2017

Harris

Ohio

Industrial Directory

MERGENT
Exclusive Provider of
Dun & Bradstreet Library Solutions

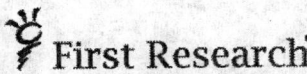
dun & bradstreet

HOOVERS™   First Research    HARRIS INFOSOURCE™

Published July 2017 next update July 2018

Publisher

Mergent Inc.
444 Madison Ave
New York, NY 10022

©Mergent Inc All Rights Reserved
2017 Mergent Business Press
ISSN 1080-2614
ISBN 978-1-68200-390-9

MERGENT
BUSINESS PRESS

TABLE OF CONTENTS

Summary of Comtents & Explanatory Notes 4
User's Guide to Listings 6

Geographic Section
County/City Cross-Reference Index 9
Firms Listed by Location City 13

Standard Industrial Classification (SIC) Section
SIC Alphabetical Index 867
SIC Numerical Index 869
Firms Listed by SIC 871

Alphabetic Section
Firms Listed by Firm Name 1091

Product Section
Product Index 1363
Firms Listed by Product Category 1389

SUMMARY OF CONTENTS

Number of Companies.. 21,371
Number of Decision Makers...................................... 53,770
Minimum Number of Employees 3

EXPLANATORY NOTES

How to Cross-Reference in This Directory

Sequential Entry Numbers. Each establishment in the Geographic Section is numbered sequentially (G-0000). The number assigned to each establishment is referred to as its "entry number." To make cross-referencing easier, each listing in the Geographic, SIC, Alphabetic and Product Sections includes the establishment's entry number. To facilitate locating an entry in the Geographic Section, the entry numbers for the first listing on the left page and the last listing on the right page are printed at the top of the page next to the city name.

Source Suggestions Welcome

Although all known sources were used to compile this directory, it is possible that companies were inadvertently omitted. Your assistance in calling attention to such omissions would be greatly appreciated. A special form on the facing page will help you in the reporting process.

Analysis

Every effort has been made to contact all firms to verify their information. The one exception to this rule is the annual sales figure, which is considered by many companies to be confidential information. Therefore, estimated sales have been calculated by multiplying the nationwide average sales per employee for the firm's major SIC/NAICS code by the firm's number of employees. Nationwide averages for sales per employee by SIC/NAICS codes are provided by the U.S. Department of Commerce and are updated annually. All sales—sales (est)—have been estimated by this method. The exceptions are parent companies (PA), division headquarters (DH) and headquarter locations (HQ) which may include an actual corporate sales figure—sales (corporate-wide) if available.

Types of Companies

Descriptive and statistical data are included for companies in the entire state. These comprise manufacturers, machine shops, fabricators, assemblers and printers. Also identified are corporate offices in the state.

Employment Data

The employment figure shown in the Geographic Section includes male and female employees and embraces all levels of the company: administrative, clerical, sales and maintenance. This figure is for the facility listed and does not include other plants or offices. It should be recognized that these figures represent an approximate year-round average. These employment figures are broken into codes A through G and used in the Product and SIC Sections to further help you in qualifying a company. Be sure to check the footnotes on the bottom of pages for the code breakdowns.

Standard Industrial Classification (SIC)

The Standard Industrial Classification (SIC) system used in this directory was developed by the federal government for use in classifying establishments by the type of activity they are engaged in. The SIC classifications used in this directory are from the 1987 edition published by the U.S. Government's Office of Management and Budget. The SIC system separates all activities into broad industrial divisions (e.g., manufacturing, mining, retail trade). It further subdivides each division. The range of manufacturing industry classes extends from two-digit codes (major industry group) to four-digit codes (product).

For example:

Industry Breakdown	Code	Industry, Product, etc.
*Major industry group	20	Food and kindred products
Industry group	203	Canned and frozen foods
*Industry	2033	Fruits and vegetables, etc.

*Classifications used in this directory

Only two-digit and four-digit codes are used in this directory.

Arrangement

1. The **Geographic Section** contains complete in-depth corporate data. This section is sorted by cities listed in alphabetical order and companies listed alphabetically within each city. A County/City Index for referencing cities within counties precedes this section.

> IMPORTANT NOTICE: It is a violation of both federal and state law to transmit an unsolicited advertisement to a facsimile machine. Any user of this product that violates such laws may be subject to civil and criminal penalties, which may exceed $500 for each transmission of an unsolicited facsimile. Mergent Inc. provides fax numbers for lawful purposes only and expressly forbids the use of these numbers in any unlawful manner.

2. The **Standard Industrial Classification (SIC) Section** lists companies under approximately 500 four-digit SIC codes. An alphabetical and a numerical index precedes this section. A company can be listed under several codes. The codes are in numerical order with companies listed alphabetically under each code.

3. The **Alphabetic Section** lists all companies with their full physical or mailing addresses and telephone number.

4. The **Product Section** lists companies under unique Harris categories. An index preceding this section lists all product categories in alphabetical order. Companies can be listed under several categories.

USER'S GUIDE TO LISTINGS

GEOGRAPHIC SECTION

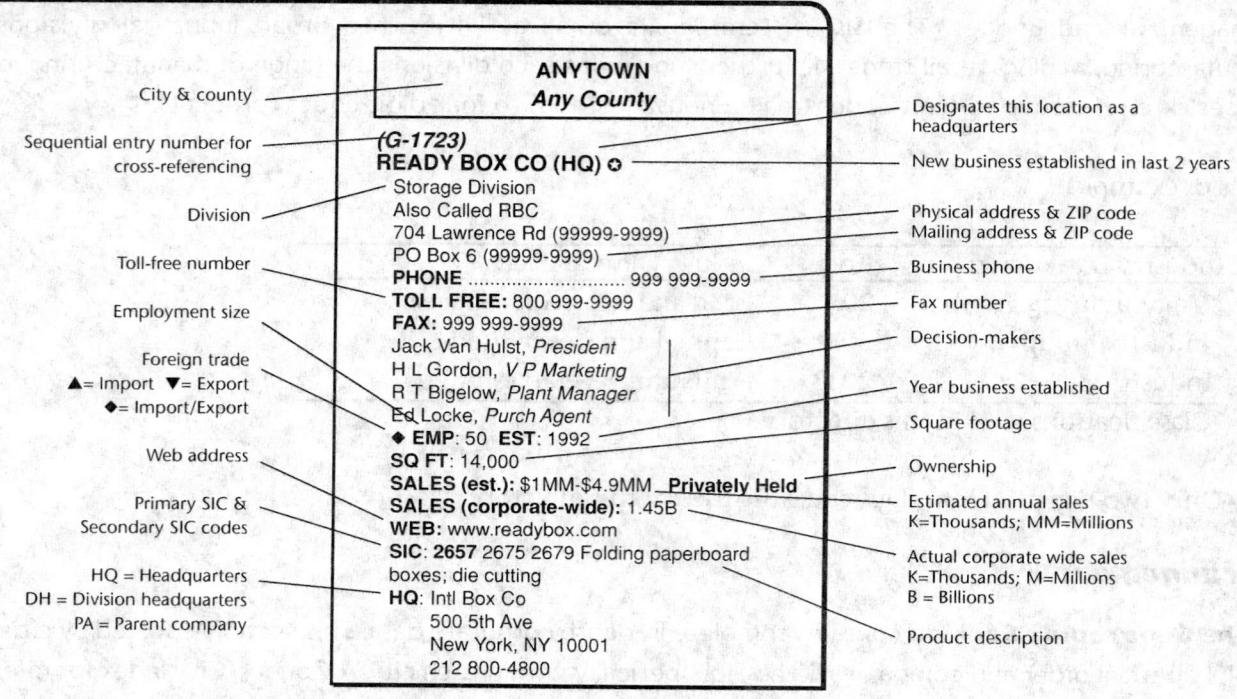

City & county

Sequential entry number for cross-referencing

Division

Toll-free number

Employment size

Foreign trade
▲= Import ▼= Export
◆= Import/Export

Web address

Primary SIC & Secondary SIC codes

HQ = Headquarters
DH = Division headquarters
PA = Parent company

Designates this location as a headquarters

New business established in last 2 years

Physical address & ZIP code

Mailing address & ZIP code

Business phone

Fax number

Decision-makers

Year business established

Square footage

Ownership

Estimated annual sales
K=Thousands; MM=Millions

Actual corporate wide sales
K=Thousands; M=Millions
B = Billions

Product description

ANYTOWN
Any County

(G-1723)
READY BOX CO (HQ) ✪
Storage Division
Also Called RBC
704 Lawrence Rd (99999-9999)
PO Box 6 (99999-9999)
PHONE 999 999-9999
TOLL FREE: 800 999-9999
FAX: 999 999-9999
Jack Van Hulst, *President*
H L Gordon, *V P Marketing*
R T Bigelow, *Plant Manager*
Ed Locke, *Purch Agent*
◆ **EMP:** 50 **EST:** 1992
SQ FT: 14,000
SALES (est.): $1MM-$4.9MM **Privately Held**
SALES (corporate-wide): 1.45B
WEB: www.readybox.com
SIC: 2657 2675 2679 Folding paperboard boxes; die cutting
HQ: Intl Box Co
500 5th Ave
New York, NY 10001
212 800-4800

SIC SECTION

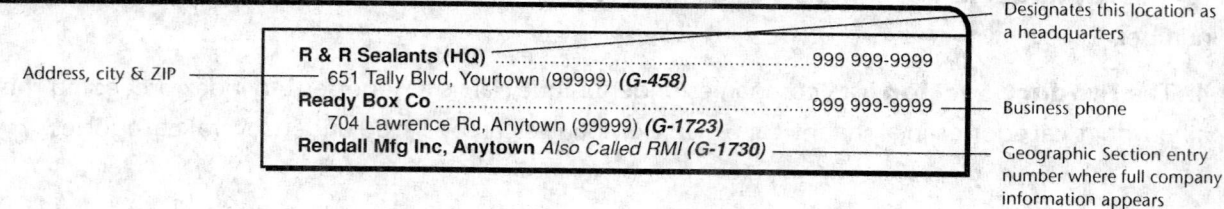

4-digit SIC number & description

Foreign trade
▲= Import ▼= Export
◆= Import/Export

City

Indicates approximate employment figure
A = over 500 employees, B = 251–500
C = 101–250, D = 51–100, E = 20–50
F = 10-19, G = 1–9

Business phone

Geographic Section entry number where full company information appears

2657-Folding Paperboard Boxes
Affordable Inds .... D...999 999-9999
Yourtown *(G-54)*
◆ **Ready Box Co** .... F....999 999-9999
Anytown *(G-1723)*

ALPHABETIC SECTION

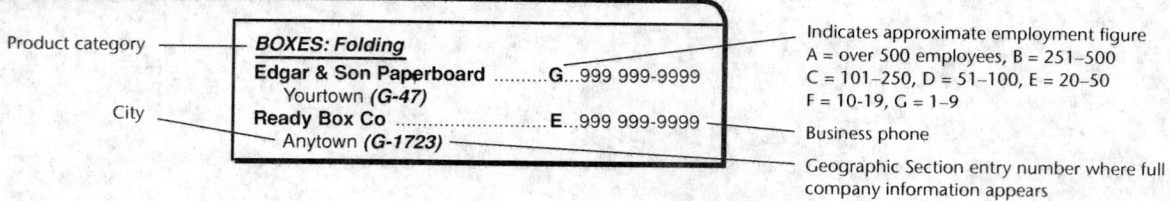

Address, city & ZIP

Designates this location as a headquarters

Business phone

Geographic Section entry number where full company information appears

R & R Sealants (HQ) 999 999-9999
651 Tally Blvd, Yourtown (99999) *(G-458)*
Ready Box Co 999 999-9999
704 Lawrence Rd, Anytown (99999) *(G-1723)*
Rendall Mfg Inc, Anytown *Also Called RMI (G-1730)*

PRODUCT SECTION

Product category

City

Indicates approximate employment figure
A = over 500 employees, B = 251–500
C = 101–250, D = 51–100, E = 20–50
F = 10-19, G = 1–9

Business phone

Geographic Section entry number where full company information appears

BOXES: Folding
Edgar & Son Paperboard ....G...999 999-9999
Yourtown *(G-47)*
Ready Box Co .... E...999 999-9999
Anytown *(G-1723)*

GEOGRAPHIC SECTION
Companies sorted by city in alphabetical order
In-depth company data listed

STANDARD INDUSTRIAL CLASSIFICATIONS
Alphabetical index of classifcation descriptions
Numerical index of classifcation descriptions
Companies sorted by SIC product groupings

ALPHABETIC SECTION
Company listings in alphabetical order

PRODUCT INDEX
Product categories listed in alphabetical order

PRODUCT SECTION
Companies sorted by product and manufacturing service classifications

Ohio
County Map

	ENTRY #		ENTRY #		ENTRY #		ENTRY #		ENTRY #

Ottawa

Clay Center	(G-4654)
Curtice	(G-7957)
Elmore	(G-9360)
Genoa	(G-10360)
Gypsum	(G-10655)
Lakeside	(G-11646)
Lakeside Marblehead (G-11647)	
Marblehead	(G-12744)
Oak Harbor	(G-15586)
Port Clinton	(G-16393)
Put In Bay	(G-16498)
Williston	(G-20420)

Paulding

Antwerp	(G-627)
Cecil	(G-2979)
Grover Hill	(G-10652)
Haviland	(G-10837)
Latty	(G-11767)
Oakwood	(G-15613)
Paulding	(G-15998)
Payne	(G-16015)

Perry

Corning	(G-7858)
Crooksville	(G-7948)
Glenford	(G-10398)
Junction City	(G-11411)
Mount Perry	(G-14590)
New Lexington	(G-14845)
Shawnee	(G-17116)
Somerset	(G-17416)
Thornville	(G-18191)

Pickaway

Ashville	(G-848)
Circleville	(G-4622)
Derby	(G-8947)
New Holland	(G-14835)
Orient	(G-15723)
Williamsport	(G-20418)

Pike

Beaver	(G-1309)
Latham	(G-11765)
Piketon	(G-16215)
Waverly	(G-19704)

Portage

Atwater	(G-898)
Aurora	(G-905)
Deerfield	(G-8771)
Diamond	(G-8959)
Garrettsville	(G-10320)
Hiram	(G-11033)
Kent	(G-11422)
Mantua	(G-12706)
Mogadore	(G-14366)
North Benton	(G-15211)
Randolph	(G-16509)
Ravenna	(G-16511)
Rootstown	(G-16718)
Streetsboro	(G-17833)
Windham	(G-20697)

Preble

Camden	(G-2484)
Eaton	(G-9298)
Eldorado	(G-9346)
Gratis	(G-10468)
Lewisburg	(G-11931)
New Paris	(G-14879)
Verona	(G-19338)
West Alexandria	(G-19778)
West Manchester	(G-20096)

Putnam

Cloverdale	(G-6536)
Columbus Grove	(G-7790)
Continental	(G-7825)
Fort Jennings	(G-9925)
Gilboa	(G-10379)
Glandorf	(G-10397)
Kalida	(G-11412)
Leipsic	(G-11867)
Ottawa	(G-15790)
Ottoville	(G-15821)
Pandora	(G-15947)

Richland

Bellville	(G-1568)
Butler	(G-2391)
Lexington	(G-11949)
Mansfield	(G-12554)
Ontario	(G-15684)
Shelby	(G-17131)
Shiloh	(G-17148)

Ross

Bainbridge	(G-1057)
Chillicothe	(G-3226)
Frankfort	(G-9998)
Londonderry	(G-12225)
Richmond Dale	(G-16650)
South Salem	(G-17449)

Sandusky

Clyde	(G-6537)
Fremont	(G-10121)
Gibsonburg	(G-10377)
Helena	(G-10895)
Millersville	(G-14300)
Vickery	(G-19361)
Woodville	(G-20724)

Scioto

Franklin Furnace	(G-10066)
Haverhill	(G-10836)
Lucasville	(G-12417)
Mc Dermott	(G-13341)
Minford	(G-14346)
New Boston	(G-14778)
Otway	(G-15826)
Portsmouth	(G-16429)
South Webster	(G-17451)
Wheelersburg	(G-20329)

Seneca

Alvada	(G-556)
Attica	(G-892)
Bettsville	(G-1668)
Bloomville	(G-1725)
Fostoria	(G-9964)
Green Springs	(G-10471)
New Riegel	(G-14946)
Old Fort	(G-15670)
Republic	(G-16579)
Tiffin	(G-18201)

Shelby

Anna	(G-619)
Botkins	(G-1949)
Fort Loramie	(G-9927)
Houston	(G-11120)
Jackson Center	(G-11336)
Kettlersville	(G-11589)
Port Jefferson	(G-16420)
Russia	(G-16760)
Sidney	(G-17164)

Stark

Alliance	(G-486)
Beach City	(G-1247)
Brewster	(G-2083)
Canal Fulton	(G-2495)
Canton	(G-2583)
East Canton	(G-9190)
East Sparta	(G-9253)
Greentown	(G-10484)
Hartville	(G-10815)
Louisville	(G-12308)
Magnolia	(G-12515)
Massillon	(G-13104)
Middlebranch	(G-13900)
Minerva	(G-14316)
Navarre	(G-14708)
North Canton	(G-15217)
North Lawrence	(G-15305)
Paris	(G-15949)
Uniontown	(G-19074)
Waynesburg	(G-19722)
Wilmot	(G-20683)

Summit

Akron	(G-12)
Barberton	(G-1092)
Bath	(G-1236)
Clinton	(G-6533)
Copley	(G-7837)
Cuyahoga Falls	(G-7960)
Fairlawn	(G-9736)
Hudson	(G-11153)
Lakemore	(G-11644)
Macedonia	(G-12433)
Munroe Falls	(G-14660)
New Franklin	(G-14823)
Northfield	(G-15462)
Norton	(G-15500)
Peninsula	(G-16032)
Richfield	(G-16612)
Sagamore Hills	(G-16778)
Silver Lake	(G-17237)
Stow	(G-17727)
Tallmadge	(G-18131)
Twinsburg	(G-18888)

Trumbull

Bristolville	(G-2098)
Brookfield	(G-2121)
Burghill	(G-2368)
Cortland	(G-7861)
Girard	(G-10380)
Hartford	(G-10814)
Hubbard	(G-11126)
Kinsman	(G-11608)
Masury	(G-13213)
Mc Donald	(G-13346)
Mesopotamia	(G-13775)
Mineral Ridge	(G-14302)
Newton Falls	(G-15128)
Niles	(G-15144)
North Bloomfield	(G-15215)
Southington	(G-17454)
Vienna	(G-19362)
Warren	(G-19515)
West Farmington	(G-20073)

Tuscarawas

Baltic	(G-1064)
Bolivar	(G-1927)
Dennison	(G-8942)
Dover	(G-8962)
Dundee	(G-9170)
Gnadenhutten	(G-10405)
Midvale	(G-14103)
Mineral City	(G-14301)
New Philadelphia	(G-14882)
Newcomerstown	(G-15107)
Port Washington	(G-16422)
Sandyville	(G-17023)
Stone Creek	(G-17724)
Strasburg	(G-17819)
Sugarcreek	(G-18014)
Uhrichsville	(G-19044)
Zoarville	(G-21370)

Union

Marysville	(G-12931)
Milford Center	(G-14181)
Raymond	(G-16576)
Richwood	(G-16659)
Unionville Center	(G-19105)

Van Wert

Convoy	(G-7831)
Middle Point	(G-13896)
Ohio City	(G-15660)
Van Wert	(G-19241)
Venedocia	(G-19321)
Willshire	(G-20651)

Vinton

Hamden	(G-10656)
Mc Arthur	(G-13328)
Ray	(G-16574)
Zaleski	(G-21261)

Warren

Carlisle	(G-2928)
Franklin	(G-10003)
Harveysburg	(G-10835)
Lebanon	(G-11773)
Maineville	(G-12520)
Mason	(G-12978)
Middletown	(G-14101)
Morrow	(G-14542)
Oregonia	(G-15722)
Pleasant Plain	(G-16370)
South Lebanon	(G-17429)
Springboro	(G-17470)
Waynesville	(G-19730)

Washington

Belpre	(G-1585)
Beverly	(G-1671)
Fleming	(G-9909)
Graysville	(G-10469)
Little Hocking	(G-12141)
Lowell	(G-12402)
Lower Salem	(G-12415)
Marietta	(G-12762)
New Matamoras	(G-14873)
Newport	(G-15126)
Reno	(G-16577)
Vincent	(G-19378)
Waterford	(G-19645)
Wingett Run	(G-20709)

Wayne

Apple Creek	(G-633)
Burbank	(G-2367)
Creston	(G-7937)
Dalton	(G-8064)
Doylestown	(G-9026)
Fredericksburg	(G-10078)
Kidron	(G-11590)
Marshallville	(G-12917)
Mount Eaton	(G-14555)
Orrville	(G-15727)
Rittman	(G-16674)
Shreve	(G-17156)
Smithville	(G-17238)
Sterling	(G-17684)
West Salem	(G-20111)
Wooster	(G-20728)

Williams

Alvordton	(G-558)
Blakeslee	(G-1708)
Bryan	(G-2273)
Edgerton	(G-9325)
Edon	(G-9339)
Montpelier	(G-14437)
Pioneer	(G-16231)
Stryker	(G-18001)
West Unity	(G-20126)

Wood

Bloomdale	(G-1719)
Bowling Green	(G-1961)
Bradner	(G-2027)
Dunbridge	(G-9168)
Grand Rapids	(G-10439)
Millbury	(G-14182)
North Baltimore	(G-15191)
Northwood	(G-15476)
Pemberville	(G-16026)
Perrysburg	(G-16060)
Portage	(G-16424)
Risingsun	(G-16672)
Rossford	(G-16737)
Walbridge	(G-19456)
Wayne	(G-19721)
West Millgrove	(G-20104)
Weston	(G-20324)

Wyandot

Carey	(G-2914)
Harpster	(G-10765)
Mc Cutchenville	(G-13340)
Nevada	(G-14743)
Sycamore	(G-18096)
Upper Sandusky	(G-19114)
Wharton	(G-20328)

GEOGRAPHIC SECTION

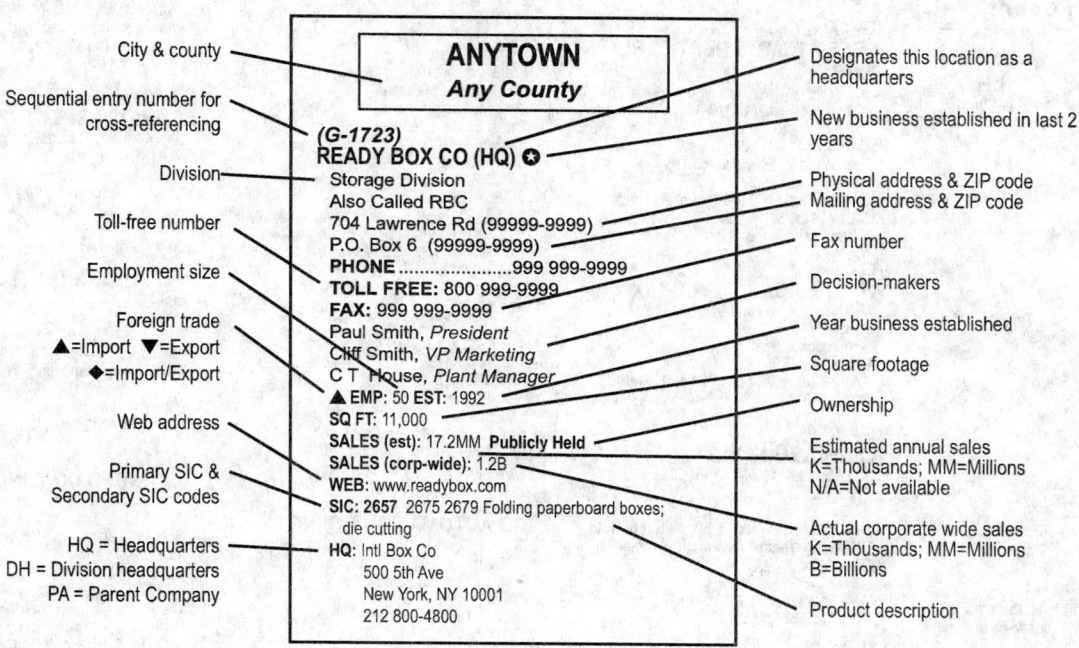

ANYTOWN
Any County

(G-1723)
READY BOX CO (HQ) ✪
Storage Division
Also Called RBC
704 Lawrence Rd (99999-9999)
P.O. Box 6 (99999-9999)
PHONE 999 999-9999
TOLL FREE: 800 999-9999
FAX: 999 999-9999
Paul Smith, *President*
Cliff Smith, *VP Marketing*
C T House, *Plant Manager*
▲ **EMP:** 50 **EST:** 1992
SQ FT: 11,000
SALES (est): 17.2MM **Publicly Held**
SALES (corp-wide): 1.2B
WEB: www.readybox.com
SIC: 2657 2675 2679 Folding paperboard boxes; die cutting
HQ: Intl Box Co
500 5th Ave
New York, NY 10001
212 800-4800

Labels (left side):
- City & county
- Sequential entry number for cross-referencing
- Division
- Toll-free number
- Employment size
- Foreign trade ▲=Import ▼=Export ◆=Import/Export
- Web address
- Primary SIC & Secondary SIC codes
- HQ = Headquarters
- DH = Division headquarters
- PA = Parent Company

Labels (right side):
- Designates this location as a headquarters
- New business established in last 2 years
- Physical address & ZIP code
- Mailing address & ZIP code
- Fax number
- Decision-makers
- Year business established
- Square footage
- Ownership
- Estimated annual sales K=Thousands; MM=Millions N/A=Not available
- Actual corporate wide sales K=Thousands; MM=Millions B=Billions
- Product description

See footnotes for symbols and codes identification.
- This section is in alphabetical order by city.
- Companies are sorted alphabetically under their respective cities.
- To locate cities within a county refer to the County/City Cross Reference Index.

IMPORTANT NOTICE: It is a violation of both federal and state law to transmit an unsolicited advertisement to a facsimile machine. Any user of this product that violates such laws may be subject to civil and criminal penalties which may exceed $500 for each transmission of an unsolicited facsimile. Harris InfoSource provides fax numbers for lawful purposes only and expressly forbids the use of these numbers in any unlawful manner.

Aberdeen
Brown County

(G-1)
HOME CITY ICE
701 Us Highway 52 (45101-7505)
PHONE 859 441-1700
EMP: 3 **EST:** 2015
SALES (est): 110.8K **Privately Held**
SIC: 2024 3556 Ice cream, packaged; molded, on sticks, etc.; ice cream manufacturing machinery

(G-2)
MAYSVILLE READY MIX CONCR
8030 Rte 52 Us (45101)
PHONE 937 795-2020
Fax: 937 795-2400
John Steele Jr, *CEO*
EMP: 6
SALES (est): 551.4K **Privately Held**
SIC: 3273 Ready-mixed concrete

Ada
Hardin County

(G-3)
ADA TECHNOLOGIES INC
805 E North Ave (45810-1809)
PHONE 419 634-7000
Fax: 419 634-7146
Bobby Suzuki, *President*
Mark Nichols, *Mfg Mgr*
Jim Swick, *Mfg Staff*
Jim Tesnow, *Purch Agent*

Mike Crisp, *Purchasing*
▲ **EMP:** 194
SQ FT: 45,000
SALES (est): 78.6MM **Privately Held**
WEB: www.adatechinc.com
SIC: 3714 Motor vehicle transmissions, drive assemblies & parts

(G-4)
AMERICAN METAL SIGN
4750 State Route 309 (45810-9716)
PHONE 267 521-2670
Ronald Klesmit, *Principal*
EMP: 3
SALES (est): 298.5K **Privately Held**
SIC: 3993 Signs & advertising specialties

(G-5)
ASSOCIATED PLASTICS CORP
502 Eric Wolber Dr (45810-1100)
PHONE 419 634-3910
Fax: 419 634-9161
Fred Wolber, *President*
Samuel W Diller, *Principal*
George Wolber, *Vice Pres*
Carie Rowe, *Human Res Mgr*
Vickie Wolber, *Corp Comm Staff*
▲ **EMP:** 70
SQ FT: 63,000
SALES (est): 16.1MM **Privately Held**
WEB: www.associatedplastics.com
SIC: 3089 Injection molded finished plastic products

(G-6)
NASG OHIO LLC
Also Called: North American Stamping Group
605 E Montford Ave (45810-1804)
P.O. Box 265 (45810-0265)
PHONE 419 634-3125
Gary Wicker, *Opers Mgr*

Michael Haughey, *Mng Member*
Nancy Stubbs, *Manager*
EMP: 11
SALES (est): 2.2MM
SALES (corp-wide): 235.1MM **Privately Held**
WEB: www.adastampings.com
SIC: 3465 Automotive stampings
PA: North American Stamping Group, Llc
119 Kirby Dr
Portland TN 37148
615 323-0500

(G-7)
WILSON SPORTING GOODS CO
217 Liberty St (45810-1135)
P.O. Box 116 (45810-0116)
PHONE 419 634-9901
Fax: 419 634-4630
Dan Riegle, *Manager*
Pam Clark, *Manager*
Mark Fisher, *Maintence Staff*
EMP: 150
SQ FT: 30,000 **Privately Held**
SIC: 3949 Balls: baseball, football, basketball, etc.
HQ: Wilson Sporting Goods Co.
8750 W Bryn Mawr Ave Fl 2
Chicago IL 60631
773 714-6400

Adamsville
Muskingum County

(G-8)
HARRISON 20 MTD BOREFINERY LLC
Also Called: Harrison Ethanol
9665 Young America Rd (43802-9721)
PHONE 740 796-4797
Wendel E Dreve, *President*
Marion Gilliland, *Manager*
EMP: 4
SALES (est): 200.2K **Privately Held**
SIC: 2869 Ethyl alcohol, ethanol

(G-9)
SHIRER BROTHERS MEATS
Also Called: Shirer Brothers Slaughter Hse
7805 Adamsville Otsego Rd (43802-9732)
PHONE 740 796-3214
Ronald Shirer, *Partner*
John Shirer, *Partner*
EMP: 5 **EST:** 1949
SQ FT: 2,000
SALES (est): 473K **Privately Held**
SIC: 2011 Meat packing plants; beef products from beef slaughtered on site

---

Addyston
Hamilton County

(G-10)
INEOS ABS (USA) LLC (DH)
356 Three Rivers Pkwy (45001-2553)
P.O. Box 39 (45001-0039)
PHONE..................................513 467-2400
Fax: 513 467-2137
Clint Herring, *Vice Pres*
Bryan Mullalley, *Opers Mgr*
Sharon Terrell, *Opers Mgr*
Duane Day, *Senior Buyer*
Baron Wair, *Buyer*
◆ **EMP:** 218
SQ FT: 372,600
SALES (est): 82MM
SALES (corp-wide): 40B **Privately Held**
SIC: 2821 Plastics materials & resins
HQ: Ineos Group Ag
      Avenue Des Uttins 3
      Rolle VD
      216 277-040

(G-11)
KIEF SIGNS
3 E Main St (45001-2520)
P.O. Box 458 (45001-0458)
PHONE..................................513 941-8800
Fax: 513 941-8800
Olivia Centrulla, *Owner*
EMP: 3
SQ FT: 2,000
SALES: 100K **Privately Held**
SIC: 3993 Signs, not made in custom sign
painting shops

Akron
Summit County

(G-12)
360 COMMUNICATIONS LLC
Also Called: Dbd
826 Minota Ave (44306-3420)
P.O. Box 7646 (44306-0646)
PHONE..................................330 329-2013
Benita Williams,
EMP: 4
SALES: 100K **Privately Held**
SIC: 2741 Miscellaneous publishing

(G-13)
48 HR BOOKS INC
2249 14th St Sw (44314-2007)
PHONE..................................330 374-6917
James Fulton, *President*
▼ **EMP:** 24 **EST:** 2007
SQ FT: 33,000
SALES (est): 3.2MM **Privately Held**
SIC: 2732 Books: printing & binding

(G-14)
69 TAPS
374 Paul Williams St (44311)
PHONE..................................330 253-4554
Susie Drandel, *Principal*
EMP: 3
SALES (est): 125.2K **Privately Held**
SIC: 2064 Candy bars, including chocolate
covered bars

(G-15)
7SIGNAL SOLUTIONS INC (PA)
526 S Main St Ste 601g (44311-4403)
PHONE..................................330 761-3515
Jeff Reedy, *CEO*
Chris Anderle, *Vice Pres*
Marvin Roush, *VP Sales*
Eric Camulli, *VP Mktg*
Veli-Pekka Ketonen, *CTO*
EMP: 20
SQ FT: 2,000
SALES (est): 3MM **Privately Held**
SIC: 3661 Telephone & telegraph appara-
tus

(G-16)
A & P TECH SERVICES INC
856 Home Ave (44310-4119)
PHONE..................................330 535-1700
John Pappano, *President*

EMP: 4
SALES: 88K **Privately Held**
SIC: 3421 Knife blades & blanks

(G-17)
A BEST TRMT & PEST CTRL SUPS
Also Called: A-Best Termite and Pest Ctrl
891 Gorge Blvd (44310-3462)
PHONE..................................330 434-5555
Fax: 330 434-1800
Todd Anderson, *President*
EMP: 6
SALES (est): 460.9K **Privately Held**
SIC: 7342 2879 5191 Pest control serv-
ices; insecticides & pesticides; pesticides

(G-18)
A PLUS SIGNS & GRAPHIX
833 E Waterloo Rd (44306-3925)
PHONE..................................330 848-4800
Bob Jacobs, *Owner*
EMP: 3
SALES (est): 184.9K **Privately Held**
SIC: 3993 Signs & advertising specialties

(G-19)
A SCHULMAN INC
1353 Exeter Rd (44306-3853)
PHONE..................................330 773-2700
EMP: 124
SALES (corp-wide): 2.5B **Publicly Held**
SIC: 2821 Plastics materials & resins
PA: A. Schulman, Inc.
      3637 Ridgewood Rd
      Fairlawn OH 44333
      330 666-3751

(G-20)
A SCHULMAN INC
1183 Home Ave (44310-2508)
PHONE..................................330 630-3315
Fax: 330 633-8138
Tom McQaide, *Project Mgr*
William Fedak, *Opers Staff*
Kim House, *Office Mgr*
Joe Ocampo, *Branch Mgr*
Tim Angel, *Manager*
EMP: 15
SQ FT: 52,766
SALES (corp-wide): 2.5B **Publicly Held**
WEB: www.aschulman.com
SIC: 2821 Molding compounds, plastics
PA: A. Schulman, Inc.
      3637 Ridgewood Rd
      Fairlawn OH 44333
      330 666-3751

(G-21)
A SCHULMAN INC
790 E Tallmadge Ave (44310-3503)
PHONE..................................330 630-0308
Fax: 330 633-8138
Ted Carpenter, *Project Mgr*
Ron Wells, *Purchasing*
Bill Sedak, *Project Engr*
Brittany Rohner, *Human Resources*
Derold Hines, *Branch Mgr*
EMP: 202
SQ FT: 104,823
SALES (corp-wide): 2.5B **Publicly Held**
WEB: www.aschulman.com
SIC: 2821 Molding compounds, plastics
PA: A. Schulman, Inc.
      3637 Ridgewood Rd
      Fairlawn OH 44333
      330 666-3751

(G-22)
A-A BLUEPRINT CO INC
2757 Gilchrist Rd (44305-4400)
PHONE..................................330 794-8803
Fax: 330 794-8348
John Scalia, *President*
Daisy Scalia, *Principal*
Joseph Brown, *Production*
Velvet Taylor, *Sales Staff*
EMP: 32
SQ FT: 30,000
SALES (est): 5.7MM **Privately Held**
WEB: www.aablueprint.com
SIC: 2791 7334 2752 2789 Typesetting;
photocopying & duplicating services;
commercial printing, offset; bookbinding &
related work; letterpress printing

(G-23)
A/C LASER TECHNOLOGIES INC
867 Moe Dr Ste F (44310-2531)
PHONE..................................330 784-3355
Fax: 330 784-3803
Jo Ann Wilson, *President*
Frank Wilson, *Treasurer*
Harry Clapp, *Manager*
Kera McAbe, *Manager*
Joelle Davis, *Executive*
EMP: 12
SQ FT: 4,100
SALES: 1.6MM **Privately Held**
WEB: www.aclaser.com
SIC: 3555 7699 5999 Printing trades ma-
chinery; printing trades machinery &
equipment repair; business machines &
equipment

(G-24)
AARON SMITH
Also Called: Apex Services
385 Rutland Ave (44305-3144)
PHONE..................................330 285-1360
Aaron Smith, *Owner*
EMP: 3
SALES: 60K **Privately Held**
SIC: 3699 Security control equipment &
systems

(G-25)
ACC AUTOMATION CO INC
475 Wolf Ledges Pkwy (44311-1199)
PHONE..................................330 928-3821
Frank Rzicznek, *Vice Pres*
William Howe, *Vice Pres*
William T Mars, *Vice Pres*
EMP: 25
SQ FT: 7,500
SALES (est): 2.3MM **Privately Held**
SIC: 8711 3536 Engineering Consulting

(G-26)
ACCU PAK MFG INC
2422 Pickle Rd (44312-4227)
PHONE..................................330 644-3015
Timothy Probst, *President*
EMP: 3
SALES (est): 220K **Privately Held**
SIC: 3565 3999 Packaging machinery;
manufacturing industries

(G-27)
ACCU-TECH MANUFACTURING CO
2691 Wingate Ave (44314-1301)
PHONE..................................330 848-8100
Fax: 330 848-8188
Slyster Downs, *President*
John Ellis, *Vice Pres*
EMP: 14
SALES (est): 2.8MM **Privately Held**
SIC: 3441 Fabricated structural metal

(G-28)
ACE PRECISION INDUSTRIES INC
925 Moe Dr (44310-2518)
PHONE..................................330 633-8523
Fax: 330 633-8525
Jerry S Wolf, *CEO*
James S Wolf, *President*
Bill Jobe, *General Mgr*
Sandy A Di Fiore, *Principal*
Doug Conrad, *Opers Mgr*
▲ **EMP:** 25 **EST:** 1974
SQ FT: 15,000
SALES (est): 5.6MM **Privately Held**
WEB: www.acebearings.com
SIC: 3599 Machine & other job shop work

(G-29)
ACRO TOOL & DIE COMPANY
Also Called: Landscape & Christmas Tree
325 Morgan Ave (44311-2494)
PHONE..................................330 773-5173
Fax: 330 773-6317
T T Thompson, *President*
Mark Weigand, *General Mgr*
Steve Wilcox, *Purchasing*
Randy Farnsworth, *QC Mgr*
M A Ross, *Engineer*
▲ **EMP:** 60
SQ FT: 27,000

SALES (est): 9.1MM **Privately Held**
WEB: www.acrotool.com
SIC: 3544 3469 0781 0811 Special dies
& tools; stamping metal for the trade;
landscape services; Christmas tree farm;
machine tools, metal cutting type; sheet
metalwork

(G-30)
ACUREN INSPECTION INC
535 Kennedy Rd Ste D (44305-4440)
PHONE..................................330 733-8160
Mike Moore, *Branch Mgr*
Stephanie Spies, *Manager*
Andrew Bowman, *Information Mgr*
Steve Hofstetter, *Information Mgr*
John Eads, *Director*
EMP: 20
SALES (corp-wide): 513MM **Privately Held**
WEB: www.hellierndt.com
SIC: 1389 Testing, measuring, surveying &
analysis services
HQ: Acuren Inspection, Inc.
      30 Main St Ste 402
      Danbury CT 06810
      203 702-8740

(G-31)
ADVANCED COATINGS INTL
2990 Gilchrist Rd # 1100 (44305-4418)
PHONE..................................330 794-6361
Steven M Johnson, *President*
▲ **EMP:** 7
SQ FT: 7,000
SALES: 500K **Privately Held**
WEB: www.advancedcoatingsinterna-
tional.com
SIC: 3479 Coating electrodes

(G-32)
ADVANCED CRYOGENIC ENTPS LLC
1034 Home Ave (44310-3502)
PHONE..................................330 922-0750
David Norton, *Mng Member*
EMP: 11 **EST:** 2006
SQ FT: 52,000
SALES: 1.2MM **Privately Held**
SIC: 7389 3679 Grinding, precision: com-
mercial or industrial; cryogenic cooling
devices for infrared detectors, masers

(G-33)
ADVANCED POLY-PACKAGING INC
1360 Exeter Rd (44306-3860)
PHONE..................................330 785-4000
EMP: 30
SALES (corp-wide): 21.4MM **Privately Held**
SIC: 2673 3565 Plastic & pliofilm bags;
packaging machinery
PA: Advanced Poly-Packaging Inc.
      1331 Emmitt Rd
      Akron OH 44306
      330 785-4000

(G-34)
AIR ENTERPRISES LLC
735 Glaser Pkwy (44306-4160)
PHONE..................................330 794-9770
John Lowe, *Regional Mgr*
John Kolar, *Vice Pres*
Gary Wolny, *Plant Mgr*
Mike Firtha, *Project Mgr*
Tim Holmes, *Project Mgr*
EMP: 21
SALES (est): 713.6K **Privately Held**
SIC: 5013 3433 Automotive supplies &
parts; heating equipment, except electric

(G-35)
AIR ENTRPRISES ACQUISITION LLC
735 Glaser Pkwy (44306-4166)
PHONE..................................330 794-9770
William M Weber, *CEO*
Richard Fleming, *Safety Dir*
Donna Drumheller, *Finance*
Glenn Swartz, *Sales Mgr*
A Malachi Mixon III,
EMP: 220
SQ FT: 100,000

▲ = Import ▼ =Export
◆ =Import/Export

SALES (est): 43.3MM **Privately Held**
SIC: 3433 Heating equipment, except electric

(G-36)
AIRBORN FLXBLE CIRCUITS NH INC
2230 Picton Pkwy (44312-4269)
PHONE....................603 537-9500
Cindy Lewis, *CEO*
Michael Fielding, *Principal*
Dean Mastantuono, *CFO*
Kristy Nebergall, *Human Res Mgr*
Michael Brustoski, *Sales Staff*
EMP: 3 EST: 1993
SALES (est): 616.8K
SALES (corp-wide): 182.3MM **Privately Held**
SIC: 3672 Printed circuit boards
HQ: Airborn Flexible Circuits Inc
11 Dohme Ave
Toronto ON M4B 1
416 752-2224

(G-37)
AKRON CENTL ENGRV MOLD MCH INC
1625 Massillon Rd (44312-4204)
PHONE....................330 794-8704
Fax: 330 794-0571
John Kaeberlein, *President*
Bob Simone, *Plant Mgr*
Frank R Muhl, *Shareholder*
EMP: 50 EST: 1969
SQ FT: 15,000
SALES (est): 10.8MM **Privately Held**
WEB: www.acemm.com
SIC: 3544 8742 4213 Industrial molds; new products & services consultants; automobiles, transport & delivery

(G-38)
AKRON COTTON PRODUCTS INC
437 W Cedar St (44307-2321)
PHONE....................330 434-7171
Fax: 330 434-7150
Michael Zwick, *President*
EMP: 9
SQ FT: 26,000
SALES: 700K **Privately Held**
WEB: www.akroncotton.com
SIC: 2211 5999 Scrub cloths; cleaning equipment & supplies

(G-39)
AKRON COUNCIL OF ENGINEERING (PA)
411 Wolf Ledges Pkwy # 105 (44311-1028)
PHONE....................330 535-8835
George Giakos, *President*
EMP: 4
SALES (est): 2.7MM **Privately Held**
SIC: 7379 3826 Computer related consulting services; spectroscopic & other optical properties measuring equipment

(G-40)
AKRON DESIGN & COSTUME CO
3425 Manchester Rd (44319-1412)
PHONE....................330 644-4849
Fax: 330 644-7425
Debbie Meridith, *Owner*
EMP: 8
SALES (est): 720.3K **Privately Held**
WEB: www.akrondesign.com
SIC: 2389 7299 Costumes; costume rental

(G-41)
AKRON ENT HEARING SERVICES INC
Also Called: Akron E N T Associates
395 E Market St (44304-1542)
PHONE....................330 762-8959
Gigi A Woodruff, *Principal*
Jackie Hamilton, *Principal*
EMP: 3
SALES (est): 388.1K **Privately Held**
SIC: 8049 3842 8011 Audiologist; hearing aids; ears, nose & throat specialist: physician/surgeon

(G-42)
AKRON EQUIPMENT COMPANY (PA)
3522 Manchester Rd Ste B (44319-1451)
P.O. Box 27027 (44319-7027)
PHONE....................330 645-3780
Edward L Mc Cartt, *Ch of Bd*
Gary A Hill, *President*
Tom Gregory, *Division Mgr*
Andrea Friede, *Corp Secy*
▼ EMP: 6 EST: 1917
SQ FT: 2,000
SALES (est): 5.6MM **Privately Held**
WEB: www.marcomfg.com
SIC: 3599 Machine shop, jobbing & repair

(G-43)
AKRON FELT & CHENILLE MFG CO
1205 George Wash Blvd (44312-3007)
PHONE....................330 733-7778
Fax: 330 733-7780
Daniel J Fanelly, *President*
Dave Watson, *Marketing Staff*
EMP: 10
SQ FT: 7,200
SALES (est): 1MM **Privately Held**
SIC: 2399 2396 5091 Emblems, badges & insignia: from purchased materials; printing & embossing on plastics fabric articles; tip printing & stamping on fabric; sporting & recreation goods

(G-44)
AKRON FOUNDRY CO (PA)
2728 Wingate Ave (44314-1300)
P.O. Box 27028 (44319-7028)
PHONE....................330 745-3101
Fax: 330 745-7999
George Ostich, *President*
Ronald C Allan, *Principal*
Geraldine Ostich, *Vice Pres*
Michael Ostich, *VP Opers*
Nimeer Daood, *Prdtn Mgr*
EMP: 175 EST: 1969
SQ FT: 100,000
SALES: 22MM **Privately Held**
WEB: www.akronfoundry.com
SIC: 3369 5063 3365 3363 Castings, except die-castings, precision; boxes & fittings, electrical; aluminum foundries; aluminum die-castings

(G-45)
AKRON GEAR & ENGINEERING INC
501 Morgan Ave (44311-2431)
P.O. Box 269 (44309-0269)
PHONE....................330 773-6608
Fax: 330 773-9005
W Thomas James III, *President*
Carl G James, *Vice Pres*
William Moore, *Vice Pres*
Michael Stohovitch, *VP Mfg*
Beverly Cookro, *Traffic Mgr*
EMP: 21 EST: 1911
SQ FT: 25,000
SALES (est): 5.7MM
SALES (corp-wide): 588.6MM **Privately Held**
WEB: www.akrongear.com
SIC: 3568 3566 3545 3462 Sprockets (power transmission equipment); gears, power transmission, except automotive; machine tool accessories; iron & steel forgings; gray & ductile iron foundries; machine shop, jobbing & repair
PA: Forge Industries, Inc.
4450 Market St
Youngstown OH 44512
330 782-8301

(G-46)
AKRON LEGAL NEWS INC
60 S Summit St (44308-1775)
PHONE....................330 296-7578
Fax: 330 376-7001
John L Burleson, *President*
Susan Maybury, *Editor*
Marlene Robinson, *Associate*
EMP: 12 EST: 1922
SQ FT: 4,000

SALES (est): 820K **Privately Held**
WEB: www.akronlegalnews.com
SIC: 2711 8111 Newspapers; legal services

(G-47)
AKRON LITHO-PRINT COMPANY INC
1026 S Main St (44311-2346)
PHONE....................330 434-3145
Fax: 330 434-3146
Pete P Ripplinger, *President*
Sharon Ripplinger, *Treasurer*
EMP: 18 EST: 1935
SQ FT: 5,500
SALES: 1.6MM **Privately Held**
WEB: www.lithoprintco.com
SIC: 2752 2759 Lithographing on metal; commercial printing, offset; letterpress printing

(G-48)
AKRON METAL ETCHING CO
463 Locust St (44307-2592)
PHONE....................330 762-7687
Fax: 330 762-7686
Lee Eisinger, *President*
Debbie Eisinger, *Corp Secy*
EMP: 5
SQ FT: 10,000
SALES (est): 400K **Privately Held**
WEB: www.textureame.com
SIC: 3479 Etching on metals

(G-49)
AKRON ORTHOTIC SOLUTIONS INC
582 W Market St (44303-1839)
PHONE....................330 253-3002
Fax: 330 253-9190
Robert McInturff, *President*
EMP: 8
SALES (est): 820.4K **Privately Held**
SIC: 3842 5999 Braces, orthopedic; orthopedic & prosthesis applications

(G-50)
AKRON PAINT & VARNISH INC
Also Called: APV Engineered Coatings
1390 Firestone Pkwy (44301-5401)
PHONE....................330 773-8911
Fax: 330 773-1028
Dave Venarge, *President*
Luhao Wu, *Managing Dir*
Lynn Kelley, *COO*
Ed Apsega, *Vice Pres*
Mike Summers, *Vice Pres*
◆ EMP: 90
SQ FT: 160,000
SALES (est): 34.6MM **Privately Held**
WEB: www.apvcoatings.com
SIC: 2851 2891 3953 Paints & paint additives; lacquers, varnishes, enamels & other coatings; adhesives & sealants; adhesives; marking devices

(G-51)
AKRON PLATING CO INC
1774 Hackberry St (44301-2493)
PHONE....................330 773-6878
Fax: 330 773-4334
Robert Ormsby Jr, *President*
Fred Beidle, *Vice Pres*
Jennifer Ormsby, *Admin Sec*
EMP: 10 EST: 1948
SQ FT: 7,500
SALES (est): 1.3MM **Privately Held**
WEB: www.akronplating.com
SIC: 3471 Electroplating of metals or formed products

(G-52)
AKRON POLYMER PRODUCTS INC
571 Kennedy Rd (44305-4425)
PHONE....................330 628-5551
Greg C Anderson, *President*
Kevin Gandee, *Vice Pres*
Michael Barnes, *QC Mgr*
▲ EMP: 43
SQ FT: 18,000
SALES (est): 14.5MM **Privately Held**
WEB: www.akronpolymer.com
SIC: 3089 3082 Extruded finished plastic products; tubes, unsupported plastic

(G-53)
AKRON PORCELAIN & PLASTICS CO (PA)
Also Called: Akron Porcelain & Plastic Co
2739 Cory Ave (44314-1308)
P.O. Box 15157 (44314-5157)
PHONE....................330 745-2159
Fax: 330 745-6688
George H Lewis Jr, *Ch of Bd*
David W Lewis, *President*
Kenneth F Burkins, *Vice Pres*
Larry Mathias, *Purchasing*
Michael B Dunphy, *Treasurer*
▲ EMP: 140 EST: 1890
SQ FT: 120,000
SALES (est): 21.1MM **Privately Held**
WEB: www.akronporcelain.com
SIC: 3089 3264 Injection molded finished plastic products; porcelain electrical supplies

(G-54)
AKRON REBAR CO (PA)
Also Called: Cleveland Rebar
809 W Waterloo Rd (44314-1527)
P.O. Box 3710 (44314-0710)
PHONE....................330 745-7100
Fax: 330 745-7272
Dennis Stump, *President*
John Tekus, *Engineer*
Kelly Strittmatter, *Manager*
EMP: 32
SQ FT: 32,600
SALES: 10.1MM **Privately Held**
WEB: www.akronrebar.com
SIC: 3441 3449 Fabricated structural metal; bars, concrete reinforcing: fabricated steel

(G-55)
AKRON SPECIAL MACHINERY INC (PA)
Also Called: Poling Group, The
2740 Cory Ave (44314-1396)
PHONE....................330 753-1077
Fax: 330 753-7308
David Poling Sr, *President*
Leon Poole, *Exec VP*
Alexander Hasbach, *Vice Pres*
John Derita, *Project Mgr*
Joseph Maite, *Project Mgr*
▼ EMP: 50 EST: 1978
SQ FT: 60,000
SALES (est): 12.9MM **Privately Held**
WEB: www.akronspecial.com
SIC: 3599 Machine shop, jobbing & repair; custom machinery

(G-56)
AKRON SPECIALIZED PRODUCTS (PA)
96 E Miller Ave (44301-1325)
PHONE....................330 762-9269
Marilyn L Tuzzio, *President*
EMP: 5
SALES (est): 1.1MM **Privately Held**
SIC: 3542 Machine tools, metal forming type

(G-57)
AKRON STEEL FABRICATORS CO
Also Called: Poling Group
3291 Manchester Rd (44319-1438)
PHONE....................330 644-0616
Fax: 330 644-0105
David Poling Sr, *President*
Timothy Wilmoth, *President*
Keith Kline, *Exec VP*
Leon Poole, *Exec VP*
Victor Flinner, *Engineer*
EMP: 30 EST: 1947
SQ FT: 28,000
SALES (est): 7.6MM **Privately Held**
WEB: www.akronsteel.com
SIC: 3491 Process control regulator valves

(G-58)
AKRON STEEL TREATING CO
336 Morgan Ave (44311-2424)
P.O. Box 2290 (44309-2290)
PHONE....................330 773-8211
Christopher Powell, *CEO*
Joseph A Powell, *President*
Jim Stewart, *Vice Pres*

GEOGRAPHIC

Vincent Pintiello, *Plant Mgr*
Steven Powell, *Controller*
EMP: 45 **EST:** 1943
SQ FT: 46,000
SALES (est): 11.3MM **Privately Held**
SIC: 3398　3479 Metal heat treating; painting, coating & hot dipping

(G-59)
AKRON THERMOGRAPHY INC
Also Called: BCT
3406 Fortuna Dr　(44312)
PHONE..............................330 896-9712
Randal S Teague, *President*
Lisa R Teague, *Corp Secy*
EMP: 30
SALES (est): 5.3MM **Privately Held**
SIC: 2752 Commercial printing, lithographic

(G-60)
AKRON VAULT COMPANY INC
Also Called: Akron Crematory
2399 Gilchrist Rd　(44305-4496)
PHONE..............................330 784-5475
Fax: 330 784-4462
Marty Ebie, *President*
Phil Kauffman, *Admin Sec*
EMP: 12 **EST:** 1944
SQ FT: 11,000
SALES (est): 1.1MM **Privately Held**
SIC: 3272 Burial vaults, concrete or precast terrazzo

(G-61)
ALCO-CHEM INC (PA)
45 N Summit St　(44308-1933)
PHONE..............................330 253-3535
Fax: 330 253-9219
Anthony Mandala Jr, *President*
Bart Mandala, *Vice Pres*
Robert Mandala, *Vice Pres*
John Mandala, *Opers Mgr*
Joanne Anderson, *Accounts Mgr*
▲ **EMP:** 34
SQ FT: 22,000
SALES (est): 27MM **Privately Held**
WEB: www.alco-chem.com
SIC: 5087　2869　2842 Janitors' supplies; industrial organic chemicals; specialty cleaning, polishes & sanitation goods

(G-62)
ALCON TOOL COMPANY
565 Lafollette St　(44311-1824)
PHONE..............................330 773-9171
Fax: 330 773-8042
Charles E Conner, *CEO*
Charles F Rankin, *President*
Ed Smith, *Traffic Mgr*
Daniel Debellis, *Engineer*
Lashaun Brown, *Accounting Dir*
▼ **EMP:** 65 **EST:** 1946
SQ FT: 100,000
SALES (est): 14.3MM **Privately Held**
WEB: www.alcontool.com
SIC: 3541 Machine tools, metal cutting type

(G-63)
ALL-TECH MANUFACTURING LTD
1477 Industrial Pkwy　(44310-2601)
PHONE..............................330 633-1095
Fax: 330 439-6311
Joseph Manijak, *Mng Member*
Frank Manijak, *Mng Member*
EMP: 40
SQ FT: 9,000
SALES (est): 5.9MM **Privately Held**
WEB: www.alltechmanufacturing.com
SIC: 3599 Machine shop, jobbing & repair

(G-64)
ALLEN RANDALL ENTERPRISES INC
70 E Miller Ave　(44301-1324)
P.O. Box 1117　(44309-1117)
PHONE..............................330 374-9850
Fax: 330 374-9853
Jim Bradshaw, *President*
EMP: 10
SQ FT: 12,500
SALES (est): 750K **Privately Held**
WEB: www.allenrandall.com
SIC: 3599 Machine shop, jobbing & repair

(G-65)
ALPHA TECHNOLOGIES SVCS LLC (DH)
3030 Gilchrist Rd　(44305-4420)
PHONE..............................330 745-1641
Barbara Davidson, *Vice Pres*
Kevin Yang, *Vice Pres*
Anthony Ferrante, *Senior Buyer*
Henry Pawlowski, *Senior Engr*
Kevin Craig, *Design Engr*
◆ **EMP:** 60
SALES (est): 24.3MM
SALES (corp-wide): 3.7B **Publicly Held**
SIC: 3823 Industrial instrmnts msrmnt display/control process variable
HQ: Dynisco Instruments Llc
　　38 Forge Pkwy
　　Franklin MA 02038
　　508 541-9400

(G-66)
AMERICAN EXECUTIVE GIFTS INC
2098 Sypher Rd Unit C　(44306-4291)
P.O. Box 1524　(44309-1524)
PHONE..............................330 645-4396
Fax: 330 645-4398
Robert R Weber, *President*
EMP: 10
SQ FT: 4,000
SALES (est): 963.1K **Privately Held**
WEB: www.aegawards.com
SIC: 3993 Advertising novelties

(G-67)
AMERICAN ORGINAL BLDG PDTS LLC
1000 Arlington Cir　(44306-3973)
PHONE..............................330 786-3000
Gordon Keller, *Opers Staff*
Edward T West, *Controller*
Dale V Wilson, *Mng Member*
Gordon F Keeler Jr, *Mng Member*
Edward West,
EMP: 15
SALES (est): 3MM **Privately Held**
SIC: 2952 Siding materials

(G-68)
AMERICAN PRINTING INC
1121 Tower Dr　(44305-1089)
PHONE..............................330 630-1121
Fax: 330 630-9797
David Hall, *President*
Steve Spinell, *Accounts Exec*
Cindy Sines, *Marketing Staff*
Jason Thomas, *Manager*
Kim Krietz, *Admin Sec*
EMP: 10 **EST:** 1928
SQ FT: 15,000
SALES (est): 1.6MM **Privately Held**
WEB: www.americanprinting.com
SIC: 2752 Commercial printing, offset

(G-69)
AMERICAN UTILITY PROC LLC
1246 Princeton St　(44301-1168)
PHONE..............................330 535-3000
Richard K Kmiecik, *Mng Member*
EMP: 34
SQ FT: 60,000
SALES (est): 3.1MM **Privately Held**
WEB: www.americanutilityprocessing.com
SIC: 3479 Aluminum coating of metal products

(G-70)
APTO ORTHOPAEDICS CORPORATION
47 N Main St　(44308-1925)
PHONE..............................330 572-7544
Thomas Olmstead, *Director*
Ritzman M D, *Director*
Steve Fening, *Director*
EMP: 28
SQ FT: 500
SALES (est): 1.3MM **Privately Held**
SIC: 3841 Surgical & medical instruments

(G-71)
ARCALLOY METAL FABRICATION
39 E Market St Ste 403　(44308-2018)
PHONE..............................800 822-9402

Michael Perkins,
EMP: 7
SALES (est): 287.9K
SALES (corp-wide): 5.9MM **Privately Held**
SIC: 3441 Fabricated structural metal
PA: American Manufacturing And Engineering Company
　　4600 W 160th St
　　Cleveland OH 44135
　　440 899-9400

(G-72)
ARCHITCTRAL RFUSE SLUTIONS LLC
525 Kennedy Rd　(44305-4425)
PHONE..............................330 733-3996
Michael Ennis, *CEO*
EMP: 4
SALES (est): 350K **Privately Held**
WEB: www.ars-llc.net
SIC: 3449 Miscellaneous metalwork

(G-73)
ARNOLDS CANDIES INC
931 High Grove Blvd　(44312-3499)
PHONE..............................330 733-4022
Fax: 330 733-5030
Ted Arnold, *President*
Gregory Dauphin, *Prgrmr*
EMP: 6
SALES (est): 30.4K **Privately Held**
SIC: 2064 Candy & other confectionery products; lollipops & other hard candy

(G-74)
ASH SEWER & DRAIN SERVICE
451 E North St　(44304-1217)
PHONE..............................330 376-9714
Greg Ash, *Owner*
EMP: 6
SALES (est): 641.6K **Privately Held**
SIC: 3272　4959 Sewer pipe, concrete; sanitary services

(G-75)
ASTER INDUSTRIES INC
275 N Arlington St Ste B　(44305-1600)
PHONE..............................330 762-7965
Kimberly Oplinger, *President*
Michael J Oplinger, *Principal*
D J Smith, *Manager*
EMP: 15
SQ FT: 14,500
SALES (est): 3.5MM **Privately Held**
WEB: www.asterind.com
SIC: 2599　3999 Bar, restaurant & cafeteria furniture; advertising display products

(G-76)
ATHENS MOLD AND MACHINE INC
1461 Industrial Pkwy　(44310-2601)
PHONE..............................740 593-6613
Fax: 740 594-7355
Jack D Thornton, *President*
Mark Thornton, *Vice Pres*
David Wickham, *Purch Agent*
Larry Pinkerton, *Sales Staff*
Marcia Wilson, *Office Mgr*
EMP: 81
SQ FT: 70,000
SALES (est): 9.5MM **Privately Held**
SIC: 3544　3599　7692 Special dies, tools, jigs & fixtures; machine shop, jobbing & repair; welding repair

(G-77)
AURIS NOBLE LLC
130 E Voris St Ste C　(44311-1536)
PHONE..............................330 685-3748
Lou Britton, *Manager*
EMP: 7
SQ FT: 12,000
SALES (corp-wide): 1.1MM **Privately Held**
SIC: 3341 Secondary precious metals; platinum group metals, smelting & refining (secondary); silver smelting & refining (secondary); iridium smelting & refining (secondary)
PA: Auris Noble, Llc
　　3045 Smith Rd Ste 700
　　Fairlawn OH 44333
　　330 321-6649

(G-78)
AUTO DEALER DESIGNS INC
303 W Bartges St　(44307-2205)
PHONE..............................330 374-7666
Fax: 330 374-0220
John Volpe, *CEO*
David Volpe, *President*
Paul Volpe, *Vice Pres*
Marilyn Volpe, *Treasurer*
Becky McGowan, *Manager*
EMP: 22
SQ FT: 16,152
SALES (est): 3.1MM **Privately Held**
WEB: www.licenseframes.com
SIC: 3993　5199 Signs & advertising specialties; advertising specialties

(G-79)
AXIS TOOL & GRINDING LLC
895 Home Ave　(44310-4115)
P.O. Box 10054　(44310-0054)
PHONE..............................330 535-4713
Thomas Burrilo, *President*
EMP: 5 **EST:** 2001
SALES (est): 478.9K **Privately Held**
SIC: 3599 Grinding castings for the trade

(G-80)
B RICHARDSON INC
Also Called: Talk of Town Silkscreen & EMB
25 Elinor Ave　(44305-4005)
PHONE..............................330 724-2122
Fax: 330 773-2577
Becky Waidmann, *President*
Herb Waidmann, *Treasurer*
EMP: 18
SQ FT: 5,000
SALES (est): 1.5MM **Privately Held**
SIC: 2262　7299 Screen printing: manmade fiber & silk broadwoven fabrics; stitching, custom

(G-81)
B W T INC
353 E Cuyahoga Falls Ave　(44310-2251)
PHONE..............................330 928-9107
EMP: 3
SALES (est): 270K **Privately Held**
SIC: 3691　5063　5531　5734 Mfg Storage Batteries Whol Electrical Equip Ret Auto/Home Supplies Ret Computers/Software

(G-82)
BABCOX MEDIA INC (PA)
3550 Embassy Pkwy　(44333-8318)
PHONE..............................330 670-1234
William E Babcox, *President*
Doug Kaufman, *Publisher*
Randy Loeser, *Publisher*
Scott Shriber, *Publisher*
Amy Antenora, *Editor*
EMP: 60
SQ FT: 40,000
SALES (est): 10.3MM **Privately Held**
WEB: www.bodyshopbusiness.com
SIC: 2721 Periodicals: publishing & printing

(G-83)
BAKER MEDIA GROUP LLC
Also Called: Akron Life
1653 Merriman Rd Ste 116　(44313-5293)
PHONE..............................330 253-0056
Don Baker Jr, *Mng Member*
EMP: 11 **EST:** 2004
SQ FT: 3,000
SALES (est): 1.2MM **Privately Held**
SIC: 2721 Magazines: publishing only, not printed on site

(G-84)
BANSAL ENTERPRISES INC
Also Called: Ink Well
1538 Home Ave　(44310-1601)
PHONE..............................330 633-9355
Usha Bansal, *President*
EMP: 10
SQ FT: 3,750
SALES (est): 1.2MM **Privately Held**
SIC: 2752　7389 Commercial printing, lithographic; advertising, promotional & trade show services

(G-85)
BARNETT SPOUTING INC
Also Called: Barney Schoolers
204 E Ralston Ave (44301-2974)
PHONE..................330 644-0853
Lynn Barnett, *President*
Mary Barnett, *Vice Pres*
EMP: 5
SALES: 350K **Privately Held**
SIC: **1761** 3949 Gutter & downspout contractor; fishing tackle, general

(G-86)
BEAVER PRODUCTIONS
2251 Cooledge Ave (44305-2162)
PHONE..................330 352-4603
Joshua Beaver, *Principal*
EMP: 4 EST: 2008
SALES (est): 283K **Privately Held**
SIC: **2741** Guides: publishing & printing

(G-87)
BEMIS COMPANY INC
Also Called: Bemis North America
1972 Akron Peninsula Rd (44313-4810)
PHONE..................330 923-5281
Jenny Frye, *Opers Staff*
William Nelson, *Project Engr*
Tom Hudson, *Branch Mgr*
Laurel E Johnson, *Manager*
Mike Hines, *Supervisor*
EMP: 28
SALES (corp-wide): 4B **Publicly Held**
SIC: **2752** 5199 2759 2672 Commercial printing, lithographic; packaging materials; commercial printing; coated & laminated paper
PA: Bemis Company, Inc.
1 Neenah Ctr Fl 4
Neenah WI 54956
920 527-5000

(G-88)
BERINGER PLATING INC
1211 Devalera St (44310-2488)
PHONE..................330 633-8409
Fax: 330 633-8447
James Beringer Jr, *President*
Alan Beringer, *Manager*
James L Beringer Sr, *Consultant*
Laura Beringer, *Admin Sec*
EMP: 8 EST: 1953
SQ FT: 21,000
SALES (est): 1.1MM **Privately Held**
WEB: www.beringerplatinginc.com
SIC: **3471** 8711 Electroplating of metals or formed products; engineering services

(G-89)
BERRAN INDUSTRIAL GROUP INC
570 Wolf Ledges Pkwy (44311-1022)
PHONE..................330 253-5800
Fax: 330 673-5235
Randy P Adair, *President*
Paul Zucik, *General Mgr*
Don Schultz, *Corp Secy*
Tom Pritchard, *Plant Mgr*
EMP: 26
SQ FT: 18,000
SALES (est): 6.1MM **Privately Held**
WEB: www.berran.com
SIC: **3599** 3441 3549 3444 Custom machinery; fabricated structural metal; metalworking machinery; sheet metalwork

(G-90)
BEST MOLD & MANUFACTURING INC
1546 E Turkeyfoot Lake Rd (44312-5350)
P.O. Box 544, Uniontown (44685-0544)
PHONE..................330 896-4084
Dave Miller, *President*
EMP: 45
SQ FT: 26,000
SALES (est): 9MM **Privately Held**
WEB: www.bestmmi.com
SIC: **3599** Machine shop, jobbing & repair

(G-91)
BF DIVERSIFIED SVCS
1516 W Exchange St (44313-7650)
PHONE..................330 869-5203
Barry Field, *President*
EMP: 9

SALES (est): 578.7K **Privately Held**
SIC: **3011** Tires & inner tubes

(G-92)
BIF CO LLC
Also Called: Bif, LLC
1405 Home Ave (44310-2514)
PHONE..................330 564-0941
Mark Schoenbaechler, *President*
EMP: 10
SQ FT: 150,000
SALES (est): 1.5MM
SALES (corp-wide): 15.2MM **Privately Held**
SIC: **3824** Impeller & counter driven flow meters
PA: Logan Machine Company
1405 Home Ave
Akron OH 44310
330 633-6163

(G-93)
BNOAT ONCOLOGY
411 Wolf Ledges Pkwy (44311-1028)
PHONE..................330 285-2537
Jill Knights, *General Mgr*
Joseph A Bauer PHD, *Principal*
EMP: 6
SALES (est): 473.1K **Privately Held**
SIC: **2834** Pharmaceutical preparations

(G-94)
BOB KING SIGN COMPANY INC
Also Called: Abl Lighting Service
1631 East Ave (44314-2645)
PHONE..................330 753-2679
Fax: 330 753-2679
Kenneth King, *President*
EMP: 3
SQ FT: 2,800
SALES (est): 350.5K **Privately Held**
WEB: www.bobkingsigns.com
SIC: **3993** 2759 7374 1799 Signs & advertising specialties; screen printing; computer graphics service; sign installation & maintenance

(G-95)
BOGIE INDUSTRIES INC LTD
Also Called: Weaver Fab & Finishing
1100 Home Ave (44310-3504)
PHONE..................330 745-3105
Jim Lauer, *President*
Marian Lauer, *Owner*
Fuzzy Helton, *Vice Pres*
Diana Helton, *Office Mgr*
EMP: 38
SQ FT: 40,000
SALES (est): 10.7MM **Privately Held**
WEB: www.weaverfab.com
SIC: **3444** 1799 3399 Sheet metalwork; coating of metal structures at construction site; powder, metal

(G-96)
BONNOT COMPANY
1301 Home Ave (44310-2654)
PHONE..................330 896-6544
Fax: 330 896-0822
George W Bain, *President*
John Negrelli, *Vice Pres*
Kris Smith, *Plant Mgr*
Kurt Houk, *Engineer*
Jovan Sutton, *Project Engr*
▼ EMP: 20
SQ FT: 20,000
SALES (est): 4.3MM **Privately Held**
WEB: www.thebonnotco.com
SIC: **3599** Custom machinery

(G-97)
BRIDGESTONE AMERICAS INC
10 E Firestone Blvd (44317-0001)
PHONE..................330 379-7000
Hang LI, *Research*
Yousof Azizi, *Engineer*
Walt Tletski, *Manager*
EMP: 31
SALES (corp-wide): 30.1B **Privately Held**
SIC: **3011** Tires & inner tubes
HQ: Bridgestone Americas, Inc.
535 Marriott Dr
Nashville TN 37214
615 937-1000

(G-98)
BRIDGESTONE PROCUREMENT HOLDIN (HQ)
381 W Wilbeth Rd (44301-2465)
P.O. Box 26611 (44319-6611)
PHONE..................337 882-1200
Gene Lavengco, *CEO*
Yuji Mochizuki, *Ch of Bd*
Tinus Grobbrlaar, *CFO*
Paul Huth, *Finance*
Greg Defrates, *Officer*
EMP: 594
SALES (est): 198.4MM
SALES (corp-wide): 30.1B **Privately Held**
SIC: **2822** Synthetic rubber
PA: Bridgestone Corporation
3-1-1, Kyobashi
Chuo-Ku TKY 104-0
368 363-001

(G-99)
BRIDGESTONE RET OPERATIONS LLC
Also Called: Firestone
1245 Firestone Pkwy (44301-1309)
PHONE..................330 379-6220
Fax: 330 379-6766
Chad Tietz, *Manager*
Terry Akon, *Manager*
EMP: 11
SQ FT: 12,000
SALES (corp-wide): 30.1B **Privately Held**
WEB: www.bfis.com
SIC: **5531** 3011 Automotive tires; tires & inner tubes
HQ: Bridgestone Retail Operations, Llc
333 E Lake St Ste 300
Bloomingdale IL 60108
630 259-9000

(G-100)
BRIGHTEYE INNOVATIONS LLC
1760 Wadsworth Rd (44320-3142)
PHONE..................800 573-0052
Josh Lefkovitz, *President*
Jacob Sheffer, *General Mgr*
EMP: 15
SQ FT: 35,000
SALES: 14MM **Privately Held**
SIC: **5023** 3089 Kitchenware; kitchenware, plastic

(G-101)
BUCHTELITE
303 Carroll St (44325-0016)
PHONE..................330 972-6184
Roger Muzger, *Principal*
Zana Salem, *Editor*
John A Messina, *Assistant VP*
Henry Nettling, *Vice Pres*
Wayne R Hill, *Assoc VP*
EMP: 22
SALES (est): 875.1K **Privately Held**
SIC: **2711** Newspapers, publishing & printing

(G-102)
BUCKEYE POST
1266 Grant St (44301-1847)
PHONE..................330 724-2800
EMP: 3
SALES (est): 143.8K **Privately Held**
SIC: **2711** Newspapers-Publishing/Printing

(G-103)
BURGHARDT MANUFACTURING INC
1524 Massillon Rd (44306-4162)
PHONE..................330 253-7590
Adam Burghardt, *President*
Amber Reider, *Office Mgr*
EMP: 9
SQ FT: 8,000
SALES (est): 1.9MM **Privately Held**
SIC: **3441** Fabricated structural metal; fabricated structural metal for bridges

(G-104)
BURGHARDT METAL FABG INC
1638 Mcchesney Rd (44306-4396)
PHONE..................330 794-1830
Fax: 330 794-8055
Craig Shuster, *President*
Cindy Archer, *Corp Secy*
EMP: 18

SQ FT: 22,000
SALES (est): 5.4MM **Privately Held**
WEB: www.burgmetalfab.com
SIC: **3449** 3441 Miscellaneous metalwork; fabricated structural metal

(G-105)
BURT MANUFACTURING COMPANY INC
Also Called: Thycurb
44 E South St (44311)
PHONE..................330 762-0061
Fax: 330 762-0914
Marvin Ricklefs, *CEO*
Bill Marzec, *Plant Mgr*
Curtis Robinson, *Purchasing*
EMP: 210
SQ FT: 120,000
SALES (est): 11.9MM
SALES (corp-wide): 34MM **Privately Held**
WEB: www.thybar.com
SIC: **3444** 3442 3564 Sheet metalwork; ventilators, sheet metal; metal roofing & roof drainage equipment; metal doors, sash & trim; blowers & fans
PA: Thybar Corporation
913 S Kay Ave
Addison IL 60101
630 543-5300

(G-106)
C E D PROCESS MINERALS INC (PA)
863 N Clvland Mssilon Rd (44333-2167)
PHONE..................330 666-5500
Leland D Cole, *Vice Pres*
Nolan E Douglas, *Treasurer*
William M Douglas, *Admin Sec*
▼ EMP: 18
SQ FT: 2,368
SALES (est): 3.4MM **Privately Held**
WEB: www.colelpa.com
SIC: **1446** Foundry sand mining

(G-107)
CALIBER MOLD AND MACHINE INC
1461 Industrial Pkwy (44310-2601)
PHONE..................330 633-8171
Jack Thornton, *President*
Thomas Thornton, *Vice Pres*
Judy Boggs, *Office Mgr*
EMP: 40
SQ FT: 12,000
SALES (est): 6.1MM **Privately Held**
WEB: www.caliber.tiremolds.com
SIC: **3544** Industrial molds

(G-108)
CANVAS 123 INC
Also Called: Pixuru
277 Oak Grove Dr (44319-2366)
PHONE..................312 805-0563
Adam Fried, *CEO*
EMP: 5 EST: 2012
SALES (est): 390K **Privately Held**
SIC: **2759** 7389 Commercial printing;

(G-109)
CAPITAL CONNECTION CABLING
1368 Crestview Ave (44320-3544)
PHONE..................330 620-6311
Garth Powell, *Owner*
EMP: 3
SALES (est): 115.2K **Privately Held**
SIC: **2298** Cable, fiber

(G-110)
CARBROS
Also Called: Associated Assoc Rdymx Con
101 W Emerling Ave (44301-1647)
PHONE..................330 375-5000
Scott Foltz, *Opers Mgr*
EMP: 15
SALES (est): 1.3MM **Privately Held**
SIC: **3273** Ready-mixed concrete

(G-111)
CARDINAL PRINTING INC
112 W Wilbeth Rd (44301-2415)
P.O. Box 678, Green (44232-0678)
PHONE..................330 773-7300
Fax: 330 773-3715

Vince Rosnack, *President*
Pam Rosnack, *Corp Secy*
Susie Anderson, *Admin Sec*
EMP: 8
SQ FT: 6,700
SALES (est): 953.2K **Privately Held**
WEB: www.electjesus.com
SIC: 2752 Commercial printing, offset

(G-112)
CARGILL INCORPORATED
2065 Manchester Rd (44314-1770)
PHONE.................................330 745-0031
Angelo Kazantzis, *Production*
Cheryl Brooks, *Purchasing*
Steven Karl, *QC Dir*
Wayne A Brown, *Manager*
EMP: 151
SALES (corp-wide): 107.1B **Privately Held**
WEB: www.cargill.com
SIC: 2899 Salt
PA: Cargill, Incorporated
15407 Mcginty Rd W
Wayzata MN 55391
952 742-7575

(G-113)
CCM WELDING INC
895 Moe Dr Ste D11 (44310-2592)
PHONE.................................330 630-2521
Fax: 330 630-1014
Charles Balogh, *President*
Alex Balogh, *Engineer*
EMP: 4
SQ FT: 4,000
SALES (est): 302.5K **Privately Held**
SIC: 3441 Fabricated structural metal

(G-114)
CCSI INC
221 Beaver St (44304-1909)
PHONE.................................800 742-8535
Frank Orlando, *Vice Pres*
EMP: 9 **EST:** 2013
SALES (est): 1.2MM **Privately Held**
SIC: 3953 Textile marking stamps, hand;
rubber or metal

(G-115)
CEC ELECTRONICS CORP
1739 Akron Peninsula Rd (44313-5157)
P.O. Box 354567, Palm Coast FL (32135-4567)
PHONE.................................330 916-8100
Fax: 330 916-8118
Dan Lujan, *President*
Valerie George, *General Mgr*
Brenda Briley, *Accountant*
EMP: 7
SQ FT: 3,000
SALES: 2.3MM **Privately Held**
WEB: www.cecelectronics.com
SIC: 3679 Electronic circuits

(G-116)
CECIL C PECK CO
1029 Arlington Cir (44306-3959)
PHONE.................................330 785-0781
Paul Stewart, *President*
▲ **EMP:** 10 **EST:** 1945
SQ FT: 8,350
SALES (est): 1.2MM **Privately Held**
WEB: www.cecilpeck.com
SIC: 3699 8711 Welding machines &
equipment, ultrasonic; designing: ship,
boat, machine & product

(G-117)
CENTER AUTOMOTIVE PARTS CO
274 E South St (44311-2162)
PHONE.................................330 434-2174
Fax: 330 434-4292
Randall Allen, *President*
EMP: 4
SALES: 1.3MM **Privately Held**
WEB: www.centerautomachine.com
SIC: 5531 3599 Automotive parts; ma-
chine shop, jobbing & repair

(G-118)
CHARLES AUTO ELECTRIC CO INC
600 Grant St (44311-1502)
PHONE.................................330 535-6269

Fax: 330 535-6280
Daniel Ardelean, *President*
Erik S Ardelean, *Vice Pres*
Mary Ardelean, *Treasurer*
EMP: 8
SQ FT: 8,000
SALES (est): 1.3MM **Privately Held**
WEB: www.charlesautoelectric.com
SIC: 3694 3621 Generators, automotive &
aircraft; alternators, automotive; starters,
for motors

(G-119)
CHARLES COSTA INC
Also Called: Costa Machine
924 Home Ave (44310-4108)
PHONE.................................330 376-3636
Fax: 330 376-3696
George Marino, *President*
Carl Prentiss, *Vice Pres*
Betty J Anderson, *Manager*
EMP: 11
SQ FT: 10,000
SALES: 1MM **Privately Held**
WEB: www.costamachine.com
SIC: 3599 Machine shop, jobbing & repair

(G-120)
CHEMEQUIP SALES INC
Also Called: R & R Engine & Machine
1004 Swartz Rd (44319-1340)
PHONE.................................330 724-8300
Fax: 330 724-4655
Jeanie Menke, *President*
EMP: 30
SQ FT: 2,500
SALES (est): 7.9MM **Privately Held**
SIC: 3519 3621 Diesel engine rebuilding;
motors & generators

(G-121)
CHEMIGON LLC
520 S Main St Ste 2511-6 (44311-1072)
PHONE.................................330 592-1875
Oliver Stahl, *Managing Prtnr*
Ann Marie Yoder, *Managing Prtnr*
EMP: 3 **EST:** 2014
SQ FT: 250
SALES: 135K **Privately Held**
SIC: 3089 8742 Plastic processing; sales
(including sales management) consultant

(G-122)
CHESTNUT HOLDINGS INC (PA)
670 W Market St (44303-1448)
PHONE.................................330 849-6503
James P McCready, *Ch of Bd*
▲ **EMP:** 2
SQ FT: 12,000
SALES (est): 148.9MM **Privately Held**
SIC: 3053 5014 5013 3714 Gaskets, all
materials; tires & tubes; wheels, motor ve-
hicle; mufflers (exhaust); motor vehicle;
exhaust systems & parts, motor vehicle

(G-123)
CHUTE SOURCE LLC
525 Kennedy Rd (44305-4425)
PHONE.................................330 475-0377
Nello Decarli, *Mng Member*
Claudio Decarli,
EMP: 15
SQ FT: 13,000
SALES (est): 2.3MM **Privately Held**
SIC: 3443 3444 Chutes & troughs; sheet
metalwork

(G-124)
CITY SCRAP & SALVAGE CO
760 Flora Ave (44314-1755)
PHONE.................................330 753-5051
Fax: 330 753-9288
Steven Katz, *CEO*
Randy Katz, *Vice Pres*
Ron Jones, *Site Mgr*
EMP: 31
SQ FT: 10,000
SALES (est): 9MM
SALES (corp-wide): 869.5MM **Publicly Held**
SIC: 5093 3341 Ferrous metal scrap &
waste; nonferrous metals scrap; second-
ary nonferrous metals
HQ: Tsb Metal Recycling Llc
1835 Dueber Ave Sw
Canton OH 44706

(G-125)
CLASSIC COUNTERTOPS LLC
1519 Kenmore Blvd (44314-1661)
PHONE.................................330 882-4220
William Blackert,
Seth Wilkerson,
EMP: 6
SQ FT: 4,700
SALES (est): 758.3K **Privately Held**
SIC: 3131 1799 Counters; counter top in-
stallation

(G-126)
CLEVELAND PIGMENT BLENDING LLC
1732 E Market St (44305-4213)
P.O. Box 149, Covington GA (30015-0149)
PHONE.................................330 794-6960
Shawn Hays, *Owner*
Don Greenwald, *Owner*
John Wagner, *General Mgr*
EMP: 6
SQ FT: 24,000
SALES (est): 899.1K **Privately Held**
SIC: 2851 Paints & allied products

(G-127)
CONSOLIDATED PATTERN WORKS INC
754 E Glenwood Ave (44310-3452)
PHONE.................................330 434-6060
Fax: 330 434-7034
James Housley, *President*
Patricia Housley, *Admin Sec*
EMP: 4 **EST:** 1966
SQ FT: 4,000
SALES: 500K **Privately Held**
WEB:
www.consolidatedpatternworksinc.com
SIC: 3999 3543 Models, except toy; indus-
trial patterns

(G-128)
CONTI TOOL & DIE INC
1333 Devalera St (44310-2453)
PHONE.................................330 633-1414
Fax: 330 633-1849
Donald L Conti, *President*
Mary Conti, *Corp Secy*
EMP: 5 **EST:** 1961
SQ FT: 4,000
SALES (est): 747.1K **Privately Held**
WEB: www.contitool.com
SIC: 3544 Special dies & tools; jigs: in-
spection, gauging & checking; jigs & fix-
tures

(G-129)
CONTITECH NORTH AMERICA INC
1144 E Market St Ste 543 (44316-1001)
PHONE.................................440 225-5363
Dave Maguire, *President*
Tim Jarvis, *Branch Mgr*
EMP: 39
SALES (corp-wide): 42.8B **Privately Held**
WEB: www.veyance.com
SIC: 5531 7538 5013 3011 Automotive &
home supply stores; general automotive
repair shops; motor vehicle supplies &
new parts; tires & inner tubes; rubber &
plastics hose & beltings
HQ: Contitech North America, Inc.
703 S Clvlnd Massillon Rd
Fairlawn OH 44333
330 664-7180

(G-130)
COS BLUEPRINT INC (PA)
590 N Main St (44310-3145)
PHONE.................................330 376-0022
Fax: 330 376-0478
Jim Scalia, *President*
Linda Scalia, *Corp Secy*
Martin Hyatt, *Vice Pres*
EMP: 13
SQ FT: 12,000
SALES: 1.5MM **Privately Held**
SIC: 2752 5999 5712 5943 Commercial
printing, offset; typewriters & business
machines; drafting equipment & supplies;
office furniture; office forms & supplies;
typesetting; bookbinding & related work

(G-131)
COUNTRY PURE FOODS INC (DH)
222 W Main St Ste 401 (44308)
PHONE.................................330 848-6875
Fax: 330 745-7838
Raymond Lee, *CEO*
Kenny Sadai, *Co-CEO*
Paul Sukalich, *Senior VP*
Liz Wilson, *Vice Pres*
Tim Hunter, *Mfg Spvr*
◆ **EMP:** 120
SALES (est): 267.9MM
SALES (corp-wide): 4.9B **Privately Held**
WEB: www.countrypurefoods.com
SIC: 2033 2037 2086 Fruit juices: fresh;
fruit juice concentrates, frozen; fruit drinks
(less than 100% juice): packaged in cans,
etc.
HQ: Sapporo International Inc.
4-20-1, Ebisu
Shibuya-Ku TKY 150-0
354 237-224

(G-132)
COUNTY OF SUMMIT
Also Called: FA Siberling Naturelm Mtro Prk
1828 Smith Rd (44313-5012)
PHONE.................................330 865-8065
Keith Shy, *Director*
EMP: 9 **Privately Held**
WEB: www.cpcourt.summitoh.net
SIC: 2531 9111 Picnic tables or benches,
park; county supervisors' & executives' of-
fices
PA: County Of Summit
650 Dan St
Akron OH 44310
330 643-2500

(G-133)
CRAIN COMMUNICATIONS INC
Also Called: Rubber & Plastics News
1725 Merriman Rd Ste 300 (44313-5283)
PHONE.................................330 836-9180
Fax: 330 836-1005
Jeannie Reall, *Editor*
Lisa Sarkis, *Editor*
Robert S Simmons, *Vice Pres*
Mary Kramer, *Vice Pres*
Ja Lewellen, *Research*
EMP: 90
SALES (corp-wide): 225MM **Privately Held**
WEB: www.crainsnewyork.com
SIC: 2711 2721 7389 Newspapers: pub-
lishing only, not printed on site; periodi-
cals; advertising, promotional & trade
show services
PA: Crain Communications, Inc.
1155 Gratiot Ave
Detroit MI 48207
313 446-6000

(G-134)
CTO INC
Also Called: Surface Systems
2035 S Main St (44301-2818)
PHONE.................................330 785-1130
Tom Gutshall, *President*
EMP: 5
SQ FT: 4,000
SALES: 708.9K **Privately Held**
WEB: www.diversifiedcoatings.com
SIC: 3479 5198 Enameling, including
porcelain, of metal products; paints, var-
nishes & supplies

(G-135)
CULT COUTURE LLC
835 Berwin St (44310-2119)
PHONE.................................330 801-9475
Royce Cleveland, *Mng Member*
EMP: 3
SALES: 130K **Privately Held**
SIC: 3961 7389 Costume jewelry;

(G-136)
CUSTOM CRAFT CONTROLS INC
1620 Triplett Blvd (44306-3308)
P.O. Box 7363 (44306-0363)
PHONE.................................330 630-9599
Fax: 330 630-3626
Kenneth Mike Dunaway, *President*

Debbie Dunaway, *President*
Eric Kirvel, *Purch Agent*
Steve Garner, *Manager*
Steve Gardner, *Info Tech Dir*
EMP: 18
SQ FT: 10,000
SALES (est): 4.3MM **Privately Held**
SIC: 3613 8711 Control panels, electric; engineering services

(G-137)
CUSTOM ENCLOSURES CORP
Also Called: Ceco Equipment Company
1951 S Main St (44301-2817)
PHONE................................330 786-9000
Fax: 330 786-9090
Chris Ehmann, *President*
EMP: 3
SQ FT: 6,330
SALES (est): 513K **Privately Held**
WEB: www.cecoequipment.com
SIC: 3444 Machine guards, sheet metal

(G-138)
CUSTOM MADE PALM TREES LLC
Also Called: Custom Made Palm Trees & Tiki
1201 Devalera St (44310-2417)
PHONE................................330 633-0063
Fax: 330 633-0063
Paul Kresowaty, *Opers Staff*
Michael A Beringer,
EMP: 3
SQ FT: 1,722
SALES (est): 182.2K **Privately Held**
WEB: www.custompalmtrees.com
SIC: 3999 Plants, artificial & preserved

(G-139)
D & D PLASTICS INC
581 E Tallmadge Ave (44310-2402)
P.O. Box 285, Tallmadge (44278-0285)
PHONE................................330 376-0668
Fax: 330 376-0901
Charles Hay, *President*
Terri Hay, *Treasurer*
EMP: 10 **EST:** 1982
SQ FT: 8,000
SALES (est): 600K **Privately Held**
SIC: 3089 Extruded finished plastic products

(G-140)
D & L MACHINE CO INC
1029 Arlington Cir (44306-3959)
PHONE................................330 785-0781
Fax: 330 785-0787
Charles Bell, *President*
Naaman Elliott, *Vice Pres*
Wendy Wiggins, *Buyer*
Lois Hawks, *Purchasing*
Terri Fogle, *Manager*
EMP: 25 **EST:** 1943
SQ FT: 18,100
SALES (est): 4.6MM **Privately Held**
SIC: 3599 Machine shop, jobbing & repair

(G-141)
DATAQ INSTRUMENTS
241 Springside Dr (44333-2432)
PHONE................................330 668-1444
Fax: 330 666-5434
John J Bowers, *President*
Karen Bowers, *Corp Secy*
Roger Lockhart, *Vice Pres*
Ken Spikowski, *Research*
Xun Chen, *Project Engr*
EMP: 15
SQ FT: 4,000
SALES (est): 3.8MM **Privately Held**
WEB: www.dataq.com
SIC: 3577 Computer peripheral equipment

(G-142)
DAVID WOLFE DESIGN INC
829 Moe Dr (44310-2516)
PHONE................................330 633-6124
Fax: 330 633-9926
David Wolfe Sr, *President*
Doug Ransdell, *Executive*
Nancy C Wolfe, *Admin Sec*
EMP: 15
SALES (est): 2MM **Privately Held**
WEB: www.davidwolfedesign.com
SIC: 7389 3089 Design, commercial & industrial; plastic processing

(G-143)
DEBS WELDING & FABRICATION
950 Rhodes Ave (44307-2262)
PHONE................................330 376-2242
Tanios Debs, *President*
EMP: 4 **EST:** 1997
SQ FT: 7,800
SALES (est): 400K **Privately Held**
SIC: 3441 Fabricated structural metal

(G-144)
DEL-TER PRECISION MACHINE INC
1038 Triplett Blvd (44306-3001)
PHONE................................330 724-9167
Fax: 330 724-8553
Terry Eddy, *President*
EMP: 5
SQ FT: 7,000
SALES (est): 587.2K **Privately Held**
SIC: 3599 Machine shop, jobbing & repair

(G-145)
DELCO CORPORATION
3300 Massillon Rd (44312-5389)
PHONE................................330 896-4220
Fax: 330 896-1608
Michael Hochschwender, *CEO*
Albert Kungl, *Vice Pres*
Dave Koszalka, *Project Mgr*
EMP: 40
SQ FT: 26,000
SALES (est): 11.8MM **Privately Held**
WEB: www.delcocorp.com
SIC: 3544 Forms (molds), for foundry & plastics working machinery; special dies & tools

(G-146)
DELCO LLC
3300 Massillon Rd (44312-5361)
PHONE................................330 896-4220
Frank Kern, *President*
Christian Kungl, *Vice Pres*
Jill McDermott, *Controller*
EMP: 35
SQ FT: 26,000
SALES (est): 1MM **Privately Held**
SIC: 3599 Machine shop, jobbing & repair

(G-147)
DESIGN FLUX TECHNOLOGIES LLC
526 S Main St Ste 108 (44311-4402)
P.O. Box 37092, Maple Heights (44137-0092)
PHONE................................216 543-6066
Terence Baptiste,
Courtney Gras,
Kent Kristensen,
Tom Vo,
EMP: 4 **EST:** 2011
SALES (est): 293.2K **Privately Held**
SIC: 3694 3621 Battery charging generators, automobile & aircraft; storage battery chargers, motor & engine generator type

(G-148)
DEXOL INDUSTRIES INC
844 E Tallmadge Ave (44310-3512)
PHONE................................330 633-4477
Fax: 330 633-4434
Marwan Ghosn, *President*
Ghassan Ghosn, *Vice Pres*
Elias Ghosn, *Shareholder*
George Ghosn, *Shareholder*
▼ **EMP:** 7
SQ FT: 12,000
SALES (est): 951.5K **Privately Held**
WEB: www.dexol.com
SIC: 3714 5013 Motor vehicle engines & parts; motor vehicle supplies & new parts

(G-149)
DIAMOND AMERICA CORPORATION
520 S Main St Ste 2456 (44311-1095)
PHONE................................330 535-3330
Fax: 330 535-3327
Jeff Schweizer, *CEO*
Kim Shaub, *Manager*
EMP: 9

SALES (est): 1.1MM **Privately Held**
WEB: www.diamondamericacorp.com
SIC: 3542 Extruding machines (machine tools), metal
PA: Akron Specialized Products Inc
96 E Miller Ave
Akron OH 44301
330 762-9269

(G-150)
DIAMOND DESIGNS INC
333 S Main St Ste B100 (44308-1205)
PHONE................................330 434-6776
Fax: 330 434-6670
Philip H Gross, *President*
Bradley Gross, *Vice Pres*
Brenda Murawski, *Office Mgr*
EMP: 8
SQ FT: 2,500
SALES (est): 1.1MM **Privately Held**
SIC: 3911 Jewelry, precious metal

(G-151)
DIDONATO PRODUCTS INC
1145 Highbrook St Ste 507 (44301-1356)
PHONE................................330 535-1119
Rudolph Didonato, *President*
Patricia Didonato, *Vice Pres*
EMP: 3
SALES (est): 265.5K **Privately Held**
SIC: 3634 Electric household cooking appliances

(G-152)
DIGITAL COLOR INTL LLC
Also Called: D C I
1653 Merriman Rd Ste 211 (44313-5276)
PHONE................................330 762-6959
Fax: 330 762-6919
Christopher Che, *CEO*
Cindy Christian, *Prdtn Mgr*
Elaine Salyer, *Accounts Mgr*
Michael Osborne, *Manager*
David Fusselman,
EMP: 43
SQ FT: 38,000
SALES (est): 8.5MM **Privately Held**
WEB: www.digitalcolorinternational.com
SIC: 7336 2653 7319 7331 Creative services to advertisers, except writers; display items, solid fiber: made from purchased materials; display advertising service; transit advertising services; direct mail advertising services; commercial printing, lithographic

(G-153)
DJ SIGNS MD LLC
224 W Exchange St Ste 290 (44302-1722)
PHONE................................330 344-6643
Gary Bollin, *Principal*
EMP: 5 **EST:** 2010
SALES (est): 248.8K **Privately Held**
SIC: 3993 Signs & advertising specialties

(G-154)
DORUM COLOR CO INC
2229 Stahl Rd (44319-1321)
PHONE................................330 773-1900
Scott Dority, *President*
EMP: 6
SQ FT: 7,000
SALES (est): 1.3MM **Privately Held**
SIC: 2865 Dyes & pigments

(G-155)
DOWCO LLC
Also Called: Finite Fibers
1374 Markle St (44306-1801)
PHONE................................330 773-6654
Keith Kleve, *President*
Todd Johnson, *Vice Pres*
Dawn Jermont, *Accounts Mgr*
Doug Terry, *Marketing Staff*
Richard Todd Downing,
▲ **EMP:** 22
SQ FT: 1,500
SALES (est): 4.6MM **Privately Held**
SIC: 2824 Nylon fibers; polyester fibers

(G-156)
DP2 ENERGY LLC
697 W Market St (44303-1450)
PHONE................................330 376-5068
Julia Norton, *Office Mgr*
EMP: 4

SALES (est): 170.8K **Privately Held**
SIC: 1389 Oil & gas wells: building, repairing & dismantling

(G-157)
DRB SYSTEMS LLC
3245 Pickle Rd (44685-5333)
P.O. Box 550, Uniontown (44685-0550)
PHONE................................330 645-3299
Fax: 330 645-2299
Dale Brott, *President*
Vincent Scovern, *Technical Mgr*
William Dietz, *Research*
James Flesher, *Engineer*
Kenneth Brott, *Treasurer*
EMP: 85
SALES (est): 20.4MM **Privately Held**
WEB: www.drbsystems.com
SIC: 7373 7371 7372 Systems software development services; custom computer programming services; prepackaged software

(G-158)
DUPONT PRFMCE ELASTOMERS LLC
Also Called: Plant 105
820 Flora Ave (44314-1722)
PHONE................................330 929-6934
Don Germano, *Branch Mgr*
EMP: 130
SALES (corp-wide): 24.5B **Publicly Held**
SIC: 2822 Synthetic rubber
HQ: Dupont Performance Elastomers L.L.C.
4417 Lancaster Pike
Wilmington DE 19805

(G-159)
E3 MATERIALS LLC
411 Wolf Ledges Pkwy (44311-1028)
PHONE................................330 972-6457
Gordon Schorr,
Wil Hemker,
EMP: 4
SALES (est): 261.5K **Privately Held**
SIC: 2899 Chemical preparations

(G-160)
EARTHQUAKER DEVICES LLC
350 W Bowery St (44307-2538)
PHONE................................330 252-9220
Jamie Stillman, *Mng Member*
Julie Robbins,
EMP: 15
SALES (est): 2MM **Privately Held**
SIC: 3931 Guitars & parts, electric & nonelectric

(G-161)
ELECTRO-MECHANICAL MFG CO INC
Also Called: Emmco
1351 S Clvlnd Mhlln Rd Ste 6 (44321)
PHONE................................330 864-0717
Fax: 330 666-2120
John Gemind, *President*
Robert Weinberg, *Manager*
Bennie L Gemind, *Admin Sec*
EMP: 4
SQ FT: 3,000
SALES (est): 557.9K **Privately Held**
WEB: www.emmcoinc.com
SIC: 3561 Pumps & pumping equipment

(G-162)
ELLET NEON SALES & SERVICE INC
Also Called: E S C
3041 E Waterloo Rd (44312-4058)
P.O. Box 6063 (44312-0063)
PHONE................................330 628-9907
Fax: 330 628-8347
Gregory Peters, *President*
Mike Croston, *Principal*
Johnathan Webb, *Principal*
Amy Yelling, *Principal*
Tom Yankovich, *VP Sls/Mktg*
EMP: 50 **EST:** 1956
SQ FT: 7,000
SALES (est): 7.9MM **Privately Held**
WEB: www.elletneon.com
SIC: 3993 Signs & advertising specialties

(G-163)
ELLORAS CAVE PUBLISHING INC
　1056 Home Ave (44310-3502)
　P.O. Box 937, Cuyahoga Falls (44223-0937)
　PHONE.....................330 253-3521
　Fax: 330 253-3531
　Patty L Marks, *CEO*
　Tina M Engler, *President*
　Raelene Gorlinsky, *Publisher*
　Christina M Brashear, *COO*
　EMP: 35
　SQ FT: 12,960
　SALES: 7MM **Privately Held**
　WEB: www.ellorascave.com
　SIC: 2741 2731 Miscellaneous publishing; book publishing

(G-164)
EMERALD PERFORMANCE MTLS LLC
　240 W Emerling Ave (44301-1620)
　PHONE.....................330 374-2418
　John Carbone, *General Mgr*
　Jeffrey Michaels, *Principal*
　Stephen Huggins, *Vice Pres*
　Jerry Lee, *Vice Pres*
　Terrence Linnert, *Vice Pres*
　EMP: 100
　SALES (corp-wide): 346.7MM **Privately Held**
　SIC: 2899 2821 Chemical preparations; plastics materials & resins
　PA: Emerald Performance Materials Llc
　　2020 Front St Ste 100
　　Cuyahoga Falls OH 44221
　　330 916-6700

(G-165)
EMERALD POLYMER ADDITIVES LLC (HQ)
　240 W Emerling Ave (44301-1620)
　PHONE.....................330 374-2424
　Tom Holleran, *President*
　EMP: 85
　SALES (est): 24.3MM
　SALES (corp-wide): 346.7MM **Privately Held**
　SIC: 2869 Industrial organic chemicals
　PA: Emerald Performance Materials Llc
　　2020 Front St Ste 100
　　Cuyahoga Falls OH 44221
　　330 916-6700

(G-166)
EMERALD SPECIALTY POLYMERS LLC
　240 W Emerling Ave (44301-1620)
　PHONE.....................330 374-2424
　Tom Holleran, *President*
　Dave Hill, *Manager*
　EMP: 30
　SALES (est): 3.4MM
　SALES (corp-wide): 346.7MM **Privately Held**
　SIC: 2821 Plastics materials & resins
　PA: Emerald Performance Materials Llc
　　2020 Front St Ste 100
　　Cuyahoga Falls OH 44221
　　330 916-6700

(G-167)
ENGINEERED PLASTICS CORP
　420 Kenmore Blvd (44301-1038)
　PHONE.....................330 376-7700
　Fax: 330 376-5811
　Jim Rauh, *President*
　Joe Raugh, *Vice Pres*
　Paullette Kray, *Manager*
　▲ EMP: 34
　SQ FT: 1,000,000
　SALES (est): 4.4MM **Privately Held**
　WEB: www.engineeredplasticscorp.com
　SIC: 3052 Plastic belting

(G-168)
ENLARGING ARTS INC
　2280 Tinkham Rd (44313-4426)
　PHONE.....................330 434-3433
　Fax: 330 464-3434
　John Welsh III, *President*
　Shirley Welsh, *Vice Pres*
　EMP: 8
　SQ FT: 10,000

SALES (est): 720K **Privately Held**
　WEB: www.enlargingarts.com
　SIC: 2752 7384 3993 7336 Commercial printing, lithographic; photofinish laboratories; signs & advertising specialties; commercial art & graphic design

(G-169)
ENTERASYS NETWORKS INC
　1093 Corsham Cir (44312-5904)
　PHONE.....................330 245-0240
　Eddie Torres, *Manager*
　EMP: 251 **Publicly Held**
　WEB: www.enterasys.com
　SIC: 3577 Computer peripheral equipment
　HQ: Enterasys Networks, Inc.
　　9 Northstern Blvd Ste 300
　　Salem NH 03079
　　603 952-5000

(G-170)
ENZYME CATALYZED POLYMERS LLC
　Also Called: Ecp
　2295 W Market St Ste D (44313-6944)
　PHONE.....................330 310-1072
　Judit Puskas, *Mng Member*
　Gabor Kaszas, *CTO*
　Matthew A Heinle,
　Susan Louscher,
　EMP: 4
　SQ FT: 1,625
　SALES (est): 121.3K **Privately Held**
　SIC: 2869 High purity grade chemicals, organic

(G-171)
EP TECHNOLOGIES LLC
　520 S Main St Ste 2455 (44311-4425)
　PHONE.....................234 208-8967
　Bob Gray, *General Mgr*
　Robert Gray,
　EMP: 14
　SALES (est): 2MM **Privately Held**
　SIC: 3845 Electrotherapeutic apparatus

(G-172)
EVENSION
　899 Moe Dr Ste 21 (44310-2599)
　PHONE.....................330 634-1430
　Brandon Ward, *Partner*
　EMP: 3 EST: 2015
　SALES (est): 148K **Privately Held**
　SIC: 3679 Electronic loads & power supplies

(G-173)
EXCHANGE PRINTING COMPANY
　969 Grant St (44311-2491)
　PHONE.....................330 773-7842
　Manuel Underdown, *President*
　Janet Bliman, *Corp Secy*
　EMP: 4 EST: 1926
　SQ FT: 8,000
　SALES (est): 370K **Privately Held**
　SIC: 2752 2759 Commercial printing, offset; letterpress printing

(G-174)
EXCHANGE SIGNS
　3152 Manchester Rd (44319-1439)
　PHONE.....................330 644-4552
　Frank Wingrove Sr, *Owner*
　EMP: 4
　SQ FT: 1,500
　SALES (est): 210K **Privately Held**
　SIC: 3993 7629 1799 Signs, not made in custom sign painting shops; electrical repair shops; sign installation & maintenance

(G-175)
EXTREME ELEMENTS
　1016 Morse St (44320-3926)
　PHONE.....................330 325-2807
　EMP: 3
　SALES (est): 230.2K **Privately Held**
　SIC: 2819 Mfg Industrial Inorganic Chemicals

(G-176)
EZ MACHINE INC
　2359 Triplett Blvd (44312-2404)
　PHONE.....................330 784-3363

Fax: 330 784-3389
　Eugene Zemlanfky, *President*
　Nancy Williams, *Office Mgr*
　EMP: 8
　SQ FT: 10,969
　SALES (est): 1MM **Privately Held**
　SIC: 3599 Machine shop, jobbing & repair

(G-177)
F M MACHINE CO
　1114 Triplett Blvd (44306-3098)
　PHONE.....................330 773-8237
　Fax: 330 773-4085
　Robert R Christian, *President*
　Joel Christian, *Vice Pres*
　Shannon Adolph, *Treasurer*
　EMP: 45 EST: 1963
　SQ FT: 36,000
　SALES (est): 12.5MM **Privately Held**
　WEB: www.fmmachine.com
　SIC: 3599 3441 Machine shop, jobbing & repair; fabricated structural metal

(G-178)
FALLS METAL FABRICATORS IND
　760 Home Ave (44310-4104)
　PHONE.....................330 253-7181
　Daniel R Pugh, *President*
　Stephanie Pugh, *Treasurer*
　Dianna Dyser, *Admin Sec*
　EMP: 13 EST: 2014
　SALES (est): 2.9MM **Privately Held**
　SIC: 3542 1542 1541 Punching, shearing & bending machines; nonresidential construction; factory construction; steel building construction; warehouse construction

(G-179)
FALLS TOOL & DIE INCORPORATED
　1416 Piedmont Ave (44310-2614)
　P.O. Box 4675 (44310-0675)
　PHONE.....................330 633-4884
　Marvin Hardy, *President*
　David Cunningham, *Controller*
　EMP: 8 EST: 1964
　SQ FT: 18,500
　SALES (est): 1.2MM **Privately Held**
　WEB: www.fallsmetalstampings.com
　SIC: 3469 3544 3465 Stamping metal for the trade; special dies & tools; automotive stampings

(G-180)
FALLS WELDING & FABG INC
　608 Grant St (44311-1502)
　PHONE.....................330 253-3437
　Ross R Holden, *President*
　Loya Candy, *Manager*
　Theresa Holden, *Admin Sec*
　▲ EMP: 7 EST: 1942
　SQ FT: 11,000
　SALES (est): 500K **Privately Held**
　WEB: www.fallsweldingandfab.com
　SIC: 3841 3537 3443 3441 Surgical & medical instruments; industrial trucks & tractors; fabricated plate work (boiler shop); fabricated structural metal

(G-181)
FAMOUS INDUSTRIES INC (HQ)
　Also Called: Johnson Contrls Authorized Dlr
　2620 Ridgewood Rd Ste 200 (44313-3507)
　PHONE.....................330 535-1811
　Fax: 330 353-5057
　Jay Blaushild, *President*
　Marc Blaushild, *Vice Pres*
　CAM Jordan, *Technical Mgr*
　EMP: 50
　SALES (est): 80.3MM **Privately Held**
　WEB: www.jfgoodco.com
　SIC: 5074 3444 5065 Plumbing & hydronic heating supplies; plumbing & heating valves; metal ventilating equipment; telephone equipment; intercommunication equipment, electronic

(G-182)
FASTENAL COMPANY
　2465 Romig Rd (44320-3826)
　PHONE.....................330 745-2996
　Scott Feathers, *Manager*
　EMP: 3
　SQ FT: 102,176

SALES (corp-wide): 3.9B **Publicly Held**
　WEB: www.fastenal.com
　SIC: 5085 5082 3471 Fasteners, industrial: nuts, bolts, screws, etc.; masonry equipment & supplies; plating & polishing
　PA: Fastenal Company
　　2001 Theurer Blvd
　　Winona MN 55987
　　507 454-5374

(G-183)
FEDEX OFFICE & PRINT SVCS INC
　322 E Exchange St (44304-1761)
　PHONE.....................330 376-6002
　Adam Mann, *Branch Mgr*
　EMP: 16
　SALES (corp-wide): 50.3B **Publicly Held**
　WEB: www.kinkos.com
　SIC: 7334 2752 Photocopying & duplicating services; commercial printing, lithographic
　HQ: Fedex Office And Print Services, Inc.
　　7900 Legacy Dr
　　Plano TX 75024
　　214 550-7000

(G-184)
FENIX FABRICATION INC
　2689 Wingate Ave (44314-1301)
　PHONE.....................330 745-8731
　Fax: 330 777-5714
　Christopher J Forgan, *President*
　Anthony Leipold, *Vice Pres*
　EMP: 37
　SALES (est): 9MM **Privately Held**
　SIC: 3441 Fabricated structural metal

(G-185)
FERRIOT INC
　1000 Arlington Cir (44306-3973)
　P.O. Box 7670 (44306-0670)
　PHONE.....................330 786-3000
　Fax: 330 786-3001
　Gordon Keeler, *CEO*
　Chip Keeler, *COO*
　Craig Ferriot, *Vice Pres*
　David Ferriot, *Vice Pres*
　Robert Brook, *Maint Spvr*
　▲ EMP: 170 EST: 1929
　SQ FT: 220,000
　SALES (est): 58MM **Privately Held**
　WEB: www.ferriot.com
　SIC: 3089 3544 Injection molding of plastics; injection molded finished plastic products; industrial molds

(G-186)
FIERY CHILLCOM
　515 E Turkeyfoot Lake Rd (44319-4102)
　PHONE.....................800 575-4180
　Rob Winings, *Principal*
　EMP: 4
　SALES (est): 300K **Privately Held**
　SIC: 3423 Hammers (hand tools)

(G-187)
FIRESTONE POLYMERS LLC (DH)
　381 W Wilbeth Rd (44301-2465)
　P.O. Box 26611 (44319-6611)
　PHONE.....................330 379-7000
　Cheryl Thomas, *Credit Mgr*
　Margaret J Koliha, *Manager*
　Hiroshi Mouri,
　◆ EMP: 73
　SALES (est): 198.4MM
　SALES (corp-wide): 30.1B **Privately Held**
　WEB: www.firesyn.com
　SIC: 3069 Latex, foamed
　HQ: Bridgestone Procurement Holdings Usa, Inc.
　　381 W Wilbeth Rd
　　Akron OH 44301
　　337 882-1200

(G-188)
FIRST MERIT
　106 S Main St Fl 6 (44308-1442)
　PHONE.....................330 849-8750
　Fax: 330 384-7271
　Paul Greig, *CEO*
　Kathleen McGraw, *Vice Pres*
　EMP: 4

SALES (est): 569.2K **Privately Held**
SIC: 3944 6311 Banks, toy; life insurance carriers

(G-189)
FIRSTNRGY NCLEAR GNRATION CORP
76 S Main St Bsmt (44308-1817)
PHONE..................................330 761-4370
Joseph J Hagan, *President*
EMP: 6
SALES (est): 492K
SALES (corp-wide): 14.5B **Publicly Held**
SIC: 3443 Nuclear reactors, military or industrial
HQ: Firstenergy Solutions Corp.
76 S Main St Bsmt
Akron OH 44308
800 736-3402

(G-190)
FLEXSYS AMERICA LP (DH)
260 Springside Dr (44333-4554)
PHONE..................................330 666-4111
Fax: 330 688-8345
Enrique Bolanos, *CEO*
James Voss, *President*
Steve Wiliamson, *Purchasing*
Frederick Ignatz-Hoover, *Adv Mgr*
Dennis Hay, *Manager*
▼ EMP: 65
SQ FT: 85,000
SALES (est): 20.4MM
SALES (corp-wide): 9B **Publicly Held**
SIC: 3069 8731 2899 2823 Reclaimed rubber & specialty rubber compounds; commercial physical research; chemical preparations; cellulosic manmade fibers; synthetic rubber; plastics materials & resins
HQ: Solutia Inc.
575 Maryville Centre Dr
Saint Louis MO 63141
423 229-2000

(G-191)
FLOWERS BAKERIES LLC
1500 Firestone Pkwy (44301-1677)
PHONE..................................330 724-1604
EMP: 49
SALES (corp-wide): 3.9B **Publicly Held**
SIC: 2051 Bread, cake & related products
HQ: Flowers Bakeries, Llc
1919 Flowers Cir
Thomasville GA 31757
229 226-9110

(G-192)
FLUENCE THERAPEUTICS
526 S Main St Ste 608c (44311-4404)
PHONE..................................216 780-5220
Shauna R Brummet, *Principal*
Warren Goldenberg, *Info Tech Mgr*
Thomas McCormick, *Info Tech Mgr*
EMP: 3
SALES (est): 169.3K **Privately Held**
SIC: 2834 Pharmaceutical preparations

(G-193)
FOUNDATION INDUSTRIES INC (PA)
Also Called: F I C
880 W Waterloo Rd Ste B (44314-1519)
PHONE..................................330 564-1250
Fax: 330 564-1251
Richard Huscroft, *President*
Terry Carey, *Sales Staff*
▼ EMP: 75
SQ FT: 109,000
SALES (est): 20.3MM **Privately Held**
WEB: www.foundationindustries.com
SIC: 3089 Engraving of plastic; injection molding of plastics

(G-194)
FRIESS EQUIPMENT INC
2222 Akron Peninsula Rd (44313-4806)
PHONE..................................330 945-9440
Fax: 330 923-5833
James Friess, *President*
EMP: 4
SQ FT: 1,000
SALES (est): 670K **Privately Held**
SIC: 5084 3599 3589 Machine tools & metalworking machinery; custom machinery; commercial cleaning equipment

(G-195)
FRIESS WELDING INC
Also Called: Summit Trailer Sales & Svcs
3342 S Main St (44319-3099)
PHONE..................................330 644-8160
Fax: 330 644-0547
Russell C Friess, *CEO*
Jeff Friess, *President*
Betty Friess, *Corp Secy*
EMP: 11 EST: 1968
SQ FT: 7,000
SALES (est): 1.1MM **Privately Held**
WEB: www.summittrailers.com
SIC: 7692 7539 5511 Welding repair; radiator repair shop, automotive; trailer repair; trucks, tractors & trailers: new & used

(G-196)
FUTURE POS OHIO INC
2561 S Arlington Rd (44319-2007)
PHONE..................................330 645-6623
Steve Pritchard, *President*
Scott Pritchard, *Vice Pres*
Sandy Silasi, *Manager*
EMP: 13
SQ FT: 3,500
SALES: 2MM **Privately Held**
WEB: www.futurepos.com
SIC: 3695 Computer software tape & disks: blank, rigid & floppy

(G-197)
GABRIEL PERFORMANCE PDTS LLC (HQ)
388 S Main St (44311-1064)
PHONE..................................440 992-3200
Seth Tomasch, *CEO*
Ken Allen, *President*
Vern Sebbio, *CFO*
Marty Zioka, *Accounting Mgr*
▲ EMP: 7
SALES (est): 4MM
SALES (corp-wide): 14.4MM **Privately Held**
WEB: www.gabepro.com
SIC: 2819 Chemicals, high purity: refined from technical grade
PA: Edgewater Capital Partners, L.P.
5005 Rockside Rd Ste 840
Independence OH 44131
216 292-3838

(G-198)
GARRO TREAD CORPORATION (PA)
Also Called: Ace Rubber Products Division
100 Beech St (44308-1916)
PHONE..................................330 376-3125
Fax: 330 376-3470
Charles Garro, *President*
Greg Garro, *Vice Pres*
EMP: 9 EST: 1980
SQ FT: 100,000
SALES: 2MM **Privately Held**
SIC: 3069 5531 Mats or matting, rubber; stair treads, rubber; floor coverings, rubber; automotive tires

(G-199)
GATEWAY INDUSTRIES
1236 Brittain Rd (44310-3704)
PHONE..................................330 633-3700
Paul Kasmar, *President*
Stephen Sweezey, *Treasurer*
▼ EMP: 5
SQ FT: 6,000
SALES (est): 1.5MM **Privately Held**
WEB: www.gatewayindustriesonline.com
SIC: 3463 Aluminum forgings

(G-200)
GEAR STAR AMERICAN PERFORMANCE
132 N Howard St (44308-1937)
PHONE..................................330 434-5216
Fax: 330 434-3634
Zack Farah, *President*
Derek Kriebel, *Principal*
◆ EMP: 6
SALES: 1.5MM **Privately Held**
SIC: 3714 5571 5013 Motor vehicle transmissions, drive assemblies & parts; motorcycle parts & accessories; motor vehicle supplies & new parts

(G-201)
GEARHART MACHINE COMPANY
1145 Highbrook St Ste 508 (44301-1356)
PHONE..................................330 253-1880
Patrick Casto, *President*
Becki Casto, *Admin Sec*
EMP: 3
SQ FT: 4,000
SALES: 100K **Privately Held**
SIC: 3599 Machine shop, jobbing & repair

(G-202)
GEHM & SONS LIMITED (PA)
825 S Arlington St (44306-2498)
PHONE..................................330 724-8423
Fax: 330 724-1939
Juanita Gehm, *President*
EMP: 6
SQ FT: 5,780
SALES (est): 2.2MM **Privately Held**
SIC: 5145 2086 5169 Syrups, fountain; carbonated beverages, nonalcoholic: bottled & canned; dry ice

(G-203)
GENERAL METALS POWDER CO (PA)
Also Called: Gempco
1195 Home Ave (44310-2576)
PHONE..................................330 633-1226
Fax: 330 630-2028
Jerry Lynch, *President*
Richard Carr, *Editor*
Barry P Alvord, *Vice Pres*
Louis L Cseko Jr, *Vice Pres*
Rick Cardarelli, *VP Mfg*
EMP: 55 EST: 1929
SQ FT: 30,000
SALES (est): 11.1MM **Privately Held**
WEB: www.gmpfriction.com
SIC: 3499 3714 3568 Friction material, made from powdered metal; motor vehicle parts & accessories; power transmission equipment

(G-204)
GENESCO INC
Also Called: Lids
2000 Brittain Rd Ste 681 (44310-4309)
PHONE..................................330 633-8179
Lee Friedman, *Branch Mgr*
EMP: 5
SALES (corp-wide): 2.8B **Publicly Held**
WEB: www.genesco.com
SIC: 2353 Hats & caps
PA: Genesco Inc.
1415 Murfreesboro Pike
Nashville TN 37217
615 367-7000

(G-205)
GENTZLER TOOL & DIE CORP (PA)
3903 Massillon Rd (44312)
P.O. Box 158, Green (44232-0158)
PHONE..................................330 896-1941
Fax: 330 896-4772
David W Gentzler, *President*
Geraldine Gentzler, *President*
David Gentzler, *Vice Pres*
David Newburner, *Plant Mgr*
Lisa Hinton, *Manager*
EMP: 20 EST: 1953
SQ FT: 20,000
SALES (est): 2.9MM **Privately Held**
SIC: 3469 3544 Metal stampings; special dies & tools

(G-206)
GOJO INDUSTRIES INC (PA)
1 Gojo Plz Ste 500 (44311-1085)
P.O. Box 991 (44309-0991)
PHONE..................................330 255-6000
Fax: 330 255-6114
Joseph Kanfer, *Ch of Bd*
Mark Lerner, *President*
Neil Wyant, *Managing Dir*
Bruce Martino, *Counsel*
Geoff Belz, *Vice Pres*
◆ EMP: 200
SQ FT: 500,000

SALES (est): 305.9MM **Privately Held**
WEB: www.gojo.com
SIC: 2842 3586 2844 Specialty cleaning, polishes & sanitation goods; measuring & dispensing pumps; toilet preparations

(G-207)
GOODYEAR TIRE & RUBBER COMPANY (PA)
200 E Innovation Way (44316-0001)
PHONE..................................330 796-2121
Fax: 330 796-3183
Richard J Kramer, *Ch of Bd*
Christopher R Delaney, *President*
Jean-Claude Kihn, *President*
Stephen R McClellan, *President*
Paul Fitzhenry, *Senior VP*
EMP: 3000 EST: 1898
SALES: 15.1B **Publicly Held**
WEB: www.goodyear.com
SIC: 3011 3052 7534 7538 Tires & inner tubes; inner tubes, all types; pneumatic tires, all types; tire & inner tube materials & related products; rubber & plastics hose & beltings; automobile hose, rubber; rubber belting; tire retreading & repair shops; rebuilding & retreading tires; general automotive repair shops; truck engine repair, except industrial; automotive repair shops; brake services; shock absorber replacement; tune-up service, automotive; motor vehicle supplies & new parts; automotive servicing equipment; automotive supplies & parts

(G-208)
GUARI INC
2215 E Waterloo Rd # 101 (44312-3818)
PHONE..................................330 733-4005
Darrell N Guariniello, *President*
Gerald J Cahill, *Principal*
Patrick J Cahill, *Principal*
India A Key, *Principal*
EMP: 4
SALES (est): 451.3K **Privately Held**
SIC: 2121 Cigars

(G-209)
H & H MACHINE SHOP AKRON INC
955 Grant St (44311-2490)
PHONE..................................330 773-3327
Fax: 330 773-6820
Henry R Haas, *President*
Debbie D'Amicone, *Vice Pres*
Don O'Brien, *Office Mgr*
Don Obrian, *Director*
Anna Haas, *Admin Sec*
EMP: 21 EST: 1959
SQ FT: 24,000
SALES (est): 4.1MM **Privately Held**
WEB: www.hhmachineshopofakron.com
SIC: 3599 7692 Machine shop, jobbing & repair; welding repair

(G-210)
H & M METAL PROCESSING CO
1414 Kenmore Blvd (44314-1600)
PHONE..................................330 745-3075
Fax: 330 745-3160
Robert McMillen, *President*
Julie West, *Manager*
Alexandra Evanko, *Shareholder*
Ben McMillen, *Shareholder*
Robert McMillen IV, *Shareholder*
EMP: 23 EST: 1942
SQ FT: 7,000
SALES: 12.2MM **Privately Held**
WEB: www.handmmetal.com
SIC: 3398 Metal heat treating

(G-211)
HALLER ENTERPRISES INC
1621 E Market St (44305-4210)
PHONE..................................330 733-9693
David Haller, *President*
Daid Haller, *Vice Pres*
Harriet Haller, *Vice Pres*
EMP: 10
SQ FT: 6,000
SALES (est): 1.1MM **Privately Held**
WEB: www.hallerenterprises.com
SIC: 2097 5999 Manufactured ice; ice

(G-212)
HAMLIN NEWCO LLC
2741 Wingate Ave (44314-1301)
PHONE.................................330 753-7791
Brian Zeh, *VP Opers*
Dave Oneil, *Safety Mgr*
Lai D Teckchandani,
Charles N Biehara,
EMP: 52
SQ FT: 110
SALES (est): 16MM Privately Held
SIC: 3469 Machine parts, stamped or
pressed metal

(G-213)
HAMLIN STEEL PRODUCTS LLC
2741 Wingate Ave (44314-1301)
PHONE.................................330 753-7791
Fax: 330 753-5577
Bob Buzzard, *Plant Mgr*
Catherine Burkhart, *Manager*
Marion Stokes, *Manager*
Lal Teckchandani,
EMP: 75 EST: 1978
SQ FT: 110,000
SALES (est): 13.7MM Privately Held
WEB: www.featherheadproductions.com
SIC: 3469 Metal stampings

(G-214)
HANGER PRSTHETCS & ORTHO INC
61 N Clvlnd Msslln Rd C (44333)
PHONE.................................330 670-8263
EMP: 7
SALES (corp-wide): 460MM Publicly
Held
SIC: 3842 Limbs, artificial
HQ: Hanger Prosthetics & Orthotics, Inc.
10910 Domain Dr Ste 300
Austin TX 78758
512 777-3800

(G-215)
HANGER PRSTHETCS & ORTHO INC
388 S Main St Ste 205 (44311-1035)
PHONE.................................330 374-9544
Frank Coptolino, *Manager*
Beth Orzell, *Manager*
EMP: 3
SALES (corp-wide): 460MM Publicly
Held
SIC: 3842 5099 Limbs, artificial; firearms
& ammunition, except sporting
HQ: Hanger Prosthetics & Orthotics, Inc.
10910 Domain Dr Ste 300
Austin TX 78758
512 777-3800

(G-216)
HARRY C LOBALZO & SONS INC (PA)
Also Called: Hobart Sales & Service
61 N Cleveland Ste A (44333)
PHONE.................................330 666-6758
Fax: 330 666-8645
Harry C Lobalzo, *President*
Rick Lobalzo, *Exec VP*
Douglas Fox, *Financial Exec*
Dana Saporito, *Mktg Dir*
Dina Saprido, *Manager*
▲ EMP: 35
SQ FT: 20,000
SALES: 5.4MM Privately Held
WEB: www.lobalzo.com
SIC: 5046 7699 3556 Commercial cook-
ing & food service equipment; bakery
equipment & supplies; restaurant equip-
ment repair; food products machinery

(G-217)
HAWK MANUFACTURING LLC
Also Called: S. C. Manufacturing
2642 Gilchrist Rd (44305-4412)
PHONE.................................330 784-6234
Fax: 330 784-7291
Leonard Errington, *Manager*
EMP: 15
SALES (corp-wide): 18.2MM Privately
Held
SIC: 3599 Machine shop, jobbing & repair

HQ: Hawk Manufacturing, Llc
380 Kennedy Rd
Akron OH 44305
330 784-3151

(G-218)
HAWK MANUFACTURING LLC (HQ)
Also Called: S. C. Manufacturing
380 Kennedy Rd (44305-4422)
PHONE.................................330 784-3151
Fax: 330 784-2208
Carl Harbert, *Partner*
Gary Worner, *Partner*
Randy Carpenter, *Safety Mgr*
EMP: 57
SQ FT: 33,624
SALES (est): 18.2MM Privately Held
SIC: 3542 3541 3599 Mechanical (pneu-
matic or hydraulic) metal forming ma-
chines; machine tools, metal cutting type;
drilling & boring machines; milling ma-
chines; machine & other job shop work;
machine shop, jobbing & repair
PA: New Growth Capital Group, Llc
380 Kennedy Rd
Akron OH 44305
216 630-0873

(G-219)
HAWK MANUFACTURING LLC
Also Called: S. C. Manufacturing
382 Kennedy Rd (44305)
PHONE.................................330 784-4815
Fax: 330 784-5606
Luke Mitchell, *General Mgr*
EMP: 11
SALES (corp-wide): 18.2MM Privately
Held
SIC: 3599 3541 Machine shop, jobbing &
repair; machine tools, metal cutting type
HQ: Hawk Manufacturing, Llc
380 Kennedy Rd
Akron OH 44305
330 784-3151

(G-220)
HENNACY MACHINE COMPANY INC
1209 Triplett Blvd (44306-3030)
PHONE.................................330 785-2940
Fax: 330 785-1993
James Hennacy, *President*
EMP: 4
SALES (est): 410K Privately Held
SIC: 3599 Machine shop, jobbing & repair

(G-221)
HERBERT MACHINE WORKS INC
1480 Industrial Pkwy (44310-2602)
PHONE.................................330 929-4297
Mathias Walter, *President*
Janet Elmore, *Manager*
Randy Jarvis, *Manager*
Todd Jarvis, *Admin Sec*
▲ EMP: 55
SQ FT: 25,000
SALES: 8MM Privately Held
SIC: 3544 Industrial molds

(G-222)
HERITAGE INDUSTRIAL FINSHG INC
1874 Englewood Ave (44312-1002)
PHONE.................................330 798-9840
Fax: 330 798-0227
Nicholas Pamboukis, *CEO*
Russell Kemppel, *President*
Roland Ciha, *General Mgr*
Agathonico Pamboukis, *Chairman*
Roberta French, *Corp Secy*
EMP: 58
SQ FT: 35,000
SALES (est): 8.2MM Privately Held
SIC: 3479 Painting of metal products

(G-223)
HERITAGE MANUFACTURING INC
Also Called: Schien Equipment Company
1600 E Waterloo Rd (44306-4103)
PHONE.................................217 854-2513
Thomas Ottersburg, *General Mgr*
Eric Bontrager, *Principal*

EMP: 5 EST: 2012
SALES (est): 1.3MM Privately Held
SIC: 3715 Trailer bodies

(G-224)
HOWDEN NORTH AMERICA INC
260 Springside Dr (44333-2433)
PHONE.................................330 867-8540
EMP: 92
SALES (corp-wide): 3.6B Publicly Held
SIC: 3564 3822 Blowers & fans; purifica-
tion & dust collection equipment; damper
operators: pneumatic, thermostatic, elec-
tric
HQ: Howden North America Inc.
2475 George Urban Blvd # 120
Depew NY 14043
803 741-2700

(G-225)
HUNNELL ELECTRIC CO INC
Also Called: Hunnell Electric Motor Repair
950 Grant St (44311-2487)
PHONE.................................330 773-8278
Michael Coughenour, *President*
Gail Coughenour, *Vice Pres*
EMP: 5
SQ FT: 10,000
SALES (est): 550K Privately Held
SIC: 7694 5063 Electric motor repair; mo-
tors, electric

(G-226)
HYDRATECS INJECTION EQP CO
430 Morgan Ave (44311-2432)
P.O. Box 26338 (44319-6338)
PHONE.................................330 773-0491
Fax: 330 773-3800
Karl Barkey, *President*
Caroline Delgado, *Manager*
Rebecca Barkey, *Admin Sec*
EMP: 4
SALES (est): 680.4K Privately Held
SIC: 3559 Rubber working machinery, in-
cluding tires

(G-227)
HYDROGEN ENERGY SYSTEMS LLC
12 E Exchange St Fl 8 (44308-1541)
PHONE.................................330 236-0358
Kevin Davis, *General Counsel*
Rosemary Ohara,
Rick Saccone,
Jeffrey Wilhite,
EMP: 5
SALES (est): 187K Privately Held
SIC: 2813 Hydrogen

(G-228)
HYGENIC ACQUISITION CO
1245 Home Ave (44310-2510)
P.O. Box 1818 (44309-1818)
PHONE.................................330 633-8460
Stewart Lorenzen, *CEO*
Earl Decarli, *President*
Jeffery Sullivan, *Engrg Dir*
Harold Baker, *VP Sls/Mktg*
Kurt Marhoefer, *CFO*
EMP: 125
SQ FT: 135,000
SALES (est): 6.6MM
SALES (corp-wide): 641.3MM Privately
Held
WEB: www.hygenic.com
SIC: 3061 3069 Mechanical rubber goods;
medical & laboratory rubber sundries &
related products
HQ: Baird Capital Partners Management
Company, Iii Llc
777 E Wisconsin Ave # 2900
Milwaukee WI 53202
414 765-3500

(G-229)
HYGENIC CORPORATION (HQ)
1245 Home Ave (44310-2575)
P.O. Box 1818 (44309-1818)
PHONE.................................330 633-8460
Fax: 330 633-9359
Marshall Dahneke, *President*
Kathy Yoder, *Senior VP*
Ralph Buster, *Vice Pres*
Dwayne Hofstatter, *Vice Pres*
Bob Poirier, *Vice Pres*

◆ EMP: 125
SQ FT: 135,000
SALES (est): 93.8MM
SALES (corp-wide): 125.7MM Privately
Held
SIC: 3069 3061 Medical & laboratory rub-
ber sundries & related products; mechani-
cal rubber goods
PA: Cogrr, Inc.
200 Park Ave Fl 20
New York NY 10166
212 370-5600

(G-230)
IMPORTERS DIRECT LLC
1559 S Main St (44301-1632)
PHONE.................................330 436-3260
Timothy Adkins, *President*
EMP: 22 EST: 2008
SQ FT: 15,400
SALES (est): 5MM Privately Held
SIC: 1731 3648 7359 3646 Sound equip-
ment specialization; stage lighting equip-
ment; sound & lighting equipment rental;
commercial indusl & institutional electric
lighting fixtures

(G-231)
IN BOX PUBLICATIONS LLC
977 Hampton Ridge Dr (44313-5087)
PHONE.................................330 592-4288
Robert Almenar, *Owner*
EMP: 3
SALES (est): 165.7K Privately Held
SIC: 2721 Periodicals

(G-232)
INDUSTRIAL TECHNOLOGIES INC
1643 Massillon Rd (44312-4204)
PHONE.................................330 434-2033
Gregg Caprez, *President*
Michelle H Caprez, *Vice Pres*
EMP: 7
SQ FT: 3,000
SALES: 800K Privately Held
SIC: 3543 Industrial patterns

(G-233)
INTEGRITY PRINT SOLUTIONS INC
567 E Turkeyfoot Lake Rd (44319-4107)
PHONE.................................330 818-0161
Gary Mosteller, *President*
EMP: 4
SALES (est): 478.7K Privately Held
WEB: www.integrityprintsolutions.com
SIC: 2752 Commercial printing, litho-
graphic

(G-234)
INTELLIROD SPINE INC
554 White Pond Dr Ste F (44320-1146)
PHONE.................................234 678-8965
Richard Navarro, *CEO*
EMP: 4
SALES (est): 410K Privately Held
SIC: 3841 Surgical & medical instruments

(G-235)
INTERNATIONAL GRINDING INC
1811 Orchard Dr (44333-1850)
PHONE.................................330 659-0220
Fax: 330 659-4476
John L Mruk, *President*
Carrie Mruk, *Vice Pres*
Jennifer Dabernig, *Shareholder*
Dave Mruk, *Shareholder*
EMP: 9
SQ FT: 7,500
SALES (est): 770K Privately Held
SIC: 3599 Machine shop, jobbing & repair

(G-236)
INVISIBLE REPAIR PRODUCTS INC
1021 Evans Ave (44305-1020)
PHONE.................................330 798-0441
Melissa L Speer, *President*
EMP: 5
SQ FT: 15,000
SALES (est): 570K Privately Held
SIC: 2891 Adhesives

(G-237)
IVAN EXTRUDERS CO INC
Also Called: Siegfried
2404 Pickle Rd (44312-4227)
PHONE..................................330 644-7400
Keith Sigfreud, *President*
EMP: 4
SQ FT: 4,500
SALES (est): 420K **Privately Held**
WEB: www.ivanextruders.com
SIC: 3452 7699 3599 Screws, metal; industrial machinery & equipment repair; machine shop, jobbing & repair

(G-238)
JADLYN INC
Also Called: Today's Bride Magazine
1930 N Clvland Mssllon Rd (44333-1817)
PHONE..................................330 670-9545
Jim Frericks, *President*
Denise Frericks, *Vice Pres*
Alec Pegler, *Sales Staff*
Colleen Ahern, *Office Mgr*
Jennifer Fyffe, *Manager*
EMP: 5
SALES: 600K **Privately Held**
WEB: www.todaysbrideshows.com
SIC: 2721 Magazines: publishing only, not printed on site

(G-239)
JILCO PRECISION MOLD & MCH CO
1245 Devalera St (44310-2457)
PHONE..................................330 633-9645
Fax: 330 633-9640
John Shepherd, *President*
Shirley Shepherd, *Admin Sec*
EMP: 6
SQ FT: 3,300
SALES: 250K **Privately Held**
SIC: 3599 Machine shop, jobbing & repair; custom machinery

(G-240)
JJC PRODUCTS INC
3670 Forest Oaks Dr (44333-9236)
PHONE..................................330 666-4582
James Costigan, *Principal*
Jerry Costigan, *Principal*
EMP: 3
SALES (est): 263.4K **Privately Held**
SIC: 3089 Plastics products

(G-241)
JONATHAN BISHOP
Also Called: Bishop International
200 Hampshire Rd (44313-4304)
PHONE..................................330 836-6947
Jonathan Bishop, *Owner*
EMP: 4
SALES: 500K **Privately Held**
WEB: www.jonathanbishop.com
SIC: 3728 Aircraft parts & equipment

(G-242)
JORDAN E ARMOUR
Also Called: Union Sewing Company
1145 Highbrook St Ste 103 (44301-1357)
PHONE..................................330 252-0290
Jordan Armour, *Owner*
EMP: 50
SQ FT: 700
SALES (est): 2.3MM **Privately Held**
SIC: 2393 Textile bags

(G-243)
JRB ATTACHMENTS LLC (DH)
820 Glaser Pkwy (44306-4133)
PHONE..................................330 734-3000
Fax: 330 734-3019
Steve Andrews, *CEO*
Paul Burton, *Vice Pres*
Gale Dilday, *Vice Pres*
Michael Flannery, *Vice Pres*
Wendell Moss, *Vice Pres*
▲ EMP: 7
SALES (est): 38MM
SALES (corp-wide): 2.3B **Privately Held**
WEB: www.paladinbrands.com
SIC: 3531 Construction machinery attachments
HQ: Paladin Brands Group, Inc.
    2800 Zeeb Rd
    Dexter MI 48130
    319 378-3696

(G-244)
JRW MANUFACTURING
667 Killian Rd (44319-2527)
PHONE..................................330 628-2994
Squires Roibert, *Principal*
EMP: 3
SALES (est): 176.9K **Privately Held**
SIC: 3999 Manufacturing industries

(G-245)
JSC EMPLOYEE LEASING CORP (PA)
1560 Firestone Pkwy (44301-1626)
PHONE..................................330 773-8971
Jack Jeter, *President*
Pam Love, *Exec VP*
Brian McCann, *Sales Executive*
Nicholas George, *Admin Sec*
EMP: 18
SQ FT: 150,000
SALES (est): 25MM **Privately Held**
WEB: www.jetersystems.com
SIC: 2522 5021 Office cabinets & filing drawers: except wood; filing units

(G-246)
K F D INC
39 Alice Dr Unit B (44319-1163)
PHONE..................................330 773-4300
David K Friddle, *President*
EMP: 3
SQ FT: 10,000
SALES (est): 332.9K **Privately Held**
WEB: www.foamedge.com
SIC: 3069 Molded rubber products

(G-247)
K K RACING CHASSIS
485 Taylor Ave (44312-3548)
PHONE..................................330 628-2930
Kenneth Kennedy, *Owner*
EMP: 3
SQ FT: 2,400
SALES (est): 214.9K **Privately Held**
SIC: 3711 Automobile assembly, including specialty automobiles

(G-248)
KAMAN FLUID POWER LLC
195 S Main St Ste 400 (44308-1314)
PHONE..................................330 315-3100
Neal Keating, *President*
EMP: 5
SALES (corp-wide): 1.8B **Publicly Held**
SIC: 3492 Hose & tube fittings & assemblies, hydraulic/pneumatic
HQ: Kaman Fluid Power, Llc
    1 Vision Way
    Bloomfield CT 06002
    860 243-7100

(G-249)
KANE SIGN CO
486 E Glenwood Ave (44310-3421)
PHONE..................................330 253-5263
Fax: 330 253-6730
Michael Kane, *Owner*
EMP: 3
SQ FT: 7,320
SALES (est): 210K **Privately Held**
WEB: www.kanesign.com
SIC: 3993 Signs & advertising specialties

(G-250)
KARDER MACHINE CO (PA)
2680 Waltham Rd (44313-4220)
PHONE..................................330 253-3377
Fax: 330 253-6320
Daniel Abraham, *President*
Genny Karder, *Corp Secy*
Gary Riffle, *Sales Staff*
EMP: 40
SQ FT: 252,000
SALES (est): 6.6MM **Privately Held**
SIC: 3599 Machine shop, jobbing & repair

(G-251)
KARMAN RUBBER COMPANY (PA)
2331 Copley Rd (44320-1499)
PHONE..................................330 864-2161
Fax: 330 864-2124
David W Mann, *President*
M Toomey, *General Mgr*
G Jay Hearty, *Vice Pres*
Greg Paxson, *Plant Mgr*
John Lynch, *Purch Agent*
EMP: 49 EST: 1945
SQ FT: 55,000
SALES (est): 7MM **Privately Held**
WEB: www.karman.com
SIC: 3069 3829 3822 3061 Molded rubber products; measuring & controlling devices; auto controls regulating residntl & coml environmt & applncs; mechanical rubber goods

(G-252)
KEN-DAL CORPORATION
644 Killian Rd (44319-2599)
PHONE..................................330 644-7118
Fax: 330 644-2703
William Keasling, *President*
Alan Place, *Vice Pres*
▲ EMP: 10 EST: 1962
SQ FT: 12,000
SALES (est): 1.4MM **Privately Held**
SIC: 3599 Machine shop, jobbing & repair

(G-253)
KENMORE DEVELOPMENT & MCH CO
1395 Kenmore Blvd (44314-1658)
PHONE..................................330 753-2274
Fax: 330 753-2401
Richard Roten, *President*
EMP: 10 EST: 1939
SQ FT: 20,000
SALES (est): 1.4MM **Privately Held**
WEB: www.allwny.com
SIC: 3599 Machine shop, jobbing & repair

(G-254)
KENMORE GEAR & MACHINE CO INC
1519 Kenmore Blvd (44314-1661)
P.O. Box 3807 (44314-0807)
PHONE..................................330 753-6671
Fax: 330 753-0371
David Ingham Jr, *President*
Pamela S Ballinger, *Vice Pres*
Gary Ballinger, *Treasurer*
EMP: 7 EST: 1926
SQ FT: 9,352
SALES (est): 1.2MM **Privately Held**
SIC: 3566 Speed changers, drives & gears

(G-255)
KENT STOW SCREEN PRINTING INC
Also Called: Mascot Shop, The
1340 Home Ave Ste F (44310-2570)
PHONE..................................330 923-5118
William C Sauders, *President*
EMP: 14
SQ FT: 3,000
SALES: 1MM **Privately Held**
SIC: 7336 2396 Silk screen design; automotive & apparel trimmings

(G-256)
KILLIAN LATEX INC
2064 Killian Rd (44312-4897)
PHONE..................................330 644-6746
Fax: 330 644-4431
Timothy J Killian, *President*
Dave Schuck, *QC Mgr*
Sara Benoit, *Executive*
Joan Faith, *Admin Sec*
Joan Killian Fisk, *Admin Sec*
▲ EMP: 15
SQ FT: 65,000
SALES (est): 3.5MM **Privately Held**
WEB: www.killianlatex.com
SIC: 3069 3087 Custom compounding of rubber materials; custom compound purchased resins

(G-257)
KILTEX CORPORATION
2064 Killian Rd (44312-4830)
PHONE..................................330 644-6746
Timothy J Killian, *President*
Joan Killian-Fisk, *Corp Secy*
EMP: 20
SALES (est): 1.9MM **Privately Held**
SIC: 3069 Custom compounding of rubber materials

(G-258)
KING MACHINE OF AKRON INC
Also Called: King Machine of NC
365 Kenmore Blvd (44301-1095)
PHONE..................................330 762-7116
Fax: 330 762-7407
Gifford Wells, *President*
Belinda Crosby, *Engineer*
John Napier, *Engineer*
Laurie Akers, *Manager*
Don Boysel, *Manager*
EMP: 33 EST: 1951
SQ FT: 28,000
SALES (est): 4.3MM **Privately Held**
SIC: 3544 Industrial molds

(G-259)
KING MODEL COMPANY
Also Called: King Castings
365 Kenmore Blvd (44301-1053)
PHONE..................................330 633-0491
Fax: 330 633-0657
Michael Wells, *President*
Gifford Wells, *President*
John Horrell, *Vice Pres*
Carol Bray, *Office Mgr*
EMP: 31
SQ FT: 15,000
SALES (est): 4.3MM **Privately Held**
WEB: www.kingcastings.com
SIC: 3999 Models, general, except toy

(G-260)
KIT MB SYSTEMS INC
Also Called: Item North America
925 Glaser Pkwy (44306-4161)
PHONE..................................330 945-4500
Eveline Nordhauss, *President*
Mike Nordhauss, *Vice Pres*
Rick Fascione, *Draft/Design*
Kevin Bable, *Project Engr*
Kevin Whittaker, *Project Engr*
▲ EMP: 30
SQ FT: 50,000
SALES (est): 9.5MM **Privately Held**
WEB: www.itemamerica.com
SIC: 3354 Shapes, extruded aluminum

(G-261)
KNAPP FOUNDRY CO INC
1207 Sweitzer Ave (44301-1389)
P.O. Box 26304 (44319-6304)
PHONE..................................330 434-0916
Fax: 330 434-0558
Charles Knapp Jr, *President*
Jeffery Knapp, *Corp Secy*
EMP: 14 EST: 1910
SQ FT: 20,000
SALES (est): 2.1MM **Privately Held**
WEB: www.knappfoundry.com
SIC: 3321 Gray iron castings

(G-262)
KOKI LABORATORIES INC
1081 Rosemary Blvd (44306-3727)
PHONE..................................330 773-7669
John J Piscitelli, *Owner*
EMP: 20
SALES (est): 3.4MM **Privately Held**
SIC: 2992 Transmission fluid: made from purchased materials

(G-263)
KURTZ BROS COMPOST SERVICES
2677 Riverview Rd (44313-4719)
PHONE..................................330 864-2621
Thomas Kurtz, *President*
EMP: 30
SALES (est): 4.3MM **Privately Held**
WEB: www.kbcompost.com
SIC: 2875 8741 Compost; management services

(G-264)
L A PRODUCTIONS CO LLC (PA)
Also Called: L A Products Co
1333 Collier Rd (44320-2409)
PHONE..................................330 666-4230
Fax: 330 867-7957
Nicholas Lamonica,
Patricia L Lamonica,
EMP: 3
SQ FT: 16,000

SALES (est): 856.5K **Privately Held**
SIC: 7699 4213 3949 Recreational vehicle repair services; aircraft & heavy equipment repair services; heavy machinery transport; sporting & athletic goods

(G-265)
LAAD SIGN & LIGHTING INC
830 Moe Dr Ste B (44310-2569)
PHONE...............................330 379-2297
Linda Nichols, *Owner*
EMP: 10
SQ FT: 1,000
SALES: 1MM **Privately Held**
SIC: 3993 Signs & advertising specialties

(G-266)
LABABIDI ENTERPRISES INC
2167 Forest Oak Dr (44312-2234)
PHONE...............................330 733-2907
Wallid Lababidi, *Owner*
EMP: 20
SALES (est): 1.8MM **Privately Held**
SIC: 3841 8011 Anesthesia apparatus; offices & clinics of medical doctors

(G-267)
LANDMARK PLASTIC CORPORATION (PA)
1331 Kelly Ave (44306-3773)
PHONE...............................330 785-2200
Fax: 330 785-9200
Robert G Merzweiler, *CEO*
Gerald D Stetham, *COO*
Paul Wallbrown, *Prdtn Mgr*
Steve Merzweiler, *Opers Staff*
Aaron Cramer, *Mfg Staff*
◆ EMP: 190
SQ FT: 200,000
SALES (est): 57.5MM **Privately Held**
WEB: www.landmarkplastic.com
SIC: 3089 Plastic containers, except foam

(G-268)
LAZER ACTION INC
1534 Brittain Rd (44310-2738)
PHONE...............................330 630-9200
Fax: 330 630-9420
Tom Frascella, *President*
Cheryl Frascella, *Vice Pres*
EMP: 5
SQ FT: 2,876
SALES (est): 679.5K **Privately Held**
WEB: www.lazeraction.com
SIC: 3577 5734 7378 7699 Computer peripheral equipment; computer peripheral equipment; computer peripheral equipment repair & maintenance; printing trades machinery & equipment repair

(G-269)
LELAND-GIFFORD INC
1029 Arlington Cir (44306-3959)
PHONE...............................330 785-9730
Robert Hartford, *President*
EMP: 9
SQ FT: 20,000
SALES (est): 1.4MM **Privately Held**
WEB: www.barkermill.com
SIC: 3541 Drilling & boring machines; milling machines

(G-270)
LENA FIORE INC
2188 Majesty Ct (44333-1286)
PHONE...............................330 468-3226
Celeste Massullo, *President*
Mary Helene Massullo, *Co-Owner*
EMP: 15
SALES: 200K **Privately Held**
WEB: www.clevelandrockscandy.com
SIC: 5023 2339 Decorative home furnishings & supplies; women's & misses' accessories

(G-271)
LIPPINCOTT & PETO INC
Also Called: Rubber World Magazine
1741 Akron Peninsula Rd (44313-5157)
P.O. Box 5451 (44334-0451)
PHONE...............................330 864-2122
Joe Lippincott, *President*
EMP: 17
SQ FT: 2,500

SALES (est): 1.9MM **Privately Held**
SIC: 2721 Trade journals: publishing only, not printed on site

(G-272)
LOCKHEED MARTIN CORPORATION
1210 Massillon Rd (44315-0001)
PHONE...............................330 796-7000
Dale P Bennett, *Branch Mgr*
EMP: 500
SALES (corp-wide): 47.2B **Publicly Held**
WEB: www.lockheedmartin.com
SIC: 3699 Countermeasure simulators, electric
PA: Lockheed Martin Corporation
6801 Rockledge Dr
Bethesda MD 20817
301 897-6000

(G-273)
LOCKHEED MARTIN CORPORATION
1210 Massillon Rd (44315-0001)
PHONE...............................330 796-2800
Jill O Reilly, *Branch Mgr*
EMP: 420
SALES (corp-wide): 47.2B **Publicly Held**
WEB: www.lockheedmartin.com
SIC: 3721 3761 Aircraft; ballistic missiles, complete; guided missiles & space vehicles, research & development; guided missiles, complete; space vehicles, complete
PA: Lockheed Martin Corporation
6801 Rockledge Dr
Bethesda MD 20817
301 897-6000

(G-274)
LOCKHEED MARTIN INTEG
1210 Massillon Rd (44315-0001)
PHONE...............................330 796-2800
Fax: 330 796-6999
Ken Kiley, *Principal*
Amalie Angel, *Business Mgr*
Dan Richardson, *Project Mgr*
Arnold Caduff, *Research*
Dan Lahurd, *Engineer*
EMP: 99
SALES (est): 21.3MM
SALES (corp-wide): 47.2B **Publicly Held**
SIC: 3699 3769 3728 3812 Electrical equipment & supplies; guided missile & space vehicle parts & auxiliary equipment; aircraft parts & equipment; search & navigation equipment
PA: Lockheed Martin Corporation
6801 Rockledge Dr
Bethesda MD 20817
301 897-6000

(G-275)
LOGAN MACHINE COMPANY (PA)
Also Called: LMC
1405 Home Ave (44310-2586)
PHONE...............................330 633-6163
Fax: 330 633-6362
Mark Schoenbaechler, *President*
Kenneth Schoenbaechler, *Vice Pres*
Clint Waggle, *Plant Mgr*
Tom Kranshan, *Project Mgr*
Shawn Schoenbaechler, *Purch Mgr*
▲ EMP: 74 EST: 1943
SQ FT: 96,000
SALES (est): 15.2MM **Privately Held**
WEB: www.loganmachine.com
SIC: 3599 3728 3544 3469 Custom machinery; machine shop, jobbing & repair; aircraft parts & equipment; special dies, tools, jigs & fixtures; metal stampings

(G-276)
LOWRY FURNACE COMPANY INC
Also Called: Hvac
663 Flora Ave (44314-1754)
PHONE...............................330 745-4822
Gregory Shiflett, *President*
EMP: 6
SQ FT: 3,000

SALES (est): 540K **Privately Held**
SIC: 1711 3444 Warm air heating & air conditioning contractor; heating systems repair & maintenance; sheet metalwork

(G-277)
LUND PRINTING CO
2962 Trenton Rd (44312-2855)
PHONE...............................330 628-4047
Fax: 330 628-4047
Norman Lund, *Owner*
EMP: 3
SQ FT: 1,400
SALES (est): 170K **Privately Held**
SIC: 2759 2752 2791 2789 Letterpress printing; commercial printing, offset; typesetting; bookbinding & related work; automotive & apparel trimmings

(G-278)
M & J MACHINE SHOP INC
2420 Pickle Rd (44312-4227)
PHONE...............................330 645-0042
Fax: 330 645-0047
James Kuts, *President*
Charlene Kuts, *Vice Pres*
Jonathan Kuts, *Admin Sec*
EMP: 10
SQ FT: 15,000
SALES (est): 200K **Privately Held**
SIC: 3599 Machine & other job shop work

(G-279)
MACK CONCRETE INDUSTRIES INC
Also Called: Mack Ready-Mix
124 Darrow Rd Ste 7 (44305-3835)
PHONE...............................330 784-7008
Fax: 330 784-6441
Ron Blanton, *Manager*
EMP: 8
SALES (corp-wide): 160.1MM **Privately Held**
SIC: 3273 Ready-mixed concrete
HQ: Mack Concrete Industries, Inc.
201 Columbia Rd
Valley City OH 44280
330 483-3111

(G-280)
MAJESTIC TRAILERS INC (PA)
Also Called: Majestic Trailer & Hitch
1750 E Waterloo Rd (44306-4104)
PHONE...............................330 798-1698
Fax: 330 798-1736
John Hughes, *Principal*
Penny Hughes, *Admin Sec*
EMP: 10
SALES (est): 1.1MM **Privately Held**
SIC: 3714 3715 Air conditioner parts, motor vehicle; truck trailers

(G-281)
MALCO PRODUCTS INC
393 W Wilbeth Rd (44301-2465)
PHONE...............................330 753-0361
Todd West, *Branch Mgr*
EMP: 50
SALES (corp-wide): 54.5MM **Privately Held**
WEB: www.malcopro.com
SIC: 2842 Specialty cleaning, polishes & sanitation goods
PA: Malco Products, Inc.
361 Fairview Ave
Barberton OH 44203
330 753-0361

(G-282)
MANUEL TAMARGO
Also Called: Perry Diesel Service
1004 Swartz Rd (44319-1340)
PHONE...............................330 456-3080
Fax: 330 456-7580
Manuel Tamargo, *Owner*
EMP: 3
SQ FT: 1,624
SALES (est): 231.8K **Privately Held**
WEB: www.perrydiesel.com
SIC: 3714 Fuel pumps, motor vehicle

(G-283)
MARAZITA GRAPHICS INC
1100 Triplett Blvd (44306-3029)
PHONE...............................330 773-6462
Fax: 330 773-6476

James J Marazita, *President*
James S Marazita, *Treasurer*
David Marazita, *Admin Sec*
EMP: 5
SALES (est): 260K **Privately Held**
WEB: www.marazitagraphics.com
SIC: 7336 2759 Silk screen design; screen printing

(G-284)
MARK-ALL ENTERPRISES LLC
Also Called: Excelsior Marking
888 W Waterloo Rd (44314-1528)
PHONE...............................800 433-3615
Fax: 330 745-2333
Bob Bussey, *Mfg Dir*
Gwenn Bull, *CFO*
David Sutter,
Robert Lux,
EMP: 22 EST: 1905
SQ FT: 32,000
SALES (est): 5.1MM **Privately Held**
WEB: www.excelsiormarking.com
SIC: 3953 2796 3999 Figures (marking devices); metal; date stamps, hand: rubber or metal; stencils, painting & marking; platemaking services; badges, metal: policemen, firemen, etc.

(G-285)
MARKETHATCH CO INC
Also Called: J G Pads
91 E Voris St (44311-1507)
P.O. Box 1151 (44309-1151)
PHONE...............................330 376-6363
Paul Joyce, *President*
Dowl Wolfe, *Controller*
EMP: 15
SQ FT: 55,000
SALES (est): 1.9MM **Privately Held**
WEB: www.jgpads.com
SIC: 3999 2759 Advertising display products; commercial printing

(G-286)
MARKHAM MACHINE COMPANY INC
160 N Union St (44304-1355)
PHONE...............................330 762-7676
Fax: 330 762-4131
James M Markham, *President*
EMP: 18
SQ FT: 13,000
SALES (est): 3.7MM **Privately Held**
SIC: 3599 Machine shop, jobbing & repair

(G-287)
MARKS BREW THRU
2455 Canton Rd (44312-5050)
PHONE...............................330 699-1755
Mark L Heldlick, *Owner*
EMP: 4
SALES (est): 282.8K **Privately Held**
SIC: 2082 Beer (alcoholic beverage)

(G-288)
MARTINOV HOME SOLUTIONS LLC
704 Mentor Rd (44303-1655)
PHONE...............................330 926-3059
Branislav Martinov, *Principal*
EMP: 3
SALES (est): 274K **Privately Held**
SIC: 3585 Parts for heating, cooling & refrigerating equipment

(G-289)
MAXION WHEELS AKRON LLC (DH)
Also Called: Hayes Lemmerz Intl-Commrcl Hwy
428 Seiberling St (44306-3205)
PHONE...............................330 794-2310
Fax: 330 794-2375
Don Polk, *President*
Steven Esau, *Vice Pres*
John A Salvette, *Vice Pres*
Eric Moraw, *Treasurer*
David Jorgensen, *Controller*
▲ EMP: 33
SALES (est): 24.8MM **Privately Held**
SIC: 3714 Motor vehicle parts & accessories

HQ: Maxion Wheels U.S.A. Llc
39500 Orchard Hill Pl # 500
Novi MI 48375
734 737-5000

(G-290)
MAXION WHEELS SEDALIA LLC
428 Seiberling St (44306-3205)
PHONE................................330 794-2300
Randy Arnst, *Branch Mgr*
Michael Michalec, *Technical Staff*
EMP: 19 Privately Held
SIC: 3291 Wheels, abrasive
HQ: Hayes Lemmerz International—
Sedalia, Llc
3610 W Main St
Sedalia MO 65301
734 737-5000

(G-291)
MCNEIL & NRM INC (HQ)
96 E Crosier St (44311-2342)
PHONE................................330 761-1855
Fax: 330 253-7022
Paul Yared, *CEO*
F H Yared, *Ch of Bd*
A Melek, *Exec VP*
A P Singh, *Exec VP*
Albert Chaoui, *Vice Pres*
◆ EMP: 65
SQ FT: 35,000
SALES (est): 24.2MM
SALES (corp-wide): 30.7MM Privately
Held
SIC: 3559 3599 3542 Rubber working
machinery, including tires; custom ma-
chinery; machine tools, metal forming
type
PA: Mcneil & Nrm Intl., Inc.
96 E Crosier St
Akron OH 44311
330 253-2525

(G-292)
MCNEIL & NRM INTL INC (PA)
96 E Crosier St (44311-2342)
PHONE................................330 253-2525
F H Yared, *Ch of Bd*
Al M Melek, *Exec VP*
R A Nelson, *CFO*
Joel Siegfried, *Treasurer*
EMP: 75
SQ FT: 35,000
SALES (est): 30.7MM Privately Held
SIC: 3559 3599 Rubber working machin-
ery, including tires; custom machinery

(G-293)
**MEASUREMENT SPECIALTIES
INC**
2236 N Cleveland Massillo (44333-1288)
PHONE................................330 659-3312
Robert Visger, *Branch Mgr*
EMP: 53
SALES (corp-wide): 12.2B Privately Held
SIC: 3829 Measuring & controlling devices
HQ: Measurement Specialties, Inc.
1000 Lucas Way
Hampton VA 23666
757 766-1500

(G-294)
**MEGGITT AIRCRAFT BRAKING
(HQ)**
Also Called: Mabsc
1204 Massillon Rd (44306-4188)
PHONE................................330 796-4400
Fax: 330 796-6230
Luke Duardogan, *President*
Paul Robinson, *General Mgr*
Tim Rogers, *General Mgr*
Mario Andreou, *Regional Mgr*
Douglas Havekost, *Vice Pres*
▲ EMP: 769
SQ FT: 733,000
SALES (est): 342.1MM
SALES (corp-wide): 2.4B Privately Held
WEB: www.meggitt-mabs.com
SIC: 3728 Brakes, aircraft; wheels, aircraft
PA: Meggitt Plc
Atlantic House Aviation Park
Christchurch BH23
120 259-7597

(G-295)
METALICO AKRON INC (HQ)
Also Called: Metalico Annaco
943 Hazel St (44305-1609)
P.O. Box 1148 (44309-1148)
PHONE................................330 376-1400
Fax: 330 376-9696
Jeffery Bauer, *General Mgr*
Melinda Reinfeld, *Controller*
Melinda Ryanfield, *Controller*
Melinda Renfeld, *Asst Controller*
Bob Toth, *Human Res Dir*
EMP: 35 EST: 1930
SQ FT: 30,000
SALES (est): 10.7MM
SALES (corp-wide): 476MM Privately
Held
WEB: www.annaco.com
SIC: 5093 4953 3341 Ferrous metal
scrap & waste; nonferrous metals scrap;
refuse systems; secondary nonferrous
metals
PA: Metalico, Inc.
135 Dermody St
Cranford NJ 07016
908 497-9610

(G-296)
MEYER DESIGN INC
100 N High St (44308-1918)
PHONE................................330 434-9176
Fax: 330 434-9110
Christopher Meyer, *President*
Ken Meyer, *Opers Staff*
EMP: 20
SQ FT: 18,000
SALES (est): 2.3MM Privately Held
WEB: www.meyerdesign.com
SIC: 3949 Playground equipment

(G-297)
MIA EXPRESS INC
3238 Robins Trce (44319-3874)
PHONE................................330 896-8180
Theodore V Sokolovic, *Principal*
EMP: 4
SALES (est): 406.4K Privately Held
SIC: 2741 Miscellaneous publishing

(G-298)
MILESTONE SERVICES CORP
551 Beacon St (44311-1805)
PHONE................................330 374-9988
Richard Drillien, *President*
George Stanley, *Treasurer*
Tamara Hanks, *Office Mgr*
EMP: 6
SQ FT: 200
SALES (est): 590K Privately Held
WEB: www.milestoneservicescorp.com
SIC: 3471 Plating & polishing

(G-299)
MODERN DESIGNS INC
310 Killian Rd (44319-2431)
P.O. Box 247, Green (44232-0247)
PHONE................................330 644-1771
Fax: 330 644-4471
Greg Boyd, *President*
Mark Boyd, *Sales Mgr*
EMP: 5
SALES: 700K Privately Held
SIC: 2541 1751 Store fixtures, wood; cabi-
net & finish carpentry

(G-300)
MOHICAN INDUSTRIES INC
1225 W Market St (44313-7107)
PHONE................................330 869-0500
Judy Dipaola, *President*
EMP: 12
SQ FT: 20,000
SALES (est): 996.1K
SALES (corp-wide): 7.9MM Privately
Held
SIC: 2822 Synthetic rubber
PA: Sovereign Chemical Company
4040 Embassy Pkwy Ste 190
Akron OH 44333
330 869-0500

(G-301)
**MONTGOMERY &
MONTGOMERY LLC**
80 N Pershing Ave (44313-6258)
PHONE................................330 858-9533

David Montgomery,
Bonnie Montgomery, *Admin Sec*
EMP: 7 EST: 2014
SALES (est): 211.1K Privately Held
SIC: 7692 Welding repair

(G-302)
MORE THAN GOURMET INC
929 Home Ave (44310-4107)
PHONE................................330 762-6652
Brad Sacks, *CEO*
Emily Maglott, *Vice Pres*
Todd McFarland, *Plant Mgr*
Marylynn Markovich, *Controller*
Jeffrey A Witherite, *VP Finance*
▲ EMP: 45
SALES: 26MM Privately Held
WEB: www.morethangourmet.com
SIC: 2032 Soups & broths: canned, jarred,
etc.

(G-303)
**MORGAN PRECISION INSTRS
LLC**
3375 Miller Park Rd (44312-5341)
PHONE................................330 896-0846
Fax: 330 896-3445
Jim Geib, *General Mgr*
George Koberlein, *Principal*
EMP: 5
SQ FT: 6,000
SALES: 520K Privately Held
WEB: www.morgangages.com
SIC: 3545 Precision measuring tools

(G-304)
MORRIS TECHNOLOGIES
1741 S Main St (44301-2428)
PHONE................................330 384-3084
Jim Morris, *Owner*
EMP: 3 EST: 2010
SALES (est): 155.2K Privately Held
SIC: 8731 3999 Commercial physical re-
search; manufacturing industries

(G-305)
MOSHER MEDICAL INC
150 Springside Dr 220b (44333-4562)
PHONE................................330 668-2252
Fax: 330 670-5306
Dan Mosher, *President*
EMP: 5
SALES (est): 707.2K Privately Held
WEB: www.moshermedical.com
SIC: 3842 Implants, surgical

(G-306)
MS SQUARED INC
2960 W Bath Rd (44333-2038)
PHONE................................330 666-0255
Fax: 330 668-2533
Mark Schill, *President*
S James Schill, *Director*
Jean Schill, *Admin Sec*
EMP: 6
SQ FT: 8,000
SALES (est): 520K Privately Held
SIC: 3679 Electronic circuits

(G-307)
**MUELLER ELECTRIC COMPANY
INC**
1208 Massillon Rd G104 (44306-4524)
P.O. Box 92922, Cleveland (44194-2922)
PHONE................................216 771-5225
Fax: 216 771-3068
Arnold Siemer, *President*
Cliff Prosek, *General Mgr*
EMP: 30 EST: 2011
SALES (est): 1.2MM
SALES (corp-wide): 210.3MM Privately
Held
SIC: 3644 3643 3694 3496 Insulators &
insulation materials, electrical; current-
carrying wiring devices; harness wiring
sets, internal combustion engines; miscel-
laneous fabricated wire products; nonfer-
rous wiredrawing & insulating; electrical
equipment & supplies
PA: Desco Corporation
7795 Walton Pkwy Ste 175
New Albany OH 43054
614 888-8855

(G-308)
MYE AUTOMOTIVE INC
1293 S Main St (44301-1302)
PHONE................................330 253-5592
John C Orr, *President*
EMP: 4
SALES (est): 945.8K
SALES (corp-wide): 558MM Publicly
Held
SIC: 3089 Pallets, plastic; stock shapes,
plastic; boxes, plastic; blow molded fin-
ished plastic products
PA: Myers Industries, Inc.
1293 S Main St
Akron OH 44301
330 253-5592

(G-309)
MYERS INDUSTRIES INC (PA)
1293 S Main St (44301-1339)
PHONE................................330 253-5592
Fax: 330 253-0035
F Jack Liebau Jr, *Ch of Bd*
R David Banyard, *President*
Virgil Jules, *Business Mgr*
Ray Cunningham, *Vice Pres*
Mark Kaiser, *Opers Mgr*
◆ EMP: 45
SQ FT: 129,000
SALES: 558MM Publicly Held
WEB: www.myersind.com
SIC: 3089 3086 3069 3052 Pallets, plas-
tic; stock shapes, plastic; boxes, plastic;
blow molded finished plastic products;
plastics foam products; packaging & ship-
ping materials, foamed plastic; insulation
or cushioning material, foamed plastic;
padding, foamed plastic; rubber automotive products; automobile hose, rubber;
tools & equipment, automotive; tire & tube
repair materials

(G-310)
**NATIONAL APPLIED CNSTR
PDTS**
3200 S Main St (44319-2435)
PHONE................................330 644-3117
Thomas Duve, *President*
Meredith Peffer, *Mktg Coord*
Carla Helsa, *Manager*
EMP: 6
SQ FT: 2,000
SALES (est): 1MM Privately Held
WEB: www.nacproducts.com
SIC: 2891 Sealing compounds, synthetic
rubber or plastic

(G-311)
**NATURAL COUNTRY FARMS
INC (DH)**
681 W Waterloo Rd (44314-1547)
PHONE................................330 753-2293
Raymond Lee, *CEO*
Tom Kolb, *Senior VP*
Paul E Sukalich, *Senior VP*
Tom Luvig, *Manager*
▲ EMP: 2
SQ FT: 67,000
SALES: 229MM
SALES (corp-wide): 4.9B Privately Held
WEB: www.countrypure.com
SIC: 2033 2037 2086 Fruit juices: fresh;
fruit juice concentrates, frozen; pasteur-
ized & mineral waters, bottled & canned

(G-312)
NERVIVE INC
526 S Main St Ste 801a (44311-4403)
PHONE................................847 274-1790
Mark K Borsody, *Principal*
Dagmar Nikles, *Principal*
EMP: 10
SALES (est): 610K Privately Held
SIC: 3841 Surgical & medical instruments

(G-313)
**NEWSOME & WORK
METALIZING CO**
258 Kenmore Blvd (44301-1000)
P.O. Box 27091 (44319-7091)
PHONE................................330 376-7144
Fax: 330 376-8424
Michael Newsome, *President*
Roger Newsome, *Vice Pres*
Gregory Newsome, *Purch Agent*

Patricia Newsome, *Treasurer*
Daniel Newsome, *Manager*
EMP: 15 **EST:** 1958
SQ FT: 10,000
SALES (est): 1.5MM **Privately Held**
WEB: www.newsome-work.com
SIC: 3471 3479 Sand blasting of metal parts; finishing, metals or formed products; painting of metal products

(G-314)
NEXT DESIGN & BUILD LLC
Also Called: Trident Polymer Solutions
3250 Doves Xing (44319-5414)
PHONE 330 907-3042
Oscar Mascarenhas, *Owner*
EMP: 3
SALES: 500K **Privately Held**
SIC: 2671 Plastic film, coated or laminated for packaging

(G-315)
NIDEC MOTOR CORPORATION
Imperial Electric
1503 Exeter Rd (44306-3889)
PHONE 575 434-0633
Fax: 330 734-3601
Bill Kuhar, *Engineer*
Thanha Tran, *Design Engr*
Sheri Brown, *Human Resources*
David Chippi, *VP Sales*
EMP: 125
SALES (corp-wide): 10B **Privately Held**
SIC: 3621 Motors, electric; generators & sets, electric
HQ: Nidec Motor Corporation
8050 West Florissant Ave
Saint Louis MO 63136

(G-316)
NORTH COAST HOLDINGS INC (PA)
768 E North St (44305-1164)
P.O. Box 9320 (44305-0320)
PHONE 330 535-7177
H A Pendleton, *Ch of Bd*
EMP: 2
SQ FT: 50,000
SALES (est): 15.7MM **Privately Held**
SIC: 3423 6512 Hand & edge tools; commercial & industrial building operation

(G-317)
NORTH COAST THEATRICAL INC (PA)
2181 Killian Rd Unit A (44312-4884)
PHONE 330 762-1768
Richard Arconti, *President*
John Kramanak, *Vice Pres*
EMP: 5
SALES (est): 738.4K **Privately Held**
SIC: 3993 7922 Signs & advertising specialties; theatrical production services

(G-318)
NORTH HILL MARBLE & GRANITE CO
448 N Howard St (44310-3185)
PHONE 330 253-2179
Fax: 330 253-5180
Miles V Buzzi II, *President*
Paul Buzzi, *Admin Sec*
EMP: 10
SQ FT: 4,000
SALES (est): 890K **Privately Held**
WEB: www.exportersindia.com
SIC: 5999 1741 3993 3281 Monuments, finished to custom order; masonry & other stonework; signs, not made in custom sign painting shops; cut stone & stone products; dimension stone

(G-319)
NORTHEAST TIRE MOLDS INC (HQ)
Also Called: Southwest Tire Molds
159 Opportunity Pkwy (44307-2202)
PHONE 330 376-6107
Christopher Sipe, *President*
Christophe Sipe, *Purchasing*
▲ **EMP:** 2
SQ FT: 29,500

SALES (est): 5.1MM
SALES (corp-wide): 118.6MM **Privately Held**
SIC: 3544 Special dies, tools, jigs & fixtures
PA: Greatoo Intelligent Equipment Inc.
Middle Section, No.5 Road, Jiedong Economic Development Area
Jieyang 51550
663 327-4082

(G-320)
NOVEX SYSTEMS LLC
2236 N Clvland Msslon Rd (44333-1288)
PHONE 330 659-3546
Michael Wheeler, *Mng Member*
Polly Wheeler,
EMP: 25
SALES (est): 2MM **Privately Held**
SIC: 2759 Commercial printing; business forms; printing; laser printing

(G-321)
NSA TECHNOLOGIES LLC
3867 Medina Rd Ste 256 (44333-4525)
PHONE 330 576-4600
Kristen Lavender, *Finance Mgr*
Vincent E Fischer,
Victor J Bierman III,
Mark W Jenney,
EMP: 150
SALES (est): 7MM **Privately Held**
SIC: 7372 8742 8731 Publishers' computer software; marketing consulting services; commercial physical research; biological research

(G-322)
OHIO BEAUTY INC
Also Called: Ohio Beauty Cut Stone
40 W Turkeyfoot Lake Rd (44319-4012)
PHONE 330 644-2241
Fax: 330 644-5559
Frank J Berenyi Jr, *President*
Sirenna Berenyi, *Vice Pres*
EMP: 7 **EST:** 1947
SQ FT: 8,000
SALES (est): 1.4MM **Privately Held**
SIC: 5032 5211 3281 1411 Brick, stone & related material; lumber & other building materials; masonry materials & supplies; sand & gravel; cut stone & stone products; dimension stone

(G-323)
OHIO GASKET AND SHIM CO INC (PA)
Also Called: Ogs Industries
976 Evans Ave (44305-1019)
PHONE 330 630-0626
Fax: 330 630-2075
John S Bader, *President*
Pam Varner, *Accounting Mgr*
Shelly Penrod, *Human Res Mgr*
Andrew Bader, *Sales Staff*
Tammy Langford, *Info Tech Mgr*
▲ **EMP:** 45 **EST:** 1959
SQ FT: 84,000
SALES (est): 19.9MM **Privately Held**
WEB: www.ogsindustries.com
SIC: 3469 3053 3599 3499 Stamping metal for the trade; gaskets, all materials; machine shop, jobbing & repair; shims, metal; packaging & labeling services

(G-324)
OHIO HICKORY HARVEST BRAND PRO
Also Called: Hickory Harvest Foods
90 Logan Pkwy (44319-1177)
PHONE 330 644-6266
Fax: 330 644-2501
Darlene Swiatkowski, *CEO*
Joseph Swiatkowski, *President*
Michael Swiatkowski, *Vice Pres*
Shellie Beck, *Office Mgr*
EMP: 32 **EST:** 1972
SQ FT: 32,000
SALES: 17.7MM **Privately Held**
WEB: www.hickoryharvest.com
SIC: 5145 5149 2099 Nuts, salted or roasted; candy; fruits, dried; food preparations

(G-325)
OHIO MECHANICAL HANDLING CO
1856 S Main St (44301-2461)
PHONE 330 773-5165
Fax: 330 773-0256
William W Burse, *President*
Robert L Burse, *Treasurer*
Karen Kavali, *Manager*
Ron Lazar, *Manager*
EMP: 10 **EST:** 1945
SQ FT: 20,000
SALES: 205.5K **Privately Held**
SIC: 3536 5084 Cranes, overhead traveling; hoists; monorail systems; materials handling machinery

(G-326)
OHIO PURE FOODS INC (DH)
681 W Waterloo Rd (44314-1587)
PHONE 330 753-2293
Raymond Lee, *CEO*
David Blair, *Senior VP*
Paul E Sukalich, *Senior VP*
Tom Kolb, *CFO*
Curtis Waiters, *Manager*
▲ **EMP:** 89
SQ FT: 100,000
SALES (est): 8.9MM
SALES (corp-wide): 4.9B **Privately Held**
SIC: 2033 2086 Fruit juices: fresh; fruit drinks (less than 100% juice): packaged in cans, etc.

(G-327)
OLDFORGE TOOLS INC (DH)
768 E North St (44305-1164)
PHONE 330 535-7177
Scott Meyer, *President*
EMP: 1
SALES (est): 3.1MM
SALES (corp-wide): 17.3MM **Privately Held**
WEB: www.kentool.com
SIC: 3423 Mechanics' hand tools
HQ: Summit Tool Company
768 E North St
Akron OH 44305
330 535-7177

(G-328)
OMNOVA SOLUTIONS INC
1380 Tech Way (44306-2572)
PHONE 330 734-1237
EMP: 84
SALES (corp-wide): 759.9MM **Publicly Held**
SIC: 2819 Industrial inorganic chemicals
PA: Omnova Solutions Inc.
25435 Harvard Rd
Beachwood OH 44122
216 682-7000

(G-329)
P C R INC
Also Called: Ruber Polymer
1135 Portage Trail Ext (44313-8283)
PHONE 330 945-7721
EMP: 10
SALES (corp-wide): 2.2MM **Privately Held**
SIC: 2952 Asphalt Felts And Coatings
PA: P C R Inc
5760 County Line Rd
Cumming GA 30040
330 945-7721

(G-330)
PACKAGING CORPORATION AMERICA
Also Called: PCA/Akron 312
708 Killian Rd Ste 1 (44319-2559)
PHONE 330 644-9542
Fax: 330 644-4053
Ralph Snyder, *Manager*
Elaine Sinopoli, *Supervisor*
EMP: 44
SALES (corp-wide): 5.7B **Publicly Held**
WEB: www.packagingcorp.com
SIC: 2653 Corrugated & solid fiber boxes
PA: Packaging Corporation Of America
1955 W Field Ct
Lake Forest IL 60045
847 482-3000

(G-331)
PACTIV LLC
708 Killian Rd (44319-2549)
PHONE 330 644-9542
Ralph Snyder, *Opers-Prdtn-Mfg*
EMP: 35 **Privately Held**
WEB: www.pactiv.com
SIC: 2653 Corrugated & solid fiber boxes
HQ: Pactiv Llc
1900 W Field Ct
Lake Forest IL 60045
847 482-2000

(G-332)
PALMER INDUSTRIES INC
Also Called: Palmer Products
920 Moe Dr (44310-2519)
PHONE 330 630-9397
Fax: 330 630-9759
Leonard Palmer Jr, *President*
Len Senior, *President*
Tom Bryant, *Plant Mgr*
Leonard R Palme, *Plant Mgr*
Leonard R Palmer, *Plant Mgr*
EMP: 7
SQ FT: 8,000
SALES (est): 1MM **Privately Held**
WEB: www.shaftsaver.com
SIC: 3599 Machine shop, jobbing & repair

(G-333)
PC SYSTEMS
Also Called: Sabbagh Tool and Equipment Co
307 Montrose Ave (44310-3815)
PHONE 330 825-7966
Dennis Sabbagh, *Owner*
EMP: 4
SQ FT: 1,200
SALES: 200K **Privately Held**
SIC: 3571 7378 5045 5734 Computers, digital, analog or hybrid; computer peripheral equipment repair & maintenance; computer peripheral equipment; computer peripheral equipment

(G-334)
PENNY PRINTING INC
2957 S Main St (44319-1857)
PHONE 330 645-2955
Robert Collier, *President*
Catherine Collier, *Corp Secy*
EMP: 3
SQ FT: 2,200
SALES: 175K **Privately Held**
SIC: 2752 Commercial printing, offset

(G-335)
PERFECT PRCISION MACHINING LTD
920 Clay St (44311-2214)
PHONE 330 475-0324
Margaret Habib, *Principal*
EMP: 9
SALES (est): 1MM **Privately Held**
SIC: 3599 Machine shop, jobbing & repair

(G-336)
PERKINELMER HLTH SCIENCES INC
520 S Main St Ste 2423 (44311-1086)
PHONE 330 825-4525
Chritine Gradisher, *Manager*
Jim Bailey, *Manager*
Paul Dudley, *Manager*
Aniket Parekh, *Software Engr*
Bryan Daugherty, *Software Dev*
EMP: 32
SALES (corp-wide): 2.1B **Publicly Held**
SIC: 2835 2836 5049 In vitro & in vivo diagnostic substances; biological products, except diagnostic; laboratory equipment, except medical or dental
HQ: Perkinelmer Health Sciences, Inc.
940 Winter St
Waltham MA 02451
617 482-9595

(G-337)
PFAHL GAUGE & MANUFACTURING CO
665 Harden Ave (44310-2421)
PHONE 330 633-8402
EMP: 4 **EST:** 1912
SQ FT: 2,000

▲ = Import ▼ =Export
◆ =Import/Export

SALES (est): 350K **Privately Held**
SIC: 3469 Mfg Metal Stampings

(G-338)
PHOENIX TECHNOLOGIES INC
825 E Tallmadge Ave (44310-3511)
PHONE...............................330 630-5888
Fax: 330 630-5788
Corneliu Phoenix Mihalca, *President*
EMP: 16
SALES (est): 1.5MM **Privately Held**
SIC: **1721** 7349 3471 Industrial painting;
cleaning service, industrial or commercial;
plating & polishing

(G-339)
PIN OAK ESTATES LTD
581 Lake Of The Wods Blvd (44333-2796)
PHONE...............................330 657-2727
John J Szalay, *Principal*
EMP: 8 EST: 2011
SALES (est): 712.4K **Privately Held**
SIC: 3452 Pins

(G-340)
PINE TOP INC
1932 Akron Peninsula Rd (44313-4810)
PHONE...............................330 929-2492
Salvatore H Crano, *President*
EMP: 3
SQ FT: 10,000
SALES (est): 351.7K **Privately Held**
SIC: **1381** 1382 Drilling oil & gas wells; oil
& gas exploration services

(G-341)
PIONEER PLASTICS CORPORATION
3330 Massillon Rd (44312-5397)
PHONE...............................330 896-2356
Fax: 330 896-3609
Ralph J Danesi Jr, *President*
Jakob Denzinger, *Principal*
David Oberholtz, *Plant Mgr*
Donna Hastings, *Persnl Dir*
David Oberholtz, *Manager*
EMP: 125
SQ FT: 45,000
SALES (est): 26.1MM **Privately Held**
SIC: 3089 Injection molding of plastics

(G-342)
PLATE-ALL METAL COMPANY INC
1210 Devalera St (44310-2483)
PHONE...............................330 633-6166
Fax: 330 633-9029
John L Burg, *President*
Charles Killinger, *Plt & Fclts Mgr*
Irene Burg, *Office Mgr*
EMP: 8
SQ FT: 6,660
SALES (est): 925.2K **Privately Held**
WEB: www.plateallmetal.com
SIC: **3471** 8711 Chromium plating of metals or formed products; engineering services

(G-343)
POLY-MET INC
1997 Nolt Dr (44312-4862)
PHONE...............................330 630-9006
Fax: 330 733-9345
Frank Moore, *President*
Laura Moore, *Vice Pres*
Carolyn Rogovy, *Vice Pres*
EMP: 14
SQ FT: 10,000
SALES (est): 500K **Privately Held**
WEB: www.poly-met.com
SIC: 3479 Hot dip coating of metals or formed products

(G-344)
PORTAGE MACHINE CONCEPTS INC
Also Called: Portage Knife Company
75 Skelton Rd (44312-1821)
PHONE...............................330 628-2343
Fax: 330 784-0701
Jeannine Lizak, *President*
Christopher Michalec, *Treasurer*
Mary Lou Govia, *Admin Sec*
W Duane Huff, *Admin Sec*
▲ EMP: 16 EST: 1981

SQ FT: 6,500
SALES (est): 3.4MM **Privately Held**
WEB: www.portageknife.com
SIC: 3549 Rotary slitters (metalworking machines)

(G-345)
POWER MEDIA INC
546 Grant St (44311-1158)
PHONE...............................330 475-0500
Jon Erisey, *President*
Mike Belofi, *Opers Staff*
Michael West, *Creative Dir*
EMP: 8
SQ FT: 11,000
SALES (est): 1.2MM **Privately Held**
SIC: **3993** 3999 Advertising novelties; advertising display products

(G-346)
PRCC HOLDINGS INC
175 Mntrose Ave W Ste 200 (44321)
PHONE...............................330 798-4790
Kenneth Bloom, *CEO*
EMP: 238
SALES (est): 14.4MM **Privately Held**
SIC: 3069 Custom compounding of rubber materials

(G-347)
PRECISION DYNAMICS INC
1270 Linden Ave (44310-1263)
PHONE...............................330 697-0611
David Burns, *President*
Lisa Burns, *Vice Pres*
EMP: 4
SALES (est): 320K **Privately Held**
SIC: 3599 Machine & other job shop work

(G-348)
PRECISION INTERNATIONAL LLC
843 N Cleveland (44322)
PHONE...............................330 793-0900
Anthony P Crisalli, *President*
Kurt Walcutt, *CFO*
EMP: 20
SALES (est): 6MM **Privately Held**
SIC: 3441 Fabricated structural metal

(G-349)
PREMIER SEALS MFG
909 W Waterloo Rd (44314-1529)
PHONE...............................330 861-1060
Fax: 330 861-1063
Robert Shultz, *Principal*
▼ EMP: 8
SALES (est): 701.9K **Privately Held**
SIC: 3999 Manufacturing industries

(G-350)
PRESSLERS MEATS INC
2553 Pressler Rd (44312-5500)
PHONE...............................330 644-5636
Fax: 330 645-1327
Roger H Pressler, *President*
Richard Pressler, *Vice Pres*
EMP: 15 EST: 1944
SQ FT: 1,800
SALES (est): 1.7MM **Privately Held**
SIC: 2011 Meat packing plants

(G-351)
PRINTING SYSTEM INC
Also Called: 48hr Books
2249 14th St Sw (44314-2007)
PHONE...............................330 375-9128
Fax: 330 375-5373
James Fulton, *President*
James T Pachell, *Principal*
EMP: 12
SALES (est): 1.3MM **Privately Held**
WEB: www.printingsystem.com
SIC: 2752 Commercial printing, offset

(G-352)
PRO-FAB INC
2570 Pressler Rd (44312-5554)
PHONE...............................330 644-0044
Fax: 330 644-0189
Anna Myers, *CEO*
Monroe W Townsend, *Vice Pres*
EMP: 20
SQ FT: 15,000

SALES (est): 6.9MM **Privately Held**
SIC: **3441** 1791 Fabricated structural
metal; structural steel erection

(G-353)
PROFESSIONAL GRINDING INC
3001 Mogadore Rd (44312-1805)
PHONE...............................330 628-3001
Fax: 330 628-0013
Richard Bobrowicz, *President*
Sharon Bobrowicz, *Corp Secy*
Donald Bobrowicz, *Vice Pres*
EMP: 7
SQ FT: 5,200
SALES (est): 520K **Privately Held**
WEB: www.professionalgrinding.com
SIC: **3552** 7389 Finishing machinery, textile; grinding, precision: commercial or industrial

(G-354)
PROGRESSIVE MANUFACTURING CO
Also Called: Progrssive Mtllizing Machining
300 Massillon Rd (44312-1914)
PHONE...............................330 784-4717
Fax: 330 784-4728
Doris Datsko, *President*
George Datsko Jr, *Corp Secy*
David Datsko, *Vice Pres*
Scott Datsko, *Sales Staff*
EMP: 8
SQ FT: 18,000
SALES (est): 1.2MM **Privately Held**
WEB: www.prorebuild.com
SIC: **3599** 3479 5084 Machine shop, jobbing & repair; painting, coating & hot dipping; industrial machinery & equipment

(G-355)
QT EQUIPMENT COMPANY (PA)
151 W Dartmore Ave (44301-2462)
PHONE...............................330 724-3055
Daniel Root, *President*
Dave Root, *Treasurer*
Kelly Stewart, *Sales Mgr*
▼ EMP: 35
SQ FT: 20,000
SALES (est): 6.3MM **Privately Held**
SIC: **7532** 5531 3713 Body shop, trucks; automotive tires; utility truck bodies

(G-356)
QUALITY INNOVATIVE PDTS LLC
787 Wye Rd (44333-2268)
PHONE...............................330 990-9888
Greg Cordray,
EMP: 5
SQ FT: 50,000
SALES (est): 235.3K **Privately Held**
SIC: 3089 Novelties, plastic

(G-357)
QUALITY MOLD INC (PA)
Also Called: Versitech Mold Div
2200 Massillon Rd (44312-4234)
PHONE...............................330 645-6653
Fax: 330 645-4828
Greg Kalikas, *President*
Stanley B Migdal, *Principal*
Jerry Candiliotis, *Vice Pres*
Mike Politis, *Vice Pres*
Bill Hines, *CFO*
▲ EMP: 100
SQ FT: 83,821
SALES (est): 86.9MM **Privately Held**
WEB: www.qualitymold.com
SIC: 3544 Industrial molds

(G-358)
QUALITY MOLDED
2200 Massillon Rd (44312-4234)
PHONE...............................330 645-6653
Greg Kalikas, *President*
Carl Sinfield, *President*
Dan Ball, *General Mgr*
EMP: 140
SQ FT: 15,000
SALES (est): 13.7MM **Privately Held**
WEB: www.newcastings.com
SIC: 3341 Aluminum smelting & refining (secondary)

(G-359)
QUANTUM TECHNOLOGIES INC
2634 S Arlington Rd # 101 (44319-2062)
PHONE...............................330 645-2762
Fax: 330 645-2768
Richard Galluch, *Principal*
Michal Piechuta, *Project Engr*
EMP: 4
SALES (est): 336.7K **Privately Held**
SIC: 3572 Computer storage devices

(G-360)
QUIKEY MANUFACTURING CO INC (PA)
1500 Industrial Pkwy (44310-2600)
PHONE...............................330 633-8106
Fax: 330 633-6670
Michael W Burns, *President*
Patrick P Burns, *Vice Pres*
Thomas Stiller, *Vice Pres*
William B Stiller, *Vice Pres*
Bonnie Marks, *Purchasing*
▲ EMP: 125
SQ FT: 50,000
SALES (est): 14.1MM **Privately Held**
WEB: www.quikey.com
SIC: 3993 Advertising novelties

(G-361)
R C A RUBBER COMPANY
1833 E Market St (44305-4214)
P.O. Box 9240 (44305-0240)
PHONE...............................330 784-1291
Fax: 330 784-2899
Sherry Price, *President*
Ennice Barnes, *Principal*
Paul H Taylor, *Principal*
Katherine Woodward, *Principal*
Shane Price, *Vice Pres*
◆ EMP: 80 EST: 1931
SQ FT: 40,000
SALES (est): 24.7MM **Privately Held**
WEB: www.rcarubber.com
SIC: 3069 Molded rubber products

(G-362)
R C MUSSON RUBBER CO
1320 E Archwood Ave (44306-2825)
P.O. Box 7038 (44306-0038)
PHONE...............................330 773-7651
Bennie D Segers, *Ch of Bd*
Frank W Rockhold, *Vice Pres*
Robert S Segers, *Vice Pres*
William J Segers, *Vice Pres*
Joseph Kostko, *Treasurer*
EMP: 20 EST: 1945
SQ FT: 40,000
SALES (est): 4.1MM **Privately Held**
WEB: www.mussonrubber.com
SIC: **3069** 5085 Mats or matting, rubber; rubber goods, mechanical

(G-363)
R W MICHAEL PRINTING CO
665 E Cuyahoga Falls Ave (44310-1552)
PHONE...............................330 923-9277
Fax: 330 923-4720
Robert Michael, *Owner*
Evelyn Michael, *Co-Owner*
EMP: 3
SQ FT: 2,000
SALES (est): 25K **Privately Held**
SIC: **2759** 2796 2791 2789 Commercial printing; platemaking services; typesetting; bookbinding & related work; commercial printing, lithographic; die-cut paper & board

(G-364)
RANDOLPH RESEARCH CO
2449 Kensington Rd (44333-2054)
PHONE...............................330 666-1667
William Hinks, *President*
Paul Ertly, *Vice Pres*
Gerald D Shook, *Vice Pres*
EMP: 3
SALES (est): 425K **Privately Held**
WEB: www.randolphresearch.com
SIC: 3562 Ball & roller bearings

(G-365)
RANDY LEWIS INC
Also Called: Acme Fence & Lumber
1053 Bank St (44305-2507)
PHONE...............................330 784-0456
Fax: 330 784-9121

G E O G R A P H I C

Randy Lewis, *President*
EMP: 10
SQ FT: 10,000
SALES: 1.2MM **Privately Held**
SIC: 3446 2499 3315 3089 Fences or posts, ornamental iron or steel; fencing, wood; chain link fencing; fences, gates & accessories: plastic; fencing

(G-366)
RAPID MOLD REPAIR & MACHINE
813 Home Ave (44310-4105)
PHONE..........................330 253-1000
Ivan Cagaric, *President*
Zelco Tomic, *Vice Pres*
EMP: 3
SQ FT: 3,700
SALES: 250K **Privately Held**
SIC: 3544 3599 Special dies & tools; custom machinery

(G-367)
RAUH POLYMERS INC
420 Kenmore Blvd (44301-1038)
PHONE..........................330 376-1120
Joseph M Rauh, *President*
James T Rauh, *Vice Pres*
▲ **EMP:** 15
SALES (est): 5MM **Privately Held**
WEB: www.rauhpolymers.com
SIC: 2821 Plastics materials & resins

(G-368)
RCM ENGINEERING COMPANY
2089 N Clvland Mssllon Rd (44333-1258)
P.O. Box 517, Bath (44210-0517)
PHONE..........................330 666-0575
Robert C Mc Dowell, *Owner*
EMP: 9 **EST:** 1903
SQ FT: 2,200
SALES (est): 725.7K **Privately Held**
SIC: 1311 1321 Natural gas production; natural gasoline production

(G-369)
REA INCORPORATED
4808 Pin Oak Rd (44333-1084)
PHONE..........................330 666-7414
Fax: 330 666-7414
Robert E Anthony, *Principal*
EMP: 3
SALES (est): 301.9K **Privately Held**
SIC: 3841 Surgical & medical instruments

(G-370)
REES WHEELCHAIR MOBILITY SVC
1615 Akron Peninsula Rd # 101 (44313-5194)
PHONE..........................330 923-2345
Stephen Rees, *Principal*
EMP: 3
SALES (est): 249.3K **Privately Held**
SIC: 3842 Wheelchairs

(G-371)
REPORTER NEWSPAPER INC
1088 S Main St (44301-1206)
P.O. Box 2042 (44309-2042)
PHONE..........................330 535-7061
Fax: 330 535-7333
William Ellis Jr, *President*
EMP: 10
SALES (est): 460K **Privately Held**
SIC: 2711 Newspapers: publishing only, not printed on site

(G-372)
RESOURCE EXCHANGE COMPANY INC
383 Abbyshire Rd (44319-3803)
PHONE..........................440 773-8915
Larry Burkette, *Principal*
Bob Buckley, *Agent*
EMP: 5
SALES (est): 388K **Privately Held**
SIC: 3641 7389 Electric lamps & parts for specialized applications;

(G-373)
RICHARDS WHL FENCE CO INC
Also Called: RICHARD'S FENCE COMPANY
1600 Firestone Pkwy (44301-1659)
PHONE..........................330 773-0423

Fax: 330 773-3513
Richard Peterson, *President*
Bill Peterson, *Vice Pres*
▲ **EMP:** 30
SQ FT: 235,000
SALES: 10.8MM **Privately Held**
SIC: 3315 5039 Chain link fencing; wire fence, gates & accessories

(G-374)
RICKS GRAPHIC ACCENTS INC
3554 S Arlington Rd (44312-5223)
PHONE..........................330 644-4455
Fax: 330 644-2676
Rick Lang, *President*
EMP: 4
SALES (est): 300K **Privately Held**
SIC: 3993 Signs & advertising specialties

(G-375)
RIVERCOR LLC
2850 Gilchrist Rd (44305-4444)
PHONE..........................330 784-1113
Fax: 330 784-1148
John Sharp, *President*
John Korzenko, *Vice Pres*
Bill Davis, *Manager*
Cindy Ede, *Manager*
EMP: 25
SQ FT: 140,000
SALES (est): 5.8MM **Privately Held**
SIC: 2679 Paper products, converted

(G-376)
ROBERT F SAMS
Also Called: Real Solution Communication
1148 Monteray Dr (44305-1770)
PHONE..........................330 990-0477
Robert F Sams, *Owner*
EMP: 5
SALES: 75K **Privately Held**
SIC: 3669 Communications equipment

(G-377)
ROCHLING AUTOMOTIVE USA LLP
2275 Picton Pkwy (44312-4270)
PHONE..........................330 400-5785
Robert Roach, *Plant Mgr*
EMP: 75
SALES (corp-wide): 1.6B **Privately Held**
SIC: 3714 Motor vehicle parts & accessories
HQ: Rochling Automotive Usa Llp
　245 Parkway E
　Duncan SC 29334
　864 486-0888

(G-378)
ROGERS INDUSTRIAL PRODUCTS INC
532 S Main St (44311-1018)
PHONE..........................330 535-3331
Fax: 330 535-4408
John Cole, *President*
John R Cole, *President*
Ted Chuchanis, *Chief Engr*
Susan Moon, *Accountant*
Brady Stalnaker, *Manager*
▲ **EMP:** 35 **EST:** 1951
SQ FT: 239,000
SALES (est): 8.2MM **Privately Held**
WEB: www.rogersusa.com
SIC: 3542 3625 3491 3643 Presses: hydraulic & pneumatic, mechanical & manual; industrial electrical relays & switches; pressure valves & regulators, industrial; current-carrying wiring devices

(G-379)
ROTOCAST TECHNOLOGIES INC
1900 Englewood Ave (44312-1004)
PHONE..........................330 798-9091
Edward W Kissel, *President*
Herb Pickrell, *General Mgr*
Bruce Kuhn, *Opers Staff*
Ken Herold, *Engineer*
Christopher Difilippo, *Finance Mgr*
EMP: 30
SQ FT: 25,000
SALES (est): 6.1MM **Privately Held**
WEB: www.rotocastmold.com
SIC: 3365 3544 Aluminum foundries; special dies, tools, jigs & fixtures

(G-380)
RUBBER CITY MACHINERY CORP
Also Called: R C M
1 Thousand Sweitzer Ave (44311)
P.O. Box 2043 (44309-2043)
PHONE..........................330 434-3500
Fax: 330 434-2244
George B Sobieraj, *President*
Daniel Abraham, *General Mgr*
Bernie Sobieraj, *Vice Pres*
Robert J Westfall, *Vice Pres*
Scott Ross, *Engineer*
▲ **EMP:** 32
SQ FT: 100,000
SALES (est): 7.7MM **Privately Held**
SIC: 3559 5084 7629 Rubber working machinery, including tires; plastics working machinery; industrial machinery & equipment; electrical repair shops

(G-381)
RUBBER WORLD MAGAZINE INC
1741 Akron Peninsula Rd (44313-5157)
PHONE..........................330 864-2122
Job Lippincott, *President*
Patrick Dimauro, *Editor*
EMP: 15
SALES (est): 880K **Privately Held**
WEB: www.rubberworld.com
SIC: 2721 Periodicals

(G-382)
RUNNER TOOL & DIE INC
Also Called: Metal Product
1678 Massillon Rd (44312-4205)
PHONE..........................330 794-8843
Fax: 330 794-8843
Jack Runner, *President*
Connie Runner, *Vice Pres*
Tracy Peterson, *Treasurer*
EMP: 7
SQ FT: 4,000
SALES (est): 940K **Privately Held**
SIC: 3599 3544 Electrical discharge machining (EDM); wire drawing & straightening dies

(G-383)
RUSCOE COMPANY (PA)
485 Kenmore Blvd (44301-1013)
P.O. Box 3858 (44314-0858)
PHONE..........................330 253-8148
Fax: 330 253-2933
Paul Michalec, *President*
Larry Musci, *General Mgr*
Betty Pfaff, *Corp Secy*
John Postan, *Plant Mgr*
Phyllis Cardinal, *Purch Dir*
EMP: 49 **EST:** 1949
SQ FT: 24,000
SALES (est): 11MM **Privately Held**
WEB: www.ruscoe.com
SIC: 2891 3297 2851 Adhesives & sealants; nonclay refractories; paints & allied products

(G-384)
RUSCOE COMPANY
219 E Miller Ave (44301-1326)
P.O. Box 3858 (44314-0858)
PHONE..........................330 253-8148
Paul Michalec, *Director*
EMP: 5
SALES (corp-wide): 11MM **Privately Held**
WEB: www.ruscoe.com
SIC: 2865 Color pigments, organic
PA: The Ruscoe Company
　485 Kenmore Blvd
　Akron OH 44301
　330 253-8148

(G-385)
RUSSELL PRODUCTS CO INC
De Valera Division
275 N Forge St Ste 1 (44304-1472)
PHONE..........................330 633-5252
Fax: 330 633-0906
Robert Evans, *Principal*
Jean Laymon, *Manager*
EMP: 21
SQ FT: 14,000

SALES (corp-wide): 6MM **Privately Held**
WEB: www.russprodco.com
SIC: 3479 3471 Painting of metal products; anodizing (plating) of metals or formed products
PA: Russell Products Co., Inc.
　275 N Forge St Ste 1
　Akron OH 44304
　330 535-9246

(G-386)
RUSSELL PRODUCTS CO INC
Also Called: Akron Anodizing & Coating Div
1066 Home Ave (44310-3502)
PHONE..........................330 535-3391
Fax: 330 535-6158
Daniel Dzurovcin, *Vice Pres*
Jerry Gray, *Opers Staff*
EMP: 9
SALES (corp-wide): 6MM **Privately Held**
WEB: www.russprodco.com
SIC: 3471 Finishing, metals or formed products; anodizing (plating) of metals or formed products
PA: Russell Products Co., Inc.
　275 N Forge St Ste 1
　Akron OH 44304
　330 535-9246

(G-387)
RUSSELL PRODUCTS CO INC
Falholt Division
1066 Home Ave (44310-3502)
PHONE..........................330 434-9163
Fax: 330 434-6605
Jerry Gray, *Vice Pres*
Peggy Russell, *CFO*
EMP: 4
SALES (corp-wide): 6MM **Privately Held**
WEB: www.russprodco.com
SIC: 3479 Painting, coating & hot dipping
PA: Russell Products Co., Inc.
　275 N Forge St Ste 1
　Akron OH 44304
　330 535-9246

(G-388)
RUSSELL PRODUCTS CO INC
Russell Division
275 N Forge St Ste 2 (44304-1472)
PHONE..........................216 267-0880
Tim Dzurovcin, *Manager*
EMP: 4
SALES (corp-wide): 6MM **Privately Held**
WEB: www.russprodco.com
SIC: 3479 Painting, coating & hot dipping
PA: Russell Products Co., Inc.
　275 N Forge St Ste 1
　Akron OH 44304
　330 535-9246

(G-389)
RUSSELL STANDARD CORPORATION
Also Called: Jasa Asphalt Russell Standard
990 Hazel St (44305-1610)
PHONE..........................330 733-9400
Robert Gunther, *Manager*
EMP: 6
SALES (corp-wide): 217.3MM **Privately Held**
WEB: www.russellstandard.com
SIC: 5032 2951 Asphalt mixture; concrete, bituminous
PA: Russell Standard Corporation
　285 Kappa Dr Ste 300
　Pittsburgh PA 15238
　412 449-0700

(G-390)
S & A INDUSTRIES CORPORATION (DH)
571 Kennedy Rd Ste R (44305-4425)
PHONE..........................330 733-6040
Greg Anderson, *President*
Blanca Garza, *Production*
Eric Hurd, *Engineer*
Randy Koehler, *Engineer*
Christopher Soulsby, *Project Engr*
▲ **EMP:** 68
SQ FT: 42,000
SALES: 21MM
SALES (corp-wide): 635.7MM **Privately Held**
SIC: 3086 Plastics foam products

HQ: Sekiso Corporation
1-3, Hinakitamachi
Okazaki AIC 444-0
564 252-121

(G-391)
S I T STRINGS CO INC
2493 Romig Rd (44320-4109)
PHONE..............................330 434-8010
Fax: 330 434-6654
Virgil Lay, *President*
Edwin Speedy, *Exec VP*
Robert C Hird, *Vice Pres*
Paulette Kelley, *Purch Agent*
Tim Pfouts, *Sales Staff*
EMP: 20
SQ FT: 16,000
SALES (est): 1.9MM **Privately Held**
WEB: www.sitstrings.com
SIC: 3931 5736 String instruments &
parts; strings, musical instrument; musical
instrument stores

(G-392)
S R TECHNOLOGIES LLC (PA)
2200 N Clvland Msslon Rd (44333-1255)
PHONE..............................330 523-7184
Frank Manning, *Mng Member*
Thomas Tedde, *Mng Member*
Marilyn Close,
▲ EMP: 4
SQ FT: 2,982
SALES (est): 881.6K **Privately Held**
SIC: 3699 Bells, electric

(G-393)
SACO LOWELL PARTS LLC
1395 Triplett Blvd (44306-3124)
PHONE..............................330 794-1535
John Daenes, *President*
Bruce Weick, *Vice Pres*
Russell Dunlap, *Vice Pres*
EMP: 21
SALES (est): 3MM **Privately Held**
WEB: www.sacolowell.com
SIC: 3469 Machine parts, stamped or
pressed metal

(G-394)
SAFAR MACHINE COMPANY
905 Brown St (44311-2211)
PHONE..............................330 644-0155
Fax: 330 434-8034
John Safar, *President*
Bruce Safar, *Vice Pres*
Julie Salopek, *Treasurer*
EMP: 10 EST: 1978
SQ FT: 5,500
SALES: 1.9MM **Privately Held**
SIC: 3599 Machine shop, jobbing & repair

(G-395)
SAINT CROIX LTD
3371 W Bath Rd (44333-2105)
P.O. Box 5229 (44334-0229)
PHONE..............................330 666-1544
Jonathan Schiesswohl, *President*
EMP: 5
SALES (est): 423.7K **Privately Held**
WEB: www.saintcroix.net
SIC: 1311 Crude petroleum production;
natural gas production

(G-396)
**SAINT-GOBAIN PRFMCE PLAS
CORP**
2664 Gilchrist Rd (44305-4412)
PHONE..............................330 798-6981
Fax: 330 798-6948
Chris Mattern, *Plant Mgr*
Sheryl Mix, *Senior Buyer*
Marc Gordin, *Controller*
Allie Krsak, *Human Res Mgr*
EMP: 200
SQ FT: 100,000
SALES (corp-wide): 185.8MM **Privately
Held**
SIC: 3061 3083 Medical & surgical rubber
tubing (extruded & lathe-cut); laminated
plastics plate & sheet
HQ: Saint-Gobain Performance Plastics
Corporation
31500 Solon Rd
Solon OH 44139
440 836-6900

(G-397)
**SCHOTT METAL PRODUCTS
COMPANY**
Also Called: Design Wheel and Hub
2225 Lee Dr (44306-4399)
PHONE..............................330 773-7873
Samuel Schott, *President*
F W Schott, *Vice Pres*
Sherry Brink, *Manager*
Paul Graham, *Admin Sec*
EMP: 100 EST: 1945
SQ FT: 90,000
SALES (est): 12.2MM **Privately Held**
SIC: 3469 3714 Stamping metal for the
trade; motor vehicle parts & accessories

(G-398)
SEAVIVAL LLC
526 S Main St Ste 518 (44311-4403)
PHONE..............................330 252-1151
Brian G Friedman, *CEO*
EMP: 5
SALES: 1,000K **Privately Held**
SIC: 3999 Manufacturing industries

(G-399)
**SERVICE IRON & STEEL
COMPANY**
1372 Kenmore Blvd (44314-1633)
PHONE..............................330 253-9147
Fax: 330 745-9423
Frank M Bernert Jr, *President*
Tom Nader, *Manager*
EMP: 3 EST: 1945
SALES (est): 240K **Privately Held**
SIC: 4225 3441 General warehousing;
fabricated structural metal

(G-400)
SHINCOR SILICONES INC (DH)
1030 Evans Ave (44305-1021)
PHONE..............................330 630-9460
Jun Hamuro, *President*
Harold Mooar, *Opers Staff*
Harry Cotsmire, *Purchasing*
Shawn Bogner, *Plant Engr*
Gaku Takeuchi, *Controller*
▲ EMP: 8
SQ FT: 51,000
SALES: 4.5MM
SALES (corp-wide): 10.9B **Privately Held**
WEB: www.shincor.com
SIC: 2822 2891 2869 Silicone rubbers;
adhesives & sealants; industrial organic
chemicals
HQ: Shin-Etsu Silicones Of America, Inc.
1150 Damar Dr
Akron OH 44305
330 630-9860

(G-401)
**SHOOK MANUFACTURED PDTS
INC (PA)**
1017 Kenmore Blvd (44314-2153)
P.O. Box 15058 (44314-5058)
PHONE..............................330 848-9780
Fax: 800 733-3882
Roy Knittle, *President*
Thomas Johns, *Vice Pres*
William Shook, *Vice Pres*
▲ EMP: 9
SQ FT: 10,000
SALES (est): 1.2MM **Privately Held**
SIC: 3545 5072 Chucks: drill, lathe or
magnetic (machine tool accessories);
hardware; screws; rivets; hand tools

(G-402)
SIMPLY CANVAS INC
1479 Exeter Rd (44306-3856)
PHONE..............................330 436-6500
Fax: 330 673-2040
Adam Fried, *President*
Linda Sager, *Manager*
EMP: 22
SALES (est): 3.3MM **Privately Held**
SIC: 2396 7384 Screen printing on fabric
articles; fabric printing & stamping;
photofinish laboratories

(G-403)
SK MACHINERY CORPORATION
487 Wellington Ave (44305-2680)
P.O. Box 2109, Stow (44224-0109)
PHONE..............................330 733-7325

Soroosh Khoshbin, *President*
▲ EMP: 4
SQ FT: 15,000
SALES: 300K **Privately Held**
SIC: 3531 Construction machinery

(G-404)
SLICE MFG LLC
1800 Triplett Blvd (44306-3311)
PHONE..............................330 733-7600
Randy Theken, *Agent*
Bobi Lekic, *Director*
EMP: 3
SALES (est): 127.2K **Privately Held**
SIC: 3313 Alloys, additive, except copper:
not made in blast furnaces

(G-405)
SMART 3D SOLUTIONS LLC
411 Wolf Ledges Pkwy # 100 (44311-1051)
PHONE..............................330 972-7840
Thomas Swiger, *Co-Owner*
EMP: 4
SQ FT: 66,500
SALES (est): 136.2K **Privately Held**
SIC: 3949 Sporting & athletic goods

(G-406)
SML INC (PA)
Also Called: Primeline Industries
4083 Embassy Pkwy (44333-1781)
PHONE..............................330 668-6555
Fax: 330 668-6510
Tejroi Naipaul, *Finance Mgr*
Lisbeth Torre, *Finance Mgr*
Kevin Larizza, *Shareholder*
Jacqueline Bebczuk, *Shareholder*
Mary Larizza, *Shareholder*
▲ EMP: 5
SQ FT: 2,000
SALES (est): 19.3MM **Privately Held**
WEB: www.primelineindustries.com
SIC: 3069 Tubing, rubber

(G-407)
**SOLDIER TECH & ARMOR RES
LLC**
3300 Massillon Rd (44312-5361)
PHONE..............................330 896-5217
Fred Kungl,
EMP: 5
SALES (est): 234.7K **Privately Held**
SIC: 3999 Manufacturing industries

(G-408)
**SOUND PUBLISHING HOLDING
INC**
Also Called: Akron Beacon Journal
44 E Exchange St (44308-1510)
PHONE..............................330 996-3000
Andrea Mathewson, *Principal*
EMP: 4
SALES (corp-wide): 620.9MM **Privately
Held**
SIC: 2711 Newspapers, publishing & print-
ing
HQ: Sound Publishing Holding, Inc.
19351 8th Ave Ne Ste 106
Poulsbo WA 98370
360 394-5800

(G-409)
SOUTH AKRON AWNING CO (PA)
763 Kenmore Blvd (44314-2196)
PHONE..............................330 848-7611
Fax: 330 753-4224
Ranell Minear, *President*
Michelle Halafa, *Vice Pres*
Kathleen Mueller, *Admin Sec*
EMP: 14 EST: 1913
SQ FT: 19,000
SALES (est): 2.2MM **Privately Held**
WEB: www.southakronawning.com
SIC: 2394 1799 7359 Awnings, fabric:
made from purchased materials; canvas
covers & drop cloths; awning installation;
tent & tarpaulin rental; party supplies
rental services

(G-410)
**SPECIALTY DRAPERY
WORKROOM**
50 S Frank Blvd (44313-7212)
PHONE..............................330 864-4190
Mark Ruby, *President*

EMP: 5
SQ FT: 4,000
SALES (est): 965.3K **Privately Held**
SIC: 2391 Curtains & draperies

(G-411)
STAMBAUGH ENGINEERING INC
1001 Heritage Ln (44333-2205)
PHONE..............................330 666-0088
Steve A Stambaugh, *President*
EMP: 3
SALES (est): 290.7K **Privately Held**
SIC: 3625 8711 Industrial controls: push
button, selector switches, pilot; engineer-
ing services

(G-412)
**STANDARD JIG BORING SVC
LLC (HQ)**
Also Called: Sjbs
3360 Miller Park Rd (44312-5388)
PHONE..............................330 896-9530
Fax: 330 896-4934
David Stuller, *Controller*
Ginger Townsend, *Mng Member*
Jeff Klusty, *Manager*
Ginger Hanson, *Executive*
Jeffrey R Wahl,
▲ EMP: 44
SQ FT: 30,000
SALES (est): 15MM
SALES (corp-wide): 114.7MM **Privately
Held**
SIC: 3599 Machine shop, jobbing & repair
PA: Ariel Corporation
35 Blackjack Road Ext
Mount Vernon OH 43050
740 397-0311

(G-413)
**STANDARD JIG BORING SVC
LLC**
3194 Massillon Rd (44312-5363)
PHONE..............................330 644-5405
George Koberlein, *Branch Mgr*
EMP: 5
SALES (corp-wide): 114.7MM **Privately
Held**
SIC: 3599 Machine shop, jobbing & repair
HQ: Standard Jig Boring Service, Llc
3360 Miller Park Rd
Akron OH 44312
330 896-9530

(G-414)
**STANDARD PATTERN WORKS
INC**
1409 Kenmore Blvd (44314-1627)
PHONE..............................330 745-2295
Fax: 330 745-2295
Harold Huth Jr, *President*
EMP: 3
SALES (est): 447.6K **Privately Held**
SIC: 3543 Industrial patterns

(G-415)
STAR PRINTING COMPANY INC
125 N Union St (44304-1390)
PHONE..............................330 376-0514
Fax: 330 376-7979
Vicki Lauck, *President*
Lynda Moore, *Corp Secy*
Paul M Lauck, *Vice Pres*
Robert D Lauck Jr, *Vice Pres*
Paul McConnaughey, *Prdtn Mgr*
EMP: 22 EST: 1932
SQ FT: 20,000
SALES (est): 3MM **Privately Held**
WEB: www.starptg.com
SIC: 2752 2759 2789 Commercial print-
ing, offset; letterpress printing; bookbind-
ing & related work

(G-416)
STATIONERY SHOP INC
30 N Summit St (44308-1941)
PHONE..............................330 376-2033
Fax: 330 376-7322
John E Steurer, *President*
EMP: 5
SQ FT: 6,000
SALES (est): 580K **Privately Held**
SIC: 2752 2759 2791 Commercial print-
ing, offset; letterpress printing; embossing
on paper; engraving; typesetting

(G-417)
STEEL STRUCTURES OF OHIO LLC
1324 Firestone Pkwy A (44301-1671)
P.O. Box 2039, New Kensington PA (15068-1439)
PHONE.................................330 374-9900
Fax: 330 374-9900
James L Rench, *Mng Member*
John Young,
EMP: 40
SQ FT: 5,000
SALES (est): 6.6MM **Privately Held**
WEB: www.steel-oh.com
SIC: 3449 Bars, concrete reinforcing: fabricated steel

(G-418)
STERLING ASSOCIATES INC
Also Called: Fastsigns
1783 Brittain Rd (44310-1801)
PHONE.................................330 630-3500
Fax: 330 630-9615
Milton L Liming, *President*
Elaine Liming, *Corp Secy*
Brent B Liming, *Vice Pres*
Todd Evans, *Executive*
EMP: 8 EST: 1962
SQ FT: 2,000
SALES (est): 1MM **Privately Held**
SIC: 3993 2721 Signs, not made in custom sign painting shops; periodicals

(G-419)
SUMMIT DRILLING COMPANY INC
152 W Dartmore Ave (44301-2450)
PHONE.................................800 775-5537
Bruce W Panning, *President*
Robert Krukow, *Corp Secy*
EMP: 16
SQ FT: 9,000
SALES: 1.3MM **Privately Held**
SIC: 1381 8748 Drilling oil & gas wells; environmental consultant

(G-420)
SUMMIT PLASTIC COMPANY (PA)
1169 Brittain Rd (44305-1004)
P.O. Box 117, Tallmadge (44278-0117)
PHONE.................................330 633-3668
Fax: 330 633-9768
Norman Belliveau, *CEO*
Jim Pfeiffer, *General Mgr*
George Collins, *Vice Pres*
Chuck Snyder, *Vice Pres*
Robin Taylor, *Accountant*
▲ **EMP:** 67 EST: 1990
SQ FT: 55,000
SALES (est): 11.3MM **Privately Held**
SIC: 3081 Unsupported plastics film & sheet

(G-421)
SUMMIT PRINTING & GRAPHICS
Also Called: Summit Printing and Graphics
1265 W Waterloo Rd (44314-1522)
PHONE.................................330 645-7644
Fax: 330 645-7246
Joe C Reinmann, *President*
EMP: 3 EST: 1976
SQ FT: 3,000
SALES (est): 240K **Privately Held**
WEB: www.summitp-g.com
SIC: 2752 Commercial printing, offset

(G-422)
SUMMIT TOOL COMPANY (HQ)
Also Called: Ken-Tools
768 E North St (44305-1164)
P.O. Box 9320 (44305-0320)
PHONE.................................330 535-7177
Fax: 216 535-1345
Douglas Romstadt, *Vice Pres*
Doug Ronstadt, *Purchasing*
Jim Rose, *Purchasing*
Don Mitchell, *Engineer*
Richard Fuller, *Asst Treas*
▲ **EMP:** 65 EST: 1932
SQ FT: 70,000
SALES (est): 17.3MM **Privately Held**
WEB: www.kenstool.com
SIC: 3423 Hand & edge tools

PA: North Coast Holdings Incorporated
768 E North St
Akron OH 44305
330 535-7177

(G-423)
SUNOCO INC
1375 Home Ave (44310-2549)
PHONE.................................216 912-2579
EMP: 27
SALES (corp-wide): 21.8B **Publicly Held**
SIC: 2911 Petroleum refining
HQ: Sunoco, Inc.
3801 West Chester Pike
Newtown Square PA 19073
215 977-3000

(G-424)
SYNERGY ALLIANCE
738 W Market St (44303-1073)
PHONE.................................330 253-9475
William Downing, *CEO*
EMP: 7
SALES (est): 821.4K **Privately Held**
WEB: www.rhdowning.com
SIC: 3465 Body parts, automobile: stamped metal

(G-425)
T J KARG COMPANY INC
1055 Evans Ave (44305-1061)
PHONE.................................330 836-0921
Fax: 330 630-2305
Thomas D Karg, *President*
William J Karg, *Vice Pres*
EMP: 7
SQ FT: 10,000
SALES (est): 750K **Privately Held**
SIC: 3599 Machine shop, jobbing & repair

(G-426)
TALLMADGE FINISHING CO INC
879 Moe Dr Ste C20 (44310-2558)
PHONE.................................330 633-7466
David Mann, *President*
Paul Cooper, *Vice Pres*
EMP: 30
SALES (est): 3MM **Privately Held**
SIC: 3069 Hard rubber & molded rubber products

(G-427)
TALLMADGE SPINNING & METAL CO
2783 Gilchrist Rd Unit A (44305-4406)
P.O. Box 58, Tallmadge (44278-0058)
PHONE.................................330 794-2277
Fax: 330 794-2270
John Sasanecki, *President*
Jacob Sasanecki, *Vice Pres*
Giovanni Catalano, *Purch Agent*
Linda Sasanecki, *Treasurer*
EMP: 15
SQ FT: 15,000
SALES (est): 3.5MM **Privately Held**
WEB: www.tsm1947.com
SIC: 3449 Miscellaneous metalwork

(G-428)
TARADON RUBBER CO INC
1441 E Turkeyfoot Lake Rd (44312-5348)
PHONE.................................330 896-3143
Fax: 330 896-3143
Donald E Brasaemle, *President*
EMP: 10
SALES: 900K **Privately Held**
WEB: www.taradon.com
SIC: 3069 3953 3061 Molded rubber products; marking devices; mechanical rubber goods

(G-429)
TARGETING CUSTOMER SAFETY INC
Also Called: TCS
1021 Galsworthy Dr (44313-8110)
PHONE.................................330 865-9593
Fax: 330 665-9084
Benny Swigert, *Partner*
Steve Zaugg, *Partner*
Neal Swigert, *Sales Mgr*
EMP: 5
SALES (est): 430K **Privately Held**
WEB: www.targetingcustomersafety.com
SIC: 3842 Personal safety equipment

(G-430)
TECH PRO INC
3030 Gilchrist Rd (44305-4420)
PHONE.................................330 923-3546
Fax: 330 923-6335
John Putman, *President*
Kay Putman, *Vice Pres*
Caroline Glaeser, *Purch Mgr*
▲ **EMP:** 28
SQ FT: 30,000
SALES (est): 2.6MM **Privately Held**
WEB: www.techpro-usa.com
SIC: 7699 3821 3829 3825 Laboratory instrument repair; laboratory apparatus & furniture; measuring & controlling devices; instruments to measure electricity; computer peripheral equipment

(G-431)
TEGRON HOLDING LLC
1208 Massillon Rd (44306-4524)
PHONE.................................330 836-2004
Jim Milan, *Engineer*
EMP: 4
SALES (corp-wide): 35.3MM **Privately Held**
SIC: 3823 5084 Controllers for process variables, all types; conveyor systems
HQ: Tegron Holding, Llc
5912b Old Highway 80
Longview TX 75604
903 759-1088

(G-432)
TEMOS INC
Also Called: Temo Candy Co
495 W Exchange St (44302-1403)
PHONE.................................330 376-7229
Lawrence C Temo, *President*
James C Temo, *Vice Pres*
EMP: 7
SQ FT: 10,000
SALES: 300K **Privately Held**
SIC: 2064 Candy & other confectionery products

(G-433)
TEMPERATURE CONTROLS COMPANY
661 Anderson Ave (44306-3101)
P.O. Box 7665 (44306-0665)
PHONE.................................330 773-6633
Fax: 330 773-7732
John Kerr, *President*
Robert J Kerr Sr, *Chairman*
James Mc Clarnon, *Vice Pres*
Robert J Kerr Jr, *Treasurer*
Lawrence Simers, *Accountant*
EMP: 15 EST: 1952
SQ FT: 12,000
SALES (est): 3.1MM **Privately Held**
WEB: www.tempcontrolco.com
SIC: 1711 7692 Mechanical contractor; warm air heating & air conditioning contractor; welding repair

(G-434)
TEMPLE ISRAEL
91 Springside Dr (44333-2428)
PHONE.................................330 762-8617
Milton I Wiskind, *President*
David Lipper, *Pastor*
Dr Davis Meckler, *Vice Pres*
Henry Nagel, *Vice Pres*
Davis Unger, *Treasurer*
EMP: 9 EST: 1866
SALES (est): 440K **Privately Held**
SIC: 8661 3625 Synagogue; switches, electric power

(G-435)
THE BEACON JOURNAL PUBG CO
Also Called: Akron Beacon Journal
44 E Exchange St (44308-1510)
P.O. Box 640 (44309-0640)
PHONE.................................330 996-3140
Fax: 330 375-9235
Andrea Mathewson, *Publisher*
Scott Babbo, *Editor*
Elissa Murray, *Editor*
Doug Oplinger, *Editor*
Mark Price, *Editor*
EMP: 410
SQ FT: 250,000

SALES (est): 53.8MM
SALES (corp-wide): 620.9MM **Privately Held**
WEB: www.ohio.com
SIC: 2711 Newspapers, publishing & printing
HQ: Sound Publishing Holding, Inc.
19351 8th Ave Ne Ste 106
Poulsbo WA 98370
360 394-5800

(G-436)
THE BOOKSELLER INC
39 Westgate Cir (44313-7401)
PHONE.................................330 865-5831
Frank Klein, *President*
Pat Klein, *Corp Secy*
Andrea A Klein, *Treasurer*
EMP: 4
SQ FT: 2,400
SALES (est): 290.7K **Privately Held**
SIC: 5932 2789 7389 Rare books; binding only: books, pamphlets, magazines, etc.; auction, appraisal & exchange services

(G-437)
THEKEN COMPANIES LLC
1800 Triplett Blvd (44306-3311)
PHONE.................................330 733-7600
Jolene Maurer, *CFO*
EMP: 25
SQ FT: 30,000
SALES (est): 1MM **Privately Held**
SIC: 3841 Surgical & medical instruments

(G-438)
THERMELECTRICITY LLC
411 Wolf Ledges Pkwy # 1 (44311-1028)
PHONE.................................330 972-8054
Erik Engeberg,
Elyse Ball,
Subramaniya Hariharan,
Mary Ellen Hinkle,
Wayne Watkins,
EMP: 5 EST: 2012
SALES (est): 309.3K **Privately Held**
SIC: 3621 Power generators

(G-439)
THERMO-RITE MFG COMPANY
Also Called: Star Fire Distributing
1355 Evans Ave (44305-1038)
PHONE.................................330 633-8680
Fax: 330 633-8701
Roy Allen, *CEO*
Barbara Lewis, *Purchasing*
Dave Williams, *Purchasing*
Ray Repasky, *Sales Mgr*
Stephanie Stankwits, *Manager*
EMP: 35 EST: 1946
SQ FT: 120,000
SALES (est): 9.1MM **Privately Held**
WEB: www.thermo-rite.com
SIC: 3429 Fireplace equipment, hardware: andirons, grates, screens

(G-440)
THIRSTY DOG BREWING CO
529 Grant St Ste 103 (44311-1184)
PHONE.................................330 252-8740
Ulo Konsen, *President*
V Erik Konsen, *Corp Secy*
John Nhaeway, *Vice Pres*
EMP: 4
SALES (est): 521.4K **Privately Held**
WEB: www.thirstydog.com
SIC: 2082 Malt beverages

(G-441)
TIMKENSTEEL CORPORATION
Also Called: Timkensteel Green Sales Office
1019 E Turkeyfoot Lake Rd (44312-5242)
PHONE.................................330 517-7300
Steven W Sorvold, *Senior Mgr*
EMP: 9
SALES (corp-wide): 869.5MM **Publicly Held**
SIC: 3312 Blast furnaces & steel mills
PA: Timkensteel Corporation
1835 Dueber Ave Sw
Canton OH 44706
330 471-7000

▲ = Import ▼=Export
◆ =Import/Export

(G-442)
TJ BELL INC
1340 Home Ave Ste E (44310-2570)
PHONE..................................330 633-3644
Thomas J Bell, *President*
Eva Bell, *Admin Sec*
EMP: 3
SQ FT: 5,000
SALES (est): 1MM **Privately Held**
WEB: www.tjbell.com
SIC: 5084 3599 Industrial machinery &
equipment; custom machinery

(G-443)
TLT-TURBO INC
2693 Wingate Ave (44314-1301)
PHONE..................................330 776-5115
John A Landis, *Director*
EMP: 6
SALES (est): 1.1MM
SALES (corp-wide): 45.1B **Privately Held**
SIC: 3564 Ventilating fans: industrial or
commercial
HQ: Tlt-Turbo Gmbh
Gleiwitzstr. 7
Zweibrucken 66482
633 280-80

(G-444)
**TRELLEBORG WHEEL SYSTEMS
AMERI (HQ)**
1501 Exeter Rd (44306-3889)
PHONE..................................866 633-8473
Fax: 330 877-0730
Ydo Doornbos, *Managing Dir*
Adam Blooenstein, *Principal*
Gregory Hower, *Principal*
▲ EMP: 40
SQ FT: 600,000
SALES (est): 55.3MM
SALES (corp-wide): 2.8B **Privately Held**
SIC: 3011 3061 Industrial tires, pneumatic;
mechanical rubber goods
PA: Trelleborg Ab
Johan Kocksgatan 10
Trelleborg 231 4
410 670-00

(G-445)
**TRI CAST LIMITED
PARTNERSHIP**
2128 Killian Rd (44312-4898)
PHONE..................................330 733-8718
John Voight, *CEO*
EMP: 24 EST: 2000
SQ FT: 18,712
SALES (est): 2.7MM **Privately Held**
WEB: www.tri-cast.com
SIC: 3321 Gray iron castings

(G-446)
TRI-CAST INC (PA)
2128 Killian Rd (44312-4898)
PHONE..................................330 733-8718
Fax: 330 733-8786
John Voight, *CEO*
Virgil Smith, *Human Res Mgr*
EMP: 30
SQ FT: 28,000
SALES (est): 2.7MM **Privately Held**
SIC: 3321 Gray iron castings; ductile iron
castings

(G-447)
TRI-WAY REBAR INC
Also Called: Clinton Supply
625 S Walnut St (44319)
P.O. Box 430, Clinton (44216-0430)
PHONE..................................330 882-8043
Jan Guy, *Manager*
EMP: 4
SALES (corp-wide): 1.5MM **Privately
Held**
SIC: 3272 Concrete products
PA: Tri-Way Rebar Inc.
625 S Walnut St
Ravenna OH 44266
330 296-9662

(G-448)
TRUMBULL INDUSTRIES INC
209 Perkins St (44304-1298)
PHONE..................................330 434-6174
Fax: 330 434-4226
Joe Reguerio, *Branch Mgr*

Joe Regueiro, *Manager*
EMP: 21
SALES (corp-wide): 112.9MM **Privately
Held**
SIC: 5074 8711 2541 Plumbing & hy-
dronic heating supplies; engineering serv-
ices; wood partitions & fixtures
PA: Trumbull Industries, Inc.
400 Dietz Rd Ne
Warren OH 44483
330 393-6624

(G-449)
**TURKEYFOOT HILL SAND &
GRAVEL**
465 E Turkeyfoot Lake Rd (44319-4105)
PHONE..................................330 899-1997
Rick Williams, *Principal*
EMP: 3
SALES (est): 173.4K **Privately Held**
SIC: 1442 Construction sand & gravel

(G-450)
TW CORPORATION
99 S Seiberling St (44305)
PHONE..................................440 461-3234
Fax: 330 784-4410
Thomas T Whims, *President*
Thomas M Seger, *Admin Sec*
EMP: 30
SQ FT: 28,000
SALES (est): 2.5MM **Privately Held**
SIC: 3365 Aerospace castings, aluminum

(G-451)
**TYLER ELECTRIC MOTOR
REPAIR**
1888 Copley Rd (44320-1570)
PHONE..................................330 836-5537
Fax: 330 869-5100
Frank S Politz, *President*
Michael E Politz, *Vice Pres*
Frank J Politz, *Treasurer*
Teresa Snyder, *Admin Sec*
EMP: 5
SQ FT: 2,700
SALES (est): 400K **Privately Held**
SIC: 7694 7699 5063 5084 Electric
motor repair; pumps & pumping equip-
ment repair; motors, electric; pumps &
pumping equipment

(G-452)
TYLER MOLD & MACHINE INC
2200 Massillon Rd (44312-4234)
PHONE..................................330 645-6653
Butch Walker, *Manager*
EMP: 30
SQ FT: 1,000
SALES (est): 789.4K
SALES (corp-wide): 86.9MM **Privately
Held**
WEB: www.tylermold.com
SIC: 7534 3544 Tire repair shop; special
dies, tools, jigs & fixtures
PA: Quality Mold, Inc.
2200 Massillon Rd
Akron OH 44312
330 645-6653

(G-453)
UNINTERRUPTED LLC
3800 Embassy Pkwy Ste 360
(44333-8389)
PHONE..................................216 771-2323
Maverick Carter, *CEO*
EMP: 15
SALES: 6MM **Privately Held**
SIC: 7372 Application computer software

(G-454)
UNION PROCESS INC
1925 Akron Peninsula Rd (44313-4896)
PHONE..................................330 929-3333
Fax: 330 929-3034
Arno Szegvari, *President*
Emery Ll, *Vice Pres*
Rick Wochele, *Chief Engr*
Anita Szegvari, *Treasurer*
Anita Goins, *Sales Staff*
▲ EMP: 35 EST: 1944
SQ FT: 30,000
SALES (est): 9.8MM **Privately Held**
WEB: www.unionprocess.com
SIC: 3541 Machine tools, metal cutting
type; grinding machines, metalworking

(G-455)
**UNITED DENTAL
LABORATORIES (PA)**
261 South Ave (44302)
P.O. Box 428, Tallmadge (44278-0428)
PHONE..................................330 253-1810
Fax: 330 253-1669
Richard Delapa Jr, *President*
R J Delapa, *Manager*
Lenny Nigh, *Manager*
EMP: 35
SQ FT: 15,000
SALES (est): 4.9MM **Privately Held**
WEB: www.uniteddentallab.com
SIC: 8072 3843 Denture production; den-
tal equipment & supplies

(G-456)
UNITED FEED SCREWS LTD
487 Wellington Ave (44305-2680)
PHONE..................................330 798-5532
Fax: 330 798-5548
Paul Norton, *President*
Joe Norton Sr, *Info Tech Dir*
▲ EMP: 10 EST: 1998
SQ FT: 14,500
SALES (est): 1.8MM **Privately Held**
WEB: www.unitedfeedscrews.com
SIC: 3061 Oil & gas field machinery rubber
goods (mechanical)

(G-457)
**UNIVERSAL PRECISION
PRODUCTS**
1480 Industrial Pkwy (44310-2602)
PHONE..................................330 633-6128
Fax: 330 633-2151
Jon Munson, *President*
Bob Munson, *Vice Pres*
EMP: 45 EST: 1946
SQ FT: 65,000
SALES (est): 7.4MM **Privately Held**
WEB: www.uppinc.com
SIC: 3554 3549 Paper industries machin-
ery; metalworking machinery

(G-458)
UNIVERSAL TIRE MOLDS INC
5127 Boyer Pkwy (44312-4272)
PHONE..................................330 253-5101
Fax: 330 253-7945
Paul Scurei, *President*
Michael R Cingel, *Vice Pres*
Harold Vance, *Treasurer*
▲ EMP: 30
SQ FT: 17,000
SALES (est): 4.8MM **Privately Held**
SIC: 3544 3599 Forms (molds), for
foundry & plastics working machinery;
machine shop, jobbing & repair

(G-459)
**UPPERROOM ACTION
MINISTRIES**
1142 Morse St (44320-3961)
PHONE..................................330 848-9246
Jimmie Rodgers, *Principal*
EMP: 4
SALES (est): 269.3K **Privately Held**
SIC: 3131 Uppers

(G-460)
UTOPIA PRODUCTS INC
3867 Medina Rd 202 (44333-4525)
PHONE..................................330 666-2602
Fax: 330 670-9733
Robert Beckett, *President*
Linda Beckett, *Vice Pres*
▲ EMP: 5
SALES (est): 430K **Privately Held**
WEB: www.utpr.com
SIC: 3999 Barber & beauty shop equip-
ment

(G-461)
**VACUUM ELECTRIC SWITCH CO
INC (PA)**
526 S Main St Ste 122 (44311-4403)
PHONE..................................330 374-5156
Fax: 330 374-5159
Cecil C Wristen, *President*
Sandra M Wristen, *Vice Pres*
EMP: 2
SQ FT: 200

SALES: 1.2MM **Privately Held**
WEB: www.vacuumelectricswitch.com
SIC: 3613 7629 Switchboards & parts,
power; electronic equipment repair

(G-462)
VALLEY RUBBER MIXING INC
115 W Bartges St (44311-1034)
PHONE..................................330 434-4442
Fax: 330 258-2016
Thomas Brennan, *President*
Tom Brenan, *Owner*
EMP: 14
SQ FT: 41,000
SALES: 2.1MM **Privately Held**
SIC: 3069 Reclaimed rubber & specialty
rubber compounds

(G-463)
VERTICAL DATA LLC
Also Called: Medtrace
2169 Chuckery Ln (44333-4742)
P.O. Box 38, Bath (44210-0038)
PHONE..................................330 289-0313
Christopher Wolff,
EMP: 15 EST: 2015
SALES: 500K **Privately Held**
SIC: 7372 Application computer software

(G-464)
**VIRTUAL HOLD TECHNOLOGY
LLC (PA)**
3875 Embassy Pkwy Ste 350
(44333-8343)
PHONE..................................330 666-1181
Fax: 330 670-2269
Wes Hayden, *CEO*
Thomas Jameson, *Exec VP*
Ted Bray, *Vice Pres*
Kevin Shinseki, *Vice Pres*
James Pavlic, *Engineer*
EMP: 80
SQ FT: 18,000
SALES (est): 20.2MM **Privately Held**
WEB: www.virtualhold.com
SIC: 7371 7372 Computer software devel-
opment & applications; prepackaged soft-
ware

(G-465)
**VULCAN MACHINERY
CORPORATION**
20 N Case Ave (44305-2598)
PHONE..................................330 376-6025
Fax: 330 376-2172
David Jacobs, *President*
Bradley J Acobs, *Vice Pres*
Bradley J Jacobs, *Vice Pres*
Gary Bradford, *Plant Mgr*
Kim Caetty, *Purch Mgr*
EMP: 25
SALES (est): 4.8MM **Privately Held**
WEB: www.vulcanmachinery.com
SIC: 3559 7299 Plastics working machin-
ery; banquet hall facilities

(G-466)
**W G LOCKHART
CONSTRUCTION CO**
800 W Waterloo Rd (44314-1528)
PHONE..................................330 745-6520
Fax: 330 745-5711
Alexander R Lockhart, *President*
Richard Stanley, *Admin Sec*
EMP: 100
SQ FT: 5,000
SALES (est): 8.1MM **Privately Held**
SIC: 1611 3273 Highway & street con-
struction; ready-mixed concrete

(G-467)
W L BECK PRINTING & DESIGN
1326 S Main St (44301-1625)
P.O. Box 1257 (44309-1257)
PHONE..................................330 762-3020
William L Beck, *President*
Vivian Shanafelt, *Treasurer*
Shirley Beck, *Admin Sec*
EMP: 6
SQ FT: 2,000
SALES (est): 630K **Privately Held**
SIC: 2754 2791 Commercial printing,
gravure; typesetting

GEOGRAPHIC

(G-468)
WARREN ENTERPRISES
1067 Winhurst Dr (44313-5814)
PHONE.................................330 836-6119
Phillip Warren, *Owner*
EMP: 3
SALES: 500K **Privately Held**
WEB: www.internetsalesman.com
SIC: 3993 Neon signs

(G-469)
WAYMAKERS INC
Also Called: Taste of Heaven Original Gourm
628 Roscoe Ave (44306-2131)
PHONE.................................330 352-1096
Ben Thurman, *President*
EMP: 3
SALES (est): 210.3K **Privately Held**
SIC: 2035 Pickles, sauces & salad dressings

(G-470)
WEST MOTORSPORTS INC
Also Called: Weldon West
1018 Ironwood Rd Ste A (44306-4217)
PHONE.................................330 350-0375
Weldon West, *President*
EMP: 3
SQ FT: 8,000
SALES (est): 324K **Privately Held**
SIC: 3312 Tool & die steel

(G-471)
WHITE INDUSTRIAL TOOL INC
Also Called: White Tool
102 W Wilbeth Rd (44301-2415)
PHONE.................................330 773-6889
Fax: 330 773-4250
Ronald White Jr, *President*
Richard White, *Vice Pres*
Christopher White, *Treasurer*
Ronald White Sr, *Shareholder*
Robert White, *Admin Sec*
EMP: 15
SQ FT: 18,000
SALES: 1.2MM **Privately Held**
WEB: www.whitetool.com
SIC: 3546 Power-driven handtools

(G-472)
WILKES ENERGY INC
17 S Main St Ste 101a (44308-1803)
PHONE.................................330 252-4560
Scott Wilkes, *President*
EMP: 4
SALES (est): 442.5K **Privately Held**
SIC: 1382 Oil & gas exploration services

(G-473)
WINSELL INCORPORATED
1720 Merriman Rd Unit J (44313-5280)
PHONE.................................330 836-7421
Fred Shockey, *CEO*
Jared Smith, *Executive Asst*
EMP: 3
SALES (est): 650.5K **Privately Held**
SIC: 2821 Plastics materials & resins

(G-474)
WMI GROUP LLC
Also Called: Ohio Metal Services
219 Annadale Ave (44304-1903)
PHONE.................................330 535-8848
Steve Riesner, *Plant Mgr*
Pat Woolard, *Manager*
John C Purdy,
EMP: 15
SQ FT: 60,000
SALES (est): 1.4MM **Privately Held**
SIC: 3545 Measuring tools & machines, machinists' metalworking type

(G-475)
YANKE BIONICS INC (PA)
303 W Exchange St (44302-1702)
PHONE.................................330 762-6411
Fax: 330 762-4110
Mark Yanke, *President*
Michele Hogan, *General Mgr*
Gary Charton, *Vice Pres*
Jean Peluso, *Purch Agent*
Jerry Bernar, *Engineer*
EMP: 44
SQ FT: 15,000

SALES (est): 10.5MM **Privately Held**
SIC: 3842 Limbs, artificial; braces, orthopedic

(G-476)
YANKE BIONICS INC
3975 Embassy Pkwy Ste 1 (44333-8321)
PHONE.................................330 668-4070
Gary Charton, *Branch Mgr*
Greg James, *Director*
EMP: 5
SALES (corp-wide): 10.5MM **Privately Held**
SIC: 3842 Limbs, artificial; braces, orthopedic
PA: Yanke Bionics Inc
303 W Exchange St
Akron OH 44302
330 762-6411

(G-477)
YES PRESS PRINTING CO
720 E Glenwood Ave Front (44310-3400)
PHONE.................................330 535-8398
Philip Freeman, *Owner*
EMP: 3
SQ FT: 2,500
SALES (est): 190K **Privately Held**
SIC: 2752 Commercial printing, offset

(G-478)
YOUR PERSONAL JEWELER INC
1262 Weathervane Ln (44313-5102)
PHONE.................................330 836-2446
Daniel Collins, *President*
Deborah Siven, *Co-Owner*
EMP: 3
SALES: 150K **Privately Held**
SIC: 5944 7631 3911 Jewelry stores; jewelry repair services; jewelry, precious metal

(G-479)
YUGO MOLD INC
1733 Wadsworth Rd (44320-3141)
PHONE.................................330 606-0710
Fax: 330 745-0914
Sam Milkovich, *Ch of Bd*
Zack Milkovich, *President*
Milo Milkovich, *Vice Pres*
EMP: 17
SQ FT: 6,050
SALES (est): 1.6MM **Privately Held**
SIC: 3544 Industrial molds

Albany
Athens County

(G-480)
HILL JAMES R & HILL EARLEY W
41085 Townsend Rd (45710-9067)
PHONE.................................740 591-4203
James R Hill, *Partner*
Early W Hill, *Partner*
Randy Hill, *Park Mgr*
EMP: 3
SALES: 110K **Privately Held**
SIC: 2082 Beer (alcoholic beverage)

Alexandria
Licking County

(G-481)
SPANISH LNGAGE PRODUCTIONS INC
3017 Mounts Rd (43001-9755)
PHONE.................................614 737-3424
Rocio Reyes-Moore, *President*
David R Moore, *CFO*
EMP: 5
SQ FT: 11,000
SALES: 700K **Privately Held**
WEB: www.spanlanpro.com
SIC: 2731 Textbooks: publishing & printing

Alger
Hardin County

(G-482)
WIWA LLC
107 N Main St (45812)
P.O. Box 398 (45812-0398)
PHONE.................................419 757-0141
Heidrun Wagner-Turczak, *President*
Jeffery Wold, *General Mgr*
Jeffrey Wold, *General Mgr*
▲ EMP: 10
SQ FT: 12,000
SALES (est): 1MM
SALES (corp-wide): 22.5MM **Privately Held**
WEB: www.wiwa.com
SIC: 3563 Spraying & dusting equipment
PA: Wiwa Wilhelm Wagner Gmbh & Co. Kg
Gewerbestr. 1-3
Lahnau 35633
644 160-90

(G-483)
WIWA LP
107 N Main St (45812)
P.O. Box 398 (45812-0398)
PHONE.................................419 757-0141
Jeffrey T Wold, *Principal*
EMP: 10
SALES (est): 1.6MM **Privately Held**
SIC: 3563 Robots for industrial spraying, painting, etc.

Alledonia
Belmont County

(G-484)
AMERICAN COAL CO
56854 Pleasant Ridge Rd (43902-9716)
PHONE.................................740 926-1372
EMP: 3
SALES (est): 131.8K **Privately Held**
SIC: 1221 Bituminous coal & lignite-surface mining

(G-485)
MAPLE CREEK MINING INC (PA)
56854 Pleasant Ridge Rd (43902-9716)
PHONE.................................740 926-9205
Fax: 740 926-9112
Robert E Murray, *President*
John Ferelli, *Vice Pres*
Michael Loiacono, *Treasurer*
Robert Moore, *Controller*
Jerry Taylor, *Director*
EMP: 1
SALES (est): 27.6MM **Privately Held**
SIC: 1222 Bituminous coal-underground mining

Alliance
Stark County

(G-486)
A J OSTER FOILS LLC
2081 Mccrea St (44601-2793)
PHONE.................................330 823-1700
Fax: 330 823-1705
Kevin Bense, *President*
Brian V Haar, *General Mgr*
Alexander B Jourdan, *General Mgr*
Robert M James, *Vice Pres*
Beth Riordan, *Safety Mgr*
▲ EMP: 53
SQ FT: 80,000
SALES (est): 15MM
SALES (corp-wide): 1.3B **Publicly Held**
SIC: 3341 3353 3471 3497 Secondary nonferrous metals; aluminum sheet, plate & foil; plating & polishing; metal foil & leaf; metals service centers & offices
HQ: A.J. Oster, Llc
301 Metro Center Blvd # 204
Warwick RI 02886
401 736-2600

(G-487)
A R SCHOPPS SONS INC
14536 Oyster Rd (44601-9243)
P.O. Box 2513 (44601-0513)
PHONE.................................330 821-8406
Fax: 330 821-5080
Robert Schopp, *President*
Joe Russo, *General Mgr*
David Schopp, *Vice Pres*
Larry Miller, *Accountant*
Mary Schopp, *Admin Sec*
▲ EMP: 50 EST: 1898
SQ FT: 3,084
SALES (est): 3.1MM **Privately Held**
WEB: www.arschopp.com
SIC: 3931 Organ parts & materials

(G-488)
ACME INDUSTRIAL GROUP INC
540 N Freedom Ave (44601-1816)
P.O. Box 2388 (44601-0388)
PHONE.................................330 821-3900
Richard Burton Jr, *President*
Cindy Hardy, *Purchasing*
Deborah Burton, *Treasurer*
Ray Maki, *Office Mgr*
EMP: 14 EST: 1952
SALES (est): 1.7MM **Privately Held**
WEB: www.acme-chrome.com
SIC: 3471 Electroplating & plating; chromium plating of metals or formed products

(G-489)
ALL COATINGS CO INC
510 W Ely St (44601-1610)
PHONE.................................330 821-3806
Scott Brothers, *President*
Wanda Lou Brothers, *Corp Secy*
EMP: 7
SQ FT: 70,000
SALES (est): 910K **Privately Held**
SIC: 2951 2851 Asphalt paving mixtures & blocks; paints & paint additives

(G-490)
ALLIANCE ABRASIVES LLC
23649 State Route 62 (44601-9027)
P.O. Box 3447 (44601)
PHONE.................................330 823-7957
Fax: 330 821-7033
Tom Boylan, *President*
Larry L Hunter, *President*
Darlene Hunter, *Corp Secy*
Jerry Reed, *Prdtn Mgr*
Jill Stryffeler, *Cust Svc Mgr*
▲ EMP: 15
SQ FT: 12,000
SALES (est): 1.6MM **Privately Held**
WEB: www.allianceabrasives.com
SIC: 3291 Abrasive products

(G-491)
ALLIANCE CASTINGS COMPANY LLC
1001 E Broadway St (44601-2602)
PHONE.................................330 829-5600
Fax: 330 823-2822
David Goodwin, *Principal*
Joe Harsh, *Administration*
▲ EMP: 20
SALES (est): 6.4MM
SALES (corp-wide): 2B **Privately Held**
WEB: www.alliancecastings.com
SIC: 3743 Railroad equipment
HQ: Amsted Rail Company, Inc.
311 S Wacker Dr Ste 5300
Chicago IL 60606
312 922-4501

(G-492)
ALLIANCE DIE DESIGN & MFG
230 Buckeye Ave (44601-1598)
P.O. Box 2604 (44601-0604)
PHONE.................................330 821-2440
Fax: 330 821-2550
Daniel Dimit, *President*
Arthur Reiber, *Corp Secy*
David Rownd, *Vice Pres*
EMP: 6
SALES: 1.3MM **Privately Held**
SIC: 3542 Presses: forming, stamping, punching, sizing (machine tools)

▲ = Import ▼=Export
◆ =Import/Export

(G-493)
ALLIANCE EQUIPMENT COMPANY INC
1000 N Union Ave (44601-1392)
PHONE..................................330 821-2291
Patricia Antonosanti, *President*
Matthew Antonosanti, *Vice Pres*
Edna Truffell, *Office Mgr*
▲ **EMP:** 11
SQ FT: 49,000
SALES (est): 1.2MM **Privately Held**
SIC: 3089 Plastic & fiberglass tanks

(G-494)
ALLIANCE FORGING GROUP LLC
12240 Rockhill Ave Ne (44601-1064)
PHONE..................................330 680-4861
David Risher, *CEO*
Alissa Bryan, *Admin Asst*
EMP: 10
SQ FT: 100,000
SALES (est): 1.6MM **Privately Held**
SIC: 3462 Ornamental metal forgings, ferrous

(G-495)
ALLIANCE PUBLISHING CO INC (HQ)
Also Called: Review, The
40 S Linden Ave (44601-2447)
P.O. Box 2180 (44601-0180)
PHONE..................................330 453-1304
Fax: 330 821-8258
Chuck Dix, *President*
Mike Brown, *Editor*
David E Dix, *Vice Pres*
R Victor Dix, *Vice Pres*
Robert C Dix, *Vice Pres*
EMP: 125 **EST:** 1888
SQ FT: 25,000
SALES (est): 36.2MM
SALES (corp-wide): 567.1MM **Privately Held**
WEB: www.alliancelink.com
SIC: 2711 2752 Newspapers, publishing & printing; commercial printing, lithographic
PA: Wooster Republican Printing Co
212 E Liberty St
Wooster OH
330 264-3511

(G-496)
ANSTINE MACHINING CORP
15835 Armour St Ne (44601-9349)
P.O. Box 3734 (44601-7734)
PHONE..................................330 821-4365
Fax: 330 821-4382
Michael Anstine, *President*
Edward Curry, *Manager*
EMP: 18
SQ FT: 23,000
SALES (est): 3.6MM **Privately Held**
SIC: 3599 3441 Machine shop, jobbing & repair; fabricated structural metal

(G-497)
BANCO DIE INC
11322 Union Ave Ne (44601-1398)
PHONE..................................330 821-8511
Fax: 330 821-7218
Michael Bresnahan, *President*
Joseph E Bender, *Vice Pres*
Patti Bresnahan, *Treasurer*
Chris Carmen, *Manager*
Martha Bender, *Admin Sec*
EMP: 15 **EST:** 1948
SQ FT: 7,500
SALES (est): 1.3MM **Privately Held**
SIC: 3544 Special dies, tools, jigs & fixtures

(G-498)
BAYLEY ENVELOPE INC
119 E State St (44601-4933)
PHONE..................................330 821-2150
Fax: 330 386-4343
Margret Mangano, *President*
Tom Babb, *Vice Pres*
Tim Vanfosson, *Vice Pres*
Michael Hoover, *Treasurer*
EMP: 5
SQ FT: 20,000
SALES (corp-wide): 580K **Privately Held**
SIC: 2677 Envelopes

PA: Luzerne Company
48941 Clctta Smthferry Rd
East Liverpool OH

(G-499)
BRIAN FRANKS ELECTRIC INC
11424 Beech St Ne (44601-8705)
PHONE..................................330 821-5457
Fax: 330 821-3522
Brian Frank, *President*
Tracy Frank, *Admin Sec*
EMP: 3
SALES (est): 250K **Privately Held**
SIC: 7694 Electric motor repair

(G-500)
C JS SIGNS
1670 Charl Ann Dr (44601-3688)
PHONE..................................330 821-7446
Fax: 330 821-7446
Christopher Liebhart, *Owner*
EMP: 6 **EST:** 1998
SALES (est): 400K **Privately Held**
SIC: 3993 Signs & advertising specialties

(G-501)
CARNATION ELC MTR REPR SLS INC
232 N Lincoln Ave (44601-1600)
PHONE..................................330 823-7116
Jim Wyman, *President*
Jennifer Wyman, *Business Mgr*
EMP: 5
SQ FT: 3,600
SALES (est): 1.7MM **Privately Held**
SIC: 7694 5999 Electric motor repair; motors, electric

(G-502)
CARNATION MACHINE & TOOL INC
14632 Oyster Rd (44601-9244)
PHONE..................................330 823-5352
Fax: 330 823-9600
A Edgar Smith Jr, *President*
Carol Smith, *Corp Secy*
Larry Haupt, *Manager*
EMP: 6
SQ FT: 4,200
SALES: 270K **Privately Held**
SIC: 3599 Machine shop, jobbing & repair

(G-503)
CENTRAL COATED PRODUCTS INC
2025 Mccrea St (44601-2794)
P.O. Box 3348 (44601-7348)
PHONE..................................330 821-9830
Fax: 330 821-3114
Thomas A Tormey, *President*
Steven T Porter, *Treasurer*
Michael Savage, *Human Resources*
Jeff Porter, *Sales Mgr*
Don Mayle, *Accounts Mgr*
▲ **EMP:** 60
SQ FT: 77,500
SALES (est): 24.5MM **Privately Held**
WEB: www.centralcoated.net
SIC: 2672 2671 Coated & laminated paper; paper coated or laminated for packaging

(G-504)
DANGO & DIENENTHAL INC
21 E Chestnut St (44601-4950)
P.O. Box 2870 (44601-0870)
PHONE..................................330 829-0277
Jorg Dienenthal, *President*
Rainer Dango, *Admin Sec*
EMP: 3
SQ FT: 19,000
SALES: 475K
SALES (corp-wide): 1.3MM **Privately Held**
SIC: 3549 Metalworking machinery
PA: Dango & Dienenthal Gmbh & Co. Kg
Hagener Str. 103
Siegen 57072
271 401-0

(G-505)
DAVIS TECHNOLOGIES INC
Also Called: Dti
837 W Main St (44601-2208)
PHONE..................................330 823-2544

Fax: 330 823-0879
Robert W Dillon, *President*
Douglas E Anderson, *Vice Pres*
James R Dillon, *Treasurer*
Richard N Dillon, *Admin Sec*
EMP: 15
SQ FT: 7,500
SALES (est): 750K **Privately Held**
WEB: www.davistechnologies.com
SIC: 8711 3625 Engineering services; control equipment, electric

(G-506)
FILNOR INC (PA)
227 N Freedom Ave (44601-1897)
P.O. Box 2328 (44601-0328)
PHONE..................................330 821-8731
Fax: 330 821-6627
Ronald L Neely, *CEO*
James C Neely, *President*
Craig Clarke, *Vice Pres*
Daren Szekely, *Vice Pres*
Dave Yarian, *Safety Mgr*
▲ **EMP:** 12 **EST:** 1970
SQ FT: 72,000
SALES (est): 8.6MM **Privately Held**
WEB: www.filnor.com
SIC: 3625 5063 Electric controls & control accessories, industrial; switches, electric power; resistors & resistor units; electrical apparatus & equipment

(G-507)
FILNOR INC
181 N Arch Ave (44601-2413)
PHONE..................................330 829-3180
Lottie Roach, *Manager*
EMP: 9
SQ FT: 7,854
SALES (corp-wide): 8.6MM **Privately Held**
WEB: www.filnor.com
SIC: 3625 Electric controls & control accessories, industrial
PA: Filnor, Inc.
227 N Freedom Ave
Alliance OH 44601
330 821-8731

(G-508)
FILNOR INC
227 N Freedom Ave (44601-1897)
P.O. Box 2328 (44601-0328)
PHONE..................................330 821-7667
Lottie Roach, *Branch Mgr*
EMP: 15
SQ FT: 5,712
SALES (corp-wide): 8.6MM **Privately Held**
WEB: www.filnor.com
SIC: 3625 3676 3643 3613 Electric controls & control accessories, industrial; electronic resistors; current-carrying wiring devices; knife switches, electric
PA: Filnor, Inc.
227 N Freedom Ave
Alliance OH 44601
330 821-8731

(G-509)
FOREPLEASURE
14461 Gaskill Dr Ne (44601-1142)
PHONE..................................330 821-1293
Kathleen Miller, *Principal*
EMP: 3
SALES (est): 212.3K **Privately Held**
SIC: 2252 Hosiery

(G-510)
GBC METALS LLC
Also Called: Olin Brass
2081 Mccrea St (44601-2704)
PHONE..................................330 823-1700
Beth Tirey, *General Mgr*
Jeff Chaney, *Info Tech Mgr*
EMP: 50
SALES (corp-wide): 1.3B **Publicly Held**
SIC: 2812 Caustic soda, sodium hydroxide
HQ: Gbc Metals, Llc
427 N Shamrock St
East Alton IL 62024
618 258-2350

(G-511)
GNW ALUMINUM INC
1356 Beeson St Ne (44601-6201)
P.O. Box 2418 (44601-0418)
PHONE..................................330 821-7955
Fax: 330 821-7911
Nathan Hoopes, *President*
Adam Hoopes, *Vice Pres*
Beatrice K Hoopes, *Treasurer*
EMP: 40
SALES (est): 9.3MM **Privately Held**
SIC: 3341 Aluminum smelting & refining (secondary)

(G-512)
HAISS FABRIPART LLC
22421 Lake Park Blvd (44601-3469)
PHONE..................................330 821-2028
Duane Stuckey, *Sales Executive*
Valerie G Giarrana, *Manager*
Lonna Roberts, *Manager*
Moritz Haiss,
EMP: 30
SQ FT: 6,600
SALES: 4MM **Privately Held**
SIC: 3599 Machine & other job shop work

(G-513)
HARTLEY MACHINE INC
22640 Hartley Rd (44601-6908)
PHONE..................................330 821-0343
Fax: 330 821-5114
Thomas Poto, *President*
Judy B Poto, *Vice Pres*
EMP: 4 **EST:** 1951
SQ FT: 5,000
SALES: 350K **Privately Held**
SIC: 3599 7692 3444 Machine shop, jobbing & repair; welding repair; sheet metalwork

(G-514)
HILLES BURIAL VAULTS INC
2145 S Union Ave (44601-4961)
PHONE..................................330 823-2251
Michael Hilles, *President*
Todd Andrie, *Admin Sec*
EMP: 3 **EST:** 1923
SQ FT: 624
SALES (est): 378.5K **Privately Held**
SIC: 3272 Burial vaults, concrete or precast terrazzo; monuments, concrete

(G-515)
HOLOPHANE LIGHTING
12720 Beech St Ne (44601-8778)
PHONE..................................330 823-5535
Steve Oyster, *Principal*
EMP: 4
SALES (est): 30.6K **Privately Held**
WEB: www.holophanelighting.com
SIC: 3646 Commercial indusl & institutional electric lighting fixtures

(G-516)
HOOPES FERTILIZER WORKS INC
9866 Freshley Ave Ne # 166 (44601-8794)
PHONE..................................330 821-3550
Steve Hoopes, *Manager*
EMP: 4
SALES (corp-wide): 1.8MM **Privately Held**
WEB: www.hooverfence.com
SIC: 2875 Fertilizers, mixing only
PA: Hoopes Fertilizer Works, Inc
24104 Us Route 30
East Rochester OH 44625
330 894-2121

(G-517)
HYKON MANUFACTURING COMPANY
163 E State St (44601-4933)
P.O. Box 3800 (44601-7800)
PHONE..................................330 821-8889
Fax: 330 821-2320
Douglas Duchon, *President*
Brenda Duchon, *Vice Pres*
EMP: 3
SQ FT: 3,000
SALES: 400K **Privately Held**
SIC: 3499 3545 Reels, cable: metal; measuring tools & machines, machinists' metalworking type

(G-518)
INNOVATIVE WLDG & DESIGN LLC
24946 Hartley Rd (44601-9015)
PHONE..................................330 581-1316
Eric Peters,
EMP: 3
SALES (est): 50.2K **Privately Held**
SIC: 7692 Welding repair

(G-519)
JARMAN PRINTING COMPANY LLC
350 S Union Ave (44601-2664)
P.O. Box 2505 (44601-0505)
PHONE..................................330 823-8585
Fax: 330 823-8575
Krista Jarvis, *Mng Member*
Randal Jarvis,
EMP: 6
SQ FT: 6,500
SALES (est): 888.5K **Privately Held**
SIC: 2752 2759 Lithographing on metal; letterpress printing

(G-520)
KARRIER COMPANY INC
1065 S Liberty Ave (44601-4061)
PHONE..................................330 823-9597
Bob Church, *Owner*
Wayne R Church, *Owner*
Holly Church, *Co-Owner*
EMP: 3 **EST:** 1998
SQ FT: 5,000
SALES (est): 230K **Privately Held**
WEB: www.karrierco.com
SIC: 3612 Vibrators, interrupter

(G-521)
KEENER RUBBER COMPANY
14700 Commerce St Ne (44601-1099)
P.O. Box 2717 (44601-0717)
PHONE..................................330 821-1880
Fax: 330 821-4246
Richard A Michelson, *CEO*
Barbara Cinson, *COO*
EMP: 28
SQ FT: 30,000
SALES (est): 5.2MM **Privately Held**
WEB: www.keenerrubber.com
SIC: 3069 Rubber bands

(G-522)
LEXINGTON ABRASIVES INC
Also Called: Sancap Abrasives
16123 Armour St Ne (44601-9301)
PHONE..................................330 821-1166
Robert Stuhlmiller, *President*
Michael A Ogline, *Principal*
Mike Chunko, *Vice Pres*
Ray Strickland, *Sls & Mktg Exec*
Cheryl M Farland, *Controller*
▲ **EMP:** 80
SQ FT: 540,000
SALES (est): 16.1MM **Privately Held**
WEB: www.sancapabrasives.com
SIC: 3291 Coated abrasive products

(G-523)
MAC MANUFACTURING INC (PA)
14599 Commerce St Ne (44601-1003)
PHONE..................................330 823-9900
Michael Conny, *Principal*
Jenny Conny, *Corp Secy*
Dan Tubbs, *Vice Pres*
▲ **EMP:** 700
SALES (est): 270.9MM **Privately Held**
SIC: 3715 5012 Truck trailers; trailers for trucks, new & used; truck bodies

(G-524)
MAC STEEL TRAILER LTD
14599 Commerce St Ne (44601-1003)
PHONE..................................330 823-9900
Michael A Conny, *Mng Member*
Tony Sparks, *Manager*
EMP: 40
SALES (est): 297.4K **Privately Held**
SIC: 3715 Truck trailers

(G-525)
MAC TRAILER MANUFACTURING INC (PA)
14599 Commerce St Ne (44601-1003)
PHONE..................................330 823-9900
Fax: 330 823-0232
Mike Conny, *President*
John Raymond, *COO*
Ben Childers, *Vice Pres*
Tay Griffith, *Vice Pres*
David Sandor, *Vice Pres*
▲ **EMP:** 238
SQ FT: 220,000
SALES (est): 149.4MM **Privately Held**
SIC: 3715 5012 5013 5015 Truck trailers; trailers for trucks, new & used; truck bodies; motor vehicle supplies & new parts; motor vehicle parts, used; trailer repair

(G-526)
MARLBORO MANUFACTURING INC
11750 Marlboro Ave Ne (44601-9798)
PHONE..................................330 935-2221
Fax: 330 935-2748
Thomas Naughton, *President*
Renee Milliken, *President*
Daniel Lough, *Vice Pres*
Patrick Whitaker, *Vice Pres*
Danny Stangelo, *Manager*
▲ **EMP:** 50 **EST:** 1960
SQ FT: 54,000
SALES (est): 12.9MM **Privately Held**
WEB: www.marlborohinge.com
SIC: 3429 Manufactured hardware (general); piano hardware

(G-527)
MILLS ALUMINUM FAB
W 23 Rd St (44601)
PHONE..................................330 821-4108
Christine Miller, *Owner*
EMP: 4
SALES (est): 320.4K **Privately Held**
SIC: 3499 Fabricated metal products

(G-528)
MORGAN ENGINEERING SYSTEMS INC
1182 E Summit St (44601-3224)
PHONE..................................330 821-4721
Beverly Montagner, *Purch Dir*
James Broch, *Branch Mgr*
EMP: 45
SALES (corp-wide): 27.5MM **Privately Held**
WEB: www.morganengineering.com
SIC: 3536 Cranes, overhead traveling
PA: Morgan Engineering Systems, Inc.
1049 S Mahoning Ave
Alliance OH 44601
330 823-6130

(G-529)
MORGAN ENGINEERING SYSTEMS INC
1049 S Mahoning Ave (44601-3212)
PHONE..................................330 823-6120
Mark Fedor, *President*
Doris Mercer, *Human Resources*
EMP: 45
SQ FT: 952
SALES (corp-wide): 27.5MM **Privately Held**
WEB: www.morganengineering.com
SIC: 3536 Hoists, cranes & monorails
PA: Morgan Engineering Systems, Inc.
1049 S Mahoning Ave
Alliance OH 44601
330 823-6130

(G-530)
MOUNT UNION PATTERN WORKS INC
920 Auld St (44601-3239)
PHONE..................................330 821-2274
Fax: 330 821-0908
Jeff Ruggles, *President*
Marjorie Ruggles, *Admin Sec*
EMP: 3
SQ FT: 10,000
SALES (est): 300K **Privately Held**
SIC: 3543 Industrial patterns

(G-531)
NORTH COAST PROFILE INC
255 E Perry St (44601-1774)
PHONE..................................330 823-7777
Dewayne Frank, *President*
EMP: 4
SALES (est): 450K **Privately Held**
SIC: 3547 3444 Ferrous & nonferrous mill equipment, auxiliary; sheet metalwork

(G-532)
P & E SALES LTD
1595 W Main St (44601-2104)
P.O. Box 382, North Benton (44449-0382)
PHONE..................................330 829-0100
Fax: 330 829-2364
Paul J Tatulinski, *President*
Ellen Tatulinski, *Vice Pres*
EMP: 8
SQ FT: 5,600
SALES (est): 550K **Privately Held**
SIC: 3053 5085 Gaskets, packing & sealing devices; gaskets & seals

(G-533)
PHILLIPS MFG & MCH CORP
118 1/2 E Ely St (44601-1809)
P.O. Box 2627 (44601-0627)
PHONE..................................330 823-9178
Fax: 330 823-3155
Deborah L Williamson, *President*
EMP: 9 **EST:** 1914
SQ FT: 20,000
SALES (est): 364.5K **Privately Held**
SIC: 3599 Machine shop, jobbing & repair

(G-534)
QUALITY OIL & GAS CORP
1654 S Union Ave (44601-4349)
P.O. Box 3756 (44601-7756)
PHONE..................................330 821-6375
Fax: 330 821-4830
Timothy J Lanzer, *President*
EMP: 6
SQ FT: 4,800
SALES (est): 1MM **Privately Held**
SIC: 1381 Drilling oil & gas wells

(G-535)
SALLY BEAUTY SUPPLY LLC
2636 W State St (44601-5699)
PHONE..................................330 823-7476
Nicole Yoder, *Manager*
Tina Houston, *Manager*
EMP: 4
SALES (corp-wide): 3.9B **Publicly Held**
WEB: www.sallybeauty.com
SIC: 5087 2844 Beauty parlor equipment & supplies; toilet preparations
HQ: Sally Beauty Supply Llc
3001 Colorado Blvd
Denton TX 76210
940 898-7500

(G-536)
SAMS GRAPHIC INDUSTRIES
611 Homeworth Rd (44601-9072)
PHONE..................................330 821-4710
Sam Schuette, *Owner*
EMP: 10
SQ FT: 6,000
SALES (est): 150K **Privately Held**
WEB: www.graphicind.com
SIC: 2796 2759 Engraving platemaking services; engraving

(G-537)
SCOTT A ZURBRUGG
Also Called: Zurbrugg Machine
6016 Union Ave Ne (44601-9449)
PHONE..................................330 821-9814
Scott A Zurbugg, *Owner*
EMP: 3 **EST:** 1990
SQ FT: 1,200
SALES (est): 159.2K **Privately Held**
SIC: 3599 Machine shop, jobbing & repair

(G-538)
SMITH MACHINE INC
20651 Lake Park Blvd (44601-3319)
PHONE..................................330 821-9898
Fax: 330 823-3051
David F Smith, *President*
Tim Smith, *General Mgr*
Eileen R Smith, *Vice Pres*
EMP: 7 **EST:** 1976

SALES: 670K **Privately Held**
SIC: 3599 Machine shop, jobbing & repair

(G-539)
STEEL EQP SPECIALISTS INC
22623 Lake Park Blvd (44601-3454)
PHONE..................................330 829-2626
Richard L Hansen, *Principal*
Fred Droliff, *Manager*
Jerry Crowl, *Director*
EMP: 25
SALES (corp-wide): 24.3MM **Privately Held**
WEB: www.seseng.com
SIC: 3599 3593 3547 Custom machinery; fluid power cylinders & actuators; rolling mill machinery
PA: Steel Equipment Specialists, Inc.
1507 Beeson St Ne
Alliance OH 44601
330 823-8260

(G-540)
STEEL EQP SPECIALISTS INC (PA)
Also Called: S.E.S.
1507 Beeson St Ne (44601-2142)
PHONE..................................330 823-8260
Fax: 330 821-6350
James R Boughton, *CEO*
T Virgil Huggett, *Ch of Bd*
Tim L Hostetler, *General Mgr*
Doris Gulyas, *Principal*
Said S Kabalan, *Principal*
▲ **EMP:** 72 **EST:** 1976
SQ FT: 32,000
SALES (est): 24.3MM **Privately Held**
WEB: www.seseng.com
SIC: 7699 3599 7629 3593 Industrial machinery & equipment repair; custom machinery; electrical repair shops; fluid power cylinders & actuators; rolling mill machinery; fabricated structural metal

(G-541)
STUCHELL PRODUCTS LLC
Also Called: Sare Plastics
14600 Commerce St Ne (44601-1033)
PHONE..................................330 821-4299
Fax: 330 821-3433
Joe Croft, *Accounts Mgr*
Bart Stuchell,
EMP: 45
SQ FT: 6,000
SALES: 3.5MM **Privately Held**
WEB: www.sareplastics.com
SIC: 3089 Injection molded finished plastic products

(G-542)
SUNAMERICACONVERTING LLC
46 N Rockhill Ave (44601-2211)
PHONE..................................330 821-6300
Amy Campbell, *Controller*
Gaby Ajram,
Howard Davison,
Russ Romocean,
▲ **EMP:** 55
SQ FT: 72,000
SALES (est): 14.8MM **Privately Held**
SIC: 2656 Paper cups, plates, dishes & utensils

(G-543)
T & W FORGE LLC
562 W Ely St (44601-6409)
PHONE..................................216 881-8600
Fax: 330 821-7309
Frank Cappello, *Treasurer*
James P Woidke, *Mng Member*
Chris Andino, *Manager*
Remigijus Belzinskas, *Admin Sec*
▲ **EMP:** 50
SALES (est): 15.7MM
SALES (corp-wide): 119.1MM **Publicly Held**
SIC: 3462 Iron & steel forgings
PA: Sifco Industries, Inc.
970 E 64th St
Cleveland OH 44103
216 881-8600

(G-544)
THOMAS ALLEN CO
1062 Parkside Dr (44601-3734)
PHONE..............................330 823-8487
Fax: 330 823-8487
Scott Celasko, *Owner*
EMP: 3
SALES (est): 216.7K **Privately Held**
SIC: 2759 Commercial printing

(G-545)
TIMKEN COMPANY
22261 Margaret Ln (44601-9099)
PHONE..............................330 471-4791
EMP: 3
SALES (corp-wide): 2.6B **Publicly Held**
SIC: 3562 Ball & roller bearings
PA: The Timken Company
4500 Mount Pleasant St Nw
North Canton OH 44720
234 262-3000

(G-546)
TRANSUE & WILLIAMS STAMPG CORP
930 W Ely St (44601-1500)
PHONE..............................330 821-5777
John Staudt, *Vice Pres*
John Beringer, *Treasurer*
Mary McGean, *Manager*
▲ EMP: 75
SALES (est): 15.9MM **Privately Held**
SIC: 3469 Stamping metal for the trade

(G-547)
TRANSUE WILLIAMS STAMPING INC (HQ)
930 W Ely St (44601-1500)
PHONE..............................330 829-5007
John Staudt, *President*
Jessy Vandygriff, *General Mgr*
John C Beringer, *Treasurer*
Kevin Gerber, *Controller*
Alison Rockwell, *Administration*
▲ EMP: 4
SQ FT: 180,000
SALES (est): 728.5K **Privately Held**
WEB: www.twstamping.com
SIC: 3469 Stamping metal for the trade
PA: Durrel Corporation
8840 Commons Blvd Ste 101
Twinsburg OH 44087
330 405-2555

(G-548)
TREMELO
884 Roseland Rd (44601-3815)
P.O. Box 3041 (44601-7041)
PHONE..............................330 823-6359
Tomas G Broone, *Owner*
EMP: 3
SALES (est): 169.1K **Privately Held**
SIC: 3931 Musical instruments

(G-549)
TRI-SEAL LLC
16125 Armour St Ne (44601-9301)
PHONE..............................330 821-1166
Paul Young, *President*
Robert Larney, *CFO*
Art Richards, *Treasurer*
David Waksman, *Admin Sec*
EMP: 4
SALES (est): 211.6K
SALES (corp-wide): 1.1B **Privately Held**
SIC: 3053 Gaskets & sealing devices
PA: Tekni-Plex, Inc.
460 E Swedesford Rd # 3000
Wayne PA 19087
484 690-1520

(G-550)
TRILOGY PLASTICS INC (PA)
2290 W Main St (44601-2272)
P.O. Box 2600 (44601-0600)
PHONE..............................330 821-4700
Stephen Osborn, *President*
Bruce Frank, *Vice Pres*
Rex Roseberry, *CFO*
EMP: 110
SQ FT: 90,000
SALES (est): 20.6MM **Privately Held**
WEB: www.trilogyplastics.com
SIC: 3089 Molding primary plastic

(G-551)
W J EGLI COMPANY INC (PA)
205 E Columbia St (44601-2563)
P.O. Box 2605 (44601-0605)
PHONE..............................330 823-3666
Fax: 330 823-0011
William J Egli, *President*
Cheryl A Stuffel, *Corp Secy*
Garth Egli, *Vice Pres*
▼ EMP: 15 EST: 1968
SQ FT: 100,000
SALES: 3.5MM **Privately Held**
WEB: www.wjegli.com
SIC: 2541 3496 3498 3444 Display fixtures, wood; miscellaneous fabricated wire products; fabricated pipe & fittings; sheet metalwork; partitions & fixtures, except wood; automotive & apparel trimmings

(G-552)
WEDGE HARDWOOD PRODUCTS
2137 Knox School Rd (44601-6923)
PHONE..............................330 525-7775
Fax: 330 525-7777
Michael Stahl, *Partner*
Jim Hahlen, *Partner*
EMP: 6
SQ FT: 7,200
SALES: 852.5K **Privately Held**
SIC: 2431 Planing mill, millwork

(G-553)
WHITACRE GREER COMPANY (PA)
1400 S Mahoning Ave (44601-3433)
PHONE..............................330 823-1610
Fax: 330 823-5502
Janet Kaboth, *CEO*
J B Whitacre Jr, *Ch of Bd*
L A Morrison, *President*
Christopher Kaboth, *Vice Pres*
Larry Johnson, *Purchasing*
EMP: 38 EST: 1916
SALES (est): 14.3MM **Privately Held**
WEB: www.wgpaver.com
SIC: 3251 3255 Paving brick, clay; clay refractories

(G-554)
WINKLE INDUSTRIES INC
2080 W Main St (44601-2187)
PHONE..............................330 823-9730
Fax: 330 823-9788
Joe Schatz, *CEO*
Jeff McCartney, *Engineer*
Dave Bentz, *Electrical Engi*
Jeffrey Parimuha, *Electrical Engi*
Beth A Felger, *Treasurer*
▲ EMP: 55
SQ FT: 85,000
SALES (est): 12.8MM **Privately Held**
WEB:
SIC: 7699 3499 5063 Industrial machinery & equipment repair; magnets, permanent: metallic; control & signal wire & cable, including coaxial

---

Alpha
Greene County

(G-555)
UNISON INDUSTRIES LLC
Also Called: Elano Machine Operations
530 Orchard Ln (45301)
P.O. Box 135 (45301-0135)
PHONE..............................937 426-4676
Fax: 937 426-9203
EMP: 85
SALES (corp-wide): 123.6B **Publicly Held**
WEB: www.unisonindustries.com
SIC: 3498 3728 3444 Tube fabricating (contract bending & shaping); aircraft parts & equipment; sheet metalwork
HQ: Unison Industries, Llc
7575 Baymeadows Way
Jacksonville FL 32256
904 739-4000

Alvada
Seneca County

(G-556)
PROFLO INDUSTRIES LLC
2679 S Us Highway 23 (44802-9707)
PHONE..............................419 436-6008
Terry Bosserman, *President*
EMP: 20
SQ FT: 12,000
SALES: 4.5MM **Privately Held**
SIC: 3728 Refueling equipment for use in flight, airplane

(G-557)
UPM INC
4777 S Us Highway 23 (44802-9702)
PHONE..............................419 595-2600
Fax: 419 595-2620
Chad Bouillon,
EMP: 4 EST: 1997
SQ FT: 5,000
SALES: 1MM **Privately Held**
SIC: 3599 Machine shop, jobbing & repair

Alvordton
Williams County

(G-558)
PIONEER FABRICATION
17455 County Road P (43501-9734)
PHONE..............................419 737-9464
Robert Sliwinski, *Principal*
EMP: 4
SALES (est): 424.2K **Privately Held**
SIC: 3444 Sheet metalwork

(G-559)
PIONEER INDUSTRIAL SYSTEMS LLC (PA)
16442 Us Highway 20 (43501-9797)
PHONE..............................419 737-9506
Todd Hendricks Sr, *President*
Steve Edwards, *Plant Mgr*
Dan Crawford, *Engineer*
Troy Martin, *Engineer*
Jerry Payton, *Engineer*
▲ EMP: 12
SQ FT: 7,500
SALES (est): 2.6MM **Privately Held**
SIC: 3599 Custom machinery

Amanda
Fairfield County

(G-560)
BUCKEYE PRODUCTS
6745 Chillicothe Lancster (43102-9508)
PHONE..............................740 969-4718
Stuart A Wharton, *Principal*
George Wharton, *Principal*
Terrence Wharton, *Principal*
EMP: 6
SQ FT: 6,000
SALES: 200K **Privately Held**
SIC: 2431 Millwork

(G-561)
CENTRAL OHIO FABRICATION LLC
8143 Bowers Rd Sw (43102-9508)
PHONE..............................740 969-2976
Bob Brown, *Mng Member*
EMP: 4
SQ FT: 4,000
SALES: 1MM **Privately Held**
SIC: 7692 Automotive welding

(G-562)
CLEAR CREEK SCREW MACHINE CORP
4900 Julian Rd Sw (43102-9514)
PHONE..............................740 969-2113
Fax: 740 969-2656
George Bartrom, *President*
EMP: 8
SQ FT: 15,000

SALES (est): 1MM **Privately Held**
SIC: 3599 3451 Machine shop, jobbing & repair; screw machine products

(G-563)
MID-WEST FABRICATING CO (PA)
Also Called: Mid West Fabricating Co
313 N Johns St (43102-9002)
PHONE..............................740 969-4411
Fax: 740 969-4433
Jennifer Johns Friel, *President*
David Gallimore, *General Mgr*
Ann Custer, *Vice Pres*
Jim Wohrer, *Purch Mgr*
Jim Wohror, *Purchasing*
◆ EMP: 125 EST: 1945
SQ FT: 280,000
SALES (est): 28.3MM **Privately Held**
WEB: www.midwestfab.com
SIC: 3714 3524 3452 Tie rods, motor vehicle; lawn & garden tractors & equipment; bolts, metal

---

Amelia
Clermont County

(G-564)
A & A SAFETY INC (PA)
1126 Ferris Rd Bldg A (45102-2376)
PHONE..............................513 943-6100
Fax: 513 943-6106
Ruth H Luttmer, *CEO*
William N Luttmer, *Vice Pres*
T R O'Bian, *Purch Agent*
Francis Luttmer, *Treasurer*
Carol Burchfield, *Accountant*
EMP: 50
SQ FT: 12,300
SALES (est): 19.3MM **Privately Held**
WEB: www.aasafetyinc.com
SIC: 7359 3993 5084 1721 Work zone traffic equipment (flags, cones, barrels, etc.); signs & advertising specialties; safety equipment; painting & paper hanging; highway & street sign installation

(G-565)
ACREO INC
3209 Marshall Dr (45102-9213)
P.O. Box 361, New Richmond (45157-0361)
PHONE..............................513 734-3327
Roger Williams, *President*
EMP: 7
SQ FT: 10,000
SALES (est): 600K **Privately Held**
SIC: 7389 3556 Design, commercial & industrial; food products machinery

(G-566)
ALL WRITE RIBBON INC
3916 Bach Buxton Rd (45102-1014)
P.O. Box 67 (45102-0067)
PHONE..............................513 753-8300
Fax: 513 753-8304
William E Lyon, *President*
Harold Wolfe, *Vice Pres*
Bill Lyon, *CFO*
Robert Sunderman, *Sales Mgr*
Valerie Roof, *Manager*
▲ EMP: 35
SQ FT: 20,000
SALES (est): 3.7MM **Privately Held**
WEB: www.allwriteribbon.com
SIC: 3955 Ribbons, inked: typewriter, adding machine, register, etc.

(G-567)
AMON INC
3214 Marshall Dr (45102-9212)
PHONE..............................513 734-1700
Fax: 513 734-1703
Derrick Campbell, *President*
Naomi Campbell, *Corp Secy*
Greg Campbell, *Vice Pres*
Daniel West, *Plant Mgr*
Donna Hinton, *Shareholder*
EMP: 13
SALES (est): 2.1MM **Privately Held**
WEB: www.amoninc.com
SIC: 3599 Machine shop, jobbing & repair

GEOGRAPHIC

(G-568)
ASAP READY MIX INC
250 Mount Holly Rd (45102-9740)
PHONE..................513 797-1774
Dan Dunham, *Principal*
EMP: 3
SALES (est): 197.5K Privately Held
SIC: 3273 Ready-mixed concrete

(G-569)
BERRY WOODWORKING
2244 Berry Rd (45102-9174)
PHONE..................513 734-6133
Fax: 513 734-2128
Charles Steelman, *Owner*
Elsa Steelman, *Co-Owner*
Chris Luck, *Manager*
EMP: 10
SALES: 600K Privately Held
SIC: 2431 Millwork

(G-570)
CINCINNATI PRINT SOLUTIONS LLC
4007 Bach Buxton Rd (45102-1047)
PHONE..................513 943-9500
Mark Johnson,
EMP: 6
SQ FT: 10,000
SALES (est): 874K Privately Held
SIC: 2752 7334 2759 Commercial printing, lithographic; photocopying & duplicating services; commercial printing

(G-571)
DACA VENDING WHOLESALE LLC
1105b W Ohio Pike (45102-1292)
PHONE..................513 753-1600
Dave Clair,
Dave St Clair,
▲ EMP: 5 EST: 1997
SALES (est): 242.7K Privately Held
SIC: 3999 3651 Slot machines; home entertainment equipment, electronic

(G-572)
DEIMLING/JELIHO PLASTICS INC
4010 Bach Buxton Rd (45102-1048)
PHONE..................513 752-6653
Fax: 513 752-6687
William Deimling, *President*
Mary Ann Deimling, *Corp Secy*
Tom Richards, *Plant Mgr*
Chad Beckett, *QC Mgr*
Jennifer Miller, *Sales Staff*
▲ EMP: 83
SQ FT: 60,000
SALES (est): 23.6MM Privately Held
WEB: www.deimling-jeliho.com
SIC: 3089 3599 Injection molding of plastics; machine shop, jobbing & repair

(G-573)
EAGLE COACH INC
Also Called: Eagle Coach Company
3344 State Route 132 (45102-2249)
PHONE..................513 797-4100
Fax: 513 797-6833
Eric Yeager, *President*
Don Worrall, *General Mgr*
Tim Lautermilch, *Principal*
Christy Kellerman, *Corp Secy*
Raj Menon, *COO*
EMP: 60
SQ FT: 150,000
SALES (est): 12.8MM Privately Held
WEB: www.eaglecoachcompany.com
SIC: 3711 Hearses (motor vehicles), assembly of

(G-574)
EAST FORK PRECISION MACHINE LL
3874 Gordon Dr (45102-1043)
PHONE..................513 753-4157
EMP: 3 EST: 2001
SALES (est): 170K Privately Held
SIC: 3599 Mfg Industrial Machinery

(G-575)
EGER PRODUCTS INC (PA)
1132 Ferris Rd (45102-1020)
PHONE..................513 753-4200
Fax: 513 753-9888
Reva Eger, *President*
Jerome Schildmeyer, *Principal*
Richard Koebbe, *Vice Pres*
Sherry Sandusjy, *Finance Mgr*
Brandon Sandusky, *Sales Mgr*
EMP: 60
SQ FT: 38,400
SALES: 28MM Privately Held
WEB: www.egerproducts.com
SIC: 3644 3544 5039 Insulators & insulation materials, electrical; forms (molds), for foundry & plastics working machinery; ceiling systems & products

(G-576)
HAMILTON SAFE AMELIA
3997 Bach Buxton Rd (45102-1013)
PHONE..................513 753-5694
Fax: 513 753-9759
Ansil Perry, *President*
William Fennessy, *Vice Pres*
EMP: 18
SQ FT: 45,000
SALES (est): 2.9MM
SALES (corp-wide): 5.3MM Privately Held
SIC: 3499 Safes & vaults, metal
PA: Hamilton Safe Co.
7775 Cooper Rd
Cincinnati OH 45242
513 874-3733

(G-577)
INDUCTIVE COMPONENTS MFG
Also Called: I C M I
1200 Ferris Rd (45102-1022)
P.O. Box 188 (45102-0188)
PHONE..................513 752-4731
Fax: 513 752-4738
Dirk W Mooibroek, *President*
Brad Hessey, *Vice Pres*
Sonja M Mooibroek, *Treasurer*
EMP: 25
SQ FT: 11,000
SALES (est): 4.3MM Privately Held
WEB: www.icmiinc.com
SIC: 3625 Electric controls & control accessories, industrial

(G-578)
JABCO & ASSOCIATES INC
1188 Ferris Rd (45102-1046)
PHONE..................513 752-0600
Fax: 513 752-6640
Mike Spicer, *President*
Tom Munninghoff, *Vice Pres*
Mike Spicer, *Plant Mgr*
EMP: 5
SQ FT: 20,000
SALES (est): 900K Privately Held
SIC: 2841 5169 Detergents, synthetic organic or inorganic alkaline; detergents

(G-579)
MARK J MYERS (PA)
Also Called: Heritage Tool & Manufacturing
80 W Main St (45102-1736)
PHONE..................513 753-7300
Mark J Myers, *Owner*
Bob Williams, *Plant Mgr*
EMP: 2
SALES (est): 1.7MM Privately Held
SIC: 3599 Machine shop, jobbing & repair

(G-580)
MOBILE CONVERSIONS INC
3354 State Route 132 (45102-2249)
PHONE..................513 797-1991
Fax: 513 797-1992
Michael G Dobbins, *President*
Steven Dobbins, *Business Mgr*
EMP: 14
SQ FT: 2,176
SALES (est): 1.8MM Privately Held
WEB: www.mobileconversions.com
SIC: 7532 2451 Van conversion; mobile homes

(G-581)
ONLINE ENGINEERING CORPORATION
3947 Bach Buxton Rd (45102-1013)
PHONE..................513 561-8878
Fax: 513 561-9944
Richard Hittinger, *President*
Jane Hittinger, *Shareholder*
▼ EMP: 6
SQ FT: 4,000
SALES (est): 750K Privately Held
WEB: www.onlineengineeringcorp.com
SIC: 3914 Stainless steel ware

(G-582)
QUEEN CITY TOOL COMPANY INC
Also Called: Queen City Bearers
3939 Bach Buxton Rd (45102-1013)
PHONE..................513 752-4200
James Erb, *President*
EMP: 3
SQ FT: 8,000
SALES (est): 421.3K Privately Held
WEB: www.bearers.com
SIC: 3599 Machine & other job shop work

(G-583)
SOLUTIONS PLUS INC
3907 Bach Buxton Rd (45102-1013)
PHONE..................513 943-9600
Fax: 513 943-9609
Charles R Weaver, *President*
Nancy D Weaver, *Vice Pres*
Bill Sechrist, *Opers Mgr*
Mike Gwin, *VP Sales*
EMP: 20
SQ FT: 15,000
SALES (est): 5.5MM Privately Held
WEB: www.spiworld.com
SIC: 2842 Industrial plant disinfectants or deodorants

(G-584)
STEWART FILMSCREEN CORP
3919 Bach Buxton Rd (45102-1013)
PHONE..................513 753-0800
Fax: 513 753-0854
Grant Stewart, *President*
Diana Ha, *Opers Mgr*
Cherie Stanton, *Engineer*
Josh Webb, *Engineer*
Manfred Freiberger, *Sales Staff*
EMP: 30
SALES (corp-wide): 30.5MM Privately Held
SIC: 3861 Screens, projection
PA: Stewart Filmscreen Corp.
1161 Sepulveda Blvd
Torrance CA 90502
310 326-1422

(G-585)
SUN CHEMICAL CORPORATION
Colors Dispersion Division
3922 Bach Buxton Rd (45102-1098)
PHONE..................513 753-9550
Fax: 513 753-8376
Edward Polaski, *General Mgr*
John Rozier, *Mfg Staff*
Lori Pennavaria, *Purchasing*
Matthew Wolfe, *Purchasing*
Jennifer Smith, *Controller*
EMP: 90
SQ FT: 7,200
SALES (corp-wide): 6.7B Privately Held
WEB: www.sunchemical.com
SIC: 2893 2865 Printing ink; cyclic crudes & intermediates
HQ: Sun Chemical Corporation
35 Waterview Blvd Ste 100
Parsippany NJ 07054
973 404-6000

(G-586)
THEDKAHN LLC
Also Called: Ufo's
15 Eagle Ct (45102-2162)
PHONE..................239 961-8757
Cristopher Konopka,
Jessica Huff,
Donald Yoest,
EMP: 3
SALES (est): 226.1K Privately Held
SIC: 2621 7389 Cigarette paper;

(G-587)
TRI-STATE FABRICATORS INC
1146 Ferris Rd (45102-1020)
PHONE..................513 752-5005
Fax: 513 752-2539
Richard Mark Vogt, *President*
Jay Richard Vogt, *Principal*
Joanne Vogt, *Principal*
Jeffrey G Vogt, *VP Mfg*
EMP: 50
SQ FT: 120,000
SALES: 5.4MM Privately Held
SIC: 3441 3444 3471 3479 Fabricated structural metal; sheet metalwork; plating & polishing; painting of metal products; fabricated pipe & fittings

(G-588)
UV DOCTOR SYSTEMS LLC
1184 Ferris Rd (45102-1046)
PHONE..................513 553-9000
Miranda Schweitzer, *General Mgr*
Todd Schweitzer, *Mng Member*
Michael Merillat,
EMP: 6
SQ FT: 8,000
SALES (est): 1.8MM Privately Held
SIC: 5064 3648 Suntanning equipment & supplies; ultraviolet lamp fixtures

Amesville
Athens County

(G-589)
APPAL ENERGY
15383 E Kasler Creek Rd (45711-9448)
P.O. Box 62 (45711-0062)
PHONE..................740 448-4605
EMP: 3 EST: 2000
SALES (est): 310K Privately Held
SIC: 2911 Biofuel Manufacturer - Biodiesel

Amherst
Lorain County

(G-590)
ALCO MANUFACTURING
105 Middle Ave (44001)
PHONE..................440 322-9166
EMP: 3 EST: 2002
SALES (est): 190K Privately Held
SIC: 3451 Mfg Screw Machine Products

(G-591)
BCT ALARM SERVICES INC
103 Milan Ave Ste 4 (44001-1492)
PHONE..................440 669-8153
Brian J Jankowski, *President*
EMP: 6
SALES (est): 630K Privately Held
SIC: 2752 Commercial printing, lithographic

(G-592)
BIRD LOFT
141 N Leavitt Rd (44001-1110)
PHONE..................440 988-2473
Elaine D Jameyson, *Principal*
EMP: 3
SALES (est): 110K Privately Held
SIC: 3999 Pet supplies

(G-593)
BRP INC
114 Hidden Tree Ln (44001-1919)
PHONE..................440 988-4398
Fax: 440 284-0271
Steve Bratos, *Principal*
Stephani Findish, *Admin Sec*
EMP: 3
SQ FT: 4,700
SALES: 130K Privately Held
WEB: www.brpracing.com
SIC: 3944 5531 Cars, play (children's vehicles); electronic toys; automotive & home supply stores

(G-594)
CHEFS PANTRY INC (DH)
Also Called: Cloverdale Food Processing
1833 Cooper Foster Pk Rd (44001-1206)
PHONE..................440 288-0146
Fax: 440 288-5008
Richard Cawrse Jr, *President*
Richard Cecil, *Corp Secy*
Angie Viglas, *Human Res Mgr*
EMP: 2

SALES (est): 1MM **Publicly Held**
WEB: www.chefspantry.com
SIC: 2053 Frozen bakery products, except bread
HQ: Advancepierre Foods, Inc.
9987 Carver Rd Ste 500
Blue Ash OH 45242
513 874-8741

(G-595)
CLOVERVALE FARMS INC (DH)
Also Called: Clovervale Foods
8133 Cooper Foster Pk Rd (44001)
PHONE..................................440 960-0146
Richard Cawrse Jr, *President*
Richard Cecil, *Corp Secy*
Suzanne Graham, *Vice Pres*
EMP: 100 EST: 1920
SQ FT: 38,000
SALES (est): 7MM **Publicly Held**
WEB: www.clovervale.com
SIC: 2099 2032 2033 2038 Gelatin dessert preparations; salads, fresh or refrigerated; puddings, except meat: packaged in cans, jars, etc.; fruits: packaged in cans, jars, etc.; frozen specialties
HQ: Advancepierre Foods, Inc.
9987 Carver Rd Ste 500
Blue Ash OH 45242
513 874-8741

(G-596)
CURRIER RICHARD & JAMES
Also Called: Amherst Party Shop
540 Mcintosh Ln (44001-3108)
PHONE..................................440 988-4132
Fax: 440 985-9002
Richard Currier, *Partner*
James Currier, *Partner*
EMP: 6
SALES (est): 760K **Privately Held**
SIC: 5921 2086 Beer (packaged); wine; bottled & canned soft drinks

(G-597)
DURAY MACHINE CO INC
400 Ravenglass Blvd (44001-2383)
PHONE..................................440 277-4119
Fax: 440 277-7192
Wayne Duray, *President*
Janet Dadas, *Corp Secy*
EMP: 10
SQ FT: 18,000
SALES (est): 1.4MM **Privately Held**
SIC: 3599 7692 Machine shop, jobbing & repair; welding repair

(G-598)
ECO FUEL SOLUTION LLC
779 Sunrise Dr (44001-1660)
PHONE..................................440 282-8592
James Bodnar, *Principal*
EMP: 3
SALES (est): 155.6K **Privately Held**
SIC: 2869 Fuels

(G-599)
JAN SQUIRES INC
7985 Leavitt Rd (44001-2709)
PHONE..................................440 988-7859
Fax: 440 988-5595
Janis Squires, *President*
Robert Squires, *Vice Pres*
EMP: 4
SQ FT: 2,400
SALES: 250K **Privately Held**
SIC: 1711 3498 Mechanical contractor; fabricated pipe & fittings

(G-600)
KTM NORTH AMERICA INC (PA)
1119 Milan Ave (44001-1319)
PHONE..................................440 985-3553
Di Stefan Pierer, *CEO*
Rod Bush, *President*
Brian Doran, *Area Mgr*
Jeremy Ketchum, *Area Mgr*
Jakob Branner, *Vice Pres*
▲ EMP: 87
SQ FT: 5,000
SALES (est): 48.4MM **Privately Held**
SIC: 5012 3751 Motorcycles; motorcycles, bicycles & parts

(G-601)
NORDSON CORPORATION
100 Nordson Dr Ms81 (44001-2454)
PHONE..................................440 985-4000
Michael Hilton, *President*
Doug Bloomfield, *Vice Pres*
Chris Park, *MIS Dir*
Ed Field, *Technology*
EMP: 500
SALES (corp-wide): 1.8B **Publicly Held**
WEB: www.nordson.com
SIC: 3563 Spraying outfits: metals, paints & chemicals (compressor)
PA: Nordson Corporation
28601 Clemens Rd
Westlake OH 44145
440 892-1580

(G-602)
NORDSON CORPORATION
555 Jackson St (44001-2496)
PHONE..................................440 988-9411
Fax: 440 988-3022
Steve Smith, *Vice Pres*
Patrick Flinn, *Engineer*
Lora Gfell, *Accounts Exec*
John Kirschner, *Manager*
Jon Erickson, *Info Tech Dir*
EMP: 432
SALES (corp-wide): 1.8B **Publicly Held**
WEB: www.nordson.com
SIC: 3563 Spraying outfits: metals, paints & chemicals (compressor); robots for industrial spraying, painting, etc.
PA: Nordson Corporation
28601 Clemens Rd
Westlake OH 44145
440 892-1580

(G-603)
NORDSON CORPORATION
300 Nordson Dr (44001-2422)
PHONE..................................440 985-4496
Fax: 770 246-9271
Jim Molosky, *Purch Agent*
Christine Schwarzmann, *Controller*
Paul Richer, *Accounts Mgr*
Sharon Krucinski, *Sales Staff*
Robert Allsop, *Marketing Mgr*
EMP: 432
SALES (corp-wide): 1.8B **Publicly Held**
SIC: 3563 Spraying outfits: metals, paints & chemicals (compressor)
PA: Nordson Corporation
28601 Clemens Rd
Westlake OH 44145
440 892-1580

(G-604)
NORDSON UV INC
Also Called: Spectral Uv Systems
555 Jackson St (44001-2408)
PHONE..................................440 985-4573
Drexel R Bunch, *Vice Pres*
Don McLane, *Vice Pres*
Herb Turner, *Plant Mgr*
Tim Harr, *Technical Mgr*
Howard Podolny, *Senior Engr*
EMP: 13
SALES: 5MM
SALES (corp-wide): 1.8B **Publicly Held**
SIC: 3826 Ultraviolet analytical instruments
PA: Nordson Corporation
28601 Clemens Rd
Westlake OH 44145
440 892-1580

(G-605)
PERSONAL STITCH MONOGRAMMING
924 Amchester Dr (44001-1254)
PHONE..................................440 282-7707
Fax: 440 282-7707
Don Szakhes, *Owner*
Cindy Szakhes, *Co-Owner*
EMP: 4
SQ FT: 1,200
SALES: 100K **Privately Held**
SIC: 2395 Embroidery & art needlework

(G-606)
POLYGON SPACESHIP
Also Called: Polygon Spaceship Games
5536 Linn Dr (44001-1221)
PHONE..................................440 506-0403
Anthony Calabro, *Partner*

Matthew Beckwith, *Partner*
Ian Zeigler, *Partner*
EMP: 3
SALES (est): 71.1K **Privately Held**
SIC: 7372 Home entertainment computer software

(G-607)
RCS BREWHOUSE
223 Church St (44001-2201)
PHONE..................................440 984-3103
Robert Pijor, *Principal*
EMP: 7
SALES (est): 598.9K **Privately Held**
SIC: 2064 Candy bars, including chocolate covered bars

(G-608)
SPEEDWAY LLC
Also Called: Speedway Superamerica 9975
712 N Leavitt Rd (44001-1133)
PHONE..................................440 988-8014
John Petis, *Branch Mgr*
EMP: 10 **Publicly Held**
WEB: www.speedwaynet.com
SIC: 1311 Crude petroleum production
HQ: Speedway Llc
500 Speedway Dr
Enon OH 45323
937 864-3000

Amsterdam
Jefferson County

(G-609)
ALLEN HARPER
1654 Township Road 266 (43903-7919)
PHONE..................................740 543-3919
Allen Harper, *CEO*
EMP: 4
SALES (est): 182.5K **Privately Held**
SIC: 1442 Construction sand & gravel

Anderson Township
Hamilton County

(G-610)
SPECTRUM BRANDS INC
7794 5 Mile Rd Ste 190 (45230-2369)
PHONE..................................513 231-0952
Matt Kirk, *Manager*
EMP: 72
SALES (corp-wide): 5.2B **Publicly Held**
SIC: 3692 Primary batteries, dry & wet
HQ: Spectrum Brands, Inc.
3001 Deming Way
Middleton WI 53562
608 275-3340

Andover
Ashtabula County

(G-611)
ADVANCED TECHNOLOGY CORP
101 Parker Dr (44003-9456)
PHONE..................................440 293-4064
Seymour S Stein, *Ch of Bd*
Sherry Epstein, *Treasurer*
Myra Brown, *Manager*
Sam Raib, *Info Tech Mgr*
Anthony Stavole, *Admin Sec*
▲ EMP: 250 EST: 1951
SQ FT: 220,000
SALES (est): 27.2MM
SALES (corp-wide): 43.6MM **Privately Held**
SIC: 3647 3469 Vehicular lighting equipment; metal stampings
HQ: Atc Lighting & Plastics, Inc.
101 Parker Dr
Andover OH 44003
440 466-7670

(G-612)
ATC GROUP INC (PA)
Also Called: Atc Lighting & Plastics
101 Parker Dr (44003-9456)
P.O. Box 1120 (44003-1120)
PHONE..................................440 293-4064
Seymour S Stein PHD, *President*
Sherry Epstein, *Treasurer*
Betty Dreyer, *Human Res Mgr*
Brown Dreyer, *Human Res Mgr*
▲ EMP: 100
SQ FT: 50,000
SALES (est): 43.6MM **Privately Held**
SIC: 3647 3089 3841 Vehicular lighting equipment; injection molded finished plastic products; surgical & medical instruments

(G-613)
ATC LIGHTING & PLASTICS INC (HQ)
Also Called: Kdlamp Company
101 Parker Dr (44003-9456)
P.O. Box 1120 (44003-1120)
PHONE..................................440 466-7670
Fax: 440 293-4591
Seymour S Stein PHD, *Ch of Bd*
James Kovach, *Manager*
▲ EMP: 155
SALES (est): 41.9MM
SALES (corp-wide): 43.6MM **Privately Held**
SIC: 3647 3714 3713 3648 Motor vehicle lighting equipment; motor vehicle parts & accessories; truck & bus bodies; lighting equipment; products of purchased glass
PA: Atc Group, Inc.
101 Parker Dr
Andover OH 44003
440 293-4064

(G-614)
ATC NYMOLD CORPORATION
101 Parker Dr (44003-9456)
PHONE..................................440 293-4064
Dr Seymour Stein, *Branch Mgr*
Jeffrey Bowers, *Data Proc Dir*
Mary Boise,
EMP: 5
SALES (corp-wide): 43.6MM **Privately Held**
WEB: www.atc-lighting-plastics.com
SIC: 3089 Plastic processing
HQ: Atc Nymold Corporation
101 Parker Dr
Andover OH 44003
440 293-4064

(G-615)
ATC NYMOLD CORPORATION (DH)
101 Parker Dr (44003-9456)
PHONE..................................440 293-4064
Seymour S Stein PHD, *President*
John Souders, *Info Tech Mgr*
EMP: 2
SQ FT: 500,000
SALES (est): 3.5MM
SALES (corp-wide): 43.6MM **Privately Held**
WEB: www.atc-lighting-plastics.com
SIC: 3089 Injection molded finished plastic products
HQ: Atc Lighting & Plastics, Inc.
101 Parker Dr
Andover OH 44003
440 466-7670

(G-616)
K D LAMP COMPANY
101 Parker Dr (44003-9456)
PHONE..................................440 293-4064
Dr Seymour Stein, *Treasurer*
Sherry Epstein, *Treasurer*
Melinda Wheeler, *Accounts Mgr*
▲ EMP: 30
SALES: 700K
SALES (corp-wide): 43.6MM **Privately Held**
SIC: 3647 Headlights (fixtures), vehicular
PA: Atc Group, Inc.
101 Parker Dr
Andover OH 44003
440 293-4064

(G-617)
LIGHTING PRODUCTS INC
101 Parker Dr (44003-9456)
P.O. Box 1120 (44003-1120)
PHONE...................................440 293-4064
Seymour S Stein PHD, *President*
Sherry Epstein, *Corp Secy*
Anthony Stavole, *Admin Sec*
EMP: 84
SALES (est): 11.1MM
SALES (corp-wide): 43.6MM **Privately Held**
WEB: www.lightingproducts.com
SIC: 3647 Motor vehicle lighting equipment
HQ: Atc Lighting & Plastics, Inc.
101 Parker Dr
Andover OH 44003
440 466-7670

(G-618)
MATHEW ODONNELL
Also Called: Model and Tool Making
6645 2nd Ave (44003-9668)
PHONE...................................440 969-4054
Matthew Odonnell, *Owner*
EMP: 3
SALES (est): 240.5K **Privately Held**
SIC: 3549 Metalworking machinery

Anna
Shelby County

(G-619)
6S PRODUCTS LLC
12800 Wenger Rd (45302-9003)
PHONE...................................937 394-7440
Genny Schroer,
Emliy Bensman,
Tracy Platsoot,
EMP: 5
SQ FT: 4,000
SALES: 850K **Privately Held**
SIC: 3089 Bottle caps, molded plastic

(G-620)
AGRANA FRUIT US INC
16197 County Road 25a (45302-9498)
P.O. Box 459, Botkins (45306-0459)
PHONE...................................937 693-3821
Nancy Jager, *Vice Pres*
Phillip Bokar, *Project Mgr*
Sean Augustus, *Opers Mgr*
Jeff Elliott, *Opers Staff*
Alice Rindler, *Personnel*
EMP: 150
SALES (corp-wide): 51.7MM **Privately Held**
SIC: 8734 2099 2087 Food testing service; food preparations; flavoring extracts & syrups
HQ: Agrana Fruit Us, Inc.
6850 Southpointe Pkwy
Brecksville OH 44141
440 546-1199

(G-621)
CHILLTEX LLC
7440 Hoying Rd (45302-9616)
PHONE...................................937 710-3308
Matt Eilerman, *Principal*
EMP: 10
SALES (est): 1.6MM **Privately Held**
SIC: 3585 Heating equipment, complete

(G-622)
ELSASS FABRICATING LTD
11385 Amsterdam Rd (45302-9766)
PHONE...................................937 394-7169
William Elsass, *President*
Bonnie Elsass, *Manager*
EMP: 4
SALES (est): 343.3K **Privately Held**
SIC: 3444 Sheet metalwork

(G-623)
HOEHNES CUSTOM WOODWORKING
9600 Amsterdam Rd (45302-9307)
PHONE...................................937 693-8008
Susan Hoehne, *Principal*
EMP: 4
SALES (est): 335.3K **Privately Held**
SIC: 2431 Millwork

(G-624)
PANEL CONTROL INC
107 Shue Dr (45302-8402)
PHONE...................................937 394-2201
Sandy Wells, *Principal*
Alan Binder, *Engineer*
EMP: 1
SQ FT: 32,000
SALES: 9.4MM **Privately Held**
SIC: 3613 Control panels, electric

Ansonia
Darke County

(G-625)
HOFMANNS LURES INC
5350 State Route 47 (45303-9796)
P.O. Box 361, Greenville (45331-0361)
PHONE...................................937 684-0338
Denis Short, *President*
EMP: 8
SQ FT: 7,200
SALES: 50K **Privately Held**
SIC: 3949 Masks: hockey, baseball, football, etc.

(G-626)
SHOOK TOOL INC
405 W High St (45303-5061)
P.O. Box 334 (45303-0334)
PHONE...................................937 337-6471
Fax: 937 337-6471
David D Shook, *President*
Darin Shook, *Vice Pres*
EMP: 5
SQ FT: 4,000
SALES: 300K **Privately Held**
SIC: 3544 Special dies, tools, jigs & fixtures

Antwerp
Paulding County

(G-627)
ANTWERP BEE-ARGUS
Also Called: Ohio Press
113 N Main St (45813-8406)
P.O. Box 1065 (45813-1065)
PHONE...................................419 258-8161
Fax: 419 258-8161
June Temple, *Partner*
Sandra Temple, *Partner*
EMP: 3
SALES (est): 177.2K **Privately Held**
SIC: 2711 Newspapers

(G-628)
ANTWERP TOOL & DIE INC
3167 County Road 424 (45813-9416)
PHONE...................................419 258-5271
Fax: 419 258-2326
Gerald A Snyder, *President*
EMP: 15
SQ FT: 10,500
SALES: 800K **Privately Held**
SIC: 3544 3545 Special dies, tools, jigs & fixtures; machine tool accessories

(G-629)
ATWOOD MOBILE PRODUCTS LLC
5406 Us 24 (45813)
PHONE...................................419 258-5531
Vincent Proaccina, *Principal*
EMP: 43
SALES (corp-wide): 687.3K **Privately Held**
SIC: 3714 Motor vehicle parts & accessories
HQ: Atwood Mobile Products Llc
1120 N Main St
Elkhart IN 46514
574 264-2131

(G-630)
K & L TOOL INC
5141 Us 24 (45813)
P.O. Box 1086 (45813-1086)
PHONE...................................419 258-2086
Fax: 419 258-2809

Kirk L Hopkins, *President*
Laurel Hopkins, *Vice Pres*
Susan Bagley, *Office Mgr*
EMP: 18
SQ FT: 4,500
SALES (est): 2.3MM **Privately Held**
SIC: 3542 3544 Bending machines; special dies & tools

(G-631)
NEW AMERICAN REEL COMPANY LLC
5278 County Road 424 A (45813-9578)
PHONE...................................419 258-2900
Mark Greenwood,
David Parisot,
▲ **EMP:** 5
SQ FT: 30,000
SALES: 400K **Privately Held**
SIC: 3499 Reels, cable: metal

(G-632)
WEST BEND PRINTING & PUBG INC
101 N Main St (45813)
P.O. Box 1008 (45813-1008)
PHONE...................................419 258-2000
Bryce Steiner, *President*
EMP: 6
SQ FT: 3,000
SALES: 350K **Privately Held**
SIC: 2752 Commercial printing, lithographic

Apple Creek
Wayne County

(G-633)
A C PRODUCTS CO
4299 S Apple Creek Rd (44606-9680)
P.O. Box 518 (44606-0518)
PHONE...................................330 698-1105
Fax: 330 698-5292
Don Olsen, *President*
David Reader, *Exec VP*
Mahlon Troyer, *Opers Mgr*
Missy Irwin, *Manager*
▼ **EMP:** 60
SQ FT: 80,000
SALES (est): 9.7MM **Privately Held**
WEB: acproductsco.com
SIC: 3261 Bathroom accessories/fittings, vitreous china or earthenware

(G-634)
COBLENTZ BROTHERS INC
7101 S Kohler Rd (44606-9613)
PHONE...................................330 857-7211
Fax: 330 857-4966
Wayne Liechty, *President*
Jonas Coblentz, *Vice Pres*
Don Yoder, *CFO*
Ray Coblentz, *Admin Sec*
EMP: 28
SQ FT: 20,100
SALES: 3.9MM **Privately Held**
SIC: 2448 2421 Pallets, wood; sawmills & planing mills, general

(G-635)
CUSTOM CUT UPS SCAPBOOKING
131 Apple Ridge Dr (44606-9594)
PHONE...................................330 698-5164
Lori Glazier, *Owner*
EMP: 3
SALES (est): 189.9K **Privately Held**
WEB: www.customcutups.net
SIC: 2782 Scrapbooks, albums & diaries

(G-636)
DES ECK WELDING
10777 E Moreland Rd (44606-9628)
PHONE...................................330 698-7271
Nelson Chupp, *Owner*
EMP: 5
SALES (est): 400K **Privately Held**
SIC: 7692 Welding repair

(G-637)
ELY ROAD REEL COMPANY LTD
9081 Ely Rd (44606-9320)
PHONE...................................330 683-1818

Fax: 330 683-1819
Marvin Weaver, *Partner*
Robert Weaver, *Partner*
Rhoda Weaver, *Admin Sec*
EMP: 25
SQ FT: 16,000
SALES: 7MM **Privately Held**
SIC: 2499 Spools, reels & pulleys: wood

(G-638)
GROSS LUMBER INC
8848 Ely Rd (44606-9799)
PHONE...................................330 683-2055
Fax: 330 682-7565
Rick Grossniklaus, *President*
Don Grossniklaus, *President*
Connie Duncan, *Manager*
EMP: 35 **EST:** 1957
SQ FT: 30,000
SALES (est): 5MM **Privately Held**
SIC: 2448 5031 5099 2426 Pallets, wood; lumber: rough, dressed & finished; wood & wood by-products; hardwood dimension & flooring mills; sawmills & planing mills, general

(G-639)
HILLCREST LUMBER LTD
8669 Zuercher Rd (44606-9651)
PHONE...................................330 359-5721
David Hershberger, *Partner*
Edward Hershberger, *Partner*
Henry Hershberger, *Partner*
EMP: 5
SQ FT: 400,000
SALES (est): 807.7K **Privately Held**
SIC: 2421 Sawmills & planing mills, general

(G-640)
JAE TECH INC
32 Hunter St (44606-9600)
PHONE...................................330 698-2000
Fax: 330 698-2007
Ian Cameron, *Principal*
Rich Schneider, *Project Mgr*
EMP: 55 **EST:** 2000
SQ FT: 37,500
SALES (est): 10.9MM **Privately Held**
WEB: www.jaetechinc.com
SIC: 3714 Axle housings & shafts, motor vehicle

(G-641)
JOHN J YODER LOGGING
6776 Mount Hope Rd (44606-9061)
PHONE...................................330 749-6324
John J Yoder, *Principal*
EMP: 3
SALES (est): 240.5K **Privately Held**
SIC: 2411 Logging

(G-642)
LE SUMMER KIDRON INC
6856 Kidron Rd (44606-9326)
P.O. Box 230, Kidron (44636-0230)
PHONE...................................330 857-2031
Glenford Steiner, *President*
EMP: 20
SALES: 11MM **Privately Held**
SIC: 2048 Livestock feeds

(G-643)
LEGGETT & PLATT INCORPORATED
Also Called: Crown North America
7315 E Lincoln Way (44606-9524)
PHONE...................................330 262-6010
EMP: 9
SALES (corp-wide): 3.9B **Publicly Held**
SIC: 3714 Mfg Motor Vehicle Parts/Accessories
PA: Leggett & Platt, Incorporated
1 Leggett Rd
Carthage MO 64836
417 358-8131

(G-644)
MAYSVILLE HARNESS SHOP LTD
8572 Mount Hope Rd (44606-9495)
PHONE...................................330 695-9977
Atlee E Yoder, *President*
EMP: 3

▲ = Import ▼=Export
◆ =Import/Export

SALES (est): 443.1K **Privately Held**
SIC: **3199** 7251 7699 Harness or harness
parts; holsters, leather; straps, leather;
shoe repair shop; harness repair shop

(G-645)
MILLWOOD INC
Also Called: Litco Wood Products
8208 S Kohler Rd (44606-9420)
PHONE................................330 857-3075
Fax: 330 857-1715
Don Smith, *Sales Staff*
Trish Rolland, *Corp Comm Staff*
Ely Miller, *Branch Mgr*
Colleen Gifford, *Manager*
EMP: 70 **Privately Held**
WEB: www.millwoodinc.com
SIC: **2448** Wood pallets & skids
PA: Millwood, Inc.
3708 International Blvd
Vienna OH 44473

(G-646)
OMEGA CEMENTING CO
3776 S Millborne Rd (44606-9757)
P.O. Box 357 (44606-0357)
PHONE................................330 695-7147
Donald Gaddis, *CEO*
EMP: 7
SQ FT: 3,000
SALES: 2.5MM **Privately Held**
SIC: **1389** 1081 7349 Well plugging &
abandoning, oil & gas; cementing oil &
gas well casings; metal mining explo-
ration & development services; cleaning
service, industrial or commercial

(G-647)
**PRECISION PRODUCTS GROUP
INC**
339 Mill St (44606-9541)
PHONE................................330 698-4711
Dave Hooe, *President*
EMP: 60
SALES (corp-wide): 77.5MM **Privately
Held**
SIC: **3495** 3493 Wire springs; steel
springs, except wire
PA: Precision Products Group, Inc.
10201 N Illinois St # 390
Indianapolis IN 46290
330 698-4711

(G-648)
REBERLAND EQUIPMENT INC
Also Called: Firovac
5963 Fountain Nook Rd (44606-9677)
PHONE................................330 698-5883
Fax: 330 698-7723
Larry Reber, *President*
Valerie Lewis, *Treasurer*
Rebecca Reber, *Admin Sec*
▲ EMP: 18
SQ FT: 10,000
SALES: 5MM **Privately Held**
WEB: www.firovac.com
SIC: **7699** 5083 3711 3713 Farm machin-
ery repair; agricultural machinery & equip-
ment; fire department vehicles (motor
vehicles), assembly of; tank truck bodies;
oil & gas field machinery

(G-649)
STEIN-WAY EQUIPMENT
12335 Emerson Rd (44606-9798)
PHONE................................330 857-8700
Fax: 330 857-8109
Oris Steiner, *General Ptnr*
EMP: 12
SQ FT: 20,000
SALES (est): 2.2MM **Privately Held**
SIC: **3523** Barn, silo, poultry, dairy & live-
stock machinery

(G-650)
TOP NOTCH LOGGING
8242 Secrest Rd (44606-9506)
PHONE................................330 466-1780
Roy Miller, *Owner*
EMP: 3
SALES (est): 237K **Privately Held**
SIC: **2411** Logging

(G-651)
**WAYNEDALE TRUSS AND
PANEL CO**
8971 Dover Rd (44606-9407)
PHONE................................330 698-7373
Fax: 330 698-2295
James Fry, *President*
Diane Fry, *Admin Sec*
EMP: 34
SQ FT: 2,000
SALES (est): 5.1MM **Privately Held**
WEB: www.waynedaletruss.com
SIC: **2439** Trusses, wooden roof; trusses,
except roof: laminated lumber

(G-652)
WEAVER PALLET LTD
9380 Ely Rd (44606-9322)
PHONE................................330 682-4022
Emery Weaver,
Andrew Weaver,
EMP: 5
SALES: 1.2MM **Privately Held**
SIC: **2448** Wood pallets & skids

(G-653)
WEAVER WOODCRAFT L L C
9652 Harrison Rd (44606-9623)
PHONE................................330 695-2150
Dave Weaver, *Principal*
EMP: 9
SALES (est): 797K **Privately Held**
SIC: **2511** Wood household furniture

Arcadia
Hancock County

(G-654)
MAASS MIDWEST MFG INC
Also Called: Dickens Foundry
19710 State Route 12 (44804-9503)
PHONE................................419 894-6424
Fax: 419 894-6424
Mike Wedge, *Ltd Ptnr*
EMP: 9
SALES (corp-wide): 10.8MM **Privately
Held**
WEB: www.maassmidwest.com
SIC: **3366** 3491 3432 Brass foundry; in-
dustrial valves; plumbing fixture fittings &
trim
PA: Maass Midwest Mfg Inc.
11283 Dundee Rd
Huntley IL 60142
847 669-5135

(G-655)
RPM CARBIDE DIE INC
202 E South St (44804-9773)
P.O. Box 278 (44804-0278)
PHONE................................419 894-6426
Fax: 419 894-6920
Eric E Metcalfe, *CEO*
Charlene Kelbley, *Purch Mgr*
Joseph E Phillips, *CFO*
Carrie Phillits, *Sales Executive*
Carrie Ritcher Phillips, *Marketing Staff*
EMP: 38
SQ FT: 18,500
SALES (est): 7MM **Privately Held**
WEB: www.rpmcarbidedie.com
SIC: **3544** Special dies & tools

Arcanum
Darke County

(G-656)
EMRICK MACHINE & TOOL
211 S Sycamore St (45304-1172)
PHONE................................937 692-5901
Rick Emrick, *Principal*
Dana Anderson, *Sales Engr*
EMP: 5
SALES (est): 300K **Privately Held**
SIC: **3599** Machine shop, jobbing & repair

(G-657)
LAVY INC
Also Called: Lavy's Marathon
1977 Gttysburg Ptsburg Rd (45304-9442)
PHONE................................937 692-8189
Sheldon Lavy, *President*
Kimberly Lavy, *Vice Pres*
EMP: 4
SQ FT: 200
SALES (est): 637.6K **Privately Held**
SIC: **2911** 5172 Gasoline blending plants;
gasoline; fuel oil

(G-658)
R J COX CO
Also Called: Cox Trailer
8903 State Route 571 (45304-9741)
PHONE................................937 548-4699
Fax: 937 548-4699
Robert J Cox, *President*
John Cox, *Vice Pres*
Joseph Cox, *Treasurer*
Kelley Cox, *Admin Sec*
EMP: 5 EST: 1949
SQ FT: 8,000
SALES (est): 600K **Privately Held**
WEB: www.rjcox.com
SIC: **3715** 5083 Trailer bodies; agricultural
machinery & equipment

(G-659)
RED BARN CABINET CO
8046 State Route 722 (45304-9409)
PHONE................................937 884-9800
Fax: 937 884-9802
Mark Angle, *President*
EMP: 6
SALES (est): 857K **Privately Held**
SIC: **2434** Wood kitchen cabinets

(G-660)
SCHWIETERMAN CY INC
4240 State Route 49 (45304-9010)
PHONE................................937 548-3965
Michael Schwieterman, *Branch Mgr*
EMP: 5
SALES (corp-wide): 6.2MM **Privately
Held**
SIC: **3531** Plows: construction, excavating
& grading
PA: Cy Schwieterman Inc
1663 Cranberry Rd
Saint Henry OH 45883
419 925-4290

Archbold
Fulton County

(G-661)
AL MEDA CHOCOLATES INC
23050 Fulton County Rd E (43502)
PHONE................................419 446-2676
Diane Taylor, *President*
Frank Taylor, *Vice Pres*
EMP: 5
SQ FT: 3,000
SALES (est): 330K **Privately Held**
SIC: **2064** Chocolate candy, except solid
chocolate

(G-662)
AMERICAN COLLOID COMPANY
Also Called: Mineral Technology Metal Cast
809 Myers St (43502-1575)
P.O. Box 195 (43502-0195)
PHONE................................419 445-9085
Greg Johnson, *Manager*
Kimberly Behnfeldt, *Clerk*
EMP: 5
SALES (corp-wide): 1.6B **Publicly Held**
WEB: www.colloid.com
SIC: **1459** Bentonite mining
HQ: American Colloid Company
2870 Forbs Ave
Hoffman Estates IL 60192

(G-663)
ARCHBOLD BUCKEYE INC
207 N Defiance St (43502-1187)
PHONE................................419 445-4466
Fax: 419 445-4177
Ross William Taylor, *President*
David Pugh, *Editor*

Sharon S Taylor, *Corp Secy*
Brent C Taylor, *Vice Pres*
Mary Huber, *Advt Staff*
EMP: 10
SQ FT: 2,800
SALES (est): 440K **Privately Held**
SIC: **2711** Newspapers: publishing only,
not printed on site

(G-664)
ARCHBOLD CONTAINER CORP
800 W Barre Rd (43502-9595)
P.O. Box 10 (43502-0010)
PHONE................................800 446-2520
Fax: 419 446-2529
Lynn Aschliman, *President*
Elvin D Yoder, *Corp Secy*
EMP: 150
SQ FT: 230,000
SALES (est): 33.4MM
SALES (corp-wide): 896.8MM **Privately
Held**
WEB: www.gbp.com
SIC: **2653** 3086 Boxes, corrugated: made
from purchased materials; packaging &
shipping materials, foamed plastic
PA: Green Bay Packaging Inc.
1700 N Webster Ave
Green Bay WI 54302
920 433-5111

(G-665)
ARCHBOLD FURNITURE CO
733 W Barre Rd (43502-9304)
PHONE................................567 444-4666
Pat McNamara, *President*
Pete Gstaldar, *Vice Pres*
Kathleen Gwinn, *Sales Staff*
Vickie Burkharg, *Manager*
Pete Gstalder, *Admin Sec*
◆ EMP: 35
SALES (est): 9MM **Privately Held**
WEB: www.archboldfurniture.com
SIC: **2511** 5712 Wood household furniture;
unassembled or unfinished furniture;
household: wood; furniture stores

(G-666)
ARROW TRU-LINE INC (PA)
2211 S Defiance St (43502-9151)
PHONE................................419 446-2785
Marvin Miller, *President*
Suzie Tule, *General Mgr*
Dave Wilson, *General Mgr*
Jack Francis, *Plant Mgr*
Brian Ziegler, *Plant Mgr*
◆ EMP: 150 EST: 1959
SQ FT: 63,000
SALES (est): 48.8MM **Privately Held**
SIC: **2431** Garage doors, overhead: wood

(G-667)
BALSER INC
502 Jackson St (43502-1411)
P.O. Box 8 (43502-0008)
PHONE................................567 444-4737
Anthony Balser, *President*
EMP: 6
SQ FT: 18,000
SALES (est): 227.1K **Privately Held**
SIC: **3479** Painting of metal products

(G-668)
CLANCYS CABINET SHOP
3751 County Road 26 (43502-9434)
PHONE................................419 445-4455
Clancy Foor, *Owner*
EMP: 25
SQ FT: 4,000
SALES: 180K **Privately Held**
WEB: www.clancyscabinets.com
SIC: **2434** Wood kitchen cabinets

(G-669)
CONAGRA BRANDS INC
La Choy Food Products Division
901 Stryker St (43502-1053)
PHONE................................419 445-8015
Mike Schiesl, *Financial Exec*
John Martinez, *Human Res Dir*
Ron Corkins, *Branch Mgr*
EMP: 398
SALES (corp-wide): 11.6B **Publicly Held**
WEB: www.conagra.com
SIC: **2032** 2099 Chinese foods: packaged
in cans, jars, etc.; food preparations

PA: Conagra Brands, Inc.
222 Merchandise Mart Plz
Chicago IL 60654
312 549-5000

(G-670)
D & G WELDING INC
302 W Barre Rd (43502-1554)
PHONE..................................419 445-5751
Fax: 419 445-1897
Dan Stuckey, *President*
Julie Stuckey, *Vice Pres*
EMP: 6 **EST:** 1956
SQ FT: 2,500
SALES: 100K **Privately Held**
SIC: 7692 1796 Welding repair; millwright

(G-671)
F & W AUTO SUPPLY
111 Depot St (43502-1236)
PHONE..................................419 445-3350
Fax: 419 445-3360
Ronald Wyse, *Owner*
EMP: 3
SQ FT: 2,000
SALES: 230K **Privately Held**
SIC: 3599 5084 Machine shop, jobbing &
repair; industrial machine parts

(G-672)
FARMLAND NEWS LLC
104 Depot St (43502-1235)
P.O. Box 240 (43502-0240)
PHONE..................................419 445-9456
Fax: 419 445-4444
Jeremy Rohrs, *Advt Staff*
Lisa Grisez, *Mng Member*
Jed W Grisez,
EMP: 10
SALES (est): 350K **Privately Held**
SIC: 2711 Newspapers: publishing only,
not printed on site

(G-673)
FM MANUFACTURING INC
300 E Mechanic St (43502-1425)
PHONE..................................419 445-0700
Ron Rupp, *President*
EMP: 9
SQ FT: 4,000
SALES (est): 1.5MM **Privately Held**
SIC: 3699 Laser systems & equipment

(G-674)
FROZEN SPECIALTIES INC
720 W Barre Rd (43502-9305)
P.O. Box 410 (43502-0410)
PHONE..................................419 445-9015
Fax: 419 445-9465
Brian Replogle, *Facilities Mgr*
Paula Gleckler, *Persnl Mgr*
Brian Riplogo, *Branch Mgr*
Dick Anderson, *Manager*
Doug Kulwicki, *Info Tech Dir*
EMP: 165
SALES (corp-wide): 27.9MM **Privately Held**
SIC: 2038 Frozen specialties
PA: Frozen Specialties, Inc.
8600 S Wilkinson Way G
Perrysburg OH 43551
419 445-9015

(G-675)
FSI/MFP INC
720 W Barre Rd (43502-9304)
PHONE..................................419 445-9015
Eugene Welka, *Principal*
Steve Dominique, *Plant Mgr*
EMP: 5
SALES (est): 263.1K **Privately Held**
SIC: 2038 Frozen specialties

(G-676)
GARDENSCAPE
Also Called: Tri State Garden Supply
56 State Rte 66 (43502)
P.O. Box 451 (43502-0451)
PHONE..................................419 445-6561
Fax: 419 445-1562
Timothy Kasmoch, *Owner*
David Kasmoch, *Facilities Dir*
EMP: 50

SALES (corp-wide): 155.1MM **Privately Held**
WEB: www.gardenscapetransport.com
SIC: 5261 2875 Nurseries & garden centers; fertilizers, mixing only
HQ: Gardenscape
And Sandy Pt Rd Rr 38
Eau Claire PA 16030
724 867-1711

(G-677)
GENDRON WHEEL LLC
400 E Lugbill Rd (43502-1564)
P.O. Box 197 (43502-0197)
PHONE..................................419 445-6060
Fax: 419 446-2631
Fred Strobel, *President*
John Gendron, *Vice Pres*
Hermann Suess, *CFO*
Dick Nagel, *Manager*
EMP: 3
SALES (est): 313.3K
SALES (corp-wide): 3.3MM **Privately Held**
WEB: www.gendroninc.com
SIC: 3842 Surgical appliances & supplies
PA: Gendron, Inc.
520 W Mulberry St Ste 100
Bryan OH 43506
419 636-0848

(G-678)
GERALD GRAIN CENTER INC
3265 County Road 24 (43502-9415)
PHONE..................................419 445-2451
Chet Phillips, *Branch Mgr*
EMP: 17
SALES (corp-wide): 32.2MM **Privately Held**
SIC: 3523 5191 Elevators, farm; animal
feeds
PA: Gerald Grain Center, Inc.
14540 County Road U
Napoleon OH 43545
800 783-8015

(G-679)
GRANITE INDUSTRIES INC
595 E Lugbill Rd (43502-1560)
PHONE..................................419 445-4733
Steve Wise, *President*
Keith Short, *Treasurer*
Mindy Borer, *Admin Sec*
◆ **EMP:** 80
SALES (est): 13.5MM **Privately Held**
WEB: www.graniteind.com
SIC: 3993 3446 2531 Signs & advertising
specialties; architectural metalwork; public building & related furniture

(G-680)
HAULOTTE US INC (DH)
Also Called: Bil-Jax
125 Taylor Pkwy (43502-9122)
PHONE..................................419 445-8915
Mike Garvaglia, *CEO*
Bernie Duque, *Vice Pres*
Darrell Nelson, *Opers Mgr*
Kyle Gerhart, *Senior Buyer*
Michael J Garavaglia, *CFO*
◆ **EMP:** 20
SQ FT: 14,700
SALES (est): 6.1MM
SALES (corp-wide): 10.3MM **Privately Held**
WEB: www.haulotteus.com
SIC: 3531 Aerial work platforms: hydraulic/elec. truck/carrier mounted
HQ: Haulotte Group
La Peronniere
L' Horme 42152
477 292-424

(G-681)
HIT TROPHY INC
4989 State Route 66 (43502-9362)
PHONE..................................419 445-5356
Fax: 419 445-6031
Tom Wyse, *President*
Abe Wyse, *Marketing Staff*
EMP: 6 **EST:** 1949
SALES: 400K **Privately Held**
WEB: www.hittrophy.com
SIC: 3499 5999 2499 Trophies, metal, except silver; trophies & plaques; trophy
bases, wood

(G-682)
LAUBER MANUFACTURING CO
3751 County Road 26 (43502-9434)
PHONE..................................419 446-2450
Fax: 419 445-6880
Bruce Lauber, *President*
Graeme O Lauber Jr, *Treasurer*
Barb Grime, *Office Mgr*
Elizabeth Grime, *Admin Sec*
EMP: 7 **EST:** 1929
SQ FT: 43,000
SALES: 1.2MM **Privately Held**
WEB: www.laubermfg.com
SIC: 2511 Wood household furniture

(G-683)
LIECHTY SPECIALTIES INC
Also Called: Industrial WD Prts Fabrication
1901 S Defiance St (43502-9438)
P.O. Box 6 (43502-0006)
PHONE..................................419 445-6696
Fax: 419 445-2802
Allen K Liechty, *President*
Virgina Liechty, *Corp Secy*
EMP: 8
SQ FT: 25,000
SALES (est): 1.3MM **Privately Held**
SIC: 2431 Millwork

(G-684)
LOCKER ROOM INC
223 N Defiance St (43502-1160)
PHONE..................................419 445-9600
Kyle Brodbeck, *President*
Tara Brodbeck, *Admin Sec*
EMP: 5
SQ FT: 2,600
SALES: 800K **Privately Held**
WEB: www.lockerroominc.com
SIC: 5941 2759 Team sports equipment;
commercial printing

(G-685)
LOGO THIS
301 Ditto St Ste E (43502-1111)
PHONE..................................419 445-1355
Dan Rychener, *President*
EMP: 6
SALES (est): 516.7K **Privately Held**
SIC: 2395 Embroidery products, except
schiffli machine

(G-686)
MATTHEWS ART GLASS
Also Called: Mark Matthews Glass
22611 State Route 2 (43502-9452)
P.O. Box 332 (43502-0332)
PHONE..................................419 335-2448
Mark Matthews, *Owner*
Ruth Matthews, *Co-Owner*
EMP: 3
SALES (est): 110K **Privately Held**
SIC: 3229 Pressed & blown glass

(G-687)
MILLER BROS PAVING INC (HQ)
1613 S Defiance St (43502-9488)
P.O. Box 30 (43502-0030)
PHONE..................................419 445-1015
Fax: 419 446-2626
Dean Miller, *President*
Bradley Dmiller, *President*
Steven A Everhart, *Corp Secy*
Robert Miller, *Vice Pres*
Doug Doblinger, *Purchasing*
EMP: 10
SQ FT: 48,000
SALES (est): 2.2MM **Privately Held**
SIC: 2951 Asphalt paving mixtures &
blocks

(G-688)
NAPOLEON SPRING WORKS INC (HQ)
111 Weires Dr (43502-9153)
P.O. Box 160 (43502-0160)
PHONE..................................419 445-1010
Robert Shram Sr, *President*
Ej Horst, *Engineer*
John Schram, *Sales Staff*
Mike Sharpe, *Manager*
Marv Buenger, *Director*
▼ **EMP:** 143 **EST:** 1960

SALES (est): 22.3MM
SALES (corp-wide): 15.8MM **Privately Held**
SIC: 3493 3429 Torsion bar springs;
builders' hardware
PA: Industries Lynx Inc
175 Rue Upper Edison
Saint-Lambert QC J4R 2
514 866-1068

(G-689)
NOFZIGER DOOR SALES INC
111 Taylor Pkwy (43502-9309)
PHONE..................................419 445-2961
Fax: 419 445-0892
Tom Rufenacht, *Manager*
EMP: 10
SALES (corp-wide): 31.9MM **Privately Held**
WEB: www.haasdoor.com
SIC: 3442 5211 Metal doors; garage
doors, sale & installation
PA: Nofziger Door Sales, Inc.
320 Sycamore St
Wauseon OH 43567
419 337-9900

(G-690)
PROGRESSIVE FURNITURE INC (HQ)
Also Called: Progressive International
502 Middle St (43502-1559)
P.O. Box 308 (43502-0308)
PHONE..................................419 446-4500
Fax: 419 825-3146
Kevin Sauder, *President*
Dan Kendrick, *Exec VP*
Mike France, *Vice Pres*
John Boring, *VP Finance*
Janys Etts, *Credit Mgr*
▲ **EMP:** 25
SQ FT: 8,000
SALES (est): 25.3MM
SALES (corp-wide): 550MM **Privately Held**
WEB: www.progressivefurniture.com
SIC: 2511 2517 5021 Bed frames, except
water bed frames: wood; dressers,
household: wood; home entertainment
unit cabinets, wood; tables, occasional;
beds; dining room furniture
PA: Sauder Woodworking Co.
502 Middle St
Archbold OH 43502
419 446-3828

(G-691)
QUADCO REHABILITATION CENTER
Also Called: Northwest Products Div
600 Oak St (43502-1579)
PHONE..................................419 445-1950
Fax: 419 446-2984
John D Miller, *Project Dir*
Phillip Zuver, *Branch Mgr*
Melody Weaver, *Supervisor*
EMP: 90
SALES (corp-wide): 445.7K **Privately Held**
SIC: 8331 2448 Vocational rehabilitation
agency; wood pallets & skids
PA: Quadco Rehabilitation Center Inc
427 N Defiance St
Stryker OH 43557
419 682-1011

(G-692)
SAUDER MANUFACTURING CO (HQ)
Also Called: Wieland
930 W Barre Rd (43502-9385)
P.O. Box 230 (43502-0230)
PHONE..................................419 445-7670
Fax: 419 446-3173
Virgil L Miller, *President*
Phil Bontrager, *President*
Beth Ehinger, *General Mgr*
Luther Gaupsche, *Vice Pres*
Willaim Ogden, *Vice Pres*
◆ **EMP:** 220 **EST:** 1945
SQ FT: 300,000

SALES (est): 92.2MM
SALES (corp-wide): 550MM **Privately Held**
WEB: www.saudermfg.com
SIC: 2531 Church furniture; chairs, portable folding
PA: Sauder Woodworking Co.
502 Middle St
Archbold OH 43502
419 446-3828

(G-693)
SAUDER WDWKG CO WELFARE TR
502 Middle St (43502-1500)
PHONE..............................419 446-2711
Doug Krieger, *Director*
EMP: 2
SALES: 16.8MM **Privately Held**
SIC: 2431 Millwork

(G-694)
SAUDER WOODWORKING CO (PA)
502 Middle St (43502-1500)
P.O. Box 156 (43502-0156)
PHONE..............................419 446-3828
Fax: 419 446-2654
Kevin J Sauder, *President*
Amy Robison, *Principal*
Maynard Sauder, *Chairman*
Wes Graber, *Area Mgr*
Brent Gingerich, *Exec VP*
◆ **EMP:** 2100
SALES (est): 550MM **Privately Held**
WEB: www.sauder.com
SIC: 2519 5021 Furniture, household; glass, fiberglass & plastic; furniture

(G-695)
SAUDER WOODWORKING CO
330 N Clydes Way (43502-9170)
PHONE..............................419 446-2711
Kevin J Sauder, *President*
Judy Rossman, *Manager*
EMP: 6
SALES (corp-wide): 550MM **Privately Held**
SIC: 2519 5021 Fiberglass & plastic furniture; furniture
PA: Sauder Woodworking Co.
502 Middle St
Archbold OH 43502
419 446-3828

(G-696)
SYSTECH HANDLING INC
120 Taylor Pkwy (43502-9309)
PHONE..............................419 445-8226
Wendell Lantz, *President*
Mike Waidelich, *Vice Pres*
Sara Gigax, *Project Mgr*
Dawn Lantz, *Office Mgr*
EMP: 12 **EST:** 1999
SQ FT: 12,500
SALES (est): 2.2MM **Privately Held**
WEB: www.systechhandling.com
SIC: 3599 8711 7692 3444 Custom machinery; engineering services; welding repair; sheet metalwork

(G-697)
T J AUTOMATION INC
U075 State Route 66 (43502-9505)
PHONE..............................419 267-5687
Fax: 419 267-3427
Tracy Hammersmith, *President*
EMP: 30
SQ FT: 12,000
SALES (est): 8.1MM **Privately Held**
SIC: 3599 Custom machinery

(G-698)
THREE CORD LLC
203 E Lugbill Rd (43502-1568)
PHONE..............................419 445-2673
Fax: 419 445-2672
Cathy King, *Mng Member*
Ron King,
Ronald D King,
EMP: 3
SQ FT: 16,000
SALES (est): 220K **Privately Held**
WEB: www.threecord.com
SIC: 2261 Screen printing of cotton broadwoven fabrics

(G-699)
WYSE ELECTRIC MOTOR REPAIR
2101 S Defiance St (43502-9150)
PHONE..............................419 445-5921
Richard J Wyse, *President*
Grace Wyse, *Corp Secy*
Patrick Wyse, *Vice Pres*
EMP: 5
SALES (est): 651.4K **Privately Held**
SIC: 7694 Electric motor repair

(G-700)
YODER & FREY INC
3649 County Road 24 (43502-9317)
P.O. Box 155 (43502-0155)
PHONE..............................419 445-2070
Robert Frey, *President*
EMP: 8 **EST:** 1947
SQ FT: 12,000
SALES (est): 1.2MM **Privately Held**
SIC: 5083 3523 Agricultural machinery & equipment; farm machinery & equipment

---

Ashland
Ashland County

(G-701)
ADVANCED CYLINDER REPAIR INC
Also Called: Signal Group
942 State Route 302 (44805-9577)
PHONE..............................419 289-0538
Fax: 419 281-5358
Kyle Sigley, *President*
EMP: 5
SQ FT: 10,000
SALES (est): 380K **Privately Held**
SIC: 3599 7699 Machine shop, jobbing & repair; hydraulic equipment repair

(G-702)
ALTEC INDUSTRIES
1236 Township Road 1175 (44805-1979)
PHONE..............................419 289-6066
Fax: 419 289-7444
Bob Donaldson, *Principal*
Jerry Moore, *Controller*
EMP: 8
SALES (est): 580.3K **Privately Held**
SIC: 3999 Atomizers, toiletry

(G-703)
AMERICARB INC
1025 Faultless Dr (44805-1248)
P.O. Box 1357 (44805-5357)
PHONE..............................419 281-5800
Matt Reineke, *President*
Leland P Reineke, *Chairman*
Pat Eckrich, *VP Opers*
Robert Babcock, *Prdtn Mgr*
Jared Cooper, *Engineer*
▲ **EMP:** 75
SQ FT: 140,000
SALES (est): 17.9MM **Privately Held**
SIC: 3624 Carbon & graphite products

(G-704)
AMERICARB INTERNATIONAL CORP
1025 Faultless Dr (44805-1248)
P.O. Box 1357 (44805-5357)
PHONE..............................419 281-5800
Fax: 419 281-0059
Matt Reineke, *CEO*
Lee Reineke, *Chairman*
Brian Guido, *Vice Pres*
Rick Mellino, *Vice Pres*
Eugene Cabonor, *CFO*
EMP: 7 **EST:** 2010
SALES (est): 682.4K **Privately Held**
SIC: 3624 Carbon & graphite products

(G-705)
ART PRINTING CO INC
147 E 2nd St (44805-2396)
PHONE..............................419 281-4371
Fax: 419 281-4371
Michael B Sattler, *President*
Judith Staley, *Corp Secy*
EMP: 5 **EST:** 1924
SQ FT: 1,500

SALES: 210K **Privately Held**
SIC: 2752 2791 2759 Commercial printing, offset; typesetting; letterpress printing

(G-706)
ASHLAND MONUMENT COMPANY INC
34 E 2nd St (44805-2399)
PHONE..............................419 281-2688
Fax: 419 281-2250
Donald Hoffman, *President*
Betty Hoffman, *Vice Pres*
EMP: 4
SQ FT: 15,000
SALES: 600K **Privately Held**
SIC: 3272 5999 Grave markers, concrete; gravestones, finished

(G-707)
ASHLAND PRECISION TOOLING LLC
1750 Baney Rd S (44805-3522)
PHONE..............................419 289-1736
Steve Englet,
John Englet,
Chris Schmid,
EMP: 52
SQ FT: 56,000
SALES (est): 9.8MM **Privately Held**
WEB: www.aptooling.com
SIC: 3562 Roller bearings & parts

(G-708)
ASHLAND PUBLISHING CO
Also Called: Ashland Times Gazette
40 E 2nd St (44805-2304)
PHONE..............................419 281-0581
Fax: 419 281-5591
Amy Adams, *Division Mgr*
Troy Dix, *General Mgr*
Dale Gerber, *CFO*
Brandy Kern, *CFO*
G Charles Dix II, *Treasurer*
EMP: 855 **EST:** 1850
SQ FT: 12,400
SALES (est): 31.5MM
SALES (corp-wide): 567.1MM **Privately Held**
WEB: www.times-gazette.com
SIC: 2711 Newspapers: publishing only, not printed on site
PA: Wooster Republican Printing Co
212 E Liberty St
Wooster OH
330 264-3511

(G-709)
ATLAS BOLT & SCREW COMPANY LLC (DH)
Also Called: Atlas Fasteners For Cnstr
1628 Troy Rd (44805-1398)
PHONE..............................419 289-6171
Fax: 419 289-2564
Robert W Moore, *President*
Robert C Gluth, *Treasurer*
Jim Gerhart, *Manager*
Robert Webb, *Admin Sec*
▲ **EMP:** 175
SQ FT: 75,000
SALES (est): 32.8MM
SALES (corp-wide): 223.6B **Publicly Held**
WEB: www.atlasfasteners.com
SIC: 3452 5085 5051 5072 Washers, metal; screws, metal; fasteners, industrial; nuts, bolts, screws, etc.; metals service centers & offices; hardware
HQ: Marmon Group Llc
181 W Madison St Ste 2600
Chicago IL 60602
312 372-9500

(G-710)
BALL BOUNCE AND SPORT INC (PA)
Also Called: Hedstrom Fitness
1 Hedstrom Dr (44805-3586)
PHONE..............................419 289-9310
Fax: 419 281-3371
James Braeunig, *CEO*
John Williams, *Vice Pres*
Michael Kelly, *CFO*
Vicky Gingery, *Controller*
John McWilliams, *VP Sales*
◆ **EMP:** 270

SQ FT: 187,000
SALES (est): 158.8MM **Privately Held**
SIC: 5092 5091 3089 Toys; fitness equipment & supplies; plastic processing

(G-711)
BARBASOL LLC
2011 Ford Dr (44805-1277)
PHONE..............................419 903-0738
Don Buckingham,
EMP: 44 **EST:** 2009
SQ FT: 80,000
SALES (est): 19.4MM **Privately Held**
SIC: 2844 Toilet preparations

(G-712)
BENDON INC (PA)
1840 Baney Rd S (44805-3524)
PHONE..............................419 207-3600
Fax: 419 207-3605
Benjamin Ferguson, *President*
Terry Gerwig, *Exec VP*
Jenny Hastings, *Exec VP*
Don Myers II, *Senior VP*
Chad Wiggins, *Senior VP*
▲ **EMP:** 54
SQ FT: 220,000
SALES (est): 36.5MM **Privately Held**
WEB: www.bendonpub.com
SIC: 2731 5999 5961 5092 Book publishing; educational aids & electronic training materials; educational supplies & equipment, mail order; educational toys

(G-713)
BOOKMASTERS INC (PA)
Also Called: Atlasbooks
30 Amberwood Pkwy (44805-9765)
PHONE..............................419 281-1802
Deb Keets, *President*
Tony Proe, *President*
Raymond Sevin, *President*
David Castro, *General Mgr*
Jon Ackerman, *Senior VP*
EMP: 122
SQ FT: 180,000
SALES (est): 58.4MM **Privately Held**
WEB: www.atlasbooks.com
SIC: 7389 2752 2731 2791 Printers' services: folding, collating; commercial printing, lithographic; book publishing; typesetting; books, periodicals & newspapers

(G-714)
BOR-IT MANUFACTURING INC
1687 Cleveland Rd (44805-1929)
P.O. Box 789 (44805-0789)
PHONE..............................419 289-6639
Fax: 419 289-6352
Michael W Albers, *President*
Michelle Albers, *Corp Secy*
Timothy Eberling, *Purchasing*
Ken Albers, *Personnel Exec*
Michelle Eberling, *Admin Sec*
▼ **EMP:** 20
SQ FT: 12,500
SALES (est): 4.9MM **Privately Held**
WEB: www.bor-it.com
SIC: 3541 Drilling & boring machines

(G-715)
BYLER TRUSS
1271 State Route 96 (44805-9357)
PHONE..............................330 465-5412
Harvey Byler, *Executive*
EMP: 4
SALES (est): 274.7K **Privately Held**
SIC: 2439 Structural wood members

(G-716)
CARTER DRAPERY SERVICE INC
1301 County Road 1356 (44805-9702)
PHONE..............................419 289-2530
John Carter, *President*
Nancy Carter, *Vice Pres*
EMP: 4
SALES: 125K **Privately Held**
SIC: 2391 Curtains & draperies

(G-717)
CENTERRA CO-OP (PA)
813 Clark Ave (44805-1967)
PHONE..............................419 281-2153
Jean Bratton, *CEO*

Gary Besancon, *Vice Pres*
Bill Rohrbaugh, *Vice Pres*
John Runion, *Opers Mgr*
Bob Mole, *Site Mgr*
EMP: 30
SALES: 174.6MM **Privately Held**
WEB: www.tc-feed.com
SIC: 5983 5261 5999 2048 Fuel oil dealers; fertilizer; feed & farm supply; bird food, prepared; gases, liquefied petroleum (propane)

(G-718)
CERTIFIED LABS & SERVICE INC
535 E 7th St (44805-2553)
PHONE..............................419 289-7462
Fax: 419 281-5157
Gary E Funkhouser, *President*
Michael C Huber, *Vice Pres*
Harret Funkhouser, *Treasurer*
Pam Huber, *Admin Sec*
EMP: 6
SQ FT: 5,000
SALES: 600K **Privately Held**
SIC: 7699 3822 3561 Pumps & pumping equipment repair; hydronic controls; pumps, domestic: water or sump

(G-719)
CHAMPION PUMP COMPANY INC
1102 Myers Pkwy (44805-1968)
P.O. Box 528 (44805-0528)
PHONE..............................419 281-4500
Jeff Hawks, *President*
Jeff McFarlin, *Engineer*
▲ **EMP:** 5
SALES (est): 621.8K **Privately Held**
WEB: www.championpump.com
SIC: 3561 Pumps, domestic: water or sump

(G-720)
CHANDLER SYSTEMS INCORPORATED
710 Orange St (44805-1725)
PHONE..............................419 281-6829
William D Chandler III, *Principal*
EMP: 7
SQ FT: 70,000
SALES (est): 1.3MM **Privately Held**
SIC: 3699 Electrical equipment & supplies

(G-721)
CHANDLER SYSTEMS INCORPORATED
Also Called: Csi Controls
220 Ohio St (44805-1639)
PHONE..............................419 281-5767
Fax: 419 289-2535
William Chandler III, *President*
Debra Vogel, *Manager*
Polly Chandler, *Admin Sec*
▲ **EMP:** 65
SQ FT: 52,000
SALES (est): 25.5MM **Privately Held**
WEB: www.chandlersystemsinc.com
SIC: 5074 3625 3823 Water purification equipment; relays & industrial controls; industrial instrmnts msrmnt display/control process variable

(G-722)
CITY OF ASHLAND
City Services
310 W 12th St (44805-1756)
P.O. Box Remont Ave (44805)
PHONE..............................419 289-8728
Fax: 419 289-9411
Jerry Mack, *Director*
EMP: 9 **Privately Held**
WEB: www.ashland-ohio.com
SIC: 3589 Garbage disposers & compactors, commercial
PA: City Of Ashland
206 Claremont Ave Ste 1
Ashland OH 44805
419 289-8170

(G-723)
COLORING BOOK SOLUTIONS LLC
426 E 8th St (44805-1952)
PHONE..............................419 281-9641

Patrick Broun, *Sales Dir*
Karen Spellman, *Cust Mgr*
Don Myers III, *Mng Member*
Jean Myers, *Manager*
Ariana Myers, *Office Admin*
EMP: 11
SQ FT: 15,000
SALES (est): 820K **Privately Held**
SIC: 2759 Commercial printing

(G-724)
CONERY MANUFACTURING INC
1380 Township Road 743 (44805-8926)
PHONE..............................419 289-1444
Fax: 419 281-0366
Scott Conery, *President*
Tim Swaisgood, *General Mgr*
Chris Shafer, *Vice Pres*
Justin Crooks, *Sales Mgr*
▲ **EMP:** 16
SQ FT: 24,000
SALES (est): 3.7MM **Privately Held**
WEB: www.conerymfg.com
SIC: 3822 Liquid level controls, residential or commercial heating

(G-725)
CONSUETUDO ABSCISUM INC
Also Called: Custom Cutting Company
921 Jacobson Ave (44805-1836)
P.O. Box 1013 (44805-7013)
PHONE..............................419 281-8002
Fax: 419 281-3453
Dwain Hochstetler, *President*
Anita Hochstetler, *Admin Sec*
EMP: 4
SQ FT: 11,000
SALES: 230K **Privately Held**
SIC: 2675 Die-cut paper & board

(G-726)
CONVERGE GROUP INC
Also Called: Hedstrom Injection
1850 Baney Rd S (44805-3524)
PHONE..............................419 281-0000
Mike Sloan, *General Mgr*
EMP: 10
SQ FT: 25,000
SALES (est): 1.5MM **Privately Held**
SIC: 3089 Injection molding of plastics

(G-727)
CUSTOM HOISTS INC (HQ)
771 County Road 30a (44805-9227)
PHONE..............................419 368-4721
Fax: 419 368-8101
Rick Hiltunen, *President*
Mike Hayes, *Design Engr*
Ron Schurman, *VP Sales*
William Wright, *VP Sales*
Marcia Harpster, *Manager*
▲ **EMP:** 165
SQ FT: 110,000
SALES (est): 42.5MM
SALES (corp-wide): 751.5MM **Publicly Held**
WEB: www.customhoists.com
SIC: 3593 Fluid power cylinders & actuators
PA: Standex International Corporation
11 Keewaydin Dr
Salem NH 03079
603 893-9701

(G-728)
DALMATIAN PRESS LLC
605 Westlake Dr (44805-4710)
PHONE..............................419 207-3600
Richard Hilicki,
▲ **EMP:** 25
SQ FT: 13,000
SALES: 1.7MM
SALES (corp-wide): 36.5MM **Privately Held**
SIC: 2731 Book publishing
PA: Bendon, Inc.
1840 Baney Rd S
Ashland OH 44805
419 207-3600

(G-729)
DR HESS PRODUCTS LLC
1000 Hedstrom Dr Ste B (44805-3587)
PHONE..............................800 718-8022
Sam Roberts, *Opers Mgr*
Dave Wurster, *Mng Member*

Scott Conery,
Terry Terwig,
Polly Tribe,
EMP: 5
SQ FT: 6,000
SALES: 420K **Privately Held**
SIC: 2834 Ointments

(G-730)
ECO-FLO PRODUCTS INC (PA)
1899 Cottage St (44805-1239)
PHONE..............................877 326-3561
Larry Donelson, *President*
Jody Bartter, *Treasurer*
EMP: 15
SQ FT: 3,000
SALES (est): 2MM **Privately Held**
SIC: 3561 Pumps & pumping equipment

(G-731)
F E MYERS CO
740 E 9th St (44805-1954)
PHONE..............................419 289-1144
Fax: 419 289-6658
Bernie Martin, *Principal*
Joe Robinson, *Purch Dir*
Brian Culler, *Engineer*
Elaine Chin, *Controller*
Corey Hinkle, *Human Res Mgr*
▲ **EMP:** 1
SALES (est): 40.6MM **Privately Held**
WEB: www.aurorapump.com
SIC: 3561 Pumps, oil well & field
HQ: Pentair Flow Technologies, Llc
1101 Myers Pkwy
Ashland OH 44805
419 289-1144

(G-732)
FARR AUTOMATION INC
58 Sugarbush Ct (44805-9737)
PHONE..............................419 289-1883
Fax: 419 895-1823
Ross Farr, *President*
Rick Martin, *Opers Mgr*
Karen Farr, *Admin Sec*
EMP: 14
SQ FT: 26,000
SALES (est): 2.4MM **Privately Held**
SIC: 3599 Custom machinery

(G-733)
FLOW CONTROL US HOLDING CORP
Also Called: Pentair Water Ashland Oper
1430 George Rd 1101 (44805-8946)
PHONE..............................419 289-1144
EMP: 3 **Privately Held**
WEB: www.pentair.com
SIC: 3561 Pumps & pumping equipment
HQ: Flow Control Us Holding Corporation
5500 Wayzata Blvd
Minneapolis MN 55416
763 545-1730

(G-734)
FOLDING CARTON SERVICE INC
608 Westlake Dr (44805-1378)
PHONE..............................419 281-4099
Fax: 419 281-4226
Mina Risha, *President*
EMP: 15
SQ FT: 24,000
SALES (est): 3.3MM **Privately Held**
SIC: 2631 Folding boxboard

(G-735)
GOOD JP
Also Called: JP Good Co
854 Willow Ln (44805-9298)
PHONE..............................419 207-8484
JP Good, *Owner*
EMP: 3
SQ FT: 2,200
SALES (est): 150K **Privately Held**
SIC: 7336 2759 2395 Silk screen design; screen printing; embroidery products, except schiffli machine

(G-736)
HARRIS WELDING AND MACHINE CO (PA)
2219 Cottage St (44805-1296)
P.O. Box 317 (44805-0317)
PHONE..............................419 281-8351
Fax: 419 281-5851

John Kochenderfer, *President*
Tracy Kochenderfer, *Corp Secy*
EMP: 10
SQ FT: 7,500
SALES (est): 1.3MM **Privately Held**
SIC: 7692 3599 Welding repair; machine shop, jobbing & repair

(G-737)
HARRIS WELDING AND MACHINE CO
2219 Cottage St (44805-1296)
PHONE..............................419 281-9623
Kacey Kline, *Branch Mgr*
EMP: 9
SALES (corp-wide): 1.3MM **Privately Held**
SIC: 3599 7692 Machine shop, jobbing & repair; welding repair
PA: Harris Welding And Machine Company
2219 Cottage St
Ashland OH 44805
419 281-8351

(G-738)
HERITAGE PRESS INC
Also Called: Northcoast Advertising
651 Sandusky St (44805-1524)
PHONE..............................419 289-9209
Fax: 419 289-9605
Ramon Dever, *President*
John Clark, *Sales Mgr*
EMP: 20 **EST:** 1959
SQ FT: 6,000
SALES (est): 2.6MM **Privately Held**
WEB: www.heritagepressinc.com
SIC: 2752 2791 Commercial printing, offset; typesetting, computer controlled

(G-739)
HESS & GAULT LUMBER CO
707 County Road 1302 (44805-9783)
PHONE..............................419 281-3105
Dan Ungerer, *Owner*
▲ **EMP:** 3
SQ FT: 9,000
SALES (est): 289.6K **Privately Held**
SIC: 2421 5032 Sawmills & planing mills, general; tile & clay products

(G-740)
HILLMAN PRECISION INC
462 E 9th St Ste 1 (44805-1908)
PHONE..............................419 289-1557
Geoff Hillman Sr, *CEO*
Geoff Hillman Jr, *President*
EMP: 16
SQ FT: 37,000
SALES (est): 1.5MM **Privately Held**
WEB: www.hillmanprecision.com
SIC: 3599 Machine shop, jobbing & repair

(G-741)
HYDROMATIC PUMPS INC
1101 Myers Pkwy (44805-1969)
PHONE..............................419 289-1144
Keith Lang, *President*
Michael Meyer, *Treasurer*
Kathy Eaken, *Manager*
▼ **EMP:** 600
SALES (est): 56MM **Privately Held**
WEB: www.pentair.com
SIC: 3561 Pumps, domestic: water or sump

(G-742)
HYNEKS MACHINE AND WELDING
Also Called: Hyneks Machine & Weld Shop
1372 State Route 603 (44805-9720)
PHONE..............................419 281-7966
Mark Hynek, *President*
EMP: 3
SALES: 700K **Privately Held**
SIC: 3599 7692 Machine shop, jobbing & repair; welding repair

(G-743)
INGRAM PRODUCTS INC
1376 Township Road 743 (44805-8926)
PHONE..............................904 778-1010
William A Irvin, *President*
William English, *Vice Pres*
Doris Irvin, *Office Mgr*
▲ **EMP:** 12
SQ FT: 5,000

SALES (est): 2.7MM **Privately Held**
WEB: www.ingramproducts.com
SIC: 3679 Electronic circuits

(G-744)
KAR-DEL PLASTICS INC
1177 Faultless Dr (44805-1250)
PHONE..................................419 289-9739
Fax: 419 281-1174
Scott Pay, *President*
Shari L Regan, *President*
Teresa Pay, *Admin Sec*
EMP: 8
SQ FT: 14,000
SALES: 800K **Privately Held**
WEB: www.kar-delplastics.com
SIC: 3089 Plastic & fiberglass tanks; plastic hardware & building products; laminating of plastic; thermoformed finished plastic products

(G-745)
KEEN PUMP COMPANY INC
471 E State Rte 250 E (44805)
PHONE..................................419 207-9400
Gregory W Keener, *President*
Frank Yuhafz, *Vice Pres*
Jody Barr, *Prdtn Mgr*
Jacob Studer, *CFO*
David Dismer, *Sales Engr*
▲ EMP: 35
SQ FT: 100,000
SALES: 7MM **Privately Held**
SIC: 3561 Pumps & pumping equipment

(G-746)
KEHL-KOLOR INC
824 Us Highway 42 (44805-9516)
P.O. Box 770 (44805-0770)
PHONE..................................419 281-3107
Fax: 419 281-4719
Jon B Kehl, *President*
Mark Kehl, *Vice Pres*
EMP: 32
SQ FT: 60,000
SALES (est): 5.5MM **Privately Held**
WEB: www.kehlkolor.com
SIC: 2752 2796 2791 2789 Commercial printing, offset; lithographic plates, positives or negatives; typesetting; bookbinding & related work

(G-747)
KEN AG INC
101 E 7th St (44805-1702)
PHONE..................................419 281-1204
Fax: 419 281-9588
Bruce Perry, *President*
Doug Patton, *General Mgr*
▲ EMP: 21 EST: 1997
SQ FT: 35,000
SALES (est): 4.7MM **Privately Held**
SIC: 2621 Milk filter disks

(G-748)
KNOWLTON MACHINE INC
726 Virginia Ave (44805-1944)
P.O. Box 656 (44805-0656)
PHONE..................................419 281-6802
Fax: 419 281-6705
James Knowlton, *President*
Tammy Frontz, *Accountant*
EMP: 6
SQ FT: 6,000
SALES (est): 604.2K **Privately Held**
WEB: www.knowltonmachine.com
SIC: 3599 1799 Machine shop, jobbing & repair; welding on site

(G-749)
LAKE ERIE FROZEN FOODS MFG CO
1830 Orange Rd (44805-1335)
PHONE..................................419 289-9204
Fax: 419 281-7624
William Buckingham, *President*
Mike Buckingham, *Vice Pres*
Brian Dill, *Plant Mgr*
Brian Jordan, *Natl Sales Mgr*
Craig Baldauf, *Manager*
▲ EMP: 40
SQ FT: 30,000

SALES (est): 9.3MM **Privately Held**
WEB: www.leffco.net
SIC: 2038 2037 2022 Snacks, including onion rings, cheese sticks, etc.; vegetables, quick frozen & cold pack, excl. potato products; cheese, natural & processed

(G-750)
LIQUI-BOX CORPORATION
1817 Masters Ave (44805-1291)
PHONE..................................419 289-9696
Fax: 419 289-6752
Sheff Sweet, *Manager*
EMP: 120
SALES (corp-wide): 497.5MM **Privately Held**
WEB: www.liquibox.com
SIC: 2673 3089 3081 2671 Plastic bags: made from purchased materials; plastic processing; unsupported plastics film & sheet; packaging paper & plastics film, coated & laminated
PA: Liqui-Box Corporation
480 Schrock Rd Ste G
Columbus OH 43229
614 888-9280

(G-751)
MAVERICK INNVTIVE SLUTIONS LLC (PA)
Also Called: Mis
532 County Road 1600 (44805-9207)
PHONE..................................419 281-7944
Keith Jackson, *President*
Mark C Valentine, *Controller*
Penny Geiser, *Manager*
Todd Meldrum, *Representative*
▲ EMP: 45
SQ FT: 50,000
SALES (est): 15.7MM **Privately Held**
SIC: 3556 3585 Food products machinery; refrigeration & heating equipment

(G-752)
MAVERICK INNVTIVE SLUTIONS LLC
532 County Road 1600 (44805-9207)
PHONE..................................419 281-7944
Jim Dygert, *Human Res Mgr*
Bruce Price, *Manager*
EMP: 30
SALES (corp-wide): 15.7MM **Privately Held**
SIC: 3441 Fabricated structural metal
PA: Maverick Innovative Solutions, Llc
532 County Road 1600
Ashland OH 44805
419 281-7944

(G-753)
MCGRAW-HILL SCHOOL EDUCATION H
Also Called: Mc Graw-Hill Educational Pubg
1250 George Rd (44805-8916)
PHONE..................................419 207-7400
Fax: 419 207-7401
Maryellen Valaitis, *Principal*
Gary Curtiss, *Maintence Staff*
Angela Oxley, *Assistant*
EMP: 401
SALES (corp-wide): 750MM **Privately Held**
WEB: www.mcgraw-hill.com
SIC: 2731 5192 Books: publishing & printing; books, periodicals & newspapers
PA: Mcgraw-Hill School Education Holdings, Llc
2 Penn Plz Fl 20
New York NY 10121
646 766-2000

(G-754)
MIDWEST CONVEYOR PRODUCTS INC
Also Called: Ashland Conveyor Products
1919 Cellar Dr (44805-1275)
PHONE..................................419 281-1235
William Waltz, *President*
Tim Swineford, *Vice Pres*
Brian Davis, *Purch Mgr*
Michael Tobias, *Sales Staff*
Matt Delac, *Marketing Mgr*
EMP: 23
SQ FT: 50,000

SALES (est): 16MM **Privately Held**
SIC: 5084 3535 Industrial machinery & equipment; belt conveyor systems, general industrial use

(G-755)
MORITZ MATERIALS INC (PA)
859 Faultless Dr (44805-1274)
P.O. Box 392 (44805-0392)
PHONE..................................419 281-0575
Fax: 419 281-9148
James Moritz, *President*
Joseph Moritz, *Vice Pres*
EMP: 22
SQ FT: 2,000
SALES (est): 2.2MM **Privately Held**
SIC: 3273 5032 Ready-mixed concrete; concrete building products

(G-756)
NATIONAL PRIDE EQUIPMENT INC
1266 Middle Rowsburg Rd (44805-2813)
P.O. Box 467 (44805-0467)
PHONE..................................419 289-2886
Fax: 419 281-5526
Charles Collins, *President*
Richard Walter, *Corp Secy*
EMP: 9
SQ FT: 11,500
SALES (est): 3.9MM **Privately Held**
WEB: www.nationalpridecarwash.com
SIC: 5046 3589 5087 Commercial equipment; car washing machinery; carwash equipment & supplies

(G-757)
NOVATEX NORTH AMERICA INC
1070 Faultless Dr (44805-1247)
PHONE..................................419 282-4264
Michael Donofrio, *Principal*
Max Shull, *Opers Mgr*
Brad Neill, *QC Mgr*
▲ EMP: 55
SALES (est): 12.8MM **Privately Held**
SIC: 3069 3085 3089 Nipples, rubber; plastics bottles; injection molded finished plastic products

(G-758)
OHIO CARBON COMPANY
Also Called: OCC
1201 Jacobson Ave (44805-1842)
PHONE..................................216 251-7274
Frank Harris, *Manager*
EMP: 4
SALES (corp-wide): 1.2MM **Privately Held**
SIC: 3991 Brushes, household or industrial
PA: The Ohio Carbon Company
W146n9300 Held Dr
Menomonee Falls WI 53051
262 250-4812

(G-759)
OHIO CARBON INDUSTRIES INC
1201 Jacobson Ave (44805-1842)
PHONE..................................419 496-2530
Fax: 419 736-3011
Will Reineke, *Owner*
EMP: 21
SALES (est): 4.4MM **Privately Held**
SIC: 3624 Carbon & graphite products

(G-760)
OHIO POWER TOOL BRUSH CO
Also Called: Opt Brush
1201 Jacobson Ave (44805-1842)
PHONE..................................419 736-3010
Lee Reineke, *President*
EMP: 5
SALES (est): 613.8K **Privately Held**
SIC: 3624 5072 Brushes & brush stock contacts, electric; hardware

(G-761)
OHIO TOOL WORKS LLC
1374 Enterprise Pkwy (44805-8926)
PHONE..................................419 281-3700
Fax: 419 281-3707
John C Hovsepian, *President*
Randy Iselt, *Vice Pres*
Michael Murphy, *Vice Pres*
David McCormic, *Plant Mgr*
Sharon Parrish, *Admin Sec*
EMP: 59

SQ FT: 45,000
SALES: 12MM **Privately Held**
WEB: www.ohiotoolworks.com
SIC: 3599 Custom machinery

(G-762)
PACKAGING CORPORATION AMERICA
Also Called: Pca/Ashland 307
929 Faultless Dr (44805-1246)
PHONE..................................419 282-5809
Fax: 419 289-6436
Dan Stefko, *Vice Pres*
John Cooney, *Safety Dir*
Doug Huff, *Production*
Rick Geething, *Financial Exec*
Jeff Kaser, *Sales Staff*
EMP: 110
SALES (corp-wide): 5.7B **Publicly Held**
WEB: www.packagingcorp.com
SIC: 2653 Corrugated & solid fiber boxes
PA: Packaging Corporation Of America
1955 W Field Ct
Lake Forest IL 60045
847 482-3000

(G-763)
PAULLIN DRIVEWAY SEALING
Also Called: Quik-Pro
1306 Wells Rd Ste A (44805-1492)
PHONE..................................419 289-2228
Fax: 419 281-3890
Lane Paullin, *President*
EMP: 3
SQ FT: 2,200
SALES (est): 220K **Privately Held**
SIC: 3069 Rubber coated fabrics & clothing

(G-764)
PENTAIR FLOW TECHNOLOGIES LLC (DH)
Also Called: Pentair Water
1101 Myers Pkwy (44805-1969)
PHONE..................................419 289-1144
Randall J Hogan, *CEO*
Linda Thompson, *General Mgr*
John L Stauch, *Exec VP*
Todd R Gleason, *Senior VP*
Frederick S Koury, *Senior VP*
◆ EMP: 277
SALES (est): 359.7MM **Privately Held**
WEB: www.aurorapump.com
SIC: 3561 Pumps, oil well & field
HQ: Flow Control Us Holding Corporation
5500 Wayzata Blvd
Minneapolis MN 55416
763 545-1730

(G-765)
PHILWAY PRODUCTS INC
521 E 7th St (44805-2553)
PHONE..................................419 281-7777
Fax: 419 289-3447
Mahendra Patel, *President*
Mina Patel, *Chairman*
Ann Knowlton, *Accounting Mgr*
Robin Goodwill, *Accounts Mgr*
EMP: 195
SQ FT: 40,000
SALES (est): 23.6MM **Privately Held**
WEB: www.philway.com
SIC: 3672 Printed circuit boards

(G-766)
PIONEER NATIONAL LATEX INC (HQ)
246 E 4th St (44805-2412)
PHONE..................................419 289-3300
Fax: 419 281-3203
Gerry Meyer, *General Mgr*
Vic Webb, *Plant Supt*
Harry Gill, *Treasurer*
Nancy Hadaway, *Controller*
Karen Dravenstott, *Cust Mgr*
▲ EMP: 100 EST: 1999
SQ FT: 58,006
SALES (est): 69MM
SALES (corp-wide): 172.4MM **Privately Held**
SIC: 3069 3944 Toys, rubber; balls, rubber; balloons, advertising & toy: rubber; games, toys & children's vehicles

PA: Continental American Corporation
5000 E 29th St N
Wichita KS 67220
316 685-2266

(G-767)
PRECISION DESIGN INC
Also Called: Ohio Electric Control
2395 Rock Rd (44805-9486)
PHONE..................................419 289-1553
Fax: 419 281-5844
Robert McMullen, *President*
EMP: 6
SQ FT: 3,000
SALES (est): 520K **Privately Held**
SIC: 3621 Control equipment for electric buses & locomotives

(G-768)
PRIMARY COLORS DESIGN CORP
1899 Cottage St (44805-1239)
PHONE..................................419 903-0403
David Vespor, *President*
David Vesper, *President*
Jeff Gierhart, *VP Sls/Mktg*
Jody Bartter, *Treasurer*
Randy Boyd, *Art Dir*
▲ **EMP:** 8
SQ FT: 5,000
SALES (est): 1.1MM
SALES (corp-wide): 2MM **Privately Held**
SIC: 2678 Stationery products
PA: Eco-Flo Products, Inc.
1899 Cottage St
Ashland OH 44805
877 326-3561

(G-769)
PURVI OIL INC
654 Us Highway 250 E (44805-9755)
PHONE..................................419 207-8234
EMP: 3 **EST:** 2014
SALES (est): 149.8K **Privately Held**
SIC: 1311 Crude petroleum & natural gas

(G-770)
R & J AG MANUFACTURING INC
Also Called: All-Plant Liquid Plant Food
821 State Route 511 (44805-9562)
PHONE..................................419 962-4707
Fax: 419 962-4534
Roger D Shopbell, *President*
Joan Shopbell, *Vice Pres*
James Shopbell, *Treasurer*
Pam Tobias, *Admin Sec*
EMP: 10
SQ FT: 5,000
SALES (est): 1.5MM **Privately Held**
SIC: 2873 5999 Nitrogenous fertilizers; farm equipment & supplies

(G-771)
RAIN DROP PRODUCTS LLC
2121 Cottage St (44805-1245)
PHONE..................................419 207-1229
Fax: 419 207-8902
Mark Williams, *President*
Ross Kette, *VP Opers*
Cory Davis, *Prdtn Mgr*
Laurie Evans, *Accounting Mgr*
Jodi Holt, *Sales Mgr*
◆ **EMP:** 30
SQ FT: 30,000
SALES (est): 5MM **Privately Held**
SIC: 3949 Water sports equipment

(G-772)
REINEKE COMPANY LLC
1025 Faultless Dr (44805-1248)
PHONE..................................419 281-5800
Matt Reineke, *CEO*
Craig Sabin, *Controller*
Carol Grim, *Manager*
EMP: 14
SQ FT: 144,000
SALES (est): 2.3MM
SALES (corp-wide): 32.8MM **Privately Held**
WEB: www.reinekecompany.com
SIC: 3714 Motor vehicle parts & accessories
PA: Bearing Technologies, Ltd.
1141 Jaycox Rd
Avon OH 44011
440 937-4770

(G-773)
ROSSI MACHINERY SERVICES INC (PA)
1529 Cottage St (44805-1226)
PHONE..................................419 281-4488
Michael Rossi, *CEO*
Chris Rossi, *President*
EMP: 4
SALES: 270K **Privately Held**
WEB: www.rossimachineryservices.com
SIC: 7349 7699 3541 3545 Building maintenance services; industrial machinery & equipment repair; machine tools, metal cutting type; machine tool accessories; rebuilt machine tools, metal forming types

(G-774)
ROTOSOLUTIONS INC
1401 Jacobson Ave (44805-1846)
PHONE..................................419 903-0800
Ralph Kirkpatrick, *CEO*
Nicole Shockley, *Office Mgr*
Chris Fitzcharles, *Manager*
Mark Kirkpatrick, *Software Engr*
EMP: 15
SALES (est): 3.2MM **Privately Held**
SIC: 3089 Injection molding of plastics

(G-775)
SANTMYER OIL CO OF ASHLAND
1011 Jacobson Ave (44805-1838)
PHONE..................................419 289-8815
Seth Resinger, *Branch Mgr*
EMP: 3
SALES (corp-wide): 104.2MM **Privately Held**
SIC: 2911 5983 Diesel fuels; jet fuels; fuel oil dealers
HQ: Santmyer Oil Co Of Ashland Inc
1055 W Old Lincoln Way
Wooster OH 44691
330 262-6501

(G-776)
SCHOONOVER INDUSTRIES INC
1440 Simonton Rd (44805-1906)
P.O. Box 69 (44805-0069)
PHONE..................................419 289-8332
Fax: 419 281-8561
Robert P Schoonover, *President*
Michael Hauenstein, *Vice Pres*
Collette Day, *Finance Mgr*
EMP: 27
SQ FT: 14,000
SALES (est): 6MM **Privately Held**
WEB: www.schoonoveronline.com
SIC: 3441 3444 Fabricated structural metal; sheet metalwork; sheet metal specialties, not stamped

(G-777)
SEPTIC PRODUCTS INC
1378 Township Road 743 (44805-8926)
PHONE..................................419 282-5933
Rod Mitchell, *President*
Dave Ratzel, *Manager*
EMP: 8
SALES (est): 1.2MM **Privately Held**
SIC: 3272 Septic tanks, concrete

(G-778)
SNYDERS-LANCE INC
2041 Claremont Ave (44805-3545)
PHONE..................................419 289-0787
Brenda Marker, *Purch Mgr*
Andre Boom, *Branch Mgr*
EMP: 205
SALES (corp-wide): 2.1B **Publicly Held**
SIC: 2052 Cookies
PA: Snyder's-Lance, Inc.
13515 Balntyn Corp Pl
Charlotte NC 28277
704 554-1421

(G-779)
STEEL CITY CORPORATION (PA)
1000 Hedstrom Dr (44805-3587)
PHONE..................................330 792-7663
Fax: 330 792-7951
Chris Shafer, *President*
Scott Vangilder, *Purch Mgr*
Jim Smith, *Natl Sales Mgr*
▲ **EMP:** 25 **EST:** 1939

SQ FT: 161,000
SALES (est): 2MM **Privately Held**
WEB: www.scity.com
SIC: 2678 Newsprint tablets & pads: made from purchased materials

(G-780)
STRAIGHTAWAY FABRICATIONS LTD
481 Us Highway 250 E (44805-9771)
PHONE..................................419 281-9440
Fax: 419 281-9447
David Bowles, *President*
Lea Myers, *Purchasing*
Josh T Aspin, *Sales Executive*
Kelly Bowles, *Manager*
EMP: 30
SQ FT: 1,500
SALES (est): 8.7MM **Privately Held**
WEB: www.straightawayfab.com
SIC: 3441 Fabricated structural metal

(G-781)
THIELS REPLACEMENT SYSTEMS INC
Also Called: Cabinet Restylers
419 E 8th St (44805-1953)
PHONE..................................419 289-6139
Fax: 419 281-4884
Eric Thiel, *President*
Denise Appleby, *Vice Pres*
Bobbie Browne, *Manager*
EMP: 56
SQ FT: 50,000
SALES (est): 7.7MM **Privately Held**
SIC: 1751 2541 5211 1799 Window & door (prefabricated) installation; cabinet & finish carpentry; cabinets, lockers & shelving; cabinets, kitchen; bathtub refinishing; gutter & downspout contractor

(G-782)
TREMCO INCORPORATED
Also Called: Tremco Glazing Solutions Group
1451 Jacobson Ave (44805-1865)
PHONE..................................419 289-2050
Fax: 419 289-6645
Ray Jackenheimer, *Safety Mgr*
Robert Gourley, *Engineer*
Peter Poirier, *Engineer*
James Mongiardo, *Manager*
Cathy Pokorny, *Manager*
EMP: 70
SALES (corp-wide): 4.8B **Publicly Held**
WEB: www.tremcoinc.com
SIC: 2891 Adhesives & sealants
HQ: Tremco Incorporated
3735 Green Rd
Beachwood OH 44122
216 292-5000

(G-783)
UNDERGROUND PROFESSIONALS
506 Us Highway 250 E (44805-9769)
PHONE..................................419 282-6400
Scott Smalley, *President*
EMP: 5
SQ FT: 20,000
SALES (est): 4.5MM **Privately Held**
WEB: www.undergroundprofessionals.com
SIC: 3532 Drills, core

(G-784)
VISTA RESEARCH GROUP LLC
Also Called: Vistanet
1554 Township Road 805 (44805-9202)
P.O. Box 321 (44805-0321)
PHONE..................................419 281-3927
James Chandler,
Barbara Chandler,
EMP: 5
SQ FT: 1,200
SALES: 500K **Privately Held**
SIC: 8748 2731 4813 Business consulting; book publishing;

(G-785)
WHITTEN STUDIOS
1180 County Road 30a (44805-9424)
P.O. Box 1623, Mansfield (44901-1623)
PHONE..................................419 368-8366
George Whitten, *Owner*
EMP: 5

SALES: 300K **Privately Held**
SIC: 3952 Canvas, prepared on frames: artists'

(G-786)
WRL OF INDIANA INC
1407 George Rd (44805-8946)
PHONE..................................419 289-8700
Joe Holson MD, *President*
Jim Rudar, *Vice Pres*
Carmen Walthour, *Manager*
Ron Wilson, *Info Tech Dir*
EMP: 600
SQ FT: 115,000
SALES (est): 42.7MM
SALES (corp-wide): 1.6B **Privately Held**
WEB: www.wilresearch.com
SIC: 8731 2899 Commercial research laboratory; chemical preparations
PA: Chemtura Corporation
1818 Market St Ste 3700
Philadelphia PA 19103
203 573-2000

(G-787)
ZEPHYR INDUSTRIES INC
600 Township Road 1500 (44805-9759)
PHONE..................................419 281-4485
Fax: 419 281-0317
Vincent Richilano, *President*
David E Richilano, *Corp Secy*
EMP: 8
SQ FT: 20,000
SALES: 625K **Privately Held**
WEB: www.zephyrindustries.com
SIC: 3365 3569 3599 Machinery castings, aluminum; firefighting apparatus & related equipment; machine shop, jobbing & repair

Ashley
Delaware County

(G-788)
IMPERIAL ON-PECE FIBRGLS POOLS
255 S Franklin St (43003-9749)
PHONE..................................740 747-2971
Fax: 614 747-2178
Charles Levings Jr, *President*
Glen Mash, *Principal*
John Mash, *Principal*
Carol Mash, *Vice Pres*
EMP: 10
SQ FT: 10,000
SALES (est): 700K **Privately Held**
WEB: www.imperial-1pc-pools.com
SIC: 3949 1799 Swimming pools, except plastic; swimming pool construction

(G-789)
INDUSTRIAL AUTOMATION SERVICE
4590 State Route 229 (43003-9712)
PHONE..................................740 747-2222
Thomas Greer, *President*
Martha Greer, *Admin Sec*
EMP: 6
SQ FT: 4,000
SALES (est): 691.8K **Privately Held**
SIC: 3544 Special dies, tools, jigs & fixtures

(G-790)
ROTARY PRODUCTS INC (PA)
117 E High St (43003)
P.O. Box 370 (43003-0370)
PHONE..................................740 747-2623
Fax: 614 747-2188
Christopher Buechel, *President*
EMP: 14 **EST:** 1958
SQ FT: 9,000
SALES (est): 1.9MM **Privately Held**
WEB: www.rotaryproductsinc.com
SIC: 3081 Vinyl film & sheet

(G-791)
ROTARY PRODUCTS INC
202 W High St (43003-9703)
P.O. Box 370 (43003-0370)
PHONE..................................740 747-2623
Chris Buechel, *President*
EMP: 15

SALES (corp-wide): 1.9MM **Privately Held**
WEB: www.rotaryproductsinc.com
SIC: 3081 Unsupported plastics film & sheet
PA: Rotary Products Inc
117 E High St
Ashley OH 43003
740 747-2623

Ashtabula
Ashtabula County

(G-792)
ALLPASS CORPORATION
2605 Crane Ave (44004-4947)
P.O. Box 489 (44005-0489)
PHONE.....................................440 998-6300
Fax: 440 998-0523
Joseph Passerell, *CEO*
David Passerell, *CEO*
Joe Passerell, *President*
Steve Passerell, *COO*
Mike Passerell, *Vice Pres*
▲ **EMP:** 12
SALES (est): 3.7MM **Privately Held**
SIC: 3443 Metal parts

(G-793)
ASHTA CHEMICALS INC
3509 Middle Rd (44004-3915)
P.O. Box 858 (44005-0858)
PHONE.....................................440 997-5221
Fax: 440 998-0286
Reginald Baxter, *President*
Jamison Baxter, *Corp Secy*
Bill Brodnick, *Vice Pres*
Richard Jackson, *Vice Pres*
Brad Westfall, *Vice Pres*
▲ **EMP:** 90
SALES (est): 47.5MM **Privately Held**
WEB: www.ashtachemicals.com
SIC: 2812 Caustic potash, potassium hydroxide; chlorine, compressed or liquefied; potassium carbonate

(G-794)
ASHTABULA RUBBER CO
2751 West Ave (44004-3100)
P.O. Box 398 (44005-0398)
PHONE.....................................440 992-2195
Fax: 440 992-7829
Nicholas J Jammal, *President*
Jeff Marano, *Plant Supt*
David Covell, *Maint Spvr*
Janice Meade, *Purch Mgr*
Kathy Acierno, *Research*
▲ **EMP:** 200 **EST:** 1945
SQ FT: 72,000
SALES (est): 42.6MM **Privately Held**
WEB: www.ashtabularubber.com
SIC: 3061 3069 3053 Mechanical rubber goods; hard rubber & molded rubber products; battery boxes, jars or parts, hard rubber; washers, rubber; molded rubber products; gaskets, all materials

(G-795)
CHROMAFLO TECHNOLOGIES CORP (PA)
2600 Michigan Ave (44004-3140)
P.O. Box 816 (44005-0816)
PHONE.....................................440 997-0081
Fax: 440 992-3613
Scott Becker, *CEO*
Brij Mohal, *Vice Pres*
Mark Skouby, *Vice Pres*
Liz Campbell, *Safety Dir*
James Ogren, *Purch Mgr*
▲ **EMP:** 160
SQ FT: 175,000
SALES (est): 46.6MM **Privately Held**
SIC: 2816 3087 2865 Inorganic pigments; custom compound purchased resins; color pigments, organic

(G-796)
CHROMAFLO TECHNOLOGIES CORP
1603 W 29th St (44004-9452)
P.O. Box B (44005)
PHONE.....................................440 997-5137
Jim Ogren, *Branch Mgr*

EMP: 110
SALES (corp-wide): 46.6MM **Privately Held**
SIC: 2816 Inorganic pigments
PA: Chromaflo Technologies Corporation
2600 Michigan Ave
Ashtabula OH 44004
440 997-0081

(G-797)
CICOGNA ELECTRIC AND SIGN CO (PA)
4330 N Bend Rd (44004-9797)
P.O. Box 234 (44005-0234)
PHONE.....................................440 998-2637
Fax: 440 992-8021
Frank Cicogna, *President*
James M Timonere, *Principal*
Brad Petro, *VP Opers*
Erin McKibbin, *Project Mgr*
Mark Woodburn, *Prdtn Mgr*
EMP: 75
SQ FT: 55,000
SALES (est): 14.5MM **Privately Held**
WEB: www.cicognasign.com
SIC: 3993 Electric signs

(G-798)
COMMUNITY RE GROUP-COMVET
3220 Station Ave (44004)
PHONE.....................................440 319-6714
James Brewington, *CEO*
EMP: 3
SALES (est): 63.3K **Privately Held**
SIC: 8211 8732 8748 1521 Specialty education; commercial sociological & educational research; testing service, educational or personnel; single-family housing construction; printed circuit boards

(G-799)
CREATIVE MILLWORK OHIO INC
1801 W 47th St (44004-5425)
P.O. Box 1157 (44005-1157)
PHONE.....................................440 992-3566
Fax: 440 992-7867
Mark Estock, *President*
Cynthia Estock, *Corp Secy*
Barbara Anthony, *Vice Pres*
Joseph Lalli, *Vice Pres*
Jo Ann Anderson, *Controller*
EMP: 45
SQ FT: 67,000
SALES (est): 7.1MM **Privately Held**
WEB: www.creativemillwork.com
SIC: 2431 Millwork; windows & window parts & trim, wood

(G-800)
CRISTAL USA INC
Also Called: Millennium
2900 Middle Rd (44004-3925)
P.O. Box 160 (44005-0160)
PHONE.....................................440 994-1400
Fax: 440 969-9214
John Hughes, *Engineer*
Jerry Jones, *Engineer*
David Price, *Engineer*
Lee Turley, *Engineer*
Sphr R Maley, *Human Resources*
EMP: 200 **Privately Held**
SIC: 2816 Titanium dioxide, anatase or rutile (pigments)
HQ: Cristal Usa Inc.
6752 Baymeadow Dr
Glen Burnie MD 21060
410 229-4441

(G-801)
DALIN AUTO SERVICE
3041 S Ridge Rd W (44004-9060)
PHONE.....................................440 997-3301
Fax: 440 997-3870
Ronald Dalin Sr, *Partner*
Judy Dalin, *Partner*
Ronald Dalin Jr, *Partner*
EMP: 3
SQ FT: 9,000
SALES: 170K **Privately Held**
SIC: 7538 7692 7699 General automotive repair shops; general truck repair; welding repair; farm machinery repair

(G-802)
DETREX CORPORATION
1100 State Rd (44004-3943)
PHONE.....................................440 997-6131
Tom Steiv, *Manager*
EMP: 48
SALES (corp-wide): 56.5MM **Publicly Held**
SIC: 2869 Laboratory chemicals, organic
PA: Detrex Corporation
1000 Belt Line Ave
Cleveland OH 44109

(G-803)
DPA INVESTMENTS INC
3050 Lake Rd E (44004-3829)
PHONE.....................................440 992-3377
Fax: 440 992-7628
Brad Loejoy, *Manager*
EMP: 5
SALES (corp-wide): 63.3MM **Privately Held**
WEB: www.usalco.com
SIC: 2899 Water treating compounds
PA: Dpa Investments, Inc.
2601 Cannery Ave
Baltimore MD 21226
410 918-2230

(G-804)
DPA INVESTMENTS INC
1741 W 47th St (44004-5423)
P.O. Box 1767 (44005-1767)
PHONE.....................................440 992-7039
Fax: 440 992-2938
Bruce Wonder, *COO*
Jack Felde, *Manager*
Rich White, *Manager*
EMP: 12
SALES (corp-wide): 63.3MM **Privately Held**
SIC: 2819 Aluminum sulfate
PA: Dpa Investments, Inc.
2601 Cannery Ave
Baltimore MD 21226
410 918-2230

(G-805)
ELCO CORPORATION
1100 State Rd (44004-3943)
PHONE.....................................440 997-6131
Gregg Luthardt, *Accountant*
Tom Steiv, *Manager*
Urban Meyer, *Administration*
EMP: 25
SALES (corp-wide): 56.5MM **Publicly Held**
WEB: www.elcocorp.com
SIC: 2869 2819 2899 Industrial organic chemicals; industrial inorganic chemicals; hydrochloric acid; chemical preparations
HQ: Elco Corporation
1000 Belt Line Ave
Cleveland OH 44109
800 321-0467

(G-806)
FARGO TOOLITE INCORPORATED
998 Stevenson Rd (44004-9675)
PHONE.....................................440 997-2442
Fax: 440 992-9770
Larry Fargo, *President*
EMP: 10
SQ FT: 13,200
SALES (est): 1.4MM **Privately Held**
WEB: www.fargomachine.com
SIC: 3544 3599 Special dies & tools; machine shop, jobbing & repair

(G-807)
FENTON MANUFACTURING INC
6600 Depot Rd (44004-9475)
PHONE.....................................440 969-1128
Dan Fenton, *President*
Melissa Fenton, *Treasurer*
EMP: 5
SQ FT: 3,200
SALES (est): 728.1K **Privately Held**
SIC: 3544 Special dies, tools, jigs & fixtures

(G-808)
G M R TECHNOLOGY INC
2131 Aetna Rd (44004-6291)
PHONE.....................................440 992-6003

Fax: 440 992-6007
Connie J Speakman, *Principal*
Sue Scheppelmann, *Sales Mgr*
Jakie Juliano, *Manager*
Rick Wilczewski, *Consultant*
William Pikor, *Technology*
▲ **EMP:** 30
SQ FT: 45,000
SALES (est): 6MM **Privately Held**
SIC: 3089 Injection molding of plastics

(G-809)
GABRIEL PERFORMANCE PDTS LLC
725 State Rd (44004-3934)
PHONE.....................................440 992-3200
Seth Tomasch, *Manager*
EMP: 4
SALES (corp-wide): 14.4MM **Privately Held**
SIC: 2819 Chemicals, high purity: refined from technical grade
HQ: Gabriel Performance Products, Llc
388 S Main St
Akron OH 44311
440 992-3200

(G-810)
GREAT LAKES PRINTING INC
2926 Lake Ave (44004-4964)
P.O. Box 245, Jefferson (44047-0245)
PHONE.....................................440 993-8781
Fax: 440 992-2834
Jeff Lampson, *President*
Mike Ski, *General Mgr*
EMP: 100
SQ FT: 2,460
SALES (est): 8.1MM **Privately Held**
SIC: 2752 2759 Commercial printing, offset; letterpress printing

(G-811)
HALMAN INC
3901 N Bend Rd (44004-9778)
P.O. Box 3108 (44005-3108)
PHONE.....................................440 992-4239
Fax: 440 992-9848
Sarah Halman, *President*
Sandra Ranck, *Corp Secy*
Bob Halman Sr, *Vice Pres*
Robert Halman Sr, *Vice Pres*
Robin Wentink, *Manager*
EMP: 14
SQ FT: 26,000
SALES (est): 2.1MM **Privately Held**
SIC: 3441 1541 Fabricated structural metal; renovation, remodeling & repairs: industrial buildings

(G-812)
HARBOR PERK LLC
1025 Bridge St (44004-3207)
PHONE.....................................440 964-9277
Jacob Sposito,
Kelly Sposito,
EMP: 6
SALES (est): 498.5K **Privately Held**
WEB: www.harborperk.com
SIC: 2095 Roasted coffee

(G-813)
ITEN INDUSTRIES INC (PA)
Also Called: Plant 2
4602 Benefit Ave (44004-5455)
P.O. Box 2150 (44005-2150)
PHONE.....................................440 997-6134
Fax: 440 992-4966
Peter D Huggins, *President*
David Riffe, *Opers Staff*
David Zandel, *Purchasing*
Bill Kane, *CFO*
Cheryl Laughlin, *Accountant*
▲ **EMP:** 190 **EST:** 1922
SQ FT: 175,000
SALES (est): 42.8MM **Privately Held**
WEB: www.itenindustries.com
SIC: 3089 Laminating of plastic; injection molded finished plastic products

(G-814)
JACKS MARINE INC
2000 Great Lakes Ave (44004-3451)
PHONE.....................................440 997-5060
Fax: 440 990-0515
Patricia Phelps, *President*
John Phelps, *Vice Pres*

GEOGRAPHIC

Ron Phelps, *Vice Pres*
EMP: 5
SQ FT: 22,200
SALES: 400K **Privately Held**
SIC: 3732 4493 5551 Boat building & repairing; boat yards, storage & incidental repair; marine supplies

(G-815)
KOSKI CONSTRUCTION CO (PA)
5841 Woodman Ave (44004-7919)
P.O. Box 1038 (44005-1038)
PHONE...............................440 997-5337
Fax: 440 992-8549
Donald R Koski, *President*
Thomas Pope, *Vice Pres*
Janet Smith, *Vice Pres*
David C Sheldon, *Treasurer*
Beverly Carey, *Accountant*
EMP: 6 **EST:** 1921
SQ FT: 3,500
SALES (est): 4.5MM **Privately Held**
SIC: 1611 1794 1771 2951 Surfacing & paving; excavation work; concrete work; asphalt & asphaltic paving mixtures (not from refineries); liquid waste, collection & disposal

(G-816)
KOSKI CONSTRUCTION CO
1149 E 5th St (44004-3513)
P.O. Box 1038 (44005-1038)
PHONE...............................440 964-8171
Bruce Schmidt, *Manager*
EMP: 4
SALES (corp-wide): 4.5MM **Privately Held**
SIC: 3531 Bituminous, cement & concrete related products & equipment
PA: Koski Construction Co (Inc)
  5841 Woodman Ave
  Ashtabula OH 44004
  440 997-5337

(G-817)
LAKE CITY PLATING LLC
1701 Lake Ave (44004-3099)
PHONE...............................440 964-3555
Fax: 440 964-2399
Todd Bendis, *CEO*
Ryan Carroll, *President*
Meloney Drable, *Manager*
EMP: 18 **EST:** 1949
SQ FT: 20,000
SALES (est): 3.2MM **Privately Held**
WEB: www.lakecityplating.com
SIC: 3471 Electroplating & plating

(G-818)
LORD CORPORATION
Also Called: Corporation Lord
4212 Ann Ave (44004-5675)
PHONE...............................440 992-0193
EMP: 153
SALES (corp-wide): 848.2MM **Privately Held**
SIC: 2891 Adhesives & sealants
PA: Lord Corporation
  111 Lord Dr
  Cary NC 27511
  919 468-5979

(G-819)
MEESE INC
Meese Orbitron Dunne
4920 State Rd (44004-6264)
P.O. Box 607 (44005-0607)
PHONE...............................440 998-1202
Robert W Dunne Jr, *President*
Dunne Robert, *CFO*
Jennifer Lemponen, *Human Res Mgr*
Erik Kozman, *Marketing Staff*
Greg Graham, *Manager*
EMP: 80
SALES (corp-wide): 90.6MM **Privately Held**
WEB: www.modroto.com
SIC: 3429 3089 3544 3444 Manufactured hardware (general); injection molded finished plastic products; special dies, tools, jigs & fixtures; sheet metalwork; miscellaneous fabricated wire products; plastics plumbing fixtures

HQ: Meese, Inc.
  535 N Midland Ave
  Saddle Brook NJ 07663
  201 796-4490

(G-820)
MFG COMPOSITE SYSTEMS COMPANY
Also Called: Mfg CSC
2925 Mfg Pl (44004-9701)
P.O. Box 675 (44005-0675)
PHONE...............................440 997-5851
Richard Morrison, *President*
Andy Juhola, *Vice Pres*
Perry Bennett, *Director*
Keith Bihary, *Director*
Dan Plona, *Director*
▼ **EMP:** 350
SALES (est): 80.6MM
SALES (corp-wide): 619.2MM **Privately Held**
SIC: 3229 2823 Glass fiber products; cellulosic manmade fibers
PA: Molded Fiber Glass Companies
  2925 Mfg Pl
  Ashtabula OH 44004
  440 997-5851

(G-821)
MODROTO
4920 State Rd (44004-6264)
PHONE...............................800 772-7659
Bob Dunne, *President*
EMP: 3 **EST:** 2015
SALES (est): 172.2K **Privately Held**
SIC: 2655 2599 5085 Fiber cans, drums & containers; carts, restaurant equipment; bins & containers, storage

(G-822)
MOHAWK FINE PAPERS INC
6800 Center Rd (44004-8947)
PHONE...............................440 969-2000
Thomas Oconnor Jr, *President*
Annmarie Mihoci, *HR Admin*
EMP: 30
SALES (corp-wide): 241.6MM **Privately Held**
WEB: www.mohawkpaper.com
SIC: 2621 Paper mills
PA: Mohawk Fine Papers Inc.
  465 Saratoga St
  Cohoes NY 12047
  518 237-1740

(G-823)
MOLDED FIBER GLASS COMPANIES (PA)
2925 Mfg Pl (44004-9445)
P.O. Box 675 (44005-0675)
PHONE...............................440 997-5851
Fax: 440 992-0542
Richard Morrison, *CEO*
Dave Denny, *President*
Pete Emrich, *General Mgr*
Wesley Shamp, *General Mgr*
Joe Wilk, *General Mgr*
▼ **EMP:** 685
SQ FT: 265,000
SALES (est): 619.2MM **Privately Held**
WEB: www.moldedfiberglass.com
SIC: 3089 Molding primary plastic; boxes, plastic; injection molding of plastics

(G-824)
MOLDED FIBER GLASS COMPANIES
Also Called: Msg Premier Molded Fiber
4401 Benefit Ave (44004-5458)
P.O. Box 675 (44005-0675)
PHONE...............................440 997-5851
Richard Morrison, *CEO*
Ivan Schwarz, *Buyer*
Pam Campbell, *CFO*
EMP: 300
SQ FT: 168,000
SALES (corp-wide): 619.2MM **Privately Held**
SIC: 3089 Molding primary plastic
PA: Molded Fiber Glass Companies
  2925 Mfg Pl
  Ashtabula OH 44004
  440 997-5851

(G-825)
MOLDED FIBER GLASS RESEARCH
1315 W 47th St (44004-5403)
PHONE...............................440 994-5100
Fax: 440 992-7395
Pete Emrich, *Vice Pres*
Janice Lipps, *Human Res Dir*
Dave Barron, *Manager*
John Oneil, *IT/INT Sup*
EMP: 20
SALES (est): 2.6MM **Privately Held**
SIC: 3229 Glass fiber products

(G-826)
NEWSPAPER HOLDING INC
Also Called: Ashtabula Star Beacon
4626 Park Ave (44004-6933)
P.O. Box 2100 (44005-2100)
PHONE...............................440 998-2323
Fax: 440 998-7938
Ed Looman, *Publisher*
Neil Frieder, *Controller*
Rich Furmage, *Advt Staff*
Jim Frustere, *Branch Mgr*
EMP: 51 **Privately Held**
WEB: www.clintonnc.com
SIC: 2711 2791 2752 Newspapers, publishing & printing; typesetting; commercial printing, lithographic
HQ: Newspaper Holding, Inc.
  425 Locust St
  Johnstown PA 15901
  814 532-5102

(G-827)
NORTHEAST BOX COMPANY
1726 Griswold Ave (44004-9213)
P.O. Box 370 (44005-0370)
PHONE...............................440 992-5500
Fax: 440 992-7820
Ronald Marchewka, *President*
Robert Jessup, *Shareholder*
Joseph Misinic, *Shareholder*
Craig Parker, *Shareholder*
Richard Selip, *Shareholder*
EMP: 55
SQ FT: 110,000
SALES (est): 15.2MM **Privately Held**
WEB: www.northeastbox.com
SIC: 2653 Boxes, corrugated: made from purchased materials

(G-828)
OUTDOOR ARMY STORE OF ASHTBULA
Also Called: Outdoor Army Navy Stores
4420 Main Ave (44004-6923)
PHONE...............................440 992-8791
Fax: 440 992-0552
William Hyland, *President*
Harmon Lustig, *Corp Secy*
EMP: 18
SQ FT: 17,000
SALES (est): 2MM **Privately Held**
SIC: 2329 5661 5941 Athletic (warmup, sweat & jogging) suits: men's & boys'; shoe stores; camping equipment

(G-829)
PENCO TOOL LLC
2621 West Ave (44004-3115)
P.O. Box 429 (44005-0429)
PHONE...............................440 998-1116
Fax: 440 992-6652
Brian Lewis, *President*
Steve Berndt, *Vice Pres*
Mary Bugdon, *Office Mgr*
EMP: 23
SQ FT: 18,450
SALES (est): 4.8MM **Privately Held**
WEB: www.deephole.com
SIC: 3544 3599 7692 Industrial molds; special dies & tools; machine shop, jobbing & repair; welding repair

(G-830)
PENDLETON MOLD & MACHINE LLC
4624 State Rd (44004-6210)
PHONE...............................440 998-0041
Steven Pendleton,
EMP: 5

SALES (est): 300K **Privately Held**
SIC: 3544 3312 Industrial molds; blast furnaces & steel mills

(G-831)
PESKA INC (PA)
Also Called: Sports & Sports
3600 N Ridge Rd E (44004-4316)
PHONE...............................440 998-4664
Steve Reichert, *President*
Edith M Reichert, *Principal*
Paul A Reichert, *Principal*
EMP: 10 **EST:** 1983
SQ FT: 6,000
SALES (est): 1.9MM **Privately Held**
SIC: 5941 2396 Sporting goods & bicycle shops; screen printing on fabric articles

(G-832)
PINNEY DOCK & TRANSPORT LLC
1149 E 5th St (44004-3513)
P.O. Box 41 (44005-0041)
PHONE...............................440 964-7186
Fax: 440 964-5210
Ricki Seaman, *Terminal Mgr*
John Mead, *Finance*
Lee Demers,
Bradley Frank,
◆ **EMP:** 33
SQ FT: 20,000
SALES (est): 516.7K
SALES (corp-wide): 13B **Publicly Held**
SIC: 3731 4491 5032 Drydocks, floating; docks, piers & terminals; limestone
PA: Kinder Morgan Inc
  1001 La St Ste 1000
  Houston TX 77002
  713 369-9000

(G-833)
PLAY ALL LLC
Also Called: Playall Trophies & Awards
4542 Main Ave (44004-6925)
PHONE...............................440 992-7529
Fax: 440 992-9192
Robert Simpson, *President*
John Simpson, *Vice Pres*
Veronica Simpson, *Treasurer*
EMP: 3
SQ FT: 2,000
SALES: 200K **Privately Held**
SIC: 3479 5999 Etching & engraving; trophies & plaques

(G-834)
PRAXAIR INC
3102 Lake Rd E (44004-3829)
PHONE...............................440 994-1000
Fax: 440 992-7241
G K Primbas, *Production*
J J Redmond, *Branch Mgr*
EMP: 99
SALES (corp-wide): 10.5B **Publicly Held**
SIC: 2813 Oxygen, compressed or liquefied; nitrogen
PA: Praxair, Inc.
  10 Riverview Dr
  Danbury CT 06810
  203 837-2000

(G-835)
REESE MACHINE COMPANY INC
2501 State Rd (44004-5235)
P.O. Box 1396 (44005-1396)
PHONE...............................440 992-3942
Fax: 440 992-5259
Dale Reese, *President*
EMP: 10
SALES (est): 1.6MM **Privately Held**
WEB: www.reesemachinecompany.com
SIC: 3599 Machine shop, jobbing & repair

(G-836)
RELOADING SUPPLIES CORP
Also Called: Ohio Guns
1040 Devon Dr (44004-2100)
PHONE...............................440 228-0367
Daryl Upole, *President*
Daryl G Upole III, *Administration*
EMP: 3 **EST:** 2012
SALES (est): 227.3K **Privately Held**
SIC: 3484 5941 Machine guns & grenade launchers; ammunition; firearms

(G-837)
REX INTERNATIONAL USA INC
Also Called: Wheeler Manufacturing
3744 Jefferson Rd (44004-9601)
P.O. Box 688 (44005-0688)
PHONE...........................800 321-7950
Fax: 440 992-2925
John Miyagawa, *President*
Jeff Jones, *Purch Mgr*
Bryan Stright, *Engineer*
Vicki Gorder, *Human Resources*
Lisa Mullins, *Sales Staff*
▲ EMP: 28
SQ FT: 22,000
SALES (est): 6.1MM
SALES (corp-wide): 45MM **Privately Held**
WEB: www.wheelerrex.com
SIC: 3423 3546 3545 3541 Hand & edge tools; power-driven handtools; machine tool accessories; pipe cutting & threading machines
PA: Rex Industries Co.,Ltd.
1-9-3, Hishiyahigashi
Higashi-Osaka OSK 578-0
729 619-887

(G-838)
SHORT RUN MACHINE PRODUCTS INC
4744 Kister Ct (44004-8974)
PHONE...........................440 969-1313
Fax: 440 969-1314
Scott Ray, *President*
Cheryl Wakeman, *Admin Sec*
EMP: 12
SALES (est): 461.1K **Privately Held**
SIC: 3599 3544 Machine & other job shop work; special dies, tools, jigs & fixtures

(G-839)
SQUIRE SHOPPE BAKERY
511 Lake Ave (44004-3261)
P.O. Box 3126 (44005-3126)
PHONE...........................440 964-3303
Dennis Peters, *Owner*
Valerie Peters, *Vice Pres*
EMP: 4
SQ FT: 4,800
SALES (est): 140K **Privately Held**
SIC: 2051 Bread, cake & related products

(G-840)
TDM LLC
1303 W 38th St (44004-5433)
PHONE...........................440 969-1442
Charles Tanzola,
EMP: 4 EST: 2014
SALES (est): 425K **Privately Held**
SIC: 3549 3442 Marking machines, metalworking; molding, trim & stripping

(G-841)
TENAN MACHINE & FABRICATING
6002 State Rd Bldg A (44004-6248)
PHONE...........................440 997-5100
Patrick Tenan, *President*
Janice Tenan, *Vice Pres*
EMP: 3
SALES: 200K **Privately Held**
SIC: 3599 Machine shop, jobbing & repair

(G-842)
THOMAS J RAFFA DDS INC
355 W Prospect Rd Ste 120 (44004-5830)
PHONE...........................440 997-5208
Thomas Raffa, *President*
EMP: 6
SQ FT: 1,200
SALES (est): 696.2K **Privately Held**
SIC: 3843 8021 Orthodontic appliances; offices & clinics of dentists

(G-843)
ULTIMATE CHEM SOLUTIONS INC
1800 E 21st St (44004-4012)
P.O. Box 1768 (44005-1768)
PHONE...........................440 998-6751
Yogi V Chokshi, *President*
EMP: 20 EST: 2010
SALES (est): 3.5MM **Privately Held**
SIC: 2869 Industrial organic chemicals

(G-844)
USALCO LLC
3050 Lake Rd E (44004-3829)
PHONE...........................440 993-2721
EMP: 4
SALES (corp-wide): 63.3MM **Privately Held**
SIC: 2911 Oils, fuel
HQ: Usalco, Llc
2601 Cannery Ave
Baltimore MD 21226
410 918-2230

(G-845)
WITT ENTERPRISES INC
2024 Aetna Rd (44004-6260)
PHONE...........................440 992-8333
Fax: 440 997-5289
Ron Kister Jr, *President*
EMP: 25
SQ FT: 600
SALES: 2MM **Privately Held**
SIC: 3471 Sand blasting of metal parts

(G-846)
YOU52
921 Bunker Hill Rd (44004-7732)
PHONE...........................440 477-7704
Scott Vargas, *Owner*
EMP: 10
SALES (est): 731.1K **Privately Held**
SIC: 3571 Electronic computers

(G-847)
ZEHRCO-GIANCOLA COMPOSITES INC (PA)
1501 W 47th St (44004-5419)
PHONE...........................440 994-6317
Fax: 440 994-6216
Anthony Giancola, *President*
Edward Brashear, *General Mgr*
Rick Degeorge, *Manager*
Dave Lyon, *Manager*
Ted Washburn, *Director*
▲ EMP: 105
SQ FT: 150,000
SALES: 26MM **Privately Held**
WEB: www.zehrco-giancola.com
SIC: 3089 Plates, plastic

Ashville
Pickaway County

(G-848)
ALERIS ROLLED PRODUCTS INC
1 Reynolds Rd (43103-9204)
P.O. Box 197 (43103-0197)
PHONE...........................740 983-2571
Sean M Stack, *CEO*
Burke Bovender, *Plant Mgr*
Pete Bednar, *Opers Staff*
Tim Shannon, *Marketing Staff*
Robert Polca, *Manager*
EMP: 59 **Privately Held**
SIC: 3341 3444 Secondary nonferrous metals; sheet metalwork
HQ: Aleris Rolled Products, Inc.
25825 Science Park Dr # 400
Beachwood OH 44122
216 910-3400

(G-849)
COLUMBUS INDUSTRIES INC (PA)
2938 State Route 752 (43103-9543)
P.O. Box 257 (43103-0257)
PHONE...........................740 983-2552
Fax: 740 983-3147
Harold T Pontius, *Ch of Bd*
Jeffrey Pontius, *President*
Terry Vourvopoulos, *President*
Gary Francis, *Regional Mgr*
Wayne Vickers, *Exec VP*
◆ EMP: 100 EST: 1965
SQ FT: 78,000
SALES (est): 186.9MM **Privately Held**
WEB: www.colind.com
SIC: 3569 Filters

(G-850)
DAILY NEEDS PERSONAL CARE LLC
11560 State Route 104 (43103-9642)
PHONE...........................614 598-8383
Suzanne Pettigrew, *Principal*
EMP: 4
SALES (est): 168.2K **Privately Held**
SIC: 2711 Newspapers, publishing & printing

(G-851)
H O FIBERTRENDS
235 State Route 674 S (43103-9794)
PHONE...........................740 983-3864
Dave Lanman, *Managing Prtnr*
James Wickline, *Partner*
EMP: 3
SALES: 130K **Privately Held**
WEB: www.hofibertrends.com
SIC: 3714 5013 Motor vehicle parts & accessories; automotive supplies & parts

(G-852)
OHIO CAST STONE CO LLC
5767 Duvall Rd (43103-9521)
PHONE...........................614 524-0666
Alan Cleary, *Principal*
EMP: 3
SALES (est): 197K **Privately Held**
SIC: 3272 Concrete products

(G-853)
OWENS CORNING SALES INC
Reynolds Rd (43103)
P.O. Box 197 (43103-0197)
PHONE...........................740 983-1300
Rodney Sawall, *Opers-Prdtn-Mfg*
Bob Polca, *Persnl Mgr*
EMP: 6
SALES (corp-wide): 5.6B **Publicly Held**
WEB: www.owenscorning.com
SIC: 3444 3354 Siding, sheet metal; aluminum extruded products
HQ: Owens Corning Sales, Llc
1 Owens Corning Pkwy
Toledo OH 43659
419 248-8000

Athens
Athens County

(G-854)
ADAMS PUBLISHING GROUP LLC (HQ)
Also Called: Apg Media of Ohio
9300 Johnson Hollow Rd (45701-9028)
PHONE...........................740 592-6612
Mark Adams, *CEO*
Robert Wallace, *CFO*
EMP: 9 EST: 2013
SALES (est): 35.7MM
SALES (corp-wide): 46.8MM **Privately Held**
SIC: 2711 Newspapers, publishing & printing
PA: Adams Publishing Group, Llc
29088 Airpark Dr
Easton MD 21601
218 348-3391

(G-855)
ALL POWER EQUIPMENT LLC (PA)
Also Called: Kubota Authorized Dealer
8880 United Ln (45701-3667)
PHONE...........................740 593-3279
Fax: 740 593-7026
Gil Elmore, *Mng Member*
EMP: 19
SQ FT: 6,000
SALES (est): 6.9MM **Privately Held**
SIC: 5261 5561 3799 5083 Lawn & garden equipment; camper & travel trailer dealers; all terrain vehicles (ATV); farm & garden machinery

(G-856)
ARTIFICIAL NEURAL SYSTEMS INC
352 Carroll Rd (45701-3312)
PHONE...........................740 593-7675
Janusz Starzyk, *Principal*
EMP: 3
SALES (est): 200.9K **Privately Held**
SIC: 3679 Electronic components

(G-857)
ATHENS TECHNICAL SPECIALISTS
Also Called: Atsi
8157 Us Highway 50 (45701-9303)
PHONE...........................740 592-2874
Fax: 740 594-2875
Ted Gilfert, *CEO*
James Gilfert, *President*
Una Gilfert, *Corp Secy*
▲ EMP: 14
SQ FT: 6,000
SALES (est): 3MM **Privately Held**
WEB: www.atsi-tester.com
SIC: 3669 8748 Traffic signals, electric; traffic consultant

(G-858)
CITY OF ATHENS
395 W State St (45701-1527)
PHONE...........................740 592-3344
Fax: 740 593-8495
Crystal Kynard, *Branch Mgr*
EMP: 21 **Privately Held**
SIC: 3589 4941 Water treatment equipment, industrial; water supply
PA: City Of Athens
8 E Washington St Ste 101
Athens OH 45701
740 592-3338

(G-859)
CRUMBS INC
Also Called: Crumbs Bakery
94 Columbus Rd (45701-1312)
PHONE...........................740 592-3803
Fax: 740 593-5451
Jeremy Bowman, *President*
Cheri Chalfant, *Manager*
EMP: 10
SALES (est): 716.4K **Privately Held**
WEB: www.crumbs.net
SIC: 2051 5461 Bakery: wholesale or wholesale/retail combined; bakeries

(G-860)
DEMEL ENTERPRISES INC
10980 Northpoint Dr (45701-8760)
PHONE...........................740 592-5800
Chris Demel, *President*
▲ EMP: 5
SALES (est): 507.8K **Privately Held**
SIC: 3991 0139 Brooms & brushes; herb or spice farm

(G-861)
DIAGNOSTIC HYBRIDS INC
2005 E State St Ste 100 (45701-2125)
PHONE...........................740 593-1784
Fax: 740 592-9820
David R Scholl PHD, *President*
James L Brown, *COO*
Gail Goodrum, *Vice Pres*
Paul D Olivo PHD, *Vice Pres*
Geoff Morgan, *CFO*
EMP: 220
SQ FT: 25,000
SALES (est): 64.4MM
SALES (corp-wide): 191.6MM **Publicly Held**
WEB: www.dhiusa.com
SIC: 2835 3841 In vitro & in vivo diagnostic substances; diagnostic apparatus, medical
PA: Quidel Corporation
12544 High Bluff Dr # 200
San Diego CA 92130
858 552-1100

(G-862)
DONKEY COFFEE & ESPRESSO
17 1/2 W Washington St (45701-2433)
PHONE...........................740 594-7353
Chris Pyle, *Owner*
Cris Pyle, *Owner*
Angie Pyle, *Principal*
EMP: 20
SALES (est): 1.5MM **Privately Held**
WEB: www.donkeycoffee.com
SIC: 2599 Bar, restaurant & cafeteria furniture

GEOGRAPHIC

(G-863)
DOUBLE B PRINTING LLC
Also Called: Minuteman Press
17 W Washington St (45701-2433)
PHONE...................................740 593-7393
William Bowers Jr,
Eric Bobo,
EMP: 4
SQ FT: 4,000
SALES (est): 385K **Privately Held**
SIC: 2752 Commercial printing, lithographic

(G-864)
ELECTRONIC VISION INC
5 Depot St (45701-2713)
PHONE...................................740 592-2433
Daniel Krivicich, *CEO*
David Burke, *President*
Julie McAfooes, *Vice Pres*
EMP: 21
SQ FT: 8,500
SALES (est): 1.5MM **Privately Held**
WEB: www.interactivefilmschool.com
SIC: 7371 3577 7372 Computer software development & applications; computer peripheral equipment; prepackaged software

(G-865)
FITNE INC
5 Depot St (45701-2713)
PHONE...................................740 592-2433
Dan Krivicich, *President*
David Burke, *General Mgr*
Julie McAfooes, *Vice Pres*
EMP: 11
SALES (est): 826.1K **Privately Held**
WEB: www.fitne.net
SIC: 7371 3577 Computer software development & applications; computer peripheral equipment

(G-866)
FUSION NOODLE CO
30 E Union St (45701-2911)
PHONE...................................740 589-5511
EMP: 8
SALES (est): 582.6K **Privately Held**
SIC: 2098 Noodles (e.g. egg, plain & water), dry

(G-867)
G & J PEPSI-COLA BOTTLERS INC
2001 E State St (45701-2125)
PHONE...................................740 593-3366
Fax: 740 592-2971
Curt Allison, *Branch Mgr*
EMP: 51
SALES (corp-wide): 490.5MM **Privately Held**
WEB: www.gjpepsi.com
SIC: 4225 5149 2086 General warehousing; beverages, except coffee & tea; carbonated beverages, nonalcoholic: bottled & canned
PA: G & J Pepsi-Cola Bottlers Inc
9435 Waterstone Blvd # 390
Cincinnati OH 45249
513 785-6060

(G-868)
GEM COATINGS LTD
5840 Industrial Park Rd (45701-8736)
PHONE...................................740 589-2998
Fax: 740 589-5987
Karry Gemmell, *Partner*
EMP: 35
SQ FT: 55,000
SALES (est): 4.6MM **Privately Held**
SIC: 3479 Coating of metals with plastic or resins

(G-869)
GLOBAL COOLING INC
Also Called: Stirling Ultracold
6000 Poston Rd (45701-9051)
PHONE...................................740 274-7900
Fax: 740 592-2695
Neill Lane, *President*
David Berchowitz, *Senior VP*
Brett Harris, *Vice Pres*
Yong-Rak Kwon, *Vice Pres*
Joseph Stoltzfus, *Controller*
◆ **EMP:** 32

SQ FT: 15,000
SALES (est): 9MM **Privately Held**
WEB: www.globalcooling.com
SIC: 3821 Freezers, laboratory

(G-870)
GUITAR DIGEST INC
23 Curtis St (45701-3724)
P.O. Box 66, The Plains (45780-0066)
PHONE...................................740 592-4614
Marc Newman, *President*
Marc Wayner, *Vice Pres*
EMP: 15
SALES (est): 1.1MM **Privately Held**
WEB: www.guitardigest.com
SIC: 2721 Periodicals

(G-871)
GUNTER ELECTRIC LLC
237 W State St (45701-1524)
PHONE...................................304 253-4671
Mary Matters,
Michael L Gunter,
EMP: 4
SQ FT: 5,184
SALES (est): 563.6K **Privately Held**
SIC: 7694 3621 Armature rewinding shops; electric motor repair; motors & generators

(G-872)
INDIE-PEASANT ENTERPRISES
Also Called: Shagbark Seed & Mill
88 Columbus Cir (45701-1370)
PHONE...................................740 590-8240
Michelle Ajamian, *Principal*
Brandon Jaeger, *Principal*
Shagbark Mill, *Principal*
EMP: 3 **EST:** 2012
SALES (est): 197.1K **Privately Held**
SIC: 2099 2041 Tortillas, fresh or refrigerated; flour & other grain mill products

(G-873)
JACKIE OS PUB BREWERY LLC
25 Campbell St (45701-2616)
PHONE...................................740 274-0777
Art Oestrike, *President*
EMP: 61
SALES (est): 7.3MM **Privately Held**
SIC: 2082 Beer (alcoholic beverage)

(G-874)
JACQUELINE L VANDYKE
Also Called: Performance Lettering & Signs
10414 State Route 550 (45701-9705)
PHONE...................................740 593-6779
Jacqueline Vandyke, *Owner*
Jackie Vandyke, *Owner*
EMP: 5
SALES: 250K **Privately Held**
SIC: 3993 5999 Signs & advertising specialties; awnings

(G-875)
MCHAPPYS DONUTS OF PARKERSBURG
Also Called: Mc Happys Donuts
384 Richland Ave (45701-3204)
PHONE...................................740 593-8744
Bonnie Boring, *Manager*
EMP: 4
SALES (corp-wide): 49.7MM **Privately Held**
WEB: www.mchappys.com
SIC: 5461 2051 Doughnuts; doughnuts, except frozen
HQ: Mchappys Donuts Of Parkersburg Inc
2515 Washington Blvd
Belpre OH 45714
740 423-6351

(G-876)
MESSENGER PUBLISHING COMPANY
Also Called: Athens Messenger, The
9300 Johnson Hollow Rd (45701-9028)
PHONE...................................740 592-6612
Fax: 740 592-4647
Clarence Brown Jr, *Ch of Bd*
Mark Policinski, *President*
Fred Weber, *Publisher*
Kathy Kerr, *Editor*
Chana Powell, *Business Mgr*
EMP: 125 **EST:** 1825
SQ FT: 25,000

SALES (est): 35.7MM
SALES (corp-wide): 46.8MM **Privately Held**
WEB: www.athensmessenger.com
SIC: 2711 2752 Newspapers, publishing & printing; commercial printing, offset
HQ: Adams Publishing Group, Llc
9300 Johnson Hollow Rd
Athens OH 45701
740 592-6612

(G-877)
MILOS WHOLE WORLD GOURMET LLC
94 Columbus Rd (45701-1312)
PHONE...................................740 589-6456
Jonathan Leal, *Mng Member*
EMP: 9
SALES (est): 1.2MM **Privately Held**
SIC: 1541 2033 Food products manufacturing or packing plant construction; canned fruits & specialties

(G-878)
MINUTEMAN PRESS OF ATHENS LLC
17 W Washington St (45701-2433)
PHONE...................................740 593-7393
William Bowers Jr,
Eric Bobo,
EMP: 3 **EST:** 1930
SQ FT: 7,000
SALES (est): 270K **Privately Held**
SIC: 2752 2759 Commercial printing, lithographic; letterpress printing

(G-879)
MITCHELL ELECTRONICS INC
1005 E State St Ste 5 (45701-2151)
P.O. Box 2626 (45701-5426)
PHONE...................................740 594-8532
Fax: 740 594-8533
Lawrence Mitchell, *President*
Joshua Jordan, *Manager*
Linda W Mitchell, *Admin Sec*
EMP: 5
SQ FT: 2,000
SALES (est): 820.4K **Privately Held**
WEB: www.mitchell-electronics.com
SIC: 3679 Electronic circuits; engineering services

(G-880)
OHIO UNIVERSITY
Also Called: Post, The
28 Union St Ground Fl (45701)
PHONE...................................740 593-4010
Fax: 740 593-0561
Dawn L Meiser, *Finance*
Jim Rodgers, *Manager*
Patrick Oconnor, *Teacher*
EMP: 130
SALES (corp-wide): 493.8MM **Privately Held**
WEB: www.zanesville.ohiou.edu
SIC: 2711 8221 Newspapers, publishing & printing; university
PA: Ohio University
1 Ohio University
Athens OH 45701
740 593-1000

(G-881)
PETRO QUEST INC (PA)
3 W Stimson Ave (45701-2679)
P.O. Box 268 (45701-0268)
PHONE...................................740 593-3800
Fax: 740 593-3865
Paul J Gerig, *President*
Christian Gerig, *Vice Pres*
Debora Jarvis, *Admin Sec*
EMP: 8
SQ FT: 2,200
SALES (est): 921.1K **Privately Held**
SIC: 1381 8111 Drilling oil & gas wells; general practice attorney, lawyer

(G-882)
PRECISION IMPRINT
26 E State St (45701-2540)
PHONE...................................740 592-5916
Fax: 740 593-6043
Randy Shoup, *Owner*
EMP: 8
SQ FT: 5,000

SALES (est): 380K **Privately Held**
WEB: www.precisionimprint.com
SIC: 2261 5136 5137 2759 Screen printing of cotton broadwoven fabrics; sportswear, men's & boys'; sportswear, women's & children's; screen printing; embroidery products, except schiffli machine

(G-883)
SENSE LABS LLC
101 S May Ave (45701-2016)
PHONE...................................740 590-0009
Benjamin L Lachman, *Mng Member*
Robin Kinney,
EMP: 2
SQ FT: 1,500
SALES: 1.5MM **Privately Held**
SIC: 3571 Electronic computers

(G-884)
SICKELS SEPTIC TANKS INC
10637 Oxley Rd (45701-8821)
PHONE...................................740 593-8302
Hildred Gwinn, *CEO*
Jack Sickel, *President*
EMP: 7
SQ FT: 2,000
SALES (est): 892K **Privately Held**
SIC: 3272 Septic tanks, concrete

(G-885)
STEWART-MACDONALD MFG CO (PA)
Also Called: Stewart McDnalds Guitar Sp Sup
21 N Shafer St (45701-2304)
PHONE...................................740 592-3021
Fax: 740 593-7922
Kay Tousley, *Principal*
Jay Hostetler, *Vice Pres*
John A Woodrow, *CFO*
Jayme Arnett, *Cust Mgr*
▲ **EMP:** 40
SQ FT: 12,000
SALES (est): 8MM **Privately Held**
WEB: www.banjoparts.com
SIC: 3931 5736 Banjos & parts; mandolins & parts; violins & parts; guitars & parts, electric & nonelectric; musical instrument stores

(G-886)
STICKY PETES MAPLE SYRUP
18216 S Canaan Rd (45701-9465)
PHONE...................................740 662-2726
Laura McManus-Berry, *Principal*
EMP: 3
SALES (est): 121.3K **Privately Held**
SIC: 2099 Maple syrup

(G-887)
SUNPOWER INC
2005 E State St Ste 104 (45701-2125)
PHONE...................................740 594-2221
Fax: 740 593-7531
Thomas Matros, *Business Mgr*
Jeffrey Hatfield, *Vice Pres*
Bill Hammer, *Research*
Steven Carpenter, *Electrical Engi*
Jeff Hatfield, *Controller*
EMP: 95
SQ FT: 16,000
SALES (est): 15.4MM
SALES (corp-wide): 3.8B **Publicly Held**
WEB: www.sunpower.com
SIC: 8731 8711 8733 3769 Commercial physical research; engineering services; physical research, noncommercial; scientific research agency; guided missile & space vehicle parts & auxiliary equipment
PA: Ametek, Inc.
1100 Cassatt Rd
Berwyn PA 19312
610 647-2121

(G-888)
TS TRIM INDUSTRIES INC
10 Kenny Dr (45701-9406)
PHONE...................................740 593-5958
Fax: 740 593-7096
Gary Griggs, *QC Mgr*
Missie Lynn, *Human Res Mgr*
Annett Porter, *Persnl Mgr*
Keith Mills, *Manager*
Earich Dean, *Manager*
EMP: 360

▲ = Import ▼=Export
◆ =Import/Export

SALES (corp-wide): 3.9B **Privately Held**
WEB: www.tstrim.com
SIC: **2399 3714** Seat covers, automobile;
motor vehicle parts & accessories
HQ: Ts Trim Industries Inc.
6380 Canal St
Canal Winchester OH 43110
614 837-4114

(G-889)
UPTOWN DOG THE INC
9 W Union St (45701-2819)
PHONE.................................740 592-4600
Fax: 740 594-9561
Mary Swintek, *President*
EMP: 8
SQ FT: 1,000
SALES (est): 750K **Privately Held**
WEB: www.uptowndogtshirts.com
SIC: **5699 2261 2759** Sports apparel;
screen printing of cotton broadwoven fab-
rics; screen printing

(G-890)
XEROX CORPORATION
35 Elliott St (45701-2608)
PHONE.................................740 592-5609
Jeffrey Wenger, *Owner*
Scott Smith, *Sales Staff*
EMP: 84
SALES (corp-wide): 10.7B **Publicly Held**
SIC: **3577** Computer peripheral equipment
PA: Xerox Corporation
201 Merritt 7
Norwalk CT 06851
203 968-3000

(G-891)
YORK PAVING CO (PA)
758 W Union St (45701-9408)
PHONE.................................740 594-3600
Cindy L Hayes, *CEO*
James Hayes, *President*
EMP: 15 EST: 1997
SALES (est): 2.2MM **Privately Held**
WEB: www.yorkpaving.com
SIC: **1771 2951** Driveway, parking lot &
blacktop contractors; asphalt paving mix-
tures & blocks

Attica
Seneca County

(G-892)
BLOOMVILLE GAZETTE INC
Also Called: Attica Hub Office
26 N Main St (44807-9001)
P.O. Box 516 (44807-0516)
PHONE.................................419 426-3491
Fax: 419 426-3491
Deb Cook, *President*
EMP: 3
SALES (est): 147.3K **Privately Held**
WEB: www.atticahub.com
SIC: **2711** Newspapers

(G-893)
BROVIG ENGINEERING INC
6090 Coder Rd (44807-9638)
P.O. Box 488 (44807-0488)
PHONE.................................419 426-1333
Fax: 419 935-2440
Fred Darling, *President*
EMP: 4
SQ FT: 10,000
SALES (est): 301K **Privately Held**
SIC: **3531 7542** Construction machinery;
truck wash

(G-894)
OMAR ASSOCIATES LLC
625 N State Route 4 (44807-9533)
PHONE.................................419 426-0610
Eric J WI, *Owner*
Heather Auburn, *Sales Staff*
EMP: 8 EST: 2001
SALES (est): 1.6MM **Privately Held**
SIC: **3556** Food products machinery

(G-895)
SENECA TILES INC
7100 S County Road 23 (44807-9796)
PHONE.................................419 426-3561

Fax: 419 426-1735
James D Fry, *President*
◆ EMP: 55
SQ FT: 150,000
SALES (est): 7.3MM **Privately Held**
WEB: www.senecatile.com
SIC: **3253** Ceramic wall & floor tile

(G-896)
SHOCK PRECAST
2467 S Township Road 197 (44807-9566)
PHONE.................................419 426-0535
Jim Shock, *Principal*
EMP: 3
SALES (est): 140K **Privately Held**
SIC: **3272** Precast terrazo or concrete
products

(G-897)
WALDOCK EQP SLS & SVC INC
(PA)
12178 E County Road 6 (44807-9793)
P.O. Box 122 (44807-0122)
PHONE.................................419 426-7771
Ronald D Waldock, *President*
Karla Waldock, *Vice Pres*
EMP: 3
SQ FT: 1,800
SALES: 100K **Privately Held**
SIC: **7692** Welding repair

Atwater
Portage County

(G-898)
HR PARTS N STUFF
2002 Industry Rd (44201-9354)
P.O. Box 67 (44201-0067)
PHONE.................................330 947-2433
Paul Ferry, *Partner*
▼ EMP: 3
SQ FT: 3,680
SALES: 170K **Privately Held**
SIC: **3599 3561** Grinding castings for the
trade; machine shop, jobbing & repair;
cylinders, pump

(G-899)
J DAVIS SALES AND ASSOC LLC
5293 Eberly Rd (44201-9783)
PHONE.................................330 947-2038
Jeffrey Davis, *Principal*
EMP: 3
SALES (est): 225.2K **Privately Held**
SIC: **2097** Manufactured ice

(G-900)
MALCOLM HYDRAULICS
6581 Waterloo Rd (44201-9508)
PHONE.................................330 819-2033
James Malcolm, *Owner*
EMP: 5
SALES (est): 347.5K **Privately Held**
SIC: **3593** Fluid power cylinders & actua-
tors

(G-901)
ORION PETRO CORPORATION
1798 State Route 183 (44201-9575)
PHONE.................................330 364-8155
Gail H West, *Manager*
EMP: 3
SALES (corp-wide): 1.2MM **Privately
Held**
SIC: **1311** Crude petroleum production;
natural gas production
PA: Orion Petro Corporation
125 N 11th St Rear
Mount Vernon IL 62864
618 244-2370

(G-902)
PYRAMID TREATING INC
3031 Sanford Rd (44201-9338)
PHONE.................................330 325-2811
Roy E Kommel Jr, *President*
Kathy Kommel, *Corp Secy*
EMP: 4
SALES (est): 456.7K **Privately Held**
SIC: **1389** Servicing oil & gas wells

(G-903)
VICTORIAN FARMS
1375 Aberagg Rd (44201-9743)
PHONE.................................330 628-9188
Kathy Cruise, *Principal*
EMP: 4
SALES (est): 319.5K **Privately Held**
SIC: **3799 4789 7999** Carriages, horse
drawn; horse drawn transportation serv-
ices; saddlehorse rental

(G-904)
WATERLOO MANUFACTURING
CO INC
6298 Waterloo Rd (44201-9702)
PHONE.................................330 947-2917
Fax: 330 947-3009
Thomas Ludlam, *President*
EMP: 4
SQ FT: 51,200
SALES: 150K **Privately Held**
WEB: www.waterloomanufacturing.com
SIC: **3629 5084** Blasting machines, elec-
trical; industrial machinery & equipment

Aurora
Portage County

(G-905)
ADVANCED INNOVATIVE MFG
INC
Also Called: A.I.M.
116 Lena Dr (44202-9202)
PHONE.................................440 759-2034
Joseph A Hawald, *President*
Mark J Hawald, *CFO*
EMP: 5
SQ FT: 14,560
SALES: 652.5K **Privately Held**
SIC: **3541** Machine tools, metal cutting
type

(G-906)
ARGOSY WIND POWER LTD
70 Aurora Industrial Pkwy (44202-8086)
P.O. Box 391641, Solon (44139-8641)
PHONE.................................440 539-1345
Jeffrey B Milbourn, *President*
Gerard J Sposato, *Exec VP*
John C Rexford, *Senior VP*
Raphael J Omerza, *Vice Pres*
John Rexford, *Engrg Mgr*
▲ EMP: 8 EST: 2011
SALES (est): 963.5K **Privately Held**
SIC: **3511** Turbines & turbine generator
sets

(G-907)
ASPHALT SERVICES & CNSTR
114 Barrington Town Sq Dr (44202-7792)
PHONE.................................330 995-6044
Fax: 330 995-0397
Lillian Jacobs, *Treasurer*
Anthony Belsito,
Andy Dorner,
EMP: 2
SQ FT: 12,000
SALES: 2MM **Privately Held**
SIC: **2951** Asphalt paving mixtures &
blocks

(G-908)
AUTOMATION PLASTICS CORP
150 Lena Dr (44202-9202)
PHONE.................................330 562-5148
Fax: 330 562-9924
Harry Smith, *President*
Dan Nunez, *Opers Mgr*
Will Wilke, *Prdtn Mgr*
Keith King, *Production*
Tressa Dewitt, *QC Mgr*
EMP: 60
SQ FT: 43,000
SALES (est): 16.2MM **Privately Held**
WEB: www.automationplastics.com
SIC: **3089 3544** Injection molding of plas-
tics; special dies, tools, jigs & fixtures

(G-909)
B & B NECESSITIES
1004 Old Barn Rd (44202-9278)
PHONE.................................330 995-0489
Wanda Jackson, *Owner*

EMP: 3
SALES (est): 268.9K **Privately Held**
SIC: **2676** Sanitary paper products

(G-910)
BARRACUDA TECHNOLOGIES
INC
2900 State Route 82 (44202-9395)
PHONE.................................216 469-1566
Kris Santin, *CEO*
EMP: 12
SALES (est): 724.9K **Privately Held**
SIC: **3644** Noncurrent-carrying wiring serv-
ices

(G-911)
BERRY PLASTICS FILMCO INC
1450 S Chillicothe Rd (44202-9282)
PHONE.................................330 562-6111
David Meldren, *President*
Judy Ciocca, *Principal*
Susan Burkholder, *Purchasing*
▲ EMP: 100
SQ FT: 85,000
SALES (est): 12.9MM
SALES (corp-wide): 6.4B **Publicly Held**
SIC: **3081** Unsupported plastics film &
sheet
HQ: Berry Plastics Corporation
101 Oakley St
Evansville IN 47710
812 424-2904

(G-912)
CANTEX INC
11444 Chamberlain Rd 1 (44202-9306)
PHONE.................................330 995-3665
Fax: 330 995-3265
Kevin McNamara, *Plant Mgr*
Dan Baughman, *Finance Mgr*
Mike Schafer, *Branch Mgr*
Henry Hawkins, *Manager*
Kay Smith, *Executive*
EMP: 60
SALES (corp-wide): 59.1B **Privately Held**
WEB: www.cantex.com
SIC: **3084 3089** Plastics pipe; fittings for
pipe, plastic
HQ: Cantex Inc.
301 Commerce St Ste 2700
Fort Worth TX 76102
817 215-7000

(G-913)
COURTAD INC
510 Cobblestone Rd (44202-9323)
PHONE.................................330 274-3100
Dennis J Courtad, *Principal*
Nick Courtad, *Engineer*
EMP: 7 EST: 2003
SALES (est): 2.1MM **Privately Held**
SIC: **3446** Architectural metalwork

(G-914)
CROCS INC
549 S Chilcthe Rd Ste 240 (44202-8857)
PHONE.................................330 954-1963
EMP: 14
SALES (corp-wide): 1.2B **Publicly Held**
SIC: **3021** Shoes, rubber or rubber soled
fabric uppers
PA: Crocs, Inc.
7477 Dry Creek Pkwy
Niwot CO 80503
303 848-7000

(G-915)
CUSTOM PULTRUSIONS INC
(HQ)
1331 S Chillicothe Rd (44202-8066)
PHONE.................................330 562-5201
Fax: 330 562-4908
Jay Lund, *CEO*
Robert Spaans, *Engineer*
Carol McCreery, *Accountant*
Kati Shannon, *Human Resources*
Dan Mornelli, *Manager*
EMP: 34
SALES (est): 17MM
SALES (corp-wide): 2.9B **Privately Held**
SIC: **3089** Injection molding of plastics
PA: Andersen Corporation
100 4th Ave N
Bayport MN 55003
651 264-5150

(G-916)
EATON CORPORATION
Synflex Division
115 Lena Dr (44202-9202)
PHONE...............................330 274-0743
Greg Ward, *Purchasing*
Iani Manas, *Engrg Dir*
Dan Tolles, *Engrg Dir*
Zach Jolly, *Engineer*
Robert Rini, *Engineer*
EMP: 210
SQ FT: 7,568 **Privately Held**
SIC: 3089 3494 3429 3052 Plastic containers, except foam; valves & pipe fittings; manufactured hardware (general); rubber & plastics hose & beltings
HQ: Eaton Corporation
1000 Eaton Blvd
Cleveland OH 44122
216 523-5000

(G-917)
EATON CORPORATION
115 Lena Dr (44202-9202)
PHONE...............................330 562-9111
Dan Tolles, *Engineer*
Doug Thornberry, *Controller*
Roy Webber, *Branch Mgr*
David Ruffing, *Manager*
EMP: 200 **Privately Held**
WEB: www.eaton.com
SIC: 2821 Thermoplastic materials
HQ: Eaton Corporation
1000 Eaton Blvd
Cleveland OH 44122
216 523-5000

(G-918)
ELECTROVATIONS INC
350 Harris Dr (44202-7536)
PHONE...............................330 274-3558
Fax: 330 995-3684
R Charles Vermerris, *President*
EMP: 25
SQ FT: 4,500
SALES (est): 2.1MM **Privately Held**
SIC: 8711 7389 3357 Engineering services; design, commercial & industrial; nonferrous wiredrawing & insulating

(G-919)
EPG INC
500 Lena Dr (44202-9245)
PHONE...............................330 995-5125
Michael Orazen, *Manager*
Gary Mike, *Director*
EMP: 80
SALES (corp-wide): 2.8B **Privately Held**
WEB: www.epgcando.com
SIC: 3053 3061 Gaskets, all materials; mechanical rubber goods
HQ: Epg, Inc.
1780 Miller Pkwy
Streetsboro OH 44241
330 995-9725

(G-920)
FREEDOM HEALTH LLC
65 Aurora Industrial Pkwy (44202-8088)
PHONE...............................330 562-0888
John Hall, *President*
Stephen Willey, *COO*
Stephen A Willey, *COO*
Steve Willey, *COO*
Vincenzo Franco, *Vice Pres*
▲ EMP: 20
SQ FT: 50,000
SALES (est): 3.6MM **Privately Held**
WEB: www.freedomhealth.com
SIC: 2023 Dietary supplements, dairy & non-dairy based

(G-921)
GE HEALTHCARE FINCL SVCS INC
1515 Danner Dr (44202-9273)
PHONE...............................312 697-3999
Donald Moon, *Plant Mgr*
Miguel Navarro, *Engineer*
Gabriel Searles, *Engineer*
Jacob Sladkey, *Electrical Engi*
Justin Bittikofer, *Marketing Staff*
EMP: 250 **Publicly Held**
SIC: 3677 Electronic coils, transformers & other inductors

HQ: Ge Healthcare Financial Services, Inc.
500 W Monroe St Fl 19
Chicago IL 60661
312 697-3999

(G-922)
GODFREY & WING INC (PA)
220 Campus Dr (44202-6663)
PHONE...............................330 562-1440
Christopher Gilmore, *President*
Brad Welch, *Corp Secy*
Karen Gilmore, *Vice Pres*
Denise Bidgood, *Accountant*
Barb Fetzer, *Accountant*
▲ EMP: 50
SQ FT: 68,000
SALES (est): 19.8MM **Privately Held**
SIC: 3479 8734 Coating of metals with plastic or resins; testing laboratories

(G-923)
GUNNISON ASSOCIATES LLC
114 Barrington Twn Sq 11 (44202-7792)
PHONE...............................330 562-5230
Dale Kowalyk,
Barbara Kowalyk,
EMP: 6
SALES (est): 12MM **Privately Held**
SIC: 3565 Packaging machinery

(G-924)
HEINENS INC
Also Called: Heinen's 8
115 N Chillicothe Rd (44202-7797)
PHONE...............................330 562-5297
Fax: 330 526-1573
Paul Otoole, *Manager*
EMP: 6
SALES (corp-wide): 357.6MM **Privately Held**
SIC: 5411 2051 Supermarkets, chain; bread, cake & related products
PA: Heinen's, Inc.
4540 Richmond Rd
Warrensville Heights OH 44128
216 475-2300

(G-925)
HOLM INDUSTRIES INC
1300 Danner Dr (44202-9284)
PHONE...............................330 562-2900
Ted McQuade, *Principal*
Ken Hodkey, *Controller*
EMP: 9
SALES (est): 1.3MM **Privately Held**
SIC: 3089 Plastics products

(G-926)
ILPEA INDUSTRIES INC
OEM/Miller
1300 Danner Dr (44202-9284)
PHONE...............................330 562-2916
Fax: 330 562-7635
John Gourley, *Opers Mgr*
Jim Severt, *Warehouse Mgr*
Mike Frys, *Purchasing*
Darrell Carson, *QC Dir*
Kathy Goode, *Personnel*
EMP: 135
SALES (corp-wide): 212.4MM **Privately Held**
WEB: www.holmindustries.com
SIC: 3089 5162 3083 Plastic containers, except foam; plastics sheets & rods; laminated plastics plate & sheet
PA: Ilpea Industries, Inc.
745 S Gardner St
Scottsburg IN 47170
812 752-2526

(G-927)
JIT PACKAGING INC (PA)
Also Called: Jit Milrob
250 Page Rd (44202)
PHONE...............................330 562-8080
Fax: 513 934-3234
David R Jones, *Chairman*
Brad Davis, *Vice Pres*
Elaine Jones, *Vice Pres*
EMP: 22
SQ FT: 60,000
SALES (est): 7.2MM **Privately Held**
SIC: 2448 5113 5085 2653 Pallets, wood; corrugated & solid fiber boxes; industrial supplies; corrugated & solid fiber boxes

(G-928)
KAPSTONE CONTAINER CORPORATION
Also Called: Filmco
1450 S Chillicothe Rd (44202-9282)
P.O. Box 239 (44202-0239)
PHONE...............................330 562-6111
Sue Burkholder, *Purchasing*
John Vamosi, *QC Dir*
Richard Pohland, *Branch Mgr*
Marianne Martone, *Director*
EMP: 106
SQ FT: 20,000
SALES (corp-wide): 3B **Publicly Held**
SIC: 3081 5199 2671 Packing materials, plastic sheet; packaging materials; packaging paper & plastics film, coated & laminated
HQ: Kapstone Container Corporation
1601 Blairs Ferry Rd Ne
Cedar Rapids IA 52402
319 393-3610

(G-929)
KARL INDUSTRIES INC
11415 Chamberlain Rd (44202-9306)
P.O. Box 181 (44202-0181)
PHONE...............................330 562-4100
Fax: 330 562-4068
Paul Tornstrom, *President*
Karen Tornstrom, *Treasurer*
EMP: 3
SQ FT: 7,000
SALES (est): 200K **Privately Held**
WEB: www.karlindustries.com
SIC: 2869 Industrial organic chemicals

(G-930)
KENT PAVERBRICK LLC
11437 Chamberlain Rd (44202-9306)
PHONE...............................330 995-7000
James Wasas, *CEO*
Robert Schultz, *Director*
EMP: 5
SQ FT: 6,000
SALES (est): 308.9K **Privately Held**
SIC: 3299 Blocks & brick, sand lime

(G-931)
KING SOFTWARE SYSTEMS
680 Briarcliff Dr (44202-9212)
PHONE...............................330 562-1135
John King, *Owner*
EMP: 3
SALES (est): 305K **Privately Held**
WEB: www.kingsoftwaresystems.com
SIC: 7372 Prepackaged software

(G-932)
LAYERZERO POWER SYSTEMS INC
1500 Danner Dr (44202-9298)
PHONE...............................440 399-9000
Milind Bhanoo, *President*
James M Galm, *Vice Pres*
Tyler Balster, *Engineer*
Linda Bell, *Controller*
Scott Ramey, *Sales Associate*
EMP: 25
SALES (est): 10.4MM **Privately Held**
WEB: www.layerzero.com
SIC: 3613 Power switching equipment

(G-933)
LINDSEY GRAPHICS INC
112 Parkview Dr (44202-8043)
PHONE...............................330 995-9241
Robert Nelson Jr, *President*
EMP: 3
SQ FT: 2,000
SALES (est): 340K **Privately Held**
WEB: www.lindseygraphics.com
SIC: 5112 2752 Stationery & office supplies; color lithography

(G-934)
LIST MEDIA INC
Also Called: Admail.net
251 W Garfield Rd Ste 284 (44202-8856)
P.O. Box 152 (44202-0152)
PHONE...............................330 995-0864
Fax: 330 995-0873
Robert Hicks, *President*
EMP: 5 EST: 1990

SALES: 4.5MM **Privately Held**
WEB: www.dm1.net
SIC: 7331 7374 7372 7371 Direct mail advertising services; data processing & preparation; application computer software; custom computer programming services; systems software development services

(G-935)
MULCH MADNESS LLC
8022 S Riverside Dr (44202-8619)
PHONE...............................330 920-9900
Tara Palladino,
EMP: 11
SALES (est): 1.7MM **Privately Held**
SIC: 2499 4212 Mulch or sawdust products, wood; truck rental with drivers

(G-936)
MYTEE PRODUCTS INC
1335 S Chillicothe Rd (44202-8066)
PHONE...............................440 591-4301
Vick Agarwalla, *President*
Prabhav Agarwalla, *Vice Pres*
◆ EMP: 10
SQ FT: 28,000
SALES (est): 5MM **Privately Held**
SIC: 5013 2824 Truck parts & accessories; vinyl fibers

(G-937)
NATURAL ESSENTIALS INC
Also Called: Bulk Apothecary
125 Lena Dr (44202-9202)
PHONE...............................330 562-8022
Gary Pellegrino, *President*
Dan Frenz, *Vice Pres*
Bryan Pellegrino, *VP Opers*
Michael Cutlip, *QA Dir*
Bruce Laake, *Controller*
▲ EMP: 30
SQ FT: 22,000
SALES (est): 19.3MM **Privately Held**
SIC: 2844 2899 Toilet preparations; oils & essential oils

(G-938)
ODYSSEY SPIRITS INC
Also Called: Odyssey Printwear
7286 N Aurora Rd (44202-9627)
PHONE...............................330 562-1523
Fax: 330 562-5496
Mark Hoehn, *President*
Laura Hoehn, *Vice Pres*
EMP: 12
SQ FT: 7,500
SALES (est): 1.5MM **Privately Held**
WEB: www.odysseyprintwear.com
SIC: 2759 5651 5699 5947 Screen printing; family clothing stores; T-shirts, custom printed; gift shop

(G-939)
OMEGA POLYMER TECHNOLOGIES INC (PA)
Also Called: Opti
1331 S Chillicothe Rd (44202-8066)
PHONE...............................330 562-5201
Ronald Baker, *President*
David Morley, *Vice Pres*
Donald Smith, *Vice Pres*
Raymond Centa, *Manager*
Ortho Prunty, *Info Tech Mgr*
EMP: 6
SALES (est): 32.7MM **Privately Held**
SIC: 3089 Injection molding of plastics

(G-940)
OMEGA PULTRUSIONS INCORPORATED
1331 S Chillicothe Rd (44202-8066)
PHONE...............................330 562-5201
Donald F Borraccini, *President*
Greg Foskey, *Vice Pres*
Tracey Roskey, *Vice Pres*
Otho Prunty, *Treasurer*
Dave Beyers, *Manager*
EMP: 140
SQ FT: 95,000
SALES: 23.6MM
SALES (corp-wide): 32.7MM **Privately Held**
SIC: 3089 Injection molding of plastics

PA: Omega Polymer Technologies, Inc.
1331 S Chillicothe Rd
Aurora OH 44202
330 562-5201

(G-941)
PVH CORP
Also Called: Van Heusen
549 S Chilcthe Rd Ste 340 (44202-6519)
PHONE..................................330 562-4440
Stephanie Lottig, *Manager*
EMP: 9
SALES (corp-wide): 8.2B **Publicly Held**
WEB: www.pvh.com
SIC: 2321 Men's & boys' dress shirts
PA: Pvh Corp.
200 Madison Ave Bsmt 1
New York NY 10016
212 381-3500

(G-942)
PYROTEK INCORPORATED
Metaullics Systems Division
355 Campus Dr (44202-6662)
PHONE..................................440 349-8800
Fax: 440 248-7100
Bob Knaser, *Opers Mgr*
Len Lutes, *Prdtn Mgr*
Rick Henderson, *Engineer*
Debbie Horn, *Credit Staff*
Tom Wurst, *Sales Staff*
EMP: 133
SALES (corp-wide): 609.3MM **Privately Held**
SIC: 3569 3624 3295 3561 Filters, general line: industrial; carbon & graphite products; graphite, natural: ground, pulverized, refined or blended; pumps & pumping equipment
PA: Pyrotek Incorporated
705 W 1st Ave
Spokane WA 99201
509 926-6212

(G-943)
RADIX WIRE COMPANY
350 Harris Dr (44202-7536)
PHONE..................................330 995-3677
Craig Hines, *Manager*
EMP: 25
SQ FT: 10,000
SALES (corp-wide): 21.5MM **Privately Held**
WEB: www.radix-wire.com
SIC: 3357 Nonferrous wiredrawing & insulating
PA: Radix Wire Co
26000 Lakeland Blvd
Cleveland OH 44132
216 731-9191

(G-944)
ROBECK FLUID POWER CO
350 Lena Dr (44202-8098)
PHONE..................................330 562-1140
Fax: 330 562-1141
Peter Becker, *President*
Ken Traeger, *Corp Secy*
Don Louis, *Opers Mgr*
Sherri Meloy, *Purchasing*
Bob Long, *Engineer*
▲ **EMP:** 65
SQ FT: 6,000
SALES (est): 71.1MM **Privately Held**
WEB: www.robeckfluidpower.com
SIC: 5084 3593 3594 3494 Hydraulic systems equipment & supplies; fluid power cylinders & actuators; fluid power pumps & motors; valves & pipe fittings

(G-945)
ROTEK INCORPORATED (DH)
1400 S Chillicothe Rd (44202-9299)
P.O. Box 312 (44202-0312)
PHONE..................................330 562-4000
Fax: 330 562-7394
Mike Drobik, *President*
Jackie Nuber, *General Mgr*
Diane Sabo, *General Mgr*
Robert Hersko, *Facilities Mgr*
Donald Basham, *Production*
▲ **EMP:** 160 **EST:** 1962
SQ FT: 132,000

SALES (est): 76.6MM
SALES (corp-wide): 44.2B **Privately Held**
WEB: www.rotek-inc.com
SIC: 3562 3462 3463 3321 Ball bearings & parts; roller bearings & parts; iron & steel forgings; nonferrous forgings; gray & ductile iron foundries
HQ: Thyssenkrupp North America, Inc.
111 W Jackson Blvd # 2400
Chicago IL 60604
312 525-2800

(G-946)
RP GATTA INC
435 Gentry Dr (44202-7538)
PHONE..................................330 562-2288
Fax: 330 562-3223
Raymond P Gatta, *President*
Katherine E Gatta, *Corp Secy*
◆ **EMP:** 24
SQ FT: 28,000
SALES: 5.3MM **Privately Held**
WEB: www.rpgatta.com
SIC: 3559 Automotive related machinery

(G-947)
SACO AEI POLYMERS INC
Also Called: Macro Meric
1395 Danner Dr (44202-9273)
PHONE..................................330 995-1600
Fax: 330 995-1699
Matt McLaughlin, *Manager*
EMP: 16
SQ FT: 28,829
SALES (corp-wide): 33.9MM **Privately Held**
WEB: www.padanaplastusa.com
SIC: 2821 Plastics materials & resins
PA: Saco Aei Polymers, Inc.
3220 Crocker Ave
Sheboygan WI 53081
920 803-0778

(G-948)
SUNSHINE PERFORMANCE GLASS INC
1455 Danner Dr (44202-9273)
PHONE..................................330 562-8600
Michael P McHugh, *President*
Todd Elozory, *Sales Mgr*
EMP: 20
SQ FT: 30,000
SALES: 1.2MM **Privately Held**
WEB: www.spgfla.com
SIC: 2221 Glass & fiberglass broadwoven fabrics

(G-949)
THORNCREEK WINERY & GARDEN
155 Treat Rd (44202-8704)
PHONE..................................330 562-9245
David Thorn, *Principal*
EMP: 4
SALES (est): 270K **Privately Held**
SIC: 2084 Wines

(G-950)
TRANSCONTINENTAL OIL & GAS
1509 Page Rd (44202-6644)
PHONE..................................330 995-0777
Calvin R Marks, *President*
EMP: 3
SQ FT: 1,800
SALES: 2.5MM **Privately Held**
SIC: 1381 Drilling oil & gas wells

(G-951)
TRELLBORG SLING PRFILES US INC (DH)
500 Lena Dr (44202-9245)
P.O. Box 639, Bristol IN (46507-0639)
PHONE..................................330 995-9725
Smitty McKee, *President*
Tom Layton, *Business Mgr*
Michael Scanlon, *Vice Pres*
Melinda Gruber, *QC Mgr*
Mike Gary, *Engineer*
EMP: 30
SQ FT: 48,588

SALES (est): 23.4MM
SALES (corp-wide): 2.8B **Privately Held**
SIC: 3089 3465 Extruded finished plastic products; automotive parts, plastic; body parts, automobile: stamped metal
HQ: Trelleborg Corporation
200 Veterans Blvd Ste 3
South Haven MI 49090
269 639-9891

(G-952)
TRUMBULL COUNTY DRY KILNS INC
475 Wheatfield Dr (44202-9200)
PHONE..................................330 562-3367
Fax: 330 898-8042
Lacy Norman, *President*
Carolyn Norman, *Corp Secy*
EMP: 11
SQ FT: 30,000
SALES (est): 770K **Privately Held**
SIC: 2421 2426 Kiln drying of lumber; flooring, hardwood; dimension, hardwood

(G-953)
UNDER ARMOUR INC
549 S Chillicothe Rd (44202-7848)
PHONE..................................330 995-9557
EMP: 5
SALES (corp-wide): 4.8B **Publicly Held**
SIC: 2329 Men's & boys' sportswear & athletic clothing
PA: Under Armour, Inc.
1020 Hull St Ste 300
Baltimore MD 21230
410 454-6428

(G-954)
VIBRATION TEST SYSTEMS INC
Also Called: V TS
10246 Clipper Cv (44202-9043)
PHONE..................................330 562-5729
Fax: 330 562-1186
Christopher Hunt, *President*
Carol Hunt, *Vice Pres*
EMP: 4
SALES (est): 495.4K **Privately Held**
SIC: 3829 Vibration meters, analyzers & calibrators

(G-955)
VIDEO PRODUCTS INC
Also Called: VPI
1275 Danner Dr (44202-8054)
PHONE..................................330 562-2622
Carl Jagatich, *President*
Tammy Kuhn, *COO*
Alan Willis, *Opers Staff*
Carl Jackson, *Engineer*
Suvidh Kankariya, *Engineer*
EMP: 60
SQ FT: 8,000
SALES: 3MM **Privately Held**
WEB: www.nti1.com
SIC: 3577 Computer peripheral equipment

(G-956)
WILLIAM THOMPSON
Also Called: Custom Boat Covers
11304 Chamberlain Rd (44202-9360)
PHONE..................................440 232-4363
Fax: 440 232-1689
William Thompson, *Owner*
EMP: 4
SQ FT: 2,500
SALES (est): 280.3K **Privately Held**
SIC: 2394 3732 Convertible tops, canvas or boat: from purchased materials; boat building & repairing

(G-957)
WORKSHOP WIRE CUT AND MCH INC
100 Francis D Kenneth Dr (44202-9275)
PHONE..................................330 995-6404
Fax: 330 995-6405
Michael W Meredith, *President*
EMP: 4
SALES (est): 614.3K **Privately Held**
SIC: 3599 Machine shop, jobbing & repair

Austinburg
Ashtabula County

(G-958)
AUSTINBURG MACHINE INC
2899 Industrial Park Dr (44010-9764)
PHONE..................................440 275-2001
Fax: 440 275-1454
Richard Pildner, *President*
Lynetta Pildner, *Corp Secy*
John Pildner, *Vice Pres*
EMP: 8
SQ FT: 8,200
SALES: 750K **Privately Held**
SIC: 3599 Machine shop, jobbing & repair

(G-959)
COLORAMIC PROCESS INC
2883 Industrial Park Dr (44010-9764)
P.O. Box 12 (44010-0012)
PHONE..................................440 275-1199
Fax: 440 275-1188
Donald Pikounik, *President*
Robert Pikounik, *President*
Fred Zust, *President*
Marilyn Pikounik, *Admin Sec*
EMP: 15 **EST:** 1959
SALES (est): 1.7MM **Privately Held**
WEB: www.coloramic.com
SIC: 2752 Cards, lithographed

(G-960)
EUCLID REFINISHING COMPNAY INC (PA)
Also Called: Surftech
2937 Industrial Park Dr (44010-9763)
PHONE..................................440 275-3356
Fax: 440 275-3358
Nicholas Cottone, *CEO*
EMP: 10
SQ FT: 15,000
SALES: 876.5K **Privately Held**
SIC: 3471 Polishing, metals or formed products; finishing, metals or formed products

(G-961)
FARIN INDUSTRIES INC
2844 Industrial Park Dr (44010-9764)
P.O. Box 185 (44010-0185)
PHONE..................................440 275-2755
Fax: 440 275-1255
Michael F Farinacci, *President*
EMP: 15
SQ FT: 10,000
SALES (est): 2.2MM **Privately Held**
SIC: 3751 Brakes, friction clutch & other: bicycle

(G-962)
FUTURE CONTROLS CORPORATION
1419 State Route 45 (44010-9749)
P.O. Box 130 (44010-0130)
PHONE..................................440 275-3191
Fax: 440 275-3192
John Williams, *President*
Philip Bunnell, *Vice Pres*
Jeremy Sutch, *Vice Pres*
Edward Kuehn, *Info Tech Mgr*
Kayla Mulo, *Admin Sec*
EMP: 41
SQ FT: 33,000
SALES (est): 7.7MM **Privately Held**
SIC: 3823 3625 3822 Temperature instruments: industrial process type; relays & industrial controls; auto controls regulating residntl & coml environmt & applncs

(G-963)
MULTI-DESIGN INC
Also Called: Twin Fin
2844 Industrial Park Dr (44010-9764)
P.O. Box 185 (44010-0185)
PHONE..................................440 275-2255
Michael F Farinacci, *President*
EMP: 4
SQ FT: 10,000
SALES (est): 336.3K **Privately Held**
WEB: www.twinfin.com
SIC: 3751 3714 Brakes, friction clutch & other: bicycle; motor vehicle parts & accessories

(G-964)
PAINESVILLE PUBLISHING CO
2883 Industrial Park Dr (44010-9764)
P.O. Box 12 (44010-0012)
PHONE...................................440 354-4142
Fax: 440 354-2519
Don Tiknovnik, *President*
Marie Baker, *Treasurer*
Tom Bain, *Manager*
EMP: 7 **EST:** 1941
SQ FT: 3,000
SALES (est): 1MM **Privately Held**
SIC: 2752 2791 2789 Commercial printing, lithographic; typesetting; bookbinding & related work

(G-965)
RTS COMPANIES (US) INC
2900 Industrial Park Dr (44010-9763)
PHONE...................................440 275-3077
Graham Lobban, *President*
▲ **EMP:** 40 **EST:** 2008
SALES (est): 8.5MM **Privately Held**
SIC: 3089 Plastic & fiberglass tanks

(G-966)
SPRING TEAM INC
2851 Industrial Park Dr (44010-9764)
P.O. Box 215 (44010-0215)
PHONE...................................440 275-5981
Russ Bryer, *President*
Robert Schultz, *Principal*
Richard Kovach, *Vice Pres*
Gary Van Buren, *Vice Pres*
Ed Hall, *Treasurer*
▼ **EMP:** 67
SQ FT: 42,000
SALES (est): 13.5MM **Privately Held**
WEB: www.springteam.com
SIC: 3496 3495 Miscellaneous fabricated wire products; wire springs

(G-967)
SURFTECH INC
2937 Industrial Park Dr (44010-9763)
PHONE...................................440 275-3356
June E Yusko, *President*
Edward Yusko Jr, *Vice Pres*
EMP: 6
SQ FT: 12,000
SALES (est): 263K
SALES (corp-wide): 876.5K **Privately Held**
WEB: www.ercsurftech.com
SIC: 3479 Coating of metals with plastic or resins
PA: Euclid Refinishing Compnay, Inc.
　　2937 Industrial Park Dr
　　Austinburg OH 44010
　　440 275-3356

Austintown
Mahoning County

(G-968)
ADYL INC
Also Called: Party On
6000 Mahoning Ave Ste 230 (44515-2225)
P.O. Box 4327 (44515-0327)
PHONE...................................330 797-8700
Debbie Simon, *President*
Kathy Lyda, *Corp Secy*
Jeffrey T Lyda, *Vice Pres*
EMP: 3
SQ FT: 10,000
SALES (est): 417.7K **Privately Held**
WEB: www.adyl.com
SIC: 2759 5699 5947 7299 Invitation & stationery printing & engraving; costumes, masquerade or theatrical; party favors; party planning service

(G-969)
BARTELLS CUPCAKERY
4555 Norquest Blvd (44515-1629)
PHONE...................................330 957-1793
EMP: 3
SALES (est): 137.9K **Privately Held**
SIC: 2053 Mfg Frozen Bakery Products

(G-970)
BOJOS CREAM
1412 S Raccoon Rd (44515-4525)
PHONE...................................330 270-3332
Bob McCalster, *Owner*
EMP: 3
SALES (est): 205.3K **Privately Held**
SIC: 2024 Ice cream, bulk

(G-971)
CAPITAL OIL & GAS INC
6075 Silica Rd (44515-1081)
PHONE...................................330 533-1828
Bruce Brocker, *President*
EMP: 6
SALES (est): 169.4K **Privately Held**
SIC: 1382 Oil & gas exploration services

(G-972)
COWLES INDUSTRIAL TOOL CO LLC
185 N Four Mile Run Rd (44515-3006)
PHONE...................................330 799-9100
David Smith, *President*
EMP: 35
SQ FT: 30,000
SALES (est): 5.1MM **Privately Held**
SIC: 3545 Tools & accessories for machine tools

(G-973)
COWLES TOOL COMPANY LLC
185 N Four Mile Run Rd (44515-3006)
PHONE...................................330 799-9100
Fax: 216 533-5740
Christine K Hoffa,
Sarah L Dziatkowics,
EMP: 4
SALES (est): 809.7K **Privately Held**
SIC: 3545 Precision measuring tools

(G-974)
HAZ-SAFE LLC
3850 Hendricks Rd (44515-1528)
P.O. Box 181, Sistersville WV (26175-0181)
PHONE...................................330 793-0900
Chuck Lisman,
Ronald L Larson,
Michael P Lewis,
EMP: 15 **EST:** 2008
SALES (est): 1.1MM **Privately Held**
SIC: 3448 Prefabricated metal buildings
PA: Precision, L.L.C.
　　843 N Cleveland Massillon
　　Akron OH 44333

(G-975)
MAHONING VALLEY FABRICATORS
3697 Oakwood Ave (44515-3030)
PHONE...................................330 793-8995
Fax: 330 793-1756
Donald J Zeisler, *President*
Donald C Zeisler, *President*
EMP: 15
SQ FT: 10,000
SALES (est): 3.2MM **Privately Held**
SIC: 3441 3599 Fabricated structural metal; machine shop, jobbing & repair

(G-976)
TRANSUE WILLIAMS STAMPING INC
207 N Four Mile Run Rd (44515-3008)
PHONE...................................330 270-0891
EMP: 4
SALES (corp-wide): 728.5K **Privately Held**
SIC: 3469 Stamping metal for the trade
HQ: Transue & Williams Stamping Co., Inc.
　　930 W Ely St
　　Alliance OH 44601
　　330 829-5007

(G-977)
WESTERN RESERVE ORTHODONTICS &
6431 Mahoning Ave (44515-2039)
PHONE...................................330 792-6826
Fax: 330 792-8493
Richard L Grope, *President*
Robert D Paul, *Area Mgr*
Kimberly Grope, *Vice Pres*
Darlene Wiant, *Manager*

Jason Lenzi, *Admin Asst*
EMP: 10
SQ FT: 8,000
SALES: 600K **Privately Held**
SIC: 3842 Prosthetic appliances

Avon
Lorain County

(G-978)
A J ROSE MFGCO (PA)
38000 Chester Rd (44011-4022)
PHONE...................................216 631-4645
Fax: 440 934-2802
Daniel T Pritchard, *President*
Douglas E Krzywicki, *Vice Pres*
Christopher Rose, *Vice Pres*
Gary Sluss, *Maint Spvr*
Cathy Curley, *Purch Mgr*
◆ **EMP:** 200 **EST:** 1922
SQ FT: 270,000
SALES (est): 99.8MM **Privately Held**
WEB: www.ajrose.com
SIC: 3465 3568 3469 Automotive stampings; pulleys, power transmission; metal stampings

(G-979)
ABC PACKAGING DIRECT LLC
2162 Clifton Way (44011-2808)
PHONE...................................440 934-1477
Jennifer Schill, *Project Mgr*
Edward D Marinac,
▲ **EMP:** 7
SALES: 950K **Privately Held**
SIC: 2671 Packaging paper & plastics film, coated & laminated

(G-980)
ACCEL CORPORATION
Also Called: Accel Color
38620 Chester Rd (44011-1074)
PHONE...................................440 327-7418
Dwight Morgan, *Manager*
EMP: 19
SALES (corp-wide): 228.1MM **Privately Held**
WEB: www.accelcolor.com
SIC: 2865 Dyes & pigments
HQ: Accel Corporation
　　38620 Chester Rd
　　Avon OH 44011

(G-981)
ACCEL CORPORATION (HQ)
Also Called: Accel Color
38620 Chester Rd (44011-1074)
PHONE...................................440 934-7711
Fax: 440 934-7717
Dwight Morgan, *CEO*
David Knowles, *President*
Mike Clabough, *Vice Pres*
Mike Gross, *Vice Pres*
Jim Jurgens, *Plant Mgr*
▲ **EMP:** 60
SALES (est): 9.4MM
SALES (corp-wide): 228.1MM **Privately Held**
WEB: www.accelcolor.com
SIC: 3087 Custom compound purchased resins
PA: Techmer Pm, Llc
　　1 Quality Cir
　　Clinton TN 37716
　　865 457-6700

(G-982)
ADVANCED POLYMER COATINGS LTD
951 Jaycox Rd (44011-1351)
P.O. Box 269 (44011-0269)
PHONE...................................440 937-6218
Fax: 440 937-5046
Donald Keehan, *Chairman*
Denise Keehan, *COO*
Mellia Hoyt, *Purch Agent*
Arthur Marshall, *Sales Staff*
▲ **EMP:** 26
SQ FT: 35,000
SALES (est): 6.1MM **Privately Held**
WEB: www.adv-polymer.com
SIC: 3081 Unsupported plastics film & sheet

(G-983)
AIRTUG LLC
1350 Chester Indus Pkwy (44011-1082)
PHONE...................................440 829-2167
Fax: 440 937-8703
David Scholtz,
EMP: 4
SALES (est): 524.5K **Privately Held**
SIC: 3728 Aircraft parts & equipment

(G-984)
AVON CONCRETE CORPORATION
930 Miller Rd (44011-1032)
PHONE...................................440 937-6264
Fax: 440 236-8452
Brock Walls, *President*
Sam Walls, *Owner*
EMP: 5
SQ FT: 8,000
SALES: 1MM
SALES (corp-wide): 1MM **Privately Held**
SIC: 3273 5211 Ready-mixed concrete; lumber & other building materials
PA: The Brock Corporation
　　26000 Sprague Rd
　　Olmsted Falls OH 44138
　　440 235-1806

(G-985)
BINDERY TECH INC
1260 Moore Rd Ste I (44011-4021)
PHONE...................................440 934-3247
Dave Sexton, *Principal*
Gordon B Loux, *Incorporator*
EMP: 14
SALES (est): 1.9MM **Privately Held**
SIC: 2789 Bookbinding & related work

(G-986)
BLUE RIBBON SCREEN GRAPHICS
1473 Hollow Wood Ln (44011-1094)
PHONE...................................216 226-6200
Patricia Boesken, *President*
EMP: 4
SQ FT: 8,000
SALES (est): 240K **Privately Held**
SIC: 2759 Screen printing; posters, including billboards: printing

(G-987)
BUDERER DRUG COMPANY INC
38530 Chester Rd Ste 400 (44011-4048)
PHONE...................................440 934-3100
Rebecca Arcaro, *Branch Mgr*
EMP: 5
SALES (corp-wide): 9.8MM **Privately Held**
SIC: 5122 2834 Drugs & drug proprietaries; animal medicines; proprietary (patent) medicines; proprietary drug products
PA: Buderer Drug Company, Inc.
　　633 Hancock St
　　Sandusky OH 44870
　　419 627-2800

(G-988)
CDI
980 Jaycox Rd (44011-1352)
PHONE...................................440 249-4178
William Carson, *Principal*
EMP: 4
SALES (est): 313.5K **Privately Held**
SIC: 3499 Fabricated metal products

(G-989)
CLEVELAND WHEELS
Also Called: Aircraft Wheels and Breaks
1160 Center Rd (44011-1208)
PHONE...................................440 937-6211
Manny Nnay Bajakfoujian, *CEO*
George Brick, *Purchasing*
Joe Mendise, *Engineer*
Otto Miller, *Engineer*
Steve Myers, *Manager*
EMP: 99
SALES (est): 6.5MM **Privately Held**
SIC: 5088 3799 Aircraft equipment & supplies; transportation equipment

(G-990)
COMPREHENSIVE LOGISTICS CO INC
1200 A Chester Indus Pkwy (44011)
PHONE..............................440 934-3517
Daryl Legg, *Branch Mgr*
EMP: 45 Privately Held
SIC: 3714 Motor vehicle transmissions, drive assemblies & parts
PA: Comprehensive Logistics Co., Inc.
4944 Belmont Ave Ste 202
Youngstown OH 44505

(G-991)
CORE TECHNOLOGY INC
1260 Moore Rd Ste E (44011-4021)
PHONE..............................440 934-9935
Fax: 440 937-6638
Jack A Redilla, *President*
Shujaat Lakhani, *Purch Mgr*
Becky Plato, *Bookkeeper*
Donna Dolezal, *Office Mgr*
Leslie Dewitt, *Manager*
▲ EMP: 10
SQ FT: 5,500
SALES: 1MM Privately Held
SIC: 3629 Power conversion units, a.c. to d.c.: static-electric

(G-992)
CUPCAKE WISHES LTD
37000 Detroit Rd (44011-1702)
PHONE..............................440 934-5550
EMP: 4
SALES (est): 218.3K Privately Held
SIC: 2051 Bread, cake & related products

(G-993)
CUTTING DYNAMICS INC (PA)
Also Called: CDI
980 Jaycox Rd (44011-1352)
PHONE..............................440 249-4662
William V Carson Jr, *President*
Marie Carson, *Corp Secy*
Wilbur S Kohring, *Vice Pres*
Wayne Beadnell, *Plant Mgr*
Rocco Deangelis, *Plant Mgr*
▲ EMP: 140 EST: 1985
SQ FT: 50,000
SALES (est): 30.8MM Privately Held
WEB: www.cuttingdynamics.com
SIC: 3599 Machine & other job shop work

(G-994)
ECP CORPORATION
Also Called: Polycase Division
1305 Chester Indus Pkwy (44011-1083)
PHONE..............................440 934-0444
Fax: 440 934-0088
Steven Began, *President*
Natasha Dean, *Vice Pres*
Kevin Whitmer, *Opers Staff*
James Mooney, *Engineer*
Judy Heitkamp, *Sales Associate*
▲ EMP: 48 EST: 1951
SQ FT: 40,000
SALES (est): 11.1MM Privately Held
WEB: www.polycase.com
SIC: 3469 Electronic enclosures, stamped or pressed metal

(G-995)
FLAVORSEAL LLC
35179 Avon Commerce Pkwy (44011-1374)
PHONE..............................440 937-3900
Jeff Binczyk, *Vice Pres*
Ken Hynes, *Vice Pres*
Corey Raub, *VP Opers*
James Smith, *Prdtn Mgr*
Shea Loper, *Purchasing*
◆ EMP: 99
SALES (est): 33.2MM Privately Held
SIC: 2673 Bags: plastic, laminated & coated

(G-996)
FREEMAN MANUFACTURING & SUP CO (PA)
1101 Moore Rd (44011-4043)
PHONE..............................440 934-1902
Fax: 440 934-7200
Gerald W Rusk, *Ch of Bd*
Lou Turco, *President*
Turco Matthew, *Vice Pres*

Matthew Turco, *Vice Pres*
Fred Cassell, *Plant Mgr*
EMP: 50
SQ FT: 110,000
SALES (est): 75.4MM Privately Held
WEB: www.freemansupply.com
SIC: 5084 3087 3543 2821 Industrial machinery & equipment; custom compound purchased resins; industrial patterns; plastics materials & resins

(G-997)
GREEN ACQUISITION LLC
Also Called: Green Bearing Co
1141 Jaycox Rd (44011-1366)
PHONE..............................440 930-7600
Laszlo Tromler,
EMP: 50
SALES (est): 3.9MM
SALES (corp-wide): 32.8MM Privately Held
SIC: 3714 Bearings, motor vehicle
PA: Bearing Technologies, Ltd.
1141 Jaycox Rd
Avon OH 44011
440 937-4770

(G-998)
JLW - TW CORP
Also Called: Suntan Supply
35350 Chester Rd (44011-1255)
PHONE..............................216 361-5940
William Gallagherr, *President*
William Gallagher, *President*
Martin F Gallagher, *Exec VP*
Jamie Carlson, *Vice Pres*
Scott A Karse, *Purch Mgr*
EMP: 7 EST: 2007
SALES (est): 1.8MM Privately Held
SIC: 3711 Motor vehicles & car bodies

(G-999)
L & W INC
Also Called: L&W Cleveland
1190 Jaycox Rd (44011-1313)
PHONE..............................734 397-6300
Steve Schafer, *Manager*
EMP: 55
SALES (corp-wide): 559.8MM Privately Held
SIC: 3469 3465 3441 3429 Stamping metal for the trade; automotive stampings; fabricated structural metal; manufactured hardware (general)
PA: L & W, Inc.
17757 Woodland Dr
New Boston MI 48164
734 397-6300

(G-1000)
MC KINLEY MACHINERY INC
1265 Lear Industrial Pkwy (44011-1364)
PHONE..............................440 937-6300
Fax: 440 937-6002
Scott Mc Kinley, *President*
EMP: 20 EST: 1980
SALES (est): 4.3MM Privately Held
SIC: 3554 5084 Die cutting & stamping machinery, paper converting; folding machines, paper; industrial machinery & equipment

(G-1001)
P M R INC
4661 Jaycox Rd (44011-2499)
PHONE..............................440 937-6241
Fax: 440 937-5752
Robert W Younglas, *President*
John Lucas, *Vice Pres*
Gay L McVeigh, *Treasurer*
Donna Shaffer, *Admin Asst*
EMP: 6 EST: 1966
SQ FT: 25,000
SALES (est): 954.8K Privately Held
SIC: 3541 Machine tools, metal cutting type

(G-1002)
PARKER-HANNIFIN CORPORATION
Parker Hannifin Corp
1160 Center Rd (44011-1297)
P.O. Box 158 (44011-0158)
PHONE..............................440 937-6211
Fax: 440 937-6416
Donald Washkewics, *CEO*

Manuel Bajaksouzian, *General Mgr*
Paul Nicholas, *Senior Buyer*
Mary L Purtell, *Personnel Exec*
Karyn Alexander, *Human Resources*
EMP: 110
SALES (corp-wide): 11.3B Publicly Held
WEB: www.parker.com
SIC: 3728 Wheels, aircraft; brakes, aircraft
PA: Parker-Hannifin Corporation
6035 Parkland Blvd
Cleveland OH 44124
216 896-3000

(G-1003)
PILGRIM-HARP CO
35050 Avon Commerce Pkwy (44011-1374)
PHONE..............................440 249-4185
William Carson, *President*
Chris Foertch, *Vice Pres*
Matt Carson, *Sales Staff*
Jason Prykuda, *Manager*
▲ EMP: 3 EST: 1999
SALES (est): 506.8K Privately Held
WEB: www.pilgrimharp.com
SIC: 3541 3312 Machine tools, metal cutting type; forgings, iron & steel

(G-1004)
PROTEC INDUSTRIES INCORPORATED
Also Called: Protech Industries
1384 Lear Industrial Pkwy (44011-1368)
PHONE..............................440 937-4142
Fax: 440 937-4162
Kurt F Van Luit, *President*
Jeff Leonard, *Vice Pres*
EMP: 6
SQ FT: 6,000
SALES (est): 785.7K Privately Held
SIC: 3089 Plastic hardware & building products

(G-1005)
QUAL-FAB INC
34250 Mills Rd (44011-2471)
PHONE..............................440 327-5000
Brice Blackman, *President*
Craig Hartzell, *General Mgr*
Gary Vanek, *Vice Pres*
Tim Glatz, *Project Mgr*
David Peter, *Project Mgr*
▼ EMP: 50
SQ FT: 80,000
SALES (est): 16.7MM Privately Held
WEB: www.qual-fab.net
SIC: 3312 3498 3433 Stainless steel; fabricated pipe & fittings; heating equipment, except electric

(G-1006)
RAILROAD BREWING COMPANY
1010 Center Rd (44011-1206)
PHONE..............................440 723-8234
Thomas R Wagner, *President*
Thomas Wager, *President*
Jerome Moore, *Vice Pres*
Tom Culler, *Treasurer*
EMP: 9
SQ FT: 4,000
SALES (est): 98.9K Privately Held
SIC: 5813 3556 Tavern (drinking places); brewers' & maltsters' machinery

(G-1007)
RDA GROUP LLC
2131 Clifton Way (44011-2809)
PHONE..............................440 724-4347
Robert Desmarais, *Principal*
EMP: 3
SALES (est): 256.4K Privately Held
SIC: 3559 Sewing machines & attachments, industrial

(G-1008)
RETEK INC
34550 Chester Rd (44011-1300)
P.O. Box 359 (44011-0359)
PHONE..............................440 937-6282
Daniel L Green, *President*
Richard L Green, *Admin Sec*
EMP: 4
SQ FT: 5,000

SALES: 2.1MM Privately Held
WEB: www.retekinc.com
SIC: 5084 3625 5085 3548 Industrial machine parts; welding machinery & equipment; resistance welder controls; resistors & resistor units; welding supplies; spot welding apparatus, electric

(G-1009)
RICHTECH INDUSTRIES INC
34000 Lear Indus Pkwy (44011-1375)
PHONE..............................440 937-4401
Fax: 440 937-4403
Kurt Van Luit, *CEO*
Jeff Leonard, *Vice Pres*
Terri Kristoff, *Marketing Staff*
Carolyn Smith, *Manager*
Jim Kodysh, *Consultant*
EMP: 9
SALES (est): 1.2MM Privately Held
WEB: www.richtech-industries.com
SIC: 3299 1799 Moldings, architectural: plaster of paris; waterproofing

(G-1010)
S & A PRECISION BEARING INC (PA)
1050 Jaycox Rd (44011-1312)
PHONE..............................440 930-7600
William Hagy, *President*
John Gross, *Controller*
▼ EMP: 5
SQ FT: 20,000
SALES (est): 550.4K Privately Held
SIC: 3714 Bearings, motor vehicle

(G-1011)
SHURTAPE TECHNOLOGIES LLC
32150 Just Imagine Dr (44011-1355)
PHONE..............................440 937-7000
Kimberly White, *Research*
John M Kahl, *Branch Mgr*
Melanie Canning, *Manager*
EMP: 350
SALES (corp-wide): 679MM Privately Held
SIC: 3083 2672 2671 3442 Laminated plastics plate & sheet; tape, pressure sensitive: made from purchased materials; masking tape: made from purchased materials; adhesive papers, labels or tapes: from purchased material; packaging paper & plastics film, coated & laminated; metal doors, sash & trim; narrow fabric mills
HQ: Shurtape Technologies, Llc
1712 8th Street Dr Se
Hickory NC 28602

(G-1012)
SHURTECH BRANDS LLC (DH)
Also Called: Duck Tape
32150 Just Imagine Dr (44011-1355)
P.O. Box 2228, Hickory NC (28603-2228)
PHONE..............................440 937-7000
C Hunt Shuford Jr, *Principal*
James B Shuford, *Principal*
Stephenson P Shuford, *Principal*
Bill Kahl, *Exec VP*
Brian Bastock, *Vice Pres*
◆ EMP: 226
SQ FT: 644,000
SALES (est): 134.9MM
SALES (corp-wide): 679MM Privately Held
SIC: 2671 Packaging paper & plastics film, coated & laminated

(G-1013)
TECHNIFAB INC
38600 Chester Rd (44011-1074)
PHONE..............................440 934-8324
Jeff Petras, *President*
John Cehovic, *Controller*
Travis Gift, *Manager*
EMP: 29 Privately Held
SIC: 3086 Plastics foam products
PA: Technifab, Inc.
1355 Chester Indus Pkwy
Avon OH 44011

(G-1014)
TECHNIFAB INC
1300 Chester Indus Pkwy (44011-1165)
Rural Route 1300 (44011)
PHONE...................................440 934-8324
Jeff Petras, *President*
EMP: 99
SALES (est): 3.6MM **Privately Held**
SIC: 3086 Insulation or cushioning material, foamed plastic

(G-1015)
TECHNIFAB INC (PA)
1355 Chester Indus Pkwy (44011-1083)
PHONE...................................440 934-8324
Fax: 440 934-3626
Jeff Petras, *President*
Lou Appleby, *Plant Mgr*
Travis Gift, *Manager*
◆ **EMP:** 30
SQ FT: 40,000
SALES (est): 7.1MM **Privately Held**
WEB: www.technifabfoam.com
SIC: 3086 Insulation or cushioning material, foamed plastic; packaging & shipping materials, foamed plastic

(G-1016)
TOMS COUNTRY PLACE INC
3442 Stoney Ridge Rd (44011-2210)
PHONE...................................440 934-4553
Fax: 440 934-4563
William Hricovec, *President*
Connie Hricovec,
EMP: 35
SQ FT: 500
SALES (est): 4.3MM **Privately Held**
WEB: www.tomscountryplace.com
SIC: 2099 Food preparations

(G-1017)
TRI-TECH MEDICAL INC
35401 Avon Commerce Pkwy
(44011-1374)
PHONE...................................800 253-8692
Fax: 440 937-5060
Don Simo, *President*
Russ Godfrey, *Principal*
Don Daviess, *Corp Secy*
Bob Gehrke, *Manager*
◆ **EMP:** 15
SQ FT: 19,000
SALES (est): 3.4MM **Privately Held**
WEB: www.tri-techmedical.com
SIC: 3841 Surgical & medical instruments

(G-1018)
WEBER ORTHOPEDIC INC
Also Called: Hely & Weber Orthopedic
1324 Chester Indus Pkwy (44011-1082)
P.O. Box 612956, Dallas TX (75261-2956)
PHONE...................................440 934-1812
Dave Ferrier, *Manager*
EMP: 7
SALES (corp-wide): 6.5MM **Privately Held**
SIC: 3842 Surgical appliances & supplies
PA: Weber Orthopedic, Inc.
　　1185 E Main St
　　Santa Paula CA 93060
　　805 525-8474

(G-1019)
WESTLAKE TOOL & DIE MFG CO
1280 Moore Rd (44011-1014)
P.O. Box 240 (44011-0240)
PHONE...................................440 934-5305
Fax: 440 934-5715
Joseph Walsh, *President*
Dwight M Allgood Jr, *Principal*
H Guy Hardy, *Principal*
Bert W Moyar, *Principal*
Seamus E Walsh, *Corp Secy*
EMP: 60
SQ FT: 65,100
SALES (est): 14.1MM **Privately Held**
SIC: 3469 Metal stampings; utensils, household: metal, except cast; machine parts, stamped or pressed metal

(G-1020)
WONDER MACHINE SERVICES INC
35340 Avon Commerce Pkwy
(44011-1374)
PHONE...................................440 937-7500
George Woyansky, *President*
Diane Woyansky, *Corp Secy*
Jeanine Woyansky, *Vice Pres*
Christopher Williams, *QC Mgr*
EMP: 30
SQ FT: 22,500
SALES (est): 5.5MM **Privately Held**
WEB: www.wondermachine.com
SIC: 3599 3541 Machine shop, jobbing & repair; machine tools, metal cutting type

(G-1021)
WOODMAN AGITATOR INC
1404 Lear Industrial Pkwy (44011-1363)
PHONE...................................440 937-9865
Fax: 440 937-9867
James Bielozer, *President*
Keith M Bielozer, *Vice Pres*
Mary Bielozer, *Vice Pres*
Dan Barone, *Plant Mgr*
◆ **EMP:** 17
SALES (est): 3.7MM **Privately Held**
WEB: www.woodmanagitator.com
SIC: 3559 Paint making machinery

Avon Lake
Lorain County

(G-1022)
1999 PVC PARTNER INC
33587 Walker Rd (44012-1145)
PHONE...................................440 930-1000
EMP: 3
SALES (est): 201.6K **Publicly Held**
WEB: www.polyone.com
SIC: 2821 Plastics materials & resins
PA: Polyone Corporation
　　33587 Walker Rd
　　Avon Lake OH 44012

(G-1023)
ALUMALLOY METALCASTING COMPANY
33665 Walker Rd (44012-1044)
PHONE...................................440 930-2222
Fax: 440 930-4854
Dennis Daniels, *President*
Chris Daniels, *Principal*
Donald C Price, *Principal*
Judy Spencer, *Principal*
EMP: 110
SQ FT: 11,000
SALES (est): 16.7MM **Privately Held**
WEB: www.alumalloy.com
SIC: 3365 Aluminum & aluminum-based alloy castings

(G-1024)
AVON LAKE PRINTING
227 Miller Rd (44012-1004)
PHONE...................................440 933-2078
Fax: 440 933-2965
Thomas Brock, *Owner*
EMP: 9
SQ FT: 8,000
SALES (est): 1MM **Privately Held**
WEB: www.avonlakeprinting.com
SIC: 2752 5943 Commercial printing, offset; office forms & supplies

(G-1025)
AVON LAKE SHEET METAL CO
33574 Pin Oak Pkwy (44012-2320)
P.O. Box 64 (44012-0064)
PHONE...................................440 933-3505
Fax: 440 933-7160
Carl Wetzig Jr, *President*
Gary Wightman, *Corp Secy*
Dennis Lightfoot, *Draft/Design*
Maureen Wightman, *Admin Mgr*
EMP: 38
SQ FT: 32,000
SALES (est): 8.8MM **Privately Held**
WEB: www.avonlakesheetmetal.com
SIC: 3444 1761 Sheet metalwork; sheet metalwork

(G-1026)
CATANIA MEDALLIC SPECIALTY
Also Called: Catania Medallic Specialities
668 Moore Rd (44012-2315)
PHONE...................................440 933-9595
Fax: 440 933-2404
Vince Frank, *President*
Trisha Frank, *Vice Pres*
▲ **EMP:** 25
SQ FT: 12,000
SALES (est): 5.3MM **Privately Held**
WEB: www.cataniainc.com
SIC: 3469 3965 3369 2395 Ornamental metal stampings; fasteners, buttons, needles & pins; nonferrous foundries; pleating & stitching

(G-1027)
CUSTOM ENGRAVING & SCREEN PRTG
690 Avon Belden Rd Ste 1b (44012-2255)
PHONE...................................440 933-2902
Fax: 440 933-2902
Gary Randall, *President*
Rebecca Randall, *Vice Pres*
EMP: 3
SALES (est): 156.1K **Privately Held**
SIC: 5947 3993 Gift shop; signs & advertising specialties

(G-1028)
ERIE SHORE INDUSTRIAL SVC CO
683 Moore Rd Ste A (44012-3504)
PHONE...................................440 933-4301
Fax: 440 933-5418
John Schmitt, *President*
Tracy Birney, *Vice Pres*
EMP: 4
SALES (est): 250K **Privately Held**
SIC: 3568 Bearings, plain

(G-1029)
FORD MOTOR COMPANY
650 Miller Rd (44012-2398)
PHONE...................................440 933-1215
Fax: 440 933-1319
Deborah S Kent, *Engineer*
Janice Goegan, *Engineer*
Mike Spencer, *Engineer*
Mark Tiberia, *Controller*
Ann Guitari, *Manager*
EMP: 2693
SALES (corp-wide): 151.8B **Publicly Held**
WEB: www.ford.com
SIC: 3713 3711 Van bodies; motor vehicles & car bodies
PA: Ford Motor Company
　　1 American Rd
　　Dearborn MI 48126
　　313 322-3000

(G-1030)
GREAT LAKES INTEGRATED INC
GL Direct
33625 Pin Oak Pkwy (44012-2321)
PHONE...................................440 892-7760
Fax: 440 808-7852
Dean Hanisko, *Div Sub Head*
Mike Trecarichi, *Project Mgr*
Neal Gallagher, *Manager*
EMP: 20
SALES (corp-wide): 25.6MM **Privately Held**
SIC: 2752 2796 Commercial printing, lithographic; lithographic plates, positives or negatives
PA: Great Lakes Integrated, Inc.
　　4005 Clark Ave
　　Cleveland OH 44109
　　216 651-1500

(G-1031)
HASHIER & HASHIER MFG
644 Moore Rd (44012-2315)
PHONE...................................440 933-4883
Fax: 440 933-3990
Frank Hashier, *President*
EMP: 6 EST: 1976
SQ FT: 6,000
SALES: 400K **Privately Held**
SIC: 3599 Machine shop, jobbing & repair

(G-1032)
HELICAL LINE PRODUCTS CO
659 Miller Rd (44012-2306)
P.O. Box 217 (44012-0217)
PHONE...................................440 933-9263
Fax: 440 933-5009
Albert C Bonds, *President*
William T Bonds, *Corp Secy*
Robert S Bonds, *Vice Pres*
▼ **EMP:** 23 EST: 1964
SQ FT: 33,000
SALES: 3MM **Privately Held**
WEB: www.helical-line.com
SIC: 3644 Pole line hardware

(G-1033)
HINKLEY LIGHTING INC (PA)
Also Called: Fredrick Ramond
33000 Pin Oak Pkwy (44012-2641)
PHONE...................................216 671-3132
Fax: 216 671-4537
Richard A Wiedemer Jr, *President*
Eric Wiedemer, *Vice Pres*
Jess Wiedemer, *Vice Pres*
Matt McKnight, *Opers Mgr*
Bob Brainard, *Engineer*
◆ **EMP:** 45 EST: 1920
SQ FT: 100,000
SALES (est): 12.4MM **Privately Held**
WEB: www.hinkleylighting.com
SIC: 3645 Residential lighting fixtures

(G-1034)
JMJ PAPER INC
Also Called: Wolfe Paper Co.
681 Moore Rd Ste D (44012-2365)
PHONE...................................216 941-8100
Jerry Jazwa, *President*
EMP: 10
SALES (est): 1.6MM **Privately Held**
SIC: 2621 Packaging paper

(G-1035)
JOHN CHRIST WINERY INC
32421 Walker Rd (44012-2226)
PHONE...................................440 933-9672
Dean Gunter, *General Mgr*
EMP: 8
SALES (est): 450K **Privately Held**
SIC: 2084 Wines

(G-1036)
KLINGSHIRN WINERY INC
33050 Webber Rd (44012-2330)
PHONE...................................440 933-6666
Lee Klingshirn, *President*
Nancy Klingshirn, *Vice Pres*
EMP: 8
SQ FT: 3,850
SALES (est): 891.3K **Privately Held**
WEB: www.klingshirnwine.com
SIC: 2084 Wines

(G-1037)
LUBRIZOL ADVANCED MTLS INC
550 Moore Rd (44012-2313)
P.O. Box 134 (44012-0134)
PHONE...................................440 933-0400
Michael Mazur, *Opers Staff*
Rick Corry, *Mfg Staff*
Lawrence Thayer, *Chief Engr*
Joeri Plusnin, *Engineer*
Dmitry Shuster, *Engineer*
EMP: 50
SALES (corp-wide): 223.6B **Publicly Held**
WEB: www.pharma.noveoninc.com
SIC: 8731 2821 2899 Commercial physical research; plastics materials & resins; chemical preparations
HQ: Lubrizol Advanced Materials Inc.
　　9911 Brecksville Rd
　　Brecksville OH 44141
　　216 447-5000

(G-1038)
M S K TOOL & DIE INC
685 Moore Rd Ste B (44012-3507)
PHONE...................................440 930-8100
Mark Roth, *President*
Michael Roth, *Vice Pres*
EMP: 6
SQ FT: 1,500

SALES: 800K **Privately Held**
SIC: 3544 Special dies, tools, jigs & fixtures

(G-1039)
MARKERS INC
33490 Pin Oak Pkwy (44012-2318)
P.O. Box 330 (44012-0330)
PHONE..................................440 933-5927
Paul Stein, *General Mgr*
Dale Hlavin, *Shareholder*
Meja Tansey, *Executive Asst*
EMP: 6
SALES (est): 480K **Privately Held**
WEB: www.markersinc.com
SIC: 2399 5261 Banners, pennants & flags; lawn & garden supplies

(G-1040)
MEXICHEM SPECIALTY RESINS INC (HQ)
33653 Walker Rd (44012-1044)
P.O. Box 277 (44012-0277)
PHONE..................................440 930-1435
Frank Tomaselli, *General Mgr*
Joe Harkelroad, *Director*
Joanne Spikowski, *Admin Sec*
◆ EMP: 27 EST: 2013
SALES (est): 87MM
SALES (corp-wide): 5.8B **Privately Held**
SIC: 2822 2821 Ethylene-propylene rubbers, EPDM polymers; polymethyl methacrylate resins (plexiglass)
PA: Mexichem, S.A.B. De C.V.
Rio San Javier No. 10
Tlalnepantla De Baz EDOMEX. 54060
555 397-8836

(G-1041)
NATIONAL FLEET SVCS OHIO LLC
607 Miller Rd (44012-2306)
P.O. Box 338 (44012-0338)
PHONE..................................440 930-5177
Tim Lariviere, *President*
Earl Fleming, *Plant Mgr*
EMP: 12
SALES (est): 504.1K **Privately Held**
SIC: 3089 7532 Automotive parts, plastic; van conversion

(G-1042)
OCEANSIDE FOODS
32859 Lake Rd (44012-1521)
PHONE..................................440 554-7810
Rich Klotz, *Principal*
EMP: 3
SALES (est): 84K **Privately Held**
SIC: 2099 Food preparations

(G-1043)
PIN OAK DEVELOPMENT LLC
32329 Orchard Park Dr (44012-2167)
PHONE..................................440 933-9862
David Rickey, *Owner*
EMP: 3
SALES (est): 217.8K **Privately Held**
SIC: 3452 Pins

(G-1044)
POLYONE CORPORATION
552 Moore Rd (44012)
PHONE..................................440 930-1000
EMP: 72 **Publicly Held**
SIC: 2821 Thermoplastic materials
PA: Polyone Corporation
33587 Walker Rd
Avon Lake OH 44012

(G-1045)
POLYONE CORPORATION
554 Moore Rd Bldg 482 (44012)
PHONE..................................440 930-3754
EMP: 68 **Publicly Held**
SIC: 2821 Plastics materials & resins
PA: Polyone Corporation
33587 Walker Rd
Avon Lake OH 44012

(G-1046)
POLYONE CORPORATION
33587 Walker Rd (44012-1145)
PHONE..................................440 933-2000
John Phillips, *Manager*
EMP: 85 **Publicly Held**

WEB: www.polyone.com
SIC: 2821 Vinyl resins
PA: Polyone Corporation
33587 Walker Rd
Avon Lake OH 44012

(G-1047)
POLYONE CORPORATION (PA)
33587 Walker Rd (44012-1145)
PHONE..................................440 930-1000
Robert M Patterson, *Ch of Bd*
Richard N Altice, *President*
Mark D Crist, *President*
Craig N Nikrant, *President*
John V Van Hulle, *President*
◆ EMP: 73
SALES: 3.3B **Publicly Held**
WEB: www.polyone.com
SIC: 2821 3087 3081 Thermoplastic materials; polyvinyl chloride resins (PVC); vinyl resins; custom compound purchased resins; resins; plastics basic shapes; unsupported plastics film & sheet

(G-1048)
RELIACHECK MANUFACTURING INC
Also Called: Ecil Met TEC
33554 Pin Oak Pkwy (44012-2320)
P.O. Box 303 (44012-0303)
PHONE..................................440 933-6162
Luis Antonio Srerie, *President*
David Updegraff, *President*
Keith Updegraff, *Purch Dir*
Laiking Crockett, *Administration*
▲ EMP: 26
SQ FT: 53,000
SALES: 6MM
SALES (corp-wide): 1.7B **Privately Held**
WEB: www.reliacheck.net
SIC: 3317 Seamless pipes & tubes
PA: Vesuvius Plc
165 Fleet Street
London EC4A
207 822-0000

(G-1049)
RYKON PLATING INC
555 Miller Rd (44012-2304)
PHONE..................................440 933-3273
Fax: 440 933-3274
Carl Kulas, *President*
EMP: 5 EST: 1949
SQ FT: 17,500
SALES (est): 581.9K **Privately Held**
WEB: www.rykon.net
SIC: 3471 Electroplating of metals or formed products

(G-1050)
SCOTT FETZER COMPANY
Also Called: Western Entps A Scott Fetzer
33672 Pin Oak Pkwy (44012-2322)
PHONE..................................440 871-2160
Fax: 440 835-3105
Jay Juneja, *Exec VP*
Dave Sack, *Prdtn Mgr*
Philip Jones, *Opers Staff*
Dale Stelmach, *Purch Mgr*
Tom Nehrenz, *Engng Exec*
EMP: 200
SALES (corp-wide): 223.6B **Publicly Held**
SIC: 3635 Household vacuum cleaners
HQ: The Scott Fetzer Company
28800 Clemens Rd
Westlake OH 44145
440 892-3000

(G-1051)
SOLUTION VENTURES INC
Also Called: Proforma Solution Ventures
31728 Commodore Ct (44012-2902)
PHONE..................................440 242-1658
EMP: 3 EST: 2006
SALES: 300K **Privately Held**
SIC: 2759 Commercial Printing

(G-1052)
SOVEREIGN STITCH
701 Jockeys Cir (44012-4042)
PHONE..................................440 829-0678
Aaron Fenton, *Mng Member*
EMP: 4 EST: 2013
SALES: 200K **Privately Held**
SIC: 2395 Embroidery & art needlework

(G-1053)
THOGUS PRODUCTS COMPANY
33490 Pin Oak Pkwy (44012-2318)
P.O. Box 330 (44012-0330)
PHONE..................................440 933-8850
Fax: 440 933-7839
Helen Thompson, *CEO*
Matthew Grantson, *President*
Scott Walton, *COO*
Kendra Gardiner, *Opers Mgr*
Megan Leibold, *Opers Mgr*
▲ EMP: 96 EST: 1958
SQ FT: 50,000
SALES (est): 39MM **Privately Held**
WEB: www.thogus.com
SIC: 3089 3494 3492 Injection molding of plastics; valves & pipe fittings; fluid power valves & hose fittings

(G-1054)
VOODOO INDUSTRIES
33640 Pin Oak Pkwy Ste 4 (44012-3510)
PHONE..................................440 653-5333
Robert Ueker, *Principal*
▲ EMP: 3
SALES (est): 233K **Privately Held**
SIC: 3999 Manufacturing industries

(G-1055)
WATTEREDGE LLC (DH)
567 Miller Rd (44012-2304)
PHONE..................................440 933-6110
Joseph P Langhenry, *President*
Erin Kobunski, *General Mgr*
◆ EMP: 64 EST: 1970
SQ FT: 65,000
SALES (est): 41.1MM
SALES (corp-wide): 2.9B **Privately Held**
WEB: www.watteredge.com
SIC: 5085 3643 5051 3052 Industrial supplies; current-carrying wiring devices; metals service centers & offices; rubber & plastics hose & beltings; miscellaneous metalwork
HQ: Coleman Cable, Llc
1530 S Shields Dr
Waukegan IL 60085
847 672-2300

(G-1056)
WOLFF TOOL & MANUFACTURING CO
Also Called: O G Bell
139 Lear Rd (44012-1904)
PHONE..................................440 933-7797
Alan Wolff, *President*
Barbara Wolff, *Vice Pres*
EMP: 10
SQ FT: 1,610
SALES (est): 1.3MM **Privately Held**
WEB: www.ogbell.com
SIC: 3425 Saw blades & handsaws

Bainbridge
Ross County

(G-1057)
COUNTRY CRUST BAKERY
4918 State Route 41 S (45612-9613)
PHONE..................................888 860-2940
EMP: 8
SALES (est): 504K **Privately Held**
SIC: 2051 Bread, cake & related products

(G-1058)
J D KNISLEY LOGGING
112 W 3rd St (45612)
PHONE..................................740 634-3207
J D Knisley, *Owner*
EMP: 5
SALES (est): 315.8K **Privately Held**
SIC: 2411 Logging

(G-1059)
JEFFREY ADAMS LOGGING INC
3656 Us Highway 50 W (45612-7504)
P.O. Box 47 (45612-0047)
PHONE..................................740 634-2286
Jeffrey A Adams, *President*
EMP: 3
SALES: 320K **Privately Held**
SIC: 2411 Logging

(G-1060)
KNAUFF BROS LOGGING & LUMBER
Also Called: Knauff Logging
494 Houseman Town Rd (45612-9408)
PHONE..................................740 634-2432
Fax: 740 634-2436
Joyce Knauff, *President*
Jonathan Knauff, *Vice Pres*
EMP: 18
SALES (est): 1.6MM **Privately Held**
SIC: 2411 Logging camps & contractors

(G-1061)
KNISLEY LUMBER
160 Potts Hill Rd (45612-9768)
P.O. Box 488 (45612-0488)
PHONE..................................740 634-2935
Fax: 740 634-2935
Mark A Knisley, *Owner*
Chris Knisley, *Director*
EMP: 15
SQ FT: 4,000
SALES: 1MM **Privately Held**
SIC: 2421 2435 2426 Sawmills & planing mills, general; hardwood veneer & plywood; hardwood dimension & flooring mills

(G-1062)
RANDY CARTER LOGGING INC
1100 Schmidt Rd (45612-9762)
PHONE..................................740 634-2604
Randy L Carter, *Principal*
EMP: 6
SALES (est): 402.4K **Privately Held**
SIC: 2411 Logging camps & contractors

Bakersville
Coshocton County

(G-1063)
MULLET ENTERPRISES INC
28003 Adams Twp Rd 101 (43803)
PHONE..................................330 897-3911
Mike Myers, *Branch Mgr*
EMP: 6
SALES (corp-wide): 8.9MM **Privately Held**
WEB: www.tmkvalley.com
SIC: 5153 2041 Grain elevators; flour & other grain mill products
PA: Mullet Enterprises, Inc
138 2nd St Nw
Sugarcreek OH 44681
330 852-4681

Baltic
Tuscarawas County

(G-1064)
ANDAL WOODWORKING
1411 Township Road 151 (43804-9627)
PHONE..................................330 897-8059
Andrew Yoder, *Principal*
EMP: 10 EST: 2008
SALES: 1.8MM **Privately Held**
SIC: 2511 Wood bedroom furniture

(G-1065)
BALTIC COUNTRY MEATS
Also Called: Baltic Meats
3320 State Route 557 (43804-9609)
PHONE..................................330 897-7025
Susie Raber, *Owner*
Dan Miller, *Owner*
EMP: 6
SALES (est): 523.6K **Privately Held**
SIC: 2011 5411 Meat packing plants; delicatessens

(G-1066)
CLARK TOWNSHIP GARAGE
2863 State Route 557 (43804-9672)
PHONE..................................330 897-4844
Nennette Yoder, *Owner*
EMP: 6
SALES (est): 261.8K **Privately Held**
SIC: 2431 Garage doors, overhead: wood

(G-1067)
COUNTRY FREEZER UNITS LLC
Also Called: Country Ice Cream Freezer
50938 Township Road 220 (43804-9502)
PHONE.....................................740 623-8658
Roy M Hershberger,
EMP: 3
SALES (est): 471.7K **Privately Held**
WEB: www.countryfreezerunits.com
SIC: 3556 Ice cream manufacturing machinery

(G-1068)
CRAWFORD MANUFACTURING COMPANY
Also Called: Miller Leasing
52496 State Route 651 (43804-9505)
PHONE.....................................330 897-1060
Jonathan D Miller, President
Mary Miller, Admin Sec
EMP: 18
SQ FT: 2,500
SALES (est): 3.7MM **Privately Held**
WEB: www.cmcservice.net
SIC: 3493 Steel springs, except wire

(G-1069)
ES STEINER DAIRY LLC
115 S Mill St (43804-9204)
PHONE.....................................330 897-5555
Stanley Mullet, President
EMP: 18
SALES: 4.6MM **Privately Held**
SIC: 2022 Cheese, natural & processed

(G-1070)
FARMERSTOWN AXLE CO
2816 State Route 557 (43804-9672)
PHONE.....................................330 897-2711
Emanuel H Yoder, Owner
▲ EMP: 5 EST: 1962
SQ FT: 8,500
SALES (est): 362.7K **Privately Held**
SIC: 3599 3799 Machine shop, jobbing & repair; carriages, horse drawn

(G-1071)
FLEX TECHNOLOGIES INC
Also Called: Poly Flex
3430 State Route 93 (43804-9705)
P.O. Box 300 (43804-0300)
PHONE.....................................330 897-6311
Fax: 330 897-7000
Gglenn Burket, Division Mgr
Brian Harrison, Manager
Ken Ziegembusch, Info Tech Mgr
EMP: 35
SQ FT: 20,000
SALES (corp-wide): 57.8MM **Privately Held**
WEB: www.flextechnologies.com
SIC: 2821 5169 3087 Molding compounds, plastics; synthetic resins, rubber & plastic materials; custom compound purchased resins
PA: Flex Technologies, Inc.
5479 Gundy Dr
Midvale OH 44653
740 922-5992

(G-1072)
GERBER & SONS INC (PA)
201 E Main St (43804)
PHONE.....................................330 897-6201
Fax: 330 897-7700
Thomas Gerber, President
Michael Gerber, President
Steven Gerber, Principal
Wayne Young, Production
Marvin Mast, Manager
EMP: 32 EST: 1905
SQ FT: 7,200
SALES (est): 8.9MM **Privately Held**
SIC: 2048 5999 Livestock feeds; farm equipment & supplies

(G-1073)
GMI HOLDINGS INC
Also Called: Genie Company, The
606 N Ray St (43804-9093)
P.O. Box 284 (43804-0284)
PHONE.....................................330 897-4424
Fax: 330 897-1115
Rick Johnson, Director
Deleila Ruble, Executive
EMP: 201

SALES (corp-wide): 3.1B **Privately Held**
WEB: www.geniecompany.com
SIC: 3699 Door opening & closing devices, electrical
HQ: Gmi Holdings, Inc.
1 Door Dr
Mount Hope OH 44660
330 821-5360

(G-1074)
HOLMES PANEL
3052 State Route 557 (43804-7504)
PHONE.....................................330 897-5040
Fax: 330 893-3825
Junior Keim, Partner
Dan Hershberger, Partner
Wayne Hershberger, Partner
EMP: 9
SQ FT: 600
SALES (est): 1.1MM **Privately Held**
SIC: 5211 2511 Lumber & other building materials; wood household furniture

(G-1075)
MONARCH IG INC
600 N Ray St (43804-9093)
P.O. Box 217, Sugarcreek (44681-0217)
PHONE.....................................330 897-2302
William Mullet, President
Jeff Yoder, General Mgr
EMP: 16
SALES (est): 1.1MM **Privately Held**
SIC: 3231 Insulating glass: made from purchased glass

(G-1076)
POLYNEW INC
3557 State Route 93 (43804-9705)
P.O. Box 318 (43804-0318)
PHONE.....................................330 897-3202
Robert Burket, President
Gail Burket, Admin Sec
EMP: 6
SQ FT: 12,000
SALES: 300K **Privately Held**
WEB: www.polynew.com
SIC: 2821 Plastics materials & resins

(G-1077)
TBONE SALES LLC
410 N Ray St (43804-8901)
P.O. Box 75 (43804-0075)
PHONE.....................................330 897-6131
Fax: 330 897-0504
Michael J Young,
Chad Schilling,
EMP: 22
SQ FT: 7,500
SALES: 3MM **Privately Held**
SIC: 5411 7549 5531 5511 Convenience stores; automotive maintenance services; automobile & truck equipment & parts; trucks, tractors & trailers: new & used; filling stations, gasoline; welding repair

(G-1078)
TRI STATE DAIRY LLC
Also Called: Es Steiner Dairy
115 S Mill St (43804-9204)
PHONE.....................................330 897-5555
Stanley Mullet,
EMP: 15
SALES (est): 1.7MM **Privately Held**
SIC: 2022 Cheese, natural & processed

(G-1079)
WOODLAND WOODWORKING
2586 Township Road 183 (43804-9613)
PHONE.....................................330 897-7282
Melvin Miller, Principal
EMP: 4 EST: 2008
SALES (est): 366.7K **Privately Held**
SIC: 2431 Millwork

Baltimore
Fairfield County

(G-1080)
BALTIMORE FABRICATORS INC
9420 Lancaster Krkersvlle (43105-9621)
P.O. Box 147 (43105-0147)
PHONE.....................................740 862-6016
Michael Stanley, President

Jeanie Hill, Office Mgr
EMP: 4
SALES (est): 537.8K **Privately Held**
SIC: 3444 Sheet metalwork

(G-1081)
CARAUSTAR INDUSTRIES INC
Ohio Paperboard
310 W Water St (43105-1276)
PHONE.....................................740 862-4167
Thomas Manley, Engineer
Anita Owens, Human Res Mgr
Jeff Peters, Manager
John Bates, Maintence Staff
EMP: 100
SALES (corp-wide): 1.5B **Privately Held**
WEB: www.newarkgroup.com
SIC: 2631 2611 Paperboard mills; pulp mills
PA: Caraustar Industries, Inc.
5000 Astell Pwdr Sprng Rd
Austell GA 30106
770 948-3101

(G-1082)
GREEN GOURMET FOODS LLC
515 N Main St (43105-1214)
P.O. Box 206 (43105-0206)
PHONE.....................................740 400-4212
Jeffrey Ware, CFO
Mitchell Adams,
Dennis Logan,
Cameron Smith,
Murray Stroud,
EMP: 30 EST: 2011
SQ FT: 150,000
SALES (est): 7.1MM **Privately Held**
SIC: 2034 Potato products, dried & dehydrated

(G-1083)
HOMEGUARD PRODUCTS INC (PA)
Also Called: Homeguard Building Products
6797 Thoreau Ln Ne (43105-9732)
PHONE.....................................616 846-0804
Marvin Hopkins, Ch of Bd
Jay Cumbers, President
Kevin Monday, Vice Pres
EMP: 2 EST: 2010
SALES (est): 1.2MM **Privately Held**
SIC: 5033 2759 Roofing & siding materials; wrappers: printing

(G-1084)
MARCUM CREW CUT INC
6080 Fisher Rd Nw (43105-9617)
PHONE.....................................740 862-3400
Mike Marcum, President
EMP: 3
SALES (est): 190K **Privately Held**
SIC: 2499 Decorative wood & woodwork

(G-1085)
PROGRESSIVE AUTOMOTIVE INC
125 W Rome St (43105-1256)
PHONE.....................................740 862-4696
Fax: 740 862-4946
Robert F Shetrone, President
EMP: 5 EST: 1976
SQ FT: 9,500
SALES (est): 719.6K **Privately Held**
WEB: www.progressiveautomotive.com
SIC: 3711 Chassis, motor vehicle

(G-1086)
RAYMOND W REISIGER
11885 Paddock View Ct Nw (43105-9556)
PHONE.....................................740 400-4090
Ray Reisiger, Principal
EMP: 4
SALES (est): 270K **Privately Held**
SIC: 3569 Filters

(G-1087)
SAKAS INCORPORATED
312 Bltmore Smerset Rd Ne (43105-9400)
P.O. Box 98 (43105-0098)
PHONE.....................................740 862-4114
Fax: 740 862-4487
Dan Sakas, CEO
Lora Sakas, President
Arla Lines, Persnl Mgr
EMP: 29 EST: 1955
SQ FT: 30,000

SALES (est): 5.2MM **Privately Held**
WEB: www.sakas.com
SIC: 3469 Machine parts, stamped or pressed metal

(G-1088)
SAWDUST
4799 Refugee Rd Nw (43105-9424)
PHONE.....................................740 862-0612
James Wagenbrenner, Owner
EMP: 8
SALES: 250K **Privately Held**
WEB: www.sawdust.com
SIC: 2431 Woodwork, interior & ornamental

(G-1089)
TIMBERMILL LTD
11015 Stoudertown Rd Nw (43105-9315)
PHONE.....................................740 862-3426
Randy Smith, Principal
EMP: 3
SALES (est): 218.4K **Privately Held**
SIC: 2421 Sawmills & planing mills, general

(G-1090)
TRI-TECH LED SYSTEMS
600 W Market St (43105-1176)
PHONE.....................................614 593-2868
EMP: 7
SQ FT: 2,000
SALES (est): 65.8K **Privately Held**
SIC: 3674 Mfg Semiconductors/Related Devices

(G-1091)
WOODEN HORSE
204 N Main St (43105-1212)
PHONE.....................................740 503-5243
Wade Messmer, Owner
Barbara Messmer, Partner
EMP: 6
SQ FT: 2,400
SALES (est): 290K **Privately Held**
SIC: 5947 5092 2426 8299 Gift, novelty & souvenir shop; toys & hobby goods & supplies; hardwood dimension & flooring mills; arts & crafts schools

---
Barberton
Summit County

(G-1092)
ACE BOILER & WELDING CO INC
2891 Newpark Dr (44203-1047)
PHONE.....................................330 745-4443
Fax: 330 745-7182
Robert Kille, President
Cynthia Kille, Shareholder
EMP: 8
SQ FT: 15,000
SALES (est): 1.1MM **Privately Held**
SIC: 3599 3441 Machine shop, jobbing & repair; fabricated structural metal

(G-1093)
ADULT DAILY LIVING LLC
3603 Highspire Dr (44203-4409)
PHONE.....................................330 612-7941
Michelle O'Connor, Principal
EMP: 3
SALES (est): 151.3K **Privately Held**
SIC: 2711 Newspapers, publishing & printing

(G-1094)
ADVERTISING IDEAS OF OHIO INC
Also Called: 1 Stop Graphics
833 Wooster Rd N (44203-1664)
PHONE.....................................330 745-6555
Fax: 330 848-4801
Robert W Jacob, President
Gene McMullen, Vice Pres
EMP: 9
SALES: 600K **Privately Held**
WEB: www.weinstallanywhere.com
SIC: 3993 Signs & advertising specialties
PA: International Installations Inc
833 Wooster Rd N
Barberton OH 44203

▲ = Import ▼=Export
◆ =Import/Export

(G-1095)
AKRON FOUNDRY CO
Also Called: Akron Electric
1025 Eagon St (44203-1603)
PHONE..................................330 745-3101
Mike Pancoe, *General Mgr*
Sukhwant Puri, *Mfg Mgr*
Lawren Hamilton, *Production*
Predrag Djeric, *Engineer*
George Sam, *Accounts Mgr*
EMP: 40
SALES (corp-wide): 22MM **Privately Held**
WEB: www.akronfoundry.com
SIC: **1731** 3699 3644 3444 Electrical work; electrical equipment & supplies; noncurrent-carrying wiring services; sheet metalwork; aluminum foundries
PA: Akron Foundry Co.
2728 Wingate Ave
Akron OH 44314
330 745-3101

(G-1096)
ALCOA INC
842 Norton Ave (44203-1715)
PHONE..................................330 848-4000
Tim Ocheltree, *Maint Spvr*
Scott Campbell, *Purch Mgr*
Jason Hallgren, *Engineer*
Dildar Mohammad, *Engineer*
Keith Humphreys, *VP Finance*
EMP: 135
SALES (corp-wide): 12.3B **Publicly Held**
SIC: **3353** Aluminum sheet & strip
PA: Arconic Inc.
390 Park Ave
New York NY 10022
212 836-2758

(G-1097)
AMERICAN MOLDING COMPANY INC
711 Wooster Rd W (44203-2444)
PHONE..................................330 620-6799
Laverne J Strohfus, *Principal*
EMP: 4
SALES (est): 339.6K **Privately Held**
SIC: **3089** Molding primary plastic

(G-1098)
ANDERSON GRAPHICS INC
711 Wooster Rd W (44203-2444)
PHONE..................................330 745-2165
Fax: 330 745-4954
John Anderson, *President*
Larry Okolish, *Treasurer*
EMP: 30 EST: 1979
SALES: 1.8MM **Privately Held**
SIC: **2752** 2759 2789 2791 Commercial printing, offset; commercial printing; bookbinding & related work; typesetting; manifold business forms

(G-1099)
ASB INDUSTRIES INC
1031 Lambert St (44203-1689)
PHONE..................................330 753-8458
Fax: 330 753-7550
Albert Kay, *President*
Peter Richter, *General Mgr*
Charles Kay, *Vice Pres*
John Lindeman, *Vice Pres*
Leonhard Holzgassner, *Associate*
EMP: 23
SQ FT: 90,000
SALES (est): 4.8MM **Privately Held**
WEB: www.asbindustries.com
SIC: **1799** 3599 3542 4215 Coating, caulking & weather, water & fireproofing; machine shop, jobbing & repair; presses: hydraulic & pneumatic, mechanical & manual; courier services, except by air

(G-1100)
AUSTIN ENGINEERING INC
Also Called: Austin Engineering Group
834 Promenade Cir (44203-4445)
PHONE..................................330 848-0815
Fax: 330 745-6050
William Babbin, *President*
EMP: 4
SALES (est): 380K **Privately Held**
SIC: **3443** Jackets, industrial: metal plate

(G-1101)
B & C RESEARCH INC
842 Norton Ave (44203-1750)
PHONE..................................330 848-4000
Fax: 330 848-9404
Bob Clements, *Ch of Bd*
Louis Bilinovich, *President*
David Sandman, *Plant Mgr*
Mike Fedevich, *Chief Engr*
Michael Kerr, *Manager*
▲ EMP: 500
SQ FT: 100,000
SALES (est): 68MM
SALES (corp-wide): 12.3B **Publicly Held**
WEB: www.bcresearch.com
SIC: **3599** Machine shop, jobbing & repair
HQ: Arconic Securities Llc
101 Cherry St Ste 400
Burlington VT 05401
802 658-2661

(G-1102)
B & P POLISHING INC
123 9th St Nw (44203-2455)
P.O. Box 408 (44203-0408)
PHONE..................................330 753-4202
Fax: 330 753-4218
Louie Vilinovach, *President*
Randy Smith, *Area Mgr*
▲ EMP: 11
SALES (est): 1.1MM **Privately Held**
SIC: **3291** Buffing or polishing wheels, abrasive or nonabrasive

(G-1103)
B&C MACHINE CO LLC
401 Newell St (44203-2018)
P.O. Box 345 (44203-0345)
PHONE..................................330 745-4013
Fax: 330 745-7189
John Beall, *Safety Mgr*
Peter Bilinovich,
Tonya Becker,
Brandon Bilinovich,
Eric Bilinovich,
EMP: 300
SQ FT: 300,000
SALES: 20MM **Privately Held**
SIC: **3599** 3714 3743 3398 Machine shop, jobbing & repair; motor vehicle parts & accessories; locomotives & parts; metal heat treating

(G-1104)
BABCOCK & WILCOX COMPANY (HQ)
20 S Van Buren Ave (44203-3585)
P.O. Box 351 (44203-0351)
PHONE..................................330 753-4511
Fax: 330 860-1093
Gregory Calvin, *President*
E James Ferland, *Chairman*
Leonard Bossart, *Regional Mgr*
Kevin Brolly, *Regional Mgr*
Fred Untch, *Regional Mgr*
◆ EMP: 1000 EST: 1967
SQ FT: 16,000
SALES (est): 833.2MM
SALES (corp-wide): 1.5B **Publicly Held**
SIC: **1629** 1711 3443 7699 Industrial plant construction; power plant construction; plumbing, heating, air-conditioning contractors; fabricated plate work (boiler shop); boilers: industrial, power, or marine; boiler & heating repair services; management services; auto controls regulating residntl & coml environmt & applncs
PA: Babcock & Wilcox Enterprises, Inc.
13024 Ballantyne Corporat
Charlotte NC 28277
704 625-4900

(G-1105)
BABCOCK & WILCOX NUCLR OPRTNS
91 Stirling Ave (44203-2600)
P.O. Box 271 (44203-0271)
PHONE..................................330 860-1010
Rod Woolsey, *Branch Mgr*
EMP: 15 **Publicly Held**
SIC: **3443** Nuclear reactors, military or industrial

HQ: Bwxt Nuclear Operations Group, Inc.
2016 Mount Athos Rd
Lynchburg VA 24504
434 522-6000

(G-1106)
BABCOCK & WILCOX POWR GENERATN
91 Stirling Ave (44203-2600)
PHONE..................................330 753-4511
Fax: 330 860-6663
Keith Curtis, *Engineer*
Doug Garlock, *Branch Mgr*
Michael A Cramer, *Technology*
EMP: 20
SALES (corp-wide): 1.5B **Publicly Held**
SIC: **3443** Nuclear reactors, military or industrial
HQ: The Babcock & Wilcox Company
20 S Van Buren Ave
Barberton OH 44203
330 753-4511

(G-1107)
BARBERTON MAGIC PRESS PRINTING
Also Called: Magic Press Printery
699 Wooster Rd N (44203-1849)
PHONE..................................330 753-9578
Fax: 330 753-9523
Richard Law, *Owner*
EMP: 4
SQ FT: 4,000
SALES: 500K **Privately Held**
SIC: **2752** 2754 Commercial printing, offset; letter, circular & form: gravure printing

(G-1108)
BARBERTON MOLD & MACHINE CO
465 5th St Ne (44203-2754)
PHONE..................................330 745-8559
Fax: 330 745-8559
Helen P Adair, *President*
Harold W Adair, *Consultant*
EMP: 4
SQ FT: 1,200
SALES: 200K **Privately Held**
SIC: **3544** Industrial molds

(G-1109)
BARBERTON PRINTCRAFT
520 Wooster Rd W (44203-2549)
PHONE..................................330 848-3000
Fax: 330 848-0703
Thomas Schleicher, *Owner*
EMP: 5 EST: 1975
SQ FT: 7,500
SALES (est): 452.1K **Privately Held**
SIC: **2752** Commercial printing, lithographic

(G-1110)
BARBERTON STEEL INDUSTRIES INC
240 E Huston St (44203-3044)
P.O. Box 350 (44203-0350)
PHONE..................................330 745-6837
Jim Kotarski, *CEO*
Jim Cecconi, *Vice Pres*
Debbie Bulgrin, *Purch Mgr*
EMP: 48
SALES (est): 15.3MM **Privately Held**
SIC: **3312** Blast furnaces & steel mills

(G-1111)
BOOKBINDERS INCORPORATED
90 16th St Sw Ste C (44203-7070)
PHONE..................................330 848-4980
Fax: 330 848-4984
Steve Heim, *President*
EMP: 6
SQ FT: 7,000
SALES (est): 665.8K **Privately Held**
WEB: www.bookbindersinc.com
SIC: **2789** Bookbinding & related work

(G-1112)
BUCKEYE ABRASIVE INC
1020 Eagon St (44203-1604)
PHONE..................................330 753-1041
Fax: 330 753-1116
Robert J Armour, *President*
Aren Hunt, *Manager*
EMP: 10

SQ FT: 14,400
SALES (est): 1.2MM **Privately Held**
SIC: **3291** Wheels, abrasive

(G-1113)
CARDINAL RUBBER COMPANY INC
939 Wooster Rd N (44203-1698)
PHONE..................................330 745-2191
Fax: 330 745-2194
Diane McConnell, *President*
Thomas R Schnee, *Vice Pres*
Diane Brookover, *Treasurer*
Diane Schnee, *VP Mktg*
Robert F Schnee Jr, *Shareholder*
▲ EMP: 30
SQ FT: 80,000
SALES: 5MM **Privately Held**
SIC: **3069** 3061 3479 2891 Molded rubber products; automotive rubber goods (mechanical); bonderizing of metal or metal products; adhesives & sealants; synthetic rubber

(G-1114)
FLOHR MACHINE COMPANY INC
Also Called: Flohrmachine.com
1028 Coventry Rd (44203-1636)
PHONE..................................330 745-3030
Fax: 330 745-4147
Ivan W Flohr, *President*
Joseph Flohr, *Principal*
Jude Flohr, *Principal*
William Flohr, *Principal*
John Leary, *Manager*
EMP: 18
SQ FT: 6,000
SALES (est): 3MM **Privately Held**
WEB: www.flohrmachine.com
SIC: **3599** Machine shop, jobbing & repair

(G-1115)
FLORENCE ALLOYS INC
Also Called: Hard Drive Co
121 Snyder Ave (44203-4007)
PHONE..................................330 745-9141
Fax: 330 745-0163
Jim Federan, *President*
EMP: 7
SQ FT: 7,700
SALES: 300K **Privately Held**
SIC: **3714** 5013 Transmissions, motor vehicle; automotive supplies & parts

(G-1116)
GARDEN ART INNOVATIONS LLC
30 2nd St Sw (44203-2620)
PHONE..................................330 697-0007
William Marthaler,
EMP: 3 EST: 2011
SALES (est): 364.9K **Privately Held**
SIC: **2844** Toilet preparations

(G-1117)
GENERAL PLASTEX INC
35 Stuver Pl (44203-2417)
PHONE..................................330 745-7775
Fax: 330 745-6939
Renee Hershberger, *President*
David Mantyla, *Sales Engr*
Anita Bader, *Executive*
EMP: 31
SQ FT: 52,500
SALES (est): 6.1MM **Privately Held**
SIC: **3452** 7699 Bolts, nuts, rivets & washers; screws, metal; industrial machinery & equipment repair

(G-1118)
GLAS ORNAMENTAL METALS INC
1559 Waterloo Rd (44203-1335)
PHONE..................................330 753-0215
Fax: 330 753-0958
Rita Glas, *Ch of Bd*
John Glas, *President*
Karol Glas, *Admin Sec*
EMP: 9
SQ FT: 6,300
SALES (est): 825K **Privately Held**
SIC: **3446** Railings, prefabricated metal

(G-1119)
GLASS SURFACE SYSTEMS INC
Also Called: G S S
24 Brown St (44203-2315)
PHONE..............................330 745-8500
Fax: 330 745-8570
Barry Jacobs, *President*
EMP: 75
SQ FT: 17,000
SALES (est): 9.4MM **Privately Held**
WEB: www.glasscoat.com
SIC: 3231 Strengthened or reinforced
glass

(G-1120)
HYCOM INC
374 5th St Nw (44203-2127)
PHONE..............................330 753-2330
Fax: 330 753-2336
Thomas J Bilinovich, *CEO*
Ralph Bowling, *President*
Chris Price, *Office Mgr*
EMP: 45
SQ FT: 126,684
SALES: 2.7MM **Privately Held**
SIC: 3498 Tube fabricating (contract bend-
ing & shaping)

(G-1121)
IDEAL DRAPERY COMPANY INC
1024 Wooster Rd N (44203-1626)
PHONE..............................330 745-9873
Fax: 330 745-1504
Barbara Parks, *President*
EMP: 17
SQ FT: 4,000
SALES (est): 968.8K **Privately Held**
SIC: 2395 7389 Decorative & novelty
stitching, for the trade; sewing contractor

(G-1122)
JOHNDOW INDUSTRIES INC
151 Snyder Ave (44203-4007)
PHONE..............................330 753-6895
Fax: 330 753-6419
Joe Dease, *President*
Drew Dawson, *Exec VP*
Sheri Clemence, *Accounting Mgr*
Mark Pfleeger, *VP Sales*
Todd Nelson, *Sales Staff*
▲ EMP: 24
SQ FT: 120,000
SALES (est): 7.3MM **Privately Held**
WEB: www.johndow.com
SIC: 3559 Automotive maintenance equip-
ment

(G-1123)
JR ENGINEERING INC (PA)
Also Called: J R Engineering
123 9th St Nw (44203-2455)
P.O. Box 1497, Norton (44203-8497)
PHONE..............................330 848-0960
Fax: 330 825-9987
Louis Bilinovich Jr, *President*
Louis Bilinovich Sr, *Corp Secy*
Brian Hien Sr, *Purch Mgr*
John Callan, *QC Mgr*
Greg Roehrich, *Sls & Mktg Exec*
◆ EMP: 215
SQ FT: 242,000
SALES (est): 70.6MM **Privately Held**
WEB: www.jr-engineering.com
SIC: 3714 Motor vehicle parts & acces-
sories

(G-1124)
LITTLERN CORPORATION
77 2nd St Sw (44203-2645)
PHONE..............................330 848-8847
Ernest L Puskas Jr, *President*
EMP: 9
SALES (est): 1.3MM **Privately Held**
WEB: www.littlern.com
SIC: 2869 2819 4226 Industrial organic
chemicals; industrial inorganic chemicals;
special warehousing & storage

(G-1125)
MADGAR GENIS CORP
Also Called: Medkeff-Nye
131 Snyder Ave (44203-4007)
P.O. Box 287 (44203-0287)
PHONE..............................330 848-6950
Fax: 330 848-6954
Normand J Madgar, *President*

James Genis, *Vice Pres*
EMP: 5
SQ FT: 7,000
SALES (est): 786.8K **Privately Held**
WEB: www.medkeff-nye.com
SIC: 3565 Packaging machinery

(G-1126)
MAG RESOURCES LLC
90 16th St Sw Ste M (44203-7070)
PHONE..............................330 294-0494
Jeff Bechdel, *Accounts Mgr*
Joseph Giovanini, *Mng Member*
Michael Giovanini,
▲ EMP: 5
SQ FT: 12,000
SALES: 700K **Privately Held**
SIC: 2591 Drapery hardware & blinds &
shades; shade, curtain & drapery hard-
ware

(G-1127)
MAGIC CITY MACHINE INC
21 4th St Nw (44203-2503)
P.O. Box 488 (44203-0488)
PHONE..............................330 825-0048
Sandor Baksa, *President*
Michael A Stobaugh, *Corp Secy*
Vicki Stobaugh, *Manager*
EMP: 10
SQ FT: 11,000
SALES: 1.2MM **Privately Held**
WEB: www.magiccitymachine.com
SIC: 3599 Machine & other job shop work

(G-1128)
**MANUFCTRING SLTONS
BRBRTON INC**
374 5th St Nw (44203-2127)
PHONE..............................330 745-4539
Mark Bilinovich, *President*
EMP: 7
SALES: 500K **Privately Held**
SIC: 3549 Metalworking machinery

(G-1129)
**MAY LIN SILICONE PRODUCTS
INC**
955 Wooster Rd W (44203-7149)
P.O. Box 335 (44203-0335)
PHONE..............................330 825-9019
Fax: 330 825-6153
Linda Weaver, *President*
Dave Weaver, *Vice Pres*
EMP: 6 EST: 1958
SQ FT: 1,800
SALES: 500K **Privately Held**
WEB: www.may-lin.com
SIC: 3069 3053 Hard rubber & molded
rubber products; rubber hardware; gas-
kets, all materials; gaskets & sealing de-
vices

(G-1130)
**MEECH STTIC ELMINATORS
USA INC**
2915 Newpark Dr (44203-1049)
PHONE..............................330 564-2000
Fax: 330 564-2005
Matt Fyffe, *General Mgr*
Pat Breitenstine, *Finance Mgr*
Vincent Defilippo, *Natl Sales Mgr*
Kevin Lipely, *Sales Mgr*
Marcel Weems, *Regl Sales Mgr*
▲ EMP: 15
SQ FT: 20,000
SALES (est): 3.3MM **Privately Held**
WEB: www.meech.com
SIC: 3823 Industrial process measurement
equipment

(G-1131)
MITCHELL PLASTICS INC
130 31st St Nw (44203-7238)
PHONE..............................330 825-2461
Fax: 330 825-6862
Mitchell E Volk, *President*
Patti Black, *Controller*
Dan Parker, *Manager*
EMP: 22
SQ FT: 15,000

SALES (est): 4.4MM **Privately Held**
WEB: www.mpicase.com
SIC: 3069 3993 Laboratory sundries:
cases, covers, funnels, cups, etc.; signs &
advertising specialties

(G-1132)
**MODEL ENGINEERING
COMPANY**
610 E State St (44203-3707)
PHONE..............................330 644-3450
Eugene Sanders, *President*
Jeff Sanders, *Vice Pres*
EMP: 4
SQ FT: 5,000
SALES: 150K **Privately Held**
WEB: www.modelengineeringco.com
SIC: 3543 3999 Industrial patterns; mod-
els, general, except toy

(G-1133)
NEIDERT FABRICATING INC
712 Wooster Rd W (44203-2420)
PHONE..............................330 753-3331
Fax: 330 753-7583
Paul Neidert, *President*
Carol Neidert, *Admin Sec*
EMP: 8
SQ FT: 9,000
SALES (est): 1.1MM **Privately Held**
SIC: 3599 3441 Machine shop, jobbing &
repair; fabricated structural metal

(G-1134)
**NORTHCOAST PRFMCE & MCH
CO**
1190 Wooster Rd N (44203-1254)
PHONE..............................330 753-7333
Fax: 330 753-7347
James Sibbio, *Owner*
EMP: 3
SALES: 150K **Privately Held**
SIC: 3599 Industrial machinery

(G-1135)
OHIO PRECISION MOLDING INC
Also Called: Opm
122 E Tuscarawas Ave (44203-2628)
PHONE..............................330 745-9393
Fax: 330 745-0825
Bruce Vereecken, *President*
Joe Vereecken, *Vice Pres*
Glenn Witchey, *Vice Pres*
Melissa Garrett, *Office Mgr*
Karen Vereecken, *Shareholder*
▲ EMP: 30
SQ FT: 30,000
SALES (est): 7.6MM **Privately Held**
WEB: www.ohioprecisionmolding.com
SIC: 3089 Injection molding of plastics

(G-1136)
**OLSON SHEET METAL CNSTR
CO**
465 Glenn St (44203-1499)
PHONE..............................330 745-8225
Fax: 330 745-7087
John Sveda, *President*
Joanne Sveda, *Admin Sec*
EMP: 6
SALES: 250K **Privately Held**
SIC: 3441 Fabricated structural metal

(G-1137)
PARATUS SUPPLY INC
635 Wooster Rd W (44203-2440)
PHONE..............................330 745-3600
John Sesic, *General Mgr*
EMP: 6
SALES (est): 1.4MM **Privately Held**
SIC: 3563 Spraying & dusting equipment

(G-1138)
**PATHFINDER COMPUTER
SYSTEMS**
345 5th St Ne (44203-2863)
PHONE..............................330 928-1961
Rodney Starcher, *President*
Chuck Rainer, *Vice Pres*
EMP: 7
SALES (est): 705.7K **Privately Held**
WEB: www.pathfindercs.com
SIC: 7372 7371 Prepackaged software;
custom computer programming services

(G-1139)
**PLASTIC MOLD TECHNOLOGY
INC**
40 Stuver Pl (44203-2416)
PHONE..............................330 848-4921
Fax: 330 848-4922
Damir Petkovic, *President*
Robin Petkovic, *Corp Secy*
EMP: 8
SQ FT: 6,500
SALES (est): 1MM **Privately Held**
WEB: www.pmtmolds.com
SIC: 3544 Industrial molds

(G-1140)
PPG INDUSTRIES INC
Also Called: P P G Chemicals Group
4829 Fairland Rd (44203-3905)
PHONE..............................330 825-0831
Fax: 330 825-2199
Randy Brillhart, *Safety Mgr*
Larry Kopowski, *Engineer*
Carl E Johnson, *Manager*
Randy Brillart, *Manager*
EMP: 24
SQ FT: 306
SALES (corp-wide): 14.7B **Publicly Held**
WEB: www.ppg.com
SIC: 2851 Paints & allied products
PA: Ppg Industries, Inc.
1 Ppg Pl
Pittsburgh PA 15272
412 434-3131

(G-1141)
PPG INDUSTRIES INC
900 Columbia Ct 16th (44203)
PHONE..............................330 825-6328
Ted Ladd, *Branch Mgr*
EMP: 4
SALES (corp-wide): 14.7B **Publicly Held**
SIC: 3999 Barber & beauty shop equip-
ment
PA: Ppg Industries, Inc.
1 Ppg Pl
Pittsburgh PA 15272
412 434-3131

(G-1142)
PRAXAIR INC
4805 Fairland Rd (44203-3913)
PHONE..............................330 825-4449
David Corley, *Plant Mgr*
Dave Corly, *Manager*
Dave Corley, *Manager*
EMP: 6
SALES (corp-wide): 10.5B **Publicly Held**
SIC: 2813 Industrial gases
PA: Praxair, Inc.
10 Riverview Dr
Danbury CT 06810
203 837-2000

(G-1143)
**PRO GRAM ENGINEERING
CORP**
475 5th St Ne (44203-2754)
P.O. Box 472 (44203-0472)
PHONE..............................330 745-1004
Fax: 330 745-8844
Kenneth Anderson, *President*
Dadan Anderson, *Vice Pres*
EMP: 9
SQ FT: 5,500
SALES (est): 1.2MM **Privately Held**
WEB: www.pro-gram.com
SIC: 3714 Motor vehicle engines & parts

(G-1144)
Q MODEL INC
711 Wooster Rd W (44203-2444)
P.O. Box 129, Mogadore (44260-0129)
PHONE..............................330 673-0473
Fax: 330 673-0603
Todd Strohfus, *President*
Laverne Strohfus, *CFO*
Paul Proctor,
EMP: 30
SQ FT: 35,000
SALES (est): 7.1MM **Privately Held**
WEB: www.qmodel.com
SIC: 3469 3069 Patterns on metal;
molded rubber products

(G-1145)
REVLIS CORPORATION
Also Called: Revlon
2845 Newpark Dr (44203-1047)
PHONE..................330 535-2108
Hal Button, *Purch Mgr*
Brad Wehman, *Sales/Mktg Mgr*
EMP: 24
SQ FT: 10,000
SALES (corp-wide): 4.2MM **Privately Held**
SIC: 2816 Inorganic pigments
PA: Revlis Corporation
255 Huntington Ave
Akron OH 44306
330 535-2108

(G-1146)
RICHARDSON PUBLISHING COMPANY
Also Called: Barberton Herald
70 4th St Nw Ste 1 (44203-8283)
P.O. Box 830 (44203-0830)
PHONE..................330 753-1068
Fax: 330 753-1021
Dave Richardson, *President*
Cathy Robertson, *Vice Pres*
EMP: 13 EST: 1923
SALES: 650K **Privately Held**
WEB: www.barbertonherald.com
SIC: 2711 Newspapers: publishing only, not printed on site

(G-1147)
RISE N SHINE YARD SIGNS
606 Grandview Ave (44203-2941)
PHONE..................330 745-5868
Mike Beal, *Principal*
EMP: 3 EST: 2010
SALES (est): 160K **Privately Held**
SIC: 3993 Signs & advertising specialties

(G-1148)
S P Z MACHINE CO
2871 Newpark Dr (44203-1047)
PHONE..................330 848-3286
Fax: 330 848-3831
Peter Zarkovacki, *Owner*
David Scott Zarkovacki, *Vice Pres*
EMP: 8
SQ FT: 50,000
SALES (est): 857.3K **Privately Held**
WEB: www.spzmachine.net
SIC: 3599 Machine shop, jobbing & repair

(G-1149)
SPECIFIED STRUCTURES INC
643 Holmes Ave (44203-2181)
PHONE..................330 753-0693
Fax: 330 753-0675
Grant Senn, *President*
EMP: 8
SQ FT: 10,000
SALES: 1MM **Privately Held**
WEB: www.specifiedstructures.com
SIC: 2434 Wood kitchen cabinets

(G-1150)
STADVEC INC
Also Called: Essco Aircraft
579 W Tuscarawas Ave (44203-2521)
PHONE..................330 644-7724
Fax: 330 644-0886
Michael Stadvec, *President*
Marjorie Stadev, *COO*
Franca Stadvec, *CFO*
Eric Sandler, *Officer*
EMP: 3
SQ FT: 11,000
SALES (est): 1.4MM **Privately Held**
WEB: www.esscoaircraft.com
SIC: 5961 7389 2759 Books, mail order (except book clubs); packaging & labeling services; laminating service; commercial printing

(G-1151)
TAHOMA ENTERPRISES INC (PA)
255 Wooster Rd N (44203-2560)
PHONE..................330 745-9016
William P Herrington, *CEO*
Steven Strouse, *Managing Dir*
Warren Flathers, *Maint Mgr*
Charles Daugherty, *Opers Staff*

Marcia Berlin, *Manager*
EMP: 100
SALES (est): 34.4MM **Privately Held**
SIC: 3069 3089 5199 5162 Reclaimed rubber (reworked by manufacturing processes); plastic processing; foams & rubber; plastics products

(G-1152)
TAHOMA RUBBER & PLASTICS INC (HQ)
Also Called: Rondy & Co.
255 Wooster Rd N (44203-2560)
PHONE..................330 745-9016
Fax: 330 745-4886
William P Herrington, *CEO*
Steven Strouse, *Managing Dir*
Bob McGovern, *Plant Mgr*
Warren Flathers, *Maint Mgr*
Charles Daugherty, *Opers Staff*
▼ EMP: 100
SQ FT: 750,000
SALES (est): 25.1MM
SALES (corp-wide): 34.4MM **Privately Held**
WEB: www.rondy.net
SIC: 3069 3089 5199 5162 Reclaimed rubber (reworked by manufacturing processes); plastic processing; foams & rubber; plastics products
PA: Tahoma Enterprises, Inc.
255 Wooster Rd N
Barberton OH 44203
330 745-9016

(G-1153)
TENNEY TOOL & SUPPLY CO
973 Wooster Rd N (44203-1625)
PHONE..................330 666-2807
Fax: 330 745-6605
David Masa, *President*
Daniel Braun, *Vice Pres*
Donald Kepple, *Admin Sec*
EMP: 16 EST: 1947
SQ FT: 11,000
SALES (est): 3.2MM **Privately Held**
WEB: www.tenneytool.com
SIC: 5085 3599 Industrial tools; machine shop, jobbing & repair

(G-1154)
TERRA COMP TECHNOLOGY
449 4th St Nw (44203-2051)
PHONE..................330 745-8912
Fax: 330 745-8912
Terry Silvester, *Owner*
EMP: 5
SALES (est): 240K **Privately Held**
WEB: www.terracomptech.com
SIC: 3571 7378 Electronic computers; computers, digital, analog or hybrid; computer maintenance & repair; computer & data processing equipment repair/maintenance; computer peripheral equipment repair & maintenance

(G-1155)
TOMMY B MANUFACTURING INC
374 5th St Nw (44203-2127)
PHONE..................330 745-4539
Thomas F Bilinovich, *Principal*
EMP: 3 EST: 2012
SALES (est): 186.6K **Privately Held**
SIC: 3999 Manufacturing industries

(G-1156)
VILLAGE PLASTICS CO
Also Called: 3d Systems
100 16th St Sw (44203-7004)
PHONE..................330 753-0100
Fax: 330 753-6610
Kevin Gerstenslager, *Principal*
Judy Hanks, *Manager*
EMP: 8
SQ FT: 22,000
SALES (est): 1.4MM **Publicly Held**
SIC: 3544 Extrusion dies
PA: 3d Systems Corporation
333 Three D Systems Cir
Rock Hill SC 29730

(G-1157)
WRIGHT TOOL COMPANY
1 Wright Pl (44203-2798)
P.O. Box 512 (44203-0512)
PHONE..................330 848-0600
Fax: 330 848-0616
Richard Wright, *Ch of Bd*
Terry G Taylor, *President*
Patricia Taylor, *Vice Pres*
Brent Smith, *Plant Supt*
Debbie Looper, *Purch Mgr*
▲ EMP: 160 EST: 1927
SQ FT: 124,000
SALES (est): 59.4MM **Privately Held**
WEB: www.wrighttool.com
SIC: 3423 3462 Hand & edge tools; wrenches, hand tools; iron & steel forgings

Barnesville
Belmont County

(G-1158)
ART WORKS
119 E Pike St (43713-1539)
PHONE..................740 425-5765
Ann Hudson, *Owner*
Brad Hudson, *Owner*
EMP: 6
SALES (est): 380K **Privately Held**
SIC: 2396 Screen printing on fabric articles

(G-1159)
BUCKEYE STEEL INCORPORATED
607 Watt Ave (43713-1272)
P.O. Box 458 (43713-0458)
PHONE..................740 425-2306
Fax: 740 425-4174
Richard W Pryor, *President*
Douglas E Kriechbaum, *Vice Pres*
Theresa Wehr, *Bookkeeper*
EMP: 10
SQ FT: 34,000
SALES (est): 4MM **Privately Held**
SIC: 1791 3441 Structural steel erection; fabricated structural metal

(G-1160)
K & J MACHINE INC
326 Fairmont Ave (43713-9669)
PHONE..................740 425-3282
Fax: 740 425-3025
Homer Luyster, *President*
Martha L Luyster, *Vice Pres*
Sharon Lucas, *Admin Sec*
EMP: 17 EST: 1971
SQ FT: 3,300
SALES (est): 1.6MM **Privately Held**
SIC: 7699 3599 7692 Aircraft & heavy equipment repair services; machine shop, jobbing & repair; welding repair

(G-1161)
SUN SHINE AWARDS
36099 Bethesda Street Ext (43713-9619)
PHONE..................740 425-2504
Danny Kimble, *Owner*
EMP: 10
SALES (est): 420.8K **Privately Held**
WEB: www.sunshineawards.com
SIC: 5999 2395 Trophies & plaques; embroidery & art needlework

(G-1162)
W O HARDWOODS INC
58098 Wright Rd (43713-9540)
PHONE..................740 425-1588
Lowell Bahmer, *President*
EMP: 3 EST: 1986
SALES (est): 245K **Privately Held**
SIC: 2421 Sawmills & planing mills, general

Batavia
Clermont County

(G-1163)
A-1 FABRICATORS FINISHERS LLC
4220 Curliss Ln (45103-3276)
PHONE..................513 724-0383
Dwayne Prather, *VP Sls/Mktg*
Stacy Lanter, *Human Res Dir*
Jason Robinson, *Marketing Staff*
Dennis Doane, *Mng Member*
Jamie Doane,
EMP: 78
SQ FT: 80,000
SALES (est): 11MM **Privately Held**
SIC: 3441 Fabricated structural metal

(G-1164)
AUTO TEMP INC
Also Called: ATI
950 Kent Rd (45103-1738)
P.O. Box 631690, Cincinnati (45263-1690)
PHONE..................513 732-6969
Fax: 513 732-6990
Frank Lauch, *CEO*
Doug Fassler, *Vice Pres*
Matt Fassler, *Vice Pres*
Jim Elcook, *Opers Staff*
John Day, *Production*
◆ EMP: 155
SQ FT: 210,000
SALES (est): 28.2MM **Privately Held**
WEB: www.autotempinc.com
SIC: 3231 Tempered glass: made from purchased glass

(G-1165)
AVENUE FABRICATING INC
1281 Clough Pike (45103-2501)
PHONE..................513 752-1911
Fax: 513 752-0044
Gretchen Nichols, *President*
Adrian Nichols, *Vice Pres*
Lauren Nichols, *Vice Pres*
Robert Nichols, *Vice Pres*
Jeff Huseman, *Sr Project Mgr*
EMP: 41
SQ FT: 17,800
SALES (est): 16MM **Privately Held**
WEB: www.avenuefabricating.com
SIC: 3499 3441 Metal ladders; fabricated structural metal

(G-1166)
B C METALS INC
4484 Hartman Ln (45103-1905)
PHONE..................513 732-9644
Fax: 513 732-9660
Harold Gatts, *President*
Kathy Gatts, *Vice Pres*
EMP: 4
SQ FT: 8,500
SALES: 380K **Privately Held**
SIC: 3599 Machine & other job shop work

(G-1167)
BALTA TECHNOLOGY INC
4350 Batavia Rd (45103-3342)
PHONE..................513 724-0247
Andy Weidner, *President*
EMP: 4
SALES (est): 45K **Privately Held**
SIC: 3822 Auto controls regulating residntl & coml environmt & applncs

(G-1168)
BECKMAN ENVIRONMENTAL SVCS INC
Also Called: Besco
4259 Armstrong Blvd (45103-1697)
PHONE..................513 752-3570
Joan Beckman, *President*
John Beckman, *Vice Pres*
EMP: 12
SQ FT: 6,700
SALES (est): 3.7MM **Privately Held**
WEB: www.beckmanenvironmental.com
SIC: 3589 7699 Sewage treatment equipment; sewer cleaning & rodding

(G-1169)
BLACK MACHINING & TECHNOLOGY
4020 Bach Buxton Rd (45103-2525)
PHONE....................................513 752-8625
Fax: 513 943-6143
Frank Black, *President*
Stephanie Standring, *Corp Secy*
Margaret Lynn Black, *Vice Pres*
EMP: 10
SALES (est): 660K **Privately Held**
SIC: 3599 Machine shop, jobbing & repair

(G-1170)
CHALLENGE TARGETS
4101 Founders Blvd (45103-3616)
P.O. Box 75040, Fort Thomas KY (41075-0040)
PHONE....................................859 462-5851
Brad Brune, *Owner*
EMP: 4
SALES: 600K **Privately Held**
SIC: 3949 Targets, archery & rifle shooting

(G-1171)
CINCHEMPRO INC
Also Called: Cincinnati Chemical Processing
458 W Main St (45103-1712)
PHONE....................................513 724-6111
Fax: 513 732-1987
John Glass, *CEO*
George Bradley, *Plant Mgr*
Gary Starmack, *Plant Mgr*
Ron Huelsman, *Chief Mktg Ofcr*
Margie Corwin, *Executive*
EMP: 105
SQ FT: 22,000
SALES (est): 19.9MM **Privately Held**
WEB: www.cinchempro.com
SIC: 2899 Chemical preparations

(G-1172)
CINCINNATI MACHINES INC
4165 Half Acre Rd (45103-3247)
PHONE....................................513 536-2432
Kelly Benz, *Buyer*
Bob Lennish, *Controller*
David Shardelow, *Finance Mgr*
Nancy Fancher, *Accountant*
Randy Roth, *Marketing Staff*
▲ EMP: 900
SALES (est): 61.9MM **Privately Held**
WEB: www.cinmac.com
SIC: 3088 Plastics plumbing fixtures

(G-1173)
CLERMONT STEEL FABRICATORS LLC
2565 Old State Route 32 (45103-3205)
PHONE....................................513 732-6033
Robert Mampe, *CEO*
Ken Miller, *Vice Pres*
Ron Hill, *Plant Mgr*
Lisa Brann, *Financial Exec*
Bridget King, *Manager*
◆ EMP: 70
SQ FT: 144,000
SALES (est): 17.8MM **Privately Held**
WEB: www.clermontsteel.com
SIC: 3441 Fabricated structural metal

(G-1174)
CORE COMPOSITES CINCINNATI LLC
4174 Half Acre Rd (45103-3250)
PHONE....................................513 724-6111
John Glass, *Principal*
Paul Grisham, *Vice Pres*
Larry McKenna, *Plant Mgr*
Dorothy Roush, *Human Res Mgr*
EMP: 847
SALES (est): 24.6MM **Publicly Held**
SIC: 3089 Molding primary plastic
PA: Core Molding Technologies, Inc.
800 Manor Park Dr
Columbus OH 43228

(G-1175)
CURTISS-WRIGHT FLOW CONTROL
Also Called: Qualtech NP
750 Kent Rd (45103-1704)
PHONE....................................513 735-2538
Mark Chatham, *Branch Mgr*
EMP: 85

SALES (corp-wide): 2.1B **Publicly Held**
SIC: 3491 3443 3599 1799 Industrial valves; plate work for the nuclear industry; machine shop, jobbing & repair; diamond drilling & sawing
HQ: Curtiss-Wright Flow Control Service Corporation
2950 E Birch St
Brea CA 92821
714 982-1898

(G-1176)
D&D DESIGN CONCEPTS INC
Also Called: W.T.nickell Co.
4360 Winding Creek Blvd (45103-1729)
PHONE....................................513 752-2191
Fax: 513 752-2354
Rick Meyer, *President*
Ray Meyer, *President*
Jaime Kinkade, *Manager*
Dave Roat, *Manager*
Violet Rogers, *Admin Asst*
EMP: 10 EST: 1960
SQ FT: 8,000
SALES (est): 1MM **Privately Held**
WEB: www.wtnickell.com
SIC: 2759 3565 Labels & seals: printing; labeling machines, industrial

(G-1177)
DELTEC INCORPORATED
4230 Grissom Dr (45103-1669)
PHONE....................................513 732-0800
Fax: 513 732-0806
Jason Dugle, *President*
Chris Dugle, *Chairman*
Greg Cossman, *Vice Pres*
Jim Gordley, *Plant Mgr*
Steve Noel, *Manager*
EMP: 46
SQ FT: 42,000
SALES: 6.2MM **Privately Held**
WEB: www.deltec-inc.com
SIC: 3499 Aerosol valves, metal

(G-1178)
EAT MOORE CUPCAKES
1212 Forest Run Dr (45103-2554)
PHONE....................................513 713-8139
Jodye Moore, *Principal*
EMP: 4
SALES (est): 166.6K **Privately Held**
SIC: 2051 Bread, cake & related products

(G-1179)
EGER PRODUCTS INC
4226 Grissom Dr (45103-1669)
PHONE....................................513 735-1400
Scott McLarin, *Branch Mgr*
Dawn Watson, *Manager*
EMP: 40
SQ FT: 2,128
SALES (corp-wide): 28MM **Privately Held**
WEB: www.egerproducts.com
SIC: 3089 Plastic processing
PA: Eger Products, Inc.
1132 Ferris Rd
Amelia OH 45102
513 753-4200

(G-1180)
ELECTRODYNE COMPANY INC
4188 Taylor Rd (45103-9736)
P.O. Box 321 (45103-0321)
PHONE....................................513 732-2822
Fax: 513 732-6953
Scott Blume, *President*
Cathy Brinkman, *Treasurer*
Ken Koch, *Sales Mgr*
▲ EMP: 14
SQ FT: 22,000
SALES (est): 2.4MM **Privately Held**
WEB: www.edyne.com
SIC: 3264 Magnets, permanent: ceramic or ferrite

(G-1181)
ELECTROFUEL INDUSTRIES INC
77 N Depot Rd (45103-2951)
PHONE....................................937 783-2846
Fax: 937 735-0236
Jerry Rearick, *President*
EMP: 3
SQ FT: 24,000

SALES: 280K **Privately Held**
SIC: 3545 Cutting tools for machine tools

(G-1182)
ELLIS & WATTS GLOBAL INDS INC
4400 Glen Willow Lake Ln (45103-2379)
PHONE....................................513 752-9000
Gina Cottrell, *President*
Diane Hoover, *Executive*
EMP: 18
SALES (est): 4.1MM
SALES (corp-wide): 223.6B **Publicly Held**
SIC: 3585 Refrigeration & heating equipment
HQ: Mitek Industries, Inc.
16023 Swinly Rdg
Chesterfield MO 63017
314 434-1200

(G-1183)
ELLIS & WATTS INTL LLC
4400 Glen Willow Lake Ln (45103-2379)
PHONE....................................513 752-9000
Fax: 513 752-4545
Richard D Porco, *President*
Richard Porco, *COO*
Kevin Morris, *QC Mgr*
Paul Behnke, *Engineer*
John Getz, *Engineer*
▲ EMP: 3
SQ FT: 172,000
SALES (est): 1.2MM **Privately Held**
WEB: www.elliswatts.com
SIC: 3585 3713 3625 3564 Air conditioning units, complete: domestic or industrial; dehumidifiers electric, except portable; heating equipment, complete; van bodies; relays & industrial controls; blowers & fans; fabricated plate work (boiler shop); mobile homes

(G-1184)
ENGINEERED MBL SOLUTIONS INC
Also Called: E M S
4350 Batavia Rd (45103-3342)
PHONE....................................513 724-0247
Bryce Johnson, *Vice Pres*
An Nguyen, *Vice Pres*
Lee Ton, *Engineer*
EMP: 15
SALES: 950K **Privately Held**
SIC: 3715 Truck trailers

(G-1185)
FOSTER MANUFACTURING
4283 Armstrong Blvd (45103-1697)
P.O. Box 458 (45103-0458)
PHONE....................................513 735-9770
Gary Foster, *President*
EMP: 4
SQ FT: 1,824
SALES (est): 348.4K **Privately Held**
WEB: www.bowholder.com
SIC: 3949 Archery equipment, general

(G-1186)
FOSTER PRODUCTS INC
Also Called: Mobile Office Solutions
4283 Armstrong Blvd (45103-1697)
P.O. Box 458 (45103-0458)
PHONE....................................513 735-9770
Gary D Foster, *President*
EMP: 4
SQ FT: 7,300
SALES (est): 420K **Privately Held**
SIC: 3441 Fabricated structural metal

(G-1187)
FREEMAN ENCLOSURE SYSTEMS LLC
4160 Half Acre Rd (45103-3250)
PHONE....................................877 441-8555
Dale Freeman, *President*
EMP: 210
SQ FT: 120,000
SALES: 28.3MM
SALES (corp-wide): 695.9MM **Publicly Held**
SIC: 3621 Motors & generators

HQ: Ies Infrastructure Solutions, Llc
800 Nave Rd Se
Massillon OH 44646
330 830-3500

(G-1188)
FREEMAN SCHWABE MACHINERY LLC
Also Called: F S
4064 Clough Woods Dr (45103-2586)
PHONE....................................513 947-2888
Greg Defisher, *CEO*
David Lees, *Vice Pres*
Lawrence Mears, *Vice Pres*
Scott Clifford, *Controller*
▲ EMP: 30
SALES (est): 7.7MM **Privately Held**
WEB: www.freemanschwabe.com
SIC: 3559 Automotive related machinery

(G-1189)
GUTTER TOPPER LTD
4111 Founders Blvd (45103-2534)
P.O. Box 349, Amelia (45102-0349)
PHONE....................................513 797-5800
Anthony Iannelli, *Partner*
Phyllis Iannelli, *Partner*
Jeff Bott, *Financial Exec*
Tony Iannelli, *Technology*
Michelle Geraci, *Executive Asst*
EMP: 7
SALES: 5MM **Privately Held**
SIC: 3444 5033 1521 Metal roofing & roof drainage equipment; roofing, siding & insulation; single-family housing construction

(G-1190)
HAMILTON FABRICATORS INC
4008 Borman Dr (45103-1681)
PHONE....................................513 735-7773
Fax: 513 735-2251
Ken Murry, *President*
Jeffrey Gileen, *Vice Pres*
EMP: 23
SALES (est): 3.1MM **Privately Held**
SIC: 3499 Safes & vaults, metal

(G-1191)
HARBISONWALKER INTL INC
4065a Clough Woods Dr (45103-2587)
PHONE....................................513 576-6240
Annette Kreiner, *Branch Mgr*
EMP: 22
SALES (corp-wide): 923MM **Privately Held**
WEB: www.hwr.com
SIC: 3255 Clay refractories
HQ: Harbisonwalker International, Inc.
1305 Cherrington Pkwy # 100
Moon Township PA 15108
412 375-6600

(G-1192)
HUHTAMAKI INC
1985 James E Sauls Sr Dr (45103-3246)
PHONE....................................513 201-1525
EMP: 320
SALES (corp-wide): 2.9B **Privately Held**
SIC: 2656 3565 Sanitary food containers; ice cream containers: made from purchased material; labeling machines, industrial
HQ: Huhtamaki, Inc.
9201 Packaging Dr
De Soto KS 66018
913 583-3025

(G-1193)
J O Y ALUMINUM PRODUCTS INC
4111 Founders Blvd (45103-2534)
P.O. Box 349, Amelia (45102-0349)
PHONE....................................513 797-1100
Fax: 513 797-1111
Anthony Iannelli, *President*
Mike Moore, *Accountant*
EMP: 15
SALES (est): 1.5MM **Privately Held**
WEB: www.guttertopper.com
SIC: 3444 Gutters, sheet metal

▲ = Import ▼=Export
◆ =Import/Export

(G-1194)
JEFF WYLER CHEVROLET INC
Also Called: Jeff Wyler Mazda
1117 State Route 32 (45103-2380)
P.O. Box 345 (45103-0345)
PHONE.............................513 752-3447
Fax: 513 753-2290
Jeffrey L Wyler, *President*
David Wyler, *Vice Pres*
Melissa Loney, *Finance Mgr*
James Simon, *Mktg Dir*
Mike Brees, *Manager*
EMP: 300
SQ FT: 90,000
SALES (est): 71.8MM **Privately Held**
SIC: 5511 7539 7538 3714 Automobiles,
new & used; automotive repair shops;
general automotive repair shops; motor
vehicle parts & accessories; top & body
repair & paint shops

(G-1195)
KABLER FARMS
4529 Elmwood Rd (45103-9495)
PHONE.............................513 732-0501
Beverly Kabler, *Owner*
Randall Kabler, *Owner*
EMP: 3
SALES (est): 160K **Privately Held**
SIC: 3949 7999 Hunting equipment; zoo-
logical garden, commercial

(G-1196)
KENNEDY CATALOGS LLC
4177 Knollview Ct (45103-2557)
PHONE.............................513 753-1518
Kennedy Stuart, *Manager*
Stuart Kennedy,
Julie Kennedy,
EMP: 3 **EST:** 2000
SALES (est): 141.3K **Privately Held**
SIC: 2741 Catalogs: publishing only, not
printed on site

(G-1197)
KENNETH HICKMAN CO
4266 Tranquility Ct (45103-3152)
PHONE.............................513 348-0016
Kenneth Hickman, *Owner*
EMP: 15
SALES (est): 1MM **Privately Held**
SIC: 3571 Electronic computers

(G-1198)
KEY RESIN COMPANY (PA)
4050 Clough Woods Dr (45103-2586)
PHONE.............................513 943-4225
Fax: 513 576-4425
Jeffrey Cain, *President*
Eric Borglum, *Vice Pres*
David Coleman, *Purch Agent*
Travis Barkey, *Research*
Joe Larger, *Finance Mgr*
▲ **EMP:** 16
SQ FT: 18,000
SALES (est): 5.4MM **Privately Held**
WEB: www.keyresin.com
SIC: 2899 Chemical preparations

(G-1199)
KIPPS GRAVEL COMPANY INC
4987 State Route 222 (45103-9782)
PHONE.............................513 732-1024
Fax: 513 732-1026
Melvin M Kipp, *President*
Judy King, *Admin Sec*
EMP: 12 **EST:** 1967
SQ FT: 5,000
SALES (est): 1.7MM **Privately Held**
SIC: 1442 1794 Gravel mining; excavation
work

(G-1200)
L & F LAUCH LLC
950 Kent Rd (45103-1738)
PHONE.............................513 732-5805
Frank Lauch, *Vice Pres*
Matt Fassler, *Vice Pres*
EMP: 6
SALES: 100K **Privately Held**
WEB: www.mootechnologies.com
SIC: 2023 2086 Concentrated milk; bottled
& canned soft drinks

(G-1201)
L A EXPRESS (PA)
1148 Marian Dr (45103-2378)
PHONE.............................513 752-6999
Mike Mueller, *Principal*
EMP: 6
SALES (est): 923.7K **Privately Held**
SIC: 3589 Car washing machinery

(G-1202)
LOUIS G FREEMAN CO
4064 Clough Woods Dr (45103-2586)
PHONE.............................513 263-1720
Louis Freeman, *Principal*
EMP: 3 **EST:** 2010
SALES (est): 201.5K **Privately Held**
SIC: 3089 Plastics products

(G-1203)
MET FAB FABRICATION AND MCH
2974 Waitensburg Pike (45103)
P.O. Box 363 (45103-0363)
PHONE.............................513 724-3715
Fax: 513 724-1336
Rod Stouder, *President*
Debbie Stouder, *Treasurer*
Debra Stouder, *Treasurer*
EMP: 6
SQ FT: 14,000
SALES: 460K **Privately Held**
WEB: www.met-fabinc.com
SIC: 3535 3599 Conveyors & conveying
equipment; machine & other job shop
work

(G-1204)
MI 2009 INC
4165 Half Acre Rd (45103-3247)
PHONE.............................513 536-2000
Dennis Smith, *CEO*
Kyle Seymour, *Div Sub Head*
Hugh C O'Donnell, *Senior VP*
David J Bertke, *Vice Pres*
Hugh C Donnell, *Vice Pres*
EMP: 3350 **EST:** 1884
SQ FT: 75,000
SALES (est): 30.6K **Privately Held**
WEB: www.milacron.com
SIC: 3559 Plastics working machinery

(G-1205)
MIDWEST MOLD & TEXTURE CORP
4270 Armstrong Blvd (45103-1670)
PHONE.............................513 732-1300
Fax: 513 732-3125
Katsumi Kawaguchi, *President*
Yoji Tatematsu, *Chairman*
Jerry Boehm, *Manager*
Susumu Kitsuta, *Manager*
Marico Cummings, *Admin Sec*
▲ **EMP:** 38
SQ FT: 20,000
SALES: 11.2MM
SALES (corp-wide): 41.5MM **Privately
Held**
WEB: www.mmtcorp.com
SIC: 3544 Forms (molds), for foundry &
plastics working machinery
PA: Tatematsu Mold Works Co.,Ltd.
27-1, Okudaosawacho
Inazawa AIC 492-8
587 326-281

(G-1206)
MILACRON LLC
4165 Half Acre Rd (45103-3247)
PHONE.............................513 536-2000
Tom Goeke, *CEO*
Dean Roberts, *President*
Ron Krisanda, *COO*
Mark Dixon, *Vice Pres*
John C Francy, *Vice Pres*
▲ **EMP:** 38
SALES (est): 7.6MM
SALES (corp-wide): 1.1B **Publicly Held**
SIC: 3089 Plastic processing
HQ: Milacron Llc
10200 Alliance Rd Ste 200
Blue Ash OH 45242
513 487-5000

(G-1207)
MILACRON MARKETING COMPANY LLC (DH)
Also Called: Wear Technology
4165 Half Acre Rd (45103-3247)
Rural Route 3010 Disney St, Cincinnati
(45209)
PHONE.............................513 536-2000
Tom Goeke, *CEO*
Jerry Newman, *Buyer*
Ben Waldman, *Engineer*
John Francy, *CFO*
Mark Wright, *Asst Treas*
◆ **EMP:** 22
SQ FT: 275,000
SALES (est): 702.7MM
SALES (corp-wide): 1.1B **Publicly Held**
SIC: 3541 Machine tools, metal cutting
type
HQ: Milacron Llc
10200 Alliance Rd Ste 200
Blue Ash OH 45242
513 487-5000

(G-1208)
MILACRON PLAS TECH GROUP LLC (DH)
4165 Half Acre Rd (45103-3247)
PHONE.............................513 536-2000
Tom Goeke, *CEO*
Dave Lawrence, *President*
Ron Krisanda, *COO*
Mark Dixon, *Vice Pres*
Richard A Oleary, *Vice Pres*
▲ **EMP:** 156
SALES: 235.4MM
SALES (corp-wide): 1.1B **Publicly Held**
SIC: 3544 Forms (molds), for foundry &
plastics working machinery
HQ: Milacron Llc
10200 Alliance Rd Ste 200
Blue Ash OH 45242
513 487-5000

(G-1209)
MOO TECHNOLOGIES INC
950 Kent Rd (45103-1738)
PHONE.............................513 732-5805
Frank Lauch, *Vice Pres*
Jackie Vann, *Opers Staff*
Gregg S Montgomery, *VP Sls/Mktg*
EMP: 5
SALES (est): 368.1K **Privately Held**
SIC: 2023 Dry, condensed, evaporated
dairy products

(G-1210)
MULTI-COLOR AUSTRALIA LLC
4053 Clough Woods Dr (45103-2587)
PHONE.............................513 381-1480
Nigel A Vinecombe, *CEO*
Mary T Fetch, *Vice Pres*
Sharon E Birkett, *CFO*
Dave McGraw, *Credit Mgr*
EMP: 388
SALES: 13.6MM
SALES (corp-wide): 810.7MM **Publicly
Held**
SIC: 2754 2752 2759 Commercial print-
ing, gravure; commercial printing, litho-
graphic; advertising literature: printing;
laser printing
PA: Multi-Color Corporation
4053 Clough Woods Dr
Batavia OH 45103
513 381-1480

(G-1211)
MULTI-COLOR CORPORATION (PA)
4053 Clough Woods Dr (45103-2587)
PHONE.............................513 381-1480
Fax: 513 381-2813
Nigel A Vinecombe, *President*
Vadis A Rodato, *President*
David G Buse, *COO*
Al Dinkins, *Plant Mgr*
Mike Julian, *Plant Mgr*
▲ **EMP:** 16
SQ FT: 277,730

SALES: 870.8MM **Publicly Held**
WEB: www.multicolorcorp.com
SIC: 2759 2679 2672 Labels & seals:
printing; labels, paper: made from purchased material; labels (unprinted),
gummed: made from purchased materials

(G-1212)
MULTI-COLOR CORPORATION
4053 Clough Woods Dr (45103-2587)
PHONE.............................513 943-0080
Ken Pizzuco, *Branch Mgr*
EMP: 60
SALES (corp-wide): 870.8MM **Publicly
Held**
WEB: www.multicolorcorp.com
SIC: 2759 2671 2754 Labels & seals:
printing; packaging paper & plastics film,
coated & laminated; commercial printing,
gravure
PA: Multi-Color Corporation
4053 Clough Woods Dr
Batavia OH 45103
513 381-1480

(G-1213)
NEWACT INC
2084 James E Sauls Sr Dr (45103-3259)
PHONE.............................513 321-5177
Fax: 513 321-5246
Rodney J Newman, *President*
Ennes Ireton III, *Vice Pres*
Tom Vale, *VP Mktg*
EMP: 17
SQ FT: 16,000
SALES (est): 9.2MM **Privately Held**
WEB: www.newactinc.com
SIC: 5085 3643 3069 Industrial supplies;
electric connectors; molded rubber prod-
ucts

(G-1214)
ON DISPLAY LLC
1250 Clough Pike (45103-2502)
PHONE.............................513 841-1600
Fax: 513 841-1622
Dave Downey, *President*
Ken Tabet, *Mktg Dir*
Brenda Schmidt, *Executive*
Donald Miller,
EMP: 20
SQ FT: 35,000
SALES (est): 4.5MM **Privately Held**
WEB: www.ondisplay.net
SIC: 3999 Advertising display products

(G-1215)
ORBIT MANUFACTURING INC
4291 Armstrong Blvd (45103-1697)
P.O. Box 144 (45103-0144)
PHONE.............................513 732-6097
Fax: 513 732-1295
James S Paul, *President*
Kathy Paul, *Corp Secy*
EMP: 25
SQ FT: 10,000
SALES (est): 4.4MM **Privately Held**
WEB: www.orbitman.com
SIC: 3089 Plastic processing

(G-1216)
PLASTIKOS CORPORATION
Also Called: Multi-Form Plastics
700 Kent Rd (45103-1704)
P.O. Box 138 (45103-0138)
PHONE.............................513 732-0961
Fax: 513 732-0906
Richard Bates, *Chairman*
EMP: 22
SQ FT: 48,000
SALES (est): 4.6MM **Privately Held**
SIC: 3089 Thermoformed finished plastic
products

(G-1217)
PRECISE PALLETS LLC
4211 Curliss Ln (45103-3221)
PHONE.............................513 560-8236
David Eyles, *Principal*
EMP: 4
SALES (est): 275.1K **Privately Held**
SIC: 2448 Pallets, wood & wood with metal

(G-1218)
PROCOAT PAINTING INC
601 W Main St Unit B (45103-1705)
PHONE.....................................513 735-2500
Steve Hickey, *Principal*
EMP: 6 EST: 2014
SALES (est): 270.3K **Privately Held**
SIC: 1721 3479 Painting & paper hanging;
   painting of metal products

(G-1219)
ROCKWELL AUTOMATION INC
1195 Clough Pike (45103-2307)
PHONE.....................................513 943-1145
Fax: 513 943-7438
Timothy Coverley, *Marketing Mgr*
Matthew Girgash, *Manager*
EMP: 20 **Publicly Held**
SIC: 3625 Relays & industrial controls
PA: Rockwell Automation, Inc.
   1201 S 2nd St
   Milwaukee WI 53204

(G-1220)
**ROSS TMBER HARVSTG FOR
MGT INC**
5300 Rapp Ln (45103-9403)
PHONE.....................................513 383-6933
Earnie Ross III, *President*
EMP: 4
SALES (est): 215.1K **Privately Held**
SIC: 2411 Logging

(G-1221)
S & K METAL POLSG & BUFFING
4194 Taylor Rd (45103-9736)
PHONE.....................................513 732-6662
Fax: 513 732-6663
Aldena Sons, *President*
Everett J Sons, *Vice Pres*
EMP: 7
SQ FT: 17,500
SALES (est): 707.7K **Privately Held**
SIC: 3471 Buffing for the trade; polishing,
   metals or formed products; finishing, met-
   als or formed products

(G-1222)
SAVOR SEASONINGS LLC
4292 Armstrong Blvd (45103-1600)
PHONE.....................................513 732-2333
Jeff Reed, *Opers Staff*
Jeff Higgins,
Shelly Higgins,
EMP: 5
SQ FT: 10,000
SALES (est): 709.9K **Privately Held**
SIC: 2099 Seasonings & spices

(G-1223)
SMOOTHIE-LICIOUS
1325 Quail Ridge Rd (45103-9537)
PHONE.....................................513 742-2260
Chris Zerhusen, *Administration*
EMP: 3
SALES (est): 132.8K **Privately Held**
SIC: 2037 Frozen fruits & vegetables

(G-1224)
SOUTHERN OHIO MFG INC
1147 Clough Pike (45103-2307)
PHONE.....................................513 943-2555
Fax: 513 943-2559
Dave Rechtin, *President*
EMP: 21
SQ FT: 13,500
SALES: 1.5MM **Privately Held**
WEB: www.sommfginc.com
SIC: 3599 Machine shop, jobbing & repair

(G-1225)
**SPECTRA-TECH
MANUFACTURING INC**
4013 Borman Dr (45103-1684)
PHONE.....................................513 735-9300
Fax: 513 735-9310
Scott Reilman, *President*
Jason Jasper, *Vice Pres*
Shirley Reilman, *Vice Pres*
Craig Wilson, *Vice Pres*
▲ EMP: 47
SQ FT: 18,000

SALES (est): 21.4MM **Privately Held**
WEB: www.spectratechmfg.com
SIC: 3613 Panelboards & distribution
   boards, electric

(G-1226)
**STRAIGHT CREEK BUSHMAN
LLC**
202 E Main St (45103-2905)
PHONE.....................................513 732-1698
Robert Stearns, *Principal*
EMP: 3 EST: 2013
SALES (est): 161.3K **Privately Held**
SIC: 1221 Bituminous coal & lignite-sur-
   face mining

(G-1227)
**SUPERIOR STEEL SERVICE
LLC**
2760 Old State Route 32 (45103-3210)
PHONE.....................................513 724-0437
Jeffrey A Brewsaugh, *Mng Member*
Debbie Jones, *Manager*
Lisa Brewsaugh, *Administration*
EMP: 15
SQ FT: 12,000
SALES (est): 3.6MM **Privately Held**
SIC: 3449 Bars, concrete reinforcing: fabri-
   cated steel

(G-1228)
**TIPTON ENVIRONMENTAL INTL
INC**
4446 State Route 132 (45103-1229)
PHONE.....................................513 735-2777
Fax: 513 735-1485
Fred Tipton, *President*
Scott Tipton, *Vice Pres*
Carol Tipton, *Purchasing*
EMP: 10
SQ FT: 3,600
SALES: 4MM **Privately Held**
WEB: www.tiptonenv.com
SIC: 3589 Water treatment equipment, in-
   dustrial

(G-1229)
TSP INC
2009 Glenn Pkwy (45103-1676)
PHONE.....................................513 732-8900
Fax: 513 732-6988
J Stuart Newman, *President*
David Hatz, *Opers Staff*
Tootie Hardman, *Office Mgr*
EMP: 25
SQ FT: 30,000
SALES (est): 18MM **Privately Held**
WEB: www.tspinc.com
SIC: 3479 3089 3081 Painting, coating &
   hot dipping; windows, plastic; thermo-
   formed finished plastic products; lenses,
   except optical: plastic; plastic film & sheet

(G-1230)
UNILOY MILACRON INC
4165 Half Acre Rd (45103-3247)
PHONE.....................................513 487-5000
Fax: 513 536-3489
John C Francy, *President*
Scotty Landers, *Opers Mgr*
Ron ABT, *Engineer*
John T Schmidt, *Project Engr*
Dave Esposito, *Electrical Engi*
◆ EMP: 52
SALES (est): 13.1MM
SALES (corp-wide): 1.1B **Publicly Held**
SIC: 2821 Plastics materials & resins
HQ: Milacron Llc
   10200 Alliance Rd Ste 200
   Blue Ash OH 45242
   513 487-5000

(G-1231)
**UNIVERSAL PACKG SYSTEMS
INC**
Also Called: Paklab
5055 State Route 276 (45103-1211)
PHONE.....................................513 732-2000
Richard Burton, *Branch Mgr*
EMP: 388

SALES (corp-wide): 139.7MM **Privately
Held**
SIC: 2844 7389 3565 2671 Cosmetic
   preparations; packaging & labeling services; bottling machinery: filling, capping,
   labeling; plastic film, coated or laminated
   for packaging
PA: Universal Packaging Systems, Inc.
   6080 Jericho Tpke
   Commack NY 11725
   631 543-2277

(G-1232)
**UNIVERSAL PACKG SYSTEMS
INC**
5069 State Route 276 (45103-1211)
PHONE.....................................513 735-4777
Rick Zellen, *Site Mgr*
EMP: 40
SALES (corp-wide): 139.7MM **Privately
Held**
SIC: 2844 7389 3565 2671 Cosmetic
   preparations; packaging & labeling serv-
   ices; bottling machinery: filling, capping,
   labeling; plastic film, coated or laminated
   for packaging
PA: Universal Packaging Systems, Inc.
   6080 Jericho Tpke
   Commack NY 11725
   631 543-2277

(G-1233)
WILSON SEAT COMPANY INC
199 Foundry Ave (45103-2606)
P.O. Box 323 (45103-0323)
PHONE.....................................513 732-2460
Fax: 513 732-3944
Michael A Wilson, *President*
Mark Wilson, *Vice Pres*
Minor E Wilson II, *Marketing Staff*
EMP: 25
SQ FT: 33,000
SALES (est): 4MM **Privately Held**
SIC: 3713 3993 Truck bodies & parts;
   signs, not made in custom sign painting
   shops

(G-1234)
**X-TREME SHOOTING
PRODUCTS LLC**
2008 Glenn Pkwy (45103-1620)
P.O. Box 829, Milford (45150-0829)
PHONE.....................................513 313-3464
C Thomas Myers, *President*
EMP: 5
SALES: 200K **Privately Held**
SIC: 3484 Small arms

(G-1235)
XOMOX CORPORATION
4576 Helmsdale Ct (45103-4000)
PHONE.....................................513 947-1200
J T Williams, *Branch Mgr*
EMP: 25
SALES (corp-wide): 2.7B **Publicly Held**
SIC: 3491 Industrial valves
HQ: Xomox Corporation
   4526 Res Frest Dr Ste 400
   The Woodlands TX 77381
   936 271-6500

Bath
Summit County

(G-1236)
ETS SOLUTION NA LLC
3900 Ira Rd (44210)
P.O. Box 1225 (44210-1225)
PHONE.....................................330 666-8696
Mark Davey, *Owner*
Connie Dague, *Principal*
EMP: 8
SALES (est): 570K **Privately Held**
SIC: 3823 Industrial instrmnts msrmnt dis-
   play/control process variable

(G-1237)
ETS SOLUTIONS USA LLC
3900 Ira Rd (44210)
P.O. Box 1225 (44210-1225)
PHONE.....................................330 666-8696
James H Rothwell, *President*
Mark Davey, *Principal*

Jim H Rothwell, *Principal*
Karen Parker, *Info Tech Mgr*
▲ EMP: 5
SALES (est): 51.5K **Privately Held**
SIC: 3829 Measuring & controlling devices

(G-1238)
LUND EQUIPMENT CO INC
2400 N Clvlnd Mssllon Rd (44210)
P.O. Box 213 (44210-0213)
PHONE.....................................330 659-4800
Fax: 330 659-9347
John Skeel, *President*
Rebecca Skeel, *Regional Mgr*
Raymond Smiley, *Vice Pres*
Rachel Conrad, *Manager*
EMP: 20
SQ FT: 5,000
SALES (est): 3.2MM **Privately Held**
WEB: www.lundkeycab.com
SIC: 3444 Sheet metalwork

(G-1239)
**MOLLARD CONDUCTING
BATONS INC**
Also Called: Lancio
2236 N Clvlnd Mssllon Rd (44210)
P.O. Box 178 (44210-0178)
PHONE.....................................330 659-7081
Robert Mollard, *President*
Kelly Kennedy, *Manager*
EMP: 13
SALES: 654.5K **Privately Held**
SIC: 2499 Carved & turned wood

(G-1240)
**WARMUS AND ASSOCIATES
INC**
Also Called: Smith Carl E Cnslting Engneers
2324 N Clvlnd Mssllon Rd (44210)
PHONE.....................................330 659-4440
Fax: 330 659-9234
Alfred T Warmus, *President*
Roy P Stype III, *Vice Pres*
Brain Warmus, *Admin Sec*
EMP: 17
SQ FT: 7,000
SALES (est): 2.2MM **Privately Held**
SIC: 8711 3441 5063 Consulting engi-
   neer; tower sections, radio & television
   transmission; electrical apparatus &
   equipment

Bay Village
Cuyahoga County

(G-1241)
**ACOUSTICAL PUBLICATIONS
INC**
Also Called: Sound and Vibration
27101 E Oviatt Rd (44140-3307)
P.O. Box 40416 (44140-0416)
PHONE.....................................440 835-0101
Fax: 440 835-9303
Jack K Mowry, *President*
Lois Mowry, *Corp Secy*
EMP: 5 EST: 1966
SQ FT: 900
SALES (est): 692.3K **Privately Held**
SIC: 2721 Magazines: publishing only, not
   printed on site

(G-1242)
BAY WEST PRODUCTS
31008 Walker Rd (44140-1405)
PHONE.....................................440 835-1991
Wayne Smith, *Owner*
EMP: 5 EST: 1978
SQ FT: 3,200
SALES (est): 290K **Privately Held**
SIC: 3599 Machine shop, jobbing & repair

(G-1243)
RESERVE INDUSTRIES INC
386 Lake Park Dr (44140-2963)
PHONE.....................................440 871-2796
John Megyimori, *President*
John Ruminsky, *Vice Pres*
EMP: 32
SQ FT: 26,000
SALES (est): 3.8MM **Privately Held**
SIC: 3089 3544 Injection molding of plas-
   tics; special dies & tools

▲ = Import ▼=Export
◆ =Import/Export

(G-1244)
ROBERT TUNEBERG
Also Called: Villager Newspaper, The
27016 Knickerbocker Rd # 1 (44140-2386)
PHONE................................440 899-9277
Fax: 440 899-1929
Robert Tuneberg, *Owner*
EMP: 4
SALES (est): 190K **Privately Held**
SIC: 2711 Newspapers, publishing & printing

(G-1245)
SCOTTS COMPANY LLC
28315 W Oviatt Rd (44140-2112)
PHONE................................440 899-9339
Jeff Sutherland, *Branch Mgr*
EMP: 40
SALES (corp-wide): 2.8B **Publicly Held**
WEB: www.scottscompany.com
SIC: 2873 Fertilizers: natural (organic), except compost
HQ: The Scotts Company Llc
14111 Scottslawn Rd
Marysville OH 43040
937 644-3729

(G-1246)
SWEET MOBILE CUPCAKERY
428 Walmar Rd (44140-1518)
PHONE................................440 465-7333
EMP: 3
SALES (est): 94.5K **Privately Held**
SIC: 2051 Bread, cake & related products

Beach City
Stark County

(G-1247)
DANIEL MEENAN
Also Called: Corell's Potato Chips
614 Pine St Nw (44608-9580)
P.O. Box 255 (44608-0255)
PHONE................................330 756-2818
Dan Meenan, *Owner*
EMP: 5 EST: 1939
SQ FT: 4,000
SALES: 300K **Privately Held**
SIC: 2096 2099 Potato chips & other potato-based snacks; food preparations

(G-1248)
MERIDIAN INDUSTRIES INC
Also Called: Kleen Test Products
9901 Chestnut Ridge Rd Nw (44608-9417)
PHONE................................330 359-5809
Fax: 330 359-5912
Pete Martin, *Plant Mgr*
Peter Morton, *Manager*
Pam Herbert, *Manager*
EMP: 50
SQ FT: 15,000
SALES (corp-wide): 374.1MM **Privately Held**
WEB: www.meridiancompanies.com
SIC: 2299 2844 Pads, fiber: henequen, sisal, istle; toilet preparations
PA: Meridian Industries, Inc.
735 N Water St Ste 630
Milwaukee WI 53202
414 224-0610

(G-1249)
MILLER CORE 2 INC
9823 Chestnut Ridge Rd Nw (44608-9480)
PHONE................................330 359-0500
Joseph Miller, *President*
Reuben Miller, *Vice Pres*
Richard Basnett, *Sales Staff*
Sue Duffield, *Office Mgr*
Linda Miller, *Admin Sec*
EMP: 8
SALES (est): 1.2MM **Privately Held**
SIC: 3567 Core baking & mold drying ovens

(G-1250)
PROGRESSIVE FOAM TECH INC
6753 Chestnut Ridge Rd Nw (44608-9464)
PHONE................................330 756-3200
Fax: 330 756-3206
Patrick Culpepper, *President*
Richard Wilson, *Vice Pres*

Kenny Albrecht, *Prdtn Mgr*
Sherry Barnhouse, *Production*
Fred Gyer, *Purch Mgr*
▲ EMP: 120
SQ FT: 100,000
SALES (est): 31.3MM **Privately Held**
WEB: www.fullback.com
SIC: 2821 Polystyrene resins

(G-1251)
STARK TRUSS COMPANY INC
Also Called: Stark Truss Beach City Lumber
6855 Chestnut Ridge Rd Nw (44608-9462)
PHONE................................330 756-3050
Fax: 330 756-2255
Jay Dickey, *Branch Mgr*
EMP: 32
SALES (corp-wide): 230.5MM **Privately Held**
WEB: www.starktruss.com
SIC: 2439 2421 Structural wood members; sawmills & planing mills, general
PA: Stark Truss Company, Inc.
109 Miles Ave Sw
Canton OH 44710
330 478-2100

Beachwood
Cuyahoga County

(G-1252)
6062 HOLDINGS LLC
Also Called: Sure To Grow
23366 Commerce Park 100b (44122-5850)
PHONE................................216 359-9005
Eric Senders, *Mng Member*
Cary Senders,
EMP: 3
SALES (est): 296.5K **Privately Held**
SIC: 3295 Minerals, ground or treated

(G-1253)
ALERIS INTERNATIONAL INC (HQ)
25825 Science Park Dr # 400
(44122-7392)
PHONE................................216 910-3400
Fax: 216 910-3650
Sean M Stack, *CEO*
Roeland Baan, *President*
Lawrence W Stranghoener, *Principal*
C Newton, *Sr Corp Ofcr*
Christopher R Clegg, *Exec VP*
▲ EMP: 39
SQ FT: 43,000
SALES (est): 1.4B **Privately Held**
SIC: 3355 3354 Bars, rolled, aluminum; aluminum extruded products

(G-1254)
ALERIS RECYCLING INC
25825 Science Park Dr # 400
(44122-7392)
PHONE................................216 910-3400
EMP: 3
SALES (est): 147.1K **Privately Held**
SIC: 3554 Paper industries machinery

(G-1255)
ALERIS RM INC
25825 Science Park Dr # 400
(44122-7323)
PHONE................................216 910-3400
EMP: 3
SALES (est): 148.2K **Privately Held**
SIC: 3355 Aluminum rolling & drawing

(G-1256)
ALERIS ROLLED PRODUCTS INC (DH)
25825 Science Park Dr # 400
(44122-7323)
PHONE................................216 910-3400
Sean M Stack, *CEO*
EMP: 8 EST: 2010
SALES (est): 309.3MM **Privately Held**
SIC: 3341 Secondary nonferrous metals

(G-1257)
AMPERSAND INTERNATIONAL INC
23775 Commerce Park (44122-5836)
PHONE................................216 831-3500

Fax: 216 831-5699
Ilya Vetrov, *President*
Chad Simmerson, *Accounts Exec*
EMP: 4
SALES (est): 652.9K **Privately Held**
WEB: www.ampersand-intl.com
SIC: 7372 Prepackaged software

(G-1258)
AUFBACKGROUNDSCREENING COM
26101 Village Ln (44122-8522)
PHONE................................216 831-4113
Marvin Goldfarb, *Principal*
EMP: 4
SALES (est): 159.4K **Privately Held**
SIC: 2899

(G-1259)
BIP PRINTING SOLUTIONS LLC
23645 Mercantile Rd Ste C (44122-5936)
PHONE................................216 832-5673
Nancy McGraw, *President*
EMP: 10
SQ FT: 13,000
SALES (est): 687.1K **Privately Held**
SIC: 2732 2789 Books: printing & binding; pamphlets: printing & binding, not published on site; trade binding services

(G-1260)
CIPAR INC (HQ)
3601 Green Rd Ste 308 (44122-5719)
PHONE................................216 910-1700
Morris Wheeler, *President*
EMP: 4
SALES (est): 420.7K **Privately Held**
SIC: 3563 Spraying & dusting equipment

(G-1261)
CLEVELAND JEWISH PUBL CO FDN
23800 Commerce Park (44122-5828)
PHONE................................216 454-8300
Barry Chesler, *Principal*
EMP: 3
SALES: 40.9K **Privately Held**
SIC: 2711 Newspapers

(G-1262)
COHESANT INC (PA)
3601 Green Rd Ste 308 (44122-5719)
PHONE................................216 910-1700
Fax: 216 910-1790
Morton A Cohen, *Ch of Bd*
Morris H Wheeler, *President*
J Stewart Nance, *President*
Steve Cohen, *Vice Pres*
David Wasserstrom, *Vice Pres*
EMP: 45
SALES (est): 20.9MM **Privately Held**
WEB: www.cohesant.com
SIC: 3563 3559 3586 Spraying outfits: metals, paints & chemicals (compressor); paint making machinery; measuring & dispensing pumps

(G-1263)
COMMONWEALTH ALUMINUM MTLS LLC
25825 Science Park Dr # 400
(44122-7323)
PHONE................................216 910-3400
EMP: 6
SALES (est): 1.1MM **Privately Held**
SIC: 3555 Printing trades machinery

(G-1264)
CONCEPT XXI INC
23600 Merc Rd Ste 101 (44122)
PHONE................................216 831-2121
Fax: 216 831-2444
Irving Kaplan, *President*
Irving Sayers, *Info Tech Dir*
Jaime Rogers, *Director*
EMP: 18
SQ FT: 2,000
SALES (est): 1.2MM **Privately Held**
WEB: www.cxxi.com
SIC: 7379 7372 Computer related consulting services; prepackaged software

(G-1265)
CORCADENCE INC
26701 Bernwood Rd (44122-7135)
PHONE................................216 702-6371
Eugene Jung, *Principal*
Subbakrishna Shankar, *COO*
EMP: 3
SALES (est): 271.6K **Privately Held**
SIC: 3829 7389 Thermometers, including digital: clinical;

(G-1266)
DIALOGUE HOUSE ASSOCIATES INC
23400 Mercantile Rd Ste 2 (44122-5948)
PHONE................................216 342-5170
Jonathon Progoff, *President*
EMP: 4
SQ FT: 1,200
SALES (est): 175K **Privately Held**
WEB: www.intensivejournal.org
SIC: 8299 2731 Personal development school; religious school; books: publishing only

(G-1267)
EATON CORPORATION
Also Called: Fluid Power Plant
1000 Eaton Blvd (44122-6058)
PHONE................................440 523-5000
Fax: 216 694-2006
Ken Narod, *District Mgr*
Ajay Ahuja, *COO*
Astrid Mozes, *Senior VP*
Scott Weisel, *Assistant VP*
William W Blausey, *Vice Pres*
EMP: 500 **Privately Held**
WEB: www.eaton.com
SIC: 3714 3824 Motor vehicle electrical equipment; mechanical & electromechanical counters & devices
HQ: Eaton Corporation
1000 Eaton Blvd
Cleveland OH 44122
216 523-5000

(G-1268)
EATON CORPORATION
Eastlake Office
1000 Eaton Blvd (44122-6058)
PHONE................................216 523-5000
Robert Decaro, *Project Mgr*
Manuel Prieto, *Project Mgr*
Keith Cozart, *Purch Mgr*
Bernie Beier, *Engineer*
Sell Craig, *Engineer*
EMP: 260 **Privately Held**
WEB: www.eaton.com
SIC: 3714 5084 Hydraulic fluid power pumps for auto steering mechanism; hydraulic systems equipment & supplies
HQ: Eaton Corporation
1000 Eaton Blvd
Cleveland OH 44122
216 523-5000

(G-1269)
EATON ELECTRICAL INC
1000 Eaton Blvd (44122-6058)
PHONE................................216 433-0616
Fax: 216 433-0545
Patrick X Donovan, *Principal*
Sam Bahr, *Buyer*
Deidrea Otts, *Director*
EMP: 15
SALES (est): 3.3MM **Privately Held**
SIC: 3559 Special industry machinery

(G-1270)
EATON LEASING CORPORATION (DH)
1000 Eaton Blvd (44122-6058)
PHONE................................216 382-2292
Richard Fearon, *President*
Billie Rawot, *Vice Pres*
Judy Griffiths, *Manager*
Timothy Brandt, *Director*
Nancy Morek, *Administration*
EMP: 6
SQ FT: 1,200

SALES (est): 47.3MM **Privately Held**
SIC: **7359** 3612 3594 3593 Equipment
rental & leasing; transformers, except
electric; fluid power pumps & motors; fluid
power cylinders & actuators; speed
changers, drives & gears; turbines & turbine generator sets
HQ: Eaton Corporation
1000 Eaton Blvd
Cleveland OH 44122
216 523-5000

(G-1271)
ENVISION RADIO MII
3733 Park East Dr Ste 222 (44122-4334)
PHONE...........................216 831-3761
Danno Wolkoss, *Owner*
Melissa Bachtel, *Marketing Mgr*
Hannah Rosenthal, *Marketing Staff*
Ryan Verardi, *Manager*
EMP: 12
SALES (est): 1.5MM **Privately Held**
WEB: www.envisionradio.com
SIC: **3663** Radio receiver networks

(G-1272)
GLOBAL FURNISHINGS INC
3659 Green Rd Ste 203 (44122-5715)
PHONE...........................216 595-0901
Colleen Porche, *President*
EMP: 3
SALES (est): 834.4K **Privately Held**
SIC: **2531** Public building & related furni-
ture

(G-1273)
GODIVA CHOCOLATIER INC
26300 Cedar Rd Ste 1035 (44122-1179)
PHONE...........................216 831-9414
Keeley Jividen, *Manager*
EMP: 24 **Privately Held**
WEB: www.godiva.com
SIC: **2066** Chocolate & cocoa products
HQ: Godiva Chocolatier, Inc.
333 W 34th St Fl 6
New York NY 10001
212 984-5900

(G-1274)
ITL LLC
Also Called: Industrial Timber and Lbr LLC
23925 Commerce Park (44122-5821)
PHONE...........................216 831-3140
Al Garceau, *Vice Pres*
Dave Allegretto, *Sales Executive*
Larry Evans,
Rich Craxton, *Administration*
EMP: 325
SALES (est): 8.3MM **Privately Held**
SIC: **2426** Lumber, hardwood dimension
HQ: Northwest Hardwoods, Inc.
820 A St Ste 500
Tacoma WA 98402

(G-1275)
JMC STEEL GROUP
3201 Entp Pkwy Ste 150 (44122)
PHONE...........................216 910-3700
Frank A Riddick III, *CEO*
Barry Zekelman, *CEO*
David W Seeger, *President*
Michael P McNamara Jr, *Vice Pres*
Michael E Mechley, *Vice Pres*
EMP: 34 EST: 2010
SALES (est): 17.1MM **Privately Held**
SIC: **3317** Steel pipe & tubes

(G-1276)
KIRTLAND CAPITAL PARTNERS
LP (PA)
Also Called: K C P
3201 Entp Pkwy Ste 200 (44122)
PHONE...........................216 593-0100
Fax: 216 593-0240
Corrie Menary, *Partner*
John Nestor, *Principal*
◆ EMP: 22
SQ FT: 4,031
SALES (est): 237.5MM **Privately Held**
SIC: **5051** 3312 3498 3494 Metals serv-
ice centers & offices; tubes, steel & iron;
fabricated pipe & fittings; valves & pipe fit-
tings; fluid power valves & hose fittings;
steel pipe & tubes

(G-1277)
MAKERGEAR LLC
23632 Merc Rd Unit G (44122)
PHONE...........................216 765-0030
Richard Pollack, *Mng Member*
EMP: 25
SALES (est): 2.8MM **Privately Held**
SIC: **3999** Education aids, devices & sup-
plies

(G-1278)
MCM IND CO INC (PA)
Also Called: McM Industries
22901 Millcreek Blvd # 250 (44122-5728)
PHONE...........................216 292-4506
Fax: 216 292-2180
Gloria Reljanovic, *CEO*
Michael Reljanovic, *President*
Jeff Ochmann, *Controller*
Josh Dalley, *Sales Mgr*
◆ EMP: 12
SQ FT: 1,000
SALES (est): 6.5MM **Privately Held**
SIC: **3496** Miscellaneous fabricated wire
products

(G-1279)
MILES PK VNTIAN BLIND SHDS
MFG
Also Called: Miles Park Window Treatments
23880 Commerce Park # 100
(44122-5830)
PHONE...........................216 239-0850
Fax: 216 581-7250
Robert M Bernstein, *President*
Bonnie Bernstein, *Treasurer*
EMP: 3 EST: 1936
SQ FT: 4,000
SALES (est): 454.6K **Privately Held**
SIC: **2591** 5719 7699 Venetian blinds;
window shades; venetian blinds; window
shades; venetian blind repair shop

(G-1280)
MILICOM LLC
23307 Commerce Park (44122-5810)
PHONE...........................216 765-8875
Shawn Naticchioni, *Buyer*
Alex Tenenbaum, *CFO*
James Harris,
EMP: 5
SALES (est): 500K **Privately Held**
SIC: **3669** Intercommunication systems,
electric

(G-1281)
MIM SOFTWARE INC (PA)
25800 Science Park Dr # 180
(44122-7311)
PHONE...........................216 896-9798
Dennis Nelson, *President*
Jerimy Brockway, *President*
Pete Simmelink, *COO*
Pete Zimmelink, *COO*
Alexandra Jorgensen, *Counsel*
EMP: 49
SALES (est): 16.3MM **Privately Held**
WEB: www.mimvista.com
SIC: **7372** Application computer software

(G-1282)
MK GLOBAL ENTERPRISES
LLC
23980 Chagrin Blvd # 204 (44122-5548)
PHONE...........................440 823-0081
Michael Krasnyansky,
EMP: 4
SQ FT: 2,000
SALES (est): 343.7K **Privately Held**
SIC: **3541** Machine tool replacement & re-
pair parts, metal cutting types

(G-1283)
NATIONAL BIOLOGICAL CORP
23700 Mercantile Rd (44122-5900)
PHONE...........................216 831-0600
Fax: 216 425-9700
Kenneth Oif, *President*
Michael Kaufman, *Vice Pres*
David Richmond, *Opers Mgr*
Lynn Keller, *Engineer*
Patti Palmer, *Controller*
▲ EMP: 50
SQ FT: 36,000

SALES (est): 9.3MM **Privately Held**
WEB: www.natbiocorp.com
SIC: **3841** 3648 Surgical & medical instru-
ments; ultraviolet lamp fixtures

(G-1284)
NICHOLS ALUMINUM-ALABAMA
LLC
25825 Science Park Dr # 400
(44122-7392)
PHONE...........................256 353-1550
Sean M Stack, *CEO*
Derrick Holtz, *Manager*
EMP: 130
SALES (est): 20.8MM **Privately Held**
SIC: **3353** Aluminum sheet, plate & foil
HQ: Uwa Acquisition Co.
397 Black Hollow Rd
Rockwood TN 37854
865 354-3626

(G-1285)
NOVACARE INC
24400 Highpoint Rd Ste 10 (44122-6027)
PHONE...........................216 704-4817
George Shamp, *President*
Margaret Shamp, *Vice Pres*
EMP: 3
SQ FT: 4,800
SALES (est): 270K **Privately Held**
SIC: **3842** 5999 7991 Limbs, artificial; ar-
tificial limbs; physical fitness facilities

(G-1286)
OHIO CLLBRTIVE LRNG SLTONS
INC (PA)
Also Called: Smart Solutions
24700 Chagrin Blvd # 104 (44122-5647)
PHONE...........................216 595-5289
Anand Julka, *President*
Griffith Beck, *Accounts Mgr*
Jonathan Pittman, *Manager*
▲ EMP: 50
SQ FT: 6,000
SALES (est): 15MM **Privately Held**
WEB: www.smartsolutionsonline.com
SIC: **7372** 8741 Business oriented com-
puter software; business management

(G-1287)
OMNOVA SOLUTIONS INC (PA)
25435 Harvard Rd (44122-6201)
PHONE...........................216 682-7000
Fax: 330 869-4227
William R Seelbach, *Ch of Bd*
Anne P Noonan, *President*
Jay T Austin, *Senior VP*
James C Lemay, *Senior VP*
Paul F Desantis, *CFO*
◆ EMP: 140 EST: 1952
SALES: 759.9MM **Publicly Held**
WEB: www.omnova.com
SIC: **2819** 2211 3069 3081 Industrial in-
organic chemicals; decorative trim & spe-
cialty fabrics, including twist weave;
roofing, membrane rubber; unsupported
plastics film & sheet; plastic film & sheet;
vinyl film & sheet

(G-1288)
OMNOVA WALLCOVERING USA
INC (HQ)
25435 Harvard Rd (44122-6201)
PHONE...........................216 682-7000
Kevin Mc Mullin, *CEO*
Micheal Hix, *CFO*
EMP: 5
SALES (est): 6.5MM
SALES (corp-wide): 759.9MM **Publicly
Held**
SIC: **2819** Industrial inorganic chemicals
PA: Omnova Solutions Inc.
25435 Harvard Rd
Beachwood OH 44122
216 682-7000

(G-1289)
ONE WISH LLC
Also Called: Audimute Soundproofing &
Medic
23945 Mercantile Rd Ste H (44122-5924)
PHONE...........................800 505-6883
Heidi Sweeney, *Marketing Staff*
Mitchell Zlotnik,
Amy Zlotnik,

EMP: 18
SQ FT: 15,000
SALES: 4MM **Privately Held**
WEB: www.medicbatteries.com
SIC: **5063** 5999 8742 1742 Batteries;
batteries, non-automotive; marketing consulting services; acoustical & insulation
work; acoustical & ceiling work; building
materials, except block or brick; concrete;
acoustical suspension systems, metal

(G-1290)
PFIZER INC
2000 Auburn Dr Ste 200 (44122-4328)
PHONE...........................216 591-0642
Andrea Maxwell, *Branch Mgr*
Monica Sturgis, *Manager*
Tonya D Brown, *Coordinator*
EMP: 60
SALES (corp-wide): 52.8B **Publicly Held**
WEB: www.pfizer.com
SIC: **2834** Pharmaceutical preparations
PA: Pfizer Inc.
235 E 42nd St
New York NY 10017
212 733-2323

(G-1291)
PROSTATE THERANOSTICS
LLC
2532 Fairwood Ct (44122-1765)
PHONE...........................216 595-1968
Zheng-Rong Lu, *Partner*
Hui Zhu, *Partner*
Todd Kaneshiro, *Principal*
EMP: 3
SALES (est): 200.4K **Privately Held**
SIC: **2835** In vitro diagnostics; in vivo diag-
nostics

(G-1292)
REAL ALLOY HOLDING INC
(HQ)
3700 Park East Dr Ste 300 (44122-4399)
PHONE...........................216 755-8800
Terry Hogan, *President*
Cris Garisek, *Treasurer*
◆ EMP: 100
SQ FT: 3,200
SALES: 1.3B
SALES (corp-wide): 1.1B **Publicly Held**
SIC: **3341** 3313 3334 Secondary nonfer-
rous metals; ferromanganese, not made
in blast furnaces; pigs, aluminum
PA: Real Industry, Inc.
15301 Ventura Blvd # 400
Sherman Oaks CA 91403
805 435-1255

(G-1293)
REAL ALLOY RECYCLING INC
(DH)
3700 Park East Dr Ste 300 (44122-4399)
PHONE...........................216 755-8900
Terry Hogan, *President*
Meg Gray, *Project Mgr*
Michael Hobey, *CFO*
EMP: 20
SQ FT: 7,000
SALES (est): 343.5MM
SALES (corp-wide): 1.1B **Publicly Held**
SIC: **3341** Secondary nonferrous metals
HQ: Real Alloy Holding, Inc.
3700 Park East Dr Ste 300
Beachwood OH 44122
216 755-8800

(G-1294)
REAL ALLOY SPECIALTY
PRODUCTS (DH)
3700 Park East Dr Ste 300 (44122-4399)
PHONE...........................216 755-8836
Fax: 216 459-1077
Terry Hogan, *President*
Michael Hobey, *CFO*
Chet Cudzilo, *Controller*
Sally Miller, *Manager*
EMP: 159
SQ FT: 36,500
SALES (est): 237.7MM
SALES (corp-wide): 1.1B **Publicly Held**
WEB: www.alumitechinc.com
SIC: **3355** Aluminum rolling & drawing;
slugs, aluminum

HQ: Real Alloy Holding, Inc.
3700 Park East Dr Ste 300
Beachwood OH 44122
216 755-8800

(G-1295)
REAL ALLOY SPECIFICATION INC (DH)
3700 Park East Dr Ste 300 (44122-4399)
P.O. Box 466, Wabash IN (46992-0466)
PHONE...................................260 563-7461
Terry Hogan, *CEO*
Steven J Demetriou, *Chairman*
Michael Hobey, *CFO*
Jason Saragin, *Director*
▲ EMP: 86
SALES (est): 39.5MM
SALES (corp-wide): 1.1B **Publicly Held**
SIC: 3334 Pigs, aluminum
HQ: Real Alloy Holding, Inc.
3700 Park East Dr Ste 300
Beachwood OH 44122
216 755-8800

(G-1296)
RELIABLE WHEELCHAIR TRANS
28899 Harvard Rd (44122-4741)
PHONE...................................216 390-3999
Lapetha Ruffin, *Principal*
EMP: 3
SALES (est): 202.9K **Privately Held**
SIC: 3842 Wheelchairs

(G-1297)
RSI COMPANY (PA)
Also Called: Worthington
24050 Commerce Park # 200 (44122-5833)
PHONE...................................216 360-9800
Fax: 216 451-9376
Steve Sords, *President*
Paul Suda, *Engineer*
Robert Sords, *CFO*
▼ EMP: 19
SQ FT: 60,000
SALES (est): 3.5MM **Privately Held**
WEB: www.rsicomp.com
SIC: 3559 3585 Recycling machinery; refrigeration & heating equipment

(G-1298)
SIATA DS INC (PA)
24665 Greenwich Ln (44122-1650)
PHONE...................................216 503-7200
Naum Simkhovich, *President*
Leible Simkhovich, *Vice Pres*
▲ EMP: 3
SALES (est): 407.6K **Privately Held**
SIC: 3444 Pipe, sheet metal

(G-1299)
SINGER PRESS
23500 Mercantile Rd Ste A (44122-5927)
PHONE...................................216 595-9400
Andrew Press, *Principal*
EMP: 4 EST: 2007
SALES (est): 313.1K **Privately Held**
SIC: 2741 Miscellaneous publishing

(G-1300)
THE CLEVELAND JEWISH PUBL CO
23880 Commerce Park Ste 1 (44122-5830)
PHONE...................................216 454-8300
Rob Certner, *Principal*
EMP: 9
SALES: 39.4K **Privately Held**
SIC: 2711 Newspapers

(G-1301)
THE EUCLID CHEMICAL COMPANY
3735 Green Rd (44122-5705)
PHONE...................................216 292-5000
EMP: 11
SALES (corp-wide): 4.8B **Publicly Held**
SIC: 2891 Adhesives & sealants
HQ: The Euclid Chemical Company
19218 Redwood Rd
Cleveland OH 44110
800 321-7628

(G-1302)
TRAPEZE SOFTWARE GROUP INC
23215 Commerce Park # 200 (44122-5803)
PHONE...................................905 629-8727
EMP: 3
SALES (corp-wide): 2.1B **Privately Held**
SIC: 7372 Prepackaged software
HQ: Trapeze Software Group, Inc.
5265 Rockwell Dr Ne
Cedar Rapids IA 52402
319 743-1000

(G-1303)
TREMCO INCORPORATED (HQ)
3735 Green Rd (44122-5730)
PHONE...................................216 292-5000
Fax: 216 765-6716
Jeffrey L Korach, *CEO*
Randall J Korach, *President*
Chuck Houk, *Division Pres*
Deryl Kratzer, *Division Pres*
Moorman Scott, *Division Pres*
◆ EMP: 300
SQ FT: 93,000
SALES (est): 508.2MM
SALES (corp-wide): 4.8B **Publicly Held**
WEB: www.tremcoinc.com
SIC: 2891 2952 1761 1752 Sealants; caulking compounds; adhesives; epoxy adhesives; roofing materials; coating compounds, tar; asphalt saturated board; roofing contractor; floor laying & floor work; paints & allied products; specialty cleaning, polishes & sanitation goods
PA: Rpm International Inc.
2628 Pearl Rd
Medina OH 44256
330 273-5090

(G-1304)
UVISIR INC
23600 Merc Rd Ste 102 (44122)
PHONE...................................216 374-9376
Guilin Mao, *President*
EMP: 3
SALES (est): 200K **Privately Held**
SIC: 3827 Optical instruments & lenses

(G-1305)
WALTER H DRANE CO INC
23811 Chagrin Blvd # 344 (44122-5525)
PHONE...................................216 514-1022
Fax: 216 752-7935
William Kenneweg, *President*
Michael Kelly, *Vice Pres*
Karen Kelly, *CFO*
Marie Skory-Ingalls, *Senior Editor*
EMP: 8 EST: 1955
SALES (est): 560K **Privately Held**
WEB: www.walterdrane.com
SIC: 2741 Technical manual & paper publishing

Beallsville
Monroe County

(G-1306)
A REED EXCAVATING LLC
52912 State Route 145 (43716-9359)
PHONE...................................740 391-4985
Adam Reed, *CEO*
Meghan Williamson, *Administration*
EMP: 9 EST: 2014
SALES (est): 412.1K **Privately Held**
SIC: 3531 Plows: construction, excavating & grading

(G-1307)
AMERICAN ENERGY CORPORATION
43521 Mayhugh Hill Rd (43716-9641)
PHONE...................................740 926-2430
Fax: 740 926-9138
Murray Ryant, *Principal*
▲ EMP: 485
SALES (est): 40.1MM **Privately Held**
SIC: 1241 1222 Coal mining services; bituminous coal-underground mining

(G-1308)
DONALD E DORNON
44592 Game Ridge Rd (43716-9318)
PHONE...................................740 926-9144
Donald E Dornon, *Principal*
EMP: 6
SALES (est): 993.4K **Privately Held**
SIC: 3531 Backhoes

Beaver
Pike County

(G-1309)
A&E MACHINE & FABRICATION INC (PA)
384 State Route 335 (45613-8000)
PHONE...................................740 820-4701
Arthur Doll, *Vice Pres*
EMP: 13
SALES: 500K **Privately Held**
SIC: 3499 Fabricated metal products

(G-1310)
BEAVER WOOD PRODUCTS
190 Buck Hollow Rd (45613)
P.O. Box 404 (45613-0404)
PHONE...................................740 226-6211
Fax: 740 226-9022
Walter Thornsberry, *Partner*
Rick Thornsberry, *Partner*
EMP: 25
SALES (est): 3.4MM **Privately Held**
SIC: 2421 2436 2435 2426 Sawmills & planing mills, general; softwood veneer & plywood; hardwood veneer & plywood; hardwood dimension & flooring mills

(G-1311)
RAMONA SOUTHWORTH
Also Called: Southworth Wood Products
2882 Adams Rd (45613-9031)
PHONE...................................740 226-8202
Ramona Southworth, *Owner*
EMP: 3
SALES: 600K **Privately Held**
SIC: 2421 Sawmills & planing mills, general

(G-1312)
WAVERLY TOOL CO LTD
2596 Glade Rd (45613-9613)
PHONE...................................740 988-4831
Fax: 740 988-4831
Roger Wiseman, *Partner*
Gary Miller, *Partner*
EMP: 4
SQ FT: 4,000
SALES (est): 310K **Privately Held**
SIC: 3544 Special dies & tools

(G-1313)
WISEMAN BROS FABG & STL LTD
2598 Glade Rd (45613-9613)
P.O. Box 307 (45613-0307)
PHONE...................................740 988-5121
Fax: 740 988-2024
Shane Wiseman,
Derek Wiseman,
EMP: 10 EST: 1995
SQ FT: 8,000
SALES (est): 2.2MM **Privately Held**
SIC: 3441 Fabricated structural metal

Beavercreek
Greene County

(G-1314)
A C HADLEY - PRINTING INC
Also Called: Hadley Printing
1530 Marsetta Dr (45432-2733)
PHONE...................................937 426-0952
Fax: 937 426-1455
Nancy Hadley, *President*
Arthur Hadley, *Vice Pres*
Scott Hadley, *Vice Pres*
Michael Hadley, *Treasurer*
EMP: 6 EST: 1959
SQ FT: 4,800
SALES: 450K **Privately Held**
SIC: 2396 2759 Automotive & apparel trimmings; thermography

(G-1315)
A SERVICE GLASS INC
1363 N Fairfield Rd (45432-2693)
PHONE...................................937 426-4920
Fax: 937 426-4532
Donald T Sullivan, *President*
Donald J Sullivan, *President*
Glenn Sullivan, *Corp Secy*
William C Sullivan, *Vice Pres*
Mark Porumb, *Manager*
EMP: 15 EST: 1959
SQ FT: 8,000
SALES (est): 1.5MM **Privately Held**
WEB: www.aserviceglass.com
SIC: 5231 3231 1793 5039 Glass; doors, glass; made from purchased glass; glass & glazing work; glass construction materials; automotive glass replacement shops

(G-1316)
ADVANT-E CORPORATION (PA)
2434 Esquire Dr (45431-2573)
PHONE...................................937 429-4288
Fax: 937 429-4309
Jason K Wadzinski, *Ch of Bd*
James E Lesch, *CFO*
Jason Boone, *Accounting Dir*
EMP: 14 EST: 1994
SQ FT: 19,000
SALES: 10.7MM **Publicly Held**
WEB: www.advant-e.com
SIC: 7372 7375 Prepackaged software; information retrieval services

(G-1317)
ANALOG BRIDGE INC
2897 Kant Pl (45431-8507)
PHONE...................................937 901-4832
Stephen Adams, *CEO*
Gregg Steinhauser, *President*
David Novak, *Vice Pres*
EMP: 3
SALES (est): 212.5K **Privately Held**
WEB: www.analogbridge.com
SIC: 3571 Electronic computers

(G-1318)
ASSISTED PATROL LLC
2130 Hedge Gate Blvd (45431-3909)
PHONE...................................937 369-0080
David Gasper, *Principal*
EMP: 3
SALES (est): 262.4K **Privately Held**
SIC: 7372 Prepackaged software; business oriented computer software

(G-1319)
ASTRO INDUSTRIES INC
4403 Dayton Xenia Rd (45432-1805)
PHONE...................................937 429-5900
Fax: 937 429-4054
Kailash Mehta, *President*
Nina Joshi, *President*
Thomas Stansell, *Purch Dir*
CHI Nguyen, *Design Engr*
Duane Ratcliff, *Sls & Mktg Exec*
EMP: 24 EST: 1967
SQ FT: 24,000
SALES (est): 14MM **Privately Held**
WEB: www.astro-ind.com
SIC: 3357 3678 3679 5063 Nonferrous wiredrawing & insulating; communication wire; coaxial cable, nonferrous; fiber optic cable (insulated); electronic connectors; electronic circuits; wiring devices; wire & cable; apparatus wire & cordage; building wire & cable

(G-1320)
AT&T GOVERNMENT SOLUTIONS INC
2940 Presidential Dr # 390 (45324-6762)
PHONE...................................937 306-3030
Kirk Dunker, *General Mgr*
David Browder, *Director*
EMP: 75
SQ FT: 1,500
SALES (corp-wide): 163.7B **Publicly Held**
SIC: 3829 8742 Measuring & controlling devices; management consulting services

GEOGRAPHIC

HQ: At&T Government Solutions, Inc.
1900 Gallows Rd Ste 105
Vienna VA 22182
703 506-5000

(G-1321)
BALL AEROSPACE & TECH CORP
2875 Presidential Dr # 180 (45324-6769)
PHONE..................................937 429-5005
Julie Maske, *Purch Agent*
Julie Burneka, *Purchasing*
Sean Barrett, *Engineer*
Tim Lawrence, *Engineer*
John Prikkel, *Engineer*
EMP: 235
SALES (corp-wide): 9B **Publicly Held**
SIC: 3812 Navigational systems & instruments
HQ: Ball Aerospace & Technologies Corporation
1600 Commerce St
Boulder CO 80301

(G-1322)
CARBIDE PROBES INC
1328 Research Park Dr (45432-2897)
PHONE..................................937 490-2994
Fax: 937 429-2103
Dan Shellabarger, *President*
Tom Terry, *General Mgr*
Roberta Lee Shellabarger, *Vice Pres*
Jason Black, *QC Mgr*
Cheryl Terry, *Treasurer*
EMP: 28
SQ FT: 10,000
SALES (est): 3MM **Privately Held**
WEB: www.carbideprobes.com
SIC: 3545 Machine tool attachments & accessories

(G-1323)
CHROME & SPEED CYCLE LLC
3490 Dayton Xenia Rd C (45432-2769)
PHONE..................................937 429-5656
Tom Rogers, *Principal*
EMP: 3 EST: 2012
SALES (est): 205.6K **Privately Held**
SIC: 3471 Finishing, metals or formed products

(G-1324)
CIRCUITS ALIVE LLC
2408 Pine Knott Dr (45431-2683)
PHONE..................................937 427-4141
Anthony J Pombo, *Principal*
EMP: 3
SALES (est): 340.6K **Privately Held**
SIC: 3679 Electronic circuits

(G-1325)
CISCO SYSTEMS INC
2661 Commons Blvd Ste 133
(45431-3704)
PHONE..................................937 427-4264
Helen Yep, *Principal*
EMP: 691
SALES (corp-wide): 49.2B **Publicly Held**
SIC: 3577 7379 Data conversion equipment, media-to-media: computer;
PA: Cisco Systems, Inc.
170 W Tasman Dr
San Jose CA 95134
408 526-4000

(G-1326)
COMMUNICATION CONCEPTS INC
508 Mill Stone Dr (45434-5840)
PHONE..................................937 426-8600
Fax: 937 429-3811
Rodger L Southworth, *President*
Marlis Southworth, *Corp Secy*
EMP: 6
SALES: 500K **Privately Held**
WEB: www.communication-concepts.com
SIC: 5961 3674 Mail order house; semiconductors & related devices

(G-1327)
CREATIVE ELECTRONIC DESIGN
2565 Celia Dr (45434-6815)
PHONE..................................937 256-5106
David Johnson, *President*

EMP: 3
SALES (est): 247.7K **Privately Held**
SIC: 5065 5063 3625 Electronic parts & equipment; electrical supplies; relays & industrial controls

(G-1328)
CREEK SMOOTHIES LLC
3195 Dayton Xenia Rd (45434-6390)
PHONE..................................937 429-1519
Creek Smoothies, *Principal*
EMP: 4
SALES (est): 311.2K **Privately Held**
SIC: 2037 Frozen fruits & vegetables

(G-1329)
DECIBEL RESEARCH INC
2661 Commons Blvd Ste 136
(45431-3704)
PHONE..................................256 705-3341
Bassem Mahafza, *Branch Mgr*
EMP: 54
SALES (corp-wide): 10.4MM **Privately Held**
SIC: 3812 Radar systems & equipment
PA: Decibel Research, Inc
325 Bob Heath
Huntsville AL 35806
256 716-0787

(G-1330)
DRS ADVANCED ISR LLC (DH)
Also Called: Technologies Inc Arlington VA
2601 Mission Point Blvd (45431-6600)
PHONE..................................937 429-7408
William J Lynn III, *CEO*
Terence J Murphy, *COO*
Sandra L Hodgkinson, *Vice Pres*
Gary Marble, *Vice Pres*
Carla K Sheets, *Purch Agent*
EMP: 150
SQ FT: 25,000
SALES (est): 100.7MM
SALES (corp-wide): 57.7MM **Privately Held**
SIC: 3812 Search & navigation equipment
HQ: Drs Defense Solutions, Llc
1 Milestone Center Ct
Germantown MD 20876
240 238-3900

(G-1331)
DRS ADVANCED ISR LLC
2601 Mission Point Blvd (45431-6600)
PHONE..................................603 429-0111
Kyle Gerlitz, *Manager*
EMP: 45
SALES (corp-wide): 57.7MM **Privately Held**
SIC: 3812 Search & navigation equipment
HQ: Drs Icas, Llc
2601 Mission Point Blvd
Beavercreek OH 45431
937 429-7408

(G-1332)
DRS ICAS LLC
2601 Miohion Point Blvd Ste 250 (45431)
PHONE..................................937 429-7408
EMP: 45
SALES (corp-wide): 57.7MM **Privately Held**
SIC: 3812 Search & navigation equipment
HQ: Drs Icas, Llc
2601 Mission Point Blvd
Beavercreek OH 45431
937 429-7408

(G-1333)
DRS SIGNAL TECHNOLOGIES INC
4393 Dayton Xenia Rd (45432)
PHONE..................................937 429-7470
Leo Torresani, *President*
Peter Oberbeck, *Vice Pres*
Bob Taylor, *Vice Pres*
Roger Witkemper, *Vice Pres*
Louis Ducheseau, *Engineer*
EMP: 30
SALES (est): 5MM
SALES (corp-wide): 57.7MM **Privately Held**
WEB: www.drs-st.com
SIC: 3825 7371 Electrical energy measuring equipment; custom computer programming services

HQ: Drs Technologies, Inc.
2345 Crystal Dr Ste 1000
Arlington VA 22202
973 898-1500

(G-1334)
EDICT SYSTEMS INC
2434 Esquire Dr (45431-2573)
PHONE..................................937 429-4288
Fax: 937 429-4309
Ason K Wadzinski, *Ch of Bd*
David McDonald, *QA Dir*
James Lesch, *CFO*
David J Rike, *VP Sales*
Greg Rupert, *Accounts Exec*
EMP: 45
SQ FT: 12,000
SALES: 10.4MM
SALES (corp-wide): 10.7MM **Publicly Held**
WEB: www.retailec.com
SIC: 7372 Prepackaged software
PA: Advant-E Corporation
2434 Esquire Dr
Beavercreek OH 45431
937 429-4288

(G-1335)
EFAB TECHNOLOGIES LLC
3086 Westminster Dr (45431-8811)
PHONE..................................937 429-1401
Piyush Shah,
Nicholas Reeder,
Andrew Sarangan,
EMP: 4
SALES (est): 127.8K **Privately Held**
SIC: 7372 Educational computer software

(G-1336)
ENVIRO POLYMERS & CHEMICALS
3045 Rodenbeck Dr Ste D (45432-2660)
P.O. Box 340278, Dayton (45434-0278)
PHONE..................................937 427-1315
Fax: 937 427-9003
Hamid T Abdulla, *President*
David Chema, *Director*
Nancy Collier, *Director*
David Hosier, *Director*
Pam Smrdel, *Director*
EMP: 4
SALES: 1MM **Privately Held**
SIC: 2899 Water treating compounds

(G-1337)
F & K CONCEPTS INC
Also Called: Fkci
462 Carthage Dr (45434-5865)
PHONE..................................937 426-6843
Fax: 937 426-9722
Fred W Booher, *President*
Don Booher, *Vice Pres*
Kay Booher, *Vice Pres*
Don G Pugmire, *Manager*
Shawnie Price, *Admin Sec*
EMP: 4
SALES: 350K **Privately Held**
WEB: www.fkci.com
SIC: 3479 5199 Engraving jewelry silverware, or metal; name plates: engraved, etched, etc.; advertising specialties

(G-1338)
FLOWERS PRINT INC
Also Called: Derby Print and Copy Shop
3783 Dayton Xenia Rd (45432-2829)
PHONE..................................937 429-3823
Fax: 937 429-3823
Vicki Flowers, *President*
Ronald Flowers, *Treasurer*
EMP: 3
SALES: 165K **Privately Held**
SIC: 2752 Commercial printing, lithographic

(G-1339)
GDC INDUSTRIES LLC
1423 Research Park Dr (45432-2842)
PHONE..................................937 367-7229
Louis Luedtke, *CEO*
EMP: 6
SQ FT: 1,000
SALES (est): 371.4K **Privately Held**
SIC: 3339 Tin-base alloys (primary)

(G-1340)
GENERAL DYNMICS MSSION SYSTEMS
2673 Commons Blvd Ste 200
(45431-3812)
PHONE..................................513 253-4770
Fax: 937 427-5799
Chris Marzilli, *President*
David Fogg, *Treasurer*
Bob Kiley, *Manager*
Julie Aslaksen, *Admin Sec*
Dawn Dozier, *Admin Asst*
EMP: 35
SALES (corp-wide): 31.3B **Publicly Held**
SIC: 3669 3812 Transportation signaling devices; search & navigation equipment
HQ: General Dynamics Mission Systems, Inc
12450 Fair Lakes Cir # 800
Fairfax VA 22033
703 263-2800

(G-1341)
GRAPHIC IMAGE
2210 Shumway Ct (45431-3018)
PHONE..................................937 320-0302
Greg Opt, *President*
Tina Opt, *Vice Pres*
EMP: 3
SQ FT: 3,500
SALES (est): 250K **Privately Held**
WEB: www.thegraphicimage.com
SIC: 7336 2791 Art design services; typesetting

(G-1342)
GRID SENTRY LLC
3915 Germany Ln (45431-1688)
PHONE..................................937 490-2101
Russ Hignite, *Mfg Mgr*
Robert Kreutzfeld, *Engineer*
Everett Trittschuh, *Project Engr*
Kim A Gilmer, *Director*
Thomas M McCann, *Engineer*
EMP: 13
SALES (est): 1.9MM **Privately Held**
SIC: 3822 Thermostats & other environmental sensors

(G-1343)
H R MACHINE
2972 Homeway Dr (45434-5709)
P.O. Box 213, Alpha (45301-0213)
PHONE..................................937 838-6289
Larry Hudson, *Owner*
EMP: 5
SALES: 160K **Privately Held**
SIC: 3544 Special dies, tools, jigs & fixtures

(G-1344)
HARRIS CORPORATION
3500 Pentagon Blvd # 300 (45431-2374)
PHONE..................................973 284-2866
Jim Wantrobski, *Branch Mgr*
EMP: 195
SALES (corp-wide): 7.4B **Publicly Held**
SIC: 3823 3812 Industrial instrmnts msrmnt display/control process variable; search & navigation equipment
PA: Harris Corporation
1025 W Nasa Blvd
Melbourne FL 32919
321 727-9100

(G-1345)
HR MACHINE LLC
2972 Homeway Dr (45434-5709)
PHONE..................................937 222-7644
Jennifer Hudson, *President*
Larry Hudson, *Vice Pres*
Melody Rainville, *Office Mgr*
EMP: 8 EST: 2010
SQ FT: 7,000
SALES: 450K **Privately Held**
SIC: 3441 3914 Fabricated structural metal; trophies, stainless steel

(G-1346)
KETCO INC
1348 Research Park Dr (45432-2818)
PHONE..................................937 426-9331
Fax: 937 426-6192
Richard D Harding, *President*
Steven Gerbic, *Vice Pres*
EMP: 20 EST: 1973

▲ = Import ▼=Export
◆ =Import/Export

SQ FT: 15,000
SALES (est): 3.7MM Privately Held
WEB: www.ketco.com
SIC: 3543 Industrial patterns

(G-1347)
LEAR ENGINEERING CORP
2942 Stauffer Dr (45434-6247)
PHONE..................................937 429-0534
Fax: 937 429-0534
Dennis M Swing, *President*
Todd Reich, *Mfg Staff*
Steve Snow, *Research*
Chris Jennings, *Engineer*
EMP: 15
SQ FT: 2,400
SALES: 2.4MM Privately Held
WEB: www.learengineering.com
SIC: 3827 Optical test & inspection equipment

(G-1348)
LEIDOS INC
Also Called: Mission Support
3745 Pentagon Blvd (45431-2369)
PHONE..................................937 431-2400
Dennis Andersh, *Vice Pres*
Dennis Anders, *Branch Mgr*
Donnelly Hoag, *Manager*
Joseph Muchnij, *Senior Mgr*
EMP: 77
SALES (corp-wide): 7B Publicly Held
WEB: www.saic.com
SIC: 8731 7371 7373 8742 Commercial physical research; energy research; environmental research; medical research, commercial; computer software development; systems engineering, computer related; training & development consultant; recording & playback apparatus, including phonograph; integrated circuits, semiconductor networks, etc.
HQ: Leidos, Inc.
    11951 Freedom Dr Ste 500
    Reston VA 20190
    571 526-6000

(G-1349)
LOCKHEED MARTIN INVESTMENTS
2940 Presidential Dr # 290 (45324-6564)
PHONE..................................937 429-0100
Joe Lanni, *Director*
EMP: 11
SALES (corp-wide): 47.2B Publicly Held
SIC: 3365 Aerospace castings, aluminum
HQ: Lockheed Martin Investments Inc
    3510 Silverside Rd Ste 3
    Wilmington DE 19810
    302 478-1583

(G-1350)
MATRIX RESEARCH INC (PA)
Also Called: Matrix Research & Engineering
1300 Research Park Dr (45432-2818)
PHONE..................................937 427-8433
Robert J Puskar, *Ch of Bd*
Robert W Hawley, *President*
James E Lutz, *CFO*
William Pierson, *Admin Sec*
EMP: 47
SQ FT: 4,000
SALES (est): 9.1MM Privately Held
SIC: 3829 8711 Measuring & controlling devices; engineering services

(G-1351)
MERKUR GROUP INC
2434 Esquire Dr (45431-2573)
PHONE..................................937 429-4288
Jason Wadzinski, *CEO*
Michael Byers, *Accounts Exec*
Carl Kroger, *Manager*
EMP: 5
SALES: 1.4MM
SALES (corp-wide): 10.7MM Publicly Held
WEB: www.merkur.com
SIC: 5734 7372 Computer & software stores; prepackaged software
PA: Advant-E Corporation
    2434 Esquire Dr
    Beavercreek OH 45431
    937 429-4288

(G-1352)
MINUTEMAN PRESS
2372 Lakeview Dr (45431-4202)
PHONE..................................937 429-8610
EMP: 3
SALES (est): 269.2K Privately Held
SIC: 2752 Commercial printing, lithographic

(G-1353)
MONARCH WATER SYSTEMS INC
689 Greystone Dr (45434-4202)
PHONE..................................937 426-5773
Toll Free:..................................888 -
Fax: 937 372-4622
Patricia A Glaser, *President*
John Glaser, *Vice Pres*
Liza Horton, *Office Mgr*
EMP: 10
SQ FT: 7,500
SALES (est): 1.6MM Privately Held
SIC: 3589 Sewage & water treatment equipment

(G-1354)
NEW TECH WELDING INC
2972 Lantz Rd (45434-6633)
PHONE..................................937 426-4801
James King, *President*
Pamela King, *Owner*
EMP: 3
SALES (est): 50K Privately Held
SIC: 7692 Welding repair

(G-1355)
ORACLE CORPORATION
3610 Pentagon Blvd # 205 (45431-6700)
PHONE..................................513 826-5632
Peter Burton, *Principal*
EMP: 191
SALES (corp-wide): 37B Publicly Held
SIC: 7372 Prepackaged software
PA: Oracle Corporation
    500 Oracle Pkwy
    Redwood City CA 94065
    650 506-7000

(G-1356)
ORACLE SYSTEMS CORPORATION
2661 Commons Blvd (45431-3704)
PHONE..................................937 427-5495
Fax: 937 426-8370
Lisa Wells, *Manager*
Tom Conte, *Manager*
Bill Hackathorne, *Technology*
EMP: 4
SALES (corp-wide): 37B Publicly Held
WEB: www.forcecapital.com
SIC: 7372 Prepackaged software
HQ: Oracle Systems Corporation
    500 Oracle Pkwy
    Redwood City CA 94065
    650 506-7000

(G-1357)
PROTECH ELECTRIC LLC
1632 Beaverbrook Dr (45432-2104)
PHONE..................................937 427-0813
John Steelman, *Mng Member*
Janet Steelman,
EMP: 12
SALES (est): 586.7K Privately Held
SIC: 4822 3495 Telegraph & other communications; wire springs

(G-1358)
QUALITY MTRLOGY STYM SOLUTIONS
425 Mill Stone Dr (45434-5837)
PHONE..................................937 431-1800
John Kolaczkowski,
EMP: 3
SALES (est): 474.8K Privately Held
SIC: 3823 Industrial instrmnts msrmnt display/control process variable

(G-1359)
RAYTHEON COMPANY
2970 Presidential Dr # 300 (45324-6752)
PHONE..................................937 429-5429
Mike Evans, *Branch Mgr*
EMP: 10

SALES (corp-wide): 24B Publicly Held
SIC: 3812 Sonar systems & equipment
PA: Raytheon Company
    870 Winter St
    Waltham MA 02451
    781 522-3000

(G-1360)
SHOPS BY TODD INC (PA)
Also Called: Occassionaly Yours
2727 Fairfld Comns W273 (45431-5748)
PHONE..................................937 458-3192
Todd Bettman, *President*
Veronica Arnett, *Admin Mgr*
Natalie Moon, *Director*
EMP: 9
SQ FT: 1,750
SALES (est): 1.1MM Privately Held
WEB: www.oygifts.com
SIC: 5947 2759 Gift shop; invitation & stationery printing & engraving

(G-1361)
SIGN WRITE
3348 Dayton Xenia Rd (45432-2747)
PHONE..................................937 559-4388
Kristine Sturr, *Principal*
EMP: 3
SALES (est): 204.4K Privately Held
SIC: 3993 Signs & advertising specialties

(G-1362)
SONALYSTS INC
2940 Presidential Dr # 160 (45324-6564)
PHONE..................................937 429-9711
EMP: 23
SALES (corp-wide): 90.3MM Privately Held
SIC: 3211 Window glass, clear & colored
PA: Sonalysts, Inc.
    215 Parkway N
    Waterford CT 06385
    860 442-4355

(G-1363)
UNISON INDUSTRIES LLC
Also Called: Elano Div
2070 Heller Dr (45434-7210)
PHONE..................................937 427-0550
Robert Hessel, *Branch Mgr*
EMP: 400
SALES (corp-wide): 123.6B Publicly Held
WEB: www.unisonindustries.com
SIC: 3728 4581 Aircraft parts & equipment; aircraft servicing & repairing
HQ: Unison Industries, Llc
    7575 Baymeadows Way
    Jacksonville FL 32256
    904 739-4000

(G-1364)
UNISON INDUSTRIES LLC
Also Called: GE
2156 Heller Dr (45434-7211)
PHONE..................................937 426-0621
Robert Hessel, *Branch Mgr*
EMP: 140
SALES (corp-wide): 123.6B Publicly Held
SIC: 3694 Ignition apparatus & distributors
HQ: Unison Industries, Llc
    7575 Baymeadows Way
    Jacksonville FL 32256
    904 739-4000

(G-1365)
WILLIAMS DESIGN & PRINTING SER
2858 Tara Trl (45434-6251)
PHONE..................................937 320-9449
Angela Williams, *Owner*
EMP: 3
SALES (est): 150K Privately Held
SIC: 2752 Commercial printing, lithographic

(G-1366)
WOOD DUCK ENTERPRISES LTD
2225 La Grange Rd (45431-3159)
PHONE..................................937 426-0506
Teresa Chromey, *Principal*
EMP: 6
SALES (est): 328.5K Privately Held
SIC: 2491 Wood products, creosoted

(G-1367)
YOUNGS PUBLISHING INC
2171 N Fairfield Rd (45431-2556)
PHONE..................................937 259-6575
Fax: 937 259-6580
Ronald K Young Sr, *President*
Ronald K Young Jr, *Vice Pres*
Tracy Walls, *Manager*
EMP: 11
SQ FT: 3,000
SALES (est): 2.4MM Privately Held
WEB: www.reforsale.org
SIC: 2721 Magazines: publishing & printing

Beavercreek
Montgomery County

(G-1368)
ALEKTRONICS INC
4095 Executive Dr (45430-1062)
PHONE..................................937 429-2118
Alan Eakle, *CEO*
Jean Gad, *General Mgr*
Sandra Howell, *Sales Mgr*
Amy Hunt, *Sales Mgr*
Debbie Stone, *Accounts Mgr*
EMP: 16
SQ FT: 4,800
SALES (est): 3.3MM Privately Held
WEB: www.alektronics.com
SIC: 3672 Printed circuit boards

(G-1369)
AVASAX LTD
Also Called: Avasax Data Recovery
3895 Oakview Dr (45430-5109)
PHONE..................................937 694-0807
Robert Mardis,
EMP: 3
SALES (est): 161.2K Privately Held
SIC: 7372 7371 Application computer software; custom computer programming services

(G-1370)
BLUESERV REPROGRAHICS LLC
3313 Seajay Dr (45430-1365)
PHONE..................................937 426-6410
Rob Mantia, *Principal*
Sheila Spinson, *Manager*
EMP: 4
SALES (est): 550.8K Privately Held
SIC: 2752 Commercial printing, lithographic

(G-1371)
BOKO PATTERNS MODELS & MOLDS
4130 Industrial Ln (45430-1019)
PHONE..................................937 426-9667
Bob Koehler, *Principal*
EMP: 5
SALES (est): 632.6K Privately Held
SIC: 3553 3543 Pattern makers' machinery, woodworking; industrial patterns

(G-1372)
CERTIFIED COMPARATOR PRODUCTS
1174 Grange Hall Rd (45430-1094)
PHONE..................................937 426-9677
Fax: 937 426-4816
Rod Murch, *President*
EMP: 6
SALES (est): 727.6K Privately Held
SIC: 5065 3545 Electronic parts & equipment; comparators (machinists' precision tools)

(G-1373)
CLINTS PRINTING INC
Also Called: Clint's Prntng
3963 Rockfield Dr (45430-1126)
PHONE..................................937 426-2771
Fax: 937 426-5613
Clinton Whittaker, *CEO*
Lucille Whittaker, *President*
Lawrence Bernard, *Vice Pres*
EMP: 6
SQ FT: 9,500

G E O G R A P H I C

SALES (est): 884.6K **Privately Held**
SIC: 2752 2791 2789 Commercial printing, lithographic; commercial printing, offset; typesetting; bookbinding & related work

(G-1374)
MEASUREMENT SPECIALTIES INC
2670 Indian Ripple Rd (45440-3605)
PHONE..........................937 427-1231
Erin May, *Engineer*
Brian Ream, *Branch Mgr*
Chanda Melville, *Manager*
EMP: 13
SALES (corp-wide): 12.2B **Privately Held**
SIC: 3674 3676 Diodes, solid state (germanium, silicon, etc.); thermistors, except temperature sensors; varistors
HQ: Measurement Specialties, Inc.
1000 Lucas Way
Hampton VA 23666
757 766-1500

(G-1375)
NAKED LIME
2405 County Line Rd (45430-1573)
PHONE..........................937 485-1932
Brooke Wood, *Principal*
Rebecca Bernard, *Editor*
Antonio Wood, *Opers Staff*
Derek Barnett, *Research*
Chris Eder, *Sales Dir*
EMP: 75
SALES (est): 6.8MM **Privately Held**
SIC: 3274 Lime

(G-1376)
NONA COMPOSITES LLC
2750 Indian Ripple Rd (45440-3638)
PHONE..........................937 490-4814
Patrick Hood, *CEO*
Benjamin Dietsch, *President*
EMP: 5
SALES (est): 252.7K **Privately Held**
SIC: 2821 3728 8711 Epoxy resins; aircraft parts & equipment; engineering services

(G-1377)
ORBITAL ATK INC
1365 Technology Ct (45430-2212)
PHONE..........................937 429-9261
Don Hairston, *Principal*
Eric Vanderhorst, *Engineer*
Ash Miller, *Design Engr*
Michael Patenaude, *Security Mgr*
Jim Common, *Manager*
EMP: 150
SALES (corp-wide): 6.5B **Publicly Held**
WEB: www.mrcwdc.com
SIC: 3728 Aircraft parts & equipment
PA: Orbital Atk, Inc.
45101 Warp Dr
Dulles VA 20166
703 406-5000

(G-1378)
PFAUDLER INC
51 Plum St Ste 260 (45440-1397)
PHONE..........................585 464-4872
Joseph M Rigot, *Director*
EMP: 3
SALES (corp-wide): 7.2B **Publicly Held**
SIC: 3559 Refinery, chemical processing & similar machinery
HQ: Pfaudler, Inc.
1000 West Ave
Rochester NY 14611
585 464-5663

(G-1379)
REYNOLDS AND REYNOLDS COMPANY
2405 County Line Rd (45430-1573)
P.O. Box 2608, Dayton (45401-2608)
PHONE..........................937 485-2805
Finbarr Oneill, *Manager*
Jeffrey Painter, *Info Tech Mgr*
EMP: 10
SALES (corp-wide): 1.4B **Privately Held**
WEB: www.reyrey.com
SIC: 2761 7372 7371 Manifold business forms; prepackaged software; custom computer programming services

HQ: The Reynolds And Reynolds Company
1 Reynolds Way
Kettering OH 45430
937 485-2000

(G-1380)
SNI INC
75 Harbert Dr Ste A (45440-5126)
PHONE..........................937 427-9447
Fax: 937 427-2446
Steven C Nuttall, *President*
EMP: 4
SQ FT: 12,000
SALES (est): 565.4K **Privately Held**
WEB: www.snitool.com
SIC: 3544 3599 Special dies & tools; machine shop, jobbing & repair

(G-1381)
SUPERIOR SODA SERVICE LLC
3626 Napanee Dr (45430-1322)
P.O. Box 341450 (45434-1450)
PHONE..........................937 657-9700
Greg Gouldbourn,
EMP: 6
SALES: 75K **Privately Held**
SIC: 5963 3441 Beverage services, direct sales; fabricated structural metal

(G-1382)
UNMANNED SOLUTIONS TECH LLC
3908 Eagle Point Dr (45430-2085)
PHONE..........................937 771-7023
Clara Tiffany, *General Mgr*
Robert Barry,
Kent Tiffany,
EMP: 6
SALES (est): 644.3K **Privately Held**
SIC: 3721 Research & development on aircraft by the manufacturer

(G-1383)
VECTOR ELECTROMAGNETICS LLC
1400 Grange Hall Rd # 500 (45430-1081)
PHONE..........................937 478-5904
Errol English, *President*
Brian Barber, *Vice Pres*
EMP: 4
SALES: 1MM **Privately Held**
SIC: 8711 3812 Electrical or electronic engineering; mining engineer; defense systems & equipment

(G-1384)
WERNLI REALTY INC
1300 Grange Hall Rd (45430-1013)
PHONE..........................937 258-7878
Richard L Schaefer, *President*
Norman Miller, *Vice Pres*
John Miltenberger, *Asst Sec*
EMP: 75
SQ FT: 20,000
SALES (est): 8.6MM **Privately Held**
SIC: 3441 6512 Building components, structural steel; nonresidential building operators

Beavercreek Township
Greene County

(G-1385)
MBM INDUSTRIES LTD
801 Space Dr (45434-7162)
PHONE..........................937 522-0719
Bradley M McWilliams,
EMP: 4 EST: 2001
SALES (est): 776.6K **Privately Held**
SIC: 3711 3827 Military motor vehicle assembly; gun sights, optical

(G-1386)
PHILLIPS COMPANIES (PA)
620 Phillips Dr (45434-7230)
P.O. Box 187, Alpha (45301-0187)
PHONE..........................937 426-5461
Richard L Phillips II, *President*
Scott Back, *General Mgr*
George E Phillips, *Chairman*
Bradley Phillips, *Vice Pres*
Jason Phillips, *Treasurer*
EMP: 20 EST: 1942

SQ FT: 2,000
SALES (est): 13.3MM **Privately Held**
WEB: www.phillipscompanies.com
SIC: 1442 6552 1794 Sand mining; gravel mining; subdividers & developers; excavation work

(G-1387)
PHILLIPS COMPANIES
Also Called: Phillips Sand & Gravel Co
620 Phillips Dr (45434-7230)
PHONE..........................937 426-5461
Richard L Phillips II, *President*
Larry Phillips, *Vice Pres*
EMP: 29
SALES (corp-wide): 13.3MM **Privately Held**
WEB: www.phillipscompanies.com
SIC: 3273 1771 Ready-mixed concrete; concrete pumping
PA: Phillips Companies
620 Phillips Dr
Beavercreek Township OH 45434
937 426-5461

(G-1388)
PHILLIPS READY MIX CO
620 Phillips Dr (45434-7230)
P.O. Box 187, Alpha (45301-0187)
PHONE..........................937 426-5151
Fax: 937 426-0659
Rick Phillips, *President*
Dennis Phillips, *Treasurer*
Larry Phillips, *Asst Sec*
EMP: 100
SALES (est): 4.2MM **Privately Held**
SIC: 1771 3273 7353 5191 Concrete pumping; ready-mixed concrete; heavy construction equipment rental; farm supplies; excavation work; construction sand & gravel

(G-1389)
PRIORITY CUSTOM MOLDING INC
840 Distribution Dr (45434-7174)
PHONE..........................937 431-8770
Fax: 937 431-8772
Carol S Williams, *President*
Dennie Williams, *Vice Pres*
Bob Abbitt, *Treasurer*
Angela Abbit, *Admin Sec*
▲ **EMP:** 18
SQ FT: 17,500
SALES (est): 2.8MM **Privately Held**
SIC: 3089 3081 Molding primary plastic; unsupported plastics film & sheet

(G-1390)
SONOCO PRODUCTS COMPANY
Sonoco Consumer Products
761 Space Dr (45434-7171)
PHONE..........................937 429-0040
Norwood Bizzell, *Manager*
EMP: 60
SALES (corp-wide): 4.7B **Publicly Held**
WEB: www.sonoco.com
SIC: 2655 5113 2891 Cans, fiber: made from purchased material; paper tubes & cores; adhesives & sealants
PA: Sonoco Products Company
1 N 2nd St
Hartsville SC 29550
843 383-7000

(G-1391)
W&W AUTOMOTIVE & TOWING INC
Also Called: W & W Automotive
680 Orchard Ln (45434-7205)
PHONE..........................937 429-1699
Fax: 937 429-8537
Regina White, *President*
EMP: 10
SQ FT: 16,000
SALES (est): 1.4MM **Privately Held**
SIC: 3711 7532 Chassis, motor vehicle; body shop, automotive

(G-1392)
WALLEN COMMERCIAL HARDWARE
832 Space Dr (45434-7161)
PHONE..........................937 426-5711
Tim Wallen, *President*

EMP: 4
SALES (est): 300K **Privately Held**
SIC: 3429 Manufactured hardware (general)

Beaverdam
Allen County

(G-1393)
HAWTHORNE SYSTEMS INC
318 W Main St (45808-9707)
PHONE..........................419 643-5861
Charles L Dale, *President*
Patricia Hemmelgarn, *Treasurer*
EMP: 10
SQ FT: 10,000
SALES (est): 890K **Privately Held**
WEB: www.hawthornesystems.com
SIC: 3523 Grain stackers

Bedford
Cuyahoga County

(G-1394)
A M CASTLE & CO
Also Called: Oliver Steel Plate
26800 Miles Rd (44146-1405)
PHONE..........................330 425-7000
Scott J Dolan, *Branch Mgr*
EMP: 65
SALES (corp-wide): 770.7MM **Publicly Held**
SIC: 5051 3444 3443 3398 Metals service centers & offices; sheet metalwork; fabricated plate work (boiler shop); metal heat treating
PA: A. M. Castle & Co.
1420 Kensington Rd # 220
Oak Brook IL 60523
847 455-7111

(G-1395)
ALS HIGH TECH INC (PA)
Also Called: Al's Electric Motor Service
135 Northfield Rd (44146-4606)
PHONE..........................440 232-7090
Fax: 330 527-2980
Elaine Ochwat, *CEO*
Dale Ochwat, *President*
Lynn O Meffen, *Corp Secy*
EMP: 11
SQ FT: 45,000
SALES: 1.2MM **Privately Held**
SIC: 7694 5063 Electric motor repair; rewinding services; electrical apparatus & equipment; motors, electric

(G-1396)
AMERICAN ACADEMIC PRESS
550 Turney Rd Apt C (44146-7328)
PHONE..........................216 906-2518
Michael Cikraji, *Owner*
Robert McGrew, *Manager*
EMP: 2
SALES (est): 95K **Privately Held**
SIC: 2731 Book publishing

(G-1397)
ANSON CO
Also Called: Effective Air
18679 Orchard Hill Dr (44146-5258)
PHONE..........................216 524-8838
EMP: 3
SQ FT: 1,200
SALES: 400K **Privately Held**
SIC: 5075 3634 Whol Heat Air Conditioning & Ventilation Equipment

(G-1398)
APEX WELDING INCORPORATED
Also Called: Apex Bulk Handlers
1 Industry Dr (44146-4413)
P.O. Box 46199, Cleveland (44146-0199)
PHONE..........................440 232-6770
Fax: 440 232-6747
D J Warner, *President*
Gary Warner, *General Mgr*
B A Danna, *Vice Pres*
EMP: 15 EST: 1947
SQ FT: 15,200

SALES (est): 3MM **Privately Held**
WEB: www.apexwelding.com
SIC: 3444 3443 Hoppers, sheet metal;
fabricated plate work (boiler shop)

(G-1399)
ART OF BEAUTY COMPANY INC (PA)
200 Egbert Rd (44146-4221)
P.O. Box 22349, Cleveland (44122-0349)
PHONE....................216 438-6363
Michael Reyzis, *President*
Leo Reyzis, *Vice Pres*
Brian Tucker, *Accountant*
Rebecca ISA, *Natl Sales Mgr*
Melissa McTee, *Mktg Coord*
◆ EMP: 15
SQ FT: 5,000
SALES (est): 3.5MM **Privately Held**
WEB: www.artofbeauty.com
SIC: 2844 Cosmetic preparations

(G-1400)
ASPEN MULLING COMPANY
Also Called: Aspen Mulling Spices
5111 Richmond Rd (44146-1353)
PHONE....................970 925-5027
David Kalen, *President*
EMP: 3
SALES (est): 164.8K
SALES (corp-wide): 16.7MM **Privately Held**
SIC: 2099 2045 Seasonings & spices;
bread & bread type roll mixes: from purchased flour
PA: Llc Brand Castle
5111 Richmond Rd Frnt
Bedford Heights OH 44146
216 292-7700

(G-1401)
AUTOMATED PACKG SYSTEMS INC
Sidepouch
25900 Solon Rd (44146-4788)
PHONE....................330 342-2000
Fax: 330 342-2440
Matt Lerner, *Exec VP*
Evan Graber, *Engineer*
Jim Lang, *Engineer*
Richard Kephart, *Design Engr*
Kevin Nau, *Design Engr*
EMP: 75
SQ FT: 59,780
SALES (corp-wide): 186.1MM **Privately Held**
WEB: www.autobag.com
SIC: 3565 2673 Packaging machinery;
bags: plastic, laminated & coated
PA: Automated Packaging Systems Inc.
10175 Philipp Pkwy
Streetsboro OH 44241
330 528-2000

(G-1402)
AUTOMATIC BACTERIAL INJECTION
Also Called: ABI
26000 Richmond Rd Ste 4 (44146-1420)
P.O. Box 389, Richfield (44286-0389)
PHONE....................216 378-1336
Fax: 216 378-1376
Lloyd Ray Parr, *President*
Thomas L Feher, *Admin Sec*
Thomas Feher, *Assistant*
EMP: 10
SALES (est): 1.5MM **Privately Held**
WEB: www.ultraclear.com
SIC: 2836 Biological products, except diagnostic

(G-1403)
BARTA VIOREL
Also Called: Cabinet Studio
26245 Broadway Ave (44146-6523)
PHONE....................440 735-1699
Fax: 440 468-3755
Viorel Barta, *Owner*
EMP: 4
SALES (est): 240K **Privately Held**
SIC: 3281 Granite, cut & shaped

(G-1404)
BASWA ACOUSTICS NORTH AMER LLC
Also Called: Sound Solutions Cnstr Svcs
21863 Aurora Rd (44146-1201)
PHONE....................216 475-7197
Ed Sellers, *Managing Prtnr*
Matt Townsend, *Partner*
▲ EMP: 12
SQ FT: 3,000
SALES (est): 3.3MM **Privately Held**
SIC: 5082 3272 General construction machinery & equipment; building materials, except block or brick: concrete

(G-1405)
BEAUTY CFT MET FABRICATORS INC
5439 Perkins Rd (44146-1856)
PHONE....................440 439-0710
Fax: 440 486-6760
Ronald Walnsch, *President*
Brian Walnsch, *Vice Pres*
Barbara Marshall, *Manager*
Mary Walnsch, *Admin Sec*
EMP: 10
SQ FT: 7,000
SALES (est): 900K **Privately Held**
WEB: www.beautycraftmetal.com
SIC: 3446 Ornamental metalwork

(G-1406)
BEDFORD PRECISION PRODUCTS INC
339 Northfield Rd 339 (44146-4639)
PHONE....................440 786-7277
Fax: 440 786-7279
John Diezic, *President*
EMP: 4
SQ FT: 3,000
SALES (est): 672.5K **Privately Held**
SIC: 3599 Machine shop, jobbing & repair

(G-1407)
BENTLEY WORLD-PACKAGING LTD
19800 Alexander Rd (44146-5346)
PHONE....................440 232-1100
Ron Skully, *Vice Pres*
EMP: 11
SALES (corp-wide): 154.8MM **Privately Held**
WEB: www.overseaspacking.net
SIC: 5113 3412 3086 Boxes & containers;
corrugated & solid fiber boxes; metal barrels, drums & pails; plastics foam products
PA: Bentley World-Packaging, Ltd.
4080 N Port Washington Rd
Milwaukee WI 53212
414 967-8000

(G-1408)
BOSS PET PRODUCTS INC (HQ)
7730 First Pl Ste E (44146-6720)
PHONE....................216 332-0832
Fax: 330 332-0838
Bruce Lancaster, *President*
▲ EMP: 12
SQ FT: 20,000
SALES (est): 1.8MM **Publicly Held**
WEB: www.bossholdings.com
SIC: 3999 Pet supplies

(G-1409)
BRAINMASTER TECHNOLOGIES INC
195 Willis St 3 (44146-3508)
P.O. Box 46725 (44146-0725)
PHONE....................440 232-6000
Thomas F Collura, *President*
Terri Collura, *Exec VP*
William Mrklas, *Vice Pres*
Sultan Ahmed, *Corp Comm Staff*
Maryjo Nero, *Manager*
EMP: 9
SALES (est): 1.2MM **Privately Held**
WEB: www.brainmaster.com
SIC: 3845 7371 Electromedical equipment; computer software development

(G-1410)
CANNON SALT & SUPPLY INC
26041 Cannon Rd (44146-1835)
PHONE....................440 232-1700
Robert Foster, *Principal*
Todd Kling, *Vice Pres*
EMP: 6
SALES (est): 1MM **Privately Held**
SIC: 3524 3423 Lawn & garden equipment; garden & farm tools, including shovels

(G-1411)
CANVAS PRODUCTS CO
634 Golden Oak Pkwy (44146-6504)
PHONE....................440 232-8716
Fax: 440 360-9086
Rudy Kastelic, *President*
EMP: 11 EST: 1955
SQ FT: 24,000
SALES: 1MM **Privately Held**
WEB: www.canvasproducts.com
SIC: 2394 Canvas & related products; tarpaulins, fabric: made from purchased materials; convertible tops, canvas or boat: from purchased materials; awnings, fabric: made from purchased materials

(G-1412)
CARR BROS INC
7177 Northfield Rd (44146-5403)
P.O. Box 46387 (44146-0387)
PHONE....................440 232-3700
Fax: 440 786-7757
Mike Carr, *Owner*
Jeanette Haines, *Office Admin*
EMP: 6
SALES (est): 159K **Privately Held**
SIC: 3273 Ready-mixed concrete

(G-1413)
CBG BIOTECH LTD CO
26400 Broadway Ave Ste A (44146-6538)
PHONE....................440 786-7667
David Camiener, *Manager*
EMP: 32 **Privately Held**
SIC: 3559 Recycling machinery
PA: Cbg Biotech, Ltd. Co.
100 Glenview Pl Apt 1003
Naples FL 34108

(G-1414)
CERTON TECHNOLOGIES INC (PA)
Also Called: Har Adhesive Technologies
60 S Park St (44146-3635)
PHONE....................440 786-7185
Fax: 440 786-7186
Joseph Cerino, *President*
Joe Cerino, *Principal*
Diane Cerino, *Vice Pres*
Geri Horvath, *Purchasing*
Debbie Voso, *Credit Staff*
EMP: 15
SQ FT: 30,000
SALES (est): 3MM **Privately Held**
SIC: 2891 2851 7699 7359 Adhesives;
paints & paint additives; professional instrument repair services; home cleaning & maintenance equipment rental services

(G-1415)
CLEVELAND TUNGSTEN INC
7650 First Pl Ste E (44146-6732)
PHONE....................440 786-0800
Fax: 440 786-0802
Taimin Li, *President*
Walter Selden, *Manager*
▲ EMP: 4
SALES (est): 729.9K **Privately Held**
SIC: 5051 3313 Miscellaneous nonferrous products; tungsten carbide powder

(G-1416)
CLOSETTEC OF NORTH EAST OHIO
5222 Richmond Rd (44146-1333)
PHONE....................216 464-0042
Don Cussari, *Principal*
EMP: 4
SALES (est): 431.1K **Privately Held**
SIC: 3553 Cabinet makers' machinery

(G-1417)
COMBINE GRINDING CO INC
7005 Krick Rd (44146-4446)
PHONE....................440 439-6148
Fax: 440 232-1350
Cynthia Musgrave, *President*
Charles Musgrave III, *Vice Pres*
EMP: 3
SQ FT: 3,200
SALES (est): 338.9K **Privately Held**
SIC: 3599 Grinding castings for the trade

(G-1418)
DENGENSHA AMERICA CORPORATION
7647 First Pl (44146-6701)
PHONE....................440 439-8081
Fax: 440 439-8217
Donald Grisez, *President*
Tom Zambelli, *Marketing Mgr*
Cheryl Hruby, *Office Mgr*
▲ EMP: 13
SALES (est): 2.9MM
SALES (corp-wide): 40.2MM **Privately Held**
WEB: www.dengensha.com
SIC: 3559 5084 Automotive related machinery; industrial machinery & equipment
PA: Dengensha Toa Co., Ltd.
1-23-1, Masugata, Tama-Ku
Kawasaki KNG 214-0
449 221-121

(G-1419)
DIVERSIFIED BRANDS
26300 Fargo Ave (44146-1310)
PHONE....................216 595-8777
Gayle Dlougon, *Principal*
EMP: 7
SALES (est): 739.3K **Privately Held**
SIC: 2819 Industrial inorganic chemicals

(G-1420)
DONE-RITE BOWLING SERVICE CO (PA)
Also Called: Paragon Machine Company
20434 Krick Rd (44146-4422)
PHONE....................440 232-3280
Fax: 440 232-3635
Robert W Gable, *CEO*
Glenn Gable, *President*
Gale Burns, *Vice Pres*
Dave Patz, *Vice Pres*
Ann Gable, *Shareholder*
▲ EMP: 22 EST: 1950
SQ FT: 20,000
SALES (est): 2.4MM **Privately Held**
WEB: www.donerite.com
SIC: 3949 1752 5091 Bowling equipment & supplies; floor laying & floor work; bowling equipment

(G-1421)
DREAM SPACE
25405 Broadway Ave (44146-6343)
PHONE....................440 945-6596
Dennis Champa, *Principal*
EMP: 7 EST: 2010
SALES (est): 785.5K **Privately Held**
SIC: 3651 Household audio & video equipment

(G-1422)
E J SKOK INDUSTRIES (PA)
26901 Richmond Rd (44146-1416)
PHONE....................216 292-7533
Fax: 216 292-7533
Edward J Skok, *President*
Richard Skok, *Corp Secy*
Kathy Skok, *Controller*
EMP: 20
SQ FT: 18,000
SALES (est): 1.9MM **Privately Held**
SIC: 2541 2434 Table or counter tops, plastic laminated; wood kitchen cabinets; vanities, bathroom: wood

(G-1423)
FERRO CORPORATION
7050 Krick Rd (44146-4416)
PHONE....................216 577-7144
Fax: 216 750-6729
Ferro Bedford, *Div Sub Head*
R Szabo, *Purchasing*
Steven Hofmeister, *Engineer*

Sally Lenhart, *Sales Mgr*
Kent Lee, *Marketing Staff*
EMP: 70
SALES (corp-wide): 1.1B **Publicly Held**
WEB: www.ferro.com
SIC: 2851 2869 2842 2836 Paint driers; industrial organic chemicals; specialty cleaning, polishes & sanitation goods; biological products, except diagnostic; industrial inorganic chemicals
PA: Ferro Corporation
 6060 Parkland Blvd # 250
 Mayfield Heights OH 44124
 216 875-5600

(G-1424)
FORD MOTOR COMPANY
7845 Northfield Rd (44146-5522)
PHONE.....................................216 587-7700
Fax: 216 587-7981
William Ferrari, *General Mgr*
Mark A Kirk, *Vice Pres*
Thomas O Laughlin, *Vice Pres*
Tom Olaughlin, *Vice Pres*
John Orem, *Vice Pres*
EMP: 817
SQ FT: 732,500
SALES (corp-wide): 151.8B **Publicly Held**
WEB: www.ford.com
SIC: 3465 Automotive stampings
PA: Ford Motor Company
 1 American Rd
 Dearborn MI 48126
 313 322-3000

(G-1425)
GREAT LAKES TEXTILES INC
11 Industry Dr (44146-4413)
PHONE.....................................440 201-1300
Evan Wake, *Manager*
EMP: 20
SALES (corp-wide): 16.6MM **Privately Held**
WEB: www.gltproducts.com
SIC: 3083 Laminated plastic sheets
PA: Great Lakes Textiles, Inc.
 6810 Cochran Rd
 Solon OH 44139
 440 439-1300

(G-1426)
GUILD INTERNATIONAL INC
7273 Division St (44146-5490)
PHONE.....................................440 232-5887
Fax: 440 232-5878
Michael Wheeler, *President*
Debby Klouda, *Buyer*
Joe Sanoro, *Engineer*
Doug Steiner, *Engineer*
Mark Wagner, *Engineer*
▲ **EMP:** 33 **EST:** 1956
SQ FT: 12,000
SALES (est): 8.9MM **Privately Held**
SIC: 3549 Coiling machinery

(G-1427)
GVC PLASTICS & METALS LLC
7051 Krick Rd (44146-4415)
PHONE.....................................440 232-9360
Greg Charatian, *Owner*
EMP: 4 **EST:** 2010
SALES (est): 374.1K **Privately Held**
SIC: 2295 Resin or plastic coated fabrics

(G-1428)
HAR EQUIPMENT SALES INC
60 S Park St (44146-3635)
PHONE.....................................440 786-7189
EMP: 5
SALES (est): 637.5K **Privately Held**
SIC: 2891 Adhesives

(G-1429)
HOME CITY ICE COMPANY
20282 Hannan Pkwy (44146-5353)
PHONE.....................................440 439-5001
Fax: 440 574-5409
Rick Wetterau, *Manager*
EMP: 11
SQ FT: 15,947
SALES (corp-wide): 305.4MM **Privately Held**
WEB: www.homecityice.com
SIC: 5999 2097 Ice; manufactured ice

PA: The Home City Ice Company
 6045 Bridgetown Rd Ste 1
 Cincinnati OH 45248
 513 574-1800

(G-1430)
I SCHUMANN & CO LLC (PA)
22500 Alexander Rd (44146-5576)
PHONE.....................................440 439-2300
Fax: 440 439-0317
Michael A Schumann, *Ch of Bd*
Scott Schumann, *President*
David Schumann, *Exec VP*
Duke Mullins, *Maint Spvr*
Don Robertson, *CFO*
◆ **EMP:** 115 **EST:** 1917
SQ FT: 150,000
SALES (est): 28.7MM **Privately Held**
WEB: www.ischumann.com
SIC: 3341 Brass smelting & refining (secondary); bronze smelting & refining (secondary); copper smelting & refining (secondary); nickel smelting & refining (secondary)

(G-1431)
INNER PRODUCTS SALES INC
Also Called: Fastsigns
5221 Northfield Rd A (44146-1110)
PHONE.....................................216 581-4141
Fax: 216 581-4908
Janice Sims, *President*
EMP: 4
SQ FT: 1,575
SALES: 300K **Privately Held**
SIC: 3993 3953 Signs & advertising specialties; marking devices

(G-1432)
INTIGRAL INC (PA)
Also Called: Est
7850 Northfield Rd (44146-5523)
PHONE.....................................440 439-0980
Fax: 440 786-1099
Jason Thomas, *President*
Jim Prete, *Exec VP*
Jamey Beard, *Vice Pres*
Dick Dietrich, *Vice Pres*
Richard Dietrich, *Vice Pres*
▲ **EMP:** 200
SQ FT: 158,000
SALES (est): 50.1MM **Privately Held**
WEB: www.edgeseal.com
SIC: 3231 Insulating glass: made from purchased glass

(G-1433)
IOPPOLO CONCRETE CORPORATION
10 Industry Dr (44146-4414)
PHONE.....................................440 439-6606
Fax: 440 232-2110
Anthony Ioppolo Jr, *President*
Dana Kernsisk, *Manager*
EMP: 20
SQ FT: 6,000
SALES (est): 3.1MM **Privately Held**
SIC: 3273 1711 7353 4959 Ready-mixed concrete; plumbing, heating, air-conditioning contractors; heavy construction equipment rental; snowplowing

(G-1434)
K C N TECHNOLOGIES LLC
Also Called: Ace Hydraulics
20637 Krick Rd (44146-5412)
PHONE.....................................440 439-4219
Brian Schuster, *General Mgr*
Gary Schuster, *Principal*
EMP: 8
SQ FT: 7,000
SALES (est): 799.8K **Privately Held**
WEB: www.acehem.com
SIC: 1799 7694 7629 Hydraulic equipment, installation & service; armature rewinding shops; electrical repair shops

(G-1435)
KADEE INDUSTRIES NEWCO INC
7160 Krick Rd Ste A (44146-4438)
PHONE.....................................440 439-8650
Fax: 440 439-6889
Brian Mullins, *President*
Joseph Scott, *Exec VP*
Rich Seaver, *Plant Mgr*

Evelyn Neal, *Engineer*
Janice M Moore, *Manager*
EMP: 10
SALES (est): 880K **Privately Held**
WEB: www.kadeeindustries.com
SIC: 3496 2273 Mats & matting; carpets & rugs

(G-1436)
KELLYS POLISHING METAL FINSHG
7010 Krick Rd (44146-4436)
PHONE.....................................440 232-8800
Danette Novak, *Principal*
EMP: 3
SALES (est): 158.5K **Privately Held**
SIC: 3471 Polishing, metals or formed products

(G-1437)
KOLTCZ CONCRETE BLOCK CO
7660 Oak Leaf Rd (44146-5554)
PHONE.....................................440 232-3630
Fax: 440 232-4506
Stanley M Koltcz, *President*
EMP: 26
SQ FT: 55,000
SALES (est): 5MM **Privately Held**
WEB: www.koltcz.com
SIC: 3271 5032 5211 Blocks, concrete or cinder: standard; masons' materials; masonry materials & supplies

(G-1438)
LAKE SHORE ELECTRIC CORP
205 Willis St (44146-3505)
PHONE.....................................440 232-0200
Fax: 216 232-5644
Michael Shane, *President*
Michael Sharne, *President*
Wayne Bussard, *Vice Pres*
Frank Dufour, *Manager*
◆ **EMP:** 25
SQ FT: 40,000
SALES (est): 17.5MM **Privately Held**
WEB: www.lake-shore-electric.com
SIC: 3625 3613 3643 3621 Control equipment; electric; switches, electric power except snap, push button, etc.; current-carrying wiring devices; motors & generators; transformers, except electric; sheet metalwork

(G-1439)
LOVEMAN STEEL CORPORATION
5455 Perkins Rd (44146-1856)
PHONE.....................................440 232-6200
Fax: 440 232-0914
Anthony Murru, *CEO*
James Loveman, *COO*
David Loveman, *Exec VP*
Rob Loveman, *Vice Pres*
John Steagall, *Vice Pres*
▼ **EMP:** 75
SQ FT: 80,000
SALES: 17MM **Privately Held**
WEB: www.lovemansteel.com
SIC: 5051 3443 Plates, metal; weldments

(G-1440)
MANTUA MANUFACTURING CO (PA)
Also Called: MANTUA BED FRAMES
7900 Northfield Rd (44146-5525)
PHONE.....................................800 333-8333
David Jaffe, *President*
Charles Bastien, *Vice Pres*
Dirk Smith, *Vice Pres*
Jeffrey Wick, *Vice Pres*
Frank Barkley, *Plant Mgr*
▲ **EMP:** 75 **EST:** 1952
SQ FT: 52,000
SALES (est): 32.8MM **Privately Held**
WEB: www.bedframes.com
SIC: 2514 Frames for box springs or bedsprings: metal

(G-1441)
MARLEN MANUFACTURING & DEV CO (PA)
5150 Richmond Rd (44146-1331)
PHONE.....................................216 292-7060
Fax: 216 292-9196
Gary Fenton, *President*

Robert L Keyes, *Principal*
David L Levine, *Principal*
R Williambashein, *Principal*
Michael Magar, *Treasurer*
▲ **EMP:** 6 **EST:** 1952
SQ FT: 45,000
SALES (est): 6.4MM **Privately Held**
SIC: 3842 Surgical appliances & supplies; adhesive tape & plasters, medicated or non-medicated

(G-1442)
MARLEN MANUFACTURING & DEV CO
Medco Coated Products
5156 Richmond Rd (44146-1331)
PHONE.....................................216 292-7546
Fax: 216 292-5900
Mark Fenton, *Manager*
EMP: 29
SALES (corp-wide): 6.4MM **Privately Held**
SIC: 2891 3842 2672 2671 Adhesives & sealants; surgical appliances & supplies; coated & laminated paper; packaging paper & plastics film, coated & laminated
PA: Marlen Manufacturing And Development Co.
 5150 Richmond Rd
 Bedford OH 44146
 216 292-7060

(G-1443)
MICROPLEX PRINTWARE CORP
100 Northfield Rd (44146-4640)
PHONE.....................................440 374-2424
Andre Fedak, *President*
Mark Merhab, *VP Sales*
Julie Swoanveck, *Accounts Mgr*
Gene Griggy, *Info Tech Mgr*
▲ **EMP:** 11
SQ FT: 12,000
SALES: 5.6MM **Privately Held**
WEB: www.microplex-usa.com
SIC: 2759 Laser printing

(G-1444)
MOLDING DYNAMICS INC
7009 Krick Rd (44146-4415)
PHONE.....................................440 786-8100
Charles F Connors III, *President*
Summer Howard, *Office Mgr*
Chuck Connors, *Manager*
EMP: 15
SQ FT: 14,000
SALES (est): 3.8MM **Privately Held**
SIC: 3089 Injection molding of plastics

(G-1445)
MORGAN ADVANCED CERAMICS INC
Also Called: Morgan Advanced Materials
232 Forbes Rd (44146-5418)
PHONE.....................................440 232-8604
Jack Gray, *Vice Pres*
John Hudak, *Vice Pres*
Kenneth Kupcak, *Purchasing*
Angelo Dellaquila, *QC Mgr*
William Hocevar, *Research*
EMP: 140
SALES (corp-wide): 1.3B **Privately Held**
WEB: www.morganelectroceramics.com
SIC: 2899 3251 Fluxes: brazing, soldering, galvanizing & welding; brick & structural clay tile
HQ: Morgan Advanced Ceramics, Inc
 2425 Whipple Rd
 Hayward CA 94544
 510 491-1100

(G-1446)
MT PLEASANT PHARMACY LLC
631 Lee Rd Apt 1228 (44146-6605)
PHONE.....................................216 672-4377
Michael Asiedu-Gyekye, *Principal*
EMP: 3
SALES (est): 240K **Privately Held**
SIC: 3842 Adhesive tape & plasters, medicated or non-medicated

(G-1447)
NEW YORK FROZEN FOODS INC (DH)
25900 Fargo Ave (44146-1302)
PHONE.....................................216 292-5655

▲ = Import ▼ =Export
◆ =Import/Export

Fax: 216 292-5978
Bruce Rosa, *President*
Donald Penn, *VP Mfg*
Mike Mahon, *Plant Mgr*
Bob Hanel, *Safety Mgr*
Brad McWithey, *Safety Mgr*
EMP: 260
SQ FT: 55,000
SALES (est): 57.5MM
SALES (corp-wide): 1.1B **Publicly Held**
WEB: www.lancaster.com
SIC: 2051 Bread, all types (white, wheat, rye, etc): fresh or frozen
HQ: T.Marzetti Company
380 Polaris Pkwy Ste 400
Westerville OH 43082
614 846-2232

(G-1448)
NOVA FILMS AND FOILS INC
11 Industry Dr (44146-4413)
P.O. Box 39055, Solon (44139-0055)
PHONE...................................440 201-1300
Steven Wake, *President*
Bruce Allaben, *Engineer*
Marinko Milos, *CFO*
Phil Davis, *Credit Mgr*
Linda Ardo, *Credit Staff*
▲ EMP: 10
SALES (est): 2.7MM **Privately Held**
WEB: www.novafilmsusa.com
SIC: 2891 Adhesives

(G-1449)
NPK CONSTRUCTION EQUIPMENT INC (HQ)
7550 Independence Dr (44146-5541)
PHONE...................................440 232-7900
Fax: 440 232-4382
Dan Tyrell, *President*
Marga Parker, *Accountant*
◆ EMP: 60
SQ FT: 150,000
SALES (est): 41.9MM **Privately Held**
WEB: www.npkce.com
SIC: 5082 3599 3546 3532 Construction & mining machinery; machine shop, jobbing & repair; power-driven handtools; mining machinery; construction machinery; cutlery
PA: Nippon Pneumatic Manufacturing Co.,Ltd.
4-11-5, Kamiji, Higashinari-Ku
Osaka OSK
669 739-100

(G-1450)
OAKWOOD INDUSTRIES INC (PA)
Also Called: Federal Metal Co
7250 Division St (44146-5406)
PHONE...................................440 232-8700
Fax: 440 232-8726
David R Nagusky, *President*
Christine Tench, *Human Res Mgr*
Karen Calo, *Manager*
Malvin E Bank, *Admin Sec*
◆ EMP: 60
SQ FT: 65,000
SALES (est): 16.2MM **Privately Held**
WEB: www.federalmetalcompany.com
SIC: 3341 3364 Brass smelting & refining (secondary); bronze smelting & refining (secondary); nonferrous die-castings except aluminum

(G-1451)
OVERSEAS PACKING LLC
Also Called: United Packaging Supply Co Div
19800 Alexander Rd (44146-5346)
PHONE...................................440 232-2917
Fax: 440 735-1007
Dean Mowery, *Controller*
Stan Gaul, *Human Resources*
Thomas Bentley,
EMP: 15
SQ FT: 52,000
SALES (est): 2.5MM **Privately Held**
WEB: www.overseaspacking.net
SIC: 2449 3412 4783 Wood containers; metal barrels, drums & pails; packing goods for shipping; crating goods for shipping

(G-1452)
PALEOMD LLC
26245 Broadway Ave Ste B (44146-6524)
PHONE...................................248 854-0031
Patricia Urcuyo, *Mng Member*
EMP: 7
SALES (est): 432.7K **Privately Held**
SIC: 2038 Pizza, frozen

(G-1453)
PINNACLE PRECISION PDTS LLC
624 Golden Oak Pkwy (44146-6504)
PHONE...................................440 786-0248
Eric Ratiaczak, *President*
EMP: 4 EST: 1999
SQ FT: 3,800
SALES (est): 250K **Privately Held**
WEB: www.pinnacleprecisioninc.com
SIC: 3541 Machine tools, metal cutting type

(G-1454)
PRINT SHOP DESIGN AND PRINT
366 Broadway Ave (44146-2604)
PHONE...................................440 232-2391
Lisa M Szabo, *Manager*
EMP: 4
SALES (est): 259.5K **Privately Held**
SIC: 2752 Commercial printing, lithographic

(G-1455)
PUHD
20806 Aurora Rd (44146-1006)
PHONE...................................216 244-3336
Chris Beard, *Owner*
EMP: 5
SALES: 1MM **Privately Held**
SIC: 2741 Miscellaneous publishing

(G-1456)
REA ELEKTRONIK INC
7307 Young Dr Ste B (44146-5385)
PHONE...................................440 232-0555
Fax: 440 232-5335
Ray Turchi, *President*
Rich Peat, *Natl Sales Mgr*
Kevin Murray, *VP Sales*
Jeff Bosch, *Regl Sales Mgr*
Bruce Roaf, *Regl Sales Mgr*
▲ EMP: 11
SQ FT: 5,400
SALES (est): 2.1MM **Privately Held**
WEB: www.rea-jet.com
SIC: 3953 5112 Marking devices; marking devices

(G-1457)
RESERVE MILLWORK INC
26881 Cannon Rd (44146-1851)
PHONE...................................216 531-6982
Fax: 216 531-5231
Tony Azzolina, *President*
Virginia Azzolina, *Vice Pres*
EMP: 28 EST: 1980
SQ FT: 18,000
SALES (est): 5.5MM **Privately Held**
WEB: www.reservemillwork.com
SIC: 2431 2434 2541 Ornamental woodwork: cornices, mantels, etc.; wood kitchen cabinets; wood partitions & fixtures

(G-1458)
S-L DISTRIBUTION COMPANY INC
26400 Broadway Ave Ste C (44146-6538)
PHONE...................................440 786-9990
EMP: 5
SALES (corp-wide): 2.1B **Publicly Held**
SIC: 2052 Pretzels
HQ: S-L Distribution Company, Inc.
1250 York St
Hanover PA 17331
717 632-4477

(G-1459)
S-L SNACKS REAL ESTATE INC
26400 Broadway Ave (44146-6537)
PHONE...................................440 786-9990
Bruce Jackson, *Manager*
EMP: 388

SALES (corp-wide): 2.1B **Publicly Held**
SIC: 2052 Cookies & crackers
HQ: S-L Snacks Real Estate, Inc.
1250 York St
Hanover PA 17331
717 632-4477

(G-1460)
SATURN PRESS INC
177 Northfield Rd (44146-4605)
PHONE...................................440 232-3344
Cindy Balamenti, *President*
Anthony Balamenti, *Vice Pres*
Biagio Belfiore, *Supervisor*
EMP: 5
SALES: 400K **Privately Held**
WEB: www.saturn-press.com
SIC: 2759 Commercial printing

(G-1461)
SEEB INDUSTRIAL INC
5182 Richmond Rd (44146-1349)
P.O. Box 382, Twinsburg (44087-0382)
PHONE...................................216 896-9016
Fax: 216 896-9267
Alex Nagy Jr, *President*
Judy Brunnett, *Office Mgr*
EMP: 9
SQ FT: 5,000
SALES: 880K **Privately Held**
WEB: www.seeb-sa.com
SIC: 3599 Machine shop, jobbing & repair

(G-1462)
SMITH-LUSTIG PAPER BOX MFG CO
22475 Aurora Rd (44146-1270)
PHONE...................................216 621-0453
Fax: 216 621-0483
Richard Ames, *President*
Ann Ames, *Vice Pres*
Graham Klintworth, *Vice Pres*
Jenna Hadavny, *Manager*
▲ EMP: 40 EST: 1932
SQ FT: 75,000
SALES (est): 7.6MM **Privately Held**
SIC: 2631 2653 Folding boxboard; boxes, corrugated: made from purchased materials

(G-1463)
T J TOOL WORKS INC
7010 Krick Rd Ste 4 (44146-4445)
PHONE...................................440 439-1388
Thomas Calkins Jr, *President*
Linda Calkins, *Admin Sec*
EMP: 3
SQ FT: 5,000
SALES (est): 511.2K **Privately Held**
SIC: 3312 7699 Forgings, iron & steel; knife, saw & tool sharpening & repair

(G-1464)
TAVENS CONTAINER INC
Also Called: Tavens Packg Display Solutions
22475 Aurora Rd (44146-1270)
PHONE...................................216 883-3333
Fax: 216 883-5316
Richard Ames, *President*
Steve Sutker, *Vice Pres*
Richard Bernheimer, *Purchasing*
Graham Klintworth, *VP Finance*
Benjamin Calkins, *Incorporator*
EMP: 60 EST: 1957
SQ FT: 87,000
SALES (est): 22.4MM **Privately Held**
WEB: www.tavens.com
SIC: 2653 3412 Boxes, corrugated: made from purchased materials; metal barrels, drums & pails

(G-1465)
THERMO FISHER SCIENTIFIC INC
1 Thermo Fisher Way (44146-6536)
PHONE...................................440 703-1400
Trey Sieger, *Safety Mgr*
Rich Pallatine, *Branch Mgr*
Mike Derrick, *Manager*
EMP: 8
SALES (corp-wide): 18.2B **Publicly Held**
WEB: www.thermo.com
SIC: 3826 Analytical instruments

PA: Thermo Fisher Scientific Inc.
168 3rd Ave
Waltham MA 02451
781 622-1000

(G-1466)
TIER ENVIRONMENTAL
7013 Krick Rd (44146-4415)
PHONE...................................440 232-9400
EMP: 19
SALES (est): 4.7MM **Privately Held**
SIC: 3822 Auto controls regulating residntl & coml environmt & applncs

(G-1467)
TMARZETTI COMPANY
Also Called: New York Frozen Foods
25900 Fargo Ave (44146-1302)
PHONE...................................216 292-5655
Mike Mahon, *Managing Dir*
Bill Vandyke, *Supervisor*
EMP: 5
SALES (corp-wide): 1.1B **Publicly Held**
SIC: 2035 Pickles, sauces & salad dressings
HQ: T.Marzetti Company
380 Polaris Pkwy Ste 400
Westerville OH 43082
614 846-2232

(G-1468)
TORQ CORPORATION
32 W Monroe Ave (44146-3693)
PHONE...................................440 232-4100
Fax: 440 232-4104
James E Taylor, *CEO*
John P Taylor, *President*
Gary Reitier, *General Mgr*
Marian Knapik, *Principal*
Gvido Kubulins, *Engineer*
▲ EMP: 29 EST: 1951
SQ FT: 22,000
SALES (est): 6.6MM **Privately Held**
WEB: www.torq.com
SIC: 3643 Current-carrying wiring devices

(G-1469)
TRUE GRINDING
20502 Krick Rd (44146-5408)
PHONE...................................440 786-7608
Mark Kerney, *President*
Jim Orban, *Vice Pres*
EMP: 3
SALES: 300K **Privately Held**
SIC: 3599 Grinding castings for the trade

(G-1470)
VDM BIOCHEMICALS LLC
5386 Majestic Pkwy Ste 9 (44146-6907)
PHONE...................................440 786-9400
Lida Gevorgyan, *Mng Member*
David Martirosyan,
EMP: 3
SALES (est): 240.7K **Privately Held**
SIC: 2833 Medicinals & botanicals

(G-1471)
VITEC INC
26901 Cannon Rd (44146-1809)
PHONE...................................216 464-4670
Fax: 216 464-5324
Richard A Wynveen, *CEO*
Michael Troyan, *Engineer*
Franz H Schubert, *Shareholder*
EMP: 11
SQ FT: 15,000
SALES (est): 2.4MM **Privately Held**
SIC: 3823 Industrial instrmnts msrmnt display/control process variable

(G-1472)
WALTON PLASTICS INC
Also Called: Wal Plax
20493 Hannan Pkwy (44146-5356)
PHONE...................................440 786-7711
Fax: 440 232-3187
Steven Wake, *CEO*
Larry Crystal, *Principal*
Marinko Milos, *CFO*
Ron Seese, *Accounts Mgr*
Phil Davis, *Manager*
▲ EMP: 21
SQ FT: 44,000
SALES (est): 7.1MM **Privately Held**
WEB: www.waltonpvc.com
SIC: 3081 Vinyl film & sheet

(G-1473)
XELLIA PHARMACEUTICALS USA LLC
200 Northfield Rd (44146-4642)
PHONE......................847 986-7984
Niess Agerbak, *Branch Mgr*
EMP: 20
SALES (corp-wide): 18.5B **Privately Held**
SIC: 2834 Pharmaceutical preparations
HQ: Xellia Pharmaceuticals Usa Llc
　　8841 Wadford Dr
　　Raleigh NC 27616
　　919 327-5500

(G-1474)
YOUNG REGULATOR COMPANY INC
7100 Krick Rd Ste A (44146-4443)
PHONE......................440 232-9452
Fax: 440 663-1830
Michael E McGuigan, *President*
Marty Gullatta, *Purch Mgr*
EMP: 20 EST: 1930
SQ FT: 40,000
SALES: 6.2MM **Privately Held**
WEB: www.youngregulator.com
SIC: 3822 1711 Air conditioning & refrigeration controls; plumbing, heating, air-conditioning contractors

(G-1475)
ZENEX INTERNATIONAL
7777 First Pl (44146-6733)
PHONE......................440 232-4155
George Kniere, *Owner*
Jason Archer, *Natl Sales Mgr*
Paul Crowther, *Regl Sales Mgr*
Ric Johnson, *Manager*
Eric Platt, *Graphic Designe*
▲ EMP: 30
SALES (est): 5MM **Privately Held**
SIC: 2813 Aerosols

Bedford Heights
Cuyahoga County

(G-1476)
ALERT STAMPING & MFG CO INC
Also Called: Paul S Blanch
24500 Solon Rd (44146-4793)
PHONE......................440 232-5020
Fax: 440 232-8417
Paul S Blanch, *President*
Dave Collura, *Business Mgr*
James D Kovacik, *Vice Pres*
Georgene Javor, *Office Mgr*
Ralph Technow, *Director*
▲ EMP: 40 EST: 1961
SQ FT: 40,000
SALES (est): 8MM **Privately Held**
SIC: 3699 3499 3641 3645 Extension cords; reels, cable: metal; lamps, fluorescent, electric; lamps, incandescent filament, electric; residential lighting fixtures

(G-1477)
ALLOY METAL EXCHANGE LLC
Also Called: Dynamic Metal Services
26000 Corbin Dr (44128)
PHONE......................216 478-0200
Brian Ducovna, *President*
Ben Henson, *Vice Pres*
Bill Mills, *Vice Pres*
George Smolinski, *Opers Staff*
Kevin Lamar, *CFO*
EMP: 25
SQ FT: 40,000
SALES (est): 10.1MM **Privately Held**
SIC: 1081 Metal mining services

(G-1478)
AMERICAN SPRING WIRE CORP (PA)
Also Called: A S W
26300 Miles Rd (44146-1072)
PHONE......................216 292-4620
Fax: 216 292-4444
Timothy W Selhorst, *CEO*
Michael L Miller, *Principal*
Greg Bokar, *COO*
William Snyder, *Vice Pres*

Peter Anselmi, *Safety Mgr*
▲ EMP: 200
SQ FT: 360,500
SALES (est): 166.1MM **Privately Held**
WEB: www.americanspringwire.com
SIC: 3272 3315 3316 3339 Concrete products; wire products, ferrous/iron: made in wiredrawing plants; wire, flat, cold-rolled strip: not made in hot-rolled mills; primary nonferrous metals; carbon & graphite products

(G-1479)
CARDINAL FSTENER SPECIALTY INC
5185 Richmond Rd (44146-1330)
PHONE......................216 831-3800
Fax: 216 292-1465
Bill Boak, *President*
Bradford Bohonus, *COO*
Wendy L Brugmann, *Exec VP*
Rick Lieberman, *Vice Pres*
Denise R Muha, *Vice Pres*
▲ EMP: 50
SQ FT: 100,000
SALES (est): 11.8MM **Privately Held**
WEB: www.cardinalfastener.com
SIC: 3965 Fasteners

(G-1480)
CLEVELAND COCA-COLA BTLG INC
25000 Miles Rd (44146-1319)
PHONE......................216 690-2653
Fax: 216 595-7971
Et Al, *President*
George M Gernhardt, *Principal*
Peter E Benzino, *Vice Pres*
Charles R Hanlon, *Treasurer*
Nio Robash, *Finance Dir*
EMP: 220 EST: 1911
SQ FT: 220,000
SALES (est): 39.9MM
SALES (corp-wide): 298.7MM **Privately Held**
SIC: 2086 Bottled & canned soft drinks
HQ: Wilmington Trust Sp Services
　　1105 N Market St Ste 1300
　　Wilmington DE 19801
　　302 427-7650

(G-1481)
CLEVELAND STEEL SPECIALTY CO
26001 Richmond Rd (44146-1435)
PHONE......................216 464-9400
Fax: 216 464-9404
Robert W Ehrhardt Sr, *President*
Robert W Ehrhardt Jr, *President*
Bob Rief, *Plant Mgr*
EMP: 30
SQ FT: 24,000
SALES (est): 8.1MM **Privately Held**
WEB: www.clevelandsteel.com
SIC: 3443 3429 3444 Metal parts; builders' hardware; sheet metalwork

(G-1482)
CWH GRAPHICS LLC
Also Called: Ink Well
23196 Miles Rd Ste A (44128-5490)
P.O. Box 22651, Cleveland (44122-0651)
PHONE......................866 241-8515
Kelvin Hunter Sr,
George F Voinovich,
EMP: 7
SQ FT: 4,000
SALES (est): 557K **Privately Held**
SIC: 2752 Commercial printing, lithographic

(G-1483)
ELECTRODATA INC
23400 Aurora Rd Ste E (44146-1738)
P.O. Box 31780, Independence (44131-0780)
PHONE......................216 663-3333
Fax: 216 663-0507
Eddy Wright, *President*
Michael Wright, *Principal*
Jim Spoth, *Corp Secy*
David Osborne, *Executive*
EMP: 15 EST: 1972
SQ FT: 11,000

SALES (est): 3.1MM **Privately Held**
WEB: www.electrodata.com
SIC: 3661 Telephone & telegraph apparatus

(G-1484)
FOOD EQUIPMENT MFG CORP
Also Called: Femc
22201 Aurora Rd (44146-1273)
PHONE......................216 672-5859
Robert Sauer, *President*
Betty Howard, *President*
Lester Weagraff, *Engineer*
Dom Castor, *Electrical Engi*
Obert Sauer, *CFO*
EMP: 20
SQ FT: 65,000
SALES (est): 6.4MM **Privately Held**
WEB: www.femc.com
SIC: 3565 Packaging machinery

(G-1485)
HALEX/SCOTT FETZER COMPANY (DH)
Also Called: Halex, A Scott Fetzer Company
23901 Aurora Rd (44146-1717)
PHONE......................440 439-1616
Fax: 440 439-1792
Gary Heeman, *President*
John Selger, *Controller*
Ross Shah, *Manager*
▲ EMP: 82
SALES (est): 16.5MM
SALES (corp-wide): 223.6B **Publicly Held**
SIC: 3699 Electrical equipment & supplies
HQ: The Scott Fetzer Company
　　28800 Clemens Rd
　　Westlake OH 44145
　　440 892-3000

(G-1486)
HOIST EQUIPMENT CO INC (PA)
26161 Cannon Rd (44146-1896)
PHONE......................440 232-0300
Fax: 440 232-0300
Nicholas Gambatesa, *CEO*
Jeffrey Sadar, *Vice Pres*
Thomas Gedeon, *Chief Engr*
Tom Giddion, *Engineer*
EMP: 30 EST: 1953
SQ FT: 40,000
SALES (est): 4.4MM **Privately Held**
WEB: www.hoistequipment.com
SIC: 3537 3535 3536 Cranes, industrial truck; engine stands & racks, metal; lift trucks, industrial: fork, platform, straddle, etc.; overhead conveyor systems; hoists

(G-1487)
LLC BRAND CASTLE (PA)
5111 Richmond Rd Frnt (44146-1354)
PHONE......................216 292-7700
Jimmy Zeilinger, *President*
Jim Shlonsky, *Vice Pres*
Bobbi Weissman, *Controller*
Brianne Moore, *Natl Sales Mgr*
Roger Hudson, *Cust Mgr*
◆ EMP: 12
SQ FT: 10,000
SALES (est): 16.7MM **Privately Held**
WEB: www.brandcastle.com
SIC: 2052 Bakery products, dry

(G-1488)
MADISON ELECTRIC PRODUCTS INC (PA)
26401 Fargo Ave (44146-1311)
PHONE......................216 391-7776
Brad Wiandt, *President*
Rob Fisher, *Vice Pres*
Sharon Miller, *Manager*
◆ EMP: 40 EST: 1988
SQ FT: 1,000
SALES (est): 6.9MM **Privately Held**
SIC: 3644 Electric conduits & fittings

(G-1489)
METRON INSTRUMENTS INC
5198 Richmond Rd (44146-1331)
PHONE......................216 332-0592
David Anderson, *President*
EMP: 8
SALES (est): 1.4MM **Privately Held**
SIC: 3826 Analytical instruments

(G-1490)
MOLDED EXTRUDED
23940 Miles Rd (44128-5425)
PHONE......................216 475-5491
Frank Novak, *Principal*
EMP: 4 EST: 2012
SALES (est): 290.2K **Privately Held**
SIC: 3089 Molding primary plastic

(G-1491)
NATIONAL PEENING
23800 Corbin Dr (44128-5454)
PHONE......................216 342-9155
Don Kvorka, *Principal*
John Shorr, *Manager*
EMP: 4
SALES (est): 428.5K **Privately Held**
SIC: 3398 Shot peening (treating steel to reduce fatigue)

(G-1492)
PARAGON ROBOTICS LLC
5386 Majestic Pkwy Ste 2 (44146-6907)
PHONE......................216 313-9299
Julian Lamb,
EMP: 3
SALES: 40K **Privately Held**
SIC: 3695 Computer software tape & disks: blank, rigid & floppy

(G-1493)
RMW INDUSTRIES INC
24869 Aurora Rd (44146-1760)
PHONE......................440 439-1971
Robyn Mays, *Principal*
EMP: 3
SALES (est): 255.6K **Privately Held**
SIC: 3999 Manufacturing industries

(G-1494)
STEVES SPORTS INC
6442 Metro Ct Ste B (44146-4777)
PHONE......................440 735-0044
Steve Baraona, *Owner*
EMP: 6 EST: 2010
SALES (est): 741.9K **Privately Held**
SIC: 2759 Screen printing

(G-1495)
TPSC INC
Also Called: Perfect Score, The
25801 Solon Rd (44146-4759)
PHONE......................440 439-9320
Fax: 440 439-9380
Ed Fraschetti, *President*
Mike Greco, *Vice Pres*
John Slater, *Chief Engr*
Megan Gross, *Admin Sec*
EMP: 15
SQ FT: 2,000
SALES: 5MM **Privately Held**
SIC: 3556 Bakery machinery

Bellaire
Belmont County

(G-1496)
BELMONT COMMUNITY HOSPITAL
Also Called: Belmont Community Health Ctr
4697 Harrison St (43906-1338)
PHONE......................740 671-1216
Garry Gould, *CEO*
KY Sohn, *Principal*
Bobbi Nesbitt, *Manager*
EMP: 275
SALES (corp-wide): 355.2MM **Privately Held**
SIC: 2599 Hospital beds
HQ: Belmont Community Hospital
　　4697 Harrison St
　　Bellaire OH 43906
　　740 671-1200

(G-1497)
CHARLES WISVARI
Also Called: Vivid Graphix
3266 Guernsey St (43906-1545)
PHONE......................740 671-9960
Fax: 740 671-1129
Charles Wisvari, *Owner*
Nancy Wisvari, *Co-Owner*
EMP: 11

▲ = Import ▼=Export
◆ =Import/Export

SQ FT: 10,500
SALES: 500K **Privately Held**
SIC: 2396 2395 5699 Screen printing on fabric articles; embroidery products, except schiffli machine; customized clothing & apparel

(G-1498)
GUMBYS LLC
2300 Belmont St (43906-1733)
PHONE................................740 671-0818
Beau Lamotte, *Branch Mgr*
EMP: 66
SALES (corp-wide): 20.8MM **Privately Held**
SIC: 3999 Cigarette & cigar products & accessories
PA: Gumby's, L.L.C.
98 E Cove Ave Ste 1
Wheeling WV 26003
304 242-0002

(G-1499)
KROGER CO
400 28th St (43906-1790)
PHONE................................740 671-5164
Fax: 740 676-6644
Kim Bartsch, *Manager*
EMP: 175
SALES (corp-wide): 115.3B **Publicly Held**
WEB: www.kroger.com
SIC: 5411 5912 5812 2052 Supermarkets, chain; drug stores & proprietary stores; eating places; cookies & crackers; bread, cake & related products
PA: The Kroger Co
1014 Vine St Ste 1000
Cincinnati OH 45202
513 762-4000

(G-1500)
PAUL/JAY ASSOCIATES
Also Called: Digital Solutions
3057 Union St (43906-1531)
P.O. Box 236 (43906-0236)
PHONE................................740 676-8776
Fax: 740 676-4441
Paul J Cramer, *Owner*
EMP: 4
SQ FT: 9,000
SALES (est): 409.9K **Privately Held**
WEB: www.digitalsolutionsusa.com
SIC: 2752 7311 7372 2791 Commercial printing, offset; advertising agencies; prepackaged software; typesetting

(G-1501)
PYROTECHNICS BY PRESUTTI INC (PA)
54911 High Ridge Rd (43906-9553)
P.O. Box 42, Saint Clairsville (43950-0042)
PHONE................................740 699-1224
Fax: 740 676-7753
Barbara P Lucas, *President*
Delphine Presutti, *President*
▲ **EMP:** 11
SQ FT: 4,000
SALES: 295.2K **Privately Held**
SIC: 2899 Fireworks

(G-1502)
XTO ENERGY INC
2358 W 23rd St (43906-9614)
PHONE................................740 671-9901
EMP: 73
SALES (corp-wide): 226B **Publicly Held**
SIC: 1311 Crude petroleum & natural gas production
HQ: Xto Energy Inc.
810 Houston St Ste 2000
Fort Worth TX 76102
817 870-2800

Bellbrook
Greene County

(G-1503)
ADVANCED ENGINE TECH LLC
Also Called: A E T
3192 Bugle Bluff Dr (45305-8856)
PHONE................................937 439-0224
Rck Pelfrey, *President*

Jordan Gartenhaus, *Engineer*
Dale Pelfrey,
EMP: 5 **EST:** 2006
SALES (est): 726.5K **Privately Held**
SIC: 2869 2992 Hydraulic fluids, synthetic base; lubricating oils & greases; oils & greases, blending & compounding

(G-1504)
COMPUTER ZOO INC
1930 N Lakeman Dr Ste 106 (45305-1200)
PHONE................................937 310-1474
Fax: 937 438-2027
EMP: 9 **EST:** 1999
SQ FT: 2,500
SALES (est): 940K **Privately Held**
SIC: 5734 3571 7372 3577 Ret Computers/Software Mfg Electronic Computers Prepackaged Software Svc Mfg Computer Peripherals Electrical Contractor

(G-1505)
D J DECORATIVE STONE INC
3180 Ferry Rd (45305-8926)
PHONE................................937 848-6462
Jamie Zimmer, *President*
EMP: 4
SALES (est): 505.2K **Privately Held**
SIC: 3281 Stone, quarrying & processing of own stone products

(G-1506)
DAIRY SHED
55 Bellbrook Plz (45305-1954)
PHONE................................937 848-3504
Roger McConnell, *Principal*
EMP: 4
SALES (est): 213.2K **Privately Held**
SIC: 2024 Ice cream, bulk

(G-1507)
ERNST ENTERPRISES INC
Also Called: Sugarcreek Ready Mix
2181 Ferry Rd (45305-9728)
PHONE................................937 848-6811
Fax: 937 848-4448
John Ernst Jr, *President*
Mark Gwin, *Sales Executive*
EMP: 25
SQ FT: 5,000
SALES (corp-wide): 191MM **Privately Held**
WEB: www.ernstconcrete.com
SIC: 3273 Ready-mixed concrete
PA: Ernst Enterprises, Inc.
3361 Successful Way
Dayton OH 45414
937 233-5555

(G-1508)
FANZ STOP
63 Bellbrook Plz (45305-1954)
PHONE................................937 310-1436
Jenniffer Simpson, *Partner*
EMP: 6
SALES (est): 762.5K **Privately Held**
SIC: 2329 2339 Men's & boys' sportswear & athletic clothing; sportswear, women's

(G-1509)
GOLDEN SPRING CO INC
2143 Ferry Rd (45305-9728)
P.O. Box 244 (45305-0244)
PHONE................................937 848-2513
Fax: 937 848-2521
Paul Smith, *President*
Rita Treser, *Corp Secy*
EMP: 10 **EST:** 1953
SQ FT: 5,100
SALES: 1MM **Privately Held**
WEB: www.golden-spring.com
SIC: 3493 Coiled flat springs

(G-1510)
N S T BATTERY
4496 W Franklin St (45305-1553)
PHONE................................937 433-9222
Linda G Mem, *Principal*
EMP: 7
SALES (est): 696.1K **Privately Held**
WEB: www.nstbattery.com
SIC: 3692 5063 5531 Primary batteries, dry & wet; batteries; batteries, automotive & truck

---

Belle Center
Logan County

(G-1511)
BELLE CENTER AIR TOOL CO INC
202 N Elizabeth St (43310-9684)
P.O. Box 37 (43310-0037)
PHONE................................937 464-7474
Fax: 937 464-4908
Carroll Doty, *President*
Ruth Doty, *Corp Secy*
▲ **EMP:** 9
SQ FT: 9,500
SALES (est): 2.8MM **Privately Held**
SIC: 5084 3532 Pneumatic tools & equipment; drills, bits & similar equipment

(G-1512)
DAN S MILLER & DAVID S MILLER
9216 County Road 97 (43310-9597)
PHONE................................937 464-9061
Dan S Miller, *Partner*
EMP: 4
SALES: 500K **Privately Held**
SIC: 2448 Pallets, wood

(G-1513)
HIGHS WELDING INC
3065 County Road 150 (43310-1107)
P.O. Box 97, Alger (45812-0097)
PHONE................................937 464-3029
Nick S High, *President*
EMP: 6
SALES (est): 554K **Privately Held**
SIC: 7692 Welding repair

(G-1514)
MILLER PALLET COMPANY
9216 County Road 97 (43310-9597)
PHONE................................937 464-4483
Dan Miller, *Owner*
David Miller, *Principal*
EMP: 3
SALES (est): 399.9K **Privately Held**
SIC: 2448 Pallets, wood

Bellefontaine
Logan County

(G-1515)
AGC AUTOMOTIVE AMERICAS
1465 W Sandusky Ave (43311-1082)
PHONE................................937 599-3131
Fax: 937 599-3322
Arkady Doorman, *Vice Pres*
Dean Wright, *Plant Mgr*
Arcadie Dorman, *Opers Staff*
Kazuhiro Sako, *Treasurer*
Dick Huber, *Controller*
▲ **EMP:** 81
SALES (est): 11.4MM **Privately Held**
SIC: 7549 1793 1799 3231 Automotive customizing services, non-factory basis; glass & glazing work; glass tinting, architectural or automotive; products of purchased glass

(G-1516)
AGC FLAT GLASS NORTH AMER INC
31 Hunter Pl (43311-3006)
PHONE................................937 292-7784
Bade Furling, *Branch Mgr*
EMP: 9
SALES (corp-wide): 11.5B **Privately Held**
SIC: 3211 Flat glass
HQ: Agc Flat Glass North America, Inc.
11175 Cicero Dr Ste 400
Alpharetta GA 30022
404 446-4200

(G-1517)
AGC FLAT GLASS NORTH AMER INC
1465 W Sandusky Ave (43311-1082)
P.O. Box 819 (43311-0819)
PHONE................................937 599-3131

Konz Jeff, *Purch Agent*
Tim Noel, *Engineer*
Kazuhiro Sako, *Treasurer*
Arcadie Dorman, *Branch Mgr*
Doug Corwin, *Manager*
EMP: 5
SQ FT: 570,000
SALES (corp-wide): 11.5B **Privately Held**
WEB: www.aptechnoglass.com
SIC: 3231 3211 Safety glass: made from purchased glass; flat glass
HQ: Agc Flat Glass North America, Inc.
11175 Cicero Dr Ste 400
Alpharetta GA 30022
404 446-4200

(G-1518)
ANKIM ENTERPRISES INCORPORATED
1221 W Sandusky Ave (43311-1046)
P.O. Box 569 (43311-0569)
PHONE................................937 599-1121
Fax: 937 599-5162
Stan Wright, *President*
Clara Wright, *Vice Pres*
EMP: 20
SQ FT: 24,000
SALES (est): 2.5MM **Privately Held**
SIC: 3678 3679 Electronic connectors; harness assemblies for electronic use: wire or cable

(G-1519)
ARDEN J NEER SR
Also Called: Neer's Engineering Labs
4859 Township Road 45 (43311-9624)
PHONE................................937 585-6733
Fax: 937 585-5083
Arden J Neer Sr, *Owner*
EMP: 12
SQ FT: 7,500
SALES: 1.1MM **Privately Held**
SIC: 1442 Construction sand mining; gravel mining

(G-1520)
AXIS CORPORATION
314 Water Ave (43311-1734)
P.O. Box 668 (43311-0668)
PHONE................................937 592-1958
Matt Oldiges, *President*
Thomas Oldiges, *Shareholder*
Linda Luebke, *Admin Sec*
EMP: 10
SQ FT: 20,000
SALES (est): 1.8MM **Privately Held**
WEB: www.axiscorporation.com
SIC: 3499 Wheels: wheelbarrow, stroller, etc.: disc, stamped metal

(G-1521)
BELLE PRINTING
118 S Main St (43311-2007)
P.O. Box 307 (43311-0307)
PHONE................................937 592-5161
Fax: 937 592-4161
Mike Joseph, *Owner*
Nancy Joseph, *Purch Agent*
EMP: 5
SQ FT: 1,500
SALES: 400K **Privately Held**
SIC: 2752 Commercial printing, lithographic; commercial printing, offset

(G-1522)
BELLEFONTAINE EXAMINER
127 E Chillicothe Ave (43311-1957)
PHONE................................937 592-3060
Thomas Hubbard, *Principal*
Matt Hammond, *Editor*
EMP: 4
SALES (est): 393.8K **Privately Held**
SIC: 2711 Newspapers, publishing & printing

(G-1523)
BUCKEYE BOXES INC
1133 W Columbus Ave (43311-1076)
PHONE................................937 599-2551
Fax: 937 599-2553
Kevin Maxam, *Manager*
EMP: 8
SALES (corp-wide): 24.9MM **Privately Held**
SIC: 2653 Corrugated & solid fiber boxes

GEOGRAPHIC

PA: Buckeye Boxes, Inc.
601 N Hague Ave
Columbus OH 43204
614 274-8484

(G-1524)
CATHIE D HUBBARD
Also Called: Publishing Company
305 E Williams Ave (43311-2449)
PHONE..............................937 593-0316
Janet Hubbard, *Owner*
EMP: 32
SALES (est): 612.5K **Privately Held**
SIC: 2711 Newspapers, publishing & print-
ing

(G-1525)
COUNTY CLASSIFIEDS
Also Called: The County Classified's
117 E Patterson Ave (43311-1912)
P.O. Box 596 (43311-0596)
PHONE..............................937 592-8847
Leah Frank, *President*
EMP: 8
SALES (est): 310K **Privately Held**
SIC: 2711 2752 2741 Job printing &
newspaper publishing combined; com-
mercial printing, lithographic; miscella-
neous publishing

(G-1526)
**DAIDO METAL BELLEFONTAINE
LLC**
1215 S Greenwood St (43311-1628)
PHONE..............................937 592-5010
Lewie Ekleberry, *Plant Mgr*
Ken Fricker, *QC Mgr*
Ray Massey, *Manager*
Duane Pittman, *Manager*
Mark Ikawa,
▲ **EMP:** 192
SQ FT: 224,000
SALES (est): 26.3MM
SALES (corp-wide): 695.6MM **Privately
Held**
WEB: www.daidometal.co.jp
SIC: 3366 Bushings & bearings
PA: Daido Metal Co., Ltd.
2-3-1, Sakae, Naka-Ku
Nagoya AIC 460-0
522 051-400

(G-1527)
**DESIGNED HARNESS SYSTEMS
INC**
Also Called: Dhs Innovations
227 Water Ave (43311-1731)
P.O. Box 37 (43311-0037)
PHONE..............................937 599-2485
Fax: 937 599-2408
Craig Lingon, *President*
David Sharp, *Project Mgr*
EMP: 10
SALES (est): 1.2MM **Privately Held**
SIC: 3714 Automotive wiring harness sets

(G-1528)
DISHTRONIX INC
2497 Township Road 55 (43311-9082)
P.O. Box 1007 (43311-6007)
PHONE..............................937 292-7981
Steven Dishop, *President*
EMP: 6
SALES (est): 679.5K **Privately Held**
SIC: 3629 8712 Electronic generation
equipment; house designer

(G-1529)
DMG TOOL & DIE LLC
1215 S Greenwood St (43311-1628)
PHONE..............................937 407-0810
John Pope, *Mfg Staff*
Thomas D Moreland, *Mng Member*
EMP: 6
SQ FT: 2,000
SALES: 13.4K **Privately Held**
SIC: 3312 Tool & die steel

(G-1530)
EWH SPECTRUM LLC
221 W Chillicothe Ave (43311-1467)
PHONE..............................937 593-8010
Fax: 937 593-2438
Robert L Robinson, *President*
Jean Robinson, *Vice Pres*
Matt Thomas, *Opers-Prdtn-Mfg*

Dave Shoffner, *Purch Mgr*
Jackie Mescher, *Director*
EMP: 74
SQ FT: 27,500
SALES (est): 16MM **Privately Held**
WEB: www.ewhspectrum.com
SIC: 3679 3694 Harness assemblies for
electronic use: wire or cable; engine elec-
trical equipment

(G-1531)
GRIT GUARD INC
3690 County Road 10 (43311-9416)
PHONE..............................937 592-9003
Fax: 937 599-2876
Luan Lamb, *President*
Chris Lamb, *Business Dir*
EMP: 5
SALES: 1.7MM **Privately Held**
SIC: 5084 2821 Plastic products machin-
ery; plastics materials & resins

(G-1532)
HBD/THERMOID INC
1301 W Sandusky Ave (43311-1082)
PHONE..............................937 593-5010
Fax: 937 593-4353
Randy Lady, *General Mgr*
Wendy Jordan, *General Mgr*
Chris Rapp, *District Mgr*
Dave Dockins, *Plant Mgr*
John Hutchins, *Purch Agent*
▼ **EMP:** 250
SALES (est): 37.5MM
SALES (corp-wide): 230.1MM **Privately
Held**
WEB: www.hbdelgin.com
SIC: 3429 3052 Manufactured hardware
(general); rubber & plastics hose & belt-
ings
PA: Hbd Industries Inc
5200 Upper Metro Pl # 110
Dublin OH 43017
614 526-7000

(G-1533)
HUBBARD PUBLISHING CO
127 E Chillicothe Ave (43311-1957)
P.O. Box 40 (43311-0040)
PHONE..............................937 592-3060
Fax: 937 592-4463
Janet Hubbard, *President*
Thomas J Hubbard, *General Mgr*
Jon B Hubbard, *Vice Pres*
EMP: 35
SQ FT: 13,000
SALES (est): 2.6MM **Privately Held**
SIC: 2711 2752 2791 Commercial printing
& newspaper publishing combined; com-
mercial printing, offset; typesetting

(G-1534)
INSTANT REPLAY
334 E Columbus Ave (43311-2002)
PHONE..............................937 592-0534
Lisa Russell, *Office Mgr*
EMP: 3
SALES (est): 247.5K **Privately Held**
SIC: 2752 Commercial printing, litho-
graphic

(G-1535)
KLB INDUSTRIES INC
Also Called: National Extrusion & Mfg Co
Orchard & Elm St (43311)
P.O. Box 460 (43311-0460)
PHONE..............................937 592-9010
Fax: 937 592-1950
Christopher A Kerns, *President*
John D Bishop, *Vice Pres*
Rick Rogers, *Plant Mgr*
Melissa Schinker, *Engineer*
Nick Benson, *Design Engr*
▲ **EMP:** 45 **EST:** 1949
SQ FT: 41,942
SALES (est): 9.1MM **Privately Held**
WEB: www.nationalextrusion.com
SIC: 3354 Aluminum extruded products

(G-1536)
MAJESTIC PLASTICS INC
811 N Main St (43311-2376)
P.O. Box 47 (43311-0047)
PHONE..............................937 593-9500
Sean Ammons, *President*
EMP: 9

SQ FT: 7,800
SALES (est): 1.5MM **Privately Held**
WEB: www.majesticplastics.com
SIC: 3089 Injection molding of plastics

(G-1537)
OHIO HARNESS LLC
227 Water Ave (43311-1731)
P.O. Box 847 (43311-0847)
PHONE..............................937 292-7355
Karen Lamb, *President*
Todd Lamb, *Vice Pres*
EMP: 20
SQ FT: 20,000
SALES: 950K **Privately Held**
SIC: 3714 7539 Automotive wiring har-
ness sets; machine shop, automotive

(G-1538)
REYNOLDS & CO INC
1515 S Main St (43311-1505)
P.O. Box 907 (43311-0907)
PHONE..............................937 592-8300
Fax: 937 592-8302
Thomas M Reynolds, *President*
EMP: 4
SALES (est): 430K **Privately Held**
WEB: www.reynolds-co.com
SIC: 5075 3589 Warm air heating & air
conditioning; water treatment equipment,
industrial

(G-1539)
SIEMENS INDUSTRY INC
811 N Main St (43311-2300)
PHONE..............................937 593-6010
Fax: 937 599-7333
Chad Miller, *Opers Mgr*
Chris Childs, *Purchasing*
Ryan Shultz, *Engineer*
Arthur Harper, *Personnel*
Larry Falk, *Director*
EMP: 100
SALES (corp-wide): 89.6B **Privately Held**
WEB: www.sea.siemens.com
SIC: 3612 3613 3643 Transformers, ex-
cept electric; switchgear & switchboard
apparatus; current-carrying wiring devices
HQ: Siemens Industry, Inc.
1000 Deerfield Pkwy
Buffalo Grove IL 60089
847 215-1000

(G-1540)
**VITAL SIGNS & ADVERTISING
LLC**
224 S Madriver St (43311-1936)
PHONE..............................937 292-7967
Pat Culp, *Owner*
EMP: 3
SALES (est): 252.4K **Privately Held**
SIC: 3993 Signs & advertising specialties

Bellevue
Huron County

(G-1541)
**AMCOR RIGID PLASTICS USA
LLC**
975 W Main St (44811-9011)
PHONE..............................419 483-4343
Dave Hoover, *Ch of Bd*
Sergey Kulayev, *General Mgr*
Michael Hodges, *Vice Pres*
William Pfeiffer, *Transptn Dir*
Matthew Schoder, *Plant Mgr*
EMP: 58
SALES (corp-wide): 9.4B **Privately Held**
SIC: 3085 Plastics bottles
HQ: Amcor Rigid Plastics Usa, Llc
10521 M 52
Manchester MI 48158

(G-1542)
**AMCOR RIGID PLASTICS USA
LLC**
Also Called: Ball Plastic Container Div
975 W Main St (44811-9011)
PHONE..............................419 483-4343
EMP: 9
SALES (corp-wide): 9.6B **Privately Held**
SIC: 3411 Mfg Metal Cans

HQ: Amcor Rigid Plastics Usa, Llc
10521 Mi State Road 52
Manchester MI 48158

(G-1543)
AMERICAN BALER CO
800 E Center St (44811-1748)
P.O. Box 29 (44811-0029)
PHONE..............................419 483-5790
Fax: 419 483-3815
Leland Boren, *CEO*
Dave Kowaleski, *President*
Frank B Cameron, *Principal*
Richard R Hollington, *Principal*
E E Moulton, *Principal*
EMP: 65 **EST:** 1945
SQ FT: 80,133
SALES (est): 32.3MM
SALES (corp-wide): 284.4MM **Privately
Held**
WEB: www.avisindustrial.com
SIC: 3569 3523 Baling machines, for
scrap metal, paper or similar material;
farm machinery & equipment
PA: Avis Industrial Corporation
1909 S Main St
Upland IN 46989
765 998-8100

(G-1544)
**AUTOMTIVE CMPNNTS
HOLDINGS LLC**
111 Hirt Dr (44811-9054)
PHONE..............................419 483-5622
Steve Nevison, *Branch Mgr*
EMP: 15
SALES (corp-wide): 151.8B **Publicly
Held**
SIC: 3714 3647 Motor vehicle parts & ac-
cessories; motor vehicle lighting equip-
ment; headlights (fixtures), vehicular
HQ: Automotive Components Holdings Llc
15303 S Commerce Dr
Dearborn MI 48120

(G-1545)
**BELLEVUE MANUFACTURING
COMPANY (PA)**
520 Goodrich Rd (44811-1139)
PHONE..............................419 483-3190
Fax: 419 483-0618
Harv Williams, *Vice Pres*
Pat Widman, *Project Mgr*
Jim Hart, *Manager*
Frank A Knapp, *Incorporator*
Ralph T Wolfrom Et Al, *Incorporator*
EMP: 94 **EST:** 1915
SQ FT: 150,000
SALES (est): 19MM **Privately Held**
WEB: www.tbmc.net
SIC: 3714 Filters: oil, fuel & air, motor vehi-
cle

(G-1546)
**BELLEVUE MANUFACTURING
COMPANY**
300 Ashford Ave (44811-1600)
PHONE..............................419 483-3190
Evelyn Hart, *Treasurer*
Charles Deluca, *Manager*
EMP: 5
SALES (corp-wide): 19.7MM **Privately
Held**
WEB: www.tbmc.net
SIC: 3714 3469 Filters: oil, fuel & air,
motor vehicle; metal stampings
PA: The Bellevue Manufacturing Company
520 Goodrich Rd
Bellevue OH 44811
419 483-3190

(G-1547)
**BUNGE NORTH AMERICA
FOUNDATION**
605 Goodrich Rd (44811-1142)
P.O. Box 369 (44811-0369)
PHONE..............................419 483-5340
Bill Miller, *Plant Mgr*
Todd Trefren, *Plant Mgr*
Jim Hartzell, *Purch Mgr*
Greg Strayer, *QC Dir*
Mike Borzenski, *Plant Engr*
EMP: 8 **Privately Held**
WEB: www.bungemarion.com

SIC: 2075 2041 Soybean oil, cake or meal; lecithin, soybean; flour & other grain mill products
HQ: Bunge North America Foundation
11720 Borman Dr
Saint Louis MO 63146
314 872-3030

(G-1548)
CAPITOL ALUMINUM & GLASS CORP
1276 W Main St (44811-9424)
PHONE..................................800 331-8268
Fax: 419 483-7830
Robert C Wagner, *Ch of Bd*
Gail P Coe, *President*
Tory J Woodard, *Corp Secy*
Dean Camp, *Vice Pres*
Tricia Norton, *Human Resources*
EMP: 55 EST: 1955
SQ FT: 75,000
SALES (est): 16.8MM **Privately Held**
WEB: www.capitol-windows.com
SIC: 3442 Metal doors; window & door frames

(G-1549)
COMPLIANCE ELEMENTS LLC
8017 State Route 269 (44811-9665)
P.O. Box 254 (44811-0254)
PHONE..................................419 217-1793
EMP: 4
SALES (est): 289.9K **Privately Held**
SIC: 2819 Mfg Industrial Inorganic Chemicals

(G-1550)
DONALD E DIDION II
Also Called: Didion's Mechanical
1027b County Road 308 (44811)
PHONE..................................419 483-2226
Fax: 419 483-4382
Donald E Didion II, *Principal*
EMP: 25
SQ FT: 20,000
SALES: 1.4MM **Privately Held**
WEB: www.didionsmech.com
SIC: 3499 8711 Fire- or burglary-resistive products; engineering services

(G-1551)
INDUSTRIAL IMAGE
5630 State Route 113 (44811-8900)
PHONE..................................419 547-1417
Jason Holcomb, *Owner*
Ericca Holcomb, *Co-Owner*
EMP: 4
SALES (est): 347.8K **Privately Held**
SIC: 3993 Signs & advertising specialties

(G-1552)
MAGNESIUM REFINING TECH INC
Also Called: Magretech
301 County Road 177 (44811-8713)
PHONE..................................419 483-9199
Fax: 419 483-8411
Alfred Lehmkukl, *Sr Corp Ofcr*
Ken Balser, *Manager*
Laura Baxter, *Administration*
EMP: 50
SALES (corp-wide): 12.1MM **Privately Held**
SIC: 3339 Magnesium refining (primary)
PA: Magnesium Refining Technologies, Inc.
29695 Pettibone Rd
Cleveland OH 44139
419 483-9199

(G-1553)
MITSUBISHI CHLS PERF PLYRS INC
Also Called: McPp
350 N Buckeye St (44811-1208)
PHONE..................................419 483-2931
Diane Sabo, *Purch Mgr*
Lee Wilson, *Branch Mgr*
EMP: 80
SALES (corp-wide): 42MM **Privately Held**
SIC: 2821 2891 Plastics materials & resins; adhesives

PA: Mitsubishi Chemical Performance Polymers, Inc.
2001 Hood Rd
Greer SC 29650
864 879-5487

(G-1554)
QUALITY WELDING INC
104 Ronald Ln (44811)
P.O. Box 273 (44811-0273)
PHONE..................................419 483-6067
Fax: 419 483-3551
Charles Tinnel, *President*
Jessica Gilbert, *Manager*
EMP: 25
SQ FT: 2,800
SALES: 1.5MM **Privately Held**
SIC: 7692 Welding repair

(G-1555)
R AND S TECHNOLOGIES INC
2474 State Route 4 (44811-9742)
PHONE..................................419 483-3691
Fax: 419 483-3691
Paul Ritz, *President*
Gary Shingledecker, *Vice Pres*
Ben Ritz, *Engineer*
EMP: 11
SQ FT: 2,400
SALES (est): 1.7MM **Privately Held**
WEB: www.r-s-t-inc.com
SIC: 3089 3599 Molding primary plastic; machine & other job shop work

(G-1556)
ROCKWARE CORP
1606 W Main St (44811-9430)
PHONE..................................419 483-5649
Matthew Williams, *Manager*
EMP: 5
SQ FT: 1,000
SALES (est): 290K **Privately Held**
SIC: 7371 7373 7372 Custom computer programming services; computer integrated systems design; application computer software

(G-1557)
SCS GEARBOX INC
739 W Main St (44811-9312)
PHONE..................................419 483-7278
Fax: 419 483-4741
Michael Sage, *President*
Craig Sage, *Vice Pres*
Mary Sage, *Admin Sec*
EMP: 11
SQ FT: 10,000
SALES (est): 1.2MM **Privately Held**
WEB: www.scsgearbox.com
SIC: 3714 Gears, motor vehicle; connecting rods, motor vehicle engine

(G-1558)
SELBRO INC
555 Goodrich Rd (44811-1140)
P.O. Box 595 (44811-0595)
PHONE..................................419 483-9918
Fax: 419 483-8128
James Seliga, *President*
Gordon Seliga, *Vice Pres*
Vicki Seliga, *Admin Sec*
EMP: 10
SQ FT: 15,000
SALES (est): 1.2MM **Privately Held**
WEB: www.selbro.com
SIC: 3546 Power-driven handtools

(G-1559)
SENECA RAILROAD & MINING CO
1075 W Main St (44811-9012)
PHONE..................................419 483-7764
Raymond Wasson, *President*
Pat Mira, *Asst Sec*
EMP: 11
SQ FT: 16,300
SALES (est): 1.5MM **Privately Held**
SIC: 3312 Rail joints or fastenings

(G-1560)
SOLAE LLC
Also Called: Solae Central Soya
300 Great Lakes Pkwy (44811)
P.O. Box 369 (44811-0369)
PHONE..................................419 483-0400
Fax: 419 483-4016

Bill Miller, *Plant Mgr*
Dale Perman, *Manager*
Raymond Bowns, *Manager*
EMP: 150
SALES (corp-wide): 24.5B **Publicly Held**
WEB: www.solae.com
SIC: 2075 Soybean oil, cake or meal
HQ: Solae Llc
4300 Duncan Ave
Saint Louis MO 63110
314 659-3000

(G-1561)
SOLAE LLC
605 Goodrich Rd (44811-1142)
PHONE..................................419 483-5340
Dale Hoffman, *Manager*
EMP: 6
SALES (est): 558.1K **Privately Held**
SIC: 2075 Soybean oil mills

(G-1562)
SPIRALCOOL COMPANY
186 Sheffield St Ste 188 (44811-1528)
P.O. Box 128 (44811-0128)
PHONE..................................419 483-2510
Fax: 419 483-1580
Richard A Hopkins, *President*
EMP: 10
SQ FT: 5,000
SALES (est): 780K **Privately Held**
SIC: 3069 Hard rubber & molded rubber products

(G-1563)
THOMAS STEEL INC
305 Elm St (44811-1543)
P.O. Box 343 (44811-0343)
PHONE..................................419 483-7540
Fax: 419 483-8400
Jake Thomas, *CEO*
Steve Roth, *President*
Lynn E Thomas, *Corp Secy*
Carl Koselke, *Vice Pres*
Chuck Gerber, *Plant Mgr*
EMP: 38
SQ FT: 50,000
SALES: 8MM **Privately Held**
WEB: www.tsifab.com
SIC: 3441 Fabricated structural metal

(G-1564)
TOWER AUTOMOTIVE OPERATIONS I
630 Southwest Rd (44811-9314)
PHONE..................................419 483-1500
Kevin Stephens, *Opers Mgr*
Craig Perry, *Materials Mgr*
Kathy Callahan, *Research*
Cherie Butz, *Engineer*
Steve Weber, *Finance*
EMP: 192
SALES (corp-wide): 1.9B **Publicly Held**
SIC: 3714 Motor vehicle body components & frame
HQ: Tower Automotive Operations Usa I Llc
17672 N Laurel Park Dr 400e
Livonia MI 48152
248 675-6000

(G-1565)
WINDSOR MOLD INC
Also Called: Precision Automotive Plastics
122 Hirt Dr (44811-9053)
PHONE..................................419 484-2400
Fax: 419 484-0035
Joe Giardina, *Branch Mgr*
EMP: 28
SALES (corp-wide): 485.1K **Privately Held**
SIC: 3089 Injection molding of plastics
HQ: Windsor Mold Inc
4035 Malden Rd
Windsor ON N9C 2
519 972-9032

(G-1566)
WINDSOR MOLD USA INC
Also Called: Autoplas Division
560 Goodrich Rd (44811-1139)
PHONE..................................419 483-0653
Fax: 419 483-5400
Brian K Moll, *President*
Matt Mignin, *Plant Mgr*
Kim Seagert, *Manager*
▲ EMP: 50

SALES (est): 11.2MM
SALES (corp-wide): 485.1K **Privately Held**
SIC: 3089 Plastic processing
HQ: Windsor Mold Inc
4035 Malden Rd
Windsor ON N9C 2
519 972-9032

(G-1567)
YORK FABRICATION & MACHINE
6964 County Road 191 (44811-8700)
PHONE..................................419 483-6275
Jerome Huff, *Owner*
EMP: 4
SQ FT: 2,200
SALES (est): 190K **Privately Held**
SIC: 3599 5531 Machine shop, jobbing & repair; automotive & home supply stores

Bellville
Richland County

(G-1568)
COLLEEN D TURNER
Also Called: Bellville Flowers and Gifts
72 Main St (44813-1021)
PHONE..................................419 886-4810
Colleen Turner, *Owner*
EMP: 4
SALES (est): 263.5K **Privately Held**
SIC: 3231 Novelties, glass: fruit, foliage, flowers, animals, etc.

(G-1569)
GATTON PACKAGING INC
99 East St (44813-1003)
PHONE..................................419 886-2577
Fax: 419 886-4990
John R Gatton, *President*
Larry Gatton, *Corp Secy*
EMP: 6
SQ FT: 10,000
SALES (est): 1.2MM **Privately Held**
SIC: 2679 Corrugated paper: made from purchased material

(G-1570)
GORMAN-RUPP COMPANY
Also Called: Division Gorman-Rupp Company
180 Hines Ave (44813-1234)
PHONE..................................419 886-3001
Fax: 419 886-2338
Michael Hill, *General Mgr*
Bryan Morris, *Purchasing*
Larry Ramey, *Design Engr*
Richard Baker, *Controller*
Jody Hastings, *Sales Dir*
EMP: 46
SQ FT: 12,000
SALES (corp-wide): 382MM **Publicly Held**
WEB: www.gormanrupp.com
SIC: 3561 Pumps & pumping equipment
PA: Gorman-Rupp Company
600 S Airport Rd
Mansfield OH 44903
419 755-1011

(G-1571)
JACKSON WELLS SERVICES
1201 Mill Rd (44813-1282)
PHONE..................................419 886-2017
Cory Jackson, *Owner*
EMP: 8
SALES (est): 591.3K **Privately Held**
SIC: 1381 Service well drilling

(G-1572)
MID-OHIO TUBING LLC
500 Main St (44813-1302)
PHONE..................................419 886-0220
EMP: 70
SALES (corp-wide): 25MM **Privately Held**
SIC: 3317 Tubes, seamless steel
PA: Mid-Ohio Tubing, Llc
145 W Elm St
Butler OH 44822
419 883-2066

(G-1573)
NORTH CENTRAL INSULATION INC (PA)
7539 State Route 13 (44813-8943)
P.O. Box 368 (44813-0368)
PHONE.................................419 886-2030
Fax: 419 886-2087
D Brent Dudgeon, *President*
Alex Melly, *Business Mgr*
John Dudgeon, *Vice Pres*
Andrew Dungeon, *Vice Pres*
Jeffrey Nelson, *Controller*
▲ EMP: 18
SQ FT: 10,000
SALES (est): 28.2MM **Privately Held**
WEB: www.nci-ins.com
SIC: 1741 1742 3231 Foundation building; insulation, buildings; products of purchased glass

(G-1574)
PJ WOODWORK LLC
16 E Ogle St (44813-1029)
PHONE.................................419 886-0008
Joel Warner, *Principal*
EMP: 4
SALES (est): 358.6K **Privately Held**
SIC: 2431 Millwork

(G-1575)
PROTEUS ELECTRONICS INC
161 Spayde Rd (44813-9011)
P.O. Box 725 (44813-0725)
PHONE.................................419 886-2296
Fax: 419 886-3563
Thomas Clabaugh, *President*
Mark Molnar, *Vice Pres*
EMP: 8
SQ FT: 3,500
SALES (est): 1.3MM **Privately Held**
WEB: www.proteuselectronics.com
SIC: 3629 Electronic generation equipment

(G-1576)
SUNBURST LIGHT CORP AMERICA
848 State Route 97 E (44813-1228)
P.O. Box 398 (44813-0398)
PHONE.................................419 886-3786
James W Gatton, *President*
Mark J Gatton, *Vice Pres*
Roma Gatton, *Treasurer*
EMP: 4
SQ FT: 1,400
SALES (est): 474.5K **Privately Held**
WEB: www.sunburstlight.com
SIC: 3648 3646 3641 Searchlights; commercial indusl & institutional electric lighting fixtures; electric lamps

Belmont
Belmont County

(G-1577)
ALANAX TECHNOLOGIES INC
40714 Cherrywood Dr (43718-9443)
PHONE.................................216 469-1545
Brian Barritt, *CEO*
Wesley Eddy, *Principal*
Robert Glitch, *CFO*
EMP: 5
SALES (est): 251.9K **Privately Held**
SIC: 7372 4899 7371 Business oriented computer software; communication signal enhancement network system; computer software development

(G-1578)
BAKER LOGGING
62683 Ok Rd (43718-9503)
PHONE.................................740 686-2817
Steve Baker, *Principal*
EMP: 3
SALES (est): 176.6K **Privately Held**
SIC: 2411 Logging

(G-1579)
GOOD WOOD INC (PA)
42591 Bina Rd (43718-9657)
P.O. Box 35 (43718-0035)
PHONE.................................740 484-1500
Fax: 740 484-1501
David Murphy, *President*

Chuck Lewis, *Treasurer*
Nancy Murphy, *Admin Sec*
▲ EMP: 6
SQ FT: 50,000
SALES (est): 1MM **Privately Held**
SIC: 2499 Novelties, wood fiber

(G-1580)
STINGRAY ENERGY SERVICES (PA)
Also Called: Stingray Pressure Pumping
42739 National Rd (43718-9669)
PHONE.................................405 648-4177
Troy Roulo, *District Mgr*
Bob Maughmer, *Mng Member*
Laurey Heilman, *Traffic Dir*
▲ EMP: 39
SALES (est): 124.2MM **Privately Held**
SIC: 1389 Gas field services

Beloit
Mahoning County

(G-1581)
BENDER ENGINEERING COMPANY
17934 Mill St (44609-9512)
P.O. Box 238 (44609-0238)
PHONE.................................330 938-2355
Dennis Patterson, *President*
Lois Patterson, *Vice Pres*
EMP: 7
SQ FT: 2,000
SALES (est): 759.6K **Privately Held**
SIC: 8711 3545 Engineering services; machine tool accessories

(G-1582)
DP OPERATING COMPANY INC
19220 State Route 62 (44609-9509)
PHONE.................................330 938-2172
Fax: 330 938-9103
Louis Dorfman, *President*
EMP: 5
SALES (est): 627.7K
SALES (corp-wide): 3.3MM **Privately Held**
SIC: 1389 Servicing oil & gas wells
PA: Dorfman Production Company
8144 Walnut Hill Ln # 1060
Dallas TX 75231
214 361-1660

(G-1583)
JENKINS MOTOR PARTS
Also Called: Carquest Auto Parts
38 Westville Lake Rd (44609-9402)
PHONE.................................330 525-4011
Fax: 330 938-0744
Thomas W Jenkins, *Owner*
EMP: 4 EST: 1949
SQ FT: 3,750
SALES (est): 511.9K **Privately Held**
SIC: 5013 7538 3599 5531 Automotive supplies & parts; engine rebuilding: automotive; machine shop, jobbing & repair; automotive parts

(G-1584)
MAHONING VALLEY MANUFACTURING
17796 Rte 62 (44609)
P.O. Box 247, Damascus (44619-0247)
PHONE.................................330 537-4492
Fax: 330 537-2606
Tony Sampedro, *CEO*
Susan Sampedro, *Vice Pres*
Marco Crestani, *VP Opers*
Joe McGonagle, *Treasurer*
EMP: 20
SQ FT: 35,000
SALES (est): 3.4MM **Privately Held**
WEB: www.mvmi.com
SIC: 3944 3469 Strollers, baby (vehicle); stamping metal for the trade

Belpre
Washington County

(G-1585)
DAVES PALLETS
710 Thomas St (45714-1929)
PHONE.................................740 525-4938
David Leek, *Principal*
EMP: 4
SALES (est): 206.1K **Privately Held**
SIC: 2448 Pallets, wood & wood with metal

(G-1586)
ELECTRNIC DSIGN FOR INDUST INC
Also Called: E D I
100 Ayers Blvd (45714-9303)
PHONE.................................740 401-4000
Fax: 740 401-4005
Larry Richards, *CEO*
Richard Wynn, *President*
Jay Pottmeyer, *Vice Pres*
Nancy Wynn, *Vice Pres*
Josh Strahler, *Sales Staff*
EMP: 21
SQ FT: 2,700
SALES: 16.5MM
SALES (corp-wide): 3.2B **Publicly Held**
SIC: 3533 5084 Oil & gas field machinery; oil refining machinery, equipment & supplies
HQ: Hy-Bon Engineering Company, Inc.
2404 Commerce Dr
Midland TX 79703
432 697-2292

(G-1587)
HEALTH BRIDGE IMAGING LLC
809 Farson St Unit 107 (45714-1067)
PHONE.................................740 423-3300
Fax: 740 423-4620
Yale Conley,
EMP: 4
SALES (est): 420K **Privately Held**
WEB: www.healthbridgeimaging.com
SIC: 3826 Analytical instruments

(G-1588)
KRATON EMPLYEES RECREATION CLB
2419 State Route 618 (45714-2086)
P.O. Box 235 (45714-0235)
PHONE.................................740 423-7571
Nanette Pettit, *Principal*
EMP: 5
SALES (est): 510.2K **Privately Held**
SIC: 2822 Synthetic rubber

(G-1589)
KRATON POLYMERS US LLC
2419 State Rd 618 (45714)
P.O. Box 235 (45714-0235)
PHONE.................................740 423-7571
Dave Cuppett, *Safety Mgr*
Tim Buttermore, *Engineer*
Dave Mongilio, *Engineer*
Vaneese Bell, *Corp Comm Staff*
Terry Cheuvront, *Business Anlyst*
EMP: 400
SALES (corp-wide): 1.7B **Publicly Held**
WEB: www.kraton.com
SIC: 2822 5169 2821 Synthetic rubber; synthetic resins, rubber & plastic materials; plastics materials & resins
HQ: Kraton Polymers U.S. Llc
15710 John F Kennedy Blvd # 300
Houston TX 77032
281 504-4700

(G-1590)
LAFARGE NORTH AMERICA INC
1684 State Route 618 (45714-2085)
PHONE.................................740 423-5900
Michael Timmons, *Manager*
EMP: 4
SALES (corp-wide): 26.6B **Privately Held**
WEB: www.lafargenorthamerica.com
SIC: 3241 5211 Cement, hydraulic; masonry materials & supplies
HQ: Lafarge North America Inc.
8700 W Bryn Mawr Li
Chicago IL 60631
703 480-3600

(G-1591)
MILLER PRSTHTICS ORTHOTICS LLC
809 Farson St Unit 108 (45714-1067)
PHONE.................................740 421-4211
Mark Miller, *CEO*
Nancy Miller, *COO*
EMP: 3
SALES (est): 209.4K **Privately Held**
SIC: 3842 Prosthetic appliances

(G-1592)
ORION ENGINEERED CARBONS LLC
11135 State Route 7 (45714-9496)
PHONE.................................740 423-9571
Donnie Loubiere, *Plant Mgr*
Dan Langler, *QC Dir*
EMP: 71 **Privately Held**
SIC: 2869 Industrial organic chemicals
HQ: Orion Engineered Carbons Llc
4501 Magnolia Cove Dr
Kingwood TX 77345
832 445-3300

(G-1593)
PIONEER CITY CASTING COMPANY
904 Campus Dr (45714-2342)
P.O. Box 425 (45714-0425)
PHONE.................................740 423-7533
Fax: 740 423-7534
Don W Simmons, *President*
EMP: 30 EST: 1946
SQ FT: 55,000
SALES (est): 7.1MM **Privately Held**
SIC: 3321 3322 Gray iron castings; malleable iron foundries

(G-1594)
POLYONE CORPORATION
2419 State Route 618 (45714-2086)
P.O. Box 219 (45714-0219)
PHONE.................................740 423-7571
David Mongilio, *Technical Mgr*
Kevin M Fogarty, *Branch Mgr*
Arlie Lowers, *Senior Mgr*
EMP: 16 **Publicly Held**
SIC: 2821 Plastics materials & resins
PA: Polyone Corporation
33587 Walker Rd
Avon Lake OH 44012

(G-1595)
WAL-BON OF OHIO INC (PA)
Also Called: Napoli's Pizza
210 Main St (45714-1612)
P.O. Box 508 (45714-0508)
PHONE.................................740 423-6351
Fax: 740 423-6700
Wayne D Waldeck, *Ch of Bd*
William D Waldeck, *President*
Neil Hinton, *Manager*
EMP: 15 EST: 1966
SQ FT: 6,000
SALES (est): 49.7MM **Privately Held**
WEB: www.napolis.com
SIC: 2051 5812 Bakery: wholesale or wholesale/retail combined; pizzeria, independent

(G-1596)
WAL-BON OF OHIO INC
Also Called: Mc Happy's Bake Shoppe
708 Main St (45714-1622)
P.O. Box 508 (45714-0508)
PHONE.................................740 423-8178
William Waldeck, *Manager*
EMP: 100
SQ FT: 8,000
SALES (corp-wide): 49.7MM **Privately Held**
WEB: www.napolis
SIC: 5461 2051 2099 Bakeries; doughnuts, except frozen; food preparations
PA: Wal-Bon Of Ohio, Inc.
210 Main St
Belpre OH 45714
740 423-6351

(G-1597)
WEEKLY CHATTER
1564 Calder Ridge Rd (45714-9467)
PHONE.................................740 336-4704
Misty Perry-Durham, *Principal*

EMP: 3
SALES (est): 113.6K Privately Held
SIC: 2711 Newspapers

Benton Ridge
Hancock County

(G-1598)
SS AUTOMOTIVE SERVICE
110 Market St (45816)
P.O. Box 114 (45816-0114)
PHONE.................................419 859-2885
Scott Sterling, Owner
EMP: 5
SALES (est): 230K Privately Held
SIC: 3599 Machine shop, jobbing & repair

Berea
Cuyahoga County

(G-1599)
A & F MACHINE PRODUCTS CO
454 Geiger St (44017-1392)
PHONE.................................440 826-0959
Fax: 440 243-3009
Fred J Helwig Sr, President
Fred J Helwig Jr, Vice Pres
Charlene Bedford, Financial Exec
EMP: 22 EST: 1960
SQ FT: 12,000
SALES (est): 6.6MM Privately Held
WEB: www.helwigpumps.com
SIC: 3561 Industrial pumps & parts

(G-1600)
ALLOY ENGINEERING COMPANY (PA)
844 Thacker St (44017-1698)
PHONE.................................440 243-6800
Fax: 440 243-6489
Lou Petonovich, President
Richard Turiczek, General Mgr
Lee Watson, Vice Pres
Eric Sistek, Plant Supt
Jan Gomes, Plant Mgr
▼ EMP: 65 EST: 1943
SQ FT: 45,000
SALES: 13.9MM Privately Held
WEB: www.alloyengineering.com
SIC: 3443 Plate work for the metalworking trade

(G-1601)
ANGEL WINDOW MFG CORP
237 Depot St (44017-1860)
PHONE.................................440 891-1006
Fax: 440 816-2037
William C Engelmann, President
Arthur Engelmann, Vice Pres
EMP: 4
SQ FT: 4,000
SALES (est): 313.6K Privately Held
SIC: 3442 Storm doors or windows, metal

(G-1602)
AUDION AUTOMATION LTD (PA)
775 Berea Industrial Pkwy (44017-2948)
PHONE.................................216 267-1911
Mark Goldman, CEO
Jimmy Bryan, Managing Dir
Ian Oroura, Director
▲ EMP: 35
SQ FT: 64,000
SALES (est): 6MM Privately Held
WEB: www.audionautomation.com
SIC: 3565 Packaging machinery; packing & wrapping machinery

(G-1603)
AUDION AUTOMATION LTD
Clamco
775 Berea Industrial Pkwy (44017-2948)
PHONE.................................216 267-1911
Mark E Goldman, CEO
Larry Boyles, Materials Mgr
Gregg Hazen, Engineer
EMP: 25
SALES (corp-wide): 6MM Privately Held
SIC: 3565 Packaging machinery

PA: Audion Automation, Ltd.
775 Berea Industrial Pkwy
Berea OH 44017
216 267-1911

(G-1604)
BEREA MANUFACTURING INC
480 Geiger St (44017-1319)
PHONE.................................440 260-0590
Ed Casper, President
Mike Pandoli, Treasurer
Earl Sunkel, Admin Sec
▲ EMP: 14
SALES (est): 1MM Privately Held
WEB: www.allwelding.com
SIC: 3599 Machine & other job shop work

(G-1605)
BEREA PRINTING COMPANY
1060 W Bagley Rd Ste 102 (44017-2938)
PHONE.................................440 243-1080
Fax: 440 234-1080
James Dettmer, President
Annette Pulling, Office Mgr
Linda Dettmer, Admin Sec
EMP: 9 EST: 1967
SQ FT: 5,500
SALES (est): 1.7MM Privately Held
WEB: www.bereaprinting.com
SIC: 2752 2759 Commercial printing, lithographic; letterpress printing

(G-1606)
CLEVELAND HOYA CORP
Also Called: Advance Lens Labs
94 Pelret Industrial Pkwy (44017-2940)
PHONE.................................440 234-5703
Fax: 440 234-4197
William Bennedict, CEO
Carolyn Gongwer, Manager
▲ EMP: 75
SALES (est): 12.4MM
SALES (corp-wide): 4.3B Privately Held
WEB: www.advancelens.com
SIC: 3827 3851 Optical instruments & lenses; ophthalmic goods
PA: Hoya Corporation
6-10-1, Nishishinjuku
Shinjuku-Ku TKY 160-0
369 114-811

(G-1607)
CLEVELAND METAL STAMPING CO
1231 W Bagley Rd Ste 1 (44017-2942)
PHONE.................................440 234-0010
Fax: 440 234-8050
Frank Ghinga, Vice Pres
Florian Ghinga, Plant Mgr
EMP: 15 EST: 1974
SQ FT: 23,000
SALES (est): 2.4MM Privately Held
SIC: 3469 Stamping metal for the trade

(G-1608)
COLORMATRIX GROUP INC (HQ)
680 N Rocky River Dr (44017-1628)
PHONE.................................216 622-0100
Stephen Newlin, Principal
EMP: 1
SALES (est): 13MM Publicly Held
SIC: 2865 2816 Dyes & pigments; inorganic pigments

(G-1609)
COLORMATRIX HOLDINGS INC
680 N Rocky River Dr (44017-1628)
PHONE.................................440 930-3162
Gerry Corrigan, Principal
EMP: 160
SALES (est): 7.6MM Publicly Held
SIC: 2865 2816 Dyes & pigments; inorganic pigments
HQ: Colormatrix Group, Inc.
680 N Rocky River Dr
Berea OH 44017

(G-1610)
DEARBORN INC
678 Front St (44017-1607)
PHONE.................................440 234-1353
Fax: 440 234-3150
Kenneth Dearborn, President
Ron Kompa, Site Mgr
Shawn Brown, Production

Stan Gregg, QA Dir
Mark Romelfanger, QC Mgr
EMP: 50
SQ FT: 30,000
SALES (est): 8.6MM Privately Held
WEB: www.dearborninc.com
SIC: 3599 Machine shop, jobbing & repair

(G-1611)
DF CONSUMER PRODUCTS
Also Called: Global Clean and Go
1220 W Bagley Rd (44017-2910)
P.O. Box 81931, Cleveland (44181-0931)
PHONE.................................440 239-4795
Aladin Ferian, President
EMP: 10
SALES: 500K Privately Held
SIC: 2819 Industrial inorganic chemicals

(G-1612)
E W WELDING & FABRICATING
336 Wyleswood Dr (44017-2443)
PHONE.................................440 826-9038
Eli Waiters, Owner
EMP: 4
SQ FT: 2,000
SALES (est): 97.4K Privately Held
SIC: 7692 3441 Welding repair; fabricated structural metal

(G-1613)
EATON CORPORATION
Also Called: Hansen Coupling Division
1000 W Bagley Rd (44017-2906)
P.O. Box 805 (44017-0805)
PHONE.................................440 826-1115
Fax: 440 826-0115
Ben Marker, Finance
Michael Blaurock, Marketing Mgr
Brett Jaffe, Branch Mgr
Mike Blaurock, Manager
Joe Mercer, Manager
EMP: 180 Privately Held
WEB: www.tuthill.com
SIC: 3494 3568 3498 Couplings, except pressure & soil pipe; pipe fittings; power transmission equipment; fabricated pipe & fittings
HQ: Eaton Corporation
1000 Eaton Blvd
Cleveland OH 44122
216 523-5000

(G-1614)
ESTABROOK ASSEMBLY SVCS INC
Also Called: Easi
700 W Bagley Rd (44017-2900)
P.O. Box 804 (44017-0804)
PHONE.................................440 243-3350
Fax: 440 243-0811
Jeffrey W Tarr, President
Rich Zsigray, Vice Pres
Fran Torok, Accounts Mgr
Kevin McKenzie, Sales Engr
Linda O'Connor, Executive
▼ EMP: 15
SQ FT: 14,000
SALES (est): 3.7MM Privately Held
SIC: 3822 Energy cutoff controls, residential or commercial types

(G-1615)
FASTENER INDUSTRIES INC
Also Called: Ohio Nut & Bolt Company Div
33 Lou Groza Blvd (44017-1237)
PHONE.................................440 891-2031
Fax: 440 243-4006
Tim Morgan, Manager
EMP: 50
SALES (corp-wide): 42.3MM Privately Held
WEB: www.on-b.com
SIC: 3452 5084 Bolts, nuts, rivets & washers; lift trucks & parts
PA: Fastener Industries, Inc.
1 Berea Commons Ste 209
Berea OH 44017
440 243-0034

(G-1616)
FLAMING RIVER INDUSTRIES INC
800 Poertner Dr (44017-2936)
PHONE.................................440 826-4488
Jeanette Ladina, President

Ron Domin, Vice Pres
Karen Raines, Purch Agent
Ken Kickel, Design Engr
Ralph A Deluca, Treasurer
▲ EMP: 18
SQ FT: 25,000
SALES (est): 4.4MM Privately Held
WEB: www.flamingriver.com
SIC: 3714 Motor vehicle engines & parts; steering mechanisms, motor vehicle

(G-1617)
GEORGE D KANAAN & ASSOCIATES
Also Called: Copy Center West Printing Co
9 N Rocky River Dr (44017-1914)
P.O. Box 420, Terra Ceia FL (34250-0420)
PHONE.................................440 243-6410
Fax: 440 243-1107
George D Kanaan, President
Carol Kanaan, Corp Secy
EMP: 5
SQ FT: 3,500
SALES (est): 572K Privately Held
WEB: www.copycenterwest.com
SIC: 2752 7311 2791 Commercial printing, offset; advertising consultant; typesetting

(G-1618)
HORIZON METALS INC
8059 Lewis Rd Ste 102 (44017-2943)
P.O. Box 38310, Olmsted Falls (44138-0310)
PHONE.................................440 235-3338
Paul Froehlich, President
James Batcha, Vice Pres
Ann Bentley, Manager
▲ EMP: 20 EST: 1997
SQ FT: 38,000
SALES (est): 6.2MM Privately Held
SIC: 3441 Fabricated structural metal

(G-1619)
HOYA OPTICAL LABS
869 W Bagley Rd (44017-2903)
PHONE.................................440 239-1924
EMP: 3
SALES (est): 192.3K Privately Held
SIC: 8734 5049 5048 3827 Testing laboratories; optical goods; optometric equipment & supplies; optical instruments & lenses

(G-1620)
HUNT IMAGING LLC (PA)
210 Sheldon Rd (44017-1234)
PHONE.................................440 826-0433
Peter J Calabrese, General Mgr
Jeff Johnson, Principal
Bob Matich, Vice Pres
Michael E Stanek, CFO
John J Margherio, Mng Member
▲ EMP: 31
SQ FT: 2,040
SALES (est): 5.5MM Privately Held
SIC: 2869 2899 Industrial organic chemicals; chemical preparations

(G-1621)
JACO MANUFACTURING COMPANY (PA)
468 Geiger St (44017-1319)
P.O. Box 619 (44017-0619)
PHONE.................................440 234-4000
Fax: 440 234-7007
Stephen C Campbell, President
Cindy Carnahan, Business Mgr
Thomas Campell, Exec VP
Anthony Lamorte, Vice Pres
Susan Sexton, Vice Pres
EMP: 100
SQ FT: 70,000
SALES (est): 19.7MM Privately Held
WEB: www.jacomfg.com
SIC: 3089 Injection molding of plastics

(G-1622)
JACO MANUFACTURING COMPANY
90 Karl St (44017-1320)
P.O. Box 619 (44017-0619)
PHONE.................................440 234-4000
Annmarie Brian, Manager
EMP: 12

GEOGRAPHIC

SQ FT: 12,000
SALES (corp-wide): 19.7MM **Privately Held**
WEB: www.jacomfg.com
SIC: 3089 3559 Injection molded finished plastic products; synthetic resin finished products; plastics working machinery
PA: Jaco Manufacturing Company
468 Geiger St
Berea OH 44017
440 234-4000

(G-1623)
JAMES F SEME
292 Karl St (44017-1371)
PHONE................................440 759-6455
James F Seme, *Owner*
EMP: 4 EST: 2012
SALES (est): 367K **Privately Held**
SIC: 2434 1799 Wood kitchen cabinets; kitchen & bathroom remodeling

(G-1624)
JOYCE MANUFACTURING CO (PA)
Also Called: Joyce Windows
1125 Berea Indus Pkwy (44017-2928)
PHONE................................440 239-9100
Fax: 440 239-1812
Russell Schmidt, *President*
John Caputo, *Corp Secy*
Todd Schmidt, *Vice Pres*
Gary Winkler, *Vice Pres*
Nikki Jacobs, *Manager*
EMP: 70 EST: 1955
SQ FT: 100,000
SALES (est): 12.3MM **Privately Held**
WEB: www.joycemfg.com
SIC: 3448 3446 3444 Prefabricated metal buildings; architectural metalwork; awnings, sheet metal

(G-1625)
MACPHERSON ENGINEERING INC
Also Called: Macpherson & Company
95 Pelret Industrial Pkwy (44017-2940)
PHONE................................440 243-6565
Fax: 440 243-2211
Bruce McPherson, *President*
EMP: 25
SALES (est): 1.8MM **Privately Held**
SIC: 3231 Reflecting glass

(G-1626)
MEDINA SUPPLY COMPANY
Also Called: Schwab Industries
661 Front St (44017-1606)
PHONE................................440 234-1321
Fax: 440 234-2351
Jerry Lance, *Manager*
Rich Brady, *Manager*
EMP: 7
SQ FT: 19,749
SALES (corp-wide): 28.6B **Privately Held**
SIC: 3271 Blocks, concrete or cinder: standard
HQ: Medina Supply Company
230 E Smith Rd
Medina OH 44256
330 723-3681

(G-1627)
MGM CONSTRUCTION INC
Also Called: MGM Roofing
1480 W Bagley Rd Ste 1 (44017-2951)
PHONE................................440 234-7660
Fax: 440 234-7073
Michael Lyon, *President*
EMP: 15 EST: 2000
SALES (est): 3.3MM **Privately Held**
SIC: 1389 1542 1761 1799 Construction, repair & dismantling services; commercial & office building contractors; roofing contractor; athletic & recreation facilities construction

(G-1628)
MR 14K INC
Also Called: C S Johns Company
370 W Bagley Rd (44017-1348)
PHONE................................440 234-6661
Fax: 440 234-2959
Matt Regotti, *President*
Mark Regotti, *Vice Pres*
EMP: 5

SQ FT: 1,000
SALES (est): 763.7K **Privately Held**
SIC: 3911 7631 Jewelry, precious metal; jewelry repair services; watch repair

(G-1629)
NORTH COAST MEDICAL EQP INC
100 Lincoln Ave (44017-1636)
PHONE................................440 243-2722
Edward Gibbs, *President*
Martha Gibbs, *Vice Pres*
EMP: 10
SQ FT: 2,694
SALES (est): 1.4MM **Privately Held**
SIC: 3844 X-ray apparatus & tubes

(G-1630)
NOSHOK INC (PA)
1010 W Bagley Rd (44017-2906)
PHONE................................440 243-0888
James B Cole, *CEO*
Jeff N Scott, *President*
Pierre Carmona, *Principal*
Christian F L Cole, *Vice Pres*
Stephen Dalziel, *Purchasing*
▲ EMP: 33
SQ FT: 50,000
SALES (est): 6.3MM **Privately Held**
WEB: www.noshok.com
SIC: 3823 Industrial instrmnts msrmnt display/control process variable

(G-1631)
OLMSTED PRINTING INC
1060 W Bagley Rd Ste 102 (44017-2938)
PHONE................................440 234-2600
Fax: 440 234-2601
Richard Bucher, *President*
Karen Bucher, *Treasurer*
EMP: 5
SALES (est): 817.3K **Privately Held**
WEB: www.olmstedprinting.com
SIC: 2752 Commercial printing, lithographic; commercial printing, offset; business forms, lithographed

(G-1632)
POLYONE CORPORATION
680 N Rocky River Dr (44017-1628)
PHONE................................216 622-0100
EMP: 4 **Publicly Held**
SIC: 2865 Dyes & pigments
PA: Polyone Corporation
33587 Walker Rd
Avon Lake OH 44012

(G-1633)
RADS LLC
Also Called: Radcliffe Steel
135 Blaze Industrial Pkwy (44017-2930)
P.O. Box 13862, Fairlawn (44334-3862)
PHONE................................330 671-0464
Douglas Radcliffe,
EMP: 19
SQ FT: 16,000
SALES (est): 3.6MM **Privately Held**
SIC: 3441 Fabricated structural metal

(G-1634)
SABRE PUBLISHING
398 W Bagley Rd Ste 210 (44017-1312)
PHONE................................440 243-4300
Keith Dunbar, *President*
EMP: 6
SALES (est): 651.3K **Privately Held**
WEB: www.sabrepublishing.com
SIC: 2721 Magazines: publishing & printing

(G-1635)
STANDBY SCREW MACHINE PDTS CO
1122 W Bagley Rd (44017-2908)
PHONE................................440 243-8200
Fax: 440 243-8310
Frederick W Marcell, *Ch of Bd*
Sal Caroniti, *President*
J Albert Lowell, *Principal*
William F Marcell, *Principal*
E J Miller, *Principal*
▲ EMP: 375 EST: 1939
SALES (est): 88.7MM **Privately Held**
WEB: www.standbyscrew.com
SIC: 3451 Screw machine products

(G-1636)
SUN ART DECALS INC
83 Dorland Ave (44017-2801)
PHONE................................440 234-9045
Fax: 440 816-0294
John J Soppelsa, *President*
Nikki Soppelsa, *Corp Secy*
James A Soppelsa, *Vice Pres*
EMP: 7
SALES (est): 690K **Privately Held**
WEB: www.sunartdecals.com
SIC: 2752 Decals, lithographed; letters, circular or form: lithographed

(G-1637)
TALENT TOOL & DIE INC
777 Berea Industrial Pkwy (44017-2948)
PHONE................................440 239-8777
Fax: 440 239-1345
Tam Pham, *Ch of Bd*
Thanh Pham, *President*
Kha Vu, *Vice Pres*
Linda Vanek, *Controller*
Young Nguyen, *Info Tech Mgr*
▲ EMP: 40
SQ FT: 80,000
SALES (est): 10.4MM **Privately Held**
WEB: www.talent-tool.com
SIC: 3469 3544 Metal stampings; special dies, tools, jigs & fixtures

(G-1638)
TELEFAST INDUSTRIES INC
777 W Bagley Rd (44017-2901)
PHONE................................440 826-0011
Fax: 440 826-3785
Jeff Liter, *President*
Deanna Ellis, *Manager*
Jake Hobrath, *Network Enginr*
▲ EMP: 65
SQ FT: 60,000
SALES (est): 22.2MM
SALES (corp-wide): 126.1MM **Privately Held**
WEB: www.telefast.com
SIC: 3452 Nuts, metal
HQ: Elgin Fastener Group, Llc
10217 Brecksville Rd
Brecksville OH 44141

(G-1639)
UNITED WIRE EDM INC
777 Berea Industrial Pkwy (44017-2948)
PHONE................................440 239-8777
Thanh Pham, *President*
Tam Pham, *President*
Tri Pham, *Shareholder*
Kha Vu, *Shareholder*
EMP: 4
SQ FT: 24,000
SALES (est): 460K **Privately Held**
SIC: 3541 Electrical discharge erosion machines

(G-1640)
VRC INC
Also Called: Vrc Manufacturers
696 W Bagley Rd (44017-1350)
PHONE................................440 243-6666
Fax: 440 826-4646
Christopher W Lovell, *CEO*
EMP: 54
SQ FT: 42,000
SALES (est): 11.2MM **Privately Held**
WEB: www.vrcmfg.com
SIC: 3599 Machine shop, jobbing & repair; custom machinery

Bergholz
Jefferson County

(G-1641)
DENOON LUMBER COMPANY LLC (PA)
571 County Highway 52 (43908-7961)
PHONE................................740 768-2220
Fax: 740 768-2856
Bill Denoon, *Opers Mgr*
Stam Patrocki, *Bookkeeper*
Richard Smith, *Sales Mgr*
Dick McCannaughy, *Officer*
Janie L Denoon,
EMP: 96

SALES (est): 11.2MM **Privately Held**
WEB: www.denoon.com
SIC: 2421 2449 2431 2426 Lumber: rough, sawed or planed; wood containers; millwork; hardwood dimension & flooring mills

(G-1642)
ROSEBUD MINING COMPANY
Also Called: Bergholz 7
9076 County Road 53 (43908-7948)
PHONE................................740 768-2097
William Denoon, *Branch Mgr*
EMP: 33
SALES (corp-wide): 672.6MM **Privately Held**
SIC: 1222 1221 Bituminous coal-underground mining; bituminous coal & lignite-surface mining
PA: Rosebud Mining Company
301 Market St
Kittanning PA 16201
724 545-6222

Berkey
Lucas County

(G-1643)
STAR DOOR & SASH CO INC
4815 Kilburn Rd (43504-9760)
PHONE................................419 841-3396
Fax: 419 841-5128
Fred Lamb, *President*
Wanda Lutheran, *Manager*
EMP: 10
SQ FT: 25,000
SALES (est): 1.5MM **Privately Held**
SIC: 2431 Doors, wood; windows, wood

Berlin
Holmes County

(G-1644)
BERLIN GARDENS GAZEBOS LTD
5045 State Rte 39 (44610)
PHONE................................330 893-3411
Atlee Raber, *Financial Exec*
EMP: 26
SALES (est): 3.3MM **Privately Held**
SIC: 2511 Wood household furniture

(G-1645)
BERLIN NATURAL BAKERY INC
5126 County Rd 120 (44610)
P.O. Box 311 (44610-0311)
PHONE................................330 893-2734
Fax: 330 893-2157
John Schrock, *President*
Cindy Widder, *Marketing Staff*
Kim Wilhelm, *Exec Dir*
Joy Von Allman, *Admin Sec*
◆ EMP: 21
SALES (est): 3.1MM **Privately Held**
WEB: www.berlinnaturalbakery.com
SIC: 2051 Bread, cake & related products

(G-1646)
BERLIN WOOD PRODUCTS INC
5039 County Rd 120 (44610)
P.O. Box 184 (44610-0184)
PHONE................................330 893-3281
Fax: 330 893-3493
John A Yoder, *President*
Arthur Yoder, *Vice Pres*
EMP: 30
SQ FT: 50,000
SALES (est): 2.3MM **Privately Held**
WEB: www.berlinwood.com
SIC: 2499 3944 Dowels, wood; tool handles, wood; wagons: coaster, express & play: children's

(G-1647)
CENTOR INC
5091 County Rd 120 (44610)
PHONE................................800 321-3391
Roger Klein, *Safety Mgr*
Brant Shaffer, *Production*
Brent Stein, *Human Res Mgr*
Mitch Stein, *Branch Mgr*

David Borter, *Manager*
EMP: 150
SALES (corp-wide): 1.5B **Privately Held**
SIC: 2631 Container, packaging & boxboard
HQ: Centor Inc.
1899 N Wilkinson Way
Perrysburg OH 43551
800 321-3391

(G-1648)
DUTCH HERITAGE WOODCRAFT
4363 State Route 39 (44610)
P.O. Box 358 (44610-0358)
PHONE..................330 893-2211
Fax: 330 893-3665
John Wengerd, *Partner*
John Schrock, *Partner*
Robert Miller, *Managing Dir*
Bryan Schrock, *Manager*
Paul Schrock, *Admin Sec*
EMP: 30
SQ FT: 20,000
SALES (est): 2MM **Privately Held**
SIC: 2511 2431 2426 Wood household furniture; millwork; hardwood dimension & flooring mills

(G-1649)
HOLMES LIMESTONE CO (PA)
4255 State Rte 39 (44610)
P.O. Box 295 (44610-0295)
PHONE..................330 893-2721
Fax: 330 893-2941
Merle Mullet, *President*
William Hummel, *Treasurer*
Wade Mullet, *Admin Sec*
EMP: 7
SQ FT: 10,000
SALES (est): 2MM **Privately Held**
WEB: www.holmeslimestone.com
SIC: 1221 Strip mining, bituminous

(G-1650)
J-J BERLIN WOODCRAFT INC (PA)
Also Called: J & J Woodcraft
4805 State Rt 39 Main St (44610)
PHONE..................330 893-9171
Roman L Kandel Jr, *President*
Naomi Kandel, *Vice Pres*
EMP: 2
SALES (est): 1.2MM **Privately Held**
WEB: www.jjwoodcraft.com
SIC: 2511 5712 Wood household furniture; furniture stores

(G-1651)
MASTERCRAFT MFG INC
6960 Dutch Country Ln (44610)
P.O. Box 415 (44610-0415)
PHONE..................330 893-3366
Fax: 330 893-3511
Les Yoder, *President*
Jennifer Dostal, *Buyer*
EMP: 30
SQ FT: 25,000
SALES (est): 3.4MM **Privately Held**
SIC: 2512 Upholstered household furniture

(G-1652)
ROBIN INDUSTRIES INC
5200 County Rd 120 (44610)
P.O. Box 330 (44610-0330)
PHONE..................330 893-3501
David Theiss, *Branch Mgr*
EMP: 23
SALES (corp-wide): 66.6MM **Privately Held**
WEB: www.robin-industries.com
SIC: 3061 3069 1481 Mechanical rubber goods; molded rubber products; mine development, nonmetallic minerals
PA: Robin Industries, Inc.
6500 Rockside Rd Ste 230
Independence OH 44131
216 631-7000

(G-1653)
WENDELL AUGUST GIFT SP & FORGE
7007 Dutch Country Ln (44610)
P.O. Box 239 (44610-0239)
PHONE..................330 893-3713
Fax: 330 893-3692
William Knecht, *Owner*

Frank W Knecht, *Owner*
EMP: 15
SALES (est): 500K **Privately Held**
SIC: 5947 3463 3462 3446 Gift, novelty & souvenir shop; nonferrous forgings; iron & steel forgings; architectural metalwork

Berlin Center
Mahoning County

(G-1654)
BERLIN BOAT COVERS
Also Called: Berlin Boat Covers Ulphostery
17740 W Akron Canfield Rd (44401-9769)
PHONE..................330 547-7600
Toll Free:..................888 -
Julie A Bowman, *Partner*
Jeffrey Bowman, *Partner*
EMP: 3
SQ FT: 3,400
SALES: 75K **Privately Held**
SIC: 2394 7641 Liners & covers, fabric: made from purchased materials; canvas boat seats; awnings, fabric: made from purchased materials; convertible tops, canvas or boat: from purchased materials; upholstery work

(G-1655)
HIGH CARD INDUSTRIES LLC
Also Called: Paragan Tool and Die
15439 W Akron Canfield Rd (44401-8766)
P.O. Box 102 (44401-0102)
PHONE..................330 547-3381
Fax: 330 547-5533
Kristi Crowe, *Controller*
Daniel F Crowe, *Mng Member*
EMP: 10
SQ FT: 16,000
SALES: 800K **Privately Held**
SIC: 3544 Special dies, tools, jigs & fixtures

(G-1656)
MASTROPIETRO WINERY INC
14558 Ellsworth Rd (44401-9742)
PHONE..................330 547-2151
Daniel Mastropietro, *President*
Marianne Mastropietro, *Vice Pres*
EMP: 8
SQ FT: 1,512
SALES (est): 676.5K **Privately Held**
WEB: www.mastropietrowinery.com
SIC: 2084 Wines

(G-1657)
OHIO STRUCTURES INC
6120 S Pricetown Rd (44401-9718)
PHONE..................330 547-7705
EMP: 35
SALES (corp-wide): 13.3MM **Privately Held**
SIC: 3441 Structural Steel Fabrication
HQ: Ohio Structures, Inc.
535 N Broad St Ste 5
Canfield OH 44406
330 533-0084

(G-1658)
OHIO WINDMILL & PUMP CO INC
8389 S Pricetown Rd (44401-9701)
PHONE..................330 547-6300
Craig Donges, *President*
EMP: 4
SALES (est): 471.7K **Privately Held**
SIC: 3523 Windmills for pumping water, agricultural

(G-1659)
WEBB MACHINE & FAB INC
15262 Hoyle Rd (44401-9785)
P.O. Box 1735, Murrells Inlet SC (29576-1735)
PHONE..................330 717-5745
William Boyer, *Owner*
EMP: 3
SQ FT: 1,914
SALES (est): 306.5K **Privately Held**
SIC: 3599 Machine shop, jobbing & repair

Berlin Heights
Erie County

(G-1660)
AUTOGATE INC
7306 Driver Rd (44814-9661)
P.O. Box 50 (44814-0050)
PHONE..................419 588-2796
Fax: 419 588-3514
Robert B Rodwancy, *Ch of Bd*
William Rodwancy, *President*
Jennifer A Kravec, *Principal*
Donald Rodwancy, *Vice Pres*
Chris Vanmeter, *Production*
EMP: 34
SQ FT: 19,000
SALES (est): 9MM **Privately Held**
WEB: www.autogate.com
SIC: 3446 Gates, ornamental metal

(G-1661)
E & R WELDING INC
32 South St (44814-9320)
PHONE..................440 329-9387
Edwin E Charles, *President*
Roberta Charles, *President*
EMP: 15
SQ FT: 28,000
SALES: 1.5MM **Privately Held**
SIC: 7692 Welding repair

(G-1662)
KERNELLS AUTMTC MACHINING INC
10511 State Rte 61 N (44814)
P.O. Box 41 (44814-0041)
PHONE..................419 588-2164
Fax: 419 588-2070
Claude Kernell, *President*
Lou Gehringer, *Engineer*
Vicky Seck, *Treasurer*
Jeff Kernell, *Admin Sec*
▲ **EMP:** 50 **EST:** 1969
SQ FT: 20,500
SALES (est): 8.1MM **Privately Held**
WEB: www.kernellsautomatic.com
SIC: 3451 Screw machine products

(G-1663)
SHAN-ROD INC
7308 Driver Rd (44814-9661)
P.O. Box 380 (44814-0380)
PHONE..................419 588-2066
Fax: 419 588-3310
Dave Hatala, *President*
Edward F Norton, *Principal*
Robert Rodwancy, *Principal*
H V Pat Shannon, *Principal*
Susan Dolesch, *Finance Dir*
EMP: 25
SALES (est): 6.4MM **Privately Held**
WEB: www.shanrod.com
SIC: 3491 Industrial valves

Bethel
Clermont County

(G-1664)
AFFORDABLE CABINET DOORS
205 S Main St (45106-1327)
PHONE..................513 734-9663
Jason Johnson, *Owner*
EMP: 4
SALES (est): 180K **Privately Held**
SIC: 2434 Wood kitchen cabinets

(G-1665)
WALNUT CREEK WOODWORKING LLC
1878 Jones Florer Rd (45106-8525)
PHONE..................513 504-3520
EMP: 3
SALES (est): 236.9K **Privately Held**
SIC: 2431 Millwork

Bethesda
Belmont County

(G-1666)
MAR-ZANE INC
Also Called: Shelly and Zans
38824 National Rd (43719-9612)
PHONE..................740 782-1240
Fax: 740 782-0032
Richard McClone, *CEO*
EMP: 4
SALES (corp-wide): 301.4MM **Privately Held**
WEB: www.zanemar.com
SIC: 2951 Asphalt paving mixtures & blocks
HQ: Mar-Zane, Inc.
3570 S River Rd
Zanesville OH 43701
740 453-0721

(G-1667)
SMITHS SAWDUST STUDIO
206 Maple Ave (43719-9609)
PHONE..................740 484-4656
Terry Smith, *Owner*
EMP: 3
SALES (est): 210K **Privately Held**
WEB: www.sawduststudio.net
SIC: 2452 Prefabricated buildings, wood

Bettsville
Seneca County

(G-1668)
CARMEUSE LIME INC
Also Called: Carmeuse Natural Chemicals
1967 W County Rd 42 (44815)
P.O. Box 708 (44815-0708)
PHONE..................419 986-5200
Fax: 419 986-2044
Thomas A Buck, *CEO*
Matt Rogish, *Safety Mgr*
Nathaniel Freeborn, *Project Engr*
Kishoore Jehan, *Human Res Mgr*
Stuart Roberts, *Office Mgr*
EMP: 49 **Privately Held**
SIC: 3274 Lime
HQ: Carmeuse Lime, Inc.
11 Stanwix St Fl 21
Pittsburgh PA 15222
412 995-5500

(G-1669)
MILLERSVILLE LIME INC 3
1967 County Rd 42 (44815)
PHONE..................419 986-2019
Steve Phagan, *Manager*
EMP: 55
SALES (est): 1.7MM **Privately Held**
SIC: 1422 Crushed & broken limestone

(G-1670)
VESUVIUS U S A CORPORATION
495 Emma St (44815)
P.O. Box 392 (44815-0392)
PHONE..................419 986-5126
Fax: 419 986-5912
Jim Stendera, *General Mgr*
Anna Cwik, *Purch Mgr*
Daniel Buxton, *Buyer*
Ashley Hampton, *Engineer*
James Head, *Manager*
EMP: 28
SALES (corp-wide): 1.7B **Privately Held**
WEB: www.vesuvius.com
SIC: 3297 Nonclay refractories
HQ: Vesuvius U S A Corporation
1404 Newton Dr
Champaign IL 61822
217 351-5000

Beverly
Washington County

(G-1671)
SCHILLING TRUSS INC
230 Stony Run Rd (45715-5051)
P.O. Box 187 (45715-0187)
PHONE..........................740 984-2396
Fax: 740 984-2396
Jeff Schilling, *President*
Charles L Schilling, *Vice Pres*
Lori Meek, *Admin Sec*
EMP: 12
SALES (est): 1.2MM **Privately Held**
SIC: 2439 Trusses, wooden roof

(G-1672)
**WATERFORD TANK
FABRICATION LTD**
203 State Route 83 (45715-8938)
P.O. Box 392, Lowell (45744-0392)
PHONE..........................740 984-4100
Matt Brook, *President*
Larry Lang,
▲ EMP: 80
SQ FT: 80,000
SALES (est): 28.3MM **Privately Held**
SIC: 3399 3441 Iron ore recovery from
open hearth slag; building components,
structural steel

Bidwell
Gallia County

(G-1673)
BOB EVANS FARMS INC
791 Farmview Rd (45614-9230)
P.O. Box 198, Rio Grande (45674-0198)
PHONE..........................740 245-5305
Donald Radkoski, *Vice Pres*
Rain McKinniss, *Manager*
EMP: 11
SALES (corp-wide): 1.3B **Publicly Held**
WEB: www.bobevans.com
SIC: 2011 Sausages from meat slaugh-
tered on site
PA: Bob Evans Farms, Inc.
8111 Smiths Mill Rd
New Albany OH 43054
614 491-2225

(G-1674)
BRAMHI INC
10282 Bulaville Pike (45614-9440)
PHONE..........................740 367-0467
Lynne B Johnson, *President*
EMP: 5
SALES (est): 414.2K **Privately Held**
SIC: 1221 Coal preparation plant, bitumi-
nous or lignite

(G-1675)
BUCKEYE METALS
185 Curr Rd (45614)
PHONE..........................740 446-9590
Gaylan Belville, *Owner*
Dori D Dunst, *Manager*
EMP: 3
SALES (est): 120K **Privately Held**
SIC: 3499 Fabricated metal products

(G-1676)
GERALD H SMITH
670 Buck Ridge Rd (45614-9204)
PHONE..........................740 446-3455
Gerald Smith, *Owner*
EMP: 3
SALES (est): 141.7K **Privately Held**
SIC: 3443 4959 Dumpsters, garbage; san-
itary services

(G-1677)
OHIO VALLEY TRACKWORK INC
39 Fairview Rd (45614-1100)
P.O. Box 153, Rio Grande (45674-0153)
PHONE..........................740 446-0181
Fax: 740 446-0270
Mike Little, *President*
Bret Little, *Vice Pres*
Adam Little, *Director*

EMP: 12
SALES (est): 3.1MM **Privately Held**
WEB: www.ohiovalleytrackwork.com
SIC: 3531 Railway track equipment

(G-1678)
RUTLAND TOWNSHIP
33325 Jessie Creek Rd (45614-9600)
P.O. Box 203, Rutland (45775-0203)
PHONE..........................740 742-2805
Opal Dyer, *Officer*
EMP: 6
SALES: 260K **Privately Held**
SIC: 2951 Asphalt paving mixtures &
blocks

(G-1679)
SOUTHERN CABINETRY INC
41 International Blvd (45614-8002)
PHONE..........................740 245-5992
Fax: 740 245-5994
Don Strieter, *President*
Lorie Strieter, *Office Mgr*
Leah Bynum, *Admin Sec*
EMP: 35
SALES (est): 5.2MM **Privately Held**
SIC: 3083 Plastic finished products, lami-
nated

Big Prairie
Holmes County

(G-1680)
**DOMETIC SANITATION
CORPORATION**
13128 State Route 226 (44611-9522)
P.O. Box 38 (44611-0038)
PHONE..........................330 439-5550
Doug Whyte, *President*
Patrick Snyder, *Sls & Mktg Exec*
Jackie Hopper, *Human Resources*
Joe Costa, *Sales Staff*
Julie Cochrane, *Marketing Staff*
▲ EMP: 75 EST: 1998
SALES (est): 11.4MM
SALES (corp-wide): 687.3K **Privately
Held**
SIC: 3089 Plastic containers, except foam
HQ: Dometic Corporation
2320 Industrial Pkwy
Elkhart IN 46516
574 294-2511

(G-1681)
**GRACE AUTOMATION
SERVICES INC**
8140 State Route 514 (44611-9692)
PHONE..........................330 567-3108
Curtis W Murray Jr, *President*
Patrick Lee, *Technician*
Brian Looney, *Technician*
EMP: 4
SALES (est): 895K **Privately Held**
WEB: www.graceautomation.com
SIC: 3663 Telemetering equipment, elec-
tronic

(G-1682)
**MANSFIELD PLUMBING PDTS
LLC**
13211 State Route 226 (44611-9584)
P.O. Box 68 (44611-0068)
PHONE..........................330 496-2301
Fax: 330 496-4475
Paul Conrad, *Manager*
EMP: 40 **Privately Held**
SIC: 1711 3088 Plumbing contractors;
plastics plumbing fixtures
HQ: Mansfield Plumbing Products Llc
150 E 1st St
Perrysville OH 44864
419 938-5211

(G-1683)
PRIDE OF HILLS MFG INC (PA)
8275 State Route 514 (44611-9692)
PHONE..........................330 567-3108
Fax: 330 567-3854
Curtis W Murray Sr, *President*
Ronald E Holtman, *Principal*
Peggy C Murray, *Corp Secy*
Dennis Justice, *Purch Mgr*
EMP: 69

SQ FT: 14,000
SALES (est): 30.5MM **Privately Held**
WEB: www.prideofthehills.com
SIC: 3533 Oil & gas field machinery

(G-1684)
**RAY H MILLER TRUCKING AND
LOG**
6054 County Road 51 (44611-9658)
PHONE..........................330 378-2131
Ray Miller, *Principal*
EMP: 3 EST: 2001
SALES (est): 202.8K **Privately Held**
SIC: 2411 Logging camps & contractors

Birmingham
Erie County

(G-1685)
CAMMANN INC
7105 State Rte 60 (44816)
P.O. Box 219 (44816-0219)
PHONE..........................440 965-4051
Fax: 440 965-4177
Henry Cammann, *CEO*
Fred W Cammann IV, *Vice Pres*
Sarah Cammann, *Treasurer*
Bob Miller, *Finance Mgr*
Sara Miller, *Personnel Exec*
▲ EMP: 10 EST: 1946
SALES (est): 1.9MM **Privately Held**
WEB: www.cammann.com
SIC: 3559 3823 3624 3549 Chemical
machinery & equipment; industrial instrm-
nts msrmnt display/control process vari-
able; carbon & graphite products;
metalworking machinery; machine tools,
metal cutting type

Blacklick
Franklin County

(G-1686)
ACTION GROUP INC
411 Reynoldsburg New (43004)
PHONE..........................614 868-8868
Fax: 614 868-6950
Frank De Nutte, *President*
Tracy A Cole, *Vice Pres*
Tracy Garner, *VP Opers*
Steve Vick, *Opers Staff*
Nancy Denutte, *Human Res Dir*
EMP: 98
SQ FT: 155,000
SALES (est): 21.8MM **Privately Held**
WEB: www.actiongroupinc.com
SIC: 3449 2541 Bars, concrete reinforc-
ing: fabricated steel; wood partitions & fix-
tures

(G-1687)
AMERICAN FOODS DIST CO LLC
7884 Dolmen Dr (43004-8539)
PHONE..........................614 218-4049
Adenike Ilesanmi, *Principal*
EMP: 3
SALES (est): 169.5K **Privately Held**
SIC: 2099 Food preparations

(G-1688)
ART BRANDS LLC
225 Business Center Dr (43004-9452)
PHONE..........................614 755-4278
Larry M Levine, *Mng Member*
EMP: 45
SQ FT: 27,000
SALES (est): 8.9MM **Privately Held**
SIC: 2759 Screen printing

(G-1689)
AUSTINS MACHINE SHOP
4295 N Waggoner Rd (43004-9732)
PHONE..........................614 855-2525
Daniel Aldridge, *Owner*
Troy Aldridge, *Sales Staff*
EMP: 20
SALES (est): 1.2MM **Privately Held**
SIC: 3599 Machine & other job shop work

(G-1690)
BESA LIGHTING CO INC
6695 Taylor Rd (43004-9614)
PHONE..........................614 475-7046
Bernd Hoffbauer, *President*
▲ EMP: 47
SQ FT: 48,500
SALES (est): 8.1MM **Privately Held**
WEB: www.besalighting.com
SIC: 3646 3645 Commercial indusl & insti-
tutional electric lighting fixtures; residen-
tial lighting fixtures

(G-1691)
BLACKLICK MACHINE CO INC
265 North St (43004-9139)
P.O. Box 105 (43004-0105)
PHONE..........................614 866-9300
Fax: 614 866-0381
John M Boggs, *President*
Morgan P Brooks, *Purchasing*
Joniece Boggs, *Admin Sec*
EMP: 10 EST: 1954
SQ FT: 7,200
SALES (est): 1.5MM **Privately Held**
SIC: 3599 Machine shop, jobbing & repair

(G-1692)
CEDAR CRAFT PRODUCTS INC
776 Reynldsbrg New Albany (43004-9690)
P.O. Box 9 (43004-0009)
PHONE..........................614 759-1600
Fax: 614 759-1418
Rick Van Walsen, *President*
Magdlen Van Walsen, *Corp Secy*
EMP: 20
SQ FT: 4,800
SALES (est): 2.5MM **Privately Held**
WEB: www.cedar-craft.com
SIC: 2441 Boxes, wood

(G-1693)
CP TECHNOLOGIES COMPANY
6615 Taylor Rd (43004-9600)
P.O. Box 639 (43004-0639)
PHONE..........................614 866-9200
Fax: 614 866-7772
Dr Charles D Amata Sr, *CEO*
Charles D Amata Jr, *President*
▲ EMP: 35
SQ FT: 31,000
SALES (est): 6.3MM **Privately Held**
WEB: www.cptechnologies.com
SIC: 3089 3544 Injection molded finished
plastic products; injection molding of plas-
tics; molding primary plastic; air mat-
tresses, plastic; special dies, tools, jigs &
fixtures

(G-1694)
CQCB INC
Also Called: Columbus Qcb, Inc.
1385 Blatt Blvd (43004)
PHONE..........................614 864-1900
Fax: 614 860-0028
Edward Paul, *President*
Dan Wheeler, *Vice Pres*
EMP: 350
SALES (est): 28MM **Privately Held**
SIC: 3412 Drums, shipping: metal

(G-1695)
**DANA OFF HIGHWAY
PRODUCTS LLC**
6635 Taylor Rd (43004-9600)
PHONE..........................614 864-1116
Terry Casto, *Branch Mgr*
EMP: 20
SALES (corp-wide): 5.8B **Publicly Held**
SIC: 3714 3599 Motor vehicle parts & ac-
cessories; machine shop, jobbing & re-
pair
HQ: Dana Off Highway Products, Llc
3939 Technology Dr
Maumee OH 43537
419 887-3000

(G-1696)
GREEN DOOR INDUSTRIES LLC
7844 Waggoner Trace Dr (43004-7182)
PHONE..........................614 558-1663
Nathan Eddy Hood, *Principal*
EMP: 3
SALES (est): 214.4K **Privately Held**
SIC: 3999 Manufacturing industries

▲ = Import ▼=Export
◆ =Import/Export

(G-1697)
HALVEY QUARTER HORSES
6230 Havens Corners Rd (43004-8728)
PHONE...................................614 648-0483
EMP: 3
SALES (est): 104.2K **Privately Held**
SIC: 3131 Quarters

(G-1698)
HUB PLASTICS INC
725 Reynoldsburg New (43004)
P.O. Box 350 (43004-0350)
PHONE...................................614 861-1791
Fax: 614 861-7176
Dennis Nielsen, *President*
Mindy Campbell, *Controller*
Heather Blackburn, *Human Res Mgr*
Glen Strickland, *Sales Mgr*
Shannon Moline, *Executive*
EMP: 70
SQ FT: 72,000
SALES (est): 12.5MM **Privately Held**
WEB: www.hubplastics.com
SIC: 3089 Plastic containers, except foam

(G-1699)
INDUSTRIAL CONTAINER SVCS LLC
1385 Blatt Blvd Gahanna A Indsutrial (43004)
PHONE...................................614 864-1900
Ron Grannan, *Principal*
Eddie Paul, *Sales Executive*
EMP: 60
SALES (corp-wide): 2.1B **Privately Held**
WEB: www.iconserv.com
SIC: 3443 3412 3411 Fabricated plate work (boiler shop); metal barrels, drums & pails; metal cans
HQ: Industrial Container Services Llc
    2400 Maitland Center Pkwy
    Maitland FL 32751
    800 273-3786

(G-1700)
LOCTOTE LLC
1010 Jackson Hole Dr (43004-6050)
PHONE...................................614 407-0882
Donald Halpern, *CEO*
EMP: 4
SALES (est): 140.1K **Privately Held**
SIC: 2393 5961 Textile bags; mail order house

(G-1701)
MARINE JET POWER INC
6740 Commerce Court Dr (43004-9200)
PHONE...................................614 759-9000
Fax: 614 759-9046
James Campbell, *President*
▲ EMP: 6
SQ FT: 7,000
SALES (est): 1MM
SALES (corp-wide): 721.6K **Privately Held**
WEB: www.ultradynamics.com
SIC: 3483 Jet propulsion projectiles
HQ: Marine Jet Power Ab
    Hansellisgatan 6
    Uppsala 754 5
    295 244-200

(G-1702)
MCGRAW-HILL GLOBAL EDUCATN LLC
860 Taylor Station Rd (43004-9540)
P.O. Box 543 (43004-0543)
PHONE...................................614 755-4151
Fax: 614 755-5680
Charles Kunkel, *Project Mgr*
Debbie Smith, *QA Dir*
Ryan Sibley, *Human Res Dir*
Becky Pennington, *Human Resources*
Mike Flowers, *Manager*
EMP: 500
SALES (corp-wide): 1.4B **Privately Held**
WEB: www.mcgraw-hill.com
SIC: 2731 Book publishing
HQ: Mcgraw-Hill Global Education, Llc
    2 Penn Plz Fl 20
    New York NY 10121
    646 766-2000

(G-1703)
PERFECTION BAKERIES INC
6720 Commerce Court Dr (43004-9200)
PHONE...................................614 866-8171
Tod Cambell, *Branch Mgr*
EMP: 57
SALES (corp-wide): 567MM **Privately Held**
SIC: 2051 Bakery: wholesale or wholesale/retail combined
PA: Perfection Bakeries, Inc.
    350 Pearl St
    Fort Wayne IN 46802
    260 424-8245

(G-1704)
REYNOLDS INDUSTRIES GROUP LLC
7463 Old River Dr (43004-7126)
PHONE...................................614 864-6199
EMP: 45 EST: 2010
SALES (est): 1.5MM **Privately Held**
SIC: 2731 Book publishing

(G-1705)
RICHARDSON WOODWORKING
3834 Mann Rd (43004-9741)
PHONE...................................614 893-8850
Craig Richardson, *President*
EMP: 6 EST: 2000
SALES: 230K **Privately Held**
SIC: 2431 Interior & ornamental woodwork & trim

(G-1706)
SCHAFER DRIVELINE LLC
6635 Taylor Rd (43004-9600)
PHONE...................................614 864-1116
Steve Rowe, *Manager*
EMP: 7
SALES (corp-wide): 28.5MM **Privately Held**
SIC: 3714 Axles, motor vehicle
HQ: Schafer Driveline Llc
    123 Phoenix Pl
    Fredericktown OH 43019
    740 694-0462

Bladensburg
Knox County

(G-1707)
DERRICK PETROLEUM INC
Market St (43005)
P.O. Box 145 (43005-0145)
PHONE...................................740 668-5711
Duane Dugan, *President*
Vickie Dugan, *Admin Sec*
EMP: 6
SQ FT: 500
SALES (est): 990K **Privately Held**
SIC: 1311 Crude petroleum production; natural gas production

Blakeslee
Williams County

(G-1708)
S & M PRODUCTS
County Rd 5 I (43505)
P.O. Box 228 (43505-0228)
PHONE...................................419 272-2054
Fax: 419 272-2404
Steve Mohre, *Owner*
Nick Mohre, *Co-Owner*
EMP: 3
SALES: 250K **Privately Held**
SIC: 2448 Pallets, wood

Blanchester
Clinton County

(G-1709)
AMERICAN SHOWA INC
960 Cherry St (45107-7883)
PHONE...................................937 783-4961
Fax: 937 783-4569
Jim Magge, *Principal*

Yoshitaka Terazawa, *Sr Corp Ofcr*
Iwan Gibby, *Plant Mgr*
Paul Reinert, *Mfg Mgr*
Jim Wiebe, *Production*
EMP: 530
SALES (corp-wide): 2.2B **Privately Held**
SIC: 3714 5812 Motor vehicle steering systems & parts; caterers
HQ: American Showa, Inc.
    707 W Cherry St
    Sunbury OH 43074
    740 965-1133

(G-1710)
BIC PRECISION MACHINE CO INC
3004 Cherry St (45107-7915)
P.O. Box 188 (45107-0188)
PHONE...................................937 783-1406
Fax: 513 722-8499
James Bellamy Jr, *Principal*
James M Bellamy, *Principal*
Vernon L Bellamy, *Principal*
Victor Burkhart Jr, *Principal*
Serah Adkins, *Manager*
EMP: 12
SQ FT: 4,000
SALES (est): 2.3MM **Privately Held**
WEB: www.bicprecision.com
SIC: 3451 Screw machine products

(G-1711)
BLANCHESTER FOUNDRY CO INC
214 Cherry St (45107-1217)
P.O. Box 126 (45107-0126)
PHONE...................................937 783-2091
Fax: 937 783-5065
Robert H Ballinger, *President*
Greg Ballinger, *President*
Mark Ballinger, *Corp Secy*
Kevin Ballinger, *Vice Pres*
EMP: 15 EST: 1947
SQ FT: 35,000
SALES (est): 1.9MM **Privately Held**
SIC: 3321 Gray iron castings

(G-1712)
CURLESS PRINTING COMPANY
202 E Main St Unit 1 (45107-1247)
P.O. Box 97 (45107-0097)
PHONE...................................937 783-2403
Fax: 937 783-4690
Donald S Hadley, *President*
Mike Homan, *General Mgr*
Parker M Beebe, *Vice Pres*
Jeff Campbell, *Plant Supt*
Rose Cooper, *Manager*
EMP: 24
SQ FT: 23,500
SALES: 1.8MM **Privately Held**
SIC: 2752 Commercial printing, lithographic

(G-1713)
FULFLO SPECIALTIES COMPANY
Also Called: True Torq
459 E Fancy St (45107-1462)
PHONE...................................937 783-2411
Fax: 937 783-4983
Thomas Ruthman, *President*
David Locaputo, *General Mgr*
Regina Waldron, *Sales Staff*
EMP: 30
SQ FT: 30,000
SALES: 4.5MM
SALES (corp-wide): 41.6MM **Privately Held**
SIC: 3494 Couplings, except pressure & soil pipe
PA: Ruthman Pump And Engineering, Inc
    1212 Streng St
    Cincinnati OH 45223
    513 559-1901

(G-1714)
J-C-R TECH INC
936 Cherry St (45107-1318)
P.O. Box 65 (45107-0065)
PHONE...................................937 783-2296
Rick Carmean, *President*
Larry Hinz, *Electrical Engi*
Caleb Maxwell, *Electrical Engi*
▲ EMP: 27 EST: 1973
SQ FT: 18,000

SALES (est): 4.5MM **Privately Held**
WEB:
SIC: 3541 7629 3544 Machine tool replacement & repair parts; metal cutting types; electrical repair shops; special dies, tools, jigs & fixtures

(G-1715)
R & R TOOL INC
1449a Middleboro Rd (45107)
PHONE...................................937 783-8665
Dan Reed, *CEO*
Daniel Reed, *CEO*
Bonnie Reed, *President*
▲ EMP: 46
SQ FT: 30,000
SALES (est): 10MM **Privately Held**
SIC: 3429 Manufactured hardware (general)

(G-1716)
RUTHMAN PUMP AND ENGINEERING
Fulflo Specialties Co
459 E Fancy St (45107-1462)
PHONE...................................937 783-2411
David Locaputo, *Manager*
EMP: 25
SALES (corp-wide): 41.6MM **Privately Held**
WEB: www.ruthmannpumpen.de
SIC: 3494 5085 3491 Valves & pipe fittings; valves & fittings; industrial valves
PA: Ruthman Pump And Engineering, Inc
    1212 Streng St
    Cincinnati OH 45223
    513 559-1901

(G-1717)
UFP BLANCHESTER LLC
Also Called: Universal Forest Products
940 Cherry St (45107-7883)
PHONE...................................937 783-2443
Matthew J Missad, *CEO*
William G Currie, *Ch of Bd*
Patrick M Webster, *President*
Michael R Cole, *CFO*
EMP: 23
SALES (est): 4.7MM **Privately Held**
SIC: 2491 Wood preserving

(G-1718)
WICO PRODUCTS INC
311 E Fancy St (45107-1456)
PHONE...................................937 783-0000
Tom Wise, *CEO*
William Wise, *President*
Joyce Wise, *Admin Sec*
EMP: 3
SALES: 300K **Privately Held**
SIC: 2493 Particleboard, plastic laminated

Bloomdale
Wood County

(G-1719)
BLOOMDALE PLASTICS CO
Also Called: Superior Trim
305 Walnut St (44817)
PHONE...................................419 454-5135
Fax: 419 454-2754
Phillip D Gardner, *President*
Charles Henry, *Principal*
Shelly Cornell, *Office Mgr*
EMP: 21
SQ FT: 12,000
SALES (est): 4.1MM **Privately Held**
SIC: 3089 3714 3713 Injection molding of plastics; motor vehicle parts & accessories; truck & bus bodies

---

Bloomingburg
Fayette County

(G-1720)
BLOOMINGBURG SPRING & WIRE FOR
83 Main St (43106-9008)
P.O. Box 158 (43106-0158)
PHONE...................................740 437-7614

Fax: 740 437-7360
James Van Horn, *President*
Rebecca Maynard, *General Mgr*
Vickie Schwarm, *General Mgr*
Tim Van Horn, *Vice Pres*
Florence Benson, *Sales Mgr*
▲ **EMP:** 20
SQ FT: 27,000
SALES (est): 3.8MM **Privately Held**
WEB: www.bloomingburgspring.com
SIC: 3495 3496 Wire springs; miscellaneous fabricated wire products

(G-1721)
VALERO RENEWABLE FUELS CO LLC
3979 State Route 238 Ne (43106-9776)
PHONE................................740 437-6211
Karl Charron, *Manager*
EMP: 68
SALES (corp-wide): 75.6B **Publicly Held**
SIC: 2869 Accelerators, rubber processing: cyclic or acyclic
HQ: Valero Renewable Fuels Company, Llc
    1 Valero Way
    San Antonio TX 78249
    210 345-2000

Bloomingdale
Jefferson County

(G-1722)
DIE-TECH MACHINE INC
1650 County Road 22a (43910-7966)
PHONE................................740 264-2426
Fax: 740 264-3645
William D Freeland, *President*
Michele Freeland, *Corp Secy*
Brett Freeland, *Vice Pres*
Ladd Merritt, *Manager*
EMP: 9
SALES: 750K **Privately Held**
SIC: 3599 Machine shop, jobbing & repair; machine & other job shop work

(G-1723)
J A H WOODWORKING LLC
39 Belvedere Dr (43910-7738)
PHONE................................740 266-6949
John Humpe III,
Brenda Humpe,
EMP: 5
SQ FT: 4,200
SALES (est): 664.6K **Privately Held**
SIC: 2431 Millwork

(G-1724)
JEFFERSON LANDMARK INC (PA)
1525 State Route 152 (43910-6903)
PHONE................................740 944-1971
Toll Free:................................888 -
Fax: 740 944-1638
Joe Rozsa, *President*
EMP: 12
SQ FT: 10,800
SALES: 21MM **Privately Held**
WEB: www.jeffersonlandmark.com
SIC: 5984 5999 2875 Liquefied petroleum gas, delivered to customers' premises; feed & farm supply; fertilizers, mixing only

Bloomville
Seneca County

(G-1725)
BU E COMP INC
7092 S State Route 19 (44818-9203)
P.O. Box 467 (44818-0467)
PHONE................................419 284-3381
Fax: 419 284-3881
Kimberline Nelferd, *President*
EMP: 6
SALES (est): 365.7K **Privately Held**
SIC: 3089 Plastics products

(G-1726)
BUECOMP INC
Also Called: Bucyrus Extruded Composites
7016 S State Route 19 (44818-9203)
P.O. Box 467, Bucyrus (44820-0467)
PHONE................................419 284-3840
Nelfred G Kimerline, *President*
Norm Tackett, *General Mgr*
Charles W Kimerline, *Corp Secy*
EMP: 32
SQ FT: 19,000
SALES (est): 4.1MM **Privately Held**
WEB: www.buecomp.com
SIC: 3089 Extruded finished plastic products

(G-1727)
EPRO INC
10890 E County Road 6 (44818-9243)
PHONE................................419 426-5053
Jim Fry, *President*
EMP: 40
SALES (est): 3.1MM **Privately Held**
SIC: 3253 Ceramic wall & floor tile

(G-1728)
HANSON AGGREGATES MIDWEST LLC
Also Called: Hanson Aggregates Mid West
4575 S County Road 49 (44818-8400)
P.O. Box 128 (44818-0128)
PHONE................................419 983-2211
Dan Lepp, *Manager*
EMP: 8
SALES (corp-wide): 16B **Privately Held**
SIC: 2951 1422 Asphalt paving mixtures & blocks; limestones, ground
HQ: Hanson Aggregates Midwest Llc
    207 Old Harrods Creek Rd
    Louisville KY 40223
    502 244-7550

Blue Ash
Hamilton County

(G-1729)
1 A LIFESAFER INC (PA)
Also Called: Ignition Interlock
4290 Glendale Milford Rd (45242-3704)
PHONE................................513 651-9560
Fax: 513 651-9563
Richard Freund, *President*
Craig Armstrong, *President*
Roy Sheram, *Senior VP*
Ed Gollar, *Vice Pres*
Chris Hansen, *Opers Mgr*
EMP: 9
SQ FT: 3,600
SALES (est): 2.7MM **Privately Held**
WEB: www.lifesafer.com
SIC: 3699 Security devices

(G-1730)
1 A LIFESAFER HAWAII INC
4290 Glendale Milford Rd (45242-3704)
PHONE................................513 651-9560
Kermes Glenn, *Principal*
EMP: 14
SALES (est): 2.6MM **Privately Held**
SIC: 3829 3714 Breathalyzers; motor vehicle parts & accessories

(G-1731)
A G RUFF PAPER SPECIALTIES CO
4320 Indeco Ct (45241-2925)
PHONE................................513 891-7990
Fax: 513 891-7992
Michael Ruff, *President*
Thomas Ruff, *President*
John Ruff, *Vice Pres*
EMP: 3
SQ FT: 20,000
SALES (est): 429.8K **Privately Held**
SIC: 2675 Die-cut paper & board

(G-1732)
ABSTRACT DISPLAYS INC
6465 Creek Rd (45242-4113)
PHONE................................513 985-9700
Fax: 513 985-9735
Michael Eng, *Vice Pres*
Karen Allendorf, *Office Mgr*

Allison Dee, *Office Admin*
Stan Dwyer, *Consultant*
Jason Eng, *Creative Dir*
EMP: 4
SALES (est): 1.5MM **Privately Held**
WEB: www.abstractdisplays.com
SIC: 5046 7389 3577 7336 Display equipment, except refrigerated; exhibit construction by industrial contractors; graphic displays, except graphic terminals; graphic arts & related design

(G-1733)
ACTEGA NORTH AMERICA INC
Also Called: Water Ink Technologies
11264 Grooms Rd Ste A (45242-1418)
PHONE................................513 489-5691
Fax: 513 489-5765
Dave Carr, *Manager*
EMP: 4 **Privately Held**
WEB: www.waterinktech.com
SIC: 2893 Printing ink
HQ: Actega North America Inc.
    950 S Chester Ave Ste B2
    Delran NJ 08075
    856 829-6300

(G-1734)
ADVANCEPIERRE FOODS INC (HQ)
Also Called: Advance Pierre Foods
9987 Carver Rd Ste 500 (45242-5563)
PHONE................................513 874-8741
Fax: 513 874-8395
John N Simons, *CEO*
Steve Booker, *President*
Tom Lavan, *President*
Walt Thurn, *President*
Brian Bauman, *Business Mgr*
▲ **EMP:** 300
SQ FT: 40,000
SALES (est): 1.4B **Publicly Held**
WEB: www.pierrefoods.com
SIC: 2013 2015 Prepared beef products from purchased beef; prepared pork products from purchased pork; chicken, processed

(G-1735)
ADVANCPERRE FOODS HOLDINGS INC (PA)
9987 Carver Rd (45242-5550)
PHONE................................800 969-2747
John N Simons Jr, *CEO*
Dean Hollis, *Ch of Bd*
Steven D Booker, *President*
Tony Schroder, *President*
Christopher D Sliva, *President*
EMP: 8
SALES (est): 1.5B **Publicly Held**
SIC: 2099 2013 Sandwiches, assembled & packaged: for wholesale market; sausages & other prepared meats

(G-1736)
ADVANTAGE PRODUCTS CORPORATION (PA)
11559 Grooms Rd (45242-1409)
PHONE................................513 489-2283
Robert Weber, *President*
Sam Weber, *Opers Staff*
Bethany Webber, *Manager*
EMP: 10
SALES (est): 1.3MM **Privately Held**
WEB: www.treds.com
SIC: 3021 Protective footwear, rubber or plastic

(G-1737)
AIR PLASTICS INC
4468 Classic Dr (45241-2208)
PHONE................................513 469-1074
Dennis E Woll, *Ch of Bd*
Christina Clonne, *Admin Sec*
EMP: 10
SQ FT: 20,000
SALES: 850K **Privately Held**
WEB: www.airplastics.com
SIC: 3089 3564 5084 Plastic & fiberglass tanks; air purification equipment; dust or fume collecting equipment, industrial; pollution control equipment, air (environmental)

(G-1738)
AKKO FASTENER INC
6855 Cornell Rd (45242-3022)
PHONE................................513 489-8300
Fax: 513 489-8366
Nancy Fernandez, *President*
Nestor Fernandez, *Vice Pres*
Terry Kimble, *Purch Mgr*
David Biddle, *Sales Executive*
Dave Biddle, *Technology*
▲ **EMP:** 23
SQ FT: 35,000
SALES (est): 6.3MM **Privately Held**
WEB: www.akkofastener.com
SIC: 3452 5072 Screws, metal; bolts; washers (hardware)

(G-1739)
ALERT SAFETY PRODUCTS INC
11435 Williamson Rd Ste C (45241-4200)
PHONE................................513 791-4790
Fax: 513 791-4792
Bill Shernick, *President*
David Fossier, *Vice Pres*
Kym Murphy, *Accounting Mgr*
EMP: 5
SALES (est): 711.1K **Privately Held**
WEB: www.alertsafetyproducts.com
SIC: 3669 Burglar alarm apparatus, electric; emergency alarms; fire alarm apparatus, electric

(G-1740)
ALIFET USA INC
Also Called: Rouse Marketing
3714 Fallentree Ln (45236-1036)
PHONE................................513 793-8033
Fax: 513 984-4417
Raymond Rouse, *President*
Pat Rouse, *Admin Sec*
EMP: 3
SQ FT: 1,500
SALES (est): 246.8K **Privately Held**
WEB: www.rousemarketing.com
SIC: 2023 Dietary supplements, dairy & non-dairy based

(G-1741)
ALL SIGNS EXPRESS INC (PA)
Also Called: Accent Signs and Graphics
6610 Corporate Dr (45242-2103)
PHONE................................513 489-7744
Robert Johnson, *President*
Earl Johnson, *Vice Pres*
Sherri Johnson, *Admin Sec*
EMP: 10
SALES: 900K **Privately Held**
WEB: www.cincinnatisigns.net
SIC: 3993 Signs & advertising specialties

(G-1742)
ALL-BILT UNIFORM CORP
4545 Malsbary Rd (45242-5624)
PHONE................................513 793-5400
Fax: 513 793-2725
EMP: 20 **EST:** 1962
SALES (est): 2.1MM
SALES (corp-wide): 194.6B **Publicly Held**
SIC: 2326 Manufacturer Of Professional Apparel
HQ: The Fechheimer Brothers Company
    4545 Malsbary Rd
    Blue Ash OH 45242
    513 793-7819

(G-1743)
AP TECH GROUP INC
11411 Williamson Rd (45241-2234)
PHONE................................513 761-8111
James Heimert, *President*
Albert C Heimert, *Vice Pres*
Todd Lee, *VP Opers*
▼ **EMP:** 15
SALES (est): 4.3MM **Privately Held**
SIC: 2499 Food handling & processing products, wood

(G-1744)
APRECIA PHARMACEUTICALS CO
10901 Kenwood Rd (45242-2813)
PHONE................................513 204-1369
Kevin O'Meara, *General Mgr*
Michael Rohlfs, *CFO*
David Harris, *Director*

EMP: 47
SQ FT: 190,000
SALES (corp-wide): 22.9MM Privately
Held
SIC: 2834 Pharmaceutical preparations
PA: Aprecia Pharmaceuticals Company
2010 Cabot Blvd W Ste F
Langhorne PA 19047
513 984-5000

(G-1745)
ARKU COIL-SYSTEMS INC
11405 Grooms Rd (45242-1407)
PHONE..................................513 985-0500
Franck Hirschmann, President
Beth Frederick, Manager
▲ EMP: 9
SALES (est): 1.9MM
SALES (corp-wide): 58.5MM Privately
Held
SIC: 3549 Wiredrawing & fabricating ma-
chinery & equipment, ex. die
PA: Arku Maschinenbau Gmbh
Siemensstr. 11
Baden-Baden 76532
722 150-090

(G-1746)
AULD LANG SIGNS INC
Also Called: Fastsigns
11109 Kenwood Rd (45242-1817)
PHONE..................................513 792-5555
Fax: 513 792-5552
Michael Langdon, President
Kathryn Langdon, Vice Pres
EMP: 4
SQ FT: 2,000
SALES (est): 525.3K Privately Held
SIC: 3993 Signs & advertising specialties

(G-1747)
BEAM MACHINES INC
5101 Creek Rd (45242-3931)
PHONE..................................513 745-4510
Tim Bell, General Mgr
EMP: 3
SALES (est): 135.4K Privately Held
SIC: 3559 Automotive related machinery

(G-1748)
**BEEBE WORLDWIDE GRAPHICS
SIGN**
Also Called: Worldwide Graphics and Sign
9933 Alliance Rd Ste 2 (45242-5662)
PHONE..................................513 241-2726
Christian Beebe, President
EMP: 6
SQ FT: 6,000
SALES (est): 901.8K Privately Held
SIC: 3993 Signs & advertising specialties

(G-1749)
BERMAN INDUSTRIES INC
10999 Reed Hartman Hwy # 204
(45242-8301)
PHONE..................................513 874-7477
Dolph Berman, President
John Berman, Plant Mgr
Becker Keltner, Manager
Janette Thompson, Admin Mgr
Nancy C Berman, Admin Sec
EMP: 10
SQ FT: 53,000
SALES (est): 1.6MM Privately Held
WEB: www.bermanindustries.com
SIC: 3089 Tableware, plastic

(G-1750)
**BEVERAGES HOLDINGS LLC
(PA)**
10300 Alliance Rd Ste 500 (45242-4767)
PHONE..................................513 483-3300
Billy William B Cyr, CEO
Daniel Sileo, VP Mfg
Katie Marx, Research
Ross A Dick, Finance Mgr
Athena Wong, VP Human Res
EMP: 33
SALES (est): 138.5MM Privately Held
SIC: 2086 2037 Fruit drinks (less than
100% juice): packaged in cans, etc.; car-
bonated beverages, nonalcoholic: bottled
& canned; fruit juice concentrates, frozen

(G-1751)
BINDUSA
6819 Ashfield Dr (45242-4108)
PHONE..................................513 247-3000
Jay Moore, CEO
EMP: 11
SALES (est): 1.6MM Privately Held
WEB: www.bindusa.com
SIC: 2789 Bookbinding & related work

(G-1752)
BLUE ASH TOOL & DIE CO INC
4245 Creek Rd (45241-2999)
PHONE..................................513 793-4530
Fax: 513 793-5969
Ronald Siderits, President
James Siderits, General Mgr
Anna Siderits, Vice Pres
Caroline Siderits, Vice Pres
Joel Donnelly, Marketing Staff
EMP: 15
SQ FT: 20,000
SALES: 829.1K Privately Held
WEB: www.batd.com
SIC: 3545 3544 Gauge blocks; machine
tool attachments & accessories; special
dies, tools, jigs & fixtures

(G-1753)
**BOSSA NOVA BEVERAGE
GROUP INC**
10300 Alliance Rd Ste 500 (45242-4767)
PHONE..................................513 483-3300
Alton Johnson, CEO
Candace Crawford, CFO
Jagadish Bandhole, Bd of Directors
▲ EMP: 10
SQ FT: 1,600
SALES (est): 655.2K
SALES (corp-wide): 138.5MM Privately
Held
SIC: 2033 Fruit juices: fresh
PA: Beverages Holdings, Llc
10300 Alliance Rd Ste 500
Blue Ash OH 45242
513 483-3300

(G-1754)
**BRAMKAMP PRINTING
COMPANY INC**
9933 Alliance Rd Ste 2 (45242-5662)
PHONE..................................513 241-1865
Fax: 513 241-4168
Larry Kuhlman, President
John Taylor, Plant Mgr
Kevin Murray, CFO
Brad Sullivan, Sales Staff
Paul Weber, Marketing Staff
EMP: 26 EST: 1921
SQ FT: 200,000
SALES (est): 4.3MM Privately Held
WEB: www.bramkamp.com
SIC: 2759 2752 Letterpress printing; com-
mercial printing, offset

(G-1755)
BROAN-NUTONE LLC
9825 Kenwood Rd Ste 301 (45242-6252)
PHONE..................................888 336-3948
EMP: 7
SALES (corp-wide): 393.7MM Privately
Held
SIC: 3634 Fans, exhaust & ventilating,
electric: household
HQ: Broan-Nutone Llc
926 W State St
Hartford WI 53027
262 673-4340

(G-1756)
BROWN PUBLISHING INC LLC
4229 Saint Andrews Pl (45236-1057)
PHONE..................................513 794-5040
Fax: 513 791-5480
Roy Brown,
EMP: 7
SALES (est): 352.8K Privately Held
SIC: 2711 Newspapers

(G-1757)
C & W CUSTOM WDWKG CO INC
6839 Ashfield Dr (45242-4108)
PHONE..................................513 891-6340
Fax: 513 891-6341
Dave Williams, Principal

Steven Cornett, Principal
Brian Cw, Project Mgr
EMP: 20
SQ FT: 3,000
SALES (est): 3MM Privately Held
WEB: www.candwcustomwoodworking.com
SIC: 2431 Millwork

(G-1758)
C A I R OHIO
10999 Reed Hartman Hwy # 207
(45242-8301)
PHONE..................................513 281-8200
Fax: 513 281-8666
C Cooper, Principal
EMP: 3
SALES (est): 106K Privately Held
SIC: 8661 2759 Religious organizations;
screen printing

(G-1759)
C M M S - RE INC
Also Called: Forward Technologies
6130 Interstate Cir (45242-1425)
PHONE..................................513 489-5111
Bradley Meyers, President
EMP: 15
SALES (corp-wide): 2.4MM Privately
Held
SIC: 3599 Machine shop, jobbing & repair
PA: C M M S - Re, Llc
6130 Interstate Cir
Blue Ash OH 45242
513 489-5111

(G-1760)
C M M S - RE LLC (PA)
Also Called: Forward Technologies
6130 Interstate Cir (45242-1425)
PHONE..................................513 489-5111
Bradley Meyers, President
Brian Collins, Vice Pres
Scott Mason, Vice Pres
Scott Mayson, Vice Pres
Andrew Schultz, Vice Pres
EMP: 11 EST: 2014
SQ FT: 6,500
SALES (est): 2.4MM Privately Held
SIC: 3365 3541 Aluminum foundries; ma-
chine tools, metal cutting: exotic (explo-
sive, etc.)

(G-1761)
**CAMARGO PHRM SVCS LLC
(PA)**
9825 Kenwood Rd Ste 203 (45242-6252)
PHONE..................................513 561-3329
Fax: 513 561-3367
Kenneth V Phelps, President
Jim Beach, COO
K Gary Barnette, Vice Pres
Steven A Castillo, Vice Pres
Lynn Gold, Vice Pres
EMP: 14
SALES (est): 1.9MM Privately Held
SIC: 2834 Proprietary drug products

(G-1762)
**CANDLE-LITE COMPANY LLC
(HQ)**
10521 Millington Ct Ste B (45242-4022)
PHONE..................................513 563-1113
Calvin Johnston, CEO
Gary Prampero, Vice Pres
Russ Elias, Senior Mgr
EMP: 60
SQ FT: 900,000
SALES (est): 206.1MM
SALES (corp-wide): 262.6MM Privately
Held
SIC: 3999 Candles
PA: Luminex Home Decor & Fragrance
Holding Corporation
10521 Millington Ct
Blue Ash OH 45242
513 563-1113

(G-1763)
CECO ENVIRONMENTAL CORP
6245 Creek Rd (45242-4104)
PHONE..................................513 458-2606
T Kroeger, Branch Mgr
EMP: 8

SALES (corp-wide): 417MM Publicly
Held
SIC: 3564 Purification & dust collection
equipment
PA: Ceco Environmental Corp.
4625 Red Bank Rd Ste 200
Cincinnati OH 45227
513 458-2600

(G-1764)
CHECK YOURSELF LLC
Also Called: Repp
4422 Carver Woods Dr # 110 (45242-5599)
PHONE..................................513 685-0868
Breeanna Bergman, Co-Owner
Adam Daniel, Co-Owner
Stephen Hartz, Co-Owner
David Volker, Co-Owner
EMP: 5 EST: 2012
SALES (est): 320K Privately Held
SIC: 7372 Application computer software

(G-1765)
**CINCINNATI THERMAL SPRAY
INC**
5901 Creek Rd (45242-4011)
PHONE..................................513 793-1037
Scott Paschke, Branch Mgr
EMP: 110
SALES (corp-wide): 27.7MM Privately
Held
SIC: 3479 Coating of metals & formed
products
PA: Cincinnati Thermal Spray, Inc.
10904 Deerfield Rd
Blue Ash OH 45242
513 793-0670

(G-1766)
CLARIANT CORPORATION
10999 Reed Hartman Hwy # 201
(45242-8319)
PHONE..................................513 791-2964
Tim Urmstom, Principal
Jerry Ogrady, Manager
EMP: 3
SALES (est): 191.8K Privately Held
SIC: 2869 Industrial organic chemicals

(G-1767)
COCA-COLA COMPANY
10151 Carver Rd Ste 500 (45242-4760)
PHONE..................................513 898-7800
John Mount, Branch Mgr
Andy O'Conner, Manager
EMP: 112
SALES (corp-wide): 41.8B Publicly Held
WEB: www.cocacola.com
SIC: 2086 Bottled & canned soft drinks
PA: The Coca-Cola Company
1 Coca Cola Plz Nw
Atlanta GA 30313
404 676-2121

(G-1768)
**COMPUTATIONAL
ENGINEERING SVCS**
10979 Reed Hartman Hwy # 210
(45242-2800)
PHONE..................................513 745-0313
Gyan Sasmal, President
EMP: 4
SQ FT: 500
SALES (est): 343.5K Privately Held
SIC: 3369 Aerospace castings, nonferrous:
except aluminum

(G-1769)
COVAP INC
10829 Millington Ct Ste 1 (45242-4023)
P.O. Box 42510, Cincinnati (45242-0510)
PHONE..................................513 793-1855
Fax: 513 793-2377
Arnold Stoller, President
Stephanie Stoller, Vice Pres
EMP: 18 EST: 1934
SQ FT: 9,000
SALES (est): 3.4MM Privately Held
WEB: www.covap.com
SIC: 5112 7331 2752 Stationery & office
supplies; mailing service; commercial
printing, lithographic

(G-1770)
CREST CRAFT COMPANY
4460 Lake Forest Dr # 232 (45242-3755)
PHONE..................................513 271-4858
Fax: 513 271-9156
Jack Johnson, *President*
Linda Stanelle, *General Mgr*
James Johnson, *Exec VP*
Michael Borellis, *CFO*
Barbara Gabbard, *Controller*
EMP: 19
SQ FT: 44,000
SALES: 2.5MM **Privately Held**
SIC: 2752 3911 3499 Lithographing on
metal; medals, precious or semiprecious
metal; novelties & giftware, including tro-
phies

(G-1771)
CRI INC
11060 Kenwood Rd Ste D (45242-1816)
PHONE..................................513 266-0882
Mike Elan, *Owner*
EMP: 5
SALES (est): 231.2K **Privately Held**
SIC: 3845 Electromedical equipment

(G-1772)
CUMMINS - ALLISON CORP
11256 Cornell Park Dr (45242-1821)
PHONE..................................513 469-2924
Jack Prather, *Manager*
EMP: 7
SALES (corp-wide): 377.1MM **Privately
Held**
WEB: www.gsb.com
SIC: 5046 3519 Commercial equipment;
internal combustion engines
PA: Cummins - Allison Corp.
852 Feehanville Dr
Mount Prospect IL 60056
847 759-6403

(G-1773)
CUSHMAN FOUNDRY LLC
5300 Creek Rd (45242-3936)
PHONE..................................513 984-5570
Fax: 513 984-5571
John C Beyersdorfer, *President*
Pam Fox, *Office Mgr*
EMP: 11
SALES (est): 1.6MM **Privately Held**
SIC: 3365 Aluminum & aluminum-based
alloy castings

(G-1774)
**DA-LITE SCREEN COMPANY
LLC**
Polacoat Divison
11500 Williamson Rd (45241-2271)
PHONE..................................574 267-8101
Fax: 513 489-4247
Keith Sterwerf, *Materials Mgr*
Bob St Martin, *Manager*
EMP: 25
SQ FT: 41,700
SALES (corp-wide): 1.3B **Privately Held**
WEB: www.dalite.com
SIC: 3861 3643 Motion picture apparatus
& equipment; current-carrying wiring de-
vices
HQ: Da-Lite Screen Company Llc
3100 N Detroit St
Warsaw IN 46582
574 267-8101

(G-1775)
DIGITEK CORP
5665 Creek Rd (45242-4005)
PHONE..................................513 794-3190
Marc E Brown, *President*
Tom Logsdon, *Purchasing*
Anna Brown, *Manager*
EMP: 10
SQ FT: 3,500
SALES (est): 2.6MM **Privately Held**
WEB: www.digitekcorp.net
SIC: 5136 5137 2253 Uniforms, men's &
boys'; uniforms, women's & children's; T-
shirts & tops, knit

(G-1776)
DOCUPROS
9933 Alliance Rd (45242-5661)
PHONE..................................513 242-7700
Fax: 513 242-2555

Bob Smith, *Owner*
EMP: 4
SALES (est): 290K **Privately Held**
WEB: www.docupros.com
SIC: 2759 Commercial printing

(G-1777)
DSK IMAGING LLC
Also Called: Allegra Marketing Print Mail
6839 Ashfield Dr (45242-4108)
PHONE..................................513 554-1797
Fax: 513 554-0343
Lance Stevens, *General Mgr*
Steve Kapuscinski, *Principal*
EMP: 10
SQ FT: 4,000
SALES (est): 1.6MM **Privately Held**
WEB: www.allegracinci.com
SIC: 8742 2752 Marketing consulting
services; commercial printing, lithographic

(G-1778)
DURBIN MINUTEMAN PRESS
11130 Kenwood Rd (45242-1818)
PHONE..................................513 791-9171
Fax: 513 792-3299
Jeff Bock,
EMP: 4
SQ FT: 3,000
SALES (est): 363.8K **Privately Held**
SIC: 2752 2759 2789 Commercial print-
ing, lithographic; commercial printing;
binding only: books, pamphlets, maga-
zines, etc.

(G-1779)
DYVERSE ENTERTAINMENT LLC
Also Called: Dyverse Marketing Solutions
10979 Reed Hartman Hwy (45242-2800)
PHONE..................................513 225-3301
Edward Cohen,
EMP: 3
SALES: 50K **Privately Held**
SIC: 3993 Signs & advertising specialties

(G-1780)
EAJ SERVICES LLC
Also Called: Nextstep Networking
4350 Glendale Milford Rd # 170
(45242-3700)
PHONE..................................513 792-3400
Fax: 513 792-3400
Brad Payne, *President*
Andrew Johnson, *Vice Pres*
Amy Hazzard, *Sales Executive*
Aaron Leopold, *Sales Executive*
Cindy Rolfes, *Office Mgr*
EMP: 18
SQ FT: 5,500
SALES: 2.4MM **Privately Held**
WEB: www.nextstepnetworking.com
SIC: 7373 7378 3571 Computer inte-
grated systems design; computer mainte-
nance & repair; electronic computers

(G-1781)
**EASTERN SHEET METAL INC
(DH)**
8959 Blue Ash Rd (45242-7800)
PHONE..................................513 793-3440
Fax: 513 793-3490
William K Stout Sr, *Ch of Bd*
William K Stout Jr, *President*
Margaret Geiger, *Treasurer*
Robert Fedders, *Admin Sec*
▲ EMP: 85 EST: 1978
SQ FT: 80,000
SALES (est): 13.5MM **Privately Held**
WEB: www.easternsheetmetal.com
SIC: 3444 Ducts, sheet metal
HQ: Johnson Controls, Inc.
5757 N Green Bay Ave
Milwaukee WI 53209
414 524-1200

(G-1782)
ELATIONS COMPANY
10300 Alliance Rd Ste 500 (45242-4767)
PHONE..................................513 483-3300
William Cyr, *President*
William Schumacher, *Vice Pres*
Tim Voelkerding, *Treasurer*
EMP: 11

SALES: 200K
SALES (corp-wide): 342.8MM **Privately
Held**
SIC: 2037 Fruit juices
PA: Beverages Holdings, Llc
10300 Alliance Rd Ste 500
Blue Ash OH 45242
513 483-3300

(G-1783)
EMC CORPORATION
9825 Kenwood Rd Ste 300 (45242-6252)
PHONE..................................513 794-9624
Fax: 513 745-0324
Stephen Swanson, *Sales Staff*
Debbie B Phipps, *Marketing Mgr*
Debbi Browning, *Marketing Staff*
Jack Garrahan, *Branch Mgr*
Steve Becker, *Manager*
EMP: 55
SALES (corp-wide): 67.1B **Publicly Held**
WEB: www.emc.com
SIC: 3572 7372 Computer storage de-
vices; prepackaged software
HQ: Emc Corporation
176 South St
Hopkinton MA 01748
508 435-1000

(G-1784)
**EMPIRE BAKERY COMMISSARY
LLC**
11243 Cornell Park Dr (45242-1811)
PHONE..................................513 793-6241
Kelly Brown,
EMP: 140 EST: 2015
SALES: 25MM **Privately Held**
SIC: 2051 Bakery: wholesale or whole-
sale/retail combined

(G-1785)
EMPRESS CHILI
9226 Hunters Creek Dr B (45242-6636)
PHONE..................................513 312-9589
Joel Miller, *Principal*
EMP: 23
SALES (est): 1.4MM **Privately Held**
SIC: 2038 Dinners, frozen & packaged

(G-1786)
**ETHICON ENDO-SURGERY INC
(HQ)**
4545 Creek Rd (45242-2839)
PHONE..................................513 337-7000
Fax: 513 483-3392
Tim Schmid, *President*
Brad Haag, *Division Mgr*
Hunter Hawver, *Division Mgr*
Rhonda Lee, *Division Mgr*
Dawn Rauen, *Division Mgr*
EMP: 1440
SQ FT: 31,330
SALES (est): 299.1MM
SALES (corp-wide): 71.8B **Publicly Held**
WEB: www.ethiconendo.com
SIC: 3841 Surgical instruments & appara-
tus
PA: Johnson & Johnson
1 Johnson And Johnson Plz
New Brunswick NJ 08933
732 524-0400

(G-1787)
ETHICON INC
Also Called: Ethicon Endo - Surgery
10123 Alliance Rd (45242-4714)
PHONE..................................513 786-7000
Frank J Ryan, *Manager*
EMP: 225
SALES (corp-wide): 71.8B **Publicly Held**
WEB: www.ethiconinc.com
SIC: 3842 Surgical appliances & supplies
HQ: Ethicon Inc.
Us Route 22
Somerville NJ 08876
732 524-0400

(G-1788)
ETHICON US LLC (DH)
4545 Creek Rd 3 (45242-2839)
PHONE..................................513 337-7000
Timothy H Schmid, *President*
Jim Bourne, *Vice Pres*
Kathy Rice, *QC Mgr*
David N Plescia, *Engineer*
Scott Bingham, *Design Engr*

EMP: 47
SALES (est): 27.5MM
SALES (corp-wide): 71.8B **Publicly Held**
SIC: 3841 Surgical instruments & appara-
tus
HQ: Ethicon Endo-Surgery, Inc.
4545 Creek Rd
Blue Ash OH 45242
513 337-7000

(G-1789)
EVERYTHINGS IMAGE INC
9933 Alliance Rd Ste 2 (45242-5662)
PHONE..................................513 469-6727
Fax: 513 469-6724
Kirk Morris, *President*
Daniel McBride, *Vice Pres*
Lisa Ruttenburg, *Manager*
Jake Runge, *Art Dir*
EMP: 15
SQ FT: 5,500
SALES (est): 1.5MM **Privately Held**
WEB: www.everythingsimage.com
SIC: 2759 Promotional printing; screen
printing

(G-1790)
EXCEL LOADING SYSTEMS LLC
675 N Deis Dr Ste 276 (45242)
PHONE..................................513 265-2936
David Shull, *President*
Alex Oswald,
Joe Williamson,
EMP: 3
SALES (est): 460.2K **Privately Held**
SIC: 3498 Pipe sections fabricated from
purchased pipe

(G-1791)
F+W MEDIA INC (HQ)
Also Called: Novel Writing Workshop
10151 Carver Rd Ste 200 (45242-4760)
PHONE..................................513 531-2690
David Nussbaum, *Ch of Bd*
Sara Domville, *President*
Allison Dolan, *Publisher*
Gary Lynch, *Publisher*
Jamie Markle, *Publisher*
▲ EMP: 265 EST: 2008
SQ FT: 250,000
SALES: 220MM **Privately Held**
WEB: www.decorativeartist.com
SIC: 2731 2721 Books: publishing only;
book clubs: publishing only, not printed on
site; magazines: publishing only, not
printed on site; trade journals: publishing
only, not printed on site
PA: New Publishing Holdings, Llc
10151 Carver Rd Ste 200
Blue Ash OH 45242
513 531-2690

(G-1792)
**FECHHEIMER BROTHERS
COMPANY (HQ)**
4545 Malsbary Rd (45242-5624)
PHONE..................................513 793-7819
Fax: 513 793-7819
Dan Dudley, *CEO*
Steven Riley, *Managing Dir*
Fred Heldman, *Senior VP*
Dan Balzofiore, *Vice Pres*
Steve Gatton, *Vice Pres*
▲ EMP: 200
SQ FT: 108,000
SALES (est): 256.4MM
SALES (corp-wide): 223.6B **Publicly
Held**
WEB: www.allbilt.com
SIC: 2311 2337 2339 5699 Men's &
boys' uniforms; policemen's uniforms:
made from purchased materials; fire-
men's uniforms: made from purchased
materials; women's & misses' suits &
coats; uniforms, except athletic: women's,
misses' & juniors'; women's & misses'
outerwear; uniforms
PA: Berkshire Hathaway Inc.
3555 Farnam St Ste 1440
Omaha NE 68131
402 346-1400

(G-1793)
FEINTOOL CINCINNATI INC (DH)
11280 Cornell Park Dr (45242-1888)
PHONE..................................513 247-0110

Fax: 513 247-0060
Christoph Trachsler, *CEO*
Ralph Hardt, *Principal*
Paul Frauchiger, *Vice Pres*
Rolf Haag, *Vice Pres*
Manfred Maier, *Facilities Mgr*
▲ EMP: 240
SALES (est): 68.5MM
SALES (corp-wide): 2.7B Privately Held
WEB: www.feintool-usa.com
SIC: 3465 Automotive stampings
HQ: Feintool U.S. Operations, Inc.
11280 Cornell Park Dr
Blue Ash OH 45242
513 247-4061

(G-1794)
FEINTOOL US OPERATIONS INC (DH)
11280 Cornell Park Dr (45242-1888)
PHONE...................513 247-4061
Richard Surico, *CEO*
Ralph E Hardt, *President*
Christoph Trachsler, *Principal*
Rick Bachman, *Vice Pres*
Tim Runyan, *Vice Pres*
▲ EMP: 250
SALES (est): 91.3MM
SALES (corp-wide): 2.7B Privately Held
SIC: 3469 3465 Metal stampings; automotive stampings
HQ: Feintool Technologie Ag
Industriering 3
Lyss BE 3250
323 875-111

(G-1795)
FLEX PRO LABEL INC
11465 Deerfield Rd (45242-2106)
PHONE...................513 489-4417
Fax: 513 489-0239
Peter Harpen, *President*
Anthony Harpen, *Corp Secy*
EMP: 3
SQ FT: 6,000
SALES: 400K Privately Held
WEB: www.flex-pro.com
SIC: 2759 Labels & seals: printing

(G-1796)
FLEXOPLATE INC
6504 Corporate Dr (45242-2101)
PHONE...................513 489-0433
Fax: 513 489-0437
Thomas M Bock, *President*
Mike Bock, *General Mgr*
Keith Ulland, *Manager*
EMP: 25
SQ FT: 10,000
SALES (est): 3.2MM Privately Held
WEB: www.flexoplate.com
SIC: 3555 2796 Printing plates; platemaking services; typesetting

(G-1797)
FLORIDA TILE INC
Florida Tile 56
10840 Millington Ct (45242-4017)
PHONE...................513 891-1122
Fax: 513 891-2508
Ian Buttress, *Principal*
EMP: 8
SQ FT: 12,000
SALES (corp-wide): 148.2MM Privately Held
WEB: www.floridatile.com
SIC: 3253 Wall tile, ceramic
PA: Florida Tile, Inc.
998 Governors Ln Ste 300
Lexington KY 40513
859 219-5200

(G-1798)
FLUID-BAG LLC
4555 Lake Forest Dr # 650 (45242-3785)
PHONE...................513 310-9550
Mark Evans, *Director*
EMP: 4 EST: 2015
SALES (est): 88.8K Privately Held
SIC: 3412 Milk (fluid) shipping containers, metal

(G-1799)
FORREST PHARMACEUTICALS
10901 Kenwood Rd (45242-2813)
PHONE...................513 791-1701

EMP: 5
SALES (est): 511.8K Privately Held
SIC: 2834 Pharmaceutical preparations

(G-1800)
FORWARD TECHNOLOGIES INC
6130 Interstate Cir (45242-1425)
PHONE...................513 489-5111
EMP: 15
SQ FT: 6,500
SALES: 500K Privately Held
SIC: 3599 Mfg Industrial Machinery

(G-1801)
G Q BUSINESS PRODUCTS
11380 Grooms Rd (45242-1406)
PHONE...................513 792-4750
Diana Queen, *President*
Gordon Queen, *Treasurer*
EMP: 8
SALES (est): 970K Privately Held
WEB: www.gqproducts.com
SIC: 5112 5199 2759 Business forms; advertising specialties; commercial printing

(G-1802)
GATE WEST COAST VENTURES LLC
Also Called: Tsjmedia
4412 Carver Woods Dr # 200 (45242-5539)
PHONE...................513 891-1000
Josh Guttman, *General Mgr*
Jose Castano, *Accounting Dir*
Brian Wiles, *Manager*
Dan Melendez, *Program Dir*
Simon Ciprianio,
EMP: 14 EST: 2005
SALES (est): 1.2MM Privately Held
SIC: 2711 Newspapers, publishing & printing

(G-1803)
GIS DYNAMICS LLC
11315 Williamson Rd (45241-2232)
PHONE...................513 847-4931
Michael Rorie,
EMP: 5
SQ FT: 2,500
SALES (est): 395.6K Privately Held
SIC: 7372 Application computer software

(G-1804)
GKN AEROSPACE CINCINNATI INC (HQ)
Also Called: Aerospace Mfg Group-Ohio
11230 Deerfield Rd (45242-2024)
PHONE...................513 489-9800
Phil Swash, *CEO*
Tom Battagli, *Senior VP*
Larry Alexander, *Vice Pres*
Mike Beck, *Vice Pres*
Robert Cohen, *Vice Pres*
▲ EMP: 158
SQ FT: 125,000
SALES (est): 46.3MM
SALES (corp-wide): 10.8B Privately Held
WEB: www.teleflex.com
SIC: 3599 Electrical discharge machining (EDM); machine shop, jobbing & repair
PA: Gkn Plc
Ipsley House
Redditch WORCS B98 0
152 751-7715

(G-1805)
HARTMANN INCORPORATED
4615 Carlynn Dr (45241-2202)
PHONE...................513 276-7318
Carolyn Hartmann, *President*
EMP: 12 EST: 2011
SALES (est): 1.4MM Privately Held
SIC: 2752 Commercial printing, offset

(G-1806)
HB FULLER COMPANY
Also Called: Adhesves Sealants Coatings Div
4450 Malsbary Rd (45242-5695)
PHONE...................513 719-3600
Louie Ybarra, *Facilities Mgr*
Todd Trushenski, *Manager*
Ralph Moeller, *Manager*
EMP: 46
SQ FT: 23,000

SALES (corp-wide): 2B Publicly Held
WEB: www.hbfuller.com
SIC: 2891 Adhesives & sealants
PA: H.B. Fuller Company
1200 Willow Lake Blvd
Saint Paul MN 55110
651 236-5900

(G-1807)
HB FULLER COMPANY
4440 Malsbary Rd (45242-5623)
PHONE...................513 719-3600
Fax: 513 891-6969
Todd Trushenski, *Branch Mgr*
EMP: 6
SALES (corp-wide): 2B Publicly Held
PA: H.B. Fuller Company
1200 Willow Lake Blvd
Saint Paul MN 55110
651 236-5900

(G-1808)
HENNIG INC
11431 Williamson Rd Ste A (45241-4216)
PHONE...................513 247-0838
Brian Smith, *Branch Mgr*
EMP: 3
SALES (corp-wide): 105.1MM Privately Held
SIC: 3444 Machine guards, sheet metal
HQ: Hennig Inc.
9900 N Alpine Rd
Machesney Park IL 61115
815 636-9900

(G-1809)
HOUSETRENDS
4601 Malsbary Rd 104 (45242-5632)
PHONE...................513 794-4103
Fax: 513 791-4140
Kevin Slattery, *Managing Prtnr*
Linda Bacher, *Publisher*
Bill Slattery, *Publisher*
Evelyn Yaus, *Publisher*
Jeremy Hensley, *Vice Pres*
EMP: 7 EST: 2011
SALES (est): 387.3K Privately Held
SIC: 2721 Magazines: publishing & printing

(G-1810)
HP INC
4440 Lake Forest Dr # 100 (45242-3758)
PHONE...................513 956-4253
Tom Janosick, *Manager*
Ron Morton, *MIS Staff*
EMP: 40
SALES (corp-wide): 48.2B Publicly Held
SIC: 3571 Personal computers (microcomputers)
PA: Hp Inc.
1501 Page Mill Rd
Palo Alto CA 94304
650 857-1501

(G-1811)
IACONO PRODUCTION SERVICES INC
Also Called: AVI Staging Technology
11420 Deerfield Rd (45242-2107)
PHONE...................513 469-5095
Michelle Moran, *Traffic Mgr*
EMP: 10
SALES (corp-wide): 6.7MM Privately Held
SIC: 3648 7359 7922 Stage lighting equipment; sound & lighting equipment rental; lighting, theatrical
PA: Iacono Production Services, Inc.
412 Central Ave
Cincinnati OH 45202
513 469-1015

(G-1812)
ILLINOIS TOOL WORKS INC
6600 Cornell Rd (45242-2033)
PHONE...................513 489-7600
Molly Dorsey, *Principal*
Robert Brigger, *Manager*
Ronald Stibich, *Manager*
EMP: 130
SALES (corp-wide): 13.6B Publicly Held
SIC: 2821 3714 2891 Polyesters; motor vehicle parts & accessories; adhesives & sealants

PA: Illinois Tool Works Inc.
155 Harlem Ave
Glenview IL 60025
847 724-7500

(G-1813)
IMERYS USA INC
9987 Carver Rd Ste 300 (45242-5563)
P.O. Box 144, Kimberly WI (54136-0144)
PHONE...................920 687-0872
John Schell, *Manager*
EMP: 20
SALES (corp-wide): 2MM Privately Held
SIC: 2672 Coated paper, except photographic, carbon or abrasive
HQ: Imerys Usa, Inc.
100 Mansell Ct E Ste 300
Roswell GA 30076
770 645-3300

(G-1814)
IMMERSUS HEALTH COMPANY LLC
4351 Creek Rd (45241-2923)
PHONE...................855 994-4325
Brian Pavlin,
EMP: 3
SALES (corp-wide): 10MM Privately Held
SIC: 3841 Surgical & medical instruments
PA: Immersus Health Company, Llc
2 Hill And Hollow Ln
Cincinnati OH 45208
855 994-4325

(G-1815)
INFINIT NUTRITION LLC
11240 Cornell Park Dr # 110 (45242-1800)
PHONE...................513 791-3500
Mark Martines, *Project Mgr*
Michael Folan, *Mng Member*
Chelsey Albrecht, *Manager*
▲ EMP: 10
SALES: 2MM Privately Held
SIC: 2023 Dietary supplements, dairy & non-dairy based

(G-1816)
INTERNATIONAL BUS MCHS CORP
Also Called: IBM
4600 Mcauley Pl Ste 200 (45242-4775)
PHONE...................513 826-1001
Bill Buechler, *Sales Mgr*
Michael Flood, *Manager*
Jim Armentrout, *Manager*
Sean Brown, *Manager*
Ron Goodin, *Manager*
EMP: 350
SALES (corp-wide): 79.9B Publicly Held
WEB: www.ibm.com
SIC: 3613 Distribution cutouts
PA: International Business Machines Corporation
1 New Orchard Rd Ste 1
Armonk NY 10504
914 499-1900

(G-1817)
INTERWEAVE PRESS LLC
10151 Carver Rd Ste 200 (45242-4760)
PHONE...................513 531-2690
EMP: 9
SALES (est): 755K Privately Held
SIC: 2741 Miscellaneous publishing

(G-1818)
JOB NEWS (PA)
10250 Alliance Rd Ste 201 (45242-4774)
PHONE...................513 984-5724
Fax: 513 984-2672
Dawna Urlakis, *Owner*
Mark Nightengale, *Vice Pres*
EMP: 8
SALES (est): 683.5K Privately Held
SIC: 2711 7311 Job printing & newspaper publishing combined; advertising agencies

(G-1819)
JOE P FISCHER WOODCRAFT
4627 Carlynn Dr (45241-2202)
PHONE...................513 530-9600
Joe P Fischer, *Owner*
EMP: 3

SALES (est): 148.3K **Privately Held**
SIC: 2431 Woodwork, interior & ornamental

(G-1820)
JPS TECHNOLOGIES INC (PA)
11110 Deerfield Rd (45242-2022)
PHONE.................................513 984-6400
Fax: 513 984-8204
Robert J Brandner, *President*
Nancy K Meyer, *Treasurer*
EMP: 10
SQ FT: 7,500
SALES (est): 10.8MM **Privately Held**
WEB: www.jpstechnologies.com
SIC: 5084 3089 Industrial machinery & equipment; plastic processing

(G-1821)
JPS TECHNOLOGIES INC
11118 Deerfield Rd (45242-2022)
PHONE.................................513 984-6400
Nancy Meyers, *Manager*
EMP: 12
SALES (corp-wide): 10.8MM **Privately Held**
WEB: www.jpstechnologies.com
SIC: 5084 3089 Industrial machinery & equipment; plastic processing
PA: Jps Technologies, Inc.
11110 Deerfield Rd
Blue Ash OH 45242
513 984-6400

(G-1822)
KARDOL QUALITY PRODUCTS LLC (PA)
9933 Alliance Rd Ste 2 (45242-5662)
PHONE.................................513 933-8206
Fax: 513 932-6900
Eric Kahn, *CEO*
Mark Bedwell, *President*
Mike Darding, *CFO*
Tom Nicolosi, *Nat'l Sales Mgr*
Mary Greenleaf, *Director*
▼ EMP: 6
SQ FT: 5,000
SALES (est): 4MM **Privately Held**
WEB: www.kardol.com
SIC: 2672 2841 2842 2821 Coated & laminated paper; soap & other detergents; specialty cleaning, polishes & sanitation goods; plastics materials & resins; paints & allied products

(G-1823)
KOLINAHR SYSTEMS INC
6840 Ashfield Dr (45242-4108)
PHONE.................................513 745-9401
Gary Jenkins, *President*
Greg Reichling, *Electrical Engi*
Cheryl Fritz, *Human Resources*
Andrew Stone, *Sales Dir*
EMP: 15
SALES (est): 6.1MM **Privately Held**
WEB: www.kolinahr.cc
SIC: 3535 5084 3565 Conveyors & conveying equipment; industrial machinery & equipment; packaging machinery

(G-1824)
LANGE PRECISION INC
6971 Cornell Rd (45242-3024)
PHONE.................................513 530-9500
Fax: 513 530-0370
Karl Lange, *President*
Robert Ayers, *QC Dir*
Drew Campbell, *Manager*
EMP: 15
SQ FT: 13,000
SALES (est): 2.8MM **Privately Held**
SIC: 3544 3599 3545 3537 Special dies, tools, jigs & fixtures; machine shop, jobbing & repair; machine tool accessories; industrial trucks & tractors; iron & steel forgings

(G-1825)
LARMAX INC
Also Called: Kwik Kopy Printing
10945 Reed Hartman Hwy # 210 (45242-2828)
PHONE.................................513 984-0783
Fax: 513 984-0171
Larry Richardson, *President*
Maxine Richardson, *Vice Pres*

EMP: 6
SQ FT: 1,500
SALES: 500K **Privately Held**
SIC: 2759 Thermography

(G-1826)
LEADEC CORP (PA)
Also Called: Vius Services Corp.
9395 Kenwood Rd Ste 200 (45242-6819)
PHONE.................................513 731-3590
Fax: 513 731-3659
William Bell, *CEO*
Donald G Morsch, *Treasurer*
Betsy Wallis, *Controller*
Kim Saylor, *Human Resources*
Vicki Yeazel, *Manager*
▲ EMP: 34
SQ FT: 18,000
SALES (est): 150MM **Privately Held**
WEB: www.premiermss.com
SIC: 7349 8741 3714 Building cleaning service; management services; motor vehicle parts & accessories

(G-1827)
LOCKES HEATING & COOLING LLC
10229 Kenwood Rd (45242-4701)
PHONE.................................513 793-1900
Steven W Locke,
EMP: 10
SQ FT: 1,000
SALES (est): 1.1MM **Privately Held**
SIC: 3585 Parts for heating, cooling & refrigerating equipment

(G-1828)
LOROCO INDUSTRIES INC (PA)
Also Called: Royal Pad Products
5000 Creek Rd (45242-3990)
PHONE.................................513 891-9544
Fax: 513 891-9549
James Lallathin, *President*
Lee Rozin, *Chairman*
Jim Myers, *CFO*
◆ EMP: 50 EST: 1898
SQ FT: 125,000
SALES (est): 13.7MM **Privately Held**
SIC: 2675 2671 3479 3544 Paperboard die-cutting; chip board, pasted, die-cut: from purchased materials; packaging paper & plastics film, coated & laminated; painting, coating & hot dipping; dies, steel rule; coated & laminated paper; paperboard mills

(G-1829)
LSI INDUSTRIES INC
Abolite Lighting
10000 Alliance Rd (45242-4706)
P.O. Box 42728, Cincinnati (45242-0728)
PHONE.................................513 793-3200
Fax: 513 793-0295
Jerry Combs, *Plant Mgr*
Dick Osborne, *Human Res Dir*
Laura Zuniga, *Accounts Mgr*
Harry Mason, *Marketing Staff*
Larry Branham, *Manager*
EMP: 50
SALES (corp-wide): 322.2MM **Publicly Held**
WEB: www.lsi-industries.com
SIC: 3648 3993 2759 3444 Lighting equipment; floodlights; public lighting fixtures; area & sports luminaries; electric signs; screen printing; labels & seals: printing; decals: printing; sheet metalwork; commercial indusl & institutional electric lighting fixtures; residential lighting fixtures
PA: Lsi Industries Inc.
10000 Alliance Rd
Blue Ash OH 45242
513 793-3200

(G-1830)
LSI INDUSTRIES INC (PA)
Also Called: LSI Graphic Solutions
10000 Alliance Rd (45242-4706)
PHONE.................................513 793-3200
Fax: 513 793-0256
Gary P Kreider, *Ch of Bd*
Dennis W Wells, *President*
Andrew J Foerster, *Exec VP*
Howard E Japlon, *Exec VP*
Sylvia Astrop, *Senior VP*

EMP: 277
SQ FT: 243,000
SALES: 322.2MM **Publicly Held**
WEB: www.lsi-industries.com
SIC: 3648 3993 Lighting equipment; floodlights; public lighting fixtures; area & sports luminaries; electric signs; light communications equipment

(G-1831)
LUMINEX HOME DECOR (PA)
Also Called: Luminex HD&f Company
10521 Millington Ct (45242-4022)
PHONE.................................513 563-1113
Calvin Johnston, *CEO*
Dawn Enright, *Manager*
EMP: 788
SALES (est): 262.6MM **Privately Held**
SIC: 5023 2844 Decorative home furnishings & supplies; toilet preparations

(G-1832)
MARKES INTERNATIONAL INC
Also Called: Alms Company
11126 Kenwood Rd Ste D (45242-1897)
PHONE.................................513 745-0241
Elizabeth Woolfenden, *Director*
Alun Cole, *Director*
EMP: 100
SALES: 1MM **Privately Held**
SIC: 3826 Analytical instruments

(G-1833)
MASTER COMMUNICATIONS INC
Also Called: Asia For Kids
4480 Lake Forest Dr # 302 (45242-3753)
P.O. Box 9096, Cincinnati (45209-0096)
PHONE.................................208 821-3473
Selina Yoon, *President*
Frederick Chen, *Vice Pres*
Gay Earlywine, *Accounts Mgr*
Debbie Miniard, *Manager*
▲ EMP: 9
SALES (est): 1.4MM **Privately Held**
WEB: www.master-comm.com
SIC: 7812 2731 Video tape production; book publishing

(G-1834)
MATDAN CORPORATION
10855 Millington Ct (45242-4019)
PHONE.................................513 794-0500
Fax: 513 794-0651
David Arand, *President*
Jan Arand, *Vice Pres*
Matt Arand, *Project Mgr*
Wes Stultz, *Cust Mgr*
▲ EMP: 35
SQ FT: 10,000
SALES (est): 8.1MM **Privately Held**
WEB: www.matdanfasteners.com
SIC: 3452 3429 Bolts, metal; manufactured hardware (general)

(G-1835)
MAVERICK CORPORATION
11379 Grooms Rd (45242-1405)
PHONE.................................513 469-9919
Fax: 513 247-2452
Eric Collins, *CEO*
Robert Gray, *President*
Brad Love, *General Mgr*
Laurie Mesing, *Controller*
Traci Denny, *Sales Staff*
EMP: 14
SQ FT: 2,300
SALES (est): 3MM **Privately Held**
SIC: 3089 3299 Thermoformed finished plastic products; ceramic fiber

(G-1836)
MAVERICK MOLDING CO
11379 Grooms Rd (45242-1405)
PHONE.................................513 469-9919
Traci Denny, *General Mgr*
Brad Love, *Principal*
Laurel Mesing, *Principal*
Jack Rubino, *Exec VP*
▲ EMP: 17
SALES: 50K **Privately Held**
SIC: 3728 Aircraft parts & equipment

(G-1837)
META MANUFACTURING CORPORATION
8901 Blue Ash Rd Ste 1 (45242-7809)
PHONE.................................513 793-6382
Fax: 513 793-6390
David Mc Swain, *President*
Pete Van Curen, *Sales Executive*
Jeff Theis, *Manager*
Mike Fennen, *Director*
EMP: 50
SQ FT: 54,000
SALES (est): 10.3MM **Privately Held**
WEB: www.metamfg.com
SIC: 3599 7692 Machine & other job shop work; welding repair

(G-1838)
METAL IMPROVEMENT COMPANY LLC
11131 Luschek Dr (45241-2434)
PHONE.................................513 489-6484
Fax: 513 489-6499
Dan Richardson, *Division Mgr*
James Groark, *General Mgr*
Brian Brown, *QC Mgr*
David Markgraf, *Manager*
Roger Catron, *Director*
EMP: 23
SQ FT: 15,031
SALES (corp-wide): 2.1B **Publicly Held**
WEB: www.mic-houston.com
SIC: 3398 3471 3341 Shot peening (treating steel to reduce fatigue); plating & polishing; secondary nonferrous metals
HQ: Metal Improvement Company, Llc
80 E State Rt 4 Ste 310
Paramus NJ 07652
201 843-7800

(G-1839)
METALEX MANUFACTURING INC (PA)
5750 Cornell Rd (45242-2083)
PHONE.................................513 489-0507
Fax: 513 489-0827
Kevin Kummerle, *CEO*
Werner Kummerle, *President*
Katherine Becker, *General Mgr*
Sue Kummerle, *Corp Secy*
Brian Lawson, *Buyer*
▲ EMP: 115
SQ FT: 120,000
SALES: 40.3MM **Privately Held**
WEB: www.metalexmfg.com
SIC: 3599 3511 3544 3769 Custom machinery; turbines & turbine generator sets; special dies, tools, jigs & fixtures; guided missile & space vehicle parts & auxiliary equipment; machine tool accessories

(G-1840)
MID-TOWN PETRO ACQUISITION LLC (PA)
9395 Kenwood Rd Ste 104 (45242-6819)
PHONE.................................219 728-5149
EMP: 2
SALES (est): 3.2MM **Privately Held**
SIC: 2911 Petroleum refining

(G-1841)
MILACRON HOLDINGS CORP (PA)
10200 Alliance Rd Ste 200 (45242-4716)
PHONE.................................513 487-5000
Ira G Boots, *Ch of Bd*
Tom J Goeke, *President*
Bruce Chalmers, *CFO*
EMP: 25
SQ FT: 22,000
SALES: 1.1B **Publicly Held**
SIC: 3544 Industrial molds; forms (molds), for foundry & plastics working machinery

(G-1842)
MILACRON LLC (DH)
10200 Alliance Rd Ste 200 (45242-4716)
PHONE.................................513 487-5000
Fax: 513 487-5086
Tom Goeke, *CEO*
John Sherman, *District Mgr*
John Gallagher, *COO*
Ron Krisanda, *COO*
Hugh O Donnell, *Senior VP*
◆ EMP: 35

▲ = Import ▼ =Export
◆ =Import/Export

SALES (est): 1.7B
SALES (corp-wide): 1.1B **Publicly Held**
SIC: 3549 2899 Metalworking machinery; correction fluid
HQ: Milacron Intermediate Holdings Inc.
3010 Disney St
Cincinnati OH 45209
513 536-2000

(G-1843)
MOLDERS WORLD INC
11471 Deerfield Rd (45242-2106)
PHONE..................................513 469-6653
Russell Bowen, *Principal*
Brandon Bowen, *Opers Mgr*
EMP: 10
SALES (est): 1MM **Privately Held**
SIC: 3089 Molding primary plastic

(G-1844)
NEW TRACK MEDIA LLC
10151 Carver Rd Ste 200 (45242-4760)
PHONE..................................513 421-6500
Stephen J Kent, *President*
W Budge Wallis, *President*
Kristi Loeffehlz, *Publisher*
Lisa O'Bryan, *Publisher*
Tina Battock, *Exec VP*
▲ **EMP:** 10
SALES (est): 1MM **Privately Held**
SIC: 2721 Magazines: publishing & printing
HQ: F+W Media, Inc.
10151 Carver Rd Ste 200
Blue Ash OH 45242
513 531-2690

(G-1845)
OLAY LLC
Also Called: Procter Gamble Olay Co - Cayey
11530 Reed Hartman Hwy (45241-2422)
PHONE..................................787 535-2191
AG Lafley, *CEO*
Ezio Garciamendez, *Plant Mgr*
EMP: 6 **EST:** 2007
SALES (est): 420.1K
SALES (corp-wide): 65.3B **Publicly Held**
SIC: 2844 Toilet preparations; cosmetic preparations
HQ: Procter & Gamble International Operations Sa
Route De St-Georges 47
Petit-Lancy GE 1213
227 096-111

(G-1846)
OMYA DISTRIBUTION LLC (DH)
9987 Carver Rd Ste 300 (45242-5563)
PHONE..................................513 387-4600
Anthony Colak, *President*
EMP: 6
SALES (est): 4MM **Privately Held**
SIC: 2819 Calcium compounds & salts, inorganic
HQ: Omya Inc.
9987 Carver Rd Ste 300
Blue Ash OH 45242
513 387-4600

(G-1847)
OMYA INDUSTRIES INC (HQ)
9987 Carver Rd Ste 300 (45242-5563)
PHONE..................................513 387-4600
Anthony Colak, *President*
John Suddarth, *Vice Pres*
Michael Phillips, *CFO*
Thomas G Turner, *CFO*
Candace Gardiner, *Finance*
◆ **EMP:** 85 **EST:** 1977
SQ FT: 21,700
SALES (est): 226.4MM **Privately Held**
SIC: 1422 Crushed & broken limestone
PA: Omya Ag
Baslerstrasse 42
Oftringen AG
627 892-929

(G-1848)
ORACLE AMERICA INC
Also Called: Sun Microsystems
9987 Carver Rd Ste 250 (45242-5553)
PHONE..................................513 381-0125
Joe Otto, *Manager*
EMP: 15
SALES (corp-wide): 37B **Publicly Held**
SIC: 3571 Minicomputers

HQ: Oracle America, Inc.
500 Oracle Pkwy
Redwood City CA 94065
650 506-7000

(G-1849)
ORACLE SYSTEMS CORPORATION
9987 Carver Rd Ste 250 (45242-5553)
PHONE..................................513 826-6000
Fax: 614 280-6573
Dale Weideling, *Vice Pres*
Adam Scott, *Accounts Exec*
Carol Beebe, *Manager*
Steve Seger, *Senior Mgr*
EMP: 50
SALES (corp-wide): 37B **Publicly Held**
WEB: www.forcecapital.com
SIC: 7372 Prepackaged software
HQ: Oracle Systems Corporation
500 Oracle Pkwy
Redwood City CA 94065
650 506-7000

(G-1850)
ORGANIZED LIGHTNING LLC
Also Called: Shelter Studios
5601 Belleview Ave (45242-7427)
PHONE..................................407 965-2730
Jonathan Weiner, *Mng Member*
EMP: 6
SQ FT: 3,500
SALES: 1MM **Privately Held**
SIC: 2741

(G-1851)
PLASTIC MOLDINGS COMPANY LLC (PA)
Also Called: P M C
9825 Kenwood Rd Ste 302 (45242-6252)
PHONE..................................513 921-5040
Fax: 513 921-5883
Dale Turner, *Vice Pres*
Louis Ripley, *VP Human Res*
George H Vincent,
Thomas R Gerdes,
Lisa Jennings,
▲ **EMP:** 75
SQ FT: 63,500
SALES (est): 31.4MM **Privately Held**
WEB: www.plasticmoldings.com
SIC: 3089 Plastic processing; injection molding of plastics

(G-1852)
PMC SMART SOLUTIONS LLC
9825 Kenwood Rd Ste 300 (45242-6252)
PHONE..................................513 921-5040
Lisa Jennings, *President*
Deborah Gerdes,
EMP: 11
SALES (est): 1.9MM **Privately Held**
SIC: 3089 Injection molded finished plastic products

(G-1853)
POSITECH CORP
11310 Williamson Rd (45241-2233)
PHONE..................................513 942-7411
Jeff Hauck, *President*
▲ **EMP:** 15
SQ FT: 12,400
SALES (est): 2.1MM **Privately Held**
WEB: www.positechcorp.com
SIC: 3599 Machine shop, jobbing & repair

(G-1854)
PRECISION ANLYTICAL INSTRS INC
Also Called: P A I
10857 Millington Ct (45242-4019)
PHONE..................................513 984-1600
Douglas G Frank, *President*
Gary Frank, *Manager*
EMP: 6
SQ FT: 2,100
SALES (est): 946.5K **Privately Held**
WEB: www.toolsforanalysis.com
SIC: 3826 Analytical instruments

(G-1855)
PRESTIGE ENTERPRISE INTL INC
11343 Grooms Rd (45242-1405)
PHONE..................................513 469-6044

Fax: 513 469-6444
Charles Gabbour, *President*
Jeff Gabbour, *Vice Pres*
Dostien Clark, *Accountant*
Chris Blum, *Marketing Staff*
◆ **EMP:** 51
SQ FT: 10,000
SALES (est): 7.1MM **Privately Held**
WEB: www.prestigefloor.com
SIC: 2426 Flooring, hardwood

(G-1856)
PROCTER & GAMBLE COMPANY
11520 Reed Hartman Hwy (45241-2422)
P.O. Box 599, Cincinnati (45201-0599)
PHONE..................................513 626-2500
Larry Bramlage, *Research*
Rob Nemeth, *Engineer*
Mylon Turk, *Engineer*
Tony Wilson, *Engineer*
Jianwei Zhang, *Senior Engr*
EMP: 800
SALES (corp-wide): 65.3B **Publicly Held**
WEB: www.pg.com
SIC: 2841 Soap & other detergents
PA: The Procter & Gamble Company
1 Procter And Gamble Plz
Cincinnati OH 45202
513 983-1100

(G-1857)
PROCTER & GAMBLE COMPANY
11530 Reed Hartman Hwy (45241-2422)
PHONE..................................513 626-2500
Fax: 513 626-3522
Kathy Kramp, *Research*
Gale Britton, *Manager*
Gregory Allspach, *Manager*
Daryl Hawkins, *Senior Mgr*
EMP: 150
SALES (corp-wide): 65.3B **Publicly Held**
WEB: www.pg.com
SIC: 2676 2844 Towels, napkins & tissue paper products; diapers, paper (disposable): made from purchased paper; feminine hygiene paper products; toilet preparations; hair preparations, including shampoos; oral preparations; deodorants, personal
PA: The Procter & Gamble Company
1 Procter And Gamble Plz
Cincinnati OH 45202
513 983-1100

(G-1858)
PROCTER & GAMBLE MFG CO
11530 Reed Hartman Hwy (45241-2422)
P.O. Box 701, Cincinnati (45202)
PHONE..................................513 626-6882
EMP: 8
SALES (corp-wide): 65.3B **Publicly Held**
SIC: 2841 Soap: granulated, liquid, cake, flaked or chip
HQ: The Procter & Gamble Manufacturing Company
1 Procter And Gamble Plz
Cincinnati OH 45202
513 983-1100

(G-1859)
PROCTOER & GAMBLE
11530 Reed Hartman Hwy (45241-2422)
P.O. Box 5584, Cincinnati (45201-5584)
PHONE..................................513 983-1100
Fax: 513 626-3145
Camille Chammas, *Manager*
EMP: 4 **EST:** 2010
SALES (est): 365.2K **Privately Held**
SIC: 2833 Medicinal chemicals

(G-1860)
PROTEIN EXPRESS LABORATORIES
Also Called: Skirdle
10931 R Hartman Hwy B (45242)
PHONE..................................513 769-9654
Zsolt Hertelendy, *Vice Pres*
EMP: 3
SALES (est): 225.7K **Privately Held**
SIC: 2836 Biological products, except diagnostic; toxins, viruses & similar substances, including venom; bacteriological media

(G-1861)
RA CONSULTANTS LLC
10856 Kenwood Rd (45242-2812)
PHONE..................................513 469-6600
Fax: 513 469-2684
John P Allen,
Marijo Flamm, *Admin Asst*
EMP: 30
SALES (est): 5MM **Privately Held**
WEB: www.raconsultsllc.com
SIC: 8711 3679 Engineering services; commutators, electronic

(G-1862)
RELADYNE INC (PA)
9395 Kenwood Rd Ste 104 (45242-6819)
PHONE..................................513 489-6000
EMP: 25
SALES (est): 347.8MM **Privately Held**
SIC: 2992 Lubricating oils & greases

(G-1863)
RSW DISTRIBUTORS LLC
Also Called: Culinary Standards
4700 Ashwood Dr Ste 200 (45241-2424)
PHONE..................................502 587-8877
George Cornett, *Controller*
Ronald Wilheim,
Mark A Littman,
EMP: 100 **EST:** 2008
SQ FT: 27,111
SALES (est): 12.6MM **Privately Held**
SIC: 2038 Frozen specialties

(G-1864)
SAMUELS PRODUCTS INC
9851 Redhill Dr (45242-5694)
PHONE..................................513 891-4456
Fax: 513 891-4520
Millard Samuels, *President*
Thomas J Samuels, *Vice Pres*
Timothy Kroger, *Sales Mgr*
William Fitzpatric, *Admin Sec*
EMP: 30 **EST:** 1903
SQ FT: 61,000
SALES (est): 4.3MM **Privately Held**
WEB: www.samuelsproducts.com
SIC: 2759 5122 Flexographic printing; bags, plastic: printing; druggists' sundries

(G-1865)
SCHOOL MAINTENANCE SUPPLY INC (PA)
10616 Millington Ct (45242)
PHONE..................................513 376-8670
Derrick Spruance, *President*
Vicky Spruance, *Corp Secy*
EMP: 5
SALES (est): 525K **Privately Held**
SIC: 2399 5013 Seat covers, automobile; seat covers

(G-1866)
SD IP HOLDINGS COMPANY
4747 Lake Forest Dr (45242-3853)
PHONE..................................513 483-3300
Billy Cyr, *President*
William Schumacher, *Senior VP*
EMP: 1
SALES (est): 15.3MM
SALES (corp-wide): 342.8MM **Privately Held**
SIC: 2086 Carbonated soft drinks, bottled & canned
HQ: Sunny Delight Beverage Co
10300 Alliance Rd Ste 500
Blue Ash OH 45242
513 483-3300

(G-1867)
SECQURE SURGICAL CORP
4480 Lake Forest Dr # 414 (45242-3740)
PHONE..................................513 769-1916
Rich Grant, *President*
EMP: 3
SQ FT: 13,000
SALES: 3MM **Privately Held**
SIC: 3841 Surgical & medical instruments

(G-1868)
SELLYOURMACCOM
11101 Kenwood Rd (45242-1817)
PHONE..................................513 965-1144
Brian Burke, *Principal*
Tyler King, *Opers Staff*

EMP: 3
SALES (est): 411.4K **Privately Held**
SIC: 2836 Culture media

(G-1869)
SHRED-IT USA LLC (DH)
11311 Cornell Park Dr # 125 (45242-1831)
PHONE..............................513 699-0845
Vincent R De Palma, *CEO*
Colette Raymond, *Exec VP*
Brenda Frank, *Vice Pres*
James Rudyk, *CFO*
Raul Acuna, *Manager*
EMP: 36
SALES (est): 522.1MM
SALES (corp-wide): 3.5B **Publicly Held**
SIC: 3589 Shredders, industrial & commercial
HQ: Shred-It Us Jv Llc
    11311 Cornell Park Dr # 125
    Blue Ash OH 45242
    513 245-8659

(G-1870)
SONOCO PRODUCTS COMPANY
Also Called: Sonoco Trident
4747 Lake Forest Dr # 100 (45242-3853)
PHONE..............................513 455-6003
Fax: 513 455-6002
Kelly Carigan, *Branch Mgr*
EMP: 57
SALES (corp-wide): 4.7B **Publicly Held**
SIC: 2631 Paperboard mills
PA: Sonoco Products Company
    1 N 2nd St
    Hartsville SC 29550
    843 383-7000

(G-1871)
SPACE DYNAMICS CORP
Also Called: Ambassador Heat Transfer
10080 Alliance Rd (45242-4706)
P.O. Box 42344, Cincinnati (45242-0344)
PHONE..............................513 792-9800
Fax: 513 792-9933
Madan L Ghai, *Ch of Bd*
Rik L Ghai, *President*
James L Lyons, *Principal*
Dolores A Yackle, *Corp Secy*
Sheila Revis, *Vice Pres*
EMP: 25 **EST:** 1961
SQ FT: 45,000
SALES: 6MM **Privately Held**
WEB: www.ambassadorco.com
SIC: 3443 3585 Heat exchangers, condensers & components; refrigeration & heating equipment

(G-1872)
SPECTRE EDM
6082 Interstate Cir (45242-1413)
PHONE..............................513 469-7700
Burt Melson, *Owner*
EMP: 5
SQ FT: 6,000
SALES: 500K **Privately Held**
SIC: 3599 Machine & other job shop work

(G-1873)
ST MEDIA GROUP INTL INC
11262 Cornell Park Dr (45242-1812)
PHONE..............................513 421-2050
Tedd Swormstedt, *President*
Robin Donovan, *Editor*
Carly Hagedon, *Editor*
Matthew Hall, *Editor*
Katie Mann, *Editor*
▲ **EMP:** 65
SQ FT: 30,000
SALES (est): 17.3MM **Privately Held**
WEB: www.signweb.com
SIC: 2721 2731 2791 Periodicals: publishing only; book publishing; typesetting

(G-1874)
STANDARD REGISTER INC
4500 Lake Forest Dr 518 (45242-3728)
PHONE..............................513 563-9700
Greg McLeod, *Manager*
EMP: 14
SALES (corp-wide): 4.6B **Privately Held**
WEB: www.stdreg.com
SIC: 2761 Manifold business forms

HQ: Standard Register, Inc.
    600 Albany St
    Dayton OH 45417
    937 221-1000

(G-1875)
STOLLE PROPERTIES INC
6954 Cornell Rd Ste 100 (45242-3001)
P.O. Box 815, Lebanon (45036-0815)
PHONE..............................513 932-8664
William Faulkner, *President*
EMP: 580
SQ FT: 1,876
SALES (est): 41.5MM
SALES (corp-wide): 60.8MM **Privately Held**
SIC: 3469 Metal stampings
PA: The Ralph J Stolle Company

    Cincinnati OH 45242
    513 489-7184

(G-1876)
SUNNY DELIGHT BEVERAGE CO (HQ)
10300 Alliance Rd Ste 500 (45242-4767)
PHONE..............................513 483-3300
Fax: 513 483-3396
Tim Voelkerding, *President*
Jeremy Weatherford, *Area Mgr*
Ellen Iobst, *Senior VP*
Keith Conover, *Production*
Greg Ogborn, *Purch Dir*
▼ **EMP:** 70
SQ FT: 20,000
SALES (est): 343.1MM
SALES (corp-wide): 348.9MM **Privately Held**
SIC: 2086 Fruit drinks (less than 100% juice): packaged in cans, etc.
PA: Brynwood Partners Vii L.P.
    8 Sound Shore Dr Ste 265
    Greenwich CT 06830
    203 622-1790

(G-1877)
SUPERIOR PRINTING INK CO INC
Also Called: Mueller Color
10861 Millington Ct Ste B (45242-4035)
PHONE..............................513 221-4707
Fax: 513 221-6209
Ed Bradley, *Principal*
EMP: 17
SQ FT: 20,000
SALES (est): 2.9MM **Privately Held**
SIC: 2899 Ink or writing fluids

(G-1878)
SURGRX INC
4545 Creek Rd (45242-2803)
PHONE..............................650 482-2400
David Clapper, *President*
Edward Unkard, *CFO*
EMP: 14 **EST:** 2000
SQ FT: 20,000
SALES (est): 1MM
SALES (corp-wide): 71.8B **Publicly Held**
WEB: www.surgrx.com
SIC: 3841 Surgical & medical instruments
HQ: Ethicon Endo-Surgery, Inc.
    4545 Creek Rd
    Blue Ash OH 45242
    513 337-7000

(G-1879)
SYRGIS HOLDINGS INC
4555 Lake Forest Dr # 650 (45242-3789)
PHONE..............................859 356-8000
Andy Harris, *CEO*
EMP: 3
SALES (est): 262.1K **Privately Held**
SIC: 2869 Industrial organic chemicals

(G-1880)
TECHNOSOFT INC
11180 Reed Hartman Hwy # 200 (45242-1824)
PHONE..............................513 985-9877
Fax: 513 985-0522
Adel Chemaly, *President*
Nabil Khater, *Vice Pres*
Harish Kumar, *Human Res Mgr*
Bishaka Ketkar, *Human Resources*
Vimal Kumar, *Human Resources*
EMP: 12

SALES (est): 1.5MM **Privately Held**
SIC: 7372 7371 Prepackaged software; custom computer programming services

(G-1881)
TEKWORX LLC
4538 Cornell Rd (45241-2425)
PHONE..............................513 533-4777
Mike Flaherty, *Managing Dir*
Larry Tillack, *Research*
EMP: 15
SALES (est): 2.1MM **Privately Held**
SIC: 8748 8711 1731 3625 Systems analysis & engineering consulting services; energy conservation engineering; energy management controls; electric controls & control accessories, industrial

(G-1882)
TOYO SEIKI USA INC
11130 Luschek Dr (45241-2434)
PHONE..............................513 546-9657
Nobukaizu Kaike, *Principal*
Saito Katsu, *Manager*
EMP: 5
SALES (est): 490.4K
SALES (corp-wide): 35.8MM **Privately Held**
SIC: 2822 Ethylene-propylene rubbers, EPDM polymers
PA: Toyo Seiki Seisaku-Sho, Ltd.
    5-15-4, Takinogawa
    Kita-Ku TKY 114-0
    339 168-181

(G-1883)
TRANS-ACC INC (PA)
11167 Deerfield Rd (45242-2021)
PHONE..............................513 793-6410
Fax: 513 793-0679
John Weinkam, *President*
Mary Weinkam, *Vice Pres*
Doug Miller, *Financial Exec*
Joe Kauffmann, *Marketing Staff*
Emily Porter, *Office Mgr*
EMP: 35
SQ FT: 27,000
SALES (est): 4.9MM **Privately Held**
SIC: 3471 3479 Finishing, metals or formed products; coating of metals & formed products

(G-1884)
TYTEK INDUSTRIES INC (PA)
4700 Ashwood Dr Ste 445 (45241-2684)
PHONE..............................513 874-7326
Fax: 513 874-7294
Chris C Tyler, *President*
Mark Sweatman, *Engineer*
Terry Mistler, *Manager*
▲ **EMP:** 4
SQ FT: 210,000
SALES (est): 798.6K **Privately Held**
WEB: www.tytekindustries.com
SIC: 3674 Photoelectric magnetic devices

(G-1885)
TYTEK MEDICAL INC
4700 Ashwood Dr Ste 445 (45241-2684)
PHONE..............................513 247-2002
Chris Tyler, *President*
EMP: 4 **EST:** 2011
SALES (est): 335.2K **Privately Held**
SIC: 3842 Bandages & dressings

(G-1886)
UNITED AIR SPECIALISTS INC (DH)
Also Called: UAS
4440 Creek Rd (45242-2802)
PHONE..............................513 891-0400
Fax: 513 891-4171
Richard Charles Larson, *President*
Robert L Kriedler, *Principal*
S F Williams, *Principal*
Pamela Curry, *Vice Pres*
Bruce A Klein, *Vice Pres*
◆ **EMP:** 150
SQ FT: 157,000
SALES: 59.7MM
SALES (corp-wide): 11.3B **Publicly Held**
WEB: www.uasinc.com
SIC: 3563 3564 Spraying & dusting equipment; air cleaning systems

HQ: Clarcor Inc.
    840 Crescent Centre Dr # 600
    Franklin TN 37067
    615 771-3100

(G-1887)
US INC
10937 Reed Hartman Hwy (45242-2858)
PHONE..............................513 791-1162
Charles Davis, *Branch Mgr*
EMP: 4
SALES (corp-wide): 3MM **Privately Held**
SIC: 1711 5023 3263 Heating & air conditioning contractors; kitchenware; commercial tableware or kitchen articles, fine earthenware
PA: Us, Inc.
    6890 Distribution Dr
    Beltsville MD 20705
    301 776-7270

(G-1888)
VALENTINE RESEARCH INC
10280 Alliance Rd (45242-4710)
PHONE..............................513 984-8900
Fax: 513 984-8976
Michael Valentine, *President*
Stephen Scholl, *Vice Pres*
Margaret Valentine, *Vice Pres*
Rick Dickerson, *Engineer*
Alice Adams, *Administration*
EMP: 45
SQ FT: 11,000
SALES (est): 11.5MM **Privately Held**
WEB: www.valentine1.com
SIC: 3812 Radar systems & equipment

(G-1889)
VENTILATION SYSTEMS JSC
Also Called: Vents - US
11013 Kenwood Rd (45242-1842)
PHONE..............................513 348-3853
EMP: 8 **Privately Held**
SIC: 3634 Fans, exhaust & ventilating, electric: household
HQ: Ventylyatsiini Systemy, Prat
    Bud. 1 Vul. Mykhaila Kotsiubynskogo
    Kyiv 01030
    444 063-625

(G-1890)
VORTEC AND PAXTON PRODUCTS
10125 Carver Rd (45242-4719)
PHONE..............................513 891-7474
David Spears, *CEO*
William Ooh, *General Mgr*
Barbara Stefl, *General Mgr*
Stan Coley, *Opers Mgr*
Brian Seifert, *Opers Staff*
EMP: 14
SQ FT: 25,000
SALES (est): 3.9MM
SALES (corp-wide): 13.6B **Publicly Held**
WEB: www.paxtonproducts.com
SIC: 3564 Blowers & fans
PA: Illinois Tool Works Inc.
    155 Harlem Ave
    Glenview IL 60025
    847 724-7500

(G-1891)
VORTEC CORPORATION
Also Called: Vortec-An Illinois TI Works Co
10125 Carver Rd (45242-4798)
PHONE..............................513 686-8210
Fax: 513 891-4092
Lois Lannigan, *President*
William OH, *General Mgr*
Barbara Stefl, *General Mgr*
Stan Coley, *Safety Dir*
Tom Long, *Controller*
EMP: 22
SALES (est): 4.1MM
SALES (corp-wide): 13.6B **Publicly Held**
WEB: www.itwvortec.com
SIC: 3585 3499 3699 3498 Refrigeration & heating equip; nozzles, spray: aerosol, paint or insecticide; electrical equipment & supplies; fabricated pipe & fittings; fabricated plate work (boiler shop); auto controls regulating residntl & coml environmt & applncs

PA: Illinois Tool Works Inc.
155 Harlem Ave
Glenview IL 60025
847 724-7500

(G-1892)
WELDPARTS INC
6500 Corporate Dr (45242-2101)
PHONE..........................513 530-0064
Fax: 513 530-0065
Mikio Kusano, *President*
Craig Napier, *Opers Mgr*
▲ **EMP:** 10 **EST:** 2000
SQ FT: 8,000
SALES (est): 2MM **Privately Held**
WEB: www.weldparts.com
SIC: 5084 3548 Welding machinery &
equipment; resistance welders, electric

(G-1893)
WESTROCK CP LLC
Also Called: Smurfit-Stone
9960 Alliance Rd (45242-5643)
P.O. Box 42363, Cincinnati (45242-0363)
PHONE..........................513 745-2400
Fax: 513 745-2436
Peter Widolff, *General Mgr*
Terrie Anderson, *Purchasing*
Teresa Lang, *Purchasing*
Lee Bolton, *Technical Mgr*
Gary Quast, *Controller*
EMP: 270
SALES (corp-wide): 14.1B **Publicly Held**
WEB: www.sto.com
SIC: 2653 3993 3412 2671 Corrugated &
solid fiber boxes; signs & advertising spe-
cialties; metal barrels, drums & pails;
packaging paper & plastics film, coated &
laminated
HQ: Westrock Cp, Llc
504 Thrasher St
Norcross GA 30071

(G-1894)
WHITEHOUSE BROS INC
4393 Creek Rd (45241-2923)
PHONE..........................513 621-2259
Joseph G Vogelsang, *President*
Gary Domsher, *Manager*
EMP: 9 **EST:** 1906
SQ FT: 1,200
SALES: 1.3MM **Privately Held**
WEB: www.whitehousebrothers.com
SIC: 3911 Jewelry, precious metal

(G-1895)
WINGATE PACKAGING SOUTH
4347 Indeco Ct (45241-2925)
PHONE..........................513 745-8600
Fax: 513 745-8603
John S Richardson, *President*
Robert W Braunschweig, *Principal*
Deborah Manczak, *Office Mgr*
Patty Metelko, *Manager*
EMP: 38
SQ FT: 44,000
SALES (est): 10.2MM **Privately Held**
WEB: www.wingateartcraft.com
SIC: 2759 Commercial printing

(G-1896)
**WITTROCK WDWKG & MFG CO
INC**
4201 Malsbary Rd (45242-5509)
PHONE..........................513 891-5800
Fax: 513 891-5802
David Wittrock, *President*
Christopher Wittrock, *Corp Secy*
Joseph Wittrock, *Vice Pres*
John Cole, *Project Mgr*
Dave Simmons, *Manager*
▲ **EMP:** 70 **EST:** 1963
SQ FT: 11,000
SALES (est): 12.9MM **Privately Held**
SIC: 2431 Millwork

(G-1897)
WOLF MACHINE COMPANY (PA)
5570 Creek Rd (45242-4004)
PHONE..........................513 791-5194
Fax: 513 791-0925
Scott E Andre, *President*
Greg Russell, *Vice Pres*
Dave Smith, *Plant Mgr*
Keith Jameson, *Purch Agent*
Ken Park, *Manager*

EMP: 35
SQ FT: 50,000
SALES (est): 39.2MM **Privately Held**
WEB: www.wolfmachine.com
SIC: 5084 3552 3556 3546 Industrial ma-
chinery & equipment; textile machinery;
food products machinery; power-driven
handtools

(G-1898)
WOODLAWN RUBBER CO
11268 Williamson Rd (45241-2281)
PHONE..........................513 489-1718
Fax: 513 489-2367
Kirk Heithaus, *President*
Donald Heithaus, *Treasurer*
EMP: 18
SQ FT: 21,000
SALES: 2MM **Privately Held**
WEB: www.woodlawnrubber.com
SIC: 3069 3061 Molded rubber products;
mechanical rubber goods

(G-1899)
WORNICK COMPANY (DH)
Also Called: Wornick Foods
4700 Creek Rd (45242-2875)
P.O. Box 42634, Cincinnati (45242-0634)
PHONE..........................800 860-4555
Jon P Geisler, *President*
Drew Willis, *General Mgr*
Scott Kaylor, *Sr Exec VP*
Jack Fields, *Vice Pres*
Doug Herald, *Vice Pres*
EMP: 277
SQ FT: 600,000
SALES (est): 248.4MM
SALES (corp-wide): 352.1MM **Privately
Held**
SIC: 2032 Baby foods, including meats:
packaged in cans, jars, etc.
HQ: Baxters Food Group Limited
Northern Preserve Works
Fochabers IV32
134 382-0393

(G-1900)
WORNICK COMPANY
Also Called: Right Away Division
4700 Creek Rd (45242-2875)
PHONE..........................513 552-7463
John Geisler, *COO*
John Burton, *Vice Pres*
John Gutzwiller, *Vice Pres*
Lee Westfield, *Vice Pres*
Kenny Worbington, *Warehouse Mgr*
EMP: 600
SALES (corp-wide): 352.1MM **Privately
Held**
SIC: 2032 Canned specialties
HQ: The Wornick Company
4700 Creek Rd
Blue Ash OH 45242
800 860-4555

(G-1901)
**WORNICK HOLDING COMPANY
INC**
4700 Creek Rd (45242-2808)
PHONE..........................513 794-9800
Jon P Geisler, *President*
Michael Hyche, *Vice Pres*
John Kowalchik, *Vice Pres*
Dustin McDulin, *CFO*
Matt Femia, *Controller*
EMP: 1368
SALES (est): 94.5MM **Privately Held**
SIC: 2032 Canned specialties
PA: Ddj Capital Management, Llc
130 Turner St Ste 600
Waltham MA 02453

(G-1902)
XEROX CORPORATION
10560 Ashview Pl (45242-3735)
PHONE..........................513 554-3200
Fax: 513 554-3267
Lonnie Stiff, *Plant Mgr*
Dennis Pauley, *Info Tech Mgr*
EMP: 500
SALES (corp-wide): 10.7B **Publicly Held**
WEB: www.xerox.com
SIC: 3861 5044 Photocopy machines; of-
fice equipment

PA: Xerox Corporation
201 Merritt 7
Norwalk CT 06851
203 968-3000

(G-1903)
XOMOX CORPORATION
Also Called: Crane Xomox
4477 Malsbary Rd (45242)
PHONE..........................513 745-6000
William Hayes, *Branch Mgr*
EMP: 6
SALES (corp-wide): 2.7B **Publicly Held**
SIC: 3491 Process control regulator valves
HQ: Xomox Corporation
4526 Res Frest Dr Ste 400
The Woodlands TX 77381
936 271-6500

(G-1904)
ZAROMET INC
10851 Millington Ct (45242-4019)
PHONE..........................513 891-0773
Tom Mettey, *President*
Anthony Catanzaro, *Vice Pres*
EMP: 4
SQ FT: 5,000
SALES (est): 453.9K **Privately Held**
WEB: www.zaromet.com
SIC: 3599 Machine shop, jobbing & repair

(G-1905)
ZOO PUBLISHING INC
11258 Cornell Park Dr # 608 (45242-1840)
PHONE..........................513 824-8297
Mark Seremet, *CEO*
Steve Buchanan, *COO*
David Fremed, *CFO*
Traci Hutmier, *Manager*
Alvin Muolic, *Producer*
▲ **EMP:** 30
SQ FT: 7,700
SALES (est): 2.3MM **Publicly Held**
SIC: 2741 Miscellaneous publishing
PA: Indiepub Entertainment, Inc.
11258 Cornell Park Dr # 608
Blue Ash OH 45242

Bluffton
Allen County

(G-1906)
**A TO Z PORTION CTRL MEATS
INC**
201 N Main St (45817-1283)
PHONE..........................419 358-2926
Fax: 419 358-8876
Lee Ann Kagy, *President*
Sean Kagy, *COO*
Ed Bucher, *Production*
EMP: 25 **EST:** 1945
SQ FT: 20,000
SALES (est): 9.4MM **Privately Held**
SIC: 5147 5142 5421 2013 Meats, fresh;
meat, frozen: packaged; meat markets,
including freezer provisioners; sausages
& other prepared meats

(G-1907)
**BLUFFTON NEWS PUBG &
PRTG CO (PA)**
Also Called: Bluffton News, The
101 S Main St (45817-1249)
P.O. Box 49 (45817-0049)
PHONE..........................419 358-8010
Fax: 419 358-8020
Thomas M Edwards, *President*
Fred Steiner, *Editor*
Marilyn Edwards, *Vice Pres*
Cathy Giddeon, *Vice Pres*
Susan Miller, *Controller*
EMP: 12
SQ FT: 4,500
SALES (est): 1.6MM **Privately Held**
SIC: 2711 2721 Job printing & newspaper
publishing combined; magazines: publish-
ing & printing

(G-1908)
**BLUFFTON PRECAST
CONCRETE CO**
8950 Dixie Hwy (45817-8566)
P.O. Box 161 (45817-0161)
PHONE..........................419 358-6946
Fax: 419 358-6258
David P Akin, *President*
Michael J Akin, *Vice Pres*
James D Akin, *Shareholder*
Carlin Porter, *Admin Sec*
EMP: 15 **EST:** 1963
SQ FT: 3,000
SALES (est): 3.7MM **Privately Held**
SIC: 3272 Concrete products; septic tanks,
concrete; burial vaults, concrete or pre-
cast terrazzo; concrete products, precast

(G-1909)
BLUFFTON STONE CO
310 Quarry Dr (45817)
PHONE..........................419 358-6941
Fax: 419 358-8247
Brent Gerken, *President*
Mike Gerken, *Corp Secy*
Cathy Schindler, *Accountant*
David Gerken, *Info Tech Mgr*
EMP: 22
SQ FT: 1,800
SALES (est): 4.2MM **Privately Held**
SIC: 1422 3274 2951 Crushed & broken
limestone; lime; asphalt paving mixtures
& blocks

(G-1910)
**COLONIAL SURFACE
SOLUTIONS INC**
Also Called: Diamond Machine and Mfg
505 E Jefferson St (45817-1349)
PHONE..........................419 358-0129
Fax: 419 358-0196
Tammy Whitlow, *Human Res Mgr*
Ryan Smith, *Manager*
EMP: 30
SQ FT: 271,000
SALES (corp-wide): 7.8MM **Privately
Held**
WEB: www.colonialsurfacesolutions.com
SIC: 3471 3398 3479 1799 Cleaning &
descaling metal products; sand blasting of
metal parts; tumbling (cleaning & polish-
ing) of machine parts; metal heat treating;
tempering of metal; painting of metal
products; coating of metal structures at
construction site
PA: Colonial Surface Solutions, Inc.
4599 Campbell Rd
Columbus Grove OH 45830
419 659-5639

(G-1911)
DIAMOND MFG BLUFFTON LTD
505 E Jefferson St (45817-1349)
P.O. Box 73 (45817-0073)
PHONE..........................419 358-0129
Brian Langhals, *General Mgr*
Tammy Whitlow, *Admin Mgr*
Janice Langhals,
Tom Langhals,
EMP: 70 **EST:** 2010
SQ FT: 120,000
SALES (est): 23.7MM **Privately Held**
SIC: 3441 Fabricated structural metal

(G-1912)
GROB SYSTEMS INC
Also Called: Machine Tool Division
1070 Navajo Dr (45817-9666)
PHONE..........................419 358-9015
Fax: 419 369-3332
Ralf Bronnenmeier, *CEO*
Jason Cartright, *President*
Michael Hutecker, *President*
William Vejnovic, *Vice Pres*
Thomas Ruf, *Project Mgr*
◆ **EMP:** 198
SQ FT: 262,000
SALES (est): 151MM
SALES (corp-wide): 276.6MM **Privately
Held**
WEB: www.grobsystems.com
SIC: 3535 7699 Robotic conveyors; indus-
trial equipment services

PA: Grob-Werke Burkhart Grob E.K.
Industriestr. 4
Mindelheim 87719
826 199-60

(G-1913)
JOHNS BODY SHOP
200 Lake Dr (45817-1383)
PHONE.....................419 358-1200
John Haldman, *Principal*
EMP: 4
SALES (est): 202.5K **Privately Held**
SIC: 7532 3713 3711 Body shop, automotive; truck & bus bodies; automobile bodies, passenger car, not including engine, etc.

(G-1914)
QUALITY READY MIX INC
Quarry Dr (45817)
PHONE.....................419 738-2817
Brian Hedding, *Manager*
EMP: 20
SALES (corp-wide): 5MM **Privately Held**
SIC: 3273 Ready-mixed concrete
PA: Quality Ready Mix, Inc
16672 County Road 66a
Saint Marys OH 45885
419 394-8870

(G-1915)
RICHLAND TWP GARAGE
8435 Dixie Hwy (45817-9543)
PHONE.....................419 358-4897
Jim Weaver, *Principal*
EMP: 4
SALES (est): 431.1K **Privately Held**
SIC: 3531 Road construction & maintenance machinery

(G-1916)
SUMIRIKO OHIO INC (HQ)
320 Snider Rd (45817-9573)
PHONE.....................419 358-2121
Fax: 419 358-9331
M Fujiwara, *Ch of Bd*
Akira Kikuta, *President*
Peter Byrne, *General Mgr*
Bill Yokas, *Senior VP*
Laura Jones, *Safety Mgr*
◆ **EMP:** 226
SQ FT: 240,000
SALES (est): 174.8MM
SALES (corp-wide): 3.6B **Privately Held**
WEB: www.dtroh.com
SIC: 3052 3069 3829 3714 Automobile hose, rubber; molded rubber products; measuring & controlling devices; motor vehicle parts & accessories
PA: Sumitomo Riko Company Limited
3-1, Higashi
Komaki AIC 485-0
568 772-121

(G-1917)
TIM BOUTWELL
Also Called: Golf Graphics
902 N Main St (45817-9710)
P.O. Box 124 (45817-0124)
PHONE.....................419 358-4653
Tim Boutwell, *Owner*
EMP: 4
SALES (est): 307.4K **Privately Held**
SIC: 5091 3993 Golf equipment; signs & advertising specialties

(G-1918)
TOWER AUTOMOTIVE OPERATIONS I
18717 County Road 15 (45817-9693)
PHONE.....................419 358-8966
Craig Westrick, *Prdtn Mgr*
James Hummer, *Purchasing*
Craig Ciola, *Engineer*
Jeff Nienberg, *Engineer*
Denise Wagner, *Human Res Dir*
EMP: 283
SALES (corp-wide): 1.9B **Publicly Held**
SIC: 3465 Automotive stampings
HQ: Tower Automotive Operations Usa I Llc
17672 N Laurel Park Dr 400e
Livonia MI 48152
248 675-6000

(G-1919)
TRIPLETT BLUFFTON CORPORATION
Also Called: Lfe Instruments
1 Triplett Dr (45817-1055)
P.O. Box 13 (45817-0013)
PHONE.....................419 358-8750
Warren J Hess, *President*
Gary Binkley, *Purchasing*
Kyle Apkarian, *CFO*
▲ **EMP:** 9
SQ FT: 150,000
SALES (est): 1MM **Privately Held**
WEB: www.triplett.com
SIC: 3825 3824 Test equipment for electronic & electrical circuits; fluid meters & counting devices

---

Boardman
Mahoning County

(G-1920)
BOARDMAN NEWS
8302 Southern Blvd Ste 2 (44512-3390)
PHONE.....................330 758-6397
Fax: 330 758-2658
Jack Darnell, *Owner*
EMP: 8
SQ FT: 3,500
SALES (est): 250K **Privately Held**
SIC: 2711 Newspapers: publishing only, not printed on site

(G-1921)
GORANT CHOCOLATIER LLC (PA)
Also Called: Gorant's Yum Yum Tree
8301 Market St (44512-6257)
PHONE.....................330 726-8821
Gary Weiss, *President*
Jack Peluse, *Plant Mgr*
Joseph M Miller, *Mng Member*
EMP: 120 **EST:** 1946
SQ FT: 60,000
SALES (est): 55MM **Privately Held**
SIC: 5441 5947 5145 3999 Candy, nut & confectionery stores; greeting cards; gift shop; candy; candles; chocolate & cocoa products

(G-1922)
PITA WRAP LLC
4721 Market St (44512-1526)
PHONE.....................330 886-8091
Marlene A Bassil, *President*
John Bassil, *Office Mgr*
EMP: 7
SQ FT: 3,700
SALES (est): 120K **Privately Held**
SIC: 2099 Food preparations

(G-1923)
POMA GL SPECIALTY WINDOWS INC
365 Mcclurg Rd Ste E (44512-6452)
PHONE.....................330 965-1000
Fax: 330 965-1011
EMP: 4
SALES (corp-wide): 11.5B **Privately Held**
SIC: 3211 Insulating glass, sealed units
HQ: Poma Glass & Specialty Windows Inc.
11175 Cicero Dr Ste 400
Alpharetta GA 30022
404 446-4200

(G-1924)
RL BEST COMPANY
723 Bev Rd (44512-6423)
PHONE.....................330 758-8601
Fax: 330 758-9413
Ted A Best, *President*
Ted Best, *President*
Mark Best, *Vice Pres*
William Kavanaugh, *Vice Pres*
Jeffrey Best, *Engineer*
EMP: 26
SQ FT: 35,000
SALES: 9MM **Privately Held**
WEB: www.rlbest.com
SIC: 3599 7539 Machine shop, jobbing & repair; machine shop, automotive

(G-1925)
TREEMEN INDUSTRIES INC
Also Called: Tii Treeman Industries
691 Mcclurg Rd (44512-6408)
P.O. Box 3777 (44513-3777)
PHONE.....................330 965-3777
Fax: 330 965-7384
George Ogletree, *President*
Daniel J Solmen, *Principal*
Violet M Ogletree, *Corp Secy*
Timothy Callahan, *Vice Pres*
Daniel Solmen, *Vice Pres*
EMP: 40
SQ FT: 35,900
SALES (est): 10.2MM **Privately Held**
WEB: www.treemen.com
SIC: 3479 3089 3646 3647 Aluminum coating of metal products; injection molding of plastics; commercial indusl & institutional electric lighting fixtures; vehicular lighting equipment

(G-1926)
ZIDIAN MANUFACTURING INC (PA)
Also Called: Summer Garden Food Mfg
500 Mcclurg Rd (44512-6405)
PHONE.....................330 965-8455
Fax: 330 965-3864
Tom Zidian, *CEO*
Michelle Gross, *Corp Secy*
Kenny Sung, *COO*
Nick Rulli, *Purch Dir*
Christian Thomas, *QA Dir*
▲ **EMP:** 7 **EST:** 2000
SALES (est): 13.5MM **Privately Held**
SIC: 2099 Sauces: gravy, dressing & dip mixes

Bolivar
Tuscarawas County

(G-1927)
AMERICAN HIGHWAY PRODUCTS LTD
11723 Strasburg Bolivar (44612-8554)
PHONE.....................330 874-3270
Fax: 330 874-3800
Scott Fier, *President*
Jason E Downing, *General Mgr*
Eric Fier, *Vice Pres*
EMP: 10 **EST:** 1978
SQ FT: 10,400
SALES (est): 2MM **Privately Held**
WEB: www.ahp1.com
SIC: 3531 Road construction & maintenance machinery

(G-1928)
BLUE JAY ENTPS OF TSCRWAS CNTY
9852 Hess Mill Rd Ne (44612-8716)
PHONE.....................330 874-2048
Leland Ervin, *President*
Brian Miller, *Vice Pres*
Tonya Ervin Miller, *Treasurer*
Karen Ervin, *Admin Sec*
EMP: 4
SALES (est): 176.8K **Privately Held**
SIC: 1459 Shale (common) quarrying

(G-1929)
CABLE MFG & ASSEMBLY INC (PA)
Also Called: CMA
10896 Industrial Pkwy Nw (44612-8990)
P.O. Box 409 (44612-0409)
PHONE.....................330 874-2900
Fax: 330 874-2373
Robert Clegg, *CEO*
Terry Williams, *President*
Thomas Spore, *Maint Spvr*
Frances Justiniano, *Accountant*
Larry Leggett, *Supervisor*
▲ **EMP:** 200
SQ FT: 61,000
SALES (est): 33MM **Privately Held**
WEB: www.cablemfg.com
SIC: 3496 Cable, uninsulated wire: made from purchased wire

(G-1930)
CHEMPURE PRODUCTS CORPORATION
148 Central Ave (44612)
PHONE.....................330 874-4300
Samuel J Lloyd, *President*
Robert Lloyd, *Vice Pres*
Karen S Lloyd, *Admin Sec*
EMP: 4
SQ FT: 10,000
SALES (est): 360K **Privately Held**
WEB: www.chempure.com
SIC: 5999 3443 Cleaning equipment & supplies; industrial vessels, tanks & containers

(G-1931)
CUSTOM DISPLAYS LLC
9838 Bimeler St Ne (44612-8805)
PHONE.....................330 454-8850
Lee Hartline,
EMP: 4
SALES (est): 190K **Privately Held**
SIC: 2441 Cases, wood

(G-1932)
DIVERSIFIED HONING INC
11064 Industrial Pkwy Nw (44612-8992)
PHONE.....................330 874-4663
Fax: 330 874-1160
William Blackwell, *President*
Shawn Blackwell, *Mfg Staff*
Bonnie L Blackwell, *Treasurer*
EMP: 21
SQ FT: 31,000
SALES (est): 300K **Privately Held**
WEB: www.diversifiedhoning.com
SIC: 3541 Honing & lapping machines

(G-1933)
ELEET CRYOGENICS INC
11132 Industrial Pkwy Nw (44612-8993)
PHONE.....................330 874-4009
Garry Sears, *President*
Tenia Sears, *Vice Pres*
Andrew Reeves, *Project Mgr*
Karrisa Reeves, *Prdtn Mgr*
Ray Himes, *Manager*
EMP: 33
SQ FT: 47,000
SALES (est): 9.3MM **Privately Held**
WEB: www.eleetcryogenics.com
SIC: 3443 7353 2761 5088 Cryogenic tanks, for liquids & gases; oil field equipment, rental or leasing; manifold business forms; tanks & tank components; trailer rental; management services

(G-1934)
FSRC TANKS INC
11029 Industrial Pkwy Nw (44612-8992)
PHONE.....................234 221-2015
Andrew Feucht, *President*
Justin Bergener, *Sales Associate*
EMP: 35
SALES (est): 1MM **Privately Held**
SIC: 1791 3443 Structural steel erection; reactor containment vessels, metal plate

(G-1935)
GEMINI FIBER CORPORATION
11145 Industrial Pkwy Nw (44612-8993)
P.O. Box 487 (44612-0487)
PHONE.....................330 874-4131
Stanley F Lakota, *President*
Aaron Lakota, *Vice Pres*
Phil Lakota, *Vice Pres*
EMP: 12
SQ FT: 15,000
SALES (est): 2.9MM **Privately Held**
WEB: www.geminifiber.com
SIC: 2679 Paper products, converted

(G-1936)
HOLDSWORTH INDUSTRIAL FABG
10407 Welton Rd Ne (44612)
P.O. Box 643, Zoar (44697-0643)
PHONE.....................330 874-3945
Fax: 330 874-3946
Randy Holdsworth, *Owner*
EMP: 6
SQ FT: 5,000

SALES (est): 492.8K **Privately Held**
SIC: **1799** 7692 Welding on site; welding repair

(G-1937)
INVENTIVE EXTRUSIONS CORP
Also Called: I E C
10882 Fort Laurens Rd Nw (44612-8942)
PHONE..................................330 874-3000
Steven Martin, *President*
Steve Martin, *Data Proc Dir*
EMP: 20
SQ FT: 12,000
SALES (est): 1.8MM **Privately Held**
SIC: **3089** 3082 Extruded finished plastic products; unsupported plastics profile shapes

(G-1938)
MYERS MACHINING INC
11789 Strasburg Bolivar (44612-8555)
PHONE..................................330 874-3005
Fax: 330 874-2158
David Myers, *President*
Brenda Myers, *Treasurer*
EMP: 15
SQ FT: 16,000
SALES (est): 2.2MM **Privately Held**
WEB: www.myersmachining.com
SIC: **3599** Machine shop, jobbing & repair

(G-1939)
NILODOR INC
10966 Industrial Pkwy Nw (44612-8991)
P.O. Box 660 (44612-0660)
PHONE..................................800 443-4321
Fax: 330 874-3366
Les W Mitson, *President*
Jeff Wilkof, *Corp Secy*
Kurt Peterson, *Vice Pres*
Kim Fellows, *Manager*
◆ EMP: 43
SQ FT: 43,000
SALES (est): 12.2MM **Privately Held**
WEB: www.nilodor.com
SIC: **2842** Deodorants, nonpersonal

(G-1940)
OSTER SAND AND GRAVEL INC
3467 Dover Zoar Rd Ne (44612-8922)
PHONE..................................330 874-3322
Fax: 330 874-1035
Dan Morrisset, *Manager*
EMP: 6
SALES (corp-wide): 3.5MM **Privately Held**
SIC: **1442** Construction sand & gravel
PA: Oster Sand And Gravel, Inc.
   5947 Whipple Ave Nw
   Canton OH 44720
   330 494-5472

(G-1941)
PAC DRILLING O & G LLC
1037 Lawnridge St Ne (44612-8873)
PHONE..................................330 874-3781
Justin L Caldwell, *Mng Member*
Jason Caldwell, *Supervisor*
EMP: 4
SALES (est): 380K **Privately Held**
SIC: **1381** Drilling oil & gas wells

(G-1942)
PREMIERE MOLD AND MACHINE CO
10882 Fort Laurens Rd Nw (44612-8942)
PHONE..................................330 874-3000
Fax: 330 874-4123
Robert L Martin, *Ch of Bd*
Garry Martin, *President*
Richard Dodez, *Admin Sec*
Marlene Miller, *Admin Sec*
EMP: 6
SQ FT: 33,000
SALES (est): 656.6K **Privately Held**
SIC: **3544** Forms (molds), for foundry & plastics working machinery

(G-1943)
PRIMARY PACKAGING INCORPORATED
10810 Industrial Pkwy Nw (44612-8990)
PHONE..................................330 874-3131
Fax: 330 874-3811
Joseph Kaplan, *CEO*
Jeffrey Thrams, *President*

David Banig, *VP Sls/Mktg*
Jim O'Brien, *Treasurer*
John Hiltner, *VP Finance*
EMP: 85
SQ FT: 50,000
SALES (est): 24.1MM **Privately Held**
WEB: www.primarypackaging.com
SIC: **2673** Plastic bags: made from purchased materials

(G-1944)
PROGRSSIVE MOLDING BOLIVAR INC
10882 Fort Laurens Rd Nw (44612-8942)
PHONE..................................330 874-3000
Robert L Martin, *Ch of Bd*
Garry Martin, *President*
James C Dukat, *Principal*
Richard D Dodez, *Principal*
Sandra K Scott, *Principal*
EMP: 110
SQ FT: 33,000
SALES (est): 17.1MM **Privately Held**
SIC: **3544** 3089 Dies, plastics forming; thermoformed finished plastic products

(G-1945)
QUILTING CREATIONS INTL
8778 Towpath Rd Ne (44612-8556)
P.O. Box 512, Zoar (44697-0512)
PHONE..................................330 874-4741
Aaron Bell, *President*
Amy Gibbons, *Assistant*
EMP: 20
SALES (est): 3.9MM **Privately Held**
WEB: www.quiltingcreations.com
SIC: **2631** 5949 Stencil board; quilting materials & supplies

(G-1946)
SPEEDWAY LLC
Also Called: Speedway Superamerica 6241
11099 State Route 212 Ne (44612-8745)
PHONE..................................330 874-4616
Paul Duerig, *President*
EMP: 11 **Publicly Held**
WEB: www.speedwaynet.com
SIC: **1311** Crude petroleum production
HQ: Speedway Llc
   500 Speedway Dr
   Enon OH 45323
   937 864-3000

(G-1947)
US TECHNOLOGY MEDIA INC
509 Water St Sw (44612-8986)
PHONE..................................330 874-3094
John Socotch, *Principal*
EMP: 10
SALES (est): 547.9K **Privately Held**
SIC: **3291** Abrasive products

(G-1948)
USA LABEL EXPRESS INC
11206 Industrial Pkwy Nw (44612-8994)
P.O. Box 518 (44612-0518)
PHONE..................................330 874-1001
Chris Helwig, *President*
Mary Helwig, *Manager*
Mary Seldenright, *Manager*
EMP: 25
SQ FT: 25,000
SALES (est): 5.2MM **Privately Held**
SIC: **2672** Labels (unprinted), gummed: made from purchased materials

Botkins
Shelby County

(G-1949)
A METALCRAFT ASSOCIATES INC
18965 State Route 219 (45306-9582)
PHONE..................................937 693-4008
Maurice Delap, *President*
EMP: 7
SALES: 300K **Privately Held**
WEB: www.metalcraftinc.net
SIC: **1542** 5031 7692 7699 Nonresidential construction; lumber, plywood & millwork; welding repair; metal reshaping & replating services; fabricated plate work (boiler shop)

(G-1950)
BOOMERANG RUBBER INC
215 S Mill St (45306-8023)
PHONE..................................937 693-4611
Fax: 937 693-3853
Mark Sultman, *President*
Bobby Brush, *General Mgr*
Chris Lotridge, *General Mgr*
Dale Zeigler, *Executive*
EMP: 22
SALES (est): 9.7MM **Privately Held**
SIC: **3069** Reclaimed rubber & specialty rubber compounds

(G-1951)
BROWN INDUSTRIAL INC
311 W South St (45306-8019)
P.O. Box 74 (45306-0074)
PHONE..................................937 693-3838
Fax: 937 693-4121
Christopher D Brown, *President*
Ruth C Brown, *Corp Secy*
Craig D Brown, *Vice Pres*
Pat Meyers, *Accountant*
EMP: 45
SQ FT: 32,000
SALES (est): 12.8MM **Privately Held**
WEB: www.brownindustrial.com
SIC: **3713** 5012 5084 7692 Truck bodies (motor vehicles); truck bodies; industrial machinery & equipment; packaging machinery & equipment; automotive welding

(G-1952)
BUCKEYE ELECTRICAL PRODUCTS
100 Commerce Dr (45306-1100)
P.O. Box 124 (45306-0124)
PHONE..................................937 693-7519
Dick Platfoot, *President*
Kevin Platfoot, *Officer*
EMP: 20
SALES (est): 3.9MM **Privately Held**
SIC: **3699** Electrical equipment & supplies

(G-1953)
RIDLEY USA INC
Also Called: Hubbard Feeds
104 Oak St (45306-8031)
P.O. Box 1105, Hopkinsville KY (42241-1105)
PHONE..................................800 837-8222
Roger Allen, *Manager*
EMP: 10
SALES (corp-wide): 306.1MM **Privately Held**
WEB: www.hubbardfeeds.net
SIC: **2048** 5191 Prepared feeds; animal feeds
HQ: Ridley Usa Inc.
   111 W Cherry St Ste 500
   Mankato MN 56001
   507 388-9400

(G-1954)
RIDLEY USA INC
Also Called: Hubbard Feeds
104 Oak St (45306-8031)
P.O. Box 460 (45306-0460)
PHONE..................................937 693-6393
Fax: 937 693-3657
Rick Duncan, *Manager*
Mark Manger, *Maintence Staff*
EMP: 45
SALES (corp-wide): 306.1MM **Privately Held**
WEB: www.hubbardfeeds.net
SIC: **2048** Prepared feeds
HQ: Ridley Usa Inc.
   111 W Cherry St Ste 500
   Mankato MN 56001
   507 388-9400

(G-1955)
T L H WINDSHIELD REPAIR
405 W South St (45306-8046)
P.O. Box 362 (45306-0362)
Dennis Berning, *Owner*
EMP: 3
SALES (est): 150.6K **Privately Held**
SIC: **3714** Windshield frames, motor vehicle

(G-1956)
T&K LASER WORKS INC
401 N Main St (45306-9547)
PHONE..................................937 693-3783
Ernest Vehorn, *Principal*
EMP: 4
SALES (est): 310.6K **Privately Held**
SIC: **3479** Etching & engraving

Bowerston
Harrison County

(G-1957)
BOWERSTON SHALE COMPANY (PA)
515 Main St (44695)
PHONE..................................740 269-2921
Fax: 740 269-5456
Mark Willard, *President*
Beth Hillyer, *Vice Pres*
Edward C Milliken, *Vice Pres*
Stephanie Price, *Accounting Mgr*
EMP: 30 EST: 1929
SQ FT: 100,000
SALES (est): 36.8MM **Privately Held**
SIC: **3255** 3251 2951 Clay refractories; brick clay: common face, glazed, vitrified or hollow; asphalt paving mixtures & blocks

(G-1958)
L J SMITH INC (HQ)
Also Called: Woodsmiths Design & Mfg
35280 Scio Bowerston Rd (44695-9731)
PHONE..................................740 269-2221
Fax: 740 269-9047
Craig Kurtz, *President*
Lowell Braunschweig, *Prdtn Mgr*
Giovanni Savastano, *Foreman/Supr*
Dan Tope, *Purch Mgr*
Sean Macsuibhne, *Purchasing*
▲ EMP: 250
SQ FT: 180,000
SALES (est): 58.2MM
SALES (corp-wide): 225MM **Privately Held**
WEB: www.ljsmith.com
SIC: **2431** Millwork; staircases, stairs & railings
PA: Mcdonough Holdings, Inc. (Fn)
   21050 N Pima Rd Ste 100
   Scottsdale AZ 85255
   602 544-5900

(G-1959)
NOLAN COMPANY
300 Boyce Dr (44695-9760)
PHONE..................................740 269-1512
Fax: 740 269-1919
Dan Chew, *Manager*
EMP: 7
SALES (corp-wide): 4.1MM **Privately Held**
SIC: **3743** 3532 Railroad equipment; mining machinery
PA: The Nolan Company
   1016 9th St Sw
   Canton OH 44707
   330 453-7922

(G-1960)
ORICA GROUND SUPPORT INC
600 Boyce Dr (44695-9801)
PHONE..................................740 269-8100
EMP: 431
SALES (corp-wide): 3.9B **Privately Held**
SIC: **3441** Building components, structural steel
HQ: Orica Ground Support Inc.
   150 Summer Ct
   Georgetown KY 40324
   502 863-6800

Bowling Green
Wood County

(G-1961)
A SCREEN PRINTED PRODUCTS
17715 N Dixie Hwy (43402-9257)
PHONE..................................419 352-1535

David L Schumacher, *Owner*
Robb First, *Data Proc Dir*
EMP: 5
SALES (est): 450K **Privately Held**
SIC: 2759 Screen printing

(G-1962)
A W S INCORPORATED
520 Hankey Ave (43402-7801)
P.O. Box 472 (43402-0472)
PHONE.............................419 352-5397
Arlyn Snyder, *President*
Judith Ann Snyder, *Corp Secy*
EMP: 2
SQ FT: 5,000
SALES: 2MM **Privately Held**
SIC: 1542 1521 2431 Commercial & office building, new construction; single-family housing construction; millwork

(G-1963)
AARDVARK GRAPHIC ENTERPRISES L
123 S Main St (43402-2910)
PHONE.............................419 352-3197
Gary Bell, *Owner*
EMP: 12
SALES (est): 896.2K **Privately Held**
SIC: 2396 Screen printing on fabric articles

(G-1964)
AARDVARK SCREEN PRTG & EMB LLC
123 S Main St (43402-2910)
P.O. Box 128 (43402-0128)
PHONE.............................419 354-6686
Toll Free:.............................888 -
Fax: 419 354-6370
Gary A Bell, *Owner*
EMP: 10
SQ FT: 3,000
SALES: 400K **Privately Held**
SIC: 2759 7311 Screen printing; advertising agencies

(G-1965)
ABSORBENT PRODUCTS COMPANY INC
2121 S Woodland Cir (43402-8832)
PHONE.............................419 352-5353
Fax: 419 352-1399
Paul Rankin, *President*
◆ **EMP:** 35
SQ FT: 54,000
SALES (est): 11.3MM
SALES (corp-wide): 70.7MM **Privately Held**
WEB: www.absorbent-products-company.com
SIC: 2676 Diapers, paper (disposable): made from purchased paper
PA: Principle Business Enterprises, Inc.
　　20189 Pine Lake Rd
　　Bowling Green OH 43402
　　419 352-1551

(G-1966)
ADVANCED SPECIALTY PRODUCTS
428 Clough St (43402-2914)
P.O. Box 210 (43402-0210)
PHONE.............................419 882-6528
Fax: 419 352-9663
Kenneth T Kujawa, *President*
Eugene Kujawa, *Vice Pres*
▼ **EMP:** 60
SQ FT: 24,000
SALES (est): 7.1MM **Privately Held**
SIC: 5082 7389 2759 Construction & mining machinery; packaging & labeling services; commercial printing

(G-1967)
ANGEL GLASS LOST
122 Meeker St (43402-2215)
PHONE.............................419 353-2831
Joel Odorisio, *President*
EMP: 4
SALES: 310K **Privately Held**
SIC: 3229 Glass furnishings & accessories

(G-1968)
APPLIED IMAGINATION INC
128 W Wooster St Ofc Ofc (43402-2846)
PHONE.............................419 352-8373

Fax: 419 353-0285
Robert Robie, *President*
Steven R Stuart, *Vice Pres*
EMP: 5
SQ FT: 2,000
SALES (est): 481K **Privately Held**
SIC: 7371 3571 7373 Custom computer programming services; electronic computers; computer integrated systems design

(G-1969)
B G NEWS
Also Called: Bg News
214 W Hall Bgsu (43403-0001)
PHONE.............................419 372-2601
Fax: 419 372-6967
Robert Bortel, *Director*
George Braatz, *Administration*
EMP: 50
SALES (est): 2MM **Privately Held**
WEB: www.bgnews.com
SIC: 2711 7313 2741 Newspapers; newspaper advertising representative; telephone & other directory publishing

(G-1970)
BARNES INTERNATIONAL INC
Henry Filters
555 Van Camp Rd (43402)
PHONE.............................419 352-7501
Fax: 419 352-0224
Brian Blair, *Vice Pres*
Scott Thomas, *Plant Mgr*
Brenda Ryan, *Controller*
Tina Schultz, *Office Mgr*
Steve Volmer, *Branch Mgr*
EMP: 60
SALES (corp-wide): 35MM **Privately Held**
WEB: www.durrautomation.com
SIC: 3677 Electronic coils, transformers & other inductors
PA: Barnes International, Inc.
　　814 Chestnut St
　　Rockford IL 61102
　　815 964-8661

(G-1971)
BASIC COATINGS LLC
400 Van Camp Rd (43402-9062)
PHONE.............................419 241-2156
Brad Betz, *General Mgr*
Nathan Daniel, *Regional Mgr*
Paul C Betz
Kellie Zdybek, *Admin Asst*
Paul Betz
EMP: 14
SALES (est): 303K
SALES (corp-wide): 138.2MM **Privately Held**
WEB: www.betco.com
SIC: 2851 Paints & allied products
PA: Betco Corporation
　　400 Van Camp Rd
　　Bowling Green OH 43402
　　419 241-2156

(G-1972)
BETCO CORPORATION LTD (HQ)
400 Van Camp Rd (43402-9062)
PHONE.............................419 241-2156
Paul C Betz, *CEO*
Tony Lyons, *CFO*
James Betz, *Admin Sec*
◆ **EMP:** 250
SALES (est): 20.4MM
SALES (corp-wide): 138.2MM **Privately Held**
SIC: 2842 Specialty cleaning, polishes & sanitation goods
PA: Betco Corporation
　　400 Van Camp Rd
　　Bowling Green OH 43402
　　419 241-2156

(G-1973)
BIO FIT ENGINEERED PRODUCTS
15500 Bio Fit Way (43402-9290)
PHONE.............................419 823-1089
Edward A Metzer, *President*
Rusty Benschoter, *Manager*
EMP: 85 **EST:** 1992
SALES (est): 6MM **Privately Held**
SIC: 2599 Furniture & fixtures

(G-1974)
BRUFIST LLC
122 1/2 S Maple St (43402-2823)
PHONE.............................330 221-4472
Martin Yungmann, *CEO*
Daniel Nawrocki,
Jeremy Rober,
EMP: 5
SALES (est): 91.3K **Privately Held**
SIC: 2082 Beer (alcoholic beverage); ale (alcoholic beverage); porter (alcoholic beverage); stout (alcoholic beverage)

(G-1975)
C & C FABRICATION INC
18237 N Dixie Hwy (43402-9322)
PHONE.............................419 354-3535
Fax: 419 353-6726
Charles H Wolford, *President*
Claudell Wolford, *Vice Pres*
EMP: 5
SQ FT: 13,800
SALES: 750K **Privately Held**
SIC: 3443 3469 Fabricated plate work (boiler shop); metal stampings

(G-1976)
CENTAUR TOOL & DIE INC
2019 Wood Bridge Blvd (43402-8913)
PHONE.............................419 352-7704
Paul E Faykosh, *President*
Jack Faykosh, *Vice Pres*
Jeff Faykosh, *Vice Pres*
Robert Shreve, *Chief Engr*
Mary Souvenier, *Controller*
EMP: 18
SQ FT: 16,400
SALES (est): 1.6MM **Privately Held**
WEB: www.centaurtool.com
SIC: 3544 Die sets for metal stamping (presses)

(G-1977)
CENTURY MARKETING CORPORATION
1145 Fairview Ave (43402-1204)
PHONE.............................419 354-2591
EMP: 3
SALES (corp-wide): 78.8MM **Privately Held**
SIC: 2759 Labels & seals: printing; flexographic printing
HQ: Century Marketing Corporation
　　12836 S Dixie Hwy
　　Bowling Green OH 43402
　　419 354-2591

(G-1978)
CENTURY MARKETING CORPORATION (HQ)
Also Called: Centurylabel
12836 S Dixie Hwy (43402-9230)
PHONE.............................419 354-2591
Fax: 419 352-9567
Albert J Caperna, *President*
Craig E Dixon, *President*
Robert Petrie, *General Mgr*
William Horner, *Corp Secy*
Melissa Desmith, *Controller*
▼ **EMP:** 150
SQ FT: 58,000
SALES (est): 21.2MM
SALES (corp-wide): 78.8MM **Privately Held**
WEB: www.centurylabel.com
SIC: 2759 2679 5046 5199 Labels & seals: printing; flexographic printing; tags & labels, paper; price marking equipment & supplies; packaging materials; commercial printing, lithographic
PA: Cmc Group, Inc.
　　12836 S Dixie Hwy
　　Bowling Green OH 43402
　　419 352-9567

(G-1979)
CENTURY SIGNS
Also Called: Mason's Century Signs
169 S Main St (43402-2910)
PHONE.............................419 352-2666
Fax: 419 353-3262
Mason Brown, *Owner*
EMP: 5
SQ FT: 1,470

SALES: 260K **Privately Held**
SIC: 3993 Signs & advertising specialties

(G-1980)
CMC DAYMARK CORPORATION
Also Called: Daymark Security Systems
12830 S Dixie Hwy (43402-9697)
PHONE.............................419 354-2591
Jeffery Palmer, *General Mgr*
Estra Miller, *Manager*
▲ **EMP:** 140
SALES (est): 24.9MM
SALES (corp-wide): 78.8MM **Privately Held**
WEB: www.centurylabel.com
SIC: 2679 5046 Labels, paper: made from purchased material; commercial equipment
PA: Cmc Group, Inc.
　　12836 S Dixie Hwy
　　Bowling Green OH 43402
　　419 352-9567

(G-1981)
CMC GROUP INC (PA)
12836 S Dixie Hwy (43402-9697)
PHONE.............................419 352-9567
Fax: 419 352-4422
Craig Dixon, *CEO*
Jeff Palmer, *President*
Albert J Caperna, *Chairman*
Tammy Corral, *Vice Pres*
Jordan E Goray, *Project Mgr*
▲ **EMP:** 76 **EST:** 1999
SQ FT: 2,268
SALES (est): 78.8MM **Privately Held**
WEB: www.centurylabel.com
SIC: 2759 Labels & seals: printing

(G-1982)
COLLEGIATE CONNECTION
1420 E Wooster St (43402-3260)
PHONE.............................419 352-8333
Jim Rood, *Owner*
Linda Rood, *Principal*
EMP: 9
SQ FT: 2,500
SALES: 490K **Privately Held**
WEB: www.collegiateconnection.com
SIC: 5699 8641 2759 2395 Sports apparel; fraternal associations; screen printing; embroidery products, except schiffli machine

(G-1983)
COOPER-STANDARD AUTOMOTIVE INC
1175 N Main St (43402-1310)
PHONE.............................419 352-3533
Fax: 419 352-1799
Bruce Meyer, *Plant Mgr*
Richard Galbraith, *Maint Spvr*
Kurt Zollinger, *QC Mgr*
Steven Ingraham, *Engineer*
Davidj Kreinbrink, *Engineer*
EMP: 350
SALES (corp-wide): 3.4B **Publicly Held**
WEB: www.cooperstandard.com
SIC: 3052 Automobile hose, rubber
HQ: Cooper-Standard Automotive Inc.
　　39550 Orchard Hill Pl
　　Novi MI 48375
　　248 596-5900

(G-1984)
DESIGN GRAPHICS GROUP INC
333 Van Camp Rd (43402-9327)
P.O. Box 675, Bradner (43406-0675)
PHONE.............................419 354-8717
Fax: 419 354-8829
Les Mintz, *President*
Cindy Sheely, *Office Mgr*
EMP: 20
SQ FT: 32,000
SALES (est): 3MM **Privately Held**
WEB: www.designgraphics.net
SIC: 2759 Screen printing

(G-1985)
DIAMONDBACK FILTERS
Also Called: Rinz-N-Reuz
11602 Sugar Ridge Rd (43402-9285)
PHONE.............................419 494-1156
Robert Fox, *Owner*
EMP: 3

SALES: 200K **Privately Held**
SIC: 3569 Filters

(G-1986)
DIGITAL AUTOMATION ASSOCIATES
310 W Gypsy Lane Rd (43402-4596)
P.O. Box 131 (43402-0131)
PHONE......................419 352-6977
Fax: 419 353-6082
Gary C Border, *President*
Erica Border, *Corp Secy*
Larry Dickson, *Purchasing*
EMP: 3
SQ FT: 6,000
SALES (est): 304.8K **Privately Held**
WEB: www.digauto.com
SIC: 8711 3491 8748 Electrical or electronic engineering; process control regulator valves; telecommunications consultant

(G-1987)
DOW JONES & COMPANY INC
1201 Brim Rd (43402-9352)
PHONE......................419 352-4696
Fax: 419 352-0274
Fred Van Der Meulen, *Plant Mgr*
Fred Vandermeulen, *Plant Mgr*
John Myers, *Foreman/Supr*
Nick Barbosa, *Opers-Prdtn-Mfg*
Abel Posada, *Director*
EMP: 25
SALES (corp-wide): 8.2B **Publicly Held**
SIC: 2711 Newspapers, publishing & printing
HQ: Dow Jones & Company, Inc.
1211 Avenue Of The Americ
New York NY 10036
609 627-2990

(G-1988)
DOWA THT AMERICA INC
2130 S Woodland Cir (43402-8832)
PHONE......................419 354-4144
Fax: 419 354-6479
Masanari Konomi, *President*
Walter Mytczynskyj, *Finance Other*
▲ EMP: 35
SALES (est): 8.5MM
SALES (corp-wide): 3.4B **Privately Held**
WEB: www.dowa-tht.com
SIC: 3398 Metal heat treating
HQ: Dowa Thermotech Co., Ltd.
19-1, Ukishimacho, Mizuho-Ku
Nagoya AIC 467-0
526 930-800

(G-1989)
GKN DRIVELINE BOWL GREEN INC
2223 Wood Bridge Blvd (43402-8873)
PHONE......................419 354-3955
Fax: 419 354-5075
Scott Sanner, *Principal*
Scott Osthimer, *Controller*
▲ EMP: 4 EST: 1998
SALES (est): 143.9K
SALES (corp-wide): 10.8B **Privately Held**
SIC: 3999 Barber & beauty shop equipment
PA: Gkn Plc
Ipsley House
Redditch WORCS B98 0
152 751-7715

(G-1990)
ISHIKAWA GASKET AMERICA INC (HQ)
828 Van Camp Rd (43402-9379)
PHONE......................419 353-7300
Fax: 419 353-8501
Toshio Matsuzaki, *President*
Chris Fix, *Controller*
▲ EMP: 10
SQ FT: 3,000
SALES (est): 1.1MM
SALES (corp-wide): 58.3MM **Privately Held**
WEB: www.ishikawaamerica.com
SIC: 3053 Gaskets & sealing devices
PA: Ishikawa Gasket Co., Ltd.
2-5-5, Toranomon
Minato-Ku TKY 105-0
335 010-371

(G-1991)
ISHIKAWA GASKET AMERICA INC
828 Van Camp Rd (43402-9379)
PHONE......................419 353-7300
Gary Stasiak, *Manager*
EMP: 190
SALES (corp-wide): 58.3MM **Privately Held**
WEB: www.ishikawaamerica.com
SIC: 3053 5085 3714 Gaskets & sealing devices; gaskets; motor vehicle parts & accessories
HQ: Ishikawa Gasket America, Inc.
828 Van Camp Rd
Bowling Green OH 43402

(G-1992)
J & K WADE LTD
Also Called: Environmental Water Engrg
109 E Wooster St Ste 3-4 (43402-2920)
P.O. Box 611 (43402-0611)
PHONE......................419 352-6163
Michael McIntosh, *President*
John Wade, *Vice Pres*
EMP: 4
SALES (est): 550K **Privately Held**
WEB: www.ewero.com
SIC: 5169 3589 Chemicals, industrial & heavy; water treatment equipment, industrial

(G-1993)
J P TOOL INC
2019 Wood Bridge Blvd (43402-8913)
PHONE......................419 354-8696
Fax: 419 354-8695
Jack Faykosh, *President*
Paul Faykosh, *Corp Secy*
Jeff Faykosh, *Vice Pres*
EMP: 3
SQ FT: 3,200
SALES (est): 200K **Privately Held**
SIC: 3544 Special dies, tools, jigs & fixtures

(G-1994)
KEL-MAR INC
436 N Enterprise St (43402-2001)
P.O. Box 424 (43402-0424)
PHONE......................419 806-4600
Fax: 419 806-4603
Burr Sterling, *President*
Chelle Bigelow, *Office Mgr*
EMP: 25
SALES (est): 1.8MM **Privately Held**
WEB: www.kel-mar.com
SIC: 3471 Finishing, metals or formed products; cleaning & descaling metal products

(G-1995)
LANDEC CORPORATION
12700 S Dixie Hwy (43402-9697)
PHONE......................419 931-1095
EMP: 88
SALES (corp-wide): 541.1MM **Publicly Held**
SIC: 2033 Fruits: packaged in cans, jars, etc.
PA: Landec Corporation
3603 Haven Ave
Menlo Park CA 94025
650 306-1650

(G-1996)
LIFE FORMATIONS INC
2029 Wood Bridge Blvd (43402-8913)
PHONE......................419 352-2101
Rodney Heiligmann, *Principal*
EMP: 11
SALES (est): 2.1MM **Privately Held**
SIC: 3559 Special industry machinery

(G-1997)
LIFEFORMATIONS INC
2029 Wood Bridge Blvd (43402-8913)
PHONE......................419 352-2101
Rodney Hailigmann, *President*
EMP: 50
SQ FT: 8,000
SALES (est): 8.6MM **Privately Held**
WEB: www.lifeformations.com
SIC: 3559 Robots, molding & forming plastics

(G-1998)
LUBRIZOL ADVANCED MTLS INC
1142 N Main St (43402-1309)
PHONE......................419 352-5565
Dennis Callan, *Principal*
John Cubberly, *Safety Mgr*
Michael Carrick, *Opers Staff*
Dave Carter, *QC Dir*
Joe Lovell, *QC Mgr*
EMP: 18
SALES (corp-wide): 223.6B **Publicly Held**
SIC: 2841 Soap & other detergents
HQ: Lubrizol Advanced Materials Inc.
9911 Brecksville Rd
Brecksville OH 44141
216 447-5000

(G-1999)
MACK INDUSTRIES
507 Derby Ave (43402-3973)
PHONE......................419 353-7081
Betsie Mack, *President*
Jeff Colvin, *Opers-Prdtn-Mfg*
Tom Setzer, *Credit Mgr*
EMP: 173
SALES (est): 20MM
SALES (corp-wide): 160.1MM **Privately Held**
WEB: www.mackconcrete.com
SIC: 3272 5211 1711 Burial vaults, concrete or precast terrazzo; masonry materials & supplies; septic system construction
PA: Mack Industries, Inc.
1321 Industrial Pkwy N # 500
Brunswick OH 44212
330 460-7005

(G-2000)
MARTIN MACHINE & TOOL INC
435 W Woodland Cir (43402-8834)
PHONE......................419 373-1711
Allen L Ahrens, *President*
Robb C Coffman, *Vice Pres*
Fred A Curtis, *Vice Pres*
W John Schobinger, *Vice Pres*
EMP: 10
SQ FT: 12,000
SALES (est): 1.4MM **Privately Held**
SIC: 3599 3544 Machine shop, jobbing & repair; special dies & tools

(G-2001)
MCCORD PRODUCTS INC
Also Called: McCord Monuments
1135 N Main St (43402-1310)
P.O. Box 646 (43402-0646)
PHONE......................419 352-3691
Fax: 419 354-8075
Kraig Hanneman, *President*
Mercene Hanneman, *Corp Secy*
Kris Hanneman, *Vice Pres*
EMP: 12 EST: 1941
SQ FT: 8,200
SALES (est): 1.2MM **Privately Held**
WEB: www.mccordproducts.com
SIC: 3995 Burial caskets; burial vaults, fiberglass

(G-2002)
MILLIGAN WORKSHOPS INC
420 Industrial Pkwy (43402-1326)
PHONE......................419 353-0099
Fax: 419 354-7493
Sandra Milligan, *President*
▲ EMP: 25
SQ FT: 15,000
SALES (est): 3.3MM **Privately Held**
WEB: www.milliganworkshops.com
SIC: 3061 3052 Automotive rubber goods (mechanical); rubber hose

(G-2003)
NOVAVISION INC (PA)
Also Called: Thermal Images
524 E Wdlnd Cir Ste 2759 (43402)
PHONE......................419 354-1427
Fax: 419 353-7908
Albert Caperna, *President*
Craig Dixon, *Vice Pres*
Mike Messmer, *Vice Pres*
Brent Norris, *Purchasing*
Josh Thilmony, *Controller*
▲ EMP: 58
SQ FT: 39,000

SALES: 12.6MM **Privately Held**
WEB: www.novavisioninc.com
SIC: 2759 3471 Flexographic printing; electroplating of metals or formed products

(G-2004)
ONE LIBERTY STREET
813 Hamilton Ct (43402-1206)
PHONE......................419 352-6298
Jim Litwin, *President*
EMP: 3
SALES (est): 83.5K **Privately Held**
SIC: 2731 Book publishing

(G-2005)
ORTHO PROSTHETIC CENTER
1224 W Wooster St (43402-2632)
PHONE......................419 352-8161
Roberto Vives, *Principal*
EMP: 3
SALES (est): 220.2K **Privately Held**
SIC: 3842 Prosthetic appliances

(G-2006)
PALMER BROS TRANSIT MIX CON (PA)
Also Called: Fostoria Concrete
12205 E Gypsy Lane Rd (43402-9516)
PHONE......................419 352-4681
Fax: 419 353-7267
Randolph G Schmeltz, *President*
Jesse Schmeltz, *Vice Pres*
EMP: 15
SQ FT: 2,000
SALES (est): 7MM **Privately Held**
SIC: 3273 Ready-mixed concrete

(G-2007)
PHOENIX TECHNOLOGIES INTL LLC
Also Called: Pti
1098 Fairview Ave (43402-1233)
PHONE......................419 353-7738
Fax: 419 354-7738
Don Hayward, *General Mgr*
Jack Ritchie, *Plant Supt*
Dennis Velkov, *Plant Mgr*
Jesse Pine, *Maint Spvr*
Jennifer Byrd, *Opers Staff*
▲ EMP: 50
SQ FT: 100,000
SALES (est): 15.1MM **Privately Held**
WEB: www.phoenixtechnologies.net
SIC: 3085 5169 Plastics bottles; synthetic resins, rubber & plastic materials

(G-2008)
PINNACLE INDUSTRIAL ENTPS INC
Also Called: Pinnacle Plastic Products
513 Napoleon Rd (43402-4822)
P.O. Box 286 (43402-0286)
PHONE......................419 352-8688
Fax: 419 354-4164
Kevin J Tearney, *President*
Mike Hagen, *Vice Pres*
Rodney Kirkpatrick, *Purch Mgr*
John Puffenberger, *Purch Mgr*
Gary Gratop, *Treasurer*
▲ EMP: 125
SQ FT: 90,000
SALES (est): 27.4MM **Privately Held**
WEB: www.pinnacleplasticproducts.com
SIC: 3089 Blow molded finished plastic products

(G-2009)
PRINCIPLE BUSINESS ENTPS INC (PA)
Also Called: Tranquility
20189 Pine Lake Rd (43402-4091)
P.O. Box 129, Dunbridge (43414-0129)
PHONE......................419 352-1551
Carol Stocking, *CEO*
Charles A Stocking, *President*
Alan Clifford, *Vice Pres*
Rob Archer, *Opers Mgr*
Lorena Roberts, *Production*
▲ EMP: 170
SQ FT: 105,000

SALES (est): 70.7MM **Privately Held**
WEB: www.pberopelock.com
SIC: 2676 3142 Diapers, paper (disposable): made from purchased paper; house slippers

(G-2010)
RAWHIDE SOFTWARE INC (PA)
Also Called: Rawhide Press
17552 W River Rd (43402-8862)
PHONE.................................419 878-0857
Steven L Mandell, *President*
EMP: 3
SALES (est): 5.1MM **Privately Held**
SIC: 7372 7371 7379 2741 Publishers' computer software; computer software development; computer related consulting services; miscellaneous publishing

(G-2011)
RECLAMATION TECHNOLOGIES INC (DH)
Also Called: Remtec International
1100 Haskins Rd (43402-9363)
PHONE.................................419 867-8990
Richard Marcus, *President*
Patricia Burns, *Managing Dir*
Tim Kearney, *Vice Pres*
Ken Logan, *Vice Pres*
Robert Tyler, *Plant Mgr*
▲ EMP: 52 EST: 1986
SQ FT: 148,000
SALES (est): 13.2MM
SALES (corp-wide): 141MM **Privately Held**
WEB: www.remtec.net
SIC: 2869 Freon
HQ: A-Gas International Limited
    Banyard Road
    Bristol
    127 537-6600

(G-2012)
RECLAMATION TECHNOLOGIES INC
Also Called: Remtec International
1100 Haskins Rd (43402-9363)
PHONE.................................419 867-8990
Richard Marcus, *President*
Tim Kearny, *Vice Pres*
EMP: 10
SALES (corp-wide): 141MM **Privately Held**
WEB: www.remtec.net
SIC: 2869 Freon
HQ: Reclamation Technologies, Inc.
    1100 Haskins Rd
    Bowling Green OH 43402
    419 867-8990

(G-2013)
REGAL BELOIT AMERICA INC
Marathon Special Products
13300 Van Camp Rd (43402)
P.O. Box 468 (43402-0468)
PHONE.................................419 352-8441
Fax: 419 352-0875
Larry Minnich, *General Mgr*
Donald Riley, *Purchasing*
Brian Mick, *Engineer*
Brian Miller, *Engineer*
Thomas Cudlike, *Manager*
EMP: 200
SALES (est): 3.2B **Publicly Held**
WEB: www.marathonelect.com
SIC: 3613 3644 Fuse mountings, electric power; noncurrent-carrying wiring services
HQ: Regal Beloit America, Inc.
    200 State St
    Beloit WI 53511
    608 364-8800

(G-2014)
ROARE-Q LLC
Also Called: Porkbelly Bbq
10232 Middleton Pike (43402-9808)
PHONE.................................419 801-4040
Charles Earl, *CEO*
Rory Earl, *COO*
Patricia Earl, *CFO*
EMP: 3 EST: 2010
SALES (est): 207.4K **Privately Held**
SIC: 2099 2087 Food preparations; glace, for glazing food

(G-2015)
ROSENBOOM MACHINE & TOOL INC
1032 S Maple St (43402-4535)
P.O. Box 408 (43402-0408)
PHONE.................................419 352-9484
Casey Mallow, *Production*
Jeff Hunker, *Engineer*
Michael Drouard, *Design Engr*
Derrik Fowler, *Branch Mgr*
Lloyd Stager, *Manager*
EMP: 47
SALES (corp-wide): 84.5MM **Privately Held**
WEB: www.rosenboom.com
SIC: 3593 3599 Fluid power cylinders, hydraulic or pneumatic; machine shop, jobbing & repair
PA: Rosenboom Machine & Tool, Inc.
    1530 Western Ave
    Sheldon IA 51201
    712 324-4854

(G-2016)
SOUTHEASTERN CONTAINER INC
307 Industrial Pkwy (43402-1347)
PHONE.................................419 352-6300
Fax: 419 352-4909
John Johnson, *Branch Mgr*
Jeff Fay, *Manager*
Christina Tucker, *Manager*
George Gater, *Maintence Staff*
EMP: 100
SALES (corp-wide): 500K **Privately Held**
SIC: 3085 3089 Plastics bottles; plastic containers, except foam
PA: Southeastern Container, Inc.
    1250 Sand Hill Rd
    Enka NC 28728
    828 350-7200

(G-2017)
TH PLASTICS INC
843 Miller Dr (43402-8601)
PHONE.................................419 352-2770
EMP: 108
SALES (corp-wide): 100.9MM **Privately Held**
SIC: 3089 Plastic processing
PA: Th Plastics, Inc.
    106 E Main St
    Mendon MI 49072
    269 496-8495

(G-2018)
UNIQUE PLASTICS LLC
13350 Bishop Rd (43402)
PHONE.................................419 352-0066
William R Anderson, *Owner*
EMP: 5
SALES (est): 574K **Privately Held**
SIC: 3089 Plastics products

(G-2019)
VEHTEK SYSTEMS INC
2125 Wood Bridge Blvd (43402-9164)
PHONE.................................419 373-8741
Christian Holzer, *Principal*
Aeric Smallwood, *Purch Mgr*
Rob Huff, *Engineer*
Alan Maag, *Controller*
Dan Trace, *Manager*
◆ EMP: 700
SALES (est): 48.2MM
SALES (corp-wide): 36.4B **Privately Held**
WEB: www.magnaint.com
SIC: 3465 Body parts, automobile: stamped metal
PA: Magna International Inc
    337 Magna Dr
    Aurora ON L4G 7
    905 726-2462

(G-2020)
WILLIAMS INDUSTRIAL SVC INC
2120 Wood Bridge Blvd (43402-9164)
PHONE.................................419 353-2120
Fax: 419 353-7712
Robert S Williams, *President*
Mary E Geremski, *Principal*
Mary Helen Nowak, *Principal*
Barry E Savage, *Principal*
Ryan Richey, *Project Mgr*
EMP: 22

SQ FT: 56,000
SALES (est): 7.6MM **Privately Held**
WEB: www.wisfurnaces.com
SIC: 3567 Industrial furnaces & ovens

(G-2021)
WIZARD GRAPHICS INC
112 S Main St (43402-2909)
PHONE.................................419 354-3098
Fax: 419 352-5294
Debra Elliott, *President*
Marge Bednar, *Bookkeeper*
EMP: 5
SQ FT: 3,000
SALES (est): 280K **Privately Held**
WEB: www.wizardgraphics.net
SIC: 2396 7299 2262 2395 Screen printing on fabric articles; stitching services; decorative finishing of manmade broadwoven fabrics; pleating & stitching

(G-2022)
WOOD COUNTY OHIO
Also Called: Laser Cartridge Express
1090 Fairview Ave (43402-1233)
PHONE.................................419 353-1227
Melinda Kale, *General Mgr*
Doug Schey, *General Mgr*
Gaile Brooker, *Manager*
EMP: 8 **Privately Held**
WEB: www.woodmrdd.org
SIC: 3955 Print cartridges for laser & other computer printers
PA: Wood County Ohio
    1 Court House Sq
    Bowling Green OH 43402
    419 354-9100

(G-2023)
XORB CORPORATION
2121 S Woodland Cir (43402-8832)
PHONE.................................419 354-6021
Ralph Temple, *President*
Paul Dunlavey, *Corp Secy*
EMP: 7
SQ FT: 10,000
SALES (est): 1MM **Privately Held**
SIC: 3599 Bellows, industrial: metal

Bradford
Miami County

(G-2024)
BOSCOTT METALS INC
138 S Miami Ave (45308-1321)
P.O. Box 23 (45308-0023)
PHONE.................................937 448-2018
Fax: 937 448-2019
Mark Quinner, *President*
EMP: 12
SQ FT: 20,000
SALES (est): 1.1MM **Privately Held**
SIC: 3365 Aluminum & aluminum-based alloy castings

(G-2025)
C F POEPPELMAN INC (PA)
Also Called: Pepcon Concrete
4755 N State Route 721 (45308-9425)
PHONE.................................937 448-2191
Fax: 937 448-2031
James Poeppelman, *President*
Fred Poeppelman, *Vice Pres*
EMP: 20 EST: 1950
SQ FT: 1,500
SALES (est): 11.8MM **Privately Held**
SIC: 1411 3273 1442 Limestone, dimension-quarrying; ready-mixed concrete; construction sand & gravel

(G-2026)
PRODUCTION PAINT FINISHERS INC
Also Called: P P F
140 Center St (45308-1202)
P.O. Box 127 (45308-0127)
PHONE.................................937 448-2627
Fax: 937 448-2995
Lawrence F Francis, *President*
Kenneth L Robertson, *Principal*
Selwyn C Jackson, *Principal*
Ronald G Smith, *Principal*
Allen J Francis, *Vice Pres*

EMP: 80 EST: 1970
SQ FT: 67,000
SALES (est): 11.3MM **Privately Held**
WEB: www.productionpaint.com
SIC: 3479 Painting of metal products

Bradner
Wood County

(G-2027)
LUCKEY FARMERS INC
2320 Bowling Green Rd E (43406-9731)
PHONE.................................419 287-3275
John Lintner, *Branch Mgr*
EMP: 3
SALES (corp-wide): 129.2MM **Privately Held**
WEB: www.luckeyfarmers.com
SIC: 2875 5191 Fertilizers, mixing only; farm supplies
PA: Luckey Farmers, Inc.
    1200 W Main St
    Woodville OH 43469
    419 849-2711

(G-2028)
MCCLAFLIN MOBILE MEDIA LLC
106 Caldwell St (43406-9784)
P.O. Box 512 (43406-0512)
PHONE.................................419 575-9367
Douglas McClaflin,
EMP: 3
SALES (est): 250.4K **Privately Held**
SIC: 3663 Radio & TV communications equipment

(G-2029)
MESTEK INC
America Wariming & Ventraling
120 Plin St (43406-7735)
P.O. Box 677 (43406-0677)
PHONE.................................419 288-2703
Fax: 419 288-2346
Todd Wightman, *Plant Mgr*
Todd Whightman, *Branch Mgr*
Derrick Kistler, *Supervisor*
EMP: 75
SALES (corp-wide): 482.1MM **Privately Held**
SIC: 3822 3564 3444 3442 Hardware for environmental regulators; blowers & fans; sheet metalwork; metal doors, sash & trim; nonferrous rolling & drawing
PA: Mestek, Inc.
    260 N Elm St
    Westfield MA 01085
    413 568-9571

(G-2030)
TRI COUNTY TARP INC
13100 State Route 23 (43406)
P.O. Box 600 (43406-0600)
PHONE.................................419 288-3350
Fax: 419 288-2372
Terrence E Augustine, *President*
Kay Augustine, *Corp Secy*
Terrence Augustin, *Executive*
EMP: 32
SQ FT: 82,000
SALES (est): 4.2MM **Privately Held**
WEB: www.tritarp.com
SIC: 2394 2542 3354 Canvas & related products; partitions for floor attachment, prefabricated: except wood; aluminum extruded products

---

Brecksville
Cuyahoga County

(G-2031)
AB RESOURCES LLC
6802 W Snowville Rd Ste E (44141-3296)
PHONE.................................440 922-1098
Fax: 440 922-1251
Chris Halvorson, *CFO*
Gordon O Yonel,
EMP: 25
SQ FT: 7,500
SALES (est): 3.9MM **Privately Held**
SIC: 1311 Crude petroleum & natural gas production

(G-2032)
ABEON MEDICAL CORPORATION
8006 Katherine Blvd (44141-4202)
PHONE...................440 262-6000
George Picha, *CEO*
Matthew Thompson, *General Mgr*
David Graves, *Engineer*
Dawn Thompson, *Engineer*
EMP: 5
SALES (est): 548.2K **Privately Held**
SIC: 3069 Medical & laboratory rubber
sundries & related products

(G-2033)
ACHILL ISLAND COMPOSITES LLC
6981 Chapel Hill Dr (44141-2717)
PHONE...................440 838-1746
James Sutter, *Principal*
EMP: 3
SALES (est): 208.5K **Privately Held**
SIC: 3089 Plastics products

(G-2034)
APPLIED MEDICAL TECHNOLOGY INC
Also Called: Amt
8006 Katherine Blvd (44141-4202)
PHONE...................440 717-4000
George J Picha, *President*
Robert J Crump, *Principal*
Tim Austin, *Manager*
Lisa Robbins, *Manager*
Dana Kaiser, *Admin Asst*
EMP: 30
SQ FT: 14,000
SALES (est): 8.4MM **Privately Held**
SIC: 3841 3083 8731 Surgical & medical
instruments; laminated plastics plate &
sheet; medical research, commercial

(G-2035)
BARNES GROUP INC
Also Called: Hyson Products
10367 Brecksville Rd (44141-3335)
PHONE...................440 526-5900
Regis Minord, *Vice Pres*
Mike Gaudiani, *Branch Mgr*
Richard Hunsicker, *Info Tech Dir*
Andreas Buchfellner, *Technology*
Jeanne Bogre, *Director*
EMP: 8
SQ FT: 53,593
SALES (corp-wide): 1.2B **Publicly Held**
WEB: www.barnesgroupinc.com
SIC: 3495 3469 Wire springs; metal
stampings
PA: Barnes Group Inc.
123 Main St
Bristol CT 06010
860 583-7070

(G-2036)
BENJAMIN MEDIA INC
10050 Brecksville Rd (44141-3219)
P.O. Box 190, Peninsula (44264-0190)
PHONE...................330 467-7588
Bernard P Krzys, *President*
Dan Waymire, *Managing Prtnr*
Russell H Frisby, *Partner*
Sharon M Bueno, *Editor*
Chris Crowell, *Editor*
▲ EMP: 28
SQ FT: 2,744
SALES (est): 4.7MM **Privately Held**
WEB: www.ttmag.com
SIC: 2721 Trade journals: publishing &
printing

(G-2037)
BLACK BOX CORPORATION
6650 W Snowville Rd Ste R (44141-4301)
PHONE...................937 438-8660
Chuck Hartley, *Branch Mgr*
EMP: 10
SALES (corp-wide): 912.6MM **Publicly Held**
SIC: 3577 Computer peripheral equipment
PA: Black Box Corporation
1000 Park Dr
Lawrence PA 15055
724 746-5500

(G-2038)
BRECKSVILLE BROADVIEW GAZETTE
Also Called: Parma Seven Hills Gazette
7014 Mill Rd (44141-1814)
PHONE...................440 526-7977
Fax: 440 526-7114
Joyce McFadden, *President*
Joyce Mc Fadden, *Publisher*
EMP: 25
SQ FT: 816
SALES (est): 1.5MM **Privately Held**
WEB: www.gazette-news.com
SIC: 2711 Newspapers

(G-2039)
C M STEPHANOFF JEWELERS INC
8718 Bradford Ln (44141-2056)
PHONE...................440 526-5890
Chris Stephanoff, *President*
Sandra Premura, *Vice Pres*
EMP: 5
SQ FT: 2,100
SALES (est): 580K **Privately Held**
SIC: 3911 7631 Bracelets, precious metal;
earrings, precious metal; necklaces, pre-
cious metal; jewelry repair services

(G-2040)
CLINICAL SPECIALTIES INC (PA)
Also Called: Csi Infusion Services
6955 Treeline Dr Ste A (44141-3373)
PHONE...................888 873-7888
Edward Rivalsky, *President*
Kevin Cunningham, *Vice Pres*
Julie Edmonds, *Manager*
EMP: 74
SQ FT: 22,000
SALES (est): 22.4MM **Privately Held**
WEB: www.csi-network.com
SIC: 2834 Intravenous solutions

(G-2041)
CLM MARKETING INC
Also Called: Cgs Aviation
4200 Royalton Rd (44141-2573)
PHONE...................440 526-8613
Fax: 440 632-1207
Chuck Slusarczyk, *President*
EMP: 6
SQ FT: 5,500
SALES (est): 741.5K **Privately Held**
WEB: www.cgsaviation.com
SIC: 3721 5088 Aircraft; aircraft equip-
ment & supplies

(G-2042)
CURTISS-WRIGHT FLOW CTRL CORP
Also Called: Sprague Products
10195 Brecksville Rd (44141-3205)
PHONE...................440 838-7690
Fax: 440 838-7699
Josh Kolenc, *Vice Pres*
Bob Atkinson, *Engineer*
Paul George, *Engineer*
Kelly Grudzinski, *Engineer*
Tony La Morte, *Engineer*
EMP: 30
SQ FT: 77,847
SALES (corp-wide): 2.1B **Publicly Held**
SIC: 3561 Pumps & pumping equipment
HQ: Curtiss-Wright Flow Control Corpora-
tion
1966 Broadhollow Rd Ste E
Farmingdale NY 11735
631 293-3800

(G-2043)
DIRECT DISPOSABLES LLC
10605 Snowville Rd (44141-3446)
P.O. Box 470451, Broadview Heights
(44147-0451)
PHONE...................440 717-3335
Kris Scott, *VP Sales*
Sharon Scott,
EMP: 7
SALES (est): 739.4K **Privately Held**
WEB: www.directdisposables.com
SIC: 2389 Disposable garments & acces-
sories

(G-2044)
EFG HOLDINGS INC (PA)
10217 Brecksville Rd (44141-3207)
PHONE...................812 717-2544
Ronald J Kiter, *President*
Ian McKenna, *CFO*
EMP: 7
SALES (est): 126.1MM **Privately Held**
SIC: 3452 Bolts, nuts, rivets & washers

(G-2045)
ELGIN FASTENER GROUP LLC
Quality Bolt & Screw
10147 Brecksville Rd (44141-3205)
PHONE...................440 717-7650
Fax: 440 717-7665
Daniel Wade, *Manager*
Joseph Ford, *Maintence Staff*
EMP: 38
SALES (corp-wide): 126.1MM **Privately Held**
SIC: 3452 Bolts, metal; screws, metal
HQ: Elgin Fastener Group, Llc
10217 Brecksville Rd
Brecksville OH 44141

(G-2046)
ELGIN FASTENER GROUP LLC (HQ)
10217 Brecksville Rd (44141-3207)
PHONE...................812 717-2544
Ron Auletta, *CEO*
Gary Goodwin, *COO*
Marty Goeree, *Vice Pres*
Tena Heller, *Treasurer*
EMP: 14
SALES (est): 126.1MM **Privately Held**
SIC: 3399 3452 Metal fasteners; bolts,
metal
PA: Efg Holdings, Inc.
10217 Brecksville Rd
Brecksville OH 44141
812 717-2544

(G-2047)
ENHANCED MFG SOLUTIONS LLC
2890 Boston Mills Rd (44141-3819)
P.O. Box 470024, Broadview Heights
(44147-0024)
PHONE...................440 476-1244
Brian Frost, *CEO*
Rick Bohn, *President*
EMP: 61
SQ FT: 2,200
SALES (est): 4.5MM **Privately Held**
SIC: 3714 Motor vehicle electrical equip-
ment

(G-2048)
EXACT CUTTING SERVICE INC
Also Called: Experimental Machine
6892 W Snwvle Rd Ste 108 (44141)
PHONE...................440 546-1319
Fax: 440 546-1322
Jerry Narduzzi, *President*
Anthony Shawan, *Vice Pres*
EMP: 20 EST: 1974
SQ FT: 20,000
SALES (est): 1.8MM **Privately Held**
WEB: www.exactcut.com
SIC: 7389 3599 Metal cutting services;
machine shop, jobbing & repair

(G-2049)
FAB TECH INC
6500 W Snowville Rd (44141-3230)
PHONE...................330 926-9556
Fax: 330 926-9562
Richard Herrilko, *President*
Gail Herrilko, *Vice Pres*
Gary Meglich, *VP Opers*
▲ EMP: 5
SQ FT: 12,000
SALES: 600K **Privately Held**
SIC: 3442 Store fronts, prefabricated,
metal

(G-2050)
FULTON MANUFACTURING INDS LLC
6600 W Snowville Rd # 6500 (44141-3257)
PHONE...................440 546-1435
Doug Perau, *Ch of Bd*
John Medas, *President*

Pete Pappas, *General Mgr*
Andrew Domonkos, *Cust Mgr*
Lisa Romaniuk, *Manager*
EMP: 34
SQ FT: 55,000
SALES (est): 5.1MM **Privately Held**
SIC: 3469 Metal stampings

(G-2051)
GENERATIONS COFFEE COMPANY LLC
60100 W Snowell (44141)
PHONE...................440 546-0901
Michael Caruso, *General Mgr*
EMP: 30
SALES (est): 3.1MM
SALES (corp-wide): 78.9MM **Publicly Held**
WEB: www.coffeeholding.com
SIC: 2095 5149 5499 Roasted coffee;
groceries & related products; coffee
PA: Coffee Holding Co., Inc.
3475 Victory Blvd Ste 4
Staten Island NY 10314
718 832-0800

(G-2052)
GLOBAL LIGHTING TECH INC
55 Andrews Cir Ste 1 (44141-3269)
PHONE...................440 922-4584
Fax: 440 922-4585
Jeffery Parker, *President*
Gordon S Kaiser, *President*
Michael Mayer, *Vice Pres*
Melanie Gerdeman, *Project Mgr*
Bret Dunham, *Project Engr*
▲ EMP: 24
SQ FT: 16,500
SALES (est): 5MM **Privately Held**
WEB: www.glthome.com
SIC: 3648 3993 Lighting equipment; signs
& advertising specialties
PA: Global Lighting Technologies Inc.
C/O: Maples & Calder Limited
George Town GR CAYMAN

(G-2053)
GLOBAL PLASTIC TECH INC
7762 Sunstone Dr (44141-2170)
PHONE...................330 963-6830
Daryl F Wene, *President*
Terry Ryan, *VP Prdtn*
Donna Delio, *Controller*
EMP: 25
SQ FT: 12,000
SALES (est): 2.3MM **Privately Held**
SIC: 3089 Injection molded finished plastic
products

(G-2054)
HANOVER PUBLISHING CO
7569 Sanctuary Cir (44141-3194)
PHONE...................440 838-0911
Agnes Thomas, *Principal*
EMP: 4 EST: 2007
SALES (est): 274.5K **Privately Held**
SIC: 2741 Miscellaneous publishing

(G-2055)
INDUSTRIAL MFG CO LLC (HQ)
8223 Brecksville Rd Ste 1 (44141-1367)
PHONE...................440 838-4700
James Benenson Jr, *CEO*
James Benenson III, *President*
Clement Benenson, *Partner*
John E Cvetic, *CFO*
Mike Mahen, *Controller*
◆ EMP: 10 EST: 1979
SQ FT: 4,700
SALES (est): 587.1MM **Privately Held**
SIC: 2542 3728 3566 Lockers (not refrig-
erated): except wood; cabinets: show, dis-
play or storage: except wood; shelving,
office & store: except wood; aircraft body
& wing assemblies & parts; aircraft as-
semblies, subassemblies & parts; speed
changers, drives & gears
PA: Summa Holdings, Inc.
8223 Brecksville Rd # 100
Cleveland OH 44141
440 838-4700

GEOGRAPHIC

(G-2056)
INTEGRATED CHEM CONCEPTS INC
Also Called: ICC
6650 W Snowville Rd Ste F (44141-4301)
PHONE................................440 838-5666
Richard H Fagher, *President*
Christine Lease, *Admin Sec*
EMP: 9
SQ FT: 9,300
SALES (est): 980K **Privately Held**
SIC: 2821 Plastics materials & resins

(G-2057)
JCB ARROWHEAD PRODUCTS INC
8223 Brecksville Rd # 100 (44141-1371)
PHONE................................440 546-4288
EMP: 3
SALES (est): 197.3K **Privately Held**
SIC: 3728 Aircraft parts & equipment

(G-2058)
KILN
7225 Fitzwater Rd (44141-1323)
PHONE................................440 717-1880
EMP: 3
SALES (est): 293.2K **Privately Held**
SIC: 3559 Kilns

(G-2059)
KNIGHT ERGONOMICS INC
Also Called: Gemini Products
6650 W Snowville Rd Ste G (44141-4301)
PHONE................................440 746-0044
Robert Haller, *President*
Nicholas Pyros, *Vice Pres*
Kate Small, *Manager*
EMP: 10
SALES: 1MM **Privately Held**
SIC: 3423 Hand & edge tools

(G-2060)
LAKE ERIE ASPHALT PAVING INC
5510 Oakes Rd (44141-2600)
PHONE................................440 526-5191
Peter Boukis, *President*
EMP: 3
SALES (est): 403.7K **Privately Held**
SIC: 2951 Asphalt paving mixtures & blocks

(G-2061)
LUBRIZOL ADVANCED MTLS INC (DH)
9911 Brecksville Rd (44141-3201)
PHONE................................216 447-5000
Fax: 216 447-5740
James L Hambrick, *CEO*
Rick Tolin, *President*
Manoj Dhar, *Business Mgr*
John J King, *Vice Pres*
Allen Park, *Project Mgr*
◆ EMP: 10
SQ FT: 380,000
SALES (est): 1.1B
SALES (corp-wide): 223.6B **Publicly Held**
WEB: www.pharma.noveoninc.com
SIC: 2899 2891 3088 2834 Chemical preparations; adhesives & sealants; plastics plumbing fixtures; pharmaceutical preparations; electronic generation equipment
HQ: The Lubrizol Corporation
29400 Lakeland Blvd
Wickliffe OH 44092
440 943-4200

(G-2062)
M & R INDUSTRIES INC
8651 Dunbar Ln (44141-2025)
PHONE................................440 897-7950
Roger D Kassouf, *Principal*
EMP: 3
SALES (est): 190.7K **Privately Held**
SIC: 3999 Manufacturing industries

(G-2063)
M/W INTERNATIONAL INC
Also Called: Mills Walls
10260 Brecksville Rd (44141-3342)
PHONE................................440 526-6900
Joseph Bucalo, *President*

Kathleen Bucalo, *Corp Secy*
Tom Davis, *VP Sales*
Lin Huttert, *Admin Sec*
▲ EMP: 18
SQ FT: 12,000
SALES: 2MM **Privately Held**
SIC: 2522 2542 1761 1751 Office furniture, except wood; partitions & fixtures, except wood; architectural sheet metal work; window & door (prefabricated) installation; glass & glazing work

(G-2064)
MAVERICK INDUSTRIES INC
5945 W Snowville Rd (44141-3266)
PHONE................................440 838-5335
Jim Urbanski, *President*
Cindy Maro, *Manager*
EMP: 10
SQ FT: 24,000
SALES (est): 1.4MM **Privately Held**
WEB: www.maverickindustries.com
SIC: 3492 5074 Hose & tube fittings & assemblies, hydraulic/pneumatic; plumbing & heating valves

(G-2065)
NATURES OWN SOURCE LLC
7033 Mill Rd (44141-1813)
PHONE................................440 838-5135
David Mansbery,
EMP: 8
SALES (est): 745.4K **Privately Held**
SIC: 2899 Desalter kits, sea water

(G-2066)
NAUTICUS INC
8080 Snowville Rd (44141-3413)
PHONE................................440 746-1290
John Agro, *President*
John Deagro, *President*
▲ EMP: 6
SALES (est): 876.5K **Privately Held**
SIC: 3732 Motorized boat, building & repairing

(G-2067)
NOVEON INCORPORATED
9921 Brecksville Rd (44141-3201)
P.O. Box 41250 (44141-0250)
PHONE................................216 447-5000
◆ EMP: 3
SALES (est): 517.3K **Privately Held**
SIC: 2841 Mfg Soap/Other Detergents

(G-2068)
NUCLEAR PLATING SERVICE INC
7935 Orianna St (44141-1317)
PHONE................................216 641-1109
Fax: 216 641-2588
Nicholas J Oleff, *President*
Frank Reale, *Product Mgr*
EMP: 35 EST: 1966
SQ FT: 16,000
SALES (est): 2.9MM **Privately Held**
SIC: 3471 Plating of metals or formed products; finishing, metals or formed products

(G-2069)
PITNEY BOWES INC
6910 Treeline Dr Ste C (44141-3366)
PHONE................................203 426-7025
Brian Philbin, *Director*
EMP: 75
SALES (corp-wide): 3.4B **Publicly Held**
SIC: 3579 7359 Postage meters; business machine & electronic equipment rental services
PA: Pitney Bowes Inc.
3001 Summer St Ste 3
Stamford CT 06905
203 356-5000

(G-2070)
PMD ENTERPRISES INC
Also Called: Caruso Coffee
6100 W Snowville Rd (44141-3238)
PHONE................................440 546-0901
Michael Caruso, *President*
Christopher Bertin, *Corp Secy*
Lisa Mann, *Manager*
▲ EMP: 15

SALES (est): 3.5MM **Privately Held**
WEB: www.carusoscoffee.com
SIC: 2095 Coffee roasting (except by wholesale grocers)

(G-2071)
SCRATCH-OFF SYSTEMS INC
6600 W Snowville Rd (44141-3257)
PHONE................................216 649-7800
Daniel Ogorek, *President*
Robert F Collett, *Principal*
Michael Hazelwood, *Principal*
Kristen Welsh, *Opers Staff*
Angela Jelovich, *Financial Exec*
▼ EMP: 20
SQ FT: 10,000
SALES (est): 6MM **Privately Held**
WEB: www.scratchoff.com
SIC: 2679 5112 2759 2754 Labels, paper: made from purchased material; stationery & office supplies; labels & seals: printing; labels: gravure printing

(G-2072)
SELECTRONICS INCORPORATED
9771 Forge Dr (44141-2825)
PHONE................................440 546-5595
Ted Liggett, *CEO*
EMP: 5
SQ FT: 600
SALES: 1MM **Privately Held**
WEB: www.selectronicsusa.com
SIC: 3674 5731 Semiconductors & related devices; radio, television & electronic stores

(G-2073)
SIEMENS INDUSTRY INC
Also Called: Rapistan Systems
6930 Treeline Dr Ste A (44141-3367)
PHONE................................440 526-2770
Fax: 440 526-0931
Charles McBride, *Manager*
EMP: 30
SALES (corp-wide): 89.6B **Privately Held**
WEB: www.sea.siemens.com
SIC: 5084 3535 Industrial machinery & equipment; conveyors & conveying equipment
HQ: Siemens Industry, Inc.
1000 Deerfield Pkwy
Buffalo Grove IL 60089
847 215-1000

(G-2074)
SUPPLIER PARK INDUSTRIES LLC
2890 Boston Mills Rd (44141-3819)
P.O. Box 470024, Broadview Heights (44147-0024)
PHONE................................440 476-1244
Brian Frost, *CEO*
Rick Bohn, *President*
EMP: 96
SQ FT: 500,000
SALES (est): 13.5MM **Privately Held**
SIC: 3714 Motor vehicle electrical equipment

(G-2075)
SYNTHETIC BODY PARTS INC
6099 Warblers Roost (44141-1751)
PHONE................................440 838-0985
Carl McMillin, *President*
EMP: 4
SALES (est): 230K **Privately Held**
SIC: 3842 Prosthetic appliances

(G-2076)
TEREX UTILITIES INC
Also Called: Cleveland Division
6400 W Snowville Rd Ste 1 (44141-3248)
PHONE................................440 262-3200
Steve Holt, *Purchasing*
Mike Greive, *Sales Engr*
Mike Dallager, *Branch Mgr*
EMP: 12
SALES (corp-wide): 4.4B **Publicly Held**
WEB: www.craneamerica.com
SIC: 7699 5084 3536 1796 Industrial machinery & equipment repair; cranes, industrial; hoists; hoists, cranes & monorails; installing building equipment

HQ: Terex Utilities, Inc.
12805 Sw 77th Pl
Tigard OR 97223
503 620-0611

(G-2077)
TURK+HILLINGER USA INC
6650 W Snowville Rd Ste W (44141-4301)
P.O. Box 41371 (44141-0371)
PHONE................................440 781-1900
Michael Mann, *President*
Christopher Grolimund, *Vice Pres*
▲ EMP: 3
SALES: 468.5K
SALES (corp-wide): 47.2MM **Privately Held**
SIC: 3621 Generating apparatus & parts, electrical
PA: Turk & Hillinger Gmbh
Fohrenstr. 20
Tuttlingen 78532
746 170-140

(G-2078)
ZEECO EQUIPMENT COMMODITY
6581 Glen Coe Dr (44141-2883)
PHONE................................440 838-1102
Zoran Stojkov, *CEO*
EMP: 5
SALES (est): 500K **Privately Held**
SIC: 3559 Chemical machinery & equipment

Bremen
Fairfield County

(G-2079)
BARCLAY PETROLEUM INC
7400 Marietta Rd Se (43107-9772)
P.O. Box 81 (43107-0081)
PHONE................................740 569-4327
Bruce Kelley, *President*
Diane Weeks, *Manager*
EMP: 4
SQ FT: 1,800
SALES (est): 426.9K **Privately Held**
SIC: 1382 1311 Oil & gas exploration services; crude petroleum production; natural gas production

(G-2080)
STUART BURIAL VAULT COMPANY
527 Ford St (43107-1111)
P.O. Box 146 (43107-0146)
PHONE................................740 569-4158
Fax: 740 569-4159
John A Boone, *President*
Mary Lyle Boone, *Vice Pres*
Barbara Westfall, *Systems Mgr*
EMP: 12
SQ FT: 16,500
SALES (est): 1.1MM **Privately Held**
SIC: 3272 Burial vaults, concrete or precast terrazzo

(G-2081)
WESTERMAN INC (DH)
245 N Broad St (43107-1003)
P.O. Box 125 (43107-0125)
PHONE................................740 569-4143
Terry A McGhee, *President*
Barry Keller, *Exec VP*
Melissa Eaton, *CFO*
◆ EMP: 185 EST: 1957
SQ FT: 150,000
SALES (est): 82.5MM
SALES (corp-wide): 2.8B **Publicly Held**
WEB: www.westermancompanies.com
SIC: 3566 Reduction gears & gear units for turbines, except automotive
HQ: Worthington Cylinder Corporation
200 W Old Wilson Bridge Rd
Worthington OH 43085
614 840-3210

(G-2082)
WORTHINGTON CYLINDER CORP
245 N Broad St (43107-1003)
P.O. Box 125 (43107-0125)
PHONE................................740 569-4143

Brian Householder, *Marketing Staff*
EMP: 191
SALES (corp-wide): 2.8B **Publicly Held**
SIC: 3443 Cylinders, pressure: metal plate
HQ: Worthington Cylinder Corporation
200 W Wlson Bridge Rd
Worthington OH 43085
614 840-3210

Brewster
Stark County

(G-2083)
BREWSTER CHEESE COMPANY (PA)
800 Wabash Ave S (44613-1464)
PHONE..............................330 767-3492
Fax: 330 767-3386
Fritz Leeman, *CEO*
Thomas Murphy, *President*
Tom Beck, *Mfg Spvr*
Steve Lambert, *Engineer*
Emil Alecusan, *CFO*
EMP: 180 **EST:** 1964
SQ FT: 78,914
SALES (est): 122.8MM **Privately Held**
SIC: 2022 Cheese, natural & processed; whey, raw or liquid

(G-2084)
BREWSTER SUGARCREEK TWP HISTO
Also Called: BREWSTER HISTORICAL SOCIETY
45 Wabash Ave S (44613-1210)
PHONE..............................330 767-0045
Robert Lucking, *Owner*
EMP: 10 **EST:** 1976
SQ FT: 3,196
SALES: 22.2K **Privately Held**
SIC: 3732 8412 Boat kits, not models; museum

(G-2085)
L & J DRIVE THRU
212 Wabash Ave N (44613-1040)
PHONE..............................330 767-2185
Lena Porter, *Principal*
EMP: 4
SALES (est): 237.9K **Privately Held**
SIC: 2086 Carbonated beverages, nonalcoholic: bottled & canned

(G-2086)
MICRO MACHINE LTD
275 7th St Sw (44613-1457)
PHONE..............................330 438-7078
Ronald Pollock, *Partner*
Harold Byer, *Partner*
EMP: 7
SALES (est): 522.3K **Privately Held**
SIC: 3599 Machine & other job shop work

Brice
Franklin County

(G-2087)
CARL C ANDRE INC
Also Called: Andre Kitchens
2894 Brice Rd (43109)
P.O. Box 62 (43109-0062)
PHONE..............................614 864-0123
Carl C Andre, *President*
EMP: 3
SQ FT: 8,000
SALES (est): 320K **Privately Held**
SIC: 2435 5211 Hardwood veneer & plywood; cabinets, kitchen

Bridgeport
Belmont County

(G-2088)
ANGELINA STONE & MARBLE LTD
55341 W Center St (43912-1216)
PHONE..............................740 633-3360

Jack McKeever, *Branch Mgr*
EMP: 6
SALES (corp-wide): 1MM **Privately Held**
SIC: 3281 Granite, cut & shaped
PA: Angelina Stone & Marble Ltd
67010 Willow Grove Rd
Saint Clairsville OH 43950
740 695-3615

(G-2089)
EVERLY CONCRETE PRODUCTS
53620 Farmington Rd (43912-9779)
PHONE..............................740 635-1415
Rich Theaker, *Principal*
EMP: 3
SALES (est): 398.8K **Privately Held**
SIC: 3272 Concrete products

(G-2090)
JERRY HAROLDS DOORS UNLIMITED (PA)
415 Hall St (43912-1343)
PHONE..............................740 635-4949
Jerry Brocht, *President*
Harold Games, *Vice Pres*
EMP: 5
SQ FT: 1,600
SALES (est): 1.9MM **Privately Held**
SIC: 5031 3446 5211 Doors; architectural metalwork; garage doors, sale & installation

(G-2091)
MAAN POWER SERVICES LLC
56346 National Rd (43912-2502)
P.O. Box 341 (43912-0341)
PHONE..............................740 609-3020
Nathan Robert Rohrig,
Aileen Rohrig,
Amy Rohrig,
Michael Rohrig,
EMP: 30
SALES (est): 2.4MM **Privately Held**
SIC: 1389 Oil field services

(G-2092)
MIKE SUPONCIC
68940 Blaine Chermont Rd (43912-9749)
PHONE..............................740 635-0654
Suponcic Mike, *Owner*
EMP: 3
SALES (est): 211.9K **Privately Held**
SIC: 3532 Mining machinery

(G-2093)
TAFLAN STEEL & WELDING INC
54364 National Rd (43912-9717)
PHONE..............................740 635-0841
Fax: 740 635-0841
James Knellinger, *President*
George Mamakos, *Corp Secy*
EMP: 5 **EST:** 1949
SQ FT: 4,800
SALES (est): 660K **Privately Held**
SIC: 3441 3446 Fabricated structural metal; railings, prefabricated metal; fences or posts, ornamental iron or steel

Brilliant
Jefferson County

(G-2094)
OPTIMUN BLINDS INC
Also Called: Optimum Blinds
204 Ohio St (43913-1125)
PHONE..............................740 598-5808
Mark Laurine, *President*
EMP: 5
SALES (est): 390K **Privately Held**
SIC: 2591 5719 Blinds vertical; vertical blinds; venetian blinds; window shades

(G-2095)
STEEL VALLEY TANK & WELDING
24 County Road 7e (43913-1079)
P.O. Box 8 (43913-0008)
PHONE..............................740 598-4994
Gary Kessler, *Owner*
EMP: 10

SALES (est): 1MM **Privately Held**
WEB: www.steelvalleytank.com
SIC: 3443 Industrial vessels, tanks & containers

(G-2096)
WORKPROS
401 Labelle St Lot 4 (43913-1175)
PHONE..............................740 512-8512
Todd Foster, *Owner*
EMP: 9
SALES: 950K **Privately Held**
SIC: 3531 Construction machinery

Brinkhaven
Knox County

(G-2097)
HILLCREST
Also Called: Hw Chair
31580 Township Rd (43006)
PHONE..............................740 824-4849
Norman Yoder, *President*
EMP: 6
SALES: 400K **Privately Held**
SIC: 2426 Chair seats, hardwood

Bristolville
Trumbull County

(G-2098)
K M B INC
Also Called: King Bros Feed & Supply
1306 State Route 88 (44402-9789)
P.O. Box 240 (44402-0240)
PHONE..............................330 889-3451
Fax: 330 889-9608
Marlene King, *President*
Rex King, *Vice Pres*
EMP: 35 **EST:** 1956
SQ FT: 4,200
SALES (est): 6.2MM **Privately Held**
WEB: www.kingbrosracing.com
SIC: 3273 5211 5261 5191 Ready-mixed concrete; lumber & other building materials; fertilizer; feed; concrete products

(G-2099)
MAHAN PACKING CO INC
6540 State Route 45 (44402-9730)
PHONE..............................330 889-2454
Fax: 330 889-9454
K Ray Mahan, *President*
Nancy Mahan, *Vice Pres*
EMP: 35 **EST:** 1958
SQ FT: 15,000
SALES (est): 5MM **Privately Held**
SIC: 2011 Meat packing plants

(G-2100)
STRUTT PRODUCTS LLC
Also Called: Fire Pit Gallery, The
6340 State Route 45 Cd (44402-9705)
PHONE..............................330 889-2727
Jason Crisp, *President*
Melissa Crisp, *Vice Pres*
Marlene Appel, *Treasurer*
Thomas Appel, *Admin Sec*
EMP: 4
SALES: 340K **Privately Held**
SIC: 3429 Fireplace equipment, hardware: andirons, grates, screens

Broadview Heights
Cuyahoga County

(G-2101)
10155 BROADVIEW BUSINESS
10155 Broadview Rd (44147-3296)
PHONE..............................440 546-1901
David M Leneghan, *Principal*
EMP: 4
SALES (est): 290.9K **Privately Held**
SIC: 3629 Power conversion units, a.c. to d.c.: static-electric

(G-2102)
ACCU-SIGN
3652 Elm Brook Dr (44147-2029)
PHONE..............................216 544-2059
Raymond C Eier, *Principal*
EMP: 3
SALES (est): 278.9K **Privately Held**
SIC: 3993 Signs & advertising specialties

(G-2103)
ACTIPRO SOFTWARE LLC
8576 Somerset Dr (44147-3422)
PHONE..............................888 922-8477
William M Henning, *President*
EMP: 3
SALES (est): 251.9K **Privately Held**
SIC: 7372 Prepackaged software

(G-2104)
BENJAMIN P FORBES COMPANY
Also Called: Forbes Chocolate
800 Ken Mar Indus Pkwy (44147-2922)
PHONE..............................440 838-4400
Fax: 440 433-1093
Keith Geringer, *President*
Mark Skvoretz, *Accountant*
▲ **EMP:** 13 **EST:** 1913
SQ FT: 16,687
SALES (est): 3.1MM **Privately Held**
SIC: 2066 Powdered cocoa

(G-2105)
BROADVIEW HEIGHTS SPOTLIGHTS
9543 Broadview Rd Bldg 7 (44147-2370)
PHONE..............................440 526-4404
Annette Phelps, *President*
EMP: 3
SALES: 14.9K **Privately Held**
SIC: 3648 Spotlights

(G-2106)
BUILDING CTRL INTEGRATORS LLC
325 Treeworth Blvd (44147-2985)
PHONE..............................440 526-6660
Jim McClintock, *Branch Mgr*
EMP: 5
SALES (corp-wide): 14.1MM **Privately Held**
SIC: 3822 Temperature controls, automatic
PA: Building Control Integrators, Llc
383 N Liberty St
Powell OH 43065
614 334-3300

(G-2107)
BUY THE PALLET LLC
8183 Twin Oaks Dr (44147-1036)
PHONE..............................440 521-0073
Joe Barto, *Principal*
EMP: 3
SALES (est): 119.9K **Privately Held**
SIC: 2448 Pallets, wood & wood with metal

(G-2108)
CLEVELAND BUSINESS SUPPLY LLC
Also Called: Total Voice Technologies
8193 Avery Rd Ste 200 (44147-1673)
PHONE..............................888 831-0088
Christopher Kikel, *President*
EMP: 5
SALES (est): 260K **Privately Held**
SIC: 8243 5044 Software training, computer; typewriter & dictation equipment; business oriented computer software

(G-2109)
CLINICL OTCMS MNGMNT SYST LLC
Also Called: Coms Interactive
9200 S Hills Blvd Ste 200 (44147-3520)
PHONE..............................330 650-9900
Edward J Tromczynski, *CEO*
Frederick T Croft, *Ch of Bd*
Tom Mohney, *Vice Pres*
Bill Stuart, *CFO*
Tom Riemenschneider, *Chief Mktg Ofcr*
EMP: 59
SQ FT: 1,400

SALES (est): 9.5MM **Privately Held**
WEB: www.comsllc.com
SIC: 7372 Business oriented computer
software

(G-2110)
HMT ASSOCIATES INC
335 Treeworth Blvd (44147-2985)
PHONE...................................216 369-0109
Patti Conti, *Principal*
Alissa Monahan, *Accounts Mgr*
EMP: 32
SALES (est): 7.2MM **Privately Held**
SIC: 3312 Hot-rolled iron & steel products

(G-2111)
J & L STEEL BAR LLC
3587 Antony Dr (44147-2048)
PHONE...................................440 526-0050
EMP: 4
SALES (est): 315.1K **Privately Held**
SIC: 3312 Bars & bar shapes, steel, hot-
rolled

(G-2112)
JL SAFETY LLC
2781 Timberwood Dr (44147-3478)
PHONE...................................440 582-5866
John Massaad, *Principal*
▲ EMP: 4 EST: 2008
SALES (est): 443K **Privately Held**
SIC: 3842 Wheelchairs

(G-2113)
MANTRA HAIRCARE LLC
305 Ken Mar Indus Pkwy (44147)
PHONE...................................440 526-3304
Jeffery Klominek,
Amy Levak,
EMP: 18
SQ FT: 10,000
SALES: 2MM **Privately Held**
SIC: 2844 Hair preparations, including
shampoos

(G-2114)
MATACO
Also Called: Machine & Tool Accessories Co
2861 E Royalton Rd (44147-2827)
PHONE...................................440 546-8355
Jeff Bubb, *Partner*
David Pajestka, *Partner*
Joseph Pajestka, *Partner*
▲ EMP: 4
SQ FT: 1,000
SALES (est): 585K **Privately Held**
WEB: www.matacoinc.net
SIC: 3541 5251 5084 3446 Machine tool
replacement & repair parts, metal cutting
types; tools; industrial machinery & equip-
ment; architectural metalwork

(G-2115)
**MATHEMATICAL BUSINESS
SYSTEMS**
1261 Valley Park Dr (44147-1643)
PHONE...................................440 237-2345
Tom Penn, *Owner*
EMP: 5
SALES: 250K **Privately Held**
SIC: 7372 Prepackaged software

(G-2116)
PROMOTIONS PLUS INC
3402 Magnolia Way (44147-3917)
PHONE...................................440 582-2855
EMP: 4
SALES (est): 280K **Privately Held**
SIC: 2329 Mfg Men's/Boy's Clothing

(G-2117)
**QUALITY IMAGE EMBROIDERY
& AP**
2643 Royalwood Rd (44147-1756)
PHONE...................................440 230-1109
Barbara Franko, *President*
Mike Franko, *Admin Sec*
EMP: 5
SQ FT: 2,000
SALES: 125K **Privately Held**
SIC: 2395 Embroidery products, except
schiffli machine

(G-2118)
SAWMILL EYE ASSOCIATES INC
8666 Scenicview Dr (44147-3476)
PHONE...................................440 724-0396
Scott P Caleodis Od, *Principal*
EMP: 3
SALES (est): 130K **Privately Held**
SIC: 2421 Sawmills & planing mills, gen-
eral

(G-2119)
SEVES GLASS BLOCK INC ✪
10576 Broadview Rd (44147-3227)
PHONE...................................440 627-6257
Anton Kava, *Managing Dir*
◆ EMP: 5 EST: 2016
SQ FT: 2,500
SALES: 150K **Privately Held**
SIC: 3299 Ornamental & architectural plas-
ter work

(G-2120)
**STEIN STEEL MILL SERVICES
INC**
1929 E Royalton Rd (44147-2867)
P.O. Box 470264 (44147-0264)
PHONE...................................440 526-9301
John Desmond, *President*
EMP: 18
SALES (est): 2.6MM **Privately Held**
SIC: 3295 Blast furnace slag

Brookfield
Trumbull County

(G-2121)
CNG FUELING LLC
1266 State Route 7 Ne F (44403-9200)
P.O. Box 4 (44403-0004)
PHONE...................................330 772-2403
Robert Nemeth, *Managing Prtnr*
Bob Nemeth, *General Mgr*
Ian Patterson, *Sales Staff*
EMP: 3
SALES (est): 360.3K **Privately Held**
SIC: 3824 Gasoline dispensing meters

(G-2122)
D & D LANDSCAPING INC
7012 Warren Sharon Rd (44403-9601)
PHONE...................................330 507-6647
Darryl Dickson, *President*
Dennis Dickson, *Vice Pres*
EMP: 3
SALES (est): 296.7K **Privately Held**
SIC: 0781 3531 Landscape services;
plows: construction, excavating & grading

(G-2123)
E-Z STOP SERVICE CENTER
Also Called: E-Z Label Co
354 Bedford Rd Se (44403-9727)
PHONE...................................330 448-2236
Frank Zurawsky, *Partner*
Dave Zurawsky, *Partner*
EMP: 60
SQ FT: 3,000
SALES (est): 5.1MM **Privately Held**
SIC: 2754 2671 Labels: gravure printing;
packaging paper & plastics film, coated &
laminated

(G-2124)
ENREVO PYRO LLC
6874 Strimbu Dr (44403-9557)
PHONE...................................203 517-5002
Philip Smith, *CEO*
EMP: 6 EST: 2012
SQ FT: 15,000
SALES (est): 198K **Privately Held**
SIC: 1311 2911 Coal pyrolysis; fractiona-
tion products of crude petroleum, hydro-
carbons

(G-2125)
IPSCO TUBULARS INC
6880 Parkway Dr (44403-9797)
PHONE...................................330 448-6772
EMP: 4
SALES (corp-wide): 454.7MM **Privately
Held**
SIC: 3498 Fabricated pipe & fittings

HQ: Ipsco Tubulars, Inc.
10120 Houston Oaks Dr
Houston TX 77064
281 949-1023

(G-2126)
SIGNS BY GEORGE
5815 Warren Sharon Rd (44403-9543)
PHONE...................................216 394-2095
Fax: 330 394-2095
George Hardin, *President*
Linda Hardin, *Corp Secy*
Dave Hardin, *Vice Pres*
EMP: 4
SALES (est): 371.6K **Privately Held**
SIC: 3993 2759 Electric signs; screen
printing

Brooklyn
Cuyahoga County

(G-2127)
AREWAY ACQUISITION INC
8525 Clinton Rd (44144-1014)
PHONE...................................216 651-9022
John Hadgis, *President*
EMP: 99
SQ FT: 100,000
SALES (est): 6.3MM **Privately Held**
SIC: 3471 Polishing, metals or formed
products

(G-2128)
AREWAY LLC
8525 Clinton Rd (44144-1014)
PHONE...................................216 651-9022
Fax: 216 634-2515
Ken Jordan, *QC Mgr*
Jeff Rabant, *Manager*
David Lazor, *Info Tech Mgr*
Gregory S Hadgis,
▲ EMP: 99
SALES (est): 28.8MM **Privately Held**
SIC: 3714 3541 Motor vehicle engines &
parts; motor vehicle transmissions, drive
assemblies & parts; buffing & polishing
machines

(G-2129)
JD NORMAN INDUSTRIES INC
4650 Tiedeman Rd (44144-2332)
PHONE...................................216 671-8000
Tim Reed, *Plant Mgr*
Chuck Wonsetler, *Engineer*
Justin Norman, *Branch Mgr*
EMP: 60
SALES (corp-wide): 128.5MM **Privately
Held**
SIC: 3469 3496 Metal stampings; miscel-
laneous fabricated wire products
PA: Jd Norman Industries, Inc.
787 W Belden Ave
Addison IL 60101
630 458-3700

Brooklyn Heights
Cuyahoga County

(G-2130)
**APPLIED METALS
TECHNOLOGIES**
1040 Valley Belt Rd (44131-1433)
PHONE...................................216 741-2440
Albert N Salvatore, *Principal*
EMP: 30
SQ FT: 30,000
SALES (est): 6.8MM **Privately Held**
SIC: 3541 Grinding machines, metalwork-
ing

(G-2131)
BEVERAGE ENGINEERING INC
4705 Van Epps Rd (44131-1013)
PHONE...................................216 641-6678
Paul L Csank, *Mng Member*
EMP: 3
SALES (est): 277.9K **Privately Held**
SIC: 3585 Beer dispensing equipment

(G-2132)
**BRILLIANT ELECTRIC SIGN CO
LTD**
4811 Van Epps Rd (44131-1082)
PHONE...................................216 741-3800
Fax: 216 741-3800
Rob Kraus, *Plant Mgr*
Skip Huber, *Foreman/Supr*
Lee Rodenfels, *Accounts Exec*
John Walsh, *Sales Staff*
James R Groh, *Mng Member*
EMP: 55
SQ FT: 55,000
SALES (est): 8MM **Privately Held**
WEB: www.brilliantsign.com
SIC: 3993 1799 Electric signs; sign instal-
lation & maintenance

(G-2133)
C T I AUDIO INC
220 Eastview Dr Ste 1 (44131-1039)
PHONE...................................440 593-1111
Fax: 440 593-5395
William Ross, *Ch of Bd*
Bob Eaton, *Chief Engr*
Gary Haythorn, *Controller*
Patti Bearce, *Credit Mgr*
Bonnie Todaro, *Human Res Dir*
EMP: 97
SQ FT: 70,000
SALES (est): 7.5MM **Privately Held**
SIC: 3651 Microphones; audio electronic
systems

(G-2134)
**CHALLENGER HARDWARE
COMPANY**
220 Eastview Dr Ste 102 (44131-1040)
P.O. Box 34001, Cleveland (44134-0701)
PHONE...................................216 591-1141
Joe Ross, *President*
▲ EMP: 12 EST: 2005
SALES (est): 2.1MM **Privately Held**
SIC: 3312 Stainless steel

(G-2135)
CI DISPOSITION CO
1000 Valley Belt Rd (44131-1433)
PHONE...................................216 587-5200
Fax: 216 587-5210
Richard N Bean, *Senior VP*
Gary Tarnowski, *Vice Pres*
Jeffrey Bahner, *Vice Pres*
Eric Lautzenheizer, *VP Sales*
Victor W Seifried, *Adv Mgr*
EMP: 38
SQ FT: 56,000
SALES (est): 8MM **Privately Held**
WEB: www.comptrolinc.com
SIC: 3699 5085 Linear accelerators; in-
dustrial supplies

(G-2136)
COVENTYA INC (DH)
4639 Van Epps Rd (44131-1049)
P.O. Box 751, Oriskany NY (13424-0751)
PHONE...................................216 351-1500
Eric Weyls, *President*
Lon Thrasher, *Exec VP*
Douglas Vogel, *Vice Pres*
Sam Polojack, *Plant Mgr*
Michael Wagner, *Opers Mgr*
▲ EMP: 45
SQ FT: 51,000
SALES (est): 11.9MM
SALES (corp-wide): 2.4MM **Privately
Held**
WEB: www.taskem.com
SIC: 2899 Chemical preparations; water
treating compounds
HQ: Coventya
7 Rue Du Cdt D Estienne D Orves
Villeneuve La Garenne 92390
147 157-300

(G-2137)
DAN NEMES AMERICAN RACING
4770 Van Epps Rd Ste 200b (44131-1031)
PHONE...................................216 749-4203
Dan Nemes, *Principal*
EMP: 5 EST: 2001
SALES (est): 340.8K **Privately Held**
SIC: 3312 Wheels

(G-2138)
DIE-MATIC CORPORATION
201 Eastview Dr (44131-1074)
PHONE...........................216 749-4656
Fax: 216 749-1160
Louie J Zeitler, *CEO*
Jerry Zeitler, *President*
John A Gorman, *Corp Secy*
Jerry Fellenstein, *Vice Pres*
Phil Fishman, *VP Mfg*
▲ EMP: 55 EST: 1958
SQ FT: 120,000
SALES (est): 16.9MM **Privately Held**
WEB: www.die-matic.com
SIC: 3469 3544 Metal stampings; special dies, tools, jigs & fixtures

(G-2139)
DIVERSIFIED AIR SYSTEMS INC (PA)
4760 Van Epps Rd (44131-1014)
PHONE...........................216 741-1700
Fax: 216 741-1700
Bob Lisi, *President*
Lisa Schoonover, *General Mgr*
Vincent Lisi, *Corp Secy*
Rita Ross, *Accounting Mgr*
Theresa Anderson, *Office Admin*
EMP: 20
SQ FT: 20,000
SALES (est): 12.2MM **Privately Held**
WEB: www.diversifiedair.com
SIC: 5084 5075 7694 Compressors, except air conditioning; compressors; air conditioning; armature rewinding shops

(G-2140)
GOODRICH CORPORATION
925 Keynote Cir Ste 300 (44131-1869)
PHONE...........................216 429-4655
Legrave Hamilton, *Branch Mgr*
Clinton Johnson, *Data Proc Exec*
EMP: 9
SALES (corp-wide): 57.2B **Publicly Held**
WEB: www.bfgoodrich.com
SIC: 3011 Tires & inner tubes
HQ: Goodrich Corporation
2730 W Tyvola Rd
Charlotte NC 28217
704 423-7000

(G-2141)
J & L BODY INC
4848 Van Epps Rd (44131-1016)
PHONE...........................216 661-2323
Fax: 216 661-2323
Mike Litteria, *President*
Rosemary Nelson, *Corp Secy*
Robert Daley, *Vice Pres*
EMP: 13
SQ FT: 16,000
SALES (est): 2.1MM **Privately Held**
SIC: 3715 7532 Truck trailers; truck painting & lettering; body shop, automotive

(G-2142)
MARLES BUSINESS SYSTEMS INC
Also Called: Marles Printing Company
1277 E Schaaf Rd (44131-1301)
P.O. Box 31478, Independence (44131-0478)
PHONE...........................440 268-8380
Fax: 216 961-8919
William Kelly, *President*
Meredith Klimaszewski, *Vice Pres*
EMP: 3
SALES (est): 744.2K **Privately Held**
SIC: 5112 2752 Business forms; commercial printing, offset

(G-2143)
NATIONAL FASTENERS INC
4581 Spring Rd (44131-1023)
PHONE...........................216 771-6473
William Fulop, *President*
EMP: 3
SALES (est): 648.3K **Privately Held**
SIC: 3399 Metal fasteners

(G-2144)
NORTH SHORE STRAPPING INC (PA)
1400 Valley Belt Rd (44131-1441)
PHONE...........................216 661-5200

Fax: 216 398-8560
Bridget A Leneghan, *President*
Kevin Leneghan, *Vice Pres*
Tony Leneghan, *Controller*
David M Leneghan, *Admin Sec*
▲ EMP: 50 EST: 1982
SQ FT: 225,000
SALES (est): 10.1MM **Privately Held**
SIC: 3081 3499 3312 2992 Unsupported plastics film & sheet; strapping, metal; wire products, steel or iron; lubricating oils & greases; enamels; lacquer: bases, dopes, thinner; lead pencils & art goods

(G-2145)
R&D MARKETING GROUP INC
Also Called: Proforma Signature Solutions
4597 Van Epps Rd (44131-1009)
PHONE...........................216 398-9100
Dave Mader, *President*
Tony Zayas, *Director*
EMP: 8 EST: 2011
SALES (est): 1.5MM **Privately Held**
SIC: 6794 2759 2752 Franchises, selling or licensing; commercial printing; commercial printing, lithographic

(G-2146)
RS INDUSTRIES INC
1455 E Schaaf Rd (44131-1321)
PHONE...........................216 524-2998
Fax: 216 524-0820
Nicholas J Russo Sr, *President*
Jason Snider, *General Mgr*
Nick Russo Jr, *CFO*
Deborah Russo, *Office Mgr*
Daniel Cook, *Manager*
EMP: 9
SALES (est): 1.3MM **Privately Held**
SIC: 5046 3556 Commercial cooking & food service equipment; food products machinery

(G-2147)
SPECTRUM INC
Also Called: Spectrum Infared
800 Resource Dr Ste 8 (44131-1875)
PHONE...........................440 951-6061
Daniel Ross, *President*
Jay Peet, *Vice Pres*
▲ EMP: 12
SALES (est): 2.5MM **Privately Held**
SIC: 3433 Gas infrared heating units

(G-2148)
TRIONETICS INC
4915 Van Epps Rd Ste B (44131-1017)
PHONE...........................216 812-3570
Eugene J Maitino, *President*
Colleen Maitino, *Office Mgr*
Tim Rusmanis, *Technology*
Allison Maitino, *Admin Asst*
EMP: 3
SQ FT: 10,800
SALES (est): 9MM **Privately Held**
SIC: 3589 Water treatment equipment, industrial

Brookpark
Cuyahoga County

(G-2149)
AM INDUSTRIAL GROUP LLC (PA)
16000 Commerce Park Dr (44142-2023)
PHONE...........................216 433-7171
Reginald Wyman, *Owner*
Luke Wootten, *Opers Mgr*
Craig Drever, *Foreman/Supr*
▲ EMP: 5
SQ FT: 5,000
SALES (est): 21.2MM **Privately Held**
WEB: www.amindustrial.com
SIC: 5084 1799 Industrial machinery & equipment; sawing & cutoff machines (metalworking machinery); rigging & scaffolding

(G-2150)
AMERICAN SOLVING INC
6519 Eastland Rd Ste 5 (44142-1347)
PHONE...........................440 234-7373
Fax: 440 234-9112

Orley Aten, *President*
Peter Bjork, *Managing Dir*
Richard Schmitt, *Area Mgr*
Andreas Bjork, *QC Mgr*
Markus M Ede, *Engineer*
▲ EMP: 6
SQ FT: 5,000
SALES (est): 510K **Privately Held**
WEB: www.americansolving.com
SIC: 3535 5084 Pneumatic tube conveyor systems; materials handling machinery; hoists

(G-2151)
AMPEX METAL PRODUCTS COMPANY (PA)
5581 W 164th St (44142-1513)
PHONE...........................216 267-9242
Fax: 216 267-1135
Andrew S Pastor, *President*
Robert Pastor, *Vice Pres*
R Hlavac, *Sales Mgr*
Beverly Pavlin, *Manager*
Gail Catcher, *Executive*
EMP: 30
SQ FT: 24,000
SALES (est): 6.6MM **Privately Held**
WEB: www.ampexmetal.com
SIC: 3469 3544 3452 3429 Metal stampings; special dies, tools, jigs & fixtures; bolts, nuts, rivets & washers; manufactured hardware (general)

(G-2152)
AXENT GRAPHICS LLC
6270 Engle Rd (44142-2106)
PHONE...........................216 362-7560
F David Weber,
F Weber,
EMP: 3
SALES (est): 290K **Privately Held**
SIC: 2759 Promotional printing; screen printing

(G-2153)
CLEVELAND INSTRUMENT CORP
6430 Eastland Rd Ste 2 (44142-1340)
PHONE...........................440 826-1800
Fax: 440 826-1649
Ryan Sullivan, *President*
EMP: 4
SQ FT: 4,000
SALES (est): 350K **Privately Held**
WEB: www.clevelandinstrument.com
SIC: 3728 3823 8734 Aircraft parts & equipment; industrial instrmnts msrmnt display/control process variable; testing laboratories

(G-2154)
CRITERION TOOL & DIE INC
Also Called: Criterion Instrument
5349 W 161st St (44142-1609)
PHONE...........................216 267-1733
Fax: 216 267-4542
Tanya Disalvo, *President*
Nilda Feliciano, *General Mgr*
Dennis M Ondercin, *Vice Pres*
Mike Pinchot, *QC Mgr*
Debi Montz, *Marketing Staff*
EMP: 40 EST: 1953
SQ FT: 20,000
SALES (est): 5.5MM **Privately Held**
WEB: www.criteriontool.com
SIC: 3599 3544 3541 Machine shop, jobbing & repair; special dies, tools, jigs & fixtures; machine tools, metal cutting type

(G-2155)
CUSTOM FLOATERS LLC
5161 W 161st St (44142-1604)
PHONE...........................216 337-9118
Dianne Malone, *Administration*
EMP: 5 EST: 2012
SALES (est): 590.7K **Privately Held**
SIC: 3465 Body parts, automobile: stamped metal

(G-2156)
DD FOUNDRY INC (PA)
15583 Brookpark Rd (44142-1618)
PHONE...........................216 362-4100
Fax: 216 481-8903
David Dolata, *CEO*
Jerry Kovatch, *President*

David Zanto, *COO*
Sandra Catlett, *CFO*
Eric Engel, *Manager*
▲ EMP: 101 EST: 1946
SQ FT: 80,000
SALES (est): 38.1MM **Privately Held**
WEB: www.precisionmetalsmiths.com
SIC: 3364 3324 3369 3365 Nonferrous die-castings except aluminum; commercial investment castings, ferrous; nonferrous foundries; aluminum foundries; steel foundries; gray & ductile iron foundries

(G-2157)
DRIVE COMPONENTS
6519 Eastland Rd Ste 106 (44142-1349)
PHONE...........................440 234-6200
Bud Zollars, *Manager*
▲ EMP: 5
SALES (est): 632.3K **Privately Held**
SIC: 3568 Power transmission equipment

(G-2158)
E L MUSTEE & SONS INC (PA)
5431 W 164th St (44142-1586)
PHONE...........................216 267-3100
Fax: 216 267-9997
Kevin Mustee, *President*
Henry Dutton, *President*
Bob Mustee, *Plant Mgr*
Steve Chomyk, *Purch Agent*
Ed Kenney, *Engineer*
▼ EMP: 86 EST: 1932
SQ FT: 140,000
SALES (est): 19.2MM **Privately Held**
WEB: www.elmustee.com
SIC: 3088 Plastics plumbing fixtures; tubs (bath, shower & laundry), plastic; shower stalls, fiberglass & plastic; bathroom fixtures, plastic

(G-2159)
FIREHOUSE SIGN CO INC
5241 W 161st St (44142-1606)
PHONE...........................216 267-5300
Fax: 440 260-7446
Scott Hales, *President*
EMP: 4
SQ FT: 2,400
SALES (est): 200K **Privately Held**
SIC: 3993 Signs & advertising specialties

(G-2160)
FORD MOTOR COMPANY
17601 Brookpark Rd (44142-1518)
P.O. Box 9900, Cleveland (44142)
PHONE...........................216 676-3989
Fax: 216 676-2503
Mike Felix, *Plant Mgr*
Randy Dougall, *Safety Mgr*
Kevin Joniak, *QC Mgr*
Andrew Kitral, *Engineer*
Mark Tiberia, *Controller*
EMP: 2832
SQ FT: 2,320,000
SALES (corp-wide): 151.8B **Publicly Held**
WEB: www.ford.com
SIC: 3714 3321 Motor vehicle parts & accessories; gray & ductile iron foundries
PA: Ford Motor Company
1 American Rd
Dearborn MI 48126
313 322-3000

(G-2161)
FOSBEL INC (HQ)
Also Called: Cetek
20600 Sheldon Rd (44142-1319)
PHONE...........................216 362-3900
Fax: 216 362-3901
Derek Scott, *President*
Sarah Burton, *CFO*
Kathlene Stevens, *CFO*
June Toddy, *CFO*
◆ EMP: 120
SALES (est): 28.2MM **Privately Held**
SIC: 7629 7692 Electrical repair shops; welding repair
PA: Fosbel Holding, Inc.
20600 Sheldon Rd
Cleveland OH 44142
216 362-3900

(G-2162)
GREENKOTE USA INC
6435 Eastland Rd (44142-1305)
PHONE......................................440 243-2865
Jaime Camacho, *Plant Mgr*
James Thomson, *CFO*
Mark Gore, *Director*
▲ **EMP:** 8
SALES (est): 1.3MM **Privately Held**
SIC: 3479 Coating of metals & formed
products

(G-2163)
H&M MTAL STAMPING ASSEMBLY INC
5325 W 140th St (44142-1759)
PHONE......................................216 898-9030
Kathryn Mabin, *President*
Lenny Hull, *Mfg Staff*
EMP: 11
SALES (est): 1.3MM **Privately Held**
SIC: 3469 Stamping metal for the trade

(G-2164)
INDUSTRIAL GRINDERS CO INC
Also Called: Industrial Grinders Machining
5261 W 137th St (44142-1810)
PHONE......................................440 237-2600
Fax: 440 237-3259
Tom Kelly, *President*
Andy Lubert, *Controller*
Gary Schreiber, *Shareholder*
EMP: 18 **EST:** 1955
SQ FT: 20,000
SALES (est): 2.4MM **Privately Held**
SIC: 3599 Machine shop, jobbing & repair

(G-2165)
K-M-S INDUSTRIES INC
Also Called: K.M.S.
6519 Eastland Rd Ste 1 (44142-1347)
PHONE......................................440 243-6680
Fax: 440 243-5667
Gerald Korman, *President*
Richard Malone Jr, *Vice Pres*
Diane Malone, *Treasurer*
Kay Teresa, *Controller*
Kay Bailey, *Manager*
EMP: 30
SQ FT: 25,000
SALES (est): 5.6MM **Privately Held**
SIC: 3599 5531 7692 Machine shop, job-
bing & repair; automotive parts; automo-
tive accessories; welding repair

(G-2166)
LAKE ERIE GRAPHICS INC
5372 W 130th St (44142-1801)
PHONE......................................216 575-1333
Fax: 216 265-0055
James K Dietz, *President*
Brain Karlak, *Prdtn Mgr*
Jim Young, *Accounts Exec*
Bob Sindelar, *Manager*
EMP: 30
SQ FT: 25,000
SALES (est): 5.9MM **Privately Held**
WEB: www.lakeeriegraphics.com
SIC: 2752 Commercial printing, offset

(G-2167)
MORSELICIOUS CUPCAKES
17341 Independence Ct (44142-3532)
PHONE......................................216 408-7508
Tina Filipkowski, *Principal*
EMP: 4 **EST:** 2010
SALES (est): 216.6K **Privately Held**
SIC: 2051 Bread, cake & related products

(G-2168)
PRINTING CONNECTION INC
5221 W 161st St (44142-1606)
PHONE......................................216 898-4878
Fax: 216 898-4891
Frank Metro, *Principal*
EMP: 6 **EST:** 2009
SALES (est): 688.7K **Privately Held**
SIC: 2752 Commercial printing, litho-
graphic

(G-2169)
ROLL-IN SAW INC
15851 Commerce Park Dr (44142-2020)
PHONE......................................216 459-9001
Fax: 216 459-9220

Donald Borman, *President*
Michael Solether, *Treasurer*
Charmaine Kizzer, *Manager*
▼ **EMP:** 10
SQ FT: 15,000
SALES (est): 1.4MM **Privately Held**
WEB: www.rollinsaw.com
SIC: 3541 Sawing & cutoff machines (met-
alworking machinery)

(G-2170)
SUPERCHARGER SYSTEMS INC
5300 W 140th St (44142-1758)
PHONE......................................216 676-5800
Timothy Fitch, *President*
EMP: 4
SQ FT: 22,000
SALES (est): 475.9K **Privately Held**
SIC: 5531 3714 Automotive parts; auto-
motive accessories; motor vehicle en-
gines & parts; axles, motor vehicle; drive
shafts, motor vehicle; motor vehicle body
components & frame

(G-2171)
VARIETY PRINTING
5707 Van Wert Ave (44142-2575)
PHONE......................................216 676-9815
Mike Fairley, *Principal*
EMP: 4
SALES (est): 362.5K **Privately Held**
SIC: 2752 Commercial printing, litho-
graphic

(G-2172)
WESTSIDE SUPPLY CO INC
5010 W 140th St (44142-1754)
PHONE......................................216 267-9353
Fax: 216 267-3823
William Swann, *President*
Bonnie McGgie, *Manager*
EMP: 4
SQ FT: 5,000
SALES (est): 679.6K **Privately Held**
SIC: 3548 Welding apparatus

Brookville
Montgomery County

(G-2173)
ADMARK PRINTING INC
310 Sycamore St (45309-1731)
PHONE......................................937 833-5111
Fax: 937 833-4627
Patrick J Bruchs, *President*
EMP: 6
SQ FT: 15,000
SALES (est): 853.6K **Privately Held**
SIC: 2752 Commercial printing, litho-
graphic

(G-2174)
ANTIQUE AUTO SHEET METAL INC
718 Albert Rd (45309-9202)
PHONE......................................937 833-4422
Fax: 937 833-4785
Raymond Gollahon, *President*
Donna Gollahon, *Corp Secy*
Lisa Lingerich, *Manager*
EMP: 40
SQ FT: 21,000
SALES (est): 6.8MM **Privately Held**
SIC: 3465 3711 3444 Automotive stamp-
ings; body parts, automobile: stamped
metal; motor vehicles & car bodies; sheet
metalwork

(G-2175)
ARLINGTON PRCSION GRINDING LLC
8909 Arlington Rd (45309-7626)
PHONE......................................937 833-1553
Theodore J Yantis, *Principal*
EMP: 3
SALES (est): 200K **Privately Held**
SIC: 3599 Grinding castings for the trade

(G-2176)
BROOKVILLE ROADSTER INC
718 Albert Rd (45309-9202)
PHONE......................................937 833-4605
Ray Gollahon, *President*

Lisa Lengerich, *Financial Exec*
Alan George, *Sales Staff*
Pete George, *Sales Staff*
EMP: 40
SALES (est): 5.8MM **Privately Held**
WEB: www.brookvilleroadster.com
SIC: 3711 5013 Automobile assembly, in-
cluding specialty automobiles; automotive
supplies & parts

(G-2177)
BROOKVILLE STAR
14 Mulberry St (45309-1828)
P.O. Box 100 (45309-0100)
PHONE......................................937 833-2545
John Gordon, *President*
Julie Harrison, *Corp Secy*
Jean Gordon, *Vice Pres*
EMP: 5
SQ FT: 4,800
SALES (est): 340K **Privately Held**
SIC: 2711 2752 Newspapers; commercial
printing, lithographic

(G-2178)
CONTEMPORARY CABINETS INC
175 Carr Dr (45309-1924)
PHONE......................................937 833-1135
Fax: 937 833-1122
Douglas Shafner, *President*
EMP: 3
SQ FT: 6,500
SALES (est): 415.2K **Privately Held**
SIC: 2434 5211 1751 Wood kitchen cabi-
nets; cabinets, kitchen; cabinet & finish
carpentry

(G-2179)
CYCLE ELECTRIC INC
8734 Dyton Grenville Pike (45309-9232)
P.O. Box 81, Englewood (45322-0081)
PHONE......................................937 884-7300
Fax: 937 884-5542
Karl Fahringer, *President*
Roxanne Fahringer, *Vice Pres*
EMP: 15
SQ FT: 8,000
SALES (est): 2MM **Privately Held**
SIC: 3694 Generators, automotive & air-
craft; voltage regulators, automotive

(G-2180)
D M TOOL & PLASTICS INC
11150 Baltimore (45309)
PHONE......................................937 962-4140
Fax: 937 884-5583
Pat Meyer, *Manager*
EMP: 15
SALES (corp-wide): 4.2MM **Privately
Held**
WEB: www.bulldogtools.com
SIC: 3089 3599 Injection molding of plas-
tics; machine shop, jobbing & repair
PA: D M Tool & Plastics, Inc.
4140 Us Route 40 E
Lewisburg OH 45338
937 962-4140

(G-2181)
DIGISOFT SYSTEMS CORPORATION
4520 Clayton Rd (45309-9332)
PHONE......................................937 833-5016
Gary E Brazier, *President*
Betty L Brazier, *Treasurer*
Christopher F Cowan, *Admin Sec*
EMP: 7
SQ FT: 600
SALES (est): 390.6K **Privately Held**
SIC: 7372 Prepackaged software

(G-2182)
ELLIOTT MFG CO
407 Albert Rd (45309-9201)
P.O. Box 255 (45309-0255)
PHONE......................................937 833-4430
Fax: 937 833-4431
Milton John Elliott, *President*
Sandra Elliott, *Admin Sec*
EMP: 14
SQ FT: 5,040
SALES: 1.6MM **Privately Held**
SIC: 3089 3544 Injection molding of plas-
tics; industrial molds

(G-2183)
FLOW DRY TECHNOLOGY INC (HQ)
379 Albert Rd (45309-9247)
P.O. Box 190 (45309-0190)
PHONE......................................937 833-2161
Douglas Leconey, *President*
Marty Kilberg, *Plant Mgr*
Csaba Gonter, *Opers Mgr*
Bob Swearingen, *Prdtn Mgr*
Tim Eustache, *Maint Spvr*
▲ **EMP:** 111
SQ FT: 65,000
SALES (est): 29.2MM
SALES (corp-wide): 33.2MM **Privately
Held**
SIC: 3053 2834 Gasket materials; drug-
gists' preparations (pharmaceuticals)
PA: Argosy Investment Partners Iv, L.P.
950 W Valley Rd Ste 2900
Wayne PA 19087
610 971-9685

(G-2184)
FTD INVESTMENTS LLC
Also Called: Flow Dry Technology, LLC
379 Albert Rd (45309-9247)
P.O. Box 190 (45309-0190)
PHONE......................................937 833-2161
Doug Le, *Principal*
EMP: 186 **EST:** 2006
SQ FT: 65,000
SALES (est): 18.8MM
SALES (corp-wide): 153.2MM **Privately
Held**
SIC: 3714 2834 Air conditioner parts,
motor vehicle; druggists' preparations
(pharmaceuticals)
PA: Blackstreet Capital Management, Llc
5425 Wisconsin Ave # 701
Chevy Chase MD 20815
240 223-1330

(G-2185)
GREEN TOKAI CO LTD (HQ)
Also Called: GTC
55 Robert Wright Dr (45309-1931)
PHONE......................................937 833-5444
Daniel Bowers, *President*
Harumitsu Yamamoto, *Corp Secy*
Dan Dowers, *Vice Pres*
Victor Wenzel, *Engineer*
Ed Creffs, *Manager*
◆ **EMP:** 525
SQ FT: 246,000
SALES (est): 191.7MM
SALES (corp-wide): 321.2MM **Privately
Held**
SIC: 3714 3069 Motor vehicle body com-
ponents & frame; rubber automotive prod-
ucts
PA: Tokai Kogyo Co.,Ltd.
4-1, Naganecho
Obu AIC 474-0
562 441-500

(G-2186)
HELLER ACQUISITIONS INC
Also Called: Life Time Embroidery
912 Salem St (45309-8226)
PHONE......................................937 833-2676
Karen Heller, *President*
Tim Heller, *President*
EMP: 3
SALES: 100K **Privately Held**
SIC: 7389 2395 7336 Embroidering of ad-
vertising on shirts, etc.; embroidery & art
needlework; silk screen design

(G-2187)
IMAGE PAVEMENT MAINTENANCE
425 Carr Dr (45309-1935)
P.O. Box 157 (45309-0157)
PHONE......................................937 833-9200
Fax: 937 833-9400
Michael Gartrell, *President*
EMP: 42
SALES (est): 4.3MM **Privately Held**
SIC: 1611 2951 1799 1771 Surfacing &
paving; asphalt paving mixtures & blocks;
parking lot maintenance; driveway con-
tractor; sweeping service: road, airport,
parking lot, etc.; tennis court construction

(G-2188)
MAR CHELE INC (PA)
Also Called: Pretzel Fest
18 Market St (45309-1815)
PHONE..................937 833-3400
Fax: 937 833-6846
Brad Good, *President*
Michelle Good, *Vice Pres*
EMP: 5
SQ FT: 1,500
SALES (est): 2.7MM **Privately Held**
SIC: 2052 Pretzels

(G-2189)
MARIETTA MARTIN MATERIALS INC
Also Called: Phillipsburg Quarry
9843 Dyton Grenville Pike (45309-8210)
PHONE..................919 781-4550
Rodney Wolford, *Manager*
EMP: 10
SALES (corp-wide): 3.8B **Publicly Held**
WEB: www.martinmarietta.com
SIC: 1442 Construction sand & gravel
PA: Martin Marietta Materials Inc
2710 Wycliff Rd
Raleigh NC 27607
919 781-4550

(G-2190)
MARIETTA MARTIN MATERIALS INC
Also Called: Martin Marietta Aggregates
9843 State Route 49 (45309-8210)
PHONE..................937 884-5814
Fax: 937 884-7703
Rodney Wolford, *Manager*
Rodney Wollford, *Manager*
EMP: 12
SALES (corp-wide): 3.8B **Publicly Held**
WEB: www.martinmarietta.com
SIC: 1422 Limestones, ground
PA: Martin Marietta Materials Inc
2710 Wycliff Rd
Raleigh NC 27607
919 781-4550

(G-2191)
MATERIALS ENGINEERING & DEV
11150 Bltmr Phlpsburg Rd (45309)
PHONE..................937 884-5118
Tracy Slemker, *President*
Dennis Meyer, *Vice Pres*
Dave Thompson, *Shareholder*
EMP: 3
SQ FT: 35,000
SALES: 150K **Privately Held**
SIC: 3842 Prosthetic appliances; limbs, artificial

(G-2192)
MC GREGOR & ASSOCIATES INC
365 Carr Dr (45309-1921)
PHONE..................937 833-6768
Fax: 937 833-4002
Larry McGregor, *President*
Don Wurst, *Vice Pres*
Steve Adams, *Finance*
Kathy Drinnon, *Human Resources*
Greg Wartinger, *Sales Dir*
▲ EMP: 120
SQ FT: 16,000
SALES (est): 14.5MM **Privately Held**
SIC: 3679 Electronic circuits

(G-2193)
MCGREGOR-SURMOUNT CORPORATION
365 Carr Dr (45309-1921)
PHONE..................937 833-6768
Fax: 937 833-0302
Larry Mc Gregor, *CEO*
Jim Bulach, *Export Mgr*
Jill Strunk, *Buyer*
Kevin Terry, *Engineer*
Elisa Snell, *Human Resources*
EMP: 190
SQ FT: 11,040
SALES (est): 39.2MM **Privately Held**
WEB: www.mcgregor-surmount.com
SIC: 3629 3672 Electronic generation equipment; printed circuit boards

(G-2194)
NORGREN INC
Also Called: IMI Precision
325 Carr Dr (45309-1929)
PHONE..................937 833-4033
Michael Vinski, *Branch Mgr*
Sheila Campbell, *Manager*
EMP: 147
SALES (corp-wide): 2B **Privately Held**
WEB: www.norgren.com
SIC: 3625 Actuators, industrial
HQ: Norgren, Inc.
5400 S Delaware St
Littleton CO 80120
303 794-5000

(G-2195)
PARKER AIRCRAFT SALES
212 Church St (45309-1407)
PHONE..................937 833-4820
Jeff Parker, *Owner*
EMP: 4
SALES (est): 250K **Privately Held**
WEB: www.parkeraircraft.com
SIC: 3724 Research & development on aircraft engines & parts

(G-2196)
PETERS CABINETRY
8766 N County Line Rd (45309-9511)
PHONE..................937 884-7514
Gary L Peters, *Owner*
EMP: 3
SALES (est): 267.8K **Privately Held**
SIC: 2434 Wood kitchen cabinets

(G-2197)
PROVIMI NORTH AMERICA INC (DH)
Also Called: Nutrition Transportation Svcs
10 Collective Way (45309-8878)
PHONE..................937 770-2400
Charles Shininger, *President*
Ken Bryant, *Vice Pres*
Kenneth Bryant, *Vice Pres*
Kyle Bryant, *Plant Mgr*
Scott Swenson, *Plant Mgr*
◆ EMP: 253
SALES (est): 211MM
SALES (corp-wide): 107.1B **Privately Held**
WEB: www.vigortone.com
SIC: 2048 5191 Prepared feeds; animal feeds
HQ: Cargill The Netherlands Holding B.V.
Evert Van De Beekstraat 378
Luchthaven Schiphol 1118
205 006-000

(G-2198)
R & J TOOL INC
10550 Upper Lewisburg (45309)
P.O. Box 118 (45309-0118)
PHONE..................937 833-3200
Fax: 937 833-3221
Richard Rohrer, *President*
Marilyn K Rohrer, *Vice Pres*
EMP: 10
SQ FT: 5,000
SALES (est): 1MM **Privately Held**
SIC: 3545 Cutting tools for machine tools

Brownsville
Licking County

(G-2199)
MIDLAND OIL CO
14687 National Rd Se (43721)
P.O. Box 43 (43721-0043)
PHONE..................740 787-2557
EMP: 3 EST: 1916
SALES: 60K **Privately Held**
SIC: 1311 Oil & Gas Producers

Brunswick
Medina County

(G-2200)
A G INDUSTRIES INC
2963 Interstate Pkwy (44212-4327)
PHONE..................330 220-0050
Albert Gawel, *President*
Josephine Gawel, *Manager*
EMP: 11
SQ FT: 4,000
SALES (est): 1.8MM **Privately Held**
SIC: 3544 Special dies, tools, jigs & fixtures

(G-2201)
A POP OF ELEGANCE LLC
4955 Neura Pkwy (44212-4741)
PHONE..................330 225-4724
Sheila Chamberlain, *Partner*
Erin Kensiki, *Partner*
Mollie Lockwood,
EMP: 5
SALES (est): 110K **Privately Held**
SIC: 2051 Cakes, pies & pastries

(G-2202)
A RAYMOND TINNERMAN MFG INC (DH)
1060 W 130th St (44212-2316)
P.O. Box 10 (44212-0010)
PHONE..................330 220-5179
Dan Kerr, *President*
Dan Dolan, *COO*
Charlese Lee, *Vice Pres*
Mike Lingo, *Vice Pres*
Jim Stith, *Plant Mgr*
EMP: 50
SQ FT: 43,000
SALES (est): 67.7MM **Privately Held**
WEB: www.tinnermanpalnut.com
SIC: 3965 Fasteners
HQ: A Raymond Gerance
129 Cours Berriat
Grenoble 38000
476 334-949

(G-2203)
AKRI TOOL CORPORATION
2927 Nationwide Pkwy (44212-2365)
PHONE..................440 237-3050
Fax: 440 237-3051
Dale Lotenero, *President*
George Felton, *Manager*
EMP: 12
SALES (est): 800K **Privately Held**
SIC: 3599 Machine shop, jobbing & repair

(G-2204)
ALPHA SINTERED METALS LLC
Also Called: Precision Made Products
1126 Industrial Pkwy N (44212-5606)
PHONE..................330 220-5800
Chad Gamble, *Prdtn Mgr*
Steve Carnahan, *QC Mgr*
Michael Roth, *Engineer*
Jessica Rogers, *Accounts Mgr*
EMP: 14
SALES (corp-wide): 5.3B **Publicly Held**
SIC: 3443 Fabricated plate work (boiler shop)
HQ: Alpha Sintered Metals, Llc
95 Mason Run Rd
Ridgway PA 15853
814 773-3191

(G-2205)
ALTERNATIVE SURFACE GRINDING
Also Called: Ring Masters
1093 Industrial Pkwy N (44212-4319)
PHONE..................330 273-3443
Kent Shutey, *President*
Dale Jarvis, *General Mgr*
EMP: 30
SALES (est): 3MM **Privately Held**
SIC: 3053 Gaskets, packing & sealing devices

(G-2206)
AVA GRAPHIX
3693 Walters Dr (44212-2744)
PHONE..................216 409-8646

Amy Von Alt, *Principal*
EMP: 3 EST: 2010
SALES (est): 257.4K **Privately Held**
SIC: 3577 Printers & plotters

(G-2207)
AVION MANUFACTURING COMPANY
2950 Westway Dr Ste 106 (44212-5666)
PHONE..................330 220-1989
Fax: 330 220-3709
Mark Ratliff, *President*
Marilyn Olah, *Office Mgr*
EMP: 4
SQ FT: 6,000
SALES (est): 689K **Privately Held**
WEB: www.avionmfg.com
SIC: 2851 3469 Paints & paint additives; machine parts, stamped or pressed metal

(G-2208)
AXESS INTERNATIONAL LLC
4641 Stag Thicket Ln (44212-5800)
PHONE..................330 460-4840
Tawfik Kashou,
EMP: 5
SALES (est): 519.8K **Privately Held**
SIC: 2522 Office furniture, except wood

(G-2209)
B & B TROPHIES & AWARDS
1317 Pearl Rd (44212-2880)
PHONE..................330 225-6193
Fax: 330 225-0833
Michael Sinclair, *Owner*
EMP: 4 EST: 1976
SALES (est): 263.5K **Privately Held**
SIC: 3914 5999 2796 Trophies; trophies & plaques; engraving on copper, steel, wood or rubber; printing plates

(G-2210)
BAKERS CHOICE DISTRIBUTING
4794 Whiteoaks Dr (44212-2448)
PHONE..................330 273-5745
James Marston, *President*
EMP: 8 EST: 1994
SALES (est): 630K **Privately Held**
SIC: 2051 Bread, cake & related products

(G-2211)
BARANY JEWELRY INC
3702 Center Rd (44212-4429)
PHONE..................330 220-4367
Elizabeth A Schlauch, *President*
Melvyn Schlauch, *Admin Sec*
EMP: 4 EST: 1969
SQ FT: 1,200
SALES: 400K **Privately Held**
WEB: www.baranyjewelers.com
SIC: 5944 7631 3911 Jewelry stores; jewelry repair services; jewelry, precious metal

(G-2212)
BEST PROCESS SOLUTIONS INC
1071 Industrial Pkwy N (44212-4319)
PHONE..................330 220-1440
Mike Desalvo, *President*
EMP: 30
SALES (est): 4.3MM **Privately Held**
SIC: 3441 Fabricated structural metal

(G-2213)
BLACKHAWK INDUSTRIES
2845 Interstate Pkwy (44212-4326)
PHONE..................918 610-4719
Bill Scheller, *Principal*
Dave Bronson, *Regional Mgr*
EMP: 14 EST: 2013
SALES (est): 1.8MM **Privately Held**
SIC: 3999 Manufacturing industries

(G-2214)
BULLSEYE ACTIVEWEAR INC
2947 Nationwide Pkwy (44212-2365)
PHONE..................330 220-1720
Fax: 330 220-1729
Susan Heiser, *President*
Jim Heiser, *Vice Pres*
Debbie Bode, *Bookkeeper*
EMP: 5

SALES: 460K **Privately Held**
WEB: www.bullseyeactivewear.com
SIC: 2759 Screen printing

(G-2215)
CCL LABEL INC
Also Called: CCL Design
2845 Center Rd (44212-2331)
PHONE.............................440 878-7000
Dean Discenza, *Mfg Mgr*
John Walsh, *Branch Mgr*
EMP: 40
SALES (corp-wide): 188.4K **Privately Held**
WEB: www.avery.com
SIC: 2672 3081 3497 2678 Adhesive papers, labels or tapes: from purchased material; gummed paper: made from purchased materials; coated paper, except photographic, carbon or abrasive; unsupported plastics film & sheet; metal foil & leaf; notebooks: made from purchased paper
HQ: Ccl Label, Inc.
　161 Worcester Rd Ste 504
　Framingham MA 01701
　508 872-4511

(G-2216)
CHALFANT MANUFACTURING COMPANY (DH)
50 Pearl Rd Ste 212 (44212-5704)
PHONE.............................330 273-3510
Gloria Slaga, *CEO*
John Slaga, *President*
F A Lennie, *Principal*
Carl W Schaefer, *Principal*
Richard C Schaefer, *Principal*
▼ **EMP:** 7
SQ FT: 55,000
SALES (est): 3MM
SALES (corp-wide): 672.8K **Privately Held**
SIC: 3643 Current-carrying wiring devices
HQ: Obo Bettermann Gmbh & Co. Kg
　Huingser Ring 52
　Menden (Sauerland) 58710
　237 389-0

(G-2217)
COLUMBIA CHEMICAL CORPORATION
1000 Western Dr (44212-4330)
PHONE.............................330 225-3200
Fax: 330 225-1499
Brett Larick, *President*
Herbert H Geduld, *Principal*
D J Hudak, *Principal*
William E Rosenberg, *Principal*
Jeff Grodecki, *Manager*
◆ **EMP:** 22
SALES (est): 8.4MM **Privately Held**
WEB: www.columbiachemical.com
SIC: 2819 Zinc chloride; tin (stannic/stannous) compounds or salts, inorganic

(G-2218)
COMPONENT MFG & DESIGN
3121 Interstate Pkwy (44212-4329)
P.O. Box 845 (44212-0845)
PHONE.............................330 225-8080
Fax: 330 225-8777
Edward C Crist, *President*
Carol McIntyre, *Manager*
EMP: 15
SQ FT: 12,000
SALES (est): 3.1MM **Privately Held**
WEB: www.cmd-tip.com
SIC: 3559 Plastics working machinery

(G-2219)
D C SYSTEMS INC
1251 Industrial Pkwy N (44212-2341)
PHONE.............................330 273-3030
Fax: 330 273-3309
Thomas E Schira, *President*
Katherine Schira, *Corp Secy*
EMP: 10
SQ FT: 22,600
SALES (est): 3.6MM **Privately Held**
SIC: 5063 3692 7699 3629 Batteries; batteries, dry cell; dry cell batteries, single or multiple cell; battery service & repair; battery chargers, rectifying or nonrotating

(G-2220)
DESTINY MANUFACTURING INC
2974 Interstate Pkwy (44212-4323)
PHONE.............................330 273-9000
Josef Schuessler, *President*
Reinhold Rock, *Corp Secy*
Bernard Karthan, *Vice Pres*
Michael Schuessler, *VP Sales*
Debbie Haber, *Manager*
▼ **EMP:** 35
SQ FT: 100,000
SALES (est): 12.4MM **Privately Held**
WEB: www.destinymfg.com
SIC: 3469 3399 Appliance parts, porcelain enameled; metal powders, pastes & flakes

(G-2221)
DIE-MENSION CORPORATION
3020 Nationwide Pkwy (44212-2360)
PHONE.............................330 273-5872
Fax: 330 273-8275
Karen Thompson, *President*
Rick Thompson, *Vice Pres*
▼ **EMP:** 12
SQ FT: 14,250
SALES: 1.6MM **Privately Held**
WEB: www.diemension.com
SIC: 3544 3469 Special dies & tools; metal stampings

(G-2222)
DYNAMIC BAR CODE SYSTEMS INC
3139 Ipswich Ct (44212-5645)
PHONE.............................330 220-5451
Bill Gregory Jr, *President*
Leslie Gregory, *Vice Pres*
EMP: 3
SQ FT: 1,300
SALES: 455K **Privately Held**
WEB: www.dynamicbarcode.com
SIC: 3565 Labeling machines, industrial

(G-2223)
ELECTRODUCT LLC
1126 Industrial Pkwy N (44212-5606)
PHONE.............................330 220-9300
EMP: 20
SQ FT: 20,000
SALES (est): 152.1K **Privately Held**
SIC: 3315 Mfg Steel Wire/Related Products

(G-2224)
FEDERAL-MOGUL VALVE TRAIN INTE
1035 Western Dr (44212-4331)
PHONE.............................330 628-6700
Fax: 330 628-6705
Mike Liebhardt, *Branch Mgr*
EMP: 20
SALES (corp-wide): 16.3B **Publicly Held**
WEB: www.trw.mediaroom.com
SIC: 3469 Metal stampings
HQ: Federal-Mogul Valve Train International Llc
　27300 W 11 Mile Rd
　Southfield MI 48034
　248 354-7700

(G-2225)
FORMATECH INC
3024 Interstate Pkwy (44212-4324)
PHONE.............................330 273-2800
Fax: 330 273-5605
Craig F Wahl, *President*
Joseph Thuener, *General Mgr*
Steve Lampshire, *Prdtn Mgr*
Lora Volpe, *Accounts Exec*
Jeff Wahl, *Mktg Dir*
▲ **EMP:** 20
SALES (est): 4.2MM **Privately Held**
WEB: www.formatechexhibits.com
SIC: 2542 2541 Counters or counter display cases: except wood; counters or counter display cases, wood

(G-2226)
FREE BIRD PUBLICATIONS LTD
1410 S Carptr Rd Apt 238 (44212)
PHONE.............................216 673-0229
Chantelle Drake, *CEO*
EMP: 3

SALES: 10K **Privately Held**
SIC: 2741 Miscellaneous publishing

(G-2227)
FREMAR INDUSTRIES INC
2808 Westway Dr (44212-5656)
PHONE.............................330 220-3700
Marcus Bauman, *CEO*
Donald Brandt, *President*
Janice Doring, *Manager*
▼ **EMP:** 30
SQ FT: 26,000
SALES (est): 5.3MM **Privately Held**
SIC: 3544 Dies, plastics forming; forms (molds), for foundry & plastics working machinery

(G-2228)
GALLEY PRINTING INC
Also Called: Galley Printing Company
2892 Westway Dr (44212-5656)
PHONE.............................330 220-5577
Fax: 330 220-5579
Richard Stitch, *CEO*
Barbara Stitch, *Corp Secy*
Deb Bernard, *Human Res Dir*
EMP: 25
SALES (est): 5.8MM **Privately Held**
SIC: 2752 Commercial printing, offset

(G-2229)
GEM INSTRUMENT CO
2832 Nationwide Pkwy (44212-2362)
P.O. Box 830 (44212-0830)
PHONE.............................330 273-6117
Fax: 330 273-4949
Spiras Arfaras, *President*
Joan Arfaras, *Vice Pres*
EMP: 15
SQ FT: 10,000
SALES (est): 1.4MM **Privately Held**
WEB: www.gem-instrument.com
SIC: 3823 3829 Digital displays of process variables; measuring & controlling devices

(G-2230)
GRIND-ALL CORPORATION
1113 Industrial Pkwy N (44212-2371)
PHONE.............................330 220-1600
Fax: 330 220-1640
Henry Matousek Sr, *President*
Mark Marcinowski, *General Mgr*
Chris Pekar, *General Mgr*
Mary Matousek, *Corp Secy*
Deborah Donze, *Vice Pres*
EMP: 48
SALES (est): 9MM **Privately Held**
WEB: www.grindall.com
SIC: 3541 Grinding machines, metalworking; honing & lapping machines

(G-2231)
GROENEVELD ATLANTIC SOUTH
1130 Industrial Pkwy N # 7 (44212-5605)
PHONE.............................330 225-4949
Yan Isscs, *President*
Glenn Isscs, *President*
▲ **EMP:** 11
SALES: 1.2MM **Privately Held**
WEB: www.groeneveldusa.com
SIC: 3569 Lubricating equipment

(G-2232)
HYDRA-TEC INC
3027 Nationwide Pkwy (44212-2361)
PHONE.............................330 225-8797
Fax: 330 225-8797
Karl Holler, *President*
Simon J Holler, *Vice Pres*
Mary E Holler, *Treasurer*
Celeste Holler, *Admin Sec*
EMP: 4
SQ FT: 2,000
SALES (est): 475.9K **Privately Held**
SIC: 3498 Tube fabricating (contract bending & shaping)

(G-2233)
ID IMAGES INC
2991 Interstate Pkwy (44212-4327)
PHONE.............................330 220-7300
Dick Yisha, *Owner*
Paul Parish, *QC Mgr*
Dan Wagar, *Engineer*

Dave Oliverio, *Sales Mgr*
Nancy Klaar, *Marketing Mgr*
EMP: 3
SALES (est): 94.5K **Privately Held**
SIC: 3577 Bar code (magnetic ink) printers

(G-2234)
ID IMAGES LLC (PA)
2991 Interstate Pkwy (44212-4327)
PHONE.............................330 220-7300
Fax: 330 220-3838
Brian Gale, *President*
▲ **EMP:** 65
SQ FT: 24,200
SALES (est): 26.1MM **Privately Held**
WEB: www.idimages.com
SIC: 2672 Adhesive papers, labels or tapes: from purchased material

(G-2235)
INTERNATIONAL MACHINING INC
2885 Nationwide Pkwy (44212-4314)
PHONE.............................330 225-1963
Fax: 330 273-6327
John Strobel, *President*
Bruce Sherman, *Vice Pres*
Leslie Salzgeber, *Accounts Mgr*
Rick Winship, *Sales Staff*
Al Snider, *Director*
EMP: 40
SQ FT: 26,000
SALES (est): 7.9MM **Privately Held**
WEB: www.imimachining.com
SIC: 3599 Machine shop, jobbing & repair

(G-2236)
KOSTER CROP TESTER INC
3077 Nationwide Pkwy (44212-2361)
PHONE.............................330 220-2116
Fax: 330 220-1636
Karl Faschian, *CEO*
Ludmilla Faschian, *President*
Wetzel Bias, *CPA*
Alice Lapp, *Office Mgr*
EMP: 4 **EST:** 1961
SQ FT: 1,440
SALES: 250K **Privately Held**
SIC: 3826 Moisture analyzers

(G-2237)
MACK INDUSTRIES INC (PA)
Also Called: Mack Transport
1321 Industrial Pkwy N # 500 (44212-6358)
PHONE.............................330 460-7005
Fax: 330 460-7023
Betsy Mack-Nespeca, *President*
Betsy Mack Nespeca, *Corp Secy*
Lee Disperoff, *Controller*
EMP: 1 **EST:** 1932
SQ FT: 40,000
SALES (est): 160.1MM **Privately Held**
WEB: www.mackconcrete.com
SIC: 3272 1771 Burial vaults, concrete or precast terrazzo; concrete work

(G-2238)
MURPHY TRACTOR & EQP CO INC
Also Called: John Deere Authorized Dealer
1240 Industrial Rd Pkwy N (44212)
PHONE.............................330 220-4999
Bob Cumberledge, *Service Mgr*
EMP: 8
SALES (corp-wide): 176.9MM **Privately Held**
SIC: 3531 5082 Construction machinery; construction & mining machinery
HQ: Murphy Tractor & Equipment Co., Inc.
　5375 N Deere Rd
　Park City KS 67219
　855 246-9124

(G-2239)
NICHOLAS PRESS SALES LLC
3077 Nationwide Pkwy (44212-2361)
PHONE.............................440 652-6604
Joyce Nicholas, *Principal*
EMP: 4
SALES (est): 280K **Privately Held**
SIC: 3469 Metal stampings

(G-2240)
OERLIKON BLZERS CATING USA INC
Also Called: Balzer's Tool Coating Co
1130 Industrial Pkwy N # 15 (44212-5605)
PHONE................................330 220-7716
Fax: 330 220-6611
Diane Hanson, *Manager*
Dan Debevec, *Manager*
Paul Faiken, *Manager*
Rich Ralkowski, *Manager*
EMP: 20
SALES (corp-wide): 2.3B Privately Held
WEB: www.balzers.com
SIC: 3479 3471 Coating of metals & formed products; finishing, metals or formed products
HQ: Oerlikon Balzers Coating Usa Inc.
1475 E Wdfield Rd Ste 201
Schaumburg IL 60173
847 619-5541

(G-2241)
PACIFIC TOOL & DIE CO
1035 Western Dr (44212-4331)
PHONE................................330 273-7363
Fax: 330 273-7362
Charles W Smith, *President*
Jeffrey Smith, *Vice Pres*
John Black, *Controller*
Joseph Cendrowski, *Sales Staff*
EMP: 14 EST: 1959
SQ FT: 20,000
SALES (est): 3MM Privately Held
SIC: 3544 Dies & die holders for metal cutting, forming, die casting; jigs & fixtures

(G-2242)
PHILPOTT INDUS PLAS ENTPS LTD
Also Called: Philpott Intl Entps Ltd
1010 Industrial Pkwy N (44212-4318)
PHONE................................330 225-3344
Stacy Bonitz, *Controller*
Russell Schabel, *Manager*
EMP: 7
SALES (est): 548.2K
SALES (corp-wide): 11.3MM Privately Held
SIC: 3089 Plastic containers, except foam; plastic hardware & building products; washers, plastic
PA: Philpott Rubber Llc
1010 Industrial Pkwy N
Brunswick OH 44212
330 225-3344

(G-2243)
PHILPOTT RUBBER LLC (PA)
Also Called: Philpott Rubber Company
1010 Industrial Pkwy N (44212-4318)
PHONE................................330 225-3344
Fax: 330 225-1999
Mike Baach, *President*
David Ferrell, *Vice Pres*
Jeffrey Rog, *Vice Pres*
Gregory C Stafford, *Vice Pres*
Russell E Schabel, *CFO*
▲ EMP: 28 EST: 1889
SQ FT: 30,000
SALES (est): 11.3MM Privately Held
WEB: www.philpottrubber.com
SIC: 3069 Medical sundries, rubber

(G-2244)
POMACON INC
2996 Interstate Pkwy (44212-4323)
PHONE................................330 273-1576
Fax: 330 273-9605
Rodger Post, *President*
EMP: 15
SQ FT: 14,000
SALES (est): 4.2MM Privately Held
WEB: www.pomacon.com
SIC: 3535 Conveyors & conveying equipment

(G-2245)
POSITOOL TECHNOLOGIES INC
2985 Nationwide Pkwy (44212-2365)
PHONE................................330 220-4002
Fax: 330 220-4119
Anthony Scardigli, *President*
EMP: 5
SQ FT: 2,500

SALES (est): 707.4K Privately Held
WEB: www.positool.com
SIC: 3544 Special dies, tools, jigs & fixtures; injection molding of plastics

(G-2246)
PRECISION EQUIPMENT LLC
1460 W 130th St Ste C (44212-2400)
PHONE................................330 220-7600
John H Nickerson III,
EMP: 3
SALES (est): 252.8K Privately Held
SIC: 5046 3537 Commercial equipment; forklift trucks

(G-2247)
PRIAMUS SYSTEM TECHNOLOGY
3061 Nationwide Pkwy (44212-2361)
PHONE................................330 273-3393
Susan Montgomery, *Principal*
EMP: 7
SALES (est): 674.6K Privately Held
SIC: 3089 Injection molding of plastics

(G-2248)
PRIME WOOD CRAFT INC (HQ)
Also Called: P W C
1120 W 130th St (44212-2317)
P.O. Box 807, West Salem (44287-0807)
PHONE................................216 738-2222
Fax: 419 853-7602
Ansir Junaid, *President*
Ijaz SA, *President*
Robert Campbell, *Owner*
Samantha Sheperd, *Office Mgr*
Olivia Bowersock, *Manager*
▲ EMP: 15
SQ FT: 60,000
SALES (est): 15.8MM Privately Held
WEB: www.primewoodcraft.com
SIC: 2448 Wood pallets & skids
PA: I.H.S. Enterprise, Inc.
5755 Granger Rd Ste 905
Independence OH 44131
216 588-9078

(G-2249)
PRISM POWDER COATINGS LTD
2890 Carquest Dr (44212-4352)
PHONE................................330 225-5626
Fax: 330 225-5688
Alex Asour, *President*
Livio Agnoletto, *Principal*
Yogesh Patel, *Principal*
Jameson Varatharaja, *Controller*
Jameson Varatharajah, *Controller*
▲ EMP: 23
SQ FT: 4,000
SALES (est): 4.8MM Privately Held
SIC: 2851 Paints & allied products

(G-2250)
QUAD FLUID DYNAMICS INC
2826 Westway Dr (44212-5656)
P.O. Box 429 (44212-0429)
PHONE................................330 220-3005
Kenneth H Oleksiak, *President*
Barbara Oleksiak, *Vice Pres*
David E Williams, *Vice Pres*
EMP: 10 EST: 1978
SQ FT: 10,000
SALES (est): 4.2MM Privately Held
WEB: www.quadfluiddynamics.com
SIC: 5085 3594 7699 Valves & fittings; fluid power pumps & motors; hydraulic equipment repair

(G-2251)
RAINBOW CULTURED MARBLE
1442 W 130th St (44212-2320)
PHONE................................330 225-3400
Carrie Fuller, *Principal*
Dale Boss, *Principal*
Michael Dornia, *Personnel Exec*
EMP: 13
SQ FT: 6,000
SALES: 1.7MM Privately Held
SIC: 3281 Bathroom fixtures, cut stone

(G-2252)
RBOOG INDUSTRIES LLC
Also Called: Slicksaw.com
3132 Ipswich Ct (44212-5644)
PHONE................................330 350-0396
Kelly Barber, *CFO*

Richard Barber,
EMP: 4
SALES: 20K Privately Held
SIC: 3546 Saws & sawing equipment

(G-2253)
REED MACHINERY INC
629 Marsh Way (44212-5522)
PHONE................................330 220-6668
John F Peterson, *Branch Mgr*
EMP: 3
SALES (corp-wide): 3.5MM Privately Held
SIC: 3545 Threading tools (machine tool accessories)
PA: Reed Machinery, Inc
10a New Bond St
Worcester MA 01606
508 595-9090

(G-2254)
ROCKSTEDT TOOL & DIE INC
2974 Interstate Pkwy (44212-4323)
PHONE................................330 273-9000
Fax: 330 651-3210
Josef Schuessler, *President*
Bernard Karthan, *Vice Pres*
Rob Prusa, *Engng Exec*
EMP: 14
SQ FT: 100,000
SALES (est): 1.4MM Privately Held
WEB: www.rockstedt.com
SIC: 3544 Special dies & tools

(G-2255)
RONLEN INDUSTRIES INC
2809 Nationwide Pkwy (44212-2363)
PHONE................................330 273-6468
Fax: 330 273-6541
Leonard Lutch, *President*
Ron Bryant, *Vice Pres*
Greg Lutch, *Vice Pres*
EMP: 26
SQ FT: 25,000
SALES (est): 9.7MM Privately Held
WEB: www.ronlen.com
SIC: 3469 3544 Stamping metal for the trade; special dies & tools

(G-2256)
SCHERBA INDUSTRIES INC
Also Called: Inflatable Images
2880 Interstate Pkwy (44212-4322)
PHONE................................330 273-3200
Fax: 330 273-3212
Robert J Scherba, *President*
Kerry Esposito, *General Mgr*
David M Scherba, *Vice Pres*
Shelley Ritley, *Info Tech Mgr*
▲ EMP: 100
SQ FT: 63,000
SALES (est): 21.2MM Privately Held
WEB: www.inflatableimages.com
SIC: 3069 3081 2394 Balloons, advertising & toy: rubber; vinyl film & sheet; canvas & related products

(G-2257)
SITEONE LANDSCAPE SUPPLY LLC
2925 Interstate Pkwy (44212-4327)
PHONE................................330 220-8691
Tom Dickey, *Purch Dir*
Dan Codeluppi, *Manager*
Dave Gobeille, *Manager*
EMP: 4
SALES (corp-wide): 1.6B Publicly Held
SIC: 5083 3494 0781 Lawn & garden machinery & equipment; sprinkler systems, field; landscape services
HQ: Siteone Landscape Supply, Llc
300 Colonial Center Pkwy # 600
Roswell GA 30076
770 255-2100

(G-2258)
STOPOL EQUIPMENT SALES LLC
1321 Industrial Pkwy N # 600
(44212-6358)
PHONE................................440 499-0030
Bob Happ, *CFO*
Rob Rando, *Accounts Exec*
EMP: 3

SALES (est): 546.1K Privately Held
SIC: 2821 3089 Molding compounds, plastics; injection molding of plastics

(G-2259)
SURTEC INC
3097 Interstate Pkwy (44212-4328)
PHONE................................440 239-9710
Karl Lindemann, *CEO*
Ray Lindemann, *President*
Debbie Midile, *Controller*
Carlos Chaves, *Info Tech Mgr*
▲ EMP: 5
SALES (est): 1.3MM
SALES (corp-wide): 6.9B Privately Held
WEB: www.cstplating.com
SIC: 2899 Plating compounds
PA: Freudenberg & Co. Kg
Hohnerweg 2-4
Weinheim 69469
620 180-0

(G-2260)
SYMATIC INC
Also Called: Ancom Business Products
2831 Center Rd (44212-2331)
PHONE................................330 225-1510
Fax: 330 225-3434
Walter H Tanner, *President*
Cindy Holton, *Vice Pres*
Jackie Wolford, *Controller*
EMP: 35
SALES (est): 4.9MM Privately Held
WEB: www.ancom-filing.com
SIC: 3579 5044 2541 2521 Paper handling machines; office equipment; wood partitions & fixtures; wood office furniture

(G-2261)
TECHNICAL TOOL & GAUGE INC
2914 Westway Dr (44212-5658)
PHONE................................330 273-1778
Jeff Butcher, *Owner*
EMP: 17
SALES (est): 1.4MM Privately Held
SIC: 3599 Machine shop, jobbing & repair

(G-2262)
TIGER CAT FURNITURE
294 Marks Rd (44212-1042)
PHONE................................330 220-7232
Audrey F Bledsoe, *Owner*
Lloyd Bledsoe, *Co-Owner*
EMP: 8 EST: 1999
SALES: 150K Privately Held
WEB: www.therustydog.com
SIC: 3999 Novelties, bric-a-brac & hobby kits

(G-2263)
TINNERMAN PALNUT ENGINEERED PR
1060 W 130th St (44212-2316)
P.O. Box 10 (44212-0010)
PHONE................................330 220-5100
Jim Finley, *Principal*
Dan Dolan, *COO*
Glen Boniface, *Manager*
Melissa Krauth, *Manager*
Lori Knapp, *Director*
▲ EMP: 23
SALES (est): 3.6MM Privately Held
SIC: 3452 Bolts, nuts, rivets & washers

(G-2264)
TURF CARE SUPPLY CORP (HQ)
50 Pearl Rd Ste 200 (44212-5703)
PHONE................................877 220-1014
Fax: 330 558-0911
William Milowitz, *President*
Mark Clark, *President*
Mark Mangan, *COO*
Frank Vetter, *COO*
Mark Austin, *Vice Pres*
▼ EMP: 254
SQ FT: 5,000
SALES (est): 169.6MM
SALES (corp-wide): 15.2B Privately Held
WEB: www.turfcaresupply.com
SIC: 2873 Nitrogenous fertilizers
PA: Platinum Equity, Llc
360 N Crescent Dr Bldg S
Beverly Hills CA 90210
310 712-1850

(G-2265)
VERSATILE AUTOMATION TECH LTD
Also Called: VA Technology
2853 Westway Dr (44212-5657)
PHONE....................................330 220-2600
James Byrne, *President*
▲ EMP: 6
SQ FT: 1,300
SALES (est): 1MM
SALES (corp-wide): 17.8MM Privately Held
SIC: 3569 5084 Robots, assembly line: industrial & commercial; robots, industrial
PA: V A Technology Limited
Halesfield 9
Telford TF7 4
195 258-5252

(G-2266)
WENTWORTH SOLUTIONS
2868 Westway Dr Ste B (44212-5661)
P.O. Box 759 (44212-0759)
PHONE....................................440 212-7696
Sean Spigtle, *President*
Anthony White, *Manager*
Jessica Spittle, *Admin Sec*
EMP: 10
SQ FT: 1,000
SALES: 2MM Privately Held
SIC: 7371 7372 Computer software writing services; prepackaged software; application computer software

(G-2267)
WENTWORTH TECHNOLOGIES LLC
2868 Westway Dr (44212-5660)
P.O. Box 283, Hinckley (44233-0283)
PHONE....................................440 212-7696
Gregory Spittle, *Partner*
Sean Spittle, *Partner*
EMP: 12
SQ FT: 1,800
SALES (est): 415.9K Privately Held
SIC: 7379 7372 ; prepackaged software; business oriented computer software; application computer software

(G-2268)
WIFI-PLUS INC
2950 Westway Dr Ste 101 (44212-5666)
PHONE....................................877 838-4195
Fax: 330 273-3437
Allen Higgins, *Managing Prtnr*
Dennis Broderick, *Partner*
Jack Nilsson, *Partner*
EMP: 6
SQ FT: 6,000
SALES (est): 935.7K Privately Held
WEB: www.wifi-plus.com
SIC: 5063 3679 Antennas, receiving, satellite dishes; antennas, receiving

(G-2269)
WIRICK PRESS INC
Also Called: Printing Partners
839 Pearl Rd (44212-2559)
PHONE....................................330 273-3488
Fax: 330 225-9932
Carl Wirick, *President*
Jerry Wirick, *Vice Pres*
EMP: 4
SQ FT: 7,000
SALES (est): 697.8K Privately Held
SIC: 2752 2759 Commercial printing, offset; letterpress printing; envelopes: printing; announcements: engraved; card printing & engraving, except greeting

(G-2270)
WM SOFTWARE INC
3660 Center Rd Ste 371 (44212-3620)
PHONE....................................330 558-0501
Fax: 330 558-0502
Micheal Monasterio, *President*
EMP: 10
SALES (est): 1.1MM Privately Held
SIC: 3695 Computer software tape & disks: blank, rigid & floppy

(G-2271)
X-PRESS TOOL INC
2845 Interstate Pkwy (44212-4326)
PHONE....................................330 225-8748

Bob Koch, *President*
EMP: 20
SALES (est): 423.3K Privately Held
SIC: 7999 3546 3545 Golf services & professionals; power-driven handtools; machine tool accessories
PA: Blackhawk Industrial Distribution, Inc.
1501 Sw Expressway Dr
Broken Arrow OK 74012

(G-2272)
ZEUS ELECTRONICS LLC
5083 Creekside Blvd (44212-1957)
PHONE....................................330 220-1571
Dan Lion, *Principal*
Patros Gatis,
Dionysios Gatis,
Stamatia Gatis,
EMP: 4
SALES: 50K Privately Held
SIC: 3679 Electronic circuits

Bryan
Williams County

(G-2273)
A-STAMP INDUSTRIES LLC
633 Commerce Dr (43506-9197)
PHONE....................................419 633-0451
Fax: 419 633-0692
Jade Croffland, *Plant Mgr*
Alison Garcia, *Asst Controller*
Kim Schumm, *Human Res Mgr*
David Vondeylen, *Mng Member*
▲ EMP: 92
SQ FT: 80,000
SALES (est): 16.5MM Privately Held
WEB: www.a-stamp.com
SIC: 3469 Metal stampings

(G-2274)
AIRMATE COMPANY
16280 County Road D (43506-9552)
PHONE....................................419 636-3184
Fax: 419 636-4210
Carol Schreder Czech, *President*
Carol Schreder, *President*
Neil Oberlin, *Vice Pres*
Ed Dewitt, *Prdtn Mgr*
Todd Moyer, *Purch Agent*
▲ EMP: 57
SQ FT: 24,000
SALES (est): 4.6MM Privately Held
WEB: www.airmatecompany.com
SIC: 3823 7311 Industrial instrmnts msrmnt display/control process variable; advertising consultant

(G-2275)
ALLIED MOULDED PRODUCTS INC
222 N Union St (43506-1450)
PHONE....................................419 636-4217
Fax: 800 237-7269
Walter Paul Troder, *President*
Brad Rupp, *Senior VP*
Tom Carlisle, *Prdtn Mgr*
Kathy Mohler, *Buyer*
Jenny Chandler, *Purchasing*
▲ EMP: 260 EST: 1958
SQ FT: 110,000
SALES (est): 72.8MM Privately Held
WEB: www.alliedmoulded.com
SIC: 3089 3699 Injection molded finished plastic products; electrical equipment & supplies

(G-2276)
ALTENLOH BRINCK & CO INC
2105 County Road 12c (43506-8301)
PHONE....................................419 636-6715
Brian Roth, *President*
Sven Kokumor, *Vice Pres*
Kit Windler, *CFO*
D Kip Winzeler, *CFO*
Kyle Flooy, *Manager*
▲ EMP: 135 EST: 1981
SQ FT: 200,000
SALES (est): 30.4MM
SALES (corp-wide): 331.7MM Privately Held
WEB: www.trufast.com
SIC: 3452 Pins

HQ: Altenloh, Brinck & Co. Us, Inc.
2105 Williams Co Rd 12 C
Bryan OH 43506
419 636-6715

(G-2277)
ALTENLOH BRINCK & CO US INC (DH)
Also Called: Trufast
2105 Williams Co Rd 12 C (43506-8301)
PHONE....................................419 636-1784
Brian Roth, *President*
Pete Garrigus, *Vice Pres*
Allyn Luce, *VP Mfg*
Kip Winzeler, *CFO*
▲ EMP: 89
SALES (est): 42.2MM
SALES (corp-wide): 331.7MM Privately Held
SIC: 3452 Screws, metal
HQ: Abc Finanzierungs- Und Beteiligungs Gmbh
Kolner Str. 71-77
Ennepetal
233 379-90

(G-2278)
ANDERSON & VREELAND INC
Also Called: Anderson Vreeland Midwest
15348 State Rte 127 E (43506)
P.O. Box 527 (43506-0527)
PHONE....................................419 636-5002
Fax: 419 636-4334
Gary Goll, *Purchasing*
Mitch Male, *Research*
Gene Lockhart, *Design Engr*
Lauren Wenz, *Finance Mgr*
Ron Grant, *Human Res Dir*
EMP: 80
SQ FT: 3,000
SALES (corp-wide): 51.4MM Privately Held
WEB: www.andersonvreeland.com
SIC: 5084 3555 3542 2796 Printing trades machinery, equipment & supplies; printing trades machinery; machine tools, metal forming type; platemaking services
PA: Anderson & Vreeland, Inc.
8 Evans St
Fairfield NJ 07004
973 227-2270

(G-2279)
ARROW TRU-LINE INC
720 E Perry St (43506-2223)
PHONE....................................419 636-7013
Fax: 419 636-7329
Curtis Anderson, *Ch of Bd*
Bill Swisher, *Manager*
EMP: 100
SALES (corp-wide): 48.8MM Privately Held
SIC: 3429 3469 3449 Builders' hardware; metal stampings; miscellaneous metalwork
PA: Arrow Tru-Line, Inc.
2211 S Defiance St
Archbold OH 43502
419 446-2785

(G-2280)
AUTOCOAT
1900 Progress Dr (43506-9323)
PHONE....................................419 636-3830
Fax: 419 636-4330
Roy Rodriguez, *Principal*
EMP: 5
SALES (est): 657.5K Privately Held
SIC: 3471 Finishing, metals or formed products

(G-2281)
BARD MANUFACTURING COMPANY INC (PA)
1914 Randolph Dr (43506-2253)
P.O. Box 607 (43506-0607)
PHONE....................................419 636-1194
Fax: 419 636-2640
William Steel, *President*
Wes Roan, *President*
Scott Bard, *Vice Chairman*
Paul Matz, *Vice Pres*
Geoffrey Mack, *Plant Mgr*
▼ EMP: 99

SALES (est): 27MM Privately Held
SIC: 3585 Refrigeration & heating equipment

(G-2282)
BEAN COUNTER LLC
1210 W High St Ste C (43506-3521)
PHONE....................................419 636-0705
Shannon Lyman, *Principal*
EMP: 3
SALES (est): 230.7K Privately Held
SIC: 3131 Counters

(G-2283)
BMC HOLDINGS INC (PA)
1914 Randolph Dr (43506-2253)
P.O. Box 607 (43506-0607)
PHONE....................................419 636-1194
Richard O Bard, *President*
James R Bard, *COO*
Paul Matz, *Treasurer*
Jon Friesen, *Sales Mgr*
EMP: 2
SQ FT: 200,000
SALES (est): 51.5MM Privately Held
WEB: www.bardhvac.com
SIC: 3433 3585 Gas burners, domestic; gas burners, industrial; oil burners, domestic or industrial; air conditioning units, complete: domestic or industrial; heat pumps, electric

(G-2284)
BP PRODUCTS NORTH AMERICA INC
Also Called: B P Exploration
710 E Wilson St (43506-1847)
P.O. Box 426 (43506-0426)
PHONE....................................419 636-2249
Larry Thiel, *Manager*
EMP: 5
SQ FT: 400
SALES (corp-wide): 183B Privately Held
WEB: www.bpproductsnorthamerica.com
SIC: 2911 Petroleum refining
HQ: Bp Products North America Inc.
501 Westlake Park Blvd
Houston TX 77079
281 366-2000

(G-2285)
BRICKER PLATING INC
612 E Edgerton St (43506-1408)
PHONE....................................419 636-1990
Fax: 419 636-1924
Tim Bricker, *President*
EMP: 6 EST: 1950
SQ FT: 4,800
SALES: 300K Privately Held
SIC: 3471 Electroplating of metals or formed products; polishing, metals or formed products

(G-2286)
BRYAN METALS LLC (DH)
1103 S Main St (43506-2440)
PHONE....................................419 636-4571
Fax: 419 636-3994
Tony Norden, *Principal*
Don Sawyer, *Plant Mgr*
Tom Carsons, *Maint Spvr*
Joyce Smith, *Manager*
Kathy Smith, *Officer*
▲ EMP: 5 EST: 1955
SQ FT: 63,000
SALES (est): 25.9MM
SALES (corp-wide): 1.3B Publicly Held
SIC: 3331 3351 Primary copper; copper & copper alloy sheet, strip, plate & products
HQ: Gbc Metals, Llc
427 N Shamrock St
East Alton IL 62024
618 258-2350

(G-2287)
BRYAN PACKAGING INC
620 E Perry St (43506-2221)
PHONE....................................419 636-2600
Fax: 419 636-5368
Leo Deiger, *President*
Cheryl Sanchez, *Human Res Dir*
EMP: 14 EST: 1998

SALES (est): 3.9MM
SALES (corp-wide): 22.7MM **Privately Held**
SIC: 2653 Boxes, corrugated: made from purchased materials
PA: Pro-Pak Industries, Inc.
1125 Ford St
Maumee OH 43537
419 729-0751

(G-2288)
BRYAN PUBLISHING COMPANY (PA)
Also Called: County Line
127 S Walnut St (43506-1718)
P.O. Box 471 (43506-0471)
PHONE............................419 636-1111
Fax: 419 636-8937
Christopher Cullis, *President*
Don Allison, *Editor*
Tom Voight, *Vice Pres*
Pam Miller, *Accounting Mgr*
Kimberly Imm, *Manager*
EMP: 80
SQ FT: 12,000
SALES: 4MM **Privately Held**
WEB: www.bryantimes.com
SIC: 2711 Newspapers, publishing & printing

(G-2289)
C E ELECTRONICS INC
2107 Industrial Dr (43506-8773)
PHONE............................419 636-6705
Garry L Courtney, *President*
Marlin Gerig, *Maint Spvr*
Joe Spallone, *Purchasing*
Robert Taylor, *Engineer*
Kevin Schroer, *Electrical Engi*
EMP: 85
SALES (est): 22.5MM **Privately Held**
WEB: www.ceelectronics.com
SIC: 3679 3672 Electronic circuits; printed circuit boards

(G-2290)
CONTINENTAL TIRE AMERICAS LLC
Also Called: Ctna Tire Plant
927 S Union Bryan (43506)
PHONE............................419 633-4221
Steve Newell, *Branch Mgr*
EMP: 5
SALES (corp-wide): 42.8B **Privately Held**
WEB: www.continentaltire.com
SIC: 3011 Tires & inner tubes
HQ: Continental Tire The Americas, Llc
1830 Macmillan Park Dr
Fort Mill SC 29707
800 450-3187

(G-2291)
COTTON PICKIN TEES & CAPS
215 W Bryan St (43506-1241)
PHONE............................419 636-3595
June Flemming, *Partner*
Ernie Flemming, *Partner*
EMP: 4
SQ FT: 2,500
SALES: 250K **Privately Held**
SIC: 2759 5699 5651 Imprinting; T-shirts, custom printed; family clothing stores

(G-2292)
CV ELECTRIC
241 Baker St (43506-1104)
PHONE............................419 630-0800
Craig A Vogel, *Principal*
EMP: 4
SALES (est): 465.6K **Privately Held**
SIC: 3699 Electrical equipment & supplies

(G-2293)
DAAVLIN DISTRIBUTING CO
205 W Bement St (43506-1264)
P.O. Box 626 (43506-0626)
PHONE............................419 636-6304
David W Swanson, *President*
Traci Hartman, *Vice Pres*
Traci L Hartman, *Vice Pres*
Tracey McKelvey, *Vice Pres*
Sandrine Woolace, *Vice Pres*
▼ **EMP:** 48
SQ FT: 24,000

SALES (est): 10MM **Privately Held**
WEB: www.daavlin.com
SIC: 3841 Surgical & medical instruments

(G-2294)
DG CUSTOM MACHINE
840 E Edgerton St (43506-1412)
PHONE............................419 636-8059
Dave Greutman, *Owner*
EMP: 3
SALES (est): 295.2K **Privately Held**
SIC: 3599 Machine shop, jobbing & repair

(G-2295)
FAYETTE INDUSTRIAL COATINGS
533 Commerce Dr Ste A (43506-7809)
PHONE............................419 636-1773
Fax: 419 636-1719
Brad Balser, *President*
Tony Baalser, *Treasurer*
EMP: 25 **EST:** 1998
SQ FT: 60,000
SALES (est): 1.8MM **Privately Held**
SIC: 3479 Painting of metal products

(G-2296)
FLUID EQUIPMENT CORP
7671 County Road E 7g (43506-9118)
P.O. Box 689 (43506-0689)
PHONE............................419 636-0777
Fax: 419 485-1431
Edward T Ward, *President*
EMP: 7
SALES (est): 687.5K **Privately Held**
SIC: 8748 8711 3823 Systems engineering consultant, ex. computer or professional; consulting engineer; fluidic devices, circuits & systems for process control

(G-2297)
G&M MEDIA PACKAGING INC
1 Toy St (43506-1853)
P.O. Box 524 (43506-0524)
PHONE............................419 636-5461
Thomas P Dillon, *President*
Jan Bjerregaard, *Manager*
▲ **EMP:** 19
SALES (est): 4.8MM **Privately Held**
SIC: 3411 3221 Food & beverage containers; bottles for packing, bottling & canning: glass
HQ: Glud & Marstrand A/S
Hedenstedvej 14
LOsning 8723
631 242-00

(G-2298)
H MACHINING INC
720 Commerce Dr (43506-9198)
PHONE............................419 636-6890
Fax: 419 636-8420
Denny Herman, *President*
Christine Shankster, *Office Mgr*
Sherrie Herman, *Admin Sec*
EMP: 11
SQ FT: 18,000
SALES (est): 1.7MM **Privately Held**
SIC: 3545 3544 Drills (machine tool accessories); special dies & tools

(G-2299)
HABITEC SEC DIVERSFD ALARM
115 N Lynn St (43506-1213)
PHONE............................419 636-1155
James Smythe, *Owner*
EMP: 4
SALES (est): 224.1K **Privately Held**
SIC: 3699 Security control equipment & systems

(G-2300)
HEALTH CARE SOLUTIONS INC
5673 State Route 15 (43506-8878)
PHONE............................419 636-4189
Kari Shininger, *Manager*
EMP: 3
SALES (corp-wide): 37.7MM **Privately Held**
SIC: 3845 Respiratory analysis equipment, electromedical

HQ: Health Care Solutions Inc
1039 Bern Rd
Reading PA 19610
610 373-5733

(G-2301)
HEARING AID CENTER OF NW OHIO
Also Called: Hearing Aid Ctr of NW Ohio The
1318 E High St Ste B (43506-8407)
PHONE............................419 636-8959
Larry Hand, *Manager*
Donald Samuelson, *Manager*
EMP: 4
SALES: 50K **Privately Held**
SIC: 3842 Hearing aids

(G-2302)
ILLINOIS TOOL WORKS INC
ITW Tomco
730 E South St (43506-2433)
PHONE............................419 636-3161
Fax: 419 633-3041
Martin Collins, *General Mgr*
Tom Mack, *Vice Pres*
Greg Thiel, *Engineer*
Tandy Roach, *Design Engr*
EMP: 270
SQ FT: 75,000
SALES (corp-wide): 13.6B **Publicly Held**
SIC: 3089 Injection molding of plastics
PA: Illinois Tool Works Inc.
155 Harlem Ave
Glenview IL 60025
847 724-7500

(G-2303)
ILLINOIS TOOL WORKS INC
Also Called: ITW Filtration Products
730 E South St (43506-2433)
PHONE............................262 248-8277
Bob Hamilton, *General Mgr*
Robert Hamilton Jr, *General Mgr*
EMP: 120
SALES (corp-wide): 13.6B **Publicly Held**
SIC: 3677 3714 3564 Filtration devices, electronic; motor vehicle parts & accessories; blowers & fans
PA: Illinois Tool Works Inc.
155 Harlem Ave
Glenview IL 60025
847 724-7500

(G-2304)
INDIGO 48 LLC
125 S Beech St (43506-1602)
P.O. Box 7158 (43506-7158)
PHONE............................419 551-6931
Mark Hillman, *General Mgr*
John D Jackson, *Principal*
EMP: 3
SALES (est): 233.9K **Privately Held**
SIC: 3471 Polishing, metals or formed products; cleaning & descaling metal products; cleaning, polishing & finishing

(G-2305)
INDUSTRIAL STEERING PDTS INC
426 N Lewis St (43506-1485)
PHONE............................419 636-3300
John E Freudenberger, *Principal*
John Freudenberger Jr, *Vice Pres*
EMP: 4
SALES (est): 462K **Privately Held**
SIC: 3714 Motor vehicle steering systems & parts

(G-2306)
INGERSOLL-RAND COMPANY
209 N Main St (43506-1319)
P.O. Box 151 (43506-0151)
PHONE............................419 633-6800
Robbie Robinson, *Vice Pres*
Kim Ford, *Finance Mgr*
J Haas, *Human Res Dir*
Larry White, *Manager*
Rick Burch, *Manager*
EMP: 50 **Privately Held**
WEB: www.ingersoll-rand.com
SIC: 3546 4225 3823 3594 Power-driven handtools; general warehousing & storage; industrial instrmnts msrmnt display/control process variable; fluid power pumps & motors; pumps & pumping equipment; hoists, cranes & monorails

HQ: Ingersoll-Rand Company
800 Beaty St Ste B
Davidson NC 28036
704 655-4000

(G-2307)
JOHNSON CONTROLS INC
918 S Union St (43506-2246)
PHONE............................419 636-4211
Kevin Cagala, *Manager*
EMP: 94 **Privately Held**
SIC: 2531 Seats, automobile
HQ: Johnson Controls, Inc.
5757 N Green Bay Ave
Milwaukee WI 53209
414 524-1200

(G-2308)
KENLEY ENTERPRISES LLC
418 N Lynn St (43506-1218)
P.O. Box 7036 (43506-7036)
PHONE............................419 630-0921
Dave Franley,
EMP: 22
SALES (est): 1MM **Privately Held**
SIC: 3549 3498 3714 Wiredrawing & fabricating machinery & equipment, ex. die; tube fabricating (contract bending & shaping); motor vehicle parts & accessories

(G-2309)
KW SERVICES LLC
527 S Union St (43506-2248)
PHONE............................419 636-3438
Fax: 419 636-0151
Kermit Caudill Jr, *General Mgr*
EMP: 6
SALES (corp-wide): 87.7MM **Privately Held**
WEB: www.koontz-wagner.com
SIC: 7694 Electric motor repair
PA: Kw Services, Llc
3801 Voorde Dr Ste B
South Bend IN 46628
574 232-2051

(G-2310)
LE SMITH COMPANY (PA)
1030 E Wilson St (43506-9358)
P.O. Box 766 (43506-0766)
PHONE............................419 636-4555
Fax: 419 636-3744
Laura Juarez, *President*
Steve Smith, *Principal*
Craig Francisco, *COO*
Mari Ivan, *COO*
Aaron Walz, *Facilities Mgr*
▲ **EMP:** 100 **EST:** 1950
SQ FT: 90,000
SALES (est): 18.8MM **Privately Held**
WEB: www.lesmith.com
SIC: 2431 5072 2541 Interior & ornamental woodwork & trim; builders' hardware; wood partitions & fixtures

(G-2311)
LEADER ENGNRNG-FABRICATION INC
County Rd D 50 (43506)
PHONE............................419 636-1731
Fax: 419 636-3183
John Hill, *Manager*
EMP: 6
SALES (corp-wide): 8.2MM **Privately Held**
WEB:
www.leaderengineeringfabrication.com
SIC: 3599 Catapults
PA: Leader Engineering-Fabrication, Inc.
695 Independence Dr
Napoleon OH 43545
419 592-0008

(G-2312)
LIBERTY DIE CASTING COMPANY
Also Called: Liberty Ornamental Products
872 E Trevitt St (43506-1498)
PHONE............................419 636-3971
Larry Barr, *President*
Scott Schafer, *Vice Pres*
Keith Dart, *Treasurer*
Scott Lotzenheiscu, *Sales Staff*
EMP: 3 **EST:** 1972
SQ FT: 16,000

SALES (est): 444.2K **Privately Held**
SIC: 3369 Zinc & zinc-base alloy castings, except die-castings

(G-2313)
MANUFACTURED HOUSING ENTPS INC
Also Called: MANSION HOMES
9302 Us Highway 6 (43506-9516)
PHONE..............................419 636-4511
Mary Jane Fitzcharles, *CEO*
Janet Rice, *Corp Secy*
Nathan Kimpel, *Vice Pres*
Robert Confer, *Purch Agent*
John Bailey, *Engineer*
EMP: 150
SQ FT: 250,000
SALES: 18.9MM **Privately Held**
WEB: www.mheinc.com
SIC: 2451 1521 Mobile homes, except recreational; single-family housing construction

(G-2314)
NOSTRUM LABORATORIES INC
705 E Mulberry St (43506-1734)
PHONE..............................419 636-1168
Grace Shen, *Marketing*
Gregory Reed, *Prdtn Mgr*
Mark Weeka, *Safety Mgr*
Steve Smith, *Purch Dir*
Sandy Yaroch, *Purch Mgr*
EMP: 46
SQ FT: 91,100
SALES (corp-wide): 23MM **Privately Held**
SIC: 2834 Pharmaceutical preparations; syrups, pharmaceutical
PA: Nostrum Laboratories Inc.
1800 N Topping Ave
Kansas City MO 64120
816 308-4900

(G-2315)
OHIO ART COMPANY (PA)
1 Toy St (43506-1853)
P.O. Box 111 (43506-0111)
PHONE..............................419 636-3141
Fax: 419 636-7614
William C Killgallon, *Ch of Bd*
Martin L Killgallon II, *President*
Larry Killgallon, *COO*
Martin L Killgallon III, *Senior VP*
John Byrer, *Plant Engr*
▲ **EMP:** 80
SQ FT: 661,000
SALES (est): 16.4MM **Privately Held**
WEB: www.world-of-toys.com
SIC: 2752 5945 Commercial printing, lithographic; toys & games

(G-2316)
OTTOKEE GROUP INC
17768 County Road H50 (43506-9429)
PHONE..............................419 636-1932
Keith Krovath, *Manager*
EMP: 6
SALES (corp-wide): 2.1MM **Privately Held**
WEB: www.archbold.org
SIC: 2875 Fertilizers, mixing only
PA: Ottokee Group, Inc.
21450 County Rd J
Archbold OH 43502
419 445-0446

(G-2317)
PAHL READY MIX CONCRETE INC (PA)
14586 Us Highway 127 Ew (43506-9754)
PHONE..............................419 636-4238
Fax: 419 636-6758
Thomas G Weber, *President*
Judy Weber, *Vice Pres*
EMP: 17
SQ FT: 500
SALES (est): 4.9MM **Privately Held**
SIC: 3273 Ready-mixed concrete

(G-2318)
PARAGON CUSTOM PLASTICS INC
402 N Union St (43506-1454)
P.O. Box 127 (43506-0127)
PHONE..............................419 636-6060

Fax: 419 636-0428
Mark Troder, *President*
Valarie Vaningen, *Manager*
EMP: 30
SQ FT: 11,000
SALES (est): 4.1MM **Privately Held**
SIC: 3086 Plastics foam products

(G-2319)
PRECISE METAL FORM INC
810 Commerce Dr (43506-8861)
P.O. Box 764 (43506-0764)
PHONE..............................419 636-5221
Fax: 419 636-2678
James Bloir, *President*
Linda Bloir, *Corp Secy*
EMP: 10
SALES (est): 1.2MM **Privately Held**
SIC: 3444 Sheet metalwork

(G-2320)
S & H AUTOMATION & EQP CO
815 Commerce Dr (43506-8862)
PHONE..............................419 636-0020
Fax: 419 636-9062
Melinda Stewart, *President*
Jimmy Stewart, *President*
EMP: 20
SALES (est): 3.3MM **Privately Held**
WEB: www.autobenders.com
SIC: 3542 Bending machines

(G-2321)
STONEY RIDGE WINERY LTD
Also Called: Stoney Ridge Farm & Winery
7144 County Road 16 (43506-9080)
PHONE..............................419 636-3500
Phillip Stotz, *President*
Sophia Stotz, *Vice Pres*
EMP: 4
SALES: 500K **Privately Held**
SIC: 2084 Wines

(G-2322)
SWIVEL-TEK INDUSTRIES LLC
417 N Lynn St (43506-1219)
P.O. Box 269 (43506-0269)
PHONE..............................419 636-7770
Joyce F Essman, *Mng Member*
Joyce Essman,
EMP: 3
SQ FT: 18,000
SALES: 600.8K **Privately Held**
WEB: www.swivel-tek.com
SIC: 3451 Custom machinery

(G-2323)
TITAN TIRE CORPORATION
Also Called: Titan Tire Corporation Bryan
927 S Union St (43506-2252)
PHONE..............................419 633-4221
Ed Lazenby, *Opers Staff*
Ann Wirth, *Purch Dir*
Ann Worth, *Purchasing*
Patricia Zuber, *Purchasing*
Keith Tarnovich, *Controller*
EMP: 400
SQ FT: 750,000
SALES (corp-wide): 1.2B **Publicly Held**
SIC: 3011 Tires & inner tubes
HQ: Titan Tire Corporation
2345 E Market St
Des Moines IA 50317

(G-2324)
TWO BANDITS BREWING CO LLC
206 Scott Dr (43506-8955)
PHONE..............................419 636-4045
Mark T W Young, *Principal*
EMP: 3
SALES (est): 84.9K **Privately Held**
SIC: 2082 Malt beverages

(G-2325)
UNIQUE-CHARDAN INC
705 S Union St (43506-2250)
PHONE..............................419 636-6900
Fax: 419 636-9292
John Weinhard, *President*
Angie Lucas, *Purchasing*
Thomas Tekiele, *CFO*
EMP: 50
SQ FT: 40,000

SALES: 4.7MM
SALES (corp-wide): 170.4MM **Publicly Held**
WEB: www.chardancorp.com
SIC: 3944 3949 3714 3086 Games, toys & children's vehicles; sporting & athletic goods; motor vehicle parts & accessories; plastics foam products; injection molded finished plastic products
PA: Unique Fabricating, Inc.
800 Standard Pkwy
Auburn Hills MI 48326
248 853-2333

(G-2326)
WEBER SAND & GRAVEL INC
14586 Us Highway 127 Ew (43506-9754)
PHONE..............................419 636-7920
Tom Weber, *President*
EMP: 8
SALES (est): 520K **Privately Held**
SIC: 1442 Construction sand & gravel

(G-2327)
WESTAR PLASTICS LLC
4271 County Road 15d (43506-9442)
PHONE..............................419 636-1333
Sean Cowen, *Marketing Mgr*
Steve Goltare, *Mng Member*
Kerri Goltare,
EMP: 7 **EST:** 1996
SQ FT: 12,000
SALES: 800K **Privately Held**
SIC: 3089 Plastic processing

(G-2328)
YANFENG US AUTOMOTIVE
918 S Union St (43506-2246)
PHONE..............................419 636-4211
Anita Olvera, *Marketing Staff*
Kevin Cagala, *Manager*
EMP: 500
SALES (corp-wide): 55MM **Privately Held**
SIC: 3089 Molding primary plastic
HQ: Yanfeng Us Automotive Interior Systems Ii Llc
5757 N Green Bay Ave
Milwaukee WI 53209
205 477-4225

Buckeye Lake
Licking County

(G-2329)
IMPACT PUBLICATIONS
Also Called: Buckeye Lake Beacon
4675 Walnut Rd (43008-7770)
P.O. Box 1542 (43008-1542)
PHONE..............................740 928-5541
Fax: 740 928-7960
Charlie Prince, *Owner*
EMP: 5
SALES (est): 197K **Privately Held**
WEB: www.buckeyelakebeacon.com
SIC: 2711 Newspapers: publishing only, not printed on site

Bucyrus
Crawford County

(G-2330)
A-1 PRINTING INC (PA)
825 S Sandusky Ave (44820-2633)
PHONE..............................419 562-3111
Fax: 419 562-0078
Dan Price, *President*
Barbara Price, *Corp Secy*
Becky Lloyd, *VP Human Res*
EMP: 14
SALES (est): 1.8MM **Privately Held**
SIC: 2752 2791 2789 2672 Commercial printing, offset; typesetting; bookbinding & related work; coated & laminated paper

(G-2331)
ADVANCED FIBER TECHNOLOGY INC
100 Crossroads Blvd (44820-1361)
PHONE..............................513 860-4446
Fax: 419 562-9062

Doug Leuthold, *President*
Mark Leuthold, *Vice Pres*
Sandi Leuthold, *Administration*
EMP: 20
SQ FT: 51,500
SALES (est): 5.2MM **Privately Held**
WEB: www.advancedfiber.com
SIC: 2821 5084 Cellulose derivative materials; paper manufacturing machinery

(G-2332)
BUCYRUS BLADES INC (HQ)
Also Called: Esco Bucyrus Inc.
260 E Beal Ave (44820-3492)
PHONE..............................419 562-6015
Fax: 419 562-8360
Calvin Collins, *CEO*
Tim Myers, *President*
Jon Owens, *Exec VP*
Nick Blauwiekel, *Senior VP*
Kevin Thomas, *Senior VP*
▲ **EMP:** 73
SQ FT: 130,000
SALES (est): 38.6MM
SALES (corp-wide): 1.4B **Privately Held**
WEB: www.bucyrusblades.com
SIC: 3531 Blades for graders, scrapers, dozers & snow plows
PA: Esco Corporation
2141 Nw 25th Ave
Portland OR 97210
503 228-2141

(G-2333)
BUCYRUS GRAPHICS INC
Also Called: Quality Printing Co
214 W Liberty St (44820-2639)
P.O. Box 454 (44820-0454)
PHONE..............................419 562-2906
Fax: 419 562-3889
W Gary Mc Kee, *President*
Judy Mc Kee, *Corp Secy*
Judy Kee, *Treasurer*
EMP: 10
SQ FT: 5,000
SALES (est): 790K **Privately Held**
SIC: 2752 Commercial printing, offset

(G-2334)
BUCYRUS PRECISION TECH INC
Also Called: B P T
200 Crossroads Blvd (44820-1363)
PHONE..............................419 563-9950
Fax: 419 563-9949
Keiji Nishio, *President*
Doug Jones, *Vice Pres*
Terry Pence, *Vice Pres*
David Provided, *Vice Pres*
Carl Faulkner, *Safety Dir*
▲ **EMP:** 189
SQ FT: 107,000
SALES (est): 59.8MM
SALES (corp-wide): 63.3MM **Privately Held**
WEB: www.bptus.com
SIC: 3714 3568 5531 Motor vehicle parts & accessories; motor vehicle transmissions, drive assemblies & parts; power transmission equipment; automotive accessories
PA: Kaneta Kogyo Co.,Ltd.
3-18-5, Takaokahigashi, Naka-Ku
Hamamatsu SZO 433-8
534 361-211

(G-2335)
CHECKMATE MARINE INC
3691 State Route 4 (44820-9466)
PHONE..............................419 562-3881
Fax: 419 562-0632
Doug Smith, *President*
Dean Reynolds, *General Mgr*
Paul Logiudice, *Vice Pres*
EMP: 17
SALES (est): 3.9MM **Privately Held**
SIC: 3732 Boat building & repairing

(G-2336)
COOPERS MILL
1414 N Sandusky Ave (44820-1330)
P.O. Box 149 (44820-0149)
PHONE..............................419 562-4215
Fax: 419 562-2405
David N Cooper, *Owner*
Sharon Sparks, *Bookkeeper*

EMP: 18
SQ FT: 17,300
SALES: 1MM Privately Held
WEB: www.coopersmill.net
SIC: 2033 5431 Jams, jellies & preserves:
packaged in cans, jars, etc.; fruit butters:
packaged in cans, jars, etc.; fruit stands
or markets; vegetable stands or markets

(G-2337)
D PICKING & CO
119 S Walnut St (44820-2325)
PHONE......................................419 562-5016
EMP: 6 EST: 1874
SQ FT: 5,000
SALES (est): 569.6K Privately Held
SIC: 3364 3931 3366 3321 Copper &
copper alloy die-castings; musical instru-
ments; copper foundries; gray & ductile
iron foundries

(G-2338)
DIAMOND WIPES INTL INC
1375 Isaac Beal Rd (44820-9604)
PHONE......................................419 562-3575
Diane Belcher, Principal
Dave Metzger, Maintence Staff
EMP: 8
SALES (corp-wide): 32.4MM Privately
Held
SIC: 3441 Fabricated structural metal
PA: Diamond Wipes International, Inc.
4651 Schaefer Ave
Chino CA 91710
909 230-9888

(G-2339)
DOOR GUYS INC
113 W Rensselaer St (44820-2215)
PHONE......................................419 562-3376
Tim Granlee, Branch Mgr
EMP: 11
SALES (corp-wide): 2.5MM Privately
Held
SIC: 2431 Garage doors, overhead: wood
PA: The Door Guys Inc
793 N Main St
Marion OH 43302
740 383-1234

(G-2340)
EAGLE CRUSHER CO INC
521 E Southern Ave (44820-3258)
P.O. Box 537, Galion (44833-0537)
PHONE......................................419 562-1183
Fax: 419 462-5382
Jeff Cullen, Plant Mgr
William Rhoades, VP Sales
Susan Cobey, Branch Mgr
EMP: 50
SQ FT: 200,000
SALES (corp-wide): 42.3MM Privately
Held
WEB: www.eaglecrusher.com
SIC: 3532 Crushing, pulverizing & screen-
ing equipment
PA: Eagle Crusher Co Inc
525 S Market St
Galion OH 44833
419 468-2288

(G-2341)
EAST SIDE FUEL PLUS
OPERATIONS
1505 N Sandusky Ave (44820-1333)
PHONE......................................419 563-0777
Bridgette J Liedorff, Principal
EMP: 5
SALES (est): 554.7K Privately Held
SIC: 2869 Fuels

(G-2342)
ERS INDUSTRIES INC
Also Called: American Ohio Locomotive
Crane
811 Hopley Ave (44820-2856)
P.O. Box 511 (44820-0511)
PHONE......................................419 562-6010
Fax: 419 562-2565
David Egner, Vice Pres
Ron Fairchild, Plant Mgr
Diana Wenninger, Purch Mgr
John Schroeder, Engineer
Mark Velazco, Engineer
EMP: 26

SALES (corp-wide): 35.1MM Privately
Held
SIC: 3531 Cranes, locomotive
PA: Ers Industries, Inc.
1005 Indian Church Rd
West Seneca NY 14224
716 675-2040

(G-2343)
ESCO CORPORATION
260 E Beal Ave (44820-3492)
PHONE......................................419 562-6015
Hughes Scott, Buyer
Robert Snader, Engineer
Alan Parrish, Project Engr
Mike Sparks, Branch Mgr
Grant Kleckner, Business Dir
EMP: 50
SALES (corp-wide): 1.4B Privately Held
SIC: 3532 Mining machinery
PA: Esco Corporation
2141 Nw 25th Ave
Portland OR 97210
503 228-2141

(G-2344)
GANYMEDE TECHNOLOGIES
CORP
Also Called: J3 Point-Of-Sale
1685 Marion Rd (44820-3116)
P.O. Box 1138 (44820-1138)
PHONE......................................419 562-5522
George Fred Fischer, President
EMP: 6
SALES (est): 445.5K Privately Held
SIC: 7371 3578 Computer software devel-
opment; calculators & adding machines

(G-2345)
GENERAL ELECTRIC COMPANY
1250 S Walnut St (44820-3266)
PHONE......................................419 563-1200
Fax: 419 563-1358
Dan Monnin, Plant Mgr
Bryon Grabenbauer, Production
Peter Gabriel, Branch Mgr
Randy Harriger, Branch Mgr
Michelle Brady, Manager
EMP: 325
SALES (corp-wide): 123.6B Publicly
Held
SIC: 3641 Lamps, fluorescent, electric
PA: General Electric Company
41 Farnsworth St
Boston MA 02210
617 443-3000

(G-2346)
GOFAST LLC
963 Hopley Ave (44820-3506)
PHONE......................................419 562-8027
Shaun Frecska, Mng Member
Chuck Pfahler, Manager
Richard Szydlyk,
EMP: 3
SALES (est): 275K Privately Held
SIC: 2033 Canned fruits & specialties

(G-2347)
HEBCO PRODUCTS INC
1232 Whetstone St (44820-3539)
PHONE......................................419 562-7987
Fax: 419 562-8577
Andrew Ason, President
Ralph Reins, Vice Pres
Matt Barringer, Engineer
EMP: 862
SALES (est): 79.4MM
SALES (corp-wide): 191MM Privately
Held
WEB: www.hebcoproducts.com
SIC: 3714 3451 3429 5013 Motor vehicle
brake systems & parts; screw machine
products; manufactured hardware (gen-
eral); automotive supplies & parts
PA: Qualitor, Inc.
1840 Mccullough St
Lima OH 45801
248 204-8600

(G-2348)
HOME SHEET METAL &
ROOFING CO
211 W Galen St (44820-2237)
P.O. Box 66 (44820-0066)
PHONE......................................419 562-7806

Terry Barney, Owner
EMP: 5
SALES: 250K Privately Held
SIC: 1761 3444 Roofing contractor; sheet
metalwork

(G-2349)
HORD ELEVATOR LLC
1016 State Route 98 (44820-9523)
P.O. Box 808 (44820-0808)
PHONE......................................419 562-5934
Robert D Hord, Manager
EMP: 12
SALES: 950K Privately Held
SIC: 3523 Elevators, farm

(G-2350)
IMASEN BUCYRUS
TECHNOLOGY INC
Also Called: I B-Tech
260 Crossroads Blvd (44820-1363)
PHONE......................................419 563-9590
Fax: 419 563-9599
Katsumi Ito, President
Joe Downing, Vice Pres
Koichi Fukui, Vice Pres
Kim Smith, Asst Sec
◆ EMP: 220 EST: 1997
SALES (est): 53.2MM
SALES (corp-wide): 1B Privately Held
SIC: 3714 Motor vehicle parts & acces-
sories
PA: Imasen Electric Industrial Co., Ltd.
1, Kakibata
Inuyama AIC 484-0
568 671-211

(G-2351)
J3 SYSTEMS LTD
Also Called: Ganymede Technology
1695 Marion Rd (44820-3116)
P.O. Box 783 (44820-0783)
PHONE......................................419 562-5522
Fred Fischer,
EMP: 7
SALES (est): 951.7K Privately Held
WEB: www.j3systems.com
SIC: 3578 5734 Point-of-sale devices;
computer & software stores

(G-2352)
LAWSON PRECISION
MACHINING INC
3981 Crestline Rd (44820-9573)
PHONE......................................419 562-1543
Gary Lawson, President
EMP: 3
SALES (est): 248K Privately Held
SIC: 3599 Custom machinery

(G-2353)
LUX CORPORATION
Also Called: C-Hawk Trailers
4613 Stetzer Rd (44820-9391)
PHONE......................................419 562-7978
Fax: 419 562-9750
Otis Shearer, President
Carol Shearer, Corp Secy
▲ EMP: 3
SALES (est): 260K Privately Held
WEB: www.c-hawktrailers.com
SIC: 3799 5599 Boat trailers; trailers &
trailer equipment; utility trailers

(G-2354)
NATIONAL LIME AND STONE CO
4580 Bethel Rd (44820-9754)
P.O. Box 69 (44820-0069)
PHONE......................................419 562-0771
Fax: 419 562-8574
Eric Johnson, Principal
Rick Dehays, Purch Agent
Delmo Arend, Sales Staff
Roger Nye, Maintence Staff
EMP: 62
SALES (corp-wide): 4B Privately Held
WEB: www.natlime.com
SIC: 1411 3281 1422 Limestone, dimen-
sion-quarrying; cut stone & stone prod-
ucts; crushed & broken limestone
PA: The National Lime And Stone Company
551 Lake Cascade Pkwy
Findlay OH 45840
419 422-4341

(G-2355)
OHIO FOAM CORPORATION (PA)
820 Plymouth St (44820-1641)
P.O. Box 208 (44820-0208)
PHONE......................................419 563-0399
Gail Potter, President
Jerry Necastro, Vice Pres
Terry Lady, Treasurer
Patty Kocher, Accounts Mgr
Pete Kessler, Sales Staff
EMP: 2 EST: 1972
SQ FT: 1,500
SALES: 13MM Privately Held
WEB: www.ohiofoam.com
SIC: 3069 Foam rubber

(G-2356)
R L RUSH TOOL & PATTERN INC
Also Called: Rush, R L Tool & Pattern
1620 Whetstone St (44820-3557)
P.O. Box 763 (44820-0763)
PHONE......................................419 562-9849
Fax: 419 562-9073
Roger Rush, President
Phyllis Rush, Admin Sec
EMP: 7
SQ FT: 7,000
SALES (est): 850K Privately Held
SIC: 3543 3469 Industrial patterns; stamp-
ing metal for the trade

(G-2357)
REGO MANUFACTURING CO INC
1870 E Mansfield St (44820-2018)
P.O. Box 838 (44820-0838)
PHONE......................................419 562-0466
Fax: 419 562-5059
Raymond L Kincaid, Ch of Bd
Claudia Kincaid, Vice Ch Bd
Ken Kincaid, President
Timothy Stenson, Treasurer
Rose Hoffman, Manager
EMP: 63 EST: 1973
SQ FT: 15,000
SALES (est): 11.7MM Privately Held
WEB: www.regoonline.com
SIC: 3911 Jewelry, precious metal

(G-2358)
RYDER-HEIL BRONZE INC
126 E Irving St (44820-1409)
P.O. Box 647 (44820-0647)
PHONE......................................419 562-2841
Fax: 419 562-8006
Herbert D Kleine, President
Shelly Acosta, Office Mgr
Aaron Atkinson, Maintence Staff
EMP: 35
SQ FT: 39,750
SALES (est): 8.4MM Privately Held
WEB: www.ryderheil.com
SIC: 3364 Brass & bronze die-castings

(G-2359)
SERVICE PDTS GROUP OF
BUCYRUS
Also Called: Wyandot Seating
118 River St (44820-1536)
P.O. Box 969 (44820-0969)
PHONE......................................419 562-4456
Fax: 419 562-5121
Phil Snyder, President
EMP: 4 EST: 1972
SQ FT: 46,000
SALES (est): 562K Privately Held
WEB: www.factorystools.com
SIC: 2522 5085 Chairs, office: padded or
plain, except wood; gaskets & seals

(G-2360)
TIMKEN COMPANY
2325 E Mansfield St (44820-2094)
PHONE......................................419 563-2200
Fax: 419 563-2233
Paul Hubacher, Plant Mgr
Keith Light, Engineer
Scott Wheeler, Engineer
Dean Hunter, Controller
Jack Yohe, Branch Mgr
EMP: 560
SQ FT: 400,000
SALES (corp-wide): 2.6B Publicly Held
SIC: 3562 Ball & roller bearings

GEOGRAPHIC

PA: The Timken Company
4500 Mount Pleasant St Nw
North Canton OH 44720
234 262-3000

(G-2361)
VAL CASTING INC
108 E Rensselaer St (44820-2320)
P.O. Box 374 (44820-0374)
PHONE...................................419 562-2499
Fax: 419 562-6561
Val Fawley, *President*
Michael Romanoff, *Vice Pres*
EMP: 30
SQ FT: 4,500
SALES (est): 3.2MM **Privately Held**
SIC: 3911 Jewelry, precious metal

(G-2362)
VASIL CO INC
Also Called: Vasil Fashions
119 E Mary St (44820-1828)
PHONE...................................419 562-2901
Margaret Ann Vasil, *Vice Pres*
Nicholas G Vasil, *Treasurer*
EMP: 8
SQ FT: 12,000
SALES (est): 831.4K **Privately Held**
SIC: 2396 2395 Screen printing on fabric
articles; art goods for embroidering,
stamped: purchased materials

(G-2363)
VELVET ICE CREAM COMPANY
Also Called: Bucyrus Ice Company
1233 Whetstone St (44820-3540)
PHONE...................................419 562-2009
Fax: 419 562-3228
Jack Rogers, *Manager*
EMP: 15
SALES (corp-wide): 14MM **Privately
Held**
WEB: www.velveticecream.com
SIC: 5143 2097 Ice cream & ices; manu-
factured ice
PA: Velvet Ice Cream Company
11324 Mount Vernon Rd
Utica OH 43080
740 892-3921

(G-2364)
W M DAUCH CONCRETE INC
900 Nevada Rd (44820-1744)
PHONE...................................419 562-6917
Fax: 419 668-1400
William Dauch, *President*
EMP: 7
SALES (est): 582.2K **Privately Held**
SIC: 3273 1771 Ready-mixed concrete;
concrete work

(G-2365)
WOOD STOVE SHED
4602 Stetzer Rd (44820-9391)
PHONE...................................419 562-1545
Patricia Garrett, *Owner*
Charles Garrett, *Co-Owner*
EMP: 3
SALES (est): 245K **Privately Held**
SIC: 3433 5075 1711 Burners, furnaces,
boilers & stokers; warm air heating equip-
ment & supplies; heating systems repair
& maintenance

(G-2366)
XT INNOVATIONS LTD
4799 Stetzer Rd (44820-9391)
PHONE...................................419 562-1989
Lane Carlisle, *Principal*
EMP: 3
SALES (est): 326.1K **Privately Held**
SIC: 2273 Carpets & rugs

Burbank
Wayne County

(G-2367)
PIPE COIL TECHNOLOGY INC
Also Called: P C T
111 Cardington Ln (44214-9426)
PHONE...................................330 256-6070
John Reece, *Chairman*
Bill Boden, *Production*

▲ EMP: 11
SALES (est): 1.7MM
SALES (corp-wide): 81.4MM **Privately
Held**
SIC: 3549 Coiling machinery
HQ: Pipe Coil Technology Limited
Armstrong Works
Newcastle-Upon-Tyne

Burghill
Trumbull County

(G-2368)
**MICHAELS TOOL SERVICE CO
INC**
8346 Milligan East Rd (44404-9729)
PHONE...................................330 772-1119
Robert F Michael, *Owner*
EMP: 4
SALES: 300K **Privately Held**
SIC: 3599 Industrial machinery

(G-2369)
PRECISION RUNNERS LLC
7186 State Route 609 (44404-9732)
PHONE...................................330 240-5988
Jason Longwell, *Owner*
EMP: 25
SALES (est): 2.4MM **Privately Held**
SIC: 3743 Tank freight cars & car equip-
ment

Burkettsville
Mercer County

(G-2370)
WERLING AND SONS INC
Also Called: Burkettsville Stockyard
100 S Plum St (45310)
PHONE...................................937 338-3281
Fax: 419 375-4187
Edward J Werling, *President*
James R Werling, *Corp Secy*
Carol Werling, *Manager*
EMP: 10 EST: 1886
SALES (est): 3.2MM **Privately Held**
WEB: www.werlingandsons.com
SIC: 5154 2011 Livestock; meat packing
plants

(G-2371)
WERLING MEATS INC
100 Plum St (45310)
PHONE...................................419 375-0037
P.O. Box 209 (45310-0209)
John Werling, *Principal*
EMP: 7
SALES (est): 254.7K **Privately Held**
SIC: 2032 Canned specialties

Burton
Geauga County

(G-2372)
ALUMINUM FENCE & MFG CO
15600 Main Market Rd (44021-9621)
PHONE...................................330 755-3323
Fax: 330 755-7811
Edward C Joseph, *President*
Maureen Joseph, *Vice Pres*
EMP: 6
SQ FT: 12,000
SALES (est): 1.2MM **Privately Held**
WEB: www.aluminumfencemfg.com
SIC: 3315 3599 3544 Chain link fencing;
machine shop, jobbing & repair; special
dies & tools

(G-2373)
DP PRODUCTS LLC
14395 Aquilla Rd (44021-9558)
P.O. Box 1062 (44021-1062)
PHONE...................................440 834-9663
Linn Ashba, *Office Mgr*
Ken Ashba,
EMP: 4
SQ FT: 12,000

SALES (est): 549.4K **Privately Held**
SIC: 2449 2441 Rectangular boxes &
crates, wood; nailed wood boxes & shook

(G-2374)
ENVIRON INTERNATIONAL COR
13801 W Center St (44021-9010)
PHONE...................................440 834-1460
Tim Barber, *Principal*
EMP: 3
SALES (est): 386.3K **Privately Held**
SIC: 3826 Environmental testing equip-
ment

(G-2375)
FONTANELLE GROUP INC
Also Called: Country Savings Magazine
13199 Longwood Ave (44021-9508)
PHONE...................................440 834-8900
Barbara Fontanelle, *President*
Benjamin Fontanelle, *Vice Pres*
EMP: 3
SALES (est): 330.5K **Privately Held**
WEB: www.countrysavingsmagazine.com
SIC: 2721 Periodicals: publishing only;
magazines: publishing & printing

(G-2376)
HEXPOL COMPOUNDING LLC
Also Called: Burton Rubber Processing
14330 Kinsman Rd (44021-9648)
PHONE...................................440 834-4644
Fax: 440 834-5524
Len McClearn, *Vice Pres*
Steven Strouse, *Vice Pres*
D Thomas, *Traffic Mgr*
John Gorrell, *Manager*
Debbie Christian, *Clerk*
EMP: 200
SALES (corp-wide): 1.2B **Privately Held**
SIC: 3087 2865 5162 2899 Custom com-
pound purchased resins; dyes & pig-
ments; resins; plastics basic shapes;
chemical preparations; adhesives &
sealants; paints & allied products
HQ: Hexpol Compounding Llc
14330 Kinsman Rd
Burton OH 44021
440 834-4644

(G-2377)
**HEXPOL COMPOUNDING LLC
(DH)**
Also Called: Hexpol Polymers
14330 Kinsman Rd (44021-9648)
P.O. Box 415000, Nashville TN (37241-
5000)
PHONE...................................440 834-4644
Tracy Garrison, *CEO*
Stephen W Chase, *General Mgr*
Peter Mollett, *General Mgr*
Glenn Thurman, *General Mgr*
Rakshit Lamba, *Vice Pres*
▲ EMP: 50
SALES (est): 490.6MM
SALES (corp-wide): 1.2B **Privately Held**
WEB: www.excel-polymers.com
SIC: 3087 2821 Custom compound pur-
chased resins; thermoplastic materials
HQ: Hexpol Holding Inc.
14330 Kinsman Rd
Burton OH 44021
440 834-4644

(G-2378)
JOES SAW SHOP
14530 Butternut Rd (44021-9528)
PHONE...................................440 834-1196
Joe Byler, *Principal*
EMP: 4
SALES (est): 325.6K **Privately Held**
SIC: 3425 Saw blades & handsaws

(G-2379)
K D HARDWOODS INC
14195 Kinsman Rd (44021-9650)
P.O. Box 177 (44021-0177)
PHONE...................................440 834-1772
Fax: 440 834-4720
Brian Snider, *President*
Cynthia Snider, *Vice Pres*
EMP: 3
SQ FT: 5,600

SALES (est): 344.2K **Privately Held**
SIC: 2431 5211 Moldings, wood: unfinished & prefinished; doors & door parts &
trim, wood; staircases, stairs & railings;
lumber products

(G-2380)
**KEN EMERICK MACHINE
PRODUCTS**
14504 Main Market Rd (44021-9615)
PHONE...................................440 834-4501
Fax: 440 834-1496
Ken Emerick, *President*
Cheryl Klatik, *General Mgr*
Pam Emerick, *Vice Pres*
EMP: 8
SQ FT: 12,500
SALES: 100K **Privately Held**
WEB: www.emerickmachine.com
SIC: 3541 Screw machines, automatic

(G-2381)
OHIO BOX & CRATE INC
Also Called: Ohio Box and Crate Co
16751 Tavern Rd (44021-9605)
PHONE...................................440 526-3133
Sarmite S Grava, *President*
Pete Grava, *Plant Mgr*
EMP: 12
SQ FT: 15,000
SALES (est): 1.8MM **Privately Held**
SIC: 2441 2448 Boxes, wood; skids, wood
& wood with metal

(G-2382)
R J DOBAY ENTERPRISES INC
Also Called: Ronald J Dobay Enterprises
14704 Main Market Rd (44021-9667)
PHONE...................................440 834-4580
EMP: 6
SALES (est): 350K **Privately Held**
SIC: 4212 1794 2421 Local Trucking Op-
erator Excavation Contractor
Sawmill/Planing Mill

(G-2383)
ROTARY TECH INC
12710 Kinsman Rd (44021-9763)
PHONE...................................440 862-8568
Kristopher Fugate, *Principal*
Chad Derbyshire, *Vice Pres*
EMP: 5
SALES (est): 167.6K **Privately Held**
SIC: 3599 Machine shop, jobbing & repair

(G-2384)
**SHALERSVILLE ASPHALT CO
(PA)**
Also Called: Ronyak Brothers Paving
14376 N Cheshire St (44021-9574)
P.O. Box 449 (44021-0449)
PHONE...................................440 834-4294
Fax: 440 834-1989
David W Ronyak, *President*
Jim Shale, *Vice Pres*
Karen Draves, *Human Resources*
Kevin Reed, *Manager*
EMP: 25
SQ FT: 2,000
SALES (est): 13.3MM **Privately Held**
SIC: 2951 Asphalt & asphaltic paving mix-
tures (not from refineries)

(G-2385)
STEPHEN M TRUDICK
Also Called: Hardwood Lumber Co
13813 Station Rd (44021)
P.O. Box 15 (44021-0015)
PHONE...................................440 834-1891
Fax: 440 834-0243
Stephen M Trudick, *Owner*
John Mullet, *Engineer*
Nancy Taddie, *Financial Exec*
Dawn Pauletter, *Office Mgr*
Jayne Shaffer, *Director*
▲ EMP: 41
SQ FT: 80,000
SALES (est): 5.6MM **Privately Held**
WEB: www.hardwood-lumber.com
SIC: 3991 2426 5031 3442 Brooms &
brushes; dimension, hardwood; lumber:
rough, dressed & finished; metal doors,
sash & trim; millwork; sawmills & planing
mills, general

▲ = Import ▼=Export
◆ =Import/Export

(G-2386)
STONEY ACRES WOODWORKING LLC
14575 Patch Rd (44021-9631)
PHONE..................................440 834-0717
Michael J Miller, *Principal*
EMP: 4 **EST:** 2009
SALES (est): 379.8K **Privately Held**
SIC: 2431 Millwork

(G-2387)
TROY CHEMICAL INDUSTRIES INC (PA)
17040 Rapids Rd (44021-9754)
P.O. Box 430 (44021-0430)
PHONE..................................440 834-4408
Fax: 440 834-1142
Lee Imhof, *President*
Joyce Pope, *Corp Secy*
Richard B Keyse, *Vice Pres*
Tibor Orszag, *Purchasing*
Joyce Imhof, *Treasurer*
▲ **EMP:** 19
SQ FT: 25,000
SALES (est): 3.4MM **Privately Held**
WEB: www.troychemical.com
SIC: 2842 Specialty cleaning preparations

(G-2388)
TROY MANUFACTURING CO
17090 Rapids Rd (44021-9754)
P.O. Box 448 (44021-0448)
PHONE..................................440 834-8262
Fax: 440 834-1137
David Cseplo, *President*
Wynne Bogert, *Vice Pres*
Charles Fath, *Vice Pres*
Richard Taylor, *Vice Pres*
Ronald Fratoe, *Manager*
EMP: 30 **EST:** 1952
SQ FT: 40,000
SALES (est): 4.7MM **Privately Held**
SIC: 3451 Screw machine products

(G-2389)
TROY PRECISION CARBIDE DIE
17720 Claridon Troy Rd (44021-9658)
PHONE..................................440 834-4477
Fax: 440 834-1643
James Dewalt, *President*
Jeff Amon, *Corp Secy*
Kelly Amon, *Vice Pres*
EMP: 12 **EST:** 1952
SQ FT: 10,000
SALES (est): 1.7MM **Privately Held**
SIC: 3599 Machine shop, jobbing & repair

(G-2390)
WB INDUSTRIES INC
16461 Messenger Rd (44021)
PHONE..................................440 708-0309
William Bertman, *Owner*
EMP: 4
SQ FT: 1,550
SALES (est): 332.5K **Privately Held**
SIC: 3589 Car washing machinery

Butler
Richland County

(G-2391)
HIGHLINE RACEWAY LLC
1766 Cassell Rd (44822-9700)
PHONE..................................419 883-2042
Kelly Donaugh, *Principal*
EMP: 3
SALES (est): 224.4K **Privately Held**
SIC: 3644 Raceways

(G-2392)
MID-OHIO TUBING LLC (PA)
145 W Elm St (44822-9783)
PHONE..................................419 883-2066
Jamie Feick, *CEO*
Wayne Riffe, *President*
EMP: 39 **EST:** 2013
SALES (est): 25MM **Privately Held**
SIC: 3317 Tubes, seamless steel

(G-2393)
MOHICAN WOOD PRODUCTS
20460 Nunda Rd (44822-9400)
PHONE..................................740 599-5655
Ivan Miller, *Owner*
EMP: 4
SQ FT: 9,792
SALES: 750K **Privately Held**
SIC: 2431 Door trim, wood; moldings, wood: unfinished & prefinished

(G-2394)
YODER WOODWORKING
21198 Swendal Rd (44822-9214)
PHONE..................................740 399-9400
Mervin Yoder, *Principal*
EMP: 4
SALES (est): 410K **Privately Held**
SIC: 2431 Millwork

Byesville
Guernsey County

(G-2395)
CALDWELL REDI MIX COMPANY
209 Pioneer Rd (43723)
PHONE..................................740 685-6554
Ruben Schafer, *President*
Allen Hill, *Manager*
EMP: 5
SALES (corp-wide): 1MM **Privately Held**
SIC: 3273 Ready-mixed concrete
PA: Caldwell Redi Mix Company
45997 Marietta Rd
Caldwell OH 43724
740 732-2906

(G-2396)
CAMBRIDGE CABLE SERVICE CO
58945 Country Club Rd (43723-9763)
P.O. Box 5 (43723-0005)
PHONE..................................740 685-5775
Kevin G Deason, *President*
Cindy Deason, *Vice Pres*
EMP: 4
SQ FT: 5,000
SALES: 1.5MM **Privately Held**
SIC: 5251 1623 5051 3315 Hardware; cable laying construction; rope, wire (not insulated); wire & fabricated wire products

(G-2397)
DAVID R HILL INC
132 S 2nd St (43723-1304)
P.O. Box 247 (43723-0247)
PHONE..................................740 685-5168
David R Hill, *CEO*
EMP: 6
SALES (est): 746.8K **Privately Held**
SIC: 1382 Geological exploration, oil & gas field

(G-2398)
DETROIT DESL RMNFCTRNG-AST INC
60703 Country Club Rd (43723-9730)
PHONE..................................740 439-7701
Roger S Penske, *Ch of Bd*
James Morrow, *President*
Mike Chuich, *Vice Pres*
Brian Pfeiffer, *Asst Controller*
Barb Menzie, *Officer*
◆ **EMP:** 500
SQ FT: 128,000
SALES (est): 153MM
SALES (corp-wide): 162B **Privately Held**
SIC: 3519 Diesel engine rebuilding
HQ: Detroit Diesel Remanufacturing Corporation
13400 W Outer Dr
Detroit MI 48239

(G-2399)
DETROIT DIESL SPECIALTY TL INC
60703 Country Club Rd (43723-9730)
PHONE..................................740 435-4452
Wayne Prouty, *President*
Damon Tauvel, *Controller*
▲ **EMP:** 30

SALES (est): 3.7MM
SALES (corp-wide): 162B **Privately Held**
WEB: www.ddre.detroitdiesel.com
SIC: 3599 Electrical discharge machining (EDM)
HQ: Detroit Diesel Corporation
13400 W Outer Dr
Detroit MI 48239
313 592-5000

(G-2400)
EAST OHIO GAS COMPANY
Also Called: Dominion East Ohio
60755 Country Club Rd (43723-9730)
PHONE..................................740 439-2721
Fax: 740 439-7782
Larry Blake, *Branch Mgr*
Greg Nicholes, *Manager*
EMP: 5
SALES (corp-wide): 11.7B **Publicly Held**
SIC: 1311 Crude petroleum & natural gas
HQ: The East Ohio Gas Company
19701 Libby Rd
Maple Heights OH 44137
800 362-7557

(G-2401)
FAMOUS INDUSTRIES INC
Also Called: L B Manufacturing
356 W Main St (43723-1123)
PHONE..................................740 685-2592
Fax: 740 685-6161
Bob Badnell, *Manager*
Gary Thompson, *Manager*
EMP: 80 **Privately Held**
WEB: www.jfgoodco.com
SIC: 3469 3585 3564 3498 Stamping metal for the trade; refrigeration & heating equipment; blowers & fans; fabricated pipe & fittings; heating equipment, except electric
HQ: Famous Industries, Inc.
2620 Ridgewood Rd Ste 200
Akron OH 44313
330 535-1811

(G-2402)
FAMOUS REALTY CLEVELAND INC
Also Called: Famous Supply
354 W Main St (43723-1123)
PHONE..................................740 685-2533
Fax: 740 685-3664
Eric St Claire, *Manager*
EMP: 11
SALES (corp-wide): 1MM **Privately Held**
SIC: 3585 5074 Heating & air conditioning combination units; plumbing fittings & supplies
PA: Famous Realty Of Cleveland, Inc.
109 N Union St
Akron OH 44304
330 762-9621

(G-2403)
HILL & ASSOCIATES INC
132 S 6th St (43723)
P.O. Box 247 (43723-0247)
PHONE..................................740 685-5168
David R Hill, *President*
EMP: 3
SALES (est): 300K **Privately Held**
SIC: 1389 Oil & gas wells: building, repairing & dismantling

(G-2404)
INTERNATIONAL PAPER COMPANY
60700 Hope Ave (43723-9740)
PHONE..................................740 439-3527
Chuck Evans, *Safety Dir*
Scott Dillon, *Plant Mgr*
EMP: 14
SALES (corp-wide): 21B **Publicly Held**
SIC: 2621 Paper mills
PA: International Paper Company
6400 Poplar Ave
Memphis TN 38197
901 419-9000

(G-2405)
ISLAND ASEPTICS LLC
100 Hope Ave (43723-9460)
P.O. Box 280 (43723-0280)
PHONE..................................740 685-2548
Jeff Campbell, *Vice Pres*

Janell Burt, *Opers Mgr*
Sandy Smith, *Controller*
Karen Skeslock, *Asst Controller*
John Kasinecz,
▲ **EMP:** 150
SQ FT: 5,000
SALES (est): 40.3MM **Privately Held**
SIC: 2656 Food containers (liquid tight), including milk cartons
HQ: Island Oasis Frozen Cocktail Co., Inc.
141 Norfolk St
Walpole MA 02081
508 660-1177

(G-2406)
KEN HARPER
Also Called: GUERNSEY INDUSTRIES
60772 Southgate Rd (43723-9731)
PHONE..................................740 439-4452
Susie Mathia, *Bookkeeper*
Ken Harper, *Exec Dir*
EMP: 110
SALES: 801.5K **Privately Held**
SIC: 8331 2511 2448 Sheltered workshop; wood household furniture; wood pallets & skids

(G-2407)
MAR-ZANE INC
59903 Vocational Rd (43723-9450)
PHONE..................................740 685-5178
Robert Hamilton, *Manager*
EMP: 3
SALES (corp-wide): 301.4MM **Privately Held**
SIC: 2951 Asphalt paving mixtures & blocks
HQ: Mar-Zane, Inc.
3570 S River Rd
Zanesville OH 43701
740 453-0721

(G-2408)
PEOPLES BANCORP INC
221 S 2nd St (43723-1303)
PHONE..................................740 685-1500
Phyllis Jeffries, *Principal*
EMP: 44
SALES (corp-wide): 166.3MM **Publicly Held**
SIC: 3578 Automatic teller machines (ATM)
PA: Peoples Bancorp Inc.
138 Putnam St
Marietta OH 45750
740 373-3155

(G-2409)
PROFESSIONAL OILFIELD SERVICES
221 1/2 S 6th St (43723-1151)
P.O. Box 247 (43723-0247)
PHONE..................................740 685-5168
David Hill, *President*
Jerry Olds, *Treasurer*
EMP: 4
SQ FT: 1,000
SALES (est): 470K **Privately Held**
SIC: 1381 Drilling oil & gas wells

(G-2410)
TIMCO INC
57051 Marietta Rd (43723-9709)
PHONE..................................740 685-2594
Tim Brown, *President*
Mark Brown, *Vice Pres*
EMP: 12
SQ FT: 2,000
SALES (est): 1.5MM **Privately Held**
WEB: www.timcoinc.net
SIC: 1381 3533 Drilling oil & gas wells; oil & gas field machinery

(G-2411)
TIMOTHY SASSER
Also Called: Triple T Fabricating
59538 Lost Rd (43723-9543)
PHONE..................................740 260-9499
Timothy Sasser, *Owner*
EMP: 5 **EST:** 2014
SALES (est): 170K **Privately Held**
SIC: 7692 Welding repair

(G-2412)
VELOCITY CONCEPT DEV GROUP LLC
8824 Clay Pike (43723-9712)
PHONE....................740 685-2637
Kathy Black, *President*
Eric Fehrman, *Branch Mgr*
EMP: 8
SALES (corp-wide): 4MM **Privately Held**
SIC: 3544 Industrial molds; special dies & tools; jigs & fixtures
PA: Velocity Concept Development Group, Llc
4393 Digital Way
Mason OH 45040
513 204-2100

(G-2413)
W P BROWN ENTERPRISES INC
57051 Marietta Rd (43723-9709)
PHONE....................740 685-2594
William P Brown, *President*
Mark Brown, *Vice Pres*
Harry Morrison, *Engineer*
Jerry Palmer, *Manager*
EMP: 6
SALES (est): 600.5K **Privately Held**
SIC: 1311 Crude petroleum production

Cable
Champaign County

(G-2414)
YOCOM BROTHERS
773 Perry Rd (43009-9634)
PHONE....................937 653-8767
Fax: 937 653-8767
Ross Yocom, *Partner*
Roger Yocom, *Partner*
EMP: 3
SQ FT: 16,000
SALES: 500K **Privately Held**
SIC: 3523 Sprayers & spraying machines, agricultural

Cadiz
Harrison County

(G-2415)
CONSOL COAL COMPANY
79285 Cadiz New Athens Rd (43907-9606)
PHONE....................740 942-4353
Brad Harvey, *President*
EMP: 60
SALES (est): 4.2MM **Privately Held**
SIC: 1241 Coal mining services

(G-2416)
DANIEL WAGNER
39170 Welsh Rd (43907-9571)
PHONE....................740 942-2928
Daniel Wagner, *Principal*
EMP: 4
SALES (est): 374.1K **Privately Held**
SIC: 3713 Dump truck bodies

(G-2417)
DARON COAL COMPANY LLC
40580 Cadiz Piedmont Rd (43907-9514)
PHONE....................614 643-0337
Fax: 740 942-2904
Charles C Ungurean,
EMP: 175
SALES (est): 6.8MM
SALES (corp-wide): 1.4B **Publicly Held**
SIC: 1221 Bituminous coal surface mining
HQ: Oxford Mining Company, Inc.
544 Chestnut St
Coshocton OH 43812
740 622-6302

(G-2418)
HARRISON NEWS HERALD INC
Also Called: Schloss Media
144 S Main St Lowr (43907-1167)
PHONE....................740 942-2118
Fax: 740 942-4667
David Schloss, *President*
Millie Pruent, *President*
EMP: 11

SALES (est): 718.6K **Privately Held**
WEB: www.harrisonnewsherald.com
SIC: 2711 Newspapers: publishing only, not printed on site

(G-2419)
MARKWEST ENERGY PARTNERS LP
Also Called: Mark West Energy
78405 Cadiz New Athens Rd (43907-9665)
PHONE....................740 942-0463
Mark West, *Branch Mgr*
EMP: 7
SALES (corp-wide): 2.5B **Publicly Held**
SIC: 1321 Natural gas liquids
HQ: Markwest Energy Partners, L.P.
1515 Arapahoe St
Denver CO 80202
303 925-9200

(G-2420)
MIH MARKETING GROUP INC
546 N Main St (43907-1276)
PHONE....................740 942-0411
Christopher J Strussion, *President*
Richard P Anoia, *Vice Pres*
EMP: 16
SQ FT: 10,000
SALES (est): 2MM **Privately Held**
SIC: 3494 Sprinkler systems, field

(G-2421)
MIZER PRINTING & GRAPHICS
160 Cunningham Ave (43907-1003)
PHONE....................740 942-3343
Fax: 740 942-3255
Thomas Mizer, *Owner*
EMP: 3
SQ FT: 1,440
SALES (est): 300.3K **Privately Held**
SIC: 2752 Commercial printing, lithographic

(G-2422)
STANLEY BITTINGER
Also Called: Bittinger Carbide
81331 Hines Rd (43907-9535)
PHONE....................740 942-4302
Fax: 740 942-3628
Stanley Bittinger, *Owner*
Sheila Bittinger, *Office Mgr*
EMP: 7
SQ FT: 1,800
SALES: 500K **Privately Held**
WEB: www.bestbur.com
SIC: 3546 5084 3545 Power-driven hand-tools; industrial machinery & equipment; machine tool accessories

Caldwell
Noble County

(G-2423)
ANTERO RESOURCES CORPORATION
44510 Marietta Rd (43724-9209)
PHONE....................303 357-7310
EMP: 110
SALES (corp-wide): 2.7B **Publicly Held**
SIC: 1382 Oil & gas exploration services
PA: Antero Resources Corporation
1615 Wynkoop St
Denver CO 80202
303 357-7310

(G-2424)
BEAR WELDING SERVICES LLC
18210 Myrtle Ake Rd (43724-9136)
PHONE....................740 630-7538
Jeremy Leonard, *Mng Member*
EMP: 10
SALES: 1.2MM **Privately Held**
SIC: 7692 Welding repair

(G-2425)
CALDWELL LUMBER & SUPPLY CO
Also Called: Do It Best
17990 Woodsfield Rd (43724-9435)
PHONE....................740 732-2306
Fax: 740 732-2307
Edward Crock, *President*
Brandon Crock, *Corp Secy*

EMP: 45 EST: 1948
SQ FT: 25,000
SALES (est): 6.3MM **Privately Held**
SIC: 5251 3273 Hardware; ready-mixed concrete

(G-2426)
CALDWELL REDI MIX COMPANY (PA)
Also Called: Caldwell Redi-Mix Concrete
45997 Marietta Rd (43724-9241)
PHONE....................740 732-2906
Reuben Schafer, *President*
EMP: 4 EST: 1958
SQ FT: 800
SALES (est): 1MM **Privately Held**
SIC: 3273 Ready-mixed concrete

(G-2427)
HL OILFIELD SERVICES LLC
19797 Harl Weiller Rd (43724-9149)
PHONE....................740 783-1156
Sandi McKown, *Office Mgr*
Todd McKown, *Manager*
EMP: 3
SALES (est): 164.6K **Privately Held**
SIC: 1389 Oil field services

(G-2428)
INTERNTNAL CNVRTER CLDWELL INC (DH)
Also Called: I-Convert
17153 Industrial Hwy (43724-9779)
PHONE....................740 732-5665
Phil Harris, *President*
Jerry Lawrence, *Vice Pres*
Craig Lemieux, *Vice Pres*
Gerry Medlin, *Vice Pres*
Mitchell Mekaelian, *Vice Pres*
◆ EMP: 176
SQ FT: 75,000
SALES (est): 29.9MM
SALES (corp-wide): 2.2B **Publicly Held**
WEB: www.ici-laminating.com
SIC: 3089 3353 3083 Laminating of plastic; aluminum sheet, plate & foil; laminated plastics plate & sheet
HQ: Packaging Dynamics Corporation
3900 W 43rd St
Chicago IL 60632
773 254-8000

(G-2429)
KING QUARRIES INC
41820 Parrish Ridge Rd (43724-8910)
PHONE....................740 732-2923
Fax: 740 732-7388
Mary King, *President*
EMP: 5 EST: 1955
SQ FT: 800
SALES (est): 765.4K **Privately Held**
SIC: 1221 Bituminous coal & lignite-surface mining

(G-2430)
MORTON BUILDINGS INC
40800 Marietta Rd (43724-9134)
PHONE....................740 783-2331
Fax: 740 783-2321
Tim Wetterhus, *Engineer*
Blake Fitzgerald, *Sales Associate*
Kevin Flood, *Manager*
EMP: 12
SALES (corp-wide): 499.4MM **Privately Held**
WEB: www.mortonbuildings.com
SIC: 3448 Farm & utility buildings
PA: Morton Buildings, Inc.
252 W Adams St
Morton IL 61550
800 447-7436

(G-2431)
R C MOORE LUMBER CO
820 Miller St (43724-1044)
P.O. Box 139 (43724-0139)
PHONE....................740 732-4950
Chad Moore, *President*
EMP: 14
SALES (corp-wide): 1.6MM **Privately Held**
WEB: www.rcmooredoorsnmore.com
SIC: 2431 5211 Doors, combination screen-storm, wood; lumber products

PA: R C Moore Lumber Co Inc
46000 County Road 56
Caldwell OH
740 732-2326

(G-2432)
SHARON STONE INC
44895 Sharon Stone Rd (43724-9534)
P.O. Box 100, Dexter City (45727-0100)
PHONE....................740 732-7100
Fax: 740 732-7774
John McCort, *President*
Robert Cunningham, *Corp Secy*
Carl Baker Jr, *Vice Pres*
EMP: 6
SQ FT: 980
SALES (est): 509.5K **Privately Held**
SIC: 1422 Limestones, ground

(G-2433)
SOUTHEAST PUBLICATIONS INC
Also Called: Journal Leader
309 Main St (43724-1321)
P.O. Box 315 (43724-0315)
PHONE....................740 732-2341
Fax: 740 732-7288
David Evans, *President*
Jack Cartener, *Director*
Ann Velgari, *Director*
EMP: 10 EST: 1941
SQ FT: 3,360
SALES: 536.5K **Privately Held**
SIC: 2711 2752 Commercial printing & newspaper publishing combined; commercial printing, lithographic

(G-2434)
UPPER SARAHSVILLE LLC
48726 Sarahsville Rd (43724-9773)
PHONE....................740 732-2071
Elizabeth Saling, *Principal*
EMP: 3
SALES (est): 174.9K **Privately Held**
SIC: 3131 Uppers

Caledonia
Marion County

(G-2435)
CLARIDON TOOL & DIE INC
Also Called: Retterer Manufacturing Company
4985 Marion Mt Gilead Rd (43314-9431)
PHONE....................740 389-1944
Karen Retterer, *President*
Ryan Fitzgerald, *Info Tech Dir*
EMP: 7
SALES: 600K **Privately Held**
WEB: www.retterer.com
SIC: 3544 Special dies & tools

(G-2436)
DIVERSIFIED TOOL SYSTEMS
5357 Mrion Wllmsport Rd E (43314-9527)
P.O. Box 249 (43314-0249)
PHONE....................419 845-2143
Fax: 419 845-3980
Robert Freeman, *Owner*
Mike Freeman, *Accountant*
EMP: 4
SQ FT: 3,500
SALES (est): 443.4K **Privately Held**
SIC: 3544 Forms (molds), for foundry & plastics working machinery

(G-2437)
GLEN-GERY CORPORATION
Also Called: Glen-Gery Caledonia Plant
5692 Rinker Rd (43314-9791)
P.O. Box 398 (43314-0398)
PHONE....................419 845-3321
Fax: 419 845-2313
Ken Hagberg, *Manager*
EMP: 90 **Privately Held**
WEB: www.glengerybrick.com
SIC: 3251 5211 3255 Brick clay: common face, glazed, vitrified or hollow; brick; clay refractories
HQ: Glen-Gery Corporation
1166 Spring St
Reading PA 19610
610 374-4011

▲ = Import ▼=Export
◆ =Import/Export

(G-2438)
INSTA-GRO MANUFACTURING INC
8217 Linn Hipsher Rd (43314-9736)
PHONE..............................419 845-3046
Fax: 419 845-3251
Allan Farrow, *President*
Brenda Shewmaker, *Manager*
EMP: 6
SALES (est): 1.1MM Privately Held
WEB: www.instagro.com
SIC: 2875 5261 Fertilizers, mixing only;
fertilizer

(G-2439)
JEFFERY A BURNS
Also Called: R & J Contracting
7430 Linn Hipsher Rd (43314-9733)
PHONE..............................419 845-2129
Jeffery A Burns, *Owner*
EMP: 5
SALES: 200K Privately Held
SIC: 3444 Sheet metalwork

(G-2440)
NAMES UNLIMITED CORP
3787 Marion Galion Rd (43314-9495)
PHONE..............................419 845-2005
Tom Cannane, *President*
EMP: 3
SQ FT: 3,000
SALES (est): 222.2K Privately Held
SIC: 3993 Signs & advertising specialties

(G-2441)
PILLSBURY COMPANY LLC
4136 Martel Rd (43314-9634)
PHONE..............................419 845-3751
Fax: 419 845-3390
Al Rodrigues, *Plant Mgr*
Heidi Duval, *QC Dir*
Craig Olinger, *Branch Mgr*
Dawn Fisher, *Director*
EMP: 75
SALES (corp-wide): 16.5B Publicly Held
WEB: www.pillsbury.com
SIC: 2041 2033 Flour & other grain mill
products; canned fruits & specialties
HQ: The Pillsbury Company Llc
1 General Mills Blvd
Minneapolis MN 55426

Cambridge
Guernsey County

(G-2442)
ACI SERVICES INC (PA)
Also Called: Gas Products
125 Steubenville Ave (43725-2212)
PHONE..............................740 435-0240
Chad Brahler, *President*
Larry Burnett, *General Mgr*
Norm Shade, *Principal*
Joe Reiheld, *Vice Pres*
Debbie Johnson, *CFO*
EMP: 40
SQ FT: 25,000
SALES: 20MM Privately Held
WEB: www.aciservices.net
SIC: 3563 Air & gas compressors including
vacuum pumps

(G-2443)
AMERICAN CULVERT & FABG CO
201 Wheeling Ave (43725-2256)
P.O. Box 757 (43725-0757)
PHONE..............................740 432-6334
Fax: 740 439-7349
Herman Rogovin, *President*
Art Rogovin, *Vice Pres*
Rod Lemasters, *MIS Mgr*
EMP: 15 EST: 1936
SQ FT: 5,000
SALES (est): 1.4MM Privately Held
SIC: 3444 3312 Pipe, sheet metal; blast
furnaces & steel mills

(G-2444)
AMG VANADIUM LLC
60790 Southgate Rd (43725-9414)
PHONE..............................740 435-4600
Hoy Frakes, *President*

William J Levy, *Vice Pres*
Rick Walters, *Opers Staff*
David Thompson, *Buyer*
David Wardle, *QC Mgr*
◆ EMP: 1
SALES (est): 4.3MM
SALES (corp-wide): 977.1MM Privately
Held
SIC: 1094 Vanadium ore mining
PA: Amg Advanced Metallurgical Group
N.V.
Strawinskylaan 1343
Amsterdam 1077
207 147-140

(G-2445)
APPALACHIAN SOLVENTS LLC
5041 Skyline Dr (43725-9729)
PHONE..............................740 680-3649
Jonathan Hudson, *Owner*
EMP: 3
SALES (est): 316.2K Privately Held
SIC: 2911 Solvents

(G-2446)
APPALACHIAN WELL SURVEYS INC
10291 Ohio Ave (43725)
P.O. Box 1058 (43725-6058)
PHONE..............................740 255-7652
Fax: 740 439-9480
Jonathan W Hudson, *President*
Mary Ann Hudson, *Vice Pres*
EMP: 8
SALES (est): 1.4MM Privately Held
SIC: 1389 Perforating well casings; survey-
ing wells; well logging

(G-2447)
BENNETT PLASTICS INC
197 N 2nd St (43725-2222)
PHONE..............................740 432-2209
Fax: 740 432-2235
Frank J Bennett Jr, *President*
EMP: 20
SALES (est): 1.2MM Privately Held
SIC: 3089 Injection molding of plastics

(G-2448)
CAMBRIDGE OHIO PRODUCTION & AS
Also Called: Copac
1521 Morton Ave (43725-2750)
PHONE..............................740 432-6383
Fax: 740 432-5865
Mike Arent, *President*
Andrew E Yandora, *Vice Pres*
Andrew Balik, *VP Sales*
EMP: 15
SQ FT: 39,500
SALES (est): 7.8MM Privately Held
SIC: 3578 3643 Accounting machines &
cash registers; current-carrying wiring de-
vices

(G-2449)
CAMBRIDGE PACKAGING INC
Also Called: Cambridge Box & Gift Shop
60794 Southgate Rd (43725-9414)
PHONE..............................740 432-3351
Fax: 740 439-5890
Larry Knellinger, *President*
Bill Knellinger, *Vice Pres*
Rick Knellinger, *Vice Pres*
Dave Garvin, *Prdtn Mgr*
Monty Young, *Maint Spvr*
EMP: 31
SQ FT: 26,000
SALES (est): 8MM Privately Held
WEB: www.cambridgepackaging.com
SIC: 2653 5199 Boxes, corrugated: made
from purchased materials; packaging ma-
terials

(G-2450)
CARRIZO OIL & GAS INC
647 Wheeling Ave (43725-2251)
PHONE..............................740 432-5463
Debbie M Soho, *Principal*
EMP: 3
SALES (corp-wide): 443.5MM Publicly
Held
SIC: 1382 Oil & gas exploration services

PA: Carrizo Oil & Gas, Inc.
500 Dallas St Ste 2300
Houston TX 77002
713 328-1000

(G-2451)
CENTRIA INC
Also Called: Centria Coil Coating Services
530 N 2nd St (43725-1214)
PHONE..............................740 432-7351
John Clark, *QC Mgr*
Kelli Hill, *Human Resources*
Gary Kehrier, *Sales Mgr*
Mike Sicklesteel, *Sales Mgr*
Doug Hileman, *Sales Staff*
EMP: 100
SALES (corp-wide): 1.6B Publicly Held
SIC: 3444 Sheet metalwork
HQ: Centria, Inc.
1005 Beaver Grade Rd # 2
Coraopolis PA 15108
412 299-8000

(G-2452)
COLGATE-PALMOLIVE COMPANY
8800 Guernsey Indus Blvd (43725-8913)
PHONE..............................212 310-2000
Fax: 740 439-7022
Chuck Bates, *Materials Mgr*
Rick Spann, *Opers-Prdtn-Mfg*
Tom Badertscher, *Engineer*
Larry Brooker, *Project Engr*
Mauricio Torres, *Financial Exec*
EMP: 250
SALES (corp-wide): 15.2B Publicly Held
WEB: www.colgate.com
SIC: 2841 Soap & other detergents
PA: Colgate-Palmolive Company
300 Park Ave Fl 5
New York NY 10022
212 310-2000

(G-2453)
CRESCENT SERVICES LLC
11137 E Pike Rd (43725-8949)
PHONE..............................405 603-1200
Susan Leonard, *Principal*
EMP: 5
SALES (est): 334.4K Privately Held
SIC: 1389 Oil & gas field services

(G-2454)
DETROIT DESL RMNFACTURING CORP
8475 Reitler Rd (43725)
PHONE..............................740 439-7701
Cheryl Meyer, *Branch Mgr*
EMP: 12
SALES (corp-wide): 162B Privately Held
SIC: 3519 Diesel engine rebuilding
HQ: Detroit Diesel Remanufacturing Corpo-
ration
13400 W Outer Dr
Detroit MI 48239

(G-2455)
DONAHUES HILLTOP ICE COMPANY
Also Called: Donahue's Hilltop Supply
1112 Highland Ave (43725-8809)
PHONE..............................740 432-3348
Fax: 740 432-6539
John Hoffman, *Owner*
John B Hoffman, *Owner*
EMP: 12
SQ FT: 8,000
SALES (est): 1.3MM Privately Held
SIC: 2097 Block ice; ice cubes

(G-2456)
ENCORE PLASTICS CORPORATION
725 Water St (43725-1241)
PHONE..............................740 432-1652
John Wilson, *Branch Mgr*
EMP: 56
SALES (corp-wide): 57.4MM Privately
Held
WEB: www.encoreplasticscorporation.com
SIC: 3089 Plastic processing
HQ: Encore Plastics Corporation
319 Howard Dr
Sandusky OH 44870
419 626-8000

(G-2457)
FEDERAL-MOGUL CORPORATION
6420 Glenn Hwy (43725-9755)
PHONE..............................740 432-2393
Steve Grilliot, *Plant Mgr*
Scott Atkinson, *Engineer*
Rick Kunko, *Controller*
Robb Junker, *Branch Mgr*
EMP: 210
SALES (corp-wide): 16.3B Publicly Held
SIC: 3053 3592 3562 5085 Gaskets &
sealing devices; oil seals, rubber; gaskets, all materials; pistons & piston rings;
ball bearings & parts; bearings; motor vehicle parts & accessories; bearings, motor
vehicle; transmission housings or parts,
motor vehicle; steering mechanisms,
motor vehicle; motor vehicle lighting
equipment
HQ: Federal-Mogul Corporation
27300 W 11 Mile Rd
Southfield MI 48034
248 354-7700

(G-2458)
GEORGETOWN VINEYARDS LLC
62920 Georgetown Rd (43725-9749)
PHONE..............................740 435-3222
Fax: 740 432-2427
John Nicolozakes, *Mng Member*
EMP: 12
SQ FT: 600
SALES (est): 64K Privately Held
SIC: 0721 2084 Vines, cultivation of; wine
cellars, bonded: engaged in blending
wines

(G-2459)
GRAHAM PACKAGING COMPANY LP
8800 Guernsey Industrial (43725-8912)
PHONE..............................740 439-4242
Jim Blume, *Plant Mgr*
Dave Echols, *Branch Mgr*
EMP: 43 Privately Held
WEB: www.grahampackaging.com
SIC: 3085 Plastics bottles
HQ: Graham Packaging Company, L.P.
700 Indian Springs Dr # 100
Lancaster PA 17601
717 849-8500

(G-2460)
H&AN LLC
Also Called: Allegra Marketing & Printing
1224 Southgate Pkwy (43725-2945)
PHONE..............................740 435-0200
Tom Heins, *Mng Member*
EMP: 4
SALES (est): 171.4K Privately Held
SIC: 2752 Commercial printing, offset

(G-2461)
KENNEDYS BAKERY INC
1025 Wheeling Ave (43725-2441)
P.O. Box 396 (43725-0396)
PHONE..............................740 432-2301
Fax: 740 432-2302
T Noralee Kennedy, *President*
Bob Kennedy, *Vice Pres*
EMP: 27 EST: 1925
SQ FT: 8,000
SALES (est): 1.2MM Privately Held
WEB: www.kennedysbakery.com
SIC: 5461 2052 2051 Bakeries; cookies &
crackers; bread, cake & related products

(G-2462)
KINGSLY COMPRESSION INC
3956 Glenn Hwy (43725-8575)
PHONE..............................740 439-0772
Jeffrey B Sable, *Branch Mgr*
Josh Peyton, *Admin Asst*
EMP: 8
SALES (corp-wide): 5MM Privately Held
WEB: www.kingslycompression.com
SIC: 3563 5084 Air & gas compressors;
processing & packaging equipment
PA: Kingsly Compression, Inc.
3750 S Noah Dr
Saxonburg PA 16056
724 524-1840

(G-2463)
LEYSHON MILLER INDUSTRIES LLC
534 N 1st St (43725-1206)
PHONE..................................740 432-2969
Phil Matthews, *Principal*
EMP: 14
SALES (est): 1.6MM **Privately Held**
SIC: 3999 Manufacturing industries

(G-2464)
LILIENTHAL SOUTHEASTERN INC
1609 N 11th St (43725-1009)
P.O. Box 580 (43725-0580)
PHONE..................................740 439-1640
Fax: 740 439-4385
Richard W Lilienthal, *President*
Mark Wharton, *Sales Staff*
EMP: 18 EST: 1875
SQ FT: 6,000
SALES (est): 2.1MM **Privately Held**
WEB: www.lilseinc.com
SIC: 2752 2782 2759 2789 Commercial printing, lithographic; blankbooks; letterpress printing; bookbinding & related work

(G-2465)
LMI CUSTOM MIXING LLC
804 Byesville Rd (43725-9327)
PHONE..................................740 435-0444
Fax: 740 735-0909
Garry Lute, *Plant Engr*
David Gingrich, *CFO*
Brian Rennicker, *Manager*
▲ EMP: 74
SQ FT: 15,000
SALES (est): 30MM
SALES (corp-wide): 172.9MM **Privately Held**
WEB: www.laureninternational.com
SIC: 2891 Rubber cement
PA: Lauren International, Ltd.
2228 Reiser Ave Se
New Philadelphia OH 44663
330 339-3373

(G-2466)
MILLER MACHINE & MFG LLC
62056 Greendale Rd (43725-9687)
PHONE..................................740 439-2283
Fax: 740 439-2673
John Miller, *Mng Member*
Sherri Miller, *Mng Member*
EMP: 3 EST: 2002
SALES: 250K **Privately Held**
SIC: 3599 Machine shop, jobbing & repair

(G-2467)
MO-TRIM INC
240 Steubenville Ave (43725-2215)
P.O. Box 850 (43725-0850)
PHONE..................................740 432-2098
Fax: 740 432-2098
Jack O Cartner, *President*
EMP: 20
SQ FT: 10,000
SALES (est): 2.9MM **Privately Held**
SIC: 3524 Lawn & garden tractors & equipment

(G-2468)
MOSSER GLASS INCORPORATED
9279 Cadiz Rd (43725-9564)
PHONE..................................740 439-1827
Fax: 740 432-7980
Timmy J Mosser, *President*
Thomas R Mosser, *President*
Sally Johnson, *Office Mgr*
Mindy Hartley, *Manager*
▲ EMP: 30 EST: 1961
SALES (est): 3.8MM **Privately Held**
WEB: www.mosserglass.com
SIC: 3229 Novelty glassware; glassware, industrial

(G-2469)
MOTRIN CORPORATION
1070 Byesville Rd (43725-8403)
P.O. Box 262 (43725-0262)
PHONE..................................740 439-2725
Jack O Cartner, *President*
EMP: 4 EST: 1967
SQ FT: 8,000

SALES (est): 396.3K **Privately Held**
SIC: 3523 Farm machinery & equipment

(G-2470)
OHIO BRIDGE CORPORATION
Also Called: U.S. Bridge
201 Wheeling Ave (43725-2256)
P.O. Box 757 (43725-0757)
PHONE..................................740 432-6334
Daniel Rogovin, *CEO*
Richard Rogovin, *Chairman*
Dan Rogovin, *Vice Pres*
Scott Flaten, *Project Engr*
Bob Donelan, *CFO*
▼ EMP: 140 EST: 1952
SQ FT: 250,000
SALES (est): 60.4MM **Privately Held**
SIC: 1622 3449 Bridge construction; bars, concrete reinforcing: fabricated steel

(G-2471)
PACKAGING MATERIALS INC
62805 Bennett Ave (43725-9490)
P.O. Box 731 (43725-0731)
PHONE..................................740 432-6337
Fax: 740 439-4718
Ronald Funk, *President*
William S Funk, *Vice Pres*
Amanda Johnson, *Controller*
▼ EMP: 38 EST: 1970
SQ FT: 48,000
SALES (est): 6MM **Privately Held**
WEB: www.pmitape.com
SIC: 3081 Unsupported plastics film & sheet; commercial printing; bags: plastic, laminated & coated

(G-2472)
PLASTIC COMPOUNDERS INC
1125 Utica Dr (43725-2578)
P.O. Box 664 (43725-0664)
PHONE..................................740 432-7371
Fax: 740 432-7374
Dick Eubanks, *President*
Phyllis Bowlin, *President*
D I C K Eubanks, *President*
Dave Carroll, *Vice Pres*
EMP: 40
SQ FT: 50,000
SALES (est): 9.3MM **Privately Held**
SIC: 2821 Melamine resins, melamine-formaldehyde

(G-2473)
QUANEX IG SYSTEMS INC
800 Cochran Ave (43725-9317)
PHONE..................................740 439-2338
Michael Hovan, *CEO*
EMP: 175
SALES (corp-wide): 928.1MM **Publicly Held**
SIC: 3061 3053 Mechanical rubber goods; gaskets, packing & sealing devices
HQ: Quanex Ig Systems, Inc.
6680 Parkland Blvd
Solon OH 44139

(G-2474)
RIDGE TOOL COMPANY
Also Called: North American Dist Ctr
9877 Brick Church Rd (43725-9420)
PHONE..................................740 432-8782
Fax: 740 439-7920
Brian Shanahan, *Opers Mgr*
Jim Carter, *Maint Spvr*
Brian Shanahann, *Manager*
EMP: 81
SALES (corp-wide): 14.5B **Publicly Held**
WEB: www.ridgid.com
SIC: 3541 Machine tools, metal cutting type
HQ: Ridge Tool Company
400 Clark St
Elyria OH 44035
440 323-5581

(G-2475)
SCHWEBEL BAKING COMPANY
8277 Georgetown Rd (43725-9706)
PHONE..................................740 435-9857
Rob Parsons, *Site Mgr*
Jim Icard, *Manager*
EMP: 9

SALES (corp-wide): 170MM **Privately Held**
WEB: www.schwebels.com
SIC: 2051 Bread, cake & related products
PA: Schwebel Baking Company
965 E Midlothian Blvd
Youngstown OH 44502
330 783-2860

(G-2476)
SLABE TOOL COMPANY
1300 Oxford Ave (43725-3012)
PHONE..................................740 439-1647
Fax: 740 435-3149
Paula Larrick, *President*
Don Larrick, *Vice Pres*
EMP: 3
SQ FT: 5,000
SALES: 300K **Privately Held**
SIC: 3544 7692 Industrial molds; dies & die holders for metal cutting, forming, die casting; welding repair

(G-2477)
SUPERIOR HARDWOODS OHIO INC
Also Called: Superior Hardwoods Cambridge
9911 Ohio Ave (43725-9307)
P.O. Box 1358 (43725-6358)
PHONE..................................740 439-2727
Fax: 740 439-3083
Fred Lander, *Manager*
EMP: 30
SALES (corp-wide): 9.3MM **Privately Held**
SIC: 2421 2426 Sawmills & planing mills, general; hardwood dimension & flooring mills
PA: Superior Hardwoods Of Ohio, Inc.
134 Wellston Indus Pk Rd
Wellston OH 45692
740 384-5677

(G-2478)
TAYLOR QUICK PRINT
1008 Woodlawn Ave A (43725-2951)
PHONE..................................740 439-2208
Brenda Taylor, *Principal*
EMP: 6
SALES (est): 844.9K **Privately Held**
SIC: 2752 Commercial printing, offset

(G-2479)
TED TIPPLE
6176 Simmons Rd (43725-9458)
PHONE..................................740 432-3263
Ted Tipple, *Principal*
EMP: 4
SALES (est): 218.5K **Privately Held**
SIC: 1221 Bituminous coal & lignite-surface mining

(G-2480)
TELLING INDUSTRIES LLC
2105 Larrick Rd (43725-3064)
PHONE..................................740 435-8900
Steve Linch, *Manager*
Jon Small, *Manager*
EMP: 70
SALES (corp-wide): 31.8MM **Privately Held**
WEB: www.tellingindustries.com
SIC: 3316 Bars, steel, cold finished, from purchased hot-rolled
PA: Telling Industries, Llc
4420 Sherwin Rd
Willoughby OH 44094
440 974-3370

(G-2481)
VARIETY GLASS INC
201 Foster Ave (43725-1219)
PHONE..................................740 432-3643
Fax: 740 432-3643
Thomas R Mosser, *President*
Timothy J Mosser, *Vice Pres*
EMP: 10 EST: 1959
SQ FT: 16,000
SALES: 2MM **Privately Held**
WEB: www.varietyglass.com
SIC: 3229 Scientific glassware

(G-2482)
W A S P INC
59100 Claysville Rd (43725-8943)
PHONE..................................740 439-2398

Jeffrey L Carpenter, *Principal*
EMP: 3
SALES (est): 394.6K **Privately Held**
SIC: 5074 3432 Plumbing & hydronic heating supplies; plumbing fixture fittings & trim

(G-2483)
ZEKELMAN INDUSTRIES INC
Also Called: Wheatland Tube Company
9208 Jeffrey Dr (43725-9417)
PHONE..................................740 432-2146
Ned Feeney, *President*
John Parks, *Mfg Staff*
Michael Welsh, *Purchasing*
Fred Schneider, *Controller*
Joe Belancic, *Sales Staff*
EMP: 104
SQ FT: 58,000
SALES (corp-wide): 637.5MM **Privately Held**
SIC: 3317 3498 5074 3644 Pipes, seamless steel; fabricated pipe & fittings; plumbing fittings & supplies; noncurrent-carrying wiring services; plumbing fixture fittings & trim; blast furnaces & steel mills
PA: Zekelman Industries, Inc.
227 W Monroe St Ste 2600
Chicago IL 60606
312 275-1600

Camden
Preble County

(G-2484)
CAMDEN READY MIX CO (PA)
478 Cmden Cllege Cornr Rd (45311-9520)
P.O. Box 5, West Alexandria (45381-0005)
PHONE..................................937 456-4539
Fax: 937 456-9247
John D Wysong, *President*
Carroll Wysong, *Vice Pres*
EMP: 10
SALES (est): 1.3MM **Privately Held**
SIC: 3273 Ready-mixed concrete

(G-2485)
MEADORS MACHINE INC
7076 N Main St (45311-9503)
PHONE..................................937 452-5571
John Meadors, *President*
EMP: 7
SALES (est): 825K **Privately Held**
SIC: 3542 Pressing machines

(G-2486)
OHIO SLITTING & STORAGE
7000 N Main St (45311-9503)
PHONE..................................937 452-1108
Doug Everhart, *President*
Matt Lankheit, *General Mgr*
Gary Macobe, *Controller*
Melinda Robinson, *Sales Staff*
EMP: 20
SALES (est): 1.1MM **Privately Held**
SIC: 3291 Abrasive products

(G-2487)
P & R HARDWOODS
2911 State Route 725 W (45311-9691)
PHONE..................................937 452-3753
Paul Personette, *Owner*
EMP: 3 EST: 2001
SALES (est): 159.4K **Privately Held**
WEB: www.palmettohardwoods.com
SIC: 2421 Sawmills & planing mills, general

(G-2488)
PRECISION WOOD PRODUCTS INC (PA)
2456 Aukerman Creek Rd (45311-9706)
P.O. Box 10 (45311-0010)
PHONE..................................937 787-3523
Fax: 937 787-4653
Lloyd W Kinzie, *President*
Glen D Knaus, *Vice Pres*
H Ronald Knaus, *Vice Pres*
Dale Swank, *Sales Executive*
Barbara Knaus, *Admin Sec*
EMP: 28 EST: 1977
SQ FT: 32,000

SALES: 2.6MM **Privately Held**
WEB: www.precisionwoodproducts.net
SIC: 2431 Doors, wood

(G-2489)
WYSONG GRAVEL CO INC
120 Cmden Cllege Cornr Rd (45311-9520)
P.O. Box 5, West Alexandria (45381-0005)
PHONE..............................937 452-1523
Tom Caden, *General Mgr*
EMP: 7
SQ FT: 3,452
SALES (corp-wide): 3.1MM **Privately Held**
SIC: 1442 Gravel mining
PA: Wysong Gravel Co Inc
2332 State Route 503 N
West Alexandria OH 45381
937 456-4539

Campbell
Mahoning County

(G-2490)
INTERNTNAL PLSTIC CMPNENTS INC
75 Mccartney Rd (44405-1071)
P.O. Box 603 (44405-0603)
PHONE..............................330 744-0625
Fax: 330 744-8330
William West, *President*
William West Jr, *Vice Pres*
EMP: 15
SQ FT: 20,000
SALES (est): 2.4MM **Privately Held**
SIC: 3089 5084 Plastic hardware & building products; industrial machinery & equipment

(G-2491)
SEACOR PAINTING CORPORATION
98 Creed Cir (44405-1277)
P.O. Box 588 (44405-0588)
PHONE..............................330 755-6361
Nicholas Frangos, *President*
EMP: 8
SALES (est): 951K **Privately Held**
SIC: 3479 Painting of metal products

(G-2492)
SUMMER GLOBAL SYSTEMS LLC
115 Creed Cir (44405-1204)
PHONE..............................330 397-1653
John Mahinis,
EMP: 4
SALES (est): 168.3K **Privately Held**
SIC: 3599 Machine & other job shop work

(G-2493)
VINDICATOR
3770 Wilson Ave (44405-1767)
PHONE..............................330 755-0135
EMP: 3
SALES (est): 118.9K **Privately Held**
SIC: 2711 Newspapers-Publishing/Printing

(G-2494)
WEST EXTRUSION LLC
75 Mccartney Rd (44405-1071)
PHONE..............................330 744-0625
William West, *Principal*
EMP: 3
SALES (est): 142K **Privately Held**
SIC: 3089 Plastic processing

Canal Fulton
Stark County

(G-2495)
AMAN & CO INC
Also Called: Met-All Industries
231 Locust St S (44614-1294)
P.O. Box 459 (44614-0459)
PHONE..............................330 854-1122
Fax: 330 854-1133
John Aman, *President*
Elizabeth Aman, *Corp Secy*
Michael Aman, *Vice Pres*

EMP: 4
SQ FT: 7,500
SALES (est): 674K **Privately Held**
SIC: 2842 Metal polish

(G-2496)
AMERICAN TRADITIONS BASKET CO
Also Called: Bayberry Co
722 Tell Dr (44614-9324)
PHONE..............................330 854-0900
Fax: 330 854-0906
Earl Houser, *President*
Carol Houser, *Corp Secy*
Daniel Houser, *Vice Pres*
▲ EMP: 20
SQ FT: 15,000
SALES (est): 2.1MM **Privately Held**
WEB: www.americantraditionsbaskets.com
SIC: 3944 5947 Baskets, toy; gift baskets

(G-2497)
ASTRO-TEC MFG INC
550 Elm Ridge Ave (44614-9369)
P.O. Box 608 (44614-0608)
PHONE..............................330 854-2209
Fax: 330 854-5376
Clayton Hopper, *President*
Stephanie Hopper, *Vice Pres*
Mark Lacey, *Plant Mgr*
Beverly Hall, *Purchasing*
Dale Lewis, *Sales Mgr*
◆ EMP: 20 EST: 1963
SQ FT: 15,328
SALES (est): 5.1MM **Privately Held**
WEB: www.astro-tec.com
SIC: 3441 Fabricated structural metal

(G-2498)
BECKY KNAPP
Also Called: Deliciously Different Candies
136 N Canal St (44614-1198)
PHONE..............................330 854-4400
Fax: 330 854-4400
Becky Knapp, *Owner*
EMP: 5
SQ FT: 1,400
SALES (est): 317.6K **Privately Held**
SIC: 5441 2064 2066 Candy, nut & confectionery stores; candy & other confectionery products; chocolate & cocoa products

(G-2499)
BIRDS EYE FOODS INC
611 Elm Ridge Ave (44614-8476)
PHONE..............................330 854-0818
Bill Gaster, *Branch Mgr*
EMP: 25
SALES (corp-wide): 2.5B **Publicly Held**
WEB: www.agrilinkfoods.com
SIC: 2096 3523 Potato chips & similar snacks; peanut combines, diggers, packers & threshers
HQ: Birds Eye Foods, Inc.
121 Woodcrest Rd
Cherry Hill NJ 08003
585 383-1850

(G-2500)
C MASSOUH PRINTING CO INC
Also Called: C Massouh Printing
590 Elm Ridge Ave (44614-9369)
PHONE..............................330 408-7330
Carl Massouh, *President*
Chris Massouh, *Vice Pres*
Steve Massouh, *VP Sales*
EMP: 10
SALES (est): 1.5MM **Privately Held**
SIC: 2752 Commercial printing, lithographic

(G-2501)
EXODUS MOLD & MACHINE INC
960 Milan St N (44614-9737)
P.O. Box 593 (44614-0593)
PHONE..............................330 854-0282
Mark White, *Principal*
EMP: 4
SALES (est): 522K **Privately Held**
WEB: www.exodusmold.com
SIC: 3544 Industrial molds

(G-2502)
GLOBECOM TECHNOLOGIES INC
8542 Kepler Ave Nw (44614-8862)
PHONE..............................330 408-7008
Robert Alto, *President*
EMP: 1
SALES: 1.1MM **Privately Held**
SIC: 3663 Radio receiver networks

(G-2503)
JONMAR GEAR AND MACHINE INC
13786 Warwick Dr Nw (44614-9738)
PHONE..............................330 854-6500
Fax: 330 854-6500
Larry Murgatroyd, *President*
Brent A Murgatroyd, *Vice Pres*
EMP: 6 EST: 2000
SQ FT: 18,000
SALES (est): 275K **Privately Held**
SIC: 3566 7699 Speed changers, drives & gears; industrial machinery & equipment repair

(G-2504)
LINDSAY PACKAGE SYSTEMS INC
6845 Erie Ave Nw (44614-8509)
P.O. Box 578 (44614-0578)
PHONE..............................330 854-4511
Fax: 330 854-0673
Tim Gesaman, *CEO*
EMP: 4
SALES: 1MM
SALES (corp-wide): 25.9MM **Privately Held**
WEB: www.lindsayconcrete.com
SIC: 3272 Precast terrazo or concrete products
PA: Lindsay Precast, Inc.
6845 Erie Ave Nw
Canal Fulton OH 44614
330 854-6282

(G-2505)
LINDSAY PRECAST INC (PA)
6845 Erie Ave Nw (44614-8509)
P.O. Box 578 (44614-0578)
PHONE..............................330 854-6282
Fax: 330 854-6664
Roland Lindsay Sr, *President*
Timothy Gesaman, *Vice Pres*
Linda Lindsay, *Treasurer*
▼ EMP: 49 EST: 1968
SQ FT: 16,400
SALES (est): 25.9MM **Privately Held**
WEB: www.lindsayconcrete.com
SIC: 3272 3699 Septic tanks, concrete; manhole covers or frames, concrete; security devices

(G-2506)
LUBE DEPOT
2185 Locust St S (44614-8437)
PHONE..............................330 854-6345
Mike Primovero, *Principal*
EMP: 3
SALES (est): 243.4K **Privately Held**
SIC: 2911 Oils, lubricating

(G-2507)
MACA MOLD & MACHINE CO INC
761 Elm Ridge Ave (44614-9380)
PHONE..............................330 854-0292
John J Addessi, *President*
EMP: 6
SALES (est): 749.7K **Privately Held**
SIC: 3999 Manufacturing industries

(G-2508)
MIDWEST KNIFE GRINDING INC
492 Elm Ridge Ave Ste 4 (44614-9369)
PHONE..............................330 854-1030
Fax: 330 854-4505
James M Richmond II, *President*
Shawna Delauder, *Sales Associate*
EMP: 10
SQ FT: 12,000
SALES (est): 2MM **Privately Held**
WEB: www.midwestknifegrinding.com
SIC: 7699 3541 3423 Knife, saw & tool sharpening & repair; machine tools, metal cutting type; hand & edge tools

(G-2509)
NEW IMAGE PLASTICS MFG CO
Also Called: Nipm
241 Market St W (44614-1014)
P.O. Box 550 (44614-0550)
PHONE..............................330 854-3010
Fax: 330 854-6770
James E Waring Sr, *Owner*
EMP: 3
SQ FT: 9,000
SALES (est): 380.1K **Privately Held**
WEB: www.newimageplastic.com
SIC: 3082 Rods, unsupported plastic; tubes, unsupported plastic

(G-2510)
PROCESS AUTOMATION SPECIALISTS
7405 Diamondback Ave Nw (44614-8106)
PHONE..............................330 247-1384
Scott Veno, *Owner*
EMP: 1
SALES: 1MM **Privately Held**
SIC: 5084 3564 Industrial machinery & equipment; dust or fume collecting equipment, industrial

(G-2511)
QUADCAST
6845 Erie Ave Nw (44614-8509)
P.O. Box 578 (44614-0578)
PHONE..............................330 854-4511
Roland C Lindsay Jr, *Principal*
EMP: 4
SALES (est): 240.2K **Privately Held**
SIC: 3273 Ready-mixed concrete

(G-2512)
RACK COATING SERVICE INC
5760 Erie Ave Nw (44614-9726)
P.O. Box 486 (44614-0486)
PHONE..............................330 854-2869
Fax: 330 854-6291
John L Hexamer, *President*
Karen Shaw, *Office Mgr*
EMP: 20 EST: 1963
SQ FT: 2,500
SALES: 1.4MM **Privately Held**
SIC: 3479 Hot dip coating of metals or formed products

(G-2513)
RICHARD PASKIET MACHINISTS
468 Etheridge Blvd S (44614-9399)
PHONE..............................330 854-4160
Fax: 330 882-3152
Richard Paskiet, *President*
Holly Paskiet, *Treasurer*
EMP: 4
SALES (est): 310K **Privately Held**
SIC: 3599 3544 Machine shop, jobbing & repair; special dies, tools, jigs & fixtures

(G-2514)
SUMMIT ENGINEERED PRODUCTS
516 Elm Ridge Ave (44614-9369)
PHONE..............................330 854-5388
Dick Lutz, *Principal*
EMP: 10
SALES (est): 1.8MM **Privately Held**
SIC: 3315 Steel wire & related products

(G-2515)
TEK GROUP INTERNATIONAL INC
Also Called: Tek Manufacturing
567 Elm Ridge Ave (44614-9369)
PHONE..............................330 706-0000
Chris Willison, *President*
Cliff Willison, *President*
EMP: 35
SQ FT: 12,000
SALES (est): 8.7MM **Privately Held**
WEB: www.tekintl.com
SIC: 3462 Automotive forgings, ferrous: crankshaft, engine, axle, etc.

(G-2516)
USA PRECAST CONCRETE LIMITED
801 Elm Ridge Ave (44614-9396)
P.O. Box 613 (44614-0613)
PHONE..............................330 854-9600
Timothy Gesaman, *President*

Jeff Augustine, *Vice Pres*
Krista Gesaman, *Vice Pres*
Wendy Potashnik, *Vice Pres*
EMP: 7
SALES (est): 293.7K **Privately Held**
SIC: 3272 Concrete products, precast

(G-2517)
WELDED TUBE PROS LLC
Also Called: Wtp Engineering
215 Market St W (44614-1014)
P.O. Box 202, Doylestown (44230-0202)
PHONE..........................330 854-2966
Fax: 330 937-0333
Bud Graham, *President*
Worth B Graham,
EMP: 3
SQ FT: 2,500
SALES (est): 592.9K **Privately Held**
WEB: www.weldedtubepros.com
SIC: 5084 3827 8711 Industrial machinery
& equipment; optical test & inspection
equipment; consulting engineer

Canal Winchester
Franklin County

(G-2518)
A K ATHLETIC EQUIPMENT INC
8015 Howe Industrial Pkwy (43110-7890)
PHONE..........................614 920-3069
Angela Katz, *President*
EMP: 25
SQ FT: 32,000
SALES (est): 4.2MM **Privately Held**
WEB: www.akathletics.com
SIC: 3086 5091 Plastics foam products;
gymnasium equipment

(G-2519)
BABBERT REAL ESTATE INV CO LTD (PA)
7415 Diley Rd (43110-8813)
P.O. Box 203 (43110-0203)
PHONE..........................614 837-8444
Ervin C Babbert, *CEO*
Chuck Babbert, *President*
Bonnie Babbert, *Corp Secy*
Ronald Babbert, *Vice Pres*
EMP: 100
SQ FT: 20,000
SALES (est): 8.6MM **Privately Held**
SIC: 3272 Liquid catch basins, tanks &
covers: concrete

(G-2520)
BIOCARE ORTHOPEDIC
8889 Basil Western Rd Nw (43110-9276)
PHONE..........................614 754-7514
Sandy Tomsic, *President*
EMP: 4
SALES (est): 343.1K **Privately Held**
SIC: 3842 Prosthetic appliances

(G-2521)
CAPSA SOLUTIONS LLC
8170 Dove Pkwy (43110-9674)
PHONE..........................614 864-9966
David Burns, *CEO*
EMP: 90
SALES (corp-wide): 47.7MM **Privately Held**
SIC: 3572 Computer storage devices
PA: Capsa Solutions Llc
4253 Ne 189th Ave
Portland OR 97230
503 766-2324

(G-2522)
DAUGHERTY MACHINE COMPANY INC
8215 Dove Pkwy (43110-7717)
P.O. Box 192, Pickerington (43147-0192)
PHONE..........................614 834-4010
Fax: 614 834-4012
Randy Tarman, *President*
Scott Crist, *Manager*
EMP: 17
SQ FT: 13,000
SALES (est): 1.5MM **Privately Held**
SIC: 3599 Machine shop, jobbing & repair

(G-2523)
E C BABBERT INC
7415 Diley Rd (43110-8813)
P.O. Box 203 (43110-0203)
PHONE..........................614 837-8444
Fax: 614 837-1198
Ervin C Babbert, *CEO*
Charles Babbert, *President*
Rick Gibbs, *Controller*
Rodney Tackett, *Sales Staff*
Christy Conkey, *Manager*
EMP: 72
SALES: 950K **Privately Held**
SIC: 3272 Liquid catch basins, tanks &
covers: concrete

(G-2524)
FIFTH AVENUE LUMBER CO
Lumbercraft
5200 Winchester Pike (43110-9723)
PHONE..........................614 833-6655
Chris Kealey, *Manager*
EMP: 67
SALES (corp-wide): 39.1MM **Privately Held**
WEB: www.straitandlamp.com
SIC: 2431 2439 2452 2435 Millwork;
trusses, wooden roof; prefabricated wood
buildings; hardwood veneer & plywood
HQ: Fifth Avenue Lumber Co (Inc)
479 E 5th Ave
Columbus OH 43201
614 294-0068

(G-2525)
HFI LLC (PA)
59 Gender Rd (43110-9733)
PHONE..........................614 491-0700
Fax: 614 491-1899
Walter Dennis Jr, *CEO*
Brad Myers, *General Mgr*
Jorge Solano, *General Mgr*
Larry Barth, *COO*
Robert S Chapell, *Vice Pres*
▲ **EMP:** 350 **EST:** 1969
SQ FT: 140,000
SALES: 240MM **Privately Held**
WEB: www.hfi-inc.com
SIC: 2396 2821 3714 3429 Automotive
trimmings, fabric; polyurethane resins;
motor vehicle parts & accessories; manu-
factured hardware (general); plastics
foam products

(G-2526)
HFI LLC
59 Gender Rd (43110-9733)
PHONE..........................614 491-0700
Walter E Dennis Jr, *CEO*
Anthony Callander, *Human Resources*
Neil Fillman, *Officer*
Jorge Veloz, *Officer*
Walter Dennis,
EMP: 200
SALES (corp-wide): 240MM **Privately Held**
WEB: www.hfi-inc.com
SIC: 2396 Automotive trimmings, fabric
PA: Hfi, Llc
59 Gender Rd
Canal Winchester OH 43110
614 491-0700

(G-2527)
HFI INC
59 Gender Rd (43110-9733)
PHONE..........................614 491-0700
Larry Barth, *Principal*
Derek Peelle, *Engineer*
EMP: 5
SALES (est): 700K **Privately Held**
SIC: 3089 Automotive parts, plastic

(G-2528)
HFI MANUFACTURING HOLDINGS LLC
Also Called: H F I
59 Gender Rd (43110-9733)
PHONE..........................614 491-0700
Walter Dennis Jr,
EMP: 5
SALES (est): 123K
SALES (corp-wide): 240MM **Privately Held**
SIC: 2821 3714 Polyurethane resins;
motor vehicle parts & accessories

PA: Hfi, Llc
59 Gender Rd
Canal Winchester OH 43110
614 491-0700

(G-2529)
KELLOGG CABINETS INC
7711 Diley Rd (43110-9616)
PHONE..........................614 833-9596
Fax: 614 833-9599
Judy A Kellogg, *CEO*
Judy Kellogg, *President*
Douglas E Kellogg, *Vice Pres*
Barry Hartman, *Project Mgr*
◆ **EMP:** 32 **EST:** 1975
SQ FT: 28,850
SALES (est): 4.7MM **Privately Held**
WEB: www.kelloggcabinets.com
SIC: 2541 2542 2522 2434 Cabinets, ex-
cept refrigerated: show, display, etc.:
wood; store fixtures, wood; partitions &
fixtures, except wood; office furniture, ex-
cept wood; wood kitchen cabinets

(G-2530)
LEAF LONO EARTH ALTERNTV FUELS
4204 Town Square Dr (43110-7757)
PHONE..........................614 829-7159
Patrick Hannon, *Owner*
EMP: 3
SALES (est): 182.4K **Privately Held**
SIC: 2869 Fuels

(G-2531)
MANIFOLD & PHALOR INC
Also Called: US Die & Mold
10385 Busey Rd Nw (43110-8883)
PHONE..........................614 920-1200
Fax: 614 866-1187
Thomas J Creek, *President*
Gene Moore, *General Mgr*
Bruce Milligan, *Vice Pres*
Jeff Fisher, *Engineer*
Brian Hintz, *Engineer*
▼ **EMP:** 45 **EST:** 1946
SQ FT: 28,800
SALES (est): 13.1MM **Privately Held**
WEB: www.manifoldphalor.com
SIC: 3441 3599 3559 Fabricated struc-
tural metal; machine shop, jobbing & re-
pair; glass making machinery: blowing,
molding, forming, etc.

(G-2532)
NIFCO AMERICA CORPORATION (HQ)
8015 Dove Pkwy (43110-9697)
PHONE..........................614 920-6800
Fax: 614 920-6998
Toshiyuki Yamamoto, *President*
Tom Day, *Vice Pres*
John Kosik, *CFO*
▲ **EMP:** 312
SQ FT: 50,000
SALES (est): 210.7MM
SALES (corp-wide): 2.2B **Privately Held**
WEB: www.nifco-us.com
SIC: 3089 Automotive parts, plastic
PA: Nifco Inc.
5-3, Hikarinooka
Yokosuka KNG 239-0
468 390-225

(G-2533)
NIFCO AMERICA CORPORATION
Also Called: Canal Winchester Facility
8015 Dove Pkwy (43110-9697)
PHONE..........................614 836-3808
Tom Day, *General Mgr*
Toshiyuku Yamamoto, *Senior VP*
John Kosik, *CFO*
Patrick Doyle, *Controller*
EMP: 250
SALES (corp-wide): 2.2B **Privately Held**
WEB: www.nifco-us.com
SIC: 3089 Automotive parts, plastic
HQ: Nifco America Corporation
8015 Dove Pkwy
Canal Winchester OH 43110
614 836-3808

(G-2534)
NURDCON LLC
Also Called: Le Nurd Mystique LLC
6645 Kodiak Dr (43110-8665)
PHONE..........................614 208-5898
Jack Stewart,
EMP: 3
SALES: 36K **Privately Held**
SIC: 2731 Book publishing

(G-2535)
OLAN PLASTICS INC
6550 Olan Dr (43110-9685)
PHONE..........................614 834-6526
Fax: 614 834-5536
Olan Long, *CEO*
James Long, *President*
Marcella Long, *Corp Secy*
Bill Moses, *Manager*
EMP: 40
SQ FT: 30,000
SALES (est): 6.9MM **Privately Held**
WEB: www.olanplastics.com
SIC: 3089 Plastic containers, except foam

(G-2536)
S & S SIGN CO
10601 Lithopolis Rd Nw (43110-8804)
PHONE..........................614 837-1511
Robert Schorr, *Owner*
EMP: 3
SALES (est): 142K **Privately Held**
SIC: 3993 Signs & advertising specialties

(G-2537)
STRAIT & LAMP LUMBER CO INC
Also Called: Lumbercraft
5200 Winchester Pike (43110-9723)
PHONE..........................614 833-6655
Fax: 614 833-6688
David Clay, *Exec VP*
Chris Kealey, *Manager*
Nate Lyons, *Manager*
EMP: 50
SALES (corp-wide): 39.1MM **Privately Held**
SIC: 2439 Trusses, wooden roof
PA: The Strait & Lamp Lumber Company
Incorporated
269 National Rd Se
Hebron OH 43025
740 928-4501

(G-2538)
TIGER OIL INC (PA)
Also Called: Tiger Construction
650 Winchester Pike (43110-9170)
PHONE..........................614 837-5552
Gerald Pfeifer, *President*
Damon Pfeifer, *Vice Pres*
Henrietta Pfeifer, *Treasurer*
EMP: 3
SALES (est): 1.3MM **Privately Held**
WEB: www.tigeroil.com
SIC: 1381 Drilling oil & gas wells

(G-2539)
TS TRIM INDUSTRIES INC
6380 Canal St (43110-9640)
PHONE..........................614 837-4114
Fax: 614 837-4127
Pat Ferren, *Vice Pres*
Jorge Veloz, *Vice Pres*
Ray Davis, *Plant Mgr*
Steve Burner, *Plant Mgr*
John Moorman, *Safety Mgr*
EMP: 9
SALES (corp-wide): 3.9B **Privately Held**
WEB: www.tstrim.com
SIC: 3465 Automotive stampings
HQ: Ts Trim Industries Inc.
6380 Canal St
Canal Winchester OH 43110
614 837-4114

(G-2540)
TS TRIM TRIMOLD INC
6380 Canal St (43110-9640)
PHONE..........................614 920-1927
Katsuhisa Keyashi, *Principal*
Andrew Geiger, *Administration*
EMP: 6
SALES (est): 802.7K **Privately Held**
SIC: 3465 Automotive stampings

▲ = Import ▼ =Export
◆ =Import/Export

(G-2541)
WILLIAM MINNIER
Also Called: Profetion Transport
3936 Cleggan St (43110-8125)
PHONE..................................614 562-8080
William L Minnier, *Principal*
EMP: 3
SALES: 100K **Privately Held**
SIC: 3715 Truck trailers

(G-2542)
WORLD HARVEST CHURCH INC (PA)
Also Called: Breakthrough Media Ministries
4595 Gender Rd (43110-9149)
P.O. Box 428 (43110-0428)
PHONE..................................614 837-1990
Fax: 614 834-1276
Rodney Parsley, *Pastor*
Darrin Endicott, *Maintenance Dir*
Andrew Sturdon, *Controller*
Scott Lee, *Director*
Debbie Baranich, *Administration*
EMP: 200
SQ FT: 200,000
SALES: 12.9MM **Privately Held**
WEB: www.breakthrough.net
SIC: 8661 7812 2731 Religious organizations; video tape production; books: publishing & printing

Canfield
Mahoning County

(G-2543)
ADVETECH INC (PA)
Also Called: Perfection In Carbide
445 W Main St (44406-1425)
PHONE..................................330 533-2227
David Scott Owens, *CEO*
David Smith, *President*
Keith Jarmusch, *CFO*
David S Owen, *Human Res Mgr*
Brian Chambers, *Manager*
EMP: 30
SQ FT: 30,000
SALES (est): 7.6MM **Privately Held**
SIC: 3421 3599 3423 3541 Knife blades & blanks; shears, hand; machine shop, jobbing & repair; knives, agricultural or industrial; machine tools, metal cutting type

(G-2544)
ADVETECH INC
451 W Main St (44406-1425)
P.O. Box 613 (44406-0613)
PHONE..................................330 533-2227
Dave Smith, *Manager*
Ted Bricker, *Manager*
EMP: 34
SALES (corp-wide): 7.6MM **Privately Held**
WEB: www.advetech.com
SIC: 3423 Knives, agricultural or industrial
PA: Advetech Inc
    445 W Main St
    Canfield OH 44406
    330 533-2227

(G-2545)
AFC COMPANY
Also Called: Canfield Industrial Park
5183 W Western Reserve Rd (44406-8112)
PHONE..................................330 533-5581
Fax: 330 533-7942
Judith Raber, *President*
EMP: 13 EST: 1915
SQ FT: 2,500
SALES (est): 1.2MM **Privately Held**
WEB: www.afcfencing.com
SIC: 6512 7389 3255 3251 Commercial & industrial building operation; grinding, precision: commercial or industrial; clay refractories; ceramic glazed brick, clay

(G-2546)
ALLOY UNLIMITED WELD
4200 W Middletown Rd (44406-9474)
PHONE..................................330 506-8375
John Kish, *Principal*
EMP: 3
SALES (est): 265.7K **Privately Held**
SIC: 7692 Welding repair

(G-2547)
ALSTART ENTERPRISES LLC
Also Called: USA Rolls
451 W Main St (44406-1425)
P.O. Box 1076 (44406-5076)
PHONE..................................330 533-3222
Kevin M Sheldon, *President*
EMP: 18 EST: 2009
SQ FT: 55,000
SALES (est): 4.9MM **Privately Held**
SIC: 3559 Plastics working machinery

(G-2548)
ALUMINUM EXTRUSION TECH LLC
6155 State Route 446 (44406-9428)
PHONE..................................330 533-3994
Andrew Ruhl, *Mng Member*
EMP: 6
SALES (est): 645.4K **Privately Held**
SIC: 3355 Extrusion ingot, aluminum: made in rolling mills

(G-2549)
BAIRD BROTHERS SAWMILL INC
7060 Crory Rd (44406-9720)
PHONE..................................330 533-3122
Fax: 330 533-0781
Paul Baird, *President*
Scott Baird, *Accountant*
Terry Davis, *Sales Staff*
Dante Dirienzo, *Sales Staff*
Terryy Baird, *Manager*
EMP: 115 EST: 1960
SQ FT: 350,000
SALES (est): 20.6MM **Privately Held**
WEB: www.bairdbros.com
SIC: 2431 Millwork; doors & door parts & trim, wood; staircases, stairs & railings; trim, wood

(G-2550)
CANFIELD COATING LLC
460 W Main St (44406-1434)
PHONE..................................330 533-3311
Ron Jandrokovic, *President*
EMP: 247
SALES (est): 25.3MM **Privately Held**
SIC: 3421 5051 Galvanizing of iron, steel or end-formed products; metals service centers & offices
PA: New Star Metals Inc.
    2250 Pratt Blvd
    Elk Grove Village IL 60007

(G-2551)
CANFIELD METAL COATING CORP
460 W Main St (44406-1434)
PHONE..................................330 702-3876
Ronald W Jandrokovic, *President*
Paul Pirko, *Vice Pres*
Clarence Newhouse Jr, *Plant Mgr*
Phil Widomski, *Controller*
George S Bokros, *Finance Dir*
EMP: 52
SALES (est): 6.5MM
SALES (corp-wide): 828.3MM **Publicly Held**
WEB: www.coilcoat.com
SIC: 3479 5051 Galvanizing of iron, steel or end-formed products; metals service centers & offices
HQ: Handy & Harman Ltd.
    1133 Westchester Ave N-222
    White Plains NY 10604

(G-2552)
DUNAWAY INC
Also Called: D I
5959 Leffingwell Rd (44406-9132)
P.O. Box 488 (44406-0488)
PHONE..................................330 533-7753
Fax: 330 533-5379
Michael Dunaway, *President*
Albert E Brennan, *Principal*
Catherine Dunaway, *Vice Pres*
Jonie Foster, *Purchasing*
EMP: 20
SQ FT: 30,000
SALES (est): 3.9MM **Privately Held**
WEB: www.dunawayinc.com
SIC: 3599 Machine shop, jobbing & repair

(G-2553)
EMPYRACOM INC
6550 Seville Dr (44406-9138)
PHONE..................................330 744-5570
Shanthi Subramanyam, *President*
Viswanath Subramanya, *Vice Pres*
EMP: 20
SQ FT: 2,500
SALES (est): 2.7MM **Privately Held**
WEB: www.empyra.com
SIC: 7379 7372 7371 Computer related consulting services; prepackaged software; business oriented computer software; computer software systems analysis & design, custom; computer software development

(G-2554)
ERIC ALLSHOUSE LLC
9666 Lisbon Rd (44406-8425)
PHONE..................................330 533-4258
EMP: 3
SALES (est): 118.1K **Privately Held**
SIC: 3561 8741 Cylinders, pump; construction management

(G-2555)
EVERFLOW EASTERN PARTNERS LP (PA)
585 W Main St (44406-9733)
P.O. Box 629 (44406-0629)
PHONE..................................330 533-2692
William A Siskovic, *President*
Everflow M Limited, *General Ptnr*
Brian A Staebler, *CFO*
EMP: 21
SQ FT: 6,400
SALES: 3.8MM **Privately Held**
SIC: 1382 1311 Oil & gas exploration services; crude petroleum & natural gas

(G-2556)
EXTREME CUSTOM SPOOLS
3711 Starrs Centre Dr (44406-8505)
PHONE..................................330 533-6936
Fax: 330 533-7017
Deborah Pecchia, *Owner*
EMP: 7
SALES (est): 380K **Privately Held**
SIC: 3089 Plastic processing

(G-2557)
HAUS MATHIAS
Also Called: Haus Cider Mill & Fruit Farm
6742 W Calla Rd (44406-9453)
PHONE..................................330 533-5305
Fax: 330 533-5305
Mathias E Haus, *Owner*
Cheryl Haus, *Co-Owner*
EMP: 5
SALES (est): 359.6K **Privately Held**
SIC: 2099 0175 2086 Cider, nonalcoholic; apple orchard; bottled & canned soft drinks

(G-2558)
IES SYSTEMS INC
464 Lisbon St (44406-1423)
P.O. Box 89 (44406-0089)
PHONE..................................330 533-6683
Fax: 330 533-7293
Mark Brucoli, *President*
Kelly Weiss, *Corp Secy*
Rob McAndrew, *Exec VP*
David Wigal, *Exec VP*
Bill Yobi, *Exec VP*
EMP: 45
SQ FT: 27,000
SALES (est): 7.5MM **Privately Held**
WEB: www.ies-us.com
SIC: 7389 3821 Design, commercial & industrial; laboratory apparatus & furniture

(G-2559)
J A DONADEE CORPORATION (PA)
535 N Broad St Ste 5 (44406-8221)
PHONE..................................330 533-3305
John A Donadee, *President*
Dave Spurio, *Vice Pres*
Bill Burnside, *Plant Supt*
Jane Donadee, *Treasurer*
Billie Delull, *Controller*
EMP: 20
SQ FT: 4,200

(G-2560)
KEEPSAKES ETC
7320 Akron Canfield Rd B (44406-9750)
PHONE..................................330 559-6716
Joann Shirilla, *Owner*
EMP: 3
SALES (est): 270.2K **Privately Held**
SIC: 2211 Blankets & blanketings, cotton

(G-2561)
LEEBAW MANUFACTURING COMPANY
3 Industrial Park Dr (44406-9738)
P.O. Box 553 (44406-0553)
PHONE..................................330 533-3368
Fax: 330 533-3917
Jeff Raymer, *General Mgr*
John C Leek, *Sales Mgr*
John Leek, *Sales Mgr*
Pati Bevan, *Marketing Staff*
Chris D'Avello, *Marketing Staff*
EMP: 18 EST: 1947
SQ FT: 20,000
SALES (est): 5MM **Privately Held**
WEB: www.leebaw.com
SIC: 3537 Industrial trucks & tractors; dollies (hand or power trucks), industrial except mining

(G-2562)
LINDE HYDRAULICS CORPORATION (HQ)
5089 W Western Reserve Rd (44406-9112)
P.O. Box 82 (44406-0082)
PHONE..................................330 533-6801
Fax: 330 533-2091
Frank Cobb, *CEO*
Dr Ferdinand Megerlin, *Ch of Bd*
Lewis P Kasper, *President*
John Kumler, *President*
David Wright, *Safety Mgr*
▲ EMP: 38
SQ FT: 80,000
SALES (est): 4.4MM
SALES (corp-wide): 17.9B **Privately Held**
WEB: www.lindeamerica.com
SIC: 3594 3566 3714 3621 Pumps, hydraulic power transfer; motors: hydraulic, fluid power or air; gears, power transmission, except automotive; motor vehicle parts & accessories; motors & generators
PA: Linde Ag
    Klosterhofstr. 1
    Munchen 80331
    893 575-701

(G-2563)
LTF ACQUISITION LLC
Also Called: Lifetime Fenders
430 W Main St (44406-1434)
PHONE..................................330 533-0111
Shirley Freed, *Personnel Exec*
Marcus Shiveley,
EMP: 14
SQ FT: 25,000
SALES (est): 2.1MM
SALES (corp-wide): 72.7MM **Privately Held**
SIC: 3465 Fenders, automobile: stamped or pressed metal
PA: Betts Company
    2843 S Maple Ave
    Fresno CA 93725
    559 498-3304

(G-2564)
MANUFACTURING DIVISION INC
445 W Main St (44406-1425)
P.O. Box 9 (44406-0009)
PHONE..................................330 533-6835
D Scott Owens, *President*
EMP: 3
SQ FT: 2,000
SALES (est): 302.3K
SALES (corp-wide): 3.4MM **Privately Held**
WEB: www.prefcommunities.com
SIC: 3592 Valves, aircraft

SALES (est): 14.7MM **Privately Held**
SIC: 1611 3441 General contractor, highway & street construction; fabricated structural metal

GEOGRAPHIC

PA: Owens-Ohio Corporation
2015 W 5th Ave
Columbus OH 43212
614 486-1148

(G-2565)
MERCERS WELDING INC
6336 W Calla Rd (44406-9452)
PHONE....................................330 533-3373
Fax: 330 533-5377
Glenn Wolford, *President*
Susan Wyand, *Treasurer*
EMP: 4
SQ FT: 1,000
SALES: 130K **Privately Held**
SIC: 7692 Welding repair

(G-2566)
MOLOROKALIN INC (DH)
Also Called: Carepoint Partners
4137 Boardman Canfield Rd LI04
(44406-8087)
PHONE....................................330 629-1332
Ralph Dimuccio, *Ch of Bd*
Leonard Holman, *President*
Greg Krieger, *Vice Pres*
John Appel, *Treasurer*
Harold Cullar, *Admin Sec*
EMP: 19
SQ FT: 5,000
SALES (est): 1.5MM **Publicly Held**
SIC: 2834 Intravenous solutions

(G-2567)
MOONLIGHTING
8627 Gibson Rd (44406-9745)
PHONE....................................330 533-3324
Peter Mazar, *Owner*
EMP: 4
SALES (est): 452.9K **Privately Held**
SIC: 3648 Outdoor lighting equipment

(G-2568)
OHIO STRUCTURES INC (HQ)
535 N Broad St Ste 5 (44406-8221)
PHONE....................................330 533-0084
Fax: 330 533-0191
John Donadee, *President*
Julie Hlebovy, *Corp Secy*
Sean Giblin, *Vice Pres*
David Spurio, *Treasurer*
Thomas Kostelic, *Admin Sec*
EMP: 50
SALES (est): 13.2MM
SALES (corp-wide): 14.7MM **Privately Held**
SIC: 3441 8711 Fabricated structural metal; engineering services
PA: J A Donadee Corporation
535 N Broad St Ste 5
Canfield OH 44406
330 533-3305

(G-2569)
PIERSANTE AND ASSOCIATES
230 Russo Dr (44406-9679)
PHONE....................................330 533-9904
Thomas S Piersante, *Principal*
EMP: 5
SALES (est): 282.2K **Privately Held**
SIC: 3494 Valves & pipe fittings

(G-2570)
PROCESS SLTIONS FOR INDUST INC
Also Called: PSI Products
480 S Broad St Ste A (44406-1688)
P.O. Box 771 (44406-0771)
PHONE....................................330 702-1685
Douglas R Holt, *President*
Diane Holt, *Vice Pres*
EMP: 4 **EST:** 1997
SQ FT: 500
SALES: 250K **Privately Held**
SIC: 2819 Industrial inorganic chemicals

(G-2571)
RANGE ONE PRODUCTS & FABG
580 W Main St (44406-9740)
P.O. Box 628 (44406-0628)
PHONE....................................330 533-1151
EMP: 11
SQ FT: 7,000

SALES (est): 83K **Privately Held**
SIC: 3599 3496 3444 Mfg Industrial Machinery Mfg Misc Fabricated Wire Products Mfg Sheet Metalwork

(G-2572)
RELATED METALS INC
6011 Deer Spring Run (44406-7609)
PHONE....................................330 799-4866
Fax: 330 793-1033
Lori Dripps, *President*
Mary Dripps, *Vice Pres*
Thomas Dripps, *Treasurer*
Lawson Dripps, *Admin Sec*
EMP: 7
SQ FT: 2,000
SALES (est): 751.7K **Privately Held**
SIC: 1761 3444 Roofing contractor; sheet metalwork; sheet metalwork

(G-2573)
SCHOEN INDUSTRIES INC
290 Southview Rd (44406-1162)
PHONE....................................330 533-6659
Fax: 330 744-4774
William Schoenfeld Sr, *President*
Robert Schoenfeld, *Treasurer*
EMP: 5
SQ FT: 8,000
SALES (est): 527.5K **Privately Held**
SIC: 3469 Kitchen fixtures & equipment, porcelain enameled

(G-2574)
SPECIAL T FOODS LLC
5529 W Middletown Rd (44406-9492)
PHONE....................................330 533-9493
Bernadette Shimek,
Tony Shimek,
EMP: 3
SALES (est): 250K **Privately Held**
SIC: 2099 Food preparations

(G-2575)
STAR EXTRUDED SHAPES INC
7055 Herbert Rd (44406-8660)
P.O. Box 553 (44406-0553)
PHONE....................................330 533-9863
Fax: 330 533-1211
Kenneth W George, *President*
Nick Mistovich, *CFO*
John Potter, *Manager*
EMP: 300
SQ FT: 143,000
SALES (est): 61.6MM **Privately Held**
SIC: 3354 Aluminum extruded products

(G-2576)
STAR FAB INC (PA)
7055 Herbert Rd (44406-8660)
P.O. Box 553 (44406-0553)
PHONE....................................330 533-9863
Kenneth W George Jr, *President*
Nick Mistovich, *CFO*
▲ **EMP:** 120
SQ FT: 100,000
SALES (est): 24.2MM **Privately Held**
WEB: www.starext.com
SIC: 3354 3479 Aluminum extruded products; painting of metal products

(G-2577)
STONEFRUIT COFFEE CO
410 W Main St (44406-1434)
PHONE....................................330 509-2787
Joshua Langenhein, *Owner*
EMP: 3
SALES (est): 117.9K **Privately Held**
SIC: 2095 Roasted coffee

(G-2578)
TETRA TECH INC
6715 Tippecanoe Rd C201 (44406-7120)
PHONE....................................330 286-3683
Dan Batrack, *CEO*
Larry Drane, *General Mgr*
EMP: 15
SALES (corp-wide): 2.5B **Publicly Held**
SIC: 8711 3822 8744 Engineering services; auto controls regulating residntl & coml environmt & applncs
PA: Tetra Tech, Inc.
3475 E Foothill Blvd
Pasadena CA 91107
626 351-4664

(G-2579)
THOROUGHBRED GT MFG LLC
6145 State Route 446 (44406-9428)
PHONE....................................330 533-0048
Nathan Miller, *Principal*
▲ **EMP:** 10
SALES (est): 790.2K **Privately Held**
SIC: 3999 Manufacturing industries

(G-2580)
TRAILEX INC
1 Industrial Park Dr (44406-9738)
P.O. Box 553 (44406-0553)
PHONE....................................330 533-6814
Fax: 330 533-9118
Kenneth George II, *President*
Tim Cooper, *Business Mgr*
Ken Montgomery, *Sales Staff*
▼ **EMP:** 10 **EST:** 1963
SQ FT: 20,000
SALES (est): 1.8MM **Privately Held**
WEB: www.trailex.com
SIC: 3715 Truck trailers

(G-2581)
UNITED EXTRUSION DIES INC
5171 W Western Reserve Rd (44406-8112)
P.O. Box 117 (44406-0117)
PHONE....................................330 533-2915
Fax: 330 533-1201
John Fritz, *President*
James Rektor, *Vice Pres*
Sharon Crawford, *Admin Sec*
EMP: 10
SQ FT: 8,000
SALES (est): 1.2MM **Privately Held**
SIC: 3544 Special dies & tools

(G-2582)
WRP ENERGY INC
12 W Main St (44406-1426)
PHONE....................................330 533-1921
Nils Johnsons, *CEO*
Kathleen Johnson, *Corp Secy*
Cindy Wilson, *Manager*
Scott W Johnson,
EMP: 5
SQ FT: 1,300
SALES (est): 331.5K **Privately Held**
SIC: 1382 Oil & gas exploration services

Canton
Stark County

(G-2583)
1455 GROUP LLC
Also Called: Ohio Print Source
6116 Market Ave N (44721-3123)
P.O. Box 227, Middlebranch (44652-0227)
PHONE....................................330 494-9074
Mike Dicato, *President*
EMP: 5 **EST:** 2008
SALES (est): 673.9K **Privately Held**
SIC: 2752 Commercial printing, lithographic

(G-2584)
A & M CREATIVE GROUP INC
1704 Ira Turpin Way Ne (44705-1415)
PHONE....................................330 452-8940
William S Henderhan, *President*
EMP: 20
SALES (est): 3.9MM **Privately Held**
SIC: 3578 Point-of-sale devices

(G-2585)
A P O HOLDINGS INC
Also Called: Air Power of Ohio
1405 Timken Pl Sw (44706-3068)
PHONE....................................330 455-8925
Fax: 330 455-9553
Eric Dunkle, *Branch Mgr*
Denny Good, *Branch Mgr*
EMP: 22
SALES (corp-wide): 25.7MM **Privately Held**
WEB: www.airpowerofohio.com
SIC: 5084 3561 3443 Compressors, except air conditioning; pumps & pumping equipment; fabricated plate work (boiler shop)

PA: A P O Holdings Inc
6607 Chittenden Rd
Hudson OH 44236
330 650-1330

(G-2586)
ACCU-RITE TOOL & DIE CO CORP
7295 Sunset Strip Ave Nw (44720-7038)
P.O. Box 2651 (44720-0651)
PHONE....................................330 497-9959
Fax: 330 497-0907
John Snyder, *President*
Susan Snyder, *Corp Secy*
Thomas Snyder, *Vice Pres*
EMP: 6
SQ FT: 5,000
SALES (est): 874K **Privately Held**
SIC: 3544 Special dies, tools, jigs & fixtures

(G-2587)
ADELMANS TRUCK PARTS CORP (PA)
Also Called: Adelman's Truck Sales
2000 Waynesburg Dr Se (44707-2194)
PHONE....................................330 456-0206
Fax: 330 456-3959
Carl Adelman, *President*
Larry Adelman, *Vice Pres*
◆ **EMP:** 30
SQ FT: 120,000
SALES (est): 8.8MM **Privately Held**
WEB: www.adelmans.com
SIC: 5013 3714 Truck parts & accessories; power transmission equipment, motor vehicle; differentials & parts, motor vehicle

(G-2588)
ADELMANS TRUCK PARTS CORP
2000 Waynesburg Dr Se (44707-2194)
PHONE....................................216 362-0500
Fax: 216 362-0106
Tim Sossa, *Manager*
David Olsen,
EMP: 17
SALES (corp-wide): 8.8MM **Privately Held**
SIC: 5013 3714 Truck parts & accessories; differentials & parts, motor vehicle
PA: Adelman's Truck Parts Corporation
2000 Waynesburg Dr Se
Canton OH 44707
330 456-0206

(G-2589)
ADVENT DRILLING INC
366 Rose Lane St Sw (44720-3556)
P.O. Box 2562 (44720-0562)
PHONE....................................330 497-2533
Charles Keeney Jr, *President*
Gary Yarnell, *Vice Pres*
Laurie Keeney, *Admin Sec*
EMP: 27
SALES: 1.9MM **Privately Held**
SIC: 1381 Drilling oil & gas wells

(G-2590)
AGGREGATE TERSORNANCE LLC
Also Called: NOOTROPICS CITY DBA
455 Navarre Rd Sw Unit H (44707)
PHONE....................................330 418-4751
Kenny L James III, *Mng Member*
EMP: 5 **EST:** 2014
SALES: 500K **Privately Held**
SIC: 2023 5499 Dietary supplements, dairy & non-dairy based; health & dietetic food stores

(G-2591)
AIRFASCO INC
2655 Harrison Ave Sw (44706-3047)
PHONE....................................330 430-6190
Dennis Dent, *CEO*
Jeff Parker, *Vice Pres*
Marlene Veobides, *Vice Pres*
Bryan Emary, *Engineer*
Tim West, *Director*
EMP: 42
SQ FT: 25,000

SALES (est): 7.6MM **Privately Held**
WEB: www.airfasco.com
SIC: 3452 Bolts, metal

(G-2592)
AIRFASCO INDS FSTNER GROUP LLC
2655 Harrison Ave Sw (44706-3047)
PHONE................................330 430-6190
Dennis Dent,
EMP: 40
SALES: 1,000K **Privately Held**
SIC: 3452 Bolts, nuts, rivets & washers

(G-2593)
AIRGAS MERCHANT GASES LLC
2505 Shepler Ave Sw (44706)
PHONE................................330 454-1330
Fax: 330 454-6774
Jody Engstrom, *Plant Mgr*
Rod Stjohn, *Plant Mgr*
Rod St John, *Branch Mgr*
Blaine Boron, *Manager*
EMP: 50
SALES (corp-wide): 163.9MM **Privately Held**
WEB: www.us.linde-gas.com
SIC: 2813 Oxygen, compressed or liquefied; nitrous oxide; acetylene; hydrogen
HQ: Airgas Merchant Gases, Llc
6055 Rckside Woods Blvd N
Cleveland OH 44131
800 242-0105

(G-2594)
AJAX TOCCO MAGNETHERMIC CORP
8984 Meridian Cir Nw (44720-8259)
PHONE................................330 818-8080
Rhonda Pernell, *Purch Mgr*
Jeff Deeter, *Engineer*
Robert Jamison, *Project Engr*
Michele Davidson, *Human Res Dir*
Dave Amos, *Manager*
EMP: 53
SALES (corp-wide): 1.2B **Publicly Held**
WEB: www.ajaxtocco.com
SIC: 3567 Industrial furnaces & ovens
HQ: Ajax Tocco Magnethermic Corporation
1745 Overland Ave Ne
Warren OH 44483
330 372-8511

(G-2595)
AK FABRICATION INC
1500 Allen Ave Se (44707-3768)
PHONE................................330 458-1037
Chris Kulenics, *President*
Stacey Griffith, *Manager*
EMP: 12
SQ FT: 10,000
SALES (est): 1.5MM **Privately Held**
SIC: 1751 3548 Carpentry work; welding apparatus

(G-2596)
AKERS IDENTITY LLC
Also Called: Akers Sign
4150 Belden Village St Nw # 503
(44718-3650)
PHONE................................330 493-0055
Richard W Akers,
EMP: 3
SALES (est): 414.5K **Privately Held**
SIC: 7389 3993 8748 Lettering & sign painting services; signs & advertising specialties; systems analysis or design

(G-2597)
ALL POWER BATTERY INC
1387 Clarendon Ave Sw # 6 (44710-2190)
PHONE................................330 453-5236
Fax: 330 453-3346
William Ferris, *President*
EMP: 6
SQ FT: 4,000
SALES: 1.5MM **Privately Held**
WEB: www.allpowerbattery.com
SIC: 7699 5013 3691 Battery service & repair; automotive batteries; lead acid batteries (storage batteries)

(G-2598)
ALLIANCE HEALTHCARE SVCS INC
5005 Whipple Ave Nw (44718-2657)
PHONE................................330 493-6747
Fax: 330 493-6947
Kimberly Winkowski, *Accounts Exec*
Jodie Pezzone-Amy, *Administration*
EMP: 88
SALES (corp-wide): 505.5MM **Publicly Held**
SIC: 3826 Magnetic resonance imaging apparatus
PA: Alliance Healthcare Services, Inc.
100 Bayview Cir Ste 400
Newport Beach CA 92660
949 242-5300

(G-2599)
ALLIANCE PETROLEUM CORPORATION (PA)
4150 Belden Village Mall (44718-2502)
PHONE................................330 493-0440
Fax: 330 493-3409
John Miller, *CEO*
Dora Silvis, *Vice Pres*
EMP: 26
SQ FT: 2,900
SALES (est): 12.5MM **Privately Held**
WEB: www.alliancepetroleumcorp.com
SIC: 1311 1382 Crude petroleum production; natural gas production; oil & gas exploration services

(G-2600)
ALWAYS BETTER COMMUNICATIONS (PA)
Also Called: ABC
4641 Dueber Ave Sw (44706-4556)
PHONE................................330 445-2220
Douglas Pauly, *President*
Bryan Witting, *Vice Pres*
Douglas Pauley, *Administration*
EMP: 12
SALES (est): 1.7MM **Privately Held**
WEB: www.alwaysbetter.net
SIC: 3663 Antennas, transmitting & communications

(G-2601)
AMBAFLEX INC
1530 Raff Rd Sw (44710-2322)
PHONE................................330 478-1858
David Spencer, *General Mgr*
◆ EMP: 22
SALES (est): 4.9MM **Privately Held**
SIC: 3535 Conveyors & conveying equipment

(G-2602)
AMERICAN ALUMINUM EXTRUSIONS
Also Called: A A E
4416 Louisville St Ne (44705-4848)
PHONE................................330 458-0300
Fax: 330 458-0400
Samuel Popa, *President*
Bill Kertes, *QC Mgr*
Scott Turner, *Controller*
Joann Tyler, *Human Resources*
George Stevenson, *VP Sales*
▲ EMP: 105
SQ FT: 240,000
SALES (est): 26.1MM **Privately Held**
WEB: www.aaeo.com
SIC: 3354 Aluminum extruded products

(G-2603)
ANCHOR FOUNDRY & MACHINE INC
4411 Louisville St Ne (44705-4847)
P.O. Box 7279 (44705-0279)
PHONE................................330 453-3441
Charles Postlewait, *President*
EMP: 3 EST: 1961
SALES (est): 312.3K **Privately Held**
SIC: 3544 3365 Industrial molds; aluminum & aluminum-based alloy castings

(G-2604)
ARCHER CORPORATION
Also Called: Archer Sign
1917 Henry Ave Sw (44706-2941)
PHONE................................330 455-9995
Jerry Archer, *CEO*
Michael Minor, *Vice Pres*
Beth Watson, *Manager*
EMP: 40
SQ FT: 70,000
SALES (est): 6.8MM **Privately Held**
WEB: www.archersign.com
SIC: 1799 3993 Sign installation & maintenance; signs & advertising specialties

(G-2605)
ARM OPCO INC
Also Called: American Road Machinery
3026 Saratoga Ave Sw (44706-2236)
PHONE................................330 868-7724
Fax: 330 868-3386
Nicholas W Ballas, *President*
Matthew D H Valentine, *Vice Pres*
Drew Likins, *Production*
Rebecca Harkless, *Manager*
▲ EMP: 40
SQ FT: 30,000
SALES (est): 18.4MM **Privately Held**
WEB: www.amroadmach.com
SIC: 3531 Blades for graders, scrapers, dozers & snow plows

(G-2606)
ARNOLD PRINTING INC
5772 West Blvd Nw (44718-1430)
PHONE................................330 494-1191
Fax: 330 477-8586
Joe Arnold, *President*
Craig Arnold, *Vice Pres*
Sue Arnold, *Admin Sec*
EMP: 4
SQ FT: 1,500
SALES: 325K **Privately Held**
SIC: 2752 Offset & photolithographic printing

(G-2607)
ASC HOLDCO INC (DH)
Also Called: Pumps Group, The
2100 International Pkwy (44720-1373)
PHONE................................330 899-0340
Ted Swaldo, *President*
Tom Blackerby, *CFO*
▲ EMP: 5
SALES (est): 45.6MM **Privately Held**
WEB: www.ucinc.com
SIC: 3714 Water pump, motor vehicle
HQ: United Components, Llc
1900 W Field Ct
Lake Forest IL 60045
812 867-4516

(G-2608)
ASSOCTED VSUAL CMMNCATIONS INC
Also Called: A V C
200 Cherry Ave Ne (44702-1129)
PHONE................................330 452-4449
Raymond Gonzalez, *President*
Paul Anthony, *Vice Pres*
Connie Anthony, *Accounts Mgr*
EMP: 25
SQ FT: 100,000
SALES: 3MM **Privately Held**
WEB: www.avcprint.com
SIC: 2759 Screen printing

(G-2609)
AULTWRKS OCCUPATIONAL MEDICINE
4650 Hills And Dales Rd N (44708-6220)
PHONE................................330 491-9675
Lisa Dyer, *Director*
Michael Furcolow, *Administration*
EMP: 15
SALES (est): 1.2MM **Privately Held**
SIC: 2834 Medicines, capsuled or ampuled

(G-2610)
AVONDALE PRINTING INC
2820 Whipple Ave Nw (44708-1566)
PHONE................................330 477-1180
Fax: 330 477-7807
Don Denham, *President*
Amber Rector, *Manager*
EMP: 3
SQ FT: 1,500
SALES (est): 432.7K **Privately Held**
WEB: www.starkrealtors.com
SIC: 2752 Commercial printing, lithographic

(G-2611)
AZZ INC
1723 Cleveland Ave Sw (44707-3646)
PHONE................................330 456-3241
Fax: 330 445-2172
Tim Myers, *Manager*
EMP: 33
SALES (corp-wide): 903.1MM **Publicly Held**
SIC: 3699 Electrical equipment & supplies
PA: Azz Inc.
3100 W 7th St Ste 500
Fort Worth TX 76107
817 810-0095

(G-2612)
AZZ INCORPORATED
1723 Cleveland Ave Sw (44707-3646)
PHONE................................330 445-2170
Mike Stroia, *Sales Mgr*
Michael Donley, *Branch Mgr*
EMP: 25
SALES (corp-wide): 903.1MM **Publicly Held**
SIC: 3479 Hot dip coating of metals or formed products
PA: Azz Inc.
3100 W 7th St Ste 500
Fort Worth TX 76107
817 810-0095

(G-2613)
B-TEK SCALES LLC
1510 Metric Ave Sw (44706-3088)
PHONE................................330 471-8900
Fax: 330 471-8909
Kraig F Brechbuhler, *President*
Eric Wolfe, *Regional Mgr*
Rei Tritt, *Corp Secy*
Andrew Brechbuhler, *Vice Pres*
Jeff Graham, *Vice Pres*
◆ EMP: 50
SQ FT: 65,000
SALES (est): 18.6MM
SALES (corp-wide): 48.1MM **Privately Held**
WEB: www.b-tek.com
SIC: 3325 7371 Steel foundries; software programming applications
PA: Brechbuhler Scales, Inc.
1424 Scales St Sw
Canton OH 44706
330 458-3060

(G-2614)
BADBOY BLASTERS INCORPORATED
1720 Wallace Ave Ne (44705-4056)
PHONE................................330 454-2699
Andrea Bandi Cain, *President*
Mark Cain, *Vice Pres*
▲ EMP: 10 EST: 2006
SQ FT: 13,000
SALES: 1.4MM **Privately Held**
SIC: 3471 Sand blasting of metal parts

(G-2615)
BALL CORPORATION
2121 Warner Rd Se (44707-2273)
PHONE................................330 244-2800
Jerry Evans, *Director*
Ed Hargager, *Director*
Bryon Jones, *Director*
Chuck Ring, *Director*
Pete Welch, *Director*
EMP: 57
SALES (corp-wide): 9B **Publicly Held**
WEB: www.sonoco.com
SIC: 2631 Paperboard mills
PA: Ball Corporation
10 Longs Peak Dr
Broomfield CO 80021
303 469-3131

(G-2616)
BARNHART PRINTING CORP
Also Called: Barnhart Publishing
1107 Melchoir Pl Sw (44707-4220)
PHONE................................330 456-2279
Fax: 330 452-4451
John F Waechter, *President*
Brent A Barnhart, *Chairman*
EMP: 18 EST: 1930
SQ FT: 10,000

SALES (est): 3.6MM **Privately Held**
WEB: www.barnhartprinting.com
SIC: 2752 2759 2789 Commercial printing, lithographic; letterpress printing;
bookbinding & related work

(G-2617)
BDI INC
417 Applegrove St Nw (44720-1617)
PHONE.................................330 498-4980
Tom Carlouzzi, *Branch Mgr*
Tom Carlozzi, *Branch Mgr*
Lori Oneil, *Manager*
EMP: 12
SALES (corp-wide): 429.5MM **Privately
Held**
SIC: 3568 Power transmission equipment
PA: Bdi, Inc.
     8000 Hub Pkwy
     Cleveland OH 44125
     216 642-9100

(G-2618)
BEAD SHOPPE AT HOME
2872 Whipple Ave Nw (44708-1532)
PHONE.................................330 479-9598
Shelley Lantz, *Owner*
EMP: 3
SALES (est): 146.6K **Privately Held**
SIC: 3999 Beads, unassembled

(G-2619)
BEATTY FOODS LLC
1117 Brant Ave Nw (44708-4008)
PHONE.................................330 327-2442
EMP: 3 EST: 2011
SALES (est): 74K **Privately Held**
SIC: 2099 Mfg Food Preparations

(G-2620)
BEN JAMES ENTERPRISES INC
4110 Southway St Sw (44706-1863)
PHONE.................................330 477-9353
Ben James, *President*
Kellie Lindsey, *Treasurer*
EMP: 4 EST: 2002
SALES (est): 739.1K **Privately Held**
SIC: 3499 Welding tips, heat resistant:
metal

(G-2621)
BETTER LIVING CONCEPTS INC
Also Called: Compu-Print
7233 Freedom Ave Nw (44720-7123)
P.O. Box 2340, North Canton (44720-0340)
PHONE.................................330 494-2213
Fax: 330 494-2214
Jeff Davies, *President*
EMP: 14
SQ FT: 5,400
SALES (est): 1MM **Privately Held**
WEB: www.betterlivingconcepts.com
SIC: 2759 Imprinting

(G-2622)
BIG KAHUNA GRAPHICS INC
Also Called: Bk Graphics
1255 Prospect Ave Sw (44706-1627)
PHONE.................................330 455-2625
Terry Lewis, *President*
EMP: 5
SALES (est): 590.6K **Privately Held**
SIC: 2396 2395 Stamping fabric articles;
pleating & stitching

(G-2623)
**BIOCURV MEDICAL
INSTRUMENTS**
245 Dryden Ct Sw (44706-1138)
PHONE.................................330 451-1628
Fax: 330 451-1611
Rich Marks, *Branch Mgr*
EMP: 3
SALES (corp-wide): 368.7K **Privately
Held**
WEB: www.biocurv.com
SIC: 2844 Oral preparations
PA: Biocurv Medical Instruments
     3054 Tuscarawas St W
     Canton OH 44708
     330 454-6621

(G-2624)
BOCOR HOLDINGS LLC
Also Called: Bocor Producing
7793 Pittsburg Ave Nw (44720-6947)
PHONE.................................330 494-1221
Robert Hutcheson, *Manager*
EMP: 4
SALES (est): 350K **Privately Held**
WEB: www.bocorproducing.com
SIC: 1382 Oil & gas exploration services

(G-2625)
**BOLONS CUSTOM KITCHENS
INC**
6287 Promler St Nw (44720-7609)
PHONE.................................330 499-0092
Guy Bolon, *CEO*
Terry Bolon, *President*
EMP: 13
SQ FT: 1,500
SALES (est): 1.7MM **Privately Held**
SIC: 5722 2599 Kitchens, complete (sinks,
cabinets, etc.); cabinets, factory

(G-2626)
BOWDIL COMPANY
2030 Industrial Pl Se (44707-2641)
PHONE.................................800 356-8663
Fax: 330 456-4625
Brite Morrow, *President*
J Britton Morrow, *Corp Secy*
Dove Hout, *Purch Mgr*
EMP: 17
SQ FT: 50,000
SALES: 2MM **Privately Held**
WEB: www.bowdil.com
SIC: 3532 3599 3398 Mining machinery;
custom machinery; metal heat treating

(G-2627)
BRAHLER INC
Also Called: Wedding Pages
4041 Batton St Nw Ste 104 (44720-7145)
PHONE.................................330 966-7730
Fax: 330 966-7709
Richard Brahler, *President*
EMP: 5
SALES (est): 311.8K **Privately Held**
SIC: 5621 2759 Bridal shops; publication
printing

(G-2628)
**BRENDEL PRODUCING
COMPANY**
8215 Arlington Ave Nw (44720-5111)
PHONE.................................330 854-4151
Frank Brendel Jr, *President*
Kay Morgan, *Office Mgr*
EMP: 8
SQ FT: 1,200
SALES (est): 603.6K **Privately Held**
SIC: 1381 1311 Directional drilling oil &
gas wells; crude petroleum & natural gas

(G-2629)
**BROOKS UTILITY PRODUCTS
GROUP**
Also Called: Brooks Meter Devices
3359 Bruening Ave Sw (44706-4100)
P.O. Box 6382 (44706-0382)
PHONE.................................330 455-0301
Susan Barringer, *Branch Mgr*
EMP: 31
SALES (corp-wide): 7.8MM **Privately
Held**
SIC: 3643 3469 Sockets, electric; elec-
tronic enclosures, stamped or pressed
metal
PA: Brooks Utility Products Group Inc
     23847 Industrial Park Dr
     Farmington Hills MI 48335
     248 477-0250

(G-2630)
BUCKEYE PAPER CO INC
5233 Southway St Sw # 523 (44706-1943)
P.O. Box 711, Massillon (44648-0711)
PHONE.................................330 477-5925
Fax: 330 477-2256
Edward N Bast Sr, *President*
Rob Bolanz, *General Mgr*
Edward Bast Jr, *Vice Pres*
Debby Olson, *Manager*
▼ EMP: 32
SQ FT: 54,000

SALES (est): 8.9MM **Privately Held**
WEB: www.buckeyepaper.com
SIC: 2679 5113 Paper products, converted; industrial & personal service
paper

(G-2631)
BUGH VINYL PRODUCTS INC
8933 Cleveland Ave Nw (44720-4565)
PHONE.................................330 305-0978
Roger Bugh, *President*
Barbara Bugh, *Vice Pres*
EMP: 8
SQ FT: 3,600
SALES (est): 1.1MM **Privately Held**
WEB: www.bughvinyl.com
SIC: 5211 3089 Fencing; fences, gates &
accessories: plastic

(G-2632)
C&H INDUSTRIES
2054 Jaquelyn Dr (44720-1134)
PHONE.................................330 899-0001
EMP: 3
SALES (est): 196K **Privately Held**
SIC: 3999 Mfg Misc Products

(G-2633)
CAGE GEAR & MACHINE LLC
1776 Gateway Blvd Se (44707-3503)
PHONE.................................330 452-1532
David Churbock, *Mng Member*
Cindy Jones, *Administration*
EMP: 12
SQ FT: 22,900
SALES (est): 1.9MM **Privately Held**
WEB: www.cage-gear.com
SIC: 3599 3566 Machine shop, jobbing &
repair; gears, power transmission, except
automotive

(G-2634)
CAMMEL SAW COMPANY INC
4898 Hills & Dales Rd Nw (44708-1495)
PHONE.................................330 477-3764
Fax: 330 477-3561
Dennis Cammel, *President*
William Leasure, *Opers Mgr*
Robert Camner, *Admin Sec*
EMP: 13
SQ FT: 10,000
SALES (est): 1.3MM **Privately Held**
WEB: www.cammelsaw.com
SIC: 7699 5072 5251 3425 Knife, saw &
tool sharpening & repair; saw blades;
tools; saws, hand: metalworking or wood-
working

(G-2635)
CAMPBELLS CANDIES
3074 Chaucer Dr Ne (44721-3670)
PHONE.................................330 493-1805
John Saner, *Owner*
EMP: 3 EST: 1969
SQ FT: 1,300
SALES (est): 144.1K **Privately Held**
SIC: 2066 5441 Chocolate candy, solid;
candy

(G-2636)
CANTON ASPHALT CO
Also Called: Superior Paving
5947 Whipple Ave Nw (44720-7692)
PHONE.................................330 499-6888
Marlene Oster, *President*
EMP: 6
SQ FT: 3,000
SALES: 1.5MM **Privately Held**
SIC: 2951 Asphalt & asphaltic paving mix-
tures (not from refineries)

(G-2637)
CANTON CABINET CO
1415 7th St Nw (44703-2923)
PHONE.................................330 455-2585
John Haslam, *Principal*
EMP: 4
SALES (est): 319.4K **Privately Held**
SIC: 2434 Wood kitchen cabinets

(G-2638)
CANTON DROP FORGE INC
4575 Southway St Sw (44706-1995)
PHONE.................................330 477-4511
Fax: 330 477-2046
Brad Ahbe, *President*

Bradly Ahbe, *President*
I H Taylor Et Al, *Principal*
J B Weida, *Principal*
James J O'Sullivan Jr, *Chairman*
◆ EMP: 300 EST: 1903
SQ FT: 245,000
SALES (est): 142.5MM **Privately Held**
WEB: www.cantondropforge.com
SIC: 3462 3463 3356 3312 Iron & steel
forgings; nonferrous forgings; nonferrous
rolling & drawing; blast furnaces & steel
mills
PA: Cordier Group Holdings Inc
     4575 Southway St Sw
     Canton OH 44706
     330 477-4511

(G-2639)
CANTON FUEL
1600 30th St Ne (44714-1628)
PHONE.................................330 455-3400
EMP: 4 EST: 2011
SALES (est): 456.7K **Privately Held**
SIC: 2869 Fuels

(G-2640)
**CANTON GEAR MFG DESIGN CO
INC**
1600 Tuscarawas St E (44707-3199)
PHONE.................................330 455-2771
Fax: 330 453-7305
Matthew Weida, *President*
Barbara Bettis, *Vice Pres*
Aj Westfall, *Office Mgr*
EMP: 10 EST: 1960
SALES (est): 2.1MM **Privately Held**
SIC: 3566 Speed changers, drives & gears

(G-2641)
**CANTON GRAPHIC ARTS
SERVICE**
800 Cleveland Ave Sw (44702-2140)
PHONE.................................330 456-9868
Ronald Wertman, *President*
Tim Toolan, *Vice Pres*
Denise Dearment, *Admin Sec*
EMP: 5 EST: 1951
SALES (est): 390K **Privately Held**
SIC: 7389 2752 2791 Engraving service;
commercial printing, lithographic; typeset-
ting

(G-2642)
**CANTON OH RUBBER SPECLTY
PRODS**
Also Called: Cors Products
1387 Clarendon Ave Sw (44710-2190)
P.O. Box 20188 (44701-0188)
PHONE.................................330 454-3847
Mark Lukosavich, *CEO*
Shirley Conradi, *Admin Mgr*
EMP: 8
SQ FT: 15,000
SALES (est): 750K **Privately Held**
SIC: 3061 2869 3069 2822 Appliance
rubber goods (mechanical); silicones;
weather strip, sponge rubber; ethylene-
propylene rubbers, EPDM polymers

(G-2643)
**CANTON OIL WELL SERVICE
INC**
7793 Pittsburg Ave Nw (44720-6947)
PHONE.................................330 494-1221
Fax: 330 494-4864
Thomas R Hutcheson, *CEO*
Kevin W Hutcheson, *President*
Robert J Hutcheson, *Principal*
James Paumier, *Vice Pres*
Seth Kienzle, *Broker*
EMP: 12 EST: 1962
SQ FT: 7,500
SALES (est): 2.2MM **Privately Held**
SIC: 1389 Servicing oil & gas wells

(G-2644)
**CANTON ORTHOTIC
LABORATORY**
811 12th St Nw (44703-1927)
PHONE.................................330 833-0955
Fax: 330 454-9568
Stephen T Simko, *President*
Ann Marie Simko, *Vice Pres*
EMP: 7 EST: 1975
SQ FT: 4,500

118   2017 Harris Ohio
Industrial Directory   ▲ = Import ▼ =Export
◆ =Import/Export

SALES (est): 583.5K **Privately Held**
SIC: 3842 Orthopedic appliances

(G-2645)
CANTON PATTERN & MOLD INC
Also Called: Canton Pattern and Mold
914 Sylvan Ct Ne (44705-1056)
P.O. Box 7295 (44705-0295)
PHONE..................................330 455-4316
Dan Ritz, *President*
EMP: 5
SQ FT: 4,300
SALES (est): 613.9K **Privately Held**
SIC: 3544 Industrial molds

(G-2646)
CANTON PLATING CO INC
903 9th St Ne (44704-1400)
PHONE..................................330 452-7808
Fax: 330 452-6851
Mark Kast, *President*
Denise Kast, *Admin Sec*
EMP: 6 **EST:** 1955
SQ FT: 3,480
SALES: 210K **Privately Held**
SIC: 3471 Electroplating of metals or
formed products

(G-2647)
CANTON SIGN CO
222 5th St Ne (44702-1262)
P.O. Box 80137 (44708-0137)
PHONE..................................330 456-7151
Fax: 330 456-7152
Timothy Franta, *President*
Mark A Franta, *Vice Pres*
EMP: 3 **EST:** 1910
SQ FT: 8,500
SALES: 400K **Privately Held**
SIC: 3993 Neon signs; name plates: ex-
cept engraved, etched, etc.: metal

(G-2648)
CANTON STERILIZED WIPING CLOTH
Also Called: Sentry Products
1401 Waynesburg Dr Se (44707-2115)
PHONE..................................330 455-5179
Fax: 330 455-2003
Robert Shapiro, *President*
Ronald Shapiro, *Vice Pres*
Debbie Starks, *Manager*
EMP: 8 **EST:** 1924
SQ FT: 42,000
SALES (est): 1.9MM **Privately Held**
SIC: 2211 5199 5113 Scrub cloths; cham-
ois leather; sponges (animal); napkins,
paper

(G-2649)
CAPITAL CHEMICAL CO
5340 Mayfair Rd (44720-1533)
PHONE..................................330 494-9535
Lon Swinehart, *President*
EMP: 25 **EST:** 1964
SQ FT: 8,000
SALES (est): 1.9MM **Privately Held**
WEB: www.royalsheeninc.com
SIC: 2842 2899 Specialty cleaning, pol-
ishes & sanitation goods; chemical prepa-
rations

(G-2650)
CARMEL TRADER PUBLISHING INC
4501 Hills & Dales Rd Nw (44708-1572)
PHONE..................................330 478-9200
Fax: 330 478-9205
Ernie Blood, *President*
Joseph Meranto, *Principal*
Karen Hought, *Vice Pres*
Melody Blood, *Treasurer*
Jonathan Blood, *Info Tech Mgr*
EMP: 30
SALES (est): 15MM **Privately Held**
SIC: 2721 2731 Magazines: publishing &
printing; book publishing

(G-2651)
CASTLEBAR CORPORATION
Also Called: CDI
406 15th St Sw (44707-4011)
PHONE..................................330 451-6511
Johnathan Adamski, *President*
EMP: 5

SALES (est): 890.2K **Privately Held**
SIC: 3313 3356 Tungsten carbide powder;
tungsten, basic shapes

(G-2652)
CHECKPOINT SYSTEMS INC
Alpha Security
1510 4th St Se (44707-3206)
PHONE..................................330 456-7776
Fax: 330 456-0462
Tom Wagner, *Opers Mgr*
Gale Essick, *Opers Staff*
Tim Williams, *Branch Mgr*
Cathy Ginella, *Administration*
EMP: 140
SALES (corp-wide): 188.4K **Privately Held**
WEB: www.checkpointsystems.com
SIC: 3089 Cases, plastic
HQ: Checkpoint Systems, Inc.
101 Wolf Dr
West Deptford NJ 08086
856 848-1800

(G-2653)
CHEMTECH INC
1712 Ira Turpin Way Ne (44705-1415)
PHONE..................................330 454-2127
Fax: 330 454-3049
Joseph Copthorne, *President*
Patricia Copthorne, *Treasurer*
EMP: 10
SQ FT: 8,000
SALES: 500K **Privately Held**
SIC: 2899 Water treating compounds

(G-2654)
CHRISTMAN FABRICATORS INC
4668 Navarre Rd Sw (44706-2337)
PHONE..................................330 477-8077
Fax: 330 477-0441
Esther Christman, *President*
Kevin Christman, *Corp Secy*
Mark Christman, *Vice Pres*
EMP: 9
SQ FT: 15,000
SALES (est): 1.8MM **Privately Held**
SIC: 3441 Fabricated structural metal

(G-2655)
CINTAS CORPORATION NO 2
3865 Highland Park Nw (44720-4537)
P.O. Box 3010 (44720-8010)
PHONE..................................330 966-7800
Fax: 330 966-7888
Allen Kocsis, *Manager*
Dawn Hlass, *Manager*
Dixie King, *Manager*
Cheryl Mitch, *Manager*
EMP: 100
SQ FT: 17,084
SALES (corp-wide): 4.9B **Publicly Held**
WEB: www.cintas-corp.com
SIC: 7218 2326 2337 Industrial uniform
supply; treated equipment supply: mats,
rugs, mops, cloths, etc.; wiping towel sup-
ply; work uniforms; uniforms, except ath-
letic: women's, misses' & juniors'
HQ: Cintas Corporation No. 2
6800 Cintas Blvd
Mason OH 45040

(G-2656)
CITY OF CANTON
Also Called: Traffic Engineering Department
2436 30th St Ne (44705-2568)
PHONE..................................330 489-3370
Byron Carson, *Superintendent*
Dan Moeglin, *Administration*
EMP: 30 **Privately Held**
WEB: www.cantonincometax.com
SIC: 3669 9111 Traffic signals, electric;
mayors' offices
PA: City Of Canton
218 Cleveland Ave Sw
Canton OH 44702
330 438-4300

(G-2657)
CLARK & SON POOL TABLE COMPANY
Also Called: Clark & Son Billiard Supply
2737 Cleveland Ave Nw (44709-3391)
PHONE..................................330 454-9153
Timothy J Clark, *Owner*
Darlene Clark, *Co-Owner*

EMP: 3
SQ FT: 6,550
SALES: 250K **Privately Held**
WEB: www.clarkandson.com
SIC: 3949 Billiard & pool equipment & sup-
plies, general

(G-2658)
CLARK OPTIMIZATION LLC
1222 Easton St Ne (44721-2455)
PHONE..................................330 417-2164
Steve Clark, *President*
Douglas B Crawford, *CFO*
EMP: 20
SALES (est): 1.4MM **Privately Held**
SIC: 2741

(G-2659)
CLARK SUBSTATIONS LLC
2240 Allen Ave Se (44707-3612)
PHONE..................................330 452-5200
Jason Harris, *Marketing Mgr*
Lawrence E Butts,
Ralph H Aldridge,
T Morris Hackney,
Carolyn M Smith,
EMP: 30
SALES (est): 3.6MM **Privately Held**
SIC: 3612 3699 3625 Distribution trans-
formers, electric; electrical equipment &
supplies; relays & industrial controls

(G-2660)
CLOVER PALLET LLC
5219 Violet Knoll Ave Ne (44705-3271)
PHONE..................................330 454-5592
Adam Rennecker, *Principal*
EMP: 3
SALES (est): 247.1K **Privately Held**
SIC: 2448 Pallets, wood & wood with metal

(G-2661)
COACH INC
4205 Belden Village Mall (44718-2503)
PHONE..................................330 491-8658
EMP: 15
SALES (corp-wide): 4.4B **Publicly Held**
SIC: 3171 Handbags, women's
PA: Coach, Inc.
10 Hudson Yards
New York NY 10001
212 594-1850

(G-2662)
COATER SERVICES INC
Also Called: Kohler Coating
1205 5th St Sw (44707-4625)
PHONE..................................330 499-1407
Herb Kohler, *President*
Richard Linc, *Controller*
Megan Soehnlen, *Mktg Coord*
▲ **EMP:** 29
SALES (est): 6MM **Privately Held**
WEB: www.kohlercoating.com
SIC: 3554 Paper industries machinery

(G-2663)
COATING CONTROL INC
825 Navarre Rd Sw (44707-4058)
PHONE..................................330 453-9136
Charles E Decker II, *President*
EMP: 5
SQ FT: 30,000
SALES (est): 664.4K **Privately Held**
WEB: www.coatingcontrol.com
SIC: 3549 Metalworking machinery

(G-2664)
COMBI PACKAGING SYSTEMS LLC
5365 E Center Dr Ne (44721-3734)
P.O. Box 9326 (44711-9326)
PHONE..................................330 456-9333
John F Fisher, *CEO*
Lisa Mackil, *Project Mgr*
Tara Withers, *Project Mgr*
Chris Pizzedaz, *Parts Mgr*
Gheorghe Vasu, *Purch Agent*
◆ **EMP:** 70
SQ FT: 119,000
SALES (est): 37.8MM **Privately Held**
WEB: www.combi.com
SIC: 3565 Packaging machinery

(G-2665)
COMMUNICATION RESOURCES INC
4786 Dressler Rd Nw Ste 3 (44718-2555)
PHONE..................................800 992-2144
Fax: 330 493-7897
Randall S Coy, *President*
Robert W Fisher, *Chairman*
Georgia A Fisher, *Vice Pres*
EMP: 25 **EST:** 1979
SQ FT: 2,000
SALES (est): 1.7MM **Privately Held**
SIC: 2731 2721 Pamphlets: publishing &
printing; periodicals

(G-2666)
CONCRETE LEVELING SYSTEMS INC
Also Called: CLS FABRICATING, INC.
5046 East Blvd Nw (44718-1212)
PHONE..................................330 966-8120
Suzanne I Barth, *CEO*
Edward A Barth, *President*
Eugene H Swearengin, *Admin Sec*
EMP: 3
SQ FT: 2,500
SALES: 3.6K **Privately Held**
SIC: 3531 Construction machinery

(G-2667)
CONTINENTAL HYDRODYNE SYSTEMS
2216 Glenmont Dr Nw (44708-2036)
PHONE..................................330 494-2740
Theodore F Savastano, *Principal*
EMP: 11
SALES (est): 1.4MM **Privately Held**
SIC: 3821 Chemical laboratory apparatus

(G-2668)
COPLEY OHIO NEWSPAPERS INC (HQ)
Also Called: Repository
500 Market Ave S (44702-2112)
PHONE..................................585 598-0030
Fax: 330 454-5745
Kevin Kampman, *President*
James Porter, *Principal*
Rich Desrosiers, *Editor*
Darryl Hudson, *CFO*
Greg Carpenter, *Human Resources*
EMP: 93
SALES (est): 45MM
SALES (corp-wide): 1.2B **Publicly Held**
WEB: www.timesreporter.com
SIC: 2711 Commercial printing & newspa-
per publishing combined
PA: New Media Investment Group Inc.
1345 Avenue Of The Americ
New York NY 10105
212 479-3160

(G-2669)
CORDIER GROUP HOLDINGS INC (PA)
4575 Southway St Sw (44706-1933)
PHONE..................................330 477-4511
James J O'Sullivan Jr, *Chairman*
John Motsay, *Vice Pres*
EMP: 1
SALES (est): 142.5MM **Privately Held**
SIC: 3462 Iron & steel forgings

(G-2670)
CRAMERS INC
4944 Southway St Sw (44706-1990)
PHONE..................................330 477-4571
Fax: 330 477-6220
Don Hoover, *President*
E Robert Schellhase, *Principal*
R C Cramer, *Principal*
Dana Cramer, *Vice Pres*
Lynn Herdlick, *Vice Pres*
EMP: 25
SQ FT: 15,000
SALES (est): 6.6MM **Privately Held**
WEB: www.cramers.com
SIC: 3444 3446 3443 3441 Sheet metal-
work; architectural metalwork; fabricated
plate work (boiler shop); fabricated struc-
tural metal

(G-2671)
CROSCO
5246 18th St Sw (44706)
PHONE..................................330 477-1999
Glenn Cross, *Principal*
EMP: 3 **EST:** 2001
SALES (est): 230K **Privately Held**
SIC: 3713 Truck beds

(G-2672)
CS PRODUCTS
1307 Gross Ave Ne (44705-1607)
PHONE..................................330 452-8566
Fax: 330 452-8567
Bill Stine, *Owner*
EMP: 5
SALES (est): 653.6K **Privately Held**
SIC: 2448 5169 Wood pallets & skids;
chemicals & allied products

(G-2673)
CUSTOM BRASS FINISHING INC
1541 Raff Rd Sw (44710-2321)
PHONE..................................330 453-0888
Fax: 330 453-2251
Jack R Vogt, *President*
Nancy M Vogt, *Vice Pres*
EMP: 9
SQ FT: 24,000
SALES (est): 553.8K **Privately Held**
SIC: 3471 Plating of metals or formed
products

(G-2674)
D & D ENERGY CO
6033 Marelis Ave Ne (44721-3160)
PHONE..................................330 495-1631
Bob Ditty, *Principal*
EMP: 10
SALES (est): 400K **Privately Held**
SIC: 1389 Oil & gas field services

(G-2675)
D & L ENERGY INC
3930 Fulton Dr Nw Ste 200 (44718-3040)
PHONE..................................330 270-1201
Fax: 330 792-9584
Ben W Lupo, *CEO*
Susan A Faith, *President*
Susan Faith, *Exec VP*
Michael McKenzie, *Opers Staff*
EMP: 23
SQ FT: 13,637
SALES (est): 6.4MM **Privately Held**
SIC: 1311 Crude petroleum & natural gas
production

(G-2676)
D ANDERSON CORP
6872 Glengarry Ave Nw (44718-4044)
P.O. Box 36205 (44735-6205)
PHONE..................................330 433-0606
Dale Anderson, *President*
Charles Brown, *Treasurer*
EMP: 2
SALES (est): 2MM **Privately Held**
SIC: 1381 Directional drilling oil & gas
wells

(G-2677)
DANNER PRESS CORP
1411 Navarre Rd Sw (44706-1624)
PHONE..................................330 454-5692
James Ilundquist, *President*
EMP: 3
SALES (est): 246.9K **Privately Held**
SIC: 2759 2752 Commercial printing;
commercial printing, lithographic

(G-2678)
**DANSCO MFG & PMPG UNIT
SVC LP**
2149 Moore Ave Se (44707-2239)
PHONE..................................330 452-3677
Dave Send, *Owner*
Lou Faulks, *Vice Pres*
Don Sibley, *Opers Mgr*
EMP: 4
SALES (est): 200K **Privately Held**
SIC: 1389 Oil field services

(G-2679)
DARK CONTINENT
817 High Ave Nw (44703-2417)
PHONE..................................330 454-7804

Dennis Adams, *Owner*
EMP: 3
SALES (est): 130.1K **Privately Held**
SIC: 2911 5169 Aromatic chemical prod-
ucts; aromatic chemicals

(G-2680)
DCC CORP (PA)
5757 Mayfair Rd (44720-1546)
P.O. Box 2288 (44720-0288)
PHONE..................................330 494-0494
Stephen G Deuble, *President*
Andy Deuble, *Vice Pres*
Daryl Miller, *Finance Mgr*
EMP: 4 **EST:** 1908
SQ FT: 16,000
SALES (est): 583.2K **Privately Held**
SIC: 6719 3999 Investment holding com-
panies, except banks; plaques, picture,
laminated

(G-2681)
DE VORE ENGRAVING CO
1017 Tuscarawas St E (44707-3154)
PHONE..................................330 454-6820
Fax: 330 454-5602
Alan J De Vore, *President*
Chris De Vore, *Vice Pres*
EMP: 6 **EST:** 1963
SQ FT: 400
SALES (est): 500K **Privately Held**
WEB: www.devoreengraving.com
SIC: 3479 Painting, coating & hot dipping

(G-2682)
DECISION SYSTEMS INC
Also Called: Midland Engineering
2935 Woodcliff Dr Nw (44718-3331)
PHONE..................................330 456-7600
Peter E Voss, *President*
E R Frederick, *Exec VP*
W Williams, *Exec VP*
Kay Wieschaus, *Treasurer*
Paul Storz, *VP Sales*
EMP: 20
SQ FT: 5,000
SALES: 49MM **Privately Held**
SIC: 3559 8711 3535 Separation equip-
ment, magnetic; engineering services;
conveyors & conveying equipment

(G-2683)
DELTA MEDIA GROUP INC
4726 Hills And Dales Rd N (44708-1571)
PHONE..................................330 493-0350
Mike Minard, *President*
EMP: 40
SALES (est): 4.3MM **Privately Held**
WEB: www.deltagroup.com
SIC: 7372 Application computer software

(G-2684)
DELTA PLATING INC
Also Called: Olymco
2125 Harrison Ave Sw (44706-3005)
PHONE..................................330 452-2300
Fax: 330 452-5425
Gregory Kalikas, *President*
Alex Sklavenitis, *Vice Pres*
Peggy Deckerd, *Controller*
William Sklavenitis, *Chief Mktg Ofcr*
David Crotsley, *Manager*
EMP: 43
SQ FT: 46,000
SALES (est): 7.2MM **Privately Held**
SIC: 3471 Electroplating of metals or
formed products; chromium plating of
metals or formed products

(G-2685)
DEVAULT INDUSTRIES LLC
3500 12th St Nw (44708-3805)
PHONE..................................330 456-6070
Dennis R Devault, *Principal*
EMP: 6
SALES (est): 791.7K **Privately Held**
SIC: 3999 Manufacturing industries

(G-2686)
DI WALT OPTICAL INC
1112 12th St Ne (44705-1120)
P.O. Box 9259 (44711-9259)
PHONE..................................330 453-8427
Fax: 330 453-7897
Marilyn Mc Dougal, *President*
Larry Dillworth, *Vice Pres*

EMP: 13
SQ FT: 3,600
SALES (est): 1.6MM **Privately Held**
SIC: 3851 Lens grinding, except prescrip-
tion: ophthalmic

(G-2687)
**DIANO CONSTRUCTION AND
SUP CO**
Also Called: Diano Supply Co
1000 Warner Rd Se (44707-3398)
PHONE..................................330 456-7229
Fax: 330 456-7470
Anthony Diano Jr, *President*
Darlene Guynup, *Vice Pres*
Mario Diano, *Sales Staff*
Neil Regal, *Manager*
EMP: 20 **EST:** 1929
SQ FT: 1,500
SALES (est): 3MM **Privately Held**
SIC: 3273 Ready-mixed concrete

(G-2688)
DIEBOLD INCORPORATED
5571 Global Gtwy (44720-1377)
PHONE..................................330 490-4000
Fax: 330 899-1452
Maryann Harowski, *Buyer*
Ron Lednik, *Buyer*
Jim Huntsman, *Technical Mgr*
Jennifer Hoffner, *Human Res Dir*
Joe Oleksik, *Manager*
EMP: 300
SALES (corp-wide): 3.3B **Publicly Held**
WEB: www.diebold.com
SIC: 3578 Automatic teller machines (ATM)
PA: Diebold Nixdorf, Incorporated
5995 Mayfair Rd
North Canton OH 44720
330 490-4000

(G-2689)
**DIEBOLD SELF SERVICE
SYSTEMS (PA)**
5995 Mayfair Rd (44720-1550)
P.O. Box 3077 (44720-8077)
PHONE..................................330 490-5099
Thomas Swidarski, *CEO*
Patrick Green, *General Mgr*
Daniel J Brien, *Vice Pres*
James L Chen, *Vice Pres*
Larry D Ingram, *Vice Pres*
▲ **EMP:** 600
SQ FT: 1,000
SALES (est): 300MM **Privately Held**
SIC: 3578 Automatic teller machines (ATM)

(G-2690)
DISCHEM INC
4252 Strausser St Nw (44720-7114)
PHONE..................................330 494-5210
Fax: 330 494-1305
Saurabh Lakhia, *President*
▼ **EMP:** 3
SQ FT: 7,500
SALES (est): 586.7K **Privately Held**
WEB: www.latexink.com
SIC: 2893 Letterpress or offset ink

(G-2691)
DLHBOWLES INC (PA)
2422 Leo Ave Sw (44706-2344)
PHONE..................................330 478-2503
John W Saxon, *CEO*
SRI Sridhara, *President*
Matthew Reese, *Vice Pres*
Dennis Whittington, *Buyer*
Melissa Stutler, *QC Mgr*
EMP: 450
SQ FT: 107,000
SALES (est): 139.3MM **Privately Held**
WEB: www.dlh-inc.com
SIC: 8711 3089 3082 Engineering serv-
ices; injection molding of plastics; tubes,
unsupported plastic

(G-2692)
DLHBOWLES INC
Also Called: Genex Mold
2422 Leo Ave Sw (44706-2344)
P.O. Box 6030 (44706-0030)
PHONE..................................330 478-2503
Fax: 330 478-2130
Debbie Hanna, *Purchasing*
Don Willis, *Enginr/R&D Mgr*
Dennis Robish, *Controller*

Tom Huskey, *Branch Mgr*
EMP: 17
SALES (corp-wide): 139.3MM **Privately
Held**
WEB: www.dlh-inc.com
SIC: 2821 Molding compounds, plastics
PA: Dlhbowles, Inc.
2422 Leo Ave Sw
Canton OH 44706
330 478-2503

(G-2693)
DLHBOWLES INC
2410 Leo Ave Sw (44706)
PHONE..................................330 479-7595
Tom Huskey, *Branch Mgr*
EMP: 30
SALES (corp-wide): 139.3MM **Privately
Held**
WEB: www.dlh-inc.com
SIC: 3089 Injection molding of plastics
PA: Dlhbowles, Inc.
2422 Leo Ave Sw
Canton OH 44706
330 478-2503

(G-2694)
DUNCAN PRESS CORPORATION
5049 Yukon St Nw (44708-5017)
PHONE..................................330 477-4529
Richard Kempthorn, *President*
Scott Duncan, *Vice Pres*
Jed Parker, *Vice Pres*
Steve Smith, *Sales Staff*
Marie Foss, *Manager*
EMP: 22 **EST:** 1958
SQ FT: 20,000
SALES (est): 2MM **Privately Held**
WEB: www.duncanpress.com
SIC: 2752 Commercial printing, litho-
graphic

(G-2695)
EDW C LEVY CO
3715 Whipple Ave Sw (44706-3535)
PHONE..................................330 484-6328
Fax: 330 484-0306
Steve Trevizo, *Opers Mgr*
Jack Sines, *Manager*
EMP: 20
SQ FT: 5,200
SALES (corp-wide): 388.3MM **Privately
Held**
WEB: www.edwclevy.com
SIC: 5093 3295 Scrap & waste materials;
minerals, ground or treated
PA: Edw. C. Levy Co.
9300 Dix
Dearborn MI 48120
313 429-2200

(G-2696)
ELECTRA TARP INC
2900 Perry Dr Sw (44706-2268)
PHONE..................................330 477-7168
Fax: 330 477-7702
Betsy Paul, *President*
Paul Bitsy, *Vice Pres*
Ruth Paul, *Manager*
EMP: 14
SQ FT: 20,000
SALES (est): 1.4MM **Privately Held**
WEB: www.electratarp.com
SIC: 2394 Tarpaulins, fabric: made from
purchased materials

(G-2697)
EMBROIDME
3611 Cleveland Ave S (44707-1447)
PHONE..................................330 484-8484
Scott Leuenberger, *Manager*
Mike Hamsher, *Manager*
EMP: 6
SALES (est): 520K **Privately Held**
SIC: 2253 T-shirts & tops, knit

(G-2698)
EVANS INDUSTRIES INC
606 Walnut Ave Ne (44702-1029)
PHONE..................................330 453-1122
Fax: 330 453-1122
Sue Ann Evans, *President*
Bevan Evans, *Corp Secy*
Carey Seigle, *CTO*
EMP: 18
SQ FT: 15,000

▲ = Import ▼ =Export
◆ =Import/Export

SALES (est): 3.2MM **Privately Held**
SIC: 3089 Plastic processing

(G-2699)
EVERHARD PRODUCTS INC (PA)
1016 9th St Sw (44707-4100)
PHONE..............................330 453-7786
Fax: 330 453-7449
G R Lucas, *Ch of Bd*
James L Anderson, *President*
Scott Anderson, *Vice Pres*
Vikki Ellington, *Purch Mgr*
Natalie Stelluto, *Purch Mgr*
▲ EMP: 119 EST: 1960
SQ FT: 154,000
SALES (est): 23.3MM **Privately Held**
WEB: www.everhard.com
SIC: 3423 Hand & edge tools

(G-2700)
FAMILY MEMORIALS
1325 Whipple Ave Nw (44708-2803)
PHONE..............................330 477-4900
Richard Miller, *Principal*
EMP: 3
SALES (est): 166.4K **Privately Held**
SIC: 1411 Granite, dimension-quarrying

(G-2701)
FIN FEATHER FUR
4080 Belden Village St Nw (44718-2541)
PHONE..............................330 493-8300
Mike Goschinski, *Branch Mgr*
EMP: 3
SALES (corp-wide): 10.8MM **Privately Held**
SIC: 3999 Furs
PA: Fin Feather Fur Outfitters-Ashland, Inc.
652 Us Highway 250 E
Ashland OH 44805
419 281-2557

(G-2702)
FINAL MACHINE
8397 Cleveland Ave Nw (44720-4819)
PHONE..............................330 966-1744
Herman Bower, *Owner*
EMP: 4
SALES (est): 317.6K **Privately Held**
SIC: 3599 Machine shop, jobbing & repair

(G-2703)
FINCOM CORPORATION (PA)
220 Market Ave S Ste 612 (44702-2171)
PHONE..............................330 456-8341
Fax: 330 430-3508
Steven P Cress, *President*
Norman Jackson, *Chairman*
Lee Dicola, *Corp Secy*
Thomas Herrick, *CFO*
EMP: 4
SALES (est): 25.6MM **Privately Held**
SIC: 6712 3599 3441 Bank holding companies; machine & other job shop work; fabricated structural metal

(G-2704)
FIRST PLACE AUTO PRODUCTS
6495 Chesham Ave Ne (44721-3506)
PHONE..............................330 493-1420
Fax: 330 493-0241
Fritz Wurgler, *Owner*
▲ EMP: 5
SQ FT: 3,500
SALES (est): 320K **Privately Held**
WEB: www.firstplaceautoproducts.com
SIC: 3714 Motor vehicle parts & accessories

(G-2705)
FOLTZ MACHINE LLC
2030 Allen Ave Se (44707-3691)
PHONE..............................330 453-9235
Fax: 330 453-3467
Lee Dicola, *Ch of Bd*
David Dicola, *President*
Linda R Polsinelli, *Vice Pres*
Dan Duffy, *Manager*
EMP: 30
SQ FT: 37,500
SALES (est): 6.6MM **Privately Held**
WEB: www.foltzmachine.com
SIC: 3599 Machine shop, jobbing & repair

(G-2706)
FORMCO INC
5175 Stoneham Rd (44720-1540)
PHONE..............................330 966-2111
Fax: 330 966-1572
Richard Bourne, *President*
Christopher Bourne, *Treasurer*
Carol Bourne, *Admin Sec*
EMP: 7 EST: 1976
SQ FT: 9,000
SALES: 500K **Privately Held**
SIC: 3069 Medical sundries, rubber

(G-2707)
FOUNDATION SYSTEMS ANCHORS INC
Also Called: F S A
2300 Allen Ave Se (44707-3673)
PHONE..............................330 454-1700
Anthony Codispoti, *President*
Karen Hawk, *Corp Secy*
Dennis Dinarda, *Vice Pres*
Maria Bertram, *Traffic Mgr*
Steve Bertram, *QC Mgr*
▲ EMP: 36
SQ FT: 2,500
SALES (est): 7.9MM **Privately Held**
WEB: www.fsabolt.com
SIC: 3449 Fabricated bar joists & concrete reinforcing bars

(G-2708)
FRITO-LAY NORTH AMERICA INC
4030 16th St Sw (44710-2354)
PHONE..............................330 477-7009
Fax: 330 477-3473
Kelly Smith, *Human Res Dir*
Mike Kulbacki, *Branch Mgr*
Jackie Blanton, *Administration*
EMP: 100
SQ FT: 36,400
SALES (corp-wide): 62.8B **Publicly Held**
WEB: www.fritolay.com
HQ: Frito-Lay North America, Inc.
7701 Legacy Dr
Plano TX 75024

(G-2709)
FUTURE PRODUCTIONS INC
4601 11th St Nw (44708-3561)
PHONE..............................330 478-0477
Brett Huntsman, *President*
EMP: 3
SALES: 264.3K **Privately Held**
SIC: 1381 Drilling oil & gas wells

(G-2710)
GALT ALLOYS INC MAIN OFC
122 Central Plz N (44702-1448)
PHONE..............................330 453-4678
Stephen R Giangiordano, *Principal*
EMP: 6
SALES (est): 376.9K **Privately Held**
SIC: 3339 Primary nonferrous metals

(G-2711)
GASPAR INC
1545 Whipple Ave Sw (44710-1373)
PHONE..............................330 477-2222
Gary W Gaspar, *President*
Chuck Clark, *Editor*
Bob F Frederick, *COO*
Wesley Morgan, *QC Mgr*
Judy Gaspar, *Admin Sec*
EMP: 55
SQ FT: 36,000
SALES (est): 17.1MM **Privately Held**
WEB: www.gasparinc.com
SIC: 3443 7692 3444 Industrial vessels, tanks & containers; heat exchangers, condensers & components; welding repair; sheet metalwork

(G-2712)
GENERAL ELECTRIC COMPANY
5555 Massillon Rd Bldg D (44720-1339)
PHONE..............................330 458-3200
June Mutter, *Manager*
EMP: 25

SALES (corp-wide): 123.6B **Publicly Held**
SIC: 3646 Commercial indusl & institutional electric lighting fixtures
PA: General Electric Company
41 Farnsworth St
Boston MA 02210
617 443-3000

(G-2713)
GERDAU MACSTEEL ATMOSPHERE ANN
Also Called: Advanced Bar Technology
1501 Raff Rd Sw (44710-2356)
PHONE..............................330 478-0314
Fax: 330 478-6554
Saminathan Ramaswamy, *Principal*
Scott C Pence, *Principal*
Barb Mraz, *Personnel*
EMP: 80
SQ FT: 31,316 **Privately Held**
WEB: www.aaimac.com
SIC: 7389 3398 Metal cutting services; metal heat treating
HQ: Gerdau Macsteel Atmosphere Annealing
209 W Mount Hope Ave # 1
Lansing MI 48910
517 782-0415

(G-2714)
GILBERT GEISER
Also Called: Protista Tool
3301 Longview Pl Nw (44720-4777)
PHONE..............................330 237-7901
Fax: 330 494-9030
Gilbert Geiser, *Owner*
EMP: 5
SALES: 105K **Privately Held**
SIC: 3523 Farm machinery & equipment; planting, haying, harvesting & processing machinery

(G-2715)
GMELECTRIC INC
4606 Southway St Sw (44706-1935)
PHONE..............................330 477-3392
George H Mountcastle, *Principal*
EMP: 6 EST: 2008
SALES: 687.6K **Privately Held**
SIC: 3694 5013 3679 Engine electrical equipment; automotive supplies & parts; harness assemblies for electronic use: wire or cable

(G-2716)
GOODWILL IDSTRS GRTR CLVLND L
2630 Atlantic Blvd Ne (44705-3730)
PHONE..............................330 456-8020
EMP: 20
SALES (corp-wide): 25.8MM **Privately Held**
SIC: 3999 Atomizers, toiletry
PA: Goodwill Industries Of Greater Cleveland And East Central Ohio, Inc.
408 9th St Sw
Canton OH 44707
330 454-9461

(G-2717)
GRACE PETROLEUM INC
5506 Keiffer Ave Nw (44706)
PHONE..............................330 484-0709
Sam Singh, *President*
EMP: 6
SALES (est): 714.9K **Privately Held**
SIC: 2911 Petroleum refining

(G-2718)
GRANGER PIPELINE CORPORATION
111 2nd St Nw Ste 202 (44702-1547)
PHONE..............................330 454-8095
Mitchell Graham, *President*
EMP: 3
SQ FT: 6,834
SALES (est): 234.3K **Privately Held**
SIC: 1389 Oil field services

(G-2719)
GREGORY INDUSTRIES INC (PA)
4100 13th St Sw (44710-1464)
PHONE..............................330 477-4800

Fax: 330 477-0626
T Stephen Gregory, *CEO*
Bob Chufar, *Regional Mgr*
Matt Gregory, *Exec VP*
Tim Porter, *Vice Pres*
Thomas Brem, *Plant Mgr*
◆ EMP: 80
SQ FT: 145,000
SALES (est): 24.1MM **Privately Held**
WEB: www.gregorycorp.com
SIC: 3499 Metal household articles

(G-2720)
GREGORY ROLL FORM INC
4100 13th St Sw (44710-1464)
PHONE..............................330 477-4800
T Stephen Gregory, *CEO*
T Raymond Gregory, *Ch of Bd*
Joseph Weaver, *CFO*
EMP: 100
SQ FT: 160,000
SALES (est): 11.4MM
SALES (corp-wide): 24.1MM **Privately Held**
WEB: www.gregorycorp.com
SIC: 3312 Iron & steel: galvanized, pipes, plates, sheets, etc.
PA: Gregory Industries, Inc.
4100 13th St Sw
Canton OH 44710
330 477-4800

(G-2721)
H-W MACHINE INC
4028 Southway St Sw (44706-1801)
PHONE..............................330 477-7221
Fax: 330 477-1360
Kris Houk, *President*
Joel Grissom, *Treasurer*
Gil Tuttle, *Office Mgr*
Millie Valentine, *Admin Sec*
EMP: 6 EST: 1944
SQ FT: 15,000
SALES (est): 600K **Privately Held**
WEB: www.hwmachine.com
SIC: 3599 Machine shop, jobbing & repair

(G-2722)
HAINES PUBLISHING INC
8050 Freedom Ave Nw (44720-6912)
P.O. Box 2117 (44720-0117)
PHONE..............................330 494-9111
William Haines Jr, *President*
Scott Southar, *General Mgr*
EMP: 65
SQ FT: 20,000
SALES: 4.1MM **Privately Held**
SIC: 2741 Directories: publishing & printing

(G-2723)
HANNON COMPANY (PA)
Also Called: Charles Rewinding Div
1605 Waynesburg Dr Se (44707-2137)
PHONE..............................330 456-4728
Fax: 330 456-3323
Thomas W Hannon, *Ch of Bd*
Tom McAllister, *President*
Gary Gonzalez, *Principal*
Carol Wood, *Principal*
Steven R Harper, *COO*
EMP: 75 EST: 1926
SQ FT: 65,000
SALES (est): 27.2MM **Privately Held**
WEB: www.hanco.com
SIC: 3621 3825 5084 3699 Motors, electric; test equipment for electronic & electrical circuits; transformers, portable: instrument; industrial machinery & equipment; electrical equipment & supplies; transformers, except electric; industrial furnaces & ovens

(G-2724)
HARRISON PAINT COMPANY (PA)
1329 Harrison Ave Sw (44706-1596)
PHONE..............................330 455-5120
Fax: 330 437-0343
Patrick Lauber, *President*
Dan Hancock, *Regional Mgr*
Steve Laizure, *VP Opers*
Pat Gorman, *Prdtn Mgr*
Gloria Tomer, *Accountant*
EMP: 27
SQ FT: 173,000

SALES (est): 4.7MM **Privately Held**
WEB: www.harrisonpaint.com
SIC: 2851 Paints & allied products

(G-2725)
HENDRICKSON USA LLC
Also Called: Hendrickson Trailer
2070 Industrial Pl Se (44707-2641)
PHONE..................................330 456-7288
Fax: 330 456-0105
Perry Bahr, *General Mgr*
John Falconer, *Project Mgr*
Dean Zimmerman, *Safety Mgr*
Eric Bauer, *Purch Mgr*
Brandon Spring, *QC Mgr*
EMP: 150
SALES (corp-wide): 1B **Privately Held**
SIC: 3537 Industrial trucks & tractors
HQ: Hendrickson Usa, L.L.C.
500 Park Blvd Ste 450
Itasca IL 60143
630 874-9700

(G-2726)
**HERCULES POLISHING &
PLATING**
4883 Southway St Sw (44706-1954)
PHONE..................................330 455-8871
Fax: 330 455-4558
Linda J Paxos, *CEO*
Nicholas Paxos, *Vice Pres*
EMP: 10
SQ FT: 20,000
SALES (est): 2MM **Privately Held**
SIC: 3471 Plating & polishing; chromium
plating of metals or formed products; pol-
ishing, metals or formed products

(G-2727)
HHI COMPANY INC (PA)
2512 Columbus Rd Ne (44705-3707)
P.O. Box 7117 (44705-0117)
PHONE..................................330 455-3983
Larry R Hunter, *President*
Judith Kay Hunter, *Vice Pres*
EMP: 3
SQ FT: 10,000
SALES (est): 1.1MM **Privately Held**
SIC: 7699 3069 Hydraulic equipment re-
pair; molded rubber products

(G-2728)
**HILAND GROUP
INCORPORATED (PA)**
Also Called: Delano Foods
7600 Supreme St Nw (44720-6920)
P.O. Box 36737 (44735-6737)
PHONE..................................330 499-8404
EMP: 65 EST: 1955
SQ FT: 10,000
SALES (est): 8.3MM **Privately Held**
SIC: 5149 2099 Whol Groceries Mfg Food
Preparations

(G-2729)
HM WIRE INTERNATIONAL INC
2125 46th St Nw (44709-1831)
P.O. Box 2153, North Canton (44720-0153)
PHONE..................................330 244-8501
Fax: 330 491-1186
Hal Marker, *President*
EMP: 5
SQ FT: 10,000
SALES (est): 490K **Privately Held**
WEB: www.hmwire.com
SIC: 3357 5051 Magnet wire, nonferrous;
miscellaneous nonferrous products

(G-2730)
HOOVER INC
8200 Freedom Ave Nw (44720-6983)
PHONE..................................330 499-9200
Fax: 330 966-5439
Lynne Dragomier, *VP Admin*
Robert Decker, *Vice Pres*
Ray Porter, *Foreman/Supr*
Ralph E Manning, *Senior Engr*
Ted Scheffler, *Controller*
EMP: 15
SALES (corp-wide): 5B **Privately Held**
SIC: 3635 Electric sweeper
HQ: Hoover Inc.
7005 Cochran Rd
Solon OH 44139
330 499-9200

(G-2731)
HUGHES CHRISTENSEN
1807 Allen Ave Se (44707-3695)
PHONE..................................330 455-2140
Hughes Christensen, *Principal*
EMP: 3
SALES (est): 338.2K **Privately Held**
SIC: 3533 Oil & gas field machinery

(G-2732)
HUNTER HYDRAULICS INC
Also Called: Hhi
2512 Columbus Rd Ne (44705-3707)
P.O. Box 7117 (44705-0117)
PHONE..................................330 455-3983
Larry R Hunter, *President*
Judith Kay Hunter, *Treasurer*
EMP: 6 EST: 1968
SQ FT: 10,000
SALES: 999K
SALES (corp-wide): 1.1MM **Privately
Held**
SIC: 3542 7699 Presses: hydraulic &
pneumatic, mechanical & manual; hy-
draulic equipment repair
PA: The Hhi Company Inc
2512 Columbus Rd Ne
Canton OH 44705
330 455-3983

(G-2733)
HYDRODEC INC (HQ)
2021 Steinway Blvd Se (44707-2644)
PHONE..................................330 454-8202
Mark McNamara, *CEO*
Sabine McGrady, *Office Mgr*
EMP: 19
SALES (est): 9.2MM
SALES (corp-wide): 43.8MM **Privately
Held**
SIC: 2911 Oils, partly refined: sold for re-
running
PA: Hydrodec Group Plc
6 Hay's Lane
London SE1 2
137 282-4750

(G-2734)
**HYDRODEC OF NORTH
AMERICA LLC**
2021 Steinway Blvd Se (44707-2644)
PHONE..................................330 454-8202
Ian Smale, *CEO*
Moynihan Colin, *Chairman*
Ellis Chris, *CFO*
Sabine McGraey, *Accounts Mgr*
▼ EMP: 29
SQ FT: 15,000
SALES (est): 9.2MM
SALES (corp-wide): 43.8MM **Privately
Held**
SIC: 2911 Oils, partly refined: sold for re-
running
HQ: Hydrodec Inc.
2021 Steinway Blvd Se
Canton OH 44707

(G-2735)
I P CONTRACTORS LLC
4974 Higbee Ave Nw Ste 11 (44718-2562)
PHONE..................................330 452-1643
Kevin Gatewood, *President*
EMP: 3
SALES (est): 182.8K **Privately Held**
SIC: 1446 Filtration sand mining

(G-2736)
I SQ R POWER CABLE CO
4300 Chamber Ave Sw (44706-3376)
P.O. Box 20149 (44701-0149)
PHONE..................................330 588-3000
Michael G Pinney, *President*
Karl Schwenk, *Director*
▲ EMP: 12
SQ FT: 8,000
SALES (est): 2.1MM **Privately Held**
SIC: 3643 Current-carrying wiring devices

(G-2737)
**INNOVATIVE PLASTIC
MACHINERY**
5252 Southway St Sw (44706-1961)
PHONE..................................330 478-1825
Fax: 330 478-2227
Abe J Kauffman, *President*

Christine Schoolcraft, *Manager*
EMP: 9
SQ FT: 27,000
SALES: 1.2MM **Privately Held**
SIC: 3559 Plastics working machinery

(G-2738)
**INTERIOR GRAPHIC SYSTEMS
LLC**
4550 Aultman Rd (44720-1525)
PHONE..................................330 244-0100
Fax: 216 244-0111
Deborah Weisburn, *Co-Owner*
Darla Miller, *Finance Mgr*
Jim Weisburn, *Mng Member*
Robert Horn, *Intrm Mgr*
EMP: 8
SQ FT: 10,000
SALES (est): 926K **Privately Held**
WEB: www.interiorgraphicsystems.com
SIC: 3993 Signs, not made in custom sign
painting shops

(G-2739)
**INTERTEX WORLD RESOURCES
INC**
4518 Fulton Dr Nw Ste 101 (44718-2391)
PHONE..................................770 214-5551
EMP: 9
SALES (corp-wide): 6MM **Privately Held**
SIC: 3011 Tires & inner tubes
PA: Intertex World Resources, Inc.
225 Maple View Dr Ste 201
Carrollton GA 30117
330 665-5533

(G-2740)
**INVUE SECURITY PRODUCTS
INC**
1510 4th St Se (44707-3206)
PHONE..................................330 456-7776
Farrokh Abadi, *President*
Gale Essick, *Mfg Mgr*
Cathy Ginella, *Admin Asst*
▼ EMP: 200
SALES (est): 14.2MM
SALES (corp-wide): 188.4K **Privately
Held**
WEB: www.checkpointsystems.com
SIC: 3699 Security devices
HQ: Checkpoint Systems, Inc.
101 Wolf Dr
West Deptford NJ 08086
856 848-1800

(G-2741)
**IRONROCK CAPITAL
INCORPORATED**
Also Called: Metropolitan Ceramics Div
1201 Millerton St Se (44707-2209)
P.O. Box 9240 (44711-9240)
PHONE..................................330 484-4887
Guy F Renkert, *President*
J G Barbour Et Al, *Principal*
C W Keplinger, *Principal*
H S Renkert, *Principal*
Clare Thomas, *Natl Sales Mgr*
▲ EMP: 100 EST: 1866
SQ FT: 100,000
SALES (est): 20.4MM **Privately Held**
WEB: www.metroceramics.com
SIC: 3253 Ceramic wall & floor tile

(G-2742)
J & K PRINTING
1728 Navarre Rd Sw (44706-1652)
PHONE..................................330 456-5306
Fax: 330 456-8206
Keith Gillilan, *Owner*
Jane Vagges, *Personnel Exec*
EMP: 5
SALES (est): 385K **Privately Held**
WEB: www.jkprint.com
SIC: 2752 2759 Commercial printing, off-
set; commercial printing

(G-2743)
J M SMUCKER COMPANY
Akron Canton Reg Aprt 7 (44720)
PHONE..................................330 497-0073
Hallie McGonigal, *Manager*
EMP: 3
SALES (corp-wide): 7.8B **Publicly Held**
WEB: www.smuckers.com
SIC: 2033 Canned fruits & specialties

PA: The J M Smucker Company
1 Strawberry Ln
Orrville OH 44667
330 682-3000

(G-2744)
**JACK R STINER MODELS &
PATTERN**
93 Spruce Dr Nw (44720-5333)
PHONE..................................330 494-1730
Scott Knisley, *President*
Sandra Stiner-Knisley, *Treasurer*
EMP: 3
SQ FT: 3,500
SALES (est): 250K **Privately Held**
SIC: 3999 3543 Models, general, except
toy; industrial patterns

(G-2745)
JANSON INDUSTRIES
1200 Garfield Ave Sw (44706-1639)
P.O. Box 6090 (44706-0090)
PHONE..................................330 455-7029
Fax: 330 455-5919
Richard Janson, *Partner*
Eric H Janson, *Partner*
Erin Wallace, *Director*
EMP: 100
SQ FT: 120,000
SALES (est): 13.6MM **Privately Held**
WEB: www.jansonindustries.com
SIC: 1799 2391 3999 Rigging & scaffold-
ing; curtains & draperies; stage hardware
& equipment, except lighting

(G-2746)
JAZ FOODS INC
Also Called: Invisible Chef, The
1818 Hopple Ave Sw (44706-1909)
PHONE..................................800 456-7115
Jill McCauley, *Owner*
EMP: 2
SQ FT: 500
SALES: 2MM **Privately Held**
SIC: 2041 Bread & bread-type roll mixes

(G-2747)
JEBCO MACHINE COMPANY INC
1311 Greenfield Ave Sw (44706-5406)
PHONE..................................330 452-2909
Fax: 330 452-9158
Gerald E Baxter, *President*
EMP: 3
SQ FT: 4,040
SALES (est): 300K **Privately Held**
SIC: 3469 Machine parts, stamped or
pressed metal

(G-2748)
JMW WELDING AND MFG
512 45th St Sw (44706-4432)
PHONE..................................330 484-2428
Fax: 330 484-2021
John Slutz, *President*
Michael Slutz, *Vice Pres*
Neal Slutz, *Treasurer*
Janet McDonald, *Human Res Mgr*
EMP: 30
SQ FT: 12,000
SALES (est): 6MM **Privately Held**
SIC: 3443 7692 Industrial vessels, tanks &
containers; dumpsters, garbage; welding
repair

(G-2749)
**JOSHUA LEIGH ENTERPRISES
INC**
2191 E Maple St (44720-3337)
PHONE..................................330 244-9200
Fax: 330 244-9200
Katie Marcus, *Branch Mgr*
EMP: 9
SALES (corp-wide): 1.7MM **Privately
Held**
SIC: 2024 Ice cream & frozen desserts
PA: Joshua Leigh Enterprises Inc
3830 Strrs Cntre Dr Ste 2
Canfield OH 44406
330 702-8270

(G-2750)
KANEL BROTHERS SUPPLY
Also Called: Kanel Brothers Church Supplies
8280 Kent Ave Ne (44721-1303)
P.O. Box 2286 (44720-0286)
PHONE..................................330 499-4802

Fax: 330 499-3550
Thomas Kanel, *Owner*
EMP: 5
SQ FT: 2,000
SALES (est): 250K **Privately Held**
WEB: www.kanelbrothers.com
SIC: 2399 Emblems, badges & insignia

(G-2751)
KERR FRICTION PRODUCTS INC
2512 Columbus Rd Ne (44705-3707)
P.O. Box 7117 (44705-0117)
PHONE..........................330 455-3983
Larry R Hunter, *President*
Judith K Hunter, *Vice Pres*
EMP: 25
SQ FT: 10,000
SALES (est): 2.2MM **Privately Held**
SIC: 3714 Motor vehicle brake systems & parts

(G-2752)
KILGORE MANUFACTURING MCH CO
2502 8th St Ne (44704-2310)
PHONE..........................330 491-1915
Eddie Mitchell Kilgore, *Principal*
EMP: 2
SALES (est): 1.8MM **Privately Held**
SIC: 3532 Mining machinery

(G-2753)
KLEBAUM MACHINERY INC
Also Called: KMC Precision Machine
1303 13th St Se (44707-3429)
P.O. Box 6084 (44706-0084)
PHONE..........................330 455-2046
Fax: 330 455-2016
Herb Klebaum, *President*
EMP: 5
SQ FT: 6,000
SALES (est): 909.5K **Privately Held**
SIC: 3555 Printing plates

(G-2754)
KLENK INDUSTRIES INC
1016 9th St Sw (44707-4108)
PHONE..........................330 453-7857
James Andreson, *President*
EMP: 100 **EST:** 1934
SQ FT: 5,000
SALES (est): 6.8MM **Privately Held**
SIC: 3421 Shears, hand; snips, tinners'

(G-2755)
KLINGSTEDT BROTHERS COMPANY
425 Schroyer Ave Sw (44702-2012)
P.O. Box 6088 (44706-0088)
PHONE..........................330 456-8319
Fax: 330 456-8310
James R Cassler, *President*
Janet Cassler, *Admin Sec*
EMP: 12 **EST:** 1912
SQ FT: 15,000
SALES: 700K **Privately Held**
WEB: www.lhtp.com
SIC: 2752 2754 Commercial printing, lithographic; rotary photogravure printing

(G-2756)
KMS 2000 INC (PA)
Also Called: P P I Graphics
315 12th St Nw (44703-1806)
P.O. Box 21220 (44701-1220)
PHONE..........................330 454-9444
Fax: 330 454-1524
Kevin Smith, *President*
Kathy Dramis, *Manager*
EMP: 14
SALES (est): 2.9MM **Privately Held**
WEB: www.ppigraphics.com
SIC: 2752 2759 Commercial printing, offset; letterpress printing

(G-2757)
KONOIL INC
6477 Frank Ave Nw (44720-8412)
PHONE..........................330 499-9811
Paul Konovsky, *President*
Donald Konovsky, *Vice Pres*
John Konovsky, *Vice Pres*
EMP: 3
SALES (est): 306.9K **Privately Held**
SIC: 1311 Crude petroleum production; natural gas production

(G-2758)
LAKE CABLE OPTICAL LAB
Also Called: Lake Cable Optical Laboratory
4837 Frank Ave Nw (44720-7425)
PHONE..........................330 497-3022
Fax: 330 497-1142
Jeff Fisher, *CEO*
EMP: 3 **EST:** 2001
SALES (est): 220.6K **Privately Held**
SIC: 3851 Ophthalmic goods

(G-2759)
LAZARS ART GLLERY CRTIVE FRMNG
2940 Woodlawn Ave Nw (44708)
PHONE..........................330 477-8351
Fax: 330 477-2310
Lazer Tarzan, *President*
Elizabeth Tarzan, *Vice Pres*
EMP: 8
SALES (est): 730K **Privately Held**
SIC: 2499 5999 Picture & mirror frames, wood; art dealers

(G-2760)
LUSTROUS METAL COATINGS INC
1541 Raff Rd Sw (44710-2321)
PHONE..........................330 478-4653
Fax: 330 478-4643
Michael Paxos, *President*
Tom Vonortas, *Exec VP*
Shirley Balista, *Manager*
EMP: 40
SQ FT: 34,000
SALES (est): 6MM **Privately Held**
WEB: www.lustrousmetal.com
SIC: 3471 Plating of metals or formed products

(G-2761)
M A C MACHINE
1111 Faircrest St Se (44707-1229)
PHONE..........................410 944-6171
Fax: 330 484-0848
Allen Craig, *Owner*
Evelyn Craig, *Vice Pres*
EMP: 6
SQ FT: 5,400
SALES (est): 390.7K **Privately Held**
SIC: 3599 Machine shop, jobbing & repair

(G-2762)
M K MORSE COMPANY (PA)
1101 11th St Se (44707-3400)
P.O. Box 8677 (44711-8677)
PHONE..........................330 453-8187
Fax: 330 453-1111
Nancy Sonner, *CEO*
James Batchelder, *President*
Sally Dale, *Owner*
Joe Dougan, *Superintendent*
Jeff Guritza, *Business Mgr*
◆ **EMP:** 277 **EST:** 1963
SQ FT: 375,000
SALES (est): 90MM **Privately Held**
WEB: www.mkmorse.com
SIC: 3425 Saw blades for hand or power saws

(G-2763)
M T SYSTEMS INC
400 Schroyer Ave Sw (44702-2013)
P.O. Box 2086, Danville IL (61834-2086)
PHONE..........................330 453-4646
Fax: 217 446-4040
Mark E Church, *President*
Robert Watson, *Engineer*
Julie Watson, *Accountant*
Bill Schnese, *Sales Mgr*
EMP: 8
SQ FT: 12,500
SALES (est): 2.1MM **Privately Held**
WEB: www.mt-systems.com
SIC: 7373 3823 3561 Computer integrated systems design; industrial instrmnts msrmnt display/control process variable; pumps & pumping equipment

(G-2764)
M TECHNOLOGIES
Also Called: Northern Mobile Electric
1818 Hopple Ave Sw (44706-1909)
PHONE..........................330 477-9009
Fax: 330 479-2541

Rodney McCauley, *Managing Prtnr*
Diane Broderick, *Partner*
Jeff Selway, *Relations*
EMP: 12
SQ FT: 6,000
SALES (est): 2MM **Privately Held**
SIC: 3625 5531 Starter, electric motor; automotive parts

(G-2765)
MACHINE COMPONENT MFG
Also Called: Brownlee Engineering & Mfg
3410 Perry Dr Nw (44708-1137)
PHONE..........................330 454-4566
Fax: 330 454-7244
Joseph R Gill, *President*
Jim Walsh, *Vice Pres*
Scott Gill, *Treasurer*
Steven Gill, *Asst Treas*
EMP: 12 **EST:** 1964
SQ FT: 12,000
SALES: 800K **Privately Held**
WEB: www.brownleemfg.com
SIC: 3491 3599 3541 3494 Industrial valves; machine shop, jobbing & repair; machine tools, metal cutting type; valves & pipe fittings

(G-2766)
MACHINE SHOP
410 Viking St Nw (44720-2466)
PHONE..........................330 494-1251
Fred Gardner, *Owner*
EMP: 4
SALES (est): 234.1K **Privately Held**
SIC: 3599 Machine shop, jobbing & repair

(G-2767)
MARATHON PETROLEUM COMPANY LP
2408 Gambrinus Rd (44706)
P.O. Box 8170 (44711-8170)
PHONE..........................330 478-5000
Sue Kreinen, *VP Opers*
Mike Armebrester, *Plant Mgr*
Heather Gustin, *Purch Mgr*
Timothy Lynn, *Purch Mgr*
Julie Vinci, *Purch Agent*
EMP: 350 **Publicly Held**
WEB: www.mapllc.com
SIC: 5172 2951 Petroleum products; asphalt paving mixtures & blocks
HQ: Marathon Petroleum Company Lp
539 S Main St
Findlay OH 45840

(G-2768)
MARCHIONE STUDIO INC
1225 Minerva Ct Nw (44703-1818)
PHONE..........................330 454-7408
Frank Marchione, *President*
EMP: 4
SQ FT: 1,200
SALES (corp-wide): 286.9K **Privately Held**
SIC: 3269 3231 Art & ornamental ware, pottery; ornamental glass: cut, engraved or otherwise decorated
PA: Marchione Studio Inc
5030 Gardendale Ave Ne
Canton OH 44714
330 454-7408

(G-2769)
MARIOS DRIVE THRU
914 12th St Ne (44704-1320)
PHONE..........................330 452-8793
Wayne Marion, *Principal*
EMP: 3
SALES (est): 230.9K **Privately Held**
SIC: 2082 Beer (alcoholic beverage)

(G-2770)
MARTZ WELL SERVICE
5101 Rocky Rill Ave Ne (44705-3269)
PHONE..........................330 323-7417
Gary L Martz, *Owner*
EMP: 3
SALES: 160K **Privately Held**
SIC: 1389 Swabbing wells; roustabout service

(G-2771)
MASSILLON PLAQUE COMPANY
5757 Mayfair Rd (44720-1546)
P.O. Box 2539 (44720-0539)
PHONE..........................330 494-4199
Fax: 330 494-5037
Daryl J Miller, *President*
Andy Deuble, *Vice Pres*
Stephen G Deuble, *Vice Pres*
Thomas M Kusits, *VP Finance*
Lance Brown, *Sales Mgr*
EMP: 11
SQ FT: 14,000
SALES: 1.4MM
SALES (corp-wide): 583.2K **Privately Held**
WEB: www.massillonplaque.com
SIC: 2796 Engraving on copper, steel, wood or rubber: printing plates
PA: Dcc Corp.
5757 Mayfair Rd
Canton OH 44720
330 494-0494

(G-2772)
MATALCO (US) INC
4420 Louisville St Ne (44705-4848)
PHONE..........................330 452-4760
EMP: 17
SQ FT: 100,000
SALES (est): 3.9MM
SALES (corp-wide): 344.1MM **Privately Held**
SIC: 3363 Aluminum die-castings
HQ: Matalco Inc
850 Intermodal Dr
Brampton ON L6T 0
905 790-2511

(G-2773)
MATRIX MANAGEMENT SOLUTIONS
5200 Stoneham Rd (44720-1584)
PHONE..........................330 470-3700
Mark Terpylak, *President*
EMP: 140
SALES (est): 10.8MM
SALES (corp-wide): 492.4MM **Publicly Held**
SIC: 7372 7373 Prepackaged software; computer integrated systems design
PA: Quality Systems, Inc.
18111 Von Karman Ave # 700
Irvine CA 92612
949 255-2600

(G-2774)
MC CONCEPTS LLC
2459 55th St Ne (44721-3425)
PHONE..........................330 933-6402
Manuel Chavarria,
EMP: 7
SALES (est): 461.8K **Privately Held**
SIC: 2095 Roasted coffee

(G-2775)
MC CULLY SUPPLY & SALES INC
5559 Fulton Dr Nw Ste A (44718-1728)
PHONE..........................330 497-2211
Fax: 330 966-5855
Toby Mc Cully, *President*
Glenn McCully, *Vice Pres*
EMP: 4
SQ FT: 1,800
SALES: 280K **Privately Held**
SIC: 3312 8742 Rail joints or fastenings; construction project management consultant

(G-2776)
MCCANN PLASTICS INC
5600 Mayfair Rd (44720-1539)
PHONE..........................330 499-1515
Fax: 330 499-8440
Michael A McCann, *President*
Berney Villers, *Plant Mgr*
David Miller, *Opers Mgr*
Carl Schmeltzer, *Maint Spvr*
Neil Slabach, *Purch Mgr*
EMP: 85
SQ FT: 157,800
SALES (est): 30.4MM **Privately Held**
WEB: www.mccannplastics.com
SIC: 3087 Custom compound purchased resins

(G-2777)
MCPHERSON WIRE CUT INC
5208 Mayfair Rd (44720-1531)
P.O. Box 649, Green (44232-0649)
PHONE...................................330 896-0267
Fax: 330 896-0370
Scott Mc Pherson, *President*
Janet Mc Pherson, *Vice Pres*
EMP: 3
SQ FT: 3,000
SALES (est): 477.3K **Privately Held**
SIC: 3599 Machine shop, jobbing & repair

(G-2778)
MEDLINE INDUSTRIES INC
3800 Commerce St Sw (44706-3367)
PHONE...................................330 484-1450
Kevin Yohman, *President*
Scott Wakser, *Principal*
EMP: 5
SALES (est): 584.1K **Privately Held**
SIC: 3999 Barber & beauty shop equipment

(G-2779)
MIDLANDS MILLROOM SUPPLY INC
1911 36th St Ne (44705-5023)
P.O. Box 7007 (44705-0007)
PHONE...................................330 453-9100
Fax: 330 453-6644
Fred Clark, *President*
Rod Cunningham, *Mfg Mgr*
Evan Smith, *Sales Staff*
Yoshi Terada, *Sales Executive*
Phil Rastok, *Manager*
▲ EMP: 28
SQ FT: 17,000
SALES: 15MM **Privately Held**
WEB: www.batch-off.com
SIC: 5084 3061 Industrial machinery & equipment; mechanical rubber goods

(G-2780)
MIDWEST INDUSTRIAL SUPPLY INC
1101 3rd St Se (44707-3230)
P.O. Box 8431 (44711-8431)
PHONE...................................330 456-3121
Fax: 330 456-3247
Robert Vitale, *President*
Steven Vitale, *Vice Pres*
Ken Crawford, *VP Mfg*
Beth Harding, *Controller*
Wes Albaugh, *Financial Exec*
▼ EMP: 70
SQ FT: 40,000
SALES (est): 35.1MM **Privately Held**
WEB: www.midwestind.com
SIC: 2899 Chemical preparations

(G-2781)
MIDWEST SIGN CTR
Also Called: Midwest Sign Center
4210 Cleveland Ave Nw (44709-2350)
PHONE...................................330 493-7330
Fax: 330 493-3733
Melvin R Lloyd, *President*
Carolyn P Lloyd, *Vice Pres*
Daniel Wells, *Art Dir*
EMP: 12
SQ FT: 3,000
SALES (est): 720K **Privately Held**
WEB: www.midwestsigncenter.com
SIC: 3993 Signs & advertising specialties

(G-2782)
MILK & HONEY
3400 Cleveland Ave Nw # 1 (44709-2784)
PHONE...................................330 492-5884
Fax: 330 492-2714
Dwayne Cornell, *Partner*
Paula Cornell, *Partner*
EMP: 15
SQ FT: 2,500
SALES (est): 916.4K **Privately Held**
SIC: 5451 5812 2066 2064 Ice cream (packaged); restaurant, lunch counter; chocolate & cocoa products; candy & other confectionery products

(G-2783)
MOBILE MINI INC
8045 Dawnwood Ave Ne (44721)
PHONE...................................303 305-9515
Anthony Day, *Branch Mgr*
EMP: 20
SALES (corp-wide): 508.6MM **Publicly Held**
WEB: www.mobilemini.com
SIC: 3448 Buildings, portable: prefabricated metal
PA: Mobile Mini, Inc.
4646 E Van Buren St # 400
Phoenix AZ 85008
480 894-6311

(G-2784)
MULTI GALVANIZING LLC
825 Navarre Rd Sw (44707-4058)
PHONE...................................330 453-1441
Charles E Decker III, *Plant Mgr*
EMP: 6
SQ FT: 30,000
SALES (est): 620K **Privately Held**
SIC: 3547 Galvanizing lines (rolling mill equipment)

(G-2785)
MURPHY TRACTOR & EQP CO INC
Also Called: John Deere Authorized Dealer
1509 Raff Rd Sw (44710-2321)
PHONE...................................330 477-9304
Chris Mears, *Branch Mgr*
EMP: 8
SALES (corp-wide): 176.9MM **Privately Held**
SIC: 3531 5082 Construction machinery; construction & mining machinery
HQ: Murphy Tractor & Equipment Co., Inc.
5375 N Deere Rd
Park City KS 67219
855 246-9124

(G-2786)
MYERS CONTROLLED POWER LLC
133 Taft Ave Ne (44720-2527)
PHONE...................................909 923-1800
Jeffery Baker, *Project Mgr*
James Fink, *Branch Mgr*
EMP: 11
SALES (corp-wide): 110.6MM **Privately Held**
SIC: 3629 Inverters, nonrotating: electrical
HQ: Myers Controlled Power, Llc
219 E Maple St 100-200e
North Canton OH 44720
330 834-3200

(G-2787)
NEW TECH
2751 Wisemill Cir Ne # 3 (44721-2160)
PHONE...................................330 494-8338
Fax: 330 494-8338
Florence Klingaman, *Owner*
John Klingaman, *Manager*
EMP: 5
SQ FT: 6,000
SALES: 295K **Privately Held**
SIC: 3599 5084 Machine shop, jobbing & repair; machine tools & accessories

(G-2788)
NICHOLAS RAY ENTERPRISES LLC
Also Called: Olympic Enterprises
3605 Mahoning Rd Ne (44705-4005)
PHONE...................................330 454-4811
Fax: 330 454-4811
Nicholas Ray,
EMP: 4 EST: 1963
SQ FT: 5,000
SALES (est): 310K **Privately Held**
SIC: 2396 Ribbons & bows, cut & sewed

(G-2789)
NOLAN COMPANY (PA)
1016 9th St Sw (44707-4108)
PHONE...................................330 453-7922
James L Anderson, *President*
Dan Chew, *Mfg Staff*
Debbie Garnet, *Accounting Mgr*
Deborah Clark, *Sales Staff*
EMP: 7
SQ FT: 52,000
SALES (est): 4.1MM **Privately Held**
SIC: 3743 3532 Railroad equipment; mining machinery

(G-2790)
NORCIA BAKERY
624 Belden Ave Ne (44704-2229)
PHONE...................................330 454-1077
Donald C Horne, *President*
Jim Butler, *Vice Pres*
EMP: 25 EST: 1920
SQ FT: 3,200
SALES (est): 3MM **Privately Held**
SIC: 2051 5461 5149 2052 Bakery: wholesale or wholesale/retail combined; bread; groceries & related products; cookies & crackers

(G-2791)
NORRIS NORTH MANUFACTURING
1500 Henry Ave Sw (44706-2852)
PHONE...................................330 691-0449
Tyler Palumbo, *Principal*
EMP: 3
SALES (est): 120.3K **Privately Held**
SIC: 3999 Manufacturing industries

(G-2792)
NORTH CANTON PLASTICS INC
6658 Promway Ave Nw (44720-7316)
PHONE...................................330 497-0071
Fax: 330 497-0269
EMP: 38
SQ FT: 26,000
SALES (est): 7.3MM **Privately Held**
SIC: 3089 Mfg Plastic Products

(G-2793)
NORTH CANTON TOOL CO
1156 Marion Ave Sw (44707-4138)
PHONE...................................330 452-0545
Fax: 330 452-5612
David Pool, *President*
Rebecca Perez, *Vice Pres*
Christine Fulton, *Analyst*
EMP: 9 EST: 1950
SQ FT: 10,000
SALES: 1MM **Privately Held**
SIC: 3599 Machine shop, jobbing & repair

(G-2794)
NORTHEASTERN OILFIELD SVCS LLC (PA)
1537 Waynesburg Dr Se (44707-2135)
PHONE...................................330 581-3304
David D Krutilek, *Principal*
Steve Stewart, *Project Mgr*
EMP: 9
SALES (est): 3.1MM **Privately Held**
SIC: 1389 Oil field services

(G-2795)
NORTHEASTERN PLASTICS INC
112 Navarre Rd Sw (44707-3950)
PHONE...................................330 453-5925
Fax: 330 453-7204
Allen Richards, *President*
EMP: 6
SQ FT: 4,800
SALES: 500K **Privately Held**
WEB: www.northeasternplastics.com
SIC: 2759 2396 Screen printing; automotive & apparel trimmings

(G-2796)
OBS INC
Also Called: OBS SPECIALTY VEHICLES
1324 Tuscarawas St W (44702-2036)
P.O. Box 6210 (44706-0210)
PHONE...................................330 453-3725
Fax: 330 453-0611
Robert Ferne, *President*
Theresa Bower, *Controller*
Bob Ferne, *Manager*
▲ EMP: 13
SQ FT: 28,000
SALES: 1.6MM **Privately Held**
SIC: 3711 7532 Mobile lounges (motor vehicle), assembly of; body shop, automotive

(G-2797)
OGC INDUSTRIES INC
934 Wells Ave Nw (44703-3500)
PHONE...................................330 456-1500
Fax: 330 456-5252
Orlando Chiarucci, *President*
EMP: 10

(G-2798)
OHIO AUTO SUPPLY COMPANY
Also Called: Professional Detailing Pdts
1128 Tuscarawas St W (44702-2086)
PHONE...................................330 454-5105
Fax: 330 454-5130
Michael Dickson, *President*
Angie Piper, *Manager*
Stanley R Rubin, *Admin Sec*
EMP: 29 EST: 1933
SQ FT: 15,000
SALES (est): 6.4MM **Privately Held**
WEB: www.ohioautosupply.com
SIC: 5013 2842 5531 3714 Automotive supplies & parts; cleaning or polishing preparations; automotive parts; motor vehicle parts & accessories

(G-2799)
OHIO GRATINGS INC (PA)
5299 Southway St Sw (44706-1992)
PHONE...................................330 477-6707
Fax: 330 477-7872
David Bartley, *Ch of Bd*
John Bartley, *President*
Shaun Eller, *General Mgr*
Ronald Lenney, *Vice Pres*
Jeff Nixlar, *Safety Mgr*
▼ EMP: 300 EST: 1970
SQ FT: 150,000
SALES (est): 98.7MM **Privately Held**
WEB: www.ohiogratings.com
SIC: 3446 3444 3441 3312 Gratings, open steel flooring; open flooring & grating for construction; sheet metalwork; fabricated structural metal; blast furnaces & steel mills

(G-2800)
OHIO L & M COMPANY INC
Also Called: Alliance Petroleum
4150 Belden Village St Nw # 410 (44718-2553)
PHONE...................................330 493-0440
John W Miller, *President*
EMP: 22
SQ FT: 2,900
SALES (est): 991.8K
SALES (corp-wide): 12.5MM **Privately Held**
WEB: www.alliancepetroleumcorp.com
SIC: 1389 1381 Servicing oil & gas wells; drilling oil & gas wells
PA: Alliance Petroleum Corporation
4150 Belden Village Mall
Canton OH 44718
330 493-0440

(G-2801)
OHIO METAL WORKING PRODUCTS
Also Called: American Carbide Tool Company
3620 Progress St Ne (44705-4438)
P.O. Box 288, Armstrong IA (50514-0288)
PHONE...................................330 455-2009
Paul Ernenwein, *President*
Barb Smith, *Prdtn Mgr*
Karen Tolbert, *Production*
Catherine Howenstine, *Admin Sec*
EMP: 35
SALES (est): 5.7MM
SALES (corp-wide): 21.5MM **Publicly Held**
SIC: 2819 Carbides
PA: Art's-Way Manufacturing Co., Inc.
5556 Highway 9
Armstrong IA 50514
712 864-3131

(G-2802)
OHIO PAPER TUBE CO
3422 Navarre Rd Sw (44706-1856)
PHONE...................................330 478-5171
Fax: 330 478-9511
William Natale Jr, *President*
Timothy Natale, *Corp Secy*
Dennis Natale, *Vice Pres*
Edith Dickinson, *Bookkeeper*
Kevin Reisinger, *Sales Dir*
EMP: 18 EST: 1968

▲ = Import ▼ =Export
◆ =Import/Export

SQ FT: 46,000
SALES (est): 4.1MM **Privately Held**
WEB: www.ohiopapertube.com
SIC: 2655 Tubes, fiber or paper: made from purchased material

(G-2803)
OHIO PRECISION INC
1239 Market Ave S (44707-3968)
PHONE..............................330 453-9710
Susan Stabler, *President*
David Boord, *Vice Pres*
EMP: 8
SALES (est): 810K **Privately Held**
SIC: 3599 Machine shop, jobbing & repair

(G-2804)
OMWP COMPANY
3620 Progress St Ne (44705-4438)
P.O. Box 7069 (44705-0069)
PHONE..............................330 453-8438
Fax: 330 453-8498
Paul Ernenwein, *President*
Steve Meuler, *Vice Pres*
Barbara Smith, *Prdtn Mgr*
Catherine Howenstine, *Admin Sec*
EMP: 35 **EST:** 1954
SQ FT: 39,000
SALES (est): 5MM **Privately Held**
WEB: www.americancarbidetool.com
SIC: 3545 Machine tool accessories; cutting tools for machine tools

(G-2805)
OSTER SAND AND GRAVEL INC (PA)
5947 Whipple Ave Nw (44720-7692)
PHONE..............................330 494-5472
Fax: 330 499-5910
Marlene Oster, *President*
Scott Oster, *Vice Pres*
Valerie Newman, *Treasurer*
EMP: 7 **EST:** 1967
SQ FT: 3,000
SALES (est): 3.5MM **Privately Held**
SIC: 1442 Construction sand & gravel

(G-2806)
PARAGRAPHICS INC
2011 29th St Nw (44709-3218)
PHONE..............................330 493-1074
Fax: 330 493-1612
James S Bosworth, *President*
Andrew Bosworth, *Vice Pres*
Peter A Bosworth, *Vice Pres*
Clark Swab, *Plant Mgr*
Judy Knapski, *Controller*
▲ **EMP:** 30
SQ FT: 18,000
SALES (est): 5.3MM **Privately Held**
WEB: www.para-inc.com
SIC: 2752 Commercial printing, lithographic

(G-2807)
PATRIOT PRECISION PRODUCTS
8817 Pleasantwood Ave Nw (44720-4759)
PHONE..............................330 966-7177
Fax: 330 494-8084
Ronald Dillard, *President*
Rick Brinkel, *Safety Mgr*
EMP: 60
SQ FT: 41,000
SALES (est): 5MM **Privately Held**
SIC: 3599 Custom machinery

(G-2808)
PATRIOT SOFTWARE INC
4883 Dressler Rd Nw # 301 (44718-3665)
PHONE..............................877 968-7147
Fax: 330 455-5451
Michael J Kappel, *President*
Todd Schmitt, *Treasurer*
Russ Corbett, *Accountant*
Don Penny, *Accountant*
Mike Wheeler, *Sales Staff*
EMP: 12
SQ FT: 1,120
SALES (est): 290.2K **Privately Held**
WEB: www.patriothr.com
SIC: 7372 Prepackaged software

(G-2809)
PATRIOT SPECIAL METALS INC
2201 Harrison Ave Sw (44706-3076)
PHONE..............................330 580-9600
Fax: 330 456-3732
Frank Carchidi, *CEO*
Rick Brown, *COO*
Paul Olah, *Vice Pres*
Mark Milliron, *Project Mgr*
Rouse Amenhauser, *Human Res Mgr*
EMP: 70
SALES (est): 15.3MM
SALES (corp-wide): 19MM **Privately Held**
SIC: 3356 Nonferrous rolling & drawing
PA: Patriot Forge Co.
280 Henry St
Brantford ON N3S 7
519 758-8100

(G-2810)
PAXOS PLATING INC
4631 Navarre Rd Sw (44706-2336)
PHONE..............................330 479-0022
Fax: 330 479-0024
Mike Paxos, *President*
Joanna Volas, *Controller*
Pete Paxos, *Manager*
EMP: 25
SQ FT: 35,000
SALES (est): 2.9MM **Privately Held**
WEB: www.paxosplating.com
SIC: 3471 Plating of metals or formed products

(G-2811)
PERMAGUIDE
2427 9th St Sw (44710-1806)
PHONE..............................330 456-8519
George Springer, *Owner*
EMP: 20
SALES (est): 1MM **Privately Held**
SIC: 2741 Maps: publishing only, not printed on site

(G-2812)
PHASE II ENTERPRISES INC
Also Called: Marino Maintenance Co
2154 Bolivar Rd Sw (44706-3055)
PHONE..............................330 484-2113
Fax: 330 484-4001
Richard Marino, *President*
EMP: 8
SQ FT: 5,200
SALES (est): 1.4MM **Privately Held**
SIC: 7349 3446 Building maintenance services; stairs, fire escapes, balconies, railings & ladders

(G-2813)
PINNACLE PRESS INC
2960 Harrisburg Rd Ne (44705-2562)
PHONE..............................330 453-7060
Robert Kettlewell, *President*
Michael Kettlewell, *Vice Pres*
Vicki Lewis, *Vice Pres*
Shelly Poyser, *Treasurer*
Shelly Kettlewell, *Personnel Exec*
EMP: 18
SQ FT: 9,700
SALES (est): 1.2MM **Privately Held**
SIC: 2752 Commercial printing, offset

(G-2814)
PJS FABRICATING INC
Also Called: Pj's
1511 Linwood Ave Sw (44710-2313)
PHONE..............................330 478-1120
Francis C Bell, *President*
Kathleen Hohler, *Corp Secy*
Harry Spurrier, *Vice Pres*
EMP: 30
SQ FT: 33,000
SALES (est): 9.4MM **Privately Held**
SIC: 3441 Fabricated structural metal

(G-2815)
PJS TOWING INC
1511 Linwood Ave Sw (44710-2313)
PHONE..............................330 478-1120
Francis Bell, *President*
EMP: 30
SALES (corp-wide): 1.1MM **Privately Held**
WEB: www.pjsfab.com
SIC: 3441 Fabricated structural metal

PA: Pj's Towing Inc
1511 Linwood Ave Sw
Canton OH 44710

(G-2816)
POWELL ELECTRICAL SYSTEMS INC
Also Called: Pemco North Canton Division
8967 Pleasantwood Ave Nw (44720-4761)
PHONE..............................330 966-1750
Fax: 330 966-1787
Sharon James, *Project Mgr*
Donald Vrudney, *Mfg Staff*
Paula Myers, *Purchasing*
Peter Crombie, *Engineer*
Allen Marshall, *Engineer*
EMP: 92
SQ FT: 41,600
SALES (corp-wide): 565.2MM **Publicly Held**
WEB: www.powl.com
SIC: 3678 5063 3699 Electronic connectors; electrical apparatus & equipment; electrical equipment & supplies
HQ: Powell Electrical Systems, Inc.
8550 Mosley Rd
Houston TX 77075
708 409-1200

(G-2817)
PPG ARCHITECTURAL FINISHES INC
Also Called: Glidden Professional Paint Ctr
4575 Tuscarawas St W (44708-5336)
PHONE..............................330 477-8165
Fax: 330 477-6313
Troy Hunter, *Manager*
Rich Brown, *Manager*
EMP: 3
SALES (corp-wide): 14.7B **Publicly Held**
WEB: www.gliddenpaint.com
SIC: 5231 2851 Paint; paints & allied products
HQ: Ppg Architectural Finishes, Inc.
1 Ppg Pl
Pittsburgh PA 15272
412 434-3131

(G-2818)
PRAXAIR INC
2225 Bolivar Rd Sw (44706-3056)
PHONE..............................330 453-9904
Fax: 330 588-2081
Ron Kalinooski, *Systems Mgr*
EMP: 25
SALES (corp-wide): 10.5B **Publicly Held**
SIC: 2813 Industrial gases
PA: Praxair, Inc.
10 Riverview Dr
Danbury CT 06810
203 837-2000

(G-2819)
PRE-MELT SYSTEMS INC
8984 Meridian Cir Nw (44720-8259)
PHONE..............................330 818-8088
Larry Areaux, *President*
EMP: 10
SQ FT: 36,000
SALES (est): 925.2K **Privately Held**
SIC: 3549 Metalworking machinery

(G-2820)
PRECISION COMPONENT INDS LLC
5325 Southway St Sw (44706-1943)
PHONE..............................330 477-1052
Patricia Gerak, *CEO*
George Melson, *Purch Mgr*
Lew Page, *Sales Executive*
David Desimio, *Manager*
Tony Jerak, *Info Tech Dir*
EMP: 30 **EST:** 1957
SQ FT: 56,000
SALES (est): 7.7MM **Privately Held**
WEB: www.precision-component.com
SIC: 3599 3544 3545 Machine shop, jobbing & repair; special dies & tools; shear knives

(G-2821)
PRIME ENGINEERED PLASTICS CORP
1505 Howington Cir Se (44707-2214)
PHONE..............................330 452-5110

Fax: 330 452-6110
Patrick M Nolan, *President*
EMP: 15
SQ FT: 14,400
SALES (est): 2.9MM **Privately Held**
SIC: 3089 Injection molding of plastics

(G-2822)
PRINT SHOP OF CANTON INC
6536 Promler St Nw (44720-7630)
PHONE..............................330 497-3212
Fax: 330 497-6306
Jeff Grametbauer, *President*
Josef K Grametbauer, *President*
Joyce Grametbauer, *Treasurer*
EMP: 8 **EST:** 1972
SQ FT: 2,600
SALES (est): 1.2MM **Privately Held**
SIC: 2752 Commercial printing, offset

(G-2823)
PRITT ENTERPRISES INC
Also Called: Craig Industries
1800 Wallace Ave Ne (44705-4058)
P.O. Box 7115 (44705-0115)
PHONE..............................330 453-2142
Fax: 330 453-0543
Steven T Pritt, *President*
EMP: 10
SQ FT: 30,000
SALES (est): 770K **Privately Held**
SIC: 3069 Medical & laboratory rubber sundries & related products; pillows, sponge rubber

(G-2824)
PRO AUDIO INNOVATIONS
4428 Whipple Ave Nw (44718-2646)
PHONE..............................330 705-5069
Dan Giarrana, *Owner*
EMP: 4
SALES (est): 1MM **Privately Held**
SIC: 3651 Audio electronic systems

(G-2825)
PRO-DECAL INC
3638 Cleveland Ave S (44707-1448)
PHONE..............................330 484-0089
Shane Branning, *President*
Robin Branning, *Corp Secy*
Kim Schott, *Vice Pres*
Michael Nowlin, *Info Tech Mgr*
EMP: 6
SQ FT: 800
SALES (est): 650K **Privately Held**
WEB: www.prodecalinc.com
SIC: 2752 3993 Decals, lithographed; signs & advertising specialties

(G-2826)
PROFESSIONAL REPORTS CORP
Also Called: PRC Printing
3976b Fulton Dr Nw (44718-3043)
P.O. Box 35791 (44735-5791)
PHONE..............................330 492-6063
Fax: 330 492-6176
David Herbert, *President*
Jack Court, *Vice Pres*
Molly J Romig, *Vice Pres*
EMP: 6
SALES (est): 200K **Privately Held**
WEB: www.prcpublishing.com
SIC: 2721 Periodicals

(G-2827)
PROFILE PLASTICS INC
1226 Prospect Ave Sw (44706-1628)
PHONE..............................330 452-7000
Bryan Knowles, *Principal*
Sandra Knowles, *Corp Secy*
Billie Farris, *Opers Mgr*
EMP: 21
SQ FT: 16,000
SALES (est): 6.7MM **Privately Held**
WEB: www.profileplastics.com
SIC: 3089 Extruded finished plastic products

(G-2828)
PROFILE PRODUCTS LLC
1525 Waynesburg Dr Se (44707-2135)
PHONE..............................330 452-2630
Fax: 330 452-2644
Lloyd De Persig, *Plant Mgr*
Lloyd Deperig, *Manager*

Archie Burgan, *Manager*
Lloyd Persig, *Manager*
EMP: 14
SALES (corp-wide): 86.9MM **Privately Held**
WEB: www.centralfiber.com
SIC: 2493 Reconstituted wood products
HQ: Profile Products Llc
750 W Lake Cook Rd # 440
Buffalo Grove IL 60089
847 215-1144

(G-2829)
QUALITY POLY CORP
3000 Atlantic Blvd Ne Rear (44705-3919)
P.O. Box 7490 (44705-0490)
PHONE..........................330 453-9559
Fax: 330 453-4073
Craig Shotwell, *President*
EMP: 16
SQ FT: 34,000
SALES (est): 2.5MM **Privately Held**
SIC: 3081 3082 Unsupported plastics film
& sheet; tubes, unsupported plastic

(G-2830)
QUARRYMASTERS INC
7761 Hill Church St Se (44730-9799)
PHONE..........................330 612-0474
Joseph A Della, *President*
Jacalyn Tutthill, *Vice Pres*
▲ **EMP:** 9
SQ FT: 1,600
SALES: 749K **Privately Held**
SIC: 3281 8742 Granite, cut & shaped;
general management consultant

(G-2831)
QUASS SHEET METAL INC
5018 Yukon St Nw (44708-5018)
PHONE..........................330 477-4841
Fax: 330 477-0091
John Angerer, *President*
Joyce Angerer, *Vice Pres*
EMP: 9 **EST:** 1936
SQ FT: 9,500
SALES (est): 1.2MM **Privately Held**
SIC: 3444 Sheet metalwork

(G-2832)
QUICKDRAFT INC
1525 Perry Dr Sw (44710-1098)
PHONE..........................330 477-4574
Matthew C Litler, *President*
Matthew C Litzler, *President*
William J Urban, *COO*
Georgia Matthews, *Credit Mgr*
Eloise Cerny, *Administration*
EMP: 45 **EST:** 1953
SQ FT: 45,000
SALES (est): 14MM
SALES (corp-wide): 36.1MM **Privately
Held**
WEB: www.quickdraft.com
SIC: 3535 3564 Conveyors & conveying
equipment; blowers & fans
PA: C.A. Litzler Holding Company
4800 W 160th St
Cleveland OH 44135
216 267-8020

(G-2833)
R H LITTLE CO
4434 Southway St Sw (44706-1894)
PHONE..........................330 477-3455
Fax: 330 477-7312
David Little, *President*
Robert Brady, *Vice Pres*
Marsha Mowery, *Office Mgr*
Genevieve Little, *Admin Sec*
EMP: 8 **EST:** 1940
SQ FT: 22,000
SALES (est): 2.5MM **Privately Held**
SIC: 3743 Railroad equipment

(G-2834)
R W SIDLEY INCORPORATED
7545 Pittsburg Ave Nw (44720-6943)
PHONE..........................330 499-5616
R W Sidley, *President*
John Higginbothem, *Manager*
EMP: 15
SALES (corp-wide): 143.8MM **Privately
Held**
SIC: 3273 Ready-mixed concrete

PA: R. W. Sidley Incorporated
436 Casement Ave
Painesville OH 44077
440 352-9343

(G-2835)
**RANDALL RICHARD & MOORE
LLC**
Also Called: Cutter Equipment Company
3710 Progress St Ne (44705-4438)
PHONE..........................330 455-8873
Lisa Speaker, *Accounts Mgr*
Gregory R Moore,
Glenn R Moore Jr,
EMP: 15 **EST:** 1998
SALES (est): 3.5MM **Privately Held**
WEB: www.cutteronline.com
SIC: 3523 Turf & grounds equipment; turf
equipment, commercial

(G-2836)
**RENEGADE WELL SERVICES
LLC**
215 Trump Ave Ne (44730-1627)
PHONE..........................330 488-6055
EMP: 3
SALES (corp-wide): 333.4MM **Privately
Held**
SIC: 1389 Servicing oil & gas wells
HQ: Renegade Well Services, Llc
3301 E Us Highway 377 # 202
Granbury TX 76049
682 936-4466

(G-2837)
REPUBLIC STEEL INC
Also Called: Canton Hot Rolled Plant
2633 8th St Ne (44705-2311)
PHONE..........................330 438-5533
John Ridgeway, *Manager*
Robert Garver, *Manager*
EMP: 200
SALES (corp-wide): 1.4B **Privately Held**
SIC: 3312 Bars & bar shapes, steel, cold-
finished: own hot-rolled; rods, iron & steel:
made in steel mills
HQ: Republic Steel Inc.
2633 8th St Ne
Canton OH 44704
330 438-5435

(G-2838)
REPUBLIC STEEL INC (DH)
2633 8th St Ne (44704-2311)
PHONE..........................330 438-5435
Fax: 330 438-5814
Jaime Vigil, *President*
M Kessler, *General Mgr*
Brent Marshall, *Area Mgr*
Noel J Huettich, *Vice Pres*
Thielens James, *Vice Pres*
◆ **EMP:** 56
SQ FT: 800,000
SALES (est): 384.5MM
SALES (corp-wide): 1.4B **Privately Held**
SIC: 3312 Bars, iron: made in steel mills;
structural shapes & pilings, steel
HQ: Grupo Simec, S.A.B. De C.V.
Av. Lazaro Cardenas No. 601 Edif. A
Guadalajara JAL. 44440
333 770-6700

(G-2839)
**REPUBLIC STORAGE SYSTEMS
LLC (HQ)**
1038 Belden Ave Ne (44705-1454)
PHONE..........................330 438-5800
Fax: 330 454-7772
Curt Carson, *Superintendent*
Clarence Jackson, *Plant Mgr*
Tom Joseph, *Engineer*
Don Oshiro, *Engineer*
Paul Phillips, *Indstl Engineer*
EMP: 147
SALES (est): 125MM
SALES (corp-wide): 1.6B **Privately Held**
SIC: 2542 3441 Lockers (not refrigerated):
except wood; shelving, office & store: ex-
cept wood; fabricated structural metal
PA: Versa Capital Management, Llc
2929 Arch St Ste 1650
Philadelphia PA 19104
215 609-3400

(G-2840)
ROBERT PEREZ CARPENTRY
430 Browning Ave Nw (44720-2340)
PHONE..........................330 497-0043
Robert Perez, *Owner*
EMP: 6
SALES (est): 310.1K **Privately Held**
SIC: 1442 Construction sand & gravel

(G-2841)
ROBERT SMART INC
Also Called: Superior Machine Co
1100 High Ave Sw (44707-4116)
PHONE..........................330 454-8881
Fax: 330 454-3003
Robert Scott Smart, *President*
Bob Smart, *Engineer*
EMP: 12 **EST:** 1939
SALES (est): 1.8MM **Privately Held**
WEB: www.superior-machine.com
SIC: 3599 Machine shop, jobbing & repair

(G-2842)
RODCO PETROLEUM INC
4600 Castlebar St Nw (44708-2139)
PHONE..........................330 477-9823
Betty O'Neill-Roderick, *President*
David W Roderick, *Corp Secy*
Morgan W Roderick Jr, *Vice Pres*
EMP: 3
SALES (est): 212.2K **Privately Held**
SIC: 1311 Crude petroleum production

(G-2843)
ROSSI CONCEPT ARTS
Also Called: Mr Neon Sign
1019 Mckinley Ave Nw (44703-2054)
P.O. Box 36144 (44735-6144)
PHONE..........................330 453-6366
Fax: 330 453-7466
Kenneth Rossi, *Owner*
EMP: 3
SQ FT: 4,000
SALES: 100K **Privately Held**
SIC: 3993 7389 Signs & advertising spe-
cialties; embroidering of advertising on
shirts, etc.

(G-2844)
**RTI INTERNATIONAL METALS
INC**
Also Called: Rti Alloys Tpd
1935 Warner Rd Se (44707-2273)
PHONE..........................330 455-4010
Cheryl Lyons, *Principal*
Chris Zbuka, *Manager*
EMP: 100
SALES (corp-wide): 12.3B **Publicly Held**
SIC: 3499 Friction material, made from
powdered metal
HQ: Rti International Metals, Inc.
5th Fl 1550 Crplis Hts Rd
Coraopolis PA 15108
412 893-0026

(G-2845)
**RTI INTERNATIONAL METALS
INC**
Also Called: Galt Alloys
208 15th St Sw (44707-4009)
PHONE..........................330 471-1844
Brian Helop, *Electrical Engi*
Bruce Whatzel, *Manager*
Crytsal Fraelich, *Manager*
Bert Newman, *Manager*
Holly Righetti, *Manager*
EMP: 78
SALES (corp-wide): 12.3B **Publicly Held**
SIC: 3312 3341 Blast furnace & related
products; secondary nonferrous metals
HQ: Rti International Metals, Inc.
5th Fl 1550 Crplis Hts Rd
Coraopolis PA 15108
412 893-0026

(G-2846)
**SHAHEEN ORIENTAL RUG CO
INC (PA)**
Also Called: Abbey Carpet
4120 Whipple Ave Nw (44718-2970)
PHONE..........................330 493-9000
Nicholas H Shaheen Jr, *President*
Dawn Shaheen, *Treasurer*
EMP: 10
SQ FT: 12,800

SALES (est): 3.2MM **Privately Held**
WEB: www.shaheenrugs.com
SIC: 5713 7217 2295 Rugs; carpet & furniture cleaning on location; tape, varnished: plastic & other coated (except
magnetic)

(G-2847)
**SHANAFELT MANUFACTURING
CO (PA)**
2600 Wnfeld Way Ne 2700 (44705)
P.O. Box 7040 (44705-0040)
PHONE..........................330 455-0315
Fax: 330 455-4487
Jon Lindseth, *Ch of Bd*
Leo Kovachic, *President*
Edwin Cassidy, *Manager*
Judy Haut, *Manager*
Joseph Sullivan, *Admin Sec*
EMP: 35
SQ FT: 50,000
SALES (est): 9.2MM **Privately Held**
WEB: www.shanafelt.com
SIC: 3537 3451 Containers (metal), air
cargo; screw machine products

(G-2848)
SHOWROOM TRACKER LLC
6543 Forestwood St Nw (44718-4208)
PHONE..........................888 407-0094
Matthew Tew,
Chris Nickless,
Matthew Nickless,
EMP: 3
SALES (est): 71.1K **Privately Held**
SIC: 7372 Business oriented computer
software

(G-2849)
**SIGNA STORTECH SYSTEMS
INC**
8990 Pleasantwood Ave Nw (44720-4762)
P.O. Box 2408 (44720-0408)
PHONE..........................214 357-0411
Fax: 330 499-1843
Gary R Smith, *CEO*
Chad Smith, *President*
EMP: 30
SQ FT: 40,000
SALES (est): 4.6MM **Privately Held**
WEB: www.signa-stortech.com
SIC: 3579 3479 3441 Sorters, filing (of-
fice); painting, coating & hot dipping; fab-
ricated structural metal

(G-2850)
SIZETEC INC
4825 Higbee Ave Nw # 103 (44718-2567)
PHONE..........................330 492-9682
Fax: 330 492-9041
Mike Tsutsumi, *President*
EMP: 3
SQ FT: 1,000
SALES (est): 380K **Privately Held**
WEB: www.sizetec.com
SIC: 3559 8711 Screening equipment,
electric; engineering services

(G-2851)
SLIMANS PRINTERY INC
Also Called: SPI Mailing
624 5th St Nw (44703-2625)
PHONE..........................330 454-9141
Samuel Sliman Jr, *President*
Judy Sliman Humphries, *Vice Pres*
Deanne Hoffman, *Mktg Dir*
EMP: 14 **EST:** 1947
SQ FT: 9,000
SALES (est): 1.2MM **Privately Held**
SIC: 2752 2759 Commercial printing, litho-
graphic; letterpress printing

(G-2852)
SOLMET TECHNOLOGIES INC
2716 Shepler Ch Ave Sw (44706-4114)
PHONE..........................330 915-4160
Fax: 330 580-5199
Joseph R Halter Jr, *President*
Jeff Davis, *General Mgr*
Lee Dicola, *Corp Secy*
Matthew Halter, *Vice Pres*
E Scott Jackson, *Vice Pres*
EMP: 50
SALES (est): 9.8MM **Privately Held**
WEB: www.solmettechnologies.com
SIC: 3462 Iron & steel forgings

▲ = Import ▼=Export
◆ =Import/Export

(G-2853)
SPECIALIZED PHARMACEUTICALS
Also Called: Qol Meds
400 Tuscarawas St W (44702-2044)
PHONE..................330 453-3067
Richard C Brunn, *Principal*
EMP: 5
SALES (est): 446.7K **Privately Held**
SIC: 2834 Pharmaceutical preparations

(G-2854)
SPECIALTY HOSE AEROSPACE CORP
7802 Freedom Ave Nw (44720-6908)
PHONE..................330 497-9650
Michael Helfer, *President*
Marjorie Onslow, *Treasurer*
Tim Henson, *Manager*
EMP: 10
SALES: 1.3MM
SALES (corp-wide): 1.4MM **Privately Held**
SIC: 3599 Hose, flexible metallic
PA: Specialty Hose Corporation
7800 Freedom Ave Nw
North Canton OH 44720
330 497-9650

(G-2855)
SPERLING RAILWAY SERVICES INC
4313 Southway St Sw (44706-1809)
PHONE..................330 479-2004
Fax: 330 479-2006
Fred Sperling, *President*
Nancy Sperling, *Corp Secy*
Warren Stryffeler, *Vice Pres*
EMP: 10
SQ FT: 17,000
SALES (est): 1.1MM **Privately Held**
WEB: www.sperlingrailway.com
SIC: 3743 Railroad equipment

(G-2856)
STARK MATERIALS INC
Also Called: Northstar Asphalt
7345 Sunset Strip Ave Nw (44720-7040)
P.O. Box 2646 (44720-0646)
PHONE..................330 497-1648
Fax: 330 497-1710
Howard Wenger, *President*
Joe Chiavari, *QC Dir*
EMP: 45
SQ FT: 1,404
SALES (est): 5.6MM **Privately Held**
SIC: 2911 2951 Asphalt or asphaltic materials, made in refineries; asphalt paving mixtures & blocks

(G-2857)
STARK READY MIX & SUPPLY CO
2905 Columbus Rd Ne (44705-3938)
P.O. Box 80449 (44708-0449)
PHONE..................330 580-4307
Fax: 330 452-1660
Douglas A Woodhall, *President*
Gerald Orn, *Treasurer*
Vincent Monteleone, *Supervisor*
EMP: 20
SQ FT: 2,250
SALES: 5.2MM
SALES (corp-wide): 60MM **Privately Held**
SIC: 3273 Ready-mixed concrete
PA: Central Allied Enterprises, Inc.
1243 Raff Rd Sw
Canton OH 44710
330 477-6751

(G-2858)
STARK TRUSS COMPANY INC (PA)
Also Called: S T C
109 Miles Ave Sw (44710-1261)
P.O. Box 80469 (44708-0469)
PHONE..................330 478-2100
Fax: 330 478-9413
Abner Yoder, *CEO*
Stephen Yoder, *President*
Javan Yoder, *Exec VP*
Todd Pallotta, *Vice Pres*
Esther Yoder, *Treasurer*
EMP: 18

SQ FT: 4,300
SALES (est): 230.5MM **Privately Held**
WEB: www.starktruss.com
SIC: 5031 2439 Lumber, plywood & millwork; trusses, wooden roof

(G-2859)
STARK TRUSS COMPANY INC
Also Called: Stark Forest Products
4933 Southway St Sw (44706-1979)
PHONE..................330 478-2100
Fax: 330 477-2267
Rob Blyer, *Branch Mgr*
EMP: 100
SALES (corp-wide): 230.5MM **Privately Held**
WEB: www.starktruss.com
SIC: 2439 2511 Structural wood members; wood household furniture
PA: Stark Truss Company, Inc.
109 Miles Ave Sw
Canton OH 44710
330 478-2100

(G-2860)
STUDIO ARTS & GLASS INC
7495 Strauss Ave Nw (44720-7103)
PHONE..................330 494-9779
Robert Joliet, *President*
Wendy Warren, *Vice Pres*
Robert Fay, *CPA*
EMP: 10
SQ FT: 7,000
SALES (est): 800K **Privately Held**
WEB: www.studioartsandglass.com
SIC: 3231 8299 Stained glass: made from purchased glass; arts & crafts schools

(G-2861)
SUAREZ CORPORATION INDUSTRIES
Biotech Research Division
7800 Whipple Ave Nw (44767-0002)
PHONE..................330 494-4282
Benjamin Suarez, *President*
Julianne Dalaynis, *Human Res Dir*
Tom Betts, *Mktg Dir*
Peggy Kerchner, *Manager*
Michael Schumacher, *MIS Dir*
EMP: 33
SALES (corp-wide): 173.8MM **Privately Held**
WEB: www.suarez.com
SIC: 3841 5091 2834 5122 Veterinarians' instruments & apparatus; fitness equipment & supplies; vitamin, nutrient & hematinic preparations for human use; vitamins & minerals
PA: Suarez Corporation Industries
7800 Whipple Ave Nw
North Canton OH 44720
330 494-5504

(G-2862)
SUAREZ CORPORATION INDUSTRIES
Edenpure Heater
7800 Whipple Ave Nw (44767-0002)
PHONE..................330 494-5504
John Carten, *Branch Mgr*
EMP: 11
SALES (corp-wide): 173.8MM **Privately Held**
SIC: 3433 Room & wall heaters, including radiators
PA: Suarez Corporation Industries
7800 Whipple Ave Nw
North Canton OH 44720
330 494-5504

(G-2863)
SUN STATE PLASTICS INC
4045 Kevin St Nw (44720-6981)
PHONE..................330 494-5220
Fax: 330 494-1231
Rick Dewees, *President*
Cheryl Santmeyer, *Manager*
EMP: 40
SQ FT: 37,000
SALES (est): 7.2MM **Privately Held**
SIC: 3089 Injection molding of plastics

(G-2864)
SUPER SIGN GUYS LLC
Also Called: Fww
5060 Navarre Rd Sw Ste C (44706-3320)
P.O. Box 36092 (44735-6092)
PHONE..................330 477-3887
Gregory Magee, *Principal*
EMP: 2
SALES (est): 268.4K **Privately Held**
SIC: 3993 Signs & advertising specialties

(G-2865)
SUSPENSION TECHNOLOGY INC
1424 Scales St Sw (44706-3081)
PHONE..................330 458-3058
Fax: 330 458-3066
David Croston, *President*
Ervin Vandenberg, *Principal*
Craig Thompson, *QC Dir*
EMP: 15
SQ FT: 12,000
SALES (est): 2.9MM **Privately Held**
WEB: www.ridesti.com
SIC: 3537 5084 Lift trucks, industrial: fork, platform, straddle, etc.; lift trucks & parts

(G-2866)
TAG SPORTSWEAR LLC
1300 Market Ave N (44714-2606)
PHONE..................330 456-8867
Richard Gattuso,
Charles Gattuso,
EMP: 5
SALES: 120K **Privately Held**
SIC: 2395 Embroidery products, except schiffli machine

(G-2867)
TECHNIBUS INC
1501 Raff Rd Sw Ste 6 (44710-2356)
PHONE..................330 479-4202
Dan Pomerleau, *President*
Keith Anthony, *Safety Mgr*
Carol Cuffman, *QA Dir*
Tammy Wile, *CFO*
Tammy Orr, *Controller*
▲ EMP: 70
SQ FT: 148,000
SALES (est): 25MM
SALES (corp-wide): 695.9MM **Publicly Held**
WEB: www.technibus.com
SIC: 3699 Electrical equipment & supplies
HQ: Ies Infrastructure Solutions, Llc
800 Nave Rd Se
Massillon OH 44646
330 830-3500

(G-2868)
TEK GEAR & MACHINE INC
1220 Camden Ave Sw (44706-1618)
PHONE..................330 455-3331
Fax: 330 455-3232
Kevin Aronhalt, *President*
Thomas Mertz, *Vice Pres*
Emil Bueno, *Treasurer*
EMP: 8
SQ FT: 6,000
SALES (est): 900K **Privately Held**
WEB: www.tekgear.net
SIC: 3599 Machine shop, jobbing & repair

(G-2869)
THE W L JENKINS COMPANY
Also Called: Chaplet & Chill Division
1445 Whipple Ave Sw (44710-1321)
PHONE..................330 477-3407
Fax: 330 477-8404
Susan E Jenkins, *President*
Kris Spark, *Manager*
EMP: 18
SQ FT: 65,000
SALES (est): 3.4MM **Privately Held**
WEB: www.wljenkinsco.com
SIC: 3699 3679 3931 3469 Electrical equipment & supplies; security devices; electronic circuits; musical instruments; metal stampings

(G-2870)
TIM L HUMBERT
Also Called: Humbert Screen Graphix
6535 Promler St Nw (44720-7626)
PHONE..................330 497-4944
Fax: 330 497-9704

Tim L Humbert, *Owner*
EMP: 11
SQ FT: 6,200
SALES (est): 886.9K **Privately Held**
SIC: 2396 2791 Screen printing on fabric articles; typesetting

(G-2871)
TIMKEN COMPANY
Also Called: Timken Aircraft Operation
5430 Lauby Rd Bldg 7 (44720-1576)
PHONE..................330 471-4300
Bob Campbell, *Manager*
EMP: 6
SALES (corp-wide): 2.6B **Publicly Held**
SIC: 3562 Ball & roller bearings
PA: The Timken Company
4500 Mount Pleasant St Nw
North Canton OH 44720
234 262-3000

(G-2872)
TIMKEN COMPANY
20th & Dueber Ave Sw (44706)
P.O. Box 6920 (44706-0920)
PHONE..................330 471-5028
Jim Wolfter, *Branch Mgr*
EMP: 4
SALES (corp-wide): 2.6B **Publicly Held**
SIC: 3562 Ball & roller bearings
PA: The Timken Company
4500 Mount Pleasant St Nw
North Canton OH 44720
234 262-3000

(G-2873)
TIMKEN COMPANY
Research Division
4500 Mount Pleasant St Nw (44720-5450)
P.O. Box 6930 (44706-0930)
PHONE..................330 471-2121
Ken Schilstra, *Engineer*
Sal Miraglia, *Manager*
Philip Chupp, *Comp Spec*
EMP: 250
SALES (corp-wide): 2.6B **Publicly Held**
SIC: 3562 Ball & roller bearings
PA: The Timken Company
4500 Mount Pleasant St Nw
North Canton OH 44720
234 262-3000

(G-2874)
TIMKEN COMPANY
Also Called: Roller Plant
786 Whipple Ave Sw (44710)
PHONE..................330 471-5043
Christopher Armstrong, *Branch Mgr*
Norm Bretz, *Manager*
EMP: 510
SALES (corp-wide): 2.6B **Publicly Held**
SIC: 3562 Ball & roller bearings
PA: The Timken Company
4500 Mount Pleasant St Nw
North Canton OH 44720
234 262-3000

(G-2875)
TIMKEN FOUNDATION
200 Market Ave N Ste 210 (44702-1437)
PHONE..................330 452-1144
Ward J Timken, *President*
EMP: 3
SALES: 8.4MM **Privately Held**
SIC: 2515 Foundations & platforms

(G-2876)
TIMKENSTEEL CORPORATION (PA)
1835 Dueber Ave Sw (44706-2728)
PHONE..................330 471-7000
Ward J Timken Jr, *Ch of Bd*
Frank A Dipiero, *Exec VP*
Tina M Beskid, *Vice Pres*
Christopher J Holding, *CFO*
EMP: 277
SALES: 869.5MM **Publicly Held**
SIC: 3312 Blast furnaces & steel mills

(G-2877)
TIMKENSTEEL CORPORATION
4511 Faircrest St Sw (44706-3513)
PHONE..................330 471-7000
Ron Balyint, *Branch Mgr*
EMP: 9

SALES (corp-wide): 869.5MM **Publicly Held**
SIC: 3317 Steel pipe & tubes
PA: Timkensteel Corporation
1835 Dueber Ave Sw
Canton OH 44706
330 471-7000

(G-2878)
TIMKENSTEEL CORPORATION
Also Called: Harrison Steel Plant
1927 Harrison Ave Sw (44706)
PHONE...................................330 438-3000
Lee Sholley, *Vice Pres*
EMP: 163
SALES (corp-wide): 869.5MM **Publicly Held**
SIC: 3312 Blast furnaces & steel mills
PA: Timkensteel Corporation
1835 Dueber Ave Sw
Canton OH 44706
330 471-7000

(G-2879)
TIMKENSTEEL CORPORATION
Also Called: Faircrest Steel Plant
4511 Faircrest St Sw (44706-3513)
PHONE...................................330 438-3000
Lee Sholley, *Branch Mgr*
Mark Gallucci, *Supervisor*
EMP: 100
SALES (corp-wide): 869.5MM **Publicly Held**
SIC: 3312 Blast furnaces & steel mills
PA: Timkensteel Corporation
1835 Dueber Ave Sw
Canton OH 44706
330 471-7000

(G-2880)
TOTAL LUBRICATION MGT CO (HQ)
3713 Progress St Ne (44705-4437)
PHONE...................................888 478-6996
Elle Donlin, *General Mgr*
Terry Ross, *Senior VP*
▲ EMP: 39 EST: 2011
SALES (est): 12.9MM
SALES (corp-wide): 3.6B **Publicly Held**
SIC: 3569 Lubrication machinery, automatic
PA: Colfax Corporation
420 Natl Bus Pkwy Fl 5
Annapolis Junction MD 20701
301 323-9000

(G-2881)
TRANSFORMER ASSOCIATES LIMITED
831 Market Ave N (44702-1175)
PHONE...................................330 430-0750
Tonya Cihon, *Manager*
Rodney Herndon,
Bonnie Tarver, *Admin Asst*
EMP: 6
SALES: 381K **Privately Held**
WEB: www.transformerassociates.com
SIC: 3612 Voltage regulating transformers, electric power

(G-2882)
TRI-K ENTERPRISES INC
935 Mckinley Ave Sw (44707-4163)
PHONE...................................330 832-7380
Fax: 330 452-4484
Robert S Black, *President*
Joan Black, *Corp Secy*
Kerry Black, *Vice Pres*
Kevin Black, *Vice Pres*
EMP: 6
SALES (est): 1MM **Privately Held**
SIC: 3451 3542 Screw machine products; presses: hydraulic & pneumatic, mechanical & manual

(G-2883)
UNI CORP
Also Called: Unitec
1300 Market Ave N (44714-2606)
PHONE...................................330 489-6500
Fax: 330 456-9403
Richard C Gattuso, *President*
Margherita Gattuso, *Corp Secy*
Marcella Petry, *Financial Exec*
▲ EMP: 20
SQ FT: 20,000

SALES (est): 2.8MM **Privately Held**
WEB: www.unitecproducts.com
SIC: 3161 3651 Cases, carrying; musical instrument cases; speaker monitors

(G-2884)
UNION METAL CORPORATION (PA)
1432 Maple Ave Ne (44705-1700)
PHONE...................................330 456-7653
Fax: 330 456-0196
Darryl Dillenback, *President*
Van Zandt Hawn, *Chairman*
Russell Harpring, *Vice Pres*
Barbara Friedman, *Safety Mgr*
Richard Wehnberg, *Purch Mgr*
◆ EMP: 248
SQ FT: 500,000
SALES (est): 81.2MM **Privately Held**
WEB: www.unionmetal.com
SIC: 3648 Public lighting fixtures

(G-2885)
UNITED ENGINEERING & FNDRY CO
1400 Grace Ave Ne (44705-2035)
PHONE...................................330 456-2761
Ronald A Martin, *President*
Jay Neisom, *Principal*
Edward Bauer, *COO*
EMP: 12
SQ FT: 5,000
SALES (est): 1.1MM **Privately Held**
SIC: 3325 Rolling mill rolls, cast steel

(G-2886)
UNITED GRINDING AND MACHINE CO
2315 Ellis Ave Ne (44705-4696)
PHONE...................................330 453-7402
Fax: 330 453-4280
Allan J Pfabe, *President*
Dennis Pfabe, *Vice Pres*
Michael Pfabe, *Purchasing*
Karen Essig, *Treasurer*
▲ EMP: 75 EST: 1967
SQ FT: 65,000
SALES (est): 12.4MM **Privately Held**
WEB: www.unitedgrinding.com
SIC: 3599 Machine shop, jobbing & repair

(G-2887)
UNITED HARD CHROME CORPORATION
2202 Gilbert Ave Ne (44705-4697)
PHONE...................................330 453-2786
Fax: 330 453-1532
Robert R Horger, *President*
Chris Seebach, *General Mgr*
Beth Horger, *Vice Pres*
Marvin Ott, *Manager*
EMP: 13 EST: 1954
SQ FT: 18,000
SALES (est): 1.1MM **Privately Held**
WEB: www.unitedhardchrome.com
SIC: 3471 Electroplating of metals or formed products

(G-2888)
UNITED ROLLS INC (DH)
Also Called: Whemco
1400 Grace Ave Ne (44705-2035)
PHONE...................................330 456-2761
Fax: 330 456-2085
J Douglas Nesom Jr, *Ch of Bd*
Robin Ingols, *President*
Ron Wilcox, *President*
Edward Bauer, *COO*
Paula Harbaugh, *Vice Pres*
◆ EMP: 130
SQ FT: 225,000
SALES (est): 33.7MM
SALES (corp-wide): 564.1MM **Privately Held**
WEB: www.ufirolls.com
SIC: 3547 3613 Rolling mill machinery; control panels, electric
HQ: Whemco Inc.
5 Hot Metal St Ste 300
Pittsburgh PA 15203
412 390-2700

(G-2889)
UNITED SURFACE FINISHING INC
2202 Gilbert Ave Ne (44705-4634)
PHONE...................................330 453-2786
Richard N Horger, *President*
Beulla P Bango, *Principal*
Francis L Petti, *Principal*
Mike Murphy, *Marketing Staff*
EMP: 3 EST: 1957
SALES (est): 382.9K **Privately Held**
SIC: 3471 Chromium plating of metals or formed products

(G-2890)
UNIVERSAL METALS CUTTING INC
2656 Harrison Ave Sw (44706)
PHONE...................................330 580-5192
Fax: 330 580-5194
Joseph Halter Jr, *President*
Lee J Dicola, *Corp Secy*
EMP: 7
SQ FT: 8,140
SALES (est): 723.6K **Privately Held**
SIC: 3312 Tubes, steel & iron

(G-2891)
US TECHNOLOGY CORPORATION
4200 Munson St Nw (44718-2981)
PHONE...................................330 455-1181
Raymond F Williams, *President*
Robert B Putnam, *Vice Pres*
Eric Williams, *Project Mgr*
Donna Torrie, *Info Tech Mgr*
Clay James, *Admin Asst*
◆ EMP: 42
SQ FT: 2,000
SALES (est): 8.4MM **Privately Held**
WEB: www.ustechnology.com
SIC: 3291 3728 Abrasive products; aircraft parts & equipment

(G-2892)
USA QUICKPRINT INC (PA)
Also Called: Quick Print
409 3rd St Sw (44702-1910)
PHONE...................................330 455-5119
Fax: 330 455-1255
Gerald Hohler, *President*
Jocelyn Hohler, *Vice Pres*
EMP: 15
SQ FT: 2,000
SALES (est): 2.4MM **Privately Held**
SIC: 2752 Commercial printing, offset

(G-2893)
V & S SCHULER ENGINEERING INC
2240 Allen Ave Se (44707-3612)
PHONE...................................330 452-5200
Fax: 330 452-8717
Brian Miller, *President*
Raymond Whaley, *Sales Mgr*
Michelle Dalpra, *Manager*
Ginny Petty, *Technology*
EMP: 100
SQ FT: 40,000
SALES (est): 27.8MM
SALES (corp-wide): 704.9MM **Privately Held**
WEB: www.vsschuler.com
SIC: 3441 3444 3312 Fabricated structural metal; sheet metalwork; blast furnaces & steel mills
HQ: Voigt & Schweitzer Llc
987 Buckeye Park Rd
Columbus OH 43207
614 449-8281

(G-2894)
V MAST MANUFACTURING INC
1712 Kimball Rd Se (44707-3618)
PHONE...................................330 409-8116
Raymond M Valentine, *President*
EMP: 3 EST: 2009
SALES (est): 213.6K **Privately Held**
SIC: 3999 Manufacturing industries

(G-2895)
VEE GEE ENTERPRISE CORPORATION
4897 Fulton Dr Nw (44718-2337)
PHONE...................................330 493-9780
Dennis L Noland, *President*
Steven T Noland, *Vice Pres*
EMP: 4
SQ FT: 3,200
SALES (est): 200K **Privately Held**
SIC: 2673 Cellophane bags, unprinted: made from purchased materials

(G-2896)
VER MICH LTD
4210 Cleveland Ave Nw (44709-2350)
PHONE...................................330 493-7330
Melvin R Lloyd, *President*
EMP: 3
SALES (est): 253.7K **Privately Held**
SIC: 2399 Fabricated textile products

(G-2897)
VERSALIFT EAST INC
4884 Corporate St Sw (44706-1907)
PHONE...................................610 866-1400
Keith W Joseph, *Branch Mgr*
EMP: 8
SALES (corp-wide): 100.4K **Privately Held**
SIC: 3534 Elevators & moving stairways
HQ: Versalift East, Inc.
2706 Brodhead Rd
Bethlehem PA 18020
610 866-1400

(G-2898)
W W CROSS INDUSTRIES INC
2510 Allen Ave Se (44707-3614)
PHONE...................................330 588-8400
Fax: 330 588-8700
Thomas Trudeau, *President*
Phillip Lattavo, *Vice Pres*
Christine Trudeau, *Treasurer*
EMP: 10
SALES (est): 1.8MM **Privately Held**
WEB: www.wwcross.com
SIC: 3965 Fasteners

(G-2899)
WACKER CHEMICAL CORPORATION
Also Called: Silmix Division
2215 International Pkwy (44720-1372)
PHONE...................................330 899-0847
Mathias Wiedemann, *Engineer*
John A Bacon, *Project Engr*
Debra May, *Human Resources*
Angela Grim, *Office Mgr*
Rainer Sextl, *Manager*
EMP: 30
SALES (corp-wide): 5.6B **Privately Held**
WEB: www.wackerchemicalcorporation.com
SIC: 2869 Silicones
HQ: Wacker Chemical Corporation
3301 Sutton Rd
Adrian MI 49221
517 264-8500

(G-2900)
WALLACE FORGE COMPANY
3700 Georgetown Rd Ne (44704-2697)
PHONE...................................330 488-1203
Fax: 330 488-1217
Dean Wallace, *President*
Sheila A Ghezzi, *Vice Pres*
William A Peterson, *Admin Sec*
▲ EMP: 65 EST: 1966
SQ FT: 55,000
SALES (est): 13.4MM **Privately Held**
WEB: www.wallaceforgecompany.com
SIC: 3462 3321 3463 3452 Iron & steel forgings; gray & ductile iron foundries; nonferrous forgings; bolts, nuts, rivets & washers; truck & bus bodies

(G-2901)
WASHINGTON LABORATORIES INC
1922 26th St Ne (44705-2160)
PHONE...................................330 452-4928
Fax: 330 452-3318
Larry Harris, *CEO*
▲ EMP: 6

SQ FT: 12,000
SALES: 1.3MM **Privately Held**
SIC: 3842 Personal safety equipment

(G-2902)
WESTERN BRANCH DIESEL INC
Also Called: John Deere Authorized Dealer
1616 Metric Ave Sw (44706-3087)
PHONE................................330 454-8800
Fax: 330 454-6126
Mike McElwain, *Branch Mgr*
EMP: 28
SQ FT: 22,400
SALES (corp-wide): 84MM **Privately Held**
WEB: www.westernbranchdiesel.com
SIC: 5084 5531 5063 3714 Engines & parts, diesel; truck equipment & parts; generators; motor vehicle parts & accessories; power transmission equipment; internal combustion engines
PA: Western Branch Diesel, Incorporated
3504 Shipwright St
Portsmouth VA 23703
757 673-7000

(G-2903)
WORTHIGNTON PRODUCTS INC
3405 Kuemerle Ct Ne (44705-5074)
PHONE................................330 452-7400
Paul Meeks, *President*
Jeffrey S Sanger, *Vice Pres*
▲EMP: 6
SQ FT: 6,000
SALES (est): 724K **Privately Held**
SIC: 3443 3429 3089 Buoys, metal; marine hardware; buoys & floats, plastic

(G-2904)
WYOMING CASING SERVICE INC
1414 Raff Rd Sw (44710-2320)
PHONE................................330 479-8785
EMP: 20
SALES (corp-wide): 224.9MM **Privately Held**
SIC: 1389 Cementing oil & gas well casings
PA: Wyoming Casing Service, Inc.
198 40th St E
Dickinson ND 58601
701 225-8521

(G-2905)
XCEL MOLD AND MACHINE INC
7661 Freedom Ave Nw (44720-6987)
PHONE................................330 499-8450
Fax: 330 499-4090
Bruce Cain, *President*
Bob Johnson, *Vice Pres*
EMP: 13
SQ FT: 25,000
SALES: 120K **Privately Held**
WEB: www.xcelmold.com
SIC: 3544 Industrial molds; special dies & tools

(G-2906)
ZEIGER INDUSTRIES
4704 Wiseland Ave Se (44707-1054)
PHONE................................330 484-4413
Fax: 330 484-0267
Donald Zeiger, *President*
Tom Zeiger, *Plant Mgr*
Andy Zeiger, *Engineer*
Sandi Zeiger, *Treasurer*
Stan Glover, *Sales Staff*
EMP: 22
SQ FT: 2,500
SALES (est): 5.6MM **Privately Held**
WEB: www.zeigerindustries.com
SIC: 3494 Valves & pipe fittings

Cardington
Morrow County

(G-2907)
3GC LLC
Also Called: Myairplane.com
5600 Sw Us 42 (43315)
PHONE................................740 703-0580
Dennis Megarry, *Owner*
EMP: 4

SALES (est): 140K **Privately Held**
SIC: 3812 Aircraft control systems, electronic

(G-2908)
BJ OILFIELD SERVICES LTD
2944 County Road 186 (43315-9344)
PHONE................................419 768-2408
Jessica Keplar, *Principal*
EMP: 3
SALES (est): 192.3K **Privately Held**
SIC: 1389 Oil field services

(G-2909)
CARDINGTON YUTAKA TECH INC (DH)
575 W Main St (43315-9796)
PHONE................................419 864-8777
Fax: 419 864-7771
Hirokazu Kawuai, *President*
Fred Razavi, *Exec VP*
Ray Welch, *Plant Mgr*
Chariss Nelson, *Purch Mgr*
Raymond Schultz, *Purchasing*
▲EMP: 750
SQ FT: 300,000
SALES (est): 233.1MM
SALES (corp-wide): 124.7B **Privately Held**
SIC: 3714 Motor vehicle parts & accessories
HQ: Yutaka Giken Co., Ltd.
508-1, Yutakacho, Higashi-Ku
Hamamatsu SZO 431-3
534 334-111

(G-2910)
GEOCORE DRILLING INC
2918 Us Highway 42 (43315-9790)
PHONE................................419 864-4011
Chad Mullin, *Owner*
EMP: 4
SALES (est): 250K **Privately Held**
SIC: 1381 Service well drilling

(G-2911)
HOFFMAN MEAT PROCESSING
157 S 4th St (43315-9726)
PHONE................................419 864-3994
Mike Hoffman, *Owner*
EMP: 7
SALES: 500K **Privately Held**
SIC: 2013 5421 Sausages & other prepared meats; meat markets, including freezer provisioners

(G-2912)
JACK GRUBER
Also Called: Industrial Machine Service
2606 County Rd Ste 184 (43315)
P.O. Box 104, Mount Gilead (43338-0104)
PHONE................................740 408-2718
Jack Gruber, *Owner*
EMP: 3 EST: 1978
SALES (est): 185.5K **Privately Held**
WEB: www.jackgruber.com
SIC: 3089 7699 Injection molded finished plastic products; industrial machinery & equipment repair

(G-2913)
PATRIOT
217 W Main St (43315-1010)
PHONE................................419 864-8411
Shannon Leary, *Owner*
EMP: 3 EST: 2014
SALES (est): 76.2K **Privately Held**
SIC: 2711 Newspapers

Carey
Wyandot County

(G-2914)
ANDERSON CO (PA)
Also Called: Specialty Wood
415 W North St (43316-1033)
P.O. Box 95 (43316-0095)
PHONE................................419 396-7056
Fax: 419 396-6676
Jim Anderson, *Owner*
Nick Klein, *Plant Mgr*
Jacqueline Anderson, *Manager*
EMP: 4 EST: 1978

SQ FT: 20,000
SALES: 639.3K **Privately Held**
SIC: 2499 Woodenware, kitchen & household

(G-2915)
CAREY PRECAST CONCRETE COMPANY
3420 Township Highway 98 (43316-9763)
P.O. Box 129 (43316-0129)
PHONE................................419 396-7142
Fax: 419 396-3511
Kathryn Beck, *President*
Dean Beck, *Corp Secy*
EMP: 6
SQ FT: 2,000
SALES (est): 390K **Privately Held**
WEB: www.careyprecast.com
SIC: 3272 Concrete products, precast

(G-2916)
CARL HUCKE
Also Called: Strongberg Hydramite
5239 State Highway 199 (43316-9421)
PHONE................................419 396-6078
Carl Hucke, *Owner*
John Hucke, *Manager*
EMP: 3
SALES (est): 196.7K **Privately Held**
SIC: 3599 Machine shop, jobbing & repair

(G-2917)
CONTINENTAL STRL PLAS INC
Also Called: CSP Carey
2915 County Rd 96 (43316)
PHONE................................419 396-1980
Mike Bishop, *Branch Mgr*
EMP: 390
SALES (corp-wide): 6.7B **Privately Held**
WEB: www.cs-plastics.com
SIC: 3089 3714 Plastic processing; motor vehicle parts & accessories
HQ: Continental Structural Plastics, Inc.
255 Rex Blvd
Auburn Hills MI 48326
248 237-7800

(G-2918)
FRUGAL SYSTEMS
21250 County Road 26 (43316-9302)
PHONE................................419 957-7863
Timothy Lee, *Partner*
EMP: 3
SALES (est): 113K **Privately Held**
SIC: 3999 Manufacturing industries

(G-2919)
HANON SYSTEMS USA LLC
581 Arrowhead Dr (43316)
PHONE................................313 920-0583
Thomas Charnesky, *Plant Mgr*
EMP: 140 **Privately Held**
SIC: 3714 3585 3699 Air conditioner parts, motor vehicle; radiators & radiator shells & cores, motor vehicle; heaters, motor vehicle; compressors for refrigeration & air conditioning equipment; heat emission operating apparatus
HQ: Hanon Systems Usa, Llc
1 Village Center Dr
Van Buren Twp MI 48111
734 710-5000

(G-2920)
MINERAL PROCESSING COMPANY
1855 County Highway 99 (43316-9722)
PHONE................................419 396-3501
Fax: 419 396-3463
Daniel Allen, *President*
John Uliveto, *Vice Pres*
Victoria C Allen, *Treasurer*
Harry Allen, *Admin Sec*
EMP: 6
SQ FT: 15,000
SALES (est): 830.3K **Privately Held**
WEB: www.mineralprocess.com
SIC: 3275 3274 Gypsum products; lime

(G-2921)
NATIONAL LIME AND STONE CO
370 N Patterson St (43316-1057)
P.O. Box 8 (43316-0008)
PHONE................................419 396-7671
Fax: 419 396-3534
J Kinsler, *Exec VP*

R Kruse, *Vice Pres*
Tim Horn, *Plant Mgr*
Rick Dehays, *Purchasing*
Chris Beeman, *VP Finance*
EMP: 130
SALES (corp-wide): 4B **Privately Held**
WEB: www.natlime.com
SIC: 1422 3291 3281 3274 Lime rock, ground; abrasive products; cut stone & stone products; lime; alkalies & chlorine; construction sand & gravel
PA: The National Lime And Stone Company
551 Lake Cascade Pkwy
Findlay OH 45840
419 422-4341

(G-2922)
OF MACHINING LLC
2140 State Rd 568 (43316)
PHONE................................419 396-7870
Michael T Fredritz, *Principal*
EMP: 5
SALES (est): 687.6K **Privately Held**
SIC: 3599 Machine shop, jobbing & repair

(G-2923)
OPS WIRELESS
807 E Findlay St (43316-1331)
PHONE................................419 396-4041
Michael R Brooks, *Owner*
Todd Dierksheide, *Manager*
EMP: 8
SQ FT: 10,500
SALES (est): 630K **Privately Held**
SIC: 3679 Video triggers, except remote control TV devices

(G-2924)
PROGRESSOR TIMES
1198 E Findlay St (43316-9760)
P.O. Box 37 (43316-0037)
PHONE................................419 396-7567
Fax: 419 396-7527
Stephen Zender, *Owner*
Amy Yeater, *Sales Staff*
EMP: 6
SALES (est): 461.1K **Privately Held**
WEB: www.theprogressortimes.com
SIC: 7313 2711 Newspaper advertising representative; newspapers

(G-2925)
PSD PARTNERS LLC (PA)
5968 State Highway 199 (43316-9422)
PHONE................................419 294-3838
Paul M Kalmbach, *Principal*
EMP: 5
SALES (est): 1.4MM **Privately Held**
SIC: 2048 Prepared feeds

(G-2926)
QUALITY PLLETS RECYCLABLES LLC
410 E Findlay St (43316-1209)
PHONE................................419 396-3244
Edward J Gretzinger, *Principal*
EMP: 4
SALES (est): 333K **Privately Held**
SIC: 2448 Pallets, wood & wood with metal

(G-2927)
TRANSGLOBAL INC (PA)
225 N Patterson St (43316-1053)
PHONE................................419 396-9079
James Schroeder, *President*
Patrick Pelphrey, *Opers Mgr*
Doug Ritter, *Natl Sales Mgr*
Jason O'Toole, *Sales Mgr*
Mark Blair, *Sales Staff*
EMP: 7
SALES (est): 1.4MM **Privately Held**
WEB: www.transglobal.com
SIC: 3799 Trailers & trailer equipment

Carlisle
Warren County

(G-2928)
BRADEN-SUTPHIN INK COMPANY
400 Industry Dr (45005-6300)
PHONE................................937 704-9047
Fax: 513 743-6122

Bill Frecercy, *Opers-Prdtn-Mfg*
Jim Leitch, *Finance*
Dan Martin, *Sales Mgr*
EMP: 25
SQ FT: 5,000
SALES (corp-wide): 27.5MM **Privately Held**
WEB: www.bsink.com
SIC: 2893 Printing ink
PA: The Braden-Sutphin Ink Company
3650 E 93rd St
Cleveland OH 44105
216 271-2300

(G-2929)
CONVERTERS/PREPRESS INC
301 Industry Dr (45005-6326)
PHONE...................937 743-0935
Fax: 937 743-0498
Mike Zimmer, *Branch Mgr*
EMP: 5
SALES (corp-wide): 3.6MM **Privately Held**
WEB: www.4cp.net
SIC: 2796 7336 Engraving platemaking services; commercial art & graphic design
PA: Converters/Prepress, Inc.
1070 Tower Ln
Bensenville IL 60106
630 860-9400

(G-2930)
DRACOOL-USA INC (PA)
30 Eagle Ct (45005-6334)
PHONE...................937 743-5899
Javier Avendano, *CEO*
Richard Ross, *VP Opers*
Scott Howard, *Sales Staff*
Daneil Manning, *Manager*
Donnie Mann, *Supervisor*
◆ **EMP:** 24
SQ FT: 20,000
SALES: 6MM **Privately Held**
SIC: 3441 Fabricated structural metal

(G-2931)
INDUSTRIAL ELECTRONIC SERVICE
Also Called: Dc- Digital
325 Industry Dr (45005-6309)
PHONE...................937 746-9750
Fax: 937 746-9074
Jim Staffan,
Pete Staffan,
EMP: 11
SQ FT: 3,700
SALES (est): 2.4MM **Privately Held**
WEB: www.ies-1.com
SIC: 3579 3993 7622 Time clocks & time recording devices; scoreboards, electric; intercommunication equipment repair

(G-2932)
KITTYHAWK MOLDING COMPANY INC
10 Eagle Ct (45005-6321)
PHONE...................937 746-3663
Fax: 937 746-5060
Wilbur V Wisecup Jr, *CEO*
Dave Holmes, *President*
Sue Little, *Corp Secy*
Anita Holmes, *Vice Pres*
EMP: 29
SQ FT: 20,500
SALES (est): 5.5MM **Privately Held**
SIC: 3089 Injection molding of plastics

(G-2933)
NARROW WAY CUSTOM TECHNOLOGY
100 Industry Dr (45005-6304)
PHONE...................937 743-1611
Fax: 937 743-1688
Timothy Williams, *President*
Cindy Williams, *Vice Pres*
EMP: 29 **EST:** 1998
SQ FT: 5,600
SALES (est): 5.3MM **Privately Held**
SIC: 3599 7629 Custom machinery; electrical repair shops

(G-2934)
PATRIOT MFG GROUP INC
512 Linden Ave (45005-3345)
PHONE...................937 746-2117

Fax: 937 746-2118
Phillip Hubbell, *President*
Michael Swigert, *Principal*
Mike Skaggs, *Manager*
EMP: 54
SALES (est): 10.1MM **Privately Held**
WEB: www.patriotmms.com
SIC: 3545 Machine tool accessories

(G-2935)
QIBCO BUFFING PADS INC (PA)
Also Called: American Buffing
301 Industry Dr Ste B (45005-6330)
PHONE...................937 743-0805
Fax: 937 743-0806
Jeff Phipps, *Vice Pres*
▲ **EMP:** 12
SALES (est): 1.5MM **Privately Held**
WEB: www.americanbuffing.com
SIC: 3291 Abrasive buffs, bricks, cloth, paper, stones, etc.

Carroll
Fairfield County

(G-2936)
ARTISAN EQUIPMENT INC
5943 Clmbus Lncster Rd Nw (43112-7700)
P.O. Box 500 (43112-0500)
PHONE...................740 756-9135
Fax: 740 756-9366
Stuart Brengman, *President*
Marsha Brengman, *Corp Secy*
Keith C Brengman, *Vice Pres*
Steven Hunt, *Personnel Exec*
Susan Rocky, *Manager*
EMP: 10
SQ FT: 12,700
SALES (est): 1.8MM **Privately Held**
WEB: www.artisanequipment.com
SIC: 3599 3469 3544 Custom machinery; machine parts, stamped or pressed metal; special dies, tools, jigs & fixtures

(G-2937)
BAINTER MACHINING COMPANY
2945 Carroll Eastern Rd (43112-9647)
PHONE...................740 756-4598
Reda L Bainter, *Treasurer*
Dan Bainter, *Systems Mgr*
EMP: 12
SALES (corp-wide): 600K **Privately Held**
SIC: 3599 Machine shop, jobbing & repair
PA: Bainter Machining Company
1230 Rainbow Dr Ne
Lancaster OH 43130
740 653-2422

(G-2938)
CRAIG BROS MACHINE CO INC
5869 Clmbus Lncster Rd Nw (43112-7703)
P.O. Box 395 (43112-0395)
PHONE...................740 756-9280
Fax: 740 756-4913
Larry E Craig, *President*
Howard W Craig, *Vice Pres*
Connie Budnick, *Assistant*
EMP: 4
SQ FT: 3,800
SALES (est): 440K **Privately Held**
SIC: 3599 Machine shop, jobbing & repair

(G-2939)
CW MACHINE WORX LTD
4805 Scooby Ln (43112-9446)
PHONE...................740 654-5304
Cameron Gabbard, *President*
Shannon Heston, *Principal*
Penny Hutchinson, *Admin Sec*
Brad D Hutchinson,
EMP: 11
SQ FT: 15,000
SALES: 3.6MM **Privately Held**
SIC: 3531 Construction machinery

(G-2940)
F C BRENGMAN AND ASSOC LLC
86 High St (43112-9793)
P.O. Box 470 (43112-0470)
PHONE...................740 756-4308
Fax: 740 756-4905
Robert Mason, *President*

Bill Mason, *Owner*
Terry Riser, *Engineer*
Kathy Snide, *Financial Exec*
Cathy Snide, *Manager*
EMP: 28 **EST:** 1949
SQ FT: 12,000
SALES (est): 5.7MM **Privately Held**
WEB: www.fcbrengman.com
SIC: 3469 Metal stampings

(G-2941)
FAIR FIELD MACHINE PRODUCTS
6215 Clmbus Lncster Rd Nw (43112-9464)
P.O. Box 410 (43112-0410)
PHONE...................740 756-4409
David Riggenbach, *President*
EMP: 12
SQ FT: 8,300
SALES: 1MM **Privately Held**
SIC: 3451 3599 Screw machine products; machine shop, jobbing & repair

(G-2942)
FAIRFIELD MACHINED PRODUCTS
6215 Clmbus Lncster Rd Nw (43112-9464)
P.O. Box 410 (43112-0410)
PHONE...................740 756-4409
David Riggenbach, *President*
Ronnie Wyne, *Corp Secy*
Frederick Marshall, *Vice Pres*
EMP: 15
SALES: 1MM **Privately Held**
SIC: 3451 Screw machine products

(G-2943)
LLOYD F HELBER
3820 Clmbus Lncster Rd Nw (43112-9720)
PHONE...................740 756-9607
Lloyd Helber, *Owner*
EMP: 20
SQ FT: 2,756
SALES (est): 825.3K **Privately Held**
SIC: 6531 5812 2754 7519 Real estate leasing & rentals; Italian restaurant; commercial printing, gravure; trailer rental; real property lessors

(G-2944)
MARTIN PAPER PRODUCTS INC
5907 Clmbus Lncster Rd Nw (43112-7700)
P.O. Box 102 (43112-0102)
PHONE...................740 756-9271
Fax: 740 756-7867
Robert A Martin, *President*
Clara R Martin, *Principal*
Christina Lefever, *Supervisor*
Ronald Martin, *Admin Sec*
EMP: 20 **EST:** 1975
SQ FT: 8,100
SALES (est): 1.6MM **Privately Held**
WEB: www.martinpartitions.com
SIC: 2653 2631 Corrugated boxes, partitions, display items, sheets & pad; paperboard mills

(G-2945)
RELIABLE MFG CO LLC
4411 Carroll Southern Rd (43112-9794)
PHONE...................740 756-9373
Emma Snodgrass,
Gordon Fink,
Susan Fosnaugh,
EMP: 6
SQ FT: 8,500
SALES (est): 1.1MM **Privately Held**
SIC: 2813 Industrial gases

(G-2946)
S J COX TOOL INC
Also Called: Cox Machine & Fabrication
3800 Old Columbus Rd Nw (43112-9672)
PHONE...................740 756-1100
Fax: 740 756-1101
Jim Cox, *President*
EMP: 4
SALES (est): 320K **Privately Held**
SIC: 3599 Machine shop, jobbing & repair

(G-2947)
STERLING GRINDING COMPANY INC
62 High St (43112-9018)
PHONE...................614 836-3412

Fax: 740 756-9266
Glenna Shy, *President*
Brenda Kirk, *Vice Pres*
John S Shy, *Vice Pres*
Donald Losasso, *Plant Mgr*
EMP: 12
SQ FT: 28,000
SALES: 1MM **Privately Held**
SIC: 3599 Machine shop, jobbing & repair

(G-2948)
SUN CLEANERS & LAUNDRY INC
Also Called: Frsteam By Sun Cleaners
3739 Old Columbus Rd Nw (43112-9673)
PHONE...................740 756-4749
Nick Babamov, *President*
Ashley Babamov, *Admin Sec*
EMP: 4
SALES (est): 187.3K **Privately Held**
SIC: 2842 Specialty cleaning, polishes & sanitation goods

(G-2949)
TECH-BOND SOLUTIONS
3775 Columbus Lancaster (43112-9720)
PHONE...................614 327-8884
Dan Meyers, *CEO*
EMP: 5
SALES (est): 606.2K **Privately Held**
SIC: 2891 5169 Glue; glue

Carrollton
Carroll County

(G-2950)
A & A DISCOUNT TIRE
5125 Canton Rd Nw (44615-9015)
PHONE...................330 863-1936
Gene Dunn, *Owner*
Bradley Salewsky, *Manager*
EMP: 6
SQ FT: 34,000
SALES (est): 605.9K **Privately Held**
SIC: 3089 5015 5531 Automotive parts, plastic; tires, used; automotive tires

(G-2951)
ALL STEEL STRUCTURES INC
Also Called: Toibox Structuctures
755 N Lisbon St (44615-9401)
PHONE...................330 312-3131
Jeremy Athey, *President*
Judy Fieldhouse, *Treasurer*
EMP: 5
SALES (est): 401.5K **Privately Held**
SIC: 3317 Steel pipe & tubes

(G-2952)
ATKORE PLASTIC PIPE CORP
Also Called: Heritage Plas An Atkore Intl
861 N Lisbon St (44615-9401)
PHONE...................330 627-8002
Mitch Colly, *Plant Mgr*
EMP: 70 **Publicly Held**
WEB: www.heritageplastics.com
SIC: 3547 Pipe & tube mills
HQ: Atkore Plastic Pipe Corporation
1202 N Bowie Dr
Weatherford TX 76086
817 594-8791

(G-2953)
CARROLL HILLS INDUSTRIES INC
540 High St Nw (44615-1116)
PHONE...................330 627-5524
Fax: 330 627-6605
Matt Champbell, *Superintendent*
Rich Pizzoferrato, *Exec Dir*
Shannan Boone, *Administration*
Vicki Brumback, *Administration*
Diana Strader, *Administration*
EMP: 60
SQ FT: 4,640
SALES: 272K **Privately Held**
SIC: 8331 3999 Sheltered workshop; barber & beauty shop equipment

---

(G-2954)
CARROLLTON PUBLISHING COMPANY
Also Called: Free Press Standard
43 E Main St (44615-1221)
P.O. Box 37 (44615-0037)
PHONE..................330 627-5591
Fax: 330 627-3195
William Peterson, *General Mgr*
Maynard Buck, *Treasurer*
EMP: 12
SQ FT: 4,800
SALES (est): 664.9K Privately Held
WEB: www.freepressstandard.com
SIC: 2711 Newspapers, publishing & printing

(G-2955)
ERNST ENTERPRISES INC
Also Called: Valley Concrete
4710 Soldiers Home Rd (44615)
P.O. Box 638 (44615-0638)
PHONE..................937 866-9441
John McAffee, *General Mgr*
EMP: 25
SALES (corp-wide): 191MM Privately Held
WEB: www.ernstconcrete.com
SIC: 3273 Ready-mixed concrete
PA: Ernst Enterprises, Inc.
3361 Successful Way
Dayton OH 45414
937 233-5555

(G-2956)
FUSION CERAMICS INC (PA)
160 Scio Rd Se (44615-9502)
P.O. Box 127 (44615-0127)
PHONE..................330 627-5821
Fax: 330 627-2082
Richard Hannon Jr, *President*
David Stanton, *General Mgr*
Dave Schneider, *Vice Pres*
John Baker, *VP Mfg*
Richard Yeager, *Buyer*
▼ EMP: 42
SQ FT: 20,000
SALES (est): 8.2MM Privately Held
WEB: www.fusionceramics.com
SIC: 2899 Frit

(G-2957)
JOHN BYLER
Also Called: JW Log and Lumber
5130 Germano Rd Se (44615-9556)
PHONE..................330 627-7635
John W Byler, *Administration*
EMP: 3 EST: 2014
SALES (est): 244.3K Privately Held
SIC: 2411 Logging

(G-2958)
JOMAC LTD
Also Called: Jones Propane Supply
182 Scio Rd Se (44615-8521)
PHONE..................330 627-7727
Fax: 330 627-2508
Richard Jones, *President*
Jack Colaprete, *Sales Associate*
Carlee Leslie, *Marketing Staff*
James Wickline, *Manager*
Lori Jones, *Admin Sec*
EMP: 7
SALES (est): 2.1MM Privately Held
WEB: www.jomacltd.com
SIC: 3441 5984 Fabricated structural metal; propane gas, bottled

(G-2959)
LAKOTA RACING
109 12th St Nw (44615-9456)
PHONE..................330 627-7255
Darlene Sample, *Owner*
EMP: 3
SALES (est): 272.7K Privately Held
WEB: www.lakotaracing.com
SIC: 3714 Motor vehicle engines & parts

(G-2960)
LIBERTY PLASTICS LLC (PA)
861 N Lisbon St (44615-9401)
PHONE..................330 627-6677
Mike Loretto, *CFO*
Larry Davis, *Controller*
Charles McCort, *Mng Member*
EMP: 8 EST: 2012

SALES: 9MM Privately Held
SIC: 2821 Polyvinyl chloride resins (PVC)

(G-2961)
M & M TOBACCO
701 Canton Rd Nw (44615-9447)
PHONE..................330 573-8543
Matt McCune, *Owner*
EMP: 4 EST: 2010
SALES (est): 350K Privately Held
SIC: 3911 Cigar & cigarette accessories

(G-2962)
NOMAC DRILLING LLC
1258 Panda Rd Se (44615-9657)
PHONE..................330 476-7040
EMP: 3
SALES (corp-wide): 1.1B Privately Held
SIC: 1381 Drilling oil & gas wells
HQ: Nomac Drilling, L.L.C.
3400 S Radio Rd
El Reno OK 73036
405 422-2754

(G-2963)
RCE HEAT EXCHANGERS LLC
3165 Folsam Rd Nw (44615-8201)
Rural Route 156cheyen, Malvern (44644)
PHONE..................330 627-0300
Mike Earl, *Managing Prtnr*
Robert Strobel, *Vice Pres*
EMP: 20
SALES (est): 4.4MM Privately Held
SIC: 3443 Heat exchangers, condensers & components

(G-2964)
ROSEBUD MINING COMPANY
Also Called: Kensington Prep Plant
95 N Lisbon St (44615-1325)
PHONE..................330 222-2334
Barry Alexin, *Chief Engr*
Randy Michell, *Manager*
EMP: 25
SALES (corp-wide): 672.6MM Privately Held
WEB: www.lore.com
SIC: 1222 1241 Bituminous coal-underground mining; coal mining services
PA: Rosebud Mining Company
301 Market St
Kittanning PA 16201
724 545-6222

(G-2965)
SEVEN RANGES MFG CORP
330 Industrial Dr Sw (44615-8569)
P.O. Box 206 (44615-0206)
PHONE..................330 627-7155
Fax: 330 627-3797
Fred D Tarr Sr, *President*
David Richard Tarr, *Vice Pres*
Kurt Fogle, *Purch Mgr*
Chris Ulman, *Manager*
EMP: 26
SQ FT: 29,000
SALES (est): 5.5MM Privately Held
WEB: www.sevenranges.com
SIC: 3469 Metal stampings

(G-2966)
SMA PLASTICS LLC
755 N Lisbon St (44615-9401)
PHONE..................330 627-1377
Charles McCort, *CEO*
EMP: 5 EST: 2015
SALES (est): 509.4K Privately Held
SIC: 2611 Pulp manufactured from waste or recycled paper

(G-2967)
T M INDUSTRIES INC
4082 Thrasher Rd Sw (44615-9516)
PHONE..................330 627-4410
Mary Sowko, *President*
John Sowko, *Vice Pres*
EMP: 4 EST: 1975
SQ FT: 2,500
SALES: 800K Privately Held
SIC: 5085 7699 3545 Tools; tool repair services; cutting tools for machine tools

(G-2968)
TWIN CITIES CONCRETE CO
1031 Kensington Rd Ne (44615-9403)
P.O. Box 400, Dover (44622-0400)
PHONE..................330 627-2158
Fax: 330 627-7576
Louis Cline, *Manager*
EMP: 5
SALES (corp-wide): 28.6B Privately Held
SIC: 3273 Ready-mixed concrete
HQ: Twin Cities Concrete Co
141 S Tuscarawas Ave
Dover OH 44622
330 343-4491

(G-2969)
WENDELL MACHINE SHOP
2076 Mobile Rd Ne (44615-9796)
PHONE..................330 627-3480
Jeff Wendell, *Owner*
EMP: 3 EST: 1992
SALES (est): 211.2K Privately Held
SIC: 3599 Machine & other job shop work

Casstown
Miami County

(G-2970)
JED TOOL COMPANY
8058 E Troy Urbana Rd (45312-9729)
PHONE..................937 857-9222
Fax: 937 857-9122
John Deford, *Owner*
EMP: 3
SALES: 100K Privately Held
SIC: 3599 Machine shop, jobbing & repair

(G-2971)
STEEL AVIATION AIRCRAFT SALES
4433 E State Route 55 (45312-9579)
PHONE..................937 332-7587
Jaime Steel, *Principal*
EMP: 7
SALES (est): 837.4K Privately Held
WEB: www.steelaviation.com
SIC: 3721 Airplanes, fixed or rotary wing

Castalia
Erie County

(G-2972)
ABJ EQUIPFIX
202 Lucas St W (44824-9254)
PHONE..................419 684-5236
Alan D Strause, *CEO*
EMP: 20
SQ FT: 7,000
SALES: 210K Privately Held
WEB: www.abjequipfix.com
SIC: 7699 3556 Industrial machinery & equipment repair; food products machinery

(G-2973)
CASTALIA TRENCHING & READY MIX
4814 State Route 269 S (44824-9359)
PHONE..................419 684-5502
Fax: 419 684-5756
Francis Winkel, *President*
James Winkel, *Corp Secy*
John Winkel, *Vice Pres*
Larry Winkel, *Vice Pres*
EMP: 10 EST: 1954
SQ FT: 8,000
SALES (est): 1.7MM Privately Held
SIC: 3273 1794 Ready-mixed concrete; excavation work

(G-2974)
ECI
8802 Portland Rd (44824-9259)
PHONE..................419 483-2738
Marvin Brenzo, *Principal*
EMP: 3 EST: 2010
SALES (est): 251.4K Privately Held
SIC: 3273 Ready-mixed concrete

(G-2975)
ERIE MATERIALS INC
Also Called: Erie Black Top
9200 Portland Rd (44824)
PHONE..................419 483-4648
Dave Misinec, *Manager*
EMP: 5
SALES (corp-wide): 45.6MM Privately Held
WEB: www.eriematerials.com
SIC: 2951 5032 Asphalt paving mixtures & blocks; paving materials
PA: Erie Materials, Inc.
4507 Tiffin Ave
Sandusky OH 44870
419 625-7374

(G-2976)
HANSON AGGREGATES EAST LLC
9220 Portland Rd (44824-9260)
PHONE..................419 483-4390
Gregory Russell, *Plant Mgr*
Tera Thornhill, *Manager*
EMP: 67
SQ FT: 3,200
SALES (corp-wide): 16B Privately Held
SIC: 1422 3274 Limestones, ground; lime
HQ: Hanson Aggregates East Llc
3131 Rdu Center Dr
Morrisville NC 27560
919 380-2500

(G-2977)
LOCKER ROOM LETTERING LTD
7316 Magill Rd (44824-9303)
PHONE..................419 359-1761
Fax: 419 684-7040
James Barton, *Owner*
EMP: 4
SQ FT: 2,500
SALES (est): 210K Privately Held
SIC: 2759 2395 5611 5621 Screen printing; embroidery products, except schiffli machine; clothing, sportswear, men's & boys'; women's sportswear; children's wear

(G-2978)
WALLSEYE CONCRETE CORP
8802 Portland Rd (44824-9259)
PHONE..................419 483-2738
Fax: 419 483-2158
Marvin Brenzo, *Manager*
EMP: 10
SALES (corp-wide): 833.3K Privately Held
SIC: 3241 5032 Portland cement; brick, stone & related material
PA: Wallseye Concrete Corp.
26000 Sprague Rd
Cleveland OH 44138
440 235-1800

Cecil
Paulding County

(G-2979)
BAKER-SHINDLER CONTRACTING CO
Also Called: Baker-Shindler Ready Mix
121 German St (45821)
PHONE..................419 399-4841
John Clellan, *Manager*
EMP: 4
SALES (corp-wide): 6.7MM Privately Held
SIC: 3273 Ready-mixed concrete
PA: The Baker-Shindler Contracting Company
525 Cleveland Ave
Defiance OH 43512
419 782-5080

Cedarville
Greene County

(G-2980)
APPLIED SCIENCES INC (PA)
141 W Xenia Ave (45314-9529)
P.O. Box 579 (45314-0579)
PHONE..............................937 766-2020
Fax: 937 766-5886
Max Lake, *President*
Inga Lake, *Vice Pres*
Robert Alig, *Senior Engr*
Benjamin Casto, *Sales Staff*
John Cushman, *Maintence Staff*
EMP: 35
SQ FT: 6,600
SALES (est): 5.6MM **Privately Held**
SIC: 8731 3624 Commercial research laboratory; carbon & graphite products

(G-2981)
MARIETTA MARTIN MATERIALS INC
Also Called: Martin Marietta Aggregates
3744 Turnbull Rd (45314-9429)
P.O. Box 577 (45314-0577)
PHONE..............................937 766-2351
Fax: 937 766-2419
Ken Holland, *Principal*
EMP: 21
SALES (corp-wide): 3.8B **Publicly Held**
WEB: www.martinmarietta.com
SIC: 1442 Sand mining
PA: Martin Marietta Materials Inc
2710 Wycliff Rd
Raleigh NC 27607
919 781-4550

(G-2982)
MARTIN MARIETTA MATERIALS INC
Also Called: Cedarville Quarry
3744 Turnbull Rd (45314-9429)
PHONE..............................937 766-2351
Brian Parks, *Manager*
EMP: 20
SALES (corp-wide): 3.8B **Publicly Held**
WEB: www.martinmarietta.com
SIC: 1423 Crushed & broken granite
PA: Martin Marietta Materials Inc
2710 Wycliff Rd
Raleigh NC 27607
919 781-4550

(G-2983)
PYROGRAF PRODUCTS INC
154 W Xenia Ave (45314-9529)
P.O. Box 579 (45314-0579)
PHONE..............................937 766-2020
Max Lake, *President*
John Mackay, *Mktg Dir*
Margy Rochon, *Manager*
Inga Lake, *Admin Sec*
EMP: 18 EST: 1996
SQ FT: 6,600
SALES (est): 2.8MM
SALES (corp-wide): 5.6MM **Privately Held**
SIC: 3624 Carbon & graphite products
PA: Applied Sciences Inc.
141 W Xenia Ave
Cedarville OH 45314
937 766-2020

Celina
Mercer County

(G-2984)
1 IRON GOLF INC
504 Maplewood Ln (45822-2964)
PHONE..............................419 662-9336
David Lake, *President*
Kathy Lake, *Vice Pres*
▲ EMP: 4
SALES: 200K **Privately Held**
SIC: 3949 Shafts, golf club

(G-2985)
ALUMACAST LLC
300 N Brandon Ave (45822-1672)
PHONE..............................419 584-1473
Fax: 419 580-0133
Cindy Reinsinger, *Manager*
Cindy Reisinger, *Manager*
Gary Holmes, *Executive*
Richard W Kaylor,
Garry Kuess,
EMP: 5
SALES (est): 320K **Privately Held**
SIC: 3363 Aluminum die-castings

(G-2986)
B HOGENKAMP & R HARLAMERT ✪
Also Called: Grand Slam Acres
3145 Hartke Rd (45822-9570)
PHONE..............................419 925-0526
Joseph Harlamert, *Partner*
Renea Harlamert, *Partner*
Bernard Hogenkamp, *Partner*
Christopher Miller, *Partner*
Jill Miller, *Partner*
EMP: 4 EST: 2017
SALES (est): 158.2K **Privately Held**
SIC: 2411 Saw logs

(G-2987)
C & M WELDING SERVICES LLC
1405 James Dr (45822-9482)
PHONE..............................419 584-0008
Charles Zehringer, *Mng Member*
Rachel Gregg, *Manager*
Mike Huelsman,
EMP: 5
SQ FT: 800
SALES: 450K **Privately Held**
SIC: 7692 5999 Welding repair; welding supplies

(G-2988)
CABINETRY BY EBBING
5765 State Route 219 (45822-9513)
PHONE..............................419 678-2191
Fax: 419 678-1035
Michael J Ebbing, *Owner*
Cindy Ebbing, *Office Mgr*
EMP: 5
SALES: 650K **Privately Held**
WEB: www.cabinetrybyebbing.com
SIC: 2434 Wood kitchen cabinets; vanities, bathroom: wood

(G-2989)
CELINA ALUM PRECISION TECH INC
Also Called: Capt
7059 Staeger Rd (45822-9395)
PHONE..............................419 586-2278
Fax: 419 586-6474
Takenori Yamaguchi, *President*
Jay James, *Senior VP*
Shelley Young, *Safety Dir*
Jason Silliman, *Plant Supt*
Siegbert Fendert, *Prdtn Mgr*
▲ EMP: 500
SQ FT: 160,000
SALES (est): 136.3MM
SALES (corp-wide): 124.7B **Privately Held**
WEB: www.capt-celina.com
SIC: 3592 Pistons & piston rings
HQ: Honda Foundry Co.,Ltd.
1620, Matoba
Kawagoe STM 350-1
492 311-521

(G-2990)
CELINA TENT INC
Also Called: Celina Industries
5373 State Route 29 (45822-9210)
PHONE..............................419 586-3610
Jeff Grieshop, *President*
Janice Grieshop, *Corp Secy*
Jonathon Reese, *Opers Mgr*
Shannon Schwieterman, *Opers Staff*
Allan Bruns, *Design Engr*
▼ EMP: 48
SQ FT: 27,000
SALES (est): 7.5MM **Privately Held**
WEB: www.celinatent.com
SIC: 2394 Tents: made from purchased materials

(G-2991)
CROWN EQUIPMENT CORPORATION
Also Called: Crown Lift Trucks
410 Grand Lake Rd (45822-1869)
PHONE..............................419 586-1100
Chuck Post, *Branch Mgr*
EMP: 719
SALES (corp-wide): 5.5B **Privately Held**
SIC: 3537 Lift trucks, industrial: fork, platform, straddle, etc.
PA: Crown Equipment Corporation
44 S Washington St
New Bremen OH 45869
419 629-2311

(G-2992)
DOLL INC
Also Called: Doll Printing
1901 Havemann Rd (45822)
PHONE..............................419 586-7880
Robert A Doll, *President*
Phyllis Doll, *Corp Secy*
Doll Smith, *Exec Dir*
Jim Scott, *Bd of Directors*
EMP: 8
SQ FT: 6,200
SALES: 800K **Privately Held**
WEB: www.dollprinting.com
SIC: 2752 Commercial printing, lithographic; commercial printing, offset

(G-2993)
E L DAVIS INC
Also Called: Davis Welding Company
6032 State Route 219 (45822-8523)
PHONE..............................419 268-2004
Edward L Davis, *President*
Phyllis Davis, *Vice Pres*
EMP: 5
SQ FT: 2,000
SALES: 550K **Privately Held**
SIC: 7692 Welding repair

(G-2994)
EIGHTH FLOOR PROMOTIONS
Also Called: Awardcraft
1 Visions Pkwy (45822-7500)
PHONE..............................419 586-6433
Dave Willis, *President*
Mike Schuffenhauer, *COO*
Les Dorfman, *Senior VP*
Heather Hoffman, *Cust Mgr*
John Helsman, *Manager*
▲ EMP: 190
SQ FT: 83,000
SALES (est): 24.3MM **Privately Held**
WEB: www.awardcraft.com
SIC: 3993 Signs & advertising specialties

(G-2995)
ERGO DESKTOP LLC
457 Grand Lake Rd (45822-1839)
P.O. Box 2116 (45822)
PHONE..............................567 890-3746
Derrick Walls, *Finance*
Kathy Sharkey, *Mng Member*
Daniel Sharkey,
EMP: 23
SQ FT: 2,500
SALES: 6MM **Privately Held**
SIC: 2522 7389 Office furniture, except wood;

(G-2996)
ESM PRODUCTS INC
5445 Behm Rd Lot 5 (45822-8146)
PHONE..............................937 492-4644
John Elliott, *President*
Tom Elliott, *Corp Secy*
Dave Elliott, *Vice Pres*
EMP: 8
SQ FT: 4,400
SALES (est): 751.7K **Privately Held**
SIC: 3312 Tool & die steel & alloys

(G-2997)
FALLEN OAK CANDLES INC
917 Lilac St (45822-1326)
PHONE..............................419 204-8162
Brian Brim, *President*
EMP: 7
SALES: 20K **Privately Held**
SIC: 3999 Manufacturing industries

(G-2998)
FUEL AMERICA
204 E Market St (45822-1733)
PHONE..............................419 586-5609
Fax: 419 586-5609
Penny Zizelman, *Principal*
EMP: 3
SALES (est): 168.1K **Privately Held**
SIC: 2869 Fuels

(G-2999)
H & S COMPANY INC
7219 Harris Rd (45822-9370)
PHONE..............................419 394-4444
Fax: 419 394-4789
Kurtis Hoelscher, *President*
Eric Schuler, *Engineer*
Kellie Hoelscher, *Finance*
EMP: 15
SQ FT: 6,480
SALES (est): 4.1MM **Privately Held**
WEB: www.wheeledtrenchers.com
SIC: 3533 3523 Oil field machinery & equipment; farm machinery & equipment

(G-3000)
HAULETTE MANUFACTURING INC
8271 Us Route 127 (45822-9416)
PHONE..............................419 586-1717
Fred Kremer, *CEO*
Steven Braun, *President*
Eric Nieberding, *Vice Pres*
Kevin Hagaman, *Plant Mgr*
Oliver Giere, *Treasurer*
EMP: 53
SQ FT: 50,000
SALES: 5.5MM **Privately Held**
WEB: www.haulette.com
SIC: 3599 3715 Machine shop, jobbing & repair; trailer bodies

(G-3001)
HEITKAMP & KREMER PRINTING
Also Called: Messenger Press
6184 State Route 274 (45822-9505)
PHONE..............................419 925-4121
Fax: 419 925-5311
Alan Kremer, *President*
Mitch Kremer, *COO*
Randy Heitkamp, *Vice Pres*
Susan Heitkamp, *Mktg Dir*
Sarah Mescher, *Mktg Dir*
EMP: 9
SALES (est): 1.5MM **Privately Held**
WEB: www.messenger-press.com
SIC: 2752 Commercial printing, lithographic

(G-3002)
HOLES CUSTOM WOODWORKING
6875 Nancy Ave (45822-9268)
PHONE..............................419 586-8171
Jane Hole, *Principal*
EMP: 4
SALES (est): 369.4K **Privately Held**
SIC: 2431 Millwork

(G-3003)
JAVANATION
108 S Main St (45822-2228)
PHONE..............................419 584-1705
Fax: 419 584-1705
Vance Nation, *Owner*
EMP: 10
SALES (est): 162.3K **Privately Held**
SIC: 3269 Pottery products

(G-3004)
JES FOODS/CELINA INC
1800 Industrial Dr (45822-1376)
PHONE..............................419 586-7446
Elaine Freed, *President*
William Freed, *Vice Pres*
Eric Freed, *Plant Mgr*
EMP: 25
SQ FT: 24,000

▲ = Import ▼ =Export
◆ =Import/Export

SALES (est): 3.9MM
SALES (corp-wide): 5.3MM **Privately Held**
WEB: www.jesfoods.com
SIC: 2033 2035 2032 Canned fruits & specialties; pickles, sauces & salad dressings; canned specialties
PA: J.E.S. Foods, Inc.
4733 Broadway Ave
Cleveland OH 44127
216 883-8987

(G-3005)
M S K PARTNERSHIP
7219 Harris Rd (45822-9370)
PHONE 419 394-4444
Shirley Hoelsher, *Partner*
Kurt Hoelsher, *Partner*
Michael Hoelsher, *Partner*
EMP: 5
SALES (est): 759.6K **Privately Held**
SIC: 3531 Entrenching machines

(G-3006)
MACHINE-PRO TECHNOLOGIES INC
1321 W Market St (45822-9285)
PHONE 419 584-0086
Fax: 419 584-0091
Tim Klosterman, *President*
Joe Sullivan, *QC Mgr*
Sandy Bettinger, *Admin Sec*
▲ **EMP:** 57
SQ FT: 24,000
SALES (est): 11.1MM **Privately Held**
WEB: www.machine-pro.com
SIC: 3599 Machine shop, jobbing & repair

(G-3007)
MCSPORTS
1945 Havemann Rd (45822-9390)
PHONE 419 586-5555
Tony Bidlack, *Manager*
EMP: 3 **EST:** 2009
SALES (est): 86.2K **Privately Held**
SIC: 7999 5941 5091 3949 Sporting goods rental; sporting goods & bicycle shops; sporting & recreation goods; sporting & athletic goods

(G-3008)
METAL CUTTING TECHNOLOGY LLC
5410 Golden Pond Rd (45822-7157)
PHONE 419 733-1236
Larry M Pond, *Mng Member*
EMP: 4
SALES: 1.5MM **Privately Held**
SIC: 3541 Machine tools, metal cutting type

(G-3009)
MIAMI VALLEY PIZZA HUT INC
1152 E Market St (45822-1934)
PHONE 419 586-5900
Fax: 419 586-9642
Karen Rowland, *Manager*
Karen Roland,
EMP: 35
SALES (corp-wide): 4.2MM **Privately Held**
SIC: 5812 2099 Pizzeria, chain; food preparations
PA: Miami Valley Pizza Hut Inc
7665 Monarch Ct Ste 111
West Chester OH 45069
513 777-8434

(G-3010)
MSK TRENCHER MFG INC
7219 Harris Rd (45822-9370)
PHONE 419 394-4444
Kurtis Hoelscher, *President*
Kellie Hoelscher, *Corp Secy*
Kellie Hoelscher, *Office Mgr*
EMP: 10
SALES (est): 2MM **Privately Held**
SIC: 3531 Construction machinery

(G-3011)
MY SCRAPBOOK PARADISE LLC
202 S Main St (45822-2229)
P.O. Box 272 (45822-0272)
PHONE 419 584-1393
Brenda Leseld, *Owner*
EMP: 3

SALES (est): 229.1K **Privately Held**
SIC: 2782 Scrapbooks

(G-3012)
PAX MACHINE WORKS INC
5139 Monroe Rd (45822-9033)
P.O. Box 338 (45822-0338)
PHONE 419 586-2337
Fax: 419 586-7123
Michael Pax, *President*
Francis J Pax, *Vice Pres*
Carol Knapke, *Human Res Mgr*
Gretchen Kifer, *Director*
Deborah Guingnch, *Bd of Directors*
▼ **EMP:** 127 **EST:** 1948
SQ FT: 326,723
SALES: 1.8MM **Privately Held**
WEB: www.paxmachine.com
SIC: 3469 Metal stampings

(G-3013)
PAX PRODUCTS INC
5097 Monroe Rd (45822-9033)
P.O. Box 257 (45822-0257)
PHONE 419 586-2337
Fax: 419 586-6932
Francis J Pax, *President*
Steven Pax, *Vice Pres*
Michael Pax, *Treasurer*
Sherry Wappelhorst, *Accountant*
Patt Ontrop, *Marketing Mgr*
EMP: 11
SQ FT: 36,500
SALES (est): 2.8MM **Privately Held**
SIC: 3569 Lubricating equipment

(G-3014)
PHI WERKES LLC
1201 Havemann Rd (45822-1391)
PHONE 419 586-9222
Scott Hoenie,
Kevin Pohlman,
EMP: 8
SQ FT: 13,800
SALES (est): 498.4K **Privately Held**
SIC: 3599 Machine shop, jobbing & repair

(G-3015)
POTTER HOUSE
108 S Main St (45822-2228)
PHONE 419 584-1705
Kimberly Nation, *Owner*
EMP: 4
SALES (est): 464.4K **Privately Held**
SIC: 3269 Firing & decorating china

(G-3016)
RENOIR VISIONS LLC
Also Called: Accents By Renoir
1 Visions Pkwy (45822-7500)
PHONE 419 586-5679
Joe Knapschaefer, *Personnel*
Tom Meyer,
Lisa Hicks, *Administration*
Kent Paxson,
Dav Willis,
EMP: 12
SQ FT: 65,000
SALES (est): 1.2MM **Privately Held**
SIC: 3993 5094 Signs & advertising specialties; jewelry & precious stones

(G-3017)
REYNOLDS AND REYNOLDS COMPANY
824 Murlin Ave (45822-2459)
P.O. Box 999 (45822-0999)
PHONE 419 584-7000
Fax: 419 584-7586
Michael Craig, *Plant Mgr*
Dan Wellman, *Plant Mgr*
Ed Hettescheimer, *QC Mgr*
Don Kramer, *Plant Engr*
Ned Lawler, *Plant Engr*
EMP: 10
SALES (corp-wide): 1.4B **Privately Held**
WEB: www.reyrey.com
SIC: 2761 2759 2752 Manifold business forms; commercial printing; commercial printing, lithographic
HQ: The Reynolds And Reynolds Company
1 Reynolds Way
Kettering OH 45430
937 485-2000

(G-3018)
SOCIETY OF THE PRECIOUS BLOOD
Also Called: Messinger Press
2860 Us Route 127 (45822-9533)
PHONE 419 925-4516
Fax: 419 925-4800
Fr James Seibert, *Branch Mgr*
EMP: 40
SALES (corp-wide): 741.5K **Privately Held**
WEB: www.cpps-preciousblood.org
SIC: 2732 8661 8211 Pamphlets: printing only, not published on site; Brethren Church; private elementary & secondary schools
PA: The Society Of The Precious Blood
431 E 2nd St
Dayton OH 45402
937 228-9263

(G-3019)
STANDARD PRINTING CO INC
Also Called: Daily Standard The
123 E Market St (45822-1730)
P.O. Box 140 (45822-0140)
PHONE 419 586-2371
Fax: 419 586-6271
Frank Snyder, *President*
Dave Hoying, *Business Mgr*
Diane Buening, *Opers-Prdtn-Mfg*
Judith Ocallaghan, *Engineer*
John Lake, *Adv Mgr*
EMP: 45
SQ FT: 20,000
SALES (est): 3.5MM **Privately Held**
WEB: www.dailystandard.com
SIC: 2711 Newspapers, publishing & printing

(G-3020)
TECH SOLUTIONS LLC
Also Called: Instantorder
658 N Main St (45822-1463)
PHONE 419 852-7190
EMP: 8
SALES: 200K **Privately Held**
SIC: 7371 5961 7372 Computer software development & applications; food, mail order; application computer software

(G-3021)
THEES MACHINE & TOOL CO
2007 State Route 703 (45822-2525)
PHONE 419 586-4766
Fax: 419 586-5776
John E Thees, *President*
Carolann Thees, *Vice Pres*
EMP: 6
SQ FT: 7,000
SALES: 275K **Privately Held**
SIC: 3599 Machine shop, jobbing & repair

(G-3022)
THIEMAN TAILGATES INC
600 E Wayne St (45822-1566)
PHONE 419 586-7727
Fax: 419 586-9724
Thomas A Thieman, *President*
Randy Counts, *Vice Pres*
Todd Thieman, *Vice Pres*
David McMurray, *Purch Mgr*
Adrian Gutierrez, *Purchasing*
EMP: 90
SQ FT: 90,000
SALES (est): 28.7MM **Privately Held**
SIC: 3537 Trucks, tractors, loaders, carriers & similar equipment

(G-3023)
TIN-SAU LLC
1406 Canterbury Dr (45822-1183)
PHONE 419 586-8886
Christopher Sauer, *Principal*
EMP: 3
SALES (est): 236.4K **Privately Held**
SIC: 3356 Tin

(G-3024)
TOUCHPINT CMPLETE SLUTIONS LLC
1978 Havemann Rd (45822-9300)
P.O. Box 252 (45822-0252)
PHONE 419 919-3222
Kam Majd, *President*

Lori Majd,
Rodney K Paxson,
EMP: 3
SALES (est): 157.4K **Privately Held**
SIC: 2511 2599 5021 5087 Racks, book & magazine: wood; bar, restaurant & cafeteria furniture; racks; restaurant supplies

(G-3025)
UNIQUE WOODMASTERS LLC
6750 Guadalupe Rd (45822-9545)
PHONE 419 268-9663
William Schoen,
Lawrence Schoen,
Robert Schoen,
EMP: 3
SALES (est): 348.1K **Privately Held**
SIC: 2434 Wood kitchen cabinets

(G-3026)
VERSA-PAK LTD
500 Staeger Rd (45822-9373)
P.O. Box 69 (45822-0069)
PHONE 419 586-5466
Fax: 419 586-1431
Tara Kathy, *Plant Mgr*
Michael Brunswick, *Manager*
Jeff Knapke, *Manager*
Neal Vogel, *Maintence Staff*
EMP: 45
SQ FT: 23,000
SALES (est): 16.7MM **Privately Held**
WEB: www.versa-pak.com
SIC: 2821 Thermoplastic materials

(G-3027)
WELDTEC INC
8319 Us Route 127 (45822-9416)
PHONE 419 394-9440
Henry B Hoskins, *President*
Anthony D Hoskins, *Treasurer*
Don Sthwieterman, *Office Mgr*
EMP: 19
SQ FT: 76,000
SALES (est): 4.5MM **Privately Held**
SIC: 3441 Fabricated structural metal

(G-3028)
WELDTEC LTD
8319 Us Route 127 (45822-9416)
PHONE 419 394-9440
Henry Hoskins, *Partner*
Tony Hoskins, *Partner*
EMP: 5
SALES (est): 696.2K **Privately Held**
SIC: 3441 Fabricated structural metal

Centerburg
Knox County

(G-3029)
COLUMBUS MOBILE WELDING
110 S Preston St (43011-9779)
PHONE 614 352-6052
David Stewart, *Principal*
EMP: 3
SALES (est): 115.4K **Privately Held**
SIC: 7692 Welding repair

(G-3030)
DANIS SWEET CUPCAKES
283 N Clayton St (43011-7089)
PHONE 614 581-8978
Christina Halley, *Manager*
EMP: 4 **EST:** 2013
SALES (est): 226.7K **Privately Held**
SIC: 2051 Bread, cake & related products

(G-3031)
TRADYE MACHINE & TOOL INC
3116a Wilson Rd (43011)
PHONE 740 625-7550
Fax: 740 625-9622
Tracy Payne, *President*
Diana Payne, *Manager*
EMP: 7
SQ FT: 12,000
SALES: 900K **Privately Held**
SIC: 3544 3599 Special dies, tools, jigs & fixtures; machine shop, jobbing & repair

GEOGRAPHIC

Centerville
Montgomery County

(G-3032)
ADAPTIVE DATA INC
93 W Franklin St (45459-4770)
PHONE............................937 436-2343
Fax: 937 436-2344
Timothy Gribler, *President*
Mike Barker, *Manager*
Jerry Gribler, *Admin Sec*
EMP: 10
SALES (est): 2.1MM Privately Held
WEB: www.adi-barcode.com
SIC: 2679 3955 3577 2671 Labels,
paper: made from purchased material;
carbon paper & inked ribbons; computer
peripheral equipment; packaging paper &
plastics film, coated & laminated

(G-3033)
**ADVANCED MEDICAL
SOLUTIONS INC**
Also Called: Next Step
7026 Corp Way Ste 116 (45459)
PHONE............................937 291-0069
Fax: 937 291-9512
Mark Abraham, *President*
EMP: 3
SALES (est): 388.2K Privately Held
SIC: 2834 3841 Medicines, capsuled or
ampuled; medical instruments & equip-
ment, blood & bone work

(G-3034)
AEROSEAL LLC (PA)
7989 S Suburban Rd (45458-2702)
PHONE............................937 428-9300
Amit Gupta, *CEO*
Vijay Kollepara, *Vice Pres*
Neal Walsh, *Vice Pres*
Aaron Newell, *Accountant*
David Benfer, *Regl Sales Mgr*
▲ EMP: 33
SALES (est): 6.5MM Privately Held
SIC: 3679 Hermetic seals for electronic
equipment

(G-3035)
**AMERICAN SPORTS DESIGN
COMPANY**
Also Called: Airborne
6551 Centervl Bus Pkwy (45459-2686)
PHONE............................937 865-5431
Michael Buenzow, *President*
Nancy Michaud, *Senior VP*
EMP: 70
SALES (est): 3.2MM
SALES (corp-wide): 44MM Privately
Held
WEB: www.huffy.com
SIC: 3949 Basketball equipment & sup-
plies, general
PA: Huffy Corporation
6551 Centervl Bus Pkwy
Centerville OH 45459
937 865-2800

(G-3036)
BAILEY & JENSEN INC
442 Yankee Trace Dr (45458-3980)
PHONE............................937 272-1784
Sharon Bailey, *CEO*
EMP: 15 EST: 2012
SALES (est): 547.9K Privately Held
SIC: 2514 Metal household furniture

(G-3037)
**BEACON AUDIO VIDEO
SYSTEMS INC**
155 N Main St (45459-4620)
PHONE............................937 723-9587
Robert R Hopper, *President*
EMP: 7
SQ FT: 5,500
SALES: 900K Privately Held
SIC: 3651 Home entertainment equipment,
electronic

(G-3038)
CARLY CO LLC
235 N Main St (45459-4617)
PHONE............................937 477-6411
Robin Grushon,
Mike Grushon,
EMP: 4
SALES: 120K Privately Held
SIC: 3633 Laundry dryers, household or
coin-operated

(G-3039)
**DIMCOGRAY CORPORATION
(PA)**
Also Called: Dimco-Gray Company
900 Dimco Way (45458-2709)
PHONE............................937 433-7600
Michael Sieron, *CEO*
T Holton, *Counsel*
Jim Daulton, *Mfg Staff*
Vince Ferraro, *Purchasing*
Katherine Hunt, *QC Mgr*
▲ EMP: 90 EST: 1924
SQ FT: 48,000
SALES (est): 10.8MM Privately Held
WEB: www.dimcogray.com
SIC: 3089 3873 3965 3625 Plastic pro-
cessing; watches, clocks, watchcases &
parts; fasteners; relays & industrial con-
trols; bolts, nuts, rivets & washers

(G-3040)
**DIVERSE ACQUISITIONS GROUP
LLC**
5021 Lausanne Dr (45458-3001)
PHONE............................888 232-1546
Shaun Ahmad, *Managing Prtnr*
Jimario Dyson, *Managing Prtnr*
Sarwar Khobaib, *Managing Prtnr*
Cameron Moore, *Managing Prtnr*
EMP: 15 EST: 2015
SALES (est): 639.5K Privately Held
SIC: 2086 Mineral water, carbonated:
packaged in cans, bottles, etc.

(G-3041)
EVOLUTION RESOURCES LLC
480 Congress Park Dr (45459-4144)
PHONE............................937 438-2390
Donald Cain, *CFO*
Chuck Biehn Jr,
▲ EMP: 3
SQ FT: 10,000
SALES: 500K Privately Held
WEB: www.evolve-now.net
SIC: 3421 5084 Knife blades & blanks;
machine tools & accessories

(G-3042)
FOUNTAIN OF YOUTH
450 N Main St Ste 100 (45459-4466)
PHONE............................937 723-9743
Estaban Pena, *Principal*
EMP: 6
SALES (est): 530.1K Privately Held
SIC: 3841 Surgical lasers

(G-3043)
HUFFY CORPORATION (PA)
Also Called: Huffy Bicycle Company
6551 Centervl Bus Pkwy (45459-2686)
PHONE............................937 865-2800
William A Smith, *President*
John Collins, *President*
H M Huffman, *Principal*
R D Hughes, *Principal*
R H McKee, *Principal*
▲ EMP: 100 EST: 1928
SQ FT: 47,000
SALES (est): 44MM Privately Held
WEB: www.huffy.com
SIC: 3949 3751 Basketball equipment &
supplies, general; motor scooters & parts

(G-3044)
MBENZTECH
5528 Liberty Bell Cir (45459-7913)
PHONE............................937 291-1527
Joseph S Johnson, *Principal*
EMP: 4
SALES: 50K Privately Held
SIC: 5045 3571 7389 Computers, periph-
erals & software; electronic computers;

(G-3045)
**TOP TIER STORAGE PRODCUTS
LLC**
6501 Centerville Business (45459-2686)
PHONE............................937 242-6133
Scott Umina, *President*
▲ EMP: 4
SQ FT: 20,000
SALES: 200K Privately Held
SIC: 3429 Door locks, bolts & checks

Chagrin Falls
Cuyahoga County

(G-3046)
1-2-3 GLUTEN FREE INC
125 Orange Tree Dr (44022-1560)
PHONE............................216 378-9233
Kim Ullner, *Principal*
EMP: 6 EST: 2007
SALES (est): 946.2K Privately Held
SIC: 2041 Flour mixes

(G-3047)
11 92 HOLDINGS LLC
8 E Washington St Ste 200 (44022-3057)
PHONE............................216 920-7790
Mike Owens, *Principal*
EMP: 30
SALES (est): 2MM
SALES (corp-wide): 8.1MM Privately
Held
SIC: 2591 Blinds vertical
PA: Vertical Knowledge Llc
8 E Washington St Ste 200
Chagrin Falls OH 44022
216 920-7790

(G-3048)
APPLELANE PRESS LLC
37 Forest Dr (44022-4114)
PHONE............................440 543-6747
Eric Beversluis, *Principal*
EMP: 3
SALES (est): 115K Privately Held
SIC: 2711 Newspapers

(G-3049)
BELKIN PRODUCTION
44 N Main St (44022-3023)
PHONE............................440 247-2722
Fax: 440 247-2722
Myron Belkin, *President*
EMP: 23 EST: 1976
SQ FT: 4,000
SALES (est): 3.6MM Privately Held
SIC: 3652 Pre-recorded records & tapes

(G-3050)
BREWER INDUSTRIES LLC
318 Bentleyville Rd (44022-2414)
PHONE............................216 469-0808
Paul Seegott, *Owner*
EMP: 4
SALES: 500K Privately Held
SIC: 2899 Chemical preparations

(G-3051)
**CHAGRIN VALLEY PUBLISHING
CO**
Also Called: Chagrin Valley Times
525 Washington St (44022-4455)
P.O. Box 150 (44022-0150)
PHONE............................440 247-5335
Fax: 440 247-5335
Harold Douthit, *President*
David Lange, *Advt Staff*
EMP: 200
SQ FT: 4,000
SALES (est): 10.5MM Privately Held
WEB: www.chagrinvalleytimes.com
SIC: 2711 Newspapers: publishing only,
not printed on site

(G-3052)
**CLEVELAND LETTER SERVICE
INC**
8351 Clover Ln (44022-3810)
PHONE............................216 781-8300
Fax: 216 781-7454
Charles E Janes, *President*
EMP: 20 EST: 1945

SQ FT: 12,000
SALES (est): 1MM Privately Held
WEB: www.clevelandletter.com
SIC: 7331 2752 2789 Addressing service;
mailing service; commercial printing, off-
set; bookbinding & related work

(G-3053)
CLICK IT CONNECT CORP (PA)
Also Called: Clickit
16 S Main St (44022-3218)
P.O. Box 2 (44022-0002)
PHONE............................440 247-4998
Danette Harlow, *COO*
EMP: 5
SALES (est): 1.1MM Privately Held
SIC: 7378 7372 7379 Computer mainte-
nance & repair; computer & data process-
ing equipment repair/maintenance;
computer peripheral equipment repair &
maintenance; application computer soft-
ware; computer related consulting serv-
ices

(G-3054)
**CORNERSTONE INDUS
HOLDINGS (PA)**
100 Park Pl (44022-4442)
PHONE............................440 893-9144
Joseph G Teague, *Ch of Bd*
Michael C Adams, *President*
Todd McCuaig, *Managing Dir*
Mark W Teague, *Shareholder*
EMP: 3
SALES (est): 8.5MM Privately Held
SIC: 3053 3644 2891 2821 Gaskets &
sealing devices; gaskets, all materials; in-
sulators & insulation materials, electrical;
adhesives & sealants; plastics materials &
resins; die-cut paper & board

(G-3055)
**DOUGLAS W & B C
RICHARDSON**
62 Wychwood Dr (44022-6853)
PHONE............................440 247-5262
Barbara C Richardson, *Principal*
EMP: 3
SALES (est): 190K Privately Held
SIC: 2992 Lubricating oils & greases

(G-3056)
E L OSTENDORF INC
Also Called: Shuler International
3425 Roundwood Rd (44022-6634)
PHONE............................440 247-7631
Ed L Ostendorf, *President*
EMP: 7
SQ FT: 12,000
SALES (est): 340.5K Privately Held
SIC: 6531 3645 Real estate agent, com-
mercial; residential lighting fixtures

(G-3057)
E-Z GRADER COMPANY
300 Industrial Pkwy Ste A (44022-4420)
P.O. Box 23608 (44023-0608)
PHONE............................440 247-7511
Fax: 440 247-0484
Jill Richards, *President*
Bruce Richards, *Vice Pres*
EMP: 8 EST: 1952
SALES (est): 922.5K Privately Held
WEB: www.ezgrader.com
SIC: 5961 2679 Educational supplies &
equipment, mail order; paperboard prod-
ucts, converted

(G-3058)
EDMAR CHEMICAL COMPANY
539 Washington St (44022-4407)
P.O. Box 598 (44022-0598)
PHONE............................440 247-9560
Fax: 440 247-9630
Jack Binder, *President*
Jack Ahern, *Treasurer*
Dan Berick, *Admin Sec*
EMP: 9 EST: 1940
SALES (est): 1.6MM Privately Held
SIC: 2841 2842 Soap: granulated, liquid,
cake, flaked or chip; fabric softeners

(G-3059)
FLIPSIDE INC (PA)
44 N Main St (44022-3023)
PHONE............................440 600-7274

Angie Cancasci, *Principal*
EMP: 4 **EST:** 1975
SALES (est): 2.6MM **Privately Held**
SIC: 2599 Bar, restaurant & cafeteria furniture

(G-3060)
INTEGRATED DEVELOPMENT & MFG (PA)
Also Called: Environmental Growth Chambers
510 Washington St (44022-4448)
P.O. Box 390 (44022-0390)
PHONE............................440 247-5100
Fax: 440 247-5100
Adrian Rule, *President*
Michael Kolbe, *General Mgr*
Tim Fanikos, *Regional Mgr*
Steven H Griggs, *Vice Pres*
Adrian Rule IV, *Vice Pres*
EMP: 16 **EST:** 1952
SQ FT: 28,000
SALES (est): 13.5MM **Privately Held**
SIC: 3822 1711 Auto controls regulating residntl & coml environmt & applncs; refrigeration contractor

(G-3061)
INVESTMENT SYSTEMS COMPANY
37840 Jackson Rd (44022-1912)
PHONE............................440 247-2865
Ronni Bialosky, *President*
EMP: 4
SALES (est): 405K **Privately Held**
WEB: www.investmentsystems.com
SIC: 7372 5045 Prepackaged software; computer software

(G-3062)
L B STEEL PLATE (PA)
68 Olive St Ste 6 (44022-3117)
PHONE............................440 893-0680
Jerry Underwood, *Mktg Dir*
Robert Richards, *Mng Member*
EMP: 4
SALES (est): 2.1MM **Privately Held**
SIC: 3449 Bars, concrete reinforcing: fabricated steel

(G-3063)
LEWIS UNLIMITED INC
165 Jackson Dr (44022-1557)
PHONE............................216 514-8282
Joseph Lewis, *President*
Nina Lewis, *Vice Pres*
EMP: 7
SQ FT: 2,500
SALES (est): 600K **Privately Held**
WEB: www.lewisunlimited.com
SIC: 3599 Machine shop, jobbing & repair

(G-3064)
MILLENNIUM ADHESIVE PDTS INC
178 E Washington St Ste 1 (44022-2978)
PHONE............................440 708-1212
Ronald Janoski, *President*
Kristian Moore, *General Mgr*
Mark Rundo, *Vice Pres*
EMP: 10
SQ FT: 7,000
SALES (est): 1.5MM **Privately Held**
WEB: www.millenniumadhesives.com
SIC: 2891 Adhesives & sealants

(G-3065)
NATIONAL DIRECTORY MORTICIANS
Also Called: Red Book
285 Park Pl (44022-4456)
P.O. Box 73 (44022-0073)
PHONE............................440 247-3561
Jack Schmidt, *President*
EMP: 3
SALES (est): 202.4K **Privately Held**
WEB: www.funeral-dir.com
SIC: 2731 Books: publishing only

(G-3066)
P P M INC
35 High Ct (44022-2863)
PHONE............................216 701-0419
Chas Gilmore, *Principal*
Cliff Nazelli, *Principal*

EMP: 10
SQ FT: 3,600
SALES (est): 1.6MM **Privately Held**
WEB: www.ppminc.com
SIC: 3825 Instruments to measure electricity

(G-3067)
PERENNIAL SOFTWARE INC
Also Called: Sedona Office
547 Washington St Ste 11 (44022-4436)
PHONE............................440 247-5602
Michael Marks, *President*
April Misseri, *Exec VP*
Bridget Perea, *Vice Pres*
Bob Faybrick, *Manager*
Laurie Goodrich, *Manager*
EMP: 15
SALES (est): 1.8MM **Privately Held**
SIC: 7372 Prepackaged software

(G-3068)
PREMIER METAL TRADING LLC
7 1/2 N Franklin St (44022-3009)
PHONE............................440 247-9494
David Glassman,
EMP: 3
SALES (est): 1.8MM **Privately Held**
SIC: 5051 3312 Ferrous metals; nonferrous metal sheets, bars, rods, etc.; sheets, metal; stainless steel

(G-3069)
SHOOK MANUFACTURED PDTS INC
3801 Wiltshire Rd (44022-1151)
PHONE............................440 247-9130
Thomas John, *Manager*
EMP: 8
SALES (corp-wide): 1.2MM **Privately Held**
SIC: 3545 Chucks: drill, lathe or magnetic (machine tool accessories)
PA: Shook Manufactured Products, Inc.
1017 Kenmore Blvd
Akron OH 44314
330 848-9780

(G-3070)
SNAPPSKIN INC
534 Manor Brook Dr (44022-4505)
PHONE............................440 318-4879
Joachim Hallwachs, *President*
EMP: 5
SQ FT: 2,000
SALES (est): 400K **Privately Held**
SIC: 3823 Digital displays of process variables

(G-3071)
THERMO KING CORPORATION
13 Orchard Cir (44022-2195)
PHONE............................478 625-7241
Steve Sherwley, *President*
C Roberts, *Div Sub Head*
D Kolb, *Research*
Julian Adams, *Manager*
Ada Morgan, *Manager*
EMP: 300 **Privately Held**
WEB: www.thermoking.com
SIC: 3585 3822 Refrigeration equipment, complete; auto controls regulating residntl & coml environmt & applncs
HQ: Thermo King Corporation
314 W 90th St
Minneapolis MN 55420
952 887-2200

(G-3072)
THERMO KING CORPORATION
13 Orchard Cir (44022-2195)
PHONE............................478 625-7241
EMP: 13
SALES (est): 1.7MM **Privately Held**
SIC: 3585 Refrigeration & heating equipment; refrigeration equipment, complete; parts for heating, cooling & refrigerating equipment
HQ: Ingersoll-Rand Company
800 Beaty St Ste B
Davidson NC 28036
704 655-4000

(G-3073)
WESTERN RESERVE FOODS LLC
325 Bell St (44022-2907)
P.O. Box 653 (44022-0653)
PHONE............................330 770-0885
Edward Gordos, *Principal*
EMP: 3
SALES (est): 245.1K **Privately Held**
SIC: 2099 Food preparations

(G-3074)
YUTEC LLC (PA)
3940 Ellendale Rd (44022-1126)
PHONE............................440 725-5353
Yuri Borsch, *Partner*
Tanya Borsch,
▲ **EMP:** 5
SQ FT: 3,500
SALES (est): 453.2K **Privately Held**
WEB: www.yutec.com
SIC: 3575 Computer terminals, monitors & components

Chagrin Falls
Geauga County

(G-3075)
ABANAKI CORPORATION (PA)
Also Called: Aerodyne
17387 Munn Rd (44023-5400)
PHONE............................440 543-7400
Fax: 440 543-7400
Mark Thomas Hobson, *President*
Karen Smidansky, *Natl Sales Mgr*
▲ **EMP:** 15
SQ FT: 7,700
SALES (est): 2.9MM **Privately Held**
WEB: www.abanaki.com
SIC: 3569 Filters

(G-3076)
AERODYNAMIC SYSTEMS
19020 Brookfield Rd (44023-9605)
P.O. Box 143, Aurora (44202-0143)
PHONE............................440 463-8820
Patrick E Ryan, *Principal*
EMP: 4
SALES (est): 343.4K **Privately Held**
SIC: 3799 Recreational vehicles

(G-3077)
BECHEM LUBRICATION TECH LLC
8401 Chagrin Rd Ste 5a (44023-4704)
P.O. Box 23609 (44023-0609)
PHONE............................440 543-9845
Isaac Tripp IV, *Treasurer*
John S Steigerwald,
▲ **EMP:** 7
SALES (est): 979K **Privately Held**
SIC: 2992 Lubricating oils

(G-3078)
BUCKEYE GEAR CO
Also Called: Skidmore Engineering Div
16354 Stone Ridge Rd (44023-1117)
PHONE............................216 292-7998
Fax: 216 292-6454
Ray Skidmore, *President*
EMP: 13 **EST:** 1957
SQ FT: 7,200
SALES (est): 2.7MM **Privately Held**
WEB: www.skidmoreengineering.com
SIC: 3566 3423 3462 Gears, power transmission, except automotive; wrenches, hand tools; iron & steel forgings

(G-3079)
CHEMPAK INTERNATIONAL LLC (PA)
10175 Queens Way Ste 8 (44023-5435)
PHONE............................440 543-8511
Jay Hole, *Director*
Patrick McCarthy,
◆ **EMP:** 4
SQ FT: 1,600
SALES (est): 1.1MM **Privately Held**
WEB: www.chempakintl.com
SIC: 2869 Laboratory chemicals, organic

(G-3080)
CLEARLY VISIBLE MOBILE WASH
8473 Tulip Ln (44023-4673)
PHONE............................440 543-9299
Charlie Kiggans, *Owner*
EMP: 3
SALES (est): 451K **Privately Held**
SIC: 3069 Washers, rubber

(G-3081)
CONSTRUCTION POLYMERS CO
8160 Devon Ct (44023-5008)
PHONE............................440 591-9018
Ronald P Raymond, *President*
Russell Raymond, *Vice Pres*
▲ **EMP:** 8
SALES (est): 660K **Privately Held**
WEB: www.kktechnologies.com
SIC: 3531 Construction machinery

(G-3082)
CONTROL ASSOCIATES INC
10205 Queens Way (44023-5409)
P.O. Box 187 (44022-0187)
PHONE............................440 708-1770
Stanley S Briggs, *President*
Steve Briggs, *Vice Pres*
Carol Abrams, *Admin Sec*
EMP: 4
SQ FT: 2,500
SALES (est): 126.6K **Privately Held**
SIC: 8711 3823 1731 3625 Industrial engineers; industrial process control instruments; electronic controls installation; relays & industrial controls

(G-3083)
CORROSION RESISTANT TECHNOLOGY
11345 Saybrook Ln (44023-9323)
PHONE............................440 543-1320
Scott Henry, *Principal*
EMP: 5
SALES (est): 437.5K **Privately Held**
SIC: 3296 Mineral wool

(G-3084)
CUT OFF BLADES INC
426 Chipping Ln (44023-6713)
PHONE............................440 543-2947
Jake Boland, *President*
EMP: 3
SALES (est): 314.7K **Privately Held**
SIC: 3421 Cutlery

(G-3085)
DYNAMIC DESIGN & SYSTEMS INC
7639 Washington St (44023-4403)
PHONE............................440 708-1010
Richard E Doerr, *President*
Marilyn N Doerr, *Vice Pres*
Beth Stewart, *Sales Executive*
Marge Sopczyk, *Office Mgr*
◆ **EMP:** 6
SQ FT: 3,000
SALES: 1.5MM **Privately Held**
SIC: 2759 2752 Screen printing; decals, lithographed; business form & card printing, lithographic

(G-3086)
ESSENTIAL SEALING PRODUCTS INC (PA)
10145 Queens Way (44023-5407)
P.O. Box 23699 (44023-0699)
PHONE............................440 543-8108
Susan Pyle, *President*
Bruce Pyle, *Vice Pres*
Pat Stipp, *Treasurer*
Bob Kauffman, *Regl Sales Mgr*
Dennis Errichiello, *MIS Mgr*
EMP: 8
SQ FT: 30,000
SALES (est): 1.3MM **Privately Held**
WEB: www.espsealing.com
SIC: 3053 Gaskets & sealing devices; packing materials

(G-3087)
ETNA PRODUCTS INCORPORATED (PA)
Also Called: Master Draw Lubricants
16824 Park Circle Dr (44023-4516)
P.O. Box 23609 (44023-0609)
PHONE..................................440 543-9845
Fax: 440 543-9845
Isaac Tripp IV, *President*
Jeanne S Tripp, *Corp Secy*
Dennis Broadwater, *Plant Mgr*
Michael Bell, *Safety Mgr*
Michael O'Connell, *Research*
◆ EMP: 30 EST: 1943
SQ FT: 35,000
SALES (est): 5.4MM Privately Held
SIC: 2992 2821 2899 Oils & greases,
blending & compounding; polyethylene
resins; chemical preparations

(G-3088)
GLOBAL GEAR LLC
8336 W Craig Dr (44023-4542)
PHONE..................................941 830-0531
Kathleen Meyer,
EMP: 4
SALES (est): 300K Privately Held
SIC: 2311 Military uniforms, men's &
youths': purchased materials

(G-3089)
GOLF DOME
8198 Washington St (44023-4506)
P.O. Box 23236 (44023-0236)
PHONE..................................440 543-1211
Fax: 440 543-6254
Larry Dolan, *Owner*
Kyle Blumenthal, *General Mgr*
EMP: 6
SALES (est): 518.2K Privately Held
SIC: 3949 Driving ranges, golf, electronic

(G-3090)
GRAPHITE SALES INC (PA)
16710 W Park Circle Dr (44023-4550)
P.O. Box 23009 (44023-0009)
PHONE..................................440 543-8221
Fax: 440 543-8221
Kevin Burmeister, *CEO*
Arthur Martin, *President*
Michael Dwaileebe, *General Mgr*
Michael Slabe, *CFO*
Edward Zsembik, *Asst Controller*
▲ EMP: 15
SQ FT: 16,000
SALES (est): 17.9MM Privately Held
WEB: www.graphitesales.com
SIC: 3624 Carbon & graphite products;
electrodes, thermal & electrolytic uses:
carbon, graphite

(G-3091)
HIGH TEMPERATURE SYSTEMS INC
16755 Park Circle Dr (44023-4562)
PHONE..................................440 543-8271
Bruno Thut, *Ch of Bd*
Kristine Thut, *President*
Paul Meyer, *Marketing Staff*
▲ EMP: 9
SQ FT: 16,000
SALES (est): 1.8MM Privately Held
WEB: www.hitemp.com
SIC: 3559 Smelting & refining machinery &
equipment

(G-3092)
HOME CARE PRODUCTS LLC (HQ)
7160 Chagrin Rd Ste 220 (44023-1135)
PHONE..................................919 693-1002
Mark Howard, *Mng Member*
Holoie Mathis, *Administration*
EMP: 3
SALES (est): 725.1K
SALES (corp-wide): 1.3MM Privately
Held
SIC: 2674 Vacuum cleaner bags: made
from purchased materials
PA: Zhao Hui Filters (Us), Inc.
7160 Chagrin Rd Ste 220
Chagrin Falls OH 44023
440 519-9300

(G-3093)
HYPER TOOL COMPANY
16829 Park Circle Dr (44023-4515)
PHONE..................................440 543-5151
Fax: 440 543-5151
Morton C Mc Clennan, *President*
Roger Clow, *General Mgr*
Donald Felton, *Vice Pres*
EMP: 18 EST: 1948
SQ FT: 12,000
SALES (est): 2.6MM Privately Held
SIC: 3541 3545 Machine tools, metal cut-
ting type; machine tool accessories

(G-3094)
IBI BRAKE PRODUCTS INC
16751 Hilltop Park Pl (44023-4500)
P.O. Box 23547 (44023-0547)
PHONE..................................440 543-7962
John Hooper, *President*
Paul Kit, *Vice Pres*
EMP: 6
SQ FT: 9,000
SALES: 2MM Privately Held
WEB: www.brakeproducts.com
SIC: 3499 5084 7389 3536 Wheels:
wheelbarrow, stroller, etc.: disc, stamped
metal; industrial machinery & equipment;
crane & aerial lift service; hoists, cranes &
monorails

(G-3095)
INTEGRATED DEVELOPMENT & MFG
8401 Washington St (44023-4511)
PHONE..................................440 543-2423
Adrian O Rule III, *Manager*
EMP: 40
SALES (corp-wide): 13.5MM Privately
Held
SIC: 3822 Auto controls regulating residntl
& coml environmt & applncs
PA: Integrated Development & Mfg
510 Washington St
Chagrin Falls OH 44022
440 247-5100

(G-3096)
INTWINE ENERGY NETWORKS LLC
8401 Chagrin Rd Ste 10a (44023-4703)
PHONE..................................216 970-5908
Dave Martin,
EMP: 5
SALES (est): 200K Privately Held
SIC: 3663 Radio & TV communications
equipment

(G-3097)
JO-BAR MANUFACTURING CORP
17259 Chillicothe Rd (44023-4619)
PHONE..................................440 232-5555
Alga Masley, *President*
Philip Schloss, *Vice Pres*
EMP: 17 EST: 1951
SQ FT: 14,000
SALES (est): 2.6MM Privately Held
SIC: 3728 Aircraft parts & equipment

(G-3098)
L HABERNY CO INC
10115 Queens Way (44023-5407)
P.O. Box 23394 (44023-0394)
PHONE..................................440 543-5999
Fax: 440 543-5122
Dale Haberny, *President*
EMP: 12
SQ FT: 7,000
SALES (est): 3.2MM Privately Held
SIC: 3567 1796 Industrial furnaces &
ovens; pollution control equipment instal-
lation

(G-3099)
LASER AUTOMATION INC
16771 Hilltop Park Pl (44023-4500)
PHONE..................................440 543-9291
Fax: 440 543-8447
John Herkes, *President*
Robert Slusher, *Mfg Staff*
Carol Scerba, *Admin Sec*
EMP: 12
SQ FT: 12,000
SALES: 950K Privately Held
WEB: www.laserautomation.com
SIC: 3699 5049 3535 Laser welding,
drilling & cutting equipment; scientific &
engineering equipment & supplies; con-
veyors & conveying equipment

(G-3100)
MAGNUS INTERNATIONAL GROUP INC (PA)
16533 Chillicothe Rd (44023-4327)
PHONE..................................216 592-8355
Theresa M Paicic, *President*
Sharon Sunderman, *President*
Eric Lofquist, *Principal*
Mark Allio, *Principal*
Scott Forster, *Vice Pres*
▲ EMP: 8
SALES (est): 60.7MM Privately Held
SIC: 4953 2048 2992 Recycling, waste
materials; prepared feeds; rust arresting
compounds, animal or vegetable oil base

(G-3101)
MAR-BAL INC (PA)
10095 Queens Way (44023-5406)
PHONE..................................440 543-7526
Fax: 440 543-4374
Scott Balogh, *CEO*
Carolyn E Balogh, *Vice Pres*
Steven Balogh, *Vice Pres*
Kevin Casey, *Vice Pres*
Eric Stump, *Plant Mgr*
▲ EMP: 93 EST: 1970
SALES (est): 45.2MM Privately Held
SIC: 3089 2821 3081 Molding primary
plastic; polyesters; unsupported plastics
film & sheet

(G-3102)
MAR-BAL INC
16930 Munn Rd (44023-5495)
PHONE..................................440 543-7526
Scott Balogh, *President*
EMP: 93
SALES (corp-wide): 45.2MM Privately
Held
WEB: www.mar-bal.com
SIC: 3089 2821 3081 Molding primary
plastic; polyesters; unsupported plastics
film & sheet
PA: Mar-Bal, Inc.
10095 Queens Way
Chagrin Falls OH 44023
440 543-7526

(G-3103)
MASTERS GROUP INC
7160 Chagrin Rd Ste 160 (44023-1182)
PHONE..................................440 893-1900
John Dublo, *President*
Jackie Jerome, *Manager*
EMP: 4
SQ FT: 500
SALES (est): 763.6K Privately Held
SIC: 1481 3399 3341 5051 Nonmetallic
mineral services; iron ore recovery from
open hearth slag; secondary nonferrous
metals; ferrous metals; iron ore

(G-3104)
MILLENNIUM ADHESIVE PRODUCTS
17340 Munn Rd (44023-5476)
PHONE..................................440 708-1212
Fax: 440 708-1212
Ron Janoski, *CEO*
EMP: 6
SALES (corp-wide): 1.2MM Privately
Held
SIC: 2891 Adhesives
PA: Millennium Adhesive Products
4401 Page Ave
Michigan Center MI 49254
800 248-4010

(G-3105)
NATIONAL POLYMER DEV CO INC
10200 Gottschalk Pkwy # 4 (44023-5470)
PHONE..................................440 708-1245
Adrian De Krom, *President*
EMP: 11
SALES (est): 1.6MM Privately Held
SIC: 2821 Plastics materials & resins

(G-3106)
NATIONAL POLYMER INC
10200 Gottschalk Pkwy (44023-5470)
P.O. Box 343, Newbury (44065-0343)
PHONE..................................440 708-1245
Adrian De Krom, *President*
Daniel Bess, *Director*
EMP: 11
SQ FT: 6,000
SALES (est): 1.7MM Privately Held
SIC: 8734 5169 2891 Testing laborato-
ries; adhesives & sealants; adhesives,
plastic

(G-3107)
NELSON ALUMINUM FOUNDRY INC
17093 Munn Rd (44023-5412)
PHONE..................................440 543-1941
Fax: 440 543-5045
Russell Nelson, *President*
Richard Vamos, *Accounting Dir*
EMP: 6 EST: 1951
SALES: 500K Privately Held
SIC: 3365 3369 Machinery castings, alu-
minum; nonferrous foundries

(G-3108)
OHIO CLASSIC STREET RODS INC
Also Called: Stainless Works
9899 Washington St (44023-5485)
PHONE..................................440 543-6593
Fax: 440 543-9183
Ronald Fuller, *President*
Geoff Masters, *General Mgr*
Paul Grabowski, *Sales Engr*
Del Borovic, *Marketing Staff*
Ellen Kliber, *Manager*
▲ EMP: 3
SALES (est): 720.1K Privately Held
SIC: 3714 5013 Exhaust systems & parts,
motor vehicle; automotive supplies &
parts

(G-3109)
P & T MILLWORK INC
10090 Queens Way (44023-5403)
PHONE..................................440 543-2151
Fax: 440 543-7651
Joe Tesauro, *CEO*
Randall Pistone, *Vice Pres*
Denise Wuertz, *Manager*
David Koci, *Admin Sec*
EMP: 21
SQ FT: 21,500
SALES (est): 2.6MM Privately Held
WEB: www.ptmillwork.com
SIC: 2499 5211 2431 Decorative wood &
woodwork; door & window products; mill-
work

(G-3110)
PADDOCK CORPORATION
Also Called: Paddock Products
8574 Washington St (44023-5369)
P.O. Box 631 (44022-0631)
PHONE..................................440 543-0631
Lisa Gorretta, *President*
Joyce Gorretta, *Vice Pres*
EMP: 9
SQ FT: 3,200
SALES: 700K Privately Held
WEB: www.paddocksaddlery.com
SIC: 5941 5961 3429 Saddlery & eques-
trian equipment; mail order house; sad-
dlery hardware

(G-3111)
PEDIAVASCULAR INC
7181 Chagrin Rd Ste 250 (44023-1130)
PHONE..................................216 236-5533
Timothy Moran, *CEO*
EMP: 15
SALES (est): 1.5MM Privately Held
SIC: 3841 Inhalation therapy equipment

(G-3112)
PHOENIX ASSOCIATES
16760 W Park Circle Dr (44023-4550)
PHONE..................................440 543-9701
Fax: 440 543-4148
Travis Hendershot, *General Mgr*
John Fisher, *Purch Mgr*
Tim Reed, *Info Tech Mgr*

Scott Janda,
EMP: 25
SQ FT: 12,000
SALES (est): 3.9MM **Privately Held**
WEB: www.intreeg.com
SIC: 3053 Gaskets, all materials

(G-3113)
POP/POS ADVANTAGE
Also Called: Poppos Advantage Group
17911 Snyder Rd Ste A (44023-1631)
PHONE..................440 543-9452
Linda White, *Owner*
EMP: 2
SALES: 1MM **Privately Held**
SIC: 3292 Asbestos textiles, except insulating material

(G-3114)
PRINTING SERVICES
16750 Park Circle Dr (44023-4563)
PHONE..................440 708-1999
Robert Roulan, *President*
Brian Pottinger, *Manager*
EMP: 25
SQ FT: 16,000
SALES (est): 1.2MM **Privately Held**
SIC: 7389 2752 Printers' services: folding, collating; commercial printing, lithographic

(G-3115)
QUBE CORPORATION
16744 W Park Circle Dr (44023-4550)
PHONE..................440 543-2393
Fax: 440 543-2393
William C Mc Coy, *President*
Steve L Clark, *Vice Pres*
EMP: 12
SQ FT: 13,000
SALES (est): 930K **Privately Held**
WEB: www.qubeinc.com
SIC: 3089 Fittings for pipe, plastic

(G-3116)
R B ROBINSON INC
Also Called: Excel Printing & Graphics
17800 Chillicothe Rd # 112 (44023-4868)
PHONE..................440 543-5547
Fax: 440 543-5298
Richard B Robinson, *President*
Donna Robinson, *Vice Pres*
EMP: 7
SQ FT: 3,000
SALES (est): 996K **Privately Held**
WEB: www.excelprint.net
SIC: 2752 2791 Commercial printing, offset; typesetting

(G-3117)
RESERVE ENERGY EXPLORATION CO
10155 Gottschalk Pkwy # 1 (44023-5465)
P.O. Box 23278 (44023-0278)
PHONE..................440 543-0770
Joseph Haas, *President*
EMP: 8
SALES (est): 1.2MM **Privately Held**
SIC: 1382 Oil & gas exploration services

(G-3118)
ROYAL ADHESIVES & SEALANTS LLC
17340 Munn Rd (44023-5476)
PHONE..................440 708-1212
EMP: 7
SALES (corp-wide): 588.6MM **Privately Held**
SIC: 2891 Sealants
PA: Royal Adhesives And Sealants Llc
2001 W Washington St
South Bend IN 46628
574 246-5000

(G-3119)
SCOTT FETZER COMPANY
Scots Tuff
16841 Park Circle Dr (44023-4515)
PHONE..................216 228-2400
Fax: 440 543-3033
Russ Anderson, *Plant Supt*
Pat McCoy, *Manager*
Fraser Murray, *Manager*
EMP: 30

SALES (corp-wide): 223.6B **Publicly Held**
SIC: 5999 3635 Cleaning equipment & supplies; household vacuum cleaners
HQ: The Scott Fetzer Company
28800 Clemens Rd
Westlake OH 44145
440 892-3000

(G-3120)
SPEED SELECTOR INC
17050 Munn Rd (44023-5494)
PHONE..................440 543-8233
Fax: 440 543-8233
George C Wick Jr, *President*
George F Howson Jr, *Vice Pres*
Craig Liechty, *CFO*
Tom Cannon, *Manager*
Cathy Rice, *Manager*
EMP: 15
SQ FT: 31,000
SALES (est): 3.7MM **Privately Held**
WEB: www.speedselector.com
SIC: 3566 Drives, high speed industrial, except hydrostatic

(G-3121)
STOCK EQUIPMENT COMPANY INC (DH)
16490 Chillicothe Rd (44023-4398)
PHONE..................440 543-6000
Fax: 440 543-5944
Robert Ciavarella, *CEO*
Jason Horn, *Business Mgr*
John Richards, *Business Mgr*
Tom Timberlake, *Vice Pres*
John Nocero, *Project Mgr*
▲ **EMP:** 240
SALES (est): 67MM **Privately Held**
WEB: www.stockequipment.com
SIC: 3535 Conveyors & conveying equipment
HQ: Schenck Process Beteiligungs Gmbh
Pallaswiesenstr. 100
Darmstadt
615 115-310

(G-3122)
STOCK FAIRFIELD CORPORATION
Also Called: Stock Equipment Company
16490 Chillicothe Rd (44023-4326)
PHONE..................440 543-6000
Robert Ciavarella, *President*
EMP: 170 **EST:** 2007
SALES (est): 40.1MM **Privately Held**
WEB: www.stockequipment.com
SIC: 5063 8711 3535 3823 Power transmission equipment, electric; electrical or electronic engineering; conveyors & conveying equipment; industrial instrmnts msrmnt display/control process variable; relays & industrial controls; industrial trucks & tractors
HQ: Stock Equipment Company, Inc.
16490 Chillicothe Rd
Chagrin Falls OH 44023
440 543-6000

(G-3123)
STOUTHEART CORPORATION (PA)
7205 Chagrin Rd Ste 4 (44023-1127)
P.O. Box 39219, Solon (44139-0219)
PHONE..................401 434-7640
Richard Burkhart, *President*
Mike Sevigny, *CFO*
EMP: 2
SQ FT: 500
SALES (est): 14MM **Privately Held**
SIC: 3351 Strip, copper & copper alloy

(G-3124)
TARKETT INC
16910 Munn Rd (44023-5411)
PHONE..................440 708-9366
Bruce Ziegler, *Director*
Joe McKenna, *Director*
Christine Bailey, *Admin Asst*
Garrett White, *Administration*
EMP: 4
SALES (corp-wide): 537K **Privately Held**
SIC: 3069 Flooring, rubber: tile or sheet

HQ: Tarkett, Inc
30000 Aurora Rd
Solon OH 44139
800 899-8916

(G-3125)
TEWELL & ASSOCIATES
10260 Washington St (44023-5478)
PHONE..................440 543-5190
James Tewell, *President*
Carolyn Tewell, *Corp Secy*
Ruth Meyer, *Manager*
EMP: 8
SQ FT: 3,500
SALES: 3.8MM **Privately Held**
WEB: www.tewell.com
SIC: 7389 2759 Brokers, contract services; screen printing

(G-3126)
THERM-O-PACKAGING SUPPLIERS
16815 Park Circle Dr (44023-4515)
PHONE..................440 543-5188
Fax: 440 543-9489
EMP: 14
SQ FT: 10,600
SALES (est): 1.5MM **Privately Held**
SIC: 2671 2657 Mfg Packaging Paper/Film Mfg Folding Paperboard Boxes

(G-3127)
TITANIUM TROUT LLC
18060 Birch Hill Dr (44023-5826)
PHONE..................440 543-3187
Kevin Donovan, *Principal*
EMP: 3
SALES (est): 20.9K **Privately Held**
SIC: 3356 Titanium

(G-3128)
TRIAD METAL PRODUCTS COMPANY
12990 Snow Rd (44023)
PHONE..................216 676-6505
Fax: 216 676-6510
Patricia Basista, *President*
Richard Basista, *President*
Wally Klubert, *President*
Bob Reynolds, *Production*
▲ **EMP:** 100 **EST:** 1945
SQ FT: 150,000
SALES (est): 20MM **Privately Held**
WEB: www.triadmetal.com
SIC: 3469 Stamping metal for the trade

(G-3129)
TRILOGY PLASTICS INC
7160 Chagrin Rd (44023-1134)
PHONE..................440 893-5522
EMP: 25
SALES (corp-wide): 20.6MM **Privately Held**
SIC: 3089 Plastic processing
PA: Trilogy Plastics, Inc.
2290 W Main St
Alliance OH 44601
330 821-4700

(G-3130)
TUNGSTEN SLTONS GROUP INTL INC
17523 Merry Oaks Trl (44023-5643)
PHONE..................440 708-3096
Hugh McIvor, *President*
Kevin McIvor, *Sales Staff*
EMP: 3 **EST:** 2012
SQ FT: 10,000
SALES: 7MM **Privately Held**
SIC: 3313 5093 Tungsten carbide powder; metal scrap & waste materials

(G-3131)
UTILITY RELAY CO LTD
Also Called: Urc
10100 Queens Way (44023-5404)
PHONE..................440 708-1000
Fax: 440 708-1177
Helmut Weiher, *Mng Member*
EMP: 42
SQ FT: 15,000

SALES (est): 10.3MM **Privately Held**
WEB: www.utilityrelay.com
SIC: 3625 Industrial electrical relays & switches

(G-3132)
VIRTUS STUNTS LLC
16320 Snyder Rd (44023-4312)
PHONE..................440 543-0472
Ted Batchelor, *Principal*
EMP: 3
SALES (est): 220.8K **Privately Held**
SIC: 2721 Television schedules: publishing only, not printed on site

(G-3133)
WHIP GUIDE CO
Also Called: Gizmo
16829 Park Circle Dr (44023-4515)
PHONE..................440 543-5151
Morton C Mc Clennan, *Partner*
Walter C Mc Clennan, *Partner*
EMP: 10
SQ FT: 10,000
SALES (est): 925.8K **Privately Held**
SIC: 3545 3366 Drilling machine attachments & accessories; copper foundries

(G-3134)
XACT SPEC INDUSTIRES LLC
Aerospace Operations
16959 Munn Rd (44023-5410)
PHONE..................440 543-8157
Peter Barnhart, *Managing Prtnr*
EMP: 9
SALES (corp-wide): 15.1MM **Privately Held**
SIC: 3599 Machine & other job shop work
PA: Xact Spec Industries Llc
16959 Munn Rd
Chagrin Falls OH 44023
440 543-8157

(G-3135)
XACT SPEC INDUSTRIES LLC (PA)
16959 Munn Rd (44023-5410)
PHONE..................440 543-8157
Fax: 440 543-4582
Peter Barnhart, *Mng Member*
EMP: 33
SQ FT: 32,000
SALES (est): 15.1MM **Privately Held**
SIC: 3599 Machine & other job shop work

(G-3136)
ZHAO HUI FILTERS (US) INC (PA)
Also Called: Zhai Hui Filters & Home Pdts
7160 Chagrin Rd Ste 220 (44023-1135)
PHONE..................440 519-9300
Cong Lawrence Lin, *President*
EMP: 5
SALES (est): 1.3MM **Privately Held**
SIC: 3569 Filters

(G-3137)
ZOOK ENTERPRISES LLC
16809 Park Circle Dr (44023-4515)
P.O. Box 419 (44022-0419)
PHONE..................440 543-1010
Fax: 440 543-1010
Alan Kohta, *Accounts Mgr*
Richard V Varos, *Mng Member*
▲ **EMP:** 30
SQ FT: 8,400
SALES (est): 6.7MM **Privately Held**
SIC: 3559 Petroleum refinery equipment

Chardon
Geauga County

(G-3138)
ADVANCED QUARTZ FABRICATION
11920 Quail Woods Dr (44024-8648)
P.O. Box 5070, Mentor (44061-5070)
PHONE..................440 350-4567
Fax: 440 205-9699
Richard R Intihar Jr, *President*
Brenda Intihar, *Corp Secy*
Stephanie Pilarczyk, *Opers Mgr*
▲ **EMP:** 12

SQ FT: 26,000
SALES (est): 1.3MM **Privately Held**
SIC: 3295 Minerals, ground or treated

(G-3139)
ALTITUDE MEDICAL INC
Po Box 770 (44024-0770)
P.O. Box 770
PHONE.....................................440 799-7701
Ray Dunning, *CEO*
EMP: 5
SALES (est): 544.8K **Privately Held**
SIC: 3841 Surgical & medical instruments

(G-3140)
ALVORDS YARD & GARDEN EQP
12089 Ravenna Rd (44024-7008)
PHONE.....................................440 286-2315
Fax: 440 286-6598
William J Alvord, *Owner*
EMP: 5
SALES (est): 388.8K **Privately Held**
SIC: 5261 7699 3546 Nurseries & garden
   centers; motorcycle repair service; saws
   & sawing equipment

(G-3141)
ARABIAN TOOLS INC
9632 Brakeman Rd (44024-8207)
PHONE.....................................440 286-3600
Fax: 440 286-3600
Frank Janek, *President*
Theresa Janek, *Vice Pres*
EMP: 3
SQ FT: 5,000
SALES: 150K **Privately Held**
SIC: 3599 Machine shop, jobbing & repair

(G-3142)
BLACK LAB LLC
11730 Ravenna Rd (44024-7005)
P.O. Box 236, Wedron IL (60557-0236)
PHONE.....................................815 313-0400
Daryl Deckard, *Mng Member*
EMP: 5
SALES (est): 507.9K
SALES (corp-wide): 535MM **Publicly
Held**
SIC: 3531 Concrete grouting equipment
HQ: Fairmount Santrol Inc.
   8834 Mayfield Rd Ste A
   Chesterland OH 44026
   440 214-3200

(G-3143)
**CHARDON CUSTOM POLYMERS
LLC**
373 Washington St (44024-1129)
PHONE.....................................440 285-2161
Marian Devoe, *President*
John Noga, *Controller*
Mitch Showers, *Sales Mgr*
EMP: 16
SALES (est): 5.2MM **Privately Held**
SIC: 3061 3069 Mechanical rubber goods;
   molded rubber products

(G-3144)
**CHARDON METAL PRODUCTS
CO**
206 5th Ave (44024-1007)
P.O. Box 67 (44024-0067)
PHONE.....................................440 285-2147
Fax: 440 286-3005
Anderson Allyn Jr, *Ch of Bd*
Duke Allyn, *President*
Aric Allyn, *Vice Pres*
Anderson Allyn III, *CFO*
Patricia White, *Controller*
EMP: 32 EST: 1945
SQ FT: 31,000
SALES (est): 8.6MM **Privately Held**
WEB: www.chardonmetal.com
SIC: 3498 3451 3599 Tube fabricating
   (contract bending & shaping); screw ma-
   chine products; machine shop, jobbing &
   repair

(G-3145)
**CHARDON PLASTICS
MACHINERY**
11680 Butternut Rd (44024-9355)
PHONE.....................................440 564-5360
Don Schindelhold, *President*
EMP: 3 EST: 1998

SALES: 375K **Privately Held**
WEB: www.chardonplastics.com
SIC: 3559 Plastics working machinery

(G-3146)
**CHARDON TOOL & SUPPLY CO
INC**
115 Parker Ct (44024-1112)
P.O. Box 291 (44024-0291)
PHONE.....................................440 286-6440
Fax: 440 286-7165
Weldon Bennett, *President*
Donna Blewett, *Principal*
Marshall Meadows, *Principal*
Andrew O'Dell, *Principal*
EMP: 35
SQ FT: 4,800
SALES: 3MM **Privately Held**
SIC: 3545 5085 Diamond cutting tools for
   turning, boring, burnishing, etc.; dia-
   monds, industrial: natural, crude

(G-3147)
CITY OF CHARDON
Also Called: Water & Sewer
201 N Hambden St (44024-1175)
PHONE.....................................440 286-2657
Fax: 440 286-7538
David Lelkl, *Manager*
EMP: 15 **Privately Held**
WEB: www.co.geauga.oh.us
SIC: 3589 Sewage & water treatment
   equipment
PA: City Of Chardon
   111 Water St Fl 2
   Chardon OH 44024
   440 286-2600

(G-3148)
DARK DIAMOND TOOLS INC
10319 Sawmill Dr (44024-8220)
P.O. Box 22, Montville (44064-0022)
PHONE.....................................440 701-6424
Fax: 440 968-3500
Richard De Francesco, *President*
Andrew Kawalec, *Vice Pres*
Cheryl De Francesco, *Treasurer*
EMP: 5
SQ FT: 2,000
SALES: 750K **Privately Held**
WEB: www.darkdiamond.net
SIC: 3545 Diamond cutting tools for turn-
   ing, boring, burnishing, etc.

(G-3149)
DEAKS FORM TOOLS INC
9954a Cutts Rd (44024-9182)
PHONE.....................................440 286-2353
George Deak, *Branch Mgr*
EMP: 3
SALES (corp-wide): 570.3K **Privately
Held**
SIC: 3312 Tool & die steel
PA: Form Deak's Tools Inc
   11836 Western Ave
   Stanton CA 90680
   714 891-5272

(G-3150)
DND PRODUCTS INC
Also Called: Maple Valley Sug Bush & Farms
13262 Chardon Windsor Rd (44024-8975)
PHONE.....................................440 286-7275
Donna Divoky, *President*
Dave Divoky, *Vice Pres*
EMP: 3
SQ FT: 1,390
SALES (est): 246.3K **Privately Held**
SIC: 3199 Safety belts, leather

(G-3151)
EGC ENTERPRISES INC
140 Parker Ct (44024-1112)
PHONE.....................................440 285-5835
Fax: 440 285-8337
Bernard L Casamento, *President*
Mary Long, *General Mgr*
Clay Miller, *Vice Pres*
Robert R Rutherford, *Vice Pres*
Dario Ortiz, *Plant Mgr*
▲ EMP: 47 EST: 1978
SQ FT: 49,000
SALES (est): 19.4MM **Privately Held**
WEB: www.egc-ent.com
SIC: 2891 3053 Sealants; gaskets, pack-
   ing & sealing devices

(G-3152)
FABCRAFT INC
344 Center St (44024-1104)
PHONE.....................................440 286-6700
John M Svoboda Sr, *President*
John M Svoboda Jr, *General Mgr*
Amy Svoboda, *Office Mgr*
EMP: 5
SQ FT: 9,600
SALES: 750K **Privately Held**
SIC: 3444 3498 Sheet metalwork; tube
   fabricating (contract bending & shaping)

(G-3153)
FIELD SPECIALTIES
11609 Claridon Troy Rd (44024-8438)
PHONE.....................................440 635-0064
David Fry, *President*
EMP: 3
SALES (est): 312.5K **Privately Held**
WEB: www.fieldspecialties.com
SIC: 3949 Track & field athletic equipment

(G-3154)
FOWLERS MILLING CO INC
12500 Fowlers Mill Rd (44024-9371)
PHONE.....................................440 286-2024
Fax: 440 286-4076
Rick Erickson, *President*
EMP: 10
SQ FT: 4,600
SALES: 600K **Privately Held**
WEB: www.fowlermill.com
SIC: 2041 5947 Flour mixes; gift baskets

(G-3155)
**GEORGIA METAL COATINGS
COMPANY**
275 Industrial Pkwy (44024-1052)
PHONE.....................................770 446-3930
George Palek, *President*
Norm Gertz, *Treasurer*
Ted Gillinger, *Office Mgr*
Harry Ginn, *Executive*
EMP: 10
SQ FT: 24,000
SALES (est): 1MM
SALES (corp-wide): 1.4B **Privately Held**
WEB: www.georgiametalcoatings.com
SIC: 3479 Etching & engraving
HQ: Nof Metal Coatings North America Inc.
   275 Industrial Pkwy
   Chardon OH 44024
   440 285-2231

(G-3156)
HI-TECH EXTRUSIONS LTD
12621 Chardon Windsor Rd (44024-8969)
PHONE.....................................440 286-4000
Fax: 440 286-3822
Matt Michalek, *Partner*
Julius Wilson, *Partner*
Donald J Michalek, *General Ptnr*
Sean Cunningham, *Prdtn Mgr*
Marcy Madar, *Manager*
EMP: 30
SQ FT: 25,000
SALES (est): 7MM **Privately Held**
WEB: www.hitechextrusions.com
SIC: 3089 Extruded finished plastic prod-
   ucts

(G-3157)
HUTTER RACING ENGINES LTD
12550 Gar Hwy (44024-8232)
PHONE.....................................440 285-2175
Fax: 440 285-2175
Ronald Hutter, *Partner*
Thalia Hutter, *Partner*
Trevor Hutter, *Partner*
EMP: 10
SQ FT: 6,000
SALES (est): 1.5MM **Privately Held**
SIC: 3599 7538 Machine shop, jobbing &
   repair; general automotive repair shops

(G-3158)
III WILLIAMS LLC
11993 Ravenna Rd Ste 12 (44024-9018)
PHONE.....................................440 721-8191
William Hurt, *President*
EMP: 2
SQ FT: 2,400
SALES: 1MM **Privately Held**
SIC: 3494 5531 Valves & pipe fittings; au-
   tomotive parts

(G-3159)
KEY MANEUVERS INC (PA)
Also Called: K.M.I. Printing
510 Center St (44024-1004)
P.O. Box 51 (44024-0051)
PHONE.....................................440 285-0774
Fax: 440 285-0774
Randy Bennett, *President*
EMP: 7
SQ FT: 3,000
SALES (est): 1MM **Privately Held**
WEB: www.kmiprinting.com
SIC: 2752 Commercial printing, litho-
   graphic

(G-3160)
KONA BLACKBIRD INC (PA)
Also Called: Black Lab Custom Products
11730 Ravenna Rd (44024-7005)
PHONE.....................................440 285-3189
Peter Hoyt, *President*
Doug Gerner, *President*
Douglas L Gerner, *President*
Daryl Deckard, *Principal*
Andrew Hoyt, *Principal*
▲ EMP: 10
SALES (est): 4.2MM **Privately Held**
WEB: www.blacklabcorp.com
SIC: 2899 3241 3251 2842 Fluxes: braz-
   ing, soldering, galvanizing & welding; ma-
   sonry cement; flooring brick, clay;
   cleaning or polishing preparations

(G-3161)
**KTS CSTM LGS/XCLSVELY YOU
INC**
602 South St Ste C-2 (44024-1459)
PHONE.....................................440 285-9803
Fax: 440 286-9600
Kevin R Temple, *President*
Melissa Temple, *Vice Pres*
EMP: 7
SQ FT: 2,800
SALES: 500K **Privately Held**
SIC: 2395 7389 Embroidery & art needle-
   work; advertising, promotional & trade
   show services

(G-3162)
KTS CUSTOM LOGOS
602 South St Ste C-2 (44024-1459)
PHONE.....................................440 285-9803
Kevin Temple, *President*
Ken Temple, *Principal*
Melissa Temple, *Vice Pres*
EMP: 7
SALES (est): 617.6K **Privately Held**
WEB: www.ktscustomlogos.com
SIC: 2395 Embroidery & art needlework

(G-3163)
LAMAR PROFORMA
12636 Mayfield Rd Ste 1 (44024-7978)
PHONE.....................................440 285-2277
Kathy McClure, *Principal*
EMP: 6
SALES (est): 560.5K **Privately Held**
SIC: 2759 Commercial printing

(G-3164)
LANXESS CORPORATION
145 Parker Ct (44024-1112)
PHONE.....................................440 279-2367
EMP: 250
SALES (corp-wide): 8.1B **Privately Held**
SIC: 3069 5169 Reclaimed rubber & spe-
   cialty rubber compounds; industrial chem-
   icals
HQ: Lanxess Corporation
   111 Parkwest Dr
   Pittsburgh PA 15275
   800 526-9377

(G-3165)
**MADISON ELECTRIC (MEPCO)
INC**
11993 Ravenna Rd Ste 12 (44024-9018)
PHONE.....................................440 279-0521
Bruce Barclay, *President*
James Ramsey, *Treasurer*
EMP: 4
SALES: 800K **Privately Held**
SIC: 3674 Infrared sensors, solid state

▲ = Import ▼ =Export
◆ =Import/Export

(G-3166)
MAPLEDALE FARM INC
Also Called: Mapledale Landscaping
12613 Woodin Rd (44024-9177)
PHONE................................440 286-3389
David P Johnson, *President*
Judy Johnson, *Corp Secy*
Arthur L Johnson Sr, *Vice Pres*
EMP: 10
SALES (est): 560K **Privately Held**
WEB: www.mapledalelandscaping.com
SIC: 0782 4959 2087 5251 Lawn & garden services; snowplowing; beverage bases, concentrates, syrups, powders & mixes; snowblowers

(G-3167)
MUNSON SALES & ENGINEERING
13260 Crows Hollow Dr (44024-9023)
PHONE................................216 496-5436
Arthur G Hollis, *Owner*
EMP: 3
SALES (est): 130K **Privately Held**
SIC: 3599 Industrial machinery

(G-3168)
NOF METAL COATINGS N AMER INC (HQ)
275 Industrial Pkwy (44024-1052)
PHONE................................440 285-2231
Fax: 440 285-5009
Shin Masuda, *President*
John Dutton, *General Mgr*
Perry Bennett, *Vice Pres*
Frederic Gheno, *Vice Pres*
Adam Stals, *Vice Pres*
▲ **EMP:** 50
SQ FT: 20,000
SALES (est): 23.6MM
SALES (corp-wide): 1.4B **Privately Held**
WEB: www.geomet.net
SIC: 2899 Chemical preparations
PA: Nof Corporation
   4-20-3, Ebisu
   Shibuya-Ku TKY 150-0
   354 246-600

(G-3169)
NORTH AMERICAN CAST STONE INC
13271 Bass Lake Rd (44024-8321)
PHONE................................440 286-1999
Richard T Rickelman, *Principal*
EMP: 5
SQ FT: 7,059
SALES (est): 662.6K **Privately Held**
WEB: www.northamericancaststone.com
SIC: 3272 Concrete products

(G-3170)
OHIO ORDNANCE WORKS INC
310 Park Dr (44024-1057)
P.O. Box 687 (44024-0687)
PHONE................................440 285-3481
Robert I Landies, *Owner*
Robert E Conroy Jr, *Vice Pres*
Al Adams, *QC Mgr*
Gary T Hershberger, *Engineer*
Josh Hershberger, *Engineer*
◆ **EMP:** 40
SALES (est): 9.4MM **Privately Held**
WEB: www.ohioordnanceworks.com
SIC: 3484 Guns (firearms) or gun parts, 30 mm. & below; revolvers or revolver parts, 30 mm. & below; rifles or rifle parts, 30 mm. & below

(G-3171)
ORWELL PRINTING
510 Center St (44024-1004)
P.O. Box 51 (44024-0051)
PHONE................................440 285-2233
Randy Bennett, *President*
Linda Kender, *Accountant*
EMP: 8 **EST:** 1948
SQ FT: 1,900
SALES (est): 1MM
SALES (corp-wide): 1MM **Privately Held**
WEB: www.orwellprinting.com
SIC: 2752 Commercial printing, lithographic; lithographing on metal

PA: Key Maneuvers Inc
   510 Center St
   Chardon OH 44024
   440 285-0774

(G-3172)
PERFORM METALS INC
124 Industrial Pkwy (44024-1049)
PHONE................................440 286-1951
Craig Rupar, *President*
Carol Rupar, *Vice Pres*
EMP: 5
SALES (est): 460K **Privately Held**
SIC: 3599 Machine shop, jobbing & repair

(G-3173)
PUDDLE SHARK STUDIOS INC
13035 Vista Pointe Dr (44024-7938)
PHONE................................440 286-2811
Dale Hodgson, *President*
◆ **EMP:** 4
SQ FT: 2,800
SALES (est): 452.7K **Privately Held**
WEB: www.puddleshark.net
SIC: 3578 Point-of-sale devices

(G-3174)
QP MANUFACTURING CO INC
215 5th Ave (44024-1001)
PHONE................................440 946-2120
John Chesnes, *Plant Mgr*
Julie Koschik, *CFO*
Mate Brkic,
Dorris Brkic,
EMP: 15
SQ FT: 74,000
SALES (est): 7.1MM **Privately Held**
SIC: 3599 Machine shop, jobbing & repair

(G-3175)
QUANTUM ENERGY LLC (PA)
10405 Locust Grove Dr (44024-8861)
P.O. Box 241506, Cleveland (44124-8506)
PHONE................................440 285-7381
Fax: 440 954-5026
Paul J Mysyk,
Harrison Schumacher,
EMP: 15
SALES (est): 2.5MM **Privately Held**
SIC: 1382 Oil & gas exploration services

(G-3176)
RICHARDS MAPLE PRODUCTS INC
545 Water St (44024-1142)
PHONE................................440 286-4160
Fax: 440 286-7203
Debra Richards, *President*
Colin Rennie, *Vice Pres*
Annette Polson, *Admin Sec*
EMP: 6 **EST:** 1910
SALES (est): 750K **Privately Held**
WEB: www.richardsmapleproducts.com
SIC: 2064 5149 Candy & other confectionery products; syrups, except for fountain use

(G-3177)
SANBORN PLASTICS CORP
415 Center St (44024-1054)
P.O. Box 267 (44024-0267)
PHONE................................440 286-4122
P Donald Sanborn, *CEO*
Mitch Sanborn, *President*
EMP: 80 **EST:** 1957
SQ FT: 40,000
SALES (est): 11.5MM **Privately Held**
SIC: 3089 3544 Injection molding of plastics; special dies, tools, jigs & fixtures

(G-3178)
SCREEN CRAFT PLASTICS
Also Called: Great Lakes Embroidery
695 South St Ste 7 (44024-1474)
P.O. Box 612 (44024-0612)
PHONE................................440 286-4060
Fax: 440 286-1306
Richard Lakatosh, *Owner*
Linda Lakatosh, *Co-Owner*
EMP: 3
SQ FT: 1,000
SALES (est): 100K **Privately Held**
SIC: 2759 Screen printing

(G-3179)
SHIFFLER EQUIPMENT SALES INC
745 South St (44024-2800)
P.O. Box 232 (44024-0232)
PHONE................................440 285-9175
John Shiffler, *CEO*
Mark C Lewis, *President*
Ed Rauckhorst, *Controller*
Greg Patterson, *Branch Mgr*
Dan Dececca, *Manager*
▲ **EMP:** 50
SQ FT: 30,000
SALES (est): 12.6MM **Privately Held**
WEB: www.shifflerequip.com
SIC: 2531 School furniture

(G-3180)
SOLON MANUFACTURING COMPANY
425 Center St (44024-1054)
P.O. Box 207 (44024-0207)
PHONE................................440 286-7149
J Timothy Dunn, *President*
Diane Popovich, *General Mgr*
George Davet, *Principal*
Steve Fowler, *Principal*
Jim Young, *Principal*
▲ **EMP:** 38
SQ FT: 30,000
SALES (est): 16.7MM **Privately Held**
WEB: www.solonmfg.com
SIC: 3823 3493 3643 3495 Pressure measurement instruments, industrial; cold formed springs; current-carrying wiring devices; wire springs; spring washers, metal

(G-3181)
TECHNISAND INC (DH)
Also Called: Santrol
11833 Ravenna Rd (44024-7006)
P.O. Box 87 (44024-0087)
PHONE................................440 285-3132
Jenniffer Deckard, *President*
William Conway, *Director*
▲ **EMP:** 3
SQ FT: 4,500
SALES (est): 106.4MM
SALES (corp-wide): 535MM **Publicly Held**
SIC: 1442 Sand mining
HQ: Fairmount Santrol Inc.
   8834 Mayfield Rd Ste A
   Chesterland OH 44026
   440 214-3200

(G-3182)
VACUUM FINISHING COMPANY
10275 Old State Rd (44024-9524)
P.O. Box 311 (44024-0311)
PHONE................................440 286-4386
Fax: 440 285-1784
John Sanker Jr, *President*
Michael J Sanker, *Corp Secy*
Steven Sanker, *Vice Pres*
EMP: 10
SQ FT: 30,000
SALES (est): 700K **Privately Held**
WEB: www.vacuumfinishing.com
SIC: 3944 3479 3471 Games, toys & children's vehicles; aluminum coating of metal products; plating & polishing

Charm
Holmes County

(G-3183)
CHARM HARNESS AND BOOT LTD
Also Called: Harness Shop
4432 County Road 70 (44617)
P.O. Box 114 (44617-0114)
PHONE................................330 893-0402
Roy A Miller, *President*
Allen Miller, *Manager*
Leroy Miller, *Manager*
EMP: 10
SQ FT: 8,000
SALES: 5MM **Privately Held**
SIC: 7251 3199 5661 7699 Shoe repair shop; harness or harness parts; shoe stores; harness repair shop

(G-3184)
RABER LUMBER CO
4112 State Rte 557 (44617)
P.O. Box 26 (44617-0026)
PHONE................................330 893-2797
Fax: 330 893-2797
Edward Raber, *Partner*
Ivan Miller, *Manager*
EMP: 7
SQ FT: 1,000
SALES (est): 952.2K **Privately Held**
SIC: 2421 2448 Sawmills & planing mills, general; pallets, wood

Chesapeake
Lawrence County

(G-3185)
CABELL HUNTINGTON
29 Candy Ln (45619-7090)
PHONE................................740 867-2665
Rhonda Crockett, *Principal*
EMP: 3
SALES (est): 207.2K **Privately Held**
SIC: 2834 Medicines, capsuled or ampuled

(G-3186)
COUNTY OF LAWRENCE
Also Called: Eastern Lawrnce Cty Watr Reclm
11100 Private Dr (45619)
P.O. Box 430 (45619-0430)
PHONE................................740 867-8700
Fax: 740 867-4292
Tim Porter, *Administration*
EMP: 10 **Privately Held**
SIC: 3589 Sewage & water treatment equipment
PA: County Of Lawrence
   115 S 5th St
   Ironton OH 45638
   740 532-3106

(G-3187)
G BIG INC (PA)
Also Called: Pickett Concrete
441 Rockwood Ave (45619-1120)
PHONE................................740 867-5758
Fax: 740 867-5758
John W Galloway, *President*
James W Galloway, *Vice Pres*
Todd A Galloway, *Vice Pres*
William Smith, *Manager*
EMP: 20 **EST:** 1960
SQ FT: 2,000
SALES (est): 2.2MM **Privately Held**
WEB: www.gbig.com
SIC: 3273 1771 Ready-mixed concrete; concrete work

(G-3188)
GERALD D DAMRON
197 Township Road 1156 (45619-8905)
PHONE................................740 894-3680
Gerald Damron, *Principal*
EMP: 4
SALES (est): 327.9K **Privately Held**
SIC: 2411 Logging

(G-3189)
PRECISION COMPONENT & MCH INC
17 Rosslyn Rd (45619)
P.O. Box 580 (45619-0580)
PHONE................................740 867-6366
Fax: 740 867-3409
Steve Chatteron, *President*
Stephanie Black, *Vice Pres*
EMP: 38
SQ FT: 24,000
SALES: 6.8MM **Privately Held**
SIC: 3069 Pump sleeves, rubber

(G-3190)
RIDGE ENTERPRISES INC
Also Called: Southern Ohio Machine Repr Sp
1940 County Road 2 (45619-7861)
P.O. Box 455 (45619-0455)
PHONE................................740 867-3456
Fax: 740 867-8910
Zimmerman Riley, *President*
Michael Riley, *Corp Secy*
EMP: 8
SQ FT: 6,000

SALES (est): 996.5K **Privately Held**
SIC: 3599 7692 3444 Machine shop, jobbing & repair; welding repair; sheet metalwork

(G-3191)
TITAN FIRE PROTECTION INC
146 Township Road 1523 (45619-8038)
PHONE.................................740 451-0838
Mitchell Kerns, *Vice Pres*
EMP: 3
SALES: 500K **Privately Held**
SIC: 3569 General industrial machinery

Cheshire
Gallia County

(G-3192)
HARSCO CORPORATION
5486 State Route 7 N (45620-9522)
P.O. Box 371 (45620-0371)
PHONE.................................740 367-7322
James D Taylor, *Manager*
EMP: 9
SQ FT: 300
SALES (corp-wide): 1.4B **Publicly Held**
SIC: 3295 Slag, crushed or ground
PA: Harsco Corporation
350 Poplar Church Rd
Camp Hill PA 17011
717 763-7064

Chesterland
Geauga County

(G-3193)
ABA GUTTERS INC
13046 Cherry Ln (44026-3025)
PHONE.................................440 729-2177
Bruce Bakula, *President*
EMP: 3
SALES (est): 280K **Privately Held**
SIC: 3444 Gutters, sheet metal

(G-3194)
ACME LABEL & TAG INC
9578 Mulberry Rd (44026-1647)
PHONE.................................440 729-1040
Dorothy R Herrick, *President*
Thomas G Herrick, *Vice Pres*
EMP: 5
SALES (est): 490K **Privately Held**
SIC: 5131 2679 Labels; labels, paper:
made from purchased material

(G-3195)
AEROTECH ENTERPRISE
8511 Mulberry Rd (44026-1437)
P.O. Box 596 (44026-0596)
PHONE.................................440 729-2616
Mike Matic, *President*
Andrea Matic, *Corp Secy*
EMP: 15
SQ FT: 6,000
SALES (est): 1.5MM **Privately Held**
SIC: 3599 Machine shop, jobbing & repair

(G-3196)
AJEH & COMPANY UNLIMITED
12497 Bentbrook Dr (44026-2404)
PHONE.................................440 729-2367
Linda McGraff, *President*
EMP: 6
SALES (est): 270K **Privately Held**
WEB: www.ajeh.com
SIC: 2791 7371 Typesetting; custom com-
puter programming services

(G-3197)
ALL FOR SHOW INC
9321 Winchester Vly (44026-3213)
PHONE.................................440 729-7186
Elaine L Sonnie, *President*
Wallace Sonnie, *Principal*
EMP: 4
SALES (est): 163.6K **Privately Held**
SIC: 2395 Embroidery & art needlework

(G-3198)
AMERICAN GRPHCAL SFTWR SYSTEMS
Also Called: American Grphcal Sftwr Systems
8000 Wedgewood Dr (44026-2162)
PHONE.................................440 729-0018
Salvatore Totino, *President*
Amy I Totino, *Corp Secy*
EMP: 3
SALES (est): 217.8K **Privately Held**
SIC: 7372 Educational computer software

(G-3199)
CHANNEL PRODUCTS INC (PA)
7100 Wilson Mills Rd (44026-1799)
PHONE.................................440 423-0113
Fax: 440 423-0891
Teresa Hack, *President*
Wayne Monaco, *Vice Pres*
Robert Greene, *Mfg Mgr*
Jeff Adams, *Facilities Mgr*
Suzanne French, *Purch Mgr*
▲ **EMP:** 80
SQ FT: 50,000
SALES (est): 15.6MM **Privately Held**
WEB: www.channelproducts.com
SIC: 3822 3679 3643 3625 Auto controls
regulating residntl & coml environmt & ap-
plncs; electronic circuits; current-carrying
wiring devices; relays & industrial con-
trols; machine tools, metal cutting type;
porcelain electrical supplies

(G-3200)
CHESTERLAND NEWS INC
8389 Mayfield Rd Ste B-4 (44026-2553)
PHONE.................................440 729-7667
Fax: 440 729-8240
Pamela Gable, *President*
EMP: 12
SALES (est): 749.5K **Privately Held**
SIC: 2711 Newspapers

(G-3201)
COMPUTER AIDED SOLUTIONS LLC
Also Called: Cas Data Loggers
8437 Mayfield Rd Ste 104a (44026-2538)
PHONE.................................440 729-2570
Laszlo Zala, *President*
Robin Brown, *Sales Associate*
Peter J Martin, *Marketing Staff*
Pete Martin,
Terry Nagy,
EMP: 20
SQ FT: 2,800
SALES (est): 4MM **Privately Held**
WEB: www.dataloggerinc.com
SIC: 3823 Data loggers, industrial process
type

(G-3202)
DEGAETANO SALES
8408 Mayfield Rd (44026-2524)
PHONE.................................440 729-8877
Nicholas Degaetano, *President*
Peg Baer, *Manager*
EMP: 3
SALES (est): 290K **Privately Held**
SIC: 3645 Chandeliers, residential

(G-3203)
ESSENCE MAKER
12819 Opalocka Dr (44026-2613)
PHONE.................................440 729-3894
Tracy Knake, *Principal*
EMP: 4 **EST:** 2010
SALES (est): 304.7K **Privately Held**
SIC: 2834 Dermatologicals

(G-3204)
FAIRMOUNT MINERALS LLC
Also Called: Fairmount Santrol
8834 Mayfield Rd Ste A (44026-2696)
P.O. Box 400 (44026)
PHONE.................................269 926-9450
Jennifer Deckard, *CEO*
EMP: 1100
SALES: 988MM **Privately Held**
SIC: 1446 Industrial sand

(G-3205)
FAIRMOUNT SANTROL HOLDINGS INC (PA)
8834 Mayfield Rd Ste A (44026-2696)
P.O. Box 87, Chardon (44024-0087)
PHONE.................................800 255-7263
Matthew F Lebaron, *Ch of Bd*
Jennifer D Deckard, *President*
Joseph D Fodo, *COO*
Gerald L Clancey, *Exec VP*
Van T Smith, *Exec VP*
◆ **EMP:** 8
SALES: 535MM **Publicly Held**
SIC: 1446 Industrial sand

(G-3206)
FAIRMOUNT SANTROL INC (HQ)
Also Called: Fairmount Minerals
8834 Mayfield Rd Ste A (44026-2696)
P.O. Box 87, Chardon (44024-0087)
PHONE.................................440 214-3200
Charles D Fowler, *CEO*
Jennifer D Deckard, *President*
William E Conway, *Chairman*
George Magaud, *Exec VP*
Joseph Fodo, *Vice Pres*
▼ **EMP:** 9
SALES (est): 299.2MM
SALES (corp-wide): 535MM **Publicly Held**
WEB: www.fairmountminerals.com
SIC: 2891 Adhesives
PA: Fairmount Santrol Holdings Inc.
8834 Mayfield Rd Ste A
Chesterland OH 44026
800 255-7263

(G-3207)
FML RESIN LLC
8834 Mayfield Rd (44026-2690)
PHONE.................................440 214-3200
Jennifer D Deckard, *President*
EMP: 27
SALES (est): 1.4MM **Privately Held**
SIC: 1442 Construction sand & gravel

(G-3208)
FML SAND LLC
8834 Mayfield Rd (44026-2690)
PHONE.................................440 214-3200
Chris Navel,
EMP: 6
SALES (est): 647.4K
SALES (corp-wide): 535MM **Publicly Held**
SIC: 1442 Common sand mining
HQ: Fairmount Santrol Inc.
8834 Mayfield Rd Ste A
Chesterland OH 44026
440 214-3200

(G-3209)
FML TERMINAL LOGISTICS LLC
8834 Mayfield Rd (44026-2690)
PHONE.................................440 214-3200
Jennifer Deckard, *President*
EMP: 71
SALES (est): 4.5MM
SALES (corp-wide): 535MM **Publicly Held**
SIC: 1442 Construction sand & gravel
HQ: Fairmount Santrol Inc.
8834 Mayfield Rd Ste A
Chesterland OH 44026
440 214-3200

(G-3210)
HF GROUP LLC (PA)
8844 Mayfield Rd (44026-2632)
PHONE.................................440 729-2445
Lori Johnson, *General Mgr*
Paul Parisi, *COO*
Steve Eisenberg, *Vice Pres*
Mark Melahn, *Vice Pres*
Tim Baker, *Plant Mgr*
EMP: 10
SQ FT: 6,000
SALES: 28MM **Privately Held**
SIC: 2732 Books: printing & binding

(G-3211)
HF GROUP LLC
8844 Mayfield Rd (44026-2632)
PHONE.................................440 729-9411
Terry Hymas, *Branch Mgr*
EMP: 550

SALES (corp-wide): 28MM **Privately Held**
SIC: 2732 Books: printing & binding
PA: Hf Group, Llc
8844 Mayfield Rd
Chesterland OH 44026
440 729-2445

(G-3212)
HF GROUP LLC
Also Called: General Book Binding
8844 Mayfield Rd (44026-2632)
PHONE.................................440 729-9411
Jim Bratton, *Branch Mgr*
Mickey Oflanagan, *Manager*
EMP: 62
SALES (corp-wide): 28MM **Privately Held**
SIC: 2732 Books: printing & binding
PA: Hf Group, Llc
8844 Mayfield Rd
Chesterland OH 44026
440 729-2445

(G-3213)
ICI BINDING CORP (PA)
8834 Mayfield Rd Ste A (44026-2696)
PHONE.................................440 729-2445
Fax: 440 729-3909
Jay Fairfield, *President*
Paul Parisi, *COO*
Steve Lund, *Controller*
EMP: 20
SALES (est): 46.1MM **Privately Held**
SIC: 2789 Bookbinding & related work

(G-3214)
MEISTERMATIC INC
12446 Bentbrook Dr (44026-2459)
PHONE.................................216 481-7773
Edward Kurnava, *President*
Joni Buzogany, *Manager*
Terry Kurnava, *Admin Sec*
EMP: 68 **EST:** 1963
SQ FT: 70,000
SALES (est): 8MM **Privately Held**
SIC: 3451 Screw machine products

(G-3215)
MIDWEST TELEMETRY INC
8251 Mayfield Rd Ste 15 (44026-2598)
PHONE.................................440 725-5718
Fax: 440 423-0053
Roger Rankin, *President*
EMP: 3 **EST:** 2012
SALES (est): 156.3K **Privately Held**
SIC: 8711 3825 Engineering services; in-
struments to measure electricity

(G-3216)
MORNING GLORY TECHNOLOGIES
12826 Morning Glory Trl (44026-2927)
PHONE.................................440 796-5076
Anthony May, *Owner*
EMP: 11
SALES: 106K **Privately Held**
SIC: 3599 Industrial machinery

(G-3217)
NITROJECTION
8430 Mayfield Rd (44026-2580)
PHONE.................................440 834-8790
Ana Leben, *Principal*
EMP: 8
SALES (est): 1MM **Privately Held**
SIC: 3089 Plastic processing

(G-3218)
ORGANON INC
7407 Cedar Rd (44026-3464)
PHONE.................................440 729-2290
EMP: 4
SALES (est): 327K **Privately Held**
SIC: 2834 Pharmaceutical preparations

(G-3219)
PATHOS LLC
Also Called: Pathos Printing
7948 Mayfield Rd (44026-2437)
PHONE.................................440 497-7278
Michael Ruddock,
EMP: 3
SALES (est): 71.1K **Privately Held**
SIC: 7372 Prepackaged software

(G-3220)
T A BACON CO
Also Called: Tabco
11655 Chillicothe Rd (44026-1927)
P.O. Box 21150, Cleveland (44121-0150)
PHONE..................................216 851-1404
Fax: 440 729-1251
Timothy Bacon, *President*
Ron Stelmarski, *Sales Mgr*
▲ EMP: 18
SQ FT: 45,000
SALES (est): 3.1MM **Privately Held**
WEB: www.tabcobodyparts.com
SIC: 3465 5013 Automotive stampings;
automotive stampings

(G-3221)
TDM FUELCELL LLC TDM LLC
12144 W Shiloh Dr (44026-2241)
PHONE..................................440 969-1442
Daniel V Judy, *President*
EMP: 3
SQ FT: 1,000
SALES (est): 297.9K **Privately Held**
SIC: 3769 Casings, missiles & missile
components: storage

(G-3222)
TRULINE INDUSTRIES INC
11685 Chillicothe Rd (44026-1927)
P.O. Box 307 (44026-0307)
PHONE..................................440 729-0140
Fax: 440 729-6022
Court Durkalski, *CEO*
Stuart Watson, *President*
Frank Durkalski, *Chairman*
Joan Durkalski, *Corp Secy*
Donald Tanski, *QC Dir*
EMP: 52 EST: 1939
SQ FT: 24,000
SALES (est): 10.2MM **Privately Held**
WEB: www.trulineind.com
SIC: 3728 Aircraft parts & equipment

(G-3223)
WESTERN RESERVE GRAPHICS
13404 Caves Rd (44026-3421)
PHONE..................................440 729-9527
Fax: 440 729-1705
Charles R Damko, *Owner*
EMP: 3
SALES: 150K **Privately Held**
SIC: 2752 Commercial printing, litho-
graphic

Chesterville
Morrow County

(G-3224)
CENTRAL OHIO ASPHALT LLC
7250a W State Rt 95 E (43317)
P.O. Box 248 (43317-0248)
PHONE..................................419 768-4211
David Porter,
Tony Porter,
EMP: 3
SALES (est): 405.8K **Privately Held**
SIC: 2951 Asphalt paving mixtures &
blocks

Chickasaw
Mercer County

(G-3225)
CHICKASAW MACHINE & TL CO INC
3050 Chickasaw Rd (45826)
PHONE..................................419 925-4325
Fax: 419 925-5804
Norbert B Tangeman, *President*
Ted Homan, *Vice Pres*
Dave Tangeman, *Vice Pres*
Beth Fortkamp, *Office Mgr*
▼ EMP: 14 EST: 1960
SQ FT: 18,000
SALES: 3.8MM **Privately Held**
SIC: 3599 Machine shop, jobbing & repair

Chillicothe
Ross County

(G-3226)
ADVANTAGE TENT FITTINGS INC
11661 Pleasant Valley Rd (45601-8315)
PHONE..................................740 773-3015
Robert Hall, *Ch of Bd*
Benjamin Hall, *President*
Barry Smith, *Sales Mgr*
Judy Williamson, *Manager*
▼ EMP: 10
SQ FT: 14,000
SALES (est): 944K **Privately Held**
WEB: www.aadvantagetent.com
SIC: 2431 5091 2394 Millwork; sporting &
recreation goods; canvas & related prod-
ucts

(G-3227)
ALL SIGNS OF CHILLICOTHE INC
559 N High St (45601-1636)
PHONE..................................740 773-5016
Fax: 740 773-5016
Sheri Oliver, *President*
Kris Oliver, *Vice Pres*
Gene Griesheimer, *Manager*
Kristine M Oliver, *Manager*
EMP: 9
SQ FT: 4,200
SALES (est): 1MM **Privately Held**
WEB: www.allsignsofohio.com
SIC: 3993 1799 Signs & advertising spe-
cialties; sign installation & maintenance

(G-3228)
BBB MUSIC LLC
20 E Water St (45601-2534)
PHONE..................................740 772-2262
Bob Green,
Sarah Lambert,
EMP: 8
SALES: 300K **Privately Held**
SIC: 3931 5736 Musical instruments; mu-
sical instrument stores

(G-3229)
BELL LOGISTICS CO
27311 Old Route 35 (45601-8110)
P.O. Box 91 (45601-0091)
PHONE..................................740 702-9830
Jon Bell, *President*
Deana Bell, *Vice Pres*
EMP: 30
SQ FT: 25,000
SALES: 10MM **Privately Held**
SIC: 3715 Truck trailers

(G-3230)
BROCK RAD & WLDG FABRICATION
Also Called: Brocks RAD Wldg Fabrication I
370 Douglas Ave (45601-3662)
PHONE..................................740 773-2540
Fax: 740 773-2541
David J Brock, *President*
Nancy Brock, *Corp Secy*
EMP: 8
SQ FT: 12,000
SALES (est): 1.2MM **Privately Held**
SIC: 7539 7692 Radiator repair shop, au-
tomotive; automotive welding

(G-3231)
CAPITAL MACHINE & FABRICATION
162 Commercial Cir (45601-3673)
PHONE..................................740 773-4976
Royce Rinehart, *Owner*
EMP: 5
SALES (est): 340K **Privately Held**
SIC: 3599 Machine & other job shop work

(G-3232)
CHILLICOTHE PACKAGING CORP
Also Called: Churmac Industries
4168 State Route 159 (45601-8695)
P.O. Box 466 (45601-0466)
PHONE..................................740 773-5800

Fax: 740 774-4270
Michael McCarty, *President*
Kevin North, *Director*
EMP: 40
SQ FT: 60,000
SALES (est): 9.2MM **Privately Held**
SIC: 2653 Pads, corrugated: made from
purchased materials

(G-3233)
CHUB GIBSONS LOGGING
391 Fyffe Hollow Rd (45601-7803)
PHONE..................................740 884-4079
EMP: 4 EST: 2005
SALES: 230K **Privately Held**
SIC: 2411 Logging

(G-3234)
CHURMAC INDUSTRIES INC
Also Called: Chillicothe Packing
4168 State Route 159 (45601-8695)
P.O. Box 205 (45601-0205)
PHONE..................................740 773-5800
Michael McCarty, *President*
Kevin North, *CFO*
EMP: 25
SQ FT: 60,000
SALES (est): 3.6MM **Privately Held**
SIC: 2631 Paperboard mills

(G-3235)
CRISPIE CREME OF CHILLICOTHE
Also Called: Grandpa Jack's
47 N Bridge St (45601-2615)
PHONE..................................740 774-3770
Richard Renison, *President*
James M Renison, *Vice Pres*
EMP: 36
SQ FT: 2,500
SALES: 500K **Privately Held**
SIC: 2051 5461 Doughnuts, except
frozen; doughnuts

(G-3236)
DEWARD PUBLISHING CO LTD
278 Scott Rd (45601-9183)
PHONE..................................800 300-9778
Daniel Degarmo, *Principal*
EMP: 4
SALES (est): 264.5K **Privately Held**
SIC: 2741 Miscellaneous publishing

(G-3237)
DOUGLAS INDUSTRIES LLC
379 Douglas Ave (45601-3663)
P.O. Box 6188 (45601-6188)
PHONE..................................740 775-2400
Lisa Diehl, *Manager*
Gloria Eyre,
Larry Eyre,
EMP: 24
SALES (est): 4.2MM **Privately Held**
SIC: 3272 Concrete products

(G-3238)
G & J ASPHALT & MATERIAL INC
379 Seney Rd (45601-8396)
PHONE..................................740 773-6358
Chad Jordan, *President*
Tricia Pardfard, *Admin Sec*
EMP: 12
SALES (est): 2.3MM **Privately Held**
SIC: 3531 Asphalt plant, including gravel-
mix type

(G-3239)
G & J PEPSI-COLA BOTTLERS INC
Also Called: Pepsico
400 E 7th St (45601-3455)
PHONE..................................740 774-2148
Fax: 740 774-1160
Henry Thrapp, *Sales & Mktg St*
John Miller, *Finance Mgr*
EMP: 45
SALES (corp-wide): 490.5MM **Privately Held**
WEB: www.gjpepsi.com
SIC: 5149 2086 Starch; bottled & canned
soft drinks

PA: G & J Pepsi-Cola Bottlers Inc
9435 Waterstone Blvd # 390
Cincinnati OH 45249
513 785-6060

(G-3240)
GANNETT CO INC
Also Called: Chillicothe Gazette
50 W Main St (45601-3103)
PHONE..................................740 773-2111
Fax: 740 772-9501
Mike Therone, *Principal*
Carl Lovern, *Vice Pres*
Donna Duffey, *Sales Mgr*
Ron Clausen, *Adv Dir*
Connie Gaul, *Personnel Assit*
EMP: 108
SALES (corp-wide): 3B **Publicly Held**
WEB: www.gannett.com
SIC: 2711 2752 Newspapers: publishing
only, not printed on site; commercial print-
ing, lithographic
PA: Gannett Co., Inc.
7950 Jones Branch Dr
Mc Lean VA 22102
703 854-6000

(G-3241)
GRAPHIC PLUS
712 Overlook Heights Ln (45601-8452)
PHONE..................................740 701-1860
Marsha Landrum, *Owner*
EMP: 3
SALES (est): 263.5K **Privately Held**
SIC: 2261 Screen printing of cotton broad-
woven fabrics

(G-3242)
HANSON AGGREGATES EAST LLC
Hanson Aggregates Davon
33 Renick Ave (45601-2895)
P.O. Box 228 (45601-0228)
PHONE..................................740 773-2172
Steve Guill, *Opers Mgr*
Leonard McFerren, *Manager*
Paul J Roeder, *Director*
EMP: 25
SALES (corp-wide): 16B **Privately Held**
SIC: 3273 3271 3272 1442 Ready-mixed
concrete; blocks, concrete or cinder: stan-
dard; concrete products; construction
sand & gravel
HQ: Hanson Aggregates East Llc
3131 Rdu Center Dr
Morrisville NC 27560
919 380-2500

(G-3243)
HERR FOODS INCORPORATED
476 E 7th St (45601-3455)
PHONE..................................740 773-8282
Fax: 740 775-8286
Shawn Martindale, *General Mgr*
Mike Cook, *Prdtn Mgr*
Scott Carmenan, *Sales/Mktg Mgr*
EMP: 40
SQ FT: 1,000
SALES (corp-wide): 451MM **Privately Held**
WEB: www.herrs.com
SIC: 2096 Potato chips & other potato-
based snacks
PA: Herr Foods Incorporated
20 Herr Dr
Nottingham PA 19362
610 932-9330

(G-3244)
HUSTON GIFTS DOLLS AND FLOWERS
Also Called: Huston Gift Shop
306 Fairway Ave (45601-1258)
PHONE..................................740 775-9141
Fax: 740 663-2881
Pamela Caldwell, *President*
James M Caldwell, *Vice Pres*
EMP: 3
SQ FT: 1,200
SALES (est): 160K **Privately Held**
SIC: 5947 3942 5992 5092 Gift shop;
dolls, except stuffed toy animals; flowers,
fresh; plants, potted; dolls; flowers, fresh

(G-3245)
INFOSIGHT CORPORATION
20700 Us Highway 23 (45601-9016)
P.O. Box 5000 (45601-7000)
PHONE..................................740 642-3600
Fax: 740 642-5001
John A Robertson, *CEO*
G D Hudelson, *President*
Becky Dolan, *General Mgr*
John Redfearn, *General Mgr*
Al Hauswirth, *Plant Mgr*
▲ EMP: 65
SQ FT: 30,000
SALES: 13.1MM **Privately Held**
WEB: www.infosight.com
SIC: 3953 Figures (marking devices),
   metal

(G-3246)
JASON C GIBSON
414 Bethel Rd (45601-8060)
PHONE..................................740 663-4520
Jason C Gibson, *Owner*
EMP: 13
SALES (est): 900K **Privately Held**
SIC: 2411 Logging

(G-3247)
JIM BUMEN CONSTRUCTION
COMPANY (PA)
3218 S Bridge St (45601-9361)
PHONE..................................740 663-2659
James Bumen, *President*
Jane Bumen, *Vice Pres*
Julie Stewart, *Admin Sec*
EMP: 6
SALES (est): 691K **Privately Held**
SIC: 3272 1542 1541 Concrete products,
   precast; commercial & office building,
   new construction; industrial buildings,
   new construction

(G-3248)
KAMAN INDUSTRIAL TECH
CORP
1404 Delano Rd (45601-8440)
PHONE..................................740 779-9201
Steven J Smidler, *Branch Mgr*
EMP: 9
SALES (corp-wide): 1.8B **Publicly Held**
SIC: 3491 Industrial valves
HQ: Kaman Industrial Technologies Corpo-
   ration
   1 Vision Way
   Bloomfield CT 06002
   860 687-5000

(G-3249)
M & M FABRICATION INC
18828 Us Highway 50 (45601-9268)
PHONE..................................740 779-3071
Fax: 740 779-3860
Gary Timmons, *President*
Greg Hopkins, *Manager*
EMP: 10
SALES (est): 2MM **Privately Held**
SIC: 3441 Fabricated structural metal

(G-3250)
MCRD ENTERPRISES LLC
Also Called: Art Tech
337 E Main St (45601-3415)
P.O. Box 368 (45601-0368)
PHONE..................................740 775-2377
Randy Drewyor,
EMP: 10
SALES (est): 1MM **Privately Held**
SIC: 3993 Signs & advertising specialties

(G-3251)
MENASHA PACKAGING
COMPANY LLC
291 S Mcarthur St (45601-3623)
PHONE..................................740 773-8204
Robert Krajci, *Manager*
Scott Heck, *Manager*
EMP: 18
SALES (corp-wide): 1.8B **Privately Held**
SIC: 2653 Sheets, corrugated: made from
   purchased materials
HQ: Menasha Packaging Company, Llc
   1645 Bergstrom Rd
   Neenah WI 54956
   920 751-1000

(G-3252)
MISCELLNOUS MTALS
FBRCTION INC
18828 Us Highway 50 (45601-9268)
PHONE..................................740 779-3071
Robert J Onda, *President*
EMP: 4
SALES (est): 502.7K **Privately Held**
SIC: 3499 Friction material, made from
   powdered metal

(G-3253)
NAW PETROLEUM SERVICE
80 Cameo Ln (45601-8536)
PHONE..................................740 464-7988
Wilby A Nelson, *Owner*
EMP: 4
SALES: 830K **Privately Held**
SIC: 1389 Oil & gas field services

(G-3254)
OPTIMAS OE SOLUTIONS LLC
101 S Mcarthur St (45601-3630)
PHONE..................................740 774-4553
Robert Hitchens, *Branch Mgr*
EMP: 8
SALES (corp-wide): 123.7MM **Privately Held**
SIC: 3965 Fasteners
HQ: Optimas Oe Solutions, Llc
   2651 Compass Rd
   Glenview IL 60026
   224 999-1000

(G-3255)
ORBIS RPM LLC
5938 State Route 159 (45601-8956)
PHONE..................................740 772-6355
Fax: 740 772-6348
Scott Smittle, *General Mgr*
EMP: 5
SALES (corp-wide): 1.8B **Privately Held**
WEB: www.orbiscorporation.com
SIC: 3081 Polypropylene film & sheet
HQ: Orbis Rpm, Llc
   1055 Corporate Center Dr
   Oconomowoc WI 53066
   262 560-5000

(G-3256)
P H GLATFELTER COMPANY
Also Called: Chillicothe Facility
232 E 8th St (45601-3364)
PHONE..................................740 772-3111
Fred Tardy, *Superintendent*
John Purdum, *Business Mgr*
John R Blind, *Vice Pres*
Jim Anderson, *Opers Mgr*
Martin Graves, *Maint Spvr*
EMP: 100
SALES (corp-wide): 1.6B **Publicly Held**
SIC: 2621 Book paper; copy paper; enve-
   lope paper; filter paper
PA: P. H. Glatfelter Company
   96 S George St Ste 520
   York PA 17401
   717 225-4711

(G-3257)
PACCAR INC
65 Kenworth Dr (45601-8829)
P.O. Box 2345 (45601-0998)
PHONE..................................740 774-5111
Brian Davis, *General Mgr*
Linda Madison, *Opers Mgr*
Straub Jack, *Materials Mgr*
Nick Corcoran, *Traffic Mgr*
Mike Seymour, *Buyer*
EMP: 2000
SALES (corp-wide): 17B **Publicly Held**
WEB: www.paccar.com
SIC: 3711 3715 3713 Truck & tractor
   truck assembly; truck trailers; truck & bus
   bodies
PA: Paccar Inc
   777 106th Ave Ne
   Bellevue WA 98004
   425 468-7400

(G-3258)
PARRY CO
33630 Old Route 35 (45601-9117)
PHONE..................................740 884-4893
Fax: 740 884-4892
Dave Merideth, *President*
Cassandra Bolt-Merideth, *Vice Pres*
EMP: 9
SQ FT: 30,000
SALES (est): 870K **Privately Held**
WEB: www.parryco.com
SIC: 1446 Industrial sand

(G-3259)
PEGASUS INDUSTRIES
104 S Mcarthur St (45601-3600)
PHONE..................................740 772-1049
Gwen Van Horn, *Principal*
EMP: 3
SALES (est): 205.5K **Privately Held**
SIC: 3999 Manufacturing industries

(G-3260)
PELLETIER BROTHERS MFG
4000 Sulphur Lick Rd (45601-8972)
PHONE..................................740 774-4704
Fax: 740 774-1252
Chris Pelletier, *President*
Mark Pelletier, *Vice Pres*
EMP: 16
SQ FT: 7,000
SALES (est): 2.3MM **Privately Held**
SIC: 3312 Ferroalloys, produced in blast
   furnaces

(G-3261)
PERKINS LOGGING LLC
361 Perkins Rd (45601-9501)
PHONE..................................740 288-7311
Roger Perkins,
EMP: 4
SALES: 1.8MM **Privately Held**
SIC: 2411 Logging

(G-3262)
PERKINS WOOD PRODUCTS
8686 Limerick Rd (45601-9508)
PHONE..................................740 884-4046
EMP: 8
SALES (est): 440K **Privately Held**
SIC: 2411 Logging

(G-3263)
PITTSBURGH GLASS WORKS
LLC
848 Southern Ave (45601-9123)
PHONE..................................740 774-7600
Jerrry Hornyak, *Manager*
Lawrence Hanchin, *Products*
EMP: 90
SALES (corp-wide): 457.8MM **Privately Held**
SIC: 3231 Insulating glass: made from pur-
   chased glass
HQ: Pittsburgh Glass Works, Llc
   30 Isabella St Ste 500
   Pittsburgh PA 15212
   412 995-6500

(G-3264)
PPG INDUSTRIES INC
Also Called: PPG Chillicothe
848 Southern Ave (45601-9123)
PHONE..................................740 774-8734
Amanda Moore, *Accountant*
EMP: 6
SALES (corp-wide): 14.7B **Publicly Held**
SIC: 2851 Paints & allied products
PA: Ppg Industries, Inc.
   1 Ppg Pl
   Pittsburgh PA 15272
   412 434-3131

(G-3265)
PPG INDUSTRIES INC
Also Called: PPG Regional Support Center
848 Southern Ave (45601-9123)
PHONE..................................740 774-7600
Fax: 740 774-7665
Melissa Wills, *Manager*
EMP: 37
SALES (corp-wide): 14.7B **Publicly Held**
SIC: 2851 Paints & allied products
PA: Ppg Industries, Inc.
   1 Ppg Pl
   Pittsburgh PA 15272
   412 434-3131

(G-3266)
PPG INDUSTRIES INC
Also Called: P P G Regional Support Center
848 Southern Ave (45601-9123)
P.O. Box 7025 (45601)
PHONE..................................740 774-7600
EMP: 12
SALES (corp-wide): 14.7B **Publicly Held**
SIC: 2851 Paints & allied products
PA: Ppg Industries, Inc.
   1 Ppg Pl
   Pittsburgh PA 15272
   412 434-3131

(G-3267)
PRC - DESOTO INTERNATIONAL
INC
Also Called: PRC Desoto International
848 Southern Ave (45601-9123)
PHONE..................................800 772-9378
EMP: 11
SALES (corp-wide): 14.7B **Publicly Held**
SIC: 2891 Adhesives & sealants
HQ: Prc - Desoto International, Inc.
   24811 Ave Rockefeller
   Valencia CA 91355
   661 678-4209

(G-3268)
PRINTEX INCORPORATED (PA)
Also Called: Printex-Same Day Printing
185 E Main St (45601-2507)
PHONE..................................740 773-0088
Fax: 740 773-0146
Jeffrey G Marshall, *President*
Gene T Marshall, *Vice Pres*
Janet Fox, *Manager*
Leila Hartland, *Manager*
Brenda Ison, *Manager*
EMP: 10 EST: 1975
SQ FT: 3,000
SALES (est): 1.6MM **Privately Held**
SIC: 2752 2732 2759 Commercial print-
   ing, lithographic; commercial printing, off-
   set; books: printing only; letterpress
   printing

(G-3269)
QC INDUSTRIAL INC
526 Red Bud Rd (45601-9002)
PHONE..................................740 642-5004
Cyndi Davis, *General Mgr*
EMP: 5
SALES (est): 588K **Privately Held**
SIC: 3441 Fabricated structural metal

(G-3270)
R L S CORPORATION
Also Called: R L S Recycling
990 Eastern Ave (45601-3658)
P.O. Box 327 (45601-0327)
PHONE..................................740 773-1440
Charles Stevens, *President*
EMP: 25 EST: 1923
SQ FT: 14,000
SALES (est): 3.3MM **Privately Held**
SIC: 5093 3341 Metal scrap & waste ma-
   terials; waste paper; secondary nonfer-
   rous metals

(G-3271)
RIFFLE MACHINE WORKS INC
(PA)
Also Called: Riffle & Sons
5746 State Route 159 (45601-8956)
PHONE..................................740 775-2838
Fax: 740 775-7028
Bob Riffle, *President*
Mark Riffle, *Vice Pres*
Mike Riffle, *Vice Pres*
Tim Riffle, *Vice Pres*
EMP: 12
SQ FT: 3,500
SALES (est): 2.6MM **Privately Held**
SIC: 3599 Machine shop, jobbing & repair

(G-3272)
RITA FISHEL INC
Also Called: Creation Sew Clever
192 S Paint St (45601-3827)
PHONE..................................740 775-1957
Fax: 740 773-2390
Rita Fishel, *President*
Ronald Fishel, *Vice Pres*
EMP: 20

SQ FT: 2,000
SALES (est): 1.4MM Privately Held
WEB: www.creationssewclever.com
SIC: 5621 5641 5949 2339 Women's clothing stores; children's wear; fabric stores piece goods; women's & misses' outerwear; girls' & children's outerwear; women's & children's clothing

(G-3273)
ROSS-CO REDI-MIX CO INC (PA)
689 Marietta Rd (45601-8437)
PHONE....................................740 775-4466
Fax: 740 775-4273
Todd Wrightsel, President
Thomas Overly, Principal
Connie Wrightsel, Corp Secy
EMP: 15 EST: 1962
SQ FT: 2,400
SALES (est): 6MM Privately Held
SIC: 3273 Ready-mixed concrete

(G-3274)
S & C NEWMAN ENTERPRISES INC
Also Called: She Said Yes Bridal & Formal
66 E Water St (45601-2544)
PHONE....................................740 772-7433
Cyndi Newman, President
EMP: 4
SALES (est): 340K Privately Held
SIC: 2335 Bridal & formal gowns

(G-3275)
SHELLY MATERIALS INC
1177 Hopetown Rd (45601-8224)
PHONE....................................740 775-4567
Rusty Scott, Manager
EMP: 19
SALES (corp-wide): 28.6B Privately Held
SIC: 1442 Gravel mining
HQ: Shelly Materials, Inc.
80 Park Dr
Thornville OH 43076
740 246-6315

(G-3276)
STANDARD CAR TRUCK COMPANY
Also Called: Barber Spring Ohio
387 Wetzel Dr (45601-2873)
P.O. Box 243 (45601-0243)
PHONE....................................740 775-6450
Scott Diehl, Branch Mgr
EMP: 75
SALES (corp-wide): 2.9B Publicly Held
SIC: 3549 3677 3743 Coil winding machines for springs; electronic coils, transformers & other inductors; freight cars & equipment
HQ: Standard Car Truck Company Inc
6400 Shafer Ct Ste 450
Rosemont IL 60018
847 692-6050

(G-3277)
STAT INDUSTRIES INC (PA)
Also Called: Stat Index Tab
137 Stone Rd (45601-9709)
PHONE....................................740 779-6561
Fax: 740 779-6566
Robert Kellough, CEO
Chris Kellough, Principal
Susanna Kellough, CFO
Robyn Kellough, Controller
EMP: 7
SQ FT: 6,000
SALES: 930K Privately Held
WEB: www.statindex.com
SIC: 2675 Index cards, die-cut: made from purchased materials

(G-3278)
STAT INDUSTRIES INC
Also Called: Stat Index Tab Company
137 Stone Rd (45601-9709)
PHONE....................................740 779-6561
Robert Kellough, President
EMP: 6
SALES (corp-wide): 930K Privately Held
WEB: www.statindex.com
SIC: 2675 Index cards, die-cut: made from purchased materials

PA: Stat Industries, Inc.
137 Stone Rd
Chillicothe OH 45601
740 779-6561

(G-3279)
SUPER FINE SHINE INC
2806 Patton Hill Rd Lot 6 (45601-3763)
PHONE....................................740 774-1700
Philip Velez, Principal
EMP: 5
SALES (est): 350.6K Privately Held
SIC: 3471 Plating & polishing

(G-3280)
TECHNOLOGY AND SERVICES INC
1336 Baum Hill Rd (45601-9179)
PHONE....................................740 626-2020
John Parks, CEO
Richmond Parks, Treasurer
▼ EMP: 8
SQ FT: 7,000
SALES (est): 1.4MM Privately Held
WEB: www.technologyandservices.com
SIC: 3953 7371 Marking devices; custom computer programming services

(G-3281)
TRIM SYSTEMS OPERATING CORP
75 Chamber Dr (45601-7612)
PHONE....................................740 772-5998
Eric Conley, Branch Mgr
Patrick Turner, Manager
Dan Neil, Director
EMP: 178
SALES (corp-wide): 662.1MM Publicly Held
SIC: 2396 Automotive & apparel trimmings
HQ: Trim Systems Operating Corp.
7800 Walton Pkwy
New Albany OH 43054
614 289-5360

(G-3282)
TRUGREEN CLEANERS LLC
1733 Anderson Station Rd (45601-7909)
PHONE....................................740 703-1063
Francis L Breeden,
EMP: 3
SALES (est): 198.2K Privately Held
SIC: 2869 Industrial organic chemicals

(G-3283)
TYKMA INC
Also Called: Tykma Electrox
370 Gateway Dr (45601-3976)
P.O. Box 917 (45601-0917)
PHONE....................................877 318-9562
David Grimes, President
Connie Hedges, General Mgr
Rick Weisbarth, Vice Pres
Adell Sams, Materials Mgr
Mark Bragg, Engineer
EMP: 21
SQ FT: 10,500
SALES (est): 6.4MM
SALES (corp-wide): 64.1MM Privately Held
WEB: www.permanentmarking.com
SIC: 3541 3555 Machine tools, metal cutting type; engraving machinery & equipment, except plates
HQ: 600 Group Incorporated
1819 N Pitcher St
Kalamazoo MI 49007
269 345-7155

(G-3284)
YSK CORPORATION
1 Colomet Rd (45601-8819)
PHONE....................................740 774-7315
Fax: 740 775-2221
Kenzaburo Matsuo, President
Reiichi Hohda, President
Ginger Rausch, QC Mgr
Les Davis, Senior Engr
Dan Turner, Senior Engr
▲ EMP: 279
SQ FT: 200,000

SALES (est): 65.1MM
SALES (corp-wide): 238.6MM Privately Held
WEB: www.yskcorp.com
SIC: 3469 Machine parts, stamped or pressed metal; household cooking & kitchen utensils, metal.,
PA: Yanagawa Seiki Co.,Ltd.
1-3-5, Shinsayama
Sayama STM 350-1
429 535-151

Cincinnati
Clermont County

(G-3285)
5ME LLC
4270 Ivy Pointe Blvd # 100 (45245-0004)
PHONE....................................513 719-1600
William A Horwarth, President
Jeffery Price, Vice Pres
Chris Chapman, CFO
EMP: 45
SALES (est): 9MM
SALES (corp-wide): 9.9MM Privately Held
SIC: 3544 8742 Special dies, tools, jigs & fixtures; business consultant
PA: 5me Holdings Llc
4270 Ivy Pointe Blvd # 100
Cincinnati OH 45245
859 534-4872

(G-3286)
5ME HOLDINGS LLC (PA)
4270 Ivy Pointe Blvd # 100 (45245-0004)
PHONE....................................859 534-4872
William A Horwath, President
EMP: 1
SALES: 9.9MM Privately Held
SIC: 3544 8742 Special dies, tools, jigs & fixtures; business consultant

(G-3287)
A & P TECHNOLOGY INC
4599 E Tech Dr (45245)
PHONE....................................513 688-3200
Andrew Head, President
Luke Domet, CFO
Keith Cnarr, Manager
EMP: 26 Privately Held
SIC: 2241 Webbing, braids & belting
PA: A & P Technology, Inc.
4595 E Tech Dr
Cincinnati OH 45245

(G-3288)
A & P TECHNOLOGY INC
4622 E Tech Dr (45245-1000)
PHONE....................................513 688-3200
Andrew Head, President
EMP: 99
SALES (est): 2.8MM Privately Held
SIC: 2241 Narrow fabric mills

(G-3289)
A & P TECHNOLOGY INC
4578 E Tech Dr (45245-1054)
PHONE....................................513 688-3200
Andrew Head, President
EMP: 99
SALES (est): 3.7MM Privately Held
SIC: 2241 Narrow fabric mills

(G-3290)
A & P TECHNOLOGY INC
4624 E Tech Dr (45245)
PHONE....................................513 688-3200
Rhonda Slominski, Branch Mgr
EMP: 31
SQ FT: 1,880 Privately Held
WEB: www.braider.com
SIC: 2241 Narrow fabric mills
PA: A & P Technology, Inc.
4595 E Tech Dr
Cincinnati OH 45245

(G-3291)
A & P TECHNOLOGY INC (PA)
4595 E Tech Dr (45245-1055)
PHONE....................................513 688-3200
Fax: 513 688-3201
Andrew A Head, President

Timothy Lofton, Prdtn Mgr
Yvonne Doyen, Purch Mgr
Sandra Ramsdell, Purch Agent
Zach Peck, Project Engr
▲ EMP: 20
SQ FT: 75,000
SALES (est): 53.9MM Privately Held
WEB: www.braider.com
SIC: 2241 Webbing, braids & belting

(G-3292)
ADGO INCORPORATED
3988 Mcmann Rd (45245-2308)
PHONE....................................513 752-6880
Fax: 513 752-5723
Robert C Reynolds, President
Rick Elliott, Vice Pres
Mike Cliett, Treasurer
Lynn Green, Sales Mgr
Gary Collier, Director
EMP: 23 EST: 1957
SQ FT: 30,000
SALES (est): 8.3MM Privately Held
WEB: www.adgoinc.com
SIC: 3613 Control panels, electric

(G-3293)
ALUFAB INC
1018 Seabrook Way (45245-1963)
PHONE....................................513 528-7281
Doug Nimmo, President
Fred Mileham, Vice Pres
▲ EMP: 6
SQ FT: 4,000
SALES: 2.2MM Privately Held
SIC: 3441 Fabricated structural metal

(G-3294)
BEACHS TREES SELECTIVE HARVEST
915 Wilma Cir (45245-2220)
PHONE....................................513 289-5976
Brian Beach, Principal
Mike Beach,
Steve Beach,
EMP: 15 EST: 2013
SQ FT: 2,500
SALES (est): 843.7K Privately Held
SIC: 2411 Logging

(G-3295)
CLIPPER PRODUCTS INC
675 Cncnnati Batavia Pike (45245-1028)
PHONE....................................513 688-7300
Fax: 513 528-7676
Gerold J Zobrist, Ch of Bd
David J Durham, President
EMP: 6
SQ FT: 16,000
SALES (est): 360K Privately Held
WEB: www.clipperproducts.com
SIC: 3161 Cases, carrying; sample cases

(G-3296)
CURTISS-WRIGHT FLOW CONTROL
Qualtech NP
4600 E Tech Dr (45245-1000)
PHONE....................................513 528-7900
Mark Chatham, Opers Staff
Tim Geers, Engineer
Marion Mitchell, Branch Mgr
Mike Wooldridge, Manager
Tami Cann, Admin Asst
EMP: 88
SALES (corp-wide): 2.1B Publicly Held
WEB: www.et.curtisswright.com
SIC: 3491 3599 3443 1799 Industrial valves; machine shop, jobbing & repair; plate work for the nuclear industry; diamond drilling & sawing
HQ: Curtiss-Wright Flow Control Service Corporation
2950 E Birch St
Brea CA 92821
714 982-1898

(G-3297)
CURTISS-WRIGHT FLOW CONTROL
Also Called: Qualtech NP
4600 E Tech Dr (45245-1000)
PHONE....................................513 528-7900
Kurt Mitchell, Branch Mgr
EMP: 88

SALES (corp-wide): 2.1B **Publicly Held**
SIC: 3491 8734 3441 Industrial valves;
testing laboratories; fabricated structural
metal
HQ: Curtiss-Wright Flow Control Service
Corporation
2950 E Birch St
Brea CA 92821
714 982-1898

(G-3298)
CURTISS-WRIGHT FLOW CTRL CORP
Also Called: Qualtech NP
4600 E Tech Dr (45245-1000)
PHONE...................................513 528-7900
Dwaine A Godfrey, *Vice Pres*
John Jolley, *Project Mgr*
Lucy Miller, *Safety Mgr*
John D Clark, *Sales Executive*
Don Clark, *Marketing Mgr*
EMP: 82
SALES (corp-wide): 2.1B **Publicly Held**
SIC: 3443 8734 Fabricated plate work
(boiler shop); testing laboratories
HQ: Curtiss-Wright Flow Control Corpora-
tion
1966 Broadhollow Rd Ste E
Farmingdale NY 11735
631 293-3800

(G-3299)
DRS MOBILE ENVIRONMNTL SVC
4043 Mcmann Rd (45245-1960)
PHONE...................................513 943-1111
Rich Reynolds, *Principal*
EMP: 5
SALES (est): 365.6K **Privately Held**
SIC: 3812 Search & navigation equipment

(G-3300)
ELECTRODYNAMICS INC
Also Called: L-3 Cmmnctions Electrodynam-
ics
3975 Mcmann Rd (45245-2307)
PHONE...................................847 259-0740
Donald A Spetter, *President*
Steven M Post, *Senior VP*
Brenda Butts, *Transptn Dir*
Deb Ridley, *Mfg Mgr*
Karen Campbell, *Mfg Staff*
EMP: 195
SQ FT: 46,000
SALES (est): 44.5MM
SALES (corp-wide): 10.5B **Publicly Held**
SIC: 3577 3812 3824 3823 Data conver-
sion equipment, media-to-media: com-
puter; flight recorders; controls, revolution
& timing instruments; counter type regis-
ters; industrial instrmnts msrmnt
display/control process variable; relays &
industrial controls
PA: L3 Technologies, Inc.
600 3rd Ave Fl 34
New York NY 10016
212 697-1111

(G-3301)
ELITE BIOMEDICAL SOLUTIONS LLC
756 Old State Route 74 C (45245-1277)
PHONE...................................513 207-0602
Jeff Smith, *CEO*
Nate Smith,
EMP: 13
SALES: 3.5MM **Privately Held**
SIC: 3841 7699 7389 Surgical & medical
instruments; medical equipment repair,
non-electric;

(G-3302)
EMITTED ENERGY INC
754 Cincinnati Batavia Pi (45245-1275)
PHONE...................................513 752-9999
Debbie Vanover, *Administration*
EMP: 3
SALES (corp-wide): 6.1MM **Privately
Held**
SIC: 3641 Electric lamps
PA: Emitted Energy, Inc.
6577 Diplomat Dr
Sterling Heights MI 48314
855 752-3347

(G-3303)
FUNTOWN PLAYGROUNDS INC
839 Cypresspoint Ct (45245-3352)
PHONE...................................513 871-8585
Fax: 513 753-6391
Orville Wright, *President*
Marty Kremer, *Vice Pres*
George Held, *Office Mgr*
EMP: 25
SALES (est): 2MM **Privately Held**
SIC: 3949 Playground equipment

(G-3304)
GENERAL DATA COMPANY INC (PA)
4354 Ferguson Dr (45245-1667)
P.O. Box 541165 (45254-1165)
PHONE...................................513 752-7978
Fax: 513 752-6947
Peter Wenzel, *President*
Jim Bacho, *Vice Pres*
James Burns, *Vice Pres*
Jim Burns, *Vice Pres*
Rick Cmar, *Vice Pres*
▲ EMP: 230
SQ FT: 45,000
SALES (est): 76.5MM **Privately Held**
WEB: www.general-data.com
SIC: 2679 5046 3264 2759 Labels,
paper: made from purchased material;
commercial equipment; printing trades
machinery, equipment & supplies; com-
mercial printing; surgical & medical instru-
ments; unsupported plastics film & sheet

(G-3305)
GENERAL DATA COMPANY INC
1004 Seabrook Way (45245-1963)
PHONE...................................513 752-7978
Peter Wenzel, *President*
EMP: 20
SALES (corp-wide): 76.5MM **Privately
Held**
SIC: 2679 Labels, paper: made from pur-
chased material
PA: General Data Company, Inc.
4354 Ferguson Dr
Cincinnati OH 45245
513 752-7978

(G-3306)
GENERAL DATA COMPANY INC
Also Called: Triangle Biomedical Sciences
1004 Seabrook Way (45245-1963)
PHONE...................................919 384-0037
Fax: 919 384-9595
Lisa Veasey, *Opers Mgr*
Tristian Lovette, *Sales Mgr*
Jack Hunnell, *Mktg Dir*
Adrienne Campbell, *Marketing Staff*
Peter Wenzel, *Branch Mgr*
EMP: 25
SALES (corp-wide): 76.5MM **Privately
Held**
SIC: 3841 Surgical & medical instruments
PA: General Data Company, Inc.
4354 Ferguson Dr
Cincinnati OH 45245
513 752-7978

(G-3307)
GENESCO INC
Also Called: Lids
4601 Estgate Blvd Ste 564 (45245)
PHONE...................................513 947-1200
Jenny Brock, *Branch Mgr*
Brandi Groneck, *Manager*
Aaron Hernandez, *Manager*
EMP: 4
SALES (corp-wide): 2.8B **Publicly Held**
WEB: www.genesco.com
SIC: 2353 Hats & caps
PA: Genesco Inc.
1415 Murfreesboro Pike
Nashville TN 37217
615 367-7000

(G-3308)
HAWKS & ASSOCIATES INC
Also Called: Hawks Tag
1029 Seabrook Way (45245-1964)
P.O. Box 541207 (45254-1207)
PHONE...................................513 752-4311
Fax: 513 752-3875
James M Hawks, *President*
Mike Bauer, *Sales Executive*

Dave Hawks, *Info Tech Mgr*
EMP: 28 EST: 1973
SQ FT: 15,000
SALES: 5.8MM **Privately Held**
WEB: www.hawkstag.com
SIC: 2759 2752 Flexographic printing;
commercial printing, lithographic

(G-3309)
HUNTER DEFENSE TECH INC
1032 Seabrook Way (45245-1963)
PHONE...................................513 943-7880
Angela Cowan, *Branch Mgr*
Beverly Carter, *Manager*
Hiram Crespo, *Manager*
Jeff Garrison, *Manager*
EMP: 150
SALES (corp-wide): 229.4MM **Privately
Held**
SIC: 3822 Auto controls regulating residntl
& coml environmt & applncs
PA: Hunter Defense Technologies, Inc.
30500 Aurora Rd Ste 100
Solon OH 44139
216 438-6111

(G-3310)
L-3 FUZING AND ORD SYSTEMS INC
3975 Mcmann Rd (45245-2307)
PHONE...................................513 943-2000
Michael T Strianese, *CEO*
Eric Ellis, *President*
Curtis Brunson, *Exec VP*
Richard A Cody, *Senior VP*
Steven M Post, *Senior VP*
EMP: 575
SQ FT: 236,000
SALES (est): 228.8MM
SALES (corp-wide): 10.5B **Publicly Held**
SIC: 3483 Arming & fusing devices for mis-
siles
PA: L3 Technologies, Inc.
600 3rd Ave Fl 34
New York NY 10016
212 697-1111

(G-3311)
L3 TECHNOLOGIES INC
Electro Fab Division
3975 Mcmann Rd (45245-2307)
PHONE...................................513 943-2000
Charls King, *General Mgr*
Charles King, *Production*
Brian Edwards, *Electrical Engi*
Brian Miracle, *Electrical Engi*
Charles Shilling, *VP Sales*
EMP: 40
SALES (corp-wide): 10.5B **Publicly Held**
WEB: www.l3circuitboards.com
SIC: 3672 Printed circuit boards
PA: L3 Technologies, Inc.
600 3rd Ave Fl 34
New York NY 10016
212 697-1111

(G-3312)
LINTECH ELECTRONICS LLC
4435 Aicholtz Rd Ste 500 (45245-1692)
P.O. Box 54436 (45254-0436)
PHONE...................................513 528-6190
Fax: 513 528-6191
John Rathbone, *Vice Pres*
Linda Rathbone,
EMP: 12
SALES (est): 1.6MM **Privately Held**
WEB: www.lintech-electronics.com
SIC: 8711 3679 Electrical or electronic en-
gineering; electronic circuits

(G-3313)
ORIGINAL MATTRESS FACTORY INC
4450 Eastgate Blvd Ste E (45245-1532)
PHONE...................................513 752-6600
Fax: 513 752-6669
Dawn Hodge, *Manager*
EMP: 3
SALES (corp-wide): 26.6MM **Privately
Held**
WEB: www.originalmattress.com
SIC: 2515 5712 Mattresses & foundations;
furniture springs; bedding & bedsprings;
mattresses

PA: The Original Mattress Factory Inc
4930 State Rd
Cleveland OH 44134
216 661-8388

(G-3314)
PRO AUDIO
671 Cncnnati Batavia Pike (45245-1002)
PHONE...................................513 752-7500
Frank Marino, *Owner*
EMP: 6
SALES (est): 493K **Privately Held**
SIC: 3651 Audio electronic systems

(G-3315)
SENCO BRANDS INC (HQ)
Also Called: Nexicor
4270 Ivy Pointe Blvd (45245-0003)
PHONE...................................513 388-2000
Fax: 513 388-3130
Ben Johansen, *CEO*
Bob Schmidt, *COO*
Ken Olson, *Buyer*
Alex Lin, *Engineer*
Nate Mullen, *Engineer*
▲ EMP: 70
SALES (est): 185.1MM
SALES (corp-wide): 912.7MM **Privately
Held**
SIC: 3546 Power-driven handtools
PA: Wynnchurch Capital, Ltd.
6250 N Rver Rd Ste 10-100
Rosemont IL 60018
847 604-6100

(G-3316)
SENCO HOLDINGS INC
4270 Ivy Pointe Blvd # 125 (45245-0003)
PHONE...................................800 543-4596
Mike Desmond, *Design Engr*
Robert Dwyer, *CFO*
Derek Johnson, *Regl Sales Mgr*
Sterling Stephenson, *Regl Sales Mgr*
Eric Habermehl, *Marketing Mgr*
EMP: 5
SALES (est): 97.7K **Privately Held**
SIC: 3452 3553 Screws, metal; furniture
makers' machinery, woodworking

(G-3317)
SENSOURCE GLOBAL SOURCING LLC
4270 Ivy Pointe Blvd (45245-0003)
PHONE...................................513 659-8283
Glenn P Rudolph,
▲ EMP: 3
SALES (est): 360.8K **Privately Held**
SIC: 3546 Power-driven handtools

(G-3318)
SMASHING EVENTS AND BAKING
693 Winding Way (45245-2421)
PHONE...................................513 415-9693
Cindy King, *Principal*
EMP: 4
SALES (est): 185K **Privately Held**
SIC: 2051 Bread, cake & related products

(G-3319)
TAKE IT FOR GRANITE LLC
3898 Mcmann Rd (45245-2347)
PHONE...................................513 735-0555
Tammy Robinson, *Manager*
Dustin Wallace,
Amy Wallace,
▲ EMP: 18
SQ FT: 12,000
SALES (est): 2MM **Privately Held**
SIC: 3281 Cut stone & stone products;
granite, cut & shaped

(G-3320)
UNITED TOOL SUPPLY INC
851 Ohio Pike Ste 101 (45245-2293)
PHONE...................................513 752-6000
Russell F Young, *President*
EMP: 6
SQ FT: 8,000
SALES: 750K **Privately Held**
SIC: 5085 3823 Industrial supplies; indus-
trial instrmnts msrmnt display/control
process variable

(G-3321)
XCITE SYSTEMS CORPORATION
675 Cncnnati Batavia Pike (45245-1028)
PHONE..............................513 965-0300
Fax: 513 528-7190
Terry A Dunlap, *President*
Gerald J Zobrist, *Chairman*
EMP: 6
SQ FT: 2,000
SALES: 950K **Privately Held**
WEB: www.xcitesystems.com
SIC: 3829 8711 Stress, strain & flaw detecting/measuring equipment; engineering services

Cincinnati
Hamilton County

(G-3322)
21ST CENTURY PRINTERS INC
326 Northland Blvd (45246-6602)
PHONE..............................513 771-4150
Cynthia Edwards, *President*
Kevin Robert Edwards, *Vice Pres*
Judy Clore, *Bookkeeper*
EMP: 4 EST: 1973
SQ FT: 900
SALES (est): 200K **Privately Held**
SIC: 2752 2791 2789 2672 Commercial printing, offset; typesetting; bookbinding & related work; coated & laminated paper

(G-3323)
3-G INCORPORATED (PA)
Also Called: Napolitano Monument
4122 Spring Grove Ave (45223-2641)
PHONE..............................513 921-4515
Fax: 513 721-2505
Gregory Napolitano, *President*
Sandra Bender, *Corp Secy*
Gary Napolitano, *Vice Pres*
Linda Ledermeier, *Manager*
EMP: 5
SQ FT: 5,000
SALES (est): 1.2MM **Privately Held**
SIC: 1751 3211 5999 Window & door installation & erection; insulating glass, sealed units; monuments & tombstones

(G-3324)
3DLT LLC
8 Peasenhall Ln (45208-1214)
PHONE..............................513 452-3358
John Hauer, *CEO*
Colin Klayer, *COO*
Tim Maggart, *CTO*
EMP: 11
SQ FT: 6,000
SALES (est): 1.1MM **Privately Held**
SIC: 2759 7374 Commercial printing; data processing & preparation

(G-3325)
3N1 MENS FASHION
481 E Kemper Rd (45246-3228)
P.O. Box 40138 (45240-0138)
PHONE..............................513 851-3610
Vinne Spence, *Partner*
EMP: 3
SALES (est): 313.2K **Privately Held**
SIC: 2326 Men's & boys' work clothing

(G-3326)
4ME GROUP LLC
6740 Clough Pike Ste 207 (45244-4038)
PHONE..............................513 898-1083
Chase Shiels, *Marketing Staff*
EMP: 3
SALES (est): 71.1K **Privately Held**
SIC: 7372 Business oriented computer software

(G-3327)
80 ACRES URBAN AGRICULTURE LLC (PA)
4535 Este Ave (45232)
PHONE..............................513 218-4387
Mike Zelkind, *President*
EMP: 7 EST: 2015
SALES (est): 1.1MM **Privately Held**
SIC: 3532 Mining machinery

(G-3328)
A & B DEBURRING COMPANY
525 Carr St (45203-1815)
PHONE..............................513 723-0777
Fax: 513 723-0444
Robert Wegman, *President*
Lance Lagaly, *Accounts Mgr*
Mike Hacker, *Manager*
EMP: 14
SQ FT: 25,000
SALES (est): 7.7MM **Privately Held**
WEB: www.abdeburr.com
SIC: 5084 3471 Metal refining machinery & equipment; polishing, metals or formed products

(G-3329)
A & E BUTSCHA CO
110 E Seymour Ave (45216-2084)
PHONE..............................513 761-1919
Fax: 513 761-7292
Daniel Hoetker, *President*
REA Hoetker, *Vice Pres*
EMP: 4
SQ FT: 30,000
SALES (est): 743.7K **Privately Held**
SIC: 3444 3446 3443 3441 Sheet metalwork; architectural metalwork; fabricated plate work (boiler shop); fabricated structural metal

(G-3330)
A AND V GRINDING INC
Also Called: Midwest Centerless Grinding
1115 Straight St 17 (45214-1735)
PHONE..............................937 444-4141
Fax: 513 541-8555
Albert Benedetti, *President*
Vera Benedetti, *Vice Pres*
EMP: 6
SQ FT: 12,500
SALES (est): 759.8K **Privately Held**
SIC: 3599 Machine shop, jobbing & repair

(G-3331)
A B & J MACHINING & FABG
Also Called: AB&j Machng Fabrictn
10330 Wayne Ave (45215-1129)
PHONE..............................513 769-5900
Fax: 513 769-5801
James J Meister, *President*
Bev Meister, *Vice Pres*
EMP: 5
SQ FT: 2,000
SALES (est): 584.4K **Privately Held**
SIC: 3599 Machine shop, jobbing & repair

(G-3332)
A B C SIGN INC
38 W Mcmicken Ave (45202-7718)
PHONE..............................513 241-8884
Fax: 513 241-8978
Cliff Meyer, *President*
Thomas Meyer, *Vice Pres*
Phil Swisher, *Manager*
EMP: 10
SQ FT: 30,500
SALES (est): 880K **Privately Held**
WEB: www.abcsign.com
SIC: 3993 2394 1799 7359 Signs & advertising specialties; awnings, fabric: made from purchased materials; sign installation & maintenance; sign rental

(G-3333)
A C KNOX INC
Also Called: Helex Division
525 Purcell Ave (45205-2341)
PHONE..............................513 921-5028
Fax: 513 921-5168
Arthur C Knox Jr, *President*
Rita Knox, *Corp Secy*
Teri Knox, *Manager*
EMP: 4 EST: 1965
SALES (est): 360K **Privately Held**
WEB: www.acknox.com
SIC: 3443 8742 8711 Heat exchangers, condensers & components; management consulting services; engineering services

(G-3334)
A DESIGNERS WORKROOM
3066 Madison Rd 3 (45209-1723)
PHONE..............................513 251-7396
Maegdlyn Morris, *Partner*
Gregory Morris, *Partner*
Lee Schmidt, *Partner*
Heather Hitson, *Manager*
EMP: 7
SALES: 180K **Privately Held**
SIC: 2391 Curtains & draperies

(G-3335)
A R JESTER CO
6781 Harrison Ave (45247-3239)
PHONE..............................513 241-1465
Fax: 513 241-4380
Randall D Jester, *President*
Pauline A Jester, *Treasurer*
EMP: 7 EST: 1939
SQ FT: 2,500
SALES: 1.4MM **Privately Held**
WEB: www.arjester.com
SIC: 5094 3911 Precious stones & metals; diamonds (gems); jewelry, precious metal

(G-3336)
A SPOON FULLA SUGAR LLC
11916 Montgomery Rd (45249-1727)
PHONE..............................513 683-0444
Mark Gallo,
EMP: 10 EST: 2009
SALES (est): 686.2K **Privately Held**
SIC: 2051 Cakes, pies & pastries

(G-3337)
A TO Z WEAR LTD
5647 Cheviot Rd (45247-7089)
PHONE..............................513 923-4662
Fax: 513 923-4044
Donna Fenstermacher, *Partner*
Gail Gilmore, *Partner*
EMP: 3
SQ FT: 1,500
SALES (est): 120K **Privately Held**
WEB: www.atozwear.com
SIC: 2395 Embroidery & art needlework

(G-3338)
A Z PRINTING INC (PA)
Also Called: A-Z Discount Printing
10122 Reading Rd (45241-3110)
PHONE..............................513 733-3900
Fax: 513 733-0770
Bruce Hassel, *President*
EMP: 6
SQ FT: 4,000
SALES (est): 559K **Privately Held**
WEB: www.azprt.com
SIC: 2759 Commercial printing

(G-3339)
A Z PRINTING INC
4077 E Galbraith Rd (45236-2323)
PHONE..............................513 745-0700
Fax: 513 733-0770
Bruce Hassle, *Owner*
EMP: 4
SALES (corp-wide): 559K **Privately Held**
WEB: www.azprt.com
SIC: 2759 7389 4783 Commercial printing; mailing & messenger services; packing & crating
PA: A Z Printing Inc
10122 Reading Rd
Cincinnati OH 45241
513 733-3900

(G-3340)
A2Z PALLETS LLC
1292 Glendale Milford Rd (45215-1209)
P.O. Box 18151 (45218-0151)
PHONE..............................513 652-9026
Ramonita Garcia, *Principal*
EMP: 4
SALES (est): 200K **Privately Held**
SIC: 2448 Pallets, wood & wood with metal

(G-3341)
AAA GALVANIZING - JOLIET INC
Also Called: Azz Galvanizing - Cincinnati
4454 Steel Pl (45209-1135)
PHONE..............................513 871-5700
Lori Wilp, *Plant Mgr*
Steve Gerhardt, *Sales Mgr*
EMP: 49
SALES (corp-wide): 903.1MM **Publicly Held**
SIC: 3479 Hot dip coating of metals or formed products; coating of metals & formed products

HQ: Aaa Galvanizing - Joliet, Inc.
625 Mills Rd
Joliet IL 60433
815 723-5000

(G-3342)
AB BONDED LOCKSMITHS INC
Also Called: Tri County Locksmith
4344 Montgomery Rd (45212-3104)
PHONE..............................513 531-7334
Fax: 513 531-6748
Russell McGurrin, *CEO*
Cindy McGurrin, *CFO*
EMP: 7 EST: 1933
SQ FT: 6,000
SALES (est): 1.4MM **Privately Held**
WEB: www.ablocks.com
SIC: 7699 3429 Locksmith shop; manufactured hardware (general)

(G-3343)
ABBY GIRL SWEETS CUPCAKERY
41 W 5th St (45202-2801)
P.O. Box 129, Fayetteville (45118-0129)
PHONE..............................513 335-0898
EMP: 4
SALES (est): 211.3K **Privately Held**
SIC: 2051 Cakes, bakery: except frozen

(G-3344)
ABEL FBRCTION PRCSION PDTS INC
Also Called: Abel Fabrication & Precision
3260 Beekman St (45223-2423)
PHONE..............................513 681-5000
Deborah Smith, *President*
Ken Smith, *Manager*
EMP: 13
SQ FT: 14,000
SALES (est): 2.3MM **Privately Held**
SIC: 3451 Screw machine products

(G-3345)
ABEL MANUFACTURING COMPANY
3474 Beekman St (45223-2425)
PHONE..............................513 681-5000
Fax: 513 681-5068
Carl Abel Jr, *President*
Mark Abel, *Vice Pres*
Michael Nagel, *Vice Pres*
Kent Smith, *Plant Mgr*
Katherine Nagel, *Treasurer*
EMP: 15 EST: 1966
SQ FT: 14,000
SALES (est): 3.2MM **Privately Held**
WEB: www.abel-usa.com
SIC: 3451 Screw machine products

(G-3346)
ABLE TOOL CORPORATION
617 N Wayne Ave (45215-2250)
PHONE..............................513 733-8989
Fax: 513 733-8994
Daniel R Hayes, *President*
Janice M Hayes, *Corp Secy*
Sara Hayes, *Vice Pres*
Robert Hollman, *Treasurer*
Andrew Hooper, *Manager*
EMP: 30
SQ FT: 22,400
SALES (est): 6.1MM **Privately Held**
WEB: www.abletool.com
SIC: 3599 3565 3545 Machine & other job shop work; packing & wrapping machinery; machine tool accessories

(G-3347)
ACCURATE GEAR MANUFACTURING CO
16 E 73rd St (45216-2038)
PHONE..............................513 761-3220
Fax: 513 761-4844
Dennis M Pauly, *President*
David Schachere, *Vice Pres*
EMP: 9
SQ FT: 10,500
SALES (est): 1.5MM **Privately Held**
SIC: 3566 Speed changers, drives & gears

(G-3348)
ACCUTECH SIGN SHOP
9316 Colerain Ave (45251-2012)
PHONE..............................513 385-3595

Sheila Pierce, *Owner*
EMP: 3 **EST:** 2001
SALES: 150K **Privately Held**
SIC: 3993 Signs & advertising specialties

(G-3349)
ACE GASKET MANUFACTURING CO
7873 Main St (45244-3158)
P.O. Box 54367 (45254-0367)
PHONE....................513 271-6321
Fax: 513 271-6359
Gregory Dietrich, *President*
Edward Dietrich, *Vice Pres*
Judith Dietrich, *Admin Sec*
EMP: 3 **EST:** 1964
SQ FT: 6,000
SALES: 500K **Privately Held**
SIC: 2899 3053 Industrial sizes; gaskets, all materials

(G-3350)
ACOUFLOW THERAPEUTICS LLC
6914 Copperglow Ct (45244-3647)
PHONE....................513 558-0073
Liran Oren,
EMP: 4
SALES (est): 177.3K **Privately Held**
SIC: 3841 Surgical & medical instruments

(G-3351)
ACTION MECHANICAL REPAIR INC
7760 Harrison Ave (45247-2469)
P.O. Box 427, Miamitown (45041-0427)
PHONE....................513 353-1046
Fax: 513 353-9601
June C Retherford, *President*
Joseph H Retherford Jr, *Vice Pres*
EMP: 4
SQ FT: 5,000
SALES: 630K **Privately Held**
SIC: 3599 Machine shop, jobbing & repair

(G-3352)
ACTIVE DAILY LIVING LLC
3308 Bishop St (45220-1858)
PHONE....................513 607-6769
Daniel E Ansel, *Principal*
EMP: 3
SALES (est): 123.7K **Privately Held**
SIC: 2711 Newspapers, publishing & printing

(G-3353)
ACUREN INSPECTION INC
502 W Crescentville Rd (45246-1222)
PHONE....................513 671-7073
Mike Ross, *District Mgr*
Ryan Raabe, *Sales Mgr*
EMP: 27
SALES (corp-wide): 513MM **Privately Held**
SIC: 1389 Testing, measuring, surveying & analysis services
HQ: Acuren Inspection, Inc.
　30 Main St Ste 402
　Danbury CT 06810
　203 702-8740

(G-3354)
AD-PRO SIGNS I LLC
11336 Dallas Blvd (45231-1357)
PHONE....................513 922-5046
Fax: 513 922-8926
Danna Moore, *Manager*
Jim Kleemeier,
EMP: 3
SQ FT: 15,000
SALES (est): 349.6K **Privately Held**
SIC: 3993 Signs & advertising specialties

(G-3355)
ADAMS CUSTOM WOODWORKING
324 W Wyoming Ave (45215-3035)
PHONE....................513 761-1395
EMP: 10 **EST:** 2008
SALES (est): 650K **Privately Held**
SIC: 2431 Mfg Millwork

(G-3356)
ADLER & COMPANY INC
Also Called: Camargo Construction
6801 Shawnee Run Rd (45243-2417)
PHONE....................513 248-1500
Fax: 513 576-8344
Harry Adler Sr, *President*
EMP: 15
SALES: 2MM **Privately Held**
SIC: 3272 Paving materials, prefabricated concrete

(G-3357)
ADRIANS PLACE
1801 Race St Ste 10 (45202-5908)
PHONE....................513 651-2154
Diana Andrade, *Owner*
EMP: 5
SALES (est): 186.6K **Privately Held**
SIC: 2052 5461 Cookies; cookies

(G-3358)
ADVANCED FITNESS INC
11875 Reading Rd (45241-1545)
P.O. Box 62751 (45262-0751)
PHONE....................513 563-1000
Mark D Pittroff, *President*
Sandra Pittroff, *Corp Secy*
EMP: 3
SALES (est): 391.2K **Privately Held**
WEB: www.adfit.com
SIC: 7331 3949 Direct mail advertising services; sporting & athletic goods

(G-3359)
ADVANCED ONSIGHT WELDING SVCS
5220 Globe Ave (45212-1536)
PHONE....................513 924-1400
Wayne Moore,
Mary Moore,
Mathew Moore,
EMP: 7
SALES: 720K **Privately Held**
SIC: 3441 7692 Fabricated structural metal; welding repair

(G-3360)
ADVANCED TECHNICAL PDTS SUP CO
508 Northland Blvd (45240-3213)
PHONE....................513 851-6858
Ben Conner, *President*
Timothy Conner, *Vice Pres*
EMP: 10
SQ FT: 15,000
SALES (est): 2MM **Privately Held**
SIC: 3479 Painting, coating & hot dipping

(G-3361)
ADVENTUROUS CHILD INC
4781 Duck Creek Rd (45227)
PHONE....................513 531-7700
Fax: 513 531-7747
Clark Kugler, *President*
Stephanie Ginter, *Manager*
EMP: 7
SQ FT: 4,000
SALES (est): 903.1K **Privately Held**
WEB: www.theadventurouschild.com
SIC: 3949 Playground equipment

(G-3362)
ADWEST TECHNOLOGIES INC
4625 Red Bank Rd Ste 200 (45227-1552)
PHONE....................513 458-2600
EMP: 5
SALES (corp-wide): 417MM **Publicly Held**
SIC: 3564 Air purification equipment
HQ: Adwest Technologies, Inc.
　4222 E La Palma Ave
　Anaheim CA 92807
　714 632-8595

(G-3363)
AFFINITY DISP EXPOSITIONS INC (PA)
Also Called: Adex International
1301 Glendale Milford Rd (45215-1210)
PHONE....................513 771-2339
Fax: 513 771-3521
Timothy Murphy, *President*
Walt Pottschmidt, *Exec VP*
Mike Murphy, *Vice Pres*

Mike Pierdiluca, *Vice Pres*
Joe Rickard, *CFO*
▲ **EMP:** 100
SQ FT: 250,000
SALES (est): 27.7MM **Privately Held**
WEB: www.adex-intl.com
SIC: 3993 Signs & advertising specialties

(G-3364)
AFFINITY DISP EXPOSITIONS INC
Also Called: Adex International
1375 Spring Park Walk (45215-0046)
PHONE....................513 771-2339
Tim Murphy, *President*
Jeff McDonough, *Info Tech Dir*
EMP: 100
SALES (corp-wide): 30.8MM **Privately Held**
WEB: www.adex-intl.com
SIC: 3993 Signs & advertising specialties
PA: Affinity Displays & Expositions, Inc.
　1301 Glendale Milford Rd
　Cincinnati OH 45215
　513 771-2339

(G-3365)
AFTER WERK
3095 Glenmore Ave (45238-2270)
PHONE....................513 661-9375
Allen Anderson, *Principal*
EMP: 4
SALES (est): 316.1K **Privately Held**
SIC: 2599 Bar, restaurant & cafeteria furniture

(G-3366)
AG ANTENNA GROUP LLC
11931 Montgomery Rd (45249)
PHONE....................513 289-6521
John Reynolds, *CEO*
James Moore, *Vice Pres*
Matt Kopeny,
EMP: 10
SQ FT: 2,500
SALES (est): 712.5K **Privately Held**
SIC: 3663 Antennas, transmitting & communications

(G-3367)
AGNONE-KELLY ENTERPRISES INC
Also Called: Thermalgraphics
11658 Baen Rd (45242-1600)
P.O. Box 428543 (45242-8543)
PHONE....................800 634-6503
Kevin Kelly, *President*
Elizabeth Kelly, *Vice Pres*
EMP: 6
SQ FT: 20,000
SALES: 1MM **Privately Held**
WEB: www.thermalg.com
SIC: 2759 Commercial printing

(G-3368)
AHEMCO LLC
Also Called: Arsco Manufacturing Company
5313 Robert Ave (45248-6214)
PHONE....................513 385-0555
Fax: 513 741-6292
Gregory Hemmert, *General Mgr*
Edward Hemmert,
EMP: 10
SQ FT: 3,000
SALES: 2MM **Privately Held**
WEB: www.arscomfg.com
SIC: 3444 Sheet metalwork

(G-3369)
AIR PRODUCTS AND CHEMICALS INC
4900 Este Ave (45232-1491)
P.O. Box 32283 (45232-0283)
PHONE....................513 242-9215
Fax: 513 242-5467
Michael Bavaro, *Purchasing*
Wayne Harding, *Engineer*
Al Hall, *Branch Mgr*
Wallace West, *Manager*
Maggie Lesure, *Manager*
EMP: 5
SALES (corp-wide): 9.5B **Publicly Held**
WEB: www.airproducts.com
SIC: 2813 Industrial gases

PA: Air Products And Chemicals, Inc.
　7201 Hamilton Blvd
　Allentown PA 18195
　610 481-4911

(G-3370)
AIRECON MANUFACTURING CORP
5271 Brotherton Rd (45227-2103)
PHONE....................513 561-5522
Fax: 513 561-0166
Joseph E Gutierrez, *President*
Timothy Kidd, *Vice Pres*
Paul Bockrath, *Sales Engr*
Thressa McCarty, *Manager*
David W Miller, *Admin Sec*
▲ **EMP:** 50
SQ FT: 30,000
SALES (est): 13.9MM **Privately Held**
WEB: www.airecon.com
SIC: 3564 Air purification equipment; dust or fume collecting equipment, industrial

(G-3371)
AIRGAS USA LLC
10031 Cncnnati Dyton Pike (45241-1003)
PHONE....................513 563-9400
Mick Higgins, *Branch Mgr*
EMP: 16
SALES (corp-wide): 163.9MM **Privately Held**
WEB: www.us.linde-gas.com
SIC: 2813 Industrial gases
HQ: Airgas Usa, Llc
　259 N Radnor Chester Rd # 100
　Radnor PA 19087
　610 687-5253

(G-3372)
AIRTX INTERNATIONAL LTD
6320 Wiehe Rd (45237-4214)
PHONE....................513 631-0660
Michael Rawlings, *Partner*
Sandy Mayer, *Office Mgr*
EMP: 10
SQ FT: 7,500
SALES (est): 1.7MM **Privately Held**
WEB: www.artxltd.com
SIC: 3563 Air & gas compressors

(G-3373)
AK STEEL CORPORATION
Sawhill Tubular
1080 Nimitzview Dr (45230-4314)
PHONE....................513 231-2552
EMP: 3
SALES (corp-wide): 5.9B **Publicly Held**
SIC: 3312 Blast Furnace-Steel Works
HQ: Ak Steel Corporation
　9227 Centre Pointe Dr
　West Chester OH 45069
　513 425-5000

(G-3374)
AKZO NOBEL PAINTS LLC
Also Called: Glidden Professional Paint Ctr
1754 Tennessee Ave (45229-1202)
PHONE....................513 242-0530
EMP: 4
SQ FT: 2,500
SALES (corp-wide): 15.2B **Publicly Held**
SIC: 2891 Mfg Adhesives/Sealants
HQ: Akzo Nobel Paints Llc
　8381 Pearl Rd
　Strongsville OH 44136
　440 297-8000

(G-3375)
ALBERT BICKEL
Also Called: CCI
7116 Leibel Rd (45248-2814)
PHONE....................513 530-5700
Albert J Bickel, *Owner*
EMP: 3
SALES (est): 140K **Privately Held**
SIC: 2741 7379 Miscellaneous publishing; computer related consulting services

(G-3376)
ALBERT BRAMKAMP PRINTING CO
4501 Greenlee Ave (45217-1803)
PHONE....................513 641-1069
Fax: 513 641-1069
Dave Bramkamp, *President*
Ed Collins, *Corp Secy*

David Bramkamp Jr, *Vice Pres*
EMP: 3
SALES: 250K **Privately Held**
SIC: 2759 Labels & seals: printing

(G-3377)
ALL CRAFT MANUFACTURING CO
Also Called: Talisman Racing
6500 Glenway Ave Side 2 (45211-4451)
PHONE....................513 661-3383
Fax: 513 661-3394
Robert W Farrell, *President*
Paula Farrell, *Vice Pres*
Becky Whitefoot, *Opers Staff*
EMP: 15
SQ FT: 3,200
SALES (est): 2MM **Privately Held**
SIC: 3599 Machine shop, jobbing & repair

(G-3378)
ALLGEIER & SON INC (PA)
6386 Bridgetown Rd (45248-2933)
PHONE....................513 574-3735
Fax: 513 598-2163
Michael Allgeier, *Owner*
Margaret A Steigerwald, *Treasurer*
EMP: 18
SQ FT: 800
SALES (est): 4.6MM **Privately Held**
SIC: 1794 1422 1795 Excavation & grading, building construction; crushed & broken limestone; wrecking & demolition work

(G-3379)
ALLIED WINDOW INC
11111 Canal Rd (45241-1861)
PHONE....................513 559-1212
Fax: 513 558-1883
David Martin, *President*
Noel Lewis, *COO*
Sonya Martin, *Vice Pres*
Richard Young, *CFO*
Robin Martin, *Sales Staff*
EMP: 40 **EST:** 1950
SQ FT: 15,000
SALES: 4.2MM **Privately Held**
WEB: www.alliedwindow.com
SIC: 3442 Storm doors or windows, metal

(G-3380)
ALLIGATOR CMPT SYSTEMS CORP
Also Called: ACS
2060 Waycross Rd (45240-2717)
P.O. Box 25306 (45225)
PHONE....................513 542-1000
Fax: 513 542-7920
James H Ernst, *President*
Jeff Ernst, *Vice Pres*
EMP: 12
SQ FT: 15,000
SALES (est): 1.3MM **Privately Held**
WEB: www.alligatortoys.com
SIC: 7993 3999 5092 Game machines; coin-operated amusement machines; amusement goods

(G-3381)
ALTERA CORPORATION
9435 Waterstone Blvd # 140 (45249-8226)
PHONE....................513 444-2021
Bernhard R Kiessling, *Manager*
EMP: 5
SALES (corp-wide): 59.3B **Publicly Held**
WEB: www.altera.com
SIC: 3674 Semiconductors & related devices
HQ: Altera Corporation
101 Innovation Dr
San Jose CA 95134
408 544-7000

(G-3382)
ALUCHEM INC (PA)
1 Landy Ln Ste 1 (45215-3489)
PHONE....................513 733-8519
Fax: 513 733-0608
Ronald P Zapletal, *President*
Bill Kist, *Senior VP*
Edward L Butera, *Vice Pres*
Matt Painter, *Vice Pres*
Ken Sierk, *Plant Mgr*
◆ **EMP:** 47
SQ FT: 200,000

SALES (est): 12MM **Privately Held**
WEB: www.aluchem.com
SIC: 3295 Minerals, ground or treated

(G-3383)
ALUMINUM EXTRUDED SHAPES INC
Also Called: AES
10549 Reading Rd (45241-2524)
PHONE....................513 563-2205
Fax: 513 563-2883
Robert E Hoeweler, *President*
EMP: 115
SQ FT: 130,000
SALES (est): 27.6MM **Privately Held**
SIC: 3354 3471 3444 Aluminum extruded products; plating & polishing; sheet metalwork

(G-3384)
AMERICAN BOTTLING COMPANY
125 E Court St Ste 820 (45202-1201)
PHONE....................513 381-4891
EMP: 70
SALES (corp-wide): 6B **Publicly Held**
SIC: 2086 Mfg Bottled/Canned Soft Drinks
HQ: The American Bottling Company
5301 Legacy Dr
Plano TX 75024
972 673-7000

(G-3385)
AMERICAN BOTTLING COMPANY
Also Called: 7 Up/ Royal Crown
5151 Fischer Ave (45217-1157)
PHONE....................513 242-5151
Fax: 513 242-4949
Mark Wendling, *Manager*
EMP: 165
SALES (corp-wide): 6.4B **Publicly Held**
WEB: www.cs-americas.com
SIC: 2086 Bottled & canned soft drinks
HQ: The American Bottling Company
5301 Legacy Dr
Plano TX 75024

(G-3386)
AMERICAN CITY BUS JOURNALS INC
Also Called: Business Courier
120 E 4th St Ste 230 (45202-4099)
PHONE....................513 337-9450
Fax: 513 621-2462
Kim Spangler, *Editor*
Douglas Bolton, *Branch Mgr*
Joe Hoffecker, *Plan/Corp Dev D*
Tara Metcalf, *Administration*
EMP: 30
SALES (corp-wide): 1.6B **Privately Held**
SIC: 2711 2741 Newspapers: publishing only, not printed on site; miscellaneous publishing
HQ: American City Business Journals, Inc.
120 W Morehead St Ste 400
Charlotte NC 28202
704 973-1000

(G-3387)
AMERICAN CRAFT BREWERY LLC
1625 Central Pkwy (45214-2423)
PHONE....................513 412-3200
Todd Agnello, *Branch Mgr*
EMP: 200
SALES (corp-wide): 906.4MM **Publicly Held**
SIC: 2082 Beer (alcoholic beverage); ale (alcoholic beverage)
HQ: American Craft Brewery Llc
1 Design Center Pl # 850
Boston MA 02210
617 368-5000

(G-3388)
AMERICAN FOODS GROUP LLC
3480 E Kemper Rd (45241-2007)
PHONE....................513 733-8898
Fax: 513 733-2045
Amanda Bedinghaus, *Vice Pres*
Lee Torres, *Manager*
EMP: 20

SALES (corp-wide): 3.8B **Privately Held**
WEB: www.americanfoodsgroup.com
SIC: 2011 2013 Beef products from beef slaughtered on site; sausages & other prepared meats
HQ: American Foods Group, Llc
500 S Washington St
Green Bay WI 54301
320 759-5900

(G-3389)
AMERICAN GUILD OF ENGLISH HAND
201 E 5th St 19001025 (45202-4152)
PHONE....................937 438-0085
Fax: 937 438-0434
Jennifer Cauhorn, *Exec Dir*
EMP: 9
SQ FT: 2,253
SALES: 778.9K **Privately Held**
WEB: www.agehr.org
SIC: 8699 7929 2741 7041 Personal interest organization; entertainers & entertainment groups; musical entertainers; music, sheet: publishing only, not printed on site; membership-basis organization hotels

(G-3390)
AMERICAN ISRAELITE CO
Also Called: American Israelite Newspaper
18 W 9th St Ste 2 (45202-2037)
PHONE....................513 621-3145
Fax: 513 621-3744
Ted Deustch, *President*
Dolores Henley, *Office Mgr*
EMP: 8
SQ FT: 1,000
SALES: 240K **Privately Held**
SIC: 2711 Newspapers: publishing only, not printed on site

(G-3391)
AMERICAN LEGAL PUBLISHING CORP
1 W 4th St Ste 300 (45202-3634)
PHONE....................513 421-4248
Fax: 513 763-3562
Stephen G Wolf, *President*
Samantha Bohnert, *Editor*
Kathy Donnermeyer, *Editor*
Zach Mullen, *Editor*
Cynthia Poweleit, *Vice Pres*
EMP: 40
SALES (est): 5MM **Privately Held**
WEB: www.amlegal.com
SIC: 2731 2741 Books: publishing only; miscellaneous publishing

(G-3392)
AMERICAN MTAL CLG CNCNNATI INC
475 Northland Blvd (45240-3210)
PHONE....................513 825-1171
Fax: 513 825-1172
James Taylor, *President*
Carol Taylor, *Vice Pres*
EMP: 3
SALES: 225K **Privately Held**
SIC: 3471 Cleaning & descaling metal products

(G-3393)
AMERICAN QUICKSILVER CO
646 Rushton Rd (45226-1124)
PHONE....................513 871-4517
Fax: 513 871-9470
Barney Pogue, *President*
Mara Pogue, *Admin Sec*
▲ **EMP:** 4 **EST:** 1993
SALES (est): 562.1K **Privately Held**
WEB: www.americanquicksilver.com
SIC: 3421 Knife blades & blanks

(G-3394)
AMERICAN WESTERN INC
Also Called: American Western Cigar Company
2575 Queen City Ave (45238-2901)
PHONE....................513 662-8802
Fred Berger, *President*
Stracie Seberling, *Manager*
EMP: 42
SQ FT: 2,000

SALES (est): 4.6MM **Privately Held**
SIC: 2121 Cigars

(G-3395)
AMERICRAFT MFG CO INC
7937 School Rd (45249-1533)
PHONE....................513 489-1047
Fax: 513 489-5288
James L Ceddia, *President*
John Pumpple, *Vice Pres*
Vincent Hartmann, *Sales Mgr*
Anne Neuville, *Director*
Deborah Hiler, *Admin Sec*
EMP: 11
SQ FT: 55,000
SALES (est): 3.6MM **Privately Held**
WEB: www.americraftmfg.com
SIC: 3564 Blowers & fans

(G-3396)
AMERIDIAN SPECIALTY SERVICES
11520 Rockfield Ct (45241-1919)
PHONE....................513 769-0150
Betty Owens, *President*
Derek Wehman, *Vice Pres*
Jim Owens, *Project Mgr*
Mike Barney, *Manager*
Ken Marsh, *Manager*
EMP: 50
SQ FT: 32,000
SALES (est): 7.9MM **Privately Held**
WEB: www.ameridiansvcs.com
SIC: 8741 1761 3441 Construction management; architectural sheet metal work; gutter & downspout contractor; fabricated structural metal

(G-3397)
AMPAC HOLDINGS LLC (DH)
Also Called: Proampac
12025 Tricon Rd (45246-1719)
PHONE....................513 671-1777
James Baker, *Senior VP*
Gene Walton, *Plant Mgr*
Eric Bradford, *CFO*
Kathy Hale, *Credit Mgr*
Greg Tucker, *Mng Member*
◆ **EMP:** 700 **EST:** 2001
SQ FT: 220,000
SALES (est): 504.1MM
SALES (corp-wide): 1.3B **Privately Held**
WEB: www.ampaconline.com
SIC: 2673 2677 3081 2674 Plastic bags: made from purchased materials; pliofilm bags: made from purchased materials; envelopes; unsupported plastics film & sheet; shopping bags: made from purchased materials; investment holding companies, except banks
HQ: Ampac Packaging, Llc
12025 Tricon Rd
Cincinnati OH 45246
513 671-1777

(G-3398)
AMPAC PACKAGING LLC (DH)
12025 Tricon Rd (45246-1719)
PHONE....................513 671-1777
John Baumann, *CEO*
Tom Geyer, *Principal*
Daniel Olander, *Opers Mgr*
Samantha Schaeper, *QA Dir*
Kathy Hale, *Accountant*
EMP: 97
SALES (est): 504.1MM
SALES (corp-wide): 1.3B **Privately Held**
SIC: 2673 Pliofilm bags: made from purchased materials
HQ: Proampac Intermediate Inc.
12025 Tricon Rd
Cincinnati OH 45246
513 671-1777

(G-3399)
AMPAC PLASTICS LLC
12025 Tricon Rd (45246-1792)
PHONE....................513 671-1777
John Q Baumann, *CEO*
James Baker, *Vice Pres*
Cristi Pruitt, *Controller*
Sally Ramirez, *Human Res Dir*
Brenda Morris, *Supervisor*
▲ **EMP:** 300 **EST:** 1965
SQ FT: 210,000

SALES (est): 27.6MM
SALES (corp-wide): 1.3B **Privately Held**
WEB: www.ampaconline.com
SIC: 2621 Packaging paper
HQ: Ampac Holdings, Llc
　　12025 Tricon Rd
　　Cincinnati OH 45246
　　513 671-1777

(G-3400)
AMPACET CORPORATION
4705 Duke Dr 400 (45249)
PHONE.................................513 247-5400
Fax: 513 247-5415
Vicky Willsey, *Manager*
EMP: 25
SALES (corp-wide): 626.1MM **Privately Held**
WEB: www.ampacet.com
SIC: 3089 5162 Coloring & finishing of plastic products; plastics materials & basic shapes
PA: Ampacet Corporation
　　660 White Plains Rd # 360
　　Tarrytown NY 10591
　　914 631-6600

(G-3401)
ANCHOR FLANGE COMPANY
Also Called: Anchor Fluid Power
3959 Virginia Ave (45227-3411)
PHONE.................................513 527-4444
Robert Coffaro, *Branch Mgr*
EMP: 10
SALES (corp-wide): 19.3MM **Privately Held**
SIC: 3462 Flange, valve & pipe fitting forgings, ferrous
PA: Anchor Flange Company
　　5553 Murray Ave
　　Cincinnati OH 45227
　　513 527-3512

(G-3402)
ANDERSON COSMETIC & VEIN INST
7794 5 Mile Rd Ste 270 (45230-2369)
PHONE.................................513 624-7900
Joseph Russell, *Owner*
EMP: 4
SALES (est): 254K **Privately Held**
SIC: 7299 3842 Personal appearance services; cosmetic restorations

(G-3403)
ANDROMEDA RESEARCH
648 Quail Run (45244-1041)
P.O. Box 222, Milford (45150-0222)
PHONE.................................513 831-9708
Fax: 513 831-7562
John Dumont, *Owner*
Adrian Rollin, *Director*
EMP: 5
SALES: 250K **Privately Held**
SIC: 3825 Test equipment for electronic & electrical circuits

(G-3404)
ANDYS MDTERRANEAN FD PDTS LLC
906 Nassau St (45206-2508)
PHONE.................................513 281-9791
Therese Hajjar,
Andy Hajjar,
Majed Hajjar,
▲ EMP: 6
SQ FT: 9,000
SALES (est): 35.4K **Privately Held**
SIC: 2099 Food preparations

(G-3405)
ANNIES MUD PIE SHOP LLC
Also Called: Funke Signature Holdings
3130 Wasson Rd Unit 4 (45209-2344)
PHONE.................................513 871-2529
Thomas Funke, *Mng Member*
Jen Louis,
EMP: 5
SQ FT: 24,000
SALES (est): 835.4K **Privately Held**
WEB: www.anniesmudpieshop.com
SIC: 5023 5719 3269 Pottery; pottery; vases, pottery

(G-3406)
ANZA INC
3265 Colerain Ave Ste 2 (45225-3301)
PHONE.................................513 542-7337
Fax: 513 542-7381
John Busse, *President*
David Burbink, *Vice Pres*
▲ EMP: 8
SQ FT: 6,000
SALES (est): 1.1MM **Privately Held**
WEB: www.anzadesign.com
SIC: 3999 Models, general, except toy

(G-3407)
APPAREL IMPRESSIONS INC
Also Called: Thanks Mom Designs
11410 Gideon Ln (45249-1654)
P.O. Box 42794 (45242-0794)
PHONE.................................513 247-0555
Gregg Devita, *President*
EMP: 3
SALES: 230K **Privately Held**
SIC: 2395 Embroidery products, except schiffli machine

(G-3408)
APPAREL SCREEN PRINTING INC
11255 Reading Rd Ste 1 (45241-4202)
PHONE.................................513 733-9495
Fax: 513 733-9498
Ronnie Thornton, *President*
Carrie Thornton, *Corp Secy*
John Guenther, *Vice Pres*
EMP: 4
SALES: 250K **Privately Held**
SIC: 2261 Screen printing of cotton broadwoven fabrics

(G-3409)
APPLIED BIOMIMETIC INC
2180 E Galbraith Rd D (45237-1625)
PHONE.................................513 558-6090
Steen Nissen, *CEO*
EMP: 7
SQ FT: 3,000
SALES (est): 1.1MM **Privately Held**
SIC: 3589 Sewage & water treatment equipment

(G-3410)
ARCHER COUNTER DESIGN INC
4433 Verne Ave (45209-1223)
PHONE.................................513 396-7526
Fax: 513 396-7450
Robert Lewis, *President*
Tony Williams, *Vice Pres*
▲ EMP: 9
SQ FT: 15,000
SALES: 810K **Privately Held**
SIC: 2541 Table or counter tops, plastic laminated

(G-3411)
ARCHITECT LOUVERS
266 W Mitchell Ave (45232-1908)
PHONE.................................513 541-5364
Joe Ray, *Owner*
EMP: 9 EST: 2007
SALES: 600K **Privately Held**
SIC: 3446 Channels, louvers & registers

(G-3412)
ARCHIVAL CONSERVATION CENTER
Also Called: Archival Conservatn Cntr
772 Crooked Stone Rd (45220-1415)
PHONE.................................513 861-3268
Okey Hatcher, *President*
Arun Khot, *President*
Yvette Hatcher, *Vice Pres*
EMP: 4
SQ FT: 1,500
SALES (est): 100K **Privately Held**
SIC: 2789 8231 Binding & repair of books, magazines & pamphlets; libraries

(G-3413)
ARIZONA BEVERAGE COMPANY LLC
644 Linn St Ste 318 (45203-1734)
PHONE.................................516 837-1999
Fax: 513 357-4754
Francie Patton, *Vice Pres*
Debbie Tufano, *Director*
John Ferolito,
Jacqueline Block-Rodriguez, *Admin Asst*
Don Vultaggio,
EMP: 62
SALES (est): 2.3MM
SALES (corp-wide): 67.8MM **Privately Held**
SIC: 2086 Iced tea & fruit drinks, bottled & canned
PA: Hornell Brewing Co., Inc.
　　60 Crossways Park Dr W # 400
　　Woodbury NY 11797
　　516 812-0300

(G-3414)
ART GUILD BINDERS INC
Also Called: Happy Booker
1068 Meta Dr (45237-5008)
PHONE.................................513 242-3000
Fax: 513 242-3004
Timothy Hugenberg, *President*
Gregory M Hugenberg, *Vice Pres*
Terry Buhr, *Office Mgr*
Donald F Cooper, *Admin Sec*
EMP: 23 EST: 1948
SQ FT: 28,000
SALES (est): 2.8MM **Privately Held**
SIC: 2782 2675 2789 Looseleaf binders & devices; die-cut paper & board; bookbinding & repairing: trade, edition, library, etc.

(G-3415)
ART WOODWORKING & MFG CO
4238 Dane Ave (45223-1856)
PHONE.................................513 681-2986
Fax: 513 681-1315
Ralph R Dickman, *President*
Michelle Clemons, *Controller*
EMP: 30
SQ FT: 23,000
SALES: 4.5MM **Privately Held**
SIC: 2431 Millwork

(G-3416)
ARTIC DIAMOND
11242 Sebring Dr (45240-2715)
PHONE.................................513 742-4921
Fax: 513 742-5666
Jeff Stahl, *President*
EMP: 5
SALES (est): 454.8K **Privately Held**
SIC: 2099 Food preparations

(G-3417)
ASCH-KLAASSEN SONICS LLC
11711 Princeton Pike # 943 (45246-2534)
PHONE.................................513 671-3226
Herbert Asch, *President*
Dan Castner, *Principal*
Rich Klaassen, *Principal*
EMP: 3
SALES (est): 178.9K **Privately Held**
SIC: 3843 Dental equipment & supplies

(G-3418)
ASHLAND LLC
3901 River Rd (45204-1033)
PHONE.................................513 557-3100
EMP: 8
SALES (corp-wide): 4.9B **Publicly Held**
SIC: 1611 1622 2821 2911 Highway & street construction; surfacing & paving; concrete construction: roads, highways, sidewalks, etc.; general contractor, highway & street construction; bridge construction; plastics materials & resins; polyesters; ester gum; thermoplastic materials; heavy distillates; oils, lubricating; paving mixtures; chemicals & allied products; noncorrosive products & materials; chemical additives; alcohols & anti-freeze compounds
HQ: Ashland Llc
　　50 E Rivercenter Blvd # 1600
　　Covington KY 41011
　　859 815-3333

(G-3419)
ASKIA INC
4303 Williamsburg Rd N (45215-5140)
PHONE.................................513 828-7443
Alioune Gueye, *President*
EMP: 3

SALES (est): 77.9K **Privately Held**
SIC: 7359 5047 5085 5063 Equipment rental & leasing; medical & hospital equipment; commercial containers; ground fault interrupters; service industry machinery

(G-3420)
ASPEC INC
5810 Carothers St (45227-2350)
PHONE.................................513 561-9922
Fax: 513 561-9925
Kerry L Bollmer, *President*
Melissa Cooper, *Manager*
EMP: 9
SQ FT: 11,000
SALES (est): 1.3MM **Privately Held**
SIC: 3089 3544 Injection molding of plastics; forms (molds), for foundry & plastics working machinery

(G-3421)
ASTRO MET INC (PA)
9974 Springfield Pike (45215-1425)
PHONE.................................513 772-1242
Fax: 513 772-9080
Donald Graham, *President*
Tom Schwetschenau, *General Mgr*
Mike Shepherd, *Mfg Mgr*
Frank Gorman, *Mfg Staff*
Marty Ankenbauer, *Controller*
EMP: 23 EST: 1961
SQ FT: 39,000
SALES (est): 3MM **Privately Held**
WEB: www.astromet.com
SIC: 3299 Ceramic fiber

(G-3422)
ASTRO QCB INC
1937 South St (45204)
PHONE.................................513 921-8811
Edward Paul, *President*
EMP: 350
SQ FT: 120,000
SALES (est): 13.6MM **Privately Held**
SIC: 3412 3089 2655 Drums, shipping: metal; plastic containers, except foam; fiber cans, drums & containers; drums, fiber: made from purchased material

(G-3423)
AT&T CORP
7875 Montgomery Rd Ofc (45236-4305)
PHONE.................................513 792-9300
Vicky Valento, *Branch Mgr*
EMP: 9
SALES (corp-wide): 163.7B **Publicly Held**
WEB: www.att.com
SIC: 4813 3661 3357 3571 Telephone communication, except radio; long distance telephone communications; voice telephone communications; data telephone communications; telephone & telegraph apparatus; telephone sets, all types except cellular radio; switching equipment, telephone; PBX equipment, manual or automatic; communication wire; fiber optic cable (insulated); electronic computers; mainframe computers; minicomputers; personal computers (microcomputers); computer peripheral equipment; microprocessors
HQ: At&t Corp.
　　1 At&T Way
　　Bedminster NJ 07921
　　800 403-3302

(G-3424)
ATK2 INC
3111 Harrison Ave (45211-5741)
PHONE.................................513 661-5869
Amy Osterfeld, *Principal*
EMP: 4
SALES (est): 177.5K **Privately Held**
SIC: 2053 Cakes, bakery: frozen

(G-3425)
ATLANTIC SIGN COMPANY INC
2328 Florence Ave (45206-2431)
PHONE.................................513 383-1504
William Yusko, *President*
Aleisa Yusko, *Corp Secy*
Larry Smith, *Vice Pres*
EMP: 15
SQ FT: 14,590

SALES (est): 2.2MM **Privately Held**
SIC: 3993 5099 Signs & advertising specialties; signs, except electric

(G-3426)
ATLAS VAC MACHINE CO LLC
9150 Reading Rd (45215-3343)
P.O. Box 42633 (45242-0633)
PHONE......................513 407-3513
Mike Oliver, *Engineer*
John Abraham, *Mng Member*
▲ EMP: 6
SQ FT: 8,800
SALES: 1.1MM **Privately Held**
SIC: 3565 Packaging machinery

(G-3427)
ATR DISTRIBUTING COMPANY
Wonderware Cincinnati
11857 Tamper Springs Dr (45240)
PHONE......................513 353-1800
Joe Murray, *Branch Mgr*
EMP: 19
SALES (corp-wide): 4.7MM **Privately Held**
SIC: 7372 Prepackaged software
PA: Atr Distributing Company
9585 Cilley Rd
Cleves OH 45002
513 353-1800

(G-3428)
AUBREY ROSE APPAREL LLC
3862 Race Rd (45211-4346)
PHONE......................513 728-2681
Raymond G Hollenkamp Jr,
EMP: 4
SALES: 547.8K **Privately Held**
SIC: 2395 Advertising, promotional & trade show services; embroidery & art needlework

(G-3429)
AURAND MANUFACTURING & EQP CO
1210 Ellis St (45223-1843)
PHONE......................513 541-7200
Fax: 513 541-3065
Ray Evers, *President*
Micheal Moeth, *General Mgr*
Mary Evers, *Corp Secy*
EMP: 6
SQ FT: 4,280
SALES: 1.8MM **Privately Held**
WEB: www.evertenterprises.com
SIC: 3589 Commercial cleaning equipment
PA: Evers Enterprises Inc
4849 Blue Rock Rd
Cincinnati OH

(G-3430)
AVERY DENNISON CORPORATION
11101 Mostellar Rd Ste 2 (45241-1882)
PHONE......................513 682-7500
Fax: 513 682-7565
Dennis Cain, *Branch Mgr*
EMP: 12
SALES (corp-wide): 6B **Publicly Held**
SIC: 2672 Adhesive backed films, foams & foils
PA: Avery Dennison Corporation
207 N Goode Ave Fl 6
Glendale CA 91203
626 304-2000

(G-3431)
B & D GRAPHICS INC
300 Township Ave (45216-2336)
PHONE......................513 641-0855
Fax: 513 641-0216
Gregory Buchtmann, *President*
Albert W Dixon III, *Vice Pres*
EMP: 5
SQ FT: 3,000
SALES: 400K **Privately Held**
SIC: 2759 Screen printing

(G-3432)
B & J BAKING COMPANY INC
4056 Colerain Ave (45223-2561)
PHONE......................513 541-2386
Fax: 513 541-7610
Steve Toleski, *President*
Tatsa Toleski, *Treasurer*
EMP: 15

SQ FT: 10,000
SALES (est): 2MM **Privately Held**
SIC: 2051 Buns, bread type: fresh or frozen

(G-3433)
B P OIL COMPANY
Also Called: BP
1201 Omniplex Dr (45240-1280)
PHONE......................513 671-4107
Fax: 513 671-3222
Pat Hoelle, *Principal*
EMP: 3
SALES (est): 258.1K **Privately Held**
SIC: 2869 Fuels

(G-3434)
BAERLOCHER PRODUCTION USA LLC
5890 Highland Ridge Dr (45232-1440)
PHONE......................513 482-6300
Fax: 513 242-9213
Ray Buehler, *CEO*
Andy Jones, *Managing Dir*
Larry Kandel, *Production*
Michael Odle, *Production*
Peace Rony, *Production*
▲ EMP: 50
SQ FT: 50,000
SALES: 12.2MM
SALES (corp-wide): 377.1MM **Privately Held**
WEB: www.baerlocher.com
SIC: 2819 Nonmetallic compounds
HQ: Baerlocher Gmbh
Freisinger Str. 1
UnterschleiBheim 85716
891 437-30

(G-3435)
BALDIE IMPORT AND EXPORT CORP
Also Called: James Alexander President
4520 Lucerne Ave (45227-2816)
PHONE......................513 503-0953
James S Alexander, *CEO*
▲ EMP: 4
SALES (est): 330K **Privately Held**
SIC: 3089 Plastic processing

(G-3436)
BARDES CORPORATION (PA)
Also Called: Ilsco
4730 Madison Rd (45227-1426)
PHONE......................513 533-6200
Fax: 513 871-4084
David Fitzgibbon, *CEO*
Merrilyn Q Bardes, *Ch of Bd*
Andrew Quinn, *President*
James E Valentine, *Treasurer*
Ron Ullett, *Manager*
▲ EMP: 300
SQ FT: 300,000
SALES (est): 120.9MM **Privately Held**
WEB: www.utilco.com
SIC: 3643 Electric connectors

(G-3437)
BARR LABORATORIES INC
5040 Duramed Rd (45213-2520)
PHONE......................513 731-9900
S Goldstein, *Principal*
Lawrence Glassman, *Senior VP*
Michael Flamm, *Vice Pres*
Patrick Brunne, *VP Opers*
Mike Balog, *Mfg Dir*
EMP: 300
SALES (corp-wide): 19.7B **Privately Held**
WEB: www.barrlabs.com
SIC: 2834 Pharmaceutical preparations
HQ: Barr Laboratories, Inc.
1090 Horsham Rd
North Wales PA 19454
215 591-3000

(G-3438)
BASF CORPORATION
4900 Este Ave (45232-1491)
PHONE......................513 482-3000
Hans Engel, *Principal*
EMP: 700
SALES (corp-wide): 60.8B **Privately Held**
SIC: 2819 Industrial inorganic chemicals

HQ: Basf Corporation
100 Park Ave
Florham Park NJ 07932
973 245-6000

(G-3439)
BASF CORPORATION
4900 Este Ave (45232-1491)
PHONE......................513 482-3000
Tasso Rigopoulos, *Manager*
EMP: 145
SALES (corp-wide): 60.8B **Privately Held**
SIC: 2869 Industrial organic chemicals
HQ: Basf Corporation
100 Park Ave
Florham Park NJ 07932
973 245-6000

(G-3440)
BAXTER BURIAL VAULT SERVICE
Also Called: Baxter-Wilbert Burial Vault
909 E Ross Ave (45217-1159)
PHONE......................513 641-1010
R Douglas Baxter, *President*
Tom Frondorf, *Manager*
Jane Minges, *Manager*
Tammy Richards, *Manager*
EMP: 25
SALES: 2.4MM **Privately Held**
SIC: 5087 3272 Concrete burial vaults & boxes; funeral directors' equipment & supplies; concrete products

(G-3441)
BAYSWATER BEVERAGES LLC
705 Wakefield Dr (45226-1324)
PHONE......................312 224-8012
Charles Hamman,
▲ EMP: 5
SALES: 80K **Privately Held**
SIC: 5963 2087 Bottled water delivery; beverage bases

(G-3442)
BECKER GALLAGHER LEGAL PUBG
8790 Governors Hill Dr # 102 (45249-1307)
PHONE......................513 677-5044
B J Becker, *President*
John Gallagher, *Vice Pres*
Julie Kershner, *Legal Staff*
EMP: 10
SQ FT: 3,000
SALES (est): 830K **Privately Held**
WEB: www.beckergallagher.com
SIC: 2741 Miscellaneous publishing

(G-3443)
BECKMAN MACHINE LLC
4684 Paddock Rd (45229-1002)
P.O. Box 37655 (45222-0655)
PHONE......................513 242-2700
Fax: 513 242-3120
Mary Kathryn Lynch, *President*
Charles Beckman, *Vice Pres*
EMP: 20
SALES (est): 3.3MM **Privately Held**
SIC: 3599 Machine shop, jobbing & repair

(G-3444)
BENCH BILLBOARD COMPANY INC
6805 Cambridge Ave (45227-3227)
PHONE......................513 271-2222
Fax: 513 271-4333
Bruce Graumlich, *President*
Billie Jones, *Vice Pres*
EMP: 3
SQ FT: 6,000
SALES (est): 422K **Privately Held**
WEB: www.bbcx.com
SIC: 7312 3993 Outdoor advertising services; signs & advertising specialties

(G-3445)
BERGHAUSEN CORPORATION
4524 Este Ave (45232-1763)
PHONE......................513 541-5631
Fax: 513 541-1169
Fritz Berghausen, *President*
Tom Dablin, *Plant Mgr*
Tom Davlin, *QC Mgr*
Chris Lewis, *Manager*

▲ EMP: 20 EST: 1863
SQ FT: 38,000
SALES (est): 5.4MM **Privately Held**
WEB: www.berghausen.com
SIC: 2843 2087 2865 Emulsifiers, except food & pharmaceutical; extracts, flavoring; food dyes or colors, synthetic

(G-3446)
BERGSTEIN OIL & GAS PARTNR
11464 Lippelman Rd # 200 (45246-4081)
PHONE......................513 771-6220
EMP: 4
SALES (est): 330K **Privately Held**
SIC: 1382 Oil/Gas Exploration Company

(G-3447)
BERNARD LABORATORIES INC
1738 Townsend St (45223-2710)
PHONE......................513 681-7373
Fax: 513 853-8152
Boyd J Piper Jr, *President*
Edward Bramlage, *Opers Mgr*
Charles Brigham II, *Admin Sec*
EMP: 22 EST: 1980
SQ FT: 30,000
SALES (est): 3.5MM **Privately Held**
WEB: www.bernardlab.com
SIC: 7389 2899 Packaging & labeling services; chemical preparations

(G-3448)
BERRY COMPANY
312 Plum St Ste 600 (45202-4809)
PHONE......................513 768-7800
Pete Luongo, *President*
Bill Mates, *Senior Mgr*
Nicholas Salisbury, *Sr Associate*
EMP: 6
SALES (est): 621.8K **Privately Held**
SIC: 2741 Directories, telephone: publishing & printing

(G-3449)
BINNS MACHINERY COMPANY
330 Railroad Ave (45217-1024)
PHONE......................513 242-3388
Fax: 513 242-8080
Jack N Binns Sr, *President*
Roger Heaton, *Exec VP*
EMP: 4
SQ FT: 3,000
SALES (est): 547.6K **Privately Held**
SIC: 3549 Metalworking machinery

(G-3450)
BIORX LLC (HQ)
Also Called: Thriverx
7167 E Kemper Rd (45249-1028)
PHONE......................866 442-4679
Fax: 513 792-3838
Jennifer Arms, *Vice Pres*
Barb Leitow, *Project Mgr*
Derrick Loudermilk, *Materials Mgr*
Lisa McEvoy, *Treasurer*
Dottie Shaw, *Accounting Mgr*
EMP: 115
SALES (est): 112.1MM
SALES (corp-wide): 4.4B **Publicly Held**
WEB: www.biorx.net
SIC: 5122 8748 2834 5047 Pharmaceuticals; business consulting; pharmaceutical preparations; intravenous solutions; medical & hospital equipment; medical equipment & supplies; skilled nursing care facilities; extended care facility; convalescent home with continuous nursing care
PA: Diplomat Pharmacy, Inc.
4100 S Saginaw St Ste A
Flint MI 48507
888 720-4450

(G-3451)
BIOWISH TECHNOLOGIES INC
2724 Erie Ave Ste B (45208-2125)
PHONE......................312 572-6700
Ian Edwards, *CEO*
Richard Carpenter, *Principal*
Russell Haack, *COO*
John Schroeder, *Vice Pres*
Jennifer Tulich, *Vice Pres*
▲ EMP: 9
SALES (est): 1.7MM **Privately Held**
SIC: 2869 Enzymes

(G-3452)
BLACK & DECKER (US) INC
Also Called: Dewalt Factory Service
2310 E Sharon Rd (45241-1844)
PHONE..................................513 772-3111
Fax: 513 772-0654
Linda Biagioni, *Vice Pres*
Bruce Brooks, *Vice Pres*
William Bruner, *Vice Pres*
Jeffrey Cooper, *Vice Pres*
John Delponti, *Vice Pres*
EMP: 5
SALES (corp-wide): 11.4B **Publicly Held**
WEB: www.dewalt.com
SIC: 3546 Power-driven handtools
HQ: Black & Decker (U.S.) Inc.
1000 Stanley Dr
New Britain CT 06053
860 885-5111

(G-3453)
BLUE CHIP PUMP INC
1045 Meta Dr (45237-5007)
PHONE..................................513 871-7867
Fax: 513 871-1170
Bruce Lipe, *President*
EMP: 3
SQ FT: 2,000
SALES (est): 190K **Privately Held**
SIC: 7699 3561 Pumps & pumping equipment repair; pumps & pumping equipment

(G-3454)
BLUE CHIP TOOL INC
11511 Goldcoast Dr (45249-1620)
PHONE..................................513 489-3561
Fax: 513 489-3823
William Riehle, *President*
Eileen Riehle, *Corp Secy*
John Kilgore, *VP Mfg*
Dennis Bain, *Production*
EMP: 12
SQ FT: 5,000
SALES (est): 1.2MM **Privately Held**
WEB: www.bluechiptool.com
SIC: 3599 Machine shop, jobbing & repair

(G-3455)
BOCK & PIERCE ENTERPRISES
Also Called: Minuteman Press
8550 Beechmont Ave # 800 (45255-4712)
PHONE..................................513 474-9500
Fax: 513 474-9501
Donald S Bock, *President*
J Joshua Pierce, *Treasurer*
EMP: 5 EST: 1997
SQ FT: 3,000
SALES (est): 858.1K **Privately Held**
WEB: www.mmpcincinnati.com
SIC: 2752 2796 2791 2789 Commercial printing, lithographic; platemaking services; typesetting; bookbinding & related work; commercial printing

(G-3456)
BODYCOTE THERMAL PROC INC
710 Burns St (45204-1904)
PHONE..................................513 921-2300
Kevin McCurdy, *Branch Mgr*
Karen Hallman, *Manager*
Pete Pitthoff, *Manager*
EMP: 46
SALES (corp-wide): 739.3MM **Privately Held**
SIC: 3398 Metal heat treating
HQ: Bodycote Thermal Processing, Inc.
12700 Park Central Dr # 700
Dallas TX 75251
214 904-2420

(G-3457)
BOHLENDER ENGRAVING COMPANY
Also Called: Bohlender Engravg
2410 Gilbert Ave (45206-3041)
PHONE..................................513 621-4095
Fax: 513 621-0733
Randy Brunk, *President*
Melanie Chafin, *Manager*
EMP: 11 EST: 1895
SQ FT: 7,500
SALES (est): 1MM **Privately Held**
SIC: 2759 2752 Commercial printing; commercial printing, lithographic

(G-3458)
BONBONNERI INC
Also Called: Bonbonneri Bakery
2030 Madison Rd Ste 1 (45208-3347)
PHONE..................................513 321-3399
Fax: 513 979-5332
Mary Pat Sullivan Pace, *President*
Sharon Butler, *Vice Pres*
Mary Lee, *Prdtn Mgr*
EMP: 16
SQ FT: 2,000
SALES (est): 1.9MM **Privately Held**
SIC: 2051 Bakery: wholesale or wholesale/retail combined

(G-3459)
BONDED PALLETS
1801 John St (45214-2411)
PHONE..................................513 541-1855
Tony Combs, *Owner*
EMP: 4
SALES (est): 404.9K **Privately Held**
SIC: 2448 Pallets, wood & wood with metal

(G-3460)
BONSAL AMERICAN INC
5155 Fischer Ave (45217-1157)
PHONE..................................513 398-7300
Fax: 513 398-1997
Marshal Lewis, *Opers-Prdtn-Mfg*
EMP: 20
SQ FT: 8,100
SALES (corp-wide): 28.6B **Privately Held**
WEB: www.bonsalamerican.com
SIC: 1442 Construction sand & gravel
HQ: Bonsal American, Inc.
625 Griffith Rd Ste 100
Charlotte NC 28217
704 525-1621

(G-3461)
BORDEN DAIRY CO CINCINNATI LLC
Also Called: H. Meyer Dairy
415 John St (45215-5481)
PHONE..................................513 948-8811
Fax: 513 948-8837
David R Meyer, *President*
Michael Campe, *Controller*
EMP: 154 EST: 1976
SALES (est): 60MM **Privately Held**
WEB: www.meyerdairy.com
SIC: 2026 2086 5143 5144 Milk processing (pasteurizing, homogenizing, bottling); bottled & canned soft drinks; dairy products, except dried or canned; poultry & poultry products

(G-3462)
BOSE CORPORATION
Also Called: Bose Showcase Store
7875 Montgomery Rd # 2422 (45236-4608)
PHONE..................................513 891-4384
Donna Davis, *Owner*
EMP: 6
SALES (corp-wide): 3B **Privately Held**
WEB: www.bose.com
SIC: 5731 3651 Radio, television & electronic stores; household audio equipment
PA: Bose Corporation
100 The Mountain Rd
Framingham MA 01701
508 879-7330

(G-3463)
BOSTON BEER COMPANY
1625 Central Pkwy (45214-2423)
PHONE..................................267 240-4429
Jeremy Roza, *Principal*
Andrea Warner, *Opers Mgr*
Amy Viessman, *Human Res Mgr*
Hayley Boles, *Natl Sales Mgr*
Carissa Sweigart, *Natl Sales Mgr*
EMP: 14
SALES (est): 199.1K **Privately Held**
SIC: 3585 Beer dispensing equipment

(G-3464)
BOYE & EMMES MACHINE TOOL CO
Also Called: Acme Turret Lathe
3640 Llewellyn Ave (45223-2336)
PHONE..................................513 541-2520
Fax: 513 541-7120

Steve Wernke, *President*
George Theobald, *Vice Pres*
EMP: 10
SQ FT: 7,500
SALES (est): 890K **Privately Held**
SIC: 3541 5084 Lathes, metal cutting & polishing; machine tool replacement & repair parts, metal cutting types; machine tools & accessories

(G-3465)
BRACE SP PRSTHTIC ORTHTIC CTRS (HQ)
111 Wellington Pl Ste 8 (45219-1758)
PHONE..................................513 421-5653
Fax: 513 763-3354
Ted Ryder, *President*
Marianne Meyer, *Business Mgr*
Patrick Flaherty, *Vice Pres*
Richard Taylor, *Vice Pres*
Douglas B Van Atta, *Vice Pres*
EMP: 15
SQ FT: 7,500
SALES (est): 1.5MM
SALES (corp-wide): 460MM **Publicly Held**
SIC: 3842 Braces, orthopedic; prosthetic appliances
PA: Hanger, Inc.
10910 Domain Dr Ste 300
Austin TX 78758
512 777-3800

(G-3466)
BRADY A LANTZ ENTERPRISES INC
Also Called: Artic Diamond
11242 Sebring Dr (45240-2715)
PHONE..................................513 742-4921
Brady A Lantz, *President*
Micah Sensenig, *Treasurer*
EMP: 4
SALES (est): 193.1K **Privately Held**
SIC: 3299 Architectural sculptures: gypsum, clay, papier mache, etc.

(G-3467)
BRENT BLEH COMPANY
Also Called: Quick Sign Works
917 Vine St (45202-1112)
PHONE..................................513 721-1100
Fax: 513 721-7446
Brent J Bleh, *Owner*
EMP: 5
SQ FT: 4,000
SALES (est): 350K **Privately Held**
SIC: 3993 7389 6531 Signs & advertising specialties; sign painting & lettering shop; real estate brokers & agents

(G-3468)
BRENT CARTER ENTERPRISES INC
Also Called: Prographics Printing Center
4404 Forest Ave (45212-3302)
PHONE..................................513 731-1440
Fax: 513 396-8045
Brent Carter, *President*
Denise Beets, *Manager*
John Jack, *Manager*
EMP: 5
SQ FT: 2,200
SALES: 700K **Privately Held**
WEB: www.prographicsprinting.com
SIC: 2752 Commercial printing, offset

(G-3469)
BRENTWOOD PRINTING & STY
8630 Winton Rd (45231-4817)
PHONE..................................513 522-2679
Fax: 513 522-2692
Scott Finke, *Owner*
Gaille Finke, *Co-Owner*
EMP: 8
SQ FT: 1,250
SALES (est): 677.7K **Privately Held**
WEB: www.brentwood-printing.com
SIC: 2752 Commercial printing, offset; lithographing on metal

(G-3470)
BREWER COMPANY
7300 Main St (45244-3015)
PHONE..................................513 576-6300
Charles W Brewer, *Opers Mgr*

Laura Graber, *Planning Mgr*
EMP: 7
SALES (corp-wide): 50MM **Privately Held**
WEB: www.thebrewerco.com
SIC: 2952 2891 Coating compounds, tar; adhesives & sealants
PA: The Brewer Company
1354 Us Route 50
Milford OH 45150
800 394-0017

(G-3471)
BREWERY X LLC
417 Warner St (45219-1167)
PHONE..................................513 240-3600
Bryon Martin,
EMP: 3
SALES (est): 148.3K **Privately Held**
SIC: 2082 Malt beverages

(G-3472)
BREWPRO INC
Also Called: Brewer Products Co
9483 Reading Rd (45215-3550)
P.O. Box 62065 (45262-0065)
PHONE..................................513 577-7200
Fax: 513 577-7210
David Brewer, *President*
James Brewer, *Vice Pres*
EMP: 6
SALES (est): 1.7MM **Privately Held**
WEB: www.brewerproducts.com
SIC: 5082 3531 7353 5169 Road construction equipment; general construction machinery & equipment; airport construction machinery; heavy construction equipment rental; adhesives & sealants; sealants

(G-3473)
BRIDGETOWN WELDERS LLC
4489 Bridgetown Rd (45211-4442)
PHONE..................................513 574-4851
Fax: 513 574-3491
Fred Coyle,
EMP: 4
SQ FT: 7,000
SALES: 200K **Privately Held**
SIC: 7692 Automotive welding

(G-3474)
BRIGHTON TRUEDGE
4955 Spring Grove Ave (45232-1925)
PHONE..................................513 771-2300
Mark Lang, *Principal*
EMP: 3
SALES (est): 459K **Privately Held**
SIC: 3443 Fabricated plate work (boiler shop)

(G-3475)
BROADWAY PRINTING LLC
530 Reading Rd (45202-1407)
PHONE..................................513 621-3429
Fax: 513 723-1349
Don Stanley,
EMP: 6
SALES (est): 518.8K **Privately Held**
SIC: 2759 Commercial printing

(G-3476)
BROADWAY WELDING & FABRICATION
25 E 76th St (45216-1611)
PHONE..................................513 821-0004
Fax: 513 821-0005
William B Schmidt, *President*
Patricia J Schmidt, *Vice Pres*
EMP: 4
SQ FT: 5,000
SALES (est): 551.6K **Privately Held**
SIC: 7692 Welding repair

(G-3477)
BROCAR PRODUCTS INC
4335 River Rd (45204-1041)
P.O. Box 42295 (45242-0295)
PHONE..................................513 922-2888
Fax: 513 922-5777
John Helmsderfer, *President*
Rick Veith, *Controller*
EMP: 21
SQ FT: 16,000

SALES: 5MM **Privately Held**
WEB: www.brocar.com
SIC: 2531 Chairs, table & arm

(G-3478)
BROCKMANS SIGNS INC
6041 Harrison Ave Ste 5 (45248-1645)
PHONE....................................513 574-6163
Fax: 513 574-0123
Alan Brockman, *President*
Carl Brockman, *Vice Pres*
Trey Canter, *Admin Sec*
EMP: 5
SALES (est): 473.5K **Privately Held**
WEB: www.brockmansigns.com
SIC: 3993 Signs & advertising specialties

(G-3479)
BRODWILL LLC
3900 Rose Hill Ave Ste C (45229-1454)
PHONE....................................513 258-2716
Rick Williams, *President*
Broderick Williams,
EMP: 8 EST: 2005
SALES (est): 379.4K **Privately Held**
SIC: 2599 Hospital furniture, except beds

(G-3480)
BROODLE BRANDS LLC
8361 Broadwell Rd Ste 100 (45244-1609)
PHONE....................................855 276-6353
Kent Arnold, *President*
EMP: 16
SQ FT: 10,000
SALES: 1MM **Privately Held**
SIC: 3411 Food & beverage containers

(G-3481)
BROOKWOOD GROUP INC
Also Called: Schauer Battery Chargers
3210 Wasson Rd (45209-2382)
PHONE....................................513 791-3030
Jonathan Chaiken, *President*
▲ EMP: 10
SQ FT: 10,000
SALES (est): 5MM **Privately Held**
WEB: www.battery-chargers.com
SIC: 3629 Battery chargers, rectifying or
nonrotating

(G-3482)
BROWER PRODUCTS INC (DH)
Also Called: Cabinet Solutions By Design
401 Northland Blvd (45240-3210)
PHONE....................................937 563-1111
Daniel C Brower, *Ch of Bd*
William Brower, *President*
Mark Frericks, *Vice Pres*
John Anderson, *Sales Staff*
Rod Kirby, *Administration*
EMP: 65
SQ FT: 125,000
SALES (est): 19MM **Privately Held**
SIC: 5031 2434 5211 3281 Kitchen cabinets; windows; doors; molding, all materials; wood kitchen cabinets; cabinets, kitchen; door & window products; lumber products; cut stone & stone products; wood partitions & fixtures
HQ: Nisbet, Inc.
11575 Reading Rd
Cincinnati OH 45241
513 563-1111

(G-3483)
BRV INC
Also Called: Boulder Daily Camera
312 Walnut St Ste 2800 (45202-4019)
P.O. Box 5380 (45201-5380)
PHONE....................................513 977-3000
Ken Lowe, *President*
EMP: 15
SALES (est): 2.2MM
SALES (corp-wide): 3B **Publicly Held**
SIC: 2711 Newspapers
HQ: Journal Media Group, Inc.
333 W State St
Milwaukee WI 53203
414 224-2000

(G-3484)
BUCKEYE FIELD SUPPLY LTD
8190 Beechmont Ave 262a (45255-6117)
PHONE....................................513 312-2343
Russell C Romme,
EMP: 3

SALES (est): 355.5K **Privately Held**
SIC: 3589 Water treatment equipment, industrial

(G-3485)
BUCKLEY MANUFACTURING COMPANY
10333 Wayne Ave Ste 1 (45215-1198)
PHONE....................................513 821-4444
Michael G Strotman, *President*
Thomas M Strotman, *Treasurer*
Tom Strotman, *Accountant*
Kathleen Strotman, *Asst Treas*
Mary Reardon, *Admin Sec*
EMP: 18 EST: 1947
SQ FT: 150,000
SALES (est): 5.8MM **Privately Held**
SIC: 3469 3714 Metal stampings; gas
tanks, motor vehicle

(G-3486)
BUILDING CTRL INTEGRATORS LLC
300 E Bus Way Ste 200 (45241)
PHONE....................................513 247-6154
Dave Milar, *Branch Mgr*
EMP: 6
SALES (corp-wide): 14.1MM **Privately Held**
WEB: www.bcicontrols.com
SIC: 3822 Temperature controls, automatic
PA: Building Control Integrators, Llc
383 N Liberty St
Powell OH 43065
614 334-3300

(G-3487)
BURNS & RINK ENTERPRISES LLC
Also Called: PES
2016 Elm St (45202-4979)
PHONE....................................513 421-7799
Chris Burns,
Tammy Burns,
EMP: 5 EST: 2009
SALES (est): 414.7K **Privately Held**
SIC: 2759 Commercial printing

(G-3488)
BUSKEN BAKERY INC
Also Called: Busken Springdale
370 W Kemper Rd (45246-3025)
PHONE....................................513 671-8454
Donna Noah, *Manager*
EMP: 6
SALES (corp-wide): 26.8MM **Privately Held**
WEB: www.busken.com
SIC: 2051 Bread, cake & related products
PA: Busken Bakery, Inc.
2675 Madison Rd
Cincinnati OH 45208
513 871-2114

(G-3489)
BUSKEN BAKERY INC
7565 Kenwood Rd Ste 104 (45236-2835)
PHONE....................................513 791-6736
Maureen Cothe, *Manager*
EMP: 6
SALES (corp-wide): 26.8MM **Privately Held**
WEB: www.busken.com
SIC: 2051 Bread, cake & related products
PA: Busken Bakery, Inc.
2675 Madison Rd
Cincinnati OH 45208
513 871-2114

(G-3490)
BUZZ SEATING INC (PA)
623 N Wayne Ave (45215-2250)
P.O. Box 31379 (45231-0379)
PHONE....................................877 263-5737
Dan Ohara, *President*
▲ EMP: 15
SQ FT: 12,982
SALES: 6.2MM **Privately Held**
WEB: www.buzzseating.com
SIC: 2521 Furniture, office: padded, upholstered or plain: wood

(G-3491)
BWAY CORPORATION
Also Called: Bwaypackaging
8200 Broadwell Rd (45244-1608)
PHONE....................................513 388-2200
Fax: 440 388-2215
Dan Chance, *Plant Mgr*
Leslie Bradshaw, *Opers Staff*
Chuck Bost, *Production*
Lon Fredericksen, *QC Mgr*
Chris Proctor, *Engineer*
EMP: 20
SALES (corp-wide): 824MM **Privately Held**
SIC: 3411 Metal cans
HQ: Bway Corporation
8607 Roberts Dr Ste 250
Atlanta GA 30350
770 645-4800

(G-3492)
BYER STEEL REBAR INC
200 W North Bend Rd (45216-1728)
PHONE....................................513 821-6400
Fax: 513 679-4470
Burke Byer, *President*
Jonas Allen, *COO*
Tom Montgomery, *Plant Supt*
Jennifer Furber, *Human Res Mgr*
Debi Debellevue, *Accounts Mgr*
EMP: 25
SQ FT: 48,000
SALES (est): 12.4MM **Privately Held**
WEB: www.absteel.com
SIC: 3499 Wheels: wheelbarrow, stroller, etc.: disc, stamped metal

(G-3493)
C J KREHBIEL COMPANY
Also Called: Cjk USA Print Possibilities
3962 Virginia Ave (45227-3412)
PHONE....................................513 271-6035
Fax: 513 271-6082
Charles W Krehbiel Jr, *CEO*
Robert C Krehbiel III, *President*
Rob Krehbiel, *Principal*
C J Krehbie, *Principal*
W H Krehbiel, *Principal*
▼ EMP: 185 EST: 1871
SQ FT: 170,000
SALES (est): 41.9MM **Privately Held**
WEB: www.cjkusa.com
SIC: 2732 Books: printing & binding

(G-3494)
CALIFORNIA GROUNDS CARE LLC
5827 Berte St (45230-7201)
PHONE....................................513 207-0244
Roberta Christ,
EMP: 3 EST: 2001
SALES (est): 220K **Privately Held**
SIC: 3524 Lawn & garden mowers & accessories

(G-3495)
CAMARGO PUBLICATIONS INC
7270 N Mingo Ln (45243-1818)
PHONE....................................513 779-7177
Fax: 513 779-2832
George Quigley Jr, *President*
Mary Quigley, *Admin Sec*
EMP: 5
SALES: 2MM **Privately Held**
SIC: 2721 Periodicals: publishing only

(G-3496)
CAPOZZOLO PRINTERS INC
4000 Hamilton Ave (45223-2602)
PHONE....................................513 542-7874
Fax: 513 542-3811
Samuel J Capozzolo II, *President*
Carmen L Capozzolo, *Corp Secy*
EMP: 4 EST: 1958
SQ FT: 13,000
SALES: 278.1K **Privately Held**
SIC: 2752 2791 Commercial printing, offset; color lithography; typesetting

(G-3497)
CARAUSTAR INDUSTRIES INC
Also Called: Cincinnati Paperboard
5500 Wooster Pike (45226-2227)
PHONE....................................513 871-7112
Fax: 513 871-7971
Allen Hall, *Plant Mgr*

Lee Sizemore, *Engineer*
Paul Nigh, *Controller*
Pam Alexander, *Human Res Mgr*
Charles Nelson, *Manager*
EMP: 45
SALES (corp-wide): 1.5B **Privately Held**
WEB: www.caraustar.com
SIC: 2631 Paperboard mills
PA: Caraustar Industries, Inc.
5000 Astell Pwdr Sprng Rd
Austell GA 30106
770 948-3101

(G-3498)
CAREY COLOR INC /CINCINNATI
1718 Central Pkwy (45214-2355)
PHONE....................................513 241-5210
Fax: 513 241-2205
Stephen O'Connor, *President*
James O'Connor, *Chairman*
Tom Carey, *Accounts Exec*
Tom Kent Jr, *Sales Staff*
Donna Stewart, *Office Mgr*
EMP: 21
SQ FT: 15,000
SALES (est): 2.2MM **Privately Held**
SIC: 2796 Color separations for printing

(G-3499)
CAREY COLOR LLC/CINCINNATI
Also Called: LLC/Owned By Partnership
1718 Central Pkwy (45214-2355)
PHONE....................................513 241-5210
Stephen O'Connor, *President*
Jim Oconnor, *Accountant*
Karen Browning, *Sales Staff*
Donna Stewart, *Office Mgr*
Doug Yancy, *Manager*
EMP: 15
SALES (est): 1.5MM
SALES (corp-wide): 7.2MM **Privately Held**
WEB: www.careydigital.com
SIC: 2759 8243 8748 Commercial printing; software training, computer; systems engineering consultant, ex. computer or professional
PA: Tech/Iii, Inc.
1330 Tennessee Ave Ste 2
Cincinnati OH 45229
513 482-7500

(G-3500)
CARGILL INCORPORATED
5204 River Rd (45233-1643)
PHONE....................................513 941-7400
Fax: 513 941-7402
Robert Mattock, *Manager*
EMP: 10
SQ FT: 12,000
SALES (corp-wide): 107.1B **Privately Held**
WEB: www.cargill.com
SIC: 2869 2899 Industrial organic chemicals; chemical preparations
PA: Cargill, Incorporated
15407 Mcginty Rd W
Wayzata MN 55391
952 742-7575

(G-3501)
CARHARTT INC
2685 Edmondson Rd (45209-1910)
PHONE....................................513 657-7130
EMP: 3
SALES (corp-wide): 1.4B **Privately Held**
SIC: 2326 Men's & boys' work clothing
PA: Carhartt, Inc.
5750 Mercury Dr
Dearborn MI 48126
313 271-8460

(G-3502)
CARLISLE AND FINCH COMPANY
4562 W Mitchell Ave (45232-1759)
PHONE....................................513 681-6080
Fax: 513 681-6226
Kurtis Finch, *CEO*
Brent R Finch, *President*
Garth Finch, *Vice Pres*
Ron Allen, *Engineer*
Thomas Wellinghoff, *Manager*
EMP: 30 EST: 1897
SQ FT: 45,000

SALES (est): 6.6MM **Privately Held**
WEB: www.carlislefinch.com
SIC: 3648 3471 3641 Searchlights; flood-lights; plating & polishing; electric lamps

(G-3503)
CARRILLO PALLETS LLC
1292 Glendale Milford Rd (45215-1209)
PHONE.....................................513 942-2210
Francisco Carrillo, *Principal*
EMP: 4 EST: 2010
SALES (est): 259.3K **Privately Held**
SIC: 2448 Pallets, wood & wood with metal

(G-3504)
CASCO MFG SOLUTIONS INC
3107 Spring Grove Ave (45225-1821)
PHONE.....................................513 681-0003
Fax: 513 853-3612
Melissa Mangold, *President*
Thomas Mangold, *Chairman*
Terri Mangold, *Vice Pres*
Jim Moore, *Opers Mgr*
Robert Woerner, *Engineer*
▲ EMP: 60 EST: 1959
SQ FT: 72,000
SALES (est): 10.6MM **Privately Held**
WEB: www.cascosolutions.com
SIC: 2515 7641 3841 2522 Mattresses, containing felt, foam rubber, urethane, etc.; upholstery work; surgical & medical instruments; office furniture, except wood; household furnishings

(G-3505)
CATALOG MERCHANDISER INC
Also Called: Portico
10525 Chester Rd Ste A (45215-1254)
PHONE.....................................888 325-9677
Fax: 513 769-8077
William Watson, *President*
Joe Tartaron, *Vice Pres*
Linda Felsheim, *Manager*
▲ EMP: 11 EST: 1997
SALES (est): 2MM **Privately Held**
SIC: 3993 Signs & advertising specialties

(G-3506)
CATERINGSTONE
6119 Kenwood Rd (45243-2307)
PHONE.....................................513 410-1064
Dr David Pensak, *CEO*
EMP: 6
SALES (est): 224.6K **Privately Held**
SIC: 2599 Carts, restaurant equipment

(G-3507)
CBD MEDIA HOLDINGS LLC (DH)
312 Plum St Ste 900 (45202-2693)
PHONE.....................................513 217-9483
Doug Myers, *President*
John P Schwing, *CFO*
EMP: 3
SALES (est): 871.9K
SALES (corp-wide): 1.5B **Privately Held**
SIC: 2741 Directories, telephone: publish-ing only, not printed on site
HQ: Local Insight Media, L.P.
　　188 Invrneco Dr W Ste 800
　　Englewood CO 80112
　　303 867-1600

(G-3508)
CDS SIGNS
11024 Reading Rd (45241-1929)
PHONE.....................................513 563-7446
Fax: 513 563-7448
Charles P Coburn, *Owner*
Charles Coburn, *Owner*
EMP: 3 EST: 1996
SQ FT: 2,000
SALES (est): 160K **Privately Held**
SIC: 2759 Commercial printing

(G-3509)
CECO ENVIRONMENTAL CORP (PA)
4625 Red Bank Rd Ste 200 (45227-1552)
PHONE.....................................513 458-2600
Fax: 513 458-2647
Jeffrey Lang, *President*
Brent Becker, *President*
Gennaro D'Alterio, *President*
Bob Christie, *General Mgr*
Richard Blum, *COO*
EMP: 5

SQ FT: 7,000
SALES: 417MM **Publicly Held**
WEB: www.effox.com
SIC: 3564 Purification & dust collection equipment

(G-3510)
CECO GROUP INC (HQ)
4625 Red Bank Rd Ste 200 (45227-1552)
PHONE.....................................513 458-2600
Jefferey Lang, *President*
Benton Cook, *CFO*
EMP: 4
SALES (est): 87.3MM
SALES (corp-wide): 417MM **Publicly Held**
SIC: 8711 3564 8734 3443 Engineering services; filters, air: furnaces, air condi-tioning equipment, etc.; testing laborato-ries; fabricated plate work (boiler shop); sheet metal specialties, not stamped; sheet metalwork
PA: Ceco Environmental Corp.
　　4625 Red Bank Rd Ste 200
　　Cincinnati OH 45227
　　513 458-2600

(G-3511)
CEEMCO INCORPORATED
3330 E Kemper Rd (45241-1538)
PHONE.....................................513 563-8822
Fax: 513 563-8830
William E Ensminger, *President*
Marty Grogan, *Vice Pres*
Eunice Hemmert, *Vice Pres*
Tester Rice, *Plant Mgr*
EMP: 59 EST: 1961
SQ FT: 30,000
SALES (est): 14.1MM **Privately Held**
WEB: www.ceemco.com
SIC: 2542 3599 Fixtures: display, office or store: except wood; machine shop, job-bing & repair

(G-3512)
CELSUS LABORATORIES INC
12150 Best Pl (45241-1569)
PHONE.....................................513 772-8130
Fax: 513 772-8132
Cornelius L Van Gorp, *President*
Cornelius Van, *General Mgr*
John Herr, *Vice Pres*
Daniel Reed, *Vice Pres*
Raymond A Stefanski, *Vice Pres*
◆ EMP: 20
SQ FT: 16,000
SALES (est): 5.5MM **Privately Held**
WEB: www.celsuslaboratories.com
SIC: 2899 Chemical preparations

(G-3513)
CENTRAL BUSINESS PRODUCTS INC
3722 Vernier Dr (45251-2433)
PHONE.....................................513 385-5899
Thomas Taulbee, *President*
EMP: 3
SALES (est): 75K **Privately Held**
SIC: 3579 Perforators (office machines)

(G-3514)
CENTRAL FABRICATORS INC
408 Poplar St (45214-2481)
PHONE.....................................513 621-1240
Fax: 513 621-1243
David J Angner, *President*
Micheal Lewis, *Vice Pres*
Daniel Meade, *Vice Pres*
EMP: 26 EST: 1945
SQ FT: 65,000
SALES: 2.5MM **Privately Held**
WEB: www.centralfabricators.com
SIC: 3443 Tanks, standard or custom fabri-cated: metal plate; vessels, process or storage (from boiler shops): metal plate; heat exchangers, plate type

(G-3515)
CENTRAL READY MIX LLC (PA)
6310 E Kemper Rd Ste 125 (45241-2370)
P.O. Box 70, Monroe (45050-0070)
PHONE.....................................513 402-5001
Toll Free:..................................888 -
Fax: 937 422-0651
John Dales, *Controller*
Ashish Goel, *Manager*

Robert Cherry,
EMP: 30 EST: 1934
SQ FT: 8,000
SALES (est): 13.7MM **Privately Held**
WEB: www.morainematerials.com
SIC: 3273 1442 Ready-mixed concrete; sand mining

(G-3516)
CENTRAL READY-MIX OF OHIO LLC
6310 E Kemper Rd Ste 125 (45241-2370)
PHONE.....................................614 252-3452
Mike Fox,
Joe Tanner,
EMP: 40
SALES (est): 2.1MM **Privately Held**
SIC: 3273 Ready-mixed concrete

(G-3517)
CENTRAL READY-MIX OHIO LLC
6310 E Kemper Rd Ste 125 (45241-2370)
PHONE.....................................614 252-3452
Michael Fuchs,
Joe Tanner,
EMP: 48
SALES (est): 5.6MM **Privately Held**
SIC: 3273 Ready-mixed concrete

(G-3518)
CENTRAL USA WIRELESS LLC
11210 Montgomery Rd (45249-2311)
PHONE.....................................513 469-1500
EMP: 28
SALES (est): 2.9MM **Privately Held**
SIC: 7622 3663 Antenna repair & installa-tion; household antenna installation & service; antennas, transmitting & commu-nications

(G-3519)
CFM INTERNATIONAL INC
1 Neumann Way (45215-1915)
PHONE.....................................513 563-4180
Pierre Fabre, *Branch Mgr*
EMP: 36
SALES (corp-wide): 14MM **Privately Held**
SIC: 3724 Aircraft engines & engine parts
PA: Cfm International, Inc.
　　6440 Aviation Way
　　West Chester OH 45069
　　513 552-2787

(G-3520)
CFM RELIGION PUBG GROUP LLC (PA)
8805 Governors Hill Dr # 400 (45249-3319)
PHONE.....................................513 931-4050
Matthew Thibeau, *President*
Don Puterbaugh, *Manager*
EMP: 32
SALES (est): 38.2MM **Privately Held**
SIC: 2721 8741 Magazines: publishing only, not printed on site; management services

(G-3521)
CHAMPION OPCO LLC (PA)
Also Called: Champion Windows Manufactur-ing
12121 Champion Way (45241-6419)
PHONE.....................................513 924-4858
Fax: 513 346-4614
Jim Mishler, *CEO*
Donald R Jones, *President*
Martin Hiedet, *VP Admin*
Joe Faisant, *CFO*
Lisa Brumfield, *Controller*
▲ EMP: 300 EST: 1953
SQ FT: 500,000
SALES (est): 516.7MM **Privately Held**
WEB: www.championfactorydirct.com
SIC: 3089 1761 3442 Window frames & sash, plastic; siding contractor; storm doors or windows, metal

(G-3522)
CHARGER CONNECTION
7779 Meadowcreek Dr (45244-2956)
PHONE.....................................888 427-5829
Larry Morgan, *Principal*
EMP: 3 EST: 2010

SALES (est): 180.2K **Privately Held**
SIC: 3621 Storage battery chargers, motor & engine generator type

(G-3523)
CHARLES J MEYERS
Also Called: American Custom Polishing
866 Suncreek Ct (45238-4837)
PHONE.....................................513 922-2866
Charles J Meyers, *Owner*
EMP: 3
SALES (est): 199.1K **Privately Held**
SIC: 3471 Polishing, metals or formed products

(G-3524)
CHATTANOOGA LASER CUTTING LLC
891 Redna Ter (45215-1110)
PHONE.....................................513 779-7200
Michelle Walker, *Manager*
Eric Hill,
EMP: 50
SQ FT: 34,000
SALES: 1.2MM **Privately Held**
WEB: www.chattanoogalaser.com
SIC: 3441 Fabricated structural metal

(G-3525)
CHC MANUFACTURING INC (PA)
10270 Wayne Ave (45215-1127)
PHONE.....................................513 821-7757
Patrick McLaughlin, *CEO*
Mark Lambert, *President*
Marty Meyer, *Purch Mgr*
Robert J Christen, *Treasurer*
Lonnie Reynolds, *Supervisor*
EMP: 21
SALES (est): 8.9MM **Privately Held**
SIC: 3446 3441 Stairs, staircases, stair treads: prefabricated metal; fabricated structural metal

(G-3526)
CHESTER LABS INC
900 Section Rd Ste A (45237)
PHONE.....................................513 458-3871
Fax: 513 458-3858
Robert King, *Principal*
Steve Tharp, *CFO*
EMP: 22
SALES (est): 3.8MM **Privately Held**
SIC: 2834 Pharmaceutical preparations

(G-3527)
CHESTER PACKAGING LLC
1900 Section Rd Ste A (45237-3308)
PHONE.....................................513 458-3840
Charlie Mills, *President*
John Deiters, *Vice Pres*
Dave Polan, *Vice Pres*
Steve Tharp, *Vice Pres*
Mike Griggs, *Purchasing*
◆ EMP: 120 EST: 1945
SQ FT: 110,000
SALES (est): 31.2MM
SALES (corp-wide): 5.6B **Privately Held**
WEB: www.chester-labs.com
SIC: 2834 2842 2841 Pharmaceutical preparations; dermatologicals; specialty cleaning, polishes & sanitation goods; soap & other detergents
PA: Medline Industries, Inc.
　　3 Lakes Dr
　　Northfield IL 60093
　　847 949-5500

(G-3528)
CHICA BANDS LLC
6216 Madison Rd (45227-1908)
P.O. Box 30537 (45230-0537)
PHONE.....................................513 871-4300
Meredith Finn, *Owner*
Marguerita Perez, *Principal*
EMP: 6
SALES (est): 522.9K **Privately Held**
SIC: 3089 Bands, plastic

(G-3529)
CHIPMAN MACHINING CO INC
2900 Spring Grove Ave (45225-2115)
PHONE.....................................513 681-8515
Fax: 513 681-8516
David Chipman, *President*
Richard Chipman, *Vice Pres*
EMP: 3

SALES: 250K **Privately Held**
SIC: 3599 Machine shop, jobbing & repair

(G-3530)
CHOICE BRANDS ADHESIVES LTD
666 Redna Ter Ste 500 (45215-1166)
PHONE..................................513 772-1234
Jeffrey Allison, *Principal*
EMP: 3
SALES (est): 308.7K **Privately Held**
SIC: 2891 Adhesives

(G-3531)
CHRIS ERHART FOUNDRY & MCH CO
1240 Mehring Way (45203-1836)
PHONE..................................513 421-6550
Fax: 513 421-6552
Daniel J Erhart, *President*
Kate Wesseling, *Purch Agent*
EMP: 30 EST: 1854
SQ FT: 40,000
SALES (est): 7MM **Privately Held**
WEB: www.erhart.com
SIC: 3321 Gray iron castings

(G-3532)
CHROMAFLO TECHNOLOGIES CORP
620 Shepherd Dr (45215-2104)
PHONE..................................513 733-5111
Diane Wills, *Supervisor*
EMP: 110
SALES (corp-wide): 46.6MM **Privately Held**
SIC: 2816 2865 3087 Inorganic pigments;
color pigments, organic; custom com-
pound purchased resins
PA: Chromaflo Technologies Corporation
2600 Michigan Ave
Ashtabula OH 44004
440 997-0081

(G-3533)
CIGARS OF CINCY
1467 Larann Ln (45215-5315)
PHONE..................................513 931-5926
Melissa St Hilaire, *Principal*
EMP: 3
SALES (est): 204.6K **Privately Held**
SIC: 2121 Cigars

(G-3534)
CIMX LLC
Also Called: Cimx Software
4625 Red Bank Rd Ste 200 (45227-1552)
PHONE..................................513 248-7700
Fax: 513 248-7711
Anthony Cuilwik, *Principal*
David Oeters, *Mktg Dir*
Kristin Cuilwik, *Manager*
Nick Stonebraker, *Software Engr*
Sam Conley, *Software Dev*
EMP: 30
SQ FT: 12,000
SALES (est): 3.3MM **Privately Held**
WEB: www.cimx.com
SIC: 7372 7371 Prepackaged software;
custom computer programming services

(G-3535)
CINCINNATI - VULCAN COMPANY
5353 Spring Grove Ave (45217-1026)
PHONE..................................513 242-5300
Fax: 513 242-4488
Garry C Ferraris, *President*
Kathy Hughes, *Office Mgr*
EMP: 60
SQ FT: 6,000
SALES (est): 14.4MM **Privately Held**
WEB: www.vulcanoil.com
SIC: 5983 2992 5171 2899 Fuel oil deal-
ers; oils & greases, blending & com-
pounding; petroleum bulk stations;
petroleum terminals; chemical prepara-
tions; specialty cleaning, polishes & sani-
tation goods; soap & other detergents
PA: Coolant Control, Inc.
5353 Spring Grove Ave
Cincinnati OH 45217
513 471-8770

(G-3536)
CINCINNATI A FLTER SLS SVC INC (PA)
Also Called: Cafco Filter
4815 Para Dr (45237-5009)
PHONE..................................513 242-3400
Fax: 513 482-4444
Edward W Flick, *CEO*
Mark Flick, *President*
Bill Rasmussen, *Sales Mgr*
Ray Cornett, *Admin Sec*
EMP: 20 EST: 1945
SQ FT: 12,500
SALES (est): 8.1MM **Privately Held**
WEB: www.cafcoairfilter.com
SIC: 5075 7349 3564 Air filters; building
component cleaning service; filters, air:
furnaces, air conditioning equipment, etc.

(G-3537)
CINCINNATI ADVG PDTS LLC (HQ)
Also Called: Wear Magic
12150 Northwest Blvd (45246-1231)
PHONE..................................513 346-7310
Fax: 513 346-7319
Bob Winget, *CFO*
Jeff Stall, *Manager*
Rick Mouty,
Jesse King,
EMP: 49
SQ FT: 40,000
SALES: 10MM
SALES (corp-wide): 261.6MM **Privately Held**
WEB: www.profillholdings.com
SIC: 2262 Screen printing: manmade fiber
& silk broadwoven fabrics
PA: Profill Holdings Llc
255 W Crescentville Rd
Cincinnati OH 45246
513 742-4000

(G-3538)
CINCINNATI AIR CONDITIONING CO
2080 Northwest Dr (45231-1700)
PHONE..................................513 721-5622
Fax: 513 345-2544
Mark Radtke, *President*
Michael Geiger, *Corp Secy*
Kenneth Wietmarschen, *Project Mgr*
Bill Wolf, *Project Mgr*
Patrick Doan, *Engineer*
EMP: 55 EST: 1939
SQ FT: 30,000
SALES (est): 18.7MM **Privately Held**
WEB: www.cincinnatiair.com
SIC: 1711 3822 Heating & air conditioning
contractors; refrigeration contractor; auto
controls regulating residntl & coml envi-
ronmt & applncs

(G-3539)
CINCINNATI ASSN FOR THE BLIND
2045 Gilbert Ave (45202-1403)
PHONE..................................513 221-8558
Toll Free:.........................888 -
Fax: 513 221-2995
John Mitchell, *CEO*
Amy Scrivner, *Development*
Jennifer Dubois, *Finance*
Ginny Backscheider, *Director*
John H Mitchell III, *Director*
EMP: 125
SQ FT: 88,000
SALES: 7.3MM **Privately Held**
SIC: 8331 8322 2891 Sheltered work-
shop; association for the handicapped;
adhesives & sealants

(G-3540)
CINCINNATI BELL ANY DSTNCE INC
221 E 4th St Ste 700 (45202-4118)
P.O. Box 2301 (45201-2301)
PHONE..................................513 397-9900
Theodore H Torbeck, *CEO*
David L Heimbach, *COO*
Shua T Duckworth, *Vice Pres*
Leigh R Fox, *CFO*
Kurt Freyberger, *CFO*
EMP: 753

SALES (est): 60.7MM
SALES (corp-wide): 1.1B **Publicly Held**
SIC: 3669 Emergency alarms
HQ: Cincinnati Bell Telephone Company
209 W 7th St Fl 1
Cincinnati OH 45202
513 565-9402

(G-3541)
CINCINNATI BELL INC
201 E 4th St (45202-4248)
PHONE..................................513 565-2210
Fax: 513 421-8624
Roy Hord, *Exec VP*
Rick Benken, *Vice Pres*
Brian G Keating, *Vice Pres*
Donald Frey, *Project Mgr*
Linda Meyer, *Project Mgr*
EMP: 14
SALES (corp-wide): 1.1B **Publicly Held**
WEB: www.broadwing.com
SIC: 2741 Directories, telephone: publish-
ing & printing
PA: Cincinnati Bell Inc.
221 E 4th St Ste 700
Cincinnati OH 45202
513 397-9900

(G-3542)
CINCINNATI BINDERY & PACKG INC
2838 Spring Grove Ave (45225-2268)
PHONE..................................859 816-0282
Emmett Grummich, *President*
EMP: 7
SALES (est): 1MM **Privately Held**
SIC: 2631 Container, packaging &
boxboard

(G-3543)
CINCINNATI BIOREFINING CORP (HQ)
470 Este Ave (45232)
PHONE..................................513 482-8800
Gary R Heminger, *President*
EMP: 5
SALES (est): 38.3MM **Publicly Held**
SIC: 2079 Edible fats & oils

(G-3544)
CINCINNATI BLACKTOP COMPANY
4992 Gray Rd (45232-1513)
P.O. Box 141100 (45250-1100)
PHONE..................................513 681-0952
Fax: 513 681-1519
Paul A Seta, *President*
EMP: 12
SQ FT: 2,500
SALES (est): 1.3MM **Privately Held**
SIC: 3241 Cement, hydraulic

(G-3545)
CINCINNATI CONVERTORS INC
1730 Cleneay Ave (45212-3506)
PHONE..................................513 731-6600
Fax: 513 731-6605
Donald Ellsworth Jr, *President*
Kristin Goltra, *COO*
Angie Holt, *Manager*
EMP: 12
SQ FT: 15,000
SALES: 2.5MM **Privately Held**
WEB: www.cincinnaticonvertors.com
SIC: 2759 Flexographic printing

(G-3546)
CINCINNATI CRT INDEX PRESS INC
119 W Central Pkwy (45202-1075)
PHONE..................................513 241-1450
Fax: 513 684-7821
Gregory Arvanetes, *President*
Mark Beattey, *General Mgr*
Mark Beatty, *General Mgr*
Joseph W Shea III, *Vice Pres*
Mike Whalel, *Manager*
EMP: 12 EST: 1892
SALES (est): 979.4K **Privately Held**
WEB: www.courtindex.com
SIC: 2711 Commercial printing & newspa-
per publishing combined

(G-3547)
CINCINNATI CTRL DYNAMICS INC
Also Called: Ccdi
4924 Para Dr (45237-5012)
PHONE..................................513 242-7300
Fax: 513 242-5691
Jeffrey Bao, *President*
Christopher Bao, *Co-Owner*
Derick Bao, *Co-Owner*
Phil Covalcine, *Plant Mgr*
Jeffrey Bad, *Director*
EMP: 8 EST: 1976
SQ FT: 20,000
SALES (est): 1MM **Privately Held**
WEB: www.ccdi1.com
SIC: 3625 3829 7373 Control equipment,
electric; measuring & controlling devices;
systems software development services

(G-3548)
CINCINNATI DRVELINE HYDRAULICS
1220 W 8th St (45203-1005)
PHONE..................................513 651-2406
Fax: 513 651-2407
Joe Klawitter, *President*
EMP: 3
SALES (est): 498.8K **Privately Held**
SIC: 3714 Drive shafts, motor vehicle

(G-3549)
CINCINNATI ENQUIRER
312 Elm St Fl 18 (45202-2721)
PHONE..................................513 721-2700
Fax: 513 768-8210
Mike Ballman, *Principal*
Katharine Vogel, *Editor*
Thomas Bernheimer, *Opers Staff*
Michael Balman, *Manager*
Robert Hartman, *Director*
EMP: 30
SALES (est): 9.3MM **Privately Held**
SIC: 2759 Commercial printing

(G-3550)
CINCINNATI GASKET PKG MFG INC
Also Called: Cincinnati Gasket & Indus GL
40 Illinois Ave (45215-5512)
PHONE..................................513 761-3458
Fax: 513 761-2994
Lawrence Uhlenbrock, *President*
Barry Ruter, *General Mgr*
Frank Duttenhofer, *Principal*
Henry D Hopf, *Principal*
Becky Knecht, *Vice Pres*
▲ EMP: 45
SQ FT: 75,000
SALES: 7.2MM **Privately Held**
WEB: www.cincinnatigasket.com
SIC: 3229 3053 Glassware, industrial;
gaskets, all materials

(G-3551)
CINCINNATI GATE SYSTEMS INC
675 Redna Ter (45215-1108)
PHONE..................................513 769-5200
Steve Williams, *President*
Anita Williams, *VP Sales*
EMP: 4
SALES (est): 430.8K **Privately Held**
WEB: www.cincinnatigate.com
SIC: 3699 Security devices

(G-3552)
CINCINNATI GEARING SYSTEMS INC (PA)
5757 Mariemont Ave (45227-4216)
PHONE..................................513 527-8600
Evans L Decamp, *President*
Walter L Rye, *Chairman*
Kenneth Kiehl, *Vice Pres*
EMP: 75 EST: 1941
SQ FT: 100,000
SALES (est): 33.5MM **Privately Held**
WEB: www.steeltreating.com
SIC: 3398 3471 Metal heat treating; plat-
ing & polishing

(G-3553)
CINCINNATI GEARING SYSTEMS INC
301 Milford Pkwy (45227)
PHONE...................513 527-8634
Kenneth Kiehl, *Vice Pres*
EMP: 140
SALES (corp-wide): 33.5MM **Privately Held**
SIC: 3462 Gears, forged steel
PA: Cincinnati Gearing Systems Incorporated
5757 Mariemont Ave
Cincinnati OH 45227
513 527-8600

(G-3554)
CINCINNATI GEARING SYSTEMS INC
5757 Mariemont Ave (45227-4216)
PHONE...................513 527-8600
Robert Rye, *Branch Mgr*
EMP: 102
SALES (corp-wide): 33.5MM **Privately Held**
WEB: www.steeltreating.com
SIC: 3714 Gears, motor vehicle
PA: Cincinnati Gearing Systems Incorporated
5757 Mariemont Ave
Cincinnati OH 45227
513 527-8600

(G-3555)
CINCINNATI GILBERT MCH TL LLC
3366 Beekman St (45223-2424)
PHONE...................513 541-4815
Fax: 513 541-4885
Rein Petry, *Vice Pres*
Bill Lane, *Safety Dir*
Ron Stites, *Purchasing*
Andy Schaffer, *Engineer*
John Rolfes, *Project Engr*
▲ EMP: 30 EST: 1995
SQ FT: 50,000
SALES (est): 5.8MM **Privately Held**
WEB: www.cincinnatigilbert.com
SIC: 3541 Machine tools, metal cutting type; drilling machine tools (metal cutting); boring mills; milling machines

(G-3556)
CINCINNATI LASER CUTTING LLC
Also Called: Cincinnati Metal Fabricating
891 Redna Ter (45215-1110)
PHONE...................513 772-6999
Eric Copeland Hill, *President*
EMP: 40
SQ FT: 45,000
SALES (est): 5.4MM **Privately Held**
WEB: www.cincylaser.com
SIC: 3699 Laser welding, drilling & cutting equipment

(G-3557)
CINCINNATI MAGAZINE
441 Vine St Ste 200 (45202-2039)
PHONE...................513 421-4300
Fax: 513 562-2746
Jay Stowe, *Publisher*
Patrice Watson, *Principal*
Kara Hagerman, *Editor*
Missy Beiting, *Opers Staff*
Danielle Johnson, *Opers Staff*
EMP: 3
SALES (est): 414.9K **Privately Held**
SIC: 2721 Periodicals

(G-3558)
CINCINNATI MARLINS INC
616 W North Bend Rd (45224-1424)
PHONE...................513 761-3320
Fax: 513 761-3880
Brian Bridgeford, *President*
Sue House, *Athletic Dir*
Ashley Yanzsa, *Assistant*
EMP: 8
SQ FT: 500
SALES: 998.4K **Privately Held**
SIC: 7997 2086 Country club, membership; swimming club, membership; soft drinks: packaged in cans, bottles, etc.

(G-3559)
CINCINNATI MEAT PROCESSING INC
3640 Muddy Creek Rd (45238-2044)
PHONE...................513 682-6000
Frank Schmitt, *General Mgr*
Glen P Napolitano, *COO*
Anita Sicke, *Manager*
◆ EMP: 80
SALES (est): 9.7MM **Privately Held**
SIC: 2013 Sausages & other prepared meats
HQ: Zwanenberg Food Group (Usa) Inc.
3640 Muddy Creek Rd
Cincinnati OH 45238
513 682-6000

(G-3560)
CINCINNATI MINE MACHINERY CO
2950 Jonrose Ave (45239-5319)
PHONE...................513 522-7777
Fax: 513 728-4041
Robert J Stenger, *President*
Ron Paolello, *General Mgr*
William D Stenger, *Treasurer*
Bobby Stenger, *Sales Staff*
Tina Hollander, *Director*
▲ EMP: 55
SQ FT: 75,000
SALES (est): 13MM **Privately Held**
WEB: www.cinmine.com
SIC: 3541 3535 Machine tools, metal cutting type; conveyors & conveying equipment

(G-3561)
CINCINNATI MOLD INCORPORATED
225 Stille Dr (45233-1646)
PHONE...................513 922-1888
Fax: 513 922-5608
Edward Korb, *President*
James Korb, *Vice Pres*
Jim Korb, *Treasurer*
EMP: 3
SALES: 500K **Privately Held**
SIC: 3544 Industrial molds

(G-3562)
CINCINNATI PATTERN COMPANY
2405 Spring Grove Ave (45214-1727)
PHONE...................513 241-9872
Fax: 513 241-9883
Michael J Ballard, *President*
Mark Banta, *Manager*
EMP: 14
SQ FT: 8,000
SALES: 1MM **Privately Held**
SIC: 3543 Foundry patternmaking

(G-3563)
CINCINNATI PRESERVING COMPANY
Also Called: Clearbrook Farms
3015 E Kemper Rd (45241-1514)
PHONE...................513 771-2000
Fax: 513 771-8381
Andrew Liscow, *CEO*
Dan Cohen, *Vice Pres*
Joseph Heinrich, *Controller*
Joe Hendricks, *Controller*
Kimberly Sueberling, *Sales Executive*
▲ EMP: 18 EST: 1924
SQ FT: 30,000
SALES: 4.3MM **Privately Held**
WEB: www.clearbrookfarms.com
SIC: 2033 Fruit pie mixes & fillings: packaged in cans, jars, etc.; preserves, including imitation: in cans, jars, etc.

(G-3564)
CINCINNATI RECREATION COMM
Also Called: Cincinnati City Boat Ramp
3540 Southside Ave (45204-1138)
PHONE...................513 921-5657
Kathy Lang, *Director*
EMP: 3
SQ FT: 2,048
SALES (est): 400K **Privately Held**
SIC: 3536 Boat lifts

(G-3565)
CINCINNATI RENEWABLE FUELS LLC
4700 Este Ave (45232-1415)
PHONE...................513 482-8800
Fax: 513 482-8858
Arunas Paliulis, *CEO*
Jeffrie Defraties, *COO*
Rajive Khosla, *CFO*
Frank Larisa, *Human Res Mgr*
◆ EMP: 75
SALES (est): 38.3MM **Publicly Held**
SIC: 2079 Edible fats & oils
HQ: Cincinnati Biorefining Corp
470 Este Ave
Cincinnati OH 45232

(G-3566)
CINCINNATI SPECIALTIES LLC
501 Murray Rd (45217-1014)
PHONE...................513 242-3300
Fax: 513 482-7315
Jim Trimbath, *Plant Engr*
Phad McCord, *Controller*
Bruce O Becker, *Manager*
Carl W Hoskins, *Supervisor*
Nancy Burrier, *Director*
EMP: 175
SQ FT: 61,020
SALES: 70MM
SALES (corp-wide): 1.3B **Privately Held**
WEB: www.pmcsg.com
SIC: 2819 Industrial inorganic chemicals
HQ: Pmc Specialties Group, Inc.
501 Murray Rd
Cincinnati OH 45217

(G-3567)
CINCINNATI VALVE COMPANY
1519 Tremont St (45214-1458)
P.O. Box 141451 (45250-1451)
PHONE...................513 471-8258
Fax: 513 471-8327
Suran Hegde, *President*
Juan Del Rincon, *Human Res Dir*
▲ EMP: 13
SQ FT: 200,000
SALES (est): 1.5MM **Privately Held**
WEB: www.lunkenheimercvc.com
SIC: 3366 Castings (except die): bronze

(G-3568)
CINCINNATI WINDOW SHADE INC (PA)
Also Called: Cincinnati Window Decor
3004 Harris Ave (45212-2404)
PHONE...................513 631-7200
Fax: 513 631-8882
James G Frederick, *President*
Janet Frederick, *Treasurer*
James M Frederick, *Admin Sec*
EMP: 16
SQ FT: 15,000
SALES (est): 4.4MM **Privately Held**
SIC: 5023 5719 2591 Window furnishings; window shades; venetian blinds; vertical blinds; window shades; venetian blinds; vertical blinds; window shades; venetian blinds; blinds vertical

(G-3569)
CINCINNATI WOOD PRODUCTS CO
2644 Colerain Ave (45214-1712)
PHONE...................513 542-0569
Tim Janson, *Owner*
EMP: 3
SALES: 100K **Privately Held**
SIC: 2431 Woodwork, interior & ornamental

(G-3570)
CINCINNATI WOODWORKS INC
2161 Elysian Pl (45219-1603)
PHONE...................513 241-6412
Fax: 513 721-8225
Charles Kussmaul, *President*
Janis Kussmaul, *Admin Sec*
EMP: 3
SQ FT: 12,000
SALES (est): 240K **Privately Held**
SIC: 2431 7532 Millwork; antique & classic automobile restoration

(G-3571)
CINCINNATTI PREMIER CANDY LLC
Also Called: Marpro
5141 Fischer Ave (45217-1157)
PHONE...................513 253-0079
Fax: 513 641-2557
Bill Ward,
Bill Clark,
Fred Runk,
Sandy Runk,
EMP: 36 EST: 1936
SQ FT: 30,000
SALES: 1.2MM **Privately Held**
WEB: www.marshmallowcone.com
SIC: 2064 2099 Candy & other confectionery products; food preparations

(G-3572)
CINCY CUPCAKES LLC
6646 Salem Rd (45230-2815)
PHONE...................513 985-4440
Amy Jones, *Manager*
EMP: 4
SALES (est): 337K **Privately Held**
SIC: 2051 Bread, cake & related products

(G-3573)
CINCY GLASS INC
3249 Fredonia Ave (45229-3309)
PHONE...................513 241-0455
Fax: 513 241-0507
Michael T Brown, *President*
Linda Hensgen, *Office Mgr*
EMP: 8
SALES (est): 1.4MM **Privately Held**
SIC: 3441 Fabricated structural metal

(G-3574)
CINEX INC
2641 Cummins St (45225-2099)
PHONE...................513 921-2825
Fax: 513 921-4755
Gary R Smith, *President*
Judith A Smith, *Corp Secy*
Ron Meyers, *Engineer*
EMP: 65
SQ FT: 35,000
SALES (est): 8.5MM **Privately Held**
SIC: 3599 Machine shop, jobbing & repair

(G-3575)
CINFAB LLC
5240 Lester Rd (45213-2522)
PHONE...................513 396-6100
Fax: 513 396-7574
Stu Cameron, *Superintendent*
Doug Agricola, *Principal*
Andrew Futscher, *Project Mgr*
Mel Phillips, *Project Mgr*
Steve Merman, *Foreman/Supr*
EMP: 140
SQ FT: 36,500
SALES (est): 37.3MM **Privately Held**
WEB: www.cinfab.com
SIC: 3444 Sheet metalwork

(G-3576)
CINN WIRE E D M INC
6850 Colerain Ave (45239-5544)
PHONE...................513 741-5402
Judith Coster, *CEO*
Robert Coster, *President*
EMP: 3
SQ FT: 3,000
SALES (est): 343.8K **Privately Held**
SIC: 3544 Special dies, tools, jigs & fixtures

(G-3577)
CINTAS CORPORATION (PA)
6800 Cintas Blvd (45262)
P.O. Box 625737 (45262-5737)
PHONE...................513 459-1200
Fax: 513 573-4035
Scott D Farmer, *CEO*
Robert J Kohlhepp, *Ch of Bd*
J Phillip Holloman, *President*
Tom Cato, *General Mgr*
Mike Flamm, *General Mgr*
◆ EMP: 1500

SALES: 4.9B **Publicly Held**
WEB: www.cintas-corp.com
SIC: **7218** 2337 2326 5084 Industrial uniform supply; uniforms, except athletic:
women's, misses' & juniors'; work uniforms; safety equipment

(G-3578)
CINTAS CORPORATION
Also Called: Cintas Uniforms AP Fcilty Svcs
5570 Ridge Ave (45213-2516)
PHONE......................................513 631-5750
Marie Seng, *Branch Mgr*
EMP: 100
SALES (corp-wide): 4.9B **Publicly Held**
SIC: **2326** 2337 7218 5084 Work uni-
forms; uniforms, except athletic: women's,
misses' & juniors'; industrial uniform sup-
ply; wiping towel supply; treated equip-
ment supply: mats, rugs, mops, cloths,
etc.; safety equipment
PA: Cintas Corporation
6800 Cintas Blvd
Cincinnati OH 45262
513 459-1200

(G-3579)
**CINTAS SALES CORPORATION
(HQ)**
6800 Cintas Blvd (45262)
PHONE......................................513 459-1200
Richard T Farmer, *Ch of Bd*
Robert J Kohlepp, *Vice Ch Bd*
Scott Farmer, *President*
Tom Thornley, *Vice Pres*
Bradley Beyer, *Opers Mgr*
EMP: 450
SALES (est): 79.7MM
SALES (corp-wide): 4.9B **Publicly Held**
SIC: **7218** 2326 5136 5137 Industrial uni-
form supply; work clothing supply; work
uniforms; uniforms, men's & boys'; uni-
forms, women's & children's
PA: Cintas Corporation
6800 Cintas Blvd
Cincinnati OH 45262
513 459-1200

(G-3580)
CITY IRON LLC
4136 Colerain Ave (45223-2560)
PHONE......................................513 721-5678
Steve Sallquist, *Principal*
Doug Bootes, *Manager*
EMP: 4
SQ FT: 13,266
SALES (est): 340.6K **Privately Held**
SIC: **3446** Fences or posts, ornamental
iron or steel

(G-3581)
CITYWIDE MATERIALS INC
Also Called: Citywide Ready Mix
5263 Wooster Pike (45226-2228)
PHONE......................................513 533-1111
Fax: 513 533-9833
Jerry Powell Jr, *Ch of Bd*
Mark Cassiere, *President*
EMP: 20
SQ FT: 560
SALES (est): 2.7MM **Privately Held**
SIC: **3273** Ready-mixed concrete

(G-3582)
**CLARKE FIRE PRTECTION PDTS
INC (HQ)**
3133 E Kemper Rd (45241-1516)
PHONE......................................513 771-2200
Fax: 513 771-0520
Dane Petrie, *Principal*
Jeff Gehlhausen, *Manager*
▲ **EMP:** 66
SALES (est): 18.4MM
SALES (corp-wide): 277.1MM **Privately
Held**
SIC: **3519** Diesel, semi-diesel or duel-fuel
engines, including marine
PA: Clarke Power Services, Inc.
3133 E Kemper Rd
Cincinnati OH 45241
513 771-2200

(G-3583)
CLARKE POWER SERVICES INC
Also Called: Clarke Fire Protection Product
3133 E Kemper Rd (45241-1516)
PHONE......................................513 771-2200
Lud Koli, *Vice Chairman*
Tom Freiwald, *Vice Pres*
Paul Loegig, *Finance*
Diane Lotz, *Human Res Dir*
Justin Strousse, *Sales Staff*
EMP: 35
SALES (corp-wide): 277.1MM **Privately
Held**
SIC: **3463** Pump, compressor, turbine &
engine forgings, except auto
PA: Clarke Power Services, Inc.
3133 E Kemper Rd
Cincinnati OH 45241
513 771-2200

(G-3584)
CLASSIC RECIPE CHILI INC
Also Called: Empress Chili
10592 Taconic Ter (45215-1125)
PHONE......................................513 771-1441
Fax: 513 771-1442
Jim Papakirk, *President*
Kevin Tuchfarber, *Manager*
EMP: 3
SQ FT: 10,000
SALES (est): 368.1K **Privately Held**
SIC: **2038** Dinners, frozen & packaged

(G-3585)
**CLAYTON MANUFACTURING
COMPANY**
Also Called: Clayton Mfg Co
3051 Exon Ave (45241-2549)
PHONE......................................513 563-1300
Fax: 513 563-1303
Margo McMartin, *General Mgr*
Ted Williams, *Engineer*
Randy Miller, *Sales Dir*
Jan Motz, *Office Mgr*
Todd Slieker, *Manager*
EMP: 12
SQ FT: 27,664
SALES (corp-wide): 128.6MM **Privately
Held**
WEB: www.claytonindustries.com
SIC: **2842** Cleaning or polishing prepara-
tions
PA: Clayton Manufacturing Company
17477 Hurley St
City Of Industry CA 91744
626 443-9381

(G-3586)
CLINE SIGNS LLC
Also Called: Fastsigns
3272 Highland Ave (45213-2508)
PHONE......................................513 396-7446
Fax: 513 396-7222
Jeff Cline, *Mng Member*
EMP: 5
SALES: 600K **Privately Held**
SIC: **3993** Signs & advertising specialties

(G-3587)
CLINICAL COMPUTING INC
205 W 4th St Ste 810 (45202-2628)
PHONE......................................513 651-3803
Fax: 513 531-8924
Barbara Robinette, *Office Mgr*
Jack N Richardson, *Manager*
EMP: 18
SALES (corp-wide): 2.1MM **Privately
Held**
WEB: www.ccl.com
SIC: **7372** 7371 Prepackaged software;
custom computer programming services
PA: Clinical Computing Plc
1 Bath Street
Ipswich IP2 8
147 369-4760

(G-3588)
**CLIPSONS METAL WORKING
INC**
Also Called: Clipson S Metalworking
127 Novner Dr (45215-1300)
PHONE......................................513 772-6393
Fax: 513 772-6394
Stuart Clipson, *President*
Patricia Clipson, *Vice Pres*

EMP: 7
SQ FT: 7,500
SALES (est): 710K **Privately Held**
SIC: **3599** 7692 3441 Machine shop, job-
bing & repair; welding repair; fabricated
structural metal

(G-3589)
CLOPAY CORPORATION
1260 W Sharon Rd (45240-2917)
PHONE......................................513 742-1984
William Weber, *Branch Mgr*
EMP: 5
SALES (corp-wide): 2B **Publicly Held**
WEB: www.clopay.com
SIC: **3081** Plastic film & sheet
HQ: Clopay Corporation
8585 Duke Blvd
Mason OH 45040
800 282-2260

(G-3590)
**CLOVERNOOK CENTER FOR
THE BLI (PA)**
7000 Hamilton Ave (45231-5240)
PHONE......................................513 522-3860
Fax: 513 728-3950
Robin Usalis, *President*
Christopher Faust, *President*
Beasy Baugh, *Vice Pres*
Betsy Baugh, *Vice Pres*
Jacqueline L Conner, *Vice Pres*
EMP: 125
SQ FT: 40,000
SALES: 8.1MM **Privately Held**
WEB: www.clovernook.org
SIC: **2656** 8322 7389 Paper cups, plates,
dishes & utensils; rehabilitation services;
fund raising organizations

(G-3591)
CLUB 513 LLC
201 E 5th St Fl 19 (45202-4162)
PHONE......................................800 530-2574
Aaron Chiles, *General Mgr*
Aaron R Chiles, *Mng Member*
Charles Chiles,
Jonathan Chiles,
London Chiles,
EMP: 6
SQ FT: 3,500
SALES: 372K **Privately Held**
SIC: **7929** 2759 5099 Entertainment
group; letterpress & screen printing; nov-
elties, durable

(G-3592)
**CMF CUSTOM METAL
FINISHERS**
7616 Anthony Wayne Ave (45216-1617)
PHONE......................................513 821-8145
John Metz, *President*
EMP: 3
SALES: 600K **Privately Held**
SIC: **3471** 3449 Finishing, metals or
formed products; miscellaneous metal-
work

(G-3593)
CNS INC (PA)
Also Called: United Graphics
3716 Montgomery Rd (45207-1131)
PHONE......................................513 631-7073
Steve Siegwald, *President*
Larry Castagno, *Corp Secy*
EMP: 5
SQ FT: 3,000
SALES: 8.7MM **Privately Held**
SIC: **2759** 2752 Business forms: printing;
commercial printing, lithographic

(G-3594)
**COATING APPLICATIONS INTL
LLC**
2860 Cooper Rd Ste 200 (45241-3368)
PHONE......................................513 956-5222
Fax: 513 956-5225
Terri Coombs, *Manager*
Bruce Rowe,
Kevin Rafferty,
EMP: 5
SQ FT: 10,500

SALES (est): 510K **Privately Held**
WEB: www.caillc.com
SIC: **2672** Enameled paper: made from
purchased paper

(G-3595)
**COCA-COLA BOTTLING CO
CNSLD**
5100 Duck Creek Rd (45227-1450)
PHONE......................................513 527-6600
Thomasina Kennedy, *Human Res Dir*
Doug Davis, *Sales Staff*
John Whitaker, *Manager*
Jim Callaway, *Info Tech Dir*
Mike McNearney, *Info Tech Mgr*
EMP: 400
SALES (corp-wide): 3.1B **Publicly Held**
WEB: www.cokecce.com
SIC: **2086** Bottled & canned soft drinks
PA: Coca-Cola Bottling Co. Consolidated
4100 Coca Cola Plz # 100
Charlotte NC 28211
704 557-4400

(G-3596)
COLDWELL WILCOX TECH LLC
3040 Forrer St (45209-1016)
PHONE......................................513 758-1010
Ross Bushman, *President*
Roger M Depperschmidt, *Controller*
James E Bushman, *Mng Member*
EMP: 4
SQ FT: 400,000
SALES (est): 543.2K
SALES (corp-wide): 33.1MM **Privately
Held**
WEB: www.coldwell-wilcox.com
SIC: **3589** Water treatment equipment, in-
dustrial
PA: Cast-Fab Technologies, Inc.
3040 Forrer St
Cincinnati OH 45209
513 758-1000

(G-3597)
COLORTREND USA LLC
620 Shepherd Dr (45215-2104)
PHONE......................................513 733-5111
Scott Becker, *President*
EMP: 3 **EST:** 2011
SALES (est): 195K **Privately Held**
SIC: **2816** Inorganic pigments

(G-3598)
COMBINED CONTAINER BOARD
7741 School Rd (45249-1529)
PHONE......................................513 530-5700
Fax: 513 530-5969
Peter Watson, *President*
Diana Tibbetts, *Vice Pres*
Chris Zimmerman, *Prdtn Mgr*
EMP: 52
SQ FT: 162,000
SALES (est): 13.1MM
SALES (corp-wide): 3.3B **Publicly Held**
WEB: www.mpc-spc.com
SIC: **2653** Sheets, corrugated: made from
purchased materials
HQ: Corrchoice, Inc.
777 3rd St Nw
Massillon OH 44647
330 833-5705

(G-3599)
COMMUNICATIONS AID INC
Also Called: University Hring Aid Assctions
222 Piedmont Ave Ste 5200 (45219-4222)
PHONE......................................513 475-8453
Stephanie Lockhart, *President*
Myles Pensak, *Director*
EMP: 10
SALES (est): 800K **Privately Held**
SIC: **5999** 3842 Communication equip-
ment; hearing aids; hearing aids

(G-3600)
**COMPLETE CYLINDER SERVICE
INC**
1240 Glendale Milford Rd (45215-1209)
PHONE......................................513 772-1500
David Kleier, *Principal*
EMP: 8 **EST:** 2012
SALES (est): 1MM **Privately Held**
SIC: **3272** Cylinder pipe, prestressed or
pretensioned concrete

(G-3601)
COMPLETE DRY FLOOD
6006 Madison Rd (45227-1818)
PHONE.....................................513 200-9274
Howard Champion, *Principal*
EMP: 3 EST: 2015
SALES (est): 107.4K **Privately Held**
SIC: 1799 3589 Post-disaster renovations;
high pressure cleaning equipment

(G-3602)
COMPOST CINCY
5800 Este Ave (45232-1442)
PHONE.....................................513 278-8178
Grant A Gibson, *Principal*
EMP: 3
SALES (est): 297.2K **Privately Held**
SIC: 2875 Compost

(G-3603)
COMPUTER SYSTEM
ENHANCEMENT
Also Called: Cse-Industrial Products Group
927 Kreis Ln (45205-2019)
PHONE.....................................513 251-6791
Spencer Morgan, *President*
James Klein, *Vice Pres*
Patricia Morgan, *Admin Sec*
EMP: 5
SQ FT: 1,200
SALES: 150K **Privately Held**
WEB: www.cse-inc.com
SIC: 7372 5085 Prepackaged software; in-
dustrial supplies

(G-3604)
CONSOLIDATED METAL PDTS
INC
1028 Depot St (45204-2073)
PHONE.....................................513 251-2624
Fax: 513 251-2488
John Bernloehr, *President*
Hugh M Gallagher Jr, *President*
Kathy Castellini, *Vice Pres*
Fred Madden, *Vice Pres*
Don Spillane, *Vice Pres*
EMP: 130 EST: 1945
SQ FT: 150,000
SALES (est): 47MM **Privately Held**
WEB: www.cmpubolt.com
SIC: 3452 3356 3316 Bolts, metal; non-
ferrous rolling & drawing; cold finishing of
steel shapes

(G-3605)
CONSUMER SOURCE INC
431 Elliott Ave (45215-5413)
PHONE.....................................513 621-7300
Carol Morgenthel, *Manager*
EMP: 7 **Privately Held**
WEB: www.apartmentguide.com
SIC: 2741 Directories: publishing only, not
printed on site
HQ: Consumer Source Inc.
3585 Engrg Dr Ste 100
Norcross GA 30092
678 421-3000

(G-3606)
CONTROL CRAFT LLC
2130 Schappelle Ln (45240-2723)
PHONE.....................................513 674-0056
Thomas Freudiger,
Ray Buller,
EMP: 10
SQ FT: 1,600
SALES (est): 1.7MM **Privately Held**
SIC: 3613 Control panels, electric

(G-3607)
CONTROLS AND SHEET METAL
INC (PA)
1051 Sargent St (45203-1858)
PHONE.....................................513 721-3610
Fax: 513 721-3658
Rick Schaible, *President*
EMP: 21 EST: 1983
SQ FT: 40,000
SALES (est): 10.4MM **Privately Held**
WEB: www.csm-inc.com
SIC: 5075 3444 Warm air heating & air
conditioning; ducts, sheet metal

(G-3608)
COOL TIMES
6127 Fairway Dr (45212-1307)
PHONE.....................................513 608-5201
Calvin Lanier, *Principal*
EMP: 4
SALES (est): 438.7K **Privately Held**
SIC: 3822 Air flow controllers, air condition-
ing & refrigeration

(G-3609)
COOLANT CONTROL INC (PA)
5353 Spring Grove Ave (45217-1095)
PHONE.....................................513 471-8770
Fax: 513 651-5245
Greg Battle, *CEO*
Garry C Ferraris, *President*
Jorge Costa, *Chairman*
Kurt Maurer, *Vice Pres*
Larry Schirmann, *CFO*
▲ EMP: 46 EST: 1975
SQ FT: 30,000
SALES (est): 12.9MM **Privately Held**
WEB: www.coolantcontrol.com
SIC: 2899 2819 Chemical preparations;
industrial inorganic chemicals

(G-3610)
COPPER MOUNTAIN
BEVERAGES LLC
1776 Mentor Ave Ste 250 (45212-3593)
PHONE.....................................513 484-9550
Steven Hatch, *Mng Member*
EMP: 5
SQ FT: 1,800
SALES (est): 430K **Privately Held**
SIC: 2086 Carbonated beverages, nonal-
coholic: bottled & canned

(G-3611)
CORNERSTONE SPCLTY WD
PDTS LLC
12020 Tramway Dr (45241-1692)
PHONE.....................................513 772-5560
Fax: 513 772-5561
Jonathon Egbert, *Engineer*
Chad Faulkner, *Engineer*
Jim Lindner, *Engineer*
Keith Shipman, *Natl Sales Mgr*
Lisa Friemoth, *Office Mgr*
EMP: 90
SQ FT: 7,500
SALES: 18MM
SALES (corp-wide): 22.3MM **Privately**
Held
WEB: www.resindek.com
SIC: 2499 Fencing, docks & other outdoor
wood structural products
PA: Universal Woods, Incorporated
2600 Grassland Dr
Louisville KY 40299
502 491-1461

(G-3612)
CORNPENTRY
2122 Schappelle Ln (45240-2723)
PHONE.....................................513 741-0594
Fax: 513 741-0225
Dean Walters, *Owner*
EMP: 6
SALES (est): 422.6K **Privately Held**
WEB: www.cornpentry.com
SIC: 3944 Games, toys & children's vehi-
cles

(G-3613)
CORPORATE DCMENT
SOLUTIONS INC
11120 Ashburn Rd (45240-3813)
PHONE.....................................513 595-8200
Mary C Percy, *President*
Harold B Percy Jr, *Vice Pres*
EMP: 15
SQ FT: 15,000
SALES (est): 2.1MM **Privately Held**
WEB: www.cdsprint.com
SIC: 7334 2752 2759 Photocopying & du-
plicating services; offset & photolitho-
graphic printing; commercial printing

(G-3614)
CORRUGATED CHEMICALS INC
3865 Virginia Ave (45227-3409)
PHONE.....................................513 561-7773
Fax: 513 527-6892

Tod Sistrunk, *Engnr/R&D Mgr*
Tony Shoemaker, *Natl Sales Mgr*
Jan Titus, *Director*
EMP: 6
SQ FT: 23,940
SALES (corp-wide): 2.6MM **Privately**
Held
WEB: www.corrugatedchemicals.com
SIC: 2869 5169 Industrial organic chemi-
cals; chemicals & allied products
PA: Corrugated Chemicals, Inc.
5410 Homberg Dr Ste 20
Knoxville TN 37919
865 588-2471

(G-3615)
COUNTER RHYTHM GROUP
397 Lombardy St (45216-2328)
PHONE.....................................513 379-6587
EMP: 3
SALES (est): 287K **Privately Held**
SIC: 3131 Counters

(G-3616)
CPG - OHIO LLC (PA)
470 Northland Blvd (45240-3211)
PHONE.....................................513 825-4800
Ben Kaufman,
Chaim Kaufman,
EMP: 51
SALES (est): 7.2MM **Privately Held**
SIC: 2671 2673 Plastic film, coated or
laminated for packaging; plastic bags:
made from purchased materials

(G-3617)
CRACO EMBROIDERY INC
37 Techview Dr (45215-1980)
PHONE.....................................513 563-6999
Fax: 513 563-8672
Bob Crable, *President*
Rick Crable, *Vice Pres*
EMP: 9
SQ FT: 1,200
SALES (est): 561.8K **Privately Held**
SIC: 2395 Emblems, embroidered

(G-3618)
CREATIVE BLAST CO
3627 Spring Grove Ave (45223-2458)
PHONE.....................................513 251-4177
Paul Shoemaker, *Owner*
EMP: 3
SQ FT: 9,000
SALES (est): 220K **Privately Held**
SIC: 5999 3993 Banners, flags, decals &
posters; signs & advertising specialties

(G-3619)
CREST GRAPHICS INC
1871 Summit Rd (45237-2803)
PHONE.....................................513 271-2200
Fax: 513 527-2234
Robert Sparks, *President*
Andy Bregger, *Vice Pres*
Mike Hickle, *Vice Pres*
Tina Schimmel, *Plant Mgr*
Gary Hill, *Sales Staff*
EMP: 16 EST: 1999
SQ FT: 22,000
SALES (est): 2.2MM **Privately Held**
WEB: www.crestgraphics.com
SIC: 2759 Commercial printing

(G-3620)
CRITICALAIRE LLC (PA)
11325 R Hartman Hwy 100 (45241)
PHONE.....................................614 499-7744
Matthew W Beecroft,
EMP: 4
SALES (est): 1.2MM **Privately Held**
SIC: 3564 Exhaust fans: industrial or com-
mercial

(G-3621)
CROWN ENVELOPE LLC
3249 E Kemper Rd Ste 1 (45241-6413)
PHONE.....................................513 771-5070
Fax: 513 771-5069
Thomas M Larke, *Mng Member*
EMP: 7
SQ FT: 15,000
SALES (est): 1.4MM **Privately Held**
WEB: www.crownenvelope.com
SIC: 2621 Envelope paper

(G-3622)
CROWN EQUIPMENT
CORPORATION
Also Called: Crown Lift Trucks
10685 Medallion Dr (45241-4827)
PHONE.....................................513 874-2600
Chris Blore, *Manager*
EMP: 85
SALES (corp-wide): 5.5B **Privately Held**
SIC: 3537 Lift trucks, industrial: fork, plat-
form, straddle, etc.
PA: Crown Equipment Corporation
44 S Washington St
New Bremen OH 45869
419 629-2311

(G-3623)
CRYOGENIC EQUIPMENT &
SVCS INC
11959 Tramway Dr Ste 1 (45241-1666)
PHONE.....................................513 761-4200
Hans Vanackere, *CEO*
Jonny Nuttin, *General Mgr*
▲ EMP: 10 EST: 1998
SQ FT: 28,000
SALES (est): 2.8MM **Privately Held**
WEB: www.cesgroup.com
SIC: 3585 Refrigeration & heating equip-
ment
PA: Cryogenic Equipment And Services Nv
Vlaswaagplein 13
Kortrijk
563 726-66

(G-3624)
CTEK TOOL & MACHINE
COMPANY
11310 Southland Rd (45240-3201)
PHONE.....................................513 742-0423
Fax: 513 742-2846
Phyllis Couch, *President*
James Couch, *Vice Pres*
Jody Stewart, *Office Mgr*
EMP: 6
SQ FT: 6,500
SALES (est): 850.9K **Privately Held**
SIC: 3599 Machine shop, jobbing & repair

(G-3625)
CUSTOM CAST MARBLEWORKS
INC
Also Called: Vanity Classics
3154 Exon Ave (45241-2548)
PHONE.....................................513 769-6505
Fax: 513 769-6510
Ron Schmidt, *President*
Jason Sieg, *Corp Secy*
Brian Schmidt, *Vice Pres*
▲ EMP: 20
SQ FT: 36,000
SALES (est): 3.7MM **Privately Held**
SIC: 3281 Marble, building: cut & shaped

(G-3626)
CUSTOM MATERIAL HDLG EQP
LLC
9089 Fontainebleau Ter (45231-4807)
PHONE.....................................513 235-5336
Stephen D Maatman,
EMP: 6
SALES (est): 440.6K **Privately Held**
SIC: 2411 Logging camps & contractors

(G-3627)
CUSTOM TOOLING COMPANY
INC
603 Wayne Park Dr (45215-2848)
PHONE.....................................513 733-5790
Fax: 513 733-1976
Thomas Brune, *President*
Charles Brune, *Vice Pres*
Debby Stevenson, *Manager*
EMP: 10
SQ FT: 5,000
SALES (est): 1.5MM **Privately Held**
WEB: www.custom-tooling.com
SIC: 3544 Special dies & tools

(G-3628)
D & A ROFAEL ENTERPRISES
INC
Also Called: Gold Star Chili-Burnet
3026 Burnet Ave (45219-2420)
PHONE.....................................513 751-4929

Fax: 513 751-4929
Ron Alsaleh, *Principal*
EMP: 5
SALES (est): 395.1K **Privately Held**
SIC: 2032 Chili with or without meat: packaged in cans, jars, etc.

(G-3629)
D & D METAL SUPPLY INC
3717 Jonlen Dr (45227-4103)
PHONE.................................513 272-1246
Fax: 513 272-5546
Richard J Merman Sr, *President*
Timothy Merman, *Corp Secy*
Richard J Merman Jr, *Vice Pres*
EMP: 14
SQ FT: 44,000
SALES (est): 2.3MM **Privately Held**
WEB: www.ddmetal-hvac.com
SIC: 3444 5051 Ducts, sheet metal; metals service centers & offices

(G-3630)
D & M SAW & TOOL INC
Also Called: Eccles Saw & Tool
2974 P G Graves Ln (45241-3155)
PHONE.................................513 871-5433
Fax: 513 871-5434
Michael Hugenberg, *President*
EMP: 9
SQ FT: 6,000
SALES (est): 930.1K **Privately Held**
SIC: 7699 5251 3423 Knife, saw & tool sharpening & repair; chainsaws; cutting dies, except metal cutting

(G-3631)
D F ELECTRONICS INC
200 Novner Dr (45215-6002)
PHONE.................................513 772-7792
Fax: 513 772-0402
Laughton Fine, *President*
Don Fine, *Plant Mgr*
Stephanie Kleinschmidt, *Purchasing*
Rene Kennedy, *Manager*
EMP: 75 EST: 1975
SQ FT: 27,000
SALES (est): 14.3MM **Privately Held**
WEB: www.dfelectronics.com
SIC: 3674 Solid state electronic devices

(G-3632)
D J KLINGLER INC
Also Called: Montgomery License Bureau
9999 Montgomery Rd (45242-5311)
PHONE.................................513 891-2284
Donna Klingler, *President*
EMP: 6 EST: 1993
SALES (est): 583.7K **Privately Held**
SIC: 3469 7299 Automobile license tags, stamped metal; personal appearance services

(G-3633)
D+H USA CORPORATION
Also Called: DH
312 Plum St Ste 500 (45202-4810)
PHONE.................................513 381-9400
Vern Anderson, *Manager*
Nancy Boesch, *Executive Asst*
EMP: 173
SALES (corp-wide): 1.2B **Privately Held**
SIC: 7372 Application computer software
HQ: D+H Usa Corporation
605 Crescent Executive Ct # 600
Lake Mary FL 32746
407 804-6600

(G-3634)
D-G CUSTOM CHROME LLC
5200 Lester Rd (45213-2522)
PHONE.................................513 531-1881
Alex Wyatt, *President*
Don Gorman, *President*
Victoria Gorman, *Vice Pres*
EMP: 58
SQ FT: 10,162
SALES (est): 9.4MM **Privately Held**
WEB: www.dgcustomchrome.com
SIC: 5013 3471 Motor vehicle supplies & new parts; plating & polishing

(G-3635)
DADCO INC (PA)
Also Called: Rpp Containers
7365 E Kemper Rd Ste D (45249-3005)
PHONE.................................513 489-2244
Scott Denoma, *President*
Eric Stein, *President*
James Bartlett, *General Mgr*
EMP: 5
SQ FT: 45,000
SALES (est): 16.4MM **Privately Held**
WEB: www.rppcontainers.com
SIC: 5085 3089 Bins & containers, storage; plastic containers, except foam

(G-3636)
DADCO INC
Also Called: Rpp Containers
12151 Best Pl (45241-6402)
PHONE.................................513 489-2244
Scott Denoma, *Branch Mgr*
EMP: 12
SALES (corp-wide): 16.4MM **Privately Held**
SIC: 3089 5085 Plastic containers, except foam; bins & containers, storage
PA: Dadco, Inc.
7365 E Kemper Rd Ste D
Cincinnati OH 45249
513 489-2244

(G-3637)
DALE KESTLER
Also Called: Apollo GL Mirror Win Screen Co
3667 Paxton Ave (45208-1558)
PHONE.................................513 871-9000
Fax: 513 871-9400
Dale Kestler, *President*
EMP: 8
SQ FT: 1,500
SALES (est): 911.8K **Privately Held**
SIC: 5231 5719 5211 3442 Glass; mirrors; door & window products; screens, door & window; screens, window, metal; glass construction materials; interior flat glass: plate or window; exterior flat glass: plate or window; mirrors & pictures, framed & unframed

(G-3638)
DANA GRAPHICS INC
2200 Dana Ave Fl 2 (45208-1025)
P.O. Box 42219 (45242-0219)
PHONE.................................513 351-4400
Fax: 513 351-2802
Jeanne M Johnson, *President*
Charles S Johnson, *CFO*
Debbie Coad, *Human Res Mgr*
▲ EMP: 5
SALES (est): 647.4K **Privately Held**
WEB: www.danagraphics.com
SIC: 2752 2759 Commercial printing, offset; letterpress printing

(G-3639)
DANIEL M BEYERBACH
2123 Auburn Ave (45219-2906)
PHONE.................................513 206-1180
Daniel M Beyerbach, *Principal*
EMP: 3
SALES (est): 187.7K **Privately Held**
SIC: 3845 Electrocardiographs

(G-3640)
DATA PROCESSING SCIENCES CORP (HQ)
Also Called: Dpsciences
2 Camargo Cyn (45243-2945)
PHONE.................................513 791-7100
Fax: 513 791-2371
Scott Q Nesbitt, *CEO*
Kurt D Loock, *President*
Stephen Vandegriff, *Vice Pres*
Timothy Shelton, *CFO*
Nadine Centers, *Accounts Mgr*
▼ EMP: 55
SQ FT: 15,000
SALES (est): 20.1MM
SALES (corp-wide): 86.4MM **Privately Held**
SIC: 5045 4813 3577 3669 Computers, peripherals & software; telephone communication, except radio; computer peripheral equipment; intercommunication systems, electric; computer rental & leasing; systems integration services

PA: Lumenate Technologies, Lp
16633 Dallas Pkwy Ste 450
Addison TX 75001
972 248-8999

(G-3641)
DAVES PRINTING
614 Riddle Rd (45220-2606)
PHONE.................................513 221-0182
David Sewell, *Principal*
EMP: 4 EST: 2009
SALES (est): 310.4K **Privately Held**
SIC: 2752 Commercial printing, lithographic

(G-3642)
DAVIS MACHINING SERVICE
602 Comet Dr (45244-1304)
PHONE.................................513 528-4917
Robert Davis, *Owner*
EMP: 5
SALES (est): 293.9K **Privately Held**
SIC: 3599 Machine shop, jobbing & repair

(G-3643)
DAYTON METAL PRODUCTS COMPANY
8296 Tidewater Ct (45255-4484)
P.O. Box 801, Dayton (45401-0801)
PHONE.................................937 849-0071
Fax: 937 849-9672
K Colin Mac Kenzie, *President*
J L Schlegel, *General Mgr*
Jennifer D Mac Kenzie, *Admin Sec*
EMP: 8
SQ FT: 12,000
SALES (est): 687K **Privately Held**
SIC: 3429 Manufactured hardware (general)

(G-3644)
DB PARENT INC
3630 E Kemper Rd (45241-2011)
PHONE.................................513 475-3265
Tom Heintz, *CFO*
EMP: 3
SALES (est): 265.4K **Privately Held**
SIC: 2819 Industrial inorganic chemicals

(G-3645)
DEBRA-KUEMPEL INC (HQ)
Also Called: De Bra - Kuempel
3976 Southern Ave (45227-3562)
P.O. Box 701620 (45270-1620)
PHONE.................................513 271-6500
Joe D Clark, *CEO*
Fred B De Bra, *Ch of Bd*
Morris H Reed, *Corp Secy*
Robert E Cupp, *Vice Pres*
John Kuempel Jr, *Vice Pres*
EMP: 80 EST: 1944
SQ FT: 20,079
SALES (est): 25.2MM
SALES (corp-wide): 7.5B **Publicly Held**
SIC: 3446 1711 3443 3441 Architectural metalwork; mechanical contractor; fabricated plate work (boiler shop); fabricated structural metal
PA: Emcor Group, Inc.
301 Merritt 7 Fl 6
Norwalk CT 06851
203 849-7800

(G-3646)
DEGUSSA INCORPORATED
620 Shepherd Dr (45215-2104)
PHONE.................................513 733-5111
Probyn Forbes, *Principal*
▲ EMP: 6 EST: 2008
SALES (est): 632.7K **Privately Held**
SIC: 2816 Inorganic pigments

(G-3647)
DELTA TRANSFORMER INC
406 Blade Ave (45216-2302)
PHONE.................................513 242-9400
Fax: 513 242-9400
Shannon Hackney, *President*
John H Juengst, *Manager*
EMP: 5
SQ FT: 5,000
SALES (est): 826.6K **Privately Held**
SIC: 3612 7629 Power transformers, electric; electrical equipment repair, high voltage

(G-3648)
DERRICK COMPANY INC
4560 Kellogg Ave (45226-2499)
PHONE.................................513 321-8122
Fax: 513 321-8125
Gary Schmid, *President*
Joe Apgar, *Principal*
Kathie Schmid, *Treasurer*
EMP: 25
SQ FT: 170,000
SALES (est): 6MM **Privately Held**
WEB: www.derrickcompany.com
SIC: 3398 3471 Metal heat treating; sand blasting of metal parts

(G-3649)
DESIGN MASTERS INC
800 Redna Ter (45215-1111)
PHONE.................................513 772-7175
Terry Masters, *President*
Scott Arand, *Manager*
EMP: 6
SALES (est): 550K **Privately Held**
SIC: 3993 7532 7319 Signs & advertising specialties; truck painting & lettering; display advertising service

(G-3650)
DESSERTS BY SANDY LLC
8071 Redhaven Ct (45247-3560)
PHONE.................................513 385-8755
Sandra Maffey, *Principal*
EMP: 4
SALES (est): 120K **Privately Held**
SIC: 2051 Cakes, pies & pastries

(G-3651)
DETAILED ATHLETIC WEAR CO INC
6272 Cleves Warsaw Pike (45233-4510)
PHONE.................................513 541-0884
Ronald G Hebert, *Owner*
EMP: 3
SALES (est): 250K **Privately Held**
SIC: 2396 Screen printing on fabric articles

(G-3652)
DEVICOR MED PDTS HOLDINGS INC
300 E Business Way Fl 5 (45241-2384)
PHONE.................................513 864-9000
Thomas D Daulton, *CEO*
Jonathan Salkin, *Exec VP*
David Nuty, *CFO*
Phil Oliver, *Controller*
EMP: 550
SALES (est): 26.2MM **Privately Held**
SIC: 3841 Surgical & medical instruments

(G-3653)
DEVICOR MEDICAL PRODUCTS INC (DH)
Also Called: Mammotone
300 E Business Way Fl 5 (45241-2384)
PHONE.................................513 864-9000
Fax: 513 864-9011
Tom Daulton, *CEO*
Jim Frontero, *Senior VP*
Gene Schrecengost, *Senior VP*
Sean Burke, *Vice Pres*
Chip Clark, *Vice Pres*
EMP: 3
SALES (est): 213.9MM
SALES (corp-wide): 16.8B **Publicly Held**
SIC: 3841 Surgical & medical instruments
HQ: Leica Biosystems Richmond, Inc.
5205 Rte 12
Richmond IL 60071
815 678-2000

(G-3654)
DIMENSION MACHINE COMPANY INC
6614 Lebanon St (45216-1931)
PHONE.................................513 242-9996
Fax: 513 242-9995
Donald P Barth, *President*
EMP: 8
SQ FT: 12,000
SALES (est): 1.3MM **Privately Held**
SIC: 3599 Machine shop, jobbing & repair

(G-3655)
DIMENSIONAL FABRICATING INC
6230 Wiehe Rd Unit 1 (45237-4200)
PHONE..........................513 482-7440
Tracy Anderson, *President*
Beverly Anderson, *Vice Pres*
EMP: 3
SQ FT: 10,000
SALES (est): 303.6K **Privately Held**
SIC: 3499 Novelties & specialties, metal

(G-3656)
DIVERSE LOGISTICS & TRNSP INC
313 Glensford Ct (45246-2376)
PHONE..........................513 305-1460
Jospeh Duckworth, *President*
EMP: 3
SALES: 950K **Privately Held**
SIC: 3715 Truck trailers

(G-3657)
DIVERSEY INC
200 Crowne Point Pl (45241-5426)
PHONE..........................513 326-8300
Fax: 513 326-8312
Scott McManis, *Finance Mgr*
Karen Aielli, *Branch Mgr*
EMP: 4
SALES (corp-wide): 6.7B **Publicly Held**
WEB: www.johnsondiversey.com
SIC: 2842 Cleaning or polishing preparations
HQ: Diversey, Inc.
2415 Cascade Pointe Blvd
Charlotte NC 28208
262 631-4001

(G-3658)
DIVERSIPAK INC (PA)
Also Called: Questmark
838 Reedy St (45202-2216)
PHONE..........................513 321-7884
Dan Kunkemoeller, *CEO*
Jennifer Kunkemoeller, *Principal*
Douglas Hearn, *Project Mgr*
Ted Trammel, *CFO*
Sherry Birkhold, *Personnel Exec*
EMP: 6
SQ FT: 15,000
SALES (est): 14.3MM **Privately Held**
WEB: www.diversipak.com
SIC: 2631 7336 Container, packaging & boxboard; package design

(G-3659)
DIVISION OVERHEAD DOOR INC (PA)
Also Called: Cincinnati Prof Door Sls Div
861 Dellway St (45229-3305)
P.O. Box 12588, Covington KY (41012-0588)
PHONE..........................513 872-0888
Robert H Mc Kibben Jr, *President*
Jim Morrison, *Corp Secy*
Pat Higgins, *Vice Pres*
EMP: 13 EST: 1942
SQ FT: 12,000
SALES (est): 1.7MM **Privately Held**
WEB: www.overheaddoors.com
SIC: 3442 2431 7699 1751 Garage doors, overhead: metal; garage doors, overhead: wood; garage door repair; garage door, installation or erection

(G-3660)
DODGE DATA & ANALYTICS LLC
Also Called: F W Dodge
7265 Kenwood Rd Ste 200 (45236-4413)
PHONE..........................513 345-8200
EMP: 5 **Privately Held**
SIC: 2741 Misc Publishing

(G-3661)
DOG DEPOT
950 S Troy Ave (45246-4632)
PHONE..........................513 771-9274
Natalie Lotspeich, *Owner*
EMP: 3
SQ FT: 500
SALES (est): 216.3K **Privately Held**
SIC: 5199 3199 Dogs; dog furnishings: collars, leashes, muzzles, etc.: leather

(G-3662)
DOMAIR TRANSMORE INC
130 Novner Dr (45215-1334)
P.O. Box 62655 (45262-0655)
PHONE..........................513 771-1516
Chris Alberts, *President*
EMP: 10
SALES (est): 453K **Privately Held**
SIC: 3231 Mirrors, truck & automobile: made from purchased glass

(G-3663)
DOMINION LIQUID TECH LLC
Also Called: D L T
3965 Virginia Ave (45227-3411)
PHONE..........................513 272-2824
Brian Young, *Vice Pres*
Daren Brown, *QC Mgr*
Stuart Schulman, *Sales Staff*
Charles Cain, *Mng Member*
Rick Burdine, *Manager*
EMP: 41
SQ FT: 54,000
SALES (est): 10.4MM **Privately Held**
SIC: 2086 2087 2033 Carbonated beverages, nonalcoholic: bottled & canned; syrups, drink; barbecue sauce: packaged in cans, jars, etc.

(G-3664)
DORAN MFG LLC
2851 Massachusetts Ave (45225-2225)
PHONE..........................513 681-5424
Tom D'Agnillo, *CFO*
Lee Demis, *Natl Sales Mgr*
Ross Ormsby, *Natl Sales Mgr*
Kay Carrubba, *Sales Staff*
EMP: 15
SQ FT: 10,000
SALES (est): 1.9MM
SALES (corp-wide): 9.7MM **Privately Held**
SIC: 5013 3714 Motor vehicle supplies & new parts; sanders, motor vehicle safety
PA: Evolving Enterprises, Inc.
2851 Massachusetts Ave
Cincinnati OH 45225
513 681-5424

(G-3665)
DOROTHY CROOKER
Also Called: Rapid Copy Printing
5984 Cheviot Rd (45247-6245)
PHONE..........................513 385-0888
Fax: 513 385-0891
Dorothy Crooker, *Owner*
EMP: 3
SALES: 150K **Privately Held**
SIC: 2752 2796 2791 Commercial printing, offset; platemaking services; typesetting

(G-3666)
DOSCHERS CANDIES INC
24 W Court St (45202-1062)
PHONE..........................513 381-8656
Fax: 513 381-0656
Gregory Clark, *President*
Harry J Doscher, *Vice Pres*
EMP: 10 EST: 1959
SALES (est): 36.1K **Privately Held**
SIC: 2064 Candy & other confectionery products

(G-3667)
DOSMATIC USA INC (PA)
3798 Round Bottom Rd (45244-2413)
PHONE..........................972 245-9765
Jeff Rowe, *President*
Wichai Wongwareetip, *Regional Mgr*
Steve Vogel, *Vice Pres*
David Heitker, *Controller*
▲ EMP: 14
SQ FT: 25,000
SALES (est): 1.8MM **Privately Held**
SIC: 3569 Liquid automation machinery & equipment

(G-3668)
DOV GRAPHICS INC (PA)
2230 Gilbert Ave (45206-2531)
PHONE..........................513 241-5150
Fax: 937 241-5326
Robert J Van Lear, *President*
Gayle Sherman, *Vice Pres*
EMP: 23 EST: 1963

SQ FT: 10,000
SALES (est): 4MM **Privately Held**
WEB: www.dovgraphics.com
SIC: 2791 2752 2759 Photocomposition, for the printing trade; commercial printing, offset; letterpress printing

(G-3669)
DOVER WIPES COMPANY
1 Procter And Gamble Plz (45202-3315)
PHONE..........................513 983-1100
Ann McKinney, *CEO*
EMP: 10
SALES (est): 2.3MM
SALES (corp-wide): 65.3B **Publicly Held**
WEB: www.pg.com
SIC: 2844 Deodorants, personal
PA: The Procter & Gamble Company
1 Procter And Gamble Plz
Cincinnati OH 45202
513 983-1100

(G-3670)
DOWNHOME INC
Also Called: Down Decor
1 Kovach Dr (45215-1000)
PHONE..........................513 921-3373
Daniel Guigui, *President*
James P Mason, *Principal*
Michael G Mason, *Principal*
▲ EMP: 45
SALES (est): 6.7MM **Privately Held**
WEB: www.downdecor.com
SIC: 2392 Pillows, bed: made from purchased materials

(G-3671)
DREIER TOOL & DIE CORP
2865 Compton Rd (45251-2633)
PHONE..........................513 521-8200
Timmothy Dreier, *President*
EMP: 4
SQ FT: 7,020
SALES: 500K **Privately Held**
SIC: 3544 Special dies & tools

(G-3672)
DTE COOL CO
105 E 4th St Ste G100 (45202-4009)
PHONE..........................513 579-0160
Tim Heineman, *General Mgr*
EMP: 3
SALES (est): 317.2K **Privately Held**
SIC: 3585 Coolers, milk & water: electric

(G-3673)
DUBOIS CHEMICALS INC (PA)
3630 E Kemper Rd (45241-2011)
PHONE..........................513 731-6350
Jeff Welsh, *CEO*
Eric Dill, *President*
Jake Harris, *Vice Pres*
Kathy Manning, *Purch Mgr*
Robert Kenney, *Purch Agent*
▼ EMP: 277
SALES (est): 221.1MM **Privately Held**
WEB: www.riversidecompany.com
SIC: 2869 Industrial organic chemicals

(G-3674)
DULLE ASSOCIATES
Also Called: Dulle Printing
5960 Glenway Ave (45238-2009)
PHONE..........................513 723-9600
Fax: 513 723-9601
Steve Dulle, *Owner*
Jim Dulle, *Co-Owner*
EMP: 4
SQ FT: 2,500
SALES (est): 355.9K **Privately Held**
WEB: www.dulleandcompany.com
SIC: 2754 Commercial printing, gravure

(G-3675)
DYNAMIC INDUSTRIES INC
3611 Woodburn Ave (45207-1019)
PHONE..........................513 861-6767
Fax: 513 861-6792
Phillip J Mitchell, *President*
Henry W Ochs, *Principal*
Frank Fountain, *Project Mgr*
Kim Richendollar, *Sls & Mktg Exec*
John Meyer, *CFO*
EMP: 33
SQ FT: 150,000

SALES (est): 6.6MM **Privately Held**
SIC: 3599 Machine shop, jobbing & repair; custom machinery

(G-3676)
DYNEON LLC
2165 Cablecar Ct (45244-4101)
PHONE..........................859 334-4500
Thomasine Miller, *Manager*
EMP: 25
SALES (corp-wide): 30.1B **Publicly Held**
WEB: www.dyneon.com
SIC: 3087 Custom compound purchased resins
HQ: Dyneon Llc
6744 33rd St N
Oakdale MN 55128

(G-3677)
E C SHAW CO
1242 Mehring Way (45203-1836)
PHONE..........................513 721-6334
Fax: 513 721-6350
Joseph Grome, *President*
Kenneth Grome, *Vice Pres*
Robert Grome, *Vice Pres*
Joann Denzler, *Cust Mgr*
Mark Coffman, *Sales Staff*
EMP: 30
SQ FT: 12,000
SALES (est): 7.8MM **Privately Held**
WEB: www.ecshaw.com
SIC: 3555 3953 3469 2821 Printing plates; marking devices; metal stampings; plastics materials & resins; platemaking services

(G-3678)
E I CERAMICS LLC
2600 Commerce Blvd (45241-1552)
PHONE..........................513 772-7001
James McIntosh, *President*
Graham J Roberts, *Mng Member*
Nancy Miller, *Manager*
▲ EMP: 60
SALES (est): 13.7MM **Privately Held**
SIC: 3297 Graphite refractories: carbon bond or ceramic bond
HQ: Ifgl Refractories Limited
Mcleod House,
Kolkata WB 70000

(G-3679)
E P S SPECIALISTS LTD INC
7875 School Rd (45249-1531)
PHONE..........................513 489-3676
Ed L Wilkson, *President*
Lee Wilkinson, *Vice Pres*
EMP: 12
SALES (est): 1MM **Privately Held**
SIC: 2821 Plastics materials & resins

(G-3680)
E Z BINDERYS
10122 Reading Rd (45241-3110)
PHONE..........................513 733-0005
Bruce Hassle, *Owner*
EMP: 3
SALES (est): 113.9K **Privately Held**
SIC: 2789 Bookbinding & related work

(G-3681)
EAGLE BURGMANN INDUSTRIES
3478 Hauck Rd (45241-4604)
PHONE..........................513 563-7325
Matt Vaupel, *Principal*
EMP: 7
SALES (est): 683.9K
SALES (corp-wide): 6.9B **Privately Held**
SIC: 3999 Manufacturing industries
HQ: Ebi Atlantic A/S
Park Alle 34
Vejen

(G-3682)
EAGLE CREEK INC
9799 Prechtel Rd (45252-2117)
PHONE..........................513 385-4442
EMP: 62
SALES (corp-wide): 12B **Publicly Held**
SIC: 3161 Luggage; traveling bags
HQ: Eagle Creek Inc
5935 Darwin Ct
Carlsbad CA 92008
760 431-6400

▲ = Import ▼=Export
◆ =Import/Export

(G-3683)
EAGLE IMAGE INC
4742 Blue Rock Rd (45247-5503)
PHONE..................513 662-3000
Richard Kessler, *President*
EMP: 10
SALES (est): 679K **Privately Held**
WEB: www.eagleimage.com
SIC: 2759 Commercial printing

(G-3684)
EAR MEDICAL CENTER INC (PA)
Also Called: Balance Disorder Institute
2121 Alpine Pl Apt 1101 (45206-2695)
PHONE..................812 537-0031
Claude P Hobeika, *President*
EMP: 14
SQ FT: 10,000
SALES (est): 2.3MM **Privately Held**
WEB: www.bdi1.com
SIC: 3842 Hearing aids

(G-3685)
EARL D ARNOLD PRINTING COMPANY
630 Lunken Park Dr (45226-1800)
PHONE..................513 533-6900
Fax: 513 533-6907
Earl D Arnold Sr, *President*
Timothy A Arnold, *Vice Pres*
Hank Majewski, *Plant Mgr*
Andy Cranmer, *Mktg Dir*
EMP: 35 EST: 1910
SQ FT: 30,000
SALES (est): 6.9MM **Privately Held**
WEB: www.arnoldprinting.com
SIC: 2752 2759 2796 2791 Commercial
printing, offset; letterpress printing;
platemaking services; typesetting; book-
binding & related work

(G-3686)
EASTGATE CUSTOM GRAPHICS LTD
4459 Mt Carmel Tobasco Rd (45244-2225)
PHONE..................513 528-7922
Fax: 513 528-7944
Donald R Hall, *Partner*
EMP: 5
SQ FT: 42,000
SALES: 458K **Privately Held**
SIC: 7336 2396 2395 Commercial art &
graphic design; automotive & apparel
trimmings; embroidery & art needlework

(G-3687)
EASY WAY LEISURE CORPORATION (PA)
Also Called: Easy Way Products
8950 Rossash Rd (45236-1210)
PHONE..................513 731-5640
Jon D Randman, *President*
Steve Coppel, *Vice Pres*
Joe Carchedi, *Prdtn Mgr*
Kim Daniels, *Controller*
Scott Szymkowicz, *VP Sales*
▼ EMP: 250
SQ FT: 100,000
SALES (est): 99.3MM **Privately Held**
WEB: www.easywayproducts.com
SIC: 2392 Cushions & pillows; chair covers
& pads: made from purchased materials

(G-3688)
EBEL-BINDER PRINTING CO
Also Called: Ebel Tape & Label
1630 Dalton Ave 1 (45214-2020)
PHONE..................513 471-1067
Fax: 513 471-5657
Thomas Heidemann, *President*
Marian Dulle, *Vice Pres*
James Dulle, *Treasurer*
EMP: 7
SQ FT: 3,000
SALES (est): 930.9K **Privately Held**
SIC: 2759 Flexographic printing; labels &
seals: printing

(G-3689)
ECO-PRINT SOLUTIONS LLC
6893 High Meadows Dr (45230-3802)
PHONE..................513 731-3106
Ben Morrison,
EMP: 3
SQ FT: 2,500

SALES: 76K **Privately Held**
WEB: www.ecoprintsolutions.com
SIC: 5085 3955 Ink, printers'; print car-
tridges for laser & other computer printers

(G-3690)
ECU CORPORATION (PA)
7209 E Kemper Rd (45249-1030)
PHONE..................513 898-9294
Mike Fox, *President*
Hank Worsley, *Vice Pres*
Bill Kubicki, *QC Mgr*
◆ EMP: 20
SQ FT: 25,000
SALES: 3MM **Privately Held**
SIC: 3585 Air conditioning units, complete:
domestic or industrial

(G-3691)
ELA HOLDING CORPORATION
Also Called: Turnkey Technology Sales
5403 Haft Rd (45247-7421)
PHONE..................513 200-1374
Eric Anevski, *Principal*
EMP: 3
SALES (est): 814.9K **Privately Held**
SIC: 7372 Business oriented computer
software

(G-3692)
ELECTRIC SERVICE CO INC
5331 Hetzell St (45227-1513)
PHONE..................513 271-6387
Fax: 513 271-0543
Helen Snyder, *President*
EMP: 34
SQ FT: 35,000
SALES (est): 6.1MM **Privately Held**
WEB: www.electricservice.com
SIC: 7629 3677 3621 Electronic equip-
ment repair; transformers power supply,
electronic type; phase or rotary convert-
ers (electrical equipment)

(G-3693)
ELYNX HOLDINGS LLC (HQ)
11500 Northlake Dr # 200 (45249-1650)
PHONE..................513 612-5969
Fax: 513 612-5977
Sharon Matthews, *President*
Steven Burchett, *Vice Pres*
Kristian Hughes, *Engineer*
Jake Jenkins, *Sales Staff*
Troy Underberg, *Manager*
EMP: 1
SALES (est): 24MM
SALES (corp-wide): 1B **Publicly Held**
SIC: 7371 7373 7372 Computer software
development; systems integration serv-
ices; prepackaged software
PA: Black Knight Financial Services, Inc.
601 Riverside Ave
Jacksonville FL 32204
904 854-5100

(G-3694)
EMERALD HILTON DAVIS LLC
Also Called: Emerald Specialties Group
2235 Langdon Farm Rd (45237-4712)
PHONE..................513 841-0057
Fax: 800 477-4565
Jim Collett, *Opers Mgr*
Rachel Stall, *Purch Agent*
Randy Palicki, *Controller*
James Donnelly, *Mng Member*
▲ EMP: 70
SALES (est): 38.2MM
SALES (corp-wide): 53.4MM **Privately Held**
SIC: 2865 Cyclic crudes & intermediates
PA: Dystar L.P
9844 Southern Pine Blvd A
Charlotte NC 28273
704 561-3000

(G-3695)
EMERALD PERFORMANCE MTLS LLC
Also Called: Emerald Hilton Davis
2235 Langdon Farm Rd (45237-4712)
PHONE..................513 841-4000
Jim Donley, *Vice Pres*
Doug Jackson, *Plant Mgr*
Theresa Hyde, *Opers Mgr*
Jerry McCluskey, *Purch Mgr*
Peggy Roundtree, *QC Mgr*

EMP: 93
SALES (corp-wide): 346.7MM **Privately Held**
SIC: 2899 Chemical preparations
PA: Emerald Performance Materials Llc
2020 Front St Ste 100
Cuyahoga Falls OH 44221
330 916-6700

(G-3696)
EMERGE HEALTH SOLUTIONS
2925 Vernon Pl Ste 100 (45219-2425)
PHONE..................513 204-5600
Trent McCracken, *President*
EMP: 5
SALES (est): 422.4K **Privately Held**
SIC: 7372 Application computer software

(G-3697)
EMERSON ELECTRIC CO
6265 Wiehe Rd (45237-4211)
PHONE..................513 631-6112
Fax: 513 631-1042
James Gilligan, *VP Sls/Mktg*
Brent Schroeder, *Branch Mgr*
EMP: 40
SQ FT: 15,000
SALES (corp-wide): 14.5B **Publicly Held**
WEB: www.gotoemerson.com
SIC: 3823 3471 3469 3465 Industrial in-
strmnts msrmnt display/control process
variable; plating & polishing; metal stamp-
ings; automotive stampings; bolts, nuts,
rivets & washers
PA: Emerson Electric Co.
8000 West Florissant Ave
Saint Louis MO 63136
314 553-2000

(G-3698)
EMERSON ELECTRIC CO
6000 Fernview Ave (45212-1312)
PHONE..................513 731-2020
Fax: 513 631-6456
William Epping, *Vice Pres*
Michael Rademacher, *Engineer*
Brent Schroeder, *Manager*
EMP: 200
SALES (corp-wide): 14.5B **Publicly Held**
WEB: www.gotoemerson.com
SIC: 3585 Air conditioning equipment,
complete; refrigeration equipment, com-
plete
PA: Emerson Electric Co.
8000 West Florissant Ave
Saint Louis MO 63136
314 553-2000

(G-3699)
EMERY OLEOCHEMICALS LLC (HQ)
4900 Este Ave (45232-1491)
PHONE..................513 762-2500
Fax: 513 482-2007
Ramesh Kana, *CEO*
Bill Kafiti, *Area Mgr*
John Debardeleben, *Business Mgr*
Joe Lynch, *Business Mgr*
Azuddin Rahman, *Senior VP*
◆ EMP: 246
SQ FT: 4,032
SALES (est): 100.4MM
SALES (corp-wide): 847.2K **Privately Held**
WEB: www.emeryoleo.com
SIC: 2899 Chemical preparations; acids
PA: Emery Oleochemicals (M) Sdn. Bhd.
Level 5 Block E Peremba Square
Shah Alam SLG 40150
333 268-686

(G-3700)
EMPIRE PRINTING INC
5877 Highland Ridge Dr (45232-1441)
PHONE..................513 242-3900
Fax: 513 242-9037
Dean Nieporte, *President*
EMP: 9 EST: 1956
SQ FT: 6,000
SALES (est): 900K **Privately Held**
SIC: 2752 2759 Commercial printing, off-
set; letterpress printing

(G-3701)
ENCLOSURE SUPPLIERS LLC
Also Called: Champion
12119 Champion Way (45241-6419)
PHONE..................513 782-3900
Fax: 513 782-3903
Dennis Manes,
▲ EMP: 30
SQ FT: 160,000
SALES (est): 11.7MM
SALES (corp-wide): 516.7MM **Privately Held**
SIC: 3448 5031 3231 Prefabricated metal
buildings; lumber, plywood & millwork;
products of purchased glass
PA: Champion Opco, Llc
12121 Champion Way
Cincinnati OH 45241
513 924-4858

(G-3702)
ENCORE DISTRIBUTING INC
Also Called: Pirtek Reading Road
8060 Reading Rd Ste 6 (45237-1423)
PHONE..................513 948-1242
Dan Pridemore, *Vice Pres*
EMP: 5 **Privately Held**
SIC: 3492 Fluid power valves & hose fit-
tings
PA: Encore Distributing, Inc.
5132 White Oak Ln
Brighton MI 48114

(G-3703)
ENERCHEM INCORPORATED
8373 Squirrelridge Dr (45243-1052)
P.O. Box 43422 (45243-0422)
PHONE..................513 745-0580
Jerrold E Radway, *President*
Larry Radway, *Vice Pres*
EMP: 4
SALES: 1.5MM **Privately Held**
SIC: 2819 8742 8732 7389 Industrial in-
organic chemicals; management consult-
ing services; market analysis, business &
economic research;

(G-3704)
ENERFAB INC (PA)
4955 Spring Grove Ave (45232-1925)
PHONE..................513 641-0500
Fax: 513 641-1821
Wendell R Bell, *CEO*
Jeffrey P Hock, *President*
Dave Herche, *Chairman*
Jeffrey R Aasch, *Exec VP*
Mark Schoettmer, *Vice Pres*
▲ EMP: 330
SQ FT: 180,000
SALES (est): 620.1MM **Privately Held**
WEB: www.enerfab.com
SIC: 3443 1629 1541 1711 Tanks, stan-
dard or custom fabricated: metal plate;
power plant construction; land reclama-
tion; industrial buildings & warehouses;
mechanical contractor; process piping
contractor; painting, coating & hot dipping

(G-3705)
ENERFAB INC
11861 Mosteller Rd (45241-1524)
PHONE..................513 771-2300
Steve Zoller, *General Mgr*
EMP: 6
SQ FT: 250,000
SALES (corp-wide): 620.1MM **Privately Held**
WEB: www.enerfab.com
SIC: 3559 Pharmaceutical machinery;
chemical machinery & equipment
PA: Enerfab, Inc.
4955 Spring Grove Ave
Cincinnati OH 45232
513 641-0500

(G-3706)
ENGINEERING METHODS INC
9352 Main St Unit 2 (45242-7645)
PHONE..................513 563-0400
Fax: 513 563-0422
William H Hibbard, *President*
Jean Terry, *Shareholder*
Julie Routt, *Administration*
EMP: 28
SQ FT: 5,000

SALES: 3MM **Privately Held**
WEB: www.engmeth.com
SIC: 7372 7373 Prepackaged software; computer-aided system services

(G-3707)
ENQUIRER PRINTING CO INC
7188 Main St (45244-3012)
PHONE..................................513 241-1956
John G Anderson, *President*
Michael W Anderson, *Vice Pres*
Steve Anderson, *Treasurer*
EMP: 10
SQ FT: 19,000
SALES: 500K **Privately Held**
SIC: 2752 Commercial printing, offset

(G-3708)
ENQUIRER PRINTING COMPANY
7188 Main St (45244-3012)
PHONE..................................513 241-1956
Steve Anderson, *Principal*
EMP: 6
SALES (est): 560K **Privately Held**
SIC: 2752 Commercial printing, lithographic

(G-3709)
ENTERPRISE MACHINE INC
Also Called: Boye & Emmes Machine
3640 Llewellyn Ave (45223-2336)
PHONE..................................513 541-4031
Steve Wernke, *President*
Sue Wernke, *Admin Sec*
EMP: 10
SQ FT: 10,000
SALES: 1MM **Privately Held**
SIC: 3363 Aluminum die-castings

(G-3710)
ENTERTRAINMENT JUNCTION
Also Called: Watson's
2721 E Sharon Rd (45241-1944)
PHONE..................................513 326-1100
Eric Mueller, *Owner*
Tom McGraw, *Sales Staff*
George Gigous, *Director*
EMP: 60
SALES (est): 5.9MM **Privately Held**
SIC: 2519 Household furniture

(G-3711)
ENVOI DESIGN INC
1332 Main St Frnt (45202-7849)
PHONE..................................513 651-4229
Fax: 513 651-5121
Denise Calmus, *President*
Steve Weinstein, *Vice Pres*
Jason Tyler, *Design Engr*
Katie Fine, *Accounts Mgr*
EMP: 7
SQ FT: 1,200
SALES (est): 632.2K **Privately Held**
WEB: www.envoidesign.com
SIC: 7336 2752 Commercial art & graphic design; graphic arts & related design; commercial printing, lithographic

(G-3712)
EP BOLLINGER LLC
Also Called: Myrlen
2664 Saint Georges Ct (45233-4290)
PHONE..................................513 941-1101
Ed P Bollinger, *Mng Member*
Kenneth F Seibel, *Mng Member*
Edward P Bollinger,
EMP: 32000
SQ FT: 22,000
SALES (est): 220.5K **Privately Held**
SIC: 2821 Plastics materials & resins

(G-3713)
EPRINTWORKSPLUS
5846 Hamilton Ave (45224-2921)
PHONE..................................513 731-3797
James Engleman, *CEO*
EMP: 3
SALES (est): 343.1K **Privately Held**
SIC: 3577 Printers & plotters

(G-3714)
EPS SPECIALTIES LTD INC
7875 School Rd 77 (45249-1531)
PHONE..................................513 489-3676
Fax: 513 489-3333
Edgar L Wilkinson, *President*

Lee Wilkinson, *Vice Pres*
▲ EMP: 12
SALES (est): 3MM **Privately Held**
WEB: www.lamlite.com
SIC: 2821 Polystyrene resins

(G-3715)
EQM TECHNOLOGIES & ENERGY INC (PA)
1800 Carillion Blvd (45240-2788)
PHONE..................................513 825-7500
Jon Colin, *CEO*
Jack S Greber, *Senior VP*
Robert Galvin, *CFO*
EMP: 19
SQ FT: 1,000
SALES: 56.2MM **Publicly Held**
SIC: 2869 Industrial organic chemicals

(G-3716)
EQUISTAR CHEMICALS LP
11530 Northlake Dr (45249-1642)
PHONE..................................513 530-4000
Fax: 513 530-4268
Garry Laaker, *Engineer*
James Thill, *Engineer*
Peter Hanik, *Branch Mgr*
Norma Maraschin, *Manager*
Bryan Pelton, *Director*
EMP: 22 **Privately Held**
SIC: 2869 Industrial organic chemicals
HQ: Equistar Chemicals, Lp
1221 Mckinney St Ste 700
Houston TX 77010

(G-3717)
ERNST CUSTOM CABINETS LLC
4686 Paddock Rd Ste 99 (45229-1042)
PHONE..................................513 376-9554
Thomas Ernst, *Principal*
EMP: 4
SALES (est): 408.4K **Privately Held**
SIC: 2434 Wood kitchen cabinets

(G-3718)
ERVAN GUTTMAN CO
8208 Blue Ash Rd Rear (45236-2188)
PHONE..................................513 791-0767
Fax: 513 891-0559
EMP: 3 EST: 1938
SQ FT: 6,000
SALES (est): 408.9K **Privately Held**
SIC: 5149 2064 5046 Mfr Candy & Baking Molds & Holiday Novelties

(G-3719)
ESTREAMZ INC
1311 Vine St (45202-7118)
PHONE..................................513 278-7836
Travis Bea, *President*
EMP: 30
SQ FT: 15,000
SALES (est): 664.4K **Privately Held**
SIC: 7379 7372 7812 ; home entertainment computer software; motion picture production & distribution; television

(G-3720)
ETHOS CORP
1045 Meta Dr (45237-5007)
PHONE..................................513 242-6336
EMP: 4
SALES (est): 401.6K **Privately Held**
SIC: 3535 Mfg Conveyors/Equipment

(G-3721)
EUROSTAMPA NORTH AMERICA INC (DH)
1440 Seymour Ave (45237-3006)
PHONE..................................513 821-2275
Gian Franco Cillario, *CEO*
Diane Obrien, *Vice Pres*
Bob Fenster, *Prdtn Mgr*
Giorgio Zucchi, *Warehouse Mgr*
Ken Cione, *Opers Staff*
▲ EMP: 95
SALES (est): 21.7MM
SALES (corp-wide): 107.4K **Privately Held**
SIC: 2752 Commercial printing, lithographic
HQ: Industria Grafica Eurostampa Spa
Viale Rimembranza 20
Bene Vagienna CN 12041
017 265-1811

(G-3722)
EVERS ENTERPRISES INC
Aurand Manufacturing & Eqp Co
1210 Ellis St (45223-1843)
PHONE..................................513 541-7200
Ray Evers, *President*
EMP: 6
SALES (corp-wide): 1.8MM **Privately Held**
WEB: www.evertenterprises.com
SIC: 3589 Commercial cleaning equipment
PA: Evers Enterprises Inc
4849 Blue Rock Rd
Cincinnati OH

(G-3723)
EVERS WELDING CO INC
4849 Blue Rock Rd (45247-5504)
P.O. Box 53426 (45253-0426)
PHONE..................................513 385-7352
Fax: 513 385-7322
Edward G Evers, *President*
Jacqueline Evers, *Corp Secy*
EMP: 40
SQ FT: 3,000
SALES (est): 5MM **Privately Held**
WEB: www.everssteel.com
SIC: 1791 3441 Structural steel erection; fabricated structural metal

(G-3724)
EVOLUTION CRTIVE SOLUTIONS INC
7107 Shona Dr (45237-3808)
PHONE..................................513 681-4450
Cathy Lindemann, *President*
Cathy Welz, *Financial Exec*
Celia Lack, *Manager*
EMP: 45
SQ FT: 22,000
SALES (est): 9.7MM **Privately Held**
WEB: www.kpbprinting.com
SIC: 2752 Color lithography

(G-3725)
EVOLUTION CRTIVE SOLUTIONS LLC
7107 Shona Dr Ste 110 (45237-3808)
PHONE..................................513 681-4450
Cathy Lindemann, *President*
Cathy Welz, *Accounting Mgr*
EMP: 25
SQ FT: 14,000
SALES: 3MM **Privately Held**
SIC: 7336 2759 5199 7389 Commercial art & graphic design; commercial printing; advertising specialties; embroidering of advertising on shirts, etc.; screen printing: manmade fiber & silk broadwoven fabrics

(G-3726)
EVONIK CORPORATION
Also Called: Coatings & Colorants
620 Shepherd Dr (45215-2104)
PHONE..................................513 554-8969
Joseph Won, *Plt & Fclts Mgr*
Larry Mason, *Engineer*
EMP: 60
SALES (corp-wide): 2.3B **Privately Held**
SIC: 2869 Industrial organic chemicals
HQ: Evonik Corporation
299 Jefferson Rd
Parsippany NJ 07054
973 929-8000

(G-3727)
EVP INTERNATIONAL LLC
Also Called: Mn8-Foxfire
10179 Wayne Ave (45215-1555)
PHONE..................................513 761-7614
Zachary Green,
EMP: 4
SQ FT: 4,000
SALES (est): 636.6K **Privately Held**
SIC: 3646 Commercial indusl & institutional electric lighting fixtures

(G-3728)
EW SCRIPPS COMPANY (PA)
312 Walnut St Ste 2800 (45202-4067)
PHONE..................................513 977-3000
Fax: 513 651-2352
Richard A Boehne, *Ch of Bd*
Adam P Symson, *COO*
William Appleton, *Senior VP*

Adam Symson, *Senior VP*
Sue Clark, *Vice Pres*
EMP: 21
SALES: 943MM **Publicly Held**
WEB: www.scripps.com
SIC: 4841 2711 4833 7375 Cable & other pay television services; newspapers; television broadcasting stations; on-line data base information retrieval

(G-3729)
EXAIR CORPORATION (PA)
11510 Goldcoast Dr (45249-1621)
P.O. Box 00766 (45264)
PHONE..................................513 671-3322
Roy O Sweeney, *CEO*
Brian Peters, *President*
Bruce Patterson, *Facilities Mgr*
Dan Preston, *Engineer*
Bob West, *CFO*
EMP: 45
SQ FT: 42,000
SALES (est): 8.4MM **Privately Held**
WEB: www.linevac.com
SIC: 3499 Nozzles, spray: aerosol, paint or insecticide

(G-3730)
EXECUTIVE SECURITY SYSTEMS INC
332 Cherry St (45246-3536)
PHONE..................................513 895-2783
Gary Michael Bender, *President*
EMP: 3
SQ FT: 2,200
SALES (est): 445.3K **Privately Held**
WEB: www.executivessi.com
SIC: 3699 Security devices

(G-3731)
EXPRESS GRAPHIC PRTG & DESIGN
9695 Hamilton Ave (45231-2351)
PHONE..................................513 728-3344
Craig Keller, *Owner*
Karla Roth, *Graphic Designe*
EMP: 8
SQ FT: 2,400
SALES (est): 858.4K **Privately Held**
WEB: www.davis411.com
SIC: 2759 Commercial printing

(G-3732)
EXPRESSIVE SCENTS BY A
1336 Behles Ave (45215-2418)
PHONE..................................513 254-5399
EMP: 3
SALES (est): 212.2K **Privately Held**
SIC: 2844 Toilet preparations

(G-3733)
EXXCITE MARKETING INC
Also Called: Exxcite Marketing Products
7949 Graves Rd (45243-3626)
PHONE..................................513 271-4550
Mary Jo Byrnes, *President*
William Stratman, *Vice Pres*
EMP: 4
SALES: 800K **Privately Held**
SIC: 2759 Promotional printing

(G-3734)
F AND W PUBLICATIONS INC
4700 E Galbraith Rd (45236-2754)
P.O. Box 36275 (45236-0275)
PHONE..................................513 531-2690
Mark Arnett, *CEO*
Karen B Callard, *General Mgr*
Maureen Bloomfield, *Editor*
Phil Graham, *Senior VP*
Patti Roberts, *Sales Staff*
EMP: 4 EST: 2015
SALES (est): 66.9K **Privately Held**
SIC: 2741 Miscellaneous publishing

(G-3735)
F K HOLDING INC (PA)
2100 Section Rd (45237-3510)
PHONE..................................513 641-1400
Franklin S Kling Jr, *CEO*
▲ EMP: 11
SALES (est): 25MM **Privately Held**
SIC: 2392 3261 3089 Household furnishings; bathroom accessories/fittings, vitreous china or earthenware; plastic kitchenware, tableware & housware

(G-3736)
FAIRY DUST LTD INC
3528 Warsaw Ave (45205-1875)
PHONE.....................513 251-0065
Fax: 513 251-2525
Diane Clark, *President*
Jennifer Clark, *Principal*
Paul Bathen, *COO*
Cindy Moning, *Office Mgr*
▲ EMP: 15
SQ FT: 7,000
SALES (est): 3MM **Privately Held**
WEB: www.fairydust.com
SIC: 2841 Soap & other detergents

(G-3737)
FAME TOOL & MFG CO INC
5340 Hetzell St (45227-1541)
PHONE.....................513 271-6387
Fax: 513 271-0456
Helen Snyder, *President*
Laddie F Snyder, *Treasurer*
EMP: 25
SQ FT: 20,000
SALES (est): 2.5MM **Privately Held**
SIC: 3544 3812 3537 Special dies, tools,
jigs & fixtures; search & navigation equip-
ment; industrial trucks & tractors

(G-3738)
**FAMILY MOTOR COACH ASSN
INC (PA)**
8291 Clough Pike (45244-2756)
PHONE.....................513 474-3622
Fax: 513 474-2332
Lana Makin, *CEO*
Pamela Kay, *Comms Dir*
Robert McMillan, *Program Mgr*
Barbara Greenwood, *Manager*
John Johnston, *Assoc Editor*
EMP: 46
SQ FT: 22,000
SALES: 3.6MM **Privately Held**
WEB: www.fmca.com
SIC: 8641 2721 Social associations; mag-
azines: publishing & printing

(G-3739)
FAMILY MOTOR COACHING INC
8291 Clough Pike (45244-2756)
PHONE.....................513 474-3622
Don Moore, *President*
Cindy Ackley, *General Mgr*
Alexis Ludwig, *Treasurer*
Don Eversmann, *Exec Dir*
EMP: 57
SQ FT: 20,000
SALES (est): 1.8MM
SALES (corp-wide): 3.6MM **Privately
Held**
WEB: www.fmca.com
SIC: 2721 Magazines: publishing only, not
printed on site
PA: Family Motor Coach Association, Inc.
8291 Clough Pike
Cincinnati OH 45244
513 474-3622

(G-3740)
FARMED MATERIALS INC
300 E Business Way # 200 (45241-2389)
PHONE.....................513 680-4046
Adam Malofsky, *CEO*
Steven Levin, *COO*
Katrina Cornish, *Vice Pres*
Chuck Joffe, *Vice Pres*
EMP: 4
SQ FT: 800
SALES (est): 170.2K **Privately Held**
SIC: 3069 2821 8731 0191 Type, rubber;
plastics materials & resins; commercial
physical research; general farms, prima-
rily crop

(G-3741)
FASTSIGNS
12125 Montgomery Rd (45249-1730)
PHONE.....................513 489-8989
William Jamison, *Principal*
EMP: 4
SALES (est): 473.7K **Privately Held**
SIC: 3993 Signs & advertising specialties

(G-3742)
FAWN CONFECTIONERY (PA)
4271 Harrison Ave (45211-3340)
PHONE.....................513 574-9612
Fax: 513 574-9651
Kathy Guenther, *CEO*
Jane Guenther, *Treasurer*
Jackie Copenhaver, *Admin Sec*
EMP: 15
SALES (est): 1.7MM **Privately Held**
WEB: www.fawnconfectionery.com
SIC: 5441 2064 2066 Candy; candy &
other confectionery products; chocolate &
cocoa products

(G-3743)
FAX MEDLEY GROUP INC
7754 Camargo Rd Ste 18 (45243-2661)
PHONE.....................513 272-1932
Michael Lowry, *President*
Rita Burgess, *Administration*
EMP: 3 EST: 1994
SALES (est): 174.4K **Privately Held**
SIC: 2741 7338 Miscellaneous publishing;
secretarial & court reporting

(G-3744)
FAXON FIREARMS LLC
11101 Adwood Dr (45240-3235)
PHONE.....................513 674-2580
Robert Faxon, *President*
Barry Faxon, *Vice Pres*
Nathanial Schueth, *Opers Staff*
Dominic Geraci, *Manager*
EMP: 4
SALES (est): 355.1K **Privately Held**
SIC: 3484 Small arms

(G-3745)
FAXON MACHINING INC
11101 Adwood Dr (45240-3235)
PHONE.....................513 851-4644
Fax: 513 851-4444
Barry A Faxon, *President*
B W Faxon, *Principal*
D K Faxon II, *Principal*
David K Faxon, *Principal*
Mark Kebe, *COO*
▲ EMP: 135
SQ FT: 155,000
SALES (est): 33.8MM **Privately Held**
WEB: www.faxon-machining.com
SIC: 3541 Drilling & boring machines

(G-3746)
FBF LIMITED
Also Called: Queen City Steel Treating Co
2980 Spring Grove Ave (45225-2146)
PHONE.....................513 541-6300
Fax: 513 541-6000
Judith T Houchens, *President*
Michael E Fourney, *Vice Pres*
William L Fourney, *Vice Pres*
Judy Rudy, *Opers Mgr*
Mike Nappi, *Engineer*
EMP: 35
SALES (est): 7.6MM **Privately Held**
WEB: www.qcst.com
SIC: 3398 Metal heat treating; brazing
(hardening) of metal

(G-3747)
**FEDERAL EQUIPMENT
COMPANY (PA)**
5298 River Rd (45233-1688)
PHONE.....................513 621-5260
Jack Davis, *CEO*
Doug P Ridenour, *President*
John Cerimele, *Vice Pres*
Jeffrey J Sterwerf, *Project Engr*
Ronald Eubanks, *Treasurer*
▲ EMP: 70
SALES (est): 25.2MM **Privately Held**
WEB: www.fecheliports.com
SIC: 3699 3728 3534 3535 Electrical
equipment & supplies; aircraft parts &
equipment; elevators & moving stairways;
conveyors & conveying equipment;
hoists, cranes & monorails; manufactured
hardware (general)

(G-3748)
FEINER PATTERN WORKS INC
11335 Sebring Dr (45240-2796)
PHONE.....................513 851-9800
Fax: 513 851-1851
Kenneth Feiner, *President*
Jimmy Feiner, *Vice Pres*
EMP: 12 EST: 1957
SQ FT: 9,000
SALES (est): 1.7MM **Privately Held**
SIC: 3543 Industrial patterns

(G-3749)
FELD PRINTING CO
6806 Main St (45244-3435)
P.O. Box 44188 (45244-0188)
PHONE.....................513 271-6806
Fax: 513 271-6828
Robert A Feld Jr, *President*
David A Feld, *Vice Pres*
William Feld, *Accounts Mgr*
Joe Mitchell, *Sales Staff*
Marilyn Feld Mitchell, *Admin Sec*
EMP: 7
SQ FT: 5,000
SALES (est): 690K **Privately Held**
WEB: www.feldprinting.com
SIC: 2761 Continuous forms, office & busi-
ness

(G-3750)
FES-OHIO INC
Also Called: Fes Incorporated
4030 Mt Carml Tbsc Rd # 227
(45255-3431)
PHONE.....................513 772-8566
Joseph Rubino, *President*
EMP: 3
SQ FT: 1,000
SALES (est): 349.7K **Privately Held**
SIC: 3822 Air conditioning & refrigeration
controls

(G-3751)
**FIEDELDEY STL FABRICATORS
INC**
8487 E Miami River Rd (45247-2208)
PHONE.....................513 353-3300
Bernard A Fiedeldey Jr, *President*
EMP: 20
SQ FT: 20,000
SALES (est): 5.9MM **Privately Held**
SIC: 3441 Fabricated structural metal

(G-3752)
**FIELD APPARATUS SERVICE &
TSTG**
Also Called: F A S T
4040 Rev Dr (45232-1914)
PHONE.....................513 353-9399
Fax: 513 353-9389
Kathy Jones, *President*
EMP: 4
SALES (est): 520K **Privately Held**
SIC: 8711 3825 Electrical or electronic en-
gineering; test equipment for electronic &
electric measurement

(G-3753)
FIELD AVIATION INC (PA)
8044 Montgomery Rd # 530 (45236-2941)
PHONE.....................513 792-2282
John Mactaggart, *CEO*
Patty Nash, *Office Mgr*
Tera Disdlier, *Manager*
Chris Clark, *Senior Mgr*
Amber Drennen, *Director*
EMP: 5
SALES (est): 35MM **Privately Held**
SIC: 3728 Aircraft parts & equipment

(G-3754)
FIELD DAILIES LLC
323 W 5th St Apt 3 (45202-2772)
PHONE.....................859 379-2120
Jim Duff, *Mng Member*
EMP: 4
SALES (est): 230K **Privately Held**
SIC: 7372 Business oriented computer
software

(G-3755)
FIELDS ASSOCIATES INC
Also Called: JCB Payroll Solutions
2134 Hatmaker St Ste 3 (45204-1948)
PHONE.....................513 426-8652
Damian Fields, *CEO*
Christine Collins, *Vice Pres*
Joseph Pierce, *Vice Pres*
Mary Smith, *Exec Sec*
EMP: 4

SALES (est): 273.4K **Privately Held**
SIC: 2051 5461 8721 Bread, cake & related products; bagels, fresh or frozen;
cakes, pies & pastries; bakeries; payroll
accounting service

(G-3756)
FINN GRAPHICS INC
220 Stille Dr (45233-1695)
PHONE.....................513 941-6161
Fax: 513 941-3880
Robert Finn, *CEO*
Dan Finn, *President*
Jack Roch, *Vice Pres*
Erin Glenn, *Sales Mgr*
Nancy Cunningham, *Accounts Exec*
EMP: 40 EST: 1940
SQ FT: 30,000
SALES (est): 6.5MM **Privately Held**
SIC: 2752 3993 2395 Commercial print-
ing, lithographic; advertising novelties;
pleating & stitching

(G-3757)
FIOMET LLC
2717 Erie Ave (45208-2103)
PHONE.....................513 519-7622
Scott Rapp, *President*
EMP: 4
SQ FT: 2,000
SALES (est): 162.8K **Privately Held**
SIC: 3829 Stress, strain & flaw
detecting/measuring equipment

(G-3758)
FISH EXPRESS
2463 Harrison Ave (45211-7957)
PHONE.....................513 661-3000
Khaled Munjed, *Principal*
EMP: 4
SALES (est): 312.7K **Privately Held**
SIC: 2741 Miscellaneous publishing

(G-3759)
FLEXOMATION LLC
11701 Chesterdale Rd (45246-3405)
PHONE.....................513 825-0555
Eric Lewis,
EMP: 14
SALES (est): 2.8MM **Privately Held**
SIC: 3549 Assembly machines, including
robotic

(G-3760)
FLIGHTLOGIX LLC
4510 Airport Rd (45226-1601)
PHONE.....................513 321-1200
Greg Herrmann,
Jay Schmalfuss,
EMP: 8
SALES (est): 990K **Privately Held**
SIC: 3721 Aircraft

(G-3761)
FLINT GROUP US LLC
Also Called: C D R Pigments Dispersions Div
410 Glendale Milford Rd (45215-1103)
PHONE.....................513 771-1900
Fax: 513 771-0651
Earl Seibert, *Safety Mgr*
Larry Bishop, *Mfg Staff*
Alan Burt, *Technical Mgr*
Michael V Luchini, *Controller*
Yvonne Wilson, *Personnel*
EMP: 60
SALES (corp-wide): 3.8B **Privately Held**
WEB: www.flintink.com
SIC: 2865 2893 Color pigments, organic;
printing ink
PA: Flint Group Us Llc
14909 N Beck Rd
Plymouth MI 48170
734 781-4600

(G-3762)
**FLOTTEMESCH ANTHONY &
SON**
8201 Camargo Rd Ste 1 (45243-1469)
PHONE.....................513 561-1212
Fax: 513 561-7788
James Flottemesch, *President*
James Flottimish Jr, *Vice Pres*
EMP: 10 EST: 1942
SQ FT: 13,000

SALES (est): 975K **Privately Held**
SIC: 2511 2434 2431 Wood household
furniture; wood kitchen cabinets; millwork

(G-3763)
FLOW CONTROL US HOLDING CORP
Also Called: General Aquatics
4030 Mount Carmel Tobasco (45255-3400)
PHONE......................................800 843-5628
Fax: 513 528-8681
Kevan Langner, *Principal*
EMP: 3 **Privately Held**
WEB: www.pentair.com
SIC: 3561 Pumps & pumping equipment
HQ: Flow Control Us Holding Corporation
5500 Wayzata Blvd
Minneapolis MN 55416
763 545-1730

(G-3764)
FLOW TECHNOLOGY INC
4444 Cooper Rd (45242-5615)
PHONE......................................513 745-6000
Bill Hayes, *President*
Bill Hays, *President*
EMP: 200
SALES (est): 12.2MM
SALES (corp-wide): 2.7B **Publicly Held**
SIC: 3491 Valves, automatic control
HQ: Xomox Corporation
4526 Res Frest Dr Ste 400
The Woodlands TX 77381
936 271-6500

(G-3765)
FLYPAPER STUDIO INC
311 Elm St Ste 200 (45202-2743)
PHONE......................................602 801-2208
Patrick Sullivan, *CEO*
Greg Head, *President*
Pat Stoner, *Treasurer*
Sunil Padiyar, *CTO*
Don Perison, *Admin Sec*
EMP: 30
SQ FT: 16,778
SALES: 1.9MM **Privately Held**
WEB: www.interactivealchemy.com
SIC: 7372 Educational computer software

(G-3766)
FOOD SPECIALTIES CO (PA)
12 Sunnybrook Dr (45237-2191)
PHONE......................................513 761-1242
Fax: 513 821-3733
Kenneth Troy, *Principal*
Patricia Furlong, *Principal*
Lucien G Strauss, *Principal*
EMP: 5 EST: 1956
SQ FT: 20,000
SALES (est): 2.4MM **Privately Held**
SIC: 2035 Mayonnaise; dressings; salad:
raw & cooked (except dry mixes)

(G-3767)
FOOT LOCKER RETAIL INC
11700 Princeton Pike D215 (45246-2526)
PHONE......................................513 671-4085
Daniel Dixon, *Branch Mgr*
EMP: 9
SALES (corp-wide): 7.7B **Publicly Held**
SIC: 3949 Sporting & athletic goods
HQ: Foot Locker Retail, Inc.
112 W 34th St Frnt 1
New York NY 10120

(G-3768)
FORCAM INC
250 E 5th St Fl 15 (45202-4119)
PHONE......................................513 878-2780
Franz Gruber, *CEO*
Emma Hamlet, *Manager*
Theresa Nick, *Manager*
EMP: 15
SQ FT: 5,000
SALES (est): 920K **Privately Held**
SIC: 7372 7371 Prepackaged software;
application computer software; computer
software development & applications

(G-3769)
FOREST CONVERTING COMPANY INC
4701 Forest Ave (45212-3399)
PHONE......................................513 631-4190
Fax: 513 631-4190

R Douglas Lojinger, *President*
EMP: 6 EST: 1949
SQ FT: 22,000
SALES: 500K **Privately Held**
SIC: 2675 Paper die-cutting; paperboard
die-cutting; cardboard cut-outs, panels &
foundations: die-cut

(G-3770)
FOREST PHARMACEUTICALS INC
3941 Brotherton Rd (45209)
PHONE......................................513 271-6800
Fax: 513 271-4795
Raymond Stafford, *Exec VP*
Terrill Howard, *Plant Mgr*
Craig Yurehak, *Plant Mgr*
Bob Tracy, *Mfg Mgr*
Aaron Reizner, *Production*
EMP: 200 **Privately Held**
WEB: www.forestpharm.com
SIC: 2834 Pharmaceutical preparations
HQ: Forest Pharmaceuticals, Inc.
400 Interpace Pkwy Ste A1
Parsippany NJ 07054
862 261-7000

(G-3771)
FOREST PHARMACEUTICALS INC
5000 Brotherton Rd (45209-1198)
PHONE......................................513 271-6800
Fax: 513 271-6801
Rob Groves, *Buyer*
David Boyle, *Purchasing*
Terry Howell, *Branch Mgr*
EMP: 105 **Privately Held**
WEB: www.forestpharm.com
SIC: 2834 Pharmaceutical preparations
HQ: Forest Pharmaceuticals, Inc.
400 Interpace Pkwy Ste A1
Parsippany NJ 07054
862 261-7000

(G-3772)
FORMICA CORPORATION (HQ)
10155 Reading Rd (45241-4805)
PHONE......................................513 786-3400
Fax: 513 786-3024
Frank Riddick, *President*
Mitchell P Quint, *President*
Davod Pallas, *COO*
Gerry Bollman, *Vice Pres*
R Gerard Bollman, *Vice Pres*
▲ EMP: 20 EST: 1913
SQ FT: 14,000
SALES (est): 290.2MM
SALES (corp-wide): 6.1B **Privately Held**
WEB: www.formica.com
SIC: 2541 2679 Counter & sink tops; table
or counter tops, plastic laminated; paper-
board products, converted
PA: Fletcher Building Limited
810 Great South Road
Auckland, 1061
952 590-00

(G-3773)
FORUM III INC
436 Mcgregor Ave (45206-2364)
PHONE......................................513 961-5123
Fax: 513 961-0320
Michael Evans, *President*
Jeffrey Crosby, *Vice Pres*
EMP: 13
SQ FT: 8,800
SALES: 500K **Privately Held**
SIC: 2434 2431 2541 Wood kitchen cabi-
nets; millwork; wood partitions & fixtures

(G-3774)
FORWARD MOVEMENT PUBLICATIONS
Also Called: Forward Day By Day
412 Sycamore St Fl 2 (45202-6202)
PHONE......................................513 721-6659
Fax: 513 721-0729
Jane Paraskevopoulos, *Personnel Exec*
Jane Paraskevotoulos, *Manager*
Richard Schmidt, *Director*
▲ EMP: 12
SALES (est): 960K **Privately Held**
WEB: www.forwarddaybyday.com
SIC: 2759 Publication printing

(G-3775)
FRAME SHOPPE
7750 Beechmont Ave (45255-4214)
PHONE......................................513 232-3970
Dorothy Green, *Owner*
EMP: 6
SALES (est): 340.1K **Privately Held**
SIC: 2499 Picture & mirror frames, wood

(G-3776)
FRAME USA
225 Northland Blvd (45246-3603)
PHONE......................................513 577-7107
Fax: 513 577-7105
Greg Clark, *CEO*
Daniel P Regenold, *Ch of Bd*
Dana Gore, *President*
Mike Billington, *Opers Mgr*
◆ EMP: 20
SQ FT: 7,000
SALES (est): 3.9MM
SALES (corp-wide): 8.1MM **Privately Held**
WEB: www.frameusa.com
SIC: 2499 5999 3499 Picture frame mold-
ing, finished; picture frames, ready made;
picture frames, metal
PA: Posterservice, Incorporated
225 Northland Blvd
Cincinnati OH 45246
513 577-7100

(G-3777)
FRANCHISE SERVICES INC
Also Called: Prographics
4404 Forest Ave (45212-3302)
PHONE......................................513 731-1440
Norman Falick, *Owner*
EMP: 8
SALES (corp-wide): 18.3MM **Privately Held**
SIC: 2752 Commercial printing, litho-
graphic
PA: Franchise Services, Inc.
26722 Plaza
Mission Viejo CA 92691
949 348-5400

(G-3778)
FRANK L HARTER & SON INC
3778 Frondorf Ave (45211-4421)
PHONE......................................513 574-1330
Fax: 513 574-5506
Michael Harter, *President*
Barb Harter, *Admin Sec*
EMP: 6 EST: 1928
SQ FT: 800
SALES: 1MM **Privately Held**
SIC: 5143 5144 5148 2099 Butter;
cheese; eggs; fresh fruits & vegetables;
salads, fresh or refrigerated

(G-3779)
FRANKLIN COVEY CO
7875 Montgomery Rd # 1202
(45236-4344)
PHONE......................................513 792-0099
Jason Mast, *Manager*
EMP: 8
SALES (corp-wide): 209.9MM **Publicly Held**
WEB: www.franklincovey.com
SIC: 2741 Miscellaneous publishing
PA: Franklin Covey Co.
2200 W Parkway Blvd
Salt Lake City UT 84119
801 817-1776

(G-3780)
FRANKLIN FUELING SYSTEMS
2715 Turpin Knoll Ct (45244-3862)
PHONE......................................513 231-7840
EMP: 3 EST: 2011
SALES (est): 174.3K **Privately Held**
SIC: 2869 Fuels

(G-3781)
FRANKS ELECTRIC INC
Also Called: Franks Electric Motor Repair
2640 Colerain Ave (45214-1712)
PHONE......................................513 542-0342
Fax: 513 542-1943
Brian Knue, *President*
Diana Grady, *Vice Pres*
EMP: 8
SQ FT: 10,000

SALES (est): 732.7K **Privately Held**
SIC: 1731 7694 5999 General electrical
contractor; electric motor repair; motors,
electric

(G-3782)
FREDERICK STEEL COMPANY LLC
Also Called: Bfs Supply
630 Glendale Milford Rd (45215-1105)
PHONE......................................513 821-6400
Burke Byer, *Principal*
Timothy Nagy, *Asst Sec*
EMP: 60 EST: 2013
SALES (est): 8.5MM
SALES (corp-wide): 86.5MM **Privately Held**
SIC: 1791 3441 Structural steel erection;
building components, structural steel
PA: Benjamin Steel Company, Inc.
777 Benjamin Dr
Springfield OH 45502
937 322-8600

(G-3783)
FRESH TABLE LLC
1801 Race St Ste 2 (45202-5917)
PHONE......................................513 381-3774
Sheila W Nolan, *Principal*
Meredith Trombly, *Manager*
EMP: 3
SALES (est): 221.6K **Privately Held**
SIC: 2099 Food preparations

(G-3784)
FRISBIE ENGINE & MACHINE CO (PA)
2635 Spring Grove Ave (45214-1731)
P.O. Box 14568 (45250-0568)
PHONE......................................513 542-1770
Reed Lee Coen, *President*
EMP: 12
SQ FT: 22,000
SALES: 1MM **Privately Held**
SIC: 3599 8742 6411 Machine shop, job-
bing & repair; management consulting
services; research services; insurance

(G-3785)
FROST ENGINEERING INC (PA)
3408 Beekman St (45223-2425)
PHONE......................................513 541-6330
Fax: 513 541-6367
Charles E Frost, *President*
Steve Meese, *Engineer*
Tom Schneider, *Sales Executive*
Krishenda Harless, *Executive Asst*
EMP: 21
SQ FT: 15,000
SALES (est): 7.2MM **Privately Held**
WEB: www.frostengineering.com
SIC: 3556 8711 Smokers, food processing
equipment; engineering services

(G-3786)
FT GROUP INC
4710 Madison Rd (45227-1426)
PHONE......................................937 746-6439
Fax: 937 746-2759
Thomas C Wortley, *CEO*
Karen Bogan, *Treasurer*
EMP: 20
SQ FT: 45,993
SALES (est): 1.9MM **Privately Held**
WEB: www.ftgroup.com
SIC: 3555 3827 2796 3825 Printing
trades machinery; microscopes, except
electron, proton & corneal; engraving on
copper, steel, wood or rubber; printing
plates; measuring instruments & meters,
electric

(G-3787)
FURNITURE BY OTMAR INC
9500 Montgomery Rd (45242-7204)
PHONE......................................513 891-5141
Fax: 513 891-5382
Harold James, *Manager*
EMP: 3
SALES (corp-wide): 1.1MM **Privately Held**
WEB: www.furniturebyotmar.com
SIC: 2511 5712 Wood household furniture;
furniture stores

PA: Furniture By Otmar, Inc.
301 Mmsburg Cnterville Rd
Dayton OH 45459
937 435-2039

(G-3788)
G & C DRAINAGE SUPPLIES INC
Also Called: Discount Dring Sups Cincinnati
200 Cavett Dr (45215-3186)
PHONE....................................513 563-8616
Fax: 513 563-8929
Larry Gorman, *Manager*
EMP: 5
SALES (corp-wide): 6.3MM **Privately Held**
SIC: 5051 3444 Pipe & tubing, steel; culverts, sheet metal
PA: G & C Drainage Supplies Inc
2600 S Arlington Rd
Akron OH 44319
330 644-0114

(G-3789)
G & J PEPSI-COLA BOTTLERS INC (PA)
9435 Waterstone Blvd # 390 (45249-8227)
PHONE....................................513 785-6060
Fax: 513 683-9467
Thomas D Heekin, *Vice Ch Bd*
Sydnor I Davis, *President*
George G Grubb, *Principal*
Stanley Kaplan, *Chairman*
Thomas R Gross, *Vice Chairman*
EMP: 10
SQ FT: 8,052
SALES (est): 490.5MM **Privately Held**
WEB: www.gjpepsi.com
SIC: 2086 Soft drinks: packaged in cans, bottles, etc.

(G-3790)
G A AVRIL COMPANY (PA)
Also Called: Brass & Bronze Ingot Division
4445 Kings Run Dr (45232-1401)
P.O. Box 32066 (45232-0066)
PHONE....................................513 641-0566
Fax: 513 641-0568
Thomas B Avril, *President*
John G Avril, *Vice Pres*
EMP: 10
SQ FT: 47,000
SALES (est): 2.1MM **Privately Held**
SIC: 3341 3356 Brass smelting & refining (secondary); bronze smelting & refining (secondary); nonferrous rolling & drawing; lead & lead alloy: rolling, drawing or extruding; tin & tin alloy: rolling, drawing or extruding; solder: wire, bar, acid core, & rosin core

(G-3791)
G A AVRIL COMPANY
White Metal Products Division
2108 Eagle Ct (45237-4754)
P.O. Box 12050 (45212-0050)
PHONE....................................513 731-5133
Fax: 513 731-5135
John Avril, *Vice Pres*
Philip V Schneider, *Manager*
EMP: 12
SQ FT: 66,782
SALES (corp-wide): 2.1MM **Privately Held**
SIC: 3356 Lead & lead alloy bars, pipe, plates, shapes, etc.; lead & lead alloy: rolling, drawing or extruding
PA: The G A Avril Company
4445 Kings Run Dr
Cincinnati OH 45232
513 641-0566

(G-3792)
G M P WELDING AND FABRICATING
11175 Adwood Dr (45240-3235)
PHONE....................................513 825-7861
Fax: 513 825-1156
Leonard J Mee, *President*
Linda Conrad, *Admin Sec*
EMP: 16 EST: 1979
SALES (est): 1.3MM **Privately Held**
SIC: 7692 Welding repair

(G-3793)
GAITWELL ORTHOTICS PEDORTHICS
1 N Commerce Park Dr # 306 (45215-3187)
PHONE....................................513 829-2217
Michael Veder, *Principal*
EMP: 3 EST: 2010
SALES (est): 140K **Privately Held**
SIC: 3842 Orthopedic appliances

(G-3794)
GALLERIA CO
1 Procter And Gamble Plz (45202-3315)
PHONE....................................513 983-1490
Camillo Pane, *CEO*
Laura Becker, *Asst Sec*
EMP: 3 EST: 2015
SALES (est): 81.8K **Publicly Held**
SIC: 2844 Cosmetic preparations
HQ: Coty Inc.
350 5th Ave Ste 2700
New York NY 10118

(G-3795)
GANNETT CO INC
Also Called: Cincinnati Enquirer, The
312 Elm St Ste 1400 (45202-2722)
PHONE....................................513 721-2700
Kimberly Harris, *Branch Mgr*
EMP: 78
SALES (corp-wide): 3B **Publicly Held**
SIC: 2711 Newspapers, publishing & printing
PA: Gannett Co., Inc.
7950 Jones Branch Dr
Mc Lean VA 22102
703 854-6000

(G-3796)
GANNETT STLLITE INFO NTWRK INC
Cincinnati Enquirer, The
312 Elm St Ste 1400 (45202-2722)
PHONE....................................513 721-2700
Margaret Buchanan, *President*
Martha Flanagan, *Publisher*
Lori Friedhoff, *Publisher*
Allen Lind, *Publisher*
Charles Brewer, *Editor*
EMP: 88
SALES (corp-wide): 3B **Publicly Held**
WEB: www.usatoday.com
SIC: 2711 Newspapers
HQ: Gannett Satellite Information Network, Llc
7950 Jones Branch Dr
Mc Lean VA 22102
703 854-6000

(G-3797)
GARDEN OF DELIGHT LLC
5540 Chandler St (45227-1636)
PHONE....................................513 300-7205
Ray Edwards, *Mng Member*
Tonia Edward,
EMP: 4
SALES: 20K **Privately Held**
SIC: 2079 7389 Edible fats & oils;

(G-3798)
GARDEN STREET IRON & METAL (PA)
2885 Spring Grove Ave (45225-2222)
PHONE....................................513 853-3700
Fax: 513 977-4264
Earl J Weber Jr, *President*
Dave Hollbroke, *General Mgr*
Margaret Weber, *Vice Pres*
Sarah Weber, *Office Mgr*
Mike Chard, *Supervisor*
EMP: 39
SQ FT: 43,000
SALES (est): 30.4MM **Privately Held**
SIC: 4953 3341 3312 Recycling, waste materials; secondary nonferrous metals; blast furnaces & steel mills

(G-3799)
GARDNER BUSINESS MEDIA INC
6925 Valley Ave (45244-3029)
PHONE....................................513 527-8800
Margaret Kline, *Manager*
Toshiro Matsuda, *Director*

David Owens, *Director*
Jeff Norgord, *Creative Dir*
EMP: 30
SQ FT: 17,600
SALES (corp-wide): 35.1MM **Privately Held**
WEB: www.gardnerweb.com
SIC: 2721 2731 Trade journals: publishing only, not printed on site; statistical reports (periodicals): publishing & printing; books: publishing & printing
PA: Gardner Business Media, Inc.
6915 Valley Ave
Cincinnati OH 45244
513 527-8800

(G-3800)
GARYS CHESECAKES FINE DESSERTS
5285 Crookshank Rd Side (45238-3372)
PHONE....................................513 574-1700
Gary Haas, *Owner*
EMP: 8
SALES (est): 580.5K **Privately Held**
SIC: 2051 Bread, cake & related products

(G-3801)
GBI CINCINNATI INC
7700 Shawnee Run Rd (45243-3120)
PHONE....................................513 841-8684
Kevin V Bevan, *President*
Robert Whiting, *CFO*
▲ **EMP:** 4
SQ FT: 16,600
SALES (est): 1MM **Privately Held**
WEB: www.gbicincinnati.com
SIC: 5084 3541 Machine tools & metalworking machinery; machine tools, metal cutting type

(G-3802)
GCI DIGITAL IMAGING INC
5031 Winton Rd (45232-1506)
PHONE....................................513 521-7446
Tom Bedacht, *President*
Tony Stickney, *Executive*
EMP: 14
SQ FT: 10,000
SALES (est): 2.4MM **Privately Held**
WEB: www.gci-digital.com
SIC: 2759 Commercial printing

(G-3803)
GE AIRCRAFT ENGINES
1 Neumann Way (45215-1915)
PHONE....................................513 243-2000
Fax: 513 771-5575
David L Joyce, *President*
Charles Blankenship, *President*
Jean Lydon-Rodgers, *President*
Bill Millhaem, *General Mgr*
Anthony Aiello, *Vice Pres*
EMP: 22
SALES (est): 10.2MM **Privately Held**
SIC: 3724 Aircraft engines & engine parts

(G-3804)
GE AVIATION SYSTEMS LLC
10270 Saint Rita Ln (45215-1215)
PHONE....................................513 470-2889
Kevin Moermond, *Engineer*
Gregory Knapp, *Finance Mgr*
EMP: 7
SALES (corp-wide): 123.6B **Publicly Held**
SIC: 3812 Aircraft control systems, electronic
HQ: Ge Aviation Systems Llc
1 Neumann Way
Cincinnati OH 45215
513 243-2000

(G-3805)
GE AVIATION SYSTEMS LLC
123 Merchant St (45246-3730)
PHONE....................................513 552-5663
David Joyce, *CEO*
EMP: 14
SALES (corp-wide): 123.6B **Publicly Held**
SIC: 3313 Alloys, additive, except copper: not made in blast furnaces
HQ: Ge Aviation Systems Llc
1 Neumann Way
Cincinnati OH 45215
513 243-2000

(G-3806)
GE AVIATION SYSTEMS LLC
Also Called: GE Aviation Services
201 W Crescentville Rd (45246-1713)
PHONE....................................513 977-1500
EMP: 128
SALES (corp-wide): 123.6B **Publicly Held**
SIC: 3812 Aircraft control systems, electronic
HQ: Ge Aviation Systems Llc
1 Neumann Way
Cincinnati OH 45215
513 243-2000

(G-3807)
GE AVIATION SYSTEMS LLC
Also Called: Morris Technologies
11988 Tramway Dr (45241-1664)
PHONE....................................513 733-1611
Gregory Morris, *Branch Mgr*
EMP: 105
SALES (corp-wide): 123.6B **Publicly Held**
SIC: 3313 Alloys, additive, except copper: not made in blast furnaces
HQ: Ge Aviation Systems Llc
1 Neumann Way
Cincinnati OH 45215
513 243-2000

(G-3808)
GE AVIATION SYSTEMS LLC (HQ)
1 Neumann Way (45215-1915)
PHONE....................................513 243-2000
R F Ehr, *President*
J B Hines, *President*
Jeff Immelt, *Chairman*
Peter Page, *Exec VP*
Charles P Blankenship Jr, *Vice Pres*
▲ **EMP:** 8
SALES (est): 273.2MM
SALES (corp-wide): 123.6B **Publicly Held**
SIC: 3812 Aircraft control systems, electronic
PA: General Electric Company
41 Farnsworth St
Boston MA 02210
617 443-3000

(G-3809)
GE HEALTH
346 Gest St (45203-1822)
PHONE....................................513 241-5955
Mark Nybo, *Manager*
EMP: 15 **Privately Held**
SIC: 2835 In vitro & in vivo diagnostic substances
HQ: Ge Healthcare Inc.
100 Results Way
Marlborough MA 01752
800 292-8514

(G-3810)
GE MILITARY SYSTEMS
1 Neumann Way (45215-1915)
PHONE....................................513 243-2000
Russ Sparks, *Vice Pres*
Jon Clapsaddle, *Prdtn Mgr*
Andrew Marovich, *Systs Prg Mgr*
EMP: 812
SALES (est): 42.3MM
SALES (corp-wide): 123.6B **Publicly Held**
SIC: 3724 Aircraft engines & engine parts
PA: General Electric Company
41 Farnsworth St
Boston MA 02210
617 443-3000

(G-3811)
GE ROLLS ROYCE FIGHTER
1 Neumann Way 318a (45215-1915)
PHONE....................................513 243-2787
Robert H Griswold, *President*
Vicki Kawecki,
EMP: 3
SALES (est): 253K
SALES (corp-wide): 123.6B **Publicly Held**
SIC: 3519 Jet propulsion engines

PA: General Electric Company
41 Farnsworth St
Boston MA 02210
617 443-3000

(G-3812)
GENERAL CHAIN & MFG CORP
3182 Beekman St (45223-2422)
PHONE..................................513 541-6005
Fax: 513 541-9290
Eric Schaumloffel, *President*
Jim Feeks Jr, *Sales Mgr*
EMP: 40 **EST:** 1919
SQ FT: 30,000
SALES (est): 8.6MM **Privately Held**
SIC: 3496 Miscellaneous fabricated wire products

(G-3813)
GENERAL ELECTRIC COMPANY
201 W Crescentville Rd (45246-1733)
PHONE..................................513 977-1500
Thomas Cooper, *Vice Pres*
Brad Mottier, *Vice Pres*
Russell Sparks, *Vice Pres*
Roy Flores, *Purch Agent*
Josh Mason, *Engineer*
EMP: 500
SALES (corp-wide): 123.6B **Publicly Held**
SIC: 7629 3769 3728 3537 Aircraft electrical equipment repair; electrical equipment repair, high voltage; guided missile & space vehicle parts & auxiliary equipment; aircraft parts & equipment; industrial trucks & tractors
PA: General Electric Company
41 Farnsworth St
Boston MA 02210
617 443-3000

(G-3814)
GENERAL ELECTRIC COMPANY
445 S Cooper Ave (45215-4565)
PHONE..................................513 948-4170
Akram Mohammad, *Marketing Mgr*
James Scott, *Office Mgr*
Carol Mase, *Manager*
Mike Eshoo, *Risk Mgmt Dir*
EMP: 8
SALES (corp-wide): 123.6B **Publicly Held**
SIC: 3724 Aircraft engines & engine parts
PA: General Electric Company
41 Farnsworth St
Boston MA 02210
617 443-3000

(G-3815)
GENERAL ELECTRIC COMPANY
1 Neumann Way (45215-1988)
PHONE..................................513 552-2000
Denise Beach, *Buyer*
Partha Sreenivasan, *Program Mgr*
Randy Bates, *Manager*
Robert Doyon, *Manager*
Diane Orr, *Senior Mgr*
EMP: 1000
SQ FT: 84,308
SALES (corp-wide): 123.6B **Publicly Held**
SIC: 4581 3724 Hangar operation; aircraft engines & engine parts
PA: General Electric Company
41 Farnsworth St
Boston MA 02210
617 443-3000

(G-3816)
GENERAL ELECTRIC INTL INC
191 Rosa Parks St (45202-2573)
PHONE..................................410 737-7228
Robert Smits, *President*
EMP: 7
SQ FT: 5,000
SALES (corp-wide): 123.6B **Publicly Held**
SIC: 8711 7629 7694 Engineering services; electrical equipment repair services; motor repair services
HQ: General Electric International, Inc.
191 Rosa Parks St
Cincinnati OH 45202
513 813-9133

(G-3817)
GENERAL MILLS INC
11301 Mosteller Rd (45241-1827)
PHONE..................................513 771-8200
Greg Parker, *Purchasing*
Dennis Meierhofer, *Engineer*
Jeanne Rockwood, *Marketing Mgr*
Jerry Kelley, *Branch Mgr*
Cathy Cranfill-Parker, *Manager*
EMP: 100
SALES (corp-wide): 16.5B **Publicly Held**
WEB: www.generalmills.com
SIC: 2043 2099 Cereal breakfast foods; food preparations
PA: General Mills, Inc.
1 General Mills Blvd
Minneapolis MN 55426
763 764-7600

(G-3818)
GENERAL MILLS INC
4100 Executive Park Dr # 11 (45241-4026)
PHONE..................................513 563-8866
Skip Korty, *Manager*
EMP: 50
SALES (corp-wide): 16.5B **Publicly Held**
WEB: www.generalmills.com
SIC: 2043 2041 Rice: prepared as cereal breakfast food; flour mixes
PA: General Mills, Inc.
1 General Mills Blvd
Minneapolis MN 55426
763 764-7600

(G-3819)
GENERAL NANO LLC
1776 Mentor Ave Ste 170 (45212-3598)
PHONE..................................513 309-5947
Edward Chan, *Exec VP*
Mark Schulz, *Engineer*
Joseph E Sprengard,
EMP: 7
SALES (est): 915.6K **Privately Held**
SIC: 3674 Microprocessors

(G-3820)
GENERAL TOOL COMPANY (PA)
101 Landy Ln (45215-3495)
PHONE..................................513 733-5500
Fax: 513 733-5604
William J Kramer Jr, *CEO*
John Cozad, *COO*
Elliot Adams, *Exec VP*
Bruce Horton, *Project Mgr*
William Watkins, *Engineer*
▲ **EMP:** 235 **EST:** 1947
SQ FT: 150,000
SALES: 45.5MM **Privately Held**
WEB: www.gentool.com
SIC: 3599 3443 3444 3544 Machine shop, jobbing & repair; fabricated plate work (boiler shop); sheet metalwork; special dies & tools; welding repair

(G-3821)
GENESIS DISPLAY SYSTEMS INC
4004 Erie Ct (45227-2110)
PHONE..................................513 561-1440
Fax: 513 561-8329
Thomas A Bove, *President*
EMP: 4
SQ FT: 13,000
SALES (est): 389K **Privately Held**
WEB: www.genesisdisplay.com
SIC: 3993 Displays & cutouts, window & lobby

(G-3822)
GERALD L HERMANN CO INC
Also Called: Master Print Center
3325 Harrison Ave (45211-5618)
PHONE..................................513 661-1818
Fax: 513 699-0378
Gerald Herrmann, *President*
Suzanne Herrmann, *Corp Secy*
Fred Krieger, *Financial Exec*
Dan Krieger, *Sales Executive*
EMP: 11
SQ FT: 7,500
SALES (est): 1MM **Privately Held**
WEB: www.addresserbasedsystems.com
SIC: 7331 2752 Addressing service; photo-offset printing

(G-3823)
GIGIS CUPCAKES OF KENWOOD
7940 Hosbrook Rd (45243)
PHONE..................................513 985-4440
Amy Jones, *Principal*
EMP: 4
SALES (est): 205.4K **Privately Held**
SIC: 2051 Bread, cake & related products

(G-3824)
GILKEY WINDOW COMPANY INC
3528 Hauck Rd (45241-1604)
PHONE..................................513 769-9663
John Gilkey, *Manager*
Rick Young, *Director*
EMP: 5
SALES (corp-wide): 18.5MM **Privately Held**
SIC: 3089 Plastic hardware & building products; windows, plastic
PA: Gilkey Window Company, Inc.
3625 Hauck Rd
Cincinnati OH 45241
513 769-4527

(G-3825)
GILKEY WINDOW COMPANY INC (PA)
3625 Hauck Rd (45241-1605)
PHONE..................................513 769-4527
Fax: 513 769-2567
John M Gilkey, *President*
Michael Vincent Gilkey, *General Mgr*
Robert Pembaur, *General Mgr*
Agustin Quirch, *Senior VP*
Sue Gilkey, *Vice Pres*
▲ **EMP:** 98
SQ FT: 56,000
SALES (est): 16.7MM **Privately Held**
SIC: 3089 Plastic hardware & building products; windows, plastic

(G-3826)
GIMINETTI BAKING COMPANY
2900 Gilbert Ave (45206-1207)
PHONE..................................513 751-7655
Fax: 513 751-7634
James Ciuccio, *President*
Constance Rice, *Sales Staff*
EMP: 20
SALES (est): 3.2MM **Privately Held**
SIC: 2051 5461 Bakery: wholesale or wholesale/retail combined; bakeries

(G-3827)
GIVAUDAN
110 E 69th St (45216-2008)
PHONE..................................513 482-2536
Mitch Lord, *Principal*
Regina Godvin, *Vice Pres*
Markus Brunnschweiler, *Plant Mgr*
Fred Wilson, *Site Mgr*
Mariann De Iturrondo, *Accountant*
EMP: 14 **EST:** 2014
SALES (est): 2.1MM **Privately Held**
SIC: 2869 Flavors or flavoring materials, synthetic; butadiene (industrial organic chemical)

(G-3828)
GIVAUDAN FLAVORS CORPORATION
100 E 69th St (45216-2008)
P.O. Box 17086 (45217-0086)
PHONE..................................513 948-8000
Andrew Herskee, *Senior VP*
Lisa Lewis, *Senior VP*
Mark Jones, *Vice Pres*
Geraldine Nicolai, *Vice Pres*
Charles Faraci, *Purch Mgr*
EMP: 300
SALES (corp-wide): 1.1B **Privately Held**
SIC: 2869 2087 Flavors or flavoring materials, synthetic; butadiene (industrial organic chemical); concentrates, flavoring (except drink)
HQ: Givaudan Flavors Corporation
1199 Edison Dr
Cincinnati OH 45216
513 948-8000

(G-3829)
GIVAUDAN FLAVORS CORPORATION
110 E 70th St (45216-2011)
PHONE..................................513 948-8000
Fax: 513 948-5439
Eric Mann, *Vice Pres*
Alain Gay, *Project Mgr*
Barri Donaghy, *Human Resources*
Ayako Hayashi, *Mktg Dir*
Jeffrey Peppet, *Marketing Staff*
EMP: 14
SALES (corp-wide): 1.1B **Privately Held**
SIC: 2087 Flavoring extracts & syrups
HQ: Givaudan Flavors Corporation
1199 Edison Dr
Cincinnati OH 45216
513 948-8000

(G-3830)
GIVAUDAN FLVORS FRAGRANCES INC (DH)
1199 Edison Dr (45216-2265)
P.O. Box 17038 (45217-0038)
PHONE..................................513 948-8000
Fax: 513 948-3214
Stefan Giezendanner, *CFO*
Tom Fong, *Finance Mgr*
EMP: 1
SALES (est): 554.4MM
SALES (corp-wide): 1.1B **Privately Held**
SIC: 2869 2087 Flavors or flavoring materials, synthetic; perfume materials, synthetic; flavoring extracts & syrups
HQ: Givaudan Roure (United States) Inc.
1199 Edison Dr
Cincinnati OH 45216
513 948-8000

(G-3831)
GIVAUDAN FRAGRANCES CORP (DH)
1199 Edison Dr Ste 1-2 (45216-2265)
PHONE..................................513 948-3428
Gilles Andrier, *CEO*
Cathy Torelli, *Senior VP*
Kathleen Slagle, *Transptn Dir*
Ashley Wesley, *Project Mgr*
Panchali Chakraborty, *Research*
◆ **EMP:** 386 **EST:** 2000
SQ FT: 78,000
SALES (est): 390.4MM
SALES (corp-wide): 1.1B **Privately Held**
SIC: 2869 Perfume materials, synthetic; flavors or flavoring materials, synthetic

(G-3832)
GIVAUDAN FRAGRANCES CORP
100 E 69th St (45216-2008)
PHONE..................................513 948-3428
Pat Otoole, *Planning Mgr*
Gary Schmidt, *Manager*
George Leskovac, *Info Tech Mgr*
Pat O'Toole, *Planning*
EMP: 260
SALES (corp-wide): 1.1B **Privately Held**
SIC: 2869 2087 Flavors or flavoring materials, synthetic; flavoring extracts & syrups
HQ: Givaudan Fragrances Corporation
1199 Edison Dr Ste 1-2
Cincinnati OH 45216
513 948-3428

(G-3833)
GIVAUDAN ROURE US INC (HQ)
Also Called: Givaudan US
1199 Edison Dr (45216-2265)
PHONE..................................513 948-8000
Michael Davis, *President*
Koichiro Maekawa, *Plant Mgr*
Michiel Paling, *Manager*
◆ **EMP:** 1
SALES (est): 554.4MM
SALES (corp-wide): 1.1B **Privately Held**
SIC: 2869 2087 Perfume materials, synthetic; flavors or flavoring materials, synthetic; flavoring extracts & syrups
PA: Givaudan Sa
Chemin De La Parfumerie 5
Vernier GE 1214
227 809-111

(G-3834)
GLASS SEALE LTD
1700 Hunt Rd (45215-3916)
PHONE.................................513 733-1464
Deborah Seale, *Principal*
EMP: 4
SALES (est): 221.4K **Privately Held**
SIC: 3231 Stained glass: made from purchased glass

(G-3835)
GLOBAL BIOCHEM
8044 Montgomery Rd (45236-2919)
PHONE.................................513 792-2218
Jeffrey Mahaffey, *COO*
▲ EMP: 5 EST: 2010
SALES (est): 491.5K **Privately Held**
SIC: 2869 2821 Ethylene glycols; ethylene glycol terephthalic acid (mylar)

(G-3836)
GLOBAL E-LUMENATION TECH
3289 Spring Grove Ave (45225-1329)
PHONE.................................513 821-8687
EMP: 3
SALES: 500K **Privately Held**
SIC: 3648 Mfg Lighting Equipment

(G-3837)
GLOBAL MANUFACTURING INDS (PA)
7710 Shawnee Run Rd (45243-3176)
PHONE.................................513 271-2180
Teodor Georgiev, *Sales Staff*
EMP: 5
SALES (est): 6.3MM **Privately Held**
SIC: 3999 Chairs, hydraulic, barber & beauty shop

(G-3838)
GLOBAL SOURCING & SUPPORT SVCS
260 E University Ave (45219-2356)
PHONE.................................513 321-0957
David Schlegeo, *Principal*
▲ EMP: 6
SALES (est): 627.2K **Privately Held**
SIC: 3599 Custom machinery

(G-3839)
GOLD STAR CHILI INC
5420 Ridge Ave (45213-2514)
PHONE.................................513 631-1990
Rusa Abusway, *Owner*
EMP: 20
SALES (corp-wide): 13.2MM **Privately Held**
SIC: 5812 2099 Chili stand; food preparations
PA: Gold Star Chili, Inc.
650 Lunken Park Dr
Cincinnati OH 45226
513 231-4541

(G-3840)
GOOD DAY TOOLS LLC
4603 Carter Ave (45212-2539)
PHONE.................................513 578-2050
Matt McFarland, *Partner*
Mark Donohoe, *Partner*
Rich McFarland, *Partner*
William Potts, *Partner*
Gene Warren, *Partner*
EMP: 5
SQ FT: 800
SALES (est): 627K **Privately Held**
SIC: 3743 Industrial locomotives & parts

(G-3841)
GOSUN INC ✪
1217 Ellis St (45223-1842)
PHONE.................................513 709-2519
Patrick Sherwin, *CEO*
Gary Star, *Treasurer*
Matt Gillespie, *Admin Sec*
EMP: 10 EST: 2016
SQ FT: 50,000
SALES: 1.1MM **Privately Held**
SIC: 3269 Cookware: stoneware, coarse earthenware & pottery

(G-3842)
GOVERNMENT ACQUISITIONS INC
720 E Pete Rose Way # 360 (45202-3576)
PHONE.................................513 721-8700
Fax: 513 721-3999
Roger Brown, *Owner*
Kathy Meece, *Project Mgr*
Javier Pardo, *Engineer*
Bobby Brown, *CFO*
Stan Jones, *CFO*
EMP: 35
SQ FT: 20,000
SALES (est): 68.6MM **Privately Held**
WEB: www.gov-acq.com
SIC: 5045 7378 3577 Computers, peripherals & software; computer software; computer maintenance & repair; computer peripheral equipment

(G-3843)
GRAETERS MANUFACTURING CO (PA)
1175 Regina Graeter Way (45216-1998)
PHONE.................................513 721-3323
Richard Graeter II, *President*
Eric T Schulze, *Principal*
Chip Graeter, *Vice Pres*
Tom Kunzelman, *Vice Pres*
James Cahill, *Treasurer*
EMP: 60 EST: 1870
SQ FT: 25,000
SALES (est): 110.8MM **Privately Held**
SIC: 2024 2051 2064 2066 Ice cream, packaged: molded, on sticks, etc.; bread, cake & related products; candy & other confectionery products; chocolate & cocoa products

(G-3844)
GRAND RAPIDS PRINTING INK CO
Also Called: Ohio Valley Ink
95 Glendale Milford Rd (45215-1142)
PHONE.................................859 261-4530
Joe Poigo, *Owner*
Steve Mangus, *Manager*
EMP: 4
SALES (corp-wide): 2.4MM **Privately Held**
WEB: www.graphicarts.org
SIC: 2893 Printing ink
PA: Grand Rapids Printing Ink Company
4920 Starr St Se
Grand Rapids MI 49546
616 241-5681

(G-3845)
GRAPHIC SOLUTIONS COMPANY
3438 Middleton Ave (45220-1627)
PHONE.................................513 484-3067
Ryan Gentry, *Principal*
EMP: 10
SQ FT: 40,000
SALES (est): 470K **Privately Held**
SIC: 2752 Commercial printing, lithographic; offset & photolithographic printing; commercial printing, offset; promotional printing, lithographic

(G-3846)
GREAT MIDWEST TOBACCO INC
Also Called: Jnj Distributors
10825 Medallion Dr (45241-4829)
PHONE.................................513 745-0450
Dennis E Harper, *President*
EMP: 3
SALES: 950K **Privately Held**
SIC: 2131 Chewing & smoking tobacco

(G-3847)
GREATER CINCINNATI BOWL ASSN
611 Mercury Dr (45244-1412)
PHONE.................................513 761-7387
Fax: 513 761-4511
Willie Dean, *President*
Joe McFarland, *Vice Pres*
Tom Taylor, *Vice Pres*
Ann Hill, *Exec Dir*
EMP: 22
SQ FT: 1,700
SALES (est): 980K **Privately Held**
SIC: 8699 2721 7933 Bowling club; periodicals; bowling centers

(G-3848)
GREEN FORWARD TECHNOLOGIES LLC
180 Linden Dr (45215-4205)
PHONE.................................513 607-9639
John Young,
Rakesh Gobing,
EMP: 5
SALES (est): 510.6K **Privately Held**
SIC: 3272 5039 Septic tanks, concrete; septic tanks

(G-3849)
GREEN RECYCLING WORKS LLC
1530 Tremont St (45214-1432)
PHONE.................................513 278-7111
Bradley Sherman, *Principal*
EMP: 5
SALES (est): 423.4K **Privately Held**
SIC: 2611 Pulp mills, mechanical & recycling processing

(G-3850)
GREENCORE USA INC
3465 Hauck Rd (45241-1601)
PHONE.................................513 645-1985
Steve Barone, *President*
Kristen Larkins, *Accountant*
▲ EMP: 75 EST: 2009
SALES (est): 4.7MM **Privately Held**
SIC: 2099 Ready-to-eat meals, salads & sandwiches

(G-3851)
GREENHILLS JOURNAL
22 Endicott St (45218-1429)
PHONE.................................513 825-2525
Ronald Otting, *Owner*
EMP: 10
SALES: 15K **Privately Held**
SIC: 2711 Newspapers, publishing & printing

(G-3852)
GREG G WRIGHT & SONS LLC
10200 Springfield Pike (45215-1116)
PHONE.................................513 721-3310
Fax: 513 721-1282
Tracey A Chriske, *Principal*
Carl A Fries,
EMP: 30
SQ FT: 34,000
SALES: 6MM **Privately Held**
WEB: www.gregwrightandsons.com
SIC: 3953 3993 Textile marking stamps, hand: rubber or metal; stencils, painting & marking; name plates: except engraved, etched, etc.: metal

(G-3853)
GRIFFIN FISHER CO INC
1126 Wliam Hward Taft Rd (45206-2031)
PHONE.................................513 961-2110
Fax: 513 961-2113
Whitney Fisher, *CEO*
Branden Fisher, *President*
EMP: 9
SQ FT: 3,800
SALES (est): 891.2K **Privately Held**
SIC: 2394 2396 2399 Convertible tops, canvas or boat: from purchased materials; automotive trimmings, fabric; seat covers, automobile

(G-3854)
GRIPPO POTATO CHIP CO INC
6750 Colerain Ave (45239-5542)
PHONE.................................513 923-1900
Fax: 513 923-3645
Ralph W Pagel II, *President*
Linda Foster, *Vice Pres*
James Pagel, *Vice Pres*
Dottie Sayler, *Treasurer*
Dorothy Saylor, *Treasurer*
EMP: 65
SQ FT: 27,000
SALES (est): 9.7MM **Privately Held**
SIC: 2096 2099 Potato chips & other potato-based snacks; food preparations

(G-3855)
GSF ENERGY LLC
10795 Hughes Rd (45251-4523)
PHONE.................................513 825-0504
Fax: 513 595-8224
John Schmitt, *President*
Daniel Bonk, *Vice Pres*
Richard Wilcox, *Facilities Mgr*
Martin Ryan, *Admin Sec*
EMP: 5
SALES (est): 1MM **Privately Held**
SIC: 2813 Industrial gases

(G-3856)
GT INDUSTRIAL SUPPLY INC
2315 Crowne Point Dr (45241-5405)
PHONE.................................513 771-7000
Michael Griffie, *President*
Stephen Tino, *Vice Pres*
EMP: 5
SALES (est): 1.1MM **Privately Held**
SIC: 2671 5063 Packaging paper & plastics film, coated & laminated; lighting fixtures

(G-3857)
GTLP HOLDINGS LLC (PA)
Also Called: Premier Southern Ticket
7911 School Rd (45249-1533)
PHONE.................................513 489-6700
Fax: 513 489-6867
Phillip R Sorensen, *President*
Kirk Schulz, *Vice Pres*
Bob Fancher, *Plant Mgr*
James Raike, *Human Res Dir*
EMP: 28
SQ FT: 35,000
SALES: 7.9MM **Privately Held**
SIC: 2752 Tag, ticket & schedule printing: lithographic

(G-3858)
GUS HOLTHAUS SIGNS INC
Also Called: Holthaus Lackner Signs
817 Ridgeway Ave (45229-3222)
P.O. Box 29373 (45229-0373)
PHONE.................................513 861-0060
Fax: 513 559-0975
Kevin Holthaus, *President*
Scott Holthaus, *Vice Pres*
Rick Souder, *Prdtn Mgr*
Charlie Holthaus, *Purch Mgr*
Jon Holthaus, *Sales Staff*
EMP: 40
SQ FT: 38,600
SALES (est): 6.9MM **Privately Held**
WEB: www.holthaussigns.com
SIC: 3993 1799 Electric signs; sign installation & maintenance

(G-3859)
H NAGEL & SON CO
Also Called: Brighton Mills
2641 Spring Grove Ave (45214-1731)
PHONE.................................513 665-4550
Brian Mitchell, *General Mgr*
Jack Diamond, *Manager*
Jessie Hensley, *Manager*
EMP: 10
SALES (corp-wide): 30MM **Privately Held**
SIC: 2041 Flour: blended, prepared or self-rising
PA: H. Nagel & Son Co.
2428 Central Pkwy
Cincinnati OH 45214
513 665-4550

(G-3860)
H NAGEL & SON CO (PA)
Also Called: Brighton Mills
2428 Central Pkwy (45214-1804)
PHONE.................................513 665-4550
Fax: 513 665-4570
William Nagel, *President*
Edward Nagel, *President*
Michael Norris, *Vice Pres*
EMP: 6
SQ FT: 2,400
SALES: 30MM **Privately Held**
SIC: 2041 Flour: blended, prepared or self-rising

(G-3861)
HADRONICS INC
4570 Steel Pl (45209-1189)
PHONE...513 321-9350
Fax: 513 321-9377
Kenneth J Green, *Ch of Bd*
Michael G Green, *President*
Pat McDonough, *President*
Jeffrey McCarty, *Vice Pres*
EMP: 56
SQ FT: 38,850
SALES (est): 9.6MM **Privately Held**
WEB: www.hadronics.com
SIC: 3471 3479 3555 3366 Plating & polishing; etching & engraving; printing trades machinery; copper foundries; blast furnaces & steel mills; platemaking services

(G-3862)
HAIR SCIENCE SYSTEMS LLC
445 Bishopsbridge Dr (45255-3951)
P.O. Box 54506 (45254-0506)
PHONE...513 231-8284
Wm Banker, *Mng Member*
Raymond Bitzer,
EMP: 5
SALES (est): 275.7K **Privately Held**
SIC: 3845 Laser systems & equipment, medical

(G-3863)
HAMILTON SAFE CO (PA)
7775 Cooper Rd (45242-7703)
PHONE...513 874-3733
Fax: 513 874-3733
Robert C Deluse, *President*
John Stroia, *President*
Greg Holbrock, *Principal*
Todd Lefevers, *Vice Pres*
David Vanschoik, *CFO*
▲ **EMP:** 19
SQ FT: 20,000
SALES (est): 5.3MM **Privately Held**
WEB: www.hamiltonproductsgroup.com
SIC: 3499 Safe deposit boxes or chests, metal; safes & vaults, metal

(G-3864)
HAMILTON SECURITY PRODUCTS CO (PA)
Also Called: Hamilton Safe
7775 Cooper Rd (45242-7703)
PHONE...513 874-3733
Robert Leslie, *CEO*
John Haining, *President*
Robert C Deluse, *Principal*
Lowell E Francois, *Principal*
H L Henkel, *Principal*
▲ **EMP:** 2
SQ FT: 20,000
SALES (est): 7.4MM **Privately Held**
SIC: 3499 Safe deposit boxes or chests, metal

(G-3865)
HANCHETT PAPER COMPANY
Also Called: Shorr Packaging
12121 Best Pl (45241-6402)
PHONE...513 782-4440
Fax: 513 936-8065
Mark Trainer, *Principal*
Greg Woolum, *Sales Mgr*
EMP: 50
SALES (corp-wide): 254.4MM **Privately Held**
SIC: 2621 Wrapping & packaging papers
PA: Hanchett Paper Company
4000 Ferry Rd
Aurora IL 60502
630 978-1000

(G-3866)
HARLAN GRAPHIC ARTS SVCS INC
4752 River Rd (45233-1633)
P.O. Box 643806 (45264-3806)
PHONE...513 251-5700
Fax: 513 251-5703
Larry Ehrman, *President*
Jeff Ehrman, *Vice Pres*
Steve Dragan, *Project Mgr*
Dan Hoffman, *Project Mgr*
Jenny Marsh, *Project Mgr*
EMP: 22 **EST:** 1980
SQ FT: 40,000

SALES (est): 3.7MM **Privately Held**
WEB: www.harlangraphics.com
SIC: 2791 Typesetting

(G-3867)
HARRAY LLC
266 W Mitchell Ave (45232-1908)
PHONE...888 568-8371
Joseph Ray, *President*
Kurt Harrington, *Vice Pres*
EMP: 6
SALES (est): 650K **Privately Held**
WEB: www.archlouvers.com
SIC: 3444 Sheet metalwork

(G-3868)
HARVEY BROTHERS INC (PA)
3492 Spring Grove Ave (45223-2417)
PHONE...513 541-2622
Fax: 513 541-2845
Stephen Kyle, *President*
Rich Hamilton, *General Mgr*
Amy Kyle, *CFO*
EMP: 12
SQ FT: 5,600
SALES (est): 2MM **Privately Held**
SIC: 3449 Miscellaneous metalwork

(G-3869)
HARVEY WHITNEY BOOKS COMPANY
Also Called: Annals of Pharmaco Therapy
8044 Montgomery Rd # 415 (45236-7925)
PHONE...513 793-3555
Fax: 513 793-3600
Harvey Whitney, *President*
Tina Whitney, *Vice Pres*
Greg Johnson, *Manager*
Donna Thordsen, *Manager*
Brenda Bailey, *Systems Mgr*
EMP: 17
SQ FT: 5,000
SALES (est): 2MM **Privately Held**
WEB: www.hwbooks.com
SIC: 2721 2731 Magazines: publishing only, not printed on site; books: publishing only

(G-3870)
HATHAWAY STAMP & IDENT CO OF C
Also Called: Hathaway Stamp Identification
635 Main St (45202-2524)
PHONE...513 621-1052
Ken Secor, *Adv Dir*
Larry Schultz, *Branch Mgr*
Lisa Ruttenberg,
EMP: 12
SALES (est): 1.4MM
SALES (corp-wide): 30.9MM **Privately Held**
SIC: 3953 3479 Marking devices; name plates: engraved, etched, etc.
PA: Volk Corporation
23936 Indl Pk Dr
Farmington Hills MI 48335
248 477-6700

(G-3871)
HATHAWAY STAMP CO
635 Main St Ste 1 (45202-2524)
PHONE...513 621-1052
Fax: 513 621-7339
Peter Ruttenberg, *President*
Robert C Ruwe, *Vice Pres*
Diane Mock, *Treasurer*
EMP: 15
SQ FT: 4,000
SALES (est): 2.2MM
SALES (corp-wide): 30.9MM **Privately Held**
WEB: www.hathawaystamps.com
SIC: 3953 3089 5999 5943 Embossing seals & hand stamps; engraving of plastic; rubber stamps; office forms & supplies; notary & corporate seals
PA: Volk Corporation
23936 Indl Pk Dr
Farmington Hills MI 48335
248 477-6700

(G-3872)
HCC INDUSTRIES
9705 Reading Rd (45215-3515)
PHONE...513 334-5585
EMP: 6

SALES (est): 704.9K **Privately Held**
SIC: 3999 Manufacturing industries

(G-3873)
HCC/SEALTRON (DH)
9705 Reading Rd (45215-3515)
PHONE...513 733-8400
Wes Hausman, *Principal*
Norman Allard, *Vice Pres*
Chris Schuh, *Engineer*
Chris Bateman, *CFO*
Mark Russell, *Finance*
EMP: 33
SQ FT: 38,000
SALES (est): 18.1MM
SALES (corp-wide): 3.8B **Publicly Held**
SIC: 3678 Electronic connectors
HQ: Hcc Industries Inc.
4232 Temple City Blvd
Rosemead CA 91770
626 443-8933

(G-3874)
HEALTHWARES MANUFACTURING
8649 E Miami River Rd (45247-2238)
PHONE...513 353-3691
Fax: 513 353-4022
Greg Overman, *President*
Dan Putz, *Manager*
Katie Wood, *Info Tech Mgr*
EMP: 10
SALES (est): 1.3MM **Privately Held**
WEB: www.healthwares.com
SIC: 3842 Wheelchairs

(G-3875)
HEARTH & HOME TECHNOLOGIES LLC
Also Called: Fireside Hearth & Homes
10025 Prncton Glendale Rd (45246-1223)
PHONE...513 874-4770
John Balanda, *Branch Mgr*
EMP: 4
SALES (corp-wide): 2.2B **Publicly Held**
SIC: 3429 Fireplace equipment; hardware: andirons, grates, screens
HQ: Hearth & Home Technologies, Llc
7571 215th St W
Lakeville MN 55044

(G-3876)
HELMART COMPANY INC
Also Called: Countertops Helmart
4960 Hillside Ave (45233-1621)
PHONE...513 941-3095
Fax: 513 941-9135
Jeff Wittwer, *President*
Mark Wittwer, *Principal*
Marlene Wittwer, *Treasurer*
EMP: 7 **EST:** 1979
SQ FT: 6,000
SALES (est): 1.6MM **Privately Held**
WEB: www.helmart.net
SIC: 5032 1411 2541 Marble building stone; granite dimension stone; table or counter tops, plastic laminated

(G-3877)
HEN OF WOODS LLC
1432 Main St (45202-7642)
PHONE...513 833-7357
Nick Marckwald,
EMP: 7
SQ FT: 9,000
SALES (est): 254.7K **Privately Held**
SIC: 2052 Cookies & crackers

(G-3878)
HENKEL CORPORATION
9435 Waterstone Blvd (45249-8226)
PHONE...513 830-0260
Debbie Singler, *Vice Pres*
Laura Soltis, *Sales Mgr*
Ann Sipe, *Sales Staff*
Daniel Henkel, *Branch Mgr*
Paige Scheidler, *Manager*
EMP: 65
SALES (corp-wide): 19.7B **Privately Held**
SIC: 2891 Adhesives & sealants
HQ: Henkel Corporation
1 Henkel Way
Rocky Hill CT 06067
860 571-5100

(G-3879)
HENTY USA
7260 Edington Dr (45249-1063)
PHONE...513 984-5590
Tylor Scott, *CEO*
Tyler Scott, *Principal*
EMP: 10
SALES (est): 100K **Privately Held**
SIC: 2392 Bags, garment storage: except paper or plastic film

(G-3880)
HERMETIC SEAL TECHNOLOGY INC
Also Called: Hst
2150 Schappelle Ln (45240-4602)
PHONE...513 851-4899
John Wendeln, *President*
EMP: 10
SALES (est): 1.7MM **Privately Held**
SIC: 3643 Connectors & terminals for electrical devices

(G-3881)
HESKAMP PRINTING CO INC
5514 Fair Ln (45227-3402)
PHONE...513 871-6770
J David Heskamp, *President*
Jane Heskamp, *Corp Secy*
EMP: 6 **EST:** 1922
SQ FT: 7,500
SALES (est): 600K **Privately Held**
SIC: 2752 2759 Commercial printing, offset; letterpress printing

(G-3882)
HILL & GRIFFITH COMPANY (PA)
1085 Summer St (45204-2037)
PHONE...513 921-1075
David Greek Jr, *President*
Dale Welsh, *Vice Pres*
Donna I Nijak, *Plant Mgr*
Sarah Dixon, *Human Res Mgr*
Mike Lawry, *Sales Mgr*
EMP: 8 **EST:** 1896
SQ FT: 15,000
SALES (est): 12.1MM **Privately Held**
SIC: 2899 2869 3565 3542 Chemical preparations; industrial organic chemicals; packaging machinery; machine tools, metal forming type

(G-3883)
HILLMAN FASTENER
10590 Hamilton Ave (45231-1457)
PHONE...513 851-6200
Fax: 513 851-4997
Rick Buller, *Principal*
Marshall Gary, *VP Sales*
John Marshall, *Mktg Dir*
▼ **EMP:** 12 **EST:** 2010
SALES (est): 5MM **Privately Held**
SIC: 3965 Fasteners

(G-3884)
HILLTOP BASIC RESOURCES INC (PA)
Also Called: Hilltop Concrete
1 W 4th St Ste 1100 (45202-3610)
PHONE...513 651-5000
Fax: 513 684-8222
John F Steele Jr, *CEO*
Kevin M Sheehan, *President*
Mike Marchioni, *General Mgr*
Brad Slabaugh, *Vice Pres*
Roger Thayer, *Opers Mgr*
EMP: 15 **EST:** 1930
SQ FT: 10,000
SALES (est): 135MM **Privately Held**
WEB: www.hilltopbasicresources.com
SIC: 1442 3273 Construction sand mining; gravel mining; ready-mixed concrete

(G-3885)
HILLTOP BASIC RESOURCES INC
Also Called: Hilltop Concrete
511 W Water St (45202-3400)
PHONE...513 621-1500
Fax: 513 684-8290
Mike Marchioni, *Manager*
EMP: 45
SQ FT: 1,758

SALES (corp-wide): 135MM **Privately Held**
WEB: www.hilltopbasicresources.com
SIC: **3273** 3272 1442 Ready-mixed concrete; concrete products; construction sand & gravel
PA: Hilltop Basic Resources, Inc.
1 W 4th St Ste 1100
Cincinnati OH 45202
513 651-5000

(G-3886)
HILLTOP STONE LLC
1 W 4th St Ste 1100 (45202-3610)
PHONE..................................513 651-5000
John Steele, *Principal*
EMP: 3
SALES (est): 390K **Privately Held**
SIC: **3272** Concrete products

(G-3887)
HOLLAENDER MANUFACTURING CO
10285 Wayne Ave (45215-1199)
P.O. Box 156399 (45215-6399)
PHONE..................................513 772-8800
Fax: 800 772-8806
Robert P Hollaender II, *CEO*
Marc E Cetrulo, *President*
Ron Crebo, *Vice Pres*
Brent Wittmeyer, *Project Mgr*
Terry Smith, *Purch Agent*
▼ EMP: 51 EST: 1946
SQ FT: 33,000
SALES (est): 13.8MM **Privately Held**
SIC: **3498** Fabricated pipe & fittings

(G-3888)
HOLLAND ASSOCTS LLC DBA ARCHOU
316 W 4th St Ste 201 (45202-2675)
PHONE..................................513 891-0006
Fax: 513 381-4954
Murray Holland,
EMP: 10
SALES (est): 3.1MM **Privately Held**
SIC: **5065** 3699 1742 Sound equipment, electronic; electric sound equipment; acoustical & insulation work; acoustical & ceiling work

(G-3889)
HOLLMANN INC
1617 W Belmar Pl (45224-1017)
PHONE..................................513 522-1800
Joseph L Hollmann, *President*
EMP: 5
SALES (est): 623.3K **Privately Held**
WEB: www.hollmanninc.com
SIC: **3523** Dairy equipment (farm)

(G-3890)
HOLTE EYEWARE
2651 Observatory Ave # 1 (45208-2040)
PHONE..................................513 321-4000
Ryan Holte, *Branch Mgr*
EMP: 5
SALES (corp-wide): 1.3MM **Privately Held**
SIC: **8042** 5999 3827 Offices & clinics of optometrists; sunglasses; optical instruments & lenses
PA: Holte Eyeware
8211 Cornell Rd Ste 510
Cincinnati OH 45249
513 489-4000

(G-3891)
HOMAN METALS LLC
1253 Knowlton St (45223-1844)
PHONE..................................513 721-5010
Doug Beckmeyer, *Sales Staff*
Marcia P Beckmeyer,
Jerome W Beckmeyer,
EMP: 8
SQ FT: 60,000
SALES (est): 2.6MM **Privately Held**
SIC: **5093** 3334 4953 3355 Scrap & waste materials; aluminum ingots & slabs; ingots (primary), aluminum; recycling, waste materials; aluminum ingot

(G-3892)
HOME CITY ICE COMPANY (PA)
6045 Bridgetown Rd Ste 1 (45248-3047)
P.O. Box 111116 (45211-1116)
PHONE..................................513 574-1800
Thomas E Sedler, *President*
Joseph H Head, *Principal*
Michael Reasbeck, *Business Mgr*
Edward T Sedler, *COO*
Kathy Winters, *Safety Dir*
EMP: 130
SQ FT: 10,000
SALES (est): 305.4MM **Privately Held**
WEB: www.homecityice.com
SIC: **2097** Ice cubes

(G-3893)
HOME CITY ICE COMPANY
11920 Kemper Springs Dr (45240-1642)
PHONE..................................513 851-4040
Fax: 513 742-7154
Jason Dugas, *Branch Mgr*
EMP: 35
SQ FT: 14,040
SALES (corp-wide): 305.4MM **Privately Held**
WEB: www.homecityice.com
SIC: **2097** Ice cubes
PA: The Home City Ice Company
6045 Bridgetown Rd Ste 1
Cincinnati OH 45248
513 574-1800

(G-3894)
HONEY BAKED HAM COMPANY LLC
Also Called: Honey Baked Ham 8401
8315 Beechmont Ave Ste 41 (45255-3193)
PHONE..................................513 474-0022
Fax: 513 474-9736
Larry Bossert, *Branch Mgr*
EMP: 6
SALES (corp-wide): 300MM **Privately Held**
SIC: **2011** Hams & picnics from meat slaughtered on site
PA: The Honey Baked Ham Company Llc
3875 Mansell Rd Ste 100
Alpharetta GA 30022
678 966-3100

(G-3895)
HONEYBAKED HAM COMPANY (PA)
11935 Mason Montgomery Rd # 200 (45249-3702)
PHONE..................................513 583-9700
Fax: 513 583-4190
Craig Kurz, *CEO*
George S Kurz, *Ch of Bd*
George J Kurz, *President*
Keith Kurz, *COO*
Dan Stewart, *Purchasing*
EMP: 25
SQ FT: 12,000
SALES (est): 73MM **Privately Held**
SIC: **5421** 2099 2024 2013 Meat markets, including freezer provisioners; food preparations; ice cream & frozen desserts; sausages & other prepared meats

(G-3896)
HONEYWELL INC
3940 Virginia Ave (45227-3412)
PHONE..................................513 272-1111
EMP: 143
SALES (corp-wide): 38.5B **Publicly Held**
SIC: **3823** Mfg Process Control Instruments
HQ: Honeywell Inc.
115 Tabor Rd
Morris Plains NJ 07950
973 455-2000

(G-3897)
HONEYWELL INTERNATIONAL INC
1280 Kemper Meadow Dr (45240-1632)
PHONE..................................513 745-7200
Naresh Subramanian, *Business Mgr*
Carlos Nazario, *Senior Engr*
Thomas Tike, *Human Res Mgr*
Steve Sena, *Marketing Mgr*
Tracy Glendy, *Branch Mgr*
EMP: 100
SALES (corp-wide): 39.3B **Publicly Held**
SIC: **7373** 7372 Computer systems analysis & design; prepackaged software
PA: Honeywell International Inc.
115 Tabor Rd
Morris Plains NJ 07950
973 455-2000

(G-3898)
HORMEL FOODS CORP SVCS LLC
4055 Executive Park Dr # 300 (45241-4020)
PHONE..................................513 563-0211
Fax: 513 563-6043
Jim Tupy, *Manager*
Rick Barghini, *Manager*
EMP: 40
SALES (corp-wide): 9.5B **Publicly Held**
SIC: **2013** Sausages & other prepared meats
HQ: Hormel Foods Corporate Services, Llc
1 Hormel Pl
Austin MN 55912
507 437-5611

(G-3899)
HORNELL BREWING CO INC
Also Called: Arizona Beverages
644 Linn St Ste 318 (45203-1734)
PHONE..................................516 812-0384
Francie Patton, *Vice Pres*
Kay Garusso, *Project Mgr*
EMP: 6
SALES (corp-wide): 67.8MM **Privately Held**
WEB: www.arizonabev.com
SIC: **2086** Bottled & canned soft drinks
PA: Hornell Brewing Co., Inc.
60 Crossways Park Dr W # 400
Woodbury NY 11797
516 812-0300

(G-3900)
HRH DOOR CORP
2136 Stapleton Ct (45240-2780)
PHONE..................................513 674-9300
Wayne Dalton, *Principal*
EMP: 31
SALES (corp-wide): 665.2MM **Privately Held**
SIC: **3442** 2431 Garage doors, overhead: metal; garage doors, overhead: wood
PA: Hrh Door Corp.
1 Door Dr
Mount Hope OH 44660
850 208-3400

(G-3901)
HUKON MANUFACTURING COMPANY
2111 Freeman Ave (45214-1820)
PHONE..................................513 721-5562
Micheal Gruenschlaeger, *Owner*
Ralph Gruenschlaeger, *Owner*
EMP: 9 EST: 1907
SALES (est): 410K **Privately Held**
SIC: **3469** Spinning metal for the trade

(G-3902)
HUNKAR TECHNOLOGIES INC (PA)
2368 Victory Pkwy Ste 210 (45206-2810)
PHONE..................................513 272-1010
Eric R Thiemann, *President*
Eric J Rulli, *General Mgr*
Mike Barker, *Vice Pres*
Jeannine Martin, *Vice Pres*
Clayton Wynn, *CFO*
EMP: 140
SQ FT: 47,000
SALES (est): 31.8MM **Privately Held**
WEB: www.hunkar.com
SIC: **3565** 3823 3577 3441 Labeling machines, industrial; controllers for process variables, all types; bar code (magnetic ink) printers; fabricated structural metal

(G-3903)
HYDE PARK LUMBER COMPANY
Also Called: Do It Best
3360 Red Bank Rd (45227-4107)
PHONE..................................513 271-1500
Fax: 513 271-6145
Mills C Judy Jr, *President*
Jeff Wessel, *Design Engr*
Vicki Clephane, *CFO*
Tim Zeeter, *Sales Executive*
Jason Raines, *Marketing Staff*
EMP: 35
SQ FT: 80,000
SALES (est): 7.3MM **Privately Held**
WEB: www.hprp.com
SIC: **5211** 2431 Lumber & other building materials; millwork
PA: The Judy Mills Company Inc
3360 Red Bank Rd
Cincinnati OH 45227
513 271-4241

(G-3904)
HYDRATECH ENGINEERED PDTS LLC
10448 Chester Rd (45215-1202)
PHONE..................................513 827-9169
Mike Wagner, *General Mgr*
Patty Nash, *Business Mgr*
Tim Meyer, *Sales Mgr*
Jim Lawton, *Sales Engr*
Amy O'Connell, *Marketing Staff*
EMP: 10
SALES (est): 2.3MM **Privately Held**
SIC: **2891** Sealing compounds for pipe threads or joints

(G-3905)
HYDRO SYSTEMS COMPANY (DH)
3798 Round Bottom Rd (45244-2498)
PHONE..................................513 271-8800
Fax: 513 271-0160
Serge Joris, *CEO*
Lindsay Ship, *Opers Staff*
J Morin, *Senior Engr*
Doug Papp, *CFO*
Romi Burroughs, *Controller*
◆ EMP: 25
SALES (est): 44.9MM
SALES (corp-wide): 6.7B **Publicly Held**
WEB: www.hydrosystemsco.com
SIC: **3586** Measuring & dispensing pumps
HQ: Opw Fluid Transfer Group
4304 Nw Mattox Rd
Kansas City MO 64150
816 741-6600

(G-3906)
I T VERDIN CO (PA)
Also Called: Verdin Company
444 Reading Rd (45202-1432)
PHONE..................................513 241-4010
Fax: 513 241-1855
F B Wersel, *CEO*
Robert R Verdin Jr, *CEO*
James R Verdin, *President*
Tom Hovey, *General Mgr*
Steve Kemme, *General Mgr*
▲ EMP: 30
SQ FT: 13,000
SALES (est): 21.2MM **Privately Held**
SIC: **3931** 3699 3873 Carillon bells; bells, electric; clocks, except timeclocks

(G-3907)
I T VERDIN CO
3900 Kellogg Ave (45226-1518)
PHONE..................................513 241-4010
Stacey Dickerson, *Branch Mgr*
EMP: 30
SQ FT: 36,722
SALES (corp-wide): 21.2MM **Privately Held**
SIC: **3931** 3699 Carillon bells; electrical equipment & supplies
PA: The I T Verdin Co
444 Reading Rd
Cincinnati OH 45202
513 241-4010

(G-3908)
I T VERDIN CO
3900 Kellogg Ave (45226-1518)
PHONE..................................513 559-3947
David Verdin, *Branch Mgr*
Tom Price, *Consultant*
Shannon Parker, *Tech/Comp Coord*
EMP: 35
SQ FT: 24,175

SALES (corp-wide): 21.2MM **Privately Held**
SIC: **3931** 3699 3873 Carillon bells; bells, electric; clocks, except timeclocks
PA: The I T Verdin Co
444 Reading Rd
Cincinnati OH 45202
513 241-4010

(G-3909)
IDEAS & AD VENTURES INC
2614 Spring Grove Ave (45214-1732)
PHONE..............................513 542-7154
Fax: 513 542-7160
Dennis P Haskamp, *President*
Patricia J Haskamp, *Corp Secy*
John H Haskamp, *Shareholder*
EMP: 6
SQ FT: 4,500
SALES (est): 530K **Privately Held**
SIC: **2752** Commercial printing, offset

(G-3910)
IFCO SYSTEMS US LLC
Also Called: I F C O Systems
10725 Evendale Dr (45241-2535)
PHONE..............................513 769-0377
Matt Mallory, *General Mgr*
Kimberly Lindsay, *Office Mgr*
Hope Singleton, *Branch Mgr*
EMP: 40
SALES (corp-wide): 5.5B **Privately Held**
SIC: **2448** Pallets, wood; skids, wood
HQ: Ifco Systems Us, Llc
3030 N Rocky Point Dr W # 300
Rocky Point FL 33607

(G-3911)
IHEARTCOMMUNICATIONS INC
8044 Montgomery Rd # 650 (45236-2919)
PHONE..............................513 241-1550
Toni Smith, *Manager*
EMP: 250
SALES (corp-wide): 6.2B **Publicly Held**
SIC: **3663** Radio receiver networks
HQ: Iheartcommunications, Inc.
200 E Basse Rd
San Antonio TX 78209
210 822-2828

(G-3912)
IMMERSUS HEALTH COMPANY LLC (PA)
2 Hill And Hollow Ln (45208-3317)
P.O. Box 8323 (45208-0323)
PHONE..............................855 994-4325
James Hadland, *Vice Pres*
Brian Pavlin,
EMP: 1
SALES: 10MM **Privately Held**
SIC: **3841** 7389 Surgical & medical instruments;

(G-3913)
IMPACKT
3700 Pocahontas Ave (45227-3821)
PHONE..............................513 559-1488
David Haynes, *Principal*
EMP: 5 EST: 2007
SALES (est): 414.9K **Privately Held**
SIC: **3565** Packaging machinery

(G-3914)
IMPERIAL ADHESIVES
6315 Wiehe Rd (45237-4213)
PHONE..............................513 351-1300
Fax: 513 351-1994
Pete Smith, *Vice Pres*
Michael Maun, *Purchasing*
David Zhang, *Technical Mgr*
John R Parker, *Treasurer*
David Tonne, *Controller*
EMP: 4
SALES (est): 400.6K **Privately Held**
SIC: **2891** Adhesives

(G-3915)
IMPERIAL POOLS INC
12090 Best Pl (45241-1569)
PHONE..............................513 771-1506
Fax: 513 771-1506
Mike Grant, *Branch Mgr*
Michael Grant, *Manager*
EMP: 68

SALES (corp-wide): 70MM **Privately Held**
SIC: **3949** Swimming pools, except plastic
PA: Imperial Pools, Inc.
33 Wade Rd
Latham NY 12110
518 786-1200

(G-3916)
INDUSTRIAL CONTAINER SVCS LLC
Also Called: Ics-Cargo Clean
1258 Knowlton St (45223-1845)
PHONE..............................513 921-2056
Gary Craig, *Branch Mgr*
EMP: 20
SALES (corp-wide): 2.1B **Privately Held**
WEB: www.iconserv.com
SIC: **3443** 3089 Fabricated plate work (boiler shop); plastic & fiberglass tanks
HQ: Industrial Container Services Llc
2400 Maitland Center Pkwy
Maitland FL 32751
800 273-3786

(G-3917)
INDUSTRIAL CONTAINER SVCS LLC
Also Called: Ics-Cargo Clean
837 Depot St (45204-2005)
PHONE..............................513 921-8811
John Stephens, *Branch Mgr*
EMP: 20
SALES (corp-wide): 2.1B **Privately Held**
WEB: www.iconserv.com
SIC: **3443** 3412 3411 Fabricated plate work (boiler shop); metal barrels, drums & pails; metal cans
HQ: Industrial Container Services Llc
2400 Maitland Center Pkwy
Maitland FL 32751
800 273-3786

(G-3918)
INDUSTRIAL THERMAL SYSTEMS INC
3914 Virginia Ave (45227-3412)
PHONE..............................513 561-2100
Robert Jackson, *President*
Susan Jackson, *Treasurer*
◆ EMP: 15
SQ FT: 34,000
SALES (est): 3.3MM **Privately Held**
SIC: **3559** 3613 Kilns; control panels, electric

(G-3919)
INDUSTRIAL WIRE ROPE SUP INC (PA)
7390 Harrison Ave (45247-2400)
P.O. Box 58149 (45258-0149)
PHONE..............................513 941-2443
Fax: 513 941-2445
Barry Stroube, *President*
James Scott Lemen, *Opers Mgr*
Matthew Hall, *Office Mgr*
John Korn, *Admin Sec*
◆ EMP: 9 EST: 1978
SQ FT: 3,000
SALES (est): 4.7MM **Privately Held**
WEB: www.industrialrope.com
SIC: **5051** 3496 Metals service centers & offices; miscellaneous fabricated wire products

(G-3920)
INGREDIENT MASTERS INC
7529 State Rd Ste A (45255-6410)
PHONE..............................513 231-7432
Scott Culshaw, *President*
Cheryl Culshaw, *Corp Secy*
▼ EMP: 7 EST: 1980
SALES: 5MM **Privately Held**
SIC: **3559** Recycling machinery

(G-3921)
INK PRODUCTION SERVICES INC
9648 Wayne Ave (45215-2259)
P.O. Box 12288 (45212-0288)
PHONE..............................513 733-9338
Fax: 513 733-9428
Jeff Wilson, *President*
Betty Wilson, *Vice Pres*
EMP: 12

SQ FT: 20,000
SALES (est): 1.2MM **Privately Held**
SIC: **2893** Printing ink

(G-3922)
INNER FIRE SPORTS LLC
2558 Madison Rd Apt 18 (45208-1144)
PHONE..............................719 244-6622
Joseph Carman, *Partner*
John Karaus, *Partner*
EMP: 3 EST: 2012
SALES (est): 140K **Privately Held**
SIC: **2389** 2329 2339 Men's miscellaneous accessories; men's & boys' sportswear & athletic clothing; women's & misses' outerwear

(G-3923)
INNOVATIVE WOODWORKING INC
1901 Ross Ave (45212-2019)
PHONE..............................513 531-1940
Fax: 513 531-1957
Robert Rodenfels, *President*
Janet A Rodenfels, *President*
Robert W Rodenfels II, *President*
EMP: 9
SQ FT: 13,000
SALES (est): 1.1MM **Privately Held**
SIC: **2522** 2521 Office bookcases, wall-cases & partitions, except wood; wood office filing cabinets & bookcases

(G-3924)
INSPIRING KIND LLC
7757 5 Mile Rd (45230-2355)
PHONE..............................513 321-1705
Fax: 513 231-1138
Mary Richmond,
EMP: 3
SALES (est): 190K **Privately Held**
SIC: **3499** Novelties & giftware, including trophies

(G-3925)
INSTRMNTATION CTRL SYSTEMS INC
Also Called: Ics Electrical Services
11355 Sebring Dr (45240-2796)
PHONE..............................513 662-2600
Fax: 513 662-2011
John Guenther, *President*
Cristein French, *Office Mgr*
EMP: 43
SQ FT: 15,500
SALES (est): 7.2MM **Privately Held**
WEB: www.icselectricalservices.com
SIC: **1731** 7629 3613 Electrical work; electric power systems contractors; electronic controls installation; fiber optic cable installation; electrical measuring instrument repair & calibration; control panels, electric

(G-3926)
INTEL INDUSTRIES LLC
773 Laverty Ln (45230-3552)
PHONE..............................614 551-5702
Thomas J Elliott, *Principal*
EMP: 6
SALES (est): 571.3K **Privately Held**
SIC: **3674** Microprocessors

(G-3927)
INTER AMERICAN PRODUCTS INC (HQ)
Also Called: Kenlake Foods
1240 State Ave (45204-1728)
PHONE..............................800 645-2233
Fax: 513 762-4565
David B Dillon, *CEO*
Rodney McMullen, *President*
Bill Lucia, *General Mgr*
Duane H Sphr, *Human Res Mgr*
Andrea Carroll, *Manager*
EMP: 27

SALES (est): 259.5MM
SALES (corp-wide): 115.3B **Publicly Held**
WEB: www.interamericanproducts.com
SIC: **2095** 2099 2033 2079 Roasted coffee; spices, including grinding; jellies, edible, including imitation: in cans, jars, etc.; preserves, including imitation: in cans, jars, etc.; salad oils, except corn: vegetable refined; concentrates, drink; processed cheese; natural cheese
PA: The Kroger Co
1014 Vine St Ste 1000
Cincinnati OH 45202
513 762-4000

(G-3928)
INTERCONTINENTAL CHEMICAL CORP (PA)
4660 Spring Grove Ave (45232-1995)
PHONE..............................513 541-7100
Fax: 513 541-6880
Cameron W Cord, *President*
Gary Valasek, *Manager*
Paul Shaver, *Admin Sec*
EMP: 30
SQ FT: 54,000
SALES (est): 3.7MM **Privately Held**
WEB: www.icc-chemicals.com
SIC: **2842** Specialty cleaning, polishes & sanitation goods

(G-3929)
INTERLUBE CORPORATION
Also Called: Lube & Chem Products
4646 Baker St (45212-2594)
PHONE..............................513 531-1777
Fax: 513 531-0193
Elmer Cleave, *President*
Elmer B Cleves, *President*
Robert Erpenbeck, *Engineer*
Tony Martini, *Manager*
EMP: 10 EST: 1969
SQ FT: 4,464
SALES (est): 1.1MM **Privately Held**
WEB: www.interlubecorporation.com
SIC: **2899** Corrosion preventive lubricant

(G-3930)
INTERNATIONAL BRAND SERVICES
Also Called: Graeter's Ice Cream
3397 Erie Ave Apt 215 (45208-1638)
PHONE..............................513 376-8209
Kellie Manning, *General Mgr*
EMP: 15
SALES (est): 910K **Privately Held**
SIC: **2024** 5812 Ice cream & ice milk; ice cream stands or dairy bars

(G-3931)
INTERNATIONAL SUPPLY CORP
Also Called: International Financial Svcs
3284 E Sharon Rd (45241-1945)
PHONE..............................513 793-0393
Fax: 513 793-4348
Ted J Day, *President*
Theodore J Day, *President*
EMP: 3
SQ FT: 2,000
SALES (est): 319K **Privately Held**
SIC: **3089** 7389 Injection molding of plastics; financial services

(G-3932)
IRON WIND METALS CO LLC
10488 Chester Rd (45215-1202)
PHONE..............................513 870-0606
Fax: 513 870-0626
Mike Noe, *Principal*
EMP: 6
SQ FT: 5,000
SALES (est): 560K **Privately Held**
WEB: www.ironwindmetals.com
SIC: **3944** 7389 Games, toys & children's vehicles; packaging & labeling services

(G-3933)
J & P INVESTMENTS INC
Also Called: Advance Printing Company
8100 Reading Rd (45237-1404)
P.O. Box 37633 (45222-0633)
PHONE..............................513 821-2299
Fax: 513 531-2313
Paul Erdman, *President*
Thomas Schamer, *Vice Pres*

Rob Barhorst, *Manager*
EMP: 13
SQ FT: 26,500
SALES: 2MM **Privately Held**
SIC: 2752 Commercial printing, offset

(G-3934)
J C EQUIPMENT SALES & LSG
2300 E Kemper Rd Unit 11a (45241-6505)
PHONE...............................513 772-7612
Fax: 513 772-7618
Jeff Combs, *President*
Chris Wells, *General Mgr*
EMP: 5
SQ FT: 2,300
SALES (est): 883K **Privately Held**
SIC: 3829 Surveying & drafting equipment

(G-3935)
J II FIRE SYSTEMS INC
3628 Harrison Ave (45211-5567)
PHONE...............................513 574-0609
June Craynon, *President*
John Craynon, *Principal*
EMP: 5
SALES (est): 1MM **Privately Held**
SIC: 3699 Security devices

(G-3936)
J M SMUCKER COMPANY
5204 Spring Grove Ave (45217-1031)
P.O. Box 599 (45201-0599)
PHONE...............................513 482-8000
Fax: 513 482-8173
Steve Landry, *Plant Mgr*
Richard Cappola, *Purchasing*
Mike Noyes, *QA Dir*
Marilyn Yager, *Plant Engr*
Rodney Dozier, *Sales Mgr*
EMP: 100
SALES (corp-wide): 7.8B **Publicly Held**
WEB: www.smuckers.com
SIC: 2099 Peanut butter
PA: The J M Smucker Company
1 Strawberry Ln
Orrville OH 44667
330 682-3000

(G-3937)
JACOBS MECHANICAL CO
4500 W Mitchell Ave (45232-1912)
PHONE...............................513 681-6800
Fax: 513 681-6855
John E Mc Donald, *President*
John McDonald, *Chief*
Dee Brisbin, *Human Resources*
Sean Lambert, *Manager*
Ray Stoehr, *Executive*
EMP: 125
SQ FT: 20,000
SALES (est): 24.4MM **Privately Held**
WEB: www.jacobsmech.com
SIC: 1711 3444 Ventilation & duct work
contractor; sheet metalwork

(G-3938)
JAKMAR INCORPORATED
3280 Hageman Ave (45241-1907)
PHONE...............................513 631-4303
William Thaman, *President*
Rick Royse, *Project Mgr*
Bernard Geyman, *Executive*
EMP: 16
SALES (est): 1.4MM **Privately Held**
SIC: 3061 Mechanical rubber goods

(G-3939)
JAMES C DENIER CO INC
Also Called: J C Denier Co
3684 Poole Rd (45251-2937)
P.O. Box 56 (45253)
PHONE...............................513 385-6272
Fax: 513 385-6272
Patrick H Denier, *President*
EMP: 4 EST: 1932
SQ FT: 6,000
SALES: 500K **Privately Held**
SIC: 5051 3446 3441 3354 Rails & accessories; architectural metalwork; fabricated structural metal; aluminum extruded products

(G-3940)
JAMES C FREE INC
Also Called: James Free Jewellers
9555 Main St Ste 1 (45242-7670)
PHONE...............................513 793-0133
Zackery Karaman, *Vice Pres*
EMP: 6
SALES (corp-wide): 3.4MM **Privately Held**
WEB: www.jamesfreejewelers.com
SIC: 3911 5944 Jewelry, precious metal; jewelry, precious stones & precious metals
PA: James C. Free, Inc.
3100 Far Hills Ave
Dayton OH 45429
937 298-0171

(G-3941)
JAMES C ROBINSON
Also Called: J C Robinson Products
442 Chestnut St Apt 1 (45203-1454)
PHONE...............................513 969-7482
James C Robinson, *Owner*
EMP: 9
SALES: 19MM **Privately Held**
SIC: 5149 7231 2842 Dried or canned foods; beauty shops; automobile polish

(G-3942)
JAPLAR GROUP INC
Also Called: Japlar Schauer
3210 Wasson Rd (45209-2382)
PHONE...............................513 791-7192
Jonathan Chaiken, *President*
▲ EMP: 15
SQ FT: 120,000
SALES (est): 2.3MM **Privately Held**
SIC: 3629 3612 3825 Battery chargers, rectifying or nonrotating; transformers, except electric; instruments to measure electricity

(G-3943)
JAY INSTRUMENTS
11501 Goldcoast Dr (45249-1620)
PHONE...............................513 733-5200
Jim Stone, *Principal*
EMP: 3 EST: 2010
SALES (est): 242.8K **Privately Held**
SIC: 3625 Control equipment, electric

(G-3944)
JERRY TOOLS INC
6200 Vine St (45216-2199)
PHONE...............................513 242-3211
Fax: 513 242-4718
David Inboldt, *President*
David Imholt, *President*
Don Daniels, *Vice Pres*
Debra Imholt, *Vice Pres*
Anthony Imholt, *Marketing Mgr*
EMP: 16 EST: 1965
SQ FT: 15,625
SALES (est): 3MM **Privately Held**
WEB: www.jerrytools.com
SIC: 3545 3452 Chucks: drill, lathe or magnetic (machine tool accessories); arbors (machine tool accessories); nuts, metal

(G-3945)
JHG RETAIL SERVICES LLC
Also Called: Phg Retail Services
319 Cooper St (45215-4710)
PHONE...............................216 447-0831
Joelle Hominy-Gertz, *President*
EMP: 14
SALES: 750K **Privately Held**
SIC: 2542 Racks, merchandise display or storage: except wood

(G-3946)
JJKB ENTERPRISES LLC
Also Called: Right Srce Cmmunications Group
6125 Montgomery Rd Unit 1 (45213-1454)
P.O. Box 36164 (45236-0164)
PHONE...............................513 731-4332
Fax: 513 297-7568
Patricia Meder, *Senior Partner*
Katy Bair, *Mng Member*
Betty Kaiser, *Graphic Designe*
EMP: 4
SQ FT: 3,000

SALES (est): 350K **Privately Held**
SIC: 8743 7374 2759 Public relations services; computer graphics service; publication printing

(G-3947)
JJS3 FOUNDATION
Also Called: Neusole Glassworks
11925 Kemper Springs Dr (45240-1643)
PHONE...............................513 751-3292
John Schiff, *Exec Dir*
EMP: 3
SALES (est): 828.4K **Privately Held**
WEB: www.neusole.com
SIC: 1542 3229 Nonresidential construction; pressed & blown glass

(G-3948)
JOE BAKER EQUIPMENT SALES
1000 Devils Backbone Rd (45233-4812)
PHONE...............................513 451-1327
Joe Baker, *Principal*
▲ EMP: 3
SALES (est): 440.2K **Privately Held**
SIC: 7538 7694 7699 Engine repair; rebuilding motors, except automotive; engine repair & replacement, non-automotive

(G-3949)
JOE BUSBY
Also Called: Laces For Less
439 S Cooper Ave (45215-4565)
P.O. Box 15726 (45215-0726)
PHONE...............................513 821-1716
Joe Busby, *Owner*
EMP: 3
SQ FT: 800
SALES: 200K **Privately Held**
WEB: www.lacesforless.com
SIC: 5131 2241 Lace fabrics; shoe laces, except leather

(G-3950)
JOE P FISCHER WOODCRAFT
8455 Greenleaf Dr (45255-5609)
PHONE...............................513 474-4316
Joe Fischer, *Principal*
EMP: 3 EST: 2008
SALES (est): 246.2K **Privately Held**
SIC: 2511 Wood household furniture

(G-3951)
JOHN F KILFOIL CO
3799 Madison Rd (45209-1123)
PHONE...............................513 791-6150
Fax: 513 791-6153
Timothy M Kilfoil, *President*
Christine Bell, *Vice Pres*
EMP: 4
SALES (est): 1.1MM **Privately Held**
SIC: 5065 3544 Electronic parts & equipment; special dies, tools, jigs & fixtures

(G-3952)
JOHN FRIEDA PROF HAIR CARE INC (DH)
2535 Spring Grove Ave (45214-1729)
PHONE...............................800 521-3189
William J Gentner, *President*
Joseph B Workman, *Vice Pres*
EMP: 40
SALES (est): 6.6MM
SALES (corp-wide): 11.9B **Privately Held**
SIC: 2844 Hair preparations, including shampoos
HQ: Kao Usa Inc.
2535 Spring Grove Ave
Cincinnati OH 45214
513 421-1400

(G-3953)
JOHN MORRELL & CO (DH)
805 E Kemper Rd (45246-2515)
P.O. Box 405020 (45240-5020)
PHONE...............................513 782-3800
Fax: 513 346-7552
Joseph B Sebring, *President*
Brad Keffaber, *General Mgr*
Mark Dorsey, *Principal*
John Pauley, *Exec VP*
Terry Wendt, *Vice Pres*
◆ EMP: 125 EST: 1957
SQ FT: 10,000

SALES (est): 145MM **Privately Held**
WEB: www.johnmorrell.com
SIC: 2011 Meat packing plants; pork products from pork slaughtered on site; bacon, slab & sliced from meat slaughtered on site; hams & picnics from meat slaughtered on site
HQ: Smithfield Foods, Inc.
200 Commerce St
Smithfield VA 23430
757 365-3000

(G-3954)
JOHN S SWIFT COMPANY INC
2524 Spring Grove Ave (45214-1730)
PHONE...............................513 721-4147
Fax: 513 721-6863
Bill Zimmerman, *Manager*
EMP: 15
SQ FT: 18,000
SALES (corp-wide): 15.7MM **Privately Held**
WEB: www.jssco.com
SIC: 2752 Commercial printing, offset
PA: John S Swift Company Incorporated
999 Commerce Ct
Buffalo Grove IL 60089
847 465-3300

(G-3955)
JOHN STEHLIN & SONS CO INC
Also Called: Stehlin, John & Sons Meats
10134 Colerain Ave (45251-4902)
PHONE...............................513 385-6164
Fax: 513 385-6165
John Stehlin, *President*
Dennis Stehlin, *Vice Pres*
Ronald Stehlin, *Vice Pres*
Richard Stehlin, *Admin Sec*
EMP: 14 EST: 1913
SQ FT: 3,600
SALES (est): 1MM **Privately Held**
SIC: 2011 5421 2013 Meat packing plants; beef products from beef slaughtered on site; pork products from pork slaughtered on site; meat & fish markets; sausages & other prepared meats

(G-3956)
JOHNSON CONTROLS INC
11648 Springfield Pike (45246-3019)
PHONE...............................513 671-6338
Lawrence W Gundler, *President*
EMP: 15 **Privately Held**
SIC: 2531 7382 Seats, automobile; security systems services
HQ: Johnson Controls, Inc.
5757 N Green Bay Ave
Milwaukee WI 53209
414 524-1200

(G-3957)
JOSEPH BERNING PRINTING CO
1850 Dalton Ave (45214-2056)
PHONE...............................513 721-0781
Fax: 513 721-0783
Michael Berning, *President*
Jim Lamping, *Opers Mgr*
Kim Fishback, *Human Res Mgr*
Carol Nelson, *Sales Staff*
EMP: 18
SQ FT: 11,800
SALES: 5MM **Privately Held**
WEB: www.josberningprinting.com
SIC: 2752 Commercial printing, lithographic

(G-3958)
JOSEPH G BETZ & SONS
4219 Saint Martins Pl (45211-5315)
PHONE...............................513 481-0322
EMP: 4 EST: 1945
SQ FT: 7,500
SALES (est): 240K **Privately Held**
SIC: 7641 2512 Reupholstery/Furniture Repair Mfg Upholstered Household Furniture

(G-3959)
JOSTENS INC
8673 Sarah Bend Dr (45251-8409)
PHONE...............................513 615-3281
Mike Beerman, *Branch Mgr*
EMP: 3
SALES (corp-wide): 13.2B **Publicly Held**
SIC: 3911 Rings, finger: precious metal

HQ: Jostens, Inc.
   3601 Minnesota Dr Ste 400
   Minneapolis MN 55435
   952 830-3300

(G-3960)
JOSTENS INC
3047 Madison Rd Ste 207 (45209-1786)
PHONE....................................513 731-5900
Tom Jans, *President*
EMP: 3
SALES (corp-wide): 13.2B **Publicly Held**
WEB: www.jostens.com
SIC: 3911 Rings, finger: precious metal
HQ: Jostens, Inc.
   3601 Minnesota Dr Ste 400
   Minneapolis MN 55435
   952 830-3300

(G-3961)
JSCS GROUP INC
Also Called: Market Direct, Inc.
690 Northland Blvd (45240-3214)
PHONE....................................513 563-4900
John Harmon, *President*
Stephanie Harmon, *President*
EMP: 5
SQ FT: 10,000
SALES: 500K **Privately Held**
WEB: www.marketdirectinc.com
SIC: 2759 7331 7336 8732 Commercial
printing; direct mail advertising services;
commercial art & graphic design; market
analysis or research

(G-3962)
JUDY MILLS COMPANY INC (PA)
3360 Red Bank Rd (45227-4107)
PHONE....................................513 271-4241
Mike Judy, *President*
EMP: 36 EST: 1922
SALES (est): 7.3MM **Privately Held**
SIC: 6512 5211 2431 Commercial & in-
dustrial building operation; lumber & other
building materials; millwork

(G-3963)
JUSTIN P STRAUB LLC
Also Called: Automation Etc
14 De Camp Ave (45216-1624)
PHONE....................................513 761-0282
Annie White,
Maggie Clezenger,
Justin Straub,
EMP: 6
SALES: 290K **Privately Held**
SIC: 3544 7699 Forms (molds), for
foundry & plastics working machinery; in-
dustrial machinery & equipment repair

(G-3964)
K & H INDUSTRIES LLC
1041 Evans St Ste 2 (45204-2019)
PHONE....................................513 921-6770
Fax: 513 921-6771
Jennifer Sharkey,
Tom Sharkey,
EMP: 15 EST: 1905
SQ FT: 60,000
SALES (est): 2.7MM **Privately Held**
WEB: www.kh-ind.com
SIC: 3469 Stamping metal for the trade

(G-3965)
K F T INC
726 Mehring Way (45203-1809)
PHONE....................................513 241-5910
Ronald Eubanks, *President*
EMP: 60
SQ FT: 45,000
SALES (est): 15.4MM **Privately Held**
WEB: www.tkf.com
SIC: 3535 1796 Conveyors & conveying
equipment; overhead conveyor systems;
millwright; machinery installation

(G-3966)
K2 PETROLEUM & SUPPLY LLC
11371 Village Brook Dr # 1321
(45249-2072)
PHONE....................................937 503-2614
Jeffery Pastor, *CFO*
EMP: 3

SALES (est): 202.6K **Privately Held**
SIC: 2911 5172 2899 5169 Petroleum refining; diesel fuel; jet fuel igniters; waxes,
except petroleum

(G-3967)
**KAFFENBARGER TRUCK EQP
CO**
3260 E Kemper Rd (45241-1519)
PHONE....................................513 772-6800
Fax: 513 772-7609
Rodney Swigert, *Manager*
Herbert Lam, *Manager*
EMP: 35
SQ FT: 18,280
SALES (corp-wide): 33.4MM **Privately
Held**
WEB: www.kaffenbarger.com
SIC: 7538 5531 3713 3532 Truck engine
repair, except industrial; truck equipment
& parts; truck bodies & parts; mining ma-
chinery; construction machinery
PA: Kaffenbarger Truck Equipment Co Inc
   10100 Ballentine Pike
   New Carlisle OH 45344
   937 845-3804

(G-3968)
KAHNY PRINTING INC
4766 River Rd (45233-1633)
PHONE....................................513 251-2911
Fax: 513 251-7004
John S Kahny, *President*
Linda Knierim, *Vice Pres*
Claire M Kahny, *Treasurer*
Susan Deters, *Manager*
EMP: 25 EST: 1956
SQ FT: 14,000
SALES (est): 4.3MM **Privately Held**
WEB: www.kahny.com
SIC: 2752 Commercial printing, offset

(G-3969)
KAISER FOODS INC (PA)
500 York St (45214-2490)
PHONE....................................513 621-2053
Fax: 513 455-8284
Ted G Kaiser, *President*
Kenneth R Hughes, *Principal*
David Kaiser, *Chairman*
Mary Kaiser, *Corp Secy*
Bob Kaiser, *Vice Pres*
▲ EMP: 20
SQ FT: 50,000
SALES (est): 7.2MM **Privately Held**
WEB: www.kaiserfoods.com
SIC: 2035 5149 Pickles, vinegar; relishes,
fruit & vegetable; relishes, vinegar; pick-
les, preserves, jellies & jams; condiments;
cookies

(G-3970)
KAISER FOODS INC
Also Called: Kaiser Pickles
2155 Kindel Ave (45214-1841)
PHONE....................................513 241-6833
Ted Kaiser, *Manager*
EMP: 16
SQ FT: 12,308
SALES (corp-wide): 7.2MM **Privately
Held**
WEB: www.kaiserfoods.com
SIC: 2035 Pickles, vinegar; relishes, fruit &
vegetable; relishes, vinegar
PA: Kaiser Foods, Inc.
   500 York St
   Cincinnati OH 45214
   513 621-2053

(G-3971)
KAM-AWARDS INC
7220 Montgomery Rd (45236-3920)
PHONE....................................513 631-5553
Fax: 513 561-5531
Robert Kast, *Owner*
EMP: 7
SALES (est): 254.9K **Privately Held**
SIC: 2396 Ribbons & bows, cut & sewed

(G-3972)
KAO USA INC (HQ)
2535 Spring Grove Ave (45214-1729)
P.O. Box 145444 (45250-5444)
PHONE....................................513 421-1400
Fax: 513 455-5373
Bill Gentner, *President*

John Nosek, *President*
David Stern, *Senior VP*
Steve Cagle, *Vice Pres*
Mark Cushman, *Vice Pres*
◆ EMP: 400 EST: 1882
SQ FT: 489,000
SALES (est): 573.9MM
SALES (corp-wide): 11.9B **Privately Held**
WEB: www.kaobrands.com
SIC: 2844 2841 Cosmetic preparations;
face creams or lotions; soap: granulated,
liquid, cake, flaked or chip
PA: Kao Corporation
   1-14-10, Nihombashikayabacho
   Chuo-Ku TKY 103-0
   336 607-111

(G-3973)
KAWS INC
Also Called: RB Tool and Manufacturing
2680 Civic Center Dr (45231-1312)
PHONE....................................513 521-8292
Kathy Schaeper, *CEO*
Al Schaeper, *President*
Christina Kid, *Manager*
EMP: 39
SQ FT: 20,000
SALES (est): 7.4MM **Privately Held**
WEB: www.rbtoolandmfg.com
SIC: 3565 Packaging machinery

(G-3974)
KDM SIGNS INC
Kdm Retail
3000 Exon Ave (45241-2550)
PHONE....................................513 769-3900
Fax: 513 769-4137
Jim Jaeger, *Financial Exec*
Lee Diss, *Branch Mgr*
EMP: 30
SALES (corp-wide): 99MM **Privately
Held**
SIC: 2541 Display fixtures, wood
PA: Kdm Signs, Inc.
   10450 Medallion Dr
   Cincinnati OH 45241
   513 769-1932

(G-3975)
KDM SIGNS INC (PA)
Also Called: Kdm Screen Printing
10450 Medallion Dr (45241-3199)
PHONE....................................513 769-1932
Fax: 513 956-3889
Robert J Kissel, *President*
Jim Brownley, *General Mgr*
Shelia Ladwig, *General Mgr*
Kathy McQueen, *Corp Secy*
Bonnie Kissel, *Plant Mgr*
EMP: 230
SQ FT: 150,000
SALES (est): 99MM **Privately Held**
WEB: www.kdmpop.com
SIC: 2759 3993 Commercial printing;
screen printing; signs & advertising spe-
cialties

(G-3976)
KEEBLER COMPANY
1 Trade St (45227-4509)
PHONE....................................513 271-3500
Fax: 513 271-3531
Sharon Maul, *Human Res Mgr*
Sam Bristle, *Manager*
EMP: 42
SALES (corp-wide): 13B **Publicly Held**
SIC: 2052 Cookies
HQ: Keebler Company
   1 Kellogg Sq
   Battle Creek MI 49017
   269 961-2000

(G-3977)
KEEBLER COMPANY
11490 Mosteller Rd (45241-1830)
PHONE....................................513 671-0880
Fax: 513 772-9560
Keith Carothers, *President*
EMP: 30
SALES (corp-wide): 13B **Publicly Held**
WEB: www.keebler.com
SIC: 2052 Cookies
HQ: Keebler Company
   1 Kellogg Sq
   Battle Creek MI 49017
   269 961-2000

(G-3978)
KELLOGG COMPANY
1 Trade St (45227-4509)
PHONE....................................513 271-3500
Jerry Morgan, *Prdtn Mgr*
Gary Blattman, *QC Dir*
Don Gallagher, *Senior Mgr*
EMP: 450
SALES (corp-wide): 13B **Publicly Held**
WEB: www.kelloggs.com
SIC: 2052 2051 Biscuits, dry; cookies;
crackers, dry; bread, cake & related prod-
ucts
PA: Kellogg Company
   1 Kellogg Sq
   Battle Creek MI 49017
   269 961-2000

(G-3979)
KELLOGG COMPANY
11490 Mosteller Rd (45241-1830)
PHONE....................................513 772-8980
Kevin Hubbard, *Controller*
Tim Duffy, *Manager*
EMP: 27
SALES (corp-wide): 13B **Publicly Held**
SIC: 2043 Cereal breakfast foods
PA: Kellogg Company
   1 Kellogg Sq
   Battle Creek MI 49017
   269 961-2000

(G-3980)
KELLOGG COMPANY
8044 Montgomery Rd # 700 (45236-2926)
PHONE....................................513 792-2700
EMP: 385
SALES (corp-wide): 13B **Publicly Held**
SIC: 2043 Cereal breakfast foods
PA: Kellogg Company
   1 Kellogg Sq
   Battle Creek MI 49017
   269 961-2000

(G-3981)
KEN HEUSER & GARY GRAVEL
473 Lenkenann Dr (45255-5049)
PHONE....................................513 752-4159
Gary Gravel, *Principal*
EMP: 3
SALES (est): 130K **Privately Held**
SIC: 1442 Construction sand & gravel

(G-3982)
**KENDALL/HUNT PUBLISHING
CO**
Also Called: Rcl Benziger
8805 Governors Hill Dr # 400
(45249-3314)
PHONE....................................877 275-4725
Lauren Comstock, *Division Mgr*
Sori Govin, *Sales Staff*
Peter Ashpostio, *Branch Mgr*
EMP: 90
SALES (corp-wide): 52.6MM **Privately
Held**
SIC: 2731 Books: publishing & printing
PA: Kendall/Hunt Publishing Company
   4050 Westmark Dr
   Dubuque IA 52002
   563 589-1000

(G-3983)
**KENNEDY INK COMPANY INC
(PA)**
5230 Wooster Pike (45226-2229)
PHONE....................................513 871-2515
Fax: 513 871-2716
Jim Scott, *President*
Donald M Kennedy, *Principal*
James H Scott, *Principal*
Ralph W Wagner, *Principal*
EMP: 15
SQ FT: 8,000
SALES (est): 2.5MM **Privately Held**
SIC: 2893 Printing ink

(G-3984)
**KENWOOD POOL
DISTRIBUTORS INC**
Also Called: Bill's Kenwood Pool & Hot Tub
8211 Blue Ash Rd (45236-1987)
PHONE....................................513 793-7080
Fax: 513 793-7081
Michael P Mahon, *President*

Terry Mahon, *Vice Pres*
EMP: 3
SQ FT: 14,000
SALES (est): 230K **Privately Held**
SIC: 5999 2519 Swimming pools, hot tubs
& sauna equipment & supplies; fiberglass
furniture, household: padded or plain

(G-3985)
KERRY FLAVOR SYSTEMS US LLC
Also Called: Kerry Ingredients & Flavours
10261 Chester Rd (45215-1581)
PHONE................................513 771-4682
Gerry Behan, *President*
EMP: 65 **Privately Held**
SIC: 2023 2079 2099 Dry, condensed,
evaporated dairy products; edible fats &
oils; food preparations; seasonings: dry
mixes
PA: Kerry Flavor Systems Us, Llc
10261 Chester Rd
Cincinnati OH 45215

(G-3986)
KETTERING ROOFING & SHTMTL
3210 Jefferson Ave Ste 1 (45220-2290)
PHONE................................513 281-6413
Fax: 513 281-6413
Timothy Kettering, *President*
Christina Kettering, *Corp Secy*
EMP: 12
SQ FT: 5,000
SALES (est): 1.3MM **Privately Held**
SIC: 1761 3444 2952 Sheet metalwork;
roofing contractor; sheet metalwork; as-
phalt felts & coatings

(G-3987)
KEY PRESS INC
2135 Central Pkwy (45214-3712)
PHONE................................513 721-1203
Jerry Koch, *President*
Rick Koch, *Vice Pres*
Larry Koch, *Manager*
EMP: 4 **EST:** 1901
SQ FT: 5,000
SALES (est): 350K **Privately Held**
SIC: 2752 2759 Lithographing on metal;
letterpress printing

(G-3988)
KILN OF HYDE PARK INC
1286 Herschel Ave (45208-3011)
PHONE................................513 321-3307
Carol Philpott, *Owner*
EMP: 15
SALES (est): 688K **Privately Held**
SIC: 5719 3269 Pottery; firing & decorat-
ing china

(G-3989)
KIMBERLY-CLARK CORPORATION
209 W 7th St (45202-2373)
PHONE................................513 864-3780
EMP: 213
SALES (corp-wide): 18.2B **Publicly Held**
SIC: 2621 Paper mills
PA: Kimberly-Clark Corporation
351 Phelps Dr
Irving TX 75038
972 281-1200

(G-3990)
KING BAG AND MANUFACTURING CO (PA)
1500 Spring Lawn Ave (45223-1699)
PHONE................................513 541-5440
Fax: 513 541-6555
Connie M Kirsch, *President*
Mary Pugh, *Business Mgr*
Ronald Kirsch Sr, *Vice Pres*
Ronald Kirsch Jr, *Vice Pres*
Chris Miller, *Prdtn Mgr*
◆ **EMP:** 25
SQ FT: 18,000
SALES (est): 12.4MM **Privately Held**
WEB: www.kingbag.com
SIC: 2221 2393 Polyethylene broadwoven
fabrics; textile bags

(G-3991)
KINSELLA MANUFACTURING CO INC
7880 Camargo Rd (45243-2652)
PHONE................................513 561-5285
Fax: 513 561-5253
George P Kinsella, *President*
John Kinsella, *Corp Secy*
Kevin Kinsella, *Vice Pres*
EMP: 10 **EST:** 1961
SQ FT: 10,000
SALES: 2MM **Privately Held**
WEB: www.kinsellakitchens.com
SIC: 5211 2541 2434 Cabinets, kitchen;
counter tops; counters or counter display
cases, wood; table or counter tops, plastic
laminated; wood kitchen cabinets

(G-3992)
KIRK & BLUM MANUFACTURING CO (DH)
4625 Red Bank Rd Ste 200 (45227-1552)
PHONE................................513 458-2600
Fax: 513 351-5475
Jeff Lang, *CEO*
L Bertoli, *Vice Pres*
Marshall Matherly, *Opers Staff*
Kyle Clark, *Engineer*
D W Blazer, *CFO*
◆ **EMP:** 200 **EST:** 1907
SQ FT: 250,000
SALES (est): 82.7MM
SALES (corp-wide): 417MM **Publicly Held**
SIC: 1761 3444 3443 Sheet metalwork;
sheet metal specialties, not stamped; fab-
ricated plate work (boiler shop)
HQ: Ceco Group, Inc.
4625 Red Bank Rd Ste 200
Cincinnati OH 45227
513 458-2600

(G-3993)
KIRWAN INDUSTRIES INC
1964 Central Ave (45214-2264)
PHONE................................513 333-0766
Ronan Kirwan, *President*
EMP: 8
SQ FT: 20,000
SALES (est): 898.1K **Privately Held**
WEB: www.kirwanindustries.com
SIC: 3441 Fabricated structural metal

(G-3994)
KITCHENS BY RUTENSCHROER INC (PA)
Also Called: Kbr
950 Laidlaw Ave (45237-5004)
PHONE................................513 251-8333
Fax: 513 244-3942
Steven Rutenschroer, *President*
Kathy Frisby, *Principal*
G Robert Hines, *Principal*
Steven D Rutenschroer, *Principal*
Helen Rutenschroer, *Vice Pres*
▲ **EMP:** 10
SQ FT: 8,000
SALES (est): 1.9MM **Privately Held**
WEB: www.kitchensbyrutenschroer.com
SIC: 5722 2519 2541 2511 Kitchens,
complete (sinks, cabinets, etc.); house-
hold furniture, except wood or metal: up-
holstered; wood partitions & fixtures;
wood household furniture; wood kitchen
cabinets

(G-3995)
KLOSTERMAN BAKING CO (PA)
4760 Paddock Rd (45229-1047)
PHONE................................513 242-5667
Fax: 513 242-3151
Kenneth Klosterman, *President*
Trent Doak, *President*
Dennis Wiltshire, *COO*
Ed Piasecki, *Vice Pres*
Chip Ray, *Transptn Dir*
EMP: 30 **EST:** 1900
SQ FT: 10,000
SALES (est): 209.5MM **Privately Held**
WEB: www.klostermanbakery.com
SIC: 2051 Bread, cake & related products;
bread, all types (white, wheat, rye, etc):
fresh or frozen; cakes, bakery: except
frozen; yeast goods, sweet: except frozen

(G-3996)
KLOSTERMAN BAKING CO
1000 E Ross Ave (45217-1191)
PHONE................................513 242-1004
Fax: 513 242-3703
Diane Bullock, *Human Res Dir*
Trent Doak, *Sales Staff*
Larry Moore, *Manager*
EMP: 85
SALES (corp-wide): 209.5MM **Privately Held**
SIC: 5149 2051 Groceries & related prod-
ucts; bread, cake & related products
PA: Klosterman Baking Co.
4760 Paddock Rd
Cincinnati OH 45229
513 242-5667

(G-3997)
KN8DESIGNS LLC
1716 Madison Rd (45206-1817)
PHONE................................859 380-5926
Nathan Ward, *Principal*
EMP: 3
SALES (est): 384.9K **Privately Held**
SIC: 2621 Printing paper

(G-3998)
KNOBLE GLASS & METAL INC (PA)
Also Called: K G M
8650 Green Rd (45255-5016)
PHONE................................513 753-1246
David Knoble, *President*
EMP: 9
SALES (est): 950.8K **Privately Held**
SIC: 3229 3354 Glass fibers, textile; alu-
minum extruded products

(G-3999)
KNOWLTON MANUFACTURING CO INC
2524 Leslie Ave (45212-4299)
PHONE................................513 631-7353
Fax: 513 631-7355
Kenneth Jenkins, *President*
Melody Ginandt, *General Mgr*
John Fricker, *Vice Pres*
Allan Marcuse, *CFO*
Evan McKlenborg, *Manager*
EMP: 15
SQ FT: 44,000
SALES (est): 2.6MM **Privately Held**
WEB: www.knowltonmfg.com
SIC: 3469 3544 Stamping metal for the
trade; special dies & tools

(G-4000)
KOEBBECO SIGNS LLC
5683 Springdale Rd (45251-1825)
PHONE................................513 923-2974
John Koebbe, *Principal*
EMP: 3
SALES (est): 163.3K **Privately Held**
WEB: www.koebbeco.net
SIC: 3993 Signs & advertising specialties

(G-4001)
KONKRETE CITY SKATEBOARDS
2109 Beechmont Ave (45230-1620)
PHONE................................513 231-0399
Maurice Richman, *Principal*
EMP: 4
SALES (est): 315.9K **Privately Held**
SIC: 3949 Skateboards

(G-4002)
KOOP DIAMOND CUTTERS INC
214 E 8th St Fl 4 (45202-2173)
PHONE................................513 621-2838
Fax: 513 621-7136
Clarence E Koop, *President*
Richard J Louis, *Treasurer*
Carol Adleta, *Sales Staff*
EMP: 10
SQ FT: 4,300
SALES (est): 1.5MM **Privately Held**
WEB: www.koopdiamondcutters.com
SIC: 3911 7631 3915 Jewelry, precious
metal; jewelry repair services; jewel cut-
ting, drilling, polishing, recutting or setting

(G-4003)
KROGER CO
11801 Chesterdale Rd (45246-3407)
PHONE................................513 671-2790
Jin Schwarz, *QC Dir*
Alan Kromer, *Controller*
Andrea Furlotte, *Human Resources*
Sean Wright, *Manager*
Mark McGrath, *Manager*
EMP: 130
SALES (corp-wide): 115.3B **Publicly Held**
SIC: 5411 2086 Supermarkets, chain; su-
permarkets, hypermarket; bottled &
canned soft drinks
PA: The Kroger Co
1014 Vine St Ste 1000
Cincinnati OH 45202
513 762-4000

(G-4004)
KROGER CO
1212 W Kemper Rd Ste 1 (45240-1774)
PHONE................................513 742-9500
Fax: 513 742-8460
Mia Doggett, *Pharmacist*
Leandrew Lloyd, *Manager*
Sam Kemp, *Manager*
Shawn Walker, *Manager*
Rita Williams, *Manager*
EMP: 183
SALES (corp-wide): 115.3B **Publicly Held**
WEB: www.kroger.com
SIC: 5411 2051 Supermarkets, chain;
bread, cake & related products
PA: The Kroger Co
1014 Vine St Ste 1000
Cincinnati OH 45202
513 762-4000

(G-4005)
KS DESIGNS INC
3044 Harrison Ave (45211-5752)
PHONE................................513 241-5953
Fax: 513 241-8374
Steven Salling, *President*
Dennis Wall, *Vice Pres*
EMP: 5 **EST:** 1981
SQ FT: 7,400
SALES (est): 541.4K **Privately Held**
WEB: www.ksdesignsinc.com
SIC: 7389 2759 Sign painting & lettering
shop; screen printing

(G-4006)
KUHLS HOT SPORTSPOT
7860 Beechmont Ave (45255-4213)
PHONE................................513 474-2282
Fax: 513 474-2287
Robert Kuhl, *Owner*
EMP: 10
SQ FT: 3,000
SALES (est): 608.1K **Privately Held**
WEB: www.kuhls.com
SIC: 2395 Embroidery & art needlework

(G-4007)
KW RIVER HYDROELECTRIC I LLC ✪
5667 Krystal Ct Ste 100 (45252-1303)
PHONE................................513 673-2251
Paul R Kling, *President*
EMP: 1 **EST:** 2016
SALES: 1MM **Privately Held**
SIC: 3511 7389 Hydraulic turbine genera-
tor set units, complete;

(G-4008)
L B MACHINE & MFG CO INC
1640 Lionel Ave (45214-1571)
PHONE................................513 471-6137
Fax: 513 471-3574
Gary Skora, *Owner*
Glenn Skora, *Vice Pres*
EMP: 8
SQ FT: 16,000
SALES: 800K **Privately Held**
SIC: 3544 3542 Special dies, tools, jigs &
fixtures; die casting machines

(G-4009)
LA MFG INC
Also Called: Brewer Products
9483 Reading Rd (45215-3550)
P.O. Box 62065 (45262-0065)
PHONE.................................513 577-7200
David Brewer, *President*
EMP: 6 **EST:** 1989
SALES (est): 500K **Privately Held**
SIC: 3569 5199 5082 General industrial machinery; nondurable goods; construction & mining machinery

(G-4010)
LAMBERT BROS INC
Also Called: Lambert Bros Nutangs
1337 Bates Ave (45225-1309)
PHONE.................................513 541-1042
Fax: 513 541-4491
Charlie Bowlin, *President*
EMP: 5
SQ FT: 3,000
SALES: 350K **Privately Held**
SIC: 3599 Machine shop, jobbing & repair

(G-4011)
LANGDON INC
9865 Wayne Ave (45215-1403)
P.O. Box 15308 (45215-0308)
PHONE.................................513 733-5955
Fax: 513 733-8050
David Sandman, *President*
Michael Sandman, *Vice Pres*
▲ **EMP:** 40
SQ FT: 42,000
SALES (est): 11.6MM **Privately Held**
WEB: www.langdonsheetmetal.com
SIC: 3444 1711 3564 3446 Ducts, sheet metal; warm air heating & air conditioning contractor; ventilation & duct work contractor; blowers & fans; architectural metalwork; fabricated plate work (boiler shop); fabricated structural metal

(G-4012)
LAROSA DIE ENGINEERING INC
3320 Robinet Dr (45238-2120)
PHONE.................................513 284-9195
Joseph Larosa, *President*
Loretta A Larosa, *Vice Pres*
EMP: 4
SQ FT: 1,800
SALES: 231K **Privately Held**
SIC: 3469 3544 Metal stampings; special dies & tools

(G-4013)
LATE FOR SKY PRODUCTION CO
3000 Robertson Ave (45209-1216)
PHONE.................................513 531-4400
Fax: 513 458-8484
Robyn L Wilson, *President*
Cy Zack, *General Mgr*
William C Schulte Jr, *Vice Pres*
Mark Hunter, *VP Mfg*
Brian Clingner, *Purchasing*
▲ **EMP:** 45
SQ FT: 60,000
SALES (est): 7.6MM **Privately Held**
WEB: www.lateforthesky.com
SIC: 3944 Board games, children's & adults'

(G-4014)
LATIN QUARTER
6904 Wooster Pike (45227-4427)
PHONE.................................513 271-5400
Fax: 513 271-5415
Victor Kleykamp, *Principal*
EMP: 4
SALES (est): 397.8K **Privately Held**
SIC: 3131 Quarters

(G-4015)
LAURENEE LTD LLC
Also Called: Deerfield Digital
3509 Harrison Ave (45211-5544)
PHONE.................................513 662-2225
Fax: 513 662-2339
Timothy R Roedersheimer, *Mng Member*
T R Roedersheimer,
Susan Mroedersheime,
EMP: 8
SQ FT: 8,500

SALES (est): 1.5MM **Privately Held**
WEB: www.deerfield-press.com
SIC: 2752 2791 Commercial printing, offset; typesetting

(G-4016)
LAZER SYSTEMS INC (PA)
850 E Ross Ave (45217-1129)
PHONE.................................513 641-4002
Kenny D Allen, *President*
Jenee Allen, *Credit Mgr*
EMP: 12
SQ FT: 12,000
SALES: 4MM **Privately Held**
SIC: 2796 2759 Color separations for printing; flexographic printing

(G-4017)
LCP TECH INC
8120 Indian Hill Rd (45243-3910)
PHONE.................................513 271-1389
David Ferguson, *President*
EMP: 5
SALES (est): 516.7K **Privately Held**
WEB: www.lcptech.com
SIC: 2992 Lubricating oils

(G-4018)
LEAN FACTORY AMERICA LLC
1859 Section Rd (45237-3305)
PHONE.................................513 297-3086
Kurt Greissinger, *Vice Pres*
Roger Sloan, *Engineer*
Brian Stansell, *Engineer*
Robert Meyer, *CFO*
Keith Chabut,
▲ **EMP:** 5
SALES (est): 858.1K
SALES (corp-wide): 10.1MM **Privately Held**
SIC: 3442 Window & door frames
PA: Orgatex Gmbh & Co. Kg
Albert-Einstein-Str. 19
Langenfeld (Rheinland) 40764
217 310-640

(G-4019)
LEE CORPORATION
Also Called: Lee Printers
12055 Mosteller Rd (45241-1589)
PHONE.................................513 771-3602
Fax: 513 771-3607
Thomas Krieg, *President*
Lee Krieg, *Vice Pres*
Ronald Krieg, *Treasurer*
Carol Krieg, *Admin Sec*
EMP: 12 **EST:** 1905
SQ FT: 35,000
SALES: 2MM **Privately Held**
WEB: www.leeprinters.com
SIC: 2752 2759 2791 2789 Commercial printing, lithographic; letterpress printing; typesetting; bookbinding & related work

(G-4020)
LEONHARDT PLATING COMPANY
5753 Este Ave (45232-1499)
PHONE.................................513 242-1410
Fax: 513 242-0411
Kerry Leonhardt, *President*
Daniel Leonhardt, *Shareholder*
Cathy Carachiolo, *Administration*
EMP: 24 **EST:** 1950
SQ FT: 20,500
SALES (est): 2.6MM **Privately Held**
WEB: www.leonhardtplating.com
SIC: 3471 2899 2851 2842 Electroplating of metals or formed products; chemical preparations; paints & allied products; specialty cleaning, polishes & sanitation goods; inorganic pigments

(G-4021)
LEYMAN MANUFACTURING CORP
Also Called: Leyman Liftgates
10335 Wayne Ave (45215-1128)
PHONE.................................513 891-6210
Fax: 513 891-4761
John Mc Henry, *President*
Robert Drews Jr, *Vice Pres*
Raymond B Leyman, *Vice Pres*
William Margroum, *Vice Pres*
Mike Durham, *Plant Mgr*
▲ **EMP:** 90 **EST:** 1940

SQ FT: 50,000
SALES (est): 22.5MM **Privately Held**
WEB: www.leymanlift.com
SIC: 3713 Truck & bus bodies

(G-4022)
LIFESTYLE NUTRACEUTICALS LTD
Also Called: Pun-U
5911 Turpin Hills Dr (45244-3857)
PHONE.................................513 376-7218
Collin Literski, *CEO*
Sam Browstein, *Principal*
Brad Bolton, *Sales Staff*
Graham Clark, *Director*
Diane Literski, *Director*
EMP: 11
SALES (est): 900K **Privately Held**
SIC: 2023 5149 8731 Dietary supplements, dairy & non-dairy based; health foods; agricultural research

(G-4023)
LIGHT VISION
1776 Mentor Ave (45212-3554)
PHONE.................................513 351-9444
Paul Graham, *Treasurer*
Mike Wodke,
Eric Begleiter,
EMP: 24
SQ FT: 3,000
SALES (est): 230.1K **Privately Held**
WEB: www.lightvision.com
SIC: 2064 Candy & other confectionery products

(G-4024)
LIGHTHOUSE YOUTH SERVICES INC
3330 Jefferson Ave (45220-2108)
PHONE.................................513 961-4080
Fax: 513 961-6578
Jeff Hollenbach, *Manager*
EMP: 17
SALES (corp-wide): 25.1MM **Privately Held**
SIC: 8322 3731 Emergency shelters; lighthouse tenders, building & repairing
PA: Lighthouse Youth Services, Inc.
401 E Mcmillan St
Cincinnati OH 45206
513 221-3350

(G-4025)
LILY TIGER PRESS
1945 Dunham Way (45238-3053)
PHONE.................................513 591-0817
Andreas Lange, *Principal*
EMP: 35
SALES (est): 1.1MM **Privately Held**
SIC: 2741 Miscellaneous publishing

(G-4026)
LINGER PHOTO ENGRAVING CORP
2230 Gilbert Ave (45206-2531)
PHONE.................................513 579-1380
Robert Vanlear, *President*
Kevin Lanigan, *Sales Staff*
EMP: 5
SALES (est): 370K **Privately Held**
SIC: 2796 Photoengraving plates, linecuts or halftones

(G-4027)
LISTERMANN MFG CO INC
Also Called: Listermann Brewery Supply
1621 Dana Ave (45207-1007)
PHONE.................................513 731-1130
Daniel Listermann, *President*
Sue Listermann, *Vice Pres*
Jason Brewer, *Sales Staff*
EMP: 8
SQ FT: 12,500
SALES: 450K **Privately Held**
WEB: www.listermann.com
SIC: 3556 Brewers' & maltsters' machinery

(G-4028)
LITHO-CRAFT LITHOGRAPHY INC
5877 Highland Ridge Dr (45232-1441)
PHONE.................................513 542-6404
Fax: 513 542-3234
Kimberly Pietrosky, *President*

EMP: 3
SQ FT: 6,000
SALES (est): 370K **Privately Held**
SIC: 2796 Lithographic plates, positives or negatives

(G-4029)
LITTLE BUSY BODIES LLC
Also Called: Boogie Wipes
1130 Findlay St (45214-2052)
PHONE.................................513 351-5700
Julie Pickin, *CEO*
Molly Wright, *Marketing Mgr*
▲ **EMP:** 50
SALES (est): 14.9MM **Privately Held**
SIC: 2676 Sanitary paper products

(G-4030)
LLOYD LIBRARY & MUSEUM
917 Plum St (45202-1081)
PHONE.................................513 721-3707
Fax: 513 721-6575
James Huizenga, *Exec Dir*
Maggie Heran, *Director*
EMP: 5
SQ FT: 21,696
SALES (est): 616K **Privately Held**
WEB: www.lloydlibrary.com
SIC: 8231 2731 Specialized libraries; public library; medical library; book publishing

(G-4031)
LMS LLC
Also Called: Kofinas Olive Oil
Kofinas Olive Oil (45230)
PHONE.................................513 981-1412
▲ **EMP:** 5
SALES (est): 259K **Privately Held**
SIC: 2079 Olive oil

(G-4032)
LONG-LOK FASTENERS CORPORATION
10630 Chester Rd (45215-1249)
PHONE.................................513 772-1880
Fax: 513 772-1888
Robert Bennett, *CEO*
Randy Ammon, *President*
James Bennett, *CFO*
Alan Batz, *Sales Staff*
Steve Hassman, *Sales Staff*
EMP: 35
SQ FT: 33,000
SALES (corp-wide): 6MM **Privately Held**
SIC: 3452 Bolts, nuts, rivets & washers
HQ: Long-Lok Fasteners Corporation
14275 Midway Rd Ste 140
Addison TX 75001
972 934-1212

(G-4033)
LOROCO INDUSTRIES INC
Royal Pad Products
10600 Evendale Dr (45241-2518)
PHONE.................................513 554-0356
Bryan Herber, *Plant Mgr*
Bryan Helber, *Manager*
EMP: 21
SALES (corp-wide): 13.7MM **Privately Held**
SIC: 7389 3554 Personal service agents, brokers & bureaus; paper industries machinery
PA: Loroco Industries, Inc.
5000 Creek Rd
Blue Ash OH 45242
513 891-9544

(G-4034)
LOW STRESS GRIND INC
12077 Mosteller Rd (45241-1528)
PHONE.................................513 771-7977
Fax: 513 771-8319
Gary A Talbot, *President*
Steve Etter, *President*
Bob Newgebaur, *Vice Pres*
John Leppard, *Treasurer*
Nancy Talbot, *Treasurer*
EMP: 19
SQ FT: 10,000
SALES (est): 1.5MM
SALES (corp-wide): 16.6MM **Privately Held**
WEB: www.mar-test.com
SIC: 3829 Measuring & controlling devices

PA: Element Materials Technology Cincinnati Inc.
1245 Hill Smith Dr
Cincinnati OH 45215
513 771-2536

(G-4035)
LPI LEGACY PLASTICS LLC
4425 Appleton St (45209-1205)
PHONE..................270 827-1318
Roger Courtney, *President*
Sharon Courtney, *Office Mgr*
EMP: 15
SALES (est): 2.4MM **Privately Held**
WEB: www.legacyplastics.com
SIC: 3089 Extruded finished plastic products

(G-4036)
LS BOMBSHELLES
3940 Vine St (45217-1965)
PHONE..................513 254-6898
Yolanda Jackson, *Owner*
EMP: 3
SALES (est): 130.4K **Privately Held**
SIC: 2844 Toilet preparations

(G-4037)
LUCKY PAWS LLC
5541 Foley Rd (45238-4613)
PHONE..................859 620-2525
Melinda Kirk, *Mng Member*
EMP: 5
SQ FT: 1,000
SALES (est): 360.3K **Privately Held**
SIC: 2047 Dog food

(G-4038)
LUKENS BLACKSMITH SHOP
30 Compton Rd (45216-1014)
PHONE..................513 821-2308
John Luken, *Owner*
EMP: 3
SQ FT: 2,700
SALES: 90K **Privately Held**
SIC: 3599 7692 Machine shop, jobbing & repair; welding repair

(G-4039)
LUMBERJACK PALLET RECYCL LLC
81 Caldwell Dr (45216-1541)
PHONE..................513 821-7543
Denise Catanzaro, *Mng Member*
EMP: 3
SQ FT: 34,500
SALES: 135.7K **Privately Held**
SIC: 4953 2448 7699 Recycling, waste materials; wood pallets & skids; pallet repair

(G-4040)
LUXFER MAGTECH INC (HQ)
Also Called: Heatermeals
2940 Highland Ave Ste 210 (45212-2402)
PHONE..................513 772-3066
Brian Purves, *CEO*
Marc Lamensdorf, *President*
Stan Smith, *VP Opers*
Deborah Simsen, *Treasurer*
Deepak Madan, *Admin Sec*
EMP: 38
SALES (est): 8.3MM
SALES (corp-wide): 414.8MM **Privately Held**
SIC: 2899 5149 Desalter kits, sea water; groceries & related products; beverages, except coffee & tea
PA: Luxfer Holdings Plc
Ancorage Gateway
Salford LANCS M50 3
161 300-0611

(G-4041)
LYNC CORP
2963 Commodore Ln Apt 2 (45251-3193)
PHONE..................513 655-7286
Travis Bea,
EMP: 22
SQ FT: 5,000
SALES (est): 1.5MM **Privately Held**
SIC: 7371 7372 7379 Computer software development & applications; application computer software; computer related maintenance services; computer related consulting services

(G-4042)
LYONDELL CHEMICAL COMPANY
11530 Northlake Dr (45249-1642)
PHONE..................513 530-4000
Norma Maraschin, *Manager*
Sarosh Hussain, *Network Tech*
EMP: 79 **Privately Held**
WEB: www.lyondell.com
SIC: 2869 2822 8731 Olefins; ethylene; polyethylene, chlorosulfonated (hypalon); commercial physical research
HQ: Lyondell Chemical Company
1221 Mckinney St Ste 300
Houston TX 77010
713 309-7200

(G-4043)
M R I EDUCATION FOUNDATION
5400 Kennedy Ave (45213-2664)
PHONE..................513 281-3400
Steve J Pomeranz MD, *President*
Michelle Inman, *Human Res Mgr*
James Kereiakes, *Shareholder*
EMP: 200
SQ FT: 5,600
SALES (est): 2.6MM **Privately Held**
SIC: 8249 2741 Medical training services; miscellaneous publishing

(G-4044)
MACHINE DEVELOPMENT CORP
Also Called: Marine Development
7707 Affinity Dr (45231-3567)
PHONE..................513 825-5885
Fax: 513 825-5886
Gary Fay, *President*
Mary Dusa, *Purchasing*
EMP: 8
SQ FT: 7,800
SALES (est): 600K **Privately Held**
SIC: 3599 Custom machinery

(G-4045)
MACHINE DOCTORS INC
3490 Mustafa Dr (45241-1668)
PHONE..................513 422-3060
Al Bradshaw, *President*
Trent Collier, *Manager*
EMP: 3
SQ FT: 5,000
SALES (est): 190K **Privately Held**
SIC: 7694 Electric motor repair

(G-4046)
MACHINE TL SLTONS UNLMITED LLC
8711 Reading Rd (45215-4800)
PHONE..................513 761-0709
Fax: 513 761-1804
Rebecca Schoch, *Controller*
E Harold Schoch,
Bruce Daniels,
George Edwards,
Herb Varin,
EMP: 15
SQ FT: 22,000
SALES (est): 1.3MM **Privately Held**
SIC: 3541 Machine tools, metal cutting type

(G-4047)
MACHINE WORKS INC
979 Redna Ter (45215-1182)
PHONE..................513 771-4600
Jerry Whitacker, *Principal*
Jerry Whitaker, *Vice Pres*
EMP: 3
SALES (est): 258.9K **Privately Held**
SIC: 3599 Machine shop, jobbing & repair

(G-4048)
MACKE BROTHERS INC
10355 Spartan Dr (45215-1220)
PHONE..................513 771-7500
Fax: 513 771-3830
Joseph D Macke Sr, *President*
Joseph D Macke Jr, *Vice Pres*
Bill Macke, *Treasurer*
Nick Macke, *Admin Sec*
EMP: 85 EST: 1908
SQ FT: 43,000

SALES (est): 8.4MM **Privately Held**
SIC: 2789 7331 Pamphlets, binding; bookbinding & repairing: trade, edition, library, etc.; mailing service

(G-4049)
MADSCO INC
Also Called: Richlen Tool Co.
7015 Mullen Rd (45247-3367)
PHONE..................513 242-4200
Fax: 513 242-0180
Wayne McGuffey, *President*
Craig Nevels, *Vice Pres*
Nick Falco, *Admin Sec*
EMP: 12
SQ FT: 9,200
SALES (est): 1.4MM **Privately Held**
SIC: 3544 Special dies & tools

(G-4050)
MAE CONSULTING
700 W Pete Rose Way 531b (45203-1896)
PHONE..................513 531-8100
Scott Risner, *General Mgr*
Denise Bartick, *Principal*
Peggy Eberhard, *Consultant*
EMP: 3
SALES: 225K **Privately Held**
WEB: www.maeconsulting.com
SIC: 7372 Prepackaged software

(G-4051)
MAGNA GROUP LLC
Also Called: Control System Upgrades
2340 Clydes Xing (45244-2839)
PHONE..................513 388-9463
Nannette Williams, *CEO*
Richard McKenzie, *President*
Gregory Smith, *Director*
EMP: 4
SALES (est): 1MM **Privately Held**
SIC: 3531 8711 Construction machinery; machine tool design

(G-4052)
MAGNA MACHINE CO (PA)
11180 Southland Rd (45240-3202)
PHONE..................513 851-6900
Scott Kramer, *President*
Elliot Adams, *President*
James Parker, *Vice Pres*
Todd Broxterman, *Design Engr*
Greg Bodenburg, *CFO*
▼ EMP: 101 EST: 1953
SQ FT: 80,000
SALES (est): 25MM **Privately Held**
WEB: www.magna-machine.com
SIC: 3556 3554 3599 Bakery machinery; paper industries machinery; machine shop, jobbing & repair

(G-4053)
MAGNETIC MKTG SOLUTIONS LLC
Also Called: Decal Impressions
2111 Kindel Ave (45214-1841)
PHONE..................513 721-3801
Fax: 513 721-3803
Bryan Vielhauer,
EMP: 3
SALES (est): 469.7K **Privately Held**
WEB: www.decalimpressions.com
SIC: 2759 3993 Screen printing; signs & advertising specialties

(G-4054)
MAIN AWNING & TENT INC
415 W Seymour Ave (45216-1862)
PHONE..................513 621-6947
Fax: 513 621-6949
Hyman Goldfarb, *President*
Leslie Goldfarb, *President*
Robert Goldfarb, *Vice Pres*
Pamela Katz, *CPA*
◆ EMP: 9 EST: 1933
SQ FT: 200,000
SALES: 1.1MM **Privately Held**
WEB: www.tentsource.com
SIC: 2394 Awnings, fabric: made from purchased materials; tents: made from purchased materials; tarpaulins, fabric: made from purchased materials

(G-4055)
MALCO LAMINATED INC
4251 Spring Grove Ave (45223-1861)
PHONE..................513 541-8300
Leo Snitzer, *President*
Mike Shavzin, *Vice Pres*
EMP: 4
SQ FT: 5,000
SALES (est): 350K **Privately Held**
SIC: 2434 2541 Wood kitchen cabinets; vanities, bathroom: wood; sink tops, plastic laminated

(G-4056)
MANUFACTURING COMPANY LLC
3468 Cornell Pl (45220-1502)
PHONE..................414 708-7583
Michael Fleisch, *Principal*
EMP: 3
SALES (est): 182.9K **Privately Held**
SIC: 3999 Manufacturing industries

(G-4057)
MAPES CONCRETE CONSTRUCTION
5691 Cheviot Rd Apt 3 (45247-7098)
PHONE..................513 245-2631
Rick Mapes, *President*
EMP: 5
SALES (est): 364.7K **Privately Held**
SIC: 3271 Concrete block & brick

(G-4058)
MARCUS JEWELERS
2022 8 Mile Rd (45244-2607)
PHONE..................513 474-4950
Fax: 513 474-4920
Mark Ogier, *Owner*
EMP: 7
SQ FT: 1,100
SALES (est): 470K **Privately Held**
SIC: 3911 5944 Jewelry, precious metal; jewelry stores

(G-4059)
MARGARET TRENTMAN
Also Called: Zip Graphics
5123 Montgomery Rd (45212-2237)
P.O. Box 12897 (45212-0897)
PHONE..................513 948-1700
Fax: 513 948-1600
Margaret Trentman, *Owner*
Richard Trentman, *Owner*
EMP: 4
SALES (est): 354.1K **Privately Held**
SIC: 2752 2791 2759 Commercial printing, lithographic; typesetting; commercial printing

(G-4060)
MARINERS LANDING INC
Also Called: Mariner's Landing Marina
7405 Forbes Rd (45233-1014)
PHONE..................513 941-3625
Fax: 513 941-9878
Pamela Tonne, *President*
David B Tonne, *Principal*
EMP: 15
SQ FT: 6,992
SALES (est): 1.2MM **Privately Held**
WEB: www.mariners-landing.com
SIC: 4493 5551 3732 Marinas; boat dealers; boat building & repairing

(G-4061)
MARKLEY ENTERPRISES LLC
Also Called: Die Craft Division
1705 Magnolia Dr (45215-1979)
PHONE..................513 771-1290
Fax: 513 771-1293
Skip Markley, *President*
Joe Ramsey, *Plant Mgr*
Ernest Pendergrass, *Sales Staff*
Mary Jo Thomas, *Manager*
▲ EMP: 22
SQ FT: 32,000
SALES (est): 6.8MM **Privately Held**
WEB: www.diecraftmachine.com
SIC: 3449 8711 3599 Miscellaneous metalwork; mechanical engineering; machine shop, jobbing & repair

(G-4062)
MARSHALLS THRIFTY PRINT INC
7244 Ohio Ave (45236-3458)
PHONE....................513 984-5513
Fax: 513 984-5519
Robert Marshall, *President*
EMP: 4 EST: 1981
SQ FT: 2,500
SALES: 750K **Privately Held**
SIC: 2752 Photo-offset printing

(G-4063)
MARTIN MARIETTA MATERIALS INC
Also Called: Kellogg Yard
4439 Kellogg Ave (45226-1540)
PHONE....................513 871-7152
Harry Charles, *Manager*
EMP: 20
SALES (corp-wide): 3.8B **Publicly Held**
WEB: www.martinmarietta.com
SIC: 1423 Crushed & broken granite
PA: Martin Marietta Materials Inc
2710 Wycliff Rd
Raleigh NC 27607
919 781-4550

(G-4064)
MARULA PUBLISHING LLC
6539 Harrison Ave Ste 154 (45247-7822)
P.O. Box 14425 (45250-0425)
PHONE....................513 549-5218
Sterlin Styles,
EMP: 3
SALES (est): 102.6K **Privately Held**
SIC: 2721 Magazines: publishing & printing

(G-4065)
MASTERPIECE PUBLISHER L P
8046 Debonair Ct (45237-1106)
PHONE....................513 948-1000
EMP: 4 EST: 2008
SALES (est): 150K **Privately Held**
SIC: 2741 Misc Publishing

(G-4066)
MATLOCK ELECTRIC CO INC (PA)
2780 Highland Ave (45212-2494)
PHONE....................513 731-9600
Fax: 513 731-9646
Joseph P Geoppinger, *President*
Thomas J Geoppinger, *Chairman*
Rick Mullaney, *Controller*
Michael Schroer, *Sales Associate*
Casey McKenna, *Manager*
EMP: 38
SQ FT: 25,000
SALES: 7.2MM **Privately Held**
WEB: www.matlockelectric.com
SIC: 7694 5063 3699 3612 Electric motor repair; rebuilding motors, except automotive; motors, electric; electrical equipment & supplies; transformers, except electric; speed changers, drives & gears

(G-4067)
MATRIX CABLE AND MOULD
11785 Highway Dr Ste 900 (45241-2087)
PHONE....................513 832-2577
Kevin Meiners, *Owner*
EMP: 5
SQ FT: 5,500
SALES (est): 210.2K **Privately Held**
SIC: 3714 3613 3089 Automotive wiring harness sets; control panels, electric; injection molding of plastics

(G-4068)
MAVERICK CHOCOLATE COMPANY
129 W Elder St (45202-7746)
PHONE....................513 381-0561
Paul Picton, *President*
EMP: 6 EST: 2013
SALES: 250K **Privately Held**
SIC: 2066 Chocolate & cocoa products

(G-4069)
MAZZELLA LIFTING TECH INC
Also Called: Mazzella Crane & Hoist Svcs
10605 Chester Rd (45215-1205)
PHONE....................513 772-4466

Fax: 513 772-7129
John Ellsworth, *Manager*
EMP: 12
SQ FT: 5,000 **Privately Held**
WEB: www.mazzellalifting.com
SIC: 3496 Woven wire products; slings, lifting: made from purchased wire
HQ: Mazzella Lifting Technologies, Inc.
21000 Aerospace Pkwy
Cleveland OH 44142
440 239-7000

(G-4070)
MCNERNEY & ASSOCIATES LLC (PA)
Also Called: P J McNerney & Associates
440 Northland Blvd (45240-3211)
PHONE....................513 241-9951
Fax: 513 825-5601
Patrick J McNerney, *President*
Jan McNerney, *Vice Pres*
Tim Egan, *Sales Executive*
Bryan Morton, *Maintence Staff*
◆ EMP: 26
SQ FT: 70,000
SALES (est): 4.8MM **Privately Held**
WEB: www.pjmcnerney.com
SIC: 2752 4783 Commercial printing, lithographic; packing goods for shipping

(G-4071)
MCNICHOLS COMPANY
3470 E Kemper Rd (45241-2007)
PHONE....................877 884-4653
Fax: 513 731-8812
Doug Leaf, *Sales Staff*
Carl Fallone, *Branch Mgr*
EMP: 3
SALES (corp-wide): 160.4MM **Privately Held**
SIC: 3441 Building components, structural steel
PA: Mcnichols Company
2502 N Rocky Point Dr # 750
Rocky Point FL 33607
877 884-4653

(G-4072)
MCSWAIN MANUFACTURING LLC
189 Container Pl (45246-1708)
PHONE....................513 671-6130
Fax: 513 671-2045
Michael Meshay, *President*
Bill Michalski, *Vice Pres*
Ann Cohron, *Accountant*
Debbie Picchione, *Human Res Mgr*
David Orth, *Director*
◆ EMP: 148
SQ FT: 70,000
SALES (est): 33.1MM
SALES (corp-wide): 1.5B **Privately Held**
SIC: 3599 Machine shop, jobbing & repair
PA: Insight Equity Holdings Llc
1400 Civic Pl Ste 250
Southlake TX 76092
817 488-7775

(G-4073)
MEASURENET TECHNOLOGY LTD
4242 Airport Rd Ste 101 (45226-1615)
PHONE....................513 396-6765
Robert Voorhees, *General Mgr*
Mark Hoffman, *Sales Dir*
Beth Voorhees, *Sales Mgr*
EMP: 10
SQ FT: 3,000
SALES (est): 1.1MM **Privately Held**
WEB: www.measurenet-tech.com
SIC: 3826 Analytical instruments

(G-4074)
MECHANICAL FINISHERS INC LLC
Also Called: Mfi
6350 Este Ave (45232-1450)
PHONE....................513 641-5419
Fax: 513 641-4193
Nico Cottone, *Principal*
EMP: 30
SALES (est): 3.4MM **Privately Held**
SIC: 3471 Decorative plating & finishing of formed products; cleaning, polishing & finishing

(G-4075)
MECHANICAL FINISHING INC
6350 Este Ave (45232-1450)
PHONE....................513 641-5419
Jerry Stenger, *President*
EMP: 20
SQ FT: 40,000
SALES (est): 1.7MM **Privately Held**
WEB: www.mechfin.com
SIC: 3471 Plating & polishing

(G-4076)
MEDERS SPECIAL TEES
618 Delhi Ave (45204-1222)
PHONE....................513 921-3800
Fax: 513 921-1864
Jerome A Meder, *Owner*
EMP: 8
SQ FT: 3,000
SALES (est): 724.2K **Privately Held**
WEB: www.lux.cinti.net
SIC: 2759 Screen printing

(G-4077)
MEDIA PROCUREMENT SERVICES INC
312 Walnut St (45202-4024)
PHONE....................513 977-3000
Kenneth Lowe, *President*
Timmy Nadeem, *Manager*
EMP: 4
SALES (est): 588K
SALES (corp-wide): 3B **Publicly Held**
WEB: www.scripps.com
SIC: 8741 5044 2679 Administrative management; office equipment; paper products, converted
HQ: Journal Media Group, Inc.
333 W State St
Milwaukee WI 53203
414 224-2000

(G-4078)
MEDIA SIGN COMPANY
2111 Kindel Ave (45214-1841)
PHONE....................513 564-9500
Fax: 513 564-9800
Joyce Mc Elroy, *President*
Robert Mc Elroy, *Vice Pres*
EMP: 4
SQ FT: 1,400
SALES: 900K **Privately Held**
WEB: www.mediasign.com
SIC: 3993 Signs & advertising specialties

(G-4079)
MEDPACE HOLDINGS INC (PA)
5375 Medpace Way (45227-1543)
PHONE....................513 579-9911
August J Troendle, *Ch of Bd*
Jesse J Geiger, *COO*
Jesse Geiger, *COO*
Susan E Burwig, *Senior VP*
Yun Le, *Vice Pres*
EMP: 7
SQ FT: 332,000
SALES: 421.5MM **Publicly Held**
SIC: 2834 8731 Pharmaceutical preparations; commercial physical research; biological research

(G-4080)
MEGGITT (ERLANGER) LLC
Also Called: Edac Composites
10293 Burlington Rd (45231-1901)
PHONE....................513 851-5550
Fax: 513 851-1926
Daniel Deutenberg, *Vice Pres*
Tom Little, *Vice Pres*
Steve Hartke, *Branch Mgr*
Victor Magliano, *Manager*
EMP: 70
SALES (corp-wide): 2.4B **Privately Held**
WEB: www.parkwayproducts.com
SIC: 3089 3544 2851 2822 Molding primary plastic; special dies, tools, jigs & fixtures; paints & allied products; synthetic rubber; molding compounds, plastics
HQ: Meggitt (Erlanger), Llc
1400 Jamike Ave
Erlanger KY 41018
859 525-8040

(G-4081)
MEIERJOHAN-WENGLER INC
10340 Julian Dr (45215-1131)
PHONE....................513 771-6074
Fax: 513 672-7183
Steve Jones, *President*
▲ EMP: 15 EST: 1941
SQ FT: 34,000
SALES (est): 2.5MM
SALES (corp-wide): 1.4B **Publicly Held**
WEB: www.plaques.net
SIC: 3366 Bronze foundry
HQ: Aurora Casket Company, Llc
10944 Marsh Rd
Aurora IN 47001
800 457-1111

(G-4082)
MEIERS WINE CELLARS INC
Also Called: John C Meier Grape Juice Co
6955 Plainfield Rd (45236-3793)
PHONE....................513 891-2900
Fax: 513 891-6370
Paul Lux, *President*
Lux Paul, *President*
Robert Manchick, *Principal*
Lucia Jack, *Vice Pres*
Jack Lucia, *Vice Pres*
▲ EMP: 29 EST: 1895
SQ FT: 20,000
SALES (est): 6.7MM
SALES (corp-wide): 44.4MM **Privately Held**
WEB: www.meierswinecellars.com
SIC: 2033 2084 2086 Fruit juices: fresh; wines; bottled & canned soft drinks
PA: Luxco, Inc.
5050 Kemper Ave
Saint Louis MO 63139
314 772-2626

(G-4083)
MELVIN STONE CO LLC
11641 Mosteller Rd Ste 2 (45241-1520)
PHONE....................513 771-0820
Susan B Salyer, *Principal*
EMP: 7
SALES (est): 760.5K **Privately Held**
SIC: 3281 Cut stone & stone products

(G-4084)
MENARD INC
2789 Cunningham Rd (45241-1390)
PHONE....................513 250-4566
EMP: 12
SALES (corp-wide): 15.5B **Privately Held**
SIC: 2431 Millwork
PA: Menard, Inc.
5101 Menard Dr
Eau Claire WI 54703
715 876-5911

(G-4085)
MERIDIAN BIOSCIENCE INC (PA)
3471 River Hills Dr (45244-3023)
PHONE....................513 271-3700
John A Kraeutler, *Ch of Bd*
Lawrence J Baldini, *Exec VP*
Slava A Elagin, *Exec VP*
Vecheslav A Elagin, *Exec VP*
Susan D Rolih, *Senior VP*
EMP: 253 EST: 1976
SQ FT: 120,000
SALES: 196MM **Publicly Held**
WEB: www.meridianbioscience.com
SIC: 2835 2834 In vitro & in vivo diagnostic substances; pharmaceutical preparations

(G-4086)
MERIDIAN LIFE SCIENCE INC (HQ)
Also Called: Viral Antigens
3471 River Hills Dr (45244-3023)
PHONE....................513 271-3700
Fax: 513 271-3762
Rick Eberly, *President*
Terry Gibson, *Vice Pres*
Lourdes Weltzien, *Vice Pres*
Deana Brunjes, *Controller*
Alex Fhvetf, *Manager*
EMP: 70
SQ FT: 34,000

SALES (est): 8.6MM
SALES (corp-wide): 196MM **Publicly
Held**
WEB: www.meridianbioscience.com
SIC: 2835 In vitro & in vivo diagnostic sub-
stances; veterinary diagnostic substances
PA: Meridian Bioscience, Inc.
3471 River Hills Dr
Cincinnati OH 45244
513 271-3700

(G-4087)
MESA INDUSTRIES INC (PA)
Also Called: Airplaco Equipment Company
4027 Eastern Ave (45226-1747)
PHONE....................513 321-2950
Fax: 513 321-8178
Terry Segerberg, *CEO*
Kent Sexton, *President*
Ken Segerberg, *Vice Pres*
James R Sexton, *Vice Pres*
Brian Karns, *Mfg Dir*
◆ EMP: 32
SQ FT: 100,000
SALES (est): 19MM **Privately Held**
WEB: www.mesa-ind.net
SIC: 3531 5085 5082 Bituminous, cement
& concrete related products & equipment;
construction & mining machinery; hose,
belting & packing

(G-4088)
MET L FAB INC
5313 Robert Ave (45248-6214)
PHONE....................513 561-4289
Fax: 513 561-2690
David Martin, *President*
EMP: 15 EST: 1959
SQ FT: 12,000
SALES (est): 2.6MM **Privately Held**
SIC: 3444 Sheet metalwork

(G-4089)
**METAL TECHNOLOGY SYSTEMS
INC**
Also Called: M T S
675 Redna Ter (45215-1108)
PHONE....................513 563-1882
Fax: 513 563-0758
Steve Williams, *President*
Perry Joyce, *Vice Pres*
Anita Williams, *Shareholder*
EMP: 5
SQ FT: 5,000
SALES: 500K **Privately Held**
SIC: 3444 Sheet metalwork

(G-4090)
**METALPHOTO OF CINCINNATI
INC**
1080 Skillman Dr (45215-1137)
PHONE....................513 772-8281
Fax: 513 772-8306
Herbert Wainer, *President*
Michael Elter, *General Mgr*
Patrick Hollis, *Vice Pres*
Richard Doerger, *VP Opers*
Lori Brown, *Cust Mgr*
EMP: 26 EST: 1959
SQ FT: 12,000
SALES (est): 3.8MM
SALES (corp-wide): 30.2MM **Privately
Held**
WEB: www.mpofcinci.com
SIC: 3993 Name plates: except engraved,
etched, etc.: metal
PA: Horizons Incorporated
18531 S Miles Rd
Cleveland OH 44128
216 475-0555

(G-4091)
**METALWORKING GROUP
HOLDINGS (PA)**
Also Called: Metalworking Group, The
9070 Pippin Rd (45251-3174)
PHONE....................513 521-4119
Mike Schmitt, *President*
Brad Brune, *Vice Pres*
Doug Watts, *CFO*
Jean Circatera, *Accountant*
Brian Dubay, *Sales Dir*
▲ EMP: 108 EST: 2000
SQ FT: 65,000
SALES (est): 27.7MM **Privately Held**
SIC: 3444 Sheet metalwork

(G-4092)
**METCUT RESEARCH
ASSOCIATES INC (PA)**
3980 Rosslyn Dr (45209-1110)
PHONE....................513 271-5100
Fax: 513 271-9511
William P Koster, *Ch of Bd*
John P Kahles, *President*
John H Clippinger, *Principal*
Robert T Keeler, *Principal*
John H More, *Principal*
EMP: 85
SQ FT: 25,000
SALES: 12.6MM **Privately Held**
WEB: www.metcut.com
SIC: 8734 3599 Metallurgical testing labo-
ratory; machine & other job shop work

(G-4093)
METLWEB
3330 E Kemper Rd (45241-1538)
PHONE....................513 563-8822
William E Ensminger, *President*
Marty Grogan, *Vice Pres*
John S George, *Data Proc Dir*
EMP: 20
SALES (est): 1.8MM **Privately Held**
SIC: 3444 3441 Sheet metalwork; fabri-
cated structural metal

(G-4094)
METRO RECYCLING COMPANY
19 W Vine St (45215-3233)
PHONE....................513 251-1800
Fax: 513 251-5239
Charles V Francis, *President*
James Sweet, *Plant Mgr*
Ben Harvey, *Purch Mgr*
Rebecca Clemons, *Human Res Mgr*
EMP: 9
SQ FT: 100,000
SALES (est): 1.6MM **Privately Held**
WEB: www.metrorecyclinginc.com
SIC: 2621 3089 4953 Paper mills; boxes,
plastic; recycling, waste materials

(G-4095)
METRODECK INC
4795 Day Rd (45252-1809)
PHONE....................513 541-4370
Fax: 513 681-4006
W Ronald Trischler, *President*
Mary Fischvogt, *Manager*
EMP: 10 EST: 1912
SQ FT: 50,000
SALES (est): 1.1MM **Privately Held**
SIC: 2542 3444 3449 5051 Shelving, of-
fice & store: except wood; sheet metal-
work; lath, expanded metal; steel; sheet
metalwork

(G-4096)
METZGER MACHINE CO
2165 Spring Grove Ave (45214-1790)
PHONE....................513 241-3360
Fax: 513 241-3361
David L Brown, *President*
Virginia Brown, *Admin Sec*
EMP: 10 EST: 1876
SQ FT: 10,000
SALES (est): 1.6MM **Privately Held**
SIC: 3599 5085 Machine shop, jobbing &
repair; industrial supplies

(G-4097)
MEYER TOOL INC (PA)
3055 Colerain Ave (45225-1827)
PHONE....................513 681-7362
Fax: 513 853-4439
Arlyn Easton, *President*
Larry Allen, *Vice Pres*
Jerry Flyr, *Vice Pres*
Ed Mayer, *Vice Pres*
Gary McGuire, *VP Mfg*
◆ EMP: 650
SQ FT: 365,000
SALES (est): 362.2MM **Privately Held**
WEB: www.meyertool.com
SIC: 3724 3599 Aircraft engines & engine
parts; machine shop, jobbing & repair

(G-4098)
MIBTACH ENTERPRISES INC
2629 Lytham Ct (45233-4295)
PHONE....................513 941-0387
William J Steioff, *President*

EMP: 4
SALES (est): 252.7K **Privately Held**
SIC: 3089 3999 Molding primary plastic;
novelties, bric-a-brac & hobby kits

(G-4099)
MICHELMAN INC
3023 E Kemper Rd Bldg 2 (45241-1509)
PHONE....................513 793-7766
Barbara Lantry-Miller, *Principal*
Phil Kreimer, *Engineer*
EMP: 20 **Privately Held**
SIC: 2869 Industrial organic chemicals
PA: Michelman, Inc.
9080 Shell Rd
Blue Ash OH 45236
513 793-7766

(G-4100)
MICRO METAL FINISHING LLC
3448 Spring Grove Ave (45225-1328)
P.O. Box 25187 (45225)
PHONE....................513 541-3095
Fax: 513 541-3099
John A Rose, *President*
Jim Moore, *Controller*
Karen Lafkas,
EMP: 61
SQ FT: 100,000
SALES: 6MM **Privately Held**
WEB: www.micrometalfinishing.com
SIC: 3471 Finishing, metals or formed
products; electroplating of metals or
formed products

(G-4101)
MICROPOWER LLC
10470 Evendale Dr (45241-2514)
PHONE....................513 382-0100
Subhan Khan,
Anis Khan,
Steve Taylor,
Harry Westerkamp,
EMP: 10
SALES (est): 1MM **Privately Held**
WEB: www.micropower.com
SIC: 3621 Power generators

(G-4102)
MICROPRESS AMERICA LLC
Also Called: Tachometer Press
4240 Minmor Dr (45217-1822)
PHONE....................513 746-0689
Todd Ea Larson, *Mng Member*
Chad S Beckett,
Marc T Hanger,
EMP: 3
SALES (est): 150K **Privately Held**
SIC: 2731 7389 Book publishing;

(G-4103)
**MICROPYRETICS HEATERS INTL
INC**
Also Called: Mhi
750 Redna Ter (45215-1109)
PHONE....................513 772-0404
Fax: 513 672-3333
Anu Vissa, *COO*
Brian Kandell, *Engineer*
Jorge Carbwood, *Marketing Staff*
Michael Stevens, *Marketing Staff*
Justin West, *Manager*
▲ EMP: 15
SALES (est): 3.7MM **Privately Held**
WEB: www.mhi-inc.com
SIC: 3567 Industrial furnaces & ovens

(G-4104)
**MICROSTRATEGY
INCORPORATED**
8044 Montgomery Rd # 700 (45236-2919)
PHONE....................513 792-2253
Mike Jonas, *Branch Mgr*
EMP: 5
SALES (corp-wide): 512.1MM **Publicly
Held**
WEB: www.microstrategy.com
SIC: 7372 7371 Application computer soft-
ware; computer software systems analy-
sis & design, custom
PA: Microstrategy Incorporated
1850 Towers Crescent Plz # 700
Tysons Corner VA 22182
703 848-8600

(G-4105)
MID-AMERICA GUTTERS INC
Also Called: Gutter Shutter Manufacturing
11820 Kemper Springs Dr # 103
(45240-1660)
PHONE....................513 671-3505
Mark Steinberg, *President*
Claire Degenhardt, *Director*
Melissa Crain, *Asst Director*
EMP: 8
SQ FT: 10,000
SALES: 1.5MM **Privately Held**
SIC: 3444 Gutters, sheet metal

(G-4106)
**MIDWEST WOODWORKING CO
INC**
4019 Montgomery Rd (45212-3694)
P.O. Box 12047 (45212-0047)
PHONE....................513 631-6684
Frank David, *President*
EMP: 20 EST: 1946
SQ FT: 60,000
SALES (est): 1.5MM **Privately Held**
SIC: 2431 2541 2434 Millwork; display
fixtures, wood; wood kitchen cabinets

(G-4107)
MIKE CLOSTERMAN
Also Called: Klosterman Signs
5620 Cheviot Rd (45247-7006)
PHONE....................513 245-9593
Mike Closterman, *Owner*
EMP: 3
SALES: 250K **Privately Held**
WEB: www.cheapersigns.com
SIC: 3993 Signs & advertising specialties

(G-4108)
MILLSTONE COFFEE INC (HQ)
1 Procter And Gamble Plz (45202-3315)
PHONE....................513 983-1100
R Kerry Clark, *President*
G W Pric, *President*
Clayton C Daley Jr, *Vice Pres*
S P Donovan Jr, *Vice Pres*
H J Kangis, *Vice Pres*
▲ EMP: 80
SALES (est): 82.2MM
SALES (corp-wide): 7.8B **Publicly Held**
WEB: www.millstone.com
SIC: 2095 Coffee roasting (except by
wholesale grocers)
PA: The J M Smucker Company
1 Strawberry Ln
Orrville OH 44667
330 682-3000

(G-4109)
MINUTEMAN PRESS
2312 E Sharon Rd (45241-1844)
PHONE....................513 772-0500
Fax: 513 772-4326
Julie Garrett, *Owner*
EMP: 5
SQ FT: 3,000
SALES: 500K **Privately Held**
WEB: www.mmprints.com
SIC: 2752 Commercial printing, litho-
graphic

(G-4110)
MINUTEMAN PRESS INC
9904 Colerain Ave (45251-1431)
PHONE....................513 741-9056
Fax: 513 741-9062
Portia Ash, *Principal*
EMP: 4
SALES (est): 355.3K **Privately Held**
SIC: 2752 Commercial printing, litho-
graphic

(G-4111)
MIRACLE DOCUMENTS
2300 Montana Ave Ste 301 (45211-3890)
PHONE....................513 651-2222
Bill Tapke, *Owner*
EMP: 3 EST: 2010
SALES (est): 160.7K **Privately Held**
SIC: 2759 Commercial printing

(G-4112)
MMP PRINTING INC
Also Called: Minuteman Press
10570 Chester Rd (45215-1204)
PHONE.................................513 381-0990
Melody Tuttle, *President*
William Tuttle, *Vice Pres*
Don Kahny, *Sales Staff*
Shannon Presley, *Sales Executive*
EMP: 23
SQ FT: 30,000
SALES (est): 4.5MM **Privately Held**
SIC: 2752 2791 2789 2759 Commercial printing, lithographic; photo-offset printing; typesetting; bookbinding & related work; commercial printing

(G-4113)
MODEL PATTERN & FOUNDRY CO
3242 Spring Grove Ave (45225-1373)
PHONE.................................513 542-2322
Fax: 513 542-7838
Shirley Kipp, *President*
David Kipp, *Corp Secy*
Kenneth Kipp, *Vice Pres*
EMP: 25 EST: 1943
SQ FT: 16,500
SALES: 1.5MM **Privately Held**
SIC: 3363 3364 3366 3365 Aluminum die-castings; brass & bronze die-castings; copper foundries; aluminum foundries

(G-4114)
MODERN DISPLAYS INC
4301 Schulte Dr (45205-2037)
PHONE.................................513 471-1639
Raymond Hafner, *President*
Eugene Hafner, *Vice Pres*
EMP: 6
SQ FT: 18,000
SALES: 500K **Privately Held**
SIC: 2759 Screen printing; advertising literature: printing

(G-4115)
MODERN ICE EQUIPMENT & SUP CO (PA)
Also Called: Modern Tour
5709 Harrison Ave (45248-1601)
PHONE.................................513 367-2101
Gary E Jerow, *President*
Shawn Messmore, *Vice Pres*
John Murphy, *Vice Pres*
Steve Schinkal, *Project Mgr*
Andrew Goderwis, *Project Engr*
◆ **EMP:** 20
SQ FT: 12,000
SALES (est): 19.9MM **Privately Held**
WEB: www.matthiesenequipment.com
SIC: 5078 3444 Refrigeration equipment & supplies; sheet metalwork

(G-4116)
MODERN MANUFACTURING INC (PA)
Also Called: M&S Machine and Manufacturing
240 Stille Dr (45233-1647)
PHONE.................................513 251-3600
Fax: 513 251-9644
Patrick Sexton, *President*
Dan Busch, *Vice Pres*
Diane Bearlaer, *Manager*
EMP: 10 EST: 2001
SQ FT: 30,000
SALES: 1.6MM **Privately Held**
WEB: www.modmfg.com
SIC: 2531 3444 3544 Public building & related furniture; sheet metal specialties, not stamped; special dies, tools, jigs & fixtures

(G-4117)
MOLECULAR RESEARCH CENTER (PA)
Also Called: MRC
5645 Montgomery Rd (45212-1846)
PHONE.................................513 841-0900
Fax: 513 841-0080
Piotr Chomczynski, *President*
Croft Edwards, *Vice Pres*
Judith Heiny, *Vice Pres*
Shirley Pohlman, *Purch Agent*
Dr Joanna Rymaszewska, *Marketing Staff*

▲ **EMP:** 19
SQ FT: 15,000
SALES (est): 1.8MM **Privately Held**
WEB: www.mrcgene.com
SIC: 2819 Industrial inorganic chemicals

(G-4118)
MOLEMAN
Also Called: Moleman Mole Trapping
1314 Pennsbury Dr (45238-3606)
P.O. Box 14785 (45250-0785)
PHONE.................................513 662-3017
Tom Schmidt, *Partner*
David Schmidt, *Partner*
Richard Schmidt, *Partner*
Sara Schmidt, *Partner*
EMP: 5
SALES (est): 429K **Privately Held**
WEB: www.themoleman.com
SIC: 2211 Moleskins

(G-4119)
MONNIG WELDING CO
521 Harriet St (45203-1886)
PHONE.................................513 241-5156
Fax: 513 241-7327
Lawrence Monnig Jr, *Partner*
EMP: 5 EST: 1875
SQ FT: 3,000
SALES (est): 300K **Privately Held**
SIC: 7692 3441 Welding repair; fabricated structural metal

(G-4120)
MONTI INCORPORATED (PA)
4510 Reading Rd (45229-1230)
PHONE.................................513 761-7775
Fax: 513 948-6858
Gavin J Narburgh, *President*
Beverly Narburgh, *Vice Pres*
Robert Duhl, *Mfg Staff*
Linda Corwin, *Controller*
John Narburgh, *Admin Sec*
▲ **EMP:** 72
SQ FT: 137,000
SALES (est): 37.7MM **Privately Held**
WEB: www.monti-inc.com
SIC: 3644 3599 Insulators & insulation materials, electrical; machine shop, jobbing & repair

(G-4121)
MOONSTRUCK GAMES INC
312 Walnut St Ste 2275 (45202-4044)
PHONE.................................513 721-3900
EMP: 5
SQ FT: 1,500
SALES (est): 210.2K **Privately Held**
SIC: 3944 5734 Mfg Games/Toys Ret Computers/Software

(G-4122)
MOR-LITE CO INC
2344 Wyoming Ave (45214-1025)
PHONE.................................513 661-8587
Fax: 513 661-8709
Donald Lauck, *President*
EMP: 4
SQ FT: 5,000
SALES: 350K **Privately Held**
SIC: 1751 1761 3444 3089 Window & door (prefabricated) installation; siding contractor; awnings, sheet metal; awnings, fiberglass & plastic combination

(G-4123)
MORRIS TECHNOLOGIES INC
11988 Tramway Dr (45241-1664)
PHONE.................................513 733-1611
Gregory M Morris, *CEO*
William G Noack, *President*
Mike Bauer, *Purchasing*
Wendell H Morris, *Treasurer*
Christopher Bruck, *Accounts Mgr*
EMP: 105
SQ FT: 25,000
SALES (est): 12MM **Privately Held**
WEB: www.morristech.com
SIC: 8711 3999 3313 3599 Mechanical engineering; models, except toy; alloys, additive, except copper: not made in blast furnaces; electrical discharge machining (EDM); surgical & medical instruments; engineering laboratory, except testing

(G-4124)
MORROW GRAVEL COMPANY INC (PA)
11641 Mosteller Rd Ste 2 (45241-1520)
PHONE.................................513 771-0820
James P Jurgensen, *President*
Tim St Clair, *CFO*
Dave Patterson, *Manager*
EMP: 20 EST: 1958
SQ FT: 15,000
SALES (est): 32.5MM **Privately Held**
SIC: 1442 1771 2951 Construction sand mining; gravel mining; blacktop (asphalt) work; asphalt & asphaltic paving mixtures (not from refineries)

(G-4125)
MORTON INTERNATIONAL LLC
Also Called: Morton Salt
5340 River Rd (45233-1645)
PHONE.................................513 941-1578
Fax: 513 941-8239
Ruben Lowrey, *Branch Mgr*
EMP: 9
SALES (corp-wide): 3.6B **Privately Held**
SIC: 1479 Salt & sulfur mining
HQ: Morton International, Llc
　　123 N Wacker Dr Ste 2400
　　Chicago IL 60606
　　312 807-2696

(G-4126)
MOSKOWITZ BROS INC
5300 Vine St (45217-1030)
PHONE.................................513 242-2100
Fax: 513 242-2107
Robert Moskowitz, *President*
Ira Moskowitz, *Principal*
Mark Moskowitz, *Vice Pres*
Linda Curtis, *VP Human Res*
EMP: 35
SQ FT: 70,000
SALES (est): 14.5MM **Privately Held**
WEB: www.moskowitzbros.com
SIC: 5093 3341 Ferrous metal scrap & waste; nonferrous metals scrap; secondary nonferrous metals

(G-4127)
MOTZ MOBILE CONTAINERS INC
3153 Madison Rd Apt 1 (45209-1399)
PHONE.................................513 772-6689
Marjorie Motz, *President*
James Motz, *Treasurer*
EMP: 5
SQ FT: 14,000
SALES (est): 430K **Privately Held**
WEB: www.flexamat.com
SIC: 1741 3272 Foundation & retaining wall construction; building materials, except block or brick: concrete

(G-4128)
MR LABEL INC
5018 Gray Rd (45232-1514)
PHONE.................................513 681-2088
Fax: 513 681-1249
Patrick H Meehan Jr, *President*
Timothy F Meehan, *Treasurer*
Brigid Hoffman, *Admin Sec*
EMP: 30
SQ FT: 19,200
SALES: 4.3MM **Privately Held**
WEB: www.mrlabel.com
SIC: 2759 2672 Flexographic printing; screen printing; coated & laminated paper

(G-4129)
MT CARMEL BREWING COMPANY
4362 Mt Carmel Tobasco Rd (45244-2338)
PHONE.................................513 519-7161
Michael Dewey, *Principal*
EMP: 7
SALES (est): 620K **Privately Held**
SIC: 2084 Wines

(G-4130)
MUEHLENKAMP PROPERTIES INC
Also Called: Paragon Metal Fabricators
4317 Kugler Mill Rd (45236-1820)
PHONE.................................513 745-0874
Fax: 513 745-9687

Joseph B Muehlenkamp III, *President*
Stanley Muehlenkamp, *Vice Pres*
Mark Muehlenkamp, *Treasurer*
EMP: 24
SQ FT: 20,000
SALES (est): 5.6MM **Privately Held**
WEB: www.paragonmetalfab.com
SIC: 3444 6531 Sheet metalwork; real estate agents & managers

(G-4131)
MULTI-COLOR CORPORATION
Also Called: Altivity Packaging
4500 Beech St (45212-3402)
PHONE.................................513 396-5600
Tom Yunker, *Senior VP*
Randy James, *Traffic Mgr*
John Gaffney, *Finance Other*
Terry Skiba, *Branch Mgr*
EMP: 150
SALES (corp-wide): 870.8MM **Publicly Held**
SIC: 2631 Container board
PA: Multi-Color Corporation
　　4053 Clough Woods Dr
　　Batavia OH 45103
　　513 381-1480

(G-4132)
MURDOCK INC
7180 Anderson Woods Dr (45244-3260)
PHONE.................................513 471-7700
Fax: 513 471-3299
Robert A Murdock, *President*
J Kelso Murdock, *Chairman*
Betty Jo Murdock, *Vice Pres*
David Blink, *Controller*
EMP: 15
SQ FT: 41,730
SALES (est): 3.4MM **Privately Held**
WEB: www.murdockfountains.com
SIC: 3431 Drinking fountains, metal

(G-4133)
MURRAY BROTHERS SHOWS INC
6282 Ashbourne Pl (45233-4454)
PHONE.................................513 941-6500
Paul Murray, *Principal*
EMP: 15 EST: 2000
SALES (est): 1.7MM **Privately Held**
SIC: 3599 Carnival machines & equipment, amusement park

(G-4134)
N K H SAFETY INC
1375 Kemper Meadow Dr # 12 (45240-1650)
PHONE.................................513 771-3839
William Huffstedder, *Principal*
John Neal, *Sr Associate*
EMP: 8
SALES (est): 810.5K **Privately Held**
SIC: 3845 Electromedical equipment

(G-4135)
N M R INC
Also Called: BP
7555 Fields Ertel Rd (45241-1750)
PHONE.................................513 530-9075
Fax: 513 563-9419
Mohamed Elnemr, *Owner*
EMP: 5
SALES (est): 404.9K **Privately Held**
WEB: www.nmr.com
SIC: 5541 2834 Filling stations, gasoline; pharmaceutical preparations

(G-4136)
NANBRANDS LLC
8405 Indian Hill Rd (45243-3703)
PHONE.................................513 313-9581
Nancy Aichholz, *Principal*
EMP: 3
SALES (est): 135.9K **Privately Held**
SIC: 2051 7389 Cakes, pies & pastries;

(G-4137)
NATIONAL ACCESS DESIGN LLC
Also Called: N A D
1924 Losantiville Ave (45237-4106)
PHONE.................................513 351-3400
Cheryl White, *President*
EMP: 13
SQ FT: 10,300

SALES: 1.2MM **Privately Held**
SIC: 2431 3442 3089 Millwork; metal
doors, sash & trim; doors, folding: plastic
or plastic coated fabric

(G-4138)
NATIONAL ADHESIVES INC
Also Called: Celtic Forms
9435 Waterstone Blvd # 200 (45249-8226)
PHONE......................................513 683-8650
Michael Roten, *President*
EMP: 10
SQ FT: 5,000
SALES (est): 931.4K **Privately Held**
SIC: 5085 2891 Adhesives, tape & plas-
ters; adhesives & sealants

(G-4139)
**NATIONAL BEDDING COMPANY
LLC**
1680 Carolina Ave (45237)
PHONE......................................513 421-4094
Mike Prude, *Branch Mgr*
EMP: 160
SALES (corp-wide): 4.2B **Privately Held**
WEB: www.sertanational.com
SIC: 2515 Box springs, assembled
HQ: National Bedding Company L.L.C.
2600 Forbs Ave
Hoffman Estates IL 60192
847 645-0200

(G-4140)
**NATIONAL MACHINE TOOL
COMPANY**
2013 E Galbraith Rd (45215-5633)
PHONE......................................513 541-6682
Fax: 513 541-6825
Harold J Rembold, *President*
Chris K Rembold, *Vice Pres*
Clifford Moore, *Marketing Staff*
EMP: 9
SQ FT: 5,998
SALES: 1MM **Privately Held**
WEB: www.keyseaters.com
SIC: 3541 Machine tools, metal cutting: ex-
otic (explosive, etc.)

(G-4141)
NATIONAL STARCH CHEMICAL
9435 Waterstone Blvd # 200 (45249-8229)
PHONE......................................513 830-0260
Fax: 513 683-5310
Michael Roten, *Principal*
John Rye, *Manager*
EMP: 4
SALES (est): 316K **Privately Held**
SIC: 2891 Adhesives & sealants

(G-4142)
NAVISTAR INC
11775 Highway Dr (45241-2005)
PHONE......................................513 733-8500
David Mannin, *Branch Mgr*
EMP: 6
SALES (corp-wide): 8.1B **Publicly Held**
WEB: www.internationaldelivers.com
SIC: 3711 Truck & tractor truck assembly
HQ: Navistar, Inc.
2701 Navistar Dr
Lisle IL 60532
331 332-5000

(G-4143)
**NEHEMIAH MANUFACTURING
CO LLC**
1130 Findlay St (45214-2052)
PHONE......................................513 351-5700
Daniel Meyer, *CEO*
Richard T Palmer, *President*
Mike Pachko, *COO*
Richard Halsey, *Vice Pres*
Dan Wall, *Vice Pres*
▲ EMP: 50
SQ FT: 33,706
SALES (est): 31.5MM **Privately Held**
SIC: 5122 2844 Toiletries; toilet prepara-
tions

(G-4144)
**NELSON PROFESSIONAL MKTG
INC**
5353 Spring Grove Ave (45217-1026)
PHONE......................................513 482-6150
Garry C Ferraris, *President*

Jorge Costa, *Exec VP*
Kurt Maurer, *Vice Pres*
Larry Schirmann, *CFO*
Mooy Frost, *Controller*
EMP: 4
SQ FT: 22,000
SALES: 120K **Privately Held**
SIC: 2899 Food contamination testing or
screening kits

(G-4145)
**NEPTUNE EQUIPMENT
COMPANY**
11082 Southland Rd (45240-3713)
PHONE......................................513 851-8008
Fax: 513 851-8009
Robert W Becker, *President*
Mary Ellen Shouse, *Corp Secy*
Ray Schwarz, *Marketing Staff*
Jarrett Lukens, *Manager*
EMP: 16
SQ FT: 4,000
SALES (est): 10MM **Privately Held**
WEB: www.neptuneequipment.com
SIC: 3825 1623 Meters: electric, pocket,
portable, panelboard, etc.; aqueduct con-
struction

(G-4146)
**NETHERLAND RUBBER
COMPANY (PA)**
2931 Exon Ave (45241-2593)
P.O. Box 62165 (45262-0165)
PHONE......................................513 733-0883
Fax: 513 733-1096
Timothy Clarke, *President*
Robert Pater, *Vice Pres*
Mike Cogozzo, *Purchasing*
Sue Clarke, *Treasurer*
Ken Berger, *Sales Mgr*
EMP: 17
SQ FT: 69,000
SALES (est): 9.7MM **Privately Held**
WEB: www.netherlandrubber.com
SIC: 5085 3053 3492 5099 Rubber
goods, mechanical; seals, industrial; gas-
kets, all materials; hose & tube fittings &
assemblies, hydraulic/pneumatic; safety
equipment & supplies; chemicals & allied
products; manufactured hardware (gen-
eral)

(G-4147)
NEURAL HOLDINGS LLC ✪
9867 Beech Dr (45231-2784)
PHONE......................................734 512-8865
Nicholas Shah, *CEO*
Paul Demott, *Principal*
Endel Maricq, *COO*
Kevin McHugh, *Vice Pres*
EMP: 4 EST: 2016
SALES (est): 98.3K **Privately Held**
SIC: 7372 Business oriented computer
software

(G-4148)
NEW PME INC
Also Called: Plant Maintenance Engineering
518 W Crescentville Rd (45246-1222)
PHONE......................................513 671-1717
Fax: 513 671-3767
Charles Walter, *President*
EMP: 30 EST: 1980
SALES (est): 3.9MM **Privately Held**
SIC: 3599 Machine shop, jobbing & repair

(G-4149)
**NEW VULCO MFG & SALES CO
LLC**
Also Called: Vulcan Oil Company
5353 Spring Grove Ave (45217-1026)
PHONE......................................513 242-2672
Garry Ferraris,
Larry Schirmann,
EMP: 60
SALES (est): 14.6MM **Privately Held**
SIC: 5983 2992 5171 2899 Fuel oil deal-
ers; oils & greases, blending & com-
pounding; petroleum bulk stations;
petroleum terminals; chemical prepara-
tions; specialty cleaning, polishes & sani-
tation goods; soap & other detergents

(G-4150)
NEWHOUSE & FAULKNER INC
Also Called: Corporate Printing
215 E 9th St (45202-2139)
P.O. Box 3587 (45201-3587)
PHONE......................................513 721-1660
George A Newhouse, *President*
Joyce Faulkner, *Vice Pres*
Joan Allen, *Manager*
EMP: 4
SQ FT: 2,500
SALES: 500K **Privately Held**
SIC: 2752 Commercial printing, offset; lith-
ographing on metal

(G-4151)
NEWMAN BROTHERS INC
5609 Center Hill Ave (45216-2340)
PHONE......................................513 242-0011
Fax: 513 242-0015
Ken Newman, *President*
Ted Oldiges, *Corp Secy*
Dick Stein, *Marketing Staff*
Libby Meirose, *Office Mgr*
EMP: 35 EST: 1882
SQ FT: 65,000
SALES (est): 7MM **Privately Held**
WEB: www.newmanbrothers.com
SIC: 3446 Architectural metalwork

(G-4152)
**NEXTGEN FIBER OPTICS LLC
(PA)**
720 E Pete Rose Way # 410 (45202-3579)
PHONE......................................513 549-4691
Richard Coleman,
EMP: 7
SALES (est): 4.3MM **Privately Held**
WEB: www.nextgenfiberoptics.com
SIC: 3229 Fiber optics strands

(G-4153)
NEXTMED SYSTEMS INC (PA)
16 Triangle Park Dr (45246-3411)
PHONE......................................216 674-0511
David Shute, *CEO*
James Bennett, *Ch of Bd*
Tony Paparella, *COO*
Wolfgang Sprie, *Finance*
Ronald Amrich, *Senior Mgr*
EMP: 44
SQ FT: 3,000
SALES (est): 3.6MM **Privately Held**
SIC: 7372 Business oriented computer
software

(G-4154)
NICKUM ENTERPRISES INC
Also Called: HI Tech Graphics
6105 Madison Rd (45227-1905)
PHONE......................................513 561-2292
Fax: 513 561-2294
Matthew Nickum, *President*
EMP: 4
SALES (est): 480K **Privately Held**
WEB: www.hitechgraphics.com
SIC: 5734 2752 Printers & plotters: com-
puters; commercial printing, lithographic

(G-4155)
**NIGERIAN ASSN PHARMACISTS
& PH**
483 Northland Blvd (45240-3210)
PHONE......................................513 861-2329
Nnodum Iheme, *Principal*
Charlene Mayes, *Manager*
EMP: 5
SALES: 194.8K **Privately Held**
SIC: 2834 Pharmaceutical preparations

(G-4156)
NILPETER USA INC
Also Called: Next
11550 Goldcoast Dr (45249-1640)
PHONE......................................513 489-4400
Nick Hughes, *Managing Dir*
Timothy Taggart, *Vice Pres*
Eric Vandenburg, *Vice Pres*
Norris Smith, *VP Mfg*
Julie McIntosh, *Purch Mgr*
◆ EMP: 110
SQ FT: 35,000

SALES (est): 39.8MM
SALES (corp-wide): 80.6K **Privately Held**
WEB: www.nilpeter.com
SIC: 3555 3554 3565 2759 Printing
trades machinery; die cutting & stamping
machinery; paper converting; packaging
machinery; commercial printing; coated &
laminated paper; packaging paper & plastics film, coated & laminated
PA: Nilpeter-Fonden
Elmedalsvej 20-22
Slagelse
585 283-11

(G-4157)
NINE GIANT BREWING LLC
3204 Nash Ave (45226-1232)
PHONE......................................510 220-5104
EMP: 3
SALES (est): 180.6K **Privately Held**
SIC: 2082 Malt beverages

(G-4158)
NITTO DENKO AVECIA INC
8560 Reading Rd (45215-5528)
PHONE......................................513 679-3000
Lindsay Biagini, *Branch Mgr*
EMP: 11
SALES (corp-wide): 6.7B **Privately Held**
SIC: 2834 Pharmaceutical preparations
HQ: Nitto Denko Avecia, Inc.
125 Fortune Blvd
Milford MA 01757

(G-4159)
NKH LIFE SAFETY LLC
4030 Mount Carmel Tobasco (45255-3431)
P.O. Box 30088 (45230-0088)
PHONE......................................513 688-7100
Fax: 513 688-0046
William Huffstedder,
EMP: 15
SALES (est): 1.7MM **Privately Held**
SIC: 3845 Defibrillator

(G-4160)
**NNODUM PHARMACEUTICALS
CORP**
483 Northland Blvd (45240-3210)
P.O. Box 19725 (45219-0725)
PHONE......................................513 861-2329
Nnodum Iheme, *President*
Peggy Iheme, *Vice Pres*
Pauline Glory, *Office Mgr*
EMP: 10
SQ FT: 8,300
SALES (est): 1.7MM **Privately Held**
WEB: www.zikspain.com
SIC: 2834 Pharmaceutical preparations

(G-4161)
NOBLE DENIM WORKSHOP
2929 Spring Grove Ave (45225-2157)
PHONE......................................513 560-5640
EMP: 4
SALES (est): 297K **Privately Held**
SIC: 2211 Denims

(G-4162)
NORTH BEND EXPRESS
3295 North Bend Rd (45239-7635)
PHONE......................................513 481-4623
Fax: 513 481-0952
Doug Pessler, *Principal*
EMP: 4
SQ FT: 410
SALES (est): 265.2K **Privately Held**
SIC: 2741 Miscellaneous publishing

(G-4163)
NORTHSIDE MEAT CO INC
2910 Sidney Ave (45225-2125)
PHONE......................................513 681-4111
Adam Nixon, *President*
Mary J Nixon, *President*
Brian Gay, *General Mgr*
EMP: 8
SQ FT: 5,000
SALES (est): 1.1MM **Privately Held**
SIC: 2011 Meat packing plants

(G-4164)
NORTON OUTDOOR ADVERTISING
5280 Kennedy Ave (45213-2620)
PHONE...................................513 631-4864
Fax: 513 631-4676
Thomas Norton, *CEO*
Daniel Norton, *President*
Steve Knapp, *Vice Pres*
Michael Norton, *Vice Pres*
Kay Malbla, *Finance Mgr*
EMP: 24 **EST:** 1949
SQ FT: 7,500
SALES (est): 3.3MM **Privately Held**
WEB: www.norton-outdoor.com
SIC: 7312 3993 Poster advertising, outdoor; billboard advertising; signs & advertising specialties

(G-4165)
NOVARTIS CORPORATION
Also Called: Novartis Vaccines & Diagnostic
1880 Waycross Rd (45240-2825)
PHONE...................................919 577-5000
EMP: 56
SALES (corp-wide): 48.5B **Privately Held**
SIC: 2834 Pharmaceutical preparations
HQ: Novartis Corporation
   1 S Ridgedale Ave 122
   East Hanover NJ 07936
   212 307-1122

(G-4166)
NOVITRAN LLC
8100 Deer Path (45243-1356)
PHONE...................................513 792-2727
Conrad Haupt, *Mng Member*
Lawrence Higvon, *Mng Member*
EMP: 5
SALES (est): 440K **Privately Held**
WEB: www.novitran.com
SIC: 3829 Transits, surveyors'

(G-4167)
NTS ENTERPRISES LTD (PA)
Also Called: Betula USA
1550 Magnolia Dr (45215-1914)
PHONE...................................513 531-1166
Stewart R Halbauer II, *CEO*
Natalie T Halbauer, *Vice Pres*
EMP: 1
SALES: 8MM **Privately Held**
SIC: 3149 5139 Athletic shoes, except rubber or plastic; footwear, athletic

(G-4168)
NURTURE BRANDS LLC
177 Wyoming Woods Ln (45215-2171)
PHONE...................................513 307-2338
Elizabeth Piocos,
EMP: 5
SALES (est): 350K **Privately Held**
SIC: 2086 Bottled & canned soft drinks

(G-4169)
NUTRALAB INC
5400 Indian Heights Dr (45243-3841)
PHONE...................................513 561-0471
Shri C Sharma, *President*
EMP: 9
SALES: 1.2MM **Privately Held**
WEB: www.nutralab.com
SIC: 2834 8731 Vitamin, nutrient & hematinic preparations for human use; food research

(G-4170)
NXSTAGE MEDICAL INC
12065 Montgomery Rd (45249-1728)
PHONE...................................513 712-1300
Jannie Heymaker, *Branch Mgr*
EMP: 5
SALES (corp-wide): 366.3MM **Publicly Held**
SIC: 3845 Electromedical equipment
PA: Nxstage Medical, Inc.
   350 Merrimack St
   Lawrence MA 01843
   978 687-4700

(G-4171)
OAK HILLS CARTON CO
6310 Este Ave (45232-1450)
PHONE...................................513 948-4200
Fax: 513 948-4203

Kenneth Kabel, *President*
Dennis Wortman, *Vice Pres*
Kim M Calah, *Executive*
EMP: 25
SQ FT: 40,000
SALES (est): 5.4MM **Privately Held**
WEB: www.oakhillscarton.com
SIC: 2679 2657 Paperboard products, converted; folding paperboard boxes

(G-4172)
OCCIDENTAL CHEMICAL CORP
4701 Paddock Rd (45229-1003)
PHONE...................................513 242-2900
Fax: 513 242-0016
Eugene Thomas, *Branch Mgr*
Luanne K Istre, *Clerk*
EMP: 29
SALES (corp-wide): 10.4B **Publicly Held**
WEB: www.oxychem.com
SIC: 2812 2874 2869 2821 Alkalies & chlorine; phosphatic fertilizers; industrial organic chemicals; plastics materials & resins; industrial inorganic chemicals; prepared feeds
HQ: Occidental Chemical Corporation
   5005 Lyndon B Johnson Fwy # 2200
   Dallas TX 75244
   972 404-3800

(G-4173)
ODACS INC
8634 Reading Rd (45215-5529)
PHONE...................................513 761-0539
Phil Barnett, *Principal*
EMP: 8
SALES (est): 1.2MM **Privately Held**
WEB: www.odacs.com
SIC: 2833 Drugs & herbs: grading, grinding & milling

(G-4174)
OHIO BIOFUELS
3613 Woodbridge Pl (45226-1730)
PHONE...................................614 886-6518
Daniel S Casey, *Principal*
EMP: 3
SALES (est): 147.6K **Privately Held**
SIC: 2911 Petroleum refining

(G-4175)
OHIO CENTECH
444 Hidden Valley Ln (45215-2542)
PHONE...................................513 477-8779
Jeff Weiss, *Principal*
EMP: 5
SALES (est): 376.4K **Privately Held**
SIC: 3281 Cut stone & stone products

(G-4176)
OHIO FEATHER COMPANY INC
1 Kovach Dr (45215-1000)
PHONE...................................513 921-3373
Fax: 513 921-3381
Gabriel Guigui, *President*
Daniel Guigui, *Vice Pres*
▲ **EMP:** 6
SALES (est): 600K **Privately Held**
SIC: 3999 Feathers & feather products

(G-4177)
OHIO FLAME HARDENING COMPANY
637 N Wayne Ave (45215-2250)
PHONE...................................513 733-5162
Fax: 513 733-5162
Robert Bokon, *President*
EMP: 24
SALES (corp-wide): 1.4MM **Privately Held**
SIC: 3398 Brazing (hardening) of metal
PA: Ohio Flame Hardening Company Inc
   4110 Columbia Rd
   Lebanon OH 45036
   513 336-6160

(G-4178)
OHIO HYDRAULICS INC
2510 E Sharon Rd Ste 1 (45241-1891)
PHONE...................................513 771-2590
Fax: 513 771-1447
John Davis, *Ch of Bd*
Kathleen Hilliard, *President*
Tamera Fair, *Corp Secy*
Dave Davis, *Vice Pres*
Robert Farwick, *Vice Pres*

EMP: 25 **EST:** 1971
SQ FT: 13,500
SALES (est): 6.5MM **Privately Held**
WEB: www.ohiohydraulics.com
SIC: 3492 3599 5084 7699 Hose & tube fittings & assemblies, hydraulic/pneumatic; flexible metal hose, tubing & bellows; hydraulic systems equipment & supplies; tank repair & cleaning services; welding repair; manufactured hardware (general)

(G-4179)
OHIO PLYWOOD BOX
5555 Vine St (45216-2343)
PHONE...................................513 242-9125
Jerry Graves, *Owner*
EMP: 4
SQ FT: 3,500
SALES: 75K **Privately Held**
SIC: 2493 Reconstituted wood products

(G-4180)
OHIO TILE & MARBLE CO (PA)
3809 Spring Grove Ave (45223-2693)
PHONE...................................513 541-4211
Fax: 513 541-2966
Sean Dowers, *President*
Ruth Dowers, *Vice Pres*
Lisa Weidmenn, *Controller*
Sharon Baird, *Sales Dir*
Clyde Dowers, *Shareholder*
▲ **EMP:** 20
SQ FT: 21,500
SALES (est): 4.8MM **Privately Held**
WEB: www.ohiotile.com
SIC: 5032 5211 3281 3253 Tile, clay or other ceramic, excluding refractory; marble building stone; tile, ceramic; masonry materials & supplies; marble, building: cut & shaped; ceramic wall & floor tile

(G-4181)
OHIO WOODWORKING CO INC
5035 Beech St (45212-2399)
PHONE...................................513 631-0870
Fax: 513 458-5021
Thomas R Frank Jr, *President*
Peggy Frank, *Admin Sec*
EMP: 8 **EST:** 1931
SQ FT: 17,000
SALES (est): 1MM **Privately Held**
WEB: www.ohiowoodworkingcompany.com
SIC: 2541 2431 Display fixtures, wood; store fixtures, wood; millwork

(G-4182)
OKEEFFES WORKING HANDS CREME
4550 Red Bank Rd (45227-2118)
P.O. Box 338, Sisters OR (97759-0338)
PHONE...................................800 275-2718
Fax: 541 549-1486
Tara Broadbent, *President*
Michael Broadbent, *Vice Pres*
Duew Orr, *Controller*
▲ **EMP:** 18
SQ FT: 7,500
SALES: 2MM **Privately Held**
WEB: www.okeeffescompany.com
SIC: 2844 Cosmetic preparations

(G-4183)
OKL CAN LINE INC
11235 Sebring Dr (45240-2714)
PHONE...................................513 825-1655
Fax: 513 825-1948
Anthony Lacey, *CEO*
Paul Henderson, *President*
Douglas Stewart, *Vice Pres*
Richard Green, *Opers Mgr*
Robin Lamgaday, *Engineer*
◆ **EMP:** 47
SQ FT: 50,000
SALES (est): 10.6MM **Privately Held**
WEB: www.oklcan.com
SIC: 3565 7699 3599 Bottling & canning machinery; industrial machinery & equipment repair; machine shop, jobbing & repair
PA: Allcan Global Services, Inc
   11235 Sebring Dr
   Cincinnati OH 45240
   513 825-1655

(G-4184)
OLIVE SMUCKERS OIL
5204 Spring Grove Ave (45217-1031)
PHONE...................................513 646-7103
EMP: 3 **EST:** 2010
SALES (est): 260K **Privately Held**
SIC: 2079 Olive oil

(G-4185)
OLIVER CHEMICAL CO INC
2908 Spring Grove Ave (45225-2154)
PHONE...................................513 541-4540
Fax: 513 541-4543
Thomas J Stiens, *President*
Bob Stiens, *General Mgr*
Robert O Stiens, *Vice Pres*
Ted Finchatten, *Purchasing*
EMP: 7 **EST:** 1938
SQ FT: 25,000
SALES (est): 670K **Privately Held**
SIC: 2842 3471 2992 2899 Sanitation preparations; metal polish; specialty cleaning preparations; plating & polishing; lubricating oils & greases; chemical preparations; soap & other detergents

(G-4186)
OMNICARE PHRM OF MIDWEST LLC (DH)
201 E 4th St Ste 900 (45202-1513)
PHONE...................................513 719-2600
Joel Gemunder, *Principal*
Kathy Kopp, *COO*
Lisa Morgenthaler, *Controller*
Charlene Francis, *Marketing Staff*
Victoria Kasten, *Manager*
EMP: 100
SALES (est): 27.7MM
SALES (corp-wide): 177.5B **Publicly Held**
SIC: 5122 5912 2834 Drugs & drug proprietaries; drug stores; pharmaceutical preparations
HQ: Neighborcare Pharmacy Services, Inc.
   201 E 4th St Ste 900
   Cincinnati OH 45202
   513 719-2600

(G-4187)
ONE CLOUD SERVICES LLC
Also Called: Zimcom Internet Solutions
1080 Nimitzview Dr (45230-4314)
PHONE...................................513 231-9500
Anne Zimmerman, *President*
Jason Huebner, *Vice Pres*
Steve Searles, *Vice Pres*
EMP: 6
SALES (est): 135.3K
SALES (corp-wide): 1.5MM **Privately Held**
SIC: 7372 Business oriented computer software
PA: Liberty Noc, Llc
   24200 Woodward Ave
   Pleasant Ridge MI 48069
   248 582-1600

(G-4188)
ONE UNIVERSAL BRANDS LLC
312 Walnut St Ste 1151 (45202-4026)
PHONE...................................513 362-4326
Rose Tilford, *President*
EMP: 4
SALES (est): 368.6K **Privately Held**
SIC: 5137 2321 Rack merchandise jobbers; men's & boys' sports & polo shirts

(G-4189)
ONETOUCHPOINT EAST CORP
Also Called: Touch Print Solution
1441 Western Ave (45214-2041)
PHONE...................................513 421-1600
Fax: 513 421-2433
Christopher A Illman, *Principal*
William Pearson, *Principal*
George Ditullio, *Purch Mgr*
Ben Griffith, *CFO*
Larry Halenkamp, *CFO*
EMP: 87 **EST:** 1935
SQ FT: 102,000

SALES (est): 17.6MM
SALES (corp-wide): 221.4MM **Privately Held**
WEB: www.bermanprinting.com
SIC: 2759 2752 2791 2789 Commercial printing; commercial printing, lithographic; typesetting; bookbinding & related work
PA: Onetouchpoint Corp.
1225 Walnut Ridge Dr
Hartland WI 53029
630 586-9002

(G-4190)
OPTIMAL OFFICE SOLUTIONS LLC
25 Merchant St Ste 135 (45246-3740)
PHONE..................................201 257-8516
Ana Vivancos, *Mng Member*
Kavous Ahmadi,
EMP: 3
SQ FT: 800
SALES: 264.1K **Privately Held**
SIC: 7372 Prepackaged software

(G-4191)
OPTIMUS LLC
4623 Wesley Ave Ste B (45212-2243)
PHONE..................................513 918-2320
John Brandt, *Principal*
Anita Curtis, *Manager*
Travis Barlow, *Director*
EMP: 35
SALES (est): 1MM **Privately Held**
SIC: 3842 Surgical appliances & supplies

(G-4192)
OPTIMZED PRDCTVITY SLTIONS LLC
Also Called: Omative North America
9435 Waterstone Blvd (45249-8226)
PHONE..................................513 444-2156
EMP: 3
SALES (est): 180K **Privately Held**
SIC: 7372 Prepackaged Software Services

(G-4193)
ORCHEM CORPORATION
4927 Beech St (45212-2315)
PHONE..................................513 874-9700
Fax: 513 874-3624
Oscar Robertson, *President*
Craig Feltner, *General Mgr*
Shana Robertson-Shaw, *Vice Pres*
Cindy Schroeder, *Accounting Mgr*
Denise Ramey, *Sales Staff*
EMP: 26
SQ FT: 80,000
SALES (est): 6.7MM **Privately Held**
WEB: www.orfoods.com
SIC: 2842 Specialty cleaning preparations; sanitation preparations

(G-4194)
ORGANIZED LIVING INC (PA)
3100 E Kemper Rd (45241-1517)
PHONE..................................513 489-9300
Fax: 513 277-3701
John D Kokenge, *CEO*
Kevin Glynn, *General Mgr*
Kevin Ball, *Principal*
Robert J Lamping, *Vice Pres*
Steve McCamley, *Vice Pres*
▲ **EMP:** 40 **EST:** 1919
SQ FT: 16,000
SALES (est): 33.5MM **Privately Held**
WEB: www.schultestorage.com
SIC: 3496 3083 3411 2542 Miscellaneous fabricated wire products; laminated plastics plate & sheet; metal cans; partitions & fixtures, except wood

(G-4195)
ORION CONTROL PANELS INC
5012 Calvert St Ste B (45209-1076)
PHONE..................................513 615-6534
Aaron Keeney, *President*
EMP: 3 **EST:** 2013
SALES (est): 290K **Privately Held**
SIC: 3625 Industrial controls: push button, selector switches, pilot

(G-4196)
ORION HOLDINGS LLC
Also Called: Orion Safety Systems
3802 Ford Cir (45227-3403)
PHONE..................................513 871-4344

Fax: 513 871-8528
Tom Hodges, *Manager*
Ilene Vickes, *Manager*
Geoffrey Mather,
Stephanie Latchford, *Administration*
▲ **EMP:** 5 **EST:** 1997
SQ FT: 11,000
SALES (est): 680.8K **Privately Held**
WEB: www.orionholdings.com
SIC: 3842 Personal safety equipment

(G-4197)
OSBORNE COINAGE COMPANY (PA)
Also Called: Doran Manufacturing Co.
2851 Massachusetts Ave (45225-2276)
PHONE..................................513 681-5424
Fax: 513 681-5604
Thomas E Stegman, *President*
Ross Ormsby, *President*
Jim Samocki, *General Mgr*
Kevin Troklus, *Purch Agent*
Randy Caskey, *Engineer*
▲ **EMP:** 70 **EST:** 1835
SQ FT: 40,000
SALES: 13MM **Privately Held**
WEB: www.doranmfg.com
SIC: 3999 3644 3613 Coins & tokens; non-currency; terminal boards; panelboards & distribution boards, electric

(G-4198)
OSTEODYNAMICS
3130 Highland Ave Fl 3 (45219-2399)
PHONE..................................405 921-9271
David Ralph, *Owner*
EMP: 4
SALES (est): 160K **Privately Held**
SIC: 3845 Electromedical equipment

(G-4199)
OTOMIK PRODUCTS INC
Also Called: Petprojekt
6919 Silverton Ave (45236-3701)
PHONE..................................877 776-5358
Jason Vap, *President*
Erik Vap, *Vice Pres*
Nancy Vap, *Treasurer*
▲ **EMP:** 5
SQ FT: 3,615
SALES: 370K **Privately Held**
SIC: 3949 3999 Sporting & athletic goods; pet supplies

(G-4200)
OTR CONTROLS LLC
40 E Mcmicken Ave (45202-6549)
PHONE..................................513 621-2197
Donna Owens, *Manager*
Howard Elliott,
Robert Burroughs, *Admin Sec*
EMP: 5
SQ FT: 3,000
SALES: 363.7K **Privately Held**
WEB: www.otrcontrols.com
SIC: 3613 3679 Control panels, electric; harness assemblies for electronic use: wire or cable

(G-4201)
OUR DAILY BREAD
1721 Logan St (45202-6949)
P.O. Box 14862 (45250-0862)
PHONE..................................513 621-6364
Fax: 513 621-3513
Tyler Pettigrew, *Exec Dir*
Ruth Vogelpohl, *Director*
Julia Sharp, *Director*
EMP: 5
SALES: 1MM **Privately Held**
SIC: 2711 8322 Newspapers, publishing & printing; individual & family services

(G-4202)
OUT ON A LIMB
5311 Springdale Rd (45251-1819)
PHONE..................................513 432-5091
Michael Niehaus, *Principal*
EMP: 3
SALES (est): 305K **Privately Held**
SIC: 3842 Limbs, artificial

(G-4203)
OUTBACK CYCLE SHACK LLC
Also Called: Pride and True Garage
7923 Blue Ash Rd (45236-2601)
PHONE..................................513 554-1048
Sean Bast, *CEO*
EMP: 3
SALES: 180K **Privately Held**
SIC: 7699 3751 Motorcycle repair service; motorcycle accessories

(G-4204)
OWEN S PRECISION GRINDING
Also Called: Owens Precisn Grindg
8383 Blue Ash Rd (45236-1986)
PHONE..................................513 745-9335
Wanda Owens, *Owner*
Patrick Glassmeyer, *Vice Pres*
Kathy Glassmyer, *Manager*
EMP: 3
SQ FT: 2,500
SALES: 450K **Privately Held**
SIC: 3599 Amusement park equipment

(G-4205)
OWL BE SWEATIN
Also Called: Hoot and Holler,
4914 Ridge Ave (45209-1035)
PHONE..................................513 260-2026
Kc Debra, *Partner*
Mallory Debra, *Partner*
EMP: 3
SALES (est): 210.3K **Privately Held**
SIC: 2339 5632 Scarves, hoods, headbands, etc.: women's; women's accessory & specialty stores

(G-4206)
P & C METAL POLISHING INC
340 Glendale Milford Rd (45215-1102)
PHONE..................................513 771-9143
Fax: 513 771-9164
Perry Pullum, *President*
Donna Williamson, *Vice Pres*
EMP: 20
SQ FT: 30,000
SALES (est): 2.4MM **Privately Held**
WEB: www.pandcmetalpolishing.com
SIC: 3471 Polishing, metals or formed products

(G-4207)
P-AMERICAS LLC
Also Called: Pepsico
2121 Sunnybrook Dr (45237-2107)
PHONE..................................513 948-5100
Fax: 513 821-3029
Chuck Lewis, *Mfg Staff*
Dave Bolger, *QC Mgr*
Tim Mund, *QC Mgr*
Paul Assum, *Sales Staff*
Bob Goodman, *Branch Mgr*
EMP: 400
SQ FT: 150,000
SALES (corp-wide): 62.8B **Publicly Held**
SIC: 2086 Carbonated soft drinks, bottled & canned
HQ: P-Americas Llc
1 Pepsi Way
Somers NY

(G-4208)
PACKAGING CORPORATION AMERICA
Also Called: PCA
791 Saint Thomas Ct (45230-3873)
PHONE..................................513 582-0690
Keith Ferrara, *Manager*
EMP: 5
SALES (corp-wide): 5.7B **Publicly Held**
SIC: 2653 Corrugated & solid fiber boxes
PA: Packaging Corporation Of America
1955 W Field Ct
Lake Forest IL 60045
847 482-3000

(G-4209)
PALETTE STUDIOS INC
2501 Woodburn Ave (45206-2202)
PHONE..................................513 961-1316
Fax: 513 961-2496
Sharon L Denight, *President*
EMP: 4
SQ FT: 3,500

SALES (est): 487.2K **Privately Held**
WEB: www.palettestudios.com
SIC: 5719 3645 Lamps & lamp shades; residential lighting fixtures

(G-4210)
PANEL-FAB INC
10520 Taconic Ter (45215-1125)
PHONE..................................513 771-1462
Fax: 513 771-4223
Robert A Harrison, *President*
Nancy J Shurlow, *Principal*
Stephen T Williford, *Vice Pres*
Carolyn Zinnecker, *Purch Mgr*
Carolyn Norris, *Purchasing*
EMP: 90 **EST:** 1979
SQ FT: 25,000
SALES (est): 40.7MM **Privately Held**
WEB: www.panel-fab.com
SIC: 3613 Control panels, electric

(G-4211)
PARAGON PRESS
2239 Fulton Ave (45206-2504)
PHONE..................................513 281-9911
Fax: 513 281-5468
James Fryman, *Owner*
EMP: 4
SALES (est): 240K **Privately Held**
SIC: 2759 2752 Letterpress printing; commercial printing, offset

(G-4212)
PATHEON PHARMACEUTICALS INC
2110 E Galbraith Rd (45237-1625)
P.O. Box 40017, College Station TX (77842-4017)
PHONE..................................513 948-7942
Claudia Hayes, *Business Mgr*
Toni Sweeney, *Vice Pres*
Laurie Fite, *Senior Buyer*
Wanda Cole, *Purch Agent*
Debbie Amos, *QA Dir*
EMP: 208
SALES (corp-wide): 1.9B **Privately Held**
SIC: 2834 Pharmaceutical preparations
HQ: Patheon Pharmaceuticals Inc.
4815 Emperor Blvd Ste 300
Durham NC 27703
919 226-3200

(G-4213)
PATIO ENCLOSURES (PA)
11949 Tramway Dr (45241-1666)
PHONE..................................513 733-4646
Ronald J Molnar, *President*
Donna Molnar, *Corp Secy*
Craig Cox, *Vice Pres*
EMP: 19
SQ FT: 10,000
SALES (est): 2.2MM **Privately Held**
SIC: 5039 2452 1521 Prefabricated structures; prefabricated wood buildings; patio & deck construction & repair

(G-4214)
PATRICIA LEE BURD
Also Called: Crosstown Bindery
310 Culvert St (45202-2229)
PHONE..................................513 302-4860
Patricia Lee Burd, *Owner*
EMP: 3
SALES (est): 110K **Privately Held**
SIC: 2789 Bookbinding & related work

(G-4215)
PATRICK J BURKE & CO
Also Called: Burke & Company
901 Adams Crossing Fl 1 (45202-1693)
PHONE..................................513 455-8200
Fax: 513 455-8212
Patrick Burke, *Owner*
Mark Miller, *Managing Dir*
Eugene Schindler, *Co-Owner*
Jamie Baker-Prewitt, *Senior VP*
Dianne Marschman, *Vice Pres*
EMP: 25
SALES (est): 2.9MM **Privately Held**
SIC: 8721 7372 Certified public accountant; prepackaged software

(G-4216)
PAUL BARTEL (PA)
Also Called: Baroque Violin Shop
1038 W North Bend Rd (45224-2241)
PHONE.................................513 541-2000
Fax: 513 541-2019
Paul Bartel, *Owner*
▲ EMP: 5
SQ FT: 2,000
SALES (est): 1.1MM **Privately Held**
WEB: www.baroqueviolinshop.com
SIC: 3931 5736 7359 7699 String instruments & parts; musical instrument stores; musical instrument rental services; musical instrument repair services

(G-4217)
PAUL WILKE & SON INC
1965 Grand Ave (45214-1505)
PHONE.................................513 921-3163
Fax: 513 921-0735
Charles S Wilke, *President*
Ed Wilke, *Vice Pres*
Edwin Wilke, *Vice Pres*
EMP: 14
SQ FT: 22,000
SALES (est): 1.8MM **Privately Held**
WEB: www.paulwilkeandson.com
SIC: 3444 3599 7692 Sheet metalwork; machine shop, jobbing & repair; welding repair

(G-4218)
PAVESTONE LLC
8479 Broadwell Rd (45244-1693)
PHONE.................................513 474-3783
Craig Willike, *General Mgr*
Jeff McKee, *Sales Staff*
Dave Lemmon, *Manager*
Dennis Potts, *Manager*
Lester Ramsey, *Manager*
EMP: 70
SQ FT: 54,837 **Privately Held**
WEB: www.pavestone.com
SIC: 3272 3281 Paving materials, prefabricated concrete; cut stone & stone products
HQ: Pavestone, Llc
3490 Piedmont Rd Ne # 1300
Atlanta GA 30305
404 926-3167

(G-4219)
PCY ENTERPRISES INC
Also Called: Young & Bertke Air Systems
3111 Spring Grove Ave (45225-1821)
PHONE.................................513 241-5566
Roger Young, *President*
Lori Morgan, *Vice Pres*
Michael Munafo, *Vice Pres*
Tim Rohrer, *Vice Pres*
Phillip C Young, *Shareholder*
EMP: 28
SQ FT: 51,000
SALES (est): 4MM **Privately Held**
WEB: www.youngbertke.com
SIC: 1761 3441 3564 3444 Sheet metalwork; fabricated structural metal; blowers & fans; sheet metalwork; fabricated plate work (boiler shop)

(G-4220)
PDMB INC
9600 Colerain Ave Ste 110 (45251-2014)
PHONE.................................513 522-7362
Donald Peak, *President*
Will Singer, *Vice Pres*
Adam Singer, *Sales Mgr*
Audrey Vuozzo, *Technical Staff*
EMP: 5
SQ FT: 1,200
SALES (est): 532.7K **Privately Held**
WEB: www.palm-tech.com
SIC: 7372 7371 Prepackaged software; custom computer programming services

(G-4221)
PEERLESS PRINTING COMPANY
2250 Gilbert Ave Ste 1 (45206-2531)
PHONE.................................513 721-4657
Fax: 513 721-0694
Ken Schrand, *President*
Paul Dimario, *Principal*
Jay Heidemann, *Principal*
Steve Lyons, *Principal*
Ryan Schrand, *Principal*

EMP: 12 EST: 1900
SQ FT: 4,400
SALES (est): 2.1MM **Privately Held**
SIC: 2752 Commercial printing, lithographic

(G-4222)
PEP PONY EXPRESS PRINTING INC
1645 Blue Rock St (45223-7500)
PHONE.................................513 542-4882
Fax: 513 542-5230
Jerry Laake, *President*
EMP: 4
SALES (est): 164.5K **Privately Held**
SIC: 5943 7334 2759 Office forms & supplies; photocopying & duplicating services; commercial printing

(G-4223)
PERFECT PROBATE
2036 8 Mile Rd (45244-2607)
PHONE.................................513 791-4100
Shawn Wood, *Owner*
EMP: 6
SALES (est): 332.2K **Privately Held**
WEB: www.perfectprobate.com
SIC: 7372 8111 Prepackaged software; legal services

(G-4224)
PERFORMANCE ABRASIVES INC
10330 Wayne Ave (45215-1129)
PHONE.................................513 733-9283
Fax: 513 769-5901
Jim Meister, *President*
Beverly Meister, *Vice Pres*
▲ EMP: 5
SQ FT: 17,000
SALES (est): 624.6K **Privately Held**
WEB: www.performanceabrasives.net
SIC: 3291 Abrasive products

(G-4225)
PERFORMANCE ELECTRONICS LTD
11529 Goldcoast Dr (45249-1620)
PHONE.................................513 777-5233
Brian Lewis, *Managing Prtnr*
Mike Monroe, *Sales Staff*
EMP: 8
SALES: 3MM **Privately Held**
WEB: www.pe-ltd.com
SIC: 3679 Electronic circuits

(G-4226)
PERFORMANCE MOTORSPORTS
2545 W Galbraith Rd (45239-4206)
PHONE.................................513 931-9999
Joe Leach, *Owner*
Joe Leacg, *Owner*
EMP: 3
SALES (est): 170K **Privately Held**
SIC: 3462 5531 Automotive & internal combustion engine forgings; automotive parts

(G-4227)
PERFORMANCE PLASTICS LTD
4435 Brownway Ave (45209-1264)
PHONE.................................513 321-8404
Fax: 513 321-0288
Tom Mendel, *President*
Edward Schauer, *COO*
Daniel King, *Production*
Anthony Malone, *Engineer*
Peggy Delany, *Sls & Mktg Exec*
EMP: 40 EST: 1982
SQ FT: 20,000
SALES (est): 11.6MM **Privately Held**
WEB: www.performanceplastics.com
SIC: 3089 Injection molding of plastics

(G-4228)
PERFUME COUNTER
11700 Princeton Pike (45246-2535)
PHONE.................................513 885-5989
Christianne Kelly, *Principal*
EMP: 3
SALES (est): 221.5K **Privately Held**
SIC: 3131 Counters

(G-4229)
PERIMETER TECHNOLOGIES INC
Also Called: Pet Stop
7669 Wooster Pike C (45227-3925)
PHONE.................................513 322-5453
Robert J Slattery, *CEO*
Blanine Bacher, *Manager*
EMP: 17
SQ FT: 2,000
SALES (est): 1.7MM **Privately Held**
SIC: 2399 3089 Pet collars, leashes, etc.: non-leather; fences, gates & accessories: plastic

(G-4230)
PETE GAIETTO & ASSOCIATES INC
1900 Section Rd (45237-3308)
PHONE.................................513 771-0903
Jordan Gaietto, *CEO*
▲ EMP: 75
SQ FT: 3,880
SALES (est): 15.4MM **Privately Held**
SIC: 2542 Office & store showcases & display fixtures

(G-4231)
PETER CREMER NORTH AMERICA LP (PA)
Also Called: Pcna
3117 Southside Ave (45204-1215)
PHONE.................................513 471-7200
Raymond Bitzer, *Managing Prtnr*
▲ EMP: 60
SALES (est): 25.6MM **Privately Held**
WEB: www.petercremerna.com
SIC: 2843 Sulfonated oils, fats or greases

(G-4232)
PETNET SOLUTIONS INC
2139 Alburn Ave (45219)
PHONE.................................865 218-2000
Danny Bingham, *Manager*
EMP: 4
SALES (corp-wide): 89.6B **Privately Held**
SIC: 2835 Radioactive diagnostic substances
HQ: Petnet Solutions, Inc.
810 Innovation Dr
Knoxville TN 37932
865 218-2000

(G-4233)
PFPC ENTERPRISES INC
5750 Hillside Ave (45233-1508)
PHONE.................................513 941-6200
Peter F Coffaro, *Ch of Bd*
James Coffaro, *President*
Gina Antrim, *Purch Agent*
Stephen Stout, *CFO*
Art Schutte, *Controller*
EMP: 300 EST: 1963
SQ FT: 52,000
SALES (est): 18.7MM **Privately Held**
WEB: www.pabcofluidpower.com
SIC: 5023 5084 3594 3535 Floor coverings; industrial machinery & equipment; pumps & pumping equipment; water pumps (industrial); hydraulic systems equipment & supplies; fluid power pumps & motors; conveyors & conveying equipment; turbines & turbine generator sets

(G-4234)
PGT HEALTHCARE LLP (HQ)
1 Procter And Gamble Plz (45202-3315)
PHONE.................................513 983-1100
David Taylor, *President*
Jon Moeller, *CFO*
Linda Clement-Holmes, *CIO*
Kathleen Fish, *CTO*
Deborah Majoras,
EMP: 3
SALES (est): 1.1MM
SALES (corp-wide): 65.3B **Publicly Held**
SIC: 2676 Towels, napkins & tissue paper products
PA: The Procter & Gamble Company
1 Procter And Gamble Plz
Cincinnati OH 45202
513 983-1100

(G-4235)
PICKENS WINDOW SERVICE INC
7824 Hamilton Ave (45231-3106)
PHONE.................................513 931-4432
Fax: 513 931-4450
Brian Pickens, *President*
Kendall Pickens, *Corp Secy*
EMP: 11
SQ FT: 10,000
SALES (est): 980K **Privately Held**
WEB: www.pickenswindowparts.com
SIC: 5211 7699 2431 Windows, storm: wood or metal; doors, storm: wood or metal; door & window repair; window screens, wood frame

(G-4236)
PILOT CHEMICAL COMPANY OHIO (PA)
2744 E Kemper Rd (45241-1818)
PHONE.................................513 326-0600
Pamela R Butcher, *CEO*
Pam Butcher, *CEO*
Michael Scott, *President*
Paul Morrisroe, *Chairman*
Robert Cellura, *Vice Pres*
◆ EMP: 30
SALES (est): 81.9MM **Privately Held**
SIC: 2843 2841 Finishing agents; detergents, synthetic organic or inorganic alkaline

(G-4237)
PILOT CHEMICAL COMPANY OHIO
606 Shepherd Dr (45215-2145)
PHONE.................................513 733-4880
Fax: 513 733-0511
Robert Cellura, *Vice Pres*
Thomas Melhorn, *Manager*
Tom Melhorn, *CTO*
EMP: 25
SQ FT: 13,820
SALES (corp-wide): 81.9MM **Privately Held**
SIC: 2843 2841 2842 Finishing agents; detergents, synthetic organic or inorganic alkaline; specialty cleaning, polishes & sanitation goods
PA: Pilot Chemical Company Of Ohio
2744 E Kemper Rd
Cincinnati OH 45241
513 326-0600

(G-4238)
PILOT CHEMICAL CORP (HQ)
2744 E Kemper Rd (45241-1818)
PHONE.................................513 326-0600
Fax: 513 326-0601
Pam Butcher, *President*
Ken Eckroth, *Vice Pres*
Susan K Leslie, *Vice Pres*
David Waisemann, *Controller*
David M Waizmann, *Finance Dir*
◆ EMP: 13
SQ FT: 10,000
SALES (est): 14.7MM
SALES (corp-wide): 81.9MM **Privately Held**
WEB: www.pilotchemical.com
SIC: 2841 2843 Detergents, synthetic organic or inorganic alkaline; surface active agents
PA: Pilot Chemical Company Of Ohio
2744 E Kemper Rd
Cincinnati OH 45241
513 326-0600

(G-4239)
PINNACLE ROLLER CO
2147 Spring Grove Ave (45214-1721)
PHONE.................................513 369-4830
Mike Brown, *Vice Pres*
Dan Dinkelacker, *Manager*
EMP: 14
SALES (est): 2MM **Privately Held**
SIC: 3069 Rubber rolls & roll coverings

(G-4240)
PIQUA MATERIALS INC (PA)
11641 Mosteller Rd Ste 1 (45241-1520)
PHONE.................................513 771-0820
James Jurgensen, *President*
Tim Saintclair, *Corp Secy*
James Jurgenson II, *Vice Pres*

▲ = Import ▼=Export
◆ =Import/Export

Anthony Ridgway, *Project Mgr*
Beth Baker, *Controller*
EMP: 31
SALES (est): 16.3MM **Privately Held**
SIC: 1422 Limestones, ground

(G-4241)
PKI INC
4500 Reading Rd (45229-1230)
PHONE..................................859 291-8680
Jeff Cox, *President*
EMP: 8
SQ FT: 10,000
SALES (est): 1.2MM **Privately Held**
WEB: www.pki-inc.com
SIC: 3479 3471 Coating of metals with
plastic or resins; sand blasting of metal
parts

(G-4242)
PLANK AND HIDE CO
721a E Sharon Rd (45241)
PHONE..................................513 378-3194
Amy Brown, *Principal*
EMP: 11 **EST:** 2014
SALES (est): 415.6K **Privately Held**
SIC: 2426 Carvings, furniture: wood

(G-4243)
PLASTIGRAPHICS INC
722 Redna Ter (45215-1109)
PHONE..................................513 771-8848
Fax: 513 771-8851
Robert Heinold, *President*
Sandy Miller, *Corp Secy*
EMP: 12
SQ FT: 6,500
SALES: 750K **Privately Held**
WEB: www.plastigraphics.com
SIC: 3993 3861 Signs & advertising spe-
cialties; graphic arts plates, sensitized

(G-4244)
PLATING SOLUTIONS
871 Redna Ter (45215-1110)
PHONE..................................513 771-1941
Cris Narburgh, *Vice Pres*
EMP: 5
SALES (est): 328.9K **Privately Held**
SIC: 3471 Plating of metals or formed
products

(G-4245)
**PLAYGROUND EQUIPMENT
SERVICE**
2980 Diehl Rd (45211-2714)
PHONE..................................513 481-3776
Eric L Schmidt, *Principal*
EMP: 6
SALES (est): 487.2K **Privately Held**
SIC: 3949 Playground equipment

(G-4246)
**PMC SPECIALTIES GROUP INC
(DH)**
501 Murray Rd (45217-1014)
PHONE..................................513 242-3300
Fax: 513 482-7373
Zetta Bouligaraki, *President*
Gordon McCullough, *Exec VP*
Ronald Pearson, *Research*
Phad McCord, *Controller*
Bruce Becker, *Manager*
◆ **EMP:** 22
SQ FT: 7,500
SALES (est): 70MM
SALES (corp-wide): 1.3B **Privately Held**
WEB: www.pmcspecialties.com
SIC: 2819 2816 Industrial inorganic chem-
icals; inorganic pigments
HQ: Plastic Services And Products
12243 Branford St
Sun Valley CA 91352
818 896-1101

(G-4247)
PMC SPECIALTIES GROUP INC
5220 Vine St (45217-1028)
PHONE..................................513 242-3300
EMP: 8
SALES (corp-wide): 1.3B **Privately Held**
SIC: 2819 2816 Industrial inorganic chem-
icals; inorganic pigments
HQ: Pmc Specialties Group, Inc.
501 Murray Rd
Cincinnati OH 45217

(G-4248)
PME OF OHIO INC (PA)
Also Called: PME- Babbit Bearings
518 W Crescentville Rd (45246-1222)
PHONE..................................513 671-1717
Charles Walter, *President*
Michelle Holt, *Controller*
Michelle McCord, *Executive*
EMP: 20
SQ FT: 20,000
SALES (est): 8.5MM **Privately Held**
WEB: www.pmebabbittbearings.com
SIC: 3599 Machine & other job shop work

(G-4249)
**POROCEL INDUSTRIES LLC
(PA)**
1 Landy Ln (45215-3405)
PHONE..................................513 733-8519
Ronald Zapletal, *President*
Ronald L Bell, *Vice Pres*
Edward L Butera, *Vice Pres*
Terrence McHugh, *Vice Pres*
William A Kist, *CFO*
◆ **EMP:** 4
SALES (est): 32.9MM **Privately Held**
WEB: www.porocel.com
SIC: 2819 Bauxite, refined

(G-4250)
**PORTER PRECISION PRODUCTS
CO (PA)**
2734 Banning Rd (45239-5504)
PHONE..................................513 385-1569
Fax: 513 923-1111
John Cipriani Jr, *President*
Mary M Cipriani, *Chairman*
Dale Warlaumont, *Corp Secy*
Vince Cipriani, *Vice Pres*
Mike Sizemore, *Plant Mgr*
EMP: 79
SQ FT: 33,200
SALES (est): 24.7MM **Privately Held**
WEB: www.porterpunch.com
SIC: 3544 Punches, forming & stamping

(G-4251)
PORTER-GUERTIN CO INC
2150 Colerain Ave (45214-1873)
P.O. Box 14177 (45250-0177)
PHONE..................................513 241-7663
Fax: 513 241-7664
James F Gentil, *President*
Kathleen Gentil, *Corp Secy*
EMP: 14
SQ FT: 12,000
SALES (est): 1.4MM **Privately Held**
SIC: 3471 Chromium plating of metals or
formed products

(G-4252)
POSITROL INC
Also Called: Positrol Workholding
3890 Virginia Ave (45227-3410)
PHONE..................................513 272-0500
Fax: 513 272-0503
David C Weber, *President*
Jonathan T Weber, *Vice Pres*
William Lorenz, *Prdtn Mgr*
Josh Pocock, *Engineer*
Adam Pendergrass, *Design Engr*
EMP: 30
SQ FT: 11,000
SALES (est): 6.4MM **Privately Held**
WEB: www.positrol.com
SIC: 3545 Machine tool attachments & ac-
cessories

(G-4253)
POSTAL UNIFORM XPRESS
1202 York St (45214-2048)
PHONE..................................513 621-4787
Dennie Fry, *President*
EMP: 99
SALES (est): 3.4MM **Privately Held**
WEB: www.postaluniformxpress.com
SIC: 2326 Work uniforms

(G-4254)
**POSTERSERVICE
INCORPORATED (PA)**
225 Northland Blvd (45246-3603)
PHONE..................................513 577-7100
Dana W Gore, *President*
Daniel P Regenold, *Chairman*

Rebecca Regenold, *Corp Secy*
Charles Mathis, *Credit Mgr*
Jeff Miller, *Manager*
▲ **EMP:** 20
SQ FT: 30,000
SALES (est): 8.1MM **Privately Held**
WEB: www.posterservice.com
SIC: 5199 2741 Posters; posters: publish-
ing & printing

(G-4255)
POWER ENGINEERING LLC
Also Called: Blue Machine
507 N Wayne Ave (45215-2871)
PHONE..................................513 793-5800
Fax: 513 793-5804
John H Burke,
Edmond Burke,
EMP: 3
SQ FT: 7,000
SALES (est): 292.5K **Privately Held**
SIC: 3541 Machine tools, metal cutting
type

(G-4256)
POWERHOUSE FACTORIES INC
1111 Saint Gregory St (45202-1770)
PHONE..................................513 719-6417
Jim Price, *Principal*
EMP: 10 **EST:** 2012
SALES (est): 902.9K **Privately Held**
SIC: 2741 Art copy: publishing & printing

(G-4257)
POWERSONIC INDUSTRIES LLC
2523 Crescentville Rd (45241-1575)
PHONE..................................513 429-2339
Jason Rampersand, *President*
EMP: 11
SALES (est): 1.3MM **Privately Held**
SIC: 3999 Manufacturing industries

(G-4258)
**PPG ARCHITECTURAL FINISHES
INC**
Glidden Professional Paint Ctr
2960 Exon Ave (45241-2521)
PHONE..................................513 563-0220
Dave Gerding, *Branch Mgr*
EMP: 10
SALES (corp-wide): 14.7B **Publicly Held**
WEB: www.gliddenpaint.com
SIC: 2891 Adhesives & sealants
HQ: Ppg Architectural Finishes, Inc.
1 Ppg Pl
Pittsburgh PA 15272
412 434-3131

(G-4259)
PPG INDUSTRIES INC
Also Called: PPG 4331
7198 Beechmont Ave (45230-4115)
PHONE..................................513 231-3200
Steve Tauber, *Manager*
EMP: 24
SALES (corp-wide): 14.7B **Publicly Held**
WEB: www.ppg.com
SIC: 2851 Paints & allied products
PA: Ppg Industries, Inc.
1 Ppg Pl
Pittsburgh PA 15272
412 434-3131

(G-4260)
PPG INDUSTRIES INC
Also Called: PPG 4333
6462 Glenway Ave (45211-5221)
PHONE..................................513 661-5220
Jim Jackson, *Manager*
EMP: 24
SALES (corp-wide): 14.7B **Publicly Held**
WEB: www.ppg.com
SIC: 2851 Paints & allied products
PA: Ppg Industries, Inc.
1 Ppg Pl
Pittsburgh PA 15272
412 434-3131

(G-4261)
PPG INDUSTRIES INC
Also Called: PPG 4339
9850 Montgomery Rd (45242-6424)
PHONE..................................513 984-6761
Steve Bryson, *Branch Mgr*
EMP: 24

SALES (corp-wide): 14.7B **Publicly Held**
WEB: www.ppg.com
SIC: 2851 Paints & allied products
PA: Ppg Industries, Inc.
1 Ppg Pl
Pittsburgh PA 15272
412 434-3131

(G-4262)
PPG INDUSTRIES INC
Also Called: PPG 4332
4600 Reading Rd (45229-1232)
PHONE..................................513 242-3050
Fax: 513 242-9597
Mike Allen, *Branch Mgr*
EMP: 24
SALES (corp-wide): 14.7B **Publicly Held**
WEB: www.ppg.com
SIC: 2851 Paints & allied products
PA: Ppg Industries, Inc.
1 Ppg Pl
Pittsburgh PA 15272
412 434-3131

(G-4263)
PRAXAIR DISTRIBUTION INC
8376 Reading Rd (45237-1407)
PHONE..................................513 821-2192
Joe R Smith, *Opers-Prdtn-Mfg*
EMP: 8
SALES (corp-wide): 10.5B **Publicly Held**
SIC: 2813 5084 5999 Carbon dioxide; dry
ice, carbon dioxide (solid); oxygen, com-
pressed or liquefied; welding machinery &
equipment; welding supplies
HQ: Praxair Distribution, Inc.
10 Riverview Dr
Danbury CT 06810
203 837-2000

(G-4264)
PRECISION SWISS LLC
9580 Wayne Ave (45215-2252)
PHONE..................................513 716-7000
Ron Hinks, *Owner*
Tatyana Hinks, *CFO*
EMP: 9
SQ FT: 17,000
SALES: 535K **Privately Held**
SIC: 3843 Dental equipment & supplies

(G-4265)
**PREFERRED GLOBAL
EQUIPMENT LLC**
7800 Redsky Dr (45249-1632)
PHONE..................................513 530-5800
Laura Grithie, *Office Mgr*
William A Decenso,
Mark Werner,
▲ **EMP:** 86
SALES (est): 43.9MM **Privately Held**
SIC: 3561 Pumps & pumping equipment

(G-4266)
PREMIER INDUSTRIES INC
5721 Dragon Way Ste 113 (45227-4518)
PHONE..................................513 271-2550
J Paul Taylor, *President*
Suzanne Gerwin, *Vice Pres*
Lori Roberts, *Admin Sec*
EMP: 40 **EST:** 1935
SQ FT: 45,000
SALES (est): 3.4MM
SALES (corp-wide): 14MM **Privately
Held**
SIC: 2656 3556 Plates, paper: made from
purchased material; food products ma-
chinery
PA: Taylor Company
5721 Dragon Way Ste 117
Cincinnati OH 45227
513 271-2550

(G-4267)
**PREMIER SOUTHERN TICKET
CO INC**
7911 School Rd (45249-1596)
PHONE..................................513 489-6700
Kirk Schulz, *President*
Jim Raike, *Human Resources*
▲ **EMP:** 38
SQ FT: 38,000
SALES (est): 3.7MM **Privately Held**
WEB: www.premiersouthern.com
SIC: 2759 Tickets: printing; tags: printing;
coupons: printing

PA: Gtlp Holdings, Llc
7911 School Rd
Cincinnati OH 45249

(G-4268)
PRIDE CAST METALS INC
2737 Colerain Ave (45225-2263)
PHONE..................................513 541-1295
Fax: 513 541-0070
Thomas Hamm, *President*
Kenneth Bechtol, *Principal*
▲ EMP: 100
SQ FT: 150,000
SALES: 20.6MM **Privately Held**
WEB: www.pridecastmetals.com
SIC: 3365 3366 3599 Aluminum & alu-
minum-based alloy castings; castings (ex-
cept die): bronze; castings (except die):
brass; machine shop, jobbing & repair

(G-4269)
PRIDE TOOL CO INC
10200 Wayne Ave (45215-1127)
P.O. Box 15627 (45215-0627)
PHONE..................................513 563-0070
Fax: 513 563-0075
David Draginoff, *CEO*
Sandra Draginoff, *Corp Secy*
Albert Harvey, *Vice Pres*
Mike Trovillo, *Vice Pres*
Margaret Gagliardo, *Manager*
EMP: 17
SQ FT: 11,500
SALES (est): 3.7MM **Privately Held**
SIC: 3599 Machine shop, jobbing & repair

(G-4270)
PRINT CRAFT INC
8045 Colerain Ave (45239-4513)
PHONE..................................513 931-6828
Fax: 513 728-7605
Mark Schuster, *President*
Dale Schuster, *Vice Pres*
EMP: 5
SQ FT: 4,400
SALES: 650K **Privately Held**
SIC: 2752 5943 5999 Commercial print-
ing, lithographic; commercial printing, off-
set; office forms & supplies; artists'
supplies & materials

(G-4271)
**PRINTERS BINDERY SERVICES
INC**
Also Called: Printers Bindery
925 Freeman Ave (45203-1109)
PHONE..................................513 821-8039
Joyce Bowman, *President*
Russ Wice, *Production*
Kelley Miller, *Admin Sec*
▲ EMP: 68
SQ FT: 80,000
SALES (est): 8.4MM **Privately Held**
WEB: www.printersbinderyohio.com
SIC: 2789 2675 Binding only: books, pam-
phlets, magazines, etc.; die-cut paper &
board

(G-4272)
**PRINTERS EMERGENCY
SERVICE LLC**
2016 Elm St Side A (45202-4979)
PHONE..................................513 421-7799
Fax: 513 651-2191
Mick Schindler, *Office Mgr*
Chris Burns,
EMP: 3
SQ FT: 1,500
SALES: 500K **Privately Held**
SIC: 2752 Letters, circular or form: litho-
graphed; commercial printing, offset

(G-4273)
PRINTMANAGEMENT LLC
3950 Virginia Ave (45227-3412)
PHONE..................................513 272-7000
Fax: 513 272-7001
Joe Desch, *CEO*
Brian Frank, *President*
Bridgette Harding, *Assistant VP*
BJ Roberts, *Opers Staff*
Jean Desch, *Human Res Mgr*
EMP: 30
SQ FT: 20,000

SALES (est): 7.2MM **Privately Held**
WEB: www.printmgmt.com
SIC: 2752 Commercial printing, litho-
graphic

(G-4274)
PRINTZONE
11974 Lebanon Rd (45241-1711)
PHONE..................................513 733-0067
Fax: 513 733-0542
B J Ariapad, *Owner*
EMP: 3
SQ FT: 1,500
SALES (est): 299.8K **Privately Held**
SIC: 2752 Commercial printing, litho-
graphic

(G-4275)
PROAMPAC LLC (PA)
12025 Tricon Rd (45246-1719)
PHONE..................................513 671-1777
Greg Tucker, *CEO*
Eric Bradford, *CFO*
EMP: 21
SALES (est): 1.3B **Privately Held**
SIC: 2671 Paper coated or laminated for
packaging

(G-4276)
**PROCESS PIGGING SYSTEMS
LLC**
1776 Mentor Ave Ste 406 (45212-3581)
PHONE..................................513 731-6005
Debby Rahal, *Manager*
Neil J O'Connor,
Gary Gervis,
EMP: 4
SQ FT: 300
SALES (est): 400K **Privately Held**
WEB: www.hps-pigging.com
SIC: 3823 Industrial instrmnts msrmnt dis-
play/control process variable

(G-4277)
**PROCTER & GAMBLE COMPANY
(PA)**
Also Called: P&G
1 Procter And Gamble Plz (45202-3393)
P.O. Box 599 (45201-0599)
PHONE..................................513 983-1100
Fax: 513 983-4381
David S Taylor, *Ch of Bd*
Steven D Bishop, *President*
Giovanni Ciserani, *President*
Gary A Coombe, *President*
Mary Lynn Ferguson-Mchugh, *President*
◆ EMP: 277 EST: 1837
SALES: 65.3B **Publicly Held**
WEB: www.pg.com
SIC: 2844 2676 3421 2842 Toilet prepa-
rations; hair preparations, including sham-
poos; oral preparations; deodorants,
personal; towels, napkins & tissue paper
products; diapers, paper (disposable):
made from purchased paper; feminine hygiene paper products; razor blades & razors; specialty cleaning preparations;
fabric softeners; soap: granulated, liquid,
cake, flaked or chip; detergents, synthetic
organic or inorganic alkaline

(G-4278)
PROCTER & GAMBLE COMPANY
6210 Center Hill Ave (45224-1708)
PHONE..................................513 983-1100
Fax: 513 983-7506
Matthew Wagner, *General Mgr*
James Miller, *Facilities Mgr*
John Herlinger, *Research*
Richard Maupin, *Research*
Bill Butsch, *Engineer*
EMP: 150
SALES (corp-wide): 65.3B **Publicly Held**
SIC: 2676 Feminine hygiene paper prod-
ucts; infant & baby paper products
PA: The Procter & Gamble Company
1 Procter And Gamble Plz
Cincinnati OH 45202
513 983-1100

(G-4279)
PROCTER & GAMBLE COMPANY
5280 Vine St (45217-1028)
PHONE..................................513 266-4375
Stan Jackson, *Design Engr*
Ed Allie, *Manager*

EMP: 26
SALES (corp-wide): 65.3B **Publicly Held**
SIC: 2752 Toilet preparations
PA: The Procter & Gamble Company
1 Procter And Gamble Plz
Cincinnati OH 45202
513 983-1100

(G-4280)
PROCTER & GAMBLE COMPANY
654 Wilmer Ave Hngr 4 (45226-1860)
PHONE..................................513 871-7557
David Tobertge, *Manager*
Greg Baynum, *Supervisor*
EMP: 45
SALES (corp-wide): 65.3B **Publicly Held**
WEB: www.pg.com
SIC: 2844 Toilet preparations
PA: The Procter & Gamble Company
1 Procter And Gamble Plz
Cincinnati OH 45202
513 983-1100

(G-4281)
PROCTER & GAMBLE COMPANY
5299 Spring Grove Ave (45217-1025)
PHONE..................................513 983-1100
Fax: 513 627-6854
John E Pepper, *Ch of Bd*
Erica Linville, *Project Mgr*
Clark Reinhard, *Opers Mgr*
Matt Smith, *Purch Mgr*
Melissa R Baker, *Purch Agent*
EMP: 133
SALES (corp-wide): 65.3B **Publicly Held**
WEB: www.pg.com
SIC: 2834 Pharmaceutical preparations
PA: The Procter & Gamble Company
1 Procter And Gamble Plz
Cincinnati OH 45202
513 983-1100

(G-4282)
PROCTER & GAMBLE COMPANY
4460 Kings Run Dr (45232)
PHONE..................................513 482-6789
Joe Kelly, *Manager*
Ricky Piedrahita, *Manager*
Eugene Daut, *Senior Mgr*
EMP: 10
SALES (corp-wide): 65.3B **Publicly Held**
SIC: 2844 Toilet preparations
PA: The Procter & Gamble Company
1 Procter And Gamble Plz
Cincinnati OH 45202
513 983-1100

(G-4283)
PROCTER & GAMBLE COMPANY
6300 Center Hill Ave Fl 2 (45224-1795)
PHONE..................................513 634-5069
Tim Fiedeldey, *Draft/Design*
Donald Culver, *Engineer*
Jeff Spaulding, *Engineer*
Steve McKinley, *Project Engr*
D L Miller, *Manager*
EMP: 500
SALES (corp-wide): 65.3B **Publicly Held**
WEB: www.pg.com
SIC: 2844 Toilet preparations
PA: The Procter & Gamble Company
1 Procter And Gamble Plz
Cincinnati OH 45202
513 983-1100

(G-4284)
PROCTER & GAMBLE COMPANY
5348 Vine St (45217-1030)
PHONE..................................513 627-7115
Fax: 513 634-3208
Alton Stephens, *Senior Buyer*
David Puthoff, *QC Mgr*
Jim Blundy, *Engineer*
Stephen Congleton, *Engineer*
Rick Horstman, *Engineer*
EMP: 500
SALES (corp-wide): 65.3B **Publicly Held**
WEB: www.pg.com
SIC: 2844 Toilet preparations
PA: The Procter & Gamble Company
1 Procter And Gamble Plz
Cincinnati OH 45202
513 983-1100

(G-4285)
PROCTER & GAMBLE COMPANY
2150 Sunnybrook Dr (45237-2181)
PHONE..................................513 948-2462
Nancy Lindemood, *Manager*
EMP: 200
SALES (corp-wide): 65.3B **Publicly Held**
WEB: www.pg.com
SIC: 2844 Toilet preparations
PA: The Procter & Gamble Company
1 Procter And Gamble Plz
Cincinnati OH 45202
513 983-1100

(G-4286)
PROCTER & GAMBLE COMPANY
2 Procter And Gamble Plz (45202-3315)
PHONE..................................513 983-1100
Jack Ryan, *General Mgr*
Kimberly Kraus, *Vice Pres*
Aron Olegnowicz, *Vice Pres*
Brian Bennings, *Project Mgr*
Charlotte Slaughter, *Project Mgr*
EMP: 500
SALES (corp-wide): 65.3B **Publicly Held**
WEB: www.pg.com
SIC: 2844 2676 2834 2841 Deodorants,
personal; hair preparations, including
shampoos; cosmetic preparations; oral
preparations; towels, napkins & tissue
paper products; diapers, paper (disposable): made from purchased paper; pharmaceutical preparations; cough
medicines; cold remedies; soap: granulated, liquid, cake, flaked or chip; detergents, synthetic organic or inorganic
alkaline; specialty cleaning preparations;
fabric softeners; shortening & other solid
edible fats; margarine & margarine oils
PA: The Procter & Gamble Company
1 Procter And Gamble Plz
Cincinnati OH 45202
513 983-1100

(G-4287)
PROCTER & GAMBLE COMPANY
5201 Spring Grove Ave (45217-1094)
PHONE..................................513 627-7779
Vinton Goure, *Project Engr*
Rich Bartonni, *Manager*
Steve Lockwood, *Manager*
Oscar Moseley, *Manager*
EMP: 4
SALES (corp-wide): 65.3B **Publicly Held**
WEB: www.pg.com
SIC: 2841 Soap & other detergents
PA: The Procter & Gamble Company
1 Procter And Gamble Plz
Cincinnati OH 45202
513 983-1100

(G-4288)
PROCTER & GAMBLE COMPANY
6280 Center Hill Ave (45224-1708)
PHONE..................................513 945-0340
Miguel A Robles, *Senior Engr*
Sarah Dia, *Manager*
Teresa Wong, *Manager*
Sharon Norton, *Admin Asst*
Susan Wilking, *Associate*
EMP: 500
SALES (corp-wide): 65.3B **Publicly Held**
WEB: www.pg.com
SIC: 2844 Toilet preparations
PA: The Procter & Gamble Company
1 Procter And Gamble Plz
Cincinnati OH 45202
513 983-1100

(G-4289)
**PROCTER & GAMBLE FAR EAST
INC (HQ)**
1 Procter And Gamble Plz (45202-3393)
PHONE..................................513 983-1100
A G Lafley, *President*
C Daley, *Principal*
Rl Antoine, *Vice Pres*
F Benvegnu, *Vice Pres*
RG Pease, *Vice Pres*
EMP: 110
SQ FT: 1,600,000

SALES (est): 100.7MM
SALES (corp-wide): 65.3B **Publicly Held**
SIC: 2842 2844 2676 Laundry cleaning preparations; fabric softeners; toilet preparations; hair preparations, including shampoos; shampoos, rinses, conditioners: hair; napkins, sanitary: made from purchased paper
PA: The Procter & Gamble Company
1 Procter And Gamble Plz
Cincinnati OH 45202
513 983-1100

(G-4290)
PROCTER & GAMBLE MFG CO (HQ)
1 Procter And Gamble Plz (45202-3393)
P.O. Box 599 (45201-0599)
PHONE..................................513 983-1100
Bob McDonald, *President*
Keith Harrison, *President*
John Jensen, *Vice Pres*
John Goodwin, *Treasurer*
Frank Bernhardt, *Info Tech Mgr*
▼ **EMP:** 15 **EST:** 1910
SQ FT: 1,600,000
SALES (est): 1.1B
SALES (corp-wide): 65.3B **Publicly Held**
SIC: 2841 2079 2099 2844 Soap: granulated, liquid, cake, flaked or chip; detergents, synthetic organic or inorganic alkaline; shortening & other solid edible fats; peanut butter; toilet preparations; cake mixes, prepared: from purchased flour
PA: The Procter & Gamble Company
1 Procter And Gamble Plz
Cincinnati OH 45202
513 983-1100

(G-4291)
PROCTER & GAMBLE PAPER PDTS CO (HQ)
1 Procter And Gamble Plz (45202-3393)
P.O. Box 599 (45201-0599)
PHONE..................................513 983-1100
David Taylor, *President*
Samuel Benedict, *Principal*
Richard R Deupree Jr, *Principal*
K Y Siddall, *Principal*
E G Nelson, *Vice Pres*
▼ **EMP:** 15
SQ FT: 1,600,000
SALES (est): 1.4B
SALES (corp-wide): 65.3B **Publicly Held**
SIC: 2676 Sanitary paper products; towels, napkins & tissue paper products; toilet paper: made from purchased paper; towels, paper: made from purchased paper
PA: The Procter & Gamble Company
1 Procter And Gamble Plz
Cincinnati OH 45202
513 983-1100

(G-4292)
PROCTER & GAMBLE PAPER PDTS CO
301 E 6th St (45202-3339)
PHONE..................................513 983-2222
EMP: 25
SALES (corp-wide): 65.3B **Publicly Held**
SIC: 2676 Sanitary paper products
HQ: The Procter & Gamble Paper Products Company
1 Procter And Gamble Plz
Cincinnati OH 45202
513 983-1100

(G-4293)
PRODUCTIVE CARBIDES INC
10265 Spartan Dr Ste K (45215-1237)
PHONE..................................513 771-7092
Fax: 513 771-7092
Lynda Wittman, *President*
Nelson Wittman, *Vice Pres*
EMP: 5 **EST:** 1982
SQ FT: 1,200
SALES (est): 200K **Privately Held**
WEB: www.productivecarbides.com
SIC: 3545 7699 Machine tool accessories; knife, saw & tool sharpening & repair

(G-4294)
PROFESSIONAL AWARD SERVICE
Also Called: ID Plastech Engraving
3901 N Bend Rd (45211-4814)
PHONE..................................513 389-3600
Fax: 513 389-3606
Ronald Jeremiah, *President*
EMP: 8
SQ FT: 3,818
SALES (est): 1.1MM **Privately Held**
WEB: www.awardsanddesign.com
SIC: 3914 7389 Silverware & plated ware; engraving service

(G-4295)
PROFESSIONAL IMAGE APPAREL INC
11444 Rockfield Ct (45241-1917)
PHONE..................................513 984-1111
Barry Hackett, *President*
EMP: 13 **EST:** 2012
SALES (est): 2MM **Privately Held**
SIC: 3161 7389 2321 2326 Clothing & apparel carrying cases; advertising, promotional & trade show services; polo shirts, men's & boys': made from purchased materials; work uniforms

(G-4296)
PROFESSIONAL IMAGE INC
11444 Rockfield Ct (45241-1917)
PHONE..................................513 984-1111
Fax: 513 984-1180
Rick Pescovitz, *President*
Charles Pescovitz, *Vice Pres*
Alfred Soliz, *Vice Pres*
Todd Gigax, *Accounts Mgr*
Kevin Mitchell, *Sales Executive*
◆ **EMP:** 16
SQ FT: 15,000
SALES (est): 4.2MM **Privately Held**
WEB: www.professional-image.com
SIC: 5199 2261 Advertising specialties; screen printing of cotton broadwoven fabrics

(G-4297)
PROFILES IN DESIGN INC
860 Dellway St (45229-3306)
PHONE..................................513 751-2212
Fax: 513 751-2160
Joe Pfaltzgraff, *President*
Gary Stacy, *Vice Pres*
Neal Glatte, *Opers Mgr*
Sarah Albert, *Admin Sec*
Michele Stacy, *Admin Asst*
EMP: 14
SQ FT: 20,000
SALES (est): 1.5MM **Privately Held**
WEB: www.profilesindesign.com
SIC: 2434 Vanities, bathroom: wood

(G-4298)
PROFT & GAMBLE
6280 Center Hill Ave (45224-1708)
PHONE..................................513 945-0340
Debbie Schurgast, *Principal*
▲ **EMP:** 7
SALES (est): 1MM **Privately Held**
SIC: 2844 Shampoos, rinses, conditioners: hair

(G-4299)
PROTECTIVE PACKG SOLUTIONS LLC
10345 S Medallion Dr (45241-4825)
PHONE..................................513 769-5777
Michael H Edlin, *CEO*
Dave Rettig, *General Mgr*
Richard B Brian, *Plant Mgr*
Cindy Garret, *Opers Mgr*
Cindy Garrett, *Manager*
EMP: 16
SALES (est): 3.8MM **Privately Held**
SIC: 3086 Plastics foam products

(G-4300)
PROTEIN EXPRESS INC
9940 Reading Rd Ste 1 (45241-3106)
PHONE..................................513 769-9654
Michael L Howell, *President*
Gary Dean, *Vice Pres*
Zsolt Hertelendy, *Vice Pres*
Charles Wendy, *Manager*

EMP: 4 **EST:** 1996
SQ FT: 4,537
SALES (est): 360K **Privately Held**
SIC: 2834 8731 Vitamin, nutrient & hematinic preparations for human use; commercial physical research

(G-4301)
PROVINCE OF ST JOHN THE BAPTIS
Also Called: St Anthony Messenger Press
28 W Liberty St (45202-6442)
PHONE..................................513 241-5615
Fax: 513 241-1197
Jeremy Harrington, *Principal*
John Koize, *Sales Dir*
Tom Bruce, *Marketing Staff*
John Feister, *CIO*
Sandy Digman, *Art Dir*
EMP: 100
SQ FT: 30,514
SALES (corp-wide): 7.2MM **Privately Held**
WEB: www.rogerbacon.org
SIC: 2721 5942 7812 2752 Magazines: publishing only, not printed on site; book stores; motion picture & video production; commercial printing, lithographic; miscellaneous publishing; book publishing
PA: The Province Of St John Baptist Order Friars Minor
1615 Vine St
Cincinnati OH 45202
513 721-4700

(G-4302)
PSA CONSULTING INC
Also Called: Cincinati Book Publicsher
19 Garfield Pl Ste 211 (45202-4309)
PHONE..................................513 382-4315
Anthony Braunsfel, *President*
EMP: 4
SALES (est): 250K **Privately Held**
SIC: 2741 Miscellaneous publishing

(G-4303)
PTC INC
625 Eden Park Dr Ste 860 (45202-6033)
PHONE..................................513 791-0330
EMP: 15
SALES (corp-wide): 1.2B **Publicly Held**
SIC: 7372 Whol Engineering Software
PA: Ptc Inc.
140 Kendrick St Ste C120
Needham MA 02494
781 370-5000

(G-4304)
Q C A INC
2832 Spring Grove Ave (45225-2220)
PHONE..................................513 681-8400
Fax: 513 681-8175
James Bosken, *President*
Andrea Winterhalter, *Vice Pres*
Amber Hines, *Sls & Mktg Exec*
EMP: 11
SQ FT: 35,000
SALES (est): 1MM **Privately Held**
WEB: www.go-qca.com
SIC: 3652 Master records or tapes, preparation of; magnetic tape (audio): prerecorded; compact laser discs, prerecorded

(G-4305)
QM SCIENTIFIC LLP
3344 Lakeview St (45211-6470)
PHONE..................................513 250-2397
Hatim Alqadah, *Research*
EMP: 3
SALES (est): 99.9K **Privately Held**
SIC: 7372 Application computer software

(G-4306)
QUALITY CONTROLS INC
3411 Church St (45244-3409)
PHONE..................................513 272-3900
Fax: 513 272-3939
Thomas M Pulskamp, *President*
Annette Pulskamp, *Admin Sec*
EMP: 11
SQ FT: 15,000
SALES (est): 2.1MM **Privately Held**
WEB: www.qualitycontrolsinc.com
SIC: 3625 3829 Motor control accessories, including overload relays; measuring & controlling devices

(G-4307)
QUALITY MECHANICALS INC
1225 Streng St (45223-2642)
PHONE..................................513 559-0998
Fax: 513 559-1146
Richard Doll, *President*
BJ Kemen, *Project Mgr*
Denise Albright, *Treasurer*
Heather Turpin, *Marketing Staff*
EMP: 35
SQ FT: 4,000
SALES (est): 7.9MM **Privately Held**
SIC: 3498 Fabricated pipe & fittings

(G-4308)
QUALITY MFG COMPANY INC
4323 Spring Grove Ave (45223-1834)
PHONE..................................513 921-4500
Fax: 513 921-4598
Edward J Bemerer, *President*
Paul A Kapper, *Corp Secy*
Richard Lipps, *Vice Pres*
EMP: 8 **EST:** 1975
SQ FT: 16,000
SALES (est): 850K **Privately Held**
SIC: 3544 Special dies, tools, jigs & fixtures

(G-4309)
QUALITY SPT & SILK SCREEN SP
Also Called: Quality Spt Silk Screen & EMB
9217 Reading Rd (45215-3415)
PHONE..................................513 769-8300
Fax: 513 769-5180
Dean J Haralamos, *Owner*
EMP: 3
SALES (est): 260.1K **Privately Held**
WEB: www.marylandsportsapparel.com
SIC: 5941 5699 2396 Sporting goods & bicycle shops; sports apparel; screen printing on fabric articles

(G-4310)
QUANTEM FBO SERVICES
1077 Celestial St (45202-1637)
PHONE..................................603 647-6763
EMP: 5 **EST:** 2013
SALES (est): 20.2K **Privately Held**
SIC: 3572 Computer storage devices

(G-4311)
QUARTER BISTRO
6904 Wooster Pike (45227-4427)
PHONE..................................513 271-5400
Adam Kleshinski, *Principal*
EMP: 3
SALES (est): 280.6K **Privately Held**
SIC: 3131 Quarters

(G-4312)
QUEBECOR WORLD JOHNSON HARDIN
3600 Red Bank Rd (45227-4142)
PHONE..................................614 326-0299
Fax: 513 527-2123
Chuck Miotke, *President*
James H Bossart, *Senior VP*
Robert Castillo, *Vice Pres*
Jeffery R Herman, *VP Finance*
Blane Ridenbaugh, *Director*
EMP: 900
SQ FT: 200,000
SALES: 100MM **Privately Held**
SIC: 2759 2752 2732 Magazines: printing; catalogs: printing; commercial printing, offset; books: printing only

(G-4313)
QUEEN CITY AWNING & TENT CO
7225 E Kemper Rd (45249-1030)
PHONE..................................513 530-9660
Fax: 513 530-0662
Peter Weingartner, *President*
Robert P Weingartner Sr, *Chairman*
Chris Herrmann, *Vice Pres*
James Weingartner, *Vice Pres*
EMP: 35 **EST:** 1877
SQ FT: 27,000
SALES (est): 4.1MM **Privately Held**
WEB: www.queencityawning.com
SIC: 2394 5712 Awnings, fabric: made from purchased materials; outdoor & garden furniture

(G-4314)
QUEEN CITY CARPETS LLC
6539 Harrison Ave 304 (45247-7822)
PHONE....................................513 823-8238
Terry Hensley, *Vice Pres*
EMP: 10 EST: 2012
SALES (est): 540.9K **Privately Held**
SIC: 2393 Cushions, except spring & carpet: purchased materials

(G-4315)
QUEEN CITY FOAM INC
3244 Mcgill Rd (45251-3207)
PHONE....................................513 741-7722
Herbert Bevelhymer, *President*
Mary Pugh, *Manager*
EMP: 5
SALES (est): 278K **Privately Held**
SIC: 2821 Polystyrene resins

(G-4316)
QUEEN CITY FORGING COMPANY
Also Called: Qcforge.com
235b Tennyson St (45226)
PHONE....................................513 321-2003
Fax: 513 321-2004
Howard R Mayer, *Ch of Bd*
George C Allen, *Principal*
John Mayer, *Vice Pres*
Andy Spires, *Prdtn Mgr*
Rick Smitson, *Traffic Mgr*
EMP: 16 EST: 1881
SQ FT: 36,000
SALES (est): 4.2MM **Privately Held**
WEB: www.qcforge.com
SIC: 3462 Iron & steel forgings

(G-4317)
QUEEN CITY OFFICE MACHINE
492 Pedretti Ave (45238-5454)
PHONE....................................513 251-7200
Fax: 513 251-2106
Ronald Swing, *Principal*
EMP: 10
SQ FT: 6,000
SALES (est): 2.2MM **Privately Held**
WEB: www.queencityoffice.com
SIC: 5112 7629 2759 Stationery & office supplies; business machine repair, electric; laser printing

(G-4318)
QUEEN CITY PALLETS
7744 Reinhold Dr (45237-2806)
PHONE....................................513 200-6426
Mike Unthank, *Partner*
Jon Lewis, *Manager*
EMP: 12
SALES (est): 1.7MM **Privately Held**
SIC: 2448 Pallets, wood

(G-4319)
QUEEN CITY REPROGRAPHICS
2863 E Sharon Rd (45241-1923)
PHONE....................................513 326-2300
Fax: 513 326-2312
Joe Herbst, *CEO*
Chris Chalifoux, *President*
Kevin Cartener, *Controller*
Dawn Hail, *Controller*
Craig Edmonston, *Sales Staff*
EMP: 105
SQ FT: 30,000
SALES (est): 16.4MM
SALES (corp-wide): 406.3MM **Publicly Held**
WEB: www.ohioblue.com
SIC: 5049 7334 7335 2752 Drafting supplies; blueprinting service; commercial photography; lithographing on metal
PA: Arc Document Solutions, Inc.
1981 N Broadway Ste 385
Walnut Creek CA 94596
925 949-5100

(G-4320)
QUEEN CITY SAUSAGE & PROVISION
1136 Straight St (45214-1736)
PHONE....................................513 541-5581
Fax: 513 541-6182
Elmer J Hensler, *President*
Dave Dramis, *General Mgr*
Pat Miller, *Sales Mgr*

Patrick Miller, *Sales Mgr*
Sandy Witt, *Sales Mgr*
EMP: 43
SQ FT: 17,000
SALES (est): 7.9MM **Privately Held**
WEB: www.queencitysausage.com
SIC: 2013 Sausages & other prepared meats

(G-4321)
QUEEN CITY SOFTWARE INC
Also Called: Qc Software
11800 Conrey Rd Ste 150 (45249-1081)
PHONE....................................513 469-1424
Fax: 513 469-1425
Rich Hite, *President*
Jerry List, *Vice Pres*
Bill Williams, *Admin Sec*
EMP: 6
SQ FT: 2,900
SALES (est): 1.1MM **Privately Held**
WEB: www.qcsoftware.com
SIC: 7371 7372 Computer software development; prepackaged software

(G-4322)
R A HELLER COMPANY
10530 Chester Rd (45215-1262)
PHONE....................................513 771-6100
Fax: 513 771-6102
Steve Heller, *President*
Laura Heller, *Admin Sec*
EMP: 11 EST: 1946
SQ FT: 20,000
SALES (est): 1.5MM **Privately Held**
WEB: www.raheller.com
SIC: 3471 3599 3545 Chromium plating of metals or formed products; machine shop, jobbing & repair; cutting tools for machine tools

(G-4323)
R C L ENTERPRISES INC
8805 Governors Hill Dr # 400 (45249-3314)
PHONE....................................972 390-6500
Sean A Hoffman, *Principal*
EMP: 3
SALES (est): 254.4K **Privately Held**
SIC: 2759 Commercial printing

(G-4324)
R E H COMPANY INC
5609 Center Hill Ave (45216-2305)
PHONE....................................513 242-0011
Ken Newman, *President*
Ted Oldieges, *Treasurer*
EMP: 52
SQ FT: 4,000
SALES (est): 4MM **Privately Held**
SIC: 3366 Castings (except die): bronze

(G-4325)
R E SMITH INC
10330 Chester Rd (45215-1225)
PHONE....................................513 771-0645
Kenneth J Koncelik, *President*
EMP: 10
SQ FT: 2,000
SALES (est): 1MM **Privately Held**
SIC: 3621 Frequency converters (electric generators)

(G-4326)
R L Y INC
Also Called: Yeager Sports
5874 Cheviot Rd (45247-6243)
PHONE....................................513 385-1950
Richard Yeager, *President*
EMP: 4
SQ FT: 3,000
SALES: 425K **Privately Held**
SIC: 3949 Sporting & athletic goods

(G-4327)
R VANDEWALLE INC
Also Called: Van Engineering Co
4030 Delhi Ave (45204-1276)
PHONE....................................513 921-2657
Robert Vandewalle, *President*
Richard Vandewalle, *Vice Pres*
EMP: 8 EST: 1942
SQ FT: 7,000
SALES: 400K **Privately Held**
SIC: 3599 Machine shop, jobbing & repair

(G-4328)
RAD TECHNOLOGIES INCORPORATED
Also Called: Precision Temp
11 Sunnybrook Dr (45237-2103)
PHONE....................................513 641-0523
Robert Muhlhauser, *CEO*
Gerry Wolters, *Principal*
Christopher Volz, *Safety Mgr*
Fred Rothzeid, *CFO*
EMP: 12
SALES (est): 1.9MM **Privately Held**
SIC: 3639 Hot water heaters, household

(G-4329)
RANDALL FOODS INC (PA)
312 Walnut St Ste 1600 (45202-4038)
PHONE....................................513 793-6525
Fax: 513 793-6143
Meredith Keating, *President*
Scott Keating, *Treasurer*
EMP: 1
SQ FT: 1,800
SALES (est): 2.4MM **Privately Held**
WEB: www.randallbeans.com
SIC: 2032 Beans, without meat: packaged in cans, jars, etc.

(G-4330)
RANDY GRAY
Also Called: Brat Printing
4142 Airport Rd Fl 1 (45226-1627)
PHONE....................................513 533-3200
Fax: 513 533-1090
Randy Gray, *Owner*
Trent Gray, *Manager*
EMP: 6
SQ FT: 9,000
SALES: 260.5K **Privately Held**
SIC: 3552 2395 2396 Textile machinery; emblems, embroidered; automotive & apparel trimmings

(G-4331)
RATECH
11110 Adwood Dr (45240-3234)
PHONE....................................513 742-2111
John Musuraca, *Owner*
Mary Smith, *Manager*
EMP: 3
SALES (est): 220K **Privately Held**
WEB: www.ratechmfg.com
SIC: 3559 Automotive maintenance equipment

(G-4332)
RBI SOLAR INC (DH)
5513 Vine St (45217-1000)
PHONE....................................513 242-2051
Rich Reilly, *President*
Jessica Abrego, *Project Mgr*
Jeff Cooley, *Project Mgr*
Bradley Fey, *Project Mgr*
Chris Lantz, *Project Mgr*
◆ EMP: 1
SALES (est): 18.7MM
SALES (corp-wide): 1B **Publicly Held**
SIC: 3433 Solar heaters & collectors
HQ: Rough Brothers Holding Co., Inc
3556 Lake Shore Rd # 100
Buffalo NY 14219
716 826-6500

(G-4333)
RCL PUBLISHING GROUP LLC
8805 Governors Hill Dr # 400 (45249-3319)
PHONE....................................972 390-6400
Rcl Benziger, *Principal*
▼ EMP: 7
SALES (est): 866.8K **Privately Held**
SIC: 2741 Miscellaneous publishing

(G-4334)
RECTO MOLDED PRODUCTS INC
4425 Appleton St (45209-1290)
PHONE....................................513 871-5544
Fax: 513 871-8495
Per Flem, *President*
EMP: 65 EST: 1913
SQ FT: 65,000

SALES (est): 12.5MM **Privately Held**
WEB: www.rectomolded.com
SIC: 3089 3083 Injection molding of plastics; laminated plastics plate & sheet

(G-4335)
REGISTERED IMAGES INC
Also Called: Patron Graphics
6545 Wiehe Rd (45237-4217)
PHONE....................................859 781-9200
Ronald Hager, *President*
Rob Eliom, *Prdtn Mgr*
EMP: 3
SQ FT: 7,500
SALES (est): 402K **Privately Held**
WEB: www.aicinsulate.com
SIC: 2796 2791 Color separations for printing; typesetting

(G-4336)
RENEE BARRETT WINERY
8129 Austin Ridge Dr (45247-1213)
PHONE....................................513 471-1340
Carl B Best, *Principal*
EMP: 4
SALES (est): 162.1K **Privately Held**
SIC: 2084 Wines

(G-4337)
RESISTFLAME ACQUISITION CORP (PA)
Also Called: Kiesling-Hess Finishing Co
7115 Miami Ave (45243-2616)
PHONE....................................513 561-5223
James J Johnston, *President*
Thomas L Applegate II, *Shareholder*
EMP: 4
SALES (est): 2.3MM **Privately Held**
SIC: 2231 2261 2262 Broadwoven fabric mills, wool; finishing plants, cotton; finishing plants, manmade fiber & silk fabrics

(G-4338)
RESOLUTE FP US INC
Also Called: Recycling Div
5535 Vine St (45217-1003)
PHONE....................................513 242-3671
Eric Vandervert, *Branch Mgr*
EMP: 434
SALES (corp-wide): 2.6B **Privately Held**
WEB: www.bowater.com
SIC: 2621 Paper mills
HQ: Resolute Fp Us Inc.
5300 Cureton Ferry Rd
Catawba SC 29704
803 981-8000

(G-4339)
RESOURCE GRAPHICS
2230 Gilbert Ave (45206-2531)
PHONE....................................513 205-2686
Gregory R Cozart, *Owner*
EMP: 3
SALES: 250K **Privately Held**
SIC: 3555 Printing trades machinery

(G-4340)
REULAND ELECTRIC CO
9620 Colerain Ave Ste 22 (45251-2018)
PHONE....................................513 825-7314
Fax: 513 825-0016
Bill Kramer, *Branch Mgr*
Jeanie Brown, *Manager*
EMP: 4
SALES (corp-wide): 42.4MM **Privately Held**
WEB: www.reuland.com
SIC: 3621 Motors, electric
PA: Reuland Electric Co.
17969 Railroad St
City Of Industry CA 91748
626 964-6411

(G-4341)
RIBS KING INC
9406 Main St (45242-7616)
PHONE....................................513 791-1942
Thomas Gregory, *President*
Evan Andrews, *Vice Pres*
Dean Gregory, *Vice Pres*
Victoria Siegel, *Vice Pres*
Nancy Foster, *Manager*
EMP: 9
SQ FT: 21,000

SALES: 7MM **Privately Held**
SIC: 2035 Seasonings & sauces, except tomato & dry

(G-4342)
RICHARD B LINNEMAN
Also Called: Sterling Industries
5642 Victory Dr (45233-4657)
PHONE..................................513 922-5537
Fax: 513 922-5537
Richard B Linneman, *Owner*
EMP: 4
SQ FT: 6,300
SALES (est): 490.8K **Privately Held**
SIC: 3556 2541 2542 Food products machinery; store fixtures, wood; fixtures, store: except wood

(G-4343)
RICHARD BENHASE & ASSOCIATES
11741 Chesterdale Rd (45246-3405)
PHONE..................................513 772-1896
Richard Benhase, *President*
Linda Benhase, *Vice Pres*
EMP: 11
SQ FT: 15,000
SALES: 800K **Privately Held**
SIC: 2521 2511 2434 Cabinets, office: wood; wood household furniture; wood kitchen cabinets

(G-4344)
RICHARDS INDUSTRIES INC
Also Called: Marwin Ball Valves Div
3170 Wasson Rd (45209-2329)
PHONE..................................513 533-7340
Fax: 513 871-0105
Bruce Broxterman, *President*
Tim Gainer, *Regional Mgr*
William Metz, *Vice Pres*
Cheryl Neiheisel, *Vice Pres*
Charles Page, *Vice Pres*
▲ **EMP:** 150
SQ FT: 150,000
SALES (est): 48MM **Privately Held**
WEB: www.richardsind.com
SIC: 3491 3494 3823 Industrial valves; pipe fittings; industrial instrmnts msrmnt display/control process variable

(G-4345)
RICKING PAPER AND SPECIALTY CO
525 Northland Blvd (45240-3233)
PHONE..................................513 825-3551
Fax: 513 825-3738
Carl Ricking Jr, *President*
Preston M Simpson, *Principal*
Carla Droll, *Vice Pres*
Karla Droll, *Vice Pres*
Julie Ricking, *Vice Pres*
EMP: 50
SQ FT: 84,000
SALES (est): 14.9MM **Privately Held**
WEB: www.ricking.com
SIC: 5113 5141 2656 Industrial & personal service paper; bags, paper & disposable plastic; towels, paper; napkins, paper; groceries, general line; cups, paper: made from purchased material

(G-4346)
RIDGE ENGINEERING INC
Also Called: Delhi Welding Co
1700 Blue Rock St (45223-2505)
PHONE..................................513 681-5500
Fax: 513 681-5550
Rob Shean, *General Mgr*
Regina Porter, *Manager*
Darrell Warren, *Manager*
EMP: 9
SQ FT: 14,000
SALES (est): 1.8MM **Privately Held**
WEB: www.ridgemetalworks.com
SIC: 7692 Welding repair

(G-4347)
RIVER CITY BODY COMPANY
2660 Commerce Blvd (45241-1552)
PHONE..................................513 772-9317
Fax: 513 772-9316
John Mc Henry, *President*
Mark Zembrodt, *General Mgr*
EMP: 11
SQ FT: 10,000

SALES (est): 1.8MM **Privately Held**
WEB: www.rivercitybody.com
SIC: 3713 Truck beds

(G-4348)
RIVER CORP
32 W Mitchell Ave (45217-1526)
P.O. Box 20206 (45220-0206)
PHONE..................................513 641-3355
Fax: 513 641-3358
Edgar Ragouzis, *President*
Charles Noe, *Vice Pres*
EMP: 3
SQ FT: 3,500
SALES (est): 329.3K **Privately Held**
SIC: 2731 2791 Books: publishing only; pamphlets: publishing only, not printed on site; typesetting

(G-4349)
RIVERSIDE CNSTR SVCS INC
218 W Mcmicken Ave (45214-2314)
PHONE..................................513 723-0900
Fax: 513 723-0990
Robert S Krejci, *President*
Timothy L Pierce, *Vice Pres*
Karen Lampson, *Office Mgr*
EMP: 32
SQ FT: 21,000
SALES (est): 6MM **Privately Held**
WEB: www.riversidearchitectural.com
SIC: 2431 1751 2434 Millwork; carpentry work; wood kitchen cabinets

(G-4350)
RIVERTOWN BREWING COMPANY LLC
607 Shepherd Dr Unit 6 (45215-2188)
PHONE..................................513 827-9280
Jason D Roeper,
Randy Schiltz,
▲ **EMP:** 20
SALES: 2MM **Privately Held**
SIC: 2082 Brewers' grain

(G-4351)
RME MACHINING CO
2900 Spring Grove Ave (45225-2115)
PHONE..................................513 541-3328
Fax: 513 541-5303
Robert Enderle, *President*
EMP: 5
SQ FT: 10,000
SALES (est): 480K **Privately Held**
SIC: 3599 3544 Machine shop, jobbing & repair; special dies & tools

(G-4352)
ROBBINS INC (PA)
Also Called: Robbins Sports Surfaces
4777 Eastern Ave (45226-2339)
PHONE..................................513 871-8988
Fax: 513 871-7998
James H Stoehr III, *Chairman*
Mike Niese, *Vice Pres*
Beth Smith, *Vice Pres*
Jonathan Turner, *Vice Pres*
John Williams, *Vice Pres*
◆ **EMP:** 28
SQ FT: 3,000
SALES (est): 74.6MM **Privately Held**
WEB: www.robbinsfloor.com
SIC: 2426 Flooring, hardwood

(G-4353)
ROBERT ESTERMAN
Also Called: Esterman Printing Services
2929 Spring Grove Ave # 100
(45225-2157)
PHONE..................................513 541-3311
Fax: 513 541-3311
Robert Esterman, *Owner*
Steve Holtmeier, *Manager*
Harry Esterman, *Representative*
EMP: 3
SQ FT: 5,000
SALES (est): 283K **Privately Held**
WEB: www.estermanprinting.com
SIC: 2759 2791 2789 Commercial printing; typesetting; bookbinding & related work

(G-4354)
ROBERT J & CINDY K HARTZ
8734 Woodview Dr (45231-5031)
P.O. Box 62046 (45262-0046)
PHONE..................................513 521-6215
Robert Hartz, *Owner*
EMP: 3
SALES: 200K **Privately Held**
SIC: 3599 Water leak detectors

(G-4355)
ROCKDALE SYSTEMS LLC
6 Rowley Ct (45246-3851)
PHONE..................................513 379-3577
Ganesh Balasubramanian, *CEO*
Adrian Thompson, *Principal*
EMP: 3
SALES (est): 218.7K **Privately Held**
SIC: 3841 Veterinarians' instruments & apparatus

(G-4356)
ROHM AND HAAS CHEMICALS LLC
Also Called: Dow Bar Roman Hosue
2000 West St (45215-3431)
PHONE..................................513 733-2100
Mark Kinnett, *Branch Mgr*
EMP: 4
SALES (corp-wide): 48.1B **Publicly Held**
SIC: 2834 Pharmaceutical preparations
HQ: Rohm And Haas Chemicals Llc
100 S Independence Mall W # 5
Philadelphia PA 19106
215 592-3000

(G-4357)
ROHM AND HAAS COMPANY
2000 West St (45215-3431)
PHONE..................................513 733-2100
Michael Feldkamp, *Purchasing*
Tom Mfarlow, *Human Res Dir*
Gary Burkins, *Branch Mgr*
EMP: 180
SQ FT: 950
SALES (corp-wide): 48.1B **Publicly Held**
WEB: www.rohmhaas.com
SIC: 2821 Plastics materials & resins
HQ: Rohm And Haas Company
100 N Independence Mall W
Philadelphia PA 19106
215 592-3000

(G-4358)
ROLCON INC
510 Station Ave (45215-5439)
PHONE..................................513 821-7259
EMP: 10
SALES (corp-wide): 3.4MM **Privately Held**
WEB: www.rolconvenix.com
SIC: 3535 3561 Conveyors & conveying equipment; cylinders, pump
PA: Rolcon, Inc
134 Carthage Ave
Cincinnati OH 45215
513 821-7259

(G-4359)
ROTEX GLOBAL LCC
Also Called: Gundlach
1230 Knowlton St (45223-1800)
PHONE..................................513 541-1236
Fax: 513 541-4888
William J Herkamp, *President*
Graeme Hill, *Managing Dir*
Steve Kirschner, *Managing Dir*
Gary Armstrong, *Vice Pres*
Mark J Moore, *Vice Pres*
◆ **EMP:** 165 **EST:** 1844
SQ FT: 150,000
SALES (est): 65.2MM
SALES (corp-wide): 1.5B **Publicly Held**
SIC: 3826 3569 Particle size analyzers; sifting & screening machines
PA: Hillenbrand, Inc.
1 Batesville Blvd
Batesville IN 47006
812 934-7500

(G-4360)
ROUGH BROTHERS MFG INC
5513 Vine St Ste 1 (45217-1022)
PHONE..................................513 242-0310
Fax: 513 242-0816
Richard Reilly, *President*

James Parris, *General Mgr*
Tom Vezdos, *General Mgr*
Kevin Caron, *Vice Pres*
Anada Bethea, *Project Mgr*
◆ **EMP:** 90
SQ FT: 100,000
SALES: 72.6MM
SALES (corp-wide): 1B **Publicly Held**
SIC: 1542 3448 Greenhouse construction; greenhouses: prefabricated metal
HQ: Rough Brothers Holding Co., Inc
3556 Lake Shore Rd # 100
Buffalo NY 14219
716 826-6500

(G-4361)
ROWLEY J F PROSTH & ORTH LAB (PA)
2729 Vine St (45219-2018)
PHONE..................................513 861-3705
Arthur C Robbin Jr, *President*
EMP: 9
SQ FT: 2,000
SALES: 1MM **Privately Held**
SIC: 3842 Limbs, artificial

(G-4362)
ROYAL SPECIALTY PRODUCTS INC
4114 Montgomery Rd (45212-3651)
PHONE..................................513 841-1267
Herbert C Brandenburg Jr, *President*
EMP: 5
SALES (est): 458.5K **Privately Held**
SIC: 3577 Printers & plotters

(G-4363)
RPI COLOR SERVICE INC
Also Called: RPI Graphic Data Solutions
1950 Radcliff Dr (45204-1823)
PHONE..................................513 471-4040
Fax: 513 244-5387
Patricia A Raker, *President*
Denise L Rellar, *Exec VP*
Karen E Rellar, *Exec VP*
Bill Engman, *Purchasing*
William E Rellar, *Treasurer*
EMP: 70 **EST:** 1980
SQ FT: 65,000
SALES: 10MM **Privately Held**
SIC: 2752 Commercial printing, lithographic

(G-4364)
RS PRO SALES LLC
1512 Eastern Ave (45202)
PHONE..................................513 699-5329
Taft Stricklind, *Mng Member*
EMP: 5
SALES (est): 545.8K **Privately Held**
SIC: 3651 3585 Household audio & video equipment; air conditioning equipment, complete

(G-4365)
RUDD EQUIPMENT COMPANY INC
11807 Enterprise Dr (45241-1511)
PHONE..................................513 321-7833
EMP: 23
SALES (corp-wide): 110.5MM **Privately Held**
SIC: 3462 Construction or mining equipment forgings, ferrous
PA: Rudd Equipment Company, Inc.
4344 Poplar Level Rd
Louisville KY 40213
502 456-4050

(G-4366)
RUMPKE TRANSPORTATION CO LLC (HQ)
10795 Hughes Rd (45251-4598)
PHONE..................................513 851-0122
William J Rumpke, *President*
Rick Dorrel, *Division Mgr*
Tim Kemper, *Division Mgr*
Richard Roberts, *Engineer*
Phil Wehrman, *CFO*
EMP: 10
SQ FT: 10,000

SALES (est): 131.2MM
SALES (corp-wide): 1.4B **Privately Held**
SIC: 3561 5084 7537 4953 Pumps & pumping equipment; hydraulic systems equipment & supplies; automotive transmission repair shops; refuse systems
PA: Rumpke Consolidated Companies, Inc.
　10795 Hughes Rd
　Cincinnati OH 45251
　800 582-3107

(G-4367)
RUMPKE TRANSPORTATION CO LLC
Also Called: Rumpke Container Service
553 Vine St (45202)
PHONE.................................513 242-4600
Jeff Rumpke, *Manager*
Bruce R Ullrey, *CIO*
EMP: 150
SALES (corp-wide): 1.4B **Privately Held**
SIC: 4953 3341 3231 2611 Recycling, waste materials; secondary nonferrous metals; products of purchased glass; pulp mills
HQ: Rumpke Transportation Company, Llc
　10795 Hughes Rd
　Cincinnati OH 45251
　513 851-0122

(G-4368)
RUSSMENTS INC
3714 Church St (45244-3005)
PHONE.................................513 602-5035
Russell Mc Murry, *President*
Kyndle Mc Murry, *Vice Pres*
Shirley Mc Murry, *Treasurer*
EMP: 1
SALES: 2MM **Privately Held**
SIC: 5084 3491 Controlling instruments & accessories; industrial valves

(G-4369)
RUTHMAN PUMP AND ENGINEERING (PA)
Also Called: Fulflo Specialties Company
1212 Streng St (45223-2643)
PHONE.................................513 559-1901
Thomas R Ruthman, *President*
David Horn, *Controller*
Tom Day, *Sales Associate*
Ed McArter, *Supervisor*
▲ **EMP:** 5
SQ FT: 45,000
SALES (est): 41.6MM **Privately Held**
WEB: www.ruthmannpumpen.de
SIC: 3561 3492 Industrial pumps & parts; control valves, fluid power; hydraulic & pneumatic

(G-4370)
RX FRAMES N LENSES LTD
4270 Boomer Rd (45247-7912)
PHONE.................................513 557-2970
Daniel Louallen, *Principal*
EMP: 3
SALES (est): 284.1K **Privately Held**
SIC: 3851 Ophthalmic goods

(G-4371)
RYKRISP LLC
4342 Centennial Dr Apt 33 (45227-2579)
PHONE.................................843 338-0750
William Leavitt, *CEO*
Robert Holden, *Principal*
Edward Slanga, *Principal*
EMP: 4
SALES: 2MM **Privately Held**
SIC: 2052 Cookies & crackers

(G-4372)
S C JOHNSON & SON INC
36 E 7th St Ste 2450 (45202-4400)
PHONE.................................513 665-3600
Jeff Johnson, *Manager*
EMP: 20
SALES (corp-wide): 4.2B **Privately Held**
WEB: www.scjohnson.com
SIC: 2842 Floor waxes; furniture polish or wax; stain removers; disinfectants, household or industrial plant
PA: S. C. Johnson & Son, Inc.
　1525 Howe St
　Racine WI 53403
　262 260-2000

(G-4373)
S J ROTH ENTERPRISES INC
Also Called: Roth Ready Mix Concrete Co
900 Kieley Pl (45217-1153)
PHONE.................................513 242-8400
Fax: 513 242-8697
Steven Roth, *President*
Darlene Royer, *Manager*
Frank J Roth, *Admin Sec*
EMP: 40
SQ FT: 1,200
SALES (est): 6.8MM **Privately Held**
SIC: 3273 Ready-mixed concrete

(G-4374)
S L C SOFTWARE SERVICES
1958 Anderson Ferry Rd (45238-3324)
PHONE.................................513 922-4303
Fax: 513 922-4439
Sandra L Gerhardt, *Owner*
EMP: 3
SQ FT: 1,000
SALES: 100K **Privately Held**
WEB: www.slcsoftware.com
SIC: 7379 7372 5063 Computer related consulting services; prepackaged software; electrical apparatus & equipment

(G-4375)
S T CUSTOM SIGNS
9493 Reading Rd (45215-3520)
PHONE.................................513 733-4227
Thomas F Harsch, *Partner*
Sandra L Pierce-Harsch, *Partner*
EMP: 3
SALES (est): 160K **Privately Held**
SIC: 8999 3993 Communication services; signs & advertising specialties

(G-4376)
SAIL MEDICAL INC
9873 Montgomery Rd (45242-6424)
PHONE.................................513 961-3144
Kenneth Sandler, *CEO*
Andrew Sandler, *COO*
Drew Sandler, *COO*
EMP: 7
SALES: 1.5MM **Privately Held**
SIC: 3845 Electromedical equipment

(G-4377)
SAKRETE INC (PA)
5155 Fischer Ave (45217-1157)
PHONE.................................513 242-3644
John G Avril, *Ch of Bd*
J Craig Avril, *President*
EMP: 20 **EST:** 1936
SQ FT: 35,000
SALES (est): 2.4MM **Privately Held**
SIC: 3273 6794 Ready-mixed concrete; patent buying, licensing, leasing

(G-4378)
SAMHAIN PUBLISHING LTD (LLC)
11821 Mason Montgomery Rd # 2 (45249-3705)
PHONE.................................513 453-4688
Christina M Brashear, *Owner*
Linda Ingmanson, *Editor*
Donna Holland, *Prdtn Mgr*
Jenn Stark, *Marketing Staff*
Mackenzie Walton, *Admin Asst*
EMP: 9
SALES (est): 977.4K **Privately Held**
SIC: 2741 Miscellaneous publishing

(G-4379)
SATURDAY KNIGHT LTD (HQ)
4330 Winton Rd (45232-1827)
PHONE.................................513 641-1400
Frank Kling, *Ch of Bd*
Jim Lewis, *President*
Julie Copenhaver, *General Mgr*
Carol Ferguson, *General Mgr*
Mike Keefner, *COO*
◆ **EMP:** 76
SQ FT: 450,000
SALES (est): 17.8MM
SALES (corp-wide): 25MM **Privately Held**
WEB: www.skltd.com
SIC: 2392 Towels, fabric & nonwoven: made from purchased materials; shower curtains: made from purchased materials

PA: F K Holding Inc
　2100 Section Rd
　Cincinnati OH 45237
　513 641-1400

(G-4380)
SAUERWEIN WELDING
605 Wayne Park Dr (45215-2848)
P.O. Box 15033 (45215-0033)
PHONE.................................513 563-2979
Fax: 513 563-1063
Donald Sauerwein, *President*
EMP: 7
SQ FT: 5,000
SALES (est): 430K **Privately Held**
SIC: 7692 Welding repair

(G-4381)
SAWBROOK STEEL CASTINGS CO (PA)
Also Called: Cushman Foundry Div
425 Shepherd Ave (45215-3114)
P.O. Box 15527 (45215-0527)
PHONE.................................513 554-1700
Fax: 513 554-0092
John C Beyersdorfer Sr, *Ch of Bd*
Michael Beyersdorfer, *President*
John C Beyersdorfer Jr, *Vice Pres*
Richard Beyersdorfer, *Vice Pres*
William Payler, *Purchasing*
▲ **EMP:** 90 **EST:** 1923
SQ FT: 523,000
SALES (est): 13.2MM **Privately Held**
WEB: www.sawbrooksteel.com
SIC: 3365 3325 3369 3341 Aluminum & aluminum-based alloy castings; alloy steel castings, except investment; nonferrous foundries; secondary nonferrous metals

(G-4382)
SC ELEARNING LLC
Also Called: Trivantis
311 Elm St Ste 200 (45202-2743)
PHONE.................................513 852-6841
Christopher Hord, *CFO*
EMP: 63
SALES (est): 1MM **Privately Held**
SIC: 7372 Prepackaged software

(G-4383)
SCALLYWAG TAG
5055 Glencrossing Way (45238-3362)
PHONE.................................513 922-4999
James Leopold, *Owner*
EMP: 4 **EST:** 2008
SALES (est): 371.5K **Privately Held**
SIC: 3845 Laser systems & equipment, medical

(G-4384)
SCHAAF CO INC
2440 Spring Grove Ave (45214-1755)
PHONE.................................513 241-7044
Fax: 513 241-2871
Walter A Smith, *President*
Chuck Smith, *Vice Pres*
Steve Lewis, *Director*
Barb Meeks, *Admin Sec*
EMP: 9
SQ FT: 6,500
SALES (est): 1MM **Privately Held**
WEB: www.schaaf.com
SIC: 2394 Canvas & related products

(G-4385)
SCHAD MEATS INC
2615 Cummins St (45225-2015)
PHONE.................................513 520-4888
Fax: 513 251-0254
Daniel Benton, *President*
EMP: 5
SQ FT: 6,000
SALES: 625K **Privately Held**
SIC: 2013 Prepared pork products from purchased pork

(G-4386)
SCHAERER MEDICAL USA INC
675 Wilmer Ave (45226-1802)
P.O. Box 645110 (45264-0301)
PHONE.................................513 561-2241
Michal Palazzola, *CEO*
Mark D Budde, *CEO*
Hans Rudolf Saegesser, *Ch of Bd*
Ted Melton, *Principal*

Jan Osborne, *Principal*
▲ **EMP:** 11 **EST:** 1965
SQ FT: 100,000
SALES (est): 2.5MM **Privately Held**
WEB: www.schaerermayfieldusa.com
SIC: 5999 3842 Medical apparatus & supplies; surgical appliances & supplies

(G-4387)
SCHENZ THEATRICAL SUPPLY INC
2959 Colerain Ave (45225-2103)
PHONE.................................513 542-6100
Fax: 513 542-0093
John J Schenz, *President*
EMP: 13
SQ FT: 15,000
SALES: 350K **Privately Held**
WEB: www.schenz.com
SIC: 2389 5999 7922 Theatrical costumes; theatrical equipment & supplies; equipment rental, theatrical

(G-4388)
SCHNEIDER INSTRUMENT CO
8115 Camargo Rd (45243-2203)
P.O. Box 43035 (45243-0035)
PHONE.................................513 561-6803
Fax: 513 527-4375
Gary Schneider, *President*
Dr Mark A Schneider, *Vice Pres*
Hattie Schneider, *Shareholder*
EMP: 13
SQ FT: 7,000
SALES (est): 2MM **Privately Held**
SIC: 3829 Measuring & controlling devices

(G-4389)
SCHOMAKER NATURAL RESOURCE
2741 Blue Rock Rd (45239-6332)
PHONE.................................513 741-1370
Joseph E Schomaker, *Owner*
EMP: 4
SALES: 130K **Privately Held**
SIC: 3524 Lawn & garden equipment

(G-4390)
SCHWAB WELDING INC
7046 Harrison Ave (45247-3208)
PHONE.................................513 353-4262
Fax: 513 353-4265
Wilbur J Schwab, *President*
James Schwab, *Vice Pres*
EMP: 3
SQ FT: 1,800
SALES: 300K **Privately Held**
SIC: 7692 3446 Welding repair; architectural metalwork

(G-4391)
SCOTT MODELS INC
607 Redna Ter Ste 400 (45215-1183)
PHONE.................................513 771-8005
Fax: 513 771-8019
Thomas Scott, *President*
Doug Fiessinger, *Marketing Staff*
Pam Jetter, *Manager*
EMP: 15
SQ FT: 10,000
SALES (est): 1.4MM **Privately Held**
WEB: www.scottmodels.com
SIC: 3999 Models, except toy

(G-4392)
SCRIPPS MEDIA INC
312 Walnut St Fl 28 (45202-4024)
PHONE.................................513 977-3000
William Appleton, *Vice Pres*
EMP: 100
SALES (est): 14.7MM
SALES (corp-wide): 3B **Publicly Held**
SIC: 2711 Newspapers
HQ: Journal Media Group, Inc.
　333 W State St
　Milwaukee WI 53203
　414 224-2000

(G-4393)
SCS CONSTRUCTION SERVICES INC
2130 Western Ave (45214-1744)
PHONE.................................513 929-0260
Jerry Back, *President*
Larry Back, *Vice Pres*

Charlie Hull, *CFO*
EMP: 45 **EST:** 2000
SQ FT: 8,000
SALES (est): 7.9MM **Privately Held**
SIC: 1542 3231 1761 3449 Commercial
& office building contractors; doors, glass:
made from purchased glass; skylight installation; curtain walls for buildings, steel;
metalware

(G-4394)
SDI INDUSTRIES
8561 New England Ct (45236-2093)
PHONE..............................513 561-4032
Edward Boll, *Principal*
EMP: 3
SALES (est): 220.8K **Privately Held**
SIC: 3999 Manufacturing industries

(G-4395)
SECURITY FENCE GROUP INC (PA)
4260 Dane Ave (45223-1855)
PHONE..............................513 681-3700
Fax: 513 681-5487
Christine Frankenstein, *President*
Angela Case, *Corp Secy*
George Frankenstein, *Vice Pres*
EMP: 37
SQ FT: 140,000
SALES (est): 11.7MM **Privately Held**
SIC: 1611 1799 3446 5039 Guardrail
construction, highways; highway & street
sign installation; fence construction; archi-
tectural metalwork; wire fence, gates &
accessories; general electrical contractor;
traffic signals, electric

(G-4396)
SECURITY SYSTEMS EQP CORP
3040 Forrer St (45209-1016)
PHONE..............................513 758-1070
James E Bushman, *Ch of Bd*
Ross Bushman, *President*
Kerry Kennedy, *Marketing Staff*
▲ **EMP:** 5
SQ FT: 80,000
SALES (est): 980.5K
SALES (corp-wide): 33.1MM **Privately Held**
WEB: www.sse-corp.com
SIC: 3556 5049 Bakery machinery; bank
equipment & supplies
PA: Cast-Fab Technologies, Inc.
3040 Forrer St
Cincinnati OH 45209
513 758-1000

(G-4397)
SEEMLESS DESIGN & PRINTING LLC
717 Linn St (45203-1703)
PHONE..............................513 871-2366
Christian Wilhelmy,
EMP: 6
SALES (est): 842.1K **Privately Held**
SIC: 2752 Commercial printing, litho-
graphic

(G-4398)
SEILKOP INDUSTRIES INC (PA)
Also Called: Epcor Foundries
425 W North Bend Rd (45216-1731)
PHONE..............................513 761-1035
Fax: 513 761-0368
Ken Seilkop, *President*
Dave Seilkop, *Vice Pres*
Paul Kiefer, *Plant Mgr*
Marilyn Seilkop, *Production*
Robin Vogel, *CFO*
EMP: 50
SQ FT: 35,000
SALES (est): 24.1MM **Privately Held**
WEB: www.epcorfoundry.com
SIC: 3363 3544 3553 3469 Aluminum
die-castings; special dies & tools; pattern
makers' machinery, woodworking; pat-
terns on metal; industrial tool grinding

(G-4399)
SEILKOP INDUSTRIES INC
Also Called: Hitech Shapes & Designs
7211 Market Pl (45216-2020)
PHONE..............................513 679-5680
Fax: 513 821-1142
Ken Seilkop, *Owner*

Marilyn Seilkop, *Prdtn Mgr*
EMP: 12
SALES (corp-wide): 24.1MM **Privately Held**
WEB: www.epcorfoundry.com
SIC: 3543 3369 3365 3363 Foundry pat-
ternmaking; nonferrous foundries; alu-
minum foundries; aluminum die-castings
PA: Seilkop Industries, Inc.
425 W North Bend Rd
Cincinnati OH 45216
513 761-1035

(G-4400)
SELBY SERVICE/ROXY PRESS INC
2020 Elm St (45202-4911)
PHONE..............................513 241-3445
Fax: 513 241-3456
Clarence Stricker, *Ch of Bd*
Robert Stricker, *President*
Bob Furnish, *Vice Pres*
Loretta Stricker, *Treasurer*
Jeanne Meinzen, *Admin Sec*
EMP: 6 **EST:** 1938
SALES (est): 580K **Privately Held**
SIC: 2752 7331 2759 Commercial print-
ing, offset; addressographing service;
mailing service; letterpress printing

(G-4401)
SELBYS UPPER DECK COMPANY
1028 Glenna Dr (45238-4321)
PHONE..............................513 451-5981
Kenneth Selby, *Principal*
EMP: 3
SALES (est): 247.9K **Privately Held**
SIC: 3131 Uppers

(G-4402)
SELECT WOODWORKING INC
427c W Seymour Ave (45216)
PHONE..............................513 948-9901
EMP: 7
SALES (est): 690K **Privately Held**
SIC: 2431 Mfg Millwork

(G-4403)
SENCO BRANDS INC
8450 Broadwell Rd (45244-1612)
PHONE..............................513 388-2833
Steve Downing, *Plant Mgr*
Arthur West, *Branch Mgr*
EMP: 22
SALES (corp-wide): 912.7MM **Privately Held**
SIC: 3546 Power-driven handtools
HQ: Senco Brands, Inc.
4270 Ivy Pointe Blvd
Cincinnati OH 45245
513 388-2000

(G-4404)
SENIOR IMPACT PUBLICATION
5980 Kugier Mill Rd (45236-2075)
PHONE..............................513 791-8800
Fax: 513 791-8847
Robert Jutze, *President*
EMP: 10
SALES (est): 450K **Privately Held**
WEB: www.seniorimpact.net
SIC: 2741 Guides: publishing only, not
printed on site

(G-4405)
SENSE DIAGNOSTICS LLC
1776 Mentor Ave Ste 411 (45212-3576)
PHONE..............................513 515-3853
Daniel Kincaid, *CEO*
Opeolu Adeoye, *Owner*
Joseph Clark,
Matthew Flaherty,
George Shaw,
EMP: 5
SALES (est): 459.8K **Privately Held**
SIC: 3841 Diagnostic apparatus, medical

(G-4406)
SERVATII INC
7161 Beechmont Ave (45230-4111)
PHONE..............................513 231-4455
Fax: 513 231-4689
Wilhelm Gottenbusch, *Owner*
Jim Lundberg, *Manager*
EMP: 10

SALES (corp-wide): 34.6MM **Privately Held**
WEB: www.servati.com
SIC: 2051 Doughnuts, except frozen
PA: Servatii, Inc.
3888 Virginia Ave
Cincinnati OH 45227
513 271-5040

(G-4407)
SERVATII INC
3774 Paxton Ave (45209-2306)
PHONE..............................513 271-5040
Fax: 513 871-1477
Becky Free, *Manager*
EMP: 13
SALES (corp-wide): 34.6MM **Privately Held**
WEB: www.servati.com
SIC: 2051 Bread, cake & related products
PA: Servatii, Inc.
3888 Virginia Ave
Cincinnati OH 45227
513 271-5040

(G-4408)
SESH COMMUNICATIONS
Also Called: N J E M A Magazine
3440 Burnet Ave Ste 130 (45229-2857)
PHONE..............................513 851-1693
Fax: 513 961-0305
Eric Kearney, *President*
Wilton Blake, *Vice Pres*
Ronda Gooden, *Vice Pres*
Jan-Michele Kearney, *Vice Pres*
Wade Lacey Sr, *Manager*
EMP: 13
SALES (est): 680K **Privately Held**
SIC: 2711 2721 Newspapers; periodicals

(G-4409)
SETCO SALES COMPANY (HQ)
5880 Hillside Ave (45233-1599)
PHONE..............................513 941-5110
Fax: 513 941-6913
Jeffrey J Clark, *President*
Jim Broz, *Vice Pres*
Joseph S Haas, *Vice Pres*
Scott Bubenhofer, *Plant Mgr*
Craig Rath, *CFO*
▲ **EMP:** 80 **EST:** 1986
SQ FT: 55,000
SALES: 30MM
SALES (corp-wide): 285.1MM **Privately Held**
SIC: 3545 7694 Machine tool accessories;
armature rewinding shops
PA: Holden Industries, Inc.
500 Lake Cook Rd Ste 400
Deerfield IL 60015
847 940-1500

(G-4410)
SEVEN HILLS FOODS LTD
Also Called: McCabe's Granola
6425 Shadyglen Rd (45243-3237)
PHONE..............................513 518-3704
Susan Muth, *CEO*
Chris Muth, *CFO*
Michael Muth, *Marketing Staff*
Jameson Muth, *CIO*
▼ **EMP:** 4
SALES: 1MM **Privately Held**
SIC: 2043 Cereal breakfast foods

(G-4411)
SHAMROCK MATERIALS INC
11641 Mosteller Rd (45241-1520)
PHONE..............................513 988-0647
Fax: 513 988-9933
James P Jurgensen, *President*
James King, *President*
David Ripple, *VP Admin*
David Groth, *Sales Staff*
EMP: 10
SQ FT: 800
SALES (est): 734.3K **Privately Held**
SIC: 1442 Construction sand & gravel

(G-4412)
SHANNON TOOL INC
3355 Hill St (45241-1934)
PHONE..............................513 563-2300
Fax: 513 563-2308
William Price, *President*
EMP: 4 **EST:** 1931

SQ FT: 10,000
SALES (est): 380K **Privately Held**
SIC: 3599 Machine shop, jobbing & repair

(G-4413)
SHARP INDUSTRIAL TOOLS INC
3348 Nandale Dr (45239-4071)
PHONE..............................513 741-9562
John R Mc Culloch, *President*
John R McCulloch, *Principal*
EMP: 7
SQ FT: 1,584
SALES (est): 440K **Privately Held**
WEB: www.sharpindustrialtools.com
SIC: 3541 3544 Machine tools, metal cut-
ting type; machine tool replacement & re-
pair parts, metal cutting types; special
dies, tools, jigs & fixtures; special dies &
tools

(G-4414)
SHAWNEE SYSTEMS INC
3616 Church St (45244-3004)
PHONE..............................513 561-9932
Richard Rogers, *President*
Warren Hensel Jr, *Vice Pres*
Richard Rogers II, *Vice Pres*
Mark Braun, *Controller*
Veronica Dickerson, *Receptionist*
▲ **EMP:** 57
SQ FT: 40,000
SALES (est): 5.2MM **Privately Held**
WEB: www.shawneesystems.com
SIC: 2761 2752 Manifold business forms;
commercial printing, lithographic

(G-4415)
SHEPHERD CHEMICAL COMPANY
2825 Highland Ave (45212-2409)
PHONE..............................513 200-6987
Gary Conrad, *General Mgr*
Steven Schwartz, *Opers Staff*
Jeanne Fisher, *Buyer*
Aaron Mehan, *Manager*
EMP: 15
SQ FT: 39,516
SALES (corp-wide): 58.2MM **Privately Held**
SIC: 2819 2869 Industrial inorganic chem-
icals; industrial organic chemicals
PA: The Shepherd Chemical Company
4900 Beech St
Norwood OH 45212
513 731-1110

(G-4416)
SIDNEY PRINTING WORKS INC
2611 Colerain Ave (45214-1777)
PHONE..............................513 542-4000
Fax: 513 542-4741
Josh Deutch, *President*
EMP: 4
SQ FT: 11,439
SALES (est): 426.8K **Privately Held**
SIC: 2752 Commercial printing, litho-
graphic

(G-4417)
SIEMENS INDUSTRY INC
Also Called: Motors & Drives Division
4620 Forest Ave (45212-3306)
PHONE..............................513 841-3100
Karl Ulreich, *Division Mgr*
Thomas Boyd, *Purchasing*
William Finley, *Research*
Steve Kroeger, *Plant Engr Mgr*
Ryan Queen, *Engineer*
EMP: 200
SQ FT: 550,000
SALES (corp-wide): 89.6B **Privately Held**
WEB: www.sea.siemens.com
SIC: 3621 Motors, electric; generators &
sets, electric
HQ: Siemens Industry, Inc.
1000 Deerfield Pkwy
Buffalo Grove IL 60089
847 215-1000

(G-4418)
SIGMATEK SYSTEMS LLC (PA)
Also Called: Sigma T E K
1445 Kemper Meadow Dr (45240-1637)
PHONE..............................513 674-0005
Fax: 513 674-0009
Ben Terreblanche, *CEO*

John Salisbury, *President*
Chris Cooper, *Principal*
Jandre Terreblanche, *Principal*
Jim Elmore, *Regional Mgr*
EMP: 65
SQ FT: 23,000
SALES (est): 20.2MM **Privately Held**
WEB: www.sigmanest.com
SIC: 7372 Prepackaged software

(G-4419)
SIGN A RAMA INC
Also Called: Sign-A-Rama
2519 Crescentville Rd (45241-1575)
PHONE.....................513 671-2213
Fax: 513 671-2214
Rebecca Carter, *Office Mgr*
Vlad Shmulevich, *Manager*
EMP: 4
SALES (corp-wide): 88.5MM **Privately Held**
WEB: www.franchisemart.com
SIC: 3993 Signs & advertising specialties
HQ: Sign A Rama Inc.
2121 Vista Pkwy
West Palm Beach FL 33411
561 640-5570

(G-4420)
SIGNALYSIS INC
539 Glenrose Ln (45244-1509)
PHONE.....................513 528-6164
Fax: 513 528-6181
Robert Neil Coleman, *President*
Kyle Coleman, *Vice Pres*
Phil Wilkin, *Shareholder*
EMP: 12
SALES (est): 2.1MM **Privately Held**
WEB: www.signalysis.com
SIC: 8711 7371 3695 7389 Consulting engineer; computer software development & applications; computer software tape & disks: blank, rigid & floppy;

(G-4421)
SIMPLE VMS LLC
7373 Beechmont Ave # 130 (45230-4100)
PHONE.....................888 255-8918
Joseph Clancy, *President*
EMP: 7 **EST:** 2011
SALES (est): 810.8K **Privately Held**
SIC: 7372 7371 8742 8748 Business oriented computer software; computer software development & applications; human resource consulting services; business consulting

(G-4422)
SIMPLY UNIQUE SNACKS LLC
4420 Haight Ave (45223-1705)
PHONE.....................513 223-7736
Steve Hofford, *President*
Tammi Hofford, *Controller*
EMP: 6
SALES (est): 435.3K
SALES (corp-wide): 1.1MM **Privately Held**
SIC: 2013 2037 2068 7389 Snack sticks, including jerky: from purchased meat; fruit juices, frozen; salted & roasted nuts & seeds;
PA: United Snacks Of America Llc

Plainview NY 11803
516 319-9448

(G-4423)
SIMS-LOHMAN INC (PA)
Also Called: Sims-Lohman Fine Kitchens Gran
6325 Este Ave (45232-1458)
PHONE.....................513 651-3510
Steve Steinman, *CEO*
John Beiersdorfer, *President*
Roger Llila, *Controller*
Crystallyn Egner, *Consultant*
▲ **EMP:** 50
SQ FT: 153,000
SALES (est): 95.7MM **Privately Held**
WEB: www.moelleringindustries.com
SIC: 5031 2435 Kitchen cabinets; hardwood veneer & plywood

(G-4424)
SK TEXTILE INC
1 Knollcrest Dr (45237-1608)
PHONE.....................323 581-8986
Fax: 323 588-2891
Kim Morris Heiman, *President*
Fe Brenade, *Controller*
Debra Centurion, *Sales Mgr*
▲ **EMP:** 105
SALES (est): 12.9MM **Privately Held**
WEB: www.sktextile.com
SIC: 2391 2211 Curtains & draperies; bedspreads, cotton

(G-4425)
SKINNY PIGGY KOMBUCHA LLC
5510 Glengate Ln (45212-2429)
PHONE.....................513 646-5753
Algirdas Aukstuolis, *Mng Member*
EMP: 3
SALES: 10K **Privately Held**
SIC: 2086 5812 Soft drinks: packaged in cans, bottles, etc.; eating places

(G-4426)
SKYLINE EXHIBITS GRTR CNCNT
9850 Prnctn Glndle Rd Ste (45246)
PHONE.....................513 671-4460
Fax: 513 860-4096
Lee Sjoquist, *President*
Kenda Sjoquist, *Vice Pres*
Art Mathews, *Sales Associate*
EMP: 5
SQ FT: 10,000
SALES: 1.5MM **Privately Held**
WEB: www.skylinecinti.com
SIC: 3993 Displays & cutouts, window & lobby; displays, paint process

(G-4427)
SMALL BUSINESS PRODUCTS
8603 Winton Rd (45231-4816)
P.O. Box 297257, Hollywood FL (33029-7257)
PHONE.....................800 553-6485
Brandi Pedersen, *Principal*
EMP: 5 **EST:** 2011
SALES (est): 550.2K **Privately Held**
SIC: 3577 Printers & plotters

(G-4428)
SMITH & MILLS SHAPERS INC
3640 Llewellyn Ave (45223-2336)
PHONE.....................513 541-4031
Steve Wernke, *President*
Suzanne Wernke, *Manager*
EMP: 10
SALES (est): 1.3MM **Privately Held**
SIC: 5084 3999 Machine tools & accessories; manufacturing industries

(G-4429)
SMITH & NEPHEW INC
5005 Barrow Ave Ste 100 (45209-1045)
PHONE.....................513 821-5888
Fax: 513 821-5878
Patrick Henrey, *Branch Mgr*
EMP: 50
SALES (corp-wide): 4.6B **Privately Held**
SIC: 3842 Surgical appliances & supplies
HQ: Smith & Nephew, Inc.
1450 E Brooks Rd
Memphis TN 38116
901 396-2121

(G-4430)
SMITH ELECTRO CHEMICAL CO
5936 Carthage Ct (45212-1103)
PHONE.....................513 351-7227
Fax: 513 351-9911
Donald W Kifer, *President*
Robert Kifer, *Vice Pres*
Teresa Kifer, *Purchasing*
EMP: 30 **EST:** 1948
SQ FT: 25,000
SALES (est): 3.6MM **Privately Held**
WEB: www.smithelectrochemical.com
SIC: 3471 Electroplating of metals or formed products; anodizing (plating) of metals or formed products

(G-4431)
SO-LOW ENVIRONMENTAL EQP CO
10310 Spartan Dr (45215-1279)
PHONE.....................513 772-9410
Fax: 513 772-0570
Walter Schum, *President*
Aaron Snyder, *General Mgr*
James Schum, *Vice Pres*
Dan Hensler, *Marketing Mgr*
Dave Collins, *Manager*
EMP: 48 **EST:** 1959
SQ FT: 66,000
SALES (est): 13.3MM **Privately Held**
WEB: www.so-low.com
SIC: 3821 3585 Laboratory apparatus & furniture; refrigeration equipment, complete

(G-4432)
SOCCER VILLAGE INC
9890 Colerain Ave (45251-1431)
PHONE.....................513 451-8500
EMP: 4
SALES (corp-wide): 2.9MM **Privately Held**
SIC: 3949 Soccer equipment & supplies
HQ: Soccer Village, Inc.
11427 Deerfield Rd
Blue Ash OH
513 489-5425

(G-4433)
SOCIALPAY LLC
312 Walnut St Ste 2275 (45202-4044)
PHONE.....................513 721-3900
Chris Burnett, *President*
Roger Ach,
EMP: 5
SQ FT: 2,200
SALES (est): 117.2K **Privately Held**
SIC: 7372 Application computer software

(G-4434)
SOFTWARE MANAGEMENT GROUP
1128 Main St Fl 6 (45202-7276)
PHONE.....................513 618-2165
Dave Nolnan, *President*
EMP: 25
SALES (est): 878.2K **Privately Held**
SIC: 7372 Prepackaged software

(G-4435)
SOLO PRODUCTS INC
838 Reedy St (45202-2216)
PHONE.....................513 321-7884
Steve Kunkemoeller, *CEO*
Doug Hearn, *CFO*
Mike Nauman, *Accounts Mgr*
Erica Stuchell-Duke, *Manager*
EMP: 12
SALES (est): 2.1MM **Privately Held**
SIC: 3086 5085 Plastics foam products; carpet & rug cushions, foamed plastic; rubber goods, mechanical

(G-4436)
SOLVAY USA INC
4775 Paddock Rd (45229-1003)
P.O. Box 29075 (45229-0075)
PHONE.....................513 482-5700
Todd Wisener, *General Mgr*
EMP: 49
SALES (corp-wide): 135.3MM **Privately Held**
WEB: www.food.us.rhodia.com
SIC: 2819 2899 Catalysts, chemical; chemical preparations
HQ: Solvay Usa Inc.
504 Carnegie Ctr
Princeton NJ 08540
609 860-4000

(G-4437)
SONUS-USA INC
222 Piedmont Ave Ste 5200 (45219-4222)
PHONE.....................513 475-8400
Dan Albrinck, *Branch Mgr*
EMP: 3
SALES (corp-wide): 2.1MM **Privately Held**
WEB: www.sonus.com
SIC: 3842 Hearing aids

HQ: Sonus-Usa, Inc.
5000 Cheshire Pkwy N # 1
Plymouth MN 55446

(G-4438)
SOUTHERN ADHSIVES COATINGS INC
Also Called: Mirror-Coat
8121 Camargo Rd (45243-2203)
P.O. Box 43250 (45243-0250)
PHONE.....................513 561-8440
Fax: 513 561-3440
Richard Williams, *President*
Muriel Williams, *Corp Secy*
Robert M Williams, *Vice Pres*
EMP: 5
SQ FT: 10,000
SALES: 2MM **Privately Held**
SIC: 2891 3451 Adhesives; sealants; screw machine products

(G-4439)
SPARKPEOPLE INC
310 Culvert St Fl 3 (45202-2229)
PHONE.....................513 651-2062
Fax: 513 241-6478
Chris Downie, *President*
Amanda Kanaga, *Senior VP*
Sean McCosh, *Vice Pres*
Kevin Carroll, *Engineer*
Paul Elfers, *Engineer*
EMP: 25
SQ FT: 15,000
SALES (est): 3.1MM **Privately Held**
SIC: 2731 Book publishing

(G-4440)
SPECIALTY LITHOGRAPHING CO
1035 W 7th St (45203-1285)
PHONE.....................513 621-0222
Fax: 513 621-0228
Elmer A Babey, *CEO*
Mark Babey, *President*
James Babey, *Vice Pres*
Carol Evans, *Admin Sec*
EMP: 17
SQ FT: 20,000
SALES (est): 2.6MM **Privately Held**
WEB: www.specialtylitho.com
SIC: 2752 Commercial printing, lithographic

(G-4441)
SPEEDWAY LLC
Also Called: Speedway Superamerica 5110
12184 Mason Rd (45249-1336)
PHONE.....................513 683-2034
Tom Giovis, *Branch Mgr*
EMP: 10 **Publicly Held**
WEB: www.speedwaynet.com
SIC: 1311 Crude petroleum production
HQ: Speedway Llc
500 Speedway Dr
Enon OH 45323
937 864-3000

(G-4442)
SPICY OLIVE LLC
2736 Erie Ave (45208-2104)
PHONE.....................513 376-9061
EMP: 3
SALES (corp-wide): 22.4MM **Privately Held**
SIC: 2079 Olive oil
PA: Spicy Olive Llc
7671 Cox Ln
West Chester OH 45069
513 847-4397

(G-4443)
SPORTSCO IMPRINTING
8277 Wicklow Ave (45236-1613)
PHONE.....................513 641-5111
Fax: 513 641-5222
Joe Eigel, *Partner*
Eric Kattus, *Partner*
EMP: 8
SQ FT: 1,800
SALES (est): 553.6K **Privately Held**
SIC: 2262 2395 Screen printing: manmade fiber & silk broadwoven fabrics; emblems, embroidered

(G-4444)
SPRING GROVE MANUFACTURING
2838 Spring Grove Ave (45225-2268)
PHONE..................513 542-0185
Jeffrey S Best, *President*
Todd M Johnson, *Vice Pres*
EMP: 10
SQ FT: 30,000
SALES (est): 956.4K **Privately Held**
SIC: 3083 Plastic finished products, laminated

(G-4445)
SPRING GROVE MANUFACTURING
Also Called: Cincinnati Bindery
2838 Spring Grove Ave (45225-2268)
PHONE..................513 542-6900
Jeff Best, *President*
EMP: 15
SALES (est): 1.1MM **Privately Held**
SIC: 2789 Bookbinding & related work

(G-4446)
SPRINGDALE BINDERY LLC
11411 Landan Ln (45246-3611)
PHONE..................513 772-8500
Fax: 513 772-1400
Steve Dehamer, *Manager*
EMP: 5
SALES (est): 592.3K **Privately Held**
SIC: 2789 Bookbinding & related work

(G-4447)
SPRINGDALE ICE CREAM BEVERAGE
11801 Chesterdale Rd (45246-3407)
PHONE..................513 699-4984
Fax: 513 671-2864
EMP: 35
SALES (est): 5.8MM **Privately Held**
SIC: 2024 0241 Mfg Ice Cream/Frozen Desert Dairy Farm

(G-4448)
SPRINGDOT INC
2611 Colerain Ave (45214-1711)
PHONE..................513 542-4000
Jeff Deutsch, *Ch of Bd*
Josh Deutsch, *President*
John Brenner, *Vice Pres*
Craig Miller, *Vice Pres*
Bill Fultz, *Traffic Mgr*
EMP: 65
SQ FT: 70,000
SALES (est): 18.6MM **Privately Held**
WEB: www.springdot.com
SIC: 2752 4899 2759 2675 Commercial printing, lithographic; color lithography; data communication services; commercial printing; die-cut paper & board; packaging paper & plastics film, coated & laminated

(G-4449)
ST BERNARD INSULATION LLC
8703 Pippin Rd (45251-3130)
PHONE..................513 266-2158
Janice Ruiz, *Mng Member*
EMP: 18 **EST:** 2014
SALES (est): 1MM **Privately Held**
SIC: 2899 5211 Insulating compounds; insulation material, building

(G-4450)
ST BERNARD SOAP COMPANY
5177 Spring Grove Ave (45217-1050)
PHONE..................513 242-2227
Fax: 513 482-2687
William Biedenharm, *President*
▲ **EMP:** 301
SALES (est): 199.8MM
SALES (corp-wide): 76.5MM **Privately Held**
WEB: www.trilliumhealthcare.com
SIC: 2841 Soap & other detergents
PA: Trillium Health Care Products Inc
2337 Parkdale Ave E
Brockville ON K6V 5
613 342-4436

(G-4451)
STAGECRAFT COSTUMING INC
Also Called: Stagecraft Theatrical
3950 Spring Grove Ave (45223-2639)
PHONE..................513 541-7150
Fax: 513 541-7151
Randy Kent, *President*
EMP: 10 **EST:** 1975
SQ FT: 20,000
SALES (est): 1MM **Privately Held**
WEB: www.stagecraftinc.com
SIC: 2389 7299 Theatrical costumes; costume rental

(G-4452)
STAN RILEYS CUSTOM DRAPERIES
7041 Vine St (45216-2031)
PHONE..................513 821-3732
Fax: 513 821-3184
Stanton J Riley Jr, *Owner*
EMP: 7 **EST:** 1971
SALES (est): 250K **Privately Held**
SIC: 2391 2392 2394 Draperies, plastic & textile: from purchased materials; household furnishings; pillows, bed: made from purchased materials; bedspreads & bed sets: made from purchased materials; canvas & related products

(G-4453)
STANDARD PUBLISHING LLC
8805 Governors Hill Dr # 400 (45249-3319)
PHONE..................513 931-4050
Fax: 513 931-0317
Peter M Esposito, *CEO*
Matthew Thibeau, *General Ptnr*
Mark Rosenbaun, *CFO*
Jennifer Vargas, *Sales Staff*
Mark Thorn, *Info Tech Dir*
▲ **EMP:** 200
SALES (est): 30.7MM
SALES (corp-wide): 34.4MM **Privately Held**
SIC: 2721 Magazines: publishing only, not printed on site
PA: Cfm Religion Publishing Group Llc
8805 Governors Hill Dr # 400
Cincinnati OH 45249
513 931-4050

(G-4454)
STANDARD REGISTER INC
9100 Centre Pnte Dr 160 (45201)
PHONE..................513 772-8860
Fax: 513 772-8871
Paul Murphey, *Branch Mgr*
EMP: 16
SALES (corp-wide): 4.6B **Privately Held**
WEB: www.stdreg.com
SIC: 2761 Manifold business forms
HQ: Standard Register, Inc.
600 Albany St
Dayton OH 45417
937 221-1000

(G-4455)
STANDARD TEXTILE CO INC (PA)
Also Called: Pridecraft Enterprises
1 Knollcrest Dr (45222-1608)
P.O. Box 371805 (45222-1805)
PHONE..................513 761-9255
Fax: 513 761-0467
Gary Heiman, *President*
Santa J Ono Lauds Gov John Kas, *President*
Norman Frankel, *Senior VP*
Kim Heiman, *Senior VP*
Steve Tracey, *Senior VP*
◆ **EMP:** 300
SQ FT: 150,000
SALES (est): 987MM **Privately Held**
WEB: www.standardtextile.com
SIC: 2389 2326 2337 2211 Hospital gowns; medical & hospital uniforms, men's; uniforms, except athletic: women's, misses' & juniors'; bandages, gauzes & surgical fabrics, cotton; surgical fabrics, cotton; draperies, plastic & textile: from purchased materials; uniforms, men's & boys'

(G-4456)
STANDEX ELECTRONICS INC (HQ)
4538 Camberwell Rd (45209-1186)
PHONE..................513 871-3777
Fax: 513 871-3779
John Meeks, *CEO*
Robert Lintz, *Vice Pres*
Chris Riccardella, *Engineer*
Shawn Davis, *Project Engr*
Ken Hay, *Controller*
▲ **EMP:** 21
SQ FT: 22,022
SALES (est): 23MM
SALES (corp-wide): 751.5MM **Publicly Held**
SIC: 3677 Electronic coils, transformers & other inductors
PA: Standex International Corporation
11 Keewaydin Dr
Salem NH 03079
603 893-9701

(G-4457)
STANDEX INTERNATIONAL CORP
Also Called: Standex Electronics
4538 Camberwell Rd (45209-1155)
PHONE..................513 871-3777
Matt Crost, *Plant Mgr*
Stacy Shinkle, *Buyer*
Steve Nunez, *Accountant*
Guy Cappello, *Sales Mgr*
John Meeks, *Branch Mgr*
EMP: 28
SALES (corp-wide): 751.5MM **Publicly Held**
SIC: 1446 Molding sand mining
PA: Standex International Corporation
11 Keewaydin Dr
Salem NH 03079
603 893-9701

(G-4458)
STARCHEM INC (PA)
3000 Disney St (45209-5028)
PHONE..................513 458-8262
Fax: 513 336-0538
Ronald Smith, *President*
Michael Tabor, *Vice Pres*
Henry Turchin, *Vice Pres*
Mark Williams, *Vice Pres*
Rich McGraw, *Plant Mgr*
EMP: 4
SQ FT: 12,000
SALES (est): 456.5K **Privately Held**
WEB: www.starchem.net
SIC: 2992 Lubricating oils & greases; cutting oils, blending: made from purchased materials

(G-4459)
STARKS PLASTICS LLC
11236 Sebring Dr (45240-2715)
PHONE..................513 541-4591
Fax: 513 541-6773
Larry Clark, *Mng Member*
Kim Clark,
EMP: 5
SQ FT: 1,400
SALES (est): 450K **Privately Held**
SIC: 3089 5046 Plastic processing; store fixtures

(G-4460)
STARR PRINTING SERVICES INC
3625 Spring Grove Ave (45223-2458)
PHONE..................513 241-7708
Fax: 513 241-7957
Robert Meade, *President*
EMP: 7
SQ FT: 5,000
SALES (est): 893.2K **Privately Held**
SIC: 2752 2759 Commercial printing, lithographic; letterpress printing

(G-4461)
STEAM ENGINE WORKS LLC
2364 Heather Hill Blvd N (45244-2667)
PHONE..................513 813-3690
David Pommert, *Owner*
EMP: 3
SALES (est): 118.7K **Privately Held**
SIC: 3511 Steam engines

(G-4462)
STEEL QUEST INC
8180 Corp Pk Dr Ste 250 (45242)
PHONE..................513 772-5030
Matthew S Kuhnell, *President*
Dave Richards, *Project Mgr*
W Kuhnell, *Manager*
EMP: 9
SQ FT: 3,500
SALES (est): 2.7MM **Privately Held**
WEB: www.steelquest.com
SIC: 3441 Fabricated structural metal

(G-4463)
STEGEMEYER MACHINE
212 Mccullough St (45226-2120)
PHONE..................513 321-5651
Fax: 513 321-6450
Richard Stegemeyer, *President*
Deanna Stegemeyer, *Admin Sec*
EMP: 7
SQ FT: 4,500
SALES (est): 375K **Privately Held**
SIC: 3599 Machine shop, jobbing & repair

(G-4464)
STELLAR SYSTEMS INC
1944 Harrison Ave (45214-1176)
PHONE..................513 921-8748
Fax: 513 921-0878
William L Spetz, *President*
Matt Spetz, *Vice Pres*
EMP: 7
SQ FT: 8,000
SALES (est): 470K **Privately Held**
WEB: www.stellarsystemsinc.com
SIC: 7371 3577 Computer software development; computer peripheral equipment

(G-4465)
STEVE SCHAEFER
Also Called: Mis Micro Information Services
9200 Montgomery Rd 23a (45242-7797)
P.O. Box 42377 (45242-0377)
PHONE..................513 792-9911
Steve Schaefer, *Owner*
Karen Schaefer, *Manager*
EMP: 4
SALES (est): 210K **Privately Held**
WEB: www.mismicro.com
SIC: 7372 Prepackaged software

(G-4466)
STEVENSON COLOR INC
535 Wilmer Ave (45226-1828)
PHONE..................513 321-7500
Thomas Stevenson, *President*
Kris Krause, *General Mgr*
Kris Kopp, *Project Mgr*
Mark Smith, *Facilities Mgr*
Tina Carter, *Production*
EMP: 190
SQ FT: 116,800
SALES (est): 35.4MM
SALES (corp-wide): 303.8MM **Privately Held**
WEB: www.stevensoncolor.com
SIC: 2796 2752 Color separations for printing; commercial printing, lithographic
HQ: Southern Graphic Systems, Llc
626 W Main St Ste 500
Louisville KY 40202
502 637-5443

(G-4467)
STEVENSON MACHINE INC
7666 Production Dr (45237-3209)
PHONE..................513 761-4121
Fax: 513 761-4124
Donald Goepper, *President*
Jim Lawton, *Finance Mgr*
Issac Deutsch, *Personnel Exec*
EMP: 11 **EST:** 1927
SQ FT: 15,000
SALES (est): 2MM **Privately Held**
WEB: www.stevensonmachine.com
SIC: 3599 3568 5085 Machine shop, jobbing & repair; power transmission equipment; power transmission equipment & apparatus

(G-4468)
STIGLERS WOODWORKS
6 Kovach Dr Ste 600 (45215-1028)
PHONE..................513 733-3009
Fax: 513 733-3755

Robert Stigler, *Owner*
EMP: 3
SQ FT: 6,000
SALES: 250K **Privately Held**
WEB: www.stiglerswoodworks.com
SIC: 2512 5712 Upholstered household
　furniture; furniture stores

(G-4469)
STINE CONSULTING INC
Also Called: Fastsigns
120 W 7th St (45202-2328)
P.O. Box 25429 (45225)
PHONE......................................513 723-4800
Fax: 513 723-4808
Stephen Stine, *President*
Christian Beebe, *Manager*
EMP: 5
SQ FT: 3,500
SALES: 823K **Privately Held**
SIC: 3993 Signs & advertising specialties

(G-4470)
STONE STATEMENTS INCORPORATED
7451 Fields Ertel Rd (45241-6083)
PHONE......................................513 489-7866
Fax: 513 489-7856
Douglas R Beyersdoerfer, *President*
▲ **EMP:** 8
SALES (est): 1.8MM **Privately Held**
WEB: www.stonestatements.com
SIC: 1411 1799 Granite dimension stone;
　counter top installation

(G-4471)
STUART COMPANY
2160 Patterson St (45214-1844)
PHONE......................................513 621-9462
Philip G Gossard, *CEO*
EMP: 15
SQ FT: 50,000
SALES: 1.1MM **Privately Held**
SIC: 2675 Die-cut paper & board

(G-4472)
STUDIO VERTU INC
1208 Central Pkwy 1 (45202-7509)
PHONE......................................513 241-9038
Mark Schmidt, *President*
Heather Schmidt, *Vice Pres*
▲ **EMP:** 35
SQ FT: 18,000
SALES (est): 3.5MM **Privately Held**
WEB: www.studiovertu.com
SIC: 3253 3281 Ceramic wall & floor tile;
　cut stone & stone products

(G-4473)
STUEBING AUTOMATIC MACHINE CO
2518 Leslie Ave (45212-4206)
PHONE......................................513 771-8028
EMP: 21 **EST:** 1892
SQ FT: 30,000
SALES (est): 3.7MM **Privately Held**
SIC: 3469 5084 Mfg Metal Stampings
　Whol Industrial Equipment

(G-4474)
SUGARS SWEETS LTD
10752 Jeff Ln (45241-3014)
PHONE......................................513 936-0104
Leslie Jones, *Owner*
EMP: 5
SALES (est): 140K **Privately Held**
SIC: 2066 Chocolate candy, solid

(G-4475)
SUMMIT DIAGNOSTIC IMAGING LLC
Also Called: Medical Imaging
7755 5 Mile Rd (45230-2355)
PHONE......................................513 233-3320
Fax: 513 233-3388
John Mattes, *General Mgr*
Patty Noll, *Mng Member*
EMP: 20 **EST:** 2000
SQ FT: 2,500
SALES (est): 2.4MM **Privately Held**
SIC: 3826 Magnetic resonance imaging
　apparatus

(G-4476)
SUN CHEMICAL CORPORATION
General Printing Ink Division
12049 Centron Pl (45246-1789)
PHONE......................................513 671-0407
Fax: 513 671-5245
Bruce Jones, *Plant Mgr*
Pat Myers, *Branch Mgr*
Stephen Bernhardt, *Manager*
Kathy Roehm, *Manager*
EMP: 60
SQ FT: 11,000
SALES (corp-wide): 6.7B **Privately Held**
WEB: www.sunchemical.com
SIC: 2893 2899 Printing ink; ink or writing
　fluids
HQ: Sun Chemical Corporation
　35 Waterview Blvd Ste 100
　Parsippany NJ 07054
　973 404-6000

(G-4477)
SUN CHEMICAL CORPORATION
Pigments Division
4526 Chickering Ave (45232-1935)
PHONE......................................513 681-5950
Fax: 513 681-3778
Brian Breidigan, *Vice Pres*
R Marino, *Vice Pres*
Dennis Keyes, *Buyer*
Jim Willits, *Purchasing*
Ryan Fulkerson, *Project Engr*
EMP: 210
SQ FT: 91,671
SALES (corp-wide): 6.7B **Privately Held**
WEB: www.sunchemical.com
SIC: 2816 2865 Inorganic pigments; cyclic
　crudes & intermediates
HQ: Sun Chemical Corporation
　35 Waterview Blvd Ste 100
　Parsippany NJ 07054
　973 404-6000

(G-4478)
SUN CHEMICAL CORPORATION
Kohl & Madden Printing Ink Div
5020 Spring Grove Ave (45232-1988)
P.O. Box 32040 (45232-0040)
PHONE......................................513 681-5950
Fax: 513 554-6023
Russ Henke, *Vice Pres*
Norm Smith, *Project Dir*
Jean Yoho, *Purch Agent*
Orly Janssen, *QC Dir*
Mike Willis, *Technical Mgr*
EMP: 39
SALES (corp-wide): 6.7B **Privately Held**
SIC: 2893 Printing ink
HQ: Sun Chemical Corporation
　35 Waterview Blvd Ste 100
　Parsippany NJ 07054
　973 404-6000

(G-4479)
SUN CHEMICAL CORPORATION
600 Redna Ter (45215-1108)
PHONE......................................513 771-4030
Fax: 513 771-1399
Steve Cornwell, *Plant Mgr*
Gloria Rutledge, *Manager*
Tim Russell, *Manager*
EMP: 44
SALES (corp-wide): 6.7B **Privately Held**
SIC: 2893 Lithographic ink
HQ: Sun Chemical Corporation
　35 Waterview Blvd Ste 100
　Parsippany NJ 07054
　973 404-6000

(G-4480)
SUN CHEMICAL CORPORATION
Sun Chmcal Corp Prfrmce Pgments
5020 Spring Grove Ave (45232-1988)
P.O. Box 16096 (45216-0096)
PHONE......................................513 681-5950
Brian Leen, *Vice Pres*
Orly Janssen, *QC Dir*
Russ Henke, *VP Sls/Mktg*
W E Breagy, *Marketing Staff*
Dianna Winfrey, *Technical Staff*
EMP: 300
SALES (corp-wide): 6.7B **Privately Held**
WEB: www.sunchemical.com
SIC: 2816 Inorganic pigments

HQ: Sun Chemical Corporation
　35 Waterview Blvd Ste 100
　Parsippany NJ 07054
　973 404-6000

(G-4481)
SUN CHEMICAL CORPORATION
5000 Spring Grove Ave (45232-1926)
PHONE......................................513 830-8667
Thad Karbowsky, *Controller*
Milt Barnes, *Branch Mgr*
EMP: 39
SALES (corp-wide): 6.7B **Privately Held**
SIC: 2893 2865 Printing ink; dyes & pig-
　ments
HQ: Sun Chemical Corporation
　35 Waterview Blvd Ste 100
　Parsippany NJ 07054
　973 404-6000

(G-4482)
SUN DRENCHED ART STUDIOS
4277 Alex Ave (45211-5348)
PHONE......................................513 375-9612
Steven Dean, *Owner*
◆ **EMP:** 4
SALES (est): 140K **Privately Held**
SIC: 3999 Framed artwork

(G-4483)
SUPER SYSTEMS INC (PA)
7205 Edington Dr (45249-1064)
PHONE......................................513 772-0060
Stephen Thompson, *President*
Scott Johnstone, *President*
Velvet Twist, *Business Mgr*
Jim Oakes, *Vice Pres*
Bill Heckman, *Project Mgr*
EMP: 45
SQ FT: 5,000
SALES (est): 6.9MM **Privately Held**
SIC: 3829 5084 Measuring & controlling
　devices; industrial machinery & equip-
　ment

(G-4484)
SUPERIOR IMAGE LLC
11875 Kemper Springs Dr (45240-1641)
P.O. Box 868, Mason (45040-0868)
PHONE......................................513 771-4565
Fax: 513 771-4561
Donald Donovan, *Mng Member*
Johanna Donovan,
EMP: 14
SQ FT: 8,000
SALES (est): 2MM **Privately Held**
WEB: www.superiorimage.com
SIC: 2395 Embroidery & art needlework

(G-4485)
SUR-SEAL CORPORATION (PA)
Also Called: Sur-Seal Gasket & Packing
6156 Wesselman Rd (45248-1204)
PHONE......................................513 574-8500
Fax: 513 574-2220
James Wilz, *President*
Paul Scherrer, *Vice Pres*
Anne Krekeler, *Buyer*
Walls Rick, *Engineer*
Elizabeth Vleamick, *Marketing Staff*
▲ **EMP:** 135
SQ FT: 67,000
SALES: 40MM **Privately Held**
WEB: www.sur-seal.com
SIC: 3053 3069 Gaskets, all materials;
　packing, rubber; molded rubber products

(G-4486)
SURFACE DYNAMICS INC
231 Northland Blvd (45246-3603)
PHONE......................................513 772-6635
Leo Glass, *Branch Mgr*
EMP: 3
SALES (corp-wide): 32.1MM **Privately Held**
SIC: 3086 Insulation or cushioning mate-
　rial, foamed plastic
HQ: Surface Dynamics, Inc
　231 Northland Blvd
　Cincinnati OH 45246

(G-4487)
SURFACE ENHANCEMENT TECH LLC
3929 Virginia Ave (45227-3411)
PHONE......................................513 561-1520

Sherry Frank, *Accounting Mgr*
Paul Prevey,
Jacqueline Pervey,
EMP: 17
SQ FT: 28,000
SALES (est): 4.2MM **Privately Held**
WEB: www.surfaceenhancement.com
SIC: 3398 Brazing (hardening) of metal

(G-4488)
SURGICAL APPLIANCE INDS INC (PA)
Also Called: AIRWAY
3960 Rosslyn Dr (45209-1195)
PHONE......................................513 271-4594
Fax: 513 271-4747
L Thomas Applegate, *Ch of Bd*
Steve McSherry, *Business Mgr*
Ginny Faught, *VP Opers*
Dave Perry, *Accountant*
Pam Rogers, *Sales Staff*
▲ **EMP:** 200 **EST:** 1893
SQ FT: 225,000
SALES (est): 58.1MM **Privately Held**
WEB: www.surgicalappliance.com
SIC: 3842 Surgical appliances & supplies;
　orthopedic appliances; braces, elastic

(G-4489)
SWEATY BANDS LLC
3802 Ford Cir (45227-3403)
PHONE......................................513 871-1222
Douglas Browning, *Managing Prtnr*
Donna Browning, *Managing Prtnr*
Lisa Fleming, *Finance Dir*
Danielle Wurtz, *Accounts Mgr*
Carla Caruso, *Sales Staff*
EMP: 20
SALES: 5MM **Privately Held**
SIC: 2396 Sweat bands, hat & cap: made
　from purchased materials

(G-4490)
T P F INC
313 S Wayne Ave (45215-4522)
P.O. Box 15171 (45215-0171)
PHONE......................................513 761-9968
Fax: 513 761-9968
Charles Stiens, *President*
Robert Stiens, *Chairman*
Charlotte Stiens, *Corp Secy*
Kenneth Stiens, *Vice Pres*
EMP: 8
SQ FT: 2,400
SALES (est): 1.2MM **Privately Held**
WEB: www.tpftherm.com
SIC: 3823 7699 Thermometers, filled sys-
　tem: industrial process type; pressure
　measurement instruments, industrial; in-
　dustrial machinery & equipment repair

(G-4491)
TAKK INDUSTRIES INC
8665 E Miami River Rd (45247-2238)
PHONE......................................513 353-4306
Fax: 513 353-4315
Joseph Overman, *President*
Gregory Overman, *Exec VP*
Ellie Linder, *Purch Agent*
Dan Putz, *Accounts Mgr*
▲ **EMP:** 16
SQ FT: 10,000
SALES (est): 2.8MM **Privately Held**
WEB: www.takk.com
SIC: 3629 3469 Static elimination equip-
　ment, industrial; metal stampings

(G-4492)
TAMBRANDS SALES CORP (HQ)
Also Called: Tampax
1 Procter And Gamble Plz (45202-3315)
PHONE......................................513 983-1100
Wolfgang C Berndt, *President*
R T Blanchard, *Vice Pres*
T A Garrett, *Vice Pres*
Mark D Ketchum, *Vice Pres*
T A Moore, *Vice Pres*
▲ **EMP:** 130 **EST:** 1936
SQ FT: 100,000
SALES (est): 169MM
SALES (corp-wide): 65.3B **Publicly Held**
WEB: www.tampax.com
SIC: 2676 Tampons, sanitary: made from
　purchased paper

PA: The Procter & Gamble Company
1 Procter And Gamble Plz
Cincinnati OH 45202
513 983-1100

(G-4493)
TARGET HOLDINGS INC
Also Called: Target World
2300 E Kemper Rd Unit 5 (45241-6505)
PHONE......................................513 474-4409
Fax: 513 772-5113
Joseph Blanco, *President*
Mark W Reis, *Principal*
Tom Blanco, *Manager*
Joseph Cowles, *Clerk*
EMP: 25
SQ FT: 13,560
SALES (est): 3.1MM **Privately Held**
SIC: 5941 7997 3499 Sporting goods &
bicycle shops; gun & hunting clubs; safes
& vaults, metal

(G-4494)
TASTE OF BELGIUM LLC
1801 Race St Ste 9 (45202-5917)
PHONE......................................513 381-3280
Jt Riley, *Managing Dir*
Chris Meibers, *Controller*
Bobbi Steberl, *Mktg Coord*
Jean F Flechet, *Principal*
Dorothy Waltenbaugh, *Executive Asst*
▲ **EMP:** 4 **EST:** 2008
SALES (est): 437.3K **Privately Held**
SIC: 2051 Bread, cake & related products

(G-4495)
TAYLOR & MOORE CO
807 Wachendorf St (45215-4743)
PHONE......................................513 733-5530
George R Taylor, *President*
EMP: 12
SQ FT: 11,898
SALES (est): 1.9MM **Privately Held**
SIC: 3585 Air conditioning units, complete:
domestic or industrial; heating & air condi-
tioning combination units

(G-4496)
TAYLOR COMPANY (PA)
5721 Dragon Way Ste 117 (45227-4518)
PHONE......................................513 271-2550
Paul Roberts, *Principal*
EMP: 2
SQ FT: 900
SALES (est): 14MM **Privately Held**
SIC: 6799 2656 Investors; plates, paper:
made from purchased material

(G-4497)
TECH/III INC (PA)
Also Called: Printing Plant
1330 Tennessee Ave Ste 2 (45229-1046)
PHONE......................................513 482-7500
Fax: 513 345-3808
James E Oconnor, *President*
Carol S Horan, *Principal*
John Troehler, *Maint Spvr*
John Hayden, *Production*
Brad Schlenk, *Sales Mgr*
EMP: 42 **EST:** 1970
SQ FT: 38,000
SALES (est): 7.2MM **Privately Held**
SIC: 2759 2671 Labels & seals: printing;
packaging paper & plastics film, coated &
laminated

(G-4498)
TECHBRITE LLC
1000 Kieley Pl (45217-1118)
PHONE......................................800 246-9977
Brett Heekin, *President*
Evan Mecklenborg, *General Mgr*
David Brown, *Vice Pres*
Katrina Huerkamp, *Purch Mgr*
Chad Cornwell, *CFO*
EMP: 22
SQ FT: 15,000
SALES (est): 5.8MM **Privately Held**
WEB: www.techbrite.com
SIC: 3646 Fluorescent lighting fixtures,
commercial

(G-4499)
TEGRATEK
500 Northland Blvd (45240-3213)
PHONE......................................513 742-5100

Fax: 513 742-5753
Thomas Mohring, *Owner*
Cliff Mohring, *Mfg Mgr*
Marilyn Mohring, *Manager*
EMP: 4 **EST:** 1976
SQ FT: 5,000
SALES (est): 449.1K **Privately Held**
SIC: 3559 3567 3599 Concrete products
machinery; heating units & devices, in-
dustrial: electric; water leak detectors

(G-4500)
TEMA ISENMANN INC (DH)
7806 Redsky Dr (45249-1632)
PHONE......................................859 252-0613
Tammy K Runyan, *Treasurer*
Karen Clendenin, *Accountant*
▲ **EMP:** 4
SQ FT: 15,000
SALES (est): 13.3MM
SALES (corp-wide): 412.5MM **Privately
Held**
WEB: www.temaisenmann.com
SIC: 3089 7389 Panels, building: plastic;
personal service agents, brokers & bu-
reaus
HQ: Steinhaus Gesellschaft Mit Beschrank-
ter Haftung
Platanenallee 46
Mulheim An Der Ruhr 45478
208 580-101

(G-4501)
TEMA SYSTEMS INC
7806 Redsky Dr (45249-1632)
PHONE......................................513 489-7811
Fax: 513 489-4817
Mike Mullins, *President*
Jeanne Miller, *Buyer*
Rex Rodebush, *Chief Engr*
Chad Mendelsohn, *Sales Mgr*
Randy Diehl, *Manager*
▲ **EMP:** 25
SQ FT: 15,000
SALES (est): 6.8MM
SALES (corp-wide): 412.5MM **Privately
Held**
WEB: www.tema.net
SIC: 3532 3599 3589 Cages, mine shaft;
mineral beneficiation equipment; custom
machinery; commercial cooking & food-
warming equipment
HQ: Siebtechnik Gmbh
Platanenallee 46
Mulheim An Der Ruhr 45478
208 580-100

(G-4502)
TESTLINK USA
11445 Century Cir W (45246-3303)
PHONE......................................513 272-1081
Paula Walker, *Principal*
EMP: 11 **EST:** 2013
SALES (est): 2.1MM **Privately Held**
SIC: 3578 Automatic teller machines (ATM)

(G-4503)
**TEVA WOMENS HEALTH INC
(DH)**
5040 Duramed Rd (45213-2520)
PHONE......................................513 731-9900
Fax: 513 731-5270
Bruce L Downey, *Principal*
Timothy J Holt, *Principal*
David J Furniss, *Senior VP*
Lawrence A Glassman, *Senior VP*
Lawrence Glassmann, *Senior VP*
EMP: 250 **EST:** 1982
SQ FT: 28,200
SALES (corp-wide): 19.7B **Privately Held**
WEB: www.barrlabs.com
SIC: 5122 2834 7389 Patent medicines;
pharmaceutical preparations; tablets,
pharmaceutical; medicines, capsuled or
ampuled; solutions, pharmaceutical;
packaging & labeling services
HQ: Teva Pharmaceuticals Usa, Inc.
1090 Horsham Rd
North Wales PA 19454
215 591-3000

(G-4504)
TH MAGNESIUM INC
9435 Waterstone Blvd (45249-8226)
PHONE......................................513 285-7568
Stephen Norris, *President*

Oliver Haun, *VP Sales*
Colleen Williams, *Director*
EMP: 6 **EST:** 2011
SALES (est): 483K **Privately Held**
SIC: 3356 Magnesium

(G-4505)
THERMOGENICS CORP
300 E Bus Way Ste 200 (45241)
PHONE......................................513 247-7963
Mark H Ingham, *Principal*
EMP: 5
SALES (est): 534K **Privately Held**
SIC: 3443 Fabricated plate work (boiler
shop)

(G-4506)
THINKWARE INCORPORATED
7611 Cheviot Rd Ste 2 (45247-4015)
PHONE......................................513 598-3300
Fax: 513 598-3315
Kevin Eickmann, *President*
Chris Bross, *Office Mgr*
EMP: 28
SQ FT: 7,500
SALES: 5.4MM **Privately Held**
WEB: www.thinkwareinc.com
SIC: 7371 7374 7372 Computer software
development; data processing & prepara-
tion; prepackaged software

(G-4507)
**THOMAS PRODUCTS CO INC
(PA)**
3625 Spring Grove Ave (45223-2458)
PHONE......................................513 756-9009
Fax: 513 756-9034
Joseph Thomas, *CEO*
Paul Green, *President*
Robert Crume, *Plant Mgr*
Patrick McHale, *Sales Staff*
EMP: 25
SQ FT: 25,000
SALES (est): 4.6MM **Privately Held**
WEB: www.tpclabels.com
SIC: 2759 3842 2761 2672 Flexographic
printing; surgical appliances & supplies;
manifold business forms; coated & lami-
nated paper; packaging paper & plastics
film, coated & laminated

(G-4508)
**THYSSENKRUPP ELEVATOR
CORP**
934 Dalton Ave (45203-1102)
PHONE......................................513 241-0222
Dave Forthuber, *Superintendent*
EMP: 54
SALES (corp-wide): 44.2B **Privately Held**
SIC: 3534 Elevators & equipment
HQ: Thyssenkrupp Elevator Corporation
11605 Haynes Bridge Rd # 650
Alpharetta GA 30009
678 319-3240

(G-4509)
TIA MARIE & COMPANY
8694 Long Ln (45231-5019)
PHONE......................................513 521-8694
Alice Huff, *Principal*
David Alford, *Principal*
Jerry Fuqua, *Accountant*
▲ **EMP:** 4
SALES (est): 160K **Privately Held**
SIC: 3161 5948 Luggage; luggage &
leather goods stores

(G-4510)
TITANIUM CONTRACTORS LTD
9400 Reading Rd (45215-3401)
PHONE......................................513 256-2152
Michael Postell, *Principal*
EMP: 3
SALES (est): 223.9K **Privately Held**
SIC: 3356 Titanium

(G-4511)
TL KRIEG OFFSET INC
10600 Chester Rd (45215-1206)
PHONE......................................513 542-1522
Fax: 513 542-5838
Terry L Krieg, *President*
Tom Schmieg, *General Mgr*
Thomas M Schaefer, *Business Mgr*
EMP: 29
SQ FT: 30,000

SALES (est): 5.2MM **Privately Held**
WEB: www.tlkriegoffset.com
SIC: 2752 2789 Commercial printing, off-
set; bookbinding & related work

(G-4512)
TOM BAD BREWING LLC
4720 Eastern Ave (45226-1893)
PHONE......................................513 871-4677
Charles Boucher,
Sheryl Gittins,
John Vojtush,
EMP: 9
SQ FT: 2,000
SALES (est): 831.5K **Privately Held**
SIC: 2082 5813 Malt beverages; ale (alco-
holic beverage); beer (alcoholic bever-
age); porter (alcoholic beverage); bars &
lounges

(G-4513)
TORMAXX CO
1150 W 8th St Ste 111 (45203-1245)
PHONE......................................513 721-6299
Fax: 513 721-2888
Gregg Sample, *President*
Ronald E Heithaus, *Principal*
EMP: 6
SQ FT: 8,000
SALES (est): 1.1MM **Privately Held**
SIC: 3545 Machine tool accessories

(G-4514)
TOUBA SATELLITE R US
4144 Hamilton Ave (45223-2248)
PHONE......................................513 853-0700
Fax: 513 853-0701
Cheika Gueye, *Owner*
EMP: 3
SALES (est): 170K **Privately Held**
WEB: www.touba-roomforrent.info
SIC: 3663 Satellites, communications

(G-4515)
**TOYOBO KUREHA AMERICA CO
LTD**
Also Called: Tk America
11630 Mosteller Rd (45241-1521)
PHONE......................................513 771-6788
Fax: 513 771-6799
Morley Thompson Jr, *Exec VP*
Zoe Enright, *Manager*
▲ **EMP:** 38
SQ FT: 120,000
SALES: 10MM
SALES (corp-wide): 2.9B **Privately Held**
SIC: 2297 Nonwoven fabrics
HQ: Kureha Ltd.
255, Oka
Ritto SGA 520-3
775 535-660

(G-4516)
TRACK-IT SYSTEMS
1776 Mentor Ave Ste 560 (45212-3583)
PHONE......................................513 522-0083
Natalie Graves, *Principal*
EMP: 5
SALES: 950K **Privately Held**
SIC: 3663 Radio & TV communications
equipment

(G-4517)
TRANE US INC
10300 Springfield Pike (45215-1118)
PHONE......................................513 771-8884
Fax: 513 772-7281
Al Fullerton, *Manager*
EMP: 50 **Privately Held**
SIC: 3585 Refrigeration & heating equip-
ment
HQ: Trane U.S. Inc.
1 Centennial Ave Ste 101
Piscataway NJ 08854
732 652-7100

(G-4518)
TRANS ASH INC
Also Called: Gibbco
320 S Wayne Ave (45215-4523)
PHONE......................................859 341-1528
Brian Keplinger, *Manager*
EMP: 10

SALES (corp-wide): 40.5MM **Privately
Held**
WEB: www.transash.com
SIC: 3295 Slag, crushed or ground
PA: Trans Ash, Inc.
　617 Shepherd Dr
　Cincinnati OH 45215
　513 733-4770

(G-4519)
TRANSDUCERS DIRECT LLC
12115 Ellington Ct (45249-1000)
PHONE.............................513 247-0601
Robert W Matthes, *President*
Lauren Matthes, *Opers Mgr*
Robert Matthes, *Human Res Mgr*
Christine Seidenman, *Human Res Mgr*
Connie Clark, *Office Mgr*
◆ EMP: 16
SALES: 3.5MM **Privately Held**
WEB: www.transducersdirect.com
SIC: 3543 5084 Industrial patterns; indus-
trial machine parts

(G-4520)
TREVED EXTERIORS
10235 Spartan Dr Ste T (45215-1243)
PHONE.............................513 771-3888
Fax: 513 771-3888
Eddie Oblinger, *Principal*
EMP: 7
SALES (est): 1.1MM **Privately Held**
SIC: 2851 Paint removers

(G-4521)
TRI-STATE BEEF CO INC
2124 Baymiller St (45214-2208)
PHONE.............................513 579-1722
Yong Woo Koo, *President*
EMP: 30
SALES (est): 6MM **Privately Held**
SIC: 2011 2013 5147 Meat packing
plants; sausages & other prepared meats;
meats & meat products

(G-4522)
TRI-STATE BELTING LTD
Also Called: Greeno Company
5525 Vine St (45217-1003)
PHONE.............................800 330-2358
Fax: 513 489-4023
Jeffrey Stagnaro, *Partner*
Shaunda Mink, *Office Mgr*
EMP: 5
SALES (est): 380K **Privately Held**
SIC: 3496 Conveyor belts

(G-4523)
**TRI-STATE SPECIAL EVENTS
INC**
614 Tafel St (45225-2330)
PHONE.............................513 221-2962
Gary Robinson, *Vice Pres*
EMP: 4
SALES: 42.1K **Privately Held**
WEB: www.tristate-events.com
SIC: 2037 Frozen fruits & vegetables

(G-4524)
TRI-STATE TOOL GRINDING INC
5311 Robert Ave Ste A (45248-7200)
PHONE.............................513 347-0100
Fax: 513 347-7842
Michael L Dinkelacker, *President*
James C Dinkelacker, *Vice Pres*
Bettey Dinkelacker, *Manager*
EMP: 22
SQ FT: 12,000
SALES (est): 2MM **Privately Held**
SIC: 3541 Boring mills

(G-4525)
**TRILLIUM HEALTH CARE
PRODUCTS**
5177 Spring Grove Ave (45217-1050)
PHONE.............................513 242-2227
Alan Gropp, *Branch Mgr*
EMP: 7
SALES (corp-wide): 76.5MM **Privately
Held**
WEB: www.trillium.cc
SIC: 2841 Soap: granulated, liquid, cake,
flaked or chip

PA: Trillium Health Care Products Inc
　2337 Parkdale Ave E
　Brockville ON K6V 5
　613 342-4436

(G-4526)
TRINITY PRINTING CO
2300 E Kemper Rd Ste A19 (45241-6501)
P.O. Box 42786 (45242-0786)
PHONE.............................513 469-1000
Fax: 513 985-0666
Thomas Schroeder, *Owner*
EMP: 12
SALES: 652.6K **Privately Held**
SIC: 2759 Commercial printing

(G-4527)
TRIPOINT INSTRUMENTS INC
7513 Hamilton Ave (45231-4307)
PHONE.............................513 702-9217
Jeff Hering, *President*
Donald Hering, *Vice Pres*
Ginger Hering, *Admin Sec*
EMP: 3
SALES (est): 384.5K **Privately Held**
WEB: www.tripointinstruments.com
SIC: 3829 Fire detector systems, non-elec-
tric

(G-4528)
TRIVANTIS CORPORATION (PA)
Also Called: Lectora
311 Elm St Ste 200 (45202-2743)
P.O. Box 1000, Memphis TN (38148-0001)
PHONE.............................513 929-0188
Fax: 513 929-0770
Lori Lynne Todd, *CEO*
Brian Kuntz, *General Mgr*
Amber Griesenstine, *COO*
Thomas S Elmer, *Vice Pres*
Tanya Seidel, *Vice Pres*
EMP: 65
SQ FT: 22,000
SALES (est): 26.1MM **Privately Held**
WEB: www.trivantis.com
SIC: 7372 7371 Publishers' computer soft-
ware; custom computer programming
services

(G-4529)
**TROYKE MANUFACTURING
COMPANY**
11294 Orchard St (45241-1996)
PHONE.............................513 769-4242
Fax: 513 769-6362
Bernard R Froehlich, *President*
Eric N Froehlich, *Vice Pres*
Gary Edmondson, *Prdtn Mgr*
Tony Adams, *Engineer*
August Foehlich, *Manager*
EMP: 12 EST: 1952
SQ FT: 40,000
SALES (est): 2.5MM **Privately Held**
SIC: 3545 Rotary tables

(G-4530)
TRU-TEX INTERNATIONAL CORP
11050 Southland Rd (45240-3713)
P.O. Box 40107 (45240-0107)
PHONE.............................513 825-8844
Fax: 513 825-8904
Ruth Henn, *CEO*
Harry G Henn, *President*
Chrisopher Henn, *Vice Pres*
EMP: 21
SQ FT: 8,000
SALES (est): 2.6MM **Privately Held**
SIC: 3544 Dies & die holders for metal cut-
ting, forming, die casting; punches, form-
ing & stamping

(G-4531)
TRUSTONE DISTRIBUTORS CO
3273 E Sharon Rd (45241-1927)
PHONE.............................513 469-0335
Stacy Weldishofer, *Vice Pres*
Randy Weldishofer,
Stacey Weldishofer,
EMP: 2
SALES (est): 1MM **Privately Held**
SIC: 3281 Stone, quarrying & processing
of own stone products

(G-4532)
TSS TECHNOLOGIES INC
10200 Chester Rd (45215-1223)
PHONE.............................513 772-7000
Brent Nichols, *Manager*
EMP: 8
SQ FT: 4,680
SALES (corp-wide): 129.5MM **Privately
Held**
SIC: 3599 Machine shop, jobbing & repair
PA: Tss Technologies, Inc.
　8800 Global Way
　West Chester OH 45069
　513 772-7000

(G-4533)
TSS TECHNOLOGIES INC
Also Called: Tools Sales & Service
1201 Hill Smith Dr (45215-1228)
PHONE.............................513 772-7000
Scott D Nichols, *Vice Pres*
Patrick Solvan, *Sales Staff*
Charles Nicols, *Branch Mgr*
Dave Ludlow, *Business Dir*
Carol McKay, *Administration*
EMP: 6
SALES (corp-wide): 129.5MM **Privately
Held**
SIC: 3599 Machine shop, jobbing & repair
PA: Tss Technologies, Inc.
　8800 Global Way
　West Chester OH 45069
　513 772-7000

(G-4534)
U S TERMINALS INC
7504 Camargo Rd (45243-3147)
PHONE.............................513 561-8145
Fax: 513 561-8755
EMP: 8
SQ FT: 16,000
SALES (est): 790K **Privately Held**
SIC: 3679 3678 Mfg Electronic Terminals
& Connectors

(G-4535)
**UNDERGROUND SPORT SHOP
INC**
1233 Findlay St Ste Frnt (45214-2012)
PHONE.............................513 751-1662
Fax: 513 487-6563
Sean Mason, *President*
Andy Wolterman, *Vice Pres*
Jim Hebert, *Admin Sec*
▲ EMP: 10
SQ FT: 12,000
SALES: 1MM **Privately Held**
WEB: www.undergroundsportshop.com
SIC: 2759 7389 5199 Screen printing;
embroidering of advertising on shirts, etc.;
advertising specialties

(G-4536)
**UNI-REF UNITED
REFRACTORIES CO**
11301 Jefferson St (45241-1965)
PHONE.............................513 563-9955
Fax: 513 563-1698
Leonard Martin, *Purchasing*
Fred Daniels, *Manager*
EMP: 20
SALES (corp-wide): 4MM **Privately Held**
SIC: 3255 3297 3433 Clay refractories;
nonclay refractories; heating equipment,
except electric
PA: Uni-Ref United Refractories Co.
　264 Valley Brook Rd
　Canonsburg PA 15317
　724 941-9390

(G-4537)
**UNITED ADVG PUBLICATIONS
INC**
Also Called: For Rent Magazine
11177 Reading Rd Ste 1 (45241-1955)
PHONE.............................513 469-8818
Fax: 513 469-8831
Betty Bohlinger, *Manager*
EMP: 5
SALES (corp-wide): 800MM **Privately
Held**
WEB: www.traderonline.com
SIC: 2721 Periodicals

HQ: United Advertising Publications, Inc.
　150 Granby St
　Norfolk VA 23510
　210 377-3116

(G-4538)
**UNITED DAIRY FARMERS INC
(PA)**
Also Called: U D F
3955 Montgomery Rd (45212-3798)
PHONE.............................513 396-8700
Fax: 513 396-8736
Brad Lindner, *President*
Frank Cogliano, *Vice Pres*
My-Linh Hartsgrove, *Plant Mgr*
Angelos Christon, *Opers Staff*
Lowell Rogers, *Opers Staff*
EMP: 200
SALES (est): 591.6MM **Privately Held**
SIC: 5411 5143 2026 2024 Convenience
stores, chain; ice cream & ices; frozen
dairy desserts; milk processing (pasteur-
izing, homogenizing, bottling); ice cream
& ice milk; filling stations, gasoline; dairy
products stores

(G-4539)
UNITED ENVELOPE LLC
4890 Spring Grove Ave (45232-1933)
PHONE.............................513 542-4700
Fax: 513 542-5260
Tim Bernstein,
EMP: 57 EST: 2009
SQ FT: 170,000
SALES (est): 13.9MM **Privately Held**
WEB: www.specialtyenvelope.com
SIC: 2677 Envelopes

(G-4540)
**UNITED STATES DRILL HEAD
CO**
5298 River Rd (45233-1688)
PHONE.............................513 941-0300
Fax: 513 941-9110
J H Nymberg Jr, *President*
D Baum, *Purchasing*
Joseph E Bashor, *Treasurer*
Mike Nymberg, *Marketing Staff*
J Keene, *Manager*
EMP: 30
SQ FT: 47,772
SALES (est): 4.5MM **Privately Held**
SIC: 3545 3363 3543 Machine tool ac-
cessories; aluminum die-castings; indus-
trial patterns

(G-4541)
UNITED-MAIER SIGNS INC
1030 Straight St (45214-1734)
PHONE.............................513 681-6600
Fax: 513 681-0818
Antony E Maier, *President*
Elvera Maier, *Vice Pres*
Michele Wocher, *Human Resources*
Gene Bare, *VP Sales*
Sally Land, *Sales Mgr*
EMP: 54 EST: 1964
SQ FT: 18,000
SALES (est): 8.2MM **Privately Held**
WEB: www.united-maier.com
SIC: 3993 1799 Signs & advertising spe-
cialties; sign installation & maintenance

(G-4542)
**UNIVERSAL PACKG SYSTEMS
INC**
Also Called: Paklab
470 Northland Blvd (45240-3211)
PHONE.............................513 674-9400
Jeff Topits, *Branch Mgr*
EMP: 388
SALES (corp-wide): 139.7MM **Privately
Held**
SIC: 2844 3565 7389 2671 Cosmetic
preparations; bottling machinery: filling,
capping, labeling; packaging & labeling
services; plastic film, coated or laminated
for packaging
PA: Universal Packaging Systems, Inc.
　6080 Jericho Tpke
　Commack NY 11725
　631 543-2277

(G-4543)
UNIVERSITY OF CINCINNATI
Also Called: U C Printing Service
2900 Rerading Rd B101 (45221-0001)
PHONE....................513 556-5042
Ken Volz, *Manager*
EMP: 17
SALES (corp-wide): 960.6MM **Privately Held**
SIC: 2752 8221 Commercial printing, lithographic; university
PA: University Of Cincinnati
2600 Clifton Ave
Cincinnati OH 45220
513 556-6000

(G-4544)
UPPER ECHELON BAR LLC
1747 Avonlea Ave (45237-6109)
PHONE....................513 531-2814
Alice Carr, *Owner*
EMP: 3
SALES (est): 225.7K **Privately Held**
SIC: 3131 Uppers

(G-4545)
US FOAM CORPORATION (PA)
7412 Jager Ct (45230-4344)
PHONE....................513 528-9800
Jerry Schoch, *President*
Todd Smith, *Sales Staff*
EMP: 3
SALES (est): 1.4MM **Privately Held**
SIC: 3086 Plastics foam products; padding, foamed plastic

(G-4546)
US GREENTECH
3607 Church St (45244-3096)
PHONE....................513 371-5520
Joe Motz, *Principal*
Adam Coleman, *Vice Pres*
Helen Motz, *Plant Mgr*
EMP: 3
SALES (est): 537.5K **Privately Held**
SIC: 2282 Manmade & synthetic fiber yarns: twisting, winding, etc.

(G-4547)
US INDUSTRIAL LUBRICANTS INC
Also Called: Oil Kraft Div
3330 Beekman St (45223-2424)
PHONE....................513 541-2225
Fax: 513 541-2293
Donald L Mattcheck, *President*
Ted Korzet, *General Mgr*
Adam Freeman, *Vice Pres*
David E Ziegler, *Vice Pres*
Shannon Schlich, *Controller*
EMP: 20
SQ FT: 45,000
SALES (est): 8MM **Privately Held**
WEB: www.usindustriallubricants.com
SIC: 2842 2992 2841 Specialty cleaning preparations; sanitation preparations; oils & greases, blending & compounding; soap & other detergents

(G-4548)
USUI INTERNATIONAL CORPORATION
88 Partnership Way (45241-1507)
PHONE....................513 448-0410
Fax: 513 539-8162
Dennis Chiu, *Engineer*
Joseph Tacinelli, *Manager*
Kenichi Aoki, *Manager*
Mike Nowell, *Manager*
EMP: 25
SALES (corp-wide): 628.4MM **Privately Held**
SIC: 3069 3564 Tubes, hard rubber; tubing, rubber; ventilating fans: industrial or commercial
HQ: Usui International Corporation
44780 Helm St
Plymouth MI 48170
734 354-3626

(G-4549)
UTC FIRE SEC AMERICAS CORP INC
14 Knollcrest Dr (45237-1635)
PHONE....................513 821-7945

Karen Lamhem, *Branch Mgr*
EMP: 3
SALES (corp-wide): 57.2B **Publicly Held**
SIC: 3669 Emergency alarms
HQ: Utc Fire & Security Americas Corporation, Inc.
8985 Town Center Pkwy
Lakewood Ranch FL 34202
941 739-4200

(G-4550)
V&P GROUP INTERNATIONAL LLC
1931 Lawn Ave (45237-6125)
PHONE....................703 349-6432
Leslie Glosby, *Manager*
EMP: 16
SALES (est): 357.8K **Privately Held**
SIC: 6531 3731 6552 8711 Real estate agents & managers; shipbuilding & repairing; subdividers & developers; engineering services; home furnishings

(G-4551)
VALLEY ASPHALT CORPORATION
7940 Main St (45244)
PHONE....................513 561-1551
Fax: 513 561-5741
Kyle Napier, *Manager*
EMP: 3
SQ FT: 800
SALES (corp-wide): 109.5MM **Privately Held**
SIC: 1611 2951 General contractor, highway & street construction; asphalt & asphaltic paving mixtures (not from refineries)
PA: Valley Asphalt Corporation
11641 Mosteller Rd
Cincinnati OH 45241
513 771-0820

(G-4552)
VALLEY ASPHALT CORPORATION
612 W Mehring Way (45202-3422)
PHONE....................513 784-1476
Buddy Cryfield, *Manager*
EMP: 3
SALES (corp-wide): 117.2MM **Privately Held**
SIC: 2951 Asphalt & asphaltic paving mixtures (not from refineries)
PA: Valley Asphalt Corporation
11641 Mosteller Rd
Cincinnati OH 45241
513 771-0820

(G-4553)
VALLEY METAL WORKS INC
698 W Columbia Ave (45215-3184)
PHONE....................513 554-1022
Fax: 513 554-1198
James Steinbeck, *President*
Kevin Graham, *President*
Joe R Rings, *COO*
Fred Horst, *Vice Pres*
James Stiebeck, *Vice Pres*
EMP: 25 EST: 1934
SQ FT: 19,000
SALES (est): 6.4MM **Privately Held**
WEB: www.valleymetalworks.com
SIC: 3444 Sheet metalwork

(G-4554)
VAN LOCK CO INC
Also Called: Vantech21
6834 Center St (45244-3404)
PHONE....................513 561-9692
Fax: 513 561-0314
James Padjen, *President*
David Kraft, *Senior Buyer*
Kathy Padjen, *VP Mktg*
Lorraine Ferone, *Admin Asst*
EMP: 10
SQ FT: 18,000
SALES (est): 3.6MM **Privately Held**
WEB: www.vanlock.com
SIC: 3429 Locks or lock sets

(G-4555)
VAN-GRINER LLC
1009 Delta Ave (45208-3103)
PHONE....................419 733-7951

Michael Griner,
Dreis Van Landuyg,
EMP: 6
SALES: 100K **Privately Held**
SIC: 2741 Miscellaneous publishing

(G-4556)
VARIFLOW EQUIPMENT INC
3834 Ridgedale Dr (45247-6947)
PHONE....................513 245-0420
Fax: 513 245-0421
Steve Weddendorf, *President*
EMP: 2
SQ FT: 1,000
SALES: 1.5MM **Privately Held**
WEB: www.variflow.com
SIC: 3585 Refrigeration & heating equipment

(G-4557)
VEEDERS MAILBOX INC
10050 Montgomery Rd # 324 (45242)
PHONE....................513 984-8749
Fax: 513 984-8745
Jenny Lamson Magro, *President*
Jonathon Margo, *Vice Pres*
EMP: 3
SQ FT: 6,386
SALES (est): 260K **Privately Held**
SIC: 3469 Boxes: tool, lunch, mail, etc.: stamped metal

(G-4558)
VEGA AMERICAS INC (HQ)
Also Called: Ohmart Vega
4170 Rosslyn Dr Ste A (45209-1193)
PHONE....................513 272-0131
Fax: 513 272-0133
Jack Rodgers, *President*
Cesar Malpica, *Regional Mgr*
Mark McDowell, *Regional Mgr*
Dan Stigler, *Regional Mgr*
Carol Ritter, *VP Admin*
◆ EMP: 200
SQ FT: 100,000
SALES (est): 147.6MM
SALES (corp-wide): 261.7MM **Privately Held**
WEB: www.ohmartvega.com
SIC: 3823 Industrial instrmnts msrmnt display/control process variable
PA: Vega Grieshaber Kg
Hauptstr. 1-5
Wolfach 77709
783 650-0

(G-4559)
VEMURI INTERNATIONAL LLC (PA)
Also Called: Queen City Paper
10600 Evendale Dr (45241-2518)
PHONE....................513 483-6300
Janet Bain, *Human Res Mgr*
Phil Holt, *Sales Staff*
Frank Horvat, *Marketing Staff*
Kevin Bain, *Manager*
Kusuma Vemuri,
◆ EMP: 8
SQ FT: 100,000
SALES (est): 9.1MM **Privately Held**
WEB: www.queencitypaper.com
SIC: 2679 Paperboard products, converted

(G-4560)
VENCO MANUFACTURING INC (HQ)
Also Called: Collins & Venco Venturo
12110 Best Pl (45241-1569)
PHONE....................513 772-8448
Fax: 513 326-5427
Larry R Collins, *President*
Terry Woosley, *General Mgr*
Ronald A Collins, *Vice Pres*
Mike Strittholt, *Treasurer*
Barbara Duke, *Admin Sec*
▲ EMP: 15
SQ FT: 35,000
SALES (est): 9.3MM
SALES (corp-wide): 18.3MM **Privately Held**
SIC: 3714 Motor vehicle parts & accessories
PA: Venco Venturo Industries Llc
12110 Best Pl
Cincinnati OH 45241
513 772-8448

(G-4561)
VENCO VENTURO INDUSTRIES LLC (PA)
Also Called: Venco/Venturo Div
12110 Best Pl (45241-1569)
PHONE....................513 772-8448
Brett Collins, *President*
Dave Foster, *Vice Pres*
Terry Woosley, *VP Opers*
Mike Strittholt, *CFO*
Larry Jones, *Sales Staff*
▲ EMP: 41
SQ FT: 100,000
SALES (est): 18.3MM **Privately Held**
WEB: www.venturo.com
SIC: 3713 5012 3714 5084 Truck bodies (motor vehicles); truck bodies; motor vehicle parts & accessories; cranes, industrial

(G-4562)
VENTURO MANUFACTURING INC
12110 Best Pl (45241-1569)
PHONE....................513 772-8448
Larry Collins, *President*
Ronald A Collins, *Vice Pres*
Sandy Riley, *Vice Pres*
Charlie Klein, *Prdtn Mgr*
Brad Clarkson, *Purch Agent*
EMP: 32
SQ FT: 5,000
SALES (est): 9MM
SALES (corp-wide): 18.3MM **Privately Held**
WEB: www.venturo.com
SIC: 3537 5084 Cranes, industrial truck; industrial machinery & equipment
PA: Venco Venturo Industries Llc
12110 Best Pl
Cincinnati OH 45241
513 772-8448

(G-4563)
VENUE LIFESTYLE & EVENT GUIDE
11959 Tramway Dr (45241-1666)
PHONE....................513 405-6822
Kim Wanamaker, *President*
Steve Wanamaker, *Vice Pres*
EMP: 15 EST: 2010
SALES (est): 1MM **Privately Held**
SIC: 2721 Magazines: publishing & printing

(G-4564)
VERO SECURITY GROUP LTD
5296 Montgomery Rd (45212-1656)
PHONE....................513 731-8376
Al Overson, *CEO*
Leonard M Watson, *President*
Kumar Chattoraj, *COO*
Derek Landers, *Sales Dir*
EMP: 6
SALES (est): 608.4K **Privately Held**
WEB: www.verosecurity.com
SIC: 3699 Security control equipment & systems

(G-4565)
VERTEX COMPUTER SYSTEMS INC
11260 Chester Rd Ste 300 (45246-4051)
PHONE....................513 662-6888
Fax: 513 662-8048
Murali Swamy, *Branch Mgr*
EMP: 15
SALES (corp-wide): 25.6MM **Privately Held**
WEB: www.vertexcs.com
SIC: 7372 Prepackaged software
PA: Vertex Computer Systems, Inc.
2245 E Enterprise Pkwy
Twinsburg OH 44087
330 963-0044

(G-4566)
VERTIFLO PUMP COMPANY
7807 Redsky Dr (45249-1636)
PHONE....................513 530-0888
Fax: 513 530-0893
Mark Werner, *President*
Phil Eldridge, *Vice Pres*
Heather Swing, *Finance Mgr*
EMP: 17
SQ FT: 18,000

SALES (est): 4.1MM **Privately Held**
WEB: www.vertiflopump.com
SIC: 3594 3561 Fluid power pumps;
pumps & pumping equipment

(G-4567)
VESI INCORPORATED
16 Techview Dr (45215-1985)
PHONE..................................513 563-6002
Greg Visconti, *CEO*
Dale Davidson, *COO*
Susan Litster, *Vice Pres*
Melinda Cramer, *Human Res Dir*
▲ EMP: 45
SQ FT: 44,500
SALES (est): 6.5MM **Privately Held**
WEB: www.vesiinc.com
SIC: 2329 2339 Men's & boys' sportswear
& athletic clothing; sportswear, women's

(G-4568)
VICAS MANUFACTURING CO INC
8407 Monroe Ave (45236-1909)
P.O. Box 36310 (45236-0310)
PHONE..................................513 791-7741
Fax: 513 791-6484
Virginia Willoughby, *President*
Stephen Kisling, *Counsel*
John Clayton, *Vice Pres*
Pon May, *Vice Pres*
Steve Newbould, *Manager*
EMP: 47 EST: 1972
SQ FT: 25,600
SALES (est): 8.4MM **Privately Held**
SIC: 3089 3599 Injection molding of plas-
tics; casting of plastic; machine shop, job-
bing & repair

(G-4569)
VIVID WRAPS LLC
12130 Royal Point Dr (45249-3306)
PHONE..................................513 515-8386
Nick Durante, *Owner*
EMP: 3
SALES: 94K **Privately Held**
SIC: 7336 3714 Commercial art & graphic
design; motor vehicle body components &
frame

(G-4570)
VOLK CORPORATION
Also Called: Hathaway
635 Main St Ste 1 (45202-2524)
PHONE..................................513 621-1052
Larry Schultz, *Branch Mgr*
EMP: 8
SALES (corp-wide): 30.9MM **Privately
Held**
WEB: www.volkcorp.com
SIC: 3953 Marking devices
PA: Volk Corporation
23936 Indl Pk Dr
Farmington Hills MI 48335
248 477-6700

(G-4571)
VULCAN INTERNATIONAL CORP
30 Garfield Pl Ste 1000 (45202-4308)
PHONE..................................513 621-2850
Fax: 513 241-8199
Benjamin Gattler, *Branch Mgr*
EMP: 9
SALES (corp-wide): 9.3MM **Publicly Held**
SIC: 3999 Barber & beauty shop equip-
ment
PA: Vulcan International Corporation
300 Delaware Ave Ste 1704
Wilmington DE 19801
302 428-3181

(G-4572)
VY INC
Also Called: Victor
37 W 7th St Fl 6 (45202-2458)
PHONE..................................513 421-8100
Fax: 513 421-8119
Victor Youkilis, *Ch of Bd*
John Youkilis, *President*
Cheryl Hussey, *Sls & Mktg Exec*
EMP: 15 EST: 1946
SQ FT: 5,000
SALES (est): 2.8MM **Privately Held**
SIC: 3911 5094 Jewelry apparel; jewelry

(G-4573)
VYA INC
Also Called: Docustar
1325 Glendale Milford Rd (45215-1210)
P.O. Box 634015 (45263-4015)
PHONE..................................513 772-5400
Fax: 513 772-5410
Jay Brokamp, *President*
Kandi O'Connor, *COO*
Terry Brokamp, *Senior VP*
Kathy Smith, *Manager*
Matt Mithoefer, *Admin Asst*
EMP: 41
SQ FT: 56,000
SALES (est): 9.6MM **Privately Held**
WEB: www.docustar.com
SIC: 2759 2675 2752 Commercial print-
ing; die-cut paper & board; commercial
printing, lithographic

(G-4574)
W H HEIMKREITER MANUFACTURING
3106 Spring Grove Ave (45225-1820)
PHONE..................................513 681-9192
Fax: 513 681-9192
William H Heimkreiter, *President*
Caroline Heimkreiter, *Treasurer*
EMP: 6
SQ FT: 5,000
SALES (est): 460K **Privately Held**
SIC: 3544 3469 Die sets for metal stamp-
ing (presses); metal stampings

(G-4575)
WAITS INSTRUMENTS LLC ◆
1337 Karahill Dr (45240-2253)
PHONE..................................513 600-5996
Matthew Waits, *CEO*
Brandy Waits, *President*
Gary Waits, *Vice Pres*
EMP: 3 EST: 2016
SALES (est): 103.6K **Privately Held**
SIC: 3931 Musical instruments; fretted in-
struments & parts

(G-4576)
WALL COLMONOY CORPORATION
940 Redna Ter (45215-1113)
P.O. Box Na Ter (45215)
PHONE..................................937 278-9111
Fax: 937 278-9118
Don Hainley, *General Mgr*
Robert Pfouts, *Engineer*
EMP: 18
SQ FT: 3,200
SALES (corp-wide): 59.3MM **Privately
Held**
WEB: www.wallcolmonoy.com
SIC: 3398 3341 Brazing (hardening) of
metal; secondary nonferrous metals
HQ: Wall Colmonoy Corporation
101 W Girard Ave
Madison Heights MI 48071
248 585-6400

(G-4577)
WALL COLMONOY CORPORATION
Aerobraze Division
940 Redna Ter (45215-1113)
PHONE..................................513 842-4200
Fax: 513 772-0149
John Sturch Jr, *General Mgr*
Julie Meeker, *Purchasing*
Norm Mannory, *Engineer*
Ken Coldfelter, *Branch Mgr*
Tim Jett, *Manager*
EMP: 55
SALES (corp-wide): 59.3MM **Privately
Held**
WEB: www.wallcolmonoy.com
SIC: 3812 Search & navigation equipment
HQ: Wall Colmonoy Corporation
101 W Girard Ave
Madison Heights MI 48071
248 585-6400

(G-4578)
WALLINGFORD COFFEE MILLS INC (PA)
11401 Rockfield Ct (45241-1971)
PHONE..................................513 771-3131
Fax: 513 771-3138

Gary Weber Sr, *President*
Michael Hoban, *VP Finance*
Mike Stratton, *Marketing Mgr*
▼ EMP: 80
SQ FT: 38,000
SALES (est): 15MM **Privately Held**
WEB: www.wallingfordcoffee.com
SIC: 2095 2099 Coffee roasting (except by
wholesale grocers); tea blending

(G-4579)
WARNER CHLCOTT PHRMCTICALS INC (PA)
1 Procter And Gamble Plz (45202-3315)
PHONE..................................513 983-1100
Mark Collar, *President*
Clayton C Daley Jr, *CFO*
Debra Jazenski, *Manager*
Axel Masschelein, *Manager*
Dan Snodgrass, *Manager*
EMP: 11 EST: 1987
SQ FT: 1,600,000
SALES (est): 259.8MM **Privately Held**
WEB: www.dash.com
SIC: 2834 Pharmaceutical preparations

(G-4580)
WAYNE SIGNER ENTERPRISES INC
Also Called: E-Z Pack
6545 Wiehe Rd (45237-4217)
PHONE..................................513 841-1351
Fax: 513 841-1396
Wayne A Signer, *CEO*
Barry Schwartz, *President*
Barbara Signer, *Vice Pres*
Teri Junker, *VP Sales*
Kim Sherman, *Accounts Mgr*
EMP: 35
SQ FT: 38,000
SALES (est): 4MM **Privately Held**
WEB: www.ezpack.com
SIC: 2631 Container, packaging &
boxboard

(G-4581)
WCM HOLDINGS INC (PA)
11500 Canal Rd (45241-1862)
PHONE..................................513 705-2100
Fax: 513 705-2138
David Herche, *CEO*
Tim Fogarty, *President*
Melvyn Fisher, *Chairman*
▲ EMP: 7
SALES (est): 111.5MM **Privately Held**
SIC: 5099 2381 3842 Safety equipment &
supplies; gloves, work: woven or knit,
made from purchased materials; clothing,
fire resistant & protective

(G-4582)
WEEKLY JUICERY
2727 Erie Ave (45208-2164)
PHONE..................................513 321-0680
EMP: 3
SALES (est): 121.2K **Privately Held**
SIC: 2711 Newspapers

(G-4583)
WELAGE CORPORATION
1925 Powers St (45223-2373)
PHONE..................................513 681-2300
Fax: 513 681-2028
David Welage, *President*
Brad Ruter, *Vice Pres*
Sean Munyon, *Project Mgr*
EMP: 15 EST: 1937
SQ FT: 15,000
SALES (est): 4MM **Privately Held**
WEB: www.welagecorp.com
SIC: 3441 3469 3544 Fabricated struc-
tural metal; metal stampings; special dies,
tools, jigs & fixtures

(G-4584)
WELCH HOLDINGS INC
8953 E Miami River Rd (45247-2232)
PHONE..................................513 353-3220
James R Welch, *President*
Ronnie L Welch, *Corp Secy*
Connie Tolson, *Human Resources*
EMP: 45
SQ FT: 3,400

SALES (est): 3.6MM **Privately Held**
WEB: www.welchsand.com
SIC: 1442 Common sand mining; gravel
mining

(G-4585)
WELSH FARMS LLC
221 E 4th St Ste 2000 (45202-4194)
PHONE..................................513 723-4487
Rosemary Welsh, *Principal*
EMP: 3
SALES (est): 140.7K **Privately Held**
SIC: 2024 Ice cream & frozen desserts

(G-4586)
WEST PHARMACEUTICAL SVCS INC
3309 Wheatcroft Dr (45239-6158)
PHONE..................................513 741-3004
Karen Beck, *Principal*
EMP: 4
SALES (corp-wide): 1.5B **Publicly Held**
SIC: 3089 Molding primary plastic
PA: West Pharmaceutical Services, Inc.
530 Herman O West Dr
Exton PA 19341
610 594-2900

(G-4587)
WESTEND BREWING LLC
5091 Orangelawn Dr (45238-5721)
PHONE..................................513 922-0289
Barbara Bain, *Principal*
EMP: 3
SALES (est): 125.5K **Privately Held**
SIC: 2082 Malt beverages

(G-4588)
WESTERN & SOUTHERN LF INSUR CO (DH)
Also Called: Western-Southern Life
400 Broadway St (45202-3341)
P.O. Box 1119 (45201-1119)
PHONE..................................513 629-1800
Fax: 513 629-1212
John F Barrett, *President*
David Dimartino, *President*
Mark Pfefferman, *President*
Elaine Reuss, *President*
Cheryl Stotts, *President*
EMP: 982 EST: 1888
SQ FT: 600,000
SALES (est): 359.9MM **Privately Held**
SIC: 6211 6311 2511 Investment firm;
general brokerage; life insurance; play
pens, children's; wood
HQ: Western & Southern Financial Group,
Inc.
400 Broadway St
Cincinnati OH 45202
866 832-7719

(G-4589)
WESTROCK CP LLC
Also Called: Smurfit Stone
414 S Cooper Ave (45215-4555)
PHONE..................................513 745-2586
Rich Branson, *Manager*
EMP: 310
SALES (corp-wide): 14.1B **Publicly Held**
SIC: 2621 Wrapping & packaging papers
HQ: Westrock Cp, Llc
504 Thrasher St
Norcross GA 30071

(G-4590)
WHEATLEY ELECTRIC SERVICE CO
2046 Ross Ave (45212-2040)
PHONE..................................513 531-4951
Fax: 513 531-5035
Dorothy Elsbrock, *President*
Jim Elsbrock, *Vice Pres*
Jim Snyder, *Manager*
EMP: 7 EST: 1934
SQ FT: 5,000
SALES (est): 1.6MM **Privately Held**
WEB: www.wheatleyelectric.com
SIC: 7694 5999 5063 Electric motor re-
pair; motors, electric; motors, electric

(G-4591)
WHITE CASTLE SYSTEM INC
3126 Exon Ave (45241-2548)
PHONE..................................513 563-2290

Fax: 513 563-8486
Jarrett Cook, *Plant Mgr*
Roy Gambrel, *Opers Mgr*
Paul Shannon, *Executive*
Dan Boger, *Maintence Staff*
EMP: 28
SALES (corp-wide): 571.7MM **Privately Held**
WEB: www.whitecastle.com
SIC: 5812 2099 Fast-food restaurant, chain; sandwiches, assembled & packaged: for wholesale market
PA: White Castle System, Inc.
555 W Goodale St
Columbus OH 43215
614 228-5781

(G-4592)
WHITWORTH KNIFE COMPANY
508 Missouri Ave (45226-1121)
PHONE.....................513 321-9177
Raymond Whitworth, *Owner*
EMP: 3
SALES: 150K **Privately Held**
SIC: 3545 Shear knives

(G-4593)
WICKTEK INC
8097 Sacred Heart Ln (45255-3122)
PHONE.....................724 329-8310
Patrick A Wick, *CEO*
Frank R Yantek, *President*
Paul R Wick, *Exec VP*
H C Stuckeman, *Vice Pres*
Robert Toye, *Vice Pres*
EMP: 25
SQ FT: 8,000
SALES (est): 2.3MM **Privately Held**
WEB: www.densicrete.com
SIC: 2899 Concrete curing & hardening compounds

(G-4594)
WILD JOES INC
Also Called: Wild Joe's Beef Jerky
2905 Jessamine St (45225-2107)
PHONE.....................513 681-9200
Fax: 513 681-9204
Micah Gaunt, *Principal*
Joe Lachenman, *Admin Sec*
▲ **EMP:** 4
SQ FT: 5,800
SALES (est): 28K **Privately Held**
WEB: www.wildjoesbeefjerky.com
SIC: 2013 Prepared beef products from purchased beef

(G-4595)
WILD PENGUIN LLC
4 Elmhurst Pl (45208-3211)
PHONE.....................513 533-4356
Jerry Sutkamp, *Managing Prtnr*
EMP: 5 EST: 2008
SALES (est): 399.2K **Privately Held**
SIC: 2024 Ice cream & frozen desserts

(G-4596)
WILLIAM POWELL COMPANY (PA)
Also Called: Powell Valve
2503 Spring Grove Ave (45214-1729)
PHONE.....................513 852-2000
Fax: 513 852-2997
David R Cowart, *President*
Rhett Demars, *Regional Mgr*
Steve Flynn, *Regional Mgr*
Brandy Cowart, *Exec VP*
Jack Brown, *Vice Pres*
▲ **EMP:** 35 EST: 1846
SALES (est): 83.7MM **Privately Held**
WEB: www.powellvalves.com
SIC: 3491 3494 Pressure valves & regulators, industrial; valves & pipe fittings

(G-4597)
WILLIS MUSIC COMPANY
11700 Princeton Pike E209 (45246-2563)
PHONE.....................513 671-3288
Robert Mooney, *Manager*
EMP: 10
SALES (corp-wide): 6.6MM **Privately Held**
WEB: www.willismusic.com
SIC: 2741 5736 Music, sheet: publishing & printing; musical instrument stores

PA: Willis Music Company
7567 Mall Rd
Florence KY 41042
859 283-2050

(G-4598)
WILLOW FROG LLC
9 Briarwood Ln (45218-1313)
PHONE.....................513 861-4834
David Otting,
Jarrod Becker,
Jennifer Bucheit,
EMP: 3 EST: 2012
SALES (est): 105K **Privately Held**
SIC: 7372 Application computer software

(G-4599)
WINE CELLAR INNOVATIONS LLC
4575 Eastern Ave (45226-1805)
PHONE.....................513 321-3733
James L Deckebach, *Owner*
Darlene Goff, *General Mgr*
Michael Berry, *Safety Dir*
Stefanie George, *Plant Mgr*
Lawrence Morley, *Opers Mgr*
▼ **EMP:** 157
SQ FT: 350,000
SALES (est): 25.4MM **Privately Held**
SIC: 2511 2541 Wood household furniture; wood partitions & fixtures

(G-4600)
WISSMAN & WOOD INCORPORATED
Also Called: Mis Solutions
7849 Palace Dr (45249-1635)
PHONE.....................513 793-6222
Micah Wissman, *President*
David Wood, *Treasurer*
EMP: 4
SALES (est): 705.8K **Privately Held**
SIC: 7372 Prepackaged software

(G-4601)
WJF ENTERPRISES LLC
Also Called: Specialty Wood Products
1347 Custer Ave (45208-2556)
PHONE.....................513 871-7320
Fax: 513 860-4044
William Funk,
EMP: 15
SQ FT: 32,000
SALES: 2MM **Privately Held**
SIC: 2448 Wood pallets & skids

(G-4602)
WM LANG & SONS COMPANY
3280 Beekman St (45223-2423)
PHONE.....................513 541-3304
Fax: 513 541-3305
Robert Schutte, *President*
Howard Schutte Jr, *Vice Pres*
Jeffrey Tuttle, *Vice Pres*
Joseph Schutte, *Admin Sec*
EMP: 18 EST: 1892
SQ FT: 16,800
SALES (est): 4.6MM **Privately Held**
SIC: 3441 Fabricated structural metal

(G-4603)
WOOD GRAPHICS INC (HQ)
Also Called: United Engraving
1270 Hill Smith Dr (45215-1297)
PHONE.....................513 771-6300
Fax: 513 771-3112
Mark Richler, *President*
Gaylord H Fill, *Corp Secy*
◆ **EMP:** 30
SQ FT: 21,500
SALES: 3.2MM
SALES (corp-wide): 128.8MM **Privately Held**
SIC: 3555 7699 2796 Printing trades machinery; industrial machinery & equipment repair; platemaking services
PA: Rotation Dynamics Corporation
8140 Cass Ave
Darien IL 60561
630 769-9255

(G-4604)
WORKFLEX SOLUTIONS LLC (PA)
7872 Cooper Rd (45242-7612)
PHONE.....................513 257-0215
Larry Schwartz, *Mng Member*
Mitesh Desai,
EMP: 8
SALES: 500K **Privately Held**
SIC: 7372 Business oriented computer software

(G-4605)
WORTHMORE FOOD PRODUCTS CO
1021 Ludlow Ave (45223-2621)
PHONE.....................513 559-1473
Fax: 513 559-0286
Phil Hock, *President*
Phil Hock III, *Vice Pres*
Richard Hock, *Admin Sec*
EMP: 12 EST: 1924
SQ FT: 15,000
SALES (est): 1.7MM **Privately Held**
SIC: 2032 Soups, except seafood: packaged in cans, jars, etc.; chili with or without meat: packaged in cans, jars, etc.; spaghetti: packaged in cans, jars, etc.; Italian foods: packaged in cans, jars, etc.

(G-4606)
WRIGHT BROTHERS INC (PA)
7825 Cooper Rd (45242-7605)
PHONE.....................513 731-2222
Fax: 513 731-2223
Charles Wright, *President*
Josh Gerdes, *General Mgr*
Samantha Trent, *CFO*
Ashley Werthaiser, *Marketing Mgr*
James Dashley, *Office Mgr*
EMP: 15
SQ FT: 15,000
SALES (est): 4MM **Privately Held**
WEB: www.expectthebest.com
SIC: 2813 3446 5084 Industrial gases; architectural metalwork; welding machinery & equipment

(G-4607)
WRIGHT BROTHERS GLOBAL GAS LLC
1930 Losantiville Ave (45237-4106)
PHONE.....................513 731-2222
Ashley Werthaiser, *President*
Neal O Willmann, *Principal*
Cyndi Blalock, *COO*
EMP: 7
SALES (est): 1.1MM **Privately Held**
SIC: 2813 Industrial gases

(G-4608)
WRIGHT WAY PATTERNS
6109 W Fork Rd (45247-5765)
PHONE.....................513 574-5776
Robert Wright, *Owner*
EMP: 4
SQ FT: 9,500
SALES (est): 264K **Privately Held**
SIC: 3543 Foundry patternmaking

(G-4609)
WRITELY SEW LLC
3862 Race Rd (45211-4346)
PHONE.....................513 728-2682
Raymond G Hollenkamp Jr,
EMP: 4
SALES: 250K **Privately Held**
SIC: 2395 Pleating & stitching

(G-4610)
WT ACQUISITION COMPANY LTD
Also Called: Waltek & Company
2130 Waycross Rd (45240-2719)
PHONE.....................513 577-7980
Brant Smith, *Partner*
Jeffrey Smith, *Partner*
Matt Furia, *Engineer*
Richard Perkins, *CFO*
EMP: 30
SQ FT: 9,000
SALES (est): 13MM **Privately Held**
SIC: 3449 3211 Curtain wall, metal; construction glass

(G-4611)
WULCO INC
Also Called: Jet Machine
6900 Steger Dr (45237-3096)
PHONE.....................513 679-2600
Adam Wulfeck, *Vice Pres*
EMP: 99
SQ FT: 80,000
SALES (corp-wide): 45.8MM **Privately Held**
SIC: 3599 Machine & other job shop work
PA: Wulco, Inc.
6899 Steger Dr Ste A
Cincinnati OH 45237
513 679-2600

(G-4612)
WULCO INC (PA)
Also Called: Jet Machine & Manufacturing
6899 Steger Dr Ste A (45237-3059)
PHONE.....................513 679-2600
Fax: 513 679-2653
Richard G Wulfeck, *President*
Chris Wulfeck, *Safety Dir*
Brad Wulfeck, *Safety Mgr*
Ken Smith, *Purch Agent*
Ken Wulfeck, *Treasurer*
▲ **EMP:** 100
SQ FT: 100,000
SALES (est): 45.8MM **Privately Held**
WEB: www.wulco.com
SIC: 3599 5085 Machine shop, jobbing & repair; industrial supplies

(G-4613)
X-3-5 LLC
Also Called: Solstreme
7621 E Kemper Rd (45249-1609)
PHONE.....................513 489-5477
Randal Sadler, *Partner*
David Necamp, *Partner*
EMP: 5
SQ FT: 7,400
SALES (est): 344.5K **Privately Held**
SIC: 3589 5084 9511 Sewage & water treatment equipment; pollution control equipment, water (environmental); air, water & solid waste management

(G-4614)
XOMOX CORPORATION
Also Called: Crane Chempharma & Energy
4444 Cooper Rd (45242-5686)
PHONE.....................936 271-6500
Fax: 513 745-6044
Joe McPeters, *Engineer*
Lisa Kobman, *Human Res Mgr*
Kelly Chalfant, *Marketing Mgr*
EMP: 27
SALES (corp-wide): 2.7B **Publicly Held**
SIC: 3491 3593 3494 Boiler gauge cocks; fluid power actuators, hydraulic or pneumatic; plumbing & heating valves
HQ: Xomox Corporation
4526 Res Frest Dr Ste 400
The Woodlands TX 77381
936 271-6500

(G-4615)
XRAY MEDIA LTD
445 Mcgregor Ave (45206-2365)
PHONE.....................513 751-9641
Arie Vandenberg, *Principal*
EMP: 4
SALES (est): 271.6K **Privately Held**
SIC: 2721 Magazines: publishing only, not printed on site

(G-4616)
XTEK INC (PA)
11451 Reading Rd (45241-2283)
PHONE.....................513 733-7800
Fax: 513 733-2990
C Jackson Cromer, *Principal*
Lewis G Gatch, *Principal*
J P Laycock, *Principal*
Frank P Petrek, *Vice Pres*
James J Raible, *Vice Pres*
◆ **EMP:** 336 EST: 1909
SQ FT: 363,440
SALES (est): 148.9MM **Privately Held**
WEB: www.xtek.com
SIC: 3568 3547 3398 3312 Power transmission equipment; rolling mill machinery; metal heat treating; wheels, locomotive & car: iron & steel

---

(G-4617)
YAGOOT
7875 Montgomery Rd # 1241
(45236-4606)
PHONE.....................513 791-6600
EMP: 3
SALES (est): 161.1K Privately Held
SIC: 2024 Mfg Ice Cream/Frozen Desert

(G-4618)
ZECH PRINTING INDUSTRIES INC
6310 Este Ave (45232-1450)
PHONE.....................937 748-2776
Fax: 513 563-1409
Kip R Zech, President
EMP: 22
SALES (est): 1.8MM Privately Held
SIC: 2759 2671 Letterpress printing; packaging paper & plastics film, coated & laminated

(G-4619)
ZIPSCENE LLC
602 Main St Ste 900 (45202-2543)
PHONE.....................513 201-5174
Sameer Mungur, CEO
Mike Grosser, President
Jonathan Richman, Vice Pres
Jen Sanning, Vice Pres
Matt Armstead, VP Sales
EMP: 62
SQ FT: 2,000
SALES (est): 12MM Privately Held
SIC: 7372 Business oriented computer software

(G-4620)
ZTS INC
5628 Wooster Pike (45227-4121)
PHONE.....................513 271-2557
Fax: 513 272-1383
Dave Zimmerman, President
Philip D Zimmerman, President
Phil Zimmerman, Principal
Marge Zimmerman, Corp Secy
▲ EMP: 10 EST: 1970
SQ FT: 8,000
SALES (est): 2MM Privately Held
SIC: 3825 Battery testers, electrical

(G-4621)
ZYGO INC
Also Called: Cincy Deli & Carryout
2832 Jefferson Ave (45219-1920)
P.O. Box 19311 (45219-0311)
PHONE.....................513 281-0888
Fax: 513 281-0777
Jim Powers, CEO
EMP: 8
SQ FT: 1,500
SALES (est): 1.1MM Privately Held
SIC: 5411 2097 Delicatessens; supermarkets, hypermarket; ice cubes

Circleville
Pickaway County

(G-4622)
ALL DO WELD & FAB LLC
28155 River Dr (43113-9726)
PHONE.....................740 477-2133
Sheng Stack, Opers Mgr
Dustin Picklesimer,
Troy S Brady,
EMP: 6
SALES: 250K Privately Held
SIC: 7692 Welding repair

(G-4623)
AMERICAN WOOD FIBERS INC
2500 Owens Rd (43113-8963)
PHONE.....................740 420-3233
Fax: 740 420-9323
Mark Roth, Manager
Mark Olter, Manager
EMP: 32
SALES (corp-wide): 101MM Privately Held
WEB: www.awf.com
SIC: 2499 Mulch or sawdust products, wood; wood flour

PA: American Wood Fibers, Inc.
9841 Broken Land Pkwy # 302
Columbia MD 21046
410 290-8700

(G-4624)
CCW GROUP PACESETTER INC
Us Highway 23 (43113)
PHONE.....................740 474-0122
Richard R Kern, President
Dennis Durand, General Mgr
Carl Eanes, Vice Pres
Donald Gott, Vice Pres
Judith Mercer, Treasurer
EMP: 230
SALES (est): 9.5MM Privately Held
WEB: www.ccwgroup.com
SIC: 4225 8741 7349 3535 General warehousing & storage; management services; building maintenance services; conveyors & conveying equipment; die-cut paper & board

(G-4625)
CIRCLEVILLE OIL CO
Also Called: Subway
224 Lancaster Pike (43113-1507)
P.O. Box 189 (43113-0189)
PHONE.....................740 477-3341
Fax: 740 420-3294
Lori Whited, Manager
EMP: 8
SALES (corp-wide): 43.7MM Privately Held
WEB: www.circlevilleoil.com
SIC: 1389 7539 5812 Construction, repair & dismantling services; brake services; sandwiches & submarines shop
PA: Circleville Oil Co (Inc)
315 Town St
Circleville OH 43113
740 474-7544

(G-4626)
CROWN PRINTING INC
118 S Scioto St (43113-1638)
PHONE.....................740 477-2511
Fax: 740 474-1290
Ronald Snyder, President
Kristy June, Office Mgr
EMP: 4 EST: 1976
SQ FT: 3,800
SALES (est): 447.8K Privately Held
WEB: www.crownprintingcorp.com
SIC: 2752 Commercial printing, offset

(G-4627)
E I DU PONT DE NEMOURS & CO
Also Called: Dupont
S Dupont Rd Rr 23 (43113)
P.O. Box 89 (43113-0089)
PHONE.....................740 474-0220
Fax: 740 474-0245
Robert Stambaugh, Superintendent
Harry Canfield, Plant Mgr
John Roberts, Safety Mgr
Judy Flattery, Rsch/Dvlpt Dir
Willard Bennett, Engineer
EMP: 50
SALES (corp-wide): 24.5B Publicly Held
WEB: www.dupont.com
SIC: 2821 3861 3081 Polyesters; polytetrafluoroethylene resins (teflon); photographic equipment & supplies; unsupported plastics film & sheet
PA: E. I. Du Pont De Nemours And Company
974 Centre Rd
Wilmington DE 19805
302 774-1000

(G-4628)
E I DU PONT DE NEMOURS & CO
Also Called: Dupont Vespel Parts and Shapes
800 Dupont Rd (43113)
PHONE.....................740 474-0635
Jason Parsons, Engineer
Cris Nesbitt, Senior Engr
Wayne Macdonald, Manager
EMP: 75
SALES (corp-wide): 24.5B Publicly Held
WEB: www.dupont.com
SIC: 2821 Plastics materials & resins

PA: E. I. Du Pont De Nemours And Company
974 Centre Rd
Wilmington DE 19805
302 774-1000

(G-4629)
FLORIDA PRODUCTION ENGRG INC
Also Called: Eg Industries
30627 Orr Rd (43113-9731)
PHONE.....................740 420-5252
Chuck Reisinger, Manager
EMP: 160
SALES (corp-wide): 575.1MM Privately Held
SIC: 3559 Plastics working machinery
HQ: Florida Production Engineering, Inc.
2 E Tower Cir
Ormond Beach FL 32174
386 677-2566

(G-4630)
GENERAL ELECTRIC COMPANY
559 E Ohio St (43113-2036)
PHONE.....................740 477-5200
Fax: 740 474-3144
Steve Abernathy, Electrical Engi
Austin Lindsey, Manager
Mike Conlee, Manager
EMP: 330
SALES (corp-wide): 123.6B Publicly Held
SIC: 3646 3641 Commercial indusl & institutional electric lighting fixtures; electric lamps
PA: General Electric Company
41 Farnsworth St
Boston MA 02210
617 443-3000

(G-4631)
GEORGIA-PACIFIC LLC
2850 Owens Rd (43113-9079)
P.O. Box 379 (43113-0379)
PHONE.....................740 477-3347
Fax: 740 474-3435
Mike Schultz, QC Dir
Debbra Saeger, Human Res Dir
Terry Gaffney, Manager
Dana Scarberry, Supervisor
Jill Banghoff, MIS Dir
EMP: 130
SALES (corp-wide): 27.3B Privately Held
WEB: www.gp.com
SIC: 2653 3412 2675 2671 Corrugated & solid fiber boxes; metal barrels, drums & pails; die-cut paper & board; packaging paper & plastics film, coated & laminated; paperboard mills
HQ: Georgia-Pacific Llc
133 Peachtree St Ne # 4810
Atlanta GA 30303
404 652-4000

(G-4632)
JM PRINTING
134 W Main St (43113-1620)
PHONE.....................740 412-8666
EMP: 4 EST: 2013
SALES (est): 417.2K Privately Held
SIC: 2752 Commercial printing, lithographic

(G-4633)
MES MATERIAL HDLG SYSTEMS LLC
28196 Scippo Creek Rd (43113-9796)
P.O. Box 370 (43113-0370)
PHONE.....................740 477-8920
Nancy Picklesimer,
EMP: 3
SALES (est): 186.9K Privately Held
SIC: 3599 5084 Industrial machinery; materials handling machinery

(G-4634)
NANOMELD LLC
18646 Us Rte 23 N (43113)
PHONE.....................740 477-5900
Michael Rhodes, General Mgr
EMP: 4
SALES (est): 584.9K Privately Held
SIC: 2299 Yarn, metallic, ceramic or paper fibers

(G-4635)
NANOSTATICS CORPORATION
18646 Us Rte 23 (43113)
PHONE.....................740 477-5900
Mark Schweizer, President
Dr John Robertson, Founder
Dr Ashley Scott, CFO
Shelby Seger, Manager
EMP: 10
SQ FT: 5,000
SALES (est): 1.1MM Privately Held
SIC: 3823 Industrial process control instruments

(G-4636)
PHIL D DE MINT
Also Called: Phil's Custom Cabinets
6345 State Route 56 E (43113-9449)
PHONE.....................740 474-7777
Fax: 740 474-7777
Phil De Mint, Owner
EMP: 4
SALES: 150K Privately Held
SIC: 2434 Wood kitchen cabinets

(G-4637)
PPG INDUSTRIES INC
559 Pittsburgh Rd (43113-9436)
PHONE.....................740 474-3161
Fax: 740 474-3167
Keith Hood, Purch Mgr
Melinda Moeslein, Research
Lesley Fetter, Human Res Mgr
Dave Moss, Branch Mgr
EMP: 210
SALES (corp-wide): 14.7B Publicly Held
SIC: 2851 Paints & allied products
PA: Ppg Industries, Inc.
1 Ppg Pl
Pittsburgh PA 15272
412 434-3131

(G-4638)
PPG INDUSTRIES INC
Also Called: PPG 5412
221 E Main St (43113-1727)
PHONE.....................740 474-3945
Fax: 740 474-3925
Darcy Pennington, Purchasing
Sandy Carnein, Manager
Terry Bridenbaugh, Manager
EMP: 24
SALES (corp-wide): 14.7B Publicly Held
WEB: www.ppg.com
SIC: 2851 Paints & allied products
PA: Ppg Industries, Inc.
1 Ppg Pl
Pittsburgh PA 15272
412 434-3131

(G-4639)
QUALITY CRAFTSMAN INC
28155 River Dr (43113-9726)
PHONE.....................740 474-9685
Fax: 740 474-4076
Cindy Davis, General Mgr
Tammy Evans Payne, Office Mgr
EMP: 10
SQ FT: 10,000
SALES: 1.8MM Privately Held
SIC: 3444 Sheet metalwork

(G-4640)
RED BARN SCREEN PRINTING & EMB
Also Called: Red Barn, The
1144 Northridge Rd (43113-9396)
PHONE.....................740 474-6657
Fax: 740 477-3153
Raymond Larry, President
Jerrilyn Stevens, President
EMP: 15
SALES (est): 1.1MM Privately Held
WEB: www.redbarntshirts.com
SIC: 2395 7336 Embroidery & art needlework; silk screen design

(G-4641)
SCIOTO COCA COLA
Also Called: Coca-Cola
387 Walnut St (43113-2225)
PHONE.....................740 474-2180
Dave Hickey, Principal
EMP: 3 EST: 2013
SALES (est): 167.5K Privately Held
SIC: 2086 Bottled & canned soft drinks

▲ = Import ▼=Export
◆ =Import/Export

(G-4642)
SHELLY COMPANY
24537 Canal Rd (43113-9691)
PHONE..........................740 474-6255
Dave McCay, *Superintendent*
Mark Martens, *Director*
EMP: 3
SALES (corp-wide): 28.6B **Privately Held**
SIC: 1611 2951 Highway & street paving contractor; concrete, bituminous
HQ: Shelly Company
80 Park Dr
Thornville OH 43076
740 246-6315

(G-4643)
SIGN SHOP
Also Called: Lighted House Numbers
3269 State Route 361 (43113-9728)
PHONE..........................740 474-1499
Tony McCammon, *Owner*
Garnet McCammon, *Co-Owner*
EMP: 4
SALES (est): 182.6K **Privately Held**
SIC: 3993 Signs & advertising specialties

(G-4644)
SUBURBAN METAL PRODUCTS INC
1050 Tarlton Rd (43113-9132)
PHONE..........................740 474-4237
Fax: 740 474-9119
Linda Kempton, *Corp Secy*
Joe Cline, *Director*
EMP: 18
SQ FT: 12,000
SALES (est): 3.6MM **Privately Held**
SIC: 3599 3441 7692 3544 Machine shop, jobbing & repair; fabricated structural metal; welding repair; special dies, tools, jigs & fixtures; sheet metalwork

(G-4645)
TANGENT AIR INC
127 Edison Ave (43113-2117)
PHONE..........................740 474-1114
Fax: 740 420-6054
John Morehead, *President*
Susan Potter, *Sales Staff*
Jerry Jones, *Admin Sec*
EMP: 38
SQ FT: 17,000
SALES (est): 6.9MM **Privately Held**
WEB: www.tangentairinc.com
SIC: 3321 3444 Cast iron pipe & fittings; sheet metalwork

(G-4646)
TECHNICOLOR USA INC
Also Called: Circleville Glass Operations
24200 Us Highway 23 S (43113-9002)
PHONE..........................614 474-8821
Fax: 740 477-6617
Jeff Snyder, *Project Mgr*
Jerry D Jones, *Engineer*
Blain Bolock, *Finance Mgr*
Vincent McGarvy, *Human Resources*
Chet Kucinski, *Manager*
EMP: 925
SQ FT: 325,000
SALES (corp-wide): 81.4MM **Privately Held**
SIC: 3651 3231 Household audio & video equipment; products of purchased glass
HQ: Technicolor Usa, Inc.
101 W 103rd St
Indianapolis IN 46290
818 260-3651

(G-4647)
TELESIS TECHNOLOGIES INC (DH)
Also Called: Telesis Marking Systems
28181 River Dr (43113-9726)
P.O. Box 1000 (43113-7000)
PHONE..........................740 477-5000
Fax: 740 477-5001
Steve Sheng, *President*
Warren K Knipple, *Vice Pres*
Angie Taylor, *Safety Dir*
Doyle Unger, *Controller*
Jennifer Ferry, *Asst Controller*
▲ EMP: 135
SQ FT: 39,900

SALES (est): 43.1MM
SALES (corp-wide): 363.4MM **Privately Held**
SIC: 3953 Cancelling stamps, hand: rubber or metal
HQ: Tyden Group Holdings Corp.
409 Hoosier Dr
Angola IN 46703
740 420-6777

(G-4648)
TRIMOLD LLC
200 Pittsburgh Rd (43113-9288)
PHONE..........................740 474-7591
Yoshimasa Okada, *President*
Steve Furnace, *Plant Mgr*
Terry Rife, *Manager*
Katsuya Kanda, *Manager*
EMP: 360
SALES (est): 77.8MM
SALES (corp-wide): 3.9B **Privately Held**
WEB: www.tstrim.com
SIC: 3089 Plastic processing
HQ: Ts Trim Industries Inc.
6380 Canal St
Canal Winchester OH 43110
614 837-4114

(G-4649)
WITTICHS CANDIES INC
Also Called: Wittich's Candy Shop
117 W High St (43113-1615)
PHONE..........................740 474-3313
Fax: 740 420-9533
Fred Wittich, *President*
EMP: 5
SQ FT: 5,000
SALES (est): 474.9K **Privately Held**
SIC: 5441 2064 Candy; candy & other confectionery products

(G-4650)
WYATT SPECIALTIES INC
4761 State Route 361 (43113-9736)
PHONE..........................614 989-5362
James Wyatt, *President*
Deborah Wyatt, *Admin Sec*
EMP: 3
SALES: 130K **Privately Held**
SIC: 3711 Automobile assembly, including specialty automobiles

<hr>

Clarington
Monroe County

<hr>

(G-4651)
DIVERSIFD OH VLLY EQPT & SRVCS
Also Called: D.O.V.E.S.
50817 State Route 556 (43915-9632)
P.O. Box 73 (43915-0073)
PHONE..........................740 458-9881
Sheila Piatt, *Finance Mgr*
Mary Rankin,
▲ EMP: 10
SALES: 1MM **Privately Held**
WEB: www.doves.com
SIC: 3441 8611 3312 5012 Fabricated structural metal; business associations; blast furnaces & steel mills; automobiles & other motor vehicles; equipment rental & leasing; industrial buildings & warehouses

<hr>

Clarksville
Clinton County

<hr>

(G-4652)
PATCHWORK PEOPLE PINS ETC
946 Pyle Rd (45113-9653)
PHONE..........................937 725-2981
Catherine Jo Streator, *Principal*
EMP: 3 EST: 2012
SALES (est): 169.9K **Privately Held**
SIC: 3452 Pins

(G-4653)
SHATZELS BACKHOE SERVICE LLC
4044 Pansy Rd (45113-8667)
PHONE..........................937 289-9630
Richard Schatzel, *Principal*
EMP: 4
SALES (est): 404K **Privately Held**
SIC: 3531 Backhoes

<hr>

Clay Center
Ottawa County

<hr>

(G-4654)
TIGER MIRROR CORPORATION
465 Main St (43408)
PHONE..........................419 855-3146
Joan Pietrowski, *President*
EMP: 5 EST: 1997
SALES (est): 162K **Privately Held**
SIC: 3231 Mirrors, truck & automobile: made from purchased glass

(G-4655)
WHITE ROCK QUARRY L P
3800 N Bolander Rd (43408)
PHONE..........................419 855-8388
Ray Advnia, *Principal*
U S Aggregates, *General Ptnr*
Robert Simpson, *General Ptnr*
Jim Fehsenseld, *Ltd Ptnr*
Heritage Group, *Ltd Ptnr*
EMP: 590
SALES (est): 13.3MM
SALES (corp-wide): 314.9MM **Privately Held**
SIC: 1422 Crushed & broken limestone
PA: Asphalt Materials, Inc.
5400 W 86th St
Indianapolis IN 46268
317 872-6010

<hr>

Clayton
Montgomery County

<hr>

(G-4656)
ANCHOR FABRICATORS INC
386 Talmadge Rd (45315-9621)
P.O. Box 99 (45315-0099)
PHONE..........................937 836-5117
Tom Saldoff, *President*
Debbie K Kesselring, *Opers Mgr*
Randee Saldoff, *Shareholder*
Marshall Ruchman, *Admin Sec*
EMP: 43
SQ FT: 60,000
SALES (est): 8.1MM **Privately Held**
WEB: www.anchorfab.com
SIC: 3471 3599 3469 Buffing for the trade; polishing, metals or formed products; machine shop, jobbing & repair; metal stampings

(G-4657)
BLACKTHORN LLC
6113 Brookville Salem Rd (45315-9701)
PHONE..........................937 836-9296
Greg Benedict, *General Mgr*
Sharon Yoakum, *Vice Pres*
Sharon Buehler, *Admin Sec*
EMP: 10 EST: 1985
SQ FT: 20,000
SALES (est): 2MM **Privately Held**
WEB: www.blackthorn-inc.com
SIC: 3053 2899 3089 3296 Gaskets, packing & sealing devices; concrete curing & hardening compounds; plastic hardware & building products; fiberglass insulation

(G-4658)
FCA LLC
6611 Hoke Rd (45315-9008)
PHONE..........................309 644-2424
Earnest Reed, *Branch Mgr*
EMP: 18
SALES (corp-wide): 159.6MM **Privately Held**
SIC: 2441 Cases, wood

PA: Fca, Llc
7601 John Deere Pkwy
Moline IL 61265
309 792-3444

(G-4659)
HOFACKER PRCSION MACHINING LLC
7560 Jacks Ln (45315-8779)
PHONE..........................937 832-7712
Jane Hofacker, *Office Mgr*
Judy King, *Office Mgr*
Fredrick Hofacker,
Jerry Henshaw,
EMP: 18 EST: 1997
SQ FT: 2,500
SALES (est): 3MM **Privately Held**
WEB: www.hofackerprecision.com
SIC: 3599 3544 Machine shop, jobbing & repair; special dies & tools; jigs & fixtures

(G-4660)
INDIAN LAKE RACEWAY LLC
6341 Silverbell Ct (45315-9750)
PHONE..........................937 837-7533
Brian C Petroziello, *Principal*
EMP: 2
SALES (est): 150.9K **Privately Held**
SIC: 3644 Raceways

(G-4661)
NORTHMONT TOOL AND GAGE INC
8741 Kimmel Rd (45315-8900)
P.O. Box 163 (45315-0163)
PHONE..........................937 836-9879
Fax: 937 836-9978
Lawrence R Cordell, *President*
Roxanne Ward, *Office Mgr*
EMP: 7
SQ FT: 15,200
SALES: 869K **Privately Held**
SIC: 3599 Machine shop, jobbing & repair

(G-4662)
SLUTERBECK TOOL & DIE INC
Also Called: Sluterbeck Tool Co
7540 Jacks Ln (45315-8779)
P.O. Box 87 (45315-0087)
PHONE..........................937 836-5736
Fax: 937 836-9769
Ronald Sluterbeck, *President*
Anne Goss, *Corp Secy*
Greg Sluterbeck, *Vice Pres*
Steve Sluterbeck, *Vice Pres*
EMP: 10
SQ FT: 6,000
SALES (est): 500K **Privately Held**
SIC: 3599 Machine shop, jobbing & repair

(G-4663)
TOM SMITH INDUSTRIES INC
Also Called: T S I
500 Smith Dr (45315-8788)
PHONE..........................937 832-1555
Fax: 937 832-1577
Annette Smith, *President*
Steven Good, *President*
Annette H Smith, *President*
Linda McGuire, *COO*
Roy Evans, *Rsch/Dvlpt Dir*
▲ EMP: 200
SQ FT: 91,000
SALES (est): 45.7MM **Privately Held**
WEB: www.tomsmithindustries.com
SIC: 3544 3089 3714 Industrial molds; injection molded finished plastic products; motor vehicle parts & accessories

<hr>

Cleveland
Cuyahoga County

<hr>

(G-4664)
1923 W 25TH ST INC
1923 W 25th St (44113-3418)
PHONE..........................216 696-7529
Richard Brown, *Principal*
EMP: 5
SALES (est): 489.8K **Privately Held**
SIC: 2653 Corrugated & solid fiber boxes

(G-4665)
3D SYSTEMS INC
7100 Euclid Ave (44103-4036)
PHONE...................................216 229-2040
Robert Heinlein, *Business Mgr*
William Lewandowski, *Vice Pres*
Doron Stern, *Engineer*
Shihong Xu, *Accountant*
Alon Avivi, *Manager*
EMP: 99
SQ FT: 4,000
SALES (est): 4.1MM **Privately Held**
SIC: 3841 Instruments, microsurgical: except electromedical

(G-4666)
4 WALLS COM LLC
4700 Lakeside Ave E 173a (44114-3863)
PHONE...................................216 432-1400
Gale Flanagan, *VP Opers*
Gretchen Ciccotti, *Marketing Staff*
Kathryn Krage, *Manager*
Ronald Soeder,
EMP: 10
SALES (est): 1.1MM **Privately Held**
SIC: 2679 Wallpaper

(G-4667)
A & W TABLE PAD CO
Also Called: Pioneer Table Pad
6520 Carnegie Ave (44103-4697)
PHONE...................................800 541-0271
Fax: 216 881-6835
Tamara Christman, *President*
EMP: 10
SQ FT: 12,000
SALES (est): 1MM **Privately Held**
WEB: www.pioneertablepads.com
SIC: 2392 Table mats, plastic & textile

(G-4668)
A AABACO PLASTICS INC
9520 Midwest Ave (44125-2463)
PHONE...................................216 663-9494
Fax: 216 663-9475
Daniel R Lee, *President*
David Lee, *Corp Secy*
Jonathan Lee, *Vice Pres*
EMP: 11
SQ FT: 25,000
SALES (est): 1.9MM **Privately Held**
WEB: www.aabacoplastics.com
SIC: 3089 Blister or bubble formed packaging, plastic; closures, plastic

(G-4669)
A C SHUTTERS INC
8119 Mansfield Ave (44105-1549)
PHONE...................................216 429-2424
Fax: 216 441-9410
Frank Was, *CEO*
Stefan Was, *President*
Mark Krejsa, *Vice Pres*
Barbara Was, *CFO*
EMP: 5
SQ FT: 10,000
SALES (est): 460K **Privately Held**
WEB: www.acshutters.com
SIC: 3442 3089 3444 2431 Shutters, door or window: metal; shutters, plastic; sheet metalwork; millwork

(G-4670)
A E F INC
Also Called: American Electric Furnace Co
24050 Commerce Park Fl 2 (44122-5833)
PHONE...................................216 360-9800
Fax: 216 360-9800
Robert Sords, *President*
Virginia Sords, *Admin Secy*
EMP: 75 EST: 1920
SQ FT: 33,000
SALES (est): 7.5MM **Privately Held**
SIC: 3567 Electrical furnaces, ovens & heating devices, exc. induction

(G-4671)
A F KRAINZ CO
1364 E 47th St (44103-1220)
PHONE...................................216 431-4341
Fax: 216 431-1117
Andrew F Krainz Jr, *Owner*
Mary Krainz, *General Mgr*
EMP: 8
SALES (est): 824.1K **Privately Held**
SIC: 2752 Commercial printing, offset

(G-4672)
A GRAPHIC SOLUTION
Also Called: Advanced Graphic Solutions
14900 Detroit Ave Ste 205 (44107-3922)
PHONE...................................216 228-7223
James Clark O'Bryan, *Owner*
EMP: 10
SALES (est): 175K **Privately Held**
WEB: www.motorsportsguide.com
SIC: 7336 8748 8243 5045 Graphic arts & related design; systems engineering consultant, ex. computer or professional; software training, computer; computer software; software, business & non-game; pleating & stitching

(G-4673)
A H MARTY CO LTD
6900 Union Ave (44105-1383)
PHONE...................................216 641-8950
Fax: 216 641-8952
Diane Champion, *President*
Tom Champion, *Vice Pres*
Albert Champion, *Sls & Mktg Exec*
Cathy Curry, *Sales Mgr*
EMP: 12 EST: 1910
SQ FT: 15,000
SALES (est): 468K **Privately Held**
SIC: 3443 Weldments

(G-4674)
A H PELZ CO
2498 Superior Ave E (44114-4227)
PHONE...................................216 861-1882
Fax: 216 861-1884
John B Cihon, *President*
Elmira Cihon, *Vice Pres*
Jim Cihon, *Treasurer*
Greg Cihon, *Admin Sec*
EMP: 8
SQ FT: 6,500
SALES (est): 941.2K **Privately Held**
WEB: www.ahpelz.com
SIC: 2782 2675 Looseleaf binders & devices; die-cut paper & board

(G-4675)
A J ROSE MFG CO
3115 W 38th St (44109-1205)
PHONE...................................216 631-4645
Fax: 216 631-8221
James Hoffman, *Plant Mgr*
Kevin Wasserman, *Engineer*
H John Warnkey, *Branch Mgr*
EMP: 183
SALES (corp-wide): 99.8MM **Privately Held**
WEB: www.ajrose.com
SIC: 3465 3568 3469 Automotive stampings; pulleys; power transmission; metal stampings
PA: A. J. Rose Mfg.Co.
　38000 Chester Rd
　Avon OH 44011
　216 631-4645

(G-4676)
A JACKS MANUFACTURING CO
1441 Chardon Rd (44117-1510)
PHONE...................................216 531-1010
Fax: 216 481-6369
Charlie Crout, *President*
Felix Tarorick, *Chairman*
Loyd Keller, *Plant Mgr*
Jim Eason, *Engineer*
David Fritz, *Controller*
▲ EMP: 21
SALES (est): 3.5MM
SALES (corp-wide): 1.2B **Publicly Held**
WEB: www.pkoh.com.cn
SIC: 3567 Industrial furnaces & ovens
HQ: Park-Ohio Industries, Inc.
　6065 Parkland Blvd Ste 1
　Cleveland OH 44124
　440 947-2000

(G-4677)
A S MANUFACTURING INC
4412 W 130th St (44135-3004)
P.O. Box 31388 (44131-0388)
PHONE...................................216 476-0656
Fax: 216 476-0656
David Ptacek, *President*
Karen Cesa, *Shareholder*
EMP: 3
SQ FT: 2,000

SALES (est): 300K **Privately Held**
WEB: www.asmfg.net
SIC: 3569 Lubricating equipment

(G-4678)
A SIGN FOR THE TIMES INC
Also Called: Signs of The Times
4100 Mayfield Rd (44121-3006)
PHONE...................................216 297-2977
Fax: 216 297-9876
Ray Bayless, *President*
Charles Bayless, *Vice Pres*
EMP: 5
SALES (est): 100K **Privately Held**
WEB: www.asignforthetimes.com
SIC: 3993 2759 Signs & advertising specialties; commercial printing

(G-4679)
A W C INC (PA)
5200 Richmond Rd (44146-1333)
PHONE...................................216 831-0550
John Turk, *President*
Steve Perney, *Treasurer*
EMP: 4 EST: 1978
SALES (est): 5MM **Privately Held**
SIC: 3423 Mechanics' hand tools

(G-4680)
A-BRITE LP
3000 W 121st St (44111-1639)
PHONE...................................216 252-2995
Fax: 216 252-2266
Hal Leitch, *President*
Herbert Gilliam, *Vice Pres*
Mojtaba Mir-Salimi, *Vice Pres*
Russ Wilson, *Finance Dir*
Michael Socha, *Maintence Staff*
EMP: 64
SQ FT: 58,000
SALES (est): 12.3MM
SALES (corp-wide): 183.8MM **Privately Held**
WEB: www.abriteplating.com
SIC: 3471 Plating & polishing
PA: App Holdings Lp
　5245 Burke St
　Windsor ON N9A 6
　519 737-6984

(G-4681)
AAA STAMPING INC
4001 Pearl Rd Uppr (44109-3198)
PHONE...................................216 749-4494
Fax: 216 749-6740
Stan Gawor, *President*
Jeffrey R Mc Intosh, *CPA*
Gwyn Gawor, *Manager*
EMP: 22
SQ FT: 25,000
SALES (est): 4.5MM **Privately Held**
SIC: 3469 Metal stampings

(G-4682)
ABBEY MACHINE PRODUCTS CO
1100 E 222nd St Ste 4 (44117-1135)
PHONE...................................216 481-0080
David L Bennett, *President*
Gregory Bennett, *Vice Pres*
Cynthia Bennett, *Controller*
EMP: 5
SQ FT: 14,000
SALES (est): 650K **Privately Held**
SIC: 3599 Machine shop, jobbing & repair

(G-4683)
ABEL METAL PROCESSING INC
2105 E 77th St (44103-4990)
PHONE...................................216 881-4156
Fax: 216 881-4417
Eugene Schoenmeyer, *President*
Joan Kern, *Vice Pres*
Jo Ann Kern, *Office Mgr*
EMP: 12 EST: 1975
SQ FT: 8,000
SALES (est): 1.6MM **Privately Held**
WEB: www.abelmetal.com
SIC: 3471 Electroplating & plating

(G-4684)
ABL PRODUCTS INC
3726 Ridge Rd (44144-1182)
PHONE...................................216 281-2400
Fax: 216 281-7753
Athel Gicei, *President*

Leslie Gicei, *Vice Pres*
EMP: 12
SALES (est): 1.8MM **Privately Held**
WEB: www.ablproducts.com
SIC: 3469 3568 Metal stampings; sprockets (power transmission equipment)

(G-4685)
ABLE ALLOY INC
3500 W 140th St (44111-2410)
PHONE...................................216 251-6110
Fax: 216 251-2739
Ken Cohen, *President*
EMP: 15
SQ FT: 12,000
SALES (est): 1.4MM **Privately Held**
SIC: 3341 Recovery & refining of nonferrous metals

(G-4686)
ABLE GRINDING CO INC
10015 Walford Ave (44102-4697)
PHONE...................................216 961-6555
Fax: 216 961-6540
Robert Urban, *President*
Mark Miller, *Plant Mgr*
Dennis Urban, *Purchasing*
Martha Urban, *Treasurer*
EMP: 4
SQ FT: 6,000
SALES (est): 1.1MM **Privately Held**
SIC: 3599 Grinding castings for the trade

(G-4687)
ABRAXUS SALT INC
5595 Ridge Rd (44129-2601)
PHONE...................................440 743-7669
John Klejka, *Principal*
EMP: 9
SALES (est): 916.7K **Privately Held**
SIC: 2899 Salt

(G-4688)
ABSOLUTELY PAPER ESTABLISHED
14000 Mont Ave (44118-1022)
PHONE...................................216 932-4822
Jermaine Golphin, *Principal*
EMP: 5
SALES (est): 208.8K **Privately Held**
SIC: 2531 Public building & related furniture

(G-4689)
ACADEMY GRAPHIC COMM INC
1000 Brookpark Rd (44109-5824)
PHONE...................................216 661-2550
Fax: 216 661-7169
James M Champion, *President*
Erik Eichenberger, *General Mgr*
Elaine Champion, *Vice Pres*
Courtney Dolinar, *VP Sales*
Jeffrey Parsons, *Accounts Exec*
EMP: 27
SQ FT: 1,400
SALES (est): 4.4MM **Privately Held**
WEB: www.visitagc.com
SIC: 2752 7336 Commercial printing, offset; graphic arts & related design

(G-4690)
ACE RUBBER STAMP & OFF SUP CO
Also Called: Royal Acme
3110 Payne Ave (44114-4504)
PHONE...................................216 771-8483
Fax: 216 771-8487
Ted Cutts, *President*
Glenn Gahagen, *Vice Pres*
Larry Harshman, *Sales Staff*
Dave Tulley, *Manager*
Matt Young, *Manager*
EMP: 35 EST: 1935
SALES (est): 3.2MM **Privately Held**
WEB: www.acerubberstamps.com
SIC: 3953 5943 Marking devices; office forms & supplies

(G-4691)
ACME BOILER CO INC
Also Called: Acme Lead Burning Company
3718 Ridge Rd (44144-1183)
PHONE...................................216 961-2471
Fax: 216 961-7455
Dawn Hammerle, *President*
Ewald Hammerle, *Corp Secy*

Hedy Hammerle, *Vice Pres*
EMP: 5
SQ FT: 3,200
SALES (est): 552.8K **Privately Held**
SIC: 7699 3443 Boiler repair shop; fabricated plate work (boiler shop)

(G-4692)
ACME DUPLICATING CO
Also Called: Acme Printing
800 Saint Clair Ave Ne (44114-1707)
PHONE..........................216 241-1241
Fax: 216 241-7300
Donald Sebold, *Owner*
Bill Oneal, *Human Res Mgr*
EMP: 7
SQ FT: 3,300
SALES (est): 420K **Privately Held**
WEB: www.namepads.com
SIC: 2752 Photolithographic printing

(G-4693)
ACME LIFTING PRODUCTS INC
Also Called: Universal Cargo
6892 W Snowville Rd Ste 2 (44141-3288)
PHONE..........................440 838-4430
Fax: 440 838-4432
Laura Davis, *President*
Arnold Davis, *Vice Pres*
EMP: 8
SQ FT: 6,000
SALES (est): 880K **Privately Held**
WEB: www.universalcargo.com
SIC: 3536 Hoisting slings

(G-4694)
ACME SPIRALLY WOUND PAPER PDTS
Also Called: Acme Paper Tube
4810 W 139th St (44135-5036)
P.O. Box 35320 (44135-0320)
PHONE..........................216 267-2950
Fax: 216 267-0239
Dan Kobrak, *CEO*
Donald H Kobak Jr, *CEO*
EMP: 17
SQ FT: 36,000
SALES (est): 8.6MM **Privately Held**
WEB: www.acmespiral.com
SIC: 2655 Tubes, fiber or paper: made from purchased material

(G-4695)
ACOR ORTHOPAEDIC INC
18530 S Miles Rd (44128-4200)
PHONE..........................216 662-4500
Fax: 216 662-4547
Greg Alaimo, *CEO*
Jeff Alaimo, *President*
Daniel Huff, *Vice Pres*
Joe Potozzak, *Purch Agent*
▲ **EMP:** 100
SQ FT: 35,000
SALES (est): 19.1MM **Privately Held**
WEB: www.acor.com
SIC: 3842 3144 3143 Orthopedic appliances; prosthetic appliances; foot appliances, orthopedic; women's footwear, except athletic; men's footwear, except athletic

(G-4696)
ACOR ORTHOPAEDIC INC
Also Called: Cleveland Prosthetic Center
18700 S Miles Rd (44128-4242)
PHONE..........................440 532-0117
Frank Zingales, *President*
EMP: 3
SALES (est): 244.3K **Privately Held**
SIC: 3842 Surgical appliances & supplies

(G-4697)
ACORN TECHNOLOGY CORPORATION
23103 Miles Rd (44128-5475)
PHONE..........................216 663-1244
Lalana Green, *President*
Robert Green, *Vice Pres*
Karl Kaups, *Manager*
EMP: 20
SQ FT: 150,000

SALES (est): 4.8MM **Privately Held**
WEB: www.acorntechnology.com
SIC: 3613 5063 3634 3429 Panel & distribution boards & other related apparatus; electrical apparatus & equipment; ceiling fans; aircraft & marine hardware, inc. pulleys & similar items

(G-4698)
ACTION INDUSTRIES LTD (PA)
12625 Berea Rd (44111-1621)
PHONE..........................216 252-7800
Fax: 216 252-7880
John E Marron, *President*
Ron Steiger, *Regional Mgr*
Guenter Plamper, *Corp Secy*
Pat Marron, *Vice Pres*
Michael Simolin, *Plant Mgr*
▲ **EMP:** 15 **EST:** 1980
SQ FT: 25,000
SALES (est): 3.9MM **Privately Held**
WEB: www.action-ind.com
SIC: 3699 2431 Door opening & closing devices, electrical; weather strip, wood

(G-4699)
AD PISTON RING COMPANY LLC
3145 Superior Ave E (44114-4342)
PHONE..........................216 781-5200
Fax: 216 781-5203
Craig Duber, *General Mgr*
Bob Lee, *Mng Member*
EMP: 10
SQ FT: 12,000
SALES (est): 980K **Privately Held**
SIC: 3592 Pistons & piston rings

(G-4700)
ADAMS MANUFACTURING COMPANY (PA)
Also Called: Dornback Furnace Division
9790 Midwest Ave (44125-2497)
PHONE..........................216 662-1600
Fax: 216 587-6807
Marty Schonberger Jr, *President*
Ruth Schonberger, *Vice Pres*
Jeffrey Dubasak, *Sales Mgr*
Lora Vee, *Manager*
▲ **EMP:** 25 **EST:** 1945
SQ FT: 80,000
SALES (est): 4.4MM **Privately Held**
WEB: www.adamsmanufacturing.com
SIC: 3585 Heating equipment, complete

(G-4701)
ADCHEM ADHESIVES INC
4111 E Royalton Rd (44147-2997)
PHONE..........................440 526-1976
Fax: 440 526-2378
Claude Dandurande, *President*
Brett Joint, *Manager*
EMP: 10
SQ FT: 15,000
SALES: 1MM **Privately Held**
WEB: www.adchemadhesives.com
SIC: 2891 Adhesives & sealants; adhesives

(G-4702)
ADCRAFT DECALS INC
7708 Commerce Park Oval (44131-2394)
PHONE..........................216 524-2934
Fax: 216 524-7569
Robert W Talion, *President*
Ciliox Rendina, *Vice Pres*
Tim Talion, *Vice Pres*
Devra Danforth, *Manager*
EMP: 31 **EST:** 1961
SQ FT: 21,200
SALES (est): 4.5MM **Privately Held**
WEB: www.adcraftdecals.com
SIC: 2759 3993 2752 2672 Screen printing; decals: printing; signs & advertising specialties; commercial printing, lithographic; coated & laminated paper; automotive & apparel trimmings

(G-4703)
ADDED EDGE ASSEMBLY INC
26800 Fargo Ave Ste A (44146-1341)
PHONE..........................216 464-4305
Fax: 216 464-4318
Kurt Kodrich, *President*
James Molle, *Manager*
Janet Kodrich, *Admin Sec*

EMP: 11
SQ FT: 3,000
SALES (est): 1MM **Privately Held**
WEB: www.addedge.com
SIC: 3549 Assembly machines, including robotic

(G-4704)
ADKINS MARLENA
Also Called: Tolento's Family Restaurant
4729 W 157th St (44135-2737)
PHONE..........................216 704-2751
Marlena Adkins, *Owner*
EMP: 4 **EST:** 2014
SALES (est): 147.5K **Privately Held**
SIC: 2599 Bar, restaurant & cafeteria furniture

(G-4705)
ADKINS & CO INC
Also Called: Adkins Printing
14541 Madison Ave (44107-4325)
PHONE..........................216 521-6323
Fax: 216 521-0237
Charles Davis, *President*
EMP: 3
SQ FT: 3,600
SALES (est): 440.1K **Privately Held**
WEB: www.adkinsprinting.com
SIC: 2752 Commercial printing, offset

(G-4706)
ADMIRAL PRODUCTS COMPANY INC
4101 W 150th St (44135-1303)
PHONE..........................216 671-0600
Fax: 216 671-2658
Vincent C Hvizda, *CEO*
Paul Hvizda, *Vice Pres*
Robert Pace, *Sales Dir*
Joe Shoemaker, *Manager*
Margaret Schroeder Hvizda, *Admin Sec*
EMP: 37 **EST:** 1948
SQ FT: 39,000
SALES (est): 10.3MM **Privately Held**
WEB: www.admiralproducts.com
SIC: 2752 2759 2754 2672 Commercial printing, offset; flexographic printing; labels: gravure printing; coated & laminated paper

(G-4707)
ADVANCE INDUSTRIES GROUP LLC
3636 W 58th St (44102-5641)
PHONE..........................216 741-1800
Jim Williams,
Jeff Stein,
EMP: 20
SQ FT: 35,000
SALES (est): 5.5MM **Privately Held**
WEB: www.advanceindustriesgroup.com
SIC: 3441 3315 Fabricated structural metal; wire & fabricated wire products

(G-4708)
ADVANCE MANUFACTURING CORP
6800 Madison Ave (44102-4099)
PHONE..........................216 333-1684
Fax: 216 961-0964
Herman Bredenbeck, *President*
Jon Bredenbeck, *President*
Kenneth Bailey, *Vice Pres*
Rick Giering, *Manager*
Kathy Goodrich, *Manager*
EMP: 48 **EST:** 1936
SQ FT: 64,000
SALES (est): 10.8MM **Privately Held**
WEB: www.advancemanuf.com
SIC: 3599 3549 Machine shop, jobbing & repair; metalworking machinery

(G-4709)
ADVANCE METAL PRODUCTS INC
3636 W 58th St (44102-5641)
PHONE..........................216 741-1800
Fax: 216 741-7153
James Williams, *President*
Ron Pribula, *Accountant*
Charlene Daum, *Office Mgr*
EMP: 18
SQ FT: 30,000

SALES: 1.5MM **Privately Held**
SIC: 3444 Sheet metalwork

(G-4710)
ADVANCE PAINT TECHNOLOGY INC
4650 W 160th St Ste 600 (44135-2613)
PHONE..........................216 676-8770
Fax: 216 676-5613
Walter Slapakovis, *President*
EMP: 6
SQ FT: 13,110
SALES (est): 70K **Privately Held**
SIC: 3479 Painting of metal products

(G-4711)
ADVANCE WIRE FORMING INC
3636 W 58th St (44102-5641)
PHONE..........................216 432-3250
Jeff Stein, *President*
EMP: 10 **EST:** 2000
SQ FT: 30,000
SALES (est): 2.1MM **Privately Held**
WEB: www.advancewireforming.com
SIC: 3315 Steel wire & related products

(G-4712)
ADVANCED FLAME HARDENING INC
1209 Marquette St (44114-3919)
PHONE..........................216 431-0370
Fax: 216 431-0515
Eleanor Syms, *Principal*
EMP: 5
SALES (est): 530.6K **Privately Held**
SIC: 3398 Brazing (hardening) of metal

(G-4713)
ADVANCED FLUIDS INC
18127 Roseland Rd (44112-1001)
PHONE..........................216 692-3050
Emil T Rosul, *President*
EMP: 7
SQ FT: 12,800
SALES (est): 1.7MM **Privately Held**
WEB: www.advancedfluids.com
SIC: 2992 Lubricating oils

(G-4714)
ADVANCED KIFFER SYSTEMS INC
4905 Rocky River Dr (44135-3245)
PHONE..........................216 267-8181
Fax: 216 267-1850
Dale C Phillip, *President*
Chester Bartosik, *Vice Pres*
Lars Eriksson, *Vice Pres*
Gary Young, *Engineer*
Walter Elbrecht, *Controller*
EMP: 16
SQ FT: 85,000
SALES (est): 3.6MM
SALES (corp-wide): 10.4MM **Privately Held**
WEB: www.aks-inc.com
SIC: 3825 Test equipment for electronic & electric measurement
PA: Kiffer Industries, Inc.
4905 Rocky River Dr
Cleveland OH 44135
216 267-1818

(G-4715)
ADVANCED LIVESCAN TECHNOLOGIES
3575 W 132nd St (44111-3418)
PHONE..........................440 759-7028
Kevin Burke, *CEO*
EMP: 5
SALES: 500K **Privately Held**
SIC: 3999 Fingerprint equipment

(G-4716)
ADVANCED MDIA PUBLICATIONS INC
Also Called: 48hourprint.com
6410 Eastland Rd Ste F (44142-1306)
PHONE..........................440 260-9910
Jim Lemmer, *Branch Mgr*
EMP: 10
SALES (corp-wide): 15.3MM **Privately Held**
WEB: www.48hourprint.com
SIC: 2721 Magazines: publishing & printing

PA: Advanced Media Corporation
159 Thomas Burgin Pkwy
Quincy MA 02169
800 844-0599

(G-4717)
ADVANCED PAPER TUBE INC
1951 W 90th St (44102-2742)
PHONE...................................216 281-5691
Fax: 216 281-6606
Leon Lasky, *President*
Norm Hensley, *Vice Pres*
Dorothy Lasky, *Vice Pres*
Patrick Lasky, *Manager*
EMP: 12
SQ FT: 27,000
SALES (est): 2.3MM **Privately Held**
WEB: www.advancedpapertube.com
SIC: 2655 Tubes, fiber or paper: made
from purchased material

(G-4718)
AERO-MED INDUSTRIES INC
1205 Brookpark Rd (44109-5827)
P.O. Box 1053, Brunswick (44212-8553)
PHONE...................................216 459-0004
Guy Weaver III, *President*
Donna Weaver, *Treasurer*
Anita Clare, *Admin Asst*
EMP: 3
SQ FT: 1,000
SALES: 350K **Privately Held**
SIC: 3599 Machine & other job shop work

(G-4719)
AEROCONTROLEX GROUP INC
(DH)
4223 Monticello Blvd (44121-2814)
PHONE...................................440 352-6182
Fax: 440 354-2912
Raymond Laubentha, *President*
Raymond Laubenthal, *President*
John Distler, *General Mgr*
Robert Henderson, *Exec VP*
Gene Mack, *Materials Mgr*
EMP: 99
SQ FT: 55,000
SALES: 19.7MM
SALES (corp-wide): 3.1B **Publicly Held**
WEB: www.aerocontrolex.com
SIC: 3492 5084 3594 Valves, hydraulic,
aircraft; industrial machinery & equip-
ment; fluid power pumps & motors
HQ: Transdigm, Inc.
4223 Monticello Blvd
Cleveland OH 44121
216 706-2939

(G-4720)
AEROLL ENGINEERING CORP
18511 Euclid Ave Rear (44112-1018)
PHONE...................................216 481-2266
Fax: 216 481-1425
Carl E Weaver III, *President*
Sherri Weaver, *Corp Secy*
EMP: 7
SQ FT: 8,000
SALES: 750K **Privately Held**
SIC: 3545 Thread cutting dies

(G-4721)
AEROMICS INC
11000 Cedar Ave Ste 270 (44106-3008)
PHONE...................................216 772-1004
Marc Pelletier, *CEO*
Walter Boron, *Ch of Bd*
John Foster, *Principal*
Frederick Jones, *Principal*
Peter Longo, *Principal*
EMP: 7
SALES (est): 300K **Privately Held**
SIC: 2834 Pharmaceutical preparations

(G-4722)
AEROQUIP-VICKERS INC (DH)
1111 Superior Ave E (44114-2522)
PHONE...................................216 523-5000
A M Cutler, *President*
J R Horst, *Vice Pres*
D E Kimmet, *Vice Pres*
J S Mitchell, *Vice Pres*
A T Dillon, *CFO*
EMP: 9
SQ FT: 21,000

SALES (est): 1.3B **Privately Held**
SIC: 3052 3492 3429 3069 Rubber hose;
plastic hose; hose & tube fittings & assemblies, hydraulic/pneumatic; clamps &
couplings, hose; keys & key blanks;
molded rubber products; parts for heating,
cooling & refrigerating equipment; aircraft
parts & equipment
HQ: Eaton Corporation
1000 Eaton Blvd
Cleveland OH 44122
216 523-5000

(G-4723)
AEROSCENA LLC
Also Called: Ascents
10000 Cedar Ave (44106-2119)
PHONE...................................800 671-1890
Mark Kohoot, *CEO*
EMP: 16 **EST:** 2010
SALES (est): 2.5MM **Privately Held**
SIC: 2844 Perfumes, natural or synthetic

(G-4724)
AEROSPACE CO INC
600 Superior Ave E (44114-2614)
PHONE...................................413 998-1637
Kent Rosenthal, *President*
EMP: 99 **EST:** 1961
SALES (est): 3.6MM **Privately Held**
SIC: 3724 Research & development on air-
craft engines & parts

(G-4725)
AEROTECH INDUSTRIES INC
1435 E 49th St (44103-1225)
PHONE...................................216 881-6660
Nicolas Tadic, *President*
EMP: 3
SQ FT: 8,000
SALES (est): 395.2K **Privately Held**
SIC: 3399 Metal fasteners

(G-4726)
AETNA PLATING CO
6511 Morgan Ave (44127-1947)
PHONE...................................216 341-9111
Fax: 216 341-4527
Peter Sobey, *President*
Joel Newman, *Admin Sec*
EMP: 15
SQ FT: 55,000
SALES: 1MM **Privately Held**
SIC: 3471 Electroplating of metals or
formed products; plating of metals or
formed products; anodizing (plating) of
metals or formed products

(G-4727)
AETNA WELDING CO INC
4613 Broadway Ave (44127-1098)
PHONE...................................216 883-1801
Fax: 216 883-1803
William Sharp, *President*
EMP: 5
SQ FT: 7,000
SALES: 300K **Privately Held**
SIC: 7692 Welding repair

(G-4728)
AFFINITY THERAPEUTICS LLC
11000 Cedar Ave (44106-3069)
P.O. Box 606044 (44106-0544)
PHONE...................................216 224-9364
Tacarra Bowens, *General Mgr*
Julius Korley,
EMP: 5
SALES (est): 574.5K **Privately Held**
SIC: 2834 Pharmaceutical preparations

(G-4729)
AFFYMETRIX INC
26111 Miles Rd (44128-5933)
PHONE...................................216 765-5000
John F Runkel Jr, *Exec VP*
Frank Maenpa, *Vice Pres*
Joe Magro, *Vice Pres*
Joann Long, *Purch Mgr*
Jim Demko, *Engineer*
EMP: 103
SALES (corp-wide): 18.2B **Publicly Held**
SIC: 3826 Analytical instruments
HQ: Affymetrix, Inc.
3450 Central Expy
Santa Clara CA 95051
408 731-5000

(G-4730)
AG INDUSTRIES INC
1 American Rd (44144-2301)
PHONE...................................216 252-7300
Fax: 216 252-6782
Jeff White, *President*
Adam Souders, *VP Opers*
Robert Taylor, *Controller*
EMP: 35
SQ FT: 30,000
SALES (est): 7.6MM
SALES (corp-wide): 2.2B **Privately Held**
SIC: 2541 Display fixtures, wood
HQ: American Greetings Corporation
1 American Rd
Cleveland OH 44144
216 252-7300

(G-4731)
AGMET LLC
5533 Dunham Rd (44137-3645)
PHONE...................................216 663-8200
Fax: 216 663-8859
Dave Crose, *Branch Mgr*
EMP: 10
SALES (corp-wide): 21.2MM **Privately
Held**
SIC: 5093 3341 Ferrous metal scrap &
waste; nonferrous metals scrap; second-
ary nonferrous metals
PA: Agmet Llc
7800 Medusa Rd
Cleveland OH 44146
440 439-7400

(G-4732)
AGRI-PRODUCTS INC
29326 Bolingbrook Rd (44124-5330)
P.O. Box 22032 (44122-0032)
PHONE...................................216 831-5890
Paul F Dickey, *President*
Kevin Dickey, *Vice Pres*
Harry Valley, *Treasurer*
W Dean Hopkins, *Admin Sec*
EMP: 3 **EST:** 1962
SALES (est): 220.1K **Privately Held**
SIC: 2048 Feed supplements

(G-4733)
AIN INDUSTRIES INC
13901 Aspinwall Ave (44110-2210)
P.O. Box 464, Avon (44011-0464)
PHONE...................................440 781-0950
Bill Kavila, *President*
Ted Black, *Corp Secy*
Steve Misch, *Vice Pres*
EMP: 6
SQ FT: 6,500
SALES (est): 945.1K **Privately Held**
SIC: 2841 5169 5087 Soap & other deter-
gents; chemicals & allied products; serv-
ice establishment equipment

(G-4734)
AIR PRODUCTS AND
CHEMICALS INC
2820 Quigley Rd (44113-4598)
PHONE...................................216 781-2801
Fax: 216 781-3616
Jerry Culbertson, *Branch Mgr*
John Cheeter, *Manager*
EMP: 15
SALES (corp-wide): 9.5B **Publicly Held**
WEB: www.airproducts.com
SIC: 2813 Industrial gases
PA: Air Products And Chemicals, Inc.
7201 Hamilton Blvd
Allentown PA 18195
610 481-4911

(G-4735)
AIR-RITE INC
Also Called: AIR RITE SERVICE SUPPLY
1290 W 117th St (44107-3096)
PHONE...................................216 228-8200
Fax: 216 228-5651
David Harris, *President*
Marilyn Harris, *Treasurer*
Dan Andolek, *Personnel Exec*
▼ **EMP:** 24
SQ FT: 28,000

SALES (est): 3.9MM **Privately Held**
WEB: www.airrite-supply.com
SIC: 7623 7699 5075 3564 Air conditioning repair; boiler & heating repair services; warm air heating equipment &
supplies; blowers & fans

(G-4736)
AIRCRAFT AND AUTO FITTINGS
CO
17120 Saint Clair Ave (44110-2531)
PHONE...................................216 486-0047
Fax: 216 486-0071
Martin Sexton, *President*
John Markulin, *Corp Secy*
EMP: 8 **EST:** 1960
SQ FT: 4,800
SALES: 450K **Privately Held**
SIC: 3599 Machine shop, jobbing & repair

(G-4737)
AIRCRAFT PLATING CORP
1106 Clark Ave (44109-1898)
PHONE...................................216 781-5845
Fax: 216 781-1409
Gerald C Ott, *President*
Brian K Ott, *Vice Pres*
Dale Dotson, *Plant Mgr*
Carol Gergen, *CFO*
EMP: 20 **EST:** 1941
SQ FT: 15,000
SALES (est): 2.1MM **Privately Held**
WEB: www.aircraftplating.com
SIC: 3471 Polishing, metals or formed
products; plating of metals or formed
products

(G-4738)
AISCO METALLIZING CORP
2996 Eggers Ave (44105-1043)
PHONE...................................216 441-7244
George E Stecz Jr, *President*
EMP: 15
SQ FT: 12,000
SALES (est): 1.9MM **Privately Held**
WEB: www.tri-a-isco.com
SIC: 3599 Machine & other job shop work;
machine shop, jobbing & repair

(G-4739)
AK-ISG STEEL COATING
COMPANY
3531 Campbell Rd (44105-1017)
PHONE...................................216 429-6901
Wilbur Ross-Chb, *Principal*
Donald Vernon, *Vice Pres*
Gene Wimmer, *Controller*
EMP: 93
SQ FT: 500,000
SALES (est): 6.6MM **Privately Held**
SIC: 3479 3471 Galvanizing of iron, steel
or end-formed products; plating & polish-
ing

(G-4740)
AKRON REBAR CO
16216 Brookpark Rd (44135-3341)
PHONE...................................216 433-0000
Fax: 216 433-0755
Tara Lopez, *Sales Staff*
Stan Shaffer, *Sales Staff*
Bill Cooper, *Branch Mgr*
EMP: 15
SALES (corp-wide): 10.1MM **Privately
Held**
WEB: www.akronrebar.com
SIC: 3316 Bars, steel, cold finished, from
purchased hot-rolled
PA: Akron Rebar Co.
809 W Waterloo Rd
Akron OH 44314
330 745-7100

(G-4741)
ALCAN CORPORATION (HQ)
6060 Parkland Blvd (44124-4225)
PHONE...................................440 460-3307
Fax: 440 423-6654
Tom Albanese, *President*
Timothy Guerra, *President*
William J Adams, *Vice Pres*
Eileen Burns Lerum, *Vice Pres*
Donald P Seberger, *Vice Pres*
◆ **EMP:** 22
SQ FT: 11,000

SALES (est): 946MM
SALES (corp-wide): 33.7B **Privately Held**
WEB: www.alcan.com
SIC: 3351 3355 3496 3357 Wire, copper
& copper alloy; wire, aluminum: made in
rolling mills; miscellaneous fabricated wire
products; nonferrous wiredrawing & insulating
PA: Rio Tinto Plc
6 St James's Square
London SW1Y
207 781-2000

(G-4742)
ALCHEMICAL TRANSMUTATION
314 E 195th St (44119-1118)
PHONE.................................216 313-8674
James Stuart Koch, *Owner*
EMP: 101
SALES (est): 4.2MM **Privately Held**
SIC: 3499 Fire- or burglary-resistive prod-
ucts

(G-4743)
ALCOA INC
3960 S Marginal Rd (44114-3835)
PHONE.................................216 391-3885
Klaus Kleinfeld, *CEO*
Tmas Mr Sigurdsson, *COO*
Kay Meggers, *Exec VP*
Gerhard Kschwendt, *Vice Pres*
Glenn Miller, *CFO*
EMP: 16
SALES (est): 1.9MM **Privately Held**
SIC: 3334 3353 1099 Primary aluminum;
aluminum sheet & strip; bauxite mining

(G-4744)
ALCOHOL & DRUG ADDICTION
SVCS
2012 W 25th St Ste 600 (44113-4119)
PHONE.................................216 348-4830
Fax: 216 861-5079
Russell Kaye, *Exec Dir*
EMP: 30
SALES: 21.4MM **Privately Held**
WEB: www.adasbcc.org
SIC: 2721 Periodicals

(G-4745)
ALCON INDUSTRIES INC
7990 Baker Ave (44102-1900)
PHONE.................................216 961-1100
Fax: 216 961-5611
Richard J Chalet, *Ch of Bd*
Donnie Farris, *Purch Agent*
Brian Gill, *CFO*
Gary Hantz, *Manager*
▲ EMP: 100 EST: 1977
SQ FT: 130,000
SALES (est): 28.8MM **Privately Held**
WEB: www.alconalloys.com
SIC: 3325 3324 3441 3369 Alloy steel
castings, except investment; steel invest-
ment foundries; fabricated structural
metal; nonferrous foundries

(G-4746)
ALERIS CORPORATION (PA)
25825 Science Park Dr # 400
(44122-7392)
PHONE.................................216 910-3400
Sean M Stack, *President*
Jeff Hoober, *President*
John Zhu, *President*
Christopher R Clegg, *Exec VP*
Ingrid Elisabeth Jorg, *Senior VP*
EMP: 3
SALES: 2.6B **Privately Held**
SIC: 3355 3354 Bars, rolled, aluminum;
aluminum extruded products

(G-4747)
ALERIS OHIO MANAGEMENT
INC (DH)
25825 Science Park Dr # 400
(44122-7392)
PHONE.................................216 910-3400
Sean M Stack, *CEO*
K Alan Di CK, *CEO*
Christopher R Clegg, *Exec VP*
Roeland Baan, *Vice Pres*
Scott A McKinley, *Vice Pres*
EMP: 16
SALES (est): 3.9MM **Privately Held**
SIC: 3555 Printing trades machinery

(G-4748)
ALERIS ROLLED PDTS SLS
CORP
25825 Science Park Dr (44122-7323)
PHONE.................................216 910-3400
Sean M Stack, *CEO*
EMP: 1 EST: 2013
SALES (est): 10.7MM **Privately Held**
SIC: 3341 Secondary nonferrous metals
HQ: Aleris Rolled Products, Inc.
25825 Science Park Dr # 400
Beachwood OH 44122
216 910-3400

(G-4749)
ALERIS ROLLED PRODUCTS
LLC (DH)
25825 Science Park Dr # 400
(44122-7323)
PHONE.................................216 910-3400
Sean M Stack, *CEO*
▲ EMP: 21
SALES (est): 121.4MM **Privately Held**
SIC: 3355 Aluminum rolling & drawing
HQ: Aleris Rolled Products, Inc.
25825 Science Park Dr # 400
Beachwood OH 44122
216 910-3400

(G-4750)
ALERT SAFETY LITE
PRODUCTS CO
24500 Solon Rd (44146-4716)
PHONE.................................440 232-5020
Alan Kovacik, *President*
Paul S Blanch, *Corp Secy*
Georgene Shingleton, *Manager*
James W Kovacik, *Admin Sec*
EMP: 15
SQ FT: 40,000
SALES (est): 2.3MM **Privately Held**
SIC: 3699 3643 Trouble lights; outlets,
electric: convenience

(G-4751)
ALFACOMP INC
Also Called: Digital Graphics
4485 Broadview Rd (44109-4373)
PHONE.................................216 459-1790
Jennifer Tripoli, *President*
Russ Tripoli, *Treasurer*
EMP: 5
SQ FT: 1,700
SALES (est): 654.4K **Privately Held**
SIC: 7336 2791 2759 Graphic arts & re-
lated design; typesetting; commercial
printing

(G-4752)
ALFRED J BUESCHER JR
17001 Shaker Blvd (44120-1633)
PHONE.................................216 752-3676
Alfred J Buescher Jr, *Owner*
EMP: 3
SALES (est): 175.4K **Privately Held**
SIC: 3612 Ignition transformers, for use on
domestic fuel burners

(G-4753)
ALFRED MACHINE CO (HQ)
29500 Solon Rd (44139-3449)
PHONE.................................440 248-4600
Art Anton, *CEO*
Keith Kainer, *Engineer*
Ed Bayer, *Manager*
EMP: 85 EST: 1964
SQ FT: 100,000
SALES (est): 6.2MM
SALES (corp-wide): 1.1B **Privately Held**
SIC: 3599 Machine shop, jobbing & repair
PA: Swagelok Company
29500 Solon Rd
Solon OH 44139
440 248-4600

(G-4754)
ALKID CORPORATION
6035 Parkland Blvd (44124-4186)
PHONE.................................216 896-3000
Jon P Marten, *CEO*
EMP: 4
SALES (est): 229.2K
SALES (corp-wide): 11.3B **Publicly Held**
SIC: 3594 Fluid power pumps

PA: Parker-Hannifin Corporation
6035 Parkland Blvd
Cleveland OH 44124
216 896-3000

(G-4755)
ALL METAL FABRICATORS INC
15400 Commerce Park Dr (44142-2011)
PHONE.................................216 267-0033
Fax: 216 267-0330
William Yankovich, *President*
Carol Yankovich, *Corp Secy*
Mike Yankovich, *Vice Pres*
EMP: 15 EST: 1978
SQ FT: 14,000
SALES (est): 2.9MM **Privately Held**
SIC: 3444 Sheet metalwork

(G-4756)
ALL OHIO COMPANIES INC
2735 Scranton Rd (44113-5181)
PHONE.................................216 420-9274
Fax: 216 420-9502
Paul Colletti, *Principal*
EMP: 15
SQ FT: 5,088
SALES (est): 2.3MM **Privately Held**
SIC: 3446 1721 1799 Gates, ornamental
metal; exterior residential painting con-
tractor; industrial painting; exterior clean-
ing, including sandblasting; steam
cleaning of building exteriors

(G-4757)
ALL OHIO THREADED ROD CO
INC
5349 Saint Clair Ave (44103-1311)
PHONE.................................216 426-1800
Fax: 216 426-1802
James Wolford, *CEO*
Rick Fien, *President*
Brian Wolford, *VP Sls/Mktg*
Raechel Sanichar, *Office Mgr*
▲ EMP: 28
SQ FT: 40,000
SALES (est): 7.6MM **Privately Held**
SIC: 3312 5085 3316 Bar, rod & wire
products; industrial supplies; cold finish-
ing of steel shapes

(G-4758)
ALL SIGNS AND DESIGNS LLC
5101 W 161st St (44142-1604)
PHONE.................................216 267-8588
Skip Collins, *President*
Carol Collins, *Vice Pres*
Melanie Collins, *Vice Pres*
EMP: 6
SQ FT: 2,500
SALES: 800K **Privately Held**
SIC: 7389 3993 Sign painting & lettering
shop; signs & advertising specialties;
electric signs

(G-4759)
ALL SPORT SERVICES
CORPORATION
3635 Perkins Ave Ste 1e (44114-4605)
PHONE.................................216 361-1965
EMP: 5
SQ FT: 11,400
SALES: 250K **Privately Held**
SIC: 3949 Reconditions Athletic Equipment

(G-4760)
ALL-SEASONS PAPER
COMPANY
6346 Eastland Rd (44142-1300)
PHONE.................................440 826-1700
Fax: 440 826-1009
Wayne Buffington, *President*
Jackie Demetriu, *Purchasing*
Jim Elersich, *Plant Engr*
Randall Buffington, *Treasurer*
EMP: 20
SQ FT: 32,000
SALES (est): 4.7MM **Privately Held**
WEB: www.allseasonspaper.com
SIC: 2672 Coated & laminated paper

(G-4761)
ALL-TYPE WELDING &
FABRICATION
7690 Bond St (44139-5351)
PHONE.................................440 439-3990

Fax: 440 439-3990
Mike Distaulo, *President*
Dennis Whitaker, *Vice Pres*
Jennifer Mangello, *Buyer*
EMP: 40
SQ FT: 34,000
SALES (est): 7.7MM **Privately Held**
WEB: www.atwf-inc.com
SIC: 3599 7692 1761 Machine & other
job shop work; welding repair; sheet met-
alwork

(G-4762)
ALLEGA CONCRETE CORP
5585 Canal Rd (44125-4874)
PHONE.................................216 447-0814
John Allega, *President*
Jim Allega, *Vice Pres*
Joe Allega, *Vice Pres*
Dennis Kramer, *Project Mgr*
Gary Thomas, *Facilities Mgr*
EMP: 35
SQ FT: 5,000
SALES (est): 8.2MM **Privately Held**
SIC: 3273 Ready-mixed concrete

(G-4763)
ALLEGA SLAG RECOVERY INC
5585 Canal Rd (44125-4874)
PHONE.................................216 447-0814
John Allega, *President*
James Allega, *Vice Pres*
Joseph Allega, *Vice Pres*
EMP: 25
SALES (est): 2.4MM **Privately Held**
SIC: 3295 Slag, crushed or ground

(G-4764)
ALLIED CONSTRUCTION PDTS
LLC (HQ)
3900 Kelley Ave (44114-4536)
PHONE.................................216 431-2600
Fax: 216 431-2601
Eileen Johnson, *President*
Mike Booth, *District Mgr*
Dave Cowen, *District Mgr*
Michael Kohler, *District Mgr*
Beau Slavens, *District Mgr*
▲ EMP: 47
SQ FT: 110,000
SALES (est): 10.7MM
SALES (corp-wide): 93.1MM **Privately
Held**
WEB: www.alliedcp.com
SIC: 3531 Construction machinery; bitumi-
nous batching plants; crushers, grinders
& similar equipment
PA: Pubco Corporation
3830 Kelley Ave
Cleveland OH 44114
216 881-5300

(G-4765)
ALLIED CONSTRUCTION PDTS
LLC
1840 E 40th St (44103-3504)
PHONE.................................216 431-2600
Leo Matthews, *Manager*
EMP: 25
SALES (corp-wide): 93.1MM **Privately
Held**
SIC: 3531 Construction machinery
HQ: Allied Construction Products Llc
3900 Kelley Ave
Cleveland OH 44114
216 431-2600

(G-4766)
ALLIED TOOL & DIE INC
16146 Puritas Ave (44135-2691)
PHONE.................................216 941-6196
Fax: 216 941-9723
Fred Montag, *President*
Edward Kern, *Engineer*
Shawn Donegan, *Sales Dir*
Walter Montag, *Shareholder*
EMP: 19 EST: 1946
SALES (est): 3.6MM **Privately Held**
SIC: 3469 3544 Metal stampings; special
dies & tools; jigs & fixtures

(G-4767)
ALLOY BLLOWS PRCISION WLDG INC
653 Miner Rd (44143-2115)
PHONE....................................440 684-3000
Fax: 440 684-3001
Michael Canty, *President*
Jim Finnucan, *Business Mgr*
Doug Isham, *Business Mgr*
Jeff Allen, *Engineer*
Connie Ward, *Engineer*
◆ EMP: 90 EST: 1935
SQ FT: 45,000
SALES (est): 17MM **Privately Held**
WEB: www.alloybellows.com
SIC: 3599 3498 3494 Bellows, industrial:
metal; machine & other job shop work;
fabricated pipe & fittings; valves & pipe fittings

(G-4768)
ALPHA PACKAGING HOLDINGS INC
Also Called: Progressive Plastics
14801 Emery Ave (44135-1476)
PHONE....................................216 252-5595
Fax: 216 252-6327
A J Busa, *Manager*
Pete Wieneke, *Maintence Staff*
EMP: 275 **Privately Held**
SIC: 3089 3085 Molding primary plastic;
plastics bottles
PA: Alpha Packaging Holdings, Inc.
1555 Page Industrial Blvd
Saint Louis MO 63132

(G-4769)
ALPHA TOOL & MOLD INC
83 Alpha Park (44143-2265)
PHONE....................................440 473-2343
Fax: 440 473-2420
Robert Pischel, *President*
William M Fumich, *Principal*
Alfred Pischel, *Principal*
Helen Pischel, *Principal*
Al Pischel, *Corp Secy*
EMP: 12
SQ FT: 8,500
SALES (est): 2.3MM **Privately Held**
SIC: 3544 Industrial molds; special dies &
tools

(G-4770)
ALPHA ZETA HOLDINGS INC (PA)
2981 Independence Rd (44115-3615)
PHONE....................................216 271-1601
Joseph T Turgeon, *CEO*
James B Krimmel, *President*
EMP: 9
SALES (est): 6.5MM **Privately Held**
SIC: 2819 2869 6799 Industrial inorganic
chemicals; industrial organic chemicals;
investors

(G-4771)
ALTERNATIVE PRESS MAGAZINE INC
1305 W 80th St Ste 214 (44102-6204)
PHONE....................................216 631-1510
Fax: 216 631-1016
Michael P Shea, *President*
Katherine Poecze, *General Mgr*
Joe Scarpelli, *General Mgr*
Jason Pettigrew, *Editor*
Deanna Zamudio, *Design Engr*
EMP: 20
SQ FT: 2,500
SALES (est): 2.5MM **Privately Held**
WEB: www.altpress.com
SIC: 2721 Magazines: publishing & printing

(G-4772)
ALUMIN NU CORP
9513 Woodland Ave (44104-2413)
P.O. Box 24359 (44124-0359)
PHONE....................................216 421-2116
Fax: 216 791-8018
Howard Kaufman, *President*
EMP: 3
SQ FT: 15,000
SALES (est): 220K **Privately Held**
WEB: www.aluminnu.com
SIC: 2842 Specialty cleaning preparations

(G-4773)
ALUMINUM BEARING CO OF AMERICA
Also Called: Albeco
4775 W 139th St (44135-5033)
PHONE....................................216 267-8560
Fax: 216 267-8570
Jane Beyer, *President*
Kerry Howcroft, *Manager*
EMP: 9 EST: 1956
SQ FT: 3,000
SALES (est): 3.4MM **Privately Held**
SIC: 5051 3429 Aluminum bars, rods, ingots, sheets, pipes, plates, etc.; manufactured hardware (general)

(G-4774)
ALUMINUM COATING MANUFACTURERS
Also Called: Alcm
7301 Bessemer Ave (44127-1817)
PHONE....................................216 341-2000
Fax: 216 341-5833
Richard Kaplan, *President*
Errol Horam, *Admin Sec*
EMP: 23
SQ FT: 50,000
SALES (est): 4.2MM **Privately Held**
WEB: www.alcm.com
SIC: 2891 2851 2952 2951 Sealants;
paints & paint additives; asphalt felts &
coatings; asphalt paving mixtures &
blocks

(G-4775)
AMAC ENTERPRISES INC
5925 W 130th St (44130-1076)
PHONE....................................216 362-1880
Dean Caimples, *Manager*
EMP: 100
SQ FT: 160,000
SALES (corp-wide): 18MM **Privately Held**
WEB: www.amacent.com
SIC: 3471 Anodizing (plating) of metals or
formed products
PA: Amac Enterprises, Inc.
5909 W 130th St
Parma OH 44130
216 362-1880

(G-4776)
AMCLO GROUP INC
2750 Grand Ave (44104-3160)
PHONE....................................216 791-8400
William Harkins, *President*
Linda Schmidt, *Vice Pres*
Karl Morganthaler, *Admin Sec*
EMP: 101
SQ FT: 39,000
SALES (est): 16.4MM **Privately Held**
WEB: www.amclo.com
SIC: 3469 3089 Stamping metal for the
trade; injection molding of plastics

(G-4777)
AMECO USA METAL FABRICATION
4600 W 160th St (44135-2630)
PHONE....................................440 899-9400
David Perkins, *General Mgr*
Thomas M McLaughlin, *Vice Pres*
Dave Kloss, *Mktg Dir*
Michael Perkins,
EMP: 9 EST: 2010
SALES (est): 438.8K
SALES (corp-wide): 5.9MM **Privately Held**
SIC: 3441 Fabricated structural metal
PA: American Manufacturing And Engineering Company
4600 W 160th St
Cleveland OH 44135
440 899-9400

(G-4778)
AMERICAN BRASS MANUFACTURING
5000 Superior Ave (44103-1299)
PHONE....................................216 431-6565
Fax: 216 431-9420
Robert Mc Conville Jr, *Chairman*
Michelle Perkins, *Personnel Exec*
▲ EMP: 30 EST: 1894
SQ FT: 40,000

SALES (est): 5.6MM **Privately Held**
WEB: www.americanbrass.com
SIC: 3432 Plumbers' brass goods: drain
cocks, faucets, spigots, etc.

(G-4779)
AMERICAN BRONZE CORPORATION
2941 Broadway Ave (44115-3692)
PHONE....................................216 341-7800
Fax: 216 341-0735
Gerald Goldstein, *President*
Joshua Goldstein, *Vice Pres*
EMP: 25 EST: 1924
SQ FT: 50,000
SALES: 10MM **Privately Held**
WEB: www.americanbronzecorp.com
SIC: 3364 Brass & bronze die-castings

(G-4780)
AMERICAN CHEMICAL PRODUCTS
5041 W 161st St (44142-1602)
PHONE....................................216 267-7722
Fax: 216 267-7721
Don Manak, *President*
Janet Metro, *Corp Secy*
Thomas McCormick, *Vice Pres*
Steve Alexander, *Engineer*
William McCormick, *Engineer*
EMP: 10
SQ FT: 10,000
SALES (est): 2.2MM **Privately Held**
SIC: 2842 Cleaning or polishing preparations

(G-4781)
AMERICAN FRICTION TECH LLC
9300 Midwest Ave (44125-2418)
PHONE....................................216 823-0861
Fax: 216 823-0866
Raven Soukup, *Materials Mgr*
Mark Havir, *QA Dir*
Paul Suvak, *Sales Executive*
Gregory C Soukup, *Mng Member*
Horst Becker,
▲ EMP: 65
SQ FT: 54,000
SALES: 15MM **Privately Held**
SIC: 3339 Primary nonferrous metals

(G-4782)
AMERICAN GREETINGS CORPORATION (HQ)
1 American Rd (44144-2398)
PHONE....................................216 252-7300
Fax: 216 252-6777
Morry Weiss, *Ch of Bd*
John W Beeder, *President*
Zev Weiss, *Co-CEO*
Jeffrey Weiss, *Co-CEO*
Mike Goulder, *Senior VP*
◆ EMP: 6000 EST: 1906
SQ FT: 1,194,414
SALES: 1.9B
SALES (corp-wide): 2.2B **Privately Held**
WEB: www.americangreetings.com
SIC: 2771 2679 2656 2678 Greeting
cards; gift wrap, paper: made from purchased material; cups, paper: made from
purchased material; plates, paper: made
from purchased material; stationery:
made from purchased materials
PA: Century Intermediate Holding Company
1 American Rd
Cleveland OH 44144
216 252-7300

(G-4783)
AMERICAN GREETINGS CORPORATION
230 W Huron Rd Ste 7228 (44113-1452)
PHONE....................................216 685-9167
Holly Evans, *Principal*
Marybeth Harper, *Admin Asst*
Rheta Kruse, *Associate*
EMP: 3
SALES (corp-wide): 2.2B **Privately Held**
SIC: 2771 Greeting cards
HQ: American Greetings Corporation
1 American Rd
Cleveland OH 44144
216 252-7300

(G-4784)
AMERICAN HOME PRODUCTS LLC (HQ)
25201 Chagrin Blvd # 350 (44122-5600)
PHONE....................................800 684-3434
Mark Mansour, *Mng Member*
Jacalyn Gilbert, *Executive Asst*
EMP: 5
SALES (est): 39MM
SALES (corp-wide): 67.9MM **Privately Held**
SIC: 2431 Millwork
PA: Mcm Capital Partners
25201 Chagrin Blvd # 360
Beachwood OH 44122
216 514-1840

(G-4785)
AMERICAN INTERIOR DESIGN INC
19561 Miles Rd (44128-4111)
PHONE....................................216 663-0606
Frank Zorman Jr, *President*
Ed Zorman, *Vice Pres*
Laura Cook, *Manager*
EMP: 15
SQ FT: 10,000
SALES (est): 1.5MM **Privately Held**
WEB: www.americaninterior.com
SIC: 2541 Cabinets, lockers & shelving

(G-4786)
AMERICAN IR MET CLEVELAND LLC
1240 Marquette St (44114-3920)
PHONE....................................216 266-0518
Michael Simms, *President*
Paul Frank, *Controller*
Terry Mahoney, *Accounts Mgr*
Tim Wilson, *Mng Member*
Keith Dougherty, *Manager*
▼ EMP: 20
SQ FT: 70,000
SALES (est): 19.3MM
SALES (corp-wide): 1.4B **Privately Held**
WEB: www.conversionresources.com
SIC: 5051 3441 Metals service centers &
offices; fabricated structural metal
HQ: Aim Specialty Materials Usa
25 Kenney Dr
Cranston RI 02920
401 463-5605

(G-4787)
AMERICAN LITHUANIAN PRESS
Also Called: DIRVA LITHUANIAN NEWSPAPER
19807 Cherokee Ave (44119-2825)
P.O. Box 19010 (44119-0010)
PHONE....................................216 531-8150
Fax: 216 531-8428
Algirdas V Matulionis, *President*
EMP: 3
SQ FT: 4,000
SALES: 51.3K **Privately Held**
SIC: 2711 Newspapers: publishing only,
not printed on site

(G-4788)
AMERICAN METAL COATINGS INC
1088 Ivanhoe Rd (44110-3207)
PHONE....................................216 451-3131
Fax: 216 451-3135
Konstantinos Dotsikas, *President*
Kathy Sansavera, *Manager*
EMP: 24
SQ FT: 50,000
SALES (est): 3.3MM **Privately Held**
SIC: 3471 Electroplating of metals or
formed products

(G-4789)
AMERICAN METAL PROC CO LLC
17001 Saranac Rd (44110-2534)
PHONE....................................216 486-4600
Jason J Lynch, *Principal*
EMP: 20
SALES (est): 2.7MM **Privately Held**
SIC: 3398 Metal heat treating

▲ = Import ▼=Export
◆ =Import/Export

(G-4790)

AMERICAN METAL TREATING CO
1043 E 62nd St (44103-1094)
PHONE....................................216 431-4492
Fax: 216 431-1508
Richard Roenn, *President*
Carol Roenn, *Corp Secy*
▲ EMP: 22 EST: 1926
SQ FT: 15,830
SALES (est): 5.2MM Privately Held
WEB: www.americanmetaltreating.com
SIC: 3398 Brazing (hardening) of metal

(G-4791)

AMERICAN MFG & ENGRG CO
7500 Grand Division Ave (44125-1235)
PHONE....................................440 899-9400
Michael Perkins, *Manager*
EMP: 3
SALES (corp-wide): 5.9MM Privately
Held
WEB: www.ameco-usa.com
SIC: 3312 Plate, steel
PA: American Manufacturing And Engineer-
ing Company
4600 W 160th St
Cleveland OH 44135
440 899-9400

(G-4792)

AMERICAN PRECISION SPINDLES (DH)
Also Called: SKF Machine Tools Service
670 Alpha Dr (44143-2123)
PHONE....................................267 436-6000
Phillip J Wykoff,
Rosemary A Wykoff,
EMP: 8
SQ FT: 10,000
SALES (est): 864.1K
SALES (corp-wide): 7.8B Privately Held
SIC: 3552 Spindles, textile
HQ: Skf Usa Inc.
890 Forty Foot Rd
Lansdale PA 19446
267 436-6000

(G-4793)

AMERICAN PROCESSING LLC
17001 Saranac Rd (44110-2534)
PHONE....................................216 486-4600
Chuck Shepard, *Manager*
EMP: 26
SALES (est): 4.6MM Privately Held
SIC: 3312 Blast furnaces & steel mills;
sheet or strip, steel, cold-rolled: own hot-
rolled; iron & steel: galvanized, pipes,
plates, sheets, etc.

(G-4794)

AMERICAN RIDE WHEELCHAIR COACH
1368 W 65th St (44102-2160)
PHONE....................................216 276-1700
C Patricia Augustine, *Principal*
EMP: 3
SALES (est): 177.4K Privately Held
SIC: 3842 Wheelchairs

(G-4795)

AMERICAN SCAFFOLDING INC
7600 Wall St Ste 200 (44125-3358)
PHONE....................................216 524-7733
Mike Tabar, *Branch Mgr*
EMP: 3
SALES (corp-wide): 12MM Privately
Held
SIC: 3499 5082 5999 Metal ladders; lad-
ders; alarm & safety equipment stores
PA: American Scaffolding, Inc.
7161 Eagle Creek Rd
Cincinnati OH
513 353-1181

(G-4796)

AMERICAN TANK & FABRICATING CO (PA)
Also Called: A T & F Co
12314 Elmwood Ave (44111-5991)
PHONE....................................216 252-1500
Fax: 216 251-4963
Terry Ripich, *Ch of Bd*
Bob Ripich, *President*
Michael Ripich, *President*

Kevin Cantrell, *Vice Pres*
Michael Puleo, *Vice Pres*
▲ EMP: 100 EST: 1940
SQ FT: 300,000
SALES (est): 39.1MM Privately Held
WEB: www.amtank.com
SIC: 3443 5051 Fabricated plate work
(boiler shop); weldments; metals service
centers & offices; iron & steel (ferrous)
products

(G-4797)

AMERILAM LAMINATING
4651 W 130th St (44135-3758)
P.O. Box 35286 (44135-0286)
PHONE....................................440 235-4687
Dan Wyman, *Owner*
Brenda Wyman, *Office Mgr*
EMP: 3
SQ FT: 3,500
SALES: 200K Privately Held
SIC: 2493 2732 Particleboard, plastic lam-
inated; textbooks: printing & binding, not
publishing

(G-4798)

AMRESCO LLC
29999 Solon Indus Pkwy (44139-4317)
P.O. Box 39098, Solon (44139-0098)
PHONE....................................440 349-2805
Doug Henley, *Opers Staff*
Vincent Yee, *Technical Mgr*
Laura Panehal, *Engineer*
Maryann Trueisky, *Human Res Mgr*
Andrew Dugan, *Sales Staff*
EMP: 200
SALES (corp-wide): 4.5B Publicly Held
WEB: www.amresco-inc.com
SIC: 2833 2899 2819 Medicinals & botan-
icals; chemical preparations; industrial in-
organic chemicals
HQ: Amresco, Llc
28600 Fountain Pkwy
Solon OH 44139
440 349-1199

(G-4799)

AMROS INDUSTRIES INC
14701 Industrial Pkwy (44135-4547)
PHONE....................................216 433-0010
Fax: 216 433-0011
Gregory Shteyngarts, *President*
Angie Helcbergier, *Office Mgr*
EMP: 22
SQ FT: 65,000
SALES (est): 4.5MM Privately Held
SIC: 7389 2821 Packaging & labeling
services; thermoplastic materials

(G-4800)

AMTANK ARMOR LLC
12314 Elmwood Ave (44111-5906)
PHONE....................................216 252-1500
Bridgette Berthelot, *Human Res Mgr*
John Mayles,
EMP: 4
SQ FT: 3,600
SALES (est): 429.1K Privately Held
SIC: 3441 Fabricated structural metal

(G-4801)

ANALIZA INC (PA)
3615 Superior Ave E 4407b (44114-4139)
PHONE....................................216 432-9050
Arnon Chait, *President*
Ian Crawford, *Vice Pres*
Tatyana Rothman, *Research*
Andrew Chervenak, *Manager*
David Jackson, *Director*
EMP: 10
SQ FT: 5,000
SALES: 350K Privately Held
SIC: 2834 Pharmaceutical preparations

(G-4802)

ANCHOR BRONZE AND METALS INC
11470 Euclid Ave Ste 509 (44106-3934)
PHONE....................................440 549-5653
Roger Moore, *President*
Tim Nielsen, *Sales Mgr*
EMP: 32
SQ FT: 42,000

SALES (est): 7MM Privately Held
SIC: 3366 5051 Copper foundries; brass
foundry; bronze foundry; castings (except
die): copper & copper-base alloy; copper;
copper products; miscellaneous nonferrous products; castings, rough: iron or
steel

(G-4803)

ANCHOR INDUSTRIES INCORPORATED
30775 Solon Indus Pkwy (44139-4338)
PHONE....................................440 473-1414
Fax: 440 473-1419
Doug Kaufman, *President*
Larry Logsdon, *Manager*
▲ EMP: 47
SALES (est): 8MM Privately Held
SIC: 3462 Automotive forgings, ferrous:
crankshaft, engine, axle, etc.

(G-4804)

ANCHOR METAL PROCESSING INC
12200 Brookpark Rd (44130-1146)
PHONE....................................216 362-6463
Fred Pfaff, *Branch Mgr*
EMP: 15
SALES (corp-wide): 8.2MM Privately
Held
SIC: 3599 1761 3444 Machine shop, job-
bing & repair; sheet metalwork; sheet
metalwork
PA: Anchor Metal Processing, Inc.
11830 Brookpark Rd
Cleveland OH 44130
216 362-1850

(G-4805)

ANCHOR METAL PROCESSING INC (PA)
11830 Brookpark Rd (44130-1103)
PHONE....................................216 362-1850
Fax: 216 362-1839
Edward Pfaff, *Ch of Bd*
Frederick Pfaff, *President*
Jeff Pfaff, *Vice Pres*
Dave Pippert, *Purchasing*
Judy Quayle, *Executive Asst*
EMP: 30
SQ FT: 46,000
SALES (est): 8.2MM Privately Held
SIC: 3599 1761 3444 Machine shop, job-
bing & repair; sheet metalwork; sheet
metalwork

(G-4806)

ANCHOR TOOL & DIE CO (PA)
Also Called: Anchor Manufacturing Group
12200 Brookpark Rd (44130-1177)
PHONE....................................216 362-1850
Fax: 216 362-7442
Frederick A Pfaff, *President*
Edward Pfaff, *Chairman*
Jeff Wilson, *Business Mgr*
Rick Gratzer, *Plant Mgr*
Barb Murawski, *Project Mgr*
▲ EMP: 261 EST: 1970
SQ FT: 350,000
SALES (est): 65MM Privately Held
WEB: www.anchor-mfg.com
SIC: 3465 3544 3469 Automotive stamp-
ings; special dies, tools, jigs & fixtures;
metal stampings

(G-4807)

ANCHOR TOOL & DIE CO
Also Called: Anchor Manufacturing Group
12200 Brookpark Rd (44130-1177)
PHONE....................................216 362-1850
Rebecca Lipowski, *Vice Pres*
Fred Pfaff, *Manager*
EMP: 100
SALES (corp-wide): 61.6MM Privately
Held
WEB: www.anchor-mfg.com
SIC: 3469 Metal stampings
PA: Anchor Tool & Die Co.
12200 Brookpark Rd
Cleveland OH 44130
216 362-1850

(G-4808)

ANDEEN-HAGERLING INC
31200 Bainbridge Rd Ste 2 (44139-2298)
PHONE....................................440 349-0370
Fax: 440 349-0359
Carl W Hagerling, *President*
Paul Sauerland, *General Mgr*
Steve Kaplan, *Vice Pres*
Carl G Andeen, *Treasurer*
John Keppler, *Manager*
EMP: 14
SQ FT: 7,600
SALES (est): 2.4MM Privately Held
WEB: www.andeen-hagerling.com
SIC: 3825 Bridges: kelvin, wheatstone,
vacuum tube, megohm, etc.; test equip-
ment for electronic & electric measure-
ment; standards & calibration equipment
for electrical measuring

(G-4809)

ANDERSON DOOR CO
18090 Miles Rd (44128-3435)
PHONE....................................216 475-5700
Fax: 216 475-2221
James B Anderson Jr, *President*
Virginia Anderson, *Corp Secy*
James B Anderson III, *Vice Pres*
Ken Buzzelli, *Manager*
EMP: 30
SQ FT: 30,000
SALES (est): 4.4MM Privately Held
SIC: 2431 3442 Garage doors, overhead:
wood; garage doors, overhead: metal

(G-4810)

ANDERSON INDUSTRIES INC
Also Called: Multiple Products Div
15501 Chatfield Ave (44111-4311)
PHONE....................................216 941-7766
Fax: 216 941-7768
William F Anderson, *President*
Joseph T Anderson, *Treasurer*
Leann Johnson, *Manager*
Joel Newman, *Admin Sec*
EMP: 11 EST: 1945
SQ FT: 22,000
SALES (est): 2MM Privately Held
WEB: www.greenssweep.com
SIC: 3469 3861 Metal stampings; photo-
graphic equipment & supplies

(G-4811)

ANDERSOUND PA SERVICE
15911 Harvard Ave (44128-2049)
PHONE....................................216 561-2636
Clarence Anderson Jr, *Owner*
EMP: 6
SALES (est): 398.5K Privately Held
SIC: 3651 Audio electronic systems

(G-4812)

ANGEL PRTG & REPRODUCTION CO
1400 W 57th St (44102-3044)
PHONE....................................216 631-5225
Fax: 216 631-8266
Frank Petkovsek, *President*
Mary Louise Petkovsek, *Vice Pres*
Nicolas Paserk, *Sales Staff*
Ted Zahnke, *Manager*
EMP: 10
SQ FT: 16,000
SALES: 1.1MM Privately Held
WEB: www.angelprinting.com
SIC: 2752 Commercial printing, offset

(G-4813)

ANGRY CUPCAKES PRODUCTIONS LLC
2300 E 95th St (44106-3452)
PHONE....................................216 229-2394
Doris Horn, *Owner*
EMP: 4
SALES (est): 152.2K Privately Held
SIC: 2051 Bread, cake & related products

(G-4814)

ANGSTROM GRAPHICS INC (PA)
4437 E 49th St (44125-1005)
PHONE....................................216 271-5300
Fax: 216 571-5344
Wayne R Angstrom, *CEO*
John Gorman, *General Mgr*
Chip Owen, *Exec VP*

Marlene Kruse, *Vice Pres*
Edward Lipp, *Vice Pres*
◆ **EMP:** 250
SQ FT: 225,000
SALES (est) 288.6MM **Privately Held**
SIC: 2721 2754 2752 Magazines: publishing & printing; commercial printing, gravure; commercial printing, lithographic

(G-4815)
ANGSTROM GRAPHICS INC MIDWEST (HQ)
4437 E 49th St (44125-1005)
PHONE.............................216 271-5300
Wayne R Angstrom, *Ch of Bd*
Rachel Malakoff, *CFO*
Tim Gailey, *Accounting Mgr*
Rhonda Perry, *VP Sales*
Bruce Macdonald, *Marketing Staff*
EMP: 295
SQ FT: 230,000
SALES (est): 55MM
SALES (corp-wide): 288.6MM **Privately Held**
SIC: 2752 7331 Commercial printing, offset; direct mail advertising services
PA: Angstrom Graphics Inc
　　4437 E 49th St
　　Cleveland OH 44125
　　216 271-5300

(G-4816)
ANGSTROM GRAPHICS SOUTHEAST (HQ)
4437 E 49th St (44125-1005)
PHONE.............................216 271-5300
Wayne R Angstrom, *Ch of Bd*
Mark Berkey, *President*
Rachel L Malakoff, *CFO*
Gian Recondo, *Manager*
◆ **EMP:** 4
SQ FT: 225,000
SALES (est): 50.8MM
SALES (corp-wide): 288.6MM **Privately Held**
WEB: www.st-ives.com
SIC: 2752 Commercial printing, lithographic
PA: Angstrom Graphics Inc
　　4437 E 49th St
　　Cleveland OH 44125
　　216 271-5300

(G-4817)
ANVIL PRODUCTS CO
4535 E 71st St (44105-5603)
PHONE.............................216 883-3740
Fax: 216 883-2740
Alex Berkes Jr, *Owner*
Aaron J Johnson, *Manager*
EMP: 3
SQ FT: 7,400
SALES: 130K **Privately Held**
SIC: 3599 Machine shop, jobbing & repair

(G-4818)
APEX ADVANCED TECHNOLOGIES LLC
4857a W 130th St (44135)
PHONE.............................216 898-1595
Dennis Hammond,
EMP: 6
SQ FT: 12,000
SALES: 400K **Privately Held**
WEB:
www.apexadvancedtechnologies.com
SIC: 2992 Lubricating oils & greases

(G-4819)
APOLLO MEDICAL DEVICES LLC
11000 Cedar Ave Ste 146 (44106-3067)
PHONE.............................440 935-5027
Fax: 440 229-8348
Patrick Leimkuehler, *CEO*
Punkaj Ahuja,
EMP: 4
SQ FT: 500
SALES (est): 262.2K **Privately Held**
SIC: 2835 In vitro diagnostics

(G-4820)
APPROVED PLUMBING CO
Also Called: Approved Plbg & Sewer Clg Co
770 Ken Mar Indus Pkwy (44147-2920)
PHONE.............................216 663-5063
Fax: 440 546-7698
Dennis Schlekie, *President*
EMP: 10 **EST:** 1940
SALES (est): 1.1MM **Privately Held**
WEB: www.approvedplumbing.com
SIC: 1711 2434 Plumbing contractors; wood kitchen cabinets

(G-4821)
ARAN INC
23500 Mercantile Rd Ste F (44122-5914)
PHONE.............................216 464-1508
Arie Teomi, *President*
Ann Teomi, *Vice Pres*
EMP: 6
SQ FT: 4,000
SALES: 650K **Privately Held**
WEB: www.expoforums.com
SIC: 2752 2789 Commercial printing, offset; bookbinding & related work

(G-4822)
ARC DRILLING INC (PA)
9551 Corporate Cir (44125-4261)
PHONE.............................216 525-0920
Lee Trem, *President*
Kevin Trem, *Vice Pres*
Shirley Conetsco, *Office Mgr*
Russ Harpring, *Branch Mgr*
Carl Duffield, *Manager*
EMP: 16 **EST:** 1947
SQ FT: 5,000
SALES (est): 2.6MM **Privately Held**
WEB: www.arcdrilling.com
SIC: 3829 3599 Thermometers, including digital: clinical; machine & other job shop work

(G-4823)
ARCELORMITTAL CLEVELAND LLC (HQ)
3060 Eggers Ave (44105-1012)
PHONE.............................216 429-6000
Micheal Rippey, *CEO*
Louis Schorsch, *CEO*
Terry Fedor, *General Mgr*
Mike Billotti, *VP Mfg*
Jim Payonk, *Project Mgr*
▲ **EMP:** 205
SQ FT: 40,000
SALES (est): 363.3MM **Privately Held**
SIC: 3312 Blast furnaces & steel mills
PA: Arcelormittal Sa
　　Boulevard D'avranches 24-26
　　Luxembourg
　　479 21 -

(G-4824)
ARCELORMITTAL CLEVELAND LLC
3060 Eggers Ave (44105-1012)
PHONE.............................216 429-6000
George Dunn, *Engineer*
Michael Frangiamore, *Engineer*
Alexander Ivanov, *Engineer*
Luke Operhall, *Engineer*
Shailesh Thakkar, *Engineer*
EMP: 30 **Privately Held**
SIC: 3325 Rolling mill rolls, cast steel
HQ: Arcelormittal Cleveland Llc
　　3060 Eggers Ave
　　Cleveland OH 44105
　　216 429-6000

(G-4825)
ARCHITECTURAL FIBERGLASS INC
8300 Bessemer Ave (44127-1839)
PHONE.............................216 641-8300
Fax: 216 641-8150
Michael Dobronos, *President*
Tanya Dobronos, *Vice Pres*
Steve Dobronos, *Sls & Mktg Exec*
Michael Doboronos, *Financial Exec*
▲ **EMP:** 30
SQ FT: 20,000
SALES (est): 5.7MM **Privately Held**
WEB: www.fiberglassafi.com
SIC: 2221 Glass & fiberglass broadwoven fabrics

(G-4826)
ARCHITECTURAL PRODUCTS DEV
6605 Clark Ave Rear 1 (44102-5330)
PHONE.............................216 631-6260
Fax: 216 631-6212
Arthur Petrauskis, *President*
Maureen Petrauskis, *Vice Pres*
Alex Braznytez, *Exec Dir*
EMP: 5
SQ FT: 17,500
SALES (est): 802.2K **Privately Held**
WEB: www.apd-inc.com
SIC: 1791 3299 Elevator front installation, metal; architectural sculptures: gypsum, clay, papier mache, etc.

(G-4827)
ARCHITECTURAL SHEET METALS LLC
1457 E 39th St (44114-4120)
PHONE.............................216 361-9952
Arthur A Petrauskis, *President*
EMP: 5
SALES (est): 710K **Privately Held**
SIC: 3444 Restaurant sheet metalwork

(G-4828)
ARDAR CO INC
12955 York Delta Dr Ste A (44133-3550)
PHONE.............................440 582-3371
Fax: 440 582-4480
Wally Marij, *President*
Irene Marij, *Corp Secy*
EMP: 5
SALES: 550K **Privately Held**
SIC: 3599 Machine shop, jobbing & repair

(G-4829)
ARISDYNE SYSTEMS INC
17909 Cleveland Pkwy Dr # 100
(44135-3236)
PHONE.............................216 458-1991
Peter Reimers, *President*
Frederick W Clarke, *Exec VP*
Paul Reinking, *Vice Pres*
Nick Berchtold, *CFO*
Cheryl Petrencsik, *Controller*
EMP: 15
SQ FT: 15,000
SALES (est): 4.2MM **Privately Held**
SIC: 3612 Saturable reactors

(G-4830)
ARKEN MANUFACTURING INC
3502 Beyerle Rd (44105-1016)
PHONE.............................216 883-6628
Donald Dostie, *President*
Ken Dostie, *Vice Pres*
EMP: 5
SQ FT: 2,500
SALES (est): 420K **Privately Held**
WEB: www.arkenusa.com
SIC: 3544 Special dies, tools, jigs & fixtures

(G-4831)
ARMATURE COIL EQUIPMENT INC
Also Called: Ace Equipment Company
4725 Manufacturing Ave (44135-2696)
PHONE.............................216 267-6366
Fax: 216 267-4361
Robert F Heran, *President*
Joseph Hamor, *Project Mgr*
Lawrence Heran, *Foreman/Supr*
Teresa Heran, *Manager*
Scott Sheran, *Manager*
EMP: 12 **EST:** 1919
SQ FT: 25,140
SALES (est): 2.5MM **Privately Held**
WEB: www.armaturecoil.com
SIC: 3549 3567 Coil winding machines for springs; industrial furnaces & ovens

(G-4832)
ARMOTEC MATERIALS CORPORATION
3825 W 150th St (44111-5806)
PHONE.............................216 476-2766
Fax: 216 476-0422
S Stryffeler, *Principal*
EMP: 3 **EST:** 2008
SALES (est): 233.5K **Privately Held**
SIC: 2241 Narrow fabric mills

(G-4833)
ARMOUR SPRAY SYSTEMS INC
210 Hayes Dr Ste I (44131-1056)
PHONE.............................216 398-3838
Fax: 216 398-0862
Michael J Mihna Jr, *President*
Michael J Mihna III, *Vice Pres*
Michelle Sokolowski, *Sales Staff*
James Nagy, *Marketing Mgr*
▲ **EMP:** 10 **EST:** 1976
SQ FT: 5,000
SALES (est): 2.3MM **Privately Held**
WEB: www.armourspray.com
SIC: 5084 3563 Industrial machinery & equipment; spraying outfits: metals, paints & chemicals (compressor)

(G-4834)
ARROW INTERNATIONAL INC (PA)
9900 Clinton Rd (44144-1097)
PHONE.............................216 961-3500
Fax: 216 961-2065
John E Gallagher, *CEO*
Edward J Maher, *Principal*
Robert E Sweeney, *Principal*
David M Delgado, *Vice Pres*
Joel Horne, *Vice Pres*
◆ **EMP:** 277
SALES (est): 249MM **Privately Held**
WEB: www.arrowgames.com
SIC: 3944 Board games, puzzles & models, except electronic

(G-4835)
ART GALVANIZING WORKS INC
3935 Valley Rd (44109-3092)
PHONE.............................216 749-0020
Fax: 216 749-0030
James Klein, *President*
Adrienne Klein, *Vice Pres*
EMP: 15 **EST:** 1935
SQ FT: 9,775
SALES (est): 1.6MM **Privately Held**
WEB: www.artgalvanizing.com
SIC: 3479 Galvanizing of iron, steel or end-formed products

(G-4836)
ART-AMERICAN PRINTING PLATES
1138 W 9th St Fl 4 (44113-1007)
PHONE.............................216 241-4420
Fax: 216 241-4420
John T Mc Sweeney, *President*
Lawrence Mc Sweeney, *Vice Pres*
John McSweeney, *Persnl Dir*
EMP: 25
SQ FT: 11,000
SALES (est): 3.4MM **Privately Held**
WEB: www.art-american.com
SIC: 2796 7336 Platemaking services; graphic arts & related design

(G-4837)
ARTHUR W GUILFORD III INC
Also Called: G A Guilford & Sons
13515 Brookpark Rd (44142-1824)
PHONE.............................216 362-1350
Fax: 216 362-6112
Arthur W Guilford III, *President*
EMP: 8
SQ FT: 5,000
SALES (est): 710K **Privately Held**
SIC: 3842 Braces, orthopedic

(G-4838)
ARTISAN TOOL & DIE CORP
4911 Grant Ave (44125-1027)
PHONE.............................216 883-2769
Fax: 216 883-2970
James Berkes, *President*
Thomas Deka, *Production*
Kristen Kotecki, *Purch Mgr*
Kristan Kaszei, *Purchasing*
David Dross, *Treasurer*
▼ **EMP:** 40
SQ FT: 65,000
SALES: 2.9MM **Privately Held**
SIC: 3469 3544 Metal stampings; special dies & tools

(G-4839)
ARTISTIC METAL SPINNING INC
Also Called: Zoia
4700 Lorain Ave (44102-3443)
PHONE..................................216 961-3336
Fax: 216 961-5119
Lorraine Hangauer, *President*
Ronald W Hangauer, *Vice Pres*
Donald E Hangauer, *Admin Sec*
EMP: 6 EST: 1930
SQ FT: 12,000
SALES (est): 948.8K **Privately Held**
SIC: 3469 Spinning metal for the trade

(G-4840)
ARZEL TECHNOLOGY INC
Also Called: Arzel Zoning Technology
4801 Commerce Pkwy (44128-5905)
PHONE..................................216 831-6068
Fax: 216 831-6074
Lenny Roth, *Senior VP*
Thomas Delt, *Vice Pres*
Leonard Roth, *Vice Pres*
Adam Bush, *Engineer*
Cathy Langer, *Marketing Staff*
▼ **EMP:** 29
SQ FT: 40,000
SALES (est): 7.3MM **Privately Held**
WEB: www.arzelzoning.com
SIC: 3823 Industrial instrmnts msrmnt display/control process variable

(G-4841)
ASCO POWER TECHNOLOGIES LP
8400 E Pleasant Valley Rd (44131-5519)
PHONE..................................216 573-7600
Bob Daniels, *General Mgr*
EMP: 35
SALES (corp-wide): 15.2B **Privately Held**
SIC: 3613 3625 Switchgear & switchboard apparatus; resistors & resistor units
HQ: Asco Power Technologies, L.P.
160 Park Ave
Florham Park NJ 07932

(G-4842)
ASCO POWER TECHNOLOGIES LP
Also Called: Avtron Loadbank
6255 Halle Dr (44125-4615)
PHONE..................................973 966-2161
Fax: 216 573-5953
Bob Daniels, *General Mgr*
Robert Dixon, *Engineer*
John Emery, *Engineer*
Diane E Niro, *Manager*
Dick Scott, *Info Tech Mgr*
EMP: 106
SALES (corp-wide): 15.2B **Privately Held**
SIC: 3613 3625 Switchgear & switchboard apparatus; resistors & resistor units
HQ: Asco Power Technologies, L.P.
160 Park Ave
Florham Park NJ 07932

(G-4843)
ASCO VALVE INC
26401 Emery Rd Ste 105 (44128-6210)
PHONE..................................216 360-0366
EMP: 13
SALES (corp-wide): 24.5B **Publicly Held**
SIC: 3625 Mfg Relays/Industrial Controls
HQ: Asco Valve, Inc.
50-60 Hanover Rd
Florham Park NJ 07932
973 966-2000

(G-4844)
ASCON TECNOLOGIC N AMER LLC
1111 Brookpark Rd (44109-5825)
PHONE..................................216 485-8350
Steven Craig, *General Mgr*
EMP: 6 EST: 2012
SALES: 10MM **Privately Held**
SIC: 3823 Industrial instrmnts msrmnt display/control process variable

(G-4845)
ASG
15700 S Waterloo Rd (44110-3814)
PHONE..................................216 486-6163
Bryon Shafer, *General Mgr*
Neil Maniccia, *Sales Executive*

Bryon Schafer, *Manager*
EMP: 12
SALES (est): 1.5MM **Privately Held**
SIC: 3423 Hand & edge tools

(G-4846)
ASHTA FORGE & MACHINE INC
3001 W 121st St (44111-1638)
PHONE..................................216 252-7000
Fax: 216 252-7601
Wayne Phelps, *President*
Karen Mason, *Corp Secy*
EMP: 20
SALES (est): 2MM **Privately Held**
SIC: 3599 Machine shop, jobbing & repair

(G-4847)
ASHTECH CORPORATION
5875 Landerbrook Dr # 140 (44124-6502)
P.O. Box 24129 (44124-0129)
PHONE..................................440 646-9911
Fax: 440 646-9911
Gerald L Deroy, *President*
EMP: 5
SQ FT: 2,000
SALES: 5MM **Privately Held**
WEB: www.ashtechcorp.com
SIC: 3535 5084 Conveyors & conveying equipment; industrial machinery & equipment

(G-4848)
ASSEMBLY SPECIALTY PDTS INC
14700 Brookpark Rd (44135-5166)
PHONE..................................216 676-5600
Fax: 216 676-6761
Erno Nagy, *President*
Don Main, *General Mgr*
Steve Konig, *COO*
Attila Nagy, *Vice Pres*
Marian Stewart, *Purch Mgr*
EMP: 22 EST: 1971
SQ FT: 33,500
SALES (est): 6.1MM **Privately Held**
WEB: www.assemblyspecialty.com
SIC: 3496 Cable, uninsulated wire: made from purchased wire

(G-4849)
ASSOCIATED PRESS REPAIR INC
5321 Saint Clair Ave (44103-1311)
PHONE..................................216 881-2288
Fax: 216 881-7909
Anthony Grbavac, *President*
Steve Grbavac, *Vice Pres*
EMP: 8
SQ FT: 24,000
SALES (est): 949.6K **Privately Held**
SIC: 3599 Machine shop, jobbing & repair

(G-4850)
AT HOLDINGS CORPORATION (DH)
23555 Euclid Ave (44117-1703)
PHONE..................................216 692-6000
Michael S Lipscomb, *Ch of Bd*
David Scaife, *Vice Pres*
Frances S St Clair, *CFO*
EMP: 3
SQ FT: 1,800,000
SALES (est): 104.9MM **Privately Held**
SIC: 3724 3728 6512 Pumps, aircraft engine; aircraft parts & equipment; commercial & industrial building operation
HQ: Eaton Corporation
1000 Eaton Blvd
Cleveland OH 44122
216 523-5000

(G-4851)
AT&F ADVANCED METALS LLC (PA)
12314 Elmwood Ave (44111-5906)
PHONE..................................330 684-1122
Jamie Pollard, *QC Mgr*
John Deily,
Terry Riplch,
▲ **EMP:** 35
SQ FT: 15,000

SALES (est): 7.1MM **Privately Held**
WEB: www.advmetals.com
SIC: 3446 3443 Railings, prefabricated metal; process vessels, industrial: metal plate

(G-4852)
AT&F NUCLEAR INC (HQ)
12314 Elmwood Ave (44111-5906)
PHONE..................................216 252-1500
Michael Ripich, *CEO*
EMP: 5
SALES (est): 1.5MM
SALES (corp-wide): 35.5MM **Privately Held**
SIC: 5051 5999 3999 Steel; welding supplies; atomizers; toiletry
PA: The American Tank & Fabricating Co
12314 Elmwood Ave
Cleveland OH 44111
216 252-1500

(G-4853)
ATHENS FOODS INC
13600 Snow Rd (44142-2546)
PHONE..................................216 676-8500
Fax: 216 676-0609
Eric Moscahlaidis, *Ch of Bd*
Scott Sumser, *President*
William Buckingham, *Vice Pres*
Jeff Swint, *Vice Pres*
Robert Tansing, *Vice Pres*
EMP: 180
SQ FT: 114,000
SALES: 27MM **Privately Held**
WEB: www.athensfoods.com
SIC: 2038 2045 Frozen specialties; prepared flour mixes & doughs

(G-4854)
ATHERSYS INC (PA)
3201 Carnegie Ave (44115-2634)
PHONE..................................216 431-9900
Fax: 216 361-9495
Gil Van Bokkelen, *Ch of Bd*
William Lehmann Jr, *President*
Cheryl Jordan, *COO*
John J Harrington, *Exec VP*
Laura K Campbell, *Senior VP*
EMP: 60
SQ FT: 45,000
SALES: 17.3MM **Publicly Held**
WEB: www.athersys.com
SIC: 2834 Pharmaceutical preparations

(G-4855)
ATLAS MACHINE PRODUCTS CO
Also Called: Atlas Portable Space Solutions
12507 Plover St (44107-5213)
PHONE..................................216 228-3688
Fax: 216 228-3689
N Medley, *President*
Ed Medley, *Corp Secy*
William Slabe, *VP Mfg*
EMP: 7 EST: 1952
SQ FT: 3,000
SALES: 300K **Privately Held**
SIC: 3451 Screw machine products

(G-4856)
ATLAS PRINTING AND EMBROIDERY
Also Called: Brian Rengh
7632 Pleasant View Dr (44134-5817)
PHONE..................................440 882-3537
Brian Rengh, *Owner*
EMP: 4 EST: 1999
SQ FT: 5,000
SALES: 280K **Privately Held**
WEB: www.atlas-printing.com
SIC: 2759 Commercial printing

(G-4857)
ATOTECH USA INC
1000 Harvard Ave (44109-3048)
PHONE..................................216 398-0550
Stephen TSE, *Engineer*
Steve Bellavita, *Branch Mgr*
EMP: 80
SALES (corp-wide): 7.3B **Publicly Held**
SIC: 2899 4225 Chemical supplies for foundries; general warehousing & storage
HQ: Atotech Usa, Llc
1750 Overview Dr
Rock Hill SC 29730

(G-4858)
AUGUST GRAPHICS INC
834 Haywood Dr (44121-3404)
PHONE..................................216 381-5503
William Burgess, *President*
EMP: 4
SALES (est): 280K **Privately Held**
SIC: 2759 Commercial printing

(G-4859)
AUSTIN FINISHING CO INC
3805 E 91st St (44105-2196)
PHONE..................................216 883-0326
Fax: 216 883-9653
Austin Smith, *President*
Nancy Smith, *Vice Pres*
Dave Smith, *Sales Staff*
EMP: 5
SQ FT: 7,200
SALES: 438K **Privately Held**
SIC: 3479 Painting of metal products

(G-4860)
AUSTIN POWDER COMPANY (DH)
25800 Science Park Dr # 300 (44122-7386)
PHONE..................................216 464-2400
Fax: 216 464-2400
William Jack Davis, *Ch of Bd*
David M Gleason, *President*
David True, *Vice Pres*
Richard Stone, *Credit Mgr*
Matt Landis, *Manager*
▲ **EMP:** 70
SQ FT: 25,000
SALES (est): 491MM
SALES (corp-wide): 504.2MM **Privately Held**
SIC: 2892 Explosives

(G-4861)
AUSTIN POWDER HOLDINGS COMPANY (HQ)
25800 Science Park Dr # 300 (44122-7311)
PHONE..................................216 464-2400
William Jack Davis, *Ch of Bd*
David M Gleason, *President*
Michael Gleason, *COO*
Randy Wicks, *Controller*
◆ **EMP:** 60
SQ FT: 25,000
SALES (est): 504.2MM **Privately Held**
WEB: www.austinpowder.com
SIC: 2892 Explosives
PA: Davis Mining & Manufacturing, Inc.
613 Front St E
Coeburn VA 24230
276 395-3354

(G-4862)
AUTO BOLT COMPANY
4740 Manufacturing Ave (44135-2640)
PHONE..................................216 881-3913
Robert Kocian, *President*
Ron Jerome, *QC Mgr*
David Morales, *Engineer*
Robert Tracy, *Controller*
Jessica Orzechowski, *Human Res Mgr*
EMP: 34
SQ FT: 64,100
SALES (est): 9.1MM **Privately Held**
SIC: 3452 Bolts, nuts, rivets & washers

(G-4863)
AUTO EXPO USA OF CLEVELAND
3250 W 117th St (44111-1701)
PHONE..................................216 889-3000
Fax: 216 941-1200
Mike Daniel, *Owner*
Majdulyn Assad,
EMP: 3
SALES (est): 140.5K **Privately Held**
SIC: 3711 Automobile assembly, including specialty automobiles

(G-4864)
AUTO-TAP INC
3317 W 140th St (44111-2428)
PHONE..................................216 671-1043
Fax: 216 671-0377
Jim Sullivan, *President*
Bill Mittas, *Manager*

G
E
O
G
R
A
P
H
I
C

Mike Peteras, *Shareholder*
Frank Suarez, *Shareholder*
EMP: 20
SQ FT: 18,000
SALES (est): 3.6MM **Privately Held**
WEB: www.auto-tap.net
SIC: 3559 2874 7692 Degreasing machines, automotive & industrial; phosphates; welding repair

(G-4865)
AUTOGRAPH INC
Also Called: Autograph Foliages
4419 Perkins Ave (44103-3543)
PHONE....................................216 881-1911
Fax: 216 881-1911
Thomas M Acklin, *Manager*
EMP: 32
SALES (corp-wide): 4.9MM **Privately Held**
WEB: www.autographfoliages.com
SIC: 3999 Foliage, artificial & preserved
PA: Autograph, Inc.
3631 Perkins Ave
Cleveland OH
216 426-6151

(G-4866)
AUTOMATED PACKG SYSTEMS INC
13555 Mccracken Rd (44125-1993)
PHONE....................................216 663-2000
Fax: 216 475-2378
John Hanks, *Business Mgr*
Yates Brad, *Opers-Prdtn-Mfg*
Amy Robinson, *Hum Res Coord*
Brad Yates, *Manager*
Pat Dale, *Supervisor*
EMP: 120
SALES (corp-wide): 186.1MM **Privately Held**
WEB: www.autobag.com
SIC: 3081 2673 Packing materials, plastic sheet; bags: plastic, laminated & coated
PA: Automated Packaging Systems Inc.
10175 Philipp Pkwy
Streetsboro OH 44241
330 528-2000

(G-4867)
AUTOMATED WHEEL LLC
8525 Clinton Rd (44144-1014)
PHONE....................................216 651-9022
Jeff Rabant, *Manager*
Gregory S Hadgis,
◆ **EMP:** 99
SALES (est): 7MM **Privately Held**
WEB: www.automatedwheel.com
SIC: 3471 Electroplating & plating; cleaning, polishing & finishing

(G-4868)
AUTOMATIC SCREW PRODUCTS CO
2070 W 7th St (44113-3690)
PHONE....................................216 241-7896
Fax: 216 241-7897
Bruce Bacik, *President*
Joanna Bacik, *Vice Pres*
▲ **EMP:** 8
SQ FT: 15,500
SALES (est): 650K **Privately Held**
SIC: 3451 Screw machine products

(G-4869)
AUTOMATIC STAMP PRODUCTS INC
1822 Columbus Rd (44113-2472)
PHONE....................................216 781-7933
Fax: 216 781-7937
Raymond L Haserodt, *Vice Pres*
David McAndrews, *Vice Pres*
Ed Dunham, *Manager*
Chuck Horvath, *Manager*
EMP: 12 **EST:** 1946
SQ FT: 44,000
SALES (est): 4.1MM **Privately Held**
WEB: www.automaticstamp.com
SIC: 3469 Metal stampings

(G-4870)
AUTOMATION FINISHING INC
3206 W 121st St (44111-1720)
PHONE....................................216 251-8805
Steve Star, *President*

EMP: 20
SALES (est): 1.3MM **Privately Held**
SIC: 3471 Electroplating & plating

(G-4871)
AVERY DENNISON CORPORATION
15939 Industrial Pkwy (44135-3321)
PHONE....................................216 267-8700
John Evola, *Purch Agent*
Michael Welch, *Engineer*
Matt Wilkinson, *Engineer*
Jennifer Grambo, *Human Res Mgr*
Matt Therrian, *Manager*
EMP: 7
SALES (corp-wide): 6B **Publicly Held**
SIC: 2672 Coated & laminated paper
PA: Avery Dennison Corporation
207 N Goode Ave Fl 6
Glendale CA 91203
626 304-2000

(G-4872)
AVIATION TECHNOLOGIES INC (DH)
1301 E 9th St Ste 3000 (44114-1871)
PHONE....................................216 706-2960
Fax: 216 706-2937
W Nicholas Howley, *CEO*
Russell Fleetwood, *CFO*
Gregory Ruful, *CFO*
Jonathan Carndall, *Controller*
EMP: 2
SQ FT: 27,000
SALES (est): 151.4MM
SALES (corp-wide): 3.1B **Publicly Held**
SIC: 3643 3678 3679 3728 Contacts, electrical; electronic connectors; liquid crystal displays (LCD); aircraft parts & equipment; search & navigation equipment; lighting equipment
HQ: Transdigm, Inc.
4223 Monticello Blvd
Cleveland OH 44121
216 706-2939

(G-4873)
AVILES CONSTRUCTION COMPANY
7011 Clark Ave (44102-5316)
PHONE....................................216 939-1084
Fax: 216 939-1086
Jose Aviles, *President*
Jose E Aviles, *President*
Alex Aviles, *Vice Pres*
Maria Aviles, *Treasurer*
Elisa E Velez, *Admin Sec*
EMP: 21
SALES (est): 4.3MM **Privately Held**
SIC: 2821 Cellulose acetate (plastics)

(G-4874)
AVITAE USA LLC
1660 W 2nd St Ste 1100 (44113-1406)
P.O. Box 93686 (44101-5686)
PHONE....................................216 416-3461
Larry Pollock, *Mng Member*
EMP: 4
SALES (est): 471K **Privately Held**
SIC: 2833 Caffeine & derivatives

(G-4875)
AVTRON AEROSPACE INC (PA)
7900 E Pleasant Valley Rd (44131-5529)
PHONE....................................216 750-5152
John Pesec, *President*
Dustin Myers, *Design Engr*
Joseph Flower, *Controller*
EMP: 113
SQ FT: 65,000
SALES (est): 31.6MM **Privately Held**
WEB: www.avtron.com
SIC: 3351 3728 Bars & bar shapes, copper & copper alloy; aircraft parts & equipment

(G-4876)
AVTRON HOLDINGS LLC
7900 E Pleasant Valley Rd (44131-5529)
PHONE....................................216 642-1230
Edward Jones, *Vice Pres*
Alfred Stanley,
James Ettamarna,
Theodore A Laufik,
Peter Taft,

EMP: 350
SQ FT: 47,707
SALES (est): 40MM **Privately Held**
SIC: 3625 3825 Electric controls & control accessories, industrial; instruments to measure electricity; test equipment for electronic & electric measurement; test equipment for electronic & electrical circuits

(G-4877)
AW FABER-CASTELL USA INC
Also Called: Creativity For Kids
9450 Allen Dr Ste B (44125-4602)
PHONE....................................216 643-4660
Fax: 216 643-4663
Jamie Gallagher, *CEO*
Phyllis Brody, *Vice Pres*
Sara McDonald, *Vice Pres*
Tom Biddel, *Safety Mgr*
Tina Dujmovic, *Engineer*
▲ **EMP:** 100
SQ FT: 85,000
SALES (est): 50.8MM
SALES (corp-wide): 335.3K **Privately Held**
WEB: www.faber-castell.com
SIC: 5092 5112 3944 Arts & crafts equipment & supplies; stationery & office supplies; writing instruments & supplies; games, toys & children's vehicles; craft & hobby kits & sets
HQ: Faber-Castell Ag
Nurnberger Str. 2
Stein 90547
911 996-50

(G-4878)
AWNING FABRI CATERS INC
10237 Lorain Ave (44111-5435)
P.O. Box 182, Avon Lake (44012-0182)
PHONE....................................216 476-4888
Fax: 216 476-0687
Todd Krupa, *President*
EMP: 7
SALES (est): 590K **Privately Held**
SIC: 2394 Awnings, fabric: made from purchased materials

(G-4879)
AXIOMED SPINE CORP (PA)
5350 Trnsp Blvd Ste 18 (44125)
PHONE....................................216 587-5566
Patrick A McBrayer, *President*
James M Kuras, *COO*
Neal Defibaugh, *Vice Pres*
Rebecca Blice, *Engineer*
Nancy Rubin, *CFO*
EMP: 15
SQ FT: 3,000
SALES (est): 1.8MM **Privately Held**
SIC: 3845 Ultrasonic scanning devices, medical

(G-4880)
B & B PAPER CONVERTERS INC
12500 Elmwood Ave Frnt (44111-5987)
PHONE....................................216 941-8100
Fax: 216 941-8174
Jerry Jazwa, *President*
Laurie Cole, *Traffic Mgr*
Cindy Wagner, *Accounts Mgr*
EMP: 12 **EST:** 1947
SQ FT: 120,000
SALES (est): 2.8MM **Privately Held**
SIC: 2621 Newsprint paper

(G-4881)
B & P SPRING PRODUCTION CO
19520 Nottingham Rd (44110-2730)
PHONE....................................216 486-4260
Fax: 216 486-0883
Ken Godnavec, *President*
Justin Ray, *General Mgr*
Lorraine Ray, *Corp Secy*
EMP: 17 **EST:** 1952
SQ FT: 13,000
SALES: 1MM **Privately Held**
SIC: 3495 Precision springs

(G-4882)
B & R MACHINE CO INC
2216 W 65th St (44102-5302)
PHONE....................................216 961-7370
Fax: 216 961-7360

William E Graham, *President*
Teala Graham, *Corp Secy*
Frank Machurey, *Administration*
EMP: 18
SQ FT: 12,000
SALES (est): 3.4MM **Privately Held**
SIC: 3545 3599 Machine tool accessories; machine shop, jobbing & repair

(G-4883)
B M C INC
17209 S Miles Rd (44128-3649)
PHONE....................................216 581-9595
Fax: 216 581-9595
Louie Smierciak, *President*
Walter Smierciak, *Admin Sec*
EMP: 3
SQ FT: 6,000
SALES (est): 338K **Privately Held**
SIC: 3599 Machine shop, jobbing & repair

(G-4884)
B Y G INDUSTRIES INC
Also Called: Guerin-Zimmerman Co
8003 Clinton Rd (44144-1004)
PHONE....................................216 961-5436
Fax: 216 961-1226
James R Brasty, *President*
John Brasty Sr, *Vice Pres*
EMP: 6
SQ FT: 10,000
SALES (est): 764K **Privately Held**
SIC: 3444 3599 Sheet metalwork; machine shop, jobbing & repair

(G-4885)
B&D PRODUCTIONS INC
2223 Willowdale Ave (44109-2840)
PHONE....................................216 961-0310
Billy A Young, *President*
Boyd Derry, *Office Mgr*
EMP: 12
SQ FT: 1,000
SALES: 250K **Privately Held**
SIC: 7389 2731 Advertising, promotional & trade show services; book publishing

(G-4886)
B-R-O-T INCORPORATED
4730 Briar Rd (44135-2595)
PHONE....................................216 267-5335
Fax: 216 267-0811
Kenneth Ott, *President*
Bob Ott, *Vice Pres*
Robert Ott, *Vice Pres*
Patricia Ott, *Treasurer*
Richard Ferraro, *Manager*
EMP: 25 **EST:** 1946
SQ FT: 22,000
SALES (est): 5.5MM **Privately Held**
WEB: www.brot-inc.com
SIC: 3444 2542 Sheet metalwork; partitions & fixtures, except wood

(G-4887)
BACK DEVELOPMENT LLC
3700 Northfield Rd Ste 11 (44122-5240)
PHONE....................................937 671-7896
Brian Back, *President*
Lauren Back, *Vice Pres*
EMP: 3
SQ FT: 2,500
SALES (est): 91.3K **Privately Held**
SIC: 2068 Salted & roasted nuts & seeds

(G-4888)
BAN-FAM INDUSTRIES INC
4740 Briar Rd (44135-5038)
PHONE....................................216 265-9588
Fax: 216 251-2458
Gary Banyasz, *President*
Frank Banyasz, *President*
Jim Banyasz, *Vice Pres*
Alice Banyasz, *Treasurer*
Chris Staab, *Treasurer*
EMP: 8
SQ FT: 15,000
SALES: 500K **Privately Held**
SIC: 3599 3594 3568 Machine shop, jobbing & repair; fluid power pumps & motors; power transmission equipment

(G-4889)
BARBS GRAFFITI INC (PA)
Also Called: Graffiti Co
3111 Carnegie Ave (44115-2632)
PHONE...................216 881-5550
Fax: 216 881-4043
Abe Miller, *President*
Barbara Miller, *Corp Secy*
▲ EMP: 40
SQ FT: 18,000
SALES (est): 6.3MM **Privately Held**
WEB: www.graffiticaps.com
SIC: 2353 2395 5136 5137 Baseball
caps; pleating & stitching; sportswear,
men's & boys'; sportswear, women's &
children's

(G-4890)
BARILE PRECISION GRINDING INC
12320 Plaza Dr (44130-1043)
PHONE...................216 267-6500
Fax: 440 237-0931
Michael Barile, *President*
Steve Lekas, *Manager*
EMP: 25
SALES: 1.4MM **Privately Held**
WEB: www.barilegrinding.com
SIC: 3599 Machine shop, jobbing & repair

(G-4891)
BARKER PRODUCTS COMPANY
1028 E 134th St (44110-2248)
P.O. Box 10845 (44110-0845)
PHONE...................216 249-0900
Fax: 216 249-3009
Hal Myers, *Manager*
Benjamin Dagley, *President*
Bill Gallagher, *General Mgr*
Dr Dieter Myers, *Vice Pres*
Christopher Sullivan, *Vice Pres*
▲ EMP: 30 EST: 1945
SALES (est): 4.4MM **Privately Held**
SIC: 3471 Electroplating of metals or
formed products

(G-4892)
BARTAN DESIGN INC
13100 Enterprise Ave (44135-5102)
PHONE...................216 267-6474
Fax: 216 267-6478
Mircea S Bartan, *President*
Rabu Bartan, *Vice Pres*
Maria Bartan, *Admin Sec*
EMP: 3
SQ FT: 8,640
SALES: 200K **Privately Held**
WEB: www.bartandesign.com
SIC: 3281 Granite, cut & shaped

(G-4893)
BARTH INDUSTRIES CO LP (PA)
12650 Brookpark Rd (44130-1154)
PHONE...................216 267-0531
Fax: 216 267-1966
Clark Neft, *President*
Richard Legan, *Exec VP*
Russ Lauer, *Vice Pres*
Don Hansinger, *Project Engr*
Anne Margaretha, *Asst Controller*
▲ EMP: 72
SQ FT: 120,700
SALES (est): 13.5MM **Privately Held**
WEB: www.barth-landis.com
SIC: 3541 3542 3535 3699 Machine
tools, metal cutting type; machine tools,
metal forming type; conveyors & convey-
ing equipment; electrical equipment &
supplies; metalworking machinery

(G-4894)
BASF CATALYSTS LLC
23800 Mercantile Rd (44122-5908)
P.O. Box 22126 (44122-0126)
PHONE...................216 360-5005
David Disantis, *Engineer*
John Ferek, *Branch Mgr*
EMP: 83
SALES (corp-wide): 60.8B **Privately Held**
SIC: 2819 8731 Industrial inorganic chem-
icals; commercial physical research
HQ: Basf Catalysts Llc
25 Middlesex Tpke
Iselin NJ 08830
732 205-5000

(G-4895)
BASF CONSTRUCTION CHEM LLC (DH)
Also Called: Degussa Construction
23700 Chagrin Blvd (44122-5506)
PHONE...................216 831-5500
John Salvatore, *President*
Frank Apicella, *Research*
Michael Pelsozy, *Research*
Donald Kehr, *Treasurer*
Sandy Sanson, *Credit Staff*
◆ EMP: 50
SALES (est): 317.4MM
SALES (corp-wide): 60.8B **Privately Held**
WEB: www.basf-admixtures.com
SIC: 2899 2851 1799 Concrete curing &
hardening compounds; epoxy coatings;
vinyl coatings, strippable; caulking (con-
struction); waterproofing
HQ: Basf Corporation
100 Park Ave
Florham Park NJ 07932
973 245-6000

(G-4896)
BASIC CASES INC
19561 Miles Rd (44128-4111)
PHONE...................216 662-3900
Fax: 216 475-8443
Kenneth Wieder, *President*
Ruth Wieder, *Treasurer*
EMP: 8
SQ FT: 22,000
SALES (est): 940.2K **Privately Held**
WEB: www.basiccases.com
SIC: 2511 2521 Wood household furniture;
wood office furniture

(G-4897)
BAY VILLAGE PRINTING INC
27209 Wolf Rd (44140-2020)
P.O. Box 40431, Bay Village (44140-0431)
PHONE...................440 892-2005
Fax: 440 892-2035
Jim Dolfi, *President*
Linda Dolfi, *Vice Pres*
EMP: 4
SQ FT: 1,700
SALES: 350K **Privately Held**
SIC: 2752 Commercial printing, offset

(G-4898)
BDI INC (PA)
Also Called: Baring Distributors
8000 Hub Pkwy (44125-5731)
PHONE...................216 642-9100
Frank L Bystricky, *CEO*
Mike Fryz, *Principal*
Chris Hawkins, *COO*
Kenneth Miko, *Vice Pres*
Bud Thayer, *Vice Pres*
▲ EMP: 188
SALES (est): 429.5MM **Privately Held**
WEB: www.bdi.com
SIC: 1389 Oil sampling service for oil com-
panies

(G-4899)
BEA-ECC APPARELS INC
1287 W 76th St (44102-2050)
PHONE...................216 650-6336
Siba Beavogui, *Principal*
EMP: 8
SALES (est): 542.1K **Privately Held**
SIC: 2311 Men's & boys' suits & coats

(G-4900)
BEACON METAL FABRICATORS INC
5425 Hamilton Ave Ste D (44114-3983)
PHONE...................216 391-7444
Fax: 216 391-4431
Kenneth Grobolsek, *President*
Robert Grobolssek, *Vice Pres*
Julie Grobolsek, *Manager*
EMP: 13
SQ FT: 11,000
SALES: 700K **Privately Held**
WEB: www.beaconmetalfab.com
SIC: 3599 3444 3446 Machine & other
job shop work; bins, prefabricated sheet
metal; railings, prefabricated metal; orna-
mental metalwork

(G-4901)
BECKERS BAKESHOP INC
13510 Miles Ave (44105-5526)
PHONE...................216 752-4161
Fax: 216 752-6602
Joe J Becker, *President*
Jaean Becker, *Assistant VP*
EMP: 12
SQ FT: 8,000
SALES (est): 1.5MM **Privately Held**
WEB: www.thebridalcafe.com
SIC: 2051 2052 Cakes, bakery: except
frozen; cookies

(G-4902)
BECKWORTH INDUSTRIES INC
Also Called: Ridgewood Brake Co
14511 Saranac Rd (44110-2336)
PHONE...................216 268-5557
Richard K Strauss, *President*
Richard K Stauss, *President*
Richard Stauss Jr, *Vice Pres*
EMP: 4 EST: 1957
SQ FT: 10,000
SALES: 85K **Privately Held**
SIC: 3625 Brakes, electromagnetic

(G-4903)
BEDFORD CABINET INC
21891 Forbes Rd Ste 102 (44146-5462)
PHONE...................440 439-4830
Fax: 440 439-5199
Bruce Smerglia, *President*
Linda Anderson, *Bookkeeper*
EMP: 5
SQ FT: 900
SALES: 1.5MM **Privately Held**
SIC: 2542 Cabinets: show, display or stor-
age: except wood

(G-4904)
BEREA HARDWOOD CO INC
18745 Sheldon Rd (44130-2472)
PHONE...................216 898-8956
Fax: 216 898-8962
James J Heusinger, *President*
▲ EMP: 5
SQ FT: 10,000
SALES (est): 900K **Privately Held**
SIC: 5031 3951 5112 Lumber: rough,
dressed & finished; ball point pens &
parts; cartridges, refill: ball point pens;
fountain pens & fountain pen desk sets;
pens &/or pencils; stationery

(G-4905)
BERGSTROM COMPANY LTD PARTNR
Also Called: Weldon Pump
640 Golden Oak Pkwy (44146-6504)
PHONE...................440 232-2282
Tony Coletto, *CEO*
Barbara Bergstrom, *Partner*
Jon Bergstrom, *Partner*
Walter T Bergstrom, *Partner*
Blane McKelvey, *General Ptnr*
EMP: 33
SQ FT: 13,600
SALES (est): 6.9MM **Privately Held**
WEB: www.weldonracing.com
SIC: 3714 3594 3586 3561 Fuel pumps,
motor vehicle; lubrication systems &
parts, motor vehicle; hydraulic fluid power
pumps for auto steering mechanism; fluid
power pumps & motors; measuring & dis-
pensing pumps; pumps & pumping equip-
ment

(G-4906)
BERNARD R DOYLES INC
Also Called: Fastsigns
2102 Saint Clair Ave Ne (44114-4047)
PHONE...................216 523-2288
Fax: 216 523-1265
Bernard R Doyle, *President*
Mary Doyle, *Vice Pres*
EMP: 5
SQ FT: 1,800
SALES (est): 586.3K **Privately Held**
SIC: 3993 7389 Signs & advertising spe-
cialties; sign painting & lettering shop

(G-4907)
BERNARD SPECIALTY CO
2800 E 55th St Frnt (44104-2861)
PHONE...................216 881-2200

(G-4908)
BERTSHERM PRODUCTS INC
1417 E 94th St (44106-1011)
P.O. Box 606147 (44106-0647)
PHONE...................440 268-8389
Mustafa Rashid, *CEO*
Julius Graves, *Senior VP*
Winston House, *Vice Pres*
EMP: 6
SALES: 75K **Privately Held**
SIC: 2844 Deodorants, personal

(G-4909)
BETA MACHINE COMPANY INC
17702 S Waterloo Rd (44119-3220)
PHONE...................216 383-0000
Fax: 216 383-0002
John Haymond, *President*
EMP: 14
SQ FT: 8,000
SALES: 300K **Privately Held**
SIC: 3599 Machine shop, jobbing & repair

(G-4910)
BETLEY PRINTING CO
Also Called: American Book Screening
3816 Cullen Dr (44105-7201)
PHONE...................216 206-5600
William T Betley, *Owner*
EMP: 3
SQ FT: 3,200
SALES (est): 274.8K **Privately Held**
SIC: 2752 2759 Business forms, litho-
graphed; letterpress printing

(G-4911)
BEVERAGE MACHINE & FABRICATORS
13301 Lakewood Hts Blvd (44107-6288)
PHONE...................216 252-5100
Fax: 216 252-7977
John D Geiger, *President*
Nancy Geiger, *Admin Sec*
EMP: 15
SQ FT: 15,000
SALES (est): 2.2MM **Privately Held**
SIC: 3599 Machine shop, jobbing & repair

(G-4912)
BIG GUS ONION RINGS INC
4500 Turney Rd (44105-6716)
PHONE...................216 883-9045
Fax: 216 883-9046
Peter George, *President*
Angela George, *Corp Secy*
Thomas George, *Vice Pres*
EMP: 20
SQ FT: 5,000
SALES (est): 4.1MM **Privately Held**
SIC: 2037 5148 2099 Vegetables, quick
frozen & cold pack, excl. potato products;
fruits, fresh; vegetables, fresh; food
preparations

(G-4913)
BLACK & DECKER CORPORATION
12100 Snow Rd Ste 1 (44130-9319)
PHONE...................440 842-9100
Fax: 440 884-3430
Mark Konecek, *Branch Mgr*
EMP: 33
SALES (corp-wide): 11.4B **Publicly Held**
WEB: www.blackanddecker.com
SIC: 3546 Power-driven handtools
HQ: The Black & Decker Corporation
701 E Joppa Rd
Towson MD 21286
410 716-3900

(G-4914)
BLAINS FOLDING SERVICE INC
4103 Detroit Ave (44113-2721)
PHONE...................216 631-4700
Fax: 216 631-4924

GEOGRAPHIC

Edward Blain, *President*
Carol Blain, *Corp Secy*
EMP: 7
SALES: 700K **Privately Held**
SIC: 2789 Binding only: books, pamphlets, magazines, etc.

(G-4915)
BLASTER CHEMICAL CO INC
8500 Sweet Valley Dr (44125-4214)
PHONE.................................216 901-5800
Fax: 216 901-5801
Tom Porter, *Chairman*
EMP: 3
SALES (est): 394.7K **Privately Held**
SIC: 2911 Petroleum refining

(G-4916)
BLASTER CORPORATION
8500 Sweet Valley Dr (44125-4214)
PHONE.................................216 901-5800
Thomas Porter, *CEO*
Tom Hrabak, *Engineer*
Ted Bradley, *Sales Dir*
George Ebert, *Manager*
Kurt Gabram, *Info Tech Mgr*
EMP: 42 **EST:** 1959
SQ FT: 20,000
SALES (est): 10.7MM **Privately Held**
WEB: www.pbblaster.com
SIC: 2911 2819 2842 2992 Fuel additives; catalysts, chemical; automobile polish; lubricating oils & greases; chemical preparations

(G-4917)
BLITZ TOOL & DIE INC
11941 Abbey Rd Ste I (44133-2663)
PHONE.................................440 237-1177
Ralph Rehner, *President*
EMP: 6
SQ FT: 3,500
SALES: 300K **Privately Held**
SIC: 3544 Special dies & tools

(G-4918)
BLOOM LAKE IRON ORE MINE LTD
200 Public Sq (44114-2316)
PHONE.................................216 694-5700
Joe Carrabba, *CEO*
Joseph A Carrabba, *President*
Laurie Brlas, *President*
Donald Gallagher, *President*
Clifford Smith, *Vice Pres*
EMP: 7404 **EST:** 2012
SALES (est): 57.6MM
SALES (corp-wide): 2.1B **Publicly Held**
SIC: 1011 Iron ore mining
PA: Cliffs Natural Resources Inc.
200 Public Sq Ste 3300
Cleveland OH 44114
216 694-5700

(G-4919)
BLUE LINE PAINTING LLC
19520 Nottingham Rd (44110-2730)
PHONE.................................440 951-2583
Sean Rogers, *Owner*
EMP: 4
SALES (est): 240K **Privately Held**
SIC: 2741 Miscellaneous publishing

(G-4920)
BOARD OF PARK COMMISSIONERS
4101 Fulton Pkwy (44144-1923)
PHONE.................................216 635-3200
Dan T Moore, *Principal*
EMP: 4
SALES (est): 187.8K **Privately Held**
SIC: 3949 Shafts, golf club

(G-4921)
BODYCOTE THERMAL PROC INC
5475 Avion Park Dr (44143-1918)
PHONE.................................440 473-2020
Ron Perkins, *Branch Mgr*
EMP: 18
SALES (corp-wide): 739.3MM **Privately Held**
SIC: 3398 Metal heat treating

HQ: Bodycote Thermal Processing, Inc.
12700 Park Central Dr # 700
Dallas TX 75251
214 904-2420

(G-4922)
BOMEN MARKING PRODUCTS INC
12905 York Delta Dr Ste A (44133-3551)
PHONE.................................440 582-0053
Fax: 440 582-0054
Joseph Mendyka, *President*
EMP: 9
SQ FT: 3,800
SALES: 700K **Privately Held**
SIC: 2796 3599 Steel line engraving for the printing trade; custom machinery

(G-4923)
BOND DISTRIBUTING LLC
Also Called: One Time
701 Beta Dr Ste 8 (44143-2337)
PHONE.................................440 461-7920
Diana Pummel, *Office Mgr*
Catherine Hartley, *Director*
Scott Fishel,
EMP: 6
SQ FT: 4,650
SALES: 832K **Privately Held**
WEB: www.onetimewood.com
SIC: 2899 Chemical preparations

(G-4924)
BONFOEY CO
1710 Euclid Ave (44115-2134)
PHONE.................................216 621-0178
Fax: 216 621-7033
Richard G Moore, *President*
Marcia Hall, *Sales/Mktg Dir*
Pamela Stropko, *Sls & Mktg Exec*
Olga Merela, *Treasurer*
Jean T Velcio, *Technology*
EMP: 15 **EST:** 1893
SQ FT: 9,300
SALES (est): 2.3MM **Privately Held**
WEB: www.bonfoey.com
SIC: 2499 5719 8999 Picture & mirror frames, wood; pictures, wall; art restoration

(G-4925)
BORDEN DAIRY COMPANY OHIO LLC
Also Called: Dairymens
3068 W 106th St (44111-1801)
PHONE.................................216 671-2300
Fax: 216 671-1169
Dale Smith, *Plant Mgr*
F David Race, *Controller*
Gina Roganish, *Credit Mgr*
Russell Dzurec, *Mng Member*
Steven Murn, *Manager*
EMP: 150 **EST:** 1923
SQ FT: 360,000
SALES (est): 52.5MM **Privately Held**
SIC: 2026 Fluid milk; milk processing (pasteurizing, homogenizing, bottling)
HQ: National Dairy, Llc
8750 N Central Expy # 400
Dallas TX 75231
469 587-0190

(G-4926)
BORMAN ENTERPRISES INC
Also Called: Cleveland Indus Training Ctr
1311 Brookpark Rd (44109-5829)
PHONE.................................216 459-9292
Donald Borman, *President*
Marybeth Borman, *Corp Secy*
Joseph Scheall, *Vice Pres*
EMP: 10
SQ FT: 13,000
SALES (est): 1.6MM **Privately Held**
WEB: www.bormanenterprises.com
SIC: 3599 8222 Machine shop, jobbing & repair; technical institute

(G-4927)
BOXIT CORPORATION (HQ)
5555 Walworth Ave (44102-4430)
PHONE.................................216 631-6900
Fax: 216 634-2319
Donald Zaas, *Ch of Bd*
Joel Zaas, *President*
Mark Cassese, *COO*
Ron Knapp, *Engineer*

John L Asimakopoulos, *CFO*
EMP: 54
SQ FT: 100,000
SALES (est): 41.4MM
SALES (corp-wide): 58.5MM **Privately Held**
SIC: 2652 2657 Setup paperboard boxes; folding paperboard boxes
PA: The Apex Paper Box Company
5555 Walworth Ave
Cleveland OH 44102
216 631-4000

(G-4928)
BOXIT CORPORATION
3000 Quigley Rd B (44113-4591)
PHONE.................................216 416-9475
Fax: 216 416-9479
Mark Cassese, *Principal*
EMP: 8
SALES (corp-wide): 58.5MM **Privately Held**
SIC: 2657 2652 Folding paperboard boxes; setup paperboard boxes
HQ: Boxit Corporation
5555 Walworth Ave
Cleveland OH 44102
216 631-6900

(G-4929)
BRADEN-SUTPHIN INK COMPANY (PA)
3650 E 93rd St (44105-2145)
PHONE.................................216 271-2300
Fax: 216 271-0515
Jim Leitch, *CEO*
Ted Zelek, *Ch of Bd*
Albert C Sutphin Jr, *President*
Tim Hennessey, *Plant Mgr*
Luis Torres, *Plant Mgr*
▲ **EMP:** 118
SQ FT: 98,000
SALES (est): 27.5MM **Privately Held**
WEB: www.bsink.com
SIC: 2893 2899 Printing ink; chemical preparations

(G-4930)
BRADLEY METAL FABRICATION LLC
17600 S Waterloo Rd (44119-3219)
PHONE.................................216 881-7400
Clint Bradley, *Mng Member*
Jamie Benak, *Manager*
EMP: 15
SQ FT: 10,000
SALES (est): 3.4MM **Privately Held**
SIC: 3441 Fabricated structural metal

(G-4931)
BRIGHT FOCUS SALES INC
2310 Superior Ave E # 225 (44114-4256)
PHONE.................................216 751-8384
Greg Shick, *President*
EMP: 15 **EST:** 2004
SALES (est): 1.8MM **Privately Held**
SIC: 3674 Light emitting diodes

(G-4932)
BROADWAY OFFSET PRINTING CO
3800 Euclid Ave (44115-2560)
PHONE.................................216 391-3800
Fax: 216 391-3819
Lawrence Kohn, *President*
Ted Kohn, *Principal*
Phyllis Kohn, *Corp Secy*
EMP: 13 **EST:** 1960
SQ FT: 14,000
SALES (est): 1.6MM **Privately Held**
SIC: 2752 Commercial printing, offset

(G-4933)
BROCO PRODUCTS INC
18624 Syracuse Ave (44110-2521)
PHONE.................................216 531-0880
Fax: 216 531-8539
Barry Brown, *President*
Joyce Brown, *Vice Pres*
Kevin Lovas, *Sales Staff*
Darrell Gorzelanczyk,
EMP: 9
SQ FT: 18,000

SALES (est): 1.8MM **Privately Held**
WEB: www.brocoproducts.com
SIC: 3559 2899 Metal finishing equipment for plating, etc.; metal treating compounds

(G-4934)
BROOKLYN MACHINE & MFG CO INC
5180 Grant Ave (44125-1065)
PHONE.................................216 341-1846
Fax: 216 341-1867
Walter Spann, *President*
Frederick Spann, *Corp Secy*
EMP: 7
SQ FT: 8,500
SALES (est): 880K **Privately Held**
SIC: 3599 Machine shop, jobbing & repair

(G-4935)
BROOKPARK LABORATORIES INC
4595 Manufacturing Ave (44135-2635)
PHONE.................................216 267-7140
Fax: 216 362-7398
Robin Ancell, *President*
Jean Roch, *General Mgr*
Susan Midolo, *Bookkeeper*
EMP: 5 **EST:** 1963
SQ FT: 1,500
SALES: 500K **Privately Held**
SIC: 3585 3812 Coolers, milk & water: electric; search & navigation equipment

(G-4936)
BROST FOUNDRY COMPANY (PA)
2934 E 55th St (44127-1207)
PHONE.................................216 641-1131
Fax: 216 641-0010
Tom Peretti, *President*
Eileen Pacholski, *Manager*
Carl Robards, *Director*
EMP: 28 **EST:** 1910
SQ FT: 45,000
SALES (est): 5.3MM **Privately Held**
WEB: www.brostfoundry.com
SIC: 3366 3365 3369 3325 Castings (except die): bronze; castings (except die): brass; aluminum & aluminum-based alloy castings; nonferrous foundries; steel foundries; steel investment foundries

(G-4937)
BROTHERS EQUIPMENT INC
Also Called: Ace
1335 E 171st St (44110-2525)
PHONE.................................216 458-0180
Drew Jurek Jr, *General Mgr*
Tracy Jurek, *Admin Sec*
EMP: 9
SALES (est): 950K **Privately Held**
SIC: 3715 Truck trailers

(G-4938)
BROTHERS PRINTING CO INC
2000 Euclid Ave (44115-2276)
PHONE.................................216 621-6050
Fax: 216 621-4202
Dotty Kaufman, *CEO*
Jay Kaufman, *President*
David Kaufman, *Treasurer*
EMP: 14 **EST:** 1925
SQ FT: 36,000
SALES (est): 1.1MM **Privately Held**
SIC: 2752 2759 Commercial printing, offset; letterpress printing

(G-4939)
BROWN MACHINE CO
16151 Puritas Ave (44135-2617)
PHONE.................................216 631-1255
Fax: 216 631-1228
Robert Brown, *Owner*
EMP: 4
SQ FT: 6,000
SALES (est): 220K **Privately Held**
SIC: 3599 Machine & other job shop work

(G-4940)
BRUENING GLASS WORKS INC
Also Called: Konys, Mark Glass Design
20157 Lake Rd (44116-1514)
PHONE.................................440 333-4768
Fax: 440 356-1522
Marc Konys, *President*

▲ = Import ▼=Export
◆ =Import/Export

Chris Konys, *Vice Pres*
EMP: 6 **EST:** 1945
SQ FT: 1,500
SALES: 290K **Privately Held**
WEB: www.brueningglass.com
SIC: 3231 5719 5712 Mirrored glass; furniture tops, glass: cut, beveled or polished; mirrors; furniture stores

(G-4941)
BRUSHES INC
5400 Smith Rd (44142-2025)
PHONE................................216 267-8084
Mary Drews, *President*
EMP: 25 **EST:** 1958
SQ FT: 9,600
SALES (est): 2.1MM **Privately Held**
SIC: 3991 Brushes, household or industrial; shaving brushes

(G-4942)
BRUSHES INC
Also Called: Malin Company
5400 Smith Rd (44142-2025)
PHONE................................216 267-8084
Fax: 216 267-9077
Leonard Defino, *President*
Jom Hauck, *Vice Pres*
▲ **EMP:** 31
SALES (est): 6MM **Privately Held**
WEB: www.brushescorp.com
SIC: 3315 Wire & fabricated wire products

(G-4943)
BUCKEYE METALS INDUSTRIES INC
3238 E 82nd St (44104-4338)
PHONE................................216 663-4300
Bruce Ison, *President*
Lowy M Marty, *Plant Supt*
Marilyn Schickler, *Sales Mgr*
EMP: 10
SQ FT: 45,000
SALES (est): 3.1MM **Privately Held**
SIC: 3469 5051 Metal stampings; steel

(G-4944)
BUCKEYE SAUCE CORPORATION (PA)
Also Called: Hot Sauce Williams Barbecue
12201 Buckeye Rd (44120-2645)
PHONE................................216 751-0440
Fax: 216 751-0468
Lemaud Williams, *President*
Essie Williams, *Vice Pres*
James Williams, *Admin Sec*
Herb Williams,
EMP: 12
SALES (est): 1.4MM **Privately Held**
SIC: 5812 2033 Barbecue restaurant; barbecue sauce: packaged in cans, jars, etc.

(G-4945)
BUD MAY INC
Also Called: Maynard Company, The
16850 Hummel Rd (44142-2131)
PHONE................................216 676-8850
Fax: 216 676-8840
John Maynard, *President*
Tom Maynard, *Vice Pres*
Joan Santoro, *Manager*
EMP: 10 **EST:** 1974
SQ FT: 18,000
SALES: 571K **Privately Held**
SIC: 3541 Grinding, polishing, buffing, lapping & honing machines; deburring machines

(G-4946)
BUFFEX METAL FINISHING INC
1935 W 96th St Ste L (44102-2600)
PHONE................................216 631-2202
Fax: 216 631-1541
Orlando R Quintana, *President*
Louis Quintana, *Vice Pres*
EMP: 11
SQ FT: 10,000
SALES: 500K **Privately Held**
SIC: 3471 Buffing for the trade; polishing, metals or formed products

(G-4947)
BULA FORGE & MACHINE INC
Also Called: B F
3001 W 121st St (44111-1638)
PHONE................................216 252-7600

Fax: 216 231-5107
Wayne Phelps, *President*
Karen Mason, *Vice Pres*
Karen Patti, *Manager*
EMP: 22
SALES: 3MM **Privately Held**
WEB: www.bulaforge.com
SIC: 3462 Iron & steel forgings

(G-4948)
BURCH PLASTICS CORP
30627 Webster Rd (44140-1107)
PHONE................................440 835-2059
Salwin Burch, *President*
EMP: 3
SALES (est): 330K **Privately Held**
SIC: 2655 Cans, composite: foil-fiber & other: from purchased fiber

(G-4949)
BURNER TECHNOLOGY UNLIMITED
7590 Independence Dr (44146-5541)
PHONE................................440 232-6181
Fax: 440 232-1834
Carl Suchovsky, *President*
Dave Hucik, *Manager*
EMP: 3
SQ FT: 2,800
SALES (est): 407.8K **Privately Held**
SIC: 3433 3823 Gas burners, industrial; combustion control instruments

(G-4950)
BURTON BOTTLING COMPANY INC
1240 E 9th St R (44199-2001)
PHONE................................216 681-0025
Bonnie L Burton, *President*
EMP: 23
SALES (est): 1.6MM **Privately Held**
SIC: 2086 3999 Carbonated soft drinks, bottled & canned; manufacturing industries

(G-4951)
BUSCHMAN CORPORATION
4100 Payne Ave Ste 1 (44103-2340)
PHONE................................216 431-6633
Fax: 216 431-5037
Tom Buschman, *CEO*
Ross Defelice, *President*
Steve Matusa, *Controller*
Chris Hughes, *Sales Staff*
Bill Wayner, *Comp Spec*
▲ **EMP:** 19
SQ FT: 90,000
SALES (est): 5.7MM **Privately Held**
WEB: www.buschmancorp.com
SIC: 3312 2679 2295 Rods, iron & steel: made in steel mills; paper products, converted; tape, varnished: plastic & other coated (except magnetic)

(G-4952)
BUSH INC
15901 Industrial Pkwy (44135-3321)
PHONE................................216 362-6700
H Russell Bush, *President*
Kim Burgess, *Sales Staff*
Kathy Bush, *Sales Staff*
Patrick Bush, *Sales Staff*
Martin King, *Sales Staff*
EMP: 23
SALES (est): 3.2MM **Privately Held**
SIC: 2759 Commercial printing

(G-4953)
BUTERA MANUFACTURING INDS
1068 E 134th St (44110-2248)
P.O. Box 349, Wickliffe (44092-0349)
PHONE................................216 761-8800
Fax: 216 761-8809
Brian Butera, *President*
Richard Butera Jr, *Opers-Prdtn-Mfg*
EMP: 6
SQ FT: 3,000
SALES (est): 657.6K **Privately Held**
SIC: 3429 Animal traps, iron or steel

(G-4954)
BUYNIX
2142 W 96th St (44102-3708)
PHONE................................216 551-3485

Virgil Tudorancea, *Owner*
EMP: 5
SALES: 41K **Privately Held**
SIC: 3579 Office machines

(G-4955)
C D C AT CITYVIEW
6606 Carnegie Ave (44103-4622)
PHONE................................216 426-2020
Jim Berish, *Director*
EMP: 35
SALES (est): 2.1MM **Privately Held**
SIC: 3826 Blood testing apparatus

(G-4956)
C L S INC
3812 W 150th St (44111-5805)
PHONE................................216 251-5011
Ron Anderson, *President*
EMP: 3 **EST:** 2008
SALES (est): 215.2K **Privately Held**
SIC: 3699 Laser welding, drilling & cutting equipment

(G-4957)
C P S ENTERPRISES INC
Also Called: Able One's Moving Company
9815 Reno Ave (44105-2723)
PHONE................................216 441-7969
Fax: 216 441-7989
Charles P Stephens, *President*
EMP: 15
SALES (est): 1.4MM **Privately Held**
SIC: 4212 2759 Moving services; commercial printing

(G-4958)
CA LITZLER CO INC
4800 W 160th St (44135-2689)
PHONE................................216 267-8020
Fax: 216 267-9856
Matthew C Litzler, *President*
William J Urban, *COO*
Julia Mayer, *Vice Pres*
J H Rogers, *Vice Pres*
P S Sprague, *Vice Pres*
▲ **EMP:** 42
SQ FT: 32,000
SALES (est): 20.4MM
SALES (corp-wide): 36.1MM **Privately Held**
WEB: www.calitzler.com
SIC: 3567 3535 3552 3549 Industrial furnaces & ovens; conveyors & conveying equipment; textile machinery; metalworking machinery; fabricated plate work (boiler shop)
PA: C.A. Litzler Holding Company
4800 W 160th St
Cleveland OH 44135
216 267-8020

(G-4959)
CA LITZLER HOLDING COMPANY (PA)
4800 W 160th St (44135-2634)
PHONE................................216 267-8020
Matthew C Litzler, *CEO*
Bill Urban, *COO*
William J Urban, *COO*
Juila L Mayer, *Vice Pres*
▲ **EMP:** 59 **EST:** 1999
SALES (est): 36.1MM **Privately Held**
SIC: 3567 Industrial furnaces & ovens

(G-4960)
CABINET CONCEPTS INC
Also Called: Custom Millwork Designs
590 Golden Oak Pkwy B (44146-6502)
PHONE................................440 232-4644
Fax: 440 232-4653
Karen Torrence, *President*
James Torrence, *Vice Pres*
Francis McCracwenl, *Office Mgr*
EMP: 7
SQ FT: 4,000
SALES (est): 881.2K **Privately Held**
SIC: 2434 Wood kitchen cabinets

(G-4961)
CABINET SYSTEMS INC
9830 York Theta Dr (44133-3533)
PHONE................................440 237-1924
Fax: 440 237-1932
John W Petrow Jr, *President*
EMP: 4

SQ FT: 10,000
SALES: 450K **Privately Held**
SIC: 2434 2521 2511 1521 Wood kitchen cabinets; cabinets, office: wood; wood household furniture; new construction, single-family houses; general remodeling, single-family houses

(G-4962)
CAILIN DEV LTD LBLTY CO
8960 70th St (44102)
PHONE................................216 408-6261
Louis Finucane, *Mng Member*
EMP: 10
SALES (est): 2MM **Privately Held**
SIC: 3523 3532 3965 3462 Farm machinery & equipment; mining machinery; straight pins: steel or brass; iron & steel forgings

(G-4963)
CAM-LEM INC
1768 E 25th St (44114-4418)
PHONE................................216 391-7750
Brian Mathewson, *CEO*
Terrell Pin, *COO*
EMP: 9
SQ FT: 1,100
SALES (est): 913.6K **Privately Held**
WEB: www.camlem.com
SIC: 3559 3544 3264 Robots, molding & forming plastics; special dies, tools, jigs & fixtures; porcelain electrical supplies

(G-4964)
CAMELOT TYPESETTING COMPANY
2570 Superior Ave E # 201 (44114-4252)
PHONE................................216 574-8973
Fax: 216 344-3026
Jack East, *Owner*
EMP: 6
SQ FT: 1,300
SALES (est): 446.6K **Privately Held**
SIC: 2791 Typesetting

(G-4965)
CANSTO COATINGS LTD
9320 Woodland Ave (44104-2410)
PHONE................................216 231-6115
Sam P Cannata, *Managing Prtnr*
EMP: 10
SALES (est): 1.3MM **Privately Held**
SIC: 2851 Paints & allied products

(G-4966)
CANSTO PAINT AND VARNISH CO
9320 Woodland Ave (44104-2489)
PHONE................................216 231-6115
Fax: 216 231-6117
Sam A Cannata Jr, *President*
Nancy G Glorioso, *Treasurer*
Katherine Wojtowicz, *Admin Sec*
EMP: 7
SQ FT: 18,000
SALES (est): 1MM **Privately Held**
SIC: 2851 Paints & paint additives; enamels; lacquer: bases, dopes, thinner; varnishes

(G-4967)
CANVAS EXCHANGE INC
2330 Denison Ave (44109-2912)
PHONE................................216 749-2233
Fax: 216 749-0987
Hank Proctor, *President*
EMP: 8
SQ FT: 5,000
SALES (est): 610K **Privately Held**
SIC: 2394 Canvas & related products

(G-4968)
CANVAS SPECIALTY MFG CO
4045 Saint Clair Ave (44103-1117)
PHONE................................216 881-0647
Fax: 216 881-6848
Carl E Heilman, *President*
EMP: 7
SQ FT: 8,500
SALES (est): 850K **Privately Held**
WEB: www.canvasspecialty.com
SIC: 2394 7699 Awnings, fabric: made from purchased materials; nautical repair services; recreational sporting equipment repair services; tent repair shop

(G-4969)
CAP DATA SUPPLY INC
15227 Triskett Rd (44111-3113)
PHONE................................216 252-2280
James De Caprio, *President*
John Thompson, *Executive*
EMP: 5
SQ FT: 3,000
SALES: 350K **Privately Held**
SIC: 3579 Word processing equipment

(G-4970)
CAPITAL ENGRAVING COMPANY
11963 Abbey Rd (44133-2635)
PHONE................................440 237-7760
Fax: 440 237-7763
Norman Andrysco, *Owner*
Ron Baldus, *CFO*
EMP: 4 EST: 1966
SALES: 200K **Privately Held**
SIC: 2796 Engraving on copper, steel,
wood or rubber: printing plates

(G-4971)
CAPITAL TOOL COMPANY
1110 Brookpark Rd (44109-5871)
PHONE................................216 661-5750
Fax: 216 661-5710
Richard Crane, *President*
EMP: 45 EST: 1962
SQ FT: 20,000
SALES (est): 7.4MM **Privately Held**
WEB: www.capitaltoolco.com
SIC: 3544 3545 3443 Special dies &
tools; jigs & fixtures; machine tool acces-
sories; fabricated plate work (boiler shop)

(G-4972)
CAPS
8300 Sweet Valley Dr # 301 (44125-4264)
PHONE................................216 524-0418
Amy Piorkowski, *Manager*
EMP: 8
SALES (est): 1.2MM **Privately Held**
SIC: 2834 Pharmaceutical preparations

(G-4973)
CARAUSTAR INDUSTRIES INC
Also Called: Cleveland Recycling Plant
3400 Vega Ave (44113-4954)
PHONE................................216 961-5060
Richard Ryan, *Opers-Prdtn-Mfg*
EMP: 10
SALES (corp-wide): 1.5B **Privately Held**
WEB: www.caraustar.com
SIC: 2679 2611 Paperboard products,
converted; pulp mills
PA: Caraustar Industries, Inc.
5000 Astell Pwdr Sprng Rd
Austell GA 30106
770 948-3101

(G-4974)
CARAVAN PACKAGING INC (PA)
6427 Eastland Rd (44142-1305)
PHONE................................440 243-4100
Fax: 440 243-4383
Fred Hitti, *President*
Chris Pisanelli, *Vice Pres*
Sue Hitti, *Treasurer*
Wesley Holcombs, *Mktg Dir*
EMP: 10 EST: 1962
SQ FT: 40,000
SALES (est): 1.9MM **Privately Held**
WEB: www.caravanpackaging.com
SIC: 4783 2441 6512 Packing & crating;
nailed wood boxes & shook; boxes, wood;
commercial & industrial building operation

(G-4975)
CARDINAL CUSTOM CABINETS LTD
8201 Almira Ave Ste 10 (44102-5400)
PHONE................................216 281-1570
Anthony Cardinal, *Partner*
James V Cardinal, *Partner*
EMP: 5
SQ FT: 9,000
SALES (est): 497.7K **Privately Held**
SIC: 2434 Wood kitchen cabinets

(G-4976)
CARDIOINSIGHT TECHNOLOGIES INC
11000 Cedar Ave Ste 210 (44106-3056)
PHONE................................216 274-2221
Patrick J Wethington, *President*
Charu Ramanathan, *Founder*
Jim Hassett, *Vice Pres*
Harold Wodlinger, *Vice Pres*
Jack Dantin, *Opers Mgr*
EMP: 9
SALES (est): 2.2MM **Privately Held**
SIC: 3845 Electrocardiographs
PA: Medtronic Public Limited Company
20 Lower Hatch Street
Dublin 2

(G-4977)
CARGILL INCORPORATED
2400 Ships Channel (44113-2673)
P.O. Box 6920 (44101-1920)
PHONE................................216 651-7200
Wayne L Streble, *Buyer*
Luba Varous, *Controller*
Bob Soupko, *Branch Mgr*
EMP: 205
SALES (corp-wide): 107.1B **Privately Held**
WEB: www.cargill.com
SIC: 1479 2899 Salt (common) mining;
chemical preparations
PA: Cargill, Incorporated
15407 Mcginty Rd W
Wayzata MN 55391
952 742-7575

(G-4978)
CARLTON NATCO
13020 Saint Clair Ave (44108-2033)
PHONE................................216 451-5588
Eugene Sizelove, *General Ptnr*
Paul Gierosky, *General Ptnr*
EMP: 3
SQ FT: 3,500
SALES (est): 632.2K **Privately Held**
SIC: 3541 5084 7629 3545 Machine
tools, metal cutting type; industrial ma-
chinery & equipment; electrical repair
shops; machine tool accessories

(G-4979)
CARMENS INSTALLATION CO
Also Called: Carmens Cstm Wndows Treat-
ments
2865 Mayfield Rd (44118-1633)
PHONE................................216 371-5633
Fax: 216 321-4051
Carmen T Montello, *President*
Rose Marie Montello, *Corp Secy*
Salvatore Montello, *Vice Pres*
Gina Montello, *Manager*
EMP: 15
SQ FT: 4,500
SALES (est): 1.7MM **Privately Held**
SIC: 1799 2211 Drapery track installation;
draperies & drapery fabrics, cotton

(G-4980)
CARMEUSE LIME INC
5400 Whiskey Is (44102-2252)
PHONE................................216 961-1010
EMP: 3 **Privately Held**
SIC: 3299 Tile, sand lime
HQ: Carmeuse Lime, Inc.
11 Stanwix St Fl 21
Pittsburgh PA 15222
412 995-5500

(G-4981)
CARNEGIE PLAS CABINETRY INC
1755 Coit Ave (44112-2018)
PHONE................................216 451-3300
Fax: 216 451-3300
Craig Warner, *President*
Lee Knox, *Manager*
EMP: 8
SQ FT: 4,500
SALES: 1MM **Privately Held**
SIC: 2434 Wood kitchen cabinets

(G-4982)
CARNEGIE PROMOTIONS INC
697 Davidson Dr (44143-2052)
PHONE................................440 442-2099

Carol Calta, *Owner*
EMP: 3
SALES (est): 238.7K **Privately Held**
SIC: 2759 Screen printing

(G-4983)
CARR BROS BLDRS SUP & COAL CO
7177 Northfield Rd (44146-5403)
PHONE................................440 232-3700
Floyd E Carr Jr, *President*
Duane Carr, *Vice Pres*
Michael Carr, *Treasurer*
Carol Sabol, *Manager*
Amy Rickleman, *Admin Sec*
EMP: 35 EST: 1892
SQ FT: 3,000
SALES (est): 4.2MM **Privately Held**
WEB: www.carrbrothers.com
SIC: 3273 Ready-mixed concrete

(G-4984)
CARRERA HOLDINGS INC
101 W Prospect Ave (44115-1093)
PHONE................................216 687-1311
James B Mooney, *Principal*
EMP: 4
SALES (est): 326.4K
SALES (corp-wide): 29.4MM **Privately Held**
SIC: 2329 2339 Knickers, dress (sepa-
rate): men's & boys'; aprons, except rub-
ber or plastic: women's, misses', juniors'
PA: Carrera Spa
Via Sant'irene 1
Caldiero VR 37042
045 613-9111

(G-4985)
CARROLL EXHIBIT AND PRINT SVCS
Also Called: Carroll Graphic
5150 Prospect Ave (44103-4324)
PHONE................................216 361-2325
Fax: 216 361-2326
John A Carroll, *President*
EMP: 4
SQ FT: 4,000
SALES (est): 468.5K **Privately Held**
SIC: 2759 7389 Screen printing; sign
painting & lettering shop

(G-4986)
CASE OHIO BURIAL CO (PA)
1720 Columbus Rd (44113-2410)
P.O. Box 26020 (44126-0020)
PHONE................................440 779-1992
Fax: 216 479-6705
Grace Caffo, *President*
Ronald Caffo, *Treasurer*
Wanda Armburger, *Admin Sec*
EMP: 13
SQ FT: 70,000
SALES (est): 1.1MM **Privately Held**
SIC: 3995 5087 Burial caskets; caskets

(G-4987)
CASE PATTERN CO INC
21691 Tungsten Rd (44117-1115)
PHONE................................216 531-0744
Fax: 216 531-8683
Timothy B Gorka, *President*
Lawrence E Gorka, *Corp Secy*
EMP: 5 EST: 1963
SQ FT: 6,000
SALES (est): 671.2K **Privately Held**
SIC: 3543 3544 Foundry patternmaking;
forms (molds), for foundry & plastics
working machinery

(G-4988)
CASE WESTERN RESERVE UNIV
10900 Euclid Ave (44106-4901)
PHONE................................216 368-2574
Fax: 216 368-4335
Debbie Andrews, *Network Enginr*
Elizabeth Keefer,
EMP: 3
SALES (est): 135.2K **Privately Held**
SIC: 3523 Farm machinery & equipment

(G-4989)
CASPA HOME PAGE INC
1501 N Marginal Rd # 166 (44114-3760)
PHONE................................216 781-0748
Charles K Newcomb, *President*

EMP: 5 EST: 1998
SALES: 500K **Privately Held**
SIC: 3324 Aerospace investment castings,
ferrous

(G-4990)
CASSELBERRY CLINIC INC
Also Called: Progressive Pain Relief
5555 Mayfield Rd (44124-2939)
PHONE................................440 995-0555
Ronald Casselberry MD, *President*
Carol Cruise, *Exec Dir*
EMP: 5
SQ FT: 2,000
SALES (est): 636.3K **Privately Held**
SIC: 2834 Medicines, capsuled or ampuled

(G-4991)
CAST SPECIALTIES INC
26711 Miles Rd (44128-5927)
PHONE................................216 292-7393
Fax: 216 292-7686
Martin Dragich, *President*
Benjamin G Ammons, *Chairman*
Michael Paskevich, *Vice Pres*
Katie Irons, *QC Mgr*
John Krisfalusy, *Controller*
EMP: 38 EST: 1960
SQ FT: 40,000
SALES (est): 10.1MM **Privately Held**
WEB: www.castspecialties.com
SIC: 3364 3363 Zinc & zinc-base alloy
die-castings; aluminum die-castings

(G-4992)
CASTALLOY INC
7990 Baker Ave (44102-1903)
PHONE................................216 961-7990
Fax: 216 961-5066
Michael Wood, *President*
Richard J Chalet, *Principal*
Russell Wood, *VP Opers*
Thomas Waldin, *Treasurer*
Joan Murphy, *Admin Sec*
▲ EMP: 55
SQ FT: 40,000
SALES (est): 13.3MM **Privately Held**
WEB: www.castalloy.com
SIC: 3324 Steel investment foundries

(G-4993)
CASTELLI MARBLE INC (PA)
1521 E 47th St (44103-2437)
PHONE................................216 361-2410
Carmelo Cario, *President*
James Laumer, *Manager*
Gina Vicio, *Admin Sec*
▲ EMP: 9
SQ FT: 10,000
SALES (est): 1.4MM **Privately Held**
SIC: 5032 3281 Marble building stone;
granite building stone; cut stone & stone
products

(G-4994)
CATHOLIC CHARITY HISPANIC OFF
2012 W 25th St Ste 507 (44113-4131)
PHONE................................216 696-2197
Fax: 216 696-2088
Maureen Dee, *Owner*
EMP: 15 EST: 2001
SALES (est): 1.2MM **Privately Held**
SIC: 2869 Alcohols, non-beverage

(G-4995)
CATS PRINTING INC
3980 Mayfield Rd (44121-2223)
PHONE................................216 381-8181
Fax: 216 381-7383
Gary Katz, *President*
Jonathon Kittredge, *Vice Pres*
Susanne Katz, *Treasurer*
EMP: 4
SQ FT: 1,000
SALES: 150K **Privately Held**
SIC: 2752 Commercial printing, litho-
graphic; commercial printing, offset

(G-4996)
CAXTON NEW STAND
812 Huron Rd E Fl 1 (44115-1126)
PHONE................................216 861-1600
Mike Marchese, *Principal*
EMP: 4

SALES (est): 212.3K **Privately Held**
SIC: 2711 5994 Newspapers, publishing & printing; newsstand

(G-4997)
CBL PRODUCTS
1661 Cumberland Rd (44118-1718)
PHONE..................................216 321-2599
Charlene Lynch, *Owner*
EMP: 3 **EST:** 2001
SALES (est): 150K **Privately Held**
SIC: 2676 Tampons, sanitary: made from purchased paper

(G-4998)
CCL LABEL INC
15939 Industrial Pkwy (44135-3321)
PHONE..................................216 676-2703
Fax: 216 676-2730
Chief Anderson, *Manager*
EMP: 150
SALES (corp-wide): 188.4K **Privately Held**
WEB: www.avery.com
SIC: 2672 3081 3497 2678 Adhesive papers, labels or tapes: from purchased material; gummed paper: made from purchased materials; coated paper, except photographic, carbon or abrasive; unsupported plastics film & sheet; metal foil & leaf; stationery products; notebooks: made from purchased paper; labels, paper: made from purchased material; tags, paper (unprinted): made from purchased paper; paperboard products, converted
HQ: Ccl Label, Inc.
161 Worcester Rd Ste 504
Framingham MA 01701
508 872-4511

(G-4999)
CDI INDUSTRIES INC
Also Called: Coaxial Dynamics
6800 Lake Abrams Dr (44130-3455)
PHONE..................................440 243-1100
Fax: 440 243-1101
Joseph D Kluha, *President*
EMP: 24
SQ FT: 16,000
SALES (est): 4.4MM **Privately Held**
WEB: www.coaxial.com
SIC: 3663 3825 3613 Receivers, radio communications; instruments to measure electricity; switchgear & switchboard apparatus

(G-5000)
CEJA PUBLISHING
3654 Atherstone Rd (44121-1358)
PHONE..................................216 319-0268
Celena Howard, *Principal*
EMP: 4
SALES (est): 145.3K **Privately Held**
SIC: 2741 Miscellaneous publishing

(G-5001)
CELCORE INC (PA)
7850 Freeway Cir Ste 100 (44130-6317)
PHONE..................................440 234-7888
William McDonald, *President*
Mark Bates, *President*
Vicky Anderson, *Treasurer*
EMP: 10
SQ FT: 8,500
SALES (est): 1MM **Privately Held**
WEB: www.celcoreinc.com
SIC: 2493 1761 Insulation & roofing material, reconstituted wood; roofing contractor

(G-5002)
CEN-TROL MACHINE CO
7601 Commerce Park Oval (44131-2303)
PHONE..................................216 524-1932
Fax: 216 524-1918
Henry J Kuska, *Principal*
Allen Straka, *Corp Secy*
Theresa Kuska, *Vice Pres*
EMP: 6 **EST:** 1964
SQ FT: 11,000
SALES: 435.3K **Privately Held**
SIC: 3599 Machine shop, jobbing & repair

(G-5003)
CENTERLESS GRINDING SERVICE
Also Called: C G S
19500 S Miles Rd (44128-4251)
PHONE..................................216 251-4100
Fax: 216 251-6880
Jim Daso, *President*
Terry Daso, *Treasurer*
EMP: 8
SQ FT: 3,632
SALES: 800K **Privately Held**
SIC: 3999 3599 Custom pulverizing & grinding of plastic materials; machine shop, jobbing & repair

(G-5004)
CENTERLESS GRINDING SOLUTIONS
7670 Hub Pkwy (44125-5707)
PHONE..................................216 520-4612
EMP: 3
SALES (est): 294.6K **Privately Held**
SIC: 3599 Grinding castings for the trade

(G-5005)
CENTRAL SYSTEMS & CONTROL
26933 Westwood Rd Ste 400 (44145-4690)
PHONE..................................440 835-0015
Thomas Ruffing, *President*
EMP: 3
SALES (est): 440.2K **Privately Held**
SIC: 3672 3625 Printed circuit boards; control equipment, electric

(G-5006)
CENTURY INTERMEDIATE HOLDG CO (PA)
1 American Rd (44144-2301)
PHONE..................................216 252-7300
Zev Weiss, *CEO*
Jeffrey Weiss, *President*
Jim Maxwell, *Director*
EMP: 15
SALES (est): 2.2B **Privately Held**
SIC: 2771 2679 2656 2678 Greeting cards; gift wrap, paper: made from purchased material; cups, paper: made from purchased material; stationery: made from purchased materials

(G-5007)
CENTURY PLATING INC
18006 S Waterloo Rd (44119-3223)
PHONE..................................216 531-4131
Fax: 216 531-5194
Peter Mooney, *President*
EMP: 9 **EST:** 1950
SQ FT: 20,000
SALES (est): 1.4MM **Privately Held**
WEB: www.centuryplating.com
SIC: 3471 Polishing, metals or formed products; plating of metals or formed products

(G-5008)
CENTURY TOOL & STAMPING INC
1510 University Rd (44113-3585)
PHONE..................................216 241-2032
Fax: 216 241-2331
William Guist Jr, *President*
William Guist LII, *Treasurer*
James Vespoli, *Treasurer*
Cathy Hoy, *Admin Sec*
EMP: 13
SQ FT: 7,800
SALES (est): 1.2MM **Privately Held**
SIC: 3599 Machine shop, jobbing & repair

(G-5009)
CERTIFIED WELDING CO
9603 Clinton Rd (44144-1083)
PHONE..................................216 961-5410
Fax: 216 961-4533
John Salisbury, *President*
Doris Ann Salisbury, *Vice Pres*
EMP: 15
SALES (est): 1MM **Privately Held**
WEB: www.cwcionline.com
SIC: 7692 3599 Welding repair; machine shop, jobbing & repair

(G-5010)
CETEK LTD
20600 Sheldon Rd (44142-1319)
PHONE..................................216 362-3900
Derek Scott, *CEO*
John Bacon, *Vice Pres*
EMP: 30
SALES (est): 2.3MM **Privately Held**
SIC: 2851 Lacquers, varnishes, enamels & other coatings

(G-5011)
CFRC WTR & ENRGY SOLUTIONS INC
850 Euclid Ave Ste 1314 (44114-3308)
P.O. Box 370151, Las Vegas NV (89137-0151)
PHONE..................................216 479-0290
Chuck Williams, *Chairman*
EMP: 5 **EST:** 2014
SQ FT: 400
SALES (est): 302.7K **Privately Held**
SIC: 3432 3491 3492 3088 Plumbing fixture fittings & trim; boiler gauge cocks; control valves, fluid power: hydraulic & pneumatic; shower stalls, fiberglass & plastic; liquid level controls, residential or commercial heating

(G-5012)
CHALFANT SEW FABRICATORS INC
Also Called: Chalfant Loading Dock Eqp
11525 Madison Ave (44102-2392)
PHONE..................................216 521-7922
Jeff Chalfant, *President*
Stephanie Chalfant, *Vice Pres*
Earl Middleton, *Engineer*
Rebecca Sandy, *Treasurer*
Donald Sanford, *Controller*
▼ **EMP:** 41 **EST:** 1940
SQ FT: 50,000
SALES (est): 8.7MM **Privately Held**
WEB: www.chalfantusa.com
SIC: 3069 2394 Sponge rubber & sponge rubber products; canvas & related products

(G-5013)
CHALK OUTLINE PICTURES
4773 Hillary Ln (44143-2910)
PHONE..................................216 291-3944
Lena Chalk, *Principal*
EMP: 3
SALES (est): 132.8K **Privately Held**
SIC: 1422 Chalk mining, crushed & broken-quarrying

(G-5014)
CHARIZMA CORP
Also Called: National Screen Production
1400 E 30th St Ste 201 (44114-4050)
P.O. Box 33520, North Royalton (44133-0520)
PHONE..................................216 621-2220
Fax: 216 621-2731
Marcy Szabados, *President*
Ken Cordle, *Human Res Mgr*
Mary Windhorst, *Human Res Mgr*
Adrian Wright, *Technical Staff*
EMP: 7 **EST:** 1980
SQ FT: 5,000
SALES (est): 450K **Privately Held**
SIC: 2396 5199 Screen printing on fabric articles; advertising specialties

(G-5015)
CHARLES C LEWIS COMPANY
1 W Interstate St Ste 200 (44146-4256)
PHONE..................................440 439-3150
Fax: 440 439-3429
Steve McCoy, *Manager*
EMP: 16
SALES (corp-wide): 10.6MM **Privately Held**
WEB: www.charleslewis.com
SIC: 3312 Plate, steel
PA: The Charles C Lewis Company
209 Page Blvd
Springfield MA 01104
413 733-2121

(G-5016)
CHARLES MESSINA
Also Called: Joseph Industries
16645 Granite Rd (44137-4301)
PHONE..................................216 663-3344
Charles Messina, *Owner*
EMP: 80
SQ FT: 170,000
SALES (est): 6.5MM **Privately Held**
SIC: 2653 Corrugated & solid fiber boxes

(G-5017)
CHARLOTTE M PETERS
3452 W 126th St (44111-3562)
PHONE..................................216 798-8997
Charlotte M Peters, *Principal*
EMP: 3
SALES (est): 220K **Privately Held**
SIC: 2721 Periodicals

(G-5018)
CHART ASIA INC
1 Infinity Corp Ctr Dr (44125-5369)
PHONE..................................440 753-1490
Samuel F Thomas, *President*
Jason Kurtis, *VP Sls/Mktg*
EMP: 176
SALES (est): 9.1MM
SALES (corp-wide): 859.1MM **Publicly Held**
WEB: www.chart-ind.com
SIC: 3443 Heat exchangers, plate type
HQ: Chart Inc
407 7th St Nw
New Prague MN 56071
952 758-4484

(G-5019)
CHART INDUSTRIES INC
5885 Landerbrook Dr # 150 (44124-4045)
PHONE..................................440 753-1490
Fax: 440 753-1491
Samuel F Thomas, *President*
Arthur S Holmes, *Principal*
Lucy Koly, *Human Res Mgr*
Cary Jeansonne, *Manager*
Robert G Turner, *Director*
EMP: 882
SALES (est): 36.9MM
SALES (corp-wide): 859.1MM **Publicly Held**
WEB: www.chart-ind.com
SIC: 3443 Heat exchangers, plate type
HQ: Chart Inc
407 7th St Nw
New Prague MN 56071
952 758-4484

(G-5020)
CHART INDUSTRIES INC (PA)
1 Infinity Corp Ctr Dr # 300 (44125-5370)
PHONE..................................440 753-1490
Samuel F Thomas, *Ch of Bd*
William C Johnson, *President*
Robert H Wolfe, *Vice Pres*
Jillian C Evanko, *CFO*
Mary C Cook,
EMP: 26
SQ FT: 32,800
SALES: 859.1MM **Publicly Held**
SIC: 3559 3569 3443 Cryogenic machinery, industrial; gas producers, generators & other gas related equipment; generators: steam, liquid oxygen or nitrogen; heat exchangers, condensers & components; cryogenic tanks, for liquids & gases

(G-5021)
CHART INTERNATIONAL INC (HQ)
1 Infinity Corp Ctr Dr (44125-5369)
PHONE..................................440 753-1490
Samuel F Thomas, *President*
Jamaal Stewart, *Engineer*
Kenneth Webster, *CFO*
Nikki Goodell, *Human Resources*
EMP: 52

SALES (est): 23.9MM
SALES (corp-wide): 859.1MM **Publicly Held**
SIC: 3443 3317 3559 3569 Heat exchangers, plate type; tanks for tank trucks, metal plate; vessels, process or storage (from boiler shops): metal plate; steel pipe & tubes; cryogenic machinery, industrial; separators for steam, gas, vapor or air (machinery)
PA: Chart Industries, Inc.
1 Infinity Corp Ctr Dr # 300
Cleveland OH 44125
440 753-1490

(G-5022)
CHARTER MANUFACTURING CO INC
Charter Steel Division
4300 E 49th St (44125-1004)
PHONE..................................216 883-3800
Greg Volovsek, *Engineer*
Kevin Burg, *Branch Mgr*
EMP: 992
SALES (corp-wide): 762.9MM **Privately Held**
WEB: www.chartermfg.com
SIC: 3312 Rods, iron & steel: made in steel mills; wire products, steel or iron
PA: Charter Manufacturing Company, Inc.
1212 W Glen Oaks Ln
Mequon WI 53092
262 243-4700

(G-5023)
CHECKPOINT SURGICAL INC
22901 Millcreek Blvd # 110 (44122-5724)
PHONE..................................216 378-9107
Leonard Cosentino, *President*
Mark Stultz, *Vice Pres*
Terri Zmina, *Opers Staff*
Don Hubbard, *VP Sales*
Paul Hargis, *Sales Dir*
EMP: 6
SALES (est): 664.4K **Privately Held**
SIC: 3845 Electromedical equipment

(G-5024)
CHEF 2 CHEF FOODS
1893 E 55th St (44103-3640)
PHONE..................................216 696-0080
EMP: 3
SALES (est): 122.2K **Privately Held**
SIC: 2038 Frozen specialties

(G-5025)
CHEMICAL SOLVENTS INC (PA)
3751 Jennings Rd (44109-2889)
PHONE..................................216 741-9310
Fax: 216 741-4080
Edward Pavlish, *Ch of Bd*
Thos A Mason, *Principal*
E H Pavlish, *Principal*
Patricia Pavlish, *Corp Secy*
Blaine Davidson, *Vice Pres*
▲ **EMP:** 45 **EST:** 1970
SQ FT: 30,000
SALES (est): 112.5MM **Privately Held**
WEB: www.chemicalsolvents.com
SIC: 5169 7349 3471 2992 Detergents & soaps, except specialty cleaning; specialty cleaning & sanitation preparations; chemical cleaning services; cleaning & descaling metal products; oils & greases, blending & compounding

(G-5026)
CHI CORPORATION (PA)
5265 Naiman Pkwy Ste H (44139-1013)
PHONE..................................440 498-2300
Fax: 440 498-2301
Diane Thome, *President*
John R Thome Sr, *Chairman*
Rob Oddo, *Purchasing*
Paul Comfort, *Engineer*
Tamera Chess, *Accounts Exec*
EMP: 11
SALES (est): 4.5MM **Privately Held**
WEB: www.chicorporation.com
SIC: 7373 3572 Systems software development services; computer tape drives & components

(G-5027)
CHIEFS MANUFACTURING & EQP CO
4325 Monticello Blvd (44121-2816)
PHONE..................................216 291-3200
William Consolo, *President*
Keith Metzung, *Vice Pres*
EMP: 5
SALES (est): 390K **Privately Held**
SIC: 3589 Car washing machinery

(G-5028)
CHILCOTE COMPANY (PA)
Also Called: Tap Packaging Solutions
2160 Superior Ave E (44114-2184)
PHONE..................................216 781-6000
Fax: 216 535-0621
Donald Fox, *Superintendent*
David W Pancoast, *Principal*
David B Chilcote, *Chairman*
Matthew Moir, *Vice Pres*
Douglas P Roof, *Controller*
▲ **EMP:** 115
SQ FT: 190,000
SALES (est): 70MM **Privately Held**
WEB: www.tap-usa.com
SIC: 2657 2782 Folding paperboard boxes; albums

(G-5029)
CHOCOLATE PIG INC (PA)
Also Called: Fantasy Candies
5338 Mayfield Rd (44124-2479)
PHONE..................................440 461-4511
Fax: 440 461-4486
Joel Fink, *President*
EMP: 6
SQ FT: 3,500
SALES (est): 2.2MM **Privately Held**
WEB: www.fantasycandies.com
SIC: 2064 5441 2066 Candy & other confectionery products; candy, nut & confectionery stores; chocolate & cocoa products

(G-5030)
CHRISTOPHER TOOL & MFG CO
30500 Carter St Frnt (44139-3580)
PHONE..................................440 248-8080
Fax: 440 248-1614
Patrick D Christopher, *President*
Craig Peck, *Vice Pres*
Larry Walker, *Vice Pres*
Brad Jorgenson, *Prdtn Mgr*
Art Cross, *Purch Mgr*
EMP: 104 **EST:** 1951
SQ FT: 48,500
SALES: 20.5MM **Privately Held**
WEB: www.christophertool.com
SIC: 3599 Machine & other job shop work

(G-5031)
CHROMATIC INC
839 E 63rd St (44103-1018)
PHONE..................................216 881-2228
Fax: 216 881-4240
Dennis L Paul, *President*
Dennis Paul, *President*
Jeff Paul, *General Mgr*
EMP: 10
SQ FT: 12,000
SALES: 900K **Privately Held**
WEB: www.chromatic.net
SIC: 3471 Chromium plating of metals or formed products; decorative plating & finishing of formed products

(G-5032)
CHROME INDUSTRIES INC
3041 Perkins Ave (44114-4626)
PHONE..................................216 771-2266
Fax: 216 771-2615
Wolfgang Hein, *President*
Roland Hein, *Vice Pres*
EMP: 4
SQ FT: 12,000
SALES: 600K **Privately Held**
SIC: 3471 Chromium plating of metals or formed products

(G-5033)
CIMINO BOX INC
Also Called: Cimino Box & Pallet Company
8500 Clinton Rd Ste 6 (44144-1001)
PHONE..................................216 961-7377
Fax: 216 961-4054

Frank Ritson, *President*
EMP: 4
SQ FT: 5,000
SALES (est): 665.3K **Privately Held**
SIC: 2448 Pallets, wood

(G-5034)
CITY GIRL MAGAZINE LLC
801 E 212th St (44119-2415)
PHONE..................................216 481-4110
Anthony Swift, *Principal*
EMP: 3
SALES (est): 112.9K **Privately Held**
SIC: 2721 Periodicals

(G-5035)
CITY OF CLEVELAND
Also Called: Printing & Reproduction Div
1735 Lakeside Ave E (44114-1118)
PHONE..................................216 664-3013
Scott Loomis, *Prdtn Mgr*
Michael Hewett, *Commissioner*
EMP: 15 **Privately Held**
SIC: 2752 9199 Commercial printing, lithographic; general government administration;
PA: City Of Cleveland
601 Lakeside Ave E Rm 210
Cleveland OH 44114
216 664-2000

(G-5036)
CITY OF CLEVELAND
Also Called: Parking Facilities
500 Lakeside Ave E (44114-1019)
PHONE..................................216 664-2711
Fax: 216 664-4005
Michael Cox, *Commissioner*
Paul Bender, *Director*
Natalie Roaniae, *Director*
EMP: 1
SALES (est): 53.3MM **Privately Held**
SIC: 3559 Parking facility equipment & supplies
PA: City Of Cleveland
601 Lakeside Ave E Rm 210
Cleveland OH 44114
216 664-2000

(G-5037)
CITY OF PARMA
Vital Statistics
6611 Ridge Rd Fl 2 (44129-5530)
PHONE..................................440 885-8816
Dennis Kish, *Manager*
EMP: 7 **Privately Held**
WEB: www.parmajustice.net
SIC: 2721 Statistical reports (periodicals): publishing & printing
PA: Parma City Of (Inc)
6611 Ridge Rd
Cleveland OH 44129
440 885-8000

(G-5038)
CITY PLATING AND POLISHING LLC
4821 W 130th St (44135-5137)
PHONE..................................216 267-8158
Fax: 216 267-8218
Randy Solganik, *Mng Member*
EMP: 7
SQ FT: 20,000
SALES (est): 899.8K **Privately Held**
WEB: www.cityplate.com
SIC: 3471 Electroplating & plating

(G-5039)
CITY VISITOR INC
Also Called: City Visitor Publications
5755 Granger Rd Ste 600 (44131-1458)
PHONE..................................216 661-6666
Rocco Dilillo, *President*
Tom Gibbons, *Editor*
Mark Timm, *Vice Pres*
Bob Zack, *Manager*
Marcia Campo, *Consultant*
EMP: 9
SQ FT: 1,500
SALES (est): 660K **Privately Held**
WEB: www.cityvisitor.com
SIC: 2721 Magazines: publishing only, not printed on site

(G-5040)
CKM VENTURES LLC (PA)
Also Called: George R Klein News
2635 Payne Ave (44114-4432)
PHONE..................................216 623-0370
Fax: 216 623-0919
Shawn Spindel, *Mng Member*
EMP: 7
SALES (est): 560K **Privately Held**
SIC: 2759 5199 Newspapers: printing; directories (except telephone): printing; maps & charts

(G-5041)
CLARK AUTO MACHINE SHOP
2597 W 41st St (44113-4808)
PHONE..................................216 939-0768
Douglas Strimpel, *Principal*
EMP: 4
SALES (est): 385.8K **Privately Held**
SIC: 3589 Service industry machinery

(G-5042)
CLASSIC LAMINATIONS INC
7703 First Pl Ste B (44146-6730)
PHONE..................................440 735-1333
Fax: 440 735-1334
James Tidd, *President*
Mike Richardson, *Sales Staff*
Donna Tidd, *Admin Sec*
EMP: 25
SQ FT: 3,800
SALES (est): 2.1MM **Privately Held**
WEB: www.classiclaminations.com
SIC: 3089 Laminating of plastic

(G-5043)
CLASSIC TOY COMPANY INC
12825 Taft Ave (44108-1635)
PHONE..................................216 851-2000
Fax: 216 851-2010
Larry Feuer, *President*
Michael Abrams, *Vice Pres*
Ira Feuer, *Vice Pres*
Jackol Dickui, *Sales Mgr*
▲ **EMP:** 3
SQ FT: 40,000
SALES (est): 230K **Privately Held**
WEB: www.classictoycompany.com
SIC: 3942 Stuffed toys, including animals

(G-5044)
CLEANLIFE ENERGY LLC
Also Called: Unibat
2400 Superior Ave E LI (44114-4236)
PHONE..................................216 661-7872
Justin Miller, *CEO*
Nathan Lowenthal, *Marketing Mgr*
Mik Miller,
▲ **EMP:** 18
SQ FT: 10,000
SALES (est): 2MM **Privately Held**
SIC: 3679 3356 Liquid crystal displays (LCD); battery metal

(G-5045)
CLEAR FOLD DOOR INC
Also Called: C F Doors
7703 First Pl Ste A (44146-6730)
PHONE..................................440 735-1351
Fax: 440 735-1353
Donald E De Roia, *President*
Rosetta A De Roia, *Corp Secy*
EMP: 5
SQ FT: 2,700
SALES (est): 831.4K **Privately Held**
WEB: www.cfdoors.com
SIC: 3089 5084 Doors, folding: plastic or plastic coated fabric; machine tools & accessories

(G-5046)
CLEARWATER ONE LLC
21400 Lorain Rd (44126-2125)
PHONE..................................216 554-4747
David Niederst, *Mng Member*
EMP: 12
SALES: 5MM **Privately Held**
SIC: 2834 Chlorination tablets & kits (water purification)

(G-5047)
CLECORR INC
Also Called: Clecorr Packaging
10610 Berea Rd Rear (44102-2595)
PHONE..................................216 961-5500

Fax: 216 961-5504
Kevin L Smith, *President*
Christopher Dye, *Vice Pres*
EMP: 29
SQ FT: 67,000
SALES (est): 6MM **Privately Held**
SIC: 2653 Boxes, corrugated: made from purchased materials

(G-5048)
CLEVELAND BAGEL COMPANY LLC
Also Called: Cleveland Bagel Company, The
4309 Larrain Ave (44113)
PHONE...................216 385-7723
Geoffry Hardman, *Principal*
Dan Herbst, *Principal*
EMP: 3
SALES (est): 125.1K **Privately Held**
SIC: 2053 Cakes, bakery: frozen

(G-5049)
CLEVELAND BEAN SPROUT INC
2675 E 40th St (44115-3508)
PHONE...................216 881-2112
Casey Chiu, *President*
Judy Chiu, *Vice Pres*
EMP: 12
SQ FT: 12,000
SALES (est): 770K **Privately Held**
SIC: 0139 0161 2052 Alfalfa farm; pea & bean farms; cookies

(G-5050)
CLEVELAND CANVAS GOODS MFG CO
1960 E 57th St (44103-3804)
PHONE...................216 361-4567
Fax: 216 361-1727
William J Morton III, *President*
Michael L Morton Jr, *Corp Secy*
Jack Morton, *Manager*
EMP: 70 EST: 1922
SQ FT: 29,500
SALES (est): 10.8MM **Privately Held**
WEB: www.clevelandcanvas.com
SIC: 2674 3161 2394 2393 Bags: uncoated paper & multiwall; vacuum cleaner bags: made from purchased materials; luggage; canvas & related products; textile bags; men's & boys' work clothing; tire cord & fabrics

(G-5051)
CLEVELAND CIRCUITS CORP
Also Called: Instrumatics
15516 Industrial Pkwy (44135-3314)
PHONE...................216 267-9020
Fax: 216 941-2228
Sumir Amin, *President*
Jay Amin, *Vice Pres*
Melody Toth, *Manager*
EMP: 25
SQ FT: 18,500
SALES (est): 1.9MM **Privately Held**
WEB: www.clevelandcircuits.com
SIC: 3679 Electronic circuits

(G-5052)
CLEVELAND CITIZEN PUBG CO
2012 W 25th St Ste 900 (44113-4124)
PHONE...................216 861-4283
Fax: 216 861-4382
Loree K Soggs, *President*
John Banno, *Vice Pres*
EMP: 8
SQ FT: 2,214
SALES: 200K
SALES (corp-wide): 505.2K **Privately Held**
WEB: www.cbctc.org
SIC: 2711 Newspapers
PA: Cleveland Building & Construction Trades Council
3250 Euclid Ave Ste 280
Cleveland OH 44115
216 361-8077

(G-5053)
CLEVELAND CONTROLS INC
1111 Brookpark Rd (44109-5825)
PHONE...................216 398-0330
Steve Craig, *President*
Anida Griffin, *Purchasing*
Jim Ransbury, *Controller*
Deirdre Storm, *Director*

EMP: 60 EST: 1942
SQ FT: 10,000
SALES (est): 6.5MM **Privately Held**
WEB: www.clevelandcontrols.com
SIC: 3823 Combustion control instruments; differential pressure instruments, industrial process type

(G-5054)
CLEVELAND COPY & PRTG SVC LLC (PA)
1835 E 30th St Fl 3 (44114-4438)
PHONE...................216 861-0324
Fax: 216 621-0686
Tina Zavesky, *Branch Mgr*
James Koelpin,
EMP: 5 EST: 1961
SALES (est): 508.8K **Privately Held**
SIC: 2759 Commercial printing

(G-5055)
CLEVELAND CSTM PLLET CRATE INC
4201 Lakeside Ave E (44114-3814)
PHONE...................216 881-1414
Fax: 216 881-1475
Gary Petric, *President*
Michael Broeckel, *Corp Secy*
Robert Mc Millan, *Vice Pres*
EMP: 38
SQ FT: 50,000
SALES (est): 6.3MM **Privately Held**
WEB: www.gmpallet.com
SIC: 2448 Pallets, wood & wood with metal; skids, wood & wood with metal

(G-5056)
CLEVELAND CUSTOM CABINETS LLC
19561 Miles Rd (44128-4111)
PHONE...................213 663-0606
EMP: 3
SALES (est): 106.9K **Privately Held**
SIC: 2434 Wood kitchen cabinets

(G-5057)
CLEVELAND DEBURRING MACHINE CO
Also Called: Cdmc
3370 W 140th St (44111-2433)
PHONE...................216 472-0200
Jeff Moell, *Manager*
Adam Mutschler,
Chris Mutschler,
EMP: 4
SALES (est): 721.5K **Privately Held**
SIC: 3541 Deburring machines

(G-5058)
CLEVELAND DIE & MFG CO
14735 Lorain Ave (44111-6104)
PHONE...................216 941-7268
Fax: 216 671-4970
Vladimir Haoui, *Plant Mgr*
David Heuser, *Director*
EMP: 7
SALES (corp-wide): 38.6MM **Privately Held**
SIC: 3544 Special dies & tools
PA: Cleveland Die & Manufacturing Co
20303 1st Ave
Middleburg Heights OH 44130
440 243-3404

(G-5059)
CLEVELAND DIE & MFG CO
20303 1st Ave (44130-2433)
PHONE...................440 243-3404
Bladimir Haoui, *Branch Mgr*
Robert Sunagel, *Info Tech Dir*
David Heuser, *Director*
EMP: 100
SALES (corp-wide): 38.6MM **Privately Held**
WEB: www.clevelanddie.com
SIC: 3465 Automotive stampings
PA: Cleveland Die & Manufacturing Co
20303 1st Ave
Middleburg Heights OH 44130
440 243-3404

(G-5060)
CLEVELAND DRAPERY STITCH INC
12890 Berea Rd (44111-1624)
PHONE...................216 252-3857
Fax: 216 252-4494
George Beckmann, *President*
Wayne Monar, *Vice Pres*
George Beckman, *CFO*
EMP: 14
SQ FT: 7,200
SALES (est): 1.2MM **Privately Held**
SIC: 2211 2221 Draperies & drapery fabrics, cotton; draperies & drapery fabrics, manmade fiber & silk

(G-5061)
CLEVELAND FP INC (PA)
12819 Coit Rd (44108-1614)
PHONE...................216 249-4900
Michael Ivany, *President*
Daniel Cleary, *General Mgr*
Joseph Gustwiller, *Opers Staff*
Jamie Justice, *Opers Staff*
Earl Youngblood, *Production*
◆ **EMP:** 90
SQ FT: 103,000
SALES (est): 26.9MM **Privately Held**
SIC: 2865 Cyclic crudes & intermediates

(G-5062)
CLEVELAND GEAR COMPANY INC (DH)
3249 E 80th St (44104-4396)
P.O. Box 70100t (44190-0001)
PHONE...................216 641-9000
Fax: 216 641-2731
Dana Lynch, *President*
John M Atkinson, *Vice Pres*
Russell Warner, *Vice Pres*
Bob Wightman, *Vice Pres*
John Turner, *Materials Mgr*
▲ **EMP:** 115
SALES (est): 21.1MM
SALES (corp-wide): 587.1MM **Privately Held**
WEB: www.clevelandgear.com
SIC: 3566 3569 Speed changers, drives & gears; gears, power transmission, except automotive; lubricating equipment
HQ: Industrial Manufacturing Company Llc
8223 Brecksville Rd Ste 1
Brecksville OH 44141
440 838-4700

(G-5063)
CLEVELAND GRANITE & MARBLE LLC
4121 Carnegie Ave (44103-4336)
PHONE...................216 291-7637
Fax: 216 241-0223
Stephen Tate, *Sales Mgr*
Denise Adomaites, *Sales Associate*
Kimberly K Lisboa, *Mng Member*
Uwe Eibich,
Frank Gotthardt,
▲ **EMP:** 33
SQ FT: 50,000
SALES (est): 3.9MM **Privately Held**
WEB: www.clevelandgranite.com
SIC: 3281 3291 Dimension stone for buildings; abrasive metal & steel products

(G-5064)
CLEVELAND HDWR & FORGING CO (PA)
Also Called: Fox Valley Forge
3270 E 79th St (44104-4306)
PHONE...................216 641-5200
Fax: 216 641-0829
William E Hoban, *Ch of Bd*
James Socha, *CFO*
▲ **EMP:** 50
SQ FT: 175,000
SALES (est): 31.6MM **Privately Held**
WEB: www.clevelandhardware.com
SIC: 3463 3799 3462 3625 Nonferrous forgings; trailers & trailer equipment; towing bars & systems; iron & steel forgings; relays & industrial controls; truck & bus bodies; manufactured hardware (general)

(G-5065)
CLEVELAND HOLLOW BORING INC
Also Called: Coomercial Forg Heat Treatment
4501 Lakeside Ave E (44114-3818)
P.O. Box 605028 (44105-0028)
PHONE...................216 883-1926
Walt Illingworgh, *Manager*
EMP: 3
SALES (corp-wide): 663.8K **Privately Held**
SIC: 3462 3398 3469 Iron & steel forgings; metal heat treating; machine parts, stamped or pressed metal
PA: Cleveland Hollow Boring, Inc
3714 E 93rd St
Cleveland OH 44105
216 883-1926

(G-5066)
CLEVELAND IRON WORKERS MEMBERS
2121 Euclid Ave Mm304 (44115-2214)
PHONE...................216 687-2290
Patrick Gaul, *Sales Associate*
Sara Bartlett, *Manager*
Valerie Clause, *Manager*
Anne Finnegan, *Manager*
Julia Zettl, *Manager*
EMP: 3
SALES (est): 247.8K **Privately Held**
SIC: 3423 Hand & edge tools

(G-5067)
CLEVELAND JEWISH PUBL CO
Also Called: Cleveland Jewish News
23880 Commerce Park Ste 1 (44122-5830)
PHONE...................216 454-8300
Fax: 216 454-8100
Rob Certner, *CEO*
Sherry Lapine, *Business Mgr*
Cynthia Dettelbach, *Exec VP*
Larry Borodkin, *Human Res Dir*
Rick Kammer, *Marketing Mgr*
EMP: 38 EST: 1964
SQ FT: 9,000
SALES (est): 2.6MM **Privately Held**
WEB: www.clevelandjewishnews.com
SIC: 2711 Newspapers: publishing only, not printed on site

(G-5068)
CLEVELAND MEDICAL DEVICES INC
Also Called: Clevemed
4415 Euclid Ave Ste 400 (44103-3757)
PHONE...................216 426-0365
Fax: 216 791-6739
Hani Kayyali, *President*
Robert N Schmidt, *Chairman*
Bryan Kolkowski, *Vice Pres*
Nelsimar Vandelli, *Vice Pres*
Ed Rapp, *Engineer*
EMP: 20
SQ FT: 9,000
SALES (est): 4.2MM **Privately Held**
WEB: www.clevemed.com
SIC: 3845 3842 Electromedical apparatus; surgical appliances & supplies

(G-5069)
CLEVELAND MENU PRINTING INC
1441 E 17th St (44114-2012)
PHONE...................216 241-5256
Fax: 216 241-5696
Tom Ramella, *President*
Gerry Ramella, *Owner*
Homas A Grabien, *Principal*
George Maxwell, *Principal*
Daniel Payne, *Principal*
▼ **EMP:** 25
SQ FT: 15,000
SALES (est): 4.5MM **Privately Held**
WEB: www.clevelandmenu.com
SIC: 2759 Menus: printing

(G-5070)
CLEVELAND METAL PROCESSING INC (PA)
20303 1st Ave (44130-2433)
P.O. Box 30249 (44130-0249)
PHONE...................440 243-3404
Juan Chahda, *President*
Liliana Chahda, *Vice Pres*

Greg Saydell, *Accounting Mgr*
Marty Curry, *Sales Associate*
EMP: 114
SQ FT: 119,000
SALES (est): 7MM **Privately Held**
SIC: 3465 3544 Automotive stampings; special dies & tools

(G-5071)
CLEVELAND OFFSET PRESS CO INC
1378 E 17th St (44114-2017)
PHONE..............................440 845-9137
Fax: 216 861-1667
Kenneth Konkol, *President*
EMP: 4
SQ FT: 1,600
SALES (est): 557.3K **Privately Held**
SIC: 2752 Commercial printing, offset

(G-5072)
CLEVELAND PLATING
1028 E 134th St (44110-2248)
PHONE..............................216 249-0300
EMP: 5
SALES (est): 609.5K **Privately Held**
SIC: 3471 Plating of metals or formed products

(G-5073)
CLEVELAND PRINTWEAR INC
13300 Madison Ave (44107-4894)
PHONE..............................216 521-5500
Fax: 216 521-9210
Michael Cannon, *President*
Karen Cannon, *Admin Sec*
EMP: 9
SQ FT: 8,000
SALES (est): 1.1MM **Privately Held**
WEB: www.clevelandprintwear.com
SIC: 2759 Screen printing

(G-5074)
CLEVELAND RANGE LLC
Also Called: Sub of Manitowoc Company
18901 Euclid Ave (44117-3351)
PHONE..............................216 481-4900
▲ **EMP:** 4 EST: 2013
SALES (est): 426K
SALES (corp-wide): 3.4B **Publicly Held**
SIC: 3556 Mfg Food Products Machinery
PA: The Manitowoc Company Inc
2400 S 44th St
Manitowoc WI 54220
920 684-4410

(G-5075)
CLEVELAND RANGE LLC (HQ)
Also Called: Manitwoc Ovens Advnced Cooking
18301 Saint Clair Ave (44110-2587)
PHONE..............................216 481-4900
Fax: 216 481-3782
Dennis O'Toole, *Vice Pres*
O McGhee, *VP Engrg*
Greg Riggle, *Engineer*
Igor Rubinov, *Engineer*
Kenneth Seketa, *Engineer*
▲ **EMP:** 204
SQ FT: 150,000
SALES (est): 69.9MM
SALES (corp-wide): 1.7B **Publicly Held**
WEB: www.clevelandrange.com
SIC: 3589 3556 3634 Commercial cooking & foodwarming equipment; food products machinery; electric housewares & fans
PA: Welbilt, Inc.
2227 Welbilt Blvd
Trinity FL 34655
727 375-7010

(G-5076)
CLEVELAND REBABBITTING SERVICE
15593 Brookpark Rd (44142-1618)
PHONE..............................216 433-0123
Fax: 216 433-7676
Kenneth Roller, *President*
Bradford Roller, *Vice Pres*
EMP: 9
SQ FT: 15,000
SALES (est): 1.4MM **Privately Held**
WEB: www.rebabbit.com
SIC: 3568 Bearings, bushings & blocks

(G-5077)
CLEVELAND ROLL FORMING CO
3170 W 32nd St (44109-1529)
PHONE..............................216 281-0202
Fax: 216 281-0204
Paul Ekey, *President*
Edward L Ekey, *Vice Pres*
Joyce Smith, *Manager*
EMP: 7
SQ FT: 11,700
SALES (est): 978.3K **Privately Held**
WEB: www.clevelandrollforming.com
SIC: 3544 Special dies, tools, jigs & fixtures

(G-5078)
CLEVELAND SMACNA
6060 Royalton Rd (44133-5104)
PHONE..............................440 877-3500
Margaret Schultz, *Principal*
EMP: 3
SALES (est): 297.1K **Privately Held**
SIC: 3585 Air conditioning condensers & condensing units

(G-5079)
CLEVELAND SPECIALTY PDTS INC
2130 W 110th St (44102-3510)
PHONE..............................216 281-8300
Manuel P Glynias, *President*
EMP: 32
SALES (est): 5.5MM **Privately Held**
SIC: 3089 Extruded finished plastic products

(G-5080)
CLEVELAND STEEL TOOL COMPANY
474 E 105th St (44108-1378)
PHONE..............................216 681-7400
Fax: 216 681-7009
Mark Dawson, *President*
Wayne Haas, *Senior VP*
Charlie Balch, *Plant Mgr*
Tony Kozak, *Plant Mgr*
Kevin Zavodny, *Purchasing*
◆ **EMP:** 26 EST: 1908
SQ FT: 25,000
SALES (est): 4.7MM **Privately Held**
WEB: www.clevelandsteeltool.com
SIC: 3544 Punches, forming & stamping; special dies & tools

(G-5081)
CLEVELAND TOOL AND MACHINE INC
5240 Smith Rd Ste 3 (44142-1700)
PHONE..............................216 267-6010
Fax: 216 267-6011
Victor Bota, *President*
Maria Bota, *Vice Pres*
Douglas Neece, *Vice Pres*
Laurentiu Taraboanta, *Engineer*
◆ **EMP:** 15
SQ FT: 30,000
SALES (est): 3.3MM **Privately Held**
WEB: www.clevtool.com
SIC: 3541 Machine tools, metal cutting type

(G-5082)
CLEVELAND TRACK MATERIAL INC (HQ)
Also Called: Cylindrical Fabrications
6917 Bessemer Ave (44127-1809)
P.O. Box 603160 (44103-0160)
PHONE..............................216 641-4000
Fax: 216 881-6910
Laurent Savornin, *CEO*
Michael Carlo, *COO*
William F Willoughby, *VP Opers*
Steve Pettry, *Safety Mgr*
Martin Newmann, *CFO*
▲ **EMP:** 100
SALES: 55MM
SALES (corp-wide): 985MM **Privately Held**
WEB: www.clevelandtrack.com
SIC: 3312 Structural & rail mill products
PA: Vossloh Ag
Vosslohstr. 4
Werdohl 58791
239 252-0

(G-5083)
CLEVELAND TRACK MATERIAL INC
6917 Bessemer Ave (44127-1809)
P.O. Box 603160 (44103-0160)
PHONE..............................216 641-4000
Wolfgang Sembach, *Vice Pres*
Kevin Gordon, *Purchasing*
Owen Jones, *Purchasing*
William Willoughby, *Branch Mgr*
Sandy Reik, *Director*
EMP: 16
SALES (corp-wide): 985MM **Privately Held**
WEB: www.clevelandtrack.com
SIC: 3312 3443 Structural & rail mill products; fabricated plate work (boiler shop)
HQ: Cleveland Track Material, Inc.
6917 Bessemer Ave
Cleveland OH 44127
216 641-4000

(G-5084)
CLEVELAND VALVE & GAUGE CO LLC
4755 W 150th St Ste H (44135-3330)
PHONE..............................216 362-1702
Fax: 216 362-6555
Shirley Trusso, *Owner*
Richard McCarthy,
EMP: 3
SALES (est): 606.8K **Privately Held**
WEB: www.clevelandvalve.com
SIC: 3491 Industrial valves

(G-5085)
CLEVELAND WELDING & FABG LLC
2175 Columbus Rd (44113-4229)
P.O. Box 450 (44107)
PHONE..............................440 364-5137
Richard K Lehmann, *Mng Member*
EMP: 3
SQ FT: 3,000
SALES (est): 44K **Privately Held**
SIC: 7692 Welding repair

(G-5086)
CLEVELAND WHISKEY LLC
1768 E 25th St (44114-4418)
PHONE..............................216 881-8481
Andrew Lix, *Chief Mktg Ofcr*
Tom Lix,
Michelle Heinz, *Relations*
EMP: 5
SALES (est): 577.6K **Privately Held**
SIC: 2085 Distilled & blended liquors

(G-5087)
CLEVELAND WIRE CLOTH & MFG CO
3573 E 78th St (44105-1517)
PHONE..............................216 341-1832
Fax: 216 341-1876
Chester F Crone, *President*
George Karnavas, *Engineer*
Scott Butler, *Plant Engr*
Joseph Sarasa, *Treasurer*
Christine Seme, *Human Res Mgr*
▲ **EMP:** 32
SQ FT: 100,000
SALES: 6.5MM **Privately Held**
WEB: www.wirecloth.com
SIC: 3496 Hardware cloth, woven wire

(G-5088)
CLIFFS & ASSOCIATES LTD
1100 Superior Ave E # 1500 (44114-2530)
PHONE..............................216 694-5700
W R Calfee, *President*
Rainald Von Bitter, *Vice Pres*
EMP: 6
SQ FT: 65,000
SALES (est): 379.1K **Privately Held**
SIC: 1011 Iron ores

(G-5089)
CLIFFS LOGAN COUNTY COAL LLC
200 Public Sq Ste 3300 (44114-2315)
PHONE..............................216 694-5700
Joseph Carrabba, *CEO*
EMP: 1

SALES (est): 2.7MM
SALES (corp-wide): 2.1B **Publicly Held**
SIC: 5989 1221 Coal; coal preparation plant, bituminous or lignite
PA: Cliffs Natural Resources Inc.
200 Public Sq Ste 3300
Cleveland OH 44114
216 694-5700

(G-5090)
CLIFFS MICHIGAN OPERATION
District 1072 Ste 1500 (44114)
PHONE..............................216 694-5303
EMP: 27
SALES (est): 4.8MM **Privately Held**
SIC: 1011 Iron ores

(G-5091)
CLIFFS MINING COMPANY (HQ)
200 Public Sq Ste 3300 (44114-2315)
PHONE..............................216 694-5700
W R Calfee, *Vice Pres*
D J Gallagher, *Vice Pres*
Laurie Brias, *CFO*
Dwayne Petish, *Treasurer*
R J Leroux, *Controller*
EMP: 15
SQ FT: 40,000
SALES (est): 9.3MM
SALES (corp-wide): 2.1B **Publicly Held**
SIC: 1011 Iron ores
PA: Cliffs Natural Resources Inc.
200 Public Sq Ste 3300
Cleveland OH 44114
216 694-5700

(G-5092)
CLIFFS MINNESOTA MINERALS CO
1100 Superior Ave E (44114-2530)
PHONE..............................216 694-5700
W R Calfee, *President*
EMP: 511
SQ FT: 65,000
SALES (est): 7.5MM
SALES (corp-wide): 2.1B **Publicly Held**
SIC: 1011 4931 Iron ore mining; electric & other services combined
PA: Cliffs Natural Resources Inc.
200 Public Sq Ste 3300
Cleveland OH 44114
216 694-5700

(G-5093)
CLIFFS NATURAL RESOURCES INC (PA)
200 Public Sq Ste 3300 (44114-2315)
PHONE..............................216 694-5700
C Lourenco Goncalves, *Ch of Bd*
Brian Baird, *Ch of Bd*
Kristy Dubitsky, *General Mgr*
Terry G Fedor, *Exec VP*
Maurice D Harapiak, *Exec VP*
EMP: 76
SALES: 2.1B **Publicly Held**
WEB: www.cliffsnaturalresources.com
SIC: 1011 Iron ore mining; iron ore pelletizing

(G-5094)
CMC PHARMACEUTICALS INC (PA)
Also Called: CMC Consulting
7100 Euclid Ave Ste 152 (44103-4036)
PHONE..............................216 600-9430
Mike Radomsky, *President*
EMP: 6
SQ FT: 1,000
SALES (est): 1.1MM **Privately Held**
SIC: 2834 Druggists' preparations (pharmaceuticals)

(G-5095)
CO PAC SERVICES INC
3113 W 110th St (44111-2753)
PHONE..............................216 688-1780
Fax: 216 688-1781
Craig Jaworski, *President*
Mike Marfeka, *Vice Pres*
Tom Maggard, *Manager*
Phil Puhala, *Admin Sec*
▲ **EMP:** 15
SQ FT: 65,000

SALES (est): 2.1MM **Privately Held**
WEB: www.copac.com
SIC: 3993 Displays & cutouts, window & lobby

(G-5096)
CODONICS INC (PA)
17991 Englewood Dr Ste D (44130-3493)
PHONE.................................216 226-1066
Fax: 440 243-1334
Peter O Botten, *CEO*
Mike Kohlberg, *General Mgr*
Michael Kolberg, *General Mgr*
Minglin LI, *General Mgr*
Alan Desantis, *Vice Pres*
◆ EMP: 154
SALES (est): 31.8MM **Privately Held**
WEB: www.codonics.com
SIC: 3571 Electronic computers

(G-5097)
COLD HEADING CO
4444 Lee Rd (44128-2902)
PHONE.................................216 581-3000
Mark Ebersbacher, *Manager*
Archie Green, *Executive*
EMP: 100
SALES (corp-wide): 50.7MM **Privately Held**
WEB: www.spst.com
SIC: 3452 Bolts, nuts, rivets & washers
HQ: The Cold Heading Co
21777 Hoover Rd
Warren MI 48089
586 497-7000

(G-5098)
COLLEGIATE DIRECTORIES INC
Also Called: National Directories College
30205 Clemens Rd Ste C (44145-1055)
P.O. Box 450640 (44145-0611)
PHONE.................................440 835-1172
Kevin Cleary, *President*
EMP: 3 EST: 1963
SALES (est): 291.3K **Privately Held**
WEB: www.customathleticdata.com
SIC: 2741 Directories: publishing only, not printed on site

(G-5099)
COLOR BAR PRINTING CENTERS INC
4576 Renaissance Pkwy (44128-5702)
PHONE.................................216 595-3939
Roger Perlmuter, *President*
Mary Ann Perlmuter, *Vice Pres*
Anita Belfi, *Personnel Exec*
EMP: 20
SQ FT: 16,248
SALES: 1.1MM **Privately Held**
SIC: 2752 Commercial printing, offset

(G-5100)
COLOR BRITE COMPANY INC
5209 Grant Ave (44125-1033)
PHONE.................................216 441-4117
Fax: 216 441-3582
Charles Pedro, *CEO*
EMP: 5
SQ FT: 10,000
SALES (est): 479.7K **Privately Held**
SIC: 1799 1761 3444 Awning installation; siding contractor; awnings, sheet metal

(G-5101)
COM-CORP INDUSTRIES INC
7601 Bittern Ave (44103-1060)
PHONE.................................216 431-6266
Fax: 216 431-5269
Thomas Stanciu, *CEO*
William Beckwith, *Vice Pres*
Kimberly Watroba, *CFO*
John Strazzanti, *Shareholder*
◆ EMP: 100
SQ FT: 150,000
SALES (est): 30.4MM **Privately Held**
SIC: 3469 Metal stampings

(G-5102)
COMCORP INC
Also Called: Sun Newspaper Div
1801 Superior Ave E (44114-2135)
PHONE.................................718 981-1234
Fax: 216 642-5527
John Urbancich, *President*
EMP: 310

SALES (est): 479.3K
SALES (corp-wide): 5.9B **Privately Held**
SIC: 2711 Newspapers: publishing only, not printed on site
PA: Advance Publications, Inc.
950 W Fingerboard Rd
Staten Island NY 10305
718 981-1234

(G-5103)
COMEX NORTH AMERICA INC (HQ)
Also Called: Comex Group
101 W Prospect Ave # 1020 (44115-1093)
PHONE.................................303 307-2100
Christopher Connor, *CEO*
Leon Cohen, *President*
Cathy Pereira, *Controller*
◆ EMP: 90
SQ FT: 2,900
SALES (est): 252.4MM
SALES (corp-wide): 11.8B **Publicly Held**
WEB: www.professionalpaintinc.com
SIC: 2851 8742 5198 5231 Paints & paint additives; paints, waterproof; paints: oil or alkyd vehicle or water thinned; corporation organizing; paints; paint brushes, rollers, sprayers; wallcoverings; paint brushes, rollers, sprayers & other supplies; wallcoverings
PA: The Sherwin-Williams Company
101 W Prospect Ave # 1020
Cleveland OH 44115
216 566-2000

(G-5104)
COMMERCIAL ELECTRIC PDTS CORP (PA)
1821 E 40th St (44103-3503)
PHONE.................................216 241-2886
Fax: 216 241-1734
Roger Meyer, *President*
Russ Arslanian, *General Mgr*
Kenneth Culp, *Vice Pres*
Char Page, *Sales Mgr*
David Jaeger, *Sales Staff*
EMP: 44 EST: 1927
SQ FT: 15,000
SALES (est): 25.7MM **Privately Held**
WEB: www.commercialelectric.com
SIC: 5085 3661 3824 1731 Power transmission equipment & apparatus; telephones & telephone apparatus; telegraph & related apparatus; mechanical & electromechanical counters & devices; general electrical contractor; industrial equipment services; electrical equipment & supplies

(G-5105)
COMMERCIAL STEEL TREATING CO
1394 E 39th St (44114-4119)
PHONE.................................216 431-8204
Fax: 216 431-5904
Jeff Seitz, *President*
Donna Seitz, *Corp Secy*
Lisa Seitz, *Admin Sec*
EMP: 10 EST: 1941
SQ FT: 36,000
SALES (est): 1.5MM **Privately Held**
SIC: 3398 3471 Metal heat treating; plating & polishing

(G-5106)
COMMERCIAL TRANSPORTATION SVCS
12487 Plaza Dr (44130-1056)
PHONE.................................216 267-2000
Allan J Miner, *President*
Ralph Napletana, *Treasurer*
Connie Roma, *Human Res Mgr*
Connie Romer, *Human Res Mgr*
Jack Miner, *Admin Sec*
EMP: 3
SQ FT: 15,000
SALES: 894.5K **Privately Held**
SIC: 7372 Prepackaged software

(G-5107)
COMMSCOPE TECHNOLOGIES LLC
1668 Sunview Rd (44124-2872)
PHONE.................................216 272-0055
Robert Andrews, *Branch Mgr*

EMP: 119 **Publicly Held**
WEB: www.andrew.com
SIC: 3663 Radio & TV communications equipment
HQ: Commscope Technologies Llc
4 Westbrook Corporate Ctr
Westchester IL 60154
708 236-6000

(G-5108)
COMMUNITY CARE NETWORK INC (PA)
1400 W 25th St Fl 2 (44113-3151)
PHONE.................................216 671-0977
David Lundeen, *President*
Christopher Cassidy, *CFO*
Lorraine Mayers, *Human Res Dir*
Bob Shafran, *Director*
EMP: 31
SALES: 3.2MM **Privately Held**
WEB: www.ccnusa.com
SIC: 3825 Network analyzers

(G-5109)
COMPANIES OF NORTH COAST LLC (HQ)
4605 Spring Rd (44131-1021)
PHONE.................................216 398-8550
Richard Petrovich, *President*
EMP: 2
SQ FT: 38,500
SALES (est): 2.8MM
SALES (corp-wide): 12.4MM **Privately Held**
SIC: 2655 3544 6719 Cans, composite: foil-fiber & other: from purchased fiber; special dies & tools; investment holding companies, except banks
PA: Unitech Holdings, Inc.
10413 N Aero Dr
Hayden ID 83835
208 772-0533

(G-5110)
COMPASS ENERGY LLC
17877 Saint Clair Ave # 1 (44110-2636)
PHONE.................................866 665-2225
Craig P Christ,
EMP: 60
SQ FT: 238,000
SALES (est): 3.7MM **Privately Held**
WEB: www.compassenergy.com
SIC: 2211 Broadwoven fabric mills, cotton

(G-5111)
COMPLIANT HEALTHCARE TECH LLC
7123 Pearl Rd Ste 305 (44130-4944)
PHONE.................................216 255-9607
Rick Ziegan, *Branch Mgr*
EMP: 15 **Privately Held**
WEB: www.chtechllc.com
SIC: 3826 Gas testing apparatus
PA: Compliant Healthcare Technologies, Llc
7123 Pearl Rd Ste 305
Cleveland OH 44130

(G-5112)
COMPLIANT HEALTHCARE TECH LLC (PA)
Also Called: C H T
7123 Pearl Rd Ste 305 (44130-4944)
PHONE.................................216 255-9607
Jason Di Marco, *Mng Member*
Patrick Dimarco, *Administration*
Scot Wederquist,
EMP: 25
SQ FT: 8,200
SALES: 7.5MM **Privately Held**
SIC: 7389 3826 Gas system conversion; gas testing apparatus

(G-5113)
COMPONENT SYSTEMS INC
Also Called: A-Wall
2245 W 114th St (44102-3517)
PHONE.................................216 252-9292
Fax: 216 889-1263
Tim Nelson, *President*
Thomas A Nelson, *Vice Pres*
Paul Much, *Purchasing*
Curtis Theriot, *Engineer*
Suzanne Reilly, *Controller*
EMP: 20
SQ FT: 26,000

SALES (est): 3.7MM **Privately Held**
WEB: www.comp-sys.com
SIC: 2542 Partitions & fixtures, except wood

(G-5114)
COMPUTER WORKSHOP INC
6100 Rockside Woods Blvd (44131-2366)
PHONE.................................216 901-0106
Fax: 216 901-0340
David Williams, *Manager*
Kim McFarland, *Manager*
EMP: 6
SALES (corp-wide): 2.6MM **Privately Held**
WEB: www.tcworkshop.com
SIC: 8243 7371 2741 Software training, computer; custom computer programming services; miscellaneous publishing
PA: The Computer Workshop Inc
5131 Post Rd Ste 102
Dublin OH 43017
614 798-9505

(G-5115)
CONN-SELMER INC
Glaesel String Instuments
1440 E 36th St Ste 501 (44114-4117)
PHONE.................................216 391-7723
Fax: 216 391-5318
EMP: 32
SALES (corp-wide): 179.6MM **Privately Held**
SIC: 3931 Mfg Musical Instruments
HQ: Conn-Selmer, Inc.
600 Industrial Pkwy
Elkhart IN 46516
574 522-1675

(G-5116)
CONSOLDATED GRAPHICS GROUP INC
Also Called: Consolidated Solutions
1614 E 40th St (44103-2319)
PHONE.................................216 881-9191
Kenneth A Lanci, *CEO*
Len Vargo, *President*
Matt Reville, *COO*
Joseph Turi, *Vice Pres*
Neil Gallagher, *VP Opers*
▲ EMP: 140
SQ FT: 75,000
SALES: 25MM **Privately Held**
SIC: 2752 2759 7331 2791 Commercial printing, lithographic; commercial printing; direct mail advertising services; typesetting; bookbinding & related work

(G-5117)
CONSOLDTED PRECISION PDTS CORP (HQ)
Also Called: Cpp Pomona
1621 Euclid Ave Ste 1850 (44115-2126)
PHONE.................................909 595-2252
James V Stewart, *CEO*
Steve Clodfelter, *President*
Debbie Comstock, *Vice Pres*
Ali Ghavami, *Vice Pres*
Benjamin Mahr, *Vice Pres*
▲ EMP: 250
SQ FT: 10,000
SALES (est): 557.3MM
SALES (corp-wide): 6B **Privately Held**
SIC: 3365 3324 Aluminum foundries; steel investment foundries
PA: Warburg Pincus Llc
450 Lexington Ave
New York NY 10017
212 878-0600

(G-5118)
CONSOLIDATED COATINGS CORP
3735 Green Rd (44122-5705)
PHONE.................................216 514-7596
Fax: 216 514-7532
Thomas C Sullivan, *Ch of Bd*
J K Milliken, *General Mgr*
Paul A Granzier, *Vice Pres*
EMP: 20 EST: 1904
SQ FT: 4,000

SALES (est): 2.7MM
SALES (corp-wide): 4.8B **Publicly Held**
WEB: www.rpmrepublic.com
SIC: 2952 5169 2891 2851 Asphalt felts
& coatings; roofing felts, cements or coatings; adhesives & sealants; adhesives & sealants; paints & allied products; specialty cleaning, polishes & sanitation goods
HQ: Republic Powdered Metals, Inc.
2628 Pearl Rd
Medina OH 44256
330 225-3192

(G-5119)
CONSOLIDATED WEB
Also Called: Consolidated Solutions
3831 Kelley Ave (44114-4537)
PHONE.............................216 881-7816
Kenneth Lanci, *President*
Dave Wasielewski, *General Mgr*
EMP: 4
SALES (est): 226.6K **Privately Held**
SIC: 2759 Commercial printing

(G-5120)
CONSTRUCTION JOURNAL LTD
Also Called: Ohio Construction News
7261 Engle Rd Ste 101 (44130-3479)
PHONE.............................440 826-4700
Fax: 440 826-0047
Sue Johnson, *Prdtn Dir*
Adrienne Gary, *VP Human Res*
Tim Blaicher, *Branch Mgr*
Ted Bliker, *Manager*
Doreen White, *Manager*
EMP: 17 **Privately Held**
WEB: www.cncnewsonline.com
SIC: 2721 Periodicals
PA: The Construction Journal Ltd
400 Sw 7th St
Stuart FL 34994

(G-5121)
CONSTRUCTION TECHNIQUES INC (HQ)
15887 Snow Rd Ste 100 (44142-2854)
PHONE.............................216 267-7310
B J Akers, *President*
Gene Pellillo, *Opers Mgr*
EMP: 15
SQ FT: 1,500
SALES (est): 848.5K
SALES (corp-wide): 2.3MM **Privately Held**
WEB: www.fabriform1.com
SIC: 2299 6794 Jute & flax textile products; patent buying, licensing, leasing
PA: Intrusion-Prepakt Incorporated
15910 Pearl Rd Ste 101
Cleveland OH
440 238-6950

(G-5122)
CONTAINERPORT GROUP INC (HQ)
1340 Depot St Ste 103 (44116-1741)
PHONE.............................440 333-2009
Fax: 440 333-1520
Frederick Hunger, *CEO*
Richard C Coleman, *President*
Russell A Graef, *President*
Jeff Horton, *General Mgr*
Kerry McIntyre, *General Mgr*
▲ EMP: 60
SQ FT: 14,000
SALES (est): 115.4MM
SALES (corp-wide): 215.4MM **Privately Held**
WEB: www.containerport.com
SIC: 3715 Truck trailers
PA: World Shipping, Inc.
1340 Depot St Ste 200
Cleveland OH 44116
440 356-7676

(G-5123)
CONTINENTAL BUSINESS ENTPS INC (PA)
Also Called: Ace Metal Stamping Company
7311 Northfield Rd (44146-6199)
PHONE.............................440 439-4400
Fax: 440 439-4410
Louis P Trolli, *President*
Lynn Di Geronimo House, *Asst Sec*
Richard L Laribee, *Asst Sec*

EMP: 17 EST: 1966
SQ FT: 33,000
SALES (est): 1.4MM **Privately Held**
SIC: 3469 3544 Stamping metal for the trade; special dies, tools, jigs & fixtures

(G-5124)
CONTINENTAL METAL PROC CO (PA)
18711 Cleveland Ave (44110)
PHONE.............................216 268-0000
Joseph Freund, *President*
Mike Freund, *Vice Pres*
Rubin Freund, *Vice Pres*
Rose Freund, *Admin Sec*
EMP: 19
SQ FT: 328,000
SALES (est): 2.9MM **Privately Held**
SIC: 3341 Aluminum smelting & refining (secondary); zinc smelting & refining (secondary)

(G-5125)
CONTINENTAL METAL PROC CO
14919 Saranac Rd (44110-2344)
PHONE.............................216 268-0000
Michael Freund, *Vice Pres*
EMP: 22
SQ FT: 320,000
SALES (corp-wide): 2.9MM **Privately Held**
SIC: 3341 Aluminum smelting & refining (secondary)
PA: Continental Metal Processing Co Inc
18711 Cleveland Ave
Cleveland OH 44110
216 268-0000

(G-5126)
CONTINENTAL PRODUCTS COMPANY
1150 E 222nd St (44117-1103)
PHONE.............................216 531-0710
Mary Ann Strebeck, *CEO*
Andy Skodnic, *Manager*
EMP: 26
SALES (corp-wide): 3.9MM **Privately Held**
WEB: www.paintdoc.com
SIC: 2851 5198 2891 Paints & paint additives; stains: varnish, oil or wax; putty; paints, varnishes & supplies; adhesives & sealants
PA: The Continental Products Company
1150 E 222nd St
Euclid OH 44117
216 383-3932

(G-5127)
CONTROL LINE EQUIPMENT INC
14750 Industrial Pkwy (44135-4548)
PHONE.............................216 433-7766
Mike Rotella, *CEO*
Robert May, *Vice Pres*
▲ EMP: 12
SQ FT: 12,000
SALES (est): 4.9MM **Privately Held**
WEB: www.control-line.com
SIC: 5084 3593 Industrial machinery & equipment; fluid power cylinders & actuators

(G-5128)
CONWAY GREENE CO INC
1400 E 30th St Ste 402 (44114-4050)
PHONE.............................216 619-8091
Fax: 216 622-1788
Barry Conway, *President*
Evalyn Greene, *Principal*
William Moller, *Finance*
Patrick Phillips, *Manager*
EMP: 7
SQ FT: 2,880
SALES (est): 967.4K **Privately Held**
WEB: www.conwaygreene.com
SIC: 2731 Book publishing

(G-5129)
COOK BONDING & MFG CO INC
701 W Schaaf Rd (44109-4638)
PHONE.............................216 661-1698
Fax: 216 661-7665
Brian Reneker, *CEO*
David M Cook, *President*

Mary Jo Knapper, *Manager*
EMP: 5 EST: 1971
SQ FT: 3,200
SALES (est): 870.5K **Privately Held**
WEB: www.cookbonding.com
SIC: 3625 Relays & industrial controls

(G-5130)
COOPER INTERCONNECT INC
Also Called: Cooper - Eaton Center
1000 Eaton Blvd (44122-6058)
PHONE.............................800 386-1911
EMP: 3 **Privately Held**
SIC: 3643 3678 Electric connectors; electronic connectors
HQ: Cooper Interconnect, Inc.
750 W Ventura Blvd
Camarillo CA 93010
805 484-0543

(G-5131)
COPERNICUS THERAPEUTICS INC
11000 Cedar Ave Ste 145 (44106-3060)
PHONE.............................216 707-1776
Fax: 216 231-9477
Joseph Ashley, *Ch of Bd*
Robert C Moen, *President*
Teo Lam, *General Mgr*
Ed Rapp, *General Mgr*
Robert Abrahart, *Vice Chairman*
EMP: 14
SQ FT: 6,000
SALES (est): 2.3MM **Privately Held**
WEB: www.cgsys.com
SIC: 2836 8731 Biological products, except diagnostic; commercial physical research

(G-5132)
COPY CATS PRINTING LLC
6659 Pearl Rd Ste 101 (44130-3840)
PHONE.............................440 345-5966
Nino Paglia, *Partner*
Donna Paglia, *Partner*
EMP: 3
SALES (est): 255.6K **Privately Held**
SIC: 2759 Commercial printing

(G-5133)
CORRO-TECH EQUIPMENT CORP
4034 W 163rd St (44135-1202)
PHONE.............................216 941-1552
Mark Burger, *President*
Mark Brown, *Corp Secy*
EMP: 4
SQ FT: 8,500
SALES (est): 515.9K **Privately Held**
SIC: 3823 1796 Industrial process control instruments; pollution control equipment installation

(G-5134)
COUNTRY PARLOUR ICE CREAM CO
12905 York Delta Dr Ste C (44133-3551)
PHONE.............................440 237-4040
Fax: 440 237-4157
Jeri Hovanec, *Principal*
Craig Hovanec, *Corp Secy*
Dave Hovanec, *Personnel Exec*
EMP: 14
SALES (est): 1.8MM **Privately Held**
SIC: 2024 2099 5143 Ice cream & frozen desserts; food preparations; dairy products, except dried or canned

(G-5135)
COUNTS CONTAINER CORPORATION
5137 W 161st St (44142-1604)
PHONE.............................216 433-4336
Fax: 216 433-0441
Roby Kountz, *President*
Vern Heiskell, *Principal*
Kimberly Kountz, *Treasurer*
Maxine Stegman, *Office Admin*
EMP: 25
SQ FT: 20,000
SALES: 5MM **Privately Held**
WEB: www.countscontainer.com
SIC: 3469 Garbage cans, stamped & pressed metal

(G-5136)
COVENTRY STEEL SERVICES INC
4200 E 71st St Ste 1 (44105-5721)
P.O. Box 25077 (44125-0077)
PHONE.............................216 883-4477
Fax: 216 883-4360
Brian Migchelbrink, *President*
Jeff Migchelbrink, *Corp Secy*
Joseph Hustosky, *Vice Pres*
EMP: 12
SQ FT: 35,000
SALES: 1MM **Privately Held**
WEB: www.coventrysteel.com
SIC: 3441 5051 Fabricated structural metal; steel

(G-5137)
COWELLS - ARROW BINGO COMPANY
9900 Clinton Rd (44144-1034)
PHONE.............................216 961-3500
John E Gallagher Jr, *President*
James Cochran, *Corp Secy*
EMP: 4
SALES (est): 200K **Privately Held**
SIC: 3944 Bingo boards (games)

(G-5138)
CPI GROUP LIMITED
Also Called: Puremonics
13858 Tinkers Creek Rd (44125-5661)
P.O. Box 25411 (44125-0411)
PHONE.............................216 525-0046
Benjamin Rosolowski,
EMP: 9
SQ FT: 2,000
SALES (est): 1.1MM **Privately Held**
SIC: 3675 8711 Electronic capacitors; electrical or electronic engineering

(G-5139)
CR LAURENCE CO INC
31600 Carter St (44139-3551)
PHONE.............................440 248-0003
Fax: 440 248-0120
Steve Newton, *Manager*
EMP: 8
SALES (corp-wide): 28.6B **Privately Held**
WEB: www.crlaurence.com
SIC: 5072 3714 Hand tools; sun roofs, motor vehicle
HQ: C.R. Laurence Co., Inc.
2503 E Vernon Ave
Vernon CA 90058
323 588-1281

(G-5140)
CRAIN COMMUNICATIONS INC
Also Called: Crain's Cleveland Business
700 W Saint Clair Ave # 310 (44113-1230)
PHONE.............................216 522-1383
Fax: 216 694-4264
Brian Tucker, *Publisher*
Cindy Goodaker, *Editor*
Dawn Donegan, *Accounts Exec*
Nicole Nolan, *Accounts Exec*
Michelle Sustar, *Marketing Staff*
EMP: 29
SALES (corp-wide): 225MM **Privately Held**
WEB: www.crainsnewyork.com
SIC: 2721 2711 Magazines: publishing only, not printed on site; newspapers
PA: Crain Communications, Inc.
1155 Gratiot Ave
Detroit MI 48207
313 446-6000

(G-5141)
CRAWFORD ACQUISITION CORP
Also Called: Famous Kiss-N-Korn Shop
16130 Saint Clair Ave (44110-3029)
PHONE.............................216 486-0702
Dan Crawford, *Owner*
Dave Crawford, *Vice Pres*
EMP: 15 EST: 1973
SQ FT: 8,000
SALES (est): 520K **Privately Held**
SIC: 2064 Popcorn balls or other treated popcorn products

(G-5142)
CROOKED RIVER COFFEE CO
761 Beta Dr Ste E (44143-2329)
PHONE..............................440 442-8330
Howard Sobel, *President*
Erv Mason, *Opers Mgr*
EMP: 3
SQ FT: 8,000
SALES (est): 592.8K **Privately Held**
WEB: www.crookedrivercoffee.com
SIC: 5149 2095 Coffee & tea; coffee roast-
ing (except by wholesale grocers)

(G-5143)
CROWNE GROUP LLC (PA)
127 Public Sq Ste 5110 (44114-1313)
PHONE..............................216 589-0198
Robert Henderson, *Mng Member*
EMP: 52
SALES (est): 1B **Privately Held**
SIC: 3559 8711 Degreasing machines, au-
tomotive & industrial; industrial engineers

(G-5144)
CSP GRAPHICS INC
1538 E 41st St (44103-2337)
PHONE..............................216 426-2660
Fax: 216 426-2661
John Filigenzi, *President*
John Bennett, *Plant Mgr*
Lisa Goodwin, *Sales Executive*
Marylyn Filigenzi, *Manager*
EMP: 13
SQ FT: 15,000
SALES (est): 2.1MM **Privately Held**
WEB: www.cspgraphics.com
SIC: 2261 Screen printing of cotton broad-
woven fabrics

(G-5145)
CT FERRY SCREW PRODUCTS I
1660 Queen Annes Gate (44145-2640)
PHONE..............................440 871-1617
EMP: 3 **EST:** 2001
SALES (est): 180K **Privately Held**
SIC: 3451 Mfg Screw Machine Products

(G-5146)
CUMMINS - ALLISON CORP
6777 Engle Rd Ste H (44130-7941)
PHONE..............................440 824-5050
Fax: 440 824-5054
David Profera, *Manager*
EMP: 8
SALES (corp-wide): 377.1MM **Privately
Held**
WEB: www.gsb.com
SIC: 5046 5087 5044 3519 Commercial
equipment; shredders, industrial & com-
mercial; check writing, signing & endors-
ing machines; internal combustion
engines
PA: Cummins - Allison Corp.
852 Feehanville Dr
Mount Prospect IL 60056
847 759-6403

(G-5147)
CURT HARLER INC
12936 Falling Water Rd (44136-4307)
PHONE..............................440 238-4556
Curt Harler, *Owner*
EMP: 5
SALES: 200K **Privately Held**
WEB: www.curtharler.com
SIC: 2721 Magazines: publishing & printing

(G-5148)
**CURTISS-WRIGHT FLOW CTRL
CORP**
Nova Machine Div
18001 Sheldon Rd (44130-2465)
PHONE..............................216 267-3200
David Linton, *CEO*
John Burk, *General Mgr*
Tim Walker, *Vice Pres*
Tim Corrigan, *Project Mgr*
Steve Suntzenich, *Opers Staff*
EMP: 84
SALES (corp-wide): 2.1B **Publicly Held**
SIC: 3452 3429 3369 3356 Bolts; metal;
washers; nuts, metal; lock washers; man-
ufactured hardware (general); nonferrous
foundries; nonferrous rolling & drawing

HQ: Curtiss-Wright Flow Control Corporation
1966 Broadhollow Rd Ste E
Farmingdale NY 11735
631 293-3800

(G-5149)
**CUSTOM CLTCH JINT HYDRLICS
INC (PA)**
3417 Saint Clair Ave Ne (44114-4186)
PHONE..............................216 431-1630
Fax: 216 431-6048
David Ballantyne, *CEO*
Donald Meintel, *President*
Elmer T Elbrecht, *Principal*
John G Roberts, *Principal*
Mary Ann Tomasch, *Principal*
EMP: 11
SQ FT: 52,000
SALES: 5.9MM **Privately Held**
WEB: www.customclutch.com
SIC: 3714 3594 3561 3492 Motor vehicle
transmissions, drive assemblies & parts;
clutches, motor vehicle; fluid power
pumps; cylinders, pump; hose & tube
couplings, hydraulic/pneumatic; power
transmission equipment; steel wire & re-
lated products

(G-5150)
CUSTOM INDUSTRIES INC
10701 Briggs Rd (44111-5330)
PHONE..............................216 251-2804
Jacob Schaufele Jr, *President*
Harold Schaufele, *Vice Pres*
John Schaufele, *Vice Pres*
Irma Schaufele, *Treasurer*
EMP: 4
SQ FT: 3,900
SALES: 550K **Privately Held**
WEB: www.customindustries.net
SIC: 3364 3369 3363 Nonferrous die-
castings except aluminum; zinc & zinc-
base alloy castings, except die-castings;
aluminum die-castings

(G-5151)
**CUSTOM RUBBER
CORPORATION**
1274 E 55th St (44103-1029)
PHONE..............................216 391-2928
Fax: 216 391-4761
William Braun, *President*
Richard Torres, *Plant Supt*
Tim Zeigler, *Plant Mgr*
Gerrick Whitworth, *Foreman/Supr*
Alice Driver, *QC Mgr*
◆ **EMP:** 75
SQ FT: 70,000
SALES: 10MM **Privately Held**
WEB: www.customrubbercorp.com
SIC: 3069 Molded rubber products

(G-5152)
CUSTOM STAMP MAKERS INC
4901 Brookpark Rd (44134-1017)
PHONE..............................216 351-1470
Sherry Miller, *President*
Kenneth Jaeger, *Corp Secy*
Mark Miller, *Vice Pres*
EMP: 5
SQ FT: 1,200
SALES: 160K **Privately Held**
SIC: 3069 Stationers' rubber sundries

(G-5153)
**CUTLER RICHARD DBA OHIO
CONTRO**
21506 Ellen Dr (44126-3008)
PHONE..............................440 892-1858
Fax: 440 892-3602
Richard Cutler, *Principal*
EMP: 3
SALES (est): 295.6K **Privately Held**
SIC: 3613 Control panels, electric

(G-5154)
**CUTTING EDGE TECHNOLOGIES
INC**
Also Called: Telos Systems
1241 Superior Ave E (44114-3204)
PHONE..............................216 574-4759
Fax: 216 241-4103
Steve Church, *CEO*
Frank J Foti, *Vice Pres*

Anthony Foti, *Admin Sec*
EMP: 50
SALES (est): 4.8MM **Privately Held**
SIC: 3679 3661 Electronic circuits; tele-
phone & telegraph apparatus

(G-5155)
CUTTING SYSTEMS INC
15593 Brookpark Rd (44142-1618)
PHONE..............................216 928-0500
Fax: 216 928-0502
Kris Asadorian, *President*
George Asadorian, *President*
Tim Keough, *Regional Mgr*
Kevan Asadolian, *Vice Pres*
Sergey Edilyan, *Vice Pres*
▲ **EMP:** 16
SQ FT: 44,500
SALES (est): 4.2MM **Privately Held**
WEB: www.cuttingsystems.com
SIC: 3541 Plasma process metal cutting
machines

(G-5156)
**CUYAHOGA CO MED EXAMINER
S OFF**
11001 Cedar Ave (44106-3022)
PHONE..............................216 721-5610
Dave Buehner, *Manager*
EMP: 5
SALES (est): 159.9K **Privately Held**
SIC: 2711 Newspapers, publishing & print-
ing

(G-5157)
**CUYAHOGA COMMUNITY
COLLEGE**
Also Called: Accounts Payable Department
700 Carnegie Ave (44115-2878)
P.O. Box 5229 (44101-0229)
PHONE..............................216 987-4744
Karen Mrak, *General Mgr*
Jerry Hourigan, *Manager*
EMP: 4
SALES (corp-wide): 99.2MM **Privately
Held**
WEB: www.tri-c.cc.oh.us
SIC: 2782 Ledger, inventory & account
books
PA: Cuyahoga Community College
700 Carnegie Ave
Cleveland OH 44115
216 987-6000

(G-5158)
**CUYAHOGA MCH CO LTD LBLTY
CO**
12301 Sprecher Ave (44135-5123)
PHONE..............................216 267-3560
Fax: 216 267-3561
Mark Pine, *Manager*
Michael L Kazimour,
EMP: 7
SALES (est): 825.4K **Privately Held**
WEB: www.cuyahogamachineco.com
SIC: 3599 5084 7699 Machine shop, job-
bing & repair; hydraulic systems equip-
ment & supplies; industrial machinery &
equipment repair; hydraulic equipment re-
pair

(G-5159)
CUYAHOGA REBUILDERS INC
5111 Brookpark Rd (44134-1047)
PHONE..............................440 846-0532
Fax: 216 635-0667
Reiner Mueller, *President*
Randolph Treudler, *Vice Pres*
EMP: 6
SQ FT: 2,500
SALES (est): 827.6K **Privately Held**
SIC: 3694 Alternators, automotive

(G-5160)
**CWRU IRLAND CNCER CTR
CELLULAR**
Also Called: Uhcmc Cellular Therapy Lab
2103 Cornell Rd Rm 6-303 (44106-3860)
PHONE..............................216 368-1007
Jane Reese, *Manager*
Stanton Gerson, *Director*
Kenneth Cooke, *Assoc Prof*
Marian Harter, *Assoc Prof*
EMP: 3

SALES (est): 500K **Privately Held**
SIC: 2869 Laboratory chemicals, organic

(G-5161)
CYBERUTILITY LLC
1599 Maywood Rd (44121-4101)
PHONE..............................216 291-8723
John Scott Minor, *Mng Member*
EMP: 8
SALES: 350K **Privately Held**
SIC: 2911 Petroleum refining

(G-5162)
D M J F INC
Also Called: Swift Print
6571 Pearl Rd (44130-3826)
PHONE..............................440 845-1155
Fax: 440 845-1158
David Fackelman, *President*
Martin Fackelman, *Vice Pres*
Yolanda Fackelman, *Vice Pres*
EMP: 4
SQ FT: 1,800
SALES: 125K **Privately Held**
SIC: 2752 Commercial printing, offset

(G-5163)
DAL-LITTLE FABRICATING INC
Also Called: Megna Plastics
11707 Putnam Ave (44105-5416)
P.O. Box 44067 (44144-0067)
PHONE..............................216 883-3323
Fax: 216 885-0026
Betty J Massielle, *President*
Joe Massielle, *President*
EMP: 8
SQ FT: 13,000
SALES (est): 580K **Privately Held**
SIC: 3229 3441 Glass fiber products; fab-
ricated structural metal

(G-5164)
DANAHER CORPORATION
6095 Parkland Blvd # 310 (44124-6140)
PHONE..............................440 995-3003
Alexander Joseph, *Principal*
Beverly Pinkney, *Admin Asst*
Chris Kastner, *Maintence Staff*
EMP: 173
SALES (corp-wide): 16.8B **Publicly Held**
SIC: 3823 Water quality monitoring & con-
trol systems
PA: Danaher Corporation
2200 Penn Ave Nw Ste 800w
Washington DC 20037
202 828-0850

(G-5165)
DANO JR LLC
6185 Ridgebury Blvd (44124-1751)
PHONE..............................440 781-5774
Louis M Giordano,
EMP: 4
SALES (est): 240.2K **Privately Held**
SIC: 3999 Candles

(G-5166)
DANTE SOLUTIONS INC
7261 Engle Rd Ste 105 (44130-3479)
PHONE..............................440 234-8477
Fax: 440 234-9140
Blake Lynn Ferguson, *President*
Andrew Freborg, *Vice Pres*
Charlie LI, *Vice Pres*
Zhichao LI, *Vice Pres*
EMP: 3
SQ FT: 900
SALES (est): 700K **Privately Held**
WEB: www.deformationcontrol.com
SIC: 8711 7372 Engineering services; ap-
plication computer software

(G-5167)
DARLING INTERNATIONAL INC
1002 Peltnine Ave (44109)
PHONE..............................216 651-9300
Lorie Shorvath, *Manager*
EMP: 18
SQ FT: 28,122
SALES (corp-wide): 3.4B **Publicly Held**
SIC: 2077 5191 Animal & marine fats &
oils; farm supplies

GEOGRAPHIC

PA: Darling Ingredients Inc.
251 Oconnor Ridge Blvd
Irving TX 75038
972 717-0300

(G-5168)
DARRAH ELECTRIC COMPANY (PA)
5914 Merrill Ave (44102-5699)
PHONE.....................216 631-0912
Fax: 216 631-0440
Robert J Darrah, *Ch of Bd*
David J Darrah, *President*
Neal A Darrah, *Corp Secy*
John A Darrah, *Vice Pres*
Thomas Pearson, *Sales Associate*
EMP: 20
SQ FT: 18,000
SALES (est): 14.5MM Privately Held
WEB: www.darrahelectric.com
SIC: 3679 3612 3674 Rectifiers, electronic; electronic circuits; power & distribution transformers; semiconductors & related devices

(G-5169)
DARRYL SMITH
Also Called: Targa Enterprises
3571 E 147th St (44120-4833)
PHONE.....................216 991-5468
Darryl Smith, *Owner*
EMP: 4
SALES (est): 168.5K Privately Held
SIC: 3496 Cages, wire

(G-5170)
DATATEX MEDIA DOLLS
7027 Columbia Rd (44138-1527)
P.O. Box 38125 (44138-0125)
PHONE.....................216 598-1000
Katherine Sanders, *President*
Denise Cefal0, *Vice Pres*
EMP: 5
SALES (est): 148.9K Privately Held
WEB: www.spiritbeach.com
SIC: 7374 3942 Computer graphics service; dolls & stuffed toys

(G-5171)
DAVRO LTD
1200 E 152nd St (44110-3333)
PHONE.....................216 258-0057
Tom Bell, *Principal*
EMP: 5
SALES (est): 371.8K Privately Held
SIC: 3471 Plating & polishing

(G-5172)
DAWN ENTERPRISES INC (PA)
Also Called: Sportwing
9155 Sweet Valley Dr (44125-4223)
PHONE.....................216 642-5506
Fax: 216 642-5505
Robert Kovach, *President*
Lawrence De Laat, *COO*
James Giglio, *Vice Pres*
David Kovach, *Vice Pres*
Tom Sable, *Purchasing*
▲ EMP: 40
SQ FT: 69,900
SALES (est): 6.4MM Privately Held
WEB: www.sportwing.com
SIC: 3089 5521 Plastic processing; used car dealers

(G-5173)
DAY-GLO COLOR CORP (DH)
4515 Saint Clair Ave (44103-1268)
PHONE.....................216 391-7070
Fax: 216 391-7751
Phil Rozick, *Vice Pres*
Kevin Sonby, *Vice Pres*
Sean O'Hara, *Production*
Jonathan Aber, *Marketing Mgr*
Wayne Likavec, *Marketing Mgr*
▲ EMP: 140
SQ FT: 36,000
SALES (est): 49.5MM
SALES (corp-wide): 4.8B Publicly Held
WEB: www.dayglo.com
SIC: 2816 2851 Inorganic pigments; lacquers, varnishes, enamels & other coatings

HQ: Republic Powdered Metals, Inc.
2628 Pearl Rd
Medina OH 44256
330 225-3192

(G-5174)
DAY-GLO COLOR CORP
4518 Hamilton Ave (44114-3854)
PHONE.....................216 391-7070
Steven Jackson, *Branch Mgr*
EMP: 140
SALES (corp-wide): 4.8B Publicly Held
SIC: 2816 2851 Inorganic pigments; lacquers, varnishes, enamels & other coatings
HQ: Day-Glo Color Corp.
4515 Saint Clair Ave
Cleveland OH 44103
216 391-7070

(G-5175)
DB REDIHEAT INC
Also Called: National Bios Fabric Company
4516 Saint Clair Ave (44103-1204)
PHONE.....................216 361-0530
David Breen, *President*
◆ EMP: 20 EST: 2011
SQ FT: 28,000
SALES: 1.7MM Privately Held
SIC: 2392 5131 2241 7389 Bags, garment storage: except paper or plastic film; textile converters; bindings, textile; sewing contractor

(G-5176)
DBHL INC (HQ)
4700 W 160th St (44135-2632)
PHONE.....................216 267-7100
Gary A Oatey, *President*
▲ EMP: 18
SALES (est): 10.9MM
SALES (corp-wide): 206.4MM Privately Held
WEB: www.dbhl.com
SIC: 5999 3088 Plumbing & heating supplies; plastics plumbing fixtures
PA: Oatey Co.
4700 W 160th St
Cleveland OH 44135
800 203-1155

(G-5177)
DCD TECHNOLOGIES INC
17920 S Waterloo Rd (44119-3222)
PHONE.....................216 481-0056
Fax: 216 481-0086
Dave Hodgson, *President*
David Norris, *QC Mgr*
Jacky Dufor, *Engineer*
Mike Palsha, *Engineer*
Kelly Sohn, *Office Mgr*
EMP: 20
SQ FT: 18,000
SALES (est): 4.5MM Privately Held
WEB: www.dcdtech.com
SIC: 3544 Dies & die holders for metal cutting, forming, die casting

(G-5178)
DCM MANUFACTURING INC (HQ)
4540 W 160th St (44135-2628)
PHONE.....................216 265-8006
Theodore Berger Jr, *President*
Theodore Berger, *Chairman*
Kevin J Berger, *Vice Pres*
Rob Knight, *VP Opers*
Eddy Cook, *Production*
◆ EMP: 50
SQ FT: 68,000
SALES (est): 13.1MM
SALES (corp-wide): 44.3MM Privately Held
SIC: 3621 3433 3714 Motors, electric; heating equipment, except electric; motor vehicle parts & accessories
PA: Dreison International, Inc.
4540 W 160th St
Cleveland OH 44135
216 362-0755

(G-5179)
DCW ACQUISITION INC
Also Called: Regol-G Industries
10646 Leuer Ave (44108-1352)
P.O. Box 608957 (44108-0957)
PHONE.....................216 451-0666
Fax: 216 451-1833
Dan Waite, *President*
EMP: 15
SQ FT: 20,000
SALES: 850K Privately Held
SIC: 7389 2394 2393 2392 Sewing contractor; canvas & related products; textile bags; household furnishings; men's & boys' work clothing

(G-5180)
DECORATIVE VENEER INC (PA)
2121 Saint Clair Ave Ne (44114-4018)
PHONE.....................216 741-5511
Michael Knoblouch, *President*
EMP: 2
SQ FT: 7,000
SALES (est): 1.3MM Privately Held
WEB: www.decorativeveneer.com
SIC: 2499 Veneer work, inlaid

(G-5181)
DEFENSE CO INC
600 Superior Ave E (44114-2614)
PHONE.....................413 998-1637
Kent Rosenthal, *President*
EMP: 99
SALES (est): 3.1MM Privately Held
SIC: 3769 Guided missile & space vehicle parts & aux eqpt, rsch & dev

(G-5182)
DELORES E OBEIRN
Also Called: O'Beirn Printing Co
13022 Kingston Way (44133-5971)
P.O. Box 81224 (44181-0224)
PHONE.....................440 582-3610
Delores E O'Beirn, *Owner*
Delores E Obeirn, *Owner*
EMP: 3
SALES: 100K Privately Held
SIC: 2752 5112 5734 2761 Lithographing on metal; business forms; software, business & non-game; manifold business forms

(G-5183)
DELTA MACHINE & TOOL CO
7575 Wall St (44125-3384)
PHONE.....................216 524-2477
Fax: 216 524-0534
Jim Kafun, *President*
Thomas Kafun, *Vice Pres*
Pat Perhala, *Office Mgr*
EMP: 10 EST: 1951
SQ FT: 12,500
SALES: 750K Privately Held
SIC: 3599 7692 3545 3544 Machine shop, jobbing & repair; welding repair; machine tool accessories; special dies, tools, jigs & fixtures

(G-5184)
DEPENDABLE STAMPING COMPANY
1160 E 222nd St (44117-1176)
PHONE.....................216 486-5522
Fax: 216 531-5900
Jeffrey N Beres, *President*
Michael Beres, *Vice Pres*
Roy Beres, *Vice Pres*
Donna Webb, *Manager*
EMP: 25
SQ FT: 20,000
SALES (est): 6.6MM Privately Held
WEB: www.dependablestamping.com
SIC: 3469 Stamping metal for the trade

(G-5185)
DESIGN SIGN INC
1723 Brookpark Rd (44109-5807)
PHONE.....................216 398-9900
Fax: 216 398-8410
Paul Sole, *President*
EMP: 8
SQ FT: 6,000
SALES (est): 1.1MM Privately Held
WEB: www.designsign.com
SIC: 3993 Signs & advertising specialties

(G-5186)
DESMOND ENGRAVING CO INC
13410 Enterprise Ave D (44135-5162)
PHONE.....................216 265-8338
William Bozak, *President*
Brett J May, *Vice Pres*
EMP: 7
SQ FT: 3,200
SALES: 350K Privately Held
SIC: 3953 Date stamps, hand: rubber or metal; figures (marking devices), metal; letters (marking devices), metal; time stamps, hand: rubber or metal

(G-5187)
DI LORIO SHEET METAL INC
5002 Clark Ave (44102-4552)
PHONE.....................216 961-3703
Fax: 216 961-4952
Anthony Di Iorio, *President*
Anna Di Iorio, *Corp Secy*
Antonio Di Iorio, *Manager*
EMP: 12
SQ FT: 34,000
SALES (est): 1.7MM Privately Held
SIC: 3444 Sheet metalwork

(G-5188)
DIAMOND HARD CHROME CO INC
6110 Grand Ave (44104-3955)
PHONE.....................216 391-3618
Fax: 216 391-4518
John R Tankovich, *President*
Robert Tankovich, *President*
EMP: 13
SQ FT: 45,000
SALES (est): 1.1MM Privately Held
SIC: 3471 Electroplating & plating; chromium plating of metals or formed products; polishing, metals or formed products

(G-5189)
DIAMOND METALS DIST INC
4635 W 160th St (44135-2629)
PHONE.....................216 898-7900
Fax: 216 898-7901
Michael Marrapese, *President*
David Palisin, *Treasurer*
Ana Pastrana-Halse, *Finance Mgr*
Sean Donovan, *Regl Sales Mgr*
Ken Sobey, *Sales Staff*
EMP: 30
SALES (est): 6.8MM Privately Held
WEB: www.diamondmetals.com
SIC: 3399 Powder, metal

(G-5190)
DIAMOND WELDING CO INC
11030 Briggs Rd (44111-5334)
PHONE.....................216 251-1679
Fax: 216 251-1768
Michael D Janosko, *President*
EMP: 4
SQ FT: 6,000
SALES: 245K Privately Held
SIC: 7692 Welding repair

(G-5191)
DIASCOPIC LLC
16173 Cleviden Rd (44112-3601)
P.O. Box 20701, Columbus (43220-0701)
PHONE.....................312 282-1800
Cary Serif, *Chairman*
EMP: 3
SALES: 25K Privately Held
SIC: 3826 Analytical instruments

(G-5192)
DIE SERVICES LTD
9200 Inman Ave (44105-2110)
PHONE.....................216 883-5800
Fax: 216 883-5807
Kenneth Raftery, *President*
EMP: 4
SALES (est): 572.7K Privately Held
SIC: 3312 Tool & die steel

(G-5193)
DIE-CUT PRODUCTS CO
Also Called: D C
1801 E 30th St (44114-4471)
PHONE.....................216 771-6994
Fax: 216 771-0777

Steve A Comet, *President*
Jenny Meaney, *General Mgr*
Liz Reinke, *Purchasing*
Arlene R Comet, *Treasurer*
Beth Comet, *Human Res Mgr*
EMP: 22
SQ FT: 10,600
SALES (est): 4MM **Privately Held**
WEB: www.diecut.com
SIC: 3069 3452 3053 3499 Washers, rubber; washers; gaskets, packing & sealing devices; gaskets & sealing devices; shims, metal; sheet metalwork

(G-5194)
DIETRICH INDUSTRIES INC
818 E 73rd St (44103-1708)
PHONE................................216 472-1511
Fax: 216 472-1517
Libby Noce, *Manager*
EMP: 51
SALES (corp-wide): 2.8B **Publicly Held**
WEB: www.dietrichmetalframing.com
SIC: 3441 Building components, structural steel
HQ: Dietrich Industries, Inc.
200 W Old Wilson Brdge Rd
Worthington OH 43085
800 873-2604

(G-5195)
DING PRODUCTS
Also Called: D'Ing Meeting Room Products
5695 Cherokee Dr (44124-3047)
PHONE................................440 442-7777
John Selvaggio, *Owner*
Anna Selvaggio, *Owner*
EMP: 8
SALES (est): 250K **Privately Held**
SIC: 2521 3651 Wood office furniture; household audio & video equipment

(G-5196)
DIRECTCONNECTGROUP LTD
Also Called: D C G
5501 Cass Ave (44102-2121)
PHONE................................216 281-2866
Robert A Durham, *Partner*
Brad Clarke, *Partner*
Scott L Durham, *Partner*
Tammy Peniston, *Partner*
James E Pinkin, *Partner*
EMP: 525
SALES (est): 23.1MM **Privately Held**
WEB: www.dcgrp.net
SIC: 7331 2752 Direct mail advertising services; mailing service; mailing list management; commercial printing, lithographic

(G-5197)
DISTILLATA COMPANY (PA)
1608 E 24th St (44114-4212)
P.O. Box 93845 (44101-5845)
PHONE................................216 771-2900
Fax: 216 771-1672
William E Schroeder, *President*
Dalphne Axline, *Principal*
R M Egan, *Principal*
J C Little, *Principal*
Herbert Buckman, *Corp Secy*
EMP: 70 EST: 1897
SQ FT: 100,000
SALES (est): 15.9MM **Privately Held**
WEB: www.distillata.com
SIC: 2899 5149 Distilled water; mineral or spring water bottling

(G-5198)
DISTRIBUTOR GRAPHICS INC
6909 Engle Rd Ste 13 (44130-3484)
PHONE................................440 260-0024
Fax: 440 362-1849
Richard Doerr, *President*
James F Gottschalk, *Vice Pres*
Robert Wilson, *Treasurer*
Kim Harris, *Administration*
EMP: 8
SQ FT: 8,500
SALES (est): 725K **Privately Held**
SIC: 2752 Commercial printing, offset

(G-5199)
DIVERSIFIED MOLD CASTINGS LLC
Also Called: Diversified Mold & Castings Co
19800 Miles Rd (44128-4118)
PHONE................................216 663-1814
Fax: 216 663-1848
Vince Costello, *Principal*
Tony Short, *Manager*
EMP: 37
SALES (est): 6.8MM **Privately Held**
SIC: 3544 Industrial molds

(G-5200)
DK & J INC
2331 Superior Ave E R (44114-4224)
PHONE................................216 357-3090
Fax: 216 357-3095
Daniel Vonalt, *President*
EMP: 3
SALES (est): 197.3K **Privately Held**
SIC: 2759 Commercial printing

(G-5201)
DLA DOCUMENT SERVICES
1240 E 9th St Rm B31 (44199-2001)
PHONE................................216 522-3535
Craig White, *Manager*
EMP: 5 **Publicly Held**
SIC: 2752 9711 Commercial printing, lithographic; national security;
HQ: Dla Document Services
5450 Carlisle Pike Bldg 9
Mechanicsburg PA 17050
717 605-2362

(G-5202)
DOG DAILY
1180 Blanchester Rd (44124-1360)
PHONE................................216 624-0735
Talun Thomas, *Principal*
EMP: 3
SALES (est): 143K **Privately Held**
SIC: 2711 Newspapers, publishing & printing

(G-5203)
DOMESTIC OIL & GAS CO INC
19600 Rockside Rd (44146-2079)
PHONE................................440 232-3150
Glenn Siegler, *President*
Randall Matheny, *Admin Sec*
EMP: 3
SQ FT: 2,000
SALES (est): 279.6K **Privately Held**
SIC: 1381 Drilling oil & gas wells

(G-5204)
DOMINION ENTERPRISES
26301 Curtiss Wright Pkwy (44143-4413)
PHONE................................216 472-1870
Michelle Dubblestyne, *Principal*
EMP: 21
SALES (corp-wide): 800MM **Privately Held**
WEB: www.traderonline.com
SIC: 2721 Periodicals
HQ: Dominion Enterprises
150 Granby St Ste 150
Norfolk VA 23510
757 351-7000

(G-5205)
DOMINO FOODS INC
Also Called: Domino Sugar
2075 E 65th St (44103-4630)
PHONE................................216 432-3222
Dan Macone, *Vice Pres*
Darrell Lubinsky, *VP Sales*
Jeffrey Bender, *Branch Mgr*
Robert Ruppe, *Manager*
Heather Baines, *Executive*
EMP: 70
SALES (corp-wide): 286.8MM **Privately Held**
WEB:
www.dominospecialtyingredients.com
SIC: 2099 7389 Sugar; packaging & labeling services
HQ: Domino Foods Inc.
99 Wood Ave S Ste 901
Iselin NJ 08830
732 590-1173

(G-5206)
DONE RIGHT ENGINE & MACHINE
12955 York Delta Dr Ste J (44133-3550)
PHONE................................440 582-1366
Fax: 440 582-2005
Rita Yanus, *Vice Pres*
Richard Yanus, *Vice Pres*
EMP: 4
SQ FT: 3,000
SALES (est): 400K **Privately Held**
SIC: 7538 3714 Engine repair; cylinder heads, motor vehicle

(G-5207)
DONEGAL BAY LTD
26055 Emery Rd Ste F (44128-6211)
PHONE................................216 360-9966
Timothy Hewitt, *President*
▲ **EMP:** 10 EST: 1995
SQ FT: 40,000
SALES (est): 958.7K **Privately Held**
WEB: www.donegalbay.com
SIC: 2389 2844 Men's miscellaneous accessories; toilet preparations

(G-5208)
DONNELLEY FINANCIAL LLC
1300 E 9th St Ste 1200 (44114-1513)
PHONE................................216 621-8384
Fax: 216 771-0108
Andrew Komer, *Manager*
EMP: 13
SALES (corp-wide): 6.9B **Publicly Held**
SIC: 2752 Commercial printing, lithographic
HQ: Donnelley Financial Llc
55 Water St Lowr L1
New York NY 10041
212 425-0298

(G-5209)
DOT-2-DOT INC
6909 Engle Rd Ste 16 (44130-3484)
PHONE................................440 891-9388
Al Tucsok, *Principal*
▲ **EMP:** 10
SALES (est): 1MM **Privately Held**
SIC: 2893 Printing ink

(G-5210)
DOUGLAS MICHALSKE
Also Called: Michalske Printing Company
5808 Clark Ave (44102-4414)
PHONE................................216 631-0567
Fax: 216 631-0568
Douglas Michalske, *Owner*
Matt Michalski, *Vice Pres*
EMP: 3
SQ FT: 4,000
SALES (est): 300.5K **Privately Held**
SIC: 2752 2759 2791 2789 Commercial printing, offset; letterpress printing; typesetting; bookbinding & related work; packaging paper & plastics film, coated & laminated

(G-5211)
DOVE DIE AND STAMPING COMPANY
15665 Brookpark Rd (44142-1668)
PHONE................................216 267-3720
Fax: 216 267-7250
Gerald Wagner, *President*
Norma Wagner, *Corp Secy*
EMP: 45
SQ FT: 42,000
SALES (est): 14.4MM **Privately Held**
WEB: www.dovedie.com
SIC: 3469 3544 Metal stampings; special dies & tools

(G-5212)
DOVE GRAPHICS INC
13500 Pearl Rd (44136-3400)
PHONE................................440 238-1800
EMP: 4 EST: 1982
SQ FT: 800
SALES: 80K **Privately Held**
SIC: 2752 Lithographic Commercial Printing

(G-5213)
DOYLE SAILMAKER
805 E 185th St (44119-2701)
PHONE................................216 486-5732
Greg Koski, *Owner*
Doyle Sailmaker, *Owner*
EMP: 5
SALES (est): 401K **Privately Held**
SIC: 3732 Sailboats, building & repairing

(G-5214)
DRABIK MANUFACTURING INC
15601 Commerce Park Dr (44142-2016)
PHONE................................216 267-4422
Fax: 216 267-4422
James Drabik, *President*
Mark Drabik, *Sales Staff*
Cathy Prest, *Manager*
EMP: 17
SQ FT: 13,000
SALES (est): 3.2MM **Privately Held**
WEB: www.drabikinc.com
SIC: 3599 7692 Machine shop, jobbing & repair; welding repair

(G-5215)
DREISON INTERNATIONAL INC (PA)
4540 W 160th St (44135-2628)
PHONE................................216 362-0755
Theodore J Berger Sr, *Ch of Bd*
Theodore Berger Jr, *President*
Marilyn J Berger, *Corp Secy*
Joe Rivera, *QC Mgr*
Whitney Slaght, *CFO*
▲ **EMP:** 190
SQ FT: 210,000
SALES (est): 44.3MM **Privately Held**
WEB: www.dreison.com
SIC: 3714 3643 3621 3561 Mufflers (exhaust), motor vehicle; current-carrying wiring devices; motors, electric; pumps & pumping equipment; purification & dust collection equipment

(G-5216)
DRG HYDRAULICS INC
18200 S Miles Rd (44128-4232)
PHONE................................216 663-9747
Fax: 216 663-4022
Don I Stetner, *President*
Mary Wise, *General Mgr*
▲ **EMP:** 35
SQ FT: 16,000
SALES (est): 7.6MM **Privately Held**
SIC: 3559 3542 Plastics working machinery; presses: hydraulic & pneumatic, mechanical & manual

(G-5217)
DUBLIN PLASTICS INC
9202 Reno Ave (44105-2125)
PHONE................................216 641-5904
Donald R Newman, *President*
James Newman, *Admin Sec*
EMP: 8
SALES: 2MM **Privately Held**
SIC: 3089 Injection molding of plastics

(G-5218)
DUBRO OIL CORPORATION
2400 Mulberry Ave (44113-1196)
PHONE................................216 696-2646
C William Roush, *President*
EMP: 3
SQ FT: 10,000
SALES (est): 205.7K **Privately Held**
SIC: 3295 2992 Graphite, natural: ground, pulverized, refined or blended; lubricating oils & greases

(G-5219)
DUCT FABRICATORS INC
Also Called: Fab3 Group
883 Addison Rd (44103-1607)
PHONE................................216 391-2400
Fax: 216 391-2404
John Haggerty, *Division Mgr*
John Sickle, *Principal*
Steven Haydu, *Principal*
Terry Negard, *Purch Agent*
EMP: 8 EST: 2011
SALES (est): 1.2MM **Privately Held**
SIC: 3444 Sheet metalwork

(G-5220)
DUCTS INC
883 Addison Rd (44103-1607)
PHONE..................................216 391-2400
Patricia Sickle Mc Elroy, *CEO*
John E Sickle Jr, *President*
John Haggerty, *Division Mgr*
Charlotte Sickle, *Chairman*
James Sickle, *Vice Pres*
EMP: 50 EST: 1962
SQ FT: 30,000
SALES (est): 3.1MM **Privately Held**
SIC: 1761 3444 Sheet metalwork; sheet metalwork

(G-5221)
DULCELICIOUS CUPCAKES AND MORE
22368 Lorain Rd (44126-2208)
PHONE..................................440 385-7706
Laura Gigante, *Principal*
EMP: 4
SALES (est): 268.5K **Privately Held**
SIC: 2051 Bread, cake & related products

(G-5222)
DUNECRAFT INC
19201 Cranwood Pkwy (44128-4043)
P.O. Box 808, Chagrin Falls (44022-0808)
PHONE..................................800 306-4168
Grant Cleveland, *President*
Bobby Sigman, *Vice Pres*
Ian Randolph, *Manager*
▲ **EMP:** 24
SALES: 5.5MM **Privately Held**
WEB: www.dunecraft.com
SIC: 3944 Science kits: microscopes, chemistry sets, etc.

(G-5223)
DURABLE PLATING CO
4404 Saint Clair Ave (44103-1188)
PHONE..................................216 391-2132
Fax: 216 391-1184
Joe Akers, *President*
Tim Akers, *Vice Pres*
Shirley Akers, *Admin Sec*
EMP: 7 EST: 1935
SQ FT: 6,500
SALES: 850K **Privately Held**
SIC: 3471 Plating of metals or formed products

(G-5224)
DURAY PLATING COMPANY INC
13701 Triskett Rd (44111-1520)
PHONE..................................216 941-5540
Fax: 216 941-5919
Kenneth R Roth, *President*
Jeffrey J Roth, *Plant Mgr*
Bruce G Roth, *Sales Mgr*
Ellie Yanky, *Director*
EMP: 25
SQ FT: 6,000
SALES (est): 1MM **Privately Held**
WEB: www.durayplatingco.com
SIC: 3471 Electroplating & plating; chromium plating of metals or formed products

(G-5225)
DURISEK ENTERPRISES INC
Also Called: Midwest Welding & Boiler Co
5200 Train Ave (44102-4525)
PHONE..................................216 281-3898
Fax: 216 281-3895
George R Durisek Sr, *President*
George R Durisek Jr, *Vice Pres*
Caroline Durisek, *Admin Sec*
EMP: 4
SQ FT: 2,800
SALES (est): 432.7K **Privately Held**
SIC: 7692 Welding repair

(G-5226)
DVUV LLC (PA)
4641 Hinckley Indus Pkwy (44109-6002)
PHONE..................................216 741-5511
Rebecca Rutherford, *Marketing Mgr*
Michael Knoblauch,
▼ **EMP:** 15
SQ FT: 20,000
SALES (est): 1.1MM **Privately Held**
SIC: 2521 Wood office furniture

(G-5227)
DYNAMIC TOOL & MOLD INC
12126 York Rd Unit N (44133-3688)
PHONE..................................440 237-8665
Dale English, *President*
John Getchell, *Vice Pres*
Adam Ziebro, *Finance Mgr*
EMP: 7
SQ FT: 3,500
SALES (est): 1MM **Privately Held**
SIC: 3544 Special dies, tools, jigs & fixtures

(G-5228)
E & E MOLD & DIE INC
4605 Manufacturing Ave (44135-2637)
PHONE..................................216 898-5853
Fax: 216 898-5856
Michael Saintz, *President*
Troy Beahr, *Vice Pres*
EMP: 6
SQ FT: 10,000
SALES (est): 630.1K **Privately Held**
SIC: 3544 Dies & die holders for metal cutting, forming, die casting; dies, plastics forming

(G-5229)
E & K PRODUCTS CO INC
3520 Cesko Ave (44109-1487)
PHONE..................................216 631-2510
Fax: 216 631-8325
Lee Klimek, *Ch of Bd*
David Klimek, *Vice Pres*
Joyce Klimek, *Admin Sec*
EMP: 8 EST: 1966
SQ FT: 25,000
SALES: 440K **Privately Held**
SIC: 3599 3444 Machine shop, jobbing & repair; sheet metalwork

(G-5230)
E B P INC
Also Called: Epic Steel
2041 W 17th St (44113-3579)
PHONE..................................216 241-2550
Fax: 216 241-3327
Dan Fremont, *President*
Arthur M Hemlock, *Principal*
Robert M Lustig, *Principal*
Neff Fremont, *Vice Pres*
Tom Eirons, *Purchasing*
EMP: 29
SQ FT: 53,500
SALES: 6.5MM **Privately Held**
WEB: www.epicsteel.com
SIC: 3441 3446 Fabricated structural metal; architectural metalwork; railings, bannisters, guards, etc.: made from metal pipe; stairs, staircases, stair treads: prefabricated metal; sheet metalwork

(G-5231)
E D M FASTAR INC
13410 Enterprise Ave (44135-5162)
PHONE..................................216 676-0100
Frank Star, *President*
EMP: 7 EST: 1999
SQ FT: 3,000
SALES (est): 600K **Privately Held**
SIC: 3544 Special dies, tools, jigs & fixtures

(G-5232)
E I DU PONT DE NEMOURS & CO
Also Called: Dupont Vespel Parts and Shapes
6200 Hillcrest Dr (44125-4624)
PHONE..................................216 901-3600
Bryan Bradford, *Engineer*
Josephine Bremenour, *Engineer*
Anthony Adetayo, *Branch Mgr*
EMP: 118
SALES (corp-wide): 24.5B **Publicly Held**
WEB: www.dupont.com
SIC: 3366 3568 Bushings & bearings; power transmission equipment
PA: E. I. Du Pont De Nemours And Company
974 Centre Rd
Wilmington DE 19805
302 774-1000

(G-5233)
E POMPILI & SONS INC
Also Called: Pompili Precast Concrete
12307 Broadway Ave (44125-1847)
PHONE..................................216 581-8080
Fax: 216 581-3910
William Pompili, *President*
EMP: 8
SQ FT: 14,500
SALES (est): 810K **Privately Held**
WEB: www.pompiliprecastconcrete.com
SIC: 3272 Concrete products, precast

(G-5234)
E T & K INC
Also Called: American Speedy Printing
9809 Running Brook Dr (44130-8217)
PHONE..................................440 888-4780
Edward Scully, *President*
Theresa Scully, *Corp Secy*
EMP: 3
SALES (est): 153.1K **Privately Held**
SIC: 2752 Commercial printing, offset

(G-5235)
E-Z ELECTRIC MOTOR SVC CORP
8510 Bessemer Ave (44127-1843)
PHONE..................................216 581-8820
Fax: 216 581-8618
Demetrius Ledgyard, *President*
Jean Ledgyard, *Director*
EMP: 13
SQ FT: 15,000
SALES: 746K **Privately Held**
SIC: 7694 Electric motor repair

(G-5236)
EAGLE ADVERTISING
4101 Commerce Ave (44103-3507)
PHONE..................................216 881-0800
Thomas M Baginski, *Owner*
EMP: 4
SALES (est): 240K **Privately Held**
SIC: 2752 5999 Offset & photolithographic printing; banners, flags, decals & posters

(G-5237)
EAGLE TOOL & DIE INC
10805 Briggs Rd (44111-5331)
PHONE..................................216 671-5055
Fax: 216 671-3060
Miroslaw Zebrowski, *President*
EMP: 3
SQ FT: 3,300
SALES: 200K **Privately Held**
SIC: 3544 Special dies & tools

(G-5238)
EAGLE WIRE WORKS INC
3173 E 66th St Fl 3 (44127-1404)
PHONE..................................216 341-8550
Fax: 216 341-6460
EMP: 10 EST: 1896
SQ FT: 30,000
SALES: 676.1K **Privately Held**
SIC: 3496 Mfg Misc Fabricated Wire Products

(G-5239)
EAST CLEVELAND RUBBER STAMP
16501 Euclid Ave (44112-1403)
PHONE..................................216 851-5050
Fax: 216 851-5051
Harold Stern, *President*
EMP: 3
SQ FT: 4,044
SALES (est): 330.7K **Privately Held**
SIC: 3953 Marking devices

(G-5240)
EAST WOODWORKING COMPANY
2044 Random Rd (44106-2320)
PHONE..................................216 791-5950
Fax: 216 791-5952
Zigmund T Hersh, *President*
Albert Hersh, *Vice Pres*
Coby Hersh, *Manager*
Ken Hersh, *Manager*
EMP: 8 EST: 1956
SQ FT: 12,400

SALES: 1.5MM **Privately Held**
WEB: www.eastwoodworking.com
SIC: 1751 2521 2522 3261 Cabinet building & installation; cabinets, office: wood; office cabinets & filing drawers: except wood; vitreous plumbing fixtures

(G-5241)
EASTWORD PUBLICATIONS DEV
Also Called: Lincoln Library Press
812 Huron Rd E Ste 401 (44115-1172)
PHONE..................................216 781-9594
Fax: 216 781-9559
Timothy Gall, *President*
Susan Bevan-Gall, *Vice Pres*
Joanne Angiolini, *Treasurer*
Richard Burns, *Manager*
Mary Hile, *Manager*
EMP: 5
SQ FT: 900
SALES (est): 17.8K **Privately Held**
WEB: www.thelincolnlibrary.com
SIC: 2731 Books-Publishing/Printing

(G-5242)
EASY SIDE PUBLISHING CO INC
Also Called: Eastside Daily News
11400 Woodland Ave (44104-2636)
PHONE..................................216 721-1674
Fax: 216 221-7145
Ulysses Glenn, *President*
EMP: 5
SQ FT: 1,311
SALES: 150K **Privately Held**
SIC: 2711 Newspapers: publishing only, not printed on site

(G-5243)
EATON AEROSPACE LLC (DH)
Also Called: E E M C O
1000 Eaton Blvd (44122-6058)
PHONE..................................216 523-5000
Alexander M Cutler, *CEO*
Bob Brlas, *Managing Dir*
Randy W Carson, *Senior VP*
R H Fearon, *CFO*
▲ **EMP:** 10
SALES (est): 224.5MM **Privately Held**
SIC: 3812 Acceleration indicators & systems components, aerospace
HQ: Eaton Hydraulics Llc
14615 Lone Oak Rd
Eden Prairie MN 55344
952 937-9800

(G-5244)
EATON AEROSPACE LLC
2000 Apollo Dr (44142-4102)
P.O. Box 818025 (44181-8025)
PHONE..................................216 523-5000
EMP: 25 **Privately Held**
SIC: 3812 Acceleration indicators & systems components, aerospace
HQ: Eaton Aerospace Llc
1000 Eaton Blvd
Cleveland OH 44122
216 523-5000

(G-5245)
EATON CORPORATION (HQ)
1000 Eaton Blvd (44122-6058)
P.O. Box 818024 (44181-8024)
PHONE..................................216 523-5000
Fax: 216 479-7092
Alexander Cutler, *Ch of Bd*
Mark McGuire, *Exec VP*
Craig Arnold, *Senior VP*
Thomas Moran, *Senior VP*
Billie Rawot, *Senior VP*
◆ **EMP:** 450
SALES: 6.9B **Privately Held**
WEB: www.eaton.com
SIC: 3625 3714 3594 3559 Motor controls & accessories; motor starters & controllers, electric; actuators, industrial; motor vehicle engines & parts; motor vehicle transmissions, drive assemblies & parts; motor vehicle steering systems & parts; pumps, hydraulic power transfer; motors: hydraulic, fluid power or air; semiconductor manufacturing machinery; personal computers (microcomputers)

(G-5246)
EATON CORPORATION
Also Called: North American Fincl Svcs Ctr
2000 Apollo Dr (44142-4102)
PHONE..................................216 416-2500
Fax: 216 416-2600
Jill Donais, *Senior VP*
Jaynee Clark, *Controller*
Linda Lynch, *Branch Mgr*
George Basel, *Admin Asst*
Jacqueline Aftoora, *Analyst*
EMP: 125 **Privately Held**
WEB: www.eaton.com
SIC: 3625 3714 3594 3559 Motor con-
trols & accessories; motor starters & con-
trollers, electric; actuators, industrial;
motor vehicle engines & parts; motor vehicle transmissions, drive assemblies &
parts; motor vehicle steering systems &
parts; pumps, hydraulic power transfer;
motors: hydraulic, fluid power or air; bag
seaming & closing machines (sewing machinery); leather working machinery; personal computers (microcomputers)
HQ: Eaton Corporation
1000 Eaton Blvd
Cleveland OH 44122
216 523-5000

(G-5247)
EATON CORPORATION
Airflex Div
9919 Clinton Rd (44144-1077)
PHONE..................................216 281-2211
Fax: 216 281-3890
Jeff Place, *Plant Mgr*
David E Schwieterman, *Plant Mgr*
Greg Lutzweiler, *Mfg Staff*
Shelly Stefancin, *Purchasing*
Don Danko, *Engineer*
EMP: 200 **Privately Held**
WEB: www.eaton.com
SIC: 3714 3625 3542 3568 Air brakes,
motor vehicle; transmission housings or
parts, motor vehicle; clutches, motor vehi-
cle; electromagnetic clutches or brakes;
brakes, metal forming; clutches, except
vehicular
HQ: Eaton Corporation
1000 Eaton Blvd
Cleveland OH 44122
216 523-5000

(G-5248)
EATON CORPORATION
6055 Rckside Woods Blvd N (44131-2301)
P.O. Box 818028 (44181-8028)
PHONE..................................888 328-6677
EMP: 217 **Privately Held**
WEB: www.eaton.com
SIC: 3625 Motor controls & accessories
HQ: Eaton Corporation
1000 Eaton Blvd
Cleveland OH 44122
216 523-5000

(G-5249)
EATON CORPORATION
Eaton Family Credit Union
333 Babbitt Rd Ste 100 (44123-1636)
PHONE..................................216 920-2000
Michael Losneck, *Branch Mgr*
EMP: 260 **Privately Held**
WEB: www.eaton.com
SIC: 3714 5084 Hydraulic fluid power
pumps for auto steering mechanism; hy-
draulic systems equipment & supplies
HQ: Eaton Corporation
1000 Eaton Blvd
Cleveland OH 44122
216 523-5000

(G-5250)
EATON CORPORATION
Also Called: NA Financial Service Center
6055 Rckside Woods Blvd N (44131-2301)
P.O. Box 818035 (44181-8035)
PHONE..................................440 826-1115
A Valore, *Manager*
EMP: 217 **Privately Held**
WEB: www.eaton.com
SIC: 3625 Relays & industrial controls
HQ: Eaton Corporation
1000 Eaton Blvd
Cleveland OH 44122
216 523-5000

(G-5251)
**EATON ELECTRIC HOLDINGS
LLC (HQ)**
1000 Eaton Blvd (44122-6058)
PHONE..................................440 523-5000
Alexander M Cutler, *CEO*
Trent Meyerhoefer, *Senior VP*
Richard Fearon, *Mng Member*
Lizbeth L Wright,
EMP: 20
SALES (est): 6.7MM **Privately Held**
SIC: 3646 Commercial indusl & institu-
tional electric lighting fixtures

(G-5252)
**EATON INDUSTRIAL
CORPORATION (DH)**
Also Called: Argo-Tech
23555 Euclid Ave (44117-1703)
PHONE..................................216 692-5456
Fax: 216 692-5293
Alexander M Cutler, *CEO*
Ken Kovalchik, *General Mgr*
Paul R Keen, *Exec VP*
James Cunningham, *Vice Pres*
Earl R Franklin, *Vice Pres*
EMP: 433
SQ FT: 1,800,000
SALES (est): 104.9MM **Privately Held**
WEB: www.atclabs.com
SIC: 3724 3728 Pumps, aircraft engine;
aircraft parts & equipment
HQ: At Holdings Corporation
23555 Euclid Ave
Cleveland OH 44117
216 692-6000

(G-5253)
**EATON USEV HOLDING
COMPANY (DH)**
1111 Suprr Eatn Ctr 173 (44114)
PHONE..................................216 523-5000
Alexander M Cutler, *CEO*
EMP: 5
SALES (est): 106MM **Privately Held**
SIC: 3592 Valves, engine
HQ: Eaton Corporation
1000 Eaton Blvd
Cleveland OH 44122
216 523-5000

(G-5254)
EATON-AEROQUIP LLC (DH)
Also Called: Eaton Global Hose
1000 Eaton Blvd (44122-6058)
PHONE..................................216 523-5000
Alexander M Cutler, *CEO*
E R Franklin, *Vice Pres*
▲ **EMP:** 220 **EST:** 1940
SQ FT: 21,000
SALES (est): 1B **Privately Held**
SIC: 3052 3492 3429 3069 Rubber hose;
plastic hose; hose & tube fittings & as-
semblies, hydraulic/pneumatic; clamps &
couplings, hose; clamps, metal; molded
rubber products; parts for heating, cooling
& refrigerating equipment; aircraft parts &
equipment
HQ: Aeroquip-Vickers, Inc.
1111 Superior Ave E
Cleveland OH 44114
216 523-5000

(G-5255)
**ECONOMY FLAME HARDENING
INC**
896 E 70th St (44103-1706)
P.O. Box 30026 (44130-0026)
PHONE..................................216 431-9333
Charles P Triplett, *President*
Chuck Kirk, *Plant Mgr*
EMP: 6
SALES (est): 574.6K **Privately Held**
SIC: 3356 Nonferrous rolling & drawing

(G-5256)
**ECONOMY STRAIGHTENING
SERVICE**
896 E 70th St (44103-1706)
PHONE..................................216 432-4410
Charles Triplett, *President*
Bob Solinski, *Vice Pres*
EMP: 5
SQ FT: 3,000

SALES (est): 510K **Privately Held**
SIC: 3356 Nonferrous rolling & drawing

(G-5257)
ECOWISE LLC
Also Called: Natgascar
17000 Saint Clair Ave (44110-2535)
PHONE..................................216 692-3700
Bradley Trembath, *President*
Kate Beckenbach, *Manager*
EMP: 5
SALES (est): 1.1MM **Privately Held**
SIC: 3563 Air & gas compressors

(G-5258)
EDGE-RITE TOOLS INC
7700 Exchange St (44125-3310)
PHONE..................................216 642-0966
Fax: 216 642-0606
John Kaput, *President*
EMP: 14
SQ FT: 3,000
SALES (est): 1.9MM **Privately Held**
SIC: 3544 3545 Special dies, tools, jigs &
fixtures; cutting tools for machine tools

(G-5259)
**EDGEWELL PER CARE BRANDS
LLC**
17120 Hawks Lookout Ln (44136-6223)
PHONE..................................440 572-1336
Bill Giermann, *Manager*
EMP: 25
SALES (corp-wide): 2.3B **Publicly Held**
WEB: www.eveready.com
SIC: 3421 Razor blades & razors
HQ: Edgewell Personal Care Brands, Llc
6 Research Dr
Shelton CT 06484
203 944-5500

(G-5260)
EG ENTERPRISE SERVICES INC
5000 Euclid Ave Ste 100 (44103-3752)
P.O. Box 18029 (44118-0029)
PHONE..................................216 431-3300
Fax: 216 431-1050
EMP: 12 **EST:** 1993
SQ FT: 10,000
SALES (est): 950K **Privately Held**
SIC: 2752 7331 7334 Commercial Offset
Printing

(G-5261)
EJ USA INC
4160 Glenridge Rd (44121-2802)
PHONE..................................216 692-3001
Richard Humkes Jr, *Manager*
EMP: 25
SQ FT: 11,397 **Privately Held**
WEB: www.ejiw.com
SIC: 3321 3322 Gray iron castings; mal-
leable iron foundries
HQ: Ej Usa, Inc.
301 Spring St
East Jordan MI 49727
800 874-4100

(G-5262)
ELCO CORPORATION (HQ)
1000 Belt Line Ave (44109-2800)
PHONE..................................800 321-0467
Fax: 216 749-7462
Doug Church, *President*
Mike Andrea, *Business Mgr*
Dave Millin, *Vice Pres*
Sam Smaldino, *Purchasing*
Bob Lunoe, *CFO*
▼ **EMP:** 61 **EST:** 1929
SQ FT: 72,000
SALES (est): 16.4MM
SALES (corp-wide): 56.5MM **Publicly
Held**
WEB: www.elcocorp.com
SIC: 2869 Industrial organic chemicals

(G-5263)
ELECTRIC CORD SETS INC (PA)
4700 Manufacturing Ave (44135-2640)
PHONE..................................216 261-1000
Robert Jericho, *Ch of Bd*
Tom Brunning, *Ch of Bd*
Sean Thrasher, *Marketing Staff*
Thomas Bruening, *Info Tech Mgr*
Karen Ammen,
▲ **EMP:** 6

SQ FT: 3,500
SALES (est): 16.5MM **Privately Held**
WEB: www.elecordset.com
SIC: 3643 Current-carrying wiring devices

(G-5264)
**ELECTRIC CTRL & MTR REPR
SVC**
6717 Saint Clair Ave (44103-1743)
PHONE..................................216 881-3143
Fax: 216 881-7657
Leslie Imeli, *President*
Zoltan Imeli, *Vice Pres*
EMP: 4
SQ FT: 1,500
SALES: 115K **Privately Held**
SIC: 7694 1731 Electric motor repair; re-
building motors, except automotive; elec-
trical work

(G-5265)
**ELECTRIC SPEED INDICATOR
CO**
12234 Triskett Rd (44111-2519)
PHONE..................................216 251-2540
Fax: 216 251-2641
Robert P Riley, *President*
Peter Riley, *General Mgr*
Coletta Riley, *Vice Pres*
EMP: 10 **EST:** 1934
SQ FT: 4,000
SALES (est): 1.3MM **Privately Held**
WEB: www.electricspeedindicator.com
SIC: 3829 7699 Geophysical & meteoro-
logical testing equipment; meteorological
instruments; meteorological instrument
repair

(G-5266)
ELECTRO-MAGWAVE INC
Also Called: E M Wave
6111 Carey Dr Ste 1 (44125-4274)
PHONE..................................216 453-1160
Frank Kim Goryance, *President*
Robert Truthan, *Vice Pres*
Anthony Zupancic, *Vice Pres*
Kim Goryance, *VP Sls/Mktg*
Tony Zupancic, *Manager*
EMP: 7
SQ FT: 6,300
SALES (est): 650K **Privately Held**
SIC: 3663 Antennas, transmitting & com-
munications

(G-5267)
**ELECTROLIZING CORPORATION
OHIO (PA)**
1325 E 152nd St (44112-2075)
P.O. Box 12007 (44112-0007)
PHONE..................................216 451-3153
Fax: 216 451-4729
Lawrence E Noble, *President*
Bill Loucks, *General Mgr*
Scott Noble, *Exec VP*
Todd Noble, *Vice Pres*
Diane Pressly, *Financial Exec*
EMP: 20
SQ FT: 20,000
SALES (est): 3.6MM **Privately Held**
WEB: www.electrohio.com
SIC: 3471 Anodizing (plating) of metals or
formed products

(G-5268)
**ELECTROLIZING CORPORATION
OHIO**
1655 Collamer Ave (44110-3201)
PHONE..................................216 451-8653
Daral Cook, *Manager*
EMP: 10
SQ FT: 12,342
SALES (corp-wide): 3.6MM **Privately
Held**
WEB: www.electrohio.com
SIC: 3471 Anodizing (plating) of metals or
formed products
PA: Electrolizing Corporation Of Ohio
1325 E 152nd St
Cleveland OH 44112
216 451-3153

GEOGRAPHIC

(G-5269)
ELECTROLUX PROFESSIONAL INC (DH)
20445 Emerald Pkwy (44135-6009)
P.O. Box 35920 (44135-0920)
PHONE....................216 898-1800
Fax: 216 898-2340
George C Weigand, *President*
Richard S Pietch, *Senior VP*
Ronald E Zajaczkowski, *Senior VP*
Maurizio Bucciarelli, *Vice Pres*
Mark W Russell, *Vice Pres*
◆ **EMP:** 25
SALES (est): 22.4MM
SALES (corp-wide): 14.1B **Privately Held**
WEB: www.electroluxprofessional.com
SIC: 3585 Air conditioning units, complete: domestic or industrial
HQ: Electrolux North America, Inc.
10200 David Taylor Dr
Charlotte NC 28262
980 236-2000

(G-5270)
ELECTROMECH TECHNOLOGIES LLC (DH)
1301 E 9th St Ste 3000 (44114-1871)
PHONE....................216 706-2960
Tariq Jesrai,
Dirkson Charles,
Bruce Graben,
Doris Harms,
▲ **EMP:** 341
SALES (est): 69.9MM
SALES (corp-wide): 3.1B **Publicly Held**
WEB: www.tyeeair.com
SIC: 3441 Fabricated structural metal
HQ: Mckechnie Aerospace Investments, Inc.
20 Pacifica Ste 200
Irvine CA
859 887-6200

(G-5271)
ELGIN FASTENER GROUP LLC
Chandler Products
1491 Chardon Rd (44117-1510)
PHONE....................216 481-4400
Pat Paulus, *Plant Mgr*
Gary Walston, *Manager*
Martin Kelp, *Info Tech Mgr*
EMP: 38
SALES (corp-wide): 126.1MM **Privately Held**
SIC: 3452 3451 3316 Bolts, nuts, rivets & washers; screw machine products; cold finishing of steel shapes
HQ: Elgin Fastener Group, Llc
10217 Brecksville Rd
Brecksville OH 44141

(G-5272)
ELITE PROPERTY GROUP LLC
3281 W 86th St (44102-4940)
PHONE....................216 316-8222
Sean Webb,
EMP: 12
SALES (est): 248.5K **Privately Held**
SIC: 8742 6719 8741 1389 Construction project management consultant; investment holding companies, except banks; construction management; construction, repair & dismantling services; real estate managers

(G-5273)
ELITE SHIP PACKAGING SYSTEM
4535 Big Met Pl (44135-1716)
PHONE....................216 502-6798
EMP: 3 **EST:** 2015
SALES (est): 160.7K **Privately Held**
SIC: 2631 Container, packaging & boxboard

(G-5274)
ELLWOOD GROUP INC
Also Called: Elwood Crankshaft Group
777 E 79th St (44103-1805)
PHONE....................216 862-6341
EMP: 3
SALES (corp-wide): 774.9MM **Privately Held**
SIC: 3599 Crankshafts & camshafts, machining

PA: Ellwood Group, Inc.
600 Commercial Ave
Ellwood City PA 16117
724 752-3680

(G-5275)
EMBROID ME
4311 Ridge Rd (44144-2714)
PHONE....................216 459-9250
Fax: 216 459-9253
Ken Grodek, *Owner*
EMP: 3
SALES (est): 120K **Privately Held**
SIC: 2395 Embroidery & art needlework

(G-5276)
EMPIRE BRASS CO
Also Called: American Brass
5000 Superior Ave (44103-1238)
PHONE....................216 431-6565
Robert Mc Connville, *President*
Robert McConville, *Administration*
▲ **EMP:** 50
SALES (est): 7.2MM **Privately Held**
WEB: www.empirebrassfaucets.com
SIC: 5074 3432 3364 Plumbing fittings & supplies; plumbing fixture fittings & trim; nonferrous die-castings except aluminum

(G-5277)
EMPIRE IRON MINING PARTNERSHIP (PA)
1100 Superior Ave E Fl 15 (44114-2530)
PHONE....................216 694-5700
Fax: 216 696-7668
David B Blake, *General Mgr*
The Cleveland-Cliffs Iron Comp, *General Ptnr*
Mittal Steel USA, *General Ptnr*
John Cotter, *Controller*
EMP: 1 **EST:** 1959
SALES (est): 84.4MM **Privately Held**
SIC: 1011 Iron ore mining; iron ore pelletizing; iron ore beneficiating

(G-5278)
EMPIRE PLOW COMPANY INC (DH)
3140 E 65th St (44127-1490)
PHONE....................216 641-2290
Fax: 216 441-4709
David Pitt, *President*
Noel Anderson, *Safety Mgr*
William Lefelhoc, *Engineer*
Ronald Elias, *Controller*
Donald Berger, *Manager*
EMP: 25 **EST:** 1840
SQ FT: 123,000
SALES (est): 22MM
SALES (corp-wide): 202.9K **Privately Held**
WEB: www.mckayempire.com
SIC: 3523 3423 Farm machinery & equipment; hand & edge tools
HQ: Ralph Mckay Industries Inc
130 Hodsman Rd
Regina SK S4N 5
306 721-9292

(G-5279)
EMX INDUSTRIES INC
4564 Johnston Pkwy (44128-2953)
PHONE....................216 518-9888
Joseph Rozgonyi, *CEO*
Debra R Shpigler, *Principal*
Bob Hausch, *Vice Pres*
Robert Hausch, *Draft/Design*
Ryan Crawford, *Engineer*
▲ **EMP:** 35
SQ FT: 20,000
SALES (est): 8.1MM **Privately Held**
WEB: www.emxinc.com
SIC: 3699 Security control equipment & systems

(G-5280)
ENERCO GROUP INC (PA)
Also Called: Mr Heater
4560 W 160th St (44135-2628)
P.O. Box 6660 (44101-1660)
PHONE....................216 916-3000
Allen Haire, *CEO*
Jeff Mack, *President*
Kevin McDonough, *Vice Pres*
Brian Vandrak, *Vice Pres*
Daniel Loprich, *Purch Dir*

▲ **EMP:** 101
SQ FT: 120,875
SALES (est): 44.6MM **Privately Held**
SIC: 3433 Gas infrared heating units

(G-5281)
ENERCO TECHNICAL PRODUCTS INC
Also Called: Mr. Heater
4560 W 160th St (44135-2628)
P.O. Box 6660 (44101-1660)
PHONE....................216 916-3000
Fax: 216 881-6699
Allen L Haire, *CEO*
John D Duross, *President*
Francis Verchick, *Vice Pres*
Carl Meermans, *VP Opers*
Don Kuse, *Sales Staff*
EMP: 180
SQ FT: 48,000
SALES (est): 21.3MM
SALES (corp-wide): 44.6MM **Privately Held**
SIC: 3433 Gas infrared heating units
PA: Enerco Group, Inc.
4560 W 160th St
Cleveland OH 44135
216 916-3000

(G-5282)
ENERSYS DELAWARE INC
12690 Elmwood Ave (44111-5912)
PHONE....................216 252-4242
Walt Sauerteig, *Branch Mgr*
EMP: 3
SALES (corp-wide): 2.3B **Publicly Held**
SIC: 3691 5063 Lead acid batteries (storage batteries); electrical apparatus & equipment
HQ: Enersys Delaware Inc.
2366 Bernville Rd
Reading PA 19605

(G-5283)
ENPROTECH INDUSTRIAL TECH LLC (DH)
4259 E 49th St (44125-1001)
PHONE....................216 883-3220
Judy Collins, *Credit Mgr*
Pedro Garcia, *Mng Member*
Ben Handshue, *Sr Project Mgr*
David Kaminowski, *Manager*
▲ **EMP:** 201
SQ FT: 96,000
SALES: 75MM
SALES (corp-wide): 43.4B **Privately Held**
WEB: www.itochu.com
SIC: 3547 3365 3599 8711 Rolling mill machinery; machinery castings, aluminum; custom machinery; engineering services; electrical repair shops
HQ: Enprotech Corp.
4259 E 49th St
Cleveland OH 44125
216 206-0080

(G-5284)
ENSIGN PRODUCT COMPANY INC
3528 E 76th St (44105-1510)
P.O. Box 27167 (44127-0167)
PHONE....................216 341-5911
Fax: 216 341-9338
Birney R Walker III, *President*
Charles Snyder, *Corp Secy*
Christopher Walker, *Vice Pres*
EMP: 6
SQ FT: 9,000
SALES (est): 840K **Privately Held**
WEB: www.ensignproductsco.com
SIC: 2992 2899 Lubricating oils & greases; chemical preparations

(G-5285)
ENTERPRISE TOOL & DIE COMPANY
4940 Schaaf Ln (44131-1008)
PHONE....................216 351-1300
Fax: 216 351-5781
Robert C Schweikert, *President*
Todd Schweikert, *Corp Secy*
Richard W Schweikert, *Vice Pres*
Len Montgomery, *Plant Mgr*
EMP: 10 **EST:** 1954
SQ FT: 10,000

SALES (est): 1.3MM **Privately Held**
WEB: www.enterprisetoolanddie.com
SIC: 3544 Dies & die holders for metal cutting, forming, die casting

(G-5286)
ENVIROFAB INC
7914 Lake Ave (44102-1992)
PHONE....................216 651-1767
Fax: 216 651-0167
Thomas J Rusnak, *President*
Richard Rusnak, *Vice Pres*
EMP: 11
SQ FT: 42,000
SALES (est): 2.2MM **Privately Held**
WEB: www.envirofab.net
SIC: 3564 Dust or fume collecting equipment, industrial

(G-5287)
EOMG HARKO HOLDINGS LLC
1500 Key Tower 127 Pub Sq (44114)
PHONE....................216 781-0083
EMP: 3
SALES (est): 84.5K
SALES (corp-wide): 1.5B **Privately Held**
SIC: 2819 Industrial inorganic chemicals
PA: Vectra Co.
120 S Central Ave Ste 200
Saint Louis MO 63105
314 797-8600

(G-5288)
EOS TECHNOLOGY INC
8525 Clinton Rd (44144-1014)
PHONE....................216 281-2999
Fax: 216 281-5548
John Hadgis, *President*
Gregory Hadgis, *Vice Pres*
EMP: 20
SALES (est): 2.5MM **Privately Held**
SIC: 3599 Machine & other job shop work

(G-5289)
EPD ENTERPRISES INC
9921 Clinton Rd (44144-1035)
PHONE....................216 961-1200
Edward Durkin, *President*
Robert Myers, *Vice Pres*
Steve Durbin, *Controller*
EMP: 75
SQ FT: 92,000
SALES (est): 5.8MM **Privately Held**
WEB: www.plasticplaters.com
SIC: 3471 Electroplating of metals or formed products

(G-5290)
EQ TECHNOLOGIES LLC
11601 Wade Park Ave (44106-4403)
PHONE....................216 548-3684
Michael Schaffer,
EMP: 6
SALES (est): 492.8K **Privately Held**
SIC: 3651 7389 Household audio & video equipment;

(G-5291)
EQUIPMENT MANUFACTURERS INTL
Also Called: E M I
16151 Puritas Ave (44135-2617)
P.O. Box 94725 (44101-4725)
PHONE....................216 651-6700
Fax: 216 524-3660
Jerry Senk, *Principal*
John Zelli, *Engineer*
R T Mackin, *Treasurer*
Bob Armstrong, *Controller*
Steve Paavola, *Controller*
▲ **EMP:** 30 **EST:** 1982
SQ FT: 65,000
SALES: 10MM **Privately Held**
WEB: www.emi-inc.com
SIC: 3559 5084 Foundry machinery & equipment; industrial machinery & equipment

(G-5292)
EQUIPSYNC LLC
4755 W 150th St (44135-3329)
P.O. Box 35288 (44135-0288)
PHONE....................216 367-6640
John Kappus, *Partner*
William Cunningham, *Partner*
Fred Kappus, *Partner*

EMP: 3
SQ FT: 14,000
SALES (est): 140K **Privately Held**
SIC: 7372 Prepackaged software; application computer software

(G-5293)
ERICHAR INC
2051 W Ridgewood Dr (44134-4305)
P.O. Box 311081 (44131-8181)
PHONE..............................216 402-2628
Dana Denallo, *President*
EMP: 3
SALES (est): 317K **Privately Held**
SIC: 2411 3999 3589 0851 Wood chips, produced in the field; custom pulverizing & grinding of plastic materials; service industry machinery; forestry services; local trucking, without storage

(G-5294)
ERIE CONTAINER CORPORATION
4700 Lorain Ave (44102-3443)
PHONE..............................216 631-1650
Fax: 216 631-1249
Frank Lipinski, *President*
Charles Lipinski, *Corp Secy*
Joseph Lipinski, *Vice Pres*
EMP: 8
SQ FT: 15,000
SALES: 400K **Privately Held**
SIC: 2655 Tubes, fiber or paper: made from purchased material

(G-5295)
ERIE LAKE PLASTIC INC
19940 Ingersoll Dr (44116-1820)
P.O. Box 16924, Rocky River (44116-0924)
PHONE..............................440 333-4880
Fax: 440 333-5231
John Derethik, *President*
Trudi Derethik, *Controller*
EMP: 18
SALES (est): 2.9MM **Privately Held**
WEB: www.lakeerieplastics.com
SIC: 3089 Extruded finished plastic products

(G-5296)
ERIE SAND & GRAVEL CO INC
Also Called: Cleveland Bulk Terminal
5400 Wiskey Is (44102)
PHONE..............................216 961-1010
Fax: 216 961-1604
EMP: 4 **Privately Held**
SIC: 1422 Crushed & broken limestone
HQ: Erie Sand & Gravel Co Inc
11 Stanwix St Fl 21
Pittsburgh PA 15222
412 995-5500

(G-5297)
ERIE SHORE MACHINE CO INC
18602 Syracuse Ave (44110-2521)
PHONE..............................216 692-1484
Fax: 216 692-1496
Lawrence G Pinter, *President*
James Pinter, *Vice Pres*
Sarah Pinter, *Admin Sec*
EMP: 6 **EST:** 1975
SQ FT: 5,000
SALES (est): 702.9K **Privately Held**
WEB: www.erieshoremachine.com
SIC: 3599 Machine shop, jobbing & repair

(G-5298)
ERIEVIEW METAL TREATING CO
Also Called: Apex Metals
4465 Johnston Pkwy (44128-2998)
PHONE..............................216 663-1780
Fax: 216 663-7782
Alex Kappos, *President*
Dennis Kappos, *Vice Pres*
Dan Hunnell, *QC Mgr*
Frank Geraci, *QC Mgr*
George Kappos Jr, *CFO*
EMP: 100 **EST:** 1961
SQ FT: 70,000
SALES (est): 14.7MM **Privately Held**
WEB: www.erieview.us
SIC: 3471 Electroplating of metals or formed products

(G-5299)
EUCLID COFFEE CO INC
17230 S Waterloo Rd (44110-3811)
PHONE..............................216 481-3330
Fax: 216 383-7269
M J Repak, *CEO*
James M Repak, *President*
EMP: 8 **EST:** 1935
SQ FT: 10,000
SALES (est): 693.7K **Privately Held**
SIC: 2095 Coffee roasting (except by wholesale grocers)

(G-5300)
EUCLID JALOUSIES INC
490 E 200th St (44119-1500)
PHONE..............................440 953-1112
Fax: 216 486-1113
Timothy Huquila, *President*
Bob Dunmire, *Vice Pres*
EMP: 7 **EST:** 1954
SQ FT: 2,400
SALES (est): 823.6K **Privately Held**
SIC: 3442 5211 Screen & storm doors & windows; windows, storm: wood or metal; doors, storm: wood or metal

(G-5301)
EUCLID MEDIA GROUP LLC (PA)
737 Bolivar Rd (44115-1246)
PHONE..............................216 241-7550
Kelli Pilch-Habel, *Marketing Staff*
Daniel N Zelman, *Mng Member*
EMP: 29
SALES (est): 3.7MM **Privately Held**
SIC: 2711 Newspapers, publishing & printing

(G-5302)
EUCLID UNIVERSAL CORPORATION
30500 Bruce Industrial B (44139-3970)
PHONE..............................440 542-0960
Fax: 440 349-4894
Scott Lantzy, *Vice Pres*
Charles Hix, *Design Engr*
▲ **EMP:** 5
SALES (est): 500K **Privately Held**
SIC: 3568 Power transmission equipment

(G-5303)
EUCLID WELDING CO INC
26670 Lakeland Blvd (44132-2644)
PHONE..............................216 289-0714
Fax: 216 289-1612
John Varljen, *Principal*
EMP: 5
SALES (est): 697.6K **Privately Held**
SIC: 7692 Welding repair

(G-5304)
EUREKA SCREW MACHINE PDTS CO
Also Called: Eureka Screw Machine Co
3960 E 91st St (44105-3964)
PHONE..............................216 883-1715
Fax: 216 883-1715
William Rubick, *President*
Irene Rubick, *Treasurer*
EMP: 6
SQ FT: 5,136
SALES (est): 657.9K **Privately Held**
SIC: 3451 Screw machine products

(G-5305)
EVANDY CO INC
5450 Dunham Rd (44137-3653)
PHONE..............................216 518-9713
Eva Dezsi, *President*
Andras Dezsi, *Vice Pres*
EMP: 5
SQ FT: 6,000
SALES: 400K **Privately Held**
SIC: 3545 Machine tool accessories

(G-5306)
EVEN-CUT ABRASIVE COMPANY
850 E 72nd St (44103-1007)
P.O. Box 714175, Columbus (43271-4175)
PHONE..............................216 881-9595
Fax: 216 881-9976
Arthur Ellison, *President*
Eileen Tilbert, *Mfg Staff*
Scott Lovett, *Plant Engr*
Gene Bernhard, *CFO*

Mike Terrell, *Sales Staff*
▲ **EMP:** 70
SQ FT: 65,000
SALES (est): 13.3MM **Privately Held**
WEB: www.evencut.com
SIC: 3291 Abrasive products

(G-5307)
EVEREADY PRINTING INC
Also Called: Weprintquick.com
20700 Miles Pkwy (44128-5506)
PHONE..............................216 587-2389
Fax: 216 587-2260
Roger Wolfson, *President*
Scott Wolfson, *Vice Pres*
Erica Paroff, *Office Mgr*
EMP: 20 **EST:** 1905
SALES (est): 4.1MM **Privately Held**
WEB: www.evereadyprint.com
SIC: 2752 Commercial printing, offset

(G-5308)
EVEREADY PRODUCTS CORPORATION
1101 Belt Line Ave (44109-2849)
PHONE..............................216 661-2755
Fax: 216 741-1391
Samuel Vandivort, *Ch of Bd*
Daniel Harrington, *President*
Terry Hermann, *Manager*
EMP: 14 **EST:** 1951
SQ FT: 36,000
SALES (est): 4.2MM **Privately Held**
WEB: www.evereadyproducts.com
SIC: 2813 Aerosols

(G-5309)
EVERYKEY INC
1988 Ford Dr (44106-3971)
PHONE..............................866 798-5577
Christopher Wentz, *CEO*
EMP: 3
SALES (est): 117K **Privately Held**
SIC: 3699 7389 Security devices;

(G-5310)
EVERYTHING IN AMERICA
Also Called: Eia
4141 Stilmore Rd (44121-3129)
PHONE..............................347 871-6872
Patrick Hadley, *Vice Pres*
EMP: 8
SALES (est): 642.9K **Privately Held**
SIC: 5211 2452 7389 Modular homes; modular homes, prefabricated, wood;

(G-5311)
EXACT-TOOL & DIE INC
5425 W 140th St (44142-1704)
PHONE..............................216 676-9140
Fax: 216 676-0091
Frank K Chesek, *CEO*
Robert Hickerson, *Business Mgr*
Mark S Klepper, *Vice Pres*
John J Melnik, *Vice Pres*
Gary Mohnickey, *Prdtn Mgr*
EMP: 35
SQ FT: 60,000
SALES (est): 9.5MM **Privately Held**
WEB: www.exact-tool.com
SIC: 3465 3469 3544 3694 Automotive stampings; metal stampings; special dies, tools, jigs & fixtures; engine electrical equipment

(G-5312)
EXCELLENT TOOL & DIE INC
10921 Briggs Rd (44111-5333)
PHONE..............................216 671-9222
Fax: 216 671-9223
John Kinsch, *President*
Edith Burnside, *President*
EMP: 6
SQ FT: 4,800
SALES: 400K **Privately Held**
SIC: 3599 Machine shop, jobbing & repair

(G-5313)
EXIKON INDUSTRIES LLC
15215 Chatfield Ave (44111-4306)
PHONE..............................216 485-2947
John T Kondilas, *Director*
EMP: 10 **EST:** 2009
SALES (est): 1.1MM **Privately Held**
SIC: 3999 Barber & beauty shop equipment

(G-5314)
EXPANSION PROGRAMS INTL
11115 Edgewater Dr (44102-6138)
PHONE..............................216 631-8544
Fax: 216 281-0828
M C Richards, *Principal*
EMP: 3
SALES (est): 258.9K **Privately Held**
SIC: 3572 Computer storage devices

(G-5315)
EXPLORYS INC
1111 Superior Ave E (44114-2522)
PHONE..............................216 767-4700
Stephen McHale, *CEO*
Charles Lougheed, *President*
Thomas Chickerella, *COO*
Anil Jain, *Senior VP*
Dave Diamond, *Vice Pres*
EMP: 67
SALES (est): 15.6MM
SALES (corp-wide): 79.9B **Publicly Held**
SIC: 7372 Prepackaged software
PA: International Business Machines Corporation
1 New Orchard Rd Ste 1
Armonk NY 10504
914 499-1900

(G-5316)
EZ BRITE BRANDS INC
806 Sharon Dr Ste C (44145-7701)
P.O. Box 40025 (44140-0025)
PHONE..............................440 871-7817
Edmond Aghajanian, *President*
Marcia Meermans, *Vice Pres*
Jill Ricker, *Office Mgr*
EMP: 15
SQ FT: 11,000
SALES (est): 3.7MM **Privately Held**
WEB: www.ezbritebrands.com
SIC: 2841 2842 Soap & other detergents; soap: granulated, liquid, cake, flaked or chip; cleaning or polishing preparations

(G-5317)
F L ENTERPRISES
Also Called: F L Distributors
4740 Briar Rd (44135-5038)
PHONE..............................216 898-5551
Fax: 216 898-5552
Fred Loeffler, *President*
Jeff Loeffler, *Vice Pres*
EMP: 4 **EST:** 1971
SQ FT: 8,400
SALES: 500K **Privately Held**
WEB: www.fldistributors.com
SIC: 3549 Metalworking machinery

(G-5318)
FABRICATION GROUP LLC
3453 W 140th St (44111-2429)
PHONE..............................216 251-1125
Patricia B Setlock, *President*
EMP: 20 **EST:** 2008
SALES (est): 6.2MM **Privately Held**
SIC: 3334 1799 3449 Primary aluminum; ornamental metal work; miscellaneous metalwork

(G-5319)
FAIRCHILD PRINTING CO
5807 Fleet Ave (44105-3495)
PHONE..............................216 641-4192
Fax: 216 641-9211
Larry Hovater, *Owner*
Suzanne Hovater, *Co-Owner*
EMP: 4 **EST:** 1933
SQ FT: 2,128
SALES: 350K **Privately Held**
SIC: 2752 Commercial printing, lithographic

(G-5320)
FAIRMONT CREAMERY LLC
1720 Willey Ave (44113-4367)
PHONE..............................216 357-2560
EMP: 3 **EST:** 2014
SALES (est): 145.8K **Privately Held**
SIC: 2021 Creamery butter

(G-5321)
FALCON INNOVATIONS INC
3316 W 118th St (44111-1723)
PHONE..............................216 252-0676
Fax: 216 252-0677

Robert A Jewell Jr, *President*
Kenneth Jewell, *Partner*
Judith Jewell, *Controller*
EMP: 6
SQ FT: 6,400
SALES: 250K **Privately Held**
SIC: 3599 Machine shop, jobbing & repair

(G-5322)
FALCON RIDGE TECHNOLOGIES LLC
Also Called: Foundatia Technologies
5055 Corbin Dr Ste 200 (44128-5462)
PHONE..................................216 674-1649
James Gehring,
Beth Gehring,
EMP: 5
SALES (est): 570K **Privately Held**
WEB: www.foundatia.com
SIC: 3571 Electronic computers

(G-5323)
FALLS STAMPING & WELDING CO
Also Called: Plant Two
1720 Fall St (44113-2416)
PHONE..................................216 771-9635
John Hall, *Foreman/Supr*
EMP: 13
SALES (corp-wide): 42.2MM **Privately Held**
WEB: www.falls-stamping.com
SIC: 3465 Automotive stampings
PA: Falls Stamping & Welding Company
2900 Vincent St
Cuyahoga Falls OH 44221
330 928-1191

(G-5324)
FARASEY STEEL FABRICATORS INC
4000 Iron Ct (44115-3582)
PHONE..................................216 641-1853
Fax: 216 641-1856
Don J Henderson, *President*
George R Henderson, *Vice Pres*
Robert L Henderson, *Vice Pres*
EMP: 15 EST: 1859
SQ FT: 14,000
SALES: 1MM **Privately Held**
WEB: www.faraseysteelfab.com
SIC: 3443 Fabricated plate work (boiler shop)

(G-5325)
FAS MACHINERY LLC
9916 Broadway Ave (44125-1635)
PHONE..................................216 472-3800
Marcia J Sadlowski, *Owner*
Aaron J Sadlowski, *General Mgr*
Robert J Sadlowski,
▼ **EMP:** 4
SQ FT: 20,000
SALES (est): 1.2MM **Privately Held**
SIC: 3599 Machine shop, jobbing & repair

(G-5326)
FASTENER INDUSTRIES INC
Buckeye Fasteners Company Div
5250 W 164th St (44142-1506)
PHONE..................................216 267-2240
Doug Campbell, *General Mgr*
EMP: 16
SALES (corp-wide): 42.3MM **Privately Held**
WEB: www.buckeyefasteners.com
SIC: 3496 5085 Wire fasteners; industrial supplies
PA: Fastener Industries, Inc.
1 Berea Commons Ste 209
Berea OH 44017
440 243-0034

(G-5327)
FAW INDUSTRIES
14837 Detroit Ave 207 (44107-3909)
PHONE..................................216 651-9595
Fred Walton, *Principal*
EMP: 3
SALES (est): 172.2K **Privately Held**
SIC: 3999 Manufacturing industries

(G-5328)
FBC CHEMICAL CORPORATION
7301 Bessemer Ave (44127-1817)
PHONE..................................216 341-2000
Derek Crawford, *Director*
EMP: 10
SALES (corp-wide): 60MM **Privately Held**
SIC: 3312 Chemicals & other products derived from coking
PA: Fbc Chemical Corporation
634 Route 228
Mars PA 16046
724 625-3116

(G-5329)
FCI INC
4661 Giles Rd (44135-3756)
PHONE..................................216 251-5200
Fax: 216 251-5206
Kenneth Edgar, *President*
Irene Edgar, *Vice Pres*
Mark George, *Plant Mgr*
Thomas Bittel, *Prdtn Mgr*
Mike Peronek, *Sales/Mktg Mgr*
EMP: 80 EST: 1958
SQ FT: 48,000
SALES (est): 14.2MM **Privately Held**
WEB: www.fci-usa.com
SIC: 3089 Plastic processing

(G-5330)
FCS GRAPHICS INC
Also Called: Forest City Specialties
2169 Saint Clair Ave Ne (44114-4018)
PHONE..................................216 771-5177
Fax: 216 771-5178
Anthony Gliozzi, *President*
Aldo Gliozzi, *Vice Pres*
EMP: 4
SQ FT: 1,600
SALES (est): 545K **Privately Held**
SIC: 2262 2395 Screen printing: man-made fiber & silk broadwoven fabrics; embroidery & art needlework

(G-5331)
FEDERAL METAL COMPANY
Also Called: FM
7250 Division St (44146-5495)
PHONE..................................440 232-8700
David R Nagusky, *CEO*
Peter Nagusky, *President*
Mike Buyarski, *COO*
Chris Greenfield, *Vice Pres*
Leo Pinkard, *Vice Pres*
EMP: 65 EST: 1913
SQ FT: 65,000
SALES (est): 15.2MM
SALES (corp-wide): 16.2MM **Privately Held**
WEB: www.federalmetalcompany.com
SIC: 3351 3364 Copper & copper alloy sheet, strip, plate & products; copper & copper alloy die-castings
PA: Oakwood Industries Inc.
7250 Division St
Bedford OH 44146
440 232-8700

(G-5332)
FEDERAL PROCESS CORPORATION (PA)
Also Called: Gasoila Thred-Taper
4520 Richmond Rd (44128-5757)
PHONE..................................216 464-6440
Fax: 216 464-2080
Jon Outcalt Jr, *President*
Jon Outcalt Sr, *Chairman*
David Anderson, *Vice Pres*
Bill Sickenberger, *Plant Mgr*
Marc Mendoza, *Project Mgr*
▲ **EMP:** 28
SQ FT: 4,000
SALES (est): 21MM **Privately Held**
WEB: www.federalprocess.com
SIC: 2891 Sealing compounds, synthetic rubber or plastic

(G-5333)
FEDEX OFFICE & PRINT SVCS INC
6901 Rockside Rd (44131-2379)
PHONE..................................216 573-1511
Tad Selders, *General Mgr*

Matt Coy, *Manager*
Jennifer Dellinger, *Senior Mgr*
EMP: 20
SALES (corp-wide): 50.3B **Publicly Held**
WEB: www.kinkos.com
SIC: 7334 2791 2789 Photocopying & duplicating services; typesetting; bookbinding & related work
HQ: Fedex Office And Print Services, Inc.
7900 Legacy Dr
Plano TX 75024
214 550-7000

(G-5334)
FENCE ONE INC
Also Called: Great Lake Fence
11111 Broadway Ave (44125-1659)
PHONE..................................216 441-2600
Fax: 216 441-4214
Michael Ely, *President*
EMP: 14 EST: 1951
SQ FT: 12,000
SALES (est): 2.7MM **Privately Held**
SIC: 1521 1799 3496 General remodeling, single-family houses; fence construction; miscellaneous fabricated wire products

(G-5335)
FERRALLOY INC
28001 Ranney Pkwy (44145-1159)
PHONE..................................440 250-1900
William Habansky Jr, *President*
Sherri Habansky, *Corp Secy*
▲ **EMP:** 27
SQ FT: 15,000
SALES (est): 10.3MM **Privately Held**
WEB: www.ferralloy.com
SIC: 5051 3599 Castings, rough: iron or steel; machine shop, jobbing & repair

(G-5336)
FERRO CORPORATION
Also Called: Porcelain Enamels
6060 Parkland Blvd # 250 (44124-4225)
PHONE..................................216 875-5600
Mark H Duesenberg, *Vice Pres*
Ann E Killian, *Vice Pres*
David Klimas, *Research*
Weinan Pan, *Research*
Robert Szabo, *Manager*
EMP: 80
SALES (corp-wide): 1.1B **Publicly Held**
SIC: 2899 Chemical preparations
PA: Ferro Corporation
6060 Parkland Blvd # 250
Mayfield Heights OH 44124
216 875-5600

(G-5337)
FERRO CORPORATION
Ferro Crmic Glz Prclan Enmel
4150 E 56th St Ste 1 (44105-4890)
P.O. Box 6550 (44101-1550)
PHONE..................................216 875-6178
Fax: 216 546-9494
John V Belcastro, *Principal*
William Newhouse, *Training Super*
EMP: 250
SALES (corp-wide): 1.1B **Publicly Held**
SIC: 2899 2851 3264 2893 Frit; lacquers, varnishes, enamels & other coatings; porcelain electrical supplies; printing ink; color lakes or toners; color pigments, organic
PA: Ferro Corporation
6060 Parkland Blvd # 250
Mayfield Heights OH 44124
216 875-5600

(G-5338)
FERRO CORPORATION
1636 Wayside Rd (44112-1233)
PHONE..................................216 481-0238
Tony Cusmai, *Plant Mgr*
Bob Given, *Office Mgr*
Paul Angus, *Manager*
EMP: 8
SALES (corp-wide): 1.1B **Publicly Held**
WEB: www.ferro.com
SIC: 2851 Paints & allied products
PA: Ferro Corporation
6060 Parkland Blvd # 250
Mayfield Heights OH 44124
216 875-5600

(G-5339)
FERROTHERM CORPORATION
4758 Warner Rd (44125-1117)
PHONE..................................216 883-9350
Fax: 216 883-8430
Haakon Egeland, *CEO*
Thor Egeland, *Exec VP*
Ron Obrzut, *Senior VP*
Brooks Lanham, *QC Dir*
Ronald Nutaitis, *QC Mgr*
▲ **EMP:** 105
SQ FT: 90,000
SALES (est): 22.8MM **Privately Held**
WEB: www.ferrotherm.com
SIC: 3462 3724 3812 3694 Turbine engine forgings, ferrous; aircraft engines & engine parts; turbines, aircraft type; search & navigation equipment; engine electrical equipment; gaskets, packing & sealing devices

(G-5340)
FERTILITY SOLUTIONS INC
11811 Shaker Blvd Ste 330 (44120-1927)
PHONE..................................216 491-0030
Fax: 216 491-0032
Susan A Rothmann, *President*
John Quigely, *Opers Mgr*
Anne D Wold, *Med Doctor*
Aletha Adams, *Manager*
EMP: 9
SQ FT: 3,000
SALES: 3.1MM **Privately Held**
WEB: www.fertilitysolutions.com
SIC: 3826 8734 8731 Analytical instruments; testing laboratories; commercial physical research

(G-5341)
FGB INTERNATIONAL LLC (PA)
7670 First Pl (44146-6714)
PHONE..................................440 359-0000
Joe Golombek,
Fairmount Investors LLP,
Edward C Smith,
EMP: 3
SQ FT: 600
SALES: 200K **Privately Held**
WEB: www.oakwoodlabs.com
SIC: 1481 Mine exploration, nonmetallic minerals

(G-5342)
FGC PLASMA SOLUTIONS LLC
11201 Cedar Ave (44106-2606)
PHONE..................................954 591-1429
Felipe Gomez Del Campo,
Joe Scott,
EMP: 5
SQ FT: 80
SALES (est): 202.2K **Privately Held**
SIC: 3728 Aircraft parts & equipment

(G-5343)
FIBERGLASS LINK INC
Also Called: Link's Auto
18607 Saint Clair Ave (44110-2617)
PHONE..................................216 531-5515
Fax: 216 531-5092
Robert Linkous, *President*
Robert Hencie, *Principal*
EMP: 3
SQ FT: 4,200
SALES (est): 316.6K **Privately Held**
SIC: 3465 Fenders, automobile: stamped or pressed metal

(G-5344)
FILLOUS & RUPPEL INC
7411 Cedar Ave (44103-4925)
PHONE..................................216 431-0470
Robert V Fillous, *President*
Leonard Fillous, *Vice Pres*
Florence Fillous, *Admin Sec*
EMP: 4 EST: 1934
SALES (est): 210K **Privately Held**
SIC: 3299 Mica products

(G-5345)
FINAL TOUCH METAL FABRICATING
2290 Scranton Rd (44113-4310)
PHONE..................................216 348-1750
Mark Koenig, *President*
Kathleen Koenig, *Vice Pres*
EMP: 3

SALES: 130K **Privately Held**
SIC: 3446 Gratings, tread: fabricated metal

(G-5346)
FINE POINTS INC
Also Called: Tekus, L Sweater Design
12620 Larchmere Blvd (44120-1110)
PHONE..................................216 229-6644
Fax: 216 231-6644
Liz Tekus, *President*
Henry Roth, *Treasurer*
EMP: 12
SQ FT: 2,000
SALES (est): 1.3MM **Privately Held**
WEB: www.finepoints.com
SIC: 2253 5949 Sweaters & sweater
coats, knit; sewing, needlework & piece
goods

(G-5347)
FINELLI ORNAMENTAL IRON CO
Also Called: Finelli Architectural Iron Co
30815 Solon Rd (44139-3485)
PHONE..................................440 248-0050
Fax: 440 248-1165
Frank Finelli, *President*
Angelo Finelli, *Vice Pres*
James Korosec, *Vice Pres*
EMP: 15
SQ FT: 15,000
SALES: 2MM **Privately Held**
WEB: www.finelliironworks.com
SIC: 3446 1751 Architectural metalwork;
railings, prefabricated metal; stairs, stair-
cases, stair treads: prefabricated metal;
gates, ornamental metal; carpentry work

(G-5348)
FINISHING TOUCH
22084 Lorain Rd (44126-3313)
PHONE..................................440 263-9264
Carolyn R Ofiara, *Owner*
EMP: 15
SALES (est): 953.4K **Privately Held**
SIC: 2335 Wedding gowns & dresses

(G-5349)
**FIRST CATHOLC SLOVAK UNION
U S (PA)**
6611 Rockside Rd (44131-2365)
P.O. Box 318013 (44131-8013)
PHONE..................................216 642-9406
Fax: 216 642-4310
Andrew M Rajec, *President*
Margaret M Perla, *Trustee*
Jerry Siman, *Trustee*
Karen E Sterling, *Trustee*
Andrew Harcar Sr, *Vice Pres*
EMP: 15
SQ FT: 7,000
SALES: 34.7MM **Privately Held**
WEB: www.fcsu.com
SIC: 6411 2711 Life insurance agents; job
printing & newspaper publishing com-
bined

(G-5350)
**FIRSTAR PRECISION
CORPORATION**
Also Called: Cnc Machine Shop
12340 Plaza Dr (44130-1043)
PHONE..................................216 362-7888
Fax: 216 362-7441
Dave Tenny, *President*
David Tenny, *President*
Joe Tako, *Corp Secy*
Mark Lisi, *Traffic Mgr*
Darreyl Hansard, *Engineer*
EMP: 32
SQ FT: 12,800
SALES (est): 6.7MM **Privately Held**
WEB: www.firstarcnc.com
SIC: 3545 Machine tool accessories

(G-5351)
FIRSTFUELCELLSCOM LLC
11163 Blossom Ave (44130-4430)
PHONE..................................440 884-2503
Diane L Sadowski, *Mng Member*
EMP: 6
SALES (est): 534.8K **Privately Held**
WEB: www.firstfuelcells.com
SIC: 3674 Fuel cells, solid state

(G-5352)
**FIVES N AMERCN COMBUSTN
INC (DH)**
4455 E 71st St (44105-5601)
PHONE..................................216 271-6000
Fax: 216 641-7852
Luigi Russo, *Ch of Bd*
Erik Paulhardt, *President*
Thomas Jonozzo, *General Mgr*
John Newby, *VP Opers*
Harold Briner, *Opers Staff*
▲ **EMP:** 244
SQ FT: 400,000
SALES (est): 105.9MM
SALES (corp-wide): 5.8MM **Privately
Held**
WEB: www.namfg.com
SIC: 3567 Industrial furnaces & ovens
HQ: Fives Inc.
23400 Halsted Rd
Farmington Hills MI 48335
248 477-0800

(G-5353)
FLASH INDUSTRIAL TECH LTD
30 Industry Dr (44146-4414)
PHONE..................................440 786-8979
Fax: 440 786-9688
Lawrence P Zajac, *Principal*
▲ **EMP:** 9
SQ FT: 18,000
SALES (est): 1.8MM **Privately Held**
SIC: 3451 Screw machine products

(G-5354)
FLEETLINE TOOL & DIE CO
7803 Harvard Ave (44105-3938)
PHONE..................................216 441-4949
Fax: 216 441-5050
Zenobivsz Buckzkowski, *Owner*
EMP: 3 **EST:** 1965
SQ FT: 1,200
SALES (est): 200K **Privately Held**
SIC: 3599 Machine shop, jobbing & repair

(G-5355)
FLEIG ENTERPRISES INC
Also Called: Smith Facing and Supply Co
940 E 67th St (44103-1724)
PHONE..................................216 361-8020
Daniel Fleig, *President*
Caroline Fleig, *Vice Pres*
EMP: 3
SQ FT: 25,000
SALES (est): 320K **Privately Held**
SIC: 3999 Custom pulverizing & grinding of
plastic materials

(G-5356)
FLEXNOVA INC
6100 Oak Tree Blvd (44131-2544)
PHONE..................................216 288-6961
Steve Rossi, *President*
EMP: 30
SQ FT: 1,000
SALES: 2MM **Privately Held**
SIC: 7372 Prepackaged software

(G-5357)
FLINT GROUP US LLC
4801 W 160th St (44135-2633)
PHONE..................................216 267-1927
Bruce Neal, *Materials Dir*
EMP: 19
SALES (corp-wide): 3.8B **Privately Held**
SIC: 2893 Printing ink
PA: Flint Group Us Llc
14909 N Beck Rd
Plymouth MI 48170
734 781-4600

(G-5358)
FLOCEL INC
4415 Euclid Ave Ste 421 (44103-3759)
PHONE..................................216 619-5903
Edward Rapp, *President*
Robert N Schmidt, *Corp Secy*
Brian M Kolkowski, *Vice Pres*
Andrew Balint, *Controller*
Jamie Nelson, *Consultant*
EMP: 5
SQ FT: 500
SALES (est): 540K **Privately Held**
WEB: www.flocel.com
SIC: 3845 Ultrasonic scanning devices,
medical

(G-5359)
FLOTBI INC
4415 Euclid Ave Ste 421 (44103-3757)
PHONE..................................216 619-5928
Matthew Mahoney, *CFO*
EMP: 4
SALES (est): 149.2K **Privately Held**
SIC: 3841 Diagnostic apparatus, medical

(G-5360)
FLOW POLYMERS LLC
12819 Coit Rd (44108-1614)
PHONE..................................216 249-4900
Mike Ivany, *President*
Martin Eble, *CFO*
Marty Ebble, *Personnel Exec*
Charles Hull, *Supervisor*
EMP: 105
SALES (est): 26.9MM
SALES (corp-wide): 38.6MM **Privately
Held**
WEB: www.flowpolymers.com
SIC: 2869 Industrial organic chemicals
PA: Polymer Solutions Group Finance, Llc
100 Park Ave Fl 31
New York NY 10017
212 771-1717

(G-5361)
FLUID SYSTEM SERVICE INC
13825 Triskett Rd (44111-1523)
P.O. Box 771414, Lakewood (44107-0057)
PHONE..................................216 651-2450
Fax: 216 651-3309
John C Balliett, *President*
D Thomas George, *Corp Secy*
EMP: 8
SALES (est): 1.3MM **Privately Held**
SIC: 3511 7699 Hydraulic turbines; hy-
draulic equipment repair

(G-5362)
FLUKE BIOMEDICAL LLC (DH)
6045 Cochran Rd (44139-3303)
PHONE..................................440 248-9300
James Lico, *President*
Roderick Jones, *General Mgr*
J G Singh, *General Mgr*
Mark Svajger, *Safety Mgr*
Xinquan Zhou, *Engineer*
▲ **EMP:** 120
SALES (est): 15.8MM
SALES (corp-wide): 6.2B **Publicly Held**
WEB: www.flukebiomedical.com
SIC: 3829 Nuclear radiation & testing ap-
paratus
HQ: Fluke Electronics Corporation
6920 Seaway Blvd
Everett WA 98203
425 446-5610

(G-5363)
FOAM SEAL INC
5109 Hamilton Ave (44114-3907)
P.O. Box 951130 (44193-0005)
PHONE..................................216 881-8111
Kenneth Dagg, *President*
Douglas Mackinzie, *President*
Michael S Sylvester, *Chairman*
Michael Griffin, *Controller*
EMP: 75 **EST:** 1971
SQ FT: 250,000
SALES (est): 11.3MM
SALES (corp-wide): 20MM **Privately
Held**
WEB: www.foam-seal.com
SIC: 3053 2891 2911 Gaskets, packing &
sealing devices; sealing compounds, syn-
thetic rubber or plastic; caulking com-
pounds; greases, lubricating
PA: Novagard Solutions, Inc.
5109 Hamilton Ave
Cleveland OH 44114
216 881-3890

(G-5364)
FOAM-TEX SOLUTIONS CORP
13981 W Parkway Rd (44135-4511)
PHONE..................................216 889-2702
Donald Abshire, *CEO*
Alan Abshire, *Vice Pres*
▲ **EMP:** 6
SQ FT: 6,700
SALES: 300K **Privately Held**
WEB: www.foam-tex.com
SIC: 2841 Soap & other detergents

(G-5365)
**FOLLOW PRINT CLUB ON
FACEBOOK**
11150 East Blvd (44106-1711)
PHONE..................................216 707-2579
EMP: 3
SALES: 210.8K **Privately Held**
SIC: 2752 Commercial printing, litho-
graphic

(G-5366)
FOOD DESIGNS INC
Also Called: Ohio City Pasta
5299 Crayton Ave (44104-2829)
PHONE..................................216 651-9221
Fax: 216 696-9203
Gary W Thomas, *President*
EMP: 10
SALES (est): 996.1K **Privately Held**
WEB: www.ohiocitypasta.com
SIC: 2099 2032 Pasta, uncooked: pack-
aged with other ingredients; ravioli: pack-
aged in cans, jars, etc.

(G-5367)
FOOTE PRINTING COMPANY
Also Called: Audit Forms
2800 E 55th St (44104-2862)
PHONE..................................216 431-1757
Fax: 216 431-9958
Michael Duhr, *President*
Karl-Heinz Duhr, *President*
Steven Duhr, *Vice Pres*
Eric Jacobson, *Vice Pres*
EMP: 12 **EST:** 1907
SQ FT: 16,000
SALES (est): 1.6MM **Privately Held**
WEB: www.auditforms.com
SIC: 2752 2759 Commercial printing, off-
set; business forms, lithographed; letter-
press printing

(G-5368)
FORD MOTOR COMPANY
7845 Northfield Rd (44146-5522)
PHONE..................................216 587-7700
Dave Buzo, *Mfg Staff*
David Boso, *Manager*
Wesley Gamble, *Manager*
Jim Schwab, *Manager*
Donna Gigliotti, *Nurse*
EMP: 2200
SALES (corp-wide): 151.8B **Publicly
Held**
WEB: www.ford.com
SIC: 3465 3714 3711 Automotive stamp-
ings; motor vehicle parts & accessories;
motor vehicles & car bodies
PA: Ford Motor Company
1 American Rd
Dearborn MI 48126
313 322-3000

(G-5369)
FOREST CITY COMPANIES INC
Also Called: Forest City Packaging
3607 W 56th St (44102-5739)
PHONE..................................216 586-5279
Anthony Galang, *President*
Ken Lewandowski, *General Mgr*
Dawn Galang, *Admin Sec*
EMP: 23
SQ FT: 42,000
SALES (est): 6.1MM **Privately Held**
WEB: www.forestcityco.com
SIC: 4783 2441 2394 Packing goods for
shipping; boxes, wood; canvas & related
products

(G-5370)
**FORGE PRODUCTS
CORPORATION**
Also Called: Forged Products
9503 Woodland Ave (44104-2487)
PHONE..................................216 231-2600
Fax: 216 231-0300
Charles E Thayer II, *President*
Thomas Thayer, *Vice Pres*
Joann Notaro, *Finance*
Priscilla Thayer, *Sales Staff*
Debbie McVaugh, *Admin Asst*
EMP: 56 **EST:** 1962
SQ FT: 31,600

SALES (est): 12.6MM **Privately Held**
WEB: www.forgeproducts.com
SIC: **3312** 3463 3462 Forgings, iron &
steel; nonferrous forgings; iron & steel
forgings

(G-5371)
FORMTEK INC
Krasny Kaplan Division
4899 Commerce Pkwy (44128-5905)
PHONE..........................216 292-6300
Roger K Steel, *Division Pres*
Ben Barnes, *Engineer*
Brian Copack, *Manager*
Dawn Studniarz, *Manager*
Ilse Boren, *Director*
EMP: 100
SALES (corp-wide): 482.1MM **Privately
Held**
WEB: www.formtekcleveland.com
SIC: **3547** 3535 Rolling mill machinery;
pipe & tube mills; conveyors & conveying
equipment
HQ: Formtek, Inc.
4899 Commerce Pkwy
Cleveland OH 44128
216 292-4460

(G-5372)
FORMTEK INC (DH)
Also Called: Krasny Kaplan Division
4899 Commerce Pkwy (44128-5905)
PHONE..........................216 292-4460
Fax: 216 292-2898
Joe Mayer, *President*
Robert Evans, *Vice Pres*
Robert Reynolds, *Vice Pres*
Dave Thompson, *Plant Mgr*
Johnny Short, *Project Mgr*
▲ EMP: 60
SQ FT: 56,000
SALES (est): 29.9MM
SALES (corp-wide): 482.1MM **Privately
Held**
WEB: www.formtekcleveland.com
SIC: **3547** 3549 3535 Pipe & tube mills;
coiling machinery; conveyors & conveying
equipment
HQ: Formtek Inc
711 Ogden Ave
Lisle IL 60532
630 285-1500

(G-5373)
FOSBEL HOLDING INC (PA)
20600 Sheldon Rd (44142-1319)
PHONE..........................216 362-3900
Derek Scott, *President*
Kathleen Stevens, *CFO*
Ritch Serowski, *Controller*
EMP: 30
SALES (est): 28.2MM **Privately Held**
SIC: **7692** Welding repair

(G-5374)
FOSECO INC (DH)
20200 Sheldon Rd (44142-1380)
P.O. Box 81227 (44181-0227)
PHONE..........................440 826-4548
Fax: 440 243-7658
Lee Plutshack, *Ch of Bd*
John S Rodgers Jr, *Vice Pres*
Roger P Stanbridge, *Vice Pres*
Cindy Janosko, *Purch Agent*
Brian Pinto, *Research*
▲ EMP: 5
SQ FT: 380,000
SALES (est): 9.1MM
SALES (corp-wide): 1.7B **Privately Held**
WEB: www.foseco.com
SIC: **2899** 3569 3547 Metal treating com-
pounds; fluxes: brazing, soldering, galva-
nizing & welding; filters; rolling mill
machinery
HQ: Vesuvius U S A Corporation
1404 Newton Dr
Champaign IL 61822
217 351-5000

(G-5375)
FOUNDRY ARTIST INC
Also Called: Studio Foundry
4404 Perkins Ave (44103-3544)
PHONE..........................216 391-9030
Mark Olitsky, *President*
Brad Grubb, *COO*

Lisa Kenion, *Vice Pres*
Craig Horstman, *Treasurer*
John Ranally, *Admin Sec*
EMP: 7
SQ FT: 3,000
SALES (est): 981.6K **Privately Held**
WEB: www.studiofoundry.com
SIC: **3366** Bronze foundry

(G-5376)
FPT CLEVELAND LLC (DH)
Also Called: Ferrous Processing and Trading
8550 Aetna Rd (44105-1607)
PHONE..........................216 441-3800
Fax: 216 441-1079
Andrew M Luntz, *President*
Jan Hemme, *Vice Pres*
Tim Pucky, *CFO*
Yale Levin,
▲ EMP: 115
SALES (est): 32MM
SALES (corp-wide): 167.5MM **Privately
Held**
SIC: **4953** 5051 5093 3341 Refuse sys-
tems; iron & steel (ferrous) products; fer-
rous metal scrap & waste; secondary
nonferrous metals
HQ: Ferrous Processing And Trading Com-
pany
3400 E Lafayette St
Detroit MI 48207
313 582-2910

(G-5377)
**FRANCK AND FRIC
INCORPORATED**
7919 Old Rockside Rd (44131-2300)
P.O. Box 31148 (44131-0148)
PHONE..........................216 524-4451
Fax: 216 524-5865
Donald R Skala Sr, *President*
Stacey Carson, *Assistant VP*
David R Skala, *Vice Pres*
Donald C Skala Jr, *Treasurer*
EMP: 51
SQ FT: 20,000
SALES (est): 7.2MM **Privately Held**
SIC: **1711** 1761 3441 3444 Ventilation &
duct work contractor; warm air heating &
air conditioning contractor; sheet metal-
work; fabricated structural metal; sheet
metalwork

(G-5378)
**FRANK J PRUCHA &
ASSOCIATES**
Also Called: Sir Speedy
6916 Daisy Ave (44131-3380)
PHONE..........................216 642-3838
Frank J Prucha Jr, *President*
Nancy H Prucha, *Vice Pres*
EMP: 4
SALES (est): 485K **Privately Held**
WEB: www.speedy77.com
SIC: **2752** 2791 2789 Commercial print-
ing, lithographic; typesetting; bookbinding
& related work

(G-5379)
FRASERNET INC
2940 Noble Rd Ste 1 (44121-2242)
PHONE..........................216 691-6686
George Fraser, *President*
Gregory Williams, *Vice Pres*
EMP: 2
SQ FT: 2,000
SALES (est): 1.2MM **Privately Held**
WEB: www.frasernet.com
SIC: **2731** Book publishing

(G-5380)
FRED W HANKS COMPANY
25018 Lakeland Blvd (44132-2628)
PHONE..........................216 731-1774
Fax: 216 731-0034
Karen Bowen, *President*
George Bowen, *Mfg Staff*
Ernest Shandle, *Treasurer*
EMP: 4
SQ FT: 7,000
SALES (est): 417.9K **Privately Held**
SIC: **3824** 3599 Water meters; machine &
other job shop work

(G-5381)
**FRESENIUS MED CARE
HLDINGS INC**
3764 Pearl Rd (44109-2714)
PHONE..........................216 661-1627
Fax: 216 739-0972
Marcia Silvers, *Manager*
Jim Barsanti, *Manager*
EMP: 7
SALES (corp-wide): 17.5B **Privately Held**
SIC: **3841** Surgical & medical instruments
HQ: Fresenius Medical Care Holdings, Inc.
920 Winter St
Waltham MA 02451

(G-5382)
**FRIENDS ORNAMENTAL IRON
CO**
1593 E 41st St (44103-2303)
PHONE..........................216 431-6710
Fax: 216 431-6710
Jim Cahlik, *President*
EMP: 4 EST: 1967
SQ FT: 7,200
SALES: 300K **Privately Held**
SIC: **5211** 1799 3496 3446 Lumber &
other building materials; ornamental metal
work; miscellaneous fabricated wire prod-
ucts; architectural metalwork; metal
doors, sash & trim

(G-5383)
FUNNY TIMES INC
2176 Lee Rd (44118-2908)
P.O. Box 18530 (44118-0530)
PHONE..........................216 371-8600
Fax: 216 371-8696
Raymond Lesser, *President*
Susan Wolpert, *Corp Secy*
Catherine Mathis, *Vice Pres*
Toby Usnik, *Exec Dir*
Kris Charles, *Director*
EMP: 6
SALES (est): 510.8K **Privately Held**
WEB: www.funnytimes.com
SIC: **2711** Newspapers: publishing only,
not printed on site

(G-5384)
FURNACE PARTS LLC
4755 W 150th St Ste C (44135-3330)
PHONE..........................216 916-9601
Fax: 216 676-5557
▲ EMP: 30
SQ FT: 15,000
SALES (est): 7.6MM **Privately Held**
SIC: **3823** Mfg Process Control Instru-
ments

(G-5385)
FURNITURE CONCEPTS INC
4925 Galaxy Pkwy Ste G (44128-5961)
PHONE..........................216 292-9100
Keith Voigt, *President*
Katie Krizek, *General Mgr*
Karyl Voigt-Walker, *Vice Pres*
Joann Ann, *Office Mgr*
Sharon Adams, *Manager*
EMP: 10
SQ FT: 1,700
SALES: 4MM **Privately Held**
SIC: **2522** 5021 7641 Office furniture, ex-
cept wood; office furniture; furniture repair
& maintenance

(G-5386)
FUTURE SCREEN INC
9009 Broadview Rd Unit B (44147-2598)
PHONE..........................440 838-5055
Fax: 440 838-1767
Eugene Gryskewich, *President*
EMP: 5
SQ FT: 2,100
SALES: 250K **Privately Held**
SIC: **2759** Screen printing

(G-5387)
FX DIGITAL MEDIA INC
Also Called: Hot Cards.com
2400 Superior Ave E # 100 (44114-4237)
PHONE..........................216 241-4040
Columbus Woodruff, *President*
Karl Edward Singleton Jr, *Manager*
EMP: 40
SQ FT: 7,000

SALES (est): 6.1MM **Privately Held**
SIC: **2752** Commercial printing, offset

(G-5388)
G T METAL FABRICATORS INC
Also Called: Acromet Metal Fabricators
12126 York Rd Unit E (44133-3688)
PHONE..........................440 237-8745
Fax: 440 237-8719
Gary Callahan, *President*
Judy Callahan, *Vice Pres*
EMP: 12
SQ FT: 9,000
SALES (est): 2.2MM **Privately Held**
WEB: www.acromet.com
SIC: **3444** Sheet metalwork

(G-5389)
G W COBB CO
3914 Broadway Ave 16 (44115-3694)
PHONE..........................216 341-0100
Fax: 216 341-1006
George W Cobb Jr, *President*
EMP: 12
SQ FT: 15,000
SALES (est): 2.1MM **Privately Held**
WEB: www.gwcobb.com
SIC: **3411** 5084 Food containers, metal;
industrial machinery & equipment

(G-5390)
**G-N SALES & MANUFACTURING
INC**
12166 York Rd Unit 3&4 (44133-3601)
PHONE..........................440 237-9014
Fax: 440 237-9015
David Gluntz, *President*
Carolyn Gluntz, *Vice Pres*
Lorrie Schurdell, *Admin Sec*
EMP: 10
SQ FT: 6,000
SALES (est): 830K **Privately Held**
SIC: **3599** Machine shop, jobbing & repair

(G-5391)
GAIL ZEILMANN
Also Called: Ultra Graphics
3560 W 105th St (44111-3838)
PHONE..........................440 888-4858
Fax: 216 251-1667
Gail Zeilmann, *Owner*
EMP: 3
SQ FT: 2,000
SALES (est): 315.8K **Privately Held**
SIC: **2759** 2396 Screen printing; automo-
tive & apparel trimmings

(G-5392)
**GALAXY BALLOONS
INCORPORATED**
11750 Berea Rd Ste 3 (44111-1603)
P.O. Box 698, Lakewood (44107-0998)
PHONE..........................216 476-3360
Fax: 216 476-3320
Terry Brizz, *President*
Nellie Elwell, *General Mgr*
Gary Fickles, *Purchasing*
Kaitlyn Kelly, *Mktg Coord*
Carol Goebelt, *Manager*
▲ EMP: 130
SQ FT: 50,000
SALES (est): 21.1MM **Privately Held**
WEB: www.galaxyballoon.com
SIC: **2752** 7336 5092 5199 Commercial
printing, offset; silk screen design; bal-
loons, novelty; advertising specialties;
signs & advertising specialties; sporting &
athletic goods

(G-5393)
GALLO DISPLAYS INC (PA)
4922 E 49th St (44125-1016)
P.O. Box 788, Twinsburg (44087-0788)
PHONE..........................216 431-9500
Fax: 216 431-1651
Don Lockwood, *President*
Sandy Bellamy, *CFO*
Phil Ridolfi, *CFO*
Mike Keefe, *Sales Mgr*
Chrissy Adamescu, *Executive*
◆ EMP: 41
SQ FT: 300,000
SALES (est): 21MM **Privately Held**
WEB: www.galloinspires.com/
SIC: **2542** 3993 Partitions & fixtures, ex-
cept wood; signs & advertising specialties

▲ = Import ▼ =Export
◆ =Import/Export

(G-5394)
GANNONS DISCOUNT BLINDS
2725 Ralph Ave (44109-5413)
PHONE...................................216 398-2761
Ray Gannon, *Owner*
EMP: 4
SALES (est): 210K Privately Held
SIC: 2591 5999 Drapery hardware &
blinds & shades; miscellaneous retail
stores

(G-5395)
GARDA ARCH FAB LLC
Also Called: Garda Archtectural Fabrication
1873 E 55th St (44103-3641)
PHONE...................................216 431-6300
Louis Tombazzi, *Mng Member*
Frank Tombazzi, *Mng Member*
◆ EMP: 9 EST: 2012
SQ FT: 30,000
SALES: 1MM Privately Held
SIC: 3315 Steel wire & related products

(G-5396)
GARDEN OF FLAVOR LLC
7501 Carnegie Ave (44103-4809)
PHONE...................................216 702-7991
Lisa Reed,
Keith Kress,
EMP: 4
SQ FT: 3,000
SALES (est): 466.3K Privately Held
SIC: 2033 Vegetable juices: packaged in
cans, jars, etc.

(G-5397)
GARFIELD ALLOYS INC (PA)
4878 Chaincraft Rd (44125)
PHONE...................................216 587-4843
Fax: 216 587-3764
Chuck Slovich, *President*
Mike Slovich Jr, *Corp Secy*
Patty Konopka, *Administration*
▼ EMP: 12 EST: 1950
SQ FT: 60,000
SALES (est): 13MM Privately Held
WEB: www.magretechinc.com
SIC: 3369 Magnesium & magnes.-base
alloy castings, exc. die-casting

(G-5398)
GARICK LLC (PA)
Also Called: Ogg Garick
13600 Broadway Ave Ste 1 (44125-1999)
PHONE...................................216 581-0100
Fax: 216 581-4712
Douglas J Alderman, *Business Mgr*
Jennifer Deckard, *Vice Pres*
Kim Eger, *Vice Pres*
John Gundlach, *Vice Pres*
P Coan, *CFO*
EMP: 20 EST: 1980
SQ FT: 3,500
SALES (est): 53.9MM Privately Held
WEB: www.garick.com
SIC: 2875 0711 2499 5091 Potting soil,
mixed; soil preparation services; mulch or
sawdust products, wood; athletic goods;
lumber scrap

(G-5399)
**GARLAND INDUSTRIES INC
(PA)**
3800 E 91st St (44105-2103)
PHONE...................................216 641-7500
David Sokol, *President*
Melvin Chrostowski, *Vice Pres*
Richard Debacco, *Vice Pres*
William Oley, *Vice Pres*
G Richard Olivier, *Vice Pres*
EMP: 8
SQ FT: 150,000
SALES (est): 238.1MM Privately Held
SIC: 2952 6512 8712 Roofing materials;
roofing felts, cements or coatings; coating
compounds, tar; commercial & industrial
building operation; architectural services

(G-5400)
GARLAND/DBS INC
3800 E 91st St (44105-2103)
PHONE...................................216 641-7500
Dave Sokol, *President*
Melvin Chrostowski, *Vice Pres*
Richard Debacco, *Vice Pres*
Dan Healy, *Plant Mgr*

Chuck Ripepi, *CFO*
EMP: 250
SALES: 59.6MM
SALES (corp-wide): 238.1MM Privately
Held
WEB: www.garlandco.com
SIC: 2952 6512 8712 Roofing materials;
roofing felts, cements or coatings; coating
compounds, tar; commercial & industrial
building operation; architectural services
HQ: The Garland Company Inc
3800 E 91st St
Cleveland OH 44105
216 641-7500

(G-5401)
GATEWAY METAL FINISHING INC
5310 W 161st St Ste J (44142-1627)
PHONE...................................216 267-2580
Fax: 216 267-3223
Edward F Eibel III, *CEO*
Ed Steele, *President*
Charles Steele, *Supervisor*
EMP: 27
SALES (est): 800K Privately Held
SIC: 3471 Finishing, metals or formed
products

(G-5402)
GE LIGHTING LLC (PA)
1975 Noble Rd Ste 338e (44112-1719)
PHONE...................................216 266-2000
Fax: 216 266-3003
Richard Simpson, *Business Mgr*
Bart McCoy, *Engineer*
Helen Rapp, *Engineer*
Victor Wong, *Finance*
William Hickey, *Natl Sales Mgr*
◆ EMP: 98
SALES (est): 87.7MM Privately Held
SIC: 3641 Sealed low-pressure gas lights

(G-5403)
**GE LIGHTING SOLUTIONS LLC
(HQ)**
1975 Noble Rd Ste 338e (44112-1719)
P.O. Box 60300, Fort Myers FL (33906-
6300)
PHONE...................................216 266-4800
Maryrose Sylvester, *President*
Agostino Renna, *President*
Shin Kimura, *Vice Pres*
Steve Germain, *Engineer*
John Hepp, *Engineer*
◆ EMP: 42
SQ FT: 20,890
SALES (est): 24.3MM
SALES (corp-wide): 123.6B Publicly
Held
WEB: www.gelcore.com
SIC: 3648 5063 Lighting equipment; light-
ing fixtures
PA: General Electric Company
41 Farnsworth St
Boston MA 02210
617 443-3000

(G-5404)
**GEAR COMPANY OF AMERICA
INC**
14300 Lorain Ave (44111-2297)
PHONE...................................216 671-5400
Fax: 216 671-5825
Edward Morel, *President*
Scott Britvec, *General Mgr*
Roy Scott, *Engineer*
Adam Scsock, *Engineer*
Carol Stoehr, *Engineer*
EMP: 60 EST: 1946
SQ FT: 96,000
SALES (est): 13.2MM Privately Held
WEB: www.gearcoa.com
SIC: 3714 3566 3462 Gears, motor vehi-
cle; gears, power transmission, except
automotive; gears, forged steel

(G-5405)
GEBAUER COMPANY
4444 E 153rd St (44128-2955)
PHONE...................................216 581-3030
Fax: 216 581-4970
John Giltinan, *Ch of Bd*
David O'Halloran, *President*
Jeff Laturell, *Vice Pres*
Steve Cherry, *Opers Staff*
John Kreft, *Engineer*

▲ EMP: 34 EST: 1957
SQ FT: 16,000
SALES (est): 11.9MM Privately Held
WEB: www.gebauerco.com
SIC: 2834 Pharmaceutical preparations

(G-5406)
GEIST CO INC
1814 W 30th St (44113-3026)
PHONE...................................216 771-2200
Fax: 216 771-7112
Thom Geist, *President*
Paul Gorman, *Vice Pres*
Sarah Gorman, *Admin Sec*
EMP: 16
SQ FT: 19,000
SALES (est): 1.6MM Privately Held
WEB: www.geistco.com
SIC: 3446 3444 Architectural metalwork;
canopies, sheet metal

(G-5407)
GELLNER ENGINEERING INC
2827 Brookpark Rd (44134-1308)
PHONE...................................216 398-8500
Fax: 216 398-8592
Dean Gellner, *President*
Carol Gellner, *Vice Pres*
EMP: 4
SQ FT: 3,300
SALES (est): 275K Privately Held
WEB: www.gellnerengineering.com
SIC: 5531 7539 3714 3519 Automotive
parts; machine shop, automotive; motor
vehicle parts & accessories; internal com-
bustion engines

(G-5408)
GEM ORNAMENTAL IRON CO
4681 Broadview Rd (44109-4619)
PHONE...................................216 661-6965
Fax: 216 661-1610
John J Klimo, *President*
Roberta Klimo, *Admin Sec*
EMP: 3 EST: 1959
SQ FT: 4,000
SALES (est): 401.6K Privately Held
SIC: 3446 Architectural metalwork; stairs,
staircases, stair treads: prefabricated
metal; railings, prefabricated metal;
fences or posts, ornamental iron or steel

(G-5409)
GEM TOOL LLC
127 Public Sq (44114-1217)
PHONE...................................216 771-8444
EMP: 6 EST: 2014
SALES (est): 727.6K Privately Held
SIC: 3545 Machine tool accessories

(G-5410)
**GENERAL ALUMINUM MFG
COMPANY (DH)**
Also Called: Gamco
6065 Parkland Blvd (44124-6119)
PHONE...................................440 947-2000
Edward Crawford, *CEO*
Bob Paulenske, *President*
Rick Steffenson, *General Mgr*
Douglas Stoops, *General Mgr*
Neil Schneider, *Senior VP*
▲ EMP: 277 EST: 1981
SQ FT: 2,000
SALES (est): 167.2MM
SALES (corp-wide): 1.2B Publicly Held
WEB: www.generalaluminum.com
SIC: 3365 3369 Aluminum & aluminum-
based alloy castings; nonferrous
foundries
HQ: Park-Ohio Industries, Inc.
6065 Parkland Blvd Ste 1
Cleveland OH 44124
440 947-2000

(G-5411)
**GENERAL AWNING COMPANY
INC**
1350 E Granger Rd (44131-1206)
PHONE...................................216 749-0110
Fax: 216 749-0113
Paul Gall, *President*
Leonard Lachner, *Manager*
EMP: 15
SQ FT: 10,000

SALES (est): 2.5MM Privately Held
WEB: www.genawning.com
SIC: 3444 1751 1761 Awnings, sheet
metal; window & door (prefabricated) installation; siding contractor

(G-5412)
GENERAL ELECTRIC COMPANY
4477 E 49th St (44125-1097)
PHONE...................................216 883-1000
Fax: 216 429-3350
John Schneider, *Purch Mgr*
Donald Mysliwec, *Enginr/R&D Mgr*
Osvaldo Alers, *Manager*
Pat Baranack, *Manager*
Dave Clemens, *Senior Mgr*
EMP: 100
SQ FT: 12,000
SALES (corp-wide): 123.6B Publicly
Held
SIC: 7629 3621 3613 3612 Electrical re-
pair shops; motors & generators;
switchgear & switchboard apparatus;
transformers, except electric; power
transmission equipment; pumps & pump-
ing equipment
PA: General Electric Company
41 Farnsworth St
Boston MA 02210
617 443-3000

(G-5413)
GENERAL ELECTRIC COMPANY
1975 Noble Rd (44112-1719)
PHONE...................................216 266-2121
Fax: 216 266-2108
John Strainic, *General Mgr*
Rich Wrightington, *General Mgr*
John Krenicki Jr, *Vice Pres*
Adrienne Woodworth, *Project Mgr*
Ryan Wood, *Facilities Mgr*
EMP: 800
SALES (corp-wide): 123.6B Publicly
Held
SIC: 3646 Commercial indusl & institu-
tional electric lighting fixtures
PA: General Electric Company
41 Farnsworth St
Boston MA 02210
617 443-3000

(G-5414)
GENERAL ELECTRIC COMPANY
18683 S Miles Rd (44128-4297)
PHONE...................................216 663-2110
Fax: 216 663-0518
John Favaloro, *Opers Mgr*
Jason Hisrich, *Production*
Kristen Frederick, *Engineer*
Heather Fuqua, *Engineer*
Sarah Tenley, *Engineer*
EMP: 70
SQ FT: 53,462
SALES (corp-wide): 123.6B Publicly
Held
SIC: 3844 Radiographic X-ray apparatus &
tubes
PA: General Electric Company
41 Farnsworth St
Boston MA 02210
617 443-3000

(G-5415)
GENERAL ELECTRIC COMPANY
1814 E 45th St (44103-2321)
PHONE...................................216 391-8741
Fax: 216 266-4838
Zoltan Toth, *Engineer*
Mike Kridle, *Manager*
EMP: 300
SALES (corp-wide): 123.6B Publicly
Held
SIC: 3641 Lamps, incandescent filament,
electric
PA: General Electric Company
41 Farnsworth St
Boston MA 02210
617 443-3000

(G-5416)
GENERAL ELECTRIC COMPANY
21800 Tungsten Rd (44117-1195)
PHONE...................................216 266-2357
Fax: 216 266-2360
Chuck Huey, *Sales Staff*
Mike Credell, *Manager*

G
E
O
G
R
A
P
H
I
C

EMP: 180
SALES (corp-wide): 123.6B **Publicly Held**
SIC: 3699 Electrical equipment & supplies
PA: General Electric Company
41 Farnsworth St
Boston MA 02210
617 443-3000

(G-5417)
GENERAL ELECTRIC COMPANY
1099 Ivanhoe Rd (44110-3293)
PHONE................................216 268-3846
Fax: 216 266-4410
Bill Cohen, *Plant Mgr*
James C Wiester, *Branch Mgr*
EMP: 100
SALES (corp-wide): 123.6B **Publicly Held**
SIC: 2819 2899 2851 Industrial inorganic chemicals; chemical preparations; paints & allied products
PA: General Electric Company
41 Farnsworth St
Boston MA 02210
617 443-3000

(G-5418)
GENERAL ENVMTL SCIENCE CORP
26000 Richmond Rd (44146-1419)
PHONE................................216 464-0680
Fax: 216 464-2720
Barton Gilbert, *President*
Elaine Gilbert, *Vice Pres*
EMP: 8
SQ FT: 20,000
SALES (est): 93.9K **Privately Held**
SIC: 2836 Bacteriological media

(G-5419)
GENERAL MOTORS LLC
5400 Chevrolet Blvd (44130-1451)
PHONE................................216 265-5000
Fax: 216 265-5279
Clayton Parsons, *Superintendent*
Al Maclaulhin, *Opers-Prdtn-Mfg*
Joyce Reed, *QC Dir*
Scott Buddie, *Engineer*
Jim Kupetz, *Engineer*
EMP: 2028
SALES (corp-wide): 166.3MM **Publicly Held**
SIC: 3711 3465 3714 2531 Motor vehicles & car bodies; body parts, automobile; stamped metal; motor vehicle parts & accessories; public building & related furniture
HQ: General Motors Llc
300 Renaissance Ctr L1
Detroit MI 48243

(G-5420)
GENERAL SHEAVE COMPANY INC
1335 Main Ave (44113-2389)
PHONE................................216 781-8120
Antun Bunjevac, *President*
EMP: 9 EST: 1951
SQ FT: 7,500
SALES (est): 1.1MM **Privately Held**
WEB: www.generalsheave.com
SIC: 3599 Machine shop, jobbing & repair

(G-5421)
GENERAL STEEL CORPORATION
3344 E 80th St (44127-1851)
PHONE................................216 883-4200
Fax: 216 883-4237
James Lamantia, *President*
Jay E Irvin, *Exec VP*
EMP: 18
SQ FT: 60,000
SALES (est): 15.6MM **Privately Held**
WEB: www.generalsteelcorporation.com
SIC: 5051 3398 3441 Metals service centers & offices; metal heat treating; fabricated structural metal

(G-5422)
GENIE REPROS INC
2211 Hamilton Ave (44114-1154)
PHONE................................216 965-0213
Fax: 216 696-6681

Barry Bishop, *President*
Pete Zupich, *Prdtn Mgr*
Don Mc Quilkin, *CPA*
Rudolph Herter, *Finance*
Michelle Toivenen, *Marketing Staff*
EMP: 20
SQ FT: 7,900
SALES (est): 3.9MM **Privately Held**
WEB: www.genierepros.com
SIC: 2752 Lithographing on metal

(G-5423)
GENT MACHINE COMPANY
445 S Green Rd (44121-2896)
PHONE................................216 481-2334
Fax: 216 481-2334
Richard W Gent Jr, *President*
Diane Gent, *Vice Pres*
Richard W Gent IV, *Vice Pres*
Andrea Plassard, *Accountant*
Tom Scharf, *CPA*
EMP: 17 EST: 1927
SQ FT: 15,000
SALES (est): 4.6MM **Privately Held**
WEB: www.gentmachine.com
SIC: 3451 Screw machine products

(G-5424)
GENVAC AEROSPACE CORP (PA)
110 Alpha Park (44143-2215)
P.O. Box 12105, Birmingham AL (35202-2105)
PHONE................................440 646-9986
Gerald T Mearini, *CEO*
Robert Kunszt, *Engineer*
Carol Ream, *Controller*
James Dayton, *CTO*
David Vance, *Info Tech Mgr*
EMP: 12
SQ FT: 18,000
SALES (est): 1.3MM **Privately Held**
WEB: www.genvacaerospace.com
SIC: 3827 2851 Optical instruments & lenses; paints & allied products

(G-5425)
GERGEL-KELLEM COMPANY INC
Also Called: Watt Printers
4544 Hinckley Indus Pkwy (44109-6010)
PHONE................................216 398-2000
Fax: 216 398-2121
John Gergel, *President*
Mike Nakonek, *Vice Pres*
EMP: 60
SQ FT: 60,000
SALES (est): 14.8MM **Privately Held**
WEB: www.wattprinters.com
SIC: 2752 Commercial printing, offset

(G-5426)
GEROW EQUIPMENT COMPANY INC
706 E 163rd St (44110-2453)
PHONE................................216 383-8800
Fax: 216 761-5260
Robert L Gerow, *CEO*
EMP: 7 EST: 1943
SQ FT: 1,500
SALES (est): 1.3MM **Privately Held**
SIC: 3561 5084 Industrial pumps & parts; heat exchange equipment, industrial

(G-5427)
GEW INC
11941 Abbey Rd Ste X (44133-2663)
PHONE................................440 237-4439
Brian Wenger, *President*
Malcolm Rae, *Managing Dir*
Dave Lyus, *Sales Staff*
David Ettinger, *Associate*
▲ EMP: 9
SALES (est): 1.5MM **Privately Held**
WEB: www.gewuv.com
SIC: 3555 Printing trades machinery

(G-5428)
GIBSON GREETINGS INC (DH)
1 American Rd (44144-2301)
PHONE................................216 252-7300
Frank J O'Connell, *Ch of Bd*
Gregory Ionna, *Exec VP*
James T Wilson, *Exec VP*
EMP: 2

SQ FT: 593,700
SALES (est): 5.9MM
SALES (corp-wide): 2.2B **Privately Held**
SIC: 2771 2679 2674 2656 Greeting cards; gift wrap, paper: made from purchased material; novelties, paper: made from purchased materials; cups, paper: made from purchased material; plates, paper: made from purchased material; napkins, paper: made from purchased paper; candles
HQ: American Greetings Corporation
1 American Rd
Cleveland OH 44144
216 252-7300

(G-5429)
GIBSON MACHINERY LLC
181 Oak Leaf Oval (44146-6156)
PHONE................................440 439-4000
Ester Schechter, *Controller*
M Lee Gibson, *Mng Member*
Larysa Gibson,
EMP: 30
SALES (est): 10MM **Privately Held**
WEB: www.gibsonmachinery.com
SIC: 3531 Construction machinery

(G-5430)
GIE MEDIA INC (PA)
5811 Canal Rd (44125-3430)
PHONE................................800 456-0707
Fax: 330 659-0823
Richard J W Foster, *CEO*
Chris Foster, *President*
Jim Gilbride, *Publisher*
Arlo Graham, *Editor*
Robert Schoenberger, *Editor*
EMP: 35 EST: 1980
SQ FT: 6,500
SALES (est): 13.2MM **Privately Held**
WEB: www.giemedia.com
SIC: 2721 2731 Magazines: publishing only, not printed on site; books: publishing only

(G-5431)
GINOS AWARDS INC
Also Called: Gino's Jewelers & Trophy Mfrs
4701 Richmond Rd Ste 300 (44128-5994)
PHONE................................216 831-5653
Fax: 216 831-8767
Gino Zavarella, *President*
▲ EMP: 50
SQ FT: 30,000
SALES (est): 8.1MM **Privately Held**
WEB: www.ginosawards.com
SIC: 3911 3993 3914 Jewelry, precious metal; signs & advertising specialties; trophies

(G-5432)
GLAUNERS WHOLESALE INC
Also Called: G & G Originals
5011 Brookpark Rd (44134-1049)
PHONE................................216 398-7088
Fax: 216 398-7452
Gregory Glauner, *President*
Monica Glauner, *Principal*
Sandy Phillips, *Principal*
EMP: 4
SQ FT: 4,000
SALES (est): 200K **Privately Held**
SIC: 2759 Screen printing

(G-5433)
GLOBAL PAYMENTS INC
21320 Hillsdale Ave (44126-2117)
PHONE................................440 356-0325
EMP: 4
SALES (corp-wide): 2.9B **Publicly Held**
SIC: 3172 Billfolds
PA: Global Payments Inc.
10 Glenlake Pkwy N Tower
Atlanta GA 30328
770 829-8000

(G-5434)
GLOBE PIPE HANGER PRODUCTS INC
14601 Industrial Pkwy (44135-4545)
PHONE................................216 362-6300
Fax: 216 267-6884
E Scot Kennedy, *Ch of Bd*
Gary Horvath, *COO*

Dale Zeleznik, *Vice Pres*
Dan Collins, *VP Sls/Mktg*
Traci Locksey, *Cust Mgr*
▲ EMP: 20
SQ FT: 30,000
SALES (est): 3.2MM **Privately Held**
WEB: www.wireproducts.com
SIC: 3569 Firefighting apparatus & related equipment

(G-5435)
GOLD PRO INC
850 Euclid Ave Ste 518 (44114-3304)
PHONE................................216 241-5143
Matthew Elkanick, *President*
Christine Elkanick, *Vice Pres*
Frank Schaefer, *Manager*
EMP: 3
SALES: 150K **Privately Held**
SIC: 3911 Jewelry, precious metal

(G-5436)
GOLUBITSKY CORPORATION
Also Called: Alvio
4364 Cranwood Pkwy (44128-4002)
PHONE................................800 552-4204
Leo Golubitsky, *President*
Alex Fonis, *Shareholder*
▲ EMP: 5
SQ FT: 6,000
SALES (est): 500K **Privately Held**
WEB: www.alvio.com
SIC: 5734 5999 3571 Computer & software stores; typewriters & business machines; electronic computers

(G-5437)
GOOCH & HOUSEGO (FLORIDA) LLC (HQ)
676 Alpha Dr (44143-2123)
PHONE................................321 242-7818
Pat Shannonhouse, *General Mgr*
Huey Ho, *Vice Pres*
Gary Catella, *VP Opers*
Jeff Luken, *Plant Mgr*
Harry Mason, *QC Mgr*
EMP: 63
SQ FT: 20,000
SALES (est): 16MM
SALES (corp-wide): 111.5MM **Privately Held**
WEB: www.neostech.com
SIC: 3827 Optical instruments & lenses
PA: Gooch & Housego Plc
Dowlish Ford
Ilminster TA19
146 025-6440

(G-5438)
GOODYEAR TIRE & RUBBER COMPANY
18901 Snow Rd (44142-1465)
PHONE................................216 265-1800
Ken Dombrowski, *General Mgr*
EMP: 200
SALES (corp-wide): 15.1B **Publicly Held**
WEB: www.goodyear.com
SIC: 5531 3011 Automotive tires; tires & inner tubes
PA: The Goodyear Tire & Rubber Company
200 E Innovation Way
Akron OH 44316
330 796-2121

(G-5439)
GORTONS INC
Specialty Products
13525 Hummel Rd (44142-2519)
PHONE................................216 362-1050
Fax: 216 362-6506
Louis Granja, *Opers-Prdtn-Mfg*
Sue Spisak, *Finance*
EMP: 36
SQ FT: 15,000
SALES (corp-wide): 5.4B **Privately Held**
WEB: www.gortons.com
SIC: 2011 Meat packing plants
HQ: Gorton's Inc.
128 Rogers St
Gloucester MA 01930
978 283-3000

(G-5440)
GOTTA GROOVE RECORDS INC
3615 Superior Ave E 4201a (44114-4185)
PHONE................................216 431-7373

▲ = Import ▼=Export
◆ =Import/Export

Vince Slusarz, *President*
EMP: 40
SALES (est): 5.1MM **Privately Held**
SIC: 2782 Account books

(G-5441)
GR GROUP SALES INC
9400 Maywood Ave (44102-4877)
P.O. Box 450931 (44145-0621)
PHONE..............................216 961-3773
Karyn Dolivka, *President*
Elizabeth Ramey, *Corp Secy*
EMP: 3
SQ FT: 6,000
SALES (est): 434K **Privately Held**
SIC: 3496 Miscellaneous fabricated wire
products

(G-5442)
GRABO INTERIORS INC
3605 Perkins Ave (44114-4632)
PHONE..............................216 391-6677
Joseph Grabo, *President*
Paul Grabo, *Vice Pres*
EMP: 6
SQ FT: 4,400
SALES (est): 500K **Privately Held**
SIC: 2511 Wood household furniture

(G-5443)
GRAFTECH INTL HOLDINGS INC
11709 Madison Ave (44107-5230)
PHONE..............................216 529-3777
Karen Narwold, *Vice Pres*
Paul Wayne, *Prdtn Mgr*
Dennis Robinson, *Human Res Mgr*
Ray Quirino, *Accounts Mgr*
Michael Zaucha, *Regl Sales Mgr*
EMP: 101
SALES (corp-wide): 14.9B **Privately Held**
SIC: 3624 Carbon & graphite products
HQ: Graftech International Holdings Inc.
6100 Oak Tree Blvd # 300
Independence OH 44131
216 676-2000

(G-5444)
GRAIN CRAFT INC
1635 Merwin Ave (44113-2421)
PHONE..............................216 621-3206
Fax: 216 621-0404
Joe E Blanton, *General Mgr*
EMP: 27
SQ FT: 20,000
SALES (corp-wide): 297.4MM **Privately
Held**
WEB: www.cerealfood.com
SIC: 2041 Flour mills, cereal (except rice)
PA: Grain Craft, Inc.
201 W Main St Ste 203
Chattanooga TN 37408
423 265-2313

(G-5445)
GRAND HARBOR YACHT SALES & SVC
Also Called: Sneller Machine Tool Division
706 Alpha Dr (44143-2125)
PHONE..............................440 442-2919
Fax: 440 442-2919
John Bennington, *President*
EMP: 6
SQ FT: 7,000
SALES (est): 889.8K **Privately Held**
WEB: www.snellermachine.com
SIC: 3599 5084 3537 3531 Machine
shop, jobbing & repair; industrial machin-
ery & equipment; industrial trucks & trac-
tors; construction machinery

(G-5446)
GRAPHIC ART SYSTEMS INC
Also Called: Grafix
5800 Pennsylvania Ave (44137-4331)
PHONE..............................216 581-9050
Fax: 216 581-9041
Jordan Katz, *President*
Hayley Ann Prendergast, *President*
Jan Andow, *General Mgr*
Karl Szelpal, *Vice Pres*
▲ **EMP:** 27 **EST:** 1963
SQ FT: 45,000
SALES: 10MM **Privately Held**
WEB: www.grafixplastics.com
SIC: 3081 Plastic film & sheet

(G-5447)
GRAPHTECH COMMUNICATIONS INC
4724 W 150th St (44135-3464)
PHONE..............................216 676-1020
Fax: 216 676-1021
Stephen L Adamson, *President*
William Kall, *Vice Pres*
EMP: 10
SQ FT: 13,500
SALES: 1MM **Privately Held**
WEB: www.graphtechcommunications.com
SIC: 2752 Commercial printing, offset

(G-5448)
GRAY & COMPANY PUBLISHERS
1588 E 40th St Ste 1b (44103-2386)
PHONE..............................216 431-2665
Fax: 216 431-7933
David Gray, *President*
EMP: 6
SALES (est): 611.1K **Privately Held**
WEB: www.grayco.com
SIC: 2731 Books: publishing only

(G-5449)
GREAT LAKES ETCHING FINSHG CO
7010 Krick Rd Ste 3 (44146-4483)
PHONE..............................440 439-3624
Fax: 440 439-6882
Ronald Pool Sr, *President*
Ronald Pool, *Owner*
Joanne Marold, *Vice Pres*
Ronald Pool III, *Vice Pres*
EMP: 11
SALES: 1MM **Privately Held**
SIC: 3479 Etching on metals

(G-5450)
GREAT LAKES GRAPHICS INC
3354 Superior Ave E (44114-4123)
PHONE..............................216 391-0077
Fax: 216 391-5102
Anthony R Lux, *President*
Diane Austin, *Controller*
James Schneider, *Accounting Dir*
EMP: 20
SQ FT: 15,000
SALES (est): 3.2MM **Privately Held**
WEB: www.greatlakesgraphicsinc.com
SIC: 3555 7336 Plates, offset; graphic arts
& related design

(G-5451)
GREAT LAKES GROUP
Also Called: Great Lakes Towing
4500 Division Ave (44102-2228)
PHONE..............................216 621-4854
Sheldon Guren, *Ch of Bd*
Ronald Rasmus, *President*
George Sogar, *Vice Pres*
Joseph Craine, *Manager*
EMP: 120
SQ FT: 6,000
SALES (est): 21.3MM **Privately Held**
SIC: 3731 4492 Shipbuilding & repairing;
marine towing services

(G-5452)
GREAT LAKES INTEGRATED INC (PA)
Also Called: Gli
4005 Clark Ave (44109-1128)
PHONE..............................216 651-1500
James R Schultz, *President*
Scot D Adkins, *President*
Carrie Spence, *President*
Anthony Sanson, *Vice Pres*
Robert J Schultz, *Vice Pres*
▲ **EMP:** 90 **EST:** 1931
SQ FT: 75,000
SALES (est): 25.6MM **Privately Held**
SIC: 2752 2796 2789 Commercial print-
ing, lithographic; lithographic plates, posi-
tives or negatives; bookbinding & related
work

(G-5453)
GREAT LAKES LITHOGRAPH
4005 Clark Ave (44109-1186)
PHONE..............................216 651-1500
Fax: 216 651-8311
Chris Donnelly, *Principal*
EMP: 12

SQ FT: 45,469
SALES (est): 1.3MM **Privately Held**
SIC: 2752 Commercial printing, litho-
graphic

(G-5454)
GREAT LAKES MANAGEMENT INC (PA)
8510 Bessemer Ave (44127-1843)
P.O. Box 811000 (44181-1000)
PHONE..............................216 883-6500
Margaret Ruebensaal, *President*
Charles M Ruebensaal Jr, *Treasurer*
David Di Biasio, *Admin Sec*
EMP: 1
SQ FT: 150,000
SALES (est): 8MM **Privately Held**
SIC: 6512 3822 Nonresidential building
operators; switches, thermostatic

(G-5455)
GREAT LAKES PUBLISHING COMPANY (PA)
Also Called: Cleveland Magazine
1422 Euclid Ave Ste 730 (44115-2001)
PHONE..............................216 771-2833
Fax: 216 781-6318
Lute Harmon Jr, *Ch of Bd*
Steve Gleydura, *Vice Pres*
Susan Harmon, *Vice Pres*
George Sedlak, *CFO*
Sarah Desmond, *Director*
EMP: 75
SQ FT: 19,000
SALES (est): 9.2MM **Privately Held**
WEB: www.clevelandmagazine.com
SIC: 2721 7374 Magazines: publishing
only, not printed on site; computer graph-
ics service

(G-5456)
GREAT LKES NROTECHNOLOGIES INC
10055 Sweet Valley Dr # 5 (44125-4246)
PHONE..............................216 520-1537
Robert N Schmidt, *Ch of Bd*
Joseph P Giuffrida, *President*
Brian M Kolkowski, *President*
Robert Schroeter, *Controller*
EMP: 20
SALES (est): 3.5MM **Privately Held**
WEB: www.glneurotech.com
SIC: 3845 Electromedical apparatus

(G-5457)
GREAT WESTERN JUICE COMPANY
Also Called: Perfection Fine Products
16153 Libby Rd (44137-1219)
PHONE..............................216 475-5770
Fax: 216 475-5772
Jack M Goldberg, *President*
William Overton, *Vice Pres*
EMP: 18
SQ FT: 30,000
SALES (est): 3.3MM **Privately Held**
SIC: 2033 2087 Fruit juices: fresh; cocktail
mixes, nonalcoholic

(G-5458)
GREATER CLEVE PIPE FTTING FUND
6305 Halle Dr (44125-4617)
PHONE..............................216 524-8334
Niel Ginley, *President*
EMP: 10
SALES: 1MM **Privately Held**
SIC: 3494 Pipe fittings

(G-5459)
GRIFFIN INDUSTRIES LLC
2254 Hamilton Ave (44114-1144)
PHONE..............................216 696-2588
Brian Conaway, *Manager*
Frank Agh, *Manager*
EMP: 3
SALES (corp-wide): 3.4B **Publicly Held**
WEB: www.griffinind.com
SIC: 2077 3441 Rendering; fabricated
structural metal
HQ: Griffin Industries Llc
4221 Alexandria Pike
Cold Spring KY 41076
859 781-2010

(G-5460)
GROFF INDUSTRIES
2201 W 110th St (44102-3511)
PHONE..............................216 634-9100
John Rusnak, *Mng Member*
EMP: 15
SALES (est): 975.4K **Privately Held**
WEB: www.groffeng.com
SIC: 3999 7389 Manufacturing industries;
packaging & labeling services

(G-5461)
GROUP INDUSTRIES INC (PA)
Also Called: Drum Parts
7580 Garfield Blvd (44125-1216)
P.O. Box 25409 (44125-0409)
PHONE..............................216 271-0702
Fax: 216 271-5044
Martin Tiernan, *Ch of Bd*
Lane A Zamin, *President*
Curtis Crowder, *Vice Pres*
Dale Zeleznik, *Vice Pres*
▲ **EMP:** 32
SQ FT: 24,000
SALES (est): 10.5MM **Privately Held**
WEB: www.drumpartsinc.com
SIC: 3429 3592 3452 Manufactured hard-
ware (general); carburetors, pistons,
rings, valves; bolts, nuts, rivets & washers

(G-5462)
GSI OF OHIO LLC
Also Called: Sidari's Italian Foods
3820 Lakeside Ave E (44114-3848)
PHONE..............................216 431-3344
Fax: 216 431-6227
Joseph Sidari, *President*
Joe Falsone, *Sales Executive*
▲ **EMP:** 65
SALES (est): 8.3MM **Privately Held**
SIC: 2099 Packaged combination prod-
ucts: pasta, rice & potato

(G-5463)
GUARANTEED FNSHG UNLIMITED INC
3200 W 121st St (44111-1720)
PHONE..............................216 252-8200
Fax: 216 252-4784
William Kozak, *CEO*
Joseph Janke, *President*
▲ **EMP:** 35
SQ FT: 50,000
SALES (est): 4.7MM **Privately Held**
SIC: 3471 Electroplating & plating

(G-5464)
GUARDIAN CO INC
2754 Woodhill Rd (44104-3661)
PHONE..............................216 721-2262
Herbert K Kubach, *President*
Kenneth Kubach, *Vice Pres*
EMP: 5
SQ FT: 15,000
SALES (est): 460K **Privately Held**
SIC: 2842 2841 2392 Waxes for wood,
leather & other materials; degreasing sol-
vent; detergents, synthetic organic or in-
organic alkaline; soap: granulated, liquid,
cake, flaked or chip; mops, floor & dust

(G-5465)
GUSTAVE JULIAN JEWELERS INC
7432 State Rd (44134-5858)
PHONE..............................440 888-1100
Fax: 440 888-3727
Jim Julian, *President*
Jayne Julian, *Corp Secy*
Edward Julian, *Vice Pres*
EMP: 7 **EST:** 1948
SQ FT: 2,400
SALES (est): 789.6K **Privately Held**
SIC: 5944 7631 3911 Silverware; jewelry
repair services; watch repair; jewelry, pre-
cious metal

(G-5466)
H & B MACHINE & TOOL INC
1390 E 40th St (44103-1102)
PHONE..............................216 431-3254
Fax: 216 431-1415
Frank Spisich, *President*
Geraldine Spisich, *Vice Pres*
EMP: 12

GEOGRAPHIC

SQ FT: 8,000
SALES (est): 1.8MM **Privately Held**
WEB: www.hb-machine.com
SIC: 3599 Machine shop, jobbing & repair

(G-5467)
H & H TRUCK PARTS LLC
5500s Cloverleaf Pkwy (44125-4815)
PHONE....................................216 642-4540
Mark Harris,
Jeff Heater,
EMP: 5
SQ FT: 12,000
SALES (est): 1MM **Privately Held**
WEB: www.hhtruckparts.com
SIC: 3713 5531 Truck bodies & parts;
   truck equipment & parts

(G-5468)
H LEFT COMPANY
4700 Spring Rd (44131-1027)
PHONE....................................216 361-6348
Sanford Leff, *Principal*
EMP: 3
SALES (est): 373.8K **Privately Held**
SIC: 3612 Fluorescent lighting transform-
   ers

(G-5469)
H P MANUFACTURING CO
3740 Prospect Ave E (44115-2706)
PHONE....................................216 361-6500
Ken Lutke, *Controller*
EMP: 63 EST: 2015
SALES (est): 3.3MM **Privately Held**
SIC: 3089 Plastics products

(G-5470)
H S PROCESSING LP
4600 Heidtman Pkwy (44105-1023)
PHONE....................................216 641-6995
Greg Glenn, *Principal*
EMP: 3
SALES (est): 167K **Privately Held**
SIC: 3316 Strip steel, cold-rolled: from pur-
   chased hot-rolled

(G-5471)
HAFCO-CASE INC
12212 Sprecher Ave (44135-5122)
PHONE....................................216 267-4644
Fax: 216 267-2527
Phyllis Tarnawsky, *President*
Natalie Tarnawsky, *Corp Secy*
Bohdan Tarnawsky, *Vice Pres*
EMP: 8 EST: 1951
SQ FT: 8,000
SALES (est): 934.7K **Privately Held**
SIC: 3599 Machine shop, jobbing & repair

(G-5472)
**HAHN MANUFACTURING
COMPANY**
5332 Hamilton Ave (44114-3984)
PHONE....................................216 391-9300
Fax: 216 391-4606
Robert E Hahn, *President*
Greg Hahn, *Vice Pres*
Laura L Hahn, *Vice Pres*
Betty Alex, *Administration*
EMP: 45 EST: 1916
SQ FT: 17,000
SALES (est): 7MM **Privately Held**
WEB: www.hahnmfg.com
SIC: 3549 3599 Metalworking machinery;
   machine shop, jobbing & repair

(G-5473)
HALVORSEN COMPANY
7500 Grand Division Ave (44125-1235)
P.O. Box 25625 (44125-0625)
PHONE....................................216 341-7500
Fax: 216 341-7557
Ross C Frick, *President*
William Patrick Clyne, *Principal*
John F Ray Jr, *Principal*
Francis J Talty, *Principal*
Slavko Paulic, *Manager*
▲ EMP: 32 EST: 1954
SQ FT: 68,000
SALES (est): 9.8MM **Privately Held**
WEB: www.halvorsenusa.com
SIC: 3441 3444 3443 Fabricated struc-
   tural metal; sheet metalwork; fabricated
   plate work (boiler shop)

(G-5474)
**HAMILTON MOLD & MACHINE
CO**
25016 Lakeland Blvd (44132-2685)
PHONE....................................216 732-8200
Fax: 216 261-9533
Dale Fleming, *President*
Bob Fleming, *Purchasing*
Don Miller, *QC Mgr*
Jim Napier, *Design Engr*
Mark Fleming, *Treasurer*
EMP: 39 EST: 1917
SQ FT: 20,000
SALES (est): 5.5MM **Privately Held**
SIC: 3544 Forms (molds), for foundry &
   plastics working machinery

(G-5475)
HANDICRAFT LLC
3407 Saint Clair Ave Ne (44114-4103)
PHONE....................................216 295-1950
Eli Gunzburg,
▼ EMP: 5
SQ FT: 8,000
SALES (est): 534.9K **Privately Held**
SIC: 2499 Decorative wood & woodwork

(G-5476)
HANG TIME GROUP INC
5340 Hamilton Ave Ste 107 (44114-3954)
PHONE....................................216 771-5885
Dave Stilson, *President*
David Stilson, *President*
Sharon Furey, *Officer*
David Stine, *Admin Sec*
EMP: 4 EST: 1997
SQ FT: 800
SALES (est): 304.9K **Privately Held**
SIC: 2395 Embroidery & art needlework

(G-5477)
**HANGER PRSTHETCS & ORTHO
INC**
6789 Ridge Rd Ste 104 (44129-5635)
PHONE....................................440 842-4251
Joe Garcia, *Principal*
EMP: 7
SALES (corp-wide): 460MM **Publicly
Held**
SIC: 3842 Limbs, artificial
HQ: Hanger Prosthetics & Orthotics, Inc.
   10910 Domain Dr Ste 300
   Austin TX 78758
   512 777-3800

(G-5478)
HANINI SEVEN OIL
6501 Denison Ave (44102-5434)
PHONE....................................216 857-0172
Amal Ajjar, *Principal*
EMP: 3
SALES (est): 258.7K **Privately Held**
SIC: 1311 Crude petroleum & natural gas

(G-5479)
HANLON INDUSTRIES INC
Also Called: Fiberglass Engineering Co
1280 E 286th St (44132-2195)
PHONE....................................216 261-7056
Fax: 216 731-2082
Bernard M Hanlon, *President*
EMP: 10
SALES (est): 605K **Privately Held**
SIC: 3089 Plastic processing

(G-5480)
**HARD CHROME PLATING
CONSULTANT**
2196 W 59th St (44102-4470)
P.O. Box 44082 (44144-0082)
PHONE....................................216 631-9090
Fax: 216 631-9091
Clarence Peger Jr, *President*
Denise Ward, *Corp Secy*
Christine Peger, *Vice Pres*
EMP: 3
SQ FT: 4,000
SALES (est): 1MM **Privately Held**
WEB: www.hard-chromesystems.com
SIC: 8742 8331 3443 Training & develop-
   ment consultant; vocational training
   agency; plate work for the metalworking
   trade

(G-5481)
HARSCO CORPORATION
Sherwood Divisions of Harsco
7900 Hub Pkwy (44125-5713)
PHONE....................................216 961-1570
Tom Hensley, *Manager*
EMP: 30
SALES (corp-wide): 1.4B **Publicly Held**
WEB: www.harsco.com
SIC: 3443 Industrial vessels, tanks & con-
   tainers
PA: Harsco Corporation
   350 Poplar Church Rd
   Camp Hill PA 17011
   717 763-7064

(G-5482)
**HARTLINE PRODUCTS COINC
(PA)**
4568 Mayfield Rd Ste 202 (44121-4050)
PHONE....................................216 291-2303
Fax: 216 291-4482
Christopher J Hart, *President*
Rebecca F Hart, *Treasurer*
Diane McGrath, *Manager*
Sandra Sable, *Director*
EMP: 5
SQ FT: 1,000
SALES (est): 2.6MM **Privately Held**
SIC: 2891 Cement, except linoleum & tile

(G-5483)
HARTLINE PRODUCTS COINC
15035 Woodworth Rd (44110-3309)
PHONE....................................216 851-7189
Ted Williams, *Plant Mgr*
EMP: 9
SALES (corp-wide): 2.6MM **Privately
Held**
SIC: 2891 3241 Cement, except linoleum
   & tile; cement, hydraulic
PA: Hartline Products Co.Inc.
   4568 Mayfield Rd Ste 202
   Cleveland OH 44121
   216 291-2303

(G-5484)
**HARVARD COIL PROCESSING
INC**
5400 Harvard Ave (44105-4828)
PHONE....................................216 883-6366
Fax: 216 883-0303
Eileen Jacobs, *President*
Robert Jacobs, *Treasurer*
Tim Thoma, *Controller*
Jeremy Jacobs, *Manager*
Doug Ridenour, *Manager*
EMP: 20
SQ FT: 2,000
SALES (est): 3.9MM **Privately Held**
WEB: www.harvardcoilprocessing.com
SIC: 3312 Blast furnaces & steel mills

(G-5485)
HATTENBACH COMPANY (PA)
5309 Hamilton Ave (44114-3909)
PHONE....................................216 881-5200
Fax: 216 881-5425
Cathy Hattenbach, *President*
Joseph G Berick, *Principal*
Dennis Bruckman, *Vice Pres*
John Heinert, *CFO*
EMP: 65 EST: 1944
SQ FT: 50,000
SALES (est): 15MM **Privately Held**
WEB: www.hattenbach.com
SIC: 1711 5078 2541 2434 Refrigeration
   contractor; commercial refrigeration
   equipment; cabinets, except refrigerated:
   show, display, etc.: wood; wood kitchen
   cabinets

(G-5486)
HBB PRO SALES (PA)
9700 Rockside Rd Ste 120 (44125-6264)
PHONE....................................216 901-7900
Jeff Hutton, *Principal*
EMP: 8
SALES (est): 1.8MM **Privately Held**
SIC: 3585 Heating equipment, complete

(G-5487)
HC STARCK (OHIO) INC
21801 Tungsten Rd (44117-1117)
PHONE....................................216 692-3990
Larry McHugh, *CEO*
Joel Hoffman, *COO*
Pete Calfo, *Senior VP*
John Durham, *Senior VP*
Dave Schwartz, *Opers Mgr*
EMP: 500
SQ FT: 150,000
SALES (est): 41.4MM **Privately Held**
SIC: 3341 Secondary nonferrous metals

(G-5488)
HCC HOLDINGS INC
4700 W 160th St (44135-2632)
PHONE....................................800 203-1155
EMP: 5
SALES (est): 402.8K
SALES (corp-wide): 206.4MM **Privately
Held**
SIC: 3444 Metal roofing & roof drainage
   equipment
PA: Oatey Co.
   4700 W 160th St
   Cleveland OH 44135
   800 203-1155

(G-5489)
HEALTH NUTS MEDIA LLC
4225 W 229th St (44126-1834)
PHONE....................................818 802-5222
Timothy Jones,
EMP: 6 EST: 2012
SALES (est): 410K **Privately Held**
SIC: 7372 7371 5999 7389 Prepackaged
   software; educational computer software;
   computer software writing services; computer software systems analysis & design,
   custom; educational aids & electronic
   training materials;

(G-5490)
**HEAT EXCHANGE INSTITUTE
INC**
1300 Sumner Ave (44115-2851)
PHONE....................................216 241-7333
John Addington, *Director*
EMP: 4
SQ FT: 5,200
SALES (est): 281.9K **Privately Held**
SIC: 8611 3699 Trade associations; elec-
   trical equipment & supplies

(G-5491)
HEAT SEAL LLC
Also Called: Ampak
4922 E 49th St (44125-1016)
PHONE....................................216 341-2022
Bryan Rakovec, *Principal*
Steve Pozsonyi, *Purchasing*
Ken Javor, *Engineer*
James Roodhouse, *Project Engr*
Tom Birkel, *Sales Mgr*
EMP: 110
SQ FT: 80,000
SALES (est): 29.8MM **Privately Held**
WEB: www.heatsealco.com
SIC: 3565 2542 Packaging machinery;
   wrapping machines; bag opening, filling &
   closing machines; vacuum packaging ma-
   chinery; fixtures, store: except wood

(G-5492)
HEATHER B MOORE INC
4502 Prospect Ave (44103-4312)
PHONE....................................216 932-5430
Heather Moore, *President*
Brian Ash, *Natl Sales Mgr*
Kate Miranda, *Representative*
EMP: 5
SQ FT: 1,000
SALES (est): 1MM **Privately Held**
WEB: www.heatherbmoore.com
SIC: 7389 3911 Apparel designers, com-
   mercial; jewelry, precious metal

(G-5493)
HEDALLOY DIE CORP
3266 E 49th St (44127-1092)
PHONE....................................216 341-3768
Fax: 216 341-5393
John Susa Jr, *President*
Joseph Susa, *General Mgr*
EMP: 12 EST: 1991
SQ FT: 10,000

SALES: 1MM **Privately Held**
SIC: 3544 Dies, steel rule; die sets for metal stamping (presses); jigs & fixtures; industrial molds

(G-5494)
HEIDTMAN STEEL PRODUCTS INC
4600 Heidtman Pkwy (44105-1023)
PHONE...................216 641-6995
David Cooley, *Manager*
EMP: 99
SALES (corp-wide): 273MM **Privately Held**
WEB: www.heidtman.com
SIC: 3444 Sheet metalwork
HQ: Heidtman Steel Products, Inc.
2401 Front St
Toledo OH 43605
419 691-4646

(G-5495)
HELLAN STRAINER COMPANY
3249 E 80th St (44104-4341)
PHONE...................216 206-4200
Jon Crowley, *President*
Jim Krava, *Project Mgr*
Brian Sullivan, *Marketing Staff*
Laurie Malicki, *CIO*
▲ **EMP:** 9
SALES (est): 2.4MM
SALES (corp-wide): 587.1MM **Privately Held**
WEB: www.hellanstrainer.com
SIC: 3569 Filters & strainers, pipeline
HQ: Industrial Manufacturing Company Llc
8223 Brecksville Rd Ste 1
Brecksville OH 44141
440 838-4700

(G-5496)
HELLER MACHINE PRODUCTS INC
1971 W 90th St (44102-2742)
PHONE...................216 281-2951
Fax: 216 281-6143
Jeff Evin, *President*
David Heller, *Vice Pres*
Mary Heller, *Vice Pres*
Joyce Evin, *Director*
Eda Heller, *Director*
EMP: 8 **EST:** 1953
SQ FT: 10,000
SALES (est): 945.4K **Privately Held**
SIC: 3451 3812 3728 3429 Screw machine products; search & navigation equipment; aircraft parts & equipment; manufactured hardware (general)

(G-5497)
HENDERSON FABRICATING CO INC
6217 Central Ave (44104-1756)
PHONE...................216 432-0404
Fax: 216 432-0404
John Henderson, *President*
John Blackburn, *Manager*
Karen Henderson, *Admin Sec*
EMP: 12
SQ FT: 8,000
SALES (est): 1.3MM **Privately Held**
SIC: 1791 3599 Structural steel erection; machine shop, jobbing & repair

(G-5498)
HENKEL CORPORATION
Cleveland Manufacturing Fcilty
18731 Cranwood Pkwy (44128-4037)
PHONE...................216 475-3600
Doug Karnf, *Vice Pres*
Cheryl Law, *Plant Mgr*
John Hanna, *Project Mgr*
Bob Sigal, *Safety Mgr*
John Dauphin, *Facilities Mgr*
EMP: 250
SALES (corp-wide): 19.7B **Privately Held**
SIC: 2891 2851 2842 Adhesives; sealants; paints & allied products; specialty cleaning, polishes & sanitation goods
HQ: Henkel Corporation
1 Henkel Way
Rocky Hill CT 06067
860 571-5100

(G-5499)
HENNINGS QUALITY SERVICE INC
3115 Berea Rd (44111-1503)
PHONE...................216 941-9120
Fax: 216 941-1128
Herbert Morrow, *President*
James Brinker, *Vice Pres*
Therese Safranek, *Manager*
EMP: 17
SQ FT: 20,000
SALES: 1.6MM **Privately Held**
SIC: 7694 Armature rewinding shops

(G-5500)
HENRY & WRIGHT CORPORATION
739 E 140th St Ste 1 (44110-2182)
PHONE...................216 851-3750
Fax: 216 851-3970
Austin W Moore, *President*
Jonathan Moore, *Vice Pres*
David Danner, *Marketing Staff*
Chuck Fetheroff, *Manager*
Russell Nieling, *Manager*
EMP: 13
SQ FT: 55,000
SALES (est): 3.5MM **Privately Held**
WEB: www.henrywright.com
SIC: 3542 3829 3823 Presses: hydraulic & pneumatic, mechanical & manual; measuring & controlling devices; industrial instrmnts msrmnt display/control process variable

(G-5501)
HENRY TOOLS INC
498 S Belvoir Blvd (44121-2351)
PHONE...................216 291-1011
Fax: 216 291-5949
Clara Henry, *Ch of Bd*
Richard Henry Sr, *President*
David Henry, *Vice Pres*
Peter Henry, *Sales Staff*
▲ **EMP:** 9
SALES (est): 1.3MM **Privately Held**
WEB: www.henrytools.com
SIC: 3724 Aircraft engines & engine parts

(G-5502)
HEPHAESTUS TECHNOLOGIES LLC
Also Called: Gray Tech International
3811 W 150th St (44111-5806)
PHONE...................216 252-0430
Fax: 216 252-8030
Helun Chahda, *CEO*
Helun Bachour Chahda, *CEO*
Eric Attel, *President*
Mario Chahda, *Vice Pres*
Jason Saliba, *Technology*
EMP: 24 **EST:** 1987
SQ FT: 20,000
SALES (est): 4.7MM **Privately Held**
WEB: www.graytechintl.com
SIC: 3599 Machine & other job shop work

(G-5503)
HERD MANUFACTURING INC
9227 Clinton Rd (44144-1088)
PHONE...................216 651-4221
Fax: 216 651-3210
Erich J Rock, *President*
Verne Campbell, *Manager*
Rita Laurenci, *Admin Sec*
EMP: 40
SQ FT: 25,000
SALES (est): 7.2MM **Privately Held**
WEB: www.herdmfg.com
SIC: 3469 3544 3599 Metal stampings; special dies & tools; custom machinery

(G-5504)
HERMAN MANUFACTURING LLC
Also Called: Walsh Manufacturing
13825 Triskett Rd (44111-1523)
PHONE...................216 251-6400
Fax: 216 251-1329
Martin Herman, *Mng Member*
Michael Herman,
EMP: 16
SQ FT: 25,000

SALES (est): 4.7MM **Privately Held**
WEB: www.walshmfg.com
SIC: 3564 3441 Dust or fume collecting equipment, industrial; fabricated structural metal

(G-5505)
HEROLD SALADS INC
17512 Miles Ave (44128-3404)
PHONE...................216 991-7500
Fax: 216 991-9565
Cathy L Herold, *President*
EMP: 25
SQ FT: 20,000
SALES (est): 4.5MM **Privately Held**
SIC: 2099 Salads, fresh or refrigerated; desserts, ready-to-mix

(G-5506)
HEXAGON INDUSTRIES INC
1135 Ivanhoe Rd (44110-3249)
PHONE...................216 249-0200
Fax: 216 249-1441
Stephen R Jackson, *President*
Peter M Jackson, *Vice Pres*
Bonita Thompson, *Human Res Dir*
▲ **EMP:** 50
SQ FT: 270,000
SALES (est): 13.1MM **Privately Held**
SIC: 3452 Bolts, nuts, rivets & washers

(G-5507)
HI CARB CORP
23610 Saint Clair Ave (44117-2591)
PHONE...................216 486-5000
Fax: 216 486-1641
John R Sonnie, *President*
Mike Bucciulli, *Engineer*
Barbara Grubelnik, *Office Mgr*
EMP: 17
SQ FT: 10,000
SALES (est): 2.9MM **Privately Held**
WEB: www.hicarb.com
SIC: 3545 Tools & accessories for machine tools

(G-5508)
HI TECMETAL GROUP INC (PA)
Also Called: Hydro-Vac
1101 E 55th St (44103-1026)
PHONE...................216 881-8100
Fax: 216 881-6811
Terence C Profughi, *President*
Harold M Baron, *Principal*
Mary C Finley, *Principal*
N M Salkover, *Principal*
Cole Coe, *Vice Pres*
EMP: 20 **EST:** 1943
SQ FT: 398,700
SALES (est): 22.9MM **Privately Held**
SIC: 3398 7692 Brazing (hardening) of metal; annealing of metal; tempering of metal; welding repair

(G-5509)
HI TECMETAL GROUP INC
Walker Heat Treating
10601 Briggs Rd (44111-5329)
PHONE...................216 941-0440
Fax: 216 941-0031
Terence Profughi, *CEO*
EMP: 15
SALES (corp-wide): 22.9MM **Privately Held**
SIC: 3398 Metal heat treating
PA: Hi Tecmetal Group Inc
1101 E 55th St
Cleveland OH 44103
216 881-8100

(G-5510)
HI TECMETAL GROUP INC
1432 E 47th St (44103-1222)
PHONE...................216 881-8100
Greg Hercik, *Manager*
EMP: 11
SALES (corp-wide): 21MM **Privately Held**
SIC: 3452 Rivets, metal
PA: Hi Tecmetal Group Inc
1101 E 55th St
Cleveland OH 44103
216 881-8100

(G-5511)
HI-TECH SOLUTIONS LLC
510 Karl Dr (44143-2544)
PHONE...................216 331-3050
Scott Bennett, *President*
EMP: 3 **EST:** 2015
SALES (est): 160.5K **Privately Held**
SIC: 3451 3489 Screw machine products; ordnance & accessories; artillery or artillery parts, over 30 mm.; guns or gun parts, over 30 mm.

(G-5512)
HIBBING TACONITE A JOINT VENTR (PA)
200 Public Sq Ste 3300 (44114-2315)
PHONE...................216 694-5700
Joseph A Carrabba, *CEO*
Laurie Brlas, *Exec VP*
Donald Gallagher, *Exec VP*
Edward M Latendresse,
Mittal S US,
▲ **EMP:** 1
SALES (est): 1.1B **Privately Held**
SIC: 1011 Iron ore mining; iron ore pelletizing; iron ore beneficiating

(G-5513)
HICKOK INCORPORATED (PA)
10514 Dupont Ave (44108-1348)
PHONE...................216 541-8060
Fax: 216 761-9879
Brian E Powers, *Ch of Bd*
Robert L Bauman, *President*
James F Allen, *VP Mfg*
George R Hart, *VP Engrg*
George Hart, *VP Engrg*
EMP: 83 **EST:** 1910
SQ FT: 37,000
SALES: 6.6MM **Publicly Held**
WEB: www.hickok-inc.com
SIC: 3823 3829 Industrial process measurement equipment; measuring & controlling devices; aircraft & motor vehicle measurement equipment

(G-5514)
HITTI ENTERPRISES INC
6427 Eastland Rd (44142-1305)
PHONE...................440 243-4100
Fred Hitti, *President*
EMP: 10
SQ FT: 40,000
SALES (est): 1.5MM **Privately Held**
SIC: 3086 6531 Packaging & shipping materials, foamed plastic; real estate agents & managers

(G-5515)
HK TECHNOLOGIES
2828 Clinton Ave (44113-2939)
PHONE...................330 337-9710
Micheal A Valore, *Principal*
EMP: 3
SALES (est): 193.4K **Privately Held**
SIC: 3999 Vibrators, electric: designed for barber & beauty shops

(G-5516)
HKM DRECT MKT CMMNICATIONS INC (PA)
Also Called: H K M
5501 Cass Ave (44102-2121)
PHONE...................216 651-9500
Fax: 216 961-6330
Rob Durham, *President*
Scott Durham, *COO*
Robert Solevenec, *Vice Pres*
Patricia Stealey, *Manager*
EMP: 135 **EST:** 1922
SQ FT: 86,000
SALES: 18MM **Privately Held**
WEB: www.hkmdirectmarket.com
SIC: 7331 2752 7375 2791 Direct mail advertising services; mailing service; mailing list management; commercial printing, lithographic; information retrieval services; typesetting; commercial printing

(G-5517)
HKM DRECT MKT CMMNICATIONS INC
5501 Cass Ave (44102-2121)
PHONE...................330 395-9538
James Jastatt, *Branch Mgr*

EMP: 20
SALES (corp-wide): 18MM **Privately Held**
WEB: www.hkmdirectmarket.com
SIC: 2759 Commercial printing
PA: Hkm Direct Market Communications, Inc.
5501 Cass Ave
Cleveland OH 44102
216 651-9500

(G-5518)
HMF ENGINEERING INC
Also Called: Hmf Racing
5111 W 164th St (44142-1505)
PHONE.............................216 631-6980
Fax: 216 631-6981
Hans Lluenger, *President*
Ray Bielo, *Financial Exec*
Jose Torres, *Financial Exec*
Brian Lambright, *Sales Staff*
Micheal Stickvitch, *Shareholder*
EMP: 4
SALES (est): 714.2K **Privately Held**
WEB: www.hmfengineering.com
SIC: 3714 Exhaust systems & parts, motor vehicle

(G-5519)
HOME CITY ICE COMPANY
10000 Broadway Ave (44125-1637)
PHONE.............................216 429-0535
Craig Thompson, *Manager*
EMP: 25
SALES (corp-wide): 305.4MM **Privately Held**
WEB: www.homecityice.com
SIC: 2097 Ice cubes
PA: The Home City Ice Company
6045 Bridgetown Rd Ste 1
Cincinnati OH 45248
513 574-1800

(G-5520)
HOME RESOLVER
11121 Magdala Dr (44130-1547)
PHONE.............................440 886-6758
Kevin Sheridan, *Principal*
EMP: 4
SALES (est): 338.9K **Privately Held**
SIC: 3621 Resolvers

(G-5521)
HOME STOR & OFF SOLUTIONS INC
Also Called: Closet Factory, The
5305 Commerce Pkwy W (44130-1274)
PHONE.............................216 362-4660
Fax: 216 362-4664
Kathy Pietrick, *President*
Robert J Pietrick Jr, *Vice Pres*
EMP: 16
SQ FT: 5,000
SALES (est): 3.1MM **Privately Held**
SIC: 5211 5712 2541 Closets, interiors & accessories; furniture stores; wood partitions & fixtures

(G-5522)
HOMELAND AG FUELS LLC
25700 Science Park Dr # 210 (44122-7319)
PHONE.............................216 763-1004
Anthony Senagore, *CEO*
J Kieran Jennings, *COO*
EMP: 3
SALES: 1,000K **Privately Held**
SIC: 2869 Industrial organic chemicals

(G-5523)
HONEYWELL INTERNATIONAL INC
6060 Rockside Woods Blvd (44131-7303)
PHONE.............................216 682-1600
EMP: 3
SALES (corp-wide): 39.3B **Publicly Held**
SIC: 3724 Aircraft engines & engine parts
PA: Honeywell International Inc.
115 Tabor Rd
Morris Plains NJ 07950
973 455-2000

(G-5524)
HORIZONS INC CAMCODE DIVISION
18531 S Miles Rd (44128-4237)
PHONE.............................216 714-0020
Melissa Van De Motter, *Managing Dir*
Nicole Pontius, *Principal*
Dan Fitzwater, *Prdtn Mgr*
Melissa Motter, *Sales Engr*
Joe Brunemann, *Sales Staff*
EMP: 20
SQ FT: 20,000
SALES (est): 1.6MM
SALES (corp-wide): 30.2MM **Privately Held**
SIC: 3861 Photographic equipment & supplies
PA: Horizons Incorporated
18531 S Miles Rd
Cleveland OH 44128
216 475-0555

(G-5525)
HORIZONS INCORPORATED (PA)
Also Called: Panam Imaging Systems
18531 S Miles Rd (44128-4237)
PHONE.............................216 475-0555
Fax: 216 587-0358
Herbert A Wainer, *President*
Dan Peck, *General Mgr*
David Kesic, *Business Mgr*
Robert Miller, *Vice Pres*
Micheal Rish, *Vice Pres*
▲ **EMP:** 115 **EST:** 1967
SQ FT: 51,000
SALES (est): 30.2MM **Privately Held**
WEB: www.horizonsisg.com
SIC: 3861 Plates, photographic (sensitized)

(G-5526)
HORSBURGH & SCOTT CO (PA)
5114 Hamilton Ave (44114-3985)
PHONE.............................216 432-5858
Fax: 216 432-5850
Lloyd G Trotter, *Ch of Bd*
Pradeep Saha, *President*
Chris Horsburg, *Vice Pres*
Ken Lonsberry, *Vice Pres*
Jadran Golem, *Buyer*
▲ **EMP:** 180
SQ FT: 240,000
SALES (est): 73.6MM **Privately Held**
WEB: www.horsburgh-scott.com
SIC: 3566 Gears, power transmission, except automotive; speed changers (power transmission equipment), except auto

(G-5527)
HORSBURGH & SCOTT CO
1441 Chardon Rd (44117-1510)
PHONE.............................216 383-2909
Vincent Iosue, *Design Engr*
Felix Tarorick, *Branch Mgr*
EMP: 9
SALES (corp-wide): 73.6MM **Privately Held**
SIC: 3566 Gears, power transmission, except automotive; speed changers (power transmission equipment), except auto
PA: The Horsburgh & Scott Co
5114 Hamilton Ave
Cleveland OH 44114
216 432-5858

(G-5528)
HOTCARDSCOM INC (PA)
2400 Superior Ave E (44114-4236)
PHONE.............................216 241-4040
John Gadd, *CEO*
Columbus Woodruff, *President*
Karl Singleton, *COO*
Nora Lane, *Mktg Dir*
Dennis Jones, *Manager*
EMP: 34
SQ FT: 15,000
SALES (est): 7.5MM **Privately Held**
WEB: www.hotcards.com
SIC: 7336 2754 Commercial art & graphic design; color printing, gravure

(G-5529)
HOUSE OF DELARA FRAGRANCES
1810 W 47th St (44102-3412)
PHONE.............................216 651-5803
Fay M Harris, *Owner*
EMP: 3 **EST:** 1987
SALES (est): 184.7K **Privately Held**
SIC: 2844 Cosmetic preparations

(G-5530)
HP MANUFACTURING COMPANY INC (PA)
Also Called: House of Plastics
3705 Carnegie Ave (44115-2750)
PHONE.............................216 361-6500
Fax: 216 361-6508
John R Melchiorre, *President*
Elmer Krizek, *Principal*
Paul Glozer, *Opers Staff*
Denny Chamberlin, *Accounts Mgr*
Cathy Lamb, *Accounts Mgr*
EMP: 63
SQ FT: 110,000
SALES (est): 10.2MM **Privately Held**
WEB: www.hpmanufacturing.com
SIC: 3089 5162 3993 3082 Plastic processing; plastics sheets & rods; signs & advertising specialties; unsupported plastics profile shapes; partitions & fixtures, except wood

(G-5531)
HPL STAMPINGS INC
4949 Galaxy Pkwy Ste W (44128-5959)
PHONE.............................440 582-9794
Ron Locktish, *Opers Mgr*
Mary Romano, *Manager*
EMP: 6
SALES (corp-wide): 5.5MM **Privately Held**
WEB: www.hplstampings.com
SIC: 3469 Stamping metal for the trade
PA: Hpl Stampings, Inc.
425 Enterprise Pkwy
Lake Zurich IL 60047
847 540-1400

(G-5532)
HPM BUSINESS SYSTEMS INC
21887 Lorain Rd 300 (44126-3330)
PHONE.............................216 520-1330
Harry P Miller, *President*
Kevin Skelly, *General Mgr*
EMP: 5
SQ FT: 1,500
SALES (est): 546.8K **Privately Held**
WEB: www.hpmweb.com
SIC: 7389 3993 Advertising, promotional & trade show services; balloons, novelty & toy; child restraint seat, automotive; rental; signs & advertising specialties; advertising novelties

(G-5533)
HUBBELL MACHINE TOOLING INC
7507 Exchange St (44125-3305)
PHONE.............................216 524-1797
Claude Petek, *CEO*
EMP: 12
SQ FT: 16,000
SALES (est): 1MM **Privately Held**
SIC: 3599 Machine shop, jobbing & repair

(G-5534)
HUDECEK CEMENT INC
6678 Big Creek Pkwy (44130-2817)
PHONE.............................216 676-0362
Carol Hudecek, *President*
Charlotte Hudecek, *Admin Sec*
EMP: 9
SALES: 750K **Privately Held**
WEB: www.hudecekcement.com
SIC: 3241 Natural cement

(G-5535)
HUDSON SUPPLY COMPANY INC
4500 Lee Rd Ste 120 (44128-2959)
PHONE.............................216 518-3000
Richard Kopittke, *President*
Neil Wine, *Sales Staff*
▲ **EMP:** 6

SALES (est): 964.6K **Privately Held**
SIC: 3545 Machine tool accessories

(G-5536)
HUGO BOSS USA INC
4600 Piderman Rd (44144)
PHONE.............................216 671-8100
Fax: 216 251-0880
Carol Burrus, *Engng Exec*
Oscar Castillo, *Office Mgr*
Bill Scott, *Manager*
EMP: 400
SALES (corp-wide): 2.8B **Privately Held**
WEB: www.hugobossusa.com
SIC: 2311 Suits, men's & boys': made from purchased materials; tailored dress & sport coats: men's & boys'; topcoats, men's & boys': made from purchased materials
HQ: Hugo Boss Usa, Inc.
55 Water St Fl 48
New York NY 10041
212 940-0600

(G-5537)
HUMPHREY COMPANY (PA)
Also Called: Euclid Beach Popcorn
20810 Miles Pkwy (44128-5508)
PHONE.............................216 662-6629
Fax: 216 662-6619
Dudley Humphrey, *President*
Elizabeth Humphrey, *Vice Pres*
Jeff Widmar, *Opers Staff*
EMP: 10
SQ FT: 11,000
SALES (est): 1.1MM **Privately Held**
SIC: 0191 2064 General farms, primarily crop; popcorn balls or other treated popcorn products

(G-5538)
HURST AUTO-TRUCK ELECTRIC
Also Called: Tuff Stuff Performance
9004 Madison Ave (44102-2715)
PHONE.............................216 961-1800
Fax: 216 961-1868
Frank Hurst, *President*
Thomas Hurst, *President*
▲ **EMP:** 4
SALES (est): 1MM **Privately Held**
WEB: www.tuffstuffperformance.com
SIC: 7539 3714 3694 3625 Automotive repair shops; alternators & generators, rebuilding & repair; motor vehicle parts & accessories; engine electrical equipment; relays & industrial controls; motors & generators; pumps & pumping equipment

(G-5539)
HUSQVARNA US HOLDING INC (HQ)
20445 Emerald Pkwy (44135-6009)
PHONE.............................216 898-1800
Richard Pietch, *Senior VP*
Ronald Zajaczkowski, *Senior VP*
George Weigand, *CFO*
Marie-Louise Wingard, *Treasurer*
▲ **EMP:** 70
SQ FT: 18,000
SALES (est): 161.8MM
SALES (corp-wide): 4.1B **Privately Held**
SIC: 3582 Dryers, laundry: commercial, including coin-operated
PA: Husqvarna Ab
Drottninggatan 2
Huskvarna 561 3
361 465-00

(G-5540)
HUTCHINSON-STEVENS INC
Also Called: Bradshaw Manufacturing
9627 Clinton Rd (44144-1029)
PHONE.............................216 281-8585
Andrew Milgram, *President*
Cara Cuddy, *Vice Pres*
EMP: 5
SQ FT: 600
SALES (est): 678.7K **Privately Held**
SIC: 3423 Soldering guns or tools, hand: electric

(G-5541)
HY-GRADE CORPORATION (PA)
3993 E 93rd St (44105-4052)
PHONE.............................216 341-7711
Fax: 216 341-8514

Michael Pemberton, *President*
Kim Gabele, *Purch Mgr*
EMP: 35
SQ FT: 25,000
SALES (est): 9.1MM **Privately Held**
WEB: www.upm.com
SIC: 5032 2952 2951 Asphalt mixture; asphalt felts & coatings; asphalt paving mixtures & blocks

(G-5542)
HYCOMP LLC
17960 Englewood Dr Ste A (44130-8496)
PHONE.................................440 234-2002
Fax: 440 234-4911
Ken Schiefer, *Area Mgr*
Andrew Boisvert, *COO*
Bill Hanna, *Mfg Mgr*
Todd Devorace, *Controller*
Brooke Hart, *Finance Mgr*
EMP: 94
SQ FT: 48,600
SALES (est): 23.6MM **Privately Held**
WEB: www.hycompinc.com
SIC: 3089 Injection molding of plastics
HQ: Sms Usa Llc
100 Sandusky St
Pittsburgh PA 15212
412 231-1200

(G-5543)
HYDROGEN 411 TECHNOLOGY LLC
7777 W 130th St (44130-7161)
PHONE.................................440 941-6760
Dan Greenberg, *Engineer*
Arnold Rusch,
EMP: 5 **EST:** 2012
SALES (est): 455.5K **Privately Held**
SIC: 3674 Fuel cells, solid state

(G-5544)
HYSTER-YALE MATERIALS HDLG INC (PA)
5875 Landerbrook Dr # 300 (44124-6511)
PHONE.................................440 449-9600
Alfred M Rankin Jr, *Ch of Bd*
Charles A Bittenbender, *Senior VP*
Rajiv K Prasad, *Senior VP*
Anthony Salgado, *Senior VP*
Stephen Karas, *Vice Pres*
EMP: 120
SALES: 2.5B **Publicly Held**
SIC: 3537 Lift trucks, industrial: fork, platform, straddle, etc.

(G-5545)
I C CONSULTANTS INC
Also Called: Icci
23564 Saint Clair Ave (44117-2513)
P.O. Box 17423 (44117-0423)
PHONE.................................216 731-9992
Walter Fasser, *President*
EMP: 10
SQ FT: 1,000
SALES (est): 1.3MM **Privately Held**
SIC: 5084 8742 3549 Industrial machinery & equipment; industrial consultant; metalworking machinery

(G-5546)
I L R INC
5240 Greenhurst Ext (44137-1128)
P.O. Box 31336 (44131-0336)
PHONE.................................216 587-2212
Fax: 216 587-1813
Robert E Gazdak, *President*
Lisa Joy Kemenyes, *Treasurer*
EMP: 5 **EST:** 1977
SQ FT: 4,000
SALES (est): 886.4K **Privately Held**
SIC: 3443 Fabricated plate work (boiler shop)

(G-5547)
I P SPECRETE INC
10703 Quebec Ave (44106-4251)
PHONE.................................216 721-2050
Fax: 216 421-0032
John Anderson, *President*
Morris Grassi, *Sales Staff*
▲ **EMP:** 5
SQ FT: 30,000

SALES (est): 990K **Privately Held**
WEB: www.specrete.com
SIC: 2899 Chemical preparations; concrete curing & hardening compounds

(G-5548)
IDENTITY HOLDING COMPANY LLC
4944 Commerce Pkwy (44128-5908)
PHONE.................................216 514-1277
EMP: 106
SALES (corp-wide): 135.1MM **Privately Held**
SIC: 3953 Marking devices
PA: Identity Holding Company, Llc
1480 Gould Dr
Cookeville TN 38506
931 432-4000

(G-5549)
IHOD USA LLC
127 Public Sq Ste 4120 (44114-1312)
PHONE.................................216 459-7179
Mark Collins,
Chris Baker,
EMP: 2
SQ FT: 2,500
SALES: 5MM **Privately Held**
SIC: 2813 Hydrogen
PA: Ihod Limited
Suite 29 Forum House
Chichester W SUSSEX

(G-5550)
IMAGE CONCEPTS INC
Also Called: AlphaGraphics Valley View
8200 Sweet Valley Dr # 107 (44125-4267)
PHONE.................................216 524-9000
Fax: 216 524-9004
Karey Zorv, *President*
Patrick Delahunty, *Vice Pres*
EMP: 10
SQ FT: 4,000
SALES (est): 1MM **Privately Held**
WEB: www.imageconceptsprint.com
SIC: 2752 Commercial printing, lithographic; business form & card printing, lithographic

(G-5551)
IMAGEIQ INC
26801 Miles Rd Ste 103 (44128-5977)
PHONE.................................855 462-4347
Timothy Kulbago, *CEO*
Zachary Kaufman, *Sales Staff*
Andrea Peters, *Office Mgr*
Britt Becknell, *Business Dir*
EMP: 10
SQ FT: 1,150
SALES (est): 1.8MM **Privately Held**
SIC: 3845 CAT scanner (Computerized Axial Tomography) apparatus

(G-5552)
IMAGEMART INC
17320 Saint Clair Ave (44110-2537)
PHONE.................................216 486-4767
Joseph Bruzas, *President*
EMP: 3
SALES (est): 325.8K **Privately Held**
SIC: 2759 Commercial printing

(G-5553)
IMALUX CORPORATION
11000 Cedar Ave Ste 250 (44106-3056)
PHONE.................................216 502-0755
Michael Burke, *President*
Bill R Sanford, *Chairman*
Paul G Amazeen, *Exec VP*
Thomas F Barnish, *CFO*
Nancy J Tresser, *Chief Mktg Ofcr*
EMP: 10
SQ FT: 1,000
SALES (est): 1.6MM **Privately Held**
WEB: www.imalux.com
SIC: 3845 Electromedical apparatus

(G-5554)
IMPACT ARMOR TECHNOLOGIES LLC
17000 Saint Clair Ave (44110-2535)
PHONE.................................216 706-2024
Dan T Moore,
Randi Deluga,
EMP: 10

SALES (est): 918K **Privately Held**
SIC: 3297 Nonclay refractories

(G-5555)
IMPERIAL COUNTERTOPS
10646 Leuer Ave (44108-1352)
P.O. Box 656, Eustis FL (32727-0656)
PHONE.................................216 851-0888
Joseph Frakes, *President*
Nancy Frakes, *Office Mgr*
EMP: 15 **EST:** 1989
SQ FT: 12,000
SALES (est): 1.6MM **Privately Held**
SIC: 5211 2541 1799 Counter tops; counter & sink tops; counter top installation

(G-5556)
IMPERIAL METAL SOLUTIONS LLC
2284 Scranton Rd (44113-4310)
PHONE.................................216 781-4094
Fax: 216 781-4166
Paul Libby, *Sales Executive*
EMP: 18
SQ FT: 23,000
SALES (est): 1.8MM **Privately Held**
SIC: 3479 Coating or wrapping steel pipe

(G-5557)
IMPERIAL METAL SPINNING CO
7600 Exchange St (44125-3308)
PHONE.................................216 524-5020
Fax: 216 524-5021
Christopher Bindel, *President*
Timothy Bindel, *Vice Pres*
EMP: 8 **EST:** 1954
SQ FT: 7,000
SALES (est): 1.5MM **Privately Held**
SIC: 3469 Spinning metal for the trade

(G-5558)
IMPRESSIONS - A PRINT SHOP
370 Alpha Park (44143-2221)
PHONE.................................440 449-6966
Fax: 440 449-6960
Mike Myers, *President*
Brenda Myers, *Admin Sec*
EMP: 3
SQ FT: 1,800
SALES (est): 180K **Privately Held**
SIC: 2759 Commercial printing

(G-5559)
IN-TOUCH CORP
Also Called: Proforma Joe Thomas Group
13500 Pearl Rd Ste 139 (44136-3428)
PHONE.................................440 268-0881
Joseph Thomas, *President*
◆ **EMP:** 3
SQ FT: 1,100
SALES (est): 315.4K **Privately Held**
SIC: 2752 5199 Commercial printing, offset; advertising specialties; packaging materials

(G-5560)
INCORPORATED TRST GSPL WK SCTY
Also Called: Union Gospel Press Division
2000 Brookpark Rd (44109-5812)
P.O. Box 6059 (44101-1059)
PHONE.................................216 749-2100
Fax: 216 749-2205
Beryl C Bidlen, *President*
Robert Andrews, *Corp Secy*
Rev Lanny C Akers, *Vice Pres*
Vera Mc Kinney, *Asst Treas*
Jonathan Hunsick, *Personnel*
EMP: 90 **EST:** 1902
SQ FT: 60,000
SALES (est): 12.6MM **Privately Held**
WEB: www.uniongospelpress.com
SIC: 2721 5942 5999 8661 Periodicals: publishing & printing; books, religious; religious goods; non-church religious organizations

(G-5561)
INCORPORATED TRUSTEES GOSPEL W
1980 Brookpark Rd (44109-5810)
P.O. Box 6059 (44101-1059)
PHONE.................................216 749-1428
Beryl Bidlen, *President*

EMP: 65
SALES (est): 5.4MM **Privately Held**
SIC: 3555 2741 Printing presses; miscellaneous publishing

(G-5562)
INDEPENDENT DIE & MFG CO
5161 W 161st St (44142-1604)
PHONE.................................216 362-6778
John Quallich, *President*
Douglas Quallich, *Treasurer*
EMP: 5
SQ FT: 2,500
SALES (est): 595.9K **Privately Held**
SIC: 3545 Cutting tools for machine tools

(G-5563)
INDEPENDENT STAMPING INC
12025 Zelis Rd (44135-4699)
PHONE.................................216 251-3500
Fax: 216 251-6868
William Nester, *President*
EMP: 25
SQ FT: 11,000
SALES (est): 4.3MM **Privately Held**
SIC: 3469 3544 Stamping metal for the trade; special dies & tools

(G-5564)
INDUSTRIAL MACHINE TOOL SVC
3560 Ridge Rd (44102-5444)
PHONE.................................216 651-1122
Fax: 216 651-2123
Ron Badovick, *President*
Roberta Badovick, *Vice Pres*
Jonathan Williamson, *Opers Mgr*
EMP: 5
SQ FT: 40,000
SALES (est): 1MM **Privately Held**
WEB: www.industrialmachinetool.com
SIC: 5084 3542 Industrial machinery & equipment; rebuilt machine tools, metal forming types

(G-5565)
INDUSTRIAL MASUREMENT CTRL INC
9901 Beechwood Dr (44133-1317)
PHONE.................................440 877-1140
Guy Baetjer, *President*
Carolyn Baetjer, *Office Mgr*
EMP: 7
SALES (est): 920.8K **Privately Held**
SIC: 3829 Measuring & controlling devices

(G-5566)
INDUSTRIAL METAL PRODUCTS
9921 York Alpha Dr (44133-3509)
PHONE.................................440 237-3506
Fax: 440 230-4102
Wayne Schreiber, *President*
Bill Hilf, *Vice Pres*
Raymond G Schreiber, *Shareholder*
EMP: 4
SQ FT: 9,400
SALES (est): 557.4K **Privately Held**
SIC: 3599 Machine shop, jobbing & repair

(G-5567)
INDUSTRIAL PACKAGING PRODUCTS
22259 Spencer Ln (44126-2523)
P.O. Box 26332 (44126-0332)
PHONE.................................440 734-2663
Charles Gantzler, *Owner*
EMP: 3
SALES (est): 256.9K **Privately Held**
SIC: 2011 Meat packing plants

(G-5568)
INFOACCESSNET LLC
8801 E Pleasant Valley Rd (44131-5510)
PHONE.................................216 328-0100
Daniel Andrew, *President*
Dan Rife, *VP Opers*
Ann McCauley, *Project Mgr*
Sierra Patterson, *Project Mgr*
Sue Rife, *Project Mgr*
EMP: 31
SQ FT: 25,000
SALES (est): 3.9MM **Privately Held**
WEB: www.infoaccess.net
SIC: 7372 Business oriented computer software

(G-5569)
INK TECHNOLOGY CORPORATION (PA)
18320 Lanken Ave (44119-3299)
PHONE..216 486-6720
Fax: 216 486-6003
Ian Walker, *President*
David Ringler, *President*
Ethel R Haff, *Principal*
Robert Jenson, *Principal*
Ernest Walker, *Principal*
◆ EMP: 20 EST: 1980
SQ FT: 20,000
SALES (est): 3MM Privately Held
WEB: www.inktechnology.com
SIC: 2893 Printing ink

(G-5570)
INNER CITY ABRASIVES LLC
7209 Saint Clair Ave 101b (44103-1769)
P.O. Box 603050 (44103-0050)
PHONE..216 391-4402
Yuri Abramovich,
EMP: 3
SALES: 250K Privately Held
WEB: www.icabrasives.com
SIC: 3291 Abrasive products

(G-5571)
INNOVATIONS IN PLASTIC INC
1643 Eddy Rd (44112-4207)
PHONE..216 541-6060
Fax: 216 851-0663
Charles Hazle, *President*
Mary Ann Hazle, *Corp Secy*
EMP: 7
SQ FT: 13,000
SALES (est): 782.9K Privately Held
SIC: 3089 Injection molded finished plastic products

(G-5572)
INNOVATIVE MEDICAL EQP LLC
29001 Cedar Rd Ste 325 (44124-6501)
PHONE..440 646-1286
Glen Guyuron, *Sls & Mktg Exec*
Brad Pulver, *Mng Member*
▲ EMP: 8
SQ FT: 1,000
SALES (est): 1.3MM Privately Held
SIC: 3841 Medical instruments & equipment, blood & bone work

(G-5573)
INSTA-PRINT INC
3101 Brookpark Rd (44134-1314)
PHONE..216 741-6500
Fax: 216 741-1181
Vincent Calo, *President*
Vincent J Calo Jr, *President*
Karen M Calo, *Vice Pres*
Dawn Calo, *Manager*
EMP: 5
SQ FT: 6,700
SALES (est): 653.8K Privately Held
SIC: 2752 Commercial printing, lithographic

(G-5574)
INTEGRAL DESIGN INC
7670 Hub Pkwy (44125-5707)
P.O. Box 25553 (44125-0553)
PHONE..216 524-0555
Fax: 216 524-9089
Robert S Liptak, *President*
Richard M Liptak, *Corp Secy*
EMP: 16
SQ FT: 8,000
SALES (est): 1.1MM Privately Held
WEB: www.integraldesigninc.com
SIC: 3089 3993 2542 2511 Thermoformed finished plastic products; signs & advertising specialties; partitions & fixtures, except wood; wood household furniture

(G-5575)
INTEGRATED POWER SERVICES LLC
Also Called: Monarch
5325 W 130th St (44130-1034)
PHONE..216 433-7808
EMP: 27
SALES (corp-wide): 1.7B Privately Held
SIC: 7694 Armature rewinding shops

HQ: Integrated Power Services Llc
3 Independence Pt Ste 100
Greenville SC 29615
864 451-5600

(G-5576)
INTER CAB CORPORATION
8551 Brookpark Rd (44129-6805)
PHONE..216 351-0770
Fax: 216 351-1455
Jamie Nagel, *President*
Stacey Rannigan, *Corp Secy*
EMP: 5
SQ FT: 12,000
SALES (est): 635.5K Privately Held
SIC: 2434 2431 Wood kitchen cabinets; millwork

(G-5577)
INTERFAST INC
4444 Lee Rd (44128-2902)
PHONE..216 581-3000
EMP: 4
SALES (corp-wide): 1.4B Publicly Held
SIC: 3965 Fasteners
HQ: Interfast Inc
2800 Matheson Blvd E
Mississauga ON L4W 4
416 674-0770

(G-5578)
INTERIOR PRODUCTS CO INC
3615 Superior Ave E 3104f (44114-4138)
PHONE..216 641-1919
Fax: 216 641-0013
Joseph J Frisse, *President*
EMP: 12
SQ FT: 14,000
SALES (est): 1.8MM Privately Held
SIC: 2521 Cabinets, office: wood

(G-5579)
INTERNATIONAL ADVG CONCEPTS
4285 W 217th St (44126-1839)
PHONE..440 331-4733
Jerome Leslie, *Owner*
EMP: 3 EST: 1980
SALES (est): 240K Privately Held
WEB: www.iaauae.org
SIC: 7311 8742 2759 Advertising agencies; marketing consulting services; commercial printing

(G-5580)
INTERNATIONAL CONT SYSTEMS LLC
Also Called: Elsons International
16601 Saint Clair Ave (44110-2951)
PHONE..216 481-8219
Earl Williams, *Vice Pres*
Wynette Bryant, *Controller*
Steven J Williams,
EMP: 15
SALES (est): 4.2MM Privately Held
SIC: 2631 Container, packaging & boxboard

(G-5581)
INTERSOFT GROUP INC
26380 Curtiss Wright Pkwy # 303 (44143-1442)
PHONE..216 765-7351
Fax: 216 381-4871
Louis Muttillo, *President*
Ursula Muttillo, *Vice Pres*
Angela Iacofano, *Project Mgr*
Joseph Muttillo, *Manager*
EMP: 10
SALES (est): 1.2MM Privately Held
SIC: 7372 Prepackaged software

(G-5582)
INTERSTATE DIESEL SERVICE INC (PA)
Also Called: Interstate-Mcbee
5300 Lakeside Ave E (44114-3916)
PHONE..216 881-0015
Fax: 216 881-0805
Alfred J Buescher, *CEO*
Ann Buescher, *President*
Brad Buescher, *COO*
▲ EMP: 125 EST: 1947
SQ FT: 70,000

SALES (est): 75.6MM Privately Held
WEB: www.interstate-mcbee.com
SIC: 5013 3714 Automotive engines & engine parts; fuel systems & parts, motor vehicle; fuel pumps, motor vehicle

(G-5583)
INTERSTATE TOOL CORPORATION
4538 W 130th St (44135-3574)
PHONE..216 671-1077
Fax: 216 671-5431
Warren Thompson, *President*
Kevin Lavelle, *Manager*
Joseph Szabo, *Manager*
EMP: 20 EST: 1962
SQ FT: 22,000
SALES (est): 5.8MM Privately Held
SIC: 5084 3545 3541 Industrial machinery & equipment; cutting tools for machine tools; machine tools, metal cutting type

(G-5584)
INTERSTATE-MCBEE LLC (PA)
5300 Lakeside Ave E (44114-3916)
PHONE..800 321-4234
Fax: 216 706-5010
Alfred J Buescher, *President*
Vic Coppola, *President*
Anne Buesther,
◆ EMP: 5
SQ FT: 25,000
SALES (est): 1.6MM Privately Held
SIC: 5999 3714 5084 Engine & motor equipment & supplies; motor vehicle engines & parts; engines & parts, diesel

(G-5585)
INX INTERNATIONAL INK CO
18001 Englewood Dr Unit P (44130-3422)
PHONE..440 239-1766
Fax: 440 239-1769
Donna Cronin, *General Mgr*
Joe Cichon, *Vice Pres*
Kyle Hurrle, *Manager*
EMP: 12
SALES (corp-wide): 1.3B Privately Held
SIC: 2893 Printing ink
HQ: Inx International Ink Co
150 N Martingale Rd # 700
Schaumburg IL 60173
630 382-1800

(G-5586)
IONBOND LLC
24270 Highpoint Rd (44122-6005)
PHONE..216 831-0880
Alan Whittaker, *Opers Mgr*
Heidi Froelich, *Branch Mgr*
EMP: 15
SALES (corp-wide): 13.1B Privately Held
SIC: 3479 Coating of metals & formed products
HQ: Ionbond Llc
1823 E Whitcomb Ave
Madison Heights MI 48071

(G-5587)
IROCK CRUSHERS LLC
5531 Canal Rd (44125-4874)
PHONE..866 240-0201
Robert Nelson, *General Mgr*
Nancy Frognowski, *Principal*
Kenneth E Taylor, *Principal*
Sean Donaghy, *Sales Executive*
John Reynolds,
▲ EMP: 5
SALES (est): 2MM Privately Held
WEB: www.irockcrushers.com
SIC: 3532 Rock crushing machinery, stationary

(G-5588)
IRVIN OSLIN INC
Also Called: Abbot Bindery
2800 E 55th St Frnt (44104-2861)
PHONE..216 361-7555
Fax: 216 361-1354
Jeff Oslin, *President*
Thomas Esper, *Vice Pres*
Darla Oslin, *Vice Pres*
EMP: 7 EST: 1953
SQ FT: 10,000

SALES (est): 590K Privately Held
WEB: www.abbotbindery.com
SIC: 2789 Binding only: books, pamphlets, magazines, etc.

(G-5589)
IRWIN ENGRAVING & PRINTING CO
5318 Saint Clair Ave # 1 (44103-1355)
PHONE..216 391-7300
Fax: 216 391-7302
Milan L Nass, *President*
Daniel Nass, *Plant Mgr*
David Nass, *VP Sales*
Martha Ness, *Admin Sec*
EMP: 9 EST: 1922
SQ FT: 16,000
SALES (est): 1MM Privately Held
SIC: 2759 2752 Engraving; commercial printing, offset

(G-5590)
ITL CALIFORNIA LLC
23925 Commerce Park (44122-5821)
PHONE..216 831-4734
Peter Tucker, *Principal*
▼ EMP: 11
SALES (est): 1.8MM Privately Held
SIC: 2411 Timber, cut at logging camp

(G-5591)
ITL CORP (DH)
Also Called: Industrial Timber & Lumber Co
23925 Commerce Park (44122-5821)
PHONE..216 831-3140
Fax: 216 831-3140
Larry Evans, *President*
Chris Whelan, *Design Engr*
▼ EMP: 30 EST: 1957
SQ FT: 10,000
SALES (est): 82.3MM Privately Held
WEB: www.itlcorp.com
SIC: 2421 2426 Kiln drying of lumber; custom sawmill; hardwood dimension & flooring mills

(G-5592)
IVAC TECHNOLOGIES CORP
Also Called: Ion Vacuum Technologies
18678 Cranwood Pkwy (44128-4036)
PHONE..216 662-4987
Fax: 216 932-6470
Bela Fischer, *President*
George Fischer, *Treasurer*
EMP: 12
SQ FT: 4,000
SALES (est): 1.4MM Privately Held
SIC: 3479 8731 Coating of metals & formed products; commercial physical research

(G-5593)
J & C INDUSTRIES INC
4808 W 130th St (44135-5138)
PHONE..216 362-8867
Fax: 216 362-8869
Bruce Jasen, *President*
Craig A Jones, *Vice Pres*
Craig Jones, *Vice Pres*
Dave Andrako, *Sales Staff*
EMP: 11
SQ FT: 16,000
SALES (est): 1.5MM Privately Held
SIC: 3599 Machine shop, jobbing & repair

(G-5594)
J AND L JEWELRY MANUFACTURING
Also Called: Bookman & Son Fine Jewelry
8803 Brecksville Rd # 6 (44141-1932)
PHONE..440 546-9988
Fax: 440 546-9930
Jeff Bookman, *President*
EMP: 7
SALES (est): 1MM Privately Held
SIC: 3911 Jewelry, precious metal

(G-5595)
J AND S TOOL INCORPORATED
15330 Brookpark Rd (44135-3332)
PHONE..216 676-8330
Fax: 216 676-8383
Vernon Justice, *President*
Donald Justice, *Vice Pres*
Carol Winchester, *Manager*
EMP: 36

▲ = Import ▼=Export
◆ =Import/Export

SQ FT: 10,000
SALES: 2MM Privately Held
SIC: 3542 5084 3544 3541 Machine tools, metal forming type; machine tools & accessories; special dies, tools, jigs & fixtures; machine tools, metal cutting type; saw blades & handsaws; hand & edge tools

(G-5596)
J B M MACHINE CO INC
Also Called: Custom Brackets
32 Alpha Park (44143-2208)
PHONE..............................440 446-0819
Fax: 440 473-1885
Michael Muzila, *President*
Patricia Muzila, *Vice Pres*
EMP: 3
SALES (est): 445.1K Privately Held
SIC: 3599 Machine shop, jobbing & repair

(G-5597)
J B STAMPING INC
7413 Associate Ave (44144-1190)
PHONE..............................216 631-0013
Fax: 216 631-1327
James P Bailey, *President*
Richard B Ginley, *Principal*
Linda G Glover, *Principal*
George Gibson, *Vice Pres*
Mary Gayle, *Manager*
EMP: 35
SQ FT: 35,000
SALES (est): 7.4MM Privately Held
WEB: www.jbstamping.com
SIC: 3469 Metal stampings

(G-5598)
J P QUALITY PRINTING INC
12614 Larchmere Blvd (44120-1110)
PHONE..............................216 791-6303
Fax: 216 791-7111
John Pathko, *President*
EMP: 5
SALES (est): 660.5K Privately Held
SIC: 2752 2759 Commercial printing, offset; letterpress printing

(G-5599)
J P SUGGINS MOBILE WELDING
2020 Saint Clair Ave Ne (44114-2013)
PHONE..............................216 566-7131
Fax: 216 861-1607
Jeffrey Hulligan, *President*
EMP: 20
SQ FT: 3,600
SALES (est): 3.5MM Privately Held
SIC: 3441 7692 Fabricated structural metal; welding repair

(G-5600)
J R M CHEMICAL INC
4881 Neo Pkwy (44128-3101)
PHONE..............................216 475-8488
Fax: 216 475-6517
Dave Czehut, *Vice Pres*
Scott Wiesler, *Vice Pres*
▲ EMP: 12
SQ FT: 12,000
SALES (est): 3.5MM Privately Held
WEB: www.soilmoist.com
SIC: 2869 Industrial organic chemicals

(G-5601)
J SCHRADER CO
4603 Fenwick Ave (44102-4597)
PHONE..............................216 961-2890
Len Gagnon, *President*
Suzanne Hartford, *Vice Pres*
EMP: 13 EST: 1922
SQ FT: 34,000
SALES (est): 2.2MM Privately Held
SIC: 3469 3645 3646 Spinning metal for the trade; table lamps; wall lamps; commercial indusl & institutional electric lighting fixtures

(G-5602)
J W HARWOOD CO (PA)
18001 Roseland Rd (44112-1109)
PHONE..............................216 531-6230
Fax: 216 531-6231
Walter B Harwood, *President*
Madeleine Harwood, *Vice Pres*
Marilyn Harwood, *Admin Sec*
EMP: 12 EST: 1934

SQ FT: 12,000
SALES (est): 2.2MM Privately Held
SIC: 3544 Special dies & tools

(G-5603)
JAB SALES INC (PA)
39 Alpha Park (44143-2202)
PHONE..............................440 446-0606
Bruce Beeth, *President*
EMP: 3
SALES (est): 345.8K Privately Held
SIC: 3441 Fabricated structural metal

(G-5604)
JACKPOT FESTIVAL & GAMING
650a E 185th St (44119-1767)
PHONE..............................216 531-3500
Fax: 216 531-2228
John Copic Jr, *President*
EMP: 5
SALES (est): 604.8K Privately Held
WEB: www.jackpotgames.biz
SIC: 3944 5199 Games, toys & children's vehicles; carnival supplies

(G-5605)
JAKPRINTS INC
3133 Chester Ave (44114-4616)
PHONE..............................877 246-3132
Jacob Edwards, *President*
Bill Rupnik, *President*
Chad Szczepanski, *COO*
Dameon Guess, *Vice Pres*
Brad Fishbaugh, *Maintenance Dir*
EMP: 127
SQ FT: 32,000
SALES (est): 26.8MM Privately Held
WEB: www.jakprints.com
SIC: 2752 Commercial printing, lithographic

(G-5606)
JAMESTOWN CONT CLEVELAND INC
4500 Renaissance Pkwy (44128-5702)
PHONE..............................216 831-3700
Fax: 216 831-3709
Glen Jenowsky, *Ch of Bd*
Jim Reminder, *Plant Mgr*
Bruce Janowsky, *Treasurer*
Mike Ihde, *Accounts Mgr*
Larry Hudson, *Sales Executive*
EMP: 350
SQ FT: 100,000
SALES (est): 38MM
SALES (corp-wide): 140.3MM Privately Held
WEB: www.jamestowncontainer.com
SIC: 2653 Corrugated boxes, partitions, display items, sheets & pad
PA: Jamestown Container Corp
14 Deming Dr
Falconer NY 14733
716 665-4623

(G-5607)
JAMISON MANUFACTURING CO
9116 Akins Rd (44133-5698)
PHONE..............................440 237-8085
Fax: 440 237-6136
Jeffrey C Jamison, *President*
Diana L Marsh, *Vice Pres*
EMP: 4 EST: 1974
SQ FT: 4,000
SALES: 300K Privately Held
SIC: 3599 Machine shop, jobbing & repair

(G-5608)
JASMINE DISTRIBUTING LTD
12117 Berea Rd (44111-1600)
PHONE..............................216 251-9420
Fax: 216 251-9426
Fady Chamoun, *Owner*
▲ EMP: 20
SALES (est): 2MM Privately Held
SIC: 2051 Breads, rolls & buns; bakery: wholesale or wholesale/retail combined

(G-5609)
JBAR A/C INC
10221 Sweet Valley Dr (44125-4249)
PHONE..............................216 447-4294
Kevin R Keogh, *CEO*
Michael Pease, *President*
Kim Pease, *Corp Secy*
▲ EMP: 16

SQ FT: 21,000
SALES (est): 2.9MM Privately Held
WEB: www.jbar-ac.com
SIC: 3714 3585 Heaters, motor vehicle; air conditioning, motor vehicle

(G-5610)
JERGENS INC (PA)
Also Called: Tooling Components Division
15700 S Waterloo Rd (44110-3898)
PHONE..............................216 486-5540
Jack H Schron Jr, *President*
Avis Kanocz, *President*
Matt Schron, *General Mgr*
Tony Filipovic, *Opers Mgr*
Duane Frager, *Opers Mgr*
▲ EMP: 195 EST: 1942
SQ FT: 104,000
SALES (est): 79.8MM Privately Held
WEB: www.jergensinc.com
SIC: 3544 3443 3452 5084 Special dies, tools, jigs & fixtures; jigs & fixtures; fabricated plate work (boiler shop); bolts, nuts, rivets & washers; machine tools & accessories; drill bushings (drilling jig); precision measuring tools

(G-5611)
JEROLD OPTICAL INC
800 Huron Rd E (44115-1121)
PHONE..............................216 781-4279
Fax: 216 781-0554
Jerold Rabnick, *CEO*
Loren Rabnick, *President*
Lisa Rabnick, *Assistant VP*
Beverly Rabnick, *Admin Sec*
EMP: 5
SQ FT: 2,000
SALES (est): 450K Privately Held
WEB: www.jeroldoptical.com
SIC: 3851 5995 Ophthalmic goods; eyeglasses, prescription

(G-5612)
JES FOODS INC (PA)
4733 Broadway Ave (44127-1007)
PHONE..............................216 883-8987
Fax: 216 883-8984
Elaine R Freed, *President*
William Freed, *Exec VP*
Jerry Mc Donald, *Vice Pres*
Dennis Friedman, *VP Finance*
Susan Zann, *Human Res Mgr*
EMP: 25
SQ FT: 7,000
SALES (est): 5.3MM Privately Held
WEB: www.jesfoods.com
SIC: 2033 Vegetables & vegetable products in cans, jars, etc.

(G-5613)
JET DOCK SYSTEMS INC
9601 Corporate Cir (44125-4261)
PHONE..............................216 750-2264
Fax: 216 750-2273
David Faber, *President*
W A Eva III, *Vice Pres*
Beverly Frollo, *Info Tech Mgr*
Jeremy Clickner, *Director*
Byron Jacobs, *Director*
▼ EMP: 30
SQ FT: 30,000
SALES (est): 7.1MM Privately Held
WEB: www.jetdock.com
SIC: 3448 Docks: prefabricated metal

(G-5614)
JEWELS BY IMG INC
5470 Mayfield Rd (44124-2986)
PHONE..............................440 461-4464
Fax: 440 461-0087
Steven Greenberg, *President*
EMP: 12
SQ FT: 5,500
SALES (est): 800K Privately Held
SIC: 3911 7631 Jewelry, precious metal; diamond setter

(G-5615)
JIM DENIGRIS & SONS LDSCPG
1520 Longwood Dr (44124-3006)
PHONE..............................440 449-5548
Fax: 440 461-7435
Anthony Denigris, *President*
EMP: 4

SALES (est): 404.6K Privately Held
SIC: 3446 0782 Architectural metalwork; lawn & garden services

(G-5616)
JJ DELONG & ASSOCIATES INC
Also Called: Jj Delong & Associates
526 Superior Ave E # 633 (44114-1905)
PHONE..............................216 861-4727
Fax: 216 861-0710
John De Long, *President*
EMP: 8
SALES (est): 913.5K Privately Held
SIC: 7361 7692 4221 7629 Employment agencies; welding repair; farm product warehousing & storage; business machine repair, electric

(G-5617)
JOB ONE CONTROL SERVICES
6893 Lantern Ln (44130-4532)
PHONE..............................216 347-0133
Ann O'Brien, *President*
EMP: 3
SALES: 15K Privately Held
SIC: 3625 Relays & industrial controls

(G-5618)
JOHN KOLESAR AND SONS INC
Also Called: Printing Partner
13437 Detroit Ave (44107-4608)
PHONE..............................216 221-7117
Fax: 216 221-1060
James Kolesar, *President*
John E Kolesar Jr, *Vice Pres*
EMP: 4
SQ FT: 1,600
SALES (est): 479.8K Privately Held
SIC: 2752 Commercial printing, offset

(G-5619)
JOHN KRUSINSKI
Also Called: Krusinski's Meat Market
6300 Heisley Ave (44105-1226)
PHONE..............................216 441-0100
Fax: 216 441-0102
John Krusinski, *Owner*
Helen Krusinski, *Office Mgr*
EMP: 10 EST: 1952
SQ FT: 10,000
SALES (est): 1.2MM Privately Held
SIC: 5147 5421 2099 2013 Meats, fresh; meat markets, including freezer provisioners; food preparations; sausages & other prepared meats

(G-5620)
JOHN P ELLIS CLINIC PODIATRY
730 Som Center Rd Ste 350 (44143-2362)
PHONE..............................440 460-0444
John P Ellis, *Owner*
EMP: 4 EST: 2015
SALES (est): 288.7K Privately Held
SIC: 2835 8071 0783 In vitro & in vivo diagnostic substances; ultrasound laboratory; surgery services; ornamental bush

(G-5621)
JOHNSON CONTROLS INC
9797 Midwest Ave (44125-2498)
PHONE..............................216 587-0100
Fax: 216 587-2256
Todd Van Denbusche, *Principal*
EMP: 60 Privately Held
SIC: 2531 Seats, automobile
HQ: Johnson Controls, Inc.
5757 N Green Bay Ave
Milwaukee WI 53209
414 524-1200

(G-5622)
JORDON AUTO SERVICE & TIRE INC
5201 Carnegie Ave (44103-4357)
PHONE..............................216 214-6528
Jordan Kaminsky, *Owner*
EMP: 7
SALES (est): 528.7K Privately Held
SIC: 2653 7539 Pallets, corrugated: made from purchased materials; automotive repair shops

(G-5623)
JOSEPH T SNYDER INDUSTRIES
9210 Loren Ave (44105-2133)
PHONE..............................216 883-6900

Gregory Snyder, *President*
Robert Snyder, *Vice Pres*
EMP: 9
SQ FT: 12,000
SALES: 2.5MM **Privately Held**
SIC: 7389 2671 2653 Packaging & labeling services; packaging paper & plastics film, coated & laminated; corrugated & solid fiber boxes

(G-5624)
JOY GLOBAL UNDERGROUND MIN LLC
6160 Cochran Rd (44139-3306)
PHONE.................................440 248-7970
Dadia Lopatkovich, *Purchasing*
Loreen Rote, *Personnel*
Herb Kinnell, *Sales Staff*
Mark Sanders, *Branch Mgr*
EMP: 15
SALES (corp-wide): 15.9B **Privately Held**
SIC: 3535 Bucket type conveyor systems
HQ: Joy Global Underground Mining Llc
  40 Pennwood Pl Ste 100
  Warrendale PA 15086
  724 779-4500

(G-5625)
JRG PERFORMANCE TECHNOLOGIES
340 Balmoral Dr (44143-1759)
PHONE.................................216 408-5974
Raymond Glumm, *Principal*
EMP: 4
SALES: 65K **Privately Held**
SIC: 3599 7389 Machine shop, jobbing & repair; business services

(G-5626)
JUST NATURAL PROVISION COMPANY
4800 Crayton Ave (44104-2822)
PHONE.................................216 431-7922
Dennis Parker, *President*
Tim Pawul, *Plant Mgr*
EMP: 6
SALES (est): 810K **Privately Held**
SIC: 2015 5144 Poultry slaughtering & processing; poultry & poultry products

(G-5627)
K & E CHEMICAL CO INC
3960 E 93rd St (44105-4050)
PHONE.................................216 341-0500
Fax: 216 341-1651
Edgar Bleick Jr, *President*
Carl Bleick, *VP Opers*
Edward Kovachy, *Treasurer*
Don Bertsch, *Manager*
EMP: 10 **EST:** 1954
SQ FT: 11,000
SALES (est): 931.7K **Privately Held**
WEB: www.klenztone.com
SIC: 2869 Industrial organic chemicals

(G-5628)
K & G MACHINE CO
26981 Tungsten Rd (44132-2992)
PHONE.................................216 732-7115
Fax: 216 732-7119
Monte Curtis, *President*
Kathy Santill, *CFO*
Kathy Sentill, *Manager*
EMP: 23 **EST:** 1953
SQ FT: 24,000
SALES (est): 3.4MM **Privately Held**
WEB: www.kandgmachine.com
SIC: 3599 3743 Machine shop, jobbing & repair; railroad equipment

(G-5629)
K S MACHINE INC
3215 Superior Ave E (44114-4344)
PHONE.................................216 687-0459
Fax: 216 687-1178
Thomas Wallace, *President*
EMP: 15
SALES (est): 2MM **Privately Held**
WEB: www.ksmachineinc.com
SIC: 3599 Machine shop, jobbing & repair

(G-5630)
K-B PLATING INC
3685 E 78th St (44105-2048)
PHONE.................................216 341-1115

Fax: 216 341-1928
David Kopea, *President*
Thomas Thome, *Vice Pres*
Doris Kopea, *Treasurer*
Gordon Loux, *Admin Sec*
EMP: 10 **EST:** 1961
SQ FT: 21,000
SALES: 1.3MM **Privately Held**
SIC: 3471 Anodizing (plating) of metals or formed products

(G-5631)
KALEIDOSCOPE MAGAZINE LLC
1677 E 40th St (44103-2304)
PHONE.................................216 566-5500
Fax: 216 391-5054
Richard J Johnson, *CEO*
Sandra Shearer, *Editor*
EMP: 20
SALES (est): 1.6MM **Privately Held**
WEB: www.kaleidoscopemagazine.net
SIC: 2721 Periodicals

(G-5632)
KAMAN AUTOMATION INC
5350 Trnsp Blvd Ste 15 (44125)
PHONE.................................216 663-0072
Rene Conti, *Manager*
EMP: 5
SALES (corp-wide): 1.8B **Publicly Held**
WEB: www.minarikdrives.com
SIC: 7694 5063 Electric motor repair; motors, electric; motor controls, starters & relays: electric
HQ: Kaman Automation, Inc.
  1 Vision Way
  Bloomfield CT 06002
  860 687-5000

(G-5633)
KARYALL-TELDAY INC
8221 Clinton Rd (44144-1008)
PHONE.................................216 281-4063
Fax: 216 281-5428
James Mindek, *President*
EMP: 20 **EST:** 1947
SQ FT: 43,000
SALES (est): 2.9MM **Privately Held**
SIC: 2851 3499 Paints & paint additives; boxes for packing & shipping, metal

(G-5634)
KASE EQUIPMENT
7400 Hub Pkwy (44125-5735)
PHONE.................................216 642-9040
Fax: 216 986-0678
Edward Hawkins, *Ch of Bd*
Partick Hawkins, *President*
Dave Hodgson, *Vice Pres*
Ed Krane, *Purch Mgr*
Gladish Gerald, *Purchasing*
▲ **EMP:** 100
SQ FT: 68,360
SALES (est): 20.4MM **Privately Held**
WEB: www.kaseequip.com
SIC: 3555 Printing trades machinery

(G-5635)
KATHY SIMECEK
Also Called: Celebrations Monogramming
9119 Running Brook Dr (44130-8231)
PHONE.................................440 886-2468
Kathy Simecek, *Owner*
Kathy Simecek, *Owner*
EMP: 3
SALES: 40K **Privately Held**
SIC: 2395 Embroidery & art needlework

(G-5636)
KAUFMAN CONTAINER COMPANY (PA)
1000 Keystone Pkwy # 100 (44135-5119)
P.O. Box 35902 (44135-0902)
PHONE.................................216 898-2000
Fax: 216 898-8940
Roger Seid, *CEO*
Ken Slater, *President*
Charles Borowiak, *Vice Pres*
Roderick Cywinski, *Vice Pres*
Jeffery Gross, *Vice Pres*
▲ **EMP:** 118 **EST:** 1910
SQ FT: 180,000
SALES (est): 66.1MM **Privately Held**
SIC: 5085 2759 Industrial supplies; plastic bottles; glass bottles; screen printing; labels & seals: printing

(G-5637)
KAWNEER COMPANY INC
4536 Industrial Pkwy (44135-4593)
PHONE.................................216 252-3203
Fax: 216 252-2850
Janice Gibson, *General Mgr*
Tom Parrish, *Manager*
Steve Shamblin, *Manager*
EMP: 14
SALES (corp-wide): 12.3B **Publicly Held**
WEB: www.kawneer.com
SIC: 3442 Metal doors
HQ: Kawneer Company, Inc.
  555 Guthridge Ct Tech
  Norcross GA 30092
  770 449-5555

(G-5638)
KAY CAPITAL COMPANY (DH)
Also Called: Advanced Vehicles
1441 Chardon Rd (44117-1510)
PHONE.................................216 531-1010
Edward Crawford, *Ch of Bd*
Felix Tarorick, *Vice Ch Bd*
Tim Dunagan, *President*
Wally Niemiec, *Purch Agent*
Jim Eason, *Chief Engr*
EMP: 5 **EST:** 1875
SQ FT: 160,000
SALES (est): 6.1MM
SALES (corp-wide): 1.2B **Publicly Held**
WEB: www.ajaxtech.com
SIC: 3542 3537 3549 3541 Machine tools, metal forming type; lift trucks, industrial: fork, platform, straddle, etc.; metalworking machinery; machine tools, metal cutting type
HQ: Park-Ohio Industries, Inc.
  6065 Parkland Blvd Ste 1
  Cleveland OH 44124
  440 947-2000

(G-5639)
KEBAN INDUSTRIES INC
Also Called: Stefan Restoration
7500 Wall St Ste 100 (44125-3357)
PHONE.................................216 446-0159
Ken Stefan, *Principal*
EMP: 7
SALES (est): 776.4K **Privately Held**
SIC: 3599 Custom machinery

(G-5640)
KEENER PRINTING INC
401 E 200th St (44119-1594)
PHONE.................................216 531-7595
Fax: 216 531-5140
Duane Pecjak, *President*
Jim Rajcan, *Manager*
EMP: 12 **EST:** 1976
SQ FT: 3,600
SALES (est): 1.9MM **Privately Held**
WEB: www.keenerprinting.com
SIC: 2752 2791 Commercial printing, offset; typesetting

(G-5641)
KEHOE BROTHERS PRINTING INC
910 W Schaaf Rd (44109-4643)
PHONE.................................216 351-4100
Thomas Kehoe Sr, *President*
Tom Kehle, *Managing Dir*
Elizabeth Kehoe, *Treasurer*
EMP: 3
SALES (est): 370K **Privately Held**
SIC: 2752 2759 Commercial printing, offset; letterpress printing

(G-5642)
KEITHLEY INSTRUMENTS INTL CORP
28775 Aurora Rd (44139-1891)
PHONE.................................440 248-0400
Joseph P Keithley, *President*
Ron Molder, *Treasurer*
Sharon Fernandize, *Credit Mgr*
Marla Mock, *Manager*
EMP: 450
SQ FT: 200,000

SALES (est): 47.3MM
SALES (corp-wide): 6.2B **Publicly Held**
WEB: www.keithley.com
SIC: 5065 3825 Electronic parts & equipment; test equipment for electronic & electric measurement
HQ: Keithley Instruments, Llc
  28775 Aurora Rd
  Solon OH 44139
  440 248-0400

(G-5643)
KELLY PLATING CO
10316 Madison Ave (44102-3594)
PHONE.................................216 961-1080
Fax: 216 961-5319
Donald J Kelly, *President*
James Kelly, *Vice Pres*
Lauralee Paukert, *Admin Sec*
EMP: 37 **EST:** 1932
SQ FT: 20,000
SALES (est): 5.3MM **Privately Held**
SIC: 3471 Electroplating of metals or formed products

(G-5644)
KENNAMETAL INC
18105 Cleveland Pkwy Dr (44135-3251)
PHONE.................................216 898-6120
Fax: 216 898-6123
Tom McNamara, *Manager*
EMP: 140
SALES (corp-wide): 2.1B **Publicly Held**
WEB: www.kennametal.com
SIC: 3545 Machine tool accessories
PA: Kennametal Inc.
  600 Grant St Ste 5100
  Pittsburgh PA 15219
  412 248-8200

(G-5645)
KENNEDY MINT INC
Also Called: Kennedy Graphics
12102 Pearl Rd Rear (44136-3398)
PHONE.................................440 572-3222
Fax: 440 572-3692
Renato Montorsi, *President*
Theresa Montorsi, *Vice Pres*
EMP: 55
SQ FT: 60,000
SALES (est): 8.4MM **Privately Held**
WEB: www.kennedysg.com
SIC: 2653 2752 7538 Corrugated boxes, partitions, display items, sheets & pad; offset & photolithographic printing; general automotive repair shops

(G-5646)
KENNICK MOLD & DIE INC
3601 Detroit Ave (44113-2791)
PHONE.................................216 631-3535
Fax: 216 631-3536
Bob Hotujac, *President*
Florence Hotujac, *Admin Sec*
EMP: 5 **EST:** 1956
SQ FT: 2,400
SALES (est): 331.2K **Privately Held**
WEB: www.kennickmold.com
SIC: 3089 Injection molded finished plastic products

(G-5647)
KENTON INDUSTRIES LTD
1278 W 9th St Ph 2 (44113-5511)
PHONE.................................915 603-2139
Keith Forster, *Principal*
EMP: 3
SALES (est): 289.2K **Privately Held**
SIC: 3999 Manufacturing industries

(G-5648)
KEREK INDUSTRIES LTD LBLTY CO
750 Beta Dr Ste A (44143-2333)
PHONE.................................440 461-1450
Fax: 440 461-1454
Tom Linsenmeier, *Prdtn Mgr*
Richard Kerek,
John Kerek,
EMP: 13
SQ FT: 22,000
SALES (est): 1.9MM **Privately Held**
WEB: www.kerekindustries.com
SIC: 3599 Machine shop, jobbing & repair

▲ = Import ▼ =Export
◆ =Import/Export

(G-5649)
KERN INC
755 Alpha Dr (44143-2124)
PHONE.....................................440 930-7315
Thomas Brock, *President*
EMP: 3
SALES (corp-wide): 134.3MM **Privately Held**
SIC: 3579 3577 Envelope stuffing, sealing & addressing machines; computer peripheral equipment
HQ: Kern, Inc.
3940 Gantz Rd Ste A
Grove City OH 43123
614 317-2600

(G-5650)
KERN MANUFACTURING INC (PA)
24050 Commerce Park (44122-5833)
PHONE.....................................216 464-5490
Alfred G Corrado, *President*
▲ EMP: 4 EST: 1970
SQ FT: 10,000
SALES (est): 20.3MM **Privately Held**
SIC: 2342 2389 Maternity bras & corsets; garter belts

(G-5651)
KEY PRINCIPAL PARTNERS CORP (HQ)
Also Called: Key Principal Investing
800 Superior Ave E # 1000 (44114-2613)
PHONE.....................................888 539-3322
John Sinnenberg, *President*
Cindy Babitt, *Vice Pres*
Samir Desai, *Vice Pres*
Patrick Rond, *Vice Pres*
Dennis Wagner, *CFO*
EMP: 15
SALES (est): 70.8MM
SALES (corp-wide): 5.3B **Publicly Held**
WEB: www.kppinvest.com
SIC: 6799 8741 3825 6726 Investors; management services; test equipment for electronic & electrical circuits; investment offices; powder, metal
PA: Keycorp
127 Public Sq
Cleveland OH 44114
216 689-3000

(G-5652)
KEYSTONE BOLT & NUT COMPANY
Also Called: Keystone Threaded Products
7600 Hub Pkwy (44125-5707)
P.O. Box 31059 (44131-0059)
PHONE.....................................216 524-9626
Fax: 216 524-7132
James W Krejci, *President*
Betsy Mitchell, *Vice Pres*
▲ EMP: 60 EST: 1919
SQ FT: 30,000
SALES (est): 13.2MM **Privately Held**
WEB: www.keystonethreaded.com
SIC: 3452 Bolts, nuts, rivets & washers

(G-5653)
KIEFER TOOL & MOLD INC
3855 W 150th St (44111-5806)
PHONE.....................................216 251-0076
John Kiefer Jr, *President*
Thomas Kiefer, *Corp Secy*
Jim Kiefer, *Vice Pres*
EMP: 15
SQ FT: 12,000
SALES: 1MM **Privately Held**
SIC: 3599 Machine shop, jobbing & repair

(G-5654)
KING MEDIA ENTERPRISES INC
Also Called: Call & Post
11800 Shaker Blvd (44120-1919)
P.O. Box 6237 (44101-1237)
PHONE.....................................216 588-6700
Don King, *President*
Shelley Shockley, *Div Sub Head*
Shanell Tritchett, *Office Mgr*
John Lenear, *Manager*
Constance Harper, *Exec Dir*
EMP: 35
SALES (est): 2.6MM **Privately Held**
SIC: 2711 Commercial printing & newspaper publishing combined

(G-5655)
KINZUA ENVIRONMENTAL INC
1176 E 38th St Ste 1 (44114-3898)
PHONE.....................................216 881-4040
Fax: 216 881-8968
Bradley R Waxman, *President*
Bradley Way, *Sls & Mktg Exec*
Matt Waxman, *Regl Sales Mgr*
Bill Levine, *Mktg Dir*
EMP: 20
SQ FT: 20,000
SALES (est): 4.6MM **Privately Held**
WEB: www.kinzuachem.com
SIC: 2842 Specialty cleaning preparations

(G-5656)
KIP-CRAFT INCORPORATED (PA)
Also Called: Schoolbelles
4747 W 160th St (44135-2631)
PHONE.....................................216 898-5500
Fax: 216 898-5520
Bruce J Carroll, *President*
Mary Carroll, *Corp Secy*
Elaine Stephens, *Vice Pres*
Kathleen Luchansky, *CFO*
Jennifer Samuel, *Accountant*
EMP: 60
SALES (est): 11.6MM **Privately Held**
WEB: www.schoolbells.com
SIC: 5699 2339 2326 Uniforms; women's & misses' outerwear; men's & boys' work clothing

(G-5657)
KIRBY SALES COMPANY INC
1920 W 114th St (44102-2344)
PHONE.....................................216 228-2400
Fax: 216 228-6287
Mike Nichols, *President*
Bud Miley, *Principal*
Jim Ramey, *COO*
H K Bell, *Vice Pres*
William Bell, *Vice Pres*
◆ EMP: 500
SALES (est): 126.7MM **Privately Held**
SIC: 3635 Household vacuum cleaners

(G-5658)
KIRK WELDING & FABRICATING
10410 Madison Ave (44102-3547)
PHONE.....................................216 961-6403
Fax: 216 631-5558
James A Baronak, *President*
George Baronak, *Corp Secy*
Rick Baronak, *Vice Pres*
EMP: 3 EST: 1933
SQ FT: 1,800
SALES (est): 170K **Privately Held**
SIC: 7692 3441 Welding repair; fabricated structural metal

(G-5659)
KIRKWOOD HOLDING INC (PA)
1239 Rockside Rd (44134-2772)
PHONE.....................................216 267-6200
Fax: 216 351-3141
L Thomas Koechley, *Principal*
Paul Hensen, *Vice Pres*
Donna Ross, *CFO*
Linda Jankowski, *Manager*
Steve McNutt, *Manager*
EMP: 7
SQ FT: 3,500
SALES (est): 37.2MM **Privately Held**
SIC: 3621 Commutators, electric motor; collector rings, for electric motors or generators

(G-5660)
KMART SUPERCENTER
17840 Bagley Rd (44130-3401)
PHONE.....................................440 974-7300
Fax: 440 974-7320
Al Keim, *Manager*
Tonia Miller, *Manager*
EMP: 4
SALES (est): 453.3K **Privately Held**
WEB: www.kmartsupercenter.com
SIC: 5912 5311 5812 5421 Drug stores; department stores; eating places; meat & fish markets; grocery stores; bread, cake & related products

(G-5661)
KNITTING MACHINERY CORP (PA)
Also Called: K M C
15625 Saranac Rd (44110-2427)
PHONE.....................................216 851-9900
Edward F Crawford, *President*
Joyce Brokos, *Office Mgr*
EMP: 5
SQ FT: 6,600
SALES (est): 4MM **Privately Held**
SIC: 3552 Knitting machines

(G-5662)
KOEHLER RUBBER & SUPPLY CO
800 W Resource Dr (44131-1837)
P.O. Box 91006 (44101-3006)
PHONE.....................................216 749-5100
Fax: 216 749-1911
Bernard Green, *President*
Betty Parsell, *Corp Secy*
Michael Ticchione, *Vice Pres*
Ted Kannen, *Consultant*
▲ EMP: 17 EST: 1917
SQ FT: 27,000
SALES: 5.5MM **Privately Held**
WEB: www.koehlerrubber.com
SIC: 3569 Lubrication equipment, industrial

(G-5663)
KOVACEVIC PRINTING INC
Also Called: Minuteman Press
6886 Pearl Rd Ste A (44130-3618)
PHONE.....................................440 887-1000
Fax: 440 887-1001
Robert Kovacevic, *President*
EMP: 4
SALES (est): 350K **Privately Held**
SIC: 2752 Commercial printing, lithographic

(G-5664)
KOVELS ANTIQUES INC
30799 Pinetree Rd 305 (44124-5903)
PHONE.....................................216 752-2252
Terry Kovel, *President*
Kim Kovel, *CFO*
EMP: 12
SALES (est): 1.4MM **Privately Held**
WEB: www.antiques.com
SIC: 2731 Book publishing

(G-5665)
KOWALSKI HEAT TREATING CO
3611 Detroit Ave (44113-2790)
PHONE.....................................216 631-4411
Fax: 216 631-8921
Robert Kowalski, *President*
Stephen Kowalski, *Vice Pres*
Carole Kowalski, *Treasurer*
Peggy Andrews, *Sales Staff*
Rhonda Branthoover, *Manager*
EMP: 13 EST: 1975
SQ FT: 11,000
SALES (est): 3.4MM **Privately Held**
WEB: www.khtheat.com
SIC: 3398 Metal heat treating

(G-5666)
KROY LLC (HQ)
Also Called: Buckeye Business Products
3830 Kelley Ave (44114-4534)
PHONE.....................................216 426-5600
Fax: 216 426-5704
Stephen Kalette, *Partner*
Elenora Grmek, *VP Opers*
Bob Overcasher, *Plant Mgr*
Mike Knack, *Purchasing*
Dee Hyer, *QC Mgr*
▲ EMP: 125
SQ FT: 110,000
SALES (est): 81.3MM
SALES (corp-wide): 93.1MM **Privately Held**
SIC: 2671 3955 2761 Packaging paper & plastics film, coated & laminated; carbon paper & inked ribbons; manifold business forms
PA: Pubco Corporation
3830 Kelley Ave
Cleveland OH 44114
216 881-5300

(G-5667)
KRUMOR INC
7655 Hub Pkwy Ste 206 (44125-5739)
PHONE.....................................216 328-9802
Fax: 216 328-9803
Robert Mikals, *President*
Herbert H Sher, *Vice Pres*
Theresa Banas, *Manager*
EMP: 10 EST: 1972
SALES (est): 2.5MM **Privately Held**
WEB: www.krumor.com
SIC: 3829 Temperature sensors, except industrial process & aircraft

(G-5668)
KYRON PLATING CORP
Also Called: Miracle Metal Finishing
1336 W 114th St (44102-1397)
P.O. Box 728 (44107-0728)
PHONE.....................................216 221-7275
Fax: 216 221-8673
Ken O'Bloy, *President*
Ken Obloy, *President*
Theresa O'Bloy, *Office Mgr*
EMP: 12 EST: 1960
SQ FT: 9,000
SALES: 700K **Privately Held**
SIC: 3471 Plating of metals or formed products

(G-5669)
L A MACHINE
3818 Trent Ave (44109)
PHONE.....................................216 651-1712
Leonard Andreasik, *Owner*
EMP: 3
SQ FT: 7,275
SALES (est): 355.8K **Privately Held**
SIC: 3599 Machine shop, jobbing & repair

(G-5670)
L B FOLDING CO INC
8110 Lake Ave (44102-1997)
PHONE.....................................216 961-0888
Richard Happensack, *President*
Geraldine Happensack, *Corp Secy*
EMP: 3
SQ FT: 25,260
SALES: 500K **Privately Held**
SIC: 2789 3554 Binding only: books, pamphlets, magazines, etc.; folding machines, paper

(G-5671)
L D KICHLER CO (PA)
Also Called: Kichler Lighting
7711 E Pleasant Valley Rd (44131-5532)
P.O. Box 318010 (44131-8010)
PHONE.....................................866 558-5706
Fax: 216 573-1000
Tony Davidson, *CEO*
Harold S Minoff, *Ch of Bd*
Barry Minoff, *Chairman*
Roy Minoff, *Vice Pres*
David Pamer, *Vice Pres*
◆ EMP: 500 EST: 1938
SQ FT: 630,000
SALES (est): 124.8MM **Privately Held**
WEB: www.kichler.com
SIC: 3645 3648 3641 Residential lighting fixtures; lighting equipment; electric lamps

(G-5672)
L-MOR INC
Also Called: Carhoff
13404 Saint Clair Ave (44110-3543)
P.O. Box 10876 (44110-0876)
PHONE.....................................216 541-2224
Fax: 216 541-4022
Lisa Morell, *President*
EMP: 10
SQ FT: 14,000
SALES (est): 2.1MM **Privately Held**
WEB: www.darlingfiresafety.com
SIC: 2842 7389 5099 Sanitation preparations; fire extinguisher servicing; safety equipment & supplies; fire extinguishers

(G-5673)
LA GRA JEWELERS INC
674 Broadway Ave (44146-3595)
PHONE.....................................440 439-5869
Fax: 440 786-0030
Joseph Graceffo, *President*
Lawrence Graceffo, *Vice Pres*
EMP: 7 EST: 1968

G E O G R A P H I C

SQ FT: 5,000
SALES (est): 887.9K **Privately Held**
WEB: www.lagra.net
SIC: 5944 3911 Jewelry, precious stones & precious metals; watches; jewelry, precious metal

(G-5674)
LACHINA PUBLISHING SVCS INC (PA)
3793 Green Rd (44122-5705)
PHONE..................................216 292-7959
Fax: 216 292-3639
Jeff Lachina, *President*
Bonnie Briggle, *Editor*
Molly Wagner, *Editor*
Tony Anselmo, *COO*
Mandy Walden, *Accounts Mgr*
EMP: 36 **EST:** 1978
SALES (est): 7.1MM **Privately Held**
WEB: www.lachina.com
SIC: 2731 Book publishing

(G-5675)
LAD TECHNOLOGY INC
730 Beta Dr Ste B (44143-2331)
PHONE..................................440 461-8002
Fax: 440 461-8004
Donna Marie Domanovics, *President*
Louis Domanovics, *Vice Pres*
EMP: 25
SQ FT: 10,000
SALES (est): 4.3MM **Privately Held**
WEB: www.ladtechnology.com
SIC: 3672 Printed circuit boards

(G-5676)
LAFARGE NORTH AMERICA INC
2500 Elm St (44113-1114)
PHONE..................................216 781-9330
Fax: 216 781-6383
Thomas Peck, *Branch Mgr*
EMP: 7
SALES (corp-wide): 26.6B **Privately Held**
WEB: www.lafargenorthamerica.com
SIC: 3241 Cement, hydraulic
HQ: Lafarge North America Inc.
8700 W Bryn Mawr Ave Ll
Chicago IL 60631
703 480-3600

(G-5677)
LAKESHORE FEED & SEED INC
5116 Clark Ave (44102-4553)
PHONE..................................216 961-5729
Fax: 216 961-1944
Marilyn Brown, *Owner*
Darnelle Brown, *Vice Pres*
EMP: 4
SALES: 330K **Privately Held**
SIC: 2047 2048 Dog food; bird food, prepared

(G-5678)
LAM PRO INC
4701 Crayton Ave Ste A (44104-2819)
PHONE..................................216 426-0661
Fax: 216 426-0662
Kerry Stewart, *President*
Pam Moore, *Opers Staff*
Debbie Dragar, *Admin Sec*
EMP: 13
SQ FT: 33,000
SALES (est): 1.9MM **Privately Held**
WEB: www.lampro.com
SIC: 3089 2789 2675 2672 Laminating of plastic; bookbinding & related work; die-cut paper & board; coated & laminated paper

(G-5679)
LAMPORTS FILTER MEDIA INC
837 E 79th St (44103-1807)
PHONE..................................216 881-2050
Fax: 216 881-8957
Walter Senney, *President*
Joyce Senney, *Vice Pres*
EMP: 15
SQ FT: 25,000
SALES (est): 116.7K **Privately Held**
WEB: www.lamports.com
SIC: 2393 Textile bags

(G-5680)
LANGENAU MANUFACTURING COMPANY
7306 Madison Ave (44102-4094)
PHONE..................................216 651-3400
Fax: 216 651-6926
W C Strangward, *President*
Dan Masterson, *Mfg Staff*
Katie Loeser, *Controller*
Anna Miller, *Technology*
EMP: 15
SQ FT: 40,000
SALES (est): 2.7MM **Privately Held**
WEB: www.langenau.com
SIC: 3432 3465 3469 3544 Plastic plumbing fixture fittings, assembly; automotive stampings; metal stampings; special dies, tools, jigs & fixtures; casket hardware

(G-5681)
LANIER & ASSOCIATES INC
Also Called: Cleveland Black Pages
1814 E 40th St Ste 1c (44103-3500)
PHONE..................................216 391-7735
Bob Lanier, *President*
Linda Lanier, *Vice Pres*
EMP: 6
SALES: 450K **Privately Held**
WEB: www.blackpagesohio.com
SIC: 2741 Directories, telephone: publishing only, not printed on site

(G-5682)
LANLY COMPANY
26201 Tungsten Rd (44132-2922)
PHONE..................................216 731-1115
Fax: 216 731-7900
Dennis W Hill, *President*
John Jencson, *Business Mgr*
David Fowle, *Vice Pres*
Robert Knierim, *Project Mgr*
Dominic Mazza, *Purch Mgr*
EMP: 44
SQ FT: 68,000
SALES (est): 13.7MM **Privately Held**
WEB: www.lanly.com
SIC: 3567 Industrial furnaces & ovens; driers & redriers, industrial process

(G-5683)
LARMCO WINDOWS INC (PA)
8400 Sweet Valley Dr # 404 (44125-4243)
PHONE..................................216 502-2832
Fax: 216 525-0014
William Simon, *Ch of Bd*
Joe Talmon, *President*
Nick Nero, *Plant Mgr*
EMP: 30
SALES (est): 5.6MM **Privately Held**
WEB: www.larmco.com
SIC: 3089 Windows, plastic; siding, plastic; doors, folding: plastic or plastic coated fabric

(G-5684)
LASER PRINTING SOLUTIONS INC
Also Called: L P S I
6040 Hillcrest Dr (44125-4620)
PHONE..................................216 351-4444
Fax: 216 351-7826
Bob Lasser, *Ch of Bd*
Mike Piaser, *President*
James G Skimin, *Opers Staff*
EMP: 14
SQ FT: 5,000
SALES (est): 1.9MM **Privately Held**
WEB: www.laserprintingsolutions.com
SIC: 2759 Laser printing

(G-5685)
LATTE LIVING
11005 Johnson Dr (44130-7352)
PHONE..................................440 364-2201
Lisa Timko, *Owner*
EMP: 4
SALES (est): 196.9K **Privately Held**
SIC: 2741

(G-5686)
LAWRENCE INDUSTRIES INC
Also Called: Arte Limited
4500 Lee Rd Ste 120 (44128-2959)
PHONE..................................216 518-1400

Arthur Kopittke, *Vice Pres*
Robert Kopittke, *Branch Mgr*
EMP: 100
SALES (corp-wide): 10.6MM **Privately Held**
WEB: www.hudsonsupply.com
SIC: 3599 3541 Machine shop, jobbing & repair; sawing & cutoff machines (metalworking machinery)
PA: Lawrence Industries Inc
4500 Lee Rd Ste 120
Cleveland OH 44128
216 518-7000

(G-5687)
LAWRENCE INDUSTRIES INC (PA)
4500 Lee Rd Ste 120 (44128-2959)
PHONE..................................216 518-7000
Lawrence A Kopittke Sr, *President*
Arthur Kopittke, *Vice Pres*
Richard J Kopittke, *Vice Pres*
◆ **EMP:** 50
SQ FT: 160,000
SALES (est): 10.6MM **Privately Held**
WEB: www.hudsonsupply.com
SIC: 3599 3541 7699 5084 Machine shop, jobbing & repair; sawing & cutoff machines (metalworking machinery); tool repair services; metalworking tools (such as drills, taps, dies, files); machine tools & metalworking machinery; industrial supplies; abrasive products

(G-5688)
LAWSONS TOWING & AUTO WRCKG
14114 Miles Ave (44128-2329)
PHONE..................................216 883-9050
EMP: 10
SALES (est): 920K **Privately Held**
SIC: 5093 3711 Whol Scrap/Waste Material Mfg Motor Vehicle/Car Bodies

(G-5689)
LAZARUS STEEL LLC
901 Addison Rd (44103-1607)
PHONE..................................216 391-3245
Timothy Harlan,
EMP: 3
SQ FT: 23,500
SALES (est): 2.4MM **Privately Held**
SIC: 3441 Fabricated structural metal

(G-5690)
LEDGE HILL SIGNS LIMITED
Also Called: Fastsigns
5369 Mayfield Rd (44124-2456)
PHONE..................................440 461-4445
Fax: 440 461-3888
Ed Davis, *Owner*
EMP: 3
SALES (est): 315.2K **Privately Held**
SIC: 3993 Signs & advertising specialties

(G-5691)
LEFCO WORTHINGTON LLC
18451 Euclid Ave (44112-1016)
PHONE..................................216 432-4422
Fax: 216 432-4424
Jennifer Viancourt, *Office Mgr*
Larry E Fulton,
EMP: 30
SQ FT: 30,000
SALES: 6.2MM **Privately Held**
WEB: www.lefcoindustries.com
SIC: 2449 4783 4226 Rectangular boxes & crates, wood; packing & crating; special warehousing & storage

(G-5692)
LEGAL NEWS PUBLISHING CO
Also Called: Daily Legal News
2935 Prospect Ave E (44115-2607)
PHONE..................................216 696-3322
Fax: 216 696-6321
Lucien B Karlovec Jr, *President*
Lisa Cech, *Editor*
Jeffrey Karlovec, *Exec VP*
Ed Mattson, *Purchasing*
Charles E Bergstresser, *Treasurer*
EMP: 28
SQ FT: 14,238

SALES (est): 3.7MM **Privately Held**
WEB: www.dln.com
SIC: 2791 2711 2752 2789 Typesetting; newspapers, publishing & printing; commercial printing, offset; bookbinding & related work; periodicals

(G-5693)
LEIMKUEHLER INC (PA)
4625 Detroit Ave (44102-2295)
PHONE..................................440 899-7842
Fax: 216 651-4057
Robert Leimkuehler, *President*
Jim Leimkuehler, *Business Mgr*
EMP: 21 **EST:** 1948
SQ FT: 10,000
SALES (est): 3.3MM **Privately Held**
SIC: 5999 3842 Orthopedic & prosthesis applications; surgical appliances & supplies

(G-5694)
LEXTECH INDUSTRIES LTD
6800 Union Ave (44105-1326)
PHONE..................................216 883-7900
David N Bortz, *President*
Gordon Weilend, *COO*
Adela Lazar, *Office Mgr*
Keith Partee, *Manager*
EMP: 6
SQ FT: 143,000
SALES (est): 800.1K **Privately Held**
WEB: www.lextechindustries.com
SIC: 3469 3568 3462 Stamping metal for the trade; power transmission equipment; iron & steel forgings

(G-5695)
LIGHTYEARMUSICCOM
5361 Pearl Rd (44129-1546)
PHONE..................................216 929-1022
Fax: 216 351-4707
Charles Polidori, *President*
▼ **EMP:** 3
SALES (est): 456.4K **Privately Held**
SIC: 3651 5999 Audio electronic systems; audio-visual equipment & supplies

(G-5696)
LINCOLN ELECTRIC COMPANY
7550 Hub Pkwy (44125-5705)
PHONE..................................216 524-8800
Christopher Mapes, *President*
EMP: 230
SALES (corp-wide): 2.2B **Publicly Held**
SIC: 3625 3823 3566 Controls for adjustable speed drives; numerical controls; industrial instrmnts msrmnt display/control process variable; speed changers, drives & gears
HQ: Lincoln Electric Company
22801 Saint Clair Ave
Euclid OH 44117
216 481-8100

(G-5697)
LINCOLN ELECTRIC COMPANY
22800 Saint Clair Ave (44117-2525)
PHONE..................................216 481-8100
Brian Sullivan, *Branch Mgr*
Greg Mueller, *Manager*
EMP: 15
SALES (corp-wide): 2.2B **Publicly Held**
WEB: www.subarc-welding.com
SIC: 3548 Welding apparatus
HQ: Lincoln Electric Company
22801 Saint Clair Ave
Euclid OH 44117
216 481-8100

(G-5698)
LINCOLN ELECTRIC HOLDINGS INC (PA)
22801 Saint Clair Ave (44117-2524)
PHONE..................................216 481-8100
Christopher L Mapes, *President*
George D Blankenship, *President*
Thomas A Flohn, *President*
Mathias Hallmann, *President*
Steven B Hedlund, *President*
EMP: 171 **EST:** 1895
SQ FT: 2,940,000

SALES: 2.2B **Publicly Held**
WEB: www.lincolnelectric.com
SIC: 3548 Welding apparatus; welding & cutting apparatus & accessories; arc welding generators, alternating current & direct current

(G-5699)
LINCOLN FOODSERVICE PDTS LLC (HQ)
1333 E 179th St (44110)
PHONE....................260 459-8200
Charlie Kingdon, *President*
Steve Deidering, *Vice Pres*
Thomas Kurgan, *Vice Pres*
Effie Lee, *Vice Pres*
James Silcox, *Vice Pres*
◆ **EMP:** 33 **EST:** 1957
SQ FT: 358,000
SALES (est): 53.6MM
SALES (corp-wide): 1.7B **Publicly Held**
WEB: www.enodisreps.com
SIC: 3556 Ovens, bakery; slicers, commercial, food; biscuit cutters (machines)
PA: Welbilt, Inc.
2227 Welbilt Blvd
Trinity FL 34655
727 375-7010

(G-5700)
LINDE LLC
6300 Halle Dr (44125-4618)
PHONE....................216 533-7256
Grzegorz Moroz, *Senior Engr*
EMP: 24
SALES (corp-wide): 17.9B **Privately Held**
SIC: 2813 Industrial gases
HQ: Linde Llc
200 Somerset Corporate Bl
Bridgewater NJ 08807
908 464-8100

(G-5701)
LINEAR TECHNOLOGY CORPORATION
7550 Lucerne Dr Ste 106 (44130-6503)
PHONE....................440 239-0817
Fax: 440 239-1466
Todd Sloan, *Manager*
EMP: 7
SALES (corp-wide): 3.4B **Publicly Held**
SIC: 3699 Electrical equipment & supplies
HQ: Linear Technology Corporation
1630 Mccarthy Blvd
Milpitas CA 95035
408 432-1900

(G-5702)
LINESTREAM TECHNOLOGIES
1468 W 9th St Ste 100 (44113-1252)
PHONE....................216 862-7874
Dave Neundorfer, *CEO*
James G Dawson, *Principal*
David Stopher, *Opers Staff*
Greg Jackson, *VP Sls/Mktg*
Gang Tian, *CTO*
EMP: 7
SALES (est): 969.7K **Privately Held**
SIC: 7372 Business oriented computer software

(G-5703)
LINSALATA CAPITAL PARTNERS FUN
5900 Landerbrook Dr # 280 (44124-4020)
PHONE....................440 684-1400
Frank Linsalata, *Partner*
Mike Anderson, *Vice Pres*
James V Guddy, *Vice Pres*
Steve Perry, *CFO*
Kurtis Zabell, *Finance Dir*
EMP: 9
SALES (est): 2.1MM **Privately Held**
WEB: www.lincap3.com
SIC: 6282 6799 3499 2676 Investment advisory service; investment research; venture capital companies; safes & vaults, metal; sanitary paper products; napkins, sanitary: made from purchased paper; tampons, sanitary: made from purchased paper; diapers, paper (disposable): made from purchased paper; scrub cloths; work garments, except raincoats: waterproof

(G-5704)
LIQUID CRYSTAL TECH LLC
24300 Solon Rd Ste 100 (44146-4794)
P.O. Box 31, Gates Mills (44040-0031)
PHONE....................440 232-8590
Tim Cicek, *Mng Member*
◆ **EMP:** 6
SQ FT: 5,000
SALES: 1MM **Privately Held**
WEB: www.liquidcrystaltechnologies.com
SIC: 3679 Liquid crystal displays (LCD)

(G-5705)
LIQUID IMAGE CORP OF AMERICA
3700 Prospect Ave E (44115-2706)
PHONE....................216 458-9800
Fax: 216 458-9804
Lea Wiertel, *President*
Michael Wiertel, *Vice Pres*
Elizabeth Wiertel, *Manager*
EMP: 7
SQ FT: 2,500
SALES (est): 1.2MM **Privately Held**
WEB: www.liquid-image.com
SIC: 3663 Digital encoders

(G-5706)
LISA MODEM
4195 Zalley Rd (44109)
PHONE....................216 551-3365
Lynn Westfall, *Owner*
EMP: 3
SALES (est): 167.5K **Privately Held**
SIC: 3661 Modems

(G-5707)
LOGAN CLUTCH CORPORATION
Also Called: Lc
28855 Ranney Pkwy (44145-1173)
PHONE....................440 808-4258
Fax: 440 431-4949
Madelon Logan, *CEO*
William A Logan, *President*
Elyse Logan, *Vice Pres*
Christina Seichko, *Accounts Mgr*
Cindy Sheferstine, *Manager*
▲ **EMP:** 30
SQ FT: 33,000
SALES (est): 8.1MM **Privately Held**
WEB: www.loganclutch.com
SIC: 3568 5085 Clutches, except vehicular; industrial supplies

(G-5708)
LOGOS ON LEE
3105 Mayfield Rd (44118-1713)
PHONE....................216 862-5226
Todd Guenther, *Principal*
EMP: 6
SALES (est): 507.9K **Privately Held**
SIC: 2759 Screen printing

(G-5709)
LOREAL USA INC
30601 Carter St (44139-3513)
P.O. Box 39608 (44139-0608)
PHONE....................440 248-3700
Rex Mason, *Principal*
Edward Lusk, *Transptn Dir*
Paul Kasper, *Opers Mgr*
EMP: 650
SALES (corp-wide): 3.2B **Privately Held**
WEB: www.lorealparisusa.com
SIC: 2844 Hair preparations, including shampoos; cosmetic preparations; perfumes & colognes
HQ: L'oreal Usa, Inc.
10 Hudson Yards Fl 30
New York NY 10001
212 818-1500

(G-5710)
LOUS SAUSAGE LTD
14723 Miles Ave (44128-2397)
PHONE....................216 752-5060
Joseph Vinciguerra,
Frank Vinciguerra,
EMP: 17
SQ FT: 7,500
SALES: 1.7MM **Privately Held**
SIC: 2013 Sausages from purchased meat

(G-5711)
LPC PUBLISHING CO
2026 Murray Hill Rd # 10 (44106-5958)
PHONE....................216 721-1800
Gail Smith, *Principal*
EMP: 4
SALES (est): 276.1K **Privately Held**
SIC: 2741 Miscellaneous publishing

(G-5712)
LUCKY THIRTEEN INC
Also Called: Lucky Thirteen Laser
7413 Associate Ave (44144-1104)
PHONE....................216 631-0013
James Bailey, *President*
James P Bailey, *Principal*
Francis J Dempsey, *Principal*
Thomas G Scheiman, *Principal*
Amelia Wurz, *Accountant*
EMP: 8
SALES (est): 1.1MM **Privately Held**
SIC: 3699 Laser welding, drilling & cutting equipment

(G-5713)
LUXCO INC
Also Called: Paramount Distillers
3116 Berea Rd (44111-1501)
PHONE....................216 671-6300
Paul A Lux, *Branch Mgr*
EMP: 40
SALES (corp-wide): 44.4MM **Privately Held**
SIC: 2085 Bourbon whiskey
PA: Luxco, Inc.
5050 Kemper Ave
Saint Louis MO 63139
314 772-2626

(G-5714)
LYNNS LOGOS INC
386 Broadway Ave (44146-2604)
PHONE....................440 786-1156
Linda Overholt, *President*
EMP: 4
SALES (est): 236.2K **Privately Held**
SIC: 2395 Embroidery products, except schiffli machine

(G-5715)
M & M DIES INC
3502 Beyerle Rd (44105-1016)
PHONE....................216 883-6628
Fax: 216 883-0237
Donald Dostie, *President*
Kenneth Dostie, *Vice Pres*
EMP: 7
SQ FT: 2,940
SALES (est): 726.9K **Privately Held**
SIC: 3364 3544 Nonferrous die-castings except aluminum; special dies & tools

(G-5716)
M & M ENGRAVING
5411 State Rd (44134-1248)
PHONE....................216 749-7166
Fax: 216 741-4810
Tom May, *Partner*
Frank Marnone, *Partner*
EMP: 3
SALES: 499K **Privately Held**
SIC: 3479 5999 Etching & engraving; trophies & plaques

(G-5717)
M B SAXON CO INC
Also Called: Saxon Jewelers
47 Alpha Park (44143-2219)
PHONE....................440 229-5006
Fax: 440 461-9671
Michael B Saxon, *President*
EMP: 15
SQ FT: 3,200
SALES (est): 1.6MM **Privately Held**
WEB: www.saxonjewelers.com
SIC: 3911 5944 5094 Jewelry, precious metal; jewelry, precious stones & precious metals; jewelry

(G-5718)
M MAZZONE & SONS BAKERY INC
Also Called: Mazzone Bakery
3519 Clark Ave (44109-1137)
PHONE....................216 631-6511

Fax: 216 281-5445
Luigi Mazzone, *President*
Frank B Mazzone, *Admin Sec*
EMP: 9
SQ FT: 6,650
SALES (est): 977.6K **Privately Held**
SIC: 2051 Bread, cake & related products

(G-5719)
M-BOSS INC
4510 E 71st St Ste 2 (44105-5638)
PHONE....................216 441-6080
William Perk, *President*
Kathy Hall, *Manager*
EMP: 20
SQ FT: 6,000
SALES (est): 4.3MM **Privately Held**
WEB: www.mbossinc.com
SIC: 3646 Ceiling systems, luminous

(G-5720)
M2M IMAGING CORPORATION
5427 Wilson Mills Rd (44143)
PHONE....................440 684-9690
Joe Flicek, *CEO*
Jon T Devries, *President*
EMP: 13
SQ FT: 2,500
SALES (est): 1.6MM **Privately Held**
SIC: 3677 Coil windings, electronic

(G-5721)
M3 TECHNOLOGIES INC
13910 Enterprise Ave (44135-5118)
PHONE....................216 898-9936
Roger May, *President*
Barry May, *Treasurer*
Danny May, *Admin Sec*
EMP: 10
SALES (est): 1.7MM **Privately Held**
WEB: www.m3technologies.com
SIC: 3444 Sheet metalwork

(G-5722)
MACE PERSONAL DEF & SEC INC (HQ)
4400 Carnegie Ave (44103-4342)
PHONE....................440 424-5321
John J McCann, *President*
Carl Smith, *CFO*
Remigijus Belzinskas, *Controller*
◆ **EMP:** 30
SQ FT: 30,000
SALES (est): 3.8MM
SALES (corp-wide): 33.7MM **Publicly Held**
SIC: 3999 5065 Self-defense sprays; security control equipment & systems
PA: Mace Security International, Inc.
4400 Carnegie Ave
Cleveland OH 44103
440 424-5321

(G-5723)
MACE SECURITY INTL INC (PA)
4400 Carnegie Ave (44103-4342)
PHONE....................440 424-5321
John J McCann, *President*
John O'Leary, *Division Pres*
Carl R Smith, *Senior VP*
Eric Crawford, *Vice Pres*
Garnett Meador, *Vice Pres*
◆ **EMP:** 19
SQ FT: 5,000
SALES (est): 33.7MM **Publicly Held**
WEB: www.securityandmore.com
SIC: 3699 3999 Security devices; self-defense sprays

(G-5724)
MACHINE INDUSTRIES INC
5200 Perkins Ave (44103-3524)
P.O. Box 603773 (44103-0773)
PHONE....................216 881-8555
Fax: 216 881-3128
Jerry Mandell, *President*
EMP: 3
SQ FT: 4,000
SALES (est): 456.9K **Privately Held**
SIC: 3599 Machine shop, jobbing & repair

(G-5725)
MACHINE PARTS INTERNATIONAL
10925 Briggs Rd (44111-5333)
PHONE....................216 251-4334

Greg Chlastosz, *President*
Kenneth Seiter, *Vice Pres*
EMP: 5
SQ FT: 3,500
SALES: 300K **Privately Held**
SIC: 3599 Machine & other job shop work

(G-5726)
MADISON GRAPHICS
13130 Detroit Ave (44107-2840)
PHONE..................................216 226-5770
Sam Salim, *Owner*
EMP: 5
SQ FT: 3,500
SALES (est): 430K **Privately Held**
SIC: 7336 2759 Silk screen design; commercial printing

(G-5727)
MADISON GROUP INC
Also Called: Logotec
15919 Industrial Pkwy (44135-3321)
PHONE..................................216 362-9000
Fax: 216 521-1744
Robert Stein, *CEO*
Matthew Stein, *President*
Gayle Stein, *Vice Pres*
EMP: 7
SQ FT: 5,000
SALES (est): 521.6K **Privately Held**
WEB: www.logotec.com
SIC: 7389 2396 5199 Embroidering of advertising on shirts, etc.; screen printing on fabric articles; advertising specialties

(G-5728)
MAGENTA INCORPORATED
3185a W 33rd St (44109-1524)
P.O. Box 228, University Heights (44118)
PHONE..................................216 571-4094
Virginia Benson, *President*
EMP: 22
SALES (est): 1MM **Privately Held**
SIC: 3641 Electric lamps & parts for specialized applications

(G-5729)
MAGNESIUM REFINING TECH INC (PA)
29695 Pettibone Rd (44139-5462)
PHONE..................................419 483-9199
Mike Slovich, *President*
Patty Konopka, *Manager*
▲ **EMP:** 40
SALES (est): 12.1MM **Privately Held**
SIC: 3339 Magnesium refining (primary)

(G-5730)
MAGNUM COMPUTERS INC
868 Montford Rd (44121-2012)
PHONE..................................216 781-1757
Dan Hanson, *President*
EMP: 10
SQ FT: 3,000
SALES (est): 1.3MM **Privately Held**
WEB: www.magnuminc.com
SIC: 5045 1731 8748 7378 Computers, peripherals & software; general electrical contractor; business consulting; computer maintenance & repair; electronic computers

(G-5731)
MAHAR SPAR INDUSTRIES INC
341 E 131st St (44108-1607)
PHONE..................................216 249-7143
Fax: 216 249-1169
Michael Mahar, *President*
Robert Schilling, *Vice Pres*
Alvin Hensel, *Treasurer*
▲ **EMP:** 6
SQ FT: 22,000
SALES: 700K **Privately Held**
SIC: 3089 Injection molding of plastics

(G-5732)
MAJESTIC STEEL MANAGEMENT CO
5300 Majestic Pkwy (44146-1744)
PHONE..................................440 786-2666
Dennis Leebow, *President*
Gene Fitch, *President*
Bruce Emmerth, *Purch Mgr*
Melissa Duda, *Human Res Mgr*
Josh Spoores, *Marketing Mgr*
EMP: 26

SALES (est): 3.8MM **Privately Held**
SIC: 8741 3312 Management services; iron & steel: galvanized, pipes, plates, sheets, etc.

(G-5733)
MAJORS WHOLESALE MED SUP LLC
Also Called: Revolution Mobility
6753 Engle Rd Ste A (44130-7935)
PHONE..................................800 376-7263
EMP: 4
SALES (est): 490K **Privately Held**
SIC: 3841 Surgical & medical instruments

(G-5734)
MALIN WIRE CO (HQ)
5400 Smith Rd (44142-2081)
PHONE..................................216 267-9080
Leonard Defino, *President*
Mary Defino, *Corp Secy*
Frank Defino, *Vice Pres*
Larry Guaruccio, *Manager*
▲ **EMP:** 2
SQ FT: 56,000
SALES (est): 2.1MM **Privately Held**
WEB: www.malinco.com
SIC: 3496 3469 Miscellaneous fabricated wire products; metal stampings

(G-5735)
MALIN WIRE CO
Also Called: Malin Co
5400 Smith Rd (44142-2081)
PHONE..................................216 267-9080
Leonard De Find, *Principal*
Al Oktavic, *Finance*
EMP: 25 **Privately Held**
WEB: www.malinco.com
SIC: 3469 Metal stampings
HQ: Malin Wire Co
5400 Smith Rd
Cleveland OH 44142
216 267-9080

(G-5736)
MALLEYS CANDIES INC
Also Called: Malley's Chocolates
13400 Brookpark Rd (44135-5145)
PHONE..................................216 529-6262
Fax: 216 529-6264
Patrick Malley, *Manager*
EMP: 25
SQ FT: 1,960
SALES (corp-wide): 55.8MM **Privately Held**
WEB: www.malleys.com
SIC: 2066 4225 5441 2064 Chocolate & cocoa products; general warehousing & storage; candy, nut & confectionery stores; candy & other confectionery products
PA: Malley's Candies
1685 Victoria Ave
Lakewood OH 44107
216 362-8700

(G-5737)
MAMA MIAS FOODS INC
Also Called: M & M Foods
3270 W 67th Pl (44102-5295)
PHONE..................................216 281-2188
Joseph Carrino, *President*
Tom Burger, *Manager*
EMP: 3
SQ FT: 12,000
SALES (est): 270.6K **Privately Held**
SIC: 2013 5147 Sausages from purchased meat; meats, cured or smoked

(G-5738)
MAMECO INTERNATIONAL INC
4475 E 175th St (44128-3599)
PHONE..................................216 752-4400
Fax: 216 752-5005
Jeff Korach, *Principal*
Ken Recko, *Manager*
EMP: 14
SQ FT: 77,000
SALES (est): 2.8MM
SALES (corp-wide): 4.8B **Publicly Held**
WEB: www.rpminc.com
SIC: 2891 2851 3069 Adhesives & sealants; paints & allied products; floor coverings, rubber

PA: Rpm International Inc.
2628 Pearl Rd
Medina OH 44256
330 273-5090

(G-5739)
MANITOWOC COMPANY INC
Also Called: Cleveland Shiprepair Company
1847 Columbus Rd (44113-2411)
PHONE..................................920 746-3332
Fax: 216 621-4885
Steve Konzel, *Manager*
Jim Diver, *Manager*
EMP: 6
SALES (corp-wide): 1.6B **Publicly Held**
WEB: www.manitowoc.com
SIC: 3731 7699 3441 3599 Cargo vessels, building & repairing; boiler repair shop; fabricated structural metal; machine shop, jobbing & repair
PA: The Manitowoc Company Inc
2400 S 44th St
Manitowoc WI 54220
920 684-4410

(G-5740)
MAR MOR INC
Also Called: Mealey Industrial Lubricants
3591 W 56th St (44102-5737)
PHONE..................................216 961-6900
Fax: 216 281-2777
Mario Pisano, *President*
EMP: 6
SQ FT: 8,500
SALES (est): 1.3MM **Privately Held**
SIC: 2992 Lubricating oils & greases

(G-5741)
MARBLE WORKS
Also Called: Outdoorwarehouse
17827 Roseland Rd (44112-1230)
PHONE..................................216 496-7745
Fax: 216 692-0042
Rich Duleba, *Owner*
EMP: 5
SQ FT: 6,500
SALES (est): 1.7MM **Privately Held**
WEB: www.polarhood.com
SIC: 3281 5149 Cut stone & stone products; baking supplies

(G-5742)
MARCUS UPPE INC
Also Called: Clicks Document Management
815 Superior Ave E # 714 (44114-2706)
PHONE..................................216 263-4000
Duane Nelson, *Accounts Mgr*
Mark Sukie, *Branch Mgr*
EMP: 60 **Privately Held**
SIC: 2759 Commercial printing
PA: Marcus Uppe Inc
320 Fort Duquesne Blvd # 300
Pittsburgh PA 15222

(G-5743)
MARICH MACHINE & TOOL CO INC
3815 Lakeside Ave E (44114-3843)
PHONE..................................216 391-5502
Fax: 216 391-6728
Andrew Marich, *President*
EMP: 9
SQ FT: 10,000
SALES (est): 1.2MM **Privately Held**
SIC: 3599 Machine shop, jobbing & repair

(G-5744)
MARK DENTAL LABORATORY
24300 Chagrin Blvd # 310 (44122-5639)
PHONE..................................216 464-6424
EMP: 8
SQ FT: 3,000
SALES (est): 470K **Privately Held**
SIC: 8072 3843 Dental Laboratory Mfg Dental Equipment/Supplies

(G-5745)
MARK TRUE ENGRAVING CO
1250 W 76th St (44102-2029)
PHONE..................................216 651-7700
Thomas Timura, *President*
Judy Mino, *Sales Mgr*
EMP: 5
SQ FT: 40,000
SALES (est): 586.8K **Privately Held**
SIC: 3469 Stamping metal for the trade

(G-5746)
MARK TRUE ENGRAVING COMPANY
3264 W 105th St (44111-2865)
PHONE..................................216 252-7422
David Timura, *Owner*
EMP: 5
SALES (est): 527K **Privately Held**
SIC: 3479 Etching & engraving

(G-5747)
MARKETING DIRECTIONS INC
Also Called: Trend Curve, The
28005 Clemens Rd (44145-1139)
P.O. Box 44475, Eden Prairie MN (55344-1475)
PHONE..................................440 835-5550
Steven Borsch, *Managing Prtnr*
Michelle Lamb, *Chairman*
EMP: 5
SALES (est): 439.6K **Privately Held**
SIC: 2721 Periodicals

(G-5748)
MARKING DEVICES INC
3110 Payne Ave (44114-4504)
PHONE..................................216 861-4498
Fax: 216 861-3451
Theodore Cutts, *President*
Sandy Forcier, *Office Mgr*
Sandy Wengstrom, *Office Mgr*
Margaret Hamge, *Relations*
EMP: 30
SALES (est): 1.8MM
SALES (corp-wide): 2.3MM **Privately Held**
WEB: www.royalacme.com
SIC: 3953 Marking devices; embossing seals & hand stamps; printing dies, rubber or plastic, for marking machines
PA: Royal Acme Corporation
3110 Payne Ave
Cleveland OH 44114
216 241-1477

(G-5749)
MARLIN MANUFACTURING CORP (PA)
12800 Corporate Dr (44130-9311)
PHONE..................................216 676-1340
Fax: 216 676-1344
Gary Kloock, *General Mgr*
John Tymkewicz, *Principal*
John H Breisch, *Principal*
Wallace B Heiser, *Principal*
John Milbum, *Purchasing*
▲ **EMP:** 70 **EST:** 1952
SQ FT: 42,000
SALES (est): 10.1MM **Privately Held**
WEB: www.marlinmfg.com
SIC: 3823 Pyrometers, industrial process type; thermocouples, industrial process type

(G-5750)
MARLIN THERMOCOUPLE WIRE INC
Also Called: Miller Wire & Cable
12800 Corporate Dr (44130-9311)
PHONE..................................440 835-1950
Fax: 440 835-2188
Ronald A Miller, *President*
David A Miller, *Vice Pres*
Joan Vargo, *Admin Sec*
▲ **EMP:** 24
SQ FT: 46,000
SALES (est): 6.6MM **Privately Held**
SIC: 3315 Wire, steel: insulated or armored

(G-5751)
MARLOW-2000 INC
Also Called: Martin Industrial Truck
13811 Enterprise Ave (44135-5115)
PHONE..................................216 362-8500
Danny E Martin, *President*
Sandra Martin, *Treasurer*
Bill Ranke, *Manager*
Sandy Martin, *Director*
EMP: 13
SQ FT: 22,000

SALES: 1MM **Privately Held**
WEB: www.mit1976.com
SIC: 5531 3537 7513 Truck equipment &
parts; forklift trucks; truck rental & leasing,
no drivers

(G-5752)
**MARTIN PULTRUSION GROUP
INC**
20801 Miles Rd Ste B (44128-4530)
PHONE................440 439-9130
Jeff Martin, *President*
William Ard, *President*
Chris Mrugacz, *Engineer*
Carol Neal, *Manager*
EMP: 6 **EST:** 1993
SQ FT: 7,360
SALES (est): 1.2MM **Privately Held**
WEB: www.martinpultrusion.com
SIC: 3544 Special dies, tools, jigs & fix-
tures

(G-5753)
MARTIN SHEET METAL INC
Also Called: Martin Cab Div
7108 Madison Ave (44102-4093)
PHONE................216 377-8200
Fax: 216 651-2079
Robert P Martin Sr, *CEO*
Pauline Martin, *Ch of Bd*
Frank Bendyck, *Principal*
Jo Wilhelm, *Purchasing*
George F Voinovich, *CFO*
EMP: 80 **EST:** 1920
SQ FT: 100,000
SALES (est): 18.3MM **Privately Held**
WEB: www.martincab.com
SIC: 3537 3713 Cabs, for industrial trucks
& tractors; truck & bus bodies

(G-5754)
**MARTINDALE ELECTRIC
COMPANY**
1375 Hird Ave (44107-3008)
P.O. Box 72419 (44192-0002)
PHONE................216 521-8567
Fax: 216 521-9476
Jim Satterthwaite, *President*
F Z Marty, *Principal*
Brian Dupris, *Vice Pres*
Jeffrey Snyder, *Vice Pres*
EMP: 48
SQ FT: 33,000
SALES (est): 10.1MM **Privately Held**
SIC: 3425 3541 Saw blades & handsaws;
machine tools, metal cutting type

(G-5755)
**MARXWARE COMPUTING
SERVICES**
4963 Schaaf Ln (44131-1034)
PHONE................216 661-5263
Mark Butler, *President*
EMP: 10
SALES (est): 757.6K **Privately Held**
SIC: 7372 Prepackaged software

(G-5756)
**MASTER CHROME SERVICE
INC**
5709 Herman Ave (44102-2195)
PHONE................216 961-2012
Fax: 216 961-3105
Gerald J Garver, *President*
Micheal J Rowe, *Vice Pres*
Charloes Rowe, *Admin Sec*
EMP: 33 **EST:** 1936
SQ FT: 10,000
SALES (est): 3.5MM **Privately Held**
SIC: 3471 Chromium plating of metals or
formed products

(G-5757)
MASTER CRAFT PRODUCTS INC
10621 Briggs Rd (44111-5329)
PHONE................216 281-5910
Fax: 216 281-5965
Jim Szente Jr, *President*
Cyndi Szente, *Treasurer*
EMP: 12
SQ FT: 4,400
SALES (est): 880K **Privately Held**
WEB: www.mastercraftdies.com
SIC: 3544 Special dies, tools, jigs & fix-
tures

(G-5758)
MASTER MFG CO INC
Also Called: Master Caster Company
9200 Inman Ave (44105-2110)
PHONE................216 641-0500
Fax: 216 641-0537
Iris Rubinfield, *President*
Jim Donofrio, *Plant Mgr*
Diane Rose, *Purchasing*
Penny Heinzmann, *Treasurer*
Bob Ptacek, *Sales Executive*
▲ **EMP:** 34
SQ FT: 10,000
SALES (est): 5.3MM **Privately Held**
SIC: 3429 2599 2392 3069 Furniture
builders' & other household hardware;
factory furniture & fixtures; household fur-
nishings; hard rubber & molded rubber
products

(G-5759)
MASTER PRINTING COMPANY
3112 Broadview Rd (44109-3390)
PHONE................216 351-2246
Fax: 216 749-2808
Donald Dobos, *President*
Russell Dobos, *Vice Pres*
David Dobos, *Treasurer*
Franklin Kotnik, *Sales Associate*
Roni Vee, *Manager*
EMP: 23 **EST:** 1928
SQ FT: 20,000
SALES (est): 4MM **Privately Held**
WEB: www.mprinting.com
SIC: 2752 Commercial printing, offset

(G-5760)
MASTER PRODUCTS COMPANY
6400 Park Ave (44105-4991)
PHONE................216 341-1740
Fax: 216 341-5555
R Jeffrey Walters, *President*
Greg Walters, *Vice Pres*
David Mitskavich, *Vice Pres*
Wil Warren, *Human Res Mgr*
Rich Fholtis, *Accounts Mgr*
EMP: 57
SQ FT: 70,000
SALES: 8MM **Privately Held**
SIC: 3452 3469 3568 Washers, metal;
stamping metal for the trade; power trans-
mission equipment

(G-5761)
**MATERION TECHNICAL MTLS
INC**
6070 Parkland Blvd (44124-4191)
PHONE................216 486-4200
Matthew Willson, *President*
Dennis Habrat, *Principal*
Daniel Skoch, *VP Admin*
Michael Anderson, *Vice Pres*
Nic Baloi, *Vice Pres*
EMP: 85
SALES (est): 18.8MM **Privately Held**
SIC: 3399 Primary metal products

(G-5762)
MAX PRO TOOLS INC
8999 W Pleasant Valley Rd (44130-7644)
PHONE................440 885-9522
Steven Kurr, *President*
EMP: 10
SALES (est): 1MM **Privately Held**
SIC: 3541 Machine tools, metal cutting
type

(G-5763)
MAYFAIR GRANITE CO INC
Also Called: Mayfair Memorial
4202 Mayfield Rd (44121-3008)
PHONE................216 382-8150
Fax: 216 382-8150
Michael J Johns Sr, *President*
Nicolette L Johns, *Corp Secy*
Michael N Johns, *Vice Pres*
Monica Johns, *Vice Pres*
Monica Montani, *Vice Pres*
EMP: 7 **EST:** 1937
SALES (est): 1MM **Privately Held**
SIC: 5999 5032 3993 Monuments, fin-
ished to custom order; granite building
stone; signs & advertising specialties

(G-5764)
**MAYFRAN INTERNATIONAL INC
(HQ)**
6650 Beta Dr (44143-2352)
PHONE................440 461-4100
Fax: 440 461-0147
Naoshige Sakai, *President*
Michael Gervasi, *General Mgr*
Karen Rebonek, *General Mgr*
Ed McManus, *Vice Pres*
Tom Neibecker, *Vice Pres*
▲ **EMP:** 239
SQ FT: 154,000
SALES: 60.8MM
SALES (corp-wide): 1.7B **Privately Held**
WEB: www.mayfran.com
SIC: 3535 Belt conveyor systems, general
industrial use
PA: Tsubakimoto Chain Co.
3-3-3, Nakanoshima, Kita-Ku
Osaka OSK 530-0
664 410-011

(G-5765)
**MAZZELLA LIFTING TECH INC
(HQ)**
21000 Aerospace Pkwy (44142-1072)
PHONE................440 239-7000
Fax: 440 239-7010
Anthony Mazzella, *CEO*
James J Mazzella, *Vice Pres*
Terry Pipik, *Plant Mgr*
Joe Stanton, *Opers Mgr*
Adam Franz, *Sales Engr*
▲ **EMP:** 80 **EST:** 1959
SQ FT: 50,000
SALES (est): 55.7MM **Privately Held**
WEB: www.mazzellalifting.com
SIC: 3496 Miscellaneous fabricated wire
products

(G-5766)
MAZZELLA LIFTING TECH INC
21000 Aerospace Pkwy (44142-1072)
PHONE................440 239-5700
Tony Mazzella, *President*
Kathleen Fay, *Controller*
EMP: 60 **Privately Held**
WEB: www.mazzellalifting.com
SIC: 3531 Backhoes, tractors, cranes,
plows & similar equipment; cranes
HQ: Mazzella Lifting Technologies, Inc.
21000 Aerospace Pkwy
Cleveland OH 44142
440 239-7000

(G-5767)
MAZZOLINI ARTCRAFT CO INC
1607 E 41st St (44103-2396)
PHONE................216 431-7529
Fax: 216 431-7531
John Mazzolini, *President*
▲ **EMP:** 11
SQ FT: 4,800
SALES (est): 1.5MM **Privately Held**
WEB: www.mazzart.com
SIC: 3299 5199 Statuary: gypsum, clay,
papier mache, metal, etc.; statuary

(G-5768)
MB DYNAMICS INC
25865 Richmond Rd (44146-1431)
PHONE................216 292-5850
Richard E Mc Cormick, *CEO*
Phillip Lehmann, *Design Engr*
Charles Mancuse, *Controller*
Dick Deemer, *Human Resources*
Edward Peterson, *Manager*
EMP: 22
SQ FT: 25,000
SALES (est): 5.8MM **Privately Held**
WEB: www.mbdynamics.com
SIC: 3829 Testing equipment: abrasion,
shearing strength, etc.

(G-5769)
**MCHAEL D GORONOK STRING
INSTRS**
10823 Magnolia Dr (44106-1807)
PHONE................216 421-4227
Michael D Goronok, *Owner*
EMP: 9
SQ FT: 8,000

SALES: 145K **Privately Held**
SIC: 3931 5099 String instruments &
parts; musical instruments

(G-5770)
MCM IND CO INC
7800 Finney Ave (44105-5125)
PHONE................216 641-6300
Bob Reid, *Engineer*
Mike Zlojutro, *Branch Mgr*
EMP: 30
SQ FT: 51,055
SALES (corp-wide): 6.5MM **Privately
Held**
SIC: 3496 Miscellaneous fabricated wire
products
PA: Mcm Ind. Co., Inc.
22901 Millcreek Blvd # 250
Beachwood OH 44122
216 292-4506

(G-5771)
**MCMATH & SHEETS UNLIMITED
INC**
Also Called: Offset Theory
4427 Mayfield Rd (44121-3633)
PHONE................216 381-0010
Fax: 216 381-0061
David Thompson, *President*
EMP: 3
SQ FT: 2,000
SALES (est): 450K **Privately Held**
SIC: 2752 Commercial printing, offset

(G-5772)
MCNAMARAS PUB INC
3498 W 146th St (44111-2209)
PHONE................216 671-8820
Gary McNamara, *CEO*
EMP: 4
SALES (est): 236.8K **Privately Held**
SIC: 2731 Book publishing

(G-5773)
MCTECH CORP
5000 Crayton Ave (44104-2826)
PHONE................216 391-7700
Fax: 216 361-2522
Linda Frazier, *Exec VP*
Scott Rediger, *Manager*
EMP: 12
SALES (corp-wide): 32.7MM **Privately
Held**
SIC: 3531 Concrete plants
PA: Mctech Corp
8100 Grand Ave Ste 100
Cleveland OH 44104
216 391-7700

(G-5774)
**MEASUREMENT COMPUTING
CORP (HQ)**
Also Called: Iotech
25971 Cannon Rd (44146-1833)
PHONE................440 439-4091
Mark Marini, *President*
Michael Grace, *Business Mgr*
Edward Ciehanosk, *Mfg Staff*
Jack Field, *Regl Sales Mgr*
Glenn Fasnacht, *Chief Mktg Ofcr*
EMP: 27
SQ FT: 30,000
SALES (est): 3.6MM
SALES (corp-wide): 1.2B **Publicly Held**
WEB: www.iotech.com
SIC: 3823 Computer interface equipment
for industrial process control
PA: National Instruments Corporation
11500 N Mopac Expy
Austin TX 78759
512 338-9119

(G-5775)
MEDCO LABS INC
Also Called: Medco Adhesive Coated Prod-
ucts
5156 Richmond Rd (44146-1331)
PHONE................216 292-7546
Gary Fenton, *President*
Marvin Magar, *Vice Pres*
Arliene Mills, *Admin Sec*
EMP: 15
SQ FT: 15,000

SALES (est): 2.8MM
SALES (corp-wide): 6.4MM **Privately Held**
WEB: www.medcocoatedproducts.com
SIC: **3842** Adhesive tape & plasters, medicated or non-medicated
PA: Marlen Manufacturing And Development Co.
5150 Richmond Rd
Bedford OH 44146
216 292-7060

(G-5776)
MEDQUEST COMMUNICATIONS INC
3800 Lkside Ave E Ste 201 (44114)
PHONE....................................216 391-9100
Fax: 216 522-9707
Mark J Goodman, *President*
Donna Paglia, *Manager*
EMP: 20
SQ FT: 3,400
SALES (est): 1.8MM **Privately Held**
WEB: www.entjournal.com
SIC: **2721** Trade journals: publishing & printing

(G-5777)
MEDTRONIC INC
5005 Rockside Rd Ste 1160 (44131-6801)
PHONE....................................216 642-1977
Fax: 216 642-1981
Larry Saunders, *Branch Mgr*
EMP: 17 **Privately Held**
SIC: **3845** Electromedical equipment
HQ: Medtronic, Inc.
710 Medtronic Pkwy
Minneapolis MN 55432
763 514-4000

(G-5778)
MEGAJOULE STORAGE INC
1768 E 25th St (44114-4418)
PHONE....................................216 496-8302
EMP: 3 EST: 2010
SALES (est): 158.1K **Privately Held**
SIC: **3691** Lead acid batteries (storage batteries)

(G-5779)
MELCOR CORPORATION (DH)
4707 Detroit Ave (44102-2216)
PHONE....................................609 393-4178
Charles Weber, *President*
Aim Karas, *Vice Pres*
James Karas, *Vice Pres*
Robert Smythe, *Vice Pres*
Scott Steurer, *Purch Mgr*
◆ EMP: 207 EST: 1996
SQ FT: 32,000
SALES (est): 17.1MM
SALES (corp-wide): 950.5MM **Privately Held**
SIC: **3674** Thermoelectric devices, solid state
HQ: Laird Technologies, Inc.
3481 Rider Trl S
Earth City MO 63045
636 898-6000

(G-5780)
MELIN TOOL COMPANY INC
5565 Venture Dr Ste C (44130-9302)
PHONE....................................216 362-4200
Fax: 216 362-4230
Mildred Rathberger, *Ch of Bd*
Mike Wochna, *President*
Jack Dean, *Plant Supt*
Dan Zuelch, *Mfg Mgr*
Sue Dimassa, *Accountant*
EMP: 70
SQ FT: 25,000
SALES (est): 18MM **Privately Held**
WEB: www.endmill.com
SIC: **3545 3541** Machine tool accessories; machine tools, metal cutting type

(G-5781)
MELINZ-REBAR INC
16226 S Waterloo Rd Ste 3 (44110-3812)
P.O. Box 19234 (44119-0234)
PHONE....................................216 531-8988
Fax: 216 531-5120
Bruno Melinz, *President*
Philip Melinz, *Vice Pres*
EMP: 20

SQ FT: 20,000
SALES (est): 4.5MM **Privately Held**
SIC: **3449** Bars, concrete reinforcing: fabricated steel

(G-5782)
MEMPHIS SMOKEHOUSE INC
Also Called: Tobacco Company
8463 Memphis Ave (44144-2126)
PHONE....................................216 351-5321
Dwight Hughes, *President*
Jim Seward, *President*
EMP: 7
SQ FT: 1,200
SALES: 3MM **Privately Held**
SIC: **2111** Cigarettes

(G-5783)
MERCURY AIR SERVICES LLC
Also Called: Air Services
5211 Secondary Dr (44135-3118)
PHONE....................................216 898-4800
Fax: 216 898-4820
Aimee Dalton, *Manager*
Tod Wulff, *Director*
Stephen Maiden, *Director*
EMP: 30 EST: 2012
SALES (est): 5.2MM **Privately Held**
SIC: **3721** Aircraft

(G-5784)
MERCURY BIOMED LLC
29001 Cedar Rd Ste 326 (44124-6501)
PHONE....................................216 777-1492
Brad Pulver, *CEO*
Brian Patrick, *Vice Pres*
EMP: 3 EST: 2015
SQ FT: 3,000
SALES (est): 206.8K **Privately Held**
SIC: **3845** Electromedical equipment

(G-5785)
MERIT FOUNDRY CO INC
2289 N Saint James Pkwy (44106-3657)
PHONE....................................216 741-4282
George R Mroz Jr, *President*
EMP: 4
SQ FT: 8,000
SALES (est): 520.4K **Privately Held**
SIC: **3365** Aluminum & aluminum-based alloy castings

(G-5786)
MET-CHEM INC
837 E 79th St (44103-1807)
PHONE....................................216 881-7900
Fax: 216 881-8950
Walter Senney, *President*
Jeff Scott, *General Mgr*
Richard Martin, *Plant Mgr*
Nicole Magnone, *Controller*
Jeff Kubiak, *VP Sales*
▲ EMP: 45
SQ FT: 25,000
SALES (est): 2.7MM **Privately Held**
SIC: **3569** Filters, general line: industrial

(G-5787)
METAL FABRICATING CORPORATION
10408 Berea Rd (44102-2506)
PHONE....................................216 631-8121
Fax: 216 631-2453
Judy Kalski, *President*
Bernard Golias Sr, *Chairman*
Joseph Golias, *Vice Pres*
Robert Golias, *Vice Pres*
Tom Hammond, *Production*
EMP: 87 EST: 1932
SQ FT: 150,000
SALES (est): 17.8MM **Privately Held**
WEB: www.metalfabricatingcorp.com
SIC: **2542 3444 3469 3443** Cabinets: show, display or storage: except wood; bins, prefabricated sheet metal; stamping metal for the trade; fabricated plate work (boiler shop); office furniture, except wood; metal household furniture

(G-5788)
METAL FINISHING NEEDS LTD
16025 Van Aken Blvd (44120-5349)
PHONE....................................216 561-6334
Thomas J Foley, *Principal*
EMP: 3

SALES (est): 136.1K **Privately Held**
SIC: **3471** Cleaning, polishing & finishing

(G-5789)
METAL-MATION INC
2391 W 38th St (44113-3838)
PHONE....................................216 651-1083
Fax: 216 651-1085
Robert Nagel, *President*
Jerry Walker, *Vice Pres*
EMP: 16
SQ FT: 2,500
SALES (est): 1.6MM **Privately Held**
WEB: www.wellwalker.com
SIC: **8748 3365** Business consulting; aluminum foundries

(G-5790)
METALCRETE INDUSTRIES INC
Also Called: Sealwall Products
4133 Payne Ave (44103-2324)
PHONE....................................440 526-5600
Ron Ford, *Branch Mgr*
Walt Landis, *Director*
EMP: 8
SALES (corp-wide): 1.2MM **Privately Held**
SIC: **2851 2891** Vinyl coatings, strippable; coating, air curing; cement, except linoleum & tile
PA: Metalcrete Industries, Inc.
4133 Payne Ave
Cleveland OH
440 526-5600

(G-5791)
METALS CRANKSHAFT GRINDING
1435 E 45th St (44103-1115)
PHONE....................................216 431-5778
Patrick Obermayer, *President*
EMP: 4
SQ FT: 6,000
SALES: 300K **Privately Held**
SIC: **3599** Machine shop, jobbing & repair

(G-5792)
METRO MECH INC
Also Called: Metalsmiths
3599 E 49th St (44105-1151)
PHONE....................................216 641-6262
Fax: 216 641-6262
Larry Zebrasky, *President*
Tom Zebrasky, *Vice Pres*
EMP: 4 EST: 1964
SQ FT: 4,000
SALES: 200K **Privately Held**
SIC: **3714 3724 3568 3544** Motor vehicle transmissions, drive assemblies & parts; aircraft engines & engine parts; power transmission equipment; special dies, tools, jigs & fixtures; construction machinery; concrete products

(G-5793)
MEYER COMPANY (PA)
Also Called: Tomlinson Industries
13700 Broadway Ave (44125-1945)
PHONE....................................216 587-3400
Fax: 800 945-9869
H F Meyer, *President*
Marianne Kives, *General Mgr*
Heidi Figas, *Corp Secy*
Donald Calkins, *Vice Pres*
Michael E Figas, *Vice Pres*
◆ EMP: 170
SQ FT: 100,000
SALES (est): 34.1MM **Privately Held**
WEB: www.tomlinsonind.com
SIC: **3556** Food products machinery

(G-5794)
MEYER PRODUCTS LLC
18513 Euclid Ave (44112-1084)
PHONE....................................216 486-1313
Fax: 216 486-1321
Andrew Outcalt, *President*
◆ EMP: 86
SALES (est): 31.8MM
SALES (corp-wide): 78MM **Privately Held**
SIC: **3531** Construction machinery; blades for graders, scrapers, dozers & snow plows; snow plow attachments

PA: The Louis Berkman Company
600 Grant St Ste 3230
Pittsburgh PA 15219
740 283-3722

(G-5795)
MFH PARTNERS INC (PA)
6650 Beta Dr (44143-2352)
P.O. Box 43038 (44143-0045)
PHONE....................................440 461-4100
J D Sullivan, *Ch of Bd*
Kevin Hatridge, *Info Tech Dir*
Carron Redena, *Exec Sec*
EMP: 10
SQ FT: 4,000
SALES (est): 59.2MM **Privately Held**
SIC: **5084 3535 3568 2296** Industrial machinery & equipment; belt conveyor systems, general industrial use; power transmission equipment; tire cord & fabrics

(G-5796)
MIC-RAY METAL PRODUCTS INC
9016 Manor Ave (44104-4524)
PHONE....................................216 791-2206
Fax: 216 791-2208
Michael Konicky Jr, *President*
Kris Konicky, *Vice Pres*
Raymond Konicky, *Treasurer*
EMP: 10 EST: 1947
SQ FT: 5,000
SALES (est): 960K **Privately Held**
SIC: **3469** Metal stampings

(G-5797)
MICELI DAIRY PRODUCTS CO (PA)
2721 E 90th St (44104-3396)
PHONE....................................216 791-6222
Fax: 216 231-2504
Joseph D Miceli, *CEO*
John J Miceli Jr, *Exec VP*
Joseph Lograsso, *Vice Pres*
Charles Surace, *Vice Pres*
Adam Csanyi, *Prdtn Mgr*
▲ EMP: 90
SQ FT: 25,000
SALES (est): 74.4MM **Privately Held**
SIC: **2022 0241** Natural cheese; milk production

(G-5798)
MICRO LAPPING & GRINDING CO
12320 Plaza Dr (44130-1060)
PHONE....................................216 267-6500
Fax: 216 267-6529
Ray Robaugh, *President*
John Dunmire, *Vice Pres*
EMP: 40
SQ FT: 25,000
SALES (est): 4.4MM **Privately Held**
SIC: **3599 3471** Grinding castings for the trade; plating & polishing

(G-5799)
MICROFORM INC
29529 Goulders Grn (44140-1271)
PHONE....................................440 899-6339
N A Shanks, *President*
EMP: 5
SQ FT: 500
SALES (est): 265.4K **Privately Held**
SIC: **3452** Bolts, nuts, rivets & washers

(G-5800)
MICROPURE FILTRATION INC
Also Called: Wfs Filter Co
837 E 79th St (44103-1807)
PHONE....................................952 472-2323
Trey Senney, *CEO*
Robert Pollmann, *President*
Marcy Pollmann, *Corp Secy*
Natalie Morris, *Webmaster*
▲ EMP: 16
SQ FT: 10,000
SALES: 750K **Privately Held**
WEB: www.micropure.com
SIC: **3677** Filtration devices, electronic

(G-5801)
MICROSHEEN CORPORATION
1100 E 222nd St Ste 1 (44117-1127)
PHONE....................................216 481-5610
Fax: 216 481-2046

Randy Hanson, *President*
Mike Elliott, *Principal*
W E Groenstein, *Vice Pres*
EMP: 10 **EST:** 1960
SQ FT: 30,000
SALES: 943.3K
SALES (corp-wide): 25.6MM **Privately Held**
WEB: www.microsheencorporation.com
SIC: 3471 Polishing, metals or formed products; anodizing (plating) of metals or formed products
PA: Interlake Industries, Inc.
    4732 E 355th St
    Willoughby OH 44094
    440 942-0800

(G-5802)
MICROSOFT CORPORATION
6050 Oak Tree Blvd # 300 (44131-6929)
PHONE..................................216 986-1440
Fax: 216 986-1445
Kerry Duncan, *Accounts Mgr*
Zachary Johnson, *Program Mgr*
Chris Caster, *Manager*
Lori Olsen, *Admin Asst*
EMP: 50
SALES (corp-wide): 85.3B **Publicly Held**
WEB: www.microsoft.com
SIC: 7372 Prepackaged software
PA: Microsoft Corporation
    1 Microsoft Way
    Redmond WA 98052
    425 882-8080

(G-5803)
MID AMERICA CHEMICAL CORP
4701 Spring Rd (44131-1025)
PHONE..................................216 749-0100
Fax: 216 749-7041
Frank J Martinek Jr, *President*
Julienne C Martinek, *Vice Pres*
Debra Matrinek, *Vice Pres*
Doris Hallaman, *Admin Sec*
EMP: 9
SQ FT: 19,000
SALES: 750K **Privately Held**
SIC: 2869 2851 Industrial organic chemicals; solvents, organic; paints & allied products; varnishes; removers & cleaners

(G-5804)
MID AMERICAN VENTURES INC
Also Called: Cookie Cupboard
7600 Wall St Ste 205 (44125-3358)
PHONE..................................216 524-0974
Fax: 216 524-9772
Richard A Pignatiello, *President*
Ellen Pignatiello, *Vice Pres*
EMP: 10
SALES (est): 1.1MM **Privately Held**
SIC: 2045 2099 Doughs, frozen or refrigerated: from purchased flour; food preparations

(G-5805)
MID-AMERICA STEEL CORP
Also Called: Mid-America Stainless
20900 Saint Clair Ave (44117-1020)
PHONE..................................800 282-3466
Fax: 216 692-3803
Jonathan Kaufman, *Vice Pres*
Joe Spellacy, *Plant Mgr*
Don Snyder, *Accountant*
Steve Feinberg, *Natl Sales Mgr*
Katherine Denner, *Sales Staff*
EMP: 50
SQ FT: 120,000
SALES (est): 72.1MM **Privately Held**
SIC: 5051 3469 3316 3312 Metals service centers & offices; sheets, metal; metal stampings; cold finishing of steel shapes; blast furnaces & steel mills

(G-5806)
MID-WEST FORGE CORPORATION (PA)
17301 Saint Clair Ave (44110-2508)
PHONE..................................216 481-3030
Robert I Gale III, *Ch of Bd*
Michael Sherwin, *Vice Ch Bd*
Paul C Gum, *President*
John T Webster, *Vice Pres*
Jerry Mejman, *Prdtn Mgr*
EMP: 150
SQ FT: 165,000

SALES (est): 36.4MM **Privately Held**
WEB: www.mid-westforge.com
SIC: 3462 Iron & steel forgings

(G-5807)
MIDWEST BOX COMPANY
9801 Walford Ave Ste C (44102-4788)
PHONE..................................216 281-9021
Fax: 216 281-5707
Susan Hecht Remer, *CEO*
Simon Tucker, *Plant Mgr*
EMP: 20 **EST:** 1964
SQ FT: 150,000
SALES (est): 7MM **Privately Held**
WEB: www.midwestbox.com
SIC: 2653 Boxes, corrugated: made from purchased materials

(G-5808)
MIDWEST COMPRESSOR CO INC (PA)
12901 Elmwood Ave (44111-5916)
PHONE..................................216 941-9200
Fax: 216 941-8801
Alex Syntax, *President*
EMP: 4
SALES (est): 638.9K **Privately Held**
WEB: www.midwestcompressor.com
SIC: 3585 1711 Compressors for refrigeration & air conditioning equipment; plumbing, heating, air-conditioning contractors

(G-5809)
MIDWEST CURTAINWALLS INC
5171 Grant Ave (44125-1031)
PHONE..................................216 641-7900
Fax: 216 641-5041
Donald F Kelly Jr, *President*
EMP: 80
SQ FT: 55,000
SALES (est): 22.5MM **Privately Held**
WEB: www.midwestcurtainwalls.com
SIC: 3449 3442 1751 Curtain wall, metal; curtain walls for buildings, steel; window & door frames; window & door (prefabricated) installation

(G-5810)
MIDWEST INDUSTRIAL PRODUCTS
7424 Bessemer Ave (44127-1820)
PHONE..................................216 771-8555
Michael Dunn, *President*
EMP: 4
SALES: 300K **Privately Held**
WEB: www.mipco.com
SIC: 2952 5033 Asphalt felts & coatings; roofing & siding materials

(G-5811)
MIDWEST PRECISION PRODUCTS
9940 York Alpha Dr (44133-3510)
PHONE..................................440 237-9500
Fax: 440 237-0303
Jim Diamond, *President*
Ella Strapko, *Buyer*
Wes Novak, *Manager*
EMP: 10
SQ FT: 25,000
SALES: 1MM **Privately Held**
WEB: www.midwestprecision.com
SIC: 2296 Fabric for reinforcing industrial belting

(G-5812)
MIKAN DIE AND TOOL LLC
13410 Enterprise Ave (44135-5162)
PHONE..................................216 265-2811
Mike Pillar, *Mng Member*
Andrew McInnes,
EMP: 5
SALES: 400K **Privately Held**
SIC: 3544 3545 Special dies & tools; machine tool accessories

(G-5813)
MILAN TOOL CORP
8989 Brookpark Rd (44129-6819)
P.O. Box 29336 (44129-0336)
PHONE..................................216 661-1078
Fax: 216 661-6946
Mark Milan, *President*
Andrew Milan, *Vice Pres*
Miles Badovick, *Prdtn Mgr*

Chris Terveek, *Accounts Mgr*
Jim Davis, *Manager*
▲ **EMP:** 30 **EST:** 1946
SQ FT: 20,000
SALES: 9.4MM **Privately Held**
SIC: 3728 3541 Aircraft body assemblies & parts; grinding machines, metalworking; machine tool replacement & repair parts; metal cutting types

(G-5814)
MILANO MONUMENTS LLC
14600 Brookpark Rd (44135-5165)
PHONE..................................216 362-1199
Fax: 216 382-6230
Bret Ninke, *Sales Staff*
Vincent Milano Jr,
▲ **EMP:** 9
SQ FT: 3,000
SALES (est): 1.4MM **Privately Held**
WEB: www.milanomonuments.com
SIC: 3281 Cut stone & stone products

(G-5815)
MILETI OPTICAL INC
Also Called: Mileti Optical & Hearing Ctr
5957 State Rd Ste 1 (44134-2872)
PHONE..................................440 884-6333
Fax: 440 888-0683
Mark Mileti, *President*
Victor Mileti, *Vice Pres*
EMP: 3 **EST:** 1962
SQ FT: 1,500
SALES (est): 491.5K **Privately Held**
SIC: 3851 5995 Ophthalmic goods; optical goods stores

(G-5816)
MILL & MOTION INC
5415 E Schaaf Rd Ste 101 (44131-1335)
PHONE..................................216 524-4000
Fax: 216 524-4000
Daniel A Hala, *President*
Albert E Hala, *Chairman*
Bruce Sidaway, *Vice Pres*
EMP: 17
SQ FT: 18,000
SALES (est): 1.5MM **Privately Held**
WEB: www.millmotion.com
SIC: 3599 8711 Machine shop, jobbing & repair; designing: ship, boat, machine & product

(G-5817)
MILLCRAFT GROUP LLC (PA)
Also Called: Deltacraft
6800 Grant Ave (44105-5628)
PHONE..................................216 441-5500
Fax: 216 641-2610
Kay Mlakar, *Ch of Bd*
Katherine Mlakar, *Ch of Bd*
Travis Mlakar, *President*
Mark Hephner, *Division Mgr*
Jack Oldiges, *Division Mgr*
EMP: 75
SQ FT: 90,000
SALES (est): 127.3MM **Privately Held**
WEB: www.deltacraft.com
SIC: 5111 5113 2679 Printing & writing paper; industrial & personal service paper; paper products, converted

(G-5818)
MILLS CUSTOMS WOODWORKS
3950 Prospect Ave E (44115-2710)
PHONE..................................216 407-3600
Paul Mills, *Principal*
EMP: 4 **EST:** 2008
SALES (est): 430.6K **Privately Held**
SIC: 2431 Millwork

(G-5819)
MINDCRAFTED SYSTEMS INC
1969 Newbury Dr (44145-3334)
PHONE..................................440 821-2245
Frank Shoemaker, *President*
EMP: 4
SALES (est): 289.6K **Privately Held**
WEB: www.mindcrafted.com
SIC: 7372 Prepackaged software

(G-5820)
MINERAL MET INC
7700 Bessemer Ave (44127-1826)
PHONE..................................216 641-3555
Fax: 216 641-5533

Anthony Demos, *President*
EMP: 8
SALES (est): 460K **Privately Held**
SIC: 3295 Minerals, ground or treated

(G-5821)
MINGS HEATING & AC
11902 Larchmere Blvd (44120-1135)
PHONE..................................216 721-2007
Ming Sing Gum, *President*
EMP: 4
SQ FT: 1,340
SALES (corp-wide): 634.9K **Privately Held**
SIC: 3444 1711 Sheet metalwork; furnace casings, sheet metal; plumbing, heating, air-conditioning contractors
PA: Ming's Heating & Air Conditioning Inc
    2469 S Taylor Rd
    Cleveland Heights OH 44118
    216 321-0578

(G-5822)
MINOR CORPORATION
1599 Maywood Rd (44121-4101)
PHONE..................................216 291-8723
John Scott Minor, *President*
EMP: 5
SALES (est): 323.9K **Privately Held**
WEB: www.bailey.com
SIC: 3661 8742 Telephone sets, all types except cellular radio; marketing consulting services

(G-5823)
MINOTAS TROPHIES & AWARDS
40 Alpha Park (44143-2208)
PHONE..................................440 720-1288
Jacqueline Minotas, *Principal*
Greg Minotas, *Principal*
EMP: 4
SALES (est): 300K **Privately Held**
SIC: 5999 5094 2499 3089 Trophies & plaques; coins, medals & trophies; engraved wood products; engraving of plastic; advertising, promotional & trade show services; engraving service

(G-5824)
MITCHELL BROS ICE CREAM INC
1867 W 25th St (44113-3406)
PHONE..................................216 861-2799
Michael Mitchell, *President*
EMP: 13
SALES (est): 1.2MM **Privately Held**
SIC: 2024 Ice cream & frozen desserts

(G-5825)
MOBILITY REVOLUTION LLC
6753 Engle Rd Ste A (44130-7935)
PHONE..................................909 980-2259
Evan Smiedt, *CEO*
Prashant Shah, *Controller*
Bradley Smiedt, *Mng Member*
▲ **EMP:** 25 **EST:** 2011
SALES (est): 2.5MM **Privately Held**
SIC: 3841 Surgical & medical instruments

(G-5826)
MODERN DESIGN STAMPING DIV
Also Called: R L Corbett Co, The
1618 Maple Rd (44121-1732)
PHONE..................................216 382-6318
R L Corbett, *President*
James P Corbett, *President*
Robert Corbett, *Vice Pres*
Paul Reik, *Admin Sec*
EMP: 4 **EST:** 1958
SALES: 250K **Privately Held**
SIC: 3599 5084 Custom machinery; hydraulic systems equipment & supplies

(G-5827)
MODERN INDUSTRIES INC
6610 Metta Ave (44103-1678)
PHONE..................................216 432-2855
Fax: 216 432-2755
Steve Seredick, *Ch of Bd*
Gregory Senn, *President*
Vee Chapman, *Administration*
EMP: 7
SQ FT: 22,000
SALES (est): 3.1MM **Privately Held**
SIC: 3599 Machine shop, jobbing & repair

(G-5828)

MODERN PIPE SUPPORTS CORP
4734 Commerce Ave (44103-3520)
P.O. Box 603544 (44103-0544)
PHONE.............................216 361-1666
Fax: 216 361-0058
Albert J Laufer, *President*
Cheryl A Laufer, *Corp Secy*
EMP: 25
SQ FT: 26,000
SALES (est): 3.4MM **Privately Held**
SIC: 3469 Metal stampings

(G-5829)

MOM TOOLS LLC
3659 Green Rd Ste 304 (44122-5715)
PHONE.............................216 283-4014
John Collier, *Mng Member*
Anthony Lockhart, *Mng Member*
EMP: 4
SALES: 50K **Privately Held**
SIC: 3544 Special dies, tools, jigs & fixtures

(G-5830)

MONARCH STEEL COMPANY INC
4650 Johnston Pkwy (44128-3219)
PHONE.............................216 587-8000
Josh Kaufman, *CEO*
Robert L Meyer, *President*
James McCracken, *Regional Mgr*
Garry Engle, *Plant Mgr*
Phil Stidham, *Plant Mgr*
▲ EMP: 40 EST: 1934
SQ FT: 118,000
SALES: 48.4MM
SALES (corp-wide): 80.8MM **Privately Held**
WEB: www.monarchsteel.com
SIC: 5051 5049 3353 Metals service centers & offices; precision tools; coils, sheet aluminum
PA: American Consolidated Industries, Inc.
    4650 Johnston Pkwy
    Cleveland OH 44128
    216 587-8000

(G-5831)

MONROE DIE & STAMPING CO
3910 E 93rd St (44105-4048)
PHONE.............................216 883-6390
Robert Brosnan, *Owner*
EMP: 7
SQ FT: 5,000
SALES (est): 371.6K **Privately Held**
SIC: 3544 Machine shop, jobbing & repair; dies & die holders for metal cutting, forming, die casting

(G-5832)

MONROE TOOL AND MFG CO
3900 E 93rd St (44105-4094)
PHONE.............................216 883-7360
Fax: 216 883-0137
Herbert C Brosnan Jr, *President*
Herbert Brosnan III, *Vice Pres*
Anne Brosnan, *CFO*
EMP: 15 EST: 1940
SQ FT: 7,200
SALES (est): 2.4MM **Privately Held**
SIC: 3599 Machine shop, jobbing & repair

(G-5833)

MOONLIGHT SPECIALTIES
4555 Renaissance Pkwy # 105
(44128-5762)
PHONE.............................216 464-6444
Ronald Rivchun, *President*
EMP: 3
SALES (est): 604.7K **Privately Held**
SIC: 7389 3993 Advertising, promotional & trade show services; signs & advertising specialties

(G-5834)

MORRISON MEDIA GROUP-CMJ LLP
11800 Shaker Blvd (44120-1919)
PHONE.............................216 973-4005
Paula D Morrsion, *Managing Prtnr*
Paula D Morrison, *Partner*
EMP: 3

SALES (est): 250K **Privately Held**
WEB: www.morrisonmediagroup.com
SIC: 2721 Magazines: publishing & printing

(G-5835)

MPC PLASTICS INC
1859 E 63rd St (44103-3832)
PHONE.............................216 881-7220
Albert Walcutt, *President*
Marshall Straight, *Controller*
EMP: 60
SQ FT: 26,000
SALES (est): 6.6MM **Privately Held**
WEB: www.mpcplastics.com
SIC: 3471 Plating & polishing

(G-5836)

MPC PLATING INC (PA)
1859 E 63rd St (44103-3832)
PHONE.............................216 881-7220
Fax: 216 881-7324
Albert N Walcutt, *President*
Rose Ann Walcutt, *Corp Secy*
Heather Piwarski, *Project Mgr*
Tyson Jump, *QC Mgr*
James Zagorsky, *Program Mgr*
▲ EMP: 49
SQ FT: 26,000
SALES (est): 14.2MM **Privately Held**
WEB: www.mpcplating.com
SIC: 3471 Electroplating of metals or formed products; anodizing (plating) of metals or formed products; buffing for the trade

(G-5837)

MPC PLATING INC
1859 E 63rd St (44103-3832)
PHONE.............................216 881-7220
Albert N Walcutt, *President*
EMP: 50
SALES (corp-wide): 14.2MM **Privately Held**
WEB: www.mpcplating.com
SIC: 3471 Chromium plating of metals or formed products
PA: M.P.C. Plating, Inc.
    1859 E 63rd St
    Cleveland OH 44103
    216 881-7220

(G-5838)

MR HEATER INC
Also Called: Heatstar
4560 W 160th St (44135-2628)
P.O. Box 44101 (44144-0101)
PHONE.............................216 916-3000
Allen L Haire, *Ch of Bd*
Jeff Mack, *President*
Kevin McDonough, *Vice Pres*
Lelia Coleman, *Director*
▲ EMP: 40
SQ FT: 100,000
SALES: 5.7MM
SALES (corp-wide): 44.6MM **Privately Held**
SIC: 3433 Gas infrared heating units
PA: Enerco Group, Inc.
    4560 W 160th St
    Cleveland OH 44135
    216 916-3000

(G-5839)

MS BARKIN COMPANY
246 E 131st St Ste 2 (44108-1646)
PHONE.............................216 761-9500
Fax: 216 761-8907
Moshe R Barkin, *Owner*
EMP: 8
SQ FT: 2,500
SALES (est): 776.2K **Privately Held**
WEB: www.msbarkinco.com
SIC: 3911 5944 Jewelry, precious metal; jewelry, precious stones & precious metals

(G-5840)

MURRAY FABRICS INC (PA)
837 E 79th St (44103-1807)
PHONE.............................216 881-4041
Fax: 216 881-5758
Walter Senney, *President*
Joyce Senney, *Admin Sec*
EMP: 10

SALES (est): 1.9MM **Privately Held**
WEB: www.murrayfabrics.com
SIC: 2258 Net & netting products

(G-5841)

MURRAY MACHINE & TOOL INC
17801 Sheldon Rd Side (44130-7992)
PHONE.............................216 267-1126
Fax: 216 433-1640
Frank P Ondercik Jr, *President*
EMP: 7 EST: 1927
SQ FT: 8,500
SALES (est): 926.5K **Privately Held**
SIC: 3599 3451 Machine shop, jobbing & repair; screw machine products

(G-5842)

MV DESIGNLABS LLC
17138 Lorain Ave Ste 201 (44111-5538)
PHONE.............................724 355-7986
Brad Hughes, *Mng Member*
Timothy Cochrane,
Jonathan Hall,
EMP: 3
SALES (est): 100K **Privately Held**
SIC: 8748 3621 Systems engineering consultant, ex. computer or professional; electric motor & generator auxillary parts

(G-5843)

MYERS AND LASCH INC
8026 Columbia Rd (44138-2022)
PHONE.............................440 235-2050
Fax: 440 235-2674
Phil Puhala, *Owner*
Mike Marhefka, *Vice Pres*
EMP: 6
SQ FT: 2,500
SALES (est): 824.3K **Privately Held**
WEB: www.myers-lasch.com
SIC: 3993 Displays & cutouts, window & lobby

(G-5844)

MYERS PRECISION GRINDING CO
19500 S Miles Rd (44128-4251)
PHONE.............................216 365-2630
Fax: 216 587-0197
Joseph Tenebria, *President*
Michelle T Tenebria, *Purch Mgr*
Ben Tenebria, *Treasurer*
Gail Myers Tenebria, *Admin Sec*
EMP: 12
SQ FT: 15,600
SALES (est): 1.9MM **Privately Held**
WEB: www.myersprecision.com
SIC: 3545 Precision tools, machinists'

(G-5845)

MYKO INDUSTRIES
896 E 70th St (44103-1706)
PHONE.............................216 431-0900
Richard Peterson, *Manager*
EMP: 3
SALES (corp-wide): 826K **Privately Held**
SIC: 1752 3241 2851 5032 Floor laying & floor work; cement, hydraulic; paints & allied products; brick, stone & related material; paints, varnishes & supplies
PA: Myko Industries
    14676 Rapids Rd
    Burton OH 44021
    216 459-9606

(G-5846)

MYSTIC CHEMICAL PRODUCTS CO
Also Called: Susan Products
3561 W 105th St (44111-3836)
PHONE.............................216 251-4416
John Gedeon Jr, *President*
John H Gedeon Sr, *Principal*
R M Gedeon, *Principal*
EMP: 9
SQ FT: 4,000
SALES (est): 1.4MM **Privately Held**
WEB: www.susanproducts.com
SIC: 2879 Pesticides, agricultural or household

(G-5847)

N J THOMAS FINE JEWELRY INC
30191 Detroit Rd (44145-1946)
PHONE.............................440 892-0656
Fax: 440 892-0656

Norman J Thomas, *President*
Manny Norman, *Vice Pres*
EMP: 4
SQ FT: 2,000
SALES (est): 19.3K **Privately Held**
SIC: 3911 7631 5944 Jewelry, precious metal; jewelry repair services; jewelry stores

(G-5848)

NACCO INDUSTRIES INC (PA)
5875 Landerbrook Dr # 300 (44124-4069)
PHONE.............................440 229-5151
Fax: 440 449-9607
Alfred M Rankin Jr, *Ch of Bd*
Louis D'Abbraccio, *Business Mgr*
Jesse L Adkins, *Counsel*
Miles B Haberer, *Counsel*
Mary D Maloney, *Counsel*
EMP: 39
SALES: 856.4MM **Publicly Held**
SIC: 3634 1221 5719 3631 Electric household cooking appliances; toasters, electric: household; irons, electric: household; coffee makers, electric: household; surface mining, lignite; kitchenware; cookware, except aluminum; household cooking equipment; microwave ovens, including portable: household

(G-5849)

NAGELE MANUFACTURING CO INC
5201 W 164th St (44142-1507)
PHONE.............................216 433-1100
Fax: 216 433-0367
EMP: 45 EST: 1956
SQ FT: 80,000
SALES: 5MM **Privately Held**
SIC: 2541 2431 1751 2511 Mfg Wood Partitions/Fixt Mfg Millwork Carpentry Contractor Mfg Wood Household Furn Mfg Wood Kitchen Cabinet

(G-5850)

NANO MARK LLC
4415 Euclid Ave (44103-3759)
PHONE.............................216 409-3104
Colin Drummond, *Partner*
EMP: 3
SALES: 25K **Privately Held**
SIC: 3845 Electromedical equipment

(G-5851)

NANOFILM LTD
6030 Carey Dr (44125-4260)
PHONE.............................216 674-1430
Scott Rickert, *President*
EMP: 35
SALES (corp-wide): 9.6MM **Publicly Held**
WEB: www.nanofilm.cc
SIC: 2869 2842 2392 Industrial organic chemicals; specialty cleaning, polishes & sanitation goods; household furnishings
HQ: Nanofilm, Ltd.
    10111 Sweet Valley Dr
    Cleveland OH 44125
    216 447-1199

(G-5852)

NATIONAL BANK NOTE COMPANY (PA)
9800 Detroit Ave Ste 1 (44102-1799)
PHONE.............................216 281-7792
Daniel L Roberts, *President*
E L Roberts, *Corp Secy*
Debbie Luster, *Vice Pres*
EMP: 5 EST: 1909
SQ FT: 3,000
SALES: 250K **Privately Held**
SIC: 2752 Commercial printing, offset

(G-5853)

NATIONAL BIAS FABRIC CO
4516 Saint Clair Ave (44103-1288)
PHONE.............................216 361-0530
Fax: 216 361-0811
James R Engelbert, *President*
Keith Engelbert, *Vice Pres*
Carol Ann Engelbert, *Admin Sec*
Barbara Seaman, *Admin Sec*
EMP: 35 EST: 1902
SQ FT: 33,000

▲ = Import ▼=Export
◆ =Import/Export

SALES (est): 3.4MM **Privately Held**
WEB: www.nationalbias.com
SIC: 2396 2631 2394 Bindings, bias:
made from purchased materials; waist-
bands, trouser; trimming, fabric; paperboard mills; canvas & related products

(G-5854)
NATIONAL BRASS COMPANY INC
3179 W 33rd St (44109-1524)
PHONE................................216 651-8530
Fax: 216 651-8532
Mirna Maalouf, *President*
EMP: 4
SQ FT: 5,000
SALES: 900K **Privately Held**
SIC: 3366 3432 Brass foundry; plumbers'
brass goods: drain cocks, faucets, spig-
ots, etc.

(G-5855)
NATIONAL ELECTRO-COATINGS INC
Also Called: National Office
15655 Brookpark Rd (44142-1619)
PHONE................................216 898-0080
Fax: 216 898-8388
Gregory R Schneider, *CEO*
Richard Corl, *President*
Robert W Schneider, *Chairman*
Teresa Corl, *Safety Dir*
Michael Schneider, *Safety Dir*
▲ EMP: 90
SQ FT: 175,000
SALES (est): 20MM **Privately Held**
WEB: www.natoffice.com
SIC: 2522 2521 1721 Office furniture, ex-
cept wood; wood office furniture; painting
& paper hanging

(G-5856)
NATIONAL FOODS PACKAGING INC
8200 Madison Ave (44102-2727)
PHONE................................216 415-7102
John Pallas, *President*
Missy Lewallen, *Office Mgr*
Nikki Johnson, *Manager*
▲ EMP: 15
SQ FT: 10,000
SALES (est): 4.6MM **Privately Held**
SIC: 2099 Syrups; vinegar

(G-5857)
NATIONAL LIME AND STONE CO
4200 E 71st St (44105-5719)
PHONE................................216 883-9840
EMP: 3
SALES (corp-wide): 4B **Privately Held**
SIC: 1422 1442 3273 1423 Crushed &
broken limestone; sand mining; gravel
mining; ready-mixed concrete; crushed &
broken granite; asphalt (native) mining
PA: The National Lime And Stone Company
551 Lake Cascade Pkwy
Findlay OH 45840
419 422-4341

(G-5858)
NATIONAL PLATING CORPORATION
6701 Hubbard Ave Ste 1 (44127-1479)
PHONE................................216 341-6707
Mark Palik, *President*
Greg Pramik, *Prdtn Mgr*
Randy Jezerinac, *Manager*
Sherrie Jezerinac, *Admin Sec*
EMP: 48
SQ FT: 100,000
SALES (est): 7.6MM **Privately Held**
SIC: 3471 Electroplating & plating

(G-5859)
NATIONAL ROLLED THREAD DIE CO
7051 Krick Rd (44146-4497)
PHONE................................440 232-8101
Paula Mau, *President*
Ronald D Mau, *VP Mfg*
Gene Kovacs, *Sales Mgr*
George Clapper, *Manager*
Goetz Arndt, *Admin Sec*
EMP: 15 EST: 1946
SQ FT: 18,000

SALES (est): 2.4MM **Privately Held**
WEB: www.nationaldie.com
SIC: 3545 Thread cutting dies

(G-5860)
NATIONAL SECURITY PRODUCTS
Also Called: Cleveland Safe Co
1636 Saint Clair Ave Ne (44114-2006)
PHONE................................216 566-9962
Fax: 216 241-3970
Mark Brajdich, *President*
EMP: 3 EST: 1978
SQ FT: 4,000
SALES: 325K **Privately Held**
WEB: www.clevelandsafe.com
SIC: 5044 5999 3499 Vaults & safes;
vaults & safes; locks, safe & vault: metal;
safe deposit boxes or chests, metal

(G-5861)
NATURE FRIENDLY PRODUCTS LLC
24050 Commerce Park # 101
(44122-5833)
PHONE................................216 464-5490
Jeri Siss, *General Mgr*
Bill Biggar,
▲ EMP: 5
SALES (est): 508.7K **Privately Held**
SIC: 2678 Stationery products

(G-5862)
NATURES SIMPLE SOLUTION INC
Also Called: Perfect Solution
1450 Som Center Rd Ste 2 (44124-2116)
PHONE................................440 567-6913
Laura Triscaro, *President*
Sharon Gambatese, *Vice Pres*
EMP: 3
SALES: 55K **Privately Held**
WEB: www.naturessimplesolution.com
SIC: 2844 Deodorants, personal

(G-5863)
NBC INDUSTRIES INC
4700 Train Ave Ste 3 (44102-4591)
PHONE................................216 651-9800
Charles Connors, *President*
EMP: 10
SQ FT: 10,000
SALES (est): 630K **Privately Held**
SIC: 3089 3544 Injection molding of plas-
tics; special dies, tools, jigs & fixtures

(G-5864)
NBW INC
4556 Industrial Pkwy (44135-4542)
PHONE................................216 377-1700
Fax: 216 377-1711
Burgess J Holt, *Chairman*
Thomas Graves, *Vice Pres*
Buck L Holt, *Treasurer*
Cherie Patton, *Accountant*
Todd Holt, *Admin Sec*
EMP: 48
SQ FT: 25,000
SALES (est): 15MM **Privately Held**
WEB: www.nbwinc.com
SIC: 1711 1796 7699 3443 Boiler setting
contractor; installing building equipment;
boiler & heating repair services; fabri-
cated plate work (boiler shop)

(G-5865)
NCM CORP
20437 Hannan Pkwy Ste 3 (44146-5384)
P.O. Box 39612 (44139-0612)
PHONE................................440 786-9870
Fax: 440 786-9872
Alfred Micklow, *President*
EMP: 8
SQ FT: 6,200
SALES (est): 620K **Privately Held**
WEB: www.ncmmachine.com
SIC: 3599 Machine shop, jobbing & repair

(G-5866)
NDI MEDICAL LLC (PA)
22901 Millcreek Blvd # 110 (44122-5724)
PHONE................................216 378-9106
Geoff Thrope, *CEO*
Leonard Cosentino, *President*
Kathryn Stager, *Exec VP*

Bob Strother, *Vice Pres*
Tina Lechman, *Project Mgr*
◆ EMP: 5
SALES (est): 2.8MM **Privately Held**
WEB: www.ndimedical.com
SIC: 3845 Electromedical equipment

(G-5867)
NEIGHBORHOOD NEWS PUBG CO
8613 Garfield Blvd (44125-1317)
P.O. Box 25400 (44125-0400)
PHONE................................216 441-2141
Fax: 216 441-0058
Ellen Psenicka, *Owner*
James Psenicka, *Owner*
Michael Psenicka, *Manager*
EMP: 5
SALES (est): 190K **Privately Held**
SIC: 2711 Newspapers

(G-5868)
NEON
15201 Euclid Ave (44112-2803)
PHONE................................216 761-4782
EMP: 3
SALES (est): 197.3K **Privately Held**
SIC: 2813 Neon

(G-5869)
NEON HEALTH SERVICES INC
4800 Payne Ave (44103-2443)
PHONE................................216 231-7700
Fax: 216 472-0518
Willie Austin, *Principal*
Cynthia Penny, *Manager*
Alonzo Barker, *CIO*
Lee Jackson, *Director*
Perry Murdock, *Administration*
EMP: 50 EST: 2010
SALES (est): 7.3MM **Privately Held**
SIC: 2813 Neon

(G-5870)
NEON LIGHT MANUFACTURING CO
12655 Coit Rd (44108-1610)
PHONE................................216 851-1000
Fax: 216 851-1166
Michael Holsman, *Principal*
EMP: 3 EST: 2010
SALES (est): 184.5K **Privately Held**
SIC: 2813 Neon

(G-5871)
NESCO INC (PA)
Also Called: Nesco Resource
6140 Parkland Blvd # 110 (44124-6106)
PHONE................................440 461-6000
Fax: 440 449-3111
Robert Tomsich, *President*
Tom Villhard, *Area Mgr*
Ken Carleton, *Business Mgr*
John Charron, *Business Mgr*
Cheryl Henry, *Business Mgr*
◆ EMP: 20
SQ FT: 55,000
SALES (est): 684.8MM **Privately Held**
SIC: 3535 3541 3544 8711 Conveyors &
conveying equipment; machine tools,
metal cutting type; special dies, tools, jigs
& fixtures; engineering services; real es-
tate managers

(G-5872)
NESTLE USA INC
7645 Granger Rd (44125-4820)
PHONE................................216 524-7738
EMP: 135
SALES (corp-wide): 88.4B **Privately Held**
SIC: 2023 Evaporated milk
HQ: Nestle Usa, Inc.
800 N Brand Blvd
Glendale CA 91203
818 549-6000

(G-5873)
NESTLE USA INC
7605 Granger Rd (44125-4820)
PHONE................................216 524-3397
EMP: 135
SALES (corp-wide): 88.4B **Privately Held**
SIC: 2023 Evaporated milk

HQ: Nestle Usa, Inc.
800 N Brand Blvd
Glendale CA 91203
818 549-6000

(G-5874)
NESTLE USA INC
Also Called: Nestle Food Service Factory
2621 W 25th St (44113-4708)
PHONE................................216 861-8350
Raymond Sirochman, *Production*
Kara Bendix, *Engineer*
George Young, *Engineer*
Ingolf Nitsch, *Branch Mgr*
EMP: 100
SALES (corp-wide): 88.4B **Privately Held**
WEB: www.nestleusa.com
SIC: 5499 2023 Health foods; dry, con-
densed, evaporated dairy products
HQ: Nestle Usa, Inc.
800 N Brand Blvd
Glendale CA 91203
818 549-6000

(G-5875)
NEUROWAVE SYSTEMS INC
2490 Lee Blvd Ste 300 (44118-1271)
PHONE................................216 361-1591
Robert N Schmidt, *CEO*
MO Modarres, *President*
Sladjana Krstic, *Purchasing*
Sankar Barua, *Engineer*
Stephane Bibian, *Engineer*
EMP: 7
SQ FT: 10,000
SALES (est): 2MM **Privately Held**
SIC: 5047 3845 Patient monitoring equip-
ment; ultrasonic scanning devices, med-
ical

(G-5876)
NEW CLEVELAND GROUP INC
2917 Mayfield Rd (44118-1604)
PHONE................................216 932-9310
Michael Goronok, *President*
Yangbing Chen, *Vice Pres*
▲ EMP: 9
SALES (est): 972.8K **Privately Held**
SIC: 3931 Musical instruments

(G-5877)
NEW ERA CONTROLS INC
11002 Edgepark Dr (44125-2240)
PHONE................................216 641-8683
Fax: 216 901-1305
Martin F Marincic, *President*
Frank Lembo, *Corp Secy*
Bob Pasquale, *Vice Pres*
EMP: 5
SQ FT: 1,000
SALES (est): 510K **Privately Held**
SIC: 3625 7373 Industrial controls: push
button, selector switches, pilot; computer
integrated systems design

(G-5878)
NEW LEAF MEDICAL INC
1768 E 25th St (44114-4418)
PHONE................................216 391-7749
Richard T Nock, *President*
EMP: 3
SALES (est): 292K **Privately Held**
SIC: 3841 Surgical & medical instruments

(G-5879)
NEW URBAN DISTRIBUTORS LLC
13940 Cedar Rd Ste 224 (44118-3204)
PHONE................................216 373-2349
Angela Underwood, *Principal*
EMP: 4
SALES (est): 184.3K **Privately Held**
SIC: 2711 Commercial printing & newspa-
per publishing combined

(G-5880)
NEWKOR INC
10410 Berea Rd (44102-2587)
PHONE................................216 631-7800
Fax: 216 631-7886
Gordon Barr, *President*
Annette Kinder, *Office Mgr*
EMP: 20
SQ FT: 23,000

SALES (est): 5.1MM **Privately Held**
WEB: www.newkor.com
SIC: 2655 Tubes, for chemical or electrical uses: paper or fiber

(G-5881)
NEXTANT AEROSPACE HOLDINGS LLC
355 Richmond Rd Ste 8 (44143-4404)
PHONE.....................216 261-9000
Kenneth C Ricci, *CEO*
Sean McGeough, *President*
Jim Miller, *President*
Edward T McDonald, *COO*
Jay Heublein, *Exec VP*
EMP: 75
SQ FT: 3,000
SALES (est): 15.5MM
SALES (corp-wide): 97.2MM **Privately Held**
WEB: www.nextantaerospace.com
SIC: 3721 Aircraft
HQ: Flight Options International, Inc.
355 Richmond Rd
Richmond Heights OH 44143
216 261-3500

(G-5882)
NIDEC INDUS AUTOMTN USA LLC
7800 Hub Pkwy (44125-5711)
PHONE.....................216 901-2400
Fax: 440 717-0133
Jim Ulrich, *Purchasing*
Ronald Whitney, *Manager*
EMP: 20
SALES (corp-wide): 10B **Privately Held**
SIC: 3566 3823 Drives, high speed industrial, except hydrostatic; industrial process control instruments
HQ: Nidec Industrial Automation Usa, Llc
7078 Shady Oak Rd
Eden Prairie MN 55344
952 995-8000

(G-5883)
NIKOLA INNOVATION LLC
1768 E 25th St (44114-4418)
PHONE.....................216 496-3022
Nick Stevovich,
EMP: 3
SALES (est): 209.5K **Privately Held**
SIC: 3751 Motorcycles, bicycles & parts

(G-5884)
NOBLE ANODIZING INC
1325 E 152nd St (44112-2014)
PHONE.....................216 268-1263
Russ Finley, *Principal*
EMP: 3
SALES (est): 130.7K **Privately Held**
SIC: 3471 Anodizing (plating) of metals or formed products

(G-5885)
NOCK AND SON COMPANY (PA)
27320 W Oviatt Rd (44140-2195)
P.O. Box 40368 (44140-0368)
PHONE.....................440 871-5525
Fax: 440 871-5581
Charles J Nock, *President*
Stephen Nock, *Vice Pres*
Michael C Nock, *Treasurer*
Patricia P Nock, *Admin Sec*
▲ EMP: 4
SQ FT: 1,200
SALES (est): 35.2MM **Privately Held**
WEB: www.nockandson.com
SIC: 3255 3297 Clay refractories; nonclay refractories

(G-5886)
NOGGIN LLC
6325 York Rd Ste 208 (44130-3030)
PHONE.....................440 305-6188
David Yeager, *CEO*
EMP: 4
SALES (est): 98.3K **Privately Held**
SIC: 7372 8731 Educational computer software; computer (hardware) development

(G-5887)
NOOK INDUSTRIES INC (PA)
4950 E 49th St (44125-1016)
PHONE.....................216 271-7900

Chirstopher Nook, *CEO*
Ronald Domeck, *President*
James Ellacott, *General Mgr*
Joseph H Nook Jr, *Chairman*
Joseph H Nook III, *COO*
▲ EMP: 160
SQ FT: 110,000
SALES (est): 35.9MM **Privately Held**
WEB: www.nookind.com
SIC: 3451 3699 3593 3568 Screw machine products; electrical equipment & supplies; fluid power cylinders & actuators; power transmission equipment; machine tool accessories

(G-5888)
NORMAN NOBLE INC
Also Called: N N I
5507 Avion Park Dr (44143-1921)
PHONE.....................216 761-5387
Fax: 216 761-0455
Kevin Noble, *Principal*
Dan Foust, *Opers Staff*
Lori Elko, *Purchasing*
Dave Saletrik, *QC Dir*
Andrae Maze, *QC Mgr*
EMP: 85
SALES (corp-wide): 103.5MM **Privately Held**
WEB: www.nnoble.com
SIC: 3599 Machine shop, jobbing & repair
PA: Norman Noble, Inc.
5507 Avion Park Dr
Highland Heights OH 44143
216 761-5387

(G-5889)
NORMAN NOBLE INC
6120 Parkland Blvd # 306 (44124-6129)
PHONE.....................216 761-2133
Daniel Haddock, *Branch Mgr*
EMP: 190
SALES (corp-wide): 103.5MM **Privately Held**
WEB: www.nnoble.com
SIC: 3599 7692 Machine shop, jobbing & repair; welding repair
PA: Norman Noble, Inc.
5507 Avion Park Dr
Highland Heights OH 44143
216 761-5387

(G-5890)
NORTH AMERICAN STEEL COMPANY
18300 Miles Rd (44128-3441)
P.O. Box 28126 (44128-0126)
PHONE.....................216 475-7300
Fax: 216 475-6143
Theodore Cohen Jr, *Owner*
EMP: 20 EST: 1945
SQ FT: 48,000
SALES (est): 2.7MM **Privately Held**
WEB: www.northamerican-steel.com
SIC: 5051 3499 3312 Steel; aerosol valves, metal; stainless steel

(G-5891)
NORTH CENTRAL PROCESSING INC (PA)
761 Stones Levee (44113-2541)
P.O. Box 93941 (44101-5941)
PHONE.....................216 623-1090
Jack Joyce, *President*
EMP: 5
SALES (est): 4MM **Privately Held**
SIC: 2895 Carbon black

(G-5892)
NORTH COAST CAMSHAFT INC
10910 Briggs Rd (44111-5332)
PHONE.....................216 671-3700
Fax: 216 671-6868
David Schultheis, *President*
EMP: 5
SQ FT: 2,000
SALES (est): 778.3K **Privately Held**
SIC: 3714 Camshafts, motor vehicle

(G-5893)
NORTH COAST COMPOSITES INC
4605 Spring Rd (44131-1021)
PHONE.....................216 398-8550
Richard L Petrovich, *President*

Robert Dahn, *General Mgr*
John Lakatos, *General Mgr*
Len Matlack, *Accountant*
Sherry Havlik, *Manager*
▲ EMP: 8
SALES (est): 1.6MM
SALES (corp-wide): 12.4MM **Privately Held**
SIC: 2655 Cans, composite: foil-fiber & other: from purchased fiber
HQ: The Companies Of North Coast Llc
4605 Spring Rd
Cleveland OH 44131
216 398-8550

(G-5894)
NORTH COAST CONTAINER CORP (PA)
Also Called: Ncc
8806 Crane Ave (44105-1622)
PHONE.....................216 441-6214
Fax: 216 441-6239
Jim Beardsley, *CEO*
Earnest C Beardsley, *CEO*
Randall D Reed, *President*
Kevin Outrich, *Superintendent*
James Drozdowski, *Vice Pres*
EMP: 82
SQ FT: 120,000
SALES (est): 27.5MM **Privately Held**
WEB: www.ncc-corp.com
SIC: 3412 Drums, shipping: metal

(G-5895)
NORTH COAST EXOTICS INC
3159 W 68th St (44102-5305)
PHONE.....................216 651-5512
Earl Gibbs Jr, *President*
EMP: 6
SQ FT: 15,000
SALES (est): 570K **Privately Held**
SIC: 7699 3714 Miscellaneous automotive repair services; motor vehicle parts & accessories

(G-5896)
NORTH COAST INSTRUMENTS INC
14615 Lorain Ave (44111-3166)
PHONE.....................216 251-2353
Fax: 216 251-6188
James Irwin, *President*
Julia W Irwin, *Treasurer*
Charlotte G Irwin, *Admin Sec*
EMP: 20
SQ FT: 20,000
SALES: 8MM **Privately Held**
SIC: 3593 Fluid power cylinders & actuators
PA: Ohio Pipe & Supply Company Incorporated
14615 Lorain Ave
Cleveland OH
216 251-2345

(G-5897)
NORTH COAST LITHO INC
4701 Manufacturing Ave (44135-2639)
PHONE.....................216 881-1952
Fax: 216 881-4432
Keith P Jaworski, *President*
Robert Strohmeyer, *General Mgr*
Stephen Davis, *Sales Staff*
EMP: 20
SQ FT: 12,000
SALES (est): 4.5MM **Privately Held**
WEB: www.northcoastlitho.com
SIC: 2752 Commercial printing, lithographic

(G-5898)
NORTH COAST MEDIA LLC
Also Called: NCM
1360 E 9th St Ste 1070 (44114-1754)
PHONE.....................216 706-3700
Kevin Stoltman, *President*
Rob Hranac, *President*
Darren Constantino, *Editor*
Steve Galperin, *Vice Pres*
Marko Saarni, *Sales Mgr*
EMP: 39
SALES (est): 7.2MM **Privately Held**
SIC: 2731 Book publishing

(G-5899)
NORTH COAST MINORITY MEDIA LLC
Also Called: North Coast Publications
1360 E 9th St (44114-1737)
PHONE.....................216 407-4327
Louis A Acosta, *Managing Dir*
EMP: 30
SALES (est): 1.1MM **Privately Held**
SIC: 2721 Magazines: publishing & printing; periodicals: publishing only

(G-5900)
NORTH SHORE STRAPPING INC
9401 Maywood Ave (44102-4852)
PHONE.....................216 661-5200
Fax: 216 961-4111
Sean Leneghan, *CFO*
Kevin Leneghan, *Manager*
EMP: 53
SALES (corp-wide): 10.1MM **Privately Held**
SIC: 3081 Unsupported plastics film & sheet
PA: North Shore Strapping Inc
1400 Valley Belt Rd
Brooklyn Heights OH 44131
216 661-5200

(G-5901)
NORTHCOAST PROCESS CONTRLS INC
6283 Sunnywood Dr (44139-3054)
P.O. Box 39071 (44139-0071)
PHONE.....................440 498-0542
Nevio E Bais, *President*
Micheal Bais, *Vice Pres*
EMP: 3
SQ FT: 2,000
SALES (est): 441.7K **Privately Held**
SIC: 3625 5065 3592 Industrial controls: push button, selector switches, pilot; electronic parts & equipment; valves

(G-5902)
NORTHCOAST TAPE & LABEL INC
24300 Solon Rd Ste 7 (44146-4794)
PHONE.....................440 439-3200
Fax: 440 439-3201
Paul Bukas, *President*
▲ EMP: 5
SQ FT: 5,000
SALES (est): 835.5K **Privately Held**
WEB: www.nclabel.com
SIC: 2672 Labels (unprinted), gummed: made from purchased materials; tape, pressure sensitive: made from purchased materials

(G-5903)
NORTHEAST BLUEPRINT & SUP CO
1230 E 286th St (44132-2138)
PHONE.....................216 261-7500
Fax: 216 261-7650
James Yurick, *President*
Timothy Yurick, *President*
Mike Rogazione, *Info Tech Mgr*
EMP: 7
SQ FT: 7,000
SALES: 1MM **Privately Held**
WEB: www.northeastblueprint.com
SIC: 7334 2752 Blueprinting service; commercial printing, lithographic; color lithography

(G-5904)
NORTHEAST MACHINE TOOL CORP
6925 Bessemer Ave Ste 1 (44127-1800)
PHONE.....................216 641-0141
Fax: 216 641-0141
Boris Vaks, *President*
Yanavak Vaks, *Treasurer*
EMP: 8
SQ FT: 6,000
SALES (est): 727.6K **Privately Held**
SIC: 3599 Machine & other job shop work

▲ = Import ▼=Export
◆ =Import/Export

(G-5905)
NORTHEAST OH NEIGHBORHOOD HEAL
8300 Hough Ave (44103-4247)
PHONE....................................216 231-7700
James Odonnell, *CFO*
Billy Foster, *Director*
Prabhleen Bhatia, *Fmly & Gen Dent*
EMP: 108
SALES (corp-wide): 23.2MM **Privately Held**
SIC: 2813 Neon
PA: Northeast Ohio Neighborhood Health
   Services, Inc.
   8300 Hough Ave
   Cleveland OH 44103
   216 231-2323

(G-5906)
NORTHEAST OHIO CONTRACTORS LLC
1873 E 55th St (44103-3641)
PHONE....................................216 269-7881
Brian Petruccelli,
EMP: 3
SQ FT: 1,000
SALES: 250K **Privately Held**
SIC: 1711 3441 Warm air heating & air
   conditioning contractor; fabricated struc-
   tural metal

(G-5907)
NORTHEAST SCENE INC
Also Called: Scene Magazine
737 Bolivar Rd (44115-1246)
PHONE....................................216 241-7550
Fax: 216 241-6275
Richard Kabat, *President*
Keith Rathbun, *Corp Secy*
EMP: 48
SQ FT: 5,300
SALES (est): 3.7MM **Privately Held**
SIC: 2721 7336 2711 Periodicals: publish-
   ing only; graphic arts & related design;
   newspapers

(G-5908)
NORTHERN BOILER COMPANY
Also Called: Northern Fabricator
3453 W 86th St (44102-4999)
PHONE....................................216 961-3033
Fax: 216 961-0443
Edward Kosman, *President*
Robert Kosman, *Vice Pres*
John Steponick, *Purchasing*
EMP: 10 EST: 1906
SQ FT: 50,000
SALES (est): 890K **Privately Held**
WEB: www.northernboiler.com
SIC: 3441 Fabricated structural metal

(G-5909)
NORTHERN CHEM BLNDING CORP INC
360 Literary Rd (44113-4560)
PHONE....................................216 781-7799
Fax: 216 781-1207
John Zemaitis, *President*
Derlene Jarrell, *Office Mgr*
▲ EMP: 9
SQ FT: 35,000
SALES (est): 1.8MM **Privately Held**
SIC: 2899 Metal treating compounds;
   water treating compounds

(G-5910)
NORTHERN INSTRUMENTS CORP LLC (HQ)
23205 Mercantile Rd (44122-5911)
PHONE....................................216 450-5073
Fax: 216 595-9560
James Henderson, *President*
Tiffany Swann, *Vice Pres*
Eugene Friedman, *Administration*
EMP: 3
SALES: 400K
SALES (corp-wide): 42.8MM **Publicly Held**
SIC: 3823 Industrial process measurement
   equipment
PA: Northern Technologies International
   Corporation
   4201 Woodland Rd
   Circle Pines MN 55014
   763 225-6600

(G-5911)
NORTHERN MACHINE TOOL CO
3453 W 86th St (44102-4917)
PHONE....................................216 961-0444
Edward Kosman, *President*
Robert Kosman, *Vice Pres*
EMP: 5
SQ FT: 50,000
SALES (est): 710K **Privately Held**
SIC: 5084 3599 Machine tools & metal-
   working machinery; machine & other job
   shop work

(G-5912)
NORTHERN STAMPING CO (PA)
6600 Chapek Pkwy (44125-1049)
PHONE....................................216 883-8888
Matthew S Friedman, *Ch of Bd*
Ron Campbell, *COO*
Scott Sheffield, *Vice Pres*
Pat Johnston, *Purch Agent*
Ian Hessel, *CFO*
◆ EMP: 120
SQ FT: 118,000
SALES (est): 285.2MM **Privately Held**
WEB: www.hilite.com
SIC: 3465 3469 Automotive stampings;
   metal stampings

(G-5913)
NORTHERN STAMPING CO
Also Called: Northern Stamping Plant 2
7750 Hub Pkwy (44125-5709)
PHONE....................................216 642-8081
Scott Sheffield, *Production*
EMP: 200
SALES (corp-wide): 285.2MM **Privately Held**
WEB: www.hilite.com
SIC: 3465 3714 Automotive stampings;
   motor vehicle parts & accessories
PA: Northern Stamping Co.
   6600 Chapek Pkwy
   Cleveland OH 44125
   216 883-8888

(G-5914)
NORTHSHORE MINING COMPANY (HQ)
Also Called: Cliffs
1100 Superior Ave E # 1500 (44114-2544)
PHONE....................................216 694-5700
Larry McCarty, *Superintendent*
Ralland W Hess, *Area Mgr*
Peter Judd, *Area Mgr*
Conor M McCue, *Area Mgr*
Matthew W REA, *Area Mgr*
◆ EMP: 1
SALES (est): 412.7MM
SALES (corp-wide): 2.1B **Publicly Held**
WEB: www.cci-northshore.com
SIC: 1011 4931 Iron ore mining; iron ore
   preparation; electric & other services
   combined
PA: Cliffs Natural Resources Inc.
   200 Public Sq Ste 3300
   Cleveland OH 44114
   216 694-5700

(G-5915)
NORTHSHORE MOLD INC
2861 E Royalton Rd (44147-2827)
PHONE....................................440 838-8212
Fax: 440 546-8311
Joseph E Pajestka Jr, *President*
Vivian Pajestka, *Vice Pres*
EMP: 7
SQ FT: 6,000
SALES (est): 676.1K **Privately Held**
SIC: 3599 3089 Machine & other job shop
   work; injection molding of plastics

(G-5916)
NORTHWIND INDUSTRIES INC
15500 Commerce Park Dr (44142-2013)
PHONE....................................216 433-0666
Fax: 216 433-1189
Garry Patla, *President*
Christine Klukan, *Vice Pres*
EMP: 27
SQ FT: 2,000

SALES (est): 3.4MM **Privately Held**
SIC: 3599 7692 3469 3444 Machine
   shop, jobbing & repair; grinding castings
   for the trade; welding repair; metal stampings; sheet metalwork; fabricated structural metal; metal heat treating

(G-5917)
NOVAGARD SOLUTIONS INC (PA)
Also Called: Soam Seal
5109 Hamilton Ave (44114-3907)
PHONE....................................216 881-3890
Fax: 216 881-6977
Michael S Sylvester, *CEO*
George Buzzy, *President*
Doug McKinzie, *VP Opers*
Terry Smith, *QC Mgr*
Ron Moeller, *CFO*
EMP: 13
SALES: 20MM **Privately Held**
SIC: 3053 2911 2891 Gaskets, packing &
   sealing devices; oils, lubricating; sealing
   compounds, synthetic rubber or plastic;
   caulking compounds

(G-5918)
NOVAK J F MANUFACTURING CO LLC
Also Called: Cleveland Church Supply
2701 Meyer Ave (44109-1532)
PHONE....................................216 741-5112
Fax: 216 271-2722
S Raum, *Sales Staff*
Sharon Campbell, *Manager*
Eleanor Rusnak,
James Rusnak,
EMP: 6 EST: 1932
SQ FT: 7,000
SALES (est): 380K **Privately Held**
WEB: www.jfnovakcompany.com
SIC: 2395 5049 Emblems, embroidered;
   religious supplies

(G-5919)
NOVAK SUPPLY LLC
2701 Meyer Ave (44109-1532)
PHONE....................................216 741-5112
EMP: 4
SALES (est): 144K **Privately Held**
SIC: 2389 Uniforms & vestments

(G-5920)
NOVOLYTE TECHNOLOGIES INC (HQ)
Also Called: Novolyte Performance
8001 E Pleasant Valley Rd (44131-5526)
PHONE....................................216 867-1040
Edward Frindt, *President*
Timothy Zappala, *Chairman*
Richard Watkins, *Vice Pres*
Andrew Egger, *Accounts Mgr*
▲ EMP: 20
SQ FT: 8,000
SALES (est): 32.3MM
SALES (corp-wide): 60.8B **Privately Held**
WEB: www.novolyte.com
SIC: 2621 Specialty or chemically treated
   papers
PA: Basf Se
   Carl-Bosch-Str. 38
   Ludwigshafen Am Rhein 67056
   621 600-

(G-5921)
NPA COATINGS INC
11110 Berea Rd Ste 1 (44102-2540)
PHONE....................................216 651-5900
Fax: 216 651-5901
Hidefumi Morita, *CEO*
Takeshi Makano, *President*
Joan Daniels, *Corp Secy*
Gary Rizzardi, *Exec VP*
Gary Prakup, *Purchasing*
▲ EMP: 180
SQ FT: 235,000
SALES: 82MM
SALES (corp-wide): 4.2B **Privately Held**
SIC: 2851 Paints & paint additives
HQ: Nippon Paint (Usa) Inc.
   300 Frank W Burr Blvd # 10
   Teaneck NJ 07666
   201 692-1111

(G-5922)
NU-DI PRODUCTS CO INC
12730 Triskett Rd (44111-2529)
PHONE....................................216 251-9070
Fax: 216 251-9089
Kenneth Bihn, *President*
Tim Bihn, *Vice Pres*
Sumant Kapoor, *Vice Pres*
David Novicky, *Vice Pres*
Joseph Sikora, *Vice Pres*
EMP: 85
SQ FT: 38,000
SALES (est): 19.3MM **Privately Held**
WEB: www.nu-di.com
SIC: 3825 5013 Engine electrical test
   equipment; testing equipment, electrical:
   automotive

(G-5923)
NUTRO CORPORATION
Also Called: Nutro Machinery
11515 Alameda Dr (44101)
PHONE....................................440 572-3800
Fax: 440 572-5584
Mark Rooney, *President*
George Wharton, *Vice Pres*
Dave Wysocki, *Project Mgr*
P J Osad, *Purch Mgr*
Mark Svec, *Project Engr*
EMP: 55
SQ FT: 65,000
SALES (est): 16.7MM **Privately Held**
WEB: www.nutro.com
SIC: 3569 3559 Liquid automation ma-
   chinery & equipment; paint making ma-
   chinery

(G-5924)
OASIS CONSUMER HEALTHCARE LLC
Also Called: Ochc
737 Bolivar Rd Ste 4500 (44115-1233)
PHONE....................................216 394-0544
Brian Sokol,
Kathy Dise,
Afif Ghannoum,
EMP: 6
SQ FT: 1,500
SALES: 1.5MM **Privately Held**
WEB: www.oasisdrymouth.com
SIC: 2844 Mouthwashes

(G-5925)
OBRIEN CUT STONE COMPANY
19100 Miles Rd (44128-4104)
PHONE....................................216 663-7800
John P O'Brien, *President*
EMP: 30
SALES (corp-wide): 4.3MM **Privately Held**
WEB: www.obriencutstone.net
SIC: 3281 Cut stone & stone products
PA: The O'brien Cut Stone Company
   19100 Miles Rd
   Cleveland OH 44128
   216 663-7800

(G-5926)
OCTAPHARMA PLASMA INC
10694 Lorain Ave (44111-5411)
PHONE....................................216 252-6811
EMP: 4
SALES (corp-wide): 1.4B **Privately Held**
SIC: 2836 Plasmas
HQ: Octapharma Plasma, Inc.
   10644 Westlake Dr
   Charlotte NC 28273
   704 654-4600

(G-5927)
OHIO ALUMINUM INDUSTRIES INC
4840 Warner Rd (44125-1193)
PHONE....................................216 641-8865
Fax: 216 641-8847
John Blemaster, *CEO*
Kurt Blemaster, *President*
Willem Der Velde, *COO*
Dave Sweeney, *Plant Mgr*
Lenny Griffin, *Purch Agent*
▲ EMP: 152
SQ FT: 78,000

G
E
O
G
R
A
P
H
I
C

SALES: 17.7MM **Privately Held**
WEB: www.ohioaluminum.com
SIC: **3365** Aluminum & aluminum-based
alloy castings

(G-5928)
OHIO AWNING &
MANUFACTURING CO
5777 Grant Ave (44105-5605)
PHONE.............................216 861-2400
Andrew Morse, *President*
Anne L Morse, *Vice Pres*
Dave Harman, *Sales Executive*
▲ EMP: 30
SQ FT: 80,000
SALES (est): 4.2MM **Privately Held**
WEB: www.ohioawning.com
SIC: **2394 3993** Canvas awnings &
canopies; electric signs

(G-5929)
OHIO BEVERAGE SYSTEMS INC
9200 Midwest Ave (44125-2416)
PHONE.............................216 475-3900
James Rickon, *President*
EMP: 15
SQ FT: 28,000
SALES (est): 2.2MM **Privately Held**
SIC: **2086** Fruit drinks (less than 100%
juice): packaged in cans, etc.

(G-5930)
OHIO BLOW PIPE COMPANY
(PA)
446 E 131st St (44108-1684)
PHONE.............................216 681-7379
Fax: 216 681-7713
Edward Fakeris, *President*
William Roberts, *Vice Pres*
David Anderson, *Purch Dir*
John McNally, *Engineer*
Lisa Kern, *CFO*
EMP: 33
SQ FT: 45,000
SALES (est): 23.9MM **Privately Held**
WEB: www.obpairsystems.com
SIC: **8711 3564 3444** Engineering serv-
ices; blowers & fans; sheet metalwork

(G-5931)
OHIO BRUSH COMPANY
2680 Lisbon Rd (44104-3188)
PHONE.............................216 791-3265
Fax: 216 791-6615
Patricia Gardner, *President*
Tom Gardner, *Vice Pres*
EMP: 19 EST: 1879
SQ FT: 14,000
SALES (est): 2.2MM **Privately Held**
WEB: www.ohiobrush.com
SIC: **3991** Brushes, household or industrial

(G-5932)
OHIO CAM & TOOL CO
23572 Saint Clair Ave (44117-2513)
PHONE.............................216 531-7900
Fax: 216 531-7901
Steve J Raab, *President*
EMP: 5 EST: 1957
SQ FT: 4,000
SALES: 325K **Privately Held**
SIC: **3541** Screw machines, automatic

(G-5933)
OHIO ENVELOPE
MANUFACTURING CO
5161 W 164th St (44142-1592)
PHONE.............................216 267-2920
Fax: 216 267-1765
David Gould III, *President*
David Gould III, *President*
Carol J Gould, *Corp Secy*
Michael Molnar, *Purchasing*
Mike Molnar, *Purchasing*
EMP: 35 EST: 1936
SQ FT: 35,000
SALES (est): 5.3MM **Privately Held**
WEB: www.ohioenvelope.com
SIC: **2759 2754 2677** Envelopes: printing;
envelopes: gravure printing; envelopes

(G-5934)
OHIO MILLS CORPORATION (PA)
Also Called: Ohio Mill Supply
1719 E 39th St (44114-4530)
PHONE.............................216 431-3979
Fax: 216 881-2266
Ronald Katz, *President*
Bob Knecht, *Sales Mgr*
EMP: 8 EST: 1983
SQ FT: 15,000
SALES (est): 1.6MM **Privately Held**
SIC: **5651 2842** Unisex clothing stores;
dusting cloths, chemically treated

(G-5935)
OKM LLC
Also Called: Ohio Knitting Mills
4701 Perkins Ave Ste 1 (44103-3525)
PHONE.............................216 272-6375
Steven Tatar, *President*
EMP: 7
SQ FT: 4,000
SALES: 100K **Privately Held**
SIC: **2253** Knit outerwear mills

(G-5936)
OLD COUNTRY SAUSAGE
KITCHEN
15711 Libby Rd (44137-1212)
PHONE.............................216 662-5988
George S Neiden, *President*
Maria Neiden, *Corp Secy*
EMP: 3
SQ FT: 4,555
SALES (est): 254.1K **Privately Held**
SIC: **2013 5421** Sausages from pur-
chased meat; meat markets, including
freezer provisioners

(G-5937)
OLD WORLD FOODS INC
3545 E 76th St (44105-1509)
P.O. Box 27382 (44127-0382)
PHONE.............................216 341-5665
Andy Emrisko, *President*
EMP: 5 EST: 1994
SALES (est): 495.2K **Privately Held**
WEB: www.oldworldfoods.com
SIC: **2037 5812** Potato products, quick
frozen & cold pack; eating places

(G-5938)
OLFACTORIUM CORP INC
Also Called: Kristine Marie's Olfactorium
12395 Mccracken Rd (44125-2967)
PHONE.............................216 663-8831
Fax: 216 663-8841
Henry Drewes, *President*
Gregory Page, *Vice Pres*
Mary Ellen Drewes, *Treasurer*
Christine Page, *Admin Sec*
EMP: 6 EST: 1980
SALES: 337.1K **Privately Held**
WEB: www.aromadeterra.com
SIC: **5999 5122 2844** Toiletries, cosmet-
ics & perfumes; cosmetics, perfumes &
hair products; toilet preparations

(G-5939)
OLIVE SERAFINO OILS
BALSAMICS
915 Worton Park Dr (44143-3327)
PHONE.............................440 773-0200
Laura Rinker, *Principal*
EMP: 3
SALES (est): 96.3K **Privately Held**
SIC: **2079** Olive oil

(G-5940)
OLYMPIC FOREST PRODUCTS
CO
2200 Carnegie Ave (44115-2621)
PHONE.............................216 421-2775
Fax: 216 421-0402
Daniel Andrews, *President*
Howard A Steindler, *Principal*
Timothy Kurcz, *Sales Mgr*
Moises Rivera, *Sales Mgr*
Bill Andrews, *Sales Staff*
EMP: 18
SQ FT: 6,300
SALES (est): 4MM **Privately Held**
WEB: www.olyforest.com
SIC: **2448** Wood pallets & skids

(G-5941)
OMNI MEDIA
1375 E 9th St Fl 10 (44114-1788)
PHONE.............................216 687-0077
Fax: 216 687-0078
Simon Badinter, *CEO*
Amy Jenyk, *Manager*
EMP: 3
SALES (est): 257K **Privately Held**
WEB: www.mediasregies.com
SIC: **3993** Signs & advertising specialties

(G-5942)
OMNI TECHNICAL PRODUCTS
INC
Also Called: Wire Lab Company
15300 Industrial Pkwy (44135-3310)
PHONE.............................216 433-1970
Fax: 216 433-0007
Robert J Fulop, *President*
Robert L Fulop, *Vice Pres*
Mark Morris, *Purch Agent*
EMP: 11
SQ FT: 20,000
SALES (est): 2MM **Privately Held**
WEB: www.wirelab.com
SIC: **3542** Mechanical (pneumatic or hy-
draulic) metal forming machines

(G-5943)
ONX USA LLC (DH)
5910 Landerbrook Dr # 250 (44124-6508)
PHONE.............................440 569-2300
Mike Cox, *CEO*
Bart Foster, *Ch of Bd*
Paul Khawaja, *President*
Wayne Kiphart, *President*
Rosalind Lehman, *CFO*
EMP: 75
SQ FT: 20,000
SALES (est): 88MM
SALES (corp-wide): 3.8B **Privately Held**
SIC: **7379 7372** Computer related consult-
ing services; business oriented computer
software
HQ: Onx Holdings Llc
5910 Landerbrook Dr # 250
Mayfield Heights OH 44124
800 559-2497

(G-5944)
OPTOQUEST INC
10000 Cedar Ave (44106-2119)
PHONE.............................216 445-3637
William J Dupps Jr, *Principal*
EMP: 7 EST: 2015
SALES (est): 90.5K **Privately Held**
SIC: **8062 3841** General medical & surgi-
cal hospitals; surgical & medical instru-
ments

(G-5945)
ORACLE CORPORATION
30500 Bruce Indus Pkwy (44139-3969)
PHONE.............................440 264-1620
EMP: 4
SALES (est): 163.3K **Privately Held**
SIC: **7372** Prepackaged software

(G-5946)
ORBYTEL PRINT AND PACKG
INC
4901 Johnston Pkwy (44128-3201)
PHONE.............................216 267-8734
Fax: 216 267-8288
Albert Uvlin, *President*
James R Bingham, *Principal*
Clarence D Finke, *Principal*
Cynthia Uvlin, *Corp Secy*
Mark Uvlin, *COO*
EMP: 8
SQ FT: 12,300
SALES (est): 1.2MM **Privately Held**
WEB: www.diagraphohio.com
SIC: **2679 5085 5084** Tags & labels,
paper; industrial supplies

(G-5947)
ORIGINAL MATTRESS FACTORY
INC (PA)
4930 State Rd (44134-1214)
PHONE.............................216 661-8388
Fax: 216 661-2337
Ron Trzcinski, *President*
Perry Doermann, *Corp Secy*

Lawrence S Carlson, *Vice Pres*
Douglas B Stroup, *Vice Pres*
David Phillips, *Sales Staff*
EMP: 4
SQ FT: 33,000
SALES (est): 26.6MM **Privately Held**
WEB: www.originalmattress.com
SIC: **2515 5712** Mattresses & foundations;
furniture springs; bedding & bedsprings;
mattresses

(G-5948)
ORLANDO BAKING COMPANY
(PA)
7777 Grand Ave (44104-3061)
PHONE.............................216 361-1872
Fax: 216 391-3469
Chester Orlando, *President*
Glenn W Eckert, *Principal*
Edna Rosenblum, *Principal*
Hattie Wagner, *Principal*
Joseph Orlando, *Vice Pres*
▲ EMP: 239 EST: 1872
SQ FT: 80,000
SALES (est): 103.2MM **Privately Held**
WEB: www.orlandobaking.com
SIC: **2051** Bread, all types (white, wheat,
rye, etc): fresh or frozen; rolls, bread type:
fresh or frozen

(G-5949)
OSBORNE INC
Also Called: Cuyahoga Concrete Products
2100 Central Furnace Ct (44115-3621)
P.O. Box 91836 (44101-3836)
PHONE.............................216 771-0010
Fax: 216 771-4503
Bill Tagalmonte, *Manager*
EMP: 29
SALES (corp-wide): 15.4MM **Privately
Held**
SIC: **5211 3273** Concrete & cinder block;
ready-mixed concrete
PA: Osborne, Inc.
7954 Reynolds Rd
Mentor OH 44060
440 942-7000

(G-5950)
OSTEOSYMBIONICS LLC
1768 E 25th St Ste 316 (44114-4418)
P.O. Box 128, Aurora (44202-0128)
PHONE.............................216 881-8500
Cynthia Brogan, *Mng Member*
Jessie San, *Case Mgr*
Valerie Hopkins, *Office Admin*
EMP: 10
SALES: 2.6MM **Privately Held**
WEB: www.osteosymbionics.com
SIC: **3842** Implants, surgical

(G-5951)
OTIS ELEVATOR COMPANY
9800 Rockside Rd Ste 1200 (44125-6270)
PHONE.............................216 573-2333
Fax: 216 573-2344
Gordy Sell, *Manager*
EMP: 73
SALES (corp-wide): 57.2B **Publicly Held**
WEB: www.otis.com
SIC: **7699 1796 3534** Elevators: inspec-
tion, service & repair; elevator installation
& conversion; elevators & equipment
HQ: Otis Elevator Company
1 Carrier Pl
Farmington CT 06032
860 674-3000

(G-5952)
OTTO KONIGSLOW MFG CO
13300 Coit Rd (44110-2285)
PHONE.............................216 851-7900
Fax: 216 851-6712
Cofer McIntosh, *CEO*
J P Lawson, *President*
EMP: 15
SQ FT: 72,500
SALES: 2MM **Privately Held**
SIC: **3724 3548** Aircraft engines & engine
parts; welding & cutting apparatus & ac-
cessories

(G-5953)
P & P MACHINE TOOL INC
26189 Broadway Ave (44146-6512)
PHONE.............................440 232-7404

Fax: 440 232-8785
Wayne Pelcarsky, *President*
Thomas Pelcarsky, *Vice Pres*
EMP: 6 **EST:** 1980
SQ FT: 4,000
SALES (est): 852.5K **Privately Held**
SIC: 3599 Machine shop, jobbing & repair

(G-5954)
P F S INCORPORATED
9861 York Alpha Dr (44133-3507)
PHONE................................440 582-1620
Fax: 440 582-9357
Ronald Miller, *President*
Rose Miller, *Vice Pres*
EMP: 4 **EST:** 1976
SQ FT: 4,800
SALES (est): 544.7K **Privately Held**
SIC: 3599 3545 Machine shop, jobbing &
repair; cutting tools for machine tools

(G-5955)
P G M DIVERSIFIED INDUSTRIES
6514 Alexandria Dr (44130-2850)
PHONE................................440 885-3500
Fax: 440 842-9228
Mark Podany, *President*
George Rowley, *Vice Pres*
Frances L Merat, *Treasurer*
EMP: 5
SALES: 260K **Privately Held**
WEB: www.pgmdi.com
SIC: 8711 3825 Consulting engineer;
measuring instruments & meters, electric

(G-5956)
P L M CORPORATION
7424 Bessemer Ave (44127-1820)
PHONE................................216 341-8008
Fax: 216 341-9150
Michael Dunn, *President*
Mary Mingus, *Admin Sec*
EMP: 9
SQ FT: 25,000
SALES (est): 1.3MM **Privately Held**
SIC: 3272 Paving materials, prefabricated
concrete

(G-5957)
P S C INC
21761 Tungsten Rd (44117-1116)
PHONE................................216 531-3375
Fax: 216 531-6751
Matthew C Litzler, *President*
Sue Glass, *General Mgr*
William J Urban, *COO*
Mike London, *Engineer*
George Barber, *Manager*
▲ **EMP:** 8 **EST:** 1970
SQ FT: 12,000
SALES (est): 1.7MM
SALES (corp-wide): 36.1MM **Privately
Held**
WEB: www.pscrfheat.com
SIC: 3567 1731 Dielectric heating equip-
ment; general electrical contractor
PA: C.A. Litzler Holding Company
4800 W 160th St
Cleveland OH 44135
216 267-8020

(G-5958)
P S SUPERIOR INC
Also Called: P S Awards
9257 Midwest Ave (44125-2415)
PHONE................................216 587-1000
Elizabeth Sudyk, *President*
Beth Sudyk, *General Mgr*
Joanne Sudyk, *Treasurer*
EMP: 11
SQ FT: 10,000
SALES (est): 825K **Privately Held**
SIC: 3499 7389 5199 Trophies, metal, ex-
cept silver; lettering service; advertising
specialties

(G-5959)
PACE CONVERTING EQP CO INC
8500 Lake Ave (44102-1912)
PHONE................................216 631-4555
Fax: 216 631-7103
Michael Chrystyna, *CEO*
Richard Jefferys, *Sales/Mktg Mgr*
EMP: 14
SQ FT: 15,000

SALES: 1.2MM **Privately Held**
WEB: www.pace-equipment.com
SIC: 3621 Phase or rotary converters
(electrical equipment)

(G-5960)
PACK LINE CORP
22900 Miles Rd (44128-5445)
PHONE................................212 564-0664
Michael Beilinson, *Principal*
Lea Katseli, *Director*
▲ **EMP:** 15
SALES (est): 441.7K
SALES (corp-wide): 11MM **Privately Held**
SIC: 3565 Packaging machinery
PA: Packline Ltd
59 Prof. Shor
Holon 58811
355 815-34

(G-5961)
PARADISE MOLD & DIE LLC
10815 Briggs Rd (44111-5331)
PHONE................................216 362-1945
Fax: 216 362-1945
Tom Edgehouse,
EMP: 3
SALES (est): 656.1K **Privately Held**
SIC: 3544 Special dies, tools, jigs & fix-
tures

(G-5962)
PARALLEL SOLUTIONS
5380 Naiman Pkwy Ste B (44139-1032)
PHONE................................440 498-9920
Keith Sherwin, *Principal*
Nancy Wright, *Consultant*
EMP: 3
SALES (est): 259K **Privately Held**
SIC: 3579 Time clocks & time recording
devices

(G-5963)
PARAMELT ARGUESO KINDT INC
12651 Elmwood Ave (44111-5911)
PHONE................................216 252-4122
David P Kindt, *President*
Ron Clarke, *Sales Staff*
Scott Pagel, *Manager*
▲ **EMP:** 7
SALES (est): 126.3K **Privately Held**
SIC: 2891 Adhesives

(G-5964)
PARAMOUNT STAMPING & WLDG CO
Also Called: Anchor Template Die Div
1200 W 58th St (44102-2118)
PHONE................................216 631-1755
Peter Kole, *President*
Gary Ash, *General Mgr*
Ed Miyoshi, *Plant Mgr*
Lisa Smith, *Purchasing*
Suzanne Ryan, *Engineer*
EMP: 100
SQ FT: 300,000
SALES (est): 15.4MM **Privately Held**
WEB: www.metalstamping99.com
SIC: 3469 3544 Stamping metal for the
trade; special dies & tools

(G-5965)
PARK CORPORATION (PA)
6200 Riverside Dr (44135-3132)
P.O. Box 8678, South Charleston WV
(25303-0678)
PHONE................................216 267-4870
Raymond P Park, *Ch of Bd*
Daniel K Park, *President*
Ricky L Bertrem, *Vice Pres*
Shelva J Davis, *Vice Pres*
Kelly C Park, *Vice Pres*
◆ **EMP:** 300
SQ FT: 2,500,000
SALES (est): 564.1MM **Privately Held**
WEB: www.parkcorp.com
SIC: 3547 1711 3443 5084 Rolling mill
machinery; boiler maintenance contractor;
mechanical contractor; boilers: industrial,
power, or marine; industrial machinery &
equipment; commercial & industrial build-
ing operation; exposition operation

(G-5966)
PARK-OHIO HOLDINGS CORP (PA)
6065 Parkland Blvd Ste 1 (44124-6145)
PHONE................................440 947-2000
Fax: 440 947-2099
Edward F Crawford, *Ch of Bd*
Matthew V Crawford, *President*
Darryl Niven, *VP Mfg*
James Nicoulin, *Materials Mgr*
Charles Smyers, *Production*
◆ **EMP:** 18
SQ FT: 20,150
SALES: 1.2B **Publicly Held**
SIC: 3462 3069 3567 3363 Iron & steel
forgings; internal combustion engine forg-
ings, ferrous; aircraft forgings, ferrous;
ordnance forgings, ferrous; molded rub-
ber products; roll coverings, rubber; rub-
ber hardware; rubber automotive
products; induction heating equipment;
aluminum die-castings; lawn & garden
tractors & equipment

(G-5967)
PARK-OHIO INDUSTRIES INC (HQ)
6065 Parkland Blvd Ste 1 (44124-6145)
PHONE................................440 947-2000
Edward F Crawford, *Ch of Bd*
Matthew V Crawford, *President*
W Scott Emerick, *CFO*
◆ **EMP:** 202
SQ FT: 60,450
SALES: 1.2B **Publicly Held**
WEB: www.pkoh.com.cn
SIC: 3462 3069 3567 3363 Iron & steel
forgings; internal combustion engine forg-
ings, ferrous; aircraft forgings, ferrous;
ordnance forgings, ferrous; molded rub-
ber products; roll coverings, rubber; rubber hardware; rubber automotive
products; induction heating equipment;
aluminum die-castings; lawn & garden
tractors & equipment
PA: Park-Ohio Holdings Corp.
6065 Parkland Blvd Ste 1
Cleveland OH 44124
440 947-2000

(G-5968)
PARK-OHIO INDUSTRIES INC
Cleveland City Forge
777 E 79th St (44103-1805)
PHONE................................216 431-2900
Fax: 216 391-4882
Gearard Statler, *Div Sub Head*
Robert Stein, *Plant Engr*
Greg Muniak, *Data Proc Mgr*
Robert Vilsack, *Admin Sec*
EMP: 35
SALES (corp-wide): 1.2B **Publicly Held**
WEB: www.pkoh.com.cn
SIC: 3462 Automotive forgings, ferrous:
crankshaft, engine, axle, etc.
HQ: Park-Ohio Industries, Inc.
6065 Parkland Blvd Ste 1
Cleveland OH 44124
440 947-2000

(G-5969)
PARK-OHIO PRODUCTS INC
7000 Denison Ave (44102-5247)
PHONE................................216 961-7200
Fax: 216 334-1090
Craig Cowan, *President*
Richard Paul Elliott, *Vice Pres*
Anthony Hall, *Vice Pres*
Robert Poeppleman, *Vice Pres*
Robert Vilsack, *Vice Pres*
▲ **EMP:** 100
SQ FT: 40,000
SALES (est): 31.6MM
SALES (corp-wide): 1.2B **Publicly Held**
WEB: www.pkoh.com.cn
SIC: 3069 Molded rubber products
HQ: Park-Ohio Industries, Inc.
6065 Parkland Blvd Ste 1
Cleveland OH 44124
440 947-2000

(G-5970)
PARKER ELWELL LTD
4205 Saint Clair Ave (44103-1121)
PHONE................................216 881-5042
Fax: 216 391-7708

Michele Minda, *Executive*
EMP: 4
SALES (est): 442.7K **Privately Held**
SIC: 3537 Industrial trucks & tractors

(G-5971)
PARKER ROYALTY PARTNERSHIP
6035 Parkland Blvd (44124-4186)
PHONE................................216 896-3000
Ravi Gudipati, *Business Mgr*
Paul Vallone, *Vice Pres*
Martin Cruvier, *Project Mgr*
Colleen Chicoine, *Buyer*
Jesus Ortiz, *QC Mgr*
EMP: 68
SALES (est): 8.4MM
SALES (corp-wide): 11.3B **Publicly Held**
SIC: 3594 Fluid power pumps & motors
PA: Parker-Hannifin Corporation
6035 Parkland Blvd
Cleveland OH 44124
216 896-3000

(G-5972)
PARKER RST-PROOF CLEVELAND INC
1688 Arabella Rd (44112-1418)
PHONE................................216 481-6680
Fax: 216 481-8645
Frederick A Fruscella, *Ch of Bd*
Sharon Bodine, *Vice Pres*
Maggie Haas, *Controller*
Connie Mareino, *Manager*
EMP: 37
SQ FT: 75,000
SALES (est): 5.5MM **Privately Held**
SIC: 3479 3471 Rust proofing (hot dip-
ping) of metals & formed products; plating
& polishing

(G-5973)
PARKER-HANNIFIN CORPORATION (PA)
6035 Parkland Blvd (44124-4186)
PHONE................................216 896-3000
Fax: 216 896-4000
Thomas L Williams, *Ch of Bd*
Lee C Banks, *President*
Yoon Chung, *President*
John R Greco, *President*
Kurt A Keller, *President*
◆ **EMP:** 500
SALES: 11.3B **Publicly Held**
WEB: www.parker.com
SIC: 3594 3593 3492 3569 Fluid power
pumps & motors; fluid power pumps; fluid
power motors; fluid power cylinders & actuators; fluid power actuators, hydraulic or
pneumatic; fluid power cylinders, hydraulic or pneumatic; control valves, fluid
power: hydraulic & pneumatic; hose &
tube fittings & assemblies,
hydraulic/pneumatic; control valves, aircraft: hydraulic & pneumatic; valves, hydraulic, aircraft; filter elements, fluid,
hydraulic line; gaskets & sealing devices;
aircraft & motor vehicle measurement
equipment

(G-5974)
PARKER-HANNIFIN CORPORATION
Also Called: Gas Turbine Fuel Systems Div
17325 Euclid Ave (44112-1247)
PHONE................................216 531-3000
Fax: 216 383-9414
Frank N Nichols, *Principal*
EMP: 125
SALES (corp-wide): 11.3B **Publicly Held**
SIC: 3494 Valves & pipe fittings
PA: Parker-Hannifin Corporation
6035 Parkland Blvd
Cleveland OH 44124
216 896-3000

(G-5975)
PARKER-HANNIFIN CORPORATION
Motion & Control Training Div
6035 Parkland Blvd (44124-4186)
PHONE................................216 531-3000
Joe Bocian, *Branch Mgr*
EMP: 600

SALES (corp-wide): 11.3B **Publicly Held**
WEB: www.parker.com
SIC: 4225 3823 3714 General warehousing & storage; industrial instrmnts msrmnt display/control process variable; motor vehicle parts & accessories
PA: Parker-Hannifin Corporation
6035 Parkland Blvd
Cleveland OH 44124
216 896-3000

(G-5976)
PARKER-HANNIFIN CORPORATION
Export Division
6035 Parkland Blvd (44124-4186)
P.O. Box 92613 (44190-0002)
PHONE....................216 896-3000
Melissa McLaughlin, *General Mgr*
EMP: 12
SALES (corp-wide): 11.3B **Publicly Held**
SIC: 3594 3593 3492 3569 Fluid power pumps; fluid power motors; fluid power cylinders, hydraulic or pneumatic; fluid power actuators, hydraulic or pneumatic; control valves, fluid power; hydraulic & pneumatic; hose & tube fittings & assemblies, hydraulic/pneumatic; control valves, aircraft; hydraulic & pneumatic; valves, hydraulic, aircraft; filter elements, fluid, hydraulic line; gaskets & sealing devices; aircraft & motor vehicle measurement equipment
PA: Parker-Hannifin Corporation
6035 Parkland Blvd
Cleveland OH 44124
216 896-3000

(G-5977)
PARKING & TRAFFIC CONTROL SEC
Also Called: Ptc Industries
13651 Newton Rd (44130-2735)
PHONE....................440 243-7565
Fax: 440 243-9242
Donald Shorts, *CEO*
Lee Shorts, *President*
EMP: 15
SQ FT: 20,000
SALES (est): 3MM **Privately Held**
WEB: www.ptcind.com
SIC: 3824 1799 8711 Mfg Fluid Meter/Counting Devices Trade Contractor Engineering Services

(G-5978)
PARMA HEIGHTS LICENSE BUREAU
6339 Olde York Rd (44130-3059)
PHONE....................440 888-0388
Fax: 440 888-0398
Dan Hughes, *Owner*
EMP: 7 **EST:** 1999
SALES (est): 569.4K **Privately Held**
SIC: 3469 Automobile license tags, stamped metal

(G-5979)
PARTHENON GLOBAL LLC
Also Called: Parthenon Globalsystems LLC
3615 Superior Ave E (44114-4138)
PHONE....................888 332-5303
Ademola Solaru, *CEO*
Tyler Virgin, *CFO*
EMP: 4
SALES (est): 98.3K **Privately Held**
SIC: 7372 Application computer software

(G-5980)
PATS NU-STYLE CLEANERS INC
Also Called: Pat's Cleaners
5851 Smith Rd (44142-2005)
PHONE....................216 676-4855
Pat Mahoney, *President*
EMP: 3
SALES (corp-wide): 351.9K **Privately Held**
SIC: 2842 Drycleaning preparations
PA: Pat's Nu-Style Cleaners Inc
21420 Lorain Rd
Cleveland OH 44126
440 331-7300

(G-5981)
PATTERSON-BRITTON PRINTING
2165 Lakeside Ave E (44114-1124)
PHONE....................216 781-7997
Harry Britton, *President*
John Britton, *Vice Pres*
EMP: 8
SQ FT: 15,000
SALES: 1.7MM **Privately Held**
SIC: 2752 Commercial printing, lithographic

(G-5982)
PAZCO INC
4500 Rockside Rd Ste 420 (44131-2180)
P.O. Box 830, Aurora (44202-0830)
PHONE....................216 447-9581
Scott Pavrish, *President*
Jeff Pavrish, *President*
EMP: 40 **EST:** 2001
SALES (est): 3.5MM **Privately Held**
WEB: www.pazco.com
SIC: 2899 8741 Plating compounds; management services

(G-5983)
PCC AIRFOILS LLC
Also Called: Sherwood Refractores
1781 Octavia Rd (44112-1410)
PHONE....................216 692-7900
Thomas Lenard, *General Mgr*
Stan Walczyk, *Div Sub Head*
Thomas Shimko, *CIO*
EMP: 150
SALES (corp-wide): 223.6B **Publicly Held**
WEB: www.pccairfoils.com
SIC: 3369 3812 3677 3543 Castings, except die-castings, precision; search & navigation equipment; electronic coils, transformers & other inductors; foundry cores
HQ: Pcc Airfoils Llc
3401 Entp Pkwy Ste 200
Cleveland OH 44122
216 831-3590

(G-5984)
PCC AIRFOILS LLC (DH)
3401 Entp Pkwy Ste 200 (44122)
PHONE....................216 831-3590
Fax: 216 766-6217
Nigel Gorman, *Managing Dir*
Salim Sitabkhan, *Vice Pres*
Cheryl Stroup, *QC Mgr*
Thomas Moreland, *Draft/Design*
Anthony Vecchio, *Engineer*
◆ **EMP:** 29
SQ FT: 14,000
SALES (est): 719.2MM
SALES (corp-wide): 223.6B **Publicly Held**
WEB: www.pccairfoils.com
SIC: 3369 Nonferrous foundries
HQ: Precision Castparts Corp.
4650 Sw Mcdam Ave Ste 300
Portland OR 97239
503 946-4800

(G-5985)
PDQ PRINTING SERVICE
1914 Clark Ave (44109-1156)
PHONE....................216 241-5443
Fax: 216 241-4251
Dorry Smotzer, *Owner*
EMP: 10
SQ FT: 3,000
SALES (est): 1.3MM **Privately Held**
SIC: 2752 Commercial printing, lithographic

(G-5986)
PEARCE INC
12026 Zelis Rd (44135-4691)
PHONE....................216 252-0550
Fax: 216 251-8340
Gerald Myatt, *President*
David Myatt, *Vice Pres*
Laurel Myatt, *Treasurer*
EMP: 11 **EST:** 1945
SQ FT: 10,000
SALES (est): 1.9MM **Privately Held**
SIC: 3555 3554 3599 Printing trades machinery; folding machines, paper; bag & envelope making machinery, paper; machine shop, jobbing & repair

(G-5987)
PECK ENGRAVING CO
14398 Detroit Ave (44107-4408)
PHONE....................216 221-1556
Richard D Zaletel Jr, *President*
Chuck Watkins, *General Mgr*
Laura Zaletel, *Corp Secy*
Patricia Tacchite, *Controller*
EMP: 20 **EST:** 1912
SQ FT: 13,536
SALES (est): 1.9MM **Privately Held**
WEB: www.peckengraving.com
SIC: 2796 2752 Engraving on copper, steel, wood or rubber; printing plates; commercial printing, lithographic

(G-5988)
PEERLESS METAL PRODUCTS INC
6017 Superior Ave (44103-1447)
PHONE....................216 431-6905
Fax: 216 431-7037
Thomas Banyas, *President*
Judy Szabo, *CFO*
EMP: 22
SQ FT: 32,000
SALES: 2MM **Privately Held**
WEB: www.peerlessmetalproducts.com
SIC: 3469 Metal stampings

(G-5989)
PEMCO INC
5663 Brecksville Rd (44131-1593)
PHONE....................216 524-2990
Fax: 216 524-2990
William John Koteles, *President*
Matt Koteles, *Vice Pres*
Ivan Kovacs, *VP Mfg*
Tom Koteles, *Purchasing*
Kathleen Koteles, *Manager*
EMP: 43 **EST:** 1942
SQ FT: 25,000
SALES: 1.2MM **Privately Held**
WEB: www.pemcomed.com
SIC: 3841 3599 3845 3545 Surgical & medical instruments; machine shop, jobbing & repair; electromedical equipment; machine tool accessories

(G-5990)
PENTON BUSINESS MEDIA INC
1100 Superior Ave E Fl 8 (44114-2530)
PHONE....................216 696-7000
Fax: 216 931-9891
David Kieselstein, *CEO*
Margaret McCartney, *General Mgr*
Nicola Allais, *CFO*
Lynne McLaughlin, *Sales Associate*
Jen Cintora, *Marketing Staff*
EMP: 1100 **EST:** 2007
SALES: 310MM **Privately Held**
SIC: 2741 7379 Miscellaneous publishing;

(G-5991)
PENTON MEDIA INC
1300 E 9th St Ste 300 (44114-1521)
PHONE....................216 696-7000
Fax: 216 931-9492
Frank Craven, *Publisher*
Steve Minter, *Publisher*
Scott Arnold, *Editor*
Steven Averett, *Editor*
Gail Bellamy, *Editor*
EMP: 650
SALES (corp-wide): 1.4B **Privately Held**
SIC: 2759 Publication printing
HQ: Penton Media, Inc.
1166 Avenue Of The Americ
New York NY 10036
212 204-4200

(G-5992)
PERFECTION METAL CO
9416 Richmond Ave (44105-4044)
PHONE....................216 641-0949
Fax: 216 641-6406
David J Eget, *President*
EMP: 4 **EST:** 1949
SQ FT: 24,000
SALES (est): 873K **Privately Held**
WEB: www.pmetal.com
SIC: 3599 5051 Machine shop, jobbing & repair; metals service centers & offices

(G-5993)
PERFUSION SOLUTIONS INC
4320 Mayfield Rd Ste 108 (44121-3601)
PHONE....................216 848-1610
William Smith, *General Mgr*
Sam Kiderman, *Principal*
Irina Tsing, *Admin Sec*
EMP: 3
SALES (est): 257.3K **Privately Held**
SIC: 3841 Surgical & medical instruments

(G-5994)
PERSONNEL SELECTION SERVICES
31517 Walker Rd (44140-1415)
PHONE....................440 835-3255
Paul Michalko, *President*
EMP: 10
SALES (est): 418.2K **Privately Held**
SIC: 1389 8071 Testing, measuring, surveying & analysis services; testing laboratories

(G-5995)
PETER ZARET & SONS VIOLINS
5767 Mayfield Rd (44124-2900)
PHONE....................440 461-1411
Fax: 440 461-1855
Peter Zaret, *President*
Zaret Lillian T, *Vice Pres*
Linda Zaret, *Admin Sec*
EMP: 5
SALES: 500K **Privately Held**
SIC: 3931 Violins & parts

(G-5996)
PETNET SOLUTIONS INC
11100 Euclid Ave (44106-1716)
PHONE....................865 218-2000
Danny Bingham, *Manager*
EMP: 4
SALES (corp-wide): 89.6B **Privately Held**
SIC: 2835 Radioactive diagnostic substances
HQ: Petnet Solutions, Inc.
810 Innovation Dr
Knoxville TN 37932
865 218-2000

(G-5997)
PETNET SOLUTIONS CLEVELAND LLC
2035 E 86th St Rm Jb-122 (44106-2963)
PHONE....................865 218-2000
Thomas Welch, *CEO*
Danny Bingham, *Manager*
EMP: 5
SALES (est): 558.7K
SALES (corp-wide): 89.6B **Privately Held**
SIC: 2835 Radioactive diagnostic substances
HQ: Petnet Solutions, Inc.
810 Innovation Dr
Knoxville TN 37932
865 218-2000

(G-5998)
PETRO GEAR CORPORATION (PA)
3901 Hamilton Ave (44114-3831)
PHONE....................216 431-2820
Herman Bronstein, *President*
Joel Bronstein, *Vice Pres*
EMP: 10
SQ FT: 40,000
SALES (est): 2MM **Privately Held**
SIC: 3566 Gears, power transmission, except automotive

(G-5999)
PETROLIANCE LLC
8500 Clinton Rd Ste 11 (44144-1001)
PHONE....................216 441-7200
Kevin McCarter, *CEO*
EMP: 113
SALES (est): 2.2MM
SALES (corp-wide): 374.8MM **Privately Held**
SIC: 2992 Lubricating oils & greases
HQ: Petroliance Llc
1009 Schieffelin Rd
Apex NC 27502
919 387-9810

(G-6000)
PHIL VEDDA & SONS INC
Also Called: Vedda Printing
12000 Berea Rd (44111-1608)
PHONE.....................................216 671-2222
Fax: 216 671-2200
Phillip Vedda, *President*
James Vedda, *Vice Pres*
Ron Jewett, *VP Opers*
Peggy Cook, *Exec Dir*
William Maglosky, *Director*
EMP: 8
SQ FT: 20,000
SALES (est): 2.8MM **Privately Held**
SIC: 2752 Commercial printing, lithographic

(G-6001)
PHILIPS MEDICAL SYSTEMS CLEVEL (HQ)
Also Called: Medical Imaging Equipment
595 Miner Rd (44143-2131)
PHONE.....................................440 247-2652
David A Dripchak, *CEO*
Arlene Burnside, *General Mgr*
Jerry C Cirino, *Exec VP*
William J Cull Sr, *Vice Pres*
Hillary Sullivan, *Vice Pres*
◆ EMP: 500
SQ FT: 495,000
SALES: 424.4MM
SALES (corp-wide): 26B **Privately Held**
SIC: 3844 5047 5137 3842 X-ray apparatus & tubes; X-ray film & supplies; instruments, surgical & medical; hospital gowns, women's & children's; surgical appliances & supplies; laboratory apparatus & furniture; electrical equipment & supplies
PA: Koninklijke Philips N.V.
High Tech Campus 5
Eindhoven 5656
402 791-111

(G-6002)
PHILLIPS CONTRACTORS SUP LLC
Also Called: Colony Hardware
1800 E 30th St (44114-4410)
PHONE.....................................216 861-5730
James D Beckett,
Ian Greenhill,
Jeffrey Williams,
EMP: 15
SQ FT: 40,000
SALES (est): 3.8MM **Privately Held**
WEB: www.pcscleveland.com
SIC: 3965 Fasteners

(G-6003)
PHILLIPS ELECTRIC CO
Also Called: Redmond Waltz Electric
4126 Saint Clair Ave (44103-1120)
PHONE.....................................216 361-0014
Fax: 216 361-6599
Jennifer Marriott, *President*
Joe Griffin, *Accounts Mgr*
Bruce Hogen, *Manager*
EMP: 15
SQ FT: 40,000
SALES (est): 2.3MM **Privately Held**
WEB: www.phillipselectric.com
SIC: 7694 5063 Electric motor repair; motors, electric

(G-6004)
PHOENIX TOOL & THREAD GRINDNG
4760 Briar Rd (44135-5038)
PHONE.....................................216 433-7008
Fax: 216 433-7067
John Biliboaca, *Owner*
EMP: 3
SALES: 250K **Privately Held**
WEB: www.phoenixthreadgrinding.com
SIC: 3451 Screw machine products

(G-6005)
PIERCE-WRIGHT PRECISION INC
13606 Enterprise Ave (44135-5112)
PHONE.....................................216 362-2870
Fax: 216 362-8229
David B Pierce, *President*
EMP: 7 EST: 1978

SQ FT: 10,000
SALES (est): 785K **Privately Held**
SIC: 3599 Machine shop, jobbing & repair

(G-6006)
PIERRES FRENCH ICE CREAM INC
6519 Carnegie Ave (44103)
PHONE.....................................216 431-2555
Fax: 216 432-0001
Sol Roth, *President*
Elliot Kaminsky, *Vice Pres*
Shelly Roth, *Vice Pres*
Harriet Roth, *Admin Sec*
▲ EMP: 25 EST: 1937
SQ FT: 75,000
SALES (est): 3.8MM **Privately Held**
SIC: 2024 Ice cream & ice milk

(G-6007)
PILE DYNAMICS INC
Also Called: Pdi
30725 Aurora Rd (44139-2735)
PHONE.....................................216 831-6131
Fax: 216 831-0916
Garland Likins, *President*
George Piscsalko, *Vice Pres*
Tim Raines, *Engineer*
Dean Cotton, *Senior Engr*
Ryan A Peee, *Senior Engr*
▲ EMP: 35 EST: 1972
SQ FT: 12,000
SALES (est): 11.1MM **Privately Held**
WEB: www.pile.com
SIC: 3825 Test equipment for electronic & electrical circuits

(G-6008)
PINNACLE GRAPHICS & IMAGING
Also Called: P G I
1138 W 9th St Ste LI (44113-1046)
PHONE.....................................216 781-1800
Fax: 216 781-1810
Dan J Nugent, *President*
EMP: 11
SQ FT: 3,000
SALES (est): 1.1MM **Privately Held**
SIC: 2796 Color separations for printing

(G-6009)
PJ BUSH ASSOCIATES INC
Also Called: Bush Integrated
15901 Industrial Pkwy (44135-3321)
PHONE.....................................216 362-6700
Fax: 216 362-7200
Kathleen Bush, *President*
Patrick J Bush, *Principal*
Tom Dennison, *Prdtn Mgr*
Laura Thompson, *Sales Staff*
Emily Koz, *Marketing Staff*
EMP: 21
SQ FT: 40,000
SALES (est): 3.6MM **Privately Held**
WEB: www.bushintegrated.com
SIC: 2759 Business forms: printing; promotional printing; screen printing

(G-6010)
PLAIN DEALER PUBLISHING CO (HQ)
Also Called: Plain Dealer, The
4800 Tiedeman Rd (44144-2336)
P.O. Box 630504, Cincinnati (45263-0504)
PHONE.....................................216 999-5000
Fax: 216 344-4122
Terrance C Z Egger, *President*
Sharon Broussard, *Editor*
Daryl Kannberg, *Editor*
Chris Quinn, *Editor*
Mark Rapp, *Editor*
EMP: 15
SQ FT: 210,000
SALES (est): 254.9MM
SALES (corp-wide): 1.6B **Privately Held**
WEB: www.plaind.com
SIC: 2711 Newspapers
PA: Advance Digital Inc.
3100 Harborside Fincl 3
Jersey City NJ 07311
201 459-2808

(G-6011)
PLAIN DEALER PUBLISHING CO
4800 Tiedeman Rd (44144-2336)
PHONE.....................................216 999-5000
Joe Bowman, *Opers Staff*
Steve Chalabian, *Manager*
Dick Fuller, *Director*
Carol Huddleston, *Director*
EMP: 900
SALES (corp-wide): 1.6B **Privately Held**
WEB: www.plaind.com
SIC: 2711 2752 Newspapers; commercial printing, lithographic
HQ: Plain Dealer Publishing Co.
4800 Tiedeman Rd
Cleveland OH 44144
216 999-5000

(G-6012)
PLASTER PROCESS CASTINGS CO
Also Called: Diversified Mold and Castings
19800 Miles Rd (44128-4118)
PHONE.....................................216 663-1814
Fax: 216 781-3152
Vince Costello, *President*
S Costello, *Vice Pres*
EMP: 30 EST: 1939
SQ FT: 7,500
SALES: 7.6MM **Privately Held**
WEB: www.plasterprocesscastings.com
SIC: 3363 3364 Aluminum die-castings; zinc & zinc-base alloy die-castings

(G-6013)
PLASTIC PLATERS LLC
Also Called: P P I
9921 Clinton Rd (44144-1086)
PHONE.....................................216 961-1200
Fax: 216 961-1263
Derrick Redding, *President*
Brad Gotts, *President*
James McKinley, *Finance Dir*
Frank Burnside, *Manager*
EMP: 150
SQ FT: 92,000
SALES (est): 21MM
SALES (corp-wide): 575.1MM **Privately Held**
WEB: www.egreeninc.com
SIC: 3471 Electroplating of metals or formed products
PA: Ernie Green Industries, Inc.
2030 Dividend Dr
Columbus OH 43228
614 219-1423

(G-6014)
PLASTIC WORKS INC
19851 Ingersoll Dr (44116-1817)
PHONE.....................................440 331-5575
Eric Kvame, *Manager*
EMP: 12
SALES (corp-wide): 1MM **Privately Held**
SIC: 3086 2671 Packaging & shipping materials, foamed plastic; packaging paper & plastics film, coated & laminated
PA: The Plastic Works Inc
10502 Mudbrook Rd
Huron OH 44839
419 433-6576

(G-6015)
PLASTRAN INC
Also Called: P T X
9841 York Alpha Dr Ste N (44133-3554)
PHONE.....................................440 237-8404
Fax: 440 237-3701
Charles Frishe, *President*
EMP: 4
SQ FT: 2,500
SALES (est): 615.3K **Privately Held**
SIC: 3443 5084 Metal parts; industrial machinery & equipment

(G-6016)
PLATFORM BEERS LLC
4125 Lorain Ave (44113-3718)
PHONE.....................................440 539-3245
Paul Benner, *Mng Member*
Justin Carson, *Mng Member*
EMP: 12
SQ FT: 5,000
SALES: 700K **Privately Held**
SIC: 2082 Near beer

(G-6017)
PLATING TEST CELL SUPPLY CO
948 Wayside Rd B (44110-2957)
PHONE.....................................216 486-8400
Fax: 216 486-8555
David E Geduld, *Owner*
EMP: 3
SQ FT: 1,000
SALES: 200K **Privately Held**
SIC: 3829 Physical property testing equipment

(G-6018)
PLUS MARK LLC
1 American Rd (44144-2398)
PHONE.....................................216 252-6770
Fax: 216 252-6774
Kurt Schoen, *President*
Dick Gygi, *President*
Christopher W Haffke, *Principal*
Chris Banning, *VP Sls/Mktg*
Gui De Mello, *Treasurer*
▲ EMP: 35
SQ FT: 1,600,000
SALES (est): 16.9MM
SALES (corp-wide): 2.2B **Privately Held**
SIC: 2621 2396 2771 Wrapping paper; automotive & apparel trimmings; greeting cards
HQ: American Greetings Corporation
1 American Rd
Cleveland OH 44144
216 252-7300

(G-6019)
POLGENIX INC
11000 Cedar Ave Ste 100 (44106-3056)
PHONE.....................................440 537-9691
Joseph Jankowski, *President*
Zhiqian Dong, *Research*
Vida M Tripodo, *Finance*
Grazyna Palczewska, *Director*
EMP: 3
SALES (est): 390.9K **Privately Held**
WEB: www.polgenixinc.com
SIC: 2834 Pharmaceutical preparations

(G-6020)
POLY PRODUCTS INC
837 E 79th St (44103-1807)
PHONE.....................................216 391-7659
Walter Senney, *President*
Joyce Senney, *Vice Pres*
EMP: 6
SQ FT: 12,000
SALES (est): 78K **Privately Held**
WEB: www.poly-products.com
SIC: 3559 3568 Refinery, chemical processing & similar machinery; bearings, bushings & blocks

(G-6021)
PORATH BUSINESS SERVICES INC
Also Called: Porath Printing
21000 Miles Pkwy (44128-5515)
PHONE.....................................216 626-0060
Fax: 216 626-0061
Gerald A Engelhart, *President*
Mindy Lapine, *Controller*
Annjoy Pickholtz, *Sales Staff*
Erich Kerstetter, *Graphic Designe*
EMP: 17
SQ FT: 5,000
SALES (est): 3.1MM **Privately Held**
SIC: 2752 7331 Commercial printing, offset; mailing service

(G-6022)
POSTLE INDUSTRIES INC
Also Called: Cermet Technologies
5500 W 164th St (44142-1512)
P.O. Box 42037 (44142-0037)
PHONE.....................................216 265-9000
Fax: 216 265-9030
John G Postle, *President*
Chris J Postle, *Vice Pres*
Keith Jansto, *Engineer*
Lisa Smith, *Accountant*
Scott Day, *Manager*
▲ EMP: 25
SQ FT: 15,000

SALES (est): 5.9MM **Privately Held**
WEB: www.postle.com
SIC: 3548 2851 Welding & cutting appara-
tus & accessories; epoxy coatings

(G-6023)
POTTERS INDUSTRIES LLC
2380 W 3rd St (44113-2509)
PHONE................................216 621-0840
Fax: 216 621-0532
Joseph Kwapinski, *VP Finance*
Bob Flanagan, *Regl Sales Mgr*
Mark Nicholson, *Regl Sales Mgr*
Bob Hooper, *Manager*
Patrick U Brady, *Manager*
EMP: 30
SALES (corp-wide): 992.1MM **Privately
Held**
WEB: www.flexolite.com
SIC: 3231 Reflector glass beads, for high-
way signs or reflectors
HQ: Potters Industries, Llc
300 Lindenwood Dr
Malvern PA 19355
610 651-4700

(G-6024)
POUCHR LLC
11470 Euclid Ave Ste 119 (44106-3934)
PHONE................................216 990-0535
Alicia Schreiber,
EMP: 4
SALES (est): 306.6K **Privately Held**
SIC: 3089 Plastic containers, except foam

(G-6025)
**PPG ARCHITECTURAL FINISHES
INC**
Also Called: Glidden Professional Paint Ctr
5480 Cloverleaf Pkwy # 5 (44125-4804)
PHONE................................216 328-1581
Jim Martinis, *Manager*
EMP: 5
SALES (corp-wide): 14.7B **Publicly Held**
WEB: www.gliddenpaint.com
SIC: 2851 Paints & allied products
HQ: Ppg Architectural Finishes, Inc.
1 Ppg Pl
Pittsburgh PA 15272
412 434-3131

(G-6026)
PPG INDUSTRIES INC
14800 Emery Ave (44135-1477)
PHONE................................216 671-7793
Dian Lind, *Branch Mgr*
EMP: 24
SALES (corp-wide): 14.7B **Publicly Held**
SIC: 2851 Paints & allied products
PA: Ppg Industries, Inc.
1 Ppg Pl
Pittsburgh PA 15272
412 434-3131

(G-6027)
**PPG INDUSTRIES OHIO INC
(HQ)**
Also Called: PPG Kansai Automotive Finishes
3800 W 143rd St (44111-4997)
PHONE................................216 671-0050
Fax: 216 252-1009
Charles E Bunch, *CEO*
Bill Silvestri, *President*
J Rich Alexander, *Vice Pres*
Randy Dewing, *Manager*
Joan Leister, *Manager*
◆ EMP: 602
SQ FT: 439,551
SALES (est): 399.9MM
SALES (corp-wide): 14.7B **Publicly Held**
WEB: www.ppgglass.com
SIC: 2851 Paints & allied products
PA: Ppg Industries, Inc.
1 Ppg Pl
Pittsburgh PA 15272
412 434-3131

(G-6028)
PPL HOLDING COMPANY
25201 Chagrin Blvd # 360 (44122-5600)
PHONE................................216 514-1840
Mark Mansour, *Bd of Directors*
EMP: 50
SALES (est): 2.3MM **Privately Held**
SIC: 2821 Thermoplastic materials

(G-6029)
PRAXAIR INC
2500 Metrohealth Dr (44109-1900)
PHONE................................216 778-5555
Ken Papa, *Manager*
EMP: 20
SALES (corp-wide): 10.5B **Publicly Held**
SIC: 2813 Industrial gases
PA: Praxair, Inc.
10 Riverview Dr
Danbury CT 06810
203 837-2000

(G-6030)
PRAXAIR INC
14788 York Rd (44133-4508)
PHONE................................440 237-8690
Brian Pasquerlo, *Superintendent*
EMP: 30
SALES (corp-wide): 10.5B **Publicly Held**
SIC: 2813 Industrial gases
PA: Praxair, Inc.
10 Riverview Dr
Danbury CT 06810
203 837-2000

(G-6031)
PRAXAIR INC
5480 Cloverleaf Pkwy # 6 (44125-4804)
PHONE................................419 652-3562
Mike Barr, *Principal*
EMP: 20
SALES (corp-wide): 10.5B **Publicly Held**
SIC: 2813 Industrial gases
PA: Praxair, Inc.
10 Riverview Dr
Danbury CT 06810
203 837-2000

(G-6032)
PRAXAIR INC
5324 Grant Ave (44125-1036)
PHONE................................440 944-8844
Don Mocarski, *Manager*
EMP: 6
SALES (corp-wide): 10.5B **Publicly Held**
SIC: 2813 Industrial gases
PA: Praxair, Inc.
10 Riverview Dr
Danbury CT 06810
203 837-2000

(G-6033)
PRECISE TOOL & MFG CORP
5755 Canal Rd (44125-3429)
PHONE................................216 524-1500
Fax: 216 524-1502
Ronald Volandt, *President*
Robert Kelbach, *Executive*
EMP: 10 EST: 1950
SQ FT: 5,200
SALES (est): 440K **Privately Held**
SIC: 3545 Cutting tools for machine tools

(G-6034)
PRECISION COATINGS INC
Also Called: Precison Coating Technology
3289 E 80th St (44104-4341)
PHONE................................216 441-0805
Fax: 216 441-0674
Dale Palik, *President*
Mike Palik, *Vice Pres*
John Gale, *Finance*
Lucille Palik, *Admin Sec*
EMP: 12 EST: 1981
SQ FT: 22,000
SALES (est): 1.4MM **Privately Held**
WEB: www.precisioncoatingsinc.org
SIC: 3479 Painting, coating & hot dipping;
coating of metals with plastic or resins

(G-6035)
**PRECISION MCHNING
SRFACING INC**
5435 Perkins Rd (44146-1856)
PHONE................................440 439-9850
David Slifka, *President*
EMP: 6
SALES (est): 701.3K **Privately Held**
WEB: www.pre-machining.com
SIC: 3599 Machine shop, jobbing & repair

(G-6036)
**PRECISION METAL PRODUCTS
INC**
7641 Commerce Park Oval (44131-2303)
PHONE................................216 447-1900
Fax: 216 447-1900
Thomas Jacin, *CEO*
George A Jacin, *President*
Robert Weisert, *QC Mgr*
Janet Breneman, *Human Res Dir*
EMP: 17 EST: 1961
SQ FT: 16,000
SALES: 7MM **Privately Held**
WEB: www.pmpstamping.com
SIC: 3469 3549 Metal stampings; assem-
bly machines, including robotic

(G-6037)
**PRECISION WELDING
CORPORATION**
7900 Exchange St (44125-3334)
P.O. Box 25548 (44125-0548)
PHONE................................216 524-6110
Fax: 216 524-0456
Dennis Nader, *President*
Randy Nader, *Vice Pres*
Shonda Compton, *Manager*
Nick Julian, *Manager*
EMP: 32
SQ FT: 26,000
SALES (est): 4.5MM **Privately Held**
SIC: 7692 3444 3441 Welding repair;
sheet metalwork; fabricated structural
metal

(G-6038)
**PRECISION WIRE PRODUCTS
INC (PA)**
Also Called: Cages By Jim
4791 W 139th St (44135-5033)
PHONE................................216 265-7580
Fax: 216 265-7585
Jim Damian Jr, *President*
EMP: 4
SQ FT: 4,500
SALES: 200K **Privately Held**
SIC: 3496 Cages, wire

(G-6039)
PREDICT INC
9555 Rockside Rd Ste 350 (44125-6283)
PHONE................................216 642-3223
Fax: 216 642-1484
Robert Jung, *CEO*
Nicholas Kroll, *President*
Jenifer Reek, *Administration*
EMP: 18
SQ FT: 20,000
SALES: 3.9MM
SALES (corp-wide): 12MM **Privately
Held**
SIC: 1389 Oil sampling service for oil com-
panies
PA: Trico Corporation
1235 Hickory St
Pewaukee WI 53072
262 691-9336

(G-6040)
PREEMPTIVE SOLUTIONS LLC
767 Beta Dr (44143-2379)
PHONE................................216 732-5895
Fax: 216 460-0680
Gabriel Torok, *CEO*
Paul Ruflin, *President*
Andy Forsyth, *Vice Pres*
Keith Peer, *Vice Pres*
Jo Ramkumar, *QA Dir*
EMP: 30
SQ FT: 4,000
SALES (est): 3.4MM **Privately Held**
WEB: www.preemptive.com
SIC: 7372 Prepackaged software

(G-6041)
**PREMIER MANUFACTURING
CORP (HQ)**
2500 Brookpark Rd Ste 200 (44134-1400)
PHONE................................216 941-9700
Fax: 216 941-9719
Paul Kara, *President*
Donald C Dawson, *President*
Bill Rush, *General Mgr*
William Rush, *Research*
John Petro, *Engineer*

◆ EMP: 78 EST: 1962
SQ FT: 170,595
SALES (est): 25.8MM
SALES (corp-wide): 459.4MM **Privately
Held**
WEB: www.premiermfg.com
SIC: 3496 3296 Miscellaneous fabricated
wire products; mineral wool
PA: Ssw Holding Company, Inc.
3501 Tulsa St
Fort Smith AR 72903
479 646-1651

(G-6042)
**PREMIER PRINTING
CORPORATION**
18780 Cranwood Pkwy (44128-4038)
PHONE................................216 478-9720
James Trombo, *President*
Jeffrey Trombo, *Vice Pres*
Coleen Keefer, *Manager*
Aldo Liberatore, *Manager*
EMP: 12
SQ FT: 10,000
SALES (est): 2.3MM **Privately Held**
WEB: www.premierprintingcorp.com
SIC: 2752 Commercial printing, offset

(G-6043)
PRESRITE CORPORATION (PA)
3665 E 78th St (44105-2048)
PHONE................................216 441-5990
Fax: 216 441-2644
Donald J Diemer, *Ch of Bd*
Chris Carman, *President*
William Berglund, *Exec VP*
George Longhour, *Vice Pres*
Roy Stainfield, *Plant Mgr*
EMP: 300
SQ FT: 180,000
SALES (est): 95.3MM **Privately Held**
WEB: www.presrite.com
SIC: 3462 Iron & steel forgings; automotive
& internal combustion engine forgings

(G-6044)
**PRESSCO TECHNOLOGY INC
(PA)**
29200 Aurora Rd (44139-1847)
PHONE................................440 498-2600
Fax: 440 498-2615
Don W Cochran, *President*
James R Bridgeland Jr, *Principal*
William C Holmes, *COO*
Jon Katz, *Vice Pres*
Ed Morgan, *Vice Pres*
▲ EMP: 90
SQ FT: 60,000
SALES (est): 16.4MM **Privately Held**
SIC: 3829 3825 Physical property testing
equipment; instruments to measure elec-
tricity

(G-6045)
**PRESSURE WASHER MFRS
ASSN**
1300 Sumner Ave (44115-2851)
PHONE................................216 241-7333
John H Addington, *Principal*
EMP: 3
SALES: 30.7K **Privately Held**
SIC: 3452 Washers

(G-6046)
PRIME CONDUIT INC (PA)
23240 Chagrin Blvd # 405 (44122-5404)
P.O. Box 22897 (44122-0897)
PHONE................................216 464-3400
Fax: 216 514-2040
Jim Abel, *President*
James Rajecki, *General Mgr*
Jeff Duricky, *Purch Mgr*
Denise Miles, *Accounting Mgr*
John Lomoro, *VP Human Res*
▲ EMP: 18
SALES (est): 14.3MM **Privately Held**
SIC: 2821 3312 Polyvinyl chloride resins
(PVC); pipes & tubes

(G-6047)
PRIME INSTRUMENTS INC
9805 Walford Ave (44102-4734)
PHONE................................216 651-0400
Fax: 216 651-5297
James R Moran, *President*

Bob Krupa, *Vice Pres*
Bill Incorvia, *Opers Staff*
Jeniffer Whalen, *Controller*
Robert Parina, *Info Tech Dir*
▲ **EMP:** 75
SQ FT: 37,000
SALES (est): 14.2MM **Privately Held**
WEB: www.primeinstruments.com
SIC: 3825 Test equipment for electronic &
electric measurement

(G-6048)
PRINCE PLATING INC
1530 E 40th St (44103-2302)
PHONE..................................216 881-7523
Mark Stover, *President*
Don Sikon, *Manager*
EMP: 62
SALES (est): 6.4MM **Privately Held**
SIC: 3471 Rechroming auto bumpers

(G-6049)
PRINT A COPY
4710 Maplecrest Ave (44134-3534)
PHONE..................................440 845-9039
Fax: 440 886-6920
Fred Zwiener, *Owner*
EMP: 3
SQ FT: 800
SALES (est): 241.2K **Privately Held**
SIC: 2752 Commercial printing, offset

(G-6050)
PRIORITY VENDING INC
3425 Prospect Ave E (44115-2617)
PHONE..................................216 361-4100
Fax: 216 361-4102
Joseph N Abraham, *President*
EMP: 5
SQ FT: 10,000
SALES (est): 774.4K **Privately Held**
WEB: www.priorityvending.com
SIC: 5962 3999 Cigarettes vending ma-
chines; cigarette & cigar products & ac-
cessories

(G-6051)
PRO ROOF WASHERS
1403 Ford Rd (44124-1432)
PHONE..................................440 521-2622
Frank Sciaulino, *Principal*
EMP: 4
SALES (est): 339.1K **Privately Held**
SIC: 3452 Washers

(G-6052)
PRODUCE PACKAGING INC
7501 Carnegie Ave (44103-4809)
PHONE..................................216 391-6129
Fax: 216 391-6131
Greg Fritz, *President*
Jerome Fritz, *Vice Pres*
Bill Ramos, *Manager*
David Reinke, *Manager*
Bill Weinmann, *Manager*
EMP: 150
SQ FT: 35,000
SALES (est): 47.8MM **Privately Held**
WEB: www.producepackagingltd.com
SIC: 3053 Packing materials

(G-6053)
PRODUCTS INNOVATORS
2567 Lafayette Dr (44118-4607)
PHONE..................................216 932-5269
Harold Isaacs, *President*
EMP: 20
SQ FT: 16,000
SALES (est): 1.2MM **Privately Held**
SIC: 3537 Trucks, tractors, loaders, carri-
ers & similar equipment

(G-6054)
**PROFESSIONAL FABRICATORS
INC**
Also Called: Pro Fab
15708 Brookpark Rd (44135-3336)
PHONE..................................216 362-1208
Fax: 216 362-8308
Paul Sutton, *President*
Louis R Sutton, *Vice Pres*
Carolyn Sutton, *Office Mgr*
EMP: 3
SQ FT: 2,500
SALES (est): 252.2K **Privately Held**
SIC: 3441 Fabricated structural metal

(G-6055)
PROFILE GRINDING INC
4593 Spring Rd (44131-1025)
PHONE..................................216 351-0600
Fax: 216 351-6278
Karen Homer, *President*
W Robert Benton, *General Mgr*
Richard Danick, *Engineer*
Cory Homer, *VP Sales*
Karla L Algeri, *Manager*
EMP: 29 **EST:** 1945
SQ FT: 20,000
SALES (est): 1.8MM **Privately Held**
WEB: www.profilegrinding.com
SIC: 3451 3599 Screw machine products;
machine shop, jobbing & repair

(G-6056)
PROPRESS INC
3135 Berea Rd Ste 1 (44111-1513)
PHONE..................................216 631-8200
Fax: 216 631-8210
Steve Forster, *President*
James Branagan, *Partner*
Teresa Tarantino, *Partner*
Barbara Brucker, *Manager*
EMP: 10
SQ FT: 3,000
SALES (est): 820K **Privately Held**
WEB: www.propressinc.com
SIC: 2741 7311 Miscellaneous publishing;
advertising agencies

(G-6057)
PROSPERITY ON PAYNE INC
1814 E 40th St Ste 5e (44103-3528)
PHONE..................................216 431-7677
Fax: 216 431-7456
Catherine Zurchin, *President*
Laura Bosse, *Vice Pres*
EMP: 3
SQ FT: 4,500
SALES (est): 80K **Privately Held**
WEB: www.prosperity.com
SIC: 3961 Jewelry apparel, non-precious
metals

(G-6058)
PROTOTYPE FABRICATORS CO
10911 Briggs Rd (44111-5300)
PHONE..................................216 252-0080
Fax: 216 252-5025
Rick Poddubny, *President*
Richard Poddubny, *President*
EMP: 8
SQ FT: 7,200
SALES: 1MM **Privately Held**
SIC: 3444 Sheet metalwork

(G-6059)
PUBCO CORPORATION (PA)
3830 Kelley Ave (44114-4534)
PHONE..................................216 881-5300
William Dillingham, *President*
Stephen R Kalette, *Vice Pres*
Michael Knack, *Purchasing*
Maria Szubski, *CFO*
Kevin Devers, *Manager*
◆ **EMP:** 85
SQ FT: 312,000
SALES (est): 93.1MM **Privately Held**
SIC: 3531 6512 3955 Construction ma-
chinery; nonresidential building operators;
carbon paper & inked ribbons

(G-6060)
**PUBLIC SAFETY OHIO
DEPARTMENT**
16945 Chagrin Blvd (44120-3725)
PHONE..................................216 283-4000
Stephanie Drake, *Branch Mgr*
EMP: 8 **Privately Held**
SIC: 3469 Automobile license tags,
stamped metal
HQ: Ohio Department Of Public Safety
1970 W Broad St Fl 5
Columbus OH 43223
614 466-3383

(G-6061)
PUCEL ENTERPRISES INC
1440 E 36th St (44114-4117)
PHONE..................................216 881-4604
Fax: 216 881-6731
Robert A Mlakar, *President*
Kathleen Cook, *Vice Pres*

Anthony F Mlakar, *Vice Pres*
Kathleen M Mlakar-Cook, *Vice Pres*
Ann Marie Mlakar-Leissa, *Vice Pres*
EMP: 55 **EST:** 1949
SQ FT: 105,000
SALES (est): 11.9MM **Privately Held**
WEB: www.pucelenterprises.com
SIC: 3499 3441 3537 3443 Furniture
parts, metal; fabricated structural metal;
industrial trucks & tractors; fabricated
plate work (boiler shop); partitions & fix-
tures, except wood; office furniture, ex-
cept wood

(G-6062)
PUEHLER TOOL CO
7670 Hub Pkwy (44125-5707)
PHONE..................................216 447-0101
Fax: 216 447-0104
William Puehler, *President*
EMP: 4
SQ FT: 9,200
SALES (est): 588.8K **Privately Held**
SIC: 3544 Special dies & tools; industrial
molds

(G-6063)
PUPPY PAWS INC
6763 Stafford Dr (44124-3612)
PHONE..................................440 461-9667
Pamela Meltzer, *President*
James Meltzer, *CFO*
EMP: 3
SQ FT: 641
SALES: 150K **Privately Held**
SIC: 3911 Collar/cuff buttons,
precious/semiprecious metal or stone

(G-6064)
PWP INC
3535 W 140th St (44111-2419)
PHONE..................................216 251-2181
Fax: 216 251-2699
Micheal Hooper, *CEO*
Ron Sathre, *Sales Mgr*
Cynthia Somogyi, *Office Mgr*
Jeanne Mummert, *Manager*
Dave Agard, *Info Tech Mgr*
▲ **EMP:** 45
SQ FT: 40,000
SALES (est): 9.3MM
SALES (corp-wide): 34.4MM **Privately
Held**
WEB: www.progresswire.com
SIC: 3496 Miscellaneous fabricated wire
products
PA: Tahoma Enterprises, Inc.
255 Wooster Rd N
Barberton OH 44203
330 745-9016

(G-6065)
PYRAMID PLASTICS INC
9202 Reno Ave (44105-2187)
PHONE..................................216 641-5904
Fax: 216 883-6996
Donald Newman, *Ch of Bd*
Mike Dezort, *President*
James E Newman, *Vice Pres*
Theresa Martin, *Finance Mgr*
Rosalyn Slade, *Clerk*
EMP: 30 **EST:** 1931
SQ FT: 10,000
SALES (est): 4.9MM **Privately Held**
SIC: 3089 Injection molded finished plastic
products

(G-6066)
**QUAKER CHEMICAL
CORPORATION**
5400 Chevrolet Blvd (44130-1451)
PHONE..................................216 265-5079
Jake Dewalt, *Manager*
EMP: 4
SALES (corp-wide): 746.6MM **Publicly
Held**
SIC: 3826 Automatic chemical analyzers
PA: Quaker Chemical Corporation
901 E Hector St
Conshohocken PA 19428
610 832-4000

(G-6067)
QUALICO INC
3201 E 66th St (44127-1403)
PHONE..................................216 271-2550

John Fry, *President*
Arlan Knopple, *Vice Pres*
Jeff Mignus, *Vice Pres*
John Grace, *Manager*
Jeff Mingus, *Executive*
EMP: 4
SQ FT: 10,000
SALES (est): 729.8K **Privately Held**
SIC: 2899 2952 Metal treating com-
pounds; rust resisting compounds; water-
proofing compounds; asphalt felts &
coatings; roofing felts, cements or coat-
ings

(G-6068)
QUALITECH ASSOCIATES INC
11324 Brookpark Rd (44130-1129)
PHONE..................................216 265-8702
Fax: 216 265-8705
Phil Kovach, *Treasurer*
EMP: 3 **EST:** 1982
SQ FT: 1,110
SALES (est): 512.4K **Privately Held**
SIC: 3821 Calibration tapes for physical
testing machines

(G-6069)
QUALITY BORATE CO LLC
3690 Orange Pl Ste 495 (44122-4465)
PHONE..................................216 896-1949
Gary McClurg,
▲ **EMP:** 10
SQ FT: 3,500
SALES (est): 1.7MM **Privately Held**
SIC: 5169 2879 Chemicals & allied prod-
ucts; agricultural chemicals

(G-6070)
QUALITY CUTTER GRINDING CO
15501 Commerce Park Dr (44142-2014)
PHONE..................................216 362-6444
Fax: 216 362-7278
Carl Scafuro, *President*
Debbie Ebert, *Treasurer*
EMP: 11
SQ FT: 13,500
SALES (est): 1.4MM **Privately Held**
SIC: 3545 7699 Cutting tools for machine
tools; knife, saw & tool sharpening & re-
pair

(G-6071)
QUALITY INDUSTRIES INC
3716 Clark Ave (44109-1198)
PHONE..................................216 961-5566
Fax: 216 961-5569
Jerry Kaplan, *President*
Jim Kaplan, *Vice Pres*
EMP: 6 **EST:** 1945
SQ FT: 12,000
SALES (est): 927.4K **Privately Held**
SIC: 3599 Machine shop, jobbing & repair

(G-6072)
QUALITY PLATING CO
1443 E 40th St (44103-1182)
P.O. Box 603247 (44103-0247)
PHONE..................................216 361-0151
Fax: 216 361-5992
Daniel Miller, *President*
▲ **EMP:** 9
SQ FT: 11,895
SALES: 865K **Privately Held**
WEB: www.qualityplatinginc.com
SIC: 3471 8711 Chromium plating of met-
als or formed products; electroplating of
metals or formed products; polishing,
metals or formed products; engineering
services

(G-6073)
**QUALITY REPLACEMENT PARTS
INC**
9099 Bank St Ste 2 (44125-3435)
PHONE..................................216 674-0200
Fax: 216 674-0202
Patricia Kuntz, *President*
Allan Kuntz, *Vice Pres*
▲ **EMP:** 4
SQ FT: 4,000
SALES (est): 270K **Privately Held**
WEB: www.qualityreplacementparts.com
SIC: 3484 Shotguns or shotgun parts, 30
mm. & below

GEOGRAPHIC

(G-6074)
QUALITY SEWING INC
5656 Dunham Rd (44137-3655)
PHONE............................216 475-0411
Domonic Armani, *President*
EMP: 3
SALES (est): 213.5K **Privately Held**
SIC: 2329 2331 2335 7219 Shirt & slack
suits: men's, youths' & boys'; women's &
misses' blouses & shirts; women's, jun-
iors' & misses' dresses; garment alter-
ation & repair shop

(G-6075)
**QUALITY STAMPING PRODUCTS
CO (PA)**
5322 Bragg Rd (44127-1283)
PHONE............................216 441-2700
Alan Nayman, *President*
Kenneth Nayman, *Vice Pres*
Nan Nayman, *Vice Pres*
Edward Marloi, *Plant Mgr*
Kevin Marxen, *Engineer*
EMP: 16 EST: 1951
SQ FT: 20,000
SALES (est): 3.1MM **Privately Held**
SIC: 3469 Stamping metal for the trade

(G-6076)
QUES INDUSTRIES INC
5420 W 140th St (44142-1703)
PHONE............................216 267-8989
Fax: 216 267-8998
Quentin Meng, *President*
Bonnie Reinhardt, *Manager*
▲ EMP: 16
SQ FT: 50,000
SALES (est): 5MM **Privately Held**
WEB: www.quesinc.com
SIC: 2899 Water treating compounds

(G-6077)
QUEZ MEDIA MARKETING INC
1138 Prospect Ave E (44115-1229)
P.O. Box 93716 (44101-5716)
PHONE............................216 910-0202
Jose A Vasquez, *CEO*
EMP: 11
SALES (est): 840K **Privately Held**
SIC: 7374 2752 7336 7371 Computer
graphics service; commercial printing, off-
set; commercial art & graphic design;
computer software systems analysis &
design, custom; direct mail advertising
services; marketing consulting services

(G-6078)
R & R COMFORT EXPERTS LLC
13370 Hathaway Rd (44125-5218)
PHONE............................216 475-3995
Robert Maglionico,
EMP: 3
SALES (est): 253.2K **Privately Held**
SIC: 3585 Heating & air conditioning com-
bination units

(G-6079)
R & R MACHINE & TOOL CO
3148 W 32nd St Ste 3 (44109-1549)
PHONE............................216 281-7609
Fax: 216 281-7609
Richard Rauske, *President*
Michelle Rauske, *Corp Secy*
EMP: 3 EST: 1969
SALES: 140K **Privately Held**
WEB: www.reinersranch.com
SIC: 3544 Special dies & tools

(G-6080)
R A K MACHINE INC
5900 Walworth Ave (44102-4461)
PHONE............................216 631-7750
Tim Bragg, *President*
Anna Sohyda, *Manager*
EMP: 15
SQ FT: 5,500
SALES (est): 2.6MM **Privately Held**
SIC: 3559 Rubber working machinery, in-
cluding tires

(G-6081)
R E MAY INC
1401 E 24th St (44114-2176)
PHONE............................216 771-6332
Fax: 216 771-0015
Betty D Pangrace, *President*
John E Pangrace, *Vice Pres*
Eric Ptak, *Prdtn Mgr*
John Lakota, *Mfg Staff*
Robert Jackson, *Sales Staff*
EMP: 16
SQ FT: 5,000
SALES (est): 1.6MM **Privately Held**
WEB: www.remay.com
SIC: 2796 Lithographic plates, positives or
negatives

(G-6082)
R F W HOLDINGS INC
1200 Smith Ct (44116-1520)
PHONE............................440 331-8300
Fax: 440 331-4810
Richard Wilber, *President*
EMP: 8
SALES (est): 540K **Privately Held**
SIC: 2394 Sails: made from purchased
materials

(G-6083)
R H INDUSTRIES INC
3155 W 33rd St (44109-1524)
PHONE............................216 281-5210
Fax: 216 281-2420
Tina Haddad, *President*
Lura Blatnica, *Manager*
Celia Santiago, *Manager*
EMP: 21
SQ FT: 10,000
SALES (est): 4.1MM **Privately Held**
SIC: 3429 3599 3511 Motor vehicle hard-
ware; machine shop, jobbing & repair; tur-
bines & turbine generator sets

(G-6084)
R M YATES CO INC
Also Called: American Carved Crystal
4452 Warner Rd (44105-5958)
PHONE............................216 441-0900
Fax: 216 441-5608
Robert M Yates Jr, *President*
Diane Yates, *Vice Pres*
EMP: 4
SQ FT: 3,500
SALES (est): 383.4K **Privately Held**
WEB: www.americancarvedcrystal.com
SIC: 3231 Products of purchased glass

(G-6085)
RADDELLS SAUSAGE
478 E 152nd St (44110-1762)
PHONE............................216 486-1944
Thomas Raddell, *Owner*
Jacob Raddell, *Manager*
EMP: 5 EST: 1958
SQ FT: 2,973
SALES (est): 280K **Privately Held**
SIC: 2013 Sausages from purchased meat

(G-6086)
RADIX WIRE CO (PA)
Also Called: Radix Wire Company, The
26000 Lakeland Blvd (44132-2638)
PHONE............................216 731-9191
Fax: 216 731-7082
Keith D Nootbaar, *President*
Jim Schaefer, *President*
Marylou Vermerris, *Chairman*
Brain Bukovec, *Vice Pres*
Steve Demko, *Vice Pres*
EMP: 60
SQ FT: 14,000
SALES (est): 21.5MM **Privately Held**
WEB: www.radix-wire.com
SIC: 3357 5051 Nonferrous wiredrawing &
insulating; cable, wire

(G-6087)
RADIX WIRE CO
26260 Lakeland Blvd (44132-2640)
PHONE............................216 731-9191
Bill Toll, *Manager*
EMP: 85
SALES (corp-wide): 21.5MM **Privately
Held**
WEB: www.radix-wire.com
SIC: 3357 Nonferrous wiredrawing & insu-
lating
PA: Radix Wire Co
26000 Lakeland Blvd
Cleveland OH 44132
216 731-9191

(G-6088)
RAGEON INC
Also Called: Let's Rage
1163 E 40th St Ste 2 (44114-3866)
PHONE............................617 633-0544
Mike Krilivsky,
EMP: 22
SALES: 2MM **Privately Held**
SIC: 2389 7389 Apparel & accessories;

(G-6089)
RAM SENSORS INC (PA)
875 Canterbury Rd (44145-1488)
PHONE............................440 835-3540
Fax: 440 835-8603
Ron Miller, *President*
Caroline J Miller, *Corp Secy*
Maureen Schiau, *Purch Dir*
Joann Miller, *Treasurer*
Keri Panigutti, *Office Mgr*
EMP: 17 EST: 1981
SQ FT: 16,000
SALES (est): 3.1MM **Privately Held**
WEB: www.ramsensors.com
SIC: 3823 3315 Temperature instruments:
industrial process type; wire, steel: insu-
lated or armored

(G-6090)
RANDYS PICKLES LLC
2203 Superior Ave E (44114-4222)
PHONE............................440 864-6611
Andrew Rainey, *CEO*
EMP: 8 EST: 2013
SQ FT: 3,000
SALES (est): 235.3K **Privately Held**
SIC: 2035 Pickles, sauces & salad dress-
ings

(G-6091)
RAY FOGG CONSTRUCTION INC
981 Keynote Cir Ste 15 (44131-1842)
PHONE............................216 351-7976
Raymon B Fogg Sr, *President*
Raymon B Fogg Jr, *Exec VP*
Michael J Merle, *Exec VP*
Richard Neiden, *Vice Pres*
Frank Kubici, *Controller*
EMP: 15
SQ FT: 5,760
SALES: 15MM **Privately Held**
SIC: 2821 Plastics materials & resins

(G-6092)
RAYS SAUSAGE INC
3146 E 123rd St (44120-3179)
PHONE............................216 921-8782
Fax: 216 921-4736
Renee Cash, *President*
Raymond Cash, *Vice Pres*
Leslie Lester, *CFO*
Ray Harvin, *Sales Staff*
Lesile Cash Lester, *Manager*
EMP: 8 EST: 1952
SQ FT: 660
SALES: 800K **Privately Held**
SIC: 2013 Sausages from purchased
meat; pork, cured: from purchased meat;
beef, dried: from purchased meat

(G-6093)
**RECOB GREAT LAKES
EXPRESS INC**
20600 Sheldon Rd (44142-1319)
PHONE............................216 265-7940
Daniel S Recob, *President*
EMP: 5
SALES (est): 334K **Privately Held**
WEB: www.rglexpress.com
SIC: 2741 Miscellaneous publishing

(G-6094)
RED DOT CORPORATION
15501 Chatfield Ave (44111-4311)
PHONE............................216 447-4294
Scott Pelot, *Production*
Michael Pease, *Branch Mgr*
EMP: 6
SALES (corp-wide): 130.2MM **Privately
Held**
SIC: 3585 Heating equipment, complete
PA: Red Dot Corporation
495 Andover Park E
Tukwila WA 98188
206 151-3840

(G-6095)
RED SEAL ELECTRIC CO
3835 W 150th St (44111-5891)
PHONE............................216 941-3900
Fax: 216 941-5305
Samuel Stryffeler, *President*
Daniel T Stryffeler, *President*
John Gibson, *Buyer*
Dave Cornish, *CFO*
Jeff Stryffeler, *Treasurer*
▲ EMP: 38 EST: 1946
SQ FT: 28,000
SALES: 10.2MM **Privately Held**
WEB: www.redseal.com
SIC: 3644 Noncurrent-carrying wiring serv-
ices; insulators & insulation materials,
electrical

(G-6096)
REDCO INSTRUMENT
659 Broadway Ave (44146-3504)
PHONE............................440 232-2132
Steve Radecky, *Owner*
EMP: 5 EST: 1973
SQ FT: 1,500
SALES (est): 536.9K **Privately Held**
SIC: 3812 Search & navigation equipment

(G-6097)
**REID ASSET MANAGEMENT
COMPANY (PA)**
Also Called: Magnus Equipment
9555 Rockside Rd Ste 350 (44125-6283)
PHONE............................216 642-3223
Fax: 440 942-8590
Pete Breeden, *Vice Pres*
Helen Stois, *Incorporator*
Norman K Austad, *Incorporator*
Norman Tischler, *Incorporator*
EMP: 1
SQ FT: 40,000
SALES (est): 9.9MM **Privately Held**
WEB: www.magnusequipment.com
SIC: 3589 Commercial cleaning equipment

(G-6098)
**REID ASSET MANAGEMENT
COMPANY**
Also Called: Predict Technologies Div
9555 Rockside Rd Ste 350 (44125-6283)
PHONE............................216 642-3223
Donald F Kautzman, *Principal*
Robert Shinn, *Project Mgr*
EMP: 40
SALES (corp-wide): 9.9MM **Privately
Held**
WEB: www.magnusequipment.com
SIC: 7389 8734 3826 5084 Industrial &
commercial equipment inspection service;
testing laboratories; analytical instru-
ments; industrial machinery & equipment
PA: Reid Asset Management Company
9555 Rockside Rd Ste 350
Cleveland OH 44125
216 642-3223

(G-6099)
**RELIABLE PATTERN WORKS
INC**
590 Golden Oak Pkwy (44146-6502)
PHONE............................440 232-8820
Fax: 440 232-8908
Stephanie Kapcio, *President*
Stephanie Kacio, *Corp Secy*
EMP: 7 EST: 1913
SQ FT: 7,500
SALES (est): 1MM **Privately Held**
WEB: www.reliablepattern.com
SIC: 3365 Aerospace castings, aluminum

(G-6100)
RENCO PRINTING INC
5261 W 161st St (44142-1606)
PHONE............................216 267-5585
Fax: 216 267-9141
Betty Marquard, *President*
Jim Marquard, *Vice Pres*
Jeff Marquard, *Admin Sec*
EMP: 3
SQ FT: 4,500
SALES: 200K **Privately Held**
SIC: 2752 Commercial printing, offset

(G-6101)
RENEGADE BRANDS LLC
3201 Enterprise Pkwy (44122-7330)
PHONE.............................216 342-4347
Cathy Horton, *CEO*
Adam Short, *VP Sales*
Dennis Nolan,
EMP: 7
SQ FT: 5,000
SALES: 4MM **Privately Held**
SIC: 2841 Soap & other detergents

(G-6102)
REPKO MACHINE INC
5081 W 164th St (44142-1599)
PHONE.............................216 267-1144
Fax: 216 267-0652
John Palmer III, *President*
Valentyna Palmer, *Admin Sec*
EMP: 9 EST: 1951
SQ FT: 16,000
SALES (est): 1.4MM **Privately Held**
WEB: www.repko.com
SIC: 3599 Machine shop, jobbing & repair

(G-6103)
REPLICA ENGINEERING INC
3483 W 140th St (44111-2418)
PHONE.............................216 252-2204
Fax: 216 252-2209
Elwyn J Price, *President*
Glyn Price, *Vice Pres*
Brian Downs, *Manager*
▲ EMP: 17
SQ FT: 9,000
SALES: 2MM **Privately Held**
WEB: www.replicaeng.com
SIC: 3561 Industrial pumps & parts

(G-6104)
REPRO ACQUISITION COMPANY LLC
Also Called: Reprocenter, The
25001 Rockwell Dr (44117-1239)
PHONE.............................216 738-3800
Fax: 216 738-3801
Ronald Smith, *Sales Executive*
▲ EMP: 40 EST: 1999
SQ FT: 32,000
SALES (est): 5.6MM **Privately Held**
WEB: www.reprocntr.com
SIC: 2752 7375 2789 Commercial print-
ing, lithographic; information retrieval
services; bookbinding & related work

(G-6105)
RESEARCH ORGANICS LLC
Also Called: Safc Cleveland
4353 E 49th St (44125-1083)
PHONE.............................216 883-8025
Fax: 216 883-1576
Rob Sternfeld, *President*
Fred Sternfeld, *Vice Pres*
Alan Larris, *Controller*
Teri Durdella, *Marketing Staff*
John Hart, *MIS Dir*
▲ EMP: 75 EST: 1966
SQ FT: 100,000
SALES (est): 22MM
SALES (corp-wide): 15.8B **Privately Held**
WEB: www.resorg.com
SIC: 2899 2869 Chemical preparations;
industrial organic chemicals
HQ: Sigma-Aldrich Corporation
3050 Spruce St
Saint Louis MO 63103
314 771-5765

(G-6106)
RESILIENCE FUND III LP (PA)
25101 Chagrin Blvd (44122-5643)
PHONE.............................216 292-0200
Michael Cavanaugh, *Partner*
Ki Mixon, *Partner*
Ted Laufik, *CFO*
Bassem Mansour, *Mng Member*
EMP: 8
SALES (est): 47MM **Privately Held**
SIC: 6799 3567 Investors; industrial fur-
naces & ovens

(G-6107)
RESOLUTE FP US INC
Also Called: Recycling Div
3400 Vega Ave (44113-4954)
PHONE.............................216 961-3900

Rich Ryan, *Principal*
EMP: 481
SALES (corp-wide): 2.6B **Privately Held**
WEB: www.bowater.com
SIC: 2621 Paper mills
HQ: Resolute Fp Us Inc.
5300 Cureton Ferry Rd
Catawba SC 29704
803 981-8000

(G-6108)
RETINAGENIX LLC
11000 Cedar Ave Ste 280 (44106-3052)
PHONE.............................440 808-9334
David Saperstein,
Marco Norchaland,
Grazyna Palczewska,
EMP: 4
SALES (est): 208.6K **Privately Held**
SIC: 2834 Pharmaceutical preparations

(G-6109)
REXON COMPONENTS INC
24500 Highpoint Rd (44122-6002)
PHONE.............................440 585-7086
Steve Fink, *Branch Mgr*
EMP: 17
SALES (corp-wide): 2.1MM **Privately Held**
WEB: www.rexon.com
SIC: 3674 Nuclear detectors, solid state
PA: Rexon Components, Inc.
24500 Highpoint Rd
Beachwood OH 44122
216 292-7373

(G-6110)
REZMANN KAROLY
Also Called: Quality Metal Works
7216 Bessemer Ave (44127-1816)
PHONE.............................216 441-4357
Fax: 216 441-4357
Karoly Rezmann, *Owner*
EMP: 3
SQ FT: 12,000
SALES (est): 257.4K **Privately Held**
SIC: 3443 3599 3469 3446 Plate work
for the metalworking trade; machine shop,
jobbing & repair; metal stampings; archi-
tectural metalwork; sheet metalwork; fab-
ricated structural metal

(G-6111)
RICHARD STEEL COMPANY INC
11110 Avon Ave (44105-4223)
P.O. Box 31516 (44131-0516)
PHONE.............................216 520-6390
Richard Jereb, *President*
EMP: 9
SQ FT: 5,000
SALES (est): 1.2MM **Privately Held**
SIC: 3441 Fabricated structural metal

(G-6112)
RICHARDS GRINDING CO INC
4914 Walworth Ave (44102-4592)
PHONE.............................216 631-7675
Fax: 216 631-9053
Richard A Oliver Sr, *President*
Betty Oliver, *Corp Secy*
Deb Luber, *Vice Pres*
Deborah Luber, *Vice Pres*
Jeff Yates, *Plant Mgr*
EMP: 14
SQ FT: 6,400
SALES (est): 1.4MM **Privately Held**
SIC: 3599 Machine shop, jobbing & repair;
grinding castings for the trade

(G-6113)
RIFT LAKE AQUATICS
16385 Heather Ln Apt 104 (44130-8324)
PHONE.............................216 221-1437
Jim Laco, *Owner*
EMP: 3
SALES (est): 40K **Privately Held**
SIC: 3499 Aquarium accessories, metal

(G-6114)
RITE MACHINE INC
13704 Enterprise Ave (44135-5114)
PHONE.............................216 267-6911
Jay Kalchoff, *President*
Adrian Kalchoff, *Corp Secy*
Dana Kalchoff, *Vice Pres*
EMP: 3 EST: 1943

SQ FT: 5,000
SALES (est): 290K **Privately Held**
SIC: 3451 Screw machine products

(G-6115)
RITIME INCORPORATED
6363 York Rd Ste 104 (44130-3031)
PHONE.............................330 273-3443
William E Avis, *President*
Jacquelyn High, *Manager*
EMP: 17
SQ FT: 10,000
SALES (est): 1.2MM **Privately Held**
WEB: www.alternativesurfacegrind.com
SIC: 3599 3542 Machine shop, jobbing &
repair; machine tools, metal forming type

(G-6116)
RITRAMA INC
341 Eddy Rd (44108-1601)
PHONE.............................216 851-7208
Fax: 216 851-1938
Mike Conklin, *Safety Dir*
Scott Ellar, *Sales Executive*
Robert Hall, *Manager*
M Santurri, *MIS Mgr*
Mark Zumerling, *MIS Mgr*
EMP: 67 **Privately Held**
WEB: www.ritrama.com
SIC: 3081 Unsupported plastics film &
sheet
HQ: Ritrama, Inc.
800 Kasota Ave Se
Minneapolis MN 55414
612 378-2277

(G-6117)
RIVER SMELTING & REF MFG CO
Also Called: River Foundry Supply
4195 Bradley Rd (44109-3779)
PHONE.............................216 459-2100
Fax: 216 749-8107
William A Grodin, *President*
James A Grodin, *Vice Pres*
Tom Villwock, *Controller*
EMP: 25
SQ FT: 70,000
SALES (est): 4.5MM
SALES (corp-wide): 45MM **Privately Held**
WEB: www.rivershell.com
SIC: 3341 Copper smelting & refining (sec-
ondary)
PA: River Recycling Enterprises, Ltd.
4195 Bradley Rd
Cleveland OH 44109
216 459-2100

(G-6118)
RIVERSIDE DRIVES INC
Also Called: Riverside Drives Disc
4509 W 160th St (44135-2627)
P.O. Box 35166 (44135-0166)
PHONE.............................216 362-1211
Fax: 216 362-6836
Bernard Dillemuth, *President*
Robert Goodwin, *General Mgr*
Kathleen Dillemuth, *Corp Secy*
David Dillemuth, *Vice Pres*
Kathy Straka, *Purchasing*
▲ EMP: 28
SQ FT: 7,500
SALES (est): 22MM **Privately Held**
WEB: www.riversidedrives.com
SIC: 5063 3699 Power transmission
equipment, electric; electrical equipment
& supplies

(G-6119)
RJR SURGICAL INC
2530 Superior Ave E # 703 (44114-4230)
PHONE.............................216 241-2804
John Redmond, *President*
Lisa Hower, *Vice Pres*
Mark Whiteaker, *Vice Pres*
EMP: 3
SQ FT: 4,000
SALES (est): 261.8K **Privately Held**
SIC: 3841 Surgical & medical instruments

(G-6120)
RML TOOL INC
15115 Chatfield Ave B (44111-4304)
PHONE.............................216 941-1615
Rick Silvaggio, *President*

EMP: 4
SALES (est): 450K **Privately Held**
SIC: 3339 Primary nonferrous metals

(G-6121)
ROBERTS DEMAND NO 3 CORP
Also Called: Electro-Plating & Fabricating
4008 E 89th St (44105-3919)
PHONE.............................216 641-0660
Les Demand, *President*
William Demand, *Vice Pres*
Chris Demand, *Manager*
Don Paukert, *Shareholder*
EMP: 15 EST: 1939
SQ FT: 13,500
SALES: 1.7MM **Privately Held**
WEB: www.molectrics.com
SIC: 3471 Cleaning & descaling metal
products; polishing, metals or formed
products

(G-6122)
ROBERTS-DEMAND CORP
Also Called: Keco Plating
17401 S Miles Rd (44128-3946)
P.O. Box 1012, Burton (44021-1012)
PHONE.............................216 581-1300
Fax: 216 581-1299
Rex Roberts, *President*
Brenda Roberts, *Vice Pres*
Albert Roberts, *Admin Sec*
EMP: 5 EST: 1946
SQ FT: 5,000
SALES (est): 430.2K **Privately Held**
SIC: 3471 Electroplating of metals or
formed products; plating of metals or
formed products; polishing, metals or
formed products; anodizing (plating) of
metals or formed products

(G-6123)
ROBERTSON MANUFACTURING CO
17917 Roseland Rd (44112-1284)
PHONE.............................216 531-8222
Fax: 216 531-0576
John S Green, *President*
Sandra Essick, *Treasurer*
Shannon Catalano, *Director*
EMP: 10 EST: 1948
SQ FT: 10,000
SALES: 4.3MM **Privately Held**
SIC: 3568 3566 Sprockets (power trans-
mission equipment); gears, power trans-
mission, except automotive

(G-6124)
ROBIN INDUSTRIES INC
Also Called: Niagara Stamping Co
4780 W 139th St (44135-5034)
PHONE.............................216 267-3554
Jack Browning, *Branch Mgr*
EMP: 4
SALES (corp-wide): 66.6MM **Privately Held**
WEB: www.robin-industries.com
SIC: 3069 3061 Molded rubber products;
mechanical rubber goods
PA: Robin Industries, Inc.
6500 Rockside Rd Ste 230
Independence OH 44131
216 631-7000

(G-6125)
ROCHLING GLASTIC COMPOSITES LP (DH)
4321 Glenridge Rd (44121-2805)
PHONE.............................216 486-0100
Fax: 216 486-1091
Georg Duffner, *CEO*
Mark Digiampietro, *General Mgr*
Ludger Bartels, *Chairman*
Kevin Streussnig, *Business Mgr*
Daniel T Coleman, *Vice Pres*
◆ EMP: 200
SQ FT: 127,000
SALES (est): 53.1MM
SALES (corp-wide): 1.6B **Privately Held**
WEB: www.glastic.com
SIC: 3089 2821 3083 3644 Thermo-
formed finished plastic products; molding
compounds, plastics; laminated plastic
sheets; noncurrent-carrying wiring serv-
ices

HQ: Rochling Engineering Plastics Se &
　　Co. Kg
　　Rochlingstr. 1
　　Haren (Ems)　49733
　　593 470-10

(G-6126)
ROCKPORT CNSTR & MTLS INC
Also Called: Rockport Ready Mix
3092 Rockefeller Ave　(44115-3612)
PHONE....................................216 432-9465
Ann Nock, *President*
Don Nichols, *Sales Staff*
EMP: 25
SALES (est): 4.4MM　Privately Held
SIC: 3273　Ready-mixed concrete

(G-6127)
ROCKWELL AUTOMATION　INC
760 Beta Dr Ste A　(44143-2334)
PHONE....................................440 604-8410
Larry Moskal, *Engineer*
Ron Fruh, *Branch Mgr*
Keith Hall, *Technology*
EMP: 40　Publicly Held
SIC: 3625　Relays & industrial controls
PA: Rockwell Automation, Inc.
　　1201 S 2nd St
　　Milwaukee WI 53204

(G-6128)
ROCKWELL AUTOMATION　INC
1 Allen Bradley Dr　(44124-6118)
PHONE....................................440 646-5000
Fax: 440 646-3083
Rich Novak, *Business Mgr*
Frank Watkins, *Business Mgr*
John Genovesi, *Vice Pres*
Scott Bohman, *Project Mgr*
Richard Collins, *Project Mgr*
EMP: 99
SQ FT: 156,653　Publicly Held
SIC: 3625　Relays & industrial controls
PA: Rockwell Automation, Inc.
　　1201 S 2nd St
　　Milwaukee WI 53204

(G-6129)
ROCKWELL AUTOMATION　INC
6680 Beta Dr　(44143-2352)
PHONE....................................440 646-7900
Fax: 440 646-7801
Steven Zink, *Business Mgr*
Wayne Foster, *Engineer*
Maureen Garnett, *Engineer*
Ned Myers, *Engineer*
Michael Bless, *Branch Mgr*
EMP: 10　Publicly Held
SIC: 3625　Relays & industrial controls
PA: Rockwell Automation, Inc.
　　1201 S 2nd St
　　Milwaukee WI 53204

(G-6130)
ROL- FAB INC
4949 Johnston Pkwy　(44128-3201)
PHONE....................................216 662-2500
Fax: 216 662-2582
Robert Hansen, *President*
Tim Organiscak, *Manager*
▼ EMP: 32
SQ FT: 70,000
SALES (est): 4.8MM　Privately Held
WEB: www.rol-fab.com
SIC: 3441　Fabricated structural metal

(G-6131)
ROME MARBLE INC
3007 Clinton Ave　(44113-2974)
PHONE....................................216 431-0334
Fernando Gonzalez, *President*
▲ EMP: 6
SQ FT: 3,000
SALES: 575K　Privately Held
WEB: www.romemarble.com
SIC: 3281　Building stone products

(G-6132)
**ROSE METAL INDUSTRIES　LLC
(PA)**
1536 E 43rd St　(44103-2310)
PHONE....................................216 881-3355
Robert B Rose, *Mng Member*
Bryan Bridgett, *Manager*
EMP: 11 EST: 1904
SQ FT: 10,000

SALES (est): 5.6MM　Privately Held
WEB: www.rosemetal.com
SIC: 3441　7692　3462　3443　Fabricated
structural metal; welding repair; iron &
steel forgings; ladles, metal plate

(G-6133)
ROSE METAL INDUSTRIES　LLC
1155 Marquette St　(44114-3919)
PHONE....................................216 426-8615
Robert Rose, *President*
EMP: 30
SALES (corp-wide): 5.6MM　Privately
Held
WEB: www.rosemetal.com
SIC: 3441　Fabricated structural metal
PA: Rose Metal Industries, Llc
　　1536 E 43rd St
　　Cleveland OH 44103
　　216 881-3355

(G-6134)
ROSENFELD JEWELRY INC
5668 Mayfield Rd　(44124-2916)
PHONE....................................440 446-0099
Fax: 440 446-0099
Henry Rosenfeld, *President*
Ruth Rosenfeld, *Vice Pres*
Arthur Rosenfeld, *Treasurer*
EMP: 8
SQ FT: 1,350
SALES (est): 1MM　Privately Held
WEB: www.rosenfeld-jewelry.com
SIC: 3911　5944　Jewelry, precious metal;
jewelry stores

(G-6135)
**ROTECH PRODUCTS
INCORPORATED**
16901 Albers Ave　(44111-4241)
PHONE....................................216 476-3722
Fax: 216 476-3680
Michael Maloney, *Principal*
Mary Maloney, *Corp Secy*
EMP: 3
SQ FT: 2,000
SALES: 500K　Privately Held
SIC: 5169　2899　Industrial chemicals; plat-
ing compounds; metal treating com-
pounds

(G-6136)
**ROYAL ACME CORPORATION
(PA)**
Also Called: Adsetting Service
3110 Payne Ave　(44114-4504)
PHONE....................................216 241-1477
Fax: 216 771-8487
Theodore D Cutts, *President*
Sandy Wengstrom, *Office Mgr*
Matt Young, *Manager*
▲ EMP: 28 EST: 1932
SALES (est): 2.3MM　Privately Held
WEB: www.royalacme.com
SIC: 3953　2791　3993　3053　Embossing
seals & hand stamps; figures (marking
devices), metal; stencils, painting & mark-
ing; seal presses, notary & hand; typeset-
ting; signs & advertising specialties;
gaskets, packing & sealing devices

(G-6137)
**ROYAL CABINET DESIGN CO
INC**
15800 Commerce Park Dr　(44142-2019)
PHONE....................................216 267-5330
Joseph Estephan, *President*
Georgette Estephan, *Corp Secy*
Elie Estephan, *Vice Pres*
EMP: 12
SALES (est): 1.8MM　Privately Held
SIC: 2434　Wood kitchen cabinets

(G-6138)
ROYAL GATEAU
4276 Pearl Rd　(44109-4235)
P.O. Box 609225　(44109-0225)
PHONE....................................216 351-3553
Michel Kahwagi, *Owner*
EMP: 3
SQ FT: 1,500
SALES (est): 130K　Privately Held
SIC: 2051　Pastries, e.g. danish; except
frozen

(G-6139)
ROYAL ICE CREAM CO
Also Called: Pierre's Ice Cream Company
6200 Euclid Ave　(44103-3724)
PHONE....................................216 432-1144
Fax: 216 432-0433
Rochelle Roth, *President*
Lawrence Bloomenthal, *Principal*
Helen Dorman, *Principal*
Jerome Ellerin, *Principal*
Frank Elliott, *Vice Pres*
◆ EMP: 85 EST: 1932
SQ FT: 16,500
SALES (est): 34.7MM　Privately Held
WEB: www.pierres.com
SIC: 2024　Ice cream & ice milk

(G-6140)
**ROYAL POWDER
CORPORATION**
4800 Briar Rd　(44135-5040)
PHONE....................................216 898-0074
Kirit Patel, *President*
EMP: 6
SQ FT: 1,300
SALES (est): 1.4MM　Privately Held
SIC: 3399　Metal powders, pastes & flakes

(G-6141)
RSB SPINE LLC
2530 Superior Ave E # 703　(44114-4200)
PHONE....................................216 241-2804
James Moran, *President*
Lisa Lower, *Opers Mgr*
Amy Turchek, *Cust Mgr*
Lisa Hower, *Manager*
John Redmond,
EMP: 13
SALES (est): 1.1MM　Privately Held
WEB: www.rsbspine.com
SIC: 3841　Surgical & medical instruments

(G-6142)
RUBBERSET COMPANY
101 W Prospect Ave　(44115-1093)
PHONE....................................800 345-4939
EMP: 3
SALES (est): 257K　Privately Held
SIC: 3563　Robots for industrial spraying,
painting, etc.

(G-6143)
RUDYS STRUDEL SHOP
Also Called: Rudy's Strudel & Bakery
5580 Ridge Rd　(44129-2305)
PHONE....................................440 886-4430
Eugenia Polatajko, *Owner*
EMP: 6 EST: 1948
SQ FT: 7,900
SALES (est): 300K　Privately Held
SIC: 2051　2052　Bread, cake & related
products; cookies & crackers

(G-6144)
RULTRACT INC
5663 Brecksville Rd　(44131-1510)
PHONE....................................216 524-2990
Janice Schilt, *President*
Dr Reiss Beg, *Vice Pres*
Phillip M Rullo Jr, *Sales Staff*
EMP: 5
SQ FT: 20,000
SALES: 1.1MM　Privately Held
WEB: www.rultract.net
SIC: 5047　3841　Instruments, surgical &
medical; surgical instruments & apparatus

(G-6145)
S & H INDUSTRIES　INC
Also Called: Keysco Tools
5200 Richmond Rd　(44146-1387)
PHONE....................................216 831-0550
Fax: 216 831-9573
John Turk, *President*
Edward Clancy, *General Mgr*
Steven Perney, *Treasurer*
▲ EMP: 30 EST: 1952
SQ FT: 23,000
SALES: 5MM　Privately Held
WEB: www.shindustries.com
SIC: 3423　Mechanics' hand tools; jacks:
lifting, screw or ratchet (hand tools)
PA: A W C Inc
　　5200 Richmond Rd
　　Cleveland OH 44146
　　216 831-0550

(G-6146)
S & H INDUSTRIES INC
14577 Lorain Ave　(44111-3156)
PHONE....................................216 831-0550
Sharon M Conrad, *Principal*
▲ EMP: 7 EST: 2010
SALES (est): 999.8K　Privately Held
SIC: 3999　Manufacturing industries

(G-6147)
**S & N ENGINEERING SVCS
CORP**
Also Called: S & N Engineering and Supply
2901 Henninger Rd　(44109-3324)
PHONE....................................216 433-1700
Nancy Novinc, *President*
EMP: 4
SQ FT: 2,400
SALES (est): 556.6K　Privately Held
SIC: 5085　3599　Industrial supplies; ma-
chine & other job shop work

(G-6148)
S & V AUTOMATICS
6511 Selma Ave　(44127-1439)
PHONE....................................216 429-2228
Paul Sperk, *Owner*
EMP: 3
SQ FT: 9,000
SALES (est): 182.8K　Privately Held
SIC: 3599　Machine shop, jobbing & repair

(G-6149)
S A LANGMACK COMPANY
Also Called: Niagara Custombilt Mfg
13400 Glenside Rd　(44110-3528)
PHONE....................................216 541-0500
Fax: 216 541-5005
Chris Langmack, *President*
John C Langmack, *Principal*
Virginia Langmack, *Corp Secy*
Clark B Langmack, *Vice Pres*
Judy Stoiner, *Manager*
EMP: 15
SQ FT: 25,000
SALES (est): 3.9MM　Privately Held
WEB: www.niagaracustom.com
SIC: 3565　3569　Bottle washing & steriliz-
ing machines; filters, general line: indus-
trial

(G-6150)
S L M INC
3148 W 32nd St Ste 3　(44109-1549)
PHONE....................................216 651-0666
Fax: 216 651-0811
Sharon Mc Guire, *President*
EMP: 6
SALES (est): 439.9K　Privately Held
SIC: 1711　3444　Warm air heating & air
conditioning contractor; sheet metal spe-
cialties, not stamped

(G-6151)
S R P M INC
30300 Bruce Industrial Pk　(44139-3921)
PHONE....................................440 248-8440
Fax: 440 248-8440
Mark Steinmeyer, *President*
Patti Macek, *Business Mgr*
Craig Steinmeyer, *Vice Pres*
Gary Rivett, *Mfg Mgr*
Brian Arthur, *QA Dir*
EMP: 30
SQ FT: 15,000
SALES (est): 6.5MM　Privately Held
WEB: www.srpm.com
SIC: 3599　Custom machinery

(G-6152)
S&P GLOBAL INC
Also Called: McGraw Hill Construction Enr
5276 W 49th St　(44134-1020)
PHONE....................................216 749-9779
Douglas L Peterson, *Manager*
EMP: 20
SALES (corp-wide): 5.6B　Publicly Held
SIC: 2741　Miscellaneous publishing
PA: S&P Global Inc.
　　55 Water St Ste Conc2
　　New York NY 10041
　　212 438-1000

(G-6153)
SABRE ENTERPRISES INC
12119 Bennington Ave (44135-3789)
PHONE...................216 941-9700
Donald C Dawson, *President*
Robert H Dawson, *Corp Secy*
EMP: 6
SQ FT: 15,000
SALES (est): 550K **Privately Held**
SIC: 3452 Bolts, nuts, rivets & washers

(G-6154)
SAFE SYSTEMS INC
Also Called: Ramzi
5401 Brookpark Rd (44129-1201)
PHONE...................216 661-1166
Christy Farhat, *President*
Kamal Farhat, *Treasurer*
Gail Doak, *Office Mgr*
EMP: 3
SALES (est): 370K **Privately Held**
SIC: 3669 1731 5013 Burglar alarm apparatus, electric; access control systems specialization; motor vehicle supplies & new parts

(G-6155)
SAINT CTHERINES METALWORKS INC (PA)
1985 W 68th St (44102-3906)
PHONE...................216 409-0576
Fax: 216 651-4465
Van Peplin, *President*
Herch Moore, *General Mgr*
EMP: 8 EST: 2001
SQ FT: 20,000
SALES (est): 500K **Privately Held**
WEB: www.scmetalworking.com
SIC: 2842 8661 Metal polish; religious organizations

(G-6156)
SAMSEL ROPE & MARINE SUPPLY CO (PA)
Also Called: Samsel Supply Company
1285 Old River Rd Uppr (44113-1279)
PHONE...................216 241-0333
Fax: 216 241-3426
Kathleen A Petrick, *President*
Larry E Nauth, *Principal*
Grace F Wilcox, *Principal*
Rosemary Woidke, *Principal*
F Michael Samsel, *Exec VP*
▲ EMP: 33
SQ FT: 100,000
SALES (est): 4.4MM **Privately Held**
WEB: www.samselsupply.com
SIC: 2394 5051 4959 5085 Canvas & related products; rope, wire (not insulated); miscellaneous nonferrous products; environmental cleanup services; industrial supplies; industrial tools; manufactured hardware (general); narrow fabric mills

(G-6157)
SANDS CO JEWELERS
26000 Chardon Rd (44143-1229)
PHONE...................216 261-8270
Fax: 216 261-9962
Steven Kozlowski, *Owner*
Dale Cook, *Manager*
EMP: 5
SALES: 400K **Privately Held**
SIC: 3911 Jewelry, precious metal

(G-6158)
SANSEI SHOWA CO LTD
31000 Bainbridge Rd (44139-2227)
PHONE...................440 248-4440
Michihiko Kobayashi, *President*
Paul Biddlestone, *Vice Pres*
John Leitz, *Engineer*
Nancy Harp, *Human Res Dir*
Andrew Palko, *Manager*
EMP: 25
SQ FT: 12,500
SALES (est): 4.3MM
SALES (corp-wide): 17.1MM **Privately Held**
WEB: www.sanseishowa.com
SIC: 3823 Industrial instrmnts msrmnt display/control process variable

PA: Sansei Denshi Co., Ltd.
1-11-8, Iwadokita
Komae TKY 201-0
334 894-131

(G-6159)
SARCOKINETICS LLC
11000 Cedar Ave Ste 265 (44106-3069)
PHONE...................414 477-9585
Julian Stelzer,
Mark Pelletier,
EMP: 3
SALES (est): 220K **Privately Held**
SIC: 2835 In vitro & in vivo diagnostic substances

(G-6160)
SARK TECHNOLOGIES LLC
Also Called: Super Inn.com
2270 Tudor Dr (44106-3210)
PHONE...................216 932-3171
Sagi Shilo, *Mng Member*
Kirk Dietrich,
Richard Dietrich,
Aviv Sack,
EMP: 4
SALES: 350K **Privately Held**
WEB: www.sarktech.com
SIC: 7372 Utility computer software

(G-6161)
SAS INSTITUTE INC
6100 Oak Tree Blvd # 400 (44131-2544)
PHONE...................216 643-6719
Fax: 216 642-4226
Christy Miller, *Manager*
EMP: 10
SALES (corp-wide): 2.1B **Privately Held**
WEB: www.sas.com
SIC: 7372 Application computer software; business oriented computer software; educational computer software
PA: Sas Institute Inc.
100 Sas Campus Dr
Cary NC 27513
919 677-8000

(G-6162)
SATELLITE GEAR INC
5135 Richmond Rd (44146-1330)
PHONE...................216 514-8668
Fax: 216 514-8671
John R Papesh, *President*
John R Papesh Jr, *Admin Sec*
EMP: 15
SQ FT: 12,000
SALES (est): 2.7MM **Privately Held**
SIC: 3462 2833 Gears, forged steel; drugs & herbs: grading, grinding & milling

(G-6163)
SAUSAGE SHOPPE
4501 Memphis Ave (44144-1912)
PHONE...................216 351-5213
Fax: 216 351-5255
Norm Heinle, *Owner*
Carol Heinle, *Co-Owner*
Jim Lange, *Sales Staff*
EMP: 4
SQ FT: 1,600
SALES (est): 316.9K **Privately Held**
WEB: www.sausageshoppe.com
SIC: 2013 5812 Sausages & other prepared meats; eating places

(G-6164)
SCHILLING ENAMELS COMPANY
12632 Triskett Rd (44111-2527)
P.O. Box 360738, Strongsville (44136-0013)
PHONE...................216 252-6242
Alfred Schilling Sr, *President*
EMP: 6
SQ FT: 5,100
SALES (est): 369.4K
SALES (corp-wide): 400K **Privately Held**
SIC: 2851 5231 Paints & allied products; paint & painting supplies
PA: Schilling Enterprises Inc
12632 Triskett Rd
Cleveland OH 44111
216 252-6242

(G-6165)
SCHILLING ENTERPRISES INC (PA)
Also Called: Schilling Enamels Company
12632 Triskett Rd (44111-2527)
P.O. Box 360738, Strongsville (44136-0013)
PHONE...................216 252-6242
Fax: 216 252-6248
Alfred Schilling Sr, *President*
Mary Ann Schilling, *Vice Pres*
Kenneth Schilling, *Treasurer*
EMP: 6
SQ FT: 5,100
SALES: 400K **Privately Held**
SIC: 2851 5231 Paints & allied products; enamels; varnishes; paint & painting supplies

(G-6166)
SCHUMANN ENTERPRISES INC
Also Called: E.C. Kitzel & Sons
4775 Manufacturing Ave (44135-2639)
PHONE...................216 267-6850
Fax: 216 267-6714
Thomas Schumann, *President*
Meredith Schumann, *Admin Sec*
Karen Capp, *Admin Asst*
EMP: 30 EST: 1927
SQ FT: 12,000
SALES (est): 4.6MM **Privately Held**
WEB: www.kitzel.com
SIC: 3545 3291 Diamond cutting tools for turning, boring, burnishing, etc.; abrasive wheels & grindstones, not artificial; diamond powder

(G-6167)
SCHWEIZER DIPPLE INC
7227 Division St (44146-5405)
PHONE...................440 786-8090
Fax: 440 786-8099
Michael J Kelley, *President*
Clark Dennis, *Exec VP*
Dennis J Clark, *Vice Pres*
James G Dwyer, *Vice Pres*
Peter A McGrogan, *Vice Pres*
EMP: 55
SQ FT: 27,000
SALES (est): 12.3MM
SALES (corp-wide): 42.6MM **Privately Held**
WEB: www.schweizer-dipple.com
SIC: 1711 3496 3444 3443 Mechanical contractor; process piping contractor; plumbing contractors; warm air heating & air conditioning contractor; miscellaneous fabricated wire products; sheet metalwork; fabricated plate work (boiler shop)
PA: Kelley Steel Erectors, Inc.
7220 Division St
Cleveland OH 44146
440 232-1573

(G-6168)
SCOTT FETZER COMPANY
Adalet
4801 W 150th St (44135-3301)
PHONE...................216 267-9000
Fax: 216 267-1681
Fred Lemke, *General Mgr*
Rob Klein, *Area Mgr*
Cherie Kmetz, *Purch Dir*
Keith Binnie, *Buyer*
Matthew Derr, *Draft/Design*
EMP: 150
SALES (corp-wide): 223.6B **Publicly Held**
WEB: www.adalet.com
SIC: 5063 3469 3357 3613 Wire & cable; metal stampings; nonferrous wiredrawing & insulating; control panels, electric; metal housings, enclosures, casings & other containers
HQ: The Scott Fetzer Company
28800 Clemens Rd
Westlake OH 44145
440 892-3000

(G-6169)
SCOTT FETZER COMPANY
Kirby Vacuum Cleaner
1920 W 114th St (44102-2391)
PHONE...................216 228-2403
Robert McBride, *President*
Dave Nicholson, *VP Admin*

John Lackner, *Vice Pres*
Joe Najm, *Opers Staff*
George Serhan, *Design Engr*
EMP: 350
SALES (corp-wide): 223.6B **Publicly Held**
SIC: 3635 Household vacuum cleaners
HQ: The Scott Fetzer Company
28800 Clemens Rd
Westlake OH 44145
440 892-3000

(G-6170)
SCOTT FETZER COMPANY
Cwp Technologies
3881 W 150th St (44111-5806)
PHONE...................216 252-1190
Tom Anderson, *Mfg Staff*
Mel Gollon, *VP Finance*
Bruce Ziegler, *Manager*
EMP: 80
SQ FT: 15,280
SALES (corp-wide): 223.6B **Publicly Held**
SIC: 3635 Household vacuum cleaners
HQ: The Scott Fetzer Company
28800 Clemens Rd
Westlake OH 44145
440 892-3000

(G-6171)
SCOTT FETZER COMPANY
875 Bassett Rd (44145-1142)
PHONE...................440 871-2160
Byron Crampton, *Manager*
EMP: 500
SALES (corp-wide): 223.6B **Publicly Held**
SIC: 3635 Household vacuum cleaners
HQ: The Scott Fetzer Company
28800 Clemens Rd
Westlake OH 44145
440 892-3000

(G-6172)
SCOTT FETZER COMPANY
Also Called: Halex
23901 Aurora Rd (44146-1717)
PHONE...................440 439-1616
Bob Zupancic, *Opers Mgr*
Cindy Martin, *Opers Staff*
Don Shymanski, *Purch Mgr*
Dennis Morgan, *Finance*
Susan Capuder, *Human Res Dir*
EMP: 120
SALES (corp-wide): 223.6B **Publicly Held**
SIC: 3635 Household vacuum cleaners
HQ: The Scott Fetzer Company
28800 Clemens Rd
Westlake OH 44145
440 892-3000

(G-6173)
SCOTT FETZER COMPANY
Meriam Process Technologies
10920 Madison Ave (44102-2526)
PHONE...................216 281-1100
Fax: 216 281-0228
Bryan Telepak, *General Mgr*
Ronald Ruiz, *Vice Pres*
Terry Weber, *Vice Pres*
Thomas Schrader, *Opers Staff*
Charemon Fee, *Buyer*
EMP: 90
SQ FT: 30,768
SALES (corp-wide): 223.6B **Publicly Held**
SIC: 3635 Household vacuum cleaners
HQ: The Scott Fetzer Company
28800 Clemens Rd
Westlake OH 44145
440 892-3000

(G-6174)
SCOTT FETZER COMPANY
Also Called: Kirby Customer Service Center
4750 W 160th St (44135-2632)
PHONE...................216 433-7797
Fax: 216 329-1272
Lou Verarvi, *Manager*
EMP: 60
SALES (corp-wide): 223.6B **Publicly Held**
SIC: 3635 Household vacuum cleaners

HQ: The Scott Fetzer Company
28800 Clemens Rd
Westlake OH 44145
440 892-3000

(G-6175)
SCOTTCARE CORPORATION (DH)
4791 W 150th St (44135-3301)
PHONE..........................216 362-0550
Fax: 216 267-6129
Deepak Malhotra, *General Mgr*
Ken Zajaczkowski, *General Mgr*
EMP: 31
SALES (est): 5.5MM
SALES (corp-wide): 223.6B **Publicly Held**
SIC: 3841 Surgical instruments & apparatus
HQ: The Scott Fetzer Company
28800 Clemens Rd
Westlake OH 44145
440 892-3000

(G-6176)
SEAFORTH MINERAL & ORE CO INC (PA)
3690 Orange Pl Ste 495 (44122-4465)
PHONE..........................216 292-5820
Gary McClurg, *Ch of Bd*
James McClurg, *President*
Vince Opaskar, *Technical Mgr*
Mary Ellen Sennet, *Manager*
▲ EMP: 15
SQ FT: 3,500
SALES (est): 25.5MM **Privately Held**
WEB: www.seaforthinc.com
SIC: 5052 3295 Nonmetallic minerals & concentrate; minerals, ground or treated

(G-6177)
SECURE MEDICAL MAIL LLC
3257 Mayfield Rd Apt 21 (44118-1864)
PHONE..........................216 269-1971
Sachin Doshi, *Co-Owner*
Ravi Patel,
Vipul Sheth,
EMP: 3
SALES (est): 153K **Privately Held**
SIC: 7372 Application computer software

(G-6178)
SECURUS MEDICAL GROUP INC
10000 Cedar Ave (44106-2119)
PHONE..........................216 445-4683
Steven Girouard, *CEO*
EMP: 5
SQ FT: 200
SALES (est): 395.6K **Privately Held**
SIC: 3841 Surgical & medical instruments

(G-6179)
SELECT SECURITY SCREEN CO LTD
1801 E 9th St Ste 1710 (44114-3198)
PHONE..........................216 362-1850
Greg Profancik, *General Mgr*
Frederick A Pfaff, *Vice Pres*
Jeffrey J Pfaff, *Vice Pres*
Edward Pfaff, *Mng Member*
Robert E Pfaff,
▲ EMP: 10
SALES (est): 1MM **Privately Held**
SIC: 3442 Screen & storm doors & windows

(G-6180)
SENECA LABEL INC
13821 Progress Pkwy (44133-4303)
PHONE..........................440 237-1600
Fax: 440 237-0427
Michael Hoopingarner, *President*
John Hoopingarner, *Vice Pres*
Paul Murdo, *Vice Pres*
Diane Tawney, *Sales Associate*
Joyce Jones, *Manager*
EMP: 35
SQ FT: 31,000
SALES (est): 5.6MM **Privately Held**
WEB: www.senecalabel.com
SIC: 2759 Flexographic printing

(G-6181)
SERVICE STATION EQUIPMENT CO (PA)
Also Called: Sseco
1294 E 55th St (44103-1029)
PHONE..........................216 431-6100
David Chrien, *President*
Diana Chrien, *Vice Pres*
Dennis Petroda, *Controller*
EMP: 10 EST: 1960
SQ FT: 45,000
SALES (est): 3.5MM **Privately Held**
WEB: www.sseqco.com
SIC: 5087 3559 Carwash equipment & supplies; petroleum refinery equipment

(G-6182)
SHAKER VALLEY FOODS INC
3304 W 67th Pl (44102-5243)
PHONE..........................216 961-8600
Fax: 216 961-8077
Dean Comber, *President*
Jeff Koutris, *Purch Mgr*
EMP: 40
SQ FT: 30,000
SALES (est): 21.6MM **Privately Held**
WEB: www.shakervalleyfoods.com
SIC: 5141 2011 Food brokers; meat packing plants

(G-6183)
SHALIX INC
10910 Briggs Rd (44111-5332)
PHONE..........................216 941-3546
David Schultheis, *President*
EMP: 10 EST: 1996
SALES (est): 1.1MM **Privately Held**
WEB: www.shalix.com
SIC: 3544 Special dies, tools, jigs & fixtures

(G-6184)
SHARP TOOL SERVICE INC
4735 W 150th St Unit H (44135-3352)
PHONE..........................330 273-4144
Fax: 330 225-4873
Richard Schirripa, *CEO*
Jeff Schirripa, *President*
Laura Schirripa, *Corp Secy*
Joe Schirripa, *Shareholder*
Rick Schirripa, *Shareholder*
EMP: 25
SQ FT: 22,000
SALES (est): 4.1MM **Privately Held**
WEB: www.sharptoolservice.com
SIC: 3545 Machine tool accessories

(G-6185)
SHEAR SERVICE INC
Also Called: Shear Service, The
3175 E 81st St (44104-4386)
PHONE..........................216 341-2700
Kim Curtis, *President*
EMP: 8
SALES: 370K **Privately Held**
SIC: 7389 3312 Metal slitting & shearing; blast furnaces & steel mills

(G-6186)
SHEFFIELD BRONZE PAINT CORP
17814 S Waterloo Rd (44119-3295)
P.O. Box 19206 (44119-0206)
PHONE..........................216 481-8330
Fax: 216 481-6606
Mel Hart, *President*
Morton Gross, *Chairman*
Bob Chamberlain, *Manager*
EMP: 20 EST: 1925
SQ FT: 100,000
SALES (est): 3.1MM **Privately Held**
WEB: www.sheffieldbronze.com
SIC: 2851 Paints & paint additives

(G-6187)
SHELLY LIQUID DIVISION
101 Mahoning Ave (44113-2500)
PHONE..........................216 781-9264
Thomas Hill, *Principal*
Dean Agonizon, *Manager*
EMP: 5 EST: 2008
SALES (est): 333.5K **Privately Held**
SIC: 1499 Asphalt mining & bituminous stone quarrying

(G-6188)
SHERIDAN WOODWORKS INC
17801 S Miles Rd (44128-4249)
PHONE..........................216 663-9333
Fax: 216 663-9585
Edward Sheridan, *President*
Fred Baker, *Manager*
EMP: 11
SQ FT: 16,000
SALES (est): 1.7MM **Privately Held**
WEB: www.sheridanwoodworks.com
SIC: 2431 1751 Millwork; cabinet building & installation

(G-6189)
SHERWIN-WILLIAMS COMPANY (PA)
101 W Prospect Ave # 1020 (44115-1075)
PHONE..........................216 566-2000
Fax: 216 566-1832
John G Morikis, *Ch of Bd*
Joel D Baxter, *President*
Robert J Davisson, *President*
David B Sewell, *President*
Jane M Cronin, *Senior VP*
EMP: 1200
SALES: 11.8B **Publicly Held**
WEB: www.sherwin.com
SIC: 5231 2851 Paint & painting supplies; wallcoverings; paints & allied products

(G-6190)
SHERWIN-WILLIAMS COMPANY
5020 Turney Rd (44125-2503)
PHONE..........................216 662-3300
Fax: 216 662-3668
Shannon Zipf, *Manager*
Chris Armbrust, *Manager*
EMP: 4
SALES (corp-wide): 11.8B **Publicly Held**
WEB: www.sherwin.com
SIC: 5231 2851 Paint & painting supplies; wallcoverings; paints & allied products; varnishes; lacquer: bases, dopes, thinner
PA: The Sherwin-Williams Company
101 W Prospect Ave # 1020
Cleveland OH 44115
216 566-2000

(G-6191)
SHERWN-WLLAMS AUTO FNSHES CORP
4440 Warrensville Ctr Rd (44128-2837)
PHONE..........................216 332-8330
Fax: 216 332-8646
Christopher Connor, *CEO*
Thomas Havlitzel, *President*
Terrence A Kacik, *Research*
Willie Harris, *Human Resources*
John Moore, *Marketing Staff*
◆ EMP: 219
SALES (est): 326.5MM
SALES (corp-wide): 11.8B **Publicly Held**
WEB: www.sherwin-automotive.com
SIC: 5231 2851 Paint & painting supplies; paints & allied products
PA: The Sherwin-Williams Company
101 W Prospect Ave # 1020
Cleveland OH 44115
216 566-2000

(G-6192)
SHERWN-WLLAMS INTL HLDINGS INC (HQ)
101 W Prospect Ave (44115-1093)
PHONE..........................216 566-2000
Henry Sherwin, *Principal*
EMP: 4
SALES (est): 820.9K
SALES (corp-wide): 11.8B **Publicly Held**
SIC: 5231 2851 Paint & painting supplies; wallcoverings; paints & allied products
PA: The Sherwin-Williams Company
101 W Prospect Ave # 1020
Cleveland OH 44115
216 566-2000

(G-6193)
SHERWOOD VALVE LLC
7900 Hub Pkwy (44125-5713)
PHONE..........................216 264-5023
Fax: 216 961-8944
Steven Greenberg, *Engineer*
Richard Gravagna, *Branch Mgr*
Michael D Devitt, *Manager*

Tom Hensley, *Manager*
Brad Alten, *Director*
EMP: 18
SALES (corp-wide): 2B **Publicly Held**
SIC: 2911 Liquefied petroleum gases, LPG
HQ: Sherwood Valve Llc
2200 N Main St
Washington PA 15301
724 225-8000

(G-6194)
SHERWOOD VALVE LLC
7900 Hub Pkwy (44125-5713)
PHONE..........................216 264-5028
Tom Hensley, *Manager*
EMP: 61
SALES (corp-wide): 2B **Publicly Held**
SIC: 3491 Automatic regulating & control valves; compressed gas cylinder valves; gas valves & parts, industrial; pressure valves & regulators, industrial
HQ: Sherwood Valve Llc
2200 N Main St
Washington PA 15301
724 225-8000

(G-6195)
SHIPPING ROOM PRODUCTS INC
19400 Saint Clair Ave (44117-1006)
P.O. Box 17120 (44117-0120)
PHONE..........................216 531-4422
Fax: 216 531-0777
Doug Painting, *President*
EMP: 4
SQ FT: 7,500
SALES (est): 360K **Privately Held**
SIC: 3499 Strapping, metal

(G-6196)
SHORELINE MACHINE PRODUCTS CO (PA)
19301 Saint Clair Ave (44117-1087)
PHONE..........................216 481-8033
Fax: 216 481-6866
Robert Arth, *President*
John J Ewers, *Principal*
Richard Kaufman, *Principal*
Joseph Frank Tekavic, *Principal*
Larry Arth, *Vice Pres*
EMP: 11 EST: 1967
SQ FT: 15,000
SALES (est): 3MM **Privately Held**
SIC: 3599 Machine shop, jobbing & repair

(G-6197)
SHREE KRUPA INC
Also Called: Gate Way News Stands
230 W Huron Rd Ste 8503 (44113-1452)
PHONE..........................216 781-6054
Ashwin Patel, *President*
Naresh Patel, *Vice Pres*
Swati Patel, *Treasurer*
Ritesh Patel, *Admin Sec*
EMP: 3
SALES: 300K **Privately Held**
SIC: 2711 Newspapers

(G-6198)
SIERRA PRECISION COMPONENTS
11941 Abbey Rd Ste E (44133-2663)
PHONE..........................440 230-9570
Fax: 440 230-2318
Daniel Baun, *President*
EMP: 4 **Privately Held**
WEB: www.sierraprecision.com
SIC: 3599 Machine shop, jobbing & repair
PA: Sierra Precision Components Inc
8511 Foxwood Ct
Poland OH 44514

(G-6199)
SIETINS PLASTICS INCORPORATED
380 Solon Rd Ste 4 (44146-3809)
PHONE..........................440 232-8515
Fax: 440 232-6829
Rhonda Caldwell, *President*
Hugh Caldwell, *Vice Pres*
EMP: 9
SQ FT: 3,960
SALES (est): 820K **Privately Held**
SIC: 3599 Machine shop, jobbing & repair

(G-6200)
SIFCO APPLIED SRFC CNCEPTS LLC (PA)
Also Called: Sifco ASC
5708 E Schaaf Rd (44131-1308)
PHONE..............................216 524-0099
Danijela Milosevic, *Research*
Sherri Beedles, *Human Res Mgr*
Phil Bauer, *Sales Mgr*
Alli Stockdale, *Mktg Coord*
Charles Allen, *Mng Member*
EMP: 34 EST: 2012
SQ FT: 18,000
SALES (est): 7.2MM Privately Held
SIC: 3471 Electroplating & plating

(G-6201)
SIFCO INDUSTRIES INC (PA)
970 E 64th St (44103-1694)
PHONE..............................216 881-8600
Fax: 216 432-6281
Norman E Wells Jr, *Ch of Bd*
Peter W Knapper, *President*
John Glover, *Vice Pres*
Steve Lacher, *Plant Mgr*
Stephanie Schulze, *Opers Mgr*
◆ EMP: 269 EST: 1916
SQ FT: 240,000
SALES: 119.1MM Publicly Held
WEB: www.sifco.com
SIC: 3724 3462 3471 Aircraft engines & engine parts; aircraft forgings, ferrous; anodizing (plating) of metals or formed products

(G-6202)
SIGN A RAMA INC
Also Called: Sign-A-Rama
731 Beta Dr Ste D (44143-2358)
P.O. Box 24272 (44124-0272)
PHONE..............................440 442-5002
Fax: 440 442-5002
Victor Baskins, *Principal*
Steve Kohn, *Manager*
EMP: 3
SALES (est): 234.4K Privately Held
SIC: 3993 Signs & advertising specialties

(G-6203)
SIGN-LITE CORPORATION
12655 Coit Rd (44108-1610)
PHONE..............................216 851-1000
Bill Holsman, *CEO*
Michael Holsman, *President*
David Kinkaid, *Sales Mgr*
Michael Bizjak, *Sales Staff*
Dane Frauenholz, *Manager*
EMP: 80
SQ FT: 41,000
SALES (est): 8.1MM Privately Held
WEB: www.sign-lite.com
SIC: 3993 Electric signs

(G-6204)
SIGNATURE SIGN CO INC
1776 E 43rd St (44103-2314)
PHONE..............................216 426-1234
Fax: 216 426-1261
Bruce Farkas, *President*
EMP: 15
SQ FT: 10,000
SALES (est): 1MM Privately Held
SIC: 1799 2499 Sign installation & maintenance; signboards, wood

(G-6205)
SINGLETON CORPORATION
3280 W 67th Pl (44102-5241)
PHONE..............................216 651-7800
Fax: 216 651-4247
Raymund Singleton, *President*
Jeff Singleton, *General Mgr*
Eric Singleton, *Vice Pres*
Dale Senkovic, *Purch Agent*
Laura Singleton, *Treasurer*
▼ EMP: 17
SQ FT: 30,000
SALES (est): 9.1MM Privately Held
WEB: www.singletoncorp.com
SIC: 5169 3559 Chemicals & allied products; anti-corrosion products; anodizing equipment; electroplating machinery & equipment

(G-6206)
SIRONRX THERAPEUTICS INC
10000 Cedar Ave (44106-2119)
PHONE..............................216 445-5588
Rahul Aras, *CEO*
EMP: 3
SALES (est): 389.4K Privately Held
SIC: 2834 Pharmaceutical preparations

(G-6207)
SKINNER MACHINING CO
23574 Saint Clair Ave (44117-2513)
PHONE..............................216 486-6636
Fax: 216 486-6637
Walter B Harwood, *President*
Carol Williams, *Office Mgr*
EMP: 8
SALES (est): 1.3MM
SALES (corp-wide): 2.2MM Privately Held
SIC: 3599 Electrical discharge machining (EDM)
PA: J W Harwood Co
18001 Roseland Rd
Cleveland OH 44112
216 531-6230

(G-6208)
SKINNYWEAR LLC
Also Called: Skinnytees
27825 Gates Ville Blvd (44124)
P.O. Box 24281, Mayfield Heights (44124-0281)
PHONE..............................216 310-5599
Alan MA,
EMP: 3
SALES: 950K Privately Held
SIC: 2341 Chemises, camisoles & teddies: women's & children's

(G-6209)
SKYBRYTE COMPANY INC
3125 Perkins Ave (44114-4627)
PHONE..............................216 771-1590
Fax: 216 771-1345
Cecil Stanley, *President*
Terry Wise, *Vice Pres*
EMP: 7 EST: 1915
SQ FT: 7,500
SALES: 1MM Privately Held
SIC: 2842 Rust removers

(G-6210)
SMART BUSINESS NETWORK INC (PA)
Also Called: Smart Business Magazine
835 Sharon Dr Ste 200 (44145-7703)
PHONE..............................440 250-7000
Fax: 440 250-7001
Fred Koury, *CEO*
David W Fazekas, *Vice Pres*
EMP: 39
SQ FT: 10,000
SALES (est): 6.2MM Privately Held
SIC: 2711 Newspapers: publishing only, not printed on site

(G-6211)
SMART SONIC CORPORATION
Also Called: Smart Snic Stencil Clg Systems
837 E 79th St (44103-1807)
PHONE..............................818 610-7900
William C Schreiber, *President*
Victor Chan, *Marketing Mgr*
Kimi Shryver, *Manager*
EMP: 8
SQ FT: 4,400
SALES (est): 1.7MM Privately Held
WEB: www.smartsonic.com
SIC: 3699 2842 3589 Cleaning equipment, ultrasonic, except medical & dental; specialty cleaning, polishes & sanitation goods; sewage & water treatment equipment

(G-6212)
SMEDLEYS BAR AND GRILL
17004 Lorain Ave (44111-5513)
PHONE..............................216 941-0124
Sean Mettler, *Principal*
EMP: 4
SALES (est): 240K Privately Held
SIC: 2085 Distilled & blended liquors

(G-6213)
SMOKEHEAL INC
5135 Spencer Rd (44124-1248)
PHONE..............................216 255-5119
Yuriy Krasnov, *President*
EMP: 3 EST: 2015
SALES (est): 123.1K Privately Held
SIC: 3999 8732 Cigar & cigarette holders; business research service

(G-6214)
SNAP RITE MANUFACTURING INC
14300 Darley Ave (44110-2172)
PHONE..............................910 897-4080
Fax: 216 851-2749
William Gray, *Safety Mgr*
Donald Acorn, *Marketing Staff*
Bill Gray, *Branch Mgr*
James Graham, *Maintence Staff*
EMP: 28
SALES (corp-wide): 18MM Privately Held
SIC: 3585 Air conditioning equipment, complete
PA: Snap Rite Manufacturing, Inc.
232 N Ida St
Coats NC 27521
910 897-4080

(G-6215)
SNYDER INTL BREWING GROUP LLC (PA)
Also Called: Sibg
1940 E 6th St Ste 200 (44114-2239)
PHONE..............................216 619-7424
Fax: 216 619-7425
Dave Snyder, *Partner*
Christopher Livingston, *Partner*
Jim Gerhig, *CFO*
EMP: 25 Privately Held
SIC: 2082 Beer (alcoholic beverage)

(G-6216)
SOBEL CORRUGATED CNTRS INC
Also Called: Miles Folding Box Co Div
1111 Superior Ave E # 1111 (44114-2522)
PHONE..............................216 475-2100
Fax: 216 475-2107
Terry Sobel, *President*
A L Kearns, *Principal*
Harry Sobel, *Principal*
Simon S Weinstein, *Principal*
Allyn David Sobel, *Exec VP*
EMP: 200
SQ FT: 148,000
SALES (est): 26.7MM Privately Held
SIC: 2653 Boxes, corrugated: made from purchased materials

(G-6217)
SOFTWARE AUTHORITY INC
6001 W Creek Rd (44131-2127)
PHONE..............................216 236-0200
George Gates, *President*
Daniel Bays, *President*
Jeff Gates, *Vice Pres*
EMP: 3
SALES (est): 209.1K Privately Held
WEB: www.softwareauthority.com
SIC: 7372 Prepackaged software

(G-6218)
SOLON GLASS CENTER INC
Also Called: Solon Glass Ctr
33001 Station St (44139-2935)
PHONE..............................440 248-5018
Fax: 440 248-4954
Roy Kucia, *President*
EMP: 10
SALES (est): 1.3MM Privately Held
WEB: www.solonglasscenter.com
SIC: 1793 3231 Glass & glazing work; products of purchased glass

(G-6219)
SOLON SPECIALTY WIRE CO
Also Called: Solon Specialty 0537
30000 Solon Rd (44139-3408)
PHONE..............................440 248-7600
Dave Haffenr, *CEO*
▲ EMP: 25
SQ FT: 180,000
SALES (est): 5.5MM
SALES (corp-wide): 3.7B Publicly Held
WEB: www.leggett.com
SIC: 3315 Wire, ferrous/iron
PA: Leggett & Platt, Incorporated
1 Leggett Rd
Carthage MO 64836
417 358-8131

(G-6220)
SONOGAGE INC
26650 Rnohance Pkwy Ste 3 (44128)
PHONE..............................216 464-1119
Fax: 216 831-3444
Alex Dybbs, *President*
EMP: 10
SALES (est): 1.8MM Privately Held
WEB: www.sonogage.com
SIC: 3841 Diagnostic apparatus, medical

(G-6221)
SOUNDWICH INC (PA)
881 Wayside Rd (44110-2961)
PHONE..............................216 486-2666
Fax: 216 486-5801
Perry Peck, *CEO*
Kevin Cleary, *President*
J Patrick Morris, *Principal*
Jeff Schroeder, *COO*
Steve Tomoba, *Vice Pres*
EMP: 80
SQ FT: 46,974
SALES (est): 31.4MM Privately Held
WEB: www.soundwich.com
SIC: 3714 Motor vehicle engines & parts

(G-6222)
SOUTH END PRINTING CO
3558 E 80th St (44105-1522)
P.O. Box 605593 (44105-0593)
PHONE..............................216 341-0669
Fax: 216 341-4411
Anthony D Dardy, *Owner*
Pat Dardy, *Co-Owner*
EMP: 3 EST: 1968
SQ FT: 2,400
SALES (est): 330.9K Privately Held
SIC: 2752 2796 2759 2791 Commercial printing, offset; lithographic plates, positives or negatives; letterpress printing; typesetting

(G-6223)
SP MOUNT PRINTING COMPANY
1306 E 55th St (44103-1302)
PHONE..............................216 881-3316
Fax: 216 881-2326
Gerald Mc Gill Sr, *Ch of Bd*
Scott C Mc Gill, *President*
Gerald McGill Jr, *Vice Pres*
Chuck Siford, *Project Mgr*
Ron Reebel, *Opers Mgr*
EMP: 25 EST: 1867
SQ FT: 45,000
SALES (est): 4.2MM Privately Held
WEB: www.spmount.com
SIC: 2752 Color lithography

(G-6224)
SPECIALTY GAS PUBLISHING INC
Also Called: Specialty Gas Report
12550 Lake Ave Apt 1312 (44107-1570)
PHONE..............................216 226-3796
Henry Grieco, *Owner*
Mike Vasilakes, *Vice Pres*
EMP: 3
SALES: 35K Privately Held
WEB: www.specgasreport.com
SIC: 2741 Miscellaneous publishing

(G-6225)
SPERZEL INC
Also Called: Sperco
15728 Industrial Pkwy (44135-3318)
PHONE..............................216 281-6868
Fax: 216 281-6810
Ronald Sperzel, *Vice Pres*
EMP: 20 EST: 1951
SQ FT: 5,000
SALES: 750K Privately Held
WEB: www.sperzel.com
SIC: 3931 String instruments & parts

(G-6226)
SPIRIT OF CLAY
828 Som Center Rd (44143-3532)
PHONE....................................440 684-0001
Kelly Strah, *Principal*
EMP: 3
SALES (est): 273.7K **Privately Held**
WEB: www.spiritofclay.net
SIC: 3269 Stoneware pottery products

(G-6227)
SPORTS CARE PRODUCTS INC
Also Called: Chemical Systems
4310 Cranwood Pkwy (44128-4002)
PHONE....................................216 663-8110
David Komocki, *Vice Pres*
EMP: 4
SALES (est): 520K **Privately Held**
WEB: www.chemicalsys.com
SIC: 2899 2911 Rifle bore cleaning compounds; oils, lubricating

(G-6228)
SPRINGCO METAL COATINGS INC (PA)
12500 Elmwood Ave (44111-5910)
PHONE....................................216 251-7023
Paul W Springer, *President*
Jason Conn, *Vice Pres*
David Starn, *Vice Pres*
EMP: 152
SQ FT: 140,000
SALES (est): 30.2MM **Privately Held**
WEB: www.springco-coatings.com
SIC: 3479 3471 Painting of metal products; coating of metals & formed products; plating & polishing

(G-6229)
SPS INTERNATIONAL INC
11880 Bellaire Rd (44135-4620)
PHONE....................................216 671-9911
Daniel J Papcun, *Owner*
EMP: 5
SQ FT: 12,000
SALES (est): 688.5K **Privately Held**
SIC: 3714 Motor vehicle parts & accessories

(G-6230)
SRC WORLDWIDE INC (HQ)
3425 Service Rd (44111-2421)
PHONE....................................216 941-6115
Marc Pignataro, *CEO*
Cary Nordan, *President*
Brian Kucia, *COO*
Jonathan Ward, *Admin Sec*
▲ EMP: 15
SQ FT: 70,000
SALES (est): 3.6MM
SALES (corp-wide): 113.6MM **Publicly Held**
SIC: 2899 Fluxes: brazing, soldering, galvanizing & welding
PA: Triangle Capital Corporation
3700 Glenwood Ave Ste 530
Raleigh NC 27612
919 719-4770

(G-6231)
STAHL GEAR & MACHINE CO
3901 Hamilton Ave (44114-3831)
PHONE....................................216 431-2820
Herman Bronstein, *President*
Joel Bronstein, *Vice Pres*
Mike Kramer, *Vice Pres*
Nikiel Walley, *Vice Pres*
Mark Bronstein, *Plant Mgr*
EMP: 50
SQ FT: 40,000
SALES: 5MM **Privately Held**
SIC: 3566 3561 3462 Gears, power transmission, except automotive; pumps & pumping equipment; iron & steel forgings

(G-6232)
STAINLESS AUTOMATION
1978 W 74th St (44102-2944)
PHONE....................................216 961-4550
Fax: 216 961-4583
Lois Martin, *Owner*
Ronald Martin, *Office Mgr*
EMP: 7
SQ FT: 3,000

SALES: 1MM **Privately Held**
WEB: www.stainlessautomation.com
SIC: 3549 3559 Metalworking machinery;

(G-6233)
STAMCO INDUSTRIES INC
26650 Lakeland Blvd (44132-2644)
PHONE....................................216 731-9333
Fax: 216 731-9338
William Sopko, *President*
Larry Reber, *General Mgr*
Dave Seward, *QC Mgr*
Tony Naglic, *Draft/Design*
Kurt Weisbarth, *Supervisor*
▲ EMP: 38
SQ FT: 130,000
SALES (est): 10MM **Privately Held**
WEB: www.stamcoind.com
SIC: 3465 Automotive stampings

(G-6234)
STANDARD MACHINE INC
1952 W 93rd St (44102-2790)
PHONE....................................216 631-4440
Fax: 216 631-2837
Jim Dopoulos, *President*
Marion R Herrington, *Principal*
Linda S Kratky, *Principal*
Eli Manos, *Principal*
Joe Nelson, *Purchasing*
EMP: 32
SQ FT: 31,000
SALES (est): 5.9MM **Privately Held**
WEB: www.standardmachineinc.com
SIC: 3599 Machine shop, jobbing & repair

(G-6235)
STANLEY ACCESS TECH LLC
Stanley Assembly Technologies
5335 Avion Park Dr (44143-1916)
P.O. Box 50400, Indianapolis IN (46250-0400)
PHONE....................................440 461-5500
John E Turpin, *Branch Mgr*
Russ Safran, *MIS Mgr*
EMP: 200
SQ FT: 40,000
SALES (corp-wide): 11.4B **Publicly Held**
WEB: www.stanleyworks.com
SIC: 3423 3546 Hand & edge tools; power-driven handtools
HQ: Stanley Access Technologies Llc
65 Scott Swamp Rd
Farmington CT 06032
860 409-6502

(G-6236)
STANLEY INDUSTRIES INC
19120 Cranwood Pkwy (44128-4088)
PHONE....................................216 475-4000
Fax: 216 475-4052
Jay Cusick, *President*
Wendy Markovitz, *Accounts Mgr*
Roger Asbury, *Office Mgr*
▼ EMP: 20 EST: 1946
SQ FT: 20,000
SALES (est): 3.3MM **Privately Held**
WEB: www.stanley-industries.com
SIC: 3599 5084 Machine shop, jobbing & repair; metal refining machinery & equipment

(G-6237)
STAR CALENDAR & PRINTING CO
4354 Pearl Rd (44109-4211)
PHONE....................................216 741-3223
Fax: 216 741-3224
Robert Cortelezzi, *President*
EMP: 6
SQ FT: 4,000
SALES (est): 570K **Privately Held**
SIC: 2752 5199 2759 Commercial printing, offset; advertising specialties; calendars; letterpress printing

(G-6238)
STAR SCREW MACHINE PRODUCTS
1531 E 41st St (44103-2303)
PHONE....................................216 361-0307
Fax: 216 361-0820
James Sanker, *President*
Pete Anastasakis, *Treasurer*
EMP: 4
SQ FT: 1,600

SALES (est): 492.5K **Privately Held**
SIC: 3451 Screw machine products

(G-6239)
STATE INDUSTRIAL PRODUCTS CORP (PA)
Also Called: State Chemical Manufacturing
5915 Landerbrook Dr # 300 (44124-4039)
PHONE....................................877 747-6986
Fax: 216 574-9433
Harold Uhrman, *President*
Robert M San Julian, *President*
William Barnett, *Corp Secy*
Brian Limbert, *COO*
John Malvic, *Vice Pres*
◆ EMP: 300 EST: 1911
SQ FT: 240,000
SALES: 107.9MM **Privately Held**
WEB: www.stateindustrial.com
SIC: 2841 5072 2842 2992 Soap: granulated, liquid, cake, flaked or chip; bolts, nuts & screws; specialty cleaning, polishes & sanitation goods; degreasing solvent; disinfectants, household or industrial plant; lubricating oils & greases; asphalt felts & coatings; chemical preparations

(G-6240)
STATE MACHINE CO INC
30400 Solon Indus Pkwy (44139-4328)
PHONE....................................440 248-1050
Fax: 440 248-1050
Christopher Catanese Jr, *President*
EMP: 7 EST: 1951
SQ FT: 6,000
SALES (est): 740K **Privately Held**
SIC: 3451 Screw machine products

(G-6241)
STATE TOOL AND DIE INC
Also Called: State Molded Plastics Division
4780 Briar Rd (44135-5038)
PHONE....................................216 267-6030
Fax: 216 267-6030
Emil J Orenick, *President*
Edward Zalar, *Exec VP*
Jeff Ambrose, *Plant Mgr*
Bill Cornell, *Prdtn Mgr*
Rich Hanzlik, *Sales Mgr*
EMP: 5 EST: 1945
SQ FT: 14,500
SALES (est): 1MM **Privately Held**
SIC: 3089 Injection molding of plastics

(G-6242)
STATUS MENS ACCESSORIES
7781 First Pl (44146-6705)
PHONE....................................440 232-6700
Scott Weger, *President*
Lee Schloss, *Vice Pres*
Mark Schloss, *Vice Pres*
▲ EMP: 6
SALES (est): 1.2MM **Privately Held**
WEB: www.statusmens.com
SIC: 2389 Men's miscellaneous accessories

(G-6243)
STD SPECIALTY FILTERS INC
837 E 79th St (44103-1807)
PHONE....................................216 881-3727
Walter Senney, *President*
Joyce P Senney, *Admin Sec*
EMP: 10
SQ FT: 25,000
SALES (est): 165.3K **Privately Held**
WEB: www.std-filters.com
SIC: 3564 3714 Filters, air: furnaces, air conditioning equipment, etc.; motor vehicle parts & accessories

(G-6244)
STEEL SERVICE PLUS LTD
6515 Juniata Ave (44103-1613)
PHONE....................................216 391-9000
Fax: 216 391-2251
Robert A Barrett, *President*
EMP: 13
SQ FT: 45,000
SALES (est): 2.2MM **Privately Held**
SIC: 3325 Steel foundries

(G-6245)
STEEL WAREHOUSE COMPANY LLC
Also Called: Steel Warehouse Ohio
4700 Heidtman Pkwy (44105-1026)
PHONE....................................216 206-2800
Jake Budzielek, *Branch Mgr*
Beth Gurband, *Clerk*
EMP: 30
SALES (corp-wide): 555.8MM **Privately Held**
SIC: 3449 Bars, concrete reinforcing: fabricated steel
PA: Steel Warehouse Company Llc
2722 Tucker Dr
South Bend IN 46619
574 236-5100

(G-6246)
STEEL WAREHOUSE OF OHIO LLC
3193 Independence Rd (44105-1045)
PHONE....................................888 225-3760
Dave Lerman, *CEO*
Mike Lerman, *President*
EMP: 60
SALES (est): 7.6MM
SALES (corp-wide): 555.8MM **Privately Held**
SIC: 3291 Abrasive metal & steel products
PA: Steel Warehouse Company Llc
2722 Tucker Dr
South Bend IN 46619
574 236-5100

(G-6247)
STEELTEC PRODUCTS LLC
13000 Saint Clair Ave (44108-2033)
PHONE....................................216 681-1114
Fax: 216 681-1120
David Bargar, *CFO*
John Bargar, *Mng Member*
Brian Bargar,
EMP: 23
SQ FT: 100,000
SALES (est): 5.6MM **Privately Held**
WEB: www.steeltecproducts.com
SIC: 3441 Fabricated structural metal

(G-6248)
STEIN INC (PA)
1929 E Royalton Rd Ste C (44147-2868)
P.O. Box 470548, Broadview Heights (44147-0548)
PHONE....................................440 526-9301
Fax: 440 526-9230
Donald Ries, *CEO*
Doug Huffnagel, *Superintendent*
Marc Glasgow, *Principal*
Joe Russo, *Vice Pres*
David Holvey, *CFO*
▲ EMP: 15
SQ FT: 17,000
SALES (est): 83.3MM **Privately Held**
WEB: www.stein.com
SIC: 3399 3312 5084 Iron ore recovery from open hearth slag; blast furnaces & steel mills; industrial machinery & equipment

(G-6249)
STEIN INC
2032 Campbell Rd (44105-1059)
P.O. Box 470548 (44147-0548)
PHONE....................................216 883-7444
Fax: 216 341-4205
Dave Bilek, *Branch Mgr*
EMP: 75
SALES (corp-wide): 83.3MM **Privately Held**
WEB: www.stein.com
SIC: 3399 3549 Iron ore recovery from open hearth slag; metalworking machinery
PA: Stein, Inc.
1929 E Royalton Rd Ste C
Cleveland OH 44147
440 526-9301

(G-6250)
STOFIEL AEROSPACE LLC
11115 Lake Ave Apt 309 (44102-1101)
PHONE....................................216 389-0084
Ronald Wilkinson, *COO*
Jason Beeman, *CFO*

Brian Stofiel,
EMP: 5 **EST:** 2015
SALES (est): 210.6K **Privately Held**
SIC: 3724 Rocket motors, aircraft

(G-6251)
STRETCHTAPE INC
3100 Hamilton Ave (44114-3701)
PHONE.................................216 486-9400
Fax: 216 486-9444
Alex F Mc Donald, *CEO*
Harry Mc Donald, *Treasurer*
Vonna Mc Donald, *Admin Sec*
▲ **EMP:** 40
SQ FT: 55,000
SALES (est): 10.1MM **Privately Held**
WEB: www.stretchtape.com
SIC: 2672 2671 3861 Adhesive papers, labels or tapes: from purchased material; packaging paper & plastics film, coated & laminated; sensitized film, cloth & paper

(G-6252)
STRIB INDUSTRIES INC
Also Called: Products Chemical
6400 Herman Ave (44102-2116)
PHONE.................................216 281-1155
Fax: 216 281-1186
John J Stibrick, *President*
▼ **EMP:** 25 **EST:** 1982
SALES (est): 5.4MM **Privately Held**
WEB: www.prod-chem.com
SIC: 2842 Cleaning or polishing preparations

(G-6253)
STRICKER REFINISHING INC
2060 Hamilton Ave (44114-1115)
PHONE.................................216 696-2906
Fax: 216 696-0535
Tom Stricker, *President*
Greg Stricker, *Treasurer*
EMP: 7
SQ FT: 4,000
SALES (est): 680K **Privately Held**
WEB: www.strickerrefinishing.com
SIC: 3471 Finishing, metals or formed products

(G-6254)
STRICTLY STITCHERY INC
Also Called: In Stitches Ctr For Ltrgcal Art
13801 Shaker Blvd Apt 4a (44120-5628)
PHONE.................................440 543-7128
Fax: 440 543-2548
Brenda Grauer, *President*
EMP: 10
SQ FT: 800
SALES: 175K **Privately Held**
SIC: 3269 5999 Art & ornamental ware, pottery; religious goods

(G-6255)
STRIPMATIC PRODUCTS INC
5301 Grant Ave Ste 200 (44125-1053)
PHONE.................................216 241-7143
Fax: 216 241-6303
William J Adler Jr, *President*
Randy Esser, *General Mgr*
Elizabeth R Adler, *Vice Pres*
Tony Scrima, *Prdtn Mgr*
Scott Baker, *Engineer*
▲ **EMP:** 29
SQ FT: 42,000
SALES: 5.7MM **Privately Held**
WEB: www.stripmatic.com
SIC: 3469 3465 3568 3498 Metal stampings; automotive stampings; power transmission equipment; fabricated pipe & fittings; copper foundries; aluminum foundries

(G-6256)
STRONG BINDERY
13015 Larchmere Blvd (44120-1147)
PHONE.................................216 231-0001
Ellen Strong, *President*
EMP: 9
SALES (est): 760.6K **Privately Held**
SIC: 2789 Bookbinding & related work

(G-6257)
STRYKER ENERGY LLC
6690 Beta Dr Ste 214 (44143-2359)
PHONE.................................440 446-9214
Mike Dodson, *Finance Mgr*

Billy Regan, *Manager*
Garry Regan,
EMP: 5
SALES (est): 946.7K **Privately Held**
SIC: 1382 Oil & gas exploration services

(G-6258)
STYNER+BIENZ US INC
12200 Brookpark Rd (44130-1146)
PHONE.................................216 362-1850
Rene Rothen, *President*
Christoph Mani, *Controller*
EMP: 3
SALES (est): 286.7K
SALES (corp-wide): 224.5MM **Privately Held**
SIC: 3465 3544 Automotive stampings; special dies, tools, jigs & fixtures
PA: Adval Tech Holding Ag
Freiburgstrasse 556
Niederwangen Bei Bern BE
319 808-444

(G-6259)
SUBURBAN MARBLE AND GRANITE CO
7818 Lake Ave (44102-1931)
PHONE.................................216 281-5557
Greg Gianvito, *Manager*
EMP: 6
SQ FT: 6,904
SALES (corp-wide): 750.1K **Privately Held**
SIC: 3281 Marble, building: cut & shaped
PA: Suburban Marble And Granite Co
26940 Bagley Rd
Olmsted Twp OH
440 235-0810

(G-6260)
SUBURBAN PRESS INC
3818 Lorain Ave (44113-3785)
PHONE.................................216 961-0766
Fax: 216 961-4372
William C Mueller, *President*
Ellen Mueller, *Corp Secy*
Paul R Mueller, *Vice Pres*
Richard M Mueller, *Vice Pres*
EMP: 24 **EST:** 1955
SALES (est): 3.9MM **Privately Held**
WEB: www.suburbanpressinc.com
SIC: 2752 2791 2789 2759 Commercial printing, offset; typesetting; bookbinding & related work; commercial printing

(G-6261)
SUMMA HOLDINGS INC (PA)
8223 Brecksville Rd # 100 (44141-1361)
PHONE.................................440 838-4700
James Benenson Jr, *Ch of Bd*
Clement C Benenson, *Co-President*
James Benenson III, *Co-President*
John E Cvetic, *CFO*
Nancy Lenhart, *Admin Sec*
◆ **EMP:** 4
SQ FT: 4,700
SALES (est): 587.1MM **Privately Held**
SIC: 2542 3462 3569 7359 Lockers (not refrigerated): except wood; cabinets: show, display or storage: except wood; shelving, office & store: except wood; gears, forged steel; lubricating systems, centralized; equipment rental & leasing; aircraft assemblies, subassemblies & parts

(G-6262)
SUMMERS ACQUISITION CORP (DH)
Also Called: Summers Rubber Company
12555 Berea Rd (44111-1619)
PHONE.................................216 941-7700
Fax: 216 941-4673
Mike Summers, *President*
William M Summers, *Chairman*
Eugene Mayo, *Vice Pres*
Gene Mayo, *Vice Pres*
Frank Tiernay, *Vice Pres*
▲ **EMP:** 26
SQ FT: 63,000
SALES: 25MM
SALES (corp-wide): 2.5B **Privately Held**
WEB: www.summersrubber.com
SIC: 5085 3429 Rubber goods, mechanical; manufactured hardware (general)

HQ: Hampton Rubber Company
1669 W Pembroke Ave
Hampton VA 23661
757 722-9818

(G-6263)
SUN POLISHING CORP
13800 Progress Pkwy Ste E (44133-4354)
PHONE.................................440 237-5525
Fax: 440 237-8110
Frank Schumacher, *President*
EMP: 8
SQ FT: 3,160
SALES: 500K **Privately Held**
SIC: 3471 Polishing, metals or formed products

(G-6264)
SUPERIOR FLUX & MFG CO
6615 Parkland Blvd (44139-4345)
PHONE.................................440 349-3000
Fax: 440 349-3003
Yehuda Baskin, *President*
Barbara Baskin, *Vice Pres*
Jeff Cantwell, *Sales Mgr*
Phil Baskin, *Sales Staff*
Benjamin Baskin, *Manager*
◆ **EMP:** 13 **EST:** 1932
SQ FT: 16,500
SALES: 3.7MM **Privately Held**
WEB: www.superiorflux.com
SIC: 2899 Fluxes: brazing, soldering, galvanizing & welding

(G-6265)
SUPERIOR HOLDING LLC (DH)
3786 Ridge Rd (44144-1127)
PHONE.................................216 651-9400
Thomas Farrel, *President*
EMP: 5
SALES (est): 19MM
SALES (corp-wide): 157.4MM **Privately Held**
SIC: 3494 5085 3492 Valves & pipe fittings; industrial supplies; fluid power valves & hose fittings

(G-6266)
SUPERIOR PNEUMATIC & MFG INC
855 Canterbury Rd (44145-1420)
P.O. Box 40420 (44140-0420)
PHONE.................................440 871-8780
Fax: 440 871-5127
Walter I Krewson Jr, *CEO*
Bradley Krewson, *President*
Robert Janusky, *Exec VP*
Anita Poshak, *Manager*
EMP: 19 **EST:** 1945
SQ FT: 10,000
SALES (est): 1.5MM **Privately Held**
WEB: www.superiorpneumatic.com
SIC: 3546 Power-driven handtools

(G-6267)
SUPERIOR PRECISION PRODUCTS
968 E 69th Pl (44103-1760)
PHONE.................................216 881-3696
Fax: 216 881-0958
Zeljko Tokic, *President*
EMP: 6
SQ FT: 16,000
SALES (est): 610K **Privately Held**
SIC: 3599 Machine shop, jobbing & repair

(G-6268)
SUPERIOR PRINTING INK CO INC
7655 Hub Pkwy Ste 205 (44125-5739)
PHONE.................................216 328-1720
Fax: 216 328-0626
Scott Allen, *Manager*
EMP: 7
SALES (corp-wide): 111.8MM **Privately Held**
SIC: 2893 2851 Printing ink; gravure ink; varnishes
PA: Superior Printing Ink Co Inc
100 North St
Teterboro NJ 07608
201 478-5600

(G-6269)
SUPERIOR PRODUCTS LLC
Also Called: Sp Medical
3786 Ridge Rd (44144-1127)
PHONE.................................216 651-9400
Tomas Sarrel, *President*
Donald L Mottinger, *President*
Tim Austin, *Managing Dir*
Gregory K Gens, *Vice Pres*
Louise Egofske, *CFO*
▼ **EMP:** 80 **EST:** 1961
SALES (est): 17.8MM **Privately Held**
WEB: www.superiorprod.com
SIC: 3451 3494 5085 3492 Screw machine products; valves & pipe fittings; industrial fittings; fluid power valves & hose fittings

(G-6270)
SUPERIOR PRODUCTS LLC
3786 Ridge Rd (44144-1127)
PHONE.................................216 651-9400
Fax: 440 602-6989
Donald L Mottinger, *President*
Tim Austin, *Managing Dir*
Gregory K Gens, *CFO*
Carolyn Gens, *Controller*
Tim Giesse, *Admin Sec*
EMP: 65
SQ FT: 75,000
SALES (est): 8.6MM
SALES (corp-wide): 157.4MM **Privately Held**
SIC: 3494 5085 3492 Valves & pipe fittings; industrial fittings; fluid power valves & hose fittings
HQ: Superior Holding, Llc
3786 Ridge Rd
Cleveland OH 44144
216 651-9400

(G-6271)
SUPERIOR STEEL STAMP CO
3200 Lakeside Ave E (44114-3750)
PHONE.................................216 431-6460
Fax: 216 431-4664
Ramzi Jammal, *President*
EMP: 4 **EST:** 1914
SALES (est): 551.8K **Privately Held**
SIC: 3469 3953 Stamping metal for the trade; marking devices

(G-6272)
SUPERIOR WELD AND FABG CO INC
15002 Woodworth Rd (44110-3310)
PHONE.................................216 249-5122
Howard Holmes, *President*
Joanne Holmes, *Manager*
EMP: 6
SQ FT: 7,000
SALES (est): 610K **Privately Held**
SIC: 3442 7692 Metal doors, sash & trim; welding repair

(G-6273)
SUPERTRAPP INDUSTRIES INC
4540 W 160th St (44135-2628)
PHONE.................................216 265-8400
Fax: 216 265-8340
Kevin Berger, *President*
James M Smith, *Principal*
Theodore Berger, *Vice Pres*
Joseph Golla, *Purchasing*
Paul Ellsworth, *Engineer*
▲ **EMP:** 83
SQ FT: 210,000
SALES (est): 20.8MM
SALES (corp-wide): 44.3MM **Privately Held**
WEB: www.supertrapp.com
SIC: 3714 Mufflers (exhaust), motor vehicle
PA: Dreison International, Inc.
4540 W 160th St
Cleveland OH 44135
216 362-0755

(G-6274)
SUPPLY TECHNOLOGIES LLC (HQ)
Also Called: I L S
6065 Parkland Blvd Ste 1 (44124-6145)
P.O. Box 248199 (44124-8199)
PHONE.................................440 947-2100

Fax: 440 947-2299
Michael L Justice, *President*
Brad Hudson, *Vice Pres*
James Smetham, *Vice Pres*
Seth Swanner, *Vice Pres*
Tom Blevins, *Opers Mgr*
▲ EMP: 150
SQ FT: 7,000
SALES (est): 40.2MM
SALES (corp-wide): 1.2B **Publicly Held**
WEB: www.deloscrew.com
SIC: 5085 3452 3469 Fasteners, indus-
trial: nuts, bolts, screws, etc.; bolts, nuts,
rivets & washers; screws, metal; nuts,
metal; stamping metal for the trade
PA: Park-Ohio Holdings Corp.
6065 Parkland Blvd Ste 1
Cleveland OH 44124
440 947-2000

(G-6275)
SURE-FOOT INDUSTRIES CORP
Also Called: Skid Guard
20260 1st Ave (44130-2430)
P.O. Box 707, Berea (44017-0707)
PHONE..........................440 234-4446
Fax: 440 234-9098
Clarence Haas, *President*
Shirley Haas, *Corp Secy*
Raymond Buckley, *Vice Pres*
Jeff Kral, *Opers Staff*
Brian Haas, *Sales Executive*
▲ EMP: 32
SQ FT: 65,000
SALES (est): 5.9MM **Privately Held**
WEB: www.surefootcorp.com
SIC: 3291 Abrasive products

(G-6276)
SURGICAL THEATER LLC
4541 Greenwold Rd (44121-4233)
PHONE..........................216 496-7884
Morvechai Avisar,
EMP: 4
SALES: 500K **Privately Held**
SIC: 3841 Surgical & medical instruments

(G-6277)
SWAGELOK COMPANY
Also Called: Flight Operations
328 Bishop Rd (44143-1446)
PHONE..........................440 442-6611
Bob Parmelee, *Manager*
EMP: 10
SALES (corp-wide): 1.1B **Privately Held**
WEB: www.swagelok.com
SIC: 4581 3494 Hangar operation; valves
& pipe fittings
PA: Swagelok Company
29500 Solon Rd
Solon OH 44139
440 248-4600

(G-6278)
SWAGELOK COMPANY
318 Bishop Rd (44143-1446)
PHONE..........................440 473-1050
Wayne Ostrosky, *Plant Mgr*
David Kallos, *QC Mgr*
Ron Edmondson, *Engineer*
Chip Falletta, *Engineer*
Jonathan Seewald, *Engineer*
EMP: 35
SALES (corp-wide): 1.1B **Privately Held**
WEB: www.swagelok.com
SIC: 3494 Valves & pipe fittings
PA: Swagelok Company
29500 Solon Rd
Solon OH 44139
440 248-4600

(G-6279)
SWAGELOK COMPANY
358 Bishop Rd (44143-1446)
PHONE..........................440 461-7714
Robin Lavigne, *Manager*
Jonathan Kobb, *Manager*
EMP: 200
SALES (corp-wide): 1.1B **Privately Held**
WEB: www.swagelok.com
SIC: 3599 Machine shop, jobbing & repair
PA: Swagelok Company
29500 Solon Rd
Solon OH 44139
440 248-4600

(G-6280)
SWIGER COIL SYSTEMS LTD
4677 Manufacturing Ave (44135-2673)
PHONE..........................216 362-7500
Fax: 216 362-1496
Michael Aladjem, *Mng Member*
▲ EMP: 190
SALES (est): 88.4MM **Privately Held**
WEB: www.swigercoil.com
SIC: 3621 3677 Electric motor & generator
parts; coils, for electric motors or genera-
tors; electronic coils, transformers & other
inductors

(G-6281)
SWIMMER PRINTING INC
Also Called: AlphaGraphics
1701 E 12th St (44114-3236)
PHONE..........................216 623-1005
Fax: 216 623-1185
Judith Swimmer, *President*
Rodrigo Abreu, *Vice Pres*
Art Coley, *Vice Pres*
Brad Swimmer, *Vice Pres*
EMP: 8
SQ FT: 3,900
SALES (est): 890K **Privately Held**
SIC: 2752 Commercial printing, litho-
graphic

(G-6282)
SYNERGY GRINDING INC
9005 Bank St (44125-3425)
PHONE..........................216 447-4000
Fax: 216 573-0661
Barbara Bissett Kitchen, *Owner*
Mark Kitchen, *Manager*
Larry Wolcott, *Manager*
EMP: 10
SALES (est): 1.2MM **Privately Held**
WEB: www.synergygrinding.com
SIC: 3541 Grinding machines, metalwork-
ing

(G-6283)
SYSTEM CONTROLS INC
4549 State Rd (44109-4786)
PHONE..........................216 351-9121
Fax: 216 351-0002
Tom Piskach, *President*
Rosemarie Piskach, *Vice Pres*
EMP: 6
SQ FT: 4,500
SALES (est): 944.4K **Privately Held**
WEB: www.systemcontrols.com
SIC: 3613 Control panels, electric

(G-6284)
SYSTEM SEALS INC (HQ)
9505 Midwest Ave (44125-2421)
PHONE..........................440 735-0200
Fax: 440 735-0288
Arnold V Engelbrechten, *President*
Jim Bell, *Controller*
Aric Camp, *VP Sales*
Julian Gigg, *Regl Sales Mgr*
▲ EMP: 60
SQ FT: 10,000
SALES (est): 9.4MM **Privately Held**
WEB: www.systemseals.com
SIC: 3953 5084 Embossing seals & hand
stamps; hydraulic systems equipment &
supplies

(G-6285)
T & B FOUNDRY COMPANY
2469 E 71st St (44104-1967)
PHONE..........................216 391-4200
Fax: 216 391-4206
Edward Pruc, *President*
Ted Pruc, *Exec VP*
Jane Pruc, *Manager*
Richard Sunderman, *Director*
EMP: 80 EST: 1992
SQ FT: 275,000
SALES (est): 1MM **Privately Held**
WEB: www.tbfoundry.com
SIC: 3321 3369 3322 Gray iron castings;
ductile iron castings; nonferrous
foundries; malleable iron foundries

(G-6286)
T & J NICKUM INC
Also Called: Kay-Dee Air & Elc Tl Repr Co
5466 Lake Ct (44114-3902)
PHONE..........................216 881-2565
Toll Free:..........................888 -
Fax: 216 881-2566
Joan Nickum, *President*
Tim Nickum Sr, *Vice Pres*
EMP: 5
SQ FT: 2,850
SALES (est): 1MM **Privately Held**
WEB: www.kaydeetools.com
SIC: 7629 5085 7694 Tool repair, electric;
tools; electric motor repair

(G-6287)
T & K WELDING CO INC
1405 E 39th St (44114-4164)
PHONE..........................216 432-0221
Fax: 216 432-0071
Bruce Komandt, *President*
Susan Komandt, *Vice Pres*
EMP: 3 EST: 1951
SQ FT: 9,000
SALES (est): 365.4K **Privately Held**
SIC: 3599 3441 Machine shop, jobbing &
repair; fabricated structural metal

(G-6288)
T D DYNAMICS INC
Also Called: Morgan Litho
4101 Commerce Ave (44103-3507)
PHONE..........................216 881-0800
Fax: 216 881-7261
Dale Fellows, *President*
Thomas M Baginski, *Vice Pres*
EMP: 10
SQ FT: 19,800
SALES (est): 880K **Privately Held**
WEB: www.morganlitho.com
SIC: 2752 Commercial printing, litho-
graphic

(G-6289)
T D GROUP HOLDINGS LLC
1301 E 9th St Ste 3710 (44114-1838)
PHONE..........................216 706-2939
Nikki Grace, *Manager*
Kenneth Kates, *Director*
Kevin Kruse, *Bd of Directors*
W Nicholas Howley,
David A Barr,
EMP: 3
SALES (est): 234.9K **Privately Held**
SIC: 3561 3563 3625 3492 Pumps &
pumping equipment; air & gas compres-
sors; relays & industrial controls; fluid
power valves & hose fittings

(G-6290)
T H E B INC
Also Called: A Quick Copy Center
3700 Kelley Ave (44114-4533)
PHONE..........................216 391-4800
Fax: 216 382-8005
Rhonda Garcia, *President*
Tom Garcia, *Admin Sec*
EMP: 7
SQ FT: 4,000
SALES (est): 753.7K **Privately Held**
SIC: 2752 Commercial printing, litho-
graphic; commercial printing, offset

(G-6291)
T&M PLASTICS CO INC
1249 W 78th St (44102-1913)
P.O. Box 602500 (44102-0500)
PHONE..........................216 651-7700
Fax: 216 631-2661
Tom Timura, *President*
Raymond Timura, *Vice Pres*
EMP: 5
SALES (est): 570K **Privately Held**
SIC: 3089 Injection molded finished plastic
products; injection molding of plastics

(G-6292)
TALAN PRODUCTS INC
18800 Cochran Ave (44110-2700)
PHONE..........................216 458-0170
Steve Peplin, *CEO*
Peter Accorti, *President*
Miguel Lugo, *Plant Mgr*
Jeff Millis, *Inv Control Mgr*
Nancy Oates, *Purch Agent*
▲ EMP: 60
SQ FT: 100,000
SALES (est): 19.5MM **Privately Held**
WEB: www.talanproducts.com
SIC: 3469 Metal stampings

(G-6293)
TALBOT DRAKE INCORPORATED
Also Called: Talbot Drake & Co
5808 Grant Ave (44105-5608)
PHONE..........................216 441-5600
Mary Morvan, *President*
EMP: 4
SQ FT: 2,034
SALES (est): 260K **Privately Held**
WEB: www.talbotdrake.com
SIC: 2731 Book publishing

(G-6294)
TAPER TOOL & BROACH INC
1066 E 222nd St (44117-1101)
PHONE..........................216 486-4435
Fax: 216 486-4456
James T Pachell, *President*
EMP: 7
SALES (est): 690K **Privately Held**
SIC: 3541 5084 Broaching machines; in-
dustrial machinery & equipment

(G-6295)
TATHAM SCHULZ INCORPORATED
Also Called: Cleveland Black Oxide
836 Broadway Ave (44115-2813)
PHONE..........................216 861-4431
Fax: 216 861-0711
David Tatham, *President*
Ken Schulz, *Vice Pres*
Richard Tatham, *Vice Pres*
Walter Johnston, *Purchasing*
Loreen Crawford, *Human Res Mgr*
EMP: 35
SQ FT: 21,000
SALES (est): 4MM **Privately Held**
WEB: www.clevelandblackoxide.com
SIC: 3471 Finishing, metals or formed
products

(G-6296)
TEAM PLASTICS INC
3901 W 150th St (44111-5810)
PHONE..........................216 251-8270
Fax: 216 251-7341
Ed Busch, *President*
Robert Timko, *CFO*
William Madar, *Treasurer*
EMP: 10
SQ FT: 14,000
SALES (est): 2.1MM **Privately Held**
SIC: 3081 Unsupported plastics film &
sheet

(G-6297)
TEAM WENDY LLC
17000 Saint Clair Ave # 5 (44110-2539)
PHONE..........................216 738-2518
Thomas J Prodouz, *President*
Dan T Moore III, *Chairman*
Robert James, *Prdtn Mgr*
Amanda Grandt, *Purchasing*
Amy Carpenter, *QC Mgr*
EMP: 60
SQ FT: 40,000
SALES (est): 12.7MM **Privately Held**
WEB: www.teamwendy.com
SIC: 3086 Padding, foamed plastic

(G-6298)
TECH INDUSTRIES INC
1313 Washington Ave (44113-2332)
PHONE..........................216 861-7337
Bruno Aldons, *President*
James Weiskittel, *Vice Pres*
Arnold Lowe, *Treasurer*
Dan Dietz, *Marketing Staff*
Lawrence A Keidel, *Manager*
EMP: 27 EST: 1953
SQ FT: 10,000
SALES (est): 3.1MM **Privately Held**
WEB: www.tech-ind.com
SIC: 3544 Special dies & tools; jigs & fix-
tures

(G-6299)
TECH READY MIX INC
5000 Crayton Ave (44104-2826)
P.O. Box 5270 (44101-0270)
PHONE..........................216 361-5000
Mark F Perkins, *President*
Janice Knight, *Principal*

EMP: 45
SALES (est): 7.3MM **Privately Held**
SIC: 3273 Ready-mixed concrete

(G-6300)
TECHNICAL MACHINE PRODUCTS INC
5500 Walworth Ave (44102-4431)
P.O. Box 920, Piqua (45356-0920)
PHONE..................................216 281-9500
Daniel P French, *Ch of Bd*
Randall Hefelfinger, *General Mgr*
Jason P McDaniel, *COO*
Dave Sledz, *Vice Pres*
Jeff Advent, *Plant Mgr*
▲ EMP: 10 EST: 1978
SALES (est): 2MM
SALES (corp-wide): 16.5MM **Privately Held**
WEB: www.techmach.com
SIC: 3559 3542 Rubber working machinery, including tires; plastics working machinery; pressing machines; presses: hydraulic & pneumatic, mechanical & manual
PA: The French Oil Mill Machinery Company
1035 W Greene St
Piqua OH 45356
937 773-3420

(G-6301)
TECHNIPLATE INC
700 E 163rd St (44110-2493)
PHONE..................................216 486-8825
Fax: 216 486-7733
Allan Stickler, *CEO*
Don Perry, *President*
Leigh Stickler, *Office Mgr*
EMP: 13
SQ FT: 13,200
SALES (est): 1.3MM **Privately Held**
WEB: www.techniplate.com
SIC: 3471 Electroplating of metals or formed products

(G-6302)
TECHNLOGY INSTALL PARTNERS LLC
13701 Enterprise Ave (44135-5113)
PHONE..................................888 586-7040
Erica Temple, *President*
Ryan Temple, *Vice Pres*
Laurie Baumholtz, *Manager*
EMP: 25
SALES (est): 2MM **Privately Held**
SIC: 3699 Security control equipment & systems

(G-6303)
TEMPCRAFT CORPORATION
3960 S Marginal Rd (44114-3835)
PHONE..................................216 391-3885
Fax: 216 391-4842
Paul Woerz, *Exec VP*
Richard Jackson, *Personnel*
Gary Zakrzeski, *Marketing Staff*
Brent Daldo, *Manager*
James Hauska, *Manager*
EMP: 225 EST: 1956
SQ FT: 100,000
SALES (est): 20MM
SALES (corp-wide): 12.3B **Publicly Held**
SIC: 3544 3543 Industrial molds; industrial patterns
HQ: Howmet Corporation
1616 Harvard Ave
Newburgh Heights OH 44105
800 242-9898

(G-6304)
TEMPEST INC
12750 Berea Rd (44111-1622)
PHONE..................................216 883-6500
Charles M Ruebensaal, *President*
Dave Dibiasio, *General Mgr*
Edward George, *General Mgr*
Tracy Cherotti, *Manager*
Stanley E Kulesa, *Manager*
EMP: 10
SQ FT: 65,000
SALES: 8MM **Privately Held**
WEB: www.tempest-eng.com
SIC: 3823 Temperature instruments: industrial process type

PA: Great Lakes Management, Inc.
8510 Bessemer Ave
Cleveland OH 44127
216 883-6500

(G-6305)
TENDON MANUFACTURING INC
20805 Aurora Rd (44146-1005)
PHONE..................................216 663-3200
Fax: 216 663-6464
Gregory F Tench, *President*
Michael J Gordon, *Corp Secy*
Eric Dedic, *Opers Staff*
Thomas Tench, *Sls & Mktg Exec*
EMP: 46
SQ FT: 36,000
SALES (est): 9.4MM **Privately Held**
WEB: www.tendon.com
SIC: 3599 3479 1761 7692 Machine shop, jobbing & repair; painting of metal products; sheet metalwork; welding repair; sheet metalwork; automotive & apparel trimmings

(G-6306)
TEREWELL INC
2683 W 14th St (44113-5215)
PHONE..................................216 334-6897
Terewell Harmon, *CEO*
EMP: 3
SALES (est): 60.7K **Privately Held**
SIC: 8082 2741 8748 8999 Home health care services; music book & sheet music publishing; testing service, educational or personnel; artists & artists' studios

(G-6307)
TERNION INC (PA)
Also Called: Skyline Trisource Exhibits
7635 Hub Pkwy Ste A (44125-5741)
PHONE..................................216 642-6180
Wendy Ressing-Seitz, *President*
Terrie Benore, *Vice Pres*
Tammy Scordo, *Marketing Staff*
Cindy Wysochanski, *Office Mgr*
Kristie Jones-Damalas, *Admin Sec*
◆ EMP: 23
SQ FT: 18,300
SALES (est): 7.3MM **Privately Held**
WEB: www.skylinees.com
SIC: 5046 3993 2542 Display equipment, except refrigerated; signs & advertising specialties; partitions & fixtures, except wood

(G-6308)
THE CLEVELAND-CLIFFS IRON CO
1100 Superior Ave E # 1500 (44114-2544)
PHONE..................................216 694-5700
J A Carrabba, *CEO*
D S Gallagher, *President*
Richard Fink, *General Mgr*
David Katsilometes, *General Mgr*
Brien Schacherer, *General Mgr*
EMP: 176
SQ FT: 40,000
SALES (est): 12.9MM
SALES (corp-wide): 2.1B **Publicly Held**
SIC: 1011 Iron ore mining; iron ore beneficiating
PA: Cliffs Natural Resources Inc.
200 Public Sq Ste 3300
Cleveland OH 44114
216 694-5700

(G-6309)
THE EUCLID CHEMICAL COMPANY (DH)
Also Called: Epoxy Chemicals
19218 Redwood Rd (44110-2799)
PHONE..................................800 321-7628
Fax: 216 531-9596
Moorman L Scott Jr, *President*
Carol Rode, *General Mgr*
Phillip Brandt, *Vice Pres*
MA Drolet, *Vice Pres*
Volkmar Harnischmacher, *Vice Pres*
◆ EMP: 20 EST: 1965
SQ FT: 5,000
SALES (est): 134.3MM
SALES (corp-wide): 4.8B **Publicly Held**
WEB: www.epoxychemicals.com
SIC: 2899 4213 Chemical preparations; trucking, except local

HQ: Tremco Incorporated
3735 Green Rd
Beachwood OH 44122
216 292-5000

(G-6310)
THE EUCLID CHEMICAL COMPANY
19218 Redwood Rd (44110-2799)
PHONE..................................216 531-9222
Glenn Strasshofer, *Branch Mgr*
EMP: 100
SALES (corp-wide): 4.8B **Publicly Held**
SIC: 2851 Paints & allied products
HQ: The Euclid Chemical Company
19218 Redwood Rd
Cleveland OH 44110
800 321-7628

(G-6311)
THE EUCLID CHEMICAL COMPANY
18900 Cochran Ave (44110)
PHONE..................................216 531-9222
EMP: 11
SALES (corp-wide): 4.8B **Publicly Held**
SIC: 2899 4225 Chemical preparations; concrete curing & hardening compounds; general warehousing & storage
HQ: The Euclid Chemical Company
19218 Redwood Rd
Cleveland OH 44110
800 321-7628

(G-6312)
THE FISCHER & JIROUCH COMPANY
4821 Superior Ave (44103-1233)
PHONE..................................216 361-3840
Fax: 216 361-0650
Robert Mattei, *President*
Salvatore Grandinetti, *Corp Secy*
Joan Mattei, *Manager*
Carloina Cretoni, *Shareholder*
EMP: 8
SQ FT: 30,000
SALES: 760K **Privately Held**
SIC: 3299 Ornamental & architectural plaster work

(G-6313)
THE GREAT LAKES BREWING CO
2516 Market Ave (44113-3434)
PHONE..................................216 771-4404
Fax: 216 771-4466
Patrick F Conway, *President*
Jonathon Satayathum, *General Mgr*
Daniel J Conway, *Corp Secy*
John Staunton, *Sales Staff*
Emmett Conway, *Marketing Staff*
▲ EMP: 85
SQ FT: 20,000
SALES (est): 29.9MM **Privately Held**
WEB: www.greatlakesbrewing.com
SIC: 2082 5813 5812 Beer (alcoholic beverage); bar (drinking places); American restaurant

(G-6314)
THE HOLTKAMP ORGAN CO
2909 Meyer Ave (44109-1584)
PHONE..................................216 741-5180
Fax: 216 741-0678
F Christian Holtkamp, *President*
Jim Sholdis, *Business Mgr*
Christian Holtkamp, *Director*
Thomas Lucchesi, *Admin Sec*
EMP: 12 EST: 1855
SQ FT: 15,700
SALES (est): 1.7MM **Privately Held**
WEB: www.holtkamporgan.com
SIC: 3931 Pipes, organ

(G-6315)
THERMAGON INC
Also Called: Laird Technologies
4707 Detroit Ave (44102-2216)
PHONE..................................216 939-2300
Fax: 216 939-2310
Tom Cochran, *President*
Richard F Gonda, *President*
Richard Hill, *Draft/Design*
Karen Foster, *Manager*
Benson Lin, *Manager*

▲ EMP: 75
SQ FT: 50,000
SALES (est): 25.6MM
SALES (corp-wide): 950.5MM **Privately Held**
WEB: www.thermagon.com
SIC: 2891 Adhesives & sealants
HQ: Laird Technologies, Inc.
3481 Rider Trl S
Earth City MO 63045
636 898-6000

(G-6316)
THERMAL INDUSTRIES INC
4920 Commerce Pkwy Ste 4 (44128-5943)
PHONE..................................216 464-0674
Ron Berna, *Manager*
EMP: 5
SALES (est): 1.2B **Privately Held**
WEB: www.thermalindustries.com
SIC: 3442 Screens, window, metal
HQ: Thermal Industries, Inc.
3700 Haney Ct
Murrysville PA 15668
724 325-6100

(G-6317)
THERMAL TREATMENT CENTER INC (HQ)
Also Called: Nettleton Steel Treating Div
1101 E 55th St (44103-1026)
PHONE..................................216 881-8100
Carmen Paponitti, *President*
Jack Luck, *Vice Pres*
Louise Profughi, *Treasurer*
EMP: 35 EST: 1945
SQ FT: 85,000
SALES (est): 6.4MM
SALES (corp-wide): 22.9MM **Privately Held**
WEB: www.htg.cc
SIC: 3398 8711 Metal heat treating; engineering services
PA: Hi Tecmetal Group Inc
1101 E 55th St
Cleveland OH 44103
216 881-8100

(G-6318)
THERMAL TREATMENT CENTER INC
Commercial Induction Division
11116 Avon Ave (44105-4257)
PHONE..................................216 883-4820
Fax: 216 881-8100
Ernie Burroughs, *Sales Staff*
Chip Gench, *Manager*
EMP: 5
SALES (corp-wide): 22.9MM **Privately Held**
WEB: www.htg.cc
SIC: 3398 Metal heat treating
HQ: Thermal Treatment Center Inc
1101 E 55th St
Cleveland OH 44103
216 881-8100

(G-6319)
THERMAL TREATMENT CENTER INC
Walker Steel Treating Division
10601 Briggs Rd (44111-5329)
PHONE..................................216 941-0440
Will Helber, *Manager*
EMP: 15
SALES (corp-wide): 21MM **Privately Held**
WEB: www.htg.cc
SIC: 3398 Metal heat treating
HQ: Thermal Treatment Center Inc
1101 E 55th St
Cleveland OH 44103
216 881-8100

(G-6320)
THERMO SYSTEMS TECHNOLOGY
2000 Auburn Dr Ste 200 (44122-4328)
PHONE..................................216 292-8250
Fax: 216 729-2973
Henry A Becker, *President*
Dale Holiday, *Vice Pres*
Neal Fenster, *Chief Engr*
Neal Senster, *Chief Engr*
EMP: 50

SALES (est): 5.4MM **Privately Held**
WEB: www.thermosys.com
SIC: **3567** 3433 Heating units & devices, industrial: electric; heating equipment, except electric

(G-6321)
THOMAS DAVID DESIGN
30799 Pinetree Rd 263 (44124-5903)
PHONE..................................614 595-0379
Jacob Radsick,
EMP: 4
SALES: 750K **Privately Held**
SIC: **3651** Household audio & video equipment

(G-6322)
THOMPSON ALUMINUM CASTING CO
Also Called: Thompson Castings
5161 Canal Rd (44125-1143)
PHONE..................................216 206-2781
Fax: 216 206-2791
Dave Oberg, *Principal*
Keith Cwiklinski, *Production*
Rick D'Amico, *QC Mgr*
Paul Danziger, *Controller*
Geraldine Basar, *Human Res Dir*
▲ EMP: 71
SQ FT: 60,000
SALES (est): 19.2MM **Privately Held**
WEB: www.thompsoncasting.com
SIC: **3364** 3369 3363 3365 Magnesium & magnesium-base alloy die-castings; magnesium & magnes.-base alloy castings, exc. die-casting; aluminum die-castings; aluminum foundries

(G-6323)
THOSE CHARC FROM CLEVE INC
Also Called: T C F C
1 American Rd (44144-2301)
PHONE..................................216 252-7300
Ed Fructembaum, *President*
William Meyer, *Vice Pres*
Thomas Schneider, *Vice Pres*
Howard Weinshenker, *Vice Pres*
Dale A Cable, *Treasurer*
EMP: 14
SQ FT: 5,000
SALES (est): 410.1K
SALES (corp-wide): 2.2B **Privately Held**
SIC: **8999** 2771 Art related services; greeting cards
HQ: American Greetings Corporation
1 American Rd
Cleveland OH 44144
216 252-7300

(G-6324)
TIG WELDING SPECIALTIES INC
13616 Enterprise Ave (44135-5112)
PHONE..................................216 621-1763
Fax: 216 621-6417
Fred Backus, *President*
Scott Backus, *Vice Pres*
EMP: 5
SQ FT: 2,000
SALES (est): 350K **Privately Held**
SIC: **7692** 3599 Welding repair; ties, form: metal

(G-6325)
TILDEN MINING COMPANY LC (PA)
1100 Superior Ave E (44114-2530)
PHONE..................................216 694-5278
John Cotter,
EMP: 580
SALES (est): 421.9MM **Privately Held**
SIC: **1011** Iron ore mining; iron ore pelletizing; iron ore beneficiating

(G-6326)
TIP PRODUCTS INC
15411 Chatfield Ave Ste 5 (44111-4300)
PHONE..................................216 252-2535
Fax: 216 252-2327
Wayne T Gielow, *President*
Rhonda Gielow, *Corp Secy*
EMP: 23 EST: 1965
SQ FT: 10,000

SALES (est): 3.9MM **Privately Held**
WEB: www.tipproducts.com
SIC: **3643** 3699 Connectors, electric cord; plugs, electric; electrical equipment & supplies

(G-6327)
TLS CORP (PA)
Also Called: Telos Alliance, The
1241 Superior Ave E (44114-3204)
PHONE..................................216 574-4759
Frank Foti, *CEO*
Timothy Carroll, *President*
Scott Stiefel, *COO*
Jim Armstrong, *Purch Mgr*
Joseph Zolyak, *Research*
◆ EMP: 48
SQ FT: 10,500
SALES (est): 8.2MM **Privately Held**
WEB: www.axiaaudio.com
SIC: **3663** 3679 3823 3661 Radio & TV communications equipment; electronic circuits; industrial instrmnts msrmnt display/control process variable; telephone & telegraph apparatus; household audio & video equipment

(G-6328)
TMW SYSTEMS INC
6085 Parkland Blvd (44124-4184)
PHONE..................................615 986-1900
Larry Sebak, *Project Mgr*
Leigh Anderson, *Human Res Mgr*
Michael Malecha, *Regl Sales Mgr*
Laura Leonardi, *Sales Staff*
Michael Wolfinger, *Sr Project Mgr*
EMP: 19
SALES (corp-wide): 2.3B **Publicly Held**
SIC: **3829** 3812 Measuring & controlling devices; navigational systems & instruments
HQ: Tmw Systems, Inc.
6085 Parkland Blvd
Mayfield Heights OH 44124
216 831-6606

(G-6329)
TO A T
Also Called: Daffy Dan's
2101 Superior Ave E (44114-2149)
PHONE..................................216 621-3322
Fax: 216 621-6744
Dan Gray, *Principal*
Ted Gibbs, *Manager*
▲ EMP: 5
SQ FT: 8,717
SALES (est): 410.2K **Privately Held**
WEB: www.daffydan.com
SIC: **3993** Signs & advertising specialties

(G-6330)
TODD INDUSTRIES INC
7300 Northfield Rd Ste 1 (44146-6106)
PHONE..................................440 439-2900
Gerald Boehnlein Sr, *President*
Gerald Boehnlein Jr, *Vice Pres*
Ed Krzywicki, *Plant Mgr*
Judith A Boehnlein, *Admin Sec*
EMP: 45
SQ FT: 45,000
SALES (est): 6.8MM **Privately Held**
WEB: www.allmachining.com
SIC: **3549** 3599 Metalworking machinery; machine shop, jobbing & repair

(G-6331)
TOM PALLAS INDUSTRIES INC
1828 Fulton Rd (44113-3036)
PHONE..................................216 622-0230
Tom Pallas, *Principal*
EMP: 8
SALES (est): 831.2K **Privately Held**
SIC: **2099** Food preparations

(G-6332)
TOMLINSON INDUSTRIES CO
13700 Brdwy Ave (44125)
PHONE..................................216 332-1595
Michael E Figas, *President*
Louis Castro, *Exec VP*
Kenneth Sidoti, *Vice Pres*
Ken Sidoi, *Plant Mgr*
Michael Ritley, *Purch Dir*
▲ EMP: 170

SALES (est): 3.1MM
SALES (corp-wide): 34.1MM **Privately Held**
SIC: **3556** Food products machinery
PA: The Meyer Company
13700 Broadway Ave
Cleveland OH 44125
216 587-3400

(G-6333)
TOOL SYSTEMS INC
71 Alpha Park (44143-2202)
PHONE..................................440 461-6363
Fax: 216 461-3367
Joseph Fortunato, *President*
Lillian A Fortunato, *Corp Secy*
EMP: 11
SQ FT: 1,300
SALES (est): 2.8MM **Privately Held**
WEB: www.toolsystemsinc.com
SIC: **5084** 3545 Machine tools & metalworking machinery; cutting tools for machine tools

(G-6334)
TOOLBOLD CORPORATION (PA)
5330 Commerce Pkwy W (44130-1273)
PHONE..................................216 676-9840
Harry Eisengrein, *CEO*
Barbara Blech, *President*
Amy Schneider, *Manager*
EMP: 6
SQ FT: 14,000
SALES (est): 5.2MM **Privately Held**
SIC: **3599** Machine shop, jobbing & repair

(G-6335)
TOOLBOLD CORPORATION
Leadfree Faucets Division
5330 Commerce Pkwy W (44130-1273)
PHONE..................................440 543-1660
Harry Eisengrein, *Branch Mgr*
EMP: 24
SALES (corp-wide): 5.2MM **Privately Held**
SIC: **3432** Faucets & spigots, metal & plastic
PA: Toolbold Corporation
5330 Commerce Pkwy W
Cleveland OH 44130
216 676-9840

(G-6336)
TOOLOVATION LLC
Also Called: Igo Home Products
23980 Mercantile Rd Uppr (44122-5944)
PHONE..................................216 514-3022
Kathy Sommers, *Accounting Dir*
Russell D Owens,
David Levine,
EMP: 3
SQ FT: 300
SALES (est): 366.5K **Privately Held**
WEB: www.igohomeproducts.com
SIC: **3423** Hand & edge tools

(G-6337)
TOP TOOL & DIE INC
15500 Brookpark Rd (44135-3334)
PHONE..................................216 267-5878
Fax: 216 267-5881
Anton Schiro, *President*
Bob Schiro, *Vice Pres*
Irma Schiro, *Treasurer*
EMP: 11
SQ FT: 12,000
SALES (est): 1.2MM **Privately Held**
SIC: **3544** Special dies & tools

(G-6338)
TOPPS PRODUCTS INC
3201 E 66th St (44127-1403)
P.O. Box 515, Stilwell KS (66085-0515)
PHONE..................................216 271-2550
Thomas Tamulewicz, *Branch Mgr*
EMP: 6 **Privately Held**
SIC: **2952** Roofing materials
PA: Topps Products, Inc.
20105 Metcalf Ave
Bucyrus KS 66013

(G-6339)
TORR METAL PRODUCTS INC
12125 Bennington Ave (44135-3729)
PHONE..................................216 671-1616
Fax: 216 671-3705

Pat Sheehan, *President*
Becky Almodovar, *Manager*
EMP: 21 EST: 1992
SQ FT: 25,000
SALES (est): 5.3MM **Privately Held**
WEB: www.torrmetal.com
SIC: **3469** 3544 Metal stampings; special dies, tools, jigs & fixtures

(G-6340)
TORTILLERIA LA BAMBA
1849 W 24th St (44113-3569)
PHONE..................................216 515-1600
Leticia Ortiz, *Principal*
EMP: 5
SALES (est): 537.1K **Privately Held**
SIC: **2099** Tortillas, fresh or refrigerated

(G-6341)
TORTILLERIA LA BAMBA LLC
1849 W 24th St (44113-3569)
PHONE..................................216 469-0410
Leticia Ortiz, *Principal*
▼ EMP: 6
SALES (est): 622.4K **Privately Held**
SIC: **2099** Tortillas, fresh or refrigerated

(G-6342)
TOTAL PLASTICS INC
17851 Englewood Dr Ste A (44130-3489)
PHONE..................................440 891-1140
Toll Free:...............................877 -
David Gabay, *Branch Mgr*
EMP: 6
SALES (corp-wide): 923.9MM **Privately Held**
WEB: www.totalplastics.com
SIC: **5162** 3089 Plastics materials & basic shapes; plastics sheets & rods; plastics film; plastic processing
HQ: Total Plastics Resources Llc
2810 N Burdick St Ste A
Kalamazoo MI 49004
269 344-0009

(G-6343)
TOTH MOLD & DIE INC
380 Solon Rd Ste 7 (44146-3809)
PHONE..................................440 232-8530
Fax: 440 232-8534
Timothy Toth, *President*
Thomas Toth, *Corp Secy*
EMP: 10
SQ FT: 6,400
SALES (est): 1MM **Privately Held**
WEB: www.tothmold.net
SIC: **3089** Injection molded finished plastic products

(G-6344)
TRACER SPECIALTIES INC
1842 Columbus Rd (44113-2412)
PHONE..................................216 696-2363
Tejinder Singh, *President*
Evagon Valez, *Admin Sec*
EMP: 8
SQ FT: 7,500
SALES (est): 937.6K **Privately Held**
SIC: **3599** Machine shop, jobbing & repair

(G-6345)
TRADEX INTERNATIONAL INC
5300 Tradex Pkwy (44102-5887)
P.O. Box 75746 (44101-4202)
PHONE..................................216 651-4788
Fax: 216 651-4770
Saji T Daniel, *President*
Philip Baseil, *COO*
Al Buccieri, *Exec VP*
Sheshank Kamalapuram, *Vice Pres*
Bill Ramey, *Opers Mgr*
▲ EMP: 65
SQ FT: 148,000
SALES (est): 23.8MM
SALES (corp-wide): 121.5B **Publicly Held**
WEB: www.tradexgloves.com
SIC: **2822** 3089 3081 3842 Butadiene-acrylonitrile, nitrile rubbers, NBR; gloves or mittens, plastic; vinyl film & sheet; radiation shielding aprons, gloves, sheeting, etc.; hair nets
PA: Cardinal Health, Inc.
7000 Cardinal Pl
Dublin OH 43017
614 757-5000

▲ = Import ▼=Export
◆ =Import/Export

(G-6346)
TRANSDIGM INC
Also Called: Aerocontrolex
4223 Monticello Blvd (44121-2814)
PHONE.................................216 291-6025
Fax: 216 382-5504
Roger Jones, *President*
Cathy Leak, *Principal*
Ray Conner, *Vice Pres*
Karri John, *Accountant*
Susan Burt, *Human Res Mgr*
EMP: 15
SALES (corp-wide): 3.1B **Publicly Held**
WEB: www.electromotion.com
SIC: 3561 3492 3563 3625 Pumps &
pumping equipment; fluid power valves &
hose fittings; air & gas compressors; re-
lays & industrial controls; alkaline cell
storage batteries; batteries, rechargeable;
lead acid batteries (storage batteries);
nickel cadmium storage batteries
HQ: Transdigm, Inc.
4223 Monticello Blvd
Cleveland OH 44121
216 706-2939

(G-6347)
TRANSDIGM INC (HQ)
Also Called: Aerocontrolex
4223 Monticello Blvd (44121-2814)
PHONE.................................216 706-2939
W Nicholas Howley, *Ch of Bd*
Raymond Laubenthal, *President*
Robert Henderson, *Exec VP*
Albert Rodriguez, *Exec VP*
Gregory Rufus, *CFO*
EMP: 8
SALES (est): 851.6MM
SALES (corp-wide): 3.1B **Publicly Held**
WEB: www.electromotion.com
SIC: 5088 3563 3625 3492 Aircraft
equipment & supplies; air & gas compres-
sors; relays & industrial controls; fluid
power valves & hose fittings; alkaline cell
storage batteries; batteries, rechargeable;
lead acid batteries (storage batteries);
nickel cadmium storage batteries; indus-
trial valves
PA: Transdigm Group Incorporated
1301 E 9th St Ste 3000
Cleveland OH 44114
216 706-2960

(G-6348)
**TRANSDIGM GROUP
INCORPORATED (PA)**
1301 E 9th St Ste 3000 (44114-1871)
PHONE.................................216 706-2960
W Nicholas Howley, *Ch of Bd*
Robert S Henderson, *Vice Chairman*
Kevin Stein, *COO*
Bernt G Iversen II, *Exec VP*
Roger V Jones, *Exec VP*
EMP: 76
SQ FT: 20,100
SALES: 3.1B **Publicly Held**
WEB: www.transdigm.com
SIC: 3728 5088 Aircraft parts & equip-
ment; aircraft equipment & supplies

(G-6349)
**TRANSTAR HOLDING COMPANY
(PA)**
5900 Landerbrook Dr Bsmt (44124-4085)
PHONE.................................800 359-3339
Monte Ahuja, *President*
Frank N Linsalata, *Chairman*
Mark A Kirk, *Vice Pres*
Stephen B Perry, *Vice Pres*
Jeffrey R Marshall, *CFO*
EMP: 6
SALES: 111.6MM **Privately Held**
SIC: 3444 3281 2952 Metal roofing & roof
drainage equipment; cut stone & stone
products; asphalt felts & coatings

(G-6350)
TRANZONIC COMPANIES
26301 Curtiss Wright Pkwy # 200
(44143-1454)
PHONE.................................440 446-0643
Ken F Vuylsteke, *President*
Ed McKiernan, *Area Mgr*
Francie Buckles, *COO*
Tom Glasser, *Vice Pres*
Frank Gancedo, *Opers Mgr*

EMP: 233
SALES (corp-wide): 360.2MM **Privately
Held**
SIC: 2676 2211 2326 2842 Sanitary
paper products; napkins, sanitary: made
from purchased paper; tampons, sanitary:
made from purchased paper; diapers,
paper (disposable): made from purchased
paper; scrub cloths; work garments, except raincoats: waterproof; sanitation
preparations, disinfectants & deodorants;
industrial plant disinfectants or deodorants; mats & matting; napping: manmade
fiber & silk broadwoven fabrics
PA: The Tranzonic Companies
26301 Curtiss Wright Pkwy # 200
Richmond Heights OH 44143
216 535-4300

(G-6351)
**TRAVELERS CUSTOM CASE
INC**
2261 E 14th St (44115-2396)
PHONE.................................216 621-8447
Fax: 216 861-5696
Kenneth Nosse, *President*
Betsy Nosse, *Business Mgr*
Elizabeth Nosse, *Admin Sec*
EMP: 10 EST: 1946
SQ FT: 18,000
SALES (est): 1.3MM **Privately Held**
WEB: www.travelerscustomcase.com
SIC: 3161 Cases, carrying

(G-6352)
TRD LEATHERS
6321 Detroit Ave (44102-3009)
PHONE.................................216 631-6233
Chuck Perez, *Owner*
▼ EMP: 4
SALES: 200K **Privately Held**
WEB: www.trdleather.com
SIC: 3199 5699 Leggings or chaps, can-
vas or leather; sports apparel

(G-6353)
TREC INDUSTRIES INC
4713 Spring Rd (44131-1025)
PHONE.................................216 741-4114
Fax: 216 741-4114
James M Trecokas, *President*
Laurel Trecokas, *Corp Secy*
Tom Erhard, *Plant Supt*
Kevin Clymer, *Mfg Staff*
Gail Shaltunuk, *Info Tech Mgr*
EMP: 22
SQ FT: 10,000
SALES (est): 4MM **Privately Held**
WEB: www.trecindustries.com
SIC: 3599 Machine shop, jobbing & repair

(G-6354)
TREMCO INCORPORATED
4475 E 175th St (44128-3411)
PHONE.................................216 752-4401
Eric Gilbert, *Engineer*
John Kadlec, *Manager*
Ken Recko, *Manager*
Mary Kuehn, *Admin Asst*
Deneen Wiley, *Assistant*
EMP: 110
SALES (corp-wide): 4.8B **Publicly Held**
WEB: www.tremcoinc.com
SIC: 2891 Sealants
HQ: Tremco Incorporated
3735 Green Rd
Beachwood OH 44122
216 292-5000

(G-6355)
**TREMONT ELECTRIC
INCORPORATED**
Also Called: Delaware Company
2112 W 7th St (44113-3622)
PHONE.................................888 214-3137
Aaron Lemieux, *CEO*
Charles Ames, *President*
Aaron Lemieux, *Principal*
Jill Lemieux, *Vice Pres*
Craig Paulette, *Marketing Staff*
EMP: 9
SALES (est): 1K **Privately Held**
WEB: www.npowerpeg.com
SIC: 3621 Motors & generators

(G-6356)
**TRENT MANUFACTURING
COMPANY**
6212 Carnegie Ave (44103-4614)
PHONE.................................216 391-1551
Fax: 216 391-1550
Lynn Gallatin, *President*
EMP: 11 EST: 1958
SQ FT: 12,000
SALES (est): 1.3MM **Privately Held**
SIC: 3991 5085 Brushes, household or in-
dustrial; brushes, industrial

(G-6357)
TRI COUNTY CONCRETE INC
Also Called: Tri County Ready Mixed Con Co
10155 Royalton Rd (44133-4426)
P.O. Box 665, Twinsburg (44087-0665)
PHONE.................................330 425-4464
Tony Farinacci, *President*
EMP: 19
SQ FT: 23,282
SALES (corp-wide): 4.2MM **Privately
Held**
SIC: 3273 Ready-mixed concrete
PA: Tri County Concrete Inc
9423 Darrow Rd
Twinsburg OH 44087
330 425-4464

(G-6358)
TRI-CRAFT INC
17941 Englewood Dr (44130-3488)
PHONE.................................440 826-1050
Fax: 440 826-0343
Kathleen Byrnes, *President*
Stephen Pilhartz, *Principal*
Josef Schuessler, *Principal*
Monica Hargis, *Vice Pres*
Frank Schmidt, *Vice Pres*
EMP: 28
SQ FT: 30,000
SALES (est): 7.6MM **Privately Held**
SIC: 3089 3544 Injection molded finished
plastic products; special dies, tools, jigs &
fixtures

(G-6359)
TRI-WELD INC
4411 Detroit Ave (44113-2761)
PHONE.................................216 281-6009
Fax: 216 281-6011
George Calogar, *President*
Betty Calogar, *Treasurer*
Ron Anz, *Manager*
EMP: 15
SQ FT: 5,800
SALES (est): 1.5MM **Privately Held**
SIC: 7692 Welding repair

(G-6360)
**TRIANGLE FASTENER
CORPORATION**
4661 Hinckley Indus Pkwy (44109-6002)
PHONE.................................734 458-1700
Fax: 216 351-5008
Troy Droste, *President*
▲ EMP: 11
SALES (est): 1.4MM **Privately Held**
SIC: 3965 Fasteners, buttons, needles &
pins

(G-6361)
**TRIANGLE MACHINE
PRODUCTS CO**
6055 Hillcrest Dr (44125-4687)
PHONE.................................216 524-5872
Fax: 216 524-1052
Raymond Scherler, *Ch of Bd*
Robb Scherler, *President*
Don Lagoni, *Vice Pres*
Randy Scherler, *Vice Pres*
Roy Scherler, *Vice Pres*
EMP: 35 EST: 1950
SQ FT: 42,000
SALES: 6.6MM
SALES (corp-wide): 38.7MM **Privately
Held**
WEB: www.trianglemachprod.com
SIC: 3451 Screw machine products
PA: Freeway Corporation
9301 Allen Dr
Cleveland OH 44125
216 524-9700

(G-6362)
TRIATRIX LLC
20006 Detroit Rd Ste 100 (44116-2406)
PHONE.................................440 263-8936
David Abood,
Allen Gerard,
EMP: 6 EST: 2004
SQ FT: 1,200
SALES (est): 427.6K **Privately Held**
SIC: 3841 Surgical & medical instruments

(G-6363)
TRIBCO INCORPORATED
18901 Cranwood Pkwy (44128-4041)
P.O. Box 202148 (44120-8119)
PHONE.................................216 486-2000
Fax: 216 486-2099
David N Bortz, *President*
Carol Lazerick, *Manager*
Dorothy Werblow, *Administration*
EMP: 40
SALES (est): 7.4MM **Privately Held**
WEB: www.tribco.com
SIC: 3499 Friction material, made from
powdered metal

(G-6364)
TRICO CORPORATION
9700 Rockside Rd Ste 430 (44125-6285)
PHONE.................................216 642-3223
Bob Young, *Branch Mgr*
EMP: 20
SALES (corp-wide): 12MM **Privately
Held**
SIC: 1389 Oil field services
PA: Trico Corporation
1235 Hickory St
Pewaukee WI 53072
262 691-9336

(G-6365)
**TRICO MACHINE PRODUCTS
CORP**
5081 Corbin Dr (44128-5413)
PHONE.................................216 662-4194
Julius Szorady Jr, *President*
James Szorady, *Vice Pres*
Mark Szorady, *Treasurer*
Jeff Udvardy, *Executive*
EMP: 10
SQ FT: 8,000
SALES (est): 1.5MM **Privately Held**
WEB: www.tricomachine.com
SIC: 3544 Dies, plastics forming

(G-6366)
TRIM TOOL & MACHINE INC
3431 Service Rd (44111-2421)
PHONE.................................216 889-1916
Fax: 216 889-1917
Dane Willis, *President*
Lisa Willis, *Office Mgr*
EMP: 20
SALES (est): 1.5MM **Privately Held**
SIC: 3544 Special dies, tools, jigs & fix-
tures

(G-6367)
TRINEL INC
5251 W 137th St (44142-1800)
PHONE.................................216 265-9190
Fax: 216 265-8630
Jimmy M Martella, *President*
Rose Martella, *Corp Secy*
Thomas A Martella, *Assistant VP*
Donna Hurley, *Office Mgr*
EMP: 12 EST: 1986
SQ FT: 22,000
SALES: 2.5MM **Privately Held**
WEB: www.trinelinc.com
SIC: 3599 Grinding castings for the trade

(G-6368)
**TRU FORM METAL PRODUCTS
INC**
12305 Grimsby Ave (44135-4843)
PHONE.................................216 252-3700
Ron Seith, *President*
EMP: 8 EST: 2001
SALES (est): 1.3MM **Privately Held**
SIC: 3444 Sheet metalwork

(G-6369)
TRUCK FAX INC
17700 S Woodland Rd (44120-1767)
PHONE..................................216 921-8866
Brian Luntz, *President*
Melissa Beesley, *Treasurer*
◆ EMP: 8
SALES (est): 983.5K **Privately Held**
SIC: 3399 7371 Iron, powdered; computer software development

(G-6370)
TRUCO INC
3033 W 44th St (44113-4817)
PHONE..................................216 631-1000
Fax: 216 281-0034
Christopher S Hoskins, *President*
Richard P Hoskins, *Chairman*
Ellen Hoskins, *Human Res Dir*
Ellen Deangelis, *Marketing Mgr*
Flo Roll, *Admin Sec*
EMP: 300 EST: 1978
SQ FT: 10,000
SALES: 54.5MM **Privately Held**
WEB: www.truco-inc.com
SIC: 2899 2952 Waterproofing compounds; roofing felts, cements or coatings

(G-6371)
TRW AUTOMOTIVE INC
Also Called: TRW Shared Services
8333 Rockside Rd (44125-6134)
P.O. Box 318076, Independence (44131-8076)
PHONE..................................216 750-2400
Shelly Peet, *Principal*
EMP: 23 **Privately Held**
SIC: 3714 Connecting rods, motor vehicle engine; steering mechanisms, motor vehicle; brake drums, motor vehicle; hydraulic fluid power pumps for auto steering mechanism
HQ: Trw Automotive Inc.
12025 Tech Center Dr
Livonia MI 48150
734 266-2600

(G-6372)
TRW AUTOMOTIVE US LLC
8333 Rockside Rd (44125-6134)
P.O. Box 94885 (44101-4885)
PHONE..................................216 750-2400
Richard Rowan, *Manager*
EMP: 50 **Privately Held**
WEB: www.trw.mediaroom.com
SIC: 3469 Metal stampings
HQ: Trw Automotive U.S. Llc
12001 Tech Center Dr
Livonia MI 48150
734 855-2600

(G-6373)
TRW AUTOMOTIVE US LLC
19501 Emery Rd (44128-4162)
PHONE..................................216 332-7100
Fax: 216 332-7080
Frank Holupka, *QC Dir*
Bernd Blankenstein, *Branch Mgr*
EMP: 405 **Privately Held**
SIC: 3469 Metal stampings
HQ: Trw Automotive U.S. Llc
12001 Tech Center Dr
Livonia MI 48150
734 855-2600

(G-6374)
TURBINE ENG CMPNENTS TECH CORP
23555 Euclid Ave (44117-1703)
PHONE..................................216 692-6173
Patrick Burk, *General Mgr*
Ken Salacienski, *Mfg Mgr*
Kevin Elkins, *Facilities Mgr*
Patti Gilmore, *HR Admin*
Robert S Cohen, *Branch Mgr*
EMP: 44 **Privately Held**
WEB: www.tectcorp.com
SIC: 3724 3728 3463 Airfoils, aircraft engine; aircraft parts & equipment; nonferrous forgings
HQ: Turbine Engine Components Technologies Corporation
1211 Old Albany Rd
Thomasville GA 31792
229 228-2600

(G-6375)
TURBO MACHINE & TOOL INC
2151 W 117th St (44111-1642)
PHONE..................................216 651-1940
Fax: 216 651-0501
Nick Stipanovich, *President*
Mary Stipanovich, *Exec VP*
EMP: 6 EST: 1980
SQ FT: 8,000
SALES (est): 530K **Privately Held**
WEB: www.turbomachineandtool.com
SIC: 3089 3599 3544 Injection molding of plastics; machine shop, jobbing & repair; special dies, tools, jigs & fixtures

(G-6376)
TURBONICS INC
4001 Pearl Rd Lowr (44109-3197)
PHONE..................................216 741-8300
Fax: 216 741-7768
Chris Jordan, *President*
Craig Mc Knight, *Treasurer*
EMP: 6
SQ FT: 25,000
SALES (est): 1.2MM **Privately Held**
WEB: www.turbonicsinc.com
SIC: 3433 Heating equipment, except electric

(G-6377)
TYLOK INTERNATIONAL INC
1061 E 260th St (44132-2877)
PHONE..................................216 261-7310
Fax: 216 261-7317
Carole Hahl, *President*
Scott Hahl, *General Mgr*
Sandy Carroll, *Vice Pres*
Vince Traina, *VP Opers*
Ray Ostanek, *Purch Mgr*
▲ EMP: 55 EST: 1955
SQ FT: 72,000
SALES (est): 15.6MM **Privately Held**
SIC: 3491 3494 3492 Pressure valves & regulators, industrial; valves & pipe fittings; hose & tube fittings & assemblies, hydraulic/pneumatic

(G-6378)
TYMEX PLASTICS INC
5300 Harvard Ave (44105-4826)
PHONE..................................216 429-8950
Fax: 216 429-8951
Michael Turkovich, *President*
Mark Simonitis, *Vice Pres*
EMP: 45
SQ FT: 160,000
SALES: 5.6MM **Privately Held**
WEB: www.tymexplastics.com
SIC: 3087 Custom compound purchased resins

(G-6379)
U S ALLOY DIE CORP
4007 Brookpark Rd (44134-1131)
PHONE..................................216 749-9700
Fax: 216 749-9707
Anthony Corrao Sr, *President*
Anthony Carrao Jr, *Vice Pres*
Rachelle Corrao, *Vice Pres*
Ron Hebebrand, *Engineer*
Dyann Corrao, *Treasurer*
EMP: 17
SQ FT: 12,000
SALES: 1.5MM **Privately Held**
SIC: 3544 3599 3541 Special dies & tools; electrical discharge machining (EDM); machine tools, metal cutting type

(G-6380)
ULTRA PRINTING & DESIGN INC
707 Brookpark Rd Ste 3 (44109-5834)
P.O. Box 31027, Independence (44131-0027)
PHONE..................................440 887-0393
Fax: 440 433-0361
Judith Juhasz, *President*
Victoria Valente, *Office Mgr*
EMP: 3
SQ FT: 2,800
SALES (est): 260K **Privately Held**
SIC: 2752 7336 Commercial printing, offset; graphic arts & related design

(G-6381)
UNDERCAR EXPRESS LLC
Also Called: U C X
18451 Euclid Ave (44112-1016)
PHONE..................................216 531-7004
Russell Martin, *Facilities Mgr*
Paul Schuck, *QC Mgr*
Joe Zorko, *Controller*
Dave Wright, *Financial Exec*
Rob Wright, *Sales Staff*
▲ EMP: 50
SQ FT: 30,000
SALES (est): 11.5MM **Privately Held**
WEB: www.ucx.com
SIC: 3714 Motor vehicle brake systems & parts

(G-6382)
UNICONTROL INC (PA)
Also Called: Hays Cleveland
1111 Brookpark Rd (44109-5825)
PHONE..................................216 398-0330
Fax: 216 398-8553
Steve Craig, *President*
Charles M Rowan, *Vice Pres*
Mark Lisi, *Purchasing*
Mark R Scoville, *Project Engr*
James Ransbury, *Controller*
▲ EMP: 67
SQ FT: 50,000
SALES (est): 9.9MM **Privately Held**
WEB: www.unicontrolinc.com
SIC: 3823 Combustion control instruments

(G-6383)
UNIQUE PAVING MATERIALS CORP
3993 E 93rd St (44105-4096)
PHONE..................................216 341-7711
Jeffrey J Higerd, *Ch of Bd*
Michael Pemberton, *President*
Don Koehler, *Business Mgr*
Donna Letizia, *Exec VP*
Don Kautzman, *Treasurer*
EMP: 41
SQ FT: 25,000
SALES (est): 13.6MM **Privately Held**
WEB: www.UniquePavingMaterials.com
SIC: 2951 Asphalt & asphaltic paving mixtures (not from refineries)

(G-6384)
UNITED FINSHG & DIE CUTNG INC
3875 King Ave (44114-3727)
PHONE..................................216 881-0239
Fax: 216 881-0653
Laurie Jacbec, *President*
Aaron Jacbec, *VP Admin*
Jim Gilbert, *Production*
EMP: 16
SALES (est): 2.3MM **Privately Held**
WEB: www.unitedfdc.com
SIC: 3544 Special dies & tools

(G-6385)
UNITED IGNITION WIRE CORP
15620 Industrial Pkwy (44135-3316)
PHONE..................................216 898-1112
Fax: 216 671-9473
Richard L Maxwell, *President*
Marie Maxwell, *Admin Sec*
▲ EMP: 8
SQ FT: 20,000
SALES: 3MM **Privately Held**
WEB: www.united-wire.com
SIC: 3694 5521 Ignition apparatus, internal combustion engines; used car dealers

(G-6386)
UNITED PRTRS & LITHOGRAPHERS
1045 French St (44113-2441)
PHONE..................................216 771-2759
Fax: 216 771-3858
Barbara Scott, *President*
Greg Scott, *Vice Pres*
EMP: 4 EST: 1952
SQ FT: 7,500
SALES: 250K **Privately Held**
SIC: 2752 Commercial printing, offset

(G-6387)
UNITED READY MIX INC
7820 Carnegie Ave (44103-4904)
PHONE..................................216 696-1600
Fax: 216 696-3210
Harvey J Newsom, *President*
Alvin Robinson, *Vice Pres*
Dwayne Newsom, *Opers Mgr*
EMP: 20
SQ FT: 4,000
SALES (est): 2.3MM **Privately Held**
WEB: www.unitedreadymix.com
SIC: 3273 Ready-mixed concrete

(G-6388)
UNITED TACONITE LLC (HQ)
Also Called: UTAC
1100 Superior Ave E # 1500 (44114-2544)
PHONE..................................218 744-7800
David H Gunning, *Vice Pres*
Gordie Popovich, *Purchasing*
Ralph Dirusso, *Treasurer*
Joyce E Washura, *Finance Dir*
Craig Hartmann, *Manager*
▼ EMP: 4
SALES (est): 424MM
SALES (corp-wide): 2.1B **Publicly Held**
SIC: 1011 Iron ore pelletizing
PA: Cliffs Natural Resources Inc.
200 Public Sq Ste 3300
Cleveland OH 44114
216 694-5700

(G-6389)
UNITED TOOL & GAGE CO
15740 Industrial Pkwy (44135-3318)
PHONE..................................216 676-1000
Fax: 216 676-1001
Bradley L Foster, *President*
Diana E Foster, *Corp Secy*
EMP: 8
SQ FT: 13,300
SALES: 750K **Privately Held**
SIC: 3599 Machine shop, jobbing & repair

(G-6390)
UNIVERSAL HEAT TREATING INC
Also Called: Universal Black Oxiding
3878 E 93rd St (44105-2148)
PHONE..................................216 641-2000
Fax: 216 641-6703
Ernie D'Amato, *CEO*
Michael D Amato, *President*
Kevin D'Amato, *Vice Pres*
EMP: 32
SQ FT: 30,000
SALES: 3.6MM **Privately Held**
SIC: 3398 Metal heat treating

(G-6391)
UNIVERSAL OIL INC
265 Jefferson Ave (44113-2594)
PHONE..................................216 771-4300
Fax: 216 771-1845
John J Purcell, *President*
Don Krance, *Sales Staff*
Paul Magyar, *Marketing Staff*
EMP: 30
SQ FT: 25,000
SALES (est): 30.9MM **Privately Held**
WEB: www.universaloil.com
SIC: 5171 2992 Petroleum bulk stations; lubricating oils

(G-6392)
UNIVERSAL STEEL COMPANY
6600 Grant Ave (44105-5692)
PHONE..................................216 883-4972
Fax: 216 341-0421
Richard W Williams, *President*
David P Miller, *Chairman*
Kevin Smith, *General Ptnr*
Jerry Kinder, *Purch Mgr*
William B Bourne III, *Treasurer*
▲ EMP: 100
SQ FT: 200,000
SALES: 23.2MM
SALES (corp-wide): 107.5MM **Privately Held**
WEB: www.univsteel.com
SIC: 3444 5051 Sheet metalwork; steel
PA: Columbia National Group, Inc.
6600 Grant Ave
Cleveland OH 44105
216 883-4972

▲ = Import ▼=Export
◆ =Import/Export

(G-6393)
UNIVERSITY CRDC & THRC GRP
11100 Euclid Ave (44106-1716)
PHONE....................................216 844-3053
Fax: 216 844-4962
Robert W Stewart, *President*
EMP: 10
SALES (est): 507.9K **Privately Held**
SIC: 8733 0783 8011 3845 Medical research; bracing & surgery services; surgeon; pacemaker, cardiac

(G-6394)
UNIVERSITY PLASTIC SURGERY
2866 W Park Blvd (44120-1811)
PHONE....................................216 778-4450
Daniel Medalie, *Owner*
EMP: 3 EST: 2015
SALES (est): 145.8K **Privately Held**
SIC: 3069 Fabricated rubber products

(G-6395)
UPDEGRAFF INC
1335 Main Ave (44113-2312)
PHONE....................................216 621-7600
David Updegraff, *President*
EMP: 3
SQ FT: 8,000
SALES (est): 250K **Privately Held**
SIC: 3599 3441 8711 Machine shop, jobbing & repair; fabricated structural metal; engineering services

(G-6396)
UPRIGHT STEEL LLC
1335 E 171st St (44110-2525)
PHONE....................................216 923-0852
Gerald Quinn, *Manager*
EMP: 20
SALES (est): 1.7MM **Privately Held**
SIC: 1791 3441 3446 Structural steel erection; concrete reinforcement, placing of; fabricated structural metal; building components, structural steel; stairs, fire escapes, balconies, railings & ladders; balconies, metal

(G-6397)
US 261 CORP
341 E 131st St (44108-1607)
PHONE....................................216 531-7143
Fax: 216 531-1169
Mike Mahar, *President*
Bob Schilling, *Corp Secy*
EMP: 5
SALES: 100K **Privately Held**
SIC: 3069 Grips or handles, rubber

(G-6398)
US BRANDS INC
23600 Mercantile Rd Ste H (44122-5965)
PHONE....................................216 595-9700
Fax: 216 595-9702
Ralph Kovel, *President*
Pat Paulus, *Vice Pres*
EMP: 4
SALES (est): 625.4K **Privately Held**
WEB: www.usbrands.com
SIC: 2721 8742 5192 Periodicals; management consulting services; books, periodicals & newspapers

(G-6399)
US COTTON LLC
15501 Industrial Pkwy (44135-3313)
PHONE....................................216 676-6400
Fax: 216 676-3681
John Levinsky, *Owner*
Cynthia Armenta, *QC Dir*
EMP: 500
SALES (corp-wide): 903.5MM **Privately Held**
WEB: www.uscotton.com
SIC: 2844 2241 Toilet preparations; cotton narrow fabrics
HQ: U.S. Cotton, Llc
531 Cotton Blossom Cir
Gastonia NC 28054
216 676-6400

(G-6400)
USA HEAT TREATING INC
4500 Lee Rd Ste B (44128-2959)
PHONE....................................216 587-4700
Fax: 216 587-0707
Forest Delaine, *President*

Norman R Fisher Jr, *President*
Norm Wilson, *General Mgr*
Jim Naliborski, *Managing Dir*
Ray Keller, *Engineer*
EMP: 26
SQ FT: 50,000
SALES (est): 5MM **Privately Held**
SIC: 3398 Metal heat treating

(G-6401)
USB CORPORATION
26111 Miles Rd (44128-5933)
PHONE....................................216 765-5000
Michael Lachman, *President*
Kathy Fortney, *Vice Pres*
Mindy Lee-Olsen, *Vice Pres*
Fred Leffler, *Vice Pres*
Frank Maenpa, *Vice Pres*
EMP: 84 EST: 1998
SQ FT: 60,000
SALES (est): 13.4MM
SALES (corp-wide): 18.2B **Publicly Held**
WEB: www.usbweb.com
SIC: 2835 2833 2834 In vitro & in vivo diagnostic substances; radioactive diagnostic substances; medicinals & botanicals; pharmaceutical preparations
HQ: Affymetrix, Inc.
3450 Central Expy
Santa Clara CA 95051
408 731-5000

(G-6402)
UTC AEROSPACE SYSTEMS
8000 Marble Ave (44105-2060)
PHONE....................................216 341-1700
Mike Brand, *Manager*
Christopher Allen, *Manager*
Stephanie Steinmetz, *Manager*
Keith Williamson, *Manager*
Michelle Frizell, *Info Tech Mgr*
EMP: 11
SALES (est): 896.8K **Privately Held**
SIC: 3728 Aircraft parts & equipment

(G-6403)
UTILITY WIRE PRODUCTS INC
3302 E 87th St (44127-1849)
PHONE....................................216 441-2180
Fax: 216 441-2184
Ronald F Anzells, *President*
Donald J Anzells, *Treasurer*
Marcia Anzells, *Admin Sec*
EMP: 15 EST: 1953
SQ FT: 48,000
SALES: 1.2MM **Privately Held**
WEB: www.utilitywire.com
SIC: 3496 Woven wire products

(G-6404)
V M MACHINE CO INC
9607 Clinton Rd (44144-1029)
P.O. Box 44510 (44144-0510)
PHONE....................................216 281-4569
Fax: 216 281-4578
Victor Mustapic, *President*
Carol Sheperd, *Admin Sec*
EMP: 4
SALES: 50K **Privately Held**
SIC: 3599 Grinding castings for the trade

(G-6405)
VACONO AMERICA LLC
1163 E 40th St Ste 301 (44114-3869)
P.O. Box 307, Hudson (44236-0307)
PHONE....................................216 938-7428
Chad Derringer, *President*
▲ EMP: 29 EST: 2011
SALES (est): 4.6MM **Privately Held**
SIC: 3479 Aluminum coating of metal products

(G-6406)
VARBROS LLC
16025 Brookpark Rd (44142-1623)
PHONE....................................216 267-5200
Fax: 216 267-5205
Joseph Dunn, *CEO*
Dave Gido, *President*
Rick Vargo, *President*
Tim Bailey, *VP Mfg*
William Huelsman, *Purch Mgr*
▼ EMP: 110 EST: 1951
SQ FT: 113,000

SALES (est): 37.6MM **Privately Held**
WEB: www.varbroscorp.com
SIC: 3469 3714 Metal stampings; motor vehicle parts & accessories

(G-6407)
VARBROS TOOL AND DIE COMPANY
16025 Brookpark Rd (44142-1623)
PHONE....................................216 267-5200
Ernest R Vargo Sr, *CEO*
Ernest R Vargo Jr, *President*
Virginia Caldwell, *Vice Pres*
Denise Huelsman, *Vice Pres*
Robert Jester, *VP Sales*
EMP: 100 EST: 1965
SQ FT: 10,000
SALES: 2MM **Privately Held**
SIC: 3544 Special dies & tools

(G-6408)
VARMLAND INC
Also Called: All Cstom Fabricators Erectors
1200 Brookpark Rd (44109-5828)
PHONE....................................216 741-1510
Fax: 216 741-1589
Erik V Schneider, *President*
Deborah Schneider, *Corp Secy*
Karl M Schneider, *Vice Pres*
Joe Weiman, *Manager*
EMP: 12 EST: 1943
SQ FT: 20,000
SALES (est): 1.4MM **Privately Held**
SIC: 3444 Sheet metal specialties, not stamped

(G-6409)
VE GLOBAL VENDING INC
Also Called: Vegv
8700 Brookpark Rd (44129-6810)
PHONE....................................216 785-2611
Aviel Dafna, *President*
Nate Stansell, *COO*
▲ EMP: 18
SALES (est): 2.4MM **Privately Held**
SIC: 3581 Automatic vending machines

(G-6410)
VERTIV CO
5900 Landerbrook Dr # 300 (44124-4020)
PHONE....................................440 460-3600
David Marsden, *Vice Pres*
Steven M Barto, *CFO*
Ron Baker, *Treasurer*
William R Calise, *Director*
James H Greene, *Director*
EMP: 7
SALES (corp-wide): 15.2B **Privately Held**
SIC: 3661 1731 Telephone & telegraph apparatus; communications specialization
HQ: Vertiv Co.
1050 Dearborn Dr
Columbus OH 43085
614 888-0246

(G-6411)
VESUVIUS U S A CORPORATION
Foseco Metallurgical
20200 Sheldon Rd (44142-1315)
PHONE....................................440 816-3051
Ken Balazs, *Purch Agent*
Dave Smith, *Research*
Andy Adams, *Engineer*
Tony Kiss, *Plant Engr*
Russ Pinzone, *Human Res Dir*
EMP: 34
SALES (corp-wide): 1.7B **Privately Held**
WEB: www.vesuvius.com
SIC: 2899 Chemical preparations
HQ: Vesuvius U S A Corporation
1404 Newton Dr
Champaign IL 61822
217 351-5000

(G-6412)
VETERANS STEEL INC
900 E 69th St (44103-1736)
PHONE....................................216 938-7476
Karen Black, *President*
EMP: 13 EST: 2014
SALES (est): 708.6K **Privately Held**
SIC: 3449 Bars, concrete reinforcing; fabricated steel

(G-6413)
VGS INC
2239 E 55th St (44103-4451)
PHONE....................................216 431-7800
Robert Comben Jr, *President*
James Huduk, *Vice Pres*
Mick Latkovich, *Vice Pres*
Donald E Carlton, *CFO*
Betty Gutman, *Controller*
EMP: 200
SQ FT: 36,000
SALES: 3.8MM **Privately Held**
SIC: 8331 2326 2311 Job training & vocational rehabilitation services; work uniforms; military uniforms, men's & youths': purchased materials

(G-6414)
VGU INDUSTRIES INC
Also Called: Vinyl Graphics
4747 Manufacturing Ave (44135-2639)
PHONE....................................216 676-9093
Fax: 216 676-8975
Brian Stransky, *President*
▲ EMP: 35
SQ FT: 40,000
SALES (est): 5.1MM **Privately Held**
SIC: 3993 2759 2396 Signs, not made in custom sign painting shops; screen printing; automotive & apparel trimmings

(G-6415)
VICS TURNING CO INC
16911 Saint Clair Ave (44110-2536)
PHONE....................................216 531-5016
Fax: 216 531-5071
John Lamovec, *President*
Ann Maher, *Corp Secy*
Victor Lamovec, *Vice Pres*
EMP: 6
SQ FT: 16,500
SALES: 260K **Privately Held**
WEB: www.vicsturning.com
SIC: 3599 Machine shop, jobbing & repair

(G-6416)
VICTORY WHITE METAL COMPANY
Also Called: Vwm Republic Metals
7930 Jones Rd (44105-3908)
P.O. Box 605217 (44105-0217)
PHONE....................................216 641-2575
Lynn Carlson, *Manager*
Lynn Carameli, *Manager*
EMP: 13
SALES (corp-wide): 42.3MM **Privately Held**
WEB: www.vwmc.com
SIC: 5051 3356 Lead; lead & zinc
PA: The Victory White Metal Company
6100 Roland Ave
Cleveland OH 44127
216 271-1400

(G-6417)
VICTORY WHITE METAL COMPANY (PA)
6100 Roland Ave (44127-1399)
PHONE....................................216 271-1400
Fax: 216 271-6430
Alex J Stanwick, *President*
Bill Clarke, *General Mgr*
Jennifer Sturman, *Admin Sec*
▲ EMP: 60 EST: 1920
SQ FT: 60,000
SALES (est): 42.3MM **Privately Held**
WEB: www.vwmc.com
SIC: 5085 3356 Valves & fittings; solder: wire, bar, acid core, & rosin core; lead & zinc; tin

(G-6418)
VICTORY WHITE METAL COMPANY
3027 E 55th St (44127-1275)
PHONE....................................216 271-7200
Fax: 216 883-0008
Tim Hess, *Manager*
EMP: 25
SQ FT: 50,000

SALES (corp-wide): 42.3MM **Privately Held**
WEB: www.vwmc.com
SIC: 3341 4941 4225 Lead smelting & refining (secondary); water supply; general warehousing & storage
PA: The Victory White Metal Company
6100 Roland Ave
Cleveland OH 44127
216 271-1400

(G-6419)
VIKING EXPLOSIVES LLC
25800 Science Park Dr (44122-7339)
PHONE..............................218 263-8845
Mike Lownds, *Vice Pres*
Bob Prittinen, *Manager*
Elaine Prittinen, *Manager*
Joel Staeth, *Info Tech Mgr*
EMP: 28
SALES (corp-wide): 22.6MM **Privately Held**
SIC: 5169 2892 Explosives; explosives
HQ: Viking Explosives Llc
25800 Science Park Dr # 300
Cleveland OH
216 464-2400

(G-6420)
VINCO MACHINE PRODUCTS INC
17601 Pennsylvania Ave (44137-4308)
PHONE..............................216 475-6708
William F Galland, *President*
Shelly Blaha, *Admin Sec*
EMP: 5 EST: 1975
SQ FT: 10,000
SALES (est): 390K **Privately Held**
SIC: 3451 Screw machine products

(G-6421)
VISI-TRAK WORLDWIDE LLC (PA)
8400 Sweet Valley Dr # 406 (44125-4244)
PHONE..............................216 524-2363
Jack Vann, *President*
Tom Vann, *Vice Pres*
Sue Thayer, *Accountant*
John T Brandon, *VP Sales*
Barbara Barrick, *Sales Staff*
EMP: 13
SQ FT: 8,050
SALES (est): 2.3MM **Privately Held**
WEB: www.visi-trakworldwide.com
SIC: 3823 Industrial instrmnts msrmnt display/control process variable

(G-6422)
VISUALY IMP EXP WM ISUES FR GR
Also Called: V I E W I N G
3041 E 121st St (44120-2965)
PHONE..............................216 561-6864
Thelia Turner, *Director*
EMP: 4
SALES (est): 308.4K **Privately Held**
WEB: www.viewing.com
SIC: 3842 Technical aids for the handicapped

(G-6423)
VITEX CORPORATION
2960 Broadway Ave (44115-3606)
PHONE..............................216 883-0920
Fax: 216 883-8055
Robert Vitek Sr, *President*
Marie Vitek, *Corp Secy*
Robert Vitek Jr, *Vice Pres*
Jessica Janca, *Administration*
EMP: 15
SQ FT: 60,000
SALES (est): 3.2MM **Privately Held**
WEB: www.vitexcorporation.com
SIC: 2842 Cleaning or polishing preparations

(G-6424)
VOCATIONAL SERVICES INC
2239 E 55th St (44103-4451)
PHONE..............................216 431-8085
Robert Comben, *President*
Donald E Carlson, *CFO*
EMP: 150
SQ FT: 17,541

SALES: 1MM **Privately Held**
SIC: 2391 2511 8331 Curtains & draperies; wood household furniture; job training & vocational rehabilitation services

(G-6425)
VOICE MEDIA GROUP INC
Also Called: Cleveland Scene
1468 W 9th St Ste 805 (44113-1299)
PHONE..............................216 241-7550
Pete Kotz, *Manager*
EMP: 70
SALES (corp-wide): 299.1MM **Privately Held**
WEB: www.ruxton.com
SIC: 2711 Newspapers: publishing only, not printed on site
PA: Voice Media Group, Inc.
969 N Broadway
Denver CO 80203
303 296-7744

(G-6426)
VOICE PRODUCTS INC
23715 Merc Rd Ste A200 (44122)
PHONE..............................216 360-0433
Michael Kaufman, *President*
EMP: 10
SALES (est): 710K **Privately Held**
WEB: www.vproducts.com
SIC: 3669 Smoke detectors

(G-6427)
VOLPE MILLWORK INC
4500 Lee Rd (44128-2963)
PHONE..............................216 581-0200
Fax: 216 581-7589
John Volpe, *President*
Christine Vegh, *Office Mgr*
William Roy Laubscher, *Shareholder*
Mary Ellen Volpe, *Shareholder*
Salvatore Volpe, *Admin Sec*
EMP: 7
SQ FT: 9,000
SALES (est): 900K **Privately Held**
SIC: 1521 2431 Single-family housing construction; millwork

(G-6428)
VON ROLL USA INC
Also Called: Von Roll Isola
4853 W 130th St (44135-5137)
PHONE..............................216 433-7474
Larry Schwener, *Branch Mgr*
EMP: 33
SALES (corp-wide): 331.8MM **Privately Held**
SIC: 3644 Insulators & insulation materials, electrical
HQ: Von Roll Usa, Inc.
200 Von Roll Dr
Schenectady NY 12306
518 344-7100

(G-6429)
VOSS INDUSTRIES INC (PA)
2168 W 25th St (44113-4172)
PHONE..............................216 771-0870
Daniel W Sedor Sr, *President*
Nicola Antonelli, *Vice Pres*
John F Fritskey, *Vice Pres*
Mark Schodowski, *VP Mfg*
Rick Baker, *Plant Mgr*
▲ EMP: 242 EST: 1957
SQ FT: 240,000
SALES (est): 55.5MM **Privately Held**
WEB: www.vossind.com
SIC: 3429 3469 3369 3499 Clamps & couplings, hose; machine parts, stamped or pressed metal; aerospace castings, nonferrous: except aluminum; strapping, metal

(G-6430)
VOSS INDUSTRIES INC
Also Called: Voss Clamp Technology Division
2168 W 25th St (44113-4172)
PHONE..............................216 771-7655
Daniel W Sedor Sr, *President*
EMP: 75
SALES (corp-wide): 60.2MM **Privately Held**
SIC: 3429 Clamps & couplings, hose

PA: Voss Industries, Inc.
2168 W 25th St
Cleveland OH 44113
216 771-0870

(G-6431)
VOYALE MINORITY ENTERPRISE LLC
5855 Grant Ave (44105-5607)
PHONE..............................216 271-3661
Jim Vojtech, *Sales Executive*
Doug Vojtech, *Manager*
Paula S Corcoran,
EMP: 20
SQ FT: 116,000
SALES (est): 4.7MM **Privately Held**
WEB: www.vmellc.com
SIC: 3499 Metal household articles

(G-6432)
VTI INSTRUMENTS CORPORATION
7525 Granger Rd Ste 7 (44125-4859)
PHONE..............................216 447-8950
Tom Sarfi, *Branch Mgr*
EMP: 4
SALES (corp-wide): 3.8B **Publicly Held**
WEB: www.vxitech.com
SIC: 3699 Electrical equipment & supplies
HQ: Vti Instruments Corporation
2031 Main St
Irvine CA 92614
949 955-1894

(G-6433)
VWM-REPUBLIC INC
Also Called: Republic Metals
6100 Roland Ave (44127-1353)
P.O. Box 605217 (44105-0217)
PHONE..............................216 271-1400
Lynn C Arameli, *Opers Mgr*
Tammy Shubert, *Personnel Exec*
Lynn Carlson, *Manager*
EMP: 15
SALES (est): 2.6MM **Privately Held**
SIC: 2816 Lead pigments: white lead, lead oxides, lead sulfate

(G-6434)
W C J CORP
1740 Columbus Rd (44113-2410)
P.O. Box 30474 (44130-0474)
PHONE..............................216 523-1135
William Chorba Jr, *President*
Jay G Wilson, *Vice Pres*
EMP: 3
SQ FT: 2,500
SALES: 400K **Privately Held**
SIC: 3479 Aluminum coating of metal products

(G-6435)
W N ALBUMS AND FRAMES INC
2160 Superior Ave E (44114-2102)
PHONE..............................800 325-5179
Steven Gregory, *Principal*
Peter Cardello, *Vice Pres*
Cheryl Earle, *Manager*
EMP: 4
SALES (est): 307.5K **Privately Held**
SIC: 2782 Albums

(G-6436)
W R G INC
Also Called: Buckeye Metals
3961 Pearl Rd (44109-3103)
PHONE..............................216 351-8494
Fax: 216 351-1984
Mike Rauch, *President*
Mildred Neumann, *Principal*
Nathan R Simon, *Principal*
Sandra L Sotos, *Principal*
Robert Rauch, *Vice Pres*
EMP: 25
SQ FT: 121,500
SALES (est): 12.3MM **Privately Held**
SIC: 5093 3341 Nonferrous metals scrap; secondary nonferrous metals

(G-6437)
WABTEC CORPORATION
4677 Manufacturing Ave (44135-2637)
PHONE..............................216 362-7500
EMP: 7

SALES (corp-wide): 2.9B **Publicly Held**
SIC: 3621 3677 Electric motor & generator parts; electronic coils, transformers & other inductors
HQ: Wabtec Corporation
1001 Airbrake Ave
Wilmerding PA 15148

(G-6438)
WABUSH MINES CLIFFS MINING CO
200 Public Sq Ste 3300 (44114-2315)
PHONE..............................216 694-5700
Terrance Taridei, *CFO*
John Tuomi, *Mng Member*
Sue McGovern, *Admin Asst*
EMP: 800
SALES (est): 14.5MM
SALES (corp-wide): 2.1B **Publicly Held**
SIC: 1011 Iron ore mining; iron ore pelletizing; iron ore beneficiating
PA: Cliffs Natural Resources Inc.
200 Public Sq Ste 3300
Cleveland OH 44114
216 694-5700

(G-6439)
WADE DYNAMICS INC
1411 E 39th St (44114-4120)
PHONE..............................216 431-8484
Fax: 216 431-1738
Dennis Wade, *President*
Peter Wade, *Vice Pres*
Denise Wade, *Treasurer*
EMP: 9
SQ FT: 6,000
SALES (est): 1.1MM **Privately Held**
WEB: www.wadedynamics.net
SIC: 3599 Machine shop, jobbing & repair

(G-6440)
WAGNER RUSTPROOFING CO INC
7708 Quincy Ave (44104-2099)
P.O. Box 31156 (44131-0156)
PHONE..............................216 361-4930
Fax: 216 361-0461
Gregory Spann, *President*
Mark Spann, *Vice Pres*
EMP: 15 EST: 1919
SQ FT: 15,000
SALES (est): 1.6MM **Privately Held**
SIC: 3334 Primary aluminum

(G-6441)
WAHCONAH GROUP INC
2295 E 55th St (44103-4452)
P.O. Box 141136 (44114-6136)
PHONE..............................216 923-0570
Isaac Crawford, *CEO*
Robert Carlston, *Senior VP*
Calvin Harris, *CFO*
EMP: 15
SQ FT: 82,000
SALES (est): 84.1K **Privately Held**
SIC: 2311 Men's & boys' suits & coats

(G-6442)
WAKE ROBIN FERMENTED FOODS LLC
1303 W 103rd St (44102-1622)
PHONE..............................216 961-9944
Patrick Murray, *Principal*
EMP: 3
SALES (est): 249.6K **Privately Held**
SIC: 2099 Food preparations

(G-6443)
WALEST INCORPORATED
Also Called: Kol-Cap Manufacturing Co
15500 Commerce Park Dr (44142-2013)
PHONE..............................216 362-8110
Fax: 216 362-1806
Mike Gorbulja, *President*
EMP: 8
SQ FT: 14,000
SALES (est): 870K **Privately Held**
WEB: www.walest.com
SIC: 3544 3599 Special dies & tools; jigs & fixtures; machine shop, jobbing & repair

▲ = Import ▼=Export
◆ =Import/Export

(G-6444)
WALLSEYE CONCRETE CORP (PA)
Also Called: Avon
26000 Sprague Rd (44138-2743)
P.O. Box 38159 (44138-0159)
PHONE...............................440 235-1800
Sandra Hill, *Corp Secy*
Brock Walls, *Vice Pres*
Kathy Matwijiw, *CPA*
EMP: 11
SQ FT: 3,400
SALES (est): 833.3K **Privately Held**
SIC: 3241 Portland cement

(G-6445)
WANASHAB INC ✪
1768 E 25th St Ste 308 (44114-4418)
PHONE...............................330 606-6675
Anthony Sterns, *CEO*
Joshua Smith, *COO*
EMP: 5 **EST:** 2016
SQ FT: 20,000
SALES (est): 210.6K **Privately Held**
SIC: 3721 Research & development on aircraft by the manufacturer

(G-6446)
WARREN CASTINGS INC
2934 E 55th St (44127-1207)
PHONE...............................216 883-2520
Fax: 216 883-2433
Willie Warren, *President*
Ernest Warren, *Executive*
EMP: 14
SALES (est): 1.4MM **Privately Held**
SIC: 3369 Castings, except die-castings, precision

(G-6447)
WARRENTON COPPER LLC
1240 Marquette St (44114-3920)
PHONE...............................636 456-3488
Herbert Black,
◆ **EMP:** 50
SQ FT: 100,000
SALES (est): 2.9MM **Privately Held**
WEB: www.warrentoncopper.com
SIC: 1021 Copper ore mining & preparation

(G-6448)
WARWICK PRODUCTS COMPANY
5350 Tradex Pkwy (44102-5887)
PHONE...............................216 334-1200
Fax: 216 334-1201
Matthew Beverstock, *President*
Tom Kunes, *Top Exec*
Susan Beverstock, *Corp Secy*
Jon Murray, *VP Sales*
Pat Bodjiak, *Manager*
▼ **EMP:** 50
SQ FT: 17,000
SALES (est): 14.8MM **Privately Held**
WEB: www.warwickproducts.com
SIC: 2653 3089 Solid fiber boxes, partitions, display items & sheets; cases, plastic

(G-6449)
WATERLOO INDUSTRIES INC
12487 Plaza Dr (44130-1056)
P.O. Box 30382 (44130-0382)
PHONE...............................800 833-8851
EMP: 3
SALES (est): 223.6K **Privately Held**
SIC: 3999 Manufacturing industries

(G-6450)
WATERLOX COATINGS CORPORATION
9808 Meech Ave (44105-4191)
PHONE...............................216 641-4877
Fax: 216 641-7213
John Wilson Hawkins, *President*
Kellie Hawkins Schaffner, *Vice Pres*
Conor Hawkins, *Manager*
▼ **EMP:** 13 **EST:** 1910
SQ FT: 40,000
SALES: 5.1MM **Privately Held**
WEB: www.waterlox.com
SIC: 2851 Paints: oil or alkyd vehicle or water thinned; varnishes; enamels; wood stains

(G-6451)
WATTERS MANUFACTURING CO INC
1931 W 47th St (44102-3413)
PHONE...............................216 281-8600
Charles D Watters, *President*
EMP: 6 **EST:** 1959
SQ FT: 2,500
SALES (est): 840.7K **Privately Held**
SIC: 3451 Screw machine products

(G-6452)
WAXMAN INDUSTRIES INC (PA)
24460 Aurora Rd (44146-1794)
PHONE...............................440 439-1830
Fax: 440 439-1262
Armond Waxman, *Ch of Bd*
Melvin Waxman, *Ch of Bd*
Larry Waxman, *President*
Laurence Waxman, *President*
Robert Feldman, *Senior VP*
▲ **EMP:** 110 **EST:** 1962
SQ FT: 21,000
SALES: 100MM **Privately Held**
WEB: www.waxmanind.com
SIC: 5072 5074 3494 3491 Hardware; plumbing & hydronic heating supplies; valves & pipe fittings; industrial valves; plumbing fixture fittings & trim

(G-6453)
WEDGEWORKS MCH TL & BORING CO
3169 E 80th St (44104-4343)
PHONE...............................216 441-1200
Fax: 216 441-1900
Bradford Braude, *President*
Sherry Braude, *Treasurer*
EMP: 6
SQ FT: 20,000
SALES (est): 759.9K **Privately Held**
SIC: 3599 Machine shop, jobbing & repair

(G-6454)
WEISKOPF INDUSTRIES CORP
731 Beta Dr Ste B (44143-2358)
P.O. Box 24390 (44124-0390)
PHONE...............................440 442-4400
Fax: 440 442-1254
Edward A Weiskopf, *President*
Geoffrey Weiskopf, *Exec VP*
Weiskopf Industries, *E-Business*
Pam Keidel, *Admin Sec*
EMP: 25
SALES (est): 3.2MM **Privately Held**
WEB: www.wicwipers.com
SIC: 2211 Tracing cloth, cotton

(G-6455)
WELDED RING PRODUCTS CO (PA)
2180 W 114th St (44102-3582)
PHONE...............................216 961-3800
Fax: 216 961-5051
James C Janosek, *President*
Gary Horvath, *Exec VP*
▲ **EMP:** 80 **EST:** 1960
SQ FT: 250,000
SALES (est): 13.1MM **Privately Held**
WEB: www.weldedring.com
SIC: 3724 Aircraft engines & engine parts

(G-6456)
WELDERS SUPPLY INC (HQ)
Also Called: Lake Erie Iron and Metal
2020 Train Ave (44113-4282)
PHONE...............................216 241-1696
Fax: 216 241-2743
Richard Osborne, *President*
Martin Hathy, *Vice Pres*
Don Watz, *Rsch/Dvlpt Dir*
Tom Kall, *Manager*
EMP: 12 **EST:** 1946
SQ FT: 8,000
SALES (est): 3.4MM
SALES (corp-wide): 11.2MM **Privately Held**
SIC: 2813 5084 5999 Oxygen, compressed or liquefied; acetylene; welding machinery & equipment; welding supplies
PA: Osair, Inc.
7001 Center St
Mentor OH 44060
440 974-6500

(G-6457)
WELKER MACHINE & GRINDING CO
718 E 163rd St (44110-2453)
PHONE...............................216 481-1360
Fax: 216 481-0858
Andy Spiranovich, *Partner*
Mark Spiranovich, *Partner*
EMP: 3 **EST:** 1966
SALES: 300K **Privately Held**
SIC: 3599 Machine shop, jobbing & repair

(G-6458)
WESTERN DIGITAL CORPORATION
2635 Butternut Ln (44124-4208)
PHONE...............................440 684-1331
Scott Schechtman, *Manager*
EMP: 6
SALES (corp-wide): 12.9B **Publicly Held**
WEB: www.wdc.com
SIC: 3572 Disk drives, computer
PA: Western Digital Corporation
3355 Michelson Dr Ste 100
Irvine CA 92612
949 672-7000

(G-6459)
WESTERN RESERVE MFG CO
9200 Inman Ave (44105-2110)
PHONE...............................216 641-0500
Iris R Rubinfield, *Partner*
Penny Heinzmann, *Partner*
Pamela Vestal, *Partner*
Diane Rose, *Manager*
EMP: 3 **EST:** 1943
SQ FT: 10,000
SALES (est): 250K **Privately Held**
SIC: 3462 3562 Flange, valve & pipe fitting forgings, ferrous; casters

(G-6460)
WHITEROCK PIGMENTS INC
1768 E 25th St (44114-4418)
PHONE...............................216 391-7765
Robert L Meyer, *CEO*
Thomas M Forman, *Chairman*
EMP: 5
SALES (est): 611.6K **Privately Held**
SIC: 2816 Titanium dioxide, anatase or rutile (pigments)

(G-6461)
WHITNEY STAINED GLASS STUDIO
5939 Broadway Ave (44127-1718)
PHONE...............................216 348-1616
Peter Billington, *President*
Glenn Billington, *Vice Pres*
Janet Lipstreu, *Director*
EMP: 9
SQ FT: 12,000
SALES (est): 276.9K **Privately Held**
WEB: www.whitneystainedglass.com
SIC: 8999 3231 Stained glass art; stained glass: made from purchased glass

(G-6462)
WILD FIRE SYSTEMS
535 Ransome Rd (44143-1993)
PHONE...............................440 442-8999
Fax: 216 368-8675
James Berilla, *Owner*
EMP: 6 **EST:** 1975
SALES (est): 583.3K **Privately Held**
SIC: 3823 7379 Computer interface equipment for industrial process control; computer related consulting services

(G-6463)
WILLIAM EXLINE INC
12301 Bennington Ave (44135-3796)
PHONE...............................216 941-0800
Fax: 216 941-4885
William B Exline, *President*
Michael P Exline, *Vice Pres*
August Tischer, *Vice Pres*
Bill Exline, *Sales Executive*
EMP: 30 **EST:** 1929
SQ FT: 35,000
SALES (est): 4.6MM **Privately Held**
WEB: www.williamexlineinc.com
SIC: 2782 Passbooks: bank, etc.; checkbooks; ledgers & ledger sheets

(G-6464)
WILLIAMS STEEL RULE DIE CO
1633 E 40th St (44103-2304)
PHONE...............................216 431-3232
Fax: 216 431-4891
Jeff Jazbec, *President*
Richard Williamson, *Purchasing*
EMP: 14 **EST:** 1961
SQ FT: 52,000
SALES (est): 1.6MM **Privately Held**
WEB: www.wsrdc.com
SIC: 3544 3953 2675 3993 Paper cutting dies; embossing seals, corporate & official; paper die-cutting; signs & advertising specialties; platemaking services; commercial printing

(G-6465)
WILSON MOBILITY LLC
17602 Deforest Ave (44128-2606)
PHONE...............................216 921-9457
Rodney Wilson, *Principal*
EMP: 3
SALES (est): 264.6K **Privately Held**
SIC: 3842 Wheelchairs

(G-6466)
WINDSOR TOOL INC
10714 Bellaire Rd (44111-5324)
PHONE...............................216 671-1900
Fax: 216 671-0004
Marc Ravas, *President*
EMP: 10
SQ FT: 5,000
SALES (est): 710K **Privately Held**
WEB: www.windsortool.com
SIC: 3544 Special dies & tools

(G-6467)
WIRE HOLDINGS LLC
Also Called: Radix Wire
26000 Lakeland Blvd (44132-2638)
PHONE...............................216 731-9191
Tony Pallotta, *Vice Pres*
Kregg Himes, *Site Mgr*
Bob Hazenfield, *Engineer*
Steve Demko, *CFO*
Margaret Eckhardt, *Controller*
EMP: 5 **EST:** 2013
SALES (est): 1MM **Privately Held**
SIC: 2298 3312 3315 Ropes & fiber cables; cable, fiber; wire products, steel or iron; wire & fabricated wire products

(G-6468)
WIRE PRODUCTS COMPANY INC (PA)
Also Called: Universal Fabrication Assembly
14601 Industrial Pkwy (44135-4595)
PHONE...............................216 267-0777
E Scot Kennedy, *President*
Winston Breeden Jr, *Exec VP*
Steve Adcock, *Vice Pres*
Dan Collins, *Vice Pres*
Gary Horvath, *Vice Pres*
EMP: 94 **EST:** 1951
SQ FT: 43,000
SALES (est): 28.1MM **Privately Held**
WEB: www.wire-products.com
SIC: 3496 Miscellaneous fabricated wire products

(G-6469)
WIRE PRODUCTS COMPANY INC
14700 Industrial Pkwy (44135-4548)
PHONE...............................216 267-0777
Dale Zeleznik, *Manager*
EMP: 225
SQ FT: 56,625
SALES (corp-wide): 31.2MM **Privately Held**
WEB: www.wire-products.com
SIC: 3495 3315 3469 Mechanical springs, precision; hangers (garment), wire; metal stampings
PA: Wire Products Company, Inc.
14601 Industrial Pkwy
Cleveland OH 44135
216 267-0777

(G-6470)
WISE WINDOW TREATMENT INC
Also Called: Wise Contracts
5293 W 137th St (44142-1810)
PHONE.....................................216 676-4080
Fax: 216 362-1201
Jerry Lang, *President*
EMP: 12
SQ FT: 5,700
SALES (est): 933K **Privately Held**
SIC: 2391 2392 Curtains & draperies; bedspreads & bed sets: made from purchased materials

(G-6471)
WLS FABRICATING CO
5405 Avion Park Dr (44143-1918)
PHONE.....................................440 449-0543
Craig Kotnik, *Vice Pres*
Susan Nash, *Manager*
▲ EMP: 30
SALES (est): 5.2MM
SALES (corp-wide): 20MM **Privately Held**
WEB: www.wlsstamping.com
SIC: 3469 Metal stampings
PA: W.L.S. Stamping Co.
3292 E 80th St
Cleveland OH 44104
216 271-5100

(G-6472)
WLS STAMPING CO (PA)
3292 E 80th St (44104-4392)
PHONE.....................................216 271-5100
Fax: 216 341-3203
Daniel C Cronin, *Ch of Bd*
Craig Kotnik, *Vice Pres*
Mike Deckert, *Plant Mgr*
Michelle Miarka, *Purch Agent*
Susan Nash, *CFO*
▲ EMP: 74 EST: 1944
SQ FT: 30,000
SALES (est): 20MM **Privately Held**
WEB: www.wlsstamping.com
SIC: 3469 3544 Stamping metal for the trade; special dies & tools

(G-6473)
WM PLOTZ MACHINE AND FORGE CO
Also Called: Peerless Pump Clveland Svc Ctr
2514 Center St (44113-1111)
PHONE.....................................216 861-0441
Fax: 216 861-3630
James W Plotz, *President*
Thomas D Plotz, *Corp Secy*
Lou Colon, *Manager*
EMP: 11 EST: 1888
SQ FT: 21,000
SALES (est): 1.8MM **Privately Held**
SIC: 3599 7699 Machine shop, jobbing & repair; pumps & pumping equipment repair

(G-6474)
WODIN INC
5441 Perkins Rd (44146-1891)
PHONE.....................................440 439-4222
Fax: 440 439-7560
R Grant Murphy, *Ch of Bd*
Kristen Holub, *Purch Mgr*
Barbara Golding, *Controller*
EMP: 35
SQ FT: 30,000
SALES (est): 10.5MM **Privately Held**
WEB: www.wodin.com
SIC: 3462 3463 3599 3965 Machinery forgings, ferrous; nonferrous forgings; machine shop, jobbing & repair; fasteners; bolts, nuts, rivets & washers; blast furnaces & steel mills

(G-6475)
WOOD-SEBRING CORPORATION
13800 Enterprise Ave (44135-5116)
PHONE.....................................216 267-3191
Fax: 216 267-4208
Joseph Kronander, *President*
Mary Kronander, *Admin Sec*
EMP: 7 EST: 1944
SQ FT: 10,000
SALES (est): 918.4K **Privately Held**
SIC: 3451 Screw machine products

(G-6476)
WOODHILL PLATING WORKS COMPANY
9114 Reno Ave (44105-2186)
PHONE.....................................216 883-1344
Fax: 216 883-1350
John W Sparano Sr, *President*
Robt Friel, *Principal*
Thomas Friel, *Principal*
James Sparano, *Vice Pres*
Jeff Sparano, *Vice Pres*
EMP: 25
SQ FT: 25,000
SALES (est): 2.6MM **Privately Held**
WEB: www.woodhillplating.com
SIC: 3471 Electroplating & plating

(G-6477)
WOODSTOCK PRODUCTS INC
2914 Broadway Ave (44115-3606)
PHONE.....................................216 641-3811
Fax: 216 341-4840
Terry Dunay, *President*
Clara Dunay, *Corp Secy*
EMP: 6
SQ FT: 5,000
SALES (est): 750.4K **Privately Held**
SIC: 2048 Feed concentrates

(G-6478)
WORLD AUTOMTN MEASUREMENT TECH
Also Called: World Systems
5710 Detroit Ave (44102-3042)
PHONE.....................................216 651-1883
Fax: 216 651-2087
Dieter Wabnitz, *President*
EMP: 10
SQ FT: 6,000
SALES (est): 89.3K **Privately Held**
SIC: 3545 3823 Gauges (machine tool accessories); industrial instrmnts msrmnt display/control process variable

(G-6479)
WORLD EXPRESS PACKAGING CORP
3607 W 56th St (44102-5739)
PHONE.....................................216 634-9000
Tony Galang, *President*
Mike Lewandowski, *Corp Secy*
Ken Lewandowski, *Vice Pres*
EMP: 3
SQ FT: 14,000
SALES (est): 363.6K **Privately Held**
SIC: 4783 2441 Packing goods for shipping; boxes, wood; cases, wood

(G-6480)
WORLD JOURNAL
1735 E 36th St (44114-4521)
PHONE.....................................216 458-0988
Yu-Chen Hsiao, *Principal*
EMP: 5
SALES (est): 265.9K **Privately Held**
SIC: 2711 Newspapers, publishing & printing

(G-6481)
WORTHINGTON CNSTR GROUP INC
3100 E 45th St Ste 400 (44127-1095)
PHONE.....................................216 472-1511
Anna Unwin, *Principal*
EMP: 1 EST: 2013
SALES (est): 2.5MM
SALES (corp-wide): 2.8B **Publicly Held**
SIC: 3446 Purlins, light gauge steel
HQ: Worthington Mid-Rise Construction Inc.
3100 E 45th St Ste 400
Cleveland OH 44127
216 472-1511

(G-6482)
WORTHINGTON MID-RISE CNSTR INC (HQ)
Also Called: Worthington Industries
3100 E 45th St Ste 400 (44127-1095)
PHONE.....................................216 472-1511
Marybeth Bosko, *President*
Michael Whitticar, *President*
Ed Musbaca, *Controller*
EMP: 40
SQ FT: 14,000

SALES (est): 4.3MM
SALES (corp-wide): 2.8B **Publicly Held**
SIC: 3446 Purlins, light gauge steel
PA: Worthington Industries, Inc.
200 W Old Wlson Bridge Rd
Worthington OH 43085
614 438-3210

(G-6483)
WORTHINGTON STEEL COMPANY
4310 E 49th St (44125-1004)
PHONE.....................................216 441-8300
Pauline Glomski, *Human Res Mgr*
Brittany Thomas, *Branch Mgr*
Mike Dort, *Manager*
Jens Strietzel, *Maintence Staff*
EMP: 175
SALES (corp-wide): 2.8B **Publicly Held**
SIC: 3316 Strip steel, cold-rolled: from purchased hot-rolled
HQ: The Worthington Steel Company
200 W Old Wlson Bridge Rd
Worthington OH 43085
614 438-3210

(G-6484)
WRIGHT DESIGNS INC (PA)
5099 Valley Woods Dr (44131-5253)
P.O. Box 31482 (44131-0482)
PHONE.....................................216 524-6662
Robert A Wright, *President*
EMP: 3 EST: 1976
SQ FT: 1,500
SALES (est): 552.3K **Privately Held**
WEB: www.brewkeeper.com
SIC: 1521 7389 2082 New construction, single-family houses; interior designer; malt beverages

(G-6485)
WYMAN-GORDON COMPANY
Also Called: Wyman Gordon
3097 E 61st St (44127-1312)
PHONE.....................................216 341-0085
Mike Sutorius, *General Mgr*
Robert Wood, *Engineer*
Tim Herron, *Branch Mgr*
Cindy Chervenak, *Info Tech Mgr*
EMP: 48
SALES (corp-wide): 223.6B **Publicly Held**
WEB: www.dropdies.com
SIC: 3462 Iron & steel forgings
HQ: Wyman-Gordon Company
244 Worcester St
North Grafton MA 01536
508 839-8252

(G-6486)
XAPC CO (PA)
Also Called: Avalon
15583 Brookpark Rd (44142-1618)
PHONE.....................................216 362-4100
Doug Ciabotti, *CEO*
Lindsey Krauth, *Human Res Mgr*
Tom Ward, *VP Sales*
▲ EMP: 85 EST: 1982
SQ FT: 36,000
SALES (est): 51.3MM **Privately Held**
SIC: 3324 Steel investment foundries

(G-6487)
XXX INTRNTIONAL AMUSEMENTS INC (PA)
3313 W 140th St D (44111-2428)
PHONE.....................................216 671-6900
Fax: 216 671-6980
Scott Moore, *President*
EMP: 24
SQ FT: 10,000
SALES (est): 4.4MM **Privately Held**
WEB: www.vgrsystems.com
SIC: 1731 2541 2517 2434 Cable television installation; wood partitions & fixtures; wood television & radio cabinets; wood kitchen cabinets

(G-6488)
YUCKON INTERNATIONAL CORP
Also Called: Ross Printing Co.
1400 E 34th St (44114-4113)
PHONE.....................................216 361-2103
EMP: 9 EST: 1947
SQ FT: 3,000

SALES: 900K **Privately Held**
SIC: 2752 2657 Lithographic Coml Print Mfg Folding Paperbrd Box

(G-6489)
ZACLON LLC
2981 Independence Rd (44115-3699)
PHONE.....................................216 271-1601
Fax: 216 271-1792
James B Krimmel, *President*
Craig Keeley, *Business Mgr*
Matthew O'Connor, *Marketing Staff*
▲ EMP: 22
SALES (est): 6.5MM **Privately Held**
SIC: 2819 2869 Industrial inorganic chemicals; industrial organic chemicals
PA: Zeta Alpha Holdings Inc
2981 Independence Rd
Cleveland OH 44115
216 271-1601

(G-6490)
ZAGAR INC
24000 Lakeland Blvd (44132-2618)
PHONE.....................................216 731-0500
Fax: 216 731-8591
John F Zagar, *President*
William Hanigan, *Vice Pres*
George Zagar, *Vice Pres*
Howard Guerin, *Controller*
Alan Fedele, *Info Tech Mgr*
◆ EMP: 25 EST: 1941
SQ FT: 50,000
SALES (est): 6.6MM **Privately Held**
WEB: www.zagar.com
SIC: 3546 3541 Power-driven handtools; machine tools, metal cutting type

(G-6491)
ZAK BOX CO INC
7100 Clark Ave (44102-5225)
P.O. Box 602697 (44102-0697)
PHONE.....................................216 961-5636
Fax: 216 961-7943
Richard Helbig, *President*
Valerie Helbig, *Vice Pres*
EMP: 5
SQ FT: 10,400
SALES (est): 400K **Privately Held**
SIC: 2441 2542 2448 Boxes, wood; shipping cases, wood: nailed or lock corner; racks, merchandise display or storage: except wood; wood pallets & skids

(G-6492)
ZAL AIR PRODUCTS INC
Also Called: Zap
1687 W Royalton Rd (44147-2413)
PHONE.....................................440 237-7155
Ed Zalar, *President*
Michele M Zalar, *Vice Pres*
Edward H Zalar III, *Admin Sec*
EMP: 4
SQ FT: 400
SALES (est): 293.8K **Privately Held**
SIC: 3491 5085 5084 Water works valves; industrial supplies; industrial machinery & equipment

(G-6493)
ZEN INDUSTRIES INC
Also Called: American Mine Door
6200 Harvard Ave (44105-4861)
PHONE.....................................216 432-3240
Fax: 216 432-3241
Kim Zenisek, *President*
Ed Ebner, *Vice Pres*
Drew McCaffrey, *Accounts Mgr*
Adam Skinner, *Manager*
EMP: 35
SQ FT: 70,000
SALES (est): 9.9MM **Privately Held**
WEB: www.minedoor.com
SIC: 3532 Mining machinery

(G-6494)
ZENITH ENERGY GROUP LLC
5069 Corbin Dr (44128-5413)
PHONE.....................................216 587-9510
Lenny Heiser,
Peter Appler,
EMP: 11
SALES (est): 2.3MM **Privately Held**
SIC: 3822 Auto controls regulating residntl & coml environmt & applncs

▲ = Import ▼=Export
◆ =Import/Export

(G-6495)
ZING PAC INC
30300 Solon Indus Pkwy (44139-4378)
PHONE................................440 248-7997
Daniel McBride, *Principal*
EMP: 3
SALES (est): 240.6K **Privately Held**
SIC: 3086 Packaging & shipping materials, foamed plastic

(G-6496)
ZIP TOOL & DIE INC
12200 Sprecher Ave (44135-5122)
PHONE................................216 267-1117
Fax: 216 267-5466
Victor De Leon, *CEO*
Wayne Dawson, *VP Mfg*
Larry Kane, *VP Engrg*
EMP: 19 EST: 1967
SQ FT: 12,000
SALES (est): 2.5MM **Privately Held**
WEB: www.ziptool.com
SIC: 3465 3469 Automotive stampings; metal stampings

(G-6497)
ZIPPITY PRINT ✪
1600 E 23rd St (44114-4208)
PHONE................................216 438-0001
Joseph P Dell'aquila, *CEO*
Dennis Dimitrov, *COO*
EMP: 3 EST: 2017
SALES (est): 201.8K **Privately Held**
SIC: 2759 Commercial printing

(G-6498)
ZIRCOA INC (PA)
31501 Solon Rd (44139-3526)
PHONE................................440 248-0500
Fax: 440 349-7209
John Kaniuk, *President*
Sherry Just, *President*
Christine Burgess, *Production*
Benjamin Demichael, *Controller*
Janet Strong, *Accounting Mgr*
▲ EMP: 130
SQ FT: 120,000
SALES (est): 27.1MM **Privately Held**
WEB: www.zircoa.com
SIC: 3339 3297 2851 Zirconium metal, sponge & granules; nonclay refractories; paints & allied products

(G-6499)
ZIRCON INDUSTRIES INC
4920 Commerce Pkwy Ste 9 (44128-5943)
PHONE................................216 595-0200
Fax: 216 595-0202
Robert Zinamon, *President*
Sidney A Zinamon, *Vice Pres*
Marlene Zinamon, *Treasurer*
EMP: 5
SALES (est): 1.1MM **Privately Held**
WEB: www.greenchem.com
SIC: 5087 2899 Cleaning & maintenance equipment & supplies; deicing or defrosting fluid

---

Cleveland Heights
Cuyahoga County

(G-6500)
MARTINI SKATE & SNOW
2122 S Taylor Rd (44118-2607)
PHONE................................216 371-0155
Michael Tirpak, *Branch Mgr*
EMP: 7 **Privately Held**
SIC: 3949 Skateboards
PA: Martini Sports Llc
8266 Golden Link Blvd Ste 14
Northfield OH 44067
330 655-0155

(G-6501)
ROBERT RAACK
2943 Berkshire Rd (44118-2443)
PHONE................................216 932-6127
Robert Raack, *Principal*
EMP: 3
SALES (est): 180K **Privately Held**
SIC: 2851 Colors in oil, except artists'

(G-6502)
UNGER KOSHER BAKERY INC
Also Called: Ungers Bakery
1831 S Taylor Rd (44118-2101)
PHONE................................216 321-7176
Fax: 216 321-0777
Marek Rosenberg, *President*
Magdalena Rosenberg, *Admin Sec*
EMP: 20 EST: 1967
SQ FT: 12,000
SALES (est): 834.4K **Privately Held**
SIC: 5461 5411 5149 2099 Bakeries; grocery stores, independent; bakery products; food preparations; bread, cake & related products

(G-6503)
WOOD TRADER INC
13429 Cedar Rd (44118-2958)
PHONE................................216 397-7671
Fax: 216 397-7566
Sara Kraber, *President*
Jack Thorp, *Vice Pres*
Leslie Kammer,
EMP: 6
SALES (est): 400K **Privately Held**
WEB: www.traderwood.com
SIC: 2499 Picture & mirror frames, wood

Cleves
Hamilton County

(G-6504)
4D SCREENPRINTING LTD
5833 Hamilton Cleves Rd (45002-9529)
PHONE................................513 353-1070
Chris Drew, *Principal*
EMP: 5
SALES (est): 548.5K **Privately Held**
SIC: 2759 Screen printing

(G-6505)
AADCO INSTRUMENTS INC
145 S Miami Ave (45002-1250)
PHONE................................513 467-1477
Fax: 513 467-9009
Fred Taphorn, *President*
Diane Tisch, *Vice Pres*
James P Tisch, *Vice Pres*
Wilbur John Tisch, *Vice Pres*
Shawn Hines, *Manager*
EMP: 3
SQ FT: 7,500
SALES (est): 431.2K **Privately Held**
WEB: www.aadcoinst.com
SIC: 3621 Motors & generators

(G-6506)
ALUMINA RLING CSTM IR WRKS INC
Also Called: ALUMINA RAILING PRODUCTS
8301 Strimple Rd (45002-9778)
PHONE................................513 353-1116
Fax: 513 353-2116
Terry Bunnell, *President*
Bruce Hinrichsen, *Manager*
Kimberly Bunnell, *Admin Sec*
EMP: 25 EST: 1994
SQ FT: 27,000
SALES (est): 2.7MM **Privately Held**
WEB: www.aluminarailing.com
SIC: 3446 Stairs, fire escapes, balconies; railings & ladders

(G-6507)
BRUEWER WOODWORK MFG CO
10000 Cilley Rd (45002-9735)
PHONE................................513 353-3505
Fax: 513 353-3177
August Bruewer, *Ch of Bd*
Ralph H Bruewer, *President*
Gary A Bruewer, *Vice Pres*
Richard M Ruffing, *Vice Pres*
Mark Grimm, *Plant Mgr*
EMP: 55
SQ FT: 155,000

SALES (est): 9.8MM **Privately Held**
SIC: 3083 2541 2435 2434 Plastic finished products, laminated; office fixtures, wood; counters or counter display cases, wood; hardwood veneer & plywood; wood kitchen cabinets; millwork; sawmills & planing mills, general

(G-6508)
CENTRAL READY MIX LLC
7340 Dry Fork Rd (45002-9431)
PHONE................................513 367-1939
Fax: 513 367-1939
Dick England, *Manager*
EMP: 8
SALES (corp-wide): 13.7MM **Privately Held**
WEB: www.morainematerials.com
SIC: 3273 Ready-mixed concrete
PA: Central Ready Mix, Llc
6310 E Kemper Rd Ste 125
Cincinnati OH 45241
513 402-5001

(G-6509)
CINCINNATI ELECTRICAL TOOL
5928 Hamilton Cleves Rd (45002-9051)
PHONE................................513 941-5000
Fax: 513 353-4040
William A Ferguson III, *Ch of Bd*
Robert Wallace, *President*
Robert A Ferguson, *Corp Secy*
Michael Baltes, *Vice Pres*
Judith Grace, *Purchasing*
EMP: 10
SQ FT: 25,000
SALES (est): 890K **Privately Held**
WEB: www.cincinnatielectrical.com
SIC: 3541 5084 Machine tool replacement & repair parts, metal cutting types; industrial machinery & equipment
PA: Jacp Inc
5928 Hamilton Cleves Rd
Miamitown OH 45041

(G-6510)
COMPLIANT ACCESS PRODUCTS LLC
5885 Hamilton Cleves Rd (45002-9529)
P.O. Box 58203, Cincinnati (45258-0203)
PHONE................................513 518-4525
Tom Reilly, *Mng Member*
EMP: 5
SALES (est): 643.7K **Privately Held**
SIC: 3354 Aluminum extruded products

(G-6511)
CONSOLIDATD ANALYTICAL SYS INC
Also Called: Cas
201 S Miami Ave (45002-1220)
PHONE................................513 542-1200
Seth Cloran, *President*
John Tish, *Corp Secy*
Jim Tish, *Vice Pres*
Thomas Brandt, *Prdtn Mgr*
Tom Platter, *Sales Mgr*
EMP: 14
SQ FT: 25,000
SALES: 1MM **Privately Held**
SIC: 8711 2452 3448 3823 Engineering services; prefabricated buildings, wood; prefabricated metal buildings; chromatographs, industrial process type; analytical instruments; analytical instruments

(G-6512)
CONVEYOR SOLUTIONS LLC
6705 Dry Fork Rd (45002-9732)
PHONE................................513 367-4845
Fax: 513 367-4846
Shawn Patton, *Sales Engr*
Sue Roth, *Manager*
Aaron Doerflein,
Robert Brinck,
James Hillgrove,
EMP: 7
SQ FT: 6,200
SALES (est): 1.7MM **Privately Held**
WEB: www.conveyorsolutionsllc.com
SIC: 3535 Belt conveyor systems, general industrial use

(G-6513)
EPOXY SYSTEMS BLSTG CATING INC
5640 Morgan Rd (45002-8720)
PHONE................................513 924-1800
Barbara Ferneding, *President*
EMP: 4 EST: 2011
SALES (est): 572.5K **Privately Held**
SIC: 2851 Epoxy coatings

(G-6514)
FDI CABINETRY LLC
5555 Dry Fork Rd (45002-9733)
P.O. Box 16, Ross (45061-0016)
PHONE................................513 353-4500
Diane Hart, *Mng Member*
EMP: 9
SQ FT: 12,000
SALES (est): 1.1MM **Privately Held**
SIC: 2434 3993 1799 3083 Wood kitchen cabinets; signs & advertising specialties; home/office interiors finishing, furnishing & remodeling; plastic finished products, laminated; millwork

(G-6515)
HANSON AGGREGATES EAST
7000 Dry Fork Rd (45002-9732)
PHONE................................513 353-1100
Tom Rodurbush, *Principal*
William Roell, *Plant Mgr*
EMP: 6
SALES (est): 280K **Privately Held**
SIC: 1442 Construction sand & gravel

(G-6516)
JAMES BUNNELL INC
7000 Dry Fork Rd (45002-9732)
PHONE................................513 353-1100
Fax: 513 367-3870
Jack Ernest, *President*
Vicki Earnst, *Corp Secy*
EMP: 10 EST: 1955
SQ FT: 1,160
SALES (est): 890K **Privately Held**
SIC: 1442 Construction sand & gravel

(G-6517)
JOHNSON PRECISION MACHINING
5919 Hamilton Cleves Rd (45002-9051)
PHONE................................513 353-4252
Fax: 513 353-3186
Mary C Hubbard, *President*
Ellis Hubbard, *Vice Pres*
EMP: 8
SQ FT: 7,500
SALES: 1MM **Privately Held**
SIC: 3599 Machine shop, jobbing & repair

(G-6518)
KINNEMYERS CORNERSTONE CAB INC
Also Called: Kinnemeyers Cornerstone Cab Co
6000 Hamilton Cleves Rd (45002-9530)
PHONE................................513 353-3030
Fax: 513 353-3299
Ken Kinnemeyer, *President*
EMP: 6
SALES: 600K **Privately Held**
SIC: 2599 2434 Cabinets, factory; wood kitchen cabinets

(G-6519)
KOHL PATTERNS
7983 Morgan Rd (45002-9709)
PHONE................................513 353-3831
Fax: 513 353-3831
Gregory A Kohl, *Partner*
William F Kohl, *Partner*
EMP: 3
SALES (est): 320K **Privately Held**
SIC: 3543 Industrial patterns

(G-6520)
L & L ORNAMENTAL IRON CO
Also Called: L & L Railings
6024 Hamilton Cleves Rd (45002-9530)
PHONE................................513 353-1930
Fax: 513 353-4830
Randy Seiler, *President*
Dean Seiler, *Vice Pres*
Debbie Seiler, *Purchasing*
EMP: 15

SQ FT: 8,000
SALES: 500K **Privately Held**
SIC: 3446 3354 2431 Ornamental metal-work; aluminum extruded products; stair railings, wood

(G-6521)
METAL MAINTENANCE INC
Also Called: Architectural Metal Maint
322 N Finley St (45002-1005)
P.O. Box 41, Addyston (45001-0041)
PHONE..................................513 661-3300
Fax: 513 467-0408
Steve Campbell, *President*
EMP: 10
SALES (est): 1.1MM **Privately Held**
WEB: www.metal-maintenance.com
SIC: 3446 Architectural metalwork

(G-6522)
POHL MACHINING INC
Also Called: Miami Machine
4901 Hamilton Cleves Rd (45002-9753)
P.O. Box 10 (45002-0010)
PHONE..................................513 353-2929
Shawna Vanderpohl, *President*
Irvin Vanderpohl, *Vice Pres*
Ray Wollenhaupt, *Opers Staff*
EMP: 48
SALES (est): 5.2MM **Privately Held**
SIC: 3599 Machine & other job shop work

(G-6523)
POLYCRAFT PRODUCTS INC
5511 Hamilton Cleves Rd (45002-9501)
PHONE..................................513 353-3334
Matt Landers, *COO*
Shawn Walker, *Branch Mgr*
EMP: 5
SALES (corp-wide): 6.4MM **Privately Held**
SIC: 3724 3061 Aircraft engines & engine parts; mechanical rubber goods
PA: Polycraft Products, Inc.
　　897 Rudolph Way
　　Greendale IN 47025
　　812 577-3400

(G-6524)
POWERCLEAN EQUIPMENT COMPANY
5945 Dry Fork Rd (45002-9794)
PHONE..................................513 202-0001
Tom Ossege, *President*
Gary Ossege, *Vice Pres*
Brent Ossege, *Manager*
EMP: 7
SALES (est): 607.7K **Privately Held**
WEB: www.powercleanequipment.com
SIC: 7359 3635 Equipment rental & leasing; household vacuum cleaners

(G-6525)
SIGNATURE SALANTS COATINGS LLC
724 Rosewynne Ct (45002-2308)
PHONE..................................513 922-8723
Ronald Roth, *Principal*
EMP: 4
SALES (est): 450.2K **Privately Held**
SIC: 2891 Sealants

(G-6526)
SPECIALTY ADHESIVE FILM CO
5838 Hamilton Cleves Rd (45002-9529)
P.O. Box 150, Aurora IN (47001-0150)
PHONE..................................513 353-1885
Fax: 513 353-1888
Jack Morline, *Manager*
EMP: 3
SALES (corp-wide): 7.2MM **Privately Held**
WEB: www.specialtyadhesive.com
SIC: 2672 2891 3083 Adhesive backed films, foams & foils; laminating compounds; laminated plastics plate & sheet
PA: Specialty Adhesive Film Co
　　10510 Randall Ave
　　Aurora IN 47001
　　812 926-0156

(G-6527)
SPURLINO MATERIALS LLC
6600 Dry Fork Rd (45002-9392)
PHONE..................................513 202-1111
Allan Roelle, *Manager*

EMP: 9
SALES (corp-wide): 27MM **Privately Held**
WEB: www.spurlino.net
SIC: 3273 Ready-mixed concrete
PA: Spurlino Materials, Llc
　　4000 Oxford State Rd
　　Middletown OH 45044
　　513 705-0111

(G-6528)
STOCK MFG & DESIGN CO INC (PA)
Also Called: Q M P
10040 Cilley Rd (45002-9735)
P.O. Box 68 (45002-0068)
PHONE..................................513 353-3600
Fax: 513 942-1071
William H Reyering, *President*
Jeremy Stock, *Managing Prtnr*
Anthony Stock, *Corp Secy*
Dennis K Stock, *Vice Pres*
John Matracia, *Engineer*
EMP: 65
SQ FT: 80,000
SALES (est): 12.3MM **Privately Held**
WEB: www.stockmfg.com
SIC: 3441 Fabricated structural metal

(G-6529)
TISCH ENVIRONMENTAL INC
145 S Miami Ave (45002-1250)
PHONE..................................513 467-9000
Fax: 513 467-9009
W John Tisch, *President*
John W Tisch, *President*
Ken Schmaltz, *Division Mgr*
James P Tisch, *Vice Pres*
Brad Liggett, *Opers Staff*
▲ EMP: 18
SQ FT: 12,000
SALES (est): 5.2MM **Privately Held**
WEB: www.tisch-env.com
SIC: 3564 Blowers & fans

(G-6530)
TRI-STATE MACHINING LLC
6088 Hamilton Cleves Rd # 2 (45002-9530)
Rural Route 6054 Bluff, Middletown (45044)
PHONE..................................513 257-9442
Shane Williams,
EMP: 3
SALES (est): 191.8K **Privately Held**
SIC: 3599 Machine & other job shop work

(G-6531)
VALLEY ASPHALT CORPORATION
5073 Kilby Rd (45002)
PHONE..................................513 353-2171
Bud Crihfield, *Manager*
EMP: 3
SALES (corp-wide): 109.5MM **Privately Held**
SIC: 2951 Asphalt & asphaltic paving mixtures (not from refineries)
PA: Valley Asphalt Corporation
　　11641 Mosteller Rd
　　Cincinnati OH 45241
　　513 771-0820

(G-6532)
W & W CUSTOM FABRICATION INC
4801 Hamilton Cleves Rd (45002-9752)
P.O. Box 288 (45002-0288)
PHONE..................................513 353-4617
Fax: 513 353-2092
Steve Webb, *President*
Mike Hutchison, *General Mgr*
EMP: 6
SALES (est): 1MM **Privately Held**
SIC: 3441 Fabricated structural metal

Clinton
Summit County

(G-6533)
ANGER PATTERN COMPANY INC
2999 S 1st St (44216-9157)
PHONE..................................330 882-6519

Fax: 330 882-6519
Richard Anger Jr, *President*
EMP: 5
SQ FT: 2,500
SALES: 500K **Privately Held**
SIC: 3543 Industrial patterns

(G-6534)
CLARK WOOD SPECIALTIES INC
9235 Shadybrook St Nw (44216-9546)
PHONE..................................330 499-8711
Fax: 330 499-0395
Paul Clark, *President*
Kimberly Ann Clark, *Vice Pres*
EMP: 8
SQ FT: 12,500
SALES (est): 1MM **Privately Held**
WEB: www.clarkwoodspecialties.com
SIC: 2431 5031 Moldings, wood: unfinished & prefinished; kitchen cabinets

(G-6535)
COMMUNITY CARE ON WHEELS
2 Kauffmans Crk (44216)
PHONE..................................330 882-5506
Cathy Jacobs, *President*
EMP: 12
SALES (est): 1.5MM **Privately Held**
SIC: 3312 Blast furnaces & steel mills

Cloverdale
Putnam County

(G-6536)
JONASHTONS
12485 State Route 634 (45827-9723)
PHONE..................................419 488-2363
Susan Knippen, *Owner*
EMP: 7
SALES (est): 310K **Privately Held**
SIC: 3599 Machine shop, jobbing & repair

Clyde
Sandusky County

(G-6537)
ARTIFLEX MANUFACTURING LLC
Also Called: Gerstco Division
550 Premier Dr (43410-2156)
PHONE..................................419 547-9211
Joe Pagniano, *Division Mgr*
Jason Morrison, *Maint Spvr*
Mark Humphrey, *Production*
Adam Chenevey, *Branch Mgr*
EMP: 12
SALES (corp-wide): 2.8B **Publicly Held**
SIC: 3465 7692 Automotive stampings; automotive welding
HQ: Artiflex Manufacturing, Llc
　　1425 E Bowman St
　　Wooster OH 44691
　　330 262-2015

(G-6538)
CLYDE TOOL & DIE INC (PA)
Also Called: Clyde Foam
524 S Church St (43410-2100)
PHONE..................................419 547-9574
Fax: 419 547-9576
Bruce G Schrader, *President*
Janice Smith, *Office Mgr*
EMP: 5
SQ FT: 30,000
SALES (est): 2.3MM **Privately Held**
WEB: www.clydetool.com
SIC: 3544 2821 Special dies & tools; molding compounds, plastics

(G-6539)
CUTTING EDGE MANUFACTURING LLC ◆
1744 W Mcpherson Hwy (43410-1052)
PHONE..................................419 547-9204
Joseph Fisher, *Principal*
EMP: 6 EST: 2016
SALES (est): 254.9K **Privately Held**
SIC: 3599 Machine & other job shop work

(G-6540)
HOFFMAN MACHINING & REPAIR LLC
1744 W Mcpherson Hwy (43410-1052)
PHONE..................................419 547-9204
William D Hoffman,
EMP: 3
SQ FT: 16,000
SALES: 300K **Privately Held**
SIC: 3499 3444 3599 7692 Metal household articles; sheet metalwork; machine shop, jobbing & repair; welding repair

(G-6541)
J TEK TOOL & MOLD INC
304 Elm St (43410-2124)
PHONE..................................419 547-9476
Fax: 419 547-6359
John Cattano, *President*
Don Young, *Plant Mgr*
EMP: 10
SQ FT: 10,000
SALES (est): 1MM **Privately Held**
WEB: www.jtektool.com
SIC: 3544 Industrial molds

(G-6542)
MIDWEST COMPOST INC
6090 State Route 101 E (43410-9720)
PHONE..................................419 547-7979
Fax: 419 547-6953
Eugene F Windau, *President*
John Steager, *Corp Secy*
Joseph Tauch, *Vice Pres*
EMP: 15
SQ FT: 2,432
SALES: 2MM **Privately Held**
SIC: 2875 Compost

(G-6543)
POLYCHEM CORPORATION
Also Called: Evergreen Plastics
202 Watertower Dr (43410-2154)
PHONE..................................419 547-1400
Fax: 419 547-4551
Mark Jeckering, *General Mgr*
Kelly Masell, *Project Engr*
Howard Lamont, *Controller*
Jeff Martinez, *Regl Sales Mgr*
Ann Dages, *Sales Staff*
EMP: 7
SALES (corp-wide): 153.7MM **Privately Held**
SIC: 3052 4953 Plastic belting; recycling, waste materials
PA: Polychem Corporation
　　6277 Heisley Rd
　　Mentor OH 44060
　　440 357-1500

(G-6544)
REVERE PLAS SYSTEMS GROUP LLC (HQ)
401 Elm St (43410-2148)
PHONE..................................419 547-6918
Rhonda Taylor, *Controller*
Rustin Shields,
EMP: 450
SALES (est): 132.9MM
SALES (corp-wide): 245.4MM **Privately Held**
SIC: 3089 Injection molded finished plastic products
PA: Revere Industries, Llc
　　16855 Suthpark Dr Ste 100
　　Westfield IN 46074
　　317 580-2420

(G-6545)
REVERE PLASTICS SYSTEMS LLC (HQ)
401 Elm St (43410-2148)
PHONE..................................419 547-6918
Rustin Shields, *General Mgr*
Kenneth Bowers, *General Mgr*
Laura Parr, *Purch Dir*
Brian Clark, *QC Mgr*
Sal Deangelo, *Project Engr*
▲ EMP: 277
SALES (est): 163.6MM
SALES (corp-wide): 245.4MM **Privately Held**
SIC: 3089 Injection molding of plastics

PA: Revere Industries, Llc
16855 Suthpark Dr Ste 100
Westfield IN 46074
317 580-2420

(G-6546)
RFS FABRICATION
Also Called: Richard Farm Shop
2515 County Road 213 (43410-9517)
PHONE.................................419 547-0650
Richard L Dickman, *Owner*
EMP: 3
SALES (est): 279K **Privately Held**
SIC: 3496 Miscellaneous fabricated wire
products

(G-6547)
SLICE OF HEAVEN BAKERY
463 N County Road 268 (43410-9759)
PHONE.................................419 656-6606
Meredith Hinds, *Principal*
EMP: 4
SALES (est): 238.2K **Privately Held**
SIC: 2051 Bakery: wholesale or whole-
sale/retail combined

(G-6548)
WHIRLPOOL CORPORATION
119 Birdseye St (43410-1397)
PHONE.................................419 547-7711
Fax: 419 547-2083
Casey Drabik, *Vice Pres*
Jennifer Hanna, *Opers Mgr*
Michael Kaser, *Opers Mgr*
Lew Robarge, *Maint Spvr*
Tom Grothouse, *Opers Staff*
EMP: 300
SQ FT: 1,500,000
SALES (corp-wide): 20.7B **Publicly Held**
WEB: www.whirlpoolcorp.com
SIC: 3633 3632 3639 3582 Household
laundry equipment; washing machines,
household: including coin-operated; freez-
ers, home & farm; refrigerators, mechani-
cal & absorption: household; dishwashing
machines, household; commercial laun-
dry equipment
PA: Whirlpool Corporation
2000 N M 63
Benton Harbor MI 49022
269 923-5000

Coldwater
Mercer County

(G-6549)
ACCUTECH FILMS INC (DH)
Also Called: Novolex
620 Hardin St (45828-8738)
P.O. Box 115 (45828-0115)
PHONE.................................419 678-8700
Fax: 419 678-2279
Fred Wampnar, *CEO*
George Thomas, *President*
Natalie Tobe, *QC Dir*
Harry Homan, *Controller*
Amy Quinter, *Accountant*
EMP: 18
SQ FT: 66,000
SALES (est): 20MM
SALES (corp-wide): 2.2B **Publicly Held**
WEB: www.accutechfilms.com
SIC: 2673 Food storage & trash bags
(plastic); plastic bags: made from pur-
chased materials
HQ: Hilex Poly Co. Llc
101 E Carolina Ave
Hartsville SC 29550
843 857-4800

(G-6550)
**ALUMETAL MANUFACTURING
COMPANY**
4555 Sr 127 (45828)
P.O. Box 166 (45828-0166)
PHONE.................................419 268-2311
Fax: 419 268-2851
Lavern W Gross, *President*
Oliver Giere, *Corp Secy*
Lou Williams, *Manager*
EMP: 21
SQ FT: 25,000

SALES: 1.5MM **Privately Held**
SIC: 3444 Mfg Sheet Metalwork

(G-6551)
**BARNSTORM BREWING
COMPANY LLC**
706 N 2nd St (45828-9779)
PHONE.................................419 852-9366
Teresa Waite, *Principal*
EMP: 5
SALES (est): 83K **Privately Held**
SIC: 2082 Malt beverages

(G-6552)
BASIC GRAIN PRODUCTS INC
Tastemorr Snack
300 E Vine St (45828-1354)
PHONE.................................614 408-3091
Jennifer Moe, *Accounts Mgr*
Carol Knapke, *Branch Mgr*
EMP: 32 **Privately Held**
WEB: www.tastemorr.com
SIC: 2096 Corn chips & other corn-based
snacks; rice chips
PA: Basic Grain Products, Inc
300310 E Vine St
Coldwater OH 45828

(G-6553)
**BASIC GRAIN PRODUCTS INC
(PA)**
Also Called: Tastemorr Snacks
300310 E Vine St (45828)
PHONE.................................419 678-2304
Carol Knapke, *President*
Amy Day, *Principal*
Ralph F Keister, *Principal*
Norm Shung, *CFO*
Jennifer Grant, *Hum Res Coord*
EMP: 68
SQ FT: 100,000
SALES (est): 17.3MM **Privately Held**
WEB: www.tastemorr.com
SIC: 2052 2099 2096 Rice cakes; food
preparations; potato chips & similar
snacks

(G-6554)
**CAMELOT MANUFACTURING
INC**
210 Butler St (45828-1103)
P.O. Box 44 (45828-0044)
PHONE.................................419 678-2603
Fax: 419 678-4106
Charles A Froning, *President*
Scott Froning, *Manager*
EMP: 15
SQ FT: 14,000
SALES (est): 2.5MM **Privately Held**
WEB: www.camelotmanufacturing.com
SIC: 3441 7692 3469 Fabricated struc-
tural metal; welding repair; metal stamp-
ings

(G-6555)
CASAD COMPANY INC
Also Called: Totally Promotional
450 S 2nd St (45828-1803)
PHONE.................................419 586-9457
Thomas R Casad, *President*
Krista Kremer, *Representative*
Mike Forlow, *Asst Cashier*
▲ EMP: 15
SQ FT: 7,000
SALES (est): 3.2MM **Privately Held**
WEB: www.casad.com
SIC: 2759 3993 Commercial printing;
signs & advertising specialties

(G-6556)
DERUIJTER INTL USA INC
120 Harvest Dr (45828-8733)
P.O. Box 90 (45828-0090)
PHONE.................................419 678-3909
Fax: 419 678-3989
Hubert Deruijter, *CEO*
Roger Deruijter, *President*
◆ EMP: 10
SQ FT: 35,000
SALES (est): 1.8MM **Privately Held**
WEB: www.deruijterusa.com
SIC: 3069 Plumbers' rubber goods

HQ: De Ruijter International B.V.
Prof. Minckelersweg 1
Waalwijk
416 674-000

(G-6557)
DUES JERSEY FARM
Also Called: Dues Lumbermill
4131 Philothea Rd (45828-9756)
PHONE.................................419 678-2102
Ken Dues, *Partner*
EMP: 5
SALES (est): 400K **Privately Held**
SIC: 2421 0241 0119 Sawmills & planing
mills, general; milk production; feeder
grains

(G-6558)
EMBEDEE LLC
Also Called: Imperial Tent Company
625 Cron St (45828-8730)
PHONE.................................419 678-7007
Mary Doll, *President*
EMP: 5
SALES (est): 600.2K **Privately Held**
WEB: www.imperialtent.com
SIC: 2394 Tents: made from purchased
materials

(G-6559)
EXCEL MACHINE & TOOL INC
212 Butler St (45828-1103)
PHONE.................................419 678-3318
Timothy Moorman, *President*
Gidget Applegate, *General Mgr*
Dale Kahlig, *Vice Pres*
Mary Bergman, *Personnel Exec*
EMP: 10
SALES (est): 1.6MM **Privately Held**
WEB: www.tubebenders.com
SIC: 3599 Machine shop, jobbing & repair

(G-6560)
FORTY NINE DEGREES LLC
149 Harvest Dr (45828-8748)
PHONE.................................419 678-0100
Michael McClurg, *President*
Brad Meyer, *Exec VP*
Paul Niekamp, *Senior VP*
Jon Lee, *Production*
Dusty Ahrens, *Design Engr*
EMP: 11
SALES (est): 2.4MM **Privately Held**
WEB: www.fortyninedegrees.com
SIC: 3993 Signs & advertising specialties

(G-6561)
**HARDIN CREEK MACHINE &
TOOL**
200 Hardin St (45828-9794)
PHONE.................................419 678-4913
Fax: 419 678-8220
Joseph Wenning, *President*
Randy Schmitz, *Vice Pres*
EMP: 10
SQ FT: 6,000
SALES: 3MM **Privately Held**
SIC: 3544 3599 Special dies & tools; ma-
chine & other job shop work

(G-6562)
HEALTH CARE PRODUCTS INC
410 Nisco St (45828-8750)
P.O. Box 116 (45828-0116)
PHONE.................................419 678-9620
Michael Bruns, *President*
Konnie Rutschillin, *Director*
Laura Link, *Admin Asst*
▲ EMP: 38
SQ FT: 50,000
SALES (est): 10.1MM **Privately Held**
WEB: www.healthcareproducts.net
SIC: 2676 Napkins, sanitary: made from
purchased paper

(G-6563)
HEMMELGARN & SONS INC
3763 Philothea Rd (45828-8710)
P.O. Box 169 (45828-0169)
PHONE.................................419 678-2351
Fax: 419 678-4922
Ronald Gross, *President*
David Koesters, *Principal*
EMP: 95 EST: 1930
SQ FT: 40,000

SALES (est): 13.3MM **Privately Held**
SIC: 2015 Egg processing

(G-6564)
HOME BAKERY
109 W Main St (45828-1702)
PHONE.................................419 678-3018
Carl Brunson, *Owner*
Bruce A Fox, *Owner*
EMP: 10
SQ FT: 3,000
SALES: 120K **Privately Held**
SIC: 2051 Bakery: wholesale or whole-
sale/retail combined

(G-6565)
HOME SERVICE STATION INC
116 S 1st St (45828-1740)
PHONE.................................419 678-2612
Larry Hausfeld, *President*
EMP: 3
SALES (est): 300K **Privately Held**
SIC: 7694 Motor repair services

(G-6566)
K VENTURES INC
Also Called: EMB Designs
211 E Main St (45828-1720)
P.O. Box 112 (45828-0112)
PHONE.................................419 678-2308
Michelle Ebbing, *President*
Mike Knapschaefer, *Corp Secy*
EMP: 10
SQ FT: 24,000
SALES (est): 950K **Privately Held**
WEB: www.designsemb.com
SIC: 5099 5137 5699 2395 Signs, except
electric; women's & children's sportswear
& swimsuits; uniforms; embroidery & art
needlework

(G-6567)
**LEFELD WELDING & STL SUPS
INC (PA)**
Also Called: Lefeld Supplies Rental
600 N 2nd St (45828-9777)
PHONE.................................419 678-2397
Fax: 419 678-8279
Stanley E Lefeld, *CEO*
Gary Lefeld, *President*
Marge Lefeld, *Controller*
Cindy Myer, *Controller*
Chuck Meyer, *Accounts Mgr*
▲ EMP: 43 EST: 1953
SQ FT: 10,400
SALES (est): 25.1MM **Privately Held**
WEB: www.lefeld.com
SIC: 5084 7353 1799 3441 Welding ma-
chinery & equipment; heavy construction
equipment rental; welding on site; fabri-
cated structural metal

(G-6568)
**MERCER COLOR
CORPORATION**
425 Hardin St (45828-8742)
P.O. Box 113 (45828-0113)
PHONE.................................419 678-8273
Fax: 419 678-3144
Mark A Baumer, *President*
Patrick J Berger, *Vice Pres*
EMP: 9
SQ FT: 12,000
SALES (est): 1.4MM **Privately Held**
SIC: 2752 Commercial printing, offset

(G-6569)
POLY WORKS
4830 State Route 219 (45828-8716)
PHONE.................................419 678-3758
Fax: 419 678-3951
Michael Buschur, *Owner*
▲ EMP: 3
SQ FT: 12,000
SALES (est): 475K **Privately Held**
SIC: 2673 Plastic bags: made from pur-
chased materials

(G-6570)
RANDALL BEARINGS INC
821 Weis St (45828-9612)
PHONE.................................419 678-2486
Jeff Hager, *Branch Mgr*
EMP: 12

SALES (corp-wide): 14MM **Privately Held**
WEB: www.randallbearings.com
SIC: 3568 3624 3366 Bearings, bushings & blocks; carbon & graphite products; copper foundries
PA: Randall Bearings, Inc.
   1046 S Greenlawn Ave
   Lima OH 45804
   419 223-1075

(G-6571)
SIGNATURE PARTNERS INC
Also Called: Signature 4 Image
149 Harvest Dr (45828-8748)
PHONE...419 678-1400
Bradley Meyer, *President*
Paul Meikemp, *Vice Pres*
Scott Wolford, *Vice Pres*
Greg Bronkena, *VP Sales*
Kelly Budde, *Manager*
▲ **EMP:** 65
SALES (est): 10MM **Privately Held**
SIC: 3479 Name plates: engraved, etched, etc.

(G-6572)
STANDARD REGISTER INC
Also Called: Wilmar
515 W Sycamore St (45828-1663)
P.O. Box 109 (45828-0109)
PHONE...419 678-6000
Fax: 419 678-6521
Bob Post, *Accounts Mgr*
Mark Travers, *Accounts Mgr*
Barry Paynter, *Branch Mgr*
Gary Patner, *Manager*
EMP: 216
SALES (corp-wide): 4.6B **Privately Held**
SIC: 2759 Commercial printing
HQ: Standard Register, Inc.
   600 Albany St
   Dayton OH 45417
   937 221-1000

(G-6573)
VAL-CO PAX INC (DH)
Also Called: Val Products
210 E Main St (45828-1751)
P.O. Box 117 (45828-0117)
PHONE...717 354-4586
Fax: 419 678-2200
Frederick Steudler, *CEO*
Steve Hough, *Vice Pres*
William Kramer, *Vice Pres*
Vincent Lefeld, *Production*
▲ **EMP:** 67 EST: 1935
SQ FT: 130,000
SALES (est): 14.9MM
SALES (corp-wide): 110.6MM **Privately Held**
SIC: 3523 3443 Hog feeding, handling & watering equipment; poultry brooders, feeders & waterers; fabricated plate work (boiler shop)
HQ: Val Products, Inc.
   2599 Old Philadelphia Pike
   Bird In Hand PA 17505
   717 392-3978

(G-6574)
WILMER
515 W Sycamore St (45828-1663)
PHONE...419 678-6000
EMP: 6
SALES (est): 804.4K **Privately Held**
SIC: 2754 Gravure Commercial Printing

Collins
Huron County

(G-6575)
GAR-NAYS WINERY
1846 Wells Rd (44826-9734)
PHONE...419 668-6802
Gary L Grose, *Administration*
EMP: 3
SALES (est): 123.7K **Privately Held**
SIC: 2084 Wines

(G-6576)
PA STRATTON & CO INC
3768 State Route 20 (44826-9514)
P.O. Box 61 (44826-0061)
PHONE...419 660-9979
Fax: 419 499-3379
Paul Stratton, *President*
Sally Stratton, *Corp Secy*
EMP: 3
SALES: 17K **Privately Held**
SIC: 3429 Furniture builders' & other household hardware

Columbia Station
Lorain County

(G-6577)
252 TATTOO (PA)
24525 Sprague Rd (44028-9601)
PHONE...440 235-6699
James Bulloch, *Owner*
EMP: 4
SALES (est): 259.9K **Privately Held**
SIC: 7299 7372 Tattoo parlor; prepackaged software

(G-6578)
ANDY PAC INC
11600 Hawke Rd (44028-9192)
P.O. Box 546 (44028-0546)
PHONE...440 748-8800
Fax: 440 748-3501
Robert A Anderson, *CEO*
Eric Anderson, *President*
Dianna Lutz, *Manager*
EMP: 4
SQ FT: 4,000
SALES: 1MM **Privately Held**
SIC: 3565 Packaging machinery

(G-6579)
AQUATIC TECHNOLOGY
26966 Royalton Rd (44028-9758)
PHONE...440 236-8330
Fax: 440 236-8336
Greg Smith, *Owner*
◆ **EMP:** 10
SQ FT: 4,300
SALES: 1.5MM **Privately Held**
WEB: www.aquatictech.com
SIC: 5999 5199 3999 Pets & pet supplies; pets & pet supplies; pet supplies

(G-6580)
ATOM BLASTING & FINISHING INC
24933 Sprague Rd (44028-9671)
PHONE...440 235-4765
Fax: 440 235-6560
Richard Ferry, *President*
Karen Widener, *Vice Pres*
▲ **EMP:** 6
SALES (est): 550K **Privately Held**
SIC: 3471 Finishing, metals or formed products; sand blasting of metal parts

(G-6581)
BOWES MILL AND CABINET LLC
33549 E Royalton Rd # 7 (44028-9307)
PHONE...440 236-3255
Tom Bowes,
EMP: 3
SALES: 100K **Privately Held**
SIC: 2434 Wood kitchen cabinets

(G-6582)
CAL SALES EMBROIDERY
13975 Station Rd (44028-9401)
PHONE...440 236-3820
Fax: 440 236-3821
Edward L Pete Houston, *Owner*
Edward L Houston, *Owner*
Pete Houston, *General Mgr*
EMP: 6
SQ FT: 1,800
SALES (est): 392.5K **Privately Held**
SIC: 2395 2396 5199 Embroidery & art needlework; screen printing on fabric articles; advertising specialties

(G-6583)
CINEEN INC
25011 Royalton Rd (44028-9404)
PHONE...440 236-3658
Yusra Suleiman, *Principal*
EMP: 4
SALES (est): 149.2K **Privately Held**
SIC: 2082 5999 Beer (alcoholic beverage); ale (alcoholic beverage); alcoholic beverage making equipment & supplies

(G-6584)
COLUMBIA CABINETS INC
33550 E Royalton Rd 4-5 (44028-9306)
PHONE...440 748-1010
Charles Dunn, *President*
EMP: 3
SQ FT: 4,000
SALES: 200K **Privately Held**
SIC: 2599 1799 Cabinets, factory; counter top installation

(G-6585)
COLUMBIA STAMPING INC
13676 Station Rd (44028-9538)
PHONE...440 236-6677
James D Galvin, *President*
Debbie Bailes, *General Mgr*
Lisa Dillinger, *General Mgr*
Ken Dillinger, *Corp Secy*
EMP: 15
SQ FT: 37,000
SALES (est): 2.7MM **Privately Held**
SIC: 3544 3542 Die sets for metal stamping (presses); die casting machines

(G-6586)
CONTROL ELECTRIC CO
12130 Eaton Commerce Pkwy (44028-9208)
PHONE...216 671-8010
Fax: 216 476-0072
Mike Vogt, *President*
Rob Horvath, *Engineer*
Bob Maugeri, *Engng Exec*
EMP: 23 EST: 1963
SQ FT: 6,800
SALES (est): 6.4MM **Privately Held**
WEB: www.controlelectric.com
SIC: 3625 8711 2542 Industrial electrical relays & switches; engineering services; partitions & fixtures, except wood

(G-6587)
DIMENSION INDUSTRIES INC
27335 Royalton Rd (44028-9159)
P.O. Box 1130 (44028-1130)
PHONE...440 236-3265
Fax: 440 236-8774
William Biljes, *President*
EMP: 12
SQ FT: 7,200
SALES (est): 1MM **Privately Held**
SIC: 3599 Machine & other job shop work

(G-6588)
DJ PALLETS
23845 Royalton Rd (44028-9458)
PHONE...216 701-9183
James Violi, *Principal*
EMP: 4
SALES (est): 393.4K **Privately Held**
SIC: 2448 Pallets, wood & wood with metal

(G-6589)
DOVE MACHINE INC
27100 Royalton Rd (44028-9048)
P.O. Box 1003 (44028-1003)
PHONE...440 864-2645
Fax: 440 236-3582
James Dove, *President*
Anna Dove, *Vice Pres*
Earl Dove, *Manager*
EMP: 15
SQ FT: 37,000
SALES (est): 2MM **Privately Held**
SIC: 3451 3714 Screw machine products; motor vehicle parts & accessories

(G-6590)
LA GANKE & SONS STAMPING CO
13676 Station Rd (44028-9538)
PHONE...216 451-0278
Fax: 216 451-0279

Charles Laganke, *President*
Paul Moses, *Vice Pres*
Kim Lorris, *Admin Sec*
EMP: 10 EST: 1961
SQ FT: 18,500
SALES (est): 1.4MM **Privately Held**
SIC: 3469 3544 Stamping metal for the trade; special dies & tools; jigs & fixtures

(G-6591)
MODERN MOLD AND TOOL
27684 Royalton Rd (44028-9073)
PHONE...440 236-9600
Fax: 440 236-8730
David Bowes, *Owner*
EMP: 7
SALES (est): 643.5K **Privately Held**
WEB: www.modernmoldandtool.com
SIC: 3599 Machine shop, jobbing & repair

(G-6592)
NOBAL ENTERPRISES INC
11470 Hawke Rd Unit 3 (44028-9805)
PHONE...440 748-0522
Paul J Novak, *President*
EMP: 5
SQ FT: 2,500
SALES: 92K **Privately Held**
SIC: 3599 Machine shop, jobbing & repair

(G-6593)
PERRONS PRINTING COMPANY
Also Called: Image Graphics
27500 Royalton Rd (44028-9713)
P.O. Box 669 (44028-0669)
PHONE...440 236-8870
Fax: 440 236-5576
Edward Perron Sr, *President*
George D Maurer Sr, *Principal*
Linda Perron, *Vice Pres*
EMP: 20
SQ FT: 10,000
SALES (est): 3.7MM **Privately Held**
SIC: 2752 7336 Commercial printing, offset; graphic arts & related design

(G-6594)
PIER TOOL & DIE INC
27369 Royalton Rd (44028-9159)
P.O. Box 452 (44028-0452)
PHONE...440 236-3188
Fax: 440 236-3193
Mario J Pierzchala, *President*
Karen Pierzchala, *Vice Pres*
Randy Pierzchala, *Plant Mgr*
EMP: 13
SQ FT: 15,000
SALES: 1.5MM **Privately Held**
SIC: 3544 Special dies & tools

(G-6595)
PRINT DIRECT FOR LESS 2 INC
27500 Royalton Rd (44028-9713)
P.O. Box 669 (44028-0669)
PHONE...440 236-8870
Linda Perron, *President*
Nellie Akalp, *Principal*
Edward M Perron Jr, *Vice Pres*
▼ **EMP:** 22
SALES (est): 4.2MM **Privately Held**
WEB: www.printdirectforless.com
SIC: 2752 Commercial printing, lithographic

(G-6596)
ROLLER SOURCE INC
34100 E Royalton Rd (44028-9759)
PHONE...440 748-4033
Steve Leuschel, *President*
George Novak, *Vice Pres*
EMP: 10
SALES: 600K **Privately Held**
WEB: www.therollersource.com
SIC: 3052 Rubber & plastics hose & beltings

(G-6597)
ROYALTON INDUSTRIES INC
12450 Eaton Commerce Pkwy (44028-9213)
PHONE...440 748-9900
William A Baltes Sr, *Ch of Bd*
William A Baltes Jr, *Treasurer*
Len Steinmeyer, *VP Sales*
Ray Dombrosky, *Sales Staff*
Jennifer Giustino, *Manager*

EMP: 10 **EST:** 1979
SQ FT: 10,000
SALES (est): 1.8MM **Privately Held**
WEB: www.royaltonindustries.com
SIC: 3599 Custom machinery

(G-6598)
RURAL URBAN RECORD INC
24487 Squire Rd (44028-9648)
P.O. Box 966 (44028-0966)
PHONE................................440 236-8982
Fax: 440 236-9198
Leonard Boise, *President*
Lee Boise, *Vice Pres*
EMP: 6
SQ FT: 1,966
SALES (est): 406.7K **Privately Held**
SIC: 2711 Newspapers

(G-6599)
SERENA SAFETY
8334 N Marks Rd (44028-9677)
PHONE................................440 572-4481
Mike Smith, *Owner*
EMP: 4
SALES (est): 571.6K **Privately Held**
SIC: 3842 Clothing, fire resistant & protective

(G-6600)
SHARC INDUSTRIES
10600 Bridle Path (44028-9699)
PHONE................................216 272-0668
Scott Thomas, *Principal*
EMP: 8
SALES (est): 969.1K **Privately Held**
SIC: 3999 Manufacturing industries

(G-6601)
SUPERIOR ENERGY SYSTEMS LLC
13660 Station Rd (44028-9538)
PHONE................................440 236-6009
Donald Fernald, *CEO*
Philip J Lombardo, *Principal*
Derek Rimko, *Vice Pres*
Mike Walters, *Vice Pres*
William J Young, *Vice Pres*
▼ **EMP:** 17
SQ FT: 14,000
SALES (est): 5.4MM **Privately Held**
WEB: www.superiorenergysystems.com
SIC: 3714 Propane conversion equipment, motor vehicle

(G-6602)
SZPAK MANUFACTURING CO INC
27500 Royalton Rd Unit 5 (44028-9713)
P.O. Box 543 (44028-0543)
PHONE................................440 236-5233
Fax: 440 236-5233
Joseph Szpak Jr, *President*
Tony Szpak, *Vice Pres*
EMP: 7
SQ FT: 2,500
SALES (est): 450K **Privately Held**
WEB: www.szpakmfg.com
SIC: 3599 Machine shop, jobbing & repair

(G-6603)
TRIAD CAPITAL AAT LLC
Also Called: American Assembly Tools
13676 Station Rd (44028-9538)
PHONE................................440 236-4163
Philip Rankin,
EMP: 4
SQ FT: 27,500
SALES (est): 321K **Privately Held**
SIC: 3546 Power-driven handtools

Columbiana
Columbiana County

(G-6604)
A PLUS POWDER COATERS INC
1384 Kauffman Ave (44408-9750)
PHONE................................330 482-4389
Fax: 330 482-1851
Robert Bertelsen, *President*
EMP: 12
SQ FT: 20,250

SALES (est): 1.3MM **Privately Held**
WEB: www.apluspowder.com
SIC: 3479 Coating of metals & formed products

(G-6605)
ALLOY MACHINING AND FABG
1028 Lower Elkton Rd (44408-8427)
P.O. Box 49 (44408-0049)
PHONE................................330 482-5543
Ed Keating, *President*
Patty Strohcket, *Manager*
EMP: 23
SALES (est): 4.1MM **Privately Held**
SIC: 3599 Machine shop, jobbing & repair

(G-6606)
BIRDFISH BREWING COMPANY LLC
16 S Main St (44408-1348)
PHONE................................330 397-4010
Joshua Dunn, *CEO*
Jared Channell, *President*
Gregory Snyder, *Vice Pres*
EMP: 5 **EST:** 2014
SQ FT: 1,250
SALES (est): 165.5K **Privately Held**
SIC: 2082 Beer (alcoholic beverage)

(G-6607)
BOARDMAN STEEL INC
156 Nulf Dr (44408-9720)
PHONE................................330 758-0951
Fax: 330 758-7267
Dave Deibel, *President*
Mary Allen, *Manager*
EMP: 55 **EST:** 1963
SQ FT: 49,000
SALES (est): 12.2MM **Privately Held**
WEB: www.boardmansteel.com
SIC: 3441 Fabricated structural metal

(G-6608)
BUCKEYE COMPONENTS LLC (PA)
1340 State Route 14 (44408-9648)
PHONE................................330 482-5163
Robert Holmes,
EMP: 29
SQ FT: 8,000
SALES (est): 2.9MM **Privately Held**
SIC: 5031 2439 Lumber, plywood & millwork; trusses, wooden roof

(G-6609)
CENTURY CONTAINER LLC
32 W Railroad St (44408-1203)
PHONE................................330 457-2367
EMP: 6
SALES (corp-wide): 92.9MM **Privately Held**
SIC: 3089 Plastic containers, except foam
HQ: Century Container, Llc
5331 State Route 7
New Waterford OH 44445
330 457-2367

(G-6610)
COBBLERS CORNER LLC
1115 Village Plz (44408-8480)
PHONE................................330 482-4005
Fax: 330 482-3703
Terry Thompson,
Jennifer Balint,
EMP: 13
SQ FT: 8,000
SALES (est): 850K **Privately Held**
SIC: 5661 3021 7251 Men's boots; women's boots; rubber & plastics footwear; shoes, rubber or rubber soled fabric uppers; footwear, custom made; shoe repair shop

(G-6611)
COL-PUMP COMPANY INC
131 E Railroad St (44408-1318)
PHONE................................330 482-1029
Fax: 330 482-1029
Thomas Bowker, *President*
Paul Rance, *Vice Pres*
Corey Bowker, *Plant Mgr*
Diana Trevena, *Human Res Mgr*
EMP: 60
SQ FT: 100,000

SALES (est): 13.2MM **Privately Held**
WEB: www.col-pump.net
SIC: 3321 Gray iron castings

(G-6612)
COLUMBIANA BOILER COMPANY LLC
200 W Railroad St (44408-1281)
PHONE................................330 482-3373
Fax: 330 482-3390
Michael J Sherwin, *President*
Wayne Good, *Vice Pres*
Chuck Gorby, *Vice Pres*
Gerianne Klepfer, *CFO*
John Bossone, *Director*
◆ **EMP:** 45 **EST:** 1894
SQ FT: 50,000
SALES: 9.5MM **Privately Held**
SIC: 1791 3443 Storage tanks, metal: erection; process vessels, industrial: metal plate
PA: Columbiana Holding Co Inc
200 W Railroad St
Columbiana OH 44408
330 482-3373

(G-6613)
COLUMBIANA HOLDING CO INC (PA)
200 W Railroad St (44408-1281)
PHONE................................330 482-3373
Thomas F Dougherty, *Ch of Bd*
John J Barrow, *Ch of Bd*
Trevor M Rummel, *Exec VP*
Gerianne Klepfer, *CFO*
Michael Sherwin, *Director*
▲ **EMP:** 4
SALES (est): 9.5MM **Privately Held**
SIC: 3443 Process vessels, industrial: metal plate

(G-6614)
COMPCO INDUSTRIES INCORPORATED (HQ)
400 W Railroad St Ste 1 (44408-1213)
PHONE................................330 482-6488
Fax: 330 482-6488
Clarence R Smith Jr, *Ch of Bd*
Eric Folsom, *President*
Gregory B Smith Sr, *President*
Robert Bachinger, *Exec VP*
Jim Morchak, *Project Mgr*
EMP: 63 **EST:** 1952
SQ FT: 200,000
SALES (est): 24.1MM **Privately Held**
WEB: www.compcoind.com
SIC: 3443 3469 3444 Tanks, standard or custom fabricated: metal plate; metal stampings; sheet metalwork
PA: S-P Company, Inc
400 W Railroad St Ste 1
Columbiana OH 44408
330 482-0200

(G-6615)
ENVELOPE 1 INC (PA)
41969 State Route 344 (44408-9421)
PHONE................................330 482-3900
Fax: 330 482-0388
Tarry Pidgeon, *CEO*
Bob Friebel, *Natl Sales Mgr*
▲ **EMP:** 90
SALES (est): 104MM **Privately Held**
SIC: 2677 Envelopes

(G-6616)
FEDERAL IRON WORKS COMPANY
42082 State Route 344 (44408-9421)
P.O. Box 150 (44408-0150)
PHONE................................330 482-5910
Fax: 330 482-5911
Edward M Sferra Jr, *President*
Marcella A Sferra, *Vice Pres*
Laura Fortunato, *Treasurer*
EMP: 20
SALES (est): 3.7MM **Privately Held**
SIC: 3446 1761 Architectural metalwork; architectural sheet metal work

(G-6617)
FOSTER PATTERN WORKS INC
1371 Kauffman Ave (44408)
P.O. Box 14 (44408-0014)
PHONE................................330 482-3612

Fax: 330 482-2872
William Huffman, *President*
Louis Huffman, *Vice Pres*
EMP: 4
SQ FT: 5,000
SALES: 280K **Privately Held**
SIC: 3543 Industrial patterns

(G-6618)
GREEN HARVEST ENERGY LLC
1340 State Route 14 (44408-9648)
P.O. Box 82, Greenford (44422-0082)
PHONE................................330 716-3068
John J Monroe, *President*
Jean Holt, *Principal*
Robert J Holmes, *Chairman*
EMP: 16
SALES: 0 **Privately Held**
SIC: 2869 Industrial organic chemicals

(G-6619)
HAYS ORCHARD & CIDER MILL LLC
3622 Middleton Rd (44408-9596)
PHONE................................330 482-2924
Fax: 330 482-3687
Todd Valendza, *Mng Member*
EMP: 15
SALES: 3MM **Privately Held**
SIC: 2099 Cider, nonalcoholic

(G-6620)
HORST PACKING INC
3535 Renkenberger Rd (44408-9763)
PHONE................................330 482-2997
David Horst, *President*
Debra Horst, *Admin Sec*
EMP: 6
SQ FT: 1,500
SALES (est): 578.9K **Privately Held**
SIC: 2011 Meat packing plants

(G-6621)
HUMTOWN PATTERN COMPANY
Also Called: Humtown Products
44708 Clmbana Wterford Rd (44408-9605)
P.O. Box 367 (44408-0367)
PHONE................................330 482-5555
Fax: 330 482-9307
Mark Lamoncha, *President*
Brandon Lamoncha, *Principal*
Bronson Lamoncha, *Principal*
Sheri Lamoncha, *Principal*
Terrie Marshall, *Principal*
EMP: 60 **EST:** 1959
SQ FT: 55,000
SALES: 10MM **Privately Held**
WEB: www.humtown.com
SIC: 3543 2759 Industrial patterns; foundry cores; commercial printing

(G-6622)
J & H MANUFACTURING LLC
1652 Columbiana Lisbon Rd (44408-9443)
P.O. Box 12 (44408-0012)
PHONE................................330 482-2636
Fax: 330 482-2638
John Kephart, *Mng Member*
▲ **EMP:** 11
SQ FT: 41,000
SALES (est): 2.1MM **Privately Held**
SIC: 3423 Hand & edge tools; screw drivers, pliers, chisels, etc. (hand tools)

(G-6623)
J&J PRECISION FABRICATORS
1341 Heck Rd (44408-9599)
PHONE................................330 482-4964
Hans Leitner, *Managing Prtnr*
John Tunning, *Manager*
EMP: 17
SQ FT: 11,500
SALES (est): 3.6MM **Privately Held**
SIC: 3312 Plate, steel

(G-6624)
MILLER CASTING INC
1634 Lower Elkton Rd (44408-9404)
P.O. Box 440 (44408-0440)
PHONE................................330 482-2923
Fax: 330 482-5044
Mike Miller, *President*
EMP: 15
SALES (est): 1.9MM **Privately Held**
SIC: 3365 Aluminum foundries

**G
E
O
G
R
A
P
H
I
C**

(G-6625)
MUNICIPAL SIGNS AND SALES INC
1219 Mcclosky Rd (44408-9510)
PHONE.................................330 457-2421
Fax: 330 457-2955
Jay Strohecker, *President*
Jean Gernert, *Vice Pres*
EMP: 5
SQ FT: 1,260
SALES: 410K Privately Held
SIC: 3993 Signs, not made in custom sign painting shops

(G-6626)
O T PACKAGING
308 Kingwood Dr (44408-1106)
PHONE.................................330 482-2224
Fax: 330 482-2250
Sue Hahn, *President*
Raymon Hahn, *Vice Pres*
Lee Hahn, *Admin Sec*
EMP: 5
SQ FT: 5,000
SALES (est): 560K Privately Held
WEB: www.clangonline.com
SIC: 5113 2752 Folding paperboard boxes; containers, paper & disposable plastic; commercial printing, lithographic

(G-6627)
OAKS WELDING INC
201 Prospect St (44408)
PHONE.................................330 482-4216
Jack Guy, *President*
Jeff Guy, *President*
Geri Rubicky, *Treasurer*
Maribell Guy, *Admin Sec*
EMP: 8
SQ FT: 11,025
SALES (est): 1.1MM Privately Held
SIC: 3599 7692 7629 Machine shop, jobbing & repair; welding repair; electrical repair shops

(G-6628)
PHD MANUFACTURING INC
44018 Clmbana Wterford Rd (44408-9481)
PHONE.................................330 482-9256
Fax: 330 482-2763
Anthony A Kopatich, *President*
Joseph J Corvino, *President*
Sue Dotson, *Controller*
Gene Hancock, *Natl Sales Mgr*
Toni Hussar, *VP Sales*
EMP: 110
SQ FT: 131,000
SALES (est): 48.5MM Privately Held
WEB: www.phd-mfg.com
SIC: 3494 Pipe fittings

(G-6629)
RANCE INDUSTRIES INC
1361 Heck Rd (44408-9599)
P.O. Box 325 (44408-0325)
PHONE.................................330 482-1745
Fax: 330 482-1727
John Rance, *President*
Brad Rance, *Senior VP*
Karen Rance, *Treasurer*
Mary Rance, *Admin Sec*
EMP: 15
SQ FT: 20,000
SALES (est): 2.2MM Privately Held
WEB: www.ranceindustries.com
SIC: 3441 Fabricated structural metal

(G-6630)
REICHARD INDUSTRIES LLC (PA)
338 S Main St (44408-1500)
PHONE.................................330 482-5511
Fax: 330 482-3743
Keith A Reichard, *President*
James E Reichard, *Chairman*
Dwayne E Reichard, *Vice Pres*
Kim Cox, *Purchasing*
James Hawkins, *Controller*
EMP: 2
SQ FT: 57,000
SALES (est): 1.4MM Privately Held
SIC: 3599 Custom machinery

(G-6631)
S-P COMPANY INC (PA)
400 W Railroad St Ste 1 (44408-1294)
PHONE.................................330 482-0200
Clarence R Smith Jr, *Ch of Bd*
Gregory B Smith, *President*
Douglas Hagy, *CFO*
EMP: 14
SQ FT: 44,000
SALES (est): 24.1MM Privately Held
SIC: 3469 3443 3498 6512 Metal stampings; tanks, standard or custom fabricated: metal plate; tube fabricating (contract bending & shaping); commercial & industrial building operation; gift shop; custom machinery

(G-6632)
SITLER PRINTER INC
707 E Park Ave (44408-1447)
PHONE.................................330 482-4463
Fax: 330 482-1076
Christine R Davis, *President*
Lee Davis, *Vice Pres*
EMP: 8 EST: 1909
SQ FT: 2,000
SALES (est): 1.3MM Privately Held
WEB: www.sitlertheprinter.com
SIC: 2752 2759 Commercial printing, offset; letterpress printing

(G-6633)
SPECIALTY CERAMICS INC
41995 State Route 344 (44408-9421)
PHONE.................................330 482-0800
Fax: 330 482-0844
Richard Ludwig, *President*
Richard F Wilk, *Corp Secy*
Jim Vaughn, *Controller*
Kevin Smith, *Sales Executive*
Kevin McClain, *Supervisor*
EMP: 100
SQ FT: 47,000
SALES (est): 27.8MM Privately Held
WEB: www.scilogs.com
SIC: 3433 3255 Logs, gas fireplace; clay refractories

(G-6634)
STAR FAB INC
400 W Railroad St Ste 8 (44408-1294)
P.O. Box 553, Canfield (44406-0553)
PHONE.................................330 482-1601
Fax: 330 533-5704
John Zepernick, *Branch Mgr*
EMP: 50
SALES (corp-wide): 24.2MM Privately Held
WEB: www.starext.com
SIC: 3354 3711 Aluminum extruded products; automobile assembly, including specialty automobiles
PA: Star Fab, Inc.
7055 Herbert Rd
Canfield OH 44406
330 533-9863

(G-6635)
TRACKER MACHINE INC
1370 Kauffman Ave (44408-9750)
PHONE.................................330 482-4086
William Niemi, *President*
EMP: 5
SALES (est): 250K Privately Held
SIC: 3544 Industrial molds

(G-6636)
UNIVERSAL PERCUSSION INC
1431 Heck Rd (44408-9599)
PHONE.................................330 482-5750
Fax: 330 482-5760
Howert Rubenstein, *President*
▲ EMP: 10
SALES (est): 760K Privately Held
WEB: www.universalpercussion.com
SIC: 3931 5736 Percussion instruments & parts; musical instrument stores

(G-6637)
VARI-WALL TUBE SPECIALISTS INC
1350 Wardingsley Ave (44408-9727)
P.O. Box 340 (44408-0340)
PHONE.................................330 482-0000
Fax: 330 482-0002
Randall Alexoff, *President*

Peter Alexoff, *Exec VP*
Robert Long, *QC Mgr*
Joe Mortellaro, *Controller*
Thomas Lodge, *Admin Sec*
▲ EMP: 100
SQ FT: 60,000
SALES (est): 20.3MM Privately Held
WEB: www.vari-wall.com
SIC: 3354 3751 3714 Shapes, extruded aluminum; motorcycles, bicycles & parts; motor vehicle parts & accessories

(G-6638)
YES MANAGEMENT INC (PA)
Also Called: Youngstown Electric Supply
44612 State Route 14 (44408-9540)
PHONE.................................330 747-8593
Fax: 330 482-5199
Lee De Rose, *President*
Lee Derose, *Research*
James Hunt, *Human Res Dir*
Bob Hildbrand, *Branch Mgr*
Randy Maas, *Branch Mgr*
EMP: 2
SQ FT: 22,000
SALES (est): 66.8MM Privately Held
WEB: www.yeselectric.com
SIC: 5063 3993 Electrical supplies; signs & advertising specialties

(G-6639)
ZARBANA ALUM EXTRUSIONS LLC
41738 Esterly Dr (44408-9448)
P.O. Box 46 (44408-0046)
PHONE.................................330 482-5092
Tom Morell, *President*
EMP: 37 EST: 2005
SALES (est): 1.6MM Privately Held
SIC: 3354 Aluminum extruded products

Columbus
Delaware County

(G-6640)
BARBEQUE INTEGRATED INC
Also Called: Smokey Bones Bbq
1481 Polaris Pkwy (43240-6002)
PHONE.................................614 430-0572
Fax: 614 430-0578
Jeremy Miller, *Branch Mgr*
EMP: 80
SALES (corp-wide): 17.2B Privately Held
WEB: www.smokeybones.com
SIC: 5812 5813 2082 Barbecue restaurant; drinking places; malt beverages
HQ: Barbeque Integrated, Inc.
2999 Ne 191st St Ste 500
Miami FL 33180
407 355-5800

(G-6641)
BRIDGESTONE FIRESTONE
8510 Orion Pl (43240-4028)
PHONE.................................614 523-2259
Steve Muscato, *Principal*
EMP: 6
SALES (est): 568.6K Privately Held
SIC: 5014 3011 Tires & tubes; tires & inner tubes

(G-6642)
BRISTOL-MYERS SQUIBB COMPANY
999 Polaris Pkwy Ste 100 (43240-2051)
PHONE.................................800 321-1335
Fax: 614 431-5644
Steve Betulius, *Branch Mgr*
EMP: 40
SALES (corp-wide): 19.4B Publicly Held
WEB: www.bms.com
SIC: 2834 Pharmaceutical preparations; drugs acting on the central nervous system & sense organs
PA: Bristol-Myers Squibb Company
345 Park Ave Bsmt Lc3
New York NY 10154
212 546-4000

(G-6643)
BROAD STREET IMAGING
2141 Polaris Pkwy (43240-2022)
PHONE.................................614 621-9100

Fax: 614 621-9107
Jill Litzinger, *Business Mgr*
Roxanne Mackey, *Office Mgr*
EMP: 9
SQ FT: 1,000
SALES (est): 1MM
SALES (corp-wide): 220.5MM Privately Held
SIC: 3841 8099 Diagnostic apparatus, medical; physical examination & testing services
HQ: Insight Health Services Corp.
5775 Wayzata Blvd Ste 400
Minneapolis MN 55416

(G-6644)
COACH INC
1500 Polaris Pkwy # 1198 (43240-2130)
PHONE.................................614 885-6184
Steve Glimcher, *Manager*
EMP: 15
SALES (corp-wide): 4.4B Publicly Held
WEB: www.coach.com
SIC: 3171 Handbags, women's
PA: Coach, Inc.
10 Hudson Yards
New York NY 10001
212 594-1850

(G-6645)
EXACT EQUIPMENT CORPORATION (HQ)
1900 Polaris Pkwy (43240-4035)
PHONE.................................215 295-2000
Robert C Enichan, *President*
Bernie Randall, *Engineer*
F Basil, *Sales Staff*
Deborah Davis, *Advt Staff*
EMP: 10
SQ FT: 9,000
SALES (est): 1.4MM
SALES (corp-wide): 2.5B Publicly Held
WEB: www.exactequipment.com
SIC: 3565 3596 3824 Packaging machinery; industrial scales; fluid meters & counting devices
PA: Mettler-Toledo International Inc.
1900 Polaris Pkwy Fl 6
Columbus OH 43240
614 438-4511

(G-6646)
FARAH JEWELERS INC
1500 Polaris Pkwy # 2156 (43240-2133)
PHONE.................................614 438-6140
Eli Hannoush, *President*
Chris Fyffe, *Sales Associate*
EMP: 18
SQ FT: 1,500
SALES (est): 2.5MM Privately Held
SIC: 3911 5944 Jewelry mountings & trimmings; jewelry stores

(G-6647)
FUSIONSTORM
Also Called: Adexis
1900 Polaris Pkwy Ste 385 (43240-4035)
PHONE.................................614 431-8000
EMP: 9
SALES (corp-wide): 279.5MM Privately Held
SIC: 7372 Prepackaged software
PA: Fusionstorm
2 Bryant St Ste 150
San Francisco CA 94105
415 623-2626

(G-6648)
HANGER PROSTHETICS & ORTHOTICS
Also Called: Hanger Clinic
1210 Gemini Pl Ste 101 (43240-6111)
PHONE.................................614 436-3516
Vinit Asar, *Ch of Bd*
Sam Liang, *President*
Sheryl Price, *Director*
EMP: 99
SALES (est): 3.2MM Privately Held
SIC: 3842 Surgical appliances & supplies

(G-6649)
HEADLEE ENTERPRISES LTD
Also Called: AlphaGraphics
9015 Antares Ave (43240-2012)
PHONE.................................614 785-0011
Chad M Headlee, *Partner*

Murray A Headlee, *Partner*
Raymond Hummons Jr, *Manager*
EMP: 8
SQ FT: 4,200
SALES (est) 1.5MM **Privately Held**
SIC: 2752 Commercial printing, lithographic

(G-6650)
HIBU INC
8415 Pulsar Pl Ste 200 (43240-4032)
PHONE..................614 468-7900
EMP: 20
SALES (corp-wide): 23K **Privately Held**
SIC: 2741 Telephone & other directory publishing
HQ: Hibu Inc.
   90 Merrick Ave Ste 530
   East Meadow NY 11554
   516 730-1900

(G-6651)
LEAF & THORN PRESS
1080 Pebble Brook Dr (43240-6040)
PHONE..................614 396-6055
Kathleen Groger, *Principal*
EMP: 3
SALES (est): 76.2K **Privately Held**
SIC: 2711 Newspapers

(G-6652)
**MCGRAW-HILL SCHOOL
EDUCATION H**
8787 Orion Pl (43240-4027)
PHONE..................614 430-4000
Fax: 614 430-6441
Chris Wiggens, *Principal*
Carla Samodulski, *Editor*
Magdalena Turner, *Editor*
Lisa Carmona, *Vice Pres*
Shelly Becker, *Buyer*
EMP: 500
SALES (corp-wide): 750MM **Privately Held**
WEB: www.mcgraw-hill.com
SIC: 2731 Book publishing
PA: Mcgraw-Hill School Education Holdings, Llc
   2 Penn Plz Fl 20
   New York NY 10121
   646 766-2000

(G-6653)
METTLER-TOLEDO INTL FIN INC
1900 Polaris Pkwy Fl 6 (43240-4055)
PHONE..................614 438-4511
Olivier Filliol, *CEO*
Rita Britz, *Asst Treas*
EMP: 4
SALES (est): 381.9K
SALES (corp-wide): 2.5B **Publicly Held**
SIC: 3596 5049 7699 3821 Industrial scales; weighing machines & apparatus; analytical instruments; professional instrument repair services; pipettes, hemocytometer; balances, laboratory; electrodes used in industrial process measurement; refractometers, except industrial process type; liquid chromatographic instruments; moisture analyzers; pH meters, except industrial process type
HQ: Mettler-Toledo, Llc
   1900 Polaris Pkwy Fl 6
   Columbus OH 43240
   614 438-4511

(G-6654)
**METTLER-TOLEDO INTL INC
(PA)**
1900 Polaris Pkwy Fl 6 (43240-4055)
PHONE..................614 438-4511
Fax: 614 438-4900
Robert F Spoerry, *Ch of Bd*
Olivier A Filliol, *President*
Jennifer McCallum, *Top Exec*
William P Donnelly, *Exec VP*
Bradley Roark, *Vice Pres*
◆ **EMP:** 276 **EST:** 1991
SALES: 2.5B **Publicly Held**
WEB: www.mt.com
SIC: 3596 3821 3826 3823 Industrial scales; laboratory measuring apparatus; balances, laboratory; analytical instruments; industrial instrmnts msrmnt display/control process variable

(G-6655)
**METTLR-TLEDO GLOBL
HLDINGS LLC (HQ)**
1900 Polaris Pkwy (43240-4035)
PHONE..................614 438-4511
Mary T Finnegan, *Treasurer*
EMP: 6 **EST:** 2010
SALES (est): 9.2MM
SALES (corp-wide): 2.5B **Publicly Held**
SIC: 3451 3826 Screw machine products; analytical instruments
PA: Mettler-Toledo International Inc.
   1900 Polaris Pkwy Fl 6
   Columbus OH 43240
   614 438-4511

(G-6656)
MICROSOFT CORPORATION
8800 Lyra Dr Ste 400 (43240-2100)
PHONE..................614 719-5900
Fax: 614 985-1832
Marrida Davis, *General Mgr*
Doug Brennan, *Sales Staff*
Dan Shea, *Manager*
Eric Savoldi, *Technical Staff*
Chris Huff, *Director*
EMP: 45
SALES (corp-wide): 85.3B **Publicly Held**
WEB: www.microsoft.com
SIC: 7372 Prepackaged software
PA: Microsoft Corporation
   1 Microsoft Way
   Redmond WA 98052
   425 882-8080

(G-6657)
OIL BAR LLC
1500 Polaris Pkwy # 2072 (43240-2132)
PHONE..................614 880-3950
Jamie Dennis, *Branch Mgr*
EMP: 14
SALES (est): 770K **Privately Held**
SIC: 2844 7299 Toilet preparations; massage parlor

(G-6658)
RENEWAL BY ANDERSEN LLC
400 Lazelle Rd Ste 1 (43240-2077)
PHONE..................614 781-9600
Jake Zahnow, *Principal*
EMP: 7
SALES (corp-wide): 2.9B **Privately Held**
SIC: 3442 2431 Screens, window, metal; millwork
HQ: Renewal By Andersen Llc
   9900 Jamaica Ave S
   Cottage Grove MN 55016
   855 871-7377

(G-6659)
**UNITED CONTROLS GROUP INC
(PA)**
400 Lazelle Rd Ste 13 (43240-4051)
PHONE..................740 936-0005
Elliott Allison, *CEO*
Juan Falcone, *General Mgr*
Brian Savinsky, *Principal*
Ken Hackworth, *Purchasing*
Paul Mayhan, *Chief Engr*
EMP: 3
SQ FT: 3,500
SALES (est): 2.8MM **Privately Held**
SIC: 3694 Engine electrical equipment

(G-6660)
UNITED CONTROLS GROUP INC
400 Lazelle Rd Ste 14 (43240-2077)
PHONE..................740 936-0005
Elliott Allison, *Principal*
EMP: 7
SALES (corp-wide): 2.8MM **Privately Held**
SIC: 3694 Engine electrical equipment
PA: United Controls Group, Inc.
   400 Lazelle Rd Ste 13
   Columbus OH 43240
   740 936-0005

(G-6661)
**VEEAM SOFTWARE
CORPORATION (PA)**
8800 Lyra Dr Ste 350 (43240-2151)
PHONE..................678 353-2140
Ratmir Timashev, *President*
Anton Antich, *Vice Pres*

Bill Botti, *Vice Pres*
Doug Hazelman, *Vice Pres*
Rick Hoffman, *Vice Pres*
EMP: 9
SALES: 90.1K **Privately Held**
SIC: 7372 Prepackaged software

(G-6662)
ZNODE INC
8415 Pulsar Pl Ste 200 (43240-4032)
P.O. Box 3162, Cedar Rapids IA (52406-3162)
PHONE..................614 468-7900
Vish Vishwanathan, *CEO*
Dan Clifford, *Sales Staff*
David Chu, *CTO*
Hugh Cathy, *Advisor*
EMP: 16
SALES (est): 1.6MM
SALES (corp-wide): 211.5K **Privately Held**
WEB: www.znode.com
SIC: 7372 Business oriented computer software
PA: Woodpro Software Inc
   2680 Shell Rd Suite 208
   Richmond BC V6X 4
   604 270-2595

Columbus
Franklin County

(G-6663)
360WATER INC
965 W 3rd Ave (43212-3109)
PHONE..................614 294-3600
Laura Tegethoff, *President*
Todd Raish, *Vice Pres*
Matthew Thomlinson, *Business Dir*
EMP: 5
SQ FT: 2,000
SALES (est): 210K **Privately Held**
WEB: www.360water.com
SIC: 8299 8742 7372 Educational service, nondegree granting: continuing educ.; human resource consulting services; educational computer software

(G-6664)
3D SYSTEMS INC
950 Taylor Station Rd K (43230-6670)
PHONE..................215 757-9611
EMP: 192 **Publicly Held**
SIC: 3571 Electronic computers
HQ: 3d Systems, Inc.
   333 Three D Systems Cir
   Rock Hill SC 29730
   803 326-3900

(G-6665)
614 MEDIA GROUP LLC
Also Called: 614 Magazine
458 E Main St (43215-5344)
PHONE..................614 488-4400
Amber Suba, *VP Sales*
Meggin Weimerskirch, *VP Sales*
Liza Worthington, *Accounts Exec*
Lindsay Arnett, *Mktg Dir*
Cortney Byus, *Marketing Mgr*
EMP: 60
SALES (est): 9.3MM **Privately Held**
SIC: 2721 Magazines: publishing & printing

(G-6666)
**A & H AUTOMOTIVE
INDUSTRIES**
Also Called: A & H Truck Parts
701 Hadley Dr (43228-1029)
P.O. Box 91256 (43209-7256)
PHONE..................614 235-1759
Alex B Rosen, *President*
Susan K Rosen, *Vice Pres*
EMP: 5
SALES (est): 938.4K **Privately Held**
WEB: www.ahautomotive.com
SIC: 5013 3714 3366 Automotive supplies & parts; motor vehicle transmissions, drive assemblies & parts; bushings & bearings, brass (nonmachined)

(G-6667)
A B SIEMER INC
150 E Campus View Blvd # 250
(43235-4648)
PHONE..................614 888-8855
Arnold B Siemer, *President*
Henry Phillips, *Controller*
EMP: 251
SALES (est): 17MM
SALES (corp-wide): 210.3MM **Privately Held**
WEB: www.descoventurecapital.com
SIC: 3442 Window & door frames
PA: Desco Corporation
   7795 Walton Pkwy Ste 175
   New Albany OH 43054
   614 888-8855

(G-6668)
**A R HARDING PUBLISHING
COMPANY**
Also Called: Fur-Fish-Game
2878 E Main St (43209-2613)
PHONE..................614 231-5735
Fax: 614 231-5735
Jeffrey A Kirn, *President*
Jeffrey A Kim, *President*
Vic Attardo, *Editor*
Mitch Cox, *Editor*
Eric Schweinhagen, *Manager*
EMP: 10
SQ FT: 1,500
SALES (est): 1.1MM **Privately Held**
WEB: www.furfishgame.com
SIC: 2721 Magazines: publishing & printing

(G-6669)
A-DISPLAY SERVICE CORP
Also Called: Signature Store Fixtures
541 Dana Ave (43223-5202)
PHONE..................614 469-1230
Fax: 614 469-0737
Anthony Grilli, *President*
Nancy Grilli, *Corp Secy*
Mario Grilli, *COO*
EMP: 10
SQ FT: 8,500
SALES (est): 1.4MM **Privately Held**
WEB: www.blueshore.com
SIC: 2541 Display fixtures, wood; showcases, except refrigerated: wood; store fixtures, wood

(G-6670)
A-Z PACKAGING COMPANY
1221 Harmon Ave (43223-3306)
PHONE..................614 444-8441
Fax: 614 444-5950
Charles Ellyson Jr, *CEO*
Jo Ann Ellyson, *President*
Charles Ellyson Sr, *Vice Pres*
Gloria Ellyson, *Treasurer*
Vanessa McNeely, *Manager*
EMP: 14
SQ FT: 12,000
SALES (est): 1.3MM **Privately Held**
SIC: 7389 2449 2448 Packaging & labeling services; wood containers; pallets, wood

(G-6671)
ABBOTT LABORATORIES
Also Called: Abbott Nutrition
585 Cleveland Ave (43215-1755)
P.O. Box 16546 (43216-6546)
PHONE..................614 624-3191
Fax: 614 624-3816
Chuck Mundy, *Principal*
Steve Nichols, *Plant Mgr*
Joe Ceddia, *Project Mgr*
Cindy Lyons, *Project Mgr*
Carol Marvin, *Project Mgr*
EMP: 550
SQ FT: 378,500
SALES (corp-wide): 20.8B **Publicly Held**
WEB: www.abbott.com
SIC: 8099 2834 2087 2086 Nutrition services; pharmaceutical preparations; flavoring extracts & syrups; bottled & canned soft drinks; canned specialties
PA: Abbott Laboratories
   100 Abbott Park Rd
   Abbott Park IL 60064
   224 667-6100

(G-6672)
ABBOTT LABORATORIES
Abbott Nutrition
3300 Stelzer Rd (43219-3034)
PHONE............................614 624-7677
Keith Wheeler, *Vice Pres*
Gloria Humphrey, *Purchasing*
Paul Johns, *Research*
Brent Hanger, *Natl Sales Mgr*
Scott Calus, *Sales Staff*
EMP: 3000
SALES (corp-wide): 20.8B **Publicly Held**
WEB: www.abbott.com
SIC: 2834 Druggists' preparations (pharmaceuticals)
PA: Abbott Laboratories
100 Abbott Park Rd
Abbott Park IL 60064
224 667-6100

(G-6673)
ABBOTT LABORATORIES
Also Called: Ross Products Division
1033 Kingsmill Pkwy (43229-1129)
P.O. Box 16546 (43216)
PHONE............................614 624-6627
Fax: 614 624-6550
Marlene Hernandez, *Manager*
EMP: 75
SALES (corp-wide): 20.8B **Publicly Held**
WEB: www.abbott.com
SIC: 2834 Druggists' preparations (pharmaceuticals)
PA: Abbott Laboratories
100 Abbott Park Rd
Abbott Park IL 60064
224 667-6100

(G-6674)
ABBOTT LABORATORIES
350 N 5th St (43215-2103)
PHONE............................614 624-3078
Nick Llukeif, *General Mgr*
EMP: 617
SALES (corp-wide): 20.8B **Publicly Held**
WEB: www.abbott.com
SIC: 2834 2844 Pharmaceutical preparations; toilet preparations
PA: Abbott Laboratories
100 Abbott Park Rd
Abbott Park IL 60064
224 667-6100

(G-6675)
ABBOTT LABORATORIES
6550 Singletree Dr (43229-1119)
PHONE............................614 624-6627
EMP: 617
SALES (corp-wide): 20.8B **Publicly Held**
WEB: www.abbott.com
SIC: 2834 Pharmaceutical preparations; druggists' preparations (pharmaceuticals); vitamin, nutrient & hematinic preparations for human use; vitamin preparations
PA: Abbott Laboratories
100 Abbott Park Rd
Abbott Park IL 60064
224 667-6100

(G-6676)
ABBOTT LABORATORIES
Also Called: Ross Products Division
6 Cleveland Ave (43215)
PHONE............................614 624-6088
David Hill, *Branch Mgr*
EMP: 2500
SALES (corp-wide): 20.8B **Publicly Held**
WEB: www.abbott.com
SIC: 2834 Druggists' preparations (pharmaceuticals)
PA: Abbott Laboratories
100 Abbott Park Rd
Abbott Park IL 60064
224 667-6100

(G-6677)
ABBOTT NUTRITION MFG INC
625 Cleveland Ave (43215-1754)
PHONE............................614 624-7485
Randy H Honaker, *Exec VP*
Steve Johnstone, *Research*
Kelly Adams, *Marketing Mgr*
Mark Goble, *Manager*
Kevin Mahan, *Exec Dir*
EMP: 27

SALES (corp-wide): 20.8B **Publicly Held**
SIC: 2834 Druggists' preparations (pharmaceuticals)
HQ: Abbott Nutrition Manufacturing Inc.
2351 N Watney Way Ste C
Fairfield CA 94533
707 399-1100

(G-6678)
ABITEC CORPORATION (HQ)
501 W 1st Ave (43215-1101)
P.O. Box 569 (43216)
PHONE............................614 429-6464
Fax: 614 421-7996
Jeff Walton, *CEO*
Anish Parikh, *Vice Pres*
P E Castello, *Traffic Mgr*
Jacob K Matthews, *Production*
C E Johnston, *Purch Agent*
▼ EMP: 20
SQ FT: 12,000
SALES (est): 36.7MM
SALES (corp-wide): 17.5B **Privately Held**
WEB: www.abiteccorp.com
SIC: 2844 2834 2869 2045 Toilet preparations; pharmaceutical preparations; industrial organic chemicals; prepared flour mixes & doughs
PA: Wittington Investments Limited
Weston Centre
London W1K 4
207 399-6565

(G-6679)
ABLE FENCE OF COLUMBUS INC
2779 E 4th Ave (43219-2824)
PHONE............................614 253-8587
Carodus Lambert, *President*
John Dages, *Vice Pres*
Michael Heffernan, *Manager*
EMP: 8
SALES (est): 1.3MM **Privately Held**
SIC: 3496 Miscellaneous fabricated wire products

(G-6680)
ABLE INDUSTRIES INC
Also Called: Able Manufacturing
870 N 20th St (43219-2421)
PHONE............................614 252-1050
Fax: 614 252-5001
Tim Dye, *President*
Brian Dye, *COO*
EMP: 5
SQ FT: 20,000
SALES (est): 909.9K **Privately Held**
WEB: www.ableindustries.net
SIC: 1611 3713 Highway & street construction; truck beds

(G-6681)
ABLE PALLET MFG & REPR
1271 Harmon Ave (43223-3306)
P.O. Box 23083 (43223-0083)
PHONE............................614 444-2115
Fax: 614 444-3766
Charles O'Hara, *President*
EMP: 11
SQ FT: 5,089
SALES (est): 986.2K **Privately Held**
SIC: 7699 2448 Pallet repair; wood pallets & skids

(G-6682)
ABLE PRINTING COMPANY
1325 Holly Ave (43212-3116)
PHONE............................614 294-4547
Fax: 614 291-3842
Patrick Davis, *President*
EMP: 5 EST: 1954
SQ FT: 13,000
SALES (est): 683.9K **Privately Held**
WEB: www.ableprintingco.com
SIC: 2759 Commercial printing

(G-6683)
ACCENT DRAPERY CO INC
Also Called: Accent Drapery Supply Co
1180 Goodale Blvd (43212-3793)
PHONE............................614 488-0741
Fax: 614 488-7809
Patrick Casbarro, *President*
Brian Whiteside, *Vice Pres*
Allyson Woods, *Mktg Coord*
EMP: 27

SQ FT: 19,500
SALES: 4MM **Privately Held**
SIC: 5714 5023 2391 Draperies; draperies; curtains & draperies

(G-6684)
ACCLAIMD INC
1275 Kinnear Rd (43212-1180)
PHONE............................614 219-9519
David Lyons, *President*
EMP: 4 EST: 2012
SALES (est): 181.7K **Privately Held**
SIC: 7372 Application computer software
PA: Eboss Online Recruitment Solutions
(Eboss) Limited
612 - 616 Wimborne Road
Bournemouth
207 183-0675

(G-6685)
ACCURATE MANUFACTURING COMPANY
1940 Lone Eagle St (43228-3626)
P.O. Box 28666 (43228-0666)
PHONE............................614 878-6510
Fax: 614 878-0933
Tom Lindblom, *CEO*
Angela Merrill, *Vice Pres*
EMP: 20
SQ FT: 10,000
SALES (est): 3.1MM **Privately Held**
SIC: 3542 3599 3548 Presses: hydraulic & pneumatic, mechanical & manual; machine shop, jobbing & repair; welding apparatus

(G-6686)
ACCUSCAN INSTRUMENTS INC
Also Called: Omni Tech Electronics
5098 Trabue Rd (43228-9391)
PHONE............................614 878-6644
Fax: 614 878-3560
R H Mandalaywala, *President*
Myrna Ocasio, *Sales/Mktg Dir*
Myrna Mandalaywala, *Manager*
Lent Christian, *Sr Software Eng*
EMP: 10
SQ FT: 10,000
SALES (est): 2.1MM **Privately Held**
WEB: www.accuscan-usa.com
SIC: 3821 Laboratory apparatus, except heating & measuring

(G-6687)
ACE PROSTHETICS INC
4971 Arlington Centre Blvd (43220-2910)
PHONE............................614 291-8325
Fax: 614 291-8342
John Alan Hays, *President*
EMP: 2
SALES: 1MM **Privately Held**
SIC: 3842 Prosthetic appliances

(G-6688)
ACER CONTRACTING LLC
3840 N High St Ste B (43214-3780)
PHONE............................702 236-5917
Christopher Garcia, *President*
EMP: 3
SALES (est): 99.8K **Privately Held**
SIC: 1389 8742 Construction, repair & dismantling services; real estate consultant

(G-6689)
ACORN PRODUCTS INC
390 W Nationwide Blvd (43215-2392)
PHONE............................614 222-4400
Fax: 614 221-8397
A Corydon Meyer, *President*
Mitch Dolloff, *Senior VP*
Hubert B Martin III, *Senior VP*
Gary W Zimmerman, *Senior VP*
John Brockelman, *Vice Pres*
EMP: 450
SQ FT: 33,000
SALES (est): 31.7MM **Privately Held**
SIC: 3423 3421 3799 3089 Garden & farm tools, including shovels; shovels, spades (hand tools); scissors, shears, clippers, snips & similar tools; hedge shears or trimmers, except power; wheelbarrows; injection molded finished plastic products; hand tools

(G-6690)
ACRODYNE MFG CO
41 Kingston Ave (43207-2438)
PHONE............................614 443-5517
Fax: 614 443-8754
Tim Burris, *President*
David Bals, *Vice Pres*
Michael R Bals, *Treasurer*
EMP: 3
SQ FT: 4,500
SALES: 400K **Privately Held**
SIC: 3599 Machine shop, jobbing & repair

(G-6691)
ACRYLICON INC
1976 Britains Ln (43224-5611)
PHONE............................614 263-2086
Fax: 614 263-0900
Greg Gruff, *President*
EMP: 3
SQ FT: 2,400
SALES: 450K **Privately Held**
WEB: www.acrylicon.com
SIC: 2542 2653 Fixtures, office: except wood; display items, solid fiber: made from purchased materials

(G-6692)
ACTUAL BREWING
655 N James Rd (43219-1837)
PHONE............................614 636-3825
Jonathan Carroll, *CEO*
EMP: 12 EST: 2015
SALES (est): 759.4K **Privately Held**
SIC: 2082 Malt beverages; malt beverage products; ale (alcoholic beverage); stout (alcoholic beverage)

(G-6693)
ACTUAL INDUSTRIES LLC
655 N James Rd (43219-1837)
PHONE............................614 379-2739
Fredrick Lee, *Principal*
EMP: 3
SALES (est): 257.3K **Privately Held**
SIC: 3999 Manufacturing industries

(G-6694)
ADB SAFEGATE AMERICAS LLC
977 Gahanna Pkwy (43230-6610)
P.O. Box 30829 (43230-0829)
PHONE............................614 861-1304
Fax: 614 864-2069
Fabiola P Le N, *Project Mgr*
Joe Pokoj, *VP Sls/Mktg*
Kelly Pfeiffer, *Human Res Mgr*
Rita Maruscak, *Human Resources*
Ben Burns, *Regl Sales Mgr*
◆ EMP: 300
SALES (est): 122.3MM
SALES (corp-wide): 67.3K **Privately Held**
WEB: www.sea.siemens.com
SIC: 3648 3812 Airport lighting fixtures: runway approach, taxi or ramp; search & navigation equipment
HQ: Adb Safegate Bvba
Leuvensesteenweg 585
Zaventem (Brucargo) 1930
272 217-11

(G-6695)
ADVANATAGE PRINT SOLUT
79 Acton Rd (43214-3301)
PHONE............................614 519-2392
Debbie Smith, *Principal*
EMP: 6 EST: 2009
SALES (est): 787.5K **Privately Held**
SIC: 2752 Commercial printing, lithographic

(G-6696)
ADVANCE SIGN GROUP LLC
5150 Walcutt Ct (43228-9641)
PHONE............................614 429-2111
Fax: 614 429-2150
Kenny Chumley, *Production*
Jeannie Biller, *Project Engr*
Danielle Anglin, *Design Engr*
Paul Rackoff, *CFO*
Karen Etnyre, *Accounting Mgr*
EMP: 50 EST: 2001
SALES (est): 7.2MM **Privately Held**
WEB: www.advancesigngroup.com
SIC: 3993 Signs & advertising specialties

(G-6697)
ADVANCED FUEL SYSTEMS INC
841 Alton Ave (43219-3710)
PHONE..................................614 252-8422
Fax: 614 252-2229
Timothy L Thickstun, *President*
Steve Thickstun, *Vice Pres*
Joanne Thickstun, *Admin Sec*
▼ EMP: 8
SQ FT: 8,500
SALES (est): 2.1MM **Privately Held**
WEB: www.advfuel.com
SIC: 3561 3728 Pumps & pumping equipment; aircraft parts & equipment

(G-6698)
ADVANTAGE PRINTING INC
1369 Royston Dr (43204-1532)
PHONE..................................614 272-8259
Rick Alford, *President*
Brenda Alford, *Corp Secy*
EMP: 2
SALES: 1MM **Privately Held**
SIC: 2752 Commercial printing, offset

(G-6699)
AEIOU SCIENTIFIC LLC
Also Called: Aeiou Diagnostics
311 Kendall Pl (43205-2016)
PHONE..................................614 325-2103
Jeffrey Spitzner, *President*
Lyn Bowman, *Chief Engr*
Brian Clark, *Director*
Anne Loucks, *Director*
EMP: 5
SALES (est): 198.4K **Privately Held**
SIC: 3841 8731 Diagnostic apparatus, medical; biological research; medical research, commercial

(G-6700)
AEP RESOURCES INC
Also Called: American Electric Power
1 Riverside Plz (43215-2355)
PHONE..................................614 716-1000
Fax: 614 223-2499
John M Adams Jr, *Principal*
EMP: 20
SALES (est): 9.5MM **Privately Held**
SIC: 3621 Power generators

(G-6701)
AEROSPACE LUBRICANTS INC
1600 Georgesville Rd (43228-3616)
PHONE..................................614 878-3600
Fax: 614 878-1600
Steven Gates, *President*
Scott Stukenberg, *General Mgr*
Melissa Wenzinger, *Manager*
EMP: 15
SQ FT: 25,000
SALES (est): 5.3MM **Privately Held**
WEB: www.aerospacelubricants.com
SIC: 2992 Lubricating oils

(G-6702)
AGRI COMMUNICATORS INC
Also Called: Ohio's Country Journal
1625 Bethel Rd Ste 203 (43220-2071)
PHONE..................................614 273-0465
Fax: 614 273-0463
Bart Johnson, *President*
Kim Lemmon, *Editor*
Marilyn Johnson, *Corp Secy*
David Conley, *Controller*
Lori Lawrence, *Marketing Staff*
EMP: 25
SQ FT: 4,000
SALES (est): 2.2MM **Privately Held**
WEB: www.ocj.com
SIC: 7313 2721 Radio, television, publisher representatives; periodicals: publishing only

(G-6703)
AGRIUM ADVANCED TECH US INC
701 Kaderly Dr (43228-1031)
PHONE..................................614 276-5103
Karl Creighton, *Branch Mgr*
EMP: 7
SALES (corp-wide): 13.6B **Privately Held**
WEB: www.cropproductionservices.com
SIC: 2873 Nitrogenous fertilizers

HQ: Agrium Advanced Technologies (U.S.) Inc.
2915 Rocky Mountain Ave # 400
Loveland CO 80538
970 292-9000

(G-6704)
AHMF INC (PA)
Also Called: Original Mattress Factory
2245 Wilson Rd (43228-9594)
PHONE..................................614 921-1223
Fax: 614 921-1227
Ronald E Trzcinski, *Ch of Bd*
Perry Doermann, *Corp Secy*
Lawrence S Carlson, *Vice Pres*
Tony Dempsey, *Vice Pres*
Jeffrey C Merill, *Vice Pres*
EMP: 20
SQ FT: 22,000
SALES (est): 4.9MM **Privately Held**
WEB: www.originalmattress.com
SIC: 2515 5712 5021 Mattresses & foundations; furniture springs; bedding & bedsprings; mattresses; mattresses

(G-6705)
AIRTEX MANUFACTURING LLLP
Also Called: Engineered Air
991 Schrock Rd Ste B (43229-1163)
PHONE..................................614 436-9693
Douglas Hannum, *Branch Mgr*
EMP: 4
SALES (corp-wide): 1.1MM **Privately Held**
SIC: 3585 Air conditioning units, complete: domestic or industrial
HQ: Airtex Manufacturing, Lllp
32050 W 83rd St
De Soto KS 66018
913 583-3181

(G-6706)
AJ STINEBURG WDWKG STUDIO LLC
4651 Tatersall Ct (43230-8327)
PHONE..................................614 526-9480
Anthony Stineburg, *Principal*
EMP: 4 EST: 2012
SALES (est): 343.1K **Privately Held**
SIC: 2431 Millwork

(G-6707)
AJAX INDUSTRIES INC
Also Called: Ajax Jaws
575 N Hague Ave (43204-1420)
PHONE..................................614 272-6944
Fax: 614 272-6945
David P De Matteo, *President*
Rocco De Matteo, *Principal*
Tony De Matteo, *Vice Pres*
Anthony Dematteo, *Vice Pres*
▲ EMP: 20
SQ FT: 10,000
SALES (est): 3.2MM **Privately Held**
WEB: www.ajaxjaws.com
SIC: 3545 Chucks: drill, lathe or magnetic (machine tool accessories)

(G-6708)
AKRON BRASS COMPANY
Also Called: Weldon Technologies
3656 Paragon Dr (43228-9750)
PHONE..................................614 529-7230
Fax: 614 527-3547
Sean Tillinghast, *Principal*
Jeff McKitrick, *Sales Engr*
Kent Clasen, *Marketing Staff*
Terry Stevenson, *Manager*
Peter Luhrs, *Director*
EMP: 46
SALES (corp-wide): 2.1B **Publicly Held**
WEB: www.v-mux.com
SIC: 3647 3699 3648 Vehicular lighting equipment; electrical equipment & supplies; lighting equipment
HQ: Akron Brass Company
343 Venture Blvd
Wooster OH 44691

(G-6709)
AKZO NOBEL COATINGS INC
1313 Windsor Ave Ste 1313 (43211-2851)
PHONE..................................614 294-3361
Paul Hoelzer, *General Mgr*
Gavin Miller, *Prdtn Mgr*
Nick Vincent, *Human Res Dir*

Edward Karper, *Marketing Mgr*
Dan Leschnik, *Manager*
EMP: 200
SALES (corp-wide): 15.9B **Privately Held**
WEB: www.nam.sikkens.com
SIC: 2851 Paints & allied products
HQ: Akzo Nobel Coatings Inc.
8220 Mohawk Dr
Strongsville OH 44136
440 297-5100

(G-6710)
AKZO NOBEL COATINGS INC
1313 Windsor Ave (43211-2851)
PHONE..................................614 294-3361
Fax: 614 421-4361
Dick Ryland, *Prdtn Mgr*
Lori Witherup, *Research*
Jeff Cattell, *Manager*
Greg Fratianne, *Manager*
Scott Hanna, *Manager*
EMP: 3
SALES (est): 81.4K **Privately Held**
SIC: 5169 2899 Chemicals & allied products; chemical preparations

(G-6711)
AKZO NOBEL COATINGS INC
1313 Windsor Ave (43211-2851)
P.O. Box 489 (43216-0489)
PHONE..................................614 294-3361
David Curl, *Opers Mgr*
Sherman Hanna, *Purchasing*
Terry Vinson, *Engineer*
John Benson, *Sales Staff*
John Wolff, *Manager*
EMP: 200
SALES (corp-wide): 15.9B **Privately Held**
WEB: www.nam.sikkens.com
SIC: 2851 8734 Paints & allied products; testing laboratories
HQ: Akzo Nobel Coatings Inc.
2031 Nelson Miller Pkwy
Louisville KY 44136
502 254-0470

(G-6712)
AKZO NOBEL INC
1313 Windsor Ave (43211-2851)
PHONE..................................205 323-5201
Lisa Young, *Human Res Mgr*
EMP: 150
SALES (corp-wide): 15.9B **Privately Held**
SIC: 2851 Paints & allied products
HQ: Akzo Nobel Inc.
525 W Van Buren St Fl 16
Chicago IL 60607
312 544-7000

(G-6713)
ALACWIN NUTRITION CORPORATION
3706 Kimberly Pkwy N (43232-8481)
PHONE..................................614 961-6479
Mary Knight, *President*
EMP: 4
SALES (est): 116.1K **Privately Held**
SIC: 2099 Food preparations

(G-6714)
ALD PRECAST CORP (PA)
400 Frank Rd (43207-2423)
PHONE..................................614 449-3366
William E Anderson, *Principal*
EMP: 5
SALES (est): 1.9MM **Privately Held**
SIC: 3272 Precast terrazo or concrete products

(G-6715)
ALGIE COMPOSITES INC
2755 Westbelt Dr (43228-3861)
PHONE..................................614 529-0477
Ian Algie, *President*
Shirley Algie, *Vice Pres*
EMP: 3
SQ FT: 7,000
SALES: 250K **Privately Held**
WEB: www.algiecompositesinc.com
SIC: 3624 5531 Fibers, carbon & graphite; speed shops, including race car supplies

(G-6716)
ALIGN ASSESS ACHIEVE LLC
900 Michigan Ave (43215-1165)
PHONE..................................614 505-6820

K M Bainbridge, *Mng Member*
Kathleen M Bainbridge, *Mng Member*
Morris Holman,
EMP: 4
SALES: 1MM **Privately Held**
SIC: 8748 2741 Educational consultant; miscellaneous publishing

(G-6717)
ALL A CART MANUFACTURING INC
2001 Courtright Rd (43232-4216)
PHONE..................................614 443-5544
Jeff Morris, *President*
Marilyn Coleman, *Manager*
▼ EMP: 15
SQ FT: 225,000
SALES (est): 5.3MM **Privately Held**
WEB: www.allacart.com
SIC: 3715 Truck trailers

(G-6718)
ALL ABOUT HOUSE
1071 Afton Rd (43221-1603)
PHONE..................................614 725-3595
Margaret Vickers, *Principal*
EMP: 5
SALES (est): 250K **Privately Held**
SIC: 3585 Room coolers, portable

(G-6719)
ALL AMERICAN TROPHY
3055 Templeton Rd Ste M (43209-2589)
PHONE..................................614 231-8824
Fax: 614 231-8921
Brian Strickler,
Randy Laymon,
EMP: 3
SALES: 200K **Privately Held**
SIC: 3914 Trophies

(G-6720)
ALL AMERICAN WELDING CO
185 Mcdowell St (43215-4011)
P.O. Box 547, Grove City (43123-0547)
PHONE..................................614 224-7752
Fax: 614 224-7257
Ken Radich, *President*
Charles Radich, *Vice Pres*
EMP: 5
SQ FT: 60,000
SALES (est): 370K **Privately Held**
SIC: 7692 3443 Welding repair; weldments

(G-6721)
ALL PRO OVRHD DOOR SYSTEMS LLC
1985 Oakland Park Ave (43224-3636)
PHONE..................................614 444-3667
Fax: 614 252-4845
Joseph Miller,
EMP: 8
SALES (est): 790K **Privately Held**
SIC: 3442 2431 Metal doors, sash & trim; door frames, wood; doors, wood

(G-6722)
ALL STAR SIGN COMPANY
112 S Glenwood Ave (43222-1406)
P.O. Box 23071 (43223-0071)
PHONE..................................614 461-9052
Fax: 614 461-0620
James E Waller, *President*
Howard Berridge, *Vice Pres*
Faye Waller, *Controller*
EMP: 32
SQ FT: 7,600
SALES (est): 4.5MM **Privately Held**
SIC: 3993 Signs & advertising specialties

(G-6723)
ALLFAB INC
2273 Williams Rd (43207-5121)
PHONE..................................614 491-4944
Fax: 614 491-5588
Lise S Roth, *President*
Russell W Roth, *Vice Pres*
EMP: 15
SQ FT: 15,000
SALES (est): 3.3MM **Privately Held**
WEB: www.allfabinc.com
SIC: 3444 Sheet metalwork

(G-6724)
ALLIED CUSTOM MOLDED PRODUCTS
1240 Essex Ave (43201-2928)
PHONE..........................614 291-0629
Fax: 614 291-8564
Kenneth Palmer, *President*
Donald O Palmer, *Vice Pres*
Linda Palmer, *Admin Sec*
EMP: 3
SQ FT: 4,500
SALES: 185K **Privately Held**
SIC: 3089 Injection molding of plastics

(G-6725)
ALLIED FABRICATING & WLDG CO
5699 Chantry Dr (43232-4799)
PHONE..........................614 751-6664
Fax: 614 868-0020
Thomas Caminiti, *CEO*
Jack Burgoon, *President*
Joseph Caminiti, *President*
Raymond Cunningham, *Vice Pres*
Gray Arthurs, *Engineer*
EMP: 34
SQ FT: 30,000
SALES (est): 7.4MM **Privately Held**
WEB: www.afaw.net
SIC: 3444 7692 3535 3441 Sheet metal specialties, not stamped; welding repair; conveyors & conveying equipment; fabricated structural metal; rubber & plastics hose & beltings

(G-6726)
ALLIED MINERAL PRODUCTS INC (PA)
2700 Scioto Pkwy (43221-4660)
PHONE..........................614 876-0244
Fax: 614 876-0981
Jon R Tabor, *President*
Ben GE, *General Mgr*
Brian Huang, *General Mgr*
Mark Rowland, *General Mgr*
Koos Heijboer, *Managing Dir*
◆ EMP: 290
SQ FT: 450,000
SALES (est): 96.1MM **Privately Held**
WEB: www.alliedmin.com
SIC: 3297 Nonclay refractories

(G-6727)
ALLYN CORP (PA)
1491 Clairmonte Rd (43221)
P.O. Box 21162 (43221-0162)
PHONE..........................614 442-3900
Larry B Anderson, *President*
EMP: 3
SALES (est): 473.2K **Privately Held**
SIC: 2819 2899 Industrial inorganic chemicals; chemical preparations

(G-6728)
ALPHA OMEGA BIOREMEDIATION LLC
2824 Fisher Rd Ste E (43204-3553)
PHONE..........................614 287-2600
John Chabray, *Partner*
Rita Lang, *Partner*
Lynn Marshall, *Partner*
EMP: 11
SALES (est): 394.9K **Privately Held**
SIC: 4959 8744 8748 2873 Environmental cleanup services; ; environmental consultant; fertilizers: natural (organic), except compost

(G-6729)
AMATECH INC
1633 Woodland Ave (43219-1135)
PHONE..........................614 252-2506
Rick Bittner, *Branch Mgr*
EMP: 20
SALES (corp-wide): 5.6MM **Privately Held**
SIC: 3086 7336 2671 Plastics foam products; package design; plastic film, coated or laminated for packaging
PA: Amatech, Inc.
   1460 Grimm Dr
   Erie PA 16501
   814 452-0010

(G-6730)
AMERICAN BOTTLING COMPANY
Also Called: Dr. Pepper 7 Up Columbus
960 Stelzer Rd (43219-3740)
PHONE..........................614 237-4201
Dan Grassbaugh, *Branch Mgr*
EMP: 100
SALES (corp-wide): 6.4B **Publicly Held**
WEB: www.cs-americas.com
SIC: 2086 Bottled & canned soft drinks
HQ: The American Bottling Company
   5301 Legacy Dr
   Plano TX 75024

(G-6731)
AMERICAN BOTTLING COMPANY
Also Called: 7 Up / R C/Canada Dry Btlg Co
950 Stelzer Rd (43219-3740)
PHONE..........................614 237-4201
Fax: 614 231-6524
Mike Stall, *Branch Mgr*
EMP: 100
SALES (corp-wide): 6.4B **Publicly Held**
WEB: www.cs-americas.com
SIC: 2086 5149 Bottled & canned soft drinks; groceries & related products
HQ: The American Bottling Company
   5301 Legacy Dr
   Plano TX 75024

(G-6732)
AMERICAN COLORSCANS INC
Also Called: ACS Commercial Graphics
5178 Sinclair Rd (43229-5437)
PHONE..........................614 895-0233
Bruce Westfall, *President*
Greg Swick, *Corp Secy*
Louise Bierdeman, *Vice Pres*
Beth Houston, *CTO*
EMP: 22
SQ FT: 4,500
SALES (est): 3MM **Privately Held**
WEB: www.colorscans.com
SIC: 7335 2752 Commercial photography; color separation, photographic & movie film; color lithography

(G-6733)
AMERICAN COMMUNITY NEWSPAPERS
5255 Sinclair Rd (43229-5042)
PHONE..........................614 888-4567
Leanne Brandell, *Principal*
Roy Gray, *Prdtn Mgr*
Charles Hause, *Controller*
EMP: 6
SALES (est): 37.8K **Privately Held**
SIC: 2711 Newspapers

(G-6734)
AMERICAN CONFECTIONS CO LLC
6291 Busch Blvd (43229-1801)
PHONE..........................614 888-8838
Bill Wilson, *Director*
EMP: 8
SALES (est): 953.2K **Privately Held**
SIC: 2026 2066 Yogurt; chocolate candy, solid

(G-6735)
AMERICAN CORRUGATED PDTS INC (PA)
4700 Alkire Rd (43228-3495)
PHONE..........................614 870-2000
Fax: 614 870-2012
Donald Youell, *CEO*
Rudy Youell, *President*
Krista Keighley, *Purch Mgr*
David Rasey, *CFO*
Amy Gothard, *Administration*
EMP: 151
SQ FT: 150,000
SALES (est): 53.8MM **Privately Held**
WEB: www.americancorrugated.com
SIC: 2653 3086 2671 2657 Corrugated & solid fiber boxes; plastics foam products; packaging paper & plastics film, coated & laminated; folding paperboard boxes

(G-6736)
AMERICAN CORRUGATED PDTS INC
Also Called: American Corrugated Michigan
4700 Alkire Rd (43228-3495)
PHONE..........................800 248-6840
Rick Carrier, *Manager*
EMP: 20
SALES (corp-wide): 53.8MM **Privately Held**
SIC: 5113 3086 2671 Corrugated & solid fiber boxes; plastics foam products; packaging paper & plastics film, coated & laminated
PA: American Corrugated Products, Inc.
   4700 Alkire Rd
   Columbus OH 43228
   614 870-2000

(G-6737)
AMERICAN ELECTRIC MOTOR SVC
900 Gray St (43201-3075)
P.O. Box 83295 (43203-0295)
PHONE..........................614 297-1600
Fax: 614 297-1643
James Stout, *President*
Alice M Stout, *Corp Secy*
EMP: 6
SALES (est): 450K **Privately Held**
SIC: 5063 7694 Motors, electric; electric motor repair

(G-6738)
AMERICAN HEALTH PACKAGING
2550 John Glenn Ave Ste A (43217-1188)
PHONE..........................614 492-8177
Fax: 614 492-1903
Ed Hancock, *President*
Diego Munoz, *Mfg Dir*
Chris Rowan, *Mfg Dir*
Kaizi Mwijage, *Opers Mgr*
Karen AHP, *Purch Agent*
EMP: 89
SQ FT: 153,000
SALES (est): 19.4MM
SALES (corp-wide): 146.8B **Publicly Held**
WEB: www.healthpack.com
SIC: 4783 2064 Packing goods for shipping; cough drops, except pharmaceutical preparations
HQ: Amerisourcebergen Drug Corporation
   1300 Morris Dr Ste 100
   Chesterbrook PA 19087
   610 727-7000

(G-6739)
AMERICAN ISOSTATIC PRESSES INC
Also Called: A I P
1205 S Columbus Arprt Rd (43207-4304)
PHONE..........................614 445-9081
Fax: 614 497-3407
Rajendra Persaud, *President*
Carol Sprang, *Principal*
Cliff Orcutt, *Vice Pres*
Paul Geuy, *Engineer*
Lisa Persaud, *Admin Sec*
▲ EMP: 16
SQ FT: 14,000
SALES (est): 4.5MM **Privately Held**
WEB: www.aiphip.com
SIC: 3821 Furnaces, laboratory

(G-6740)
AMERICAN LED-GIBLE INC
1776 Lone Eagle St (43228-3655)
PHONE..........................614 851-1100
Fax: 614 851-1121
Charles R Morrison, *President*
Robin L Morrison, *CFO*
▲ EMP: 15
SQ FT: 7,000
SALES: 1.3MM **Privately Held**
WEB: www.ledgible.com
SIC: 3993 Electric signs

(G-6741)
AMERICAN ORTHOPEDICS INC (PA)
1151 W 5th Ave (43212-2529)
PHONE..........................614 291-6454
Richard F Nitsch, *President*

Ronald Kidd, *President*
Zachary Ruhl, *Vice Pres*
Linda Kreuter, *Accounting Mgr*
Barbara Berndt, *Manager*
EMP: 22
SQ FT: 7,000
SALES: 4MM **Privately Held**
SIC: 3842 Prosthetic appliances; limbs, artificial; braces, orthopedic

(G-6742)
AMERICAN WHISTLE CORPORATION
6540 Huntley Rd Ste B (43229-1088)
PHONE..........................614 846-2918
Fax: 614 846-4821
Ray Giesse, *CEO*
Diane Serraglio, *President*
EMP: 14 EST: 1957
SQ FT: 5,000
SALES (est): 1.1MM **Privately Held**
WEB: www.americanwhistle.com
SIC: 3949 Sporting & athletic goods

(G-6743)
AMERIGRAPH LLC
2727 Harrison Rd (43204-3514)
PHONE..........................614 278-8000
Fax: 614 278-9400
Dirk C Grizzle, *Principal*
EMP: 6
SALES (est): 457.3K **Privately Held**
SIC: 2759 Commercial printing

(G-6744)
AMERITECH PUBLISHING INC
Also Called: SBC
2550 Corp Exchange Dr # 310 (43231-7659)
PHONE..........................614 895-6123
David Lobdell, *Manager*
EMP: 75
SALES (corp-wide): 163.7B **Publicly Held**
SIC: 2741 Directories, telephone: publishing only, not printed on site
HQ: Ameritech Publishing, Inc.
   23500 Northwestern Hwy
   Southfield MI 48075
   800 996-4609

(G-6745)
AMPSCO DIVISION
2301 Fairwood Ave (43207-2768)
PHONE..........................614 444-2181
Fax: 614 443-7564
Dennis J Leukart, *President*
Matthew Leukart, *CFO*
EMP: 19 EST: 1960
SQ FT: 250,000
SALES: 1.2MM
SALES (corp-wide): 73MM **Privately Held**
WEB: www.superior-dietool.com
SIC: 3599 Machine shop, jobbing & repair
PA: Superior Production Llc
   2301 Fairwood Ave
   Columbus OH 43207
   614 444-2181

(G-6746)
AMSOIL INC
707 Hadley Dr (43228-1029)
PHONE..........................614 274-9851
Fax: 614 274-9852
Scott Davis, *Manager*
Joel Parsons, *Manager*
EMP: 8
SALES (corp-wide): 120.9MM **Privately Held**
WEB: www.amsoil.com
SIC: 2992 3589 2873 3714 Lubricating oils & greases; water filters & softeners, household type; fertilizers: natural (organic), except compost; motor vehicle parts & accessories
PA: Amsoil Inc.
   925 Tower Ave
   Superior WI 54880
   715 392-7101

(G-6747)
AMT MACHINE SYSTEMS LIMITED
1760 Zollinger Rd Ste 2 (43221-2848)
PHONE..........................740 965-2693

Gregory Knight, *Partner*
Eric Ribble, *Partner*
Howard Ubert, *Partner*
Denise Courter, *Controller*
Dennis R Pugh,
EMP: 10
SQ FT: 2,000
SALES (est): 1.1MM **Privately Held**
WEB: www.amtmachinesystems.com
SIC: 3451 Screw machine products

(G-6748)
AMT MACHINE SYSTEMS LTD
50 W Broad St Ste 1200 (43215-5907)
PHONE................................614 635-8050
Dennis R Pugh, *CEO*
Howard Ubert, *Principal*
▲ **EMP:** 12 **EST:** 2009
SALES (est): 1.2MM **Privately Held**
SIC: 3599 Custom machinery

(G-6749)
AMTEKCO INDUSTRIES INC (HQ)
1205 Refugee Rd (43207-2114)
PHONE................................614 228-6590
Fax: 614 737-8017
Earl B Sisson, *President*
Hugh E Kirkwood Jr, *President*
John McCormick, *President*
Ollie Rossman, *President*
Bruce Wasserstrom, *Vice Pres*
EMP: 100
SALES: 25.5MM
SALES (corp-wide): 776.3MM **Privately Held**
WEB: www.amtekco.com
SIC: 3469 2541 Kitchen fixtures & equipment: metal, except cast aluminum; cabinets, except refrigerated: show, display, etc.: wood
PA: The Wasserstrom Company
477 S Front St
Columbus OH 43215
614 737-8472

(G-6750)
AMTEKCO INDUSTRIES INC
33 W Hinman Ave (43207-1809)
PHONE................................614 228-6525
Fax: 614 443-4807
Ron Bower, *President*
EMP: 6
SALES (corp-wide): 776.3MM **Privately Held**
WEB: www.amtekco.com
SIC: 2541 3469 Wood partitions & fixtures; metal stampings
HQ: Amtekco Industries Inc
1205 Refugee Rd
Columbus OH 43207
614 228-6590

(G-6751)
ANADEM INC
3620 N High St Ste 201 (43214-3643)
PHONE................................614 262-2539
Will Kuhlmann, *CEO*
Mike Cheadle, *Vice Pres*
EMP: 7
SALES (est): 510K **Privately Held**
SIC: 2741 Miscellaneous publishing

(G-6752)
ANALYNK WIRELESS LLC
790 Cross Pointe Rd (43230-6685)
PHONE................................614 755-5091
Tom Mackessy, *President*
Robert Longest, *President*
Dougals Cox, *Vice Pres*
William Mahoney, *Vice Pres*
Rick Catlett, *Engineer*
◆ **EMP:** 5
SQ FT: 5,000
SALES (est): 700K **Privately Held**
WEB: www.analynk.com
SIC: 3663 Radio receiver networks; receiver-transmitter units (transceiver); receivers, radio communications; antennas, transmitting & communications

(G-6753)
ANCHOR CORPORATION
2160 Cloverleaf St E (43232-4166)
P.O. Box 294, Groveport (43125-0294)
PHONE................................614 836-9590
Michael W Brumm, *President*

Suzie Dillon, *Office Mgr*
EMP: 3
SQ FT: 2,000
SALES (est): 265K **Privately Held**
SIC: 2899 1711 Water treating compounds; plumbing, heating, air-conditioning contractors

(G-6754)
ANCHOR PATTERN COMPANY
748 Frebis Ave (43206-3709)
PHONE................................614 443-2221
Fax: 614 443-1189
Wilbur S Smith III, *President*
Barbara L Smith, *Corp Secy*
EMP: 6 **EST:** 1967
SQ FT: 4,000
SALES: 1.2MM **Privately Held**
SIC: 3312 Tool & die steel

(G-6755)
ANDERSON CONCRETE CORP (PA)
Also Called: Buckeye Ready Mix
400 Frank Rd (43207-2456)
P.O. Box 398 (43216-0398)
PHONE................................614 443-0123
Fax: 614 443-4001
Douglas Anderson, *President*
Richard D Anderson, *Exec VP*
Bill Feltz, *Vice Pres*
William Feltz, *Vice Pres*
Rod Jenkins, *QC Mgr*
EMP: 130
SALES (est): 16.2MM **Privately Held**
WEB: www.andersonconcrete.com
SIC: 3273 Ready-mixed concrete

(G-6756)
ANDERSON GLASS CO INC
2816 Morse Rd (43231-6094)
PHONE................................614 476-4877
Fax: 614 471-4330
Bradley Anderson, *President*
Helena Anderson, *Vice Pres*
George Deniro, *Opers Staff*
Judy Mullen, *Office Mgr*
EMP: 30 **EST:** 1949
SQ FT: 32,000
SALES: 4MM **Privately Held**
WEB: www.andersonglassco.com
SIC: 5039 3231 3229 Exterior flat glass: plate or window; interior flat glass: plate or window; products of purchased glass; pressed & blown glass

(G-6757)
ANHEUSER-BUSCH LLC
700 Schrock Rd (43229-1159)
PHONE................................614 847-6213
Fax: 614 847-6497
Jeremy Curren, *Safety Dir*
Bradley Kelly, *Safety Dir*
Ron Morgan, *Plant Mgr*
Joan Woerner, *Plant Mgr*
Jennifer Eckstein, *Opers Mgr*
EMP: 500 **Privately Held**
WEB: www.hispanicbud.com
SIC: 2082 Malt beverages
HQ: Anheuser-Busch, Llc
1 Busch Pl
Saint Louis MO 63118
314 632-6777

(G-6758)
ANNES AUNTIE PRETZELS
125 Easton Town Ctr (43219-6075)
PHONE................................614 418-7021
Fax: 614 882-2766
Marty Pete, *Owner*
Sharron Wheeler, *Owner*
EMP: 22
SALES (est): 413.6K **Privately Held**
SIC: 5461 2052 Pretzels; pretzels

(G-6759)
ANTHONY-THOMAS CANDY COMPANY (PA)
Also Called: Anthony-Thomas Candy Shoppes
1777 Arlingate Ln (43228-4114)
P.O. Box 21865 (43221-0865)
PHONE................................614 274-8405
Fax: 614 274-0019
Tom Zanetos, *CEO*
Joseph Zanetos, *President*

Gregory Zanetos, *General Mgr*
Agnes Zanetos, *Corp Secy*
Steve Scully, *Plant Mgr*
▲ **EMP:** 125 **EST:** 1907
SQ FT: 152,000
SALES (est): 58.9MM **Privately Held**
WEB: www.anthony-thomas.com
SIC: 2064 5441 2068 2066 Candy & other confectionery products; candy, nut & confectionery stores; salted & roasted nuts & seeds; chocolate & cocoa products

(G-6760)
ANTHONY-THOMAS CANDY COMPANY
Also Called: Anthony Thomas Candy Shoppes
4636 W Broad St (43228-1611)
PHONE................................614 870-8899
Gregory Zanetos, *Exec VP*
Tom Zanetos, *Vice Pres*
Steve Scully, *Prdtn Mgr*
Joe Zanetos, *Branch Mgr*
EMP: 4
SALES (corp-wide): 58.9MM **Privately Held**
WEB: www.anthony-thomas.com
SIC: 2064 5441 Candy & other confectionery products; candy, nut & confectionery stores
PA: Anthony-Thomas Candy Company
1777 Arlingate Ln
Columbus OH 43228
614 274-8405

(G-6761)
APEX FIRE SERVICES LLC
449 Industry Dr (43204-6234)
PHONE................................614 274-6400
Donald G Zender, *Mng Member*
EMP: 6
SQ FT: 4,500
SALES (est): 200K **Privately Held**
SIC: 3842 Clothing, fire resistant & protective

(G-6762)
APPIAN MANUFACTURING CORP
Also Called: Necco American
2025 Camaro Ave (43207-1716)
PHONE................................614 445-2230
Fax: 614 445-2236
Fran A Vendetta, *President*
Ron Whitaker, *Production*
Ryan Lauer, *Engineer*
Eric Schmidt, *Human Resources*
Amber McAtee, *Manager*
▲ **EMP:** 30
SQ FT: 40,000
SALES (est): 7.8MM **Privately Held**
WEB: www.appian.com
SIC: 3441 3498 Fabricated structural metal; fabricated pipe & fittings

(G-6763)
APPLE INC
4070 The Strand E (43219-6130)
PHONE................................614 478-5592
Steve Lunetta, *Marketing Staff*
Bill Davanzo, *Branch Mgr*
EMP: 4
SALES (corp-wide): 215.6B **Publicly Held**
WEB: www.apple.com
SIC: 3571 Electronic computers
PA: Apple Inc.
1 Infinite Loop
Cupertino CA 95014
408 996-1010

(G-6764)
APPLICATION LINK INC
4449 Easton Way Fl 2 (43219-7005)
PHONE................................614 934-1735
Michael Reed, *President*
EMP: 15
SQ FT: 2,000
SALES (est): 1.6MM **Privately Held**
WEB: www.applicationlink.com
SIC: 7372 5045 7371 Business oriented computer software; computers, peripherals & software; custom computer programming services

(G-6765)
APPLIED EXPERIENCE LLC
1003 Kinnear Rd (43212-1150)
PHONE................................614 943-2970
EMP: 7
SALES (est): 136.4K **Privately Held**
SIC: 7389 7373 8711 3599 Drafting service, except temporary help; computer integrated systems design; engineering services; machine & other job shop work

(G-6766)
AQUA SCIENCE INC
1877 E 17th Ave (43219-1006)
PHONE................................614 252-5000
Fax: 614 257-0008
Dan L Smucker, *President*
Darrell L Miller Jr, *Vice Pres*
Joan Miller, *Manager*
Bradley Whitt, *Manager*
EMP: 34
SQ FT: 28,000
SALES (est): 10.4MM **Privately Held**
SIC: 2899 Water treating compounds

(G-6767)
AQUACALC LLC
Also Called: Jbs Instruments
1700 Joyce Ave (43219-1026)
PHONE................................916 372-0534
Greg Ruszovan, *President*
EMP: 3
SQ FT: 3,500
SALES (est): 128K **Privately Held**
SIC: 3823 Flow instruments, industrial process type

(G-6768)
ARCELORMITTAL COLUMBUS LLC
1800 Watkins Rd (43207-3440)
PHONE................................614 492-6800
Donald Riesbeck, *QC Mgr*
Michael Rippey, *Mng Member*
Brian Stack, *Manager*
▲ **EMP:** 113
SQ FT: 350,000
SALES (est): 14.6MM **Privately Held**
SIC: 3479 3471 3398 Galvanizing of iron, steel or end-formed products; plating & polishing; metal heat treating
HQ: Arcelormittal Usa Llc
1 S Dearborn St Ste 1800
Chicago IL 60603
312 346-0300

(G-6769)
ARCELORMITTAL OBETZ LLC
4300 Alum Creek Dr (43207-4519)
PHONE................................614 492-8287
Rodney Mott, *President*
Robert Dalrymple, *Vice Pres*
John Goodwin, *Vice Pres*
Brian Pole, *Vice Pres*
Brian Stack, *Vice Pres*
EMP: 25
SQ FT: 83,600
SALES (est): 3.3MM **Privately Held**
SIC: 3312 Iron & steel: galvanized, pipes, plates, sheets, etc.
HQ: Arcelormittal Usa Llc
1 S Dearborn St Ste 1800
Chicago IL 60603
312 346-0300

(G-6770)
ARDENT MILLS LLC
4200 Sullivant Ave (43228-4325)
PHONE................................614 274-2545
Fax: 614 274-0068
Richard Hooper, *Plant Mgr*
Richard Baillie, *Branch Mgr*
Dan Srouse, *Manager*
EMP: 32
SALES (corp-wide): 30.3B **Publicly Held**
WEB: www.conagra.com
SIC: 2041 5153 Flour; grain elevators
HQ: Ardent Mills Llc
1875 Lawrence St Ste 1400
Denver CO 80202
800 851-9618

(G-6771)
ARESGEAR
1807 Obrien Rd (43228-3866)
PHONE................................518 966-2737

Jacob Sebens, *Principal*
EMP: 3
SALES (est): 150K **Privately Held**
SIC: 5699 2326 Belts, apparel: custom; work garments, except raincoats: water-proof

(G-6772)
ARMADA POWER LLC
230 West St Ste 150 (43215-2785)
PHONE............................614 204-9341
Kathyayani Mahadevan, *Principal*
EMP: 8 **EST:** 2014
SQ FT: 2,000
SALES (est): 478.6K **Privately Held**
SIC: 7371 3663 Computer software systems analysis & design, custom; light communications equipment; telemetering equipment, electronic

(G-6773)
ART COLUMBUS MEMORIAL INC
606 W Broad St (43215-2712)
PHONE............................614 221-9333
Fax: 614 221-7288
Steve Streamer, *Sales Mgr*
Mel Lee, *Manager*
EMP: 8
SQ FT: 5,000
SALES (corp-wide): 2.2MM **Privately Held**
SIC: 3272 Monuments, concrete
PA: Art Columbus Memorial Inc
766 Greenlawn Ave
Columbus OH 43223
614 443-5778

(G-6774)
ART TEES INC
39 S Yearling Rd (43213-1823)
PHONE............................614 338-8337
Fax: 614 338-8767
Mitchell Hirsch, *CEO*
David Hirsch, *President*
Zelda Hirsch, *Corp Secy*
EMP: 4
SQ FT: 20,000
SALES: 480K **Privately Held**
SIC: 2759 5941 3993 2791 Screen printing; sporting goods & bicycle shops; signs & advertising specialties; typesetting; automotive & apparel trimmings

(G-6775)
ASHLAND INC
1979 Atlas St (43228-9645)
PHONE............................800 283-4823
EMP: 219
SALES (corp-wide): 5.3B **Publicly Held**
SIC: 2869 Mfg Industrial Organic Chemicals
PA: Ashland Inc.
50 E Rivercenter Blvd # 1600
Covington KY 41011
859 815-3333

(G-6776)
ASHLAND SPECIALTY INGREDIENTS
1979 Atlas St (43228-9645)
PHONE............................614 529-3311
EMP: 54
SALES (corp-wide): 34.3MM **Privately Held**
SIC: 2844 Bath salts
PA: Ashland Specialty Ingredients
5200 Laser Pkwy
Dublin OH 43017
302 594-5000

(G-6777)
ASIST INC
Also Called: Asist Translation Services
4891 Sawmill Rd Ste 200 (43235-7266)
PHONE............................614 451-6744
Fax: 614 451-1349
Elena Tsinman, *President*
Heather Latscha, *Human Res Dir*
Wayne Chilicki, *Regl Sales Mgr*
EMP: 12
SQ FT: 8,000
SALES (est): 1.4MM **Privately Held**
WEB: www.asisttranslations.com
SIC: 7389 2791 Translation services; typesetting

(G-6778)
ASPHALT SERVICES OHIO INC
4579 Poth Rd (43213-1327)
PHONE............................614 864-4600
Edward Minhinnick, *President*
EMP: 5
SALES (est): 490K **Privately Held**
SIC: 1771 3241 Blacktop (asphalt) work; cement, hydraulic

(G-6779)
ASSEMBLY MACHINING WIRE PDTS
Also Called: A M W
2375 Refugee Park (43207-2173)
PHONE............................614 443-1110
Fax: 614 443-2149
Gregory Allan Donovan, *President*
EMP: 7
SQ FT: 10,000
SALES: 350K **Privately Held**
SIC: 3599 Machine shop, jobbing & repair

(G-6780)
AT&T CORP
150 E Gay St Ste 4a (43215-3130)
PHONE............................614 223-8236
Connie Browning, *President*
Cari Walters, *Assistant VP*
Michael Kehoe, *Vice Pres*
Steven Kleinknecht, *Sls & Mktg Exec*
Susan Mentes, *Sls & Mktg Exec*
EMP: 1000
SALES (corp-wide): 163.7B **Publicly Held**
WEB: www.att.com
SIC: 7629 4813 2741 Telecommunication equipment repair (except telephones); telephone communication, except radio; miscellaneous publishing
HQ: At&T Corp.
1 At&T Way
Bedminster NJ 07921
800 403-3302

(G-6781)
ATCHLEY SIGNS & GRAPHICS
1616 Transamerica Ct (43228-9332)
PHONE............................614 421-7446
Derek Atchley, *Co-Owner*
Christine Atchley, *Co-Owner*
EMP: 9
SALES: 750K **Privately Held**
SIC: 3993 7389 Signs & advertising specialties; printed circuitry graphic layout

(G-6782)
ATLAPAC CORP
2901 E 4th Ave Ste 5 (43219-2896)
PHONE............................614 252-2121
Fax: 614 252-7289
James R Staeck, *President*
Mike Mc Coy, *CFO*
Mike McCoy, *CFO*
▲ **EMP:** 70 **EST:** 1964
SQ FT: 50,000
SALES (est): 11MM **Privately Held**
WEB: www.atlapaccorp.com
SIC: 2673 5113 Bags: plastic, laminated & coated; cellophane bags, unprinted: made from purchased materials; bags, paper & disposable plastic

(G-6783)
ATLAS GEAR AND MACHINE CO
Also Called: A Jack' S Industries
575 N Hague Ave (43204-1420)
PHONE............................614 272-6944
David P De Matteo, *President*
Rocco D Matteo, *Manager*
EMP: 5
SQ FT: 10,000
SALES (est): 462.8K **Privately Held**
SIC: 3599 Machine shop, jobbing & repair

(G-6784)
ATLAS INDUSTRIAL CONTRS LLC (HQ)
5275 Sinclair Rd (43229-5042)
PHONE............................614 841-4500
Fax: 614 841-4510
George Ghanem, *President*
Rich Wine, *Division Mgr*
Peter Lamonica, *Vice Pres*
Gary Martin, *Vice Pres*

Dan Hodge, *Safety Dir*
EMP: 300
SQ FT: 20,000
SALES: 130MM
SALES (corp-wide): 39MM **Privately Held**
WEB: www.atlascos.com
SIC: 1731 3498 1796 Electrical work; fabricated pipe & fittings; machine moving & rigging
PA: Gmg Holdings, Llc
5275 Sinclair Rd
Columbus OH 43229
614 841-4500

(G-6785)
AUBURN DAIRY PRODUCTS INC
2200 Cardigan Ave (43215-1092)
PHONE............................614 488-2536
Douglas A Smith, *President*
Martin Lavine, *Vice Pres*
Thomas G Michaelides, *Treasurer*
G Frederick Smith, *Admin Sec*
EMP: 31
SQ FT: 10,300
SALES (est): 4.2MM
SALES (corp-wide): 43.5MM **Privately Held**
SIC: 2026 5143 Whipped topping, except frozen or dry mix; dairy products, except dried or canned
PA: Instantwhip Foods, Inc.
2200 Cardigan Ave
Columbus OH 43215
614 488-2536

(G-6786)
AULD COMPANY
1003 Kinnear Rd (43212-1150)
PHONE............................614 454-1010
Fax: 614 755-2329
Daniel Auld, *President*
Douglas Auld, *Vice Pres*
Jason Gleim, *Webmaster*
EMP: 40
SQ FT: 9,000
SALES (est): 3.3MM **Privately Held**
WEB: www.theauldcompany.com
SIC: 3993 3479 3089 3369 Name plates: except engraved, etched, etc.: metal; name plates: engraved, etched, etc.; injection molding of plastics; white metal castings (lead, tin, antimony), except die

(G-6787)
AULD CRAFTERS INC
175 Cleveland Ave Rear (43215-1926)
PHONE............................614 221-6825
Fax: 614 221-6434
Linda Weltlich, *President*
Chris Carioti, *Vice Pres*
John Carioti, *Vice Pres*
Gary Weltlich, *Vice Pres*
EMP: 3 **EST:** 1935
SQ FT: 7,500
SALES: 450K **Privately Held**
SIC: 5999 3911 5947 Trophies & plaques; pearl jewelry, natural or cultured; gift, novelty & souvenir shop

(G-6788)
AULD TECHNOLOGIES LLC
2030 Dividend Dr (43228-3847)
PHONE............................614 755-2853
Elizabeth Judy, *Mng Member*
EMP: 17
SALES (est): 3.6MM **Privately Held**
SIC: 3993 Signs & advertising specialties

(G-6789)
AUSTIN FOAM PLASTICS INC
Also Called: A F P Ohio
2200 International St (43228-4630)
PHONE............................614 921-0824
Fax: 614 527-7881
Dan Berona, *Manager*
EMP: 25
SALES (corp-wide): 48.7MM **Privately Held**
WEB: www.austinfoam.com
SIC: 3086 7336 Insulation or cushioning material, foamed plastic; package design
PA: Austin Foam Plastics, Inc.
2933 A W Grimes Blvd
Pflugerville TX 78660
512 251-6300

(G-6790)
AUTOMATION SOLUTIONS INC
505 S Parkview Ave # 206 (43209-1676)
PHONE............................614 235-4060
Rolf Kates, *President*
Ellen Kates, *Vice Pres*
EMP: 2
SALES: 1MM **Privately Held**
SIC: 3565 5084 Packaging machinery; industrial machinery & equipment

(G-6791)
AUTOMTIQ MSUREMENT SYSTEMS LLC
797 Gatehouse Ln (43235-1731)
PHONE............................614 431-2667
Vincent Phillips, *Mng Member*
C Vincent Phillips, *Mng Member*
Gary W James,
EMP: 3 **EST:** 2000
SALES (est): 330K **Privately Held**
SIC: 3825 Test equipment for electronic & electric measurement

(G-6792)
AVER INC
41 S High St Ste 1400 (43215-3406)
PHONE............................877 841-2775
Nick Augustinos, *President*
Katty Detore, *Human Resources*
Susan Dora, *Manager*
Bryce Glass, *Manager*
Steven Sutters, *Manager*
EMP: 3
SALES: 110K **Privately Held**
SIC: 7372 Application computer software; business oriented computer software

(G-6793)
AVOTRONICS POWERTRAIN INC
4200 Regent St (43219-6229)
PHONE............................614 537-0261
Ugo Nwoke, *CEO*
EMP: 4
SALES (est): 305.3K **Privately Held**
SIC: 3566 Speed changers, drives & gears

(G-6794)
AVURE AUTOCLAVE SYSTEMS INC (DH)
Also Called: ABB Autoclave Systems
3721 Corp Dr (43231)
PHONE............................614 891-2732
Fax: 614 891-4568
Jerry Toops, *President*
◆ **EMP:** 20
SQ FT: 20,000
SALES (est): 2.2MM
SALES (corp-wide): 122.3MM **Privately Held**
WEB: www.avureae.com
SIC: 3823 5084 Pressure measurement instruments, industrial; industrial machinery & equipment
HQ: Flow International Corporation
23500 64th Ave S
Kent WA 98032
253 850-3500

(G-6795)
B & G TOOL COMPANY
4832 Kenny Rd (43220-2793)
PHONE............................614 451-2538
Fax: 614 451-3355
Francis Plahuta, *President*
Francis Bud Plahuta, *President*
James Plahuta, *Vice Pres*
Mike Plahuta, *Plant Mgr*
Steve Plahuta, *Admin Sec*
EMP: 9 **EST:** 1965
SQ FT: 3,800
SALES: 1.2MM **Privately Held**
SIC: 3599 3312 Machine shop, jobbing & repair; tool & die steel

(G-6796)
B B BRADLEY COMPANY INC
2699 Scioto Pkwy (43221-4658)
PHONE............................614 777-5600
Fax: 614 777-5631
Bruce Beaty, *President*
EMP: 7

SALES (corp-wide): 5.1MM **Privately Held**
WEB: www.bbbradley.com
SIC: **3086** 5199 Packaging & shipping materials, foamed plastic; packaging materials
PA: The B B Bradley Company Inc
7755 Crile Rd
Painesville OH 44077
440 354-2005

(G-6797)
B&A HOLSTIC FOOD AND HERBS
Also Called: Holistic Foods Herbs and Books
6031 E Main St (43213-3356)
PHONE......................614 747-2885
Sonya Robinson, *Principal*
Ahrayah Robinson, *Principal*
John Robinson, *Principal*
EMP: 10
SALES: 250K **Privately Held**
SIC: **2833** Drugs & herbs: grading, grinding & milling

(G-6798)
B-F PROCESSING LLC
Also Called: B-F Processing Corporation
180 E Broad St Lbby (43215-3750)
PHONE......................614 225-4000
C Robert Kidder, *President*
EMP: 3
SALES (est): 20.7K **Publicly Held**
SIC: **2869** Industrial organic chemicals
HQ: Hexion Inc.
180 E Broad St Fl 26
Columbus OH 43215
614 225-4000

(G-6799)
BABCOCK & WILCOX MEGTEC
835 N Cassady Ave (43219-2203)
PHONE......................614 258-9501
Mark Stouffer, *Research*
Mike Hunter, *Manager*
Nick Strow, *Manager*
Bill Vogelhuber, *Manager*
Diana Dumitrecu, *Administration*
EMP: 110
SALES (corp-wide): 1.5B **Publicly Held**
WEB: www.megtec.com
SIC: **3564** 2899 3674 3624 Blowers & fans; air purification equipment; chemical preparations; bay oil; semiconductors & related devices; carbon & graphite products; specialty cleaning, polishes & sanitation goods
HQ: Babcock & Wilcox Megtec
830 Prosper St
De Pere WI 54115
920 336-5715

(G-6800)
BABCOCK & WILCOX MEGTEC
Also Called: Solvent Recovery Division
2120 Citygate Dr (43219-3566)
PHONE......................614 340-4154
Bill Greenwood, *Project Mgr*
David Evan, *Manager*
EMP: 5
SALES (corp-wide): 1.5B **Publicly Held**
SIC: **2911** Solvents
HQ: Babcock & Wilcox Megtec
830 Prosper St
De Pere WI 54115
920 336-5715

(G-6801)
BAISE ENTERPRISES INC
Also Called: Baise Quality Printing
695 Koebel Ave Frnt (43207-7103)
PHONE......................614 444-3171
Troy Baise, *President*
EMP: 5
SQ FT: 10,000
SALES (est): 501.1K **Privately Held**
WEB: www.baisequalityprinting.com
SIC: **2759** 2791 2789 2752 Commercial printing; typesetting; bookbinding & related work; commercial printing, lithographic

(G-6802)
BAKE ME HAPPY LLC
116 E Moler St (43207)
PHONE......................614 477-3642

Letha Pugh,
Wendy Miller Pugh,
EMP: 3 EST: 2013
SQ FT: 2,800
SALES (est): 623.9K **Privately Held**
SIC: **5142** 5149 2051 Bakery products, frozen; crackers, cookies & bakery products; pies, bakery: except frozen

(G-6803)
BAKER WELDING LLC
2901 Eastport Ave Bldg 95 (43219)
P.O. Box 20403, Circleville (43113)
PHONE......................614 252-6100
Ray Baker, *Owner*
EMP: 4
SQ FT: 10,060
SALES: 675K **Privately Held**
SIC: **7692** Welding repair

(G-6804)
BALL CORPORATION
2690 Charter St (43228-4600)
PHONE......................614 771-9112
Fax: 614 771-5340
Paul Scott, *Safety Dir*
Dan Griffit, *Plant Mgr*
Carol Stockett, *Purchasing*
Mike Johnson, *QC Mgr*
John Ficek, *Engineer*
EMP: 65
SALES (corp-wide): 9B **Publicly Held**
WEB: www.ball.com
SIC: **3411** Metal cans
PA: Ball Corporation
10 Longs Peak Dr
Broomfield CO 80021
303 469-3131

(G-6805)
BANNER METALS GROUP INC
1308 Holly Ave (43212-3115)
PHONE......................614 291-3105
Fax: 614 291-3125
John E O'Brien III, *CEO*
Wm Seidensticker Et Al, *Principal*
F M Jaeger, *Principal*
James H Kennedy, *Principal*
C Bronson Jones, *Vice Pres*
EMP: 70
SQ FT: 70,000
SALES (est): 15.2MM **Privately Held**
WEB: www.bannerstamping.com
SIC: **3469** 3544 Metal stampings; special dies & tools; jigs & fixtures; jigs: inspection, gauging & checking

(G-6806)
BARBARA A EISENHARDT
7726 Cloister Dr (43235-1461)
PHONE......................614 436-9690
Barbara A Eisenhardt, *Principal*
EMP: 3
SALES (est): 133K **Privately Held**
SIC: **2711** Newspapers, publishing & printing

(G-6807)
BARR ENGINEERING INCORPORATED
5710 Westbourne Ave (43213-1400)
PHONE......................614 892-0162
Enoch Chipukaizer, *CEO*
Margaret Henry, *Consultant*
EMP: 15
SALES (corp-wide): 9.1MM **Privately Held**
SIC: **8711** 8734 8748 1799 Construction & civil engineering; civil engineering; structural engineering; testing laboratories; traffic consultant; lighting consultant; core drilling & cutting; nonmetallic minerals development & test boring; architectural services; architectural engineering
PA: Barr Engineering Incorporated
2800 Corp Exchange Dr # 240
Columbus OH 43231
614 714-0299

(G-6808)
BARR ENGINEERING INCORPORATED (PA)
Also Called: National Engrg Archtctral Svcs
2800 Corp Exchange Dr # 240 (43231-7628)
PHONE......................614 714-0299

Jawdat Siddiqi, *President*
Enoch Chipukaizer, *Principal*
Robin Lamb, *Principal*
Margaret Henry, *Marketing Staff*
EMP: 35
SQ FT: 1,500
SALES (est): 9.1MM **Privately Held**
SIC: **8711** 8713 8734 1799 Construction & civil engineering; surveying services; testing laboratories; core drilling & cutting; nonmetallic minerals development & test boring

(G-6809)
BARRY BROTHERS ELECTRIC
1100 Leona Ave (43201-3039)
PHONE......................614 299-8187
Fax: 614 299-1683
Boyce A Barry, *Owner*
EMP: 4
SQ FT: 1,000
SALES (est): 266.8K **Privately Held**
SIC: **7694** 3625 Electric motor repair; electric controls & control accessories, industrial

(G-6810)
BARTEK SYSTEMS
6155 Chinaberry Dr (43213-3323)
PHONE......................614 759-6014
Heywood Hampton, *Principal*
EMP: 5
SALES (est): 511.5K **Privately Held**
SIC: **3578** Cash registers

(G-6811)
BARTLEY OFFIE
Also Called: Capital Tool Grinding Co
3760 E 5th Ave (43219-1807)
PHONE......................614 235-9050
Offie Bartley, *Owner*
EMP: 4
SQ FT: 10,500
SALES (est): 297.6K **Privately Held**
SIC: **3599** Machine shop, jobbing & repair

(G-6812)
BASF CORPORATION
9565 Logistics Ct (43217-0001)
PHONE......................614 662-5682
EMP: 4
SALES (corp-wide): 60.8B **Privately Held**
SIC: **2869** 2819 2899 2843 Industrial organic chemicals; industrial inorganic chemicals; antifreeze compounds; surface active agents; pharmaceutical preparations; vitamin preparations; agricultural chemicals
HQ: Basf Corporation
100 Park Ave
Florham Park NJ 07932
973 245-6000

(G-6813)
BASINGER INC
2222 Wilson Rd (43228-9386)
PHONE......................614 771-8300
Robert Lee Basinger, *Principal*
EMP: 2
SALES: 2.7MM **Privately Held**
SIC: **2759** Financial note & certificate printing & engraving

(G-6814)
BASS INTERNATIONAL SFTWR LLC (PA)
Also Called: Onevuex
4449 Easton Way Ste 200 (43219-7005)
PHONE......................877 227-0155
Darrel F Bass,
EMP: 5
SQ FT: 400
SALES (est): 1.4MM **Privately Held**
SIC: **7372** Business oriented computer software

(G-6815)
BEAM TECHNOLOGIES INC
629 N High St Fl 6 (43215-2025)
PHONE......................800 648-1179
Alex Frommeyer, *CEO*
Alexander Curry, *COO*
Daniel Dykes, *CTO*
EMP: 9
SALES (est): 1.2MM **Privately Held**
SIC: **3841** Surgical & medical instruments

(G-6816)
BECK & ORR INC
3097 W Broad St (43204-1306)
PHONE......................614 276-8809
Fax: 614 276-5515
Roland L Bowman, *President*
EMP: 3 EST: 1888
SQ FT: 2,700
SALES: 175K **Privately Held**
SIC: **2782** Looseleaf binders & devices

(G-6817)
BECKENHORST PRESS INC
960 Old Henderson Rd (43220-3723)
P.O. Box 14273 (43214-0273)
PHONE......................614 451-6461
Jeffrey D Hamm, *President*
Bryan Babcock, *Sales Staff*
Craig Courtney, *Director*
EMP: 4
SQ FT: 8,500
SALES (est): 433.6K **Privately Held**
WEB: www.beckenhorstpress.com
SIC: **2741** Music, sheet: publishing only, not printed on site

(G-6818)
BECKMAN XMO
376 Morrison Rd Ste D (43213-1447)
PHONE......................614 864-3305
Tracy Beckman, *Principal*
Scott Taylor, *Prdtn Mgr*
David Schultz, *Accounts Exec*
Craig Faist, *Manager*
Bob Moyer, *Consultant*
EMP: 14
SALES (est): 2.2MM **Privately Held**
SIC: **2752** Commercial printing, lithographic

(G-6819)
BEESIGN SIGNS INC
3079 W Broad St Ste 2 (43204-1376)
PHONE......................614 449-3233
Ted Eisleben, *President*
Betty Lippold, *Vice Pres*
EMP: 3
SQ FT: 5,000
SALES: 130K **Privately Held**
SIC: **3993** Signs & advertising specialties

(G-6820)
BEGASHAW & ASSOCIATES
33 S James Rd Ste 203 (43213-1065)
PHONE......................614 329-1630
Seisu Begashaw, *Partner*
EMP: 3
SALES (est): 172.5K **Privately Held**
SIC: **2741** Telephone & other directory publishing

(G-6821)
BENCHMARK ARCHTECTURAL SYSTEMS
Also Called: Kingspan Benchmark
720 Marion Rd (43207-2553)
PHONE......................614 444-0110
Russel Shiels, *President*
Ilhan Eser, *Vice Pres*
John Parisi, *Credit Mgr*
Jeff Irwin, *Accounts Mgr*
William Sandahl, *Regl Sales Mgr*
▲ EMP: 40
SQ FT: 96,000
SALES (est): 9.6MM **Privately Held**
WEB: www.kingspanpanels.us
SIC: **3448** Prefabricated metal buildings
HQ: Kingspan Insulated Panels Inc.
726 Summerhill Dr
Deland FL 32724
386 626-6789

(G-6822)
BENDEL INC (PA)
4120 The Strand (43219-6121)
PHONE......................614 478-9013
Henri Bendel, *President*
EMP: 9
SALES (est): 4.5MM **Privately Held**
SIC: **3545** Machine tool accessories

(G-6823)
BETTER THAN SEX ICE CREAM LLC
Also Called: BTS Ice Cream
1352 Parsons Ave (43206-3643)
PHONE..........................614 444-5505
Troy Harris, *President*
EMP: 5
SQ FT: 800
SALES (est): 200K Privately Held
SIC: 2024 Ice cream & frozen desserts

(G-6824)
BEVERLY SNIDER
Also Called: Wedding Plantation
3900 Noe Bixby Rd (43232-6164)
PHONE..........................614 837-5817
Fax: 614 833-2921
Beverly Snider, *Owner*
EMP: 6
SQ FT: 2,400
SALES (est): 313.5K Privately Held
SIC: 5621 3652 Bridal shops; dress shops; pre-recorded records & tapes

(G-6825)
BEXLEY FABRICS INC
2476 E Main St (43209-2441)
P.O. Box 124, Galloway (43119-0124)
PHONE..........................614 231-7272
Edward E Goldin, *Owner*
EMP: 8
SALES (est): 555.3K Privately Held
SIC: 2295 Sleeving, textile: saturated

(G-6826)
BEXLEY PEN COMPANY INC
2840 Fisher Rd Ste B (43204-3551)
PHONE..........................614 351-9988
Fax: 614 351-9989
Howard Levy, *President*
Steven Vandyke, *Vice Pres*
▲ EMP: 5
SQ FT: 2,200
SALES (est): 575.1K Privately Held
WEB: www.bexleypen.com
SIC: 3951 3599 Pens & mechanical pencils; machine shop, jobbing & repair

(G-6827)
BIG DRUM USA LTD
5706 Westbourne Ave (43213-1400)
PHONE..........................614 626-0843
Timothy Miller,
EMP: 4
SQ FT: 4,800
SALES (est): 662.6K Privately Held
SIC: 3556 Ice cream manufacturing machinery

(G-6828)
BIG NOODLE LLC
687 Kenwick Rd (43209-2592)
PHONE..........................614 558-7170
Christina Providence, *Principal*
EMP: 3
SALES (est): 201.1K Privately Held
SIC: 2098 Noodles (e.g. egg, plain & water), dry

(G-6829)
BIO-BLOOD COMPONENTS INC
1393 N High St (43201-2459)
PHONE..........................614 294-3183
Fax: 614 294-2214
Jane Hancock, *Manager*
Shelly Heckert, *Manager*
EMP: 30
SALES (corp-wide): 17.3MM Privately Held
SIC: 8099 2836 Blood bank; biological products, except diagnostic
PA: Bio-Blood Components, Inc.
5700 Pleasant View Rd
Memphis TN 38134
901 384-6250

(G-6830)
BIOBENT HOLDINGS LLC
Also Called: Biobent Polymers
1275 Kinnear Rd Ste 239 (43212-1180)
PHONE..........................513 658-5560
Keith Masavage, *CEO*
Michele Cole, *Principal*
Curtis Crocker,

Ross Youngs,
EMP: 6 EST: 2012
SALES (est): 491K Privately Held
SIC: 2821 Plastics materials & resins

(G-6831)
BIOBENT HOLDINGS LLC
Also Called: Biobent Polymers
1275 Kinnear Rd Ste 239 (43212-1180)
PHONE..........................513 658-5560
Keith Masavage, *CEO*
Michele Cole, *Principal*
Curtis Crocker, *Principal*
Ross Youngs, *Principal*
EMP: 6 EST: 2012
SALES (est): 771.4K Privately Held
SIC: 2821 Plastics materials & resins

(G-6832)
BISON BUILDERS LLC
Also Called: Cabinet Guys, The
6999 Huntley Rd Ste M (43229-1031)
PHONE..........................614 636-0365
David Needs, *Mng Member*
Jason Myers,
David Sprangue,
EMP: 18
SALES (est): 1.6MM Privately Held
SIC: 1522 2434 5031 Hotel/motel & multi-family home renovation & remodeling; vanities, bathroom: wood; kitchen cabinets

(G-6833)
BIZZY BEE PRINTING INC
Also Called: Innovative Computer Forms
1500 W 3rd Ave Ste 106 (43212-2887)
PHONE..........................614 771-1222
Fax: 614 771-0051
Chris Schmelzer, *President*
Rick Schmelzer, *Treasurer*
Rosemary Schmelzer, *Admin Sec*
EMP: 6
SALES (est): 705.4K Privately Held
SIC: 2759 Commercial printing

(G-6834)
BJ EQUIPMENT LTD
Also Called: Rent-A-John
4522 Lockbourne Rd (43207-4231)
P.O. Box 753 (43216-0753)
PHONE..........................614 497-1776
Fax: 614 497-4114
William Reynolds Jr, *President*
Bonnie Jean Reynolds, *Corp Secy*
Cassie A Reynolds, *Marketing Staff*
Boby Neff, *Manager*
EMP: 15
SALES (est): 1.6MM Privately Held
SIC: 7359 3444 3443 3431 Equipment rental & leasing; sheet metalwork; fabricated plate work (boiler shop); metal sanitary ware

(G-6835)
BJOND INC
1463 Briarmeadow Dr (43235-1612)
PHONE..........................614 537-7246
Kenneth Leachman, *CEO*
EMP: 8
SALES (est): 298.3K Privately Held
SIC: 7372 7389 Business oriented computer software;

(G-6836)
BLACCO SPLCING RGGING LOFT INC (PA)
1976 Alum Creek Dr (43207-1711)
PHONE..........................614 444-2888
Fax: 614 444-2951
Boyd C Black, *CEO*
Bart Black, *President*
EMP: 3 EST: 1956
SQ FT: 22,500
SALES (est): 2.9MM Privately Held
SIC: 3496 Slings, lifting: made from purchased wire

(G-6837)
BLACK & DECKER (US) INC
1948 Schrock Rd (43229-1563)
PHONE..........................614 895-3112
Fax: 614 895-3187
Dave Burica, *Manager*
EMP: 7

SALES (corp-wide): 11.4B Publicly Held
WEB: www.dewalt.com
SIC: 3546 Power-driven handtools
HQ: Black & Decker (U.S.) Inc.
1000 Stanley Dr
New Britain CT 06053
860 885-5111

(G-6838)
BLACKBURNS FABRICATION INC
2467 Jackson Pike (43223-3846)
PHONE..........................614 875-0784
Fax: 614 875-0337
Mark A Blackburn, *President*
Edsel L Blackburn Sr, *Vice Pres*
Carolyn Blackburn, *Admin Sec*
Kim Green, *Admin Sec*
EMP: 30
SQ FT: 50,000
SALES (est): 9.2MM Privately Held
WEB: www.blackburnsfab.com
SIC: 3441 5051 Fabricated structural metal; structural shapes, iron or steel

(G-6839)
BLACKWOOD SHEET METAL INC
844 Kerr St (43215-1499)
PHONE..........................614 291-3115
Fax: 614 291-2919
Diana Blackwood Newby, *President*
Charles Newby, *Vice Pres*
EMP: 8 EST: 1908
SQ FT: 10,000
SALES: 550K Privately Held
SIC: 7692 3443 Welding repair; fabricated plate work (boiler shop)

(G-6840)
BLADE MANUFACTURING CO INC
915 Distribution Dr Ste A (43228-1009)
PHONE..........................614 294-1649
Fax: 614 294-8437
Michael F Callahan, *President*
Thomas J Callahan, *Corp Secy*
Michelle M Callahan, *Vice Pres*
Marc Callahan, *VP Sales*
▲ EMP: 10 EST: 1946
SQ FT: 10,000
SALES (est): 1.1MM Privately Held
WEB: www.blademfg.com
SIC: 3425 7389 Saw blades & handsaws; saw blades for hand or power saws; grinding, precision: commercial or industrial

(G-6841)
BMD BLASTING
1840 Federal Pkwy (43207-5709)
PHONE..........................614 580-9468
Michael Bradford, *Owner*
EMP: 4
SQ FT: 4,000
SALES (est): 186K Privately Held
SIC: 3471 Plating & polishing

(G-6842)
BMI MACHINE INC
Also Called: Butler Machine
8354 Fairway Dr (43235-1155)
PHONE..........................614 785-7020
Fax: 614 785-7023
Robert I Davidson, *President*
Diane L Leatherbury, *Purch Mgr*
EMP: 3
SALES (est): 365.4K Privately Held
SIC: 3599 Machine & other job shop work

(G-6843)
BODYCOTE THERMAL PROC INC
Columbus Div
1515 Universal Rd (43207-1770)
PHONE..........................614 444-1181
Fax: 614 444-0421
David Nelson, *Plant Engr Mgr*
David Hollingsworth, *Sales Mgr*
Marc Walters, *Branch Mgr*
Keith A Engwall, *Director*
EMP: 45
SQ FT: 26,000

SALES (corp-wide): 739.3MM Privately Held
WEB: www.mic-houston.com
SIC: 3398 Metal heat treating
HQ: Bodycote Thermal Processing, Inc.
12700 Park Central Dr # 700
Dallas TX 75251
214 904-2420

(G-6844)
BOGGS & ASSOCIATES INC
3555 E Fulton St (43227-1195)
PHONE..........................614 237-0600
Fax: 614 237-0102
Stephan Boggs, *President*
Vicki Boggs, *Corp Secy*
EMP: 6
SQ FT: 5,000
SALES (est): 786.5K Privately Held
SIC: 3599 Machine shop, jobbing & repair

(G-6845)
BOICH COMPANIES LLC
41 S High St Ste 3750s (43215-3406)
PHONE..........................614 221-0101
Wayne M Boich, *CEO*
Brian T Murphy, *CFO*
EMP: 7
SALES (est): 330.8K Privately Held
SIC: 1241 Coal mining services

(G-6846)
BOOKCOLOR BINDERY SERVICES
1685 Woodland Ave (43219-1135)
PHONE..........................614 252-2941
Glenn Morrow, *CEO*
Norris Joe, *Treasurer*
EMP: 20
SQ FT: 11,000
SALES (est): 950K Privately Held
WEB: www.bookcolorbindery.com
SIC: 2789 Binding only: books, pamphlets, magazines, etc.

(G-6847)
BORDEN BAKERS INC
4723 Reed Rd (43220-3051)
PHONE..........................614 457-9800
Michael Borden, *Principal*
EMP: 4
SALES (est): 150K Privately Held
SIC: 2051 Bakery: wholesale or wholesale/retail combined

(G-6848)
BORDEN CHEMICAL INC
180 E Broad St (43215-3707)
PHONE..........................614 225-4000
Fax: 614 225-4742
Lesa Frantz, *Principal*
EMP: 33
SALES (est): 4.9MM Privately Held
SIC: 2891 Adhesives & sealants

(G-6849)
BORDEN CHEMICAL FOUNDRY LLC
180 E Broad St Fl 24 (43215-3760)
PHONE..........................614 225-4000
Earl Freeman, *Area Mgr*
William Stoll, *Exec VP*
Timothy Zappala, *Exec VP*
Jeff McWilliams, *Senior VP*
Kamal Aboshama, *Vice Pres*
EMP: 20
SALES (est): 3.2MM Publicly Held
SIC: 2869 Industrial organic chemicals
HQ: Hexion Inc.
180 E Broad St Fl 26
Columbus OH 43215
614 225-4000

(G-6850)
BOSE CORPORATION
Also Called: Bose Showcase Store
155 Easton Town Ctr Fl 1 (43219-6075)
PHONE..........................614 475-8565
Fax: 614 475-8896
Jim Pearsall, *Manager*
EMP: 9
SALES (corp-wide): 3B Privately Held
WEB: www.bose.com
SIC: 5731 3651 Radio, television & electronic stores; household audio equipment

▲ = Import ▼=Export
◆ =Import/Export

PA: Bose Corporation
100 The Mountain Rd
Framingham MA 01701
508 879-7330

(G-6851)
BOYCE LTD
2173 S James Rd (43232-3850)
PHONE..............................614 236-8901
Troy M Boyce, *Principal*
EMP: 3
SALES (est): 253.4K **Privately Held**
SIC: 1799 1521 7532 0782 Home/office interiors finishing, furnishing & remodeling; single-family home remodeling, additions & repairs; interior repair services; lawn services; construction, repair & dismantling services; roof repair

(G-6852)
BPM REALTY INC
195 N Grant Ave Fl 2a (43215-2855)
PHONE..............................614 221-6811
Frederick W Ziegler, *Ch of Bd*
John M Ziegler, *President*
Gloria McCoy, *Accountant*
EMP: 27
SQ FT: 43,000
SALES (est): 3MM **Privately Held**
WEB: www.buckeyepm.com
SIC: 7331 2752 Mailing service; commercial printing, offset

(G-6853)
BRADEN-SUTPHIN INK COMPANY
2272 S High St (43207-2432)
PHONE..............................614 443-9100
Kevin Preston, *Manager*
EMP: 6
SALES (corp-wide): 27.5MM **Privately Held**
WEB: www.bsink.com
SIC: 2893 5085 Printing ink; ink, printers'
PA: The Braden-Sutphin Ink Company
3650 E 93rd St
Cleveland OH 44105
216 271-2300

(G-6854)
BRENDONS FIBER WORKS
306 E Jeffrey Pl (43214-1714)
PHONE..............................614 353-6599
Laura K Brendon, *Principal*
EMP: 3
SALES (est): 172.9K **Privately Held**
SIC: 3296 Mineral wool

(G-6855)
BREWER COMPANY
472 Brehl Ave (43223-1973)
P.O. Box 23054 (43223-0054)
PHONE..............................614 279-8688
Fax: 614 279-7201
Jack Donnelly, *Sales Staff*
Bill Ison, *Manager*
EMP: 20
SQ FT: 55,000
SALES (corp-wide): 50MM **Privately Held**
WEB: www.thebrewerco.com
SIC: 2952 2951 2891 Asphalt felts & coatings; asphalt paving mixtures & blocks; adhesives & sealants
PA: The Brewer Company
1354 Us Route 50
Milford OH 45150
800 394-0017

(G-6856)
BREWERY REAL ESTATE PARTNR
467 N High St (43215-2007)
PHONE..............................614 224-9023
EMP: 4
SALES (est): 196.7K **Privately Held**
SIC: 2082 Beer (alcoholic beverage)

(G-6857)
BREWPUB RESTAURANT CORP
Also Called: Barley's Brewing Company
467 N High St (43215-2007)
PHONE..............................614 228-2537
Fax: 614 224-2739
Leonard Kolada, *President*
Bertolo Jason, *Manager*

Angelo Signorino, *Manager*
Ian Boyland, *Asst Mgr*
Joseph Colburn, *Executive*
EMP: 60
SALES (est): 1.7MM **Privately Held**
SIC: 5812 2082 Chicken restaurant; malt beverages

(G-6858)
BRIDGE COMPONENTS INCORPORATED
3476 Millikin Ct (43228-9765)
P.O. Box 1228, Dublin (43017-6228)
PHONE..............................614 873-0777
Neil Spears, *President*
EMP: 7
SALES (est): 1MM **Privately Held**
WEB: www.bridgecomponentsinc.com
SIC: 2824 3449 Elastomeric fibers; bars, concrete reinforcing: fabricated steel

(G-6859)
BRIDGE COMPONENTS INDS INC
3476 Millikin Ct (43228-9765)
PHONE..............................614 873-0777
Tyler Spears, *President*
EMP: 6
SALES (est): 794K **Privately Held**
SIC: 3312 Railroad crossings, steel or iron

(G-6860)
BRIGHTON COLLECTIBLES LLC
217 Easton Town Ctr (43219-6077)
PHONE..............................614 418-7561
Jerry Kohl, *Branch Mgr*
EMP: 34
SALES (corp-wide): 378.3MM **Privately Held**
SIC: 3199 Corners, luggage: leather
PA: Brighton Collectibles, Llc
14022 Nelson Ave
City Of Industry CA 91746
626 961-9381

(G-6861)
BRILISTA FOODS COMPANY INC (PA)
Also Called: Krema Nut Co
1000 Goodale Blvd (43212-3827)
PHONE..............................614 299-4132
Fax: 614 299-1636
Michael Giunta, *President*
David Block, *Vice Pres*
Brian Giunta, *Vice Pres*
Peggy Giunta, *Vice Pres*
John Walters, *Manager*
EMP: 8
SQ FT: 8,500
SALES (est): 943.4K **Privately Held**
WEB: www.krema.com
SIC: 2038 Snacks, including onion rings, cheese sticks, etc.

(G-6862)
BRILLIANT COLORWORKS LLC
2940 E 14th Ave (43219-2304)
PHONE..............................800 566-4162
Jim Kaminiski, *Principal*
EMP: 4
SALES (est): 353.6K **Privately Held**
SIC: 3479 Painting of metal products

(G-6863)
BRISKHEAT CORPORATION (PA)
4800 Hilton Corporate Dr (43232-4150)
PHONE..............................614 294-3376
Fax: 614 294-2672
Domenic Federico, *CEO*
James Zins, *Corp Secy*
Sorina Sok, *Purch Mgr*
Ken Jones, *Purchasing*
Joe Barille, *Financial Exec*
▲ **EMP:** 159
SQ FT: 40,000
SALES (est): 57.8MM **Privately Held**
WEB: www.bhthermal.com
SIC: 3585 Heating equipment, complete

(G-6864)
BRISKHEAT CORPORATION
460 E Starr Ave (43201-3695)
PHONE..............................614 429-3232
John Vanvleet, *President*
Ken Jones, *Purchasing*

EMP: 58
SALES (corp-wide): 57.8MM **Privately Held**
SIC: 3567 Heating units & devices, industrial: electric
PA: Briskheat Corporation
4800 Hilton Corporate Dr
Columbus OH 43232
614 294-3376

(G-6865)
BROAD STREET ENERGY COMPANY
1515 Lake Shore Dr # 225 (43204-3896)
PHONE..............................614 228-0326
William E Arthur, *President*
Geoffrey W Arthur, *Corp Secy*
EMP: 5
SQ FT: 3,100
SALES: 3.8MM **Privately Held**
SIC: 1311 Crude petroleum & natural gas production
PA: Broad Street Financial Company
1515 Lake Shore Dr # 225
Columbus OH 43204
614 228-0326

(G-6866)
BROAD STREET FINANCIAL COMPANY (PA)
Also Called: Broadstreet Energy Company
1515 Lake Shore Dr # 225 (43204-3896)
PHONE..............................614 228-0326
William E Arthur, *Ch of Bd*
Geoff Arthur, *Exec VP*
Dan Kosikowski, *Comptroller*
EMP: 5
SQ FT: 3,100
SALES: 3.8MM **Privately Held**
SIC: 1311 6799 6722 Crude petroleum & natural gas production; real estate investors, except property operators; management investment, open-end

(G-6867)
BRON-SHOE COMPANY
Also Called: American Bronzing Company
1313 Alum Creek Dr (43209-2760)
PHONE..............................614 252-0967
Fax: 614 252-4602
Robert J Kaynes Jr, *President*
Susan Lantz, *Treasurer*
EMP: 25 **EST:** 1949
SQ FT: 40,000
SALES (est): 3.1MM **Privately Held**
WEB: www.abcbronze.com
SIC: 7389 3471 Bronzing, baby shoes; plating of metals or formed products

(G-6868)
BROWNIE POINTS INC
5712 Westbourne Ave (43213-1400)
PHONE..............................614 860-8470
Lisa King, *President*
EMP: 5
SQ FT: 1,326
SALES (est): 609.5K **Privately Held**
WEB: www.browniepointsinc.com
SIC: 2066 5149 Chocolate & cocoa products; bakery products

(G-6869)
BSA INDUSTRIES INC
Also Called: Select Optical
6510 Huntley Rd (43229-1012)
PHONE..............................614 846-5515
Delbert M Lothes, *CFO*
M Lothes, *CFO*
EMP: 70
SQ FT: 20,000
SALES (est): 11.5MM
SALES (corp-wide): 938.9MM **Privately Held**
SIC: 3827 3851 Lenses, optical: all types except ophthalmic; ophthalmic goods
HQ: Essilor Laboratories Of America, Inc.
13515 N Stemmons Fwy
Dallas TX 75234
972 241-4141

(G-6870)
BUCKEYE BOXES INC (PA)
601 N Hague Ave (43204-1498)
PHONE..............................614 274-8484
Fax: 614 274-7381
Craig Hoyt, *President*

Ken Churchill, *Vice Pres*
Judd Hauenstein, *Vice Pres*
Jim Mullins, *Prdtn Mgr*
John Strickler, *Purchasing*
▲ **EMP:** 60 **EST:** 1966
SQ FT: 100,000
SALES (est): 24.9MM **Privately Held**
SIC: 2673 2653 3993 2675 Bags: plastic, laminated & coated; cellophane bags, unprinted: made from purchased materials; boxes, corrugated: made from purchased materials; signs & advertising specialties; die-cut paper & board; paperboard mills

(G-6871)
BUCKEYE BOXES INC
601 N Hague Ave (43204-1498)
PHONE..............................614 274-8484
Fax: 419 626-9635
Ed Wells, *General Mgr*
EMP: 30
SALES (corp-wide): 24.9MM **Privately Held**
SIC: 5113 2653 Industrial & personal service paper; corrugated & solid fiber boxes
PA: Buckeye Boxes, Inc.
601 N Hague Ave
Columbus OH 43204
614 274-8484

(G-6872)
BUCKEYE CSTM SCREEN PRINT EMB
Also Called: Seymour, Lloyd
3822 Elbern Ave (43213-1723)
PHONE..............................614 237-0196
Lloyd Seymour, *Owner*
EMP: 10
SQ FT: 1,800
SALES (est): 456.7K **Privately Held**
SIC: 2759 2752 Screen printing; commercial printing, lithographic

(G-6873)
BUCKEYE METAL WORKS INC
3240 Petzinger Rd (43232-3912)
PHONE..............................614 239-8000
Fax: 614 239-8877
Denny Arthurs, *President*
Walt Daniel, *Vice Pres*
Matt Daniel, *Project Mgr*
EMP: 17
SQ FT: 15,000
SALES (est): 3.6MM **Privately Held**
SIC: 3444 Sheet metalwork

(G-6874)
BUCKEYE RACEWAY LLC
4050 W Broad St (43228-1449)
PHONE..............................614 272-7888
EMP: 7 **EST:** 2014
SALES (est): 489.7K **Privately Held**
SIC: 3644 Raceways

(G-6875)
BUCKEYE STAMPING COMPANY
Also Called: Buckeye Shapeform
555 Marion Rd (43207-2501)
PHONE..............................614 445-0059
Fax: 614 445-8224
Jon Hettinger, *Ch of Bd*
C A Morningstar, *President*
Ken Tumblison, *President*
Larry Doza, *Corp Secy*
Don Cotter, *Manager*
EMP: 60 **EST:** 1902
SQ FT: 80,000
SALES (est): 17MM **Privately Held**
SIC: 3469 3443 3089 3449 Electronic enclosures, stamped or pressed metal; containers, shipping (bombs, etc.): metal plate; plastic hardware & building products; miscellaneous metalwork; metal cans; luggage

(G-6876)
BURTON METAL FINISHING INC
1711 Woodland Ave (43219-1137)
PHONE..............................614 252-9523
Fax: 614 252-6172
Dallas Burton, *CEO*
Victoria Burton, *Corp Secy*
Scott Burton, *Vice Pres*
EMP: 25
SQ FT: 5,000

SALES (est): 5.9MM **Privately Held**
WEB: www.burton-metal-finishing.com
SIC: 3559 Metal finishing equipment for plating, etc.

(G-6877)
BUSCH PROPERTIES INC
1103 Schrock Rd Ste 200 (43229-1179)
P.O. Box 29229 (43229-0229)
PHONE....................................614 888-0946
Fax: 614 888-0946
Sherral Butler, *Director*
Ralph Chizzonite, *Director*
EMP: 6
SALES (corp-wide): 5.1B **Publicly Held**
WEB: www.abconference.com
SIC: 3411 Aluminum cans
HQ: Busch Properties, Inc.
1 Busch Pl
Saint Louis MO
757 253-3943

(G-6878)
BUSINESS FIRST COLUMBUS INC (DH)
303 W Nationwide Blvd (43215-3894)
PHONE....................................614 461-4040
Fax: 614 365-2980
Whitney Shaw, *President*
Don Deperro, *Publisher*
Sue Ellen Gabel, *Business Mgr*
James Breiner, *Div Sub Head*
Tim Harvey, *Counsel*
EMP: 20
SQ FT: 7,300
SALES (est): 3MM
SALES (corp-wide): 1.6B **Privately Held**
WEB: www.businessfirstofcolumbus.com
SIC: 2711 Newspapers: publishing only, not printed on site
HQ: American City Business Journals, Inc.
120 W Morehead St Ste 400
Charlotte NC 28202
704 973-1000

(G-6879)
BUSINESS IDNTIFICATION SYSTEMS
Also Called: Sign-A-Rama
6185 Huntley Rd Ste M (43229-1094)
PHONE....................................614 841-1255
Fax: 614 841-7366
Stephen M Thompson, *President*
EMP: 6
SQ FT: 5,200
SALES (est): 656.6K **Privately Held**
SIC: 3993 5999 Signs & advertising specialties; banners, flags, decals & posters

(G-6880)
BYERS SIGN CO
2940 E 14th Ave (43219-2304)
PHONE....................................614 561-1224
Ted Byers, *Owner*
EMP: 3
SALES (est): 276.5K **Privately Held**
SIC: 3993 Signs & advertising specialties

(G-6881)
C & J JEWELERS INC
Also Called: Continental Jwly Replacement
175 Cleveland Ave Frnt (43215-1925)
PHONE....................................614 221-8588
John Carioti, *President*
Chris Carioti, *Vice Pres*
EMP: 5
SQ FT: 7,000
SALES: 700K **Privately Held**
SIC: 3911 Jewelry, precious metal

(G-6882)
C AND O ELECTRIC MOTOR SERVICE
3105 Hillgate Rd (43207-3720)
PHONE....................................614 491-6387
Augie Watson, *President*
Randy Watson, *Vice Pres*
Carol Watson, *Treasurer*
Laura Watson, *Admin Sec*
EMP: 5
SQ FT: 3,000
SALES: 400K **Privately Held**
SIC: 5999 7694 Motors, electric; electric motor repair

(G-6883)
C J SMITH MACHINERY SERVICE
3000 E Main St Ste B (43209-3717)
PHONE....................................614 348-1376
Tim Gallen, *President*
EMP: 3
SALES (est): 223.1K **Privately Held**
SIC: 3589 Service industry machinery

(G-6884)
C P R DRAIN CLEANING INC
2168 Eakin Rd (43223-3220)
PHONE....................................614 279-3445
Fax: 614 279-7030
Dave Turberville, *President*
Kenneth Ilderton Jr, *Vice Pres*
EMP: 12
SALES (est): 1.2MM **Privately Held**
SIC: 3999 Pipe cleaners

(G-6885)
C SOLTESZ CO
4374 Dublin Rd (43221-5001)
PHONE....................................614 529-5494
Mary Soltesz, *Principal*
EMP: 4
SALES (est): 341K **Privately Held**
SIC: 2819 Nuclear fuel scrap, reprocessing

(G-6886)
CABINTPAK KITCHENS OF COLUMBUS
Also Called: Cabinet Works
899 King Ave (43212-2646)
PHONE....................................614 294-4646
Linda Owens, *President*
C Joseph Call, *President*
Christopher Morley, *Vice Pres*
James Owens, *Vice Pres*
EMP: 5
SQ FT: 3,600
SALES: 500K **Privately Held**
SIC: 2514 1751 Kitchen cabinets: metal; cabinet & finish carpentry

(G-6887)
CADBURY SCHWEPPES BOTTLING
950 Stelzer Rd (43219-3740)
PHONE....................................614 238-0469
John Ferrante, *Principal*
EMP: 4
SALES (est): 237.5K **Privately Held**
SIC: 2086 Bottled & canned soft drinks

(G-6888)
CALGON CARBON CORPORATION
835 N Cassady Ave (43219-2203)
PHONE....................................614 258-9501
Tim Duckwall, *Prdtn Mgr*
Chuck Hegenberger, *QA Dir*
Maria Damico, *HR Admin*
Steven Butterworth, *Natl Sales Mgr*
Maria D'Amico, *Branch Mgr*
EMP: 110
SALES (corp-wide): 514.2MM **Publicly Held**
SIC: 2819 Charcoal (carbon), activated
PA: Calgon Carbon Corporation
3000 Gsk Dr
Moon Township PA 15108
412 787-6700

(G-6889)
CALLAHAN CUTTING TOOLS INC
Also Called: Blade Manufacturing Co, The
915 Distribution Dr Ste A (43228-1009)
PHONE....................................614 294-1649
Marc A Callahan, *Principal*
EMP: 5
SALES (est): 580.1K **Privately Held**
SIC: 3425 Machine tools, metal cutting type; saw blades & handsaws

(G-6890)
CALLCOPY INC (DH)
Also Called: Uptivity
555 S Front St (43215-5668)
PHONE....................................614 340-3346
Fax: 614 358-2803
Jeff Canter, *CEO*

Jonathan Dunham, *Exec VP*
Matt Madzia, *Vice Pres*
Richard Snow, *Vice Pres*
Susan Terry, *Vice Pres*
EMP: 6
SQ FT: 12,000
SALES (est): 11.7MM
SALES (corp-wide): 918.9MM **Privately Held**
WEB: www.callcopy.com
SIC: 7371 7372 5045 Computer software development & applications; prepackaged software; computer software
HQ: Incontact, Inc.
75 W Towne Ridge Pkwy # 1
Sandy UT 84070
801 320-3200

(G-6891)
CAMELOT CELLARS WINERY
901 Oak St (43205-1204)
PHONE....................................614 441-8860
Charles Frobose, *Principal*
EMP: 5
SALES (est): 446.2K **Privately Held**
WEB: www.camelotcellars.com
SIC: 2084 Wines, brandy & brandy spirits

(G-6892)
CAMTON MECHANICAL INC
4531 Ellery Dr (43227-2541)
PHONE....................................614 864-7620
Frank Cardinale, *President*
Anthony Cardinale, *Vice Pres*
Dorothy J Cardinale, *Treasurer*
EMP: 3
SALES (est): 272.1K **Privately Held**
SIC: 3559 1796 Automotive maintenance equipment; machinery installation

(G-6893)
CAP & ASSOCIATES INCORPORATED
445 Mccormick Blvd (43213-1526)
PHONE....................................614 863-3363
Fax: 614 863-3603
Charlene A Prosnik, *CEO*
Randy Griffith, *President*
Jason Prosnik, *President*
Joseph Chaulk, *Exec VP*
Ken Louis, *Opers Mgr*
◆ EMP: 170
SQ FT: 110,000
SALES: 49.3MM **Privately Held**
WEB: www.cap-associates.com
SIC: 2541 2542 Store fixtures, wood; shelving, office & store, wood; fixtures, store: except wood

(G-6894)
CAP CITY DIRECT LLC
3203 E 11th Ave (43219-3735)
PHONE....................................614 252-6245
Levi Gibson, *General Mgr*
Jacqueline R Beal,
EMP: 17
SQ FT: 5,000
SALES (est): 2.6MM **Privately Held**
SIC: 2759 7331 Financial note & certificate printing & engraving; direct mail advertising services

(G-6895)
CAPEHART ENTERPRISES LLC
Also Called: Minuteman Press
1724 Northwest Blvd B1 (43212-2246)
PHONE....................................614 769-7746
Gerald C Capehart, *Mng Member*
EMP: 15
SQ FT: 1,500
SALES (est): 44K **Privately Held**
SIC: 2752 5199 8742 Commercial printing, lithographic; advertising specialties; marketing consulting services

(G-6896)
CAPITAL CITY AVIATION INC
2160 West Case Rd Unit 15 (43235-2539)
PHONE....................................614 459-2541
Jason Seavolt, *President*
Joseph Makarich, *Vice Pres*
Ruben Padro, *Treasurer*
Brad Guthrie, *Director*
William Westfall, *Director*
EMP: 12
SQ FT: 800

SALES (est): 253.3K **Privately Held**
SIC: 3721 Aircraft

(G-6897)
CAPITAL CITY AWNING COMPANY
577 N 4th St (43215-2183)
PHONE....................................614 221-5404
Fax: 614 365-9420
Timothy Kellogg, *President*
Michael Mc Connell, *Vice Pres*
Michael McConnell, *Vice Pres*
Frank Collette, *Project Mgr*
Brian Graham, *Marketing Staff*
EMP: 50 EST: 1944
SQ FT: 25,600
SALES (est): 6MM **Privately Held**
WEB: www.capitalcityawning.com
SIC: 2394 2393 Awnings, fabric: made from purchased materials; canvas bags; cushions, except spring & carpet: purchased materials

(G-6898)
CAPITAL CITY ENERGY GROUP INC
1335 Dublin Rd Ste 122d (43215-1000)
PHONE....................................614 485-3110
Todd E Crawford, *Ch of Bd*
Timothy S Shear, *President*
William D Faith, *Treasurer*
EMP: 3
SALES: 675.2K **Privately Held**
SIC: 1382 Oil & gas exploration services

(G-6899)
CAPITAL PROSTHETIC & (PA)
4678 Larwell Dr (43220-3621)
PHONE....................................614 451-0446
Fax: 614 451-2126
David J Kozersky, *President*
Patricia W Kozersky, *Corp Secy*
Lisa Crawford, *Manager*
EMP: 12 EST: 1982
SQ FT: 3,200
SALES (est): 2.9MM **Privately Held**
SIC: 3842 Limbs, artificial; braces, orthopedic

(G-6900)
CAPITAL PROSTHETIC &
4678 Larwell Dr (43220-3621)
PHONE....................................614 451-0446
Lisa Crawford, *Branch Mgr*
EMP: 3
SALES (corp-wide): 2.9MM **Privately Held**
SIC: 3842 Limbs, artificial
PA: Capital Prosthetic And Orthotic Center, Inc.
4678 Larwell Dr
Columbus OH 43220
614 451-0446

(G-6901)
CAPITAL RESIN CORPORATION
324 Dering Ave (43207-2956)
PHONE....................................614 445-7177
Fax: 614 445-7290
Judithe Wensinger, *CEO*
Daniel Yinger, *COO*
Matt Ducay, *Mfg Dir*
Jon Gehman, *Project Mgr*
Ann Tyler, *Opers Staff*
▲ EMP: 76
SQ FT: 6,000
SALES (est): 34.6MM **Privately Held**
WEB: www.capitalresin.com
SIC: 2821 2819 Plastics materials & resins; acrylic resins; polyurethane resins; melamine resins, melamine-formaldehyde; inorganic acids, except nitric & phosphoric

(G-6902)
CAPITAL TRACK COMPANY INC
1364 Cardwell Sq S (43229-9022)
PHONE....................................614 595-5088
Matt Caldwell, *President*
EMP: 4
SQ FT: 16,000
SALES (est): 530K **Privately Held**
WEB: www.capitaltrack.com
SIC: 3555 Printing trades machinery

(G-6903)
CAPITOL CITICOM INC
2225 Citygate Dr Ste A (43319-3651)
PHONE...................................614 472-2679
Fax: 614 472-3246
Daniel J Oakes, *President*
Gail E Oakes, *Vice Pres*
Kelly Koons, *Accounts Mgr*
Stephanie Pitstick, *Accounts Mgr*
Scott Bryant, *Manager*
EMP: 20
SQ FT: 11,500
SALES (est): 3.2MM **Privately Held**
WEB: www.citicomprint.com
SIC: 7374 7372 7389 7334 Data processing service; publishers' computer software; printers' services: folding, collating; photocopying & duplicating services

(G-6904)
CARBOGENE USA LLC
2252 Sedgwick Dr (43220-5430)
PHONE...................................215 378-4306
Cynthia Coleman, *Manager*
Qingjia Jeff Yao,
EMP: 3
SALES (est): 150K **Privately Held**
SIC: 2836 Biological products, except diagnostic

(G-6905)
CARDINAL BUILDERS INC
4409 E Main St (43213-3061)
PHONE...................................614 237-1000
Fax: 614 237-0569
Tim Coady, *President*
Tim Kane, *Shareholder*
EMP: 25 EST: 1965
SQ FT: 22,000
SALES: 6.5MM **Privately Held**
WEB: www.cardinalbuilders.com
SIC: 3541 1521 1522 1799 Machine tool replacement & repair parts, metal cutting types; general remodeling, single-family houses; hotel/motel & multi-family home renovation & remodeling; kitchen & bathroom remodeling; siding contractor

(G-6906)
CARDINAL HEALTH 414 LLC
2215 Citygate Dr Ste D (43319-3589)
PHONE...................................614 473-0786
Scott Lucas, *Branch Mgr*
EMP: 9
SALES (corp-wide): 121.5B **Publicly Held**
SIC: 2835 2834 Radioactive diagnostic substances; pharmaceutical preparations
HQ: Cardinal Health 414, Llc
7000 Cardinal Pl
Dublin OH 43017
614 757-5000

(G-6907)
CARENECTION LLC
1103 Schrock Rd Ste 205 (43229-1179)
PHONE...................................614 468-6045
William Hannan, *CFO*
Ellie Ibarra, *Accountant*
EMP: 3
SALES (est): 78.2K **Privately Held**
SIC: 7372 Prepackaged software

(G-6908)
CARING THINGS INC
435 W State St (43215-4010)
P.O. Box 693, Grove City (43123-0693)
PHONE...................................614 749-9084
Ryan McManus, *CEO*
Shaun Young, *COO*
Lee Wang, *Chief Engr*
Andi Sie, *Product Mgr*
EMP: 4
SQ FT: 300
SALES (est): 108.2K **Privately Held**
SIC: 7372 Prepackaged software

(G-6909)
CARLAS CAKE POPS CNFCTIONS LLC
1561 Old Leonard Ave (43219-2580)
P.O. Box 32055 (43232-0055)
PHONE...................................614 321-9280
Carla Lewis, *CEO*
Derrick Lewis, *Business Mgr*
EMP: 3 EST: 2015

SALES (est): 118.5K **Privately Held**
SIC: 2051 Cakes, bakery: except frozen

(G-6910)
CAROL J GUILER
Also Called: A-1 Welding & Sandblasting
1359 E 5th Ave (43219-2458)
PHONE...................................614 252-6920
Carol Guiler, *Owner*
EMP: 5
SQ FT: 5,500
SALES (est): 170K **Privately Held**
SIC: 7692 Welding repair

(G-6911)
CAROLYN CHEMICAL COMPANY
1601 Woodland Ave (43219-1135)
PHONE...................................614 252-5000
Dan Smucker, *President*
EMP: 13
SALES (est): 1.4MM **Privately Held**
SIC: 2842 Rug, upholstery, or dry cleaning detergents or spotters

(G-6912)
CARROLL DISTRG & CNSTR SUP INC
2929 E 14th Ave (43219-2303)
PHONE...................................614 564-9799
Chris Kreuzer, *Branch Mgr*
EMP: 6
SALES (corp-wide): 75.9MM **Privately Held**
SIC: 5082 3444 Contractors' materials; concrete forms, sheet metal
PA: Carroll Distributing & Construction Supply, Inc.
205 S Iowa Ave
Ottumwa IA 52501
641 683-1888

(G-6913)
CARRY GRANDVIEW OUT
710 Neil Ave (43215-1612)
PHONE...................................614 487-0305
Jeffery Norris, *Owner*
EMP: 4 EST: 2008
SALES (est): 213.1K **Privately Held**
SIC: 2082 Beer (alcoholic beverage)

(G-6914)
CARTOON BOOKS INC
523 S 4th St (43206-1103)
P.O. Box 16973 (43216-6900)
PHONE...................................614 224-4487
Vijaya Iyer, *President*
Jeff Smith, *Treasurer*
▲ EMP: 4
SQ FT: 1,410
SALES (est): 270K **Privately Held**
WEB: www.boneville.com
SIC: 2741 Miscellaneous publishing

(G-6915)
CARYNS CUISINE
155 N Remington Rd (43209-1444)
PHONE...................................614 237-4143
Caryn Shapiro, *Principal*
EMP: 4 EST: 2010
SALES (est): 195.2K **Privately Held**
SIC: 2051 Cakes, bakery: except frozen

(G-6916)
CATHOLIC DIOCESE OF COLUMBUS
Also Called: Catholic Times
197 E Gay St Ste 4 (43215-3229)
PHONE...................................614 224-5195
Fax: 614 241-2518
Teresa Ianaggi, *Manager*
EMP: 9
SALES (corp-wide): 5.9MM **Privately Held**
WEB: www.colscss.org
SIC: 2711 Newspapers
PA: Catholic Diocese Of Columbus
198 E Broad St
Columbus OH 43215
614 224-2251

(G-6917)
CC & SJ OF OHIO INC
4764 W Broad St (43228-1613)
PHONE...................................614 878-7291
Charles Thompson, *President*

EMP: 3
SALES (est): 125K **Privately Held**
SIC: 2599 Food wagons, restaurant

(G-6918)
CENTRAL OHIO METAL STAMPI
1055 Claycraft Rd (43230-6637)
P.O. Box 307776 (43230-7776)
PHONE...................................614 861-3332
Fax: 614 861-0837
John Davidson, *President*
Pennie Davidson, *Corp Secy*
Lawrence Davidson, *Vice Pres*
EMP: 25
SQ FT: 25,000
SALES (est): 5.8MM **Privately Held**
WEB: www.centralohiometalstamping.com
SIC: 3469 Stamping metal for the trade

(G-6919)
CENTRAL OIL ASPHALT CORP (PA)
8 E Long St Ste 400 (43215-2914)
PHONE...................................614 224-8111
Fax: 614 224-4713
F L Shafer, *President*
Alton E Bonnr, *Vice Pres*
C H Knowlton Jr, *Director*
EMP: 7
SQ FT: 4,600
SALES (est): 5.1MM **Privately Held**
SIC: 2951 Asphalt & asphaltic paving mixtures (not from refineries)

(G-6920)
CERTIFIED OIL COMPANY INC
949 King Ave (43212-2662)
PHONE...................................614 421-7500
Peter Lacaillade, *Ch of Bd*
David Hogan, *COO*
EMP: 107
SQ FT: 24,500
SALES (est): 16.3MM
SALES (corp-wide): 49.8MM **Privately Held**
SIC: 2911 Gasoline blending plants
PA: Certified Oil Corporation
949 King Ave
Columbus OH 43212
614 421-7500

(G-6921)
CERTIFIED WALK IN TUBS
Also Called: Home Pro
926 Freeway Dr N (43229-5424)
PHONE...................................614 436-4848
Skyler Alexander, *Partner*
EMP: 17
SALES (est): 1MM **Privately Held**
SIC: 5999 3088 Plumbing & heating supplies; plastics plumbing fixtures

(G-6922)
CHARACTERISTIC SOLUTIONS LLC
Also Called: Discus Sofware
829 Bethel Rd Ste 105 (43214-1903)
PHONE...................................614 360-2424
Bob Roush, *General Mgr*
Susan Iacobacci, *Engineer*
Scot Morris, *Sales Mgr*
Jake Hart, *Marketing Mgr*
Dan Sokol, *Mng Member*
EMP: 3
SQ FT: 1,500
SALES: 300K **Privately Held**
SIC: 3695 Computer software tape & disks: blank, rigid & floppy

(G-6923)
CHC MANUFACTURING INC
2343 Glass Brook Dr (43228)
PHONE...................................614 527-1606
Dan Blank, *Branch Mgr*
EMP: 4
SALES (corp-wide): 8.9MM **Privately Held**
SIC: 3446 3441 Stairs, staircases, stair treads: prefabricated metal; fabricated structural metal
PA: Chc Manufacturing, Inc.
10270 Wayne Ave
Cincinnati OH 45215
513 821-7757

(G-6924)
CHEP (USA) INC
2130 New World Dr (43207-3433)
PHONE...................................614 497-9448
Matt Mallory, *Manager*
EMP: 50
SALES (corp-wide): 5.5B **Privately Held**
SIC: 2448 Wood pallets & skids
HQ: Chep (U.S.A.) Inc.
5897 Windward Pkwy
Alpharetta GA 30005
770 379-6900

(G-6925)
CHERYL A LUCAS
Also Called: It's Sew Much More
388 Morrison Rd (43213-1430)
PHONE...................................614 755-2100
Cheryl A Lucas, *Owner*
Greg Brown, *Owner*
EMP: 4
SQ FT: 2,400
SALES: 150K **Privately Held**
SIC: 2395 Embroidery & art needlework

(G-6926)
CHEZ RAMA RESTAURANT
3669 E Livingston Ave (43227-2243)
PHONE...................................614 237-9315
Mouhamadou Toure, *Owner*
EMP: 4
SALES: 350K **Privately Held**
SIC: 2099 Food preparations

(G-6927)
CHRIS NCKEL CSTM LTHERWORK LLC
80 E Kelso Rd (43202-2312)
PHONE...................................614 262-2672
Paul Nickel, *Principal*
EMP: 3
SALES (est): 183K **Privately Held**
SIC: 3356 Nickel

(G-6928)
CHRONICLE YOUR LIFE STORY
123 S Virginialee Rd (43209-2051)
PHONE...................................614 456-7576
Naomi Kayne, *Principal*
EMP: 3
SALES (est): 159.8K **Privately Held**
SIC: 2711 Newspapers

(G-6929)
CIGS N SUCH
1864 Hard Rd (43235-1996)
PHONE...................................614 389-6115
Pablo Lima, *Manager*
EMP: 4
SALES (est): 330.9K **Privately Held**
SIC: 3911 Cigar & cigarette accessories

(G-6930)
CITI 2 CITI LOGISTICS
Also Called: Abacus Biodiesel Complex
6031 E Main St (43213-3356)
PHONE...................................614 306-4109
Kenneth Turner, *Principal*
EMP: 50
SALES: 950K **Privately Held**
SIC: 2999 Petroleum & coal products

(G-6931)
CITY DOG
510 E Main St (43215-5311)
PHONE...................................614 228-3647
Becky S Hinga, *Principal*
EMP: 4
SALES (est): 497K **Privately Held**
SIC: 3999 Pet supplies

(G-6932)
CITYNET OHIO LLC
343 N Front St Ste 400 (43215-2266)
PHONE...................................614 364-7881
James Martin, *Mng Member*
EMP: 30
SALES (est): 1.4MM **Privately Held**
SIC: 7372 Prepackaged software

(G-6933)
CLARK GRAVE VAULT COMPANY (PA)
Also Called: C.T.L. Steel Division
375 E 5th Ave (43201-2819)
P.O. Box 8250 (43201-0250)
PHONE................................614 294-3761
Fax: 614 299-2324
David Beck, *President*
David A Beck II, *Vice Pres*
Douglas A Beck, *Vice Pres*
Mark Beck, *Vice Pres*
Darrell Kovacs, *Purch Agent*
EMP: 140
SQ FT: 300,000
SALES (est): 53.8MM Privately Held
SIC: 3995 3316 Grave vaults, metal; strip
steel, flat bright, cold-rolled: purchased
hot-rolled; sheet, steel, cold-rolled: from
purchased hot-rolled

(G-6934)
CLASSIC STONE COMPANY INC
4090 Janitrol Rd (43228-1396)
PHONE................................614 833-3946
R G Reitter, *President*
Steven Waits, *CFO*
Gary Cantwall, *Sales Mgr*
EMP: 10
SQ FT: 20,000
SALES (est): 1MM Privately Held
WEB: www.classicstonecompany.com
SIC: 3281 Cut stone & stone products

(G-6935)
CLEAN WATER CONDITIONING
305 Sumption Dr (43230-1639)
PHONE................................614 475-4532
Frank Moeckel, *Owner*
EMP: 3
SALES: 75K Privately Held
SIC: 3589 5074 Swimming pool filter &
water conditioning systems; plumbing &
hydronic heating supplies

(G-6936)
CLEOBROTHERS & COMPANY LLC
200 E Campus View Blvd (43235-4678)
PHONE................................614 985-3639
Ken Hughes, *QA Dir*
Innocent A Nweze, *Mng Member*
Frank Fabish,
EMP: 10
SQ FT: 200
SALES (est): 631K Privately Held
SIC: 2834 Pharmaceutical preparations

(G-6937)
CLEVELAND PLANT AND FLOWER CO
2370 Marilyn Ln (43219-1792)
P.O. Box 30837, Gahanna (43230-0837)
PHONE................................614 478-9900
Fax: 614 478-9905
Brian Davis, *Manager*
EMP: 20
SQ FT: 3,000
SALES (corp-wide): 42.3MM Privately Held
WEB: www.cpfco.com
SIC: 5193 5992 3999 Flowers, fresh;
florists' supplies; flowers, fresh; candles
PA: The Cleveland Plant And Flower Company
12920 Corporate Dr
Cleveland OH 44130
216 898-3500

(G-6938)
CLEVEX INC (PA)
1275 Kinnear Rd Ste 223 (43212-0017)
PHONE................................614 675-3757
Doug Myers, *President*
EMP: 4
SALES (est): 550.4K Privately Held
SIC: 3841 Surgical & medical instruments

(G-6939)
CLIMATERIGHT LLC
Also Called: Climateright Air
777 Manor Park Dr (43228-9522)
PHONE................................800 725-4628
Todd Arend, *CEO*
EMP: 5

SALES (est): 255.2K Privately Held
SIC: 3585 Room coolers, portable

(G-6940)
CLUSTER SOFTWARE INC
2674 Billingsley Rd (43235-1924)
PHONE................................614 760-9380
Kailasnath Murthy, *President*
Vishwa Vedula, *Vice Pres*
EMP: 11
SALES (est): 1.5MM Privately Held
WEB: www.clustersoft.com
SIC: 7372 Prepackaged software

(G-6941)
COALESCENCE LLC
3455 Millennium Ct (43219-5550)
PHONE................................614 861-3639
Angela N Cauley, *CEO*
Suzy Godfrey, *Finance Dir*
Kermit Montague, *Manager*
Ian Blount,
▲ EMP: 39
SQ FT: 35,000
SALES (est): 26MM Privately Held
WEB: www.coalescencellc.com
SIC: 2099 Baking powder & soda, yeast &
other leavening agents; seasonings &
spices; sauces: gravy, dressing & dip
mixes; sugar

(G-6942)
COCA-COLA COMPANY
2455 Watkins Rd (43207-3488)
PHONE................................614 491-6305
Fax: 614 497-6485
Angelica Uribe-Miller, *District Mgr*
Eric Bacher, *Project Mgr*
Richard Rutherford, *Project Mgr*
Terrance McGann, *Opers Mgr*
Greg McCoy, *Warehouse Mgr*
EMP: 120
SALES (corp-wide): 41.8B Publicly Held
WEB: www.cocacola.com
SIC: 2086 Bottled & canned soft drinks
PA: The Coca-Cola Company
1 Coca Cola Plz Nw
Atlanta GA 30313
404 676-2121

(G-6943)
COCA-COLA COMPANY
4500 Groves Rd (43232-4106)
PHONE................................614 863-7200
Doug Davis, *Manager*
EMP: 85
SQ FT: 150,000
SALES (corp-wide): 41.8B Publicly Held
WEB: www.colasic.net
SIC: 2086 Bottled & canned soft drinks
PA: The Coca-Cola Company
1 Coca Cola Plz Nw
Atlanta GA 30313
404 676-2121

(G-6944)
COLORTECH GRAPHICS & PRINTING (PA)
4000 Business Park Dr (43204-5023)
PHONE................................614 766-2400
C Wayne Booker, *President*
Patrick Dahn, *VP Sales*
Jamie Deroll, *Sales Mgr*
Marie Bowman, *Accounts Mgr*
EMP: 19
SQ FT: 1,600
SALES (est): 2.1MM Privately Held
WEB: www.colortechdesign.com
SIC: 7334 2791 Photocopying & duplicating services; typesetting

(G-6945)
COLUMBIA ENERGY GROUP
200 Civic Center Dr (43215-4138)
PHONE................................614 460-4683
Robert Skaggs Jr, *President*
Robert Skaggs, *President*
Gary W Pottorff, *Vice Pres*
Gary Smith, *Controller*
EMP: 2
SALES (est): 984.9MM
SALES (corp-wide): 4.4B Publicly Held
WEB: www.nisource.com
SIC: 4922 1311 1731 Natural gas transmission; crude petroleum production;
electric power systems contractors

PA: Nisource Inc.
801 E 86th Ave
Merrillville IN 46410
877 647-5990

(G-6946)
COLUMBIA GAS METER SHOP
5315 Fisher Rd (43228-9511)
PHONE................................614 460-5519
Patrick Donnelly, *Principal*
EMP: 12
SALES (est): 588.2K Privately Held
SIC: 1311 Crude petroleum & natural gas

(G-6947)
COLUMBUS ALIVE INC
34 S 3rd St (43215-4201)
PHONE................................614 221-2449
Fax: 614 221-2456
Sarah Sally Crane, *President*
Andy Downing, *Editor*
Greg Glasser, *Accounts Exec*
EMP: 15
SALES (est): 575.2K
SALES (corp-wide): 648.7MM Privately
Held
WEB: www.columbusdispatch.com
SIC: 2711 Newspapers: publishing only,
not printed on site
PA: The Dispatch Printing Company
62 E Broad St
Columbus OH 43215
614 461-5000

(G-6948)
COLUMBUS BRIDE
34 S 3rd St (43215-4201)
PHONE................................614 888-4567
Fax: 614 561-8746
Ray Tatrocki, *General Mgr*
Randy Beyer, *Controller*
Leanne Brandell, *Executive*
EMP: 60
SQ FT: 1,000
SALES (est): 4.9MM Privately Held
WEB: www.columbusalive.com
SIC: 2721 7389 Periodicals: publishing
only; convention & show services

(G-6949)
COLUMBUS COATINGS COMPANY
1800 Watkins Rd (43207-3440)
PHONE................................614 492-6800
Brian R Stack, *General Mgr*
John Wray, *Plant Mgr*
Bob Nye, *Purchasing*
Robert Broderick, *Treasurer*
James Lawrence, *Manager*
EMP: 100
SQ FT: 350,000
SALES (est): 10.6MM Privately Held
SIC: 3479 3398 3471 Galvanizing of iron,
steel or end-formed products; metal heat
treating; plating & polishing

(G-6950)
COLUMBUS ELECTRICAL WORKS CO
777 N 4th St (43215-1596)
PHONE................................614 294-4651
Fax: 614 294-3731
Lon Johnson, *President*
Joe Johnson, *Vice Pres*
Jack Quisno, *Manager*
EMP: 11
SQ FT: 28,000
SALES (est): 1.2MM Privately Held
SIC: 5063 7694 Motors, electric; electric
motor repair

(G-6951)
COLUMBUS FIRE FIGHTERS UNION
379 W Broad St (43215-2756)
PHONE................................614 481-8900
Scott Main, *Principal*
EMP: 4
SALES: 114.2K Privately Held
SIC: 3711 Fire department vehicles (motor
vehicles), assembly of

(G-6952)
COLUMBUS GASKET AND SUP CO LLC
1875 Lone Eagle St (43228-3647)
PHONE................................614 878-6041
EMP: 3
SALES (est): 85.1K Privately Held
SIC: 3053 Gaskets, all materials

(G-6953)
COLUMBUS GASKET CO INC
Also Called: Columbus Gasket & Supply
1875 Lone Eagle St (43228-3692)
PHONE................................614 878-6041
Fax: 614 878-1590
James K Green, *President*
Dan Bauer, *Purchasing*
Kimberly Skiva, *Manager*
▲ EMP: 9
SQ FT: 14,000
SALES: 1.2MM Privately Held
WEB: www.columbusgasket.com
SIC: 3053 3069 Gaskets, all materials;
molded rubber products

(G-6954)
COLUMBUS HEATING & VENT CO
182 N Yale Ave (43222-1127)
PHONE................................614 274-1177
Fax: 614 274-7873
Charles R Gulley, *President*
Greogy Yoak, *President*
Michael Blythe, *Corp Secy*
Anthony Staten, *Director*
Mikel Plythe, *Admin Sec*
EMP: 135 EST: 1874
SALES (est): 23.6MM Privately Held
WEB: www.columbusheat.com
SIC: 1711 3585 Warm air heating & air
conditioning contractor; ventilation & duct
work contractor; furnaces, warm air: electric

(G-6955)
COLUMBUS HUMUNGOUS APPAREL LLC
Also Called: Hc Apparel
2913 Manola Dr Ste 100 (43209-3261)
PHONE................................614 824-2657
Jamal Moore,
EMP: 4
SALES: 300K Privately Held
SIC: 2759 Screen printing

(G-6956)
COLUMBUS INSTRUMENTS INTL CORP
950 N Hague Ave (43204-2121)
PHONE................................614 276-0593
Fax: 614 276-0529
Jan A Czekajewski, *President*
Laura Damas, *Vice Pres*
David Leonard, *Purch Mgr*
Tim Hans, *Engineer*
Ken Kober, *Sales Mgr*
◆ EMP: 48
SQ FT: 19,460
SALES (est): 10.1MM Privately Held
WEB: www.colinst.com
SIC: 3826 Analytical instruments

(G-6957)
COLUMBUS INTERNATIONAL CORP
200 E Campus View Blvd # 200
(43235-4678)
PHONE................................614 323-1086
Rajeev Kumar, *President*
EMP: 18
SQ FT: 2,000
SALES: 1MM Privately Held
WEB: www.americanbusiness.com
SIC: 7372 Business oriented computer
software

(G-6958)
COLUMBUS JACK CORPORATION
2222 S 3rd St (43207-2402)
PHONE................................614 228-0185
Fax: 614 444-9337
Richard Drexler, *CEO*
Gene Albrecht, *Vice Pres*

TAC Kensler, *CFO*
Karen Hart, *Asst Treas*
Maria Conley, *Comms Mgr*
EMP: 52
SQ FT: 50,000
SALES (est): 4.2MM
SALES (corp-wide): 24MM **Privately Held**
WEB: www.columbusjack.com
SIC: 3728 3542 Aircraft parts & equipment; presses: hydraulic & pneumatic, mechanical & manual
PA: Quality Products, Inc.
2222 S 3rd St
Columbus OH 43207
614 228-0185

(G-6959)
COLUMBUS KOMBUCHA COMPANY LLC
930 Freeway Dr N (43229-5424)
PHONE....................614 262-0000
Russell Pinto, *Sales Mgr*
Michael Iannarino,
EMP: 8
SQ FT: 5,000
SALES: 1.5MM **Privately Held**
SIC: 2082 Malt beverages

(G-6960)
COLUMBUS MACHINE WORKS INC
2491 Fairwood Ave (43207-2709)
PHONE....................614 409-0244
Fax: 614 409-0245
Michael Stacey, *President*
Mike Hansell, *Vice Pres*
John Harm, *Project Engr*
Diana Stacey, *Treasurer*
Ken McMullen, *Sales Associate*
EMP: 11
SQ FT: 3,729
SALES (est): 1.1MM **Privately Held**
WEB: www.columbusmachine.com
SIC: 3599 Machine shop, jobbing & repair

(G-6961)
COLUMBUS MESSENGER COMPANY (PA)
Also Called: Madison Messenger
3500 Sullivant Ave (43204-1887)
PHONE....................614 272-5422
Fax: 614 272-0684
Phillip Daubel, *Owner*
Douglas Henry, *Sales Staff*
Kristy Zurbrick, *Advt Staff*
EMP: 25
SQ FT: 4,000
SALES (est): 1.9MM **Privately Held**
SIC: 2711 Newspapers: publishing only, not printed on site

(G-6962)
COLUMBUS PIPE AND EQUIPMENT CO
Also Called: Steel Warehouse Division
763 E Markison Ave (43207-1390)
P.O. Box 7843 (43207-0843)
PHONE....................614 444-7871
Fax: 614 444-0949
Bruce Jay Silberstein, *President*
Jonathan Silberstein, *Vice Pres*
Mike Denoewer, *CFO*
Jeff Sapo, *Controller*
Helen Johnson, *Manager*
EMP: 15
SQ FT: 50,000
SALES (est): 7.5MM **Privately Held**
SIC: 5082 7692 5074 Construction & mining machinery; welding repair; plumbing fittings & supplies

(G-6963)
COLUMBUS PROCESSING CO LLC
4300 Alum Creek Dr (43207-4519)
PHONE....................614 492-8287
Roger Wolf, *President*
Bob Broderick, *Treasurer*
Roger A Wolf, *Manager*
EMP: 4
SALES (est): 482.6K **Privately Held**
SIC: 3312 Iron & steel: galvanized, pipes, plates, sheets, etc.

(G-6964)
COLUMBUS ROOF TRUSSES INC (PA)
2525 Fisher Rd (43204-3588)
PHONE....................614 272-6464
Fax: 614 272-6469
Tony Iacovetta, *President*
Rose A Pritchard, *Corp Secy*
Eugene R Iacovetta, *Vice Pres*
Rose Iacovetta, *Admin Sec*
EMP: 30
SQ FT: 51,000
SALES (est): 4.1MM **Privately Held**
SIC: 2439 Trusses, wooden roof; trusses, except roof: laminated lumber

(G-6965)
COLUMBUS SERUM CO
7570 Donora Ln (43235-1920)
PHONE....................614 793-0615
EMP: 3
SALES (est): 151.9K **Privately Held**
SIC: 2836 Serums

(G-6966)
COLUMBUS SIGN COMPANY (PA)
1515 E 5th Ave (43219-2483)
PHONE....................614 252-3133
Fax: 614 252-2494
Michael Hoy, *President*
Michael S Hoy, *President*
EMP: 30 EST: 1911
SQ FT: 15,000
SALES (est): 4.4MM **Privately Held**
WEB: www.columbussign.com
SIC: 3993 Neon signs; signs, not made in custom sign painting shops

(G-6967)
COLUMBUS STEEL CASTINGS CO
Also Called: Columbus Castings
2211 Parsons Ave (43207-2448)
PHONE....................614 444-2121
Rick Mavrakis, *President*
Ernie Pierce, *Chairman*
Jack Thomas, *Chairman*
Mike Clary, *Area Mgr*
Michael Yaus, *COO*
▲ **EMP:** 750
SALES (est): 228.8MM
SALES (corp-wide): 349.7MM **Privately Held**
WEB: www.columbussteel.com
SIC: 3325 Steel foundries
HQ: Columbus Holdings Inc
50 Tice Blvd Ste 340
Woodcliff Lake NJ

(G-6968)
COLUMBUS STEELMASTERS INC
660 Concrea Rd (43219-1822)
PHONE....................614 231-2141
Fax: 614 231-2444
Brenda Neale, *CEO*
Steven Neale, *President*
EMP: 12
SQ FT: 17,000
SALES: 1MM **Privately Held**
SIC: 3444 Sheet metal specialties, not stamped

(G-6969)
COLUMBUS-SPORTS PUBLICATIONS
Also Called: Buckeye Sports Bulletin
1350 W 5th Ave Ste 30 (43212-2907)
P.O. Box 12453 (43212-0453)
PHONE....................614 486-2202
Fax: 614 486-3650
Frank L Moskowitz, *President*
EMP: 13
SQ FT: 1,250
SALES (est): 843.2K **Privately Held**
WEB: www.buckeyesports.com
SIC: 2711 Newspapers: publishing only, not printed on site

(G-6970)
COMDOC INC
330 W Spring St Ste 100 (43215-2346)
PHONE....................330 899-8000

Fax: 614 224-3260
Larry Frank, *Vice Chairman*
Ted Madick, *Vice Pres*
Frank Pacetta, *Vice Pres*
Paul Dipronio, *Director*
EMP: 3
SALES (corp-wide): 10.7B **Publicly Held**
SIC: 2759 Commercial printing
HQ: Comdoc, Inc.
3458 Massillon Rd
Uniontown OH 44685
330 896-2346

(G-6971)
COMMERCIAL LUBRICANTS INC
2854 Johnstown Rd (43219-1772)
PHONE....................614 475-5952
Fax: 614 817-8703
Jim Vannett, *Branch Mgr*
EMP: 5 **Privately Held**
SIC: 2992 5172 Lubricating oils & greases; lubricating oils & greases
PA: Commercial Lubricants Inc.
2846 E 37th St
Cleveland OH 44115

(G-6972)
COMMISSARY BREWING
1400 Dublin Rd (43215-1009)
PHONE....................614 636-3164
EMP: 3 EST: 2015
SALES (est): 75.4K **Privately Held**
SIC: 2082 Malt beverages

(G-6973)
COMPUTER ALLIED TECHNOLOGY CO
3385 Somerford Rd (43221-1438)
PHONE....................614 457-2292
Mark Taylor, *President*
Pat Taylor, *Treasurer*
EMP: 7
SALES (est): 630K **Privately Held**
SIC: 7371 3569 Computer software development & applications; robots, assembly line: industrial & commercial

(G-6974)
COMPUTERCRAFTS
2936 Brownlee Ave (43209-3060)
PHONE....................614 231-7559
John Rogers, *Owner*
EMP: 4
SALES (est): 154.9K **Privately Held**
SIC: 2741 Miscellaneous publishing

(G-6975)
COMPUWARE CORPORATION
8351 N High St Ste 200 (43235-1501)
PHONE....................614 847-8212
Deepti Rudraraju, *QA Dir*
Jerry Lobenstein, *Engineer*
David Diley, *Branch Mgr*
MO Seck, *Sr Project Mgr*
EMP: 100
SALES (corp-wide): 1.3B **Privately Held**
WEB: www.compuware.com
SIC: 7371 7372 Computer software development; prepackaged software
HQ: Compuware Corporation
1 Campus Martius Fl 4
Detroit MI 48226
313 227-7300

(G-6976)
CONCEPT 9 INC
1604 Clara St (43211-2664)
PHONE....................614 294-3743
Fax: 614 294-4563
Kenneth J Nienkirchen, *Ch of Bd*
Karl Nienkirchen, *President*
Kris Nienkirchen, *Vice Pres*
EMP: 6
SQ FT: 5,000
SALES (est): 559.8K **Privately Held**
SIC: 2759 Screen printing

(G-6977)
CONTECH ENGNERED SOLUTIONS LLC
1103 Schrock Rd Ste 105 (43229-1179)
PHONE....................614 477-1171
EMP: 3 **Privately Held**
SIC: 3444 Sheet metalwork

HQ: Contech Engineered Solutions Llc
9025 Ctr Pinte Dr Ste 400
West Chester OH 45069
513 645-7000

(G-6978)
CONTRACT LIGHTING INC
1207 Grandview Ave (43212-3449)
PHONE....................614 746-7022
Andrew Brooks, *Principal*
Mary Fey, *Project Mgr*
Brigid Lare, *Cust Mgr*
Drew Schulte, *Sales Associate*
Jason Donnellon, *Contractor*
EMP: 4
SALES (est): 504.8K **Privately Held**
SIC: 3645 5063 Residential lighting fixtures; lighting fixtures

(G-6979)
CONVAULT OF OHIO INC
841 Alton Ave (43219-3710)
P.O. Box 89, Reynoldsburg (43068-0089)
PHONE....................614 252-8422
Tim Thickstun, *President*
Steven Thickstun, *Corp Secy*
Joanne Thickstun, *Vice Pres*
Kenneth Thickstun, *Vice Pres*
EMP: 9
SALES: 1.5MM **Privately Held**
SIC: 3443 Fuel tanks (oil, gas, etc.): metal plate

(G-6980)
COOKIE BOUQUETS INC
6665 Huntley Rd Ste F (43229-1045)
PHONE....................614 888-2171
Fax: 614 841-3950
Christian McCoy, *President*
EMP: 7
SQ FT: 4,500
SALES (est): 380K **Privately Held**
WEB: www.cookiebouquets.com
SIC: 5461 5947 2052 Cookies; gift baskets; cookies & crackers

(G-6981)
COPIER RESOURCES INC
Also Called: Cri Digital
4800 Evanswood Dr (43229-6207)
P.O. Box 14824 (43214-0824)
PHONE....................614 268-1100
Fax: 614 268-6646
Scott Di Francesco, *President*
Debra Berry, *Manager*
EMP: 6
SQ FT: 4,000
SALES (est): 1.5MM **Privately Held**
WEB: www.cridigital.net
SIC: 7629 7359 5734 3575 Electrical repair shops; office machine rental, except computers; computer & software stores; cathode ray tube (CRT), computer terminal; mailing machines; photocopy machines

(G-6982)
CORE AUTOMOTIVE TECH LLC (HQ)
800 Manor Park Dr (43228-9762)
PHONE....................614 870-5000
Ed Stehle, *Sales Staff*
Richard Redding, *Manager*
Alan Golding,
Darlene Thompson, *Analyst*
Terrence O'Donovan,
EMP: 1
SQ FT: 15,000
SALES: 130.5MM **Publicly Held**
SIC: 3714 5521 Motor vehicle body components & frame; used car dealers

(G-6983)
CORE MOLDING TECHNOLOGIES INC (PA)
800 Manor Park Dr (43228-9762)
PHONE....................614 870-5000
James L Simonton, *Ch of Bd*
Kevin L Barnett, *President*
Terrence J O'Donovan, *Vice Pres*
William R Ringling, *Vice Pres*
Robert P Price, *VP Opers*
EMP: 333
SQ FT: 338,000
SALES: 174.8MM **Publicly Held**
SIC: 3089 Molding primary plastic

(G-6984)
CORE QUANTUM TECHNOLOGIES INC
1275 Kinnear Rd (43212-1180)
PHONE................................614 214-7210
Ted Greene, *CEO*
Kristie Melnik, *COO*
EMP: 4
SALES (est): 419K **Privately Held**
SIC: 2835 In vitro & in vivo diagnostic substances

(G-6985)
CORPORATE ELEVATOR LLC
35 E Gay St Ste 218 (43215-8128)
PHONE................................614 288-1847
Ivan Isreal, *Principal*
EMP: 15
SALES (est): 480.5K **Privately Held**
SIC: 8243 7372 7371 Repair training, computer; application computer software; educational computer software; custom computer programming services

(G-6986)
CORPORATE SUPPLY LLC
Also Called: Golfpremiums.com
3608 Sugar Loaf Ct (43221-5255)
P.O. Box 3784, Dublin (43016-0403)
PHONE................................614 876-8400
James Lemmon, *Mng Member*
Jeff Minor, *Consultant*
EMP: 3
SALES: 200K **Privately Held**
WEB: www.corporatesupply.com
SIC: 2759 5112 Promotional printing; office filing supplies

(G-6987)
COSTUME SPECIALISTS INC (PA)
211 N 5th St Ste 100 (43215-2722)
PHONE................................614 464-2115
Fax: 614 464-2114
Wendy C Goldstein, *President*
Jay Christopher, *Prdtn Mgr*
Steven Hudson, *Purch Agent*
EMP: 31
SQ FT: 34,500
SALES (est): 2.8MM **Privately Held**
WEB: www.cospec.com
SIC: 2389 7299 5699 Theatrical costumes; costume rental; costumes, masquerade or theatrical

(G-6988)
COSTUME SPECIALISTS INC
211 N 5th St Ste 100 (43215-2722)
PHONE................................614 464-2115
Fax: 614 237-6379
Vickie Little, *Manager*
Tracy Liberatore, *Admin Asst*
EMP: 5
SALES (corp-wide): 2.8MM **Privately Held**
WEB: www.cospec.com
SIC: 2389 7299 5699 Theatrical costumes; costume rental; costumes, masquerade or theatrical
PA: Costume Specialists, Inc.
211 N 5th St Ste 100
Columbus OH 43215
614 464-2115

(G-6989)
COTT SYSTEMS INC
2800 Corp Exchange Dr # 300 (43231-1678)
PHONE................................614 847-4405
Fax: 614 847-3737
Deborah A Ball, *CEO*
Karen L Bailey, *Exec VP*
Jodie Bare, *Vice Pres*
Bob Mains, *Vice Pres*
Richard J Miller, *Vice Pres*
EMP: 77
SQ FT: 20,000
SALES (est): 16.4MM **Privately Held**
WEB: www.cottsystems.com
SIC: 7373 7371 2789 Computer integrated systems design; computer software development & applications; beveling of cards

(G-6990)
COULTER VENTURES LLC (PA)
Also Called: Rogue Fitness
1080 Steelwood Rd (43212-1360)
PHONE................................614 358-6190
Alex Steinker, *Editor*
Jonathan Hotaling, *Project Mgr*
Mano Sergakis, *Mfg Staff*
Jonathan Harder, *Engineer*
Christian Hermosilla, *Engineer*
▼ EMP: 48
SQ FT: 25,000
SALES (est): 17.2MM **Privately Held**
SIC: 3949 Sporting & athletic goods

(G-6991)
COUNTERTOP SALES
5767 Westbourne Ave (43213-1488)
PHONE................................614 626-4476
Phillip Holbrook, *President*
EMP: 11
SALES (est): 1.1MM **Privately Held**
SIC: 2541 Counter & sink tops

(G-6992)
COW INDUSTRIES INC (PA)
Also Called: Central Ohio Welding
1875 Progress Ave (43207-1781)
PHONE................................614 443-6537
Fax: 614 443-9600
John Burns, *President*
Michael Netto, *Vice Pres*
Danny Perkins, *Prdtn Mgr*
Matthew Nicol, *Purch Mgr*
Mike Burns, *Purch Agent*
EMP: 40
SQ FT: 80,000
SALES (est): 6.4MM **Privately Held**
WEB: www.cowind.com
SIC: 3499 3444 Machine bases, metal; sheet metalwork

(G-6993)
COX INTERIOR INC
Also Called: Cox's Interior Supply
2220 Citygate Dr (43219-3565)
PHONE................................614 473-9169
Fax: 614 861-9504
Lora B Bland, *Manager*
Tim Mays, *Manager*
EMP: 8
SALES (corp-wide): 206.9MM **Privately Held**
WEB: www.coxinterior.com
SIC: 2431 Millwork
PA: Cox Interior, Inc.
1751 Old Columbia Rd
Campbellsville KY 42718
270 789-3129

(G-6994)
COZMYK ENTERPRISES INC
3757 Courtright Ct (43227-2250)
PHONE................................614 231-1370
Fax: 614 231-1371
Alan L Cozmyk, *President*
Christopher J Minnillo, *Principal*
Cheryl Dutiel, *Manager*
EMP: 15
SQ FT: 20,000
SALES (est): 4.1MM **Privately Held**
WEB: www.cozmyk.com
SIC: 3446 Architectural metalwork; ornamental metalwork

(G-6995)
CPI INDUSTRIAL CO
2300 Parsons Ave (43207-2467)
P.O. Box 7867 (43207-0867)
PHONE................................614 445-0800
Fax: 614 491-5963
Mark T Owens, *President*
Susan Flannigan, *Corp Secy*
Vince Paul, *Admin Sec*
Don Adams, *Administration*
EMP: 22
SALES (est): 5.7MM **Privately Held**
SIC: 2851 Epoxy coatings

(G-6996)
CPMM SERVICES GROUP INC
3785 Indianola Ave (43214-3754)
PHONE................................614 447-0165
Fax: 614 447-0203
Dan Dimitroff, *President*
EMP: 15

SQ FT: 12,500
SALES (est): 1.6MM **Privately Held**
WEB: www.cpmmservices.com
SIC: 7331 2752 7374 Mailing list compilers; mailing service; commercial printing, offset; data processing service

(G-6997)
CRANE BLENDING CENTER
2141 Fairwood Ave (43207-1753)
P.O. Box 1058 (43216-1058)
PHONE................................614 542-1199
Phil Stobart, *President*
EMP: 40
SALES (est): 2.6MM **Privately Held**
SIC: 2821 Mgf

(G-6998)
CRANE PLASTICS MFG LTD
2141 Fairwood Ave (43207-1779)
PHONE................................614 754-3700
Fax: 614 449-5694
Tim Tait, *Principal*
Mark Mace, *Controller*
Joe Ewing, *Sales Mgr*
Gregory Scott Evans, *Technical Staff*
EMP: 5
SALES (est): 670K **Privately Held**
SIC: 2821 Plastics materials & resins

(G-6999)
CRAWFORD PRODUCTS INC
3637 Corporate Dr (43231-7997)
PHONE................................614 890-1822
Fax: 614 890-1876
William A Crawford, *CEO*
Kevin P Crawford, *President*
Scott Stauch, *Vice Pres*
Dave Wampler, *Sales Mgr*
Michael Bangert, *Regl Sales Mgr*
▲ EMP: 21
SQ FT: 12,500
SALES (est): 15MM **Privately Held**
WEB: www.crawfordproducts.com
SIC: 5085 3452 Fasteners, industrial: nuts, bolts, screws, etc.; bolts, nuts, rivets & washers

(G-7000)
CRITICALAIRE LLC
6155 Huntley Rd Ste A (43229-1096)
PHONE................................513 475-3800
EMP: 13 **Privately Held**
SIC: 3564 Exhaust fans: industrial or commercial
PA: Criticalaire, Llc
11325 R Hartman Hwy 100
Cincinnati OH 45241

(G-7001)
CROWN DIELECTRIC INDS INC
Also Called: Crown Auto Top Mfg Co
830 W Broad St (43222-1421)
PHONE................................614 224-5161
Fax: 614 221-1384
Anthony Gurvis, *President*
Andrew M Kauffman, *Principal*
Ron Gurvis, *Vice Pres*
Andy Kauffman, *Controller*
EMP: 105 EST: 1931
SQ FT: 2,000
SALES (est): 6.9MM **Privately Held**
SIC: 2394 2399 2273 5013 Convertible tops, canvas or boat: from purchased materials; seat covers, automobile; automobile floor coverings, except rubber or plastic; automotive supplies & parts; automotive parts

(G-7002)
CRYSTAL ART IMPORTS INC (PA)
Also Called: Crystal Classics
6185 Huntley Rd Ste K (43229-1094)
PHONE................................614 505-6001
Bruno Bergman, *CEO*
Maxine Stotler, *President*
Andy Fry, *Sales Staff*
▲ EMP: 10
SALES (est): 3.1MM **Privately Held**
SIC: 5947 3231 5719 Gift shop; ornamental glass: cut, engraved or otherwise decorated; kitchenware

(G-7003)
CURVES AND MORE WOODWORKING
2002 Zettler Rd (43232-3834)
PHONE................................614 239-7837
Steven Blake, *Principal*
EMP: 6 EST: 2007
SALES (est): 634.6K **Privately Held**
SIC: 2431 Millwork

(G-7004)
CUSTOM RETAIL GROUP LLC
Also Called: Crg Worldwide
6311 Busch Blvd (43229-1802)
PHONE................................614 409-9720
Colin Leveque, *Mng Member*
EMP: 9 EST: 2013
SQ FT: 25,000
SALES (est): 1.7MM **Privately Held**
SIC: 3993 Displays, paint process

(G-7005)
CUSTOM SIGN CENTER INC
3200 Valleyview Dr (43204-2080)
PHONE................................614 279-6700
Tim W Sheehy, *President*
Teryl Fox, *Vice Pres*
Judy Ramsburg, *Vice Pres*
Amy Guile, *Project Mgr*
Thad King, *Design Engr*
EMP: 50
SQ FT: 40,000
SALES (est): 9.4MM **Privately Held**
WEB: www.customsigncenter.com
SIC: 3993 Signs & advertising specialties

(G-7006)
D M PALLET SERVICE INC
2019 Rathmell Rd (43207-5012)
PHONE................................614 491-0881
Fax: 614 491-2192
Dexter Mounts II, *President*
Dexter Mounts Sr, *Corp Secy*
EMP: 16
SQ FT: 800
SALES (est): 2MM **Privately Held**
SIC: 2448 Pallets, wood

(G-7007)
DAIKIN APPLIED AMERICAS INC
739 N Wilson Rd (43204-1463)
PHONE................................614 351-9862
EMP: 9
SALES (corp-wide): 17.4B **Privately Held**
SIC: 3585 5075 Refrigeration & heating equipment; warm air heating & air conditioning
HQ: Daikin Applied Americas Inc.
13600 Industrial Pk Blvd
Minneapolis MN 55441
763 553-5330

(G-7008)
DAILY REPORTER
580 S High St Ste 316 (43215-5659)
PHONE................................614 224-4835
Ed Frederickson, *President*
Dan Shillingburg, *Vice Pres*
Jeff Zeigler, *Sales Executive*
Chad Roush, *Info Tech Mgr*
EMP: 25 EST: 1896
SQ FT: 5,500
SALES: 1.9MM
SALES (corp-wide): 14.6MM **Privately Held**
WEB: www.sourcenews.com
SIC: 2711 Newspapers, publishing & printing
PA: Calcomco, Inc.
5544 S Red Pine Cir
Kalamazoo MI 49009
313 885-9228

(G-7009)
DALLAS INSTANTWHIP INC
Also Called: Instantwhip National Office
2200 Cardigan Ave (43215-1092)
PHONE................................614 488-2536
EMP: 18
SQ FT: 10,300
SALES (est): 1.9MM **Privately Held**
SIC: 2026 5143 Mfg & Whol Refrigerated Dairy Products

▲ = Import ▼=Export
◆ =Import/Export

(G-7010)
DAN WILZYNSKI
Also Called: Edge Makers
2000 Fairwood Ave (43207-1607)
PHONE..........................800 531-3343
Dan Wilzynski, *Partner*
Lisa Wilzynski, *Partner*
Mari Sander, *Facilities Mgr*
EMP: 3
SQ FT: 6,400
SALES: 350K **Privately Held**
SIC: 3421 5085 3541 Cutlery; industrial
supplies; machine tools, metal cutting
type

(G-7011)
DANITE HOLDINGS LTD
Also Called: Danite Sign Co
1640 Harmon Ave (43223-3321)
PHONE..........................614 444-3333
Fax: 614 444-3026
Tim McCord, *President*
C William Klausman, *Partner*
Tom Seymore, *COO*
Jeremy McCord, *Purchasing*
Jill Waddell, *Sales Executive*
EMP: 50
SQ FT: 33,500
SALES (est): 8MM **Privately Held**
WEB: www.danitesign.com
SIC: 3993 1799 Signs & advertising spe-
cialties; neon signs; sign installation &
maintenance

(G-7012)
DASKAL ENTERPRISE LLC (PA)
Also Called: Laser Cutting Shapes
6522 Singletree Dr (43229-1119)
PHONE..........................614 848-5700
Scott Vogel, *Opers Mgr*
Vadim Daskal, *Mng Member*
EMP: 8 **EST:** 2008
SQ FT: 3,000
SALES (est): 1MM **Privately Held**
SIC: 3699 Laser systems & equipment

(G-7013)
DATA POWER SOLUTIONS
Also Called: Current Technology
804 Hedley Pl (43230-1617)
P.O. Box 30842 (43230-0842)
PHONE..........................614 471-1911
Fax: 614 471-9390
David Michael Beck, *Owner*
EMP: 3
SALES (est): 240K **Privately Held**
SIC: 3825 1731 5045 Instruments to
measure electricity; computer installation;
computers, peripherals & software

(G-7014)
DAVID BOSWELL
Also Called: Noun Research and Dev Svcs
1777 Franklin Park S (43205-2217)
PHONE..........................614 441-2497
David Boswell, *Owner*
EMP: 50
SALES (est): 1.6MM **Privately Held**
SIC: 3714 3669 3829 3812 Motor vehicle
body components & frame; burglar alarm
apparatus, electric; measuring & control-
ling devices; search & navigation equip-
ment

(G-7015)
DAVIS LASER PRODUCTS
2700 E 6th Ave (43219-2754)
PHONE..........................614 252-7711
John Davis, *Owner*
EMP: 4
SALES (est): 107K **Privately Held**
SIC: 3571 7378 Electronic computers;
computer maintenance & repair

(G-7016)
DEADBOLT SOFTWARE
43 Amazon Pl (43214-3501)
PHONE..........................614 679-2093
Todd Cooperider, *President*
EMP: 4
SALES (est): 330K **Privately Held**
SIC: 7372 Prepackaged software

(G-7017)
DEE PRINTING INC
4999 Transamerica Dr (43228-9381)
P.O. Box 132 (43216-0132)
PHONE..........................614 777-8700
Fax: 614 777-9624
Dorothy J Murnane, *President*
EMP: 14
SQ FT: 4,000
SALES (est): 1.8MM **Privately Held**
SIC: 2759 7311 Letterpress printing; ad-
vertising agencies

(G-7018)
DELILLE OXYGEN COMPANY (PA)
772 Marion Rd (43207-2595)
P.O. Box 7809 (43207-0809)
PHONE..........................614 444-1177
Fax: 614 444-0733
Joseph R Smith, *Ch of Bd*
Tom Smith, *President*
Richard F Carlile, *Principal*
Jim Smith, *Vice Pres*
Josh Weinmann, *Vice Pres*
EMP: 30
SQ FT: 20,000
SALES (est): 19.8MM **Privately Held**
WEB: www.delille.com
SIC: 2813 5085 Acetylene; welding sup-
plies

(G-7019)
DELITE FRUIT JUICES
185 N Yale Ave (43222-1146)
PHONE..........................614 470-4333
Chad Carney, *Owner*
EMP: 4
SALES (est): 327K **Privately Held**
SIC: 2086 Bottled & canned soft drinks

(G-7020)
DELL FIXTURES INC
321 Dering Ave (43207-2955)
PHONE..........................614 449-1750
Fax: 614 449-1755
Donald C Koch, *President*
Rich Clemons, *Vice Pres*
Thomas M Koch, *Treasurer*
Julie Clemons, *Admin Sec*
▲ **EMP:** 20
SQ FT: 64,000
SALES (est): 2.9MM **Privately Held**
WEB: www.dellfixtures.com
SIC: 2541 1799 2542 Store & office dis-
play cases & fixtures; counter top installa-
tion; fixtures, store: except wood

(G-7021)
DELPHIA CONSULTING LLC
250 E Broad St Ste 1150 (43215-3773)
PHONE..........................614 421-2000
Fax: 614 487-0600
Brian Delphia, *CEO*
Tony Diblasi, *COO*
Kim Kocher, *COO*
Alexander Main, *COO*
Syed Naqvi, *Manager*
EMP: 4
SALES (est): 660.5K **Privately Held**
SIC: 8742 7372 Human resource consult-
ing services; business oriented computer
software

(G-7022)
DESTINATION DONUTS LLC
59 Spruce St (43215-1622)
PHONE..........................614 370-0754
Heather Morris, *President*
EMP: 4
SQ FT: 364
SALES (est): 163.4K **Privately Held**
SIC: 2051 Cakes, bakery: except frozen

(G-7023)
DEVRIES & ASSOCIATES INC
Also Called: Fastsigns
5117 E Main St (43213-2410)
PHONE..........................614 860-0103
Tom Devries, *Principal*
Mary Devries, *Vice Pres*
EMP: 6
SALES (corp-wide): 1MM **Privately Held**
SIC: 3993 Signs & advertising specialties

PA: Devries & Associates Inc
5117 E Main St
Westerville OH 43081
614 860-0103

(G-7024)
DEWITT GROUP INC
Also Called: Capital Office Supply
777 Dearborn Park Ln E (43085-5716)
PHONE..........................614 847-5919
Bill Dewitt, *Ch of Bd*
Jory Dewitt, *Corp Secy*
Jay Etheridge, *Manager*
Bill Witt, *Manager*
EMP: 10
SQ FT: 9,000
SALES (est): 3.6MM **Privately Held**
SIC: 5112 2752 Stationery & office sup-
plies; commercial printing, offset

(G-7025)
DIAMOND INNOVATIONS INC (DH)
6325 Huntley Rd (43229-1007)
P.O. Box 568, Worthington (43085-0568)
PHONE..........................614 438-2000
Fax: 614 438-2931
Mark Schweizer, *President*
Jess Miller, *COO*
Susan Mann, *Vice Pres*
Carl Liebert, *Mfg Mgr*
Linda Piper, *Purchasing*
▲ **EMP:** 406
SALES (est): 134.4MM
SALES (corp-wide): 9.8B **Privately Held**
WEB: www.diamondinnovations.com
SIC: 3291 Abrasive products
HQ: Sanrip Ab
Mossvagen 10
Sandviken
262 600-00

(G-7026)
DIRAMED LLC
1275 Kinnear Rd (43212-1180)
PHONE..........................614 487-3660
William Shane, *President*
Robert Schlegall, *Chairman*
Justina Penrod, *Opers Staff*
EMP: 10
SALES: 700K **Privately Held**
SIC: 2835 In vitro & in vivo diagnostic sub-
stances

(G-7027)
DIRCKSEN AND ASSOCIATES INC
3452 E Livingston Ave (43227-2219)
P.O. Box 13662 (43213-0662)
PHONE..........................614 238-0413
Fax: 614 238-0437
Daniel W Dircksen, *President*
EMP: 6 **EST:** 1983
SALES (est): 620K **Privately Held**
SIC: 3728 5088 Military aircraft equipment
& armament; transportation equipment &
supplies

(G-7028)
DISANTE SOCKS
1540 Westwood Ave (43212-2767)
PHONE..........................614 481-3243
Donna Ruscitti, *Principal*
EMP: 4
SALES (est): 355.8K **Privately Held**
SIC: 2252 Socks

(G-7029)
DISCOVER PUBLICATIONS
6427 Busch Blvd (43229-1862)
PHONE..........................614 785-1111
Leo Zupam, *Principal*
Catherine Zupan, *Opers Staff*
John Peck, *Marketing Staff*
Tony Sylvester, *Office Mgr*
Katie Pack, *Manager*
EMP: 9
SALES (est): 884.8K **Privately Held**
SIC: 2741 Miscellaneous publishing

(G-7030)
DISPATCH PRINTING COMPANY
Also Called: CM Printing
5253 Sinclair Rd (43229-5042)
PHONE..........................614 885-6020
Fax: 614 885-6102

Colleen Bennett, *Sales Staff*
Roy Gray, *Manager*
EMP: 50
SALES (corp-wide): 648.7MM **Privately
Held**
WEB: www.columbusmonthly.com
SIC: 2711 2752 2721 Commercial printing
& newspaper publishing combined; com-
mercial printing, lithographic; periodicals
PA: The Dispatch Printing Company
62 E Broad St
Columbus OH 43215
614 461-5000

(G-7031)
DISTINCTIVE SURFACES LLC
5158 Sinclair Rd (43229-5415)
PHONE..........................614 431-0898
Jonathan Ruper, *Mng Member*
EMP: 18
SALES (est): 1.5MM **Privately Held**
SIC: 2434 Wood kitchen cabinets

(G-7032)
DISTRICT BREWING CO INC
Also Called: Columbus Brewing Co
2555 Harrison Rd (43204-3511)
PHONE..........................614 224-3626
Susie Edwards, *President*
Jennifer White, *General Mgr*
Ben Pridgeon, *Vice Pres*
EMP: 5
SQ FT: 6,000
SALES: 500K **Privately Held**
SIC: 2082 Beer (alcoholic beverage)

(G-7033)
DLZ OHIO INC (HQ)
6121 Huntley Rd (43229-1003)
PHONE..........................614 888-0040
A James Siebert, *President*
Vikram Rajadhyaksha, *Chairman*
P V Rajadhyaksha, *COO*
David Cutlip, *Vice Pres*
Laurie Johnson, *Vice Pres*
EMP: 200
SQ FT: 45,000
SALES (est): 25.1MM
SALES (corp-wide): 93MM **Privately
Held**
SIC: 8711 1382 8712 8713 Consulting
engineer; civil engineering; geophysical
exploration, oil & gas field; architectural
services; surveying services
PA: Dlz Corporation
6121 Huntley Rd
Columbus OH 43229
614 888-0040

(G-7034)
DNO INC
Also Called: Fresh Health
3650 E 5th Ave (43219-1805)
PHONE..........................614 231-3601
Fax: 614 231-5032
Anthony Dinovo, *President*
Carol Dinovo, *Vice Pres*
James Griffin, *Manager*
Alex Dinovo, *Director*
EMP: 80
SQ FT: 10,000
SALES: 24MM **Privately Held**
WEB: www.dnoinc.com
SIC: 5148 2099 Fresh fruits & vegetables;
fruits, fresh; salads, fresh or refrigerated

(G-7035)
DOUGLAS J HALL
Also Called: Doug Hall Electric
815 E Hudson St (43211-1133)
PHONE..........................614 261-8871
Douglas J Hall, *Owner*
EMP: 3
SALES: 100K **Privately Held**
WEB: www.dheco.com
SIC: 3663 Telemetering equipment, elec-
tronic

(G-7036)
DR PEPPER SNAPPLE GROUP INC
950 Stelzer Rd (43219-3740)
PHONE..........................614 237-4201
Dean Purcell, *Vice Pres*
Elizabeth Trilikis, *Buyer*
Terrie Gregory, *Finance*

Jeff Karla, *Human Res Mgr*
Allen Hartman, *VP Sales*
EMP: 100
SALES (corp-wide): 6.4B **Publicly Held**
SIC: 2086 Bottled & canned soft drinks
PA: Dr Pepper Snapple Group, Inc.
    5301 Legacy Dr
    Plano TX 75024
    972 673-7000

(G-7037)
DR PEPPER SNAPPLE GROUP INC
960 Stelzer Rd (43219-3740)
PHONE..............................614 237-4201
Dan Grassbaugh, *Branch Mgr*
EMP: 100
SALES (corp-wide): 6.4B **Publicly Held**
SIC: 2086 Soft drinks: packaged in cans, bottles, etc.; carbonated beverages, non-alcoholic: bottled & canned
PA: Dr Pepper Snapple Group, Inc.
    5301 Legacy Dr
    Plano TX 75024
    972 673-7000

(G-7038)
DRAGON BEVERAGE INC
1945 Judwick Dr (43229-5305)
PHONE..............................614 506-5592
Igor Svishevskiy, *Principal*
EMP: 3
SALES: 124.2K **Privately Held**
SIC: 2086 Bottled & canned soft drinks

(G-7039)
DRAKE BROTHERS LTD
1215 Forsythe Ave (43201-3202)
PHONE..............................415 819-4941
EMP: 7
SALES (est): 502.6K **Privately Held**
SIC: 2084 Wines

(G-7040)
DURE FOODS US LLC
6967 Alum Creek Dr (43217-1244)
PHONE..............................614 409-9030
Bud Mackillop, *Purch Mgr*
Rob Malcolm, *Purchasing*
Crystal Clayton, *Manager*
Burt Bruffet,
EMP: 15
SQ FT: 50,000
SALES (est): 2.1MM
SALES (corp-wide): 1.7MM **Privately Held**
SIC: 2096 Potato chips & similar snacks
PA: Dure Foods Limited
    120 Roy Blvd
    Brantford ON N3R 7
    519 753-5504

(G-7041)
DYNAMIC POLYMERS LLC
950 Taylor Station Rd M (43230-6670)
PHONE..............................614 575-1222
Fax: 614 575-9222
Colleen Kanpp, *Office Mgr*
Vicky Perkins, *Manager*
Judy Sheu,
▲ **EMP:** 7
SQ FT: 20,000
SALES: 19MM **Privately Held**
WEB: www.kentek-usa.com
SIC: 3089 Plastic containers, except foam

(G-7042)
E & E SCREEN PRTG & CSTM EMB
901 Robinwood Ave Ste G (43213-1781)
PHONE..............................614 235-2177
EMP: 4
SALES (est): 210K **Privately Held**
SIC: 2262 Screen Printing Embroidery

(G-7043)
E RETAILING ASSOCIATES LLC
Also Called: Customized Girl
2282 Westbrooke Dr (43228-9416)
PHONE..............................614 300-5785
Claire Stinedurf, *Production*
Taj Schaffnit, *Mng Member*
Stephanie Schaffnit, *Manager*
Marty Laroche, *CTO*
Jeff Benzenberg, *Director*
EMP: 64

SALES (est): 8.6MM **Privately Held**
WEB: www.customisegirl.com
SIC: 8748 5961 2253 Business consulting; ; T-shirts & tops, knit

(G-7044)
E-WASTE SYSTEMS (OHIO) INC
1033 Brentnell Ave # 300 (43219-2192)
PHONE..............................614 824-3057
George Pardos, *CEO*
Steve Hollinshead, *CFO*
EMP: 7
SALES (est): 752.3K **Privately Held**
SIC: 3861 Photocopy machines

(G-7045)
EASTERN RESERVE DEVELOPMENT
3888 Stonewater Dr (43221-5931)
PHONE..............................614 319-3179
Bruce Smith, *CEO*
Gerald Picker, *President*
EMP: 3
SALES: 2MM **Privately Held**
SIC: 1382 Oil & gas exploration services

(G-7046)
EDUCATIONAL PUBLISHER INC
1091 W 1st Ave (43212-3601)
PHONE..............................614 485-0721
Robert Sims, *President*
EMP: 5
SALES (est): 45.7K **Privately Held**
SIC: 2741 Miscellaneous publishing

(G-7047)
EDWARDS ELECTRICAL & MECH
685 Grandview Ave (43215-1119)
PHONE..............................614 485-2003
Fax: 614 485-2518
Matt Snyder, *Branch Mgr*
EMP: 40
SALES (corp-wide): 66.8MM **Privately Held**
WEB: www.edwards-elec.com
SIC: 2752 1711 Commercial printing, lithographic; mechanical contractor
HQ: Edwards Electrical & Mechanical Inc
    2350 N Shadeland Ave
    Indianapolis IN 46219
    317 543-3460

(G-7048)
EFCO CORP
Also Called: Economy Forms
3900 Zane Trace Dr (43228-3833)
PHONE..............................614 876-1226
Fax: 614 876-1228
James Grubb, *Plant Mgr*
Jim Grubb, *Plant Mgr*
Robert Thrash, *Plant Mgr*
Jim Davis, *Manager*
EMP: 26
SALES (corp-wide): 227.7MM **Privately Held**
SIC: 5051 7353 4225 3444 Steel; heavy construction equipment rental; general warehousing; concrete forms, sheet metal; miscellaneous fabricated wire products; fabricated plate work (boiler shop)
HQ: Efco Corp
    1800 Ne 46th Ave
    Des Moines IA 50313
    515 266-1141

(G-7049)
ELASTANCE IMAGING LLC
226 E Beechwold Blvd (43214-2120)
PHONE..............................614 579-9520
William Timmons, *President*
EMP: 4
SALES (est): 149.2K **Privately Held**
SIC: 3845 8731 Magnetic resonance imaging device, nuclear; ultrasonic medical equipment, except cleaning; ultrasonic scanning devices, medical; biotechnical research, commercial; medical research, commercial

(G-7050)
ELASTOSTAR RUBBER CORP
7030 Huntley Rd Ste B (43229-1053)
PHONE..............................614 841-4400
Ghanshyam Dungarani, *President*

Hiren Jetani, *Vice Pres*
EMP: 20
SALES (est): 2.7MM **Privately Held**
SIC: 2822 Synthetic rubber

(G-7051)
ELBERN PUBLICATIONS
3120 Elbern Ave (43209-2075)
P.O. Box 9497 (43209-0497)
PHONE..............................614 235-2643
Fax: 614 237-2637
Evelyn Becker, *Vice Pres*
EMP: 3
SALES (est): 153.1K **Privately Held**
SIC: 2741 Miscellaneous publishing

(G-7052)
ELEVATOR BREWING COMPANY LLC
165 N 4th St (43215-2906)
PHONE..............................614 679-2337
Richard Stevens, *Mng Member*
EMP: 8 **EST:** 2009
SQ FT: 13,000
SALES (est): 1.2MM **Privately Held**
SIC: 2082 Beer (alcoholic beverage)

(G-7053)
ELITE FIRE SERVICES LLC
1520 Harmon Ave Ste 667 (43223-3361)
PHONE..............................614 586-4255
Carol Nabors, *Office Mgr*
Sean Overbeck,
Rod Bishop,
Rob Callihan,
Doug Patterson,
EMP: 12
SQ FT: 850
SALES (est): 3.1MM **Privately Held**
SIC: 3569 Firefighting apparatus & related equipment

(G-7054)
ELYTUS LTD
40 E Columbus St (43206-2051)
PHONE..............................614 824-4985
Drew Clauson, *Info Tech Mgr*
Paul Organ, *Technology*
Matthew Hollis,
Alan Dillman,
EMP: 11
SALES (est): 1.7MM **Privately Held**
SIC: 7372 Utility computer software

(G-7055)
EMBROIDERY DESIGN GROUP LLC
2564 Billingsley Rd (43235-1990)
PHONE..............................614 798-8152
Mary Bandeen, *Mng Member*
EMP: 13
SALES (est): 958K **Privately Held**
WEB: www.embroiderydesigngroup.com
SIC: 2395 Embroidery & art needlework

(G-7056)
EMBROIDME CO
950 Taylor Station Rd U (43230-6671)
PHONE..............................614 933-9194
Fax: 614 933-9196
Dave Foresta, *Principal*
EMP: 6
SALES (est): 746.6K **Privately Held**
SIC: 2759 5699 5949 Screen printing; customized clothing & apparel; sewing & needlework

(G-7057)
ENGINEERED MARBLE INC
4064 Fisher Rd (43228-1020)
PHONE..............................614 308-0041
Fax: 614 308-0043
Jeff Schmidt, *President*
Jeff Klein, *Vice Pres*
EMP: 6
SQ FT: 6,100
SALES: 400K **Privately Held**
WEB: www.engineeredstone.com
SIC: 3281 Marble, building: cut & shaped

(G-7058)
ENGINEERED PROFILES LLC
Also Called: Crane Plastics
2141 Fairwood Ave (43207-1753)
PHONE..............................614 754-3700

Tim Tait, *General Mgr*
Timothy T Miller, *Principal*
Matt Fenneman, *Vice Pres*
Jared Kentner, *Plant Engr*
Adam Wachter, *CFO*
EMP: 200
SQ FT: 300,000
SALES: 55.6MM
SALES (corp-wide): 179.4MM **Privately Held**
WEB: www.craneplasticsmfg.com
SIC: 3089 Extruded finished plastic products
HQ: The Crane Group Companies Limited
    330 W Spring St Ste 200
    Columbus OH 43215
    614 754-3000

(G-7059)
ENLYTON LTD
1216 Kinnear Rd (43212-1154)
PHONE..............................614 888-9220
Jeffrey R Bergen, *CEO*
EMP: 5
SALES (est): 575.8K **Privately Held**
SIC: 2835 In vitro & in vivo diagnostic substances

(G-7060)
ENNOVEA MEDICAL LLC
2030 Dividend Dr (43228-3847)
PHONE..............................855 997-2273
Vinc Ellerbrock, *CFO*
Larry Jutte, *Mng Member*
Robert Deans,
EMP: 3
SALES: 150K
SALES (corp-wide): 575.1MM **Privately Held**
SIC: 3841 Surgical & medical instruments; diagnostic apparatus, medical
PA: Ernie Green Industries, Inc.
    2030 Dividend Dr
    Columbus OH 43228
    614 219-1423

(G-7061)
ENTROCHEM INC
1245 Kinnear Rd (43212-1155)
PHONE..............................614 946-7602
Jim McGuire, *President*
EMP: 10
SALES (est): 1.8MM **Privately Held**
SIC: 2891 Adhesives

(G-7062)
ENTROTECH INC
1245 Kinnear Rd (43212-1155)
PHONE..............................614 946-7602
James E McGuire Jr, *President*
Elizebeth Maag, *Principal*
Dave Bragg, *Vice Pres*
Jim Koch, *Vice Pres*
Doug Davis, *Controller*
▲ **EMP:** 18
SQ FT: 6,000
SALES (est): 6.7MM **Privately Held**
WEB: www.entrotech.net
SIC: 3081 Plastic film & sheet

(G-7063)
EP FERRIS & ASSOCIATES INC
880 King Ave (43212-2654)
PHONE..............................614 299-2999
Fax: 614 299-2992
Edward P Ferris, *Ch of Bd*
Heather Mackling, *Senior Engr*
Dane Sommer, *Design Engr*
Sean G Gillilan, *Manager*
Matthew Ferris, *Director*
EMP: 3 **EST:** 1987
SALES (est): 144.6K **Privately Held**
SIC: 8742 8711 1389 Management consulting services; construction & civil engineering; testing, measuring, surveying & analysis services

(G-7064)
ERNIE GREEN INDUSTRIES INC (PA)
Also Called: Eg Industries
2030 Dividend Dr (43228-3847)
PHONE..............................614 219-1423
Ernie Green, *President*
Samuel Morgan, *Exec VP*
▲ **EMP:** 4

SQ FT: 7,000
SALES (est): 575.1MM **Privately Held**
WEB: www.egreeninc.com
SIC: **3714** 3089 3471 3469 Motor vehicle
wheels & parts; motor vehicle body components & frame; motor vehicle engines &
parts; motor vehicle transmissions, drive
assemblies & parts; injection molded finished plastic products; automotive parts,
plastic; chromium plating of metals or
formed products; metal stampings

(G-7065)
ERNST ENTERPRISES INC
711 Stimmel Rd (43223-2905)
PHONE..............................614 443-9456
John C Ernst Jr, *Branch Mgr*
EMP: 46
SALES (corp-wide): 191MM **Privately
Held**
SIC: **5211** 3273 Cement; ready-mixed
concrete
PA: Ernst Enterprises, Inc.
3361 Successful Way
Dayton OH 45414
937 233-5555

(G-7066)
**ESSILOR LABORATORIES AMER
INC**
Also Called: Top Network
3671 Interchange Rd (43204-1499)
PHONE..............................614 274-0840
Fax: 614 274-5414
Kathryn Rismiller, *Treasurer*
Don Lepore, *Manager*
Judy Ellis, *Manager*
Steve Hile, *Manager*
Wayne Phelps, *Manager*
EMP: 50
SALES (corp-wide): 938.9MM **Privately
Held**
WEB: www.crizal.com
SIC: **3851** 5049 Eyeglasses, lenses &
frames; optical goods
HQ: Essilor Laboratories Of America, Inc.
13515 N Stemmons Fwy
Dallas TX 75234
972 241-4141

(G-7067)
ESSROC CEMENT CORP
1550 Williams Rd (43207-5108)
PHONE..............................614 497-2001
Larry Moore, *Branch Mgr*
EMP: 3
SALES (corp-wide): 16B **Privately Held**
WEB: www.essroc.com
SIC: **3241** 5032 Cement, hydraulic; ce-
ment
HQ: Essroc Cement Corp.
3251 Bath Pike
Nazareth PA 18064
610 837-6725

(G-7068)
**EUROPIA GOURMET FOODS
LLC**
672 N High St (43215-1547)
PHONE..............................614 460-3000
Olympia Hiotis, *Owner*
EMP: 5
SQ FT: 1,300
SALES (est): 248.9K **Privately Held**
WEB: www.europiagourmet.com
SIC: **2084** Wines

(G-7069)
EV LIQUIDS LLC
Also Called: Enso Vapors
192 Oak St (43235-6447)
PHONE..............................614 622-9617
Alan Pfeuffer, *Co-Owner*
EMP: 4
SALES (est): 171.1K **Privately Held**
SIC: **2131** Chewing & smoking tobacco

(G-7070)
**EVANS ADHESIVE
CORPORATION LTD (PA)**
925 Old Henderson Rd (43220-3779)
PHONE..............................614 451-2665
Fax: 614 451-1373
Rusty Thompson, *CEO*
George S Hoster, *Partner*

Tambera M Schueler, *Partner*
C Rusty Thompson, *General Ptnr*
Jeff Kriegel, *VP Admin*
◆ EMP: 32 EST: 1900
SQ FT: 70,000
SALES (est): 9.6MM **Privately Held**
WEB: www.evansadhesive.com
SIC: **2891** 2821 Adhesives; glue; adhe-
sives, paste; cement, linoleum & tile; plas-
tics materials & resins

(G-7071)
**EVANS ADHESIVE
CORPORATION LTD**
925 Old Henderson Rd (43220-3779)
PHONE..............................614 451-2665
Jim Feltner, *Manager*
EMP: 7
SALES (corp-wide): 9.6MM **Privately
Held**
WEB: www.evansadhesive.com
SIC: **2891** Adhesives
PA: Evans Adhesive Corporation, Ltd.
925 Old Henderson Rd
Columbus OH 43220
614 451-2665

(G-7072)
EVANS CREATIVE GROUP LLC
Also Called: Columbus Underground
11 E Gay St (43215-3101)
PHONE..............................614 657-9439
Anne Evans,
Walker Evans,
EMP: 9
SQ FT: 2,600
SALES (est): 385.1K **Privately Held**
SIC: **2741**

(G-7073)
EXPONENTIA US INC
424 Beecher Rd Ste A (43230-3510)
PHONE..............................614 944-5103
Gira Suvramani, *President*
Veera Murugappan, *Controller*
EMP: 30
SQ FT: 5,200
SALES (est): 4.8MM **Privately Held**
SIC: **7372** Publishers' computer software

(G-7074)
EYE CENTER (PA)
Also Called: Ohio Eye Associates
262 Neil Ave (43215-7309)
PHONE..............................614 228-3937
Peter Utrata, *Principal*
Grace Kim, *Ophthalmology*
Mary Delong, *Administration*
EMP: 25
SQ FT: 2,200
SALES (est): 3.9MM **Privately Held**
WEB: www.eyesurgerycenterofohio.com
SIC: **3841** 8011 Eye examining instru-
ments & apparatus; offices & clinics of
medical doctors

(G-7075)
**FACILITIES MANAGEMENT EX
LLC**
Also Called: Fmx
1515 Lake Shore Dr # 100 (43204-4939)
PHONE..............................844 664-4400
Jeffery Wilkins, *CEO*
Brian Gregory, *COO*
EMP: 11 EST: 2014
SQ FT: 3,200
SALES (est): 452.2K **Privately Held**
SIC: **7372** Application computer software;
business oriented computer software

(G-7076)
FAIRCHILD LABS LLC
2243 S James Rd (43232-3853)
PHONE..............................614 235-7040
Fax: 614 235-7245
Jay Fellows,
Steve Russo,
EMP: 12
SQ FT: 2,500
SALES (est): 1.6MM **Privately Held**
WEB: www.meritpad.com
SIC: **2891** Adhesives

(G-7077)
FBG BOTTLING GROUP LLC
Also Called: Frostop
1523 Alum Creek Dr (43209-2712)
PHONE..............................614 554-4646
Mike Gutter, *President*
EMP: 12
SALES (est): 2.2MM **Privately Held**
SIC: **2086** Bottled & canned soft drinks

(G-7078)
FCX PERFORMANCE INC (PA)
Also Called: Jh Instruments
3000 E 14th Ave (43219-2355)
PHONE..............................614 324-6050
Thomas Cox, *CEO*
Jeff Caswell, *President*
Don G Reece, *President*
Amory Roach, *Area Mgr*
Russell S Frazee, *COO*
▲ EMP: 40
SQ FT: 44,000
SALES (est): 227.9MM **Privately Held**
WEB: www.fcxperformance.com
SIC: **5084** 5085 3494 Instruments & con-
trol equipment; industrial supplies; valves
& fittings; valves & pipe fittings

(G-7079)
**FEDEX OFFICE & PRINT SVCS
INC**
4157 Morse Xing (43219-6015)
PHONE..............................614 478-1180
Fax: 614 478-1183
Ehren Cruz, *Branch Mgr*
EMP: 4
SALES (corp-wide): 50.3B **Publicly Held**
SIC: **2752** Commercial printing, litho-
graphic
HQ: Fedex Office And Print Services, Inc.
7900 Legacy Dr
Plano TX 75024
214 550-7000

(G-7080)
**FEDEX OFFICE & PRINT SVCS
INC**
180 N High St (43215-2403)
PHONE..............................614 621-1100
Leslie Benners, *CFO*
Joe Hunt, *Accounts Exec*
Trocon Brown, *Branch Mgr*
EMP: 32
SALES (corp-wide): 50.3B **Publicly Held**
WEB: www.kinkos.com
SIC: **7334** 2791 Photocopying & duplicat-
ing services; typesetting
HQ: Fedex Office And Print Services, Inc.
7900 Legacy Dr
Plano TX 75024
214 550-7000

(G-7081)
**FERGUSON FIRE FABRICATION
INC**
1640 Clara St (43211-2628)
PHONE..............................614 299-2070
Dan Tober, *Branch Mgr*
EMP: 15
SALES (corp-wide): 20.8B **Privately Held**
SIC: **3312** 3999 5074 Wheels; atomizers,
toiletry; plumbing fittings & supplies
HQ: Ferguson Fire & Fabrication, Inc.
2750 S Towne Ave
Pomona CA 91766
909 517-3085

(G-7082)
FIFTH AVENUE FRET SHOP LLC
1597 W 5th Ave (43212-2310)
PHONE..............................614 481-8300
Fax: 614 481-8346
Phil Maneri, *Owner*
Olive Smith, *Treasurer*
EMP: 3
SQ FT: 900
SALES (est): 279.7K **Privately Held**
WEB: www.fretshop.com
SIC: **3931** 5736 5932 7699 Guitars &
parts, electric & nonelectric; string instru-
ments; musical instruments, secondhand;
musical instrument repair services

(G-7083)
FILAMENT LLC
1507 Chambers Rd Fl 1 (43212-1568)
PHONE..............................614 732-0754
Arfaan Rampersaud,
Cynthia Rampersaud,
EMP: 5 EST: 2014
SALES (est): 376.7K **Privately Held**
SIC: **2835** 2851 3826 3841 In vitro diag-
nostics; paints & paint additives; ultravio-
let analytical instruments; laser scientific
& engineering instruments; diagnostic ap-
paratus, medical

(G-7084)
FIMM USA INC
5454 Alkire Rd (43228-3606)
PHONE..............................253 243-1522
Enrico Spinelli, *President*
Fabio Meli, *Manager*
◆ EMP: 19
SQ FT: 120,000
SALES (est): 3.5MM **Privately Held**
SIC: **3991** Brooms & brushes

(G-7085)
FINE LINE GRAPHICS CORP (PA)
1481 Goodale Blvd (43212-3402)
P.O. Box 163370 (43216-3370)
PHONE..............................614 486-0276
Fax: 614 486-5012
James Basch, *President*
Mark Carro, *Principal*
Gregory Davis, *Vice Pres*
Allie Davis, *VP Human Res*
Tracy Phares, *Human Res Mgr*
▲ EMP: 151
SQ FT: 42,000
SALES (est): 39MM **Privately Held**
SIC: **2752** 7331 Commercial printing, off-
set; business forms, lithographed; mailing
service

(G-7086)
FINISHMASTER INC
Also Called: Autobody Supply Company
212 N Grant Ave (43215-2642)
PHONE..............................614 228-4328
James Volpe, *Branch Mgr*
EMP: 68
SALES (corp-wide): 1.3B **Privately Held**
SIC: **3563** 5013 5198 Air & gas compres-
sors including vacuum pumps; automotive
supplies; paints, varnishes & supplies;
paints; lacquers; enamels
HQ: Finishmaster, Inc.
115 W Washington St Fl 7
Indianapolis IN 46204
317 237-3678

(G-7087)
FIRE BALL PRESS
27 E 5th Ave (43201-4510)
PHONE..............................614 280-0100
Dough Holmes, *Owner*
EMP: 4 EST: 2013
SALES (est): 234.9K **Privately Held**
SIC: **2741** 7336 Miscellaneous publishing;
commercial art & graphic design

(G-7088)
FIREHOUSE FOODS
917 E Whittier St (43206-1584)
PHONE..............................614 592-8115
Shehabel Nuwara, *Principal*
EMP: 6
SALES (est): 459.2K **Privately Held**
SIC: **2099** Food preparations

(G-7089)
FISHEL COMPANY
Johnson Brothers Construction
1600 Walcutt Rd (43228-9394)
PHONE..............................614 850-4400
Fax: 614 850-4419
Ed Evans, *Manager*
Angi Storino, *IT/INT Sup*
EMP: 65

G
E
O
G
R
A
P
H
I
C

SALES (corp-wide): 301.8MM **Privately Held**
WEB: www.fishelco.com
SIC: 1623 8711 1731 3612 Telephone & communication line construction; electric power line construction; cable television line construction; gas main construction; engineering services; electrical work; transformers, except electric
PA: The Fishel Company
1366 Dublin Rd
Columbus OH 43215
614 274-8100

(G-7090)
FLAG LADY INC
Also Called: Flag Lady's Flag Store, The
4567 N High St (43214-2042)
PHONE..............................614 263-1776
Fax: 614 263-1719
Mary Leavitt, *President*
Lori Leavitt Watson, *Treasurer*
EMP: 9
SQ FT: 5,000
SALES (est): 1.5MM **Privately Held**
WEB: www.flagladyinc.com
SIC: 5999 2399 Flags; flags, fabric

(G-7091)
FLORIDA TILE INC
Florida Tile 59
7029 Huntley Rd Ste B (43229-1059)
PHONE..............................614 436-2511
Fax: 614 436-2566
Brian Cotterman, *Sales Staff*
Jason Tackett, *Branch Mgr*
Jason Reikowsky, *Asst Mgr*
EMP: 8
SALES (corp-wide): 148.2MM **Privately Held**
WEB: www.floridatile.com
SIC: 3253 Wall tile, ceramic
PA: Florida Tile, Inc.
998 Governors Ln Ste 300
Lexington KY 40513
859 219-5200

(G-7092)
FORD PIPING AND BREWRY SVC LLC
1742 Kenny Rd (43212-1384)
PHONE..............................614 284-2409
Bryant Ford,
EMP: 3
SALES (est): 202.7K **Privately Held**
SIC: 3556 Brewers' & maltsters' machinery

(G-7093)
FORMWARE INC
3441 Winchester Pike (43232-5566)
PHONE..............................614 231-9387
Fax: 614 231-1478
James J Vatter, *President*
Margaret Kessler, *Corp Secy*
EMP: 9
SQ FT: 5,200
SALES (est): 730K **Privately Held**
SIC: 2434 2541 Wood kitchen cabinets; table or counter tops, plastic laminated; cabinets, except refrigerated: show, display, etc.: wood

(G-7094)
FORTIN WELDING & MFG INC
Also Called: Fortin Ironworks
944 W 5th Ave (43212-2657)
PHONE..............................614 291-4342
Dan Fortin, *President*
Margaret V Gundy, *Corp Secy*
Danny Coffman, *Vice Pres*
Fred Fortin, *Vice Pres*
John Fortin, *Vice Pres*
EMP: 39 EST: 1946
SQ FT: 60,000
SALES (est): 10.6MM **Privately Held**
WEB: www.fortinironworks.com
SIC: 3449 3446 Miscellaneous metalwork; ornamental metalwork

(G-7095)
FORTNER UPHOLSTERING INC
2624 Johnstown Rd (43219-2309)
PHONE..............................614 475-8282
Fax: 614 475-8283
David F Fortner Jr, *President*
Glen McAllister, *President*

Wanda L Fortner, *Principal*
E J Silberman, *Principal*
Diana Orum, *Corp Secy*
EMP: 16
SQ FT: 7,000
SALES (est): 3.7MM **Privately Held**
WEB: www.fortnerinc.com
SIC: 5712 2512 7641 3429 Furniture stores; upholstered household furniture; reupholstery & furniture repair; reupholstery; furniture builders' & other household hardware

(G-7096)
FRANKLIN ART GLASS STUDIOS
222 E Sycamore St (43206-2198)
PHONE..............................614 221-2972
Fax: 614 221-5223
Gary L Helf, *Ch of Bd*
Andrea Reid, *Vice Pres*
Mike S Sal, *Sales Mgr*
Mike Stone, *Sales Staff*
▲ **EMP:** 30 EST: 1900
SQ FT: 55,000
SALES (est): 3.6MM **Privately Held**
WEB: www.franklinartglass.com
SIC: 3231 5231 5945 Stained glass: made from purchased glass; glass, leaded or stained; hobby, toy & game shops

(G-7097)
FRANKLIN COMMUNICATIONS INC
Also Called: Wsny FM
4401 Carriage Hill Ln (43220-3837)
PHONE..............................614 459-9769
Fax: 614 821-9595
Edward K Christian, *CEO*
Alan Goodman, *President*
John Marocchi, *Chief Engr*
EMP: 65
SQ FT: 10,000
SALES (est): 2MM
SALES (corp-wide): 142.5MM **Publicly Held**
WEB: www.sagacommunications.com
SIC: 4832 2711 Radio broadcasting stations; newspapers
HQ: Saga Communications Of New England, Inc.
73 Kercheval Ave Ste 201
Grosse Pointe Farms MI 48236
313 886-7070

(G-7098)
FRANKLIN FIELD SERVICE
7065 Huntley Rd (43229-1055)
PHONE..............................614 885-1779
David Nunez, *President*
EMP: 3
SALES (est): 187.5K **Privately Held**
SIC: 3398 Metal heat treating

(G-7099)
FRED D PFENING COMPANY (PA)
1075 W 5th Ave (43212-2691)
PHONE..............................614 294-5361
Fax: 614 294-1633
Fred D Pfening Jr, *CEO*
Fred D Pfening III, *President*
Ed Brackman, *Vice Pres*
William F Kearns, *Vice Pres*
Darren Adams, *Project Engr*
EMP: 41 EST: 1919
SQ FT: 55,000
SALES (est): 9.3MM **Privately Held**
WEB: www.pfening.com
SIC: 3535 3585 3556 Pneumatic tube conveyor systems; air conditioning units, complete: domestic or industrial; mixers, commercial, food

(G-7100)
FRED D PFENING COMPANY
Also Called: Plant 2
1075 W 5th Ave (43212-2691)
PHONE..............................614 294-5361
John Legg, *Branch Mgr*
EMP: 7
SALES (corp-wide): 9.3MM **Privately Held**
WEB: www.pfening.com
SIC: 3556 Bakery machinery

PA: The Fred D Pfening Company
1075 W 5th Ave
Columbus OH 43212
614 294-5361

(G-7101)
FRENCH QUARTER LLC
6210 Busch Blvd (43229-1804)
PHONE..............................614 781-0588
Tom Logsdon, *Principal*
EMP: 3
SALES (est): 278.1K **Privately Held**
SIC: 3131 Quarters

(G-7102)
FULL GOSPEL BAPTIST TIMES
Also Called: Oakley Full Gospel Baptist Ch
3415 El Paso Dr (43204-1448)
PHONE..............................614 279-3307
Fax: 614 279-4045
Laverne Palmore, *Administration*
EMP: 4
SALES (est): 273.7K **Privately Held**
SIC: 2711 Newspapers

(G-7103)
G & D LEASING SERVICES INC
870 N 20th St (43219-2421)
PHONE..............................303 457-9189
William Dye, *President*
EMP: 10
SALES (est): 52.4K **Privately Held**
SIC: 3531 Log splitters

(G-7104)
G & J PEPSI-COLA BOTTLERS INC
Also Called: Pepsico
1241 Gibbard Ave (43219-2438)
PHONE..............................614 253-8771
Fax: 614 253-3306
Russ Morton, *Vice Pres*
Thomas Pendrey, *Branch Mgr*
Dan Foster, *Info Tech Mgr*
EMP: 550
SQ FT: 200,000
SALES (corp-wide): 490.5MM **Privately Held**
WEB: www.gjpepsi.com
SIC: 2086 Carbonated soft drinks, bottled & canned
PA: G & J Pepsi-Cola Bottlers Inc
9435 Waterstone Blvd # 390
Cincinnati OH 45249
513 785-6060

(G-7105)
G2 PRINT PLUS
3787 Interchange Rd (43204-1485)
PHONE..............................614 276-0500
Fax: 614 276-0501
George Wallace, *General Ptnr*
EMP: 10
SALES (est): 2.1MM **Privately Held**
WEB: www.g2printplus.com
SIC: 2759 Commercial printing

(G-7106)
GECECO INC
6416 Plankton Dr (43213-3471)
PHONE..............................614 861-4479
Guido Epelbaum, *President*
Barbara Epelbaum, *Vice Pres*
EMP: 25 EST: 1960
SQ FT: 16,000
SALES (est): 2.8MM **Privately Held**
WEB: www.gececo.com
SIC: 3524 3999 Lawn & garden equipment; lawn ornaments

(G-7107)
GEN III
2300 Lockbourne Rd (43207-2167)
PHONE..............................614 737-8744
John McCormick, *President*
Eric Wasserstrom, *President*
EMP: 4
SALES (est): 1.2MM **Privately Held**
SIC: 3441 Fabricated structural metal

(G-7108)
GENERAL THEMING CONTRS LLC
Also Called: GTC Artist With Machines
3750 Courtright Ct (43227-2253)
PHONE..............................614 252-6342
Fax: 614 252-6297
Richard D Rogovin, *Principal*
Joe Barton, *Controller*
Steve Urell, *Sales Staff*
Rob Davis, *Sr Project Mgr*
Erin Fisher, *Manager*
EMP: 105
SQ FT: 60,000
SALES (est): 17.9MM **Privately Held**
WEB: www.theming.net
SIC: 7389 7336 2759 2396 Sign painting & lettering shop; commercial art & graphic design; commercial printing; automotive & apparel trimmings

(G-7109)
GENERALS BOOKS
Also Called: The General's Books
522 Norton Rd (43228-2617)
P.O. Box 28685 (43228-0685)
PHONE..............................614 870-1861
Fax: 614 870-7881
David Roth, *President*
Robin Patricia Roth, *President*
EMP: 8
SQ FT: 1,980
SALES (est): 919.5K **Privately Held**
WEB: www.bluegraymagazine.com
SIC: 2721 Magazines: publishing only, not printed on site

(G-7110)
GEORGE WESTON CO
1020 Claycraft Rd Ste D (43230-6684)
PHONE..............................614 868-7565
Fax: 614 868-9350
Jeff Clark, *Principal*
EMP: 4
SALES (est): 202.3K **Privately Held**
SIC: 2051 Cakes, bakery: except frozen

(G-7111)
GEORGIA-PACIFIC LLC
1975 Watkins Rd (43207-3443)
PHONE..............................614 491-9100
Fax: 614 491-3880
Kurt Miller, *Manager*
EMP: 40
SALES (corp-wide): 27.3B **Privately Held**
WEB: www.gp.com
SIC: 2821 Plastics materials & resins
HQ: Georgia-Pacific Llc
133 Peachtree St Ne # 4810
Atlanta GA 30303
404 652-4000

(G-7112)
GFS CHEMICALS INC
851 Mckinley Ave (43222-1148)
P.O. Box 245, Powell (43065-0245)
PHONE..............................614 224-5345
Fax: 614 225-1175
John Reed, *Opers Mgr*
Jay West, *Opers Mgr*
Theodore Elliott, *Engineer*
Timothy Fecher, *Engineer*
Angie Miller, *Human Res Mgr*
EMP: 60
SALES (corp-wide): 22.4MM **Privately Held**
WEB: www.gfschemicals.com
SIC: 2819 2899 2869 Chemicals, reagent grade: refined from technical grade; chemical preparations; industrial organic chemicals
PA: Gfs Chemicals, Inc.
3041 Home Rd
Powell OH 43065
740 881-5501

(G-7113)
GFS CHEMICALS INC
800 Mckinley Ave (43222-1107)
PHONE..............................740 881-5501
Fax: 740 881-5989
EMP: 52
SALES (corp-wide): 22.4MM **Privately Held**
SIC: 2819 Chemicals, reagent grade: refined from technical grade

PA: Gfs Chemicals, Inc.
3041 Home Rd
Powell OH 43065
740 881-5501

(G-7114)
GFS CHEMICALS INC
800 Kaderly Dr (43228-1034)
PHONE..................................614 351-5347
Fax: 614 224-2688
Rob Pierron, *Plant Mgr*
John Pringle, *Manager*
Liza Tallon, *Director*
EMP: 60
SALES (corp-wide): 22.4MM **Privately Held**
SIC: 2819 Chemicals, reagent grade: refined from technical grade
PA: Gfs Chemicals, Inc.
3041 Home Rd
Powell OH 43065
740 881-5501

(G-7115)
GLASS AXIS
610 W Town St (43215-4446)
PHONE..................................614 291-4250
Carl Gortzig, *Vice Pres*
Mary C Mills, *Vice Pres*
Shawn Everette, *Facilities Mgr*
Rex Brown, *Exec Dir*
Chuck Goding, *Director*
EMP: 5
SQ FT: 12,700
SALES (est): 573.9K **Privately Held**
WEB: www.glassaxis.org
SIC: 3229 Pressed & blown glass

(G-7116)
GLAXOSMITHKLINE LLC
741 Chaffin Rdg (43214-2905)
PHONE..................................937 623-2680
EMP: 26
SALES (corp-wide): 34.3B **Privately Held**
SIC: 2834 Pharmaceutical preparations
HQ: Glaxosmithkline Llc
5 Crescent Dr
Philadelphia PA 19112
215 751-4000

(G-7117)
GLAXOSMITHKLINE LLC
359 Garden Rd (43214-2133)
PHONE..................................614 570-5970
EMP: 26
SALES (corp-wide): 34.3B **Privately Held**
SIC: 2834 Pharmaceutical preparations
HQ: Glaxosmithkline Llc
5 Crescent Dr
Philadelphia PA 19112
215 751-4000

(G-7118)
GLISTER INC
Also Called: Kingswood Company, The
3065 Switzer Ave (43219-2369)
PHONE..................................614 252-6400
Kristie Nicolosi, *President*
EMP: 6
SALES (est): 590K **Privately Held**
SIC: 2842 Specialty cleaning, polishes & sanitation goods

(G-7119)
GLOBAL COAL SALES GROUP LLC (HQ)
41 S High St Ste 3750s (43215-3406)
PHONE..................................614 221-0101
Wayne M Boich, *Mng Member*
▼ EMP: 6
SALES (est): 24.1MM **Privately Held**
SIC: 1241 Coal mining services
PA: Global Mining Holding Company, Llc
41 S High St
Columbus OH 43215
614 221-0101

(G-7120)
GLOBAL MINING HOLDING CO LLC (PA)
41 S High St (43215-6170)
PHONE..................................614 221-0101
Brian Murphy, *Mng Member*
EMP: 3
SALES (est): 24.1MM **Privately Held**
SIC: 1241 Coal mining services

(G-7121)
GLOBAL TRUCKING LLC
3723 Ellerdale Dr (43230-4086)
PHONE..................................614 598-6264
Ayan Abdirizak, *Mng Member*
EMP: 10
SALES (est): 438.2K **Privately Held**
SIC: 3537 Trucks, tractors, loaders, carriers & similar equipment

(G-7122)
GOLDEN DYNAMIC INC
950 Taylor Station Rd M (43230-6670)
PHONE..................................614 575-1222
Judy Sheu, *President*
Coleen Knapp, *Office Mgr*
▲ EMP: 7
SALES (est): 847.2K **Privately Held**
WEB: www.goldendynamic.com
SIC: 3291 Abrasive grains

(G-7123)
GONGWER NEWS SERVICE INC (PA)
Also Called: Michigan Report
17 S High St Ste 630 (43215-3413)
PHONE..................................614 221-1992
Fax: 614 221-7844
Alan A Miller, *President*
Scott Miller, *Assistant VP*
J W Chalfant, *Relations*
Melissa Dilley, *Relations*
EMP: 11
SQ FT: 3,200
SALES (est): 1.5MM **Privately Held**
WEB: www.gongwer-oh.com
SIC: 2721 8111 Periodicals: publishing only; legal services

(G-7124)
GONGWER NEWS SERVICE INC (HQ)
17 S High St Ste 630 (43215-3413)
PHONE..................................614 221-1992
Alan Miller, *President*
EMP: 5
SQ FT: 2,100
SALES (est): 848.3K
SALES (corp-wide): 1.5MM **Privately Held**
WEB: www.gongwer.com
SIC: 2721 Periodicals: publishing only
PA: Gongwer News Service Inc
17 S High St Ste 630
Columbus OH 43215
614 221-1992

(G-7125)
GOODALE AUTO-TRUCK PARTS INC
1100 E 5th Ave (43201-3000)
PHONE..................................614 294-4777
Fax: 614 294-1637
Jason Comer, *President*
James N Miller, *Principal*
Herbert S Peterson, *Principal*
Earle E Weimer, *Principal*
Nick Comer, *Vice Pres*
EMP: 25 EST: 1931
SQ FT: 36,000
SALES: 3.6MM **Privately Held**
WEB: www.goodale1.com
SIC: 3714 Transmissions, motor vehicle

(G-7126)
GRAFFITI FOODS LIMITED
333 Outerbelt St (43213-1529)
PHONE..................................614 759-1921
Lisa Hughes, *Manager*
Ronna Maciejewski, *Manager*
Philip E Griesinger,
EMP: 13
SQ FT: 7,600
SALES (est): 2.3MM **Privately Held**
SIC: 2099 Food preparations

(G-7127)
GRAHAM FORD POWER PRODUCTS
850 Harmon Ave (43223-2410)
PHONE..................................614 801-0049
EMP: 5
SQ FT: 3,200

SALES (est): 450K **Privately Held**
SIC: 3519 5084 Mfg Internal Combustion Engines Whol Industrial Equipment

(G-7128)
GRANDON MFG CO INC
530 Dow Ave (43211-2674)
PHONE..................................614 294-2694
Fax: 614 294-2696
Bonnie May, *President*
Brian May, *General Mgr*
EMP: 3
SQ FT: 4,000
SALES: 200K **Privately Held**
SIC: 3554 Die cutting & stamping machinery, paper converting

(G-7129)
GRANDVIEW GRIND
1423 Grandview Ave (43212-2853)
PHONE..................................614 485-9005
Samantha J Demint, *Principal*
EMP: 3
SALES (est): 319.5K **Privately Held**
SIC: 3599 Grinding castings for the trade

(G-7130)
GREAT OPPURTUNITIES INC
Also Called: Sportsales
1750 Idlewild Dr (43232-2917)
PHONE..................................614 868-1899
Fax: 614 868-5077
Raymond Pribish, *President*
EMP: 4
SQ FT: 6,000
SALES: 500K **Privately Held**
SIC: 2262 5091 2395 Screen printing: manmade fiber & silk broadwoven fabrics; sporting & recreation goods; embroidery products, except schiffli machine

(G-7131)
GREEN ROOM BREWING LLC
1101 N 4th St (43201-3683)
PHONE..................................614 596-3655
Jim W Baldrick,
David Spencer,
EMP: 7
SALES (est): 274.4K **Privately Held**
SIC: 5813 2082 Bars & lounges; near beer

(G-7132)
GURINA COMPANY
1379 River St (43222-1120)
PHONE..................................614 279-3891
Burton L Smith, *President*
Donald L Smith, *Vice Pres*
EMP: 7
SQ FT: 9,300
SALES: 760.2K **Privately Held**
SIC: 1711 7699 7692 Boiler setting contractor; boiler repair shop; welding repair

(G-7133)
H & E MACHINE COMPANY
1646 Fairwood Ave (43206-3711)
PHONE..................................614 443-7635
Fax: 614 443-0278
John Hanna, *President*
Janice A Hanna, *Admin Sec*
EMP: 10
SQ FT: 8,000
SALES (est): 1.5MM **Privately Held**
SIC: 3451 Screw machine products

(G-7134)
H & L WELDING SERVICE INC
3756 Agler Rd (43219-3605)
P.O. Box 117, Baltimore (43105-0117)
PHONE..................................740 862-3520
Harold Mullins, *President*
EMP: 3
SQ FT: 2,000
SALES (est): 244.1K **Privately Held**
SIC: 7692 Welding repair

(G-7135)
H ROSEN USA LLC
1195 Technology Dr (43230-6606)
PHONE..................................614 354-6707
EMP: 200
SALES (corp-wide): 79.3MM **Privately Held**
SIC: 3999 Atomizers, toiletry

PA: H. Rosen Usa, Llc
14120 Interdrive E
Houston TX 77032
281 442-8282

(G-7136)
H Y O INC
Also Called: Pengywn
2550 W 5th Ave (43204-3815)
PHONE..................................614 488-2861
Jim Kime, *President*
Sheila Kime, *Corp Secy*
Charles Hoskins, *Supervisor*
EMP: 11
SQ FT: 20,000
SALES (est): 1.3MM **Privately Held**
WEB: www.pengwyn.com
SIC: 3531 3594 Snow plow attachments; fluid power pumps & motors

(G-7137)
HACKMAN FRAMES LLC
502 Schrock Rd (43229-1028)
PHONE..................................614 841-0007
Fax: 614 841-0445
Craig Hackman,
EMP: 15
SQ FT: 14,000
SALES (est): 1.2MM **Privately Held**
WEB: www.hackmanframes.com
SIC: 2499 Picture & mirror frames, wood

(G-7138)
HAKE HEAD LLC
Also Called: Maramor Chocolates
1855 E 17th Ave (43219-1006)
PHONE..................................614 291-2244
Diane Myers, *Sales Mgr*
Rita Harshe, *Accounts Mgr*
Michael Ryan, *Mng Member*
Ben Spicer,
▲ EMP: 25
SQ FT: 30,000
SALES (est): 6.1MM **Privately Held**
WEB: www.maramor.com
SIC: 2064 Candy & other confectionery products

(G-7139)
HAMILTON TANKS LLC
2200 Refugee Rd (43207-2898)
PHONE..................................614 445-8446
Fax: 614 445-7248
Stephen Meeker, *President*
Bob Morrison, *Draft/Design*
Joshua Kindig, *Engineer*
Michael Penny, *Mktg Dir*
Michael Davis, *Technology*
EMP: 17
SQ FT: 30,000
SALES (est): 9.7MM **Privately Held**
WEB: www.hamiltontanks.com
SIC: 3443 Tanks, lined: metal plate
PA: Meeker Equipment Co., Inc.
4381 Front Mountain Rd
Belleville PA 17004
215 361-2900

(G-7140)
HANG-IT-ALL CURTAIN SYSTEM LLC
89 S Burgess Ave (43204-3252)
PHONE..................................614 275-0954
Megan Mateer, *President*
EMP: 3 EST: 2014
SALES (est): 198.9K **Privately Held**
SIC: 3089 Window screening, plastic

(G-7141)
HANG-UPS INSTLLATION GROUP INC
3751 April Ln (43227-3371)
P.O. Box 9811 (43209-0811)
PHONE..................................614 239-7004
Fax: 614 239-7668
Mark Russell, *President*
Christine Russell, *Corp Secy*
EMP: 3
SQ FT: 3,000
SALES (est): 500K **Privately Held**
SIC: 7389 2591 Interior decorating; drapery hardware & blinds & shades

GEOGRAPHIC

(G-7142)
HANGER PRSTHETCS & ORTHO INC
1357 Dublin Rd (43215-7046)
PHONE..............................614 481-8338
Tim Riedinger, *Manager*
EMP: 16
SALES (corp-wide): 460MM **Publicly Held**
SIC: 3842 Surgical appliances & supplies
HQ: Hanger Prosthetics & Orthotics, Inc.
10910 Domain Dr Ste 300
Austin TX 78758
512 777-3800

(G-7143)
HANSON CONCRETE PRODUCTS OHIO
Also Called: Hanson Pipe & Products
1500 Haul Rd (43207-1888)
PHONE..............................614 443-4846
Terry Feather, *Manager*
EMP: 35
SALES (corp-wide): 6MM **Privately Held**
SIC: 1771 3441 3272 Concrete work; fabricated structural metal; concrete products
PA: Hanson Concrete Products Ohio, Inc
6055 150th St W
Saint Paul MN 55124
612 432-6050

(G-7144)
HARPER ENGRAVING & PRINTING CO (PA)
2626 Fisher Rd (43204-3561)
P.O. Box 426 (43216-0426)
PHONE..............................614 276-0700
Fax: 614 276-5557
Donald Mueller, *President*
Brian Regenye, *Natl Sales Mgr*
Merle Finchbrown, *Manager*
Sherry Jacobs, *Manager*
Joel E Radout, *Manager*
EMP: 73
SQ FT: 40,000
SALES (est): 12.7MM **Privately Held**
WEB: www.harperengraving.com
SIC: 2759 2752 Commercial printing; commercial printing, offset

(G-7145)
HARRIS PAPER CRAFTS INC
266 E 5th Ave (43201-2818)
PHONE..............................614 299-2141
Fax: 614 299-2423
Richard Potts, *President*
EMP: 10
SALES (est): 1MM **Privately Held**
SIC: 2679 2796 2789 2675 Paper products, converted; platemaking services; bookbinding & related work; die-cut paper & board

(G-7146)
HAZELBAKER INDUSTRIES LTD
Also Called: Wellnitz
1661 Old Henderson Rd (43220-3644)
PHONE..............................614 276-2631
Fax: 614 276-7718
David Buell, *President*
Donald Crites, *Vice Pres*
Joseph Hazelbaker, *Vice Pres*
James Cramer, *Treasurer*
K Robert Evenson Jr, *Treasurer*
EMP: 45
SQ FT: 2,500
SALES (est): 5.8MM **Privately Held**
WEB: www.wellnitz.com
SIC: 3271 5211 3272 Concrete block & brick; masonry materials & supplies; concrete products

(G-7147)
HEARTLAND GROUP HOLDINGS LLC (HQ)
4001 E 5th Ave (43219-1812)
PHONE..............................614 441-4001
EMP: 30
SALES (est): 19.5MM
SALES (corp-wide): 407.4MM **Privately Held**
SIC: 3559 Oil Refinery That Recycles Used Motor Oils Into Recycled Base Oils

PA: Warren Distribution, Inc.
727 S 13th St
Omaha NE 68102
402 341-9397

(G-7148)
HELENA CHEMICAL COMPANY
800 Distribution Dr (43228-1004)
PHONE..............................614 275-4200
Helena Cwu, *Branch Mgr*
EMP: 9
SALES (corp-wide): 62.3B **Privately Held**
WEB: www.helenachemical.com
SIC: 5191 2819 Fertilizers & agricultural chemicals; seeds & bulbs; chemicals, high purity: refined from technical grade
HQ: Helena Chemical Company
255 Schilling Blvd # 200
Collierville TN 38017
901 761-0050

(G-7149)
HENDERSON PARTNERS LLC
4424 N High St (43214)
PHONE..............................614 883-1310
Timothy Rollins, *Principal*
EMP: 5
SALES (est): 470K **Privately Held**
SIC: 6411 3699 Patrol services, insurance; security control equipment & systems

(G-7150)
HENRY BUSSMAN
Also Called: Minuteman Press
70 S 4th St (43215-4315)
PHONE..............................614 224-0417
Fax: 614 224-0418
Henry Bussman, *Owner*
EMP: 4
SQ FT: 950
SALES (est): 500K **Privately Held**
SIC: 2752 7334 2789 Photo-offset printing; photocopying & duplicating services; bookbinding & related work

(G-7151)
HERITAGE MARBLE OF OHIO INC
Also Called: Heritage Marbles
7086 Huntley Rd (43229-1022)
PHONE..............................614 436-1464
Fax: 614 436-9874
Gene Daniels, *President*
Jim Franklin, *Controller*
EMP: 25
SQ FT: 22,000
SALES (est): 1.9MM **Privately Held**
WEB: www.heritagemarble.com
SIC: 3281 1411 Marble, building: cut & shaped; dimension stone

(G-7152)
HEXION INC (DH)
180 E Broad St Fl 26 (43215-3707)
PHONE..............................614 225-4000
Fax: 614 225-4127
Craig O Morrison, *Ch of Bd*
Joseph P Bevilaqua, *COO*
John P Auletto, *Exec VP*
Douglas A Johns, *Exec VP*
George F Knight, *CFO*
EMP: 277
SALES (est): 3.4B **Publicly Held**
WEB: www.hexion.com
SIC: 2821 Thermosetting materials; acrylic resins; epoxy resins; melamine resins, melamine-formaldehyde
HQ: Hexion Llc
180 E Broad St Fl 26
Columbus OH 43215
614 225-4000

(G-7153)
HEXION LLC (DH)
180 E Broad St Fl 26 (43215-3707)
PHONE..............................614 225-4000
Craig O Morrison, *CEO*
William H Carter, *Exec VP*
Kyle Henagan, *Engineer*
George Knight, *Treasurer*
Howard Rochon, *Tax Mgr*
◆ **EMP:** 100
SQ FT: 200,000

SALES (est): 3.4B **Publicly Held**
SIC: 2821 2899 Thermosetting materials; chemical preparations
HQ: Hexion Holdings Llc
180 E Broad St
Columbus OH 43215
614 225-4000

(G-7154)
HI LITE PLASTIC PRODUCTS
Also Called: Capital Toe Grinding
3760 E 5th Ave (43219-1807)
PHONE..............................614 235-9050
Offie Bartley, *Owner*
EMP: 6
SALES (est): 522.5K **Privately Held**
SIC: 3089 Kitchenware, plastic

(G-7155)
HIGH LVEL FSHION ATHLETES FOOT
5200 E Main St (43213-2411)
PHONE..............................614 577-8800
Salah Alsakir, *General Mgr*
EMP: 3
SALES (est): 330.9K **Privately Held**
SIC: 2326 Men's & boys' work clothing

(G-7156)
HIGHLIGHTS PRESS INC
1800 Watermark Dr (43215-1048)
P.O. Box 18360 (43218-0360)
PHONE..............................614 487-2767
Cheri Routzahn, *Treasurer*
Sherry Routzahn, *Controller*
EMP: 3
SQ FT: 1,000
SALES (est): 308.7K **Privately Held**
SIC: 2731 Book publishing

(G-7157)
HILLEARY-WHITAKER INC
Also Called: Kwik Kopy Printing
2646 Billingsley Rd (43235-1924)
PHONE..............................614 766-4694
Fax: 614 766-0545
Stephen Whitaker, *President*
EMP: 3
SALES (est): 451.9K **Privately Held**
SIC: 2752 2791 7334 Commercial printing, lithographic; typesetting; photocopying & duplicating services

(G-7158)
HILTI INC
Also Called: Hc 142
818 N Rose Ave (43219-2525)
PHONE..............................614 258-8384
Fax: 614 258-8389
Marty Rack, *Manager*
EMP: 13
SALES (corp-wide): 4.6B **Privately Held**
SIC: 3399 3545 5082 Metal fasteners; tools & accessories for machine tools; drill bits, metalworking; drills (machine tool accessories); contractors' materials
HQ: Hilti, Inc.
7250 Dallas Pkwy Ste 1000
Plano TX 75024
800 879-8000

(G-7159)
HIRSCHVOGEL INCORPORATED
2230 S 3rd St (43207-2431)
PHONE..............................614 340-5657
Fax: 614 445-7335
Felix Schmieder, *President*
Robert Hartwell, *VP Mfg*
Michael Gruskiewicz, *Opers Mgr*
Bob Sonntag, *Maint Spvr*
Jackie Harding, *Purch Mgr*
◆ **EMP:** 150
SQ FT: 155,000
SALES (est): 45.4MM
SALES (corp-wide): 999.2MM **Privately Held**
WEB: www.hirschvogel.com
SIC: 3714 Motor vehicle parts & accessories
PA: Hirschvogel Holding Gmbh
Dr.-Manfred-Hirschvogel-Str. 6
Denklingen 86920
824 329-10

(G-7160)
HITE PARTS EXCHANGE INC
2235 Mckinley Ave (43204-3400)
PHONE..............................614 272-5115
Fax: 614 272-9808
Thomas A Blake, *President*
Chris Allred, *Sales Staff*
Dona Blake, *Admin Sec*
EMP: 30
SQ FT: 14,000
SALES (est): 4.4MM **Privately Held**
WEB: www.hiteparts.com
SIC: 5013 3714 3625 3594 Automotive supplies & parts; pumps, oil & gas; clutches; motor vehicle engines & parts; clutches, motor vehicle; relays & industrial controls; fluid power pumps & motors; carburetors, pistons, rings, valves; power transmission equipment

(G-7161)
HJ SYSTEMS INC
230 N Central Ave (43222-1001)
PHONE..............................614 351-9777
James E Stang, *President*
EMP: 10
SQ FT: 20,000
SALES (est): 800K **Privately Held**
WEB: www.hjsystemsinc.com
SIC: 2431 Millwork

(G-7162)
HONEYWELL
2199 Dividend Dr (43228-3805)
PHONE..............................614 850-8228
Matthew Chretien, *Principal*
EMP: 3
SALES (est): 357.9K **Privately Held**
SIC: 3724 Aircraft engines & engine parts

(G-7163)
HONEYWELL INTERNATIONAL INC
2080 Arlingate Ln (43228-4112)
PHONE..............................614 850-5000
Larry Anderson, *VP Admin*
Richard Cary, *Plant Mgr*
David Moore, *Plant Mgr*
Bob Fresco, *Electrical Engi*
Mike Ogle, *CFO*
EMP: 200
SALES (corp-wide): 39.3B **Publicly Held**
WEB: www.honeywell.com
SIC: 3829 3674 Pressure transducers; semiconductors & related devices
PA: Honeywell International Inc.
115 Tabor Rd
Morris Plains NJ 07950
973 455-2000

(G-7164)
HONEYWELL INTERNATIONAL INC
2080 Arlingate Ln (43228-4112)
PHONE..............................614 850-5000
Brad Forry, *Branch Mgr*
EMP: 84
SALES (corp-wide): 39.3B **Publicly Held**
SIC: 3829 3674 Pressure transducers; semiconductors & related devices
PA: Honeywell International Inc.
115 Tabor Rd
Morris Plains NJ 07950
973 455-2000

(G-7165)
HONEYWELL LEBOW PRODUCTS
Also Called: Honeywell Senfopec
2080 Arlingate Ln (43228-4112)
PHONE..............................614 850-5000
Phil Geraffo, *Vice Pres*
▲ **EMP:** 200
SALES (est): 15.8MM
SALES (corp-wide): 39.3B **Publicly Held**
WEB: www.honeywell.com
SIC: 3829 Measuring & controlling devices
PA: Honeywell International Inc.
115 Tabor Rd
Morris Plains NJ 07950
973 455-2000

(G-7166)
HOOKAH RUSH
2422 N High St (43202-2924)
PHONE................................614 267-6463
EMP: 4
SALES (est): 365.3K **Privately Held**
SIC: 2131 Smoking tobacco

(G-7167)
HOPCO RESOURCES INC
2829 E Dblin Granville Rd (43231-4037)
PHONE................................614 882-8533
Fax: 614 882-8434
Gary Hopkins, *President*
Gary W Hopkins, *President*
Kenneth Hopkins, *Vice Pres*
EMP: 5
SQ FT: 1,800
SALES (est): 710.2K **Privately Held**
SIC: 1311 Crude petroleum production;
natural gas production

(G-7168)
HOSTER GRAPHICS COMPANY INC
Also Called: Advance Graphics
1349 Delashmut Ave (43212-3103)
PHONE................................614 299-9770
Frank Hoster, *President*
Naomi Tuttle, *Vice Pres*
Curt Smith, *Cust Mgr*
EMP: 13
SQ FT: 10,000
SALES (est): 2.6MM **Privately Held**
WEB: www.advancecolumbus.com
SIC: 2752 7334 Commercial printing, off-
set; photocopying & duplicating services

(G-7169)
HUMBLE CONSTRUCTION CO
3441 Morse Rd (43231-6183)
PHONE................................614 888-8960
Gary Slagle, *Safety Dir*
EMP: 22
SALES (corp-wide): 19.1MM **Privately Held**
SIC: 3499 3312 1521 Aerosol valves,
metal; blast furnaces & steel mills; single-
family housing construction
PA: Humble Construction Co.
1180 Carlisle Ave
Bellefontaine OH 43311
937 465-6035

(G-7170)
HUNG PHAM
5291 Westpointe Plaza Dr (43228-9131)
PHONE................................614 850-9695
Pham Hung, *Owner*
EMP: 5
SALES (est): 317.8K **Privately Held**
SIC: 3999 Fingernails, artificial

(G-7171)
HUNTERS HIGHTECH ENERGY SYSTM
2059 Big Tree Dr (43223-3292)
PHONE................................614 275-4777
James E Hunter,
EMP: 3
SALES: 150K **Privately Held**
SIC: 1711 5074 3674 Solar energy con-
tractor; heating equipment & panels,
solar; photovoltaic devices, solid state

(G-7172)
HYPE SOCKS
33 N 3rd St (43215-3514)
PHONE................................614 506-5248
J Michael Wintermantel, *Principal*
EMP: 4
SALES (est): 88.8K **Privately Held**
SIC: 2252 Socks

(G-7173)
HYPER TECH RESEARCH INC
539 Industrial Mile Rd (43228-2412)
PHONE................................614 481-8050
Fax: 614 481-4080
Michael Tomsic, *President*
David Doll, *Principal*
Trent Wieber, *Project Engr*
Lawrence Walley, *CFO*
John Phillips, *Senior Mgr*
EMP: 16

SQ FT: 50,000
SALES (est): 3.6MM **Privately Held**
WEB: www.hypertechresearch.com
SIC: 3674 Semiconductors & related de-
vices

(G-7174)
HYPODERMIC DESIGNS LLC
3089 1/2 W Broad St Apt C (43204-1373)
P.O. Box 526, Worthington (43085-0526)
PHONE................................614 203-4048
Robin Keenan, *COO*
Anthony Gower, *CFO*
EMP: 3
SALES (est): 98.2K **Privately Held**
SIC: 2759 Letterpress & screen printing

(G-7175)
HYTEC AUTOMOTIVE IND LLC
4419 Equity Dr (43228-3856)
PHONE................................614 527-9370
Denis Bruncak, *CEO*
Timothy Zahler, *President*
◆ EMP: 10
SQ FT: 40,000
SALES (est): 1.2MM **Privately Held**
SIC: 3714 Water pump, motor vehicle

(G-7176)
HYTEC-DEBARTOLO LLC
Also Called: Hytec Automotive
4419 Equity Dr (43228-3856)
PHONE................................614 527-9370
Mike Minichello, *Controller*
Denis Bruncak,
▲ EMP: 17
SQ FT: 34,600
SALES (est): 3.1MM
SALES (corp-wide): 33.1MM **Privately Held**
WEB: www.debartoloholdings.com
SIC: 3714 Water pump, motor vehicle
PA: Debartolo Holdings, Llc
15436 N Florida Ave # 200
Tampa FL 33613
813 908-8400

(G-7177)
I A B F INC
Also Called: Industrial Aluminum Foundry
1890 Mckinley Ave (43222-1004)
PHONE................................614 279-4498
Fax: 614 279-4499
Andrew B Kientz, *President*
G Jenkins, *Manager*
EMP: 8 EST: 1966
SQ FT: 7,500
SALES (est): 550K **Privately Held**
SIC: 3365 3369 Aluminum & aluminum-
based alloy castings; nonferrous
foundries

(G-7178)
I H SCHLEZINGER INC
Also Called: Schlezinger Metals
1041 Joyce Ave (43219-2448)
P.O. Box 83624 (43203-0624)
PHONE................................614 252-1188
Fax: 614 252-1180
Kenneth Cohen, *President*
Jackie Ames, *Vice Pres*
Jack Joseph, *Vice Pres*
John Miller, *Vice Pres*
Donald Zulanch, *Vice Pres*
EMP: 42
SQ FT: 9,000
SALES (est): 13.6MM **Privately Held**
WEB: www.ihschlezinger.com
SIC: 3341 5093 Secondary nonferrous
metals; ferrous metal scrap & waste

(G-7179)
I HEART CUPCAKES
372 Hanton Way (43213-4435)
PHONE................................614 787-3896
Stacee Streifel, *Principal*
EMP: 4
SALES (est): 158.9K **Privately Held**
SIC: 2051 Bread, cake & related products

(G-7180)
IC3D LLC
421 W State St (43215-4008)
PHONE................................614 260-5631
Michael Cao, *Principal*
EMP: 5

SALES (est): 422.9K **Privately Held**
SIC: 8731 2821 Computer (hardware) development; plastics materials & resins

(G-7181)
ICC SAFETY SERVICE INC
1070 Leona Ave (43201-3039)
PHONE................................614 261-4557
Tiffany Adair, *President*
Christopher Duger, *Vice Pres*
EMP: 6
SQ FT: 3,900
SALES (est): 888.6K **Privately Held**
SIC: 3271 Blocks, concrete: insulating

(G-7182)
IMAGE PRINT INC
6417 Busch Blvd (43229-1862)
PHONE................................614 430-8470
Fax: 614 430-8471
Bill Lang, *President*
EMP: 3
SQ FT: 1,700
SALES (est): 213.6K **Privately Held**
SIC: 2752 Commercial printing, offset

(G-7183)
IMAGING CENTER EAST MAIN
500 E Main St 2nd (43215-5369)
PHONE................................614 566-8120
Shawn Sharp, *Manager*
EMP: 4
SALES (est): 364.6K **Privately Held**
SIC: 3845 Ultrasonic scanning devices,
medical

(G-7184)
IMMIGRATION LAW SYSTEMS INC
1620 E Broad St Ste 107 (43203-2012)
PHONE................................614 252-3078
Fax: 614 252-8140
Bernard Boiston, *President*
EMP: 3
SALES (est): 218.3K **Privately Held**
WEB: www.ilssys.com
SIC: 2741 7371 Miscellaneous publishing;
custom computer programming services

(G-7185)
INDUSTRIAL PATTERN & MFG CO
899 N 20th St (43219-2420)
PHONE................................614 252-0934
Fax: 614 252-9233
Thomas C Birkefeld, *President*
Charles J Birkefeld, *Vice Pres*
Jay Hrun, *Vice Pres*
Jay Thrun, *Engineer*
Donna Birkefeld, *Executive*
EMP: 12 EST: 1947
SQ FT: 5,000
SALES (est): 2.1MM **Privately Held**
WEB: www.industrialpattern.com
SIC: 3543 Industrial patterns

(G-7186)
INFANT FOOD PROJECT INC
638 S Hampton Rd (43213-2728)
P.O. Box 91169 (43209-7169)
PHONE................................614 239-5763
Victor Alexander, *Principal*
EMP: 3
SALES (est): 184.4K **Privately Held**
SIC: 2099 Food preparations

(G-7187)
INHANCE TECHNOLOGIES LLC
6575 Huntley Rd Ste D (43229-1039)
PHONE................................614 846-6400
Fax: 614 846-7042
Tom Gardener, *Opers-Prdtn-Mfg*
EMP: 18
SQ FT: 7,500
SALES (corp-wide): 8.9MM **Privately Held**
WEB: www.fluoroseal.com
SIC: 3089 Plastic containers, except foam
PA: Inhance Technologies Llc
16223 Park Row Ste 100
Houston TX 77084
800 929-1743

(G-7188)
INLAND PRODUCTS INC (PA)
599 Frank Rd (43223-3813)
PHONE................................614 443-3425
Gary H Baas, *President*
Tom Pegan, *Controller*
David Bass, *Finance Dir*
EMP: 26 EST: 1867
SQ FT: 40,000
SALES (est): 5.4MM **Privately Held**
SIC: 2077 5159 Grease rendering, inedi-
ble; tallow rendering, inedible; bone meal,
except as animal feed; meat meal & tank-
age, except as animal feed; hides

(G-7189)
INSKEEP BROTHERS INC
Also Called: Inskeep Brothers Printers
3193 E Dblin Granville Rd (43231-4035)
PHONE................................614 898-6620
Fax: 614 898-6625
Jeff Inskeep, *President*
Paula Inskeep, *Vice Pres*
EMP: 15
SQ FT: 11,000
SALES (est): 2MM **Privately Held**
WEB: www.inskeepbrothers.com
SIC: 2759 Commercial printing

(G-7190)
INSTALLED BUILDING PDTS LLC
Swan Freedom
1320 Mckinley Ave Ste A (43222-1155)
PHONE................................614 308-9900
Jeff Phipps, *Purchasing*
Mark Lomax, *Branch Mgr*
Todd Hite, *Director*
EMP: 35
SALES (corp-wide): 862.9MM **Publicly Held**
SIC: 2511 2514 3231 3442 Whatnot
shelves: wood; medicine cabinets & vani-
ties: metal; mirrored glass; shutters, door
or window: metal
HQ: Installed Building Products Llc
495 S High St Ste 50
Columbus OH 43215
614 221-3399

(G-7191)
INSTANT IMPRESSIONS INC
Also Called: Elektro Kopy
4499 Kenny Rd (43220-4034)
P.O. Box 20788 (43220-0788)
PHONE................................614 538-9844
Fax: 614 538-9845
Chris Donnelly, *Director*
EMP: 3
SALES (corp-wide): 3.5MM **Privately Held**
WEB: www.instantimpressions.com
SIC: 7334 2759 Photocopying & duplicat-
ing services; commercial printing
PA: Instant Impressions, Inc.
4078 Anson Dr
Hilliard OH 43026
614 527-6925

(G-7192)
INSTANTWHIP CONNECTICUT INC (PA)
2200 Cardigan Ave (43215-1092)
PHONE................................614 488-2536
Clifton J Smith, *Ch of Bd*
Douglas A Smith, *President*
John Beck, *Vice Pres*
Thomas Fleming, *Vice Pres*
Albert Gardner, *Vice Pres*
EMP: 18 EST: 1946
SQ FT: 10,300
SALES (est): 3.1MM **Privately Held**
SIC: 2026 5143 Whipped topping, except
frozen or dry mix; dairy products, except
dried or canned

(G-7193)
INSTANTWHIP DETROIT INC (PA)
2200 Cardigan Ave (43215-1092)
PHONE................................614 488-2536
Clifton J Smith, *Ch of Bd*
Douglas A Smith, *President*
Fred Smith, *Vice Pres*
Thomas G Michaelides, *Treasurer*
G Fredrick Smith, *Admin Sec*
EMP: 18 EST: 1936

SALES (est): 2.8MM **Privately Held**
SIC: 2026 Whipped topping, except frozen
or dry mix

(G-7194)
INSTANTWHIP DETROIT INC
Also Called: Instant Whip Detroit
2200 Cardigan Ave (43215-1092)
PHONE.............................800 544-9447
Ken Parks, *Manager*
EMP: 15
SALES (corp-wide): 2.8MM **Privately
Held**
SIC: 2026 5143 Cream, whipped; dairy
products, except dried or canned
PA: Instantwhip Detroit Inc
2200 Cardigan Ave
Columbus OH 43215
614 488-2536

(G-7195)
INSTANTWHIP FOODS INC (PA)
2200 Cardigan Ave (43215-1092)
PHONE.............................614 488-2536
Fax: 614 488-0307
Douglas A Smith, *President*
Thomas G Michaelides, *Treasurer*
Diana De'santis, *Credit Mgr*
Ken Temple, *Manager*
EMP: 18 EST: 1934
SQ FT: 10,300
SALES (est): 43.5MM **Privately Held**
WEB: www.instantwhip.com
SIC: 6794 8741 2026 5143 Franchises,
selling or licensing; administrative man-
agement; fluid milk; whipped topping, ex-
cept frozen or dry mix; dairy products,
except dried or canned

(G-7196)
**INSTANTWHIP OF BUFFALO INC
(HQ)**
2200 Cardigan Ave (43215-1092)
PHONE.............................614 488-2536
Douglas A Smith, *President*
John Beck, *Vice Pres*
Thomas G Michaelides, *Treasurer*
G Frederick Smith, *Admin Sec*
EMP: 10
SQ FT: 10,300
SALES (est): 1.9MM
SALES (corp-wide): 43.5MM **Privately
Held**
SIC: 2026 5143 Whipped topping, except
frozen or dry mix; dairy products, except
dried or canned
PA: Instantwhip Foods, Inc.
2200 Cardigan Ave
Columbus OH 43215
614 488-2536

(G-7197)
**INSTANTWHIP PRODUCTS CO
PA (HQ)**
Also Called: Instantwhip of Pennsylvania
2200 Cardigan Ave (43215-1092)
PHONE.............................614 488-2536
Douglas A Smith, *President*
EMP: 18
SQ FT: 20,300
SALES (est): 1.4MM
SALES (corp-wide): 43.5MM **Privately
Held**
SIC: 2026 5143 Whipped topping, except
frozen or dry mix; dairy products, except
dried or canned
PA: Instantwhip Foods, Inc.
2200 Cardigan Ave
Columbus OH 43215
614 488-2536

(G-7198)
**INSTANTWHIP-CHICAGO INC
(PA)**
2200 Cardigan Ave (43215-1092)
PHONE.............................614 488-2536
Clifton J Smith, *Ch of Bd*
Douglas A Smith, *President*
Jim Ring, *Vice Pres*
Thomas G Michaelides, *Treasurer*
Diana Desantis, *Manager*
EMP: 36
SQ FT: 10,300
SALES (est): 6.7MM **Privately Held**
SIC: 2026 Fluid milk; cream, whipped;
whipped topping, except frozen or dry mix

(G-7199)
**INSTANTWHIP-SYRACUSE INC
(PA)**
2200 Cardigan Ave (43215-1092)
PHONE.............................614 488-2536
Clifton J Smith, *Ch of Bd*
Douglas A Smith, *President*
Raymond Winslow, *Vice Pres*
Thomas G Michaelides, *Treasurer*
G Frederick Smith, *Admin Sec*
EMP: 17
SQ FT: 10,300
SALES (est): 1.6MM **Privately Held**
SIC: 2026 Whipped topping, except frozen
or dry mix

(G-7200)
INSULPRO INC
4650 Indianola Ave (43214-1884)
PHONE.............................614 262-3768
Fax: 614 262-3769
Greg Freed, *President*
Nicole Newman, *Manager*
EMP: 10
SALES (est): 1.4MM **Privately Held**
SIC: 3494 Line strainers, for use in piping
systems

(G-7201)
INTELLINETICS INC
2190 Dividend Dr (43228-3806)
PHONE.............................614 388-8908
Fax: 614 850-2789
A Michael Chretien, *Ch of Bd*
Matthew L Chretien, *President*
Thomas D Moss, *Engineer*
Kendall D Gill, *CFO*
EMP: 15
SQ FT: 6,000
SALES (est): 2.6MM **Privately Held**
SIC: 7372 Prepackaged software; busi-
ness oriented computer software

(G-7202)
**INTERFACE LOGIC SYSTEMS
INC**
Also Called: Weighing Division
3311 E Livingston Ave (43227-1923)
PHONE.............................614 236-8388
Fax: 614 236-8122
Eli Sneward, *President*
Charles Libicki, *Senior VP*
Charles Wenger, *Vice Pres*
Harold Cheney, *Treasurer*
EMP: 9
SQ FT: 3,500
SALES (est): 1MM **Privately Held**
WEB: www.interfacelogic.com
SIC: 7629 3596 Electrical measuring in-
strument repair & calibration; scales &
balances, except laboratory

(G-7203)
**INTERIOR DNNAGE SPCIALITES
INC**
470 E Starr Ave (43201-3695)
PHONE.............................614 291-0900
Fax: 614 291-0929
Georgina Stevenson, *President*
Scott Stevenson, *Vice Pres*
EMP: 14
SQ FT: 35,000
SALES (est): 1.7MM **Privately Held**
WEB: www.idsinc-columbus.com
SIC: 3086 Plastics foam products

(G-7204)
INTERLINE BRANDS INC
2375 International St (43228-4622)
PHONE.............................614 527-9475
Fax: 614 527-9478
John Liapakis, *Manager*
EMP: 7
SALES (corp-wide): 94.6B **Publicly Held**
SIC: 3661 Carrier equipment, telephone or
telegraph
HQ: Interline Brands, Inc.
701 San Marco Blvd
Jacksonville FL 32207
904 421-1400

(G-7205)
**INTERNATIONAL BEVERAGE
WORKS**
5636 Moorgate Dr (43235-2506)
PHONE.............................614 798-5398
Fax: 614 798-5336
June M Slater, *President*
Jeff Slater, *Vice Pres*
Robert B Slater Jr, *Vice Pres*
EMP: 3
SALES (est): 419.6K **Privately Held**
SIC: 3585 5046 5078 Soda fountain &
beverage dispensing equipment & parts;
restaurant equipment & supplies; refriger-
ated beverage dispensers

(G-7206)
INTERNATIONAL PRODUCTS
Also Called: Ipsg
2701 Charter St Ste A (43228-4639)
PHONE.............................614 334-1500
EMP: 3
SALES (corp-wide): 2.9B **Privately Held**
SIC: 3571 Electronic computers
HQ: International Products Sourcing Group,
Inc.
4119 Leap Rd
Hilliard OH 43026
614 850-3000

(G-7207)
**INTERNATIONAL TRADE GROUP
INC**
2920 North Star Rd (43221-2961)
P.O. Box 800, Oxford (45056-0800)
PHONE.............................614 486-4634
James E Reider, *CEO*
EMP: 5
SALES (est): 591.1K **Privately Held**
SIC: 8742 5084 3469 3672 Management
consulting services; industrial machinery
& equipment; metal stampings; printed
circuit boards

(G-7208)
**INTERNTNAL TCHNCAL
CATINGS INC**
Also Called: Itc Manufacturing
845 E Markison Ave (43207-1388)
PHONE.............................614 449-6669
Judith Fernandez, *Branch Mgr*
EMP: 75
SALES (corp-wide): 61.5MM **Privately
Held**
SIC: 3496 3479 Shelving, made from pur-
chased wire; painting, coating & hot dip-
ping
PA: International Technical Coatings, Inc.
110 S 41st Ave
Phoenix AZ 85009
602 415-1400

(G-7209)
INTERSTATE TRUCKWAY INC
5440 Renner Rd (43228-8941)
PHONE.............................614 771-1220
Willy Walraven, *Branch Mgr*
EMP: 32
SALES (corp-wide): 68.6MM **Privately
Held**
WEB: www.itdsdedicated.com
SIC: 3799 5012 Trailers & trailer equip-
ment; automobiles & other motor vehicles
PA: Interstate Truckway Inc
1755 Dreman Ave
Cincinnati OH 45223
513 542-5500

(G-7210)
IPA LTD
Also Called: Zed Digital
700 Taylor Rd Ste 290 (43230-3539)
PHONE.............................614 523-3974
Sumithra Jagannath, *President*
EMP: 13 EST: 2014
SQ FT: 1,500
SALES (est): 267.4K **Privately Held**
SIC: 7371 7373 2741 7374 Custom com-
puter programming services; computer in-
tegrated systems design; ; computer
graphics service

(G-7211)
IRONFAB LLC
1771 Progress Ave (43207-1749)
PHONE.............................614 443-3900
Joey Stepleton, *President*
Paula Decker, *Manager*
Barbara Green, *Manager*
EMP: 13
SALES (est): 3.3MM **Privately Held**
SIC: 3441 Fabricated structural metal

(G-7212)
ISCO INC
6360 Fiesta Dr (43235-5205)
PHONE.............................614 792-2206
Fax: 614 792-1559
Brian D Amerine, *President*
Ivan R Amerine, *Chairman*
Kris Joseph, *Manager*
EMP: 10
SQ FT: 19,000
SALES (est): 930K **Privately Held**
WEB: www.iscoinc.com
SIC: 3599 Machine & other job shop work

(G-7213)
**ISOSTATIC PRESSING SVCS
LLC**
1205 S Columbus Arprt Rd (43207-4304)
PHONE.............................614 370-2140
Kenneth A Sprang,
EMP: 5
SALES (est): 456.9K **Privately Held**
SIC: 3398 Metal heat treating

(G-7214)
ISP CHEMICALS LLC
1979 Atlas St (43228-9645)
PHONE.............................614 876-3637
Dr Paul Taylor, *Director*
EMP: 70
SALES (corp-wide): 124.7MM **Privately
Held**
SIC: 2834 Pharmaceutical preparations
HQ: Isp Chemicals Llc
455 N Main St
Calvert City KY 42029
270 395-4165

(G-7215)
ITG BRANDS LLC
6740 Huntley Rd (43229-1064)
PHONE.............................614 431-0044
EMP: 3
SALES (corp-wide): 35.8B **Privately Held**
SIC: 2111 Cigarettes
HQ: Itg Brands, Llc
714 Green Valley Rd
Greensboro NC 27408
336 335-7000

(G-7216)
J AMERICA LLC
580 N 4th St Ste 620 (43215-2125)
PHONE.............................614 914-2091
EMP: 4
SALES (corp-wide): 9.1MM **Privately
Held**
SIC: 2329 2396 2395 Men's & boys'
sportswear & athletic clothing; automotive
& apparel trimmings; screen printing on
fabric articles; embroidery products, ex-
cept schiffli machine
HQ: J. America, Llc
1200 Mason Ct
Webberville MI 48892
517 521-2525

(G-7217)
J E JOHNSON PALLETT INC
1465 E 17th Ave (43219-1082)
P.O. Box 11623 (43211-0623)
PHONE.............................614 424-9663
Fax: 614 424-9665
EMP: 8 EST: 1991
SQ FT: 20,000
SALES (est): 730K **Privately Held**
SIC: 2448 5999 Rebuilds & Recycles
Wood Pallets

(G-7218)
**J LIU OF UPPER ARLINGTON
INC**
7765 Wavetree Ct (43235-4529)
PHONE.............................614 313-1268

Jiechun Liu, *Principal*
EMP: 6
SALES (est): 531.9K **Privately Held**
SIC: 3131 Uppers

(G-7219)
J S C PUBLISHING
958 King Ave (43212-2655)
PHONE..................................614 424-6911
Joe Paxton, *Owner*
EMP: 6
SALES (est): 225K **Privately Held**
SIC: 2731 Pamphlets: publishing & printing

(G-7220)
JACK PINE STUDIO
420 1/2 E 5th Ave (43201-2877)
PHONE..................................614 291-0699
Jack Pine, *Owner*
EMP: 3
SALES (est): 52.9K **Privately Held**
SIC: 3229 Glass tubes & tubing

(G-7221)
JACOBI CARBONS INC
432 Mccormick Blvd (43213-1525)
PHONE..................................215 546-3900
Bill Eubanks, *President*
Patty Augustyn, *Sales Mgr*
Bonnie Roth, *Accounts Mgr*
▲ **EMP:** 35
SALES (est): 12.1MM
SALES (corp-wide): 11.3B **Privately Held**
SIC: 2895 Carbon black
HQ: Jacobi Carbons Ab
Slojdaregatan 1
Kalmar 393 5
480 417-550

(G-7222)
JAIN AMERICA FOODS INC (HQ)
Also Called: Jain Americas
1819 Walcutt Rd Ste 1 (43228-9149)
PHONE..................................614 850-9400
Anil Jain, *CEO*
Nerinder Gupta, *COO*
John Donovan, *CFO*
Jon Silver, *Regl Sales Mgr*
Mita Ramanathan, *Manager*
◆ **EMP:** 7
SQ FT: 30,000
SALES (est): 26.4MM **Privately Held**
SIC: 3086 2821 3081 Plastics foam products; molding compounds, plastics; polyvinyl film & sheet

(G-7223)
JAIN AMERICA HOLDINGS INC ✪
1819 Walcutt Rd Ste 1 (43228-9149)
PHONE..................................614 850-9400
Anil Jain, *CEO*
Nerinder Gupta, *COO*
Viresh Tater, *Opers Mgr*
◆ **EMP:** 100 **EST:** 2016
SQ FT: 30,000
SALES (est): 20MM
SALES (corp-wide): 616.1MM **Privately Held**
SIC: 3086 2821 3081 Plastics foam products; molding compounds, plastics; polyvinyl film & sheet
PA: Jain Irrigation Systems Limited
Jain Plastic Park,
Jalgaon MH 42500
257 225-8022

(G-7224)
JAMES EASTWOOD
663 Harmon Plz (43223-3341)
PHONE..................................614 444-1340
James Eastwood, *Owner*
EMP: 4
SQ FT: 3,000
SALES (est): 291.7K **Privately Held**
SIC: 3599 Machine shop, jobbing & repair

(G-7225)
JAMES MCGUIRE
190 Ziegler Ave (43207-3752)
PHONE..................................614 483-9825
James McGuire, *Principal*
EMP: 3
SALES (est): 210.1K **Privately Held**
SIC: 3081 Unsupported plastics film & sheet

(G-7226)
JAMES OSHEA
326 Richards Rd (43214-3740)
PHONE..................................614 262-3188
James Oshea, *Principal*
EMP: 3
SALES (est): 161K **Privately Held**
SIC: 2711 Newspapers

(G-7227)
JANSZEN LOUDSPEAKER LTD
480 Trade Rd (43204-6241)
PHONE..................................614 448-1811
Sungok Yoon, *President*
David A Janszen, *Mng Member*
EMP: 3
SALES: 150K **Privately Held**
WEB: www.janszenloudspeaker.com
SIC: 3651 Speaker systems; household audio equipment

(G-7228)
JAX WAX INC
3145 E 17th Ave (43219-2329)
PHONE..................................614 476-6769
Jack Minor, *President*
EMP: 10 **EST:** 1993
SQ FT: 5,600
SALES (est): 1.7MM **Privately Held**
WEB: www.jaxwax.com
SIC: 2842 Specialty cleaning, polishes & sanitation goods; automobile polish

(G-7229)
JE GROTE COMPANY INC (PA)
1160 Gahanna Pkwy (43230-6615)
PHONE..................................614 868-8414
Fax: 614 863-1647
James E Grote, *Ch of Bd*
Bob Grote, *President*
Tom Mathues, *Vice Pres*
John Seifert, *Safety Mgr*
David Waterman, *Mfg Spvr*
◆ **EMP:** 100
SQ FT: 73,500
SALES (est): 32.1MM **Privately Held**
WEB: www.grotecompany.com
SIC: 3589 3556 Cooking equipment, commercial; food products machinery

(G-7230)
JET CONTAINER COMPANY
1033 Brentnell Ave # 100 (43219-2190)
PHONE..................................614 444-2133
Fax: 614 444-8822
Stephen J Schmitt, *Vice Pres*
Mike Schmitt, *CFO*
Cleo Grant, *Bookkeeper*
Richard Prohl, *Mng Member*
EMP: 47
SQ FT: 175,000
SALES (est): 13MM **Privately Held**
WEB: www.jetcontainer.com
SIC: 2653 Boxes, corrugated: made from purchased materials

(G-7231)
JET FUEL TECH INC
100 E Broad St Fl 16 (43215-3607)
PHONE..................................614 463-1986
Perry Jeter Jr, *Owner*
EMP: 3
SALES (est): 164.4K **Privately Held**
SIC: 2911 Jet fuels

(G-7232)
JETCOAT LLC
472 Brehl Ave (43223-1973)
P.O. Box 23054 (43223-0054)
PHONE..................................800 394-0047
Dawn Fulton, *Accountant*
David L Thorson, *Mng Member*
Gary Roshon, *Manager*
EMP: 20
SQ FT: 5,000
SALES (est): 4.9MM
SALES (corp-wide): 92.9MM **Privately Held**
WEB: www.sealmaster.net
SIC: 2891 Sealants
PA: Thorworks Industries, Inc.
2520 Campbell St
Sandusky OH 44870
419 626-4375

(G-7233)
JKI SALES
3815 Gabrielle Dr (43234)
PHONE..................................614 581-5498
John Kanoski, *Principal*
EMP: 4
SALES (est): 140K **Privately Held**
SIC: 2389 Apparel & accessories

(G-7234)
JLS FUNERAL HOME
2322 Randy Ct (43232-8470)
PHONE..................................614 625-1220
Jimmie Spurlock, *Principal*
EMP: 10
SALES (est): 420K **Privately Held**
SIC: 2396 5087 7389 Veils & veiling: bridal, funeral, etc.; cemetery & funeral directors' equipment & supplies;

(G-7235)
JMAC INC (PA)
200 W Nationwide Blvd # 1 (43215-2561)
PHONE..................................614 436-2418
John P McConnell, *Ch of Bd*
Michael A Priest, *President*
George N Corey, *Principal*
Tod Wynkoop, *Accountant*
▲ **EMP:** 18
SQ FT: 6,000
SALES (est): 96MM **Privately Held**
WEB: www.j-mac.com
SIC: 3325 5198 7999 5511 Steel foundries; paints; ice skating rink operation; automobiles, new & used; financial management for business

(G-7236)
JOB NEWS USA
150 E Campus View Blvd # 120 (43235-6602)
PHONE..................................614 310-1700
Marsha Olivieri, *Principal*
Mary C Griffith, *Accounts Mgr*
EMP: 12
SALES (est): 496.7K **Privately Held**
SIC: 2711 Newspapers, publishing & printing

(G-7237)
JOE PAXTON
Also Called: Graphic Awards
960 King Ave (43212-2655)
PHONE..................................614 424-9000
Fax: 614 424-9005
Joe Paxton, *Owner*
Brett Paxton, *Vice Pres*
Diana Blessing, *Sales Dir*
Steve Baden, *Graphic Designe*
EMP: 5
SQ FT: 5,100
SALES: 900K **Privately Held**
WEB: www.graphicawards.net
SIC: 2759 5999 3993 Screen printing; trophies & plaques; signs & advertising specialties

(G-7238)
JOHN B ALLEN
2346 Brandon Rd (43221-3803)
PHONE..................................614 488-7122
John B Allen, *Owner*
EMP: 5
SALES (est): 440.3K **Privately Held**
WEB: www.allen-systems.com
SIC: 3679 3674 7371 Electronic circuits; computer logic modules; computer software development

(G-7239)
JOHNNY ON THE SPOT INC (PA)
4522 Lockbourne Rd (43207-4231)
P.O. Box 753 (43216-0753)
PHONE..................................614 497-1776
William A Reynolds, *President*
EMP: 20
SQ FT: 6,300
SALES: 750K **Privately Held**
SIC: 7359 3799 3713 Portable toilet rental; trailers & trailer equipment; tank truck bodies

(G-7240)
JOHNSON BROTHERS HOLDINGS LLC
Also Called: Qkardz.com
717 Oak St (43205-1011)
P.O. Box 83282 (43203-0282)
PHONE..................................614 868-5273
Nathan K Johnson Sr, *Mng Member*
Beaux Johnson,
EMP: 4 **EST:** 2007
SALES: 100K **Privately Held**
SIC: 7336 1731 4813 7389 Commercial art & graphic design; telephone & telephone equipment installation; local & long distance telephone communications; presorted mail service; flags & banners; fabric printing & stamping

(G-7241)
JOHNSONS REAL ICE CREAM CO
Also Called: Wilcoxon, James H Jr
2728 E Main St (43209-2534)
PHONE..................................614 231-0014
Fax: 614 231-5450
James H Wilcoxon Jr, *President*
EMP: 20
SQ FT: 4,600
SALES (est): 1.1MM **Privately Held**
SIC: 5812 5143 2024 Ice cream stands or dairy bars; dairy products, except dried or canned; ice cream & frozen desserts

(G-7242)
JOHNSTON-MOREHOUSE-DICKEY CO
4647 Poth Rd (43213-1396)
PHONE..................................614 866-0452
Glenn Dupilka Jr, *Manager*
EMP: 5
SALES (corp-wide): 34.3MM **Privately Held**
SIC: 2299 3089 5082 Narrow woven fabrics: linen, jute, hemp & ramie; plastic hardware & building products; contractors' materials
PA: Johnston-Morehouse-Dickey Co Inc
5401 Progress Blvd
Bethel Park PA 15102
412 833-7100

(G-7243)
JOINT VUE LLC
1275 Kinnear Rd (43212-1180)
PHONE..................................614 640-3350
Ray Wasielewski,
EMP: 5
SALES (est): 366.9K **Privately Held**
SIC: 3842 Surgical appliances & supplies

(G-7244)
JOSEPH A PANICO & SONS INC (PA)
4605 E 5th Ave (43219-1819)
PHONE..................................614 235-3188
John E Panico, *President*
Joe Panico, *Vice Pres*
EMP: 4
SALES (est): 450.1K **Privately Held**
WEB: www.panico.org
SIC: 3993 Advertising novelties

(G-7245)
JOSEPH T RYERSON & SON INC
555 N Yearling Rd (43213-1395)
P.O. Box 145484, Cincinnati (45250-5484)
PHONE..................................513 542-5800
Fax: 513 542-4413
Edward J Lehner, *President*
Mark Oswald, *General Mgr*
Phil Kennedy, *Sales Staff*
Kurt Balder, *Clerk*
EMP: 80
SQ FT: 480,000
SALES (corp-wide): 2.8B **Publicly Held**
SIC: 5051 3444 Iron & steel (ferrous) products; aluminum bars, rods, ingots, sheets, pipes, plates, etc.; sheet metalwork
HQ: Joseph T. Ryerson & Son, Inc.
227 W Monroe St Fl 27
Chicago IL 60606
312 292-5000

(G-7246)
JRS HYDRAULIC & WELDING
Also Called: J R S Hydraulic & Welding
2774 Groveport Rd (43207-3149)
PHONE..................................614 497-1100
J R Stansell, *Owner*
EMP: 3
SQ FT: 1,500
SALES (est): 120K **Privately Held**
SIC: 7692 7699 3599 Welding repair; hy-
draulic equipment repair; machine shop,
jobbing & repair

(G-7247)
JUANA WILLIAMS
Also Called: Revelation Fmly Child Care Ctr
2850 Fisher Rd (43204-3538)
PHONE..................................614 351-9844
Juana Williams, *Principal*
EMP: 4
SQ FT: 3,000
SALES (est): 179.6K **Privately Held**
SIC: 2048 Feed premixes

(G-7248)
JUDITH LEIBER LLC (PA)
4300 E 5th Ave (43219-1816)
PHONE..................................614 449-4217
Wanda Ucet, *Payroll Mgr*
Mary Gleason,
EMP: 20 EST: 2000
SALES: 19MM **Privately Held**
SIC: 3171 Women's handbags & purses

(G-7249)
K B PRINTING
Also Called: Bizzy Bee
1199 Goodale Blvd (43212-3730)
PHONE..................................614 771-1222
Fax: 614 228-3041
Chris Schmelzer, *Principal*
EMP: 5 EST: 2010
SALES (est): 270K **Privately Held**
SIC: 2752 Commercial printing, litho-
graphic

(G-7250)
K EFFS INC
2117 S High St (43207-2428)
PHONE..................................614 443-0586
Fax: 614 443-7818
K R Gay, *President*
Kenneth Robert Gay, *President*
Elizabeth Sue Gay, *Vice Pres*
Elizabeth Gay, *Controller*
EMP: 15
SQ FT: 35,000
SALES (est): 2.7MM **Privately Held**
WEB: www.keffs.net
SIC: 3496 Shelving, made from purchased
wire

(G-7251)
KARN MEATS INC
Also Called: Central Market Specialty Meats
922 Taylor Ave (43219-2558)
PHONE..................................614 252-3712
Fax: 614 252-8273
Richard Karn, *President*
Mike Furr, *Purch Mgr*
Lora Leach, *Office Mgr*
Duff Klamfoth, *Maintence Staff*
EMP: 50
SQ FT: 50,000
SALES (est): 8.2MM **Privately Held**
SIC: 2011 2013 Meat packing plants;
sausages & other prepared meats

(G-7252)
KCG INC
Also Called: Magnum Products
3939 E 5th Ave (43219-1810)
PHONE..................................614 238-9450
Fax: 614 238-9465
Mitch Swick, *Sales Staff*
Todd Wellman, *Sales Executive*
Ed Hook, *Manager*
EMP: 5
SALES (corp-wide): 361.4MM **Privately
Held**
WEB: www.kcg-inc.com
SIC: 3272 5032 2891 Building materials,
except block or brick: concrete; drywall
materials; adhesives & sealants

PA: Kcg, Inc.
15720 W 108th St Ste 100
Lenexa KS 66219
913 438-4142

(G-7253)
KEEBLER COMPANY
200 E Campus View Blvd # 200
(43235-4678)
PHONE..................................614 836-3094
Ray Mangini, *Manager*
EMP: 50
SQ FT: 6,000
SALES (corp-wide): 13B **Publicly Held**
WEB: www.keebler.com
SIC: 2052 Cookies
HQ: Keebler Company
1 Kellogg Sq
Battle Creek MI 49017
269 961-2000

(G-7254)
**KENAN ADVANTAGE GROUP
INC**
Also Called: Advantage Truck Trailers
500 Manor Park Dr (43228-9396)
PHONE..................................614 878-4050
Rick Brinkman, *Vice Pres*
Dan Peckinpaugh, *Manager*
EMP: 34
SALES (corp-wide): 1.7B **Privately Held**
SIC: 3715 Truck trailers
PA: The Kenan Advantage Group Inc
4366 Mount Pleasant St Nw
North Canton OH 44720
877 999-2524

(G-7255)
KENDALL HOLDINGS LTD (PA)
Also Called: Phpk Technologies
2111 Builders Pl (43204-4886)
PHONE..................................614 486-4750
Richard Coleman, *Partner*
Ken Krienbrink, *Vice Pres*
Steve Willming, *Design Engr*
Julie Battles, *Controller*
Tim Savely, *Marketing Mgr*
EMP: 45
SQ FT: 60,000
SALES (est): 10.8MM **Privately Held**
SIC: 3443 8711 Fabricated plate work
(boiler shop); engineering services

(G-7256)
**KENOSHA BEEF
INTERNATIONAL LTD**
Birchwood Meats & Provisions
1821 Dividend Dr (43228-3848)
PHONE..................................614 771-1330
Fax: 614 771-9590
Ken Fudy, *Principal*
Ken Fude, *COO*
Mike Marquardt, *Vice Pres*
Troy Maynard, *Opers Staff*
Marty Roberts, *Chief Mktg Ofcr*
EMP: 107
SQ FT: 10,000
SALES (corp-wide): 184.3MM **Privately
Held**
WEB: www.bwfoods.com
SIC: 5147 2013 Meats & meat products;
sausages & other prepared meats
PA: Kenosha Beef International, Ltd.
3111 152nd Ave
Kenosha WI 53144
800 541-1684

(G-7257)
KENWEL PRINTERS INC
4272 Indianola Ave (43214-2891)
PHONE..................................614 261-1011
Fax: 614 268-3299
David G Starner, *President*
Michael Fisher, *Senior VP*
Mike Fisher, *Vice Pres*
Michael O Hull, *Vice Pres*
Doug Shroyer, *Controller*
EMP: 36 EST: 1969
SQ FT: 15,000
SALES (est): 7.5MM **Privately Held**
WEB: www.kenwel.com
SIC: 2752 2789 2759 Commercial print-
ing, offset; bookbinding & related work;
commercial printing

(G-7258)
KEVER INCORPORATED
Also Called: Kever Printing & Promotions
4581 Poth Rd (43213-1327)
PHONE..................................614 552-9000
Fax: 614 552-9001
Maureen Egan-Simons, *President*
Roger Simons, *Corp Secy*
EMP: 5
SQ FT: 6,000
SALES (est): 500K **Privately Held**
WEB: www.keverinc.com
SIC: 2752 Commercial printing, offset

(G-7259)
KEY BLUE PRINTS INC
6180 Cleveland Ave (43231-1614)
PHONE..................................614 899-6180
Fax: 614 899-6786
Kristin Kinney, *Branch Mgr*
EMP: 3
SALES (corp-wide): 29.1MM **Privately
Held**
SIC: 3555 Printing presses
PA: Key Blue Prints, Inc.
195 E Livingston Ave
Columbus OH 43215
614 228-3285

(G-7260)
KEY FINISHES LLC
727 Harrison Dr (43204-3507)
PHONE..................................614 351-8393
James H McCurdy, *CFO*
Tod Powers,
Robert Johnson,
▲ EMP: 9
SALES (est): 880K **Privately Held**
SIC: 3399 Powder, metal

(G-7261)
**KEYSTONE GRANITE AND TILE
INC**
2747 Westbelt Dr (43228-3861)
PHONE..................................614 541-9749
Ahmet Ozcan, *Principal*
Mustafa Kol, *Principal*
EMP: 9
SALES (est): 296.2K **Privately Held**
SIC: 3281 Curbing, granite or stone

(G-7262)
**KIRK EXCAVATING &
CONSTRUCTION**
821 Stimmel Rd (43223-2907)
P.O. Box 8, Grove City (43123-0008)
PHONE..................................614 444-4008
Fax: 614 444-4408
Charles Kirk, *President*
Tamara Pleskach, *Vice Pres*
Pam Schmittler, *Controller*
Tamara Pleshach, *Manager*
EMP: 20
SALES (est): 7.8MM **Privately Held**
SIC: 1794 1381 Excavation work; direc-
tional drilling oil & gas wells

(G-7263)
KISSICAKES - N-SWEETS LLC
7660 Silver Fox Dr (43235-1835)
PHONE..................................614 940-2779
George T Kissi, *Principal*
EMP: 6
SALES (est): 439.5K **Privately Held**
SIC: 2053 Cakes, bakery: frozen

(G-7264)
KLOSTERMAN BAKING CO
2655 Courtright Rd (43232-4838)
PHONE..................................614 338-8111
Fax: 614 338-8114
Ron Hostelley, *Manager*
EMP: 6
SALES (corp-wide): 209.5MM **Privately
Held**
SIC: 2051 Breads, rolls & buns
PA: Klosterman Baking Co.
4760 Paddock Rd
Cincinnati OH 45229
513 242-5667

(G-7265)
KOKOSING MATERIALS INC
4755 S High St (43207-4028)
P.O. Box 334, Fredericktown (43019-0334)
PHONE..................................614 491-1199
Fax: 614 491-1638
Bill Burgett, *President*
Bob Bailey, *Vice Pres*
EMP: 50
SALES (est): 5.7MM **Privately Held**
SIC: 2951 Asphalt & asphaltic paving mix-
tures (not from refineries)

(G-7266)
KRAFT OF WRITING
46 Webster Park Ave (43214-3513)
PHONE..................................614 620-2476
EMP: 6
SALES (est): 487.2K **Privately Held**
SIC: 2022 Processed cheese

(G-7267)
KRIGBAUM INC
Also Called: Signs By Tomorrow
76 N Stygler Rd (43230-2435)
PHONE..................................614 478-6472
Fax: 614 478-6473
Richard Krigbaum, *President*
Marilyn Krigbaum, *Vice Pres*
EMP: 20
SQ FT: 2,400
SALES (est): 1.7MM **Privately Held**
WEB: www.krigbaum.com
SIC: 3993 Signs & advertising specialties

(G-7268)
**KRISPY KREME DOUGHNUT
CORP**
Also Called: Krispy Kreme 322
3690 W Dblin Granville Rd (43235-7987)
PHONE..................................614 798-0812
Fax: 614 798-0861
James Lewis, *Manager*
EMP: 12
SQ FT: 2,158
SALES (corp-wide): 518.7MM **Privately
Held**
WEB: www.kkreme.com
SIC: 5461 2051 Doughnuts; pastries, e.g.
danish: except frozen
HQ: Krispy Kreme Doughnut Corp
259 S Stratford Rd
Winston Salem NC 27103
336 724-2484

(G-7269)
**KROEHLER FURNITURE MFG
CO INC**
4300 E 5th Ave (43219-1816)
P.O. Box 1178, Conover NC (28613-1178)
PHONE..................................828 459-9865
Jay Schottenstein, *Ch of Bd*
David Fadlowki, *General Mgr*
David Sadlowski, *Vice Pres*
Larry Wright, *Plant Mgr*
David Zimmer, *Purchasing*
▲ EMP: 400
SQ FT: 300,000
SALES (est): 58MM **Privately Held**
SIC: 2512 Upholstered household furniture

(G-7270)
KROGER CO
Also Called: Columbus Bakery
457 Cleveland Ave (43215-1725)
P.O. Box 83586 (43203-0586)
PHONE..................................614 462-2000
Fax: 614 462-2043
John Masa, *Managing Dir*
Jerry Moore, *Safety Mgr*
Jerry Jenkins, *Purchasing*
Greg Gruenwald, *QC Dir*
Bobby Nguyen, *Engineer*
EMP: 60
SALES (corp-wide): 115.3B **Publicly
Held**
SIC: 5411 2099 2096 2052 Supermar-
kets, chain; food preparations; potato
chips & similar snacks; cookies & crack-
ers
PA: The Kroger Co
1014 Vine St Ste 1000
Cincinnati OH 45202
513 762-4000

▲ = Import ▼=Export
◆ =Import/Export

(G-7271)
KROGER CO
3417 N High St (43214-4051)
PHONE......................614 263-1766
Fax: 614 263-1798
John Ettenhofer, *Branch Mgr*
Melissa Prince Jr, *Pharmacist*
Molly Davis, *Executive*
EMP: 180
SALES (corp-wide): 115.3B **Publicly Held**
WEB: www.kroger.com
SIC: 5411 5912 2051 Supermarkets, chain; drug stores & proprietary stores; bread, cake & related products
PA: The Kroger Co
1014 Vine St Ste 1000
Cincinnati OH 45202
513 762-4000

(G-7272)
KROGER CO
7000 E Broad St (43213-1519)
PHONE......................614 575-3742
Fax: 614 575-3746
Denise Maynard, *Branch Mgr*
Denise Kirkwood, *Manager*
EMP: 250
SALES (corp-wide): 115.3B **Publicly Held**
WEB: www.kroger.com
SIC: 5411 5912 2051 Supermarkets, chain; drug stores & proprietary stores; bread, cake & related products
PA: The Kroger Co
1014 Vine St Ste 1000
Cincinnati OH 45202
513 762-4000

(G-7273)
KRONOS INCORPORATED
1 Easton Oval Ste 350 (43219-6043)
PHONE......................614 528-2200
Fax: 614 478-1806
Edward Wycuff, *Accounts Mgr*
Deb Garberson, *Manager*
EMP: 18
SALES (corp-wide): 1.3B **Privately Held**
WEB: www.kronos.com
SIC: 7372 Prepackaged software
HQ: Kronos Incorporated
297 Billerica Rd
Chelmsford MA 01824
978 250-9800

(G-7274)
KYRON TOOL AND MACHINE CO INC
2900 Banwick Rd (43232-3838)
PHONE......................614 231-6000
Fax: 614 294-1673
Charles P Haueisen, *President*
Randal Hauesein, *Vice Pres*
Rosemary Hauesein, *Treasurer*
Jacky Kellogg, *Manager*
EMP: 10 **EST:** 1949
SQ FT: 50,000
SALES (est): 1.4MM **Privately Held**
SIC: 3599 Machine shop, jobbing & repair

(G-7275)
L BRANDS INC
Limited
3 Limited Pkwy (43230-1467)
P.O. Box 182145 (43218-2145)
PHONE......................614 479-2000
Fax: 614 224-4002
EMP: 117
SALES (corp-wide): 12.1B **Publicly Held**
SIC: 5641 2389 Ret Child's/Infant's Wear Mfg Apparel/Accessories
PA: L Brands, Inc.
3 Limited Pkwy
Columbus OH 43230
614 415-7000

(G-7276)
L C G MACHINE & TOOL INC
2923 Grasmere Ave (43224-4155)
PHONE......................614 261-1651
Lowell C Garrett, *CEO*
▼ **EMP:** 3
SALES: 80K **Privately Held**
SIC: 3469 Machine parts, stamped or pressed metal

(G-7277)
L H MARSHALL CO
1601 Woodland Ave (43219-1135)
PHONE......................614 294-6433
Fax: 614 294-0297
Dorothy B Roberts, *President*
Courtney Roberts, *Vice Pres*
Chris Dale, *Opers Mgr*
Janet Forgue, *Treasurer*
Cynthia R Padilla, *Admin Sec*
EMP: 18 **EST:** 1927
SALES (est): 4.3MM **Privately Held**
WEB: www.lhmarshall.com
SIC: 3829 Thermocouples
PA: The Roberts Group Inc
2646 Alliston Ct
Columbus OH 43220
614 486-0497

(G-7278)
L3 AVIATION PRODUCTS INC
Also Called: Goodrich Avionics
1105 Schrock Rd Ste 800 (43229-1154)
PHONE......................614 825-2001
Billie Stevens, *Manager*
EMP: 60
SALES (corp-wide): 10.5B **Publicly Held**
SIC: 3812 8711 Aircraft flight instruments; gyroscopes; automatic pilots; aircraft; radar systems & equipment; engineering services
HQ: L3 Aviation Products, Inc.
5353 52nd St Se
Grand Rapids MI 49512
616 977-6837

(G-7279)
LA VOZ HISPANIA NEWSPAPER
3552 Sullivant Ave (43204-1106)
PHONE......................614 274-5505
Alex Flores, *President*
EMP: 3
SQ FT: 960
SALES (est): 223.7K **Privately Held**
SIC: 2711 Newspapers, publishing & printing

(G-7280)
LAIRD PLASTICS INC
Also Called: Branch 49
2220 International St (43228-4630)
PHONE......................614 272-0777
Fax: 614 272-1677
Edward Bartlett, *Sales Staff*
Roger Plizga, *Manager*
EMP: 10
SALES (corp-wide): 446.4MM **Privately Held**
SIC: 5162 3089 Plastics materials; plastics sheets & rods; plastics film; windows, plastic
PA: Laird Plastics, Inc.
5800 Campus Circle Dr E
Irving TX 75063
469 299-7000

(G-7281)
LAMBERT SHEET METAL INC
Also Called: Lsmi
3776 E 5th Ave (43219-1807)
PHONE......................614 237-0384
Fax: 614 237-0384
Carl Lambert, *President*
Betty Lambert, *Vice Pres*
EMP: 15
SQ FT: 10,000
SALES (est): 3.4MM **Privately Held**
WEB: www.smcco.org
SIC: 3444 Sheet metal specialties, not stamped

(G-7282)
LANCASTER COMMERCIAL PDTS LLC
2353 Westbrooke Dr (43228-9557)
P.O. Box 870, Worthington (43085-0870)
PHONE......................740 286-5081
Kenneth Evans, *President*
◆ **EMP:** 34
SALES (est): 16.9MM **Privately Held**
SIC: 5085 3089 Industrial supplies; injection molding of plastics

(G-7283)
LANDON VAULT COMPANY
1477 Frebis Ave (43206-3763)
PHONE......................614 443-5505
Martin Pehrson, *President*
Randy Howard, *Superintendent*
Autumn Epperson, *Admin Sec*
EMP: 15 **EST:** 1920
SQ FT: 3,600
SALES: 1.2MM **Privately Held**
SIC: 3272 Burial vaults, concrete or pre-cast terrazzo

(G-7284)
LANG STONE COMPANY INC (PA)
4099 E 5th Ave (43219-1812)
P.O. Box 360747 (43236-0747)
PHONE......................614 235-4099
Fax: 614 224-5264
E Dean Coffman, *President*
Bryan Bragg, *COO*
Joan First, *VP Admin*
Joann Coffman, *Vice Pres*
Tom Coffman, *Vice Pres*
▲ **EMP:** 55 **EST:** 1856
SQ FT: 10,000
SALES (est): 20.3MM **Privately Held**
WEB: www.langstone.com
SIC: 5032 5211 3281 3272 Building stone; marble building stone; granite building stone; lumber & other building materials; masonry materials & supplies; cut stone & stone products; concrete products; crushed & broken limestone

(G-7285)
LANZ PRINTING CO INC
257 Cleveland Ave (43215-2107)
PHONE......................614 221-1724
Fax: 614 221-1734
Michael Llaneza, *President*
Mary Llaneza, *Vice Pres*
EMP: 3 **EST:** 1968
SQ FT: 10,000
SALES: 450K **Privately Held**
SIC: 2752 Commercial printing, offset

(G-7286)
LAPHAM-HICKEY STEEL CORP
753 Marion Rd (43207-2554)
PHONE......................614 443-4881
James Derry, *COO*
Gary West, *Plant Mgr*
George Keel, *Safety Mgr*
Casey Stedman, *Accounts Mgr*
Joni Fritz, *Sales Associate*
EMP: 25
SQ FT: 110,000
SALES (corp-wide): 305.3MM **Privately Held**
WEB: www.lapham-hickey.com
SIC: 5051 3443 3441 3398 Steel; fabricated plate work (boiler shop); fabricated structural metal; metal heat treating; blast furnaces & steel mills
PA: Lapham-Hickey Steel Corp.
5500 W 73rd St
Chicago IL 60638
708 496-6111

(G-7287)
LASTING IMPRESSION LLC
4415 Berthstone Dr (43231-8722)
PHONE......................614 806-1186
Kayla Davila,
EMP: 5
SALES (est): 390.1K **Privately Held**
SIC: 2599 Bar furniture

(G-7288)
LATORRE CONCRETE CNSTR INC
850 N Cassady Ave (43219-2298)
PHONE......................614 257-1401
Mark Latorre, *President*
Anthony Latorre, *Admin Sec*
EMP: 25
SQ FT: 11,000
SALES: 2MM **Privately Held**
WEB: www.latorreconcrete.com
SIC: 3272 Concrete products

(G-7289)
LEAR CORPORATION
2181 International St (43228-4631)
PHONE......................614 850-8630
Joe Mauri, *Manager*
EMP: 15
SALES (corp-wide): 18.5B **Publicly Held**
WEB: www.lear.com
SIC: 2531 Seats, automobile
PA: Lear Corporation
21557 Telegraph Rd
Southfield MI 48033
248 447-1500

(G-7290)
LEGENDARY INK INC
1559 Granville St (43203-1719)
PHONE......................614 766-5101
Steve Wolever, *President*
Nick Arnold, *Manager*
EMP: 3
SALES (est): 310K **Privately Held**
SIC: 2759 Commercial printing

(G-7291)
LENS AC (PA)
4265 Diplomacy Dr (43228-3834)
PHONE......................888 248-5367
Fax: 614 291-8154
Peter Clarkson, *CEO*
Philip Dietrich, *Principal*
Elise Laase, *Buyer*
Kelli Ford, *Accounting Dir*
Amanda Jones, *Business Anlyst*
▲ **EMP:** 21
SALES (est): 5.6MM **Privately Held**
SIC: 3827 5048 Optical instruments & lenses; contact lenses

(G-7292)
LIEBERT CORPORATION (DH)
Also Called: Vertiv
1050 Dearborn Dr (43085-4709)
P.O. Box 29186 (43229-0186)
PHONE......................614 888-0246
Fax: 614 841-6973
Steve Hassell, *President*
Robert P Bauer, *President*
Robert Yopko, *President*
Dominique Fourrier, *General Mgr*
Kevin Harris, *Managing Dir*
◆ **EMP:** 1300
SQ FT: 330,000
SALES (est): 1B
SALES (corp-wide): 15.2B **Privately Held**
WEB: www.liebert.com
SIC: 3585 3613 7629 Air conditioning equipment, complete; regulators, power; electronic equipment repair
HQ: Vertiv Group Corporation
1050 Dearborn Dr
Columbus OH 43085
614 888-0246

(G-7293)
LIEBERT NORTH AMERICA INC
Also Called: Vertiv
1050 Dearborn Dr (43085-4709)
P.O. Box 29186 (43229-0186)
PHONE......................614 888-0246
Robert P Bauer, *President*
James Good, *Vice Pres*
Don Morris, *Credit Staff*
EMP: 1800
SQ FT: 22,000
SALES (est): 187.7MM
SALES (corp-wide): 15.2B **Privately Held**
WEB: www.gotoemerson.com
SIC: 3699 3585 Electrical equipment & supplies; refrigeration & heating equipment
HQ: Liebert Corporation
1050 Dearborn Dr
Columbus OH 43085
614 888-0246

(G-7294)
LIFE SUPPORT DEVELOPMENT LTD
777 Dearborn Park Ln R (43085-5746)
PHONE......................614 221-1765
Cheryl Krueger, *President*
David Zamore, *Treasurer*
Dillon Beck, *Director*
EMP: 8

SALES (est): 1MM **Privately Held**
SIC: 2086 Fruit drinks (less than 100% juice): packaged in cans, etc.

(G-7295)
LIGHTING SOLUTIONS GROUP LLC
Also Called: Specgrade Led
153 Outerbelt St (43213-1548)
PHONE..................................614 868-5337
Doug Lauck, *Mng Member*
Rick Nathans,
▲ EMP: 10
SALES (est): 844.4K **Privately Held**
SIC: 3648 Lighting equipment

(G-7296)
LIND STONEWORKS LTD
175 Oberlin Ct N (43230-2872)
PHONE..................................614 866-9733
Fax: 614 866-9732
James E Lind, *Partner*
Vincent Lind, *Partner*
▲ EMP: 12
SQ FT: 17,000
SALES (est): 1.6MM **Privately Held**
SIC: 3281 Cut stone & stone products

(G-7297)
LINDE GAS NORTH AMERICA LLC
Also Called: Lifegas
7029 Huntley Rd (43229-1099)
PHONE..................................614 846-7048
Fax: 614 846-7085
Cindy Fenton, *Branch Mgr*
EMP: 19
SALES (corp-wide): 17.9B **Privately Held**
SIC: 2813 Nitrogen; oxygen, compressed or liquefied
HQ: Linde Gas North America Llc
　　200 Somerset Corp Blvd # 7000
　　Bridgewater NJ 08807
　　908 464-8100

(G-7298)
LINEBACKER INC
1275 Kinnear Rd (43212-1180)
PHONE..................................614 340-1446
David A Sybert MD, *CEO*
Curt Sybert, *Director*
EMP: 4
SALES (est): 215.1K **Privately Held**
SIC: 3999 Manufacturing industries

(G-7299)
LINEN CARE PLUS INC
84 N Glenwood Ave (43222-1241)
PHONE..................................614 224-1791
Fax: 614 224-2738
Lindsey Hayman, *Owner*
Pam Conruly, *Owner*
EMP: 10 EST: 1979
SALES (est): 854.4K **Privately Held**
SIC: 3582 7218 7213 Dryers, laundry: commercial, including coin-operated; industrial launderers; linen supply

(G-7300)
LIQUI-BOX CORPORATION (PA)
480 Schrock Rd Ste G (43229-1092)
PHONE..................................614 888-9280
Ken Swanson, *President*
Greg Gard, *Senior VP*
Anthony Rizzo, *Senior VP*
Dave Klopp, *Vice Pres*
Lou Marmo, *CFO*
◆ EMP: 65 EST: 1963
SQ FT: 63,000
SALES (est): 497.5MM **Privately Held**
WEB: www.liquibox.com
SIC: 2673 3585 3089 3081 Plastic bags: made from purchased materials; soda fountain & beverage dispensing equipment & parts; plastic containers, except foam; blow molded finished plastic products; injection molded finished plastic products; plastic film & sheet; mineral or spring water bottling

(G-7301)
LITTLE GHOST ROASTERS
247 1/2 King Ave (43201)
PHONE..................................614 325-2065
Wyatt Burk, *Principal*
EMP: 4

SQ FT: 750
SALES (est): 116.1K **Privately Held**
SIC: 2095 5812 Roasted coffee; American restaurant

(G-7302)
LOCKHEED MARTIN CORPORATION
2720 Airport Dr Ste 100 (43219-2219)
PHONE..................................614 418-1930
Tony Donato, *Manager*
EMP: 5
SALES (corp-wide): 47.2B **Publicly Held**
WEB: www.lockheedmartin.com
SIC: 7372 7371 Application computer software; computer software systems analysis & design, custom
PA: Lockheed Martin Corporation
　　6801 Rockledge Dr
　　Bethesda MD 20817
　　301 897-6000

(G-7303)
LOFT VIOLIN SHOP
4604 N High St (43214-2002)
PHONE..................................614 267-7221
David Schlub, *Owner*
Richard C Schlub, *Partner*
Jennifer Short, *General Mgr*
Jim Hofstetter, *Education*
EMP: 14
SALES (est): 2MM **Privately Held**
WEB: www.theloftviolinshop.com
SIC: 7699 5736 3931 7359 Musical instrument repair services; musical instrument stores; string instruments; musical instruments; musical instrument rental services

(G-7304)
LONG SIGN CO
979 E 5th Ave (43201-3064)
PHONE..................................614 294-1057
John Long, *Owner*
EMP: 3
SALES (est): 280.3K **Privately Held**
SIC: 3993 Signs & advertising specialties

(G-7305)
LOUIS INSTANTWHIP-ST INC (PA)
2200 Cardigan Ave (43215-1092)
P.O. Box 333 (43216-0333)
PHONE..................................614 488-2536
Douglas A Smith, *President*
Thomas G Michaelides, *Treasurer*
G Frederick Smith, *Admin Sec*
EMP: 18
SQ FT: 10,300
SALES (est): 1MM **Privately Held**
SIC: 2026 5143 Whipped topping, except frozen or dry mix; dairy products, except dried or canned

(G-7306)
LVD ACQUISITION LLC (HQ)
Also Called: Oasis International
222 E Campus View Blvd (43235-4634)
PHONE..................................614 861-1350
John Kucharik, *CEO*
Di CK Fulk, *Vice Pres*
Nancy Howard, *Human Res Mgr*
Jon McKee, *Accounts Mgr*
E Russell, *Manager*
▲ EMP: 50
SQ FT: 15,000
SALES (est): 331.4K
SALES (corp-wide): 4B **Privately Held**
WEB: www.tripalmint.com
SIC: 3585 Coolers, milk & water: electric
PA: Patriarch Partners, Llc
　　1 Liberty Plz Rm 3500
　　New York NY 10006
　　212 825-0550

(G-7307)
M & W WELDING INC
72 N Glenwood Ave (43222-1241)
PHONE..................................614 224-0501
Fax: 614 224-0502
Ernest D Whitehead Jr, *President*
EMP: 5
SQ FT: 6,000
SALES (est): 194.7K **Privately Held**
SIC: 7692 3441 Welding repair; fabricated structural metal

(G-7308)
M G 3D
320 E Weber Rd (43202-1452)
PHONE..................................614 262-0956
Mike Grigsby, *Owner*
EMP: 12
SALES (est): 544.6K **Privately Held**
WEB: www.mg-3d.com
SIC: 3944 Science kits: microscopes, chemistry sets, etc.

(G-7309)
M M A AUTHENTICS LLC
576 Georgesville Rd (43228-2402)
PHONE..................................614 274-1141
Patricia Sincic-Disabato, *Mng Member*
Michael Disabato,
EMP: 5
SALES: 900K **Privately Held**
SIC: 2389 Men's miscellaneous accessories

(G-7310)
M WEB TYPE INC
3500 Sullivant Ave (43204-1105)
PHONE..................................614 272-8973
Phil Daubel, *President*
EMP: 3 EST: 1971
SQ FT: 16,000
SALES (est): 391.4K
SALES (corp-wide): 1.9MM **Privately Held**
WEB: www.columbusmessenger.com
SIC: 2791 Typesetting
PA: The Columbus Messenger Company
　　3500 Sullivant Ave
　　Columbus OH 43204
　　614 272-5422

(G-7311)
MACHINE TOOL REBUILDERS INC
2042 Leonard Ave (43219-2105)
PHONE..................................614 228-1070
Fax: 614 228-1857
Mark Coleman, *CEO*
Janis Bowling, *Principal*
▲ EMP: 3
SQ FT: 6,400
SALES (est): 463.2K **Privately Held**
SIC: 3542 7699 Rebuilt machine tools, metal forming types; industrial machinery & equipment repair

(G-7312)
MACWOOD INC
Also Called: Macwood Custom Woodworking
397 Martha Ave (43223-1984)
PHONE..................................614 279-7676
Fax: 614 279-6161
Mike McDonald, *President*
EMP: 3 EST: 1953
SQ FT: 2,800
SALES: 250K **Privately Held**
WEB: www.macwood.com
SIC: 2521 2541 Cabinets, office: wood; cabinets, except refrigerated: show, display, etc.: wood

(G-7313)
MAD METAL WLDG FABRICATION LLC
3435 Polley Rd (43221-4705)
PHONE..................................614 256-4163
Timothy Heer, *Principal*
EMP: 4
SALES (est): 474.5K **Privately Held**
SIC: 3499 Fabricated metal products

(G-7314)
MAGNEXT LTD
7100 Huntley Rd Unit 1 (43229-1076)
PHONE..................................614 406-4136
Dmitri Troianovski, *President*
Tim Gerhard, *Opers Mgr*
Alex Mindelin, *Chief Engr*
Jim Essex, *Sales Staff*
Geoffrey Seefeldt, *Sales Staff*
EMP: 7 EST: 2005
SQ FT: 10,000
SALES: 1.4MM **Privately Held**
SIC: 3572 Computer storage devices

(G-7315)
MAGNUM MACHINE WORKS LLC
3680 E 5th Ave Unit D (43219-1831)
PHONE..................................614 231-4880
Mike Young,
EMP: 3
SALES (est): 368.5K **Privately Held**
SIC: 3599 Machine shop, jobbing & repair

(G-7316)
MAPSYS INC (PA)
Also Called: MAP SYSTEMS AND SOLUTIONS
920 Michigan Ave (43215-1165)
PHONE..................................614 255-7258
Steve Bernard, *President*
Paul Neal, *Corp Secy*
Jim Heiberger, *Vice Pres*
Terry Payne, *Vice Pres*
Scott Abrams, *Engineer*
EMP: 30
SQ FT: 6,000
SALES: 20.3MM **Privately Held**
WEB: www.mapsysinc.com
SIC: 7372 7371 5045 Business oriented computer software; custom computer programming services; computers, peripherals & software

(G-7317)
MARATHON AT SAWMILL
Also Called: Sawmill Marathon
7200 Sawmill Rd (43235-5964)
PHONE..................................614 734-0836
Fax: 614 761-0644
Donald Spangler, *Owner*
EMP: 10
SALES (est): 590K **Privately Held**
SIC: 2421 Sawmills & planing mills, general

(G-7318)
MARFO COMPANY (PA)
Also Called: Trading Corp of America
799 N Hague Ave (43204-1424)
PHONE..................................614 276-3352
Fax: 614 276-2279
Bill Giovanello, *CEO*
Cheryl Beery, *President*
Carol Gatzke, *Vice Pres*
Carla Jay, *Buyer*
Mary Montgomery, *Buyer*
EMP: 100
SQ FT: 41,000
SALES (est): 21.9MM **Privately Held**
WEB: www.marsala.com
SIC: 5094 3911 Jewelry; jewelry apparel

(G-7319)
MARS PETCARE US INC
Also Called: Masterfoods USA
5115 Fisher Rd (43228-9146)
P.O. Box 28146 (43228-0146)
PHONE..................................614 878-7242
Goodwyn Morgan, *Principal*
George Rosko, *Purch Mgr*
Melissa Mutz, *Purch Agent*
Nicole Thrower, *Engineer*
Oscar Harrell, *Human Res Mgr*
EMP: 25
SQ FT: 175,000
SALES (corp-wide): 35B **Privately Held**
SIC: 2047 Dog & cat food
HQ: Mars Petcare Us, Inc.
　　315 Cool Springs Blvd
　　Franklin TN 37067
　　615 807-4626

(G-7320)
MARSHALLTOWN PACKAGING INC
601 N Hague Ave (43204-1422)
PHONE..................................641 753-5272
Gary Bolar, *President*
▲ EMP: 9
SQ FT: 54,000
SALES (est): 1.3MM
SALES (corp-wide): 24.9MM **Privately Held**
SIC: 2653 Corrugated & solid fiber boxes
PA: Buckeye Boxes, Inc.
　　601 N Hague Ave
　　Columbus OH 43204
　　614 274-8484

(G-7321)
MARTINA METAL LLC
1575 Shawnee Ave (43211-2643)
PHONE..................................614 291-9700
Fax: 614 291-2064
Terry Kiliany, *CFO*
Greg Stewart, *Mng Member*
EMP: 20 EST: 1962
SQ FT: 12,500
SALES (est): 2.1MM
SALES (corp-wide): 121MM **Privately Held**
WEB: www.martinametal.com
SIC: 1761 3444 3441 3364 Sheet metalwork; sheet metalwork; fabricated structural metal; nonferrous die-castings except aluminum
PA: Sauer Holdings, Inc.
30 51st St
Pittsburgh PA 15201
412 687-4100

(G-7322)
MARVIN MIX
3113 Kentwood Pl (43227-3444)
P.O. Box 24851 (43224-0851)
PHONE..................................614 774-9337
EMP: 3
SALES (est): 187.4K **Privately Held**
SIC: 3273 Mfg Ready-Mixed Concrete

(G-7323)
MATERIALS SCIENCE INTL INC
1660 Georgesville Rd (43228-3613)
PHONE..................................614 870-0400
Fax: 614 878-6000
Neil Crabbe, *President*
William F Bailey, *Vice Pres*
Steve Dahms, *Vice Pres*
John Cherup, *Site Mgr*
Nathan Gallant, *Engineer*
▲ EMP: 30
SQ FT: 12,500
SALES (est): 3.9MM **Privately Held**
SIC: 3479 Aluminum coating of metal products

(G-7324)
MATHEWS PRINTING COMPANY
1250 S Front St (43206-3437)
P.O. Box 188 (43216-0188)
PHONE..................................614 444-1010
Fax: 614 444-2182
Robert Mathews, *President*
Lynn Mullins, *Plant Mgr*
EMP: 16
SQ FT: 15,000
SALES (est): 3.5MM **Privately Held**
WEB: www.mathewsprintingcompany.com
SIC: 2752 Offset & photolithographic printing

(G-7325)
MATTHEW R COPP (PA)
2291 Scioto Harper Dr (43204-3495)
PHONE..................................614 276-8959
Matthew R Copp, *Principal*
EMP: 5
SALES (est): 508.8K **Privately Held**
SIC: 2741 Miscellaneous publishing

(G-7326)
MATTHEW WARREN INC
Also Called: Capital Spring
2000 Jetway Blvd (43219-1673)
PHONE..................................614 418-0250
Fax: 614 418-0260
William Hunsucker, *Principal*
Hoyt Lolla, *Business Mgr*
Terri Hudnall, *Manager*
EMP: 47
SALES (corp-wide): 115.4MM **Privately Held**
SIC: 3493 3495 Steel springs, except wire; wire springs
HQ: Matthew Warren, Inc.
9501 Tech Blvd Ste 401
Rosemont IL 60018
847 349-5760

(G-7327)
MATVEST INC
Also Called: Bermex
1380 Dublin Rd Ste 200 (43215-1025)
PHONE..................................614 487-8720
Fax: 614 487-8783

Mark Everly, *General Mgr*
David Mack, *Opers Mgr*
Chris Covey, *Branch Mgr*
EMP: 30
SALES (corp-wide): 12MM **Privately Held**
WEB: www.bermexinc.com
SIC: 3545 7389 Machine tool accessories; meter readers, remote
PA: Matvest, Inc.
37244 S Groesbeck Hwy A
Clinton Township MI 48036
586 461-2051

(G-7328)
MAUSER USA LLC
1410 Blatt Blvd (43230-6627)
PHONE..................................614 856-5982
Brad Strawser, *General Ptnr*
John Waddell, *Controller*
Penny Evans, *Accounts Mgr*
Amy Strawser, *Manager*
EMP: 25 EST: 1985
SQ FT: 70,000
SALES (est): 5.7MM **Privately Held**
SIC: 3412 Metal barrels, drums & pails

(G-7329)
MCCLELLAN RAND L
65 E State St (43215-4213)
PHONE..................................614 462-4782
Rand L McClellan, *Principal*
EMP: 3 EST: 2010
SALES (est): 202.6K **Privately Held**
SIC: 3131 Rands

(G-7330)
MCGILL AIRCLEAN LLC
1777 Refugee Rd (43207-2119)
PHONE..................................614 829-1200
Fax: 614 542-2616
James D McGill, *President*
Jerry Childress, *Natl Sales Mgr*
T J Shay, *Sales Mgr*
Tj Shay, *Sales Mgr*
Paul R Hess, *Mng Member*
◆ EMP: 70
SQ FT: 15,000
SALES (est): 20.3MM
SALES (corp-wide): 62.8MM **Privately Held**
WEB: www.mcgillairclean.com
SIC: 3564 1796 Precipitators, electrostatic; pollution control equipment installation
HQ: United Mcgill Corporation
1 Mission Park
Groveport OH 43125
614 829-1200

(G-7331)
MCGILL AIRFLOW LLC
2400 Fairwood Ave (43207-2708)
PHONE..................................614 829-1200
Fax: 614 542-2620
Ed Kromer, *Manager*
EMP: 15
SALES (corp-wide): 62.8MM **Privately Held**
WEB: www.mcgillairflow.com
SIC: 3444 Sheet metalwork
HQ: Mcgill Airflow Llc
1 Mission Park
Groveport OH 43125
614 829-1200

(G-7332)
MCGILL AIRPRESSURE LLC
Also Called: McGill Airclean
1777 Refugee Rd (43207-2119)
PHONE..................................614 882-5455
James D McGill, *Manager*
D McGill, *Manager*
Norman Boyer, *Director*
Paul R Hess,
EMP: 5
SQ FT: 75,500
SALES (est): 1MM
SALES (corp-wide): 62.8MM **Privately Held**
WEB: www.mcgillairpressure.com
SIC: 3443 3567 3296 Fabricated plate work (boiler shop); industrial furnaces & ovens; mineral wool

HQ: United Mcgill Corporation
1 Mission Park
Groveport OH 43125
614 829-1200

(G-7333)
MCGILL AIRSILENCE LLC
2400 Fairwood Ave (43207-2708)
PHONE..................................614 443-0192
James D McGill, *Manager*
Norman Boyer, *Director*
EMP: 10
SQ FT: 30,000
SALES (est): 1.4MM
SALES (corp-wide): 62.8MM **Privately Held**
WEB: www.mcgillairsilence.com
SIC: 3625 Noise control equipment
HQ: United Mcgill Corporation
1 Mission Park
Groveport OH 43125
614 829-1200

(G-7334)
MCGLAUGHLN OIL COMPNY/FAS LUBE (PA)
3750 E Livingston Ave (43227-2246)
PHONE..................................614 231-2518
Fax: 614 231-7431
Steve Theodor, *President*
Dana Cheney, *Controller*
Teresa Mc Cormick, *Admin Sec*
EMP: 20
SQ FT: 4,000
SALES (est): 19.5MM **Privately Held**
SIC: 2992 Lubricating oils & greases

(G-7335)
MCGLENNON METAL PRODUCTS INC
940 N 20th St (43219-2423)
PHONE..................................614 252-7114
Fax: 614 252-4141
Thomas Saldoff, *President*
Charlotte Collins, *Controller*
Robin Lemon, *Manager*
EMP: 15
SQ FT: 22,000
SALES (est): 3MM **Privately Held**
WEB: www.mcglennonmetal.com
SIC: 3469 Spinning metal for the trade

(G-7336)
MCL INC
Also Called: McL Whitehall
5240 E Main St (43213-2501)
PHONE..................................614 861-6259
Fax: 614 861-4005
Jim Bell, *Manager*
EMP: 60
SALES (corp-wide): 48.2MM **Privately Held**
WEB: www.mclcafe.com
SIC: 2051 Bakery: wholesale or wholesale/retail combined
PA: Mcl, Inc.
2730 E 62nd St
Indianapolis IN 46220
317 257-5425

(G-7337)
MCLEOD BAR GROUP LLC
234 King Ave (43201-2776)
PHONE..................................614 299-2099
Matthew McLeod,
EMP: 15
SALES (est): 522.5K **Privately Held**
SIC: 2599 Bar, restaurant & cafeteria furniture

(G-7338)
MCNEIL GROUP INC
Also Called: Pinnacle Metal Products
1701 Woodland Ave (43219-1137)
PHONE..................................614 298-0300
Fax: 614 298-0305
Susan McNeil, *President*
Michael McNeil, *Vice Pres*
EMP: 32
SQ FT: 41,000
SALES (est): 9.8MM **Privately Held**
SIC: 3441 Fabricated structural metal

(G-7339)
MCNEIL HOLDINGS LLC
1701 Woodland Ave (43219-1137)
PHONE..................................614 298-0300
Michael R McNeil,
EMP: 6 EST: 1998
SALES (est): 670K **Privately Held**
SIC: 3441 Fabricated structural metal

(G-7340)
MEDFORALL LLC
1500 W 3rd Ave Ste 111 (43212-2816)
PHONE..................................614 947-0791
Ali Rahimi, *President*
EMP: 4
SALES (est): 298.4K **Privately Held**
SIC: 3845 7373 Electromedical equipment; patient monitoring apparatus; systems software development services

(G-7341)
MEDRANO USA INC ✪
4311 Janitrol Rd Ste 500 (43228-1390)
PHONE..................................614 272-5856
Gerardo Fernandez, *CEO*
EMP: 125 EST: 2016
SQ FT: 700
SALES: 1.3MM **Privately Held**
SIC: 3537 Platforms, stands, tables, pallets & similar equipment

(G-7342)
METALS RECOVERY SERVICES LLC
1400 Norton Rd (43228-3631)
PHONE..................................614 870-0364
Bill Bailey, *Manager*
EMP: 3
SALES (corp-wide): 303K **Privately Held**
SIC: 3341 4924 Silver recovery from used photographic film;
PA: Metals Recovery Services Llc
1660 Georgesville Rd
Columbus OH 43228
614 888-9272

(G-7343)
METTLER-TOLEDO LLC
Toledo Scales & Systems
6600 Huntley Rd (43229-1048)
PHONE..................................614 841-7300
Fax: 614 841-7295
Wade Long, *General Mgr*
Dave Tatman, *Opers Mgr*
Paul Hillerich, *Production*
Al Herold, *Opers-Prdtn-Mfg*
Tom Rice, *Engrg Mgr*
EMP: 170
SQ FT: 71,000
SALES (corp-wide): 2.5B **Publicly Held**
WEB: www.mtnw.com
SIC: 3596 Industrial scales
HQ: Mettler-Toledo, Llc
1900 Polaris Pkwy Fl 6
Columbus OH 43240
614 438-4511

(G-7344)
MEYER MACHINE TOOL COMPANY
3434 E 7th Ave (43219-1735)
PHONE..................................614 235-0039
Fax: 614 338-1996
Richard A Meyer, *Owner*
Sheryl Meyer, *Principal*
EMP: 5
SQ FT: 5,500
SALES: 350K **Privately Held**
SIC: 3542 3544 Machine tools, metal forming type; special dies & tools

(G-7345)
MICKES QUALITY MACHINING
488 Trade Rd (43204-6241)
PHONE..................................614 746-6639
Mickes Frank Jr, *Principal*
EMP: 3
SALES (est): 253.3K **Privately Held**
SIC: 3599 Machine shop, jobbing & repair

(G-7346)
MICRO CENTER CORPORATION
747 Bethel Rd (43214-1901)
PHONE..................................614 326-8500
Fax: 614 481-4433

John Baker, *Principal*
EMP: 8
SALES (est): 800K **Privately Held**
SIC: 3571 Electronic computers

(G-7347)
MICRO INDUSTRIES CORPORATION
2270 Port Rd (43217)
PHONE..................................740 548-7878
Russ Diehl, *Branch Mgr*
EMP: 10
SALES (corp-wide): 17.1MM **Privately Held**
WEB: www.microindustries.com
SIC: 3674 Semiconductor circuit networks
PA: Micro Industries Corporation
8399 Green Meadows Dr N
Westerville OH 43081
740 548-7878

(G-7348)
MID WEST DRY SIFT
3441 Merrydawn Dr (43221-4559)
PHONE..................................614 946-3797
Stephen Concilla, *Owner*
Josh Chapman, *Owner*
EMP: 3
SALES (est): 50K **Privately Held**
SIC: 2759 Screen printing

(G-7349)
MID-OHIO ELECTRIC CO
1170 Mckinley Ave (43222-1113)
PHONE..................................614 274-8000
Fax: 614 274-1671
Cynthia Langhirt, *President*
Bruce A Langhirt, *Vice Pres*
Vince Langhirt, *Vice Pres*
Bret Law, *Accountant*
Bob Calkins, *Sales Staff*
EMP: 26
SQ FT: 13,800
SALES (est): 5.8MM **Privately Held**
WEB: www.mid-ohioelectric.com
SIC: 7694 5063 7629 8711 Electric motor repair; motors, electric; circuit board repair; generator repair; electrical or electronic engineering

(G-7350)
MIDDLETON LEE ORIGINAL DOLLS (HQ)
2400 Corporate Exch Dr (43231-7605)
Fax: 614 901-0517
▲ **EMP:** 17
SQ FT: 18,000
SALES (est): 1.3MM
SALES (corp-wide): 8.2MM **Privately Held**
SIC: 3942 5945 5947 Mfg Dolls/Stuffed Toys Ret Hobbies/Toys/Games Ret Gifts/Novelties
PA: First Time Design Limited
2350 S 170th St
New Berlin WI 53151
262 364-5200

(G-7351)
MIDWEST MOTOR SUPPLY CO (PA)
Also Called: Kimball Midwest
4800 Roberts Rd (43228-9791)
P.O. Box 2470 (43216-2470)
PHONE..................................800 233-1294
Fax: 614 219-6101
Patrick J McCurdy Jr, *President*
A Glenn McClelland, *Principal*
Charles McCurdy, *Vice Pres*
Chas McCurdy, *Vice Pres*
David McCurdy, *Vice Pres*
▲ **EMP:** 200
SQ FT: 85,000
SALES (est): 152.5MM **Privately Held**
WEB: www.kimballmidwest.com
SIC: 3965 3399 8742 Fasteners; metal fasteners; materials mgmt. (purchasing, handling, inventory) consultant

(G-7352)
MIDWEST QUALITY BEDDING INC
3860 Morse Rd (43219-3014)
PHONE..................................614 504-5971
EMP: 3

SALES (est): 150K **Privately Held**
SIC: 2515 Mattresses & bedsprings

(G-7353)
MILLS LED LLC (PA)
81 S 5th St Ste 201 (43215-4323)
PHONE..................................800 690-6403
Rodney Nespeca, *Mng Member*
EMP: 4
SALES: 1MM **Privately Held**
SIC: 3646 Commercial indusl & institutional electric lighting fixtures

(G-7354)
MILLS LED LLC
655 N Cassady Ave (43219-2720)
PHONE..................................800 690-6403
Michael Hawkins, *Branch Mgr*
EMP: 5
SALES (corp-wide): 1MM **Privately Held**
SIC: 3646 Commercial indusl & institutional electric lighting fixtures
PA: Mills Led, Llc
81 S 5th St Ste 201
Columbus OH 43215
800 690-6403

(G-7355)
MILLWOOD INC
1886 Williams Rd (43207-5113)
PHONE..................................614 409-9680
Fax: 614 409-9755
Greg Rank, *Plant Mgr*
Connie Starr, *Manager*
EMP: 22 **Privately Held**
WEB: www.millwoodinc.com
SIC: 2448 Pallets, wood; cargo containers, wood
PA: Millwood, Inc.
3708 International Blvd
Vienna OH 44473

(G-7356)
MINIMALLY INVASIVE DEVICES INC
Also Called: Mid
1275 Kinnear Rd (43212-1180)
PHONE..................................614 484-5036
Wayne Poll, *CEO*
Caroline Crisafulli, *Vice Pres*
Trudie Seeger, *Vice Pres*
Kenneth Jones, *CFO*
Jim Bobbitt, *VP Sales*
EMP: 25
SALES (est): 4.1MM **Privately Held**
SIC: 3841 Surgical & medical instruments

(G-7357)
MINUTEMAN PRESS
265 Lincoln Cir Ste C (43230-3084)
PHONE..................................614 337-2334
Fax: 614 337-2655
Jeff Remy, *Owner*
EMP: 3
SALES (est): 210K **Privately Held**
SIC: 2752 Commercial printing, lithographic

(G-7358)
MMF INCORPORATED (PA)
Also Called: MILLS METAL FINISHING
1977 Mcallister Ave (43205-1614)
PHONE..................................614 252-2522
Fax: 614 252-0071
Brian L Mills, *President*
Cheryl Camp, *Vice Pres*
Foster Mills, *Director*
Steven Mills, *Shareholder*
EMP: 11
SQ FT: 9,400
SALES: 2.1MM **Privately Held**
SIC: 3471 Plating of metals or formed products; polishing, metals or formed products

(G-7359)
MMF INCORPORATED
Rainbow Custom Powder Coaters
1977 Mcallister Ave (43205-1614)
PHONE..................................614 252-2522
Brian Mills, *Manager*
EMP: 14

SALES (corp-wide): 2.1MM **Privately Held**
SIC: 3471 Plating of metals or formed products; polishing, metals or formed products
PA: Mmf Incorporated
1977 Mcallister Ave
Columbus OH 43205
614 252-2522

(G-7360)
MOBILE MINI INC
871 Buckeye Park Rd (43207-2586)
PHONE..................................614 449-8655
Fax: 614 449-8656
Sean Roche, *Manager*
EMP: 12
SALES (corp-wide): 508.6MM **Publicly Held**
WEB: www.mobilemini.com
SIC: 3448 3441 3412 7359 Prefabricated metal buildings; fabricated structural metal; metal barrels, drums & pails; equipment rental & leasing
PA: Mobile Mini, Inc.
4646 E Van Buren St # 400
Phoenix AZ 85008
480 894-6311

(G-7361)
MOBILE SOLUTIONS LLC
149 N Hamilton Rd (43213-1308)
PHONE..................................614 286-3944
Darryl Crockett,
EMP: 10
SQ FT: 2,500
SALES (est): 374.7K **Privately Held**
SIC: 3711 Cars, electric, assembly of

(G-7362)
MOJO SPORTSGEAR
5765 Westbourne Ave (43213-1488)
PHONE..................................614 864-6656
Mark Witte, *Owner*
Adam Hollett, *Info Tech Mgr*
EMP: 6
SALES (est): 481.5K **Privately Held**
SIC: 2759 Screen printing

(G-7363)
MOK INDUSTRIES LLC
4449 Easton Way (43219-6093)
PHONE..................................614 934-1734
William Mook,
EMP: 4
SQ FT: 3,000
SALES (est): 360.3K **Privately Held**
WEB: www.mokindustries.fuzing.com
SIC: 3674 Solar cells

(G-7364)
MOMENTIVE PERFORMANCE
180 E Broad St (43215-3707)
PHONE..................................281 325-3536
Douglas A Johns, *Branch Mgr*
EMP: 4
SALES (corp-wide): 2.2B **Publicly Held**
SIC: 2899 Chemical preparations
HQ: Momentive Performance Materials Worldwide Inc.
260 Hudson River Rd
Waterford NY 12188
281 325-3536

(G-7365)
MOMENTIVE PERFORMANCE MTLS INC (PA)
180 E Broad St (43215-3707)
PHONE..................................614 986-2495
Craig O Morrison, *CEO*
Dale N Plante, *President*
Deepak Kumar, *Top Exec*
Nathan E Fisher, *Exec VP*
Anthony B Greene, *Exec VP*
▼ **EMP:** 277
SALES (est): 2.6B **Privately Held**
SIC: 2821 2869 Thermosetting materials; silicones

(G-7366)
MONITORTECH CORP
661 N James Rd (43219-1837)
PHONE..................................614 231-0500
Robert Mullowney, *General Mgr*
Jeff York, *Principal*
Sarah Gunther, *Office Mgr*

Tom Mundy, *Software Engr*
Eric Norris, *Comp Tech*
EMP: 5
SALES (est): 1.4MM **Privately Held**
SIC: 3823 Industrial process control instruments

(G-7367)
MONKS COPY SHOP INC (PA)
47 E Gay St (43215-3103)
PHONE..................................614 885-7228
Fax: 614 885-1171
Edward M Smith, *President*
EMP: 3
SQ FT: 15,718
SALES (est): 2.1MM **Privately Held**
WEB: www.monkscopyshop.com
SIC: 7334 2752 Photocopying & duplicating services; commercial printing, lithographic

(G-7368)
MORCAST PRECISION INC
1615 Woodland Ave (43219-1135)
PHONE..................................614 258-5071
Fax: 614 258-5281
Doug Moran, *President*
Donald Young, *Vice Pres*
EMP: 5
SQ FT: 20,000
SALES (est): 581.3K **Privately Held**
SIC: 3543 Foundry patternmaking

(G-7369)
MORI SHUJI
Also Called: Geodyne One
3755 Mountview Rd (43220-4801)
PHONE..................................614 459-1296
Shuji Mori, *Owner*
EMP: 7
SALES (est): 381.4K **Privately Held**
WEB: www.geodyneone.com
SIC: 1382 Oil & gas exploration services

(G-7370)
MORRISON MEDICAL
3735 Paragon Dr (43228-9751)
PHONE..................................614 461-4400
Marshall Witzel, *Partner*
Donald Evans, *Principal*
Lena Smith, *Mktg Dir*
Scarlet Gray, *Director*
Thompson Della, *Executive*
EMP: 24
SQ FT: 4,700
SALES (est): 4.3MM **Privately Held**
WEB: www.morrisonmed.com
SIC: 3841 Surgical & medical instruments; probes, surgical

(G-7371)
MORRISON SIGN COMPANY INC
2757 Scioto Pkwy (43221-4658)
PHONE..................................614 276-1181
Fax: 614 274-6048
David Morrison, *President*
Helen Morrison, *Corp Secy*
EMP: 27
SQ FT: 18,000
SALES (est): 4.3MM **Privately Held**
WEB: www.morrisonsigns.com
SIC: 3993 2759 Signs, not made in custom sign painting shops; screen printing

(G-7372)
MRS INDUSTRIAL INC
Also Called: M R S
2583 Harrison Rd (43204-3511)
PHONE..................................614 308-1070
Fax: 614 308-1075
Scott J Cosgrove, *President*
Scott Cosgrove, *President*
Ronald L Belford, *Vice Pres*
Kenneth Michael Cosgrove, *Vice Pres*
Debbie Andrix, *Manager*
▲ **EMP:** 24
SQ FT: 60,000
SALES (est): 5.9MM **Privately Held**
SIC: 3444 Sheet metalwork

(G-7373)
MULTIPRESS INC
1250 Refugee Ln (43207-2112)
PHONE..................................614 228-0185
Fax: 614 228-2358
Michael Pfister, *Principal*

EMP: 4
SALES (est) 587.8K **Privately Held**
SIC: 3542 Presses: hydraulic & pneumatic, mechanical & manual

(G-7374)
MURPHY TRACTOR & EQP CO INC
Also Called: John Deere Authorized Dealer
2121 Walcutt Rd (43228-9575)
PHONE..................................614 876-1141
Michael R Slinger, *Vice Pres*
Tim Murphy, *CFO*
Mike Slinger, *Manager*
EMP: 8
SALES (corp-wide): 176.9MM **Privately Held**
SIC: 3531 5082 Construction machinery; construction & mining machinery
HQ: Murphy Tractor & Equipment Co., Inc.
5375 N Deere Rd
Park City KS 67219
855 246-9124

(G-7375)
MVP PHARMACY
1931 Parsons Ave (43207-2364)
PHONE..................................614 449-8000
Joseph F Miccio, *Administration*
EMP: 4
SALES (est): 270.9K **Privately Held**
SIC: 2834 Pharmaceutical preparations

(G-7376)
MY CATERED TABLE LLC
1871 N High St (43210-1105)
PHONE..................................614 882-7323
Kimberly Scaggs, *Partner*
EMP: 6
SALES (est): 446.3K **Privately Held**
SIC: 3541 Milling machines

(G-7377)
N WASSERSTROM & SONS INC (HQ)
Also Called: Wasserstrom Marketing Division
2300 Lockbourne Rd (43207-6111)
PHONE..................................614 228-5550
Fax: 614 443-6499
William Wasserstrom, *President*
John H Mc Cormick, *Senior VP*
Craig Dietz, *Vice Pres*
Jim Scott, *Purchasing*
Rosie Bonlarron, *Accounts Exec*
◆ EMP: 250 EST: 1933
SQ FT: 175,000
SALES (est): 145MM
SALES (corp-wide): 776.3MM **Privately Held**
SIC: 3556 5046 3444 Food products machinery; restaurant equipment & supplies; sheet metalwork
PA: The Wasserstrom Company
477 S Front St
Columbus OH 43215
614 737-8472

(G-7378)
N WASSERSTROM & SONS INC
Also Called: Select Seating
862 E Jenkins Ave (43207-1317)
PHONE..................................614 737-5410
Fax: 614 737-5430
Greg Pell, *Manager*
Brad McCormick, *Manager*
EMP: 100
SALES (corp-wide): 776.3MM **Privately Held**
SIC: 2511 2531 Wood household furniture; public building & related furniture
HQ: N. Wasserstrom & Sons, Inc.
2300 Lockbourne Rd
Columbus OH 43207
614 228-5550

(G-7379)
NANO INNOVATIONS LLC
Also Called: Nano Fabrix
2121 Riverside Dr (43221-4052)
PHONE..................................614 203-5706
Andy Dickson,
EMP: 5 EST: 2012
SALES (est): 451.1K **Privately Held**
SIC: 2821 Plastics materials & resins

(G-7380)
NANOFIBER SOLUTIONS INC
1275 Kinnear Rd (43212-1180)
PHONE..................................614 559-9065
Ross Kayuha, *CEO*
Tyler Groehl, *Research*
Devan Ohst, *Research*
Nolan Kleinhenz, *Marketing Mgr*
Jason Chakroff, *Manager*
EMP: 9
SQ FT: 20,000
SALES: 550K **Privately Held**
SIC: 2834 2835 Liniments; in vitro & in vivo diagnostic substances

(G-7381)
NANOTECH WEST LAB
1381 Kinnear Rd Ste 100 (43212-1178)
PHONE..................................614 688-3055
Robert Davis, *Director*
▲ EMP: 10
SALES (est): 1.3MM **Privately Held**
SIC: 2869 Laboratory chemicals, organic

(G-7382)
NATIONAL ELECTRIC COIL INC (PA)
Also Called: N E C Columbus
800 King Ave (43212-2644)
P.O. Box 370 (43216-0370)
PHONE..................................614 488-1151
Fax: 614 488-2063
Robert Barton, *CEO*
Beant Nindra, *President*
William Wentz, *General Mgr*
Athena Amaxas, *Principal*
Brian Damant, *Business Mgr*
◆ EMP: 300
SQ FT: 500,000
SALES (est): 69.9MM **Privately Held**
WEB: www.national-electric-coil.com
SIC: 7694 Electric motor repair

(G-7383)
NATIONAL FRUIT VEGETABLE TECH
Also Called: Fresh Vegetable Technology
250 Civic Center Dr (43215-5086)
P.O. Box 67, Baltimore (43105-0067)
PHONE..................................740 400-4055
Fax: 740 862-3444
Daniel Cashman, *CEO*
Mitch Adams, *Ch of Bd*
Keith Stoll, *VP Mfg*
Bart Adams, *Sales Mgr*
Richard Cashman, *Shareholder*
EMP: 50
SQ FT: 150,000
SALES (est): 6.9MM **Privately Held**
SIC: 2037 Fruits, quick frozen & cold pack (frozen)

(G-7384)
NATIONAL MOLD REMEDIATION
3923 E Main St (43213-2948)
PHONE..................................614 231-6653
Lynn Edelman, *President*
EMP: 5
SALES (est): 374.7K **Privately Held**
SIC: 3544 Industrial molds

(G-7385)
NBBI
1055 Crupper Ave (43229-1108)
PHONE..................................614 888-8320
David Trent, *Analyst*
EMP: 3
SALES (est): 326.1K **Privately Held**
SIC: 3433 Boilers, low-pressure heating: steam or hot water

(G-7386)
NEON HUSSY LLC
237 E 12th Ave (43201-2216)
PHONE..................................513 374-7644
Jess Mishos, *Principal*
EMP: 3
SALES (est): 123.2K **Privately Held**
SIC: 2813 Neon

(G-7387)
NETWORK PRINTING & GRAPHICS
443 Crestview Rd (43202-2244)
PHONE..................................614 230-2084

Cathy Ann Dawson, *President*
EMP: 10
SQ FT: 7,500
SALES (est): 1.1MM **Privately Held**
SIC: 2752 7331 2791 2789 Commercial printing, lithographic; direct mail advertising services; typesetting; bookbinding & related work; commercial printing

(G-7388)
NEWALL ELECTRONICS INC
1803 Obrien Rd (43228-3866)
PHONE..................................614 771-0213
Martha Sullivan, *President*
Danny Donaldson, *Vice Pres*
Vincent A Inendino, *Vice Pres*
Alison Roelke, *Vice Pres*
Debbie Norris, *Opers Mgr*
▲ EMP: 14
SQ FT: 7,000
SALES (est): 2.6MM
SALES (corp-wide): 2.9B **Privately Held**
WEB: www.newall.com
SIC: 3829 Measuring & controlling devices
HQ: Custom Sensors & Technologies, Inc.
1461 Lawrence Dr
Thousand Oaks CA 91320
805 716-0322

(G-7389)
NEWMAST MKTG & COMMUNICATIONS
Also Called: Printing Company, The
2060 Integrity Dr N (43209-2726)
PHONE..................................614 837-1200
Fax: 614 837-0752
Terry L Wike, *President*
EMP: 20 EST: 1898
SQ FT: 15,000
SALES (est): 1.2MM **Privately Held**
SIC: 7336 2752 Silk screen design; commercial printing, offset

(G-7390)
NEWS REEL INC
Also Called: News Reel Mag By & For Blind
5 E Long St Ste 1001 (43215-2915)
PHONE..................................614 469-0700
Kate Sniderman, *President*
Ed Eames, *President*
Tom Lykins, *Vice Pres*
Patty Silver, *Vice Pres*
Jeffrey Gardner, *Treasurer*
EMP: 3
SALES: 61.2K **Privately Held**
SIC: 3652 8399 Magnetic tape (audio): prerecorded; community development groups

(G-7391)
NEXT DAY SIGNS LLC
6403 Nicholas Dr (43235-5204)
PHONE..................................614 764-7446
Cheryl A Raudabaugh, *Managing Prtnr*
Amanda B Martin, *Marketing Staff*
EMP: 3
SALES: 300K **Privately Held**
WEB: www.nextdaysignscols.com
SIC: 3993 Signs & advertising specialties

(G-7392)
NICKLAUS MACHINE CO
3975 Karl Rd (43224-2124)
PHONE..................................614 262-7223
Roger F Nicklaus, *Owner*
EMP: 3
SQ FT: 3,000
SALES: 140K **Privately Held**
SIC: 3599 Machine shop, jobbing & repair

(G-7393)
NIIDEX ENTERPRISE LLC
3314 Morse Rd Ste 215 (43231-6100)
PHONE..................................614 653-8526
Hanad Duale,
Nur Mohamed,
▲ EMP: 4
SALES (est): 270K **Privately Held**
SIC: 2035 Seasonings & sauces, except tomato & dry

(G-7394)
NO SURPRISES SOFTWARE INC
536 S Wall St Fl 1 (43215-5794)
PHONE..................................855 462-6448
Robert Friedman, *CEO*

EMP: 8 EST: 2012
SALES: 875.4K
SALES (corp-wide): 45.8MM **Privately Held**
SIC: 7372 Prepackaged software
PA: Mitratech Holdings, Inc.
5001 Plaza On The Lk
Austin TX 78746
512 382-7322

(G-7395)
NOISE SUPPRESSION TECHNOLOGIES
Also Called: Nsti
4182 Fisher Rd (43228-1024)
PHONE..................................614 275-1818
Fax: 614 258-4452
Daniel F Belcher, *CEO*
Christen Whitt, *Office Mgr*
EMP: 10
SQ FT: 5,000
SALES (est): 1.5MM **Privately Held**
WEB: www.noisesuppression.com
SIC: 3625 Noise control equipment

(G-7396)
NOM NOM NOM
2818 Banwick Rd (43232-3805)
PHONE..................................614 302-4815
Johnna McDonald, *Owner*
EMP: 4 EST: 2013
SALES (est): 119.7K **Privately Held**
SIC: 2047 Dog food

(G-7397)
NORDIC LIGHT AMERICA INC
426 Mccormick Blvd (43213-1525)
PHONE..................................614 981-9497
Kenneth Johansson, *President*
EMP: 10
SQ FT: 96,000
SALES (est): 1.6MM
SALES (corp-wide): 594.9MM **Privately Held**
SIC: 7389 3646 Interior design services; ceiling systems, luminous
HQ: Nordic Light Ab
Servicegatan 13
Skelleftea 931 7
910 733-790

(G-7398)
NORSE DAIRY SYSTEMS LP
1740 Joyce Ave (43219-1026)
P.O. Box 1869 (43216-1869)
PHONE..................................614 421-5297
Scott Fullbright, *Partner*
Cindy Linkiewicz, *Vice Pres*
Harry Seniea, *Vice Pres*
Jack Frysztak, *Plant Mgr*
Steven Krotz, *Plant Mgr*
▼ EMP: 340
SALES (est): 71.1MM
SALES (corp-wide): 35.2B **Privately Held**
WEB: www.norse.com
SIC: 3556 2052 2656 Ice cream manufacturing machinery; cones, ice cream; ice cream containers: made from purchased material
HQ: Interbake Foods Llc
3951 Westerre Pkwy # 200
Henrico VA 23233
804 755-7107

(G-7399)
NORTH COAST SECURITY GROUP LLC
750 E Long St Ste 3000 (43203-1874)
PHONE..................................614 887-7255
Micheal Cudgel, *Co-Owner*
Malik Abdul-Zahir, *Co-Owner*
EMP: 4
SALES (est): 189.8K **Privately Held**
SIC: 8748 7372 7371 7373 Systems engineering consultant, ex. computer or professional; operating systems computer software; custom computer programming services; systems engineering, computer related; value-added resellers, computer systems

(G-7400)
NORTH HIGH BREWING LLC
1125 Cleveland Ave (43201-2900)
PHONE..................................614 407-5278
Timothy Ward,

Gavin Meyers,
EMP: 10 **EST:** 2011
SALES (est): 1.2MM **Privately Held**
SIC: 2082 Near beer

(G-7401)
NORTH SHORE STONE INC
915 Manor Park Dr (43228-9522)
PHONE..................................614 870-7531
Fax: 614 870-7538
Denny Hamond, *President*
Cliff Hammond, *Vice Pres*
Willard Jakeway, *Treasurer*
Steve Keefe, *Director*
EMP: 15
SQ FT: 1,280
SALES (est): 880K **Privately Held**
WEB: www.northshorestone.com
SIC: 1411 Limestone & marble dimension
stone

(G-7402)
NORTHEAST CABINET CO LLC
6063 Taylor Rd (43230-3211)
PHONE..................................614 759-0800
James P Yankle, *Principal*
EMP: 8
SALES (est): 1MM **Privately Held**
SIC: 2434 Wood kitchen cabinets

(G-7403)
NORTHWOOD ENERGY CORPORATION
941 Chatham Ln Ste 100 (43221-2471)
PHONE..................................614 457-1024
Ralph W Talmage, *President*
Tyna A Anderson, *Managing Dir*
Frederick H Kennedy, *Principal*
Joan S Talmage, *Principal*
Holly Clemens, *Vice Pres*
EMP: 20
SQ FT: 5,000
SALES: 31.4MM **Privately Held**
SIC: 1311 Crude petroleum production;
natural gas production

(G-7404)
NOXGEAR LLC
2264 Green Island Dr (43228-9432)
PHONE..................................937 248-1860
Tom Walters, *CEO*
EMP: 3
SALES (est): 297.6K **Privately Held**
SIC: 2329 Vests (suede, leatherette, etc.),
sport: men's & boys'

(G-7405)
NUCON INTERNATIONAL INC (PA)
7000 Huntley Rd (43229-1035)
P.O. Box 29151 (43229-0151)
PHONE..................................614 846-5710
J Louis Kovach, *President*
Joseph C Enneking, *Vice Pres*
Larry Shaffer, *Project Mgr*
Alex Seyerle, *Purch Agent*
Luke Primel, *QA Dir*
▲ **EMP:** 11
SQ FT: 22,000
SALES (est): 9.1MM **Privately Held**
WEB: www.nucon-int.com
SIC: 5199 8711 8734 3829 Charcoal;
pollution control engineering; pollution
testing; nuclear radiation & testing appa-
ratus; earth science services

(G-7406)
NUTS ARE GOOD INC (PA)
Also Called: Buffalo Peanuts
Busch Blvd (43229)
PHONE..................................586 619-2400
Daniel B Levy, *President*
EMP: 12
SQ FT: 10,000
SALES: 3MM **Privately Held**
SIC: 2068 5145 Salted & roasted nuts &
seeds; nuts, salted or roasted

(G-7407)
NUVOX
111 N 4th St (43215-3116)
PHONE..................................614 232-9115
Andrea Kelly, *Principal*
EMP: 3
SALES (est): 198.3K **Privately Held**
SIC: 3355 Aluminum rolling & drawing

(G-7408)
OASIS EMBROIDERY
6663 Huntley Rd Ste R (43229-1040)
PHONE..................................614 785-7266
Scott Wise, *Owner*
EMP: 3
SALES (est): 176.9K **Privately Held**
SIC: 2395 Embroidery & art needlework

(G-7409)
OBERFIELDS LLC
Also Called: Marble Cliff Block & Bldrs Sup
4033 Alum Creek Dr (43207-5138)
PHONE..................................614 491-7643
Fax: 614 491-1877
Randy Tackett, *Manager*
EMP: 50
SALES (corp-wide): 17MM **Privately
Held**
SIC: 3271 5211 3272 Blocks, concrete or
cinder: standard; masonry materials &
supplies; concrete products
PA: Oberfield's, Llc
528 London Rd
Delaware OH 43015
740 369-7644

(G-7410)
OBERFIELDS LLC
1165 Alum Creek Dr (43209-2719)
PHONE..................................614 252-0955
Chris Buttke, *Sales/Mktg Mgr*
Don Mankins, *Manager*
EMP: 15
SALES (corp-wide): 17MM **Privately
Held**
SIC: 3272 3271 2531 Concrete products;
concrete block & brick; public building &
related furniture
PA: Oberfield's, Llc
528 London Rd
Delaware OH 43015
740 369-7644

(G-7411)
OCEAN PROVIDENCE COLUMBUS LLC
3699 Interchange Rd (43204-1499)
PHONE..................................614 272-5973
EMP: 3 **EST:** 2013
SALES (est): 275.8K **Privately Held**
SIC: 2048 0913 Fish food; shellfish

(G-7412)
OCTSYS SECURITY CORP
Also Called: O S C
341 S 3rd St Ste 100-42 (43215-5463)
P.O. Box 1071 (43216-1071)
PHONE..................................614 470-4510
Vincent King, *Ch of Bd*
Esther Brandon, *Human Resources*
EMP: 9
SALES (est): 710.1K **Privately Held**
SIC: 3089 3999 Identification cards, plas-
tic; stereographs, photographic

(G-7413)
OFA SERVICES INC
2130 Stella Ct Ste 200 (43215-1011)
PHONE..................................614 884-1203
Doug Cole, *President*
Bobby Barnitz, *Vice Pres*
David Saboia, *Treasurer*
EMP: 12
SQ FT: 3,700
SALES (est): 881.7K **Privately Held**
SIC: 2731 6733 8611 Books: publishing
only; trusts, except educational, religious,
charity: management; business associa-
tions

(G-7414)
OHIO ANODIZING COMPANY INC
915 N 20th St (43219-2422)
PHONE..................................614 252-7855
Fax: 614 258-2178
Jim Hoyle, *President*
Keith Willike, *Treasurer*
EMP: 16
SQ FT: 50,000
SALES: 2MM **Privately Held**
SIC: 3471 Finishing, metals or formed
products; anodizing (plating) of metals or
formed products

(G-7415)
OHIO ASSOCIATION REALTORS INC
200 E Town St (43215-4608)
PHONE..................................614 228-6675
Fax: 614 228-2601
Robert E Fletcher, *CEO*
Robin Jennings, *VP Opers*
Lisa Picklesimer, *Marketing Staff*
Cherie Murray, *CTO*
Carl Horst, *Director*
EMP: 25 **EST:** 1911
SQ FT: 15,168
SALES: 4.4MM **Privately Held**
WEB: www.ohiorealtor.com
SIC: 8611 2721 Trade associations; trade
journals: publishing & printing

(G-7416)
OHIO CAST STONE CO LLC
45 W Barthman Ave (43207-1887)
P.O. Box 7852 (43207-0852)
PHONE..................................614 444-2278
Fax: 740 983-2034
Alan Cleary, *Principal*
EMP: 5
SALES (est): 360K **Privately Held**
SIC: 3272 Concrete products

(G-7417)
OHIO CHEMICAL TWO
8132 Linden Leaf Cir (43235-4617)
PHONE..................................614 482-8073
Megan E Horvath, *Principal*
EMP: 3
SALES (est): 298.8K **Privately Held**
SIC: 2869 Laboratory chemicals, organic

(G-7418)
OHIO DEPARTMENT TRANSPORTATION
1606 W Broad St (43223-1202)
PHONE..................................614 351-2898
Paul A Trapasso, *Branch Mgr*
EMP: 20 **Privately Held**
SIC: 9621 3669 Regulation, administration
of transportation; ; transportation signal-
ing devices
HQ: Ohio Department Of Transportation
1980 W Broad St
Columbus OH 43223
614 466-7170

(G-7419)
OHIO DESIGNER CRAFTSMEN ENTPS (HQ)
Also Called: OHIO CRAFT MUSEUM
1665 W 5th Ave (43212-2315)
PHONE..................................614 486-7119
Fax: 614 486-7110
Sharon Kokot, *Director*
EMP: 12 **EST:** 1963
SQ FT: 2,000
SALES: 899.9K
SALES (corp-wide): 1MM **Privately Held**
SIC: 5947 8741 2721 Artcraft & carvings;
management services; periodicals: pub-
lishing only
PA: Ohio Designer-Craftsmen
1665 W 5th Ave
Columbus OH 43212
614 486-7119

(G-7420)
OHIO DISTINCTIVE ENTERPRISES
Also Called: Ohio Distinctive Software
6500 Fiesta Dr (43235-5201)
PHONE..................................614 459-0453
Fax: 614 457-2488
Stanford Apseloff, *President*
Timothy M Clark, *Corp Secy*
Glen Apseloff, *Vice Pres*
EMP: 20
SQ FT: 12,000
SALES (est): 2.7MM **Privately Held**
WEB: www.ohio-distinctive.com
SIC: 7372 Prepackaged software

(G-7421)
OHIO FOAM CORPORATION
1513 Alum Creek Dr (43209-2712)
PHONE..................................614 252-4877
Fax: 614 252-1213
Peter Kesler, *Accounts Mgr*

Sheila Bennett, *Office Mgr*
Phil Johnson, *Branch Mgr*
EMP: 8
SALES (corp-wide): 13MM **Privately
Held**
WEB: www.ohiofoam.com
SIC: 3069 3086 Foam rubber; plastics
foam products
PA: Ohio Foam Corporation
820 Plymouth St
Bucyrus OH 44820
419 563-0399

(G-7422)
OHIO MANUFACTURING EXT PARTNR
Also Called: Ohmep
77 S High St (43215-6108)
PHONE..................................614 644-8788
Beth Colbert, *Partner*
EMP: 3
SALES: 950K **Privately Held**
SIC: 3999 Manufacturing industries

(G-7423)
OHIO NEWS NETWORK
Also Called: Ohio News Network, The
770 Twin Rivers Dr (43215-1127)
PHONE..................................614 460-3700
Fax: 614 280-6305
Tom Greidorn, *General Mgr*
Vince Jones, *Vice Pres*
Thomas Banks, *Engineer*
Scott Brandenburg, *Accounts Exec*
Molly Pensyl, *Accounts Exec*
EMP: 80
SALES (est): 3.7MM **Privately Held**
WEB: www.onnnews.com
SIC: 7383 2711 4841 News syndicates;
newspapers; cable & other pay television
services

(G-7424)
OHIO NEWSPAPER SERVICES INC
Also Called: Adohio
1335 Dublin Rd Ste 216b (43215-1000)
PHONE..................................614 486-6677
Andy Blizzard, *Advt Staff*
Chris Dixon, *Advt Staff*
Sue Bazzoli, *Manager*
Jason Sanford, *Manager*
Frank Deaner, *Exec Dir*
EMP: 11
SALES: 370.3K **Privately Held**
WEB: www.classifiedsohio.com
SIC: 7313 2711 Newspaper advertising
representative; newspapers, publishing &
printing
PA: Ohio News Media Association Ad Ohio
1335 Dublin Rd Ste 216b
Columbus OH 43215
614 486-6677

(G-7425)
OHIO NEWSPAPERS FOUNDATION
1335 Dublin Rd Ste 216b (43215-1000)
PHONE..................................614 486-6677
Al Sahafa, *Principal*
EMP: 5
SALES: 360.5K **Privately Held**
SIC: 2711 Newspapers, publishing & print-
ing

(G-7426)
OHIO PACKING COMPANY (PA)
1306 Harmon Ave (43223-3365)
PHONE..................................614 445-0627
Fax: 614 237-0885
Walter Wilke Jr, *President*
Carla Jones, *Vice Pres*
James Wilke, *Treasurer*
Ronald Wilke, *Exec Dir*
Edward Wilke Jr, *Admin Sec*
EMP: 90 **EST:** 1907
SQ FT: 70,000
SALES (est): 14.9MM **Privately Held**
SIC: 2011 Meat packing plants; pork prod-
ucts from pork slaughtered on site; cured
meats from meat slaughtered on site;
luncheon meat from meat slaughtered on
site

(G-7427)
OHIO PACKING COMPANY
1306 Harmon Ave (43223-3365)
PHONE..............................614 445-0627
Jim Wilke, *Manager*
EMP: 80
SALES (corp-wide): 14.9MM **Privately Held**
SIC: 2011 2013 Meat packing plants; sausages & other prepared meats
PA: The Ohio Packing Company
1306 Harmon Ave
Columbus OH 43223
614 445-0627

(G-7428)
OHIO PROCESSORS INC (HQ)
2200 Cardigan Ave (43215-1092)
PHONE..............................740 852-9243
Clifton J Smith, *Ch of Bd*
Douglas A Smith, *President*
Thomas G Michaelides, *Treasurer*
G Frederick Smith, *Admin Sec*
EMP: 4
SQ FT: 10,300
SALES (est): 2.9MM
SALES (corp-wide): 43.5MM **Privately Held**
SIC: 2026 5143 Whipped topping, except frozen or dry mix; dairy products, except dried or canned
PA: Instantwhip Foods, Inc.
2200 Cardigan Ave
Columbus OH 43215
614 488-2536

(G-7429)
OHIO PSYCHLOGY PBLICATIONS INC
Also Called: National Psychologist, The
620 Taylor Station Rd F (43230-6699)
PHONE..............................614 861-1999
Fax: 614 861-1996
Martin Saeman, *President*
Marilyn L Saeman, *Treasurer*
John Thomas, *Accounting Dir*
EMP: 5
SALES (est): 300K **Privately Held**
WEB: www.nationalpsychologist.com
SIC: 2731 Book publishing

(G-7430)
OHIO STATE PLASTICS
1917 Joyce Ave (43219-1029)
PHONE..............................614 299-5618
Fax: 614 299-5634
Dwayne Margin, *Manager*
John Fry, *Manager*
EMP: 17
SALES (est): 164.4K
SALES (corp-wide): 17.3B **Privately Held**
WEB: www.cccllc.com
SIC: 2656 Food containers (liquid tight), including milk cartons
HQ: Consolidated Container Company, Llc
3101 Towercreek Pkwy Se
Atlanta GA 30339
678 742-4600

(G-7431)
OHIO STATE UNIVERSITY
Also Called: Osu Arabidopsis Resource
1060 Carmack Rd Rm 39 (43210-1002)
PHONE..............................614 292-7656
Robert Tabita, *Director*
EMP: 40
SALES (corp-wide): 5.1B **Privately Held**
WEB: www.ohio-state.edu
SIC: 2869 8221 Laboratory chemicals, organic; university
PA: The Ohio State University
Student Acade Servi Bldg
Columbus OH 43210
614 292-6446

(G-7432)
OHIO STATE UNIVERSITY
Also Called: Osu Industrial Welding Sy
1248 Arthur E Adams Dr (43221-3560)
PHONE..............................614 292-4139
Richard A Miller, *Chairman*
EMP: 32
SALES (corp-wide): 5.1B **Privately Held**
WEB: www.ohio-state.edu
SIC: 7692 8221 Welding repair; university

PA: The Ohio State University
Student Acade Servi Bldg
Columbus OH 43210
614 292-6446

(G-7433)
OHIO STATE UNIVERSITY
Also Called: Assistive Technology of Ohio
2050 Kenny Rd Fl 9 (43221-3502)
PHONE..............................614 293-3600
Dena Truman, *Manager*
EMP: 7
SALES (corp-wide): 5.1B **Privately Held**
WEB: www.ohio-state.edu
SIC: 3842 8322 Technical aids for the handicapped; individual & family services
PA: The Ohio State University
Student Acade Servi Bldg
Columbus OH 43210
614 292-6446

(G-7434)
OHIO STATE UNIVERSITY
Also Called: O S U Press
1070 Carmack Rd Rm 180 (43210-1002)
PHONE..............................614 292-6930
Fax: 614 292-2065
Tara Cythers, *Editor*
Malcolm Litchfield, *Director*
Kathy Edwards, *Administration*
EMP: 13
SALES (corp-wide): 5.1B **Privately Held**
WEB: www.ohio-state.edu
SIC: 8221 2721 University; periodicals
PA: The Ohio State University
Student Acade Servi Bldg
Columbus OH 43210
614 292-6446

(G-7435)
OHIO TRAILER SUPPLY INC
Also Called: Ots
2966 Westerville Rd (43224-4563)
PHONE..............................614 471-9121
Fax: 614 476-1494
Jet Chrysler, *President*
EMP: 7
SQ FT: 8,000
SALES (est): 1MM **Privately Held**
WEB: www.ohiotrailer.com
SIC: 5013 7692 Trailer parts & accessories; welding repair

(G-7436)
OHIO WIRE FORM & SPRING CO
2270 S High St (43207-2432)
PHONE..............................614 444-3676
Fax: 614 444-4443
Stephen A Van Horn, *President*
P E Van Horn Jr, *Chairman*
Samuel E Van Horn, *Vice Pres*
Carl Hall, *Plant Mgr*
Sharon Ward, *Safety Mgr*
EMP: 17 EST: 1947
SQ FT: 43,800
SALES (est): 4.2MM **Privately Held**
WEB: www.ohiowireform.com
SIC: 3496 3495 Miscellaneous fabricated wire products; wire springs

(G-7437)
OHIO WOOD RECYCLING INC
Also Called: Dm Pallet Service
2019 Rathmell Rd (43207-5012)
PHONE..............................614 491-0881
Dexter Mounts, *President*
EMP: 20
SALES (est): 1.3MM **Privately Held**
SIC: 2448 Pallets, wood

(G-7438)
OHLINGER PUBLISHING SVCS INC
28 W Henderson Rd (43214-2628)
PHONE..............................614 261-5360
Monica Ohlinger, *President*
Donna Petersch, *Principal*
EMP: 10
SALES (est): 659.7K **Privately Held**
SIC: 2741 Miscellaneous publishing

(G-7439)
OIL BAR LLC (PA)
2740 Eastland Mall (43232-4960)
PHONE..............................614 501-9815
Ernest E Dennis Jr,

EMP: 4
SALES: 250K **Privately Held**
SIC: 2899 Oils & essential oils

(G-7440)
OLD TRAIL PRINTING COMPANY
100 Fornoff Rd (43207-2475)
PHONE..............................614 443-4852
Fax: 614 443-7742
Mary Held, *Owner*
Jeff Lampert, *Sales Mgr*
Dave Held, *Shareholder*
Michael Held, *Shareholder*
Susan Horn, *Shareholder*
EMP: 125 EST: 1924
SQ FT: 55,000
SALES (est): 24.8MM **Privately Held**
WEB: www.oldtrailprinting.com
SIC: 2752 2791 2789 2759 Commercial printing, offset; letters, circular or form: lithographed; typesetting; bookbinding & related work; commercial printing

(G-7441)
OLENTANGY EYE AND LASER A
3525 Olentngy Rvr Rd # 5310 (43214-3938)
PHONE..............................614 267-4122
Debbie Riegel, *Office Mgr*
EMP: 4
SALES (est): 479.6K **Privately Held**
SIC: 3841 Surgical lasers

(G-7442)
OMNITECH ELECTRONICS INC
5090 Trabue Rd (43228-9391)
PHONE..............................800 822-1344
Fax: 614 878-3560
Bogdan Zaleski, *President*
Paul Zaleski, *Managing Dir*
EMP: 12
SQ FT: 22,500
SALES: 800K **Privately Held**
SIC: 3826 Analytical instruments

(G-7443)
OPEN HOUSE MAGAZINE INC
1537 Guilford Rd (43221-3850)
PHONE..............................614 523-7775
Michael A Schadek, *President*
EMP: 3 EST: 1994
SALES (est): 300.9K **Privately Held**
WEB: www.openhousemag.com
SIC: 2721 6531 Magazines: publishing & printing; real estate agents & managers

(G-7444)
OPTICAL DISTRIBUTION CORP
401 N Front St Ste 350 (43215-2249)
PHONE..............................937 405-7280
Dave Delle Donne, *President*
Michael R Morosky, *Vice Pres*
Susannah Evans, *Info Tech Mgr*
Timothy O Neal, *Admin Sec*
▲ EMP: 16
SQ FT: 11,500
SALES: 3.6MM **Privately Held**
WEB: www.rodenstockusa.com
SIC: 3851 Eyeglasses, lenses & frames

(G-7445)
ORANGE BARREL MEDIA LLC
250 N Hartford Ave (43222-1100)
PHONE..............................614 294-4898
Peter Scantland, *Principal*
James Wooster, *Opers Staff*
Adam Borchers, *CFO*
Danielle Williamson, *VP Sales*
Lorin Wolf, *Accounts Exec*
EMP: 25
SALES (est): 2.5MM **Privately Held**
WEB: www.orangebarrelmedia.com
SIC: 3993 7312 Signs & advertising specialties; outdoor advertising services

(G-7446)
ORIGINAL MATTRESS FACTORY INC
851 W 5th Ave (43212-2632)
PHONE..............................614 291-8085
Fax: 614 291-9929
Richard Flynn, *Manager*
EMP: 3

SALES (corp-wide): 26.6MM **Privately Held**
SIC: 2515 Mattresses, innerspring or box spring
PA: The Original Mattress Factory Inc
4930 State Rd
Cleveland OH 44134
216 661-8388

(G-7447)
OSI GLOBAL SOURCING LLC
2575 Ferris Rd (43224-2540)
PHONE..............................614 471-4800
Tom Martini, *President*
EMP: 130
SALES (est): 4.4MM **Privately Held**
SIC: 2821 Plastics materials & resins

(G-7448)
OUR HEART HEALTH CARE SVCS LLC
1336 E Main St (43205-2081)
PHONE..............................614 943-5216
Erica Coit,
Leroy Kendrick,
Jackie Tunrbo,
EMP: 3 EST: 2010
SALES (est): 103.7K **Privately Held**
SIC: 2086 Fruit drinks (less than 100% juice): packaged in cans, etc.

(G-7449)
OUR NINE LLC
Also Called: Midwest Graphics
6740 Huntley Rd Ste F (43229-1037)
PHONE..............................614 844-6655
Geoff Binkley, *Prdtn Mgr*
Gayle May, *Software Dev*
EMP: 4 EST: 2012
SQ FT: 2,032
SALES (est): 487.1K **Privately Held**
SIC: 2752 Commercial printing, lithographic

(G-7450)
OUTLOOK PUBLISHING INC
815 N High St Ste I (43215-6424)
PHONE..............................614 268-8525
Malcolm Riggle, *President*
▲ EMP: 14
SALES: 466.2K **Privately Held**
SIC: 2711 Newspapers: publishing only, not printed on site

(G-7451)
P S PLASTICS INC
2020 Britains Ln (43224-5612)
PHONE..............................614 262-7070
Fax: 614 262-0408
John Pyers, *President*
Rob Sutliff, *Corp Secy*
Pat Rickard, *Sales Staff*
EMP: 11
SQ FT: 6,700
SALES: 500K **Privately Held**
SIC: 3089 Plastic processing

(G-7452)
P-AMERICAS LLC
Also Called: Pepsico
1241 Gibbard Ave (43219-2438)
PHONE..............................614 253-8771
Dale Watkins, *CFO*
EMP: 123
SALES (corp-wide): 62.8B **Publicly Held**
SIC: 2086 Carbonated soft drinks, bottled & canned
HQ: P-Americas Llc
1 Pepsi Way
Somers NY

(G-7453)
PACTIV LLC
2120 Westbelt Dr (43228-3820)
PHONE..............................815 547-1200
EMP: 53
SQ FT: 104,000 **Privately Held**
SIC: 2656 Mfg Sanitary Food Containers
HQ: Pactiv Llc
1900 W Field Ct
Lake Forest IL 60045
847 482-2000

(G-7454)
PACTIV LLC
2120 Westbelt Dr (43228-3820)
P.O. Box 28147 (43228)
PHONE.................................614 771-5400
Joe Deal, *Opers Mgr*
Ed Steeberger, *Opers Mgr*
Lynn Morgan, *Purch Agent*
Gary White, *Buyer*
Toni Caniglia, *Human Res Dir*
EMP: 240 **Privately Held**
WEB: www.pactiv.com
SIC: 2631 7389 Paperboard mills; packaging & labeling services
HQ: Pactiv Llc
1900 W Field Ct
Lake Forest IL 60045
847 482-2000

(G-7455)
PAKRA LLC
449 E Mound St (43215-5514)
PHONE.................................614 477-6965
Rini Das, *Mng Member*
Pamela Schmdt- Cavaliero,
Anne Claire France,
Ashish Shah,
Michelle Stewart,
EMP: 10
SQ FT: 900
SALES: 100K **Privately Held**
WEB: www.pakragames.com
SIC: 7372 8331 8249 8742 Business oriented computer software; educational computer software; job training & vocational rehabilitation services; business training services; management consulting services

(G-7456)
PANACEA PRODUCTS CORPORATION (PA)
Also Called: J-Mak Industries
2711 International St (43228-4604)
PHONE.................................614 850-7000
Fax: 614 850-7111
Frank A Paniccia, *President*
Louis Calderone, *Principal*
Fred Pagura, *Principal*
Jim Fancelli, *Vice Pres*
Gregg Paniccia, *Vice Pres*
◆ **EMP:** 40
SALES (est): 30.5MM **Privately Held**
WEB: www.panac.com
SIC: 3496 2542 5051 Miscellaneous fabricated wire products; shelving, made from purchased wire; shelving, office & store: except wood; metals service centers & offices

(G-7457)
PANACEA PRODUCTS CORPORATION
1825 Joyce Ave (43219-1027)
PHONE.................................614 429-6320
Frank Panancea, *Branch Mgr*
EMP: 54
SALES (corp-wide): 30.5MM **Privately Held**
WEB: www.panac.com
SIC: 3496 3423 2542 Miscellaneous fabricated wire products; hand & edge tools; partitions & fixtures, except wood
PA: Panacea Products Corporation
2711 International St
Columbus OH 43228
614 850-7000

(G-7458)
PAPEL COUTURE
Also Called: PC
6522 Singletree Dr (43229-1119)
PHONE.................................614 848-5700
Vadim Daskal, *Owner*
Scott Vogel, *General Mgr*
EMP: 6
SQ FT: 600
SALES: 1MM **Privately Held**
SIC: 2759 Invitation & stationery printing & engraving
PA: Daskal Enterprise, Llc
6522 Singletree Dr
Columbus OH 43229
614 848-5700

(G-7459)
PAPER VAULT
869 Montrose Ave (43209-2451)
PHONE.................................614 859-5538
Darci Bonnington, *Principal*
EMP: 3 **EST:** 2013
SALES (est): 160K **Privately Held**
SIC: 3272 Burial vaults, concrete or precast terrazzo

(G-7460)
PAPWORTH PRINTS
4355 Boulder Creek Dr (43230-6327)
PHONE.................................614 428-6137
William Papworth, *Principal*
EMP: 6
SALES (est): 610.7K **Privately Held**
SIC: 2752 Commercial printing, lithographic

(G-7461)
PARAGON WOODWORKING LLC
800 Reynolds Ave (43201-3767)
PHONE.................................614 402-1459
Larry Griggs, *Mng Member*
EMP: 3
SALES: 300K **Privately Held**
SIC: 2431 Millwork

(G-7462)
PARKER-HANNIFIN CORPORATION
Tube Fittings Division
3885 Gateway Blvd (43228-9723)
PHONE.................................614 279-7070
Fax: 614 279-7685
Wendy Moore, *Safety Mgr*
Ted Amling, *Engineer*
Dan Domanowski, *Engineer*
Nathan Green, *Engineer*
Eric Grimes, *Engineer*
EMP: 120
SALES (corp-wide): 11.3B **Publicly Held**
WEB: www.parker.com
SIC: 3494 5074 Pipe fittings; plumbing fittings & supplies
PA: Parker-Hannifin Corporation
6035 Parkland Blvd
Cleveland OH 44124
216 896-3000

(G-7463)
PATIO PRINTING INC
Also Called: Patio Print & Promotions
6663 Huntley Rd Ste S (43229-1040)
PHONE.................................614 785-9553
Fax: 614 785-9549
Dieter Thellmann, *President*
Margit Thellmann, *Vice Pres*
EMP: 7
SQ FT: 1,400
SALES (est): 982.1K **Privately Held**
WEB: www.patioprinting.com
SIC: 2752 Commercial printing, offset

(G-7464)
PATIO ROOM FACTORY INC
2659 Beulah Rd (43211-1012)
PHONE.................................614 449-7900
Fax: 614 263-1094
Walter Renz, *President*
Mark Yates, *Treasurer*
EMP: 5
SALES (est): 500K **Privately Held**
SIC: 3444 Awnings & canopies

(G-7465)
PATRIOT CONSULTING LLC
Also Called: Patriot Distributing
20 E Frambes Ave (43201-1406)
PHONE.................................614 554-6455
Robert Packey,
EMP: 3
SALES: 150K **Privately Held**
SIC: 3646 Commercial indusl & institutional electric lighting fixtures

(G-7466)
PATS DELICIOUS LLC
737 Parkwood Ave (43219-2517)
PHONE.................................614 441-7047
Patricia Okoro, *CEO*
EMP: 4
SALES (est): 127.7K **Privately Held**
SIC: 2096 Potato chips & similar snacks

(G-7467)
PAUL PETERSON COMPANY (PA)
950 Dublin Rd (43215-1169)
P.O. Box 1510 (43216-1510)
PHONE.................................614 486-4375
Fax: 614 486-5517
Paul Peterson Jr, *CEO*
Parr Peterson, *President*
Andrew J White Jr, *Principal*
Richard L Miller, *Principal*
Grant S Richards, *Principal*
EMP: 47
SALES (est): 15.2MM **Privately Held**
WEB: www.ppco.net
SIC: 1611 1799 3669 5084 Guardrail construction, highways; highway & street sign installation; waterproofing; traffic signals, electric; safety equipment; work zone traffic equipment (flags, cones, barrels, etc.)

(G-7468)
PAUL PETERSON SAFETY DIV INC
950 Dublin Rd (43215-1169)
P.O. Box 1510 (43216-1510)
PHONE.................................614 486-4375
Paul Peterson Jr, *President*
Colette Peterson, *Corp Secy*
Gary Boylan, *Vice Pres*
Parr Peterson, *Vice Pres*
EMP: 30
SQ FT: 3,800
SALES (est): 180.7K
SALES (corp-wide): 15.2MM **Privately Held**
WEB: www.ppco.net
SIC: 3993 5999 7359 Signs, not made in custom sign painting shops; safety supplies & equipment; work zone traffic equipment (flags, cones, barrels, etc.)
PA: The Paul Peterson Company
950 Dublin Rd
Columbus OH 43215
614 486-4375

(G-7469)
PAULA AND JULIES COOKBOOKS LLC
6034 Mcnaughten Grove Ln (43213-5103)
PHONE.................................614 863-1193
Paula Weinstein, *Principal*
EMP: 3
SALES (est): 167.5K **Privately Held**
SIC: 2741 Miscellaneous publishing

(G-7470)
PAULG CORPORATION
1601 W 5th Ave (43212-2310)
PHONE.................................914 662-9837
Jeff Hartman, *Vice Pres*
EMP: 40
SALES (est): 1.3MM **Privately Held**
SIC: 3499 Novelties & giftware, including trophies

(G-7471)
PEARSON EDUCATION INC
4350 Equity Dr (43228-4801)
PHONE.................................614 876-0371
Janet Fauser, *Prdtn Mgr*
Heather Ganan, *Production*
Joanne Toscano, *Marketing Staff*
Sheila Hickle, *Branch Mgr*
John Campbell, *Manager*
EMP: 14
SALES (corp-wide): 5.6B **Privately Held**
SIC: 2721 Periodicals
HQ: Pearson Education, Inc.
1 Lake St
Upper Saddle River NJ 07458
201 236-7000

(G-7472)
PEARSON EDUCATION INC
445 Hutchinson Ave # 400 (43235-5677)
PHONE.................................614 841-3700
Tim Richards, *President*
Ann Davis, *Editor*
Bruce Johnson, *Manager*
EMP: 17
SALES (corp-wide): 5.6B **Privately Held**
WEB: www.phgenit.com
SIC: 2721 Periodicals

HQ: Pearson Education, Inc.
1 Lake St
Upper Saddle River NJ 07458
201 236-7000

(G-7473)
PECO II INC
7060 Huntley Rd (43229-1082)
PHONE.................................614 431-0694
Rich Powell, *Opers Mgr*
EMP: 55
SALES (corp-wide): 123.6B **Publicly Held**
WEB: www.peco2.com
SIC: 3661 8711 7372 3822 Telephone & telegraph apparatus; engineering services; prepackaged software; auto controls regulating residntl & coml environmt & applncs; relays & industrial controls
HQ: Peco Ii, Inc.
601 Shiloh Rd
Plano TX 75074
972 284-8449

(G-7474)
PEEBLES - HERZOG INC
50 Hayden Ave (43222-1019)
PHONE.................................614 279-2211
Fax: 614 279-2321
Michael B Herzog, *President*
Michael Lauffer, *Vice Pres*
Jane Hampton, *Treasurer*
Lynn Slimmer, *Personnel Exec*
EMP: 9
SQ FT: 6,500
SALES (est): 884.2K **Privately Held**
WEB: www.peeblesherzog.com
SIC: 3931 7699 Pipes, organ; organ tuning & repair

(G-7475)
PEGGYS PRIDE
183 E Rich St (43215-5218)
PHONE.................................614 464-2511
Fax: 614 464-4351
Bill Welch, *President*
Carrie Welch, *Manager*
EMP: 3
SALES (est): 180K **Privately Held**
SIC: 2013 Sausages & other prepared meats

(G-7476)
PENNANT COMPANIES (PA)
2000 Bethel Rd Ste D (43220-5810)
P.O. Box 188, Sabina (45169-0188)
PHONE.................................614 451-1782
Chuck Foster, *CEO*
Larry Martin, *CFO*
EMP: 405
SQ FT: 200
SALES (est): 51.4MM **Privately Held**
WEB: www.pennantcompanies.com
SIC: 3465 Moldings or trim, automobile: stamped metal

(G-7477)
PEPSI-COLA METRO BTLG CO INC
Also Called: Pepsico
2553 N High St (43202-2555)
PHONE.................................614 261-8193
Al Vogt, *Manager*
EMP: 115
SALES (corp-wide): 62.8B **Publicly Held**
WEB: www.pbg.com
SIC: 2086 Carbonated soft drinks, bottled & canned
HQ: Pepsi-Cola Metropolitan Bottling Company, Inc.
1111 Westchester Ave
White Plains NY 10604
914 767-6000

(G-7478)
PERCUVISION LLC
2030 Dividend Dr (43228-3847)
PHONE.................................614 891-4800
Errol Singh, *CEO*
Earl Singh, *COO*
Rick Karr, *Vice Pres*
Allen Stock, *Vice Pres*
David Busick, *Commissioner*
EMP: 18
SQ FT: 7,500

SALES (est): 2.3MM **Privately Held**
SIC: 3841 Surgical & medical instruments

(G-7479)
PERFORMANCE RESEARCH INC
Also Called: PRI Marine
3328 Westerville Rd (43224-3700)
PHONE......................................614 475-8300
Fax: 614 475-8299
Robert M Proffit, *President*
EMP: 7 EST: 1953
SQ FT: 10,000
SALES (est): 650K **Privately Held**
SIC: 3519 Marine engines

(G-7480)
PETROLIANCE
2854 Johnstown Rd (43219-1772)
PHONE......................................614 475-5952
EMP: 3 EST: 2010
SALES (est): 130K **Privately Held**
SIC: 2992 Mfg Lubricating Oils/Greases

(G-7481)
PHARMAFORCE INC (DH)
960 Crupper Ave (43229-1109)
PHONE......................................614 436-2222
Peter Stoelzle, *President*
Gopal Anyarambhatla, *Vice Pres*
Timothy Lutz, *Mfg Dir*
Derrick Bennett, *Site Mgr*
Quinn Parks, *Opers Staff*
EMP: 30
SQ FT: 80,000
SALES (est): 37.1MM
SALES (corp-wide): 8.4B **Privately Held**
WEB: www.pharmaforceinc.com
SIC: 2834 Pharmaceutical preparations
HQ: Luitpold Pharmaceuticals, Inc.
5 Ramsey Rd
Shirley NY 11967
631 924-4000

(G-7482)
PHILADELPHIA INSTANTWHIP INC (HQ)
2200 Cardigan Ave (43215-1092)
PHONE......................................614 488-2536
Douglas A Smith, *President*
Tom Willard, *General Mgr*
Thomas G Michaelides, *Treasurer*
G Frederick Smith, *Admin Sec*
EMP: 4
SALES (est): 821.6K
SALES (corp-wide): 43.5MM **Privately Held**
SIC: 2026 5143 Whipped topping, except frozen or dry mix; dairy products, except dried or canned
PA: Instantwhip Foods, Inc.
2200 Cardigan Ave
Columbus OH 43215
614 488-2536

(G-7483)
PHOTO-TYPE ENGRAVING COMPANY
2500 Harrison Rd (43204-3510)
PHONE......................................614 308-1900
Fax: 614 308-5600
Doug Rittenhouse, *Branch Mgr*
EMP: 15
SALES (corp-wide): 37.5MM **Privately Held**
SIC: 2791 Photocomposition, for the printing trade
PA: The Photo-Type Engraving Company
2141 Gilbert Ave
Cincinnati OH 45206
513 281-0999

(G-7484)
PHOTO-TYPE ENGRAVING COMPANY
2500 Harrison Rd (43204-3510)
PHONE......................................614 308-7914
Doug Rittenhouse, *Opers Staff*
Dave Olberding, *Manager*
EMP: 15
SALES (corp-wide): 34.1MM **Privately Held**
WEB: www.phototype.com
SIC: 2791 Photocomposition, for the printing trade

PA: The Photo-Type Engraving Company
2141 Gilbert Ave
Cincinnati OH 45206
513 281-0999

(G-7485)
PIECE OF CAKE
772 N High St Ste 104 (43215-1457)
PHONE......................................614 421-0399
Brian Hopopt, *Manager*
EMP: 8 EST: 2002
SALES (est): 1.2MM **Privately Held**
SIC: 3556 Ovens, bakery

(G-7486)
PITT PLASTICS INC (DH)
3980 Groves Rd Ste A (43232-4172)
PHONE......................................614 868-8660
Terry Callow, *Treasurer*
Sandy Wood, *Office Mgr*
EMP: 65
SQ FT: 120,000
SALES (est): 58.3MM
SALES (corp-wide): 1.1B **Privately Held**
SIC: 2821 2673 Polyethylene resins; bags: plastic, laminated & coated
HQ: Pitt Plastics, Inc.
1400 E Atkinson Ave
Pittsburg KS 66762
620 231-4030

(G-7487)
PJS WHOLESALE INC
2551 Westbelt Dr (43228-3826)
PHONE......................................614 402-9363
Azmi Azzam Alhamouri, *Principal*
Mahmoud T Almahmoud, *Principal*
▲ EMP: 6 EST: 2009
SALES (est): 515.1K **Privately Held**
SIC: 2253 T-shirts & tops, knit

(G-7488)
PLAIN DEALER PUBLISHING CO
155 E Broad St Fl 23 (43215-3609)
PHONE......................................614 228-8200
Fax: 614 228-6872
Reginald Fields, *Manager*
EMP: 5
SALES (corp-wide): 1.6B **Privately Held**
WEB: www.plaind.com
SIC: 2711 7383 Newspapers; news syndicates
HQ: Plain Dealer Publishing Co.
4800 Tiedeman Rd
Cleveland OH 44144
216 999-5000

(G-7489)
PLASKOLITE LLC (PA)
Also Called: Plaskolite Continental
1770 Joyce Ave (43219-1026)
P.O. Box 1497 (43216-1497)
PHONE......................................614 294-3281
Fax: 614 297-7288
Mitchell P Grindley, *President*
Tyler Dockery, *Buyer*
Andrew Dunn, *Purchasing*
Matt Gutman, *Purchasing*
Robert Bower, *Accounting Dir*
▲ EMP: 238 EST: 1950
SQ FT: 650,000
SALES (est): 166.8MM **Privately Held**
WEB: www.plaskolite.com
SIC: 2821 Plastics materials & resins

(G-7490)
PLASKOLITE LLC
Also Called: Retail Display Group
1770 Joyce Ave (43219-1026)
P.O. Box 1497 (43216-1497)
PHONE......................................614 294-7294
Fax: 614 297-7232
James R Dunn, *Branch Mgr*
EMP: 280
SALES (corp-wide): 166.8MM **Privately Held**
WEB: www.plaskolite.com
SIC: 2821 3083 Acrylic resins; laminated plastics plate & sheet
PA: Plaskolite Llc
1770 Joyce Ave
Columbus OH 43219
614 294-3281

(G-7491)
PLASMACARE INC
3840 E Main St (43213-2947)
PHONE......................................614 231-5322
Douglas Bogue, *Branch Mgr*
EMP: 6
SALES (corp-wide): 548.5MM **Privately Held**
SIC: 2836 Plasmas
HQ: Plasmacare, Inc.
2410 Lillyvale Ave
Los Angeles CA 90032
323 225-2221

(G-7492)
PLASTIC SELECTION GROUP INC (PA)
Also Called: P S G
692 N High St Ste 310 (43215-1581)
PHONE......................................614 464-2008
Fax: 614 464-1585
Frank William Dickinson, *President*
Bill Dickinson, *President*
Stephen Gibson, *Sls & Mktg Exec*
Amanda Coulter, *Sales Staff*
Dee Walker, *Director*
▼ EMP: 5
SQ FT: 1,500
SALES: 3.2MM **Privately Held**
WEB: www.go2psg.com
SIC: 2821 Plastics materials & resins

(G-7493)
PLASTIC SUPPLIERS INC (PA)
2450 Marilyn Ln (43219-1721)
PHONE......................................614 471-9100
Fax: 614 471-9033
Peter Driscoll, *Ch of Bd*
George L Thomas, *President*
Dave Dittman, *Vice Pres*
Erich Emhuff, *Vice Pres*
Robert Scholz, *VP Opers*
◆ EMP: 29 EST: 1949
SQ FT: 7,500
SALES (est): 92.5MM **Privately Held**
WEB: www.plasticsuppliers.com
SIC: 3081 Unsupported plastics film & sheet

(G-7494)
PLASTIC SUPPLIERS INC
2400 Marilyn Ln (43219-1721)
P.O. Box 360478 (43236-0478)
PHONE......................................614 475-8010
Fax: 614 475-0264
EMP: 93
SALES (corp-wide): 93.3MM **Privately Held**
SIC: 3081 Mfg Unsupported Plastic Film/Sheet
PA: Plastic Suppliers, Inc.
2887 Johnstown Rd
Columbus OH 43219
614 471-9100

(G-7495)
PLASTIC SUPPLIERS INC
2450 Marilyn Ln (43219-1721)
PHONE......................................614 475-8010
Fax: 614 475-0264
Jim Allen, *Branch Mgr*
EMP: 25
SALES (corp-wide): 92.5MM **Privately Held**
WEB: www.plasticsuppliers.com
SIC: 3081 Plastic film & sheet
PA: Plastic Suppliers, Inc.
2450 Marilyn Ln
Columbus OH 43219
614 471-9100

(G-7496)
PLATINUM PRODUCTIONS INC
Also Called: Ron Roth Advertising
8100 N High St (43235-6400)
PHONE......................................614 888-7771
Ron Foth, *President*
Marty Nowak, *VP Prdtn*
Todd King, *Art Dir*
EMP: 45
SQ FT: 13,500
SALES (est): 5.4MM **Privately Held**
WEB: www.platinumproductions.com
SIC: 3993 Advertising artwork

(G-7497)
PLAZA AT SAWMILL PL
6472 Sawmill Rd (43235)
PHONE......................................614 889-6121
Fax: 614 889-6163
Dan McGrath, *Principal*
EMP: 9
SALES (est): 561.8K **Privately Held**
SIC: 2421 Sawmills & planing mills, general

(G-7498)
PLC CONNECTIONS LLC
673 N Wilson Rd (43204-1461)
PHONE......................................614 279-1796
◆ EMP: 15
SQ FT: 7,000
SALES (est): 1.6MM **Privately Held**
SIC: 3229 Mfg Fiber-Optic Components

(G-7499)
PLCC2 LLC
Also Called: PLC Connections
673 N Wilson Rd (43204-1461)
PHONE......................................614 279-1796
Tammy Bergman, *Accountant*
Tadashi Miyashita, *Mng Member*
Michael Obrian,
◆ EMP: 8 EST: 2014
SQ FT: 7,000
SALES (est): 553.4K **Privately Held**
SIC: 3678 8711 Electronic connectors; engineering services

(G-7500)
PLOTT GRAPHIC DIRECTIONS INC
859 Harmony Dr (43230-4390)
PHONE......................................614 475-0217
Fax: 614 475-0137
Elizabeth Plott, *President*
James Galliher, *Vice Pres*
Barbara Pike, *Office Mgr*
EMP: 8
SQ FT: 3,500
SALES: 500K **Privately Held**
WEB: www.gdi324.com
SIC: 2791 Typesetting, computer controlled

(G-7501)
PMJ PARTNERS LLC
Also Called: Bucktask
281 Lenappe Dr (43214-3171)
PHONE......................................201 360-1914
Paul Weiss,
EMP: 4
SALES: 50K **Privately Held**
SIC: 7372 7389 Application computer software;

(G-7502)
POLKADOT CUPCAKERY LIMITED
2926 Hayden Run Plz (43235-7261)
PHONE......................................614 304-1368
EMP: 4
SALES (est): 240.7K **Privately Held**
SIC: 2051 Bread, cake & related products

(G-7503)
POLYCEL INCORPORATED
Also Called: Amatech Polycell
1633 Woodland Ave (43219-1135)
PHONE......................................614 252-2400
Fax: 614 252-2422
David Amatangelo, *Principal*
Steve Mina, *Sls & Mktg Exec*
EMP: 22 EST: 1980
SALES (est): 3.7MM **Privately Held**
WEB: www.polycel-inc.com
SIC: 3086 Plastics foam products

(G-7504)
POPS PRINTED APPAREL LLC
1758 N High St Unit 2 (43201-4422)
PHONE......................................614 372-5651
Austin Pence, *Mng Member*
Chad Campagna,
EMP: 6
SQ FT: 2,000
SALES: 200K **Privately Held**
SIC: 2759 Screen printing

(G-7505)
POSM SOFTWARE LLC
4925 Sharon Hill Dr (43235-3451)
PHONE.................................859 274-0041
Robert Katter, *Principal*
EMP: 6
SALES (est): 421.1K **Privately Held**
SIC: 7372 Prepackaged software

(G-7506)
POWER ACQUISITION LLC (HQ)
835 Goodale Blvd (43212-3824)
PHONE.................................614 228-5000
John B Simmons, *CEO*
J Michael Kirksey, *CFO*
Megan Wajda, *Administration*
EMP: 3
SALES (est): 66.7MM
SALES (corp-wide): 1.4B **Privately Held**
SIC: 3694 7538 7537 Distributors, motor
vehicle engine; diesel engine repair: auto-
motive; automotive transmission repair
shops
PA: Oep Capital Advisors, L.P.
510 Madison Ave Fl 19
New York NY 10022
212 277-1552

(G-7507)
PPAFCO INC
1096 Ridge St (43215-1154)
PHONE.................................614 488-7259
Fax: 614 488-7219
Laura Bowman, *President*
EMP: 14
SQ FT: 15,000
SALES: 950K **Privately Held**
SIC: 3089 3069 5074 Fittings for pipe,
plastic; nipples, rubber; pipes & fittings,
plastic

(G-7508)
PPG ARCHITECTURAL FINISHES INC
Also Called: Glidden Professional Paint Ctr
2840 N High St (43202-1102)
PHONE.................................614 846-0097
Fax: 614 846-0488
Mike Stevens, *Manager*
EMP: 4
SALES (corp-wide): 14.7B **Publicly Held**
WEB: www.gliddenpaint.com
SIC: 2891 Adhesives
HQ: Ppg Architectural Finishes, Inc.
1 Ppg Pl
Pittsburgh PA 15272
412 434-3131

(G-7509)
PPG INDUSTRIES INC
Also Called: PPG 5537
5548 N Hamilton Rd (43230-1322)
PHONE.................................614 939-2365
Donna Matthews, *Branch Mgr*
EMP: 24
SALES (corp-wide): 14.7B **Publicly Held**
WEB: www.ppg.com
SIC: 2851 Paints & allied products
PA: Ppg Industries, Inc.
1 Ppg Pl
Pittsburgh PA 15272
412 434-3131

(G-7510)
PPG INDUSTRIES INC
Also Called: PPG 5404
2840 N High St (43202-1102)
PHONE.................................614 268-2609
Robert Seagle, *Branch Mgr*
Bill Stygler, *Manager*
EMP: 24
SALES (corp-wide): 14.7B **Publicly Held**
WEB: www.ppg.com
SIC: 2851 Paints & allied products
PA: Ppg Industries, Inc.
1 Ppg Pl
Pittsburgh PA 15272
412 434-3131

(G-7511)
PR SIGNS & SERVICE
3049 E 14th Ave (43219)
PHONE.................................614 252-7090
Philip Radke, *Principal*
EMP: 5

SALES (est): 366.9K **Privately Held**
SIC: 3993 Signs & advertising specialties

(G-7512)
PRAXAIR DISTRIBUTION INC
450 Greenlawn Ave (43223-2611)
PHONE.................................614 443-7687
Fax: 740 443-1915
Pratt Thompson, *Manager*
EMP: 19
SALES (corp-wide): 10.5B **Publicly Held**
SIC: 2813 Industrial gases
HQ: Praxair Distribution, Inc.
10 Riverview Dr
Danbury CT 06810
203 837-2000

(G-7513)
PRECISION APPLIED COATINGS
3021 E 4th Ave Ste B (43219-2888)
PHONE.................................614 252-8711
Michael R Gramke,
Scott J Gramke,
Tadd D Gruenewald,
▲ EMP: 7
SALES (est): 605K **Privately Held**
SIC: 3479 Painting, coating & hot dipping

(G-7514)
PREISSER INC
Also Called: PIP Printing
3560 Millikin Ct Ste A (43228-9809)
P.O. Box 827, Dublin (43017-6827)
PHONE.................................614 345-0199
Fax: 740 548-0299
Gail Preisser, *President*
Thomas Preisser, *Corp Secy*
Richard Ayers, *Sales Staff*
Kris Davis, *Sales Staff*
John Konrad, *Marketing Staff*
EMP: 20 EST: 1974
SALES (est): 4.6MM **Privately Held**
SIC: 2752 2791 Commercial printing, off-
set; typesetting

(G-7515)
PRESS CHEMICAL & PHRM LAB
2700 E Main St Ste 102 (43209-2536)
P.O. Box 9103 (43209-0103)
PHONE.................................614 863-2802
Pearson Press, *President*
Phea Press, *Corp Secy*
Paul Wherry, *Vice Pres*
EMP: 3
SQ FT: 600
SALES (est): 320K **Privately Held**
SIC: 2819 2833 Industrial inorganic chem-
icals; organic medicinal chemicals: bulk,
uncompounded

(G-7516)
PRESTRESS SERVICES INDS LLC (PA)
2250 N Hartford Ave (43222)
P.O. Box 55436, Lexington KY (40555-5436)
PHONE.................................859 299-0461
Martin Cohen, *Mng Member*
Scott Ramsden, *Manager*
Barry Barger,
Greg Harville,
Richard Hudnall,
EMP: 250
SALES (est): 93.8MM **Privately Held**
SIC: 3272 Concrete products

(G-7517)
PRIME EQUIPMENT GROUP INC
Also Called: Diversfied Mch Pdts Gnsvlle GA
2000 E Fulton St (43205-2534)
PHONE.................................614 253-8590
Fax: 614 253-6966
Joseph Gasbarro, *President*
Nicholas Gasbarro, *President*
Kirk Reis, *Research*
Kathleen Drum, *Engineer*
Geoff Moss, *Engineer*
◆ EMP: 100
SALES (est): 47MM **Privately Held**
WEB: www.primeequipmentgroup.com
SIC: 3556 Poultry processing machinery

(G-7518)
PRINT SYNDICATE LLC
901 W 3rd Ave Ste A (43212-3131)
PHONE.................................614 519-0341

Jarred Mullins, *Manager*
EMP: 15
SALES (est): 2.6MM **Privately Held**
SIC: 2752 Commercial printing, litho-
graphic

(G-7519)
PRINTED IMAGE
Also Called: The Printed Image
41 S Grant Ave (43215-3979)
PHONE.................................614 221-1412
Cathleen Siech, *President*
Vicki Hamer, *Vice Pres*
Karen Norton, *Consultant*
EMP: 10
SALES (est): 1.4MM **Privately Held**
WEB: www.printedimage.com
SIC: 2752 2791 2789 Commercial print-
ing, offset; typesetting; bookbinding & re-
lated work

(G-7520)
PRISM PRINTS INC
Also Called: Prism Prints T-Shirts
5765 Westbourne Ave (43213-1488)
PHONE.................................614 294-4981
Fax: 614 294-0185
Laurence Seitzer, *President*
Kristin Seitzer, *Admin Sec*
EMP: 7 EST: 1974
SQ FT: 5,500
SALES (est): 500K **Privately Held**
SIC: 2261 Screen printing of cotton broad-
woven fabrics

(G-7521)
PRO PRINTING INC
4191 W Broad St (43228-1651)
PHONE.................................614 276-8366
Sherri Sykes, *President*
Danielle Slone, *Consultant*
EMP: 5
SALES (est): 580K **Privately Held**
SIC: 2752 Commercial printing, litho-
graphic

(G-7522)
PROCESS MACHINERY INC
860 Kaderly Dr (43228-1034)
PHONE.................................614 278-1055
Rose Savage, *Branch Mgr*
EMP: 19
SALES (corp-wide): 29.9MM **Privately Held**
SIC: 3569 Filters
PA: Process Machinery, Inc.
1636 Isaac Shelby Dr
Shelbyville KY 40065
502 633-5665

(G-7523)
PROFILE IMAGING COLUMBUS LLC
Also Called: Profile Discovery
46 N High St Ste 200 (43215-3010)
PHONE.................................614 222-2888
Larry Kotterman, *President*
Linda F Wong, *Opers Staff*
Andrew Keck, *Info Tech Dir*
EMP: 3 EST: 2005
SALES (est): 407.2K **Privately Held**
SIC: 7372 Prepackaged software

(G-7524)
PROFORM GROUP INC
1715 Georgesville Rd (43228-3619)
PHONE.................................614 332-9654
Missy Reed, *QC Mgr*
Joe Vannata, *Branch Mgr*
Cherri Haywood, *Director*
EMP: 52
SALES (corp-wide): 55.9MM **Privately Held**
SIC: 3713 Truck bodies & parts
PA: Proform Group, Inc.
4400 Don Cayo Dr
Muskogee OK 74403
918 682-8666

(G-7525)
PROVIDENCE REES INC
2111 Builders Pl (43204-4886)
P.O. Box 12535 (43212-0535)
PHONE.................................614 833-6231
Fax: 614 487-6184
Leo Steger, *Corp Secy*

Billy Parsley, *Corp Secy*
Herbert Brown, *Vice Pres*
John Oneal, *Opers Mgr*
Lee Nichols, *Production*
EMP: 35
SQ FT: 36,000
SALES: 4.7MM **Privately Held**
SIC: 3496 8711 Wire winding; engineering
services

(G-7526)
PUBLISHING GROUP LTD
781 Northwest Blvd # 202 (43212-3874)
PHONE.................................614 572-1240
Fax: 614 572-1241
Chuck Steie, *CEO*
Chuck Stein, *CEO*
Dave Prosser, *President*
Garth Bishop, *Editor*
Kathy Gillis, *Vice Pres*
EMP: 10
SALES: 1.5MM **Privately Held**
WEB: www.pubgroupltd.com
SIC: 2721 7389 2741 5199 Magazines:
publishing & printing; trade journals: pub-
lishing & printing; trade show arrange-
ment; art copy: publishing & printing;
advertising specialties

(G-7527)
PUREBRED PUBLISHING INC
1224 Alton Darby Creek Rd C
(43228-9813)
PHONE.................................614 339-5393
John Mocier, *President*
Seph Johnson, *General Mgr*
Seth Spencer, *Vice Pres*
EMP: 5
SALES (est): 357.6K
SALES (corp-wide): 962K **Privately Held**
WEB: www.brownswissusa.com
SIC: 2741 Miscellaneous publishing
PA: American Guernsey Association
1224 Alton Darby Creek Rd
Columbus OH 43228
614 864-2409

(G-7528)
Q T COLUMBUS LLC
1330 Stimmel Rd (43223-2917)
PHONE.................................800 758-2410
Daniel Root, *President*
Dave Root, *Treasurer*
EMP: 6
SALES (est): 706.8K
SALES (corp-wide): 6.3MM **Privately Held**
WEB: www.qtequipment.com
SIC: 7532 5531 3713 Body shop, trucks;
automotive tires; utility truck bodies
PA: Q.T. Equipment Company
151 W Dartmore Ave
Akron OH 44301
330 724-3055

(G-7529)
QLEANAIR SCANDINAVIA INC
7670 Whitewood Ct (43235-1756)
PHONE.................................614 323-1272
David Schneider, *President*
Amanda Helms-Myers, *Manager*
EMP: 5
SALES (est): 351K **Privately Held**
SIC: 3822 7389 Building services monitor-
ing controls, automatic;

(G-7530)
QPI MULTIPRESS INC
2222 S 3rd St (43207-2402)
PHONE.................................614 228-0185
Fax: 614 228-8340
Richard Drexler, *CEO*
Theodore P Schwartz, *President*
Larry Bondurant, *Purchasing*
TAC Kensler, *CFO*
Doug Brooke, *Manager*
EMP: 7
SQ FT: 55,000
SALES (est): 577.4K
SALES (corp-wide): 24MM **Privately Held**
WEB: www.quality-products.com
SIC: 3542 Presses: hydraulic & pneumatic,
mechanical & manual

PA: Quality Products, Inc.
2222 S 3rd St
Columbus OH 43207
614 228-0185

(G-7531)
QUAD/GRAPHICS INC
4051 Fondorf Dr (43228-1025)
PHONE......................................614 276-4800
Pat Seymour, *Human Res Dir*
Norm Phristoffersem, *Manager*
EMP: 250
SALES (corp-wide): 4.3B **Publicly Held**
WEB: www.vertisinc.com
SIC: 7311 2791 2752 Advertising agen-
cies; typesetting; commercial printing, lith-
ographic
PA: Quad/Graphics Inc.
N61w23044 Harrys Way
Sussex WI 53089
414 566-6000

(G-7532)
QUADRA - TECH INC
864 E Jenkins Ave (43207-1317)
PHONE......................................614 445-0690
Fax: 614 443-2024
Alan Wasserstrom, *CEO*
John H McCormick, *President*
Zigler Robert, *Sales Mgr*
Robert Zigler, *Sales Mgr*
Howard Hickman, *Telecom Exec*
EMP: 85
SQ FT: 125,000
SALES (est): 14.7MM
SALES (corp-wide): 776.3MM **Privately
Held**
WEB: www.quadra-techinc.com
SIC: 2599 Carts, restaurant equipment
PA: The Wasserstrom Company
477 S Front St
Columbus OH 43215
614 737-8472

(G-7533)
QUALCO LLC
2211 S James Rd (43232-3852)
PHONE......................................614 257-7408
Ryan Patenaude, *Manager*
Michael Gibbs,
EMP: 3 **EST:** 2004
SQ FT: 12,000
SALES (est): 410K **Privately Held**
SIC: 2542 Fixtures: display, office or store:
except wood

(G-7534)
**QUALITY BAKERY COMPANY
INC**
Also Called: Mountain Top Frozen Pies Div
50 N Glenwood Ave (43222-1206)
P.O. Box 453 (43216-0453)
PHONE......................................614 224-1424
Fax: 614 224-8652
Jeff Waller, *Manager*
EMP: 50
SQ FT: 32,836
SALES (corp-wide): 1.1B **Publicly Held**
WEB: www.marzetti.com
SIC: 2051 Bread, cake & related products
HQ: The Quality Bakery Company Inc
380 Polaris Pkwy Ste 400
Westerville OH 43082
614 846-2232

(G-7535)
QUALITY PRODUCTS INC (PA)
2222 S 3rd St (43207-2402)
PHONE......................................614 228-0185
David Somers, *CEO*
Richard Drexler, *Ch of Bd*
Karen Hart, *President*
Jason I Drexler, *CFO*
TAC Kensler, *CFO*
EMP: 67 **EST:** 1988
SQ FT: 45,000
SALES: 24MM **Privately Held**
WEB: www.quality-products.com
SIC: 3542 3569 Presses: hydraulic &
pneumatic, mechanical & manual; jacks,
hydraulic

(G-7536)
QUALITY RUBBER STAMP INC
3314 Refugee Rd (43232-4810)
PHONE......................................614 235-2700

Fax: 614 235-3031
John J Lawler, *President*
EMP: 8
SQ FT: 4,000
SALES: 900K **Privately Held**
WEB: www.qualityrubberstamp.com
SIC: 3953 3083 2396 2395 Numbering
stamps, hand: rubber or metal; plastic fin-
ished products, laminated; screen printing
on fabric articles; embroidery & art
needlework; emblems, embroidered;
platemaking services

(G-7537)
**QUALITY STITCH EMBROIDERY
INC**
3892 E Broad St (43213-1128)
PHONE......................................614 237-0480
Steve Fowler, *President*
EMP: 5
SQ FT: 1,500
SALES: 250K **Privately Held**
WEB: www.quality-stitch.com
SIC: 2395 Embroidery products, except
schiffli machine

(G-7538)
**QUALITY-SERVICE PRODUCTS
INC**
528 E Hudson St (43202-2766)
PHONE......................................614 447-9522
Fax: 614 263-1478
Nelson N Jeck Sr, *CEO*
Nelson N Jeck Jr, *President*
Jo Ann Jeck, *Corp Secy*
EMP: 11
SQ FT: 8,200
SALES (est): 1.8MM **Privately Held**
SIC: 3085 Plastics bottles

(G-7539)
QUICKSTITCH PLUS LLC
124 Granville St (43230-3043)
PHONE......................................614 476-3186
Michele Uber, *Principal*
Scott Uber, *Sales Staff*
EMP: 4
SALES (est): 338.5K **Privately Held**
SIC: 2395 Embroidery & art needlework

(G-7540)
QUIKRETE COMPANIES INC
Also Called: THE QUIKRETE COMPANIES
INC
6225 Huntley Rd (43229-1005)
PHONE......................................614 885-4406
Fax: 614 436-5931
D Winchester, *Vice Pres*
Phil Wegmiller, *Opers Mgr*
Robert Miller, *Branch Mgr*
John Ihlendorf, *Manager*
EMP: 35
SQ FT: 10,000 **Privately Held**
WEB: www.quikrete.com
SIC: 3272 3241 2899 Dry mixture con-
crete; cement, hydraulic; chemical prepa-
rations
HQ: The Quikrete Companies Llc
3490 Piedmont Rd Ne # 1300
Atlanta GA 30305
404 634-9100

(G-7541)
R & J BARDON INC
4676 Larwell Dr (43220-3621)
PHONE......................................614 457-5500
Chris Swearingen, *President*
Leslie Swearingen, *Vice Pres*
EMP: 9
SQ FT: 3,000
SALES: 850K **Privately Held**
SIC: 2752 Commercial printing, offset

(G-7542)
R & S MONITIONS INC
181 Rosslyn Ave (43214-1474)
PHONE......................................614 846-0597
Ron Herman, *President*
Sherry Herman, *Vice Pres*
EMP: 6
SALES (est): 544.4K **Privately Held**
SIC: 3482 5941 Small arms ammunition;
firearms

(G-7543)
R D COOK COMPANY LLC
Also Called: Cook, R D Company
883 E Hudson St (43211-1163)
PHONE......................................614 262-0550
Fax: 614 262-0256
Robert Cook,
▲ **EMP:** 5
SQ FT: 10,000
SALES: 750K **Privately Held**
WEB: www.robmcook.com
SIC: 2541 2511 Cabinets, except refriger-
ated: show, display, etc.: wood; counters
or counter display cases, wood; wood
household furniture

(G-7544)
R DESIGN & PRINTING CO
30 E 4th Ave (43201-3502)
PHONE......................................614 299-1420
Fax: 614 299-1422
David Ramirez, *CEO*
Juli Rogers, *President*
EMP: 4
SALES (est): 637.8K **Privately Held**
SIC: 2752 Commercial printing, litho-
graphic

(G-7545)
RADON BE GONE INC
4319 Indianola Ave (43214-2220)
PHONE......................................614 268-4440
Bill Dzackowitz, *President*
EMP: 3
SALES (est): 262.7K **Privately Held**
SIC: 3564 Air cleaning systems

(G-7546)
RAIL ROAD CORPORATION
Also Called: North Fork Southern
4881 Trabue Rd (43228-9613)
PHONE......................................614 771-2102
Ron Pauly, *Manager*
EMP: 5
SALES (est): 234.9K **Privately Held**
SIC: 3743 Train cars & equipment, freight
or passenger

(G-7547)
RAM PRODUCTS INC
1091 Stimmel Rd (43223-2911)
PHONE......................................614 443-4634
Fax: 614 443-4813
John Pelleriti, *President*
Richard Pelleriti Jr, *General Mgr*
Richard Dawson, *Vice Pres*
Anne Pelleriti, *Treasurer*
EMP: 12
SQ FT: 8,000
SALES (est): 2.2MM **Privately Held**
SIC: 3542 Presses: hydraulic & pneumatic,
mechanical & manual; presses: forming,
stamping, punching, sizing (machine
tools)

(G-7548)
RAPID MR INTERNATIONAL LLC
1500 Lake Shore Dr # 310 (43204-3936)
PHONE......................................614 486-6300
Fax: 614 486-6400
Titus Lanz, *General Mgr*
Florian Odoj, *General Mgr*
Dania Parsons, *Manager*
Ulrike Haase,
EMP: 7
SALES (est): 550K **Privately Held**
WEB: www.rapidmri.com
SIC: 3677 Electronic coils, transformers &
other inductors

(G-7549)
RAY RIESER TROPHY CO
3852 Sullivant Ave (43228-2125)
PHONE......................................614 279-1128
Fax: 614 279-2224
Freddie Rieser, *Owner*
EMP: 4
SQ FT: 2,500
SALES (est): 250K **Privately Held**
SIC: 5999 3499 Trophies & plaques; tro-
phies, metal, except silver

(G-7550)
RED BARAKUDA LLC
4439 Shoupmill Dr (43230-1489)
PHONE......................................614 596-5432

Isaiah Wambari,
EMP: 7
SALES (est): 347K **Privately Held**
SIC: 3949 7389 Flies, fishing: artificial;

(G-7551)
REDI-QUIK SIGNS INC
123 E Spring St (43215-2516)
PHONE......................................614 228-6641
Fax: 614 228-6642
Larry Rausch, *CEO*
Skip Rausch, *President*
David Rausch, *Treasurer*
EMP: 3
SALES (est): 280K **Privately Held**
WEB: www.rediquik.com
SIC: 3993 Signs & advertising specialties

(G-7552)
REGAL SPRING CO
2140 Eakin Rd Ste J (43223-6258)
PHONE......................................614 278-7761
Fax: 614 278-7765
Robert Forby, *Owner*
EMP: 5
SQ FT: 22,000
SALES (est): 313.3K **Privately Held**
SIC: 3495 Wire springs

(G-7553)
**REGAL TECHNOLOGY
CORPORATION**
3860 Bramford Rd (43220-4770)
P.O. Box 21207 (43221-0207)
PHONE......................................614 272-7644
Vonne Linse, *President*
Jim Linse, *General Mgr*
Mary K Linse, *Exec VP*
John Linse, *Manager*
EMP: 5
SALES (est): 1MM **Privately Held**
WEB: www.regal-technology.com
SIC: 2892 Explosives

(G-7554)
RENITE COMPANY
Also Called: Renite Lubrication Engineers
2500 E 5th Ave (43219-2700)
P.O. Box 30830 (43230-0830)
PHONE......................................614 253-5509
Fax: 614 253-1333
Stephen M Halliday, *Ch of Bd*
Eugene F Cook, *Vice Pres*
Leo L Harding, *VP Sales*
Becky Christy, *Office Mgr*
Francis E Cook, *Admin Sec*
EMP: 15
SALES (est): 4MM **Privately Held**
WEB: www.renite.com
SIC: 2992 3569 Lubricating oils &
greases; lubrication equipment, industrial

(G-7555)
RESAURUS COMPANY INC
240 Outerbelt St Ste A (43213-1589)
PHONE......................................614 751-9352
Fax: 614 751-9939
Douglas Sapp, *President*
Michael Compton, *Vice Pres*
Kevin Havens, *Engrg Dir*
Carly Sparrow, *Treasurer*
Dave Schubert, *Controller*
EMP: 17
SQ FT: 13,000
SALES (est): 1.2MM **Privately Held**
SIC: 3944 5092 Games, toys & children's
vehicles; toys

(G-7556)
**RESEARCH AND
DEVELOPMENT GROUP**
Also Called: R & D Group
1208 E Hudson St (43211-1308)
PHONE......................................614 261-0454
Fax: 614 261-0455
John Wells, *President*
Martha Wells, *Admin Sec*
EMP: 4
SQ FT: 3,200
SALES (est): 75K **Privately Held**
SIC: 2741 2759 Miscellaneous publishing;
commercial printing

(G-7557)
RESOLUTE FP US INC
Also Called: Recycling Div
995 Marion Rd (43207-2557)
PHONE.....................................614 443-6300
Sylvain-Yves Longval, *Owner*
Angie Henk, *Manager*
EMP: 434
SALES (corp-wide): 2.6B Privately Held
WEB: www.bowater.com
SIC: 2621 Paper mills
HQ: Resolute Fp Us Inc.
5300 Cureton Ferry Rd
Catawba SC 29704
803 981-8000

(G-7558)
RESOURCE FUELS LLC (PA)
41 S High St Ste 3750s (43215-3406)
PHONE.....................................614 221-0101
Fax: 614 233-6354
Brian Murphy, *CFO*
Donald J Drabant,
EMP: 5 EST: 1998
SQ FT: 3,000
SALES (est): 1.5MM Privately Held
SIC: 1241 Coal mining services

(G-7559)
REX AUTOMATION INC
2211 Aspenwood Ln (43235-2756)
PHONE.....................................614 766-4672
John Rex, *President*
Kelly Carlson, *Opers Mgr*
Kia Weller, *Marketing Staff*
Merle Rex, *Admin Sec*
EMP: 4
SQ FT: 1,425
SALES (est): 430K Privately Held
SIC: 3625 Relays & industrial controls

(G-7560)
REYNOLDS METALS COMPANY LLC
Also Called: Reynolds Residential Service
868 Goodale Blvd (43212)
PHONE.....................................614 228-7390
James B Schomaker, *Branch Mgr*
EMP: 14
SALES (corp-wide): 3.4B Publicly Held
SIC: 3411 Food containers, metal
HQ: Reynolds Metals Company, Llc
390 Park Ave
New York NY 10022
212 518-5400

(G-7561)
RICHARDS AND SIMMONS INC
33 W Schreyer Pl (43214-2615)
PHONE.....................................614 268-3909
Thomas Simmons, *President*
EMP: 3
SALES (est): 337.3K Privately Held
SIC: 2671 5999 Plastic film, coated or laminated for packaging; packaging materials: boxes, padding, etc.

(G-7562)
RICKLY HYDROLOGICAL CO
1700 Joyce Ave (43219-1026)
PHONE.....................................614 297-9877
Fax: 614 297-9878
Michael Rickly, *Owner*
John Harrison, *Info Tech Dir*
EMP: 24
SALES (est): 4MM Privately Held
SIC: 3823 Industrial process measurement equipment

(G-7563)
RICKLY HYDROLOGICAL COMPANY
1700 Joyce Ave (43219-1026)
PHONE.....................................614 297-9877
Michael Rickly, *President*
Jerry Morrison, *Sales Staff*
William H Rickly, *Admin Sec*
EMP: 6
SQ FT: 5,200
SALES (est): 600K Privately Held
WEB: www.rickly.com
SIC: 3829 Gauging instruments, thickness ultrasonic

(G-7564)
RIMROCK HOLDINGS CORPORATION (HQ)
1700 Jetway Blvd (43219-1675)
PHONE.....................................614 471-5926
Tom Dejong, *President*
Robert E Archer, *Vice Pres*
Dave Voves, *Engineer*
EMP: 50
SALES (est): 16.4MM
SALES (corp-wide): 2.2B Publicly Held
SIC: 3563 3569 3443 3541 Spraying outfits: metals, paints & chemicals (compressor); robots, assembly line: industrial & commercial; ladles, metal plate; machine tools, metal cutting type
PA: Lincoln Electric Holdings, Inc.
22801 Saint Clair Ave
Cleveland OH 44117
216 481-8100

(G-7565)
RJM STAMPING CO
1641 Universal Rd (43207-1704)
PHONE.....................................614 443-1191
Fax: 614 443-3308
Laura L Lloyd, *President*
Floyd Lloyd, *Vice Pres*
Carl Nixon, *Project Mgr*
Kekky Womax, *Engineer*
EMP: 12
SQ FT: 9,016
SALES: 1MM Privately Held
WEB: www.rjmstamping.com
SIC: 3469 Metal stampings

(G-7566)
RNM HOLDINGS INC
2350 Refugee Park (43207-2173)
PHONE.....................................614 444-5556
Matt Milton, *President*
Danielle Wills, *Office Mgr*
EMP: 11
SALES (corp-wide): 38.3MM Privately Held
SIC: 7353 5084 3536 Heavy construction equipment rental; cranes, industrial; hoists; cranes, overhead traveling; cranes & monorail systems; cranes, industrial plant
PA: Rnm Holdings, Inc.
550 Conover Dr
Franklin OH 45005
937 704-9900

(G-7567)
ROADSAFE TRAFFIC SYSTEMS INC
1350 Stimmel Rd (43223-2917)
PHONE.....................................614 274-9782
Fax: 614 533-9926
Steve Fisher, *Manager*
Chuck Clevina, *Manager*
EMP: 6
SALES (corp-wide): 679.1MM Privately Held
SIC: 3531 Construction machinery
PA: Roadsafe Traffic Systems, Inc.
8750 W Bryn Mawr Ave # 400
Chicago IL 60631
773 724-3300

(G-7568)
ROBERT C BOST ASSOCIATES INC (HQ)
1783 Kenny Rd (43212-1311)
PHONE.....................................301 206-9466
A Gregory Roberts, *President*
EMP: 11
SALES (est): 1.8MM
SALES (corp-wide): 8.4MM Privately Held
SIC: 3625 Noise control equipment
PA: Ketchum & Walton Co.
1783 Kenny Rd
Columbus OH
614 486-5961

(G-7569)
ROBERTS GROUP INC (PA)
2646 Alliston Ct (43220-4287)
PHONE.....................................614 486-0497
Dorothy B Roberts, *President*
Gina Tomilonus, *Production*
EMP: 2

SALES (est): 4.3MM Privately Held
SIC: 3829 3299 Thermocouples; stucco

(G-7570)
ROBEY TOOL & MACHINE
1593 E 5th Ave (43219-2572)
PHONE.....................................614 251-0412
Wilbur N Robey, *Owner*
EMP: 5
SQ FT: 5,500
SALES (est): 9MM Privately Held
SIC: 3599 Machine & other job shop work

(G-7571)
RONS TEXSTYLES LLC
457 Thorburn Pl (43230-6847)
PHONE.....................................513 936-9975
Ron Melser, *Owner*
Tim Malling, *Opers Mgr*
Ron ABT, *Engineer*
Tim Thalheimer, *Info Tech Dir*
James Polce, *Administration*
EMP: 3
SQ FT: 400
SALES: 500K Privately Held
SIC: 2326 5023 Work uniforms; linens, table

(G-7572)
ROOF DIE TOOL & MACHINE INC
2000 S High St (43207-2425)
PHONE.....................................614 444-6253
Fax: 614 444-0068
Robert L Roof, *President*
George Holzpfel, *Vice Pres*
Tony Stockton, *Opers Mgr*
Jim Middleton, *Engineer*
Margaret Roof, *Treasurer*
EMP: 4
SQ FT: 6,000
SALES: 350K Privately Held
SIC: 3599 Machine shop, jobbing & repair

(G-7573)
ROSE PRODUCTS AND SERVICES INC
545 Stimmel Rd (43223-2901)
PHONE.....................................614 443-7647
Fax: 614 443-2771
Robert Roth, *President*
Sue Brennan, *Manager*
EMP: 50 EST: 1926
SQ FT: 50,000
SALES (est): 7.9MM Privately Held
SIC: 5087 2842 Janitors' supplies; specialty cleaning preparations

(G-7574)
ROXANE LABORATORIES INC
1809 Wilson Rd (43228-9579)
P.O. Box 16532 (43216-6532)
PHONE.....................................614 276-4000
Fax: 614 274-0974
Michael Raya, *CEO*
Brian Hoffmann, *President*
Glenn Marina, *Vice Pres*
Randy Wilson, *Vice Pres*
Michael Williams, *Project Mgr*
EMP: 127
SALES: 500MM
SALES (corp-wide): 1.4B Privately Held
SIC: 2834 Druggists' preparations (pharmaceuticals)
HQ: Eurohealth (U.S.A.), Inc
401 Industrial Way W
Eatontown NJ 07724
732 542-1191

(G-7575)
ROY L BAYES
Also Called: Bayes, Roy Products
1593 Harrisburg Pike (43223-3611)
PHONE.....................................614 274-6729
Roy L Bayes, *Owner*
EMP: 3
SQ FT: 8,000
SALES (est): 199.5K Privately Held
SIC: 2541 5091 Showcases, except refrigerated: wood; sporting & recreation goods

(G-7576)
RR DONNELLEY & SONS COMPANY
Also Called: Bowne of Columbus
41 S High St Ste 3750 (43215-6161)
PHONE.....................................614 221-8385

Fax: 614 221-8427
Bob Licker, *Sales Staff*
Ron Wymr, *Manager*
EMP: 8
SALES (corp-wide): 6.9B Publicly Held
SIC: 2791 Typesetting
PA: R. R. Donnelley & Sons Company
35 W Wacker Dr Ste 3650
Chicago IL 60601
312 326-8000

(G-7577)
RTZ MANUFACTURING CO
6530 Huntley Rd (43229-1070)
P.O. Box 289, Worthington (43085-0289)
PHONE.....................................614 848-8366
Fax: 614 848-7641
Zoe Rosser, *President*
Ty Rosser, *Vice Pres*
EMP: 9
SQ FT: 3,000
SALES: 900K Privately Held
SIC: 3599 Custom machinery

(G-7578)
RUTLAND PLASTIC TECH INC
777 Dearborn Park Ln N (43085-5716)
PHONE.....................................614 846-3055
Fax: 614 846-3943
Guy Lewis, *Manager*
EMP: 5
SALES (corp-wide): 34.6MM Privately Held
WEB: www.rutlandinc.com
SIC: 3087 3089 2759 Custom compound purchased resins; plastic processing; screen printing
PA: Rutland Group, Inc.
10021 Rodney St
Pineville NC 28134
704 553-0046

(G-7579)
RUTOBO INC
Also Called: Allegra Print & Imaging
4279 E Main St (43213-3032)
PHONE.....................................614 236-2948
Fax: 614 236-2951
Tom Boder, *CEO*
Penny Dowling, *Accounts Mgr*
Brad Alexander, *Manager*
EMP: 5
SQ FT: 2,800
SALES (est): 517.5K Privately Held
SIC: 2752 Commercial printing, offset

(G-7580)
RXPERT CONSULTANTS LLC
4719 Reed Rd Ste 250 (43220-3051)
PHONE.....................................614 579-9384
Julia Rhoades, *President*
EMP: 5
SALES (est): 204.5K Privately Held
SIC: 2011 8748 Meat packing plants; business consulting

(G-7581)
S BECKMAN PRINT & G
Also Called: Beckman Xmo
376 Morrison Rd Ste D (43213-1447)
PHONE.....................................614 864-2232
Fax: 614 864-3305
Tracy Beckman, *President*
Jackie Russer, *Manager*
Pam Taylor, *Manager*
David Potts, *Art Dir*
EMP: 21
SQ FT: 4,100
SALES (est): 3.5MM Privately Held
WEB: www.sbeckmanprint.com
SIC: 2752 Commercial printing, lithographic

(G-7582)
S&S SIGN SERVICE
485 Ternstedt Ln (43228-2128)
PHONE.....................................614 279-9722
Robert Sherry, *CEO*
EMP: 6
SALES (est): 651.7K Privately Held
SIC: 3993 Signs & advertising specialties

(G-7583)
SAFECOR HEALTH LLC (PA)
Also Called: R S C
4060 Business Park Dr B (43204-5046)
PHONE.................................781 933-8780
Rob Mains, *Vice Pres*
Hilary Schnieders, *Opers Spvr*
Susan Blatti, *QC Mgr*
Doug Moore, *CFO*
Kris Krock, *Accounts Mgr*
EMP: 10
SALES (est): 23.7MM **Privately Held**
SIC: 7389 2834 Packaging & labeling
services; pharmaceutical preparations

(G-7584)
SAFELITE GLASS CORP (DH)
Also Called: Safelite Autoglass
7400 Safelite Way (43235-5086)
P.O. Box 182827 (43218-2827)
PHONE.................................614 210-9000
Fax: 614 761-4987
George T Haymaker Jr, *Ch of Bd*
Dan Wislon, *President*
Dan H Wilson, *President*
Paul Jurgensen, *Division Mgr*
Anthony Batts, *General Mgr*
▲ EMP: 700
SALES (est): 1.6B
SALES (corp-wide): 2.9B **Privately Held**
WEB: www.safelite.com
SIC: 3231 Windshields, glass: made from
purchased glass
HQ: Safelite Group, Inc
7400 Safelite Way
Columbus OH 43235
614 210-9000

(G-7585)
SAFELITE GROUP INC (DH)
Also Called: Safelite Autoglass
7400 Safelite Way (43235-5086)
P.O. Box 182827 (43218-2827)
PHONE.................................614 210-9000
Fax: 614 761-4992
Thomas Feeney, *CEO*
Michelle Beiter, *President*
Ron Duncan, *President*
Paul Groves, *President*
Kerry Hurff, *President*
▲ EMP: 1000
SALES (est): 2.2B
SALES (corp-wide): 2.9B **Privately Held**
WEB: www.safelitegroup.com
SIC: 7536 3231 6411 Automotive glass
replacement shops; windshields, glass:
made from purchased glass; insurance
claim processing, except medical
HQ: Belron Sa
Boulevard Prince Henri 9b
Luxembourg
274 788-60

(G-7586)
SAFEWHITE INC
1275 Kinnear Rd Ste 237 (43212-1180)
PHONE.................................614 340-1450
Ray Shealy, *President*
Mark Shary, *Chairman*
Alan Fermier, *Vice Pres*
Ada Sierraalta, *Director*
Gary Musso, *Security Dir*
EMP: 5
SQ FT: 500
SALES (est): 844.2K **Privately Held**
SIC: 2836 Biological products, except diag-
nostic

(G-7587)
SALINDIA LLC
2756 Eastland Mall (43232-4901)
PHONE.................................614 501-4799
Afsal Koya, *Principal*
EMP: 4
SALES (est): 26.6K **Privately Held**
SIC: 2389 Men's miscellaneous acces-
sories

(G-7588)
SALSBURY INDUSTRIES INC
2300 Rickenbacker Pkwy (43217-5001)
PHONE.................................614 409-1600
EMP: 7

SALES (corp-wide): 66.6MM **Privately
Held**
SIC: 3444 Mail (post office) collection or
storage boxes, sheet metal
PA: Salsbury Industries, Inc.
1010 E 62nd St
Los Angeles CA 90001
323 846-6700

(G-7589)
SAMMY S AUTO DETAIL
3514 Cleveland Ave (43224-2908)
PHONE.................................614 263-2728
Sam Cavin, *CEO*
EMP: 10
SALES (est): 882.9K **Privately Held**
SIC: 3589 7538 Car washing machinery;
general automotive repair shops

(G-7590)
SAVARE CORPORATION (PA)
230 West St Ste 700 (43215-2663)
PHONE.................................614 255-2878
Giovanni Luigi Boffelli, *CEO*
EMP: 7
SQ FT: 52,650
SALES: 28.9MM **Privately Held**
SIC: 2891 Adhesives

(G-7591)
**SAVKO PLASTIC PIPE &
FITTINGS**
Also Called: Bath & Brass Emporium The
683 E Lincoln Ave (43229-5021)
PHONE.................................614 885-8420
Fax: 614 885-4470
Chuck Savko, *President*
Andrew C Puskas, *President*
Mitch Ellis, *Vice Pres*
Lindo Spinosi, *Vice Pres*
EMP: 13
SQ FT: 9,000
SALES (est): 2.5MM **Privately Held**
WEB: www.savko.com
SIC: 3084 5719 5074 Plastics pipe; bath
accessories; plumbing & hydronic heating
supplies

(G-7592)
SAWMILL CROSSING
6700 Allister Way (43235-7913)
PHONE.................................614 766-1685
Jennifer Harrison, *Principal*
EMP: 3
SALES (est): 261.9K **Privately Held**
SIC: 2421 Sawmills & planing mills, gen-
eral

(G-7593)
SAWMILL EYE ASSOCIATES INC
6500 Sawmill Rd (43235-4942)
PHONE.................................614 734-2685
Scott P Caleodis, *Principal*
EMP: 3
SALES (est): 277.5K **Privately Held**
SIC: 2421 Sawmills & planing mills, gen-
eral

(G-7594)
SCAREFACTORY INC
2905 E 4th Ave (43219-2827)
PHONE.................................614 252-8000
David Fachman, *President*
EMP: 15
SQ FT: 38,000
SALES (est): 1.8MM **Privately Held**
WEB: www.scarefactory.com
SIC: 3999 Theatrical scenery

(G-7595)
SCHELL SCENIC STUDIO INC
841 S Front St 843 (43206-2578)
PHONE.................................614 444-9550
Fax: 614 444-9554
Gustav Schell, *President*
Philip G Schell, *Vice Pres*
Rick Redfern, *Manager*
Ed Twynham, *Manager*
Lance Jones, *Admin Asst*
EMP: 7
SQ FT: 20,000
SALES: 750K **Privately Held**
WEB: www.schellscenic.com
SIC: 3999 7922 Theatrical scenery;
scenery rental, theatrical

(G-7596)
**SCHODORF TRUCK BODY &
EQP CO**
885 Harmon Ave (43223-2411)
P.O. Box 23322 (43223-0322)
PHONE.................................614 228-6793
Fax: 614 228-6775
Joe Schodorf, *President*
Paul F Schodorf, *Vice Pres*
Mattday Schodorfwinches, *Parts Mgr*
EMP: 40
SQ FT: 52,000
SALES (est): 10.3MM **Privately Held**
WEB: www.schodorftruck.com
SIC: 5012 3713 3211 Truck bodies; truck
bodies (motor vehicles); flat glass

(G-7597)
SCHOLZ & EY ENGRAVERS INC
1558 Parsons Ave (43207-1252)
PHONE.................................614 444-8052
Fax: 614 444-8452
Kevin Scholz, *President*
Stephen Scholz, *Principal*
EMP: 13 EST: 1950
SQ FT: 3,100
SALES (est): 425K **Privately Held**
SIC: 3479 5947 5094 5199 Engraving
jewelry silverware, or metal; name plates:
engraved, etched, etc.; gift shop; jewelry;
gifts & novelties

(G-7598)
SCHOOL PRIDE LIMITED
3511 Johnny Appleseed Ct (43231-4985)
PHONE.................................614 568-0697
Daren Brown, *President*
Janet Brown, *Business Mgr*
Andrew Atkinson, *Sales Mgr*
Brian Beck, *Sales Mgr*
Caleb Schafrath, *Sales Mgr*
EMP: 30
SALES (est): 2.3MM **Privately Held**
WEB: www.schoolpride.com
SIC: 2399 Banners, pennants & flags

(G-7599)
**SCI ENGINEERED MATERIALS
INC**
2839 Charter St (43228-4607)
PHONE.................................614 486-0261
Daniel Rooney, *Ch of Bd*
Michael K Barna, *Vice Pres*
Jeremy Young, *Opers Mgr*
Gerald S Blaskie, *CFO*
EMP: 24
SQ FT: 32,000
SALES (est): 5.4MM **Privately Held**
WEB: www. superconductivecomp.com
SIC: 3674 Semiconductors & related de-
vices

(G-7600)
**SCIOTO CERAMIC PRODUCTS
INC**
854 Curleys Ct (43235-2161)
PHONE.................................614 436-0405
Patrick J Langdale, *President*
James D Roullard, *Vice Pres*
EMP: 45
SQ FT: 48,000
SALES (est): 3.6MM **Privately Held**
SIC: 3299 Ceramic fiber

(G-7601)
SCIOTO READYMIX CO
1500 Williams Rd (43207-5108)
PHONE.................................614 491-0773
Ken Bolen, *Principal*
EMP: 3
SALES (est): 316.1K **Privately Held**
SIC: 3273 Ready-mixed concrete

(G-7602)
SCORECARDS UNLIMITED LLC
Also Called: Golf Dsign Screcards Unlimited
6334 Huntley Rd (43229-1008)
PHONE.................................614 885-0796
Susan Siegrist, *Sales Mgr*
Paul Filing, *Mng Member*
Paul J Filing, *Manager*
Brian Miller, *Manager*
EMP: 8

SALES (est): 890K **Privately Held**
WEB: www.golfdesign.com
SIC: 2752 Commercial printing, offset

(G-7603)
**SCREEN PRINTING SHOW
HOUSE**
853 N Nelson Rd (43219-2732)
PHONE.................................614 252-2202
Fax: 614 252-2255
Joseph A Call, *President*
James B Call, *Vice Pres*
EMP: 5
SQ FT: 7,000
SALES: 663K **Privately Held**
SIC: 2261 Screen printing of cotton broad-
woven fabrics

(G-7604)
SCRIPTEL CORPORATION
2174 Dividend Dr (43228-3806)
PHONE.................................614 276-8402
Fax: 614 276-7615
Wayne Barphel, *President*
Robert Kable, *Principal*
Winston Towers, *Vice Pres*
Ray Murphy, *Buyer*
Edward Kutyd, *Controller*
▲ EMP: 17
SALES (est): 4.5MM **Privately Held**
SIC: 3577 Computer peripheral equipment
PA: Sutisoft Inc.
4984 El Camino Real Ste 2
Los Altos CA 94022
650 969-7884

(G-7605)
SEALANT SOLUTIONS
947 E Johnstown Rd (43230-1851)
PHONE.................................614 599-8000
Donald McDaniels, *Principal*
EMP: 4
SALES (est): 246.4K **Privately Held**
SIC: 2891 Sealants

(G-7606)
SEEKIRK INC
2420 Scioto Harper Dr (43204-3480)
PHONE.................................614 278-9200
Fax: 614 278-9257
Douglas Seeley, *CEO*
Pamela Seeley, *Treasurer*
EMP: 14 EST: 1982
SQ FT: 11,000
SALES (est): 2.6MM **Privately Held**
WEB: www.seekirk.com
SIC: 3823 Annunciators, relay & solid state
types

(G-7607)
SELECTEON CORPORATION
777 W Swan St (43212-3864)
PHONE.................................614 228-8008
Thomas J Ward, *President*
Cecil Robinson, *General Mgr*
Mark Rodrian, *Project Mgr*
EMP: 20
SQ FT: 10,000
SALES (est): 4.4MM **Privately Held**
SIC: 3569 Assembly machines, non-metal-
working

(G-7608)
SENTEK CORPORATION
1160b Alum Creek Dr (43209-2720)
PHONE.................................614 586-1123
Niklas Almstedt, *President*
Ann Almstedt, *Vice Pres*
EMP: 7 EST: 1999
SQ FT: 9,000
SALES (est): 810K **Privately Held**
WEB: www.sentekcorp.com
SIC: 3547 8748 Ferrous & nonferrous mill
equipment, auxiliary; systems analysis &
engineering consulting services

(G-7609)
**SERMONIX
PHARMACEUTICALS ✪**
142 S Remington Rd (43209-1868)
PHONE.................................614 864-4919
David Portman, *CEO*
Miriam Portman, *COO*
EMP: 3 EST: 2016
SALES (est): 203.4K **Privately Held**
SIC: 2834 Pills, pharmaceutical

(G-7610)
SEVAN AT-NDUSTRIAL PNT ABR LTD
1555 Alum Creek Dr (43209-2712)
PHONE..................................614 258-4747
Dan Birt, *Principal*
EMP: 4
SALES (est): 551.5K **Privately Held**
SIC: 5085 2842 5012 Abrasives; automobile polish; automobiles & other motor vehicles

(G-7611)
SEVELL + SEVELL INC
939 N High St (43201-2553)
PHONE..................................614 341-9700
Steve Sevell, *President*
Beverly Sevell, *Admin Sec*
EMP: 5
SALES (est): 350K **Privately Held**
WEB: www.sevell.com
SIC: 2741 2759 7336 7374 Miscellaneous publishing; commercial printing; graphic arts & related design; computer graphics service; information retrieval services; direct mail advertising services

(G-7612)
SEVENTH SON BREWING CO
1101 N 4th St (43201-3683)
PHONE..................................614 783-4217
EMP: 4
SALES (est): 369.6K **Privately Held**
SIC: 2082 Ale (alcoholic beverage)

(G-7613)
SEXTANT GROUP INC
4041 N High St Ste 204 (43214-3248)
PHONE..................................614 429-3606
EMP: 3 **Privately Held**
SIC: 3812 Sextants
PA: The Sextant Group Inc
700 Waterfront Dr
Pittsburgh PA 15222

(G-7614)
SHADETREE SYSTEMS LLC
6317 Busch Blvd (43229-1802)
PHONE..................................614 844-5990
Lori Groomer, *Sales Staff*
Shirley Garnham, *Info Tech Dir*
Marvin Williams,
Dwayne Williams,
◆ EMP: 19
SQ FT: 19,000
SALES (est): 3.6MM **Privately Held**
WEB: www.shadetreesystems.com
SIC: 3444 Canopies, sheet metal

(G-7615)
SHENET LLC
50 W Broad St Ste 12000 (43215-3301)
PHONE..................................614 563-9600
Sally Haimbaugh,
EMP: 25
SALES (est): 1.7MM **Privately Held**
SIC: 3663 Radio & TV communications equipment

(G-7616)
SHIP PRINT E SELL
3145 Kingsdale Ctr (43221)
PHONE..................................614 459-1205
Fax: 614 459-1713
Mark Heimrich, *Partner*
Charles Groezinger, *Partner*
John Pugh, *Partner*
EMP: 3
SALES: 170K **Privately Held**
SIC: 2752 Commercial printing, lithographic

(G-7617)
SHOEMAKER ELECTRIC COMPANY
Also Called: Shoemaker Industrial Solutions
831 Bonham Ave (43211-2999)
PHONE..................................614 294-5626
Fax: 614 294-6330
Fred N Kletrovets, *President*
Derrick Crowe, *Electrical Engi*
Teri Richardson, *Treasurer*
Russ Richardson, *Manager*
Betty Kletrovets, *Admin Sec*
▲ EMP: 29 EST: 1935

SQ FT: 16,000
SALES (est): 7.4MM **Privately Held**
WEB: www.shoemakerindustrial.com
SIC: 7694 5063 Electric motor repair; motors, electric

(G-7618)
SHRED-IT USA LLC
Also Called: Shred-It Columbus
1784 Dividend Dr (43228-3845)
PHONE..................................614 231-7470
Brian Chadwick, *Branch Mgr*
EMP: 3
SALES (corp-wide): 3.5B **Publicly Held**
SIC: 3589 Shredders, industrial & commercial
HQ: Shred-It Usa Llc
11311 Cornell Park Dr # 125
Blue Ash OH 45242
513 699-0845

(G-7619)
SIEMENS INDUSTRY INC
977 Gahanna Pkwy (43230-6610)
PHONE..................................614 573-8212
Michael Morrow, *Branch Mgr*
EMP: 87
SALES (corp-wide): 89.6B **Privately Held**
SIC: 3822 Air conditioning & refrigeration controls
HQ: Siemens Industry, Inc.
1000 Deerfield Pkwy
Buffalo Grove IL 60089
847 215-1000

(G-7620)
SIGNAGE CONSULTANTS INC
870 E 5th Ave (43201-2960)
PHONE..................................614 297-7446
Elizabeth Navarro, *President*
Elizabeth Navagrro, *President*
EMP: 6
SQ FT: 8,000
SALES (est): 675.2K **Privately Held**
WEB: www.signageconsultants.com
SIC: 3993 7336 Signs, not made in custom sign painting shops; graphic arts & related design

(G-7621)
SIGNCOM INCORPORATED
527 W Rich St (43215-4903)
PHONE..................................614 228-9999
Fax: 614 228-4326
Jim Hartley, *President*
Bret Gilmore, *Controller*
Bruce M Sommerfelt, *Sales Mgr*
Bruce Sommerfelt, *Sales Mgr*
Melody Ward, *Office Mgr*
EMP: 25
SALES: 2.7MM **Privately Held**
WEB: www.signcom.cc
SIC: 3993 Electric signs

(G-7622)
SIMEX INC
181 Pleasants Indus Park (43224)
P.O. Box 247230 (43224-7230)
PHONE..................................304 665-1104
Mark Savan, *President*
EMP: 5
SALES (est): 1MM **Privately Held**
SIC: 2591 Window shades

(G-7623)
SIMON & SCHUSTER INC
Also Called: Silver, Burdett & Ginn
4350 Equity Dr (43228-4801)
P.O. Box 2500, Lebanon IN (46052-3009)
PHONE..................................614 876-0371
Sheila Hickle, *Director*
EMP: 140
SALES (corp-wide): 13.1B **Publicly Held**
WEB: www.digonsite.com
SIC: 2731 2741 Books: publishing & printing; textbooks: publishing & printing; miscellaneous publishing
HQ: Simon & Schuster, Inc.
1230 Ave Of The Americas
New York NY 10020
212 698-7000

(G-7624)
SIMPSON STRONG-TIE COMPANY INC
2600 International St (43228-4617)
PHONE..................................614 876-8060
Fax: 614 876-0636
Tiffany Weethee, *Purch Mgr*
Shane Vilasineekul, *Engineer*
Sharon Bott, *Human Res Dir*
Rick Reid, *Sales Staff*
Dave Williams, *Branch Mgr*
EMP: 120
SALES (corp-wide): 860.6MM **Publicly Held**
SIC: 5082 3643 3452 Construction & mining machinery; current-carrying wiring devices; bolts, nuts, rivets & washers
HQ: Simpson Strong-Tie Company Inc.
5956 W Las Positas Blvd
Pleasanton CA 94588
925 560-9000

(G-7625)
SINNERS N SAINTS LLC
1515 Alum Creek Dr (43209-2712)
PHONE..................................614 231-7467
EMP: 3
SALES (est): 230K **Privately Held**
SIC: 3751 7699 Mfg Motorcycles/Bicycles Repair Services

(G-7626)
SKEELES MANUFACTURING CORP
4040 Fondorf Dr (43228-1026)
PHONE..................................614 274-4700
Fax: 614 274-4721
Fred Skeeles, *President*
Jonathan Skeeles, *Vice Pres*
Rebecca Skeeles, *Vice Pres*
Anna Bell, *Exec Dir*
EMP: 18
SQ FT: 15,000
SALES (est): 2.4MM **Privately Held**
WEB: www.skeelesinc.com
SIC: 2541 Counter & sink tops

(G-7627)
SODA PIG LLC ✪
790 Kerr St (43215-1559)
PHONE..................................646 241-7126
Marvin Wise,
Robert Malko,
Brannan McGill,
EMP: 3 EST: 2016
SALES (est): 76K **Privately Held**
SIC: 7372 Application computer software

(G-7628)
SOFTCHOICE CORPORATION
300 Marconi Blvd Ste 303 (43215-2329)
PHONE..................................614 224-4123
Chandran Rajaratnam, *President*
EMP: 3
SALES (corp-wide): 1.3MM **Privately Held**
WEB: www.softchoice.com
SIC: 7372 Prepackaged software
HQ: Softchoice Corporation
314 W Superior St Ste 400
Chicago IL 60654

(G-7629)
SOFTURA LEGAL SOLUTIONS LLC ✪
1555 Lake Shore Dr (43204-3825)
PHONE..................................614 220-5611
Dennis Meadors, *CFO*
Brian Deas,
EMP: 5 EST: 2016
SALES (est): 117.2K **Privately Held**
SIC: 7372 Business oriented computer software

(G-7630)
SOMERSET GALLERIES INC
Also Called: Mica Laminates
1144 S 4th St (43206-2686)
PHONE..................................614 443-0003
Kenneth G Haas, *President*
Maxine Haas, *Corp Secy*
Aaron Haas, *Vice Pres*
Leonard Haas, *Vice Pres*
EMP: 3
SQ FT: 10,000

SALES: 100K **Privately Held**
SIC: 3083 Laminated plastics plate & sheet

(G-7631)
SONOCO PRODUCTS COMPANY
444 Mccormick Blvd (43213-1525)
PHONE..................................614 759-8470
Greg Ickes, *Principal*
EMP: 30
SALES (corp-wide): 4.7B **Publicly Held**
WEB: www.sonoco.com
SIC: 2631 2671 2653 2655 Paperboard mills; packaging paper & plastics film, coated & laminated; corrugated & solid fiber boxes; fiber cans, drums & similar products; injection molded finished plastic products; extruded finished plastic products; reels, plywood
PA: Sonoco Products Company
1 N 2nd St
Hartsville SC 29550
843 383-7000

(G-7632)
SOUTH SIDE AUDIO LLC
2501 S High St Frnt Frnt (43207-2998)
PHONE..................................614 453-0757
Donavin Gleaton,
Michael Cumpston,
EMP: 3
SALES (est): 240K **Privately Held**
SIC: 3651 Audio electronic systems

(G-7633)
SOUTHWEST GREENS OHIO LLC
1781 Westbelt Dr (43228-3811)
PHONE..................................614 389-6042
Rick Dodson,
Kate Dodson,
EMP: 10
SQ FT: 1,500
SALES (est): 1.9MM **Privately Held**
WEB: www.southwestgreensohio.com
SIC: 3299 Synthetic stones, for gem stones & industrial use

(G-7634)
SPECIAL DESIGN PRODUCTS INC
500 Industrial Mile Rd (43228-2413)
PHONE..................................614 272-6700
Fax: 614 272-6844
Nancy Evanichko, *President*
Stan Evanichko, *Vice Pres*
Mike Zogleman, *Director*
Suzette King, *Shareholder*
EMP: 45
SALES (est): 10.3MM **Privately Held**
WEB: www.specialdesignproducts.com
SIC: 3086 Packaging & shipping materials, foamed plastic

(G-7635)
SPECIALTY FILMS INC
2887 Johnstown Rd (43219-1719)
PHONE..................................614 471-9100
Howard Callaghan Jr, *President*
Steve H Dudley, *Treasurer*
Peter E Driscoll, *Director*
Cynthia Decker, *Administration*
EMP: 35
SQ FT: 7,500
SALES (est): 2.9MM
SALES (corp-wide): 92.5MM **Privately Held**
WEB: www.plasticsuppliers.net
SIC: 3081 Plastic film & sheet
PA: Plastic Suppliers, Inc.
2450 Marilyn Ln
Columbus OH 43219
614 471-9100

(G-7636)
SPECIALTY NAMEPLATE CORP
4670 Groves Rd (43232-4164)
PHONE..................................614 444-6876
Fax: 614 444-6589
Frank Schreck, *General Mgr*
Kathy Entsminger, *Vice Pres*
Ty Whitfield, *Controller*
Denise Crawford, *Admin Sec*
EMP: 14
SQ FT: 7,600

G
E
O

SALES (est): 1.3MM **Privately Held**
WEB: www.extendedresources.com
SIC: 3993 Name plates: except engraved, etched, etc.: metal

(G-7637)
SPECIALTY PRINTING AND PROC
4670 Groves Rd (43232-4164)
PHONE................................614 322-9035
Fax: 614 322-9036
Frank Schreck, *Owner*
Kathy Entsminger, *Marketing Staff*
EMP: 17 **EST:** 2000
SALES (est): 3.4MM **Privately Held**
WEB: www.extendedresources.net
SIC: 2759 Screen printing

(G-7638)
SPECIALTY SERVICES INC
1382 Ohlen Ave (43211-2640)
PHONE................................614 421-1599
Fax: 614 421-1616
Michael Melton, *President*
Joann Melton, *Corp Secy*
EMP: 8
SQ FT: 10,200
SALES (est): 700K **Privately Held**
SIC: 2521 2511 Cabinets, office: wood; wood household furniture

(G-7639)
SPECIALTY TECHNOLOGY & RES
Also Called: Star
1150 Milepost Dr (43228-9388)
PHONE................................614 870-0744
Girish Dubey, *President*
Darla Bushell, *Manager*
Brent Kibarger, *Manager*
EMP: 6
SQ FT: 4,500
SALES (est): 1.8MM **Privately Held**
WEB: www.starseal.com
SIC: 2951 8731 Paving mixtures; commercial physical research

(G-7640)
SPECTROGLASS CORP
1380 Holly Ave (43212-3115)
PHONE................................614 297-0412
EMP: 3 **EST:** 2002
SALES (est): 230K **Privately Held**
SIC: 2295 Mfg Coated Fabrics

(G-7641)
SPECTRUM DYNAMICS INC
1951 Hampshire Rd (43221-4116)
PHONE................................614 486-3223
Steven Caton, *President*
EMP: 4
SALES (est): 50K **Privately Held**
SIC: 3599 Machine & other job shop work

(G-7642)
SPECTRUM MFG & SLS INC (PA)
1951 Hampshire Rd (43221-4116)
PHONE................................614 486-3640
Fax: 614 486-3640
Steven Caton, *President*
EMP: 2
SQ FT: 4,000
SALES (est): 1.3MM **Privately Held**
SIC: 5084 3599 Industrial machine parts; machine shop, jobbing & repair

(G-7643)
SPEEDWAY LLC
Also Called: Speedway Superamerica 2034
2875 Stelzer Rd (43219-3132)
PHONE................................614 418-9325
Josh Dillinger, *Branch Mgr*
EMP: 10 **Publicly Held**
WEB: www.speedwaynet.com
SIC: 1311 Crude petroleum production
HQ: Speedway Llc
500 Speedway Dr
Enon OH 45323
937 864-3000

(G-7644)
SPILLMAN COMPANY
1701 Moler Rd (43207-1684)
P.O. Box 7847 (43207-0847)
PHONE................................614 444-2184

Fax: 614 444-1231
Ted Coons, *CEO*
Don McNutt, *President*
Theodore W Coons, *Principal*
Lynn Coons, *Treasurer*
Abby Aitchison, *Sales Mgr*
◆ **EMP:** 34 **EST:** 1948
SQ FT: 37,000
SALES (est): 6.6MM **Privately Held**
WEB: www.spillmanform.com
SIC: 1771 5084 3446 Concrete work; cement making machinery; architectural metalwork

(G-7645)
SPIRIT AVIONICS LTD
Also Called: Spirit Aeronautics
4808 E 5th Ave (43219-1853)
PHONE................................614 358-0333
Tony Bailey, *President*
Rick Ochs, *Partner*
Steve Wathen, *Partner*
Brian Jay, *QC Mgr*
John Marihugh, *Controller*
EMP: 13
SQ FT: 15,000
SALES (est): 4.5MM **Privately Held**
WEB: www.spiritavionics.com
SIC: 7629 4581 2396 3629 Aircraft electrical equipment repair; aircraft servicing & repairing; automotive trimmings, fabric; electronic generation equipment; aircraft engines & engine parts; electronic parts & equipment

(G-7646)
SPRING WORKS INC
801 Distribution Dr (43228-1003)
PHONE................................614 351-9345
Fax: 614 351-0595
Edgar Weil, *CEO*
Art Neu, *QC Mgr*
EMP: 20
SQ FT: 27,000
SALES (est): 3.4MM **Privately Held**
WEB: www.thespringworks.com
SIC: 3495 Mechanical springs, precision

(G-7647)
SRICO INC
2724 Sawbury Blvd (43235-4579)
PHONE................................614 799-0664
Fax: 614 799-2116
SRI Sriram, *President*
Judith C Sriram, *Vice Pres*
Andrea Pollick, *Research*
Susan Carmichael, *Manager*
EMP: 8
SQ FT: 3,600
SALES (est): 804.6K **Privately Held**
WEB: www.srico.com
SIC: 3229 8731 Fiber optics strands; electronic research

(G-7648)
SRM GRAPHICS INC
Also Called: Concept Wear
950 Oakland Park Ave (43224-3310)
PHONE................................614 263-4433
Fax: 614 263-4449
Stephen Miller, *President*
Linda Saup, *Admin Sec*
EMP: 3
SQ FT: 2,400
SALES (est): 309.9K **Privately Held**
WEB: www.conceptwear.com
SIC: 2759 Screen printing

(G-7649)
SSP TENNESSEE LLC
Also Called: Solstice Sleep Products
2652 Fisher Rd Ste A (43204-3576)
PHONE................................614 279-8850
EMP: 3
SALES (est): 146.3K **Privately Held**
SIC: 2515 Mattresses & bedsprings

(G-7650)
STANDARD ENERGY COMPANY
1105 Schrock Rd Ste 602 (43229-1174)
PHONE................................614 885-1901
Gerald S Jacobs, *President*
Donna Sanger, *Vice Pres*
Denise Amspoker, *Admin Sec*
EMP: 4
SQ FT: 3,400

SALES (est): 370K **Privately Held**
SIC: 1382 1311 6798 Oil & gas exploration services; crude petroleum production; natural gas production; realty investment trusts

(G-7651)
STAR JET LLC
4130 E 5th Ave (43219-1802)
PHONE................................614 338-4379
Gordon Macswain, *Info Tech Dir*
Robert Austin,
EMP: 15
SALES (est): 1MM **Privately Held**
WEB: www.starjet.com
SIC: 3721 Aircraft

(G-7652)
STAR NEWSPAPER
1472 Dobson Sq N (43229-1366)
PHONE................................614 622-5930
Joseph Owusu Ansah, *Owner*
EMP: 3
SALES (est): 0 **Privately Held**
SIC: 2711 7389 Newspapers;

(G-7653)
STAR SEAL OF OHIO INC
1400 Walcutt Rd (43228-9194)
PHONE................................614 870-1590
Fax: 614 870-0598
Dr Sudhir Dubey, *President*
Girish Dubey, *Chairman*
Darla Bushell, *Opers Mgr*
EMP: 6
SALES (est): 1.4MM **Privately Held**
SIC: 2951 Coal tar paving materials (not from refineries)

(G-7654)
STARECASING SYSTEMS INC
2822 Fisher Rd (43204-3538)
PHONE................................312 203-5632
Ryan Otoole, *President*
EMP: 9
SALES (est): 1MM **Privately Held**
SIC: 2435 Hardwood plywood, prefinished

(G-7655)
STEER & GEAR INC
Also Called: Steer & Gear
1000 Barnett Rd (43227-1188)
PHONE................................614 231-4064
Fax: 614 231-5712
Gerald Ries, *President*
Susan Ries, *Vice Pres*
Linda Clites, *Purchasing*
Carmen Clites, *Administration*
EMP: 35
SALES (est): 5.1MM **Privately Held**
WEB: www.steerandgear.com
SIC: 3714 Power steering equipment, motor vehicle

(G-7656)
STEP IT UP LLC ✪
580 N 4th St (43215-2106)
PHONE................................720 289-1520
Bob Myers,
EMP: 5 **EST:** 2017
SALES (est): 117.2K **Privately Held**
SIC: 7372 Application computer software

(G-7657)
STOCKER & SITLER INC
4770 Indianola Ave (43214-1862)
PHONE................................614 888-9588
Judson K Byrd, *President*
William A Grubaugh, *Vice Pres*
John Erwin, *Treasurer*
Susan Newbaur, *Manager*
EMP: 4 **EST:** 1969
SALES (est): 215K
SALES (corp-wide): 21.7MM **Privately Held**
SIC: 1311 Crude petroleum production; natural gas production
HQ: Stocker & Sitler Oil Company Inc
4770 Indianola Ave
Columbus OH 43214
614 888-9588

(G-7658)
STOCKER & SITLER OIL COMPANY (HQ)
4770 Indianola Ave (43214-1862)
PHONE................................614 888-9588
Judson K Byrd, *President*
EMP: 4
SALES (est): 596.6K
SALES (corp-wide): 21.7MM **Privately Held**
SIC: 1311 1389 Crude petroleum & natural gas production; pumping of oil & gas wells
PA: Cgas Inc
110 E Wilson Bridge Rd # 250
Worthington OH 43085
614 975-4697

(G-7659)
STONEWARE PALACE LTD
3560 Mountshannon Rd (43221-5237)
PHONE................................614 529-6974
Sherri Lynn, *President*
Ben Wingeier, *Vice Pres*
Leslie Golan, *Marketing Staff*
EMP: 3
SALES (est): 40K **Privately Held**
WEB: www.stonewarepalace.com
SIC: 3269 Stoneware pottery products

(G-7660)
STREAMSAVVY LLC
629 N High St Fl 4 (43215-2025)
PHONE................................614 256-7955
Christopher Kessler, *CEO*
EMP: 4
SALES (est): 98.3K **Privately Held**
SIC: 7372 Application computer software

(G-7661)
STRONG M LLC
2046 Leonard Ave (43219-2105)
PHONE................................614 329-8025
Cathy Calendine, *Executive*
Michael Paterson,
EMP: 17
SALES (est): 1.6MM **Privately Held**
SIC: 3825 Radio frequency measuring equipment

(G-7662)
STRONGBASICS LLC
35 E Gay St Ste 322 (43215-8128)
PHONE................................716 903-6151
Narasimha Vyakaranamkan,
EMP: 5
SALES (est): 540K **Privately Held**
SIC: 7371 7372 7379 Computer software development; application computer software; computer related consulting services

(G-7663)
STUDS N HIP HOP
2032 E Hudson St (43211-2328)
PHONE................................614 477-0786
Tiffany Herding, *Owner*
EMP: 5 **EST:** 2014
SALES (est): 93.8K **Privately Held**
SIC: 7221 2759 Photographer, still or video; screen printing

(G-7664)
STYLE-LINE INCORPORATED (PA)
Also Called: Chelsea House Fabrics
901 W 3rd Ave Ste A (43212-3131)
P.O. Box 2706 (43216-2706)
PHONE................................614 291-0600
Fax: 614 291-0700
Laura R Prophater, *President*
William H Prophater, *Vice Pres*
EMP: 35
SQ FT: 54,000
SALES (est): 5.8MM **Privately Held**
SIC: 5023 5131 2391 1799 Venetian blinds; vertical blinds; window shades; window covering parts & accessories; drapery material, woven; curtains, window: made from purchased materials; drapery track installation

(G-7665)
SUBURBAN STL SUP CO LTD PARTNR
Also Called: Suburban Steel of Indiana
1900 Deffenbaugh Ct (43230-8604)
PHONE.....................................317 783-6555
Mark Debellis, *President*
EMP: 8
SALES (corp-wide): 12.4MM **Privately Held**
WEB: www.suburbansteelsupply.com
SIC: 3441 Fabricated structural metal
PA: Suburban Steel Supply Co. Limited
    Partnership
    1900 Deffenbaugh Ct
    Gahanna OH 43230
    614 737-5501

(G-7666)
SUCCESS PRO PUBLICATIONS
3137 Houston Dr (43207-3330)
PHONE.....................................614 497-5674
Lori Whitmore, *Principal*
EMP: 3
SALES (est): 135.9K **Privately Held**
SIC: 2741 Miscellaneous publishing

(G-7667)
SUNRISE FOODS INC
1157 Baumock Burn Dr (43235-2167)
PHONE.....................................614 276-2880
Fax: 614 276-2838
Mark Pl Sr, *President*
Martin Blaine, *Controller*
EMP: 48
SQ FT: 38,000
SALES (est): 11.4MM **Privately Held**
WEB: www.sunrisefoods.org
SIC: 2038 2013 2035 2099 Ethnic foods,
    frozen; frozen meats from purchased
    meat; pickles, sauces & salad dressings;
    food preparations

(G-7668)
SUPERIOR TASTING PRODUCTS INC
Also Called: Graeter's Ice Cream
2555 Bethel Rd (43220-2224)
PHONE.....................................614 442-0622
Maurice E Levine, *President*
Troy Packham, *Vice Pres*
Nick Whitney, *Manager*
EMP: 40
SALES (est): 3.8MM **Privately Held**
SIC: 2024 5451 Ice milk, bulk; ice cream
    (packaged)

(G-7669)
SUPERIOR WELDING CO
906 S Nelson Rd (43205-3098)
PHONE.....................................614 252-8539
Fax: 614 252-9451
Steve Shipley, *President*
Sandra R Shipley, *Vice Pres*
EMP: 17
SQ FT: 22,000
SALES (est): 2.4MM **Privately Held**
WEB: www.superiorweldingcompany.com
SIC: 3441 Fabricated structural metal

(G-7670)
SUPPLY TECHNOLOGIES LLC
590 Claycraft Rd (43230-5319)
PHONE.....................................614 759-9939
Bill Bennett, *Finance*
Thomas Gisczinski, *Manager*
Anthony Denny, *Manager*
EMP: 15
SALES (corp-wide): 1.2B **Publicly Held**
WEB: www.deloscrew.com
SIC: 3452 Bolts, nuts, rivets & washers
HQ: Supply Technologies Llc
    6065 Parkland Blvd Ste 1
    Cleveland OH 44124
    440 947-2100

(G-7671)
SWEET GS CUPCAKERY LTD
3820 Turnock Gln (43230-3494)
PHONE.....................................419 610-8507
Brittany Griffin, *Principal*
EMP: 4
SALES (est): 176.8K **Privately Held**
SIC: 2051 Bread, cake & related products

(G-7672)
SYSCOM ADVANCED MATERIALS INC
1275 Kinnear Rd (43212-1180)
PHONE.....................................614 487-3626
Joseph W Reed, *President*
EMP: 12
SALES: 1.3MM **Privately Held**
SIC: 3479 Metal coating & allied service

(G-7673)
T E MARTINDALE ENTERPRISES
Also Called: A & M Ornamental Mfg Co
2840 E 5th Ave (43219-2849)
PHONE.....................................614 253-6826
Fax: 614 253-4957
Troy Martindale, *President*
Linda Martindale, *Treasurer*
EMP: 4
SQ FT: 2,500
SALES: 140K **Privately Held**
SIC: 3599 3446 Machine & other job shop
    work; architectural metalwork

(G-7674)
TAG
2226 Wilson Rd (43228-9386)
PHONE.....................................614 921-1732
Yon Deweese, *Owner*
EMP: 4 EST: 2011
SALES: 500K **Privately Held**
SIC: 2759 Screen printing

(G-7675)
TAMARKIN COMPANY
4780 W Broad St (43228-1613)
PHONE.....................................614 878-8942
Debra B Krasnow, *Principal*
EMP: 5
SALES (est): 304.2K **Privately Held**
SIC: 2836 Vaccines & other immunizing
    products

(G-7676)
TARAHILL INC
Also Called: Pet Goods Mfg
3985 Groves Rd (43232-4138)
PHONE.....................................706 864-0808
Floyd E Seal, *President*
Sharon Barfield, *Accountant*
Becky Young, *Sales Staff*
◆ EMP: 20
SALES (est): 2.8MM **Privately Held**
WEB: www.petgoodsmfg.com
SIC: 3199 Dog furnishings: collars,
    leashes, muzzles, etc.: leather

(G-7677)
TARIGMA CORPORATION
Also Called: Ooteksofpak
6161 Busch Blvd Ste 110 (43229-2553)
PHONE.....................................614 436-3734
J Declan Smith, *President*
Keith Sarbaugh, *CFO*
Aaron Grant, *Software Engr*
Howard Free, *Prgrmr*
Winthrop Worcester, *Admin Sec*
EMP: 10
SQ FT: 1,000
SALES (est): 1MM **Privately Held**
WEB: www.tarigma.com
SIC: 7372 Prepackaged software

(G-7678)
TARRIER FOODS CORP
2700 International St # 100 (43228-4640)
PHONE.....................................614 876-8594
Fax: 614 876-3038
Timothy A Tarrier, *President*
Chuck Zigler, *General Mgr*
Julia A Grooms, *Principal*
Ann Tarrier, *Principal*
Jordan T Tarrier, *Project Dir*
EMP: 42
SQ FT: 54,000
SALES (est): 23.2MM **Privately Held**
WEB: www.tarrierfoods.com
SIC: 5149 5145 2099 Dried or canned
    foods; nuts, salted or roasted; candy;
    food preparations

(G-7679)
TARRIER STEEL COMPANY INC
1379 S 22nd St (43206-3083)
PHONE.....................................614 444-4000

Fax: 614 444-0883
Todd Tarrier, *President*
Shelly Parrish, *Manager*
EMP: 41 EST: 1920
SQ FT: 36,000
SALES (est): 19.9MM **Privately Held**
SIC: 3441 3446 Fabricated structural
    metal; ornamental metalwork

(G-7680)
TDS CUSTOM CABINETS LLC
1819 Walcutt Rd Ste A (43228-9149)
PHONE.....................................614 517-2220
Paula Sauer, *Vice Pres*
Dustin Sauer, *Project Mgr*
Terry Sauer, *Mng Member*
EMP: 6
SQ FT: 36,000
SALES: 3.4MM **Privately Held**
SIC: 2434 Wood kitchen cabinets

(G-7681)
TEAM INC
Tsi Manufacturing
3005 Silver Dr (43224-3945)
PHONE.....................................614 263-1808
Sam Dematteo, *Vice Pres*
Sam Dematio, *Mfg Spvr*
Aaron Hipwell, *QC Mgr*
EMP: 12
SALES (corp-wide): 1.2B **Publicly Held**
SIC: 3398 Metal heat treating
HQ: Team, Inc.
    5095 Paris St
    Denver CO 80239
    720 579-0660

(G-7682)
TEAM COOPERHEAT MQS
5764 Westbourne Ave (43213-1400)
PHONE.....................................614 501-7304
Sam Dematteo, *Principal*
EMP: 3
SALES (est): 231.6K **Privately Held**
SIC: 3398 Metal heat treating

(G-7683)
TECH-SONIC INC
2710 Sawbury Blvd (43235-1821)
PHONE.....................................614 792-3117
Byoung Ou, *President*
Hyun Ou, *Treasurer*
EMP: 14
SALES (est): 2MM **Privately Held**
SIC: 3548 3699 Electric welding equip-
    ment; generators, ultrasonic

(G-7684)
TECHNICAL ARTISTRY INC
Also Called: Tech Art Productions
1945 Corvair Ave (43207-1719)
P.O. Box 1239, Hilliard (43026-6239)
PHONE.....................................614 299-7777
Tim McLaughlin, *CEO*
Jeremy Andrews, *Prdtn Mgr*
EMP: 6
SALES: 350K **Privately Held**
WEB: www.techartproductions.com
SIC: 5063 7929 5099 7359 Lighting fix-
    tures; entertainment service; video &
    audio equipment; sound & lighting equip-
    ment rental; speaker systems

(G-7685)
TEKDOG INC
132 Northwoods Blvd Ste A (43235-4726)
PHONE.....................................614 737-3743
Jason Keller, *President*
Kerry Kicos, *Opers Staff*
EMP: 5
SALES (est): 240K **Privately Held**
SIC: 8331 7372 8243 Job training serv-
    ices; prepackaged software; business ori-
    ented computer software; software
    training, computer

(G-7686)
TEX-VENT CO
6100 Huntley Rd (43229-1004)
PHONE.....................................614 299-1902
Fax: 614 299-5488
EMP: 3 EST: 2010
SALES (est): 150K **Privately Held**
SIC: 3559 Mfg Misc Industry Machinery

(G-7687)
THAMES COMPANY LTD
Also Called: Relativity Digital Systems
50 W Broad St Ste 1133 (43215-3301)
PHONE.....................................614 228-4869
Michael Di Cuccio, *President*
Michael Dicuccio, *Prgrmr*
EMP: 5
SQ FT: 1,000
SALES (est): 576.6K **Privately Held**
WEB: www.relativityds.com
SIC: 3575 Computer terminals

(G-7688)
THATCHER ENTERPRISES CO LTD
Also Called: Fastsigns
205 E Broad St (43215-3701)
PHONE.....................................614 228-2013
Fax: 614 228-2218
Michael Thatcher, *Owner*
Lynn Thatcher, *Co-Owner*
EMP: 5
SQ FT: 1,600
SALES (est): 691.7K **Privately Held**
SIC: 3993 Signs & advertising specialties

(G-7689)
THE GUARDTOWER INC
Also Called: Shield Laminating
3600 Trabue Rd (43204-3609)
PHONE.....................................614 488-4311
Fax: 614 488-4337
Lynn Bartells, *President*
EMP: 10
SALES (est): 820K **Privately Held**
SIC: 3944 5945 Games, toys & children's
    vehicles; models, toy & hobby

(G-7690)
THE HARTMAN CORP
Also Called: Hartman Baseball Cards
3216 Morse Rd (43231-6132)
PHONE.....................................614 475-5035
Fax: 614 475-0794
Larry Hartman, *President*
Gary Hartman, *Vice Pres*
Linda Hartman, *Admin Sec*
EMP: 6
SQ FT: 6,500
SALES (est): 874.1K **Privately Held**
SIC: 5999 5941 5947 3993 Trophies &
    plaques; bowling equipment & supplies;
    trading cards: baseball or other sports,
    entertainment, etc.; signs & advertising
    specialties

(G-7691)
THE MAGIC SEAL PAPER PDTS CO
Also Called: Magic Seal Packaging Products
850 Williams Ave (43212-3848)
P.O. Box 12399 (43212-0399)
PHONE.....................................614 299-1185
Fax: 614 299-1466
Thomas N Walker, *President*
Tammy Sexton, *Admin Sec*
▼ EMP: 12
SQ FT: 33,000
SALES: 2MM **Privately Held**
SIC: 2679 Wrappers, paper (unprinted):
    made from purchased material

(G-7692)
THERMAL SOLUTIONS INC
3005 Silver Dr (43224-3945)
PHONE.....................................614 263-1808
Mike Urban, *Principal*
Pat Dunn, *Manager*
Ed Winters, *Manager*
EMP: 3
SALES (est): 194.6K **Privately Held**
SIC: 3398 Metal heat treating

(G-7693)
THURNS BAKERY & DELI
541 S 3rd St (43215-5721)
PHONE.....................................614 221-9246
Fax: 614 221-3510
Marilyn Plank, *President*
Bill Plank, *Vice Pres*
Chris Plank, *Vice Pres*
Dan Plank, *Vice Pres*
EMP: 25 EST: 1972
SQ FT: 2,100

SALES (est): 1.1MM **Privately Held**
SIC: **5461** 5149 2051 Bakeries; bakery products; bread, cake & related products

(G-7694)
TIMBERTECH LIMITED
2141 Fairwood Ave (43207-1753)
PHONE..614 443-4891
EMP: 10
SALES (corp-wide): 1.2B **Publicly Held**
SIC: **3089** Plastic hardware & building products
HQ: Timbertech Limited
894 Prairie Rd
Wilmington OH 45177
937 655-8766

(G-7695)
TIS INCORPORATED
Also Called: Universitees
2114 N High St (43201-1110)
PHONE..614 291-3950
Oliver Roberts, *Branch Mgr*
EMP: 5
SALES (corp-wide): 40.6MM **Privately Held**
WEB: www.tisbookui.com
SIC: **2253** T-shirts & tops, knit
PA: T.I.S. Incorporated
5005 N St Rd 37 Business
Bloomington IN 47404
812 332-3307

(G-7696)
TKS INDUSTRIAL COMPANY
1939 Refugee Rd (43207-1743)
PHONE..614 444-5602
Fax: 614 444-5603
Mark Swedni, *Branch Mgr*
EMP: 65
SALES (corp-wide): 1.8B **Privately Held**
WEB: www.tks-america.com
SIC: **3559** Metal finishing equipment for plating, etc.
HQ: Tks Industrial Company
901 Tower Dr Ste 150
Troy MI 48098
248 786-5000

(G-7697)
TMARZETTI COMPANY
Also Called: Allen Milk Division
1709 Frank Rd (43223-3726)
P.O. Box 453 (43216-0453)
PHONE..614 279-8673
Fax: 614 279-5674
Tom Deschler, *Vice Pres*
Michael Schumacher, *QA Dir*
Jim Weimerskirch, *Accounting Mgr*
Fred Davison, *Manager*
Foster Hartman, *Manager*
EMP: 133
SALES (corp-wide): 1.1B **Publicly Held**
SIC: **2024** 2023 Yogurt desserts, frozen; canned cream
HQ: T.Marzetti Company
380 Polaris Pkwy Ste 400
Westerville OH 43082
614 846-2232

(G-7698)
TOM JAMES COMPANY
1156 Dublin Rd Ste 101 (43215-1095)
PHONE..614 488-8400
Bruce Bays, *Manager*
EMP: 11
SALES (corp-wide): 317.5MM **Privately Held**
SIC: **2311** Suits, men's & boys': made from purchased materials
PA: Tom James Company
263 Seaboard Ln
Franklin TN 37067
615 771-1122

(G-7699)
TORAH TECH INC
2671 E Main St (43209-2533)
PHONE..614 570-6298
William Goldberg, *President*
EMP: 3
SALES (est): 35K **Privately Held**
SIC: **7372** Publishers' computer software

(G-7700)
TORSO
772 N High St Ste 100 (43215-1457)
PHONE..614 421-7663
Scott Rousku, *Owner*
EMP: 4
SALES (est): 433.7K **Privately Held**
WEB: www.torsoonline.com
SIC: **2329** Men's & boys' sportswear & athletic clothing

(G-7701)
TOTAL TENNIS INC
Also Called: TTI Sports Equipment
1733 Cardiff Rd (43221-3806)
PHONE..614 488-5004
Fax: 614 488-5004
James Lathrop, *President*
Sally Ann Lathrop, *Vice Pres*
EMP: 7
SALES: 1MM **Privately Held**
SIC: **3949** 5091 Tennis equipment & supplies; sporting & recreation goods

(G-7702)
TOYO SYSTEM USA INC
2216 Citygate Dr (43219-3565)
PHONE..614 414-0515
Hideki Shoji, *President*
Henry Kim, *Vice Pres*
EMP: 9 EST: 2013
SALES (est): 735.9K **Privately Held**
SIC: **3692** Primary batteries, dry & wet

(G-7703)
TRANE US INC
2300 Citygate Dr Ste 100 (43219-3664)
PHONE..614 473-3131
Fax: 614 473-3141
Al Fullerton, *District Mgr*
Jeff Coston, *Project Mgr*
Matt Beecroft, *Opers Staff*
Bob Eckweiler, *Natl Sales Mgr*
Randy Katz, *Sales Mgr*
EMP: 150 **Privately Held**
SIC: **3585** Refrigeration & heating equipment
HQ: Trane U.S. Inc.
1 Centennial Ave Ste 101
Piscataway NJ 08854
732 652-7100

(G-7704)
TRANE US INC
Also Called: Trane National Account Service
2300 Citygate Dr Ste 250 (43219-3664)
PHONE..614 473-8701
EMP: 61 **Privately Held**
SIC: **3585** Refrigeration & heating equipment
HQ: Trane U.S. Inc.
1 Centennial Ave Ste 101
Piscataway NJ 08854
732 652-7100

(G-7705)
TRANSCONTINENTAL ELECTRIC LLC
3155 Wareham Rd (43221-2245)
PHONE..614 496-4379
Eric Odita, *Principal*
EMP: 4 EST: 2012
SALES (est): 221.1K **Privately Held**
SIC: **3612** Power transformers, electric

(G-7706)
TRANSMET CORPORATION
4290 Perimeter Dr (43228-1036)
PHONE..614 276-5522
Fax: 614 276-3299
Douglas Shull, *President*
Debbie Worthington, *Accounts Mgr*
Tom Fee, *Manager*
Robin Gates, *Administration*
Henry Rumemper, *Maintence Staff*
▼ EMP: 8
SQ FT: 17,000
SALES (est): 1.9MM **Privately Held**
WEB: www.transmet.com
SIC: **3399** Flakes, metal; powder, metal

(G-7707)
TRANSPORT CONTAINER CORP
950 Augusta Glen Dr (43235-5097)
PHONE..614 459-8140

Fax: 614 459-9165
Peter F Demarco, *President*
Cynthia Demarco, *Corp Secy*
EMP: 4
SALES: 500K **Privately Held**
SIC: **2655** Fiber cans, drums & containers

(G-7708)
TREVI TECHNOLOGY INC
1029 Dublin Rd (43215-1199)
PHONE..614 754-7175
Brent Ludington, *Principal*
▲ EMP: 3
SALES (est): 371.3K **Privately Held**
SIC: **3827** Optical instruments & apparatus

(G-7709)
TRI-STATE SUPPLY CO INC
3840 Fisher Rd (43228-1016)
PHONE..614 272-6767
Jim Bruce, *Principal*
EMP: 10 EST: 1950
SQ FT: 10,000
SALES (est): 1.1MM **Privately Held**
SIC: **2531** 2493 5046 Public building & related furniture; blackboards, wood; bulletin boards, wood; bulletin boards, cork; partitions

(G-7710)
TRIO INSULATED GLASS INC
1094 Mckinley Ave (43222-1111)
PHONE..614 276-1647
Fax: 614 276-0545
Timothy Marburger, *President*
Paul Marburger, *Corp Secy*
David Marburger, *Vice Pres*
Mark Marburger, *Vice Pres*
EMP: 5 EST: 1974
SQ FT: 8,500
SALES (est): 390K **Privately Held**
SIC: **3231** Insulating glass: made from purchased glass

(G-7711)
TRU-CHEM COMPANY INC
6645 Singletree Dr (43229-1120)
PHONE..614 888-2436
Fax: 614 761-8010
William S Bartley Jr, *President*
Judith Kenoyer, *Manager*
EMP: 12
SALES (est): 1.5MM **Privately Held**
WEB: www.truchem.com
SIC: **2819** Industrial inorganic chemicals

(G-7712)
TRULITE GL ALUM SOLUTIONS LLC
Arch Ohio
2395 Setterlin Dr (43228-9499)
PHONE..614 876-1057
Fax: 614 876-1832
David Kruse, *President*
Leon Silverstein, *General Mgr*
Dave Converse, *Manager*
EMP: 85
SQ FT: 135,000 **Privately Held**
SIC: **3449** Miscellaneous metalwork
PA: Trulite Glass & Aluminum Solutions, Llc
403 Westpark Ct Ste 201
Peachtree City GA 30269

(G-7713)
TRUTECH CABINETRY
2121 S James Rd (43232-3829)
PHONE..614 338-0680
Nick Willis, *Owner*
EMP: 8
SALES: 850K **Privately Held**
SIC: **2434** Wood kitchen cabinets

(G-7714)
TURN-KEY INDUSTRIAL SVCS LLC
820 Distribution Dr (43228-1004)
PHONE..614 274-1128
Gregory Less, *Mng Member*
EMP: 52
SQ FT: 10,000
SALES: 7.6MM **Privately Held**
SIC: **7692** 3441 Automotive welding; building components, structural steel

(G-7715)
TURN-KEY TUNNELING INC
1247 Stimmel Rd (43223-2915)
PHONE..614 275-4832
Christine Froehrlich, *President*
Deborah Tingler, *President*
Michael J Fusco, *Principal*
Brian Froehrlich, *Vice Pres*
Alice Blevins, *Treasurer*
EMP: 35
SALES (est): 9.6MM **Privately Held**
SIC: **3531** Tunnelling machinery

(G-7716)
U S FUEL DEVELOPMENT CO (PA)
Also Called: General Equipped Products
1445 Goodale Blvd (43212-3402)
PHONE..614 486-0614
Harold B Epler Jr, *President*
EMP: 1
SQ FT: 800
SALES (est): 1.2MM **Privately Held**
SIC: **6552** 1311 1381 6792 Subdividers & developers; crude petroleum & natural gas; drilling oil & gas wells; oil royalty traders

(G-7717)
U S HAIR INC
3727 E Broad St (43213-1127)
PHONE..614 235-5190
Tom Jeon, *President*
EMP: 6
SALES (est): 388.8K **Privately Held**
WEB: www.ushairbeauty.com
SIC: **3999** Hair & hair-based products

(G-7718)
UIC ENERGY LLC
3000 Corp Exchange Dr # 600 (43231-7689)
PHONE..614 839-0250
EMP: 4
SALES (corp-wide): 4.2MM **Privately Held**
SIC: **3674** 3648 Solar cells; lighting equipment
HQ: Uic Energy, Llc
101 N Plains Industrl Rd
Wallingford CT 06492
860 436-5600

(G-7719)
UNITED CONVERTING INC
3960 Groves Rd Unit B (43232-4137)
PHONE..614 863-9972
Preecha Inthisarn, *President*
John Malaby, *Vice Pres*
EMP: 3
SQ FT: 16,000
SALES: 800K **Privately Held**
SIC: **3081** Plastic film & sheet

(G-7720)
UNITED MCGILL
1777 Refugee Rd (43207-2119)
PHONE..614 829-1226
EMP: 6
SALES (est): 1.2MM **Privately Held**
SIC: **3589** Service Industry Machinery, Nec, Nsk

(G-7721)
UNITED SECURITY SEALS INC (PA)
Also Called: United Seal Company
2000 Fairwood Ave (43207-1607)
P.O. Box 7852 (43207-0852)
PHONE..614 443-7633
Fax: 614 443-4875
Herbert Cook, *President*
Daniel P Sander, *Principal*
Bryan Kern, *Opers Staff*
Mari Sander, *Marketing Mgr*
Susan George, *Director*
EMP: 30 EST: 1900
SQ FT: 20,000
SALES (est): 2.5MM **Privately Held**
SIC: **3312** 3089 Bar, rod & wire products; plastic processing

(G-7722)
UNIVERSAL EQUIPMENT MFG
2140 Advance Ave (43207-1722)
PHONE..............................614 586-1780
Pat Seymour, *Principal*
EMP: 4
SALES (est): 250K **Privately Held**
SIC: 3523 Farm machinery & equipment

(G-7723)
UNIVERSAL FABG CNSTR SVCS INC
Also Called: UNI-Facs
1241 Mckinley Ave (43222-1114)
PHONE..............................614 274-1128
Steve Finkel, *President*
Robert Watts, *Treasurer*
Jodi Sinclair, *Director*
▲ EMP: 86
SQ FT: 120,000
SALES (est): 25.1MM **Privately Held**
WEB: www.unifacs.com
SIC: 1541 3441 3599 1799 Renovation, remodeling & repairs: industrial buildings; building components, structural steel; expansion joints (structural shapes), iron or steel; catapults; sandblasting of building exteriors

(G-7724)
UNIVERSAL PALLETS INC (PA)
659 Marion Rd (43207-2552)
P.O. Box 77455 (43207-7455)
PHONE..............................614 444-1095
Mike Afaghi, *President*
EMP: 3
SALES (est): 1.6MM **Privately Held**
SIC: 2448 Pallets, wood & wood with metal

(G-7725)
UNIVERSAL PALLETS INC
611 Marion Rd (43207-2552)
PHONE..............................614 444-1095
Mike Afaghi, *Branch Mgr*
EMP: 20
SALES (corp-wide): 1.6MM **Privately Held**
SIC: 5031 2448 Pallets, wood; cargo containers, wood
PA: Universal Pallets Inc.
　　659 Marion Rd
　　Columbus OH 43207
　　614 444-1095

(G-7726)
UNIVERSITY SPORTS PUBLICATIONS
1265 Indianola Ave (43201-2838)
PHONE..............................614 291-6416
Michael Shavefels, *CEO*
EMP: 20
SALES (est): 549.2K **Privately Held**
SIC: 2711 2721 Newspapers; periodicals

(G-7727)
US GOVERNMENT PUBLISHING OFF
Also Called: Book Store
200 N High St Rm 207 (43215-2408)
PHONE..............................614 469-5657
EMP: 3 **Publicly Held**
SIC: 2759 5942 9199 Commercial Printing Ret Books
HQ: Us Government Publishing Office
　　732 N Capitol St Nw
　　Washington DC 20401
　　202 512-0000

(G-7728)
USTEK INCORPORATED
4663 Executive Dr Ste 3 (43220-3627)
PHONE..............................614 538-8000
Fax: 614 538-8002
Robert M Simon, *President*
Amy Holbrook, *Sales Mgr*
Wendy Simon, *Admin Sec*
▲ EMP: 4
SQ FT: 650
SALES: 3.8MM **Privately Held**
WEB: www.ustek.com
SIC: 3674 Semiconductors & related devices

(G-7729)
V & C ENTERPRISES CO
Also Called: Printed Image, The
41 S Grant Ave (43215-3979)
PHONE..............................614 221-1412
Cathleen Siech, *Principal*
Vicki Hamer, *Principal*
EMP: 7
SALES (est): 778.7K **Privately Held**
SIC: 2752 Commercial printing, lithographic

(G-7730)
V & S COLUMBUS GALANIZING LLC
987 Buckeye Park Rd (43207-2596)
PHONE..............................614 449-8281
Fax: 614 443-6375
Werner Niehaus, *President*
Brian Miller, *Mng Member*
Cheryl Williams, *Clerk*
EMP: 90
SALES (est): 14.6MM **Privately Held**
WEB: www.hotdipgalv.com
SIC: 3479 Galvanizing of iron, steel or end-formed products

(G-7731)
VALLEY VITAMINS II INC
4449 Easton Way Fl 2 (43219-7005)
PHONE..............................330 533-0051
Adam Crouch, *CEO*
EMP: 26
SALES: 950K **Privately Held**
SIC: 2833 Medicinals & botanicals

(G-7732)
VAN DYKE CUSTOM IRON INC
311 Outerbelt St (43213-1529)
PHONE..............................614 860-9300
Fax: 614 863-9670
John Van Dyke, *President*
Darrell V Dyke, *Vice Pres*
Darrell Van Dyke, *Vice Pres*
Michael V Dyke, *VP Opers*
Michael Van Dyke, *VP Opers*
EMP: 6
SQ FT: 6,000
SALES (est): 620K **Privately Held**
SIC: 1521 3446 General remodeling, single-family houses; architectural metalwork

(G-7733)
VECTRA INC (HQ)
3950 Business Park Dr (43204-5021)
PHONE..............................614 351-6868
Fax: 614 351-6899
Craig Taylor, *President*
Chris Snyder, *Vice Pres*
Jill Taylor, *Vice Pres*
Ken Leachman, *CFO*
Vicki Jones, *Human Resources*
◆ EMP: 17
SQ FT: 186,000
SALES (est): 59.6MM
SALES (corp-wide): 4.6B **Privately Held**
WEB: www.msbv.com
SIC: 2752 4225 Commercial printing, lithographic; general warehousing & storage
PA: Taylor Corporation
　　1725 Roe Crest Dr
　　North Mankato MN 56003
　　507 625-2828

(G-7734)
VERTIV CO (DH) ✪
1050 Dearborn Dr (43085-1544)
PHONE..............................614 888-0246
Rob Johnson, *CEO*
Stephen Liang, *President*
Frank Simpkins, *CFO*
EMP: 8 EST: 2016
SALES: 4.4B
SALES (corp-wide): 15.2B **Privately Held**
SIC: 3823 Computer interface equipment for industrial process control
HQ: Vertiv Group Corporation
　　1050 Dearborn Dr
　　Columbus OH 43085
　　614 888-0246

(G-7735)
VERTIV GROUP CORPORATION (DH)
Also Called: Cortes NP Acquisition Corp
1050 Dearborn Dr (43085-1544)
PHONE..............................614 888-0246
Rob Johnson, *President*
Stephen H Liang, *Group VP*
Matthew S Dean, *Vice Pres*
Eva M Kalawski, *Vice Pres*
Gary Niederpruem, *Vice Pres*
EMP: 1000
SALES (est): 5.9B
SALES (corp-wide): 15.2B **Privately Held**
SIC: 3679 3585 Power supplies, all types: static; air conditioning units, complete: domestic or industrial
HQ: Platinum Equity Partners, Llc
　　360 N Crescent Dr South
　　Beverly Hills CA 90210
　　310 712-1850

(G-7736)
VESCO MEDICAL LLC
692 N High St Ste 205 (43215-1569)
PHONE..............................614 914-5991
Tom Hancock, *Branch Mgr*
EMP: 11
SALES (corp-wide): 1.5MM **Privately Held**
SIC: 3841 Surgical & medical instruments
PA: Vesco Medical, Llc
　　4400 Chavenelle Rd
　　Dubuque IA 52002
　　614 914-5991

(G-7737)
VETERAN INDUSTRIES LLC
147 Lake Bluff Dr (43235-4642)
PHONE..............................937 751-2133
Charles Witt,
EMP: 3
SALES (est): 182K **Privately Held**
SIC: 3357 Nonferrous wiredrawing & insulating

(G-7738)
VF OUTDOOR LLC
4025 Gramercy St (43219-6078)
PHONE..............................614 337-1147
EMP: 4
SALES (corp-wide): 12B **Publicly Held**
SIC: 3949 Sporting & athletic goods
HQ: Vf Outdoor, Llc
　　2701 Harbor Bay Pkwy
　　Alameda CA 94502
　　510 618-3500

(G-7739)
VIA VECCHIA WINERY
485 S Front St (43215-5625)
PHONE..............................614 469-4940
Michael Elmer, *Owner*
EMP: 4
SALES (est): 355K **Privately Held**
SIC: 2084 Wines, brandy & brandy spirits

(G-7740)
VICTORY POSTCARDS INC
Also Called: Victory Postcards & Souvenirs
1005 Old Henderson Rd (43220-3701)
PHONE..............................614 764-8975
Fax: 614 764-8074
Scott Armstrong, *President*
Kimberly Armstrong, *Vice Pres*
EMP: 6
SALES: 900K **Privately Held**
SIC: 2759 5099 Post cards, picture: printing; souvenirs

(G-7741)
VIRGINIA AIR DISTRIBUTORS INC
2821 Silver Dr (43211-1052)
PHONE..............................614 262-1129
Ken Baker, *CEO*
EMP: 8
SALES (corp-wide): 69MM **Privately Held**
SIC: 3585 Parts for heating, cooling & refrigerating equipment
PA: Virginia Air Distributors Inc
　　2501 Waterford Lake Dr
　　Midlothian VA 23112
　　804 379-1610

(G-7742)
VISIONARY SIGNS LLC
6155 Huntley Rd Ste C (43229-1096)
PHONE..............................614 504-5899
Bill Hennessy, *Owner*
EMP: 3
SALES (est): 370.8K **Privately Held**
SIC: 3993 Signs & advertising specialties

(G-7743)
VISTA INDUSTRIAL PACKAGING LLC
Also Called: Vista Packaging & Logistics
4700 Fisher Rd (43228-9752)
PHONE..............................800 454-6117
Tina Defluiter, *Opers Mgr*
Sarah Eckhoff, *Accounting Mgr*
Martha J Cahall,
J Matthew Cahall,
Kyle A Cahall,
EMP: 65
SQ FT: 350,000
SALES (est): 25.5MM **Privately Held**
SIC: 4783 7389 4226 2679 Packing & crating; inspection & testing services; special warehousing & storage; pressed fiber & molded pulp products except food products

(G-7744)
VOIGT & SCHWEITZER LLC (HQ)
987 Buckeye Park Rd (43207-2596)
PHONE..............................614 449-8281
Fax: 614 443-8851
Werner Niehaus, *President*
Brian Miller, *Senior VP*
James Arahill, *Opers Mgr*
Michael Trivelloni, *Opers Mgr*
▲ EMP: 12
SQ FT: 55,000
SALES: 88.4MM
SALES (corp-wide): 704.9MM **Privately Held**
WEB: www.hotdipgalvanizing.com
SIC: 3479 Galvanizing of iron, steel or end-formed products; hot dip coating of metals or formed products
PA: Hill & Smith Holdings Plc
　　Westhaven House
　　Solihull W MIDLANDS B90 4
　　121 704-7430

(G-7745)
W B COAL COMPANY INC
17 S High St Ste 1220 (43215-3441)
PHONE..............................614 221-0101
Wayne Boich, *President*
Max Sovell, *Vice Pres*
EMP: 10 EST: 1974
SQ FT: 3,000
SALES (est): 548.9K **Privately Held**
WEB: www.boich.com
SIC: 1221 Strip mining, bituminous

(G-7746)
W W WILLIAMS COMPANY LLC (DH)
835 Goodale Blvd (43212-3870)
PHONE..............................614 228-5000
Fax: 614 228-4490
Alan Gatlin, *CEO*
Tom Stocker, *Opers Staff*
Greg Wainer, *Sales Mgr*
Tom Ikegami, *Sales Staff*
Dennis Behning, *Manager*
EMP: 60 EST: 1981
SQ FT: 75,000
SALES: 66.7MM
SALES (corp-wide): 1.4B **Privately Held**
SIC: 3694 7538 7537 Distributors, motor vehicle engine; diesel engine repair: automotive; automotive transmission repair shops
HQ: Power Acquisition Llc
　　835 Goodale Blvd
　　Columbus OH 43212
　　614 228-5000

(G-7747)
WALKER MAGNETICS GROUP INC
Also Called: Walker National
2195 Wright Brothers Ave (43217-1157)
PHONE..............................614 492-1614
Fax: 614 481-0040

Doug Bailey, *Mktg Dir*
Larry Staats, *Manager*
EMP: 26
SALES (corp-wide): 55.4MM **Privately Held**
WEB: www.walkermagnet.com
SIC: 3499 Magnets, permanent: metallic
HQ: Walker Magnetics Group, Inc.
60 Solferino St Ste C
Worcester MA 01604
508 853-3232

(G-7748)
WALKER NATIONAL INC
2195 Wright Brothers Ave (43217-1157)
PHONE................................614 492-1614
Richard Longo, *President*
Deborah Krikorian, *CFO*
Laurie Efteves, *Accountant*
Joy Keller, *Credit Staff*
Doug Bailey, *Executive*
◆ **EMP:** 30
SALES: 8MM
SALES (corp-wide): 55.4MM **Privately Held**
WEB: www.walkernational.com
SIC: 3499 7699 Magnets, permanent: metallic; industrial equipment services
HQ: Walker Magnetics Group, Inc.
60 Solferino St Ste C
Worcester MA 01604
508 853-3232

(G-7749)
WARLOCK INC
Also Called: Custom Welding
2179 Citygate Dr (43219-3564)
PHONE................................614 471-4055
Scott Rogers, *President*
EMP: 5 **EST:** 1979
SQ FT: 3,500
SALES (est): 310K **Privately Held**
SIC: 7692 Welding repair

(G-7750)
WASSERSTROM COMPANY (PA)
Also Called: National Smallwares
477 S Front St (43215-5677)
PHONE................................614 737-8472
Fax: 614 228-2165
Rodney Wasserstrom, *President*
Dave Lewellen, *General Mgr*
Mark Medonich, *General Mgr*
David A Tumen, *Principal*
Shelly Meyers, *Exec VP*
◆ **EMP:** 395 **EST:** 1902
SQ FT: 250,000
SALES (est): 776.3MM **Privately Held**
WEB: www.wasserstrom.com
SIC: 5087 3566 5021 5046 Restaurant supplies; speed changers, drives & gears; office furniture; commercial cooking & food service equipment; office supplies; kitchenware

(G-7751)
WASSERSTROM COMPANY
National Office Warehouse Div
2777 Silver Dr (43211-1054)
PHONE................................614 228-2233
Fax: 614 737-8557
Mike Burroughs, *General Mgr*
EMP: 10
SQ FT: 70,000
SALES (corp-wide): 776.3MM **Privately Held**
WEB: www.wasserstrom.com
SIC: 5044 5112 5021 2752 Office equipment; office supplies; office furniture; commercial printing, offset
PA: The Wasserstrom Company
477 S Front St
Columbus OH 43215
614 737-8472

(G-7752)
WATKINS PRINTING COMPANY
1401 E 17th Ave (43211-2849)
PHONE................................614 297-8270
Fax: 614 291-1961
Tamara Watkins Green, *Co-Owner*
David Watkins, *Vice Pres*
Eric Watkins, *Vice Pres*
Arnie Schwed, *Manager*
Debra Llewellyn, *Info Tech Dir*
EMP: 45

SQ FT: 35,000
SALES (est): 9.7MM **Privately Held**
WEB: www.watkinsprinting.com
SIC: 2752 2791 2789 Commercial printing, offset; typesetting; bookbinding & related work

(G-7753)
WATSON ELECTRIC MOTOR SVC INC
536 Stockbridge Rd (43207-3965)
PHONE................................614 836-9904
Fax: 614 836-0158
Maria Swonger, *President*
Mike Watson, *Principal*
Patricia Hacker, *Accounts Mgr*
Helen Watson, *Admin Sec*
EMP: 10
SQ FT: 4,800
SALES (est): 690K **Privately Held**
SIC: 7694 5063 Electric motor repair; rebuilding motors, except automotive; motors, electric

(G-7754)
WEENK LABS LLC
221 N 4th St (43215-2510)
PHONE................................614 448-0160
Stephan Smith,
EMP: 5
SALES (est): 320.8K **Privately Held**
SIC: 3944 Electronic games & toys

(G-7755)
WELCH PACKAGING GROUP INC
Also Called: Welch Packaging Columbus
4700 Alkire Rd (43228-3495)
PHONE................................614 870-2000
Fax: 614 491-4044
Michael Compton, *Vice Pres*
John Hewer, *Branch Mgr*
EMP: 33
SALES (corp-wide): 160.2MM **Privately Held**
SIC: 2621 7389 Wrapping & packaging papers; packaging & labeling services
PA: Welch Packaging Group, Inc.
1020 Herman St
Elkhart IN 46516
574 295-2460

(G-7756)
WELDING CONSULTANTS INC
889 N 22nd St (43219-2426)
PHONE................................614 258-7018
Fax: 614 258-1996
William A Svekric Sr, *President*
William Svekric Jr, *Vice Pres*
EMP: 6
SQ FT: 4,800
SALES (est): 975.6K **Privately Held**
SIC: 8742 8734 8711 7692 Management consulting services; testing laboratories; engineering services; welding repair; measuring & controlling devices

(G-7757)
WELDON
3834 Zane Trace Dr (43228-3831)
PHONE................................330 263-9533
John Wingo, *Manager*
EMP: 3
SALES (est): 251.9K **Privately Held**
SIC: 3679 Electronic components

(G-7758)
WEST-WARD PHARMACEUTICALS CORP
1809 Wilson Rd (43228-9579)
PHONE................................614 276-4000
EMP: 5
SALES (corp-wide): 1.4B **Privately Held**
SIC: 2834 Chlorination tablets & kits (water purification)
HQ: West-Ward Pharmaceuticals Corp.
401 Industrial Way W
Eatontown NJ 07724
732 542-1191

(G-7759)
WESTROCK CP LLC
1015 Marion Rd (43207-2558)
PHONE................................614 445-6850
Fax: 614 445-7877

Rich Simon, *General Mgr*
EMP: 34
SALES (corp-wide): 14.1B **Publicly Held**
WEB: www.sto.com
SIC: 2631 Paperboard mills
HQ: Westrock Cp, Llc
504 Thrasher St
Norcross GA 30071

(G-7760)
WHEEL GROUP HOLDINGS LLC
Also Called: Wheel One
2901 E 4th Ave Ste 3 (43219-2896)
PHONE................................614 253-6247
Joseph Nantle, *Office Mgr*
Phillip Johnson, *Manager*
Joseph Mantle, *Manager*
EMP: 6
SALES (corp-wide): 34.7MM **Privately Held**
SIC: 3714 3452 Wheel rims, motor vehicle; nuts, metal
PA: Wheel Group Holdings, Llc
1903 E Jay St
Ontario CA 91764
888 399-8885

(G-7761)
WHITE CASTLE SYSTEM INC (PA)
555 W Goodale St (43215-1104)
P.O. Box 1498 (43216-1498)
PHONE................................614 228-5781
Fax: 614 464-0596
Edgar W Ingram III, *Ch of Bd*
Bette Everson, *President*
Elizabeth Ingram, *President*
Shelly Frazier, *General Mgr*
Gail Gurney, *General Mgr*
▲ **EMP:** 275
SQ FT: 143,000
SALES (est): 571.7MM **Privately Held**
WEB: www.whitecastle.com
SIC: 5812 5142 2051 2013 Fast-food restaurant, chain; meat, frozen: packaged; bread, cake & related products; sausages & other prepared meats

(G-7762)
WHITS FROZEN CUSTARD OF UPPER
2124 Arlington Ave (43221-4314)
PHONE................................614 230-2213
Chad Wells, *Manager*
EMP: 3
SALES (est): 160K **Privately Held**
SIC: 3131 Uppers

(G-7763)
WILLIAM A WEIDINGER JEWELRY
Also Called: Weidingr, Wm A Gldsmth-Jwlry
1458 W 5th Ave (43212-2400)
PHONE................................614 481-8866
William A Weidinger, *Owner*
EMP: 5
SQ FT: 1,300
SALES (est): 468.3K **Privately Held**
SIC: 3911 Jewelry, precious metal

(G-7764)
WILLIAM DARLING COMPANY INC
615 Hilliard Rome Rd A (43228-9475)
PHONE................................614 878-0085
Fax: 614 878-0761
William J Darling, *President*
Kathy Moss, *Purchasing*
EMP: 6
SQ FT: 1,500
SALES (est): 1.2MM **Privately Held**
SIC: 5084 3545 Industrial machinery & equipment; cutting tools for machine tools

(G-7765)
WILSONART LLC
2500 International St (43228-4601)
PHONE................................614 876-1515
Buddy Mohler, *Enginr/R&D Mgr*
EMP: 30
SALES (corp-wide): 6.6B **Privately Held**
WEB: www.wilsonart.com
SIC: 2821 2541 Plastics materials & resins; table or counter tops, plastic laminated

HQ: Wilsonart Llc
2501 Wilsonart Dr
Temple TX 76504
254 207-7000

(G-7766)
WINSTON CAMPBELL LLC
1777 Mckinley Ave (43222-1050)
PHONE................................614 274-7015
Jonathan Edwards,
EMP: 3
SALES (est): 502K **Privately Held**
SIC: 3441 Fabricated structural metal

(G-7767)
WK BRICK COMPANY
Also Called: Ceramitec
970 Claycraft Rd (43230-6634)
P.O. Box 361034 (43236-1034)
PHONE................................614 416-6700
Luke Castilli, *Partner*
EMP: 4
SALES (est): 263.2K **Privately Held**
WEB: www.ceramitec.com
SIC: 3251 Ceramic glazed brick, clay

(G-7768)
WOLF METALS INC
1625 W Mound St (43223-1809)
PHONE................................614 461-6361
Fax: 614 461-1813
James Wolf, *President*
Donna Wolf, *Vice Pres*
Mike Wolf, *Plant Mgr*
Leigh Wolf, *Admin Sec*
EMP: 6 **EST:** 1974
SQ FT: 10,000
SALES (est): 750K **Privately Held**
SIC: 3444 Sheet metal specialties, not stamped

(G-7769)
WOLFDEN PRODUCTS INC
Also Called: Wolf Composite Solutions
3991 Fondorf Dr (43228-1025)
PHONE................................614 219-6990
Alex Wolford, *President*
Bethany Wolford, *Office Mgr*
▼ **EMP:** 7
SQ FT: 53,000
SALES: 1MM **Privately Held**
WEB: www.wolfdenproducts.com
SIC: 3624 Fibers, carbon & graphite

(G-7770)
WOLFDEN PRODUCTS LLC
3991 Fondorf Dr (43228-1025)
PHONE................................614 219-6990
Alex Wolford, *CEO*
EMP: 4 **EST:** 2000
SALES (est): 319.2K **Privately Held**
SIC: 3624 Fibers, carbon & graphite

(G-7771)
WOLFE ASSOCIATES INC
Also Called: DISPATCH PRINTING
34 S 3rd St (43215-4201)
PHONE................................614 461-5000
John F Wolfe, *President*
Nancy W Lane, *Vice Pres*
William C Wolfe Jr, *Vice Pres*
James H Gilmore, *CFO*
A K Pierce Jr, *Treasurer*
EMP: 4
SALES: 4.3MM **Privately Held**
SIC: 2759 Newspapers: printing

(G-7772)
WOMENS IMAGING CENTER LLC
921 Jasonway Ave (43214-2352)
PHONE................................614 457-7660
Mike D'Eramo, *President*
EMP: 30
SALES (est): 3.5MM **Privately Held**
WEB: www.womensimagingcenter.com
SIC: 3829 Measuring & controlling devices

(G-7773)
WORDCROSS ENTERPRISES INC
Also Called: Christian Happenings Magazine
735 Taylor Rd Ste 230 (43230-6546)
PHONE................................614 410-4140
Fax: 614 410-4150

Edward J Novak, *President*
Andy Fry, *Sales Mgr*
Dave Arnold, *Marketing Staff*
Cynthia Novak, *Shareholder*
Mary Brennan, *Administration*
EMP: 15
SQ FT: 3,300
SALES (est): 1.3MM **Privately Held**
WEB: www.christianhappenings.com
SIC: 2721 7336 Magazines: publishing only, not printed on site; graphic arts & related design

(G-7774)
WORLD WIDE RECYCLERS INC
3131 S Hamilton Rd (43232-5654)
PHONE..............................614 554-3296
Jeffery May Sr, *President*
EMP: 14
SALES: 1MM **Privately Held**
SIC: 2611 5064 Pulp mills, mechanical & recycling processing; electric household appliances

(G-7775)
WORTHINGTON CYLINDER CORP
1085 Dearborn Dr (43085-1542)
PHONE..............................614 438-7900
Fax: 614 438-7967
Matt Lockard, *Vice Pres*
Jim Stevning, *Finance*
Dusty McClintock, *Sales Staff*
Natalie Bunevich, *Marketing Mgr*
Michael Whalen, *Business Anlyst*
EMP: 196
SALES (corp-wide): 2.8B **Publicly Held**
SIC: 3443 Cylinders, pressure: metal plate
HQ: Worthington Cylinder Corporation
200 W Old Wlson Bridge Rd
Worthington OH 43085
614 840-3210

(G-7776)
WORTHINGTON INDUSTRIES INC
2170 West Case Rd (43235-7527)
PHONE..............................614 438-3113
Paul Spreng, *Manager*
EMP: 12
SALES (corp-wide): 2.8B **Publicly Held**
WEB: www.worthingtonindustries.com
SIC: 3316 Strip steel, cold-rolled: from purchased hot-rolled
PA: Worthington Industries, Inc.
200 W Old Wlson Bridge Rd
Worthington OH 43085
614 438-3210

(G-7777)
WORTHINGTON INDUSTRIES INC
Also Called: Worthington Steel Div
1127 Dearborn Dr (43085-4920)
PHONE..............................614 438-3190
Fax: 614 438-3283
James Brocksmith, *Managing Dir*
Dave Dauphin, *Managing Dir*
Frank Roberto, *Principal*
Robert J Borel, *Engineer*
Dawn Byrnes, *Human Res Dir*
EMP: 12
SALES (corp-wide): 2.8B **Publicly Held**
WEB: www.worthingtonindustries.com
SIC: 3316 Cold finishing of steel shapes
PA: Worthington Industries, Inc.
200 W Old Wlson Bridge Rd
Worthington OH 43085
614 438-3210

(G-7778)
WORTHNGTION STELPAC SYSTEMS LLC (HQ)
1205 Dearborn Dr (43085-4769)
PHONE..............................614 438-3205
Mark Russell, *CEO*
EMP: 250
SALES (est): 54.6MM
SALES (corp-wide): 2.8B **Publicly Held**
SIC: 3325 5051 Steel foundries; metals service centers & offices
PA: Worthington Industries, Inc.
200 W Old Wlson Bridge Rd
Worthington OH 43085
614 438-3210

(G-7779)
WYMAN WOODWORKING
389 Robinwood Ave (43213-1752)
PHONE..............................614 338-0615
Marc Wyman, *Principal*
EMP: 4 **EST:** 2008
SALES (est): 445.5K **Privately Held**
SIC: 2431 Millwork

(G-7780)
YABOS TACOS
3051 Northwest Blvd (43221-2233)
PHONE..............................614 824-2485
Scott Boles, *Principal*
EMP: 3
SALES (est): 291.9K **Privately Held**
SIC: 3131 Uppers

(G-7781)
YACHIYO OF AMERICA INC (DH)
2285 Walcutt Rd (43228-9575)
PHONE..............................614 876-3220
Poshio Yanada, *CEO*
Jason Armstrong, *Production*
Michael Schoener, *Purch Mgr*
Bill Taylor, *Purch Mgr*
Kirk Bohanan, *QC Mgr*
▲ **EMP:** 98
SALES (est): 203.7MM
SALES (corp-wide): 124.7B **Privately Held**
SIC: 3714 3089 3465 Acceleration equipment, motor vehicle; novelties, plastic; automotive stampings
HQ: Yachiyo Industry Co., Ltd.
393, Kashiwabara
Sayama STM 350-1
429 551-211

(G-7782)
YARN SHOP INC
1125 Kenny Centre Mall (43220-4036)
PHONE..............................614 457-7836
Joyce Lewis, *President*
EMP: 5
SALES: 300K **Privately Held**
SIC: 2281 5949 Yarn spinning mills; knitting goods & supplies

(G-7783)
YEMANEH MUSIE
Also Called: Red Sea Truck Line
2734 Rosedale Ave (43204-2762)
PHONE..............................614 506-3687
Musie Yemaneh, *Owner*
EMP: 3
SQ FT: 625
SALES: 500K **Privately Held**
SIC: 4212 3537 4789 Animal transport; trucks: freight, baggage, etc.: industrial, except mining; car loading

(G-7784)
YI XING INC
850 Busch Ct (43229-1792)
PHONE..............................614 785-9631
EMP: 5
SALES: 100K **Privately Held**
SIC: 2759 2396 Commercial Printing Mfg Auto/Apparel Trimming

(G-7785)
ZAHLER ENTERPRISES LLC
129 Beacon Run W (43228-1556)
PHONE..............................614 870-7872
Janet Zahler, *Opers Mgr*
Todd T Zahler,
EMP: 4
SALES (est): 339.7K **Privately Held**
SIC: 2273 Mats & matting

(G-7786)
ZANER-BLOSER INC (HQ)
1400 Goodale Blvd Ste 200 (43212-3777)
P.O. Box 16764 (43216-6764)
PHONE..............................614 486-0221
Fax: 614 487-2699
Robert Page, *President*
Thomas Mason, *Treasurer*
Jennifer Ayers, *Accountant*
Lee Shaler, *Sales Associate*
Charlotte Cannizzaro, *Consultant*
▲ **EMP:** 68
SQ FT: 15,000

SALES (est): 83.8MM
SALES (corp-wide): 216.4MM **Privately Held**
WEB: www.zaner-bloser.com
SIC: 5192 5049 8249 2731 Books; school supplies; correspondence school; book publishing
PA: Highlights For Children, Inc.
1800 Watermark Dr
Columbus OH 43215
614 486-0631

(G-7787)
ZENOS ACTIVEWEAR INC
1354 Parsons Ave (43206-3643)
PHONE..............................614 443-0070
Steve White, *President*
David White, *Corp Secy*
Ed White, *Senior VP*
Robert White, *Vice Pres*
EMP: 5
SALES: 400K **Privately Held**
WEB: www.zenosactivewear.com
SIC: 2261 2759 2396 Screen printing of cotton broadwoven fabrics; screen printing; automotive & apparel trimmings

(G-7788)
ZIMMER INC
6816 Lauffer Rd (43231-1623)
PHONE..............................614 508-6000
Fax: 614 508-6001
Scott Klebunde, *Branch Mgr*
EMP: 104
SALES (corp-wide): 7.6B **Publicly Held**
SIC: 3842 Surgical appliances & supplies
HQ: Zimmer, Inc.
1800 W Center St
Warsaw IN 46580
330 343-8801

(G-7789)
ZYVEX PERFORMANCE MTLS INC (HQ)
Also Called: Zyvex Technologies
1255 Kinnear Rd Ste 100 (43212-1162)
PHONE..............................614 481-2222
Lance Criscuolo, *President*
Matt Palmisciano, *VP Opers*
Mike Nemeth, *VP Bus Dvlpt*
Cristy Fletcher, *Office Mgr*
EMP: 21
SALES (est): 2.3MM
SALES (corp-wide): 4.6MM **Privately Held**
WEB: www.zyvexpro.com
SIC: 3624 Carbon & graphite products
PA: Ocsial Llc
1804 Embarcadero Rd # 202
Palo Alto CA 94303
415 906-5271

Columbus Grove
Putnam County

(G-7790)
BOGART IMPRINTING
303 Taft St (45830-1153)
PHONE..............................419 659-2840
Michael Bogart, *Owner*
EMP: 3
SQ FT: 1,700
SALES (est): 164.4K **Privately Held**
WEB: www.bogart-tribute.net
SIC: 2752 Decals, lithographed

(G-7791)
BUCKEYE TRACTOR COMPANY CORP
11313 Slabtown Rd (45830-9302)
P.O. Box 97 (45830-0097)
PHONE..............................419 659-2162
Fax: 419 659-2082
Lynn Graham, *President*
Mike Graham, *Sales Staff*
▼ **EMP:** 8
SQ FT: 11,200
SALES (est): 1.4MM **Privately Held**
WEB: www.buctraco.com
SIC: 3523 5261 Farm machinery & equipment; nurseries & garden centers

(G-7792)
COAT ALL
4599 Campbell Rd (45830-9403)
PHONE..............................419 659-2757
Dennis Schroeder, *Owner*
EMP: 3
SALES (est): 149.4K **Privately Held**
WEB: www.calmcoat.com
SIC: 3479 Metal coating & allied service

(G-7793)
COLONIAL SURFACE SOLUTIONS INC (PA)
4599 Campbell Rd (45830-9403)
PHONE..............................419 659-5639
Tom Langhals, *President*
Gene Heitmeyer, *General Mgr*
Brian Langhals, *Facilities Mgr*
Tammy Whitlow, *Human Res Mgr*
Chad Sellman, *Manager*
EMP: 51
SQ FT: 750
SALES (est): 7.8MM **Privately Held**
WEB: www.colonialsurfacesolutions.com
SIC: 3479 3471 3398 1799 Painting of metal products; cleaning & descaling metal products; sand blasting of metal parts; tumbling (cleaning & polishing) of machine parts; metal heat treating; tempering of metal; coating of metal structures at construction site

(G-7794)
GROVE ENGINEERED PRODUCTS INC
201 E Cross St (45830-1302)
PHONE..............................419 659-5939
Larry Clymer, *President*
▲ **EMP:** 6
SALES: 6MM **Privately Held**
WEB: www.groveengineeredproducts.com
SIC: 2241 3011 Spindle banding; tire & inner tube materials & related products

(G-7795)
H & K PRODUCTS INC
10246 Road P (45830-9733)
PHONE..............................419 659-5110
Fax: 419 659-5110
Sandra Sue Nordhaus, *President*
Jeff Nordhaus, *Corp Secy*
Don Nordhaus, *Vice Pres*
EMP: 5 **EST:** 1951
SQ FT: 14,130
SALES: 334.1K **Privately Held**
WEB: www.sassafrastea.com
SIC: 2099 Tea blending

(G-7796)
NATIONAL LIME AND STONE CO
18264 State Route 189 (45830-9207)
PHONE..............................419 642-6690
Nick Morris, *Branch Mgr*
EMP: 3
SALES (corp-wide): 4B **Privately Held**
WEB: www.natlime.com
SIC: 1422 Crushed & broken limestone
PA: The National Lime And Stone Company
551 Lake Cascade Pkwy
Findlay OH 45840
419 422-4341

(G-7797)
PRODUCTION PRODUCTS INC
200 Sugar Grove Ln (45830-9627)
PHONE..............................419 659-2978
Sam Modica, *Principal*
Grace Viers, *Principal*
Heather Caligiuri, *Controller*
Emily Peck, *Human Resources*
▼ **EMP:** 76
SQ FT: 20,000
SALES (est): 20MM **Privately Held**
SIC: 3469 3548 Metal stampings; electric welding equipment; arc welders, transformer-rectifier; arc welding generators, alternating current & direct current
PA: Midway Products Group, Inc.
1 Lyman E Hoyt Dr
Monroe MI 48161

▲ = Import ▼ =Export
◆ =Import/Export

(G-7798)
WITT-GOR INC
108 S High St 110 (45830-1241)
P.O. Box 125 (45830-0125)
PHONE.....................419 659-2151
Fax: 419 659-2154
W N Witteborg Sr, *President*
William N Witteborg Sr, *President*
Arlene M Witteborg, *Corp Secy*
EMP: 5
SQ FT: 8,000
SALES (est): 517K **Privately Held**
SIC: 2541 5713 2542 Display fixtures, wood; floor covering stores; partitions & fixtures, except wood

Concord Township
Lake County

(G-7799)
RANPAK CORP (PA)
7990 Auburn Rd (44077-9701)
P.O. Box 8004 (44077-8004)
PHONE.....................440 354-4445
Fax: 440 639-2198
Stephen A Kovach, *President*
Frank Marino, *General Mgr*
Joe Vitale, *Vice Pres*
Keith Oress, *Plant Mgr*
Tom Cassano, *Materials Mgr*
◆ **EMP:** 110
SQ FT: 162,000
SALES (est): 98.3MM **Privately Held**
WEB: www.ranpak.com
SIC: 2621 Packaging paper

Conneaut
Ashtabula County

(G-7800)
B C MACHINING INC
502 E Main Rd (44030-8673)
PHONE.....................440 593-4763
Neil Burger, *President*
Terrance Crowe, *Vice Pres*
EMP: 3
SALES (est): 437.3K **Privately Held**
WEB: www.bcmachininginc.com
SIC: 3599 Machine shop, jobbing & repair

(G-7801)
CASCADE OHIO INC
Also Called: C W Ohio
1209 Maple Ave (44030-2120)
PHONE.....................440 593-5800
Fax: 440 593-4545
Nicholas N Noirot, *President*
Gary C Trapp, *Vice Pres*
Gary Trapp, *CFO*
Dave Punkar, *Controller*
Harlan Smith, *Maintence Staff*
▲ **EMP:** 282
SQ FT: 250,000
SALES (est): 83.9MM **Privately Held**
WEB: www.cwohio.com
SIC: 2431 3442 Windows & window parts & trim, wood; louver windows, glass, wood frame; windows, wood; metal doors, sash & trim

(G-7802)
CITY OF CONNEAUT
Also Called: Conneaut Township Park
480 Lake Rd (44030-1460)
PHONE.....................440 599-7071
Bruce Mitchell, *Superintendent*
EMP: 6 **Privately Held**
SIC: 2531 Picnic tables or benches, park
PA: City Of Conneaut
294 Main St
Conneaut OH 44030
440 593-7413

(G-7803)
CONTINENTAL STRL PLAS INC
333 Gore Rd (44030-2909)
PHONE.....................440 945-4800
Jessica Van Epps, *Materials Mgr*
Dave Murtha, *Branch Mgr*
Kim Zitny, *Director*
EMP: 246

SALES (corp-wide): 6.7B **Privately Held**
SIC: 3089 Plastic processing
HQ: Continental Structural Plastics, Inc.
255 Rex Blvd
Auburn Hills MI 48326
248 237-7800

(G-7804)
GAMCO COMPONETS GROUP LLC
1370 Chamberlain Blvd (44030-1100)
PHONE.....................440 593-1500
Linda Kold, *Counsel*
Edward Crawford, *Mng Member*
EMP: 9
SALES (est): 1MM
SALES (corp-wide): 1.2B **Publicly Held**
WEB: www.pkoh.com.cn
SIC: 3465 Automotive stampings
HQ: Park-Ohio Industries, Inc.
6065 Parkland Blvd Ste 1
Cleveland OH 44124
440 947-2000

(G-7805)
GENERAL ALUMINUM MFG COMPANY
1370 Chamberlain Blvd (44030-1100)
PHONE.....................440 593-6225
Fax: 440 593-6269
Dennis Reinhart, *Superintendent*
Gary McLaughlin, *Plant Mgr*
Ron Maurer, *Engineer*
Michelle Brehm, *Controller*
Mike Verzella, *Finance Mgr*
EMP: 300
SALES (corp-wide): 1.2B **Publicly Held**
SIC: 3365 3369 Aluminum & aluminum-based alloy castings; nonferrous foundries
HQ: General Aluminum Mfg. Company
6065 Parkland Blvd
Cleveland OH 44124
440 947-2000

(G-7806)
GENERAL ELECTRIC COMPANY
880 Maple Ave (44030-2113)
P.O. Box 688 (44030-0688)
PHONE.....................440 593-1156
Fax: 440 593-6802
Jeff Adams, *Manager*
Mike Kehoe, *Manager*
EMP: 140
SALES (corp-wide): 123.6B **Publicly Held**
SIC: 3641 5719 Electric lamps; lighting, lamps & accessories
PA: General Electric Company
41 Farnsworth St
Boston MA 02210
617 443-3000

(G-7807)
HARBOR INDUSTRIAL CORP
859 W Jackson St (44030-2255)
PHONE.....................440 599-8366
Fax: 440 599-8386
Michael D Legeza, *President*
Dale Hoskins, *Admin Sec*
EMP: 18
SQ FT: 92,000
SALES (est): 3.2MM **Privately Held**
SIC: 3089 Plastic hardware & building products

(G-7808)
HMT INC (PA)
360 Commerce St (44030-2200)
P.O. Box 88 (44030-0088)
PHONE.....................440 599-7005
Fax: 440 599-7575
Darrell Maukonen, *President*
Nancy Grable, *Office Mgr*
EMP: 8
SQ FT: 5,000
SALES (est): 847K **Privately Held**
WEB: www.hmt.com
SIC: 3398 Metal heat treating

(G-7809)
HRH DOOR CORP
Also Called: Wayne - Dalton Plastics
1001 Chamberlain Blvd (44030-1168)
PHONE.....................440 593-5226
Charles Adam, *Manager*

EMP: 76
SALES (corp-wide): 665.2MM **Privately Held**
WEB: www.waynedalton.com
SIC: 2431 3089 3083 Millwork; extruded finished plastic products; laminated plastics plate & sheet
PA: Hrh Door Corp.
1 Door Dr
Mount Hope OH 44660
850 208-3400

(G-7810)
INDEPENDENT CAN COMPANY
1049 Chamberlain Blvd (44030-1168)
PHONE.....................440 593-5300
Edward Crawford, *Plant Mgr*
Kevin Clinton, *Opers Mgr*
Nancy Kalinowski, *Branch Mgr*
Steve Nine, *Manager*
Mike Wulfeck, *Manager*
EMP: 32
SALES (corp-wide): 63.3MM **Privately Held**
WEB: www.independentcan.com
SIC: 3411 Tin cans
PA: Independent Can Company
1300 Brass Mill Rd
Belcamp MD 21017
410 272-0090

(G-7811)
KELLYS WELDING & FABRICATING
285 N Amboy Rd (44030-3098)
PHONE.....................440 593-6040
Fax: 440 599-7598
Herbert Kelly Jr, *President*
EMP: 8
SALES (est): 803.6K **Privately Held**
SIC: 7692 3441 1799 1542 Welding repair; fabricated structural metal; welding on site; nonresidential construction

(G-7812)
LAKESIDE CUSTOM PLATING INC
373 Commerce St (44030-2288)
PHONE.....................440 599-2035
Fax: 440 599-2580
Tracy McBride, *President*
Trevor McBride, *Vice Pres*
Betty McBride, *Admin Sec*
EMP: 5
SALES: 300K **Privately Held**
SIC: 3471 Plating of metals or formed products

(G-7813)
LIGHTNING MOLD & MACHINE INC
509 W Main Rd (44030-2975)
PHONE.....................440 593-6460
Fax: 440 593-6460
Ronald R Newhart, *President*
Loretta Newhart, *Corp Secy*
Erik Newhart, *Vice Pres*
EMP: 10
SQ FT: 2,700
SALES (est): 1.2MM **Privately Held**
SIC: 3544 3599 Industrial molds; custom machinery

(G-7814)
LUKJAN METAL PRODUCTS INC (PA)
645 Industry Rd (44030-3045)
P.O. Box 357 (44030-0357)
PHONE.....................440 599-8127
Fax: 440 593-6237
Anatol Lukjanczuk, *President*
Elena Kelly, *Vice Pres*
Gary Ring, *Sls & Mktg Exec*
Janis Howland, *Human Res Dir*
Brenda Sembower, *Human Res Dir*
EMP: 140 **EST:** 1964
SQ FT: 100,000
SALES (est): 35.5MM **Privately Held**
WEB: www.lukjan.com
SIC: 3312 3444 Blast furnaces & steel mills; ducts, sheet metal

(G-7815)
MARKKO VINEYARD
4500 S Ridge Rd W (44030-9712)
PHONE.....................440 593-3197
Fax: 440 599-7022
Arnulf Esterer, *Owner*
Thomas H Hubbard, *Partner*
EMP: 4
SQ FT: 4,000
SALES: 180K **Privately Held**
WEB: www.markko.com
SIC: 0172 2084 Grapes; wines

(G-7816)
MODERN ENGINEERING
527 W Adams St (44030-2272)
PHONE.....................440 593-5414
David Mc Laughlin, *Owner*
David McLaughlin, *Plant Mgr*
EMP: 6
SALES: 500K **Privately Held**
SIC: 3469 3599 Machine parts, stamped or pressed metal; machine shop, jobbing & repair

(G-7817)
PRINTCRAFT INC
866 W Jackson St (44030-2256)
PHONE.....................440 599-8903
Fax: 440 593-6213
Richard Truran, *CEO*
Thomas Truran, *President*
EMP: 8 **EST:** 1943
SQ FT: 3,000
SALES (est): 983.2K **Privately Held**
SIC: 2752 2759 Commercial printing, offset; letterpress printing

(G-7818)
S AND S TOOL INC
576 Blair St (44030-1463)
P.O. Box 127 (44030-0127)
PHONE.....................440 593-4000
Fax: 440 593-6910
Paul Sedmak, *President*
Joe Sedmak, *Vice Pres*
EMP: 8
SQ FT: 5,000
SALES (est): 1.1MM **Privately Held**
SIC: 3599 Machine shop, jobbing & repair

(G-7819)
SECONDARY MACHINING SERVICES
539 Center Rd (44030-2308)
P.O. Box 296 (44030-0296)
PHONE.....................440 593-1272
Fax: 440 593-6174
Art Distelrath Jr, *President*
Amy Distelrath, *Vice Pres*
Madelon L Distelrath, *Treasurer*
EMP: 7
SALES: 100K **Privately Held**
SIC: 3599 Machine shop, jobbing & repair

(G-7820)
THE GAZETTE PRINTING CO INC
Also Called: Gazette Publishing
218 Washington St (44030-2605)
P.O. Box 212 (44030-0212)
PHONE.....................440 593-6030
Fax: 440 593-6061
John Lampson, *Principal*
EMP: 9
SALES (corp-wide): 12.1MM **Privately Held**
WEB: www.gazetteprinting.com
SIC: 2752 2711 Commercial printing, offset; newspapers
PA: The Gazette Printing Co Inc
46 W Jefferson St
Jefferson OH 44047
440 576-9125

(G-7821)
VESUVIUS U S A CORPORATION
Also Called: Foseco Metallurgical
1100 Maple Ave (44030-2119)
PHONE.....................440 593-1161
Nabeel Khan, *Managing Dir*
Frank Corpuz, *VP Opers*
David Lawrie, *Plant Mgr*
Kirk Ericson, *Purch Agent*
Tony Midea, *Technical Mgr*
EMP: 22

SALES (corp-wide): 1.7B **Privately Held**
WEB: www.vesuvius.com
SIC: 2899 Chemical preparations
HQ: Vesuvius U S A Corporation
　　1404 Newton Dr
　　Champaign IL 61822
　　217 351-5000

Conover
Miami County

(G-7822)
CAVEN AND SONS MEAT PACKING CO
7850 E Us Rte 36 (45317)
P.O. Box 400 (45317-0400)
PHONE..............................937 368-3841
Fax: 937 368-3849
Howard Caven, *President*
Victor Caven, *Vice Pres*
Dean Caven, *Treasurer*
Helen Caven, *Admin Sec*
EMP: 15 EST: 1951
SALES (est): 1.1MM **Privately Held**
SIC: 2011 5147 5421 2013 Meat packing plants; meats, fresh; meat markets, including freezer provisioners; sausages & other prepared meats

(G-7823)
CONOVER LUMBER COMPANY INC
Also Called: Staely Custom Crating
7960 N Alcony Conover Rd (45317-9763)
P.O. Box 464 (45317-0464)
PHONE..............................937 368-3010
Fax: 937 368-3034
John D Staley, *President*
Jackie Wagner, *Manager*
EMP: 14
SQ FT: 3,584
SALES (est): 3.5MM **Privately Held**
SIC: 5211 2421 Lumber products; flooring (dressed lumber), softwood

(G-7824)
MAGNUM MOLDING INC
7435 N Bollinger Rd (45317-9738)
P.O. Box 459 (45317-0459)
PHONE..............................937 368-3040
Fax: 937 368-3050
Greg Gross, *President*
EMP: 9
SQ FT: 7,000
SALES (est): 1.6MM **Privately Held**
SIC: 3089 3544 Injection molding of plastics; industrial molds

Continental
Putnam County

(G-7825)
CONTINENTAL TURF SYSTEMS INC
21801 Road E16 (45831-9003)
P.O. Box 467, Kalida (45853-0467)
PHONE..............................419 596-4409
Fax: 419 542-2816
Scott Lane, *President*
EMP: 6
SQ FT: 12,000
SALES (est): 346.8K **Privately Held**
SIC: 4953 3559 Recycling, waste materials; recycling machinery

(G-7826)
HELENA CHEMICAL COMPANY
200 N Main St (45831-9172)
PHONE..............................419 596-3806
Wayne Nossfinger, *Branch Mgr*
EMP: 6
SALES (corp-wide): 62.3B **Privately Held**
SIC: 2819 5191 Chemicals, high purity: refined from technical grade; fertilizers & agricultural chemicals; seeds & bulbs
HQ: Helena Chemical Company
　　255 Schilling Blvd # 200
　　Collierville TN 38017
　　901 761-0050

(G-7827)
LIEBRECHT MANUFACTURING
Also Called: Liebrecht Excavating
Rd H 13 (45831)
PHONE..............................419 596-3501
Sylvester Liebrecht Jr, *Owner*
EMP: 5 EST: 1961
SALES (est): 604.1K **Privately Held**
WEB: www.farmdrainage.com
SIC: 3632 3799 3531 1794 Freezers, home & farm; trailers & trailer equipment; excavators: cable, clamshell, crane, derrick, dragline, etc.; excavation work

(G-7828)
SOCAR OF OHIO INC (PA)
21739 Road E16 (45831-9003)
PHONE..............................419 596-3100
Fax: 419 596-3120
Ken Charles, *President*
Cary Andrews, *Vice Pres*
Donald G Smith, *Treasurer*
John Morris, *Asst Treas*
Mary Hoffman, *Human Res Dir*
EMP: 89
SQ FT: 90,000
SALES (est): 5.2MM **Privately Held**
SIC: 3441 2439 Joists, open web steel: long-span series; structural wood members

(G-7829)
VERHOFF MACHINE & WELDING INC
7300 Road 18 (45831-8826)
PHONE..............................419 596-3202
Fax: 419 596-3220
Edward Verhoff, *President*
Leonard J Verhoff, *Principal*
Joseph Verhoff, *Vice Pres*
Eric Mohr, *Opers Mgr*
Roger Verhoff, *Maint Spvr*
EMP: 120 EST: 1955
SQ FT: 150,000
SALES (est): 22.7MM **Privately Held**
WEB: www.verhoff.com
SIC: 3599 3469 3444 3443 Machine shop, jobbing & repair; metal stampings; sheet metalwork; fabricated plate work (boiler shop); fabricated structural metal; manufactured hardware (general)

(G-7830)
WOLLAM AG CENTER INC
202 N Main St (45831-9172)
P.O. Box 190 (45831-0190)
PHONE..............................419 596-3896
Lester Wollam, *President*
Patricia M Wollam, *Treasurer*
Kathyrn Wollam, *Admin Sec*
EMP: 10 EST: 1928
SQ FT: 5,000
SALES (est): 1.1MM **Privately Held**
SIC: 5999 3274 Farm equipment & supplies; agricultural lime

Convoy
Van Wert County

(G-7831)
DECOR AT 124
7944 Kings Church Rd (45832-9005)
PHONE..............................260 319-4213
Robert Johnson, *President*
Ron Greenwood, *Vice Pres*
Connie Johnson, *Treasurer*
EMP: 4
SALES: 30K **Privately Held**
SIC: 5949 2512 Fabric stores piece goods; upholstered household furniture

(G-7832)
LINCOLN CANDLE COMPANY INC
6588 Pollock Rd (45832-8834)
PHONE..............................419 749-4224
Jeffery Thomas, *President*
Cathy Thomas, *Vice Pres*
EMP: 4
SQ FT: 7,000
SALES (est): 292.4K **Privately Held**
WEB: www.lincolncandleco.com
SIC: 3999 Candles

Coolville
Athens County

(G-7833)
AMERICAN DOLL ACCESSORIES
24924 Brimstone Rd (45723-9477)
PHONE..............................740 590-8458
Janice Middleton, *Principal*
EMP: 3
SALES (est): 121.7K **Privately Held**
SIC: 3021 Rubber & plastics footwear

(G-7834)
M & G TRUSS RAFTERS
Also Called: Lock-N-Logs Log Homes
26077 Congrove St (45723-8112)
PHONE..............................740 667-3166
Fax: 740 667-3166
Richard N Gillian, *Owner*
EMP: 3
SQ FT: 900
SALES: 300K **Privately Held**
SIC: 2439 Trusses, wooden roof

(G-7835)
MIDDLETON LLYD DOLLS INC (PA)
Also Called: Middlton Lloyd Doll Fctry Outl
23689 Mountain Bell Rd (45723-9463)
PHONE..............................740 989-2082
Fax: 740 667-9721
Janice Middleton, *President*
Lloyd Middleton, *President*
Janice Middleton, *Vice Pres*
EMP: 7
SQ FT: 8,000
SALES (est): 1.6MM **Privately Held**
WEB: www.lloydmiddleton.com
SIC: 3942 5945 5092 Dolls, except stuffed toy animals; doll parts; hobby, toy & game shops; dolls

(G-7836)
MURPHY JAMES CONSTRUCTION LLC
4146 N Torch Rd (45723-9730)
PHONE..............................740 667-3626
Fax: 740 667-3626
Linney Murphy,
James Murphy,
EMP: 20
SALES (est): 450K **Privately Held**
SIC: 3241 Masonry cement

Copley
Summit County

(G-7837)
A M SCHEFFER SIGNS FAB
1089 S Clvland Mssllon Rd (44321-1659)
PHONE..............................330 666-6674
Michael Scheffer, *Principal*
EMP: 3
SALES (est): 251.8K **Privately Held**
SIC: 3993 Signs & advertising specialties

(G-7838)
AKRON DISPERSIONS INC
3291 Sawmill Rd (44321-1637)
P.O. Box 4195 (44321-0195)
PHONE..............................330 666-0045
Fax: 330 666-7842
Michael Giustino, *CEO*
James Finn, *President*
Diane Hunsicker, *Principal*
Donna Brown, *Admin Mgr*
Katie Yungashick, *Admin Mgr*
▲ EMP: 25
SQ FT: 56,000
SALES (est): 8.5MM **Privately Held**
WEB: www.akrondispersions.com
SIC: 2819 2899 Industrial inorganic chemicals; chemical preparations

(G-7839)
ALL FIRED UP PNT YOUR OWN POT
30 Rothrock Loop (44321-1331)
PHONE..............................330 865-5858
Janelle Wertz, *Owner*
Kristopher Wertz, *Co-Owner*
EMP: 6
SALES (est): 488.7K **Privately Held**
SIC: 3269 5719 Pottery products; pottery

(G-7840)
BLOCH PRINTING COMPANY
3569 Copley Rd (44321-1646)
PHONE..............................330 576-6760
David Bloch, *President*
Maria Bloch, *Vice Pres*
EMP: 6 EST: 1977
SALES (est): 1.1MM **Privately Held**
WEB: www.blochprinting.com
SIC: 5112 2752 Business forms; computer & photocopying supplies; commercial printing, lithographic

(G-7841)
CARAUSTAR INDUSTRIES INC
202 Montrose West Ave # 315 (44321-2923)
PHONE..............................330 665-7700
EMP: 37
SALES (corp-wide): 1.5B **Privately Held**
WEB: www.caraustar.com
SIC: 2631 2679 2655 3275 Paperboard mills; folding boxboard; paperboard products, converted; tubes, fiber or paper: made from purchased material; cores, fiber: made from purchased material; gypsum products; wallboard, gypsum; injection molded finished plastic products; extruded finished plastic products
PA: Caraustar Industries, Inc.
　　5000 Astell Pwdr Sprng Rd
　　Austell GA 30106
　　770 948-3101

(G-7842)
COMPETITIVE PRESS INC
144 Scenic View Dr (44321-1343)
PHONE..............................330 289-1968
▲ EMP: 4 EST: 2010
SALES (est): 343.4K **Privately Held**
SIC: 2741 Miscellaneous publishing

(G-7843)
COPLEY FIRE & RESCUE ASSN
Also Called: COPLEY TOWNSHIP FIRE DEPT
1540 S Clvland Mssllon Rd (44321-1908)
PHONE..............................330 666-6464
Chief Joseph Ezzi, *Principal*
Joseph Ezzi, *Principal*
EMP: 24
SALES: 22.3K **Privately Held**
SIC: 3711 Fire department vehicles (motor vehicles), assembly of

(G-7844)
DOW CORNING CORPORATION
3835 Copley Rd (44321-1617)
PHONE..............................330 319-1127
Jeff Clapp, *Branch Mgr*
EMP: 125
SALES (corp-wide): 48.1B **Publicly Held**
WEB: www.dowcorning.com
SIC: 2869 Silicones
HQ: Dow Corning Corporation
　　2200 W Salzburg Rd
　　Auburn MI 48611
　　989 496-4000

(G-7845)
DOWNING ENTERPRISES INC
Also Called: Downing Exhibits
1287 Centerview Cir (44321-1632)
PHONE..............................330 666-3888
William Downing Jr, *CEO*
Michael Carano, *President*
Ross Haffey, *Corp Secy*
Karen Gallaher, *Exec VP*
David Hocevar, *Purch Agent*
▲ EMP: 100
SQ FT: 144,000
SALES: 20MM **Privately Held**
WEB: www.downingexhibits.com
SIC: 3993 Signs & advertising specialties

▲ = Import ▼=Export
◆ =Import/Export

(G-7846)
ERIK V LAMB
1638 S Clvland Mssllon Rd (44321-1910)
P.O. Box 5223, Akron (44334-0223)
PHONE....................................330 962-1540
Erik V Lamb, *Principal*
EMP: 3
SALES: 35K **Privately Held**
SIC: 2844 7389 Toilet preparations;

(G-7847)
GLAXOSMITHKLINE LLC
4273 Ridge Crest Dr (44321-3067)
PHONE....................................330 608-2365
EMP: 26
SALES (corp-wide): 34.3B **Privately Held**
SIC: 2834 Pharmaceutical preparations
HQ: Glaxosmithkline Llc
5 Crescent Dr
Philadelphia PA 19112
215 751-4000

(G-7848)
J J MERLIN SYSTEMS INC
1245 S Cleveland Massillo (44321-1676)
PHONE....................................330 666-8609
Robert Stroupe, *President*
EMP: 7
SALES (est): 880K **Privately Held**
SIC: 2992 Lubricating oils

(G-7849)
JRF INDUSTRIES LTD
3675 Copley Rd (44321-1645)
PHONE....................................330 665-3130
Jim Ripley, *Principal*
EMP: 3
SALES (est): 246.4K **Privately Held**
SIC: 3999 Manufacturing industries

(G-7850)
MULTIBASE INC
3835 Copley Rd (44321-1671)
PHONE....................................330 666-0505
Fax: 330 666-7419
Brian Schell, *President*
Gifford Shearer, *President*
Thomas G Tangney, *Vice Pres*
Joseph Rinaldi, *Treasurer*
Gifford Sheare, *Executive*
▲ EMP: 85
SQ FT: 160,000
SALES (est): 27.6MM
SALES (corp-wide): 48.1B **Publicly Held**
WEB: www.multibase.com
SIC: 2821 Plastics materials & resins
HQ: Dow Corning Corporation
2200 W Salzburg Rd
Auburn MI 48611
989 496-4000

(G-7851)
NEWTECH MATERIALS & ANALYTICAL
618 Tresham Ct (44321-1297)
PHONE....................................330 329-1080
Haiming Xiao, *Partner*
EMP: 3
SALES (est): 331K **Privately Held**
SIC: 3823 Industrial instrmnts msrmnt display/control process variable

(G-7852)
PREFERRED COMPOUNDING CORP (PA)
175 Montrose West Ave # 200
(44321-2762)
PHONE....................................330 798-4790
Fax: 330 798-4795
Ken Bloom, *President*
Michael Magno, *COO*
Andrew Chan, *Vice Pres*
Joe Hudson, *Vice Pres*
Scott Lieberman, *Vice Pres*
▲ EMP: 109
SQ FT: 70,000
SALES (est): 82MM **Privately Held**
WEB: www.preferredperforms.com
SIC: 3069 Custom compounding of rubber materials

(G-7853)
PVS CHEMICAL SOLUTIONS INC
3149 Copley Rd (44321-2127)
P.O. Box 4143 (44321-0143)
PHONE....................................330 666-0888
Bob Vorhees, *Manager*
Ron Gray, *Manager*
EMP: 10
SQ FT: 27,596
SALES (corp-wide): 487.5MM **Privately Held**
SIC: 2819 5169 Sulfur chloride; chemicals & allied products
HQ: Pvs Chemical Solutions, Inc.
10900 Harper Ave
Detroit MI 48213
313 921-1200

(G-7854)
SHELLY COMPANY
3350 Sawmill Rd (44321-1635)
PHONE....................................330 666-1125
Joe Casto, *Manager*
EMP: 4
SALES (corp-wide): 28.6B **Privately Held**
SIC: 3648 Miners' lamps
HQ: Shelly Company
80 Park Dr
Thornville OH 43076
740 246-6315

(G-7855)
SOFTPOINT INDUSTRIES
988 Traci Ln (44321-1466)
PHONE....................................330 668-2645
Richard Porter, *Principal*
EMP: 3 EST: 2008
SALES (est): 224.7K **Privately Held**
SIC: 3999 Manufacturing industries

(G-7856)
SPORTSARTCOM
939 Traci Ln (44321-1467)
PHONE....................................330 903-0895
Philip Ferguson, *Partner*
Jeff Ferguson, *Principal*
EMP: 8
SALES (est): 670K **Privately Held**
WEB: www.sportsart.com
SIC: 2752 Lithographing on metal

(G-7857)
VISION GRAPHICS
Also Called: Signal Graphics Printing
3545 Copley Rd (44321-1608)
PHONE....................................330 665-4451
Fax: 330 665-4868
Eric Schultz, *President*
Steve Hall, *Agent*
Todd Vranken, *Graphic Designe*
EMP: 5
SQ FT: 2,000
SALES (est): 708.1K **Privately Held**
SIC: 2752 Commercial printing, offset

Corning
Perry County

(G-7858)
ALTEIRS OIL INC
140 W Main St (43730-9588)
P.O. Box 415 (43730-0415)
PHONE....................................740 347-4335
Leo Alteir, *President*
Pat Sikorski, *Treasurer*
EMP: 3
SALES (est): 243.7K **Privately Held**
SIC: 1382 Oil & gas exploration services

(G-7859)
ALTHEIRS OIL INC
140 E Main St (43730-9550)
P.O. Box 415 (43730-0415)
PHONE....................................740 347-4335
Fax: 740 347-4324
Leo Altier, *President*
EMP: 6 EST: 2010
SALES (est): 448.3K **Privately Held**
SIC: 1389 Oil & gas field services

(G-7860)
ALTIER BROTHERS INC
155 Walnut St (43730)
P.O. Box 430 (43730-0430)
PHONE....................................740 347-4329
Fax: 740 347-4625
Louis Altier, *President*
EMP: 17
SQ FT: 5,000
SALES (est): 1.6MM **Privately Held**
SIC: 1389 Oil field services

Cortland
Trumbull County

(G-7861)
BACCONIS LICKETY SPLIT
4194 Greenville Rd (44410-9750)
PHONE....................................330 924-0418
Abbey L Bacconi, *Principal*
EMP: 3
SALES (est): 206.6K **Privately Held**
SIC: 2024 Ice cream, bulk

(G-7862)
BORTNICK TRACTOR SALES INC
6192 Warren Rd (44410-9736)
PHONE....................................330 924-2555
Dana W Harju, *Principal*
EMP: 14
SALES (est): 2.2MM **Privately Held**
SIC: 3524 5261 3541 Grass catchers, lawn mower; lawn & garden equipment; saws & sawing machines

(G-7863)
CONCRETE CNSTR MCHY CO LLC
5210 State Route 46 (44410-9607)
PHONE....................................330 638-1515
Doug Roper,
Ward Roper,
John Thellman,
EMP: 4
SALES (est): 701.9K **Privately Held**
SIC: 3531 Construction machinery

(G-7864)
CONTROL TRANSFORMER INC
Also Called: Geneva Rubber Company
3701 Warren Meadville Rd (44410-9423)
PHONE....................................330 637-6015
Fax: 330 637-2180
William J Martin, *President*
Joseph Whaley, *Sales Mgr*
Matt Dieter, *Sales Staff*
Shane Fonderlin, *Sales Staff*
Joe Whaley, *Sales Staff*
▲ EMP: 45 EST: 2002
SQ FT: 30,000
SALES: 18MM
SALES (corp-wide): 1.2B **Publicly Held**
WEB: www.control-transformer.com
SIC: 3612 Power transformers, electric
HQ: Ajax Tocco Magnethermic Corporation
1745 Overland Ave Ne
Warren OH 44483
330 372-8511

(G-7865)
CORTLAND HARDWOOD PRODUCTS LLC
234 N Mecca St (44410-1039)
PHONE....................................330 638-3232
Fax: 330 638-1965
Dave Denman, *Mng Member*
Dorothy Denman,
Janet L Jewett,
EMP: 25
SQ FT: 20,000
SALES (est): 3.2MM **Privately Held**
SIC: 2431 Millwork; doors & door parts & trim, wood

(G-7866)
CUBIC BLUE INC
2934 Warren Meadville Rd (44410-9321)
PHONE....................................330 638-2999
Joseph Teffner, *President*
Donna Meadows, *Vice Pres*
EMP: 3

SQ FT: 1,800
SALES: 400K **Privately Held**
SIC: 3544 Industrial molds

(G-7867)
CUSTOM COUNTER TOPS & SPC CO
161 W Main St (44410-1482)
PHONE....................................330 637-4856
Fax: 330 638-6430
Amil Roscoe, *President*
Ronald Roscoe, *Vice Pres*
Patty Roscoe, *Treasurer*
Margaret M Roscoe, *Admin Sec*
EMP: 4 EST: 1962
SQ FT: 10,000
SALES (est): 470K **Privately Held**
WEB: www.mainstvideo.com
SIC: 5211 2541 Cabinets, kitchen; counters or counter display cases, wood

(G-7868)
EXTREME CASTER SERVICES INC
3333 Niles Cortland Rd Ne (44410-1786)
PHONE....................................330 637-9030
John C Grundy, *Principal*
EMP: 5
SALES (est): 477.6K **Privately Held**
SIC: 3562 Casters

(G-7869)
HOWLAND PRINTING INC
3117 Niles Cortland Rd Ne (44410-1737)
PHONE....................................330 637-8255
Fax: 330 637-8188
Norma Harned, *President*
EMP: 7
SQ FT: 1,500
SALES (est): 775.9K **Privately Held**
SIC: 2752 Commercial printing, offset

(G-7870)
LAKESIDE SPORT SHOP INC
2115 Wlson Sharpsville Rd (44410-9384)
PHONE....................................330 637-2862
Fax: 330 637-2862
John C Wallace, *President*
J W Wallace, *Vice Pres*
EMP: 5
SQ FT: 2,048
SALES (est): 373.7K **Privately Held**
SIC: 1389 5941 Fishing for tools, oil & gas field; sporting goods & bicycle shops; fishing equipment

(G-7871)
LAWBRE CO
Also Called: Architechual Etc
3311 Warren Meadville Rd (44410-8808)
PHONE....................................330 637-3363
Christopher Riekert, *President*
Jan Haines, *Office Mgr*
EMP: 6
SQ FT: 5,000
SALES (est): 481.7K **Privately Held**
WEB: www.lawbre.com
SIC: 3944 Games, toys & children's vehicles; dollhouses & furniture

(G-7872)
NUFLUX LLC
2395 State Route 5 (44410-9217)
PHONE....................................330 399-1122
Robert White, *President*
Rob Whaite, *General Mgr*
William M West, *Mng Member*
EMP: 7
SALES (est): 3.1MM **Privately Held**
SIC: 3399 3312 Metal powders, pastes & flakes; electrometallurgical steel

(G-7873)
PARROT ENERGY COMPANY
180 Portal Dr (44410-1521)
P.O. Box 92 (44410-0092)
PHONE....................................330 637-0151
Natale Pestalozzi, *Owner*
EMP: 4
SALES (est): 230K **Privately Held**
SIC: 1381 Drilling oil & gas wells

(G-7874)
QUANTUM INTEGRATION LLC
1980 Niles Cortland Rd Ne (44410-9405)
PHONE..................................330 609-0355
Andre Camelli, *Principal*
EMP: 3
SALES (est): 188.5K **Privately Held**
SIC: 3572 Computer storage devices

(G-7875)
SPECIALTY TECHNOLOGIES INC
3470 Warren Meadville Rd (44410-9434)
P.O. Box 216 (44410-0216)
PHONE..................................330 638-0744
Bryan Unger, *Branch Mgr*
EMP: 6
SALES (corp-wide): 932.5K **Privately Held**
SIC: 2992 Lubricating oils & greases
PA: Specialty Technologies Inc
2852a Old Ferry Rd Sw
Supply NC 28462
910 256-1298

(G-7876)
VENOM EXTERMINATING LLC
40 Monte Ln (44410-2010)
P.O. Box 321 (44410-0321)
PHONE..................................330 637-3366
Paul Antonchak, *Principal*
EMP: 3
SALES (est): 204.3K **Privately Held**
SIC: 2836 Venoms

Coshocton
Coshocton County

(G-7877)
AK STEEL CORPORATION
Also Called: Coshocton Stainless
17400 State Route 16 (43812-9268)
P.O. Box 190 (43812-0190)
PHONE..................................740 829-2206
Chad Neighbor, *Safety Mgr*
Terry Cooper, *Engineer*
Ronald Miller, *Engineer*
William Netta, *Engineer*
Fred Williams, *Engineer*
EMP: 584
SALES (corp-wide): 5.8B **Publicly Held**
WEB: www.ketnar.org
SIC: 3312 3316 Blast furnaces & steel
mills; cold finishing of steel shapes
HQ: Ak Steel Corporation
9227 Centre Pointe Dr
West Chester OH 45069
513 425-4200

(G-7878)
ANNIN & CO
700 S 3rd St (43812-2062)
PHONE..................................740 622-4447
Vane Scott III, *Production*
Rick Payne, *Manager*
Scott Vane III, *Manager*
EMP: 100
SQ FT: 15,000
SALES (corp-wide): 154MM **Privately Held**
WEB: www.annin.com
SIC: 2399 5999 3446 3429 Flags, fabric;
banners, flags, decals & posters; architectural metalwork; manufactured hardware (general)
PA: Annin & Co.
105 Eisenhower Pkwy # 203
Roseland NJ 07068
973 228-9400

(G-7879)
ANSELL HEALTHCARE PRODUCTS LLC
925 Chestnut St (43812-1302)
PHONE..................................740 622-4311
Randy Killebrew, *Prdtn Mgr*
D R Scholfield, *Marketing Staff*
Allan Roman, *Manager*
EMP: 70
SALES (corp-wide): 1.5B **Privately Held**
WEB: www.ansellpro.com
SIC: 3842 3069 Gloves, safety; rubber
coated fabrics & clothing; aprons, vulcanized rubbed or rubberized fabric

HQ: Ansell Healthcare Products Llc
111 Wood Ave S Ste 210
Iselin NJ 08830
732 345-5400

(G-7880)
ANSELL HEALTHCARE PRODUCTS LLC
Also Called: Cpp
925 Chestnut St (43812-1302)
PHONE..................................740 295-5414
EMP: 160
SALES (corp-wide): 1.6B **Privately Held**
SIC: 3842 2326 3069 Mfg Surgical Appliances Mfg Men/Boy Work Clothng Mfg
Fabrcatd Rubber Prdt
HQ: Ansell Healthcare Products Llc
111 Wood Ave S Ste 210
Iselin NJ 08830
732 345-5400

(G-7881)
BAIRD CONCRETE PRODUCTS INC
15 Locust St (43812-1136)
P.O. Box 1028 (43812-5028)
PHONE..................................740 623-8600
Fax: 740 623-0200
John Baird, *President*
Cynthia Albertson, *Corp Secy*
Tom Albertson, *Vice Pres*
Margie Baird, *Vice Pres*
EMP: 10
SQ FT: 13,700
SALES: 1.6MM **Privately Held**
SIC: 3272 Building materials, except block
or brick: concrete

(G-7882)
BEACH COMPANY
Also Called: Standard Advertising Co
240 Browns Ln (43812-2067)
P.O. Box 518 (43812-0518)
PHONE..................................740 622-0905
Fax: 740 622-3646
James M Beach, *President*
Esward Beach, *Vice Pres*
Scott King, *Purch Dir*
Beverly M Beach, *Treasurer*
Margret Beach, *Admin Sec*
EMP: 14
SQ FT: 24,000
SALES (est): 2.1MM **Privately Held**
WEB: www.thebeachcompany.com
SIC: 2752 Calendars, lithographed

(G-7883)
BRYDET DEVELOPMENT CORPORATION
16867 State Route 83 (43812-9460)
P.O. Box 199, Conesville (43811-0199)
PHONE..................................740 623-0455
Paul E Bryant, *President*
Ron Deeter, *Principal*
Doug Share, *Engineer*
Julie Pepper, *Controller*
George Sarvay, *Rsch/Dvlpt Mgr*
▼ **EMP:** 50
SQ FT: 4,500
SALES (est): 9.6MM **Privately Held**
WEB: www.brydet.com
SIC: 3532 Auger mining equipment

(G-7884)
COSHOCTON COUNTY ADVERTISER
550 Main St (43812-1612)
PHONE..................................740 295-3435
Erica Harirson, *President*
Yazeed Atiya, *Accounting Mgr*
Lorne Zdhelnik, *Human Res Dir*
Mario Balettie, *Personnel Exec*
EMP: 5
SALES: 500K
SALES (corp-wide): 818.8MM **Privately Held**
WEB: www.oshkoshinfo.com
SIC: 2711 Newspapers: publishing only,
not printed on site
HQ: Journal Community Publishing Group,
Inc.
600 Industrial Dr
Waupaca WI 54981
715 258-8450

(G-7885)
COSHOCTON ETHANOL LLC
18137 County Road 271 (43812-9465)
PHONE..................................740 623-3046
Mike Fedor, *Mng Member*
EMP: 42
SALES (est): 5.7MM **Privately Held**
SIC: 2869 Ethyl alcohol, ethanol

(G-7886)
COSHOCTON INDUSTRIES INC (PA)
605 N 15th St (43812-1496)
PHONE..................................740 622-4734
Fax: 740 623-0422
James R Harris, *President*
Angela Wilt, *Manager*
EMP: 4
SQ FT: 17,500
SALES (est): 2.1MM **Privately Held**
WEB: www.jnindustries.com
SIC: 3599 Machine shop, jobbing & repair

(G-7887)
CRABAR/GBF INC
Also Called: Ennis Business Forms of Ohio
24170 Hangar Ct (43812-9225)
P.O. Box 730 (43812-0730)
PHONE..................................740 622-0222
Fax: 740 622-8120
Joe Fyte, *Manager*
Roger Hermiller, *Manager*
EMP: 29
SALES (corp-wide): 568.9MM **Publicly Held**
WEB: www.ennis.com
SIC: 2752 Business form & card printing,
lithographic
HQ: Crabar/Gbf, Inc.
68 Vine St
Leipsic OH 45856
419 943-2141

(G-7888)
DJ & WOODIES VINYL FRONTIER
2339 County Road 16 (43812-9454)
PHONE..................................740 623-2818
Fax: 740 622-5319
Donna Woodie, *Co-Owner*
Kevin Woodie, *Co-Owner*
EMP: 5 **EST:** 1999
SQ FT: 3,200
SALES (est): 424.8K **Privately Held**
SIC: 3442 5211 5031 Window &
door frames; siding; roofing, siding & insulation; lumber, plywood & millwork

(G-7889)
EXCELLO FABRIC FINISHERS INC
802 S 2nd St (43812-1916)
P.O. Box 848 (43812-0848)
PHONE..................................740 622-7444
Fax: 740 622-8547
Edward L Lee, *Ch of Bd*
Kevin Lee, *President*
Charles Milligan, *Principal*
Lawrence Burns, *Principal*
Eugene Weir, *Principal*
EMP: 10 **EST:** 1966
SQ FT: 1,000
SALES (est): 1.6MM **Privately Held**
WEB: www.excellofabric.com
SIC: 2295 Waterproofing fabrics, except
rubberizing

(G-7890)
FESLERS REFINISHING
315 Main St (43812-1510)
PHONE..................................740 622-4849
EMP: 4
SALES (est): 130K **Privately Held**
SIC: 7641 2511 Reupholstery/Furniture
Repair Mfg Wood Household Furniture

(G-7891)
FRANCISCO JAUME
Also Called: Coshocton Orthopedic Center
311 S 15th St Ste 206 (43812-1875)
P.O. Box 490 (43812-0490)
PHONE..................................740 622-1200
Francisco Jaume, *Owner*
EMP: 6

SALES (est): 313.7K **Privately Held**
SIC: 3842 8011 Surgical appliances &
supplies; offices & clinics of medical doctors

(G-7892)
GANNETT CO INC
Also Called: Coshocton Tribune
550 Main St (43812-1612)
P.O. Box 10 (43812-0010)
PHONE..................................740 295-3435
Fax: 740 295-3460
Rick Szabrak, *General Mgr*
EMP: 22
SQ FT: 5,000
SALES (corp-wide): 3B **Publicly Held**
WEB: www.gannett.com
SIC: 2711 2752 Newspapers: publishing
only, not printed on site; commercial printing, lithographic
PA: Gannett Co., Inc.
7950 Jones Branch Dr
Mc Lean VA 22102
703 854-6000

(G-7893)
GENERAL ELECTRIC COMPANY
1350 S 2nd St (43812-1980)
PHONE..................................740 623-5366
Fax: 740 622-2812
David A Kadri, *Engineer*
Elaine Henninger, *VP Human Res*
Debbie Dutton, *Marketing Staff*
Ted Murdaugh, *Marketing Staff*
Ted Torbeck, *Marketing Staff*
EMP: 70
SALES (corp-wide): 123.6B **Publicly Held**
SIC: 3083 Plastic finished products, laminated
PA: General Electric Company
41 Farnsworth St
Boston MA 02210
617 443-3000

(G-7894)
GRO2 BAGS & ACCESSORIES LLC
1760 Buena Vista Dr (43812-3005)
PHONE..................................740 622-0928
Laura Grogro,
EMP: 3
SALES (est): 203.9K **Privately Held**
SIC: 3171 7389 Women's handbags &
purses;

(G-7895)
HOPEWELL INDUSTRIES INC (PA)
637 Chestnut St (43812-1212)
PHONE..................................740 622-3563
Fax: 740 622-3531
Heather Kendall, *Principal*
Diane Williams, *Safety Mgr*
EMP: 70 **EST:** 1971
SQ FT: 14,000
SALES: 1MM **Privately Held**
WEB: www.hopewellind.org
SIC: 8331 7349 2789 0782 Sheltered
workshop; building maintenance services;
bookbinding & related work; lawn & garden services

(G-7896)
KRAFT HEINZ FOODS COMPANY
1660 S 2nd St (43812-1977)
PHONE..................................740 622-0523
Sanjay Khosla, *Exec VP*
Joe L Kistler, *Safety Mgr*
Emil Pisch, *Engineer*
Zachary Edwards, *Project Engr*
Richard R Leggett, *Financial Analy*
EMP: 500
SQ FT: 120,000
SALES (corp-wide): 26.4B **Publicly Held**
WEB: www.kraftfoods.com
SIC: 2013 Sausages & other prepared
meats
HQ: Kraft Heinz Foods Company
1 Ppg Pl Ste 3200
Pittsburgh PA 15222
412 456-5700

(G-7897)
MCWANE INC
Clow Water Systems Company
2266 S 6th St (43812-8906)
P.O. Box 6001 (43812-6001)
PHONE..................................740 622-6651
Fax: 740 622-8551
Frank Eschleman, *President*
Jeff Otterstedt, *Vice Pres*
Mike Parker, *Safety Dir*
Chris Balo, *Opers Mgr*
Terry Crozier, *Foreman/Supr*
EMP: 400
SALES (corp-wide): 1.2B Privately Held
WEB: www.mcwane.com
SIC: 3321 5085 5051 3444 Cast iron
pipe & fittings; industrial supplies; pipe &
tubing, steel; sheet metalwork; fabricated
structural metal; blast furnaces & steel
mills
PA: Mcwane, Inc.
2900 Highway 280 S # 300
Birmingham AL 35223
205 414-3100

(G-7898)
MFC DRILLING INC
Also Called: Medina Fuel
46281 Us Highway 36 (43812-8707)
P.O. Box 715 (43812-0715)
PHONE..................................740 622-5600
James S Aslanides, *President*
Randy Matheny, *Vice Pres*
Jackie Wilkins, *Administration*
EMP: 10
SQ FT: 2,200
SALES (est): 940K Privately Held
SIC: 1311 Crude petroleum & natural gas;
crude petroleum production

(G-7899)
**MUSKINGUM GRINDING & MCH
CO**
2155 Otsego Ave (43812-9401)
P.O. Box 396 (43812-0396)
PHONE..................................740 622-4741
Fax: 740 622-2966
Jeff Mulett, *President*
Janel Richards, *Corp Secy*
EMP: 10 EST: 1945
SQ FT: 14,000
SALES (est): 1.1MM Privately Held
SIC: 3599 Machine shop, jobbing & repair

(G-7900)
NEOLA INC
632 Main St (43812-1613)
PHONE..................................740 622-5341
Fax: 740 622-2557
Scott Westhoven, *Opers Staff*
Amanda Clapp, *Research*
Sam Kalbaugh, *Corp Comm Staff*
Richard Clapp, *Manager*
Jim Conner, *Consultant*
EMP: 14
SALES (corp-wide): 1.6MM Privately
Held
WEB: www.neola.com
SIC: 2731 Book publishing
PA: Neola Inc.
3914 Clk Pnte Trl Ste 103
Stow OH 44224
330 926-0514

(G-7901)
**NGO DEVELOPMENT
CORPORATION**
Also Called: Energy Corportive
504 N 3rd St (43812-1113)
P.O. Box 662 (43812-0662)
PHONE..................................740 622-9560
Fax: 740 622-8388
Scott Kees, *Manager*
EMP: 12
SALES (corp-wide): 34.7MM Privately
Held
SIC: 1382 4923 5984 Oil & gas explo-
ration services; gas transmission & distri-
bution; propane gas, bottled
HQ: Ngo Development Corporation
1500 Granville Rd
Newark OH 43055
740 344-3790

(G-7902)
**NORTH AMERICAN AUGER
MINING**
1816 Bayberry Ln (43812-3127)
PHONE..................................740 622-8782
David Glover, *President*
Chris Glover, *Corp Secy*
EMP: 4
SALES (est): 321K Privately Held
WEB: www.augermining.com
SIC: 1241 Coal mining services

(G-7903)
NOVELTY ADVERTISING CO INC
Also Called: Kenyon Co
1148 Walnut St (43812-1769)
P.O. Box 250 (43812-0250)
PHONE..................................740 622-3113
Fax: 740 622-5286
Gregory Coffman, *President*
Mark Clark, *Vice Pres*
James McConnel, *Vice Pres*
Dick Emerson, *Marketing Staff*
Thad Coffman,
◆ EMP: 50 EST: 1895
SQ FT: 100,000
SALES (est): 11.7MM Privately Held
WEB: www.noveltyadv.com
SIC: 2752 5199 Calendars, lithographed;
advertising specialties

(G-7904)
OFCO INC
Also Called: Ohio Fabricators
111 N 14th St (43812-1710)
P.O. Box 218 (43812-0218)
PHONE..................................740 622-5922
Marcia Bush, *CEO*
Harold R Shaw, *President*
Marsha Bush, *Manager*
Bob Crown, *Info Tech Mgr*
▲ EMP: 65
SQ FT: 50,000
SALES (est): 14.5MM Privately Held
WEB: www.ohfab.com
SIC: 3496 Wire cloth & woven wire prod-
ucts

(G-7905)
**OXFORD MIN CMPANY-
KENTUCKY LLC**
544 Chestnut St (43812-1209)
PHONE..................................740 622-6302
EMP: 183
SALES (est): 97.1MM
SALES (corp-wide): 1.4B Publicly Held
SIC: 1221 Strip mining, bituminous
HQ: Westmoreland Resource Partners, Lp
9540 Maroon Cir Unit 200
Englewood CO 80112
614 643-0337

(G-7906)
**OXFORD MINING COMPANY INC
(DH)**
544 Chestnut St (43812-1209)
P.O. Box 427 (43812-0427)
PHONE..................................740 622-6302
Fax: 740 623-0365
Charles C Ungurean, *President*
Gregory J Honish, *Senior VP*
Daniel M Maher, *Senior VP*
Thomas T Ungurean, *Vice Pres*
Jeffrey M Gutman, *CFO*
EMP: 6
SQ FT: 3,200
SALES (est): 238.9MM
SALES (corp-wide): 1.4B Publicly Held
SIC: 1221 Strip mining, bituminous
HQ: Westmoreland Resource Partners, Lp
9540 Maroon Cir Unit 200
Englewood CO 80112
614 643-0337

(G-7907)
**OXFORD MINING COMPANY
LLC**
544 Chestnut St (43812-1209)
PHONE..................................740 622-6302
EMP: 5
SALES (est): 374.4K Privately Held
SIC: 1241 Coal mining services

(G-7908)
SANCAST INC
535 Clow Ln (43812-9782)
PHONE..................................740 622-8660
Fax: 740 622-8663
Don Hutchins, *Principal*
Nancy Foster, *Principal*
John Fox, *Principal*
Julie Starcher, *Principal*
Don Popernik, *Corp Secy*
EMP: 50
SQ FT: 56,000
SALES (est): 11.9MM
SALES (corp-wide): 2.9B Publicly Held
SIC: 3321 3322 Ductile iron castings; gray
iron castings; malleable iron foundries
HQ: Standard Car Truck Company Inc
6400 Shafer Ct Ste 450
Rosemont IL 60018
847 692-6050

(G-7909)
SHAWNE SPRINGS WINERY
20093 County Road 6 (43812-9149)
PHONE..................................740 623-0744
Randy Hall, *Principal*
EMP: 4
SALES (est): 287.1K Privately Held
SIC: 2084 Wines

(G-7910)
SPRINT PRINT INC
Also Called: Market Media Creations
520 Main St (43812-1612)
PHONE..................................740 622-4429
Fax: 740 622-3604
Jeff Eikenberry, *President*
EMP: 9
SQ FT: 6,000
SALES (est): 770K Privately Held
SIC: 2752 7319 Commercial printing, litho-
graphic; poster advertising service, ex-
cept outdoor

(G-7911)
STEVEN MERCER INC
Also Called: Signmaker Shop, The
801 Walnut St (43812-1623)
P.O. Box 26 (43812-0026)
PHONE..................................740 623-0033
Fax: 740 623-0034
Steven Mercer, *President*
EMP: 4
SQ FT: 5,500
SALES (est): 320K Privately Held
SIC: 7389 3993 Sign painting & lettering
shop; signs & advertising specialties

(G-7912)
T JS OIL & GAS INC
Also Called: R & K Industrial Supply
23191 County Road 621 (43812-8903)
PHONE..................................740 623-0192
Rodney F Adams, *President*
Kathy A Adams, *Corp Secy*
Jeffrey D Adams, *Vice Pres*
EMP: 4
SQ FT: 5,600
SALES (est): 909.4K Privately Held
SIC: 1311 5084 5261 Crude petroleum
production; natural gas production; petro-
leum industry machinery; lawnmowers &
tractors

(G-7913)
THOMAS J WEAVER INC (PA)
Also Called: Coshocton Pallet & Door Co
1501 Kenilworth Ave (43812-2430)
P.O. Box 412 (43812-0412)
PHONE..................................740 622-2040
Thomas J Weaver, *President*
EMP: 12 EST: 1963
SALES (est): 3.2MM Privately Held
SIC: 1542 1541 1521 2448 Commercial
& office building, new construction; indus-
trial buildings, new construction; new con-
struction, single-family houses; pallets,
wood; boxes, wood; metal doors

(G-7914)
**WESTMORELAND RESOURCES
GP LLC**
544 Chestnut St (43812-1209)
P.O. Box 427 (43812-0427)
PHONE..................................740 622-6302
Charles Ungurean, *Manager*

EMP: 12
SALES (est): 2.5MM
SALES (corp-wide): 1.4B Publicly Held
SIC: 1221 Bituminous coal & lignite-sur-
face mining
PA: Westmoreland Coal Company
9540 Maroon Cir Unit 200
Englewood CO 80112
855 922-6463

(G-7915)
WESTROCK CP LLC
Also Called: Smurfit-Stone Container
500 N 4th St (43812-1119)
PHONE..................................740 622-0581
Fax: 740 622-5297
M L Tripp, *Opers-Prdtn-Mfg*
Randall Hothem, *Enginr/R&D Mgr*
Wes Enlow, *Manager*
Robert Smith, *Data Proc Mgr*
Al Miller, *Programmer Anys*
EMP: 265
SALES (corp-wide): 14.1B Publicly Held
WEB: www.smurfit-stone.com
SIC: 2631 2621 Corrugating medium;
paper mills
HQ: Westrock Cp, Llc
504 Thrasher St
Norcross GA 30071

(G-7916)
WILEYS FINEST LLC
545 Walnut St Ste B (43812-1656)
P.O. Box 1665 (43812-6665)
PHONE..................................740 622-1072
Sam Wiley, *Principal*
Shane Griffiths, *Principal*
EMP: 3
SALES (est): 180K Privately Held
SIC: 2077 2023 2079 5499 Animal fats,
oils & meals; dietary supplements; dairy &
non-dairy based; edible fats & oils; health
foods

Covington
Miami County

(G-7917)
AEROVENT INC
800 S High St (45318-1170)
PHONE..................................937 473-3789
Fax: 937 473-3793
Bob Day, *Principal*
EMP: 3
SALES (est): 340.7K Privately Held
SIC: 3999 5088 5099 Manufacturing in-
dustries; aircraft equipment & supplies;
durable goods

(G-7918)
ARENS CORPORATION (PA)
395 S High St (45318-1121)
P.O. Box 69 (45318-0069)
PHONE..................................937 473-2028
Gary Godfrey Sr, *President*
Nadine Sanders, *Corp Secy*
Ginger Godfrey, *Vice Pres*
Jean Devlin, *Advt Staff*
Carol Wood, *Advt Staff*
EMP: 17 EST: 1954
SQ FT: 2,000
SALES (est): 1.7MM Privately Held
WEB: www.arenspub.com
SIC: 2711 2721 2752 Newspapers: pub-
lishing only, not printed on site; maga-
zines: publishing only, not printed on site;
commercial printing, offset

(G-7919)
ARENS CORPORATION
Also Called: Arens Publications & Printing
22 N High St (45318-1306)
PHONE..................................937 473-2028
Fax: 937 473-2500
Gary Godfrey, *Financial Exec*
Connie Didier, *Manager*
EMP: 6
SALES (corp-wide): 1.7MM Privately
Held
WEB: www.arenspub.com
SIC: 2711 2721 2752 Newspapers: pub-
lishing only, not printed on site; maga-
zines: publishing only, not printed on site;
commercial printing, offset

PA: The Arens Corporation
395 S High St
Covington OH 45318
937 473-2028

(G-7920)
B K PLASTICS INC
1400 Mote Dr (45318-1217)
P.O. Box 250 (45318-0250)
PHONE.....................................937 473-2087
Fax: 937 473-3597
Robert Robbins, *President*
Al Weaver, *Safety Mgr*
Karen Robbins, *Treasurer*
EMP: 6
SQ FT: 12,000
SALES (est): 1.2MM **Privately Held**
SIC: 2673 Plastic bags: made from pur-
chased materials

(G-7921)
D & D CLASSIC AUTO
RESTORATION
Also Called: D&D Classic Restoration
2300 Mote Dr (45318-1200)
PHONE.....................................937 473-2229
Fax: 937 473-5433
Dale Sotsing, *President*
Rodger James, *Vice Pres*
Mark Kennison, *Admin Sec*
EMP: 22
SQ FT: 8,000
SALES (est): 1.2MM **Privately Held**
WEB: www.ddclassic.com
SIC: 7389 3711 5521 7532 Automobile
recovery service; motor vehicles & car
bodies; automobiles, used cars only; tops
(canvas or plastic), installation or repair:
automotive

(G-7922)
FAB-TECH MACHINE INC
Also Called: Fabtech Machine
2 W Spring St (45318-1324)
PHONE.....................................937 473-5572
Randy Garber, *President*
EMP: 5
SALES (est): 250K **Privately Held**
SIC: 3599 7692 Machine shop, jobbing &
repair; welding repair

(G-7923)
GENERAL FILMS INC
645 S High St (45318-1182)
PHONE.....................................888 436-3456
Fax: 937 473-2403
Tim Weikert, *President*
Tony Slade, *Managing Dir*
Roy J Weikert, *Chairman*
Tom Granata, *Vice Pres*
Kenneth Bruce, *VP Mfg*
EMP: 80
SQ FT: 55,000
SALES (est): 31.1MM **Privately Held**
WEB: www.generalfilms.com
SIC: 3081 2673 Polyethylene film; plastic
& pliofilm bags

(G-7924)
HAROLD FLORY
Also Called: Flory Cabinetry
5225 W Myers Rd (45318-8714)
PHONE.....................................937 473-3030
Harold Flory, *Owner*
EMP: 5
SQ FT: 2,500
SALES (est): 200K **Privately Held**
SIC: 2434 0119 Wood kitchen cabinets;
feeder grains

(G-7925)
L & C PLASTIC BAGS INC
500 Dick Minnich Dr (45318-1263)
P.O. Box 214 (45318-0214)
PHONE.....................................937 473-2968
Fax: 937 473-5334
Rodney Sprenkel, *President*
EMP: 20 EST: 1967
SQ FT: 9,000
SALES: 500K **Privately Held**
WEB: www.lcplastics.com
SIC: 2673 Plastic bags: made from pur-
chased materials

(G-7926)
MCMILLION LOCK & KEY
8822 N Rangeline Rd (45318-9638)
PHONE.....................................937 473-5342
Jennifer McMillion, *Manager*
EMP: 9
SALES (est): 1.1MM **Privately Held**
SIC: 2421 4225 Sawdust & shavings;
warehousing, self-storage

(G-7927)
PBM COVINGTON LLC
400 Hazel St (45318-1724)
PHONE.....................................937 473-2050
Scott F Jamison, *Mng Member*
Larry Hensler, *Manager*
EMP: 14
SALES (est): 2.1MM **Privately Held**
SIC: 2834 Vitamin, nutrient & hematinic
preparations for human use

Crestline
Crawford County

(G-7928)
ANTHONY-LEE SCREEN PRTG
INC
401 S Thoman St (44827-1849)
P.O. Box 292 (44827-0292)
PHONE.....................................419 683-1861
Fax: 419 683-2209
Donald W Grady, *President*
Lisa Grady, *Vice Pres*
Lisa Grady-Clerk, *Vice Pres*
Mike Grady, *Site Mgr*
Sandra J Grady, *Treasurer*
EMP: 11
SQ FT: 20,000
SALES (est): 1.7MM **Privately Held**
SIC: 2759 Screen printing

(G-7929)
FOWLER PRODUCTS INC
810 Colby Rd (44827-1799)
PHONE.....................................419 683-4057
Fax: 419 683-3620
Mark Fowler, *President*
Phyllis Fowler, *Chairman*
Darrell Baker, *Sales Staff*
Jean E Cole, *Shareholder*
Marcia A Dishon, *Shareholder*
▲ EMP: 18
SQ FT: 52,000
SALES (est): 3.8MM **Privately Held**
WEB: www.fowler-inc.com
SIC: 3089 3829 3084 3083 Extruded fin-
ished plastic products; measuring & con-
trolling devices; plastics pipe; laminated
plastics plate & sheet

(G-7930)
INTERSTATE SIGN PRODUCTS
INC
432 E Main St (44827-1118)
P.O. Box 187 (44827-0187)
PHONE.....................................419 683-1962
Fax: 419 683-3729
Robin Wittmer, *President*
EMP: 6
SQ FT: 4,000
SALES (est): 990K **Privately Held**
WEB: www.interstate911.com
SIC: 5085 3993 Signmaker equipment &
supplies; letters for signs, metal

(G-7931)
LINKS COUNTRY MEATS
7252 Leesville Rd (44827-9455)
PHONE.....................................419 683-2195
Mike Link, *Owner*
Janice Link, *Co-Owner*
EMP: 5
SQ FT: 6,500
SALES (est): 220K **Privately Held**
SIC: 2011 5147 5421 Meat packing
plants; meats, fresh; food & freezer plans,
meat

(G-7932)
NIESE FARMS
7506 Cole Rd (44827-9742)
PHONE.....................................419 347-1204
Patrick Niese, *Partner*

EMP: 7
SQ FT: 2,150
SALES (est): 366.5K **Privately Held**
SIC: 2043 Oatmeal: prepared as cereal
breakfast food

(G-7933)
PITTSBURGH GLASS WORKS
LLC
5066 Lincoln Hwy (44827-9605)
P.O. Box 269 (44827-0269)
PHONE.....................................419 683-2400
Mark Soderberg, *QC Dir*
Richard Krehnobi, *Engineer*
William Page, *Accounting Dir*
Robert Halsey, *Human Res Dir*
Tony Hartman, *Human Res Dir*
EMP: 300
SALES (corp-wide): 457.8MM **Privately
Held**
SIC: 2851 Paints & allied products
HQ: Pittsburgh Glass Works, Llc
30 Isabella St Ste 500
Pittsburgh PA 15212
412 995-6500

(G-7934)
PITTSBURGH GLASS WORKS
LLC
Also Called: Pgw
5064 Lincoln Hwy (44827-9605)
PHONE.....................................419 569-7521
Praveen Vavaidya, *Plant Mgr*
EMP: 170
SALES (corp-wide): 457.8MM **Privately
Held**
SIC: 3711 Automobile assembly, including
specialty automobiles
HQ: Pittsburgh Glass Works, Llc
30 Isabella St Ste 500
Pittsburgh PA 15212
412 995-6500

(G-7935)
PPG INDUSTRIES INC
Also Called: Satellite
5066 Lincoln Hwy (44827-9605)
P.O. Box 269 (44827-0269)
PHONE.....................................419 683-2400
Fax: 419 526-7537
Dave Kimble, *Plant Mgr*
Dan Couch, *Site Mgr*
Llew Wheaton, *Manager*
EMP: 24
SALES (corp-wide): 14.7B **Publicly Held**
WEB: www.ppg.com
SIC: 2851 3211 3231 3229 Paints & al-
lied products; paints & paint additives;
coating, air curing; lacquers, varnishes,
enamels & other coatings; flat glass;
strengthened or reinforced glass; windshields, glass: made from purchased
glass; glass fiber products; fiber optics
strands; alkalies & chlorine; chlorine,
compressed or liquefied; caustic soda,
sodium hydroxide; plastics materials &
resins
PA: Ppg Industries, Inc.
1 Ppg Pl
Pittsburgh PA 15272
412 434-3131

(G-7936)
SUNRISE COOPERATIVE INC
3000 W Bucyrus St (44827-1674)
P.O. Box 870, Fremont (43420-0870)
PHONE.....................................419 683-4600
Steve Neise, *Branch Mgr*
EMP: 40
SALES (corp-wide): 46.5MM **Privately
Held**
SIC: 3315 3465 2542 Baskets, steel wire;
wire products, ferrous/iron: made in wire-
drawing plants; automotive stampings;
partitions & fixtures, except wood
PA: Sunrise Cooperative, Inc.
2025 W State St Ste A
Fremont OH 43420
419 332-6468

Creston
Wayne County

(G-7937)
ACCURATE AUTOMATIC MFG
LTD
141 Factory St (44217)
P.O. Box 4441 (44217-4441)
PHONE.....................................330 435-4575
Fax: 330 435-1630
James Bush,
EMP: 4
SALES (est): 593.6K **Privately Held**
SIC: 3999 Manufacturing industries

(G-7938)
CANAAN COUNTRY MEATS
11970 Canaan Center Rd (44217-9767)
PHONE.....................................330 435-4778
Ryan Lily, *Owner*
EMP: 4
SALES (est): 180K **Privately Held**
SIC: 2011 Meat packing plants

(G-7939)
FRANK CSAPO
Also Called: Frank Csapo Oil & Gas Producer
157 Myers St (44217-9704)
PHONE.....................................330 435-4458
Frank Csapo, *Owner*
EMP: 6
SALES (est): 700.8K **Privately Held**
SIC: 1381 Drilling oil & gas wells

(G-7940)
LISA ARTERS
117 Maple Ave (44217-9691)
PHONE.....................................330 435-1804
EMP: 3 EST: 2010
SALES (est): 116.7K **Privately Held**
SIC: 2711 Newspapers-Publishing/Printing

(G-7941)
MELLOTT BRONZE INC
4634 E Sterling Rd (44217-9241)
PHONE.....................................330 435-6304
Fax: 330 435-4600
Ron Mellott, *President*
Ed Mellott, *Vice Pres*
Linda Mellott, *Admin Sec*
EMP: 13
SQ FT: 11,800
SALES (est): 2.3MM **Privately Held**
SIC: 3599 Machine shop, jobbing & repair

(G-7942)
OHIO FARMS PACKING CO LTD
2416 E West Salem Rd (44217-9650)
PHONE.....................................330 435-6400
David Mullet, *Mng Member*
EMP: 4
SALES (est): 523.6K **Privately Held**
SIC: 2011 Veal from meat slaughtered on
site

(G-7943)
SHRINER SHEET METAL INC
196 S Main St (44217-9799)
P.O. Box 3331 (44217-3331)
PHONE.....................................330 435-6735
Fax: 330 435-6003
Fred Shriner, *President*
Karen Shriner, *Admin Sec*
EMP: 16 EST: 1953
SQ FT: 1,800
SALES (est): 2.4MM **Privately Held**
SIC: 1711 3444 Warm air heating & air
conditioning contractor; sheet metalwork

(G-7944)
WHITEFEATHER MEATS LLC
14079 Cleveland Rd (44217-9658)
PHONE.....................................330 435-6300
Fax: 330 435-6253
Don Perkins, *Vice Pres*
Fred Perkins,
Bunny Perkins,
EMP: 9
SALES (est): 880K **Privately Held**
WEB: www.whitefeathermeats.com
SIC: 2011 Meat packing plants

Cridersville
Auglaize County

(G-7945)
HAWTHORNE-SEVING INC
320 W Main St (45806-2215)
PHONE..................................419 643-5531
Fax: 419 643-4762
Charles L Dale, *President*
EMP: 46 **EST:** 1950
SQ FT: 10,000
SALES (est): 6.9MM **Privately Held**
SIC: 3535 3556 Conveyors & conveying equipment; food products machinery
PA: E S Industries Inc
110 Brookview Ct
Lima OH 45801
419 643-2625

(G-7946)
KATIES LIGHT HOUSE LLC
300 Dupler Ave (45806-2304)
PHONE..................................419 645-5451
Fax: 419 645-5452
Richard Lavy,
EMP: 23
SALES (est): 2MM **Privately Held**
WEB: www.katieslighthouse.com
SIC: 3229 Bulbs for electric lights

(G-7947)
UNITED FIRE APPARATUS CORP
204 S Gay St (45806-2312)
P.O. Box 2066 (45806-0066)
PHONE..................................419 645-4083
Darrel A Chapman, *President*
Sonja Chapman, *Admin Sec*
EMP: 5 **EST:** 1963
SQ FT: 9,000
SALES: 867K **Privately Held**
SIC: 3711 3569 5012 5087 Fire department vehicles (motor vehicles), assembly of; firefighting apparatus; trucks, commercial; firefighting equipment

Crooksville
Perry County

(G-7948)
ALFMAN LOGGING LLC
4499 Township Road 448 Ne (43731-9740)
PHONE..................................740 982-6227
EMP: 6
SALES (est): 488K **Privately Held**
SIC: 2411 Logging camps & contractors

(G-7949)
BEAUMONT BROTHERS STONEWARE (PA)
Also Called: Beaumont Brothers Pottery
410 Keystone St (43731-1034)
PHONE..................................740 982-0055
Fax: 740 982-8484
Roger Beaumont, *President*
Margie Beaumont, *Vice Pres*
EMP: 2
SQ FT: 14,000
SALES (est): 1.4MM **Privately Held**
WEB: www.beaumontbrotherspottery.com
SIC: 3269 Stoneware pottery products

(G-7950)
I CERCO INC
416 Maple Ave (43731-1305)
P.O. Box 151 (43731-0151)
PHONE..................................740 982-2050
Fax: 740 982-9396
Gary Troyer, *Engineer*
Mick Pease, *Branch Mgr*
EMP: 75
SALES (corp-wide): 58.1MM **Privately Held**
WEB: www.cercollc.com
SIC: 3255 3567 3297 Clay refractories; industrial furnaces & ovens; nonclay refractories
PA: I Cerco Inc
453 W Mcconkey St
Shreve OH 44676
330 567-2145

(G-7951)
OLD MILL POWER EQUIPMENT
100 China St (43731-1112)
P.O. Box 28 (43731-0028)
PHONE..................................740 982-3246
Edward Gamble, *Owner*
EMP: 4
SALES (est): 322.7K **Privately Held**
SIC: 3751 Bicycles & related parts

(G-7952)
PCC AIRFOILS LLC
101 China St (43731-1111)
P.O. Box 206 (43731-0206)
PHONE..................................740 982-6025
Fax: 330 868-7236
Robert Lake, *QC Dir*
Trey Mason, *Engineer*
Ryan Thrush, *Systems Staff*
EMP: 300
SALES (corp-wide): 223.6B **Publicly Held**
WEB: www.pccairfoils.com
SIC: 3369 3728 Castings, except die-castings, precision; aircraft parts & equipment
HQ: Pcc Airfoils Llc
3401 Entp Pkwy Ste 200
Cleveland OH 44122
216 831-3590

(G-7953)
PETRO WARE INC
Also Called: Swingle Drilling
713 Keystone St (43731-1039)
P.O. Box 220 (43731-0220)
PHONE..................................740 982-1302
Fax: 740 982-9875
Mark B Swingle, *President*
James R Swingle, *Vice Pres*
Dan Swingle, *Purch Mgr*
Rick Emmert, *Engineer*
EMP: 54
SQ FT: 2,000
SALES (est): 11.2MM **Privately Held**
SIC: 3569 3264 Filters, general line: industrial; porcelain electrical supplies

(G-7954)
TEMPLE OIL & GAS COMPANY
Also Called: Speed-O-Print
6626 Ceramic Rd Ne (43731-9419)
P.O. Box 70 (43731-0070)
PHONE..................................740 452-7878
Fax: 740 982-5191
Robert Swingle, *President*
Bob Swingle, *General Mgr*
Wendy Gorbi, *Office Mgr*
EMP: 8
SQ FT: 8,000
SALES (est): 1.6MM **Privately Held**
SIC: 1381 1311 Directional drilling oil & gas wells; natural gas production

Croton
Licking County

(G-7955)
OHIO FRESH EGGS LLC (PA)
11212 Croton Rd (43013-9725)
P.O. Box 247 (43013-0247)
PHONE..................................740 893-7200
Donald Hersey, *General Mgr*
Gary Bethel, *Mng Member*
▲ **EMP:** 6
SQ FT: 5,000
SALES (est): 123.5MM **Privately Held**
SIC: 5144 2015 Eggs; egg processing

Cumberland
Guernsey County

(G-7956)
KING LIMESTONE INC
53681 Spencer Rd (43732-9709)
PHONE..................................740 638-3942
Fax: 740 638-2407
Duane King, *President*
EMP: 19
SQ FT: 1,200
SALES (est): 1.9MM **Privately Held**
SIC: 1422 Crushed & broken limestone

Curtice
Ottawa County

(G-7957)
GREAT LAKES MACHINE AND TOOL
10705 Jerusalem Rd (43412-9419)
PHONE..................................419 836-2346
EMP: 3 **EST:** 2005
SALES (est): 210K **Privately Held**
SIC: 3531 Mfg Construction Machinery

(G-7958)
OTTAWA PRODUCTS CO
Also Called: None
1602 N Curtice Rd Ste A (43412-9507)
PHONE..................................419 836-5115
Fax: 419 836-5111
Jeffery Hepner, *President*
George F Wasmer, *Chairman*
Daryl Hildreth, *Director*
Bruce Miller, *Director*
EMP: 20
SQ FT: 19,000
SALES (est): 1.2MM **Privately Held**
WEB: www.ottawaproducts.com
SIC: 3429 3469 Clamps, metal; spinning metal for the trade

(G-7959)
TAT MACHINE AND TOOL LTD
1313 S Cousino Rd (43412-9100)
P.O. Box 184 (43412-0184)
PHONE..................................419 836-7706
Fax: 419 836-6060
Thomas A Truman, *Partner*
Joan C Truman, *Partner*
EMP: 8
SQ FT: 7,500
SALES (est): 579.6K **Privately Held**
SIC: 3599 Machine shop, jobbing & repair

Cuyahoga Falls
Summit County

(G-7960)
4R ENTERPRISES INCORPORATED
Also Called: Radioshack
700 Portage Trl (44221-3057)
PHONE..................................330 923-9799
EMP: 6
SQ FT: 2,000
SALES (est): 726.8K **Privately Held**
SIC: 5731 3826 3821 7389 Ret Radio/Tv/Electronics Mfg Analytical Instr Mfg Lab Apparatus/Furn Business Services Engineering Services

(G-7961)
ACU-SERVE CORP
2020 Front St Ste 205 (44221-3257)
PHONE..................................330 923-5258
Fax: 330 928-2848
Angie Barone, *President*
Timothy Barone, *Vice Pres*
EMP: 9
SALES (est): 1.1MM **Privately Held**
SIC: 7372 6411 Prepackaged software; medical insurance claim processing, contract or fee basis

(G-7962)
ADVANCED HOLDING DESIGNS INC
Also Called: Ahd
3332 Cavalier Trl (44224-4906)
PHONE..................................330 928-4456
Fax: 330 928-8633
Mark Smrekar, *President*
Anne Daugherty, *Manager*
EMP: 13
SQ FT: 12,000
SALES (est): 1.8MM **Privately Held**
WEB: www.ahd-flex-e-on.com
SIC: 3545 Collets (machine tool accessories); chucks: drill, lathe or magnetic (machine tool accessories)

(G-7963)
ALDEN SAND & GRAVEL CO INC
Also Called: Alden Excavating
2486 Northampton Rd (44223-2712)
PHONE..................................330 928-3249
Connie Ensign, *President*
Robert E Alden III, *Corp Secy*
EMP: 11 **EST:** 1963
SQ FT: 1,200
SALES (est): 980K **Privately Held**
WEB: www.aldenexcavating.com
SIC: 1442 1794 Sand mining; gravel & pebble mining; excavation work

(G-7964)
AMERICHEM INC
155 E Steels Corners Rd (44224-4919)
PHONE..................................330 926-3185
Michael Roberts, *Production*
Richard Allison, *QC Dir*
Mary Thomas, *Human Res Dir*
Bill Nagel, *Branch Mgr*
Rod Manfull, *Manager*
EMP: 50
SQ FT: 78,214
SALES (corp-wide): 209.9MM **Privately Held**
WEB: www.americhem.com
SIC: 2865 2816 Color pigments, organic; inorganic pigments
PA: Americhem, Inc.
2000 Americhem Way
Cuyahoga Falls OH 44221
330 929-4213

(G-7965)
AMERICHEM INC (PA)
2000 Americhem Way (44221-3303)
PHONE..................................330 929-4213
Fax: 330 929-4144
Matthew Hellstern, *CEO*
Thomas Weigl, *Managing Dir*
Mark Juve, *Editor*
Matthew Miklos, *Vice Pres*
Diane Shields, *Vice Pres*
▲ **EMP:** 100 **EST:** 1941
SQ FT: 83,000
SALES (est): 209.9MM **Privately Held**
WEB: www.americhem.com
SIC: 2865 2851 2819 2816 Color pigments, organic; paints & allied products; industrial inorganic chemicals; inorganic pigments

(G-7966)
AMH HOLDINGS LLC
3773 State Rd (44223-2603)
PHONE..................................330 929-1811
Ira D Kleinman, *Ch of Bd*
Thomas N Chieffe, *President*
Warren J Arthur, *Senior VP*
Stephen E Graham, *CFO*
John F Haumesser, *VP Human Res*
EMP: 2400
SQ FT: 70,000
SALES (est): 207.8MM **Privately Held**
SIC: 3355 3444 Coils, wire aluminum: made in rolling mills; siding, sheet metal
PA: Associated Materials Group, Inc.
1 Maritime Plz Fl 12
San Francisco CA 94111

(G-7967)
AMH HOLDINGS II INC
3773 State Rd (44223-2603)
PHONE..................................330 929-1811
Thomas N Chieffe, *CEO*
John Haumesser, *VP Human Res*
EMP: 8402
SALES (est): 228.8MM **Privately Held**
SIC: 3355 Coils, wire aluminum: made in rolling mills

(G-7968)
APPLETON GRP LLC
4441 Hickory Trl (44224-3678)
PHONE..................................330 689-1904
EMP: 108
SALES (corp-wide): 24.5B **Publicly Held**
SIC: 3823 Mfg Process Control Instruments
HQ: Appleton Grp Llc
9377 W Higgins Rd
Rosemont IL 60018
847 268-6024

GEOGRAPHIC

(G-7969)
APPLIED VISION CORPORATION (PA)
2020 Vision Ln (44223-4706)
PHONE...................................330 926-2222
Fax: 330 926-2250
Amir Novini, *CEO*
Jeff Hartung, *President*
Mike Kress, *President*
Brian Baird, *Vice Pres*
Darren Hench, *Vice Pres*
EMP: 62 EST: 1997
SQ FT: 80,000
SALES (est): 15.6MM Privately Held
WEB: www.applied1.com
SIC: 3577 Magnetic ink & optical scanning devices

(G-7970)
ASCOT VALLEY FOODS LLC (PA)
Also Called: Bunny B
205 Ascot Pkwy (44223-3701)
PHONE...................................330 376-9411
Keith A Kropp, *CEO*
Erin Debney, *Manager*
EMP: 8
SQ FT: 4,000
SALES (est): 2.7MM Privately Held
WEB: www.bunnyb.com
SIC: 2038 Snacks, including onion rings, cheese sticks, etc.

(G-7971)
ASSOCIATED MATERIALS LLC (DH)
3773 State Rd (44223-2603)
P.O. Box 2010, Akron (44309-2010)
PHONE...................................330 929-1811
Erik D Ragatz, *Ch of Bd*
Brian C Strauss, *President*
William L Topper, *Exec VP*
Philippe Bourbonniere, *Senior VP*
Adam D Casebere, *Senior VP*
EMP: 277
SQ FT: 63,000
SALES: 1.1B Privately Held
WEB: www.associatedmaterials.com
SIC: 3089 5033 5031 3442 Plastic hardware & building products; siding, plastic; windows, plastic; fences, gates & accessories: plastic; roofing & siding materials; siding, except wood; roofing, asphalt & sheet metal; insulation materials; windows; kitchen cabinets; metal doors, sash & trim

(G-7972)
ASSOCIATED MTLS HOLDINGS LLC
3773 State Rd (44223-2603)
P.O. Box 2010, Akron (44309-2010)
PHONE...................................330 929-1811
Ira D Kleinman, *Ch of Bd*
James Bussman, *Exec VP*
Warren Arthur, *Senior VP*
Paul Pratt, *Vice Pres*
Scott Harcek, *VP Opers*
EMP: 2000
SALES (est): 201.6MM Privately Held
SIC: 3089 5033 5031 5063 Plastic hardware & building products; siding, plastic; windows, plastic; fences, gates & accessories: plastic; roofing & siding materials; siding, except wood; roofing, asphalt & sheet metal; insulation materials; windows; kitchen cabinets; wire & cable; metal doors, sash & trim
PA: Associated Materials Group, Inc.
　1 Maritime Plz Fl 12
　San Francisco CA 94111

(G-7973)
ATA TOOLS INC
238 Marc Dr (44223-2651)
PHONE...................................330 928-7744
Peter McManeny, *CEO*
Steven Lukaszewicz, *Business Mgr*
Ed Boggs, *Senior VP*
Tim Dunn, *Buyer*
Jeff Pallone, *Sales Dir*
EMP: 100
SALES (est): 24.5MM Privately Held
SIC: 3542 Brakes, metal forming

(G-7974)
BEECH ARMAMENT LLC
105 Marc Dr (44223-2629)
PHONE...................................330 962-4694
Martin Beech,
EMP: 3
SALES (est): 114.3K Privately Held
SIC: 3484 Small arms

(G-7975)
BOURBON PLASTICS INC (PA)
111 Stow Ave Ste 100 (44221-2560)
P.O. Box 23, Bourbon IN (46504-0023)
PHONE...................................574 342-0893
Jerry Garrison, *CEO*
Richard Bennett, *President*
Mike Albert, *Vice Pres*
Ray Brown, *Opers Staff*
Michael W Albert, *CFO*
EMP: 27
SQ FT: 25,000
SALES (est): 2.5MM Privately Held
WEB: www.bourbonplastics.com
SIC: 3644 3089 Insulators & insulation materials, electrical; injection molded finished plastic products

(G-7976)
CARTWRIGHT CONSTRUCTION INC
Also Called: Cartwright Cnstr H B A C
4898 Wild Lake Rd (44224)
PHONE...................................330 929-3020
Fax: 330 929-1305
Darrell Cartwright, *President*
Margarett Cartwright, *Vice Pres*
EMP: 3
SALES (est): 300K Privately Held
SIC: 3585 1711 Heating & air conditioning combination units; heating & air conditioning contractors

(G-7977)
CENTRAL GRAPHICS INC
1658 State Rd (44223-1304)
PHONE...................................330 928-7080
David Soulsby, *President*
Joe Kist, *Mktg Dir*
Jeff Loofboro, *Manager*
EMP: 5
SALES (est): 631.5K Privately Held
WEB: www.sign-central.com
SIC: 3993 Signs & advertising specialties

(G-7978)
CHAMPION WEBBING COMPANY INC
2748 2nd St (44221-2202)
PHONE...................................330 920-1007
Fax: 330 920-1745
Tong Choi, *President*
EMP: 4 EST: 1979
SQ FT: 7,000
SALES (est): 400K Privately Held
SIC: 2241 Webbing, woven

(G-7979)
CHILD EVNGELISM FELLOWSHIP INC
641 Acorn Pl (44221-1001)
PHONE...................................440 218-4982
EMP: 41
SALES (corp-wide): 28.6MM Privately Held
SIC: 2752 Commercial printing, lithographic
PA: Child Evangelism Fellowship Incorporated
　17482 Highway M
　Warrenton MO 63383
　636 456-4321

(G-7980)
CIRCLE PRIME MANUFACTURING
2114 Front St (44221-3220)
P.O. Box 112 (44222-0112)
PHONE...................................330 923-0019
Fax: 330 923-8249
James Mothersbaugh, *President*
Jeanette Federico, *General Mgr*
Dale Mitchell, *Vice Pres*
Robert Mothersbaugh, *Vice Pres*
Chris Zentz, *Materials Mgr*
EMP: 27

SQ FT: 50,000
SALES (est): 5.1MM Privately Held
WEB: www.circleprime.com
SIC: 8731 3672 3812 3663 Commercial physical research; printed circuit boards; antennas, radar or communications; radio broadcasting & communications equipment; electrical equipment & supplies; engineering services

(G-7981)
COLTENE/WHALEDENT INC (HQ)
235 Ascot Pkwy (44223-3701)
PHONE...................................330 916-8800
Fax: 330 916-7077
Nick Huber, *Ch of Bd*
Martin Schaufelberger, *Ch of Bd*
Jerry Sullivan, *President*
Stephen Mallinson, *Managing Dir*
Joseph Fasano, *Vice Pres*
▲ EMP: 222
SQ FT: 89,000
SALES (est): 44.5MM
SALES (corp-wide): 158.8MM Privately Held
SIC: 3843 Dental equipment & supplies
PA: Coltene Holding Ag
　Feldwiesenstrasse 20
　AltstAtten SG 9450
　717 575-472

(G-7982)
CORTAPE INC
60 Marc Dr (44223-2628)
PHONE...................................330 929-6700
Erik W Akins, *Ch of Bd*
Matthew Mc Clellan, *President*
◆ EMP: 17
SQ FT: 25,000
SALES (est): 5.6MM Privately Held
WEB: www.cortape.com
SIC: 2672 Tape, pressure sensitive: made from purchased materials; labels (unprinted), gummed: made from purchased materials

(G-7983)
CREATIVE FUELS LLC
1093 Foxglove Cir (44223-2797)
PHONE...................................330 923-2222
Robert Dirgo,
EMP: 10
SALES (est): 790.7K Privately Held
WEB: www.creativefuelsllc.com
SIC: 2869 Industrial organic chemicals

(G-7984)
CUSTOM CRAFT DRAP INC
1924 Portage Trl (44223-1743)
PHONE...................................330 929-5728
Geraldine Course, *President*
Donald Stock, *Vice Pres*
EMP: 4 EST: 1977
SQ FT: 800
SALES (est): 441.1K Privately Held
SIC: 2211 5714 Draperies & drapery fabrics, cotton; draperies

(G-7985)
D A STIRLING INC
2740 Hudson Dr (44221-1971)
PHONE...................................330 923-3195
Fax: 330 923-3115
Donald L Glenny, *President*
Dana Glenny, *Admin Sec*
Dana Shoff, *Admin Sec*
EMP: 5
SQ FT: 10,000
SALES (est): 581.8K Privately Held
WEB: www.dastirling.com
SIC: 3544 2675 Dies, steel rule; die-cut paper & board

(G-7986)
DBCR INC
Also Called: G.S. Steel Company
3400 Cavalier Trl (44224-4908)
PHONE...................................330 920-1900
Donald E Potoczek, *President*
Beth Potoczek, *Treasurer*
EMP: 20
SALES (est): 4.4MM Privately Held
SIC: 3541 7389 7692 Plasma process metal cutting machines; metal cutting services; welding repair

(G-7987)
DENTRONIX INC
235 Ascot Pkwy (44223-3701)
PHONE...................................330 916-7300
Fax: 330 916-7333
Jerry Sullivan, *President*
Joseph Fasano, *Treasurer*
EMP: 50
SQ FT: 16,000
SALES: 5.5MM
SALES (corp-wide): 158.8MM Privately Held
WEB: www.dentronix.com
SIC: 3843 5047 3842 3841 Orthodontic appliances; dental equipment & supplies; surgical appliances & supplies; surgical & medical instruments; analytical instruments; laboratory apparatus & furniture
HQ: Coltene/Whaledent Inc.
　235 Ascot Pkwy
　Cuyahoga Falls OH 44223
　330 916-8800

(G-7988)
E3 DIAGNOSTICS INC
3420 Cavalier Trl Ste C (44224-4967)
PHONE...................................330 926-0594
Kristin Wysmierski, *Branch Mgr*
EMP: 4 Privately Held
SIC: 3845 Audiological equipment, electromedical
HQ: E3 Diagnostics, Inc.
　3333 N Kennicott Ave
　Arlington Heights IL 60004
　847 459-1770

(G-7989)
ECONO PRODUCTS INC
Also Called: Graphic Arts Rubber
101 Ascot Pkwy (44223-3355)
PHONE...................................330 923-4101
Fax: 330 923-4464
Harry Millward, *Manager*
EMP: 12
SQ FT: 19,000
SALES (corp-wide): 6.6MM Privately Held
SIC: 3069 2891 2796 Reclaimed rubber & specialty rubber compounds; adhesives & sealants; platemaking services
PA: Econo Products, Inc.
　159 Huxley Way
　Victor NY 14564
　585 288-7550

(G-7990)
EMERALD PERFORMANCE MTLS LLC (PA)
2020 Front St Ste 100 (44221-3257)
PHONE...................................330 916-6700
Fax: 330 916-6734
Robert Culp, *Vice Pres*
Chris O'Neil, *Vice Pres*
Julie O Vaughn, *Vice Pres*
Becki L Watson, *CFO*
Jim Warholic, *Treasurer*
◆ EMP: 35
SALES (est): 346.7MM Privately Held
SIC: 2821 Plastics materials & resins; thermosetting materials

(G-7991)
ENDODENT INC
235 Ascot Pkwy (44223-3701)
PHONE...................................626 359-5715
Jerry Sullivan, *President*
Nicolas M Lenz, *General Mgr*
EMP: 34
SQ FT: 10,000
SALES (est): 3.4MM Privately Held
WEB: www.endodent.com
SIC: 3843 Dental tools

(G-7992)
ESSENTIAL WONDERS INC
2926 State Rd Ste 202 (44223-1244)
PHONE...................................888 525-5282
Tom Osbourne, *President*
EMP: 6
SQ FT: 50,000
SALES: 600K Privately Held
SIC: 2095 Roasted coffee

(G-7993)
EXACT PIPE TOOLS
141 Broad Blvd Ste 201 (44221-3817)
PHONE..................................330 922-8150
Mike Stone, *Owner*
EMP: 5 EST: 2014
SALES (est): 636.5K
SALES (corp-wide): 3.3MM **Privately Held**
SIC: 3429 Manufactured hardware (general)
PA: Exact Tools Oy
    Sarkiniemientie 5d
    Helsinki 00210
    943 667-50

(G-7994)
F M P ENTERPRISES INC
1871 12th St (44223-2401)
PHONE..................................330 920-8059
Jon McMannis, *President*
John Pappano, *Vice Pres*
EMP: 5
SQ FT: 7,000
SALES (est): 360K **Privately Held**
SIC: 3011 Tires & inner tubes

(G-7995)
FACTS INC
2737 Front St (44221-1904)
PHONE..................................330 928-2332
Fax: 330 928-3018
Albert H Curry, *President*
Piyush Dhawan, *Managing Dir*
Thomas W Fisher III, *Vice Pres*
Kel Hess, *Engineer*
John Watts, *Engineer*
EMP: 20
SQ FT: 10,000
SALES (est): 3.6MM **Privately Held**
WEB: www.facts-inc.com
SIC: 7371 3823 Computer software systems analysis & design, custom; industrial process control instruments

(G-7996)
FALLS STAMPING & WELDING CO (PA)
2900 Vincent St (44221-1954)
P.O. Box 153 (44222-0153)
PHONE..................................330 928-1191
Fax: 330 928-1196
David Cesar, *CEO*
Rick Boettner, *Chairman*
Kenneth J Laino, *Counsel*
Kellie Smith, *Materials Mgr*
Dallas Griffith, *QC Mgr*
EMP: 125 EST: 1919
SQ FT: 95,000
SALES (est): 42.2MM **Privately Held**
WEB: www.falls-stamping.com
SIC: 3465 3469 3544 3711 Automotive stampings; stamping metal for the trade; special dies, tools, jigs & fixtures; chassis, motor vehicle; motor vehicle parts & accessories; welding repair

(G-7997)
FLEX-E-ON INC
3332 Cavalier Trl (44224-4906)
PHONE..................................330 928-4496
Fax: 330 928-5181
Mark Smrekar, *President*
EMP: 10
SQ FT: 12,000
SALES (est): 890K **Privately Held**
WEB: www.flexeonrehabclinics.com
SIC: 3545 Chucks: drill, lathe or magnetic (machine tool accessories); mandrels

(G-7998)
FOX TOOL CO INC
1471 Main St (44221-4926)
PHONE..................................330 928-3402
Fax: 330 928-8220
Nathan Fox, *President*
EMP: 22
SQ FT: 5,120
SALES (est): 2.1MM **Privately Held**
SIC: 7699 3545 Knife, saw & tool sharpening & repair; cutting tools for machine tools

(G-7999)
FRESH LOOK LASER EYE CTRS LLC
789 Graham Rd (44221-1045)
PHONE..................................614 885-2745
Charles H Davis, *Mng Member*
Kathy Calvelli, *Director*
EMP: 3
SALES (est): 218.4K **Privately Held**
SIC: 3851 Eyeglasses, lenses & frames

(G-8000)
FRONTLINE INTERNATIONAL INC
187 Ascot Pkwy (44223-3747)
PHONE..................................330 861-1100
Fax: 330 861-1105
John W Palazzo, *President*
Giovanni Brienza, *Vice Pres*
Bevan Evans, *Sls & Mktg Exec*
Zack Palazzo, *Sales Mgr*
Trevor Stretch, *Manager*
▼ EMP: 15
SQ FT: 30,000
SALES (est): 4.2MM **Privately Held**
WEB: www.frontlineii.com
SIC: 3589 Cooking equipment, commercial

(G-8001)
FUSE CHICKEN LLC
1127 Portage Trl (44223-2101)
PHONE..................................330 338-7108
Jon Fawcett, *Mng Member*
▼ EMP: 4 EST: 2012
SQ FT: 5,000
SALES (est): 420.5K **Privately Held**
SIC: 3625 Electric controls & control accessories, industrial

(G-8002)
GENERAL DIE CASTERS
4607 Dresher Trl (44224-2006)
PHONE..................................330 678-2528
James Mathias, *Principal*
EMP: 3
SALES (est): 153.4K **Privately Held**
SIC: 3544 Special dies & tools

(G-8003)
GENTEK BUILDING PRODUCTS INC (DH)
Also Called: Revere Building Products
3773 State Rd (44223-2603)
PHONE..................................800 548-4542
Thomas Chieffe, *CEO*
Michael Caporale, *President*
D Keith Lavanway, *Vice Pres*
Ira Kleinman, *Director*
▲ EMP: 18
SQ FT: 8,000
SALES (est): 229.1MM **Privately Held**
WEB: www.gentekinc.com
SIC: 3444 3089 Siding, sheet metal; downspouts, sheet metal; siding, plastic
HQ: Associated Materials, Llc
    3773 State Rd
    Cuyahoga Falls OH 44223
    330 929-1811

(G-8004)
GOJO INDUSTRIES INC
Also Called: Production
3783 State Rd (44223-2698)
P.O. Box 991, Akron (44309-0991)
PHONE..................................330 255-6000
Bob Potvin, *Vice Pres*
Cindy Simko, *Production*
Steven Zammarrelli, *Production*
Richard Holmes, *Engineer*
Kevin Hagen, *Accountant*
EMP: 50
SALES (corp-wide): 305.9MM **Privately Held**
WEB: www.gojo.com
SIC: 2842 Specialty cleaning, polishes & sanitation goods
PA: Gojo Industries, Inc.
    1 Gojo Plz Ste 500
    Akron OH 44311
    330 255-6000

(G-8005)
GOJO INDUSTRIES INC
3901 Lippman Pkwy (44224-4993)
PHONE..................................330 922-4522

Nicole Koharik, *COO*
Evelyn David, *Research*
Gregory Leonhard, *Engineer*
Stephanie Onderko, *Engineer*
John Hooker, *Controller*
EMP: 125
SALES (corp-wide): 305.9MM **Privately Held**
SIC: 2842 3586 2844 Specialty cleaning, polishes & sanitation goods; measuring & dispensing pumps; toilet preparations
PA: Gojo Industries, Inc.
    1 Gojo Plz Ste 500
    Akron OH 44311
    330 255-6000

(G-8006)
HARBOR CASTINGS INC
2508 Bailey Rd (44221-2585)
PHONE..................................231 733-1053
Tom Braum, *Branch Mgr*
EMP: 34
SALES (corp-wide): 14.2MM **Privately Held**
WEB: www.harbor-castings.com
SIC: 3324 3325 Steel investment foundries; alloy steel castings, except investment
PA: Harbor Castings, Inc.
    2508 Bailey Rd
    Cuyahoga Falls OH 44221
    330 499-7178

(G-8007)
HARBOR CASTINGS INC (PA)
2508 Bailey Rd (44221-2585)
PHONE..................................330 499-7178
Fax: 330 499-2018
C Richard Lynham, *CEO*
Steve Krajci, *Manager*
Kim Wilkinson, *Administration*
EMP: 45 EST: 1992
SQ FT: 13,000
SALES (est): 14.2MM **Privately Held**
WEB: www.harbor-castings.com
SIC: 3324 3369 3325 Steel investment foundries; nonferrous foundries; steel foundries

(G-8008)
HARWOOD RUBBER PRODUCTS INC
1365 Orlen Ave (44221-2957)
PHONE..................................330 923-3256
Fax: 330 923-1171
Richard Harwood, *President*
Frank Batton, *General Mgr*
Lundy Mills, *Corp Secy*
John H Eblen, *Vice Pres*
Kitty Brown, *Director*
EMP: 30 EST: 1952
SQ FT: 22,000
SALES (est): 4MM **Privately Held**
WEB: www.harwoodrubber.com
SIC: 3479 3061 Coating of metals with plastic or resins; mechanical rubber goods

(G-8009)
HOWARD B CLAFLIN CO
2475 2nd St (44221-2707)
PHONE..................................330 928-1704
Howard B Claflin, *President*
Howard Claflin, *Owner*
Marge Claflin, *Bookkeeper*
Bruce Claflin, *Sales Mgr*
EMP: 6
SQ FT: 3,600
SALES: 300K **Privately Held**
SIC: 2655 2599 Reels (fiber), textile: made from purchased material; boards: planning, display, notice

(G-8010)
INNOVATED HEALTH LLC
2241 Front St Fl 1 (44221-2509)
P.O. Box 963 (44223-0963)
PHONE..................................330 858-0651
Fred Guerra, *Mng Member*
EMP: 9
SQ FT: 2,000
SALES (est): 650K **Privately Held**
SIC: 2023 Dietary supplements, dairy & non-dairy based

(G-8011)
INTER-ION INC
157 Ascot Pkwy (44223-3747)
PHONE..................................330 928-9655
Fax: 330 928-9654
Adam Antonas, *President*
Panos Panayiotou, *Exec VP*
Ken Craft, *Project Mgr*
Panos Williams, *Purchasing*
Mary Timura, *CPA*
EMP: 25
SQ FT: 25,000
SALES (est): 3.3MM **Privately Held**
WEB: www.inter-ion.com
SIC: 3479 Painting, coating & hot dipping

(G-8012)
J&J PRECISION MACHINE LTD
1474 Main St (44221-4927)
PHONE..................................330 923-5783
Fax: 330 923-5905
Hans R Leitner, *CEO*
Hans Leitner, *CEO*
EMP: 38
SALES (est): 7.1MM **Privately Held**
SIC: 3441 7699 Building components, structural steel; industrial machinery & equipment repair

(G-8013)
JAY-EM AEROSPACE CORPORATION
75 Marc Dr (44223-2627)
PHONE..................................330 923-0333
Michael E Bell Sr, *CEO*
Gregory Norman, *President*
Michael Saltis, *General Mgr*
John Heidt, *Mfg Dir*
Brian Hodor, *Plant Mgr*
EMP: 25
SQ FT: 34,000
SALES (est): 9.9MM **Privately Held**
WEB: www.jay-em.com
SIC: 3728 3599 Wheels, aircraft; brakes, aircraft; machine shop, jobbing & repair

(G-8014)
JJB ENGINEER
2695 N Haven Blvd Ste 10 (44223-2123)
PHONE..................................330 807-0671
Edward Sheehan, *President*
EMP: 5
SALES (est): 751.1K **Privately Held**
SIC: 3519 Internal combustion engines

(G-8015)
JULIUS ZORN INC
Also Called: Juzo
3690 Zorn Dr (44223-3580)
P.O. Box 1088 (44223-1088)
PHONE..................................330 923-4999
Fax: 330 916-9165
Anne Rose Zorn, *President*
Walter Zorn, *COO*
Petra Zorn, *Vice Pres*
Nancy Schnarr, *Purch Mgr*
Raymond Gornik, *CFO*
▲ EMP: 75
SQ FT: 30,000
SALES (est): 33.8MM
SALES (corp-wide): 77.6MM **Privately Held**
WEB: www.juzousa.com
SIC: 5047 3842 Medical & hospital equipment; hosiery, support; supports: abdominal, ankle, arch, kneecap, etc.; socks, stump
PA: Julius Zorn Gmbh
    Juliusplatz 1
    Aichach 86551
    825 190-1142

(G-8016)
KENNETH J MOORE
3775 Wyoga Lake Rd (44224-4945)
PHONE..................................330 923-8313
Kenneth Moore, *Principal*
EMP: 3
SALES (est): 200K **Privately Held**
SIC: 3993 Signs & advertising specialties

(G-8017)
KEUCHEL & ASSOCIATES INC
Also Called: Spunfab
175 Muffin Ln (44223-3359)
PHONE..................................330 945-9455

GEOGRAPHIC

Fax: 330 945-7588
Ken Keuchel, *President*
Herbert W Keuchel, *Principal*
Richard W Staehle, *Principal*
Herb Keuchel, *Shareholder*
◆ **EMP:** 50
SQ FT: 40,000
SALES (est): 7.8MM **Privately Held**
WEB: www.spunfab.com
SIC: 2241 8711 Narrow fabric mills; con-
sulting engineer

(G-8018)
KOLPIN OUTDOORS
CORPORATION
Also Called: Premier OEM
3479 State Rd (44223-2553)
PHONE..................................330 328-0772
James Nagy, *President*
EMP: 3
SALES (est): 104.1K **Privately Held**
SIC: 3799 All terrain vehicles (ATV); off-
road automobiles, except recreational ve-
hicles

(G-8019)
KYOCERA SGS PRECISION
TOOLS
2824 2nd St (44221-1901)
PHONE..................................330 688-6667
John Haag, *Branch Mgr*
EMP: 37
SQ FT: 29,973
SALES (corp-wide): 78.5MM **Privately
Held**
WEB: www.sgstool.com
SIC: 3545 Cutting tools for machine tools
PA: Kyocera Sgs Precision Tools
55 S Main St
Munroe Falls OH 44262
330 688-6667

(G-8020)
LINDEN INDUSTRIES INC
137 Ascot Pkwy (44223-3355)
PHONE..................................330 928-4064
Peter Tilgner, *President*
Ken Erwin, *Vice Pres*
Bob Hughey, *CFO*
Robert Hughey, *Controller*
Scott Erwin, *Sales Executive*
EMP: 42
SQ FT: 26,000
SALES (est): 9.9MM **Privately Held**
WEB: www.lindenindustries.com
SIC: 3559 5084 Plastics working machin-
ery; robots, molding & forming plastics; in-
dustrial machinery & equipment

(G-8021)
MADAEN NATURAL PRODUCTS
INC
Also Called: One With Nature
141 Broad Blvd Lowr (44221-3817)
PHONE..................................800 600-1445
▲ **EMP:** 3
SALES (est): 250K **Privately Held**
SIC: 2844 Mfg Toilet Preparations

(G-8022)
MAIN STREET GOURMET LLC
Also Called: Main Street Cambritt Cookies
170 Muffin Ln (44223-3358)
PHONE..................................330 929-0000
Fax: 330 920-8329
Dan Maurer, *Research*
Marla Kuba, *Controller*
Robert Braun,
David Choe,
Steven Marks,
EMP: 108
SQ FT: 60,000
SALES (est): 67.6MM **Privately Held**
WEB: www.mainstreetgourmet.com
SIC: 2053 2099 2052 2051 Frozen bak-
ery products, except bread; food prepara-
tions; cookies & crackers; bread, cake &
related products

(G-8023)
MAJIC TOUCH
4133 State Rd (44223-2611)
PHONE..................................330 923-8259
Keione Artite, *Owner*
EMP: 6

SALES (est): 512.5K **Privately Held**
SIC: 3589 Car washing machinery

(G-8024)
MARTZ MOLD & MACHINE INC
1365 Munroe Falls Ave (44221-3535)
PHONE..................................330 928-2159
Fax: 330 928-8124
Dennis I Martz, *President*
M Dennis Martz, *Vice Pres*
William Martz, *Vice Pres*
EMP: 4 **EST:** 1944
SQ FT: 6,800
SALES (est): 521.4K **Privately Held**
SIC: 3544 Industrial molds

(G-8025)
MCKINNON PRINTING INC
Also Called: McKinnon A Co
2845 Hickory Cv (44223-1288)
PHONE..................................330 929-5769
Fax: 330 929-3256
Timothy Mc Kinnon, *President*
Janice Harry, *Prdtn Mgr*
Beth Mc Kinnon, *Treasurer*
Andrew Mc Kinnon, *Shareholder*
Marjean Mc Kinnon, *Shareholder*
EMP: 18
SQ FT: 6,500
SALES (est): 2.2MM **Privately Held**
SIC: 2752 Commercial printing, offset

(G-8026)
MEGA BRIGHT LLC
2251 Front St (44221-2567)
PHONE..................................330 577-8859
LI Coffee, *Managing Dir*
Bill Wang, *Director*
EMP: 10
SQ FT: 5,000
SALES (est): 975.9K **Privately Held**
SIC: 3645 3646 Residential lighting fix-
tures; commercial indusl & institutional
electric lighting fixtures

(G-8027)
MOORE MC MILLEN HOLDINGS
1850 Front St (44221)
PHONE..................................330 745-3075
Robert S Mc Millen, *President*
EMP: 85
SQ FT: 19,141
SALES (est): 7.2MM **Privately Held**
SIC: 3398 Metal heat treating

(G-8028)
NANOTRONICS IMAGING INC
(PA)
2251 Front St Ste 109-111 (44221-2567)
P.O. Box 306 (44222-0306)
PHONE..................................330 926-9809
Matthew Putnam, *CEO*
Brian Fink, *President*
John Putman, *President*
Vann Walke, *COO*
Caroline Glaeser, *Manager*
EMP: 33
SALES (est): 3MM **Privately Held**
WEB: www.nanotronicsimaging.com
SIC: 3826 Analytical instruments

(G-8029)
NIKKICAKES
806 Myrtle Ave (44221-4104)
PHONE..................................330 606-5745
Nicole Longfellow, *Principal*
EMP: 4 **EST:** 2010
SALES (est): 242.5K **Privately Held**
SIC: 2051 Bakery: wholesale or whole-
sale/retail combined

(G-8030)
OHIO SPORTING GOODS LLC
Also Called: Blue Target Firearms
2769 Front St (44221-1904)
PHONE..................................330 548-5911
Sean Gordon, *Principal*
EMP: 3
SQ FT: 15,000
SALES (est): 188K **Privately Held**
SIC: 3949 Shooting equipment & supplies,
general

(G-8031)
PARADISE INC
Also Called: ALCOHOLICS ANONYMOUS
1710 Front St (44221-4712)
PHONE..................................330 928-3789
Tim Crawford, *President*
EMP: 5 **EST:** 1951
SALES: 198.5K **Privately Held**
SIC: 2511 Club room furniture: wood

(G-8032)
PATRIOT ENERGY LLC
1574 Main St (44221-4937)
PHONE..................................330 923-4442
Fax: 330 923-3712
John A Shutsa,
EMP: 99
SALES (est): 11.3MM **Privately Held**
SIC: 2869 Industrial organic chemicals

(G-8033)
PNEUMATIC SCALE
CORPORATION (DH)
Also Called: Pneumatic Scale Angelus
10 Ascot Pkwy (44223-3325)
PHONE..................................330 923-0491
Timothy J Sulllivan, *CEO*
William J Morgan, *President*
Robert H Chapman, *Chairman*
Frank Zepf, *Business Mgr*
Paul Kearney, *Exec VP*
◆ **EMP:** 225 **EST:** 1895
SQ FT: 102,000
SALES (est): 102.2MM
SALES (corp-wide): 1.9B **Privately Held**
WEB: www.pneumaticscale.com
SIC: 3565 3569 3535 Packaging machin-
ery; bottling machinery: filling, capping, la-
beling; centrifuges, industrial; conveyors
& conveying equipment
HQ: Barry-Wehmiller Companies, Inc.
8020 Forsyth Blvd
Saint Louis MO 63105
314 862-8000

(G-8034)
POLYMERICS INC (PA)
2828 2nd St (44221-1953)
PHONE..................................330 434-6665
Fax: 330 929-8819
C Robert Samples, *Ch of Bd*
Joe Arhar, *President*
Pat Eckman, *Plant Mgr*
Mike Arnold, *Technical Mgr*
Connie Richards, *Human Res Mgr*
▲ **EMP:** 50
SQ FT: 24,000
SALES (est): 15.3MM **Privately Held**
WEB: www.polymericsinc.com
SIC: 3069 2819 2891 2865 Custom com-
pounding of rubber materials; industrial
inorganic chemicals; adhesives &
sealants; cyclic crudes & intermediates;
paints & allied products; plastics materials
& resins

(G-8035)
PREMIER UV PRODUCTS LLC
1738 Front St (44221-4712)
PHONE..................................330 715-2452
Michael Forsyth, *Manager*
James R Nagy,
EMP: 4
SALES (est): 340K **Privately Held**
WEB: www.premieruv.com
SIC: 3799 All terrain vehicles (ATV)

(G-8036)
PREMIERE MEDICAL
RESOURCES INC
2750 Front St (44221-1969)
PHONE..................................330 923-5899
Joseph Chase, *Principal*
EMP: 17
SALES (est): 3.2MM **Privately Held**
SIC: 3069 Medical sundries, rubber

(G-8037)
PROSPECT MOLD & DIE
COMPANY
1100 Main St (44221-4922)
PHONE..................................330 929-3311
Bruce W Wright, *CEO*
Brandon Wenzlik, *President*
Jeff Glick, *Vice Pres*

Jim Vanmeter, *Engineer*
Thomas M Orr, *CFO*
▲ **EMP:** 100 **EST:** 1945
SQ FT: 100,000
SALES (est): 94.7MM **Privately Held**
WEB: www.prospectmold.com
SIC: 5084 3544 Industrial machinery &
equipment; forms (molds), for foundry &
plastics working machinery

(G-8038)
QUALITY CRAFT MACHINE INC
137 Ascot Pkwy (44223-3355)
PHONE..................................330 928-4064
Fax: 330 940-4443
Peter Tilgner, *President*
EMP: 15
SQ FT: 8,900
SALES (est): 1.4MM **Privately Held**
WEB: www.qcraft.com
SIC: 3599 Machine & other job shop work

(G-8039)
R T R SLOTTING & MACHINE
INC
2742 2nd St (44221-2202)
PHONE..................................330 929-2608
Fax: 330 929-1849
Richard A Hamlet, *President*
Roland Steinlechner, *Corp Secy*
Timothy Hamlet, *Vice Pres*
EMP: 3
SQ FT: 4,500
SALES (est): 385.9K **Privately Held**
SIC: 3599 Machine shop, jobbing & repair

(G-8040)
RECYCLING EQP SOLUTIONS
CORP
276 Remington Rd Ste C (44224-4900)
PHONE..................................330 920-1500
Gary Gaither, *President*
Mary Gaither, *Vice Pres*
▼ **EMP:** 8
SALES (est): 1.1MM **Privately Held**
SIC: 3542 Mechanical (pneumatic or hy-
draulic) metal forming machines

(G-8041)
REUTHER MOLD & MFG CO INC
(PA)
Also Called: Reuther Mold & Manufacturing
1225 Munroe Falls Ave (44221-3598)
PHONE..................................330 923-5266
Fax: 330 923-9930
Karl A Reuther II, *President*
John Bendetto, *Vice Pres*
John Benedetto, *Vice Pres*
Dave Kolb, *Safety Mgr*
Karen Thompson, *Accountant*
EMP: 60 **EST:** 1950
SQ FT: 61,000
SALES (est): 14.4MM **Privately Held**
WEB: www.reuthermold.com
SIC: 3544 3599 Industrial molds; machine
shop, jobbing & repair

(G-8042)
RMS EQUIPMENT LLC
Also Called: RMS Equipment Company
1 Vision Ln (44223-4710)
PHONE..................................330 564-1360
Armand Massary, *President*
Susan Fattore, *Credit Mgr*
▲ **EMP:** 20
SQ FT: 50,000
SALES (est): 320.9K
SALES (corp-wide): 1.3B **Privately Held**
WEB: www.rmsequip.com
SIC: 3559 Rubber working machinery, in-
cluding tires
HQ: Pettibone L.L.C.
27501 Bella Vista Pkwy
Warrenville IL 60555
630 353-5000

(G-8043)
SENNECO GLASS INC (PA)
1730 Newberry St (44221-4018)
PHONE..................................330 825-7717
Fax: 330 922-8244
Richard Sennebogen, *President*
EMP: 4
SQ FT: 4,000

SALES: 266K **Privately Held**
WEB: www.senneglass.com
SIC: 3714 Motor vehicle parts & accessories

(G-8044)
SILICON USA INC
1220 Orlen Ave (44221-2956)
P.O. Box 1079, Ravenna (44266-1079)
PHONE....................................330 928-6217
Walter Garot, *Principal*
▲ EMP: 5 EST: 2008
SALES (est): 501.8K **Privately Held**
SIC: 3965 Fasteners

(G-8045)
SILICONE SOLUTIONS INC
338 Remington Rd (44224-4916)
PHONE....................................330 920-3125
David M Brassard, *President*
Natalie Mitchen, *Purch Mgr*
Joe Iatonna, *Engineer*
Lorraine R Brassard, *Treasurer*
Laurie Brassard, *Manager*
EMP: 10 EST: 1996
SQ FT: 10,000
SALES: 1.4MM **Privately Held**
WEB: www.siliconesolutions.com
SIC: 2869 2891 Silicones; adhesives & sealants

(G-8046)
SIMON & SIMON BLUE POND INC
Also Called: Blue Pawn
2211 Harding Rd (44223-1131)
PHONE....................................330 928-2298
Frank T Simon, *President*
EMP: 3
SALES (est): 299.1K **Privately Held**
WEB: www.bluepawn.com
SIC: 3271 Blocks, concrete: landscape or retaining wall

(G-8047)
SMITH TRUCK CRANES & EQP CO
307 Munroe Falls Ave (44221-2827)
PHONE....................................330 929-3303
Fax: 330 929-9551
Timothy Smith, *President*
Rosemary Malloy, *Administration*
▲ EMP: 10
SQ FT: 14,000
SALES (est): 2MM **Privately Held**
SIC: 3441 Railroad car racks, for transporting vehicles: steel

(G-8048)
SPECTRUM PLASTICS CORPORATION
99 E Ascot Ln (44223-3788)
PHONE....................................330 926-9766
Fax: 330 926-9767
Mohammad Malik, *President*
▲ EMP: 9
SQ FT: 25,000
SALES (est): 1.9MM **Privately Held**
SIC: 3089 Injection molding of plastics

(G-8049)
SPUNFAB LTD (PA)
175 Muffin Ln (44223-3359)
PHONE....................................330 945-9455
Tom Carone, *VP Opers*
Kenneth Keuchel,
Erin Hunt, *Administration*
Herb Keuchel,
◆ EMP: 6
SALES (est): 1.6MM **Privately Held**
SIC: 2241 Manmade fiber narrow woven fabrics

(G-8050)
STEELASTIC COMPANY LLC
1 Vision Ln (44223-4710)
PHONE....................................330 633-0505
Fax: 330 633-0527
Carl Spengler, *Purch Mgr*
Richard Baggett, *Electrical Engi*
Jeffrey Kristofeld, *VP Finance*
Zachary Boaz, *Sales Dir*
Laura Hickle, *Accounts Mgr*
▲ EMP: 46 EST: 1970
SQ FT: 34,500

SALES (est): 27.5MM
SALES (corp-wide): 1.3B **Privately Held**
WEB: www.pettibone.com
SIC: 3559 Automotive related machinery
HQ: Pettibone L.L.C.
27501 Bella Vista Pkwy
Warrenville IL 60555
630 353-5000

(G-8051)
SUMMIT MILLWORK LLC
1619 Main St (44221-4047)
PHONE....................................330 920-4000
Robert Doing, *Sales Mgr*
Keith Hall, *Sales Associate*
David Keenan,
EMP: 8
SQ FT: 30,000
SALES (est): 940K **Privately Held**
WEB: www.summitmillwork.com
SIC: 2431 Millwork

(G-8052)
SWIFT TOOL INC
1420 Ritchie St (44221-4931)
PHONE....................................330 945-6973
Fax: 330 945-6977
Doug Genova, *President*
EMP: 5
SQ FT: 3,500
SALES (est): 664.9K **Privately Held**
SIC: 3599 Custom machinery

(G-8053)
TECHNICOTE INC
70 Marc Dr (44223-2628)
PHONE....................................330 928-1476
Fax: 330 928-5261
Dave Bolanz, *Manager*
Dave Holt, *Maintence Staff*
EMP: 45
SALES (corp-wide): 84.6MM **Privately Held**
WEB: www.technicote.com
SIC: 2891 Adhesives
PA: Technicote, Inc.
222 Mound Ave
Miamisburg OH 45342
800 358-4448

(G-8054)
TERRASOURCE GLOBAL CORPORATION
Also Called: Cuyahoga Falls Plant
601-607 Munroe Falls Ave (44221)
PHONE....................................330 923-5254
Fax: 330 923-7199
EMP: 60
SQ FT: 60,000
SALES (corp-wide): 1.6B **Publicly Held**
SIC: 3532 Mfg Mining Machinery
HQ: Terrasource Global Corporation
100 N Broadway Ste 1600
Saint Louis MO 63102
618 641-6966

(G-8055)
THE EWART-OHLSON MACHINE CO
1435 Main St (44221-4926)
P.O. Box 359 (44222-0359)
PHONE....................................330 928-2171
Fax: 330 928-9018
Brian L Ewart, *President*
David Achauer, *General Mgr*
David L Ewart, *Chairman*
Earl Norrod, *Vice Pres*
Karen Sims, *Office Mgr*
▲ EMP: 28
SQ FT: 39,000
SALES (est): 4.7MM **Privately Held**
WEB: www.ewart-ohlson.com
SIC: 3599 Machine shop, jobbing & repair

(G-8056)
THICKEMZ ENTERTAINMENT LLC
Also Called: Amoney Train Music
1268 Wellingshire Cir (44221-5146)
PHONE....................................404 399-4255
Laurice Adams Simmons, *CEO*
Larenzo Adams, *Vice Pres*
Shantell M Florence, *Admin Sec*
EMP: 3

SALES (est): 48.9K **Privately Held**
SIC: 7922 2741 7389 Theatrical talent & booking agencies; theatrical production services; concert management service; ; artists' agents & brokers;

(G-8057)
TRM MANUFACTURING INC
601 Munroe Falls Ave (44221-3437)
PHONE....................................330 769-2600
Yong-Chang Tang, *CEO*
Anna White, *Controller*
EMP: 24
SALES (est): 5.9MM **Privately Held**
SIC: 3462 Iron & steel forgings

(G-8058)
TUFFY MANUFACTURING
140 Ascot Pkwy (44223-3743)
PHONE....................................330 940-2356
EMP: 3 EST: 2014
SALES (est): 177.2K **Privately Held**
SIC: 5521 5013 3999 Automobiles, used cars only; automotive servicing equipment; manufacturing industries

(G-8059)
ULTRA TECH MACHINERY INC
297 Ascot Pkwy (44223-3701)
PHONE....................................330 929-5544
Fax: 330 923-7527
Don Hagarty, *President*
Jim Hagarty, *Vice Pres*
Robert Hagarty, *Vice Pres*
David Monter, *Engineer*
Kim Hoover, *Senior Engr*
▲ EMP: 30
SQ FT: 11,000
SALES (est): 7.8MM **Privately Held**
WEB: www.utmachinery.com
SIC: 3599 7389 Machine shop, jobbing & repair; design, commercial & industrial

(G-8060)
ULTRATECH POLYMERS INC
280 Ascot Pkwy (44223-3346)
PHONE....................................330 945-9410
Fax: 330 945-9470
Anthony Kerkimis, *President*
John Herhold, *Vice Pres*
John Brown, *Treasurer*
Kelli Coleman, *Controller*
Vilie Kerkimis, *Office Mgr*
EMP: 15
SQ FT: 4,000
SALES (est): 1.5MM **Privately Held**
WEB: www.ultratechpolymers.com
SIC: 3083 Laminated plastics plate & sheet

(G-8061)
V-ASH MACHINE COMPANY
1220 Orlen Ave (44221-2956)
PHONE....................................216 267-3400
Fax: 216 267-1195
Vaden Ashley Jr, *President*
EMP: 4
SQ FT: 9,400
SALES: 160K **Privately Held**
SIC: 3599 Machine shop, jobbing & repair

(G-8062)
WIN CD INC
Also Called: Win Plex
3333 Win St (44223-3790)
PHONE....................................330 929-1999
David K Pulk, *President*
Sindy Platner, *Controller*
EMP: 18
SQ FT: 42,000
SALES (est): 5.9MM **Privately Held**
WEB: www.winplasticextrusions.com
SIC: 3089 Extruded finished plastic products

(G-8063)
YOUNGS SCREENPRINTING & EMBRO
1245 Munroe Falls Ave (44221-3533)
PHONE....................................330 922-5777
Penny Young, *Owner*
EMP: 5
SALES (est): 370.6K **Privately Held**
SIC: 2752 Commercial printing, lithographic

Dalton
Wayne County

(G-8064)
C & D MANUFACTURING INC
374 Eckard Rd (44618-9160)
PHONE....................................330 828-8357
Fax: 330 828-8357
David Wengerd, *President*
Cheryl Wengerd, *Vice Pres*
EMP: 3
SQ FT: 5,000
SALES (est): 410K **Privately Held**
SIC: 3599 Machine shop, jobbing & repair

(G-8065)
CROSCO WOOD PRODUCTS
1543 Zuercher Rd (44618-9776)
PHONE....................................330 857-0228
Crist H Miller, *Owner*
Lee Miller, *Manager*
EMP: 5
SALES (est): 371.4K **Privately Held**
SIC: 5211 2499 Lumber & other building materials; lumber products; decorative wood & woodwork

(G-8066)
DALTON VEAL
14978 Arnold Rd (44618-9228)
PHONE....................................330 828-8337
Lawrence Good, *President*
Andy Hershberger, *Manager*
EMP: 3
SALES (est): 159.8K **Privately Held**
SIC: 2011 0191 Veal from meat slaughtered on site; general farms, primarily crop

(G-8067)
DENDRATEC LTD
1417 Zuercher Rd (44618-9776)
PHONE....................................330 473-4878
Clarence Jennings, *Principal*
EMP: 6
SALES (est): 647.7K **Privately Held**
SIC: 2431 Millwork

(G-8068)
EGR PRODUCTS COMPANY INC (PA)
55 Eckard Rd (44618-9664)
PHONE....................................330 833-6554
Fax: 330 828-2565
Jeffery Daley, *President*
Jerome T Daley, *President*
Mary Ann Daley, *Vice Pres*
Ronald Thornberry, *Purchasing*
EMP: 13
SQ FT: 30,000
SALES: 2.4MM **Privately Held**
WEB: www.egrproducts.com
SIC: 3694 3714 Generators, automotive & aircraft; alternators, automotive; motors, starting: automotive & aircraft; motor vehicle parts & accessories

(G-8069)
GEDCO INC
Also Called: American Barricade
130 Briarwood Dr (44618-9789)
P.O. Box 202 (44618-0202)
PHONE....................................330 828-2044
Greg Donhue, *President*
Greg Donahoe, *Opers Staff*
EMP: 4
SALES: 225K **Privately Held**
SIC: 3993 Signs & advertising specialties

(G-8070)
HRH DOOR CORP
Also Called: Wayne - Dalton Rolling Doors
14512 Lincoln Way E (44618-9014)
PHONE....................................330 828-2291
Bill Hammer, *Manager*
EMP: 185
SALES (corp-wide): 665.2MM **Privately Held**
WEB: www.waynedalton.com
SIC: 3442 3446 Metal doors, sash & trim; architectural metalwork

PA: Hrh Door Corp.
1 Door Dr
Mount Hope OH 44660
850 208-3400

(G-8071)
J & L DOOR
13505 Bodine Rd (44618-9710)
PHONE.................................330 684-1496
Les Troyer, *Partner*
Joel Troyer, *Partner*
EMP: 3
SALES: 500K **Privately Held**
WEB: www.jldoor.com
SIC: 2434 Wood kitchen cabinets

(G-8072)
J HORST MANUFACTURING CO
Also Called: 2cravealloys
279 E Main St (44618-9601)
P.O. Box 507 (44618-0507)
PHONE.................................330 828-2216
Fax: 330 828-8107
Roland Horst, *President*
Mary Steiner, *Principal*
Richard Horst, *Vice Pres*
Dave Forrer, *Opers Mgr*
Todd Fiscus, *Purchasing*
EMP: 53 **EST:** 1963
SQ FT: 78,000
SALES: 12MM **Privately Held**
WEB: www.jhorst.com
SIC: 3599 3441 3549 3547 Machine
shop, jobbing & repair; fabricated struc-
tural metal; metalworking machinery;
rolling mill machinery; plating & polishing

(G-8073)
LAKE REGION OIL INC
26 N Cochran St (44618)
P.O. Box 499 (44618-0499)
PHONE.................................330 837-4767
Fax: 330 828-8158
Howard J Wenger, *President*
EMP: 15
SQ FT: 1,800
SALES (est): 1.7MM **Privately Held**
SIC: 1311 Crude petroleum production;
natural gas production

(G-8074)
MASSILLON MATERIALS INC (PA)
26 N Cochran St (44618)
P.O. Box 499 (44618-0499)
PHONE.................................330 837-4767
Howard J Wenger, *President*
EMP: 16
SQ FT: 6,000
SALES (est): 2.8MM **Privately Held**
SIC: 1442 Sand mining; gravel mining

(G-8075)
NEISS BODY & EQUIPMENT CORP
17485 Old Lincoln Way (44618-9692)
PHONE.................................330 828-2409
Fax: 330 828-2509
John M Neiss, *President*
Marla Neiss, *Corp Secy*
EMP: 7 **EST:** 1935
SQ FT: 12,000
SALES (est): 1.1MM **Privately Held**
WEB: www.neissbody.com
SIC: 3713 Truck bodies (motor vehicles)

(G-8076)
P GRAHAM DUNN INC (PA)
630 Henry St (44618-9280)
PHONE.................................330 828-2105
Paul Dunn, *President*
Joe Knutson, *President*
Robert Shetler, *Vice Pres*
Patrick Helmuth, *CFO*
Leanna Dunn, *Treasurer*
▲ **EMP:** 85
SQ FT: 100,000
SALES (est): 17.1MM **Privately Held**
SIC: 2511 Wood household furniture

(G-8077)
PETER GRAHAM DUNN INC
1417 Zuercher Rd (44618-9776)
PHONE.................................330 816-0035
Fax: 330 857-5455
Peter G Dunn, *President*

Leanna Dunn, *Corp Secy*
Elisa Stoyle, *Office Mgr*
▲ **EMP:** 50
SQ FT: 36,000
SALES: 9.3MM **Privately Held**
WEB: www.pgrahamdunn.com
SIC: 3499 5199 Novelties & giftware, in-
cluding trophies; advertising specialties

(G-8078)
PIONEER EQUIPMENT COMPANY
Also Called: Wengerd's Machine
16875 Jericho Rd (44618-9657)
PHONE.................................330 857-6340
Wayne H Wengerd, *President*
Esther Wengird, *Manager*
◆ **EMP:** 18
SALES (est): 3.9MM **Privately Held**
SIC: 3523 3312 Farm machinery & equip-
ment; blast furnaces & steel mills

(G-8079)
WAYNEDALE TRUSS & PANEL CO
93 Lake Dr (44618-9720)
PHONE.................................330 683-4471
Dianne Fry, *Principal*
EMP: 3
SALES (est): 265.2K **Privately Held**
SIC: 2439 Structural wood members

(G-8080)
WENGER PIPELINE CONSTRUCTION
14945 Lincoln Way E (44618-9730)
P.O. Box 526 (44618-0526)
PHONE.................................330 828-8803
Leonard Wenger, *President*
Sharon Wenger, *Corp Secy*
Dan Hershberger, *Office Mgr*
Paul Hershberger, *Office Mgr*
EMP: 23
SQ FT: 7,500
SALES (est): 2.8MM **Privately Held**
SIC: 1389 Oil field services

(G-8081)
YOST CANDY CO
Also Called: Kiddi Pops
51 N Cochran St (44618)
PHONE.................................330 828-2777
Fax: 330 828-8296
Sofie Yost, *President*
Catherine S Farris, *Corp Secy*
Earl Yost, *Vice Pres*
Joseph Yost, *Vice Pres*
EMP: 35 **EST:** 1937
SQ FT: 45,000
SALES (est): 4.1MM **Privately Held**
WEB: www.yostcandy.com
SIC: 2064 Lollipops & other hard candy

(G-8082)
ZIMMERMAN STEEL & SUP CO LLC
18543 Davis Rd (44618-9697)
PHONE.................................330 828-1010
Nancy Zimmerman, *CFO*
David Zimmerman,
EMP: 10
SQ FT: 11,700
SALES (est): 2.1MM **Privately Held**
SIC: 3499 Fire- or burglary-resistive prod-
ucts

Danville
Knox County

(G-8083)
B & J DRILLING COMPANY INC
13911 Millersburg Rd (43014-9697)
PHONE.................................740 599-6700
William Samples, *President*
EMP: 3 **EST:** 1963
SQ FT: 3,200
SALES (est): 497.7K **Privately Held**
SIC: 1311 Natural gas production

(G-8084)
BESL SPECIALIZED CARRIER
Also Called: Gns
16559 Skyline Dr (43014-8620)
PHONE.................................740 599-6305
Glenn Nyharto, *Owner*
EMP: 3
SALES (est): 261.5K **Privately Held**
SIC: 3799 Transportation equipment

(G-8085)
CAMPHIRE DRILLING INC
8 Ross St (43014)
P.O. Box 28 (43014-0028)
PHONE.................................740 599-6928
George E Camphire, *President*
Janet Camphire, *Vice Pres*
EMP: 4 **EST:** 1966
SALES: 180K **Privately Held**
SIC: 1381 Directional drilling oil & gas
wells

(G-8086)
CAROL MICKLEY (PA)
Also Called: Unocal
2 Richard St (43014)
P.O. Box J
PHONE.................................740 599-7870
Carol Mickley, *President*
▲ **EMP:** 3
SALES (est): 1MM **Privately Held**
SIC: 1311 7992 Crude petroleum produc-
tion; public golf courses

(G-8087)
DUNAGAN LOGGING
16844 Pritchard Rd (43014-8000)
PHONE.................................740 599-9368
Sue Dunagan, *Owner*
EMP: 3
SALES (est): 143.1K **Privately Held**
WEB: www.thesunlink.com
SIC: 2411 Logging camps & contractors

(G-8088)
ELECTROWARMTH PRODUCTS LLC
513 Market St (43014)
P.O. Box A (43014-0601)
PHONE.................................740 599-7222
Dan Grindle, *President*
Beulah Grindle, *Vice Pres*
▲ **EMP:** 4 **EST:** 1939
SQ FT: 6,500
SALES (est): 499.4K **Privately Held**
SIC: 3699 Heat emission operating appa-
ratus

(G-8089)
LYNN LYONS
Also Called: Horseshoe Drive Thru
803 Market St (43014)
P.O. Box 27 (43014-0027)
PHONE.................................740 599-7811
Lynn Lyons, *Owner*
EMP: 5
SALES (est): 250.9K **Privately Held**
WEB: www.lynnlyonsnh.com
SIC: 2086 Carbonated beverages, nonal-
coholic: bottled & canned

(G-8090)
MCFADDEN LOGGING
305 S Mickley St (43014)
P.O. Box L (43014-0612)
PHONE.................................740 599-6902
Jim McFadden, *Owner*
EMP: 3
SALES (est): 200K **Privately Held**
SIC: 2411 5099 Logging; logs, hewn ties,
posts & poles

(G-8091)
SHROCK PREFAB LLC
23403 College Hill Rd (43014-9634)
PHONE.................................740 599-9401
Joseph Shrock,
EMP: 11
SALES: 950K **Privately Held**
SIC: 3448 Trusses & framing: prefabri-
cated metal

(G-8092)
VALLEY VIEW PALLETS PARTNERS
22414 Hostetler Rd (43014-9638)
PHONE.................................740 393-9282
Ephraim Yoder, *Principal*
EMP: 4
SALES (est): 686.4K **Privately Held**
SIC: 2448 Pallets, wood & wood with metal

(G-8093)
YOUNGS LOCKER SERVICE INC
Also Called: Youngs Locker Serv & Meat Proc
16201 Nashville Rd (43014-9738)
P.O. Box Y (43014-0625)
PHONE.................................740 599-6833
Fax: 740 599-2943
Lawrence Payne, *President*
EMP: 10
SQ FT: 10,000
SALES: 190K **Privately Held**
SIC: 2011 4222 2013 Meat packing
plants; warehousing, cold storage or re-
frigerated; sausages & other prepared
meats

Dayton
Greene County

(G-8094)
ADVANCED PROPELLER SYSTEMS
1297 Windsor Dr (45434-8019)
PHONE.................................937 409-1038
William Jeffrey, *Owner*
EMP: 3
SALES (est): 221.7K **Privately Held**
SIC: 3366 7389 Propellers; business serv-
ices

(G-8095)
AIR FORCE US DEPT OF
4225 Logistics Ave (45433-5769)
PHONE.................................937 656-2354
EMP: 254 **Publicly Held**
SIC: 9711 7372 Air Force; business ori-
ented computer software
HQ: United States Department Of The Air
Force
1000 Air Force Pentagon
Washington DC 20330

(G-8096)
ANTHONY BUSINESS FORMS INC
3160 Plainfield Rd (45432-3713)
P.O. Box 24754 (45424-0754)
PHONE.................................937 253-0072
Fax: 937 253-8107
Katherine D Harrah, *President*
EMP: 12
SQ FT: 6,000
SALES (est): 2.4MM **Privately Held**
WEB: www.anthonybusinessforms.com
SIC: 5112 2754 2759 2791 Business
forms; labels: gravure printing; envelopes:
printing; typesetting; manifold business
forms; commercial printing, lithographic

(G-8097)
CABLE AND CTRL SOLUTIONS LLC
4726 Springfield St (45431-1045)
PHONE.................................937 254-2227
Bob Day, *General Mgr*
EMP: 3
SALES (est): 422K **Privately Held**
SIC: 3496 3629 Cable, uninsulated wire:
made from purchased wire; electronic
generation equipment

(G-8098)
CAPITAL PRECISION MACHINE & TL
1865 Radio Rd (45431-1034)
PHONE.................................937 258-1176
Paul Powers Sr, *Owner*
Cliff Smith, *Owner*
EMP: 15
SQ FT: 10,000

▲ = Import ▼=Export
◆ =Import/Export

SALES (est): 940K **Privately Held**
WEB: www.cpmtool.com
SIC: 3544 Special dies, tools, jigs & fixtures

(G-8099)
CASSADY WOODWORKS INC
446 N Smithville Rd (45431-1080)
PHONE...............................937 256-7948
Fax: 937 256-1832
Tom Joch, *President*
Dave Davis, *Vice Pres*
Janet Rosser, *Manager*
EMP: 25
SQ FT: 12,000
SALES: 7.9MM **Privately Held**
WEB: www.cassadywoodworks.com
SIC: 2541 2431 2441 Wood partitions & fixtures; display fixtures, wood; millwork; nailed wood boxes & shook

(G-8100)
D & B INDUSTRIES INC
5031 Linden Ave Ste B (45432-1893)
PHONE...............................937 253-8658
Fax: 937 253-2225
Brent Gillott, *President*
Brent Grotegut, *Technology*
EMP: 7
SQ FT: 5,000
SALES (est): 944.5K **Privately Held**
WEB: www.d-bindustries.com
SIC: 3599 Machine & other job shop work

(G-8101)
DAILY SQUAWK LLC
3214 Bob White Pl (45431-3364)
PHONE...............................937 426-6247
Daniel W Ross, *Principal*
EMP: 3
SALES (est): 121.1K **Privately Held**
SIC: 2711 Newspapers, publishing & printing

(G-8102)
DAYTON ENVIRONMENTAL
1621 Pence Pl (45432-3315)
PHONE...............................937 478-1536
Anthony Lombardo, *Owner*
EMP: 14
SALES (est): 420K **Privately Held**
SIC: 2844 Cosmetic preparations

(G-8103)
DAYTON INDUSTRIAL DRUM INC
1880 Radio Rd (45431-1099)
PHONE...............................937 253-8933
Fax: 937 253-8656
David Hussong, *President*
Phillip Sievering, *General Mgr*
Ruth M Hussong, *Corp Secy*
Kylene Hussong, *Vice Pres*
David Kotchka, *Sales Associate*
EMP: 25
SQ FT: 25,000
SALES (est): 4.6MM **Privately Held**
WEB: www.daytonindustrialdrum.com
SIC: 7699 5085 5113 2673 Industrial equipment services; drums, new or reconditioned; industrial & personal service paper; bags: plastic, laminated & coated; fiber cans, drums & similar products

(G-8104)
DLA DOCUMENT SERVICES
4165 Communications Blvd (45433-5601)
PHONE...............................937 257-6014
Leonard Xavier, *Director*
EMP: 25 **Publicly Held**
SIC: 2752 9711 Commercial printing, lithographic; national security
HQ: Dla Document Services
5450 Carlisle Pike Bldg 9
Mechanicsburg PA 17050
717 605-2362

(G-8105)
G W SMITH AND SONS INC
1700 Spaulding Rd (45432-3728)
PHONE...............................937 253-5114
Fax: 937 253-9363
Victor W Smith Jr, *President*
Michael Fitzharris, *Vice Pres*
▲ EMP: 22 EST: 1939
SQ FT: 45,000

SALES (est): 7.8MM
SALES (corp-wide): 746.6MM **Publicly Held**
WEB: www.gwsmithandsons.com
SIC: 2992 Lubricating oils & greases
PA: Quaker Chemical Corporation
901 E Hector St
Conshohocken PA 19428
610 832-4000

(G-8106)
GREEN MACHINE TOOL INC
1865 Radio Rd (45431-1034)
PHONE...............................937 253-0771
Fax: 937 253-0727
Eugene Green, *President*
Mary Ann Green, *Vice Pres*
EMP: 12
SQ FT: 12,000
SALES: 1MM **Privately Held**
SIC: 3599 3544 Machine shop, jobbing & repair; forms (molds), for foundry & plastics working machinery

(G-8107)
GREENE COUNTY
Also Called: Green County Wtr Sup & Trtmnt
1122 Beaver Valley Rd (45434-7014)
PHONE...............................937 429-0127
Fax: 937 427-5325
Ken French, *Manager*
Lyndon Kendrick, *Manager*
EMP: 8 **Privately Held**
WEB: www.greeneworks.com
SIC: 3589 4941 Sewage & water treatment equipment; water supply
PA: Greene County
35 Greene St
Xenia OH 45385
937 562-5006

(G-8108)
HEARTH PRODUCTS CONTROLS CO
3050 Plainfield Rd (45432-3711)
PHONE...............................937 436-9800
Fax: 937 436-9803
Greg Stech, *Vice Pres*
Jim Karns, *Purch Mgr*
Mike Adkins, *Engineer*
John Wagner, *Natl Sales Mgr*
Jennifer Combs, *Accounts Mgr*
▲ EMP: 18
SQ FT: 8,400
SALES (est): 4.8MM **Privately Held**
WEB: www.hearthproductscontrols.com
SIC: 3491 Process control regulator valves

(G-8109)
ITT CORPORATION
Wright Ptrson A Frce Base (45433)
PHONE...............................937 256-1705
Steve Gaffney, *Branch Mgr*
EMP: 58
SALES (corp-wide): 2.4B **Publicly Held**
WEB: www.ittind.com
SIC: 3625 Control equipment, electric
HQ: Itt Llc
1133 Westchester Ave N-100
White Plains NY 10604
914 641-2000

(G-8110)
LAU INDUSTRIES INC (DH)
Also Called: Supreme Fan/Industrial Air
4509 Springfield St (45431-1042)
PHONE...............................937 476-6500
Fax: 937 254-9519
Damian Macaluso, *President*
Dan Disser, *Vice Pres*
Christopher Wampler, *Vice Pres*
Ritch Mumpower, *Engineer*
Calvin Heard, *Human Resources*
▼ EMP: 125
SQ FT: 50,000
SALES (est): 206.9MM **Privately Held**
WEB: www.lauparts.com
SIC: 3564 Ventilating fans: industrial or commercial
HQ: Johnson Controls, Inc.
5757 N Green Bay Ave
Milwaukee WI 53209
414 524-1200

(G-8111)
MANTYCH METALWORKING INC
3175 Plainfield Rd (45432-3712)
PHONE...............................937 258-1373
Fax: 937 258-3771
Kathleen Mantych, *CEO*
Colleen Mantych, *President*
Cristy Mantych, *Vice Pres*
Eric Gill, *Purchasing*
Matt Orr, *Manager*
EMP: 24 EST: 1971
SQ FT: 24,000
SALES (est): 4.2MM **Privately Held**
WEB: www.mantych.net
SIC: 3599 3444 Machine shop, jobbing & repair; sheet metalwork

(G-8112)
MIAMI VALLEY LIGHTING LLC
1065 Woodman Dr (45432-1423)
PHONE...............................937 224-6000
Teresa Sloan, *General Mgr*
Joyce Reives, *Mng Member*
Shanda Donley, *Manager*
Dave Hinnan,
EMP: 7
SQ FT: 1,500
SALES: 9MM
SALES (corp-wide): 13.5B **Publicly Held**
WEB: www.dpl.com
SIC: 3648 Street lighting fixtures
HQ: Dpl Inc.
1065 Woodman Dr
Dayton OH 45432
937 331-4063

(G-8113)
MIAMI VLY MFG & ASSEMBLY INC
1889 Radio Rd (45431-1034)
PHONE...............................937 254-6665
Fax: 937 254-6575
Joseph S Rosenkranz, *President*
EMP: 12
SQ FT: 5,000
SALES: 1MM **Privately Held**
SIC: 3599 Machine & other job shop work

(G-8114)
MULCH MAN
Also Called: Mulch Man Greenline Products
4595 Fairpark Ave (45431)
PHONE...............................937 866-5370
Fax: 937 435-0347
John Randall, *Principal*
EMP: 20
SALES (est): 2MM **Privately Held**
SIC: 2499 Mulch, wood & bark

(G-8115)
POI HOLDINGS INC (HQ)
Also Called: Phase One
3203 Plainfield Rd (45432-3736)
PHONE...............................937 253-7377
Fax: 937 253-3877
Frederick Ewing, *President*
John Schreiner, *Vice Pres*
Stephen Barker, *Director*
Rick Yanez, *Director*
EMP: 15
SQ FT: 7,500
SALES (est): 2.4MM
SALES (corp-wide): 25.4MM **Privately Held**
SIC: 3821 3823 Laboratory apparatus & furniture; flow instruments, industrial process type
PA: Vacuum Instrument Corporation
2101 9th Ave Ste A
Ronkonkoma NY 11779
631 737-0900

(G-8116)
SALLEY TOOL & DIE CO
3180 Plainfield Rd Ste 1 (45432-3740)
PHONE...............................937 258-3333
Fax: 937 258-9355
Stephen Salley, *Owner*
EMP: 13
SALES (est): 1.3MM **Privately Held**
SIC: 3728 3599 Military aircraft equipment & armament; machine shop, jobbing & repair

(G-8117)
STEINBARGER PRECISION CNC INC
3100 Plainfield Rd Ste A (45432-3725)
PHONE...............................937 252-0322
EMP: 3 EST: 1998
SQ FT: 2,500
SALES: 300K **Privately Held**
SIC: 3599 Machine Shop

(G-8118)
TOASTMASTERS INTERNATIONAL
1854 Redleaf Ct (45432-4103)
PHONE...............................937 429-2680
Dan Reeves, *Treasurer*
EMP: 10
SALES (corp-wide): 34.1MM **Privately Held**
WEB: www.d70toastmasters.org
SIC: 8299 2721 Educational service, non-degree granting: continuing educ.; magazines: publishing only, not printed on site
PA: Toastmasters International
23182 Arroyo Vis
Rcho Sta Marg CA 92688
949 858-8255

(G-8119)
TOOL SERVICE CO INC
Also Called: Ohio Industrial Supply
4620 Tall Oaks Dr (45432-3241)
P.O. Box 292165 (45429-0165)
PHONE...............................937 254-4000
Fax: 937 254-6353
Dwayne Jones, *President*
Scott Gooch, *Vice Pres*
Gregory Jones, *VP Prdtn*
Shirley Jones, *Admin Sec*
Denise Gooch, *Asst Sec*
EMP: 5
SQ FT: 6,400
SALES (est): 450K **Privately Held**
SIC: 3541 5084 Grinding, polishing, buffing, lapping & honing machines; machine tool replacement & repair parts, metal cutting types; machine tools & metalworking machinery

(G-8120)
UCR LLC
Also Called: Spare Parts Warehouse
1332 Woodman Dr Ste 2 (45432-3444)
PHONE...............................937 253-8898
Daniel Thompson, *CEO*
Gary Klosterman, *Purch Agent*
EMP: 19
SQ FT: 10,000
SALES (est): 6.2MM **Privately Held**
WEB: www.ucrnet.com
SIC: 7378 7373 3577 Computer maintenance & repair; systems integration services; local area network (LAN) systems integrator; computer peripheral equipment

(G-8121)
UNISON INDUSTRIES LLC
Elano Div
2455 Dayton Xenia Rd (45434-7148)
PHONE...............................937 426-0621
Fax: 937 427-0288
Linda Revis, *Materials Mgr*
Alex Byrd, *Engineer*
Greg Engler, *Engineer*
Michael Lockhart, *Engineer*
Mike Stout, *Engineer*
EMP: 400
SALES (corp-wide): 123.6B **Publicly Held**
WEB: www.unisonindustries.com
SIC: 3728 4581 3714 3498 Aircraft parts & equipment; aircraft servicing & repairing; motor vehicle parts & accessories; fabricated pipe & fittings; steel pipe & tubes
HQ: Unison Industries, Llc
7575 Baymeadows Way
Jacksonville FL 32256
904 739-4000

(G-8122)
UNISON INDUSTRIES LLC
Also Called: Elano Div
2455 Dayton Xenia Rd (45434-7148)
PHONE...............................937 426-0621

GEOGRAPHIC

Ed Mayer, *Manager*
EMP: 600
SALES (corp-wide): 123.6B **Publicly Held**
WEB: www.unisonindustries.com
SIC: 3498 Tube fabricating (contract bending & shaping)
HQ: Unison Industries, Llc
7575 Baymeadows Way
Jacksonville FL 32256
904 739-4000

Dayton
Montgomery County

(G-8123)
4 OVER LLC
7801 Technology Blvd (45424-1574)
PHONE..............................937 610-0629
Frank Johnston, *Vice Pres*
Jeff Hanson, *Supervisor*
EMP: 10
SALES (corp-wide): 173.3MM **Privately Held**
SIC: 2752 Commercial printing, lithographic
HQ: 4 Over, Llc
5900 San Fernando Rd D
Glendale CA 91202
818 246-1170

(G-8124)
5 AXIS GRINDING INC
86 Westpark Rd (45459-4813)
PHONE..............................937 312-9797
Scott Ameduri, *President*
Barbara Ameduri, *Admin Sec*
EMP: 7
SALES (est): 970.2K **Privately Held**
SIC: 3556 Cutting, chopping, grinding, mixing & similar machinery

(G-8125)
A & B IRON & METAL COMPANY
329 Washington St (45402-2541)
PHONE..............................937 228-1561
Fax: 937 222-4766
Greg Thoma, *President*
Joseph Caperna, *President*
Brion Haynes, *General Mgr*
Rosalia Caperna, *Vice Pres*
EMP: 15
SQ FT: 500
SALES: 2MM **Privately Held**
SIC: 5093 4953 3341 3231 Scrap & waste materials; refuse systems; secondary nonferrous metals; products of purchased glass

(G-8126)
A & W SPRING CO INC
1000 E 2nd St Ste 8 (45402-1370)
PHONE..............................937 222-7284
EMP: 4 **EST:** 1973
SQ FT: 1,800
SALES (est): 320K **Privately Held**
SIC: 3495 Mfg Wire Springs

(G-8127)
AABEL PLUMBING INC
440 Congress Park Dr (45459-4125)
PHONE..............................937 434-4343
Charles Norman, *President*
EMP: 25
SQ FT: 16,000
SALES (est): 2.1MM **Privately Held**
SIC: 3261 Vitreous plumbing fixtures

(G-8128)
ABSOLUTE SMILE LLC
4469 Far Hills Ave (45429-2405)
PHONE..............................937 293-9866
EMP: 4
SALES (est): 454.4K **Privately Held**
SIC: 3843 Mfg Dental Equipment/Supplies

(G-8129)
ACCU JET CORP
Also Called: Accu-Jet Div of First Tool
612 Linden Ave (45403-2513)
PHONE..............................937 252-9931
Robert Davis, *President*
Lisa Davis, *Vice Pres*

Doug Rambow, *Engineer*
Scott Boshart, *Manager*
EMP: 30
SALES (est): 2.1MM **Privately Held**
SIC: 3545 5251 Machine tool accessories; tools

(G-8130)
ACCU-GRIND & MFG CO INC
272 Leo St (45404-1006)
P.O. Box 117, Laura (45337-0117)
PHONE..............................937 224-3303
Fax: 937 224-3450
Jeff Heisey, *President*
EMP: 34
SQ FT: 39,500
SALES (est): 4.8MM **Privately Held**
SIC: 3541 Grinding machines, metalworking

(G-8131)
ACCUMULUS SOFTWARE
6708 Innsbruck Dr (45459-1224)
P.O. Box 750171 (45475-0171)
PHONE..............................937 435-0861
Eric Greenrose, *President*
EMP: 4
SALES (est): 176.5K **Privately Held**
SIC: 7372 Prepackaged software

(G-8132)
ACCURACY PRODUCTS INC
2551 Thunderhawk Ct (45414-3466)
PHONE..............................937 454-2240
Fax: 937 454-5337
Larry F Andersen, *President*
Darrell Cook, *Vice Pres*
Scott Warner, *Vice Pres*
Candice Long, *Treasurer*
EMP: 18
SQ FT: 14,500
SALES (est): 3MM **Privately Held**
SIC: 3451 Screw machine products

(G-8133)
ACCUTECH PLASTIC MOLDING INC
5015 Kitridge Rd (45424-4433)
P.O. Box 24272 (45424-0272)
PHONE..............................937 233-0017
Fax: 937 233-6877
William Stoddard Jr, *President*
EMP: 7 **EST:** 1977
SQ FT: 6,000
SALES (est): 1.1MM **Privately Held**
SIC: 3089 Injection molding of plastics

(G-8134)
ACTION RUBBER CO INC
601 Fame Rd (45449-2355)
PHONE..............................937 866-5975
Ron Mc Croson, *President*
EMP: 10
SQ FT: 12,500
SALES (est): 770K **Privately Held**
WEB: www.actionrubber.com
SIC: 3069 Molded rubber products

(G-8135)
ACUREN INSPECTION INC
705 Albany St (45417-3460)
PHONE..............................937 228-9729
Jim Bailey, *President*
EMP: 52
SALES (corp-wide): 513MM **Privately Held**
SIC: 1389 Testing, measuring, surveying & analysis services
HQ: Acuren Inspection, Inc.
30 Main St Ste 402
Danbury CT 06810
203 702-8740

(G-8136)
ADENA TOOL CORPORATION
4201 Little York Rd (45414-2507)
PHONE..............................937 890-8428
Fax: 937 387-0881
Gary Van Gundy, *President*
Joyce Mueller, *Vice Pres*
Chad Massie, *Engineer*
Stephen Barnes, *Treasurer*
Steve Smith, *Controller*
▲ **EMP:** 56
SQ FT: 54,000

SALES (est): 6.1MM **Privately Held**
WEB: www.drtusa.com
SIC: 3544 Special dies, tools, jigs & fixtures
PA: Drt Holdings, Inc.
618 Greenmount Blvd
Dayton OH 45419

(G-8137)
ADEPT MANUFACTURING CORP
511 N Findlay St (45404-2205)
PHONE..............................937 222-7110
Fax: 937 222-7134
Mike Mueller, *President*
Sandy Mueller, *Treasurer*
EMP: 10
SQ FT: 18,000
SALES (est): 1.4MM **Privately Held**
SIC: 3544 Special dies, tools, jigs & fixtures

(G-8138)
ADVANCED GRAPHICS OF DAYTON
207 Air St (45404-1805)
PHONE..............................937 228-2221
Fax: 937 228-3523
Kimberly Kuns, *President*
Karen A Schmitt, *Vice Pres*
EMP: 4
SQ FT: 7,500
SALES: 150K **Privately Held**
SIC: 2752 Commercial printing, lithographic

(G-8139)
AERO PATTERN WORKS
2725 Stonequarry Rd (45414-1411)
PHONE..............................937 890-3720
Jack Haws, *Owner*
EMP: 3
SALES (est): 100K **Privately Held**
SIC: 3543 Industrial patterns

(G-8140)
AHLSTROM WEST CARROLLTON LLC
1 S Elm St (45449-1732)
PHONE..............................937 859-3621
Cameron Lonergar, *President*
Alan P Berens, *Vice Pres*
Bob Scancella, *Vice Pres*
Jeff Whitt, *Facilities Mgr*
Tom Bray, *Mfg Staff*
▲ **EMP:** 120
SQ FT: 100,000
SALES (est): 21.3MM
SALES (corp-wide): 409MM **Privately Held**
WEB: www.wcparchment.com
SIC: 2621 2672 Parchment paper; coated & laminated paper
PA: Ahlstrom Usa Inc.
2 Elm St
Windsor Locks CT 06096
860 654-8300

(G-8141)
AIR CLEANING SOLUTIONS
8613 N Main St (45415-1329)
P.O. Box 13103 (45413-0103)
PHONE..............................937 832-3600
Jim O'Bryan, *Owner*
Jim Obryan, *Owner*
EMP: 3
SALES (est): 325.2K **Privately Held**
SIC: 3564 Filters, air: furnaces, air conditioning equipment, etc.

(G-8142)
AIRGAS USA LLC
1223 Mccook Ave (45404-1011)
PHONE..............................937 228-8594
Kevin Little, *Branch Mgr*
Julie Rengers, *Manager*
EMP: 21
SQ FT: 9,600
SALES (corp-wide): 163.9MM **Privately Held**
WEB: www.us.linde-gas.com
SIC: 5169 5084 5984 2813 Industrial gases; gases, compressed & liquefied; welding machinery & equipment; liquefied petroleum gas dealers; industrial gases

HQ: Airgas Usa, Llc
259 N Radnor Chester Rd # 100
Radnor PA 19087
610 687-5253

(G-8143)
ALFRED NICKLES BAKERY INC
201 Pritz Ave (45403-2521)
PHONE..............................937 256-3762
Fax: 937 256-4365
Gary Huffman, *Manager*
EMP: 16
SALES (corp-wide): 205MM **Privately Held**
SIC: 2051 Bakery, for home service delivery
PA: Alfred Nickles Bakery, Inc.
26 Main St N
Navarre OH 44662
330 879-5635

(G-8144)
ALL SYSTEMS COLOUR INC
2032 S Alex Rd Ste A (45449-4023)
PHONE..............................937 859-9701
George Dick, *President*
EMP: 4
SALES (est): 427.4K
SALES (corp-wide): 14MM **Privately Held**
WEB: www.allsystemscolour.com
SIC: 2732 2752 Books: printing & binding; commercial printing, lithographic
PA: Four Colour Imports, Ltd.
2410 Frankfort Ave Ste 1
Louisville KY 40206
502 896-9644

(G-8145)
ALLEY CAT DESIGNS INC
919 Senate Dr (45459-4017)
PHONE..............................937 885-7950
Fax: 937 291-8805
Ron Dallessandris, *President*
Joyce Dallessandris, *Vice Pres*
Mariana Neal, *Vice Pres*
Patty Dallessandris, *Admin Sec*
EMP: 8
SQ FT: 2,800
SALES (est): 660K **Privately Held**
WEB: www.alleycatworldwide.com
SIC: 3552 2395 Printing machinery, textile; embroidery products, except schiffli machine

(G-8146)
ALLIANCE INDUS MASKING INC
204 S Ludlow St Ste 201 (45402-2341)
PHONE..............................937 681-5569
Donald Gray, *President*
EMP: 3
SALES (est): 148.1K **Privately Held**
SIC: 2675 Cutouts, cardboard, die-cut: from purchased materials

(G-8147)
ALLIANCE TORQUE CONVERTERS INC
5915 Wolf Creek Pike (45426-2439)
PHONE..............................937 222-3394
Donald G Gray, *Principal*
EMP: 9
SALES (est): 1.3MM **Privately Held**
SIC: 3621 Torque motors, electric

(G-8148)
ALLIED SILK SCREEN INC
2740 Thunderhawk Ct (45414-3464)
PHONE..............................937 223-4921
Dennis Brzozowski, *President*
David Brzozowski, *Vice Pres*
EMP: 7
SQ FT: 10,000
SALES: 200K **Privately Held**
WEB: www.alliedsilkscreen.com
SIC: 2759 Screen printing

(G-8149)
ALRO STEEL CORPORATION
Also Called: Arlo Aluminum & Steel
821 Springfield St (45403-1252)
PHONE..............................937 253-6121
Fax: 937 253-6126
Tim Elliott, *Manager*
David Zontek, *Manager*
EMP: 40

2017 Harris Ohio
Industrial Directory

▲ = Import ▼=Export
◆ =Import/Export

SQ FT: 120,000
SALES (corp-wide): 1.6B Privately Held
WEB: www.alro.com
SIC: 5051 3441 3317 3316 Steel; fabricated structural metal; steel pipe & tubes; cold finishing of steel shapes; blast furnaces & steel mills
PA: Alro Steel Corporation
3100 E High St
Jackson MI 49203
517 787-5500

(G-8150)
AMERICAN AERO COMPONENTS LLC
2601 W Stroop Rd Unit 60 (45439-1929)
PHONE...................937 367-5068
Ajitesh Kakade, MIS Mgr
EMP: 3
SQ FT: 50,000
SALES (est): 130.9K Privately Held
SIC: 3451 3599 3721 3724 Screw machine products; machine & other job shop work; aircraft; aircraft engines & engine parts; aircraft parts & equipment

(G-8151)
AMERICAN BOTTLING COMPANY
7 Up Bottling Co of Dayton
3131 Transportation Rd (45404-2372)
PHONE...................937 236-0333
Fax: 937 236-9324
Michael Eichner, Manager
Christine Durr, Manager
Mike Eichner, Manager
Scott Jackson, Manager
Jim Maloney, Telecom Exec
EMP: 100
SQ FT: 100,000
SALES (corp-wide): 6.4B Publicly Held
WEB: www.cs-americas.com
SIC: 2086 Bottled & canned soft drinks
HQ: The American Bottling Company
5301 Legacy Dr
Plano TX 75024

(G-8152)
AMERICAN CITY BUS JOURNALS INC
Also Called: Dayton Business Journal
40 N Main St Ste 800 (45423-1053)
PHONE...................937 528-4400
Fax: 937 222-8595
Dave Smith, Publisher
John Hancock, Editor
Caleb Stephens, Editor
Jane Applegate, Engineer
Neil Arthur, Manager
EMP: 26
SALES (corp-wide): 1.6B Privately Held
SIC: 2711 7313 Newspapers: publishing only, not printed on site; newspaper advertising representative
HQ: American City Business Journals, Inc.
120 W Morehead St Ste 400
Charlotte NC 28202
704 973-1000

(G-8153)
AMERICAN CONCRETE PRODUCTS
Also Called: American Brick & Block
1433 S Euclid Ave (45417-3839)
PHONE...................937 224-1433
Fax: 937 224-8387
Lee Snyder, President
Lee E Snyder, Treasurer
Merrill Durig, Sales Mgr
EMP: 11
SQ FT: 10,000
SALES: 750K Privately Held
SIC: 3271 5211 Blocks, concrete or cinder: standard; brick

(G-8154)
AMERICAN INDUS MAINTENENCE
605 Springfield St (45403-1248)
PHONE...................937 254-3400
Fax: 937 254-3489
Marvin Price, President
Cari Price, President
EMP: 8
SQ FT: 19,000

SALES: 1.1MM Privately Held
SIC: 5231 3471 Paint & painting supplies; sand blasting of metal parts

(G-8155)
AMERICAN RESCUE TECHNOLOGY
2780 Culver Ave (45429-3724)
PHONE...................937 293-6240
Fax: 937 293-7049
Richard S Michalo, President
Scott Strawser, Manager
▲ EMP: 10
SQ FT: 11,000
SALES (est): 3.7MM Privately Held
WEB: www.genesisrescue.com
SIC: 5084 3569 Industrial machinery & equipment; firefighting apparatus & related equipment

(G-8156)
AMERICAN WOODWORK SPECIALTY CO
Also Called: A W S C O
4301 N James H Mcgee Blvd (45417-9537)
PHONE...................937 263-1053
Fax: 937 263-6542
Michael E Knapp, President
Janine A Knapp, Treasurer
EMP: 35
SQ FT: 120,000
SALES (est): 4.2MM Privately Held
WEB: www.awsco.com
SIC: 2431 3442 3231 Window frames, wood; louver windows, glass, wood frame; metal doors, sash & trim; products of purchased glass

(G-8157)
AMERIWATER LLC
3345 Stop 8 Rd (45414-3425)
PHONE...................937 461-8833
Fax: 937 461-1988
Diane Dolan, CEO
James Baker, Vice Pres
Becky Betta, Purch Agent
Barbara Westfall, Manager
Brian Bowman, Administration
▲ EMP: 47
SQ FT: 48,000
SALES (est): 15.9MM
SALES (corp-wide): 38.7MM Privately Held
WEB: www.ameriwater.com
SIC: 3589 Water treatment equipment, industrial
HQ: Suez International
Tour Cb 21
Courbevoie 92400
146 256-000

(G-8158)
ANGELL-DEMMEL NORTH AMER CORP (PA)
Also Called: Alutrim North America
1516 Stanley Ave (45404-1113)
PHONE...................937 461-5800
Fax: 937 586-6031
John S Turner, President
David Benner, Vice Pres
Billy Newton, Production
Michael Truitt, Production
Ann Ashley, Purch Agent
▲ EMP: 80
SQ FT: 50,000
SALES (est): 43.1MM Privately Held
WEB: www.angellmfg.com
SIC: 3469 3465 3089 2752 Metal stampings; moldings or trim, automobile: stamped metal; plastic processing; commercial printing, lithographic; packaging paper & plastics film, coated & laminated; automotive & apparel trimmings

(G-8159)
ANGSTRON MATERIALS INC
1240 Mccook Ave (45404-1059)
PHONE...................937 331-9884
Meishio Jang, President
David Burton, Exec VP
Bor Z Jang, Vice Pres
Nilo Joson, Prdtn Mgr
WEI Xiong, Research
EMP: 4

SALES (est): 1MM Privately Held
SIC: 3624 Carbon & graphite products

(G-8160)
APEX TOOL GROUP LLC
762 W Stewart St (45417-3971)
PHONE...................937 222-7871
Fax: 937 228-0422
EMP: 200
SALES (corp-wide): 17.3B Privately Held
WEB: www.cooperhandtools.com
SIC: 3546 Power-driven handtools
HQ: Apex Tool Group, Llc
14600 York Rd Ste A
Sparks MD 21152

(G-8161)
APS-MATERIALS INC (PA)
Also Called: A P S
4011 Riverside Dr (45405-2364)
P.O. Box 1106 (45401-1106)
PHONE...................937 278-6547
Fax: 937 278-4352
Michael C Wilson, President
Phil Chitty, General Mgr
Joseph T Cheng, Chairman
Robert Willson, VP Opers
Michael Willson, Plant Mgr
▲ EMP: 65 EST: 1975
SQ FT: 50,000
SALES (est): 17.1MM Privately Held
WEB: www.apsmaterials.com
SIC: 3479 2899 2851 Painting, coating & hot dipping; chemical preparations; paints & allied products

(G-8162)
APS-MATERIALS INC
Also Called: Ceranode Division
153 Walbrook Ave (45405-2343)
PHONE...................937 278-6547
Michael Wilson, Purch Mgr
Monty King, Engineer
Philip Chitty, Manager
EMP: 50
SALES (corp-wide): 17.1MM Privately Held
WEB: www.apsmaterials.com
SIC: 3479 Painting, coating & hot dipping
PA: Aps-Materials, Inc.
4011 Riverside Dr
Dayton OH 45405
937 278-6547

(G-8163)
ARGROV BOX CO
6030 Webster St (45414-3434)
P.O. Box 305, Middletown (45042-0305)
PHONE...................937 898-1700
Fax: 937 898-1770
Kenneth Eppich, President
Dean Timmons, COO
Judith Eppich, Vice Pres
Diane Jennings, Admin Mgr
EMP: 14
SQ FT: 42,400
SALES (est): 1.3MM Privately Held
SIC: 2653 5113 Boxes, corrugated: made from purchased materials; boxes & containers

(G-8164)
ARMSTRONG S PRINTING EX LLC
8810 Grovecreek Ct (45458-3372)
PHONE...................937 276-7794
James A Armstrong, Principal
EMP: 4
SALES (est): 342.3K Privately Held
SIC: 2752 Commercial printing, lithographic

(G-8165)
ASHTON PUMPMATIC INC
7670 Mcewen Rd (45459-3908)
P.O. Box 750783 (45475-0783)
PHONE...................937 424-1380
John Kelch, President
Jeanne E Kelch, Vice Pres
Luceille Rucker, Manager
EMP: 4
SQ FT: 6,000

SALES (est): 600K Privately Held
WEB: www.pumpmatic.com
SIC: 5047 3821 Instruments, surgical & medical; clinical laboratory instruments, except medical & dental

(G-8166)
ASSOCIATED MATERIALS LLC
Also Called: Alside Supply Center
3361 Needmore Rd (45414-4311)
PHONE...................937 236-5679
Dough Singleton, Manager
Tommie Walters, Manager
EMP: 5 Privately Held
WEB: www.associatedmaterials.com
SIC: 3444 5031 5211 Metal flooring & siding; lumber, plywood & millwork; door & window products
HQ: Associated Materials, Llc
3773 State Rd
Cuyahoga Falls OH 44223
330 929-1811

(G-8167)
ASTERENA CORPORATION
1413 Verna Ct (45458-9715)
PHONE...................937 605-6470
Sreeharshan Nambiar, President
Ponon Dileep Kumar, Vice Pres
Jayendran Moorkoth Arakkalath, Admin Sec
EMP: 3
SALES (est): 128.2K Privately Held
SIC: 7372 Utility computer software

(G-8168)
ATLAS PRODUCE LLC
104 Salem Ave (45406-5801)
P.O. Box 61091 (45406-9091)
PHONE...................937 223-1446
Sylvester Ballard,
EMP: 5
SALES (est): 223K Privately Held
WEB: www.sylresources.com
SIC: 2051 Bakery: wholesale or wholesale/retail combined

(G-8169)
ATS ASSEMBLY AND TEST INC
Advanced Assembly Automation
313 Mound St (45402-8370)
PHONE...................937 222-3030
Fax: 937 222-2931
John Hazelrigg, Purch Mgr
Robert Ussery, Engineer
Arnie Hinojosa, Sr Project Mgr
Bill Budde, Director
James Rice, Director
EMP: 395
SALES (corp-wide): 750.9MM Privately Held
WEB: www.assembly-testww.com
SIC: 3569 3825 Assembly machines, non-metalworking; instruments to measure electricity
HQ: Ats Assembly And Test, Inc.
313 Mound St
Dayton OH 45402
937 222-3030

(G-8170)
ATS ASSEMBLY AND TEST INC (HQ)
313 Mound St (45402-8370)
PHONE...................937 222-3030
David McAusland, Ch of Bd
Bob Bricker, Project Mgr
John Gajda, Project Mgr
Scott Harris, Project Mgr
John Hazelrigg, Materials Mgr
▲ EMP: 277
SQ FT: 140,000
SALES (est): 113.1MM
SALES (corp-wide): 750.9MM Privately Held
WEB: www.assembly-testww.com
SIC: 3599 Machine shop, jobbing & repair
PA: Ats Automation Tooling Systems Inc
730 Fountain St Suite 2b
Cambridge ON N3H 4
519 653-4483

(G-8171)
AUGUST INCORPORATED
354 Congress Park Dr (45459-4133)
PHONE...................937 434-2520
Lee Fister Jr, President

Judith W Fister, *Vice Pres*
David Idle, *Vice Pres*
Jane Luther, *CFO*
EMP: 20
SQ FT: 20,000
SALES (est): 2.6MM **Privately Held**
WEB: www.augustinc.com
SIC: 2521 Wood office furniture

(G-8172)
AUTO-VALVE INC
1707 Guenther Rd (45417-9398)
PHONE....................................937 854-3037
Fax: 937 854-3039
Raymond Clark, *President*
Tim Claude, *Mfg Mgr*
Richard Henderson, *Foreman/Supr*
Nick Schuyler, *Engineer*
Daniel M Guire, *Design Engr*
EMP: 38
SQ FT: 17,800
SALES (est): 7.4MM **Privately Held**
WEB: www.autovalve.com
SIC: 3728 3494 Aircraft parts & equipment; valves & pipe fittings

(G-8173)
AUTOMATION SYSTEMS DESIGNS INC
Also Called: A S D
6222 Webster St (45414-3438)
PHONE....................................937 387-0351
Fax: 937 387-0357
Sunny Kullar, *Principal*
Sukhi Kullar, *CFO*
EMP: 20
SQ FT: 17,000
SALES (est): 9.1MM **Privately Held**
WEB: www.asddayton.com
SIC: 3535 Robotic conveyors

(G-8174)
AUTOMATION TECHNOLOGY INC
1900 Troy St (45404-2194)
PHONE....................................937 233-6084
Fax: 937 233-7813
Robert Storar, *CEO*
Jeff Storar, *President*
N Chris Storar, *Corp Secy*
Joe Palcic, *Senior Buyer*
Shirley Minnix, *Buyer*
EMP: 25
SQ FT: 20,000
SALES (est): 5.3MM **Privately Held**
SIC: 3625 3825 3829 3823 Actuators, industrial; test equipment for electronic & electrical circuits; measuring & controlling devices; industrial instrmnts msrmnt display/control process variable

(G-8175)
AVION TOOL CORPORATION
2624 Keenan Ave (45414-4998)
P.O. Box 13551 (45413-0551)
PHONE....................................937 278-0779
Fax: 937 278-3672
Paul Molnar, *President*
EMP: 16 **EST:** 1947
SQ FT: 11,000
SALES (est): 1.7MM **Privately Held**
SIC: 3724 Aircraft engines & engine parts

(G-8176)
AWESOME YOGURT LLC
3337 Lenox Dr (45429-1509)
PHONE....................................937 643-0879
Naomi Fogel, *Owner*
EMP: 5
SALES (est): 348.8K **Privately Held**
SIC: 2024 Yogurt desserts, frozen

(G-8177)
B & P COMPANY INC
97 Compark Rd (45459-4801)
P.O. Box 41184 (45441-0184)
PHONE....................................937 298-0265
Fax: 937 298-8064
Margaret Wright, *President*
James Wright, *General Mgr*
Neal Phillips, *Manager*
EMP: 9
SQ FT: 13,000
SALES: 2MM **Privately Held**
WEB: www.frownies.com
SIC: 2844 Cosmetic preparations

(G-8178)
B C WILSON INC
85 Compark Rd (45459-4801)
PHONE....................................937 439-1866
Fax: 937 439-1986
EMP: 5
SQ FT: 6,000
SALES (est): 682.7K **Privately Held**
SIC: 3544 7389 Mfg Dies/Tools/Jigs/Fixtures Business Services

(G-8179)
B S F INC (PA)
8895 N Dixie Dr (45414-1803)
P.O. Box 459, Vandalia (45377-0459)
PHONE....................................937 890-6121
Fax: 937 890-0974
Kathryn Keel, *President*
Chris Bright, *Principal*
Jackie Frank, *Principal*
Eric Metzger, *Principal*
Sarah Gayman, *Editor*
EMP: 10 **EST:** 1974
SQ FT: 2,000
SALES (est): 1.8MM **Privately Held**
SIC: 3498 3568 Couplings, pipe: fabricated from purchased pipe; couplings, shaft: rigid, flexible, universal joint, etc.

(G-8180)
BACKGROUND MUSIC & SOUND INC
8529 N Dixie Dr Ste 325 (45414-2497)
PHONE....................................937 898-9871
Fax: 937 898-9871
Sal Chirico Sr, *President*
EMP: 8
SQ FT: 2,900
SALES (est): 670K **Privately Held**
SIC: 1731 5065 3651 Sound equipment specialization; sound equipment, electronic; intercommunication equipment, electronic; sound reproducing equipment

(G-8181)
BAR CODES UNLIMITED INC
683 Miamisburg Ctrvl 21 Ste (45459)
PHONE....................................937 434-2633
Jay Dring, *President*
Karen Dring, *Vice Pres*
Craig Dring, *Treasurer*
Anthony Scrimenti, *VP Sales*
Ryan Hartley, *Technology*
EMP: 4
SALES (est): 620K **Privately Held**
WEB: www.bcuinc.com
SIC: 5046 2759 8742 Commercial equipment; labels & seals: printing; industry specialist consultants

(G-8182)
BASETEK LLC
35 Irongate Park Dr (45459-4616)
PHONE....................................877 712-2273
EMP: 4
SALES (corp-wide): 5MM **Privately Held**
SIC: 5032 3531 Concrete & cinder block; construction machinery
PA: Basetek, Llc
14975 White Rd
Middlefield OH 44062
877 712-2273

(G-8183)
BAUMER HHS CORP
10570 Success Ln (45458-3561)
PHONE....................................937 886-3160
Joe Madren, *President*
Nadeem Jadon, *General Mgr*
Kim Deady, *Controller*
Kim Rupert, *Controller*
Brian Bohm, *Sales Mgr*
EMP: 21
SQ FT: 9,000
SALES: 9.6MM **Privately Held**
WEB: www.hhsamerica.com
SIC: 3579 Binding machines, plastic & adhesive
HQ: Baumer Hhs Gmbh
Adolf-Dembach-Str. 19
Krefeld 47829
215 144-020

(G-8184)
BELTON FOODS
2701 Thunderhawk Ct (45414-3445)
P.O. Box 13605 (45413-0605)
PHONE....................................937 890-7768
Fax: 937 890-7780
David V Sipos, *President*
Ted Dorow, *Vice Pres*
Cindy Gillespie, *Vice Pres*
Don Fox, *Sales Mgr*
Eleanor Sipos, *Shareholder*
EMP: 27 **EST:** 1949
SQ FT: 24,800
SALES (est): 10.2MM **Privately Held**
SIC: 2087 2086 2035 Concentrates, drink; syrups, flavoring (except drink); bottled & canned soft drinks; pickles, sauces & salad dressings

(G-8185)
BENCHWORKS JEWELERS INC
133 E Franklin St (45459-5915)
PHONE....................................937 439-4243
Fax: 937 439-4120
George Steberl, *President*
Tari Steberl, *Vice Pres*
EMP: 4
SQ FT: 1,462
SALES (est): 411K **Privately Held**
WEB: www.benchworksjewelers.com
SIC: 3911 5944 7631 Jewelry, precious metal; jewelry stores; jewelry repair services

(G-8186)
BETA INDUSTRIES INC (PA)
2860 Culver Ave (45429-3794)
PHONE....................................937 299-7385
Fax: 937 299-0468
William B Walcott, *President*
Carol Dunton, *Vice Pres*
Kenneth Walcott, *Vice Pres*
Wanda King, *Purchasing*
Maggie N Melton, *Finance*
EMP: 22
SQ FT: 12,600
SALES (est): 3.4MM **Privately Held**
SIC: 3599 Machine shop, jobbing & repair; custom machinery; electrical equipment & supplies

(G-8187)
BEVCLEAN PRODUCTS INC
3975 Dayton Park Dr (45414-4422)
PHONE....................................937 233-5000
Noel G Luhn, *President*
Darlene Siembida, *Manager*
Frank Luhn, *Director*
EMP: 3
SQ FT: 42,000
SALES (est): 417.9K **Privately Held**
SIC: 2842 Specialty cleaning preparations

(G-8188)
BIOFOCUS INC (PA)
3345 Old Salem Rd (45415-1232)
PHONE....................................937 890-3068
Onno Van De Stolpe, *CEO*
Daisy Hom, *Asst Sec*
EMP: 6
SALES: 16.4MM **Privately Held**
SIC: 2833 2899 Medicinals & botanicals; chemical preparations

(G-8189)
BLAIRS CNC TURNING INC
245 Leo St (45404-1005)
P.O. Box 2840 (45401-2840)
PHONE....................................937 461-1100
Fax: 937 461-6411
James Trochelman, *President*
Marina Trochelman, *Vice Pres*
EMP: 7
SQ FT: 13,100
SALES: 650K **Privately Held**
SIC: 3541 Lathes

(G-8190)
BLANG ACQUISITION LLC
Also Called: Kap Signs
1608 Kuntz Rd (45404-1234)
PHONE....................................937 223-2155
Fax: 937 223-7603
Dave Williams, *Sales Mgr*
John D Blang, *Mng Member*
Jack Brooks, *Manager*
EMP: 15
SQ FT: 12,000
SALES (est): 1.4MM **Privately Held**
WEB: www.kapsigns.com
SIC: 2499 5999 5199 3993 Signboards, wood; letters, wood; banners; decals; decals; posters; signs & advertising specialties

(G-8191)
BOOKFACTORY LLC
2302 S Edwin C Moses Blvd (45417-4662)
PHONE....................................937 226-7100
Fax: 614 388-5635
Judy Thaller, *Accounting Mgr*
Tessin Farmer, *Sales Executive*
Ashley Myers, *Sales Executive*
Robin Cordes, *Manager*
Samantha Gilliam, *Manager*
▼ **EMP:** 30
SQ FT: 20,000
SALES (est): 4.9MM **Privately Held**
SIC: 5942 2678 2731 2789 Book stores; memorandum books, notebooks & loose-leaf filler paper; book publishing; textbooks: publishing & printing; books: publishing & printing; bookbinding & related work

(G-8192)
BP PRODUCTS NORTH AMERICA INC
Also Called: B P Exploration
621 Brandt St (45404-2226)
PHONE....................................937 461-3621
Peter Whitson, *General Mgr*
Allen Cook, *Manager*
EMP: 4
SALES (corp-wide): 183B **Privately Held**
WEB: www.bpproductsnorthamerica.com
SIC: 2911 Petroleum refining
HQ: Bp Products North America Inc.
501 Westlake Park Blvd
Houston TX 77079
281 366-2000

(G-8193)
BRANHAM MOTORSPORTS LLC
1690 Thomas Paine Pkwy (45459-2539)
PHONE....................................937 428-6040
Daniel J Branham, *President*
EMP: 4 **EST:** 2011
SALES (est): 290K **Privately Held**
SIC: 3799 All terrain vehicles (ATV)

(G-8194)
BRIDGITS BATH LLC
1226 Pursell Ave (45420-1974)
PHONE....................................937 259-1960
Joan Speicher,
Anne Ruhland,
Lawrence Speicher,
EMP: 7 **EST:** 2008
SALES (est): 480K **Privately Held**
SIC: 3261 7389 Soap dishes, vitreous china; bathroom accessories/fittings, vitreous china or earthenware;

(G-8195)
BRIGHT EYES INC (PA)
Also Called: Bright Eyes Optical
5135 N Dixie Dr (45414-3944)
PHONE....................................937 277-9991
Mark Willinger, *President*
EMP: 3
SQ FT: 3,000
SALES (est): 392.8K **Privately Held**
SIC: 3827 Lenses, optical: all types except ophthalmic

(G-8196)
BRINKMAN TOOL & DIE INC
325 Kiser St (45404-1621)
PHONE....................................937 222-1161
Fax: 937 222-2079
John Brinkman Sr, *President*
Charlene Brinkman, *Corp Secy*
John C Brinkman Jr, *Vice Pres*
Charles L Brinkman Sr, *Shareholder*
▲ **EMP:** 30 **EST:** 1913
SQ FT: 24,000
SALES (est): 4.8MM **Privately Held**
WEB: www.brinkmantool.com
SIC: 3544 Special dies & tools; jigs & fixtures; industrial molds

GEOGRAPHIC

(G-8197)
BROADWAY COMPANIES INC (PA)
6161 Ventnor Ave (45414-2651)
P.O. Box 13418 (45413-0418)
PHONE...........................937 890-1888
Fax: 937 890-9846
Karin Gaiser, *President*
Debra Doyle, *Vice Pres*
Earl Debinport, *Accounting Mgr*
Maressa Bokelman, *IT/INT Sup*
EMP: 23
SQ FT: 5,000
SALES: 3MM **Privately Held**
SIC: 3544 Industrial molds

(G-8198)
BROCKMAN JIG GRINDING SERVICE
1535 Stanley Ave (45404-1112)
P.O. Box 71, Englewood (45322-0071)
PHONE...........................937 220-9780
Fax: 937 220-9698
Rex Brockman, *Owner*
EMP: 3
SQ FT: 1,000
SALES: 100K **Privately Held**
SIC: 3599 7389 Grinding castings for the trade; grinding, precision: commercial or industrial

(G-8199)
BROWDER TOOL CO INC
Also Called: B T C
5924 Executive Blvd (45424-1419)
PHONE...........................937 233-6731
Gerald Kozuh, *President*
Dave Kozuh, *Corp Secy*
Betty Kozuh, *Vice Pres*
EMP: 5
SQ FT: 2,600
SALES (est): 350K **Privately Held**
SIC: 3544 Special dies & tools

(G-8200)
BT INVESTMENTS II INC
Also Called: Farquhar Heating and Air
601 Congress Park Dr (45459-4007)
P.O. Box 751475 (45475-1475)
PHONE...........................937 434-4321
William E O'Neill, *President*
Theresa Oneill, *Vice Pres*
EMP: 8
SALES (est): 572.8K **Privately Held**
SIC: 1711 4961 3444 1799 Plumbing, heating, air-conditioning contractors; warm air heating & air conditioning contractor; steam supply systems, including geothermal; elbows, for air ducts, stovepipes, etc.: sheet metal; insulation of pipes & boilers

(G-8201)
BTA ENTERPRISES INC
4090 Little Richmond Rd (45417-9453)
PHONE...........................937 277-0881
Fax: 937 277-2420
Billy T Atherton, *President*
Dusty Atherton, *Vice Pres*
EMP: 7 EST: 1984
SALES (est): 940K **Privately Held**
SIC: 3089 Automotive parts, plastic

(G-8202)
BUDDE SHEET METAL WORKS INC (PA)
305 Leo St (45404-1083)
PHONE...........................937 224-0868
Fax: 937 224-1356
Thomas Budde, *President*
William R Budde Jr, *Corp Secy*
Stephen L Budde, *Vice Pres*
Bill Campbell, *Project Mgr*
Neil Pardo, *Foreman/Supr*
EMP: 25
SQ FT: 20,000
SALES: 7.8MM **Privately Held**
WEB: www.buddesheetmetal.com
SIC: 1761 3444 1711 Sheet metalwork; sheet metalwork; plumbing, heating, air-conditioning contractors

(G-8203)
C & M RUBBER CO INC
414 Littell Ave (45419-3608)
PHONE...........................937 299-2782
Fax: 937 299-2790
James McCloskey, *President*
Eric Weber, *Vice Pres*
EMP: 15
SQ FT: 10,000
SALES: 1MM **Privately Held**
WEB: www.cmrubber.com
SIC: 3069 Molded rubber products

(G-8204)
C G EGLI INC
515 Springfield St (45403-1246)
P.O. Box 82 (45404-0082)
PHONE...........................937 254-8898
Fax: 937 298-1941
Christian G Egli, *President*
EMP: 5
SQ FT: 14,000
SALES (est): 751.4K **Privately Held**
SIC: 3599 Machine & other job shop work

(G-8205)
C-LINK ENTERPRISES LLC
Also Called: Southern Ohio Kitchens
1825 Webster St (45404-1147)
PHONE...........................937 222-2829
Lisa J Buckner,
Lisa Buckner,
Nathan Buckner,
EMP: 10
SQ FT: 25,000
SALES: 1.2MM **Privately Held**
WEB: www.johnrgardner.com
SIC: 1521 2514 5722 General remodeling, single-family houses; kitchen cabinets: metal; kitchens, complete (sinks, cabinets, etc.)

(G-8206)
CAC ENERGY LTD
1025 N Main St (45405-4213)
PHONE...........................937 867-5593
Ifeanyi Nwanoro, *CEO*
Chikere Umez-Eronini, *COO*
Charles Opoku Fordjour, *CFO*
EMP: 3 EST: 2015
SALES (est): 170K **Privately Held**
SIC: 1311 5172 6799 8742 Crude petroleum & natural gas; diesel fuel; engine fuels & oils; commodity contract trading companies; management consulting services

(G-8207)
CADENZA ENTERPRISES LLC
Also Called: Sgo Designer Glass
6533 Halberd Ct (45459-1308)
PHONE...........................937 428-6058
John Root,
EMP: 5
SALES: 100K **Privately Held**
SIC: 3231 Products of purchased glass

(G-8208)
CALVIN LANIER
5363 Birdland Ave (45417-8848)
PHONE...........................937 952-4221
Calvin Lanier, *Owner*
EMP: 25
SALES (est): 898K **Privately Held**
SIC: 3423 7389 Plumbers' hand tools;

(G-8209)
CAPITAL CORE INC
1025 N Keowee St (45404-1519)
PHONE...........................800 223-1884
Len Twansmith, *Principal*
Ben Brinkman, *Manager*
EMP: 3
SALES (corp-wide): 17.1MM **Privately Held**
SIC: 3714 Motor vehicle transmissions, drive assemblies & parts
PA: Capital Core, Inc.
    3790 E 5th Ave
    Columbus OH 43219
    614 464-1884

(G-8210)
CARGILL INCORPORATED
3201 Needmore Rd (45414-4321)
PHONE...........................937 236-1971
Wade Richards, *Maint Spvr*
Rick Arnett, *Research*
Cecilia Vocke, *Human Res Dir*
Sheila Willhoite, *Branch Mgr*
EMP: 49
SALES (corp-wide): 107.1B **Privately Held**
WEB: www.cargill.com
SIC: 2046 2087 2041 Corn starch; corn syrup, dried or unmixed; flavoring extracts & syrups; flour & other grain mill products
PA: Cargill, Incorporated
    15407 Mcginty Rd W
    Wayzata MN 55391
    952 742-7575

(G-8211)
CARR SUPPLY CO
4800 Webster St (45414-4850)
PHONE...........................937 276-2555
Fax: 937 276-9540
Steve Shepherd, *Principal*
Steve Werling, *Manager*
EMP: 8
SALES (corp-wide): 2.7B **Privately Held**
SIC: 5999 5722 5074 3432 Plumbing & heating supplies; household appliance stores; plumbing & hydronic heating supplies; plumbing fixture fittings & trim
HQ: Carr Supply Co.
    1415 Old Leonard Ave
    Columbus OH 43219
    614 252-7883

(G-8212)
CARRIER CORPORATION
6050 Milo Rd (45414-3418)
PHONE...........................937 275-0645
Tim Spencer, *Project Mgr*
Dan Reekers, *Manager*
Kim Cotter, *Manager*
EMP: 24
SALES (corp-wide): 57.2B **Publicly Held**
WEB: www.carrier.com
SIC: 3585 1711 Refrigeration & heating equipment; heating & air conditioning contractors
HQ: Carrier Corporation
    17900 Bee Line Hwy
    Jupiter FL 33478
    561 796-2000

(G-8213)
CARSON-SAEKS INC (PA)
Also Called: Karen Carson Creations
2601 Timber Ln (45414-4733)
P.O. Box 13297 (45413-0297)
PHONE...........................937 278-5311
Fax: 937 278-9848
William Smith, *Ch of Bd*
Terrence Mollaun, *President*
Paul Lynch, *General Mgr*
Jeff Smith, *Vice Pres*
Laura Bowman, *Manager*
▲ EMP: 41
SQ FT: 20,000
SALES (est): 7.2MM **Privately Held**
WEB: www.karencarson.com
SIC: 2869 Perfume materials, synthetic

(G-8214)
CASSIS PACKAGING CO
1235 Mccook Ave (45404-2812)
PHONE...........................937 223-8563
Fax: 937 223-6535
Sheila Cassis, *President*
William Wilson, *General Mgr*
Cassandra Cassis, *Vice Pres*
EMP: 13 EST: 1957
SQ FT: 26,000
SALES: 1MM **Privately Held**
WEB: www.cassispackaging.com
SIC: 2449 4783 Rectangular boxes & crates, wood; crating goods for shipping; packing goods for shipping

(G-8215)
CATECH INC
80 Westpark Rd A (45459-4813)
PHONE...........................937 439-0432
Fax: 937 439-9251
Kevin Hickey, *CEO*
Lanny K Wiggins, *President*
Tim Hauxwell, *Treasurer*
Stephen Blatchford, *Admin Sec*
EMP: 21

SQ FT: 8,000
SALES (est): 1.7MM **Privately Held**
WEB: www.endolite.com
SIC: 3842 5999 Prosthetic appliances; orthopedic & prosthesis applications

(G-8216)
CB MANUFACTURING & SLS CO INC
4475 Infirmary Rd (45449)
PHONE...........................937 866-5986
Charles Biehn, *Manager*
EMP: 60
SALES (corp-wide): 41.4MM **Privately Held**
WEB: www.cbmfg.com
SIC: 3423 Hand & edge tools
PA: Cb Manufacturing & Sales Co., Inc.
    4455 Infirmary Rd
    Miamisburg OH 45342
    937 866-5986

(G-8217)
CECO MACHINE & TOOL
5727 Webster St (45414-3520)
PHONE...........................937 264-3047
Steve Beck, *Owner*
Denis Beck, *Co-Owner*
Greg Beck, *Manager*
EMP: 5
SQ FT: 5,000
SALES (est): 1MM **Privately Held**
SIC: 3315 Steel wire & related products

(G-8218)
CELSTAR GROUP INC (PA)
40 N Main St Ste 1730 (45423-1002)
PHONE...........................937 224-1730
Fax: 937 224-9455
Robert H Brethen, *President*
Jonas Gruenberg, *Admin Sec*
EMP: 2
SALES (est): 26.5MM **Privately Held**
SIC: 3229 Glass fiber products

(G-8219)
CEMEX MATERIALS LLC
1504 N Gettysburg Ave (45417-9518)
PHONE...........................937 268-6706
Anthony Cox, *Manager*
B Holloway, *Manager*
EMP: 100
SALES (corp-wide): 12B **Privately Held**
WEB: www.rinkermaterials.com
SIC: 3272 5211 Concrete products; masonry materials & supplies
HQ: Cemex Materials, Llc
    1501 Belvedere Rd
    West Palm Beach FL 33406
    561 833-5555

(G-8220)
CEMEX MATERIALS LLC
4385 N James H Mcgee Blvd (45417-9537)
PHONE...........................937 268-6706
Dennis Paulsgrove, *Branch Mgr*
EMP: 20
SALES (corp-wide): 12B **Privately Held**
WEB: www.rinkermaterials.com
SIC: 3272 Concrete products; furniture, church: concrete
HQ: Cemex Materials, Llc
    1501 Belvedere Rd
    West Palm Beach FL 33406
    561 833-5555

(G-8221)
CENTERLINE TOOL & MACHINE
1330 E 2nd St (45403-1021)
PHONE...........................937 222-3600
Fax: 937 222-3610
Michael A Gambrell, *Owner*
EMP: 5
SQ FT: 8,000
SALES: 700K **Privately Held**
SIC: 3544 3599 Forms (molds), for foundry & plastics working machinery; industrial molds; machine & other job shop work

(G-8222)
CERTIFIED HEAT TREATING INC (PA)
4475 Infirmary Rd (45449)
P.O. Box 354
PHONE..............................937 866-0245
Fax: 937 865-5785
Joseph Biehn, *President*
Larry Destro, *CFO*
David Livingood, *Human Res Mgr*
Vernon Fravier, *Info Tech Mgr*
EMP: 20 **EST:** 1970
SQ FT: 20,000
SALES (est): 2.4MM **Privately Held**
WEB: www.certifiedindustrialservices.com
SIC: 3398 Metal heat treating

(G-8223)
CERTIFIED SERVICE INC
2876 Culver Ave (45429-3726)
PHONE..............................937 643-0393
Donald Groves, *President*
Mike Groves, *Vice Pres*
EMP: 5 **EST:** 1959
SQ FT: 15,000
SALES: 520K **Privately Held**
WEB: www.certifiedservice.com
SIC: 3585 Compressors for refrigeration & air conditioning equipment

(G-8224)
CESO INC (PA)
8534 Yankee St Ste 2b (45458-1889)
PHONE..............................937 435-8584
Fax: 937 435-3307
David Oakes, *President*
James I Weprin, *Principal*
Tina Gunter, *Human Res Dir*
Chris Broshears, *Manager*
EMP: 51
SQ FT: 30,000
SALES (est): 15.7MM **Privately Held**
SIC: 8711 3674 8712 Civil engineering; light emitting diodes; architectural services

(G-8225)
CHAOS ENTERTAINMENT
Also Called: CD / Dvd Distribution
7570 Mount Whitney St (45424-6944)
PHONE..............................937 520-5260
Melvin Higgins,
EMP: 8
SALES: 10K **Privately Held**
SIC: 3561 Pumps & pumping equipment

(G-8226)
CHECKPOINT SYSTEMS INC
7620 Mcewen Rd (45459-3908)
PHONE..............................937 281-1304
George Babich Jr, *Branch Mgr*
EMP: 128
SALES (corp-wide): 188.4K **Privately Held**
SIC: 3699 Security control equipment & systems
HQ: Checkpoint Systems, Inc.
　　101 Wolf Dr
　　West Deptford NJ 08086
　　856 848-1800

(G-8227)
CHELSEA MACHINE SERVICE INC
2401 Valley Pike Ste 1 (45404-2686)
PHONE..............................937 233-6330
Pete Zimmerman, *Manager*
EMP: 5
SALES (corp-wide): 432.9K **Privately Held**
SIC: 3599 7699 Machine shop, jobbing & repair; industrial machinery & equipment repair
PA: Chelsea Machine Service Inc
　　2651 Camino Pl W
　　Dayton OH 45420
　　937 233-6330

(G-8228)
CHEMCORE INC
20 Madison St (45402-2106)
P.O. Box 802 (45401-0802)
PHONE..............................937 228-6118
Fax: 937 395-1104
Mike Klaus, *CEO*

Reiff Lorenz, *President*
Geoffrey Lorenz, *Vice Pres*
Lewis McBride, *Mfg Dir*
Thomas Borchers, *Treasurer*
EMP: 10
SALES (est): 1.5MM **Privately Held**
SIC: 5169 2869 Chemical additives; industrial organic chemicals

(G-8229)
CINDERELLA
2700 Mmsburg Cntrville Rd (45459)
PHONE..............................937 312-9969
James Paek, *Manager*
EMP: 3
SALES (est): 232.4K **Privately Held**
SIC: 2311 Tuxedos: made from purchased materials

(G-8230)
CINTAS CORPORATION NO 2
903 Brandt St Bldg A (45404-2231)
PHONE..............................937 236-1506
James Lois, *Manager*
EMP: 4
SALES (corp-wide): 4.9B **Publicly Held**
WEB: www.cintas-corp.com
SIC: 3589 Shredders, industrial & commercial
HQ: Cintas Corporation No. 2
　　6800 Cintas Blvd
　　Mason OH 45040

(G-8231)
CIRCUIT CENTER
4738 Gateway Cir (45440-1724)
PHONE..............................513 435-2131
Fax: 937 435-7698
Michael Kerr, *Principal*
EMP: 7
SALES (est): 664.6K **Privately Held**
SIC: 3672 Printed circuit boards

(G-8232)
CITIZENS USA
3651 Wright Way Rd (45424-5165)
PHONE..............................937 280-2001
Pendra Snyder, *Personnel Exec*
EMP: 3
SALES (est): 106.8K **Privately Held**
SIC: 2711 Newspapers, publishing & printing

(G-8233)
CNR MARKETING LTD
Also Called: Proforma Cnr Marketing
3149 Far Hills Ave (45429-2511)
PHONE..............................937 293-1030
Connie Muzechuk, *Vice Pres*
Nicole Merkle, *VP Sls/Mktg*
Ron Muzechuk, *Mng Member*
EMP: 5
SQ FT: 775
SALES: 1.2MM **Privately Held**
SIC: 2759 5199 Commercial printing; advertising specialties

(G-8234)
COACH TOOL & DIE INC
5728 Webster St (45414-3521)
PHONE..............................937 890-4716
Dave Hollon, *President*
Gregg Kopp, *Vice Pres*
EMP: 6
SALES: 900K **Privately Held**
SIC: 3544 Jigs & fixtures

(G-8235)
COCA-COLA BOTTLING CO CNSLD
1000 Coca Cola Blvd (45424-6375)
PHONE..............................937 878-5000
Fax: 937 879-1005
Bob Tiootson, *Manager*
Diana Huffman, *Manager*
EMP: 95
SALES (corp-wide): 3.1B **Publicly Held**
WEB: www.colasic.net
SIC: 5149 2086 Soft drinks; carbonated beverages, nonalcoholic: bottled & canned
PA: Coca-Cola Bottling Co. Consolidated
　　4100 Coca Cola Plz # 100
　　Charlotte NC 28211
　　704 557-4400

(G-8236)
COLBY WOODWORKING INC
1912 Lucille Dr (45404-1109)
P.O. Box 138 (45404-0138)
PHONE..............................937 224-7676
Steven L Colby, *President*
EMP: 5
SALES (est): 288.3K **Privately Held**
SIC: 2499 1751 Decorative wood & woodwork; cabinet building & installation

(G-8237)
COMBINED TECH GROUP INC
6061 Milo Rd (45414-3417)
PHONE..............................937 274-4866
Fax: 937 274-1881
Kurtis Vanburen, *President*
Gary Mayo, *Vice Pres*
Tina Vanburen, *Vice Pres*
Brian Greene, *Opers Mgr*
Chris Bautista, *Engineer*
EMP: 28
SQ FT: 50,000
SALES (est): 6.2MM **Privately Held**
WEB: www.comtechgrp.com
SIC: 3549 Assembly machines, including robotic

(G-8238)
COMMCONNECT
915 E Central Ave (45449-1820)
PHONE..............................937 414-0505
Fax: 937 859-4450
Scott Dilworth, *Principal*
EMP: 7
SALES (est): 883.7K **Privately Held**
SIC: 3351 Wire, copper & copper alloy

(G-8239)
COMMERCIAL MTAL FBRICATORS INC
150 Commerce Park Dr (45404-1273)
PHONE..............................937 233-4911
Fax: 937 233-8960
Patrick Dakin, *President*
James D Utrecht, *Principal*
Molly Dakin, *Controller*
EMP: 40 **EST:** 1954
SALES (est): 12.8MM **Privately Held**
WEB: www.cmfweb.com
SIC: 3441 3444 3443 Fabricated structural metal; sheet metalwork; fabricated plate work (boiler shop)

(G-8240)
COMPOSITE ADVANTAGE LLC
401 Kiser St (45404-1639)
PHONE..............................937 723-9031
Andy Loff, *Vice Pres*
Josh Driver, *Plant Mgr*
Brian Patrick, *Opers Mgr*
Scott Reeve, *Mng Member*
Lori Bishop, *Manager*
EMP: 50
SQ FT: 46,000
SALES: 7MM **Privately Held**
SIC: 3089 Plastic & fiberglass tanks

(G-8241)
COMPOSITE TECHNOLOGIES CO LLC
401 N Keowee St (45404-1602)
PHONE..............................937 228-2880
Missy Hindman, *Purch Agent*
Mary Serrano, *Purch Agent*
Nick Pitstick, *Engineer*
Ron Richter, *Engineer*
Sharon Harrington, *Human Res Mgr*
EMP: 80
SQ FT: 100,000
SALES (est): 16.8MM
SALES (corp-wide): 130.1MM **Privately Held**
WEB: www.soininternational.com
SIC: 3089 Plastic containers, except foam
PA: Soin International, Llc
　　1129 Miamsbg Ctrvl Rd 1 Ste
　　Dayton OH 45449
　　937 427-7646

(G-8242)
CONTAINER MANUFACTURING LTD
6450 Poe Ave Ste 511 (45414-2677)
P.O. Box 750455 (45475-0455)
PHONE..............................937 264-2370
Ralph P Stodd, *President*
James Wilkins, *Exec VP*
EMP: 5
SQ FT: 2,100
SALES (est): 738K **Privately Held**
SIC: 3411 Beer cans, metal; beverage cans, metal: except beer

(G-8243)
CONTECH BRIDGE SOLUTIONS LLC
Also Called: Bridgetek
7941 New Carlisle Pike (45424-1507)
PHONE..............................937 878-2170
Fax: 937 878-8780
Jim Feltner, *Manager*
EMP: 12 **Privately Held**
SIC: 3272 Concrete products
HQ: Contech Bridge Solutions Llc
　　9025 Cntrpinte Dr Ste 400
　　West Chester OH 45069

(G-8244)
COUCH BUSINESS DEVELOPMENT INC
Also Called: Fordyce Custom Finishing
32 Bates St (45402-1326)
PHONE..............................937 253-1099
David Couch, *President*
EMP: 16
SQ FT: 49,250
SALES: 1MM **Privately Held**
SIC: 2541 2491 1751 Display fixtures, wood; store fixtures, wood; millwork, treated wood; store fixture installation

(G-8245)
COX MEDIA GROUP OHIO INC (DH)
1611 S Main St (45409-2547)
PHONE..............................937 225-2000
Fax: 937 225-7352
Emily Chambers, *President*
Rick Cassano, *Editor*
Michelle Everhart, *Editor*
Michelle Fong, *Editor*
Rick Gillette, *Editor*
EMP: 550
SQ FT: 150,000
SALES (est): 135.3MM
SALES (corp-wide): 32.4B **Privately Held**
WEB: www.daytondailynews.com
SIC: 2711 Newspapers, publishing & printing

(G-8246)
COX NEWSPAPERS LLC
Also Called: Dayton Daily News
1611 S Main St (45409-2547)
PHONE..............................937 225-2000
John M Dyer, *Branch Mgr*
EMP: 60
SALES (corp-wide): 32.4B **Privately Held**
SIC: 2711 Newspapers
HQ: Cox Newspapers, Inc.
　　6205 Peachtree Dunwoody
　　Atlanta GA 30328

(G-8247)
COX PUBLISHING HQ
1611 S Main St (45409-2547)
PHONE..............................937 225-2000
Michael Joseph, *Principal*
Marc Pendleton, *Editor*
Mary Mendenhall, *Controller*
Ron Fowler, *Consultant*
EMP: 9
SALES (est): 643.3K **Privately Held**
SIC: 2741 Miscellaneous publishing

(G-8248)
CREATIVE DESIGN MARBLE INC
7901 S Suburban Rd (45458-2702)
PHONE..............................937 434-8892
Fax: 937 434-8892
Eric Maxel, *President*
Paul M Maxel, *Vice Pres*

Zelda Maxel, *Treasurer*
EMP: 5
SQ FT: 4,000
SALES (est): 410K **Privately Held**
SIC: 3281 Cut stone & stone products;
marble, building: cut & shaped; granite,
cut & shaped

(G-8249)
CREATIVE FOAM DAYTON MOLD
3337 N Dixie Dr (45414-5645)
PHONE....................937 279-9987
EMP: 4 **EST:** 2013
SALES (est): 268.4K **Privately Held**
SIC: 3544 Industrial molds

(G-8250)
CREATIVE IMPRESSIONS INC
4611 Gateway Cir (45440-1713)
PHONE....................937 435-5296
Fax: 937 435-0544
Dennis C Carter, *President*
Linda S Carter, *Vice Pres*
EMP: 10
SQ FT: 7,500
SALES (est): 2.2MM **Privately Held**
SIC: 2752 Commercial printing, litho-
graphic

(G-8251)
CRG PLASTICS INC
2661 Culver Ave (45429-3721)
PHONE....................937 298-2025
Fax: 937 298-8074
Jerry Wenzke, *President*
Nancy Wenzke, *Treasurer*
Darlene Baker, *Office Mgr*
▲ **EMP:** 11
SQ FT: 8,000
SALES: 1.1MM **Privately Held**
SIC: 2821 3089 Polytetrafluoroethylene
resins (teflon); molding primary plastic

(G-8252)
CRITICAL PATIENT CARE INC
4738 Gateway Cir Ste B (45440-1724)
PHONE....................937 434-5455
Marie Cosgrove, *CEO*
▲ **EMP:** 3
SQ FT: 2,000
SALES (est): 431.6K **Privately Held**
SIC: 3845 Electromedical equipment

(G-8253)
CRYSTAL SPIRITS LLC
827 S Patterson Blvd (45402-2622)
PHONE....................937 228-0201
Tom Rabasek, *Managing Prtnr*
Chris Finke, *Partner*
Jim Rabasek, *Partner*
Marty Clarke, *CFO*
EMP: 5 **EST:** 2010
SALES (est): 343.9K **Privately Held**
SIC: 2085 Vodka (alcoholic beverage)

(G-8254)
CSV INC
Also Called: Beverage Dock
2080 E Rahn Rd (45440-2535)
PHONE....................937 438-1142
Cosmo Savino, *President*
EMP: 11
SALES (est): 1.1MM **Privately Held**
SIC: 2086 5921 Bottled & canned soft
drinks; beer (packaged)

(G-8255)
CTC PLASTICS
401 N Keowee St (45404-1602)
PHONE....................937 228-9184
Vishal Soin, *CEO*
Mike Dematto, *COO*
William R Senften, *CFO*
EMP: 306 **EST:** 2012
SALES: 32.8MM
SALES (corp-wide): 130.1MM **Privately
Held**
SIC: 3089 Injection molding of plastics
PA: Soin International, Llc
1129 Miamsbg Ctrvl Rd 1 Ste
Dayton OH 45449
937 427-7646

(G-8256)
CUDA COMPOSITES LLC
1788 S Metro Pkwy (45459-2520)
PHONE....................937 499-0360
David Havens, *President*
EMP: 5
SALES (est): 87.4K **Privately Held**
SIC: 3083 3728 Thermosetting laminates:
rods, tubes, plates & sheet; aircraft parts
& equipment

(G-8257)
CUSTOM BLIND CORPORATION
Also Called: Castle Blinds and Draperies
2895 Culver Ave (45429-3725)
PHONE....................937 643-2907
Fax: 937 643-1119
Douglas Mainard, *President*
EMP: 12
SQ FT: 6,000
SALES (est): 1.3MM **Privately Held**
SIC: 2591 5023 1521 Drapery hardware
& blinds & shades; vertical blinds; single-
family home remodeling, additions & re-
pairs

(G-8258)
**CUSTOM DUCT & SUPPLY CO
INC**
912 Cincinnati St (45417-4098)
PHONE....................937 228-2058
Jerry Sharp Sr, *President*
Martha Sharp, *Vice Pres*
EMP: 4
SQ FT: 6,000
SALES: 500K **Privately Held**
SIC: 5075 3444 Warm air heating & air
conditioning; ducts, sheet metal

(G-8259)
**CUSTOM MANUFACTURING
SOLUTIONS (PA)**
1129 Miamisburg Centervil (45449-4007)
PHONE....................937 372-0777
Raj Soin, *CEO*
Mike Collinsworth, *President*
Kim Upton, *Accountant*
EMP: 45
SQ FT: 82,000
SALES (est): 8.8MM **Privately Held**
WEB: www.cusmfgsol.com
SIC: 3449 Miscellaneous metalwork

(G-8260)
CUSTOM METAL SHEARING INC
80 Commerce Park Dr (45404-1212)
PHONE....................937 233-6950
Fax: 937 233-6951
Robert Colby, *President*
Kitty Colby, *Vice Pres*
Marlene Colby, *Vice Pres*
Richard Colby, *Vice Pres*
EMP: 13
SQ FT: 20,000
SALES: 1MM **Privately Held**
WEB: www.custommetalshearing.com
SIC: 3444 7389 2819 Sheet metalwork;
metal slitting & shearing; aluminum oxide

(G-8261)
CUSTOM NICKEL LLC
45 N Clinton St (45402-1346)
PHONE....................937 222-1995
Fax: 937 222-2060
Kevin M McHugh,
EMP: 6
SALES (est): 520K **Privately Held**
SIC: 3471 Electroplating & plating

(G-8262)
CYBER TECH TOOLING
9378 Taylorsville Rd (45424-6346)
PHONE....................937 320-2298
Robert J Seibert, *Principal*
EMP: 5
SALES (est): 598.6K **Privately Held**
SIC: 3545 Tools & accessories for machine
tools

(G-8263)
D & J MACHINE SHOP
442 Todd St (45403-2905)
PHONE....................937 256-2730
Chuck Lehman, *Owner*
EMP: 6

SQ FT: 2,200
SALES: 100K **Privately Held**
WEB: www.djmachineshop.com
SIC: 3599 Machine shop, jobbing & repair

(G-8264)
D C M INDUSTRIES INC
1901 E 5th St (45403-2347)
P.O. Box 1942 (45401-1942)
PHONE....................937 254-8500
Sam Nicolosi, *President*
EMP: 12
SQ FT: 10,000
SALES: 600K **Privately Held**
SIC: 3678 3679 Electronic connectors;
transducers, electrical

(G-8265)
DAISYS PILLOWS LLC
Also Called: Manfacturing
4694 Free Pike (45416-1200)
PHONE....................937 776-6968
Daisy Peterson,
EMP: 3
SALES (est): 201.5K **Privately Held**
SIC: 3949 Sporting & athletic goods

(G-8266)
DAVID ESRATI
Also Called: Next Wave Marketing Innovation
100 Bonner St (45410-1306)
PHONE....................937 228-4433
Fax: 937 228-4111
David Esrati, *Owner*
Paul Stebel, *Administration*
EMP: 3
SQ FT: 1,700
SALES: 350K **Privately Held**
WEB: www.the-next-wave.com
SIC: 7311 7336 8742 3993 Advertising
agencies; graphic arts & related design;
marketing consulting services; signs &
advertising specialties; commercial pho-
tography; motion picture & video produc-
tion

(G-8267)
DAY-HIO PRODUCTS INC
709 Webster St (45404-1527)
PHONE....................937 445-0782
Fax: 937 445-0721
John L Lenz, *President*
Harley Hilderbrandt, *Manager*
▲ **EMP:** 20
SQ FT: 15,000
SALES (est): 2.5MM **Privately Held**
SIC: 3451 Screw machine products

(G-8268)
DAYTON BAG & BURLAP CO
448 Huffman Ave (45403-2506)
PHONE....................937 253-1722
Fax: 937 253-1726
Dave Barcus, *Branch Mgr*
EMP: 10
SALES (corp-wide): 41.2MM **Privately
Held**
SIC: 4225 2299 General warehousing &
storage; burlap, jute
PA: The Dayton Bag & Burlap Co
322 Davis Ave
Dayton OH 45403
937 258-8000

(G-8269)
DAYTON BINDERY SERVICE INC
3757 Inpark Dr (45414-4417)
PHONE....................937 235-3111
Fax: 937 235-5070
Charles Bridges, *CEO*
Kimberley Mikesell, *President*
Marianne Keadey, *Purch Mgr*
Pat Behnken, *Controller*
EMP: 20
SALES (est): 1.1MM **Privately Held**
SIC: 2789 Bookbinding & related work

(G-8270)
DAYTON CITY PAPER NEW LLC
Also Called: Impact Weekly
126 N Main St Ste 240 (45402-1766)
PHONE....................937 222-8855
Fax: 937 222-6113
Paul Noah, *Publisher*
Mehdi Adineh, *Mng Member*
Reach Dayton, *Director*

EMP: 10
SALES (est): 670.8K **Privately Held**
WEB: www.impactweekly.com
SIC: 2711 Newspapers

(G-8271)
**DAYTON CLUTCH & JOINT INC
(PA)**
2005 Troy St 1 (45404-2936)
P.O. Box 163 (45404-0163)
PHONE....................937 236-9770
Fax: 937 236-4987
Keith Knight, *President*
Foyd Carlotton, *Manager*
Nancy Knight, *Admin Sec*
EMP: 16 **EST:** 1956
SQ FT: 16,000
SALES: 3.4MM **Privately Held**
WEB: www.daytonclutch.com
SIC: 3714 Motor vehicle parts & acces-
sories

(G-8272)
DAYTON COATING TECH LLC
1926 E Siebenthaler Ave (45414-5334)
PHONE....................937 278-2060
Fax: 937 278-2061
Bethany Paxson, *Business Mgr*
George Korenyi-Both,
EMP: 6
SQ FT: 15,000
SALES (est): 951.3K **Privately Held**
WEB: www.webdct.com
SIC: 3479 Etching & engraving

(G-8273)
**DAYTON FORGING HEAT
TREATING**
215 N Findlay St (45403-1200)
P.O. Box 1629 (45401-1629)
PHONE....................937 253-4126
Fax: 937 253-0409
Eric Wilson, *President*
Phyllis Todd, *Vice Pres*
Martha Todd Wilson, *Vice Pres*
Richard Markham, *Controller*
Justin Moore, *Accounting Mgr*
EMP: 65
SQ FT: 100,000
SALES (est): 23.6MM **Privately Held**
WEB: www.daytonforging.com
SIC: 3462 3398 Iron & steel forgings; ma-
chinery forgings, ferrous; metal heat treat-
ing

(G-8274)
DAYTON FRUIT TREE LABEL CO
Also Called: Dayton Garden Labels
1225 Ray St (45404-1656)
PHONE....................937 223-4650
Fax: 937 223-7066
Richard Joyner, *President*
Bryan Rosencrance, *Accounts Exec*
▲ **EMP:** 2 **EST:** 1898
SQ FT: 8,000
SALES: 1MM **Privately Held**
WEB: www.daytongardenlabels.com
SIC: 2671 Packaging paper & plastics film,
coated & laminated

(G-8275)
DAYTON GEAR & TOOL CO INC
500 Fame Rd (45449-2387)
PHONE....................937 866-4327
Fax: 937 866-0408
Thomas R Baird, *President*
Dan Ervin, *General Mgr*
Jerry Scott, *Project Mgr*
Adam Baird, *Opers Staff*
Joyce Thomas, *Office Mgr*
EMP: 20 **EST:** 1946
SQ FT: 3,000
SALES (est): 5.8MM **Privately Held**
WEB: www.daytongear.com
SIC: 3566 Gears, power transmission, ex-
cept automotive

(G-8276)
**DAYTON HAWKER
CORPORATION**
2844 Culver Ave (45429-3726)
PHONE....................937 293-8147
Fax: 937 293-9351
William Darrow, *President*
▲ **EMP:** 10

SQ FT: 12,000
SALES (est): 1.8MM **Privately Held**
WEB: www.hawkermfg.com
SIC: 3553 3841 3915 Lathes, wood turning: including accessories; forceps, surgical; pin stems

(G-8277)
DAYTON LAMINA
CORPORATION (DH)
Also Called: Anchor Lamina America
500 Progress Rd (45449-2326)
P.O. Box 39 (45449)
PHONE....................937 859-5111
David Turpin, *President*
John Vecore, *General Mgr*
Rick Chapman, *Regional Mgr*
James Whitaker, *Plant Supt*
Paul Coddington, *Project Mgr*
EMP: 3
SALES (est): 274.7MM
SALES (corp-wide): 2B **Privately Held**
SIC: 3544 6719 Special dies, tools, jigs & fixtures; investment holding companies, except banks
HQ: Misumi Investment Usa Corporation
500 Progress Rd
Dayton OH 45449
937 859-5111

(G-8278)
DAYTON LASER & AESTHETIC
MEDIC
6611 Clyo Rd Ste E (45459-2785)
PHONE....................937 208-8282
Lisa Smith, *Principal*
EMP: 8
SALES (est): 679.3K **Privately Held**
SIC: 2834 8011 Medicines, capsuled or ampuled; physicians' office, including specialists

(G-8279)
DAYTON MAILING SERVICES
INC
100 S Keowee St (45402-2241)
P.O. Box 2436 (45401-2436)
PHONE....................937 222-5056
Fax: 937 222-2696
Christine Soward, *President*
Mark Kuns, *Accounts Exec*
Tom Cooper, *Manager*
Natalie Bisnow, *Info Tech Mgr*
Dennis Hale, *Info Tech Mgr*
EMP: 30
SQ FT: 100,000
SALES (est): 9MM **Privately Held**
WEB: www.daytonmailing.com
SIC: 7331 2759 Mailing service; commercial printing

(G-8280)
DAYTON MOLDED URETHANES
LLC
Also Called: D M U
3337 N Dixie Dr (45414-5645)
PHONE....................937 279-9987
Fax: 937 279-1910
William Palmer, *President*
Dennis McCreight, *Controller*
Joy Palmer, *Admin Sec*
EMP: 75
SQ FT: 50,000
SALES (est): 12MM
SALES (corp-wide): 186.8MM **Privately Held**
WEB: www.daypp.com
SIC: 3081 Unsupported plastics film & sheet
PA: Creative Foam Corporation
300 N Alloy Dr
Fenton MI 48430
574 546-4238

(G-8281)
DAYTON PATTERN INC
5591 Wadsworth Rd (45414-3446)
P.O. Box 13779 (45413-0779)
PHONE....................937 277-0761
Fax: 937 277-2414
Erik Zimmer, *President*
Janice Zimmer, *Corp Secy*
EMP: 6 **EST:** 1965
SQ FT: 7,000

SALES: 800K **Privately Held**
SIC: 3543 Industrial patterns

(G-8282)
DAYTON POLYMERIC
PRODUCTS INC
3337 N Dixie Dr (45414-5645)
PHONE....................937 279-9987
William Johnson, *Ch of Bd*
Loney Abney, *President*
Lisa S Pierce, *Principal*
Dennis McCreight, *Controller*
EMP: 60
SQ FT: 55,000
SALES (est): 7.3MM **Privately Held**
SIC: 3086 Plastics foam products

(G-8283)
DAYTON PRECISION PUNCH
4900 Webster St (45414-4831)
PHONE....................937 275-8700
Fax: 937 275-9522
Mike Casella, *Principal*
EMP: 5
SALES (est): 521.6K
SALES (corp-wide): 44.3MM **Privately Held**
SIC: 3545 Machine tool attachments & accessories
PA: Fc Industries, Inc.
4900 Webster St
Dayton OH 45414
937 275-8700

(G-8284)
DAYTON PROGRESS
CORPORATION (DH)
500 Progress Rd (45449-2351)
PHONE....................937 859-5111
Fax: 937 859-5353
David Turpin, *President*
Timothy Burkhart, *President*
John Vecore, *General Mgr*
Tommy Baughman, *Regional Mgr*
Rick Chapman, *Regional Mgr*
▲ **EMP:** 525
SALES (est): 203.5MM
SALES (corp-wide): 2B **Privately Held**
WEB: www.daytonpunch.com
SIC: 3544 3545 3495 3493 Punches, forming & stamping; machine tool accessories; wire springs; steel springs, except wire
HQ: Dayton Lamina Corporation
500 Progress Rd
Dayton OH 45449
937 859-5111

(G-8285)
DAYTON PROGRESS INTL CORP
500 Progress Rd (45449-2326)
PHONE....................937 859-5111
Alan Shaffer, *President*
Bill Mills, *Vice Pres*
David Turpin, *Vice Pres*
Randy S Wissinger, *Vice Pres*
Bob Hedrick, *Marketing Staff*
EMP: 6
SALES (est): 510K
SALES (corp-wide): 2B **Privately Held**
WEB: www.daytonpunch.com
SIC: 3544 Special dies, tools, jigs & fixtures
HQ: Dayton Progress Corporation
500 Progress Rd
Dayton OH 45449
937 859-5111

(G-8286)
DAYTON SAFE COMPANY
Also Called: A-Door Lock Shop
1803 Webster St Ste A (45404-1153)
PHONE....................937 461-3900
Fax: 937 461-4044
Elliot Nagler, *Ch of Bd*
Sara Nagler, *President*
EMP: 5 **EST:** 1968
SQ FT: 17,500
SALES (est): 610.2K **Privately Held**
SIC: 3499 7699 5999 Safes & vaults, metal; locksmith shop; vaults & safes

(G-8287)
DAYTON STENCIL WORKS
COMPANY
Also Called: Datono Products
113 E 2nd St (45402-1753)
P.O. Box 126 (45401-0126)
PHONE....................937 223-3233
Fax: 937 223-5301
Edward Jauch, *President*
David Jauch, *General Mgr*
Larry Horwath, *Vice Pres*
Mike Bertke, *Purch Agent*
John Jauch, *Treasurer*
EMP: 20
SQ FT: 18,000
SALES: 2MM **Privately Held**
WEB: www.daytonstencil.com
SIC: 3949 3953 3544 5085 Golf equipment; marking devices; special dies, tools, jigs & fixtures; industrial supplies

(G-8288)
DAYTON TOOL CO INC
1825 E 1st St (45403-1129)
PHONE....................937 222-5501
Fax: 937 222-5505
Larry Beam, *President*
Richard L Wiegand, *Vice Pres*
Elizabeth Jacoby, *Program Mgr*
EMP: 44 **EST:** 1950
SQ FT: 28,500
SALES (est): 5.2MM **Privately Held**
SIC: 3544 3469 Special dies & tools; metal stampings

(G-8289)
DAYTON WEEKLY NEWS
Also Called: MWC Publishing Co
118 Salem Ave (45406-5803)
PHONE....................937 223-8060
Fax: 937 223-9964
Donald Black, *President*
EMP: 4
SALES (est): 444.6K **Privately Held**
SIC: 8743 2711 Public relations & publicity; newspapers, publishing & printing

(G-8290)
DAYTON WHEEL CONCEPTS
INC
Also Called: Dayton Wire Wheel
115 Compark Rd (45459-4803)
PHONE....................937 438-0100
Fax: 937 438-1215
Brad Cruchleo, *General Mgr*
Sam Warwar, *Principal*
Mark Abernathy, *Safety Mgr*
Pam Good, *Opers Staff*
Rob Moore, *Opers Staff*
▲ **EMP:** 30 **EST:** 1953
SQ FT: 150,000
SALES (est): 6.3MM **Privately Held**
WEB: www.dwpco.com
SIC: 3714 Wheels, motor vehicle

(G-8291)
DAYTON WIRE PRODUCTS INC
7 Dayton Wire Pkwy (45404-1282)
PHONE....................937 236-8000
Fax: 937 236-8300
David Leiser, *President*
Brian Schissler, *Vice Pres*
Mike Ferguson, *Manager*
EMP: 40
SQ FT: 62,500
SALES (est): 8MM **Privately Held**
WEB: www.daytonwireproducts.com
SIC: 3496 3993 Miscellaneous fabricated wire products; signs & advertising specialties

(G-8292)
DAYTON WRIGHT COMPOSITE
3251 Mccall St (45417-1907)
P.O. Box 69, Englewood (45322-0069)
PHONE....................937 469-3962
John Prikkel, *President*
EMP: 3
SALES (est): 94.1K **Privately Held**
SIC: 3299 Mica products

(G-8293)
DAYTON-PHOENIX GROUP INC
(PA)
1619 Kuntz Rd (45404-1240)
PHONE....................937 496-3900
Fax: 937 496-3969
Gale Kooken, *President*
Roger Fleming, *Vice Pres*
John Murphy, *Vice Pres*
Xung T Bui, *Engineer*
Rob Snyder, *Design Engr*
◆ **EMP:** 242
SQ FT: 640,000
SALES (est): 143.1MM **Privately Held**
WEB: www.dayton-phoenix.com
SIC: 3621 3743 Motors & generators; railroad equipment; locomotives & parts

(G-8294)
DEALS
5522 Springboro Pike (45449-2804)
PHONE....................937 293-7429
Richard Hale, *Principal*
EMP: 4
SALES (est): 280.2K **Privately Held**
SIC: 3643 Outlets, electric: convenience

(G-8295)
DEBAN ENTERPRISES INC
611 Congress Park Dr (45459-4007)
PHONE....................937 426-4235
Elias Aboujaoude, *President*
Hilda Aboujaoude, *Manager*
EMP: 4
SQ FT: 1,250
SALES: 400K **Privately Held**
WEB: www.deban.com
SIC: 3823 Industrial instrmnts msrmnt display/control process variable

(G-8296)
DELMA CORP
Also Called: Dayton Manufacturing Company
3327 Elkton Ave (45403-1357)
PHONE....................937 253-2142
Fax: 937 253-5888
Robert J Davis, *President*
Mary W Davis, *Principal*
Lisa D Houseman, *Principal*
Lisa Davis, *Corp Secy*
Robert Rouhier, *Vice Pres*
EMP: 65
SQ FT: 52,000
SALES (est): 14.8MM **Privately Held**
WEB: www.daytonmanufacturing.com
SIC: 3444 Metal housings, enclosures, casings & other containers; casings, sheet metal

(G-8297)
DELTA CONTROL INC (PA)
2532 Nordic Rd (45414-3422)
P.O. Box 13612 (45413-0612)
PHONE....................937 277-3444
Fax: 937 277-9641
Michaela Grafton, *President*
EMP: 5
SQ FT: 2,500
SALES (est): 1.2MM **Privately Held**
SIC: 7389 3625 8711 Water softener service; industrial controls: push button, selector switches, pilot; engineering services

(G-8298)
DEM TECHNOLOGY LLC
755 Albany St (45417-3460)
PHONE....................937 223-1317
Fax: 937 228-1380
Evan Morgan, *Vice Pres*
David M Morgan,
EMP: 4
SQ FT: 10,000
SALES (est): 475.8K **Privately Held**
SIC: 3999 Barber & beauty shop equipment

(G-8299)
DEPUY ORTHOPAEDICS INC
2747 Armstrong Ln (45414-4225)
PHONE....................937 274-5850
David Smith, *Branch Mgr*
EMP: 28
SALES (corp-wide): 71.8B **Publicly Held**
SIC: 3842 Orthopedic appliances

HQ: Depuy Orthopaedics, Inc.
700 Orthopaedic Dr
Warsaw IN 46582
574 267-8143

(G-8300)
DESIGN PATTERN WORKS INC
2312 E 3rd St (45403-2015)
PHONE.................................937 252-0797
Fax: 937 252-5667
George Weckler, President
James Weckler, Vice Pres
EMP: 8 EST: 1977
SALES (est): 1MM Privately Held
SIC: 3543 Industrial patterns

(G-8301)
DESIGN TECH INC
1531 Keystone Ave (45403-3335)
PHONE.................................937 254-7000
Fax: 937 254-7720
EMP: 4
SQ FT: 12,000
SALES: 400K Privately Held
SIC: 3543 3599 Manufactures Industrial
Patterns & Job Machine Shop

(G-8302)
DGL WOODWORKING INC
5931 Wolf Creek Pike (45426-2439)
PHONE.................................937 837-7091
Fax: 937 854-7568
Derek Grauduss, President
Rita Cochran, Office Mgr
EMP: 10
SQ FT: 10,000
SALES: 820K Privately Held
WEB: www.dglwoodworking.com
SIC: 2522 2434 1751 Cabinets, office: ex-
cept wood; desks, office: except wood;
wood kitchen cabinets; cabinet & finish
carpentry

(G-8303)
**DIGITAL MEDIA INTEGRATION
LLC**
9090 State Route 48 B (45458-5125)
PHONE.................................937 305-5582
Philip R Lee,
EMP: 3
SQ FT: 1,100
SALES (est): 317.8K Privately Held
SIC: 3651 Audio electronic systems

(G-8304)
DIGITAL SHORTS INC
136 N Saint Clair St # 100 (45402-1774)
PHONE.................................937 228-1700
Fax: 937 222-3950
Edmund Grant, President
Donna Tubis, Office Mgr
EMP: 3
SALES (est): 310K Privately Held
SIC: 2759 Commercial printing

(G-8305)
DIK JAXON PRODUCTS CO
Also Called: Jaxon's
6195 Webster St (45414-3447)
PHONE.................................937 890-7350
Fax: 937 890-2535
Barry Jackson, President
EMP: 3
SQ FT: 5,400
SALES (est): 335.1K Privately Held
SIC: 2099 Emulsifiers, food

(G-8306)
**DISALVOS DELI & ITALIAN
STORE**
Also Called: Disalvo Deli & Italian Store
1383 E Stroop Rd (45429-4925)
PHONE.................................937 298-5053
Fax: 937 395-0341
Rinaldo S Disalvo, Owner
Matthew Booth, Director
EMP: 5
SALES (est): 433.8K Privately Held
WEB: www.disalvosdeli.com
SIC: 2032 5812 5499 Italian foods: pack-
aged in cans, jars, etc.; caterers; gourmet
food stores

(G-8307)
**DOLING & ASSOCIATES DENTAL
LAB**
3318 Successful Way (45414-4318)
PHONE.................................937 254-0075
Fax: 937 254-3256
Ted Doling, President
Joe Wiener, Vice Pres
Joyce Doling, Finance Mgr
EMP: 25
SQ FT: 3,000
SALES (est): 1.5MM Privately Held
SIC: 8072 3842 Dental laboratories; crown
& bridge production; surgical appliances
& supplies

(G-8308)
DONALD MARLO
Also Called: Mac Advertising Co
5003 Brock Ln (45415-3429)
PHONE.................................937 836-4880
Donald Marlo, Owner
EMP: 3
SALES (est): 188.6K Privately Held
SIC: 3993 Signs & advertising specialties

(G-8309)
DOW CHEMICAL COMPANY
555 Gaddis Blvd (45403-1406)
PHONE.................................937 254-1550
EMP: 16
SALES (corp-wide): 57B Publicly Held
SIC: 2821 3081 3086 2879 Mfg Plastics
Specialty Chemicals & Agricultural Prod-
ucts
PA: The Dow Chemical Company
2030 Dow Ctr
Midland MI 48674
989 636-1000

(G-8310)
**DRAGOON TECHNOLOGIES INC
(PA)**
Also Called: Dragoonitcn
900 Senate Dr (45459-4017)
PHONE.................................937 439-9223
Kathy Appenzeller, CEO
Dan Simich, Electrical Engi
Elizabeth Appenzeller, Accounts Mgr
Christy Clark, Manager
EMP: 6
SQ FT: 51,000
SALES (est): 1.9MM Privately Held
WEB: www.dragoontech.com
SIC: 3812 Radar systems & equipment

(G-8311)
DRAWN METALS CORP
331 Congress Park Dr (45459-4127)
P.O. Box 750758 (45475-0758)
PHONE.................................937 433-6151
Fax: 937 433-4734
Gary Mertler, President
Lorin A Mertler, Chairman
EMP: 12
SQ FT: 10,000
SALES (est): 1.9MM Privately Held
SIC: 3499 Strapping, metal

(G-8312)
DRT MEDICAL LLC
618 Greenmount Blvd (45419-3271)
PHONE.................................937 298-7391
Julie Smith, Principal
Michael Rauch, Purch Agent
EMP: 8
SALES (est): 910K Privately Held
SIC: 3841 Surgical & medical instruments

(G-8313)
DRT MFG CO (HQ)
618 Greenmount Blvd (45419-3271)
PHONE.................................937 297-6670
Fax: 937 297-6740
Gary L Van Gundy, President
Gregory S Martin, Senior VP
Tony Cornacchione, Plant Mgr
Dallas Brill, Purchasing
Tom Scarpelli, Purchasing
✪ EMP: 170 EST: 1949
SQ FT: 106,000
SALES (est): 27MM Privately Held
WEB: www.drtusa.com
SIC: 3544 3545 Special dies & tools; ma-
chine tool accessories

(G-8314)
**DUPONT ELECTRONIC
POLYMERS LP**
1515 Nicholas Rd (45417-6712)
PHONE.................................937 268-3411
Ellen Kullman, Ch of Bd
Craig F Binetti, President
Charles Holiday, Partner
James C Borel, Exec VP
David G Bills, Senior VP
EMP: 65
SALES (est): 14.1MM
SALES (corp-wide): 24.5B Publicly Held
WEB: www.dupont.com
SIC: 3571 Electronic computers
PA: E. I. Du Pont De Nemours And Com-
pany
974 Centre Rd
Wilmington DE 19805
302 774-1000

(G-8315)
**DYNAPOINT TECHNOLOGIES
INC**
475 Progress Rd (45449-2323)
P.O. Box 355 (45449)
PHONE.................................937 859-5193
Fax: 937 859-4498
Jeffrey G Beatty, President
Jerry Frame, Opers Mgr
Amanda Bafs, Administration
EMP: 23 EST: 1969
SQ FT: 14,000
SALES (est): 4.1MM Privately Held
WEB: www.dynapoint1.com
SIC: 3599 Machine shop, jobbing & repair

(G-8316)
E3 DIAGNOSTICS INC
Also Called: E3 Gordon Stowe
74 Marco Ln (45458-3817)
PHONE.................................937 435-2250
Fax: 937 435-2921
Alan Michelson, Sales/Mktg Mgr
Maura Benton, Accounts Mgr
Christine Koss, Admin Sec
EMP: 8 Privately Held
SIC: 3845 3651 Audiological equipment,
electromedical; household audio & video
equipment
HQ: E3 Diagnostics, Inc.
3333 N Kennicott Ave
Arlington Heights IL 60004
847 459-1770

(G-8317)
EASTMAN KODAK COMPANY
3000 Research Blvd (45420-4003)
PHONE.................................937 259-3000
Fax: 937 259-3385
Randy Vandagriff, President
Kirstie Black, Senior Buyer
Kenneth Harrington, Engineer
Glen Kowal, Engineer
Robert Egerman, Design Engr
EMP: 20
SALES (corp-wide): 1.8B Publicly Held
SIC: 3355 3577 5043 Aluminum rolling &
drawing; computer peripheral equipment;
projection apparatus, motion picture &
slide
PA: Eastman Kodak Company
343 State St
Rochester NY 14650
585 724-4000

(G-8318)
ECO-GROUPE INC (PA)
6161 Ventnor Ave (45414-2651)
PHONE.................................937 898-2603
William Gaiser, CEO
Karin Gaiser, President
Kelly Ferguson, Vice Pres
Steve Ferguson, Manager
Susan Bokelman, Info Tech Dir
EMP: 25
SALES (est): 58.8MM Privately Held
SIC: 3085 Plastics bottles

(G-8319)
**EDGEWELL PER CARE BRANDS
LLC**
973 S Perry St (45402-2526)
P.O. Box 10488 (45402-7488)
PHONE.................................937 228-0105

Mike Davis, Purchasing
Kenneth Schriber, Branch Mgr
EMP: 100
SALES (corp-wide): 2.4B Publicly Held
SIC: 3421 Razor blades & razors
HQ: Edgewell Personal Care Brands, Llc
6 Research Dr
Shelton CT 06484
203 944-5500

(G-8320)
EDWARD S EVELAND
6175 Falkland Dr (45424-3819)
PHONE.................................937 233-6568
Ed Eveland, Principal
EMP: 3
SALES (est): 214.5K Privately Held
SIC: 3721 Aircraft

(G-8321)
**ELECTRICAL CONTROL
SYSTEMS**
Also Called: E C S
3731 W Alex Bell Rd (45449-1920)
PHONE.................................937 859-7136
Fax: 937 859-3831
Nicholas Vendel Jr, President
Kirk Vendel, Vice Pres
Jean Vendel, Admin Sec
EMP: 5
SQ FT: 15,000
SALES (est): 740K Privately Held
SIC: 3613 3469 Control panels, electric;
electronic enclosures, stamped or
pressed metal

(G-8322)
**ELECTRO POLISH COMPANY
INC**
332 Vermont Ave (45404-1597)
PHONE.................................937 222-3611
Fax: 937 222-2988
Kent Kumbroch, President
Stuart Price, Vice Pres
EMP: 28 EST: 1949
SQ FT: 8,000
SALES (est): 4.1MM Privately Held
WEB: www.electro-polish.com
SIC: 3471 Finishing, metals or formed
products

(G-8323)
ELECTRO-LINE INC
118 S Terry St (45403-2312)
P.O. Box 1688 (45401-1688)
PHONE.................................937 461-5683
Fax: 937 461-0533
Bruce Jump, President
Jeffrey J Bucher, Vice Pres
Ruth Ford, Admin Sec
EMP: 15 EST: 1958
SQ FT: 15,000
SALES: 1.8MM Privately Held
WEB: www.electroline.com
SIC: 3679 5065 Electronic circuits; elec-
tronic parts & equipment

(G-8324)
**ELLIOTT TOOL TECHNOLOGIES
LTD (PA)**
1760 Tuttle Ave (45403-3428)
PHONE.................................937 253-6133
Fax: 937 253-9189
Joseph W Smith, President
Roger Lall, General Mgr
John Stoll, Area Mgr
Robert Columbus, Vice Pres
Jim Ireton, Vice Pres
EMP: 68
SQ FT: 37,000
SALES (est): 17.8MM Privately Held
WEB: www.elliott-tool.com
SIC: 7359 3542 5072 3541 Equipment
rental & leasing; machine tools, metal
forming type; hand tools; machine tools,
metal cutting type; fabricated pipe & fit-
tings

(G-8325)
ENCON INC (HQ)
6161 Ventnor Ave (45414-2651)
P.O. Box 13418 (45413-0418)
PHONE.................................937 898-2603
Karin S Gaiser, CEO
Kelly Ferguson, Vice Pres

Therese McNea-Wiley, *Vice Pres*
Debra Doyle, *Treasurer*
◆ **EMP:** 140
SQ FT: 50,000
SALES (est): 55MM
SALES (corp-wide): 58.8MM **Privately Held**
SIC: 3085 3089 Plastics bottles; plastic containers, except foam
PA: The Eco-Groupe Inc
6161 Ventnor Ave
Dayton OH 45414
937 898-2603

(G-8326)
ENERGY STORAGE TECHNOLOGIES
Also Called: Vacupanel
7610 Mcewen Rd (45459-3908)
PHONE....................937 312-0114
Fax: 937 312-1277
C William Swank, *President*
Michael Fisher, *CFO*
Robert Hussey, *Controller*
Kim Buckingham, *Director*
EMP: 50
SALES (est): 5.6MM **Privately Held**
SIC: 3086 Insulation or cushioning material, foamed plastic

(G-8327)
ENKON LLC
6161 Ventnor Ave (45414-2651)
P.O. Box 13418 (45413-0418)
PHONE....................937 898-2603
Debra L Doyle,
EMP: 14
SALES (est): 2.5MM
SALES (corp-wide): 58.8MM **Privately Held**
SIC: 3089 Injection molding of plastics
PA: The Eco-Groupe Inc
6161 Ventnor Ave
Dayton OH 45414
937 898-2603

(G-8328)
EPIX TUBE CO INC (PA)
5800 Wolf Creek Pike (45426-2438)
P.O. Box 187, West Alexandria (45381-0187)
PHONE....................937 529-4858
Paul Kasperski, *President*
Angela Salazar, *CFO*
David Steuart, *Controller*
EMP: 57
SALES (est): 23.5MM **Privately Held**
SIC: 2599 5531 Factory furniture & fixtures; automotive accessories

(G-8329)
EQUIPMENT CONCEPTS
400 Linden Ave Ste 14 (45403-2558)
PHONE....................937 291-9734
Fax: 937 258-1755
David L Franer, *Owner*
EMP: 3
SQ FT: 2,000
SALES (est): 293.8K **Privately Held**
SIC: 3568 3544 7389 Power transmission equipment; clutches, except vehicular; collars, shaft (power transmission equipment); special dies & tools; design services

(G-8330)
EQUIPMENT SPCALISTS DAYTON LLC
5595 Webster St (45414-3516)
PHONE....................937 415-2151
Stephen Hart, *Partner*
Teresa Hart, *Partner*
EMP: 3
SQ FT: 2,000
SALES (est): 123.2K **Privately Held**
SIC: 2841 7699 Soap & other detergents; industrial machinery & equipment repair; pumps & pumping equipment repair; agricultural equipment repair services

(G-8331)
ERNST ENTERPRISES INC (PA)
Also Called: Ernst Concrete
3361 Successful Way (45414-4317)
PHONE....................937 233-5555
Fax: 937 233-9203

John C Ernst Jr, *President*
Bob Hines, *Principal*
David Ernst, *Vice Pres*
Steve Harvey, *Data Proc Exec*
David Stomberger, *Exec Dir*
EMP: 20
SQ FT: 6,300
SALES (est): 191MM **Privately Held**
WEB: www.ernstconcrete.com
SIC: 3273 Ready-mixed concrete

(G-8332)
ESTEE MOLD & DIE INC
1467 Stanley Ave (45404-1171)
PHONE....................937 224-7853
Fax: 937 228-0257
Dan Rinehart, *President*
Gerhard Triftshouser, *Shareholder*
Werner Triftshouser, *Shareholder*
EMP: 20 **EST:** 1945
SQ FT: 28,000
SALES (est): 6MM **Privately Held**
WEB: www.esteemold.com
SIC: 3544 Industrial molds

(G-8333)
EUGENE STEWART
Also Called: Spectrum Printing & Design
5671 Webster St (45414-3518)
PHONE....................937 898-1117
Fax: 937 898-1116
Eugene Stewart, *Owner*
EMP: 8
SQ FT: 6,000
SALES (est): 987K **Privately Held**
SIC: 2791 7336 2789 2752 Typesetting; art design services; bookbinding & related work; commercial printing, lithographic

(G-8334)
EVANS BAKERY INC
700 Troy St (45404-1851)
PHONE....................937 228-4151
Fax: 937 228-6910
Edward William Evans, *President*
Rose Mary Evans, *Vice Pres*
EMP: 8
SQ FT: 1,600
SALES (est): 370K **Privately Held**
SIC: 5461 2051 Bakeries; doughnuts; bakery: wholesale or wholesale/retail combined

(G-8335)
EVIL CORPORATION CORPORATION
Also Called: Prospeed SEC Doorjamb Systems
116 Front St (45402-1331)
PHONE....................937 902-5921
Kim Pollard, *President*
EMP: 3 **EST:** 2015
SALES (est): 146.2K **Privately Held**
SIC: 2431 Door frames, wood

(G-8336)
EXCITON INC
5271 Split Rail (45429-1962)
PHONE....................937 252-2989
Fax: 937 258-3937
Richard Steppel, *President*
Judith Steppel, *Corp Secy*
Lawrence Knaak, *Vice Pres*
Carrie Brown, *Office Mgr*
EMP: 10
SQ FT: 5,000
SALES (est): 1.9MM **Privately Held**
WEB: www.exciton.com
SIC: 2865 Dyes & pigments

(G-8337)
EXITO MANUFACTURING
4738 Gateway Cir Ste E (45440-1724)
PHONE....................937 291-9871
Eric Fernandez,
EMP: 7
SALES (est): 836K **Privately Held**
SIC: 3544 3542 3728 3714 Special dies, tools, jigs & fixtures; machine tools, metal forming type; aircraft parts & equipment; motor vehicle parts & accessories

(G-8338)
FAST FAB AND LASER LLC
401 Kiser St (45404-1639)
P.O. Box 327 (45409-0327)
PHONE....................937 224-3048
Martha Rodgers, *President*
Sim Rodgers, *Vice Pres*
EMP: 13
SQ FT: 22,000
SALES (est): 1.2MM **Privately Held**
SIC: 3599 Machine shop, jobbing & repair

(G-8339)
FEDEX OFFICE & PRINT SVCS INC
1189 Mmsburg Cntrville Rd (45459)
PHONE....................937 436-0677
EMP: 30
SALES (corp-wide): 47.4B **Publicly Held**
SIC: 7334 2791 2789 Photocopying Services Typesetting Services Bookbinding/Related Work
HQ: Fedex Office And Print Services, Inc.
7900 Legacy Dr
Dallas TX 75024
214 550-7000

(G-8340)
FERNANDES ENTERPRISES LLC (PA)
Also Called: Fourjay Industries
2801 Ontario Ave (45414-5136)
PHONE....................937 890-6444
Vernon Fernandes, *President*
Jim Gamble, *Opers Mgr*
Melonnie Demido, *Manager*
▲ **EMP:** 18
SQ FT: 9,600
SALES (est): 2.7MM **Privately Held**
SIC: 3699 Electric sound equipment

(G-8341)
FIDELITY ORTHOPEDIC INC (PA)
8514 N Main St (45415-1325)
PHONE....................937 228-0682
Fax: 937 228-8193
Hillmo Hodzic, *President*
Suzan Brandelik, *Accounting Mgr*
Adam Murka, *Director*
Mark Murka, *Director*
EMP: 5 **EST:** 1929
SQ FT: 4,000
SALES (est): 663.8K **Privately Held**
WEB: www.fidelityorthopedic.com
SIC: 3842 Limbs, artificial; braces, orthopedic

(G-8342)
FIRST TOOL CORP
612 Linden Ave (45403-2589)
PHONE....................937 254-6197
Fax: 937 254-0625
Robert J Davis, *President*
Amy Howard, *General Mgr*
Pauline Miller, *Principal*
Seymour D Ramby, *Principal*
Bill Valentine, *Foreman/Supr*
EMP: 50 **EST:** 1966
SQ FT: 60,000
SALES (est): 13.7MM **Privately Held**
WEB: www.firsttoolcorp.com
SIC: 3542 3544 Machine tools, metal forming type; jigs & fixtures

(G-8343)
FISCHER ENGINEERING COMPANY
8220 Expansion Way (45424-6382)
PHONE....................937 754-1750
Fax: 937 754-1754
Glenn N Fischer, *President*
Justin Hartman, *General Mgr*
Sharon Howard, *Office Mgr*
EMP: 4 **EST:** 1976
SQ FT: 14,400
SALES (est): 938.6K **Privately Held**
WEB: www.fischerengr.com
SIC: 8711 3829 Consulting engineer; measuring & controlling devices

(G-8344)
FIVE POINTS DISTILLERY LLC
122 Van Buren St (45402-2934)
PHONE....................937 776-4634
Murphy Laselle, *Principal*

EMP: 3
SQ FT: 5,000
SALES (est): 177.9K **Privately Held**
SIC: 2085 Rye whiskey

(G-8345)
FLEET GRAPHICS INC
1701 Thomas Paine Pkwy (45459-2540)
PHONE....................937 252-2552
Fax: 937 252-2105
Scott Waggoner, *President*
Val R Waggoner, *Vice Pres*
Bob Brogan, *Accounts Exec*
K Waggoner, *Accounts Exec*
Ron Holland, *Director*
EMP: 9
SQ FT: 6,000
SALES (est): 2.3MM **Privately Held**
WEB: www.fleetgraphicsinc.com
SIC: 3571 2752 Computers, digital, analog or hybrid; commercial printing, lithographic

(G-8346)
FLOWSERVE CORPORATION
2200 E Monument Ave (45402-1362)
PHONE....................937 226-4568
Fax: 937 226-4177
Bill Fredrickson, *Vice Pres*
Howard D Wynn, *Vice Pres*
Charles Power, *Marketing Staff*
John Carano, *Branch Mgr*
R O Blackwood, *Director*
EMP: 55
SALES (corp-wide): 3.9B **Publicly Held**
SIC: 3561 Pumps & pumping equipment
PA: Flowserve Corporation
5215 N Oconnor Blvd Connor
Irving TX 75039
972 443-6500

(G-8347)
FORM-A-CHIP INC
Also Called: Kneiss Saw & Tool Supply
2069 Webster St (45404-1143)
PHONE....................937 223-4135
Fax: 937 223-6073
Joe Tischler, *President*
EMP: 6
SQ FT: 4,600
SALES (est): 883.3K **Privately Held**
SIC: 5072 3425 7699 Power tools & accessories; saw blades; saw blades & handsaws; professional instrument repair services

(G-8348)
FORTERRA PIPE & PRECAST LLC
1504 N Gettysburg Ave (45417-9518)
PHONE....................937 268-6707
EMP: 20
SALES (corp-wide): 14.4B **Privately Held**
SIC: 3272 Mfg Concrete Products
HQ: Forterra Pipe & Precast, Llc
511 E John Carpenter Fwy
Irving TX 75062
469 458-7973

(G-8349)
FORTERRA PIPE & PRECAST LLC
Also Called: Hanson Pipe & Precast Hamburg
1504 N Gettysburg Ave (45417-9518)
PHONE....................937 268-6707
Kevin Sams, *Manager*
Kevin Sam, *Manager*
EMP: 3
SALES (corp-wide): 141.7MM **Publicly Held**
SIC: 1771 5211 3272 Concrete work; masonry materials & supplies; concrete products
HQ: Forterra Pipe & Precast, Llc
511 E John Carpenter Fwy
Irving TX 75062
469 458-7973

(G-8350)
FRANKLIN IRON & METAL CORP
1939 E 1st St (45403-1131)
PHONE....................937 253-8184
Fax: 937 253-2030
Jack Edelman, *President*
Greg Clouse, *General Mgr*
Debra Edelman, *Treasurer*

2017 Harris Ohio
Industrial Directory

▲ = Import ▼=Export
◆ =Import/Export

▲ **EMP:** 105
SQ FT: 60,000
SALES (est): 51.3MM **Privately Held**
SIC: 5093 3341 3312 Scrap & waste materials; secondary nonferrous metals; blast furnaces & steel mills

(G-8351)
FRIED DADDY
Also Called: American Sports Center
448 N Union Rd (45417-7614)
PHONE................................937 854-4542
Fred Fry, *Owner*
Charles Roberts, *General Mgr*
EMP: 5
SALES (est): 100K **Privately Held**
SIC: 5941 5999 3993 2396 Sporting goods & bicycle shops; trophies & plaques; signs & advertising specialties; automotive & apparel trimmings

(G-8352)
FRIENDS SERVICE CO INC
4604 Salem Ave (45416-1712)
PHONE................................800 427-1704
Kenneth J Schroeder, *Branch Mgr*
EMP: 15
SALES (corp-wide): 30MM **Privately Held**
SIC: 5112 5021 5087 2752 Stationery & office supplies; furniture; service establishment equipment; commercial printing, lithographic; office equipment
PA: Friends Service Co., Inc.
2300 Bright Rd
Findlay OH 45840
419 427-1704

(G-8353)
FRIES MACHINE & TOOL INC
5729 Webster St (45414-3520)
PHONE................................937 898-6432
Arland Fries, *CEO*
Tony E Fries, *President*
Lisa A Fries, *Corp Secy*
EMP: 12
SQ FT: 4,000
SALES (est): 1MM **Privately Held**
SIC: 3599 Machine shop, jobbing & repair

(G-8354)
FUKUVI USA INC
7631 Progress Ct (45424-6378)
PHONE................................937 236-7288
Fax: 937 236-7289
S Yagi, *President*
Chris Addeo, *General Mgr*
K Takagi, *Vice Pres*
Tricia L Holt, *Controller*
T Page, *Controller*
▲ **EMP:** 65
SQ FT: 84,000
SALES (est): 15MM
SALES (corp-wide): 330.8MM **Privately Held**
WEB: www.fukuvi-usa.com
SIC: 3089 Plastic kitchenware, tableware & houseware
PA: Fukuvi Chemical Industry Co., Ltd.
33-66, Sanjuhasshacho
Fukui FKI 918-8
776 388-001

(G-8355)
FURNITURE BY OTMAR INC (PA)
301 Mmsburg Cnterville Rd (45459)
PHONE................................937 435-2039
Fax: 937 435-2010
Josef Otmar IV, *President*
Alberto Otmar, *Vice Pres*
EMP: 12 **EST:** 1960
SQ FT: 10,000
SALES (est): 1.1MM **Privately Held**
WEB: www.furniturebyotmar.com
SIC: 2511 5712 Wood household furniture; furniture stores

(G-8356)
GADJETS INC
Also Called: Associated Technical Sales
3629 N Dixie Dr (45414-5232)
P.O. Box 13419 (45413-0419)
PHONE................................937 274-2111
Fax: 937 274-7302
Adryana Southerland, *President*

EMP: 8 **EST:** 1947
SQ FT: 9,280
SALES (est): 350K **Privately Held**
WEB: www.gadjets.com
SIC: 3542 3089 Presses: hydraulic & pneumatic, mechanical & manual; fittings for pipe, plastic

(G-8357)
GAUNTLET AWARDS & ENGRAVING
9153 N Dixie Dr (45414-1859)
P.O. Box 267, Vandalia (45377-0267)
PHONE................................937 890-5811
Fax: 937 890-6014
Vickie Akers, *Owner*
EMP: 4
SQ FT: 4,000
SALES (est): 318K **Privately Held**
SIC: 5999 7389 5199 3993 Trophies & plaques; engraving service; advertising specialties; signs & advertising specialties; bolts, nuts, rivets & washers; packaging paper & plastics film, coated & laminated

(G-8358)
GE AVIATION SYSTEMS LLC
Also Called: Tdi
6800 Poe Ave (45414-2530)
PHONE................................937 898-9600
Fax: 937 898-8431
Deanne Hartman, *General Mgr*
Shawn Conrad, *Opers Staff*
Jeff Hollowell, *Engineer*
Kevin McGray, *Finance*
Bob Englet, *Sales Staff*
▲ **EMP:** 150 **EST:** 1987
SQ FT: 100,000
SALES (est): 46.6MM **Privately Held**
SIC: 3511 3724 Turbines & turbine generator sets & parts; aircraft engines & engine parts

(G-8359)
GE AVIATION SYSTEMS LLC
6800 Poe Ave (45414-2530)
PHONE................................937 898-9600
EMP: 198
SALES (corp-wide): 123.6B **Publicly Held**
SIC: 3812 Aircraft control systems, electronic
HQ: Ge Aviation Systems Llc
1 Neumann Way
Cincinnati OH 45215
513 243-2000

(G-8360)
GEDICO INTERNATIONAL INC
Also Called: Largemachining.com
4050 Grafix Blvd (45417-9578)
PHONE................................937 274-2167
Fax: 937 274-1301
George E Dorin, *President*
Donald J Smith, *Vice Pres*
EMP: 7 **EST:** 1945
SQ FT: 20,000
SALES: 300K **Privately Held**
WEB: www.gedico.com
SIC: 3555 3599 Printing trades machinery; machine shop, jobbing & repair

(G-8361)
GEM CITY ENGINEERING CO (PA)
Also Called: Gem City Engineering & Mfg
401 Leo St (45404-1009)
PHONE................................937 223-5544
James Whalen, *CEO*
David D Harry, *President*
Don King, *Project Mgr*
Jerry Cook, *Mfg Mgr*
Lori Anderson, *Buyer*
EMP: 120 **EST:** 1936
SQ FT: 250,000
SALES (est): 34.6MM **Privately Held**
WEB: www.gemcity.com
SIC: 3544 3549 3569 Special dies & tools; metalworking machinery; assembly machines, non-metalworking

(G-8362)
GEM CITY METAL TECH LLC
1825 E 1st St (45403-1129)
PHONE................................937 252-8998

Fax: 937 252-7565
Dennis Mc Wright, *CFO*
Scott Warren, *Accounting Mgr*
Dennis Nystrom, *Mng Member*
Don Nystron, *Mng Member*
Norb Overla,
EMP: 49
SQ FT: 53,000
SALES (est): 14.6MM **Privately Held**
SIC: 3356 3444 3444 3469 Nonferrous rolling & drawing; architectural metalwork; sheet metalwork; spinning metal for the trade; machine tools, metal forming type

(G-8363)
GENEVA GEAR & MACHINE INC
339 Progress Rd (45449-2321)
PHONE................................937 866-0318
Fax: 937 866-7706
Otto G Takacs Jr, *President*
EMP: 15
SQ FT: 12,700
SALES: 2MM **Privately Held**
SIC: 3568 3566 3462 Power transmission equipment; gears, power transmission, except automotive; iron & steel forgings

(G-8364)
GINKO VOTING SYSTEMS LLC (PA)
Also Called: Ginko Systems
600 Progress Rd (45449-2300)
PHONE................................937 291-4060
Franklin Dunkin, *CEO*
Lawrence Whitehead, *Vice Pres*
J R Dunkin, *Opers Staff*
EMP: 1
SQ FT: 12,000
SALES (est): 3.4MM **Privately Held**
SIC: 3578 3695 Automatic teller machines (ATM); computer software tape & disks: blank, rigid & floppy

(G-8365)
GLEASON METROLOGY SYSTEMS CORP (HQ)
Also Called: Gleason M & M Precision
300 Progress Rd (45449-2322)
PHONE................................937 384-8901
Fax: 937 859-4452
Douglas Beerck, *General Mgr*
Terry Turner, *Exec VP*
Stuart Piper, *Vice Pres*
Kevin Gilbert, *Purch Agent*
Carol Wilson, *Credit Staff*
◆ **EMP:** 50
SQ FT: 68,000
SALES (est): 6.9MM
SALES (corp-wide): 1B **Privately Held**
SIC: 3829 3823 3769 3621 Measuring & controlling devices; industrial instrmnts msrmnt display/control process variable; guided missile & space vehicle parts & auxiliary equipment; motors & generators; computer peripheral equipment; machine tool accessories
PA: Gleason Corporation
1000 University Ave
Rochester NY 14607
585 473-1000

(G-8366)
GLEN D LALA
Also Called: Innovative Creations
2610 Willowburn Ave (45417-9434)
P.O. Box 328, Springboro (45066-0328)
PHONE................................937 274-7770
Fax: 937 274-0727
Glen D Lala, *Owner*
EMP: 6
SQ FT: 12,000
SALES (est): 186K **Privately Held**
SIC: 2759 7699 Screen printing; printing trades machinery & equipment repair

(G-8367)
GLOBAL MANUFACTURING SOLUTIONS
2001 Kuntz Rd (45404-1221)
PHONE................................937 236-8315
Charles M Woods, *President*
William Bankes, *Vice Pres*
Jack L Cobb, *Director*
Fred Seger, *Director*
EMP: 13
SQ FT: 46,000

SALES (est): 1.3MM **Privately Held**
WEB: www.globalms.com
SIC: 3082 8734 5947 5199 Unsupported plastics profile shapes; product testing laboratory, safety or performance; gifts & novelties; foams & rubber

(G-8368)
GLOBE MOTORS INC (HQ)
2275 Stanley Ave (45404-1226)
PHONE................................334 983-3542
Fax: 937 229-8531
Steven McHenry, *CEO*
Charles Conway, *Engineer*
Danny Kottmyer, *Project Engr*
William Gillespie, *CFO*
Thomas Carroll, *Admin Sec*
▲ **EMP:** 150
SALES (est): 127.9MM
SALES (corp-wide): 232.4MM **Publicly Held**
WEB: www.globe-motors.com
SIC: 3621 Motors & generators
PA: Allied Motion Technologies Inc.
495 Commerce Dr Ste 3
Amherst NY 14228
716 242-8634

(G-8369)
GLOBE MOTORS INC
1944 Troy St (45404-2159)
PHONE................................937 228-3171
Fax: 937 229-0499
Tom Miller, *Finance Mgr*
Bob Ryan, *Marketing Staff*
Dick Peacock, *Manager*
Jerry Birch, *Manager*
Steve Partollo, *Manager*
EMP: 125
SALES (corp-wide): 232.4MM **Publicly Held**
WEB: www.globe-motors.com
SIC: 3621 3369 3365 Motors & generators; nonferrous foundries; aluminum foundries
HQ: Globe Motors, Inc.
2275 Stanley Ave
Dayton OH 45404
334 983-3542

(G-8370)
GLOBE MOTORS INC
2275 Stanley Ave (45404-1226)
PHONE................................937 228-3171
Steve McHenry, *Branch Mgr*
EMP: 100
SALES (corp-wide): 232.4MM **Publicly Held**
WEB: www.globe-motors.com
SIC: 3621 Motors, electric
HQ: Globe Motors, Inc.
2275 Stanley Ave
Dayton OH 45404
334 983-3542

(G-8371)
GLOBE PRODUCTS INC (PA)
5051 Kitridge Rd (45424-4433)
PHONE................................937 233-0233
Fax: 937 233-5290
James E Kroencke, *CEO*
Scott Kroencke, *President*
Don Knight, *Plant Mgr*
Pat Dolgas, *Engineer*
Roger Dosland, *Finance*
▲ **EMP:** 20 **EST:** 1919
SQ FT: 100,000
SALES (est): 2.8MM **Privately Held**
WEB: www.globe-usa.com
SIC: 3599 Custom machinery

(G-8372)
GLT INC (PA)
3341 Successful Way (45414-4317)
PHONE................................937 237-0055
Kevin Knight, *CEO*
Jeff Banford, *Vice Pres*
Vince Hinde, *Vice Pres*
Chris Knight, *Vice Pres*
Brad Labensky, *Vice Pres*
◆ **EMP:** 12
SQ FT: 75,000
SALES (est): 11.3MM **Privately Held**
WEB: www.gltonline.com
SIC: 3541 Machine tools, metal cutting type

(G-8373)
GMD INDUSTRIES LLC
Also Called: Production Screw Machine
1414 E 2nd St (45403-1023)
PHONE...................................937 252-3643
Fax: 937 252-1667
Greg Macpherson, *Business Mgr*
Mark Michaels, *Purch Agent*
Theresa Nichols, *Human Res Dir*
Rada Garfora, *Sales Engr*
Mark Denlinger, *Marketing Staff*
▼ EMP: 65
SQ FT: 35,000
SALES (est): 10.7MM **Privately Held**
WEB: www.psmco.com
SIC: 3599 Machine shop, jobbing & repair

(G-8374)
GO CUPCAKE
5017 Rolling Woods Trl (45429-1110)
PHONE...................................937 299-4985
Jennifer Cox, *Principal*
EMP: 4
SALES (est): 244.9K **Privately Held**
SIC: 2051 Bread, cake & related products

(G-8375)
GOVERNMENT SPECIALTY
PDTS LLC (PA)
9588 Quailwood Trl (45458-9630)
PHONE...................................937 672-9473
John Hetzel,
EMP: 1
SALES: 3.2MM **Privately Held**
SIC: 2311 Military uniforms, men's &
youths': purchased materials

(G-8376)
GRANT JOHN
Also Called: J & D Printing
2715 Culver Ave (45429-3723)
PHONE...................................937 298-0633
Fax: 937 298-0634
John Grant, *Owner*
EMP: 3
SQ FT: 1,100
SALES: 200K **Privately Held**
SIC: 2752 2796 2789 2759 Commercial
printing, offset; platemaking services;
bookbinding & related work; commercial
printing

(G-8377)
GRB HOLDINGS INC
131 Janney Rd (45404-1225)
P.O. Box 173 (45404-0173)
PHONE...................................937 236-3250
David Gitridge, *President*
David Gutridge, *President*
EMP: 80 EST: 1913
SQ FT: 50,000
SALES: 15MM **Privately Held**
WEB: www.behmquartz.com
SIC: 3295 3471 Minerals, ground or
treated; plating & polishing

(G-8378)
GREEN LEAF PRINTING AND
DESIGN
1001 E 2nd St Ste 2485 (45402-1498)
PHONE...................................937 222-3634
Larry Blevins, *Principal*
EMP: 4
SALES (est): 407.7K **Privately Held**
SIC: 2752 Commercial printing, litho-
graphic

(G-8379)
GREEN TOKAI CO LTD
3700 Inpark Dr (45414-4418)
PHONE...................................937 237-1630
EMP: 3
SALES (corp-wide): 321.2MM **Privately**
Held
SIC: 3714 Motor vehicle parts & acces-
sories
HQ: Green Tokai Co., Ltd.
55 Robert Wright Dr
Brookville OH 45309
937 833-5444

(G-8380)
GREGORY STONE CO INC
1860 N Gettysburg Ave (45417-9585)
PHONE...................................937 275-7455

Fax: 937 275-4521
Thomas L Call, *President*
Jackie K Call, *Vice Pres*
EMP: 9
SQ FT: 7,000
SALES (est): 1.9MM **Privately Held**
SIC: 5211 1411 Masonry materials & sup-
plies; limestone, dimension-quarrying

(G-8381)
H & H SCREEN PROCESS INC
1220 Wyoming St (45410-1912)
PHONE...................................937 253-7520
Robert Hess, *President*
Aileen Hess, *Vice Pres*
EMP: 4
SQ FT: 2,400
SALES: 200K **Privately Held**
SIC: 2396 2395 2759 Screen printing on
fabric articles; embroidery & art needle-
work; screen printing

(G-8382)
H GERSTNER & SONS INC
Also Called: Gerstner International
20 Gerstner Way (45402-8408)
PHONE...................................937 228-1662
Fax: 937 228-8557
John Campbell, *President*
John Scott Campbell Jr, *Vice Pres*
Nancy Campbell, *Admin Sec*
EMP: 15 EST: 1906
SQ FT: 30,000
SALES (est): 1.3MM **Privately Held**
WEB: www.gerstnerusa.com
SIC: 2441 Nailed wood boxes & shook;
tool chests, wood

(G-8383)
HAM SIGNS LLC
6020 N Dixie Dr (45414-4018)
PHONE...................................937 454-9111
Fax: 937 890-6727
Larry Miller,
EMP: 5
SALES (est): 420K **Privately Held**
SIC: 3993 7532 Signs & advertising spe-
cialties; truck painting & lettering

(G-8384)
HANGER PRSTHETCS & ORTHO
INC
Also Called: Orpro Prosthetics & Orthotics
1 Elizabeth Pl Ste 300 (45417-3445)
PHONE...................................937 228-5462
Jim Babcock, *Materials Mgr*
Randy Daniel, *Branch Mgr*
Sheryl Price, *Director*
EMP: 15
SALES (corp-wide): 460MM **Publicly**
Held
SIC: 3842 5999 Prosthetic appliances; or-
thopedic appliances; orthopedic & pros-
thesis applications
HQ: Hanger Prosthetics & Orthotics, Inc.
10910 Domain Dr Ste 300
Austin TX 78758
512 777-3800

(G-8385)
HARBOR FREIGHT TOOLS USA
INC
1941 Needmore Rd (45414-3807)
PHONE...................................937 415-0770
Fax: 937 415-0844
Vance Moore, *Manager*
EMP: 20
SALES (corp-wide): 2.4B **Privately Held**
SIC: 7699 7389 5084 3423 Tool repair
services; hand tool designers; compres-
sors, except air conditioning; hand & edge
tools
PA: Harbor Freight Tools Usa, Inc.
26541 Agoura Rd
Calabasas CA 91302
818 836-5000

(G-8386)
HAYES METALFINISHING INC
Also Called: Quality Black Oxide
2617 Stanley Ave (45404-2732)
PHONE...................................937 228-7550
Fax: 937 228-4062
Phillip Hayes, *President*
Kathy Hayes, *Vice Pres*
EMP: 5

SQ FT: 3,106
SALES (est): 494.3K **Privately Held**
SIC: 3471 Finishing, metals or formed
products

(G-8387)
HAYES RECONDITIONING
GROUP
Also Called: A R C of Dayton
1301 Robert Dickey Pkwy (45409-2122)
PHONE...................................937 299-8013
Tim Hayes, *CEO*
EMP: 3
SALES: 120K **Privately Held**
SIC: 2396 Automotive & apparel trimmings

(G-8388)
HEC INVESTMENTS INC
4800 Wadsworth Rd (45414-4224)
PHONE...................................937 278-9123
Lynne Henson, *President*
Shane Miller, *Exec VP*
William Tallman, *Director*
▲ EMP: 144 EST: 1975
SQ FT: 12,000
SALES (est): 24.8MM **Privately Held**
WEB: www.superiorabrasives.com
SIC: 3291 Abrasive products

(G-8389)
HESS ADVANCED SOLUTIONS
LLC
7415 Chambersburg Rd (45424-3921)
P.O. Box 17669 (45417-0669)
PHONE...................................937 829-4794
Frederick Edmonds, *CEO*
EMP: 8
SQ FT: 15,000
SALES (est): 319.7K **Privately Held**
SIC: 3699 1731 8711 1711 Electrical
equipment & supplies; electrical work;
heating & ventilation engineering; heating
& air conditioning contractors; heating
equipment & panels, solar

(G-8390)
HOCKER TOOL AND DIE INC
5161 Webster St (45414-4227)
PHONE...................................937 274-3443
Fax: 937 274-5860
Ronald S Hocker, *President*
William K Hocker, *Vice Pres*
Gloria Graeter, *Office Mgr*
EMP: 14
SQ FT: 12,000
SALES: 1.8MM **Privately Held**
WEB: www.hockertoolanddie.com
SIC: 3599 Machine shop, jobbing & repair

(G-8391)
HOLLYWOOD GAMING AT
DAYTON RAC
777 Hollywood Blvd (45414-3698)
PHONE...................................937 235-7800
EMP: 4 EST: 2015
SALES (est): 269K **Privately Held**
SIC: 3644 Raceways

(G-8392)
HOME CITY ICE COMPANY
1020 Gateway Dr (45404-2281)
PHONE...................................937 461-6028
Fax: 937 461-2637
Kyle Kenny, *Sales Executive*
Joel Heck, *Manager*
EMP: 25
SALES (corp-wide): 305.4MM **Privately**
Held
WEB: www.homecityice.com
SIC: 2097 5999 Manufactured ice; ice
PA: The Home City Ice Company
6045 Bridgetown Rd Ste 1
Cincinnati OH 45248
513 574-1800

(G-8393)
HOUSE OF 10000 PICTURE
FRAMES
2210 Wilmington Pike (45420-1433)
PHONE...................................937 254-5541
Fax: 937 254-0244
William Heath, *Owner*
Karen Wysong, *Sales Staff*
EMP: 9
SQ FT: 4,000

SALES: 450K **Privately Held**
SIC: 5999 5719 2499 Picture frames,
ready made; pictures, wall; picture frame
molding, finished

(G-8394)
HTEC SYSTEMS INC
561 Congress Park Dr (45459-4036)
PHONE...................................937 438-3010
Peter A Flaherty, *President*
Phillip Hayden, *Chairman*
Christopher Hayden, *Corp Secy*
Pete Lieser, *Engineer*
EMP: 10
SQ FT: 4,000
SALES: 3MM **Privately Held**
WEB: www.htecsystems.com
SIC: 8711 7389 1629 3599 Engineering
services; design services; industrial plant
construction; custom machinery

(G-8395)
HUBER HEIGHTS LICENSE
BUREAU
6134 Chambersburg Rd (45424-3857)
PHONE...................................937 233-7560
Fax: 937 233-6441
Mike Foley, *Owner*
Elizabeth Bolner, *Owner*
EMP: 15
SALES (est): 1.2MM **Privately Held**
SIC: 3469 Automobile license tags,
stamped metal

(G-8396)
HUESTON INDUSTRIES INC
3020 Production Ct (45414-3514)
PHONE...................................937 264-8163
Michael Parin, *President*
John Parin, *Manager*
EMP: 8
SQ FT: 5,100
SALES: 1.2MM **Privately Held**
SIC: 3625 Noise control equipment

(G-8397)
HUNTER TOOL AND DIE
COMPANY
2104 E 1st St (45403-1207)
PHONE...................................937 256-9798
Fax: 937 256-3391
Mike Barok, *President*
Diane Barok, *Corp Secy*
EMP: 4
SALES: 450K **Privately Held**
SIC: 3544 Special dies, tools, jigs & fix-
tures

(G-8398)
HYDE PARK ELECTRONICS LLC
1875 Founders Dr (45420-4017)
PHONE...................................937 252-2121
Fax: 937 258-5830
Piyush Shah, *Engineer*
Mark Waggoner, *Engineer*
Tracey Murphy, *Manager*
Greg Nelson,
▲ EMP: 70
SQ FT: 33,000
SALES (est): 9.8MM
SALES (corp-wide): 241K **Privately Held**
WEB: www.squared.com
SIC: 3625 Electric controls & control ac-
cessories, industrial
HQ: Schneider Electric Usa, Inc.
800 Federal St
Andover MA 01810
978 975-9600

(G-8399)
HYLAND MACHINE COMPANY
Also Called: Hyland Screw Machine Products
1900 Kuntz Rd (45404-1251)
P.O. Box 133 (45404-0133)
PHONE...................................937 233-8600
Fax: 937 233-7067
Forest Hyland, *President*
Dan Hyland, *Vice Pres*
Mitch Lambert, *Plant Mgr*
Brian Hyland, *Sales Staff*
▲ EMP: 27 EST: 1928
SQ FT: 42,000
SALES (est): 7.1MM **Privately Held**
WEB: www.hylandmach.com
SIC: 3451 Screw machine products

(G-8400)
IDX CORPORATION
2875 Needmore Rd (45414-4301)
PHONE.............................937 401-3225
David Mueller, *General Mgr*
EMP: 150
SALES (corp-wide): 454.7MM **Privately Held**
SIC: 3083 2521 3999 2511 Plastic finished products, laminated; wood office furniture; plaques, picture, laminated; wood household furniture; wood kitchen cabinets; millwork
PA: Idx Corporation
1 Rider Trail Plaza Dr
Earth City MO 63045
314 739-4120

(G-8401)
INDEPENDENT AWNING & CANVAS CO
324 Jones St (45410-1104)
PHONE.............................937 223-9661
Fax: 937 223-7043
Fred Utzinger III, *President*
Shirley Utzinger, *Corp Secy*
EMP: 7
SQ FT: 5,400
SALES: 575.2K **Privately Held**
SIC: 2394 Awnings, fabric: made from purchased materials

(G-8402)
INDUSTRIAL FIBERGLASS SPC INC
Also Called: Fiber Systems
521 Kiser St (45404-1641)
PHONE.............................937 222-9000
Theodore Morton, *Ch of Bd*
Diana Hall, *President*
Janice Morton, *Corp Secy*
Diana Partin, *Purchasing*
Rose Marie Wiliams, *Accounting Mgr*
EMP: 35 EST: 1978
SQ FT: 122,000
SALES (est): 6.5MM **Privately Held**
WEB: www.ifs-frp.com
SIC: 3229 1799 Glass fiber products; service station equipment installation, maintenance & repair

(G-8403)
INLAND MANUFACTURING LLC
6785 W 3rd St (45417-7837)
PHONE.............................937 835-0220
Penelope Norton, *Office Mgr*
Ronald Norton,
EMP: 3
SALES (est): 215.7K **Privately Held**
SIC: 3484 Rifles or rifle parts, 30 mm. & below

(G-8404)
INNOMARK COMMUNICATIONS LLC
6700 Homestretch Rd (45414-2516)
PHONE.............................937 454-5555
Robert Fares, *Plant Mgr*
Rob Jones, *Manager*
EMP: 42
SALES (corp-wide): 126.2MM **Privately Held**
SIC: 2752 2789 Commercial printing, offset; bookbinding & related work
PA: Innomark Communications Llc
3233 S Tech Blvd
Miamisburg OH 45342
937 427-6100

(G-8405)
INNOVATIVE PLASTIC MOLDERS LLC
7438 Webster St (45414-5816)
PHONE.............................937 898-3775
Brian O' Leary, *Mng Member*
Dave Stelmat, *Manager*
EMP: 50
SQ FT: 12,800
SALES (est): 11.3MM **Privately Held**
SIC: 3544 Special dies, tools, jigs & fixtures

(G-8406)
INNOVATIVE RETAIL DISPLAYS INC
2127 Troy St (45404-2162)
P.O. Box 156 (45404-0156)
PHONE.............................937 237-7708
Jackie Simpson, *CEO*
Michael Ely, *President*
Craig Simpson, *Vice Pres*
▲ EMP: 19
SQ FT: 12,000
SALES: 1.1MM **Privately Held**
SIC: 2541 Store & office display cases & fixtures; cabinets, lockers & shelving

(G-8407)
INNOVATIVE VEND SOLUTIONS LLC
2048 S Alex Rd (45449-4042)
PHONE.............................866 931-9413
Patrick McDonald, *Principal*
EMP: 24
SALES (est): 5.2MM **Privately Held**
SIC: 3581 Automatic vending machines

(G-8408)
INNOVATIVE WELD SOLUTIONS LTD
1701 Farr Dr (45404-2286)
PHONE.............................937 545-7695
Anthony Ananthanarayanan,
EMP: 8
SQ FT: 8,000
SALES: 150K **Privately Held**
SIC: 8733 3691 Scientific research agency; storage batteries

(G-8409)
INSIGNIA SIGNS INC
300 Gargrave Rd (45449-2464)
PHONE.............................937 866-2341
Rick Dobson, *President*
Dan McBride, *Principal*
Chip Heck, *Prdtn Mgr*
EMP: 8
SALES (est): 972.2K **Privately Held**
SIC: 3993 7336 Signs & advertising specialties; graphic arts & related design

(G-8410)
INSTANTWHIP-DAYTON INC (PA)
Also Called: Tiller Foods
5820 Executive Blvd (45424-1451)
PHONE.............................937 235-5930
Fax: 937 235-5936
Donald Tiller Jr, *President*
William B Tiller, *Vice Pres*
David Yost, *Admin Sec*
▲ EMP: 15
SQ FT: 15,000
SALES (est): 1.7MM **Privately Held**
SIC: 2026 2023 5143 Half & half; cream substitutes; dairy products, except dried or canned

(G-8411)
INSTANTWHIP-DAYTON INC
Also Called: Tiller Foods
967 Senate Dr (45459-4017)
PHONE.............................937 435-4371
Fax: 937 435-1408
David Yost, *General Mgr*
EMP: 6
SALES (corp-wide): 1.7MM **Privately Held**
SIC: 2026 2023 Half & half; cream substitutes
PA: Instantwhip-Dayton, Inc.
5820 Executive Blvd
Dayton OH 45424
937 235-5930

(G-8412)
INSTRUCTION & DESIGN CONCEPTS
441 Maple Springs Dr (45458-9232)
PHONE.............................937 439-2698
Fran Kick, *Owner*
EMP: 5
SALES: 156.7K **Privately Held**
WEB: www.kickitin.com
SIC: 8748 2731 8732 7336 Educational consultant; book publishing; educational research; commercial art & graphic design; management consulting services;

(G-8413)
INTEGRITY MANUFACTURING CORP
3723 Inpark Dr (45414-4417)
P.O. Box 312 (45404-0312)
PHONE.............................937 233-6792
Fax: 937 233-7957
Richard L Halderman, *President*
Kevin Halderman, *General Mgr*
Gretchen Halderman, *Vice Pres*
Keith Halderman, *Manager*
EMP: 20
SQ FT: 11,950
SALES (est): 4.2MM **Privately Held**
WEB: www.integrity-mfg.com
SIC: 3451 3599 Screw machine products; machine shop, jobbing & repair

(G-8414)
INTEGRITY PRINTING
912 N Main St (45405-4633)
PHONE.............................937 331-5390
Fax: 937 331-5391
Greg Jones, *Owner*
EMP: 5 EST: 1990
SALES (est): 260K **Privately Held**
SIC: 2759 Commercial printing

(G-8415)
INTERNATIONAL BUSINESS SOLUTIO
Also Called: Ibsa
432 Windsor Park Dr (45459-4111)
PHONE.............................937 853-0348
Mike Luckett, *Senior VP*
Karen Stensland, *Manager*
Amy Cooper, *Director*
Mark McKinney,
Roger Courson,
EMP: 19
SQ FT: 2,500
SALES (est): 2.1MM **Privately Held**
WEB: www.ibsaonline.com
SIC: 2759 Business forms: printing

(G-8416)
INTERNATIONAL FINISHING LLC
2223 S Dixie Dr (45409-2014)
P.O. Box 290 (45409-0290)
PHONE.............................937 293-3340
Daniel J O'Connor, *President*
Maryann Weber, *Administration*
EMP: 5
SQ FT: 4,200
SALES (est): 920.9K **Privately Held**
WEB: www.internationalfinishing.com
SIC: 3559 Metal finishing equipment for plating, etc.

(G-8417)
INTERNATIONAL LAMINATING CORP
1712 Springfield St Ste 2 (45403-1447)
PHONE.............................937 254-8181
Raymond P Horan, *President*
Debbie Zengel, *General Mgr*
Debbie Burnett, *Mfg Staff*
Jack Parente, *Consultant*
EMP: 20
SQ FT: 25,000
SALES (est): 3.3MM **Privately Held**
WEB: www.intlam.com
SIC: 3083 Laminated plastics plate & sheet

(G-8418)
J T E CORP
5675 Webster St (45414-3518)
PHONE.............................937 454-1112
Fax: 937 454-1102
James Thorstenson, *President*
Jack Thornburg, *Vice Pres*
Thorstenson James, *Administration*
EMP: 4
SQ FT: 2,000
SALES (est): 499.3K **Privately Held**
WEB: www.jtecor.com
SIC: 3599 3548 Machine shop, jobbing & repair; welding & cutting apparatus & accessories

(G-8419)
JAFFE & GROSS JEWELRY COMPANY
3951 Far Hills Ave (45429-2438)
PHONE.............................937 461-9450
Fax: 937 461-9260
Lawrence Jaffe, *President*
Linda Matthews, *Corp Secy*
Beth Darmour, *Manager*
EMP: 3
SALES: 1.6MM **Privately Held**
WEB: www.jaffejewelry.com
SIC: 5944 5094 7389 3911 Jewelry, precious stones & precious metals; jewelry & precious stones; appraisers, except real estate; jewelry, precious metal

(G-8420)
JAMES C FREE INC (PA)
Also Called: James Free Jewelers
3100 Far Hills Ave (45429-2512)
PHONE.............................937 298-0171
Fax: 937 298-2872
Michael S Karaman, *President*
Beth Crawford, *Buyer*
Joe Helm, *Sales Mgr*
Scott Hannig, *Sales Staff*
Stephanie Potter, *Office Mgr*
▲ EMP: 20
SQ FT: 6,000
SALES (est): 3.4MM **Privately Held**
WEB: www.jamesfreejewelers.com
SIC: 3911 5944 Jewelry, precious metal; jewelry, precious stones & precious metals

(G-8421)
JAMES R EATON
535 Clareridge Ln (45458-2602)
PHONE.............................937 435-7767
EMP: 3
SALES (est): 285.8K **Privately Held**
SIC: 3625 Mfg Relays/Industrial Controls

(G-8422)
JANEWAY SIGNS INC
Also Called: Fastsigns
7825 Waynetowne Blvd (45424-2063)
PHONE.............................937 237-8433
Fax: 937 237-8436
Larry Miller, *President*
Wayne Beisner, *General Mgr*
EMP: 5
SQ FT: 1,500
SALES: 350K **Privately Held**
SIC: 3993 Signs & advertising specialties

(G-8423)
JBK MANUFACTURING LLC
Also Called: J B K Manufacturing & Dev
2127 Troy St (45404-2162)
PHONE.............................937 233-8300
Fax: 937 426-8585
Carol Brabender, *Accountant*
Kenneth Nutter, *Mng Member*
Bill Bowling, *Director*
Robert W Nutter,
▲ EMP: 30
SQ FT: 20,000
SALES (est): 6.6MM **Privately Held**
WEB: www.jbkmfg.com
SIC: 3599 Machine shop, jobbing & repair

(G-8424)
JC ROOFING SUPPLY (PA)
1535 Keystone Ave (45403-3335)
PHONE.............................937 258-9999
Fax: 937 258-0842
Gerald Jayne, *Owner*
Austin Bauer, *Manager*
EMP: 2
SQ FT: 2,000
SALES (est): 2.8MM **Privately Held**
SIC: 3531 Roofing equipment

(G-8425)
JEFF BONHAM ELECTRIC INC
3647 Wright Way Rd (45424-5165)
PHONE.............................937 233-7662
Jeff Bonham, *President*
Bryan Farlow, *Vice Pres*
EMP: 22
SQ FT: 1,500

GEOGRAPHIC

SALES (est): 4.6MM **Privately Held**
WEB: www.jeffbonhamelectric.com
SIC: **1731** 3613 Electrical work; panel &
distribution boards & other related apparatus; fuses, electric

(G-8426)
JEFFREY L BECHT INC
Also Called: Sign Dynamics
2781 Thunderhawk Ct (45414-3445)
PHONE................................937 264-2070
Jeffrey L Becht, *President*
Jessica Bennham, *Project Mgr*
Nate Bucher, *Project Mgr*
John Smith, *Project Mgr*
Connie Rismiller, *Opers Mgr*
EMP: 3
SQ FT: 6,000
SALES (est): 769.5K **Privately Held**
WEB: www.signdynamics.com
SIC: **3993** Signs & advertising specialties

(G-8427)
JEFFS BAKERY
210 Groveview Ave (45415-2305)
PHONE................................937 890-9703
Jeff Morris, *Principal*
EMP: 5
SALES (est): 275.1K **Privately Held**
SIC: **2051** Bakery: wholesale or whole-
sale/retail combined

(G-8428)
JOYCE/DAYTON CORP (HQ)
3300 S Dixie Dr Ste 101 (45439-2318)
P.O. Box 635789, Cincinnati (45263-5789)
PHONE................................937 294-6261
Fax: 937 294-7631
Michael Harris, *President*
Tim Hummel, *Opers Staff*
Victor Lianas, *Purchasing*
Eric Claudepierre, *Engineer*
Roy Mead, *Engineer*
▲ EMP: 30 EST: 1893
SQ FT: 20,000
SALES (est): 27.1MM
SALES (corp-wide): 2.4B **Publicly Held**
SIC: **3569** Jacks, hydraulic
PA: Graham Holdings Company
1300 17th St N Ste 1700
Arlington VA 22209
703 345-6300

(G-8429)
JULIE MAYNARD INC
Also Called: Consolidated Vehicle Converter
4991 Hempstead Station Dr (45429-5159)
PHONE................................937 443-0408
Julie Maynard, *President*
Tim Prugh, *Corp Secy*
Marcia Prugh, *Vice Pres*
Lisa Brandt, *Office Mgr*
▲ EMP: 10
SQ FT: 20,000
SALES (est): 2.3MM **Privately Held**
SIC: **3714** 3566 Motor vehicle parts & ac-
cessories; speed changers, drives &
gears

(G-8430)
JUNEBUGS CUPCAKED
2423 Mmsburg Cntrville Rd (45459)
PHONE................................937 723-9040
Michael Stewart, *Principal*
EMP: 7
SALES (est): 602.9K **Privately Held**
SIC: **2053** Cakes, bakery: frozen

(G-8431)
JUST BUSINESS INC
Also Called: Onstage Publications
1612 Prosser Ave Ste 100 (45409-2041)
PHONE................................866 577-3303
Norman L Orlowski, *President*
Garett Orlowski, *Vice Pres*
Ashlie Steadman, *Production*
Kyle Orlowski, *VP Sales*
Lee Mardis, *Accounts Mgr*
EMP: 14 EST: 2001
SQ FT: 2,000
SALES: 2MM **Privately Held**
WEB: www.jusbiz.com
SIC: **8742** 2731 7311 Marketing consult-
ing services; book publishing; advertising
consultant

(G-8432)
K & B ACQUISITIONS INC
Also Called: Mehaffie Pie Company
3013 Linden Ave (45410-3028)
PHONE................................937 253-1163
Fax: 937 253-1111
Greg Hay, *President*
Jim Columbus, *Vice Pres*
Bruce Kouse, *Vice Pres*
Steve Columbus, *Plant Mgr*
Barb Columbus, *Treasurer*
EMP: 10 EST: 1930
SQ FT: 9,000
SALES (est): 650K **Privately Held**
SIC: **2051** 5461 Pies, bakery: except
frozen; pies

(G-8433)
K & R PRETZEL CO
1700 Flesher Ave (45420-3231)
PHONE................................937 299-2231
Kathleen Glaze, *Owner*
EMP: 3
SALES (est): 183.6K **Privately Held**
SIC: **2052** Pretzels

(G-8434)
KEITHLEY ENTERPRISES INC
Also Called: Bucher Printing
3425 Garianne Dr (45414-2221)
PHONE................................937 890-1878
Randy Keithley, *President*
Sherry Keithley, *Admin Sec*
EMP: 9
SQ FT: 5,000
SALES: 500K **Privately Held**
SIC: **2752** 2759 2679 Commercial print-
ing, offset; letterpress printing; labels,
paper: made from purchased material

(G-8435)
KELLEY COMMUNICATION DEV
Also Called: Kelley Bible Books
2312 Candlewood Dr (45419-2825)
P.O. Box 292113 (45429-0113)
PHONE................................937 298-6132
Robert Kelley, *Owner*
EMP: 7
SALES (est): 315.7K **Privately Held**
WEB: www.kcdev.com
SIC: **2731** Books: publishing only

(G-8436)
KENDALL & SONS COMPANY
Also Called: Kendall Printing
510 Xenia Ave (45410-1824)
PHONE................................937 222-6996
Fax: 937 222-6998
Michael Kendall, *President*
Brian Kendall, *Principal*
Elma Kendall, *Corp Secy*
Susan Kendall, *Vice Pres*
Eff Smith, *Administration*
EMP: 5
SQ FT: 3,800
SALES (est): 680.1K **Privately Held**
SIC: **2752** 4731 Commercial printing, litho-
graphic; freight transportation arrange-
ment

(G-8437)
KENNEDY INK COMPANY INC
110 Vermont Ave (45404-1522)
PHONE................................937 461-5600
Fax: 937 461-5600
James Bishop, *Manager*
EMP: 4
SALES (corp-wide): 2.5MM **Privately
Held**
SIC: **2893** 5085 Printing ink; ink, printers'
PA: Kennedy Ink Company, Inc.
5230 Wooster Pike
Cincinnati OH 45226
513 871-2515

(G-8438)
KENWORTH OF DAYTON
7740 Center Point 70 Blvd (45424-6367)
PHONE................................937 235-2589
Fax: 937 235-2589
Randy Pennington, *Principal*
Jim Buhrlage, *Store Mgr*
EMP: 16
SALES (est): 2.9MM **Privately Held**
SIC: **3519** Internal combustion engines

(G-8439)
KERF WATERJET LTD
313 E Helena St (45404-1031)
PHONE................................937 254-9711
Jon Wickersham, *Partner*
David Kleinfelder, *Partner*
EMP: 3
SQ FT: 3,500
SALES: 700K **Privately Held**
WEB: www.kerfwaterjet.com
SIC: **3599** Machine & other job shop work

(G-8440)
KESSLER SIGN COMPANY
5804 Poe Ave (45414-3442)
PHONE................................937 898-0633
Fax: 740 898-7407
Robert Kessler, *President*
Leslie Newlun, *Marketing Staff*
Aaron Hillis, *Supervisor*
Nichole Keylor, *Executive Asst*
EMP: 4
SALES (corp-wide): 7.4MM **Privately
Held**
WEB: www.kesslersignco.com
SIC: **3993** 7312 1799 Signs, not made in
custom sign painting shops; outdoor ad-
vertising services; sign installation &
maintenance
PA: Kessler Sign Company
2669 National Rd
Zanesville OH 43701
740 453-0668

(G-8441)
KIMMATT CORP
Also Called: Best Glass
326 Troy St (45404-1856)
PHONE................................937 228-3811
Fax: 937 228-0282
Susan Ballweg, *President*
Matthew Ballweg, *Vice Pres*
Larry Ballweg, *Treasurer*
Karla Flaming, *Admin Sec*
EMP: 8
SQ FT: 5,000
SALES (est): 1MM **Privately Held**
SIC: **1793** 3496 3231 Glass & glazing
work; screening, woven wire: made from
purchased wire; strengthened or rein-
forced glass; mirrored glass

(G-8442)
KISTLER INSTRUMENT CORP
3061 Dorf Dr (45439-7902)
PHONE................................937 268-5920
Bob Hendricks, *Principal*
EMP: 3
SALES (est): 155.3K **Privately Held**
SIC: **1446** Molding sand mining

(G-8443)
KNOBLE TOOL CORP
1535 Stanley Ave (45404-1112)
PHONE................................937 461-4040
Tom Biegel, *President*
EMP: 25
SQ FT: 20,000
SALES (est): 1.3MM **Privately Held**
SIC: **3545** 3544 Gauges (machine tool ac-
cessories); special dies & tools

(G-8444)
**KOLHFAB CSTM PLSTIC
FBRICATION**
2025 Webster St (45404-1143)
PHONE................................937 237-2098
Bernie Kohlbarg, *CEO*
EMP: 6
SALES: 600K **Privately Held**
SIC: **2399** Emblems, badges & insignia

(G-8445)
KOMATEC TOOL & DIE INC
1415 E 2nd St (45403-1022)
PHONE................................937 252-1133
Donald Koman, *President*
Kevin Stewart, *Admin Sec*
EMP: 4
SQ FT: 3,000
SALES: 250K **Privately Held**
SIC: **3599** Machine shop, jobbing & repair

(G-8446)
KRDC INC
Also Called: Martin-Palmer TI & Die Co Div
90 Vermont Ave (45404-1521)
PHONE................................937 222-2332
Fax: 937 222-2332
Richie Blevins, *President*
Kenneth R Syx, *Vice Pres*
Rick Syx, *Vice Pres*
EMP: 8
SQ FT: 12,500
SALES: 700K **Privately Held**
SIC: **3599** 3544 Machine & other job shop
work; special dies, tools, jigs & fixtures

(G-8447)
KROGER CO
1934 Needmore Rd (45414-3808)
PHONE................................937 277-0950
Fax: 937 277-6393
Pete Gerger, *Manager*
EMP: 150
SALES (corp-wide): 115.3B **Publicly
Held**
WEB: www.kroger.com
SIC: **5411** 5992 5912 2052 Supermar-
kets, chain; florists; drug stores & propri-
etary stores; cookies & crackers; bread,
cake & related products
PA: The Kroger Co
1014 Vine St Ste 1000
Cincinnati OH 45202
513 762-4000

(G-8448)
KUSTOM CASES LLC
130 Oxford Ave (45402-6149)
PHONE................................240 380-6275
Mike Smith, *CEO*
EMP: 4
SALES (est): 197.3K **Privately Held**
SIC: **2051** 7389 Bakery: wholesale or
wholesale/retail combined;

(G-8449)
L3 TECHNOLOGIES INC
3155 Res Blvd Ste 101 (45420)
PHONE................................937 223-3285
Fax: 937 425-6680
Walker Larimer, *Branch Mgr*
EMP: 7
SALES (corp-wide): 10.5B **Publicly Held**
SIC: **3812** Navigational systems & instru-
ments
PA: L3 Technologies, Inc.
600 3rd Ave Fl 34
New York NY 10016
212 697-1111

(G-8450)
LAB-PRO INC
11019 Cold Spring Dr (45458-4518)
PHONE................................937 434-9600
Joseph Jobe, *President*
EMP: 9
SALES: 8MM **Privately Held**
SIC: **3448** 5039 Prefabricated metal build-
ings; prefabricated buildings

(G-8451)
LAHM-TROSPER INC
Also Called: Lahm Tool
1030 Springfield St (45403-1350)
P.O. Box 336 (45401-0336)
PHONE................................937 252-8791
Fax: 937 252-0373
James Trosper, *President*
Jennifer Kovach, *Manager*
EMP: 17
SQ FT: 10,000
SALES (est): 4.1MM **Privately Held**
SIC: **3541** 3544 Machine tools, metal cut-
ting type; special dies, tools, jigs & fix-
tures

(G-8452)
LASERMARK LLC
530 N Union Rd (45417-7615)
P.O. Box 10308 Ambe, Cincinnati (45241)
PHONE................................513 312-9889
Charles Mark, *Agent*
Sherman McGill,
Ron Norton,
EMP: 3

SALES (est): 150K **Privately Held**
SIC: 5092 5734 3949 Video games; software, computer games; pigeons, clay
(targets)

(G-8453)
LAVISH LYFE MAGAZINE
19 Colgate Ave (45417-8944)
PHONE................................937 938-5816
Ryan Pope, *Principal*
EMP: 3
SALES (est): 184.3K **Privately Held**
SIC: 2721 Periodicals

(G-8454)
**LAWRENCE TECHNOLOGIES
INC**
2571 Timber Ln (45414-4731)
PHONE................................937 274-7771
Fax: 937 274-7775
Lawrence J Richards, *President*
Linda Heider, *Vice Pres*
▲ EMP: 8
SQ FT: 5,000
SALES (est): 1.4MM **Privately Held**
WEB: www.lawrencetechnologies.com
SIC: 3714 3728 3569 8711 Motor vehicle
parts & accessories; aircraft parts &
equipment; filters; professional engineer

(G-8455)
LENCO INDUSTRIES INC
3301 Klepinger Rd (45406-1823)
PHONE................................937 277-9364
John L Lenz, *President*
Robert Wagner, *Vice Pres*
EMP: 50 EST: 1955
SQ FT: 15,000
SALES (est): 4.9MM **Privately Held**
WEB: www.lenzinc.com
SIC: 3451 Screw machine products

(G-8456)
LENZ INC
Also Called: Lenz Company
3301 Klepinger Rd (45406-1823)
P.O. Box 1044 (45401-1044)
PHONE................................937 277-9364
Fax: 937 277-6516
Robert Wagner, *President*
Grace Campbell, *Human Resources*
Rick Brown, *Sales Staff*
EMP: 50
SQ FT: 15,000
SALES (est): 6.5MM **Privately Held**
WEB: www.thelenz.com
SIC: 6531 3089 Real estate brokers &
agents; fittings for pipe, plastic

(G-8457)
LEWARK METAL SPINNING INC
2746 Keenan Ave (45414-4912)
PHONE................................937 275-3303
Fax: 937 275-5111
Larry W Lewark, *President*
Pete Hagenbuch, *President*
Mickey Click, *General Mgr*
Brian Henderson, *General Mgr*
Rachael Lewark, *Human Res Mgr*
EMP: 50
SQ FT: 35,000
SALES (est): 15MM **Privately Held**
WEB: www.lewarkmetalspinning.com
SIC: 3499 3469 Friction material, made
from powdered metal; spinning metal for
the trade

(G-8458)
LION APPAREL INC (HQ)
7200 Poe Ave Ste 400 (45414-2798)
PHONE................................937 898-1949
Fax: 937 898-9204
Steve Schwartz, *CEO*
Stephen A Schwartz, *President*
Mark Berliant, *Principal*
Mark Jahnke, *Principal*
Stephen Schwartz, *Principal*
◆ EMP: 150 EST: 1930
SQ FT: 37,000

SALES (est): 237.1MM
SALES (corp-wide): 87.8MM **Privately
Held**
WEB: www.lionprotectivesystems.com
SIC: 2311 Firemen's uniforms: made from
purchased materials; military uniforms,
men's & youths': purchased materials; policemen's uniforms: made from purchased
materials
PA: Lion Group, Inc.
7200 Poe Ave Ste 400
Dayton OH 45414
937 898-1949

(G-8459)
LORD CORPORATION
Mechanical Products Division
4644 Wadsworth Rd (45414-4220)
PHONE................................937 278-9431
Fax: 937 278-6286
Carol Williams, *Purchasing*
Michael Rogers, *Personnel*
Janet Eastep, *Manager*
Miriam Zietlow, *Director*
Gary Kelly, *Maintence Staff*
EMP: 150
SQ FT: 30,000
SALES (corp-wide): 848.2MM **Privately
Held**
WEB: www.lordcorp.com
SIC: 3545 3769 Machine tool accessories;
guided missile & space vehicle parts &
auxiliary equipment
PA: Lord Corporation
111 Lord Dr
Cary NC 27511
919 468-5979

(G-8460)
LORENZ CORPORATION (PA)
Also Called: Show What You Know
501 E 3rd St (45402-2280)
P.O. Box 802 (45401-0802)
PHONE................................937 228-6118
Fax: 937 223-2042
Geoffrey R Lorenz, *Ch of Bd*
Reiff Lorenz, *President*
Jean A Shafferman, *Editor*
Tom Borchers, *Corp Secy*
Barbara Meaks, *Vice Pres*
▲ EMP: 68 EST: 1890
SQ FT: 55,000
SALES (est): 9.1MM **Privately Held**
WEB: www.lorenz.com
SIC: 2741 5049 2721 Music, sheet: pub-
lishing only, not printed on site; school
supplies; periodicals: publishing only

(G-8461)
**M & R ELECTRIC MOTOR SVC
INC**
1516 E 5th St (45403-2397)
PHONE................................937 222-6282
Fax: 937 222-1901
Charles Mader, *Corp Secy*
Ronald Mader, *Vice Pres*
Anthony Mader, *Vice Pres*
Craig Mader, *Treasurer*
EMP: 28 EST: 1949
SQ FT: 8,000
SALES: 4MM **Privately Held**
SIC: 5063 7694 Motors, electric; electric
motor repair

(G-8462)
**M J COATES CONSTRUCTION
CO**
9809 Saddle Creek Trl (45458-9729)
P.O. Box 41231 (45441-0231)
PHONE................................937 886-9546
Martin J Coates, *President*
Toni Coates, *Bookkeeper*
EMP: 11
SALES (est): 670K **Privately Held**
WEB: www.mjcoateshomes.com
SIC: 1442 1521 Gravel & pebble mining;
new construction, single-family houses

(G-8463)
**M J COATES CONSTRUCTION
CO (PA)**
Also Called: Mj Coates Homes
9809 Saddle Creek Trl (45458-9729)
P.O. Box 41231 (45441-0231)
PHONE................................937 886-9546
Fax: 937 293-6698

Marty Coates, *President*
Toni Coates, *Admin Sec*
EMP: 3
SQ FT: 2,000
SALES: 4.5MM **Privately Held**
SIC: 1522 1442 Residential construction;
gravel mining

(G-8464)
**M T M MOLDED PRODUCTS
COMPANY**
3370 Obco Ct (45414-3500)
P.O. Box 13117 (45413-0117)
PHONE................................937 890-7461
Fax: 937 890-1747
William J Minneman, *Ch of Bd*
Steve Minneman, *President*
Allen Minneman, *Vice Pres*
Steve Osborne, *Safety Mgr*
Mike Luksic, *Engineer*
▼ EMP: 25
SQ FT: 38,000
SALES (est): 6.4MM **Privately Held**
WEB: www.mtmmolded.com
SIC: 3089 Cases, plastic; molding primary
plastic

(G-8465)
M21 INDUSTRIES LLC
Also Called: Module 21 Bldg Company
721 Springfield St (45403-1250)
P.O. Box 4044 (45401-4044)
PHONE................................937 781-1377
Fax: 937 781-1375
Jeffrey Levine, *CEO*
Wolfgang Dalichau, *President*
David Allen, *Vice Pres*
Rusty Brown, *Vice Pres*
Don Carter, *Vice Pres*
EMP: 90
SQ FT: 230,000
SALES (est): 10.6MM **Privately Held**
WEB: www.m21industries.com
SIC: 2541 2431 Office fixtures, wood; win-
dows, wood

(G-8466)
**MACHINE PRODUCTS
COMPANY**
5660 Webster St (45414-3596)
PHONE................................937 890-6600
Fax: 937 890-1916
Robert C Appenzeller, *President*
Rebecca A Cain, *Corp Secy*
David Mansfield, *Purch Agent*
Curtis Bailey, *Engrg Mgr*
Jeff Hutchins, *Engineer*
EMP: 35 EST: 1956
SQ FT: 40,000
SALES (est): 6.7MM **Privately Held**
WEB: www.mpcdayton.com
SIC: 3599 3825 3694 Machine shop, job-
bing & repair; instruments to measure
electricity; engine electrical equipment

(G-8467)
MACHINEX OF DAYTON INC
10 Davis Ave (45403-2999)
PHONE................................937 252-7021
Fax: 937 252-7218
William Brownsberger, *President*
Janet M Brownsberger, *Treasurer*
EMP: 4
SQ FT: 10,000
SALES: 125.1K **Privately Held**
SIC: 3599 Machine shop, jobbing & repair

(G-8468)
MADSEN WIRE PRODUCTS INC
101 Madison St (45402-1711)
P.O. Box 98, Orland IN (46776-0098)
PHONE................................937 829-6561
Gary Stephens, *President*
▲ EMP: 50
SALES (est): 3.1MM **Privately Held**
SIC: 3315 Wire & fabricated wire products

(G-8469)
MAGNUM TOOL CORP
1407 Stanley Ave (45404-1110)
PHONE................................937 228-0900
Fax: 937 228-8954
Christopher S Grooms, *President*
Gregory S Grooms, *Corp Secy*
Cindy Sands, *Office Mgr*
◆ EMP: 8

SQ FT: 6,000
SALES: 720K **Privately Held**
SIC: 3544 Special dies & tools; jigs & fix-
tures; industrial molds

(G-8470)
MAHLE BEHR DAYTON LLC
1720 Webster St (45404-1128)
PHONE................................937 369-2900
Rob Baker, *Branch Mgr*
EMP: 350 **Privately Held**
SIC: 3714 Air conditioner parts, motor vehi-
cle
HQ: Mahle Behr Dayton L.L.C.
1600 Webster St
Dayton OH 45404
937 369-2900

(G-8471)
MAHLE BEHR DAYTON LLC (DH)
1600 Webster St (45404-1144)
PHONE................................937 369-2900
Willm Uhlenbecker, *CEO*
Ing Heinz K Junker, *Ch of Bd*
Wolf Hennig Scheider, *President*
Bruce Moorehouse, *Vice Pres*
Stephen Kemp, *Engineer*
◆ EMP: 93
SALES: 272.4MM **Privately Held**
SIC: 3714 Motor vehicle parts & acces-
sories
HQ: Mahle Behr Gmbh & Co. Kg
Mauserstr. 3
Stuttgart
711 501-0

(G-8472)
MAHLE BEHR USA INC
Also Called: Behr Dayton Thermal Products
1600 Webster St (45404-1144)
PHONE................................937 369-2000
Wilhelm Baum, *Principal*
Mark Autio, *Engineer*
Dan Byrne, *Engineer*
Robert Smell, *Engineer*
Ellyn Chaney, *Manager*
EMP: 2000 **Privately Held**
SIC: 3443 3585 Heat exchangers, con-
densers & components; refrigeration &
heating equipment
HQ: Mahle Behr Usa Inc.
2700 Daley Dr
Troy MI 48083
248 743-3700

(G-8473)
**MAHLE INDUSTRIES
INCORPORATED**
Also Called: Delphi-T - Vandalia Ptc
1600 Webster St (45404-1144)
PHONE................................937 890-2739
Samuel Cicatello, *Branch Mgr*
EMP: 30 **Privately Held**
SIC: 3714 Motor vehicle parts & acces-
sories
HQ: Mahle Industries, Incorporated
23030 Mahle Dr
Farmington Hills MI 48335
248 305-8200

(G-8474)
MANCOR OHIO INC (HQ)
1008 Leonhard St (45404-1666)
PHONE................................937 228-6141
Art Church, *Ch of Bd*
Dale Harper, *President*
Joe Rimkus, *CFO*
Dino Bigbee, *Supervisor*
Dwayne Roseberry, *Supervisor*
EMP: 50
SALES (est): 61.3MM
SALES (corp-wide): 68.8MM **Privately
Held**
SIC: 3713 Truck bodies & parts
PA: Mancor Canada Inc
2485 Speers Rd
Oakville ON L6L 2
905 827-3737

(G-8475)
MANCOR OHIO INC
600 Kiser St (45404-1644)
PHONE................................937 228-6141
George McNight, *General Mgr*
Richard Meissner, *Plant Mgr*
Ray Kemphues, *Engineer*

EMP: 55
SALES (corp-wide): 68.8MM **Privately Held**
SIC: 3713 Truck bodies & parts
HQ: Mancor Ohio Inc.
　　1008 Leonhard St
　　Dayton OH 45404
　　937 228-6141

(G-8476)
MAR-VEL TOOL CO INC
858 Hall Ave (45404-1142)
PHONE...................................937 223-2137
Fax: 937 223-2131
John G Glaser, *President*
Brett R Glaser, *Vice Pres*
EMP: 25
SQ FT: 23,000
SALES (est): 2.4MM **Privately Held**
SIC: 3544 Special dies & tools; jigs & fixtures

(G-8477)
MARCO PRINTED PRODUCTS CO
Also Called: Marco's Papers
25 W Whipp Rd (45459-1811)
PHONE...................................937 433-7030
Fax: 937 433-7767
Gary Ihle, *President*
Margaret Ihle, *Treasurer*
Karen Ihle, *Manager*
David Ihle, *Admin Sec*
EMP: 20
SQ FT: 7,000
SALES (est): 1.9MM **Privately Held**
WEB: www.marcopaper.com
SIC: 2752 Commercial printing, lithographic

(G-8478)
MARCO PRINTED PRODUCTS CO INC (PA)
Also Called: Marco's Paper
14 Marco Ln (45458-3857)
PHONE...................................937 433-5680
Fax: 937 433-0496
R Gary Ihle, *President*
Margaret Ihle, *Treasurer*
David Ihle, *Admin Sec*
EMP: 5 EST: 1971
SQ FT: 3,200
SALES (est): 2.3MM **Privately Held**
SIC: 7331 2752 5111 Mailing service; commercial printing, offset; printing paper

(G-8479)
MAXTOOL COMPANY LIMITED
2946 Production Ct (45414-3537)
PHONE...................................937 415-5776
Mack Hufford, *President*
Chris Harlamert,
Herbert McClellan Hufford II,
EMP: 4
SQ FT: 1,000
SALES (est): 440K **Privately Held**
SIC: 3544 Special dies, tools, jigs & fixtures

(G-8480)
MCO SOLUTIONS INC
8820 Sugarcreek Pt (45458-2832)
PHONE...................................937 205-9512
Nympha Clark, *President*
EMP: 2
SALES: 2MM **Privately Held**
SIC: 3812 Defense systems & equipment

(G-8481)
MDF ENTERPRISES LLC
Also Called: Universal Tool Technology
821 Hall Ave (45404-1101)
PHONE...................................937 640-3436
Marjorie Farmer, *CFO*
EMP: 5
SALES (est): 507.9K **Privately Held**
SIC: 3544 Special dies, tools, jigs & fixtures

(G-8482)
MEASUREMENT SPECIALTIES INC
10522 Success Ln (45458-3561)
PHONE...................................937 885-0800
Fax: 937 885-0140

Mike Campbell, *President*
Sean Quinn, *Vice Pres*
Catherine Campbell, *Admin Sec*
EMP: 15
SQ FT: 13,500
SALES (est): 1.7MM **Privately Held**
SIC: 7699 8734 3559 Industrial machinery & equipment repair; calibration & certification; screening equipment, electric

(G-8483)
MELS LIFE LIKE HAIR
Also Called: Mel's Lifelike Hair
6140 N Main St (45415-3174)
PHONE...................................937 278-9486
Melvin P Garber, *Partner*
EMP: 3
SQ FT: 1,589
SALES (est): 181.5K **Privately Held**
SIC: 3999 7241 Hair & hair-based products; barber shop selling wigs; hair stylist, men

(G-8484)
MERIT MOLD & TOOL PRODUCTS
4648 Gateway Cir (45440-1714)
PHONE...................................937 435-0932
Fax: 937 435-6743
James Reynolds, *President*
Dan Robinson, *Controller*
EMP: 8 EST: 1979
SQ FT: 10,000
SALES (est): 689.1K **Privately Held**
SIC: 3599 Machine shop, jobbing & repair

(G-8485)
MERRICK MANUFACTURING II LLC
844 Hall Ave (45404-1101)
PHONE...................................937 222-7164
Stephen Smith, *Mng Member*
EMP: 4
SQ FT: 8,000
SALES: 500K **Privately Held**
SIC: 5087 3465 3469 Firefighting equipment; automotive stampings; metal stampings

(G-8486)
METAL BRITE POLISHING
2445 Neff Rd Unit 4 (45414-5067)
PHONE...................................937 278-9739
Michael Barr, *Owner*
EMP: 12
SALES (est): 85K **Privately Held**
SIC: 3471 Plating of metals or formed products

(G-8487)
METOKOTE CORPORATION
8040 Center Point 70 Blvd (45424-6373)
PHONE...................................937 235-2811
Fax: 937 235-0492
Frank Zack, *Branch Mgr*
EMP: 104
SALES (corp-wide): 14.7B **Publicly Held**
WEB: www.metokote.com
SIC: 3479 Coating of metals with plastic or resins
HQ: Metokote Corporation
　　1340 Neubrecht Rd
　　Lima OH 45801
　　419 996-7800

(G-8488)
MEYERS PRINTING & DESIGN INC
254 Leo St (45404-1006)
PHONE...................................937 461-6000
Gregory Meyers, *President*
EMP: 8 EST: 1999
SALES (est): 750K **Privately Held**
WEB: www.mpdink.com
SIC: 2759 Commercial printing

(G-8489)
MIAMI STEEL FABRICATORS INC
1525 Manchester Rd (45449-1933)
PHONE...................................937 299-5550
Eugene Crase, *President*
Kevin Mc Coy, *Corp Secy*
EMP: 5
SQ FT: 1,800

SALES (est): 470K **Privately Held**
SIC: 3441 Fabricated structural metal

(G-8490)
MIAMI VALLEY GASKET CO INC
Also Called: Focke Rubber Products Div
1222 E 3rd St (45402-2255)
PHONE...................................937 228-0781
Fax: 937 228-9252
Robin Cunningham, *President*
Jim Focke, *Vice Pres*
Elaine Cunningham, *Manager*
Paul Purcell, *Manager*
EMP: 25 EST: 1948
SQ FT: 29,000
SALES (est): 4.9MM **Privately Held**
WEB: www.miamivalleygasket.com
SIC: 3053 Gaskets, all materials

(G-8491)
MIAMI VALLEY PUNCH & MFG
3425 Successful Way (45414-4319)
PHONE...................................937 237-0533
Kamlesh Trivedi, *President*
Sangita Trivedi, *Treasurer*
EMP: 20
SQ FT: 21,000
SALES (est): 3.7MM **Privately Held**
SIC: 3544 7699 Punches, forming & stamping; industrial equipment services

(G-8492)
MIAMI VLY PACKG SOLUTIONS INC
1752 Stanley Ave (45404-1117)
P.O. Box 296 (45404-0296)
PHONE...................................937 224-1800
James Williams, *President*
Donald Chmiel, *Vice Pres*
Kenneth Phegley, *Vice Pres*
EMP: 19
SQ FT: 6,000
SALES (est): 2.5MM **Privately Held**
SIC: 2653 Corrugated & solid fiber boxes

(G-8493)
MICRO SYSTEMS DEVELOPMENT INC
419 E 6th St (45402-2927)
PHONE...................................937 438-3567
EMP: 5
SQ FT: 1,250
SALES (est): 694.6K **Privately Held**
SIC: 3829 Manufacturer Of Measuring And Controlling Devices

(G-8494)
MICROSUN LAMPS LLC
7890 Center Point 70 Blvd (45424-6369)
PHONE...................................888 328-8701
Bob Conner, *CEO*
EMP: 3 EST: 2014
SALES (est): 176.9K **Privately Held**
SIC: 5719 3645 Lighting, lamps & accessories; desk lamps

(G-8495)
MIDWEST EXPOSURE MAGAZINE
1509 S Smithville Rd (45410-3243)
PHONE...................................937 626-6738
Clois E Williams, *Owner*
Damien Elder, *Vice Pres*
◆ **EMP:** 3
SALES (est): 103.1K **Privately Held**
SIC: 2721 7389 Magazines: publishing & printing;

(G-8496)
MIDWEST IRON AND METAL CO
461 Homestead Ave (45417-3921)
P.O. Box 546 (45401-0546)
PHONE...................................937 222-5992
Fax: 937 222-5233
Joel Frydman, *CEO*
Farley Frydman, *President*
Bert Appel, *Principal*
Judy Griffith, *Principal*
Miriam Jacobs, *Principal*
EMP: 65
SQ FT: 150,000
SALES (est): 18.5MM **Privately Held**
SIC: 3341 5093 Secondary nonferrous metals; scrap & waste materials

(G-8497)
MIDWEST SPRAY BOOTHS
7672 Mcewen Rd (45459-3908)
PHONE...................................937 439-6600
Michael Fondy, *Owner*
EMP: 3
SALES (est): 309K **Privately Held**
SIC: 5013 3444 Body repair or paint shop supplies, automotive; booths, spray: prefabricated sheet metal

(G-8498)
MIDWEST TOOL & ENGINEERING CO
112 Webster St (45402-1388)
PHONE...................................937 224-0756
Fax: 937 224-0757
JB McCarthy, *President*
Robert Cammerer, *President*
JB McCarthy, *President*
Dr Richard Cammerer, *Corp Secy*
Lisa Carroll, *Office Mgr*
EMP: 20 EST: 1920
SQ FT: 27,750
SALES (est): 3.6MM **Privately Held**
WEB: www.themidwesttool.com
SIC: 3544 3594 3545 Special dies & tools; jigs & fixtures; fluid power pumps & motors; machine tool accessories

(G-8499)
MIKE-SELLS POTATO CHIP CO (HQ)
333 Leo St (45404-1080)
P.O. Box 115 (45404-0115)
PHONE...................................937 228-9400
Fax: 937 461-5707
Dennis Franklin, *General Mgr*
D W Mikesell, *Principal*
Martha J Mikesell, *Principal*
Philip Kazer, *Exec VP*
Joe Gauthier, *Vice Pres*
EMP: 30
SQ FT: 95,000
SALES (est): 65.7MM **Privately Held**
SIC: 2096 5145 Potato chips & other potato-based snacks; snack foods; pretzels; corn chips
PA: Mike-Sell's West Virginia, Inc.
　　333 Leo St
　　Dayton OH 45404
　　937 228-9400

(G-8500)
MIKES AUTOMOTIVE LLC
7581 Brandt Pike Unit B (45424-2337)
PHONE...................................937 233-1433
Mike Leonard, *Mng Member*
EMP: 5
SQ FT: 45,000
SALES: 290K **Privately Held**
SIC: 7692 7539 Welding repair; automotive repair shops

(G-8501)
MILLAT INDUSTRIES CORP (PA)
4901 Croftshire Dr (45440-1721)
P.O. Box 931188, Cleveland (44193-1449)
PHONE...................................937 434-6666
Fax: 937 434-8190
Greg Millat, *President*
Robert Millat, *Chairman*
Diana Newport, *Accountant*
Kevin Lowry, *Director*
▲ **EMP:** 100
SQ FT: 99,000
SALES (est): 56.5MM **Privately Held**
WEB: www.millatindustries.com
SIC: 3769 3599 3714 Guided missile & space vehicle parts & auxiliary equipment; machine shop, jobbing & repair; motor vehicle parts & accessories

(G-8502)
MILLAT INDUSTRIES CORP
7611 Center Pt I 70 Blvd (45424)
PHONE...................................937 535-1500
Fax: 937 535-1504
Yogi Singhal, *Principal*
EMP: 32
SALES (corp-wide): 56.5MM **Privately Held**
SIC: 3714 Motor vehicle parts & accessories

PA: Millat Industries, Corp.
4901 Croftshire Dr
Dayton OH 45440
937 434-6666

(G-8503)
MILLER INDUSTRIES INC
139 Auto Club Dr (45402-2501)
PHONE..................................937 293-2223
Douglas Thoma, *Branch Mgr*
EMP: 5
SALES (corp-wide): 601.1MM **Publicly Held**
WEB: www.swansenauctions.com
SIC: 3713 Automobile wrecker truck bodies
PA: Miller Industries, Inc.
8503 Hilltop Dr
Ooltewah TN 37363
423 238-4171

(G-8504)
MISUMI INVESTMENT USA CORP (HQ)
500 Progress Rd (45449-2326)
PHONE..................................937 859-5111
Ryusei Ono, *President*
Randy S Wissinger, *VP Finance*
Sawato Hayashi, *Admin Sec*
EMP: 2
SALES: 106.2MM
SALES (corp-wide): 2B **Privately Held**
SIC: 6719 3544 Investment holding companies, except banks; die sets for metal stamping (presses)
PA: Misumi Group Inc.
2-5-1, Koraku
Bunkyo-Ku TKY 112-0
358 057-050

(G-8505)
MOLD CRAFTERS INC
1531 Keystone Ave (45403-3335)
PHONE..................................937 426-3179
Tony E Carver, *President*
Ann L Carver, *Vice Pres*
EMP: 3
SALES: 372.5K **Privately Held**
SIC: 3544 Industrial molds

(G-8506)
MONAGHAN & ASSOCIATES INC
Also Called: Monaghan Tooling Group
30 N Clinton St (45402-1327)
PHONE..................................937 253-7706
Fax: 937 259-9241
Scott Monaghan, *President*
David C Monaghan, *Principal*
Dan Knight, *Technical Mgr*
Mike Galloway, *Engineer*
Franz Stark, *Regl Sales Mgr*
EMP: 20
SALES (est): 4.1MM **Privately Held**
WEB: www.monaghaninc.com
SIC: 3545 5084 3541 Machine tool accessories; industrial machinery & equipment; machine tools, metal cutting type

(G-8507)
MONCO ENTERPRISES INC (PA)
1507 Kuntz Rd (45404-1232)
PHONE..................................937 461-0034
Fax: 937 461-6554
Phil Hartje, *General Mgr*
Joe Akakpo, *Facilities Mgr*
Kamarr Gage, *Manager*
Tom Digiovanna, *Info Tech Mgr*
Elvia Thomas, *Director*
EMP: 700
SQ FT: 50,000
SALES: 286.4K **Privately Held**
SIC: 8331 2789 Sheltered workshop; community service employment training program; bookbinding & related work

(G-8508)
MORNING PRIDE MFG LLC (HQ)
Also Called: Honeywell First Responder Pdts
1 Innovation Ct (45414-3967)
PHONE..................................937 264-2662
Fax: 937 264-0075
William L Grilliot, *President*
Cathy Black, *President*
Craig Barnes, *Plant Mgr*
Jimmie Baker, *Purch Agent*
John Hodac, *QA Dir*

▲ **EMP:** 521
SQ FT: 56,000
SALES (est): 277.7MM
SALES (corp-wide): 39.3B **Publicly Held**
WEB: www.morningpride.com
SIC: 3842 2326 Respirators; men's & boys' work clothing
PA: Honeywell International Inc.
115 Tabor Rd
Morris Plains NJ 07950
973 455-2000

(G-8509)
MORNING PRIDE MFG LLC
4978 Riverton Dr (45414-3964)
PHONE..................................937 264-1726
Patrick Walls, *Supervisor*
EMP: 3
SALES (corp-wide): 39.3B **Publicly Held**
SIC: 3842 Respirators
HQ: Morning Pride Mfg Llc
1 Innovation Ct
Dayton OH 45414
937 264-2662

(G-8510)
MORTON INTERNATIONAL LLC
Also Called: Western Ohio Hall Service
312 Mound St (45402-8325)
PHONE..................................937 222-3860
Jim Benton, *Branch Mgr*
EMP: 5
SALES (corp-wide): 3.6B **Privately Held**
SIC: 3764 Guided missile & space vehicle propulsion unit parts
HQ: Morton International, Llc
123 N Wacker Dr Ste 2400
Chicago IL 60606
312 807-2696

(G-8511)
MOSHER MACHINE & TOOL CO INC
1420 Springfield St (45403-1497)
PHONE..................................937 258-8070
Fax: 937 258-2838
Kevin Mosher, *President*
Michael Mosher, *Vice Pres*
Greg Mosher, *QC Dir*
EMP: 25
SQ FT: 13,000
SALES (est): 4.6MM **Privately Held**
WEB: www.moshermachine.com
SIC: 3451 3599 Screw machine products; machine shop, jobbing & repair

(G-8512)
MOUND MANUFACTURING CENTER INC
33 Commerce Park Dr (45404-1211)
PHONE..................................937 236-8387
Fax: 937 236-8390
Albert J Hodapp III, *President*
Steve Priser, *Vice Pres*
EMP: 12
SQ FT: 9,000
SALES (est): 1.6MM **Privately Held**
SIC: 8711 3599 Machine tool design; machine shop, jobbing & repair

(G-8513)
MRS ELECTRONIC INC
2149 Winners Cir (45404-1176)
PHONE..................................937 660-6767
Franz Hoffmann, *CEO*
Guenther Doergeloh, *COO*
EMP: 12
SQ FT: 3,000
SALES (est): 151.8K **Privately Held**
SIC: 3714 Motor vehicle electrical equipment

(G-8514)
MULLINS RUBBER PRODUCTS INC
2949 Valley Pike (45404-2693)
P.O. Box 24830 (45424-0830)
PHONE..................................937 233-4211
William D Mullins, *Principal*
Dennis Mullins, *Vice Pres*
William R Mullins Jr, *Vice Pres*
Charles Patton, *Safety Mgr*
EMP: 52 **EST:** 1939
SQ FT: 75,000

SALES (est): 8.7MM **Privately Held**
WEB: www.mullinsrubber.com
SIC: 3069 Molded rubber products

(G-8515)
MV INNOVATIVE TECHNOLOGIES LLC
Also Called: Optonicus
711 E Monu Ave Ste 102 (45402)
PHONE..................................937 221-7639
EMP: 5
SALES (est): 788.3K **Privately Held**
SIC: 3699 Mfg Electrical Equipment/Supplies

(G-8516)
MY LADY MUFFINS LLC
2475 N Snyder Rd (45426-4429)
PHONE..................................937 854-5317
Bernice Logan,
EMP: 3
SQ FT: 350
SALES (est): 229.2K **Privately Held**
SIC: 2051 Bread, cake & related products

(G-8517)
NAOMI KIGHT
Also Called: Kight Creations
132 Marson Dr (45405-2921)
PHONE..................................937 278-0040
Naomi Kight, *Owner*
EMP: 3
SALES: 38.5K **Privately Held**
SIC: 2732 Book printing

(G-8518)
NATIONAL CENTER FOR COMPOSITE
Also Called: NATIONAL COMPOSITE CENTER
2000 Composite Dr (45420-1493)
PHONE..................................937 297-9450
Fax: 937 297-9440
Louis A Luedtke, *President*
Peter G Haley, *Chairman*
Michael D Melton, *VP Opers*
Lisa Novelli, *VP Opers*
Crystal Yexley, *Manager*
EMP: 22
SQ FT: 200,000
SALES (est): 2.2MM **Privately Held**
SIC: 3272 Concrete stuctural support & building material

(G-8519)
NATIONAL OILWELL VARCO LP
Also Called: Chemineer
5870 Poe Ave (45414-3442)
PHONE..................................978 687-0101
Daniel Margolien, *General Mgr*
EMP: 35
SALES (corp-wide): 7.2B **Publicly Held**
WEB: www.chemineer.com
SIC: 3569 3531 Liquid automation machinery & equipment; construction machinery
HQ: National Oilwell Varco, L.P.
1530 W Sam Houston Pkwy N
Houston TX 77043
713 960-5100

(G-8520)
NATIONAL OILWELL VARCO LP
Also Called: Chemineer
5870 Poe Ave (45414-3442)
P.O. Box 1123 (45401-1123)
PHONE..................................937 454-3200
Fax: 937 454-3230
Joel Staff, *Partner*
Patty Breig, *Opers Staff*
Robert Strong, *Research*
Eric Janz, *Engineer*
Beau Blakeley, *Design Engr*
EMP: 38
SALES (corp-wide): 7.2B **Publicly Held**
WEB: www.chemineer.com
SIC: 3556 3554 Food products machinery; paper industries machinery
HQ: National Oilwell Varco, L.P.
1530 W Sam Houston Pkwy N
Houston TX 77043
713 960-5100

(G-8521)
NATIONAL PALLET & MULCH LLC
3550 Intercity Dr (45424-5124)
PHONE..................................937 237-1643
Gary Manson,
EMP: 10
SALES (est): 1.5MM **Privately Held**
SIC: 2499 Mulch or sawdust products, wood

(G-8522)
NDC TECHNOLOGIES INC
8001 Technology Blvd (45424-1568)
PHONE..................................937 233-9935
Bromley Beadle, *President*
EMP: 115
SALES (corp-wide): 1.6B **Privately Held**
SIC: 3823 Industrial process control instruments
HQ: Ndc Technologies, Inc.
5314 Irwindale Ave
Irwindale CA 91706
626 960-3300

(G-8523)
NEVELS PRECISION MACHINING LLC
2770 Thunderhawk Ct (45414-3464)
PHONE..................................937 387-6037
Ted J Nevels, *President*
EMP: 3
SALES (est): 449.5K **Privately Held**
SIC: 3599 Machine & other job shop work

(G-8524)
NOBLE TOOL CORP
1535 Stanley Ave (45404-1112)
PHONE..................................937 461-4040
Fax: 937 461-1943
Thomas Biegel, *President*
Nick Rosenkranz, *Vice Pres*
Eddy Moorehouse, *Project Mgr*
John Rosenkranz, *Draft/Design*
Kevin Huntsberger, *Manager*
EMP: 31
SQ FT: 7,500
SALES (est): 5MM **Privately Held**
WEB: www.nobletool.com
SIC: 3599 Machine shop, jobbing & repair

(G-8525)
NON-FERROUS CASTING CO
736 Albany St (45417-3486)
P.O. Box 364 (45409-0364)
PHONE..................................937 228-1162
Fax: 937 228-1163
James D Claffey Jr, *Principal*
EMP: 6 **EST:** 1954
SQ FT: 12,000
SALES: 1MM **Privately Held**
SIC: 3366 3365 Brass foundry; bronze foundry; masts, cast aluminum

(G-8526)
NORTH DIXIE PARTS & SERVICE
3507 N Dixie Dr (45414-5231)
P.O. Box 444, Tipp City (45371-0444)
PHONE..................................937 275-0933
Fax: 937 275-2870
Jim Watson, *President*
Sharon Brown, *President*
Larry Brown, *Vice Pres*
EMP: 8
SQ FT: 3,510
SALES (est): 1.3MM **Privately Held**
SIC: 3677 Transformers power supply, electronic type; filtration devices, electronic

(G-8527)
NORTH-WEST TOOL CO
2725 Kearns Ave (45414-5546)
P.O. Box 13115 (45413-0115)
PHONE..................................937 278-7995
Fax: 937 278-7997
John Uhrig Jr, *President*
Joyce Uhrig, *Corp Secy*
EMP: 5
SQ FT: 13,000
SALES: 500K **Privately Held**
SIC: 3545 Cutting tools for machine tools; tool holders

(G-8528)
NORTHMONT SIGN CO INC
8400 N Main St (45415-1322)
PHONE..937 890-0372
Fax: 937 890-4506
Lee Hodges, *President*
Richard Hodges, *Vice Pres*
Vicki Walker, *Treasurer*
Judy Hodges, *Admin Sec*
EMP: 5
SQ FT: 5,000
SALES: 500K Privately Held
WEB: www.northmontsign.com
SIC: 2796 3993 5099 Engraving
platemaking services; signs & advertising
specialties; rubber stamps

(G-8529)
NORTHROP GRMMN SPCE & MSSN SYS
1900 Founders Dr Ste 202 (45420-1182)
PHONE..937 259-4956
Terrance A Brim, *Principal*
Mark Thullen, *Chief Engr*
Paul Ward, *Engineer*
Matt Neely, *Manager*
Matt Walker, *Software Engr*
EMP: 60 Publicly Held
WEB: www.trw.com
SIC: 7372 7374 Prepackaged software;
data processing & preparation
HQ: Northrop Grumman Space & Mission
Systems Corp.
6377 San Ignacio Ave
San Jose CA 95119
703 280-2900

(G-8530)
NORWOOD MEDICAL
2055 Winners Cir (45404-1182)
PHONE..937 228-4101
EMP: 3
SALES (est): 88.8K Privately Held
SIC: 3469 3599 Metal stampings; air in-
take filters, internal combustion engine,
except auto

(G-8531)
NORWOOD MEDICAL
2101 Winners Cir (45404-1176)
P.O. Box 3806 (45401-3806)
PHONE..937 228-4101
Ken Hammelgarn, *Manager*
EMP: 125
SALES (corp-wide): 44.6MM Privately
Held
WEB: www.norwoodtool.com
SIC: 3469 Metal stampings
PA: Norwood Tool Company
2122 Winners Cir
Dayton OH 45404
937 228-4101

(G-8532)
NORWOOD TOOL COMPANY (PA)
Also Called: Norwood Medical
2122 Winners Cir (45404-1148)
P.O. Box 3806 (45401-3806)
PHONE..937 228-4101
Fax: 937 228-1608
Kenneth Hemmelgarn Sr, *President*
Kenneth J Hemmelgarn Sr, *President*
Brian Hemmelgarn, *Vice Pres*
Chad Bacik, *Project Mgr*
Mark Kramer, *Project Mgr*
EMP: 75
SQ FT: 65,000
SALES (est): 44.6MM Privately Held
WEB: www.norwoodtool.com
SIC: 3599 3469 Machine shop, jobbing &
repair; metal stampings

(G-8533)
NOVA CREATIVE GROUP INC
168 W Franklin St (45459-4750)
PHONE..937 291-8653
Fax: 937 434-0400
Daniel Schlegel, *President*
J C King, *Vice Pres*
Larry Knapp, *Vice Pres*
Cheryl Kinnison, *Project Mgr*
Shannon Lipp, *Project Mgr*
EMP: 10
SQ FT: 5,000

SALES (est): 1MM Privately Held
WEB: www.novacreative.com
SIC: 7336 2752 Graphic arts & related de-
sign; offset & photolithographic printing

(G-8534)
NTECH INDUSTRIES INC
5475 Kellenburger Rd (45424-1013)
PHONE..707 467-3747
John Mayfield, *President*
EMP: 18
SQ FT: 1,600
SALES (est): 1.6MM
SALES (corp-wide): 2.3B Publicly Held
WEB: www.ntechindustries.com
SIC: 3523 Farm machinery & equipment
PA: Trimble Inc.
935 Stewart Dr
Sunnyvale CA 94085
408 481-8000

(G-8535)
NUFAB SHEET METAL
4750 Hempstead Station Dr (45429-5164)
PHONE..937 235-2030
Greg McAfee, *Owner*
Brad Frank, *Manager*
EMP: 3
SQ FT: 3,960
SALES (est): 302.2K Privately Held
WEB: www.nufabsheetmetal.com
SIC: 3444 Sheet metalwork

(G-8536)
NUMATX INC
4668 Gateway Cir (45440-1714)
PHONE..937 435-8178
Mark D Swinford, *President*
EMP: 3
SALES (est): 280K Privately Held
SIC: 3545 Tools & accessories for machine
tools

(G-8537)
OAKLEY INC
1421 Springfield St # 2 (45403-1435)
P.O. Box 8302, Mason (45040-5302)
PHONE..949 672-6560
Sheila Oakley, *Branch Mgr*
EMP: 52 Privately Held
SIC: 3851 Ophthalmic goods
HQ: Oakley, Inc.
1 Icon
Foothill Ranch CA 92610
949 951-0991

(G-8538)
OBERFIELDS LLC
10075 Sheehan Rd (45458-4301)
PHONE..937 885-3711
Bruce Loris, *President*
EMP: 7
SALES (corp-wide): 17MM Privately
Held
SIC: 3272 Concrete products, precast
PA: Oberfield's, Llc
528 London Rd
Delaware OH 43015
740 369-7644

(G-8539)
OERLIKON FRICTION SYSTEMS
220 Janney Rd (45404-1265)
PHONE..937 233-7002
Mark Weldron, *Branch Mgr*
EMP: 20
SALES (corp-wide): 2.3B Privately Held
SIC: 3465 5084 Automotive stampings;
tool & die makers' equipment
HQ: Oerlikon Friction Systems (Us) Inc.
240 Detrick St
Dayton OH 45404
937 449-4000

(G-8540)
OERLIKON FRICTION SYSTEMS (HQ)
240 Detrick St (45404-1699)
P.O. Box 745 (45401-0745)
PHONE..937 449-4000
Fax: 937 425-7585
Eric A Schueler, *President*
Terry Nels, *Vice Pres*
John Parker, *CFO*
Mark Szporka, *Director*
◆ EMP: 160

SQ FT: 115,000
SALES: 28.3MM
SALES (corp-wide): 2.3B Privately Held
WEB: www.johnston-pump.com
SIC: 3714 Transmission housings or parts,
motor vehicle
PA: Oc Oerlikon Corporation Ag, Pfaffikon
Churerstrasse 120
PfAffikon SZ 8808
583 609-696

(G-8541)
OERLIKON FRICTION SYSTEMS
Also Called: Plant 5
240 Detrick St (45404-1699)
PHONE..937 233-9191
Joe Caffano, *Branch Mgr*
EMP: 20
SALES (corp-wide): 2.3B Privately Held
SIC: 3465 Automotive stampings
HQ: Oerlikon Friction Systems (Us) Inc.
240 Detrick St
Dayton OH 45404
937 449-4000

(G-8542)
OHI-TEC MANUFACTURING INC
3015 Production Ct (45414-3514)
PHONE..937 882-6144
Timothy Ozvath, *President*
EMP: 20
SQ FT: 36,000
SALES (est): 3MM Privately Held
SIC: 3469 Stamping metal for the trade

(G-8543)
OHIO GRAPHIC SUPPLY INC
530 W Whipp Rd (45459-2947)
PHONE..937 433-7537
Fax: 937 223-6965
Jo Ann Ruja, *President*
EMP: 3
SQ FT: 3,000
SALES (est): 370K Privately Held
SIC: 3555 5734 Printing trades machinery;
computer tapes

(G-8544)
OHIO METAL FABRICATING INC
6057 Milo Rd (45414-3417)
PHONE..937 233-2400
Gary Brandeberry, *President*
Leta Brandeberry, *Principal*
Craig Simpson, *Vice Pres*
Todd Back, *Mfg Mgr*
Gary Burdette, *Engineer*
EMP: 8
SQ FT: 18,000
SALES (est): 950K Privately Held
WEB: www.gcmetalspinning.com
SIC: 3542 Spinning machines, metal

(G-8545)
OHIO METAL PRODUCTS COMPANY
35 Bates St (45402-1395)
PHONE..937 228-6101
Fax: 937 228-6494
John D Moore, *President*
Janet A Simpson, *Corp Secy*
John Smith, *Mfg Mgr*
EMP: 30 EST: 1909
SQ FT: 32,000
SALES (est): 5.6MM Privately Held
WEB: www.ohio-metal.com
SIC: 3451 3471 Screw machine products;
plating & polishing

(G-8546)
OHIO TOOL & JIG GRIND INC
5724 Webster St (45414-3521)
PHONE..937 415-0692
Fax: 937 415-0713
David A Brinker, *President*
Craig Price, *Mfg Mgr*
Tom Farrell, *QC Mgr*
EMP: 35
SQ FT: 2,000
SALES: 1MM Privately Held
SIC: 3544 Special dies, tools, jigs & fix-
tures

(G-8547)
OLWIN METAL FABRICATION LLC
2514 Nordic Rd (45414-3422)
PHONE..937 277-4501
Derick Olwin, *Mng Member*
EMP: 4
SALES (est): 524.6K Privately Held
SIC: 3499 Fabricated metal products

(G-8548)
OMEGA AUTOMATION INC
2850 Needmore Rd (45414-4300)
PHONE..937 890-2350
Fax: 937 277-7757
Marybeth Krystofik, *President*
Alan King, *Chairman*
Doug Pund, *Plant Mgr*
Dale Rudisill, *Mfg Staff*
Karen Ebert, *Controller*
EMP: 55
SQ FT: 31,000
SALES (est): 12.4MM
SALES (corp-wide): 17.7MM Privately
Held
SIC: 3549 3569 3829 Assembly ma-
chines, including robotic; robots, assem-
bly line: industrial & commercial; physical
property testing equipment
HQ: Omega International, Inc
6192 Webster St
Dayton OH 45414
937 890-2350

(G-8549)
OMEGA INTERNATIONAL INC (HQ)
6192 Webster St (45414-3436)
PHONE..937 890-2350
Alan King, *Ch of Bd*
Karen Ebert, *Controller*
EMP: 50
SQ FT: 30,000
SALES (est): 17.4MM
SALES (corp-wide): 17.7MM Privately
Held
SIC: 3829 3599 3549 3569 Physical
property testing equipment; machine
shop, jobbing & repair; assembly ma-
chines, including robotic; robots, assem-
bly line: industrial & commercial

(G-8550)
OMEGA TOOL & DIE INC
Also Called: Omega Tool and Die
2850 Needmore Rd (45414-4302)
PHONE..937 890-2350
Fax: 937 890-2352
Geo Howdieshell, *President*
Charlie Browning, *Engineer*
Karen Ebert, *Controller*
Joanna Moncivaiz, *Controller*
Angel Harbaum, *Accountant*
EMP: 45 EST: 1970
SQ FT: 30,000
SALES (est): 5MM
SALES (corp-wide): 17.7MM Privately
Held
WEB: www.omega-company.com
SIC: 3599 3544 Machine shop, jobbing &
repair; special dies, tools, jigs & fixtures
HQ: Omega International, Inc
6192 Webster St
Dayton OH 45414
937 890-2350

(G-8551)
OPTIMUS LLC (PA)
Also Called: Optimus Prosthetics
8517 N Dixie Dr Ste 300 (45414-6400)
PHONE..937 454-1900
Steve Phillips, *CFO*
Beth Warren, *Marketing Mgr*
John Brandt,
Scott R Schall,
EMP: 3
SALES: 180K Privately Held
SIC: 3842 Surgical appliances & supplies

(G-8552)
OREGON VILLAGE PRINT SHOPPE
Also Called: Oregon Printing
29 N June St (45403-1015)
PHONE..937 222-9418

Fax: 937 222-9436
Judd Plattenburg, *President*
Bob Allbery, *Vice Pres*
Amanda Pond, *Marketing Staff*
Anita Miller, *Admin Asst*
Kelly Ritteman, *Admin Asst*
EMP: 15 **EST:** 1974
SQ FT: 5,300
SALES (est): 1.6MM **Privately Held**
WEB: www.oregonprinting.com
SIC: 2752 Commercial printing, offset

(G-8553)
OSCAR HICKS
Also Called: Hobby Printing
9860 Atchison Rd (45458-9206)
PHONE......................937 435-4350
Oscar Hicks, *Owner*
EMP: 3
SALES (est): 124.4K **Privately Held**
SIC: 2752 Commercial printing, litho-
graphic

(G-8554)
OTTER GROUP LLC
Also Called: Yale Industries
2725 Needmore Rd (45414-4207)
PHONE......................937 315-1199
EMP: 18
SALES (est): 2MM **Privately Held**
SIC: 3448 3442 5031 Mfg Mfg & Dist
Windows Doors Awnings Patio Covers&
Patio Rooms

(G-8555)
OUTLOOK TOOL INC
360 Fame Rd (45449-2313)
PHONE......................937 235-6330
Eric Staeuble, *President*
Ted Nevels, *Admin Sec*
EMP: 6
SQ FT: 3,200
SALES: 550K **Privately Held**
SIC: 3599 Machine shop, jobbing & repair

(G-8556)
OUTTA BOX DISPENSERS LLC
Also Called: Otb
811 E 4th St (45402-2227)
PHONE......................937 221-7106
John Bongiorno, *Vice Pres*
Michael J Emoff,
Mary J Miller,
EMP: 4
SALES (est): 373.3K **Privately Held**
WEB: www.outtathebox.com
SIC: 3578 Point-of-sale devices

(G-8557)
OVASE MANUFACTURING LLC
Also Called: Global Tool
1990 Berwyck Ave (45414-5556)
PHONE......................937 275-0617
Michelle Easterling, *Manager*
Joe Kamil,
EMP: 28
SALES (est): 5.3MM **Privately Held**
WEB: www.globaltoolmfg.com
SIC: 3545 Machine tool attachments & ac-
cessories

(G-8558)
P J TOOL COMPANY INC
1115 Springfield St (45403-1420)
PHONE......................937 254-2817
Fax: 937 254-2836
Paul Hedrick, *President*
Jim Fedor, *Corp Secy*
EMP: 6
SQ FT: 2,600
SALES (est): 889.3K **Privately Held**
SIC: 3599 3544 Machine shop, jobbing &
repair; special dies, tools, jigs & fixtures

(G-8559)
P3 SECURE LLC
Also Called: 4everready
926 W Fairview Ave (45406-2806)
PHONE......................937 610-5500
Felecia Greene, *Principal*
Jared Greene, *Principal*
Addie Keaton Harris, *Principal*
Marion Harris, *Principal*
Richard Harris,
EMP: 25

SALES (est): 1.7MM **Privately Held**
WEB: www.p3securellc.com
SIC: 2032 Canned specialties

(G-8560)
PA & JJS FRUITY SMILES INC
Also Called: Edible Arrangements
4015 Far Hills Ave (45429-2413)
PHONE......................937 449-0999
Amanda Bosworth, *President*
EMP: 8
SQ FT: 1,900
SALES: 540K **Privately Held**
SIC: 2064 Fruit, chocolate covered (except
dates)

(G-8561)
**PACKAGES ANYTHING
ANYWHERE**
4085 E Town And Cntry Rd (45429-2831)
PHONE......................937 298-1939
Fax: 937 298-8656
Cathy Klawon, *President*
EMP: 4
SQ FT: 750
SALES: 300K **Privately Held**
SIC: 3086 Packaging & shipping materials,
foamed plastic

(G-8562)
PACKAGING PLUS INC
1235 Mccook Ave (45404-1011)
PHONE......................304 429-5900
Karen Wasley, *President*
Sheila Cassis, *Vice Pres*
EMP: 4
SQ FT: 6,000
SALES (est): 300.5K **Privately Held**
SIC: 4783 5199 3949 2448 Packing
goods for shipping; packaging materials;
sporting & athletic goods; wood pallets &
skids; nailed wood boxes & shook

(G-8563)
PARCO INC
2747 Culver Ave (45429-3723)
PHONE......................937 296-0356
Fax: 937 296-0182
Mark Paxson, *President*
Lisa Peltz, *Admin Sec*
EMP: 12
SQ FT: 1,500
SALES: 500K **Privately Held**
SIC: 3599 Machine shop, jobbing & repair

(G-8564)
PARTS UNLIMITED
5221 Shiloh Springs Rd (45426-3905)
PHONE......................937 558-1527
Jack Daniel, *Owner*
EMP: 3
SALES: 200K **Privately Held**
SIC: 3599 Machine shop, jobbing & repair

(G-8565)
**PATIENTSS CONSUMERS PHRM
INC**
Also Called: P&C Pharma
955 Congress Park Dr (45459-4009)
PHONE......................937 813-7800
Joe D'Silva, *Principal*
EMP: 5 **EST:** 2015
SALES (est): 303.4K **Privately Held**
SIC: 3559 Pharmaceutical machinery

(G-8566)
PAVE TECHNOLOGY CO
2751 Thunderhawk Ct (45414-3451)
PHONE......................937 890-1592
Fax: 937 890-5165
Walter D Wood, *Ch of Bd*
Brad Boomershine, *Vice Pres*
Kasey Gueth, *Buyer*
John Holloway, *QC Mgr*
Adam Habig, *Engineer*
▲ **EMP:** 45
SQ FT: 20,000
SALES (est): 9.4MM **Privately Held**
WEB: www.pavetechnology.com
SIC: 3643 3089 Current-carrying wiring
devices; injection molding of plastics

(G-8567)
PAXAR CORPORATION
7801 Technology Blvd (45424-1574)
PHONE......................937 681-4541
Fax: 937 235-3761
Phil Warren, *Manager*
Lynn McCoy, *Director*
EMP: 9
SALES (corp-wide): 6B **Publicly Held**
WEB: www.paxar.com
SIC: 2679 2752 2675 2672 Tags, paper
(unprinted): made from purchased paper;
commercial printing, lithographic; die-cut
paper & board; coated & laminated paper;
packaging paper & plastics film, coated &
laminated; narrow fabric mills
HQ: Paxar Corporation
524 Route 303
Orangeburg NY 10962
845 398-3229

(G-8568)
PDQ TECHNOLOGIES INC
2608 Nordic Rd (45414-3424)
PHONE......................937 274-4958
Fax: 937 274-4969
Robert Adams, *Administration*
EMP: 13
SQ FT: 20,000
SALES (est): 1.5MM **Privately Held**
SIC: 3469 Machine parts, stamped or
pressed metal

(G-8569)
PENTAGEAR PRODUCTS LLC
6161 Webster St (45414-3435)
PHONE......................937 660-8182
Marvin Nicholson,
EMP: 12
SALES (est): 868.2K **Privately Held**
SIC: 3566 7389 Speed changers, drives &
gears;

(G-8570)
**PEPSI-COLA METRO BTLG CO
INC**
526 Milburn Ave (45404-1678)
PHONE......................937 461-4664
Tim Trant, *General Mgr*
Cheryl Fuson, *Human Res Mgr*
Richard Hargenrader, *Sales Executive*
Phillip Beach, *Manager*
Michael Sidenstick, *Manager*
EMP: 300
SQ FT: 115,000
SALES (corp-wide): 62.8B **Publicly Held**
WEB: www.joy-of-cola.com
SIC: 2086 5149 Soft drinks: packaged in
cans, bottles, etc.; groceries & related
products
HQ: Pepsi-Cola Metropolitan Bottling Com-
pany, Inc.
1111 Westchester Ave
White Plains NY 10604
914 767-6000

(G-8571)
PERMA-FIX OF DAYTON INC
300 Cherokee Dr (45417-8113)
PHONE......................937 268-6501
Fax: 937 268-5734
Brad Malatesta, *President*
Richard Kelecy, *Vice Pres*
Andy Owens, *QC Mgr*
Alison Arrowsmith, *Manager*
Kim Black, *Manager*
EMP: 42 **EST:** 1941
SQ FT: 25,000
SALES (est): 6.8MM
SALES (corp-wide): 6.8MM **Privately
Held**
SIC: 4953 2992 Recycling, waste materi-
als; lubricating oils & greases
PA: Ogm, Ltd.
2480 Jackson Pike
Columbus OH 43223
614 539-8238

(G-8572)
**PHILLIPS SHTMTL
FABRICATIONS**
1215 Ray St (45404-1656)
PHONE......................937 223-2722
Robert Holmes, *President*
Donald F Holmes, *President*

▲ **EMP:** 5
SQ FT: 6,000
SALES: 290K **Privately Held**
SIC: 3444 Sheet metalwork

(G-8573)
PHOENIX METAL WORKS INC
Also Called: Phoenix Metal Fabricators
2528 Ashcraft Rd (45414-3402)
PHONE......................937 274-5555
Fax: 937 274-0866
Carl Abshire, *President*
Randy Abshire, *General Mgr*
Marcia Russell, *Safety Mgr*
Chris Abshire, *Purchasing*
EMP: 9
SQ FT: 10,000
SALES (est): 1.2MM **Privately Held**
WEB: www.phoenixdayton.com
SIC: 3441 Fabricated structural metal

(G-8574)
PHOENIX TRINITY MFG INC
1883 Sthtown Blvd Ste 102 (45439)
PHONE......................937 619-0172
Brian Williams, *President*
Tiffany Williams, *Treasurer*
EMP: 7 **EST:** 2011
SQ FT: 6,000
SALES: 900K **Privately Held**
SIC: 3999 Barber & beauty shop equip-
ment

(G-8575)
PIEDMONT CHEMICAL CO INC
1516 Silver Lake Dr (45458-3529)
PHONE......................937 428-6640
Ed Kren, *Principal*
EMP: 3
SALES (est): 221.3K **Privately Held**
SIC: 3471 Cleaning, polishing & finishing

(G-8576)
PIETRA NATURALE INC
9308 Dayton Lebanon Pike (45458-3839)
PHONE......................937 438-8882
Fax: 937 438-8360
Michael Carnevale Jr, *President*
Chip Carnevale, *Vice Pres*
Robert Carnevale, *Vice Pres*
Michael Ricky Carnevale, *Treasurer*
Sonja L Bowing, *Admin Sec*
EMP: 12
SQ FT: 15,000
SALES (est): 1.4MM **Privately Held**
WEB: www.pietranaturale.com
SIC: 3281 1799 Cut stone & stone prod-
ucts; marble, building: cut & shaped;
counter top installation

(G-8577)
PITCO PRODUCTS INC
120 N Terry St (45403-1029)
PHONE......................513 228-7245
Fax: 937 228-7247
Ralph Pippenger, *President*
Geoff Hoefflin, *General Mgr*
EMP: 10 **EST:** 1958
SQ FT: 6,000
SALES: 1MM **Privately Held**
WEB: www.pitcoproducts.com
SIC: 3728 3544 Aircraft assemblies, sub-
assemblies & parts; special dies & tools

(G-8578)
**PLATING TECHNOLOGY INC
(PA)**
1525 W River Rd (45417-6740)
PHONE......................937 268-6882
Fax: 937 268-7209
Jody Pollack Blazar, *Owner*
Bruce A Lowman, *Principal*
Robert E Patterson, *Principal*
Roger B Turrell, *Principal*
Zack Moore, *Purch Mgr*
▲ **EMP:** 55 **EST:** 1953
SQ FT: 190,000
SALES (est): 17.2MM **Privately Held**
WEB: www.platingtech.com
SIC: 3471 3469 Electroplating of metals or
formed products; machine parts, stamped
or pressed metal

(G-8579)
PLATING TECHNOLOGY INC
1525 W River Rd (45417-6740)
PHONE..937 268-6788
Fax: 614 449-2584
Dana Hubbard, *Manager*
EMP: 15
SQ FT: 5,265
SALES (corp-wide): 17.2MM **Privately Held**
WEB: www.platingtech.com
SIC: 3471 Plating of metals or formed products
PA: Plating Technology, Inc.
　　1525 W River Rd
　　Dayton OH 45417
　　937 268-6882

(G-8580)
POWER MANAGEMENT INC (PA)
420 Davis Ave (45403-2912)
PHONE..937 222-2909
Fax: 937 258-5495
Reece Powers, *President*
EMP: 28
SQ FT: 24,000
SALES (est): 3.1MM **Privately Held**
SIC: 6512 6513 2752 7331 Nonresidential building operators; apartment building operators; offset & photolithographic printing; mailing service; management consulting services; commercial nonphysical research

(G-8581)
PRECISION AIRCRAFT COMPONENTS
2787 Armstrong Ln (45414-4225)
PHONE..937 278-0264
Fax: 937 278-4466
Emsy Little Jr, *CEO*
Huck Lewis, *Sales Executive*
Debbie Croneberg, *Office Mgr*
Debbie Reichert, *Manager*
Jonathan Hurlow, *Admin Sec*
EMP: 25
SQ FT: 17,500
SALES (est): 5.1MM **Privately Held**
SIC: 3728 Aircraft assemblies, subassemblies & parts

(G-8582)
PRECISION ENERGY & TECH LLC
Also Called: P E T
2000 Composite Dr (45420-1493)
PHONE..937 558-2708
Thomas J Willis,
EMP: 5
SQ FT: 200,000
SALES: 3.7MM **Privately Held**
WEB: www.petfc.com
SIC: 3674 Fuel cells, solid state

(G-8583)
PRECISION FINISHING SYSTEMS
6101 Webster St (45414-3435)
PHONE..937 415-5794
Barbara Lipuma, *Principal*
EMP: 14
SALES (est): 2MM **Privately Held**
SIC: 3471 Cleaning, polishing & finishing

(G-8584)
PRECISION GAGE & TOOL COMPANY
375 Gargrave Rd (45449-2465)
PHONE..937 866-9666
Fax: 937 866-9661
Gwen Waltz, *CEO*
Vicki Waltz, *President*
Jeff Arnold, *General Mgr*
Leslie Heaton, *Vice Pres*
Larry Haverstock, *Draft/Design*
EMP: 24 EST: 1929
SQ FT: 16,000
SALES (est): 4.3MM **Privately Held**
WEB: www.pgtgage.com
SIC: 3545 Gauges (machine tool accessories)

(G-8585)
PRECISION MANUFACTURING CO INC
2149 Valley Pike (45404-2542)
PHONE..937 236-2170
Fax: 937 236-6023
Faye Ledwick, *CEO*
Dorothy Preston, *Plant Mgr*
Bryan Camp, *Prdtn Mgr*
Kim Weaver, *Prdtn Mgr*
Ginger Webb, *Prdtn Mgr*
EMP: 70
SQ FT: 30,000
SALES (est): 13MM **Privately Held**
WEB: www.precmfgco.com
SIC: 3679 Harness assemblies for electronic use: wire or cable

(G-8586)
PRECISION MFG & ASSEMBLY LLC
2240 Richard St (45403-2551)
PHONE..937 252-3507
William Bill Duckro, *Mng Member*
Joe Duckro, *Manager*
Joeseph Duckro,
EMP: 65
SALES: 2.2MM **Privately Held**
SIC: 3089 Automotive parts, plastic

(G-8587)
PRECISION MTAL FABRICATION INC (PA)
191 Heid Ave (45404-1217)
PHONE..937 235-9261
Fax: 937 233-0906
Jim Hackenberger, *President*
John Limberg, *Corp Secy*
Drew Hackenberger, *QC Mgr*
Mike Desch, *Sales Staff*
Rick Miller, *Manager*
EMP: 53
SQ FT: 30,000
SALES (est): 6.8MM **Privately Held**
WEB: www.premetfab.com
SIC: 7692 3444 Welding repair; sheet metalwork

(G-8588)
PRECISION PRESSED POWDERED MET
1522 Manchester Rd (45449-1933)
PHONE..937 433-6802
Fax: 937 433-1729
David Warner, *President*
Stephen G England, *Chairman*
Elizabeth Kingsborough, *Manager*
EMP: 14
SQ FT: 7,000
SALES (est): 1.6MM **Privately Held**
SIC: 3469 Machine parts, stamped or pressed metal

(G-8589)
PREMIER PRINTING AND PACKG INC
Also Called: Minuteman Press
90 Compark Rd Ste A (45459-4967)
PHONE..937 436-5290
Fax: 937 436-5298
Frederic Polizzi, *President*
EMP: 5
SALES: 550K **Privately Held**
SIC: 2752 Commercial printing, lithographic

(G-8590)
PRESTIGE PRINTING
5888 Executive Blvd (45424-1451)
PHONE..937 236-8468
Fax: 937 236-9350
Jack Schaadt, *Owner*
EMP: 4
SQ FT: 2,440
SALES: 400K **Privately Held**
SIC: 2752 Commercial printing, lithographic

(G-8591)
PRIDE INVESTMENTS LLC
Also Called: American Heat Treating
1346 Morris Ave (45417-3829)
PHONE..937 461-1121
Fax: 937 461-1166

Lawrence Gray, *Owner*
Theresa Carney, *Manager*
Dale Barham, *Maintence Staff*
EMP: 15
SQ FT: 32,000
SALES (est): 2MM **Privately Held**
SIC: 3398 Metal heat treating

(G-8592)
PRIME CONTROLS INC
4528 Gateway Cir (45440-1712)
PHONE..937 435-8659
Larry Tucker, *President*
Jim A Michud, *President*
Jim Michaud, *Corp Secy*
David Smith, *Vice Pres*
Lance Smith, *Safety Mgr*
EMP: 5
SQ FT: 3,000
SALES (est): 610K **Privately Held**
WEB: www.primecontrols.com
SIC: 3625 5084 Relays & industrial controls; instruments & control equipment

(G-8593)
PRIME MANUFACTURING CORP (HQ)
1619 Kuntz Rd (45404-1240)
PHONE..937 496-3900
Gale Kooken, *President*
Roger Fleming, *Vice Pres*
Jeff Mueller, *Vice Pres*
Chloe Reynolds, *Purchasing*
Christy Fox, *Treasurer*
EMP: 7
SALES (est): 630.4K
SALES (corp-wide): 143.1MM **Privately Held**
WEB: www.primemfg.com
SIC: 3743 Railroad equipment; refrigeration & heating equipment
PA: Dayton-Phoenix Group, Inc.
　　1619 Kuntz Rd
　　Dayton OH 45404
　　937 496-3900

(G-8594)
PRIME PRINTING INC (PA)
8929 Kingsridge Dr (45458-1621)
P.O. Box 751591 (45475-1591)
PHONE..937 438-3707
Fax: 937 291-3597
Gary Smith, *President*
Dan Cornelius, *Vice Pres*
Tim Cox, *Vice Pres*
Jason Martin, *Vice Pres*
EMP: 33
SQ FT: 12,000
SALES (est): 1.6MM **Privately Held**
WEB: www.primedigitalprinting.com
SIC: 2752 2796 2791 2789 Commercial printing, offset; platemaking services; typesetting; bookbinding & related work

(G-8595)
PRINTPOINT PRINTING INC
150 S Patterson Blvd (45402-2421)
PHONE..937 223-9041
Fax: 937 223-4820
Mike Munch, *President*
Diane Woods, *Office Mgr*
Kathy Munch, *Manager*
EMP: 7 EST: 1976
SQ FT: 13,000
SALES (est): 690K **Privately Held**
WEB: www.printpointprinting.com
SIC: 2752 Commercial printing, lithographic

(G-8596)
PRINTPROD INC
419 Bainbridge St (45410-1167)
PHONE..937 228-2181
Fax: 937 228-3832
Robert Flaute Jr, *President*
Michael Flaute, *Office Mgr*
EMP: 14
SQ FT: 12,000
SALES (est): 1.7MM **Privately Held**
WEB: www.printprodinc.com
SIC: 2752 Tags, lithographed

(G-8597)
PROCESS DEVELOPMENT CORP
6060 Milo Rd (45414-3418)
PHONE..937 890-3388
Fax: 937 890-3377
Cliff Blacke, *President*
Shiela Warner, *Manager*
EMP: 24
SQ FT: 42,000
SALES (est): 5.7MM **Privately Held**
WEB: www.processdev.com
SIC: 3559 3599 3582 3548 Automotive related machinery; machine & other job shop work; commercial laundry equipment; welding apparatus

(G-8598)
PRODUCTION DESIGN SERVICES INC (PA)
Also Called: Pdsi Technical Services
401 Fame Rd (45449-2398)
PHONE..937 866-3377
Fax: 937 866-3437
John H Schultz, *President*
Jeffrey R Schultz, *Vice Pres*
Pat Moore, *Plant Mgr*
Jim Hite, *Engineer*
Kevin Sizemore, *Engineer*
EMP: 76
SQ FT: 48,000
SALES (est): 17.1MM **Privately Held**
WEB: www.p-d-s-i.com
SIC: 3569 8711 7363 3823 Robots, assembly line: industrial & commercial; industrial engineers; mechanical engineering; temporary help service; industrial instrmnts msrmnt display/control process variable; machine tool accessories; special dies, tools, jigs & fixtures

(G-8599)
PROFILE DIGITAL PRINTING LLC
5449 Marina Dr (45449-1833)
PHONE..937 866-4241
Terry Harmeyer, *General Mgr*
Tom Helmers, *Principal*
Carol Fiorentino, *Prdtn Mgr*
June Helmers,
EMP: 25
SALES (est): 4.2MM **Privately Held**
WEB: www.profiledpi.com
SIC: 7334 2759 2752 Photocopying & duplicating services; commercial printing; commercial printing, lithographic

(G-8600)
PROFOUND LOGIC SOFTWARE INC
396 Congress Park Dr (45459-4149)
PHONE..937 439-7925
Alex Roytman, *President*
Brian May, *Info Tech Mgr*
EMP: 9
SALES (est): 965.2K **Privately Held**
SIC: 7372 Prepackaged software

(G-8601)
PROGRESSIVE PRINTERS INC
884 Valley St (45404-2066)
PHONE..937 222-1267
Fax: 937 222-6697
Dennis Livesay, *President*
Sharon L Staggs, *Vice Pres*
Phil Bondi, *Opers Mgr*
Birdie Livesay, *Mfg Staff*
Mike Lafferty, *Accounts Mgr*
EMP: 55 EST: 2004
SQ FT: 26,000
SALES (est): 17.3MM **Privately Held**
WEB: www.progressiveprinters.com
SIC: 2752 2759 Commercial printing, lithographic; commercial printing

(G-8602)
PROSTAR MACHINE & TOOL CO
2039 Webster St (45404-1143)
PHONE..937 223-1997
Fax: 937 223-8805
EMP: 8
SQ FT: 3,000
SALES: 300K **Privately Held**
SIC: 3599 Machine Shop Jobbing And Repair

(G-8603)
PUTNAM PLASTICS INC
Also Called: Farm Products Division
255 S Alex Rd (45449-1910)
PHONE..............................937 866-6261
Fax: 937 866-9365
Gary Spacht, *General Mgr*
Sherry Miller, *Manager*
EMP: 8
SALES (corp-wide): 6.6MM **Privately Held**
WEB: www.putnamplasticsinc.com
SIC: 5199 5113 3081 Packaging materials; industrial & personal service paper; polyethylene film
PA: Putnam Plastics Inc
30 W Stardust Rd
Cloverdale IN 46120
765 795-6102

(G-8604)
PUTTCO INC
2613 Oakley Ave (45419-2351)
PHONE..............................937 299-1527
Frank Puthoff, *President*
EMP: 3
SALES (est): 184.1K **Privately Held**
SIC: 2396 Fabric printing & stamping

(G-8605)
Q M C PLEASANTS INC
Also Called: Quality Machine
5648 Wadsworth Rd (45414-3412)
PHONE..............................937 278-7302
Fax: 937 278-0302
David Pleasant Jr, *President*
David K Pleasant Sr, *President*
Deborah Pleasant, *Admin Sec*
EMP: 3
SQ FT: 2,800
SALES (est): 350.1K **Privately Held**
SIC: 3599 Machine shop, jobbing & repair

(G-8606)
QUALITY QUARTZ
ENGINEERING INC
131 Janney Rd (45404-1225)
PHONE..............................937 236-3250
Fax: 937 236-3254
Tyler Shumard, *Sales Mgr*
Bea Stapleton, *Accounts Mgr*
Gary Zimmermen,
◆ EMP: 52
SQ FT: 55,000
SALES (est): 10.6MM **Privately Held**
SIC: 3679 Quartz crystals, for electronic application
PA: Quality Quartz Engineering, Incorporated
8484 Central Ave
Newark CA 94560

(G-8607)
QUEEN CITY POLYMERS INC
Also Called: Qc Plastics
365 Leo St (45404-1007)
PHONE..............................937 236-2710
Fax: 937 236-1718
Greg Hendon, *Manager*
Greg Hendren, *Manager*
EMP: 5
SALES (corp-wide): 6.5MM **Privately Held**
WEB: www.qcpinc.com
SIC: 5162 3089 Plastics materials & basic shapes; plastic processing
PA: Queen City Polymers, Inc.
6101 Schumacher Park Dr
West Chester OH 45069
513 779-0990

(G-8608)
R & H SIGNS UNLIMITED INC
3048 Wilmington Pike (45429-4002)
PHONE..............................937 293-3834
Fax: 937 293-3835
Brian Hodell, *Vice Pres*
Phyllis Ruber, *Treasurer*
Tami Hodell, *Admin Sec*
EMP: 5
SALES (est): 540.5K **Privately Held**
SIC: 3993 Signs & advertising specialties

(G-8609)
R D BAKER ENTERPRISES INC
Also Called: Alpha Water Conditioning Co
765 Liberty Ln (45449-2134)
PHONE..............................937 461-5225
Bill Miller, *Branch Mgr*
EMP: 6
SALES (corp-wide): 4.3MM **Privately Held**
WEB: www.daytonwatersystems.com
SIC: 5999 8734 5074 Water purification equipment, household type; water testing laboratory; water softeners
PA: R. D. Baker Enterprises, Inc.
765 Liberty Ln
Dayton OH 45449
937 461-5225

(G-8610)
R L TECHNOLOGIES INC (PA)
1711 Mccall St (45402-8036)
P.O. Box 17250 (45417-0250)
PHONE..............................937 321-5544
Tanya Epps, *President*
Harry Mayo, *Vice Pres*
EMP: 5
SALES (est): 699.2K **Privately Held**
SIC: 3965 Fasteners

(G-8611)
R M WELDING PRODUCTS
1944 Stanley Ave (45404-1121)
PHONE..............................937 260-4510
Michael W Buckley, *Owner*
EMP: 4
SALES (est): 35.9K **Privately Held**
SIC: 7692 5999 Welding repair; safety supplies & equipment

(G-8612)
R S C SALES COMPANY
1347 E 4th St (45402-2235)
PHONE..............................423 581-4916
Richard Carper, *President*
Scott Carper, *Vice Pres*
▲ EMP: 20
SQ FT: 22,000
SALES (est): 1.9MM **Privately Held**
SIC: 2752 5013 7336 Commercial printing, offset; automotive supplies & parts; silk screen design

(G-8613)
R WEIR INC
Also Called: Fastsigns
978 Mmsburg Cnterville Rd (45459)
PHONE..............................937 438-5730
Fax: 937 438-5733
Ronald Weir, *President*
EMP: 5
SQ FT: 1,980
SALES: 300K **Privately Held**
WEB: www.rweir.com
SIC: 3993 5999 Signs & advertising specialties; banners, flags, decals & posters

(G-8614)
RAM PRECISION INDUSTRIES INC
Also Called: R A M Precision Tool
11125 Yankee St Ste A (45458-3698)
PHONE..............................937 885-7700
Fax: 937 885-7727
Richard Mount, *CEO*
Mark Anticoli, *Engineer*
John Slouffan, *Sales Mgr*
Cathy Morgan, *Accounts Mgr*
Rick Scarpelli, *Marketing Staff*
▲ EMP: 85
SQ FT: 55,000
SALES (est): 16.8MM **Privately Held**
WEB: www.rampaintball.com
SIC: 3599 Machine shop, jobbing & repair

(G-8615)
RAM TOOL INC
1944 Neva Dr (45414-5525)
PHONE..............................937 277-0717
Fax: 937 277-4083
Robert Coblentz, *President*
Forrest Lemaster, *President*
Michelle Polum, *VP Admin*
EMP: 7
SQ FT: 4,000

SALES (est): 630K **Privately Held**
WEB: www.ramtoolohio.com
SIC: 3544 Special dies, tools, jigs & fixtures

(G-8616)
RAMBASEK REALTY INC
Also Called: Crystal Water Company
827 S Patterson Blvd (45402-2622)
PHONE..............................937 228-1189
Fax: 937 228-3817
Tom Rambasek, *President*
Nancy F Rambasek, *Treasurer*
EMP: 19
SQ FT: 16,000
SALES (est): 3.2MM **Privately Held**
SIC: 5149 5963 2899 7359 Water, distilled; bottled water delivery; distilled water; equipment rental & leasing

(G-8617)
RANDD ASSOC PRTG &
PROMOTIONS
330 Progress Rd (45449-2322)
PHONE..............................937 294-1874
Rick Dobson, *President*
Pam Dobson, *Corp Secy*
Rhonda Fultz, *Accounting Mgr*
EMP: 7
SQ FT: 3,200
SALES (est): 1MM **Privately Held**
WEB: www.randdassociates.com
SIC: 2752 5199 Commercial printing, offset; advertising specialties

(G-8618)
READY TECHNOLOGY INC
Also Called: Standard Die Supply
630 Kiser St (45404-1644)
PHONE..............................937 228-8181
Fax: 937 228-2928
Troy Todd, *Plant Mgr*
Kelly Romer, *Branch Mgr*
EMP: 14
SALES (corp-wide): 16.6MM **Privately Held**
WEB: www.readytech.net
SIC: 3542 5084 Machine tools, metal forming type; tool & die makers' equipment
HQ: Ready Technology, Inc.
333 Progress Rd Unit A
Dayton OH 45449
937 866-7200

(G-8619)
READY TECHNOLOGY INC (HQ)
333 Progress Rd Unit A (45449-2490)
PHONE..............................937 866-7200
Fax: 937 866-7226
Michael Danly, *President*
Kelly Romer, *Plant Mgr*
Steve Thompson, *Plant Mgr*
Jim Pecqueux, *Controller*
Carleen Thompson, *Sales Executive*
▲ EMP: 14 EST: 1981
SQ FT: 10,000
SALES (est): 3.6MM
SALES (corp-wide): 16.6MM **Privately Held**
WEB: www.readytech.net
SIC: 3542 5084 3544 Machine tools, metal forming type; bending machines; metalworking tools (such as drills, taps, dies, files); special dies, tools, jigs & fixtures
PA: Danly Corporation
3121 Commodore Plz Ph 5
Miami FL 33133
305 285-0111

(G-8620)
REECES LAS VEGAS SUPPLIES (PA)
5425 Fishburg Rd (45424-7500)
PHONE..............................937 274-5000
Fax: 937 274-5300
Reece Powers, *Partner*
Janice Powers, *Partner*
Bill Jarvis, *Manager*
EMP: 4
SALES (est): 750K **Privately Held**
SIC: 3581 3599 Automatic vending machines; amusement park equipment

(G-8621)
REEL IMAGE
2520 Blackhawk Rd (45420-3902)
PHONE..............................937 296-9036
J Osborne, *Principal*
EMP: 5
SALES (est): 468.7K **Privately Held**
SIC: 2721 Periodicals

(G-8622)
REELFLYRODCOM
7635 Wilmington Pike D (45458-5425)
PHONE..............................937 434-8472
Todd Mikesell, *Owner*
EMP: 3 EST: 2009
SALES (est): 259.3K **Privately Held**
SIC: 3949 7999 Reels, fishing; outfitters, recreation

(G-8623)
RELY-ON MANUFACTURING INC
955 Springfield St (45403-1347)
PHONE..............................937 254-0118
Marsha Mosher, *President*
Peter T Mosher, *Vice Pres*
EMP: 6
SALES (est): 700K **Privately Held**
SIC: 3599 Machine shop, jobbing & repair

(G-8624)
REMNANT ROOM
1915 S Alex Rd (45449-4002)
PHONE..............................937 938-7350
Mike Daugherty, *Owner*
EMP: 3
SALES (est): 267.2K **Privately Held**
SIC: 2273 Carpets & rugs

(G-8625)
RENCO MOLD INC
2801 Ome Ave (45414-5118)
PHONE..............................937 233-3233
Fax: 937 274-6790
Marvin Evans, *President*
Glenn Renner, *Admin Sec*
EMP: 6
SQ FT: 3,000
SALES (est): 606.4K **Privately Held**
SIC: 3544 Special dies & tools

(G-8626)
REPUBLIC EDM SERVICES INC
5660 Wadsworth Rd (45414-3412)
PHONE..............................937 278-7070
Fax: 937 278-7411
Gary D Schinder, *President*
Kim S Schinder, *Corp Secy*
EMP: 3
SQ FT: 2,000
SALES: 250K **Privately Held**
SIC: 3541 Electron-discharge metal cutting machine tools

(G-8627)
REX AMERICAN RESOURCES
CORP (PA)
7720 Paragon Rd (45459-4050)
PHONE..............................937 276-3931
Stuart A Rose, *Ch of Bd*
Zafar Rizvi, *President*
Douglas L Bruggeman, *CFO*
Edward M Kress, *Admin Sec*
EMP: 102
SQ FT: 7,500
SALES: 453.8MM **Publicly Held**
WEB: www.rexstore.com
SIC: 2869 6531 Fuels; ethyl alcohol, ethanol; real estate leasing & rentals

(G-8628)
REX M & KIM P BELLVILLE
4121 Cleveland Ave (45410-3403)
PHONE..............................937 256-2526
Cody Bellville, *Partner*
EMP: 15
SALES (est): 1MM **Privately Held**
SIC: 2047 Dog & cat food

(G-8629)
REYNOLDS AND REYNOLDS
COMPANY
354 Mound St (45402-8325)
P.O. Box 2608 (45401-2608)
PHONE..............................937 485-4771
David R Holmes, *President*

GEOGRAPHIC

Virginia Stuckey, *Technical Mgr*
Gary Mathes, *Engineer*
Tom McDermott, *Accounts Exec*
Bob Adams, *Manager*
EMP: 7
SQ FT: 1,575
SALES (corp-wide): 1.4B **Privately Held**
WEB: www.reyrey.com
SIC: 2759 5045 Business forms: printing;
computers & accessories, personal &
home entertainment
HQ: The Reynolds And Reynolds Company
1 Reynolds Way
Kettering OH 45430
937 485-2000

(G-8630)
REYNOLDS AND REYNOLDS
COMPANY
115 S Ludlow St (45402-1812)
P.O. Box 2237 (45401-2237)
PHONE.............................937 449-4039
Melinda Vaughn, *Principal*
Thomas Barras, *Vice Pres*
Austin Floyd, *Engineer*
Nicole Case, *Sales Staff*
Penny Barkley, *Manager*
EMP: 50
SALES (corp-wide): 1.4B **Privately Held**
WEB: www.reyrey.com
SIC: 2761 Manifold business forms
HQ: The Reynolds And Reynolds Company
1 Reynolds Way
Kettering OH 45430
937 485-2000

(G-8631)
RICHARD A SCOTT
8000 Allison Ave (45415-2205)
PHONE.............................937 898-1592
Richard A Scott, *Principal*
EMP: 3
SALES (est): 210.7K **Privately Held**
SIC: 3566 Speed changers, drives & gears

(G-8632)
RITE WAY BLACK & DEBURR
INC
1138 E 2nd St (45403-1092)
PHONE.............................937 224-7762
Fax: 937 224-4706
Cecil W Parker, *President*
James Parker, *Vice Pres*
Diana Spencer, *Vice Pres*
Joyce Parker, *Purchasing*
EMP: 5
SQ FT: 6,000
SALES (est): 380K **Privately Held**
SIC: 3471 3479 Plating & polishing; etch-
ing & engraving

(G-8633)
RIXAN ASSOCIATES INC
7560 Paragon Rd (45459-5317)
PHONE.............................937 438-3005
Fax: 937 438-0130
Stephen Harris, *President*
Aaron Harris, *Chairman*
Beatrice Harris, *Corp Secy*
David Ryan, *Vice Pres*
Jeff Conrad, *Engineer*
EMP: 20 **EST:** 1959
SQ FT: 14,000
SALES (est): 12.6MM **Privately Held**
WEB: www.rixan.com
SIC: 5084 3569 5065 Robots, industrial;
robots, assembly line: industrial & com-
mercial; electronic parts

(G-8634)
RLFSHOP LLC
Also Called: Shopsmith
6530 Poe Ave (45414-2527)
PHONE.............................937 898-6070
Fax: 937 898-9762
Wes Powell, *Manager*
Robert L Folkerth,
▲ **EMP:** 3
SALES (est): 425.2K **Privately Held**
SIC: 3553 Woodworking machinery

(G-8635)
RMT CORPORATION
2552 Titus Ave (45414-4217)
PHONE.............................513 942-8308
Fax: 937 274-6366

Brent Shreiner, *President*
Joe Rieger, *Engineer*
EMP: 10
SQ FT: 1,267
SALES (est): 1.6MM **Privately Held**
SIC: 3544 Special dies, tools, jigs & fix-
tures

(G-8636)
ROBBINS & MYERS INC
5870 Poe Ave Ste A (45414-3442)
P.O. Box 1123 (45401-1123)
PHONE.............................937 454-3200
Kathy Morland, *Human Res Mgr*
Chris Cleveland, *Sales Staff*
Kevin Brown, *Branch Mgr*
EMP: 17
SALES (corp-wide): 7.2B **Publicly Held**
SIC: 3533 Oil & gas field machinery
HQ: Robbins & Myers, Inc.
10586 N Highway 75
Willis TX 77378
936 890-1064

(G-8637)
ROBS WELDING
TECHNOLOGIES LTD
2920 Production Ct (45414-3537)
PHONE.............................937 890-4963
Fax: 937 890-1948
Dean Shoup, *Partner*
Rob Shoup, *Partner*
Cheryl Shoup, *Office Mgr*
EMP: 9
SQ FT: 10,000
SALES: 1.5MM **Privately Held**
WEB: www.robsweldingtech.com
SIC: 3312 3441 1799 Tool & die steel;
fabricated structural metal; welding on
site

(G-8638)
RONALD T DODGE CO
Also Called: Dodge Company
55 Westpark Rd (45459-4812)
PHONE.............................937 439-4497
Fax: 937 439-1704
Ronald J Versic, *President*
Linda J Versic, *Treasurer*
EMP: 10
SQ FT: 8,000
SALES (est): 1.8MM **Privately Held**
WEB: www.rtdodge.com
SIC: 2869 8731 High purity grade chemi-
cals, organic; commercial research labo-
ratory

(G-8639)
RPA ELECTRONIC DISTRS INC
Also Called: R P A
122 S Terry St (45403-2340)
P.O. Box 1001 (45401-1001)
PHONE.............................937 223-7001
Fax: 937 461-7315
R Paul Perkins Jr, *Principal*
William Watson, *Vice Pres*
Sandy Strawser, *Treasurer*
Alicia Dearth, *Office Mgr*
Bajump Jump, *Info Tech Mgr*
EMP: 12
SQ FT: 9,000
SALES (est): 4MM **Privately Held**
SIC: 5065 3679 Electronic parts; elec-
tronic circuits

(G-8640)
RUBBER-TECH INC
5208 Wadsworth Rd (45414-3592)
PHONE.............................937 274-1114
Fax: 937 274-1798
Forest Back, *President*
L Irene Back, *Corp Secy*
Irene L Back, *Treasurer*
EMP: 17
SQ FT: 10,000
SALES (est): 3.2MM **Privately Held**
WEB: www.rubber-tech.com
SIC: 3069 3061 Molded rubber products;
mechanical rubber goods

(G-8641)
RYANWORKS INC
Also Called: Woodcraft
175 E Alex Bell Rd # 264 (45459-2701)
PHONE.............................937 438-1282
Fax: 937 438-0119

Alan Ryan, *President*
EMP: 16
SALES: 1MM **Privately Held**
WEB: www.ryanworks.com
SIC: 5084 2499 Woodworking machinery;
decorative wood & woodwork

(G-8642)
S & R SHEET METAL
320 Gargrave Rd (45449-2464)
P.O. Box 186, Miamisburg (45343-0186)
PHONE.............................937 865-9236
Fax: 937 865-9237
Jeffrey Cooper, *Partner*
Harold Urban, *Partner*
EMP: 5
SQ FT: 5,200
SALES: 500K **Privately Held**
SIC: 3444 Sheet metalwork

(G-8643)
S & S PRINTING SERVICE INC
Also Called: William A Selz
505 Hunter Ave (45404-1569)
PHONE.............................937 228-9411
Fax: 937 222-3823
Ken Selz, *President*
Betty Selz, *Treasurer*
EMP: 5
SQ FT: 3,600
SALES: 300K **Privately Held**
SIC: 2752 Commercial printing, offset

(G-8644)
S F MOCK & ASSOCIATES LLC
105 Westpark Rd (45459-4814)
PHONE.............................937 438-0196
Stephen F Mock,
EMP: 10
SALES (est): 391.3K **Privately Held**
SIC: 2761 5611 2759 Manifold business
forms; men's & boys' clothing stores;
business forms: printing

(G-8645)
SAMPLE MACHINING INC
Also Called: Bitec
220 N Jersey St (45403-1220)
PHONE.............................937 258-3338
Fax: 937 258-3840
Beverly Bleicher, *President*
Kevin Bleicher, *Vice Pres*
Jeremy Royse, *QC Mgr*
Robert Bleicher, *Engineer*
Becky Bleicher, *Finance Mgr*
EMP: 45
SQ FT: 19,000
SALES: 7MM **Privately Held**
WEB: www.bitecsmi.com
SIC: 3599 8734 Custom machinery; test-
ing laboratories

(G-8646)
SCARLETT KITTY LLC
Also Called: Scarlett Ktty Bath Made Pretty
2786 Wilmington Pike (45419-2141)
PHONE.............................678 438-3796
Joy Coleman, *CEO*
EMP: 10 **EST:** 2014
SQ FT: 3,000
SALES (est): 325.1K **Privately Held**
SIC: 2844 Depilatories (cosmetic)

(G-8647)
SCHUERHOLZ PRINTING INC
3540 Marshall Rd (45429-4916)
PHONE.............................937 294-5218
Fax: 937 294-4958
Charles Schuerholz, *President*
EMP: 7
SQ FT: 4,500
SALES (est): 605K **Privately Held**
WEB: www.schuerholzgraphics.com
SIC: 2752 7336 Commercial printing, off-
set; graphic arts & related design

(G-8648)
SCIENCE/ELECTRONICS INC
Also Called: Earth and Atmospheric Sciences
521 Kiser St (45404-1641)
PHONE.............................937 224-4444
Fax: 937 224-4434
Ted Morton, *CEO*
Janice Morton, *CFO*
Melanie Shockey, *Office Mgr*
EMP: 15

SQ FT: 90,000
SALES (est): 1.8MM **Privately Held**
SIC: 5049 3829 Scientific instruments;
measuring & controlling devices

(G-8649)
SCOTTS COMPANY LLC
20 Innovation Ct (45414-3968)
PHONE.............................937 454-2782
Kevin Laughlin, *Manager*
EMP: 15
SALES (corp-wide): 2.8B **Publicly Held**
WEB: www.scottscompany.com
SIC: 2873 Fertilizers: natural (organic), ex-
cept compost
HQ: The Scotts Company Llc
14111 Scottslawn Rd
Marysville OH 43040
937 644-3729

(G-8650)
SCREEN WORKS INC (PA)
3970 Image Dr (45414-2524)
PHONE.............................937 264-9111
Fax: 937 264-9100
Jeff Cottrell, *Principal*
Greg Brubaker, *Opers Mgr*
Linda Flaugher, *Purch Agent*
Beth Nealeigh, *Human Res Mgr*
Kevin Shehee, *Marketing Staff*
EMP: 46
SQ FT: 42,000
SALES (est): 8.6MM **Privately Held**
WEB: www.screenworksinc.com
SIC: 7336 5199 7389 3993 Silk screen
design; advertising specialties; embroi-
dering of advertising on shirts, etc.; signs
& advertising specialties; automotive &
apparel trimmings

(G-8651)
SEEBACH INC
Also Called: Seebach Tools & Molds Mfg
2622 Keenan Ave (45414-4910)
PHONE.............................937 275-3565
Fax: 937 275-7485
Mark Seebach, *CEO*
James Seebach, *President*
Carl Seebach, *Vice Pres*
EMP: 14
SQ FT: 9,600
SALES: 700K **Privately Held**
WEB: www.seebach.com
SIC: 3599 Machine shop, jobbing & repair

(G-8652)
SELECT INDUSTRIES
CORPORATION
Also Called: Select International Corp.
60 Heid Ave (45404-1216)
P.O. Box 887 (45401-0887)
PHONE.............................937 233-9191
Mark Wogoman, *President*
Robert Whited, *Principal*
Kelly Wogoman, *Chairman*
Alan Fidler, *Engineer*
Blanca Geisert, *Accounting Mgr*
◆ **EMP:** 200
SQ FT: 250,000
SALES (est): 56.1MM **Privately Held**
SIC: 3469 Metal stampings; capacitor or
condenser cans & cases, stamped metal;
electronic enclosures, stamped or
pressed metal; automobile license tags,
stamped metal
PA: Select International Corp.
60 Heid Ave
Dayton OH 45404
937 233-9191

(G-8653)
SELECT INTERNATIONAL CORP
(PA)
60 Heid Ave (45404-1216)
P.O. Box 887 (45401-0887)
PHONE.............................937 233-9191
Kelly Wogomanceo, *CEO*
Mark Wogoman, *Vice Pres*
Debbie Lambdin, *Purch Agent*
Tom Landon, *Chief Engr*
Ken Porr, *Engineer*
EMP: 3
SALES (est): 56.1MM **Privately Held**
SIC: 3465 1799 Automotive stampings;
welding on site

354   2017 Harris Ohio
Industrial Directory   ▲ = Import ▼ =Export
◆ =Import/Export

(G-8654)
SHILOH HOTGLASS
274 Briarcliff Rd (45415-3423)
P.O. Box 230 (45415)
PHONE..................................937 274-7222
Thomas Chapman, *Owner*
EMP: 3
SALES: 85K **Privately Held**
SIC: 3231 Art glass: made from purchased glass

(G-8655)
SHILOH INDUSTRIES INC
5988 Executive Blvd Ste B (45424-1413)
PHONE..................................937 236-5100
Fax: 937 236-7789
John Dixon, *President*
David W Dixon, *Vice Pres*
Charles Broome, *Manager*
Pam Studebaker, *Executive*
EMP: 18
SQ FT: 18,000
SALES (est): 3.6MM **Privately Held**
SIC: 3679 3089 Electronic circuits; injection molding of plastics

(G-8656)
SHORE TO SHORE INC (DH)
8170 Washington Vlg Dr (45458-1848)
PHONE..................................937 866-1908
Howard Kurdin, *President*
John Lau, *Exec VP*
Bobette Jerome, *Project Mgr*
Jo Clark, *QC Mgr*
Chuck Rowland, *CFO*
▲ EMP: 100
SQ FT: 30,000
SALES (est): 130MM
SALES (corp-wide): 188.4K **Privately Held**
WEB: www.shr2shr.com
SIC: 2679 2241 Labels, paper: made from purchased material; labels, woven
HQ: Checkpoint Systems, Inc.
101 Wolf Dr
West Deptford NJ 08086
856 848-1800

(G-8657)
SIGN CONNECTION INC
90 Compark Rd Ste B (45459-4967)
PHONE..................................937 435-4070
Fax: 937 435-4071
Jane Fiehrer, *President*
EMP: 4
SALES (est): 511.2K **Privately Held**
SIC: 3993 Signs & advertising specialties

(G-8658)
SIGN TECHNOLOGIES LLC
Also Called: Signetics
2001 Kuntz Rd (45404-1221)
PHONE..................................937 439-3970
Fax: 937 438-9666
Shari Brown, *Finance Mgr*
EMP: 6
SQ FT: 6,000
SALES (est): 490K **Privately Held**
WEB: www.signetics1.com
SIC: 2499 Signboards, wood

(G-8659)
SIMON ELLIS SUPERABRASIVES
501 Progress Rd (45449-2325)
PHONE..................................937 226-0683
Fax: 937 226-0684
David Rawson, *President*
Thomas Greene, *Vice Pres*
Theresa Tsmcatee, *Office Mgr*
Beverly Greene, *Admin Sec*
EMP: 9
SQ FT: 5,000
SALES (est): 1.1MM **Privately Held**
WEB: www.simonellis.com
SIC: 3423 Hand & edge tools

(G-8660)
SKIN
333 Wayne Ave (45410-1115)
PHONE..................................937 222-0222
Fax: 937 222-8665
Iris Goldflies, *President*
Gary Golgflies, *Vice Pres*
EMP: 4

SALES: 260K **Privately Held**
SIC: 2844 Face creams or lotions

(G-8661)
SNYDER CONCRETE PRODUCTS INC
Also Called: Snyder Brick and Block
1433 S Euclid Ave (45417-3839)
PHONE..................................937 224-1433
Fax: 937 299-4318
Chip Lytel, *Manager*
EMP: 9
SALES (corp-wide): 13.3MM **Privately Held**
WEB: www.snyderonline.com
SIC: 5032 3271 Brick, except refractory; concrete & cinder building products; blocks, concrete or cinder: standard
PA: Snyder Concrete Products, Inc.
2301 W Dorothy Ln
Moraine OH 45439
937 885-5176

(G-8662)
SOUTHERN EXPRESS LUBES INC
3781 Salem Ave (45406-1651)
PHONE..................................937 278-5807
Dwayne Mowen, *Manager*
EMP: 15
SALES (corp-wide): 8.7MM **Privately Held**
WEB: www.selubes.com
SIC: 2843 Oils & greases
PA: Southern Express Lubes, Inc.
8520 Conn Ave Ste 200
Chevy Chase MD
301 657-0774

(G-8663)
SOUTHERN ORNAMENTAL IRON CO (PA)
4267 Salem Ave (45416-1704)
PHONE..................................937 278-4319
Fax: 937 278-5250
Steven Davis, *President*
EMP: 7 EST: 1961
SQ FT: 4,000
SALES (est): 739.8K **Privately Held**
WEB: www.mwdpc.com
SIC: 3446 Architectural metalwork

(G-8664)
SOUTHWESTERN OHIO INSTRUCTION
Also Called: S O I T A
1205 E 5th St (45402-2221)
PHONE..................................937 746-6333
Fax: 513 746-1029
Dave Mc Williams, *Corp Secy*
Larry Pogue, *Exec Dir*
David Gibson, *Director*
EMP: 10
SQ FT: 2,000
SALES: 459.4K **Privately Held**
WEB: www.soita.org
SIC: 7372 Educational computer software

(G-8665)
SPACE AGE COATINGS LLC
Also Called: Space Age Concepts
4825 Wolf Creek Pike (45417-9439)
P.O. Box 26488 (45426-0488)
PHONE..................................937 275-5117
Gerald Blessing, *CEO*
Linda Yarvel, *Vice Pres*
Dean Blessing,
EMP: 3
SQ FT: 4,000
SALES (est): 218.6K **Privately Held**
WEB: www.spaceagecoating.com
SIC: 7699 3544 Metal reshaping & replating services; special dies, tools, jigs & fixtures

(G-8666)
SPAOS INC (PA)
Also Called: Superior Printing and Off Sup
6012 N Dixie Dr (45414-4018)
PHONE..................................937 890-0783
Fax: 937 898-7873
Jack Roberts, *President*
Bonnie Roberts, *Corp Secy*
EMP: 6

SALES (est): 944.5K **Privately Held**
SIC: 2752 5943 Commercial printing, offset; office forms & supplies

(G-8667)
SPECTRACAM LTD
1112 E Race Dr (45404)
PHONE..................................937 223-3805
Joseph Wendling, *Mng Member*
EMP: 7 EST: 1998
SQ FT: 6,300
SALES (est): 790K **Privately Held**
SIC: 3544 3543 Special dies, tools, jigs & fixtures; industrial patterns

(G-8668)
SPECTRON INC
132 S Terry St (45403-2340)
P.O. Box 3518 (45401-3518)
PHONE..................................937 461-5590
Fax: 937 461-5594
Betty Burnett, *President*
Jeff Bucher, *President*
EMP: 6 EST: 1966
SQ FT: 4,000
SALES (est): 737.3K **Privately Held**
WEB: www.spectroninc.com
SIC: 3679 Electronic circuits

(G-8669)
SPECTRUM EMBROIDERY INC
332 Gargrave Rd (45449-2464)
PHONE..................................937 847-9905
Randy Russell, *President*
Donna Russell, *Vice Pres*
EMP: 3
SALES (est): 338.9K **Privately Held**
SIC: 2759 2395 Promotional printing; embroidery products, except schiffli machine

(G-8670)
SPIEGLER BRAKE SYSTEMS USA LLC
1699 Thomas Paine Pkwy (45459-2538)
PHONE..................................937 291-1735
Matthias Schaub, *Mng Member*
John Lucas, *Manager*
▲ EMP: 6
SQ FT: 3,500
SALES (est): 985.6K **Privately Held**
SIC: 3751 5571 Motorcycles, bicycles & parts; motorcycle parts & accessories

(G-8671)
SPITFIRE TECHNOLOGIES LLC
110 N Main St (45402-1795)
PHONE..................................937 463-7729
Joseph Krebs, *CPA*
EMP: 4 EST: 2013
SQ FT: 2,500
SALES (est): 220K **Privately Held**
SIC: 7372 Application computer software

(G-8672)
SRC LIQUIDATION LLC (PA)
600 Albany St (45417-3405)
P.O. Box 1167 (45401-1167)
PHONE..................................937 221-1000
Fax: 937 221-1205
F David Clarke III, *Ch of Bd*
Landen Williams, *President*
Joseph Morgan, *COO*
Coleen Hart, *Project Mgr*
Jeff Murakami, *Project Mgr*
◆ EMP: 600
SALES (est): 1.2B **Privately Held**
WEB: www.stdreg.com
SIC: 2761 2672 2677 2759 Manifold business forms; labels (unprinted); gummed: made from purchased materials; envelopes; promotional printing

(G-8673)
SS METAL FABRICATORS INC
423 Rita St (45404-2716)
P.O. Box 157 (45404-0157)
PHONE..................................937 226-9957
Jim Shanks, *President*
Tony Shanks, *Vice Pres*
EMP: 5
SQ FT: 10,000
SALES: 620K **Privately Held**
SIC: 3441 Fabricated structural metal

(G-8674)
STAFFORD GAGE & TOOL INC
4606 Webster St (45414-4826)
PHONE..................................937 277-9944
Fax: 937 277-9239
Judy Stafford, *President*
Jean Stafford, *Vice Pres*
EMP: 12 EST: 1947
SQ FT: 10,500
SALES (est): 1.2MM **Privately Held**
WEB: www.sgandt.com
SIC: 3599 Machine shop, jobbing & repair

(G-8675)
STANCO PRECISION MANUFACTURING
Also Called: Ss Industries
1 Walbrook Ave (45405-2341)
PHONE..................................937 274-1785
Fax: 937 274-1743
Stephen P Stanoikovich, *President*
Steve Strader, *General Mgr*
Rhonda Stanoikovich, *Manager*
▲ EMP: 9
SQ FT: 8,000
SALES (est): 1.1MM **Privately Held**
WEB: www.stancoprecision.com
SIC: 3599 3544 Machine shop, jobbing & repair; special dies & tools

(G-8676)
STANDARD REGISTER INC
600 Albany St (45417-3442)
PHONE..................................860 870-2063
Jim Miller, *Manager*
Kevin Daley, *Technology*
EMP: 24
SALES (corp-wide): 4.6B **Privately Held**
WEB: www.stdreg.com
SIC: 2761 2759 2752 Manifold business forms; commercial printing; commercial printing, lithographic
HQ: Standard Register, Inc.
600 Albany St
Dayton OH 45417
937 221-1000

(G-8677)
STANDARD REGISTER INC
7755 Paragon Rd Ste 101 (45459-4052)
PHONE..................................732 356-0081
Fax: 937 439-5463
Brian Clark, *Manager*
EMP: 11
SALES (corp-wide): 4.6B **Privately Held**
WEB: www.stdreg.com
SIC: 2761 Manifold business forms
HQ: Standard Register, Inc.
600 Albany St
Dayton OH 45417
937 221-1000

(G-8678)
STANDARD REGISTER INC
600 Albany St (45417-3442)
PHONE..................................480 763-1900
Maryann Kulakowski, *Manager*
EMP: 5
SALES (corp-wide): 4.6B **Privately Held**
WEB: www.stdreg.com
SIC: 2761 Manifold business forms
HQ: Standard Register, Inc.
600 Albany St
Dayton OH 45417
937 221-1000

(G-8679)
STANDARD REGISTER INC
220 E Monument Ave (45402-1287)
PHONE..................................937 228-5800
Camille Palladino, *Principal*
John Odonnell, *Marketing Staff*
Becky Graham, *Admin Asst*
EMP: 5
SALES (corp-wide): 4.6B **Privately Held**
SIC: 5112 2754 2789 2761 Stationery & office supplies; commercial printing, gravure; bookbinding & related work; manifold business forms; commercial printing, lithographic
HQ: Standard Register, Inc.
600 Albany St
Dayton OH 45417
937 221-1000

(G-8680)
STANDARD REGISTER INC
2222 Philadelphia Dr (45406)
PHONE.............................866 541-0937
EMP: 3
SALES (corp-wide): 4.6B Privately Held
SIC: 2754 Commercial printing, gravure
HQ: Standard Register, Inc.
600 Albany St
Dayton OH 45417
937 221-1000

(G-8681)
STARWIN INDUSTRIES INC
3387 Woodman Dr (45429-4100)
PHONE.............................937 293-8568
Fax: 937 299-0698
Norman Staub, CEO
Rick Little, President
John Whitaker, General Mgr
Mark Belt, Vice Pres
Bill Anderson, Project Mgr
EMP: 40
SQ FT: 30,000
SALES (est): 7.5MM Privately Held
WEB: www.starwin-ind.com
SIC: 3599 7372 Machine shop, jobbing &
repair; prepackaged software

(G-8682)
STATE OF OHIO DAYTON RACEWAY
4701 Wagner Ford Rd (45414-4421)
PHONE.............................937 237-7802
EMP: 3
SALES (est): 198.9K Privately Held
SIC: 3644 Raceways

(G-8683)
STECK MANUFACTURING CO INC
1115 S Broadway St Ste 1 (45417-3940)
PHONE.............................937 222-0062
Fax: 937 222-6666
John Brill, President
Rick Vogel, Vice Pres
Ryan Steberl, Opers Staff
Cindy Barnett, Marketing Mgr
Ray Steck, Manager
▲ EMP: 16 EST: 1945
SQ FT: 14,300
SALES: 4MM Privately Held
WEB: www.steckmfg.com
SIC: 3714 3599 Motor vehicle parts & ac-
cessories; machine shop, jobbing & repair

(G-8684)
STOLLE MACHINERY COMPANY LLC
Also Called: Ultra Punch
7425 Webster St (45414-5817)
PHONE.............................937 859-4644
Fax: 937 859-7357
Keith Gilmore, Manager
EMP: 20
SALES (corp-wide): 256.7MM Privately
Held
SIC: 3544 3496 Punches, forming &
stamping; dies & die holders for metal
cutting, forming, die casting; miscella-
neous fabricated wire products
PA: Stolle Machinery Company, Llc
6949 S Potomac St
Centennial CO 80112
303 708-9044

(G-8685)
STORECOM EQUIPMENT LLC
1150 E Dixie Dr (45449-1922)
PHONE.............................800 356-0368
Fax: 937 428-9710
Bonnie Farmer, General Mgr
Abbey Farmer, Prdtn Mgr
EMP: 3 EST: 2010
SALES: 400K Privately Held
SIC: 3669 Emergency alarms

(G-8686)
SUBURBAN NEWPAPERS OF DAYTON
Also Called: Huber Heights Courier
7089 Taylorsville Rd A (45424-3180)
PHONE.............................937 236-4990
Fax: 937 236-4176
Greg Smart, Principal

EMP: 5
SALES (corp-wide): 45.6MM Privately
Held
WEB: www.tcnewsnet.com
SIC: 2711 Commercial printing & newspa-
per publishing combined
HQ: Suburban Newpapers Of Dayton Inc
3085 Woodman Dr Ste 170
Dayton OH
937 294-7000

(G-8687)
SUGAR CREEK PACKING CO
1241 N Gettysburg Ave (45417-9513)
PHONE.............................937 268-6601
Fax: 937 268-6603
Steve Shutte, Opers-Prdtn-Mfg
Timothy Sparks, Executive
EMP: 350
SQ FT: 20,000
SALES (corp-wide): 739.8MM Privately
Held
WEB: www.sugarcreek.com
SIC: 2013 2011 Bacon, side & sliced: from
purchased meat; meat packing plants
PA: Sugar Creek Packing Co.
2101 Kenskill Ave
Wshngtn Ct Hs OH 43160
740 335-7440

(G-8688)
SULZER TRANSMISSION TECH
260 Detrick St (45404-1699)
PHONE.............................937 449-4000
EMP: 3 EST: 2011
SALES (est): 178.7K Privately Held
SIC: 3465 Automotive stampings

(G-8689)
SUPERIOR MACHINING INC
2946 Lindale Ave (45414-5521)
PHONE.............................937 236-9619
Fax: 937 236-5819
Thomas Gilhooly, CEO
James Lewis, President
EMP: 32
SQ FT: 16,764
SALES (est): 3.4MM Privately Held
WEB: www.superior-machining-inc.com
SIC: 3541 Milling machines

(G-8690)
SUPPLIER INSPECTION SVCS INC (PA)
2941 S Gettysburg Ave (45439-7912)
PHONE.............................937 263-7097
Fax: 937 263-2165
Paul A Bowell, President
Steve Anklen, Opers Mgr
Gary Blanford, Opers Mgr
Ernest Henderson, Opers Mgr
Dan Henning, Opers Mgr
EMP: 20
SQ FT: 50,000
SALES (est): 5.8MM Privately Held
WEB: www.sis-inspection.net
SIC: 3545 7389 Machine tool accessories;
inspection & testing services

(G-8691)
SURE TOOL & MANUFACTURING CO
429 Winston Ave (45403-1400)
PHONE.............................937 253-9111
Fax: 937 253-9761
Jerrald Kuriger, President
Ruth Kuriger, Corp Secy
Russell B Kuriger, Vice Pres
Beryl R Kuriger, Controller
EMP: 23 EST: 1969
SQ FT: 14,000
SALES (est): 2.2MM Privately Held
WEB: www.suretool.com
SIC: 3544 Special dies & tools

(G-8692)
SWIGART REFINISHING COMPANY
2021 E 3rd St (45403-1994)
PHONE.............................937 254-1141
Fax: 937 254-7877
Ralph Swigart Jr, President
EMP: 3
SQ FT: 8,000

SALES: 140K Privately Held
SIC: 7641 2511 Antique furniture repair &
restoration; furniture refinishing; furniture
repair & maintenance; reupholstery; wood
household furniture

(G-8693)
SYSTECH ENVIRONMENTAL CORP (DH)
3085 Woodman Dr Ste 300 (45420-1159)
PHONE.............................800 888-8011
Fax: 937 643-1203
Thomas J Sponiger, Vice Ch Bd
David Cheney, President
Thomas Moore, Vice Pres
Dana Dunstan, Project Mgr
Julie Hubart, Research
◆ EMP: 20
SQ FT: 10,000
SALES (est): 21.1MM
SALES (corp-wide): 26.6B Privately Held
WEB: www.sysenv.com
SIC: 2869 Fuels
HQ: Lafarge North America Inc.
8700 W Bryn Mawr Ave Ll
Chicago IL 60631
703 480-3600

(G-8694)
SYSTEMAX MANUFACTURING INC
6450 Poe Ave Ste 200 (45414-2655)
PHONE.............................937 368-2300
Tammy Moore, Warehouse Mgr
Linda Owens, Accounting Mgr
Jennifer Harlow, Accountant
Pam Shablin, Sales Mgr
Skip Murray, Mktg Dir
▲ EMP: 200
SQ FT: 185,000
SALES (est): 22MM Publicly Held
WEB: www.systemax.com
SIC: 5045 5961 7373 3577 Computers,
peripherals & software; computer periph-
eral equipment; printers, computer; com-
puters & accessories, personal & home
entertainment; computers & peripheral
equipment, mail order; systems integra-
tion services; computer peripheral equip-
ment; electronic computers
PA: Systemax Inc.
11 Harbor Park Dr
Port Washington NY 11050

(G-8695)
T & L CUSTOM SCREENING INC
3464 Successful Way (45414-4320)
PHONE.............................937 237-3121
Fax: 937 237-3146
Louise Edwards, President
Tonya Snapp, Corp Secy
Stephanie Edwards, Office Mgr
EMP: 7
SQ FT: 6,500
SALES: 390K Privately Held
SIC: 2759 5199 2395 2396 Commercial
printing; advertising specialties; embroi-
dery products, except schiffli machine;
automotive & apparel trimmings

(G-8696)
T & R WELDING SYSTEMS INC
1 Janney Rd (45404-1263)
PHONE.............................937 228-7517
Fax: 937 228-7707
Mike Bozzo, President
▼ EMP: 15
SQ FT: 15,000
SALES (est): 3.4MM Privately Held
SIC: 3496 7692 Miscellaneous fabricated
wire products; welding repair

(G-8697)
TABTRONICS INC
2153 Winners Cir (45404-1150)
PHONE.............................937 222-9969
Fax: 937 222-9121
Thomas Biel, President
Kelly McKoy, Manager
Cindy Biel, Admin Sec
EMP: 16
SQ FT: 9,000

SALES (est): 5.2MM Privately Held
WEB: www.pedtke.com
SIC: 3625 Relays & industrial controls;
electric controls & control accessories, industrial

(G-8698)
TALECRIS PLASMA RESOURCES
3909 Salem Ave (45406-1526)
PHONE.............................937 275-5996
Regina McMahan, Manager
EMP: 5
SALES (est): 638.8K Privately Held
SIC: 2836 Plasmas

(G-8699)
TANNING
7109 Taylorsville Rd (45424-3101)
PHONE.............................937 233-4554
Tay Wazt, Owner
EMP: 3
SALES (est): 216.2K Privately Held
SIC: 2861 7299 Dyeing materials, natural;
softwood distillates; miscellaneous per-
sonal service; tanning salon

(G-8700)
TARGET PRINTING & GRAPHICS
233 Leo St (45404-1005)
PHONE.............................937 228-0170
Kris Willetts, President
Phyllis Swigart, Corp Secy
Kiela Willets, Vice Pres
EMP: 6
SQ FT: 12,000
SALES (est): 658K Privately Held
SIC: 2752 2791 2789 2721 Commercial
printing, offset; typesetting; bookbinding &
related work; periodicals

(G-8701)
TARGETED CMPUND MONITORING LLC
531 E 3rd St (45402-2280)
PHONE.............................513 461-3535
Todd Dockum,
EMP: 4
SALES (est): 162.8K Privately Held
SIC: 3826 Automatic chemical analyzers

(G-8702)
TARK INC (PA)
420 Congress Park Dr (45459-4125)
PHONE.............................937 434-6766
Joe McCarthy, CEO
Jim McCarthy, President
John Basnett, Vice Pres
Donna McCarthy, Vice Pres
John Koverman, Treasurer
EMP: 42
SQ FT: 600
SALES (est): 9.6MM Privately Held
WEB: www.tarkinc.com
SIC: 3561 Pumps & pumping equipment

(G-8703)
TATE LYLE INGRDNTS AMRICAS LLC
5600 Brentlinger Dr (45414-3512)
PHONE.............................937 236-5906
Todd Davis, Plant Mgr
Keith Oliger, Foreman/Supr
Marie Carmack, Buyer
Charles Kraft, Branch Mgr
Celi Duran, Manager
EMP: 75
SALES (corp-wide): 3.4B Privately Held
SIC: 2899 2819 2087 Chemical prepara-
tions; industrial inorganic chemicals; fla-
voring extracts & syrups
HQ: Tate & Lyle Ingredients Americas Llc
2200 E Eldorado St
Decatur IL 62521
217 423-4411

(G-8704)
TATE LYLE INGRDNTS AMRICAS LLC
5584 Webster St (45414-3517)
PHONE.............................937 235-4074
Araceli Duran, Manager
Celi Duran, Manager
EMP: 86

SALES (corp-wide): 3.4B **Privately Held**
SIC: **2046** Wet corn milling
HQ: Tate & Lyle Ingredients Americas Llc
2200 E Eldorado St
Decatur IL 62521
217 423-4411

(G-8705)
TC PRECISION MACHINE INC
2540 Ashcraft Rd (45414-3402)
PHONE..................................937 278-3334
Thomas J Trick, *President*
Cheryl Herick, *Admin Sec*
EMP: 4
SQ FT: 4,800
SALES (est): 471K **Privately Held**
SIC: **3599 7389** Machine shop, jobbing & repair; grinding, precision: commercial or industrial

(G-8706)
TE BROWN LLC (PA)
1205 Lamar St (45404-1658)
P.O. Box 89 (45404)
PHONE..................................937 223-2241
Teddy Brown, *President*
Kimberly Morgan, *Office Mgr*
EMP: 4
SQ FT: 10,000
SALES (est): 1.1MM **Privately Held**
SIC: **7699 3823** Industrial equipment services; temperature measurement instruments, industrial

(G-8707)
TEC DESIGN & MANUFACTURING INC
4549 Gateway Cir (45440-1711)
PHONE..................................937 435-2147
John A Hudock, *President*
Raj Shah, *Controller*
EMP: 14
SQ FT: 13,000
SALES (est): 890K **Privately Held**
SIC: **3542 3469** Machine tools, metal forming type; machine parts, stamped or pressed metal

(G-8708)
TEKNOL INC (PA)
Also Called: Rubber Seal Products
5751 Webster St (45414-3520)
P.O. Box 13387 (45413-0387)
PHONE..................................937 264-0190
Fax: 937 890-6320
Kent Von Behren, *President*
David Rants, *Sales Mgr*
R Von Behren, *Shareholder*
▲ EMP: 57 EST: 1976
SQ FT: 60,000
SALES: 31MM **Privately Held**
WEB: www.rubber-seal.com
SIC: **2899 2891 5198 2851** Chemical preparations; sealants; paints, varnishes & supplies; paints & allied products

(G-8709)
TESSEC LLC
5679 Webster St (45414-3518)
PHONE..................................937 985-3552
David Evans, *President*
EMP: 21
SALES (est): 4.2MM **Privately Held**
SIC: **3364 3721** Nonferrous die-castings except aluminum; motorized aircraft

(G-8710)
TESSEC MANUFACTURING SVCS LLC
5679 Webster St (45414-3518)
PHONE..................................937 985-3552
David Evans, *President*
EMP: 21
SALES (est): 760.3K **Privately Held**
SIC: **3452 3541 3544 3721** Bolts, nuts, rivets & washers; machine tools, metal cutting type; special dies, tools, jigs & fixtures; aircraft; guided missiles & space vehicles; tanks & tank components

(G-8711)
THOMAS CABINET SHOP INC
321 Gargrave Rd (45449-2465)
PHONE..................................937 847-8239
Fax: 937 847-8577
Jon Thomas, *President*

Cherie Thomas, *Corp Secy*
Don Thomas, *Vice Pres*
EMP: 10
SQ FT: 11,800
SALES: 1.5MM **Privately Held**
SIC: **1542 1751 2541 2434** Commercial & office buildings, renovation & repair; cabinet building & installation; wood partitions & fixtures; wood kitchen cabinets

(G-8712)
THREAD-RITE TOOL & MFG INC
1200 E 1st St (45403-1008)
PHONE..................................937 222-2836
Fax: 937 222-9603
Timothy D Turner, *President*
Joseph J Wilson, *Vice Pres*
EMP: 4
SQ FT: 10,000
SALES: 630K **Privately Held**
SIC: **7389 3599** Grinding, precision: commercial or industrial; machine shop, jobbing & repair

(G-8713)
THREE BOND INTERNATIONAL INC
101 Daruma Pkwy (45439-7908)
PHONE..................................937 610-3000
EMP: 50 **Privately Held**
SIC: **2891** Adhesives; glue
HQ: Three Bond International, Inc.
6184 Schumacher Park Dr
West Chester OH 45069
513 779-7300

(G-8714)
THRIFT TOOL INC
5916 Milo Rd (45414-3416)
PHONE..................................937 275-3600
Fax: 937 275-3611
Walter Jones, *President*
Jeff Jones, *Vice Pres*
EMP: 6
SQ FT: 8,000
SALES (est): 114.3K **Privately Held**
SIC: **3312** Tool & die steel & alloys

(G-8715)
THT PRESSES INC
Also Called: Tht Presses
7475 Webster St (45414-5817)
PHONE..................................937 898-2012
Fax: 937 890-1530
Mike Thieman, *President*
Ron Swarts, *Chief Engr*
Rick Kamm, *Engineer*
Larry Siefring, *Engineer*
Lori Lawson, *Human Res Mgr*
▲ EMP: 25 EST: 1977
SQ FT: 51,000
SALES (est): 5.6MM **Privately Held**
WEB: www.thtpresses.com
SIC: **3542** Die casting machines; pressing machines

(G-8716)
TIPP MACHINE & TOOL INC (HQ)
4201 Little York Rd (45414-2507)
PHONE..................................937 890-8428
Richard L Snell, *Ch of Bd*
Gary Van Gundy, *President*
Charles E Snell, *Principal*
Robert J Moorman, *Principal*
Viola M Snell, *Principal*
EMP: 124
SQ FT: 52,000
SALES (est): 14.2MM **Privately Held**
WEB: www.tippmachine.com
SIC: **3544 3599 7389** Special dies & tools; industrial molds; jigs & fixtures; machine shop, jobbing & repair; grinding, precision: commercial or industrial

(G-8717)
TIPP STONE INC
8172 Meeker Rd (45414-1911)
P.O. Box 367, Troy (45373-0367)
PHONE..................................937 890-4051
Thomas Eidemiller, *President*
EMP: 3 EST: 1966
SQ FT: 480
SALES (est): 301.3K **Privately Held**
SIC: **1442** Sand mining; gravel mining

(G-8718)
TOMCO MACHINING INC
4962 Riverton Dr (45414-3964)
PHONE..................................937 264-1943
Fax: 937 264-3038
Kathy J Tomasiak, *Ch of Bd*
James W Tomasiak, *President*
De Wayne Sutton, *Manager*
EMP: 20
SQ FT: 15,000
SALES: 2MM **Privately Held**
WEB: www.tomcoaero.com
SIC: **3498** Tube fabricating (contract bending & shaping)

(G-8719)
TOOLCRAFT PRODUCTS INC
1265 Mccook Ave (45404-2800)
P.O. Box 482 (45401-0482)
PHONE..................................937 223-8271
Fax: 937 223-1408
Mark W Klug, *President*
Thomas W Thompson, *Vice Pres*
Dan Denlinger, *Purch Agent*
Mark W Newton, *Engineer*
Cherilynn M O'Malley, *CFO*
EMP: 68 EST: 1939
SQ FT: 56,000
SALES (est): 12.5MM **Privately Held**
WEB: www.toolcraftproducts.com
SIC: **3544** Die sets for metal stamping (presses)

(G-8720)
TOOLRITE MANUFACTURING INC
5370 Wadsworth Rd (45414-3523)
PHONE..................................937 278-1962
Fax: 937 278-1963
David Tangeman, *President*
Tim Ryan, *Vice Pres*
Cindy Loy, *Manager*
EMP: 12
SQ FT: 4,500
SALES: 2.2MM **Privately Held**
SIC: **3544** Special dies, tools, jigs & fixtures

(G-8721)
TORSION CONTROL PRODUCT
840 W Spring Valley Pike (45458-3251)
PHONE..................................248 597-9997
Bob McLain, *Principal*
EMP: 4
SALES (est): 148.4K **Privately Held**
SIC: **3493** Steel springs, except wire

(G-8722)
TREADWAY MANUFACTURING LLC
5667 Webster St (45414-3518)
PHONE..................................937 264-8447
Kenny Treadway, *CEO*
EMP: 8
SALES (est): 673K **Privately Held**
SIC: **3999** Manufacturing industries

(G-8723)
TRIANGLE PRECISION INDUSTRIES
1650 Delco Park Dr (45420-1392)
PHONE..................................937 299-6776
Fax: 937 299-7340
Gerald D Schriml, *President*
Paul S Holzinger, *Vice Pres*
Mark Behnken, *Site Mgr*
EMP: 57
SQ FT: 23,400
SALES (est): 10.2MM **Privately Held**
WEB: www.triangleprecision.com
SIC: **3599 7692 3446 3444** Machine shop, jobbing & repair; welding repair; architectural metalwork; sheet metalwork; fabricated plate work (boiler shop); fabricated structural metal

(G-8724)
TRIFECTA TOOL & ENGRG LLC
4648 Gateway Cir (45440-1714)
PHONE..................................937 291-0933
Fax: 937 435-8947
Bret West, *CEO*
Bret West MBR-Ceo, *Principal*
Yogi Ferstl, *Project Mgr*
Cory Borrello,

▲ EMP: 9
SQ FT: 15,000
SALES (est): 1.4MM **Privately Held**
WEB: www.trifectatool.com
SIC: **3089** Automotive parts, plastic; injection molding of plastics

(G-8725)
TRILO INC
Also Called: Alien Workshop
2947 Boulder Ave (45414-4846)
PHONE..................................937 276-4288
Fax: 937 276-5532
Chris Carter, *President*
Mike Hill, *Vice Pres*
▲ EMP: 7
SQ FT: 20,000
SALES (est): 1.6MM **Privately Held**
WEB: www.burton.com
SIC: **3949 5941** Skateboards; skateboarding equipment

(G-8726)
TRIMBLE INC
Trimble Engineering
5475 Kellenburger Rd (45424-1013)
PHONE..................................937 233-8921
Karl Ramstrom, *President*
Chris Shephard, *Branch Mgr*
EMP: 11
SALES (corp-wide): 2.3B **Publicly Held**
WEB: www.trimble.com
SIC: **3812** Navigational systems & instruments
PA: Trimble Inc.
935 Stewart Dr
Sunnyvale CA 94085
408 481-8000

(G-8727)
TRIMBLE INC
5475 Kellenburger Rd (45424-1013)
PHONE..................................937 245-5951
Jody Carter, *Manager*
EMP: 70
SALES (corp-wide): 2.3B **Publicly Held**
SIC: **3663**
PA: Trimble Inc.
935 Stewart Dr
Sunnyvale CA 94085
408 481-8000

(G-8728)
TRIUMPH TOOL LLC
229 Leo St (45404-1005)
PHONE..................................937 222-6885
EMP: 3
SALES (est): 403.2K **Privately Held**
SIC: **3599 7699** Mfg Industrial Machinery Repair Services

(G-8729)
TROJON GEAR INC
418 San Jose St (45403-1419)
P.O. Box 1507 (45401-1507)
PHONE..................................937 254-1737
Fax: 937 254-3029
Charles Trochelman, *President*
Tom Landis, *General Mgr*
Chuck Randall, *General Mgr*
Candace Trochelman, *Vice Pres*
Michael Reed, *QC Mgr*
EMP: 18
SQ FT: 18,000
SALES: 1.3MM **Privately Held**
WEB: www.trojon-gear.com
SIC: **3599 7389 3566 3724** Machine & other job shop work; machine shop, jobbing & repair; metal cutting services; grinding, precision: commercial or industrial; speed changers, drives & gears; gears, power transmission, except automotive; aircraft engines & engine parts; gears, motor vehicle; screw machine products

(G-8730)
TROY VALLEY PETROLEUM
201 Valley St (45404-1864)
PHONE..................................937 604-0012
Amarjid Singh, *Principal*
EMP: 3
SQ FT: 2,248
SALES (est): 401K **Privately Held**
SIC: **2911** Petroleum refining

GEOGRAPHIC

(G-8731)
TRU-FAB INC
4751 Gateway Cir (45440-1787)
PHONE....................................937 435-1733
Fax: 937 435-2411
Steven Dudley, *President*
Ed Parker, *Vice Pres*
EMP: 14
SQ FT: 13,000
SALES (est): 1.1MM Privately Held
SIC: 3441 Fabricated structural metal

(G-8732)
TRUECHOICEPACK CORP
1285 Lyons Rd Ste H (45458-1859)
PHONE....................................937 630-3832
Heena Rathore, *President*
Christopher Che, *Chairman*
Rakesh Rathore, *COO*
Chris Decker, *Sales Staff*
Alyssa Yates, *Admin Asst*
EMP: 44
SALES (est): 1.8MM
SALES (corp-wide): 9.6MM Privately
Held
SIC: 3089 3086 8748 7389 Blister or
bubble formed packaging, plastic; pack-
aging & shipping materials, foamed plas-
tic; business consulting; field warehousing
PA: Che International Group, Llc
9435 Waterstone Blvd # 140
Cincinnati OH 45249
513 444-2072

(G-8733)
TWEEN BRANDS INC
Also Called: Limited Too 937
2700 Mmsburg Cntrville Rd (45459)
PHONE....................................937 435-6928
EMP: 14
SALES (corp-wide): 4.7B Publicly Held
SIC: 2361 Mfg Girl/Youth Dresses/Blouses
HQ: Tween Brands, Inc.
8323 Walton Pkwy
New Albany OH 43054
614 775-3500

(G-8734)
**TWIN DESIGN AP PROMOTIONS
LTD**
5785 Far Hills Ave (45429-2207)
PHONE....................................937 732-6798
Dixie Scott, *Owner*
Nancy Honshell, *Owner*
EMP: 3
SALES (est): 170K Privately Held
SIC: 7389 2395 2211 Design services;
embroidery & art needlework; apparel &
outerwear fabrics, cotton

(G-8735)
TWIN TOOL LLC
4648 Gateway Cir (45440-1714)
PHONE....................................937 435-8946
Cory Corello, *President*
Corey Corrello,
EMP: 5 EST: 2000
SALES (est): 809.1K Privately Held
WEB: www.twintool.com
SIC: 3541 Machine tools, metal cutting
type

(G-8736)
**U S CHROME CORPORATION
OHIO**
107 Westboro St (45417-4055)
PHONE....................................937 224-0548
Fax: 937 224-5695
Donald J Johnson, *Plant Supt*
Greg Santo, *Branch Mgr*
EMP: 12
SQ FT: 8,000
SALES (corp-wide): 30.4MM Privately
Held
SIC: 3471 Electroplating of metals or
formed products
HQ: U S Chrome Corporation Of Ohio
175 Garfield Ave
Stratford CT
937 224-0548

(G-8737)
UMAT LLC
272 Leo St (45404-1006)
P.O. Box 117, Laura (45337-0117)
PHONE....................................937 224-3303
Chrisanne Heisey,
Chrisanne C Heisey,
Jeff Heisey,
EMP: 30
SQ FT: 33,000
SALES: 2.5MM Privately Held
SIC: 3599 3544 Machine shop, jobbing &
repair; special dies, tools, jigs & fixtures

(G-8738)
UNITHERM INC
2601 Timber Ln (45414-4733)
P.O. Box 1189, Lebanon (45036-5189)
PHONE....................................937 278-1900
Fax: 937 932-4774
Ronald D Messer, *President*
Brian Messer, *Software Dev*
EMP: 5
SQ FT: 12,000
SALES: 899.4K Privately Held
SIC: 2672 Adhesive papers, labels or
tapes: from purchased material

(G-8739)
**UNIVERSAL TOOL
TECHNOLOGY LLC**
3488 Stop 8 Rd (45414-3428)
P.O. Box 31249 (45437-0249)
PHONE....................................937 222-4608
Waldemar Boehmer, *General Mgr*
Todd Ballard, *Vice Pres*
Debbie Toney, *CFO*
Jacqueline Cwiek, *Office Mgr*
Michael Farmer,
EMP: 45
SQ FT: 45,000
SALES (est): 3.4MM Privately Held
WEB: www.universal-systems.net
SIC: 3544 3599 Special dies & tools; die
sets for metal stamping (presses); jigs &
fixtures; industrial molds; machine shop,
jobbing & repair

(G-8740)
US AEROTEAM INC
2601 W Stroop Rd Unit 60 (45439-1929)
PHONE....................................937 458-0344
Fax: 937 458-0331
Suhas Kakde, *President*
Jim Zahora, *COO*
Jeff Maag, *Vice Pres*
Dennis Sparks, *VP Opers*
Heather Marsh, *HR Admin*
EMP: 48
SALES (est): 15MM Privately Held
WEB: www.usaeroteam.com
SIC: 3724 3728 3769 Aircraft engines &
engine parts; aircraft parts & equipment;
guided missile & space vehicle parts &
auxiliary equipment

(G-8741)
VETZ USA INC
7174 Montague Rd (45424-3046)
PHONE....................................937 237-8764
Danny Owens, *President*
EMP: 3
SALES (est): 187.6K Privately Held
SIC: 2869 Industrial organic chemicals

(G-8742)
VIBRONIC
5208 Wadsworth Rd (45414-3508)
PHONE....................................937 274-1114
Leah Lach, *Branch Mgr*
EMP: 17
SALES (est): 1.7MM Privately Held
SIC: 2822 Synthetic rubber

(G-8743)
VIKING GROUP INC
2806 Wayne Ave (45420-1837)
PHONE....................................937 443-0433
Todd Rodger, *President*
Thomas J Williams, *Vice Pres*
EMP: 6
SQ FT: 1,200

SALES (est): 938.7K Privately Held
SIC: 3569 3491 3669 2899 Sprinkler systems, fire: automatic; automatic regulating
& control valves; fire alarm apparatus,
electric; fire retardant chemicals

(G-8744)
VULCAN TOOL COMPANY
730 Lorain Ave (45410-2400)
PHONE....................................937 253-6194
Fax: 937 253-1062
Dan Kuchenbuch, *Principal*
Tom Schell, *Mfg Staff*
Jeff Smith, *Engineer*
Mary Martin, *Manager*
▲ EMP: 7 EST: 1916
SQ FT: 90,000
SALES (est): 1.2MM Privately Held
WEB: www.vulcancut.com
SIC: 3544 3542 3541 3643 Special dies
& tools; jigs & fixtures; machine tools,
metal forming type; machine tools, metal
cutting type; current-carrying wiring de-
vices

(G-8745)
WARRIOR TECHNOLOGIES INC
7320 Kings Run Rd (45459-3420)
PHONE....................................937 438-0279
Charles J Hardin, *President*
Stephanie McCabe, *Vice Pres*
EMP: 5
SQ FT: 26,000
SALES (est): 420K Privately Held
SIC: 3599 1799 Machine shop, jobbing &
repair; welding on site

(G-8746)
WATKINS GRINDING INC
1245 Leonhard St (45404-1661)
PHONE....................................937 461-4487
Fax: 937 461-9221
Dennis W Watkins, *President*
Lois Watkins, *Admin Sec*
EMP: 3
SQ FT: 3,800
SALES (est): 240K Privately Held
SIC: 3599 Machine shop, jobbing & repair

(G-8747)
**WATSON HARAN & COMPANY
INC**
Also Called: Manoranjan Shaffer & Heidkamp
1500 Yankee Park Pl (45458-1878)
PHONE....................................937 436-1414
Angie Shaffer, *Manager*
EMP: 6
SALES (corp-wide): 807K Privately Held
WEB: www.hwcocpa.com
SIC: 8721 2759 Certified public account-
ant; financial note & certificate printing &
engraving
PA: Watson Haran & Company Inc
7600 Olentangy River Rd # 100
Columbus OH 43235
614 847-2333

(G-8748)
WAYNE SPORTING GOODS
7101 Taylorsville Rd (45424-3101)
PHONE....................................937 236-6665
Fax: 937 236-6687
Rick Breitfield, *Owner*
Marcia Breitfield, *Co-Owner*
EMP: 5 EST: 1976
SQ FT: 3,300
SALES: 400K Privately Held
SIC: 5941 3552 2262 Team sports equip-
ment; embroidery machines; screen print-
ing: manmade fiber & silk broadwoven
fabrics

(G-8749)
**WEBER JEWELERS
INCORPORATED**
Also Called: F & J Manufacturing
3155 Far Hills Ave (45429-2522)
PHONE....................................937 643-9200
Fred Weber, *Manager*
EMP: 3
SQ FT: 1,500
SALES (corp-wide): 1.3MM Privately
Held
WEB: www.weberjewelers.com
SIC: 3911 Jewelry, precious metal

PA: Weber Jewelers Incorporated
3109 Far Hills Ave
Dayton OH
937 643-9600

(G-8750)
WELDCRAFT PRODUCTS CO
1933 Kuntz Rd (45404-1222)
P.O. Box 122 (45404-0122)
PHONE....................................937 233-6141
Fax: 937 233-2166
Nancy Massey, *President*
Tiana Bilbrey, *Office Mgr*
EMP: 12 EST: 1953
SQ FT: 19,500
SALES (est): 3.6MM Privately Held
SIC: 3499 7692 Machine bases, metal;
welding repair

(G-8751)
WELDMENTS INC
167 Heid Ave (45404-1217)
PHONE....................................937 235-9261
Fax: 937 235-9265
James Hackenberger, *President*
John Limberg, *Corp Secy*
Chuck Kraft, *Vice Pres*
Carol Stewart, *Accountant*
EMP: 12
SQ FT: 10,000
SALES (est): 1.5MM
SALES (corp-wide): 6.8MM Privately
Held
WEB: www.weldments.com
SIC: 7692 1799 Welding repair; welding
on site
PA: Precision Metal Fabrication, Inc.
191 Heid Ave
Dayton OH 45404
937 235-9261

(G-8752)
WENDLING PATTERNS INC
2121 Jergens Rd (45404-1291)
PHONE....................................937 233-7770
Fax: 937 233-3282
James Wendling, *President*
EMP: 9 EST: 1928
SQ FT: 4,800
SALES (est): 1.2MM Privately Held
SIC: 3543 Industrial patterns

(G-8753)
**WEST CARROLLTON
CONVERTING INC**
400 E Dixie Dr (45449-1827)
PHONE....................................937 859-3621
Pierce J Lonergan, *President*
Alan P Berens, *Vice Pres*
◆ EMP: 80
SALES (est): 12MM Privately Held
WEB: www.friendgrp.com
SIC: 2621 Paper mills

(G-8754)
WESTROCK CP LLC
7032 N Dixie Dr (45414-3126)
PHONE....................................937 898-2115
Julie Robinson, *Branch Mgr*
EMP: 213
SALES (corp-wide): 14.1B Publicly Held
WEB: www.smurfit-stone.com
SIC: 2621 2796 Wrapping & packaging
papers; platemaking services
HQ: Westrock Cp, Llc
504 Thrasher St
Norcross GA 30071

(G-8755)
WESTROCK MWV LLC
Consumer & Office Products Div
10 W 2nd St (45402-1791)
P.O. Box 72, Miamisburg (45343-0072)
PHONE....................................937 495-6323
Fax: 937 461-0318
Patricia B Robinson, *Manager*
Kelly Silverman, *Executive*
EMP: 680
SALES (corp-wide): 14.1B Publicly Held
WEB: www.meadwestvaco.com
SIC: 2678 Stationery products
HQ: Westrock Mwv, Llc
501 S 5th St
Richmond VA 23219
804 444-1000

(G-8756)
WESTWOOD FBRCTION SHTMETAL INC
1752 Stanley Ave (45404-1117)
P.O. Box 13531 (45413-0531)
PHONE......................937 837-0494
Fax: 937 837-2704
Larry Highlander, *President*
Sandy Svenund, *Manager*
EMP: 9
SQ FT: 25,000
SALES (est): 2.1MM **Privately Held**
WEB: www.westwoodfabrication.com
SIC: 3441 Fabricated structural metal

(G-8757)
WFSR HOLDINGS LLC
220 E Monument Ave (45402-1287)
PHONE......................877 735-4966
Tim Tatman, *President*
Tom Koenig, *CFO*
▲ EMP: 2000
SALES (est): 156.1MM
SALES (corp-wide): 1.2B **Privately Held**
SIC: 2752 2754 2759 2761 Commercial printing, lithographic; commercial printing, gravure; commercial printing; manifold business forms; bookbinding & related work; typesetting
PA: Src Liquidation Llc
600 Albany St
Dayton OH 45417
937 221-1000

(G-8758)
WILLET ENTERPRISES
Also Called: Cavalon Drapery Cleaners
1945 Southtown Blvd Ste A (45439-1985)
PHONE......................937 298-8622
Fax: 937 885-0103
Ed Willett, *Owner*
EMP: 6
SQ FT: 4,200
SALES (est): 210K **Privately Held**
SIC: 7216 7699 2391 Curtain cleaning & repair; awning repair shop; draperies, plastic & textile: from purchased materials

(G-8759)
WILSON CONCRETE PRODUCTS INC (PA)
10075 Sheehan Rd (45458-4301)
PHONE......................937 885-7965
Fax: 937 885-7984
David L Wilson, *President*
Robert Wilson, *Treasurer*
Linda Wilson, *Manager*
EMP: 30 EST: 1946
SQ FT: 45,000
SALES (est): 3.3MM **Privately Held**
SIC: 3272 5211 Concrete products; lumber & other building materials

(G-8760)
WILSON SIGN CO INC
300 Hamilton Ave (45403-2450)
PHONE......................937 253-2246
Fax: 937 253-5008
David Wilson, *President*
Lattie B Wilson, *CFO*
EMP: 16 EST: 1969
SQ FT: 17,000
SALES (est): 1.5MM **Privately Held**
SIC: 3993 7629 Electric signs; electrical equipment repair, high voltage

(G-8761)
WINKLER CO INC
Also Called: Oakwood Register, The
435 Patterson Rd (45419-4344)
P.O. Box 572 (45409-0572)
PHONE......................937 294-2662
Dolores Winkler, *President*
Lance A Winkler, *Vice Pres*
Dana M Winkler, *Treasurer*
Beth Brownridge, *Accounts Mgr*
Vicky Holloway, *Accounts Exec*
EMP: 6
SQ FT: 2,700
SALES (est): 430.1K **Privately Held**
WEB: www.oakwoodregister.com
SIC: 2711 2791 Newspapers: publishing only, not printed on site; typesetting

(G-8762)
WINSTON HEAT TREATING INC
711 E 2nd St (45402-1319)
P.O. Box 1551 (45401-1551)
PHONE......................937 226-0110
Fax: 937 226-1061
John L Reger, *President*
Hillary Ramsey, *Admin Asst*
Travis Hixson, *Assistant*
EMP: 33
SQ FT: 26,000
SALES (est): 8.3MM **Privately Held**
WEB: www.winstonht.com
SIC: 3398 Metal heat treating

(G-8763)
WISCO PRODUCTS INCORPORATED
109 Commercial St (45402-2297)
PHONE......................937 228-2101
Fax: 937 228-2407
Mark Paxson, *President*
Kyle Paxson, *Opers Mgr*
EMP: 30
SQ FT: 23,000
SALES (est): 5.8MM **Privately Held**
WEB: www.wiscoproducts.com
SIC: 3469 3089 Metal stampings; caps, plastic

(G-8764)
WOODBURN PRESS LLC
405 Littell Ave (45419-3609)
P.O. Box 329 (45409-0329)
PHONE......................937 293-9245
Fax: 937 293-9401
John O'Brien, *President*
Linda O'Brien, *Owner*
Mike O'Brien, *Owner*
BJ Obrien, *Vice Pres*
EMP: 6
SQ FT: 10,000
SALES (est): 721.3K **Privately Held**
WEB: www.woodburnpress.com
SIC: 2731 2741 Book publishing; posters: publishing & printing

(G-8765)
WURTH ELECTRONICS ICS INC
Also Called: Wurth Elecktronik
7496 Webster St (45414-5816)
PHONE......................937 415-7700
Fax: 937 415-7710
France Hoffmann, *President*
Tracy Hayes, *Manager*
EMP: 11
SQ FT: 14,000
SALES (est): 2.7MM
SALES (corp-wide): 11.8B **Privately Held**
SIC: 3672 Printed circuit boards
HQ: Wurth Group Of North America Inc.
93 Grant St
Ramsey NJ 07446
201 818-8877

(G-8766)
YODER INDUSTRIES INC (PA)
2520 Needmore Rd (45414-4204)
PHONE......................937 278-5769
Fax: 937 278-6321
Ron Zeverka, *President*
Janet E Roush, *Principal*
Ron Veverka, *Principal*
J B Yoder, *Principal*
Charles W Slicer, *Chairman*
EMP: 110 EST: 1956
SQ FT: 32,000
SALES (est): 13MM **Privately Held**
WEB: www.yoderindustries.com
SIC: 3369 3363 3365 3471 Nonferrous foundries; aluminum die-castings; aluminum foundries; plating & polishing; testing laboratories; nonferrous die-castings except aluminum

(G-8767)
YODER INDUSTRIES INC
3009 Production Ct (45414-3514)
PHONE......................937 890-4322
Fax: 937 890-1220
John Ridder, *Manager*
Gary Burner, *Manager*
EMP: 35

SALES (corp-wide): 13MM **Privately Held**
SIC: 3364 3365 Nonferrous die-castings except aluminum; aluminum foundries
PA: Yoder Industries, Inc.
2520 Needmore Rd
Dayton OH 45414
937 278-5769

(G-8768)
ZIMMER ENTERPRISES INC (PA)
Also Called: Kettering Monogramming
911 Senate Dr (45459-4017)
PHONE......................937 428-1057
Fax: 937 428-5857
Jeffrey Zimmer, *President*
Patricia M Zimmer, *Vice Pres*
Donna Johnson, *Credit Mgr*
Karen Kennedy, *Sales Staff*
Kate Parker,
▲ EMP: 24
SALES: 10.1MM **Privately Held**
WEB: www.pbj-sport.com
SIC: 5137 2395 Women's & children's clothing; embroidery products, except schiffli machine

---

De Graff
Logan County

(G-8769)
PRECISION CUSTOM PRODUCTS INC
4590 County Road 35 (43318-9770)
PHONE......................937 585-4011
Fax: 937 585-4440
James Kerg Jr, *CEO*
Dawn Beelman, *CFO*
Daniel McMahon, *Sales Mgr*
Scott Frey, *Marketing Staff*
Hazel Lambert, *Manager*
EMP: 26
SQ FT: 30,000
SALES: 4.4MM **Privately Held**
WEB: www.pcplastics.com
SIC: 3089 Injection molded finished plastic products

(G-8770)
SUPERIOR MACHINE AND TOOL
7726 Crowl Rd (43318-9562)
PHONE......................937 308-5771
Andrea Smith, *Owner*
EMP: 4
SQ FT: 2,500
SALES (est): 184.2K **Privately Held**
SIC: 3599 Machine shop, jobbing & repair

Deerfield
Portage County

(G-8771)
CHEVRON AE RESOURCES LLC
1823 State Route 14 (44411)
P.O. Box 160 (44411-0160)
PHONE......................330 654-4343
EMP: 30
SALES (corp-wide): 129.9B **Publicly Held**
SIC: 1311 1382 Crude Petroleum/Natural Gas Production Oil/Gas Exploration Services
HQ: Chevron Ae Resources Llc
1000 Commerce Dr Fl 4
Pittsburgh PA 15275
800 251-0171

(G-8772)
DEERFIELD FARMS SERVICE INC
9041 U S Route 224 (44411-8715)
PHONE......................800 589-8606
EMP: 75 EST: 1959
SALES (est): 11.6MM **Privately Held**
SIC: 2873 Mfg Nitrogenous Fertilizers

(G-8773)
FOUNDER SERVICE & MFG CO
Also Called: Founder's Service Co
879 State Route 14 (44411-9777)
P.O. Box 56, North Benton (44449-0056)
PHONE......................330 584-7759
Fax: 330 584-9022
Doug Stanley, *President*
Thad Stanley, *Admin Sec*
EMP: 13
SQ FT: 8,000
SALES (est): 1.9MM **Privately Held**
SIC: 3543 3544 Foundry cores; forms (molds), for foundry & plastics working machinery

(G-8774)
MIDWEST FIREWORKS MFG CO II
8550 State Route 224 (44411-8743)
PHONE......................330 584-7000
Fax: 330 584-6000
EMP: 4
SALES (est): 309.8K **Privately Held**
SIC: 2899 Fireworks

Defiance
Defiance County

(G-8775)
ADVANTAGE POWDER COATING INC (PA)
2090 E 2nd St Ste 102 (43512-8648)
PHONE......................419 782-2363
Fax: 419 782-0400
Joellen Hornish, *President*
Sam Hornish, *Vice Pres*
Denny Elwer, *Personnel Exec*
April P Hahn, *Office Mgr*
Mike Ketcham, *CIO*
EMP: 70
SQ FT: 51,000
SALES (est): 7MM **Privately Held**
SIC: 3479 Painting, coating & hot dipping

(G-8776)
AL-FE HEAT TREATING INC
Also Called: Al-Fe Heat Treating Defiance
2066 E 2nd St (43512-8654)
PHONE......................419 782-7200
Fax: 419 782-7251
Paul Christensen, *Regl Sales Mgr*
Ernie Lackner, *Branch Mgr*
John Holifield, *Manager*
EMP: 27
SALES (corp-wide): 45.6MM **Privately Held**
WEB: www.al-fe.com
SIC: 3398 Metal heat treating
PA: Al-Fe Heat Treating Inc
6920 Pointe Inverness Way # 140
Fort Wayne IN 46804
260 747-9422

(G-8777)
ALLTEL COMMUNICATIONS CORP
1007 N Clinton St Ste 1 (43512-4608)
PHONE......................419 784-3808
Thomas Zimmerman, *Manager*
EMP: 4
SALES (corp-wide): 163.7B **Publicly Held**
SIC: 4813 4812 5065 5063 Local & long distance telephone communications; cellular telephone services; telephone equipment; telephone & telegraph wire & cable; data processing service; application computer software
HQ: Alltel Communications Corp
66 N 4th St
Newark OH 43055
740 349-8551

(G-8778)
ARONIT MACHINE LLC
2018 Baltimore St (43512-1918)
PHONE......................419 782-4740
John E Postema,
EMP: 10
SALES: 780K **Privately Held**
SIC: 3569 Filters

(G-8779)
ARPS DAIRY INC
220 N Clinton St (43512-1810)
P.O. Box 803 (43512-0803)
PHONE.............................419 782-9116
Fax: 419 782-5243
Stephen L Boomer, *President*
Dennis Roehrig, *Plant Mgr*
Mark Weidenhamer, *Sales Staff*
Marlene Miller, *Manager*
EMP: 18 EST: 1936
SQ FT: 10,000
SALES: 5.1MM **Privately Held**
WEB: www.arpsdairy.com
SIC: 2026 Milk processing (pasteurizing,
homogenizing, bottling)

(G-8780)
BAKER-SHINDLER
CONTRACTING CO (PA)
Also Called: Baker-Shindler Builders Sup Co
525 Cleveland Ave (43512-3546)
P.O. Box 488 (43512-0488)
PHONE.............................419 782-5080
Fax: 419 784-2643
Douglas Shindler, *President*
EMP: 23 EST: 1921
SQ FT: 8,500
SALES (est): 6.7MM **Privately Held**
SIC: 1542 1541 3273 Specialized public
building contractors; industrial buildings,
new construction; ready-mixed concrete

(G-8781)
BARBS CUSTOM EMBROIDERY
14845 State Route 111 (43512-8616)
PHONE.............................419 393-2226
Barbara Brink, *Principal*
EMP: 3
SALES (est): 127.2K **Privately Held**
SIC: 2395 Embroidery & art needlework

(G-8782)
BRUNSWICK EYE & CONTACT
LENS C
2011 S Clinton St (43512-3222)
PHONE.............................419 439-3381
EMP: 3
SALES (est): 180K **Privately Held**
SIC: 3851 Mfg Ophthalmic Goods

(G-8783)
CBS BORING AND MCH CO INC
2064 E 2nd St (43512-8654)
PHONE.............................419 784-9500
Fax: 419 784-9502
Todd Chupick, *Opers Staff*
Dave Hodell, *Manager*
EMP: 35
SALES (corp-wide): 20.5MM **Privately
Held**
WEB: www.cbsboring.com
SIC: 3599 Machine shop, jobbing & repair
PA: C.B.S. Boring And Machine Company,
Inc.
33750 Riviera
Fraser MI 48026
586 294-7540

(G-8784)
CHIEF GENERAL OFFICE
1340 W High St Ste E (43512-5307)
PHONE.............................419 782-0950
EMP: 3
SALES (est): 711.6K **Privately Held**
SIC: 3421 Table & food cutlery, including
butchers'

(G-8785)
DEFIANCE METAL PRODUCTS
CO (PA)
21 Seneca St (43512-2274)
P.O. Box 447 (43512-0447)
PHONE.............................419 784-5332
Fax: 419 782-0148
Stephen Mance, *CEO*
Sam Strausbaugh, *President*
Robert Thomas, *General Mgr*
Jeff Behlke, *Vice Pres*
Rick Creedmore, *Vice Pres*
▲ EMP: 475
SQ FT: 165,000

SALES (est): 373.9MM **Privately Held**
SIC: 3465 3443 3544 Automotive stampings; fabricated plate work (boiler shop);
special dies & tools

(G-8786)
DEFIANCE METAL PRODUCTS
CO
6728 N State Route 66 (43512-6731)
PHONE.............................419 784-5332
Rick W Williams, *VP Sales*
Cecilia Montalvo-Silburn, *Manager*
EMP: 275
SALES (corp-wide): 373.3MM **Privately
Held**
SIC: 3465 Automotive stampings
PA: Defiance Metal Products Co.
21 Seneca St
Defiance OH 43512
419 784-5332

(G-8787)
DEFIANCE METAL PRODUCTS
WI INC
Also Called: Medalist Laserfab
21 Seneca St (43512-2274)
PHONE.............................920 426-9207
Steve Mance, *CEO*
Joel Staffaroni, *Engineer*
Ken Daiff, *CFO*
Debbie Lembcke, *Controller*
Michael Schoendorf, *Admin Sec*
EMP: 115
SQ FT: 36,000
SALES (est): 29.8MM
SALES (corp-wide): 373.9MM **Privately
Held**
WEB: www.mlaserfab.com
SIC: 3441 3498 Fabricated structural
metal; fabricated pipe & fittings; pipe fit-
tings, fabricated from purchased pipe;
pipe sections fabricated from purchased
pipe
PA: Defiance Metal Products Co.
21 Seneca St
Defiance OH 43512
419 784-5332

(G-8788)
DEFIANCE PUBLISHING CO
Also Called: Defiance Crescent News, The
624 W 2nd St (43512-2161)
P.O. Box 249 (43512-0249)
PHONE.............................419 784-5441
Fax: 419 784-1492
Albert E Dix, *President*
Charles Dix, *President*
Brett Belew, *District Mgr*
Mickie Butler, *District Mgr*
Greg Meyers, *District Mgr*
EMP: 855 EST: 1888
SQ FT: 9,000
SALES (est): 37.6MM
SALES (corp-wide): 567.1MM **Privately
Held**
WEB: www.crescent-news.com
SIC: 2711 Newspapers, publishing & print-
ing
PA: Wooster Republican Printing Co
212 E Liberty St
Wooster OH
330 264-3511

(G-8789)
DOMINION LABELS & FORMS
232 Adams St (43512-1702)
P.O. Box 825 (43512-0825)
PHONE.............................419 784-1041
Bill Papenhagen, *Owner*
EMP: 3
SALES: 500K **Privately Held**
SIC: 2759 Commercial printing

(G-8790)
GENERAL MOTORS LLC
26427 State Route 281 (43512-6781)
PHONE.............................419 782-2244
Fax: 419 784-7502
Dave Heeter, *Purch Mgr*
Vick Vernace, *Purchasing*
Suheb Hag, *Plant Engr Mgr*
Brian Buss, *Engineer*
A J Grohman, *Engineer*
EMP: 4000

SALES (corp-wide): 166.3MM **Publicly
Held**
SIC: 3321 3322 3365 3369 Gray iron
castings; malleable iron foundries; aluminum & aluminum-based alloy castings;
nonferrous foundries
HQ: General Motors Llc
300 Renaissance Ctr L1
Detroit MI 48243

(G-8791)
GODFREY & WING INC
2066 E 2nd St (43512-8654)
PHONE.............................419 980-4616
John Horvath, *Branch Mgr*
EMP: 12
SALES (corp-wide): 19.8MM **Privately
Held**
SIC: 3823 Absorption analyzers: infrared,
X-ray, etc.: industrial
PA: Godfrey & Wing Inc.
220 Campus Dr
Aurora OH 44202
330 562-1440

(G-8792)
GT TECHNOLOGIES INC
Also Called: Defiance Operations
1125 Precision Way (43512-1946)
PHONE.............................419 782-8955
Joe Molnar, *Plant Mgr*
Rich Stratton, *Human Res Mgr*
EMP: 140
SALES (corp-wide): 221MM **Privately
Held**
SIC: 3714 3562 3599 3398 Motor vehicle
engines & parts; ball & roller bearings;
machine shop, jobbing & repair; metal
heat treating
HQ: Gt Technologies, Inc.
5859 E Executive Dr
Westland MI 48185
734 467-8371

(G-8793)
HILLTOP PRINTING
1815 Baltimore St (43512-1913)
PHONE.............................419 782-9898
Fax: 419 784-2596
Verle L Harner, *Owner*
EMP: 6
SQ FT: 5,000
SALES (est): 280K **Privately Held**
SIC: 2759 Commercial printing

(G-8794)
HUBBARD COMPANY
612 Clinton St (43512-2637)
P.O. Box 100 (43512-0100)
PHONE.............................419 784-4455
Fax: 419 782-1662
E Keith Hubbard, *Ch of Bd*
Thomas K Hubbard, *President*
Debe Mesker, *Purch Agent*
Jean A Hubbard, *Treasurer*
Dick Anderson, *Sales Staff*
EMP: 44 EST: 1906
SQ FT: 20,000
SALES (est): 7.2MM **Privately Held**
WEB: www.hubbardcompany.com
SIC: 5943 5192 2752 2732 Office forms
& supplies; books; commercial printing,
offset; book printing; book publishing

(G-8795)
JOHNS MANVILLE
CORPORATION
925 Carpenter Rd (43512-1765)
PHONE.............................419 784-7000
Brian Siler, *Warehouse Mgr*
Jason Brown, *Production*
David Morris, *Production*
Janet Spitnale, *Purch Agent*
Steve Thieroff, *Plant Engr*
EMP: 600
SALES (corp-wide): 223.6B **Publicly
Held**
WEB: www.jm.com
SIC: 3296 Fiberglass insulation
HQ: Johns Manville Corporation
717 17th St Ste 800
Denver CO 80202
303 978-2000

(G-8796)
JOHNS MANVILLE
CORPORATION
3rd And Perry (43512)
P.O. Box 158 (43512-0158)
PHONE.............................419 784-7000
Fax: 419 784-7097
Jerry Henry, *President*
Susan Thiel, *District Mgr*
Roger Snow, *Plant Mgr*
Ted Guelde, *Plt & Fclts Mgr*
Janet Spitnale, *Purch Agent*
EMP: 200
SALES (corp-wide): 223.6B **Publicly
Held**
SIC: 3296 Mineral wool
HQ: Johns Manville Corporation
717 17th St Ste 800
Denver CO 80202
303 978-2000

(G-8797)
JOHNS MANVILLE
CORPORATION
408 Perry St Plant 02 2 Plant (43512)
PHONE.............................419 878-8111
Ronald Bick, *Engineer*
Randy Engel, *Engineer*
Warren Schultz, *Plant Engr*
Craig McKibben, *Manager*
Rhonda Francis, *Manager*
EMP: 224
SALES (corp-wide): 223.6B **Publicly
Held**
WEB: www.jm.com
SIC: 3296 Mineral wool
HQ: Johns Manville Corporation
717 17th St Ste 800
Denver CO 80202
303 978-2000

(G-8798)
KIRK & BLUM MANUFACTURING
CO
Also Called: Kirk and Blum
24226 Bowman Rd (43512-6819)
PHONE.............................419 782-9885
Fax: 419 782-9888
George Nelson, *Manager*
EMP: 38
SALES (corp-wide): 417MM **Publicly
Held**
SIC: 1761 3444 3443 Sheet metalwork;
sheet metal specialties, not stamped; fab-
ricated plate work (boiler shop)
HQ: The Kirk & Blum Manufacturing Com-
pany
4625 Red Bank Rd Ste 200
Cincinnati OH 45227
513 458-2600

(G-8799)
KOESTER MACHINED
PRODUCTS CO
136 Fox Run Dr (43512-1394)
PHONE.............................419 782-0291
Fax: 419 782-1150
Michael Koester, *President*
Lawrence Derge, *Engineer*
Robert Hagen, *Engineer*
Brad Schlachter, *Engineer*
Mike Brown, *Project Engr*
EMP: 15
SQ FT: 21,000
SALES: 771K **Privately Held**
SIC: 3599 Machine shop, jobbing & repair

(G-8800)
M W SOLUTIONS LLC
1802 Baltimore St Ste B (43512-2081)
PHONE.............................419 782-1611
Matthew Winzeler, *Mng Member*
EMP: 10 EST: 2010
SALES: 2MM **Privately Held**
SIC: 3089 3694 3559 Automotive parts,
plastic; alternators, automotive; automo-
tive electrical equipment; automotive re-
lated machinery

(G-8801)
MARC V CONCEPTS INC
Also Called: Figley Stamping Company
401 Agnes St (43512-3072)
PHONE.............................419 782-6505
Christopher Slee, *President*

Rick Behnfeldt, *Vice Pres*
▼ **EMP:** 10 **EST:** 1993
SQ FT: 23,000
SALES (est): 1MM **Privately Held**
WEB: www.figleystamping.com
SIC: 3469 Metal stampings

(G-8802)
MARTIN DIESEL INC
27809 County Road 424 (43512-8147)
P.O. Box 1000 (43512-1000)
PHONE.............................419 782-9911
Fax: 419 782-6741
James M Martin Jr, *President*
Cliff Martin, *Vice Pres*
Phil Schaadt, *Parts Mgr*
Brian Martin, *Sls & Mktg Exec*
EMP: 21
SQ FT: 17,500
SALES (est): 4.1MM **Privately Held**
WEB: www.martindiesel.com
SIC: 3621 5013 5531 5084 Generators &
sets, electric; automotive supplies &
parts; truck equipment & parts; engines &
parts, diesel

(G-8803)
MEEKS PASTRY SHOP
315 Clinton St (43512-2113)
PHONE.............................419 782-4871
William Meek, *Owner*
EMP: 6
SQ FT: 2,500
SALES (est): 512.5K **Privately Held**
SIC: 2051 5461 Bread, cake & related
products; pastries

(G-8804)
MESSERMAN CORP
Also Called: Messerman Machine Co
407 Agnes St (43512-3072)
P.O. Box 116 (43512-0116)
PHONE.............................419 782-1136
Fax: 419 782-1248
Jeff Behlke, *President*
Jeffrey Pahl, *Vice Pres*
EMP: 5 **EST:** 1952
SQ FT: 5,000
SALES (est): 462.8K **Privately Held**
SIC: 3599 Custom machinery; machine
shop, jobbing & repair

(G-8805)
MINUTEMAN PRESS
214 Clinton St (43512-0017)
P.O. Box 1010 (43512-1010)
PHONE.............................419 782-8002
David D Lawson, *Owner*
Jake Smith, *Accounts Mgr*
EMP: 4
SQ FT: 1,000
SALES (est): 300K **Privately Held**
SIC: 2752 Commercial printing, litho-
graphic

(G-8806)
**MOUNTAIN FILTRATION
SYSTEMS**
26705 Blanchard Rd (43512-8984)
PHONE.............................419 395-2526
Larry Moore, *Manager*
EMP: 3
SALES (corp-wide): 503.7K **Privately
Held**
SIC: 3589 5074 Water filters & softeners,
household type; water heaters & purifica-
tion equipment
PA: Mountain Filtration Systems Inc
907 Isaacs Creek Rd
Lost Creek WV

(G-8807)
NOSTALGIC IMAGES INC
26012 Nostalgic Rd (43512-7108)
PHONE.............................419 784-1728
William Westrick, *President*
Deborah Collins, *General Mgr*
Clay W Balyeat, *Principal*
Lynda Sue Westrick, *Principal*
Jason Westrick, *Marketing Staff*
▲ **EMP:** 24
SQ FT: 60,000
SALES (est): 5.4MM **Privately Held**
WEB: www.nostalgicimages.com
SIC: 3499 Picture frames, metal

(G-8808)
OMNISOURCE CORPORATION
Omnisource Defiance Division
880 Linden St (43512-2776)
PHONE.............................419 784-5669
Fax: 419 782-1949
John Lero, *Branch Mgr*
EMP: 30
SALES (corp-wide): 7.7B **Publicly Held**
WEB: www.omnisource.com
SIC: 3462 Iron & steel forgings
HQ: Omnisource Corporation
7575 W Jefferson Blvd
Fort Wayne IN 46804
260 422-5541

(G-8809)
**SENSORYEFFECTS FLAVOR
COMPANY**
Also Called: Sensory Effects
136 Fox Run Dr (43512-1394)
PHONE.............................419 782-5010
Brett Keezer, *Branch Mgr*
EMP: 24
SALES (corp-wide): 553.2MM **Publicly
Held**
SIC: 2087 Extracts, flavoring
HQ: Sensoryeffects Flavor Company
231 Rock Indus Prk Dr
Bridgeton MO 63044
314 291-5444

(G-8810)
**SENSORYFFCTS POWDR
SYSTEMS INC**
136 Fox Run Dr (43512-1394)
PHONE.............................419 783-5518
Charles A Nicolais, *CEO*
Mark Miller, *General Mgr*
Bob Switzer, *Vice Pres*
Aric Diehl, *Purch Agent*
Joan Haselman, *Research*
◆ **EMP:** 70 **EST:** 1870
SQ FT: 160,000
SALES (est): 25.7MM
SALES (corp-wide): 553.2MM **Publicly
Held**
WEB: www.diehlinc.com
SIC: 2099 Food preparations
HQ: Sensoryeffects, Inc.
13723 Rverport Dr Ste 201
Maryland Heights MO 63043
314 291-5444

(G-8811)
SUPERIOR BAR PRODUCTS INC
1710 Spruce St (43512-2457)
PHONE.............................419 784-2590
Fax: 419 784-2621
Mark Crandall, *President*
Sandy Crandall, *Trustee*
Wes Wittenmyer, *Vice Pres*
Deb Wittenmyer, *Treasurer*
EMP: 6
SQ FT: 7,000
SALES: 600K **Privately Held**
SIC: 3451 Screw machine products

(G-8812)
TRESSLERS PLUMBING LLC
9170 State Route 15 (43512-8642)
P.O. Box 433 (43512-0433)
PHONE.............................419 784-2142
Fax: 419 784-2142
Doug Tressler,
Terry Tressler,
EMP: 7
SALES (est): 545.2K **Privately Held**
SIC: 1481 Pumping or draining, nonmetal-
lic mineral mines

(G-8813)
**WERE ROLLING PRETZLE
COMPANY**
1500 N Clinton St Ste 144 (43512-4102)
PHONE.............................419 784-0762
Angela Quinones, *Manager*
EMP: 6
SALES (est): 282.4K **Privately Held**
SIC: 2051 Breads, rolls & buns

(G-8814)
WERLOR INC
Also Called: Werlor Waste Control
1420 Ralston Ave (43512-1380)
PHONE.............................419 784-4285
Fax: 419 782-9188
Gerald Wertz, *President*
Judy Wertz, *Corp Secy*
Mark Hageman, *Vice Pres*
Tom Taylor, *Vice Pres*
Casey Wertz, *Vice Pres*
EMP: 40
SQ FT: 8,000
SALES (est): 5.5MM **Privately Held**
WEB: www.werlor.com
SIC: 4212 2875 Garbage collection &
transport, no disposal; compost

Delaware
Delaware County

(G-8815)
ACI INDUSTRIES LTD (PA)
970 Pittsburgh Dr (43015-3872)
PHONE.............................740 368-4160
Fax: 740 764-7803
Ralph Paglieri, *CEO*
Scott H Fischer, *President*
Shreelal Bhatter, *Vice Pres*
Helen Harper, *Vice Pres*
Michael Blanton, *Plant Mgr*
◆ **EMP:** 49
SQ FT: 225,000
SALES: 3.8MM **Privately Held**
WEB: www.aci-industries.com
SIC: 3341 5093 3339 Secondary nonfer-
rous metals; scrap & waste materials; pri-
mary nonferrous metals

(G-8816)
**ACI INDUSTRIES CONVERTING
LTD (HQ)**
Also Called: J and J Sales
970 Pittsburgh Dr (43015-3872)
PHONE.............................740 368-4160
Fax: 740 368-4181
Mike Paglieri, *General Ptnr*
Mark Arcaro, *Vice Pres*
Todd Zimdars, *VP Opers*
John T Griffo, *Controller*
Cathy Arcaro, *Manager*
◆ **EMP:** 33
SQ FT: 232,000
SALES (est): 2.7MM
SALES (corp-wide): 3.8MM **Privately
Held**
SIC: 2676 5113 Towels, napkins & tissue
paper products; towels, paper
PA: Aci Industries, Ltd.
970 Pittsburgh Dr
Delaware OH 43015
740 368-4160

(G-8817)
ADJUSTABLE KICKER LLC
45 River St (43015-2196)
PHONE.............................740 362-9170
Fax: 740 362-7518
Tim Colatruglio,
Ernest Massert,
EMP: 3
SALES (est): 474.1K **Privately Held**
WEB: www.adjustablekicker.com
SIC: 3444 Concrete forms, sheet metal

(G-8818)
**AFTERMARKET PARTS
COMPANY LLC**
2338 Us Highway 42 S (43015-9502)
PHONE.............................740 369-1056
John Hankins, *Branch Mgr*
EMP: 302
SALES (corp-wide): 1.5B **Privately Held**
SIC: 3711 Buses, all types, assembly of
HQ: The Aftermarket Parts Company Llc
3229 Sawmill Pkwy
Delaware OH 43015
888 333-6224

(G-8819)
AG DESIGNS LLC
1165 Dunham Rd (43015-8689)
PHONE.............................614 506-2849

Matthew Ayers,
EMP: 4
SALES: 18K **Privately Held**
SIC: 3993 5999 7336 7389 Letters for
signs, metal; banners, flags, decals &
posters; commercial art & graphic design;

(G-8820)
**AMERICAN FLANGE & MFG CO
INC**
425 Winter Rd (43015-8903)
PHONE.............................740 549-6073
David B Fischer, *Branch Mgr*
EMP: 7
SALES (corp-wide): 3.3B **Publicly Held**
SIC: 3466 Crowns & closures
HQ: American Flange & Manufacturing Co.
Inc.
290 Fullerton Ave
Carol Stream IL 60188
630 665-7900

(G-8821)
**API MACHINING FABRICATION
INC**
377 London Rd (43015-2444)
P.O. Box 326 (43015-0326)
PHONE.............................740 369-0455
Fax: 740 363-1244
Arthur Main, *President*
EMP: 4
SQ FT: 6,900
SALES: 350K **Privately Held**
SIC: 3356 3999 Nonferrous rolling & draw-
ing; identification plates

(G-8822)
**ASSOCIATED HYGIENIC PDTS
LLC**
2332 Us Highway 42 S (43015-9502)
PHONE.............................770 497-9800
Dale Hanshaw, *Principal*
EMP: 375
SALES (corp-wide): 5.6B **Privately Held**
WEB: www.ahp-dsg.com
SIC: 2211 Diaper fabrics
HQ: Associated Hygienic Products Llc
1029 Old Creek Rd
Greenville NC 27834
770 476-3594

(G-8823)
ATTIA APPLIED SCIENCES INC
Also Called: Taasi
548 W Central Ave (43015-1421)
PHONE.............................740 369-1891
Yosry Attia, *President*
Vera Attia, *Vice Pres*
EMP: 11 **EST:** 1985
SALES (est): 1.9MM **Privately Held**
SIC: 2899 Chemical preparations

(G-8824)
AUTO CORE SYSTEMS
2097 London Rd Unit A (43015-8485)
PHONE.............................740 362-5599
Chuck Dodeci, *Principal*
EMP: 3
SALES (est): 198.4K **Privately Held**
SIC: 3471 Cleaning & descaling metal
products

(G-8825)
**BLACK WING SHOOTING
CENTER LLC**
3722 Marysville Rd (43015-9527)
PHONE.............................740 363-7555
Rex Gore, *President*
John Richardson, *Store Mgr*
EMP: 9
SALES (est): 1.2MM **Privately Held**
WEB: www.blackwingsc.com
SIC: 7999 3949 Shooting facilities &
archery lanes; bases, baseball

(G-8826)
BUNS OF DELAWARE INC
Also Called: Buns Restaurant & Bakery
14 W Winter St (43015-1919)
PHONE.............................740 363-2867
Fax: 740 363-1756
Vasili Konstantinidis, *President*
EMP: 40
SQ FT: 11,184

GEOGRAPHIC

SALES (est): 1.1MM **Privately Held**
SIC: 5812 5461 7299 2051 Eating
places; bakeries; banquet hall facilities;
bread, cake & related products

(G-8827)
CAROLINA COLOR CORP OHIO
100 Colomet Dr (43015-3846)
P.O. Box 690 (43015-0690)
PHONE....................................740 363-6622
Fax: 740 363-6833
J A Carter, *President*
Matt Barr, *Chairman*
Terry Jordon, *Treasurer*
EMP: 25
SQ FT: 35,000
SALES (est): 4.4MM **Privately Held**
WEB: www.carolinacolor.com
SIC: 3089 Coloring & finishing of plastic
products

(G-8828)
CAROLINA COLOR CORPORATION
100 Colomet Dr (43015-3846)
P.O. Box 690 (43015-0690)
PHONE....................................740 363-6622
Jeff Smik, *Branch Mgr*
Bryan Ball, *Manager*
EMP: 25
SALES (corp-wide): 8.7MM **Privately Held**
SIC: 3088 Plastics plumbing fixtures
PA: Carolina Color Corporation
100 E 17th St
Salisbury NC 28144
704 637-7000

(G-8829)
CAST METALS TECHNOLOGY INC (PA)
Also Called: C M Tech
550 Liberty Rd (43015-8806)
PHONE....................................740 363-1690
Jerome Harmeyer, *President*
Madelyn C Harmeyer, *Chairman*
Vera Maruli, *CFO*
EMP: 5
SALES (est): 8.8MM **Privately Held**
WEB: www.castmetalstec.com
SIC: 3365 Aluminum foundries

(G-8830)
CCONLY INC
320 London Rd Ste 414 (43015-6405)
PHONE....................................614 607-2288
Jon Ko, *Principal*
▲ EMP: 10 EST: 2010
SALES (est): 1.3MM **Privately Held**
SIC: 2452 Chicken coops, prefabricated,
wood

(G-8831)
CEDEE CEDAR INC (PA)
Also Called: Cedar Woodworking
3903 Us Highway 42 S (43015-9517)
PHONE....................................740 363-3148
Carl Reynolds, *CEO*
Kris Bargram, *Manager*
EMP: 10
SALES: 500K **Privately Held**
SIC: 2434 Wood kitchen cabinets

(G-8832)
CHARTER NEX FILMS - DELAWARE
1188 S Houk Rd (43015-3857)
PHONE....................................740 369-2770
Fax: 740 369-1889
David Timm, *President*
Kathy Bolhous, *Principal*
Herb Pack, *Plant Mgr*
Thomas Ziolkowski, *CFO*
EMP: 45
SALES: 20.7MM
SALES (corp-wide): 80.2MM **Privately Held**
WEB: www.optimumplastics.com
SIC: 3081 2673 Unsupported plastics film
& sheet; plastic & pliofilm bags
HQ: Charter Nex Holding Company
1264 E High St
Milton WI 53563

(G-8833)
CHARTER NEX HOLDING COMPANY
1188 S Houk Rd (43015-3857)
PHONE....................................740 369-2770
Kevin Keneally, *Branch Mgr*
EMP: 45
SALES (corp-wide): 80.2MM **Privately Held**
SIC: 3081 2673 Unsupported plastics film
& sheet; plastic & pliofilm bags
HQ: Charter Nex Holding Company
1264 E High St
Milton WI 53563

(G-8834)
CHERHIRE CHOPPERS
4059 State Route 37 E A (43015-9461)
P.O. Box 843, Grove City (43123-0843)
PHONE....................................740 362-0695
Scott Malenky, *Principal*
EMP: 4
SALES (est): 250.4K **Privately Held**
SIC: 3751 Motorcycles & related parts

(G-8835)
DELA-GLASSWARE LTD LLC
130 N Liberty St (43015-1721)
PHONE....................................740 369-6737
Fax: 614 369-3362
EMP: 7
SQ FT: 5,000
SALES (est): 530K **Privately Held**
SIC: 3211 6513 5211 Mfg Insulating
Glass

(G-8836)
DELAWARE GAZETTE COMPANY
Also Called: Mid Ohio Net
40 N Sandusky St Ste 202 (43015-1973)
PHONE....................................740 363-1161
Fax: 614 363-6262
Roy Brown, *President*
Walter D Thomson II, *President*
Art Ruth, *General Mgr*
Matt Emmons, *Editor*
Thomas T Thomson, *Treasurer*
EMP: 96 EST: 1818
SQ FT: 20,000
SALES (est): 4.3MM **Privately Held**
WEB: www.delgazette.com
SIC: 2711 Newspapers, publishing & printing

(G-8837)
DELOHIO TECH
2061 State Route 521 (43015-8754)
PHONE....................................740 816-5628
Tom Davis, *President*
EMP: 12
SALES (est): 308.8K **Privately Held**
SIC: 3571 Electronic computers

(G-8838)
DIVERSE MFG SOLUTIONS LLC
970 Pittsburgh Dr Ste 22 (43015-3872)
PHONE....................................740 363-3600
Carl Stover,
EMP: 10
SALES (est): 237K **Privately Held**
SIC: 3542 Sheet metalworking machines

(G-8839)
DOMESTIC CASTING COMPANY LLC
620 Liberty Rd (43015-9387)
PHONE....................................717 532-6615
Jerry Harmeyer, *Mng Member*
Michael Heyne,
Tom James,
EMP: 115
SALES (est): 31.9MM **Privately Held**
WEB: www.domesticcasting.com
SIC: 3321 Gray iron castings; ductile iron
castings

(G-8840)
ELECTRIMOTION INC
1484 Dale Ford Rd (43015-9633)
PHONE....................................740 362-0251
David Leahy, *President*
EMP: 4 EST: 2000

SALES (est): 586.7K **Privately Held**
SIC: 3651 Home entertainment equipment,
electronic

(G-8841)
ELF ATOCHEM NA OH
421 London Rd (43015-2493)
PHONE....................................740 363-1351
Fax: 614 363-0302
Carole Krouse, *Principal*
EMP: 3
SALES (est): 190.4K **Privately Held**
SIC: 2819 Industrial inorganic chemicals

(G-8842)
EMERSON NETWORK POWER
975 Pittsburgh Dr (43015-2858)
PHONE....................................740 833-8630
Robert Howard, *Project Mgr*
Brian Cogar, *Engineer*
Phillip Kukelhan, *Engineer*
Chris Crawford, *Branch Mgr*
Bill Campbell, *Manager*
EMP: 10
SALES (corp-wide): 15.2B **Privately Held**
SIC: 3613 Switchgear & switchboard apparatus
HQ: Vertiv Services, Inc.
610 Executive Campus Dr
Westerville OH 43082
614 841-6400

(G-8843)
ENGINEERED MTLS SYSTEMS INC
Also Called: E M S
100 Innovation Ct (43015-7532)
PHONE....................................740 362-4444
Todd Irion, *President*
Janet G Feeny, *Corp Secy*
Lou Morris, *Corp Secy*
Teresa Peck, *Purchasing*
Alan Brown, *Research*
▲ EMP: 45
SQ FT: 20,000
SALES (est): 15.1MM **Privately Held**
SIC: 2891 Adhesives & sealants

(G-8844)
FEDERAL HEATH SIGN COMPANY LLC
1020 Pittsburgh Dr Ste B (43015-3878)
PHONE....................................740 369-0999
Mark Watt, *Plant Mgr*
Dave Rayburn, *Safety Mgr*
Ken Hermes, *Plt & Fclts Mgr*
Leif Olson, *Sales Executive*
EMP: 70 **Privately Held**
WEB: www.zimsign.com
SIC: 3993 Electric signs
PA: Federal Heath Sign Company, Llc
4602 North Ave
Oceanside CA 92056

(G-8845)
FOUR NATURES KEEPERS INC
4651 Marysville Rd (43015-9528)
PHONE....................................740 363-8007
Willis J Whittaker, *President*
Nancy Pintavalli, *Admin Sec*
EMP: 10
SALES (est): 757.3K **Privately Held**
SIC: 2048 Bird food, prepared

(G-8846)
FRISCHCO INC
Also Called: Dairy Clean
715 Sunbury Rd (43015-9396)
PHONE....................................740 363-7537
Jim Frisch, *Manager*
EMP: 3
SALES (est): 170.8K **Privately Held**
SIC: 2052 Cones, ice cream

(G-8847)
GREIF INC (PA)
425 Winter Rd (43015-8903)
P.O. Box 8014 (43015-8014)
PHONE....................................740 549-6000
Michael J Gasser, *Ch of Bd*
Peter G Watson, *President*
Deeanne Marlow, *President*
Timothy L Bergwall, *Division Pres*
Ole G Rosgaard, *Division Pres*
EMP: 50 EST: 1877

SALES: 3.3B **Publicly Held**
WEB: www.greif.com
SIC: 2653 2449 2655 3412 Corrugated &
solid fiber boxes; boxes, corrugated:
made from purchased materials; shipping
cases & drums, wood: wirebound & plywood; barrels, wood: coopered; fiber
cans, drums & similar products; drums,
fiber: made from purchased material; fiber
cans, drums & containers; drums, shipping: metal; plastic containers, except
foam; paper bags: made from purchased
materials

(G-8848)
GREIF INC
Also Called: Grief Brothers
366 Greif Pkwy (43015-8260)
PHONE....................................740 657-6500
Jim Craig, *Vice Pres*
Kevin Kling, *Opers Mgr*
Kathy King, *Manager*
Michael Domansky, *Director*
Gina Filonenko, *Director*
EMP: 46
SALES (corp-wide): 3.3B **Publicly Held**
WEB: www.greif.com
SIC: 2449 2655 3412 2653 Shipping
cases & drums, wood: wirebound & plywood; barrels, wood: coopered; drums,
fiber: made from purchased material; fiber
cans, drums & containers; drums, shipping: metal; boxes, corrugated: made
from purchased materials; paper bags:
made from purchased materials; plastic
containers, except foam
PA: Greif, Inc.
425 Winter Rd
Delaware OH 43015
740 549-6000

(G-8849)
GREIF INC
Also Called: Independent Container
366 Greif Pkwy (43015-8260)
PHONE....................................740 657-6500
Max Marley, *General Mgr*
Roger Conway, *General Mgr*
Denard Tucker, *Vice Pres*
EMP: 90
SQ FT: 113,400
SALES (corp-wide): 3.3B **Publicly Held**
WEB: www.greif.com
SIC: 2653 Corrugated boxes, partitions,
display items, sheets & pad
PA: Greif, Inc.
425 Winter Rd
Delaware OH 43015
740 549-6000

(G-8850)
GREIF INC
425 Winter Rd (43015-8903)
PHONE....................................740 549-6000
Ronald C Bogart, *Manager*
C Bogart, *Manager*
EMP: 15
SALES (corp-wide): 3.3B **Publicly Held**
WEB: www.greif.com
SIC: 2449 Shipping cases & drums, wood:
wirebound & plywood
PA: Greif, Inc.
425 Winter Rd
Delaware OH 43015
740 549-6000

(G-8851)
GREIF INC
425 Winter Rd (43015-8903)
PHONE....................................740 549-6000
EMP: 51
SALES (corp-wide): 3.3B **Publicly Held**
SIC: 2653 Corrugated & solid fiber boxes
PA: Greif, Inc.
425 Winter Rd
Delaware OH 43015
740 549-6000

(G-8852)
GREIF INC
366 Greif Pkwy (43015-8260)
PHONE....................................937 548-4111
Tony Perotin, *Branch Mgr*
EMP: 64

SALES (corp-wide): 3.3B **Publicly Held**
WEB: www.greif.com
SIC: 2655 Fiber cans, drums & similar
products
PA: Greif, Inc.
425 Winter Rd
Delaware OH 43015
740 549-6000

(G-8853)
GREIF BROS CORP OHIO INC
425 Winter Rd (43015-8903)
PHONE..................................740 549-6000
Ronald Brown, *Senior VP*
Glenna Steck, *HR Admin*
Michael Barilla, *Info Tech Mgr*
Jan Stimmel, *Admin Asst*
EMP: 11
SALES (est): 1.6MM
SALES (corp-wide): 3.3B **Publicly Held**
SIC: 2655 Ammunition cans or tubes,
board laminated with metal foil
PA: Greif, Inc.
425 Winter Rd
Delaware OH 43015
740 549-6000

(G-8854)
GREIF PACKAGING LLC (HQ)
366 Greif Pkwy (43015-8260)
PHONE..................................740 549-6000
Brian Dum, *CEO*
Michael J Gasser, *Chairman*
Tony Lutes, *Opers Mgr*
Jay Burns, *Manager*
▲ EMP: 88
SALES (est): 274.5MM
SALES (corp-wide): 3.3B **Publicly Held**
SIC: 3086 Packaging & shipping materials,
foamed plastic
PA: Greif, Inc.
425 Winter Rd
Delaware OH 43015
740 549-6000

(G-8855)
GREIF PAPER PACKG & SVCS
LLC
425 Winter Rd (43015-8903)
P.O. Box 675, Massillon (44648-0675)
PHONE..................................740 549-6000
Brian Dum, *Credit Mgr*
Chip Shew, *Manager*
Matt Patton,
EMP: 99
SALES (est): 20.6MM
SALES (corp-wide): 3.3B **Publicly Held**
SIC: 2631 Paperboard mills
PA: Greif, Inc.
425 Winter Rd
Delaware OH 43015
740 549-6000

(G-8856)
GREIF U S HOLDINGS INC
425 Winter Rd (43015-8903)
PHONE..................................740 549-6000
David B Fisher, *President*
John K Dieker, *Treasurer*
Gary R Martz, *Admin Sec*
EMP: 4
SALES (est): 357.5K
SALES (corp-wide): 3.3B **Publicly Held**
SIC: 2653 Corrugated & solid fiber boxes
PA: Greif, Inc.
425 Winter Rd
Delaware OH 43015
740 549-6000

(G-8857)
HARRIS INSTRUMENT
CORPORATION
155 Johnson Dr (43015-8500)
PHONE..................................740 369-3580
Fax: 740 369-2653
John Harris, *President*
David E Harris, *Owner*
W S Centers, *Prdtn Mgr*
Michael Latimer, *Prdtn Mgr*
Gary E Saum, *Shareholder*
EMP: 9 EST: 1979
SQ FT: 10,000

SALES: 1.5MM **Privately Held**
WEB: www.harris-instrument.com
SIC: 3825 3827 3829 3824 Resistance
measuring equipment; test equipment for
electronic & electrical circuits; optical instruments & apparatus; measuring & controlling devices; fluid meters & counting
devices; industrial instrmnts msrmnt dis-
play/control process variable; relays & industrial controls

(G-8858)
HDI ROCK DRILLING GROUP
LTD
3955 Klondike Rd (43015-8862)
PHONE..................................740 369-2968
Alan F Hooper, *Owner*
EMP: 3
SALES (est): 195.4K **Privately Held**
SIC: 3541 Drilling & boring machines

(G-8859)
HENKEL CORPORATION
Also Called: Henkel Surface Technologies
421 London Rd (43015-2493)
P.O. Box 363 (43015-0363)
PHONE..................................740 363-1351
Michael V Biondolillo, *Senior VP*
Scott Link, *Opers Staff*
Carole Krouse, *Purchasing*
Mike Quail, *VP Sls/Mktg*
Tony Neal, *Branch Mgr*
EMP: 46
SQ FT: 1,634
SALES (corp-wide): 19.7B **Privately Held**
SIC: 2841 2842 Detergents, synthetic or-
ganic or inorganic alkaline; specialty
cleaning, polishes & sanitation goods
HQ: Henkel Corporation
1 Henkel Way
Rocky Hill CT 06067
860 571-5100

(G-8860)
HOME CITY ICE COMPANY
150 Johnson Dr (43015-8699)
PHONE..................................419 562-4953
Fax: 513 598-7160
Bryan Stuckman, *Manager*
EMP: 10
SALES (corp-wide): 305.4MM **Privately**
Held
WEB: www.homecityice.com
SIC: 2024 2097 Ice cream & frozen
desserts; manufactured ice
PA: The Home City Ice Company
6045 Bridgetown Rd Ste 1
Cincinnati OH 45248
513 574-1800

(G-8861)
INNO-PAK HOLDING INC
1932 Pittsburgh Dr (43015-3868)
PHONE..................................740 363-0090
Jonathan Sill, *President*
Gary Bechtold, *Vice Pres*
Diane Dewald, *Credit Mgr*
Christopher Sill, *Admin Sec*
▲ EMP: 5
SQ FT: 55,000
SALES (est): 1.3MM **Privately Held**
WEB: www.innopak.com
SIC: 2671 5162 Paper coated or lami-
nated for packaging; plastics products

(G-8862)
INTERNATIONAL PAPER
COMPANY
865 Pittsburgh Dr (43015-2860)
PHONE..................................740 363-9882
EMP: 147
SALES (corp-wide): 21B **Publicly Held**
SIC: 2653 2899 2671 2631 Boxes, corru-
gated: made from purchased materials;
ink or writing fluids; packaging paper &
plastics film, coated & laminated; paper-
board mills
PA: International Paper Company
6400 Poplar Ave
Memphis TN 38197
901 419-9000

(G-8863)
INTERNATIONAL PAPER
COMPANY
875 Pittsburgh Dr (43015-2860)
P.O. Box 8005 (43015-8005)
PHONE..................................740 369-7691
Jim Kugler, *Production*
Melanie Miley, *Purchasing*
Jason Belgya, *Design Engr*
Barbara Russo, *Cust Mgr*
David Harbaugh, *Manager*
EMP: 172
SALES (corp-wide): 21B **Publicly Held**
WEB: www.internationalpaper.com
SIC: 2653 Boxes, corrugated: made from
purchased materials
PA: International Paper Company
6400 Poplar Ave
Memphis TN 38197
901 419-9000

(G-8864)
KELLOGG COMPANY
124 Hyatts Rd (43015-8961)
PHONE..................................614 855-3437
EMP: 703
SALES (corp-wide): 13B **Publicly Held**
SIC: 2043 Cereal breakfast foods
PA: Kellogg Company
1 Kellogg Sq
Battle Creek MI 49017
269 961-2000

(G-8865)
KHEMPCO BLDG SUP CO LTD
PARTNR (PA)
Also Called: Arlington-Blaine Lumber Co
130 Johnson Dr (43015-8699)
PHONE..................................740 549-0465
Fax: 614 294-3163
Donny Bowman, *Partner*
Richard Robinson, *Partner*
James D Klingbeil Jr, *General Ptnr*
Michael Michalski, *Controller*
EMP: 100
SALES (est): 22.7MM **Privately Held**
SIC: 5031 5211 2439 2431 Lumber:
rough, dressed & finished; building mate-
rials, exterior; building materials, interior;
lumber & other building materials;
trusses, except roof: laminated lumber;
trusses, wooden roof; doors, wood; hard-
ware

(G-8866)
KRAMER EXPLORATION
COMPANY
170 W Lincoln Ave (43015-1627)
PHONE..................................740 362-1805
Terry M Kramer, *President*
EMP: 5 EST: 1978
SALES (est): 390.8K **Privately Held**
SIC: 1311 Crude petroleum production;
natural gas production

(G-8867)
LARCOM & MITCHELL LLC
1800 Pittsburgh Dr (43015-3870)
PHONE..................................740 595-3750
Charles Mitchell, *Principal*
EMP: 13
SALES (est): 2.4MM **Privately Held**
SIC: 3599 Flexible metal hose, tubing &
bellows

(G-8868)
LIBERTY CASTING COMPANY
LLC (PA)
550 Liberty Rd (43015-8670)
PHONE..................................740 363-1941
Rick Vaught, *Vice Pres*
Eddie Cimini, *Foreman/Supr*
Melanie Rose, *Purch Agent*
Terry Geisen, *VP Sls/Mktg*
Viera Maruli, *CFO*
EMP: 70
SQ FT: 400,000
SALES (est): 28.4MM **Privately Held**
SIC: 3321 Gray iron castings; ductile iron
castings

(G-8869)
LIBERTY CASTING COMPANY
LLC
407 Curtis St (43015-2439)
P.O. Box 1368 (43015-8368)
PHONE..................................740 363-1941
Lonnie Buckner, *Manager*
EMP: 55
SALES (corp-wide): 28.4MM **Privately**
Held
SIC: 7699 7692 5085 Cleaning services;
welding repair; industrial supplies
PA: Liberty Casting Company Llc
550 Liberty Rd
Delaware OH 43015
740 363-1941

(G-8870)
LUVATA OHIO INC (DH)
1376 Pittsburgh Dr (43015-3814)
PHONE..................................740 363-1981
Fax: 740 363-3847
Jyrki Vesaluoma, *CEO*
Jussi Helavirta, *Ch of Bd*
Dirk Greywitt, *Vice Pres*
Ron Beal, *Mfg Staff*
Bonita Rizzo, *Engineer*
▲ EMP: 100
SQ FT: 60,000
SALES (est): 18.6MM
SALES (corp-wide): 423.9K **Privately**
Held
WEB: www.luvata.com/ohio
SIC: 3548 Welding & cutting apparatus &
accessories; electric welding equipment
HQ: Luvata Fabrication Oy
Vaisalantie 2
Espoo
104 255-700

(G-8871)
MIDWEST ACOUST-A-FIBER INC
487 London Rd (43015-2849)
PHONE..................................740 363-6247
Steve Pollock, *President*
EMP: 35
SALES (corp-wide): 80MM **Privately**
Held
WEB: www.acoust-a-fiber.com
SIC: 3296 Mineral wool
PA: Midwest Acoust-A-Fiber, Inc.
759 Pittsburgh Dr
Delaware OH 43015
740 369-3624

(G-8872)
NATIONAL LIME AND STONE CO
Also Called: National Lime Stone Clmbus
Reg
2406 S Section Line Rd (43015-9518)
P.O. Box 537 (43015-0537)
PHONE..................................740 548-4206
Fax: 614 363-0325
Michael Geckle, *Site Mgr*
Chris Barks, *Opers Staff*
Carolyn Coder, *Office Mgr*
EMP: 40
SALES (corp-wide): 4B **Privately Held**
WEB: www.natlime.com
SIC: 1422 Crushed & broken limestone
PA: The National Lime And Stone Company
551 Lake Cascade Pkwy
Findlay OH 45840
419 422-4341

(G-8873)
NATIONAL METAL SHAPES INC
425 S Sandusky St Ste 1 (43015-3604)
PHONE..................................740 363-9559
Fax: 614 363-3000
John Vogel, *President*
Chris Washek, *General Mgr*
Donna Reynolds, *Manager*
▲ EMP: 25
SQ FT: 85,000
SALES (est): 6.8MM **Privately Held**
SIC: 3354 Aluminum extruded products

(G-8874)
NEU PROSTHETICS &
ORTHOTICS
2848 Jericho Pl (43015-3175)
PHONE..................................740 363-3522
William Neu, *Info Tech Mgr*
EMP: 3

SALES: 600K **Privately Held**
SIC: 3842 Prosthetic appliances

(G-8875)
NUTRIMIR LLC
Also Called: Nutrimir Personalized Wellness
408 Tipperary Loop (43015-7190)
PHONE..............................614 600-2478
Cameron Rink,
Savita Khanna,
Sashwati Roy,
Chandan Sen,
EMP: 4
SALES (est): 156.7K **Privately Held**
SIC: 2834 Vitamin, nutrient & hematinic
   preparations for human use

(G-8876)
OBERFIELDS LLC (PA)
528 London Rd (43015-2850)
P.O. Box 362 (43015-0362)
PHONE..............................740 369-7644
Fax: 614 363-7644
Bruce Loris, *President*
Todd Shepherd, *General Mgr*
Joe Mahler, *Vice Pres*
Darrick Collins, *Plant Mgr*
Mark Selhorst, *Opers Mgr*
EMP: 70 **EST:** 1961
SQ FT: 52,000
SALES (est): 17MM **Privately Held**
SIC: 3272 Concrete products, precast

(G-8877)
OLD VILLAGE
2878 Jericho Pl (43015-3175)
PHONE..............................614 791-8467
Fax: 614 798-0935
Thomas Sweitzer, *CEO*
Steven Sweitzer, *President*
Darlyne Sweitzer, *Vice Pres*
EMP: 10
SALES (est): 935.4K **Privately Held**
SIC: 3911 5944 Jewelry, precious metal;
   jewelry, precious stones & precious met-
   als

(G-8878)
PPG INDUSTRIES OHIO INC
760 Pittsburgh Dr (43015-3811)
PHONE..............................740 363-9610
Stoever Greg, *Finance Mgr*
James Boyd, *Branch Mgr*
EMP: 44
SALES (corp-wide): 14.7B **Publicly Held**
WEB: www.ppgglass.com
SIC: 2851 Paints & allied products
HQ: Ppg Industries Ohio, Inc.
   3800 W 143rd St
   Cleveland OH 44111
   216 671-0050

(G-8879)
**PRECISION TOWER PRODUCTS
LLC**
435 Park Ave (43015-2431)
P.O. Box 129 (43015)
PHONE..............................740 362-7876
George Anasis,
EMP: 8
SALES: 1MM **Privately Held**
SIC: 3441 Building components, structural
   steel

(G-8880)
PRICE FARMS ORGANICS LTD
4838 Warrensburg Rd (43015-8589)
PHONE..............................740 369-1000
Tom Price, *Mng Member*
Tricia Kalmar,
EMP: 12
SQ FT: 1,000
SALES (est): 698K **Privately Held**
WEB: www.pricebarnes.org
SIC: 2875 Compost

(G-8881)
RB&W MANUFACTURING LLC
Also Called: Delo Screw Products
700 London Rd (43015-8637)
PHONE..............................740 363-1971
EMP: 4

SALES (corp-wide): 1.2B **Publicly Held**
WEB: www.pkoh.com.cn
SIC: 5085 3452 3469 Fasteners, industrial: nuts, bolts, screws, etc.; bolts, nuts,
   rivets & washers; screws, metal; nuts,
   metal; stamping metal for the trade
HQ: Rb&W Manufacturing Llc
   10080 Wellman Rd
   Streetsboro OH 44241
   234 380-8540

(G-8882)
REDBUILT LLC
200 Colomet Dr (43015-2873)
PHONE..............................740 363-0870
Peter Mellbolm, *General Mgr*
Ron Butler, *Opers Staff*
Kevin Piatt, *Purch Mgr*
Dallas Anderson, *Info Tech Mgr*
EMP: 20
SALES (corp-wide): 1.8B **Privately Held**
SIC: 2439 3441 Trusses, wooden roof;
   fabricated structural metal
HQ: Redbuilt Llc
   200 E Mallard Dr
   Boise ID 83706
   866 859-6757

(G-8883)
RJW TRUCKING COMPANY LTD
Also Called: Henderson Trucking
124 Henderson Ct (43015-8479)
PHONE..............................740 363-5343
Jack Henderson, *Mng Member*
Shaun Henderson,
EMP: 25
SALES (est): 2.1MM **Privately Held**
SIC: 1442 4212 Construction sand &
   gravel; local trucking, without storage;
   dump truck haulage

(G-8884)
SAM DONG OHIO INC
801 Pittsburgh Dr (43015-2860)
PHONE..............................740 363-1985
Jong, *General Mgr*
Michael Galyk, *Info Tech Mgr*
▲ **EMP:** 75
SALES (est): 25.2MM
SALES (corp-wide): 436.5MM **Privately
Held**
SIC: 3331 Primary copper
PA: Sam Dong Co.,Ltd.
   816 - 41 Samyang-Ro, Daeso-Myeon
   Umsong 27673
   438 794-072

(G-8885)
SANDRA WEDDINGTON
Also Called: Blend of Seven Winery
1400 Stratford Rd (43015-2922)
PHONE..............................740 417-4286
Sandra Weddington, *Owner*
EMP: 6
SALES (est): 550.2K **Privately Held**
SIC: 2084 5182 5921 Wines; wine; wine

(G-8886)
**SAVARE SPECIALTY ADHESIVES
LLC**
1201 S Houk Rd (43015-3876)
P.O. Box 20344, Columbus (43220-0344)
PHONE..............................614 255-2648
Domenico Boffelli, *CEO*
Biagio Savare, *Vice Pres*
Tim Pione, *Mng Member*
Tom Carr,
◆ **EMP:** 45
SALES: 28.9MM
SALES (corp-wide): 28.9MM **Privately
Held**
SIC: 2891 Adhesives
PA: Savare Corporation
   230 West St Ste 700
   Columbus OH 43215
   614 255-2878

(G-8887)
SHRED AWAY
227 Rockmill St (43015-4288)
PHONE..............................740 363-6327
Kim Srail, *Principal*
EMP: 3
SALES (est): 261.5K **Privately Held**
SIC: 3559 Tire shredding machinery

(G-8888)
SKY CLIMBER LLC (PA)
Also Called: Sky Climber Wind Solutions
1800 Pittsburgh Dr (43015-3870)
PHONE..............................740 203-3900
George Anasis, *CEO*
Kelly Winkler, *President*
Todd King, *General Mgr*
Tom Warchol, *General Mgr*
Robert Eddy, *VP Admin*
◆ **EMP:** 25
SQ FT: 55,000
SALES (est): 8MM **Privately Held**
WEB: www.skyclimber.com
SIC: 3446 Scaffolds, mobile or stationary:
   metal

(G-8889)
SKY CLIMBER FASTENERS LLC
1800 Pittsburgh Dr (43015-3870)
PHONE..............................740 816-9830
Donald Rice, *General Mgr*
Kelly Winkler, *Vice Pres*
EMP: 3 **EST:** 2015
SQ FT: 100,000
SALES (est): 124.8K **Privately Held**
SIC: 3429 Metal fasteners

(G-8890)
**SKY CLIMBER WIND
SOLUTIONS LLC**
1800 Pittsburgh Dr (43015-3870)
PHONE..............................740 203-3900
George Anasis,
EMP: 3
SALES (est): 280K **Privately Held**
SIC: 3446 Scaffolds, mobile or stationary:
   metal

(G-8891)
SUPPLY TECHNOLOGIES LLC
Also Called: Delo Screw Products
700 London Rd (43015-8637)
PHONE..............................740 363-1971
Jane Scroggins, *Controller*
Mike Grella, *Sales Mgr*
EMP: 70
SALES (corp-wide): 1.2B **Publicly Held**
WEB: www.deloscrew.com
SIC: 3451 Screw machine products
HQ: Supply Technologies Llc
   6065 Parkland Blvd Ste 1
   Cleveland OH 44124
   440 947-2100

(G-8892)
UTILITY SOLUTIONS INC
327 Curtis St (43015-2439)
PHONE..............................740 369-4300
Trent Hertzfeld, *President*
Mike Killian, *Vice Pres*
EMP: 3
SQ FT: 6,000
SALES (est): 530.2K **Privately Held**
SIC: 3084 Plastics pipe

(G-8893)
**V & P HYDRAULIC PRODUCTS
LLC**
1700 Pittsburgh Dr (43015-3869)
PHONE..............................740 203-3600
Fax: 740 548-6206
Jeff Braumiller, *Purchasing*
Melanie Crane, *Controller*
Laura Scott, *Controller*
Melanie Kirk, *Accountant*
Brad Scott, *Mng Member*
EMP: 70
SQ FT: 45,000
SALES (est): 18.2MM **Privately Held**
WEB: www.vphyd.com
SIC: 3593 Fluid power cylinders, hydraulic
   or pneumatic

(G-8894)
WANNER METAL WORX INC
525 London Rd (43015-2849)
P.O. Box 1004 (43015-7104)
PHONE..............................740 369-4034
Fax: 614 369-4321
Craig Wanner, *President*
Rick Wanner, *Exec VP*
Richard Wanner Jr, *Vice Pres*
Frank Lewis, *Plant Mgr*
Randy Archer, *VP Sales*

EMP: 50
SQ FT: 250,000
SALES (est): 13MM **Privately Held**
WEB: www.wannermetalworx.com
SIC: 3446 Stairs, staircases, stair treads:
   prefabricated metal; balconies, metal

(G-8895)
WATERFORD SIGNS INC
288 S Sandusky St Ste C (43015-2697)
PHONE..............................740 362-7446
Tim Moore, *President*
Debbie Moore, *Corp Secy*
EMP: 3
SALES: 500K **Privately Held**
SIC: 3993 Signs & advertising specialties

(G-8896)
**WHITESIDE MANUFACTURING
CO**
309 Hayes St (43015-2189)
P.O. Box 322 (43015-0322)
PHONE..............................740 363-1179
Fax: 740 369-1082
Kirt Whiteside, *CEO*
Robert Whiteside, *President*
Heather Murphy, *General Mgr*
Rick Yates, *Vice Pres*
Don Brimhall, *Purchasing*
▲ **EMP:** 40
SQ FT: 75,000
SALES (est): 12.5MM **Privately Held**
WEB: www.whitesidemfg.com
SIC: 3537 3429 Platforms, stands, tables,
   pallets & similar equipment; manufactured
   hardware (general)

Dellroy
Carroll County

(G-8897)
BEUCLER BROTHERS INC
Also Called: Bbi Well Service
7237 Flint Rd Sw (44620-9648)
PHONE..............................330 735-2267
Louis Beucler, *President*
EMP: 4
SALES (est): 353.3K **Privately Held**
SIC: 1311 Crude petroleum production

Delphos
Allen County

(G-8898)
A & J WOODWORKING INC
808 Ohio St (45833-1824)
PHONE..............................419 695-5655
Fax: 419 695-1173
Arnold Mohler, *President*
Jill Mohler, *Corp Secy*
Jeff Mohler, *Vice Pres*
Marc Dulebohn, *Manager*
EMP: 8
SALES: 1.1MM **Privately Held**
SIC: 1751 2541 2434 2431 Cabinet
   building & installation; wood partitions &
   fixtures; wood kitchen cabinets; millwork

(G-8899)
AERO PRINTING INC
710 Elida Ave (45833-1737)
P.O. Box 68 (45833-0068)
PHONE..............................419 695-2931
Fax: 419 695-9930
Carl Core Jr, *President*
Dave Core, *Vice Pres*
Laura Basinger, *Graphic Designe*
Brooke Tibbs, *Graphic Designe*
EMP: 4
SQ FT: 2,100
SALES (est): 563.5K **Privately Held**
WEB: www.aeroprinting.com
SIC: 2752 Commercial printing, litho-
   graphic

(G-8900)
AIRGAS INC
11713b Delphs Spncrvle Rd (45833-9221)
PHONE..............................419 695-7085
Tom Hobaugh, *Manager*
EMP: 3

SALES (corp-wide): 163.9MM **Privately Held**
WEB: www.airgas.com
SIC: 2873 Anhydrous ammonia
HQ: Airgas, Inc.
    259 N Radnor Chester Rd # 100
    Radnor PA 19087
    610 687-5253

(G-8901)
BABY LOVE PRENATAL IMAGING LLC ✪
727 W 2nd St (45833-1614)
PHONE..................................419 905-7935
John Parent, *Co-Owner*
Valerie Parent, *Co-Owner*
EMP: 4 EST: 2016
SALES (est) 149.2K **Privately Held**
SIC: 3841 Diagnostic apparatus, medical

(G-8902)
BETTER LIVING SUNROOMS NW OHIO
205 S Pierce St (45833-1924)
PHONE..................................419 692-4526
EMP: 4
SALES (est) 290K **Privately Held**
SIC: 3448 1521 Mfg Prefabricated Metal Buildings Single-Family House Construction

(G-8903)
BUNGE NORTH AMERICA FOUNDATION
234 S Jefferson St (45833-1820)
P.O. Box 485 (45833-0485)
PHONE..................................419 692-6010
Tony Matney, *Facilities Mgr*
Tim Hodson, *Opers-Prdtn-Mfg*
Mel Holder, *Financial Exec*
EMP: 55 **Privately Held**
WEB: www.bungemarion.com
SIC: 2075 Soybean oil, cake or meal
HQ: Bunge North America Foundation
    11720 Borman Dr
    Saint Louis MO 63146
    314 872-3030

(G-8904)
DELPHOS HERALD INC (PA)
405 N Main St (45833-1598)
PHONE..................................419 695-0015
Fax: 419 692-7704
Murray Cohen, *Ch of Bd*
Ray Geary, *Treasurer*
EMP: 83 EST: 1962
SQ FT: 14,000
SALES: 1.1MM **Privately Held**
WEB: www.delphosherald.com
SIC: 2711 2752 Newspapers, publishing & printing; commercial printing, offset

(G-8905)
DELPHOS HERALD INC
Eagle Print
405 N Main St (45833-1598)
PHONE..................................419 695-0015
Fax: 419 695-4675
Murray Cohen, *Owner*
Jeff Easterday, *General Mgr*
Denny Klausing, *Vice Pres*
Marg Ashby, *Systems Mgr*
EMP: 60
SALES (corp-wide): 1.1MM **Privately Held**
WEB: www.delphosherald.com
SIC: 2711 2789 2752 Newspapers, publishing & printing; bookbinding & related work; commercial printing, offset
PA: Herald Delphos Inc
    405 N Main St
    Delphos OH 45833
    419 695-0015

(G-8906)
DRAPERY STITCH OF DELPHOS
50 Summers Ln (45833-1791)
P.O. Box 307 (45833-0307)
PHONE..................................419 692-3921
Fax: 419 692-4050
Donald Beckman, *President*
Cheryl Beckman, *Vice Pres*
Karen Bensman, *Office Mgr*
EMP: 25
SQ FT: 18,000

SALES: 1MM **Privately Held**
WEB: www.draperystitch.com
SIC: 2391 Curtains & draperies

(G-8907)
DTR EQUIPMENT INC
1430 N Main St (45833-1150)
P.O. Box 163, Kalida (45853-0163)
PHONE..................................419 692-3000
Robert T Horstman, *President*
Richard A Horstman, *Vice Pres*
Sandy Kinstle, *Controller*
▲ EMP: 12
SQ FT: 40,000
SALES: 267K **Privately Held**
WEB: www.rthprocessing.com
SIC: 3069 Mats or matting, rubber

(G-8908)
ETC ENTERPRISES LLC
330 Sunderland Rd S (45833-9768)
PHONE..................................417 262-6382
Tim Arheit,
EMP: 4
SALES (est) 269.1K **Privately Held**
SIC: 3822 5063 5065 Refrigeration controls (pressure); switches, thermostatic; refrigeration thermostats; switches, except electronic; transformers, electronic

(G-8909)
KNIPPEN CHRYSLER DODGE JEEP
800 W 5th St (45833-9212)
PHONE..................................419 695-4976
Fax: 419 692-7913
Ronald Knippen, *President*
John Klausing, *Treasurer*
Ronald Baumgarte, *Admin Sec*
▲ EMP: 22
SQ FT: 13,500
SALES (est) 7.7MM **Privately Held**
WEB: www.knippenchrysler.com
SIC: 5511 7538 5521 3714 Pickups, new & used; general automotive repair shops; general truck repair; used car dealers; motor vehicle parts & accessories; truck rental & leasing, no drivers; automotive & home supply stores

(G-8910)
KRENDL MACHINE COMPANY
1201 Spencerville Rd (45833-2381)
PHONE..................................419 692-3060
Fax: 419 695-9301
Jack Krendl, *President*
Lori Presston, *COO*
Jeffrey Krendl, *Vice Pres*
Joseph Krendl, *Vice Pres*
Kyle Goedde, *Plant Supt*
▼ EMP: 70 EST: 1958
SQ FT: 55,000
SALES (est) 14MM **Privately Held**
WEB: www.krendlmachine.com
SIC: 3599 3827 3432 Machine & other job shop work; optical instruments & lenses; plumbing fixture fittings & trim

(G-8911)
LAKEVIEW FARMS INC
1700 Gressel Dr (45833-9152)
PHONE..................................419 695-9925
Phil Baldauf, *Plant Mgr*
Mark Howell, *Purch Dir*
Sharon Freitag, *Purchasing*
Robert Williams, *Technical Mgr*
Melissa Mc Clurg, *Human Res Mgr*
EMP: 95
SALES (corp-wide): 108.6MM **Privately Held**
SIC: 2026 Cream, sour
PA: Lakeview Farms, Llc
    1600 Gressel Dr
    Delphos OH 45833
    419 695-9925

(G-8912)
LAKEVIEW FARMS LLC
1600 Gressel Dr (45833-9153)
P.O. Box 98 (45833-0098)
PHONE..................................419 695-9925
Fax: 262 857-2276
Pat Denor, *Branch Mgr*
Robert Graves, *Manager*
EMP: 50

SALES (corp-wide): 108.6MM **Privately Held**
SIC: 2026 2022 Cream, sour; cheese spreads, dips, pastes & other cheese products
PA: Lakeview Farms, Llc
    1600 Gressel Dr
    Delphos OH 45833
    419 695-9925

(G-8913)
LAKEVIEW FARMS LLC (PA)
1600 Gressel Dr (45833-9153)
P.O. Box 98 (45833-0098)
PHONE..................................419 695-9925
Fax: 419 695-9900
Ernest E Graves, *President*
Melissa McFadden, *Business Mgr*
John Kopilchack, *Vice Pres*
Scott Hageman, *Plant Mgr*
Brian Smith, *Plant Mgr*
EMP: 140
SQ FT: 36,250
SALES (est) 108.6MM **Privately Held**
SIC: 2026 2099 2022 Cream, sour; dips, sour cream based; dips, except cheese & sour cream based; gelatin dessert preparations; cheese, natural & processed

(G-8914)
LION CLOTHING INC
Also Called: Sports Loft
206 N Main St (45833-1767)
PHONE..................................419 692-9981
Carol Odenweller, *President*
John F Odenweller, *Corp Secy*
EMP: 4
SQ FT: 4,000
SALES (est) 641.9K **Privately Held**
WEB: www.lionsclothing.com
SIC: 5611 5941 7336 2395 Clothing, sportswear, men's & boys'; sporting goods & bicycle shops; silk screen design; emblems, embroidered

(G-8915)
NR LEE RESTORATION LTD
7470 Grone Rd (45833-9107)
PHONE..................................419 692-2233
Nathan R Lee, *President*
EMP: 6 EST: 2007
SALES (est) 925.3K **Privately Held**
SIC: 3259 1761 1741 Roofing tile, clay; roofing contractor; tuckpointing or restoration

(G-8916)
R T H PROCESSING INC
1430 N Main St (45833-1150)
P.O. Box 466 (45833-0466)
PHONE..................................419 692-3000
Fax: 419 692-1401
Ted Horstman, *President*
Rick Horstman, *Vice Pres*
Sandy Kinstle, *Controller*
◆ EMP: 100
SQ FT: 50,000
SALES (est): 17.3MM
SALES (corp-wide): 712.6MM **Privately Held**
WEB: www.rthprocessing.com
SIC: 3069 5941 Mats or matting, rubber; exercise equipment
HQ: Ultimate Rb, Inc.
    1430 N Main St
    Delphos OH 45833
    419 692-3000

(G-8917)
SAW SIEFKER MILL
4700 Good Rd (45833-9748)
PHONE..................................419 339-1956
Ronald Siefker, *Partner*
Dan Siefker, *Partner*
Gary Siefker, *Partner*
Ken Siefker, *Partner*
EMP: 7
SQ FT: 20,000
SALES (est): 710.6K **Privately Held**
SIC: 2421 Sawmills & planing mills, general

(G-8918)
TECH-E-Z LLC
446 E Cleveland St (45833-1903)
PHONE..................................419 692-1700

EMP: 5 EST: 2006
SALES (est) 280K **Privately Held**
SIC: 5734 5045 7378 7372 Ret/Whol Tech Prod & Svcs

(G-8919)
TOLEDO MOLDING & DIE INC
900 Gressel Dr (45833-9154)
PHONE..................................419 692-6022
Fax: 419 692-2130
Lori Doty, *Human Res Dir*
Jack Ruhe, *Manager*
EMP: 130
SALES (corp-wide): 426.5MM **Privately Held**
WEB: www.tmdinc.com
SIC: 3089 3714 Injection molding of plastics; motor vehicle parts & accessories
PA: Toledo Molding & Die, Inc.
    1429 Coining Dr
    Toledo OH 43612
    419 470-3950

(G-8920)
TOLEDO MOLDING & DIE INC
Also Called: Delphos Plant 2
24086 State Route 697 (45833-9203)
P.O. Box 393 (45833-0393)
PHONE..................................419 692-6022
Fax: 419 692-8058
Craig Norbeck, *Plant Mgr*
Troy Burns, *Engineer*
Steve Cleaves, *Engineer*
Brian Hohenbrink, *Engineer*
Robert Whitney, *Engineer*
EMP: 85
SALES (corp-wide): 426.5MM **Privately Held**
WEB: www.tmdinc.com
SIC: 5031 3714 Molding, all materials; motor vehicle parts & accessories
PA: Toledo Molding & Die, Inc.
    1429 Coining Dr
    Toledo OH 43612
    419 470-3950

(G-8921)
TRI-TECH MFG LLC
7404 State Route 66 (45833-9527)
PHONE..................................419 238-0140
William Evans, *Mng Member*
EMP: 3
SALES: 300K **Privately Held**
SIC: 3524 Lawn & garden mowers & accessories

(G-8922)
ULTIMATE RB INC (DH)
1430 N Main St (45833-1150)
PHONE..................................419 692-3000
Marvin Wool, *President*
Nathan Miller, *Accountant*
EMP: 16
SALES (est): 17.5MM
SALES (corp-wide): 712.6MM **Privately Held**
SIC: 3069 Mats or matting, rubber
HQ: Dash Multi-Corp, Inc.
    2500 Adie Rd
    Maryland Heights MO 63043
    314 432-3200

(G-8923)
UNVERFERTH MFG CO INC
24309 State Route 697 (45833-9202)
PHONE..................................419 695-2060
Dave Unverferth, *Manager*
Paul Niemeyer, *Executive*
EMP: 55
SALES (corp-wide): 164MM **Privately Held**
WEB: www.unverferth.com
SIC: 3523 Farm machinery & equipment
PA: Unverferth Manufacturing Company, Inc.
    601 S Broad St
    Kalida OH 45853
    419 532-3121

(G-8924)
US GREENFIBER LLC
1601 Gressel Dr (45833-9150)
P.O. Box 435 (45833-0435)
PHONE..................................419 692-7015
Todd Wannemacher, *Manager*
EMP: 17 **Privately Held**

WEB: www.us-gf.com
SIC: 2493 Insulation board, cellular fiber
HQ: Us Greenfiber, Llc
　　5500 77 Center Dr Ste 100
　　Charlotte NC 28217
　　704 379-0640

(G-8925)
US METALCRAFT INC
101 S Franklin St (45833-1936)
P.O. Box 308 (45833-0308)
PHONE.............................419 692-4962
Fax: 419 695-0235
Joel Birkmeier, *President*
Steve Birkmeier, *Treasurer*
Debra Altenburger, *Sales Mgr*
Amy Wannemacher, *Office Mgr*
◆ EMP: 21
SQ FT: 20,000
SALES (est): 4.5MM **Privately Held**
WEB: www.usmetalcraft.com
SIC: 3365 Aluminum & aluminum-based
alloy castings

(G-8926)
VAN WERT MACHINE INC
Also Called: Progressive Tool Division
210 E Cleveland St (45833-1941)
P.O. Box 40 (45833-0040)
PHONE.............................419 692-6836
Fax: 419 695-0480
Jesse F Hitchcock, *President*
Gloria Bechtol, *Corp Secy*
Donald E Bechtol, *Vice Pres*
Lorna Baker, *Bookkeeper*
EMP: 17 EST: 1961
SQ FT: 18,600
SALES (est): 2.3MM **Privately Held**
SIC: 3544 Special dies & tools

(G-8927)
VANAMATIC COMPANY
701 Ambrose Dr (45833-9179)
PHONE.............................419 692-6085
Fax: 419 692-3260
Jay Winhover, *General Mgr*
James N Wiltsie Jr, *Chairman*
Jeff Wiltsie, *Co-President*
Perry Wiltsie, *Co-President*
Patricia M Morris, *CFO*
EMP: 85 EST: 1954
SQ FT: 75,000
SALES: 13MM **Privately Held**
WEB: www.vanamatic.com
SIC: 3451 Screw machine products

Delta
Fulton County

(G-8928)
AXLE SURGEONS OF NW OHIO
811 Helvetia St (43515-1407)
PHONE.............................419 822-5775
Mike Irelan, *Owner*
EMP: 3
SALES (est): 548.7K **Privately Held**
SIC: 3714 Axles, motor vehicle

(G-8929)
BEAVERSON MACHINE INC
11600 County Road 10 2 (43515-9748)
PHONE.............................419 923-8064
Fax: 419 923-0558
Ralph Beaverson, *President*
James Beaverson, *Vice Pres*
EMP: 6
SQ FT: 3,000
SALES (est): 863.6K **Privately Held**
SIC: 3498 Tube fabricating (contract bend-
ing & shaping)

(G-8930)
DELTA TOOL & DIE STL BLOCK INC
5226 County Road 6 (43515-9648)
PHONE.............................419 822-5939
Fax: 419 822-3781
John Gilders, *President*
EMP: 13 EST: 1999
SQ FT: 27,500
SALES (est): 2.1MM **Privately Held**
SIC: 3544 3469 Jigs & fixtures; metal
stampings

(G-8931)
EDW C LEVY CO
Also Called: Fulton Mill Services
6565 County Road 9 (43515-9449)
P.O. Box 86 (43515-0086)
PHONE.............................419 822-8286
Paul Ruffner, *Manager*
EMP: 30
SALES (corp-wide): 388.3MM **Privately Held**
WEB: www.edwclevy.com
SIC: 4212 3295 Dump truck haulage; min-
erals, ground or treated
PA: Edw. C. Levy Co.
　　9300 Dix
　　Dearborn MI 48120
　　313 429-2200

(G-8932)
FORREST MACHINE SHOP
204 Main St (43515-1312)
PHONE.............................419 822-5847
Steve Forrest, *Owner*
EMP: 3
SALES (est): 272.7K **Privately Held**
SIC: 3599 Machine shop, jobbing & repair

(G-8933)
FULTON COUNTY PROCESSING LTD
7800 State Route 109 (43515-9335)
P.O. Box 67 (43515-0067)
PHONE.............................419 822-9266
Fax: 419 822-0408
James J Vanpoppel, *General Ptnr*
▲ EMP: 75
SALES: 36.4MM **Privately Held**
WEB: www.fcpltd.com
SIC: 3312 Blast furnaces & steel mills

(G-8934)
GB MANUFACTURING COMPANY (PA)
1120 E Main St (43515)
P.O. Box 8 (43515-0008)
PHONE.............................419 822-5323
Fax: 419 822-5765
Nelson U Reyes, *President*
Annette Y Petree, *Vice Pres*
Mark Ries, *Vice Pres*
Michael Pechette, *CFO*
Becky Sattler, *Human Res Mgr*
▲ EMP: 53
SQ FT: 50,000
SALES (est): 36.9MM **Privately Held**
WEB: www.gbmfg.com
SIC: 3469 Metal stampings

(G-8935)
GLENN HUNTER & ASSOCIATES INC
1222 County Road 6 (43515-9644)
PHONE.............................419 822-3744
Fax: 419 822-3512
James Clark, *Ch of Bd*
Glenn Hunter, *President*
Dean Daenens, *General Mgr*
Janel Withzler, *Manager*
Sue Pollitt, *Executive*
▼ EMP: 75
SQ FT: 2,500
SALES (est): 23.1MM **Privately Held**
SIC: 3559 Recycling machinery

(G-8936)
INDUSTRIAL REPAIR & MFG INC (PA)
1140 E Main St Ste A (43515-8401)
PHONE.............................419 822-4232
Toll Free:.............................877　-
William H Toedter, *President*
Peggy J Toedter, *Vice Pres*
▲ EMP: 42
SQ FT: 48,000
SALES (est): 6MM **Privately Held**
SIC: 7699 7363 3443 Industrial equip-
ment services; truck driver services; con-
tainers, shipping (bombs, etc.): metal
plate

(G-8937)
LINDE LLC
6744 County Road 10 (43515-9453)
P.O. Box 99 (43515-0099)
PHONE.............................419 822-3909

Mike Murphy, *Manager*
EMP: 7
SALES (corp-wide): 17.9B **Privately Held**
SIC: 2813 Industrial gases
HQ: Linde Llc
　　200 Somerset Corporate Bl
　　Bridgewater NJ 08807
　　908 464-8100

(G-8938)
LYNN JAMES CONTRACTING LLC
12490 County Road 5 (43515-9720)
PHONE.............................419 467-4505
EMP: 5
SALES: 200K **Privately Held**
SIC: 2951 1771 Mfg Asphalt
Mixtures/Blocks Concrete Contractor

(G-8939)
NORTH STAR BLUESCOPE STEEL LLC
6767 County Road 9 (43515-9449)
PHONE.............................419 822-2399
Fax: 419 822-2276
Miguel Alvarez, *President*
Jeff Joldrichsen, *Vice Pres*
Dave Rintoul, *Plant Mgr*
Steve Duda, *Purch Mgr*
Timothy Mitchell, *QC Mgr*
◆ EMP: 345
SQ FT: 600,000
SALES (est): 218.7MM
SALES (corp-wide): 6.7B **Privately Held**
WEB: www.nsbhp.com
SIC: 3312 Hot-rolled iron & steel products
PA: Bluescope Steel Limited
　　L 11 120 Collins St
　　Melbourne VIC 3000
　　180 080-0789

(G-8940)
TWIN POINT INC (PA)
Also Called: Workman Electronics
11955 County Road 10 2 (43515-9748)
PHONE.............................419 923-7525
Fax: 419 923-7145
Jerry Twining, *CEO*
▲ EMP: 13
SALES (est): 947.1K **Privately Held**
SIC: 3679 Electronic circuits

(G-8941)
WORTHINGTON INDUSTRIES INC
Worthington Steel Division
6303 County Road 10 (43515-9453)
PHONE.............................419 822-2500
Fax: 419 822-2502
Tom Campana, *Vice Pres*
Ryan Lamb, *Safety Dir*
Erwin Lakia, *Engineer*
Don Gerdes, *Human Res Dir*
Jeff Leeper, *Manager*
EMP: 100
SALES (corp-wide): 2.8B **Publicly Held**
WEB: www.worthingtonindustries.com
SIC: 3312 Iron & steel: galvanized, pipes,
plates, sheets, etc.
PA: Worthington Industries, Inc.
　　200 W Old Wilson Bridge Rd
　　Worthington OH 43085
　　614 438-3210

Dennison
Tuscarawas County

(G-8942)
ALSCO METALS CORPORATION (DH)
1309 Deer Hill Rd (44621-9350)
PHONE.............................740 983-2571
Paul Carpenter, *Plant Mgr*
Scott A McKinley, *Treasurer*
Peter Ingermi, *Director*
Christopher R Clegg, *Director*
◆ EMP: 30
SQ FT: 10,000
SALES (est): 45.7MM **Privately Held**
SIC: 3444 3089 3479 Siding, sheet metal;
siding, plastic; painting of metal products

(G-8943)
CAM CO INC (PA)
6270 Wolf Run Rd Se (44621-8914)
PHONE.............................740 922-4533
Fax: 740 922-6734
Randy Leishman, *President*
Daniel Leishman, *Corp Secy*
David Leishman, *Vice Pres*
EMP: 1
SALES: 1.4MM **Privately Held**
SIC: 1221 Auger mining, bituminous

(G-8944)
CLAPP & HANEY BRAZED TOOL CO
901 Race St (44621-1509)
P.O. Box 105 (44621-0105)
PHONE.............................740 922-3515
Fax: 740 922-3563
Richard Liggett, *Partner*
Tom Benner, *Partner*
EMP: 20
SALES (est): 3.6MM **Privately Held**
SIC: 3545 3599 Cutting tools for machine
tools; machine shop, jobbing & repair

(G-8945)
KENNETH MC BETH
Also Called: Blackstone Mining
514 Stillwater Ave (44621-1350)
PHONE.............................740 922-9494
Kenneth Mc Beth, *Owner*
EMP: 5
SALES (est): 369.5K **Privately Held**
SIC: 1221 Bituminous coal surface mining

(G-8946)
SERVICES ACQUISITION CO LLC
Also Called: Tank Services
4412 Pleasant Vly Rd Se (44621-9038)
P.O. Box 71 (44621-0071)
PHONE.............................330 479-9267
James Milano, *CEO*
EMP: 5 EST: 2014
SALES (est): 882.8K **Privately Held**
SIC: 3731 Tankers, building & repairing

Derby
Pickaway County

(G-8947)
PETTITS PALLETS INC
11812 London Rd (43117)
PHONE.............................614 351-4920
Brenda Pettit, *President*
Tim Pettit, *Vice Pres*
EMP: 7
SALES (est): 679.3K **Privately Held**
SIC: 2448 Pallets, wood

Deshler
Henry County

(G-8948)
CAST METALS INCORPORATED
104 W North St (43516-1164)
P.O. Box 87 (43516-0087)
PHONE.............................419 278-2010
Fax: 419 278-2430
Tom Downer, *President*
EMP: 33
SQ FT: 22,500
SALES (est): 6.2MM **Privately Held**
WEB: www.castmetals.com
SIC: 3321 Gray iron castings; ductile iron
castings

(G-8949)
DESHLER METAL WORKING CO INC
140 S East Ave (43516-1302)
PHONE.............................419 278-0472
Fax: 419 278-0472
Judee Suber, *President*
EMP: 4
SQ FT: 11,000
SALES (est): 380.3K **Privately Held**
SIC: 3469 Spinning metal for the trade

▲ = Import　▼=Export
◆ =Import/Export

(G-8950)
ENVIROSCAPE EMC
300 S Chestnut St (43516-1049)
PHONE..............................419 278-2000
Ken Deitering, *Principal*
EMP: 8
SALES (est): 1.4MM **Privately Held**
SIC: 3572 Computer storage devices

(G-8951)
GRAMINEX LLC
2 300 County Rd C (43516)
PHONE..............................419 278-1023
Fax: 419 278-1042
Justin Ritter, *Manager*
Ed Wyszumiala, *Manager*
EMP: 15
SALES (corp-wide): 3.5MM **Privately
Held**
WEB: www.gmtfinechemicalssa.com
SIC: 2834 2833 Extracts of botanicals:
powdered, pilular, solid or fluid; medici-
nals & botanicals
PA: Graminex, L.L.C.
95 Midland Rd
Saginaw MI 48638
989 797-5502

(G-8952)
YARNELL BROS INC
103 E North St (43516-1283)
P.O. Box 81 (43516-0081)
PHONE..............................419 278-2831
Fax: 419 278-2331
Ron Yarnell, *President*
Richard L Yarnell, *Corp Secy*
Dave Yarnell, *Vice Pres*
EMP: 4 EST: 1948
SQ FT: 5,000
SALES (est): 461.1K **Privately Held**
SIC: 2048 Alfalfa or alfalfa meal, prepared
as animal feed

Dexter City
Noble County

(G-8953)
AMES COMPANIES INC
21460 Ames Ln (45727-9702)
PHONE..............................740 783-2535
Fax: 740 783-0305
Jim Basham, *Branch Mgr*
Jeff Sanford, *Manager*
EMP: 20
SALES (corp-wide): 2B **Publicly Held**
WEB: www.ames.com
SIC: 3423 Garden & farm tools, including
shovels
HQ: The Ames Companies Inc
465 Railroad Ave
Camp Hill PA 17011
717 737-1500

(G-8954)
B&N COAL INC
38455 Marietta Rte (45727)
P.O. Box 100 (45727-0100)
PHONE..............................740 783-3575
Fax: 740 783-5455
Carl Baker, *President*
Bob Cunningham, *Corp Secy*
Roger Osborne, *Vice Pres*
EMP: 64 EST: 1962
SQ FT: 21,000
SALES: 18MM **Privately Held**
SIC: 1221 8711 Strip mining, bituminous;
engineering services

(G-8955)
**BELDEX LAND COMPANY LLC
(PA)**
Also Called: Belpre Sand and Gravel Com-
pany
38455 State Rte 821 S (45727)
P.O. Box 100 (45727-0100)
PHONE..............................740 783-3575
Carl Baker, *Mng Member*
David Skinner, *Mng Member*
EMP: 6
SALES (est): 1MM **Privately Held**
SIC: 1442 Construction sand & gravel

(G-8956)
DEXTER HARDWOODS INC
145 Jefferson St (45727)
PHONE..............................740 783-4141
Kenton Byrd, *President*
Carl Baker Jr, *Principal*
Robert P Cunningham, *Corp Secy*
Kevin Cimore, *Manager*
EMP: 4
SQ FT: 10,000
SALES: 1.5MM **Privately Held**
SIC: 2421 Lumber: rough, sawed or planed

(G-8957)
SHARON STONE CO
County Road 10 (45727)
P.O. Box 100 (45727-0100)
PHONE..............................740 374-3236
Carl Baker, *Owner*
EMP: 4
SALES (est): 238.5K **Privately Held**
SIC: 3295 5032 Slag, crushed or ground;
stone, crushed or broken

(G-8958)
WARREN DRILLING CO INC
Also Called: Warren Trucking
305 Smithson St (45727-9749)
P.O. Box 103 (45727-0103)
PHONE..............................740 783-2775
Fax: 740 783-0016
Dan R Warren, *President*
Lewis D Warren, *Principal*
Paul H Warren, *Principal*
W T Warren, *Principal*
Randy C Warren, *Vice Pres*
EMP: 110 EST: 1939
SALES (est): 27.5MM **Privately Held**
WEB: www.warrendrilling.biz
SIC: 1381 Directional drilling oil & gas
wells

Diamond
Portage County

(G-8959)
RINKER MATERIALS
4200 Universal Dr (44412-9700)
PHONE..............................330 654-2511
Chris Rowland, *Principal*
EMP: 5 EST: 1963
SALES (est): 446.7K **Privately Held**
SIC: 3273 Ready-mixed concrete

Donnelsville
Clark County

(G-8960)
BEACH MANUFACTURING CO
118 N Hampton Rd (45319-5011)
P.O. Box 129 (45319-0129)
PHONE..............................937 882-6372
Fax: 937 882-6153
Ted Beach, *President*
Louis Beach, *Principal*
Carrie M Ridenaur, *Principal*
Kevin Mallory, *Exec VP*
Joya Bartlett, *Bookkeeper*
EMP: 120
SQ FT: 20,000
SALES (est): 30.3MM **Privately Held**
WEB: www.beachmfgco.com
SIC: 3714 3231 Motor vehicle parts & ac-
cessories; mirrors, truck & automobile:
made from purchased glass

(G-8961)
**ECON-O-MACHINE PRODUCTS
INC**
160 E Main St (45319-5042)
P.O. Box 153 (45319-0153)
PHONE..............................937 882-6307
Fax: 937 882-6416
Annabelle Blumenschein, *President*
Roger A Blumenschein, *President*
Doug Blumenschein, *Vice Pres*
EMP: 3
SQ FT: 8,440

SALES (est): 280K **Privately Held**
SIC: 3599 3549 7694 3621 Machine
shop, jobbing & repair; metalworking machinery; armature rewinding shops; motors & generators

Dover
Tuscarawas County

(G-8962)
A W TIPKA OIL & GAS INC
2421 Johnstown Rd Ne (44622-7579)
PHONE..............................330 364-4333
Fax: 330 364-1219
Alan W Tipka, *President*
James Schumacher, *CFO*
EMP: 7
SALES (est): 460K **Privately Held**
SIC: 1389 Servicing oil & gas wells

(G-8963)
**ALLIED MACHINE & ENGRG
CORP (PA)**
120 Deeds Dr (44622-9652)
P.O. Box 36 (44622-0036)
PHONE..............................330 343-4283
Fax: 330 602-3400
Bill Stokey, *CEO*
Terry Koester, *Regional Mgr*
Janine Garber, *Exec VP*
Michael A Stokey, *Exec VP*
Steve Stokey, *Exec VP*
▲ EMP: 250 EST: 1933
SALES (est): 54.5MM **Privately Held**
WEB: www.alliedmachine.com
SIC: 3545 Machine tool attachments & ac-
cessories

(G-8964)
**ARIZONA CHEMICAL COMPANY
LLC**
875 Harger St (44622-9441)
PHONE..............................330 343-7701
Matthew Hess, *Safety Mgr*
Robert Hammond, *Production*
Mario Maffei, *Research*
Mark Ewing, *Engineer*
Tom Wiegand, *Engineer*
EMP: 115
SQ FT: 3,000
SALES (corp-wide): 1.7B **Publicly Held**
WEB: www.arizonachemical.com
SIC: 2861 2911 2821 2819 Wood distilla-
tion products; fractionation products of
crude petroleum, hydrocarbons; plastics
materials & resins; industrial inorganic
chemicals
HQ: Arizona Chemical Company, Llc
4600 Touchton Rd E # 1500
Jacksonville FL 32246
904 928-8700

(G-8965)
BAERLOCHER USA LLC (DH)
3676 Davis Rd Nw (44622-9771)
PHONE..............................330 364-6000
Fax: 330 343-7025
Ray Buehler, *CEO*
David Keubel, *CFO*
Mary Newton, *Controller*
Judy Loibl, *Human Res Dir*
Janet Whitman, *Sales Staff*
▲ EMP: 10
SQ FT: 10,000
SALES (est): 45MM
SALES (corp-wide): 377.1MM **Privately
Held**
SIC: 2819 Nonmetallic compounds
HQ: Baerlocher Gmbh
Freisinger Str. 1
UnterschleiBheim 85716
891 437-30

(G-8966)
BAIR BODIES & TRAILERS INC
4562 Bair Rd Nw (44622-7070)
PHONE..............................330 343-4853
Lynn Corpman, *President*
D Corpman, *Vice Pres*
EMP: 3
SALES (est): 262.5K **Privately Held**
WEB: www.bairbodies.com
SIC: 3713 Truck bodies & parts

(G-8967)
BARKETT FRUIT CO INC (PA)
Also Called: Farmer Smiths Market
1213 E 3rd St (44622-1227)
PHONE..............................330 364-6645
Fax: 330 364-7683
William Barkett, *CEO*
James Barkett, *President*
Thomas Barkett, *Vice Pres*
Ronald Barkett, *Treasurer*
EMP: 36
SQ FT: 20,000
SALES (est): 13.5MM **Privately Held**
WEB: www.barkettfruit.com
SIC: 5148 5143 5144 2099 Vegetables;
fruits; dairy products, except dried or
canned; eggs; salads, fresh or refriger-
ated

(G-8968)
**BELDEN & BLAKE
CORPORATION**
1748 Saltwell Rd Nw (44622-7471)
PHONE..............................330 602-5551
Fax: 330 602-5554
Tim McConah, *Branch Mgr*
EMP: 30
SQ FT: 4,500
SALES (corp-wide): 59.8MM **Privately
Held**
WEB: www.beldenblake.com
SIC: 1311 1389 4922 5082 Crude petro-
leum production; natural gas production;
oil field services; natural gas transmis-
sion; oil field equipment; oil & gas explo-
ration services
HQ: Belden & Blake Corporation
1001 Fannin Ste 800
Houston TX 77002
713 659-3500

(G-8969)
BLICK TOOL & DIE INC
117 E Front St (44622-2951)
PHONE..............................330 343-1277
Fax: 330 364-8558
James E Blickensderfer, *President*
Beth Blickensderfer, *Vice Pres*
EMP: 5
SQ FT: 6,000
SALES: 200K **Privately Held**
SIC: 3544 Special dies, tools, jigs & fix-
tures

(G-8970)
**BREITENBACH WINE CELLAR
INC**
Also Called: Breitenbach Bed & Breakfast
5934 Old Route 39 Nw (44622-7787)
PHONE..............................330 343-3603
Fax: 330 343-8290
Cynthia Bixler, *President*
Susan Gerber, *Accountant*
Jennifer Kohler, *Sales Staff*
Anita Davis, *Manager*
EMP: 8
SALES (est): 909.1K **Privately Held**
WEB: www.breitenbachwine.com
SIC: 2084 5812 7011 Wines; eating
places; bed & breakfast inn

(G-8971)
**COMMERCIAL HONING LLC
(PA)**
Also Called: Commercial Fluid Power
2997 Progress St (44622-9639)
PHONE..............................330 343-8896
Steve Kohl, *Safety Mgr*
Valerie Woodburn, *Controller*
Marge Nowak, *Human Res Mgr*
Jeff Headley, *Mng Member*
Rich Finnicum,
▲ EMP: 60
SQ FT: 15,000
SALES (est): 25.5MM **Privately Held**
SIC: 3599 3471 3317 Machine shop, job-
bing & repair; plating & polishing; steel
pipe & tubes

(G-8972)
**COMMERCIAL HONING OHIO
INC (PA)**
2997 Progress St (44622-9639)
PHONE..............................330 343-8896
Fax: 330 343-6391

(PA)=Parent Co (HQ)=Headquarters (DH)=Div Headquarters
✪ = New Business established in last 2 years

2017 Harris Ohio
Industrial Directory

367

GEOGRAPHIC

Jeff Headlee Mgr Member, *Principal*
Jeff Headlee, *Mng Member*
EMP: 60 **EST:** 1950
SALES (est): 9.6MM **Privately Held**
WEB: www.commercial-honing.com
SIC: 3492 Fluid power valves & hose fittings

(G-8973)
COMMERCIAL HONING OHIO INC
Commercial Fluid Power
2997 Progress St (44622-9639)
PHONE............................330 343-8896
Melvin White, *Branch Mgr*
EMP: 25
SALES (corp-wide): 9.6MM **Privately Held**
WEB: www.commercial-honing.com
SIC: 3593 Fluid power cylinders, hydraulic or pneumatic
PA: Commercial Honing Of Ohio, Inc.
　2997 Progress St
　Dover OH 44622
　330 343-8896

(G-8974)
CYCLONE SUPPLY COMPANY INC (PA)
524 River St (44622-1935)
P.O. Box 706 (44622-0706)
PHONE............................330 204-0313
Tim Levengood, *President*
Dewain Horn, *Exec VP*
Dewain Horne, *Vice Pres*
EMP: 3
SQ FT: 60,000
SALES (est): 726K **Privately Held**
SIC: 3533 Oil & gas field machinery

(G-8975)
DEFLECTO LLC
303 Oxford St Ste A (44622-1977)
PHONE............................330 602-0840
David Maurer, *Accounts Mgr*
John Jordan, *Branch Mgr*
EMP: 34
SALES (corp-wide): 592.6MM **Privately Held**
SIC: 3089 Plastic hardware & building products
HQ: Deflecto, Llc
　7035 E 86th St
　Indianapolis IN 46250
　317 849-9555

(G-8976)
DIRECT ACTION CO INC
Also Called: Dac
6668 Old State Rte 39 Nw (44622)
P.O. Box 2205 (44622-1000)
PHONE............................330 364-3219
Fax: 330 364-6522
Randy Jacobs, *President*
James Rhodes, *Vice Pres*
Carol Frazier, *Marketing Staff*
Kayleigh Keller, *Technology*
EMP: 15
SQ FT: 2,000
SALES: 760K **Privately Held**
WEB: www.directaction.com
SIC: 5122 2048 Vitamins & minerals; feed supplements

(G-8977)
DORIS KIMBLE
Also Called: Red Hill Development Company
3596 State Route 39 Nw (44622-7232)
PHONE............................330 343-1226
Doris Kimble, *Owner*
Pete Gutwein, *Manager*
EMP: 20
SALES: 3MM **Privately Held**
SIC: 1381 Drilling oil & gas wells

(G-8978)
DOVER CABINET INC
1568 State Route 39 Nw (44622-7346)
PHONE............................330 343-9074
Fax: 330 364-2586
John A Perkowski, *President*
EMP: 18
SQ FT: 16,000
SALES (est): 2.1MM **Privately Held**
SIC: 2434 Wood kitchen cabinets

(G-8979)
DOVER CHEMICAL CORPORATION (HQ)
3676 Davis Rd Nw (44622-9771)
PHONE............................330 343-7711
Fax: 330 364-1579
Dwain S Colvin, *President*
Matt Fender, *Business Mgr*
Jack Teat, *Exec VP*
Chuck Fletcher, *Vice Pres*
Kim Sangha, *Vice Pres*
▲ **EMP:** 170 **EST:** 1949
SQ FT: 260,000
SALES (est): 113.2MM
SALES (corp-wide): 886.7MM **Privately Held**
WEB: www.doverchem.com
SIC: 2819 2869 2899 Industrial inorganic chemicals; industrial organic chemicals; chemical preparations
PA: Icc Industries Inc.
　460 Park Ave Fl 7
　New York NY 10022
　212 521-1700

(G-8980)
DOVER HIGH PRFMCE PLAS INC
Also Called: Dhpp
140 Williams Dr Nw (44622-7662)
PHONE............................330 343-3477
Fax: 330 343-7642
Mary L Schwab, *President*
Tim Fisher, *General Mgr*
George Maksim, *Treasurer*
Kevin Kirkland, *Persnl Dir*
Paul Palmer, *Mktg Dir*
EMP: 36
SQ FT: 60,000
SALES (est): 9.1MM **Privately Held**
WEB: www.dhpp.net
SIC: 3559 Plastics working machinery
PA: Jastin Inc
　1112 Glen Dr Ne
　New Philadelphia OH

(G-8981)
DOVER MACHINE CO
2208 State Route 516 Nw (44622-7081)
PHONE............................330 343-4123
Fax: 330 343-0558
Wayne Amistadi, *President*
EMP: 14 **EST:** 1955
SQ FT: 10,000
SALES: 740K **Privately Held**
SIC: 3599 7692 3544 Machine shop, jobbing & repair; welding repair; special dies, tools, jigs & fixtures

(G-8982)
DOVER TANK AND PLATE COMPANY
5725 Crown Rd Nw (44622-9649)
P.O. Box 70 (44622-0070)
PHONE............................330 343-4443
Fax: 330 364-3125
David Lawless, *President*
Earl Lawless, *Vice Pres*
Joseph Lawless, *Vice Pres*
Luke Lawless, *Treasurer*
EMP: 45 **EST:** 1922
SQ FT: 40,000
SALES (est): 17.7MM **Privately Held**
WEB: www.dovertank.com
SIC: 3441 3446 3444 3443 Fabricated structural metal; architectural metalwork; sheet metalwork; fabricated plate work (boiler shop)

(G-8983)
E I DU PONT DE NEMOURS & CO
1929 Tremont St (44622-1078)
PHONE............................330 364-6002
Donald Burge, *Branch Mgr*
EMP: 177
SALES (corp-wide): 24.5B **Publicly Held**
WEB: www.dupont.com
SIC: 2879 Agricultural chemicals
PA: E. I. Du Pont De Nemours And Company
　974 Centre Rd
　Wilmington DE 19805
　302 774-1000

(G-8984)
ERNEST WARTHER AND SONS INC
327 Karl Ave (44622-2767)
PHONE............................330 343-7513
Steve Cunningham, *President*
Joan Warther, *Corp Secy*
Carol Moreland, *Purchasing*
EMP: 12 **EST:** 1946
SQ FT: 14,000
SALES: 1.2MM **Privately Held**
SIC: 3421 5947 2431 Table cutlery, except with handles of metal; carving sets; gift shop; millwork

(G-8985)
EXTREME TRAILERS LLC
317 E Broadway St (44622-1914)
P.O. Box 233, Alliance (44601)
PHONE............................330 440-0026
Lelie Smith, *President*
Shawn Ellwood, *Materials Mgr*
EMP: 6
SQ FT: 100,000
SALES: 3MM **Privately Held**
SIC: 3715 Truck trailers

(G-8986)
G A SPRING ADVERTISING
Also Called: Pro-Print Business Center
2101 N Wooster Ave (44622-2403)
P.O. Box 673 (44622-0673)
PHONE............................330 343-9030
Fax: 330 343-9030
Gerald A Spring, *Owner*
EMP: 4
SQ FT: 12,000
SALES: 180K **Privately Held**
SIC: 5112 2752 Stationery & office supplies; business form & card printing, lithographic

(G-8987)
GENERAL ELECTRIC COMPANY
200 W Broadway St (44622-1958)
PHONE............................330 343-8841
Fax: 330 364-0203
Mary Blenn, *Plant Mgr*
Dan Carter, *Purch Mgr*
Jim Ostberg, *Engineer*
Scott Carbaugh, *Branch Mgr*
Terry Glass, *Manager*
EMP: 100
SALES (corp-wide): 123.6B **Publicly Held**
SIC: 3357 3356 3496 3339 Appliance fixture wire, nonferrous; tungsten, basic shapes; miscellaneous fabricated wire products; primary nonferrous metals; ferroalloy ores, except vanadium
PA: General Electric Company
　41 Farnsworth St
　Boston MA 02210
　617 443-3000

(G-8988)
GRAPHIC PUBLICATIONS INC
123 W 3rd St (44622-2968)
PHONE............................330 343-4377
Michael Mast, *President*
Hunter Bargin, *Principal*
EMP: 60
SALES (est): 1.4MM **Privately Held**
SIC: 2711 Newspapers, publishing & printing

(G-8989)
GREER STEEL COMPANY
624 Boulevard St (44622-2027)
P.O. Box 1900, Morgantown WV (26507-1900)
PHONE............................330 343-8811
Fax: 330 343-1700
John R Raese, *President*
George Whalen, *VP Admin*
James R Harpster, *Vice Pres*
Scott Rummell, *Plant Mgr*
Linda Pisony, *Purchasing*
◆ **EMP:** 150
SALES (est): 47.5MM
SALES (corp-wide): 132MM **Privately Held**
WEB: www.greerlimestone.com
SIC: 3316 Strip steel, cold-rolled: from purchased hot-rolled

PA: Greer Industries, Inc.
　570 Canyon Rd
　Morgantown WV 26508
　304 296-2549

(G-8990)
HANNON COMPANY
Charles Rewinding Division
801 Commercial Pkwy (44622-3152)
P.O. Box 398 (44622-0398)
PHONE............................330 343-7758
Fax: 330 343-5650
Thomas E Krocker, *Division Mgr*
Thomas E Krockr, *Division Mgr*
Craig Stewart, *Marketing Staff*
Tim J Welch, *Manager*
EMP: 14
SQ FT: 12,200
SALES (corp-wide): 27.2MM **Privately Held**
WEB: www.hanco.com
SIC: 7629 5063 7699 7694 Electrical repair shops; motors, electric; motor controls, starters & relays: electric; welding equipment repair; electric motor repair; machine shop, jobbing & repair
PA: The Hannon Company
　1605 Waynesburg Dr Se
　Canton OH 44707
　330 456-4728

(G-8991)
HVAC INC
Also Called: Dover Phila Heating & Cooling
133 W 3rd St (44622-2933)
PHONE............................330 343-5511
Fax: 330 343-7469
David Kinsey, *President*
Dana Moser, *General Mgr*
James Moser, *Corp Secy*
EMP: 12
SQ FT: 10,000
SALES (est): 1.2MM **Privately Held**
WEB: www.hvac-inc.com
SIC: 1711 3444 Warm air heating & air conditioning contractor; sheet metalwork

(G-8992)
INCA PRESSWOOD-PALLETS LTD (PA)
3005 Progress St (44622-9640)
P.O. Box 248 (44622-0248)
PHONE............................330 343-3361
Fax: 330 364-4734
Wolfgang Ketzer, *Partner*
Hans Inselkammer, *Partner*
Matt Doughty, *Plant Mgr*
Rae Powell, *Admin Asst*
▲ **EMP:** 35
SQ FT: 45,000
SALES (est): 6.2MM **Privately Held**
SIC: 2448 Pallets, wood

(G-8993)
INDUSTRIAL FINISHERS INC
3690 State Route 800 Ne (44622-7999)
P.O. Box 482 (44622-0482)
PHONE............................330 343-7797
Fax: 330 343-7793
Paul Neiger, *President*
Tommie Wahl, *Corp Secy*
EMP: 4
SQ FT: 12,000
SALES (est): 125K **Privately Held**
WEB: www.industrial-finishers.com
SIC: 3479 Painting, coating & hot dipping

(G-8994)
J & J TOOL & DIE INC
203 W 4th St (44622-2905)
PHONE............................330 343-4721
Fax: 330 343-0427
Scott Sherer, *President*
Carol Belt, *Corp Secy*
Mary Sherer, *Vice Pres*
EMP: 7
SQ FT: 5,000
SALES (est): 375.1K **Privately Held**
SIC: 3544 Special dies & tools

(G-8995)
KIM PHILLIPS SIGN CO LLC
Also Called: Signs To Go
812 Boulevard St (44622-2008)
PHONE............................330 364-4280
Fax: 330 343-5860

Kim Phillips, *Principal*
EMP: 4
SALES (est): 442.4K **Privately Held**
SIC: 1522 3993 Residential construction;
signs & advertising specialties

(G-8996)
KRUZ INC
Also Called: Ravens Sales & Service
6332 Columbia Rd Nw (44622-7676)
P.O. Box 525 (44622-0525)
PHONE...................................330 878-5595
Fax: 330 878-7345
Todd Abel, *Sales Executive*
Rufus Hall, *Manager*
Patty Fisher, *Manager*
EMP: 30
SALES (corp-wide): 10.9MM **Privately
Held**
WEB: www.kruz.com
SIC: 3713 Dump truck bodies
PA: Kruz Inc.
1201 W Culver Rd
Knox IN 46534
574 772-6673

(G-8997)
LAVANDER BRIDAL SALON
218 W 3rd St (44622-2965)
PHONE...................................330 602-0333
Karen Stokey, *Owner*
EMP: 10
SALES (est): 912.1K **Privately Held**
SIC: 2335 Bridal & formal gowns

(G-8998)
MARLITE INC
609 S Tuscarawas Ave (44622-2345)
PHONE...................................330 343-6621
Darryl Rosser, *Branch Mgr*
EMP: 150
SALES (corp-wide): 532.5MM **Privately
Held**
SIC: 2542 Partitions & fixtures, except
wood
HQ: Marlite, Inc.
1 Marlite Dr
Dover OH 44622
330 343-6621

(G-8999)
MARLITE INC (DH)
1 Marlite Dr (44622-2361)
PHONE...................................330 343-6621
Fax: 330 343-7296
Daryl Rosser, *President*
T J Rine, *Business Mgr*
Mark Jutte, *Vice Pres*
Greg Leary, *Vice Pres*
Greg Triplett, *Vice Pres*
◆ **EMP:** 150
SQ FT: 450,000
SALES (est): 60.3MM
SALES (corp-wide): 532.5MM **Privately
Held**
WEB: www.marlite.com
SIC: 2542 Partitions & fixtures, except
wood
HQ: Nudo Products, Inc.
1500 Taylor Ave
Springfield IL 62703
217 528-5636

(G-9000)
MARMON HIGHWAY TECH LLC
6332 Columbia Rd Nw (44622-7676)
P.O. Box 525 (44622-0525)
PHONE...................................330 878-5595
EMP: 40
SQ FT: 2,725
SALES (corp-wide): 210.8B **Publicly Held**
SIC: 7539 3714 Automotive Repair Mfg
Motor Vehicle Parts/Accessories
HQ: Marmon Highway Technologies Llc
5915 Chalkville Rd 300
Birmingham AL 35235
205 508-2000

(G-9001)
METEOR SEALING SYSTEMS LLC
Also Called: Meteor Automotive
400 S Tuscarawas Ave (44622-2342)
PHONE...................................330 343-9595
Joerg Busse, *Vice Pres*

Ray Buffington, *Purch Mgr*
Daniel Brown, *Engineer*
Michael Frustaci, *Engineer*
Chris Sprague, *Engineer*
▲ **EMP:** 155
SALES (est): 47.4MM **Privately Held**
WEB: www.meteor-sealingsystems.com
SIC: 3069 Tubing, rubber
HQ: Meteor Gummiwerke K.H. Badje Gmbh
& Co. Kg
Ernst-Deger-Str. 9
Bockenem 31167
506 725-0

(G-9002)
MILLER WELDING INC
2718 Broad Run Dar Rd Nw (44622-7705)
PHONE...................................330 364-6173
Fax: 330 364-6983
C Delon Miller, *President*
Robin Miller, *Vice Pres*
E Pauline Miller, *Treasurer*
EMP: 7
SQ FT: 1,320
SALES (est): 1MM **Privately Held**
SIC: 7692 Welding repair

(G-9003)
MINTEQ INTERNATIONAL INC
5864 Crown Street Ext Nw (44622)
PHONE...................................330 343-8821
Carl Laib, *Safety Mgr*
Ron Nanni, *Branch Mgr*
Matt Shuck, *Manager*
Jeff Rickard, *Director*
Terry Stephan, *Director*
EMP: 32
SQ FT: 150,000
SALES (corp-wide): 1.6B **Publicly Held**
WEB: www.minteq.com
SIC: 3297 3255 3251 Brick refractories;
clay refractories; brick & structural clay
tile
HQ: Minteq International Inc.
35 Highland Ave
Bethlehem PA 18017
724 794-3000

(G-9004)
MR TRAILER SALES INC
1565 Steel Hill Rd Nw (44622)
P.O. Box 562 (44622-0562)
PHONE...................................330 339-7701
Sharon Rostad, *President*
Roger Rostad, *Vice Pres*
Don Rostad, *Director*
EMP: 8
SALES (est): 910K **Privately Held**
SIC: 3715 5012 5531 7519 Truck trailers;
trailers or vans for transporting horses;
trailers for passenger vehicles; automo-
tive & home supply stores; trailer rental;
utility trailers

(G-9005)
NATURAL GAS CONSTRUCTION INC
Also Called: Ngc Red Hill
1737 Red Hill Rd Nw (44622-7113)
PHONE...................................330 364-9240
Miles Pillar, *President*
Kathy Pillar, *Treasurer*
EMP: 3
SALES: 1MM **Privately Held**
SIC: 1389 Gas field services

(G-9006)
NEXT SALES LLC
3258 Dogwood Ln Nw (44622-6822)
PHONE...................................330 704-4126
Michael R Ludwig, *Principal*
EMP: 8 EST: 2012
SALES (est): 916.5K **Privately Held**
SIC: 3275 Acoustical plaster, gypsum

(G-9007)
R & J CYLINDER & MACHINE INC
2155 Progress St (44622-9654)
PHONE...................................330 364-8263
Fax: 330 364-8264
Ronald Sandy, *President*
Jeffrey Shepherd, *Vice Pres*
Mark Salisbury, *Engineer*
Pam Adams, *Human Resources*
Bill Kreidler, *Sales Staff*

EMP: 53
SQ FT: 33,500
SALES (est): 9.9MM **Privately Held**
WEB: www.rjcylinder.com
SIC: 3593 3599 Fluid power cylinders, hy-
draulic or pneumatic; machine & other job
shop work

(G-9008)
R & J PRINTING ENTERPRISES INC
Also Called: Newhouse Printing Company
111 N Walnut St (44622-2939)
P.O. Box 280 (44622-0280)
PHONE...................................330 343-1242
Fax: 330 343-8106
John S Carpenter, *President*
Stephanie Carpenter, *Mktg Coord*
Michael Schaller, *Art Dir*
EMP: 15 EST: 1917
SQ FT: 7,500
SALES (est): 1.6MM **Privately Held**
SIC: 2752 Commercial printing, offset

(G-9009)
RANGE RSURCES - APPALACHIA LLC
1748 Saltwell Rd Nw (44622-7471)
PHONE...................................330 866-3301
Woody McDaniels, *Manager*
EMP: 41
SALES (corp-wide): 1.1B **Publicly Held**
WEB: www.gl-energy.com
SIC: 1382 Oil & gas exploration services
HQ: Range Resources - Appalachia, Llc.
3000 Town Center Blvd
Canonsburg PA 15317
724 743-6700

(G-9010)
REAM AND HAAGER LABORATORY
179 W Broadway St (44622-1916)
P.O. Box 706 (44622-0706)
PHONE...................................330 343-3711
Tim Levengood, *President*
EMP: 13
SQ FT: 4,300
SALES: 580K **Privately Held**
SIC: 8748 8734 0711 1389 Business
consulting; water testing laboratory; soil
testing services; pipe testing, oil field
service

(G-9011)
SCHINDLERS BROAD RUN CHESE HSE
6011 Old Route 39 Nw (44622-7788)
PHONE...................................330 343-4108
Fax: 330 343-1092
Chad Schindler, *President*
Nancy Schindler, *Treasurer*
EMP: 10 EST: 1933
SQ FT: 16,600
SALES (est): 1.2MM **Privately Held**
WEB: www.broadruncheese.com
SIC: 2022 5451 5947 Natural cheese;
cheese; gift shop

(G-9012)
SCHOOL HOUSE WINERY LLC
455 Schneiders Crssng Rd (44622-6922)
PHONE...................................330 602-9463
Jennifer Jagunic, *Principal*
EMP: 5 EST: 2009
SALES (est): 186K **Privately Held**
SIC: 8299 2084 Schools & educational
service; wines, brandy & brandy spirits

(G-9013)
SCHWAB INDUSTRIES INC (HQ)
2301 Progress St (44622-9641)
PHONE...................................330 364-4411
Fax: 330 343-2899
Jerry A Schwab, *President*
Jerry Gwinn, *General Mgr*
David A Schwab, *Vice Pres*
Mary Lynn Hites, *Treasurer*
Tracy Herb, *Manager*
EMP: 15 EST: 1950
SQ FT: 2,500

SALES (est): 70.2MM
SALES (corp-wide): 28.6B **Privately Held**
WEB: www.schwabindustries.com
SIC: 3273 5031 5032 Ready-mixed con-
crete; lumber, plywood & millwork; con-
crete & cinder block
PA: Crh Public Limited Company
Stonemason' S Way
Dublin 16
140 410-00

(G-9014)
SHELLY MATERIALS INC
2301 Progress St (44622-9641)
P.O. Box 400 (44622-0400)
PHONE...................................330 364-4411
Dave Moreland, *Branch Mgr*
EMP: 4
SALES (corp-wide): 28.6B **Privately Held**
SIC: 1422 Crushed & broken limestone
HQ: Shelly Materials, Inc.
80 Park Dr
Thornville OH 43076
740 246-6315

(G-9015)
SMITH CONCRETE CO (PA)
Also Called: Division of Selling Materials
2301 Progress St (44622-9641)
P.O. Box 356, Marietta (45750-0356)
PHONE...................................740 373-7441
Fax: 740 373-7446
Mike Murphy, *General Mgr*
Amelia Fouss, *Manager*
EMP: 50 EST: 1922
SQ FT: 2,000
SALES (est): 5.6MM **Privately Held**
WEB: www.smithconcreteco.com
SIC: 3272 3273 1442 Dry mixture con-
crete; ready-mixed concrete; construction
sand & gravel

(G-9016)
SNYDER MANUFACTURING INC
3001 Progress St (44622-9640)
P.O. Box 188 (44622-0188)
PHONE...................................330 343-4456
Fax: 330 343-7396
Dennis Snyder, *President*
Joe Hildebrand, *Purch Agent*
Ken Metzger, *Manager*
Goerge Mokodean, *Admin Sec*
▲ **EMP:** 60
SQ FT: 50,000
SALES (est): 14.1MM **Privately Held**
SIC: 3083 Laminated plastics plate & sheet

(G-9017)
SNYDER MANUFACTURING CO LTD
3001 Progress St (44622-9640)
P.O. Box 188 (44622-0188)
PHONE...................................330 343-4456
Dennis Snyder, *Partner*
George Mokodean, *Controller*
EMP: 3
SQ FT: 50,000
SALES (est): 488K **Privately Held**
WEB: www.snyderman.com
SIC: 7359 6512 3083 3081 Equipment
rental & leasing; commercial & industrial
building operation; laminated plastics
plate & sheet; unsupported plastics film &
sheet; broadwoven fabric mills, manmade

(G-9018)
SPEEDWAY LLC
Also Called: Speedway Superamerica 6243
225 S Wooster Ave (44622-1942)
PHONE...................................330 343-9469
Bobbi Ward, *Branch Mgr*
EMP: 10 **Publicly Held**
WEB: www.speedwaynet.com
SIC: 1311 Crude petroleum production
HQ: Speedway Llc
500 Speedway Dr
Enon OH 45323
937 864-3000

(G-9019)
SUGARCREEK LIME SERVICE
Also Called: M B Trucking
2068 Gordon Rd Nw (44622-7741)
PHONE...................................330 364-4460
Matthew Beachy, *Owner*
EMP: 8 EST: 1979

SALES (est): 715.5K Privately Held
SIC: 3274 Lime

(G-9020)
T V SPECIALTIES INC
Also Called: Dover Tower Company, The
320 W 3rd St (44622-3199)
PHONE................................330 364-6678
Fax: 330 364-7700
Clifford R Border, *CEO*
Jeffrey C Border, *President*
Naomi Border, *Treasurer*
EMP: 10
SQ FT: 67,000
SALES (est): 1.8MM Privately Held
WEB: www.tvspecialties.com
SIC: 5064 3663 5731 5065 Radios; tele-
vision sets; radio & TV communications
equipment; radio, television & electronic
stores; radio parts & accessories; televi-
sion parts & accessories

(G-9021)
TWIN CITIES CONCRETE CO (DH)
141 S Tuscarawas Ave (44622-1951)
PHONE................................330 343-4491
Fax: 330 364-7548
Jerry Schwab, *President*
Jerry Gwinn, *General Mgr*
David Schwab, *Vice Pres*
Bill Trumbull, *Vice Pres*
Mary Lynn Schwab, *Treasurer*
EMP: 17 **EST:** 1949
SQ FT: 1,500
SALES (est): 20.7MM
SALES (corp-wide): 28.6B Privately Held
SIC: 3273 5072 Ready-mixed concrete;
builders' hardware
HQ: Schwab Industries, Inc.
2301 Progress St
Dover OH 44622
330 364-4411

(G-9022)
UNION CAMP CORP
875 Harger St (44622-9441)
PHONE................................330 343-7701
Fax: 330 364-2674
Carl Springer, *Purch Mgr*
Gary Craig, *Director*
▲ **EMP:** 4
SALES (est): 508.8K Privately Held
SIC: 2819 Industrial inorganic chemicals

(G-9023)
VALLEY PRINTING & GRAPHICS
226 W 2nd St (44622-2907)
P.O. Box 400, Sugarcreek (44681-0400)
PHONE................................330 364-5010
Fax: 330 364-1198
Steve Middaugh, *Owner*
Mandy Middaugh, *Comp Spec*
EMP: 9
SQ FT: 5,000
SALES (est): 775.9K Privately Held
SIC: 2752 Commercial printing, litho-
graphic

(G-9024)
WARTHERS MUSIC BOX BELLS
Also Called: Warther Woodworking
115 W Front St (44622-2937)
PHONE................................330 343-4706
Dan Warther, *Owner*
EMP: 3
SALES (est): 125K Privately Held
WEB: www.wartherwoodworking.com
SIC: 5999 2499 Alarm & safety equipment
stores; decorative wood & woodwork

(G-9025)
ZIMME ORTHO SURGI PRODU INC (HQ)
200 W Ohio Ave (44622-9642)
PHONE................................800 321-5533
Fax: 330 343-0995
Kenneth R Coonce, *Vice Pres*
James T Crines, *Vice Pres*
Ian Dawson, *Marketing Mgr*
Joyce Elkins, *Manager*
Ulrich Berger, *Info Tech Dir*
▲ **EMP:** 100
SALES (est): 39.9MM
SALES (corp-wide): 7.6B Publicly Held
SIC: 3842 Orthopedic appliances

PA: Zimmer Biomet Holdings, Inc.
345 E Main St
Warsaw IN 46580
574 267-6131

Doylestown
Wayne County

(G-9026)
AMISH TIMBER FRAMERS
11627 Hametown Rd (44230-9316)
PHONE................................330 658-5699
Fax: 330 658-5690
Jj Orr, *Owner*
EMP: 10
SALES (est): 1.1MM Privately Held
WEB: www.amishtimberframers.com
SIC: 2439 Timbers, structural: laminated
lumber

(G-9027)
BUCKEYE SEALCOATING
40 W Marion St (44230-1239)
P.O. Box 117 (44230-0117)
PHONE................................330 658-3377
William Gallagher, *Owner*
Jeffrey Gallager, *Vice Pres*
Jeffrey Goldstein, *Sls & Mktg Exec*
EMP: 10
SQ FT: 3,600
SALES (est): 580K Privately Held
WEB: www.buckeyesealcoating.com
SIC: 2951 Asphalt paving mixtures &
blocks

(G-9028)
COUNTER CONCEPTS INC
15535 Portage St (44230-1130)
PHONE................................330 848-4848
Fax: 330 745-4371
Shawn Green, *President*
Kathy Kabaski, *Principal*
William Blackbart, *Vice Pres*
EMP: 16
SALES (est): 1.5MM Privately Held
WEB: www.counterconcepts.com
SIC: 2541 3083 Counters or counter dis-
play cases, wood; plastic finished prod-
ucts, laminated

(G-9029)
MID-WEST POLY PAK INC
89 E Marion St (44230-1454)
P.O. Box 35 (44230-0035)
PHONE................................330 658-2921
Fax: 330 658-2939
Dan Large, *President*
Julie Meeks, *Principal*
Sandra S Hubiak, *Vice Pres*
EMP: 25
SQ FT: 26,000
SALES (est): 7.6MM Privately Held
WEB: www.midwestpolypak.com
SIC: 2673 Plastic & pliofilm bags

(G-9030)
STORAGE BUILDINGS UNLIMITED
12321 Hollow Ridge Rd (44230-9765)
PHONE................................216 731-0010
Steve Rosser, *Branch Mgr*
EMP: 5
SALES (corp-wide): 1.2MM Privately Held
SIC: 3448 Prefabricated metal buildings
PA: Storage Buildings Unlimited Inc
278 Main St
Wadsworth OH
330 334-5803

(G-9031)
T J TARGET
235 Bailey Ct (44230-1596)
P.O. Box 171 (44230-0171)
PHONE................................330 658-3057
Janet Siebeneck, *Owner*
EMP: 4
SALES (est): 351.5K Privately Held
SIC: 2621 5941 5091 Specialty papers;
sporting goods & bicycle shops; sporting
& recreation goods

Dresden
Muskingum County

(G-9032)
DRESDEN SPECIALTIES INC (PA)
Also Called: Social Supper
305 Main St (43821)
P.O. Box 110 (43821-0110)
PHONE................................740 754-2451
Fax: 740 754-2456
M Dean Cole, *CEO*
Donna R Cole, *President*
EMP: 4 **EST:** 1956
SALES (est): 558.2K Privately Held
WEB: www.socialsupper.com
SIC: 3231 5947 5699 2752 Decorated
glassware: chipped, engraved, etched,
etc.; gift shop; formal wear; commercial
printing, offset; letterpress printing; auto-
motive & apparel trimmings

(G-9033)
MINING RECLAMATION INC
15953 State Route 60 S (43821-9657)
P.O. Box 555 (43821-0555)
PHONE................................740 327-5555
John Shupert, *President*
EMP: 15 **EST:** 1997
SALES (est): 1MM Privately Held
SIC: 1081 Metal mining services

Dublin
Franklin County

(G-9034)
A GRADE NOTES INC (PA)
6385 Shier Rings Rd Ste 1 (43016-1261)
P.O. Box 4175 (43016-0617)
PHONE................................614 766-9999
Fax: 614 299-4222
Gary Vander Stoep, *CEO*
Kathy Gatton Eshelman, *President*
Rita Wood, *Corp Secy*
David Kiess, *Vice Pres*
Tracy Deal, *Manager*
EMP: 8
SQ FT: 1,000
SALES (est): 1MM Privately Held
WEB: www.gradeanotes.com
SIC: 2752 7334 Commercial printing, litho-
graphic; photocopying & duplicating serv-
ices

(G-9035)
ABHUSHAN LLC
2815 Festival Ln (43017-2363)
PHONE................................614 789-0632
Fax: 614 789-0748
Tina Joshi, *Principal*
▲ **EMP:** 4
SALES (est): 340K Privately Held
SIC: 3423 Jewelers' hand tools

(G-9036)
ADNA INC
6866 Mcdougal Ct (43017-8898)
PHONE................................614 397-4974
Rama P Ramenujam, *President*
EMP: 1
SALES: 1MM Privately Held
SIC: 2819 Chemicals, reagent grade: re-
fined from technical grade

(G-9037)
ADVANCED PRGRM RESOURCES INC (PA)
Also Called: Touchmark
2715 Tuller Pkwy (43017-2310)
PHONE................................614 761-9994
Fax: 614 761-3397
Danial Chacho, *CEO*
Larry Dado, *President*
Douglas Heagren, *Treasurer*
Jennifer Heagren, *Director*
Karen Smith, *Administration*
EMP: 47
SQ FT: 5,100

SALES (est): 4.3MM Privately Held
SIC: 7379 7373 8742 7372 Computer related consulting services; systems integration services; management consulting
services; application computer software;
custom computer programming services

(G-9038)
AFI BRANDS LLC
Also Called: Ripple Swimwear
5575 Hayden Run Blvd (43016-7725)
PHONE................................614 999-6426
Joanne Hopkins, *Mng Member*
EMP: 3
SALES (est): 300K Privately Held
SIC: 2329 2331 Men's & boys' sportswear
& athletic clothing; women's & misses'
blouses & shirts

(G-9039)
ALKON CORPORATION
6750 Crosby Ct (43016-7644)
PHONE................................614 799-6650
Fax: 614 793-0608
Mark Marino, *Branch Mgr*
Chad Eldridge, *Info Tech Mgr*
EMP: 35
SALES (corp-wide): 24.2MM Privately Held
WEB: www.alkoncorp.com
SIC: 3491 3082 5084 5085 Industrial
valves; unsupported plastics profile
shapes; industrial machinery & equip-
ment; industrial supplies
PA: Alkon Corporation
728 Graham Dr
Fremont OH 43420
419 355-9111

(G-9040)
ALPPS LTD
8226 Glencullen Ct (43017-8637)
PHONE................................614 804-3772
Keith Johanns,
Jun Liu,
Galal Walker,
EMP: 3
SALES (est): 116.2K Privately Held
SIC: 7372 Business oriented computer
software

(G-9041)
ALTRASERV LLC
6365 Old Avery Rd Ste 3 (43016-9293)
P.O. Box 355 (43017-0355)
PHONE................................614 889-2500
Dorothy Moran, *President*
EMP: 6
SQ FT: 3,000
SALES (est): 482.4K Privately Held
SIC: 2095 Roasted coffee

(G-9042)
AMERICAN MITSUBA CORPORATION
4140 Tuller Rd Ste 106 (43017-5013)
PHONE................................989 779-4962
Kenichi Hirano, *Branch Mgr*
EMP: 5
SALES (corp-wide): 2.8B Privately Held
SIC: 3621 Motors, electric
HQ: American Mitsuba Corporation
2945 Three Leaves Dr
Mount Pleasant MI 48858
989 779-4962

(G-9043)
AMERICAN MITSUBA CORPORATION
4140 Tuller Rd Ste 106 (43017-5013)
PHONE................................989 779-4962
EMP: 5
SALES (corp-wide): 2.5B Privately Held
SIC: 3621 Mfg Motors/Generators
HQ: American Mitsuba Corporation
2945 Three Leaves Dr
Mount Pleasant MI 48858
989 773-0377

(G-9044)
AMERICAN RODPUMP LTD
5201 Indian Hill Rd (43017-9708)
PHONE................................440 987-9457
John Van Krevel, *President*
EMP: 3

▲ = Import ▼=Export
◆ =Import/Export

SALES (est): 271.7K **Privately Held**
SIC: 1311 Crude petroleum & natural gas

(G-9045)
APPALACHIAN FUELS LLC (PA)
6375 Riverside Dr Ste 200 (43017-5045)
PHONE.................................606 928-0460
Steven Addington, *President*
Maryland Runyan, *Accounts Mgr*
Gwen Myers, *Manager*
EMP: 8
SALES (est): 16.3MM **Privately Held**
SIC: 1241 Coal mining services

(G-9046)
AQ PRODUCTIONS INC
5945 Wilcox Pl Ste B (43016-8713)
PHONE.................................614 486-7700
Fax: 614 486-7730
Ronald Stiebler, *President*
Susan Trego, *Treasurer*
EMP: 3
SQ FT: 1,500
SALES (est): 21.9K **Privately Held**
WEB: www.aqproductions.com
SIC: 3993 Signs & advertising specialties

(G-9047)
ASHLAND LLC
Also Called: Ashland Distribution
5200 Blazer Pkwy (43017-3309)
P.O. Box 2219, Columbus (43216-2219)
PHONE.................................614 790-3333
Fax: 614 790-3173
Leonard R Gelosa, *Senior VP*
Ted Harris, *Vice Pres*
Fred Good, *Vice Pres*
Thomas Henderson, *Opers Mgr*
Micheal Brown, *Engineer*
EMP: 150
SALES (corp-wide): 4.9B **Publicly Held**
WEB: www.ashland.com
SIC: 2899 5169 Chemical preparations;
chemicals & allied products
HQ: Ashland Llc
50 E Rivercenter Blvd # 1600
Covington KY 41011
859 815-3333

(G-9048)
ASHLAND SPECIALTY INGREDIENTS (PA)
Also Called: Ashland Spcalty Ingredients GP
5200 Laser Pkwy (43017)
PHONE.................................302 594-5000
James J O'Brien, *CEO*
EMP: 75 EST: 2015
SALES (est): 34.3MM **Privately Held**
SIC: 2844 Shampoos, rinses, conditioners:
hair

(G-9049)
ASK CHEMICALS LP
495 Metro Pl S Ste 250 (43017-5319)
PHONE.................................614 763-0384
Frank Coenen, *CEO*
Stefan Sommer, *Chairman*
Scott Hoertz, *COO*
Randy Helmick, *Senior VP*
Linda Kilby, *Opers Mgr*
◆ EMP: 150
SQ FT: 3,200
SALES (est): 105.4MM **Privately Held**
SIC: 2899 Chemical preparations
HQ: Ask Chemicals Gmbh
Reisholzstr. 16-18
Hilden 40721
211 711-030

(G-9050)
AUTOMATION AND CTRL TECH INC
Also Called: Act
6141 Avery Rd (43016-8761)
P.O. Box 3667 (43016-0338)
PHONE.................................614 495-1120
Fax: 614 495-1121
Charles Totel, *President*
Dave Pond, *COO*
Michael Iaquinta, *Vice Pres*
Charles Bayles, *QC Dir*
Ron Geiger, *Director*
EMP: 26
SQ FT: 21,000

SALES (est): 6.9MM **Privately Held**
WEB: www.autocontroltech.com
SIC: 3829 3823 Measuring & controlling
devices; industrial instrmnts msrmnt dis-
play/control process variable

(G-9051)
AXIS LED GROUP LLC
6810 Avery Rd (43017-2803)
PHONE.................................614 633-7955
Adam Harmon,
EMP: 1
SALES: 6MM **Privately Held**
SIC: 3229 Bulbs for electric lights

(G-9052)
BAMBECK INC
Also Called: Signs By Tomorrow
4362 Tuller Rd (43017-5029)
PHONE.................................614 766-1000
Fax: 614 766-2700
Mike Bambeck, *President*
EMP: 3
SALES (est): 238.8K **Privately Held**
SIC: 3993 Signs & advertising specialties

(G-9053)
BANDON CORP
8420 Kilbirnie Ct (43017-9732)
PHONE.................................614 766-7243
Ronald A Kramer, *President*
EMP: 7
SALES (est): 711.9K **Privately Held**
SIC: 3714 Motor vehicle parts & acces-
sories

(G-9054)
BIOMETRIC INFORMATION MGT LLC
6059 Frantz Rd Ste 102 (43017-3322)
PHONE.................................614 456-1296
Bill Webb, *CEO*
David W Babner,
EMP: 5
SALES (est): 862.7K **Privately Held**
SIC: 3674 Semiconductors & related de-
vices

(G-9055)
BITES BAKING COMPANY LLC
8090 Summerhouse Dr W (43016-7066)
PHONE.................................614 457-6092
Diane Steiger, *Principal*
EMP: 4
SALES (est): 225.7K **Privately Held**
SIC: 2051 Bread, cake & related products

(G-9056)
CAKE LLC
6724 Perimeter Loop Rd # 254
(43017-3202)
PHONE.................................614 592-7681
Lesley Blake, *Agent*
EMP: 7
SALES (est): 310.3K **Privately Held**
SIC: 7372 Home entertainment computer
software

(G-9057)
CARDINAL HEALTH INC (PA)
7000 Cardinal Pl (43017-1091)
PHONE.................................614 757-5000
Fax: 614 757-6000
David Schlotterbeck, *CEO*
George S Barrett, *Ch of Bd*
Kirk Bantz, *Exec VP*
Stephen T Falk, *Exec VP*
Steve Falk, *Exec VP*
EMP: 2800
SALES: 121.5B **Publicly Held**
WEB: www.cardinal.com
SIC: 5122 5047 8741 3842 Drugs, pro-
prietaries & sundries; pharmaceuticals;
druggists' sundries; blood plasma; surgi-
cal equipment & supplies; hospital equip-
ment & supplies; management services;
surgical appliances & supplies

(G-9058)
CARDINAL HEALTH 414 LLC (HQ)
7000 Cardinal Pl (43017-1091)
PHONE.................................614 757-5000
George S Barrett, *CEO*
Lisa Ashby, *President*

Shelley Bird, *Exec VP*
Mark Blake, *Exec VP*
Nick Augustinos, *Senior VP*
▲ EMP: 155 EST: 1974
SQ FT: 60,967
SALES (est): 242MM
SALES (corp-wide): 121.5B **Publicly Held**
WEB: www.syncor.com
SIC: 2834 2835 Pharmaceutical prepara-
tions; radioactive diagnostic substances
PA: Cardinal Health, Inc.
7000 Cardinal Pl
Dublin OH 43017
614 757-5000

(G-9059)
CARDINAL HEALTH TECH LLC (HQ)
7000 Cardinal Pl (43017-1091)
PHONE.................................614 757-5000
Lisa Ashby, *President*
EMP: 8
SALES (est): 4.3MM
SALES (corp-wide): 121.5B **Publicly Held**
SIC: 3571 Electronic computers
PA: Cardinal Health, Inc.
7000 Cardinal Pl
Dublin OH 43017
614 757-5000

(G-9060)
CENTRAL OHIO ORTHTIC PRSTHETIC
248 Bradenton Ave (43017-7593)
PHONE.................................614 659-1580
Brenda K Fowler, *Principal*
EMP: 3
SALES (est): 205.7K **Privately Held**
SIC: 3842 Orthopedic appliances

(G-9061)
CENTURY BIOTECH PARTNERS INC
7765 Dublin Rd (43017-9192)
PHONE.................................614 746-6998
Jinji Yue, *CFO*
EMP: 3
SALES: 250K **Privately Held**
SIC: 3845 Ultrasonic scanning devices,
medical

(G-9062)
CHAMPA VENTURES LLC
6314 Belvedere Green Blvd (43016-8582)
P.O. Box 425 (43017-0425)
PHONE.................................614 726-1801
Champa Fernando, *Principal*
EMP: 3
SALES (est): 135.4K **Privately Held**
SIC: 2051 Bakery products, partially
cooked (except frozen)

(G-9063)
COLUMBUS MARBLE PRODUCTS INC
6843 Bowles Ct (43017-8575)
PHONE.................................614 766-2786
Fax: 614 258-4405
Tim Fallon, *President*
Charlie Hummel, *Vice Pres*
Steve Patterson, *Manager*
EMP: 14
SQ FT: 30,000
SALES: 1.2MM **Privately Held**
SIC: 3281 Marble, building: cut & shaped;
bathroom fixtures, cut stone

(G-9064)
COMMAND ALKON INCORPORATED
6750 Crosby Ct (43016-7644)
PHONE.................................614 799-0600
Randy Willaman, *Branch Mgr*
EMP: 60
SALES (corp-wide): 101.9MM **Privately Held**
WEB: www.commandalkon.com
SIC: 3823 7371 3625 Industrial process
measurement equipment; custom com-
puter programming services; relays & in-
dustrial controls

PA: Command Alkon Incorporated
1800 Intl Pk Dr Ste 400
Birmingham AL 35243
205 879-3282

(G-9065)
COMPUTER WORKSHOP INC (PA)
5131 Post Rd Ste 102 (43017-1161)
PHONE.................................614 798-9505
Fax: 614 798-9535
Thelma Tippie, *President*
Terri Williams, *COO*
Kim McFarland, *Financial Exec*
Abbey Williams, *Marketing Staff*
Shawn Quigley, *Consultant*
EMP: 20
SALES (est): 2.6MM **Privately Held**
WEB: www.tcworkshop.com
SIC: 8243 7371 2741 Operator training,
computer; custom computer programming
services; miscellaneous publishing

(G-9066)
CRIMSON GATE CONSULTING CO (PA)
3274 Heatherstone Ct (43017-1806)
PHONE.................................614 805-0897
Brent Dyke, *CEO*
Brian Rogers, *Project Mgr*
Haixuan Zhu, *Manager*
Glenn Foote, *Director*
EMP: 4
SQ FT: 300
SALES (est): 901.9K **Privately Held**
SIC: 8742 7372 Business consultant; busi-
ness oriented computer software; educa-
tional computer software; operating
systems computer software

(G-9067)
DAISHIN INDUSTRIAL CO
6490 Shier Rings Rd Ste E (43016-6907)
PHONE.................................614 766-9535
Takeshi Okamaura, *President*
Aaron Schroeder, *Manager*
▲ EMP: 3
SALES (est): 395.8K **Privately Held**
SIC: 3842 Braces, elastic

(G-9068)
DIOCESAN PUBLICATIONS INC OHIO (PA)
6161 Wilcox Rd (43016-1264)
PHONE.................................614 718-9500
Fax: 614 718-2989
Robert Zielke, *President*
Donald Zielke, *Treasurer*
Brian Bastic, *Sales Mgr*
EMP: 35
SALES (est): 7.8MM **Privately Held**
SIC: 2759 2741 Letterpress printing; mis-
cellaneous publishing

(G-9069)
DUBLIN MILLWORK CO INC
7575 Fishel Dr S (43016-8821)
PHONE.................................614 889-7776
Fax: 614 889-8206
Wilbur C Strait, *Ch of Bd*
Scott Evisol, *General Mgr*
Nathan Bishop, *Warehouse Mgr*
Scott Ebersole, *Manager*
Chuck Dearth, *Info Tech Mgr*
EMP: 30 EST: 1981
SQ FT: 100,000
SALES (est): 4.5MM
SALES (corp-wide): 39.1MM **Privately Held**
WEB: www.dublinmillwork.com
SIC: 5031 2431 Trim, sheet metal; doors
& windows; millwork
PA: The Strait & Lamp Lumber Company
Incorporated
269 National Rd Se
Hebron OH 43025
740 928-4501

(G-9070)
DUNCAN DENTAL LAB LLC
6175 Shamrock Ct Ste A (43016-1200)
PHONE.................................614 793-0330
Fax: 614 932-9155
Gary Duncan, *Owner*
Brunhilde J Duncan, *Principal*

EMP: 4
SALES (est): 563.6K **Privately Held**
SIC: 3843 8072 Dental equipment & supplies; dental laboratories

(G-9071)
EBISYN MEDICAL INC
6474 Weston Cir W (43016-7724)
PHONE..........................609 759-1101
Dipanjan Nag, *President*
Jessica Morton, *Vice Pres*
EMP: 6 EST: 2014
SALES (est): 313.5K **Privately Held**
SIC: 3841 Diagnostic apparatus, medical

(G-9072)
ECO CHEM ALTERNATIVE FUELS LLC
565 Metro Pl S Ste 300 (43017-5382)
PHONE..........................614 764-3835
EMP: 5 EST: 2011
SALES (est): 316.6K **Privately Held**
SIC: 2869 Fuels

(G-9073)
EVERRIS NA INC (DH)
4950 Blaver Pkwy (43017)
PHONE..........................800 492-8255
Raymond Simpson, *Principal*
David Lunt, *VP Finance*
Brenda Collins, *Finance Spvr*
EMP: 30
SALES (est): 39.8MM
SALES (corp-wide): 5.6B **Privately Held**
SIC: 2873 Nitrogenous fertilizers

(G-9074)
EVERRIS NA INC (DH)
4950 Blazer Pkwy (43017-3305)
PHONE..........................614 726-7100
Ariana Cohen, *President*
Hadia Lefavre, *Exec VP*
Dana Pearson, *Marketing Mgr*
Martin Shroyer, *Manager*
◆ EMP: 25
SQ FT: 73,000
SALES (est): 40.5MM
SALES (corp-wide): 5.6B **Privately Held**
WEB: www.everris.com
SIC: 1479 Fertilizer mineral mining; fertilizer mineral mining

(G-9075)
EXACT SOFTWARE NORTH AMER LLC (DH)
5455 Rings Rd Ste 100 (43017-7519)
PHONE..........................978 539-6186
Lisa Wise, *General Mgr*
Mariette Hoogenboom, *Finance Mgr*
Mitchell Alcon,
Alex Braverman,
James A Workman,
EMP: 170
SQ FT: 30,000
SALES (est): 63.9MM
SALES (corp-wide): 145.4K **Privately Held**
WEB: www.exactamerica.com
SIC: 7371 7372 5045 2759 Computer software development; prepackaged software; computer software; letterpress printing
HQ: Exact Holding B.V.
Molengraaffsingel 33
Delft 2629
152 613-714

(G-9076)
FEDEX OFFICE & PRINT SVCS INC
6735 Avery Muirfield Dr (43016-7251)
PHONE..........................614 356-1639
Fax: 614 356-1641
Staci Clark, *Branch Mgr*
EMP: 4
SALES (corp-wide): 50.3B **Publicly Held**
SIC: 2752 Commercial printing, lithographic
HQ: Fedex Office And Print Services, Inc.
7900 Legacy Dr
Plano TX 75024
214 550-7000

(G-9077)
FRANKLIN ELECTRIC CO INC
555 Metro Pl N
PHONE..........................614 794-2266
EMP: 563
SALES (corp-wide): 949.8MM **Publicly Held**
SIC: 3621 Motors, electric
PA: Franklin Electric Co., Inc.
9255 Coverdale Rd
Fort Wayne IN 46809
260 824-2900

(G-9078)
GEOFFREY SMITH
Also Called: Fastsigns
2829 Festival Ln (43017-2363)
PHONE..........................614 793-1996
Fax: 614 793-8119
Geoffrey Smith, *Owner*
EMP: 5
SALES (est): 320K **Privately Held**
SIC: 3993 Signs & advertising specialties

(G-9079)
GOLD MINE INC
4951 Gillingham Way (43017-8644)
P.O. Box 385 (43017-0385)
PHONE..........................614 378-8308
Ajay Pahouja, *President*
EMP: 4
SALES (est): 470K **Privately Held**
SIC: 3911 Jewelry, precious metal

(G-9080)
GRANDMAS FRUIT CAKES
Also Called: Sister Sweet Shoppe The
45 N High St (43017-1130)
P.O. Box 1007 (43017-6007)
PHONE..........................614 761-1118
Fax: 614 761-0078
Craig Sonksen, *Owner*
Christopher Wernli, *Vice Pres*
▼ EMP: 8
SQ FT: 1,208
SALES (est): 477.1K **Privately Held**
WEB: www.grandmasfruitcakes.com
SIC: 2051 Bread, cake & related products

(G-9081)
GUILD ASSOCIATES INC (PA)
Also Called: Guild Biosciences
5750 Shier Rings Rd (43016-1234)
PHONE..........................614 798-8215
Fax: 614 798-1972
Dominic Dinovo, *President*
Dolores D Novo, *Treasurer*
Robert L Freeburn II, *Manager*
EMP: 45
SQ FT: 53,000
SALES (est): 15.8MM **Privately Held**
SIC: 8731 3559 Chemical laboratory, except testing; biotechnical research, commercial; chemical machinery & equipment

(G-9082)
GUILD ASSOCIATES INC
Also Called: Guild Biosciences
4412 Tuller Rd (43017-5033)
PHONE..........................843 573-0095
Dominic Dinovo, *President*
Nick Dinovo, *Manager*
EMP: 7
SALES (corp-wide): 15.8MM **Privately Held**
SIC: 8731 3559 Chemical laboratory, except testing; chemical machinery & equipment
PA: Guild Associates, Inc.
5750 Shier Rings Rd
Dublin OH 43016
614 798-8215

(G-9083)
HARTCO PRINTING COMPANY (PA)
Also Called: Hartco Products, The
4106 Delancy Park Dr (43016-7246)
PHONE..........................614 761-1292
Carlton W Hartley, *President*
Frank Woodcox, *General Mgr*
Louann Hartley, *Vice Pres*
EMP: 8 EST: 1955
SQ FT: 9,900

SALES (est): 1MM **Privately Held**
WEB: www.hartcoprinting.com
SIC: 2752 Commercial printing, offset

(G-9084)
HIDAKA USA INC
5761 Shier Rings Rd (43016-1233)
PHONE..........................614 889-8611
Fax: 614 889-6551
Yoshihiro Hidaka, *President*
Kazumi Fukasawa, *Manager*
Diane Rosso, *Manager*
Mikihiro Hidaka, *Admin Sec*
▲ EMP: 40
SQ FT: 90,000
SALES (est): 14.8MM **Privately Held**
WEB: www.hidakausainc.com
SIC: 3444 3469 Sheet metalwork; machine parts, stamped or pressed metal

(G-9085)
HOMESTAT FARM LTD (PA)
6065 Frantz Rd Ste 206 (43017-3372)
PHONE..........................614 718-3060
Bill Stadtlander, *Maintenance Dir*
John Hulsizer, *Plant Mgr*
Lance Archibald, *Mng Member*
Mendy Crofford, *Manager*
EMP: 3
SQ FT: 1,152
SALES (est): 9MM **Privately Held**
WEB: www.homestatfarm.com
SIC: 5141 2099 Food brokers; food preparations

(G-9086)
HUSKY ENERGY
Also Called: Husky Marketing and Supply Co
5550 Blazer Pkwy Ste 200 (43017-3478)
PHONE..........................614 766-5633
Jerry Miller, *Manager*
Claudio Ingaramo, *Manager*
Greg Lake, *CIO*
EMP: 14
SALES (corp-wide): 9.5B **Privately Held**
SIC: 2911 Petroleum refining
PA: Husky Energy Inc
707 8 Ave Sw
Calgary AB T2P 1
403 298-6111

(G-9087)
HUSKY MARKETING AND SUPPLY CO
Also Called: Husky Energy
5550 Blazer Pkwy Ste 200 (43017-3478)
PHONE..........................614 210-2300
Scott Howard, *General Mgr*
Sherry Glover, *Manager*
EMP: 40
SALES (est): 143.9K
SALES (corp-wide): 9.5B **Privately Held**
SIC: 1321 1382 Natural gasoline production; oil & gas exploration services
HQ: Husky Oil Operations Limited
707 8 Ave Sw
Calgary AB T2P 1
403 298-6111

(G-9088)
IMPRESSIONS TO GO LLC
6121 Pirthshire St (43016-6705)
PHONE..........................614 760-0600
Fax: 614 760-9239
Michael Kenny, *Mng Member*
Debra Kenny, *Manager*
Richard L Bibart,
EMP: 3
SQ FT: 1,800
SALES (est): 200K **Privately Held**
WEB: www.impressionstogo.com
SIC: 3993 Signs & advertising specialties

(G-9089)
INJOY FOODS LLC
4860 Calloway Ct (43017-8605)
PHONE..........................614 798-2033
Kathleen Pierce, *Principal*
EMP: 3
SALES (est): 169.9K **Privately Held**
SIC: 2099 Food preparations

(G-9090)
INTERSTATE GAS SUPPLY INC (PA)
6100 Emerald Pkwy (43016-3248)
PHONE..........................614 659-5000
Fax: 614 659-5993
Scott White, *President*
Jim Baich, *COO*
Doug Austin, *Exec VP*
Mike Gatt, *Vice Pres*
Jason Moore, *Vice Pres*
EMP: 93
SQ FT: 100,000
SALES (est): 1.4B **Privately Held**
WEB: www.igsenergy.com
SIC: 1311 Natural gas production

(G-9091)
JASSTEK INC
555 Metro Pl N Ste 100 (43017-1389)
PHONE..........................614 808-3600
Sulakshana Singh, *President*
Ravi Paruchuri, *COO*
Praveen Tummala, *CFO*
Ankit Tarik, *Human Res Mgr*
EMP: 11
SQ FT: 1,200
SALES (est): 829.4K **Privately Held**
SIC: 7371 7372 7379 8748 Custom computer programming services; computer software development & applications; business oriented computer software; ; systems engineering consultant, ex. computer or professional

(G-9092)
JOHN STIEG & ASSOCIATES
8621 Kirkhill Ct (43017-9610)
PHONE..........................614 889-7954
John Stieg, *Owner*
EMP: 4
SALES (est): 395.3K **Privately Held**
WEB: www.buckeyesales.com
SIC: 3429 Manufactured hardware (general)

(G-9093)
KAD HOLDINGS INC
Also Called: Minuteman Press
5887 Karric Square Dr (43016-4243)
PHONE..........................614 792-3399
Fax: 614 792-5303
Kenneth A Davis, *President*
Ken Davis, *Principal*
EMP: 3
SALES (est): 493.3K **Privately Held**
SIC: 2752 2791 2789 Commercial printing, lithographic; typesetting; bookbinding & related work

(G-9094)
KASAI NORTH AMERICA INC
655 Metro Pl S Ste 560 (43017-3382)
PHONE..........................614 356-1494
Yoichi Yamaguchi, *Branch Mgr*
EMP: 14
SALES (corp-wide): 2B **Privately Held**
SIC: 3089 3714 3429 Injection molded finished plastic products; motor vehicle parts & accessories; manufactured hardware (general)
HQ: Kasai North America, Inc.
1020 Volunteer Pkwy
Manchester TN 37355
931 728-4122

(G-9095)
KEHLER ENTERPRISES INC
323 W Bridge St (43017-2124)
PHONE..........................614 889-8488
Eric N Kehler, *President*
Darian Kehler, *Admin Sec*
Diane Kehler, *Admin Sec*
EMP: 3
SALES: 340K **Privately Held**
SIC: 3955 5734 Print cartridges for laser & other computer printers; printers & plotters: computers

(G-9096)
KENTROX INC (HQ)
5800 Innovation Dr (43016-3271)
PHONE..........................614 798-2000
Richard S Cremona, *CEO*
Charlie Vogt, *Ch of Bd*
Jeffrey S Estuesta, *President*

Eric Langille, *President*
William Pollack, *COO*
▲ EMP: 100
SALES (est): 7.3MM **Publicly Held**
SIC: 3661 Telephone central office equipment, dial or manual

(G-9097)
KREMA PRODUCTS INC (PA)
Also Called: Krema Peanut Butter
45 N High St (43017-1130)
P.O. Box 715 (43017-0815)
PHONE..................................614 889-4824
Craig Sonksen, *CEO*
Brent Morgan, *COO*
Leah McChesney, *Director*
EMP: 3
SQ FT: 600
SALES (est): 6.5MM **Privately Held**
WEB: www.kremaproducts.com
SIC: 2099 5159 5441 5961 Peanut butter; nuts & nut by-products; nuts; gift items, mail order

(G-9098)
L C SYSTEMS INC
6135 Memorial Dr Ste 106f (43017-9005)
P.O. Box 437249, Louisville KY (40253-7249)
PHONE..................................614 235-9430
Steve Brown, *President*
Deborah Brown, *Corp Secy*
EMP: 4
SALES (est): 680.1K **Privately Held**
WEB: www.lc-systems.com
SIC: 3444 Ventilators, sheet metal

(G-9099)
LEPPERT COMPANIES INC
8779 Tartan Fields Dr (43017-8771)
PHONE..................................614 889-2818
Matthew Leppert, *Principal*
EMP: 3
SALES (est): 170K **Privately Held**
SIC: 2421 Furniture dimension stock, softwood

(G-9100)
LSP TECHNOLOGIES INC
6145 Scherers Pl (43016-1284)
PHONE..................................614 718-3000
Fax: 614 718-3007
Jeff L Dulaney, *President*
David Lahrman, *Vice Pres*
Mark O'Loughlin, *Vice Pres*
Mark Oloughlin, *Draft/Design*
Sherry Diamond, *Accountant*
EMP: 22
SQ FT: 18,000
SALES (est): 5.6MM **Privately Held**
WEB: www.lspt.com
SIC: 3724 Aircraft engines & engine parts

(G-9101)
MANCHIK ENGINEERING & CO
7070 Avery Rd (43017-2808)
PHONE..................................740 927-4454
Joseph D Manchik, *Owner*
EMP: 5
SALES (est): 200K **Privately Held**
SIC: 7389 3663 Design services; radio broadcasting & communications equipment

(G-9102)
MERCURIO BIOTEC LLC
4150 Tuller Rd Ste 23 (43017-5014)
PHONE..................................214 507-8031
Carlton Anderson, *CEO*
Luis Alcalde, *General Counsel*
Samuel Riega,
Milton Sanchez-Parodi,
Marvin Slepian,
EMP: 10 EST: 2015
SALES (est): 409.5K **Privately Held**
SIC: 2834 Pharmaceutical preparations

(G-9103)
MIRUS ADAPTED TECH LLC
288 Cramer Creek Ct (43017-2584)
PHONE..................................614 402-4585
Stephan Mertik, *Mng Member*
EMP: 20
SALES (est): 1.4MM **Privately Held**
SIC: 1731 7372 Electrical work; home entertainment computer software

(G-9104)
MODULAR ASSEMBLY INNOVATIONS (PA)
600 Stonehenge Pkwy # 100 (43017-6027)
PHONE..................................614 389-4860
Billy R Vickers, *President*
EMP: 14
SALES (est): 61.4MM **Privately Held**
SIC: 3559 Automotive related machinery

(G-9105)
MONITOR MAPBOARD SYSTEMS LLC
565 Metro Pl S Ste 300 (43017-5382)
P.O. Box 2029 (43017-7029)
PHONE..................................614 761-9985
Vincent Blaeser, *President*
Gene Hosler, *Principal*
EMP: 4 EST: 2002
SQ FT: 50
SALES (est): 259.1K **Privately Held**
SIC: 3823 Panelboard indicators, recorders & controllers: receiver

(G-9106)
MONITORED THERAPEUTICS INC
5940 Venture Dr Ste C (43017-2248)
P.O. Box 322 (43017-0322)
PHONE..................................614 761-3555
William Zimlich, *CEO*
William Ross, *Ch of Bd*
Michael Taylor, *Vice Pres*
Steve Han, *CTO*
EMP: 6
SALES (est): 487.8K **Privately Held**
SIC: 3845 7372 7389 Electromedical equipment; business oriented computer software;

(G-9107)
MUIRFIELD WINE COMPANY LLC
Also Called: Tutto Vino
7154 Muirfield Dr (43017-3801)
PHONE..................................614 799-9222
Raj Hora, *Managing Prtnr*
EMP: 8
SALES (est): 690K **Privately Held**
SIC: 2084 Wine cellars, bonded: engaged in blending wines

(G-9108)
N8 MEDICAL INC
6000 Memorial Dr (43017-9767)
PHONE..................................614 537-7246
David Richards, *CEO*
Kenneth B Leachman, *Principal*
Bruce Halpryn, *COO*
EMP: 4
SALES (est): 1MM **Privately Held**
SIC: 2834 Pharmaceutical preparations

(G-9109)
NATIONAL GLASS SERVICE GROUP
5500 Frantz Rd Ste 100 (43017-3545)
PHONE..................................614 652-3699
Patric Fransko, *Principal*
EMP: 10
SALES (est): 750K **Privately Held**
SIC: 2671 Packaging paper & plastics film, coated & laminated

(G-9110)
NAVIDEA BIOPHARMACEUTICALS INC
5600 Blazer Pkwy Ste 200 (43017-7550)
PHONE..................................614 793-7500
Fax: 614 793-7520
Michael M Goldberg, *President*
Jed A Latkin, *COO*
Frederick O Cope, *Senior VP*
Thomas J Klima, *Senior VP*
William J Regan, *Senior VP*
EMP: 57
SQ FT: 25,000
SALES: 21.9MM **Privately Held**
WEB: www.neoprobe.com
SIC: 2835 In vitro & in vivo diagnostic substances

(G-9111)
NEIL BARTON
Also Called: Vendfriend
8215 Dublin Rd (43017-9712)
PHONE..................................614 889-9933
Neil Barton, *Owner*
Susan Barton, *Partner*
EMP: 8
SALES (est): 729.4K **Privately Held**
SIC: 3589 Water treatment equipment, industrial

(G-9112)
NEW BAKERY OF ZANESVILLE LLC
1 Dave Thomas Blvd (43017-5452)
P.O. Box 256 (43017-0256)
PHONE..................................614 764-3100
EMP: 345 EST: 2015
SALES (est): 9.6MM
SALES (corp-wide): 1.4B **Privately Held**
SIC: 2051 Bread, cake & related products
HQ: East Balt Ohio, Llc
3005 E Pointe Dr
Zanesville OH 43701
740 454-6876

(G-9113)
NEXEO SOLUTIONS LLC
5200 Blazer Pkwy (43017-3309)
PHONE..................................800 531-7106
Tom Konop, *District Mgr*
Pat Martinezwong, *Facilities Mgr*
George White, *Facilities Mgr*
Janet Gibson, *Senior Buyer*
Jim Mason, *Senior Buyer*
EMP: 17
SALES (corp-wide): 1B **Publicly Held**
SIC: 5169 5162 2821 Industrial chemicals; plastics materials & basic shapes; plastics materials & resins
HQ: Nexeo Solutions, Llc
3 Waterway Square Pl # 1000
The Woodlands TX 77380

(G-9114)
NEXERGY INC (HQ)
Also Called: Iccnexergy
5115 Prkcnter Ave Ste 275 (43017)
PHONE..................................614 351-2191
Phil Glandon, *CEO*
Geo McConnaughey, *Principal*
Earl Sala, *Principal*
Jr Robert Whitesell, *Principal*
Joe Dougherty, *COO*
▲ EMP: 155
SQ FT: 46,000
SALES (est): 33.2MM **Privately Held**
WEB: www.nexergy.com
SIC: 3679 Harness assemblies for electronic use: wire or cable

(G-9115)
OHIO LOGOS INC
Also Called: Ohio Tods
4384 Tuller Rd (43017-5031)
PHONE..................................614 717-0833
Fax: 614 717-0836
Evert Stewart, *President*
Roger Rose, *Manager*
EMP: 9
SALES (est): 999.1K
SALES (corp-wide): 1.5B **Publicly Held**
WEB: www.interstatelogos.com
SIC: 3993 Signs & advertising specialties
HQ: Interstate Logos, L.L.C.
16560 Old Perkins Rd W
Baton Rouge LA 70810

(G-9116)
PAPER OCCASIONS
55 S High St Ste A (43017-2118)
PHONE..................................614 761-8880
Kim Price, *Principal*
EMP: 3
SALES (est): 241.4K **Privately Held**
SIC: 2759 5943 Invitation & stationery printing & engraving; stationery stores

(G-9117)
PARALLEL TECHNOLOGIES INC
4868 Blazer Pkwy (43017-3302)
PHONE..................................614 798-9700
Fax: 614 798-1701
Joseph Redman, *President*
Martin B Jacobs, *Senior VP*

Sarah Redman, *Personnel Exec*
Todd Poling, *Manager*
EMP: 80
SQ FT: 8,500
SALES (est): 15.2MM **Privately Held**
WEB: www.paralleltech.com
SIC: 1623 7372 Telephone & communication line construction; business oriented computer software
PA: R C I Communications Inc
4868 Blazer Pkwy
Dublin OH 43017
614 798-9700

(G-9118)
PAYCARD USA INC
5854 Whitebark Pine Trl (43016-7456)
PHONE..................................702 216-6801
Jim Hammer, *President*
EMP: 12
SALES (est): 1.2MM **Privately Held**
SIC: 2675 Cards: die-cut & unprinted: made from purchased materials

(G-9119)
PEARL TECH CORPORATION (PA)
545 Metro Pl S Ste 100 (43017-5353)
PHONE..................................614 284-8357
Sirisha Nagireddi, *President*
Ben Nagireddi, *Vice Pres*
EMP: 4 EST: 2011
SQ FT: 2,000
SALES (est): 682.7K **Privately Held**
SIC: 7371 7372 Computer software development & applications; business oriented computer software

(G-9120)
PEEBLES CREATIVE GROUP INC
4260 Tuller Rd Ste 200 (43017-5026)
PHONE..................................614 487-2011
Doug Peebles, *Principal*
EMP: 9
SQ FT: 3,500
SALES (est): 802.8K **Privately Held**
WEB: www.peeblescreativegroup.com
SIC: 2741 2759 Miscellaneous publishing; commercial printing

(G-9121)
PEERLESS-WINSMITH INC
Peerless Winsmith
5200 Upper Metro Pl # 110 (43017-5378)
PHONE..................................330 399-3651
Fax: 330 393-6041
Don Fox, *Safety Mgr*
Jim Hynes, *Controller*
Paul Petrich, *Manager*
Vince Rossi, *Manager*
Linda Truran, *Info Tech Mgr*
EMP: 328
SALES (corp-wide): 230.1MM **Privately Held**
WEB: www.peerlesswinsmith.com
SIC: 3621 Motors & generators
HQ: Peerless-Winsmith, Inc.
5200 Upper Metro Pl # 110
Dublin OH 43017
614 526-7000

(G-9122)
PEERLESS-WINSMITH INC (HQ)
Also Called: Ohio Electric Motors
5200 Upper Metro Pl # 110 (43017-5378)
PHONE..................................614 526-7000
R L Greely, *Ch of Bd*
Joe Humenick, *General Mgr*
Mike Feschak, *CFO*
R0bert A Sirak, *Treasurer*
M T Clancey, *Admin Sec*
▲ EMP: 3
SALES (est): 152.4MM
SALES (corp-wide): 230.1MM **Privately Held**
WEB: www.peerlesswinsmith.com
SIC: 3621 3566 3634 3812 Motors & generators; speed changers (power transmission equipment), except auto; electric household cooking utensils; magnetic field detection apparatus; separation equipment, magnetic

PA: Hbd Industries Inc
5200 Upper Metro Pl # 110
Dublin OH 43017
614 526-7000

(G-9123)
PENTAGON PROTECTION USA LLC
5500 Frantz Rd Ste 100 (43017-3545)
PHONE................................614 734-7240
Sam Elzein, *President*
EMP: 10
SQ FT: 2,000
SALES (est): 2MM **Privately Held**
SIC: 1793 3699 Glass & glazing work; security control equipment & systems

(G-9124)
PFIZER INC
8192 Bibury Ln (43016-7440)
PHONE................................614 496-0990
Todd Keiner, *Principal*
EMP: 225
SALES (corp-wide): 52.8B **Publicly Held**
SIC: 2834 Pharmaceutical preparations
PA: Pfizer Inc.
235 E 42nd St
New York NY 10017
212 733-2323

(G-9125)
PIADA SAWMILL LLC
6495 Sawmill Rd Unit Ts (43017-9007)
PHONE................................614 389-2069
EMP: 9 **EST:** 2011
SALES (est): 946.2K **Privately Held**
SIC: 2421 Sawmills & planing mills, general

(G-9126)
PRO ONCALL TECHNOLOGIES LLC
Also Called: Digital & Analog Design
4374 Tuller Rd Ste B (43017-5030)
PHONE................................614 761-1400
David Myers, *Sales/Mktg Mgr*
EMP: 15
SALES (corp-wide): 25.6MM **Privately Held**
SIC: 5065 3661 Telephone equipment; communication equipment; telephone & telegraph apparatus
PA: Pro Oncall Technologies, Llc
12125 Ellington Ct
Cincinnati OH 45249
513 489-7660

(G-9127)
PROFESSIONAL PLASTICS CORP
4863 Rays Cir (43016-6069)
PHONE................................614 336-2498
Mark Casey, *VP Sales*
EMP: 3
SALES (est): 231.2K **Privately Held**
SIC: 3089 Plastics products

(G-9128)
PROFORMA PRINT & IMAGING
655 Metro Pl S Ste 600 (43017-3394)
PHONE................................216 520-8400
Jim Pfaff, *Owner*
EMP: 7
SALES (est): 261.7K **Privately Held**
SIC: 2752 Commercial printing, lithographic

(G-9129)
QUESTLINE INC
5500 Frantz Rd Ste 156 (43017-3548)
PHONE................................614 255-3166
David Reim, *CEO*
Robert L Hines, *COO*
EMP: 36
SQ FT: 8,000
SALES (est): 4.7MM **Privately Held**
SIC: 2741 Business service newsletters: publishing & printing

(G-9130)
REICHARD SOFTWARE CORP
Also Called: Reichard Controls
655 Metro Pl S Ste 600 (43017-3394)
PHONE................................614 537-8598
Steven Reichard, *President*

EMP: 3
SQ FT: 1,200
SALES (est): 310K **Privately Held**
WEB: www.reichard.com
SIC: 7372 7371 Prepackaged software; custom computer programming services

(G-9131)
RESIDENTS OF SAWMILL PARK
2765 Sawmill Park Dr (43017-1872)
PHONE................................614 659-6678
Fax: 614 659-6679
Jennifer Offner, *Principal*
EMP: 9
SALES (est): 891.8K **Privately Held**
SIC: 2421 Sawmills & planing mills, general

(G-9132)
RESIDUE NATIONAL LLC
3100 Wakeshire Dr (43017-1741)
PHONE................................614 309-8963
Rena Tesler, *Principal*
EMP: 3
SALES (est): 162.6K **Privately Held**
SIC: 2911 Residues

(G-9133)
RIKENKAKI AMERICA CORPORATION
5985 Wilcox Pl Ste D (43016-6798)
PHONE................................614 336-2744
Tetsuo Watanabe, *President*
Akiko Rogas, *Accountant*
▲ **EMP:** 3
SALES (est): 396.5K **Privately Held**
SIC: 3711 5012 Motor vehicles & car bodies; automobile auction

(G-9134)
ROBERT W JOHNSON INC (PA)
Also Called: Diamond Cellar, The
6280 Sawmill Rd (43017-1470)
PHONE................................614 336-4545
Fax: 614 336-4555
R Andrew Johnson, *CEO*
Ron Croft, *Vice Pres*
Barb Tomcik, *Vice Pres*
Laura Schmidbauer, *Buyer*
Amanda Peace, *Finance Asst*
EMP: 70 **EST:** 1946
SQ FT: 23,000
SALES (est): 11.9MM **Privately Held**
SIC: 5944 3911 Jewelry, precious stones & precious metals; jewelry, precious metal

(G-9135)
RUSCILLI REAL ESTATE SERVICES
5100 Prkcnter Ave Ste 100 (43017)
PHONE................................614 923-6400
Fax: 614 923-3301
Timothy Kelton, *President*
Timothy D Kelton, *President*
David C Wade, *Treasurer*
EMP: 10 **EST:** 1978
SQ FT: 1,000
SALES (est): 1.3MM **Privately Held**
WEB: www.ruscillire.com
SIC: 6531 1389 Real estate brokers & agents; real estate agent, commercial; roustabout service

(G-9136)
SAGINOMIYA AMERICA INC
655 Metro Pl S Ste 700 (43017-3661)
PHONE................................614 766-7390
Shane Smith, *Engineer*
Gretchen Durthaler, *Shareholder*
◆ **EMP:** 12
SALES (est): 2.3MM **Privately Held**
SIC: 3829 Testing equipment: abrasion, shearing strength, etc.

(G-9137)
SAINT-GOBAIN PRFMCE PLAS CORP
Also Called: Medex
6250 Shier Rings Rd (43016-1270)
PHONE................................614 889-2220
Fax: 614 889-2651
Dale Gallogly, *Engineer*
Ralph Dickman, *Branch Mgr*
Mark Anthony, *Info Tech Mgr*
J Thompson, *Info Tech Mgr*

Gerald Cannon, *IT/INT Sup*
EMP: 300
SALES (corp-wide): 185.8MM **Privately Held**
SIC: 3061 Mechanical rubber goods
HQ: Saint-Gobain Performance Plastics Corporation
31500 Solon Rd
Solon OH 44139
440 836-6900

(G-9138)
SALIENT SYSTEMS INC
4393 Tuller Rd Ste K (43017-5106)
PHONE................................614 792-5800
Fax: 614 792-5888
Robert Bower, *President*
Grant Midgley, *Opers Mgr*
Walt Spicker, *Senior Engr*
Michael Handler, *Manager*
S Harrison, *Manager*
EMP: 24
SQ FT: 16,000
SALES (est): 4.6MM
SALES (corp-wide): 483.5MM **Publicly Held**
WEB: www.salientsystems.com
SIC: 3674 8742 Microprocessors; business consultant
HQ: L. B. Foster Rail Technologies, Inc.
415 Holiday Dr Ste 1
Pittsburgh PA 15220
412 928-3400

(G-9139)
SAWMILL STATION
3062 Sawdust Ln (43017-1695)
PHONE................................614 434-6147
EMP: 3
SALES (est): 180.4K **Privately Held**
SIC: 2421 Sawmills & planing mills, general

(G-9140)
SCHUSTER BEVERAGE MARKETING
3231 Cranston Dr (43017-1920)
PHONE................................614 764-1420
Fax: 614 764-1016
Douglas Schuster, *President*
EMP: 5
SALES (est): 472.7K **Privately Held**
SIC: 2721 2082 Periodicals: publishing only; malt beverages

(G-9141)
SCORPION CASE MFG LLC
329 Clover Ln (43017-1301)
PHONE................................614 274-7246
Eric Epstine, *Manager*
Michael Pierce,
EMP: 10
SQ FT: 5,000
SALES: 500K **Privately Held**
WEB: www.scorpioncase.com
SIC: 2441 Shipping cases, wood:.nailed or lock corner

(G-9142)
SENSETRONICS LLC
8407 Gleneagles Ct (43017-9728)
PHONE................................614 292-2833
Lloyd Brandon, *Principal*
Stephen Lee,
EMP: 3
SALES (est): 152.5K **Privately Held**
SIC: 3845 8731 Electromedical equipment; biotechnical research, commercial

(G-9143)
SERTEK LLC
6399 Shier Rings Rd (43016-3213)
PHONE................................614 504-5828
Vicky Flanery, *Office Mgr*
Dave Crites, *Manager*
Tim Schiff,
EMP: 100
SALES (est): 34.5MM **Privately Held**
SIC: 3312 Blast furnaces & steel mills

(G-9144)
SMITHS MEDICAL ASD INC
5200 Upper Metro Pl # 200 (43017-5379)
P.O. Box 8106 (43016-2106)
PHONE................................800 796-8701
Guy Smith, *VP Engrg*

Dave Donars, *Engineer*
Ann Heser, *Controller*
Rob Sweitzer, *Sales Staff*
Eller Erock, *Manager*
EMP: 23
SALES (corp-wide): 4.1B **Privately Held**
WEB: www.smith-medical.com
SIC: 3842 Surgical appliances & supplies
HQ: Smiths Medical Asd, Inc.
6000 Nathan Ln N Ste 100
Plymouth MN 55442
763 383-3000

(G-9145)
SMITHS MEDICAL ASD INC
6250 Shier Rings Rd (43016-1270)
PHONE................................614 889-2220
Tod Wiget, *Engineer*
Terry Wcislo, *Accountant*
Heather Wise, *Manager*
Pat Toll, *Maintence Staff*
EMP: 242
SALES (corp-wide): 4.1B **Privately Held**
SIC: 3841 IV transfusion apparatus
HQ: Smiths Medical Asd, Inc.
6000 Nathan Ln N Ste 100
Plymouth MN 55442
763 383-3000

(G-9146)
SMITHS MEDICAL NORTH AMERICA
5200 Upper Metro Pl (43017-5377)
PHONE................................614 210-7300
Srini Seshadri, *President*
Rob White, *Vice Pres*
EMP: 8 **EST:** 2010
SALES (est): 1MM **Privately Held**
SIC: 3841 5047 Surgical & medical instruments; medical & hospital equipment

(G-9147)
SMITHS MEDICAL PM INC (PA)
Also Called: BCI International
5200 Upper Metro Pl # 200 (43017-5379)
PHONE................................614 210-7300
Jeff McCaulley, *President*
Anna Kardon, *Business Mgr*
Don Alexander, *Vice Pres*
Jeff Baker, *Vice Pres*
Mark Sanderson, *Vice Pres*
◆ **EMP:** 10 **EST:** 1976
SQ FT: 55,600
SALES (est): 42.7MM **Privately Held**
SIC: 3841 5047 Diagnostic apparatus, medical; electro-medical equipment

(G-9148)
SOCCER FIRST INC (PA)
6490 Dublin Park Dr (43016-8490)
PHONE................................614 889-1115
Fax: 614 791-3006
Allen S Shepherd III, *President*
EMP: 7
SALES (est): 673.9K **Privately Held**
WEB: www.soccerfirst.net
SIC: 3949 Soccer equipment & supplies

(G-9149)
STANLEY STEEMER INTL INC (PA)
Also Called: Stanley Steemer Carpet Cleaner
5800 Innovation Dr (43016-3271)
P.O. Box 8004 (43016-2004)
PHONE................................614 764-2007
Fax: 614 764-1506
Wesley C Bates, *CEO*
Jack A Bates, *President*
Justin Bates, *President*
Bill Bradley, *General Mgr*
Ron Cochran, *General Mgr*
▲ **EMP:** 250
SQ FT: 55,000
SALES: 234.1MM **Privately Held**
WEB: www.stanley-steemer.com
SIC: 7217 3635 6794 5713 Carpet & furniture cleaning on location; upholstery cleaning on customer premises; household vacuum cleaners; franchises, selling or licensing; carpets

(G-9150)
SUTPHEN CORPORATION (PA)
6450 Eiterman Rd (43016-8711)
P.O. Box 158, Amlin (43002-0158)
PHONE................................800 726-7030

2017 Harris Ohio
Industrial Directory

▲ = Import ▼=Export
◆ =Import/Export

Fax: 614 889-0874
Drew Sutphen, *President*
Thomas C Sutphen, *Chairman*
Julie S Phelps, *Vice Pres*
Greg Mallon, *CFO*
Jill Dorne, *Controller*
◆ **EMP:** 180
SQ FT: 90,000
SALES (est): 49.5MM **Privately Held**
WEB: www.sutpheneast.com
SIC: 3711 5087 Fire department vehicles (motor vehicles), assembly of; firefighting equipment

(G-9151)
SYMANTEC CORPORATION
545 Metro Pl S Ste 100 (43017-5353)
PHONE......................................614 793-3060
Eric Hentshel, *Branch Mgr*
EMP: 5
SALES (corp-wide): 3.6B **Publicly Held**
WEB: www.symantec.com
SIC: 7372 Business oriented computer software
PA: Symantec Corporation
350 Ellis St
Mountain View CA 94043
650 527-8000

(G-9152)
SYNSEI MEDICAL
6474 Weston Cir W (43016-7724)
PHONE......................................609 759-1101
Dipanjan Nag, *Partner*
EMP: 3
SALES (est): 152.2K **Privately Held**
SIC: 3845 Electrocardiographs

(G-9153)
TAUPE HOLDINGS CO
7758 Deercrest Ct (43016-9280)
PHONE......................................614 330-4600
Emmanuel Bate, *CEO*
Ajuseh Fortaboh, *President*
EMP: 3
SQ FT: 1,600
SALES (est): 94K **Privately Held**
SIC: 7349 7382 3991 4731 Building & office cleaning services; protective devices, security; street sweeping brooms, hand or machine; freight transportation arrangement

(G-9154)
TECHNICAL SALES & SOLUTION
4361 Wyandotte Woods Blvd (43016-8661)
PHONE......................................614 793-9612
Bob Kollins, *Principal*
EMP: 4
SALES (est): 310K **Privately Held**
SIC: 3699 Electrical welding equipment

(G-9155)
TOTAL SUPPLY SOLUTIONS LLC
4177 Wyandotte Woods Blvd (43016-9611)
P.O. Box 4136 (43016-0598)
PHONE......................................614 989-6665
Tony Majeed, *Managing Prtnr*
Chris Harpster, *Partner*
EMP: 3
SALES (est): 337.5K **Privately Held**
SIC: 3663 5731 ; consumer electronic equipment

(G-9156)
TRU COMFORT MATTRESS
8994 Mediterra Pl (43016-6098)
PHONE......................................614 595-8600
Samuel Wang, *Administration*
EMP: 5
SALES (est): 533.3K **Privately Held**
SIC: 2515 Mattresses & foundations

(G-9157)
TURNER LIGHTNING PROTECTION CO
5193 Dry Creek Dr (43016-9727)
PHONE......................................614 738-6225
Bob Turner, *President*
Mike Adams, *Vice Pres*
EMP: 5
SALES (est): 600K **Privately Held**
WEB: www.lightningpro.com
SIC: 3643 Current-carrying wiring devices

(G-9158)
UNITED TRADE PRINTERS LLC
94 N High St Ste 290 (43017)
PHONE......................................614 326-4829
Greg Hensel, *President*
▼ **EMP:** 20
SQ FT: 6,000
SALES (est): 5MM **Privately Held**
SIC: 2752 Commercial printing, lithographic

(G-9159)
UNMANNED SCIENCE INC
565 Metro Pl S Ste 300 (43017-5382)
PHONE......................................614 581-9893
Benjamin Hofecker, *CEO*
Terry Hofecker, *Chief Engr*
EMP: 5
SALES (est): 203.2K **Privately Held**
SIC: 3812 Defense systems & equipment

(G-9160)
USV OPTICAL INC
Also Called: J C Penney Optical
5083 Tuttle Crossing Blvd (43016-1533)
PHONE......................................614 717-0238
Sharon Mc Guire, *Manager*
EMP: 6
SALES (corp-wide): 345.8MM **Privately Held**
WEB: www.ntouchcomm.net
SIC: 3851 Ophthalmic goods
HQ: Usv Optical, Inc.
1 Harmon Dr Glen Oaks Par
Glendora NJ 08029

(G-9161)
VARO ENERGY SERVICES LLC
2751 Tuller Pkwy (43017-2317)
PHONE......................................914 437-6906
Tina Scanlon, *Manager*
Jeffrey A Himmel,
Tomothy P Burnham,
EMP: 3
SALES (est): 119.9K **Privately Held**
SIC: 3443 Industrial vessels, tanks & containers

(G-9162)
VIDA VE CORP
8210 Timber Mist Ct (43017-8673)
PHONE......................................614 203-2607
Kellie Smith-Hoover, *President*
Jeff Hoover, *Principal*
Barb Macdonald, *Principal*
EMP: 3
SALES (est): 180.3K **Privately Held**
SIC: 3612 Power transformers, electric

(G-9163)
VIOTEC LLC
5970 Pirthshire St (43016-6706)
P.O. Box 12743, Green Bay WI (54307-2743)
PHONE......................................614 596-2054
Michael Baenen,
EMP: 3
SALES (est): 121.3K **Privately Held**
SIC: 3699 Security devices

(G-9164)
VISIONTECH AUTOMATION LLC
6682 Weston Cir W (43016-7901)
PHONE......................................614 554-2013
Rakesh Mohan, *Partner*
EMP: 4
SQ FT: 2,000
SALES: 500K **Privately Held**
SIC: 3621 8711 Generating apparatus & parts, electrical; consulting engineer

(G-9165)
WEASTEC INCORPORATED
6195 Enterprise Ct (43016-3293)
PHONE......................................614 734-9645
EMP: 5
SALES (corp-wide): 240.5MM **Privately Held**
SIC: 3711 Automobile assembly, including specialty automobiles
HQ: Weastec, Incorporated
1600 N High St
Hillsboro OH 45133
937 393-6800

(G-9166)
WONDER-SHIRTS INC
7695 Crawley Dr (43017-8820)
PHONE......................................917 679-2336
Matthew Mohr, *President*
EMP: 6 **EST:** 2002
SALES (est): 588.2K **Privately Held**
SIC: 2253 T-shirts & tops, knit

(G-9167)
Z TRACK MAGAZINE
6142 Northcliff Blvd (43016-6713)
PHONE......................................614 764-1703
Robert Clue, *President*
Robert J Kluz II, *Publisher*
EMP: 3
SALES (est): 232.2K **Privately Held**
SIC: 2721 5945 Periodicals; hobby, toy & game shops

Dunbridge
Wood County

(G-9168)
BLAKO INDUSTRIES INC
10850 Middleton Pike (43414)
PHONE......................................419 246-6172
Fax: 419 833-5733
Ed Long, *President*
Paul J Leahy, *Principal*
Charles Hansen, *Vice Pres*
Jeff Briner, *Controller*
EMP: 28
SQ FT: 21,000
SALES (est): 6.6MM **Privately Held**
WEB: www.blako.com
SIC: 3081 Polyethylene film

(G-9169)
GELOK INTERNATIONAL CORP
Pine Lake Rd Pn Lk In Par (43414)
P.O. Box 69 (43414-0069)
PHONE......................................419 352-1482
Fax: 419 352-8340
Charles Stocking, *President*
Micheal Kirby, *CFO*
Richard Lavoie, *Sales Mgr*
Tim Brand, *IT/INT Sup*
Carol Stocking, *Admin Sec*
◆ **EMP:** 15
SQ FT: 20,000
SALES (est): 4MM **Privately Held**
WEB: www.gelok.com
SIC: 3842 Surgical appliances & supplies

Dundee
Tuscarawas County

(G-9170)
A & M KILN DRY LTD
10836 Lower Trail Rd Nw (44624-8922)
PHONE......................................330 852-0505
Andrew Raber, *Partner*
Duane Rabe, *Partner*
Abe Raber, *Partner*
EMP: 10
SALES (est): 950K **Privately Held**
SIC: 3559 2435 Kilns; plywood, hardwood or hardwood faced

(G-9171)
DANIELS AMISH COLLECTION LLC (PA)
9190 Massillon Rd (44624-9412)
PHONE......................................330 359-0400
Fax: 330 695-9340
Christopher Karman, *Mng Member*
Daniel Yoder,
EMP: 20
SQ FT: 25,000
SALES: 20MM **Privately Held**
SIC: 2519 Fiberglass furniture, household: padded or plain

(G-9172)
DUTCH LEGACY LLC
2425 Us Route 62 (44624-9233)
PHONE......................................330 359-0270
Aaron Garber,
EMP: 8

SQ FT: 20,000
SALES: 12MM **Privately Held**
SIC: 2511 Wood household furniture

(G-9173)
HOLMES PRCUT/TROYER IMPRINTING
7540 Peabody Kent Rd (44624-9248)
PHONE......................................330 359-0000
EMP: 3
SALES (est): 305.7K **Privately Held**
SIC: 2759 Imprinting

(G-9174)
LITTLE COTTAGE COMPANY
6673 State Route 515 (44624-9254)
P.O. Box 455, Berlin (44610-0455)
PHONE......................................330 893-4212
Daniel Schlabach, *President*
Lisa Schlabach, *Vice Pres*
EMP: 4
SALES (est): 664.1K **Privately Held**
WEB: www.littlecottagecompany.com
SIC: 3944 5945 Games, toys & children's vehicles; hobby, toy & game shops

(G-9175)
LJ WOODWORKING
9035 Senff Rd (44624-9414)
PHONE......................................330 359-3216
Fax: 330 698-3200
Ray Yoder Jr, *Owner*
EMP: 9
SALES (est): 1.1MM **Privately Held**
SIC: 2431 Millwork

(G-9176)
MILLWOOD INC
Also Called: Millwood Pallet Co
18279 Dover Rd (44624-9425)
PHONE......................................330 359-5220
Fax: 330 359-5781
Jim Caughey, *Manager*
EMP: 30 **Privately Held**
WEB: www.millwoodinc.com
SIC: 2448 Pallets, wood; cargo containers, wood
PA: Millwood, Inc.
3708 International Blvd
Vienna OH 44473

(G-9177)
MILLWOOD WHOLESALE INC
7969 Township Road 662 (44624-9602)
PHONE......................................330 359-6109
Fax: 330 620-6208
David Miller, *President*
EMP: 10
SALES: 1MM **Privately Held**
SIC: 1751 2431 2511 5021 Carpentry work; millwork; kitchen & dining room furniture; chairs

(G-9178)
NORTH VIEW WOODWORKING
8454 State Route 93 Nw (44624-8722)
PHONE......................................330 359-6286
Robert Miller, *Principal*
EMP: 4
SALES (est): 493.8K **Privately Held**
SIC: 2431 Millwork

(G-9179)
PRO FAB INDUSTRIES INC
9368 Massillon Rd (44624-9412)
P.O. Box 322, Mount Eaton (44659-0322)
PHONE......................................317 297-0461
Fax: 330 359-5012
Scott R Lowrie, *Principal*
William Harder, *Research*
Mike Joyce, *Project Engr*
Rich Mazon, *CFO*
Keith R Rudy, *Manager*
EMP: 4
SALES (est): 265.5K **Privately Held**
SIC: 5271 3441 Mobile homes; fabricated structural metal

(G-9180)
SONIC DRILLING
9406 Massillon Rd (44624-9412)
PHONE......................................330 359-0079
Jim Nidzgorski, *Principal*
EMP: 4
SALES (est): 503.9K **Privately Held**
SIC: 3541 Drilling & boring machines

(G-9181)
TRAIL CABINET
2270 Township Road 415 (44624-9654)
PHONE..................................330 893-3791
Robert Miller, *Principal*
EMP: 4
SALES (est): 311.7K **Privately Held**
SIC: 2434 Wood kitchen cabinets

(G-9182)
TRAILWAY WOOD
3173 Township Road 414 (44624-9274)
PHONE..................................330 893-9966
Jonas Miller, *Owner*
EMP: 14
SALES: 3MM **Privately Held**
SIC: 2511 Tables, household: wood

(G-9183)
TROYERS TRAIL BOLOGNA INC
6552 State Route 515 (44624-9226)
PHONE..................................330 893-2414
Fax: 330 893-3058
Dale Troyer, *President*
Darrin Troyer, *Vice Pres*
Greg Troyer, *Vice Pres*
Kevin Troyer, *Vice Pres*
Kenneth Troyer, *Treasurer*
EMP: 21 **EST:** 1925
SQ FT: 1,050
SALES: 4.5MM **Privately Held**
SIC: 2011 5411 Cured meats from meat slaughtered on site; grocery stores, independent

(G-9184)
TWIN OAKS BARN
3337 Us Route 62 (44624-9270)
PHONE..................................330 893-3126
Melvin Miller, *Owner*
EMP: 10
SALES: 1.5MM **Privately Held**
SIC: 2452 3999 Prefabricated buildings, wood; lawn ornaments

(G-9185)
WALNUT CREEK LUMBER CO LTD
10433 Pleasant Hill Rd Nw (44624-8775)
PHONE..................................330 852-4559
Fax: 330 852-2561
Dennis A Raber, *President*
EMP: 22
SQ FT: 864
SALES (est): 5MM **Privately Held**
SIC: 5031 2421 Lumber: rough, dressed & finished; custom sawmill

(G-9186)
WINESBURG HARDWOOD LUMBER CO
2871 Us Route 62 (44624-9236)
PHONE..................................330 893-2705
Fax: 330 893-3667
Robert Coblentz, *Partner*
Levi Coblentz, *Partner*
Owen Coblentz, *Partner*
EMP: 25
SQ FT: 4,000
SALES (est): 3.9MM **Privately Held**
SIC: 2448 Pallets, wood

Dunkirk
Hardin County

(G-9187)
DIAMOND PLASTICS INC
211 W Geneva St (45836-1090)
P.O. Box 99 (45836-0099)
PHONE..................................419 759-3838
Fax: 419 759-3843
EMP: 82
SQ FT: 70,000
SALES (est): 8.9MM **Privately Held**
SIC: 3089 Mfg Plastic Products

(G-9188)
NORTH COAST CUSTOM MOLDING INC
211 W Geneva St (45836-1008)
PHONE..................................419 905-6447
Fax: 419 396-6745

Jim Braeunig, *President*
Chad Erick Miller, *Vice Pres*
Jane Miller, *Vice Pres*
Ronald Coleman, *Prdtn Mgr*
Ed Hunker, *QC Mgr*
EMP: 15
SQ FT: 9,700
SALES (est): 2.2MM **Privately Held**
SIC: 3089 Molding primary plastic

(G-9189)
OLDAKER MANUFACTURING CORP
Also Called: Oldaker M F G
301 N Main St (45836-1087)
PHONE..................................419 759-3551
Fax: 419 759-3312
Linda Ream, *President*
Patrick M Ream, *President*
Patty Miller, *Controller*
John M Tudor, *Agent*
EMP: 8
SQ FT: 9,000
SALES (est): 1.1MM **Privately Held**
WEB: www.testleads.net
SIC: 3699 Lead-in wires, electric lamp

East Canton
Stark County

(G-9190)
BARBCO INC
315 Pekin Dr Se (44730-9462)
P.O. Box 30189, Canton (44730-0189)
PHONE..................................330 488-9400
Fax: 330 488-2022
Anthony R Barbera, *Principal*
John F Boggins, *Principal*
Richard C Kettler, *Principal*
Anthony Barbera, *Vice Pres*
David Barbera, *Vice Pres*
▲ **EMP:** 46
SQ FT: 15,000
SALES (est): 19.1MM **Privately Held**
WEB: www.barbco.com
SIC: 3531 3541 Tunnelling machinery; drilling & boring machines

(G-9191)
DLHBOWLES INC
336 Wood St S (44730-1348)
P.O. Box 6030, Canton (44706-0030)
PHONE..................................330 488-0716
Fax: 330 488-0719
Debbie Seaburn, *Branch Mgr*
EMP: 75
SALES (corp-wide): 126.6MM **Privately Held**
WEB: www.dlh-inc.com
SIC: 3089 3082 Injection molding of plastics; tubes, unsupported plastic
PA: Dlhbowles, Inc.
　　2422 Leo Ave Sw
　　Canton OH 44706
　　330 478-2503

(G-9192)
FOLTZ & FOLTZ LTD PARTNERSHIP
Also Called: Tkg Operating
4700 Ravenna Ave Se (44730-9733)
PHONE..................................330 488-1898
Robert Foltz, *Partner*
Dwain Foltz, *Partner*
EMP: 5
SQ FT: 5,000
SALES (est): 432.9K **Privately Held**
SIC: 1311 Crude petroleum & natural gas

(G-9193)
FTS INTERNATIONAL INC
1520 Wood Ave Se (44730-9591)
PHONE..................................330 754-2375
Richard Jelley, *Branch Mgr*
EMP: 303 **Privately Held**
SIC: 1389 Measurement of well flow rates, oil & gas
PA: Fts International, Inc.
　　777 Main St Ste 3000
　　Fort Worth TX 76102

(G-9194)
KOCH KNIGHT LLC (DH)
5385 Orchardview Dr Se (44730-9568)
P.O. Box 30070 (44730-0070)
PHONE..................................330 488-1651
Fax: 330 488-1656
Mike Graeff, *President*
Mathew Phayer, *Vice Pres*
Jeremy Heestand, *Project Mgr*
Roy Williams, *Project Mgr*
Greg Carle, *Opers Mgr*
◆ **EMP:** 80
SALES (est): 26.5MM
SALES (corp-wide): 27.3B **Privately Held**
WEB: www.kochknight.com
SIC: 2911 5172 5169 4922 Petroleum refining; petroleum products; chemicals & allied products; natural gas transmission; crude petroleum production; natural gas production; refinery, chemical processing & similar machinery
HQ: Koch-Glitsch, Lp
　　4111 E 37th St N
　　Wichita KS 67220
　　316 828-5110

(G-9195)
OSNABURG QUILT FIBR ART GUILD
6855 Orchardview Dr Se (44730-9428)
PHONE..................................330 488-2591
Susan Jean Burgess, *Principal*
EMP: 4 **EST:** 2010
SALES (est): 285.9K **Privately Held**
SIC: 2211 Osnaburgs

(G-9196)
RECON SYSTEMS LLC (PA)
330 Wood St S (44730-1348)
P.O. Box 30100 (44730-0100)
PHONE..................................330 484-8444
Brandon Ballos,
Rod Tussant,
EMP: 6
SALES (est): 814.9K **Privately Held**
WEB: www.reconsystems.com
SIC: 3714 Rebuilding engines & transmissions, factory basis

(G-9197)
RESCO PRODUCTS INC
6878 Osnaburg St Se (44730-9529)
P.O. Box 30169 (44730-0169)
PHONE..................................330 488-1226
Paul Jeremiah, *Purch Agent*
Kurt Bletzacker, *Manager*
EMP: 65
SQ FT: 1,500
SALES (corp-wide): 192.1MM **Privately Held**
SIC: 3255 Ladle brick, clay
PA: Resco Products, Inc.
　　1 Robinson Plz Ste 300
　　Pittsburgh PA 15205
　　412 494-4491

East Fultonham
Muskingum County

(G-9198)
CHESTERHILL STONE CO
Also Called: Shelly Materials
6305 Saltillo Rd (43735)
P.O. Box 28 (43735-0028)
PHONE..................................740 849-2338
Fax: 740 849-2599
George Hill, *Superintendent*
EMP: 29
SALES (corp-wide): 9MM **Privately Held**
SIC: 1422 Crushed & broken limestone
PA: Chesterhill Stone Co
　　773 E State Route 60 Ne
　　Mcconnelsville OH

East Liberty
Logan County

(G-9199)
C & F FABRICATIONS INC
3100 State St (43319)
P.O. Box 258 (43319-0258)
PHONE..................................937 666-3234
Fax: 937 666-6275
William D Mercer, *CEO*
Betty J Mercer, *President*
W Douglas Mercer, *Treasurer*
Karen Lyon, *Controller*
EMP: 20 **EST:** 1959
SQ FT: 26,000
SALES (est): 1.1MM **Privately Held**
SIC: 3496 Miscellaneous fabricated wire products

(G-9200)
GREAT LAKES ASSEMBLIES LLC
11590 Tr 298 (43319)
PHONE..................................937 645-3900
Fax: 937 645-3991
Billy R Vickers, *President*
William Buchanan, *Controller*
Kathy Carrington, *Executive Asst*
EMP: 70
SQ FT: 90,000
SALES (est): 61.2MM
SALES (corp-wide): 61.4MM **Privately Held**
WEB: www.gla-llc.com
SIC: 3711 Automobile assembly, including specialty automobiles
PA: Modular Assembly Innovations
　　600 Stonehenge Pkwy # 100
　　Dublin OH 43017
　　614 389-4860

(G-9201)
HARDING MACHINE ACQUISITION CO
Also Called: Global Precision Parts
13060 State Route 287 (43319-9439)
P.O. Box 752, Van Wert (45891-0752)
PHONE..................................937 666-3031
Fax: 937 666-6155
Dave Kriegel, *Ch of Bd*
Todd Kriegel, *President*
Susan Mosier, *CFO*
Yolanda Von Lehmden, *Controller*
Jessica Wooten, *Controller*
EMP: 75
SALES (est): 13.2MM **Privately Held**
SIC: 3451 Screw machine products

(G-9202)
NISSIN BRAKE OHIO INC
25790 State Route 287 (43319-9500)
PHONE..................................937 642-7556
Hannah Martell, *Engineer*
Aaron Riesen, *Branch Mgr*
EMP: 27
SALES (corp-wide): 1.4B **Privately Held**
SIC: 3714 Motor vehicle brake systems & parts
HQ: Nissin Brake Ohio, Inc.
　　1901 Industrial Dr
　　Findlay OH 45840
　　419 420-3800

East Liverpool
Columbiana County

(G-9203)
ASHCO
1250 Saint George St # 3 (43920-3400)
PHONE..................................330 385-2400
Fax: 330 386-5880
Robert L Ash, *Owner*
Robert Lord, *Manager*
Don Saga, *Manager*
EMP: 2
SALES: 1MM **Privately Held**
SIC: 3556 Food products machinery

(G-9204)
C A JOSEPH CO (PA)
13712 Old Frdericktown Rd (43920-9531)
PHONE....................330 385-6869
Fax: 330 385-5038
Charles Chuck Joseph, *President*
Chris Joseph, *Vice Pres*
Mike Joseph, *Vice Pres*
▲ EMP: 8
SQ FT: 200,000
SALES (est): 4.1MM **Privately Held**
WEB: www.cajoseph.com
SIC: 3089 3599 Plastic processing; machine shop, jobbing & repair

(G-9205)
CAMPBELL SIGNS & APPAREL LLC
47366 Y And O Rd (43920-8747)
PHONE....................330 386-4768
Jodi H Campbell, *CFO*
Jeff Campbell,
EMP: 15
SQ FT: 9,600
SALES: 12MM **Privately Held**
SIC: 3993 2759 2395 Signs & advertising specialties; screen printing; embroidery & art needlework

(G-9206)
CAROLEX COMPANY INC
761 Dresden Ave (43920-4346)
PHONE....................330 386-9529
Fax: 330 386-9535
Clyde McClellon, *President*
EMP: 50
SALES (est): 4MM **Privately Held**
SIC: 3253 Ceramic wall & floor tile

(G-9207)
COLUMBIANA METRO HSING AUTH
Also Called: C M H A
325 Moore St (43920-2572)
PHONE....................330 385-6662
Brenda Simmons, *Manager*
Tom Snow, *Exec Dir*
EMP: 32
SALES (est): 1.6MM **Privately Held**
WEB: www.colmha.org
SIC: 2531 Public building & related furniture

(G-9208)
COMMERCIAL DECAL OF OHIO INC
46686 Y And O Rd (43920-9710)
P.O. Box 2747 (43920-0747)
PHONE....................330 385-7178
Fax: 330 385-9762
David Dunn, *President*
EMP: 25
SQ FT: 11,000
SALES (est): 2MM **Privately Held**
SIC: 2759 Decals: printing

(G-9209)
CUSTOM CRANKSHAFT INC
1730 Annesley Rd (43920-9410)
PHONE....................330 382-1200
Fax: 330 382-1209
Scott Watson, *President*
EMP: 35
SALES (est): 4.4MM **Privately Held**
SIC: 3599 Crankshafts & camshafts, machining

(G-9210)
D JOHNSON SERVICES
50579 Fisher Ave (43920-9564)
PHONE....................330 386-4588
David M Johnson, *Owner*
EMP: 7
SALES (est): 422.4K **Privately Held**
SIC: 3312 Bars, iron: made in steel mills

(G-9211)
DC MUSIC
15765 State Route 170 # 9 (43920-9070)
PHONE....................330 385-0468
Dave Byers, *Owner*
EMP: 3
SALES (est): 386K **Privately Held**
SIC: 3931 Musical instruments

(G-9212)
DECARIA BROTHERS INC
104 E 5th St (43920-3031)
PHONE....................330 385-0825
Erin McCart, *Principal*
EMP: 6
SALES (est): 930.3K **Privately Held**
SIC: 2836 Vaccines & other immunizing products

(G-9213)
DELTA MANUFACTURING INC
Also Called: Twister Displays
49207 Clctta Smthferry Rd (43920-9570)
P.O. Box 2704 (43920-0704)
PHONE....................330 386-1270
Fax: 330 386-0418
Harry Smith, *President*
Jeff Smith, *Vice Pres*
EMP: 15 EST: 1972
SQ FT: 800,000
SALES (est): 3MM **Privately Held**
WEB: www.twisterdisplay.com
SIC: 3599 Amusement park equipment

(G-9214)
ENVIRO CREST SERVICES INC
Also Called: E C S
16977 Park Way (43920-9447)
PHONE....................330 932-0345
Betty Weber, *Owner*
Vincent P Weber, *Treasurer*
George Stairs, *Admin Sec*
EMP: 3
SQ FT: 2,000
SALES: 750K **Privately Held**
WEB: www.envirocrestservices.com
SIC: 3677 8748 Filtration devices, electronic; business consulting

(G-9215)
FARNSWORTH ENGINEERING
313 Smith St (43920-3005)
P.O. Box 105 (43920-5105)
PHONE....................330 385-1745
Fax: 330 385-1443
Brian Farnsworth, *Owner*
Brenda McSwegin, *Office Mgr*
EMP: 10
SQ FT: 30,000
SALES (est): 871.5K **Privately Held**
WEB: www.farnsworthengineering.com
SIC: 3599 8711 7692 Custom machinery; machine shop, jobbing & repair; industrial engineers; welding repair

(G-9216)
GROWMARK FS LLC
1080 Elmwood St (43920-3510)
PHONE....................330 386-7626
Jan Punningham, *Manager*
Kevin Black, *Manager*
Gina Delsanto, *Commissioner*
Cindy Fletcher, *Executive*
Megan Hoffman, *Administration*
EMP: 12
SALES (corp-wide): 7B **Privately Held**
WEB: www.growmarkfs.com
SIC: 2875 4225 4221 Fertilizers, mixing only; general warehousing & storage; farm product warehousing & storage
HQ: Growmark Fs, Llc
308 Ne Front St
Milford DE 19963
302 422-3002

(G-9217)
HALLS WELDING & SUPPLIES INC
49037 Clctta Smthferry Rd (43920-9206)
PHONE....................330 385-9353
Fax: 330 385-1882
James Hall, *President*
Alicia Hall, *Vice Pres*
Gregory Hall, *Vice Pres*
Alicia McGown, *Purchasing*
EMP: 4
SQ FT: 4,410
SALES (est): 570K **Privately Held**
WEB: www.hallswelding.com
SIC: 5084 1799 3699 3548 Welding machinery & equipment; welding on site; electrical equipment & supplies; welding apparatus

(G-9218)
I CERCO INC
48400 Huston Rd (43920-9652)
PHONE....................304 387-0178
Byron Anderson, *Branch Mgr*
EMP: 68
SALES (corp-wide): 58.1MM **Privately Held**
SIC: 3567 Ceramic kilns & furnaces
PA: I Cerco Inc
453 W Mcconkey St
Shreve OH 44676
330 567-2145

(G-9219)
INNOVATIVE CERAMIC CORP
Also Called: Quality Stamp Co
432 Walnut St (43920-3130)
PHONE....................330 385-6515
Fax: 330 385-6510
Orville Steininger, *President*
EMP: 3
SQ FT: 5,000
SALES (est): 379.4K **Privately Held**
WEB: www.innovativeceramic.com
SIC: 3953 Pads, inking & stamping

(G-9220)
JOE BARRETT
Also Called: Barrett & Sons Pallet & Lbr Co
13583 Old Frdericktown Rd (43920-8941)
PHONE....................216 385-2384
Roberta J Barrett, *Principal*
EMP: 4 EST: 2012
SALES (est): 315.3K **Privately Held**
SIC: 2448 Pallets, wood & wood with metal

(G-9221)
KENTAK PRODUCTS COMPANY
1308 Railroad St (43920-3430)
P.O. Box 979 (43920-5979)
PHONE....................330 386-3700
Doug Gomoll, *President*
Pat Tittle, *Regional Mgr*
Cheryl Smith, *Production*
EMP: 60
SALES (corp-wide): 9MM **Privately Held**
SIC: 3082 3052 Tubes, unsupported plastic; plastic hose
PA: Kentak Products Company
1230 Railroad St
East Liverpool OH 43920
330 382-2000

(G-9222)
KENTAK PRODUCTS COMPANY (PA)
1230 Railroad St (43920-3406)
PHONE....................330 382-2000
Fax: 330 532-2112
Otto H Gomoll Jr, *Ch of Bd*
Douglas A Gomoll, *President*
William Mays, *Exec VP*
John Crago, *Plant Mgr*
Pat Pittle, *Purch Mgr*
▲ EMP: 45
SQ FT: 50,000
SALES: 9MM **Privately Held**
SIC: 3082 3052 Tubes, unsupported plastic; plastic hose

(G-9223)
KEYSTONE PRINTING CO
648 Saint Clair Ave (43920-3077)
P.O. Box 993 (43920-5993)
PHONE....................330 385-9519
Fax: 330 385-9519
Craig Kidd, *President*
Dale Kidd, *Vice Pres*
EMP: 3
SQ FT: 2,250
SALES: 150K **Privately Held**
SIC: 2752 Commercial printing, lithographic

(G-9224)
LARRY C WHITE
Also Called: TV Facts
101 E 6th St Ste D (43920-3087)
P.O. Box 8000 (43920-7708)
PHONE....................330 386-3228
Larry C White, *Owner*
EMP: 3

SALES (est): 170K **Privately Held**
SIC: 2721 2791 2752 Magazines: publishing & printing; television schedules: publishing & printing; typesetting; commercial printing, lithographic

(G-9225)
OHIO VALLEY HERBAL PRODUCTS
1250 Saint George St # 5 (43920-3400)
PHONE....................330 382-1229
Marina Schaum, *President*
EMP: 3
SALES (est): 385.9K **Privately Held**
WEB: www.wilderb.com
SIC: 2833 Drugs & herbs: grading, grinding & milling

(G-9226)
PWS WELDING & MTG
14533 E Liverpool Rd (43920-9733)
PHONE....................330 385-6922
Fax: 330 385-6959
Betty Caudill, *Owner*
EMP: 11 EST: 2012
SALES (est): 1.7MM **Privately Held**
SIC: 3317 3548 8734 3699 Welded pipe & tubes; welding & cutting apparatus & accessories; welded joint radiographing; electrical welding equipment

(G-9227)
SH BELL COMPANY
2217 Michigan Ave (43920-3637)
PHONE....................412 963-9910
Fax: 330 385-8120
Tim Bowersock, *Safety Mgr*
Adam Bell, *Sales Mgr*
Vince Monte, *Sales Staff*
Rusty Davis, *Manager*
Mark Pease, *Manager*
EMP: 37
SALES (corp-wide): 25.3MM **Privately Held**
SIC: 3479 4226 4225 Aluminum coating of metal products; special warehousing & storage; general warehousing & storage
PA: S.H. Bell Company
644 Alpha Dr
Pittsburgh PA 15238
412 963-9910

(G-9228)
WALLOVER ENTERPRISES INC
Also Called: Woco
1032 Pennsylvania Ave (43920-3561)
PHONE....................440 238-9250
Fax: 330 385-9975
Bill Cutri, *Vice Pres*
David Pristic, *Purchasing*
Joseph Early, *Sales Staff*
EMP: 10 **Privately Held**
SIC: 5172 2992 Petroleum products; lubricating oils & greases
HQ: Wallover Oil Company Incorporated
21845 Drake Rd
Strongsville OH 44149
440 238-9250

East Palestine
Columbiana County

(G-9229)
CARDINAL WELDING INC
895 E Taggart St (44413-2465)
P.O. Box 405 (44413-0405)
PHONE....................330 426-2404
Fax: 330 426-2403
Daniel Shofstahl, *President*
EMP: 6
SQ FT: 25,000
SALES (est): 1.1MM **Privately Held**
SIC: 7692 3411 Welding repair; metal cans

(G-9230)
CARLSON AIRCRAFT INC
Also Called: Sky-Tek
51028 State Route 14 (44413-9747)
P.O. Box 88 (44413-0088)
PHONE....................330 426-3934
Mary Carlson, *President*
EMP: 4

GEOGRAPHIC

SALES (est): 290K **Privately Held**
SIC: **3721 7699** Aircraft; aircraft & heavy
equipment repair services

(G-9231)
COLD DUCK SCREEN PRTG &
EMB CO
540 Sugar Camp Dr (44413-1680)
PHONE................................330 426-1900
Fax: 330 426-4077
John A Campagna, *Owner*
John Campagna, *Owner*
Connie Campagna, *Co-Owner*
EMP: 3
SQ FT: 2,400
SALES (est): 260.6K **Privately Held**
WEB: www.coldduckscreenprinting.com
SIC: **2759 2752 7389 2791** Screen print-
ing; commercial printing, offset; sewing
contractor; typesetting

(G-9232)
CUSTOMIZED VINYL SALES
50814 Hadley Rd (44413-9738)
PHONE................................330 518-3238
Lauren McCambridgegruber, *Principal*
EMP: 6
SALES (est): 607.6K **Privately Held**
SIC: **3089** Fences, gates & accessories:
plastic

(G-9233)
DILWORTH MACHINE
51552 Chain School Rd (44413-9742)
PHONE................................330 427-1706
Fax: 330 427-1735
William Dilworth, *Owner*
◆ EMP: 18
SQ FT: 10,000
SALES (est): 1.3MM **Privately Held**
SIC: **3599** Machine shop, jobbing & repair

(G-9234)
DUNCAN BROTHERS DRILLING
INC (PA)
1264 Howell Ave (44413-9784)
P.O. Box 8 (44413-0008)
PHONE................................330 426-9507
Mark Duncan, *President*
EMP: 10
SQ FT: 2,500
SALES (est): 2.5MM **Privately Held**
SIC: **1241** Mining services: bituminous

(G-9235)
DUNCAN BROTHERS DRILLING
INC
1264 Howell Ave (44413-9784)
P.O. Box 8 (44413-0008)
PHONE................................330 426-9507
Mark Duncan, *President*
EMP: 10
SALES (corp-wide): 2.5MM **Privately**
Held
SIC: **1241** Mining services: bituminous
PA: Duncan Brother's Drilling Inc
　　1264 Howell Ave
　　East Palestine OH 44413
　　330 426-9507

(G-9236)
E J BOGNAR INC
51887 E Taggart St (44413-2471)
P.O. Box 6 (44413-0006)
PHONE................................330 426-9292
Fax: 330 426-9292
Mike Livingston, *Manager*
John Chambers, *Manager*
EMP: 12
SQ FT: 5,000
SALES (corp-wide): 12.3MM **Privately**
Held
WEB: www.ejbognar.com
SIC: **1459** Fire clay mining
PA: E. J. Bognar, Inc.
　　733 Washington Rd Fl 5
　　Pittsburgh PA 15228
　　412 344-9900

(G-9237)
E R ADVANCED CERAMICS INC
Also Called: US Group
600 E Clark St (44413-2430)
P.O. Box 270 (44413-0270)
PHONE................................330 426-9433

John Hayday, *President*
David A Early, *Exec VP*
Dawn Carsey, *Purch Agent*
Michael Dematteo, *CFO*
◆ EMP: 34
SQ FT: 68,274
SALES: 4.2MM **Privately Held**
WEB: www.usstoneware.com
SIC: **3531 3269 3547 3821** Construction
machinery; grinding media, pottery; rolling
mill machinery; particle size reduction ap-
paratus, laboratory; filters; industrial
pumps & parts

(G-9238)
EAST PALESTINE DECORATING
LLC
870 W Main St (44413-1328)
PHONE................................330 426-9600
Pam Moore, *Executive*
Walter O'Malley,
Patrick Gaughan,
▲ EMP: 10
SALES (est): 297K **Privately Held**
SIC: **3231** Decorated glassware: chipped,
engraved, etched, etc.

(G-9239)
EXOCHEM CORPORATION
90 Kemple Dr (44413-1501)
PHONE................................330 426-9898
Randy Meraldi, *President*
EMP: 19
SALES (corp-wide): 11.5MM **Privately**
Held
SIC: **2399** Cheese bandages, made from
purchased materials
PA: Exochem Corporation
　　2421 E 28th St
　　Lorain OH 44055
　　800 807-7464

(G-9240)
KENTAK PRODUCTS COMPANY
795 E Martin St (44413-2437)
P.O. Box 979, East Liverpool (43920-5979)
PHONE................................330 532-6211
Virginia Pickens, *Manager*
EMP: 5
SALES (corp-wide): 9MM **Privately Held**
SIC: **3082 3052** Tubes, unsupported plas-
tic; plastic hose
PA: Kentak Products Company
　　1230 Railroad St
　　East Liverpool OH 43920
　　330 382-2000

(G-9241)
LIQUID LUGGERS LLC
183 Edgeworth Ave (44413-1554)
PHONE................................330 426-2538
Lynn Neely, *Principal*
EMP: 50
SALES (est): 8.9MM **Privately Held**
SIC: **3443** Tanks for tank trucks, metal
plate

(G-9242)
MX SPRING INC
Also Called: Fcr Suspension
39 Wilderson Ave (44413-1163)
PHONE................................330 426-4600
EMP: 5
SALES (est): 310K **Privately Held**
SIC: **3799** Transportation Equipment, Nec,
Nsk

(G-9243)
RBS MFG INC
145 E Martin St (44413-2337)
P.O. Box 430 (44413-0430)
PHONE................................330 426-9486
Dennis Garrett, *Principal*
John Wade, *Purch Mgr*
Rick Severs, *VP Sales*
Leslie Allcorn, *Office Mgr*
EMP: 19
SALES (est): 2.5MM **Privately Held**
SIC: **3999** Manufacturing industries

(G-9244)
ROBERT MAYO INDUSTRIES
Also Called: Mayo, R A Industries
157 E Martin St (44413-2315)
PHONE................................330 426-2587
Robert A Mayo, *Owner*

EMP: 6 EST: 1963
SQ FT: 1,500
SALES: 767.4K **Privately Held**
SIC: **2512 7641** Upholstered household
furniture; reupholstery & furniture repair

(G-9245)
STROHECKER INCORPORATED
213 N Pleasant Dr (44413-2497)
PHONE................................330 426-3143
Fax: 330 426-3143
Richard Strohecker, *President*
Tony J Moran, *Vice Pres*
John Felger, *Engineer*
Sharen Williams, *Office Mgr*
▲ EMP: 40 EST: 1947
SQ FT: 4,000
SALES: 11MM **Privately Held**
WEB: www.strohecker.com
SIC: **3567 3443** Industrial furnaces &
ovens; metal parts

(G-9246)
TEST MARK INDUSTRIES INC
995 N Market St (44413-1109)
PHONE................................330 426-2200
William F Tyger, *President*
Martin R Napolitano, *Corp Secy*
William Quinlan, *Director*
EMP: 12
SQ FT: 8,500
SALES (est): 3.4MM **Privately Held**
WEB: www.testmark.net
SIC: **5049 3829** Laboratory equipment,
except medical or dental; physical prop-
erty testing equipment

(G-9247)
TUBETECH INC (PA)
Also Called: Tubetech North America
900 E Taggart St (44413-2424)
P.O. Box 470 (44413-0470)
PHONE................................330 426-9476
Fax: 330 426-4175
Steve Oliphant, *CEO*
Stephen D Oliphant, *CEO*
Jon Roscow, *President*
Richard Downey, *Corp Secy*
Bonnie Evans, *Traffic Mgr*
EMP: 26
SQ FT: 80,000
SALES (est): 3.6MM **Privately Held**
WEB: www.tubetechnorthamerica.com
SIC: **3317 3471** Tubes, wrought: welded
or lock joint; plating of metals or formed
products

(G-9248)
UNITY TUBE INC
1862 State Route 165 (44413-9737)
P.O. Box 425 (44413-0425)
PHONE................................330 426-4282
Dennis Kuhns, *President*
Lisa Travis, *Info Tech Mgr*
EMP: 18
SALES (est): 4.1MM **Privately Held**
WEB: www.unitytube.com
SIC: **3498** Tube fabricating (contract bend-
ing & shaping)

(G-9249)
WAYNES PRECISION MACHINE
INC
Also Called: Wayne's Precision Mach Shop
354 N Liberty St (44413-2334)
PHONE................................330 426-4626
Fax: 330 426-6620
Dave Myers, *President*
EMP: 3
SQ FT: 5,000
SALES: 250K **Privately Held**
SIC: **3599** Machine shop, jobbing & repair

East Rochester
Columbiana County

(G-9250)
HOOPES FERTILIZER WORKS
INC (PA)
24104 Us Route 30 (44625-9701)
P.O. Box 74 (44625-0074)
PHONE................................330 894-2121
Fax: 330 894-2947

Terry Hoopes, *President*
EMP: 5 EST: 1956
SQ FT: 30,000
SALES (est): 1.8MM **Privately Held**
WEB: www.hoopesfence.com
SIC: **2875 5191** Fertilizers, mixing only;
fertilizers & agricultural chemicals

(G-9251)
SUMMIT WELL SERVICES INC
28050 Speidel Rd (44625-9764)
P.O. Box 129, Hanoverton (44423-0129)
PHONE................................330 223-1074
Alfred S Levine, *President*
Russell Miller, *Vice Pres*
Sandy Samoro, *Admin Sec*
EMP: 6
SALES (est): 610K **Privately Held**
SIC: **1382** Oil & gas exploration services

(G-9252)
VANGUARD OIL & GAS
28050 Speidel Rd (44625-9764)
P.O. Box 129, Hanoverton (44423-0129)
PHONE................................330 223-1074
Alfred Levine, *Owner*
EMP: 5
SALES (est): 340K **Privately Held**
SIC: **1389** Oil & gas field services

East Sparta
Stark County

(G-9253)
ADAMS FABRICATING INC
10125 Sandyville Ave (44626)
P.O. Box 325 (44626-0325)
PHONE................................330 866-2986
Fax: 330 866-2986
Bill Adams, *President*
Elizabeth Adams, *Corp Secy*
Stephen Adams, *Vice Pres*
EMP: 4
SQ FT: 5,600
SALES: 350K **Privately Held**
SIC: **3312** Plate, steel; structural shapes &
pilings, steel

(G-9254)
CLARK SON ACTN LIQUIDATION
INC
10233 Sandyville Ave Se (44626-9333)
PHONE................................330 866-9330
Jona Rosks, *Principal*
Darrell Johnson, *Manager*
Jennifer Warner, *Manager*
▼ EMP: 8
SALES (est): 610K **Privately Held**
SIC: **2434** Wood kitchen cabinets

(G-9255)
SLATS AND NAILS INC
10465 Sandyville Ave Se (44626-9336)
P.O. Box 245, Sandyville (44671-0245)
PHONE................................330 866-1008
Fax: 330 866-1008
Richard Fioretto, *President*
Nicholas Incarnato, *Vice Pres*
Miklos Fioretto, *Treasurer*
EMP: 3
SQ FT: 80,000
SALES (est): 5.6MM **Privately Held**
SIC: **2448** Pallets, wood

Eastlake
Lake County

(G-9256)
2-M MANUFACTURING
COMPANY
34560 Lakeland Blvd (44095-5221)
PHONE................................440 269-1270
Fax: 440 269-1171
Mirko Cukelj, *President*
Katherine Cukelj, *Corp Secy*
Sandy Palmer, *Manager*
EMP: 25
SALES (est): 4.4MM **Privately Held**
SIC: **3599** Machine shop, jobbing & repair

(G-9257)
ADVANCED CONTROLS INC
34300 Lakeland Blvd Frnt (44095-5237)
PHONE..................................440 354-5413
Fax: 440 354-5702
Paul O'Connor, *President*
EMP: 20
SQ FT: 15,000
SALES (est): 3.9MM **Privately Held**
WEB: www.advancedcontrols.com
SIC: 3613 Control panels, electric

(G-9258)
AGILE SIGN & LTG MAINT INC
35280 Lakeland Blvd (44095-5302)
PHONE..................................440 918-1311
Tim Ruff, *President*
EMP: 17
SALES (est): 1,000K **Privately Held**
WEB: www.agilesign.com
SIC: 3993 Signs & advertising specialties

(G-9259)
BLACK DIAMND ECO SOLUTIONS LLC
34355 Melinz Pkwy (44095-4033)
PHONE..................................877 892-3370
Scott Janda, *Mng Member*
Timothy Reed, *Mng Member*
EMP: 3 EST: 2013
SQ FT: 5,000
SALES (est): 232.7K **Privately Held**
SIC: 3089 Plastic containers, except foam

(G-9260)
C & D TOOL INC
35595 Curtis Blvd Unit F (44095-4100)
PHONE..................................440 942-8463
Duane Seelinger, *President*
EMP: 5
SQ FT: 2,000
SALES: 475K **Privately Held**
SIC: 3544 Industrial molds

(G-9261)
C STONEMAN CORPORATION
Also Called: Stoneman Welding
100 E Shore Blvd (44095-1906)
PHONE..................................440 942-3325
Fax: 216 481-4479
Chuck Stoneman, *President*
EMP: 3
SQ FT: 11,831
SALES (est): 219.1K **Privately Held**
SIC: 7692 1799 Welding repair; welding
on site

(G-9262)
CHAGRIN METAL FABRICATING INC
34201 Melinz Pkwy Unit B (44095-4018)
PHONE..................................440 946-6342
Fax: 440 946-4570
Bob Munaretto, *President*
Anthony Munaretto, *Principal*
EMP: 4
SALES (est): 320K **Privately Held**
SIC: 3444 Sheet metalwork

(G-9263)
CONSOLDTED PRECISION PDTS CORP
Also Called: Cpp Cleveland
34000 Lakeland Blvd (44095-5215)
PHONE..................................440 953-0053
Corey Demidovich, *Opers Mgr*
Nathan Prussing, *Opers Mgr*
Sam Henninger, *Engineer*
Wesley Shimizu, *Engineer*
Daniel Wise, *Engineer*
EMP: 31
SALES (corp-wide): 6B **Privately Held**
SIC: 3369 Castings, except die-castings,
precision
HQ: Consolidated Precision Products Corp.
1621 Euclid Ave Ste 1850
Cleveland OH 44115
909 595-2252

(G-9264)
DEPENDABLE GEAR CORP
1422 E 363rd St (44095-4136)
PHONE..................................440 942-4969
John Luckay Jr, *President*
EMP: 4

SQ FT: 400
SALES: 150K **Privately Held**
WEB: www.dependablegear.com
SIC: 3566 3568 3462 Speed changers,
drives & gears; pulleys, power transmission; construction or mining equipment
forgings, ferrous

(G-9265)
DIE CO INC
1889 E 337th St (44095-5231)
PHONE..................................440 942-8856
Fax: 440 946-4295
Donald G Hawk, *President*
Michael T Hawk, *Vice Pres*
Dave Coffee, *QC Mgr*
Donna Corrigan, *Admin Sec*
▲ EMP: 48
SQ FT: 35,000
SALES (est): 10.2MM **Privately Held**
WEB: www.diecoinc.com
SIC: 3469 3496 3471 3429 Metal stamp-
ings; miscellaneous fabricated wire prod-
ucts; plating & polishing; manufactured
hardware (general); metal heat treating

(G-9266)
DIVERSIFIED MCH COMPONENTS LLC
34099 Melinz Pkwy Unit D (44095-4001)
PHONE..................................440 942-5701
Gregory J O'Brien, *Mng Member*
EMP: 28
SALES (est): 6.2MM **Privately Held**
SIC: 3545 Machine tool accessories

(G-9267)
EAGLEHEAD MANUFACTURING CO
35280 Lakeland Blvd (44095-5302)
PHONE..................................440 951-0400
Ray Westfall, *Principal*
EMP: 8 EST: 2009
SALES (est): 969.3K **Privately Held**
SIC: 3999 Manufacturing industries

(G-9268)
ENPAC LLC
34355 Melinz Pkwy (44095-4033)
PHONE..................................440 975-0070
Fax: 440 975-0047
Thomas Carter, *Vice Pres*
Brian Walters, *Vice Pres*
Tammy Thompson, *Opers Mgr*
Dawn Lariccia, *Purch Mgr*
Larry Stanek, *Engineer*
◆ EMP: 50
SQ FT: 66,500
SALES (est): 11.7MM **Privately Held**
SIC: 3089 Plastic containers, except foam

(G-9269)
ENPRESS LLC
34899 Curtis Blvd (44095-4015)
PHONE..................................440 510-0108
Fax: 440 510-0202
Douglas Honer, *Owner*
Anne Melita, *Manager*
Timothy Reid,
▼ EMP: 40
SALES (est): 9.9MM **Privately Held**
WEB: www.enpress.com
SIC: 3089 Injection molding of plastics

(G-9270)
EUCLID PRECISION GRINDING CO
35400 Lakeland Blvd (44095-5304)
PHONE..................................440 946-8888
Fax: 440 946-8474
Eric Barbe, *President*
Mary Lu Grycan, *Admin Sec*
EMP: 6 EST: 1945
SQ FT: 9,600
SALES (est): 1MM **Privately Held**
WEB: www.euclidprecision.com
SIC: 3599 Machine shop, jobbing & repair

(G-9271)
GOULD ELECTRONICS INC (PA)
34929 Curtis Blvd Ste 100 (44095-4056)
PHONE..................................440 953-5000
Fax: 440 953-5133
D P Burgess, *Vice Pres*
Kerji Kataqiri, *Vice Pres*

John L Monaco, *Vice Pres*
Stephen Kohut, *Opers Staff*
William Wonders, *VP Human Res*
◆ EMP: 245
SQ FT: 450,000
SALES (est): 143.6MM **Privately Held**
WEB: www.gould.com
SIC: 3825 3497 3613 3691 Instruments
to measure electricity; logic circuit testers;
oscillographs & oscilloscopes; copper foil;
power circuit breakers; storage batteries;
semiconductors & related devices

(G-9272)
GRIP FORCE LLC
990 Quentin Rd (44095-2836)
P.O. Box 222, Willoughby (44096-0222)
PHONE..................................440 497-7014
Frank Royce, *Principal*
EMP: 3 EST: 2010
SALES (est): 262.4K **Privately Held**
SIC: 3494 Well adapters

(G-9273)
HIGH QUALITY TOOLS INC (PA)
34940 Lakeland Blvd (44095-5226)
PHONE..................................440 975-9684
Fax: 440 975-9685
Mirko Cukelj, *President*
Bryan Heartz, *General Mgr*
Chuck Thaw, *Vice Pres*
Joe Fortney, *Sales Associate*
▲ EMP: 12
SQ FT: 3,000
SALES: 5.5MM **Privately Held**
WEB: www.hqtinc.com
SIC: 5085 3545 Industrial tools; tools &
accessories for machine tools

(G-9274)
HOLMBURY INC
33801 Curtis Blvd Ste 104 (44095-4036)
PHONE..................................440 578-1070
Al Pacosky, *President*
Al Pocosky, *General Mgr*
Len Bieder, *Opers Staff*
Tom Nadsady, *Sales Mgr*
Neil Robins, *Sales Staff*
▲ EMP: 5
SALES (est): 1.1MM **Privately Held**
WEB: www.holmburyusa.com
SIC: 3568 Joints & couplings

(G-9275)
INDUSTRIAL SHAFT AND MFG INC
34201 Melinz Pkwy Unit A (44095-4018)
PHONE..................................440 942-9104
Cleo Engbert, *President*
John Engbert, *Treasurer*
EMP: 4
SQ FT: 3,000
SALES: 180K **Privately Held**
SIC: 3599 Machine shop, jobbing & repair

(G-9276)
INTELLITRONIX CORPORATION
34099 Melinz Pkwy Unit E (44095-4001)
PHONE..................................440 210-7645
Fax: 216 521-9794
Paul Spivak, *President*
Chris Jones, *Vice Pres*
EMP: 20
SQ FT: 15,000
SALES (est): 3.7MM **Privately Held**
SIC: 3621 Motors & generators

(G-9277)
JONES PRINTING SERVICES INC
1519 E 367th St Ste 1 (44095-5351)
PHONE..................................440 946-7300
Fax: 440 946-7302
James E Jones, *President*
Bob Jones, *President*
Todd Beebe, *Prdtn Mgr*
Ralph Jones, *Treasurer*
EMP: 5
SALES: 700K **Privately Held**
WEB: www.printwithjones.com
SIC: 2752 Commercial printing, litho-
graphic

(G-9278)
KILROY COMPANY (PA)
Also Called: Trust Technologies
34929 Curtis Blvd Ste 104 (44095-4053)
PHONE..................................440 951-8700
Fax: 440 543-1694
William S Kilroy II, *Ch of Bd*
Brett Jaffe, *President*
Mike Campbell, *President*
Paul Cardinale, *President*
Marty Cole, *Plant Mgr*
EMP: 75
SQ FT: 20,000
SALES (est): 27MM **Privately Held**
WEB: www.trust-tech.com
SIC: 3544 3549 3545 3541 Jigs & fix-
tures; metalworking machinery; machine
tool accessories; machine tools, metal
cutting type; sheet metalwork; nonferrous
rolling & drawing

(G-9279)
KYNTROL HOLDINGS INC (PA)
34700 Lakeland Blvd (44095-5223)
PHONE..................................440 220-5990
Wayne Foley, *President*
EMP: 1
SALES (est): 1.6MM **Privately Held**
SIC: 3593 Fluid power actuators, hydraulic
or pneumatic

(G-9280)
KYNTROL LLC (HQ)
Also Called: Comptroll
34700 Lakeland Blvd (44095-5223)
PHONE..................................440 951-2333
Carl Richter, *Vice Pres*
Pamela Bregitzer, *HR Admin*
Wayne Foley, *Mng Member*
EMP: 7
SALES (est): 1.6MM **Privately Held**
SIC: 3593 Fluid power actuators, hydraulic
or pneumatic
PA: Kyntrol Holdings Inc.
34700 Lakeland Blvd
Eastlake OH 44095
440 220-5990

(G-9281)
LANGE EQUIPMENT
Also Called: Unit Dle
1585 E 361st St Unit D (44095-5329)
PHONE..................................440 953-1621
Fax: 440 729-8110
Dick Lang, *Owner*
EMP: 5
SALES (est): 337.6K **Privately Held**
SIC: 3559 Metal finishing equipment for
plating, etc.

(G-9282)
MIDWEST PRECISION LLC
34700 Lakeland Blvd (44095-5223)
PHONE..................................440 951-2333
Fax: 440 951-2336
Carl Richter, *President*
Steve Zuzek, *Plant Mgr*
Eddie Schwartz, *Purch Mgr*
Dale King, *Engineer*
Scott Huling, *Electrical Engi*
EMP: 52 EST: 2010
SQ FT: 38,000
SALES (est): 12.9MM **Privately Held**
WEB: www.midwestllc.com
SIC: 3451 Screw machine products

(G-9283)
MRD SOLUTIONS LLC
34201 Melinz Pkwy Unit A (44095-4018)
PHONE..................................440 942-6969
Nicholas Merlini,
Eugene Rapp,
EMP: 8
SALES (est): 1.6MM **Privately Held**
SIC: 3541 Machine tools, metal cutting
type

(G-9284)
NATIONAL BULLET CO
34971 Glen Dr (44095-2622)
PHONE..................................800 317-9506
Fax: 440 951-7761
Nick Sasso, *CEO*
Ken M Bayko, *President*
EMP: 9
SQ FT: 2,000

GEOGRAPHIC

SALES: 850K **Privately Held**
WEB: www.nationalbullet.com
SIC: 3482 5941 Small arms ammunition; sporting goods & bicycle shops

(G-9285)
POLYMER & STEEL TECH INC
34899 Curtis Blvd (44095-4015)
PHONE...........................440 510-0108
Douglas Horner, *President*
Janda Scott, *President*
Pat Gothro, *Vice Pres*
Larry Stanek, *Engineer*
Timothy D Reed, *CFO*
▼ EMP: 50
SQ FT: 66,000
SALES (est): 8.4MM **Privately Held**
WEB: www.enpac.com
SIC: 3089 Plastic containers, except foam

(G-9286)
SAWYER RESEARCH PRODUCT
35400 Lakeland Blvd (44095-5304)
PHONE...........................440 951-1480
Fax: 440 951-1480
Gary R Johnson, *Principal*
Paul R Hevey, *Manager*
EMP: 3
SALES (est): 377.9K **Privately Held**
SIC: 3679 Electronic components

(G-9287)
STAINLESS SPECIALTIES INC
33240 Lakeland Blvd (44095-5205)
PHONE...........................440 942-4242
Dennis O'Brien, *President*
Joan Podmore, *Vice Pres*
EMP: 25
SQ FT: 26,000
SALES (est): 4.9MM **Privately Held**
WEB: www.stainless-specialties.com
SIC: 3441 3312 Fabricated structural metal; blast furnaces & steel mills

(G-9288)
STEVENS AUTO GLAZE AND SEC LL
36250 Lkeland Blvd Unit 3 (44095)
PHONE...........................440 953-2900
Fax: 440 953-4473
Jeff Stevens, *President*
Joyce Stevens, *Corp Secy*
EMP: 2
SALES: 1MM **Privately Held**
SIC: 5531 5013 5169 3559 Automotive accessories; automotive supplies & parts; chemicals & allied products; automotive maintenance equipment

(G-9289)
STONEBROOK MACHINE
1572 E 365th St (44095-5325)
PHONE...........................440 951-5013
Donna Bowersock, *Owner*
EMP: 4
SQ FT: 3,000
SALES: 510K **Privately Held**
SIC: 3399 Metal fasteners

(G-9290)
SUBURBAN MANUFACTURING CO
1924 E 337th St (44095-5229)
PHONE...........................440 953-2024
Fax: 440 953-2318
Richard E Grice, *President*
Brian Nuibe, *Opers Staff*
Vicki Fazekas, *Manager*
Roxanne Putnam, *Manager*
EMP: 60
SQ FT: 31,000
SALES: 11.4MM **Privately Held**
WEB: www.submfg.com
SIC: 3599 3546 3469 3561 Machine shop, jobbing & repair; power-driven handtools; metal stampings; pumps & pumping equipment; fluid power pumps; fluid power cylinders & actuators

(G-9291)
SUMMERS ACQUISITION CORP
1857 E 337th St Unit B (44095-5231)
PHONE...........................440 946-5611
Richard Brown, *Branch Mgr*
EMP: 3

SALES (corp-wide): 2.5B **Privately Held**
WEB: www.summersrubber.com
SIC: 5085 3429 Rubber goods, mechanical; manufactured hardware (general)
HQ: Summers Acquisition Corporation
12555 Berea Rd
Cleveland OH 44111
216 941-7700

(G-9292)
T & D FABRICATING INC
1489 E 363rd St (44095-4137)
PHONE...........................440 951-5646
Fax: 440 953-3941
Dallas Adkins, *President*
Helen Adkins, *Corp Secy*
Todd Adkins, *Vice Pres*
EMP: 20
SALES (est): 5.7MM **Privately Held**
WEB: www.tdfabricating.com
SIC: 3469 3498 3354 3351 Metal stampings; fabricated pipe & fittings; aluminum extruded products; copper rolling & drawing; steel pipe & tubes; welding machinery & equipment

(G-9293)
TRI-TECH RESEARCH LLC
Also Called: Watts Acquisition Company II
34099 Melinz Pkwy Unit K (44095-4001)
PHONE...........................440 946-6122
Fax: 440 946-6127
Ridley Watts, *Mng Member*
EMP: 16
SQ FT: 12,000
SALES: 1.3MM **Privately Held**
SIC: 3625 8711 Electric controls & control accessories, industrial; engineering services

(G-9294)
TYMOCA PARTNERS LLC
Also Called: Federal Gear
33220 Lakeland Blvd (44095-5205)
PHONE...........................440 946-4327
Fax: 440 946-8018
Stephanie Ritt, *Bookkeeper*
David Hegenbarth,
EMP: 10
SALES (est): 2.3MM **Privately Held**
SIC: 3566 Speed changers, drives & gears

(G-9295)
UNITED MACHINE AND TOOL INC
1956 E 337th St (44095-5229)
PHONE...........................440 946-7677
Fax: 440 946-9729
Martha Klatt, *CEO*
Harry Klatt, *President*
EMP: 8 EST: 1965
SQ FT: 10,000
SALES (est): 490K **Privately Held**
WEB: www.unitedmachineandtool.com
SIC: 3599 Machine shop, jobbing & repair

(G-9296)
UNIVERSAL PROTOTYPE PRODUCT CO
36781 Lake Shore Blvd (44095-1146)
PHONE...........................440 953-3550
Fax: 440 953-8099
Ivan Nogalo, *President*
EMP: 3
SQ FT: 2,500
SALES: 270K **Privately Held**
SIC: 3599 Machine shop, jobbing & repair

(G-9297)
WEBER TECHNOLOGIES INC
34000 Melinz Pkwy (44095-4054)
PHONE...........................440 946-8833
Wim Huijs, *CEO*
EMP: 25 EST: 1901
SQ FT: 54,000
SALES (est): 3.6MM
SALES (corp-wide): 751.5MM **Publicly Held**
WEB: www.weber-tech.com
SIC: 3469 3471 3444 Stamping metal for the trade; perforated metal, stamped; spinning metal for the trade; finishing, metals or formed products; sheet metalwork

HQ: Enginetics Corporation
7700 New Carlisle Pike
Huber Heights OH 45424
937 878-3800

Eaton
Preble County

(G-9298)
ABBY INDUSTRIES LLC
346 Frizzell Ave (45320-9375)
PHONE...........................513 502-9865
Abigail Dahlinghaus, *Principal*
EMP: 3 EST: 2012
SALES (est): 240.1K **Privately Held**
SIC: 3999 Manufacturing industries

(G-9299)
AUKERMAN J F STEEL RULE DIE
5582 Ozias Rd (45320-9716)
P.O. Box 374 (45320-0374)
PHONE...........................937 456-4498
Fax: 937 456-9908
John F Aukerman Jr, *President*
EMP: 7
SALES (est): 101.2K **Privately Held**
SIC: 3544 Dies, steel rule

(G-9300)
BRUBAKER METALCRAFTS INC
209 N Franklin St (45320-1819)
PHONE...........................937 456-5834
Fax: 937 456-5786
Paul Brubaker, *President*
Ashley Myers, *Corp Secy*
Wilma Brubaker, *Admin Sec*
EMP: 7 EST: 1973
SQ FT: 3,000
SALES: 300K **Privately Held**
WEB: www.brubakertinware.com
SIC: 3229 Lantern globes

(G-9301)
BULLEN ULTRASONICS INC
1301 Miller Williams Rd (45320-8507)
PHONE...........................937 456-7133
Fax: 937 456-2779
Mary A Bullen, *President*
Thomas Fote, *Manager*
Mary A Moreland, *Admin Sec*
▲ EMP: 65 EST: 1969
SQ FT: 4,748
SALES (est): 12.1MM **Privately Held**
SIC: 3599 Machine shop, jobbing & repair

(G-9302)
CAMDEN CONCRETE PRODUCTS
Also Called: Shawnee Molds
4952 State Route 732 W (45320-9574)
PHONE...........................937 456-1229
Fax: 937 456-6456
Everett J Gilbert,
Patricia Gilbert,
▼ EMP: 6
SALES: 450K **Privately Held**
SIC: 3544 Industrial molds

(G-9303)
CORNERSTONE MANUFACTURING INC
861 Us Route 35 (45320-8638)
P.O. Box 682 (45320-0682)
PHONE...........................937 456-5930
Fax: 937 456-9268
Ronnie J Kutter, *President*
Patricia Kutter, *Vice Pres*
Trisha Kutter, *Vice Pres*
EMP: 9
SQ FT: 4,000
SALES: 1MM **Privately Held**
SIC: 3544 Special dies & tools

(G-9304)
DAILY AGENCY INC
309 N Barron St (45320-1705)
PHONE...........................937 456-9808
Fax: 937 456-1813
William Daily, *President*
Rick Daily, *Corp Secy*
EMP: 15
SQ FT: 3,000

SALES (est): 793K **Privately Held**
WEB: www.dailyagency.com
SIC: 6531 2711 Real estate agents & managers; newspapers, publishing & printing

(G-9305)
ELECTRO-CAP INTERNATIONAL INC
1011 W Lexington Rd (45320-9290)
P.O. Box 87 (45320-0087)
PHONE...........................937 456-6099
Fax: 937 456-7323
W Nelson Hardin, *President*
Amy Swallows, *Sales Mgr*
Janet L Hardin, *Admin Sec*
EMP: 18
SQ FT: 10,000
SALES (est): 2.6MM **Privately Held**
WEB: www.electro-cap.com
SIC: 3089 5047 Caps, plastic; hospital equipment & furniture

(G-9306)
FIRST IMPRESSION WEAR
120 E Main St (45320-1744)
PHONE...........................937 456-3900
Fax: 937 456-9050
Pat Taylor, *Principal*
EMP: 3
SALES (est): 267.3K **Privately Held**
SIC: 2759 Screen printing

(G-9307)
GRILL
100 Morton Rd (45320-1633)
PHONE...........................937 673-6768
EMP: 3 EST: 2014
SALES (est): 119.9K **Privately Held**
SIC: 3625 Motor controls & accessories

(G-9308)
HEART WARMING CANDLES
6806 Cumbersville St (45320)
PHONE...........................937 456-2720
Carol Gardner, *Owner*
EMP: 3
SALES (est): 93K **Privately Held**
SIC: 3999 Candles

(G-9309)
HENNY PENNY CORPORATION (PA)
1219 Us Route 35 (45320-8621)
P.O. Box 60 (45320-0060)
PHONE...........................937 456-8400
Fax: 937 456-8553
Steve Cobb, *CEO*
Rob Connelly, *President*
John Olsen, *Opers Mgr*
Glenn Ford, *Purchasing*
Jim Shepard, *Purchasing*
◆ EMP: 508
SQ FT: 400,000
SALES (est): 175.6MM **Privately Held**
SIC: 3589 Cooking equipment, commercial; food warming equipment, commercial

(G-9310)
I DREAM OF CAKES
995 Camden Rd (45320-9511)
PHONE...........................937 533-6024
Julie Rosfeld, *Principal*
EMP: 6
SALES (est): 159K **Privately Held**
SIC: 5461 2041 Bakeries; flour & other grain mill products

(G-9311)
INTERNATIONAL PAPER COMPANY
900 State Route 35 W (45320-8647)
PHONE...........................937 456-4131
Dale Whitman, *Production*
John Winters, *Branch Mgr*
Paul L Stoffregen, *Manager*
Paul Stoffregen, *Manager*
EMP: 120
SALES (corp-wide): 21B **Publicly Held**
SIC: 2653 Boxes, corrugated: made from purchased materials

PA: International Paper Company
6400 Poplar Ave
Memphis TN 38197
901 419-9000

(G-9312)
KEE PRINTING INC
118 W Monfort St (45320-1422)
PHONE..................................937 456-6851
Fax: 937 456-4316
Richard McKee, *Owner*
Carol Fewell, *Manager*
EMP: 4
SQ FT: 3,000
SALES: 275K **Privately Held**
SIC: 2752 2759 5999 Commercial printing, offset; letterpress printing; rubber stamps

(G-9313)
KRAMER POWER EQUIPMENT CO
2388 State Route 726 N (45320-9217)
PHONE..................................937 456-2232
Fax: 937 456-2282
Joseph Kramer, *President*
C Jason Kramer, *Vice Pres*
Andrew L Kramer, *Opers Staff*
Sharon Kramer, *Office Mgr*
Bill Salyers, *Supervisor*
EMP: 18
SQ FT: 20,000
SALES: 1.1MM **Privately Held**
WEB: www.kramerusa.com
SIC: 3599 3444 3441 7692 Machine shop, jobbing & repair; sheet metalwork; fabricated structural metal; welding repair

(G-9314)
LAM RESEARCH CORPORATION
Also Called: Silfex
950 S Franklin St (45320-9421)
PHONE..................................937 472-3311
Mike Snell, *General Mgr*
Patrick Bach, *Business Mgr*
Steve Joslin, *Opers Mgr*
Kristi Douglas, *Human Resources*
Steve Proia, *Manager*
EMP: 220
SALES (corp-wide): 5.8B **Publicly Held**
WEB: www.lamrc.com
SIC: 3559 Semiconductor manufacturing machinery
PA: Lam Research Corporation
4650 Cushing Pkwy
Fremont CA 94538
510 572-0200

(G-9315)
LAS MOTOR SPORTS
1694 Eaton Lewisburg Rd (45320-9756)
PHONE..................................937 456-2441
EMP: 3 EST: 2003
SALES (est): 150K **Privately Held**
SIC: 3599 Mfg Industrial Machinery

(G-9316)
LEE PLASTIC COMPANY LLC
1100 Us Route 35 (45320-8620)
P.O. Box 271 (45320-0271)
PHONE..................................937 456-5720
Fax: 937 456-5799
Patricia Kutter, *CEO*
Ron Kutter, *Director*
EMP: 8
SQ FT: 8,000
SALES: 750K **Privately Held**
SIC: 3089 Injection molding of plastics

(G-9317)
MARK COTTLE
Also Called: Tecmar Industries
11 Kastrup Dr (45320-2607)
PHONE..................................937 787-4791
Mark Cottle, *Owner*
EMP: 3
SQ FT: 6,500
SALES (est): 160K **Privately Held**
SIC: 3599 Machine & other job shop work

(G-9318)
MARK DAILY
807 N Maple St (45320-1532)
PHONE..................................937 369-5358
EMP: 3

SALES (est): 120K **Privately Held**
SIC: 2711 Newspapers, publishing & printing

(G-9319)
NEATON AUTO PRODUCTS MFG INC (HQ)
975 S Franklin St (45320-9400)
PHONE..................................937 456-7103
Fax: 937 456-1437
Naoki Horikawa, *President*
David Gulling, *Exec VP*
Kazuhiro Watanabe, *Vice Pres*
Joe Weaver, *Plant Mgr*
Dave Dunfee, *Prdtn Mgr*
▲ **EMP:** 277
SQ FT: 500,000
SALES (est): 111.6MM
SALES (corp-wide): 1.1B **Privately Held**
WEB: www.neaton.com
SIC: 3714 Motor vehicle parts & accessories; steering mechanisms, motor vehicle
PA: Nihon Plast Co.,Ltd.
3507-15, Yamamiya
Fujinomiya SZO 418-0
544 586-830

(G-9320)
PARKER-HANNIFIN CORPORATION
Tube Fittings Division
725 N Beech St (45320-1499)
PHONE..................................937 456-5571
Fax: 937 456-5696
Dave Stover, *Prdtn Mgr*
Jay Studer, *Mfg Mgr*
Debrah Burleson, *Purchasing*
Paul Farno, *Purchasing*
Tom Fox, *QC Dir*
EMP: 400
SALES (corp-wide): 11.3B **Publicly Held**
WEB: www.parker.com
SIC: 3494 5074 3498 3492 Pipe fittings; couplings, except pressure & soil pipe; plumbing & heating valves; plumbing fittings & supplies; tube fabricating (contract bending & shaping); fluid power valves & hose fittings
PA: Parker-Hannifin Corporation
6035 Parkland Blvd
Cleveland OH 44124
216 896-3000

(G-9321)
REGISTER HERALD OFFICE
200 Eaton Lewisburg Rd # 105 (45320-1191)
PHONE..................................937 456-5553
Fax: 937 456-3558
Darron Newman, *Principal*
EMP: 15 EST: 2002
SALES (est): 812.8K **Privately Held**
SIC: 2711 Newspapers, publishing & printing

(G-9322)
SEVEN MILE CREEK CORPORATION
315 S Beech St (45320-2311)
P.O. Box 155 (45320-0155)
PHONE..................................937 456-3320
William Cressell, *President*
Marqueeta Cressell, *Admin Sec*
EMP: 14 EST: 1935
SQ FT: 3,850
SALES (est): 350K **Privately Held**
WEB: www.sevenmilecreek.com
SIC: 2399 2392 2393 2326 Aprons, breast (harness); shower curtains: made from purchased materials; textile bags; men's & boys' work clothing

(G-9323)
SILFEX INC
950 S Franklin St (45320-9421)
PHONE..................................937 472-3311
Martin Anstice, *CEO*
Rhoel Ramos, *Project Mgr*
Colleen Friedsberg, *Mfg Mgr*
Marianna Gunsalus, *Production*
Randi Hollen, *Production*
▲ **EMP:** 142

SALES (est): 43.9MM
SALES (corp-wide): 5.8B **Publicly Held**
SIC: 3674 Semiconductors & related devices
PA: Lam Research Corporation
4650 Cushing Pkwy
Fremont CA 94538
510 572-0200

(G-9324)
TIMKENSTEEL CORPORATION
Also Called: St Clair Plant
401 Industrial Dr (45320-2255)
PHONE..................................937 456-8002
Fax: 937 456-8015
Jeremy Linder, *Principal*
Michael Ziarko, *Plant Mgr*
EMP: 67
SALES (corp-wide): 869.5MM **Publicly Held**
SIC: 3312 Blast furnaces & steel mills
PA: Timkensteel Corporation
1835 Dueber Ave Sw
Canton OH 44706
330 471-7000

Edgerton
Williams County

(G-9325)
AIR-WAY MANUFACTURING COMPANY
303 W River St (43517-9670)
PHONE..................................419 298-2366
Fax: 419 298-3164
Ronald Hamm, *CEO*
Kim De Young, *General Mgr*
Kim Deyoung, *General Mgr*
Lynn Lyman, *Marketing Staff*
Pam Nester, *Office Mgr*
EMP: 150
SALES (corp-wide): 64MM **Privately Held**
WEB: www.air-way.com
SIC: 3492 Hose & tube fittings & assemblies, hydraulic/pneumatic
PA: Air-Way Manufacturing Company Inc
586 N Main St
Olivet MI 49076
269 749-2161

(G-9326)
BUILDING CONCEPTS INC (PA)
Also Called: Cardinal Truss & Components
444 N Michigan Ave (43517-9811)
P.O. Box 579 (43517-0579)
PHONE..................................419 298-2371
Fax: 419 298-2667
William H Lutterbein, *President*
Dennis Imbrock, *Vice Pres*
Donald C Landel, *Vice Pres*
EMP: 16 EST: 1924
SQ FT: 14,000
SALES (est): 3.1MM **Privately Held**
WEB: www.lutterbein.com
SIC: 5211 1521 2439 Lumber & other building materials; single-family housing construction; trusses, wooden roof

(G-9327)
EDGERTON FORGE INC (HQ)
257 E Morrison St (43517-9302)
PHONE..................................419 298-2333
Fax: 419 298-3487
Richard Horton, *CEO*
Skip Dietrick, *President*
Pam Fitzcharles, *General Mgr*
Mark A Cluadio, *Vice Pres*
Gordon Miller, *Vice Pres*
EMP: 54
SQ FT: 70,000
SALES (est): 14.8MM
SALES (corp-wide): 284.4MM **Privately Held**
WEB: www.edgertonforge.com
SIC: 3462 3714 3423 Iron & steel forgings; motor vehicle parts & accessories; hand & edge tools
PA: Avis Industrial Corporation
1909 S Main St
Upland IN 46989
765 998-8100

(G-9328)
ELLIOTT OREN PRODUCTS INC
113 Industrial Dr (43517-9666)
PHONE..................................419 298-0015
Leo Font, *Prdtn Mgr*
Matthew Elliott, *Branch Mgr*
EMP: 16
SALES (corp-wide): 6MM **Privately Held**
WEB: www.orenelliottproducts.com
SIC: 3451 Screw machine products
PA: Oren Elliott Products, Inc.
128 W Vine St
Edgerton OH 43517
419 298-2306

(G-9329)
ELLIOTT OREN PRODUCTS INC (PA)
128 W Vine St (43517-8606)
P.O. Box 638 (43517-0638)
PHONE..................................419 298-2306
Fax: 419 298-3545
June Elliott, *President*
Oren Elliott, *Vice Pres*
Matthew Elliott, *Prdtn Mgr*
Crystal Yazvac, *Engineer*
Steven Ellliott, *Manager*
EMP: 39
SQ FT: 24,000
SALES (est): 6MM **Privately Held**
WEB: www.orenelliottproducts.com
SIC: 3675 3451 3469 Electronic capacitors; screw machine products; metal stampings

(G-9330)
FERGUSON TOOLS INC
103 Industrial Dr (43517-9666)
PHONE..................................419 298-2327
Fax: 419 298-2455
William Ferguson, *President*
Darrin Ferguson, *Vice Pres*
Markc Ferguson, *Vice Pres*
Kathy Ferguson, *Admin Sec*
EMP: 30
SQ FT: 10,000
SALES (est): 5.3MM **Privately Held**
WEB: www.fergusontools.com
SIC: 3545 Machine tool accessories

(G-9331)
FLEGAL BROTHERS INC
104 Industrial Dr (43517-9666)
PHONE..................................419 298-3539
Douglas Flegal, *President*
EMP: 15
SALES: 500K **Privately Held**
SIC: 2611 4213 Pulp mills, mechanical & recycling processing; trucking, except local

(G-9332)
MATSU OHIO INC
228 E Morrison St (43517-9389)
PHONE..................................419 298-2394
Dave Rutila, *President*
Art Artuso, *President*
Galliano Tiberini, *Vice Pres*
Richard Ponpey, *Branch Mgr*
Barbara Lane, *Manager*
▲ **EMP:** 122
SQ FT: 220,000
SALES (est): 31.7MM
SALES (corp-wide): 62MM **Privately Held**
SIC: 3465 Body parts, automobile: stamped metal
PA: Matsu Manufacturing Inc
7657 Bramalea Rd
Brampton ON L6T 5
905 291-5000

(G-9333)
MIDWEST STAMPING & MFG CO
228 E Morrison St (43517-9389)
PHONE..................................419 298-2394
Fax: 419 724-6971
John Carney, *Principal*
EMP: 9
SALES (est): 692.4K **Privately Held**
SIC: 3999 Manufacturing industries

(G-9334)
ROBERTSON EDM LLC
9294 State Route 249 (43517-9556)
PHONE..................................419 658-2219

Ronald Walker, *Mng Member*
Jeffrey Robertson,
EMP: 5
SALES: 675K **Privately Held**
SIC: 3599 Machine shop, jobbing & repair

(G-9335)
RURAL PRODUCTS INC
6266 Us Highway 6 (43517-9710)
PHONE..............................419 298-2677
Fax: 419 298-2148
John Curry, *President*
EMP: 4 **EST:** 1963
SALES (est): 400K **Privately Held**
SIC: 3451 3544 Screw machine products;
　special dies & tools

(G-9336)
STAFFORD GRAVEL INC
4225 Co Rd 79 (43517)
P.O. Box 340 (43517-0340)
PHONE..............................419 298-2440
Fax: 419 298-2774
Gerry Weber, *Principal*
EMP: 6
SALES (est): 587.1K **Privately Held**
SIC: 1442 Construction sand & gravel

(G-9337)
STARK TRUSS COMPANY INC
400 Component Dr (43517)
P.O. Box 535 (43517-0535)
PHONE..............................419 298-3777
Fax: 419 298-2726
Duane Miller, *Branch Mgr*
EMP: 75
SQ FT: 45,000
SALES (corp-wide): 230.5MM **Privately
Held**
WEB: www.starktruss.com
SIC: 2439 2511 2411 Trusses, wooden
　roof; wood household furniture; logging
PA: Stark Truss Company, Inc.
　　109 Miles Ave Sw
　　Canton OH 44710
　　330 478-2100

(G-9338)
WEBER SAND & GRAVEL INC
2702 County Road 3b (43517-9692)
PHONE..............................419 298-2388
Fax: 419 298-2363
Thomas B Weber, *President*
Judy Weber, *Vice Pres*
EMP: 11
SQ FT: 2,000
SALES (est): 818.5K **Privately Held**
SIC: 1442 Common sand mining; gravel
　mining

Edon
Williams County

(G-9339)
AGRIDRY LLC
3460 Us Highway 20 (43518-9733)
P.O. Box 336 (43518-0336)
PHONE..............................419 459-4399
Bruce Silcott, *Office Mgr*
Eli P Troyer, *Mng Member*
EMP: 45
SALES (est): 11.9MM **Privately Held**
SIC: 3567 1541 Driers & redriers, indus-
　trial process; grain elevator construction

(G-9340)
**DIMENSION HARDWOOD
VENEERS INC**
509 Woodville St (43518)
PHONE..............................419 272-2245
Fax: 419 272-2406
Paul Horstman, *President*
▲ **EMP:** 50 **EST:** 1977
SQ FT: 56,000
SALES (est): 8.4MM **Privately Held**
SIC: 2435 Hardwood veneer & plywood

(G-9341)
L & L MACHINE INC
2919 County Road 2l (43518-9771)
PHONE..............................419 272-5000
Fax: 419 272-5025
Laurie Lehman, *CEO*

Michael Lehman, *President*
EMP: 11
SQ FT: 40,000
SALES: 1.5MM **Privately Held**
SIC: 3599 Machine shop, jobbing & repair

(G-9342)
**NORTHWEST MOLDED
PLASTICS**
14372 County Road 4 (43518-9765)
PHONE..............................419 459-4414
Fax: 419 459-4333
Richard L Lemmon, *Owner*
EMP: 9 **EST:** 1976
SQ FT: 25,000
SALES (est): 550K **Privately Held**
WEB: www.comtech2000.com
SIC: 3089 Molding primary plastic

(G-9343)
PLAS-TEC CORP
601 W Indiana St (43518-9645)
PHONE..............................419 272-2731
Fax: 419 272-2733
Kenneth Sharlow, *General Mgr*
Terry Carter, *Purch Dir*
Dennis Cox, *Treasurer*
Troy Brock, *Maintence Staff*
EMP: 60
SQ FT: 85,000
SALES (est): 16.4MM **Privately Held**
WEB: www.plasteccorp.com
SIC: 3089 Injection molded finished plastic
　products

(G-9344)
PTC ENTERPRISES INC
3047 County Road K (43518-9551)
PHONE..............................419 272-2524
Fax: 419 272-2721
Bill Patton, *President*
David C Newcomer, *Principal*
Joyce Psurny, *Manager*
▲ **EMP:** 50
SALES (est): 8.6MM **Privately Held**
SIC: 3089 Bearings, plastic

(G-9345)
**S R T PROSTHETICS &
ORTHOTICS**
6868 State Route 49 (43518-9713)
PHONE..............................419 272-3102
Samuel Santa Rita, *Owner*
EMP: 3
SALES (est): 239.9K **Privately Held**
SIC: 3842 Orthopedic appliances

Eldorado
Preble County

(G-9346)
MIAMI VALLEY PLASTICS INC
310 S Main St (45321-9731)
PHONE..............................937 273-3200
Fax: 937 273-2690
George W Halderman, *CEO*
▲ **EMP:** 35
SQ FT: 2,569
SALES (est): 6.3MM **Privately Held**
SIC: 3089 Injection molding of plastics

(G-9347)
**OLDE SCHLHUSE VNYRD
WINERY LLC**
8538 State Route 726 (45321-9734)
P.O. Box 230 (45321-0230)
PHONE..............................937 273-6023
Angela S Zdobinski, *Owner*
EMP: 4
SALES (est): 287.9K **Privately Held**
SIC: 2084 Wines

(G-9348)
SUDS
160 Main Cross (45321)
PHONE..............................937 273-6007
Martin Ridge, *Principal*
EMP: 4
SALES (est): 366.4K **Privately Held**
SIC: 2599 Bar, restaurant & cafeteria furni-
　ture

Elida
Allen County

(G-9349)
**A & D WOOD PRODUCTS INC
(PA)**
4220 Sherrick Rd (45807-9783)
PHONE..............................419 331-8859
Joseph Peters, *President*
EMP: 9 **Privately Held**
SIC: 2448 Pallets, wood

(G-9350)
**AIRCRAFT DYNAMICS
CORPORATION**
418 E Kiracofe Ave (45807-1030)
P.O. Box 3038, Lima (45807-0038)
PHONE..............................419 331-0371
Fax: 419 331-7349
Jack D Jones, *President*
Alice White, *Corp Secy*
Steve Jones, *Exec VP*
Doug Thackery, *Vice Pres*
Mel Utrup, *Sales Mgr*
EMP: 18
SQ FT: 12,000
SALES (est): 2.4MM **Privately Held**
WEB: www.aircraftdynamics.com
SIC: 7359 3546 Equipment rental & leas-
　ing; power-driven handtools

(G-9351)
LIMA MILLWORK INC
4251 East Rd (45807-1534)
PHONE..............................419 331-3303
Fax: 419 331-4731
Mark Niemeyer, *President*
Thelma Neimeyer, *Vice Pres*
EMP: 26
SQ FT: 16,000
SALES: 3.5MM **Privately Held**
SIC: 2431 2511 2434 3281 Millwork;
　wood household furniture; wood kitchen
　cabinets; cut stone & stone products;
　wood partitions & fixtures; wood office fur-
　niture

(G-9352)
LIMA PIPE ORGAN CO INC
408 E Kiracofe Ave (45807-1030)
P.O. Box 3023 (45807-0023)
PHONE..............................419 331-5461
Larry Holycross, *President*
Tom Holycross, *Vice Pres*
EMP: 4
SQ FT: 3,500
SALES: 250K **Privately Held**
WEB: www.limapipeorgan.com
SIC: 3931 7699 Pipes, organ; organ tun-
　ing & repair

(G-9353)
ORICK STAMPING
614 E Kiracofe Ave (45807-1034)
PHONE..............................419 331-0600
Fax: 419 331-1552
Paul Orick, *CEO*
Greg Orick, *President*
Monica Orick, *Exec VP*
Bob Sheffield, *QC Mgr*
Amy Ricker, *Human Resources*
EMP: 80
SQ FT: 100,000
SALES (est): 29.3MM **Privately Held**
WEB: www.oricktool.com
SIC: 3469 3544 Metal stampings; special
　dies, tools, jigs & fixtures

(G-9354)
PATTON INDUSTRIES INC
Also Called: Dimensional Equipment Div
1950 Beery Rd (45807-9514)
PHONE..............................419 331-5658
Fax: 419 331-2235
James E Patton, *President*
Sherry Patton, *Corp Secy*
Sandra L Patton, *Vice Pres*
EMP: 5
SQ FT: 40,000
SALES: 400K **Privately Held**
SIC: 5084 3599 Metalworking machinery;
　machine shop, jobbing & repair

(G-9355)
**PETERS FAMILY ENTERPRISES
INC**
5959 Allentown Rd (45807-9413)
P.O. Box 3133 (45807-0133)
PHONE..............................419 339-0555
Dave Peters, *President*
EMP: 8
SALES (est): 1MM **Privately Held**
SIC: 2499 Decorative wood & woodwork

(G-9356)
RANGE KLEEN MFG INC
4240 East Rd (45807-1533)
P.O. Box 696, Lima (45802-0696)
PHONE..............................419 331-8000
Fax: 419 331-4538
Patrick O'Connor, *President*
Ron Moots, *Maintenance Dir*
Karen Griff, *Plant Mgr*
Becky Hesseling, *Prdtn Mgr*
T Clutter, *Sales Staff*
▲ **EMP:** 403
SQ FT: 50,000
SALES (est): 73.1MM **Privately Held**
WEB: www.rangekleen.com
SIC: 3365 3469 Cooking/kitchen utensils,
　cast aluminum; metal stampings

(G-9357)
SHELDON ON SITE INC
4848 Gomer Rd (45807-9507)
PHONE..............................419 339-1381
Sheldon Bowman, *President*
Rebecca Bowman, *Admin Sec*
EMP: 5
SALES: 200K **Privately Held**
SIC: 7694 7699 Electric motor repair; en-
　gine repair & replacement, non-automo-
　tive

(G-9358)
SIEFKER SAWMILL
8705 W State Rd (45807-8730)
PHONE..............................419 339-1956
Gary Siefker, *Partner*
Dan Siefker, *Partner*
Ken Siefker, *Partner*
Ron Siefker, *Partner*
EMP: 8
SALES (est): 780K **Privately Held**
SIC: 2421 2426 Sawmills & planing mills,
　general; lumber, hardwood dimension

(G-9359)
**ULRICH RUBBER STAMP
COMPANY**
Also Called: Tebben Rubber Stamp Company
2130 Larkspur Dr (45807-1489)
PHONE..............................419 339-9939
Fax: 419 339-1457
Jack Ulrich, *President*
Sally Ulrich, *Vice Pres*
EMP: 3 **EST:** 1953
SALES: 75K **Privately Held**
SIC: 2791 3953 7389 Typesetting; em-
　bossing seals & hand stamps;

Elmore
Ottawa County

(G-9360)
ALVIN L ROEPKE
Also Called: Vision Quest
329 Rice St (43416-9404)
P.O. Box 197 (43416-0197)
PHONE..............................419 862-3891
Fax: 419 862-1750
Alvin L Roepke, *Owner*
EMP: 16
SQ FT: 5,400
SALES: 850K **Privately Held**
SIC: 7336 2759 3993 2284 Silk screen
　design; screen printing; signs & advertis-
　ing specialties; embroidery thread

(G-9361)
CALVIN J MAGSIG
Also Called: Elmore Mfg Co
343 Clinton St (43416-7703)
P.O. Box 32 (43416-0032)
PHONE..............................419 862-3311
Calvin J Magsig, *Owner*

EMP: 7
SQ FT: 15,000
SALES: 600K **Privately Held**
SIC: 3599 3494 Machine shop, jobbing & repair; valves & pipe fittings

(G-9362)
CHIPMATIC TOOL & MACHINE INC
212 Ottawa St (43416-7710)
P.O. Box 87 (43416-0087)
PHONE..................................419 862-2737
Fax: 419 862-2769
Mike Detzel, *President*
Bob Babjack, *General Mgr*
John Hansen, *Purch Mgr*
Duane Glase, *Purch Agent*
Chris Lajoie, *QC Mgr*
EMP: 67
SQ FT: 30,000
SALES (est): 11.1MM **Privately Held**
WEB: www.chipmatic.com
SIC: 3599 8711 7692 3544 Machine shop, jobbing & repair; mechanical engineering; welding repair; special dies, tools, jigs & fixtures

(G-9363)
MACHINING TECHNOLOGIES INC (PA)
Also Called: M T
468 Maple St (43416-9423)
P.O. Box 287 (43416-0287)
PHONE..................................419 862-3110
Fax: 419 862-2107
William M Van Dorn, *CEO*
Thomas C Van Dorn, *CFO*
Yangsayam J Mahapanyawongs, *Controller*
Beverly Corne, *Accountant*
Tony Haines, *Sales Mgr*
▲ EMP: 41
SQ FT: 32,000
SALES (est): 8.4MM **Privately Held**
SIC: 3082 3545 Unsupported plastics profile shapes; precision tools, machinists'

(G-9364)
MARTIN INDUSTRIES INC
473 Maple St (43416-9402)
P.O. Box 569 (43416-0569)
PHONE..................................419 862-2694
Fax: 419 862-3560
Tim Gerkensmeyer, *President*
EMP: 30
SQ FT: 10,000
SALES (est): 4.8MM **Privately Held**
SIC: 3069 3061 Hard rubber & molded rubber products; mechanical rubber goods

(G-9365)
MATERION BRUSH INC
14710 W Prtage River S Rd (43416-9500)
PHONE..................................419 862-2745
Fax: 419 862-4000
Daniel Skoch, *VP Admin*
Thomas Piazza, *Vice Pres*
Andrew Sandor, *VP Opers*
Steve Deuschle, *Opers Mgr*
Wm Smith, *Purch Mgr*
EMP: 700
SQ FT: 100,000
SALES (corp-wide): 969.2MM **Publicly Held**
WEB: www.brushwellman.com
SIC: 3339 3369 3341 Beryllium metal; nonferrous foundries; secondary nonferrous metals
HQ: Materion Brush Inc.
6070 Parkland Blvd Ste 1
Mayfield Heights OH 44124
216 486-4200

Elyria
Lorain County

(G-9366)
3M COMPANY
1301 Lowell St (44035-4864)
PHONE..................................440 323-6161
Michael Flannery, *Purch Dir*
Michael Burns, *Engineer*
Gretchen Mueller, *Engineer*

Daniel Finkel, *Plant Engr*
George Hrabik, *Branch Mgr*
EMP: 170
SALES (est): 3.7MM **Privately Held**
SALES (corp-wide): 30.1B **Publicly Held**
WEB: www.mmm.com
SIC: 3089 2823 Sponges, plastic; cellulosic manmade fibers
PA: 3m Company
3m Center Bldg 22011w02
Saint Paul MN 55144
651 733-1110

(G-9367)
ALCO MANUFACTURING CORP LLC (PA)
10584 Middle Ave (44035-7812)
PHONE..................................440 458-5165
Fax: 440 458-6821
Kevin Koepp, *President*
Martina Mutz, *Sales Mgr*
EMP: 50
SALES (est): 19.4MM **Privately Held**
SIC: 3542 Machine tools, metal forming type

(G-9368)
ALEXIS CONCRETE ENTERPRISE INC
672 Sugar Ln (44035-6310)
PHONE..................................440 366-0031
Edward Machovia, *President*
Jennifer Elbert, *Manager*
EMP: 11 EST: 2000
SALES (est): 1.6MM **Privately Held**
SIC: 3273 Ready-mixed concrete

(G-9369)
ALLEN KENARD PRINTING INC
501 Clark St (44035-6109)
PHONE..................................440 323-7405
Fax: 440 323-3379
Fred A Rice, *President*
Judy L Rice, *Corp Secy*
EMP: 10
SQ FT: 10,000
SALES (est): 930K **Privately Held**
SIC: 2752 Commercial printing, offset

(G-9370)
AMERICAN COMMODORE TUXEDOS
3433 Midway Mall (44035-2449)
PHONE..................................440 324-2889
Jose Rodriguez, *Manager*
EMP: 4
SALES (est): 99.2K **Privately Held**
SIC: 7299 2311 Clothing rental services; tuxedos: made from purchased materials

(G-9371)
AMERICAN FLUID POWER INC
144 Reaser Ct (44035-6285)
PHONE..................................877 223-8742
Robert Weltman, *COO*
EMP: 7
SALES: 610K **Privately Held**
SIC: 3542 Machine tools, metal forming type; bending machines

(G-9372)
AMIDAC WIND CORPORATION
151 Innovation Dr (44035-1675)
PHONE..................................213 973-4000
Ameer Alghusain, *CEO*
EMP: 5 EST: 2015
SALES (est): 330.6K **Privately Held**
SIC: 3643 Lightning protection equipment

(G-9373)
ANDRAS CORP
840 Infirmary Rd (44035-4819)
PHONE..................................440 323-2528
Ken Andras, *President*
EMP: 5 EST: 1964
SQ FT: 10,000
SALES: 500K **Privately Held**
SIC: 3272 Burial vaults, concrete or precast terrazzo

(G-9374)
APPLIED ENGNEERED SURFACES INC
535 Ternes Ln (44035-6286)
PHONE..................................440 366-0440
Lauren Yoakam, *President*

EMP: 17
SALES (est): 3.7MM **Privately Held**
SIC: 3441 Fabricated structural metal

(G-9375)
ARNCO CORPORATION
860 Garden St (44035-4877)
PHONE..................................800 847-7661
Fax: 440 322-1001
Arlene P Tengel, *Principal*
William E Smith, *Corp Secy*
Ron Bayus, *Mfg Dir*
Michael McNulty, *Plant Mgr*
Dale Nichols, *Purchasing*
▲ EMP: 250
SALES: 44.2MM
SALES (corp-wide): 1.8B **Privately Held**
WEB: www.arncocorp.com
SIC: 3661 3829 3644 3429 Telephones & telephone apparatus; measuring & controlling devices; noncurrent-carrying wiring services; manufactured hardware (general); nonferrous wiredrawing & insulating
PA: Audax Group, L.P.
101 Huntington Ave # 2450
Boston MA 02199
617 859-1500

(G-9376)
ATTRACTIVE KITCHENS & FLRG LLC
536 Cleveland St (44035-4055)
PHONE..................................440 406-9299
Byron Slater,
EMP: 5
SQ FT: 5,000
SALES: 2MM **Privately Held**
SIC: 2499 5211 1752 Woodenware, kitchen & household; counter tops; wood floor installation & refinishing

(G-9377)
AVAIL VAPOR LLC
641 Chestnut Commons Dr (44035-9609)
PHONE..................................440 365-5440
EMP: 3
SALES (corp-wide): 70.1MM **Privately Held**
SIC: 2111 Cigarettes
PA: Avail Vapor, Llc
820 Southlake Blvd
North Chesterfield VA 23236
804 419-2180

(G-9378)
B&B DISTRIBUTORS LLC
Also Called: Builders Straight Edge
150 Keep Ct Ste A (44035-2215)
PHONE..................................440 324-1293
George Hovanitz,
EMP: 10
SALES (est): 1.1MM **Privately Held**
SIC: 3353 Aluminum sheet, plate & foil

(G-9379)
BASF CATALYSTS LLC
120 Pine St (44035-5228)
P.O. Box 4017 (44036-2017)
PHONE..................................440 322-3741
Fax: 440 329-2404
Gregory Menz, *Maint Spvr*
Darryl L Ferguson, *Mfg Staff*
Richard Olechnowicz, *QC Dir*
Noemi Trent, *Engineer*
Randolph C Turk, *Branch Mgr*
EMP: 263
SALES (corp-wide): 60.8B **Privately Held**
SIC: 2819 Industrial inorganic chemicals
HQ: Basf Catalysts Llc
25 Middlesex Tpke
Iselin NJ 08830
732 205-5000

(G-9380)
BENDIX SPCER FNDTION BRAKE LLC (DH)
901 Cleveland St (44035-4153)
PHONE..................................440 329-9709
Eddie Wilkinson, *President*
Aaron Schwass, *Vice Pres*
Mehmet Kocaarslan, *Buyer*
Greg Mazzella, *Buyer*
Fred Stephens, *Accountant*
▲ EMP: 101

SALES (est): 75.3MM **Privately Held**
SIC: 3714 Air brakes, motor vehicle; brake drums, motor vehicle; motor vehicle brake systems & parts
HQ: Knorr Brake Holding Corporation
748 Starbuck Ave
Watertown NY 13601
315 786-5356

(G-9381)
BEST FAB CO
936 Taylor St (44035-6234)
PHONE..................................440 328-3254
Joe Jingle, *President*
EMP: 8
SQ FT: 9,200
SALES (est): 1.1MM **Privately Held**
SIC: 3441 Fabricated structural metal

(G-9382)
BIRGE HEAVY INDUSTRIES LTD
322 Furnace St (44035-5065)
PHONE..................................440 821-3249
Anthony Birge,
EMP: 20
SQ FT: 3,250
SALES (est): 950K **Privately Held**
SIC: 3999 Manufacturing industries

(G-9383)
BUCKEYE MOLDED PRODUCTS LTD
443 Oberlin Elyria Rd (44035-7761)
PHONE..................................440 323-2244
Fax: 440 323-2205
Carl R Kennedy, *Mng Member*
Susan Tursivio, *Manager*
Fred Hugunin,
EMP: 10
SQ FT: 20,000
SALES (est): 860K **Privately Held**
WEB: www.buckeyemoldedproducts.com
SIC: 3624 Brush blocks, carbon or molded graphite

(G-9384)
BUCKEYE STATE WELDING & FABG (PA)
131 Buckeye St (44035-5216)
P.O. Box 837 (44036-0837)
PHONE..................................440 322-0319
Fax: 440 323-7620
Kenneth E Reddinger, *President*
Christopher R Reddinger, *Corp Secy*
Patrick J Reddinger, *Vice Pres*
Richard Radichi, *Accountant*
EMP: 9
SQ FT: 12,000
SALES (est): 3.3MM **Privately Held**
SIC: 3599 Machine shop, jobbing & repair

(G-9385)
BUCKEYE STATE WELDING & FABG
175 Woodford Ave (44035-5436)
P.O. Box 837 (44036-0837)
PHONE..................................440 322-0344
Fax: 440 323-6817
Chris Reddinger, *Owner*
EMP: 22
SALES (corp-wide): 3.3MM **Privately Held**
SIC: 3548 Welding & cutting apparatus & accessories
PA: Buckeye State Welding & Fabricating Inc
131 Buckeye St
Elyria OH 44035
440 322-0319

(G-9386)
CA PICARD SURFACE ENGRG INC
1206 E Broad St (44035-6308)
PHONE..................................440 366-5400
Fax: 440 366-5404
Mark Sink, *President*
Dave Smith, *Sales Mgr*
Peg Lieberman, *Executive Asst*
Sarah Phillips, *Admin Asst*
▲ EMP: 12
SQ FT: 7,000

SALES (est): 1.8MM
SALES (corp-wide): 50.7MM **Privately Held**
SIC: 3469 5051 Machine parts, stamped or pressed metal; foundry products
HQ: Carl Aug. Picard Gmbh
　　Haster Aue 9
　　Remscheid 42857
　　219 189-30

(G-9387)
CABLETEK WIRING PRODUCTS INC
1150 Taylor St (44035-6281)
PHONE..............................800 562-9378
Stan Leonowigh, *President*
EMP: 25
SALES (est): 3.2MM **Privately Held**
SIC: 3444 Metal housings, enclosures, casings & other containers

(G-9388)
CASCADE PATTERN COMPANY INC
519 Ternes Ln (44035-6286)
PHONE..............................440 323-4300
Fax: 440 365-8458
Charles A Petek, *CEO*
Rick Petek, *President*
Nick Petek, *Vice Pres*
Dick Lakocy, *Purchasing*
Scott Harsany, *Engineer*
EMP: 32
SALES (est): 6.3MM **Privately Held**
WEB: www.cascadepattern.com
SIC: 3543 Industrial patterns

(G-9389)
CASCADE PLATING INC
Also Called: Lake Plating
210 Abbe Rd S (44035-6240)
PHONE..............................440 366-4931
Greg Lake, *President*
EMP: 3
SQ FT: 10,800
SALES (est): 343.7K **Privately Held**
SIC: 3471 Plating of metals or formed products

(G-9390)
CASTCO INC
527 Ternes Ln (44035-6286)
P.O. Box 1368, Delaware (43015-8368)
PHONE..............................440 365-2333
Dan Petek, *CEO*
EMP: 45
SALES (est): 7.5MM **Privately Held**
WEB: www.castco.com
SIC: 3321 Gray & ductile iron foundries

(G-9391)
CASTEK ALUMINUM INC
527 Ternes Ln (44035-6286)
PHONE..............................440 365-2333
Fax: 440 365-2334
Daniel C Petek, *President*
EMP: 40
SALES (est): 8.6MM **Privately Held**
SIC: 3365 Aluminum foundries

(G-9392)
CHALFANT MANUFACTURING COMPANY
7005 W River Rd S (44035-7058)
PHONE..............................440 323-9870
Fax: 440 323-1925
John Slaga, *Branch Mgr*
EMP: 17
SALES (corp-wide): 672.8K **Privately Held**
SIC: 3643 Current-carrying wiring devices
HQ: Chalfant Manufacturing Company
　　50 Pearl Rd Ste 212
　　Brunswick OH 44212
　　330 273-3510

(G-9393)
CHEMTURA CORPORATION
Also Called: Ingredient Technology Division
110 Liberty Ct (44035-2237)
PHONE..............................440 324-6060
Fax: 440 324-2747
Ronald Nicolson, *Opers-Prdtn-Mfg*
Ronald Delikat, *Purch Mgr*
John Cassidy, *Branch Mgr*

Dave Karolak, *Manager*
Damon Gambino, *Supervisor*
EMP: 50
SQ FT: 10,000
SALES (corp-wide): 1.6B **Privately Held**
WEB: www.cromptoncorp.com
SIC: 2099 Emulsifiers, food
PA: Chemtura Corporation
　　1818 Market St Ste 3700
　　Philadelphia PA 19103
　　203 573-2000

(G-9394)
CITY ELYRIA COMMUNICATION
851 Garden St (44035-4874)
PHONE..............................440 322-3329
Larry Showalter, *Superintendent*
EMP: 6
SALES (est): 378.6K **Privately Held**
SIC: 3669 Traffic signals, electric

(G-9395)
CLONDALKIN GROUP
Cleveland Plastic Films
41740 Schadden Rd (44035-2231)
PHONE..............................440 324-2222
James Hendershot, *COO*
Dwayne Nicholas, *Branch Mgr*
Ken Miller, *Exec Dir*
EMP: 3 **Privately Held**
SIC: 3081 Polyethylene film
HQ: Clondalkin Group
　　2000 Market St Ste 2810
　　Philadelphia PA 19103
　　215 440-0570

(G-9396)
COCA-COLA COMPANY
1410 Lake Ave (44035-3124)
PHONE..............................440 324-3335
Fax: 440 324-4419
Scott Dickerhoff, *Manager*
EMP: 52
SALES (corp-wide): 41.8B **Publicly Held**
WEB: www.colasic.net
SIC: 2086 Bottled & canned soft drinks
PA: The Coca-Cola Company
　　1 Coca Cola Plz Nw
　　Atlanta GA 30313
　　404 676-2121

(G-9397)
CONSUN FOOD INDUSTRIES INC
Also Called: Sunshine Farms Dairy
123 Gateway Blvd N (44035-4923)
PHONE..............................440 322-6301
Dennis Walter, *President*
EMP: 60
SALES (corp-wide): 13.8MM **Privately Held**
SIC: 2026 Fluid milk
PA: Consun Food Industries, Inc.
　　123 Gateway Blvd N
　　Elyria OH 44035
　　440 322-6301

(G-9398)
CREATIVE POWDER COATINGS
6412 Gateway Blvd S (44035-5442)
PHONE..............................440 322-8197
Mark Brown, *CEO*
Gail Brown, *Treasurer*
EMP: 3
SQ FT: 6,000
SALES (est): 307K **Privately Held**
SIC: 3479 Painting of metal products

(G-9399)
CRYSTAL KOCH FINISHING INC
Also Called: Koch Crystal Finishing
630 Sugar Ln (44035-6310)
PHONE..............................440 366-7526
Fax: 440 783-3299
Elizabeth Koch, *President*
EMP: 5
SQ FT: 6,000
SALES (est): 491.9K **Privately Held**
SIC: 7699 3471 Scientific equipment repair service; plating & polishing

(G-9400)
CUSTOM ALUMINUM BOXES
330 10th St (44035-7031)
PHONE..............................440 864-2664
Mark Morales, *Principal*

EMP: 4
SALES (est): 460.2K **Privately Held**
SIC: 2631 Folding boxboard

(G-9401)
DENNE INDUSTRIES INC
Also Called: Rec Enterprises
650 Sugar Ln (44035-6310)
PHONE..............................440 365-0600
Fax: 440 365-3606
Robert Casper, *President*
Kristie Natale, *Office Mgr*
EMP: 20
SQ FT: 7,500
SALES (est): 3.5MM **Privately Held**
SIC: 3316 Cold finishing of steel shapes

(G-9402)
DIAMOND PRODUCTS LIMITED
1111 Taylor St (44035-6245)
PHONE..............................440 323-4616
Don Williams, *Purch Agent*
Tracey Howe, *Manager*
Karl Moller, *Manager*
EMP: 10
SALES (corp-wide): 64.1MM **Privately Held**
WEB: www.diamondproducts.com
SIC: 3545 Machine tool accessories
PA: Diamond Products, Limited
　　333 Prospect St
　　Elyria OH 44035
　　440 323-4616

(G-9403)
DIAMONDS PRODUCTS LLC
1250 E Broad St (44035-6311)
PHONE..............................440 323-4616
Andrew Jedrick, *General Mgr*
Barney Oldfield, *Vice Pres*
Karl Moller,
▲ EMP: 7
SALES (est): 877.3K **Privately Held**
SIC: 3545 Diamond cutting tools for turning, boring, burnishing, etc.

(G-9404)
DICKS COUNTER D M
275 Warden Ave (44035-2649)
PHONE..............................440 322-3312
Horace Dicks, *Principal*
EMP: 3
SALES (est): 181.8K **Privately Held**
SIC: 3131 Counters

(G-9405)
DIY HOLSTER LLC
7836 Oberlin Rd (44035-1910)
PHONE..............................419 921-2168
EMP: 8
SALES (est): 970.3K **Privately Held**
SIC: 3199 5072 5961 Holsters, leather; hardware; tools & hardware, mail order

(G-9406)
DONCASTERS GROUP LTD
Also Called: Nelson Stud Welding
7900 W Ridge Rd (44035-1952)
P.O. Box 4019 (44036-2019)
PHONE..............................440 329-0400
William M Ellis, *President*
EMP: 6 EST: 2011
SALES (est): 810.1K **Privately Held**
SIC: 3826 Laser scientific & engineering instruments
HQ: Doncasters Group Limited
　　Millennium Court
　　Burton-On-Trent STAFFS DE14
　　133 286-4900

(G-9407)
DURA-LINE CORPORATION
860 Garden St (44035-4826)
PHONE..............................440 322-1000
Steven Sminth, *Branch Mgr*
EMP: 49
SALES (corp-wide): 5.8B **Privately Held**
SIC: 3084 Plastics pipe
HQ: Dura-Line Corporation
　　11400 Parkside Dr Ste 300
　　Knoxville TN 37934
　　865 218-3460

(G-9408)
DYNATECH SYSTEMS INC
161 Reaser Ct (44035-6285)
P.O. Box 1589 (44036-1589)
PHONE..............................440 365-1774
Fax: 440 365-1717
Sue A Everett, *President*
EMP: 25
SQ FT: 5,000
SALES (est): 3MM **Privately Held**
WEB: www.diamonddrillbit.com
SIC: 3425 5085 Saw blades & handsaws; industrial supplies

(G-9409)
E C S CORP
Also Called: Elyria Concrete Step Company
8015 Murray Ridge Rd (44035-2071)
PHONE..............................440 323-1707
Everett G Goad, *President*
Betty Goad, *Vice Pres*
Gary Goad, *Vice Pres*
Thomas R Goad, *Vice Pres*
Leanne Odel, *Admin Sec*
EMP: 13 EST: 1957
SQ FT: 9,300
SALES: 745.9K **Privately Held**
SIC: 3446 3272 Grillwork, ornamental metal; steps, prefabricated concrete

(G-9410)
E D M ELECTROFYING INC
34 Artemas Ct (44035-6167)
PHONE..............................440 322-8900
Fax: 440 322-9480
Timothy Koba, *President*
Jennifer Koba, *Vice Pres*
EMP: 5
SQ FT: 2,800
SALES: 380K **Privately Held**
WEB: www.electrofyingedm.com
SIC: 3541 3544 Electrical discharge erosion machines; special dies, tools, jigs & fixtures; industrial molds

(G-9411)
ELCOR INC
640 Sugar Ln (44035-6310)
P.O. Box 376, Amherst (44001-0376)
PHONE..............................440 365-5941
Fax: 440 365-4809
Jerry Mucha, *President*
Robert Zahratka, *Corp Secy*
Glen Hersteck, *Vice Pres*
Michael Lotito, *Opers Mgr*
Bill Parmentar, *CFO*
EMP: 23
SQ FT: 7,500
SALES (est): 1.5MM **Privately Held**
WEB: www.elcor.net
SIC: 3694 3699 Harness wiring sets, internal combustion engines; electrical equipment & supplies

(G-9412)
ELYRIA COPY CENTER INC
325 Lake Ave (44035-4903)
PHONE..............................440 323-4145
Fax: 440 323-8692
Summit Dukeman, *President*
EMP: 5
SQ FT: 2,000
SALES: 300K **Privately Held**
SIC: 2752 7334 Commercial printing, offset; photocopying & duplicating services

(G-9413)
ELYRIA MANUFACTURING CORP (PA)
Also Called: EMC Precision Machining
145 Northrup St (44035-6163)
P.O. Box 479 (44036-0479)
PHONE..............................440 365-4171
Fax: 216 365-4000
Larry Harrison, *President*
Bradley R Ohlemacher, *President*
Robert Graney, *COO*
Samuel Tarantino, *Plant Mgr*
Tracy Farriss, *Prdtn Mgr*
▲ EMP: 54 EST: 1925
SQ FT: 86,000
SALES (est): 12.2MM **Privately Held**
WEB: www.elyriamfg.com
SIC: 3451 Screw machine products

(G-9414)
ELYRIA MTAL SPNNING FBRICATION
7511 W River Rd S (44035-6972)
P.O. Box 992 (44036-0992)
PHONE.....................440 323-8068
Fax: 440 323-6942
Don Didomenico, *President*
Jennifer Didomenico, *Vice Pres*
EMP: 6 EST: 1962
SQ FT: 14,000
SALES (est): 1.1MM Privately Held
SIC: 3469 3599 Spinning metal for the trade; machine shop, jobbing & repair

(G-9415)
ELYRIA PATTERN CO INC
6785 W River Rd S (44035-7052)
PHONE.....................440 323-1526
Fax: 440 323-8673
James A Schroeder, *President*
James W Schroeder, *Vice Pres*
EMP: 7
SALES: 500K Privately Held
SIC: 3543 Industrial patterns

(G-9416)
ELYRIA PLATING CORPORATION
118 Olive St (44035-4000)
PHONE.....................440 365-8300
Fax: 440 365-8966
Kevin J Flanigan, *CEO*
E F Gookins, *President*
Ed Manuel, *Plant Mgr*
Steve Fleming, *Controller*
EMP: 40 EST: 1937
SQ FT: 35,000
SALES (est): 4.5MM Privately Held
SIC: 3471 Electroplating of metals or formed products

(G-9417)
ELYRIA SPRING & SPECIALTY INC
123 Elbe St (44035-4879)
PHONE.....................440 323-5502
John Turk, *President*
Rich Osberg, *General Mgr*
Brian King, *Purch Mgr*
Jay Ogan, *QC Mgr*
John Neiding, *Draft/Design*
EMP: 45
SQ FT: 8,858
SALES (est): 9.2MM Privately Held
WEB: www.elyriaspring.com
SIC: 3495 3496 3493 3469 Wire springs; miscellaneous fabricated wire products; steel springs, except wire; metal stampings; automotive stampings

(G-9418)
EMC PRECISION MACHINING II LLC (PA)
145 Northrup St (44035-6147)
P.O. Box 479 (44036-0479)
PHONE.....................440 365-4171
Jack Zeman,
EMP: 20 EST: 2010
SALES (est): 13.9MM Privately Held
SIC: 3599 Machine & other job shop work

(G-9419)
ENERCON SYSTEMS INC
Also Called: Eco Waste Solutions USA
300 Huron St (44035-4880)
PHONE.....................305 213-3997
Steve Meldrum, *President*
EMP: 3
SALES (est): 105.1K
SALES (corp-wide): 1.3MM Privately Held
SIC: 3532 3533 3991 Mining machinery; oil & gas field machinery; brooms & brushes
PA: Eco Burn Inc
5195 Harvester Rd Suite 14
Burlington ON L7L 6
905 634-7022

(G-9420)
ENGELHARD CORP
120 Pine St (44035-5228)
PHONE.....................440 322-3741
Fax: 440 322-1591
Al Brightwell, *Principal*

▲ EMP: 8
SALES (est): 878.3K Privately Held
SIC: 2819 Industrial inorganic chemicals

(G-9421)
ENVELOPE MART OF OHIO INC
1540 Lowell St (44035-4869)
P.O. Box 808 (44036-0808)
PHONE.....................440 365-8177
Fax: 800 214-1733
Robert T Thompson, *President*
Chris Arnold, *President*
EMP: 50
SALES (est): 9MM Privately Held
SIC: 5112 2677 Envelopes; envelopes

(G-9422)
ES THERMAL INC
Also Called: Brown Fired Heater Div
300 Ceran (44035)
P.O. Box 4030 (44036-4030)
PHONE.....................440 323-3291
David Hoecke, *President*
John Somodi, *Vice Pres*
Keith Phillips, *Chief Engr*
Jonathan Phillips, *Project Engr*
Donald Linden, *Manager*
EMP: 25 EST: 1974
SQ FT: 48,000
SALES (est): 6MM Privately Held
SIC: 3433 Oil burners, domestic or industrial

(G-9423)
FELLER TOOL CO INC
194 Morgan Ave (44035-2638)
PHONE.....................440 324-6277
Fax: 440 324-2352
Doug Feller, *President*
Deborah Feller, *Vice Pres*
EMP: 10 EST: 1959
SQ FT: 2,400
SALES (est): 700K Privately Held
SIC: 3544 3599 Special dies & tools; machine shop, jobbing & repair

(G-9424)
GASFLUX COMPANY
32 Hawthorne St (44035-4008)
P.O. Box 1170 (44036-1170)
PHONE.....................440 365-1941
Fax: 440 365-3495
William K Farquhar, *Ch of Bd*
Robert C Farquhar, *President*
Richard Hoffman, *Vice Pres*
Bill Linden, *Opers Mgr*
Mary Ann Farquhar, *Treasurer*
◆ EMP: 8 EST: 1938
SQ FT: 20,000
SALES (est): 1.7MM Privately Held
WEB: www.gasflux.com
SIC: 2899 Fluxes: brazing, soldering, galvanizing & welding

(G-9425)
GATEWAY INDUSTRIAL PDTS INC
160 Freedom Ct (44035-2245)
P.O. Box 95 (44036-0095)
PHONE.....................440 324-4112
Fax: 440 365-8326
Peter Delaporte, *President*
Gayle Delaporte, *General Mgr*
Eric Porte, *Engineer*
Rose Snyder, *Controller*
Denise Ames, *Sales Staff*
▼ EMP: 15
SQ FT: 25,000
SALES (est): 3.3MM Privately Held
WEB: www.gatewayindustrial.com
SIC: 3089 2431 Window screening, plastic; doors & door parts & trim, wood

(G-9426)
GOODMAN DISTRIBUTION INC
160 Liberty Ct (44035-2237)
PHONE.....................440 324-4071
Alan Fayer, *Manager*
EMP: 5
SALES (corp-wide): 17.4B Privately Held
SIC: 3585 Heating & air conditioning combination units
HQ: Goodman Distribution, Inc.
1426 Ne 8th Ave
Ocala FL 34470
352 620-2727

(G-9427)
GREBER MACHINE TOOL INC
Also Called: Custom Powdr Coating By Greber
313 Clark St (44035-6105)
PHONE.....................440 322-3685
Fax: 440 322-4559
Ken Greber, *President*
Steve Axford, *General Mgr*
Tammy Greber, *Treasurer*
EMP: 7
SQ FT: 600
SALES (est): 640K Privately Held
WEB: www.greberracing.com
SIC: 3479 7692 Coating of metals & formed products; welding repair

(G-9428)
HAWTHORNE CARAVAN & ASSOC LLC
Also Called: Caravan Protective Cases
25 Hawthorne St (44035-4007)
P.O. Box 1506 (44036-1506)
PHONE.....................440 366-9065
Fax: 440 366-1809
Charles R Patton, *President*
EMP: 13
SALES (est): 2MM Privately Held
WEB: www.caravancases.com
SIC: 2441 3469 3412 3161 Shipping cases, wood: nailed or lock corner; metal stampings; metal barrels, drums & pails; luggage; wood partitions & fixtures

(G-9429)
HUDAK MACHINE & TOOL INC
144 Eady Ct (44035-4124)
PHONE.....................440 366-8955
Fax: 440 366-8955
Frank P Hudak Jr, *President*
Barbara Schmittgen, *Corp Secy*
EMP: 3
SALES: 130K Privately Held
WEB: www.absolutemachine.com
SIC: 3544 3599 Jigs & fixtures; machine shop, jobbing & repair

(G-9430)
HY-TECH PRODUCTS
125 Abbe Rd S (44035-4101)
PHONE.....................440 537-1257
Fax: 440 365-2560
Ron Priddy, *Owner*
EMP: 12
SQ FT: 10,000
SALES (est): 980.7K Privately Held
SIC: 3089 Injection molding of plastics

(G-9431)
HYDRO-AIRE INC
Also Called: Lear Romec
241 Abbe Rd S (44035-6239)
P.O. Box 4014 (44036-2014)
PHONE.....................440 323-3211
Fax: 440 322-3378
Jay Higgs, *President*
Valentino Camardo, *Engineer*
David Hunger, *Engineer*
Gary Krock, *Engineer*
Dan Walsh, *Engineer*
EMP: 236
SALES (corp-wide): 2.7B Publicly Held
WEB: www.craneco.com
SIC: 3494 Valves & pipe fittings
HQ: Hydro-Aire, Inc.
3000 Winona Ave
Burbank CA 91504

(G-9432)
INTERNATIONAL MULTIFOODS CORP
6325 Gateway Blvd S (44035-5447)
PHONE.....................440 323-5100
Fax: 440 323-3256
Mike Phippen, *Branch Mgr*
EMP: 6
SALES (corp-wide): 7.8B Publicly Held
SIC: 2051 Bakery: wholesale or wholesale/retail combined
HQ: International Multifoods Corporation
1 Strawberry Ln
Orrville OH 44667
330 682-3000

(G-9433)
INTERTEK MACHINING & WLDG INC
6805 W River Rd S (44035-7054)
PHONE.....................440 323-3325
Mort Guerine, *President*
Dave W Dennis, *Vice Pres*
Andrea Monschein, *CFO*
EMP: 13
SQ FT: 24,000
SALES (est): 2.3MM Privately Held
WEB: www.intertekmachandweld.com
SIC: 3599 Machine shop, jobbing & repair

(G-9434)
INVACARE CANADIAN HOLDINGS LLC
1 Invacare Way (44035-4190)
PHONE.....................440 329-6000
EMP: 3 EST: 2015
SALES (est): 99.2K
SALES (corp-wide): 1B Publicly Held
SIC: 3842 Surgical appliances & supplies
PA: Invacare Corporation
1 Invacare Way
Elyria OH 44035
440 329-6000

(G-9435)
INVACARE CORPORATION (PA)
1 Invacare Way (44035-4190)
P.O. Box 4028 (44036-2028)
PHONE.....................440 329-6000
Fax: 440 365-8227
Matthew E Monaghan, *Ch of Bd*
Amy Lowrie, *General Mgr*
John Brumley, *Business Mgr*
Dean J Childers, *Senior VP*
Anthony C Laplaca, *Senior VP*
◆ EMP: 662
SQ FT: 50,000
SALES: 1B Publicly Held
WEB: www.invacare.com
SIC: 3842 2514 2813 Surgical appliances & supplies; wheelchairs; personal safety equipment; beds, including folding & cabinet, household: metal; industrial gases; oxygen, compressed or liquefied

(G-9436)
INVACARE CORPORATION
Also Called: Invacare It & Financial Svcs
1320 Taylor St (44035-6250)
PHONE.....................800 333-6900
Paula Basa, *Technology*
Mia Yu, *Analyst*
EMP: 97
SALES (corp-wide): 1B Publicly Held
SIC: 3842 2514 2813 Surgical appliances & supplies; wheelchairs; personal safety equipment; beds, including folding & cabinet, household: metal; industrial gases; oxygen, compressed or liquefied
PA: Invacare Corporation
1 Invacare Way
Elyria OH 44035
440 329-6000

(G-9437)
INVACARE CORPORATION
1200 Taylor St (44035-6248)
PHONE.....................440 329-6000
Fax: 440 365-7480
Kent Kluth, *Vice Pres*
Sue L MA, *Vice Pres*
Sekar Venkataraman, *Purch Mgr*
Emit Reynolds, *Engineer*
James Feriance, *Development*
EMP: 14
SQ FT: 13,000
SALES (corp-wide): 1B Publicly Held
WEB: www.invacare.com
SIC: 3842 Wheelchairs; walkers
PA: Invacare Corporation
1 Invacare Way
Elyria OH 44035
440 329-6000

(G-9438)
INVACARE HOLDINGS CORPORATION
Also Called: Invacare Holdings Inc
1 Invacare Way (44035-4190)
PHONE.....................440 329-6000
Gerald Blouch, *CEO*

GEOGRAPHIC

A Malachi Mixon III, *Ch of Bd*
Joseph B Richey II, *President*
Anthony C Laplaca, *Senior VP*
▲ EMP: 3
SALES (est): 450.5K
SALES (corp-wide): 1B **Publicly Held**
SIC: 3842 2514 3841 Surgical appliances
& supplies; wheelchairs; personal safety
equipment; beds, including folding & cabi-
net, household: metal; inhalation therapy
equipment
HQ: Invacare International Corporation
1 Invacare Way
Elyria OH 44035
440 329-6000

(G-9439)
INVACARE INTERNATIONAL
CORP (HQ)
1 Invacare Way (44035-4190)
PHONE....................................440 329-6000
Sharon Corbett, *Principal*
EMP: 3
SALES (est): 19.2MM
SALES (corp-wide): 1B **Publicly Held**
SIC: 3842 2514 3841 Surgical appliances
& supplies; wheelchairs; personal safety
equipment; beds, including folding & cabi-
net, household: metal; inhalation therapy
equipment
PA: Invacare Corporation
1 Invacare Way
Elyria OH 44035
440 329-6000

(G-9440)
INVACARE RESPIRATORY CORP
899 Cleveland St (44035-4100)
PHONE....................................440 329-6000
Fax: 440 365-6822
Jeff Steiss, *Corp Comm Staff*
Annette Soule, *Program Mgr*
Randy Moore, *Director*
Dale A La Porte, *Admin Sec*
▲ EMP: 35
SALES: 1.5MM
SALES (corp-wide): 1B **Publicly Held**
WEB: www.invacare.com
SIC: 3841 Surgical & medical instruments
PA: Invacare Corporation
1 Invacare Way
Elyria OH 44035
440 329-6000

(G-9441)
J & M PRECISION DIE CAST INC
1329 Taylor St (44035-6249)
PHONE....................................440 365-7388
Michael Prokop, *President*
EMP: 12
SQ FT: 8,000
SALES: 1.2MM
SALES (corp-wide): 13.5MM **Privately
Held**
SIC: 3363 Aluminum die-castings
PA: Rhenium Alloys, Inc.
38683 Taylor Pkwy
North Ridgeville OH 44035
440 365-7388

(G-9442)
J M SMUCKER COMPANY
6325 Gateway Blvd S (44035-5447)
PHONE....................................440 323-5100
Mike Phippen, *Branch Mgr*
EMP: 36
SALES (corp-wide): 7.8B **Publicly Held**
WEB: www.smuckers.com
SIC: 2045 2099 2051 Cake mixes, pre-
pared: from purchased flour; food prepa-
rations; bread, cake & related products
PA: The J M Smucker Company
1 Strawberry Ln
Orrville OH 44667
330 682-3000

(G-9443)
JOE GONDA COMPANY INC
Also Called: Gonda Wood Products
40196 Butternut Ridge Rd (44035-7904)
P.O. Box 282, Grafton (44044-0282)
PHONE....................................440 458-6000
Fax: 440 458-6160
Michael Gonda, *President*
Patricia Marie Gonda, *Corp Secy*
EMP: 11

SQ FT: 7,500
SALES (est): 1.5MM **Privately Held**
SIC: 2448 2449 Pallets, wood; skids,
wood; wood containers

(G-9444)
JUDCO INC
7501 W River Rd S (44035-6972)
P.O. Box 358 (44036-0358)
PHONE....................................440 322-6604
Patrick J Judge, *President*
Robert A Judge, *Vice Pres*
Sherry Rumph, *Treasurer*
Patricia G Judge, *Admin Sec*
EMP: 9
SQ FT: 11,500
SALES (est): 1.2MM **Privately Held**
WEB: www.judco-inc.com
SIC: 3993 5087 Signs, not made in cus-
tom sign painting shops; cleaning & main-
tenance equipment & supplies

(G-9445)
KASTLER & REICHLIN INC
Also Called: Phoenix Mold & Die
710 Taylor St (44035-6230)
PHONE....................................440 322-0970
Fax: 440 322-3668
James Kastler, *President*
Dawn Reichlin, *General Mgr*
Karen Meyes, *QC Dir*
James Reichlin, *Treasurer*
EMP: 50
SALES (est): 3.8MM **Privately Held**
SIC: 3544 3599 Special dies, tools, jigs &
fixtures; machine & other job shop work

(G-9446)
KELCH MANUFACTURING CORP
626 Sugar Ln (44035-6396)
PHONE....................................440 366-5060
Fax: 440 366-0713
Franklyn S Kelch, *President*
Joan Kelch, *Vice Pres*
EMP: 7
SQ FT: 9,000
SALES (est): 350K **Privately Held**
SIC: 3469 3544 Metal stampings; dies,
plastics forming; diamond dies, metal-
working

(G-9447)
KEYGHOBAD VENTURES LLC
Also Called: Nanobio Systems
141 Innovation Dr Ste 320 (44035-1673)
PHONE....................................440 366-3278
Seyamak Keyghobad, *CEO*
Andrea Stamp, *Vice Pres*
EMP: 4
SQ FT: 1,094
SALES (est): 104.8K **Privately Held**
SIC: 3845 Automated blood & body fluid
analyzers, except laboratory

(G-9448)
L C SMITH CO
196 Morgan Ave (44035-2638)
PHONE....................................440 327-1251
Fax: 440 353-0974
Francis Fife, *President*
Sheila Smith, *Vice Pres*
A Smith, *Mfg Staff*
Steve Krone, *Purchasing*
Jack Smith, *Manager*
EMP: 3 EST: 1948
SQ FT: 4,200
SALES: 500K **Privately Held**
WEB: www.lcsmith.net
SIC: 3545 3715 Measuring tools & ma-
chines, machinists' metalworking type;
trailer bodies

(G-9449)
LAKESIDE INDUSTRIAL PDTS
CORP
115 Preston St (44035-3929)
PHONE....................................440 366-0052
Thomas Nielsen, *President*
EMP: 5
SQ FT: 7,000
SALES (est): 420K **Privately Held**
SIC: 3341 Secondary nonferrous metals

(G-9450)
LAUREN YOAKAM
Also Called: Applied Engineered Surface
591 Ternes Ln (44035-6271)
PHONE....................................440 365-3952
Lauren Yoakam, *Owner*
John Yoakam, *Engineer*
EMP: 8
SALES (est): 520K **Privately Held**
SIC: 3441 Fabricated structural metal

(G-9451)
LEAR MFG CO INC
147 Freedom Ct (44035-2245)
PHONE....................................440 324-1111
Bonnie Lear, *President*
EMP: 15 EST: 2014
SALES: 600K **Privately Held**
SIC: 3452 Nuts, metal

(G-9452)
LEGGETT & PLATT
INCORPORATED
Also Called: Leggett & Platt 0640
377 Woodland Ave (44035-3217)
PHONE....................................440 322-4865
John Forest, *Branch Mgr*
EMP: 50
SALES (corp-wide): 3.7B **Publicly Held**
WEB: www.leggett.com
SIC: 2515 Mattresses & bedsprings
PA: Leggett & Platt, Incorporated
1 Leggett Rd
Carthage MO 64836
417 358-8131

(G-9453)
LIQUID SHOCK GAMES LLC
621 49th St (44035-2401)
PHONE....................................386 627-0840
Mark Kellogg,
EMP: 3
SALES (est): 115.8K **Privately Held**
SIC: 7372 7371 7389 Home entertain-
ment computer software; computer soft-
ware development;

(G-9454)
LORAIN COUNTY AUTO
SYSTEMS INC
101 Liberty Ct (44035-2238)
PHONE....................................248 442-6800
Thomas Rockwell, *CFO*
EMP: 60
SALES (corp-wide): 552.7MM **Privately
Held**
SIC: 3714 Motor vehicle engines & parts
HQ: Lorain County Automotive Systems,
Inc.
7470 Industrial Pkwy Dr
Lorain OH 44053
440 960-7470

(G-9455)
LORAIN MODERN PATTERN INC
159 Woodbury St (44035-4011)
PHONE....................................440 365-6780
Todd R Roth, *President*
Sheila Kelly, *Vice Pres*
Paul Luikart, *Vice Pres*
Sheila I Kelly-Roth, *Vice Pres*
EMP: 10
SQ FT: 5,500
SALES: 550K **Privately Held**
WEB: www.lorainmodern.com
SIC: 3543 Industrial patterns

(G-9456)
LOWER LIMB CENTERS LLC
1100 Abbe Rd N Ste D (44035-1667)
PHONE....................................440 365-2502
Mark I Winters, *Principal*
EMP: 3
SALES (est): 254K **Privately Held**
SIC: 3842 Limbs, artificial

(G-9457)
LTI POWER SYSTEMS
10800 Middle Ave Hngr B (44035-7893)
PHONE....................................440 327-5050
Robert J Morog, *CEO*
Chuck Wallace, *Engineer*
Christy Farkas, *VP Finance*
Chris Desimone, *Accounts Mgr*
George Weiss, *Director*

▼ EMP: 20
SQ FT: 35,000
SALES (est): 2MM **Privately Held**
WEB: www.ltipowersystems.com
SIC: 3612 Specialty transformers

(G-9458)
MARATHON INDUSTRIAL CNTRS
INC
100 Freedom Ct (44035-2245)
PHONE....................................440 324-2748
Richard L Sipley, *President*
▼ EMP: 12
SQ FT: 30,000
SALES (est): 1.4MM **Privately Held**
SIC: 3443 Industrial vessels, tanks & con-
tainers

(G-9459)
MASTER BOLT & MFG INC
811 Taylor St (44035-6231)
PHONE....................................440 323-5529
Fax: 440 323-2468
Vickie Plas, *General Mgr*
Paul L Millet, *Principal*
Tamala Taylor, *Sales Staff*
Paul Klug, *Admin Sec*
▲ EMP: 30
SQ FT: 30,000
SALES: 3.6MM **Privately Held**
WEB: www.masterbolt.com
SIC: 3462 Railroad wheels, axles, frogs or
other equipment: forged

(G-9460)
MENTOR RADIO LLC
151 Innovation Dr Ste 320 (44035-1677)
PHONE....................................216 265-2315
Eric M Sadowski, *President*
Richard Myers, *Prdtn Mgr*
EMP: 3
SALES (est): 280K **Privately Held**
WEB: www.mentorradio.com
SIC: 3663 Radio & TV communications
equipment

(G-9461)
METAL FORMING LUBRICANTS
INC
10800 Middle Ave Hngr A (44035-7890)
P.O. Box 989 (44036-0989)
PHONE....................................440 458-5730
Glen Boepple, *President*
Michael Richwalsky, *Vice Pres*
Dean Worden, *Vice Pres*
EMP: 6
SQ FT: 13,000
SALES (est): 1.3MM **Privately Held**
WEB: www.mflube.com
SIC: 2992 Oils & greases, blending & com-
pounding

(G-9462)
METRO DESIGN INC
10740 Middle Ave (44035-7816)
P.O. Box 248 (44036-0248)
PHONE....................................440 458-4200
Fax: 440 324-3410
Jeffery Kraps, *President*
EMP: 14
SQ FT: 10,000
SALES: 2MM **Privately Held**
SIC: 3599 7699 3844 Custom machinery;
machine shop, jobbing & repair; X-ray
equipment repair; X-ray apparatus &
tubes

(G-9463)
MINUTEMAN PRESS OF ELYRIA
631 Abbe Rd S (44035-7243)
PHONE....................................440 365-9377
Fax: 440 365-8889
Donna Stein, *Owner*
Brenda Woodring, *Partner*
EMP: 4
SQ FT: 1,100
SALES (est): 371.7K **Privately Held**
SIC: 2752 Commercial printing, litho-
graphic

(G-9464)
ML ERECTORS LLC
827 Walnut St (44035-3352)
PHONE....................................440 328-3227
Matthew J Loftin, *Mng Member*

EMP: 7
SQ FT: 26,000
SALES: 1.2MM **Privately Held**
SIC: 2759 Publication printing

(G-9465)
MULTILINK INC
Also Called: Multifab
580 Ternes Ln (44035-6252)
PHONE...............................440 366-6966
Fax: 440 366-6802
Steven Kaplan, *President*
Bernadette Golas, *COO*
Mike French, *Senior VP*
Kathy Kaplan, *Vice Pres*
Will Lundstrom, *Vice Pres*
▲ EMP: 140
SQ FT: 110,000
SALES (est): 147.4MM **Privately Held**
WEB: www.multilinkbroadband.com
SIC: 5063 3829 Wire & cable; cable testing machines

(G-9466)
NATIONAL MOLDED PRODUCTS INC
147 Kenwood St (44035-4009)
PHONE...............................440 365-3400
Fax: 440 365-2900
Robert E Brown, *President*
Charlene Brown, *Corp Secy*
Brian Brown, *Vice Pres*
EMP: 30
SQ FT: 33,000
SALES: 1.5MM **Privately Held**
SIC: 3089 Injection molding of plastics

(G-9467)
NELSON STUD WELDING INC (DH)
7900 W Ridge Rd (44035-1952)
P.O. Box 4019 (44036-2019)
PHONE...............................440 329-0400
Fax: 440 329-0526
Ken Caratelli, *President*
Linda Loosli, *General Mgr*
David Bubar, *Vice Pres*
Debbie Hunnel, *Vice Pres*
Jim King, *Vice Pres*
◆ EMP: 277 EST: 2000
SALES (est): 199.9MM **Privately Held**
SIC: 3452 3548 Bolts, nuts, rivets & washers; welding apparatus
HQ: Doncasters 456 Limited
Millennium Court
Burton-On-Trent STAFFS
133 286-4900

(G-9468)
NORTH COAST RIVET INC
700 Sugar Ln (44035-6312)
P.O. Box 1441 (44036-1441)
PHONE...............................440 366-6829
Fax: 440 365-8261
Wesley L Shirley, *CEO*
Kathy Shirley, *Admin Sec*
EMP: 19
SQ FT: 6,000
SALES (est): 1MM **Privately Held**
SIC: 3452 Rivets, metal

(G-9469)
OAK TREE INTL HOLDINGS INC
1209 Lowell St (44035-4803)
PHONE...............................702 462-7295
EMP: 17
SALES (corp-wide): 1.5MM **Privately Held**
SIC: 2834 Pharmaceutical preparations
PA: Oak Tree International Holdings, Inc.
9550 S Eastrn Ave Ste 253
Las Vegas NV 89123
702 462-7295

(G-9470)
OHIO DISPLAYS INC
Also Called: Odi
825 Leona St (44035-2300)
PHONE...............................216 961-5600
Fax: 216 961-7869
Thomas R Mc Kay, *Ch of Bd*
Judy Miller, *Vice Pres*
Vincent Papa, *Project Mgr*
Sam Cheraso, *Accounts Exec*
Carl Rappaport, *Accounts Exec*
EMP: 15

SQ FT: 70,000
SALES (est): 2.3MM **Privately Held**
WEB: www.ohiodisplays.com
SIC: 3993 2542 Displays, paint process; partitions & fixtures, except wood

(G-9471)
OHIO METALLURGICAL SERVICE INC
Also Called: Ohiomet
1033 Clark St (44035-6257)
P.O. Box 1228 (44036-1228)
PHONE...............................440 365-4104
Fax: 440 365-9527
Donald S Gaydosh, *President*
John Gaydosh, *President*
R E Baird, *Principal*
William D Latiano, *Principal*
Glenn E Shoemaker, *Principal*
EMP: 69
SQ FT: 50,000
SALES: 10MM **Privately Held**
WEB: www.ohiomet.com
SIC: 3398 Metal heat treating

(G-9472)
OHIO SCREW PRODUCTS INC
818 Lowell St (44035-4876)
P.O. Box 4027 (44036-2027)
PHONE...............................440 322-6341
Fax: 440 322-0750
Edward N Imbrogno, *Ch of Bd*
Daniel Imbrogno, *President*
Jim Fetcko, *President*
Dan Imbrogno, *President*
Elmer Brown, *Vice Pres*
EMP: 75 EST: 1945
SQ FT: 65,000
SALES: 23.7MM **Privately Held**
WEB: www.ohioscrew.com
SIC: 3541 3451 Screw machines, automatic; screw machine products

(G-9473)
P P E INC
Also Called: Elyria Plastic Products
710 Taylor St (44035-6230)
PHONE...............................440 322-8577
Fax: 440 322-7979
Jim Kastler, *President*
R Stephen Laux, *Principal*
James M Reichlin, *Principal*
Joyce Salasky, *Purchasing*
Patrick Reichlin, *Engineer*
▲ EMP: 75
SQ FT: 6,000
SALES (est): 21.5MM **Privately Held**
WEB: www.elyriapp.com
SIC: 3089 Injection molded finished plastic products

(G-9474)
P-AMERICAS LLC
Also Called: Pepsico
925 Lorain Blvd (44035-2819)
PHONE...............................440 323-5524
EMP: 123
SALES (corp-wide): 62.8B **Publicly Held**
SIC: 2086 Carbonated soft drinks, bottled & canned
HQ: P-Americas Llc
1 Pepsi Way
Somers NY

(G-9475)
PARKER-HANNIFIN CORPORATION
Gresen Hydraulics
520 Ternes Ln (44035-6266)
P.O. Box 4026 (44036-2026)
PHONE...............................440 366-5100
Fax: 440 366-5253
Kurt Boey, *Engineer*
John Darmstadt, *Engineer*
Ray Wetzel, *Engineer*
Winnie Wong, *Design Engr*
Steven Myers, *Office Mgr*
EMP: 300
SALES (corp-wide): 11.3B **Publicly Held**
WEB: www.parker.com
SIC: 3492 Control valves, fluid power: hydraulic & pneumatic
PA: Parker-Hannifin Corporation
6035 Parkland Blvd
Cleveland OH 44124
216 896-3000

(G-9476)
PARKER-HANNIFIN CORPORATION
Fluid Systems Division
711 Taylor St (44035-6229)
P.O. Box 4032 (44036-4032)
PHONE...............................440 284-6277
Fax: 440 322-6094
Don Secord, *Human Res Dir*
Eric Mitchell, *Manager*
Eric Arndt, *Manager*
Geoff Turner, *Manager*
Thomas Dorinsky, *Senior Mgr*
EMP: 200
SALES (corp-wide): 11.3B **Publicly Held**
WEB: www.parker.com
SIC: 3728 3724 Aircraft assemblies, sub-assemblies & parts; aircraft engines & engine parts
PA: Parker-Hannifin Corporation
6035 Parkland Blvd
Cleveland OH 44124
216 896-3000

(G-9477)
PERFECTIONS FABRICATORS INC
680 Sugar Ln (44035-6310)
PHONE...............................440 365-5850
Fax: 440 365-5851
James Ennes, *President*
David Ennes, *President*
Laurie Diaringer, *Office Mgr*
EMP: 10 EST: 1973
SQ FT: 27,000
SALES (est): 907.5K **Privately Held**
SIC: 3441 Fabricated structural metal

(G-9478)
PLASTIC ENTERPRISES INC (PA)
41520 Schadden Rd (44035-2227)
PHONE...............................440 324-3240
Fax: 440 324-3243
John Leonowich, *President*
William Kaatz, *Vice Pres*
Carole Torres, *Purch Dir*
EMP: 22
SQ FT: 35,000
SALES (est): 4.6MM **Privately Held**
WEB: www.plastic-enterprises.com
SIC: 3089 3544 Injection molding of plastics; special dies, tools, jigs & fixtures

(G-9479)
PLASTO-TECH CORPORATION
708 Lowell St (44035-4843)
P.O. Box 226, Wooster (44691-0226)
PHONE...............................440 323-6300
Fax: 440 323-6313
Bala Venkataraman, *President*
Laks Venkataraman, *Vice Pres*
Dean Yoder, *Purch Mgr*
Thomas Woodruff, *Treasurer*
Tammy Rodriguez, *Office Mgr*
EMP: 11
SQ FT: 50,000
SALES (est): 1.9MM
SALES (corp-wide): 20.7MM **Privately Held**
WEB: www.plasto-tech.com
SIC: 3082 Unsupported plastics profile shapes
PA: Magni- Power Company
5511 E Lincoln Way
Wooster OH 44691
330 264-3637

(G-9480)
PRECISE MODELS INC
195 Canterbury Rd (44035-1720)
PHONE...............................440 365-5701
Paul Schneider, *President*
Rita Malanowski, *Corp Secy*
EMP: 8 EST: 1960
SQ FT: 10,500
SALES (est): 582.5K **Privately Held**
SIC: 3999 Miniatures

(G-9481)
QUALITY BLOW MOLDING INC
635 Oberlin Elyria Rd (44035-7727)
PHONE...............................440 458-6550
Fax: 440 458-6551
Ronald E Matcham, *President*

Mary Anne Matcham, *Admin Sec*
EMP: 90
SQ FT: 30,000
SALES: 10.5MM **Privately Held**
SIC: 3089 Blow molded finished plastic products

(G-9482)
R V SPA LLC
42345 Oberlin Elyria Rd (44035-7415)
PHONE...............................440 284-4800
Bill Gates, *Principal*
EMP: 4
SALES (est): 353.5K **Privately Held**
SIC: 3799 Recreational vehicles

(G-9483)
REAL ALLOY SPECIALTY PRODUCTS
320 Huron St (44035-4829)
PHONE...............................440 322-0072
Randy Collins, *Manager*
EMP: 28
SALES (corp-wide): 1.1B **Publicly Held**
SIC: 3341 Aluminum smelting & refining (secondary)
HQ: Real Alloy Specialty Products, Inc
3700 Park East Dr Ste 300
Beachwood OH 44122
216 755-8836

(G-9484)
REBUILDING & FABRICATING INC
41821 Oberlin Rd (44035)
PHONE...............................440 322-0844
Fax: 440 323-8541
Joseph A Yusko, *President*
EMP: 5
SQ FT: 20,000
SALES (est): 590K **Privately Held**
SIC: 3559 Plastics working machinery

(G-9485)
RECOGNITION ROBOTICS INC (PA)
151 Innovation Dr (44035-1675)
PHONE...............................440 590-0499
Simon Melikian, *CEO*
Joe Cyrek, *Vice Pres*
EMP: 19
SALES (est): 10.7MM **Privately Held**
SIC: 3569 8742 Robots, assembly line: industrial & commercial; automation & robotics consultant

(G-9486)
RIDGE TOOL COMPANY (DH)
Also Called: Ridgid
400 Clark St (44035-6100)
P.O. Box 4023 (44036-2023)
PHONE...............................440 323-5581
Fax: 440 329-4551
B J Jones, *Principal*
Mark Downie, *Vice Pres*
Mark Hersh, *Vice Pres*
Toni Miller, *Vice Pres*
Cathy Raible, *Vice Pres*
◆ EMP: 800 EST: 1922
SQ FT: 600,000
SALES (est): 367.7MM
SALES (corp-wide): 14.5B **Publicly Held**
WEB: www.ridgid.com
SIC: 3541 3423 3547 3546 Machine tools, metal cutting type; pipe cutting & threading machines; hand & edge tools; rolling mill machinery; power-driven hand-tools

(G-9487)
RIDGE TOOL COMPANY
321 Sumner St (44035-6125)
PHONE...............................440 329-4737
Ron Farkas, *Manager*
EMP: 20
SALES (corp-wide): 14.5B **Publicly Held**
WEB: www.ridgid.com
SIC: 3823 Industrial instrmnts msrmnt display/control process variable
HQ: Ridge Tool Company
400 Clark St
Elyria OH 44035
440 323-5581

(G-9488)
RIDGE TOOL MANUFACTURING CO
400 Clark St (44035-6100)
P.O. Box 4023 (44036-2023)
PHONE.................................440 323-5581
Fred Pond, *President*
Scott Garfield, *Vice Pres*
Ralph Shaw, *CFO*
Ron Schade, *Credit Mgr*
Kevin Jakubec, *MIS Dir*
EMP: 1400
SQ FT: 400,000
SALES (est): 70.7MM
SALES (corp-wide): 14.5B **Publicly Held**
WEB: www.ridgid.com
SIC: 3541 3423 3547 3546 Machine tools, metal cutting type; hand & edge tools; rolling mill machinery; power-driven handtools; machine tool accessories; metal stampings
HQ: Ridge Tool Company
　　400 Clark St
　　Elyria OH 44035
　　440 323-5581

(G-9489)
RPM INDUSTRIES
1444 Lowell St (44035-4867)
PHONE.................................440 268-8077
Erik Vanover, *Principal*
EMP: 3
SALES (est): 185.1K **Privately Held**
SIC: 3999 Manufacturing industries

(G-9490)
S A E MANUFACTURING
7880 W River Rd S (44035-6938)
PHONE.................................440 322-9026
Mark Klier, *President*
Kevin Fenik, *Vice Pres*
EMP: 4
SQ FT: 6,000
SALES (est): 450K **Privately Held**
SIC: 3599 Machine & other job shop work

(G-9491)
SELZER TOOL & DIE INC
163 Kenwood St (44035-4096)
P.O. Box 1017 (44036-1017)
PHONE.................................440 365-4124
Fax: 440 365-4125
David Selzer, *President*
Donna Selzer, *President*
Dale Selzer, *Vice Pres*
EMP: 3
SQ FT: 8,000
SALES (est): 300K **Privately Held**
SIC: 3599 7692 3544 Machine shop, jobbing & repair; welding repair; special dies, tools, jigs & fixtures

(G-9492)
SHALMET CORPORATION
164 Freedom Ct (44035-2245)
PHONE.................................440 236-8840
Fax: 440 324-6975
Hugh O Donnell, *Branch Mgr*
Dave Blyth, *Director*
EMP: 9
SALES (corp-wide): 1.8B **Publicly Held**
SIC: 3471 Polishing, metals or formed products
HQ: Shalmet Corporation
　　116 Pinedale Indus Rd
　　Orwigsburg PA 17961
　　570 366-1414

(G-9493)
SMART MICROSYSTEMS LTD
141 Innovation Dr (44035-1673)
PHONE.................................440 366-4257
Matt Apanius, *President*
Monica Tarasco,
EMP: 10
SALES (est): 720K **Privately Held**
SIC: 3674 Microcircuits, integrated (semiconductor)

(G-9494)
SMOKIN GUNS LLC
41458 Griswold Rd (44035-2351)
PHONE.................................440 324-4003
Cory Eden, *President*
Melvin Eden, *Assistant VP*
Mary Melvin, *Vice Pres*

Mary Eden, *Exec Dir*
EMP: 3 EST: 2014
SALES: 70K **Privately Held**
SIC: 3484 7997 5941 Guns (firearms) or gun parts, 30 mm. & below; gun club, membership; firearms

(G-9495)
SORTA 4 U LLC
267 Bon Air Ave (44035-4115)
PHONE.................................440 365-0091
EMP: 3
SALES (est): 190K **Privately Held**
SIC: 3448 Mfg Prefabricated Metal Buildings

(G-9496)
SUZIN L CHOCOLATIERS
230 Broad St (44035-5502)
PHONE.................................440 323-3372
Fax: 440 323-6627
Suzin Stefanelli, *Owner*
EMP: 12
SQ FT: 26,000
SALES (est): 1.2MM **Privately Held**
WEB: www.suzinl.com
SIC: 2064 5441 5947 Chocolate candy, except solid chocolate; candy; gift shop

(G-9497)
SWARTZ MANUFACTURING INC
820 Walnut St (44035-3353)
PHONE.................................440 284-0297
Fax: 440 322-1589
Ira Swartz, *President*
Alissa Swartz, *Vice Pres*
EMP: 5
SQ FT: 10,000
SALES: 500K **Privately Held**
WEB: www.swartzmfg.com
SIC: 3599 Machine shop, jobbing & repair

(G-9498)
SYMRISE INC
110 Liberty Ct (44035-2237)
PHONE.................................440 324-6060
Gary Golden, *Safety Mgr*
Aileen Alvear, *Sales Staff*
John Cassidy, *Branch Mgr*
Suzanne Blanchette, *Director*
Bret Markel, *Maintence Staff*
EMP: 150
SALES (corp-wide): 3B **Privately Held**
WEB: www.symriseinc.com
SIC: 2869 Perfume materials, synthetic
HQ: Symrise Inc.
　　300 North St
　　Teterboro NJ 07608
　　201 462-5559

(G-9499)
TBH INTERNATIONAL
150 Ridge Circle Ln Apt A (44035-8711)
PHONE.................................440 323-4651
Thomas Heffner, *President*
Amy Heffner, *Vice Pres*
EMP: 3 EST: 2009
SALES (est): 230K **Privately Held**
SIC: 3861 Photographic equipment & supplies

(G-9500)
TEZ TOOL & FABRICATION INC
115 Buckeye St (44035-5216)
PHONE.................................440 323-2300
Fax: 440 323-2213
Matt Tezmer, *President*
EMP: 5
SQ FT: 4,900
SALES (est): 553.6K **Privately Held**
SIC: 3089 Injection molded finished plastic products

(G-9501)
THE RELIABLE SPRING WIRE FRMS
300 Abbe Rd S (44035-6276)
P.O. Box 58 (44036-0058)
PHONE.................................440 365-7400
Fax: 440 366-0747
Richard McBride, *President*
Lucille Roselli, *Engineer*
Patty Hartman, *Accounting Mgr*
Sybil McBride, *Admin Sec*
EMP: 41 EST: 1937
SQ FT: 34,000

SALES (est): 8.6MM **Privately Held**
WEB: www.reliablespring.com
SIC: 3495 3469 Wire springs; mechanical springs, precision; metal stampings

(G-9502)
TILLMANS ENTP -SIGNS SHIP LLC
810 Taylor St (44035-6232)
PHONE.................................440 281-9340
Pamela Melia,
EMP: 5
SALES (est): 250.1K **Privately Held**
SIC: 3993 7389 Letters for signs, metal;

(G-9503)
TTR MANUFACTURING
740 Sugar Ln (44035-6312)
PHONE.................................440 366-5005
EMP: 3 EST: 2010
SALES (est): 297.1K **Privately Held**
SIC: 3999 Manufacturing industries

(G-9504)
ULTRA MACHINE INC
Also Called: Silver Machine Co
530 Lowell St (44035-4862)
PHONE.................................440 323-7632
Fax: 440 323-7636
Thomas C Guignette, *President*
Paul Guignette, *Manager*
EMP: 7
SQ FT: 2,500
SALES (est): 681.2K **Privately Held**
WEB: www.ultramachine.com
SIC: 3599 Machine shop, jobbing & repair

(G-9505)
UNITED INITIATORS INC (HQ)
555 Garden St (44035-4870)
PHONE.................................440 326-2416
Ed Hoozemans, *CEO*
Onofrio Palazzolo, *General Mgr*
Ivan Velikanovic, *General Mgr*
William Clements, *Vice Pres*
Karen Barnes, *Opers Mgr*
◆ EMP: 63
SQ FT: 40,000
SALES (est): 68.6MM
SALES (corp-wide): 225.1MM **Privately Held**
SIC: 2819 2869 Catalysts, chemical; industrial organic chemicals
PA: United Initiators Gmbh
　　Dr.-Gustav-Adolph-Str. 3
　　Pullach I. Isartal 82049
　　897 442-20

(G-9506)
US MACHINE PRCSION GRNDING LLC
880 Taylor St (44035-6232)
PHONE.................................440 284-0711
Arrie Pritchard,
Leonard Miller,
EMP: 4
SALES: 850K **Privately Held**
SIC: 3559 Sewing machines & hat & zipper making machinery

(G-9507)
VECTRON INC
201 Perry Ct (44035-6149)
PHONE.................................440 323-3369
Fax: 440 323-3139
Robert Pustay, *President*
Suzie Pope, *Purchasing*
Cheryl Larkey, *Human Res Dir*
EMP: 100
SQ FT: 48,000
SALES (est): 11.9MM **Privately Held**
SIC: 3599 3471 Machine shop, jobbing & repair; plating & polishing

(G-9508)
VTD SYSTEMS INC
7600 W River Rd S (44035-6934)
PHONE.................................440 323-4122
Fax: 440 323-4128
Robert Vilagi Jr, *President*
Marcia Logan, *Sls & Mktg Exec*
EMP: 20
SQ FT: 5,100
SALES (est): 3.5MM **Privately Held**
WEB: www.vtdsystems.com
SIC: 3599 Machine shop, jobbing & repair

(G-9509)
WAYNE PAK LTD
214 Brace Ave (44035-2662)
PHONE.................................440 323-8744
Marcie Difranco, *Manager*
Ron Young,
Diane Butler,
EMP: 15
SQ FT: 22,000
SALES: 2.5MM **Privately Held**
SIC: 3089 Plastic containers, except foam

(G-9510)
WESTVIEW CONCRETE CORP
Also Called: Avon Concrete
40105 Butternut Ridge Rd (44035-7903)
PHONE.................................440 458-5800
Fax: 440 236-5813
John Walls, *Vice Pres*
EMP: 20
SQ FT: 1,202
SALES (corp-wide): 9.3MM **Privately Held**
SIC: 3273 5211 Ready-mixed concrete; masonry materials & supplies
PA: Westview Concrete Corp.
　　26000 Sprague Rd
　　Olmsted Falls OH 44138
　　440 235-1800

(G-9511)
WOOSTER BRUSH COMPANY
870 Infirmary Rd (44035-4899)
PHONE.................................440 322-8081
Rick Dice, *Branch Mgr*
Freeman Barui, *Manager*
EMP: 6
SALES (corp-wide): 80.8MM **Privately Held**
SIC: 3991 Paint & varnish brushes
PA: The Wooster Brush Company
　　604 Madison Ave
　　Wooster OH 44691
　　330 264-4440

(G-9512)
ZAYTRAN CORPORATION
41535 Schadden Rd (44035-2226)
P.O. Box 1660 (44036-1660)
PHONE.................................440 324-2814
Fax: 440 324-3552
Theodore Zajac Jr, *President*
J C Wm Tattersall, *Principal*
Theodore Zajac Sr, *Chairman*
Monica Parker, *Vice Pres*
Jerry Williams, *Engineer*
EMP: 42
SQ FT: 80,000
SALES (est): 9.7MM **Privately Held**
WEB: www.zaytran.com
SIC: 3593 3492 Fluid power actuators, hydraulic or pneumatic; fluid power cylinders, hydraulic or pneumatic; fluid power valves & hose fittings

---

Englewood
Montgomery County

(G-9513)
CMI TECHNOLOGY INC
65 Haas Dr (45322-2842)
PHONE.................................937 832-2000
John Howard, *President*
Lisa S Pierce, *Principal*
EMP: 17
SQ FT: 12,000
SALES (est): 3MM **Privately Held**
WEB: www.crossroadsmachine.com
SIC: 3599 3544 Machine shop, jobbing & repair; special dies, tools, jigs & fixtures

(G-9514)
CREATIVE COUNTERTOPS OHIO LLC
477 E Wenger Rd (45322-2831)
PHONE.................................937 540-9450
Joe Kunk,
EMP: 10
SQ FT: 10,000
SALES: 1MM **Privately Held**
SIC: 3281 Granite, cut & shaped

(G-9515)
CREATIVE MICROSYSTEMS INC
Also Called: Civica CMI
52 Hillside Ct (45322-2745)
PHONE...................................937 836-4499
Fax: 937 836-1036
James T Hodges, *CEO*
Susan M Neuman, *Corp Secy*
Missy Matherne, *Purchasing*
David Swigart, *Finance*
Mark Buchanan, *VP Sales*
EMP: 80 EST: 1979
SQ FT: 14,400
SALES (est): 12MM Privately Held
WEB: www.creativemicrosystems.com
SIC: 7373 7372 Systems integration services; prepackaged software

(G-9516)
DISPLAY DYNAMICS INC
1 Display Point Dr (45315-8857)
P.O. Box 27, Clayton (45315-0027)
PHONE...................................937 832-2830
Fax: 937 832-3543
Veit Von Parker, *President*
Jacqueline Parker, *Vice Pres*
David Wells, *Prdtn Mgr*
EMP: 15
SQ FT: 40,000
SALES (est): 1.8MM Privately Held
WEB: www.disdyn.com
SIC: 7389 2541 7319 1751 Exhibit construction by industrial contractors; store fixtures, wood; display advertising service; cabinet & finish carpentry; partitions & fixtures, except wood; millwork

(G-9517)
DRIVEN INNOVATIONS LLC
140 Harrisburg Dr (45322-2836)
PHONE...................................330 818-7681
William Royer,
Martin Vance,
EMP: 6
SQ FT: 11,000
SALES (est): 276.8K Privately Held
SIC: 3634 Electric housewares & fans

(G-9518)
EATON COMPRSR FABRICATION INC
Also Called: Polar Air
1000 Cass Dr (45315-8844)
PHONE...................................877 283-7614
Fax: 937 540-1150
Matt Cain, *President*
Bonita Reyna, *Sales Associate*
◆ EMP: 25
SQ FT: 50,000
SALES (est): 9.5MM Privately Held
SIC: 3563 Air & gas compressors

(G-9519)
ETI TECH INC
75 Holiday Dr (45322-2706)
PHONE...................................937 832-4200
Bill McLendon, *President*
Kay O'Diam, *Business Mgr*
Jeff Hartman, *CFO*
EMP: 13
SQ FT: 23,000
SALES (est): 3.8MM
SALES (corp-wide): 911.5K Privately Held
WEB: www.enginetictech.com
SIC: 3812 3679 8711 3629 Search & navigation equipment; electronic circuits; engineering services; electronic generation equipment; machine shop, jobbing & repair; aircraft parts & equipment
PA: Eti Mission Controls Llc
    75 Holiday Dr
    Englewood OH 45322
    937 832-4200

(G-9520)
FRYES SOCCER SHOPPE
709 Taywood Rd (45322-1822)
PHONE...................................937 832-2230
Fax: 937 832-1733
Don Frye, *Owner*
EMP: 5
SQ FT: 2,400

SALES (est): 440.3K Privately Held
WEB: www.fryesoccer.com
SIC: 5941 2261 Soccer supplies; screen printing of cotton broadwoven fabrics

(G-9521)
GALACTIC PRECISION MFG LLC
345 Huls Dr (45315-8983)
PHONE...................................937 540-1800
Roger Mears,
Sivaram Gogineni,
Urmila Nath,
EMP: 3
SALES (est): 321.6K Privately Held
SIC: 3599 Crankshafts & camshafts, machining

(G-9522)
HART & COOLEY INC
1 Lau Pkwy (45315-8754)
PHONE...................................937 832-7800
Bob McDonald, *Branch Mgr*
EMP: 250 Privately Held
SIC: 3446 Registers (air), metal
HQ: Hart & Cooley, Inc.
    5030 Corp Exch Blvd Se
    Grand Rapids MI 49512
    616 656-8200

(G-9523)
HINKLE FINE FOODS INC
130 Harrisburg Dr (45322-2836)
PHONE...................................937 836-3665
Fax: 937 836-3665
Benny S Hinkle, *President*
Micheal Beller, *Principal*
Craig Frost, *Principal*
Marlene M Hinkle, *Admin Sec*
EMP: 8
SQ FT: 8,200
SALES (est): 1.4MM Privately Held
SIC: 2035 Seasonings & sauces, except tomato & dry; dressings, salad: raw & cooked (except dry mixes)

(G-9524)
IMAGE INDUSTRIES INC
Also Called: Secret Image Promotion
305 Smith Dr (45315-8705)
PHONE...................................937 832-7969
Fax: 937 832-8838
Bill Michael, *President*
Steve Baldwin, *Manager*
EMP: 7
SQ FT: 4,000
SALES (est): 780.9K Privately Held
WEB: www.secretimage.com
SIC: 2791 7336 Typesetting; silk screen design

(G-9525)
INNOVATIVE BUS CMPT SOLUTIONS
Also Called: I B C S
303 Shady Tree Ct (45315-9652)
PHONE...................................937 832-3969
Kent L Crabtree, *President*
Hoyng Bob, *COO*
EMP: 4
SQ FT: 2,400
SALES (est): 320K Privately Held
WEB: www.spasalon.com
SIC: 7372 Prepackaged software

(G-9526)
INTERNATIONAL BELLOWS
2 Ferrari Ct (45315-8988)
PHONE...................................937 832-4501
Fax: 937 832-4701
Thomas Armstrong, *President*
Greg Furlong, *Vice Pres*
Tony Riggs, *Vice Pres*
Martin Sherry, *Vice Pres*
Cheri Romans, *Plant Mgr*
EMP: 10
SQ FT: 4,800
SALES (est): 1.2MM Privately Held
SIC: 3599 Bellows, industrial: metal

(G-9527)
JACK A BYTE MLTMDIA GAMING LLC
Also Called: Jackabyte
893 S Main St 375 (45322-2814)
PHONE...................................937 321-1716
Sheri Yarbrough,

EMP: 5
SALES (est): 340.3K Privately Held
SIC: 7372 Home entertainment computer software

(G-9528)
KENT SWIGART
Also Called: Swigart Electric
301 W Wenger Rd (45322-1829)
PHONE...................................937 836-5292
Kent Swigart, *Owner*
Nevin E Swigart Sr, *Owner*
EMP: 3
SALES (est): 378.7K Privately Held
SIC: 7694 1799 3599 Electric motor repair; welding on site; machine shop, jobbing & repair

(G-9529)
KING KOLD INC
331 N Main St (45322-1333)
PHONE...................................937 836-2731
Fax: 937 836-5919
Douglas Smith, *President*
Robert L Smith, *Corp Secy*
Nancy Beckman, *Office Mgr*
EMP: 25
SQ FT: 5,210
SALES (est): 2.2MM Privately Held
SIC: 2038 2013 2011 5142 Frozen specialties; cooked meats from purchased meat; meat packing plants; fish, frozen: packaged

(G-9530)
LITEFLEX LLC (PA)
100 Holiday Dr (45322-2707)
P.O. Box 69 (45322-0069)
PHONE...................................937 836-7025
John Prikkel III, *President*
James Dean, *General Mgr*
Daniel Chien, *Vice Pres*
Geoff Scowen, *Engineer*
Ray Blatz, *CFO*
▲ EMP: 30
SQ FT: 70,000
SALES (est): 16.8MM Privately Held
SIC: 3493 Leaf springs: automobile, locomotive, etc.

(G-9531)
METRO TOOL & DIE CO INC
11974 Putnam Rd (45322-9721)
PHONE...................................937 836-8242
Fax: 937 836-1190
Michael Black, *CEO*
Karen Hergenrather, *Office Mgr*
EMP: 5 EST: 1959
SQ FT: 10,000
SALES: 500K Privately Held
SIC: 3544 Special dies & tools

(G-9532)
MEXUS HOLDINGS INC
140 Harrisburg Dr (45322-2836)
PHONE...................................937 832-2307
John N Adams, *President*
Geraldina Adams, *Vice Pres*
Michelle Hatton, *Bookkeeper*
EMP: 18
SALES (est): 1.8MM Privately Held
SIC: 3089 Injection molding of plastics

(G-9533)
MIDWEST METROLOGY LLC
341 Smith Dr (45315-8705)
PHONE...................................937 832-0965
Bill Sierschula,
EMP: 3 EST: 1999
SQ FT: 2,400
SALES (est): 400.6K Privately Held
WEB: www.midwest-metrology.com
SIC: 7699 3825 Industrial equipment services; test equipment for electronic & electric measurement

(G-9534)
NANOLAP TECHNOLOGIES LLC
85 Harrisburg Dr (45322-2835)
PHONE...................................877 658-4949
George Chang, *President*
George Shuai, *Sales Mgr*
EMP: 22
SQ FT: 19,000

SALES: 6MM Privately Held
SIC: 3291 Abrasive products; coated abrasive products; sandpaper

(G-9535)
NEWSPAPER SOLUTIONS LLC
116 Old Carriage Dr (45322-1168)
P.O. Box 398, Vandalia (45377-0398)
PHONE...................................937 694-9370
Douglas Gibson, *Mng Member*
EMP: 5
SALES: 25K Privately Held
SIC: 2711 Newspapers

(G-9536)
NISSIN PRECISION N AMER INC
375 Union Rd (45315-8802)
P.O. Box 399 (45322-0399)
PHONE...................................937 836-1910
Todd Shimizu, *President*
Kevin McCarthy, *General Mgr*
Mike Greer, *Vice Pres*
Cathy Sayer, *Vice Pres*
Akio Yamamoto, *Vice Pres*
▲ EMP: 80
SALES (est): 18.7MM
SALES (corp-wide): 78.7MM Privately Held
WEB: www.epinei.com
SIC: 3663 3444 Television broadcasting & communications equipment; sheet metalwork
PA: Nissin Kogyo Co.,Ltd.
    1-1-1, Tsukinowa
    Otsu SGA 520-2
    775 453-011

(G-9537)
PROSTHETIC DESIGN INC
Also Called: Pdi
700 Harco Dr (45315-8793)
PHONE...................................937 836-1464
Fax: 937 832-5361
Tracy Slemker, *President*
Larry Lang, *General Mgr*
Don Mason, *Business Mgr*
Bob Carpenter, *Engineer*
Robert Carpenter, *Engineer*
▲ EMP: 4
SALES (est): 1.8MM Privately Held
WEB: www.prostheticdesign.com
SIC: 3842 5999 Prosthetic appliances; orthopedic & prosthesis applications

(G-9538)
RATLIFF METAL SPINNING CO INC
40 Harrisburg Dr (45322-2834)
PHONE...................................937 836-3900
Fax: 937 836-3999
Michael K Ratliff, *President*
James D Ratliff, *Vice Pres*
Robin K Ratliff, *Treasurer*
Robin N Ratliffsammons, *Treasurer*
Ardis Ratliff, *Personnel Exec*
EMP: 30
SQ FT: 40,000
SALES: 5.3MM Privately Held
WEB: www.ratliffmetal.com
SIC: 3499 Friction material, made from powdered metal

(G-9539)
SK TECH INC
200 Metro Dr (45315-8700)
PHONE...................................937 836-3535
Fax: 937 832-8898
Nobuyoshi Saigusa, *President*
Hideki Kawase, *President*
Hidki Kawase, *Principal*
Masatoshi Watanabe, *Vice Pres*
Paula Graef, *Accountant*
▲ EMP: 160
SQ FT: 48,000
SALES (est): 56.9MM Privately Held
SIC: 3694 Engine electrical equipment

(G-9540)
T K L LETTERING
300 W National Rd Ste C (45322-1442)
PHONE...................................937 832-2091
Fax: 937 832-2091
R Thomas Penny, *Owner*
EMP: 3

GEOGRAPHIC

SALES (est): 128.6K **Privately Held**
SIC: 5941 5699 2759 Sporting goods & bicycle shops; sports apparel; screen printing

(G-9541)
UNIFIED SCRN & CRUSH-OH INC
Also Called: Ohio Wire Cloth
200 Cass Dr (45315-8834)
P.O. Box 280 (45322-0280)
PHONE..................937 836-3201
Tom Lentsch, *President*
Michele Kleason, *Treasurer*
EMP: 6
SQ FT: 10,000
SALES: 900K
SALES (corp-wide): 14.2MM **Privately Held**
SIC: 3496 5082 7699 Wire cloth & woven wire products; mining machinery & equipment, except petroleum; welding equipment repair
PA: Unified Screening & Crushing - Mn, Inc.
3350 Highway 149
Eagan MN 55121
651 454-8835

(G-9542)
VALUE ADDED PACKAGING INC
44 Lau Pkwy (45315-8777)
PHONE..................937 832-9595
Fax: 937 832-9696
Jarod D Wenrick, *President*
Marcus Selman, *Materials Mgr*
Shannon Kitchen, *Marketing Mgr*
Tim Goodwin, *Office Mgr*
Gary Swartout, *Manager*
EMP: 15
SQ FT: 20,000
SALES (est): 4.5MM **Privately Held**
WEB: www.4vapack.com
SIC: 2653 Boxes, corrugated: made from purchased materials

(G-9543)
VANTAGE SPECIALTY INGREDIENTS
707 Harco Dr (45315-8854)
PHONE..................937 264-1222
Fax: 937 264-1225
Louis Frischling, *President*
Patrick Bruegeman, *President*
Arica McCracken, *Business Mgr*
Stephen Greenberg PHD, *Vice Pres*
Jeremy Vance, *Foreman/Supr*
▲ **EMP:** 24
SALES: 4.5MM **Privately Held**
WEB: www.lipotechnologies.com
SIC: 2869 Industrial organic chemicals

(G-9544)
WAGONER STORES INC (PA)
Also Called: Wagoners Red Wing Shs Fabrics
324 Union Blvd (45322-2115)
PHONE..................937 836-3636
Fax: 937 832-0336
Carl Wagoner, *President*
Hazel Wagoner, *Vice Pres*
▲ **EMP:** 4
SQ FT: 4,000
SALES (est): 1.2MM **Privately Held**
SIC: 5331 5311 5661 2326 Variety stores; department stores; men's shoes; men's & boys' work clothing; sewing, needlework & piece goods; hats & caps

Enon
Clark County

(G-9545)
HALLMARK INDUSTRIES INC (PA)
Also Called: Miller, Jim Furniture
6711 Dyton Springfield Rd (45323-1217)
P.O. Box 386 (45323-0386)
PHONE..................937 864-7378
Fax: 937 864-1122
James Odell Miller, *President*
Diane E Miller, *Vice Pres*
EMP: 25
SQ FT: 54,000

SALES (est): 2.8MM **Privately Held**
SIC: 2512 5712 Living room furniture: upholstered on wood frames; furniture stores

(G-9546)
HALLMARK INDUSTRIES INC
Also Called: Hallmark Manufacturing
6711 Dyton Springfield Rd (45323-1217)
P.O. Box 386 (45323-0386)
PHONE..................937 864-7378
James Miller, *President*
EMP: 19
SALES (corp-wide): 2.8MM **Privately Held**
SIC: 2512 Living room furniture: upholstered on wood frames
PA: Hallmark Industries, Inc.
6711 Dyton Springfield Rd
Enon OH 45323
937 864-7378

(G-9547)
HARDWOOD STORE INC
340 Enon Rd (45323-1004)
PHONE..................937 864-2899
John B Clark, *President*
Lisa L Clark, *Vice Pres*
Eric Shoopman, *Opers Mgr*
Cheryl Lewis, *Director*
EMP: 6
SQ FT: 16,000
SALES (est): 654.2K **Privately Held**
WEB: www.thelumberstore.com
SIC: 2499 5211 Decorative wood & woodwork; lumber products

(G-9548)
PROMAC INC
350 Conley Dr (45323-1002)
P.O. Box 158 (45323-0158)
PHONE..................937 864-1961
Fax: 937 864-1179
Russell Foster, *President*
Leslie Webb, *Bookkeeper*
Ralph Bailey, *Sales Staff*
EMP: 25
SQ FT: 22,000
SALES (est): 3.5MM **Privately Held**
SIC: 3599 3544 Machine shop, jobbing & repair; special dies, tools, jigs & fixtures

(G-9549)
SEEPEX INC
511 Speedway Dr (45323-1057)
P.O. Box 951454, Cleveland (44193-0016)
PHONE..................937 864-7150
Fax: 937 864-7157
Mike Dillon, *President*
Daniel Lakovic, *President*
Peter McGarian, *Managing Dir*
Ulrich Seeberger, *Managing Dir*
Bruce Stark, *Regional Mgr*
◆ **EMP:** 115
SQ FT: 35,000
SALES: 34.5MM
SALES (corp-wide): 137.4MM **Privately Held**
WEB: www.seepex.com
SIC: 3586 3561 Measuring & dispensing pumps; pumps & pumping equipment
PA: Seepex Gmbh
Scharnholzstr. 344
Bottrop 46240
204 199-60

(G-9550)
SPEEDWAY LLC (HQ)
500 Speedway Dr (45323-1056)
P.O. Box 1500, Springfield (45501-1500)
PHONE..................937 864-3000
Fax: 937 863-6722
Anthony R Kenney, *President*
Mary Johnson, *General Mgr*
Seth Rostoser, *General Mgr*
Richard Worley, *General Mgr*
Michael Eargood, *Regional Mgr*
EMP: 742
SALES (est): 3.5B **Publicly Held**
WEB: www.speedwaynet.com
SIC: 5411 5541 2869 Convenience stores, chain; filling stations, gasoline; fuels

Etna
Franklin County

(G-9551)
ALICE BEOUGHER
Also Called: Wagram
13255 National Rd Sw (43068-3396)
PHONE..................740 927-2470
Alice Beougher, *Owner*
EMP: 3
SALES (est): 222.4K **Privately Held**
WEB: www.wagram.com
SIC: 3942 Miniature dolls, collectors'

(G-9552)
TERRY A JOHNSON
15094 Palmer Rd Sw (43068-3326)
PHONE..................614 561-0706
Terry A Johnson, *Principal*
EMP: 5 **EST:** 2010
SALES (est): 270K **Privately Held**
SIC: 2048 Prepared feeds

(G-9553)
WAIBEL ELECTRIC CO INC
133 Humphries Dr (43068-6801)
PHONE..................740 964-2956
Fax: 614 964-1265
Carl H Waibel Jr, *President*
Sherry Waibel, *Corp Secy*
EMP: 16
SQ FT: 5,200
SALES: 1MM **Privately Held**
WEB: www.waibelelectric.com
SIC: 1731 3621 General electrical contractor; motors & generators

Etna
Licking County

(G-9554)
AN BAICEIR BAKERY
116 Reader Ct (43062-9800)
PHONE..................740 739-0501
Katrina Sheily, *Owner*
EMP: 9
SALES: 24K **Privately Held**
SIC: 2051 Bread, cake & related products

(G-9555)
BEST LIGHTING PRODUCTS INC (DH)
1213 Etna Pkwy (43062-8041)
PHONE..................740 964-0063
Fax: 740 964-1132
Jeffrey S Katz, *CEO*
George Jue, *President*
Lynne Bauman, *CFO*
Jeff Murphy, *VP Sales*
Howard Hopkins, *Accounts Mgr*
◆ **EMP:** 55 **EST:** 1997
SQ FT: 60,000
SALES (est): 12.3MM **Privately Held**
WEB: www.bestlighting.net
SIC: 3646 5063 Commercial indusl & institutional electric lighting fixtures; electrical apparatus & equipment
HQ: Wafra Investment Advisory Group Inc.
345 Park Ave Fl 4100
New York NY 10154
212 515-7600

(G-9556)
GUADALUPE PUBLISHING INC
60 Dellenbaugh Loop (43062-9642)
PHONE..................614 450-2474
William Taylor, *Principal*
EMP: 4
SALES (est): 210.7K **Privately Held**
SIC: 2741 Miscellaneous publishing

(G-9557)
JELD-WEN INC
Also Called: Jeld-Wen Millwork Masters
91 Heritage Dr (43062-9805)
PHONE..................740 964-1431
Fax: 740 964-1473
EMP: 136
SALES (corp-wide): 22.5B **Publicly Held**
SIC: 2431 Millwork

HQ: Jeld-Wen, Inc.
440 S Church St Ste 400
Charlotte NC 28202
800 535-3936

(G-9558)
JOULES ANGSTROM UV PRINTING (PA)
104 Heritage Dr (43062-8042)
PHONE..................740 964-9113
Patrick T Carlisle, *President*
Jeff Curtis, *Sales Staff*
Danny Davis, *Sales Staff*
Jerry Duclos, *Marketing Staff*
Kevin Kirchner, *Marketing Staff*
EMP: 24
SQ FT: 30,000
SALES (est): 7.7MM **Privately Held**
SIC: 2899 Chemical preparations

(G-9559)
LESS COST LIGHTING INC
1213 Etna Pkwy (43062-8041)
P.O. Box 394 (43018-0394)
PHONE..................866 633-6883
Michael Katz, *President*
Dale McCain, *President*
INA Katz, *Accountant*
Steve Smithson, *Sales Mgr*
Stephen Smitson, *Manager*
EMP: 15
SALES: 4MM **Privately Held**
SIC: 3646 Commercial indusl & institutional electric lighting fixtures

(G-9560)
REX BURNETT
26 1st Ave Sw (43062-9441)
PHONE..................740 927-4669
Rex Burnett, *Owner*
EMP: 3
SALES (est): 245.5K **Privately Held**
SIC: 3444 Awnings & canopies

(G-9561)
RIDGE CORPORATION
1201 Etna Pkwy (43062-8041)
PHONE..................614 421-7434
Gary A Grandominico, *Principal*
Rodger Cooper, *Facilities Mgr*
Barry Shumaker, *Maint Spvr*
Kyle Gaines, *Purch Mgr*
Crystal Hill, *Engineer*
▲ **EMP:** 91
SALES (est): 21.6MM **Privately Held**
SIC: 3443 Liners/lining

(G-9562)
SCARRED HANDS WOOD CREATIONS
8484 Hazelton Etna Rd Sw (43062-9491)
PHONE..................740 975-2835
EMP: 4
SALES (est): 179.8K **Privately Held**
SIC: 2431 Millwork

Euclid
Cuyahoga County

(G-9563)
ABC REFRESHMENTS LLC
19541 Roseland Ave (44117-1374)
PHONE..................866 382-5575
Thomas McGinty, *Mng Member*
Patrick McGinty,
EMP: 15
SQ FT: 10,000
SALES (est): 1.8MM **Privately Held**
SIC: 2096 2024 Potato chips & similar snacks; ice cream & frozen desserts

(G-9564)
ADVANCED EQUIPMENT SYSTEMS LLC
22800 Lakeland Blvd (44132-2606)
PHONE..................216 289-6505
Fax: 216 289-4552
Frederic W Starr, *President*
EMP: 8
SQ FT: 65,000
SALES: 1.5MM **Privately Held**
SIC: 3535 Conveyors & conveying equipment

(G-9565)
AMD PLASTICS LLC (PA)
27600 Lakeland Blvd (44132-2152)
PHONE..................................216 289-4862
Fax: 216 289-4863
Pete Hottois, *President*
EMP: 19
SQ FT: 50,000
SALES (est): 3.5MM **Privately Held**
WEB: www.amdnet.com
SIC: 3089 Thermoformed finished plastic products

(G-9566)
AMERICAN PUNCH CO INC
1655 Century Corners Pkwy (44132-3321)
PHONE..................................216 731-4501
Fax: 216 731-3790
Robert Olson, *President*
Larry Kern, *Opers Mgr*
Charles William Olson, *Controller*
Marlo Slusarski, *Human Res Mgr*
Paul Cassidy, *Sales Engr*
EMP: 21
SQ FT: 12,000
SALES (est): 4MM **Privately Held**
WEB: www.americanpunchco.com
SIC: 3599 3544 3421 Machine shop, jobbing & repair; special dies, tools, jigs & fixtures; cutlery

(G-9567)
BIC MANUFACTURING INC
Also Called: A-D Machine
26420 Cntury Corners Pkwy (44132-3310)
PHONE..................................216 531-9393
Fax: 216 531-8214
David D Carr, *President*
Gene Schein, *General Mgr*
James McNamara, *Vice Pres*
Tom Levicky, *CFO*
Candy Kosteonik, *Manager*
EMP: 45
SQ FT: 42,000
SALES (est): 9.2MM **Privately Held**
SIC: 3599 Machine shop, jobbing & repair

(G-9568)
BOYER SIGNS & GRAPHICS INC
21611 Tungsten Rd (44117-1115)
PHONE..................................216 383-7242
Fax: 216 383-7271
Clyde Boyer, *CEO*
Mike Boyer, *President*
Alghea Boryk, *Office Mgr*
April Jurija, *Manager*
EMP: 24
SQ FT: 22,000
SALES: 2.1MM **Privately Held**
WEB: www.boyersigns.com
SIC: 3993 1799 Signs & advertising specialties; neon signs; sign installation & maintenance

(G-9569)
CALIFORNIA CERAMIC SUPPLY CO
Also Called: R Molds
19451 Roseland Ave Ste A (44117-1324)
PHONE..................................216 531-9185
Fax: 216 531-0070
EMP: 6 EST: 1950
SQ FT: 12,000
SALES (est): 380K **Privately Held**
SIC: 5945 3544 3275 Ret Hobbies/Toys/Games Mfg Dies/Tools/Jigs/Fixtures Mfg Gypsum Products

(G-9570)
CARE CABINETRY INC
1410 Chardon Rd Frnt (44117-1543)
PHONE..................................216 481-7445
Fax: 216 383-6986
Zolton Michal, *Vice Pres*
Michal Zolton, *Treasurer*
EMP: 5
SQ FT: 7,000
SALES (est): 480K **Privately Held**
SIC: 2434 Wood kitchen cabinets

(G-9571)
CENTER LINE MACHINING LLC
25700 Lakeland Blvd (44132-2635)
PHONE..................................216 289-6828
Fax: 440 946-2128

Marin Grman, *Mng Member*
Tusan Grman, *Mng Member*
EMP: 4
SALES: 700K **Privately Held**
SIC: 3541 Machine tool replacement & repair parts, metal cutting types

(G-9572)
CLEVELAND PLASTIC FABRICAT
25861 Tungsten Rd (44132-2817)
PHONE..................................216 797-7300
Fax: 216 486-7302
Mitchell Opalich, *President*
Lorraine Simer, *Vice Pres*
John Harrel, *Sales Staff*
Judy Pintar, *Office Mgr*
EMP: 18
SQ FT: 21,500
SALES (est): 1.6MM **Privately Held**
WEB: www.clevelandplastic.com
SIC: 3599 3498 3561 3089 Machine shop, jobbing & repair; tube fabricating (contract bending & shaping); pumps & pumping equipment; fittings for pipe, plastic; industrial supplies; industrial fittings; pipes & fittings, plastic

(G-9573)
CONTINENTAL PRODUCTS COMPANY (PA)
1150 E 222nd St (44117-1103)
P.O. Box 17215 (44117-0215)
PHONE..................................216 383-3932
Fax: 216 289-1745
Miriam Strebeck, *Ch of Bd*
Emerson O McArthur III, *President*
Michael McArthur, *Manager*
EMP: 20 EST: 1916
SQ FT: 4,000
SALES (est): 3.9MM **Privately Held**
WEB: www.paintdoc.com
SIC: 2851 Paints & paint additives; stains: varnish, oil or wax; putty

(G-9574)
DETROIT FLAME HARDENING CO
Also Called: Cleveland Flame Hardening
24951 Tungsten Rd (44117-1237)
PHONE..................................216 531-4273
Fax: 216 738-2205
Greg Bybee, *General Mgr*
EMP: 5
SQ FT: 7,000
SALES (corp-wide): 2.9MM **Privately Held**
WEB: www.detroitflame.com
SIC: 3398 Metal heat treating
PA: Detroit Flame Hardening Company Inc
17644 Mount Elliott St
Detroit MI
313 891-2936

(G-9575)
E D M SERVICES INC
21724 Saint Clair Ave (44117-1026)
PHONE..................................216 486-2068
Fax: 216 486-4636
Clifford Griffin, *President*
Nancy Griffin, *Corp Secy*
Louis Kapel, *Vice Pres*
▲ EMP: 3
SQ FT: 4,400
SALES (est): 300.7K **Privately Held**
SIC: 3599 3544 Electrical discharge machining (EDM); special dies, tools, jigs & fixtures

(G-9576)
EAGLEHEAD MANUFACTURING CO
Also Called: Dejak Machine Tool Company
23555 Euclid Ave (44117-1703)
PHONE..................................216 692-1240
Fax: 216 692-1156
Harris Phillips, *CEO*
Ray Westfall, *President*
C Roger Cotman, *Shareholder*
EMP: 28
SQ FT: 25,000
SALES (est): 3.3MM **Privately Held**
SIC: 3965 Fasteners

(G-9577)
EDZPLACE
400 E 255th St (44132-1010)
PHONE..................................216 289-4834
Eddie Anderson, *Principal*
EMP: 3
SALES (est): 205.2K **Privately Held**
SIC: 2836 Culture media

(G-9578)
EUCLID BREWING COMPANY LLC
22408 Lake Shore Blvd (44123-1313)
PHONE..................................216 289-5100
Douglas Fry, *Principal*
EMP: 4
SALES (est): 75.4K **Privately Held**
SIC: 2082 Malt beverages

(G-9579)
EUCLID HEAT TREATING CO
Also Called: E H T Company
1408 E 222nd St (44117-1108)
PHONE..................................216 481-8444
Fax: 216 481-3473
John H Vanas, *President*
Dan Lipnicki, *Vice Pres*
Steve Pitt, *Plant Mgr*
Deidra Minerd, *Human Res Mgr*
Roger Robbins, *Manager*
EMP: 55 EST: 1946
SQ FT: 45,000
SALES (est): 14MM **Privately Held**
WEB: www.euclidheattreating.com
SIC: 3398 1711 Metal heat treating; plumbing, heating, air-conditioning contractors

(G-9580)
EUCLID STEEL & WIRE INC
Also Called: ES&w
25030 Lakeland Blvd (44132-2628)
P.O. Box 770850, Lakewood (44107-0038)
PHONE..................................216 731-6744
Fax: 216 731-6747
Donald J Anzells, *President*
Daniel R Corcoran, *Principal*
Charles D Mc Bride, *Principal*
T P Mc Mahon, *Principal*
Lynn Lemmo, *Controller*
EMP: 12
SQ FT: 10,400
SALES (est): 1.2MM **Privately Held**
SIC: 3315 Wire, steel: insulated or armored

(G-9581)
GLOBAL GLASS BLOCK INC
23570 Lakeland Blvd (44132-2613)
PHONE..................................216 731-2333
Fax: 216 731-3832
Anthony Lacorte, *President*
▲ EMP: 8
SALES (est): 798K **Privately Held**
SIC: 3229 5039 Blocks & bricks, glass; glass construction materials

(G-9582)
GUARDIAN TECHNOLOGIES LLC
Also Called: Germ Guardian
26251 Bluestone Blvd # 7 (44132-2826)
PHONE..................................216 706-2250
Tina Reynolds, *Accountant*
David Brickner, *Mng Member*
Charles A Waldorff Jr, *Manager*
Richard Farone,
▲ EMP: 24
SQ FT: 72,000
SALES: 36.6MM **Privately Held**
WEB: www.guardiantechnologies.com
SIC: 3564 3585 Air purification equipment; humidifiers & dehumidifiers

(G-9583)
H C STARCK INC
1250 E 222nd St (44117-1114)
PHONE..................................216 692-6990
Richard M Corry, *CEO*
Carol Gilmurray, *Managing Dir*
John Hribar, *QC Mgr*
Branden Melich, *Draft/Design*
Adolfo Leal, *Project Engr*
EMP: 30 **Privately Held**
SIC: 3339 Primary nonferrous metals

HQ: H. C. Starck Inc.
45 Industrial Pl
Newton MA 02461
617 630-5800

(G-9584)
H C STARCK INC
21801 Tungsten Rd (44117-1117)
PHONE..................................216 692-3990
Pete Calfo, *Vice Pres*
Joe Hoffman, *Vice Pres*
Bobby Woods, *Production*
Ken J Wuchte, *Production*
Paula Yuen, *Buyer*
EMP: 300 **Privately Held**
WEB: www.hcstarck.com
SIC: 3356 3313 3339 Tungsten, basic shapes; molybdenum silicon, not made in blast furnaces; rhenium refining (primary)
HQ: H. C. Starck Inc.
45 Industrial Pl
Newton MA 02461
617 630-5800

(G-9585)
HACIENDA PUBLICATIONS LLC
20970 Wilmore Ave (44123-2818)
PHONE..................................216 202-5440
Robin Boyd,
EMP: 3
SALES (est): 102.6K **Privately Held**
SIC: 2721 Periodicals: publishing & printing

(G-9586)
INTERGROUP INTERNATIONAL LTD
1111 E 200th St (44117-1134)
PHONE..................................216 965-0257
Neil Gloger, *Partner*
Sarah Gatanas, *Partner*
Caroline Brichford, *Controller*
Sandy Jewell, *Manager*
EMP: 70
SQ FT: 130,000
SALES (est): 19.9MM **Privately Held**
SIC: 2821 Plastics materials & resins

(G-9587)
J W HARRIS CO INC
Also Called: Harris Products Group, The
22801 Saint Clair Ave (44117-2524)
PHONE..................................216 481-8100
David Nangle, *President*
▲ EMP: 10 EST: 2013
SALES (est): 4.6MM
SALES (corp-wide): 2.2B **Publicly Held**
SIC: 5051 3398 Copper; brazing (hardening) of metal
HQ: J. W. Harris Co., Inc.
4501 Quality Pl
Mason OH 45040
513 754-2000

(G-9588)
JBJ TECHNOLOGIES INC
185 E 280th St (44132-1306)
PHONE..................................216 469-7297
Michael Johnston, *Senior VP*
EMP: 11
SALES (est): 1.3MM **Privately Held**
SIC: 3599 Machine shop, jobbing & repair

(G-9589)
LINCOLN ELECTRIC COMPANY (HQ)
22801 Saint Clair Ave (44117-1199)
PHONE..................................216 481-8100
Fax: 216 486-1363
Steven B Hedlund, *President*
Christopher L Mapes, *Chairman*
Frederick G Stueber, *Exec VP*
Geoffrey P Allman, *Senior VP*
Anthony Battle, *Senior VP*
◆ EMP: 3200
SQ FT: 2,658,410
SALES (est): 1.4B
SALES (corp-wide): 2.2B **Publicly Held**
WEB: www.subarc-welding.com
SIC: 3548 Arc welding generators, alternating current & direct current; electrodes, electric welding
PA: Lincoln Electric Holdings, Inc.
22801 Saint Clair Ave
Cleveland OH 44117
216 481-8100

GEOGRAPHI

(G-9590)
LINCOLN ELECTRIC INTL HOLDG CO (HQ)
22801 Saint Clair Ave (44117-2524)
PHONE...................216 481-8100
Dave Snider, *General Mgr*
John Stropki, *Chairman*
William Dotson, *District Mgr*
Bob Blackstock, *Business Mgr*
Wayne Deatsch, *Foreman/Supr*
▲ EMP: 29
SALES (est): 352.3MM
SALES (corp-wide): 2.2B **Publicly Held**
SIC: 3548 Welding apparatus
PA: Lincoln Electric Holdings, Inc.
22801 Saint Clair Ave
Cleveland OH 44117
216 481-8100

(G-9591)
MART PLUS FUEL
21820 Lake Shore Blvd (44123-1707)
PHONE...................216 261-0420
Anil Uppal, *Principal*
EMP: 3
SALES (est): 191.5K **Privately Held**
SIC: 2869 Fuels

(G-9592)
MECHANICAL DYNAMICS ANALIS LTD
Also Called: Renewal Parts Maintenance
1250 E 222nd St (44117-1114)
PHONE...................440 946-0082
Fax: 440 946-5524
John L Vanderhoef, *CEO*
EMP: 21
SALES (corp-wide): 34.5B **Privately Held**
SIC: 7699 3568 3053 Industrial machinery & equipment repair; power transmission equipment; gaskets, packing & sealing devices
HQ: Mechanical Dynamics & Analysis, Ltd.
19 British American Blvd
Latham NY 12110
518 399-3616

(G-9593)
MESOCOAT INC
Also Called: Mesocoat Advanced Coating Tech
24112 Rockwell Dr (44117-1252)
PHONE...................216 453-0866
Fax: 216 404-0054
Stephen Goss, *CEO*
Anupam Ghilyal, *Vice Pres*
Max Matteson, *Manager*
▲ EMP: 18
SALES (est): 748.8K
SALES (corp-wide): 1MM **Publicly Held**
SIC: 3479 1799 5169 7699 Coating of metals & formed products; coating, rust preventive; aluminum coating of metal products; corrosion control installation; anti-corrosion products; industrial equipment services; industrial equipment cleaning
PA: Abakan Inc
2665 S Byshr Dr Ste 450
Miami FL 33133
786 206-5368

(G-9594)
MULLIN PRINT SOLUTIONS
84 E 197th St (44119-1002)
PHONE...................216 383-2901
Kevin Mullin, *Principal*
EMP: 4
SALES (est): 343K **Privately Held**
SIC: 2752 Commercial printing, lithographic

(G-9595)
NORTH AMERICAN PLAS CHEM INC (PA)
Also Called: Noramco
1400 E 222nd St (44117-1108)
PHONE...................216 531-3400
Fax: 216 531-3401
James Popela, *Principal*
EMP: 35
SQ FT: 25,000

SALES (est): 19.5MM **Privately Held**
WEB: www.nap-bag.com
SIC: 2673 2671 Plastic & pliofilm bags; packaging paper & plastics film, coated & laminated

(G-9596)
ORTHOTIC AND PROSTETIC SPC
20650 Lakeland Blvd (44119-3241)
PHONE...................216 531-2773
Fax: 216 531-5376
Richard Gaudio, *President*
Tom Heckman, *Vice Pres*
Jeff Gerl, *Admin Sec*
EMP: 15
SQ FT: 7,200
SALES: 1.3MM **Privately Held**
SIC: 3842 Surgical appliances & supplies; braces, elastic; splints, pneumatic & wood

(G-9597)
PIKE MACHINE PRODUCTS CO
23460 Lakeland Blvd (44132-2699)
PHONE...................216 731-1880
Fax: 216 731-7097
Louis D Pike, *President*
Phyllis Bauer, *Vice Pres*
Barbara Pike, *Vice Pres*
EMP: 30 EST: 1943
SQ FT: 10,000
SALES: 1MM **Privately Held**
SIC: 3599 3645 3451 3398 Machine shop, jobbing & repair; residential lighting fixtures; screw machine products; metal heat treating

(G-9598)
POWDERMET INC (PA)
24112 Rockwell Dr (44117-1252)
PHONE...................216 404-0053
Andrew Sherman, *President*
Brian Doud, *Engineer*
Mark Grogan, *Engineer*
Allen Rister, *Engineer*
Sharon Pealer, *Office Mgr*
EMP: 50
SQ FT: 7,800
SALES: 1.4MM **Privately Held**
WEB: www.powdermetinc.com
SIC: 3399 Powder, metal

(G-9599)
POWDERMET POWDER PRODUCTION
24112 Rockwell Dr Ste D (44117-1252)
PHONE...................216 404-0053
Andrew Sherman, *CEO*
EMP: 10
SALES (est): 834.4K **Privately Held**
SIC: 3821 Crushing & grinding apparatus, laboratory

(G-9600)
PPG INDUSTRIES OHIO INC
Also Called: Pretreatment & Specialty Pdts
23000 Saint Clair Ave (44117-2503)
PHONE...................216 486-5300
Jim Driddy, *Principal*
Matt Brady, *Vice Pres*
Stan Zaharewicz, *Plant Mgr*
EMP: 66
SALES (corp-wide): 14.7B **Publicly Held**
WEB: www.ppgglass.com
SIC: 2851 Paints & allied products
HQ: Ppg Industries Ohio, Inc.
3800 W 143rd St
Cleveland OH 44111
216 671-0050

(G-9601)
PRECISION HYDRAULIC CONNECTORS
Also Called: PHC Divison Bic Manufacturing
26420 Cntury Corners Pkwy (44132-3310)
PHONE...................440 953-3778
Patrick De Capua, *President*
EMP: 15
SQ FT: 12,000
SALES (est): 1MM **Privately Held**
SIC: 3599 Machine & other job shop work

(G-9602)
QCSM LLC
Also Called: Columbia Industries
23582 Saint Clair Ave (44117-2513)
PHONE...................216 531-5960
John Quigley,
EMP: 3
SALES (est): 253.8K **Privately Held**
SIC: 3593 3451 8711 3599 Fluid power cylinders & actuators; fluid power cylinders, hydraulic or pneumatic; screw machine products; mechanical engineering; machine & other job shop work

(G-9603)
R & A SPORTS INC
Also Called: Adler Team Sports
23780 Lakeland Blvd (44132-2615)
PHONE...................216 289-2254
Fax: 216 289-6392
John Domo, *President*
Richard Domo, *Vice Pres*
Ruth Ann Domo, *Admin Sec*
EMP: 25
SQ FT: 16,000
SALES: 3.9MM **Privately Held**
SIC: 5091 5136 5137 2396 Sporting & recreation goods; sportswear, men's & boys'; sportswear, women's & children's; screen printing on fabric articles

(G-9604)
RISHER & CO
27011 Tungsten Rd (44132-2990)
PHONE...................216 732-8351
Fax: 216 732-7331
William J Risher, *President*
Josh Mann, *Regional Mgr*
Brandon Plumlee, *Sales Mgr*
Jo Ann McNaughgon, *Manager*
Joanne Smith, *Manager*
EMP: 18 EST: 1942
SQ FT: 27,000
SALES (est): 2.8MM **Privately Held**
SIC: 3599 Machine shop, jobbing & repair

(G-9605)
S C INDUSTRIES INC
24460 Lakeland Blvd (44132-2622)
P.O. Box 32307 (44132-0307)
PHONE...................216 732-9000
Earl Lauridsen, *President*
Gayle Wakefield, *Office Mgr*
▲ EMP: 20
SQ FT: 10,000
SALES (est): 5.1MM **Privately Held**
SIC: 3366 7389 Bushings & bearings; grinding, precision: commercial or industrial

(G-9606)
SEME & SON AUTOMOTIVE INC
1320 E 260th St (44132-2816)
PHONE...................216 261-0066
Fax: 216 289-0994
Frank Seme, *President*
Julie Seme, *General Mgr*
EMP: 4
SQ FT: 15,940
SALES (est): 553.6K **Privately Held**
WEB: www.seme-now.com
SIC: 3599 7538 Machine shop, jobbing & repair; engine rebuilding: automotive

(G-9607)
SUNSET INDUSTRIES INC
1272 E 286th St (44132-2191)
PHONE...................216 731-8131
Fax: 216 731-8716
Ivan Hauptman, *President*
Peter Hauptman, *Vice Pres*
Clem Hren, *Vice Pres*
Rudy Hren, *Treasurer*
Frank Hren, *Shareholder*
EMP: 28
SQ FT: 14,500
SALES (est): 5.2MM **Privately Held**
WEB: www.sunsetindustries.com
SIC: 3599 3812 3594 Machine shop, jobbing & repair; search & navigation equipment; fluid power pumps & motors

(G-9608)
TECH-MED INC
Also Called: Shaker Numeric Mfg
1080 E 222nd St (44117-1101)
PHONE...................216 486-0900
Fax: 216 486-0904
Gary White, *President*
Andy Misiak, *Engineer*
Carty White, *Admin Sec*
EMP: 15 EST: 1953
SQ FT: 10,000
SALES (est): 2.6MM **Privately Held**
WEB: www.shakernumeric.com
SIC: 3469 Machine parts, stamped or pressed metal

(G-9609)
TECHALLOY INC
22801 Saint Clair Ave (44117-2524)
PHONE...................410 633-9300
George Blankenship, *President*
Henry Lopes, *Vice Pres*
Richard Perlick, *Vice Pres*
Carl Reed, *Vice Pres*
Kurt Slacik, *Vice Pres*
▲ EMP: 50
SALES (est): 5.9MM
SALES (corp-wide): 2.2B **Publicly Held**
SIC: 3548 Welding wire, bare & coated
PA: Lincoln Electric Holdings, Inc.
22801 Saint Clair Ave
Cleveland OH 44117
216 481-8100

(G-9610)
TERMINAL OPTICAL LAB
26215 Tungsten Rd (44132-2998)
PHONE...................216 289-7722
Fax: 216 289-1967
Rick Milam, *Principal*
EMP: 3
SALES (est): 300.1K **Privately Held**
SIC: 3851 Ophthalmic goods

(G-9611)
TRI COUNTY DOOR SERVICE INC
21701 Tungsten Rd (44117-1116)
PHONE...................216 531-2245
Fax: 216 531-2248
Peter Look, *President*
Frank A Cigoy, *Vice Pres*
EMP: 11 EST: 1968
SQ FT: 10,000
SALES (est): 1.3MM **Privately Held**
WEB: www.tricountydoor.com
SIC: 3442 1751 Garage doors, overhead: metal; carpentry work

(G-9612)
TRUST MANUFACTURING LLC
20080 Saint Clair Ave (44117-1015)
PHONE...................216 531-8787
Paul S Novosel, *President*
Mark Graham, *Sales Staff*
Alex Manuk, *Manager*
Jose Padilla, *Manager*
Tim Corgan,
EMP: 15
SALES (est): 3.6MM **Privately Held**
SIC: 3429 Manufactured hardware (general)

Fairborn
Greene County

(G-9613)
ALI INDUSTRIES INC
Also Called: Abrasive Leaders & Innovators
747 E Xenia Dr (45324-8761)
PHONE...................937 878-3946
Terry Ali, *President*
Christopher Ali, *Vice Pres*
Lee Kockentiet, *VP Finance*
Phillip Ali, *VP Sales*
Viola Ali, *Admin Sec*
◆ EMP: 200
SQ FT: 260,360
SALES (est): 93.5MM **Privately Held**
WEB: www.gatorgrit.com
SIC: 3291 Abrasive products

(G-9614)
ALL SRVICE PLASTIC MOLDING INC
611 Yllow Sprng Frfeld Rd (45324)
PHONE...................................937 415-3674
Julie Bodenmiller, *Warehouse Mgr*
Keller Phillip, *Branch Mgr*
EMP: 43
SALES (corp-wide): 47.7MM **Privately Held**
SIC: 3089 Injection molding of plastics
PA: All Service Plastic Molding, Inc.
900 Fall Creek Dr
Vandalia OH 45377
937 890-0322

(G-9615)
BENS WELDING SERVICE INC
605 Middle St (45324-4828)
PHONE...................................937 878-4052
Fax: 937 878-4052
James Pile, *President*
Lisa Pile, *Admin Sec*
EMP: 4
SQ FT: 2,000
SALES (est): 350K **Privately Held**
SIC: 7692 7699 Welding repair; lawn
mower repair shop

(G-9616)
CEDAR CHEST
405 W Main St (45324-4816)
PHONE...................................937 878-9097
Bobby Jasoniski, *Owner*
EMP: 3
SALES (est): 189.5K **Privately Held**
SIC: 2499 Decorative wood & woodwork

(G-9617)
CEMEX USA INC
2600 Paramount Pl (45324-6819)
PHONE...................................937 879-8350
Fax: 937 879-8374
Don Clem, *Principal*
Butch Valentine, *Sales Mgr*
Gary Warner, *Supervisor*
EMP: 14
SALES (est): 2.5MM **Privately Held**
SIC: 3273 Ready-mixed concrete

(G-9618)
CURTISS-WRIGHT CONTROLS
2600 Paramount Pl Ste 200 (45324-6816)
PHONE...................................937 252-5601
Ron Taulton, *Branch Mgr*
Gorky Chin, *Manager*
Paul Davis, *Manager*
Julie Trotter, *Manager*
Eric Freeman, *Info Tech Dir*
EMP: 50
SALES (corp-wide): 2.1B **Publicly Held**
SIC: 8711 8731 3769 3625 Engineering
services; commercial physical research;
guided missile & space vehicle parts &
auxiliary equipment; relays & industrial
controls
HQ: Curtiss-Wright Controls Electronic Sys-
tems, Inc.
28965 Avenue Penn
Santa Clarita CA 91355
661 702-1494

(G-9619)
DOMICONE PRINTING INC
854 Kauffman Ave (45324-3842)
P.O. Box 1 (45324-0001)
PHONE...................................937 878-3080
Fax: 937 878-7899
Fred Domicone, *President*
EMP: 5
SQ FT: 2,000
SALES: 600K **Privately Held**
WEB: www.domiconeprinting.com
SIC: 2752 7334 2759 Commercial print-
ing, offset; photocopying & duplicating
services; invitations; printing; announce-
ments; engraved

(G-9620)
ERNST ENTERPRISES INC
Also Called: Valley Concrete Division
5325 Medway Rd (45324-9765)
PHONE...................................937 878-9378
Fax: 937 878-1484
John Macfee, *General Mgr*
EMP: 16

SALES (corp-wide): 191MM **Privately Held**
WEB: www.ernstconcrete.com
SIC: 3273 Ready-mixed concrete
PA: Ernst Enterprises, Inc.
3361 Successful Way
Dayton OH 45414
937 233-5555

(G-9621)
FONDRIEST ENVIRONMENTAL INC
2091 Exchange Ct (45324-6355)
PHONE...................................937 426-2151
Fax: 937 426-1125
Liz Fondriest, *CEO*
Steven Fondriest, *President*
Elizabeth Fondriest, *COO*
EMP: 12
SALES: 6.5MM **Privately Held**
WEB: www.fondriest.com
SIC: 3823 Water quality monitoring & con-
trol systems

(G-9622)
FOX LITE INC
8300 Dayton Rd (45324-5944)
PHONE...................................937 864-1966
Fax: 937 864-7010
Douglas Hoy, *President*
Mark Hopkins, *Vice Pres*
Walter Hoy, *Vice Pres*
John Duchesne, *Engineer*
Frank A Fox, *Comptroller*
▼ **EMP:** 30
SQ FT: 74,000
SALES (est): 6MM **Privately Held**
WEB: www.foxlite.com
SIC: 3089 Plastic hardware & building
products; windows, plastic

(G-9623)
GLAWE MANUFACTURING CO INC
Also Called: Glawe Awnings
851 Zapata Dr (45324-5165)
PHONE...................................937 754-0064
Fax: 937 754-1780
L Vernon Schaefer, *President*
Thomas R Fridley, *Vice Pres*
Katherine Schaefer, *Vice Pres*
V Schaefer, *Vice Pres*
EMP: 20 EST: 1877
SQ FT: 20,500
SALES (est): 2.1MM **Privately Held**
WEB: www.glaweawnings.com
SIC: 2394 7359 Canvas & related prod-
ucts; equipment rental & leasing

(G-9624)
HILLTOP BASIC RESOURCES INC
5325 Medway Rd (45324-9765)
PHONE...................................937 878-8631
Fax: 937 878-8518
West Johnson, *Manager*
EMP: 25
SALES (corp-wide): 135MM **Privately Held**
WEB: www.hilltopbasicresources.com
SIC: 3273 1442 Ready-mixed concrete;
construction sand mining
PA: Hilltop Basic Resources, Inc.
1 W 4th St Ste 1100
Cincinnati OH 45202
513 651-5000

(G-9625)
HONEYWELL INTERNATIONAL INC
1232 Dytn Yllow Sprng Rd (45324-6360)
PHONE...................................937 754-4134
EMP: 60
SALES (corp-wide): 39B **Publicly Held**
SIC: 3822 3669 Mfg Environmntl Controls
Mfg Communications Equip
PA: Honeywell International Inc.
101 Columbia Rd
Morristown NJ 07950
973 455-2000

(G-9626)
LASERLINC INC
777 Zapata Dr (45324-5160)
PHONE...................................937 318-2440

Fax: 937 318-2445
Dan Dixon, *President*
Jeff Kohler, *Vice Pres*
Jack Weiss, *Vice Pres*
Marc Waldron, *Accounts Mgr*
Joey Kenyon, *Sales Staff*
▲ **EMP:** 20
SQ FT: 19,000
SALES (est): 5.3MM **Privately Held**
WEB: www.laserlinc.com
SIC: 3826 Analytical instruments

(G-9627)
NUVASIVE MANUFACTURING LLC
1 Herald Sq (45324-5153)
PHONE...................................937 343-0400
Todd Tuckett, *Branch Mgr*
EMP: 20
SQ FT: 40,000
SALES (corp-wide): 962MM **Publicly Held**
SIC: 3845 Ultrasonic scanning devices,
medical
HQ: Nuvasive Manufacturing, Llc
7475 Lusk Blvd
San Diego CA 92121
858 909-1800

(G-9628)
P & B ELECTRIC
1835 Successful Dr (45324-9236)
PHONE...................................937 754-4695
Leonard Porter, *Principal*
EMP: 7
SALES (est): 1.1MM **Privately Held**
SIC: 3699 Electrical equipment & supplies

(G-9629)
RAPISCAN SYSTEMS HIGH ENERGY I
Also Called: Aracor
514 E Dytn Yllow Sprng Rd (45324-6432)
PHONE...................................937 879-4200
Fax: 937 879-3935
Robert Armistead, *President*
EMP: 4
SALES (corp-wide): 829.6MM **Publicly Held**
WEB: www.aracor.com
SIC: 3845 Electromedical equipment
HQ: Rapiscan Systems High Energy In-
spection Corporation
520 Almanor Ave
Sunnyvale CA 94085
408 733-7780

(G-9630)
STADCO INC
Also Called: STADCO AUTOMATICS
632 Yllow Sprng Frfeld Rd (45324)
PHONE...................................937 878-0911
Fax: 937 878-0810
Dennis C Trammell, *President*
Catherine Carter, *General Mgr*
Kenneth Wilson, *Vice Pres*
Jeffrey Lyon, *Director*
EMP: 45 EST: 1948
SQ FT: 42,000
SALES: 5.3MM **Privately Held**
WEB: www.stadcoautomatics.com
SIC: 3451 3541 Screw machine products;
machine tools, metal cutting type

(G-9631)
SURFACE RECOVERY TECH LLC
833 Zapata Dr (45324-5165)
PHONE...................................937 879-5864
Thomas Brooks, *Mng Member*
EMP: 15
SQ FT: 20,000
SALES (est): 1.5MM **Privately Held**
SIC: 3441 Fabricated structural metal

(G-9632)
TEE CREATIONS
Also Called: Tca Graphics
701 N Broad St Ste C (45324-5262)
PHONE...................................937 878-2822
Fax: 937 878-2860
Mike Brown, *Owner*
EMP: 9 EST: 1962
SQ FT: 5,000

SALES: 500K **Privately Held**
WEB: www.tcagraphics.com
SIC: 2396 5699 Screen printing on fabric
articles; sports apparel

(G-9633)
VMETRO INC (DH)
Also Called: V Metro
2600 Paramount Pl Ste 200 (45324-6816)
PHONE...................................281 584-0728
James H Gerberman, *President*
Teresa Grubbs, *Accounts Mgr*
▲ **EMP:** 6
SQ FT: 18,371
SALES (est): 1.9MM
SALES (corp-wide): 2.1B **Publicly Held**
WEB: www.vmetro.com
SIC: 3825 3672 3577 5065 Test equip-
ment for electronic & electric measure-
ment; printed circuit boards; computer
peripheral equipment; electronic parts &
equipment
HQ: Curtiss-Wright Controls, Inc.
15801 Brixham Hill Ave # 200
Charlotte NC 28277
704 869-4600

(G-9634)
VOLTAGE REGULATOR SALES & SVCS
Also Called: Electronic Services
590 E Dayton Dr (45324-5120)
PHONE...................................937 878-0673
Sarah Ruth Barnette, *Treasurer*
▼ **EMP:** 4
SQ FT: 5,000
SALES (est): 622.1K **Privately Held**
WEB: www.gen-powercontrols.com
SIC: 7629 3612 Electrical repair shops;
voltage regulating transformers, electric
power

(G-9635)
WCR INC (PA)
Also Called: W C R
2377 Commerce Center Blvd B
(45324-6378)
PHONE...................................937 223-0703
Fax: 937 223-2818
Kim Andreasen, *CEO*
Brad Stevens, *Owner*
Greg Pinasco, *Vice Pres*
Ying Yang, *Prdtn Mgr*
Jeremy Foley, *Sales Mgr*
◆ **EMP:** 32 EST: 2007
SQ FT: 54,000
SALES (est): 39.9MM **Privately Held**
WEB: www.wcr-regasketing.com
SIC: 3443 Fabricated plate work (boiler
shop)

(G-9636)
ZWF GOLF LLC
Also Called: Gem City Golf Club
920 N Broad St (45324)
PHONE...................................937 767-5621
Zachary Fink, *General Mgr*
Troy Martin, *Superintendent*
EMP: 20
SQ FT: 185
SALES: 600K **Privately Held**
SIC: 3949 Shafts, golf club

Fairfield
Butler County

(G-9637)
AAA LAMINATING & BINDERY
7209 Dixie Hwy (45014-5544)
PHONE...................................513 860-2680
Gerald Randall, *Owner*
EMP: 3
SALES (est): 396.2K **Privately Held**
SIC: 2789 Bookbinding & related work

(G-9638)
AGFA CORPORATION
6104 Monastery Dr (45014-4460)
PHONE...................................513 829-6292
James Dixon, *Branch Mgr*
EMP: 220

SALES (corp-wide): 530.5MM **Privately Held**
SIC: 3861 Photographic equipment & supplies
HQ: Agfa Corporation
10 S Academy St
Greenville SC 29601
800 526-5441

(G-9639)
AKRO TOOL CO INC
240 Donald Dr (45014-3007)
PHONE.............................513 858-1555
Ken Johnson, *President*
Donna Johnson, *Treasurer*
EMP: 8
SQ FT: 10,000
SALES (est): 1MM **Privately Held**
SIC: 3544 Special dies, tools, jigs & fixtures

(G-9640)
ALBA MANUFACTURING INC
8950 Seward Rd (45011-9109)
PHONE.............................513 874-0551
Tom Moon, *President*
Thomas N Inderhees, *President*
Mike Kroger, *Vice Pres*
Jerry Heneerlight, *Safety Mgr*
Mike Kees, *Purchasing*
EMP: 52
SQ FT: 67,000
SALES (est): 30.3MM **Privately Held**
WEB: www.albamfg.com
SIC: 3535 5084 3312 Conveyors & conveying equipment; conveyor systems; blast furnaces & steel mills

(G-9641)
AMERICAN INKS AND COATINGS CO
575 Quality Blvd (45014-2294)
PHONE.............................513 552-7200
EMP: 14
SALES (corp-wide): 3.8B **Privately Held**
SIC: 2893 2752 3999 Printing ink; lithographing on metal; atomizers, toiletry
HQ: American Inks And Coatings Company
3400 N Hutchinson St
Pine Bluff AR 71602
870 247-2080

(G-9642)
AMERICAN MANUFACTURING & EQP
Also Called: Cincinnati Retread Systems
4990 Factory Dr (45014-1945)
PHONE.............................513 829-2248
Fax: 513 829-2394
Albert Penter, *President*
Albert Penter Jr, *Vice Pres*
Ty Penter, *Purchasing*
Carol Penter, *Treasurer*
EMP: 9
SQ FT: 12,000
SALES (est): 1.4MM **Privately Held**
WEB: www.cincinnatitreadsystems.com
SIC: 3559 3714 3564 Tire retreading machinery & equipment; motor vehicle parts & accessories; blowers & fans

(G-9643)
AREA WIDE PROTECTIVE INC
9500 Le Saint Dr (45014-2253)
PHONE.............................513 321-9889
Fax: 513 321-9891
EMP: 48
SALES (corp-wide): 111.4MM **Privately Held**
SIC: 3669 7381 7382 Mfg Communications Equip Detective/Armor Car Svcs Security System Svcs
HQ: Area Wide Protective, Inc.
826 Overholt Rd
Kent OH 44240
330 644-0655

(G-9644)
AVI FOOD SYSTEMS INC
4175 Port Union Rd Ste B (45014-2278)
PHONE.............................513 860-4191
Fax: 513 870-4572
Mark Chandler, *Manager*
EMP: 47

SALES (corp-wide): 659.4MM **Privately Held**
WEB: www.avifoodsystems.com
SIC: 3581 Automatic vending machines
PA: Avi Food Systems, Inc.
2590 Elm Rd Ne
Warren OH 44483
330 372-6000

(G-9645)
BETH OTTO INDEPENDENT CASE EXA
544 Walter Ave (45014-1656)
PHONE.............................513 868-0484
Beth Otto, *Principal*
EMP: 3
SALES (est): 255.7K **Privately Held**
SIC: 3523 Farm machinery & equipment

(G-9646)
BK TOOL COMPANY INC
300 Security Dr (45014-4243)
PHONE.............................513 870-9622
Fax: 513 870-9742
Bernie Brown, *Vice Pres*
Robert Reed Jr, *Treasurer*
EMP: 17
SQ FT: 10,200
SALES (est): 2.4MM **Privately Held**
SIC: 3544 Special dies, tools, jigs & fixtures

(G-9647)
BROWN-CAMPBELL COMPANY
555 Quality Blvd (45014-2294)
PHONE.............................513 860-3564
Chris Chioini, *COO*
John Puthoff, *Warehouse Mgr*
Charles Wilhelm, *Sales/Mktg Mgr*
EMP: 20
SQ FT: 5,000
SALES (corp-wide): 63.7MM **Privately Held**
WEB: www.brown-campbell.com
SIC: 3446 Gratings, open steel flooring
PA: Brown-Campbell Company
11800 Investment Dr
Shelby Township MI 48315
586 884-2180

(G-9648)
BYRON PRODUCTS INC
3781 Port Union Rd (45014-2207)
PHONE.............................513 870-9111
Fax: 513 870-9285
Mark Byron, *CEO*
Rick Henry, *President*
Mary Cole, *CFO*
Mary Henry, *Human Resources*
Mike Pavelka, *Manager*
▲ EMP: 70
SQ FT: 44,000
SALES: 9.5MM **Privately Held**
WEB: www.byronproducts.com
SIC: 3398 Metal heat treating

(G-9649)
CALVARY INDUSTRIES INC (PA)
9233 Seward Rd (45014-5407)
PHONE.............................513 874-1113
Fax: 513 860-6184
John P Morelock Jr, *CEO*
Ivan Byers, *President*
John Connor, *General Mgr*
Kimberly Fraley, *General Mgr*
Austin Morelock, *General Mgr*
▲ EMP: 48
SQ FT: 100,000
SALES (est): 16.3MM **Privately Held**
WEB: www.calvaryindustries.com
SIC: 2819 5169 Industrial inorganic chemicals; chemicals & allied products

(G-9650)
CARBOLINE COMPANY
3905 Port Union Rd Ste B (45014-2276)
PHONE.............................513 896-1919
Steve Hook, *Manager*
EMP: 3
SALES (corp-wide): 4.8B **Publicly Held**
SIC: 3479 Painting of metal products
HQ: Carboline Company
2150 Schuetz Rd
Saint Louis MO 63146
314 644-1000

(G-9651)
CARR TOOL COMPANY
575 Security Dr (45014-4269)
PHONE.............................513 825-2900
Patricia Blum, *CEO*
Alex Blum, *President*
D F Cote, *Opers Mgr*
Michael Carr, *Manager*
Missy Mann, *Administration*
EMP: 30
SQ FT: 13,000
SALES (est): 7.1MM **Privately Held**
WEB: www.carrtool.com
SIC: 3532 Mining machinery

(G-9652)
CENTRAL DESIGN SERVICES
5417 Dixie Hwy (45014-4107)
PHONE.............................513 829-7027
Donald C Blust, *Owner*
EMP: 4
SQ FT: 2,000
SALES (est): 221.2K **Privately Held**
SIC: 7641 2512 Reupholstery; upholstered household furniture

(G-9653)
CIMA INC
4416 Dixie Hwy (45014-1114)
PHONE.............................513 682-5900
Tom Uhl, *President*
▲ EMP: 30
SALES (est): 4.9MM **Privately Held**
WEB: www.cima-kdt.com
SIC: 3561 7363 Industrial pumps & parts; temporary help service

(G-9654)
CINCINNATI BABBITT INC
9217 Seward Rd (45014-5407)
PHONE.............................513 942-5088
Fax: 513 942-5277
Louis M Patterson, *President*
Dale A Frye, *Corp Secy*
Mike Yenke, *Cust Svc Mgr*
Steve Foster, *Manager*
▲ EMP: 15
SQ FT: 20,000
SALES (est): 2.3MM **Privately Held**
WEB: www.cinbab.com
SIC: 3599 Machine shop, jobbing & repair

(G-9655)
CINTI TAN COMPANY
6600 Dixie Hwy Ste N (45014-5400)
PHONE.............................513 874-8267
Dan Caskey, *President*
Kevin Carson, *President*
EMP: 30
SALES (est): 1.5MM **Privately Held**
SIC: 3648 Sun tanning equipment, incl. tanning beds

(G-9656)
CKS SOLUTION INCORPORATED (PA)
4293 Muhlhauser Rd (45014-5450)
PHONE.............................513 947-1277
Peter Sung, *President*
James Braun, *CFO*
Jennifer Harris, *Cust Mgr*
▲ EMP: 35
SQ FT: 72,000
SALES (est): 6.3MM **Privately Held**
SIC: 3679 Liquid crystal displays (LCD)

(G-9657)
CPC LOGISTICS INC
Also Called: Pds
8695 Seward Rd (45011-9716)
PHONE.............................513 874-5787
Fax: 513 682-7555
Scott Morman, *President*
Donald Ufferman, *President*
Jan Ufferman, *Corp Secy*
EMP: 51 EST: 1972
SALES (est): 2.1MM **Privately Held**
WEB: www.cpc.com
SIC: 8742 7363 3674 Transportation consultant; help supply services; semiconductors & related devices

(G-9658)
DETROIT FLAME HARDENING CO
Also Called: Cincinnati Flame Hardening Co
375 Security Dr (45014-4250)
PHONE.............................513 942-1400
Fax: 513 942-1414
Allen Leach, *Manager*
EMP: 10
SALES (corp-wide): 2.9MM **Privately Held**
WEB: www.detroitflame.com
SIC: 3398 Metal heat treating
PA: Detroit Flame Hardening Company Inc
17644 Mount Elliott St
Detroit MI
313 891-2936

(G-9659)
FORCE CONTROL INDUSTRIES INC
3660 Dixie Hwy (45014-1105)
PHONE.............................513 868-0900
Fax: 513 868-2105
James C Besl, *President*
Steve Wissel, *General Mgr*
Robert Briede, *Principal*
Joseph E Besl, *Exec VP*
Jerry Boyd, *Purch Agent*
▲ EMP: 60
SQ FT: 60,000
SALES (est): 17.5MM **Privately Held**
WEB: www.forcecontrol.com
SIC: 3568 3714 3594 3566 Power transmission equipment; clutches, except vehicular; drives: belt, cable or rope; motor vehicle parts & accessories; fluid power pumps & motors; speed changers, drives & gears

(G-9660)
G & W PRODUCTS LLC
8675 Seward Rd (45011-9716)
PHONE.............................513 860-4050
Gary Johns, *CEO*
Wayde Hunker, *President*
Douglas Henderson, *Vice Pres*
Randy Sagraves, *Vice Pres*
Doug Keehn, *Engineer*
▲ EMP: 125
SQ FT: 120,000
SALES (est): 39.6MM **Privately Held**
WEB: www.gandwinc.com
SIC: 2541 3441 3469 Cabinets, lockers & shelving; fabricated structural metal; metal stampings

(G-9661)
GOTCHA COVERED
4854 Factory Dr (45014-1915)
PHONE.............................513 829-7555
Gregg Faestel, *Owner*
EMP: 5
SQ FT: 7,200
SALES (est): 290K **Privately Held**
SIC: 5719 2396 Window shades; screen printing on fabric articles

(G-9662)
GWP HOLDINGS INC
8675 Seward Rd (45011-9716)
PHONE.............................513 860-4050
Wayde Hunker, *CEO*
Douglas Henderson, *Vice Pres*
Elizabeth Sargent, *Purch Dir*
Sue Stidham, *Controller*
▲ EMP: 80
SQ FT: 120,000
SALES (est): 13.7MM **Privately Held**
WEB: www.g-w-a.com
SIC: 3441 3479 3446 3469 Floor posts, adjustable: metal; building components, structural steel; railroad car racks, for transporting vehicles: steel; painting, coating & hot dipping; architectural metalwork; metal stampings; sheet metalwork; partitions & fixtures, except wood

(G-9663)
H S MORGAN LIMITED PARTNERSHIP (PA)
3158 Production Dr (45014-4228)
PHONE.............................513 870-4400
Thadius Jaroszewicz, *Mng Member*
James Vanderzwaag,

EMP: 2
SALES (est): 69.1MM **Privately Held**
SIC: 2521 2522 Panel systems & partitions (free-standing), office: wood; panel systems & partitions, office: except wood

(G-9664)
HAMILTON AIR PRODUCTS INC
3143 Production Dr (45014-4227)
PHONE...............................513 874-4030
Fax: 513 874-3967
Stephen Cornell, *President*
Harvey Henkel, *Corp Secy*
Robert C Deluse, *Vice Pres*
Brian Strautman, *Vice Pres*
Scott Detherage, *Plant Mgr*
EMP: 7
SQ FT: 20,000
SALES: 2MM
SALES (corp-wide): 11.3MM **Privately Held**
SIC: 3535 Pneumatic tube conveyor systems
PA: Hamilton Products Group, Inc.
7775 Cooper Rd
Cincinnati OH 45242
513 753-7773

(G-9665)
HIPSY LLC
4951 Dixie Hwy (45014-2994)
PHONE...............................513 403-5333
Lerin Buggs, *Branch Mgr*
EMP: 9
SALES (corp-wide): 654K **Privately Held**
SIC: 2339 Scarves, hoods, headbands, etc.: women's
PA: Hipsy Llc
5321 Cleves Warsaw Pike
Cincinnati OH 45238
513 403-5333

(G-9666)
HONEYMOON PAPER PRODUCTS INC (PA)
7100 Dixie Hwy (45014-5543)
PHONE...............................513 755-7200
Fax: 513 755-7200
Betty Lou Cundall, *Principal*
David Reed, *Accounts Mgr*
John Kennedy, *Sales Staff*
Dottie Miesse, *Office Mgr*
EMP: 70
SQ FT: 68,000
SALES (est): 14.6MM **Privately Held**
WEB: www.honeymoonpaper.com
SIC: 2675 2653 Die-cut paper & board; corrugated & solid fiber boxes

(G-9667)
HOWDEN AMERICAN FAN COMPANY (DH)
2933 Symmes Rd (45014-2001)
PHONE...............................513 773-0103
Greg Card, *President*
Dave Nadler, *Vice Pres*
Kathy Parry, *Vice Pres*
Jeff Robinson, *Vice Pres*
▲ EMP: 103
SALES (est): 50.6MM
SALES (corp-wide): 51.6MM **Privately Held**
SIC: 3564 Exhaust fans: industrial or commercial; turbo-blowers, industrial; blowing fans: industrial or commercial; ventilating fans: industrial or commercial
HQ: Flakt Woods Group Sa
Avenue Louis-Casai 18
GenCve GE
223 093-800

(G-9668)
INNOMARK PERM DISPLY GRP LLC
Also Called: Innomark Communications
420 Distribution Cir (45014-5473)
PHONE...............................513 285-1040
Brian Herres, *VP Opers*
Thom House, *VP Opers*
Bill Witters, *Controller*
Paul Molyneaux, *Mng Member*
Bill Snyder, *Sr Project Mgr*
▲ EMP: 15
SQ FT: 17,000

SALES (est): 3.7MM
SALES (corp-wide): 126.2MM **Privately Held**
SIC: 2653 Corrugated boxes, partitions, display items, sheets & pad
HQ: Prestige Display And Packaging Llc
420 Distribution Cir
Fairfield OH 45014

(G-9669)
IWATA BOLT USA INC
102 Iwata Dr (45014-2298)
PHONE...............................513 942-5050
Fax: 513 942-5566
Yoshiko Jarosz, *Marketing Staff*
Nick Hiraga, *Branch Mgr*
EMP: 14
SALES (corp-wide): 34MM **Privately Held**
WEB: www.iwatabolt.com
SIC: 3452 Bolts, metal
PA: Iwata Bolt Usa Inc.
7131 Orangewood Ave
Garden Grove CA 92841
714 897-0800

(G-9670)
J FELDKAMP DESIGN BUILD LTD
3239 Profit Dr (45014-4239)
PHONE...............................513 870-0601
Jody Feldkamp, *President*
Robert Boggs, *Principal*
Jonathan Feldkamp, *Vice Pres*
Elisa Feldkamp, *CFO*
Steve Habard, *Manager*
EMP: 42
SQ FT: 18,000
SALES: 3.7MM **Privately Held**
SIC: 1711 3499 Heating & air conditioning contractors; plumbing contractors; aerosol valves, metal

(G-9671)
JOHNSON-NASH METAL PDTS INC
9265 Seward Rd (45014-5407)
PHONE...............................513 874-7022
Fax: 513 874-2700
Craig Johnson, *CEO*
Charles Johnson, *President*
Colleen Johnson, *Chairman*
Carol Johnson Dreyer, *Corp Secy*
Charles Bell, *Engineer*
EMP: 15
SQ FT: 21,000
SALES (est): 3MM **Privately Held**
WEB: www.johnsonnash.com
SIC: 3444 Sheet metalwork

(G-9672)
KNE LLC
12 Suffolk Ct (45014-3818)
PHONE...............................859 356-1690
Tom Elias, *Principal*
EMP: 4
SALES (est): 360.3K **Privately Held**
SIC: 3421 Table & food cutlery, including butchers'

(G-9673)
KOCH FOODS OF CINCINNATI LLC
4100 Port Union Rd (45014-2293)
PHONE...............................513 874-3500
Fax: 513 874-3501
Gary Tallent, *Superintendent*
Ted Davis, *Vice Pres*
Bernice Aryetey, *Transptn Dir*
Jason Abner, *Plant Mgr*
Tina Hurley, *Purch Agent*
EMP: 1
SALES (est): 28MM
SALES (corp-wide): 1.8B **Privately Held**
SIC: 2099 Food preparations
PA: Koch Foods Incorporated
1300 W Higgins Rd
Flowood MS 39232
601 732-8911

(G-9674)
KOCH MEAT CO INC
Also Called: Cooked Foods
4100 Port Union Rd (45014-2293)
PHONE...............................513 874-3500

Monty Lobb, *Human Res Mgr*
Brian Reisen, *Manager*
EMP: 400
SALES (corp-wide): 1.8B **Privately Held**
SIC: 5142 5144 2015 Packaged frozen goods; poultry & poultry products; poultry slaughtering & processing
HQ: Koch Meat Co., Inc.
1300 Higgins Rd Ste 100
Park Ridge IL 60068
847 384-8018

(G-9675)
KOLE SPECIALTIES INC
4695 Industry Dr Ste A (45014-1965)
PHONE...............................513 829-1111
John W Kole, *President*
Joyce Kole, *Treasurer*
EMP: 3
SQ FT: 11,000
SALES: 100K **Privately Held**
SIC: 3599 Machine shop, jobbing & repair

(G-9676)
L&M SHEET METAL LTD
5010 Factory Dr (45014-1919)
PHONE...............................513 858-6173
Fax: 513 829-2690
Keith Mobley, *Partner*
Terry Lawson, *Partner*
EMP: 5
SQ FT: 4,125
SALES: 361.2K **Privately Held**
SIC: 3444 Sheet metalwork

(G-9677)
LCMF INC
Also Called: Original Mattress Factory
7010 Fairfield Bus Ctr (45014)
PHONE...............................513 860-9988
Fax: 513 860-9979
Phill Wilkes, *Partner*
EMP: 50
SALES (est): 4.8MM **Privately Held**
SIC: 2515 Mattresses & bedsprings

(G-9678)
MACHINTEK CO
3721 Port Union Rd (45014-2200)
PHONE...............................513 551-1000
Fax: 513 942-4441
Roger Hasler, *President*
Vaughn Burckard, *Principal*
Louis Solimine, *Admin Sec*
▲ EMP: 65
SQ FT: 37,000
SALES (est): 15MM **Privately Held**
WEB: www.machintek.com
SIC: 3599 Machine shop, jobbing & repair

(G-9679)
MASS-MARKETING INC
7209 Dixie Hwy (45014-5544)
PHONE...............................513 860-6200
Fax: 513 874-0800
Donald J Mueller, *President*
Betsy Engle, *Vice Pres*
Lance Miller, *Vice Pres*
Francine Ris, *Vice Pres*
Betsy Engoe, *Manager*
◆ EMP: 140
SQ FT: 25,000
SALES (est): 15.8MM **Privately Held**
WEB: www.donmueller.com
SIC: 2752 Commercial printing, lithographic

(G-9680)
MASTER-HALCO INC
620 Commerce Center Dr (45011-8664)
PHONE...............................513 869-7600
Paul Smith, *Manager*
EMP: 35
SALES (corp-wide): 43.4B **Privately Held**
WEB: www.fenceonline.com
SIC: 3315 5051 Steel wire & related products; fence gates posts & fittings: steel; steel
HQ: Master-Halco, Inc.
3010 Lbj Fwy Ste 800
Dallas TX 75234
972 714-7300

(G-9681)
MATLY DIGITAL SOLUTIONS LLC
6625 Dixie Hwy Ste E (45014-5490)
PHONE...............................513 860-3435
George Matly, *Branch Mgr*
EMP: 5
SALES (corp-wide): 2.5MM **Privately Held**
SIC: 2741 7389 Business service newsletters: publishing & printing; personal service agents, brokers & bureaus
PA: Matly Digital Solutions, Llc
3432 Preston Hwy
Louisville KY 40213
502 375-2525

(G-9682)
MB MANUFACTURING CORP
2904 Symmes Rd (45014-2035)
PHONE...............................513 682-1461
Greg Kelley, *Principal*
Diane Mizer, *Manager*
EMP: 9 EST: 2003
SALES (est): 1.1MM **Privately Held**
SIC: 2421 Lumber: rough, sawed or planed

(G-9683)
MCNEILUS TRUCK AND MFG INC
8997 Lesaint Dr (45014)
PHONE...............................513 874-2022
Ken Shurboff, *Branch Mgr*
EMP: 23
SALES (corp-wide): 6.2B **Publicly Held**
WEB: www.mcneiluscompanies.com
SIC: 3713 3531 Cement mixer bodies; concrete plants
HQ: Mcneilus Truck And Manufacturing, Inc.
524 County Rd 34 E
Dodge Center MN 55927
614 868-0760

(G-9684)
MIDWEST CONTAINER CORPORATION
375 Northpointe Dr (45014-5474)
PHONE...............................513 870-3000
Fax: 513 870-3001
Mike Brunst, *Owner*
Terry Pater, *Vice Pres*
Terry Evans, *Plant Mgr*
Barry Ludwick, *Controller*
Kathy Henry, *Cust Svc Mgr*
EMP: 20
SQ FT: 52,200
SALES (est): 4.6MM **Privately Held**
SIC: 2653 Boxes, corrugated: made from purchased materials

(G-9685)
MIDWEST SPECIALTY PDTS CO INC
280 Northpointe Dr (45014-5443)
PHONE...............................513 874-7070
Fax: 513 874-7503
Michael Brunst, *President*
Steven Huesman, *Corp Secy*
Thomas Brunst, *Vice Pres*
Mark Poynter, *Mktg Dir*
▲ EMP: 18 EST: 1965
SQ FT: 52,000
SALES (est): 3.9MM **Privately Held**
SIC: 2655 Tubes, fiber or paper: made from purchased material

(G-9686)
MOBILE MINI INC
4444 Dixie Hwy (45014-1114)
PHONE...............................513 353-9800
Jason Clemons, *Branch Mgr*
EMP: 20
SALES (corp-wide): 508.6MM **Publicly Held**
WEB: www.mobilemini.com
SIC: 3448 Buildings, portable: prefabricated metal
PA: Mobile Mini, Inc.
4646 E Van Buren St # 400
Phoenix AZ 85008
480 894-6311

GEOGRAPHIC

(G-9687)
MOSS VALE INC
160 Donald Dr B (45014-3018)
P.O. Box 18759 (45018-0759)
PHONE.....................................513 939-1970
Fax: 513 939-1972
Timothy J Morris, *President*
Janet Morris, *Corp Secy*
EMP: 18
SALES (est): 800K **Privately Held**
SIC: 3498 Tube fabricating (contract bending & shaping)

(G-9688)
MT PLEASANT BLACKTOPPING INC
3199 Production Dr (45014-4227)
PHONE.....................................513 874-3777
Fax: 513 874-3796
William House, *CEO*
Benjamin House, *President*
Anna House, *Vice Pres*
Luke Crosby, *Manager*
EMP: 8 **EST:** 1952
SQ FT: 3,200
SALES (est): 2.2MM **Privately Held**
SIC: 1623 1771 2951 Sewer line construction; water main construction; blacktop (asphalt) work; concrete repair; asphalt & asphaltic paving mixtures (not from refineries)

(G-9689)
MULHERN BELTING INC
310 Osborne Dr (45014-2247)
PHONE.....................................201 337-5700
Fax: 513 874-8376
George Oboer, *Manager*
Terry Crandol, *Manager*
Scott Horvath, *Manager*
EMP: 25
SQ FT: 10,000
SALES (corp-wide): 19MM **Privately Held**
SIC: 3021 3535 Rubber & plastics footwear; conveyors & conveying equipment
PA: Mulhern Belting, Inc.
148 Bauer Dr
Oakland NJ 07436
201 337-5700

(G-9690)
NORTHEND GEAR & MACHINE INC
475 Security Dr (45014-4251)
PHONE.....................................513 860-4334
Fax: 513 860-0899
Dan Rockenfelder, *President*
Duane Ratcliff, *Corp Secy*
David Shope, *Vice Pres*
Mark Miller, *Foreman/Supr*
Susan Mc Daniel, *Controller*
EMP: 15
SQ FT: 18,000
SALES (est): 2.2MM **Privately Held**
WEB: www.northendgear.com
SIC: 3599 Machine shop, jobbing & repair

(G-9691)
NORTHERN PRECISION INC
3245 Production Dr (45014-4232)
PHONE.....................................513 860-4701
Fax: 513 860-4706
Harold W Jarvis, *President*
Dane A Kerby, *Senior VP*
Sherry Kerby, *Manager*
EMP: 15
SQ FT: 5,000
SALES (est): 2.8MM **Privately Held**
SIC: 3599 Machine & other job shop work

(G-9692)
OBERSONS NURS & LANDSCAPES INC
Also Called: Obersons Snow and Ice MGT
3951 River Rd (45014-1008)
PHONE.....................................513 894-0669
Chad Oberson, *President*
EMP: 11
SQ FT: 7,000
SALES (est): 2.1MM **Privately Held**
SIC: 0782 7349 2899 Lawn & garden services; building maintenance services; salt

(G-9693)
OCS INTELLITRAK INC
8660 Seward Rd (45011-9716)
PHONE.....................................513 742-5600
Fax: 513 714-4173
Thomas D Robertson, *President*
Charles P Tabler, *President*
Michelle Tabler, *Purch Mgr*
Brent Yeager, *Electrical Engi*
Tom Robertson, *Manager*
▲ **EMP:** 12
SQ FT: 14,500
SALES (est): 5MM
SALES (corp-wide): 46.6MM **Privately Held**
WEB: www.intellitrak.com
SIC: 3535 Conveyors & conveying equipment
PA: Lico, Inc.
9230 E 47th St
Kansas City MO 64133
816 356-0660

(G-9694)
P & G PRECISION LLC
3955 Kraus Ln (45014-5841)
PHONE.....................................513 738-3500
Mark Puckett,
EMP: 5
SQ FT: 7,500
SALES: 500K **Privately Held**
WEB: www.pgprecision.com
SIC: 3599 Machine shop, jobbing & repair

(G-9695)
PACIFIC INDUSTRIES USA INC
8955 Seward Rd (45011-9109)
PHONE.....................................513 860-3900
Fax: 513 860-3953
Toru Nishimura, *President*
Yasu Okumura, *General Mgr*
Bill Earley, *Sales Mgr*
James Johnson, *Manager*
Brad Bush, *Systs Prg Mgr*
◆ **EMP:** 25
SQ FT: 53,000
SALES (est): 4.9MM
SALES (corp-wide): 913.4MM **Privately Held**
SIC: 3714 Motor vehicle wheels & parts
PA: Pacific Industrial Co., Ltd.
100, Kyutokucho
Ogaki GIF 503-0
584 911-111

(G-9696)
PACIFIC MANUFACTURING OHIO INC
8955 Seward Rd (45011-9109)
PHONE.....................................513 860-3900
Fax: 513 642-0056
Toshiteru Ando, *President*
Kazuya Hayashi, *Exec VP*
Jason Marcum, *Mfg Mgr*
Eugene Bonsu, *Mfg Spvr*
Lea A Legg, *Production*
▲ **EMP:** 450
SALES (est): 188.7MM
SALES (corp-wide): 913.4MM **Privately Held**
SIC: 3714 3469 Motor vehicle parts & accessories; metal stampings
PA: Pacific Industrial Co., Ltd.
100, Kyutokucho
Ogaki GIF 503-0
584 911-111

(G-9697)
PACKAGING CORPORATION AMERICA
Also Called: PCA
3840 Port Union Rd (45014-2202)
PHONE.....................................513 860-1145
Susan Gardner, *Project Mgr*
Robert Apodaca, *Design Engr*
Theresa Keene, *Marketing Staff*
Dave Snyder, *Marketing Staff*
Tim Remy, *Manager*
EMP: 4
SALES (corp-wide): 5.7B **Publicly Held**
SIC: 2653 Corrugated & solid fiber boxes
PA: Packaging Corporation Of America
1955 W Field Ct
Lake Forest IL 60045
847 482-3000

(G-9698)
PANELMATIC INC (PA)
258 Donald Dr (45014-3072)
P.O. Box 181446 (45018-1446)
PHONE.....................................513 829-3666
Richard P Leach, *President*
Rich Baley, *General Mgr*
Kevin Koch, *General Mgr*
Cory Jones, *Vice Pres*
Dave Adamson, *CFO*
EMP: 2
SALES (est): 21,180
SALES (est): 32MM **Privately Held**
WEB: www.panelmatic.com
SIC: 3613 Control panels, electric; cubicles (electric switchboard equipment)

(G-9699)
PANELMATIC CINCINNATI INC
258 Donald Dr (45014-3072)
PHONE.....................................513 829-1960
Fax: 513 829-3931
Richard E Dooley, *President*
J P Stiffler Jr, *Vice Pres*
David D Adamson, *CFO*
Gary Packer, *Sales Engr*
Crystal Murray, *Admin Sec*
EMP: 24 **EST:** 1962
SQ FT: 21,300
SALES (est): 4.1MM
SALES (corp-wide): 32MM **Privately Held**
WEB: www.panelmatic.com
SIC: 3613 8711 Control panels, electric; designing: ship, boat, machine & product
PA: Panelmatic, Inc.
258 Donald Dr
Fairfield OH 45014
513 829-3666

(G-9700)
PEASE INDUSTIES INC
7100 Dixie Hwy (45014-5543)
PHONE.....................................513 870-3600
Fax: 513 870-3618
David H Pease Jr, *Ch of Bd*
Leonard W Cavens, *President*
David A Aluise, *Vice Pres*
Neil W Jackman, *Vice Pres*
Rodney K Sawall, *VP Mfg*
EMP: 352
SQ FT: 220,000
SALES (est): 38.8MM
SALES (corp-wide): 2.2B **Privately Held**
WEB: www.peasedoors.com
SIC: 3442 3089 2431 Metal doors; doors, folding; plastic or plastic coated fabric; doors, wood; door frames, wood
PA: Pella Corporation
102 Main St
Pella IA 50219
641 621-1000

(G-9701)
PERFECTION PRINTING
9560 Le Saint Dr (45014-2253)
PHONE.....................................513 874-2173
Fax: 513 870-5842
Steve Myers, *President*
Scott Myers, *Vice Pres*
Joe Myers, *Treasurer*
Diana Haverland, *Manager*
EMP: 14
SQ FT: 10,000
SALES: 1.4MM **Privately Held**
WEB: www.perfectionprinting.com
SIC: 2759 Commercial printing

(G-9702)
PERKINS & MARIE CALLENDERS LLC
Also Called: Foxtail Foods
6880 Fairfield Bus Ctr Dr (45014)
PHONE.....................................513 881-7900
Fax: 513 881-7910
Hank Larkins, *Vice Pres*
Jeffrey Davis, *Prdtn Mgr*
Steve Dattilio, *Warehouse Mgr*
Sarah Evans, *QA Dir*
Larry Stroup, *Plant Engr*
EMP: 130
SALES (corp-wide): 588.8MM **Privately Held**
WEB: www.perkinsrestaurants.com
SIC: 2051 Bread, cake & related products

HQ: Perkins & Marie Callender's, Llc
6075 Poplar Ave Ste 800
Memphis TN 38119
901 766-6400

(G-9703)
PPG INDUSTRIES INC
Also Called: PPG 4338
726 Nilles Rd (45014-3604)
PHONE.....................................513 829-6006
Fax: 513 829-7610
Rick Smith, *Branch Mgr*
EMP: 24
SALES (corp-wide): 14.7B **Publicly Held**
WEB: www.ppg.com
SIC: 2851 Paints & allied products
PA: Ppg Industries, Inc.
1 Ppg Pl
Pittsburgh PA 15272
412 434-3131

(G-9704)
PREMIER CONSTRUCTION COMPANY
9361 Seward Rd (45014-5409)
PHONE.....................................513 874-2611
Fax: 513 874-4893
Jan Gilkey, *President*
Dennis Long, *Manager*
EMP: 35 **EST:** 1959
SQ FT: 10,000
SALES (est): 8.2MM **Privately Held**
SIC: 5031 1751 2452 Lumber: rough, dressed & finished; plywood; carpentry work; panels & sections, prefabricated, wood

(G-9705)
PRESTIGE DISPLAY AND PACKG LLC (HQ)
420 Distribution Cir (45014-5473)
PHONE.....................................513 285-1040
Fax: 513 942-4521
Jeff Laking, *General Mgr*
Bill Witters, *Controller*
Victor Nelsen, *Human Res Dir*
Dave McGinnis, *Info Tech Mgr*
Gary P Boens,
▲ **EMP:** 16
SQ FT: 200,000
SALES (est): 4.9MM
SALES (corp-wide): 126.2MM **Privately Held**
WEB: www.prestigedisplay.com
SIC: 2653 Corrugated boxes, partitions, display items, sheets & pad
PA: Innomark Communications Llc
3233 S Tech Blvd
Miamisburg OH 45342
937 427-6100

(G-9706)
QUALITY GOLD INC (PA)
500 Quality Blvd (45014-2292)
P.O. Box 18490 (45018-0490)
PHONE.....................................513 942-7659
Michael Langhammer, *CEO*
Jason Langhammer, *COO*
Jonathon Driggs, *Opers Staff*
Bonnie Cassett, *Purch Mgr*
Dennis Horn, *Controller*
▲ **EMP:** 270
SQ FT: 110,000
SALES (est): 55.6MM **Privately Held**
WEB: www.qgold.com
SIC: 3339 5944 Gold refining (primary); silver refining (primary); clock & watch stores

(G-9707)
QUEEN CITY TOOL WORKS INC
125 Constitution Dr Ste 2 (45014-2256)
PHONE.....................................513 874-0111
Fax: 513 874-7779
Martin Oehler, *President*
Tim Mayes, *Vice Pres*
EMP: 6
SQ FT: 5,200
SALES: 1.4MM **Privately Held**
WEB: www.queencitywebhosting.com
SIC: 3544 3599 Special dies, tools, jigs & fixtures; machine & other job shop work

(G-9708)
R K METALS LTD
3235 Homeward Way (45014-4237)
PHONE......................................513 874-6055
Fax: 513 874-3212
Thomas McKee IV,
K C McKee,
EMP: 30 **EST:** 1997
SQ FT: 45,000
SALES (est): 6MM **Privately Held**
WEB: www.rkmetals.net
SIC: 3469 Metal stampings

(G-9709)
R K S TOOL & DIE INC
200 Security Dr (45014-4244)
PHONE......................................513 870-0225
Richard Strecker, *President*
David J Strecker, *Corp Secy*
Keith Pipton, *Opers Staff*
EMP: 3
SQ FT: 7,000
SALES (est): 366.5K **Privately Held**
WEB: www.rks-toolanddie.com
SIC: 3544 Special dies & tools

(G-9710)
REUSS MEATS INC
Also Called: Premier Meats
3765 Port Union Rd (45014-2207)
P.O. Box 188025 (45018-8025)
PHONE......................................513 874-3200
James E Kite, *President*
Andy Stroehlein, *Purchasing*
Michelle Gravens, *Controller*
Tom Koeninger, *VP Sales*
Gaylene Smith, *Marketing Staff*
EMP: 12
SQ FT: 5,000
SALES (est): 1.6MM
SALES (corp-wide): 49.1MM **Privately Held**
WEB: www.premieremeats.com
SIC: 2011 Meat packing plants
PA: The Ellenbee-Leggett Company Inc
3765 Port Union Rd
Fairfield OH 45014
513 874-3200

(G-9711)
RIVER CITY PHARMA
8695 Seward Rd (45011-9716)
PHONE......................................513 870-1680
Danny Smith, *President*
Jason Smith, *Vice Pres*
EMP: 75
SALES (est): 5.7MM **Privately Held**
SIC: 2834 5122 Pharmaceutical preparations; pharmaceuticals

(G-9712)
RODERER ENTERPRISES INC
Also Called: Fastsigns
6560 Dixie Hwy Ste E (45014-2238)
PHONE......................................513 942-3000
Fax: 513 860-8752
Richard A Roderer Jr, *President*
Steven Roderer, *Info Tech Dir*
EMP: 5
SQ FT: 1,400
SALES (est): 320K **Privately Held**
SIC: 3993 Signs & advertising specialties

(G-9713)
ROYAL WELDING INC
5000 Factory Dr (45014-1919)
PHONE......................................513 829-9353
Brett Barthel, *President*
Tom Klette, *Vice Pres*
Federico Robles, *Project Engr*
EMP: 4
SALES (est): 1.3MM **Privately Held**
SIC: 3441 Fabricated structural metal

(G-9714)
SCHOBER USA INC
4690 Industry Dr (45014-1923)
PHONE......................................513 489-7393
Karl Schober, *President*
Carl Schober, *President*
▲ **EMP:** 4
SQ FT: 2,000

SALES: 1.1MM
SALES (corp-wide): 1.6MM **Privately Held**
WEB: www.schoberusa.com
SIC: 3545 Precision tools, machinists'
PA: Schober Bau Gmbh
Dorfstr. 3
Konigstein/Sachs. Schw. 01824
350 216-8053

(G-9715)
SEA BIRD PUBLICATIONS INC
311 Nilles Rd Ste B (45014-2621)
PHONE......................................513 869-2200
Ginger Byrd, *Owner*
EMP: 4
SALES (est): 239.2K **Privately Held**
SIC: 2741 Miscellaneous publishing

(G-9716)
SHEET ANGLE BAR MET FBRICATION
4875 Factory Dr (45014-1914)
PHONE......................................513 829-8600
Fax: 513 829-8600
Carl Johnson, *Owner*
Eve Johnson, *Co-Owner*
EMP: 4
SQ FT: 12,000
SALES (est): 285K **Privately Held**
SIC: 1761 7692 3714 3444 Sheet metalwork; welding repair; motor vehicle parts & accessories; sheet metalwork; aluminum extruded products

(G-9717)
SIEB & MEYER AMERICA INC
3975 Port Union Rd (45014-2203)
PHONE......................................513 563-0860
Axel Schroeter, *President*
John G Endres, *Treasurer*
EMP: 14
SQ FT: 10,000
SALES (est): 2.7MM
SALES (corp-wide): 34.9MM **Privately Held**
WEB: www.pmcelectronics.com
SIC: 3625 5063 Relays & industrial controls; electrical apparatus & equipment; motors, electric; motor controls, starters & relays: electric
PA: Sieb & Meyer Ag
Auf Dem Schmaarkamp 21
Luneburg 21339
413 120-30

(G-9718)
SIGNIFICANT IMPRESSIONS INC
Also Called: Hightech Signs
4050 Thunderbird Ln (45014-2234)
PHONE......................................513 874-5223
Fax: 513 874-5224
Robert Steiner, *President*
Sarah Steiner, *Co-Owner*
Janet L Steiner, *Vice Pres*
Kris Rutherford, *Sales Staff*
Lisa Brennan, *Manager*
EMP: 5
SQ FT: 8,000
SALES (est): 750K **Privately Held**
SIC: 3993 Signs & advertising specialties

(G-9719)
SKYLINE CHILI INC (PA)
4180 Thunderbird Ln (45014-2235)
PHONE......................................513 874-1188
Fax: 513 874-3591
Kevin R Mc Donnell, *President*
Philip M Lewis, *Senior VP*
Kenneth E Davis, *Vice Pres*
Charles L Harnist, *Vice Pres*
Jim Konves, *Vice Pres*
EMP: 120 **EST:** 1949
SQ FT: 42,000
SALES (est): 51MM **Privately Held**
WEB: www.skylinechili.com
SIC: 5812 2038 6794 5149 Restaurant, family: chain; frozen specialties; franchises, selling or licensing; groceries & related products; dried or canned foods; canned goods: fruit, vegetables, seafood, meats, etc.; canned specialties

(G-9720)
SOFTWARE TO SYSTEMS INC
640 Glenna Dr (45014-2719)
PHONE......................................513 893-9888
Fax: 513 893-9888
Vicki Humphreys, *President*
Jason Cigarran, *Vice Pres*
EMP: 8
SALES (est): 653.1K **Privately Held**
WEB: www.software2sys.com
SIC: 7372 Prepackaged software

(G-9721)
SOUTHERN GLAZERS WINE & SPRT
Also Called: Just Cheking Cash
4305 Muhlhauser Rd Ste 4 (45014-2265)
PHONE......................................513 755-7082
Fax: 513 755-8094
Andrea Fisher, *Sales Mgr*
John Roberts, *Manager*
EMP: 55
SALES (corp-wide): 5.3B **Privately Held**
WEB: www.glazer.com
SIC: 2082 Beer (alcoholic beverage)
HQ: Southern Glazer's Wine And Spirits Of Texas, Llc
2001 Diplomat Dr
Farmers Branch TX 75234
972 277-2000

(G-9722)
SPEEDWAY LLC
Also Called: Speedway Superamerica 3389
5010 Dixie Hwy (45014)
PHONE......................................513 829-3223
EMP: 10 **Publicly Held**
WEB: www.speedwaynet.com
SIC: 1311 Crude petroleum production
HQ: Speedway Llc
500 Speedway Dr
Enon OH 45323
937 864-3000

(G-9723)
TEDIA COMPANY INC
1000 Tedia Way (45014-2003)
PHONE......................................513 874-5340
Hoon Choi, *President*
Elinora Park, *Chairman*
Chris Dendy, *Vice Pres*
John F Terbot II, *Vice Pres*
Chandra Senanayake, *Production*
◆ **EMP:** 88
SQ FT: 48,500
SALES (est): 37.3MM **Privately Held**
WEB: www.tedia.com
SIC: 2869 Solvents, organic

(G-9724)
TERON LIGHTING INC
33 Donald Dr Uppr (45014-3022)
PHONE......................................513 858-6004
Fax: 513 829-1527
Micheal Bellos, *President*
David Bellos, *Principal*
Brandon Mundell, *Engineer*
Jon Grahm, *Controller*
▲ **EMP:** 45
SQ FT: 51,100
SALES (est): 9.7MM
SALES (corp-wide): 124.8MM **Privately Held**
WEB: www.teronlight.com
SIC: 3646 Fluorescent lighting fixtures, commercial
PA: L. D. Kichler Co.
7711 E Pleasant Valley Rd
Cleveland OH 44131
866 558-5706

(G-9725)
THE-FISCHER-GROUP
20282052 Bohlke Blvd (45014)
PHONE......................................513 285-1281
Vannessa Fisher, *Manager*
EMP: 21
SALES (est): 3.7MM **Privately Held**
SIC: 3915 Lapidary work, contract or other

(G-9726)
TSR MACHINERY SERVICES INC
100 Security Dr (45014-4245)
PHONE......................................513 874-9697

Todd Routh, *President*
Mike Clifford, *Engineer*
Lisa Routh, *Treasurer*
Fred Brown, *Bookkeeper*
Bruce Duncan, *Sales Staff*
EMP: 26
SQ FT: 26,000
SALES (est): 3.2MM **Privately Held**
SIC: 3541 Grinding machines, metalworking

(G-9727)
UNLIMITED PROMOTIONS INC
1120 Hicks Blvd Ste 1 (45014-9401)
P.O. Box 181147 (45018-1147)
PHONE......................................513 844-2211
Mark Johnston, *President*
EMP: 8
SALES (est): 912K **Privately Held**
SIC: 2759 Screen printing

(G-9728)
VERITIV OPERATING COMPANY
Also Called: International Paper
375 Distribution Cir (45014-5442)
PHONE......................................513 242-0800
Gary Burkert, *Branch Mgr*
EMP: 133
SALES (corp-wide): 8.3B **Publicly Held**
SIC: 2621 Paper mills
HQ: Veritiv Operating Company
1000 Abernathy Rd
Atlanta GA 30328
770 391-8200

(G-9729)
VIBRA FINISH CO
8411 Seward Rd (45011-8651)
PHONE......................................513 870-6300
Fax: 513 870-6311
Haskel Hall, *President*
Wilma Hall, *Finance*
EMP: 20
SALES (corp-wide): 4.1MM **Privately Held**
WEB: www.vibrafinish.com
SIC: 3291 Abrasive products
PA: Vibra Finish Co.
2220 Shasta Way
Simi Valley CA 93065
805 578-0033

(G-9730)
WAKE NATION
201 Joe Nuxhall Way (45014-1036)
PHONE......................................513 887-9253
Peter Kennedy, *Owner*
▲ **EMP:** 10 **EST:** 2009
SALES (est): 938.9K **Privately Held**
SIC: 3949 Water sports equipment

(G-9731)
WATCH-US INC
4450 Dixie Hwy (45014-1114)
PHONE......................................513 829-8870
Fax: 513 858-7812
Dan Graf, *President*
Jason Frazer, *Controller*
▲ **EMP:** 20
SQ FT: 90,000
SALES (est): 8.6MM **Privately Held**
WEB: www.watch-us.com
SIC: 3944 Games, toys & children's vehicles; automobile & truck models, toy & hobby

(G-9732)
WHOLESALE BAIT CO INC (PA)
2619 Bobmeyer Rd (45014-1217)
P.O. Box 15006, Hamilton (45015-0006)
PHONE......................................513 863-2380
Gregory Fessel, *CEO*
Anthony G Fessel, *President*
Marc Fessel, *CFO*
Benjamin Fessel, *Director*
EMP: 18 **EST:** 1950
SQ FT: 18,000
SALES (est): 5.3MM **Privately Held**
WEB: www.waxworms.com
SIC: 5199 3949 Bait, fishing; sporting & athletic goods

GEOGRAPHIC

(G-9733)
WORKSTREAM INC (HQ)
Also Called: Hamilton Sorter
3158 Production Dr (45014-4228)
PHONE.................................513 870-4400
Fax: 513 870-4475
Thadius Jaroszewicz, *CEO*
Rich Mealey, *President*
Ron Sebastian, *Asst Controller*
Brad Quick, *Cust Mgr*
Dimitri Zelepuhin, *Info Tech Mgr*
▼ EMP: 60
SQ FT: 50,000
SALES (est): 26.5MM **Privately Held**
SIC: 2521 2522 Panel systems & parti-
tions (free-standing), office: wood; panel
systems & partitions, office: except wood

(G-9734)
**WYSONG CONCRETE
PRODUCTS LLC**
2138 Resor Rd (45014-3861)
PHONE.................................513 874-3109
John A Wysong, *Principal*
EMP: 5 EST: 2001
SALES (est): 523.7K **Privately Held**
SIC: 3272 Concrete products

(G-9735)
**ZEBEC OF NORTH AMERICA
INC**
210 Donald Dr (45014-3007)
P.O. Box 181570 (45018-1570)
PHONE.................................513 829-5533
Ed Synder, *President*
Chris Snyder, *Vice Pres*
Scott Snyder, *Vice Pres*
Danielle Koroschetz, *Office Mgr*
▲ EMP: 35
SQ FT: 7,000
SALES (est): 3.6MM **Privately Held**
WEB: www.zebec.com
SIC: 3949 5091 Sporting & athletic goods;
sporting & recreation goods

Fairlawn
Summit County

(G-9736)
A SCHULMAN INC (PA)
3637 Ridgewood Rd (44333-2699)
PHONE.................................330 666-3751
Fax: 330 668-7204
Joseph M Gingo, *Ch of Bd*
Gary A Miller, *COO*
Gustavo P Rez, *COO*
Rainer R Schewe, *Exec VP*
Brent Middleton, *Vice Pres*
EMP: 77 EST: 1928
SQ FT: 34,000
SALES: 2.5B **Publicly Held**
WEB: www.aschulman.com
SIC: 2821 Plastics materials & resins;
molding compounds, plastics

(G-9737)
AKRO POLYCHEM INC
150 N Miller Rd Ste 300b (44333-3780)
PHONE.................................330 864-0360
Dave Murphy, *President*
▲ EMP: 3 EST: 2004
SALES (est): 320.6K **Privately Held**
SIC: 2296 Tire cord & fabrics

(G-9738)
ASI INVESTMENT HOLDING CO
3550 W Market St (44333-2658)
PHONE.................................330 666-3751
Joseph Gingo, *President*
Ron Andref, *Vice Pres*
Gary Elek, *Vice Pres*
Barry Rhodes, *Vice Pres*
Robert Stefanko, *CFO*
EMP: 80
SALES (est): 6.5MM
SALES (corp-wide): 2.5B **Publicly Held**
WEB: www.aschulman.com
SIC: 2821 Elastomers, nonvulcanizable
(plastics)
PA: A. Schulman, Inc.
   3637 Ridgewood Rd
   Fairlawn OH 44333
   330 666-3751

(G-9739)
AURIS NOBLE LLC (PA)
3045 Smith Rd Ste 700 (44333-4458)
PHONE.................................330 321-6649
Patrick Deeringer, *COO*
Patrick Darringer, *COO*
Lou Britton, *Plant Mgr*
EMP: 2
SQ FT: 2,000
SALES (est): 1.1MM **Privately Held**
SIC: 3341 Secondary precious metals;
platinum group metals, smelting & refining
(secondary); silver smelting & refining
(secondary); iridium smelting & refining
(secondary)

(G-9740)
BEKAERT CORPORATION
3200 W Market St Ste 303 (44333-3326)
P.O. Box 92688t, Cleveland (44190-0002)
PHONE.................................330 835-5124
David Best, *Branch Mgr*
EMP: 35
SALES (corp-wide): 451MM **Privately
Held**
WEB: www.bekaert.com
SIC: 3315 Wire & fabricated wire products;
fencing made in wiredrawing plants
HQ: Bekaert Corporation
   1395 S Marietta Pkwy Se 500-100
   Marietta GA 30067
   770 421-8520

(G-9741)
BEKAERT CORPORATION
3200 W Market St Ste 303 (44333-3326)
PHONE.................................330 867-3325
Fax: 330 873-3424
Cuvelier Mike, *Controller*
Andre Minjauw, *Sales Executive*
Terese Crapanzano, *Branch Mgr*
Greg Faber, *Manager*
David Foust, *Manager*
EMP: 6
SQ FT: 11,000
SALES (corp-wide): 451MM **Privately
Held**
WEB: www.bekaert.com
SIC: 3315 Wire & fabricated wire products;
fencing made in wiredrawing plants
HQ: Bekaert Corporation
   1395 S Marietta Pkwy Se 500-100
   Marietta GA 30067
   770 421-8520

(G-9742)
**BEKAERT NORTH AMERICA
MGT CORP (HQ)**
3200 W Market St Ste 303 (44333-3326)
PHONE.................................330 867-3325
Rick McWhirt, *President*
Bert Degraeve, *Chairman*
David Best, *CFO*
Ken Gillette, *Controller*
Mike Adams, *Manager*
◆ EMP: 20
SALES (est): 700.8MM
SALES (corp-wide): 451MM **Privately
Held**
SIC: 3315 Wire & fabricated wire products
PA: Bekaert Sa Nv
   Bekaertstraat 2
   Zwevegem 8550
   567 661-11

(G-9743)
BKT USA INC
2660 W Market St Ste 100 (44333-4209)
PHONE.................................330 836-1090
Minoo Mehta, *President*
Loudan Hammersmith, *Manager*
▲ EMP: 15
SQ FT: 3,000
SALES: 2.8MM
SALES (corp-wide): 474.5MM **Privately
Held**
SIC: 5531 3011 Automotive tires; tires &
inner tubes
HQ: Bkt Exim Limited
   C/15,Trade World, Kamala Mills Com-
   pound
   Mumbai MH 40001

(G-9744)
**BUCKEYE CORRUGATED INC
(PA)**
Also Called: B C I
822 Kumho Dr Ste 400 (44333-9298)
PHONE.................................330 576-0590
Fax: 330 576-0600
Douglas A Bosnik, *President*
Robert Butterfield, *President*
Robert Bailey, *Prdtn Mgr*
Don Laurie, *Prdtn Mgr*
Mark A Husted, *CFO*
EMP: 9 EST: 1958
SQ FT: 11,000
SALES (est): 196.7MM **Privately Held**
WEB: www.buckeyecorrugated.com
SIC: 2653 Boxes, corrugated: made from
purchased materials

(G-9745)
CEP HOLDINGS LLC
3560 W Market St Ste 340 (44333-2687)
PHONE.................................330 665-2900
Lisa Burns, *Manager*
Mark Hamlin Jr,
James Van Tiem,
EMP: 5
SALES (est): 606.8K **Privately Held**
SIC: 3069 3089 Hard rubber & molded
rubber products; extruded finished plastic
products

(G-9746)
**COLLABORATIVE FOR
ADAPTIVE LIF**
Also Called: Calm
3250 W Market St Ste 205 (44333-3320)
PHONE.................................216 513-0572
Megan Ordway, *President*
Sara Bouchard, *Admin Sec*
EMP: 3
SALES (est): 117.4K **Privately Held**
SIC: 3841 7389 Surgical & medical instru-
ments;

(G-9747)
**CONTITECH NORTH AMERICA
INC (DH)**
703 S Clvnd Massilon Rd (44333-3023)
PHONE.................................330 664-7180
Francisco Hidalgo, *CEO*
Susan Galdamez, *Opers Mgr*
Martin Stein, *Draft/Design*
Val Moreno, *Sales Mgr*
Timothy Hoppenworth, *Accounts Mgr*
▲ EMP: 17
SALES (est): 17.7MM
SALES (corp-wide): 42.8B **Privately Held**
WEB: www.contitech-usa.com
SIC: 3061 Mechanical rubber goods
HQ: Contitech Ag
   Vahrenwalder Str. 9
   Hannover 30165
   511 938-02

(G-9748)
CONTITECH USA INC (DH)
Also Called: Continental Contitech
703 S Clvland Mssillon Rd (44333-3023)
PHONE.................................330 664-7000
Jim Hill, *President*
Bret Hall, *General Mgr*
Mark Robuck, *Area Mgr*
Michael Hoying, *Business Mgr*
Donna Campagna, *Vice Pres*
◆ EMP: 16
SQ FT: 100,000
SALES (est): 9.5MM
SALES (corp-wide): 42.8B **Privately Held**
WEB: www.veyance.com
SIC: 3069 Molded rubber products
HQ: Contitech North America, Inc.
   703 S Clvnd Massillon Rd
   Fairlawn OH 44333
   330 664-7180

(G-9749)
ELIOKEM INC
Also Called: Eliokem Materials and Concepts
175 Ghent Rd (44333-3330)
PHONE.................................330 734-1100
Jerry Perfinger, *Branch Mgr*
Regina Matranga, *Manager*
EMP: 50
SQ FT: 103,766

SALES (corp-wide): 759.9MM **Publicly
Held**
WEB: www.eliokem.com
SIC: 2822 Synthetic rubber
HQ: Eliokem, Inc.
   175 Ghent Rd
   Fairlawn OH 44333
   330 734-1100

(G-9750)
FRISBY PRINTING COMPANY
Also Called: Minuteman Press
3571 Brookwall Dr Unit C (44333-9295)
PHONE.................................330 665-4565
Fax: 330 665-4521
Parris Frisby, *President*
EMP: 3
SQ FT: 1,600
SALES: 400K **Privately Held**
SIC: 2752 Commercial printing, litho-
graphic

(G-9751)
GVS INC
3406 S Smith Rd (44333-3008)
PHONE.................................330 310-8275
Greg Vlasenko, *President*
Alexander Vlasenko, *Opers Mgr*
Olga Vlasenko, *Accountant*
EMP: 4
SALES: 400K **Privately Held**
SIC: 3537 Aircraft engine cradles

(G-9752)
**HGGC CITADEL PLAS
HOLDINGS INC (HQ)**
3637 Ridgewood Rd (44333-3123)
PHONE.................................330 666-3751
Mike Huff, *CEO*
Kevin Andrews, *President*
Jason Jimerson, *Vice Pres*
Amy Rodgers, *Vice Pres*
Mario Sandoval, *Vice Pres*
EMP: 7
SALES (est): 19.4MM
SALES (corp-wide): 2.5B **Publicly Held**
SIC: 2821 Plastics materials & resins
PA: A. Schulman, Inc.
   3637 Ridgewood Rd
   Fairlawn OH 44333
   330 666-3751

(G-9753)
HPC HOLDINGS LLC (DH)
Also Called: Composite Group, The
3637 Ridgewood Rd (44333-3123)
PHONE.................................330 666-3751
Terry Morgan, *CEO*
Tom Meola, *CFO*
Chris Coxe, *Manager*
EMP: 14
SALES (est): 143.2MM
SALES (corp-wide): 2.5B **Publicly Held**
SIC: 2821 2655 Molding compounds,
plastics; cans, composite: foil-fiber &
other: from purchased fiber
HQ: Bulk Molding Compounds, Inc.
   1600 Powis Ct
   West Chicago IL 60185
   630 377-1065

(G-9754)
ICO TECHNOLOGY INC
3550 W Market St (44333-2658)
PHONE.................................330 666-3751
Jennifer K Beeman, *Principal*
EMP: 3 EST: 2014
SALES (est): 168.1K **Privately Held**
SIC: 3089 Extruded finished plastic prod-
ucts

(G-9755)
**KOROSEAL INTERIOR
PRODUCTS LLC (PA)**
3875 Embassy Pkwy Ste 110 (44333-8334)
PHONE.................................330 668-7600
Rich Runkel, *CEO*
Bill Calhoun, *General Mgr*
Thomas Roche, *General Mgr*
John Farrell, *COO*
Eric Wroldsen, *Exec VP*
EMP: 114

SALES (est): 100MM Privately Held
SIC: 3081 3089 3069 Floor or wall covering, unsupported plastic; battery cases, plastic or plastic combination; wallcoverings, rubber

(G-9756)
LEADER PUBLICATIONS INC
Also Called: West Side Leader
3075 Smith Rd Ste 204 (44333-4454)
PHONE....................330 665-9595
Fax: 330 665-9590
Clark Burns, General Mgr
EMP: 20
SALES (est): 1.1MM Privately Held
WEB: www.akron.com
SIC: 2711 Newspapers: publishing only, not printed on site

(G-9757)
OMNOVA OVERSEAS INC (HQ)
175 Ghent Rd (44333-3330)
PHONE....................330 869-4200
Kevin M McMullen, CEO
J L Heckel, President
William Gorenc Jr, Counsel
Marvin L Isles, Exec VP
James Lambert, Vice Pres
EMP: 120
SALES (est): 6.5MM
SALES (corp-wide): 759.9MM Publicly Held
SIC: 2295 Chemically coated & treated fabrics
PA: Omnova Solutions Inc.
25435 Harvard Rd
Beachwood OH 44122
216 682-7000

(G-9758)
PROFUSION INDUSTRIES LLC (PA)
822 Kumho Dr Ste 202 (44333-5105)
PHONE....................800 938-2858
Fax: 330 664-8931
Jon Golden, President
Jack Woodyard, Vice Pres
William Hatch, CFO
EMP: 8
SALES (est): 27.2MM Privately Held
SIC: 3081 3089 Unsupported plastics film & sheet; extruded finished plastic products

(G-9759)
SANCTUARY SOFTWARE STUDIO INC
3560 W Market St Ste 100 (44333-2660)
PHONE....................330 666-9690
Michael J Terry, President
Stacey Simonton, Manager
Nicholas Cross, Software Engr
Donald Fuldauer, Software Engr
Ryan Maffit, Software Engr
EMP: 28
SQ FT: 2,200
SALES (est): 2MM Privately Held
WEB: www.sancsoft.com
SIC: 7372 7371 Prepackaged software; computer software development

(G-9760)
SPECILTY FBRICS CONVERTING INC (DH)
703 S Clvland Mssillon Rd (44333-3023)
PHONE....................706 637-3000
Mark Daniels, President
Ienne Bond, Executive Asst
▲ EMP: 45
SQ FT: 330,000
SALES (est): 26.8MM
SALES (corp-wide): 42.8B Privately Held
SIC: 2399 2281 Hand woven apparel; yarn spinning mills
HQ: Contitech Ag
Vahrenwalder Str. 9
Hannover 30165
511 938-02

(G-9761)
SSP INDUSTRIAL GROUP INC
3560 W Market St Ste 300 (44333-2687)
PHONE....................330 665-2900
Richard M Hamlin, President
Mark Hamlin Jr, President

James D Van Tiem, Corp Secy
James Gaul, Admin Sec
▲ EMP: 9
SALES (est): 1.4MM Privately Held
SIC: 3465 3412 3411 8742 Automotive stampings; metal barrels, drums & pails; food & beverage containers; management consulting services

(G-9762)
SUNPRENE COMPANY
Also Called: Asi Investments Holding Co
3550 W Market St (44333-2658)
PHONE....................330 666-3751
Terry Haines, President
Anthony Johnson, Project Mgr
Robert Helteman, Opers Mgr
Rene Rombouts, Director
EMP: 120
SALES (est): 11.4MM Privately Held
SIC: 2821 Elastomers, nonvulcanizable (plastics)

(G-9763)
SWAROVSKI US HOLDING LIMITED
3265 W Market St Ste 544 (44333-3346)
PHONE....................330 867-2201
Dave Holland, Branch Mgr
EMP: 5
SALES (corp-wide): 4.2B Privately Held
SIC: 3961 Costume jewelry
HQ: Swarovski U.S. Holding Limited
1 Kenney Dr
Cranston RI 02920
401 463-6400

(G-9764)
TCP INC
Also Called: Sir Speedy
2747 Crawfis Blvd Ste 108 (44333-2886)
PHONE....................330 836-4239
Fax: 330 836-2523
Thomas Delehanty, President
Connie Delehanty, Vice Pres
EMP: 5
SQ FT: 4,000
SALES (est): 830.2K Privately Held
WEB: www.printplususa.com
SIC: 2752 2761 2677 2671 Commercial printing, lithographic; manifold business forms; envelopes; packaging paper & plastics film, coated & laminated

Fairport Harbor
Lake County

(G-9765)
GEORGE WHALLEY COMPANY
Also Called: Cft Systems
1180 High St Ste 1 (44077-6921)
PHONE....................216 453-0099
Fax: 216 481-6666
George M Whalley, President
Howard M Whalley, Vice Pres
Kim Whalley, Manager
EMP: 20
SQ FT: 25,000
SALES (est): 3.9MM Privately Held
WEB: www.coolantfedtooling.com
SIC: 3545 Machine tool accessories; tool holders; cutting tools for machine tools

(G-9766)
JM PERFORMANCE PRODUCTS INC
Also Called: J & M Machine
1234 High St (44077-5559)
PHONE....................440 357-1234
Fax: 440 357-1129
John Stoneback, President
Linda Stoneback, Vice Pres
Andy Rrowy, Manager
EMP: 19
SQ FT: 19,500
SALES (est): 2.5MM Privately Held
WEB: www.jmmachineinc.com
SIC: 3545 Milling machine attachments (machine tool accessories)

(G-9767)
LYONDELL CHEMICAL COMPANY
110 3rd St (44077-5837)
PHONE....................440 352-9393
Jim Hillier, Facilities Mgr
Brian Luthardt, Production
Greg Fuhrman, Plant Engr
Michael Step, Enginr/R&D Mgr
Chris Cain, Manager
EMP: 42 Privately Held
WEB: www.lyondell.com
SIC: 2869 Industrial organic chemicals
HQ: Lyondell Chemical Company
1221 Mckinney St Ste 300
Houston TX 77010
713 309-7200

(G-9768)
MJM INDUSTRIES INC
1200 East St (44077-5571)
PHONE....................440 350-1230
Fax: 440 350-1360
Thomas Roulston, Ch of Bd
Lois Roulston, Vice Ch Bd
Eric Wachob, President
Collen Costa, QC Dir
Peter Wanek, Sales Mgr
▲ EMP: 58
SQ FT: 35,500
SALES (est): 13.8MM Privately Held
WEB: www.mjmindustries.com
SIC: 3643 Current-carrying wiring devices

(G-9769)
OURPETS COMPANY (PA)
1300 East St (44077-5573)
PHONE....................440 354-6500
Steven Tsengas, Ch of Bd
Konstantine S Tsengas, COO
Scott R Mendes, CFO
Kathleen R Homyock, VP Sales
Gabriella Chessman, VP Mktg
▲ EMP: 54
SQ FT: 64,000
SALES: 27MM Publicly Held
WEB: www.our-pets.com
SIC: 3999 Pet supplies

(G-9770)
QUARTZ SCIENTIFIC INC (PA)
Also Called: Qsi
819 East St (44077-5596)
P.O. Box 1129 (44077-8129)
PHONE....................360 574-6254
James R Atwell Jr, President
David North, Accounting Mgr
Paula Weber, Accountant
EMP: 25
SQ FT: 44,000
SALES (est): 2.8MM Privately Held
WEB: www.qsiquartz.com
SIC: 3679 Quartz crystals, for electronic application

(G-9771)
RAMPE MANUFACTURING COMPANY
Also Called: Torque Transmission
1246 High St (44077-5559)
PHONE....................440 352-8995
Fax: 440 352-6998
John N Rampe, CEO
John W Rampe, President
Russ Needhammer, Plant Mgr
Joe Alberts, Purch Mgr
Joe Alberts-, Purch Mgr
EMP: 17 EST: 1947
SQ FT: 40,000
SALES (est): 1.9MM Privately Held
WEB: www.torquetrans.com
SIC: 3568 Power transmission equipment

(G-9772)
RITCHIE FOODS LLC
212 High St (44077-5827)
PHONE....................440 354-7474
Erik Ritchie, Principal
EMP: 3
SALES (est): 247.3K Privately Held
SIC: 2099 Food preparations

Farmersville
Montgomery County

(G-9773)
QUALITY DRBLE INDUS FLOORS INC
5005 Frmrsvll Germntwn Pa (45325-9268)
PHONE....................937 696-2833
Scott Carmack, President
Douglas Emrick, Vice Pres
EMP: 20
SALES: 1.4MM Privately Held
SIC: 5713 7389 3996 Floor covering stores; ; hard surface floor coverings

Fayette
Fulton County

(G-9774)
C & K MACHINE CO INC
604 N Park St (43521-9718)
P.O. Box 478 (43521-0478)
PHONE....................419 237-3203
Fax: 419 237-9012
Ken Cassaubon, President
EMP: 7
SALES (est): 597.6K Privately Held
SIC: 3599 Machine shop, jobbing & repair

(G-9775)
K P PRECISION TOOL AND MCH CO
606 N Park St (43521)
PHONE....................419 237-2596
Fax: 419 237-2594
Aaron Lee Kerns, President
EMP: 5
SQ FT: 7,500
SALES (est): 644.8K Privately Held
SIC: 3544 3599 Special dies & tools; machine shop, jobbing & repair

(G-9776)
LAROSE INDUSTRIES LLC
Also Called: CRA-Z-Art, Palmer Paint
40 E Industrial Pkwy (43521)
PHONE....................419 237-1600
Lawrence Rosen, Branch Mgr
EMP: 21
SALES (corp-wide): 54.7MM Privately Held
SIC: 5092 3944 3269 Arts & crafts equipment & supplies; craft & hobby kits & sets; stationery articles, pottery
PA: Larose Industries Llc
1578 Sussex Tpke
Randolph NJ 07869
973 543-2037

(G-9777)
PHANTOM FIREWORKS INC
25840 Us Highway 20 (43521-9511)
PHONE....................419 237-2185
Laurie Beaverson, Manager
EMP: 5
SALES (corp-wide): 23.2MM Privately Held
WEB: www.bjalan.com
SIC: 5999 2899 Fireworks; fireworks
PA: Phantom Fireworks, Inc
555 Martin L King Jr Blvd
Youngstown OH 44502
330 746-1064

(G-9778)
QUALITY TUBE SERVICE INC
701 E Industrial Pkwy (43521)
P.O. Box 331 (43521-0331)
PHONE....................419 237-3014
Fax: 419 237-2620
Melvin Jones, President
Joyce Fruchey, Vice Pres
C Fruchey, Personnel
Jim Jones, Sales Staff
Pauline Jones, Admin Sec
EMP: 10
SQ FT: 22,000
SALES: 1MM Privately Held
SIC: 7389 3498 Metal cutting services; fabricated pipe & fittings

GEOGRAPHIC

(G-9779)
RJR & ASSOCIATES INC
21550 County Road L (43521-9707)
PHONE...............................419 237-2220
Jon Rupp, *President*
Debra Rupp, *Corp Secy*
Jack Rupp, *Vice Pres*
EMP: 9
SQ FT: 6,600
SALES (est): 910K **Privately Held**
WEB: www.rjrassociates.net
SIC: 5999 5083 7692 Feed & farm sup-
ply; livestock equipment; welding repair

(G-9780)
TRW AUTOMOTIVE INC
Also Called: TRW Automotive Fayette Plant
705 N Fayette St (43521-9586)
PHONE...............................419 237-2511
Gary Predki, *General Mgr*
Dave Anderson, *Plant Mgr*
Rachel Konrad, *Safety Mgr*
Lynn Barnhart, *Mfg Staff*
Lee Riches, *Controller*
EMP: 212 **Privately Held**
SIC: 3714 Motor vehicle parts & acces-
sories
HQ: Trw Automotive Inc.
12025 Tech Center Dr
Livonia MI 48150
734 266-2600

Fayetteville
Brown County

(G-9781)
DEUCE MACHINING LLC
3088 Us Highway 50 (45118-9012)
P.O. Box 57 (45118-0057)
PHONE...............................513 875-2291
Tim Boggs, *Principal*
EMP: 7
SALES (est): 779.6K **Privately Held**
SIC: 3599 Machine shop, jobbing & repair

(G-9782)
**G B WELDING & METAL FABG
CO**
3288 Mcmullen Rd (45118-9748)
PHONE...............................937 444-2091
Greg Boler, *President*
Karen Boler, *Admin Sec*
EMP: 4
SALES (est): 264.6K **Privately Held**
SIC: 7692 Welding repair

(G-9783)
KILEY MACHINE COMPANY INC
4196 Anderson State Rd (45118-9777)
PHONE...............................513 875-3223
Dennis E Kiley, *President*
EMP: 8
SALES: 150K **Privately Held**
SIC: 3599 Custom machinery

(G-9784)
KILEY MOLD COMPANY LLC
4200 Anderson State Rd (45118-9098)
PHONE...............................513 875-3223
Dennis Kiley,
Jerome Kiley,
EMP: 7
SALES (est): 983.7K **Privately Held**
SIC: 2821 Molding compounds, plastics

(G-9785)
**WIEDERHOLD WLDG &
FABRICATION**
Also Called: W W F
1843 Us Highway 50 (45118-9661)
PHONE...............................513 875-3755
Dan Wiederhold, *Owner*
EMP: 4
SALES (est): 125K **Privately Held**
SIC: 3548 Welding apparatus

Felicity
Clermont County

(G-9786)
L C LIMING & SONS INC
Also Called: L & L Plastics
3200 State Route 756 (45120-9766)
PHONE...............................513 876-2555
Fax: 513 876-2555
James C Liming, *President*
Margaret Laubach, *Treasurer*
EMP: 8
SQ FT: 9,250
SALES (est): 1.6MM **Privately Held**
WEB: www.landlplastics.com
SIC: 3089 6515 Injection molding of plas-
tics; mobile home site operators

Findlay
Hancock County

(G-9787)
**ADVANCE NOVELTY
INCORPORATED**
101 Stanford Pkwy (45840-1731)
P.O. Box 846 (45839-0846)
PHONE...............................419 424-0363
Fax: 419 424-2129
Tom Heimann, *Principal*
EMP: 7 EST: 2007
SALES (est): 648.6K **Privately Held**
SIC: 5092 3944 Toys & games; games,
toys & children's vehicles

(G-9788)
**ADVANCED DRAINAGE
SYSTEMS INC**
401 Olive St (45840-5358)
PHONE...............................419 424-8324
Steve Farrow, *Plant Mgr*
Jason Duty, *Engineer*
Bruce Rush, *Branch Mgr*
EMP: 36
SALES (corp-wide): 1.2B **Publicly Held**
WEB: www.ads-pipe.com
SIC: 3084 3083 Plastics pipe; laminated
plastics plate & sheet
PA: Advanced Drainage Systems, Inc.
4640 Trueman Blvd
Hilliard OH 43026
614 658-0050

(G-9789)
ALLEGRA PRINT & IMAGING
701 W Sandusky St (45840-2325)
P.O. Box 609 (45839-0609)
PHONE...............................419 427-8095
Karl Heminger, *Owner*
Shari Lthielen, *Accounts Mgr*
Mary F Fleming, *Manager*
Diana Lynch, *Manager*
EMP: 12
SALES (est): 1MM **Privately Held**
SIC: 2752 Commercial printing, offset

(G-9790)
ARCHIES TOO
2145 S Lake Ct (45840-1245)
PHONE...............................419 427-2663
Mike Miller, *Owner*
EMP: 70
SALES (est): 4.1MM **Privately Held**
WEB: www.archiefans.com
SIC: 2024 Ice cream & frozen desserts

(G-9791)
AUTOLIV NISSIN BRAKE
2001 Industrial Dr (45840-5444)
P.O. Box 886 (45839-0886)
PHONE...............................419 425-6725
Robert Bisciotti, *President*
EMP: 450
SALES: 150MM
SALES (corp-wide): 10B **Publicly Held**
SIC: 3714 Motor vehicle brake systems &
parts
HQ: Autoliv Asp, Inc.
1000 W 3300 S
Ogden UT 84401
801 625-4800

(G-9792)
BALL CORPORATION
1800 Production Dr (45840-5445)
PHONE...............................419 423-3071
Karen Clark, *Purch Mgr*
Sarzin Satari, *Engineer*
Rob Miles, *VP Mktg*
Hank Schroeder, *Manager*
Dennis Sharninghouse, *Manager*
EMP: 151
SALES (corp-wide): 9B **Publicly Held**
SIC: 3411 Food & beverage containers
PA: Ball Corporation
10 Longs Peak Dr
Broomfield CO 80021
303 469-3131

(G-9793)
**BALL METAL BEVERAGE CONT
CORP**
Also Called: Ball Metal Beverage Cont Div
12340 Township Rd 99 E (45840)
P.O. Box 1046 (45839-1046)
PHONE...............................419 423-3071
Fax: 419 425-4721
Dean Christiansen, *Purchasing*
Dennis Sharninghouse, *Purchasing*
Tom Starr, *Plant Engr*
Jedd Osborn, *Controller*
Kathy Rumgay, *Personnel*
EMP: 204
SALES (corp-wide): 9B **Publicly Held**
SIC: 3411 Beer cans, metal
HQ: Ball Metal Beverage Container Corp.
9300 W 108th Cir
Westminster CO 80021
303 469-5511

(G-9794)
**BALLINGER INDUSTRIES INC
(PA)**
2500 Fostoria Ave (45840-8732)
PHONE...............................419 422-4533
Jon Ballinger, *President*
Jeff Bisbee, *Plant Mgr*
EMP: 18
SALES (est): 54.8MM **Privately Held**
WEB: www.fabco-inc.com
SIC: 3531 Construction machinery

(G-9795)
BIRD CORPORATION
Also Called: Envirnmntal Archtctral Signage
100 Stanford Pkwy (45840-1732)
PHONE...............................419 424-3095
Fax: 419 422-1442
Jay Morehart, *President*
John Schafer, *Vice Pres*
EMP: 6
SALES (est): 212.5K **Privately Held**
SIC: 1799 3993 Sign installation & mainte-
nance; signs & advertising specialties

(G-9796)
BLANCHARD PIPE LINE CO LLC
539 S Main St (45840-3229)
PHONE...............................419 422-2121
Gary R Heminger, *President*
EMP: 1
SALES (est): 1.2MM **Publicly Held**
SIC: 2911 Petroleum refining
PA: Marathon Petroleum Corporation
539 S Main St
Findlay OH 45840

(G-9797)
**BLANCHARD REFINING
COMPANY LLC**
539 S Main St (45840-3229)
PHONE...............................419 422-2121
Gary R Heminger, *CEO*
Timothy Griffith, *Treasurer*
EMP: 1 EST: 2012
SALES (est): 44.7MM **Publicly Held**
SIC: 2911 Petroleum refining
PA: Marathon Petroleum Corporation
539 S Main St
Findlay OH 45840

(G-9798)
**BLANCHARD TERMINAL
COMPANY LLC**
539 S Main St (45840-3229)
PHONE...............................419 422-2121
Gary R Heminger, *President*

EMP: 1
SALES (est): 1.9MM **Publicly Held**
SIC: 2911 Petroleum refining
PA: Marathon Petroleum Corporation
539 S Main St
Findlay OH 45840

(G-9799)
BOEHR PRINT
2703 N Main St Ste 1 (45840-4039)
PHONE...............................419 358-1350
Fax: 419 358-4974
Grandy Ramond, *Owner*
Jeff Boehr, *Owner*
EMP: 3
SQ FT: 3,600
SALES: 130K **Privately Held**
SIC: 2752 Commercial printing, litho-
graphic

(G-9800)
**BOSSERMAN AUTOMOTIVE
ENGRG LLC**
Also Called: Aircraft-Refuelers.com
18919 Olympic Dr (45840-9453)
PHONE...............................419 722-2879
Terry Bosserman, *President*
EMP: 6 EST: 2012
SALES (est): 666.3K **Privately Held**
SIC: 3713 Tank truck bodies

(G-9801)
BREAD KNEADS INC
510 S Blanchard St (45840-5951)
PHONE...............................419 422-3863
Kelley Smith, *President*
EMP: 9
SALES (est): 748.4K **Privately Held**
SIC: 5411 5149 2099 2051 Deli-
catessens; groceries & related products;
food preparations; bread, cake & related
products

(G-9802)
**BRINKMAN TURKEY FARMS INC
(PA)**
Also Called: Brinkman's Country Corner
16314 State Route 68 (45840-9245)
PHONE...............................419 365-5127
Fax: 419 365-1284
Larry Brinkman, *President*
Joe Ray Brinkman, *Vice Pres*
Patty Bauman, *Bookkeeper*
EMP: 18
SQ FT: 6,000
SALES (est): 7.8MM **Privately Held**
WEB: www.brinkmanfarms.com
SIC: 5411 2015 2013 0253 Grocery
stores, independent; turkey, processed:
canned; chicken, processed: canned; pre-
pared beef products from purchased beef;
prepared pork products from purchased
pork; turkey farm; soybeans; corn

(G-9803)
**BROWN COMPANY OF FINDLAY
LTD**
243 Stanford Pkwy (45840-1733)
P.O. Box 1625 (45839-1625)
PHONE...............................419 425-3002
Melvin J Brown, *President*
Cheryl Grace, *Manager*
EMP: 20
SALES (est): 3.9MM **Privately Held**
SIC: 3089 7389 Injection molding of plas-
tics; inspection & testing services

(G-9804)
CASCADE CUT STONE
41 Township Highway 87 (45839)
P.O. Box 120 (45839-0120)
PHONE...............................419 422-4341
EMP: 3 EST: 2009
SALES (est): 150K **Privately Held**
SIC: 3281 Mfg Cut Stone/Products

(G-9805)
**CENTENNIAL SCREEN
PRINTING**
1785 S Romick Pkwy (45840-5461)
PHONE...............................419 422-5548
Fax: 419 422-5548
Ron Pehrson, *Partner*
Kathryn Pehrson, *Partner*
EMP: 4

SQ FT: 32,000
SALES: 260K Privately Held
SIC: 2759 Screen printing

(G-9806)
CENTREX PLASTICS LLC (PA)
814 W Lima St (45840-2312)
P.O. Box 707 (45839-0707)
PHONE................................419 423-1213
Terrence L Reinhart, President
Nick Reinhart, Opers Mgr
Joshua McCartney, Engineer
Lynn Otto, CTO
Gina Todd, Admin Asst
◆ EMP: 189
SALES: 76.7MM Privately Held
SIC: 3089 Injection molded finished plastic
products

(G-9807)
CHATELAIN PLASTICS INC
413 N Main St (45840-3541)
P.O. Box 1464 (45839-1464)
PHONE................................419 422-4323
Fax: 419 422-1122
Jim Chatelain, President
Karen Detert, Treasurer
Lynnette Saucedo, Graphic Designe
EMP: 5 EST: 1947
SQ FT: 2,400
SALES (est): 470K Privately Held
SIC: 3089 5162 3993 Boxes, plastic;
plastics materials; signs, not made in cus-
tom sign painting shops

(G-9808)
CLARK RM INC
400 Crystal Ave (45840-4770)
PHONE................................419 425-9889
Fax: 419 425-9887
Marshall Clark, Manager
EMP: 40
SALES (corp-wide): 5.6MM Privately
Held
SIC: 2491 2449 2448 2441 Structural
lumber & timber, treated wood; wood con-
tainers; wood pallets & skids; nailed wood
boxes & shook
PA: Clark Rm Inc
1110 Summerlin Dr
Douglas GA
912 384-2590

(G-9809)
CLASSIC SIGN COMPANY INC
112 Lagrange St (45840-1600)
PHONE................................419 420-0058
Patrick Gaswint, President
Lisa Gaswint, Admin Sec
EMP: 7
SQ FT: 10,000
SALES: 1.5MM Privately Held
SIC: 3993 Signs & advertising specialties

(G-9810)
CONTROL INDUSTRIES INC
1700 Fostoria Ave Ste 300 (45840-6281)
P.O. Box 889, Urbana (43078-0889)
PHONE................................937 653-8018
Fax: 937 653-7694
James Long, President
James B Long, Vice Pres
EMP: 6 EST: 1962
SQ FT: 3,200
SALES (est): 530K Privately Held
SIC: 3663 Receiver-transmitter units
(transceiver)

(G-9811)
**COOPER TIRE & RUBBER
COMPANY (PA)**
701 Lima Ave (45840-2388)
PHONE................................419 423-1321
Fax: 419 424-4305
Bradley E Hughes, CEO
Thomas P Capo, Ch of Bd
Stephen Zamansky, Senior VP
Ginger M Jones, CFO
Brenda S Harmon, Officer
◆ EMP: 1000
SALES: 2.9B Publicly Held
WEB: www.coopertire.com
SIC: 3011 Automobile tires, pneumatic;
truck or bus tires, pneumatic; motorcycle
tires, pneumatic; retreading materials, tire

(G-9812)
**COOPER TIRE & RUBBER
COMPANY**
900 Lima Ave (45840-2320)
PHONE................................419 424-4202
P Rooney, Branch Mgr
EMP: 21
SALES (corp-wide): 2.9B Publicly Held
SIC: 3011 Automobile tires, pneumatic
PA: Cooper Tire & Rubber Company Inc
701 Lima Ave
Findlay OH 45840
419 423-1321

(G-9813)
**COOPER TIRE & RUBBER
COMPANY**
1625 Lake Casscade Pkwy (45840)
P.O. Box 550 (45839-0550)
PHONE................................419 424-4384
John Ebert, Manager
EMP: 60
SALES (corp-wide): 2.9B Publicly Held
WEB: www.coopertire.com
SIC: 3011 Tires & inner tubes
PA: Cooper Tire & Rubber Company Inc
701 Lima Ave
Findlay OH 45840
419 423-1321

(G-9814)
**COOPER TIRE VHCL TEST CTR
INC (HQ)**
701 Lima Ave (45840-2315)
PHONE................................419 423-1321
Brad Hughes, President
Stephen O Schrooder, Treasurer
James E Kline, Admin Sec
▲ EMP: 23
SQ FT: 2,500
SALES (est): 2.6MM
SALES (corp-wide): 2.9B Publicly Held
SIC: 3011 4225 Automobile tires, pneu-
matic; truck or bus tires, pneumatic; gen-
eral warehousing & storage
PA: Cooper Tire & Rubber Company Inc
701 Lima Ave
Findlay OH 45840
419 423-1321

(G-9815)
CWC PARTNERS LLC
228 Stadium Dr (45840-2246)
PHONE................................567 208-1573
Cary Cox,
EMP: 4
SALES: 200K Privately Held
SIC: 0762 2084 5182 5921 Vineyard
management & maintenance services;
wines; wine; wine; dried fruit

(G-9816)
**DIETSCH BROTHERS
INCORPORATED (PA)**
400 W Main Cross St (45840-3317)
PHONE................................419 422-4474
Fax: 419 424-5597
Jeffery Dietsch, President
Erika Dietsch, General Mgr
Richard Dietsch, Vice Pres
Thomas Dietsch, Vice Pres
Sherrie Dietsch, Manager
EMP: 40
SQ FT: 12,000
SALES: 4.2MM Privately Held
WEB: www.dietschs.com
SIC: 2066 2024 5441 Chocolate & cocoa
products; ice cream & frozen desserts;
confectionary

(G-9817)
DJM PLASTICS LTD
Also Called: DLM Plastics
1530 Harvard Ave (45840-1737)
PHONE................................419 424-5250
Jo A Gligher, Plant Engr
Robert Coghill, Treasurer
Mike Longbach, CTO
Lucas Kunk, Director
Matt Badertscher,
◆ EMP: 10
SALES (est): 1.6MM Privately Held
SIC: 3089 3081 Plastic processing; un-
supported plastics film & sheet

(G-9818)
DOW CHEMICAL COMPANY
3441 N Main St (45840-4299)
PHONE................................419 423-6500
Fax: 419 423-6581
Greg Fields, Personnel
John Harrison, Branch Mgr
Chris Conner, Info Tech Mgr
EMP: 150
SQ FT: 250,000
SALES (corp-wide): 48.1B Publicly Held
WEB: www.dow.com
SIC: 3081 Plastic film & sheet
PA: The Dow Chemical Company
2030 Dow Ctr
Midland MI 48674
989 636-1000

(G-9819)
**ELEKTRON N MAGNESIUM
AMER INC**
115 Stanford Pkwy (45840-1731)
PHONE................................419 424-8878
Connie Kempf, Manager
EMP: 24
SALES (corp-wide): 414.8MM Privately
Held
WEB: www.magnesium-elektron.com
SIC: 3364 Magnesium & magnesium-base
alloy die-castings
HQ: Magnesium Elektron North America,
Inc.
1001 College St
Madison IL 62060
618 452-5190

(G-9820)
FABCO INC (HQ)
616 N Blanchard St (45840-5706)
P.O. Box 673 (45839-0673)
PHONE................................419 421-4740
Fax: 419 422-2263
Lynn Roeder, Principal
Kelly Cullum, Vice Pres
Keith Kuchera, Safety Mgr
Derek Warren, Purch Agent
Timothy A Jones, CFO
▲ EMP: 50
SQ FT: 35,000
SALES (est): 25.9MM
SALES (corp-wide): 54.8MM Privately
Held
WEB: www.fabco-inc.com
SIC: 3531 3535 3444 3443 Construction
machinery; bucket or scarifier teeth; buck-
ets, excavating: clamshell, concrete,
dragline, etc.; conveyors & conveying
equipment; sheet metalwork; fabricated
plate work (boiler shop); fabricated struc-
tural metal
PA: Ballinger Industries, Inc.
2500 Fostoria Ave
Findlay OH 45840
419 422-4533

(G-9821)
**FACTORY DIRECT
INTERNATIONAL**
337 S Main St Ste 400 (45840-3332)
P.O. Box 773 (45839-0773)
PHONE................................419 425-9636
L Kent Rogers, Owner
◆ EMP: 20
SQ FT: 7,000
SALES (est): 1.3MM Privately Held
WEB: www.fdizone.com
SIC: 2673 2253 3021 2353 Bags: plastic,
laminated & coated; shirts (outerwear),
knit; shoes, plastic soles molded to fabric
uppers; hats, caps & millinery

(G-9822)
**FINDLAY AMERICAN
PROSTHETIC &**
12474 County Road 99 (45840-9736)
PHONE................................419 424-1622
Fax: 419 424-5744
Jeremy Berman, President
EMP: 6
SALES (est): 440K Privately Held
WEB: www.fapoc.com
SIC: 3842 3841 Braces, orthopedic; med-
ical instruments & equipment, blood &
bone work

(G-9823)
FINDLAY MACHINE & TOOL INC
Also Called: Fmt
2000 Industrial Dr (45840-5443)
P.O. Box 1562 (45839-1562)
PHONE................................419 434-3100
Fax: 419 422-0072
Joseph Kirk, President
Kolleen Kirk, President
George Hay, Vice Pres
Andrew Rill, Vice Pres
Ken Cobb, Purchasing
EMP: 45
SQ FT: 200,000
SALES (est): 12.3MM Privately Held
WEB: www.fmtinc.com
SIC: 3559 Degreasing machines, automo-
tive & industrial

(G-9824)
FINDLAY PALLET INC
300 Bell Ave (45840)
PHONE................................419 423-0511
Robert Reed, President
EMP: 9
SALES (est): 660K Privately Held
SIC: 2448 Cargo containers, wood & wood
with metal; skids, wood & wood with
metal

(G-9825)
**FINDLAY PRODUCTS
CORPORATION**
2045 Industrial Dr (45840-5444)
P.O. Box 1006 (45839-1006)
PHONE................................419 423-3324
Fax: 419 423-1375
James E Hoyt, President
Lloyd A Miller, Vice Pres
Sherry Siffer, Accountant
Paul Banner, Manager
Louie Bonifaf, Manager
▲ EMP: 130
SQ FT: 224,000
SALES (est): 38.3MM Privately Held
SIC: 3465 3469 Automotive stampings;
metal stampings
PA: Midway Products Group, Inc.
1 Lyman E Hoyt Dr
Monroe MI 48161

(G-9826)
FLEETMASTER EXPRESS INC
5250 Distribution Dr (45840-9814)
PHONE................................419 425-0666
Rob Mahlman, Branch Mgr
EMP: 235
SALES (corp-wide): 67.7MM Privately
Held
SIC: 2741 Miscellaneous publishing
PA: Fleetmaster Express, Incorporated
1814 Hollins Rd Ne
Roanoke VA 24012
540 344-8834

(G-9827)
**FREUDENBERG-NOK GENERAL
PARTNR**
555 Marathon Blvd (45840-1790)
P.O. Box 269 (45839-0269)
PHONE................................419 427-5221
Roy Sehroeder, General Mgr
EMP: 170
SALES (corp-wide): 6.9B Privately Held
WEB: www.freudenberg-nok.com
SIC: 3053 3492 Gaskets, all materials;
fluid power valves & hose fittings
HQ: Freudenberg-Nok General Partnership
47690 E Anchor Ct
Plymouth MI 48170
734 451-0020

(G-9828)
FRIENDS SERVICE CO INC (PA)
Also Called: Friends Business Source
2300 Bright Rd (45840-5432)
PHONE................................419 427-1704
Fax: 419 425-9432
Kenneth J Schroeder, President
Dale Alt, President
Betsy Hughes, Vice Pres
Peg Schroeder, Human Res Dir
Linda Mignin, Accounts Exec
EMP: 79
SQ FT: 65,000

SALES: 30MM **Privately Held**
WEB: www.friendsoffice.com
SIC: 5112 5021 5044 5087 Stationery & office supplies; furniture; office equipment; janitors' supplies; photolithographic printing

(G-9829)
G S WIRING SYSTEMS INC (HQ)
1801 Production Dr (45840-5446)
P.O. Box 1045 (45839-1045)
PHONE..............................419 423-7111
George Suzuki, *President*
Shinichi Inagaki, *President*
Yukinobu Ukai, *Treasurer*
Annette Edgington, *Accountant*
Masami Kunimi, *Sales Mgr*
▲ **EMP:** 3
SQ FT: 72,000
SALES (est): 143.5MM
SALES (corp-wide): 238.1MM **Privately Held**
WEB: www.gswiring.com
SIC: 3714 5013 Automotive wiring harness sets; motor vehicle supplies & new parts
PA: G.S.Electech,Inc.
58-1, Hirako, Yoshiwaracho
Toyota AIC 473-0
565 782-800

(G-9830)
GARSITE/PROGRESS LLC
1005 Lima Ave (45840-2321)
PHONE..............................419 424-1100
Greg McDermott, *Branch Mgr*
Benson Steve, *Manager*
EMP: 14
SALES (corp-wide): 1.8B **Publicly Held**
SIC: 3728 Refueling equipment for use in flight, airplane
HQ: Garsite/Progress Llc
539 S 10th St
Kansas City KS 66105
913 342-5600

(G-9831)
GILLIG CUSTOM WINERY INC
1720 Northridge Rd (45840-1905)
PHONE..............................419 202-6057
EMP: 3 **EST:** 2015
SALES (est): 157.9K **Privately Held**
SIC: 2084 Wines

(G-9832)
GOULD FIRE PROTECTION INC
633 Bristol Dr (45840-6909)
PHONE..............................419 957-2416
Arthur Gould, *President*
James Amos, *Vice Pres*
EMP: 6
SALES: 550K **Privately Held**
SIC: 3569 Sprinkler systems, fire: automatic

(G-9833)
GRAHAM PACKG PLASTIC PDTS INC
170 Stanford Pkwy 7 (45840-1732)
PHONE..............................419 421-8037
John Linde, *Principal*
EMP: 180
SALES (corp-wide): 9B **Publicly Held**
SIC: 3085 Plastics bottles
HQ: Graham Packaging Plastic Products Inc.
1 Seagate Ste 10
Toledo OH 43604
717 849-8500

(G-9834)
GSW MANUFACTURING INC
1801 Production Dr (45840-5446)
P.O. Box 1045 (45839-1045)
PHONE..............................419 423-7111
Fax: 419 423-8999
Yukinobu Ukai, *President*
Gregg Dugranrut, *Purch Mgr*
Jeffrey Marok, *QC Mgr*
Chris Morman, *Engineer*
Brett Rice, *Engineer*
▲ **EMP:** 412
SQ FT: 72,000

SALES (est): 143.5MM
SALES (corp-wide): 238.1MM **Privately Held**
WEB: www.gswiring.com
SIC: 3714 3694 Automotive wiring harness sets; engine electrical equipment
HQ: G S Wiring Systems, Inc
1801 Production Dr
Findlay OH 45840
419 423-7111

(G-9835)
HAMLET PROTEIN INC
5289 Hamlet Dr (45840)
P.O. Box 240 (45839-0240)
PHONE..............................567 525-5627
Julie A Taylor, *Principal*
▲ **EMP:** 20
SALES (est): 5.1MM **Privately Held**
SIC: 2048 Prepared feeds
HQ: Hamlet Protein A/S
Saturnvej 51
Horsens 8700
756 310-20

(G-9836)
HANCOR HOLDING CORPORATION (HQ)
401 Olive St (45840-5358)
PHONE..............................419 422-6521
Steven Anderson, *President*
Barbara Mewhorter, *Vice Pres*
John Haughawout, *CFO*
John Maag, *CFO*
Rich Martorano, *Controller*
◆ **EMP:** 330
SQ FT: 27,000
SALES (est): 173MM
SALES (corp-wide): 1.2B **Publicly Held**
SIC: 3084 Plastics pipe
PA: Advanced Drainage Systems, Inc.
4640 Trueman Blvd
Hilliard OH 43026
614 658-0050

(G-9837)
HANCOR INC
Also Called: Hantech
433 Olive St (45840-5358)
P.O. Box 1047 (45839-1047)
PHONE..............................419 424-8225
Fax: 419 424-8371
Clark Inniger, *Manager*
Phillips Matthews, *MIS Staff*
Kathi Lyon, *Administration*
EMP: 70
SALES (corp-wide): 1.2B **Publicly Held**
SIC: 3089 3084 2821 Septic tanks, plastic; plastics pipe; plastics materials & resins
HQ: Hancor, Inc.
4640 Trueman Blvd
Hilliard OH 43026
614 658-0050

(G-9838)
HANCOR INC
12370 Jackson Township Rd (45839)
P.O. Box 1047 (45839-1047)
PHONE..............................419 424-8222
Fax: 419 424-5208
Steve Ferell, *Manager*
EMP: 100
SALES (corp-wide): 1.2B **Publicly Held**
SIC: 3084 Plastics pipe
HQ: Hancor, Inc.
4640 Trueman Blvd
Hilliard OH 43026
614 658-0050

(G-9839)
HIGH QUALITY PLASTICS
2000 Fostoria Ave (45840-9775)
P.O. Box 269 (45839-0269)
PHONE..............................419 422-8290
Fax: 419 422-8557
Frits Vanderklooster, *Principal*
Jeff Emmitt, *Manager*
EMP: 7
SALES (est): 614.5K **Privately Held**
SIC: 3053 Gaskets, packing & sealing devices

(G-9840)
HOLTGREVEN SCALE & ELEC CORP
Also Called: Loadmaster Scale Mfgr
420 E Lincoln St (45840-4945)
PHONE..............................419 422-4779
Fax: 419 422-9036
Leonard Holtgreven, *President*
Mark Holtgreven, *Vice Pres*
Jenice Fullington, *Manager*
▲ **EMP:** 17 **EST:** 1958
SQ FT: 20,000
SALES (est): 4.1MM **Privately Held**
WEB: www.loadmasterscale.com
SIC: 3596 Industrial scales; truck (motor vehicle) scales

(G-9841)
HOMESTEAD COLLECTIONS
11300 Township Rd 99 (45840)
PHONE..............................419 422-8286
Fax: 419 420-0110
Bonnie Schey, *Partner*
Kreg Schey, *Partner*
EMP: 3
SALES (est): 355.7K **Privately Held**
SIC: 2499 Decorative wood & woodwork

(G-9842)
HOUSE OF AWARDS AND SPORTS
419 N Main St (45840-3378)
PHONE..............................419 422-7877
Fax: 419 422-7776
Jeff Crawford, *President*
Karen Crawford, *Vice Pres*
EMP: 7
SQ FT: 3,500
SALES (est): 862.6K **Privately Held**
SIC: 3949 5091 Sporting & athletic goods; sporting & recreation goods

(G-9843)
HOUSE OF HINDENACH
408 N Main St (45840-3542)
PHONE..............................419 422-0392
Fax: 419 422-7220
Donald W Hindenach, *Owner*
EMP: 4
SQ FT: 4,500
SALES: 400K **Privately Held**
SIC: 5731 3651 7622 1731 Consumer electronic equipment; audio electronic systems; speaker systems; communication equipment repair; radio repair & installation; home entertainment repair services; sound equipment specialization

(G-9844)
JAQUAS MONOGRAMMING & DESIGN
Also Called: Jacqua's Monogramming & Design
1016 Tiffin Ave Ste E (45840-6269)
PHONE..............................419 422-2244
Fax: 419 422-3043
Patrick Jaqua, *President*
EMP: 4
SALES (est): 211.6K **Privately Held**
SIC: 2395 Embroidery products, except schiffli machine

(G-9845)
JIM H NIEMEYER
1004 W Sandusky St (45840-2332)
PHONE..............................419 422-2465
Jim Neimeyer, *Owner*
EMP: 15
SALES (est): 985.2K **Privately Held**
SIC: 2024 Ice cream & frozen desserts

(G-9846)
JK-CO LLC
16960 E State Route 12 (45840-9744)
PHONE..............................419 422-5240
Fax: 419 422-5260
Joseph L Kurtz, *President*
C Leon Thornton, *Vice Pres*
Chuck Brothers, *Buyer*
▼ **EMP:** 45
SQ FT: 40,000
SALES (est): 11.7MM **Privately Held**
SIC: 3743 4789 Railroad car rebuilding; railroad car repair

(G-9847)
KENNEDY PRINTING CO
Also Called: Accurate Mail
1631 Broad Ave (45840-2718)
PHONE..............................419 422-1802
Fax: 419 422-3076
Mark Keesey, *President*
Rodger Clark, *Office Mgr*
Carla Towers, *Administration*
EMP: 18
SQ FT: 7,200
SALES (est): 1.7MM **Privately Held**
SIC: 2752 Commercial printing, offset

(G-9848)
KROGER CO
Also Called: Kroger 00510
101 6th St (45840-5143)
PHONE..............................419 423-2065
Fax: 419 423-8976
Richard Redick, *Branch Mgr*
Kendra A Fultz, *Pharmacist*
Ming Yu, *Manager*
EMP: 75
SALES (corp-wide): 115.3B **Publicly Held**
WEB: www.kroger.com
SIC: 5411 5912 2051 Supermarkets, chain; proprietary (non-prescription medicine) stores; bread, cake & related products
PA: The Kroger Co
1014 Vine St Ste 1000
Cincinnati OH 45202
513 762-4000

(G-9849)
KUSS FILTRATION INC (PA)
2150 Industrial Dr (45840-5402)
PHONE..............................419 423-9040
Fax: 419 423-8474
Hasnain R Merchant, *CEO*
Nick Galambos, *Ch of Bd*
Scott Salsburey, *Principal*
George Starring, *Principal*
Julie Graber, *Business Mgr*
▲ **EMP:** 400
SQ FT: 100,000
SALES (est): 199.9MM **Privately Held**
SIC: 3569 Filters, general line: industrial

(G-9850)
LAWFT (PA)
1016 N Blanchard St (45840-4719)
PHONE..............................419 422-5293
Verl Warnimont, *Owner*
EMP: 4 **EST:** 2012
SALES (est): 518.4K **Privately Held**
SIC: 2326 Work uniforms

(G-9851)
LEGACY FARMERS COOPERATIVE (PA)
6566 County Road 236 (45840-9769)
PHONE..............................419 423-2611
Fax: 419 423-9706
Andrew Jones, *Ch of Bd*
Marvin Maas, *Vice Ch Bd*
Mark Sunderman, *President*
Steve Rodman, *Division Mgr*
William Tong, *Vice Pres*
EMP: 15
SQ FT: 10,000
SALES (est): 278.4MM **Privately Held**
SIC: 5153 5191 5984 2875 Grains; farm supplies; seeds: field, garden & flower; fertilizer & fertilizer materials; liquefied petroleum gas dealers; fertilizers, mixing only; prepared feeds; flour & other grain mill products

(G-9852)
LFG SPECIALTIES LLC
16406 E Us Route 224 (45840-9761)
PHONE..............................419 424-4999
De Arment,
Steve Martin,
EMP: 50
SQ FT: 3,000
SALES (est): 8.6MM
SALES (corp-wide): 12.9B **Privately Held**
WEB: www.lfgspecialties.com
SIC: 3585 2899 Evaporative condensers, heat transfer equipment; flares

HQ: The Shaw Group Inc
4171 Essen Ln
Baton Rouge LA 70809

(G-9853)
MANUFCTRING BUS DEV SLTONS LLC
6000 Fostoria Ave (45840-9776)
P.O. Box 1811 (45839-1811)
PHONE..............................419 294-1313
Felicia M Briggs, *President*
Brian J Robertson, *Vice Pres*
EMP: 22
SQ FT: 250,000
SALES (est): 1.8MM Privately Held
WEB: www.mbdsna.com
SIC: 3559 Automotive related machinery

(G-9854)
MARATHON OIL COMPANY
539 S Main St (45840-3229)
P.O. Box 151 (45839-0151)
PHONE..............................419 422-2121
Fax: 419 421-3522
George Shaffner, *Senior VP*
Christiane Fox, *Vice Pres*
Virginia King, *Vice Pres*
John Beardslee, *Project Mgr*
Ricky Jones, *Project Mgr*
EMP: 27
SALES (corp-wide): 4.6B Publicly Held
WEB: www.marathonoilcompany.com
SIC: 2911 Petroleum refining
HQ: Marathon Oil Company
5555 San Felipe St # 2017
Houston TX 77056
713 629-6600

(G-9855)
MARATHON PETROLEUM COMPANY LP (HQ)
539 S Main St (45840-3229)
P.O. Box 1 (45839-7836)
PHONE..............................419 422-2121
Gary Heminger, *CEO*
Ronald G Becker, *President*
Brad Allsop, *Partner*
Mary Ellen Peters, *Partner*
J Michael Wilder, *Partner*
◆ EMP: 10
SQ FT: 621,000
SALES (est): 19.9B Publicly Held
WEB: www.maplic.com
SIC: 5172 2951 2865 Gasoline; asphalt paving mixtures & blocks; cyclic crudes & intermediates

(G-9856)
MARATHON PETROLEUM CORPORATION (PA)
539 S Main St (45840-3229)
PHONE..............................419 422-2121
Fax: 330 273-0972
Gary R Heminger, *Ch of Bd*
Rodney P Nichols, *Exec VP*
Raymond L Brooks, *Senior VP*
Thomas M Kelley, *Senior VP*
C Michael Palmer, *Senior VP*
EMP: 277
SALES: 63.3B Publicly Held
SIC: 2911 5172 Petroleum refining; gasoline

(G-9857)
MARATHON PETROLEUM SUPPLY LLC
539 S Main St (45840-3229)
PHONE..............................419 422-2121
Gary Heminger, *Mng Member*
EMP: 2000
SALES (est): 57.3MM Publicly Held
SIC: 2911 Petroleum refining
PA: Marathon Petroleum Corporation
539 S Main St
Findlay OH 45840

(G-9858)
MARBEE INC
Also Called: Marbee Printing & Graphic Art
2703 N Main St Ste 1 (45840-4039)
PHONE..............................419 422-9441
Fax: 419 423-8521
Randy Raymond, *President*
Teresa Raymond, *Corp Secy*
EMP: 6

SQ FT: 3,600
SALES (est): 889.5K Privately Held
WEB: www.marbeeprinting.com
SIC: 2752 2759 Commercial printing, off-set; commercial printing

(G-9859)
MC BROWN INDUSTRIES INC
10534 Township Road 128 (45840-9315)
PHONE..............................419 963-2800
Fax: 419 963-5505
Lester Brown III, *President*
Dan Brown, *Vice Pres*
EMP: 10
SQ FT: 15,000
SALES (est): 690K Privately Held
SIC: 3441 3599 Fabricated structural metal; machine shop, jobbing & repair

(G-9860)
MICHIGAN SUGAR COMPANY
Also Called: Findlay Terminal
1343 Greenwood St (45840-1660)
PHONE..............................419 423-1666
Fax: 419 423-7741
Jay Roszatycki, *Mfg Staff*
Westley Thomas, *Branch Mgr*
Kevin Romzek, *Maintence Staff*
EMP: 5
SALES (corp-wide): 600MM Privately Held
SIC: 4225 2063 General warehousing & storage; beet sugar
PA: Michigan Sugar Company
122 Uptown Dr Unit 300
Bay City MI 48708
989 686-0161

(G-9861)
MIDWEST LASER SYSTEMS INC
Also Called: MLS Systems
1101 Commerce Pkwy (45840-1997)
PHONE..............................419 424-0062
Fax: 419 424-3568
William J Hunter, *President*
Rob Robenalt, *Opers Staff*
Gene Rupp, *Project Engr*
Aaron Goodwin, *Manager*
Daniel J Lucke, *Manager*
EMP: 40
SQ FT: 50,000
SALES (est): 7.4MM Privately Held
WEB: www.mlssystems.com
SIC: 3599 3549 Custom machinery; metalworking machinery

(G-9862)
MILL CRAFT MCH & FABRICATION
1500 Morrical Blvd (45840-1574)
PHONE..............................419 422-6346
Fred Osborn, *President*
Theresa Osborn, *Treasurer*
EMP: 3
SALES (est): 240K Privately Held
SIC: 3599 Machine shop, jobbing & repair

(G-9863)
MILLSTREAM PRESS INC
1631 Broad Ave (45840-2718)
P.O. Box 1361 (45839-1361)
PHONE..............................419 422-9745
Fax: 419 422-8099
Mark Keesey, *President*
Gene Wyse, *Sales Staff*
EMP: 18 EST: 1979
SQ FT: 6,500
SALES (est): 2.8MM Privately Held
WEB: www.millstreampress.com
SIC: 2752 Commercial printing, offset

(G-9864)
MITEC POWERTRAIN INC
4000 Fostoria Ave (45840-8733)
PHONE..............................567 525-5606
Tim Hall, *President*
▲ EMP: 30
SQ FT: 100,000
SALES (est): 8.3MM
SALES (corp-wide): 156.4MM Privately Held
SIC: 3714 Motor vehicle parts & accessories

PA: Mitec Automotive Ag
Rennbahn 25
Eisenach 99817
369 168-40

(G-9865)
MOLTEN NORTH AMERICA CORP (HQ)
1835 Industrial Dr (45840-5440)
P.O. Box 1451 (45839-1451)
PHONE..............................419 425-2700
Fax: 419 425-2915
Hiddaki Miyamoto, *President*
Toshikazu Yamate, *Vice Pres*
Guy Crawford, *QC Mgr*
Satoshi Nakamura, *Engineer*
Satoshi Saito, *Accounting Mgr*
▲ EMP: 189
SQ FT: 100,814
SALES: 21.9MM
SALES (corp-wide): 399.6MM Privately Held
SIC: 3089 Automotive parts, plastic
PA: Molten Corporation
1-8, Yokogawashimmachi, Nishi-Ku
Hiroshima HIR 733-0
822 921-381

(G-9866)
NATIONAL LIME AND STONE CO
9860 County Road 313 (45840-9003)
P.O. Box 120 (45839-0120)
PHONE..............................419 423-3400
Fax: 419 423-1313
Gary Eisenhart, *Credit Mgr*
Tim Federici, *Sales Staff*
Denny Swick, *Branch Mgr*
Jeannine Clark, *Director*
EMP: 31
SALES (corp-wide): 4B Privately Held
WEB: www.natlime.com
SIC: 3273 1422 Ready-mixed concrete; crushed & broken limestone
PA: The National Lime And Stone Company
551 Lake Cascade Pkwy
Findlay OH 45840
419 422-4341

(G-9867)
NICHIDAI AMERICA CORPORATION
Also Called: N A C
15630 E State Route 12 # 4 (45840-7771)
PHONE..............................419 423-7511
Yuzuru Mishimura, *President*
Kiyoshi Naaadawa, *Vice Pres*
EMP: 26
SALES (est): 3.2MM Privately Held
SIC: 3312 Tool & die steel & alloys

(G-9868)
NISSIN BRAKE OHIO INC (HQ)
1901 Industrial Dr (45840-5442)
P.O. Box 886 (45839-0886)
PHONE..............................419 420-3800
Itsuo Miyake, *President*
Keith Dunnigan, *Business Mgr*
Kaoru Sakaguchi, *COO*
Takayuki Ueno, *Senior VP*
Ron Hall, *Vice Pres*
▲ EMP: 670
SQ FT: 228,000
SALES (est): 143.9MM
SALES (corp-wide): 1.4B Privately Held
WEB: www.nissinbrake.com
SIC: 3714 Motor vehicle brake systems & parts
PA: Nissin Kogyo Co., Ltd.
801, Kazawa
Tomi NAG 389-0
268 631-230

(G-9869)
NORTHWEST INSTALLATIONS INC
1903 Blanchard Ave (45840-6472)
P.O. Box 1563 (45839-1563)
PHONE..............................419 423-5738
Tracy Lopez, *President*
Douglas Laplant, *CFO*
John Garcia, *Manager*
EMP: 23
SQ FT: 7,000

SALES (est): 3.9MM Privately Held
WEB: www.northwestinstallationsltd.com
SIC: 1796 3444 3443 3441 Machinery installation; sheet metalwork; fabricated plate work (boiler shop); fabricated structural metal

(G-9870)
OHIO CONVEYOR AND SUPPLY INC
1310 N Main St (45840-3703)
P.O. Box 678 (45839-0678)
PHONE..............................419 422-3825
Fax: 419 422-4490
John R Snyder, *President*
Annette Bowden, *Corp Secy*
Joseph P Snyder, *Vice Pres*
EMP: 5 EST: 1944
SQ FT: 15,000
SALES: 1MM Privately Held
SIC: 3463 Mechanical power transmission forgings, nonferrous

(G-9871)
OLD MILL CUSTOM CABINETRY CO
Also Called: Diversified Woodworking
310 E Crawford St (45840-4807)
PHONE..............................419 423-8897
Fax: 419 422-9897
Robert Chiow, *President*
Diana Chiow, *Treasurer*
EMP: 4
SQ FT: 7,500
SALES (est): 428.8K Privately Held
SIC: 2434 1799 Wood kitchen cabinets; vanities, bathroom: wood; kitchen cabinet installation

(G-9872)
OLDE MAN GRANOLA LLC
7227 W State Route 12 (45840-8802)
PHONE..............................419 819-9576
Fay Plaza, *Opers Staff*
Rebecca Green, *Manager*
Mark Plaza, *Manager*
Kelly Green, *Exec Dir*
Trevor Plaza, *Exec Dir*
EMP: 10 EST: 2013
SALES (est): 581.2K Privately Held
SIC: 2043 7389 Granola & muesli, except bars & clusters;

(G-9873)
OPERATIONAL SUPPORT SVCS LLC
1850 Industrial Dr (45840-5439)
P.O. Box 178 (45839-0178)
PHONE..............................419 425-0889
Fax: 419 425-0756
Donald J Holtgraven,
Gary Franks,
Paul Yates,
EMP: 15
SQ FT: 5,000
SALES (est): 5.2MM Privately Held
SIC: 2655 Fiber shipping & mailing containers

(G-9874)
OTTAWA OIL CO INC
Also Called: Findlay Party Mart
1100 Trenton Ave (45840-1920)
PHONE..............................419 425-3301
Fax: 419 425-3301
Karen Roberts, *Manager*
Brian Leer, *Manager*
Brian Vanleer, *Manager*
EMP: 11
SALES (corp-wide): 71.1MM Privately Held
WEB: www.putnamnet.com
SIC: 1389 Pumping of oil & gas wells
PA: Ottawa Oil Co., Inc.
10305 State Route 224
Ottawa OH
419 523-6441

(G-9875)
P & A INDUSTRIES INC
600 Crystal Ave (45840-4600)
P.O. Box 1446 (45839-1446)
PHONE..............................419 422-7070
Fax: 419 422-7646
Matt Bowman, *Prdtn Mgr*

Dale Rampe, *Mfg Staff*
Stan Haselman, *QC Dir*
Dean Treier, *Financial Exec*
Jennifer Warnecke, *Human Resources*
EMP: 200 **Privately Held**
SIC: 3465 3469 Automotive stampings;
metal stampings
HQ: P & A Industries, Inc.
1 Lyman E Hoyt Dr
Monroe MI 48161
734 241-7242

(G-9876)
PARKINS ASPHALT SEALING
1710 Olney Ave (45840-1451)
PHONE....................419 422-2399
Jim Heldman, *Owner*
Pat Heldman, *Principal*
EMP: 5
SALES (est): 424.1K **Privately Held**
SIC: 2851 1771 Paints, asphalt or bitumi-
nous; driveway contractor

(G-9877)
PARTITIONS PLUS LLC
12517 County Road 99 (45840-9736)
PHONE....................419 422-2600
Brian Robinson, *Office Mgr*
EMP: 13
SQ FT: 40,000
SALES (est): 4MM **Privately Held**
SIC: 5046 2541 5021 Partitions; wood
partitions & fixtures; racks

(G-9878)
PIECO INC (PA)
Also Called: Superior Trim
2151 Industrial Dr (45840-5429)
P.O. Box 118 (45839-0118)
PHONE....................419 422-5335
Fax: 419 422-8180
Michael Gardner, *President*
Tim Gross, *Plant Mgr*
Gary Sinski, *Plant Mgr*
Jeff Coleman, *Program Mgr*
EMP: 50 **EST:** 1997
SQ FT: 50,000
SALES (est): 39.3MM **Privately Held**
WEB: www.suptrim.com
SIC: 2396 Automotive trimmings, fabric;
furniture trimmings, fabric; trimming, fab-
ric

(G-9879)
PMC ACQUISITIONS INC (PA)
2040 Industrial Dr (45840-5443)
PHONE....................419 429-0042
Duane Jebbett, *President*
EMP: 3 **EST:** 2014
SALES (est): 25MM **Privately Held**
SIC: 3081 6719 Plastic film & sheet; in-
vestment holding companies, except
banks

(G-9880)
**PREMIER MATERIAL CONCEPTS
LLC**
2040 Industrial Dr (45840-5443)
P.O. Box 1123 (45839-1123)
PHONE....................419 429-0042
Duane Jebbett, *CEO*
Tom Miller, *General Mgr*
Roger Jean, *Vice Pres*
Eric Short, *Vice Pres*
Christy Kisseverth, *Accountant*
EMP: 65 **EST:** 2014
SALES: 25MM **Privately Held**
SIC: 3081 Plastic film & sheet
PA: Pmc Acquisitions, Inc.
2040 Industrial Dr
Findlay OH 45840
419 429-0042

(G-9881)
PUKKA INC (PA)
Also Called: Pukka Headwear
337 S Main St Fl 4 (45840-3373)
P.O. Box 773 (45839-0773)
PHONE....................419 429-7808
Shawn Rogers, *CEO*
Tate Miller, *President*
Andrea Rogers, *Vice Pres*
David Pruss, *CFO*
John Bond, *VP Sales*
▲ **EMP:** 48 **EST:** 2003

SALES (est): 6.9MM **Privately Held**
SIC: 2353 Caps: cloth, straw & felt

(G-9882)
REITER DAIRY OF AKRON INC
10456 State Route 224 W (45840-1907)
PHONE....................419 424-5060
Fax: 419 423-1243
Ed Bazile, *Manager*
EMP: 20 **Publicly Held**
SIC: 2026 2024 Milk processing (pasteur-
izing, homogenizing, bottling); ice cream,
bulk
HQ: Reiter Dairy Of Akron, Inc.
1961 Commerce Cir
Springfield OH 45504
937 323-5777

(G-9883)
ROKI AMERICA CO LTD
2001 Production Dr (45840-5450)
P.O. Box 1044 (45839-1044)
PHONE....................419 424-9713
Fax: 419 424-3352
Takaya Shimada, *CEO*
Toshifumi Sasamori, *President*
Hiromitsu Shimada Jr, *Chairman*
Bob Funkhouser, *Vice Pres*
Akira Terada, *Plant Mgr*
▲ **EMP:** 350
SQ FT: 177,000
SALES (est): 193.4MM **Privately Held**
WEB: www.filtechusa.com
SIC: 3714 Filters: oil, fuel & air, motor vehi-
cle; power transmission equipment, motor
vehicle
PA: Roki Holdings Co.,Ltd.
2396, Futamata, Futamatacho, Ten-
ryu-Ku
Hamamatsu SZO
539 260-545

(G-9884)
ROWMARK LLC (PA)
5409 Hamlet Dr (45840)
P.O. Box 1605 (45839-1605)
PHONE....................419 425-8974
Fax: 419 425-0501
Duane E Jebbett, *CEO*
Thomas Miller, *Senior VP*
Myrth Van Den Brandt, *Opers Mgr*
Jeremy Horne, *Purch Agent*
Samantha Stacy, *Engineer*
◆ **EMP:** 100
SQ FT: 65,000
SALES: 35MM **Privately Held**
WEB: www.rowmark.com
SIC: 3089 3083 Extruded finished plastic
products; laminated plastics plate & sheet

(G-9885)
ROWMARK LLC
Also Called: Premier Material Concepts
2040 Industrial Dr (45840-5443)
PHONE....................419 429-0042
EMP: 75
SALES (corp-wide): 79.6MM **Privately
Held**
SIC: 3089 Mfg Plastic Products
PA: Rowmark Llc
5409 Hamlet Dr
Findlay OH 45840
419 425-8974

(G-9886)
ROYAL MFG
2447 Tiffin Ave (45840-8672)
PHONE....................419 902-8222
James Herrington, *Principal*
EMP: 4
SALES: 750K **Privately Held**
SIC: 3999 Manufacturing industries

(G-9887)
SANOH AMERICA INC (HQ)
1849 Industrial Dr (45840-5440)
P.O. Box 1626 (45839-1626)
PHONE....................419 425-2600
Fax: 419 420-7103
Masahiko Mizukami, *President*
Eric Carroll, *Vice Pres*
Jeff Hook, *Vice Pres*
Ronald Frisch, *CFO*
Ronald J Curry, *VP Mktg*
▲ **EMP:** 70
SQ FT: 303,000

SALES (est): 289.8MM
SALES (corp-wide): 1.1B **Privately Held**
WEB: www.sanoh-america.com
SIC: 3498 Tube fabricating (contract bend-
ing & shaping)
PA: Sanoh Industrial Co.,Ltd.
1-23-23, Ebisu
Shibuya-Ku TKY 150-0
357 938-411

(G-9888)
**SAUSSER STEEL COMPANY
INC**
230 Crystal Ave (45840-4796)
PHONE....................419 422-9632
Fax: 419 422-9691
Joe W Sausser, *President*
Dorothy M Garlow, *Corp Secy*
Larry Cherry, *Vice Pres*
Donald Hutton, *Vice Pres*
Saunders Scobys, *Asst Treas*
▲ **EMP:** 19 **EST:** 1941
SQ FT: 500,000
SALES (est): 3.8MM **Privately Held**
WEB: www.saussersteel.com
SIC: 3441 5084 5051 3446 Fabricated
structural metal; welding machinery &
equipment; steel; architectural metalwork;
sheet metalwork; fabricated plate work
(boiler shop)

(G-9889)
SIGNED BY JOSETTE LLC
303 E Sandusky St (45840-4941)
PHONE....................419 796-9632
Josette Brinkman,
EMP: 3 **EST:** 2007
SALES (est): 229.9K **Privately Held**
SIC: 3993 Signs & advertising specialties

(G-9890)
SMOKE RINGS INC
Also Called: Butt Hut
1928 Tiffin Ave (45840-6753)
PHONE....................419 420-9966
Fax: 419 420-1765
Jean Dove, *President*
EMP: 7
SALES (est): 550K **Privately Held**
WEB: www.smokerings.com
SIC: 2131 5993 Chewing & smoking to-
bacco; tobacco stores & stands

(G-9891)
**SONOCO PRTECTIVE
SOLUTIONS INC**
1900 Industrial Dr (45840-5441)
P.O. Box 714 (45839-0714)
PHONE....................419 420-0029
EMP: 5
SALES (corp-wide): 4.9B **Publicly Held**
SIC: 2671 Manufactures Packaging Paper
And Film
HQ: Sonoco Protective Solutions, Inc.
1 N 2nd St
Hartsville SC 29550
843 383-7000

(G-9892)
**SONOCO PRTECTIVE
SOLUTIONS INC**
1900 Industrial Dr (45840-5441)
P.O. Box 714 (45839-0714)
PHONE....................419 420-0029
Rod Williams, *Branch Mgr*
EMP: 100
SQ FT: 100,000
SALES (corp-wide): 4.7B **Publicly Held**
WEB: www.createccorp.com
SIC: 3089 3086 2821 Blister or bubble
formed packaging, plastic; plastics foam
products; plastics materials & resins
HQ: Sonoco Protective Solutions, Inc.
1 N 2nd St
Hartsville SC 29550
843 383-7000

(G-9893)
SOUTHSIDE WOLFIES
546 6th St (45840-5148)
PHONE....................419 422-5450
Fax: 419 422-5450
Shawn Lalji, *Owner*
EMP: 3

SALES (est): 196.6K **Privately Held**
SIC: 2068 Salted & roasted nuts & seeds

(G-9894)
SQUARE ONE SOLUTIONS LLC
Also Called: Brown Box Company
105 Jefferson St (45840)
PHONE....................419 425-5445
Stephen Chan, *President*
Kary Chan,
Kathryn Lewis,
Giannina Riblet,
EMP: 13
SQ FT: 7,000
SALES (est): 2.4MM **Privately Held**
SIC: 2653 Boxes, corrugated: made from
purchased materials

(G-9895)
STONECO INC (DH)
1700 Fostoria Ave Ste 200 (45840-6218)
P.O. Box 865 (45839-0865)
PHONE....................419 422-8854
Fax: 419 429-3444
John T Bearss, *President*
Don Weber, *Vice Pres*
Jack Zouhary, *Admin Sec*
EMP: 110
SQ FT: 34,000
SALES (est): 52MM
SALES (corp-wide): 28.6B **Privately Held**
WEB: www.stoneco.net
SIC: 2951 1411 Asphalt & asphaltic paving
mixtures (not from refineries); limestone,
dimension-quarrying
HQ: S. E. Johnson Companies, Inc
1360 Ford St
Maumee OH 43537
419 893-8731

(G-9896)
STREAMSIDE MATERIALS LLC
7440 Township Road 95 (45840-9659)
PHONE....................419 423-1290
Randall Tucker, *CEO*
Brian Halm, *Director*
EMP: 6 **EST:** 2015
SALES (est): 282.3K **Privately Held**
SIC: 8742 1442 Materials mgmt. (purchas-
ing, handling, inventory) consultant; con-
struction sand & gravel

(G-9897)
STREICHERS ENTERPRISES INC
Also Called: Streicher's Quickprint
109 S Main St (45840-3423)
PHONE....................419 423-8606
Fax: 419 423-9222
Thomas Day, *President*
Tammy Day, *Admin Sec*
Michael Streicher, *Admin Sec*
EMP: 5
SQ FT: 4,000
SALES: 500K **Privately Held**
SIC: 2752 Commercial printing, offset

(G-9898)
SUMMERS ACQUISITION CORP
16406 E Us Route 224 (45840-9761)
PHONE....................419 423-5800
Gary Porcello, *Branch Mgr*
EMP: 5
SALES (corp-wide): 2.5B **Privately Held**
WEB: www.summersrubber.com
SIC: 5085 3498 3441 3429 Industrial
supplies; fabricated pipe & fittings; fabri-
cated structural metal; manufactured
hardware (general); rubber & plastics
hose & beltings
HQ: Summers Acquisition Corporation
12555 Berea Rd
Cleveland OH 44111
216 941-7700

(G-9899)
T & S ENTERPRISES
1616 Bliss Ave (45840-1512)
P.O. Box 305 (45839-0305)
PHONE....................419 424-1122
Sharon A Nagy, *Owner*
Michael P Nagy, *Opers Mgr*
EMP: 20
SQ FT: 60,000

SALES (est): 1.4MM **Privately Held**
SIC: 3596 3643 Scales & balances, except laboratory; connectors & terminals for electrical devices

(G-9900)
TEXSTONE INDUSTRIES
433 Oak Ave (45840-4750)
PHONE....................................419 722-4664
EMP: 3
SALES (est): 168.6K **Privately Held**
SIC: 3999 Manufacturing industries

(G-9901)
TH PLASTICS INC
1640 Westfield Dr (45840)
PHONE....................................419 425-5825
EMP: 15
SALES (corp-wide): 100.6MM **Privately Held**
SIC: 3089 Mfg Plastic Products
PA: Th Plastics, Inc.
106 E Main St
Mendon MI 49072
419 425-5825

(G-9902)
TH PLASTICS INC
101 Bentley Ct (45840-1799)
PHONE....................................419 425-5825
Stacy McCoy, *Buyer*
Maurisa Meyers, *Purchasing*
Elizabeth Mitchell, *Branch Mgr*
EMP: 115
SALES (corp-wide): 100.6MM **Privately Held**
SIC: 3089 Aquarium accessories, plastic
PA: Th Plastics, Inc.
106 E Main St
Mendon MI 49072
419 425-5825

(G-9903)
THUNDER DREAMER PUBLISHING
2500 Crystal Ave (45840-4462)
PHONE....................................419 424-2004
Daniel Gerschutz, *President*
Deborah Gerschutz, *Vice Pres*
EMP: 3
SALES (est): 171K **Privately Held**
SIC: 2741 Music, sheet: publishing & printing

(G-9904)
VALFILM LLC
3441 N Main St (45840-4206)
PHONE....................................419 423-6500
Alberto Geronomi, *Principal*
Sara Geronimi, *Principal*
EMP: 50
SALES (est): 14.8MM **Privately Held**
SIC: 3081 Plastic film & sheet

(G-9905)
WABASH NATIONAL CORPORATION
2000 Fostoria Ave (45840-9775)
PHONE....................................419 434-9409
EMP: 201
SALES (corp-wide): 1.8B **Publicly Held**
SIC: 3715 Truck trailers
PA: Wabash National Corporation
1000 Sagamore Pkwy S
Lafayette IN 47905
765 771-5300

(G-9906)
WAXLER MACHINE TOOL COMPANY
535 6th St (45840-5100)
PHONE....................................419 422-1240
Dennis B Waxler, *Owner*
EMP: 3
SQ FT: 2,200
SALES (est): 100K **Privately Held**
SIC: 3599 7692 Machine shop, jobbing & repair; welding repair

(G-9907)
WERK-BRAU COMPANY
2800 Fostoria Ave (45840-8757)
P.O. Box 545 (45839-0545)
PHONE....................................419 422-2912
Fax: 419 422-7207

Paul Ballinger, *CEO*
Jon Ballinger, *President*
Jim Greulich, *Vice Pres*
Keith Kashera, *Safety Mgr*
Keith Kuchera, *Safety Mgr*
▲ EMP: 66
SQ FT: 104,000
SALES (est): 28.8MM
SALES (corp-wide): 54.8MM **Privately Held**
WEB: www.werkbrau.com
SIC: 3531 3412 Buckets, excavating: clamshell, concrete, dragline, etc.; backhoe mounted, hydraulically powered attachments; construction machinery attachments; metal barrels, drums & pails
PA: Ballinger Industries, Inc.
2500 Fostoria Ave
Findlay OH 45840
419 422-4533

(G-9908)
WHIRLPOOL CORPORATION
4901 N Main St (45840-9780)
PHONE....................................419 423-8123
Fax: 419 423-6044
Jeff Noelcorporate, *President*
John Siefker, *Project Mgr*
Linda Kessler, *Materials Mgr*
Forrest Frank, *Facilities Mgr*
Tom Buckleitner, *Opers Staff*
EMP: 100
SALES (corp-wide): 20.7B **Publicly Held**
WEB: www.whirlpoolcorp.com
SIC: 3639 3632 Dishwashing machines, household; household refrigerators & freezers
PA: Whirlpool Corporation
2000 N M 63
Benton Harbor MI 49022
269 923-5000

Fleming
Washington County

(G-9909)
ANDERSON ENERGY INC
12959 State Route 550 (45729-5229)
P.O. Box 327, Vincent (45784-0327)
PHONE....................................740 678-8608
Den Anderson, *President*
EMP: 7
SALES (est): 348.5K **Privately Held**
SIC: 1381 Drilling oil & gas wells

(G-9910)
AZA ENTERPRISES LLC
1149 Fisher Ridge Rd (45729-5001)
PHONE....................................740 678-8482
EMP: 5
SALES: 350K **Privately Held**
SIC: 3325 Steel Foundry

(G-9911)
BT ENERGY CORPORATION (PA)
1635 Warren Chapel Rd (45729-5089)
P.O. Box 60, Marietta (45750-0060)
PHONE....................................740 373-6134
Jugal K Taneja, *CEO*
Eddie Beale, *President*
A Theodore Stautberg Jr, *President*
R Stuyvesant Pierrepont, *VP Finance*
EMP: 1 EST: 1981
SQ FT: 4,000
SALES (est): 1.3MM **Privately Held**
SIC: 1311 Crude petroleum production; natural gas production

(G-9912)
DECKER WELL SERVICE LLC
14165 State Route 550 (45729-5049)
P.O. Box 91 (45729-0091)
PHONE....................................740 678-2970
Fax: 740 678-2924
Dean Decker,
Cheryl Decker,
EMP: 3
SALES (est): 270K **Privately Held**
SIC: 1389 Oil field services; gas field services

(G-9913)
PINE RIDGE PROCESSING
Also Called: Pine Ridge Meat Processing
4559 Anderson Rd (45729-5148)
PHONE....................................740 749-3166
Douglas Sprague, *Owner*
EMP: 3
SQ FT: 1,800
SALES (est): 160K **Privately Held**
SIC: 2011 5421 Beef products from beef slaughtered on site; meat markets, including freezer provisioners

(G-9914)
STONEBRIDGE OPERATING CO LLC
1635 Warren Chapel Rd (45729-5089)
P.O. Box 60, Marietta (45750-0060)
PHONE....................................740 373-6134
Charlotte Dolak, *Marketing Staff*
E Biehl,
EMP: 1
SALES (est): 1.3MM **Privately Held**
WEB: www.stonebridgeoperating.com
SIC: 1311 Crude petroleum & natural gas
PA: Bt Energy Corporation
1635 Warren Chapel Rd
Fleming OH 45729
740 373-6134

Fletcher
Miami County

(G-9915)
CREATIA INC
7990 Sodom Ballou Rd (45326-8772)
PHONE....................................937 368-3100
Tim Deaton, *Branch Mgr*
EMP: 5 **Privately Held**
SIC: 7336 2262 Commercial art & graphic design; screen printing: manmade fiber & silk broadwoven fabrics
PA: Creatia, Inc.
8989 Lostcreek Shelby Rd
Fletcher OH 45326

Flushing
Belmont County

(G-9916)
GLENN MICHAEL BRICK
Also Called: Go For Broke Amusement
108 Wood St (43977-9727)
PHONE....................................740 391-5735
Glenn M Brick, *Owner*
EMP: 11
SALES: 2.7MM **Privately Held**
SIC: 4212 7993 7699 3578 Mail carriers, contract; juke boxes; automated teller machine (ATM) repair; automatic teller machines (ATM)

Forest
Hardin County

(G-9917)
AEROVATION TECH HOLDINGS LLC
11651 Township Rd 81 (45843)
PHONE....................................567 208-5525
Eric Barger,
EMP: 9
SALES (est): 470K **Privately Held**
SIC: 8711 3721 Aviation &/or aeronautical engineering; research & development on aircraft by the manufacturer

(G-9918)
BUCKEYE MCH FABRICATORS INC
610 E Lima St (45843-1182)
PHONE....................................419 273-2521
Fax: 419 273-2874
D Ray Marshall, *President*
Neil Boyd, *Vice Pres*
Brad Richards, *Production*
Michelle Cole, *VP Finance*

Jerry Perry, *Sales Staff*
EMP: 50 EST: 1974
SQ FT: 65,000
SALES (est): 10.3MM **Privately Held**
SIC: 3599 Machine shop, jobbing & repair; custom machinery

(G-9919)
DPI INC
110 N Davis St (45843-1010)
PHONE....................................419 273-1400
Fax: 419 273-2234
EMP: 6
SQ FT: 7,000
SALES (est): 520K **Privately Held**
SIC: 3199 5699 5713 Mfg Of Leather Steering Wheel Covers A Ret Of Embroidered Apparel & A Ret & Whol Of Carpets

(G-9920)
DUFF QUARRY INC
3798 State Route 53 (45843-9379)
PHONE....................................419 273-2518
Fax: 419 273-3286
James E Duff, *President*
EMP: 10
SALES (corp-wide): 2.2MM **Privately Held**
SIC: 1422 Crushed & broken limestone
PA: Duff Quarry Inc
9042 State Route 117
Huntsville OH 43324
937 686-2811

(G-9921)
HEMPY WATER CONDITIONING INC (PA)
505 Smith St (45843-1055)
P.O. Box 40 (45843-0040)
PHONE....................................419 273-2531
Fax: 419 273-2605
Paul N Staley, *President*
Jeff Knedler, *Principal*
Justin Wagner, *Vice Pres*
James Weber, *Vice Pres*
Regina Spiegel, *Treasurer*
EMP: 8
SQ FT: 6,000
SALES: 2.3MM **Privately Held**
SIC: 3589 Water treatment equipment, industrial

(G-9922)
SHELLY MATERIALS INC
3798 State Route 53 (45843-9379)
PHONE....................................419 273-2510
Norman Cochran, *Branch Mgr*
EMP: 6
SALES (corp-wide): 28.6B **Privately Held**
SIC: 2951 Asphalt paving mixtures & blocks
HQ: Shelly Materials, Inc.
80 Park Dr
Thornville OH 43076
740 246-6315

(G-9923)
TRIUMPH THERMAL SYSTEMS LLC (HQ)
200 Railroad St (45843-9193)
PHONE....................................419 273-2511
Michael Perhay, *President*
John R Bartholdson, *Senior VP*
Doug Nemura, *Purch Mgr*
Allen Musgrave, *Senior Buyer*
Chris Clay, *Buyer*
EMP: 115
SQ FT: 125,000
SALES (est): 29.9MM
SALES (corp-wide): 3.8B **Publicly Held**
WEB: www.triumph-thermal.com
SIC: 3728 3443 Aircraft parts & equipment; heat exchangers, condensers & components
PA: Triumph Group, Inc.
899 Cassatt Rd Ste 210
Berwyn PA 19312
610 251-1000

(G-9924)
VTS CO LTD
607 E Lima St (45843-1180)
PHONE....................................419 273-4010
Lloyd Swavel, *President*
EMP: 7

SALES (est): 839K Privately Held
SIC: 3089 Extruded finished plastic products

Fort Jennings
Putnam County

(G-9925)
BCFAB INC (PA)
Also Called: Buckeye Custom Fab
15751 Road 19 (45844-9739)
PHONE..............................419 532-2899
Fax: 419 532-2900
Mike Siebeneck, *Managing Prtnr*
Dan Wehri, *Partner*
Mark Wehri, *Principal*
EMP: 7
SALES (est): 700K Privately Held
SIC: 3441 Fabricated structural metal

(G-9926)
G & S CUSTOM TOOLING LLC
18406 Road 20 (45844-9106)
PHONE..............................419 286-2888
German Darrin, *Administration*
EMP: 4
SALES (est): 348K Privately Held
SIC: 3544 Special dies & tools

Fort Loramie
Shelby County

(G-9927)
CROWN EQUIPMENT CORPORATION
Also Called: Crown Lift Trucks
300 S Tower St (45845)
P.O. Box 379 (45845-0379)
PHONE..............................937 295-4062
Sheryl Gray, *Branch Mgr*
EMP: 70
SALES (corp-wide): 5.5B Privately Held
SIC: 3537 Lift trucks, industrial: fork, platform, straddle, etc.
PA: Crown Equipment Corporation
44 S Washington St
New Bremen OH 45869
419 629-2311

(G-9928)
CUSTOM FOAM PRODUCTS INC (PA)
900 Tower Dr (45845-8712)
PHONE..............................937 295-2700
Fax: 937 295-3777
Nick Fullenkamp, *Owner*
Steve Sherman, *Vice Pres*
Susan Kunk, *Manager*
EMP: 20
SQ FT: 48,000
SALES (est): 3.2MM Privately Held
SIC: 3086 Plastics foam products

(G-9929)
EDWARDS MACHINE SERVICE INC
8800 State Route 66 (45845-9806)
P.O. Box 33 (45845-0033)
PHONE..............................937 295-2929
Fax: 937 295-3148
Thomas Edwards, *President*
Ronald Edwards, *Treasurer*
Ann Chaney, *Office Mgr*
EMP: 10
SQ FT: 7,500
SALES (est): 1.1MM Privately Held
WEB: www.edwardsmachine.net
SIC: 3542 Rebuilt machine tools, metal forming types

(G-9930)
FIVE STAR MACHINE & TOOL
403 S Main St (45845-8716)
PHONE..............................937 420-2170
Jeff Albers, *President*
Michelle Albers, *Admin Sec*
EMP: 4
SALES: 200K Privately Held
SIC: 3469 Machine parts, stamped or pressed metal

(G-9931)
FORT LORAMIE CAST STONE PDTS
120 S Main St (45845-9781)
P.O. Box 322 (45845-0322)
PHONE..............................937 420-2257
Fax: 937 295-2641
Charles Wendeln, *President*
Theodore Wendeln, *Corp Secy*
John Wendeln, *Vice Pres*
EMP: 3 EST: 1928
SQ FT: 20,000
SALES: 450K Privately Held
WEB: www.caststoneproducts.com
SIC: 3272 5231 5211 Concrete products; paint; lumber & other building materials

(G-9932)
INDUSTRIAL MACHINING SERVICES
700 Tower Dr (45845-8769)
P.O. Box 228 (45845-0228)
PHONE..............................937 295-2022
John B Puthoff, *President*
Dana Meyer, *General Mgr*
Teresa P Puthoff, *Manager*
EMP: 40
SQ FT: 13,500
SALES: 9.1MM Privately Held
WEB: www.ims-spi.com
SIC: 3544 Special dies, tools, jigs & fixtures

(G-9933)
JEFFREY BRANDEWIE
Also Called: National Thermoform
30 E Park St (45845-9301)
PHONE..............................937 726-7765
Jeffrey Brandewie, *Principal*
EMP: 3
SALES (est): 150K Privately Held
SIC: 3089 Plastics products

(G-9934)
PARTNERS IN RECOGNITION INC
405 S Main St (45845-8716)
PHONE..............................937 420-2150
Gregory Short, *President*
Angela Speelman, *Vice Pres*
◆ **EMP:** 28
SQ FT: 10,000
SALES (est): 2.9MM Privately Held
WEB: www.partnersinrecognition.com
SIC: 3999 Identification plates

(G-9935)
R C FAMILY WOOD PRODUCTS
5590 State Route 47 (45845)
PHONE..............................937 295-2393
Rick Schulze, *President*
Cindy Schulze, *Vice Pres*
EMP: 5
SQ FT: 1,664
SALES (est): 781.6K Privately Held
SIC: 2448 Pallets, wood; skids, wood

(G-9936)
ROL - TECH INC
Also Called: Marwil
4814 Calvert Dr (45845)
P.O. Box 12872, Dallas TX (75225-0872)
PHONE..............................214 905-8050
Roberto Diaz Del Castillo, *President*
Mark Lang, *Principal*
Zachary Gillett, *Vice Pres*
Deb Gehle, *Manager*
▲ **EMP:** 170
SALES (est): 35.7MM Privately Held
SIC: 3545 Machine tool accessories

(G-9937)
SCHMITMEYER INC
Also Called: G W Tool & Die Co
195 Ben St (45845)
P.O. Box 227 (45845-0227)
PHONE..............................937 295-2091
Fax: 937 295-2210
Jarett Schmitmeyer, *President*
Nicole Schmitmeyer, *Vice Pres*
Eric Grimm, *Prgrmr*
EMP: 9 EST: 1946
SQ FT: 7,200

SALES (est): 790K Privately Held
WEB: www.g-wtool.com
SIC: 3599 3544 Machine shop, jobbing & repair; special dies & tools

(G-9938)
SELECT-ARC INC
600 Enterprise Dr (45845)
P.O. Box 259 (45845-0259)
PHONE..............................937 295-5215
Fax: 937 295-5217
Dale Stager, *President*
Scott Sager, *Vice Pres*
Melvin Seitz, *QC Mgr*
Ottmar Marko, *CFO*
Bob Hopkins, *Regl Sales Mgr*
◆ **EMP:** 125
SQ FT: 67,000
SALES (est): 32.9MM Privately Held
WEB: www.select-arc.com
SIC: 3548 6719 Welding apparatus; personal holding companies, except banks

(G-9939)
SHARP ENTERPRISES INC
Also Called: A & B Printing
400 Enterprise Dr (45845)
P.O. Box 2 (45845-0002)
PHONE..............................937 295-2965
Fax: 937 295-3566
James R Sharp, *President*
Mark Bornhorst, *Manager*
EMP: 19
SQ FT: 8,000
SALES (est): 3.9MM Privately Held
SIC: 2752 Commercial printing, offset

(G-9940)
SOUTH SIDE DRIVE THRU
9204 Hilgefort Rd (45845-9717)
PHONE..............................937 295-2927
Ken Barhorst, *Owner*
Mary Barhorst, *Co-Owner*
EMP: 6
SALES (est): 305.1K Privately Held
SIC: 2082 Beer (alcoholic beverage)

(G-9941)
STUDIO ELEVEN INC (PA)
301 S Main St (45845-8755)
P.O. Box 315 (45845-0315)
PHONE..............................937 295-2225
Fax: 937 295-2225
Tom Barhorst, *President*
Frances A Barhorst, *Corp Secy*
Frances A Brhorst, *Treasurer*
Joyce Vehorn, *Sales Executive*
Paige Turner, *Mktg Coord*
▲ **EMP:** 20
SALES (est): 2.2MM Privately Held
WEB: www.studioeleven.net
SIC: 2759 Screen printing

(G-9942)
TOOLING TECH HOLDINGS LLC (HQ)
100 Enterprise Dr (45845)
PHONE..............................937 295-3672
Tony Seger, *CEO*
EMP: 4 EST: 2011
SALES (est): 34.6MM
SALES (corp-wide): 126.3MM Privately Held
SIC: 3089 Thermoformed finished plastic products
PA: Gennx360 Capital Partners, L.P.
590 Madison Ave Fl 27
New York NY 10022
212 257-6772

(G-9943)
TOOLING TECHNOLOGY LLC (PA)
Also Called: Tooling Tech Group
100 Enterprise Dr (45845)
P.O. Box 319 (45845-0319)
PHONE..............................937 295-3672
Fax: 937 295-3677
Anthony Seger, *CEO*
Scott Nestor, *Draft/Design*
Jeff Bradshaw, *Engineer*
Aaron Barhorst, *Sales Staff*
James Meyer, *Marketing Staff*
EMP: 80
SQ FT: 42,000

SALES (est): 33.5MM Privately Held
SIC: 3544 3363 3365 3322 Special dies, tools, jigs & fixtures; aluminum die-castings; aluminum foundries; malleable iron foundries

(G-9944)
WAYNE TRAIL TECHNOLOGIES INC
203 E Park St (45845-9303)
P.O. Box 257 (45845-0257)
PHONE..............................937 295-2120
Fax: 937 295-2642
David M Knapke, *President*
Craig Olberding, *Safety Mgr*
Brooke Broerman, *Purchasing*
Dave Ruhenkamp, *Purchasing*
Mike Bollheimer, *Engineer*
EMP: 100 EST: 1962
SQ FT: 82,000
SALES (est): 32.3MM
SALES (corp-wide): 2.2B Publicly Held
WEB: www.waynetrail.com
SIC: 3728 3599 7692 3544 Aircraft parts & equipment; tubing, flexible metallic; machine shop, jobbing & repair; welding repair; special dies, tools, jigs & fixtures
PA: Lincoln Electric Holdings, Inc.
22801 Saint Clair Ave
Cleveland OH 44117
216 481-8100

Fort Recovery
Mercer County

(G-9945)
BUCKEYE DESIGN & ENGR SVC LLC
2600 Wabash Rd (45846-9500)
P.O. Box 168 (45846-0168)
PHONE..............................419 375-4241
James Westgerdes, *Partner*
EMP: 6
SALES (est): 908K Privately Held
WEB: www.buckeyedesign.com
SIC: 3089 Injection molding of plastics

(G-9946)
COOPER FARMS INC (PA)
2321 State Route 49 (45846-9501)
P.O. Box 339 (45846-0339)
PHONE..............................419 375-4116
James R Cooper, *President*
Brian Donley, *General Ptnr*
Gary A Cooper, *Vice Pres*
Vic Cooper, *Project Mgr*
Dave Hoffhenes, *Purch Mgr*
EMP: 100 EST: 1940
SQ FT: 38,000
SALES (est): 32.6MM Privately Held
WEB: www.cooperfarms.com
SIC: 2048 5191 Poultry feeds; feed

(G-9947)
COOPER FARMS INC
Also Called: Cooper Farms East Mill
2351 Wabash Rd (45846-9586)
PHONE..............................419 375-4119
Bill Alig, *Manager*
EMP: 64
SALES (corp-wide): 32.6MM Privately Held
SIC: 2048 Poultry feeds
PA: Cooper Farms, Inc.
2321 State Route 49
Fort Recovery OH 45846
419 375-4116

(G-9948)
COOPER FARMS INC
3310 State Route 49 (45846-9507)
P.O. Box 339 (45846-0339)
PHONE..............................419 375-4619
Fax: 419 375-4037
Gary Cooper, *COO*
Tim Beckwith, *Accounting Mgr*
Dave Garman, *Accounting Mgr*
Dianne Cooper, *Sales Staff*
Tina Brackel, *Pub Rel Dir*
EMP: 17

▲ = Import ▼=Export
◆ =Import/Export

SALES (corp-wide): 32.6MM **Privately Held**
WEB: www.cooperfarms.com
SIC: 2048 5191 5153 Poultry feeds; feed; grains
PA: Cooper Farms, Inc.
2321 State Route 49
Fort Recovery OH 45846
419 375-4116

(G-9949)
FORT RECOVERY EQUIPMENT INC
1201 Industrial Dr (45846-8046)
P.O. Box 646 (45846-0646)
PHONE..................................419 375-1006
Fax: 419 375-4404
Cyril G Le Fevre, *President*
Helen Le Fevere, *Vice Pres*
Greg Le Fevre, *Vice Pres*
Chad Guggenbiller, *CFO*
◆ EMP: 50 EST: 1970
SQ FT: 30,000
SALES (est): 12.4MM **Privately Held**
WEB: www.fortrecoveryequipment.com
SIC: 5083 3523 Livestock equipment; barn, silo, poultry, dairy & livestock machinery

(G-9950)
FORT RECOVERY EQUITY INC (PA)
2351 Wabash Rd (45846-9586)
P.O. Box 307 (45846-0307)
PHONE..................................419 375-4119
Fax: 419 375-4838
William Glass, *CEO*
Arnie Sumner, *President*
EMP: 33
SQ FT: 15,000
SALES (est): 29.5MM **Privately Held**
SIC: 2015 5153 Egg processing; grain elevators

(G-9951)
FORT RECOVERY INDUSTRIES INC (PA)
2440 State Route 49 (45846-9501)
P.O. Box 638 (45846-0638)
PHONE..................................419 375-4121
Fax: 419 375-4194
Wesley M Jetter, *Ch of Bd*
Dean Jetter, *COO*
Barry Hounshell, *VP Mfg*
Jack Baughman, *Plant Mgr*
Tony Thees, *Site Mgr*
◆ EMP: 234 EST: 1945
SQ FT: 120,000
SALES (est): 47.7MM **Privately Held**
WEB: www.fortrecoveryindustries.com
SIC: 3432 3363 3429 Plumbing fixture fittings & trim; aluminum die-castings; manufactured hardware (general)

(G-9952)
FORT RECOVERY INDUSTRIES INC
1200 Industrial Park Dr (45846)
PHONE..................................419 375-3005
Randy Petit, *Manager*
EMP: 30
SALES (corp-wide): 47.7MM **Privately Held**
WEB: www.fortrecoveryindustries.com
SIC: 3432 Plumbing fixture fittings & trim
PA: Fort Recovery Industries, Inc.
2440 State Route 49
Fort Recovery OH 45846
419 375-4121

(G-9953)
GS WOOD & METAL COATING LLC
2096 Saint Joe Rd (45846-9711)
P.O. Box 593 (45846-0593)
PHONE..................................419 375-7708
Gary Steinbrunner, *Principal*
EMP: 4
SALES (est): 349.8K **Privately Held**
SIC: 3479 Painting, coating & hot dipping

(G-9954)
HOME IDEA CENTER INC
1100 Commerce St (45846-8003)
P.O. Box 649 (45846-0649)
PHONE..................................419 375-4951
Fax: 419 375-4032
Dan Schoen, *President*
Travis Laux, *Vice Pres*
Stacy Laux, *Controller*
EMP: 18
SQ FT: 12,000
SALES: 2MM **Privately Held**
SIC: 2599 Cabinets, factory

(G-9955)
J & M MANUFACTURING CO INC
284 Railroad St (45846)
P.O. Box 547 (45846-0547)
PHONE..................................419 375-2376
Fax: 419 375-2708
Michael Grieshop, *President*
Jeff Grieshop, *Vice Pres*
Eric Fullenkamp, *Engineer*
Joshua Gaerke, *Engineer*
Jeremy Post, *Engineer*
◆ EMP: 200 EST: 1950
SQ FT: 400,000
SALES: 62.7MM **Privately Held**
WEB: www.jm-inc.com
SIC: 3523 Farm machinery & equipment

(G-9956)
JR MANUFACTURING INC (PA)
900 Industrial Dr W (45846-8043)
P.O. Box 478 (45846-0478)
PHONE..................................419 375-8021
Fax: 419 375-0019
Jeff Roessner, *President*
Tomo Yamamoto, *President*
Greg Lefevre, *Vice Pres*
Dave Lamm, *Plant Mgr*
Lavern Grube, *Project Mgr*
▲ EMP: 130
SQ FT: 48,000
SALES (est): 29.6MM **Privately Held**
WEB: www.jrmanufacturing.net
SIC: 3315 3441 Steel wire & related products; fabricated structural metal

(G-9957)
JW MANUFACTURING
317 Watkins Rd (45846-9125)
PHONE..................................419 375-5536
Josh Wuebker, *Principal*
EMP: 3
SALES (est): 381.1K **Privately Held**
SIC: 3999 Manufacturing industries

(G-9958)
ROESSNER HOLDINGS INC
Also Called: Suspension Feeder
482 State Route 119 (45846-9563)
P.O. Box 369, Saint Henry (45883-0369)
PHONE..................................419 356-2123
Jeffrey D Roessner, *President*
Tim Roessner, *Manager*
EMP: 6
SQ FT: 5,000
SALES: 450K **Privately Held**
SIC: 3555 Printing trades machinery

(G-9959)
STEVE VORE WELDING AND STEEL
Also Called: Vores Steve Welding & Steel
3234 State Route 49 (45846-9507)
P.O. Box 37 (45846-0037)
PHONE..................................419 375-4087
Fax: 419 375-2466
Stephen Vore, *President*
Margaret Henderson, *Office Mgr*
EMP: 10
SQ FT: 5,400
SALES: 836.9K **Privately Held**
SIC: 3312 7692 1799 3444 Structural shapes & pilings, steel; welding repair; welding on site; sheet metalwork; fabricated plate work (boiler shop); fabricated structural metal

(G-9960)
SUSPENSION FEEDER CORPORATION
482 State Route 119 (45846-9563)
P.O. Box 369, Saint Henry (45883-0369)
PHONE..................................419 763-1377
Gregory G Baron, *President*
Roberta Baron, *Treasurer*
EMP: 10
SQ FT: 12,000
SALES: 1MM **Privately Held**
SIC: 3555 Printing trades machinery

(G-9961)
V H COOPER & CO INC (HQ)
Also Called: Cooper Foods
2321 State Route 49 (45846-9501)
P.O. Box 339 (45846-0339)
PHONE..................................419 375-4116
Fax: 419 375-4200
James R Cooper, *President*
Gary A Cooper, *COO*
Neil Diller, *CFO*
Anada E Cooper, *Treasurer*
Dale Siebeneck, *Director*
EMP: 150
SQ FT: 4,400
SALES (est): 124MM
SALES (corp-wide): 256.7MM **Privately Held**
WEB: www.cooperfoods.com
SIC: 0253 2015 2011 Turkeys & turkey eggs; chicken slaughtering & processing; pork products from pork slaughtered on site; hams & picnics from meat slaughtered on site
PA: Cooper Hatchery, Inc.
22348 Road 140
Oakwood OH 45873
419 594-3325

(G-9962)
WABASH RIVER CONSERVANCY
Also Called: Wabash River Conservancy Dst
14574 State Route 49 (45846-9104)
PHONE..................................419 375-2577
Walter Broeing, *President*
Don Rose, *Vice Pres*
John Portcamp, *Treasurer*
EMP: 4 EST: 1999
SALES: 27.8K **Privately Held**
SIC: 3823 Water quality monitoring & control systems

(G-9963)
WESTGERDES CABINETS
2664 Sawmill Rd (45846-9707)
PHONE..................................419 375-2113
Robert Westgerdes, *Owner*
EMP: 3
SQ FT: 8,200
SALES (est): 150K **Privately Held**
SIC: 2434 Wood kitchen cabinets

Fostoria
Seneca County

(G-9964)
ALPHA COATINGS INC
622 S Corporate Dr W (44830-9447)
PHONE..................................419 435-5111
Fax: 419 435-5441
Terence White, *President*
Sean Sterling, *Vice Pres*
Chad Hall, *QC Dir*
Donna Mason, *Accountant*
EMP: 115
SQ FT: 48,000
SALES (est): 16.3MM **Privately Held**
WEB: www.alpha-coatings.com
SIC: 3479 2891 Coating of metals & formed products; adhesives & sealants

(G-9965)
ALPHA COATINS INC
431 E North St (44830-2828)
P.O. Box 1006 (44830-1006)
PHONE..................................419 436-6144
Fax: 419 436-9709
Terry White, *Principal*
EMP: 4

SALES (est): 249.6K **Privately Held**
SIC: 3714 Motor vehicle parts & accessories

(G-9966)
ARCHER-DANIELS-MIDLAND COMPANY
Also Called: ADM
608 Findlay St (44830-1850)
PHONE..................................419 435-6633
Fax: 419 435-6472
Dale Anderbury, *Manager*
EMP: 45
SALES (corp-wide): 62.3B **Publicly Held**
WEB: www.admworld.com
SIC: 2048 2077 2075 Cereal-, grain-, & seed-based feeds; animal & marine fats & oils; soybean oil mills
PA: Archer-Daniels-Midland Company
77 W Wacker Dr Ste 4600
Chicago IL 60601
312 634-8100

(G-9967)
B & B PALLET CO
885 S State Route 587 (44830-9501)
PHONE..................................419 435-4530
Steve Bugner, *Owner*
EMP: 3
SALES (est): 204.5K **Privately Held**
SIC: 2448 Pallets, wood & wood with metal

(G-9968)
B&D TRUCK PARTS SLS & SVCS LLC
1498 Perrysburg Rd (44830-1351)
PHONE..................................419 701-7041
Bill J Bowling,
EMP: 6
SALES (est): 330K **Privately Held**
SIC: 8999 3751 Artists & artists' studios; motorcycle accessories

(G-9969)
DAILY FOSTORIA REVIEW CO
Also Called: Review Times, The
113 E Center St (44830-2905)
P.O. Box 947 (44830-0947)
PHONE..................................419 435-6641
Fax: 419 435-9073
Dean Kieffer, *Principal*
EMP: 200
SALES (est): 5.4MM **Privately Held**
SIC: 2711 Newspapers: publishing only, not printed on site

(G-9970)
FABRICATION SHOP INC
1395 Buckley St (44830-9459)
PHONE..................................419 435-7934
Fax: 419 435-4951
Bill Cronauer, *President*
Deborah Cronauer, *Vice Pres*
Al Hager, *Facilities Mgr*
EMP: 18
SQ FT: 15,000
SALES (est): 2.2MM **Privately Held**
SIC: 7692 3443 3544 Welding repair; fabricated plate work (boiler shop); special dies & tools

(G-9971)
FENIX LLC (HQ)
319 S Vine St (44830-1843)
P.O. Box 946 (44830-0946)
PHONE..................................419 739-3400
Steven Wray, *President*
Anand Bhagwat, *Plant Mgr*
Kevin G Shumaker, *CFO*
Douglas Stearns, *VP Sales*
Erma Kummerer, *Supervisor*
▲ EMP: 13
SQ FT: 141,000
SALES (est): 8.6MM
SALES (corp-wide): 12MM **Privately Held**
WEB: www.Fenixllc.com
SIC: 3315 Wire products, ferrous/iron: made in wiredrawing plants
PA: The Seneca Wire Group Inc
319 S Vine St
Fostoria OH 44830
419 435-9261

GEOGRAPHIC

(G-9972)
FILMTEC INC
1120 Sandusky St (44830-2761)
PHONE....................................419 435-1819
Fax: 419 435-9215
John P Hollingsworth, *President*
Jo Hollingsworth, *Vice Pres*
Paul Taylor, *Purchasing*
EMP: 20
SQ FT: 44,000
SALES (est): 3.7MM **Privately Held**
WEB: www.filmtecinc.com
SIC: 3549 Wiredrawing & fabricating machinery & equipment, ex. die

(G-9973)
FOSTORIA BSHNGS INSLATORS CORP
602 S Corporate Dr W D (44830-9456)
P.O. Box 1064 (44830-1064)
PHONE....................................419 435-7514
Philip C John, *President*
▲ EMP: 6
SALES (est): 750K **Privately Held**
SIC: 3612 Transformers, except electric

(G-9974)
FOSTORIA BUSHINGS INC
Also Called: FB Ins
602 S Corporate Dr W (44830-9456)
P.O. Box 1064 (44830-1064)
PHONE....................................419 435-7514
Fax: 419 435-7580
Philip C John, *President*
▲ EMP: 9
SALES (est): 1.2MM **Privately Held**
SIC: 3612 Transformers, except electric

(G-9975)
FOSTORIA ETHANOL LLC
Also Called: Poet Brfining- Fostoria 23200
2111 Sandusky St (44830-2790)
PHONE....................................419 436-0954
Fax: 419 436-0986
Art Thomas, *General Mgr*
Jeff Broin, *Principal*
Ty Oliver, *Manager*
EMP: 40
SALES (est): 15.7MM
SALES (corp-wide): 4.3B **Privately Held**
SIC: 2869 Ethyl alcohol, ethanol
PA: Poet, Llc
4615 N Lewis Ave
Sioux Falls SD 57104
605 965-2200

(G-9976)
FOSTORIA FOCUS INC
112 N Main St (44830-2223)
P.O. Box 1158 (44830-1158)
PHONE....................................419 435-6397
Fax: 419 435-0101
Donald P Miller, *President*
Jodi Walters, *Accounts Exec*
John Irwin, *Director*
Charles Knight, *Director*
EMP: 11
SALES (est): 472.2K **Privately Held**
WEB: www.fostoriafocus.com
SIC: 2711 Newspapers

(G-9977)
FOSTORIA MACHINE PRODUCTS
425 S Union St (44830-2342)
P.O. Box 883 (44830-0883)
PHONE....................................419 435-4262
Fax: 419 435-5022
Bill Derck, *Owner*
EMP: 7 EST: 1954
SQ FT: 3,000
SALES (est): 673.1K **Privately Held**
SIC: 3544 3451 Special dies & tools; screw machine products

(G-9978)
FOSTORIA MONUMENT CO (PA)
Also Called: Tri County Marble & Granite
701 Van Buren St (44830-1538)
PHONE....................................419 435-0373
Fax: 419 435-1151
Gregory A Smith, *President*
Saundra Smith, *Admin Sec*
EMP: 3
SQ FT: 2,000
SALES (est): 941K **Privately Held**
SIC: 3281 5099 Monument or burial stone, cut & shaped; signs, except electric

(G-9979)
FRAM GROUP OPERATIONS LLC
Honeywell
1600 N Union St (44830-1958)
P.O. Box 880 (44830-0880)
PHONE....................................419 436-5827
Eric Ashleman, *Opers Mgr*
Jeff Leiter, *Buyer*
Gary Zulauf, *Research*
David Smith, *Engineer*
Joe Hensey, *Human Res Mgr*
EMP: 900 **Privately Held**
WEB: www.honeywell.com
SIC: 3714 3264 Motor vehicle parts & accessories; porcelain electrical supplies
HQ: Fram Group Operations Llc
1900 W Field Ct
Lake Forest IL 60045

(G-9980)
INNOVATION PLASTICS LLC
1150 State St (44830-3007)
PHONE....................................513 818-1771
Trinity Elam,
Chad Elam,
EMP: 20
SALES (est): 1MM **Privately Held**
SIC: 3089 4953 Casting of plastic; recycling, waste materials

(G-9981)
LARSON MANUFACTURING CO INC
616 N Corporate Dr W (44830-9400)
PHONE....................................419 435-9400
Fax: 419 435-0273
Roger Haseley, *Manager*
EMP: 11
SALES (corp-wide): 166.2MM **Privately Held**
WEB: www.larsondoors.com
SIC: 3442 5031 Storm doors or windows, metal; lumber, plywood & millwork
HQ: Larson Manufacturing Company, Inc.
2333 Eastbrook Dr
Brookings SD 57006
605 692-6115

(G-9982)
LINDE LLC
405 E Zeller Rd (44830-3243)
PHONE....................................419 435-8153
Simon Douglas, *Branch Mgr*
EMP: 50
SALES (corp-wide): 17.9B **Privately Held**
SIC: 2813 Industrial gases
HQ: Linde Llc
200 Somerset Corporate Bl
Bridgewater NJ 08807
908 464-8100

(G-9983)
MACHINE TOOL & FAB CORP
1401 Sandusky St (44830-2774)
PHONE....................................419 435-7676
Dick Kiser, *President*
Jim W Bodart, *Engineer*
EMP: 19
SQ FT: 20,400
SALES (est): 3.4MM **Privately Held**
WEB: www.machinetoolandfab.com
SIC: 3599 3441 3442 Custom machinery; fabricated structural metal; hangar doors, metal

(G-9984)
MACHINE TOOL DESIGN & FAB LLC
1401 Sandusky St (44830-2774)
PHONE....................................419 435-7676
Christopher Eastman, *Mng Member*
EMP: 19
SALES (est): 727.6K
SALES (corp-wide): 1.1MM **Privately Held**
SIC: 3544 7699 Special dies, tools, jigs & fixtures; metal reshaping & replating services
PA: Eastman Holding Llc
1185 W Parkway Blvd
Aurora OH 44202
419 435-7676

(G-9985)
MENNEL MILLING COMPANY
319 S Vine St (44830-1843)
P.O. Box 806 (44830-0806)
PHONE....................................419 436-5130
Donald J Mennel, *Branch Mgr*
Scott Flick, *Manager*
EMP: 6
SALES (corp-wide): 69.4MM **Privately Held**
WEB: www.troyelevator.com
SIC: 2041 Flour & other grain mill products
PA: The Mennel Milling Company
320 Findlay St
Fostoria OH 44830
419 435-8151

(G-9986)
NATIONAL ELEC CARBN PDTS INC
200 N Town St (44830-2835)
PHONE....................................419 435-8182
Fax: 419 436-5990
Rick J Clark, *VP Prdtn*
Jarred Jacoby, *Facilities Mgr*
Dale Bracy, *Maint Spvr*
Henry C Robinson, *Engineer*
Greg Smith, *Finance Mgr*
EMP: 100
SALES (corp-wide): 1.3B **Privately Held**
WEB: www.nationalspecialties.com
SIC: 3624 Carbon & graphite products
HQ: National Electrical Carbon Products, Inc.
251 Forrester Dr
Greenville SC 29607
864 458-7777

(G-9987)
NEON PAINTBRUSH
461 W Lytle St Lot 153 (44830-3412)
PHONE....................................419 436-1202
Joseph McCartney, *Administration*
EMP: 3
SALES (est): 155.6K **Privately Held**
SIC: 2813 Neon

(G-9988)
NIPPON STL SMKIN CRNKSHAFT LLC
Also Called: Nsi Crankshaft
1815 Sandusky St (44830-2754)
PHONE....................................419 435-0411
Makoto Tsuruhara, *President*
Tim Hasegawa, *Exec VP*
Jim Siebenaller, *Facilities Mgr*
Frank Provino III, *Production*
Amy Craun, *Purch Mgr*
EMP: 13
SQ FT: 225,000
SALES (est): 3.9MM
SALES (corp-wide): 41.9B **Privately Held**
SIC: 3599 3714 Crankshafts & camshafts, machining; crankshaft assemblies, motor vehicle
HQ: Nippon Steel & Sumitomo Metal U.S.A., Inc.
1251 Ave Of The Ave Fl 23
New York NY 10020
212 486-7150

(G-9989)
NONNIES GOODIES LLC
3352 N County Road 39 (44830-9540)
PHONE....................................419 435-4685
Linda Otte, *Principal*
EMP: 6 EST: 2010
SALES (est): 360.1K **Privately Held**
SIC: 2052 Cookies

(G-9990)
NORTON MANUFACTURING CO INC
455 W 4th St (44830-1864)
P.O. Box 1127 (44830-1127)
PHONE....................................419 435-0411
Fax: 419 435-3881
Theodore Lorensen, *Manager*
EMP: 12
SALES (est): 1.1MM **Privately Held**
SIC: 3999 Manufacturing industries

(G-9991)
ROPPE CORPORATION
1602 N Union St (44830-1958)
PHONE....................................419 435-8546
Brent Fike, *General Mgr*
Donald P Miller, *Principal*
Chip Deringer, *Vice Pres*
Judy Miller, *Vice Pres*
Doug Michelsen, *VP Opers*
◆ EMP: 260
SALES (est): 72.9MM
SALES (corp-wide): 146.8MM **Privately Held**
SIC: 3069 Flooring, rubber: tile or sheet
PA: Roppe Holding Company
1602 N Union St
Fostoria OH 44830
419 435-8546

(G-9992)
ROPPE HOLDING COMPANY
J Miller and Co
106 N Main St (44830-2223)
PHONE....................................419 435-6601
Fax: 419 435-2217
Jessica Sheridan, *Manager*
EMP: 8
SALES (corp-wide): 146.8MM **Privately Held**
WEB: www.roppe.com
SIC: 3089 3069 Extruded finished plastic products; rubber floor coverings, mats & wallcoverings; wallcoverings, rubber; tile, rubber; stair treads, rubber
PA: Roppe Holding Company
1602 N Union St
Fostoria OH 44830
419 435-8546

(G-9993)
SANDY CREEK MINING CO INC
522 S Poplar St (44830-3054)
P.O. Box 88 (44830-0088)
PHONE....................................419 435-5891
Fax: 419 435-6690
Patrick Woodruff, *President*
Jason Woodruff, *General Mgr*
▲ EMP: 4 EST: 1996
SALES (est): 535.6K **Privately Held**
WEB: www.sandycreekmining.com
SIC: 1481 Mine exploration, nonmetallic minerals

(G-9994)
SCHREINER CSTM STAIRS & MLLWK
1415 Sandusky St (44830-2774)
P.O. Box 750 (44830-0750)
PHONE....................................419 435-8935
Melvin Schreiner, *President*
Shirley Schreiner, *Corp Secy*
Greg Schreiner, *Vice Pres*
EMP: 5
SQ FT: 5,000
SALES (est): 640.2K **Privately Held**
SIC: 2431 Millwork

(G-9995)
SENECA MILLWORK INC
300 Court Pl (44830-2453)
P.O. Box 429 (44830-0429)
PHONE....................................419 435-6671
Fax: 419 435-5688
Donald Miller, *President*
Christopher Iannantuono, *General Mgr*
Mark J Baker, *Principal*
Judy R Miller, *Principal*
Angela K Gillett, *Vice Pres*
EMP: 50 EST: 1873
SQ FT: 120,000
SALES (est): 7.1MM **Privately Held**
WEB: www.senecamillwork.com
SIC: 2431 Moldings, wood: unfinished & prefinished; floor baseboards, wood

(G-9996)
SENECA WIRE GROUP INC (PA)
319 S Vine St (44830-1843)
P.O. Box 946 (44830-0946)
PHONE....................................419 435-9261
Steven Wray, *President*
Kevin G Shumaker, *CFO*
Douglas Stearns, *VP Sales*
EMP: 3

SALES (est): 12MM **Privately Held**
SIC: 3315 Wire products, ferrous/iron: made in wiredrawing plants

(G-9997)
TIME IS MONEY
1280 North Dr (44830-9780)
PHONE...............................419 701-6098
EMP: 3 EST: 1999
SALES (est): 230K **Privately Held**
SIC: 3559 7389 Mfg Misc Industry Machinery

Frankfort
Ross County

(G-9998)
CONVEYOR METAL WORKS INC
2717 Bush Mill Rd (45628-9791)
PHONE...............................740 477-8700
Fax: 740 477-6940
Scott P Kadish, *President*
Christy Wolfe, *Vice Pres*
Tom Furne, *Manager*
EMP: 20 EST: 2000
SQ FT: 30,000
SALES (est): 5.4MM **Privately Held**
WEB: www.conveyormetalworks.com
SIC: 3535 Conveyors & conveying equipment

(G-9999)
JAY TACKETT
Also Called: T R C
387 Musselman Station Rd (45628-9761)
PHONE...............................740 779-1715
Jay Takett, *Owner*
Preston Tackett, *Vice Pres*
EMP: 5
SQ FT: 4,000
SALES: 200K **Privately Held**
SIC: 3955 5112 3861 2899 Print cartridges for laser & other computer printers; inked ribbons; photographic equipment & supplies; chemical preparations

(G-10000)
LIGHTLE ENTERPRISES OHIO LLC (PA)
22 E Springfield St (45628-8013)
P.O. Box 329 (45628-0329)
PHONE...............................740 998-5363
Zachary Winegar, *Sales Mgr*
David Lightle,
Dixie Lightle,
EMP: 4
SALES (est): 1MM **Privately Held**
SIC: 3669 7359 5099 Pedestrian traffic control equipment; work zone traffic equipment (flags, cones, barrels, etc.); reflective road markers

(G-10001)
LIGHTLE ENTERPRISES OHIO LLC
23 E Walnut St (45628)
P.O. Box 329 (45628-0329)
PHONE...............................740 998-5363
Dixie Lightle,
David Lightle,
EMP: 4
SQ FT: 2,880
SALES (corp-wide): 1MM **Privately Held**
SIC: 3669 5099 Pedestrian traffic control equipment; reflective road markers
PA: Lightle Enterprises Of Ohio, Llc
22 E Springfield St
Frankfort OH 45628
740 998-5363

(G-10002)
ROCAL INC (PA)
3186 County Road 550 (45628-9503)
PHONE...............................740 998-2122
Fax: 740 998-2073
Robert Lightle, *President*
Tom Baldwin, *Plant Mgr*
Andrew Blazar, *Plant Mgr*
Amy Kerns, *Purch Mgr*
John Hirsch, *Engineer*
▲ EMP: 90
SQ FT: 200,000

SALES (est): 23.4MM **Privately Held**
SIC: 3993 Signs, not made in custom sign painting shops

Franklin
Warren County

(G-10003)
119C LANDIS DISPLAY CO
Also Called: C L D
346 Beam Dr (45005-2008)
PHONE...............................937 307-9499
Charles H Landis Jr, *Owner*
Charlie Landis, *Owner*
EMP: 5
SALES: 178.6K **Privately Held**
SIC: 2541 Store & office display cases & fixtures

(G-10004)
3-D TECHNICAL SERVICES INC
Also Called: 3-Dmed
255 Industrial Dr (45005-4429)
PHONE...............................937 746-2901
Fax: 513 746-5071
Robert Aumann, *President*
Bill Wurzelbacher, *Opers Mgr*
Ashley Albanese, *Sales Staff*
Becky Larson, *Sales Staff*
Jennifer Theriault, *Info Tech Mgr*
EMP: 25
SQ FT: 15,000
SALES (est): 3.4MM **Privately Held**
WEB: www.3-dtechnicalservices.com
SIC: 7389 2542 3999 Building scale models; design, commercial & industrial; partitions & fixtures, except wood; models, general, except toy

(G-10005)
ADVANCED WELDING CO
901 N Main St (45005-1650)
PHONE...............................937 746-6800
Fax: 937 746-4390
Tony Ling, *Owner*
EMP: 20
SQ FT: 8,000
SALES: 500K **Privately Held**
SIC: 3443 3599 7692 3444 Fabricated plate work (boiler shop); machine & other job shop work; welding repair; sheet metalwork

(G-10006)
AM GENERAL LLC
2000 Watkins Glen Dr (45005-2392)
PHONE...............................937 704-0160
Alasdair Young, *Chief Engr*
Jose Ochoa, *Engineer*
Charles M Hall, *Branch Mgr*
EMP: 4 **Privately Held**
SIC: 3711 3714 Military motor vehicle assembly; motor vehicle parts & accessories
HQ: Am General Llc
105 N Niles Ave
South Bend IN 46617
574 237-6222

(G-10007)
AMPLE INDUSTRIES INC
4000 Commerce Center Dr (45005-1897)
PHONE...............................937 746-9700
Fax: 513 746-2234
Gregory K Pratt, *President*
William Akers Sr, *Vice Pres*
Vic Crainish, *Controller*
Ty Gardner, *Manager*
Stewart Whitlow, *Manager*
EMP: 210
SQ FT: 108,000
SALES (est): 31MM
SALES (corp-wide): 2.9B **Privately Held**
WEB: www.ampleindustries.com
SIC: 2657 Paperboard backs for blister or skin packages
PA: Huhtamaki Oyj
Miestentie 9
Espoo 02100
106 867-000

(G-10008)
ATLAS ROOFING CORPORATION
Gypsum & Roofing Div
675 Oxford Rd (45005-3678)
PHONE...............................937 746-9941
Fax: 937 746-1528
Scott Harkinson, *COO*
Andy McLaughlin, *VP Mfg*
Kathy Cahall, *QC Mgr*
Rick Bielecki, *Plant Engr*
Robert Cipriano, *VP Human Res*
EMP: 170
SALES (corp-wide): 857.2MM **Privately Held**
WEB: www.atlasroofing.com
SIC: 3086 2951 2952 Insulation or cushioning material, foamed plastic; asphalt paving mixtures & blocks; asphalt felts & coatings
HQ: Atlas Roofing Corporation
802 Highway 19 N Ste 190
Meridian MS 39307
601 484-8900

(G-10009)
BOND MACHINE COMPANY INC
921 N Main St (45005-1650)
PHONE...............................937 746-4941
Fax: 937 746-1352
David Bond, *President*
Steve Bond, *Corp Secy*
John Bond Jr, *Vice Pres*
Gary Estes, *Director*
Tom Bond, *Admin Sec*
EMP: 14 EST: 1968
SQ FT: 12,000
SALES: 2.1MM **Privately Held**
WEB: www.bondmachineco.com
SIC: 3599 Machine shop, jobbing & repair

(G-10010)
BORAL BRICKS INC
Also Called: BORAL BRICKS INC.
250 Industrial Dr (45005-4430)
PHONE...............................937 294-1548
Fax: 937 746-7167
Troy Vaughn, *Manager*
EMP: 7
SALES (corp-wide): 3.1B **Privately Held**
WEB: www.boralbricks.com
SIC: 3251 Structural brick & blocks
HQ: Boral Bricks Llc
200 Mansell Ct E Ste 305
Roswell GA 30076
770 645-4500

(G-10011)
CAST PLUS INC
415 Oxford Rd (45005-3639)
PHONE...............................937 743-7278
Fax: 937 743-5741
Maurice R Meeker, *President*
Richard Devaney, *Vice Pres*
Scott Meeker, *Sales Executive*
Brad Cox, *Executive*
EMP: 35
SQ FT: 40,000
SALES (est): 6MM **Privately Held**
WEB: www.castplus.com
SIC: 3479 Coating of metals & formed products

(G-10012)
CHENEY PULP AND PAPER COMPANY
1000 Anderson St (45005-2571)
P.O. Box 215 (45005-0215)
PHONE...............................937 746-9991
Fax: 937 746-3884
Mark Snyder, *President*
Donald A Davies, *Principal*
Marry Chase, *Manager*
Tony Priest, *Maintence Staff*
▲ EMP: 30 EST: 1924
SQ FT: 30,000
SALES (est): 9.4MM **Privately Held**
WEB: www.cheneypulp.com
SIC: 2611 Pulp made from rags, bagassse, hemp or other fiber base

(G-10013)
CONTAINER GRAPHICS CORP
1 Miller St (45005-4455)
PHONE...............................937 746-5666

Fax: 937 746-4186
Steve Woods, *Branch Mgr*
EMP: 21
SALES (corp-wide): 75.1MM **Privately Held**
WEB: www.containergraphics.com
SIC: 3544 Dies, steel rule
PA: Container Graphics Corp.
114 Ednbrgh S Dr Ste 104
Cary NC 27511
919 481-4200

(G-10014)
COUNTER- ADVICE INC
7002 State Route 123 (45005-2358)
PHONE...............................937 291-1600
Fax: 937 291-3502
Brian Donley, *President*
Stephanie Gottschling, *Office Mgr*
EMP: 13
SQ FT: 13,000
SALES: 2.1MM **Privately Held**
WEB: www.counteradvice.com
SIC: 2541 Counter & sink tops

(G-10015)
COUNTRY TIN
228 S Main St (45005-2226)
PHONE...............................937 746-7229
EMP: 3 EST: 2004
SALES (est): 160K **Privately Held**
SIC: 3645 Mfg Residential Lighting Fixtures

(G-10016)
COX MEDIA GROUP OHIO INC
5000 Commerce Center Dr (45005-7200)
PHONE...............................937 743-6700
Barbara Parker, *Branch Mgr*
Julie Campbell, *Admin Mgr*
EMP: 3
SALES (corp-wide): 32.4B **Privately Held**
WEB: www.daytondailynews.com
SIC: 2711 Newspapers, publishing & printing
HQ: Cox Media Group Ohio, Inc.
1611 S Main St
Dayton OH 45409
937 225-2000

(G-10017)
DAYTON DAILEY NEWS
5000 Commerce Center Dr (45005-7200)
PHONE...............................937 743-2387
Joe Mc Kinnon, *Principal*
Barbara Parker, *Purchasing*
Julie Campbell, *Admin Mgr*
Stan Richmond, *Executive*
EMP: 12
SALES (est): 1.6MM **Privately Held**
SIC: 2711 Newspapers, publishing & printing

(G-10018)
DCS TECHNOLOGIES CORPORATION (PA)
6501 State Route 123 (45005-4519)
PHONE...............................937 743-4060
Fax: 513 743-4056
Phil Denlinger, *President*
Ned M Denlinger, *Vice Pres*
Paul Daniels, *Accounts Mgr*
Doug Roemer, *Accounts Mgr*
Paul Shaffer, *Accounts Mgr*
EMP: 33
SQ FT: 15,000
SALES (est): 3.8MM **Privately Held**
WEB: www.dcs-tech.com
SIC: 2759 Laser printing

(G-10019)
F & G TOOL AND DIE CO
130 Industrial Dr (45005-4428)
PHONE...............................937 746-3658
Dick Smith, *Branch Mgr*
EMP: 22
SALES (corp-wide): 10.7MM **Privately Held**
SIC: 3542 3469 Machine tools, metal forming type; metal stampings
PA: F & G Tool And Die Co.
3024 Dryden Rd
Moraine OH 45439
937 294-1405

GEOGRAPHIC

(G-10020)
F P C PRINTING INC
Also Called: Franklin's Printing
119 Art Ave (45005-1601)
PHONE.............................937 743-8136
Michael Patrick, *President*
Kathleen Patrick, *Corp Secy*
Chad Patrick, *Vice Pres*
EMP: 6 EST: 1928
SQ FT: 10,000
SALES (est): 739.2K **Privately Held**
SIC: 2752 Commercial printing, litho-
graphic

(G-10021)
FAURECIA EXHAUST SYSTEMS INC
Also Called: Franklin Mfg Div
2301 Commerce Center Dr (45005-1896)
PHONE.............................937 743-0551
Fax: 937 743-0393
Carlos Pires, *Plant Mgr*
Keith Ross, *Production*
Julie Price, *Purchasing*
Parker Sykes, *Branch Mgr*
Mark Dishun, *Manager*
EMP: 400
SALES (corp-wide): 271.8MM **Privately Held**
WEB: www.franklin.faurecia.com
SIC: 3714 3053 Exhaust systems & parts,
motor vehicle; manifolds, motor vehicle;
gaskets, packing & sealing devices
HQ: Faurecia Exhaust Systems, Llc
543 Matzinger Rd
Toledo OH 43612
419 727-5000

(G-10022)
FERCO TECH LLC
291 Conover Dr (45005-1944)
P.O. Box 607 (45005-0607)
PHONE.............................937 746-6696
Fax: 937 746-7177
Bryan Perkins, *President*
Earl Larkin, *Co-CEO*
Vincent Bebko, *Plant Mgr*
Randy Harris, *Engineer*
Jim Clemons, *CFO*
EMP: 120
SQ FT: 30,000
SALES (est): 25.3MM
SALES (corp-wide): 121.4MM **Privately Held**
SIC: 3728 Aircraft parts & equipment
PA: Novaria Group, L.L.C.
6300 Ridglea Pl Ste 800
Fort Worth TX 76116
817 381-3810

(G-10023)
FRANKLIN CABINET COMPANY INC
2500 Commerce Center Dr (45005-1816)
PHONE.............................937 743-9606
Fax: 937 743-8148
Mark Duncan, *President*
Fred Alcorn, *Manager*
EMP: 29
SQ FT: 50,000
SALES (est): 4.7MM **Privately Held**
SIC: 3083 2541 2599 2531 Plastic fin-
ished products, laminated; cabinets, lock-
ers & shelving; bar, restaurant & cafeteria
furniture; public building & related furni-
ture; upholstered household furniture;
wood kitchen cabinets

(G-10024)
GENERAL ENGINE PRODUCTS LLC
2000 Watkins Glen Dr (45005-2392)
P.O. Box 488 (45005-0488)
PHONE.............................937 704-0160
Fax: 513 704-1874
Charles M Hall, *President*
Daniel J Dell'orto, *Vice Pres*
Brian Culp, *Controller*
Jeffery Adams, *Director*
Robin Wellman, *Administration*
▲ EMP: 80
SALES (est): 15.8MM **Privately Held**
WEB: www.amgmil.com
SIC: 3519 Diesel engine rebuilding

HQ: Am General Llc
105 N Niles Ave
South Bend IN 46617
574 237-6222

(G-10025)
GREEN POINT METALS INC (PA)
Also Called: GPM
301 Shotwell Dr (45005-4659)
PHONE.............................937 743-4075
Fax: 937 743-4098
Brian D Williamson, *CEO*
Doug Everhart, *President*
Travis Hearn, *Vice Pres*
Matt Lankheit, *Maint Spvr*
Joe Routson, *Purch Mgr*
EMP: 35
SQ FT: 150,000
SALES (est): 8.5MM **Privately Held**
WEB: www.greenpointmetals.com
SIC: 3441 Fabricated structural metal

(G-10026)
H & W SCREW PRODUCTS INC
335 Industrial Dr (45005-4431)
PHONE.............................937 866-2577
Fax: 937 746-0843
Robert E Wray, *President*
Wendy Wray, *Treasurer*
Richard Carlisle, *Admin Sec*
EMP: 13
SQ FT: 10,000
SALES (est): 1MM **Privately Held**
SIC: 3451 Screw machine products

(G-10027)
HOMECARE MATTRESS INC
303 Conover Dr (45005-1957)
PHONE.............................937 746-2556
Debbie Lipps, *President*
P Scott Lipps, *Vice Pres*
Scott Lipps, *Manager*
EMP: 15
SQ FT: 6,000
SALES (est): 3.3MM **Privately Held**
SIC: 3448 2515 5047 5712 Ramps: pre-
fabricated metal; mattresses & founda-
tions; medical & hospital equipment;
mattresses

(G-10028)
HUHTAMAKI INC
4000 Commerce Center Dr (45005-1897)
PHONE.............................937 746-9700
Bob Fairchild, *President*
Paul Huckins, *Vice Pres*
Hubert Hausoul, *Opers Staff*
Deborah Nix, *Auditing Mgr*
Chris Berta, *Manager*
EMP: 320
SALES (corp-wide): 2.9B **Privately Held**
SIC: 2656 3565 Sanitary food containers;
ice cream containers: made from pur-
chased material; labeling machines, in-
dustrial
HQ: Huhtamaki, Inc.
9201 Packaging Dr
De Soto KS 66018
913 583-3025

(G-10029)
IKO PRODUCTION INC
1200 S Main St (45005-2781)
PHONE.............................937 746-4561
Fax: 513 746-5283
Wayne Johnson, *Sales Mgr*
David Foulkes, *Branch Mgr*
EMP: 47
SQ FT: 100,000
SALES (corp-wide): 40.8MM **Privately Held**
SIC: 2952 3083 Roofing felts, cements or
coatings; laminated plastics plate & sheet
HQ: Iko Production, Inc.
120 Hay Rd
Wilmington DE 19809
302 764-3100

(G-10030)
KEMPER AUTOMOTIVE
1380 E 2nd St (45005-1850)
P.O. Box 188 (45005-0188)
PHONE.............................800 783-8004
Mike Kemper, *Partner*
Ron Kemper, *Partner*
EMP: 6

SQ FT: 11,000
SALES (est): 683.3K **Privately Held**
WEB: www.kemperautomotive.com
SIC: 2396 5531 Automotive & apparel
trimmings; automotive accessories

(G-10031)
KNOX MACHINERY INC
375 Industrial Dr (45005-4431)
PHONE.............................937 743-2641
Toll Free:.............................877 -
Fax: 937 743-2642
Gregory J Knox, *President*
Connie Leplant, *Manager*
EMP: 15
SQ FT: 10,000
SALES (est): 3.1MM **Privately Held**
WEB: www.knoxmachinery.com
SIC: 3545 Cutting tools for machine tools

(G-10032)
LEGACY FINISHING INC
415 Oxford Rd (45005-3639)
P.O. Box 249 (45005-0249)
PHONE.............................937 743-7278
Tom Custer, *Principal*
Kevin Dickerson, *Production*
Dick Meeker, *Benefits Mgr*
Christine Fischer, *Office Mgr*
Scott Meeker, *Manager*
EMP: 9
SALES (est): 1.6MM **Privately Held**
SIC: 3399 Powder, metal

(G-10033)
LYNX CHEMICAL
370 Industrial Dr (45005-4432)
PHONE.............................513 856-9161
William Schmidt,
EMP: 4
SALES (corp-wide): 3.4MM **Privately Held**
SIC: 2899 Chemical supplies for foundries
PA: Lynx Chemical
2184 Schlichter Dr
Hamilton OH 45015
317 774-1333

(G-10034)
MARBLE ARCH PRODUCTS INC
263 Industrial Dr (45005-4429)
PHONE.............................937 746-8388
Fax: 937 743-5634
Mike Rundle, *President*
Keenan Beauchamp, *Treasurer*
EMP: 14
SQ FT: 15,000
SALES (est): 2.9MM **Privately Held**
WEB: www.marblearchproducts.com
SIC: 3088 Plastics plumbing fixtures

(G-10035)
MCS MIDWEST LLC (PA)
3876 Hendrickson Rd (45005-9726)
PHONE.............................513 217-0805
Stanley J Streeter,
EMP: 18
SALES (est): 4.8MM **Privately Held**
SIC: 3089 7699 Garbage containers, plas-
tic; agricultural equipment repair services

(G-10036)
MIAMI VALLEY PAPER LLC
Also Called: Miami Wabash
413 Oxford Rd (45005-3639)
P.O. Box 5651, Hartford CT (06102-5651)
PHONE.............................937 746-6451
Howard Harper, *Vice Pres*
Rita Sortman, *Purchasing*
Bill Naser, *Manager*
EMP: 19
SALES (corp-wide): 102.4MM **Privately Held**
SIC: 2631 2672 Paperboard mills; coated
& laminated paper
HQ: Miami Valley Paper Llc
108 Main St Ste 3
Norwalk CT 06851
203 847-8500

(G-10037)
MIRACLE WELDING INC
Also Called: Miracle Air
141 Industrial Dr Ste 200 (45005-4427)
PHONE.............................513 746-9977
Fax: 513 746-9398

David Miracle, *President*
Faun Miracle, *Vice Pres*
EMP: 6 EST: 1978
SQ FT: 12,000
SALES (est): 1MM **Privately Held**
WEB: www.miraclewelding.com
SIC: 3599 3441 Machine & other job shop
work; fabricated structural metal

(G-10038)
NATION COATING SYSTEMS INC
501 Shotwell Dr (45005-4663)
PHONE.............................937 746-7632
Toll Free:.............................888 -
Fax: 937 746-7658
Larry F Grimenstein, *President*
Lois Grimenstein, *Corp Secy*
Jim Drumm, *Vice Pres*
Mark Simpson, *Plant Mgr*
EMP: 8
SALES (est): 1.1MM **Privately Held**
WEB: www.nationcoatingsystems.com
SIC: 3479 Painting, coating & hot dipping

(G-10039)
NC WORKS INC
3500 Commerce Center Dr (45005-7202)
PHONE.............................937 514-7781
Simon Chen, *President*
Mikio Nishizu, *Principal*
Travis Couch, *Controller*
▲ EMP: 25 EST: 2010
SALES (est): 4.2MM **Privately Held**
SIC: 2299 Automotive felts; carpet cush-
ions, felt
PA: Fehrer Enterprise Corporation.
1, Miao-Pu Lane, Shau Shin Lee,
Tainan City
658 362-16

(G-10040)
NIKTEC LLC
127 Industrial Dr (45005-4427)
PHONE.............................513 282-3747
Nicholas Campbell,
▼ EMP: 7
SALES (est): 550.8K **Privately Held**
SIC: 7629 3679 Electrical repair shops;
electronic circuits

(G-10041)
NOVOLEX HOLDINGS INC
Also Called: Burrows Paper Corroc Div
2000 Commerce Center Dr (45005-1477)
PHONE.............................937 746-1933
Fax: 937 746-8515
Michael Ward, *Purchasing*
Jef Hall, *Manager*
EMP: 337
SQ FT: 106,000
SALES (corp-wide): 2.2B **Publicly Held**
WEB: www.burrowspaper.com
SIC: 2621 2656 2653 Tissue paper; sani-
tary food containers; boxes, corrugated:
made from purchased materials
HQ: Novolex Holdings, Inc.
101 E Carolina Ave
Hartsville SC 29550
843 857-4800

(G-10042)
OLIVAMED CORPORATION
401 Shotwell Dr (45005-4660)
PHONE.............................937 401-0821
Bernard Speeckaert, *President*
Vayan Peck, *General Mgr*
Franco Grasso, *Principal*
Joseph Hopple, *Administration*
◆ EMP: 9
SQ FT: 2,000
SALES (est): 1.5MM **Privately Held**
SIC: 2079 Olive oil

(G-10043)
P R U INDUSTRIES INC
8401 Claude Thomas Rd (45005-1497)
PHONE.............................937 746-8702
James Riling, *President*
Marcie Marks, *Vice Pres*
Mark See, *Vice Pres*
EMP: 10
SALES: 4MM
SALES (corp-wide): 5.4MM **Privately Held**
SIC: 2448 Wood pallets & skids

▲ = Import ▼=Export
◆ =Import/Export

PA: Industrial Holdings Group, Inc
7755 Paragon Rd Ste 104
Dayton OH 45459
937 434-8100

(G-10044)
PFIZER INC
160 Industrial Dr (45005-4428)
PHONE...................................937 746-3603
Nancy Steele, *Vice Pres*
Fred Haller, *Manager*
Toni Brothers, *Director*
Ron Groh, *Director*
EMP: 146
SALES (corp-wide): 52.8B **Publicly Held**
WEB: www.pfizer.com
SIC: 2834 2833 2844 2099 Pharmaceutical preparations; drugs acting on the cardiovascular system, except diagnostic; drugs affecting parasitic & infective diseases; veterinary pharmaceutical preparations; antibiotics; hair preparations, including shampoos; toilet preparations; oral preparations; cake fillings, except fruit
PA: Pfizer Inc.
235 E 42nd St
New York NY 10017
212 733-2323

(G-10045)
PHARMACIA HEPAR LLC
160 Industrial Dr (45005-4428)
PHONE...................................937 746-3603
Fax: 513 746-9855
Fred J Haller, *President*
Rhonda Meadows, *Manager*
Adam Panstingel, *Manager*
David Rohling, *Manager*
EMP: 72
SQ FT: 35,000
SALES (est): 9.4MM
SALES (corp-wide): 52.8B **Publicly Held**
WEB: www.pfizer.com
SIC: 2833 2834 Medicinal chemicals; pharmaceutical preparations
PA: Pfizer Inc.
235 E 42nd St
New York NY 10017
212 733-2323

(G-10046)
QUALITY ARCHITECTURAL AND FABR
8 Shotwell Dr (45005-4600)
PHONE...................................937 743-2923
Fax: 513 743-2926
Demida Davis, *President*
Theodosa L Davis, *Vice Pres*
Bruce Hinrichsen, *Engineer*
Rhonda King, *Office Mgr*
EMP: 18
SQ FT: 15,000
SALES (est): 3.9MM **Privately Held**
SIC: 3446 Architectural metalwork

(G-10047)
QUEST TECHNOLOGIES INC
Also Called: Quest Lasercut
600 Commerce Center Dr (45005-7205)
PHONE...................................937 743-1200
John Wenning, *President*
Mike Wolters, *Vice Pres*
EMP: 10
SQ FT: 12,000
SALES (est): 1.8MM **Privately Held**
SIC: 3599 3499 7389 Machine & other job shop work; fire- or burglary-resistive products; metal cutting services

(G-10048)
R L DRAKE COMPANY
230 Industrial Dr (45005-4496)
PHONE...................................937 746-4556
Ronald E Wysong, *Ch of Bd*
Blonder Tongue, *Senior VP*
Michael Brubaker, *Vice Pres*
Steve Koogler, *Vice Pres*
Steve Morgan, *Vice Pres*
EMP: 79 EST: 1943
SQ FT: 90,000

SALES (est): 8.6MM **Privately Held**
WEB: www.rldrake.com
SIC: 3663 3651 Radio broadcasting & communications equipment; television broadcasting & communications equipment; space satellite communications equipment; household audio & video equipment

(G-10049)
RIVERVIEW PACKAGING INC
101 Shotwell Dr (45005-4653)
P.O. Box 155 (45005-0155)
PHONE...................................937 743-9530
Fax: 937 743-8340
Joan K Ferrell, *President*
Marshall D Ruchman, *Principal*
Robert S Ferrell, *Corp Secy*
Randal T Ferrell, *Vice Pres*
Billy Birchfield, *Office Mgr*
EMP: 40
SQ FT: 75,000
SALES (est): 9.1MM **Privately Held**
SIC: 2653 Boxes, corrugated: made from purchased materials

(G-10050)
RNM HOLDINGS INC (PA)
550 Conover Dr (45005-1953)
PHONE...................................937 704-9900
Matt Milton, *President*
Stephen F Marsee, *President*
Steven Harris, *Vice Pres*
Donald Elliot Jr, *VP Opers*
Herbert Horn, *VP Opers*
▲ EMP: 41
SQ FT: 13,500
SALES (est): 38.3MM **Privately Held**
WEB: www.crane1services.com
SIC: 3531 Crane carriers

(G-10051)
ROTATION DYNAMICS CORPORATION
Also Called: Rotadyne
315 Industrial Dr (45005-4431)
PHONE...................................937 746-4069
Fax: 937 746-2854
Ed Nykiel, *Mktg Dir*
Pat Lakes, *Office Mgr*
EMP: 10
SALES (corp-wide): 128.8MM **Privately Held**
SIC: 3555 Printing trades machinery
PA: Rotation Dynamics Corporation
8140 Cass Ave
Darien IL 60561
630 769-9255

(G-10052)
SERVING VETERANS MOBILITY INC
303 Conover Dr (45005-1957)
PHONE...................................937 746-4788
Debra Lipps, *Vice Pres*
EMP: 8
SALES (est): 235K **Privately Held**
SIC: 3999 Wheelchair lifts

(G-10053)
SHUR FIT DISTRIBUTORS INC
Also Called: Shur-Form Laminates Division
221 N Main St (45005-1629)
PHONE...................................937 746-0567
Fax: 513 746-8010
Paul Gross, *President*
Hershal Nichol, *Vice Pres*
Kent Gross, *Treasurer*
EMP: 30
SQ FT: 58,000
SALES (est): 3.7MM **Privately Held**
SIC: 2541 Table or counter tops, plastic laminated

(G-10054)
SRS MANUFACTURING CORP
395 Industrial Dr (45005-4431)
PHONE...................................937 746-3086
Fax: 937 746-0148
Carlos Robinson, *President*
Kevin Robinson, *Manager*
Sally Fitzgerald, *Admin Mgr*
EMP: 18
SQ FT: 12,000
SALES: 2.2MM **Privately Held**
SIC: 3599 Machine & other job shop work

(G-10055)
SUN CHEMICAL CORPORATION
General Printing Ink Division
125 Jaygee Dr (45005-4446)
PHONE...................................937 743-8055
Mike Grotha, *Branch Mgr*
EMP: 20
SQ FT: 22,500
SALES (corp-wide): 6.7B **Privately Held**
WEB: www.sunchemical.com
SIC: 2893 Printing ink
HQ: Sun Chemical Corporation
35 Waterview Blvd Ste 100
Parsippany NJ 07054
973 404-6000

(G-10056)
SUNSTAR ENGRG AMERICAS INC
Also Called: Sunstar Sprockets
700 Watkins Glen Dr (45005-2394)
PHONE...................................937 743-9049
Naoki Achiwa, *Principal*
EMP: 13 **Privately Held**
SIC: 3751 Motorcycles, bicycles & parts
HQ: Sunstar Engineering Americas Inc.
85 S Pioneer Blvd
Springboro OH 45066

(G-10057)
TAPCO HOLDINGS INC
200 Shotwell Dr (45005-4656)
PHONE...................................800 771-4486
Joseph Kelley, *Branch Mgr*
EMP: 6
SALES (corp-wide): 974.8MM **Publicly Held**
WEB: www.atlanticshuttersystems.com
SIC: 3089 Shutters, plastic
HQ: Tapco Holdings, Inc.
29797 Beck Rd
Wixom MI 48393
248 668-6400

(G-10058)
TECH-WAY INDUSTRIES INC
301 Industrial Dr (45005-4431)
P.O. Box 517 (45005-0517)
PHONE...................................937 746-1004
Fax: 513 746-3867
Kenneth Parker, *CEO*
Robin Parker, *Principal*
Brian Kress, *Vice Pres*
Paula Miles, *Purch Dir*
Ricki Heronemus, *Controller*
EMP: 55 EST: 1964
SQ FT: 90,000
SALES (est): 15.1MM **Privately Held**
SIC: 3089 Injection molding of plastics

(G-10059)
TOTAL QUALITY MACHINING INC
10 Shotwell Dr (45005-4600)
PHONE...................................937 746-7765
Fax: 937 746-9609
Theodosa Davis, *President*
Jim Evans, *Purchasing*
Demida Davis, *Treasurer*
Rhonda King, *Accounts Mgr*
EMP: 14
SQ FT: 25,000
SALES (est): 1.2MM **Privately Held**
WEB: www.totalqualitymachining.com
SIC: 3599 Machine shop, jobbing & repair

(G-10060)
TRI STATE PALLET INC (PA)
8401 Claude Thomas Rd # 57 (45005-1475)
PHONE...................................937 746-8702
Fax: 937 746-8703
John Sickinger, *President*
EMP: 19
SALES (est): 2MM **Privately Held**
SIC: 2448 Pallets, wood & wood with metal

(G-10061)
VALUED RELATIONSHIPS INC
Also Called: V R I
1400 Commerce Center Dr B (45005-7203)
PHONE...................................800 860-4230
Chris Hendriksen, *CEO*
Andy Schoonover, *Managing Prtnr*

Salli Duncan, *Vice Pres*
Rich Filler, *CFO*
Dan Vogel, *CFO*
EMP: 331
SQ FT: 10,000
SALES (est): 55.8MM **Privately Held**
WEB: www.monitoringcare.com
SIC: 3845 Patient monitoring apparatus

(G-10062)
WAFFLE HOUSE INC
6840 Franklin Lebanon Rd (45005-4558)
PHONE...................................937 746-6830
Fax: 937 746-6830
Steve Foreman, *Branch Mgr*
Mike Buck, *Manager*
EMP: 20
SALES (corp-wide): 752.9MM **Privately Held**
SIC: 2096 5145 Potato chips & similar snacks; snack foods
PA: Waffle House, Inc.
5986 Financial Dr
Norcross GA 30071
770 729-5700

(G-10063)
WALTER F STEPHENS JR INC
415 South Ave (45005-3647)
PHONE...................................937 746-0521
Fax: 513 746-0947
Ruth Ann Stephens, *Ch of Bd*
Carla Baker, *President*
Walter F Stephens Jr, *President*
Diane Stephens Maloney, *Corp Secy*
Patty Gleason, *Vice Pres*
EMP: 50
SQ FT: 45,000
SALES (est): 6.8MM **Privately Held**
SIC: 5999 2389 5122 5023 Police supply stores; uniforms & vestments; toiletries; toothbrushes, except electric; kitchenware; uniforms, men's & boys'; mattresses & foundations

(G-10064)
WALTHER ENGRG & MFG CO INC
Also Called: Walther EMC
3501 Shotwell Dr (45005-4667)
PHONE...................................937 743-8125
Chris Walther, *President*
Phil Fensel, *Vice Pres*
Mike Carbaugh, *VP Mfg*
Anthony Ridenour, *Engineer*
Kim Lamoureua, *Accountant*
EMP: 49
SQ FT: 35,000
SALES (est): 10.8MM **Privately Held**
WEB: www.waltheremc.com
SIC: 3714 Motor vehicle parts & accessories

(G-10065)
WAYTEK CORPORATION
400 Shotwell Dr (45005-4661)
PHONE...................................937 743-6142
Fax: 513 743-8041
Stephen P Foley, *President*
William Le May, *Chairman*
William Crawford, *Vice Pres*
Sylvia Kessler, *Admin Sec*
Cathy Pavao, *Administration*
▲ EMP: 42
SQ FT: 32,000
SALES (est): 12.4MM **Privately Held**
WEB: www.waytekcorp.com
SIC: 2672 2891 Coated & laminated paper; adhesives & sealants

> **Franklin Furnace**
> *Scioto County*

(G-10066)
BRUCE BOX CO INC
2146 Junior Rd (45629-9049)
P.O. Box 35 (45629-0035)
PHONE...................................740 533-0670
Fax: 740 533-2393
Keith Bruce, *President*
Joyce Bruce, *President*
Sharon Bruce, *Vice Pres*
Debbie Crabtree, *Admin Sec*

EMP: 3
SQ FT: 3,500
SALES: 330K **Privately Held**
SIC: 2653 Corrugated & solid fiber boxes

(G-10067)
CECIL CAUDILL TRAILER SLS INC
6679 Gallia Pike (45629-8986)
PHONE...................740 574-0704
Richard Caudill, *President*
EMP: 10
SALES (est): 1.3MM **Privately Held**
SIC: 3792 5561 Travel trailers & campers; camper & travel trailer dealers

(G-10068)
CHAFFIN ELECTRONICS INC
4170 Gallia Pike (45629-8812)
PHONE...................740 354-9896
Fax: 740 354-9462
Gregory Chaffin, *President*
EMP: 3
SALES (est): 411.6K **Privately Held**
SIC: 5063 3672 Electrical apparatus & equipment; printed circuit boards

(G-10069)
G & J PEPSI-COLA BOTTLERS INC
Also Called: Pepsico
4587 Gallia Pike (45629-8777)
P.O. Box 299 (45629-0299)
PHONE...................740 354-9191
Fax: 740 354-9217
Don Chalfant, *VP Sales*
Robert Ross, *Branch Mgr*
EMP: 350
SALES (corp-wide): 490.5MM **Privately Held**
WEB: www.gjpepsi.com
SIC: 2086 5149 Carbonated soft drinks, bottled & canned; groceries & related products
PA: G & J Pepsi-Cola Bottlers Inc
   9435 Waterstone Blvd # 390
   Cincinnati OH 45249
   513 785-6060

(G-10070)
WOODWORKS UNLIMITED
330 Lambro Ln (45629-8994)
PHONE...................740 574-4523
Gregory Chaffin, *Owner*
EMP: 4
SALES (est): 358.3K **Privately Held**
SIC: 2431 Millwork

Frazeysburg
Muskingum County

(G-10071)
CALVARY CHRISTIAN CH OF OHIO
Also Called: Frazeysburg Restaurant & Bky
338 W 3rd St (43822-9785)
PHONE...................740 828-9000
Rev Scott Egbert, *President*
Robert McGraw, *Vice Pres*
Mari Anne Holbrook, *Treasurer*
Faith O'Leary, *Manager*
Faith Oleary, *Manager*
EMP: 40
SQ FT: 2,500
SALES: 55.4K **Privately Held**
SIC: 2051 8661 5541 0241 Bakery: wholesale or wholesale/retail combined; Christian & Reformed Church; filling stations, gasoline; milk production

(G-10072)
DK MANFCTURING FRAZEYSBURG INC (HQ)
119 W 2nd St (43822-9675)
P.O. Box 409 (43822-0409)
PHONE...................740 828-3291
Allen L Handlan, *Principal*
Brad Williams, *Vice Pres*
Nancy Campbell, *Purchasing*
Sharron Adair, *Manager*
Joe Stone, *Manager*
EMP: 38

SALES (est): 14.1MM
SALES (corp-wide): 24.6MM **Privately Held**
SIC: 3089 Injection molded finished plastic products
PA: Dak Enterprises, Inc.
   18062 Timber Trails Rd
   Marysville OH 43040
   740 828-3291

(G-10073)
H & D DRILLING CO INC
11183 Pleasant Valley Rd (43822-9507)
PHONE...................740 745-2236
Harold Donaker, *CEO*
Wanda Donaker, *Corp Secy*
EMP: 5
SALES (est): 472K **Privately Held**
SIC: 1381 Drilling oil & gas wells

(G-10074)
H & S DRILLING CO INC
101 E 3rd St (43822-9652)
P.O. Box 40 (43822-0040)
PHONE...................740 828-2411
Robert Hullhorst, *President*
Thomas Hullhorst, *Treasurer*
EMP: 3
SQ FT: 2,500
SALES (est): 150K **Privately Held**
SIC: 1311 1382 1794 Crude petroleum production; oil & gas exploration services; excavation work

(G-10075)
LONGABERGER COMPANY
Also Called: Longaberger Baskets
5563 Raiders Rd (43822-9431)
PHONE...................740 828-4000
Fax: 740 828-4144
Kimi Longaberger, *CEO*
Rachel Schmidt, *COO*
Joe Dinan, *Safety Mgr*
Boone Birkhimer, *Facilities Mgr*
R Longaberger-Sch, *Manager*
EMP: 3600
SALES (corp-wide): 113.9MM **Publicly Held**
WEB: www.longaberger.com
SIC: 2449 Baskets: fruit & vegetable, round stave, till, etc.
HQ: The Longaberger Company
   5563 Raiders Rd
   Frazeysburg OH 43822
   740 322-5000

(G-10076)
R & J DRILLING COMPANY INC
18586 Pinewood Trl (43822-9502)
P.O. Box 86 (43822-0086)
PHONE...................740 763-3991
Ronald F Moran, *President*
Brenda Moran, *Manager*
EMP: 5 EST: 1958
SQ FT: 6,000
SALES: 240K **Privately Held**
SIC: 1389 1381 Oil field services; directional drilling oil & gas wells

(G-10077)
WALNUT HILL SHOP
17388a Frampton Rd (43822)
PHONE...................740 828-3346
Mary Kanuckel, *Owner*
EMP: 3
SALES (est): 100K **Privately Held**
SIC: 2395 Embroidery & art needlework

Fredericksburg
Wayne County

(G-10078)
BILL HALL WELL SERVICE
10180 James Rd (44627-9538)
PHONE...................330 695-4671
Bill Hall, *Owner*
EMP: 3
SALES (est): 140K **Privately Held**
SIC: 1389 Swabbing wells; gas field services; oil field services

(G-10079)
CABINET SPECIALTIES INC
10738 Criswell Rd (44627-9719)
PHONE...................330 695-3463
Fax: 330 695-4008
Ivan Weaver, *President*
Robert Weaver, *Vice Pres*
EMP: 20
SQ FT: 15,000
SALES (est): 1.9MM **Privately Held**
SIC: 2434 Wood kitchen cabinets

(G-10080)
CHORE ANDEN
Also Called: Hickory Lane Welding
11461 Salt Creek Rd (44627-9755)
PHONE...................330 695-2300
Aden Chore, *Owner*
EMP: 8
SALES (est): 665.3K **Privately Held**
SIC: 7692 Welding repair

(G-10081)
COUNTRY COMFORT WOODWORKING
2 Mi Sw Of Mt Eaton (44627)
PHONE...................330 695-4408
Crist Miller, *Principal*
EMP: 3
SALES (est): 404.4K **Privately Held**
SIC: 2431 Millwork

(G-10082)
CRISWELL FURNITURE
8139 Criswell Rd (44627-9709)
PHONE...................330 695-2082
EMP: 4
SALES (est): 230K **Privately Held**
SIC: 2511 Mfg Wooden Furniture

(G-10083)
DUTCH DESIGN PRODUCTS LLC
8216 State Route 241 (44627-9638)
PHONE...................330 674-1167
Barbara Hershberger, *Owner*
EMP: 22
SALES: 950K **Privately Held**
SIC: 2521 Wood office furniture

(G-10084)
DUTCH VALLEY WOODCRAFT LTD
5833 Township Road 610 (44627-9640)
PHONE...................330 695-2364
Levi A Weaver, *Principal*
EMP: 3
SALES (est): 221.5K **Privately Held**
SIC: 2511 Wood household furniture

(G-10085)
EVEN HEAT MFG LTD
8241 Tr 601 (44627)
PHONE...................330 695-9351
John R Slater, *CEO*
▲ EMP: 10
SQ FT: 6,700
SALES (est): 1.2MM **Privately Held**
SIC: 3469 Metal stampings

(G-10086)
FARMSTEAD ACRES WOODWORKING
9106 County Road 201 (44627-9402)
PHONE...................330 695-6492
Lester J Wengerd, *Principal*
EMP: 4 EST: 2010
SALES (est): 371.3K **Privately Held**
SIC: 2431 Millwork

(G-10087)
HOLMES PRINTING SOLUTIONS LLC
8757 County Road 77 (44627-9446)
PHONE...................330 234-9699
Phillip Holmes, *President*
Lonnie Yoder, *Manager*
EMP: 4
SALES (est): 310K **Privately Held**
SIC: 2752 Commercial printing, lithographic

(G-10088)
MILLER CRIST
Also Called: Crosco Wood Products
10258 S Kansas Rd (44627-9754)
PHONE...................330 359-7877
Fax: 330 359-7878
Crist Miller, *Owner*
Cris Miller, *Principal*
Rosanna Miller, *Manager*
EMP: 16
SQ FT: 8,000
SALES (est): 1.4MM **Privately Held**
SIC: 2435 Hardwood plywood, prefinished

(G-10089)
MRS MLLERS HMMADE NOODLES LTD
9140 County Road 192 (44627-9436)
P.O. Box 289 (44627-0289)
PHONE...................330 694-5814
Leon Miller, *Partner*
Esther Miller, *Partner*
Maria Miller, *Principal*
▲ EMP: 10
SQ FT: 11,000
SALES (est): 1.1MM **Privately Held**
WEB: www.mrsmillersnoodles.com
SIC: 2098 Noodles (e.g. egg, plain & water), dry

(G-10090)
PREMIUM PANEL & TREAD
4910 Harrison Rd (44627-9500)
PHONE...................330 695-9979
Daniel Shetler, *Owner*
EMP: 5
SALES (est): 520.7K **Privately Held**
SIC: 2431 Millwork; stair railings, wood

(G-10091)
QUALITY FABRICATIONS LLC
7108 Township Road 569 (44627-9410)
PHONE...................330 695-2478
Ivan Hochstetler, *Principal*
Sam Yoder, *Manager*
EMP: 5
SALES: 1.3MM **Privately Held**
SIC: 2512 Living room furniture: upholstered on wood frames

(G-10092)
ROBIN INDUSTRIES INC
Also Called: Fredericksburg Facility
300 W Clay St (44627)
P.O. Box 242 (44627-0242)
PHONE...................330 695-9300
Dave Wingett, *Principal*
Dean Dahinden, *Exec VP*
Amy Davis, *Purchasing*
Leonard Lorman, *Engineer*
Polly Yoder, *Personnel*
EMP: 170
SALES (corp-wide): 66.6MM **Privately Held**
WEB: www.robin-industries.com
SIC: 3069 3061 Molded rubber products; mechanical rubber goods
PA: Robin Industries, Inc.
   6500 Rockside Rd Ste 230
   Independence OH 44131
   216 631-7000

(G-10093)
SALT CREEK LUMBER COMPANY INC
11657 Salt Creek Rd (44627-9755)
PHONE...................330 695-3500
Fax: 330 695-3500
Norman Boerman, *President*
Shirley Boerman, *Vice Pres*
EMP: 6
SQ FT: 8,000
SALES (est): 690K **Privately Held**
SIC: 5031 2421 Lumber: rough, dressed & finished; sawmills & planing mills, general

(G-10094)
YODER WINDOW & SIDING LTD
Also Called: Glass Specialties
7165 Fredericksburg Rd (44627-9808)
PHONE...................330 857-4530
Derryl Troyer, *Manager*
EMP: 5
SALES (corp-wide): 2MM **Privately Held**
SIC: 3211 Flat glass

PA: Yoder Window & Siding, Ltd.
7846 Harrison Rd
Fredericksburg OH 44627
330 695-6960

(G-10095)
YODER WINDOW & SIDING LTD
(PA)
Also Called: Yoder Window and Siding
7846 Harrison Rd (44627-9798)
PHONE..........................330 695-6960
Jonas Yoder, *Partner*
Derryl R Troyer, *Partner*
Jonas M Yoder, *Partner*
EMP: 13
SQ FT: 6,500
SALES (est): 2.1MM **Privately Held**
SIC: 2431 1751 1761 Windows, wood;
window & door (prefabricated) installation;
gutter & downspout contractor; siding
contractor

Fredericktown
Knox County

(G-10096)
BENCHMARK CABINETS
97 Mount Vernon Ave (43019-7700)
PHONE..........................740 694-1144
Fax: 740 694-7022
Wesley Crum, *Owner*
EMP: 32
SQ FT: 29,000
SALES (est): 3MM **Privately Held**
WEB: www.benchmark-cabinets.com
SIC: 2434 2541 Wood kitchen cabinets;
counter & sink tops

(G-10097)
COUNTRY MANUFACTURING
INC
333 Salem Ave Ext (43019-9186)
P.O. Box 104 (43019-0104)
PHONE..........................740 694-9926
Fax: 740 694-5088
Joe Chattin, *President*
Karen Gay Chattin, *Corp Secy*
Chad Chattin, *Vice Pres*
EMP: 15
SQ FT: 15,000
SALES (est): 2.8MM **Privately Held**
WEB: www.countrymfg.com
SIC: 3524 Lawn & garden equipment

(G-10098)
DANA OFF HIGHWAY
PRODUCTS LLC
123 Phoenix Pl (43019-9162)
PHONE..........................740 694-2055
Fax: 740 694-0437
John Stolher, *Controller*
Terry Casto, *Branch Mgr*
Jeff Coffing, *Maintence Staff*
EMP: 200
SALES (corp-wide): 5.8B **Publicly Held**
SIC: 3714 Motor vehicle parts & acces-
sories
HQ: Dana Off Highway Products, Llc
3939 Technology Dr
Maumee OH 43537
419 887-3000

(G-10099)
DEE-JAYS CSTM BUTCHERING
PROC
17460 Ankneytown Rd (43019-8015)
PHONE..........................740 694-7492
Fax: 740 694-5380
Mike Jessee, *Owner*
Jenny Jessee, *Co-Owner*
EMP: 6
SALES (est): 300K **Privately Held**
SIC: 2011 Meat packing plants

(G-10100)
DIVELBISS CORPORATION
9778 Mount Gilead Rd (43019-9161)
PHONE..........................800 245-2327
Fax: 740 694-9035
Terry L Divelbiss, *President*
Alan Divelbiss, *Vice Pres*
Robert Chapin, *QC Mgr*

Donald Divelbiss, *Engineer*
Shawn Reynolds, *Design Engr*
EMP: 39 **EST:** 1974
SQ FT: 17,000
SALES (est): 8.3MM **Privately Held**
WEB: www.divelbiss.com
SIC: 3625 Relays & industrial controls

(G-10101)
EDWARDS SHEET METAL
WORKS INC
Also Called: Edwards Culvert Co
10439 Sparta Rd (43019-9025)
P.O. Box 239 (43019-0239)
PHONE..........................740 694-0010
Richard Well, *President*
Catherine Chris Well, *Corp Secy*
Hector Frazier, *Vice Pres*
Sandy Casto, *Manager*
EMP: 12 **EST:** 1907
SQ FT: 8,000
SALES: 1MM **Privately Held**
SIC: 3444 Culverts, sheet metal; pipe,
sheet metal

(G-10102)
FOOTE FOUNDRY LLC
283 N Main St (43019-1111)
PHONE..........................740 694-1595
Fax: 740 694-6893
Bob Bert, *Controller*
Ron Cross, *CPA*
Joseph E Locanti, *Mng Member*
Todd Colman, *Controller*
EMP: 65
SQ FT: 70,000
SALES (est): 11.6MM **Privately Held**
WEB: www.footefoundry.com
SIC: 3321 Gray & ductile iron foundries

(G-10103)
FT PRECISION INC
Also Called: Ftp
9731 Mount Gilead Rd (43019-9167)
PHONE..........................740 694-1500
Fax: 740 694-5500
Tamami Nishimura, *President*
Ben Beeber, *President*
James Wagner, *QC Mgr*
Kevin Allerding, *Manager*
Lein Coenets, *Manager*
▲ **EMP:** 512
SQ FT: 150,000
SALES (est): 199.6MM
SALES (corp-wide): 347.4MM **Privately**
Held
WEB: www.ftprecision.com
SIC: 3714 Motor vehicle parts & acces-
sories
PA: Tanaka Seimitsu Kogyo Co.,Ltd.
2-7-10, Shinjohommachi
Toyama TYM 930-0
764 517-651

(G-10104)
INDUSTRIAL AND MAR ENG SVC
CO
Also Called: Imesco
13843 Armentrout Rd (43019-9717)
PHONE..........................740 694-0791
Theresa C Chandler, *CEO*
Bill Hawkins, *Prdtn Mgr*
Scott C Chandler, *Manager*
EMP: 10
SQ FT: 7,200
SALES (est): 950K **Privately Held**
WEB: www.imescomfg.com
SIC: 3613 3625 3479 3993 Control pan-
els, electric; switchgear & switchgear ac-
cessories; generator control & metering
panels; control circuit relays, industrial;
name plates: engraved, etched, etc.;
signs & advertising specialties; motors &
generators

(G-10105)
LAGC LTD
11729 Leedy Rd (43019-9289)
PHONE..........................419 886-2141
Donnie Cataldo, *Principal*
EMP: 4
SALES (est): 312.6K **Privately Held**
SIC: 1311 Crude petroleum & natural gas

(G-10106)
M H LOGGING & LUMBER
14582 Montgomery Rd (43019-9772)
PHONE..........................740 694-1988
Mark Hulse, *Owner*
EMP: 3
SALES (est): 347.2K **Privately Held**
SIC: 2411 Logging

(G-10107)
OHIO COMMUNITY MEDIA
59 W College St (43019-1042)
PHONE..........................740 848-4064
Leslie Bronstein, *Principal*
EMP: 3
SALES (est): 105.5K **Privately Held**
SIC: 2711 Newspapers, publishing & print-
ing

(G-10108)
OPTIONS PLUS
INCORPORATED
143 Tuttle Ave (43019-1029)
PHONE..........................740 694-9811
Fax: 740 694-1245
Camilyn Jo Meleca, *President*
Melissa Chattin, *Vice Pres*
▼ **EMP:** 10 **EST:** 1976
SQ FT: 25,000
SALES (est): 1.5MM **Privately Held**
WEB: www.optionsplus.com
SIC: 3444 3496 Sheet metalwork; miscel-
laneous fabricated wire products

(G-10109)
SCHAFER DRIVELINE LLC (HQ)
123 Phoenix Pl (43019-9162)
PHONE..........................740 694-0462
Bipin Doshi, *Principal*
Jim Hall, *Engineer*
Matthew McClain, *Controller*
Stanley Blenke, *Manager*
▲ **EMP:** 50
SQ FT: 110,000
SALES (est): 13MM
SALES (corp-wide): 28.5MM **Privately**
Held
SIC: 3714 Axles, motor vehicle
PA: Schafer Industries, Inc.
4701 Nimtz Pkwy
South Bend IN 46628
574 234-4116

(G-10110)
TD LANDSCAPE INC
16780 Pinkley Rd (43019-9302)
PHONE..........................740 694-0244
Scott Huvler, *President*
EMP: 15
SALES (est): 645K **Privately Held**
SIC: 3523 Grounds mowing equipment

(G-10111)
TENDA HORSE PRODUCTS LLC
18400 N Liberty Rd (43019-9742)
P.O. Box 614, Mount Vernon (43050-0614)
PHONE..........................740 694-8836
Todd Mizer,
EMP: 3
SALES (est): 339.5K **Privately Held**
WEB: www.tendahorse.com
SIC: 2048 Mineral feed supplements

(G-10112)
TEXMASTER TOOLS INC
143 Tuttle Ave (43019-1029)
P.O. Box 132 (43019-0132)
PHONE..........................740 965-8778
Fax: 740 965-8782
John Capoccia, *President*
EMP: 18
SQ FT: 25,000
SALES (est): 4.2MM **Privately Held**
SIC: 5072 3429 Hardware; manufactured
hardware (general)

(G-10113)
U M D AUTOMATED SYSTEMS
INC
9855 Salem Rd (43019-9301)
P.O. Box 317 (43019-0317)
PHONE..........................740 694-8614
Fax: 740 694-8619
Don Rogers, *President*
Laura Rogers, *Vice Pres*

Ben Potter, *Project Mgr*
Brad Walls, *Safety Mgr*
Shane Taylor, *Facilities Mgr*
EMP: 72
SQ FT: 55,000
SALES (est): 20MM **Privately Held**
SIC: 3441 Fabricated structural metal

(G-10114)
UMD CONTRACTORS INC
9855 Salem Rd (43019-9301)
P.O. Box 228 (43019-0228)
PHONE..........................740 694-8614
Don Rogers, *President*
Bill Vick, *Accounts Mgr*
EMP: 13
SALES (est): 2.2MM **Privately Held**
SIC: 3011 Tires & inner tubes

(G-10115)
VILLAGE WOODWORKING
8033 Ridge Rd (43019-9473)
PHONE..........................740 326-4461
Menno R Yoder, *Principal*
EMP: 3
SALES (est): 369.8K **Privately Held**
SIC: 2431 Millwork

(G-10116)
WARD/KRAFT FORMS OF OHIO
INC
700 Salem Ave Ext (43019-9188)
P.O. Box 211 (43019-0211)
PHONE..........................740 694-0015
Fax: 740 694-0960
Harold E Kraft, *President*
Robert A Horton, *Vice Pres*
David Young, *Treasurer*
Daryl Roller, *VP Mktg*
Fred Mitchelson, *Admin Sec*
EMP: 80
SQ FT: 41,400
SALES (est): 5.6MM
SALES (corp-wide): 88.9MM **Privately**
Held
WEB: www.wardkraft.com
SIC: 2759 Commercial printing
HQ: Ward-Kraft, Inc.
2401 Cooper St
Fort Scott KS 66701
800 821-4021

Freeport
Harrison County

(G-10117)
BOND QUARTERS HORSES
23574 Cadiz Rd (43973-8602)
PHONE..........................614 354-4028
EMP: 3
SALES (est): 171.1K **Privately Held**
SIC: 3131 Quarters

(G-10118)
FREEPORT PRESS INC (PA)
121 E Main St (43973-9355)
P.O. Box 198 (43973-0198)
PHONE..........................740 658-3315
Fax: 740 658-3727
David G Pilcher, *President*
Roy Clore, *Opers Mgr*
Renny Glazer, *Safety Mgr*
Terry Hockenberry, *Production*
Tom Dixon, *Purch Dir*
EMP: 150
SQ FT: 36,000
SALES (est): 30MM **Privately Held**
WEB: www.freeportpress.com
SIC: 2759 Commercial printing

(G-10119)
ROSEBUD MINING COMPANY
28490 Birmingham Rd (43973-9754)
PHONE..........................740 658-4217
EMP: 35
SALES (corp-wide): 672.6MM **Privately**
Held
SIC: 1222 Bituminous coal-underground
mining
PA: Rosebud Mining Company
301 Market St
Kittanning PA 16201
724 545-6222

(G-10120)
SCHROCK WOODWORKING
71444 Grapevine Rd (43973-8909)
PHONE..................................740 489-5229
Eli Schrock, *Owner*
EMP: 4
SALES: 400K **Privately Held**
SIC: 2434 Wood kitchen cabinets

Fremont
Sandusky County

(G-10121)
A BUN IN OVEN
1011 Hayes Ave (43420-2816)
PHONE..................................419 559-3056
Brooke Huber, *Principal*
EMP: 4 EST: 2011
SALES (est): 173K **Privately Held**
SIC: 2051 Bakery: wholesale or wholesale/retail combined

(G-10122)
ABC INOAC EXTERIOR SYSTEMS LLC
1410 Motor Ave (43420-1437)
PHONE..................................419 334-8951
Fax: 419 332-1866
Angelo Cesta, *Branch Mgr*
EMP: 250
SALES (corp-wide): 131MM **Privately Held**
SIC: 3082 Unsupported plastics profile shapes
PA: Abc Inoac Exterior Systems Llc
24175 Northwestern Hwy
Southfield MI 48075
248 619-6057

(G-10123)
ACTION PRINTING & PHOTOGRAPHY
626 Grant St (43420-2259)
PHONE..................................419 332-9615
Dan Laity, *Owner*
EMP: 4
SALES: 180K **Privately Held**
SIC: 2752 Commercial printing, offset

(G-10124)
ALKON CORPORATION (PA)
728 Graham Dr (43420-4073)
PHONE..................................419 355-9111
Mark Winter, *President*
Wayne Morroney, *President*
Prakash Jog, *Vice Pres*
Mark Radloff, *Vice Pres*
Dave Kowalski, *Opers Mgr*
▲ EMP: 60
SQ FT: 40,000
SALES (est): 24.2MM **Privately Held**
WEB: www.alkoncorp.com
SIC: 3491 3082 5084 5085 Valves, nuclear; tubes, unsupported plastic; industrial machinery & equipment; pistons & valves; valves & fittings; fluid power valves & hose fittings

(G-10125)
ART FREMONT IRON CO
307 E State St (43420-4151)
P.O. Box 652 (43420-0652)
PHONE..................................419 332-5554
Fax: 419 332-3982
Robert C Leaser, *Owner*
EMP: 4 EST: 1946
SQ FT: 5,000
SALES: 240K **Privately Held**
SIC: 3444 3446 Casings, sheet metal; architectural metalwork

(G-10126)
ATLAS INDUSTRIES INC (PA)
1750 E State St (43420-4056)
PHONE..................................419 355-1000
Fax: 419 355-9000
Jerald F Clark, *President*
Roman G Burnor Jr, *Principal*
J S Heyman, *Principal*
Merwyn G Leatherman, *Principal*
Stephen Clark, *COO*
▲ EMP: 134 EST: 1938
SQ FT: 150,000

SALES (est): 165.3MM **Privately Held**
WEB: www.atlasindustries.com
SIC: 3599 Crankshafts & camshafts, machining; custom machinery

(G-10127)
BAP MANUFACTURING INC
601 N Stone St Ste 1 (43420-1566)
PHONE..................................419 332-5041
Fax: 419 332-7277
W Scott Brown, *President*
Steven P Rich, *General Mgr*
EMP: 30
SQ FT: 10,000
SALES: 1.2MM **Privately Held**
WEB: www.bapman.com
SIC: 3545 Cutting tools for machine tools

(G-10128)
BEMIS COMPANY INC
730 Industrial Dr (43420-8678)
PHONE..................................419 334-9465
Fax: 419 332-5796
Russell John, *Engineer*
Ryan Richter, *Plant Engr*
Lynne Russell, *Human Res Dir*
Ken Zeop, *Sales Staff*
William Kraut, *Manager*
EMP: 20
SALES (corp-wide): 4B **Publicly Held**
SIC: 2671 2672 Packaging paper & plastics film, coated & laminated; coated & laminated paper
PA: Bemis Company, Inc.
1 Neenah Ctr Fl 4
Neenah WI 54956
920 527-5000

(G-10129)
BENCHMARK PRINTS
2252 W State St (43420-1439)
PHONE..................................419 332-7640
Fax: 419 332-7090
Kenn Bower, *Owner*
EMP: 11
SQ FT: 5,700
SALES (est): 590K **Privately Held**
WEB: www.benchmarkprints.com
SIC: 2759 5611 5199 Screen printing; men's & boys' clothing stores; advertising specialties

(G-10130)
BERLEKAMP PLASTICS INC
2587 County Road 99 (43420-9316)
PHONE..................................419 334-4481
Fax: 419 334-9094
Kenneth Berlekamp Jr, *President*
Sandra Berlekamp, *Corp Secy*
Kathy Macallister, *Office Mgr*
EMP: 15 EST: 1929
SQ FT: 12,000
SALES (est): 2.6MM **Privately Held**
WEB: www.berlekamp.com
SIC: 3089 Injection molding of plastics

(G-10131)
BOMB MFG LLC
530 S Taft Ave (43420-3234)
PHONE..................................419 559-9689
Kenneth F Flower, *CEO*
EMP: 4
SALES: 500K **Privately Held**
SIC: 3999 Manufacturing industries

(G-10132)
BURKETT INDUSTRIES INC
507 Vine St (43420-3493)
PHONE..................................419 332-4391
Fax: 419 332-5010
Richard B Burkett, *President*
Teresa Burkett, *Treasurer*
EMP: 5 EST: 1870
SQ FT: 5,600
SALES (est): 728.7K **Privately Held**
WEB: www.burkettindustrieselectric.com
SIC: 1731 3643 General electrical contractor; lightning protection equipment

(G-10133)
C A KUSTOMS
524 N Stone St (43420-1531)
PHONE..................................419 332-4395
Clay Keim, *Owner*
Dawn Keim, *Bookkeeper*
EMP: 3

SALES: 200K **Privately Held**
WEB: www.cakustoms.com
SIC: 3993 Signs & advertising specialties

(G-10134)
CARBO FORGE INC
150 State Route 523 (43420-9364)
PHONE..................................419 334-9788
Jeffrey Woitha, *President*
Jeffrey Witham, *President*
Shane Willer, *Production*
Troy Lewis, *Engineer*
Rich Egbert, *Controller*
EMP: 44 EST: 1920
SQ FT: 90,000
SALES (est): 9MM **Privately Held**
WEB: www.carboforge.com
SIC: 3462 Iron & steel forgings

(G-10135)
CENTEC CAST METAL PRODUCTS
501 Knapp St (43420-2514)
P.O. Box 645 (43420-0645)
PHONE..................................419 355-1414
Fax: 419 355-1422
James R Labenne, *President*
Richard Brown, *Corp Secy*
EMP: 9
SQ FT: 15,000
SALES: 1.1MM **Privately Held**
WEB: www.centeccast.com
SIC: 2796 Platemaking services

(G-10136)
CENTURY DIE COMPANY LLC
215 N Stone St (43420-1505)
PHONE..................................419 332-2693
Fax: 419 332-7126
Mark Curtis, *Manager*
Timothy Myers,
EMP: 58
SALES (est): 13.9MM **Privately Held**
SIC: 3544 Industrial molds

(G-10137)
CHRISTY MACHINE COMPANY
118 Birchard Ave (43420-3008)
P.O. Box 32 (43420-0032)
PHONE..................................419 332-6451
Fax: 419 332-8800
Randy Fielding, *President*
Newhope Vineyard, *Finance Mgr*
EMP: 11
SQ FT: 7,000
SALES (est): 1.1MM **Privately Held**
WEB: www.christydispensers.com
SIC: 3556 Food products machinery

(G-10138)
CLARK ASSOCIATES INC
702 W State St Ste A (43420-2592)
PHONE..................................419 334-3838
Fax: 419 334-3838
Gerald E Clark, *President*
Garry E Clark, *Vice Pres*
Jean Clark, *Sales Staff*
EMP: 4
SQ FT: 3,500
SALES: 300K **Privately Held**
SIC: 2752 5045 Offset & photolithographic printing; computers & accessories, personal & home entertainment

(G-10139)
CROWN BATTERY MANUFACTURING CO (PA)
1445 Majestic Dr (43420-9190)
P.O. Box 990 (43420-0990)
PHONE..................................419 332-0563
Fax: 419 334-7416
Hal Hawk, *President*
JB Blackwelder, *Vice Pres*
Scott Macina, *VP Human Res*
Ann Woolf, *Human Res Mgr*
Bill Bessire, *Admin Sec*
◆ EMP: 450 EST: 1926
SQ FT: 220,000
SALES: 222.1MM **Privately Held**
WEB: www.crownbattery.com
SIC: 3691 Storage batteries

(G-10140)
CUSTOM SEAL INC
Also Called: Custom Seal Roofing
708 Graham Dr (43420-4073)
P.O. Box 1290 (43420-8290)
PHONE..................................419 334-1020
Fax: 419 334-3211
Steven Mayle, *President*
Robert L Mayle, *Vice Pres*
Mike Ribbe, *Finance Mgr*
Annette Cronin, *Office Mgr*
Jordy Speak, *Manager*
▼ EMP: 25
SQ FT: 10,000
SALES (est): 5.1MM **Privately Held**
WEB: www.customseal.com
SIC: 2952 Roofing materials

(G-10141)
DECKER CUSTOM WOOD LLC
Also Called: Decker Custom Wood Working
505 W Mcgormley Rd (43420-8672)
PHONE..................................419 332-3464
Adam Decker,
Jim Britner,
EMP: 6
SQ FT: 3,500
SALES: 200K **Privately Held**
WEB: www.deckerwoodworking.com
SIC: 2493 Reconstituted wood products

(G-10142)
DENNIS CONSTUCTION SANITATION
Also Called: J D'S Pre Cast
1201 Siler St (43420-3557)
PHONE..................................419 332-8301
Fax: 419 332-9589
A James Dennis, *Owner*
EMP: 7 EST: 1973
SALES (est): 472.8K **Privately Held**
SIC: 1794 1711 3272 Excavation work; plumbing contractors; septic tanks, concrete

(G-10143)
ENERGY MANUFACTURING LTD
1830 Old Oak Harbour Rd (43420)
P.O. Box 1127, Fostoria (44830-1127)
PHONE..................................419 355-9304
Leslie Lipski, *CFO*
Richard Norton,
EMP: 6
SQ FT: 40,000
SALES (est): 964.1K **Privately Held**
SIC: 3586 Oil pumps, measuring or dispensing; gasoline pumps, measuring or dispensing

(G-10144)
ENGLER PRINTING CO
808 W State St (43420-2538)
PHONE..................................419 332-2181
Fax: 419 332-9080
Jay Engler, *Owner*
Marilyn Engler, *Co-Owner*
EMP: 9 EST: 1952
SQ FT: 4,000
SALES (est): 530K **Privately Held**
SIC: 2752 Commercial printing, offset

(G-10145)
FIRST CHOICE PACKAGING INC (PA)
Also Called: First Choice Packg Solutions
1501 W State St (43420-1629)
PHONE..................................419 333-4100
Fax: 419 334-6564
Paul W Tomick, *President*
Frank Wolfinger, *Vice Pres*
Charlie Bently, *Purchasing*
Greg Walters, *Design Engr*
Joyce Menekey, *Admin Sec*
EMP: 105
SALES (est): 33.2MM **Privately Held**
WEB: www.firstchoicepackaging.com
SIC: 3089 7389 Thermoformed finished plastic products; packaging & labeling services

(G-10146)
FREMONT COMPANY (PA)
802 N Front St (43420-1917)
PHONE..................................419 334-8995
Fax: 419 334-8120

Richard L Smith, *President*
Jim Fox, *COO*
Jeff Diehr, *Vice Pres*
Christopher Smith, *Vice Pres*
Mike Hayes, *QA Dir*
▼ EMP: 55
SQ FT: 250,000
SALES (est): 42.6MM **Privately Held**
WEB: www.fremontcompany.com
SIC: 2033 Vegetables: packaged in cans, jars, etc.

(G-10147)
FREMONT COMPANY
802 N Front St (43420-1917)
PHONE...................................419 334-8995
Jerry Schuett, *Manager*
EMP: 40
SALES (corp-wide): 42.6MM **Privately Held**
WEB: www.fremontcompany.com
SIC: 2033 Vegetables: packaged in cans, jars, etc.
PA: The Fremont Company
802 N Front St
Fremont OH 43420
419 334-8995

(G-10148)
FREMONT CUTTING DIES INC
3179 Us 20 E (43420-9014)
PHONE...................................419 334-5153
Gregory Abdoo, *President*
EMP: 9
SQ FT: 1,000
SALES (est): 1.2MM **Privately Held**
SIC: 3544 Die springs

(G-10149)
FREMONT FLASK CO
1000 Wolfe Ave (43420-1670)
P.O. Box 594 (43420-0594)
PHONE...................................419 332-2231
Fax: 419 332-2446
Carl W Yeager Jr, *President*
John Yeager, *Treasurer*
James Yeager, *Admin Sec*
EMP: 16
SQ FT: 20,000
SALES (est): 2.4MM **Privately Held**
WEB: www.wwsusa.net
SIC: 3559 Foundry machinery & equipment

(G-10150)
FREMONT PLASTIC PRODUCTS INC
2101 Cedar St (43420-1015)
PHONE...................................419 332-6407
Fax: 419 322-3934
Brian Beth, *President*
Duane Spencer, *Plant Mgr*
Mike Moore, *CFO*
EMP: 250
SQ FT: 180,000
SALES (est): 38.8MM
SALES (corp-wide): 104.7MM **Privately Held**
WEB: www.theplasticsgroup.net
SIC: 3089 3944 3714 3661 Blow molded finished plastic products; games, toys & children's vehicles; motor vehicle parts & accessories; telephone & telegraph apparatus; farm machinery & equipment; metal stampings
PA: The Plastics Group Inc
7409 S Quincy St
Willowbrook IL 60527
630 325-1210

(G-10151)
GANNETT CO INC
News Herald
1700 Cedar St (43420-1114)
P.O. Box 550, Port Clinton (43452-0550)
PHONE...................................419 332-5511
Fax: 419 898-7451
David Barth, *General Mgr*
C George-Dealer, *Principal*
Gary L Watson, *Division Pres*
EMP: 18
SALES (corp-wide): 3B **Publicly Held**
WEB: www.gannett.com
SIC: 2711 Newspapers: publishing only, not printed on site

PA: Gannett Co., Inc.
7950 Jones Branch Dr
Mc Lean VA 22102
703 854-6000

(G-10152)
GANNETT STLLITE INFO NTWRK LLC
News Messenger, The
1800 E State St Ste B (43420-4083)
P.O. Box 1230 (43420-8230)
PHONE...................................419 334-1012
Fax: 419 332-9750
Steve Avery, *Mfg Staff*
Roger Buoen, *Asst Mgr*
Kent Gardner, *Asst Mgr*
Scott Gillespie, *Asst Mgr*
Susan Hopper, *Asst Mgr*
EMP: 60
SQ FT: 2,792
SALES (corp-wide): 3B **Publicly Held**
WEB: www.usatoday.com
SIC: 2711 2752 Newspapers; commercial printing, lithographic
HQ: Gannett Satellite Information Network, Llc
7950 Jones Branch Dr
Mc Lean VA 22102
703 854-6000

(G-10153)
GARVIN TOOL & DIE INC
3000 State Route 412 (43420-9599)
PHONE...................................419 334-2392
Fax: 419 332-5050
William Garvin, *President*
Ted Gardin, *Vice Pres*
Joe Garvin, *Shareholder*
EMP: 5 EST: 1965
SQ FT: 2,048
SALES (est): 550K **Privately Held**
WEB: www.garvintools.com
SIC: 3544 Special dies & tools

(G-10154)
GENERAL CUTLERY INC (PA)
1918 N County Road 232 (43420-9595)
PHONE...................................419 332-2316
Fax: 419 334-7119
David Reitz, *President*
Carleton R Reitz, *Vice Pres*
Donna Shoemaker, *Admin Sec*
EMP: 12 EST: 1945
SQ FT: 25,000
SALES (est): 1.6MM **Privately Held**
SIC: 3421 Cutlery

(G-10155)
GRAHAM PACKAGING COMPANY LP
725 Industrial Dr (43420-8679)
PHONE...................................419 334-4197
Rick Van, *Manager*
EMP: 43 **Privately Held**
WEB: www.grahampackaging.com
SIC: 3085 3089 Plastics bottles; plastic containers, except foam
HQ: Graham Packaging Company, L.P.
700 Indian Springs Dr # 100
Lancaster PA 17601
717 849-8500

(G-10156)
GRAHAM PACKAGING PET TECH INC
725 Industrial Dr (43420-8679)
PHONE...................................419 334-4197
Lance Novotny, *Manager*
Van Engeoenhoven, *Manager*
Lance Lovotny, *Manager*
EMP: 113
SALES (corp-wide): 9B **Publicly Held**
SIC: 3085 Plastics bottles
HQ: Graham Packaging Pet Technologies Inc.
1 Seagate Ste 10
Toledo OH
717 849-8500

(G-10157)
GREEN BAY PACKAGING INC
Fremont Division
2323 Commerce Dr (43420-1052)
PHONE...................................419 332-5593
Fax: 419 332-5713

Paul Martin, *General Mgr*
Peter Tilleman, *Engineer*
Brian Walker, *Engineer*
Sandy Clark, *Human Res Dir*
Bill Lamb, *Human Res Dir*
EMP: 129
SALES (corp-wide): 896.8MM **Privately Held**
WEB: www.gbp.com
SIC: 2653 3412 Boxes, corrugated: made from purchased materials; metal barrels, drums & pails
PA: Green Bay Packaging Inc.
1700 N Webster Ave
Green Bay WI 54302
920 433-5111

(G-10158)
INDUSTRIAL HANGER CONVEYOR CO
886 N County Road 232 (43420-9145)
P.O. Box 30, Clyde (43410-0030)
PHONE...................................419 332-2661
Paul W Fishbaugh, *President*
Donna Fishbaugh, *Admin Sec*
EMP: 4
SALES (est): 1.1MM **Privately Held**
WEB: www.industrialhanger.com
SIC: 3599 3441 3444 Machine shop, jobbing & repair; fabricated structural metal; sheet metalwork

(G-10159)
INTERNATIONAL AUTOMOTIVE
400 S Stone St (43420-2658)
PHONE...................................419 332-1587
Robert S Miller, *President*
Terri Nagy, *Buyer*
Craig Wahl, *Engineer*
EMP: 273 **Privately Held**
WEB: www.iaaawards.com
SIC: 3089 Automotive parts, plastic
HQ: International Automotive Components Group North America, Inc.
28333 Telegraph Rd
Southfield MI 48034
248 455-7000

(G-10160)
JOSEPH B STINSON CO
2300 Napoleon Rd (43420-2644)
P.O. Box 71 (43420-0071)
PHONE...................................419 334-4151
Adair Van Nette, *President*
EMP: 4
SALES (est): 400K **Privately Held**
SIC: 7389 3569 Design, commercial & industrial; assembly machines, non-metalworking

(G-10161)
JS FABRICATIONS INC
1400 E State St (43420-4061)
PHONE...................................419 333-0323
Jack Swint, *President*
EMP: 8
SALES (est): 1.3MM **Privately Held**
SIC: 3441 1795 1721 Fabricated structural metal; demolition, buildings & other structures; industrial painting

(G-10162)
KRAFT HEINZ FOODS COMPANY
Also Called: Quality Assurance
1200n N 5th St (43420)
PHONE...................................419 332-7357
Fax: 419 332-3973
Scott Ellithorpe, *Traffic Mgr*
Daniel Ross, *Purchasing*
Jennifer Bower, *Engineer*
Tony Bascone, *Asst Controller*
Bob Jurski, *Branch Mgr*
EMP: 41
SALES (corp-wide): 26.4B **Publicly Held**
SIC: 3556 Choppers, commercial, food
HQ: Kraft Heinz Foods Company
1 Ppg Pl Ste 3200
Pittsburgh PA 15222
412 456-5700

(G-10163)
LESHER PRINTERS INC
810 N Wilson Ave (43420-2271)
P.O. Box 565 (43420-0565)
PHONE...................................419 332-8253
Fax: 419 332-2601

Emiel J Cool, *CEO*
Gary Cool, *President*
Sally Herr, *Admin Sec*
EMP: 28 EST: 1949
SQ FT: 24,000
SALES: 3MM **Privately Held**
WEB: www.lesherprinters.com
SIC: 2759 Commercial printing

(G-10164)
LIGHT CRAFT MANUFACTURING INC
Also Called: Light Craft Direct
220 Sullivan Rd (43420-9671)
PHONE...................................419 332-0536
Fax: 419 332-0987
Jeffery R Matt, *President*
Susan L Wright, *Corp Secy*
Kenneth A Matt, *Vice Pres*
▲ EMP: 10
SQ FT: 14,370
SALES (est): 1.9MM **Privately Held**
WEB: www.lightcraftmfg.com
SIC: 3646 Commercial indusl & institutional electric lighting fixtures

(G-10165)
LINE TOOL & DIE INC
933 Napoleon St (43420-2323)
PHONE...................................419 332-2931
Fax: 419 332-4325
Albert Mader, *President*
EMP: 3 EST: 1920
SQ FT: 2,500
SALES (est): 500.6K **Privately Held**
SIC: 3544 3599 Special dies, tools, jigs & fixtures; machine shop, jobbing & repair

(G-10166)
LOCKER KONNECTION SERVICES LLC
405 Jackson St (43420-2315)
P.O. Box 457 (43420-0457)
PHONE...................................419 334-3956
Larry Spann, *President*
EMP: 6
SALES (est): 652K **Privately Held**
SIC: 3444 Sheet metalwork

(G-10167)
LOUIS G FREEMAN CO
911 Graham Dr (43420-4086)
PHONE...................................419 334-9709
EMP: 50
SALES (corp-wide): 8.3MM **Privately Held**
SIC: 3312 3544 Blast Furnace-Steel Works Mfg Dies/Tools/Jigs/Fixtures
PA: Louis G Freeman Co Inc
911 Graham Dr
Fremont OH 43420
419 334-9709

(G-10168)
LUDLOW COMPOSITES CORPORATION
Also Called: Crown Mats & Mating
2100 Commerce Dr (43420-1048)
PHONE...................................419 332-5531
Fax: 419 332-5531
Vincent J Dephillips, *President*
B Randall Dobbs, *President*
Joann Northcott, *Vice Pres*
Barry Payne, *Vice Pres*
Chris Tricozzi, *Vice Pres*
◆ EMP: 180
SQ FT: 190,000
SALES (est): 47.7MM **Privately Held**
SIC: 3069 3081 Mats or matting, rubber; latex, foamed; vinyl film & sheet

(G-10169)
MARK CARPENTER INDUSTRIES INC
Also Called: Mc Industries
2300 Napoleon Rd (43420-2644)
PHONE...................................419 294-4568
Fax: 419 355-8083
Mark Stephan, *President*
Donna Stephan, *Treasurer*
EMP: 8
SQ FT: 10,000
SALES: 600K **Privately Held**
SIC: 3559 Foundry machinery & equipment

GEOGRAPHIC

(G-10170)
MICHIGAN SUGAR COMPANY
1101 N Front St (43420-1922)
PHONE..............................419 332-9931
David Noble, *Vice Pres*
Mark Flegenheimer, *Manager*
EMP: 10
SALES (corp-wide): 600MM **Privately Held**
SIC: 2063 Beet sugar
PA: Michigan Sugar Company
122 Uptown Dr Unit 300
Bay City MI 48708
989 686-0161

(G-10171)
O E MEYER CO
1005 Everett Rd (43420-1432)
PHONE..............................419 332-6931
Fax: 419 332-6044
Eric Wharton, *Branch Mgr*
Terry Toney, *Manager*
EMP: 8
SALES (corp-wide): 55.7MM **Privately Held**
WEB: www.oemeyer.com
SIC: 3548 Welding & cutting apparatus & accessories
PA: O. E. Meyer Co.
3303 Tiffin Ave
Sandusky OH 44870
419 625-1256

(G-10172)
OMNIMOLD LLC
Also Called: Fremont Plastic Molds
4711 N State Route 19 (43420-8910)
PHONE..............................419 332-4466
Fax: 419 332-2494
Daryl Damschroder, *Vice Pres*
Ken Recker, *Vice Pres*
Mark Wendt, *Safety Mgr*
Larry Camp, *Branch Mgr*
Bill Raubenolt, *Manager*
EMP: 75
SALES (corp-wide): 12.7MM **Privately Held**
WEB: www.midwesttoolinggroup.com
SIC: 3544 3599 Dies & die holders for metal cutting, forming, die casting; machine & other job shop work
PA: Omnimold, Llc
100 Park Pl
Chagrin Falls OH

(G-10173)
ORBIS RPM LLC
2100 Cedar St (43420-1008)
PHONE..............................419 355-8310
Jay Neundorfer, *Branch Mgr*
EMP: 10
SALES (corp-wide): 1.6B **Privately Held**
WEB: www.cartonplast.com
SIC: 3081 Polypropylene film & sheet
HQ: Orbis Rpm, Llc
1055 Corporate Center Dr
Oconomowoc WI 53066
262 560-5000

(G-10174)
PALMER BROS TRANSIT MIX CON
210 N Stone St (43420)
PHONE..............................419 332-6363
Fax: 419 332-6030
Chuck Rapp, *Manager*
EMP: 10
SALES (corp-wide): 7MM **Privately Held**
SIC: 3273 Ready-mixed concrete
PA: Palmer Bros Transit Mix Concrete Inc
12205 E Gypsy Lane Rd
Bowling Green OH 43402
419 352-4681

(G-10175)
PLASTICS GROUP INC
Also Called: Fremont Plastic Products
2101 Cedar St (43420-1007)
PHONE..............................630 325-1210
Dwayne Center, *Manager*
EMP: 250
SALES (corp-wide): 104.7MM **Privately Held**
WEB: www.theplasticsgroup.net
SIC: 3089 Molding primary plastic

PA: The Plastics Group Inc
7409 S Quincy St
Willowbrook IL 60527
630 325-1210

(G-10176)
PRECISION MACHINE & TOOL CO
1016 N 5th St (43420-3932)
PHONE..............................419 334-8405
Fax: 419 334-4502
Ken Ambrozy, *President*
Carolyn Ambrozy, *Corp Secy*
Eric Kizer, *Engineer*
Charles Marietta, *Engineer*
Daniel Garza, *Project Engr*
EMP: 17 **EST:** 1979
SQ FT: 11,500
SALES (est): 3MM **Privately Held**
WEB: www.pmtcompany.com
SIC: 3599 Custom machinery

(G-10177)
PROFESSIONAL SUPPLY INC
Also Called: Worthington Energy Innovations
504 Liberty St (43420-1929)
PHONE..............................419 332-7373
Fax: 419 332-6816
Thomas E Kiser, *President*
Dave Engeman, *Treasurer*
Steven Frederick, *Manager*
EMP: 18 **EST:** 1979
SQ FT: 9,600
SALES (est): 6.2MM **Privately Held**
WEB: www.professionalsupplyinc.com
SIC: 3585 1711 Refrigeration & heating equipment; plumbing, heating, air-conditioning contractors

(G-10178)
REXAM BEVERAGE CAN COMPANY
2145 Cedar St (43420-1007)
PHONE..............................419 334-4461
Tom Schaefer, *Plant Mgr*
Larry Brown, *Engineer*
Jeff Hill, *Personnel*
Robin Wuertz, *Manager*
EMP: 131
SALES (corp-wide): 9B **Publicly Held**
SIC: 3411 3444 3412 3354 Metal cans; sheet metalwork; metal barrels, drums & pails; aluminum extruded products
HQ: Rexam Beverage Can Company
8770 W Bryn Mawr Ave Fl 8
Chicago IL 60631
773 399-3000

(G-10179)
RJM TOOL
1718 Sycamore St (43420-2258)
PHONE..............................419 355-0900
Fax: 419 355-0900
Robert Mason, *Owner*
EMP: 3
SALES: 100K **Privately Held**
SIC: 3599 Machine & other job shop work

(G-10180)
ROOTS POULTRY INC
3721 W State St (43420-9771)
PHONE..............................419 332-0041
Fax: 419 332-5885
Mark Damschroder, *CEO*
Annette Damschroder, *General Mgr*
EMP: 19
SQ FT: 8,000
SALES: 2.2MM **Privately Held**
WEB: www.rootspoultry.com
SIC: 2015 5144 5499 Chicken, processed: cooked; poultry & poultry products; eggs & poultry

(G-10181)
ROWEND INDUSTRIES INC
1035 Napoleon St Ste 101 (43420-2390)
PHONE..............................419 333-8300
Robert Jablonski, *President*
EMP: 8
SALES (est): 824K **Privately Held**
SIC: 3999 Barber & beauty shop equipment

(G-10182)
SEAWIN INC
728 Graham Dr (43420-4073)
PHONE..............................419 355-9111
Fax: 419 355-9211
Prakash Jog, *President*
Mark Radloff, *QC Dir*
EMP: 60
SALES (est): 5.4MM
SALES (corp-wide): 24.2MM **Privately Held**
WEB: www.seawin.com
SIC: 3491 Industrial valves
PA: Alkon Corporation
728 Graham Dr
Fremont OH 43420
419 355-9111

(G-10183)
STANDARD TECHNOLOGIES LLC
2641 Hayes Ave (43420-9715)
PHONE..............................419 332-6434
Fax: 419 332-1199
Max Valentine, *President*
Andy Price, *Sales Dir*
EMP: 75 **EST:** 1916
SQ FT: 35,000
SALES (est): 15.9MM **Privately Held**
SIC: 3444 Sheet metalwork

(G-10184)
STYLE CREST INC (HQ)
2450 Enterprise St (43420-8553)
P.O. Box A (43420-0555)
PHONE..............................419 332-7369
Thomas Kern, *CEO*
Henry Valle, *President*
Phillip Burton, *Corp Secy*
William Goad, *Exec VP*
Bryan T Kern, *Exec VP*
◆ **EMP:** 277
SALES (est): 155.2MM
SALES (corp-wide): 162.7MM **Privately Held**
SIC: 3089 5075 5031 8361 Siding, plastic; warm air heating & air conditioning; building materials, exterior; building materials, interior; residential care
PA: Style Crest Enterprises, Inc.
2450 Enterprise St
Fremont OH 43420
419 355-8586

(G-10185)
STYLE CREST ENTERPRISES INC (PA)
2450 Enterprise St (43420-8553)
P.O. Box A (43420-0555)
PHONE..............................419 355-8586
Thomas L Kern, *CEO*
Henry Valle, *President*
Phillip Burton, *Corp Secy*
Bryan T Kern, *Exec VP*
Stephen Crokie, *Mfg Spvr*
EMP: 82
SQ FT: 40,000
SALES (est): 162.7MM **Privately Held**
SIC: 3089 5075 Plastic hardware & building products; awnings, fiberglass & plastic combination; siding, plastic; warm air heating & air conditioning

(G-10186)
TECHNIFORM INDUSTRIES INC
2107 Hayes Ave (43420-2695)
PHONE..............................419 332-8484
Fax: 419 334-5222
Clifford A Robinette, *President*
Paul Reinhart, *Project Mgr*
Thomas Messina, *Engineer*
Michael Robinette, *Sales Mgr*
Jon Mistor, *Office Mgr*
EMP: 30
SQ FT: 16,000
SALES (est): 8.6MM **Privately Held**
WEB: www.techniform-plastics.com
SIC: 3083 3599 Thermoplastic laminates: rods, tubes, plates & sheet; custom machinery

(G-10187)
THE FREMONT KRAUT COMPANY
724 N Front St (43420-1915)
PHONE..............................419 332-6481
Fax: 419 334-5087
Russell G Sorg, *President*
Jan Sorg, *Corp Secy*
Orland H Hasselbach, *Vice Pres*
Richard L Smith, *VP Sales*
EMP: 70 **EST:** 1906
SALES: 3MM
SALES (corp-wide): 42.6MM **Privately Held**
WEB: www.fremontcompany.com
SIC: 2033 Canned fruits & specialties
PA: The Fremont Company
802 N Front St
Fremont OH 43420
419 334-8995

(G-10188)
TRUE KOTE INC
2132 E Cole Rd (43420-8754)
PHONE..............................419 334-8813
Donald C Bayless, *President*
Marie Bayless, *Corp Secy*
EMP: 8
SQ FT: 2,500
SALES: 500K **Privately Held**
SIC: 1752 3544 Floor laying & floor work; dies, steel rule

(G-10189)
TW TANK LLC
721 Graham Dr (43420-4074)
PHONE..............................419 334-2664
EMP: 5 **Privately Held**
SIC: 3443 Mfg Fabricated Plate Work

(G-10190)
TW TANK LLC
721 Graham Dr (43420-4074)
PHONE..............................419 334-2664
EMP: 5 **Privately Held**
SIC: 7692 Welding Repair

(G-10191)
UNICAN OHIO LLC
4600 Oak Harbor Rd (43420-9373)
PHONE..............................419 636-5461
Kim Miller, *Plant Mgr*
Stig Rasmussen, *Mng Member*
▲ **EMP:** 5
SQ FT: 100,000
SALES (est): 1.2MM **Privately Held**
SIC: 3412 Metal barrels, drums & pails

(G-10192)
UNIQUE FABRICATIONS INC
2520 Hayes Ave (43420-2639)
PHONE..............................419 355-1700
Fax: 419 355-0104
Karl Honsperger, *President*
Anthony Doble, *Vice Pres*
Wayne Doble, *Vice Pres*
Ed Gebhart, *Purchasing*
Kay Wilson, *Purchasing*
EMP: 17
SQ FT: 12,000
SALES: 4.6MM **Privately Held**
WEB: www.uniquefabrications.com
SIC: 3441 Fabricated structural metal

(G-10193)
WAHL REFRACTORY SOLUTIONS LLC
767 S State Route 19 (43420-9260)
PHONE..............................419 334-2658
Fax: 419 334-9445
Timothy M Albertson, *President*
Cornerstone Industrial Group, *Managing Prtnr*
Sarah Herman, *Controller*
Alex George, *Sales Mgr*
Gilles Mercier, *Sales Staff*
▲ **EMP:** 65
SALES (est): 16.7MM **Privately Held**
SIC: 3255 3297 Clay refractories; mortars, clay refractory; plastic fire clay bricks; nonclay refractories

(G-10194)
WELLYS HORSERADISH
Also Called: Welly's Horseradish Co
141 N Monroe St (43420-2347)
PHONE..............................419 334-3134
Roger Frantz, *President*
Craig Frantz, *Vice Pres*
Kay Frantz, *Vice Pres*
EMP: 3
SQ FT: 4,000
SALES: 70K **Privately Held**
WEB: www.wellyshorseradish.com
SIC: 2035 Horseradish, prepared

(G-10195)
WOODBRIDGE GROUP
827 Graham Dr (43420-4075)
PHONE..............................419 334-3666
Fax: 419 334-2922
Lucy Mathia, *Human Res Dir*
Mike Kohout, *Manager*
Jeff Humenick, *Manager*
EMP: 150
SALES (corp-wide): 3.7B **Publicly Held**
SIC: 3069 3714 Hard rubber & molded
rubber products; motor vehicle parts & ac-
cessories
HQ: Woodbridge Company Limited, The
65 Queen St W Suite 2400
Toronto ON M5H 2
416 364-8700

Fresno
Coshocton County

(G-10196)
CHILI LOGGING LTD
30240 County Road 10 (43824-9021)
PHONE..............................740 545-9502
Leroy Troyer, *Principal*
EMP: 3
SALES (est): 185.8K **Privately Held**
SIC: 2411 Logging

(G-10197)
PEARL VALLEY CHEESE INC
54760 Township Road 90 (43824-9796)
P.O. Box 68 (43824-0068)
PHONE..............................740 545-6002
Fax: 740 545-7703
John E Stalder, *President*
Sally Ellis, *Corp Secy*
Charles Ellis, *Manager*
John Grace, *Technology*
EMP: 20
SQ FT: 8,000
SALES (est): 6.2MM **Privately Held**
WEB: www.pearlvalleycheese.com
SIC: 2022 Natural cheese

(G-10198)
PRECISION INC
33725 County Road 10 (43824-9018)
PHONE..............................330 897-8860
Dan Miller, *President*
Martha Miller, *Admin Sec*
EMP: 4
SQ FT: 400
SALES (est): 100K **Privately Held**
SIC: 7389 3599 Design, commercial & in-
dustrial; electrical discharge machining
(EDM)

(G-10199)
SUPERFINE MANUFACTURING INC
33715 County Road 10 (43824-9018)
PHONE..............................330 897-9024
Fax: 330 897-8014
Dan Miller, *Owner*
EMP: 10
SALES (est): 1.2MM **Privately Held**
WEB: www.superfineinc.com
SIC: 3999 Forms: display, dress & show

(G-10200)
THOMAS HORA
Also Called: Deer Valley Woodworking
32441 County Rd Ste 12 (43824)
PHONE..............................740 622-1386
Thomas Hora, *Owner*
EMP: 3

SALES (est): 170K **Privately Held**
SIC: 2511 2541 Wood household furniture;
wood partitions & fixtures

(G-10201)
TROYERS PALLET SHOP
31052 Township Road 227 (43824-8801)
PHONE..............................330 897-1038
Atlee Troyer, *Owner*
EMP: 3 EST: 2001
SALES (est): 262.1K **Privately Held**
SIC: 2448 Pallets, wood & wood with metal

Gahanna
Franklin County

(G-10202)
ADVANCED PLASTIC SYSTEMS INC
990 Gahanna Pkwy (43230-6613)
PHONE..............................614 759-6550
Fax: 614 759-6758
Wolfegang Doerschlag, *President*
James Mott, *CFO*
Diana Netzer, *Accountant*
Dianna Metzger, *Office Mgr*
Lori Planton, *Technical Staff*
EMP: 17
SQ FT: 25,000
SALES (est): 3.2MM **Privately Held**
SIC: 3089 Plastic processing

(G-10203)
AJA INDUSTRIES LLC
3857 Wintergreen Blvd (43230-1058)
PHONE..............................614 216-9566
John D Chubb,
Tina L Chubb,
▲ **EMP:** 3
SALES: 169.9K **Privately Held**
SIC: 3599 7389 Custom machinery;

(G-10204)
ARCHITCTRAL IDENTIFICATION INC (PA)
1170 Claycraft Rd (43230-6640)
PHONE..............................614 868-8400
Fax: 614 866-4614
William J Cooke, *President*
Barbara B Cooke, *Corp Secy*
James W Cooke, *COO*
Robert C Barnhart Jr, *Vice Pres*
Keri Schroeder, *Project Mgr*
EMP: 20
SQ FT: 5,000
SALES (est): 2MM **Privately Held**
WEB: www.archid.net
SIC: 3993 8748 Signs & advertising spe-
cialties; electric signs; signs, not made in
custom sign painting shops; systems
analysis or design

(G-10205)
BUSINESS FNCTNALITY FORMS SVCS
4367 Grays Market Dr (43230-5425)
PHONE..............................614 557-9420
Kenyetta Bagby, *Principal*
EMP: 3
SALES: 3K **Privately Held**
SIC: 2754 Business form & card printing,
gravure

(G-10206)
DEEMSYS INC
800 Cross Pointe Rd Ste A (43230-6688)
PHONE..............................614 322-9928
Vijiayarani Benjamin, *Ch of Bd*
Jacob Benjamin, *President*
Dexter Benjamin, *Vice Pres*
Rt Rajan, *Manager*
EMP: 82
SQ FT: 5,100
SALES: 5.7MM **Privately Held**
WEB: www.deemsysinc.com
SIC: 8748 2741 7373 8299 Business
consulting; ; systems software develop-
ment services; educational service, non-
degree granting: continuing educ.;
computer software development & appli-
cations

(G-10207)
FRANKIE TATUM
Also Called: Tatum Landscaping & Lawncare
3604 Watt Rd (43230-1157)
P.O. Box 30148, Columbus (43230-0148)
PHONE..............................614 216-1556
Frankie Tatum, *Owner*
Kathy Tatum, *Principal*
EMP: 3
SALES (est): 114.9K **Privately Held**
SIC: 0783 3271 0782 Spraying services,
ornamental tree; blocks, concrete: land-
scape or retaining wall; garden planting
services

(G-10208)
HANGER PRSTHETCS & ORTHO INC
471 Morrison Rd Ste E (43230-5308)
PHONE..............................614 471-8210
Fax: 614 471-8239
Tim Riedlinger, *Manager*
EMP: 3
SALES (corp-wide): 460MM **Publicly Held**
SIC: 3842 Limbs, artificial
HQ: Hanger Prosthetics & Orthotics, Inc.
10910 Domain Dr Ste 300
Austin TX 78758
512 777-3800

(G-10209)
HEAT TREATING INC
675 Cross Pointe Rd (43230-6689)
PHONE..............................614 759-9963
Rod Ingram, *Vice Pres*
EMP: 7 EST: 2009
SALES (est): 631.5K **Privately Held**
SIC: 3398 Metal heat treating

(G-10210)
HEXION INC
630 Morrison Rd Ste 300 (43230-5318)
PHONE..............................614 759-6227
Debra Dutton, *Branch Mgr*
Dina Wonn, *Manager*
EMP: 52 **Publicly Held**
SIC: 2821 Thermosetting materials
HQ: Hexion Inc.
180 E Broad St Fl 26
Columbus OH 43215
614 225-4000

(G-10211)
HOLLYWOOD IMPRINTS LLC
1000 Morrison Rd Ste D (43230-6669)
PHONE..............................614 501-6040
Elvis Doss,
Davidee Doss,
Kim Mitchem,
EMP: 14
SALES (est): 1.2MM **Privately Held**
SIC: 7336 2396 7319 Silk screen design;
fabric printing & stamping; screen printing
on fabric articles; poster advertising serv-
ice, except outdoor

(G-10212)
INK WELL
969 Claycraft Rd (43230-6635)
PHONE..............................614 861-7113
Fax: 614 863-5534
Barbara Seay, *Owner*
EMP: 5
SQ FT: 3,000
SALES (est): 330K **Privately Held**
SIC: 2752 Commercial printing, litho-
graphic

(G-10213)
INTO GREAT BRANDS INC
Also Called: Motorkote & Dura Lube
1010 Taylor Station Rd A (43230-6676)
PHONE..............................888 771-5656
Bill Beichner, *CEO*
Lance Balistrere, *Vice Pres*
James Dolin Jr, *CFO*
Elizabeth Dean, *Accounts Mgr*
▼ **EMP:** 10
SQ FT: 15,000
SALES (est): 1.9MM **Privately Held**
WEB: www.motorkote.com
SIC: 2992 Oils & greases, blending & com-
pounding

(G-10214)
K PETROLEUM INC (PA)
81 Mill St Ste 205 (43230-1718)
PHONE..............................614 532-5420
Jam Khorrami, *President*
EMP: 10
SQ FT: 3,000
SALES: 7.6MM **Privately Held**
WEB: www.kpetroleum.com
SIC: 1382 Oil & gas exploration services

(G-10215)
KAHIKI FOODS INC
1100 Morrison Rd (43230-6645)
PHONE..............................614 322-3180
Fax: 614 751-0039
Alan L Hoover, *President*
Bob Helland, *Vice Pres*
Tim Tsao, *Vice Pres*
Jim Triskett, *Warehouse Mgr*
Chris Overholt, *QC Mgr*
▲ **EMP:** 160
SQ FT: 119,000
SALES (est): 47.8MM
SALES (corp-wide): 298.7MM **Privately Held**
WEB: www.kahiki.com
SIC: 2038 Frozen specialties
PA: Abarta, Inc.
200 Alpha Dr
Pittsburgh PA 15238
412 963-6226

(G-10216)
LA BOIT SPECIALTY VEHICLES (PA)
700 Cross Pointe Rd (43230-6685)
PHONE..............................614 231-7640
Gil Blais, *President*
Ryan Depriest, *General Mgr*
Samson Cheng, *CFO*
Jody Blais, *Sales Executive*
Ann Blais, *Manager*
EMP: 35
SQ FT: 18,000
SALES (est): 9.1MM **Privately Held**
WEB: www.laboit.com
SIC: 3711 3713 Ambulances (motor vehi-
cles), assembly of; ambulance bodies

(G-10217)
MAUSER USA LLC
1410 Blatt Blvd (43230-6627)
PHONE..............................614 856-5982
Mike Tanner, *Plant Mgr*
EMP: 45
SALES (corp-wide): 6.6B **Privately Held**
SIC: 3412 Barrels, shipping: metal
HQ: Mauser Usa, Llc
2 Tower Center Blvd 20-1
East Brunswick NJ 08816
732 353-7100

(G-10218)
MCNEILUS TRUCK AND MFG INC
1130 Morrison Rd (43230-6646)
P.O. Box 30777 (43230-0777)
PHONE..............................614 868-0760
Fax: 614 868-0498
Paul Ellingen, *Manager*
Kem Satterfield, *Manager*
EMP: 6
SALES (corp-wide): 6.2B **Publicly Held**
WEB: www.mcneiluscompanies.com
SIC: 3713 5082 Cement mixer bodies;
concrete processing equipment
HQ: Mcneilus Truck And Manufacturing,
Inc.
524 County Rd 34 E
Dodge Center MN 55927
614 868-0760

(G-10219)
MIDDLETON PRINTING CO INC
81 Mill St Ste 300 (43230-1718)
PHONE..............................614 294-7277
Fax: 614 294-7449
David H Stewart, *President*
Reno Camerucci, *Vice Pres*
Laura Firestone, *Manager*
EMP: 9 EST: 1950
SQ FT: 14,000

GEOGRAPHIC

SALES (est): 1.5MM **Privately Held**
WEB: www.middletonprinting.com
SIC: 2752 2791 2759 Commercial printing, offset; typesetting; commercial printing

(G-10220)
MILNOT COMPANY
735 Taylor Rd Ste 200 (43230-6274)
PHONE.................................888 656-3245
Craig A Steinke, *CEO*
William J Bond, *Vice Pres*
John Halll, *Vice Pres*
Alain Souligny, *CFO*
Connie Huck, *Controller*
▼ EMP: 4
SALES (est): 470.7K
SALES (corp-wide): 7.8B **Publicly Held**
WEB: www.milnot.com
SIC: 2023 2032 Dry, condensed, evaporated dairy products; condensed milk; canned specialties
PA: The J M Smucker Company
　1 Strawberry Ln
　Orrville OH 44667
　330 682-3000

(G-10221)
MRC GLOBAL (US) INC
700 Taylor Rd (43230-3318)
PHONE.................................614 475-4033
Steven Park, *Branch Mgr*
EMP: 11
SALES (corp-wide): 3B **Publicly Held**
SIC: 1311 Crude petroleum & natural gas
HQ: Mrc Global (Us) Inc.
　1301 Mckinney St Ste 2300
　Houston TX 77010
　877 294-7574

(G-10222)
NETPARK LLC
1182 Claycraft Rd (43230-6640)
PHONE.................................614 866-2495
Jon Schmidt, *President*
Patricia Bell, *CFO*
Douglas Fortman, *Programmer Anys*
Daniel Gump, *Director*
EMP: 10
SALES (est): 937.4K **Privately Held**
SIC: 7372 Business oriented computer software

(G-10223)
NETWORK COMMUNICATIONS INC
Also Called: Apartment Finder Magazine
467 Waterbury Ct Ste B (43230-5313)
PHONE.................................614 934-1919
EMP: 150
SALES (corp-wide): 1.3B **Privately Held**
SIC: 2741 Misc Publishing
HQ: Network Communications, Inc.
　2 Sun Ct Ste 300
　Norcross GA 30092
　678 346-9300

(G-10224)
NIAGARA BOTTLING LLC
1700 Eastgate Pkwy (43230-8602)
PHONE.................................614 751-7420
Randell Presnell, *Principal*
▲ EMP: 14
SALES (est): 2.6MM **Privately Held**
SIC: 2086 Bottled & canned soft drinks

(G-10225)
PAHUJA INC
Also Called: Alloy Polymers
1125 Gahanna Pkwy (43230-6612)
PHONE.................................614 864-3989
Cathy Stimpert, *Vice Pres*
Matt Collier, *Engineer*
Shawn Heartman, *Engineer*
Peter Ploumidis, *Manager*
EMP: 60
SALES (corp-wide): 59.4MM **Privately Held**
WEB: www.alloypolymers.com
SIC: 2821 3089 Polypropylene resins; extruded finished plastic products
PA: Pahuja, Inc.
　3310 Deepwater Trml Rd
　Richmond VA 23234
　804 200-6624

(G-10226)
PERFECTION PACKAGING INC
885 Claycraft Rd (43230-6850)
PHONE.................................614 866-8558
James W Cox, *President*
Evelyn Cox, *Vice Pres*
EMP: 3
SALES (est): 37.5K **Privately Held**
WEB: www.perfectionpkg.com
SIC: 2671 3577 Packaging paper & plastics film, coated & laminated; paper coated or laminated for packaging; bar code (magnetic ink) printers

(G-10227)
R&S CARBON TRADING LLC
146 N Hamilton Rd Ste 127 (43230-2600)
PHONE.................................614 264-3083
Roger D Kinney, *Mng Member*
Sean Kinney,
▼ EMP: 4
SQ FT: 525
SALES (est): 1MM **Privately Held**
WEB: www.rscarbon.com
SIC: 3624 Carbon & graphite products

(G-10228)
RIBBON TECHNOLOGY CORPORATION
Also Called: Ribtec
825 Taylor Station Rd (43230-6654)
P.O. Box 30758 (43230-0758)
PHONE.................................614 864-5444
Fax: 614 864-5305
Kevin Jackson, *President*
Scott Palmer, *Corp Secy*
Terry Boyd, *Manager*
▼ EMP: 11
SQ FT: 40,000
SALES (est): 1.6MM
SALES (corp-wide): 7.5MM **Privately Held**
WEB: www.ribtec.com
SIC: 3357 Building wire & cable, nonferrous
HQ: Ribbon Technology Corporation
　825 Taylor Station Rd
　Gahanna OH 43230
　614 864-5444

(G-10229)
RIBBON TECHNOLOGY CORPORATION (DH)
Also Called: River Technology
825 Taylor Station Rd (43230-6654)
PHONE.................................614 864-5444
John Norder, *President*
Scott Palmer, *Corp Secy*
Scott Palmar, *Controller*
John Solomon, *Manager*
▼ EMP: 11
SQ FT: 40,000
SALES (est): 1.6MM
SALES (corp-wide): 7.5MM **Privately Held**
SIC: 2299 Yarn, metallic, ceramic or paper fibers
HQ: Dynamic-Materials Limited
　Brookhill Industrial Estate
　Nottingham NOTTS
　177 386-3100

(G-10230)
ROMANOFF ELC RESIDENTIAL LLC
1288 Research Rd (43230-6625)
PHONE.................................614 755-4500
Matthew Romanoff, *CEO*
EMP: 50
SALES (est): 172.3K
SALES (corp-wide): 7.5MM **Privately Held**
SIC: 3699 Household electrical equipment
PA: The Romanoff Group Llc
　1288 Research Rd
　Gahanna OH 43230
　614 755-4500

(G-10231)
SCOTTS COMPANY LLC
710 Cross Pointe Rd (43230-6685)
P.O. Box 307574 (43230-7574)
PHONE.................................614 863-3920
Mike McClung, *Branch Mgr*
EMP: 20

SALES (corp-wide): 2.8B **Publicly Held**
WEB: www.scottscompany.com
SIC: 2873 Fertilizers: natural (organic), except compost
HQ: The Scotts Company Llc
　14111 Scottslawn Rd
　Marysville OH 43040
　937 644-3729

(G-10232)
SIGN A RAMA
Also Called: Sign-A-Rama
64 Granville St (43230-3064)
PHONE.................................614 337-6000
Fax: 614 337-2295
Bill Martin, *Owner*
EMP: 4 EST: 1999
SALES (est): 230K **Privately Held**
SIC: 3993 Signs & advertising specialties

(G-10233)
SJPM INC
Also Called: Metcalf Design & Printing Ctr
264 Agler Rd (43230-2546)
PHONE.................................614 475-4571
Fax: 614 475-6004
Beverly Metcalf, *President*
David Metcalf, *Vice Pres*
Jeff Metcalf, *Manager*
Jane Schmidt, *Manager*
EMP: 5
SQ FT: 1,200
SALES (est): 520K **Privately Held**
SIC: 2752 7336 2791 Commercial printing, lithographic; graphic arts & related design; typesetting

(G-10234)
SNOW AVIATION INTL INC
949 Creek Dr (43230)
PHONE.................................614 588-2452
Fax: 614 492-7678
Harry T Snow, *President*
Bill Fergusson, *Exec VP*
Lucky Ekman, *Vice Pres*
Richard Heybes, *Vice Pres*
Donald Smith, *Vice Pres*
EMP: 129
SQ FT: 28,000
SALES: 10MM **Privately Held**
WEB: www.snowaviation.com
SIC: 3721 3728 3724 Aircraft; aircraft assemblies, subassemblies & parts; aircraft engines & engine parts

(G-10235)
SPECTRAMED INC
275 W Johnstown Rd (43230-2732)
PHONE.................................740 263-3059
Richard Fisher, *President*
Glendevore Borad, *Sales Staff*
Matt Favazzo, *Sales Staff*
Nathan Fisher, *Manager*
Teresa Biber, *Director*
▲ EMP: 10
SQ FT: 3,000
SALES (est): 2.3MM **Privately Held**
WEB: www.spectramedonline.com
SIC: 3624 Electrodes, thermal & electrolytic uses: carbon, graphite

(G-10236)
SPHON ASSOCIATES INC
962 Bryn Mawr Dr (43230-3843)
PHONE.................................614 741-4002
Alicia Holloway, *Principal*
EMP: 3
SALES (est): 180K **Privately Held**
SIC: 2421 Building & structural materials, wood

(G-10237)
SURPLUS FREIGHT INC (PA)
501 Morrison Rd Ste 100 (43230-3541)
PHONE.................................614 235-7660
David Belford, *CEO*
Alf Karzia, *President*
Douglas A Hanby, *Principal*
Mike Mess, *Treasurer*
EMP: 7
SALES (est): 4.1MM **Privately Held**
SIC: 3537 Trucks: freight, baggage, etc.: industrial, except mining

(G-10238)
THOMPSON PARTNERS INC
Also Called: Tpi Medical
82 Mill St Ste A (43230-3058)
P.O. Box 307687 (43230-7687)
PHONE.................................866 475-2500
Garret Thompson, *President*
Michele Thompson, *Manager*
EMP: 4
SALES (est): 270K **Privately Held**
SIC: 3841 Surgical & medical instruments

(G-10239)
TIMKEN COMPANY
1027 Greythorne Pl (43230-6216)
PHONE.................................614 476-3934
EMP: 3
SALES (est): 207.9K **Privately Held**
SIC: 3562 Ball & roller bearings

(G-10240)
VICTORY DIRECT LLC
750 Cross Pointe Rd Ste M (43230-6692)
PHONE.................................614 626-0000
Glen Morrow, *Sales Executive*
Joe King, *Mng Member*
EMP: 7
SALES: 1MM **Privately Held**
SIC: 7331 2752 Direct mail advertising services; business form & card printing, lithographic

---

Galena
Delaware County

(G-10241)
ERIC MONDENE
4278 Harlem Rd (43021-9667)
PHONE.................................740 965-2842
Eric Mondene, *Principal*
EMP: 4
SALES (est): 268.1K **Privately Held**
SIC: 3423 Carpenters' hand tools, except saws: levels, chisels, etc.

(G-10242)
GALENA VAULT LTD
4909 Harlem Rd (43021-9302)
PHONE.................................740 965-2200
Marcia Jo M Eisenbrown, *Owner*
EMP: 3
SALES (est): 367K **Privately Held**
SIC: 3272 Burial vaults, concrete or precast terrazzo

(G-10243)
HALLS SHEET METAL FABRICATION
Also Called: Hall's Sheet Metal Fabricating
10001 Center Village Rd (43021-9002)
PHONE.................................740 965-9264
Fax: 740 965-8286
James Hall, *President*
Mary Hall, *Admin Sec*
EMP: 4
SQ FT: 6,000
SALES (est): 638.4K **Privately Held**
WEB: www.hallsheetmetal.com
SIC: 3444 Sheet metalwork

(G-10244)
JCP SIGNS & GRAPHIX INC
12920 Gorsuch Rd (43021-8620)
PHONE.................................740 965-3058
John W Petten, *President*
EMP: 3
SALES (est): 207.7K **Privately Held**
SIC: 3993 Signs & advertising specialties

(G-10245)
K-O-K PRODUCTS INC
700 S 3 Bs And K Rd (43021-9725)
PHONE.................................740 548-0526
Frank Biancone, *Ch of Bd*
Joe Minadeo, *President*
Sandra Ann Biancone, *Vice Pres*
EMP: 15 EST: 1926
SQ FT: 32,000
SALES: 2.5MM **Privately Held**
WEB: www.kokproducts.com
SIC: 2842 5087 Bleaches, household: dry or liquid; specialty cleaning preparations; service establishment equipment

(G-10246)
LEXINGTON PROSTHETIC ORTOTICS
7035 Dustin Rd (43021-9475)
PHONE..................................803 939-0097
Michael Russell, *President*
Judith Russell, *Corp Secy*
R Micheal Russell, *Director*
EMP: 5
SALES (est): 380K **Privately Held**
SIC: 3842 Braces, orthopedic

(G-10247)
MASON PRODUCING INC
10010 Center Village Rd (43021-8605)
PHONE..................................740 913-0686
EMP: 3
SALES (est): 141.4K **Privately Held**
SIC: 1311 Crude petroleum & natural gas

(G-10248)
MIDWEST INDUSTRIAL SPECIALTIES
5521 Summer Blvd (43021-9549)
PHONE..................................740 815-0541
Steven B Davis, *Mng Member*
EMP: 3
SALES: 250K **Privately Held**
SIC: 3544 Dies & die holders for metal cutting, forming, die casting

(G-10249)
SHADES OF SUGAR LTD
5939 Lakewood Dr (43021-9626)
PHONE..................................614 776-5998
John Johnson, *Principal*
EMP: 3
SALES (est): 124.9K **Privately Held**
SIC: 2052 Cookies & crackers

Galion
Crawford County

(G-10250)
A & G MANUFACTURING CO INC (PA)
Also Called: A G Mercury
280 Gelsanliter Rd (44833-2234)
P.O. Box 935 (44833-0935)
PHONE..................................419 468-7433
Fax: 419 468-3990
Arvin Shifley, *President*
Glen Shifley Sr, *Principal*
Doug Shifley, *Treasurer*
Jim Streib, *Sales Mgr*
Karin Baldwin, *Accounts Mgr*
▲ EMP: 40
SQ FT: 100,000
SALES (est): 10.4MM **Privately Held**
WEB: www.agmercury.com
SIC: 3599 7692 3446 3444 Machine shop, jobbing & repair; welding repair; architectural metalwork; sheet metalwork; fabricated plate work (boiler shop); fabricated structural metal

(G-10251)
A & G MANUFACTURING CO INC
165 Gelsanliter Rd (44833)
PHONE..................................419 468-7433
Arvin Shifley, *Branch Mgr*
EMP: 70
SALES (corp-wide): 10.4MM **Privately Held**
WEB: www.agmercury.com
SIC: 3599 Machine shop, jobbing & repair
PA: A. & G. Manufacturing Co., Inc.
280 Gelsanliter Rd
Galion OH 44833
419 468-7433

(G-10252)
ALEXANDER WILBERT VAULT CO (PA)
134 Harding Way W (44833-1726)
P.O. Box 177 (44833-0177)
PHONE..................................419 468-3477
Fax: 419 468-5176
C Phillip Longstreth, *President*
Sean Longstreth, *Vice Pres*
EMP: 9

SALES: 700K **Privately Held**
SIC: 3272 Burial vaults, concrete or precast terrazzo

(G-10253)
AMERICAN STEEL GRAVE VAULT CO
799 Newberry Dr (44833-1146)
PHONE..................................419 468-6715
Fax: 419 468-2292
Brent Kingseed, *President*
Al Kingseed, *Vice Pres*
Mary Kingseed, *Admin Sec*
EMP: 10 EST: 1908
SQ FT: 46,300
SALES: 720.6K **Privately Held**
SIC: 3995 Grave vaults, metal

(G-10254)
BAILLIE LUMBER CO LP
3953 County Road 51 (44833)
PHONE..................................419 462-2000
Russel Jones, *Branch Mgr*
EMP: 40
SALES (corp-wide): 281.9MM **Privately Held**
SIC: 5031 2426 2421 Lumber: rough, dressed & finished; hardwood dimension & flooring mills; sawmills & planing mills, general
PA: Baillie Lumber Co., L.P.
4002 Legion Dr
Hamburg NY 14075
800 950-2850

(G-10255)
BROTHERS BODY AND EQP LLC
352 South St Bldg 24 (44833-2742)
P.O. Box 926 (44833-0926)
PHONE..................................419 462-1975
Michael Horn, *President*
Tim Horn, *General Mgr*
▲ EMP: 15
SQ FT: 30,000
SALES (est): 4MM **Privately Held**
WEB: www.brothersbande.com
SIC: 3713 Truck bodies & parts

(G-10256)
CARTER MACHINE COMPANY INC (PA)
Also Called: Hydranamics
820 Edward St (44833-2223)
PHONE..................................419 468-3530
Fax: 419 468-9185
Juanita Carter, *Ch of Bd*
Andrea Carter, *President*
E V Keeler, *Principal*
Larry Korbas, *Director*
EMP: 5 EST: 1941
SALES (est): 11.6MM **Privately Held**
SIC: 3593 3498 3471 Fluid power cylinders, hydraulic or pneumatic; fabricated pipe & fittings; plating & polishing

(G-10257)
CASS FRAMES INC
6052 State Route 19 (44833-9771)
P.O. Box 625 (44833-0625)
PHONE..................................419 468-2863
James Cass, *President*
Bart Cass, *Vice Pres*
Delores Cass, *Admin Sec*
EMP: 9
SQ FT: 4,200
SALES (est): 1.4MM **Privately Held**
SIC: 2499 Picture & mirror frames, wood; picture frame molding, finished

(G-10258)
CENTRAL STATE ENTERPRISES INC
1331 Freese Works Pl (44833-9368)
PHONE..................................419 468-8191
Fax: 419 468-8663
Donald E Kuenzli Jr, *President*
Sandra Kuenzli, *Corp Secy*
Tresa Osowski, *Manager*
EMP: 37
SQ FT: 28,000
SALES (est): 7.7MM **Privately Held**
SIC: 3599 Machine shop, jobbing & repair

(G-10259)
CMI HOLDING COMPANY CRAWFORD
1310 Freese Works Pl (44833-9368)
PHONE..................................419 468-9122
Fax: 419 468-8364
Kevin Hessey, *President*
Brad Hessey, *Vice Pres*
Keith Hummel, *Vice Pres*
Joleen Shey, *Purch Agent*
Laurie Schroeder, *Marketing Staff*
◆ EMP: 70
SALES (est): 14.4MM
SALES (corp-wide): 60MM **Privately Held**
WEB: www.crawfordmachineinc.com
SIC: 3432 Plumbing fixture fittings & trim; plumbers' brass goods: drain cocks, faucets, spigots, etc.
HQ: Sloan L Tramec L C
534 E 48th St
Holland MI 49423
616 395-5600

(G-10260)
COTTONWOOD PALLET INC
Also Called: Cotton Wood Pallet Co
9541 Mrral Krkptrick Rd E (44833-9789)
PHONE..................................419 468-9703
Eugene Stewart, *President*
Christopher Stewart, *Vice Pres*
EMP: 4
SALES (est): 397.3K **Privately Held**
SIC: 2448 Pallets, wood

(G-10261)
COVERT MANUFACTURING INC (PA)
328 S East St (44833-2729)
P.O. Box 608 (44833-0608)
PHONE..................................419 468-1761
Fax: 419 468-2188
Kym Fox, *President*
Teri Williams, *President*
Donald L Covert Sr, *Principal*
Martha Covert, *Sr Corp Ofcr*
Steve Lamontagne, *Mktg Dir*
▲ EMP: 108
SQ FT: 300,000
SALES (est): 65.9MM **Privately Held**
WEB: www.covertmfg.com
SIC: 3545 Machine tool accessories

(G-10262)
CRASE COMMUNICATIONS INC
120 Harding Way E Ste 104 (44833-1927)
PHONE..................................419 468-1173
Fax: 419 462-1155
Edward Crase, *President*
Linda Crase, *Corp Secy*
EMP: 13
SALES (est): 1.4MM **Privately Held**
WEB: www.crasecommunications.com
SIC: 1731 3661 Telephone & telephone equipment installation; toll switching equipment, telephone

(G-10263)
DINKMAR INC
9357 Township Road 48 (44833-9801)
PHONE..................................419 468-8516
Fax: 419 468-8417
David Dinkel, *President*
EMP: 5
SQ FT: 5,200
SALES (est): 400K **Privately Held**
SIC: 3589 5084 Vacuum cleaners & sweepers, electric: industrial; industrial machinery & equipment

(G-10264)
DYENAMO DISTRIBUTING
6124 State Route 19 (44833-8931)
P.O. Box 759 (44833-0759)
PHONE..................................419 462-9474
Fax: 419 462-9466
Ken Dye, *Owner*
EMP: 12
SALES (est): 560K **Privately Held**
SIC: 2759 Promotional printing

(G-10265)
E & E NAMEPLATES INC
760 E Walnut St (44833-2133)
PHONE..................................419 468-3617

Fax: 419 468-4231
Mike Enders, *Co-Owner*
Michelle Montague, *Vice Pres*
EMP: 12 EST: 1976
SQ FT: 4,500
SALES (est): 1MM **Privately Held**
SIC: 2759 Screen printing

(G-10266)
EAGLE CRUSHER CO INC (PA)
525 S Market St (44833-2612)
P.O. Box 537 (44833-0537)
PHONE..................................419 468-2288
Fax: 419 468-4840
Susanne Cobey, *President*
Bob Hamilton, *Vice Pres*
Shawn Jury, *Vice Pres*
Scott Carpenter, *Purch Mgr*
Chris Chartier, *Purch Agent*
◆ EMP: 75
SQ FT: 40,000
SALES (est): 42.3MM **Privately Held**
WEB: www.eaglecrusher.com
SIC: 3535 3532 3589 3531 Conveyors & conveying equipment; crushing, pulverizing & screening equipment; sewage & water treatment equipment; construction machinery

(G-10267)
ELLIOTT MACHINE WORKS INC
1351 Freese Works Pl (44833-9368)
P.O. Box 955 (44833-0955)
PHONE..................................419 468-4709
Fax: 419 468-4642
Richard Ekin, *President*
Brad Ekin, *Vice Pres*
Brent Ekin, *VP Opers*
EMP: 48 EST: 1968
SQ FT: 54,000
SALES: 8MM **Privately Held**
WEB: www.elliottmachine.com
SIC: 3713 3443 3537 Truck bodies (motor vehicles); tanks for tank trucks, metal plate; trucks: freight, baggage, etc.: industrial, except mining; truck trailers, used in plants, docks, terminals, etc.

(G-10268)
GALION LLC
515 N East St (44833-2142)
P.O. Box 447 (44833-0447)
PHONE..................................419 468-5214
Richard Voorde, *CEO*
Jon Amos, *QC Mgr*
Karen Grove, *Human Res Mgr*
Paula K Turner, *Human Res Mgr*
Stephen Koch, *Mng Member*
EMP: 105
SQ FT: 60,000
SALES (est): 51MM **Privately Held**
WEB: www.galion.net
SIC: 3482 3444 Small arms ammunition; sheet metalwork

(G-10269)
GALION CANVAS PRODUCTS CO (PA)
385 S Market St (44833-2608)
PHONE..................................419 468-5333
Fax: 419 468-4168
Steve Siclair, *Owner*
EMP: 6
SQ FT: 5,000
SALES: 445K **Privately Held**
WEB: www.galioncanvasproducts.com
SIC: 7359 2394 Tent & tarpaulin rental; canvas & related products; tarpaulins, fabric: made from purchased materials; awnings, fabric: made from purchased materials; tents: made from purchased materials

(G-10270)
GALION PACKAGING CO INC
340 S East St (44833-2731)
PHONE..................................419 468-2548
Fax: 419 468-2548
David La Chance, *President*
Richard Lachance, *Vice Pres*
EMP: 5
SQ FT: 15,000
SALES (est): 896.9K **Privately Held**
SIC: 2631 Container, packaging & boxboard; packaging board

(G-10271)
GEYERS MARKETS INC
Geyer's Market 5
230 Portland Way N (44833-1631)
PHONE..........................419 468-9477
Fax: 419 468-1826
Jeff Wagner, *Manager*
EMP: 80
SALES (corp-wide): 60MM **Privately
Held**
SIC: 5411 2051 Grocery stores, independent; bread, cake & related products
PA: Geyers' Markets, Inc.
　131 Iberia St
　Mount Gilead OH 43338
　419 683-2925

(G-10272)
**GINNYS CUSTOM FRAMING
GALLERY**
Also Called: Gathering Place
1135 Cherington Dr (44833-1004)
PHONE..........................419 468-7240
Ginny Barr, *Owner*
Donald Barr, *Co-Owner*
EMP: 3
SQ FT: 1,600
SALES (est): 150K **Privately Held**
SIC: 2499 Picture frame molding, finished

(G-10273)
**GLEDHILL ROAD MACHINERY
CO**
765 Portland Way S (44833-2326)
P.O. Box 567 (44833-0567)
PHONE..........................419 468-4400
Garland Gledhill, *Ch of Bd*
Michael D Rarick, *President*
Curt Gledhill, *Engineer*
Jim Springer, *Plant Engr*
Sherrie Dill, *Treasurer*
EMP: 50
SQ FT: 57,000
SALES (est): 17.8MM **Privately Held**
WEB: www.gledhillonline.com
SIC: 3531 Road construction & maintenance machinery; snow plow attachments

(G-10274)
GLEN-GERY CORPORATION
3785 Cardington Iberia Rd (44833)
PHONE..........................419 468-4890
Joe Wishan, *Branch Mgr*
EMP: 78 **Privately Held**
WEB: www.glengerybrick.com
SIC: 3251 Brick clay: common face,
glazed, vitrified or hollow
HQ: Glen-Gery Corporation
　1166 Spring St
　Reading PA 19610
　610 374-4011

(G-10275)
HYDRANAMICS INC
Also Called: Hydranamics Div Carter Mch Co
820 Edward St (44833-2223)
PHONE..........................419 468-3530
Juanita Carter, *Ch of Bd*
Andrea Carter, *President*
Mike Drake, *Superintendent*
Dick Jacobs, *Buyer*
EMP: 86
SALES (est): 7.1MM
SALES (corp-wide): 11.6MM **Privately
Held**
WEB: www.hydranamics.com
SIC: 3593 3547 Fluid power cylinders, hydraulic or pneumatic; rolling mill machinery
PA: Carter Machine Company, Inc.
　820 Edward St
　Galion OH 44833
　419 468-3530

(G-10276)
IBERIA FIREARMS INC
3929 State Route 309 (44833-9408)
P.O. Box 236, Iberia (43325-0236)
PHONE..........................419 468-3746
James Cole, *President*
Jane Cole, *Corp Secy*
EMP: 4
SALES (est): 220K **Privately Held**
SIC: 3484 Guns (firearms) or gun parts, 30
mm. & below

(G-10277)
JUST PLASTICS INC
869 Smith St (44833-2761)
P.O. Box 645 (44833-0645)
PHONE..........................419 468-5506
Fax: 419 468-7740
Judy Eckstein, *President*
Harold Tranxler, *Accountant*
Mark Detwiler, *Manager*
Steve Eckstein, *Shareholder*
EMP: 40
SQ FT: 11,000
SALES (est): 5.8MM **Privately Held**
SIC: 3089 Injection molded finished plastic
products

(G-10278)
KNOX COUNTY PRINTING CO
Also Called: Knox County Citizen
129 Harding Way E (44833-1902)
PHONE..........................740 848-4032
Fax: 740 694-4555
Donald E Clark, *President*
Richard Brenneman, *Owner*
EMP: 5
SQ FT: 1,000
SALES: 109.1K **Privately Held**
SIC: 2711 2752 Commercial printing &
newspaper publishing combined; commercial printing, lithographic

(G-10279)
LINDEN MONUMENTS
104 Linden Dr (44833-1526)
PHONE..........................419 468-4130
Charles E Jackson, *Owner*
EMP: 3
SALES (est): 234.9K **Privately Held**
SIC: 3281 5999 Monument or burial stone,
cut & shaped; monuments & tombstones

(G-10280)
MWE OF OHIO
146 Rensch Ave (44833-2349)
PHONE..........................419 777-7192
Tim A Monaco, *Principal*
EMP: 5
SALES (est): 758.1K **Privately Held**
SIC: 3089 Garbage containers, plastic

(G-10281)
**PARTNERS MANUFACTURING
GROUP**
9357 Township Road 48 (44833-9801)
PHONE..........................419 468-8516
Jeff Dinkel, *President*
Dave Dinkel, *Corp Secy*
Norm Dinkel, *Vice Pres*
EMP: 4
SQ FT: 7,500
SALES: 280K **Privately Held**
SIC: 3315 Steel wire & related products

(G-10282)
**PIPELINE AUTOMATION SYSTE
INC**
215 Harding Way W (44833-1728)
PHONE..........................419 462-8833
EMP: 1
SALES: 1MM **Privately Held**
SIC: 3547 Mfg Misc Products

(G-10283)
**PRINTS & PAINTS FLR CVG CO
INC**
Also Called: My Floors By Prints and Paints
888 Bucyrus Rd (44833-1549)
PHONE..........................419 462-5663
Fax: 419 468-3877
Gary Frankhouse Sr, *President*
Sandra Frankhouse, *Exec VP*
Anns Walter, *Purchasing*
Gary Frankhose Jr, *Treasurer*
Steve Frankhouse, *Admin Sec*
EMP: 23
SQ FT: 14,000
SALES (est): 4.4MM **Privately Held**
WEB: www.printsandpaints.com
SIC: 3996 5231 2295 1743 Asphalted-
felt-base floor coverings: linoleum, carpet;
paint; laminating of fabrics; tile installation, ceramic

(G-10284)
SAUTTER BROTHERS
Also Called: Sautter Bros Machine & Fabg
6443 Brandt Rd (44833-9395)
PHONE..........................419 468-7443
John M Sautter, *Partner*
Thomas E Sautter, *Partner*
EMP: 4
SQ FT: 100,000
SALES (est): 487.9K **Privately Held**
SIC: 3441 0116 0115 Fabricated structural metal; soybeans; corn

(G-10285)
SCENIC SCREEN
4463 State Route 309 (44833-9616)
PHONE..........................419 468-3110
Judy Sanders, *Owner*
EMP: 3
SQ FT: 1,000
SALES (est): 135.2K **Privately Held**
SIC: 2262 Screen printing: manmade fiber
& silk broadwoven fabrics

(G-10286)
SCHILLING GRAPHICS INC (PA)
275 Gelsanliter Rd (44833-2235)
P.O. Box 978 (44833-0978)
PHONE..........................419 468-1037
Fax: 419 468-7999
Douglas Schilling, *President*
Eric Dilgard, *Engineer*
Geoff Weinstock, *Sales Mgr*
Frank Brito, *Marketing Staff*
Laura Peoples, *Manager*
EMP: 33 **EST:** 1963
SQ FT: 20,000
SALES (est): 9.3MM **Privately Held**
SIC: 2752 3552 3555 2759 Decals, lithographed; silk screens for textile industry;
printing trades machinery; commercial
printing; packaging paper & plastics film,
coated & laminated; automotive & apparel
trimmings

(G-10287)
SHOWPLACE INC
Also Called: Showplace Rental
201 S Market St (44833-2629)
PHONE..........................419 468-7368
Fax: 419 462-8533
Jacob Webb, *Manager*
EMP: 5
SALES (corp-wide): 11.9MM **Privately
Held**
WEB: www.showplaceinc.biz
SIC: 3679 7359 Electronic circuits; stores
& yards equipment rental
PA: Showplace, Inc
　611 Bellefontaine Ave
　Marion OH 43302
　740 382-8891

(G-10288)
SPEEDWAY LLC
Also Called: Speedway Superamerica 3187
746 Harding Way W (44833-1616)
PHONE..........................419 468-9773
Carl Schieber, *Branch Mgr*
EMP: 10 **Publicly Held**
WEB: www.speedwaynet.com
SIC: 1311 Crude petroleum production
HQ: Speedway Llc
　500 Speedway Dr
　Enon OH 45323
　937 864-3000

(G-10289)
STARKEY MACHINERY INC
254 S Washington St (44833-2616)
P.O. Box 207 (44833-0207)
PHONE..........................419 468-2560
Fax: 419 468-1698
James D Starkey, *President*
Michelle Starkey, *Corp Secy*
Don Starkey, *Vice Pres*
Mindy Scherer, *Office Mgr*
EMP: 20 **EST:** 1881
SQ FT: 30,000
SALES (est): 4.1MM **Privately Held**
WEB: www.starkeymachinery.com
SIC: 3559 5084 3594 3544 Clay working
& tempering machines; industrial machinery & equipment; fluid power pumps &
motors; special dies, tools, jigs & fixtures;
machine tools, metal forming type

(G-10290)
VULCAN PRODUCTS CO INC
208 S Washington St (44833-2616)
P.O. Box 216 (44833-0216)
PHONE..........................419 468-1039
Fax: 419 468-3904
Ralph Chamberlin, *President*
EMP: 13
SALES (est): 1.7MM **Privately Held**
SIC: 3451 Screw machine products

Gallipolis
Gallia County

(G-10291)
BCMR PUBLICATIONS LLC
1140 2nd Ave (45631-1751)
PHONE..........................740 441-7778
EMP: 4 **EST:** 2009
SALES (est): 266.7K **Privately Held**
SIC: 2741 Miscellaneous publishing

(G-10292)
BIG RIVER ELECTRIC INC
299 Upper River Rd (45631-1838)
P.O. Box 244 (45631-0244)
PHONE..........................740 446-4360
Fax: 740 446-7384
Kelly Counts, *President*
Debra Barcus, *Corp Secy*
Geraldine Counts, *Vice Pres*
Paula Counts, *Manager*
EMP: 6
SQ FT: 8,500
SALES: 1MM **Privately Held**
SIC: 5999 7694 5063 Motors, electric;
electric motor repair; motors, electric

(G-10293)
**CREMEANS CONCRETE AND
SUP CO**
161 Georges Creek Rd (45631-8535)
P.O. Box 475 (45631-0475)
PHONE..........................740 446-1142
Fax: 740 446-1143
John Cremeans, *President*
Carol Cremeans, *Treasurer*
Barbara Ebersbach, *Office Mgr*
EMP: 6
SALES (est): 719.9K **Privately Held**
SIC: 3273 Ready-mixed concrete

(G-10294)
**ELECTROCRAFT ARKANSAS
INC**
250 Mccormick Rd (45631-8745)
PHONE..........................501 268-4203
James Elsner, *CEO*
Logan D Delany Jr, *Ch of Bd*
Douglas Cook, *Plant Mgr*
Jarrett Hamrick, *Materials Mgr*
Johnny Hodges, *Maint Spvr*
▲ **EMP:** 65
SQ FT: 50,000
SALES (est): 12.9MM
SALES (corp-wide): 130MM **Privately
Held**
WEB: www.agimotors.com
SIC: 3621 Electric motor & generator parts
HQ: Electrocraft, Inc.
　1 Progress Dr
　Dover NH 03820
　603 742-3330

(G-10295)
ELECTROCRAFT OHIO INC
250 Mccormick Rd (45631-8745)
PHONE..........................740 441-6200
Fax: 740 441-6309
James Elsner, *President*
Mike Karsonovich, *President*
Dan Radosavljevic, *President*
Terry McKinniss, *General Mgr*
Logan D Delany Jr, *Principal*
▲ **EMP:** 225
SQ FT: 160,000
SALES (est): 47.7MM
SALES (corp-wide): 130MM **Privately
Held**
SIC: 3625 Relays & industrial controls

HQ: Electrocraft, Inc.
1 Progress Dr
Dover NH 03820
603 742-3330

(G-10296)
ENGINEERED METAL PRODUCTS
2160 Eastern Ave (45631-1823)
PHONE..................................740 446-9211
Daniel Swannigan, *CEO*
John Hovack Controller, *Controller*
EMP: 9
SALES (est): 432.8K **Privately Held**
SIC: 3462 Iron & steel forgings

(G-10297)
GALLIPOLIS VAULT CO INC
1050 State Route 141 (45631)
PHONE..................................740 446-3357
Fax: 740 446-0666
Ralph Martin, *President*
EMP: 9 EST: 1946
SQ FT: 22,000
SALES (est): 1.3MM **Privately Held**
SIC: 3272 3281 Concrete products; septic
tanks, concrete; burial vaults, stone

(G-10298)
GKN SINTER METALS LLC
Also Called: Precision Forged Products
2160 Eastern Ave (45631-1823)
PHONE..................................740 441-3203
John Thomas, *Materials Mgr*
Gary Williams, *Purchasing*
David Knotts, *Engineer*
Jim McKinney, *Engineer*
Shad Williams, *Engineer*
EMP: 130
SALES (corp-wide): 10.8B **Privately Held**
SIC: 3312 3568 3462 Sinter, iron; power
transmission equipment; iron & steel forg-
ings
HQ: Gkn Sinter Metals, Llc
2200 N Opdyke Rd
Auburn Hills MI 48326
248 296-7832

(G-10299)
HANGER PRSTHETCS & ORTHO INC
Also Called: Hanger Clinic
1168 Jackson Pike (45631-2600)
PHONE..................................740 446-6879
Fax: 740 446-2499
Kevin Allen, *Branch Mgr*
EMP: 4
SALES (corp-wide): 460MM **Publicly Held**
SIC: 3842 Surgical appliances & supplies
HQ: Hanger Prosthetics & Orthotics, Inc.
10910 Domain Dr Ste 300
Austin TX 78758
512 777-3800

(G-10300)
HEARTLAND PUBLICATIONS LLC
Gallipolis Daily Tribune
825 3rd Ave (45631-1624)
PHONE..................................740 446-2342
Fax: 740 446-3008
Chuck Gozey, *Publisher*
Stephanie Filson, *Editor*
Sammy Lopez, *Branch Mgr*
Jim Freeland, *Branch Mgr*
Dave Killgallon, *Director*
EMP: 11
SALES (corp-wide): 1.4B **Privately Held**
WEB: www.heartlandpublications.com
SIC: 2759 2711 Publication printing; news-
papers, publishing & printing
HQ: Heartland Publications, Llc
4500 Lyons Rd
Miamisburg OH 45342
860 664-1075

(G-10301)
JM LOGGING INC
1624 Graham School Rd (45631-8002)
PHONE..................................740 441-0941
J M Clagg, *Owner*
EMP: 3 EST: 2010
SALES (est): 235.2K **Privately Held**
SIC: 2411 Logging

(G-10302)
KING KUTTER II INC
Also Called: Sfs Truck Sales & Parts
2150 Eastern Ave (45631-1823)
P.O. Box 786 (45631-0786)
PHONE..................................740 446-0351
Fax: 740 446-2859
James Phillip Fraley, *President*
Jeff Fraley, *Vice Pres*
Debbie Frally, *Manager*
Deborah Swain, *Admin Sec*
▲ **EMP:** 50
SQ FT: 160
SALES (est): 17.2MM **Privately Held**
SIC: 5521 3713 Trucks, tractors & trailers:
used; truck & bus bodies

(G-10303)
KSN CLEARING LLC
736 2nd Ave (45631-1514)
P.O. Box 796, Marietta (45750-0796)
PHONE..................................304 269-3306
Kristine Frame,
EMP: 15
SALES (est): 452.4K **Privately Held**
SIC: 1389 7389 Grading oil & gas well
foundations;

(G-10304)
MARION CALDWELL
1262 Lincoln Pike Rear (45631)
PHONE..................................740 446-1042
Caldwell Marion, *Owner*
EMP: 3
SALES (est): 160K **Privately Held**
SIC: 3523 Driers (farm): grain, hay & seed

(G-10305)
MASSIE PUBLISHING LLC
460 2nd Ave (45631-1157)
PHONE..................................740 446-4543
Marilyn Massie, *Principal*
EMP: 4
SALES (est): 130K **Privately Held**
SIC: 2741 Miscellaneous publishing

(G-10306)
O-KAN MARINE REPAIR INC
267 Upper River Rd (45631-1838)
PHONE..................................740 446-4686
Fax: 740 446-4203
Chris Preston, *President*
Randy Canaday, *General Mgr*
Tessa Haggerty, *General Mgr*
Jay Hall Jr, *Vice Pres*
Sandra Neal, *Treasurer*
EMP: 34
SALES (est): 5MM **Privately Held**
WEB: www.okanmarinerepair.com
SIC: 3731 3732 Shipbuilding & repairing;
barges, building & repairing; boat building
& repairing

(G-10307)
PIP AND HUDS LLC
334 2nd Ave (45631-1414)
PHONE..................................740 208-5519
EMP: 4
SALES (est): 329.4K **Privately Held**
SIC: 2752 Commercial printing, offset

(G-10308)
RIVERVIEW PRODUCTIONS INC
Also Called: Unique Expressions
652 Jackson Pike (45631-1389)
P.O. Box 624, Wellston (45692-0624)
PHONE..................................740 441-1150
Thomas Meadows, *Chairman*
EMP: 9
SALES (est): 472.1K **Privately Held**
SIC: 5261 2611 Nurseries; pulp mills, me-
chanical & recycling processing

(G-10309)
SHELLY MATERIALS INC
1248 State Route 7 N (45631-9475)
PHONE..................................740 446-7789
Trevor Small, *Manager*
EMP: 4
SALES (corp-wide): 28.6B **Privately Held**
SIC: 2951 Asphalt & asphaltic paving mix-
tures (not from refineries)
HQ: Shelly Materials, Inc.
80 Park Dr
Thornville OH 43076
740 246-6315

(G-10310)
THOMAS DO-IT CENTER INC (PA)
Also Called: Thomas Rental
176 Mccormick Rd (45631-8745)
PHONE..................................740 446-2002
Fax: 740 446-6761
Jim Thomas, *President*
Lee Cyrus, *President*
Jay Hall, *Principal*
Marlene Hall, *Vice Pres*
▲ **EMP:** 45
SQ FT: 85,000
SALES (est): 14MM **Privately Held**
SIC: 5211 5251 7359 2439 Lumber &
other building materials; lumber products;
hardware; builders' hardware; equipment
rental & leasing; lawn & garden equip-
ment rental; trusses, wooden roof

(G-10311)
VSL SIGNS
1049 Blazer Rd (45631-9067)
PHONE..................................740 441-7578
Vernon Bing, *Principal*
EMP: 3
SALES (est): 225.8K **Privately Held**
SIC: 3993 Signs & advertising specialties

Galloway
Franklin County

(G-10312)
EL NUEVO NARANJO
6142 Glenworth Ct (43119-8559)
PHONE..................................614 863-4212
James Diaz De Leon, *Principal*
EMP: 4
SALES (est): 345.4K **Privately Held**
SIC: 3421 Table & food cutlery, including
butchers'

(G-10313)
EM INNOVATIONS INC
6106 Bausch Rd (43119-9382)
P.O. Box 262 (43119-0262)
PHONE..................................614 853-1504
Connie Lewis, *President*
Jane Parr, *Corp Secy*
Joel Culp, *Vice Pres*
Spencer Fullerton, *Sales Dir*
Tom Parr, *Shareholder*
▲ **EMP:** 4
SALES (est): 401.6K **Privately Held**
WEB: www.eminnovations.com
SIC: 3841 Surgical & medical instruments

(G-10314)
GNI ERECTORS
8907 Stillwater Dr (43119-9082)
PHONE..................................614 465-7260
Steven Nash, *Owner*
EMP: 5 EST: 1994
SALES: 200K **Privately Held**
SIC: 3444 Sheet metalwork

(G-10315)
SNYDERS TOOL & DIE INC
6481 W Broad St (43119-9390)
PHONE..................................614 878-2205
Fax: 614 878-5502
William R Frey, *President*
EMP: 3
SQ FT: 3,000
SALES (est): 290K **Privately Held**
SIC: 3544 Special dies & tools

Gambier
Knox County

(G-10316)
KENYON REVIEW
104 College Dr Fl 2 (43022-5003)
PHONE..................................740 427-5208
Fax: 740 427-3077
David Lynn, *CEO*
Meg Galipault, *COO*
Susan Morse, *Persnl Dir*
Sarah St Clair, *Supervisor*
Kim Novak, *Director*
EMP: 6
SALES (est): 778.2K **Privately Held**
WEB: www.kenyonreview.com
SIC: 2721 Magazines: publishing & printing

(G-10317)
SMALL SAND & GRAVEL INC
10229 Killduff Rd (43022-9657)
P.O. Box 617 (43022-0617)
PHONE..................................740 427-3130
Michael W Small, *President*
Wiiliam T Small, *Treasurer*
Sharon Mills, *Office Mgr*
Carol Small, *Admin Sec*
EMP: 35
SALES (est): 8.6MM **Privately Held**
SIC: 1442 Sand mining; gravel mining

(G-10318)
SMALLS ASPHALT PAVING INC
10229 Killduff Rd (43022-9657)
P.O. Box 552 (43022-0552)
PHONE..................................740 427-4096
Robert E Small, *President*
Michael Small, *Vice Pres*
William T Small, *Treasurer*
Carol Small, *Admin Sec*
EMP: 25
SALES (est): 2.5MM **Privately Held**
SIC: 1771 2951 1611 Blacktop (asphalt)
work; asphalt paving mixtures & blocks;
highway & street construction

(G-10319)
YODERS CIDER BARN
Also Called: Yoder's Cider Barn
3361 Martinsburg Rd (43022-9737)
PHONE..................................740 668-4961
Sheldon Yoder, *Owner*
Steve Yoder, *Manager*
▲ **EMP:** 10
SALES (est): 1.1MM **Privately Held**
SIC: 2023 2033 Condensed, concentrated
& evaporated milk products; jams, includ-
ing imitation: packaged in cans, jars, etc.

Garrettsville
Portage County

(G-10320)
EDGEWELL PER CARE BRANDS LLC
10545 Freedom St (44231-9237)
PHONE..................................330 527-2191
Pat Wilson, *Opers Mgr*
Ronald R Taylor, *Branch Mgr*
EMP: 70
SQ FT: 50,000
SALES (corp-wide): 2.3B **Publicly Held**
WEB: www.eveready.com
SIC: 3421 Razor blades & razors
HQ: Edgewell Personal Care Brands, Llc
6 Research Dr
Shelton CT 06484
203 944-5500

(G-10321)
ENERGIZER BATTERY MFG INC
10545 Freedom St (44231-9237)
PHONE..................................330 527-2191
Matt Smith, *Principal*
Brady Wagers, *Opers Spvr*
EMP: 3
SALES (est): 333.2K **Privately Held**
SIC: 3999 Manufacturing industries

(G-10322)
GRNTWRX LLC
8205 Clover Ln (44231-1060)
PHONE..................................440 478-6160
Nicholas Hadzinsky,
EMP: 3
SALES (est): 156K **Privately Held**
SIC: 3452 Bolts, nuts, rivets & washers

(G-10323)
HARRISON MCH & PLASTIC CORP (PA)
11614 State Route 88 (44231-9105)
P.O. Box 1826, Hiram (44234-1826)
PHONE..................................330 569-3128
Bryson Swanda, *President*
Timothy Swanda, *Vice Pres*

GEOGRAPHIC

Bob Maynard, *Controller*
Debra Swanda, *Manager*
Robert Maynard, *CTO*
EMP: 25
SQ FT: 30,000
SALES (est): 4.7MM **Privately Held**
SIC: 3089 3444 3084 Plastic processing;
sheet metalwork; plastics pipe

(G-10324)
**HERMANN PICKLE COMPANY
(PA)**
11964 State Route 88 (44231-9115)
P.O. Box 347 (44231-0347)
PHONE.................................330 527-2696
Fax: 330 527-2327
Larry Hermann, *President*
Ruth Hermann, *Treasurer*
Karl Hermann, *Manager*
EMP: 28
SALES (est): 5.7MM **Privately Held**
SIC: 2033 Canned fruits & specialties; veg-
etables: packaged in cans, jars, etc.

(G-10325)
JC ELECTRIC
9717 State Route 88 (44231-9746)
P.O. Box 304 (44231-0304)
PHONE.................................330 760-2915
Jason Carmichael, *Owner*
EMP: 22
SALES (est): 2.9MM **Privately Held**
SIC: 1731 3699 1521 Electrical work;
door opening & closing devices, electrical;
single-family home remodeling, additions
& repairs

(G-10326)
KECAMM LLC
10404 Industrial Dr (44231-9764)
PHONE.................................330 527-2918
Cheryl A Macek, *CEO*
George Macek, *President*
Darrin Macek, *Manager*
EMP: 7
SQ FT: 10,000
SALES (est): 718.7K **Privately Held**
SIC: 3479 5084 Bonderizing of metal or
metal products; paint spray equipment, in-
dustrial

(G-10327)
KECOAT LLC
10610 Freedom St (44231-9763)
PHONE.................................330 527-0215
Darrin Macek, *Mng Member*
EMP: 17
SQ FT: 10,000
SALES (est): 3.1MM **Privately Held**
SIC: 3441 Fabricated structural metal

(G-10328)
L & P MACHINE COMPANY
8488 State Route 305 (44231-9755)
PHONE.................................330 527-2753
Fax: 330 527-2753
Terry Allen, *Owner*
EMP: 4 **EST:** 1967
SQ FT: 10,000
SALES (est): 350.6K **Privately Held**
WEB: www.lpmachine.net
SIC: 3599 Machine shop, jobbing & repair;
custom machinery

(G-10329)
MACHINE TEK SYSTEMS INC
10400 Industrial Dr (44231-9764)
P.O. Box 187 (44231-0187)
PHONE.................................330 527-4450
Fax: 330 527-5353
Tim Paul, *President*
EMP: 33
SQ FT: 22,000
SALES (est): 5.4MM **Privately Held**
SIC: 3544 3599 3451 Special dies, tools,
jigs & fixtures; machine shop, jobbing &
repair; screw machine products

(G-10330)
MEGA PLASTICS CO
10610 Freedom St (44231-9763)
PHONE.................................330 527-2211
Ronald Porter, *President*
Wendi Porter, *Vice Pres*
EMP: 20 **EST:** 1998
SQ FT: 25,000

SALES: 1.8MM **Privately Held**
SIC: 3089 Plastic processing

(G-10331)
MODERN STORE FIXTURES INC
10421 Industrial Dr (44231-9764)
PHONE.................................330 427-6906
Michael E Diskin, *President*
Dan Trahey, *Vice Pres*
▲ **EMP:** 14
SQ FT: 70,000
SALES: 1.4MM **Privately Held**
WEB: www.modernstorefixtures.com
SIC: 3089 2542 Closures, plastic; fixtures,
store: except wood

(G-10332)
PREMIER PROD SVC INDS INC
10384 Industrial Dr C (44231-9263)
PHONE.................................330 527-0333
Fax: 330 372-5629
Heidi Piecuch, *President*
Brian Piecuch, *Vice Pres*
EMP: 4 **EST:** 1989
SQ FT: 5,000
SALES (est): 625.9K **Privately Held**
SIC: 3599 Machine & other job shop work;
machine shop, jobbing & repair

(G-10333)
**SUPERIOR QUALITY MACHINE
CO**
10500 Industrial Dr (44231-9250)
P.O. Box 303 (44231-0303)
PHONE.................................330 527-7146
Fax: 330 569-2049
Joe Kenesky, *Owner*
▲ **EMP:** 20
SQ FT: 11,000
SALES (est): 2MM **Privately Held**
SIC: 3599 Machine shop, jobbing & repair

(G-10334)
THERM-O-LINK INC (PA)
10513 Freedom St (44231-9244)
PHONE.................................330 527-2124
Fax: 330 527-2123
Ronald M Krisher, *Ch of Bd*
David Campbell, *President*
Thomas C B Letson, *Principal*
Mike Frigo, *VP Opers*
Gregory Carr, *QC Mgr*
▲ **EMP:** 100
SQ FT: 125,000
SALES (est): 41.2MM **Privately Held**
WEB: www.tolwire.com
SIC: 3357 3496 Nonferrous wiredrawing &
insulating; miscellaneous fabricated wire
products

(G-10335)
VILLAGER PUBLISHING CO INC
Also Called: Villager Weekly
8088 Main St (44231-1214)
P.O. Box 331 (44231-0331)
PHONE.................................330 527-5761
Jody Schroath, *President*
Roy Pancost, *Publisher*
Roy Tancost, *Co-Owner*
Shelby Berzinskas, *Advt Staff*
Heidi Pittman-Collin, *Office Mgr*
EMP: 3
SALES (est): 237.6K **Privately Held**
SIC: 2711 2752 Newspapers; commercial
printing, lithographic

(G-10336)
WOOD KRAFT
8928 Ely Rd (44231-9613)
PHONE.................................440 487-4634
Kenneth Bender, *Principal*
EMP: 4
SALES (est): 222.7K **Privately Held**
SIC: 2022 Processed cheese

(G-10337)
**Z AND M SCREW MACHINE
PRODUCTS**
10232 Hopkins Rd (44231-9011)
PHONE.................................330 467-5822
EMP: 5
SQ FT: 3,500
SALES (est): 320K **Privately Held**
SIC: 3451 Mfg Screw Machine Products

Gates Mills
Cuyahoga County

(G-10338)
TRANSDERMAL INC
Also Called: Lasercap
938 Chestnut Run (44040-9761)
PHONE.................................440 241-1846
Robert Haber, *President*
▲ **EMP:** 10
SALES (est): 550K **Privately Held**
SIC: 3841 3699 Diagnostic apparatus,
medical; laser systems & equipment

Geneva
Ashtabula County

(G-10339)
**ADRIA SCIENTIFIC GL WORKS
CO**
2683 State Route 534 S (44041)
P.O. Box 673 (44041-0673)
PHONE.................................440 474-6691
Fax: 440 474-5362
Milan Krmpotic, *President*
Brigitte Krmpotic, *Corp Secy*
EMP: 6
SQ FT: 18,000
SALES: 500K **Privately Held**
SIC: 3229 Scientific glassware

(G-10340)
ADVANCED TIME SYSTEMS
4591 Cork Cold Springs Rd (44041-9674)
PHONE.................................440 466-2689
Charles McFarland, *Owner*
Christa McFarland, *Principal*
EMP: 3
SALES: 300K **Privately Held**
WEB: www.advtime.com
SIC: 3579 Time clocks & time recording
devices

(G-10341)
AITKEN PRODUCTS INC
566 N Eagle St (44041-1099)
P.O. Box 151 (44041-0151)
PHONE.................................440 466-5711
Fax: 440 466-5716
Suzanne Aitken Shannon, *President*
Louis J Doria, *Principal*
Thomas A Grabien, *Principal*
Sue Aitken, *Vice Pres*
Nancy Carmack, *Manager*
EMP: 8 **EST:** 1957
SQ FT: 50,000
SALES (est): 1.5MM **Privately Held**
SIC: 3634 3433 Heating units, electric (ra-
diant heat): baseboard or wall; gas in-
frared heating units

(G-10342)
AMERICAN GUARD CO INC
Also Called: Technical Engineered Products
150 D Termination Ave (44041-1173)
PHONE.................................440 354-1400
Fax: 440 354-3255
Jerry Leeds, *President*
James Paul, *Vice Pres*
▲ **EMP:** 14
SQ FT: 15,000
SALES (est): 2.1MM **Privately Held**
SIC: 3469 Metal stampings

(G-10343)
ARC RUBBER INC
100 Water St (44041-1192)
PHONE.................................440 466-4555
Fax: 440 466-2048
Robert Johnson Jr, *President*
Robert Johnson III, *Vice Pres*
Josephine Johnson, *Admin Sec*
EMP: 10 **EST:** 1965
SQ FT: 20,000
SALES (est): 1.7MM **Privately Held**
WEB: www.arcrubber.com
SIC: 3069 3061 Molded rubber products;
mechanical rubber goods

(G-10344)
CLASSIC EXHAUST
805 Pro Gram Pkwy (44041-1172)
PHONE.................................440 466-5460
Fax: 440 466-8997
Scott Thompson, *Partner*
Dwayne Hudson, *Partner*
EMP: 4
SQ FT: 6,200
SALES (est): 350K **Privately Held**
SIC: 3714 Exhaust systems & parts, motor
vehicle

(G-10345)
DWAYNE BENNETT INDUSTRIES
Also Called: Bennett Displays
6708 N Ridge Rd W (44041-7663)
PHONE.................................440 466-5724
Fax: 440 466-7871
Dwayne Bennett, *Owner*
EMP: 6
SALES (est): 459.2K **Privately Held**
SIC: 2542 3441 Racks, merchandise dis-
play or storage: except wood; fabricated
structural metal

(G-10346)
**ELSTER PERFECTION
CORPORATION (DH)**
436 N Eagle St (44041-1157)
PHONE.................................440 428-1171
Fax: 440 428-3568
Barry O'Connell, *President*
Jason Knaus, *Engineer*
Timothy Stevens, *Finance Dir*
James Hugo, *Manager*
◆ **EMP:** 100 **EST:** 1944
SQ FT: 75,000
SALES (est): 51.7MM
SALES (corp-wide): 39.3B **Publicly Held**
WEB: www.perfectioncorp.com
SIC: 3498 3089 3429 3312 Fabricated
pipe & fittings; fittings for pipe, plastic;
manufactured hardware (general); blast
furnaces & steel mills; plastics pipe; lami-
nated plastics plate & sheet
HQ: Elster American Meter Company, Llc
208 S Rogers Ln
Raleigh NC 27610
800 257-9754

(G-10347)
FERRANTE WINE FARM INC
558 Rte 307 (44041)
PHONE.................................440 466-8466
Fax: 440 466-7370
Nicholas Ferrante, *President*
Nicholas Ferrante, *Principal*
Mary Jo Ferrante, *Principal*
Peter Ferrante, *Principal*
Charles Rehor, *Principal*
EMP: 40
SQ FT: 3,023
SALES (est): 2.4MM **Privately Held**
WEB: www.ferrantewinery.com
SIC: 0172 2084 5812 Grapes; wines; eat-
ing places

(G-10348)
**H & H ENGINEERED MOLDED
PDTS**
436 N Eagle St (44041-1157)
PHONE.................................440 415-1814
Fax: 440 248-7130
Barry O Connell, *President*
Roy Sutterfield, *President*
Tim Stevens, *Treasurer*
EMP: 55
SQ FT: 26,000
SALES (est): 6MM
SALES (corp-wide): 39.3B **Publicly Held**
WEB: www.perfectioncorp.com
SIC: 3089 Injection molding of plastics
HQ: Elster Perfection Corporation
436 N Eagle St
Geneva OH 44041
440 428-1171

(G-10349)
HADLOCK PLASTICS LLC
110 N Eagle St (44041-1196)
PHONE.................................440 466-4876
Fax: 440 466-9396
Terry Morgan, *President*
Marvin Benjamin, *Plant Mgr*

Jerry Lillie, *Facilities Mgr*
Tim Clark, *QA Dir*
Jim Haynes, *Engineer*
▲ **EMP:** 107
SQ FT: 110,000
SALES (est): 26.8MM
SALES (corp-wide): 2.5B **Publicly Held**
WEB: www.hadlockplastics.com
SIC: 3089 Injection molded finished plastic products
HQ: Hpc Holdings, Llc
   3637 Ridgewood Rd
   Fairlawn OH 44333

(G-10350)
HDT EXPEDITIONARY SYSTEMS INC
5455 Route 307 W (44041)
PHONE..............................440 466-6640
James Maurer, *President*
Chris Justus, *Manager*
Michael Schultz, *Info Tech Mgr*
EMP: 17
SALES (corp-wide): 229.4MM **Privately Held**
SIC: 3585 3564 3433 Air conditioning units, complete: domestic or industrial; filters, air: furnaces, air conditioning equipment, etc.; heating equipment, except electric
HQ: Hdt Expeditionary Systems, Inc.
   30500 Aurora Rd Ste 100
   Solon OH 44139
   216 438-6111

(G-10351)
HUNDLEY CELLARS LLC
6451 N River Rd W (44041-9312)
PHONE..............................843 368-5016
Larry Hundley,
EMP: 5
SALES (est): 370.5K **Privately Held**
SIC: 2084 7389 Wines;

(G-10352)
LOUIS ARTHUR STEEL COMPANY (PA)
185 Water St (44041-1199)
P.O. Box 229 (44041-0229)
PHONE..............................440 997-5545
Fax: 440 992-9726
J Trombley Kanicki, *President*
Andy Housel, *General Mgr*
J Matthew Kanicki, *Vice Pres*
Matthew Kanicki, *Vice Pres*
Sandra Kanicki, *Vice Pres*
EMP: 8 **EST:** 1949
SQ FT: 80,000
SALES (est): 11.2MM **Privately Held**
SIC: 3441 5051 3444 3443 Fabricated structural metal; steel; sheet metalwork; fabricated plate work (boiler shop)

(G-10353)
NORTH COAST VOICE MAG
143 S Cedar St (44041-1657)
P.O. Box 118 (44041-0118)
PHONE..............................440 415-0999
L Carol Stouder, *Principal*
EMP: 4
SALES (est): 162.4K **Privately Held**
SIC: 2711 Newspapers

(G-10354)
OLD MILL WINERY INC
403 S Broadway (44041-1844)
PHONE..............................440 466-5560
Fax: 440 466-2099
Al Snyder, *Partner*
Joanne Snyder, *Partner*
EMP: 12
SALES (est): 1.3MM **Privately Held**
SIC: 2084 Wines

(G-10355)
PHILLIPS & SONS WELDING & FABG
6720 N Ridge Rd W (44041)
PHONE..............................440 428-1625
Steven Phillips, *Owner*
EMP: 3
SQ FT: 20,000
SALES: 350K **Privately Held**
SIC: 7692 3441 Welding repair; fabricated structural metal

(G-10356)
PRIDE OF GENEVA
72 W Main St (44041-1226)
PHONE..............................440 466-5695
Curtis Hall, *Principal*
EMP: 3
SALES (est): 129.9K **Privately Held**
SIC: 2711 Newspapers, publishing & printing

(G-10357)
TEGAM INC (PA)
10 Tegam Way (44041-1144)
PHONE..............................440 466-6100
Fax: 440 466-6110
Andrew Brush, *CEO*
Adam Fleder, *President*
Jacque Kato'schaefer, *Accountant*
EMP: 43
SQ FT: 28,600
SALES (est): 9.1MM **Privately Held**
WEB: www.tegam.com
SIC: 3829 7629 Measuring & controlling devices; electrical measuring instrument repair & calibration

(G-10358)
VIRANT FAMILY WINERY INC
541 Atkins Rd (44041-8352)
PHONE..............................440 466-6279
Charles Virant, *CEO*
Frank Virant, *President*
Martha Virant, *Treasurer*
Holly Virant, *Admin Sec*
EMP: 4 **EST:** 1998
SQ FT: 1,338
SALES (est): 110K **Privately Held**
WEB: www.starbeacon.com
SIC: 2084 Wines

(G-10359)
WINERY AT SPRING HILL INC
6062 S Ridge Rd W (44041-8375)
P.O. Box 47 (44041-0047)
PHONE..............................440 466-0626
Richard Trice, *Principal*
Jeffrey Piotrowski, *CFO*
EMP: 15
SALES (est): 1.6MM **Privately Held**
SIC: 2084 Wines, brandy & brandy spirits

Genoa
Ottawa County

(G-10360)
GRAYMONT DOLIME (OH) INC
21880 W State Route 163 (43430-1679)
P.O. Box 158 (43430-0158)
PHONE..............................419 855-8682
Stephane Godin, *Principal*
J Graham Weir, *Chairman*
Mike Brown, *Vice Pres*
Richard Marks, *Vice Pres*
Allen Walsh, *Plant Mgr*
▼ **EMP:** 54
SALES (est): 11MM
SALES (corp-wide): 211.6MM **Privately Held**
SIC: 3274 Lime
PA: Graymont Inc
   301 S 700 E 3950
   Salt Lake City UT 84102
   801 262-3942

(G-10361)
JBI CORPORATION
22325 State Route 51 W (43430-1123)
PHONE..............................419 855-3389
Fax: 419 855-3226
John Badger, *Ch of Bd*
Joseph Badger, *President*
Florence Badger, *Corp Secy*
EMP: 10
SQ FT: 7,500
SALES (est): 1.5MM **Privately Held**
WEB: www.jbicorp.com
SIC: 8711 3544 8734 Engineering services; consulting engineer; jigs & fixtures; testing laboratories

(G-10362)
RCR PARTNERSHIP
Also Called: Paul Blausey Farms
424 N Martin Williston Rd (43430-9786)
PHONE..............................419 340-1202
Chad Gargas,
EMP: 6 **EST:** 2013
SALES (est): 758.6K **Privately Held**
SIC: 3443 Farm storage tanks, metal plate

(G-10363)
RIVERSIDE MCH & AUTOMTN INC (PA)
1240 N Genoa Clay Ctr Rd (43430-1206)
PHONE..............................419 855-8308
Fax: 419 855-8427
Gerald Giesler, *CEO*
Jerry Giesler, *President*
Lester Meyer, *Vice Pres*
Glenn Burger, *Plant Mgr*
Gary Kapp, *Purchasing*
EMP: 60
SQ FT: 30,000
SALES (est): 9.7MM **Privately Held**
WEB: www.riverside-machine.com
SIC: 3599 3549 Machine shop, jobbing & repair; machine & other job shop work; metalworking machinery

Georgetown
Brown County

(G-10364)
BROWN CNTY BD MNTAL RTARDATION
325 W State St Ste A2 (45121-1262)
PHONE..............................937 378-4891
Theresa Armstrong, *Principal*
Lena Bradford, *Principal*
EMP: 35
SQ FT: 100,000
SALES (est): 131.9K **Privately Held**
SIC: 8331 3993 2396 Sheltered workshop; signs & advertising specialties; automotive & apparel trimmings

(G-10365)
SGT S DRIVE THRU
3468 State Route 125 (45121-8411)
PHONE..............................937 378-3813
Danny Pangallo, *Manager*
EMP: 4
SALES (est): 227.9K **Privately Held**
SIC: 2082 Beer (alcoholic beverage)

(G-10366)
THOMAS ENTPS OF GEORGETOWN
Also Called: Thomas Welding & Repair
933 S Main St (45121-8409)
PHONE..............................937 378-6300
Fax: 937 378-6300
Keith D Thomas, *President*
EMP: 3
SQ FT: 1,820
SALES: 450K **Privately Held**
SIC: 7692 3599 Welding repair; machine shop, jobbing & repair

(G-10367)
WATSON MEEKS AND COMPANY
10402 W Fork Rd (45121-8260)
P.O. Box 21700 (45121-0700)
PHONE..............................937 378-2355
William C Meeks, *Partner*
Richard M Watson, *Partner*
EMP: 4
SQ FT: 2,800
SALES (est): 558.4K **Privately Held**
SIC: 3931 8711 Keyboard instruments & parts; carillon bells; consulting engineer

Germantown
Montgomery County

(G-10368)
ABSOLUTE CNC MACHINING LLC
2643 Dyton Grmantown Pike (45327-9625)
P.O. Box 47 (45327-0047)
PHONE..............................937 855-0406
Thomas Hodge,
EMP: 3
SQ FT: 1,500
SALES (est): 345K **Privately Held**
SIC: 3599 Machine & other job shop work

(G-10369)
HOSLER MAPS INC
115 N Plum St (45327-1359)
PHONE..............................937 855-4173
Fax: 937 855-4174
Gene Hosler, *President*
Susie Hosler, *President*
EMP: 3
SQ FT: 9,000
SALES: 385K **Privately Held**
SIC: 3613 Panel & distribution boards & other related apparatus

(G-10370)
L & H PRINTING
Also Called: L & H Printing Co
34 W Market St (45327-1354)
PHONE..............................937 855-4512
Nancy Havens, *Mng Member*
EMP: 4
SALES (est): 160K **Privately Held**
SIC: 8351 2752 Child day care services; commercial printing, lithographic

(G-10371)
OHIO ENGINEERING AND MFG SLS
Also Called: O E M Sales
11610 State Route 725 (45327-9760)
PHONE..............................937 855-6971
Harold Melampy, *President*
Harold E Melampy, *President*
Pamela S Melampy, *Treasurer*
EMP: 5
SQ FT: 4,400
SALES: 200K **Privately Held**
SIC: 5051 3599 Stampings, metal; grinding castings for the trade

(G-10372)
PIQUA CONCRETE CORP
9151 Township Park Dr (45327-8711)
PHONE..............................937 855-0410
Hank Ernst, *Branch Mgr*
EMP: 6
SALES (corp-wide): 10.8MM **Privately Held**
SIC: 5211 5032 3273 Cement; concrete & cinder building products; ready-mixed concrete
PA: Piqua Concrete Corp
   8395 Piqua Lockington Rd
   Piqua OH 45356
   937 773-0841

(G-10373)
POINT SOURCE INC
7996 Butter St (45327)
PHONE..............................937 855-6020
Fax: 937 855-6020
EMP: 12
SQ FT: 3,000
SALES: 1.2MM **Privately Held**
SIC: 8731 3827 Commercial Physical Research Mfg Optical Instruments/Lenses

(G-10374)
THOMAS D EPPERSON
Also Called: Epco
7440 Weaver Rd (45327-9390)
P.O. Box 19 (45327-0019)
PHONE..............................937 855-3300
Fax: 937 855-3330
Thomas D Epperson, *Owner*
EMP: 7
SQ FT: 2,104

GEOGRAPHIC

SALES (est): 649.4K **Privately Held**
SIC: 3751 Motorcycle accessories; motorcycles & related parts

Gettysburg
Darke County

(G-10375)
NORCOLD INC
1 Century Dr (45328)
P.O. Box 295 (45328-0295)
PHONE..................................937 447-2241
Fax: 937 497-3074
Al Keller, *QC Dir*
Steve Hemmelgarn, *Research*
Jim Shaw, *Manager*
EMP: 200
SALES (corp-wide): 523.2MM **Privately Held**
SIC: 3822 3632 Refrigeration controls
(pressure); household refrigerators &
freezers
HQ: Norcold Inc.
600 S Kuther Rd
Sidney OH 45365

(G-10376)
WHOLESALE CARPET OUTLET INC
301 E Main St (45328)
PHONE..................................937 447-4265
Ronald Lynch, *President*
EMP: 4
SALES (est): 324.3K **Privately Held**
SIC: 2273 Carpets & rugs

Gibsonburg
Sandusky County

(G-10377)
HENDERSON BUILDERS INC
1610 County Road 90 (43431-9717)
PHONE..................................419 665-2684
David R Henderson Jr, *President*
Kim Henderson, *Admin Sec*
EMP: 5
SALES (est): 583.6K **Privately Held**
SIC: 1521 2791 General remodeling, sin-
gle-family houses; typesetting, computer
controlled

(G-10378)
UNIVERSAL GROUND CULLET INC
Also Called: Fast Blast
400 Cedar St (43431-1165)
PHONE..................................419 637-2630
Robert Bambascurd, *Owner*
EMP: 6
SALES (corp-wide): 928.8K **Privately Held**
SIC: 3291 Abrasive products
PA: Universal Ground Cullet Inc
6407 Wolf Rd
Cleveland OH
216 267-8057

Gilboa
Putnam County

(G-10379)
HILLSIDE WINERY
221 Main St (45875-9757)
PHONE..................................419 456-3108
Lou Schaublin, *Principal*
EMP: 7
SALES (est): 636.3K **Privately Held**
SIC: 2084 Wines, brandy & brandy spirits

Girard
Trumbull County

(G-10380)
A J CONSTRUCTION CO
870 Shannon Rd (44420-2046)
PHONE..................................330 539-9544
Fax: 330 539-9545
Anthony Guerrieri, *President*
EMP: 6
SALES (est): 661.2K **Privately Held**
SIC: 2541 Cabinets, except refrigerated:
show, display, etc.: wood; cabinets, lock-
ers & shelving; counter & sink tops; coun-
ters or counter display cases, wood

(G-10381)
ALTRONIC LLC (DH)
712 Trumbull Ave (44420-3443)
PHONE..................................330 545-9768
Fax: 330 545-9005
Bruce R Beeghly, *President*
Joseph Lepley, *Vice Pres*
Richard R Pisani, *Vice Pres*
Richard P Schook, *Vice Pres*
Dimitri Wallick, *Vice Pres*
▲ EMP: 150
SQ FT: 80,000
SALES (est): 37.8MM **Privately Held**
WEB: www.altroniccontrols.com
SIC: 3694 3823 3613 3625 Ignition sys-
tems, high frequency; temperature instru-
ments: industrial process type; control
panels, electric; relays & industrial con-
trols
HQ: Hoerbiger Holding Ag
Baarerstrasse 18
Zug ZG
415 601-000

(G-10382)
AMEX DIES INC
932 N State St (44420-1796)
PHONE..................................330 545-9766
Fax: 330 545-6701
Ted Dudzik, *President*
Sam Bates, *General Mgr*
Donna Covelli, *Bookkeeper*
EMP: 17
SQ FT: 6,000
SALES (est): 1.6MM **Privately Held**
SIC: 3544 Extrusion dies

(G-10383)
BRAINARD RIVET COMPANY
Also Called: BUCKEYE FASTENERS COM-
PANY
222 Harry St (44420-1759)
P.O. Box 30 (44420-0030)
PHONE..................................330 545-4931
Fax: 330 545-2827
Patrick Finnegan, *President*
Judy Volpe, *General Mgr*
Linda Kerekes, *Corp Secy*
Chris Morrison, *Mfg Mgr*
Janice Hughes, *Purch Agent*
EMP: 34
SQ FT: 61,000
SALES: 6.3MM
SALES (corp-wide): 42.3MM **Privately Held**
WEB: www.brainardrivet.com
SIC: 3452 Bolts, nuts, rivets & washers
PA: Fastener Industries, Inc.
1 Berea Commons Ste 209
Berea OH 44017
440 243-0034

(G-10384)
CHECKERED EXPRESS INC
2501 W Liberty St (44420-3112)
PHONE..................................330 530-8169
Csaba Bujdoso, *President*
EMP: 15
SALES (est): 1.6MM **Privately Held**
SIC: 2741 Miscellaneous publishing

(G-10385)
DAFFINS CANDIES (PA)
Also Called: Daffin Candies
39 W Liberty St (44420-2842)
PHONE..................................330 545-0325
Fax: 330 545-0325

Joseph Costello, *President*
Dorothy Costello, *Vice Pres*
Mary Ward, *Manager*
EMP: 5
SQ FT: 4,000
SALES (est): 1MM **Privately Held**
SIC: 2064 5947 Chocolate candy, except
solid chocolate; gift shop

(G-10386)
FIRE FAB CORPORATION
999 Trumbull Ave (44420-3448)
Rural Route 999 Trumbu (44420)
PHONE..................................330 759-9834
Fax: 330 759-8949
Ernie Nicholas, *President*
Mary Nicholas, *Corp Secy*
Jamie Wilcox, *Accountant*
EMP: 6
SQ FT: 18,000
SALES: 1.1MM **Privately Held**
SIC: 3569 Sprinkler systems, fire: auto-
matic

(G-10387)
FIRE FOE CORP
999 Trumbull Ave (44420-3400)
PHONE..................................330 759-9834
Earnest A Nicholas, *President*
Thomas Spain, *Safety Dir*
Jamie Wilcox, *Controller*
Mary Nicholas, *Admin Sec*
EMP: 35
SQ FT: 18,000
SALES: 4.5MM **Privately Held**
WEB: www.firefoe.com
SIC: 3569 7699 Sprinkler systems, fire:
automatic; fire control (military) equipment
repair

(G-10388)
FIVE STAR GRAPHICS INC
201 W Liberty St (44420-2846)
PHONE..................................330 545-5077
Fax: 330 545-5077
John Penza, *CEO*
Samuel Penza, *Vice Pres*
Robert Penza, *Treasurer*
James Penza, *Admin Sec*
EMP: 5
SQ FT: 14,400
SALES (est): 518.8K **Privately Held**
WEB: www.fivestargraphics.net
SIC: 2759 Screen printing

(G-10389)
GAS ANALYTICAL SERVICES INC
1688 Shannon Rd (44420-1121)
PHONE..................................330 539-4267
Bernie Vogel, *Manager*
EMP: 3
SALES (corp-wide): 23.5MM **Privately Held**
SIC: 1389 Gas field services
HQ: Gas Analytical Services, Inc.
8444 Water St
Stonewood WV 26301
304 623-0020

(G-10390)
GIRARD MACHINE COMPANY INC
700 Dot St (44420-1701)
P.O. Box 298 (44420-0298)
PHONE..................................330 545-9731
Fax: 330 545-6164
Carl Malito, *President*
Donald Malito, *Vice Pres*
Jeff Hinebaugh, *QC Mgr*
Robert Malito, *Admin Sec*
EMP: 50 EST: 1948
SQ FT: 60,000
SALES: 13.7MM **Privately Held**
SIC: 3559 3599 Foundry, smelting, refin-
ing & similar machinery; machine shop,
jobbing & repair

(G-10391)
MARSH TECHNOLOGIES INC
30 W Main St Ste A (44420-2513)
PHONE..................................330 545-0085
Fax: 330 545-2157
Sandra G Marsh, *President*
EMP: 12
SQ FT: 10,000

SALES (est): 1.2MM **Privately Held**
WEB: www.marshtechnologies.com
SIC: 3544 Special dies, tools, jigs & fix-
tures

(G-10392)
PETTIT W T & SONS CO INC
1670 Keefer Rd (44420-1434)
PHONE..................................330 539-6100
Fax: 330 539-4472
Francis Poe, *President*
Daniel De Genova, *Vice Pres*
EMP: 8
SQ FT: 57,000
SALES (est): 1.4MM **Privately Held**
WEB: www.wtpettit.com
SIC: 3469 7389 Metal stampings; metal
slitting & shearing

(G-10393)
ROCKYS HINGE CO
1660 Harding Ave (44420-1514)
PHONE..................................330 539-6296
Fax: 330 539-4462
Rocky Shamlin, *Owner*
EMP: 6
SQ FT: 3,072
SALES (est): 481.7K **Privately Held**
WEB: www.rockyhin.ipower.com
SIC: 5251 3944 Hardware; child restraint
seats, automotive

(G-10394)
RW SIDLEY INC
200 Mill St (44420-2858)
PHONE..................................330 545-1964
Fax: 330 545-1068
Robert Sidley, *Owner*
EMP: 3
SQ FT: 1,664
SALES (est): 256.6K **Privately Held**
SIC: 3273 5211 5261 Ready-mixed con-
crete; cement; concrete & cinder block;
lawn & garden supplies

(G-10395)
SOFT TOUCH WOOD LLC
Also Called: Soft Tuch Furn Repr Rfinishing
1560 S State St (44420-3315)
PHONE..................................330 545-4204
Fax: 330 288-0083
Terry Chudakoff, *President*
Bob Leer, *Manager*
EMP: 40
SQ FT: 5,000
SALES (est): 2MM **Privately Held**
WEB: www.softtouchwood.com
SIC: 7641 2531 Furniture refinishing; pub-
lic building & related furniture

(G-10396)
STANCORP INC
712 Trumbull Ave (44420-3443)
PHONE..................................330 545-6615
Fax: 330 545-6726
Bruce R Beeghly, *President*
J D Beeghly, *Vice Pres*
Richard Pisani, *Treasurer*
Donna Gbur, *Asst Sec*
EMP: 4
SQ FT: 1,200
SALES (est): 576.9K **Privately Held**
WEB: www.stancorp.com
SIC: 6411 3823 Property & casualty insur-
ance agent; industrial instrmnts msrmnt
display/control process variable

Glandorf
Putnam County

(G-10397)
FIELD GYMMY INC
138-143 S Main St (45848)
P.O. Box 121, Ottawa (45875-0121)
PHONE..................................419 538-6511
Fax: 419 538-6365
Dennis Nienberg, *President*
Thomas Russell, *Corp Secy*
Melvin Nienberg, *Vice Pres*
Thomas Nienberg, *Vice Pres*
Ken Elchinger, *Sales Staff*
EMP: 8
SQ FT: 15,300

▲ = Import ▼=Export
◆ =Import/Export

SALES (est): 590K **Privately Held**
WEB: www.fieldgymmy.com
SIC: 3523 3713 3563 3531 Farm machinery & equipment; truck & bus bodies; air & gas compressors; construction machinery

Glenford
Perry County

(G-10398)
JAMES RYAN SOLOMAN
Also Called: Buildcret Concrete
5471 High Point Rd (43739-9727)
PHONE...................................740 659-2304
Ryan Solomon, *Owner*
EMP: 3
SALES (est): 156.7K **Privately Held**
SIC: 1442 Construction sand & gravel

(G-10399)
PLASTIC REGRINDERS INC
3161 Cooperriders Rd Nw (43739-9648)
PHONE...................................740 659-2346
Fax: 740 659-9629
George West, *President*
Sharon West, *Corp Secy*
EMP: 4
SALES (est): 330K **Privately Held**
SIC: 2821 Plastics materials & resins

(G-10400)
PREMIER SILICA LLC
Also Called: Glassrock Plant
2446 State Route 204 (43739)
PHONE...................................740 659-2241
Fax: 740 659-2348
Paul Currant, *Maint Mgr*
Jennifer Mulherin, *Financial Exec*
Wayn Dailey, *Manager*
EMP: 40
SALES (corp-wide): 3.8B **Publicly Held**
SIC: 3295 1446 Minerals, ground or treated; industrial sand
HQ: Premier Silica Llc
5205 N O Connor Blvd # 200
Irving TX 75039
972 444-9001

(G-10401)
VAN BURENS WELDING & MACHINE
11496 Cherry Hill Rd (43739-9620)
P.O. Box 85 (43739-0085)
PHONE...................................740 787-2636
Daniel V Buren, *Owner*
Daniel Van Buren, *Owner*
Jonathan Van Buren, *Co-Owner*
EMP: 4
SALES (est): 200K **Privately Held**
SIC: 7692 3542 Welding repair; machine tools, metal forming type

Glenmont
Holmes County

(G-10402)
BRIAR HILL STONE COMPANY
12470 State Route 520 (44628-9702)
P.O. Box 457 (44628-0457)
PHONE...................................330 377-5100
Fax: 330 377-5110
Frank Waller, *President*
Lowell M Shope, *General Mgr*
Connie D Scott, *Vice Pres*
Jerry Parsons, *Purchasing*
Ed Gales, *Manager*
EMP: 30
SQ FT: 4,000
SALES (est): 3.8MM **Privately Held**
WEB: www.briarhillstone.com
SIC: 3281 Stone, quarrying & processing of own stone products

Glouster
Athens County

(G-10403)
C & B LOGGING INC
9821 State Route 13 Se (45732-9623)
PHONE...................................740 347-4844
George J Post, *President*
Cameron Post, *Vice Pres*
EMP: 5
SALES (est): 507.1K **Privately Held**
SIC: 2411 0139 Logging camps & contractors; hay farm

(G-10404)
FROG RANCH FOODS LTD
5 S High St (45732-1051)
PHONE...................................740 767-3705
Craig Cornett, *President*
Kristi Hewitt, *CFO*
Kristi N Kay Hewitt, *CFO*
EMP: 10
SQ FT: 10,000
SALES: 1MM **Privately Held**
WEB: www.frogranch.com
SIC: 2099 Food preparations

Gnadenhutten
Tuscarawas County

(G-10405)
DAVID COX
Also Called: Dave's Welding & Excavation
9664 Gilmore Rd Se (44629-9637)
PHONE...................................740 254-4858
David Cox, *Owner*
Patricia Cox, *Co-Owner*
EMP: 3 EST: 1968
SALES: 200K **Privately Held**
SIC: 1794 7692 3444 Excavation work; welding repair; sheet metalwork

(G-10406)
ECHO DRILLING INC
Also Called: Crude Oil Buyer
367 Echo Rd Se (44629-9654)
PHONE...................................740 254-4127
Kenneth Ebersbach, *Branch Mgr*
EMP: 5
SALES (corp-wide): 1.3MM **Privately Held**
SIC: 1381 Drilling oil & gas wells
PA: Echo Drilling Inc
11 Crestview Mnr
Newcomerstown OH 43832
740 498-8560

(G-10407)
FIVECOAT LUMBER INC
2400 Larson Rd Se (44629-9500)
P.O. Box 871 (44629-0871)
PHONE...................................740 254-4681
Fax: 740 254-4617
John Fivecoat, *President*
Carl Fivecoat, *Vice Pres*
Dawn Fivecoat, *Manager*
Karen Fivecoart, *Admin Sec*
EMP: 15
SALES (est): 773.6K **Privately Held**
SIC: 2421 5211 Lumber: rough, sawed or planed; planing mill products & lumber

(G-10408)
MILLWOOD LUMBER INC
Also Called: Millwood Logging
2400 Larson Rd Se (44629-9500)
P.O. Box 871 (44629-0871)
PHONE...................................740 254-4681
Jeffery Miller, *President*
Michael Malara, *General Mgr*
EMP: 22
SALES (est): 2.5MM **Privately Held**
WEB: www.millwoodlumber.com
SIC: 2411 Logging

(G-10409)
PEMJAY INC
318 E Tuscarawas Ave (44629)
P.O. Box 669 (44629-0669)
PHONE...................................740 254-4591
Fax: 740 254-4036

Yolanda Jagunic, *Ch of Bd*
David Jagunic, *President*
Mark Dummermuth, *Vice Pres*
Nancy Rainsberg, *Treasurer*
Laura Granato, *Manager*
EMP: 23
SQ FT: 8,000
SALES (est): 5.6MM **Privately Held**
WEB: www.pemjay.com
SIC: 3312 Structural & rail mill products

(G-10410)
PLYMOUTH FOAM INCORPORATED
1 Souther Gateway St (44629)
P.O. Box 177 (44629-0177)
PHONE...................................740 254-1188
Brent Marshall, *Plant Mgr*
Chris Coleman, *Manager*
Thomas Groth, *Manager*
Rob Mann, *Manager*
EMP: 45
SALES (corp-wide): 34.7MM **Privately Held**
SIC: 3086 Plastics foam products
PA: Plymouth Foam Llc
1800 Sunset Dr
Plymouth WI 53073
608 807-1688

(G-10411)
STOCKER CONCRETE COMPANY
7574 Us Hwy 36 Se (44629)
P.O. Box 176 (44629-0176)
PHONE...................................740 254-4626
Thomas Stocker, *President*
Jeffrey Stocker, *Corp Secy*
Bryan Stocker, *Vice Pres*
William Stocker, *Shareholder*
EMP: 12
SQ FT: 15,000
SALES (est): 880K
SALES (corp-wide): 2.2MM **Privately Held**
SIC: 3273 5032 5211 3271 Ready-mixed concrete; concrete building products; masonry materials & supplies; concrete & cinder block; concrete block & brick; construction sand & gravel
PA: Stocker Sand & Gravel Co
Rr 36
Gnadenhutten OH 44629
740 254-4635

(G-10412)
STOCKER SAND & GRAVEL CO (PA)
Rr 36 (44629)
PHONE...................................740 254-4635
Fax: 740 254-9108
Bill Stocker, *President*
Jeffrey Stocker, *President*
Thomas Stocker, *Corp Secy*
Bryan Stocker, *Vice Pres*
Shane Casimir, *Manager*
EMP: 12 EST: 1933
SQ FT: 3,000
SALES: 2.2MM **Privately Held**
SIC: 1442 3271 Common sand mining; gravel mining; blocks, concrete or cinder: standard

Goshen
Clermont County

(G-10413)
CARGILL INCORPORATED
1976 Woodville Pike (45122-9469)
PHONE...................................513 625-2863
Ronald Young, *President*
EMP: 9
SALES (corp-wide): 107.1B **Privately Held**
WEB: www.cargill.com
SIC: 2044 Rice milling
PA: Cargill, Incorporated
15407 Mcginty Rd W
Wayzata MN 55391
952 742-7575

(G-10414)
DANDY PRODUCTS INC
3314 State Route 131 (45122-8511)
PHONE...................................513 625-3000
Fax: 513 625-2600
Daniel R Reed, *President*
Colleen Reed, *Vice Pres*
Detty Reed, *Admin Sec*
EMP: 10
SQ FT: 15,000
SALES (est): 1.7MM **Privately Held**
SIC: 3069 Floor coverings, rubber; mats or matting, rubber; wallcoverings, rubber

(G-10415)
G S LINK & ASSOCIATES
1881 Main St (45122-9763)
PHONE...................................513 722-2457
S T Link, *Partner*
Goethe S Link, *Principal*
EMP: 5
SQ FT: 5,000
SALES (est): 290K **Privately Held**
SIC: 2752 Commercial printing, lithographic

(G-10416)
LAB QUALITY MACHINING INC
6311 Roudebush Rd (45122-9571)
PHONE...................................513 625-0219
Fax: 513 625-9042
James Brath, *President*
Linda A Brath, *Principal*
EMP: 6
SQ FT: 5,200
SALES: 400K **Privately Held**
WEB: www.labqualitymachining.com
SIC: 3544 Special dies, tools, jigs & fixtures

(G-10417)
TRIUMPHANT ENTERPRISES INC
7096 Hill Station Rd (45122-9728)
PHONE...................................513 617-1668
Richard G Hughes Sr, *President*
Jewell A Hughes, *Vice Pres*
EMP: 25
SALES (est): 4.9MM **Privately Held**
SIC: 3537 Trucks: freight, baggage, etc.: industrial, except mining

Grafton
Lorain County

(G-10418)
ADVANCE WEIGHT SYSTEM INC
409 Main St (44044-1205)
P.O. Box 6 (44044-0006)
PHONE...................................440 926-3691
Fax: 440 926-2142
Clarence G Lahl Jr, *President*
Roland Seaburn, *Vice Pres*
Martha Lahl, *Treasurer*
EMP: 10
SQ FT: 3,000
SALES: 400K **Privately Held**
WEB: www.advancew8.com
SIC: 3596 Weighing machines & apparatus

(G-10419)
ARTISAN MOLD CO INC
1021 Commerce Dr 219 (44044-1279)
P.O. Box 219 (44044-0219)
PHONE...................................440 926-4511
Fax: 440 366-5808
Jerry Winson, *President*
John T Winson, *Vice Pres*
Gail Philion, *Admin Sec*
EMP: 4
SALES: 620K **Privately Held**
SIC: 3089 Injection molding of plastics

(G-10420)
BANKS MANUFACTURING COMPANY
40259 Banks Rd (44044-9750)
PHONE...................................440 458-8661
Fax: 440 458-4471
Tim Boyd, *President*
Sheila Boyd, *Vice Pres*
EMP: 10 EST: 1948
SQ FT: 10,000

SALES: 954.2K **Privately Held**
WEB: www.banksmfg.com
SIC: **1799** 1721 3441 Sandblasting of building exteriors; industrial painting; fabricated structural metal

(G-10421)
COMMTECH SOLUTIONS INC
38900 Arbor Ct (44044-1056)
PHONE..................................440 458-4870
Alan Gauvreau, *President*
EMP: 1
SALES: 1.8MM **Privately Held**
SIC: **3661** Communication headgear, telephone

(G-10422)
CREATIVE WOODWORKS
16940 Indian Hollow Rd (44044-9232)
PHONE..................................440 355-8155
Larry Babb, *Owner*
EMP: 4
SQ FT: 1,500
SALES: 67.3K **Privately Held**
SIC: **2521** Wood office furniture

(G-10423)
CUSTOMCHROME PLATING INC
Also Called: Custom Chrome Plating
963 Mechanic St (44044-1416)
PHONE..................................440 926-3116
Jon E Wright, *President*
EMP: 15
SQ FT: 12,500
SALES: 1MM **Privately Held**
SIC: **3471** Chromium plating of metals or formed products

(G-10424)
EATON CORPORATION
Also Called: Eaton Township
12043 Avon Belden Rd (44044-9417)
PHONE..................................440 748-2236
Linda Spitzer, *Principal*
EMP: 3 **Privately Held**
WEB: www.eaton.com
SIC: **3625** Motor controls & accessories
HQ: Eaton Corporation
　　1000 Eaton Blvd
　　Cleveland OH 44122
　　216 523-5000

(G-10425)
EATON FABRICATING COMPANY INC
1009 Mcalpin Ct (44044-1322)
PHONE..................................440 926-3121
Fax: 440 926-3406
Ray D Roach Jr, *President*
Lloyd H Roach Sr, *Principal*
Jack Schulman, *Principal*
Chris Woconish, *Engineer*
▲ EMP: 50
SQ FT: 40,600
SALES (est): 10.7MM **Privately Held**
WEB: www.eatonfabricating.com
SIC: **3599** 3444 3443 Machine shop, jobbing & repair; sheet metalwork; fabricated plate work (boiler shop)

(G-10426)
GENERAL PLUG AND MFG CO (PA)
455 Main St (44044-1257)
P.O. Box 26 (44044-0026)
PHONE..................................440 926-2411
Fax: 440 926-3305
D Wallace Weil, *President*
Jim Tyree, *General Mgr*
Gerald L Jenkins, *Vice Pres*
Jacques Cote, *Plant Mgr*
Jason Holstein, *Engineer*
▲ EMP: 125 EST: 1955
SQ FT: 70,000
SALES (est): 35.2MM **Privately Held**
WEB: www.generalplug.com
SIC: **3494** 3599 3643 Pipe fittings; machine shop, jobbing & repair; current-carrying wiring devices

(G-10427)
GRAFTON READY MIX CONCRET INC
1155 Elm St (44044-1303)
P.O. Box 37 (44044-0037)
PHONE..................................440 926-2911
Fax: 440 926-3813
Jeffrey Riddell, *President*
John Wilson, *Opers Mgr*
EMP: 22
SQ FT: 15,000
SALES: 1.4MM
SALES (corp-wide): 10.9MM **Privately Held**
WEB: www.graftonreadymix.com
SIC: **3273** 5032 5211 Ready-mixed concrete; brick, stone & related material; concrete mixtures; masonry materials & supplies
PA: Consumeracq, Inc.
　　2509 N Ridge Rd E
　　Lorain OH 44055
　　440 277-9305

(G-10428)
GREAT WORKS PUBLISHING INC
Also Called: Donze Enterprises
1080 Cleveland St (44044-1319)
PHONE..................................440 926-1100
Fax: 440 926-2882
Christoher Donze, *President*
EMP: 15
SALES (est): 689.2K **Privately Held**
SIC: **2741** Music, sheet: publishing & printing

(G-10429)
GREEN FUEL TODAY
11 April Hill Dr (44044-9607)
PHONE..................................440 925-7820
EMP: 4
SALES (est): 256K **Privately Held**
SIC: **2869** Fuels

(G-10430)
HOTEND WORKS INC
18153 Indian Hollow Rd (44044-9672)
PHONE..................................440 787-3181
Benjamin Becker, *Managing Dir*
EMP: 3
SALES (est): 135.4K **Privately Held**
SIC: **3555** Printing trades machinery

(G-10431)
JESCO PRODUCTS INC
11811 Robson Rd (44044-9157)
PHONE..................................440 233-5828
Fax: 440 233-5849
Eva Squires, *President*
Mary Jane Taylor, *Corp Secy*
EMP: 3
SQ FT: 800
SALES (est): 428.1K **Privately Held**
WEB: www.jescoproducts.com
SIC: **3599** Machine shop, jobbing & repair

(G-10432)
KEY MARKETING GROUP
11185 Arrowhead Dr (44044-9774)
PHONE..................................440 748-3479
David Pataky, *Owner*
Judy Pataky, *Co-Owner*
EMP: 4
SALES (est): 269.5K **Privately Held**
SIC: **7336** 2759 Graphic arts & related design; commercial printing

(G-10433)
LUDWIG MUSIC PUBLISHING CO
1080 Cleveland St (44044-1319)
PHONE..................................440 926-1100
Christopher Donze, *President*
Kaprice Holloway, *General Mgr*
EMP: 12
SQ FT: 7,000
SALES (est): 830.5K **Privately Held**
WEB: www.ludwigmusic.com
SIC: **2741** Music, sheet: publishing only, not printed on site

(G-10434)
PALLET PROS
12500 Island Rd (44044-9550)
PHONE..................................440 537-9087

EMP: 3
SALES (est): 130K **Privately Held**
SIC: **2448** Mfg Wood Pallets/Skids

(G-10435)
POWER GROUNDING SOLUTIONS LLC
1001 Commerce Dr (44044-1278)
P.O. Box 66 (44044-0066)
PHONE..................................440 926-3219
Margaret McMillen, *President*
▲ EMP: 4
SQ FT: 10,000
SALES: 584.4K **Privately Held**
SIC: **3643** Current-carrying wiring devices

(G-10436)
SOUNDPROOF
15400 Highland Dr (44044-9028)
PHONE..................................440 864-8864
John Schneider, *Owner*
EMP: 5
SALES: 30K **Privately Held**
SIC: **3651** Household audio & video equipment

(G-10437)
SULO ENTERPRISES INC
Also Called: Magna Products
1017 Commerce Dr (44044-1279)
P.O. Box 97 (44044-0097)
PHONE..................................440 926-3322
Fax: 440 926-2403
Lowell L Snider, *President*
Suzanne Snider, *Vice Pres*
Robert Alford, *Manager*
Steven Snider, *Admin Secy*
▲ EMP: 16
SQ FT: 6,000
SALES: 13.5MM **Privately Held**
WEB: www.shop-mag.com
SIC: **3499** Magnets, permanent: metallic

(G-10438)
UNITED CIRCUITS INC
1000 Commerce Dr (44044-1271)
PHONE..................................440 926-1000
Fax: 440 922-8289
Frank Schubert, *President*
Barbara Schubert, *Corp Secy*
Gary W Jump, *Vice Pres*
Rick Schubert, *Mfg Staff*
EMP: 10 EST: 1982
SQ FT: 17,000
SALES (est): 740K **Privately Held**
SIC: **3672** Printed circuit boards

Grand Rapids
Wood County

(G-10439)
A+ ENGINEERING FABRICATION INC
17562 Beech St (43522-9728)
P.O. Box 470 (43522-0470)
PHONE..................................419 832-0748
Fax: 419 832-1821
David Arno, *President*
Linda Arno, *Vice Pres*
Ryan Arno, *Draft/Design*
Teri Miller, *Manager*
EMP: 15
SQ FT: 23,500
SALES (est): 4.7MM **Privately Held**
WEB: www.aplusengineering.com
SIC: **3441** 3599 8711 Fabricated structural metal; machine shop, jobbing & repair; engineering services

(G-10440)
INDUSTRIAL APPLICATION SVS
13453 Woodbrier Ln (43522-9681)
PHONE..................................419 875-5093
Marty Anderson, *President*
EMP: 4
SALES (est): 405.9K **Privately Held**
WEB: www.industrialapp.com
SIC: **3629** 7389 Electrical industrial apparatus; business services

(G-10441)
LAKE WOOD PRODUCT INC (PA)
13020 Box Rd (43522-9233)
PHONE..................................419 832-0150
Jay Thomas, *President*
Donald W Pullen, *President*
Heidi Thomas, *Vice Pres*
Patty Miller, *Admin Sec*
EMP: 5
SQ FT: 11,648
SALES: 400K **Privately Held**
SIC: **2448** Pallets, wood; skids, wood

(G-10442)
PARAMOUNT PRODUCTS
10550 Prov Neap Swan Rd (43522-9668)
P.O. Box 429, Neapolis (43547-0429)
PHONE..................................419 832-0235
Fax: 419 832-1534
Roger A Kosch, *President*
Carolyn Kosch, *Corp Secy*
George Walker, *Sales Mgr*
EMP: 5
SQ FT: 10,000
SALES (est): 796.8K **Privately Held**
WEB: www.paramountproducts.com
SIC: **2992** Lubricating oils & greases

(G-10443)
PIONEER HI-BRED INTL INC
15180 Henry Wood Rd (43522-9772)
PHONE..................................419 748-8051
Scott Millikan, *Manager*
EMP: 35
SQ FT: 6,000
SALES (corp-wide): 24.5B **Publicly Held**
WEB: www.pioneer.com
SIC: **5191** 5153 2075 2041 Seeds: field, garden & flower; corn; soybeans; soybean oil mills; flour & other grain mill products
HQ: Pioneer Hi-Bred International, Inc.
　　7100 Nw 62nd Ave
　　Johnston IA 50131
　　515 535-3200

(G-10444)
Q S I FABRICATION
10333 Us Route 24 (43522-9350)
PHONE..................................419 832-1680
Tom Zitzelberger, *President*
Pete Wiederhold, *Sales Mgr*
EMP: 7
SQ FT: 400
SALES (est): 351.4K **Privately Held**
SIC: **3441** Fabricated structural metal

(G-10445)
SAYLOR PRODUCTS CORPORATION
17484 Saylor Ln (43522-9792)
PHONE..................................419 832-2125
Fax: 419 832-0710
Gregory Westhoven, *President*
Sherlly Price, *Manager*
EMP: 10 EST: 1902
SQ FT: 550
SALES (est): 1.4MM
SALES (corp-wide): 6.9MM **Privately Held**
SIC: **3644** Electric conduits & fittings
PA: Saylor Technical Products, Llc
　　17484 Saylor Ln
　　Grand Rapids OH 43522
　　713 884-0564

(G-10446)
SEEBURGER GREENHOUSE
Also Called: Usc Metal Fabricators
11480 Us Route 24 (43522-9341)
PHONE..................................419 832-1834
Larry Seeburger, *Owner*
EMP: 5
SALES (est): 160K **Privately Held**
SIC: **0181** 3441 Bedding plants, growing of; flowers: grown under cover (e.g. greenhouse production); fabricated structural metal

Grand River
Lake County

(G-10447)
ACTUATION KONGSBERG SYSTEMS II
Also Called: Kongsberg Automotive
301 Olive St (44045-8221)
P.O. Box 98 (44045-0098)
PHONE..................................440 639-8778
Martin Whate, *Branch Mgr*
EMP: 17
SALES (est): 311.6K
SALES (corp-wide): 25.6MM **Privately Held**
WEB: www.teleflexfluidsystems.com
SIC: 3714 Motor vehicle parts & accessories
PA: Kongsberg Actuation Systems Ii, Inc.
1 Firestone Dr
Suffield CT 06078
860 668-1285

(G-10448)
FREDEBAUGH WELL DRILLING CO
714 Lakeshore Blvd (44045)
PHONE..................................440 357-6924
Fax: 440 357-6091
H Fredebaugh Sr, *President*
Mark Fredebaugh, *Vice Pres*
Patricia Fredebaugh, *Admin Sec*
EMP: 15
SQ FT: 2,500
SALES (est): 2.4MM **Privately Held**
SIC: 1381 Drilling oil & gas wells

(G-10449)
GRAND RIVER ASPHALT
6 Coast Guard Rd (44045)
P.O. Box 249 (44045-0249)
PHONE..................................440 352-2254
Jerome T Osborne, *President*
EMP: 4
SALES (est): 530K **Privately Held**
SIC: 2951 Asphalt & asphaltic paving mixtures (not from refineries)

(G-10450)
HOGAN AWNING INC
503 Lake Shore Blvd (44045)
P.O. Box 599 (44045-0599)
PHONE..................................440 352-4033
James Hogan, *President*
EMP: 7
SQ FT: 7,200
SALES (est): 410K **Privately Held**
SIC: 2394 Convertible tops, canvas or boat: from purchased materials; sails: made from purchased materials; awnings, fabric: made from purchased materials; canvas boat seats

(G-10451)
JED INDUSTRIES INC
320 River St (44045-8214)
P.O. Box 369 (44045-0369)
PHONE..................................440 639-9973
Fax: 440 639-9796
Donald Nye, *President*
Barb Nye, *Manager*
EMP: 25
SQ FT: 27,000
SALES (est): 4MM **Privately Held**
WEB: www.jedindustries.com
SIC: 3599 5084 Machine & other job shop work; industrial machinery & equipment

(G-10452)
OSBORNE MATERIALS COMPANY (PA)
1 Williams St (44045-8253)
P.O. Box 248 (44045-0248)
PHONE..................................440 357-7026
Harold T Larned, *President*
Gary D Bradler, *President*
David Baczek, *Accountant*
▼ **EMP:** 1
SQ FT: 2,500
SALES (est): 3.8MM **Privately Held**
SIC: 1442 Sand mining; gravel mining

(G-10453)
SUMITOMO ELC CARBIDE MFG INC (DH)
Also Called: Master Tool Div
210 River St (44045-8249)
P.O. Box 188 (44045-0188)
PHONE..................................440 354-0600
Fax: 440 354-6372
Yasuhisa Hashimoto, *President*
Roger Raines, *Prdtn Mgr*
Rick Ropos, *Engineer*
Matt Snyder, *Controller*
Takahiro Kimura, *Admin Sec*
EMP: 10
SQ FT: 25,000
SALES (est): 13.2MM
SALES (corp-wide): 25B **Privately Held**
SIC: 3541 3546 3545 3544 Machine tools, metal cutting type; power-driven handtools; machine tool accessories; special dies, tools, jigs & fixtures; hand & edge tools
HQ: Sumitomo Electric Carbide Inc
1001 E Business Center Dr
Mount Prospect IL 60056
847 635-0044

(G-10454)
TWINSBURG DEVELOPMENT CORP (PA)
1 Williams St (44045-8253)
P.O. Box 249 (44045-0249)
PHONE..................................440 357-5562
Harold T Larned, *President*
Jerome T Osborne, *Principal*
Michael E Osborne, *Principal*
EMP: 1
SQ FT: 2,500
SALES: 1MM **Privately Held**
SIC: 1442 Sand mining; gravel mining

Granville
Licking County

(G-10455)
CARTER EVANS ENTERPRISES INC
Also Called: Pacer's Embroidery Barn
3354 Battee Rd (43023-9796)
PHONE..................................614 920-2276
Fax: 614 920-2277
EMP: 3
SQ FT: 2,500
SALES: 180K **Privately Held**
SIC: 2395 5949 Embroidery Or Art Needlework & Ret Embroidery Supplies

(G-10456)
CPIC AUTOMOTIVE INC
1226 Weaver Dr (43023-1257)
PHONE..................................740 587-3262
Cameron Cofer, *Vice Pres*
EMP: 3
SQ FT: 15,000
SALES (est): 156K **Privately Held**
SIC: 3296 Fiberglass insulation

(G-10457)
DOWNEY ENTERPRISES INC
Also Called: John Downey Company
2087 Jones Rd (43023-9542)
P.O. Box 565 (43023-0565)
PHONE..................................740 587-4258
John Downey, *President*
EMP: 5
SQ FT: 1,500
SALES: 140K **Privately Held**
SIC: 7217 2721 Carpet & upholstery cleaning; magazines: publishing & printing

(G-10458)
ERATH VENEER CORP VIRGINIA
2825 Hallie Ln B (43023-9256)
PHONE..................................540 483-5223
Michael G Erath, *Chairman*
Rbobert C Moore, *Corp Secy*
C M Rbobert Jr, *CFO*
Neely Bowling, *Human Res Dir*
◆ **EMP:** 14
SALES (est): 1.9MM **Privately Held**
WEB: www.erathveneer.com
SIC: 2435 Veneer stock, hardwood

(G-10459)
HOLOPHANE CORPORATION (HQ)
3825 Columbus Rd Bldg A (43023-8604)
PHONE..................................866 759-1577
Fax: 740 349-4486
Vernon J Nagel, *CEO*
Rick Clark, *Vice Pres*
Randy Crothers, *VP Sls/Mktg*
Latanya Riley, *Accounting Mgr*
Valerie Rivir, *Cust Mgr*
◆ **EMP:** 163
SALES (est): 865MM
SALES (corp-wide): 3.2B **Publicly Held**
SIC: 3646 3648 Commercial indusl & institutional electric lighting fixtures; outdoor lighting equipment
PA: Acuity Brands, Inc.
1170 Peachtree St Ne
Atlanta GA 30309
404 853-1400

(G-10460)
MCDONALD & WOODWARD PUBG CO
431b E College St (43023)
PHONE..................................740 321-1140
Fax: 740 321-1141
Jerry Mc Donald, *President*
Gavin Faulkner, *Vice Pres*
Trish Newcomb, *Admin Sec*
EMP: 3
SALES (est): 210K **Privately Held**
WEB: www.mwpubco.com
SIC: 2731 Book publishing

(G-10461)
MERITOR INC
Also Called: Arvinmrtor Commerical Vhcl Sys
4009 Columbus Rd Ste 111 (43023-8623)
PHONE..................................740 348-3498
Jim Corll, *Engineer*
Brian Hayes, *Engineer*
R S Shea, *Engineer*
Mike Deep, *Manager*
Michelle Hansen, *Analyst*
EMP: 157
SALES (corp-wide): 3.2B **Publicly Held**
WEB: www.arvinmeritor.com
SIC: 3714 3713 Axles, motor vehicle; truck & bus bodies
PA: Meritor, Inc.
2135 W Maple Rd
Troy MI 48084
248 435-1000

(G-10462)
MILESTONE VENTURES LLC (PA)
Also Called: Milestone Veneer
2924 Hallie Ln (43023-9516)
PHONE..................................317 908-2093
Dittmar Schaefer, *Mng Member*
John J McHugh III, *Mng Member*
Bernd Merkel, *Mng Member*
EMP: 3
SALES (est): 1.9MM **Privately Held**
SIC: 2411 Veneer logs

(G-10463)
OOGEEP
1718 Columbus Rd (43023-1234)
PHONE..................................740 587-0410
Rhonda Reda, *Principal*
Mark Bruce, *Comms Dir*
EMP: 4
SALES (est): 320.4K **Privately Held**
SIC: 1381 Drilling oil & gas wells

(G-10464)
OWENS CORNING SALES LLC
Owens Corning Science and Tech
2790 Columbus Rd (43023-1200)
PHONE..................................740 587-3562
Fax: 740 321-7677
Frank O'Brien Bernin, *Vice Pres*
David Roth, *Vice Pres*
Warren Wolf, *Vice Pres*
Beth Ansley, *Opers Dir*
Paul Borders, *Plant Mgr*
EMP: 400
SALES (corp-wide): 5.6B **Publicly Held**
WEB: www.owenscorning.com
SIC: 8731 2221 Commercial physical research; broadwoven fabric mills, manmade
HQ: Owens Corning Sales, Llc
1 Owens Corning Pkwy
Toledo OH 43659
419 248-8000

(G-10465)
PHOENIX GRAPHIX PUBG SVCS LLC
444 N Pearl St (43023-1302)
PHONE..................................740 587-3659
Judy Blair, *Project Mgr*
Wendy Hollinger,
EMP: 4
SALES: 250K **Privately Held**
SIC: 2741 Miscellaneous publishing

(G-10466)
RED VETTE PRINTING COMPANY
75 Fern Hill Dr (43023-9102)
P.O. Box 725, Newark (43058-0725)
PHONE..................................740 364-1766
Fax: 740 349-9378
Denna Brown, *President*
EMP: 5
SALES: 250K **Privately Held**
WEB: www.redvetteprinting.com
SIC: 2752 Commercial printing, lithographic

(G-10467)
THERMAL VISIONS INC (PA)
Also Called: Threshhold
83 Stone Henge Dr (43023-9532)
PHONE..................................740 587-4025
Dwight Musgrave, *President*
Dean Musgrave, *Admin Sec*
▲ **EMP:** 5
SQ FT: 11,000
SALES: 17MM **Privately Held**
WEB: www.thermalvisions.com
SIC: 3086 Packaging & shipping materials, foamed plastic

Gratis
Preble County

(G-10468)
TOLSON PALLET MFG INC
10240 State Rte 122 (45330)
P.O. Box 151 (45330-0151)
PHONE..................................937 787-3511
Fax: 937 787-4662
Keith Tolson, *President*
Brent Tolson, *Vice Pres*
EMP: 10 **EST:** 1969
SQ FT: 30,000
SALES: 2.5MM **Privately Held**
SIC: 2448 Pallets, wood; skids, wood

Graysville
Washington County

(G-10469)
HARMON JOHN
Also Called: Harmon, John K
36300 Greenbrier Rd (45734-9725)
PHONE..................................740 934-2032
John Harmon, *Owner*
EMP: 4
SALES (est): 259.4K **Privately Held**
SIC: 1389 Servicing oil & gas wells

(G-10470)
WHITACRE ENTERPRISES INC
35651 State Route 537 (45734-7002)
PHONE..................................740 934-2331
Koy Whitacre, *President*
EMP: 16
SQ FT: 7,000
SALES (est): 2MM **Privately Held**
SIC: 5411 1382 Convenience stores, independent; oil & gas exploration services

Green Springs
Seneca County

(G-10471)
JAMES W CUNNINGHAM
Also Called: Electrical Machinery & Repair
125 Baker St (44836-9306)
PHONE....................................419 639-2111
Fax: 419 639-2113
EMP: 15 EST: 1954
SQ FT: 15,000
SALES (est): 670K Privately Held
SIC: 7694 Electric Motor Repair

Greenfield
Highland County

(G-10472)
ADIENT US LLC
Also Called: Johnson Controls
1147 N Washington St (45123-9782)
PHONE....................................937 383-5200
Fax: 937 981-4450
Joe Jones, Prdtn Mgr
Al Cabose, Network Mgr
Greg Galloway, Network Mgr
EMP: 250
SQ FT: 65,000 Privately Held
SIC: 2531 Seats, automobile
HQ: Adient Us Llc
    49200 Halyard Dr
    Plymouth MI 48170
    734 254-5000

(G-10473)
**AMERICAN MADE
CORRUGATED PACKG**
Also Called: A M C P
1100 N 5th St (45123)
P.O. Box 186 (45123-0186)
PHONE....................................937 981-2111
Fax: 937 981-2113
Arden Fife, President
Melvin Smith, Vice Pres
Pat Mc Allister, Treasurer
EMP: 15
SQ FT: 21,000
SALES (est): 2.4MM Privately Held
SIC: 2653 5113 Boxes, corrugated: made
from purchased materials; corrugated &
solid fiber boxes

(G-10474)
C-MOLD INC
175 Industrial Park Dr (45123-9000)
PHONE....................................937 981-7797
Fax: 937 981-7125
Chuck Winkle, Owner
Orlando Brown, Vice Pres
Bill Beatty, Treasurer
Steve Lewis, Admin Sec
EMP: 30
SQ FT: 21,500
SALES (est): 5.4MM Privately Held
SIC: 3089 Injection molding of plastics

(G-10475)
CORVAC COMPOSITES LLC
1025 N Washington St (45123-9780)
PHONE....................................248 807-0969
James Fitzell, CEO
Christine Black, Controller
EMP: 9
SALES (corp-wide): 157.9MM Privately
Held
SIC: 3089 Thermoformed finished plastic
products
HQ: Corvac Composites, Llc
    4450 36th St Se
    Kentwood MI 49512
    616 281-4026

(G-10476)
GMI COMPANIES INC
Woodware Furniture
512 S Washington St (45123-1645)
PHONE....................................937 981-0244
George L Leasure, President
Karen Kurtz, Administration
EMP: 3

SALES (corp-wide): 22.9MM Privately
Held
SIC: 2531 2493 2599 2541 Blackboards,
wood; bulletin boards, cork; bulletin
boards, wood; boards: planning, display,
notice; showcases, except refrigerated:
wood; panel systems & partitions (free-
standing), office: wood; panel systems &
partitions, office: except wood
PA: Gmi Companies, Inc.
    2999 Henkle Dr
    Lebanon OH 45036
    513 932-3445

(G-10477)
GMI COMPANIES INC
Also Called: Waddell A Div GMI Companies
512 S Washington St (45123-1645)
P.O. Box 18 (45123-0018)
PHONE....................................937 981-7724
Fax: 937 981-2918
Tom Septor, Opers Staff
Tom Septer, Manager
Kevin Smiertka, Manager
John Stone, Manager
EMP: 25
SALES (corp-wide): 22.9MM Privately
Held
WEB: www.ghent.com
SIC: 2541 Showcases, except refrigerated:
wood; store fixtures, wood
PA: Gmi Companies, Inc.
    2999 Henkle Dr
    Lebanon OH 45036
    513 932-3445

(G-10478)
**GREENFIELD RESEARCH INC
(PA)**
347 Edgewood Ave (45123-1149)
P.O. Box 239 (45123-0239)
PHONE....................................937 981-7763
Fax: 937 981-3763
Michael Penn, President
Robert Snider, Corp Secy
Bob Snider, Treasurer
Chris Lewis, Controller
Gary Pristas, Human Res Dir
▼ EMP: 150 EST: 1966
SQ FT: 60,000
SALES (est): 42.1MM Privately Held
WEB: www.greenfieldresearch.com
SIC: 2396 Automotive & apparel trimmings;
automotive trimmings, fabric

(G-10479)
GREENFIELD RESEARCH INC
324 S Washington St (45123-1437)
PHONE....................................937 876-9224
Michael Penn, President
EMP: 5
SALES (corp-wide): 42.1MM Privately
Held
SIC: 2396 Automotive trimmings, fabric
PA: Greenfield Research, Inc.
    347 Edgewood Ave
    Greenfield OH 45123
    937 981-7763

(G-10480)
HISEY BELLS
Also Called: Inter Valley Communication
581 Capps Rd (45123-8356)
PHONE....................................740 333-7669
Dave Hisey, Owner
EMP: 3
SALES: 80K Privately Held
WEB: www.hiseybells.com
SIC: 3931 Bells (musical instruments)

(G-10481)
JETTS EMBROIDERIES
Also Called: Jett's Professional Embroidery
1060 Jefferson St (45123-8319)
PHONE....................................937 981-3716
Carla Jett, Owner
Ted Jett, Manager
EMP: 3
SALES: 180K Privately Held
SIC: 2395 2396 Embroidery & art needle-
work; screen printing on fabric articles

(G-10482)
LETTER SHOP
247 Jefferson St (45123-1345)
PHONE....................................937 981-3117

Steve Pearce, Owner
EMP: 3
SQ FT: 6,300
SALES: 280K Privately Held
SIC: 2752 Commercial printing, offset

Greenford
Mahoning County

(G-10483)
SPOTTED HORSE STUDIO INC
6385 State Rte 165 (44422)
P.O. Box 5 (44422-0005)
PHONE....................................330 533-2391
William Baird, President
EMP: 3
SALES (est): 210K Privately Held
SIC: 3993 Signs & advertising specialties

Greentown
Stark County

(G-10484)
ACTION SIGN INC
3140 Stage St (44630)
P.O. Box 341 (44630-0341)
PHONE....................................330 966-0390
Fax: 330 966-9517
George Manos, President
EMP: 3
SALES (est): 327.7K Privately Held
SIC: 3993 Signs, not made in custom sign
painting shops

(G-10485)
CANRON MANUFACTURING INC
3979 State St Nw (44630)
P.O. Box 356 (44630-0356)
PHONE....................................330 497-1131
Fax: 330 497-6086
John Kettering, President
Heidi Michel, Vice Pres
EMP: 10 EST: 1981
SQ FT: 15,000
SALES (est): 2.7MM Privately Held
SIC: 3496 Miscellaneous fabricated wire
products

(G-10486)
EXCALIBUR EXPLORATION INC
9720 Cleveland Ave Nw (44630)
P.O. Box 362 (44630-0362)
PHONE....................................330 966-7003
Fax: 330 966-4818
David E Harker, President
Kurt Tyuluman, Vice Pres
Jennifer N Harker, Treasurer
EMP: 3
SALES (est): 549.9K Privately Held
WEB: www.excaliburexploration.com
SIC: 1311 Crude petroleum production;
natural gas production

Greenville
Darke County

(G-10487)
ACTION PROSTHETICS LLC
1498 N Broadway St Ste 3 (45331-2454)
PHONE....................................937 548-9100
Karl Burk, Owner
EMP: 3
SALES (est): 250K Privately Held
SIC: 3842 Surgical appliances & supplies

(G-10488)
**ANDERSONS MARATHON
ETHANOL LLC**
5728 Sebring Warner Rd N (45331-9800)
PHONE....................................937 316-3700
Neill McKinstary, President
EMP: 40
SALES (est): 9.3MM Privately Held
SIC: 2869 Ethyl alcohol, ethanol

(G-10489)
BASF CORPORATION
1175 Martin St (45331-1886)
PHONE....................................937 547-6700
Fax: 937 547-6778
Martin Borgerding, Engineer
Jim Bero, Branch Mgr
EMP: 150
SALES (corp-wide): 60.8B Privately Held
WEB: www.basf.com
SIC: 2869 Industrial organic chemicals
HQ: Basf Corporation
    100 Park Ave
    Florham Park NJ 07932
    973 245-6000

(G-10490)
**BROTHERS PUBLISHING CO
LLC**
Also Called: Early Bird, The
5312 Sebring Warner Rd (45331-8787)
PHONE....................................937 548-3330
Fax: 937 548-3376
Ryan Berry, Editor
Carol Mikesell, Office Mgr
Keith Foutz, Mng Member
EMP: 45 EST: 1898
SALES (est): 2.4MM Privately Held
SIC: 2711 2791 7331 Newspapers: pub-
lishing only, not printed on site; typeset-
ting; mailing list compilers

(G-10491)
**CALMEGO SPECIALIZED PDTS
LLC**
1569 Martindale Rd (45331-9696)
PHONE....................................937 669-5620
Clarence Neels,
EMP: 10
SALES (est): 1.1MM Privately Held
SIC: 3366 Copper foundries

(G-10492)
CARR SUPPLY CO
900 Sater St (45331-1637)
PHONE....................................937 316-6300
Stive Werling, Manager
EMP: 5
SALES (corp-wide): 2.7B Privately Held
SIC: 5722 5074 3432 1521 Air condition-
ing room units, self-contained; plumbing
fittings & supplies; plumbing fixture fittings
& trim; single-family home remodeling,
additions & repairs
HQ: Carr Supply Co.
    1415 Old Leonard Ave
    Columbus OH 43219
    614 252-7883

(G-10493)
CLASSIC REPRODUCTIONS
5315 Meeker Rd (45331-9751)
P.O. Box 916 (45331-0916)
PHONE....................................937 548-9839
Fax: 937 548-0287
Thomas Jeffers, Owner
Kelly Jeffers, Finance Mgr
Ronda King, Sales Staff
EMP: 8
SQ FT: 48,000
SALES (est): 813.7K Privately Held
WEB: www.classicreproductions.com
SIC: 3714 Motor vehicle parts & acces-
sories; motor vehicle body components &
frame

(G-10494)
**COMMERCIAL PRTG OF
GREENVILL**
314 S Broadway St (45331-1905)
PHONE....................................937 548-3835
Fax: 937 548-3835
Jeff Campbell, Owner
Joan Brante, Principal
Marian Campbell, Admin Sec
EMP: 8
SQ FT: 2,200
SALES (est): 460K Privately Held
SIC: 2752 Commercial printing, litho-
graphic

(G-10495)
CONTINENTAL CARBONIC PDTS INC
198 Continental Dr (45331-8809)
PHONE...................................937 316-6160
EMP: 3
SALES (corp-wide): 5.4B Privately Held
SIC: 2813 Dry ice, carbon dioxide (solid)
HQ: Continental Carbonic Products, Inc.
3985 E Harrison Ave
Decatur IL 62526
217 428-2068

(G-10496)
CROMWELL ALEENE
Also Called: Mock Shoppe
101 W Main St (45331-1401)
PHONE...................................937 547-2281
Aleene Cromwell, Owner
EMP: 3
SQ FT: 500
SALES (est): 75K Privately Held
SIC: 3199 Novelties, leather

(G-10497)
D A FITZGERALD CO INC
1045 Sater St (45331-1638)
P.O. Box 206 (45331-0206)
PHONE...................................937 548-0511
Fax: 937 548-2544
Don S Fitzgerald, President
Janice Fitzgerald, Corp Secy
Scott Fitzgerald, Admin Sec
EMP: 9
SQ FT: 10,000
SALES (est): 770K Privately Held
SIC: 3544 Special dies & tools; jigs & fix-
tures

(G-10498)
FOUREMANS SAND & GRAVEL INC
2791 Wildcat Rd (45331-9453)
PHONE...................................937 547-1005
Gary B Foureman, President
John Foureman, Vice Pres
Susan Foureman, Treasurer
EMP: 6 EST: 1953
SQ FT: 14,000
SALES: 380K Privately Held
SIC: 1442 1794 Gravel mining; excavation
& grading, building construction

(G-10499)
FRAM GROUP OPERATIONS LLC
Honeywell
851 Jackson St (45331-1277)
PHONE...................................937 316-3000
Fax: 937 316-3389
Bob Rhodes, Purch Mgr
William Lefevre, Draft/Design
Todd Hickman, Engineer
Gary Osterfield, Engineer
Bernie Salles, Manager
EMP: 4 Privately Held
WEB: www.honeywell.com
SIC: 3714 3264 Filters: oil, fuel & air,
motor vehicle; spark plugs, porcelain
HQ: Fram Group Operations Llc
1900 W Field Ct
Lake Forest IL 60045

(G-10500)
FRIENDS OF BEARS MILL INC
6450 Arcanum Bearsmill Rd (45331-9617)
PHONE...................................937 548-5112
Fax: 937 547-6044
Terry Clark, President
EMP: 4
SQ FT: 8,000
SALES: 110.5K Privately Held
WEB: www.bearsmill.com
SIC: 2041 5947 Flour mills, cereal (except
rice); gift shop

(G-10501)
G S K INC
915 Front St (45331-1606)
P.O. Box 358 (45331-0358)
PHONE...................................937 547-1611
Fax: 937 547-0029
Jack Besecker, CEO
Chris Besecker, President
Patricia Besecker, Corp Secy
Leanne Murphy, Manager

EMP: 9
SQ FT: 6,600
SALES (est): 1.6MM Privately Held
SIC: 3089 2631 7389 Plastic processing;
paperboard mills; packaging & labeling
services

(G-10502)
GE INTELLIGENT PLATFORMS INC
5438 S State Route 49 (45331-3317)
PHONE...................................937 459-5404
David Benton, Branch Mgr
EMP: 3
SALES (corp-wide): 123.6B Publicly
Held
SIC: 3625 Numerical controls
HQ: Ge Intelligent Platforms, Inc.
2500 Austin Dr
Charlottesville VA 22911
434 978-5000

(G-10503)
GOSPEL TRUMPET PUBLISHING
5065 S State Route 49 (45331-9750)
P.O. Box 1139 (45331-9139)
PHONE...................................937 548-9876
Fax: 937 548-9876
Susan Mutch, Owner
EMP: 3
SALES: 88.9K Privately Held
SIC: 2741 Miscellaneous publishing

(G-10504)
GREENVILLE TECHNOLOGY INC (HQ)
5755 State Route 571 (45331-9692)
P.O. Box 974 (45331-0974)
PHONE...................................937 548-3217
Fax: 937 548-1574
YAF Nakao, President
James Heiser, Exec VP
William Laframboise, Vice Pres
Akihiko Hirano, Treasurer
Kazuhiko Tani, Treasurer
▲ EMP: 672
SQ FT: 300,000
SALES: 20MM
SALES (corp-wide): 11.4MM Privately
Held
WEB: www.gtioh.com
SIC: 3089 Injection molded finished plastic
products
PA: Moriroku Holdings Company, Ltd.
1-1-1, Minamiaoyama
Minato-Ku TKY 107-0
334 036-102

(G-10505)
ICON ENERGY SYSTEMS INC
5261 S State Route 49 (45331-1035)
PHONE...................................937 423-4786
Mark L Heiser, President
EMP: 3
SALES: 950K Privately Held
SIC: 1311 Crude petroleum & natural gas

(G-10506)
JAFE DECORATING CO INC
1250 Martin St (45331-1870)
PHONE...................................937 547-1888
Fax: 937 547-1760
Randy O'Dell, President
EMP: 28
SQ FT: 36,000
SALES (est): 4.5MM Privately Held
SIC: 3231 Decorated glassware: chipped,
engraved, etched, etc.

(G-10507)
JOSH L DERKSEN
200 N Broadway St (45331-2223)
PHONE...................................937 548-0080
Josh Derksen, Principal
EMP: 3
SALES (est): 558.5K Privately Held
SIC: 3714 Mufflers (exhaust), motor vehi-
cle

(G-10508)
KLOCKNER PENTAPLAST AMER INC
Witt Plastics
1671 Martindale Rd (45331-9681)
PHONE...................................937 548-7272

Bob Kramer, Plant Mgr
Todd Geyer, Site Mgr
Cindy Farley, Purch Dir
Sue Shroyer, Human Res Mgr
Susan Sharoyer, Manager
EMP: 80 Privately Held
WEB: www.kpafilms.com
SIC: 3081 Plastic film & sheet
HQ: Klockner Pentaplast Of America, Inc.
3585 Kloeckner Rd
Gordonsville VA 22942
540 832-1400

(G-10509)
KNITTING MACHINERY CORP
607 Riffle Ave (45331-1612)
P.O. Box 902 (45331-0902)
PHONE...................................937 548-2338
Bob Rice, Prdtn Mgr
Chester Rice, Manager
Marilyn Rice, Manager
Robert Rice, Manager
EMP: 10
SALES (corp-wide): 4MM Privately Held
SIC: 3552 Knitting machines
PA: Knitting Machinery Corp.
15625 Saranac Rd
Cleveland OH 44110
216 851-9900

(G-10510)
MARKWITH TOOL COMPANY INC
Also Called: Millmcrawley
5261 S State Route 49 (45331-1035)
PHONE...................................937 548-6808
Fax: 937 548-7051
Merlin Miller, President
Maxine Miller, Vice Pres
Karen Delk, Controller
EMP: 13
SQ FT: 32,500
SALES (est): 1.8MM Privately Held
WEB: www.markwithtool.com
SIC: 3599 Custom machinery; machine
shop, jobbing & repair

(G-10511)
MIAMI VALLEY PRESS INC
6132 Kruckeburg Rd (45331-9210)
PHONE...................................937 547-0771
Gerald Flora, President
Jane Flora, Vice Pres
EMP: 5 EST: 2001
SALES (est): 470K Privately Held
SIC: 2754 2759 2752 Invitations: gravure
printing; envelopes: printing; business
form & card printing, lithographic

(G-10512)
NEW CAN COMPANY INC
1367 Sater St (45331-1640)
PHONE...................................937 547-9050
Fax: 937 547-3155
Jamie Jamieson, Branch Mgr
EMP: 4
SALES (corp-wide): 7.9MM Privately
Held
SIC: 3999 Barber & beauty shop equip-
ment
HQ: The New Can Company Inc
1 Mear Rd
Holbrook MA 02343
781 767-1650

(G-10513)
POLYONE CORPORATION
1050 Landsdowne Ave (45331-8382)
PHONE...................................937 548-1395
Julie A McAlindon, Manager
Zoya Sotirova, Manager
Celeste Bassuk, Director
EMP: 100 Publicly Held
WEB: www.spartech.com
SIC: 3081 3089 Unsupported plastics film
& sheet; plastic containers, except foam;
plastic kitchenware, tableware & house-
ware
PA: Polyone Corporation
33587 Walker Rd
Avon Lake OH 44012

(G-10514)
POLYONE CORPORATION
1050 Landsdowne Ave (45331-8382)
PHONE...................................800 727-4338

John Dimino, Plant Mgr
Mark Huffman, Executive
EMP: 121 Publicly Held
WEB: www.spartech.com
SIC: 3081 Plastic film & sheet
PA: Polyone Corporation
33587 Walker Rd
Avon Lake OH 44012

(G-10515)
POLYONE CORPORATION
Also Called: Spartech Plastics
1050 Landsdowne Ave (45331-8382)
PHONE...................................937 548-2133
Ed Baker, Purchasing
Jack Laux, QC Dir
Julie A McAlindon, Manager
EMP: 50 Publicly Held
SIC: 3081 Packing materials, plastic sheet
PA: Polyone Corporation
33587 Walker Rd
Avon Lake OH 44012

(G-10516)
RAMCO ELECTRIC MOTORS INC
5763 Jysville St Johns Rd (45331-9678)
PHONE...................................937 548-2525
Fax: 937 548-9706
Dave Dunaway, President
Dan Weaver, General Mgr
Jay Sanner, Engineer
Corey Schmidt, Project Engr
Dennis Eckstein, Controller
EMP: 85
SQ FT: 30,000
SALES (est): 23.9MM Privately Held
WEB: www.ramcorotors.com
SIC: 3621 3625 3363 Electric motor &
generator parts; rotors, for motors; relays
& industrial controls; aluminum die-cast-
ings

(G-10517)
REBSCO INC
4362 Us Route 36 (45331-9754)
P.O. Box 370 (45331-0370)
PHONE...................................937 548-2246
Fax: 937 548-8506
Tyeis L Baker-Baumann, President
EMP: 15 EST: 1965
SQ FT: 23,000
SALES: 2.1MM Privately Held
WEB: www.rebsco.com
SIC: 1542 2431 3448 3443 Commercial
& office building contractors; millwork;
prefabricated metal buildings; tanks, stan-
dard or custom fabricated: metal plate

(G-10518)
REESERS MACHINE INC
2624 Fox Rd (45331-9467)
PHONE...................................937 548-5847
Fax: 937 548-5847
Daniel Reeser, President
Dan Reeser, President
Linda Reeser, Corp Secy
EMP: 4
SQ FT: 5,000
SALES: 500K Privately Held
SIC: 3599 Machine shop, jobbing & repair

(G-10519)
RIEGLE COLORS
3566 N Creek Dr (45331-3006)
PHONE...................................937 548-8444
James Riegle, Owner
EMP: 5
SALES (est): 220K Privately Held
WEB: www.rieglecolors.com
SIC: 2329 Riding clothes:, men's, youths' &
boys'

(G-10520)
ROBERT WINNER SONS INC
Also Called: Winners Meat Farm
2259 State Route 502 (45331-9442)
PHONE...................................937 548-7513
Mike Winner, Branch Mgr
EMP: 4
SALES (corp-wide): 33.9MM Privately
Held
SIC: 0213 2011 Hogs; pork products from
pork slaughtered on site

GEOGRAPHIC

PA: Robert Winner Sons, Inc.
8544 State Route 705
Yorkshire OH 45388
419 582-4321

(G-10521)
RUSSELL L GARBER (PA)
Also Called: Garber Farms
4891 Clark Station Rd (45331-9562)
PHONE......................937 548-6224
Russell L Garber, *Owner*
Etta Garber, *Co-Owner*
EMP: 8
SALES (est): 1.1MM **Privately Held**
WEB: www.garberfarms.com
SIC: 0161 2448 Vegetables & melons; melon farms; rooted vegetable farms; lettuce & leaf vegetable farms; pallets, wood

(G-10522)
SPECIALIZED CASTINGS LTD
1569 Martindale Rd (45331-9696)
PHONE......................937 669-5620
Clarence Neels, *CEO*
Jeffrey Deitering, *President*
▼ **EMP:** 15
SQ FT: 50,000
SALES: 1.5MM **Privately Held**
WEB: www.spcastings.com
SIC: 3334 Primary aluminum

(G-10523)
ST HENRY TILE CO INC
Also Called: Wayne Builders Supply
5410 S State Route 49 (45331-1032)
PHONE......................937 548-1101
Fax: 937 548-6814
Mike Homan, *Manager*
EMP: 12
SALES (corp-wide): 30MM **Privately Held**
SIC: 3271 5211 3272 Concrete block & brick; masonry materials & supplies; concrete products, precast
PA: The St Henry Tile Co Inc
281 W Washington St
Saint Henry OH 45883
419 678-4841

(G-10524)
STATELINE POWER CORP
Also Called: Southeast Diesl Acquisition Sub
650 Pine St (45331-1625)
PHONE......................937 547-1006
Tom Tracy III, *President*
Andrew Heindl, *Mktg Coord*
Kirk Harman, *Manager*
EMP: 15
SQ FT: 45,000
SALES: 7.1MM
SALES (corp-wide): 27.9MM **Privately Held**
WEB: www.statelinepower.com
SIC: 3569 3621 Gas producers, generators & other gas related equipment; gas generators; motors & generators; power generators
HQ: Tradewinds Power Corp.
5820 Nw 84th Ave
Doral FL 33166
305 592-9745

(G-10525)
TREATY CITY INDUSTRIES INC
Also Called: T C I
945 Sater St (45331-1636)
P.O. Box 39 (45331-0039)
PHONE......................937 548-9000
Fax: 937 548-0414
Mike Jones, *President*
Sherri Jones, *Treasurer*
EMP: 19
SQ FT: 40,000
SALES (est): 3MM **Privately Held**
SIC: 3053 3469 Gaskets, packing & sealing devices; metal stampings

(G-10526)
WALLS BROS ASPHALT CO INC (PA)
Also Called: Walls Asphalt Manufacturing
3690 Hllnsburg Sampson Rd (45331-9721)
PHONE......................937 548-7158
Fax: 937 548-1129
Perry Walls, *President*
James Jergensen, *Chairman*

EMP: 4 **EST:** 1961
SQ FT: 1,900
SALES (est): 721.3K **Privately Held**
SIC: 2951 1611 Asphalt & asphaltic paving mixtures (not from refineries); general contractor, highway & street construction

(G-10527)
WHIRLPOOL CORPORATION
1701 Kitchen Aid Way (45331-8331)
PHONE......................937 548-4126
Fax: 937 547-2827
Bill Good, *Plant Mgr*
Lou Morris, *Materials Mgr*
Jerry Boolman, *Facilities Mgr*
Jeff Postel, *Opers Staff*
John Heck, *QC Dir*
EMP: 375
SALES (corp-wide): 20.7B **Publicly Held**
WEB: www.whirlpoolcorp.com
SIC: 3634 Electric household cooking appliances
PA: Whirlpool Corporation
2000 N M 63
Benton Harbor MI 49022
269 923-5000

(G-10528)
WHIRLPOOL CORPORATION
1301 Sater St (45331-1640)
PHONE......................937 547-0773
EMP: 175
SALES (corp-wide): 20.7B **Publicly Held**
SIC: 3633 Household laundry machines, including coin-operated
PA: Whirlpool Corporation
2000 N M 63
Benton Harbor MI 49022
269 923-5000

(G-10529)
WOLF G T AWNING & TENT CO
3352 State Route 571 (45331-3229)
P.O. Box 248 (45331-0248)
PHONE......................937 548-4161
Susan Miles, *President*
Maurie Miles, *Vice Pres*
EMP: 10 **EST:** 1896
SALES (est): 910.5K **Privately Held**
SIC: 7359 2394 Tent & tarpaulin rental; canvas & related products

---

Greenwich
Huron County

(G-10530)
F SQUARED INC
9 Sunset Dr (44837-1020)
PHONE......................419 752-7273
William Shipman, *President*
Patricia Shipman, *Corp Secy*
EMP: 6
SALES: 450K **Privately Held**
SIC: 3825 Electrical power measuring equipment

(G-10531)
JOHNSON BROS RUBBER CO INC
Also Called: Johnson Bros Greenwich
41 Center St (44837-1049)
PHONE......................419 752-4814
Fax: 419 752-7705
Ken Bostic, *Manager*
EMP: 30
SALES (corp-wide): 54.4MM **Privately Held**
SIC: 5199 3743 3634 3545 Foams & rubber; railroad equipment; electric housewares & fans; machine tool accessories; gaskets, packing & sealing devices
PA: Johnson Bros. Rubber Co., Inc.
42 W Buckeye St
West Salem OH 44287
419 853-4122

(G-10532)
K & L DIE & MANUFACTURING
7541 Olvsburg Ftchvlle Rd (44837)
PHONE......................419 895-1301
Fax: 419 895-1348
Karl Kinstle, *President*
Lu Kinstle, *Corp Secy*

EMP: 5
SQ FT: 5,000
SALES (est): 655.8K **Privately Held**
SIC: 3469 3544 3441 Stamping metal for the trade; special dies & tools; tower sections, radio & television transmission

(G-10533)
LAKEPARK INDUSTRIES INC
Also Called: Midway Products Group
40 Seminary St (44837-1040)
PHONE......................419 752-4471
Fax: 419 752-0340
James Hoyt, *President*
Lloyd A Miller, *Vice Pres*
Jeff Price, *Plant Mgr*
Jeanne Carpenter, *QC Mgr*
Nilesh Soni, *QC Mgr*
EMP: 150
SQ FT: 60,000
SALES (est): 27.9MM **Privately Held**
SIC: 3469 3465 Metal stampings; automotive stampings
PA: Midway Products Group, Inc.
1 Lyman E Hoyt Dr
Monroe MI 48161

(G-10534)
QUALITY MOLD INC
Also Called: Versitech Mold
49 N Kniffin St (44837-1103)
PHONE......................419 752-4511
Fax: 419 752-6913
Thomas Tanler, *Manager*
EMP: 70
SALES (corp-wide): 86.9MM **Privately Held**
WEB: www.qualitymold.com
SIC: 3599 3544 Machine shop, jobbing & repair; special dies, tools, jigs & fixtures
PA: Quality Mold, Inc.
2200 Massillon Rd
Akron OH 44312
330 645-6653

(G-10535)
RICHLAND LAMINATED COLUMNS LLC
8252 State Route 13 (44837-9638)
PHONE......................419 895-0036
Elmer Sensenig,
EMP: 10
SQ FT: 40,000
SALES (est): 2MM **Privately Held**
SIC: 2439 Arches, laminated lumber

(G-10536)
S C MACHINE
116 Us Highway 224 W (44837-9400)
PHONE......................419 752-6961
Fax: 419 752-6962
Steve Chuburko, *Owner*
EMP: 4
SALES (est): 309.6K **Privately Held**
WEB: www.scmachine.com
SIC: 3599 Machine shop, jobbing & repair

(G-10537)
TIMBERLANE WOODWORKING
8425 Olvsburg Ftchvlle Rd (44837)
PHONE......................419 895-9945
Wilmer Martin, *Principal*
EMP: 4 **EST:** 2008
SALES (est): 444.6K **Privately Held**
SIC: 2431 Millwork

Grove City
Franklin County

(G-10538)
ADVANCE APEX INC (PA)
Also Called: Advance Cnc Machining
2375 Harrisburg Pike (43123-1057)
PHONE......................614 539-3000
Jeremy J Hamilton, *President*
Chet Colopy, *Vice Pres*
Travis Hamilton, *Sales Mgr*
Tricia Hulse, *Sales Staff*
Melanie Bowles, *Mktg Dir*
▲ **EMP:** 31
SQ FT: 40,000

SALES (est): 6.7MM **Privately Held**
WEB: www.advancemachining.com
SIC: 3599 Machine shop, jobbing & repair

(G-10539)
ADVANCE INDUSTRIAL MFG INC
1996 Longwood Ave (43123-1218)
P.O. Box 1296 (43123-6296)
PHONE......................614 871-3333
Fax: 614 871-3339
James Wintzer, *President*
Katherine L Larimore, *Corp Secy*
Nancy Keppler, *Controller*
Dana Kaegs, *Sales Staff*
Dr Christopher Wintzer, *Director*
EMP: 49
SQ FT: 35,000
SALES: 6MM **Privately Held**
SIC: 3441 3443 3449 Fabricated structural metal; fabricated plate work (boiler shop); miscellaneous metalwork

(G-10540)
AIM ATTACHMENTS
1720 Feddern Ave (43123-1206)
PHONE......................614 539-3030
Fax: 614 539-3001
Dennis Hamilton, *Owner*
Travis Morrow, *Regl Sales Mgr*
▼ **EMP:** 20 **EST:** 2008
SALES (est): 2.9MM **Privately Held**
WEB: www.aimattachments.com
SIC: 3531 Construction machinery attachments

(G-10541)
ALL PACK SERVICES LLC
3442 Grant Ave (43123-2513)
PHONE......................614 935-0964
Billie Jo Grubb, *Accountant*
Brian Householder,
Tom Pack,
EMP: 13 **EST:** 2013
SALES: 60K **Privately Held**
SIC: 7349 3613 Building maintenance services; time switches, electrical switchgear apparatus

(G-10542)
AMERICAN AWARDS INC
2380 Harrisburg Pike (43123-1058)
PHONE......................614 875-1850
Fax: 614 875-1915
Steve Gibson, *President*
Gary Gibson, *Corp Secy*
EMP: 13
SQ FT: 6,500
SALES (est): 1MM **Privately Held**
WEB: www.awardsohio.com
SIC: 5094 3993 Trophies; signs & advertising specialties

(G-10543)
AMIR INTERNATIONAL FOODS INC
3504 Broadway (43123-1941)
PHONE......................614 332-1742
Basel Said, *Principal*
EMP: 6
SALES (est): 220K **Privately Held**
SIC: 2099 Food preparations

(G-10544)
ARMOUR-ECKRICH MEATS LLC
6130 Enterprise Pkwy (43123-9286)
PHONE......................614 539-9600
Fax: 614 539-5475
Gene Adams, *Principal*
EMP: 7 **Privately Held**
SIC: 3556 Meat, poultry & seafood processing machinery
HQ: Armour-Eckrich Meats Llc
4225 Naperville Rd # 600
Lisle IL 60532
630 281-5000

(G-10545)
BARBS EMBROIDERY
2700 Brunswick Dr (43123-2122)
PHONE......................614 875-9933
Barbara Cantrell, *Principal*
EMP: 3
SALES (est): 95.7K **Privately Held**
SIC: 2395 Embroidery & art needlework

(G-10546)
BOEHM INC (PA)
Also Called: Geauge Decal
2050 Hardy Parkway St (43123-1214)
PHONE..................................614 875-9010
Fax: 614 875-7055
Robert R Boehm, *CEO*
Stuart Reeve, *President*
Mary Larkin, *Managing Dir*
Lisa Boehm, *Vice Pres*
Michael Hutchinson, *Vice Pres*
EMP: 30
SQ FT: 12,000
SALES: 8.1MM **Privately Held**
WEB: www.boehminc.com
SIC: 2672 2752 5112 2759 Coated &
laminated paper; commercial printing, lith-
ographic; writing instruments & supplies;
decals: printing; marking devices

(G-10547)
BRICOLAGE INC
2989 Lewis Centre Way (43123-1782)
PHONE..................................614 853-6789
Phillip G Lilly, *President*
Chad Pond, *General Mgr*
EMP: 9
SALES (est): 1.4MM **Privately Held**
SIC: 2434 3399 2821 2752 Wood kitchen
cabinets; metal fasteners; plastics materi-
als & resins; commercial printing, litho-
graphic

(G-10548)
BUCK EQUIPMENT INC
1720 Feddern Ave (43123-1206)
PHONE..................................614 539-3039
Fax: 614 539-3040
Dennis Hamilton, *CEO*
Steve Sunderland, *Controller*
Lee Nanzo, *Accounts Mgr*
Jamie Odell, *Sales Executive*
Chris Nichols, *Manager*
▲ EMP: 35
SQ FT: 60,000
SALES (est): 9.1MM **Privately Held**
WEB: www.buckequipment.com
SIC: 3531 3743 3441 5088 Logging
equipment; railroad equipment; fabricated
structural metal; railroad equipment &
supplies

(G-10549)
**CLIENTRAX TECHNOLOGY
SOLUTIONS**
Also Called: Clientrax Software
3347 Mcdowell Rd (43123-2907)
PHONE..................................614 875-2245
Michael Mantkowski, *President*
EMP: 10 EST: 1987
SALES (est): 605K **Privately Held**
WEB: www.clientrax.com
SIC: 7372 Prepackaged software

(G-10550)
CONCORD FABRICATORS INC
6511 Seeds Rd (43123-8431)
PHONE..................................614 875-2500
Fax: 614 875-5940
Gary Hammel, *President*
Chuck Purdom, *Vice Pres*
Jerry Miller, *Purchasing*
Sheila Corbin, *Human Res Mgr*
Sheila Inboden, *Office Mgr*
EMP: 23
SQ FT: 21,500
SALES (est): 10MM **Privately Held**
SIC: 1791 3441 Structural steel erection;
fabricated structural metal

(G-10551)
**CROWN EQUIPMENT
CORPORATION**
Also Called: Crown Lift Trucks
2100 Southwest Blvd (43123-1898)
PHONE..................................614 274-7700
Fax: 740 928-4232
Rusty Edwards, *Manager*
Aaron Burak, *Representative*
EMP: 65
SALES (corp-wide): 5.5B **Privately Held**
WEB: www.okisys.com
SIC: 3537 Lift trucks, industrial: fork, plat-
form, straddle, etc.

PA: Crown Equipment Corporation
44 S Washington St
New Bremen OH 45869
419 629-2311

(G-10552)
CUMMINS BRIDGEWAY LLC
2297 Southwest Blvd Ste K (43123-1822)
PHONE..................................614 604-6000
Paul Lesteshen, *General Mgr*
Dan Ogg, *Branch Mgr*
Jerry Martin, *Manager*
EMP: 30
SALES (corp-wide): 17.5B **Publicly Held**
WEB: www.bridgewaypower.com
SIC: 5084 3519 Engines & parts, diesel;
internal combustion engines
HQ: Cummins Bridgeway, Llc
21810 Clessie Ct
New Hudson MI 48165
248 573-1600

(G-10553)
DEERFIELD VENTURES INC
Also Called: Ink Well
2224 Stringtown Rd (43123-3926)
P.O. Box 305 (43123-0305)
PHONE..................................614 875-0688
David Keil, *President*
Anna Keil, *Corp Secy*
EMP: 8 EST: 1982
SQ FT: 3,000
SALES (est): 1.1MM **Privately Held**
SIC: 2752 Commercial printing, litho-
graphic

(G-10554)
DIMENSIONS THREE INC
6157 Enterprise Pkwy (43123-9539)
PHONE..................................614 539-5180
Tony Hart, *President*
Michael Charnier, *Vice Pres*
John Casey, *Treasurer*
EMP: 5 EST: 1997
SQ FT: 4,500
SALES (est): 322K **Privately Held**
SIC: 2395 Pleating & stitching

(G-10555)
DYNAMP LLC
3735 Gantz Rd Ste D (43123-4849)
PHONE..................................614 871-6900
Fax: 614 871-6910
Brad Seavoy, *General Mgr*
Sherman Christopher, *COO*
Farid Masri, *Engineer*
Robert Mills, *Project Engr*
David Shepard, *VP Sales*
▲ EMP: 27
SQ FT: 16,000
SALES (est): 5.4MM **Privately Held**
SIC: 3825 Current measuring equipment

(G-10556)
EJ USA INC
1855 Feddern Ave (43123-1207)
PHONE..................................614 871-2436
Fax: 614 871-3773
Brian Hall, *Sales/Mktg Mgr*
Greg Probasco, *Branch Mgr*
Greg Alderdice, *Manager*
EMP: 6 **Privately Held**
WEB: www.ejiw.com
SIC: 3321 Manhole covers, metal
HQ: Ej Usa, Inc.
301 Spring St
East Jordan MI 49727
800 874-4100

(G-10557)
**ELECTR-GNRAL PLAS CORP
CLUMBUS**
6200 Enterprise Pkwy (43123-9286)
PHONE..................................614 871-2915
Fax: 614 871-2914
Patrick A Castro Sr, *President*
Patrick A Castro Jr, *Vice Pres*
S Skell, *VP Opers*
Kevin O'Harra, *Maintence Staff*
EMP: 8
SQ FT: 36,400
SALES (est): 1.9MM **Privately Held**
SIC: 3089 Plastic processing

(G-10558)
FABCON COMPANIES LLC
3400 Jackson Pike (43123-8993)
PHONE..................................614 875-8601
Fax: 614 871-6962
Michael Lejeune, *CEO*
Jim Houtman, *Vice Pres*
Jeff Prewitt, *Vice Pres*
Rick Link, *Plant Mgr*
James Cetovich, *Sales & Mktg St*
EMP: 100
SQ FT: 40,000
SALES (corp-wide): 220MM **Privately
Held**
SIC: 3272 Prestressed concrete products
PA: Fabcon Companies, Llc
6111 Highway 13 W
Savage MN 55378
952 890-4444

(G-10559)
GRAMAG LLC
2999 Lewis Centre Way (43123-1782)
PHONE..................................614 875-8435
Robert M Adams, *Principal*
EMP: 50 **Privately Held**
WEB: www.gramagtsys.com
SIC: 2531 Seats, automobile
PA: Gramag Llc
41700 Gardenbrook Rd # 150
Novi MI

(G-10560)
GREEN CORP MAGNETIC INC
4342 Mcdowell Rd (43123-4000)
PHONE..................................614 801-4000
Fax: 614 539-0474
Stephen Green, *President*
▲ EMP: 20
SALES (est): 3.1MM **Privately Held**
WEB: www.greencorp.com
SIC: 3542 Magnetic forming machines

(G-10561)
HALCORE GROUP INC (HQ)
Also Called: Horton Emergency Vehicles
3800 Mcdowell Rd (43123-4022)
PHONE..................................614 539-8181
Fax: 614 539-8165
John Slawson, *President*
Bruce Temple, *Vice Pres*
Dan Sisson, *Prdtn Mgr*
Don Hunter, *Opers Staff*
Rick Smith, *Production*
▼ EMP: 171 EST: 1997
SQ FT: 110,000
SALES (est): 73MM **Publicly Held**
WEB: www.hortonambulance.com
SIC: 3713 Ambulance bodies

(G-10562)
HOLLINGSWORTH SIGNS INC
Also Called: Hollingswrth Otdoor Buying Svc
4423 Broadway (43123-3078)
P.O. Box 488 (43123-0488)
PHONE..................................614 875-2825
Al Hollingsworth, *President*
EMP: 3
SQ FT: 2,200
SALES (est): 242.6K **Privately Held**
SIC: 3993 Signs & advertising specialties;
advertising artwork

(G-10563)
HORTON ENTERPRISES INC
3800 Mcdowell Rd (43123-4022)
PHONE..................................614 539-8181
EMP: 3
SALES (est): 280K **Privately Held**
SIC: 3711 Mfg Motor Vehicle/Car Bodies

(G-10564)
**INSTANTWHIP-COLUMBUS INC
(HQ)**
3855 Marlane Dr (43123-9224)
P.O. Box 249 (43123-0249)
PHONE..................................614 871-9447
Fax: 614 871-8759
Douglas A Smith, *President*
Tom G Michaelides, *Senior VP*
Vinson Lewis, *Vice Pres*
Ken Temple, *Controller*
G Fredrick Smith, *Admin Sec*
EMP: 32
SQ FT: 10,300

SALES (est): 5.1MM
SALES (corp-wide): 43.5MM **Privately
Held**
SIC: 2026 5143 2023 8741 Whipped topping, except frozen or dry mix; dairy products, except dried or canned; dietary
supplements, dairy & non-dairy based;
management services
PA: Instantwhip Foods, Inc.
2200 Cardigan Ave
Columbus OH 43215
614 488-2536

(G-10565)
**INTEGRATED SYSTEMS
PROFESSIONA**
Also Called: Isp
4110 Demorest Rd (43123-9549)
PHONE..................................614 875-0104
Tony Brackman, *Principal*
Mark Sell
EMP: 3 EST: 2015
SALES (est): 270.9K **Privately Held**
SIC: 3357 Fiber optic cable (insulated)

(G-10566)
JOE SESTITO
Also Called: Varsity Sporting Goods
5553 Spring Hill Rd (43123-8907)
PHONE..................................614 871-7778
Joe Sestito, *Owner*
EMP: 7
SALES (est): 293.3K **Privately Held**
SIC: 5941 5699 2752 Sporting goods &
bicycle shops; miscellaneous apparel &
accessories; commercial printing

(G-10567)
KERN INC (DH)
3940 Gantz Rd Ste A (43123-4845)
PHONE..................................614 317-2600
Thomas Brock, *President*
Todd Russell, *Vice Pres*
Rick Stepp, *CFO*
Debbie Ferguson, *Accountant*
▲ EMP: 25
SQ FT: 30,000
SALES (est): 7MM
SALES (corp-wide): 134.3MM **Privately
Held**
SIC: 3579 3577 Envelope stuffing, sealing
& addressing machines; computer periph-
eral equipment
HQ: Kern Ag
Hunigenstrasse 16
Konolfingen BE
317 903-535

(G-10568)
KIRK WILLIAMS COMPANY INC
2734 Home Rd (43123-1701)
P.O. Box 189 (43123-0189)
PHONE..................................614 875-9023
Fax: 614 871-9214
James K Williams Jr, *President*
James K Williams III, *Corp Secy*
Nic Williams, *Project Mgr*
Patrick Williams, *Project Mgr*
Steve Woodward, *Project Mgr*
EMP: 80
SQ FT: 40,000
SALES (est): 31.3MM **Privately Held**
WEB: www.kirkwilliamsco.com
SIC: 1711 3564 3444 Mechanical con-
tractor; warm air heating & air condition-
ing contractor; ventilation & duct work
contractor; blowers & fans; sheet metal-
work

(G-10569)
LOGITECH INC
6423 Seeds Rd (43123-9524)
PHONE..................................614 871-2822
Fax: 614 871-4744
Kirk Wallace, *President*
Bill Gedwill, *Sls & Mktg Exec*
David W Ritchie III, *Treasurer*
Greg Rhine, *VP Sales*
Mary Meador, *Manager*
▲ EMP: 20
SQ FT: 32,400
SALES (est): 6MM **Privately Held**
SIC: 3535 5084 Conveyors & conveying
equipment; conveyor systems

(G-10570)
MAGIC DRAGON MACHINE INC
3451 Grant Ave (43123-2512)
PHONE..................................614 539-8004
Richard Burket, *President*
EMP: 6
SQ FT: 4,000
SALES: 360K **Privately Held**
SIC: 3711 Automobile assembly, including specialty automobiles

(G-10571)
MERRILL CORPORATION
3400 Southpark Pl Ste H (43123-4857)
PHONE..................................614 801-4700
Fax: 614 801-4796
Robert Cook, *Branch Mgr*
EMP: 150
SALES (corp-wide): 579.3MM **Privately Held**
SIC: 2711 Job printing & newspaper publishing combined
PA: Merrill Corporation
1 Merrill Cir
Saint Paul MN 55108
651 646-4501

(G-10572)
MID OHIO SCREEN PRINT INC
4163 Kelnor Dr (43123-2960)
PHONE..................................614 875-1774
Fax: 614 875-1827
Mike Haughn, *President*
Steven Haughn, *Treasurer*
EMP: 6
SQ FT: 18,000
SALES: 800K **Privately Held**
SIC: 2759 Screen printing

(G-10573)
MIDWEST METAL PRODUCTS LLC
3945 Brookham Dr (43123-9741)
PHONE..................................614 539-7322
Fax: 614 539-7319
Howard H Hatmaker Sr, *President*
Linda Hatmaker,
EMP: 25
SALES (est): 2.8MM **Privately Held**
SIC: 3444 Sheet metalwork

(G-10574)
MOHAWK INDUSTRIES INC
3565 Urbancrest Indus Dr (43123-1766)
PHONE..................................800 837-3812
Gary Miller, *Branch Mgr*
EMP: 156
SALES (corp-wide): 8.9B **Publicly Held**
WEB: www.mohawkind.com
SIC: 2273 3253 Finishers of tufted carpets & rugs; smyrna carpets & rugs, machine woven; ceramic wall & floor tile
PA: Mohawk Industries, Inc.
160 S Industrial Blvd
Calhoun GA 30701
706 629-7721

(G-10575)
MURRAY DISPLAY FIXTURES LTD
3721 Thistlewood Dr Ste B (43123-8123)
PHONE..................................614 554-9461
Todd Murray, *Partner*
EMP: 1 EST: 2006
SALES: 1.4MM **Privately Held**
SIC: 2541 Store & office display cases & fixtures

(G-10576)
NATIONAL WELDING & TANKER REPR
2036 Hendrix Dr (43123-1215)
PHONE..................................614 875-3399
Fax: 614 875-4227
Bryan Baker, *President*
EMP: 9
SALES (est): 313.9K **Privately Held**
SIC: 7692 7699 7389 9621 Welding repair; tank repair & cleaning services; inspection & testing services; licensing, inspection: transportation facilities, services

(G-10577)
NATIONAL WELDING & TANKER REPR
2036 Hendrix Dr (43123-1215)
PHONE..................................614 875-3399
John Watterson, *President*
Nicole Watterson, *Vice Pres*
EMP: 5
SALES (est): 310K **Privately Held**
SIC: 7692 Welding repair

(G-10578)
NEXUS VISION GROUP LLC
2156 Southwest Blvd (43123-1893)
PHONE..................................866 492-6499
Jerry Shaw,
▲ EMP: 30
SALES (est): 4.9MM **Privately Held**
SIC: 3851 Eyeglasses, lenses & frames

(G-10579)
OH-LI COMMERCIAL CLEANING LLC
1905 Lake Crest Dr (43123-4895)
PHONE..................................614 390-3628
Ray West, *Mng Member*
EMP: 5
SALES (est): 217.7K **Privately Held**
SIC: 3589 Commercial cleaning equipment

(G-10580)
OLDE HOME MARKET LLC
2517 Old Home Rd (43123-1773)
PHONE..................................614 738-3975
Steven Garner, *CEO*
EMP: 4
SQ FT: 3,000
SALES (est): 180K **Privately Held**
SIC: 2051 Bread, cake & related products; bakery: wholesale or wholesale/retail combined

(G-10581)
OWENS CORNING SALES LLC
3750 Brookham Dr Ste K (43123-4850)
PHONE..................................614 539-0830
Fax: 614 539-0839
Lynda Wininger, *Opers Mgr*
Anne Depaaew, *Manager*
Marques Warner, *Manager*
EMP: 50
SALES (corp-wide): 5.6B **Publicly Held**
WEB: www.owenscorning.com
SIC: 3296 Mineral wool
HQ: Owens Corning Sales, Llc
1 Owens Corning Pkwy
Toledo OH 43659
419 248-8000

(G-10582)
PARABELLUM ARMAMENT CO LLC
3142 Broadway Ste 200 (43123-1780)
PHONE..................................614 557-5987
Andrew Edge, *Mng Member*
Dave Waldmann,
EMP: 5
SALES: 530K **Privately Held**
SIC: 3484 Small arms; machine guns or machine gun parts, 30 mm. & below; shotguns or shotgun parts, 30 mm. & below

(G-10583)
POSSIBLE PLASTICS INC
1620 Feddern Ave Bldg B (43123-1200)
PHONE..................................614 277-2100
Shawn Lind, *CEO*
Cheryl Lind, *President*
EMP: 4
SQ FT: 5,000
SALES (est): 492.7K **Privately Held**
WEB: www.possibleplastics.com
SIC: 3089 5046 Plastic processing; store fixtures & display equipment

(G-10584)
PPG INDUSTRIES INC
Also Called: PPG 5539
2362 Stringtown Rd (43123-3927)
PHONE..................................614 277-0620
Jeff Baker, *Manager*
EMP: 3

SALES (corp-wide): 14.7B **Publicly Held**
WEB: www.ppg.com
SIC: 2851 Paints & allied products
PA: Ppg Industries, Inc.
1 Ppg Pl
Pittsburgh PA 15272
412 434-3131

(G-10585)
PRESTRESS SERVICES INDS LLC
3350 Jackson Pike (43123-8875)
PHONE..................................614 871-2900
Kevin Chesshir, *General Mgr*
EMP: 23
SQ FT: 1,000
SALES (est): 3MM
SALES (corp-wide): 93.8MM **Privately Held**
SIC: 3272 Prestressed concrete products
PA: Prestress Services Industries Llc
2250 N Hartford Ave
Columbus OH 43222
859 299-0461

(G-10586)
PROCTER & GAMBLE COMPANY
2200 Southwest Blvd (43123-2854)
PHONE..................................410 527-5735
EMP: 205
SALES (corp-wide): 65.3B **Publicly Held**
WEB: www.pg.com
SIC: 2841 2676 2844 2079 Soap: granulated, liquid, cake, flaked or chip; detergents, synthetic organic or inorganic alkaline; towels, napkins & tissue paper products; diapers, paper (disposable): made from purchased paper; deodorants, personal; hair preparations, including shampoos; cosmetic preparations; oral preparations; shortening & other solid edible fats; margarine & margarine oils; pharmaceutical preparations; cough medicines; cold remedies
PA: The Procter & Gamble Company
1 Procter And Gamble Plz
Cincinnati OH 45202
513 983-1100

(G-10587)
PVM INCORPORATED
3515 Grove City Rd (43123-3054)
PHONE..................................614 871-0302
Fax: 614 871-5559
Gary Curry, *President*
EMP: 8
SQ FT: 10,000
SALES (est): 780K **Privately Held**
SIC: 3599 Machine shop, jobbing & repair

(G-10588)
REXNORD INDUSTRIES LLC
3655 Brookham Dr (43123-4852)
PHONE..................................614 675-1800
Fax: 614 675-1898
Anita Cordle, *Principal*
EMP: 58
SALES (corp-wide): 1.9B **Publicly Held**
SIC: 3568 Chain, power transmission
HQ: Rexnord Industries, Llc
247 W Freshwater Way # 200
Milwaukee WI 53204
414 643-3000

(G-10589)
RICHARDSON SUPPLY LLC
2080 Hardy Parkway St (43123-1214)
PHONE..................................614 539-3033
Jeff Richardson, *Managing Prtnr*
Keith Howard, *Manager*
John H Fisher III,
Sharon Fisher,
Carol Cunningham, *Clerk*
EMP: 7
SALES (est): 1.7MM **Privately Held**
WEB: www.richardsonsupply.com
SIC: 2759 Screen printing

(G-10590)
RUBEX INC
Also Called: Edge Adhesives-Oh
3709 Grove City Rd (43123-3020)
PHONE..................................614 875-6343
Dave Burger, *CEO*
Paul Swingle, *Plant Mgr*
▼ EMP: 13

SALES (est): 2.9MM **Privately Held**
SIC: 2891 Adhesives & sealants
PA: Edge Adhesives Holdings, Inc.
5117 Northeast Pkwy
Fort Worth TX 76106
817 232-2026

(G-10591)
S&T AUTOMOTIVE AMERICA LLC
3900 Gantz Rd (43123-4834)
PHONE..................................248 649-1020
JW Park,
EMP: 4
SQ FT: 175,000
SALES: 2MM **Privately Held**
SIC: 3089 Automotive parts, plastic

(G-10592)
SC SOLUTIONS INC
4119 Ashgrove Dr (43123-3377)
PHONE..................................614 317-7119
Amanda J Moore, *CEO*
Sara A Dugan, *COO*
Carolina E Petri, *Risk Mgmt Dir*
EMP: 3
SALES: 1.5K **Privately Held**
WEB: www.scsbooks.com
SIC: 2731 2721 2741 Book publishing; periodicals: publishing & printing; technical papers: publishing & printing

(G-10593)
SHELLY MATERIALS INC
3300 Jackson Pike (43123-8875)
PHONE..................................614 801-9105
Craig Ferguson, *Branch Mgr*
EMP: 5
SALES (corp-wide): 28.6B **Privately Held**
SIC: 3272 Building materials, except block or brick: concrete
HQ: Shelly Materials, Inc.
80 Park Dr
Thornville OH 43076
740 246-6315

(G-10594)
SHERWIN-WILLIAMS COMPANY
3875 Brookham Dr (43123-4827)
PHONE..................................614 539-8456
Timothy Sandor, *Manager*
EMP: 20
SALES (corp-wide): 11.8B **Publicly Held**
WEB: www.sherwin.com
SIC: 5231 2851 Paint & painting supplies; wallcoverings; paints & allied products; varnishes; lacquer: bases, dopes, thinner
PA: The Sherwin-Williams Company
101 W Prospect Ave # 1020
Cleveland OH 44115
216 566-2000

(G-10595)
SIMMONS COMPANY
3960 Brookham Dr (43123-9741)
PHONE..................................614 871-8088
Fax: 614 871-8096
Williamson Barry, *Principal*
EMP: 4
SALES (est): 372.3K **Privately Held**
SIC: 2511 Wood bedroom furniture

(G-10596)
SNYDERS-LANCE INC
4000 Gantz Rd Ste E (43123-4844)
PHONE..................................614 856-4616
Erroll Elliott, *Manager*
EMP: 4
SALES (corp-wide): 2.1B **Publicly Held**
WEB: www.lancesnacks.com
SIC: 2052 2064 Cookies; crackers, dry; soda crackers; candy bars, including chocolate covered bars; granola & muesli, bars & clusters
PA: Snyder's-Lance, Inc.
13515 Balntyn Corp Pl
Charlotte NC 28277
704 554-1421

(G-10597)
SOUND COMMUNICATIONS INC
3474 Park St (43123-2530)
P.O. Box 1148 (43123-6148)
PHONE..................................614 875-8500
Fax: 614 875-8179
Garry Stephenson, *President*

James Jacobs, *General Mgr*
Toni Vanhorn, *Vice Pres*
Jim Capriotti, *Manager*
Jacque Ramsey, *Info Tech Dir*
EMP: 17
SQ FT: 6,000
SALES (est): 4.3MM **Privately Held**
WEB: www.soundcommunications.com
SIC: 3669 7382 7338 Intercommunication systems, electric; security systems services; secretarial & court reporting

(G-10598)
STANDARD REGISTER INC
3125 Lewis Centre Way (43123-1784)
PHONE.............................614 277-7500
Jeff Wise, *Branch Mgr*
EMP: 166
SALES (corp-wide): 4.6B **Privately Held**
SIC: 2759 Commercial printing
HQ: Standard Register, Inc.
600 Albany St
Dayton OH 45417
937 221-1000

(G-10599)
STANDARD REGISTER INC
3545 Urbancrest Indus (43123-1766)
PHONE.............................937 221-3347
Fax: 614 539-8519
Wesley Thompson, *Manager*
EMP: 60
SALES (corp-wide): 4.6B **Privately Held**
WEB: www.stdreg.com
SIC: 2761 Manifold business forms
HQ: Standard Register, Inc.
600 Albany St
Dayton OH 45417
937 221-1000

(G-10600)
STRAWSER HYDRANT MAINTENANCE
4391 Club Trail Ln (43123-8152)
PHONE.............................614 875-1514
Brad Strawser, *President*
Donald Strawser, *Vice Pres*
EMP: 6
SALES (est): 530K **Privately Held**
SIC: 3429 Fireplace equipment, hardware: andirons, grates, screens

(G-10601)
TIGERPOLY MANUFACTURING INC
6231 Enterprise Pkwy (43123-9271)
PHONE.............................614 871-0045
Fax: 614 871-2576
Seiji Shiga, *President*
Michael S Crane, *Principal*
Yasuhiko Tomita, *Principal*
Pete Rensch, *Opers Staff*
Brenda Kowal, *Production*
▲ **EMP:** 350
SQ FT: 196,000
SALES (est): 94.1MM
SALES (corp-wide): 339.2MM **Privately Held**
SIC: 3089 3714 3621 3061 Blow molded finished plastic products; motor vehicle parts & accessories; motors & generators; mechanical rubber goods
PA: Tigers Polymer Corporation
1-4-1, Higashimachi, Shinsenri
Toyonaka OSK 560-0
668 341-551

(G-10602)
TMARZETTI COMPANY
Also Called: Marzetti Distribution Center
5800 N Meadows Dr (43123-8600)
PHONE.............................614 277-3577
Joyce Decker, *Purch Mgr*
Jake Dean, *Research*
Shelba Jackson, *Branch Mgr*
Jeff Burkhart, *Manager*
Stephanie Gleason, *Manager*
EMP: 122
SALES (corp-wide): 1.1B **Publicly Held**
SIC: 4225 2035 General warehousing & storage; pickles, sauces & salad dressings
HQ: T.Marzetti Company
380 Polaris Pkwy Ste 400
Westerville OH 43082
614 846-2232

(G-10603)
TOOLTEX INC
6160 Seeds Rd (43123-8603)
PHONE.............................614 539-3222
Fax: 614 539-3223
Paul Spurgeon, *President*
Ray Kautz, *Accounting Mgr*
EMP: 15
SQ FT: 140,000
SALES (est): 4.3MM **Privately Held**
WEB: www.tooltex.com
SIC: 3559 Plastics working machinery

(G-10604)
TOSOH AMERICA INC (HQ)
3600 Gantz Rd (43123-1895)
PHONE.............................614 539-8622
Fax: 614 539-8722
Jan Top, *President*
Jim Shaffer, *Treasurer*
Dan Rowell, *Controller*
Jessica Newsome, *Accounting Mgr*
Lisa Lee, *Accountant*
▲ **EMP:** 350
SQ FT: 250,000
SALES (est): 236.4MM
SALES (corp-wide): 6.4B **Privately Held**
SIC: 5169 3564 5052 Industrial chemicals; blowers & fans; diagnostic equipment, medical; coal & other minerals & ores
PA: Tosoh Corporation
3-8-2, Shiba
Minato-Ku TKY 105-0
354 275-103

(G-10605)
TOSOH SMD INC
2050 Southpark Pl (43123-4819)
PHONE.............................614 875-7912
Jason Akers, *Manager*
EMP: 5
SALES (corp-wide): 6.4B **Privately Held**
SIC: 3499 Aerosol valves, metal
HQ: Tosoh Smd Inc.
3600 Gantz Rd
Grove City OH 43123
614 875-7912

(G-10606)
TOSOH SMD INC (DH)
3600 Gantz Rd (43123-1895)
PHONE.............................614 875-7912
Fax: 614 875-0031
Marten Blazic, *President*
Ken Gay, *Vice Pres*
Andrew Smith, *Engineer*
Kirk Holcomb, *Project Engr*
Dan Rowell, *Controller*
▲ **EMP:** 207
SQ FT: 250,000
SALES (est): 77.2MM
SALES (corp-wide): 6.4B **Privately Held**
WEB: www.tsmd.com
SIC: 3499 Aerosol valves, metal
HQ: Tosoh America, Inc.
3600 Gantz Rd
Grove City OH 43123
614 539-8622

(G-10607)
TRIMTEC SYSTEMS LTD
2455 Harrisburg Pike (43123-1453)
PHONE.............................614 820-0340
Fax: 614 820-0431
Bonnie Biers, *Manager*
Jeffrey Wagner,
EMP: 18
SQ FT: 22,000
SALES (est): 3.6MM **Privately Held**
WEB: www.trimtecsystems.com
SIC: 2431 Ornamental woodwork: cornices, mantels, etc.

(G-10608)
TURNER PRESSURE
3997 Thistlewood Dr (43123-9048)
PHONE.............................614 871-7775
Dale Turner, *Principal*
EMP: 5 **EST:** 2006
SQ FT: 1,200
SALES (est): 290K **Privately Held**
SIC: 3822 Steam pressure controls, residential or commercial type

(G-10609)
UNITED ULTRA VIOLET INC
3280 Hrrsbrg Gvl Rd (43123-9166)
PHONE.............................614 875-8088
Fax: 614 875-6388
Mike Chamier, *President*
John Casey, *Corp Secy*
EMP: 12
SQ FT: 12,000
SALES (est): 2.2MM **Privately Held**
SIC: 3577 3497 Graphic displays, except graphic terminals; foil, laminated to paper or other materials

(G-10610)
WOODCOR AMERICA INC (PA)
Also Called: Cedar America
2965 Columbus St Ste C (43123-2808)
P.O. Box 668 (43123-0668)
PHONE.............................614 277-2930
Ted Gawel, *President*
Thane Bock, *Corp Secy*
Kerry Lind, *Vice Pres*
Amy Happ, *Engineer*
Brian Kinn, *Controller*
▲ **EMP:** 5
SQ FT: 12,000
SALES (est): 1.4MM **Privately Held**
WEB: www.cedaramerica.com
SIC: 2499 Applicators, wood

(G-10611)
Z M O COMPANY INC (PA)
Also Called: Z M O Oil
4188 Alkire Rd (43123-1004)
PHONE.............................614 875-0230
Fax: 614 875-0230
Ronald Johnson, *President*
Don Schaffner, *Vice Pres*
Doris Johnson, *Treasurer*
Marie Schaffner, *Admin Sec*
EMP: 6
SALES: 768.6K **Privately Held**
SIC: 2834 Liniments

Groveport
Franklin County

(G-10612)
AMSTED INDUSTRIES INCORPORATED
Griffin Wheel
3900 Bixby Rd (43125-9510)
PHONE.............................614 836-2323
Fax: 614 836-2377
Joe Cuske, *Plant Mgr*
Mark S Shirley, *Plant Mgr*
Chris Grys, *Production*
Jesse Lepart, *Research*
Carrie Goss, *Personnel*
EMP: 181
SALES (corp-wide): 2B **Privately Held**
SIC: 3321 5088 3743 3714 Railroad car wheels & brake shoes, cast iron; railroad equipment & supplies; railroad equipment; motor vehicle parts & accessories
PA: Amsted Industries Incorporated
180 N Stetson Ave
Chicago IL 60601
312 645-1700

(G-10613)
AMSTED RAIL COMPANY INC
3900 Bixby Rd (43125-9510)
PHONE.............................614 836-2323
Richard Goehring, *Manager*
EMP: 12
SALES (corp-wide): 2B **Privately Held**
SIC: 3743 Railroad equipment
HQ: Amsted Rail Company, Inc.
311 S Wacker Dr Ste 5300
Chicago IL 60606
312 922-4501

(G-10614)
AS AMERICA INC
Also Called: American Standard Brands
6600 Port Rd Ste 200 (43125-9129)
PHONE.............................614 497-9384
Joe Coleman, *Manager*
EMP: 125
SQ FT: 1,000,000

SALES (corp-wide): 16.1B **Privately Held**
SIC: 3432 Plumbing fixture fittings & trim
HQ: As America, Inc.
1 Centennial Ave Ste 101
Piscataway NJ 08854
732 980-3000

(G-10615)
ASTELLAS PHARMA US INC
5650 Green Pointe Dr N (43123-1054)
PHONE.............................614 409-2953
John Babec, *Branch Mgr*
EMP: 29
SALES (corp-wide): 11.7B **Privately Held**
WEB: www.ambisome.com
SIC: 2834 Pharmaceutical preparations
HQ: Astellas Pharma Us, Inc.
1 Astellas Way
Northbrook IL 60062
800 888-7704

(G-10616)
BELL OHIO INC
Also Called: Bell Incorporated
Ste 100 (43125)
PHONE.............................605 332-6721
Benjamin Graham, *President*
Elaine Johnson, *Accounts Mgr*
EMP: 10 **EST:** 2015
SALES: 12MM
SALES (corp-wide): 60.7MM **Privately Held**
SIC: 2657 Folding paperboard boxes
PA: Bell Incorporated
617 W Algonquin St
Sioux Falls SD 57104
605 332-6721

(G-10617)
C & R INC (PA)
5600 Clyde Moore Dr (43125-1081)
PHONE.............................614 497-1130
Ronald E Murphy, *President*
Christina M Murphy, *Corp Secy*
Phillip Lee Mc Kitrick, *Vice Pres*
Toni Simmions, *Manager*
EMP: 47
SALES (est): 9.7MM **Privately Held**
WEB: www.crproducts.com
SIC: 3444 7692 3443 3312 Sheet metal specialties, not stamped; welding repair; fabricated plate work (boiler shop); blast furnaces & steel mills

(G-10618)
CENTRAL OHIO PAPER & PACKG INC
Also Called: Breckenridge Paper & Packaging
5885 Green Pointe Dr S C (43125-2004)
PHONE.............................614 492-8956
Tony Lowe, *Branch Mgr*
EMP: 5
SALES (corp-wide): 5.1MM **Privately Held**
WEB: www.breckpack.com
SIC: 2671 Paper coated or laminated for packaging
PA: Central Ohio Paper & Packaging, Inc.
2350 University Dr E
Huron OH 44839
419 621-9239

(G-10619)
CREATIVE TOOL & DIE
244 Main St (43125-1124)
PHONE.............................614 836-0080
Fax: 614 836-3544
James Newman Jr, *Partner*
Anita Raisley, *Partner*
EMP: 6
SQ FT: 2,600
SALES (est): 694.5K **Privately Held**
WEB: www.creativetooldie.com
SIC: 3599 Machine shop, jobbing & repair

(G-10620)
EVOQUA WATER TECHNOLOGIES LLC
6300 Commerce Center Dr (43125-1183)
PHONE.............................614 491-4000
Charlene Fortney, *Purchasing*
Becky Cherry, *Cust Svc Dir*
Jim Campbell, *Manager*
EMP: 20

SALES (corp-wide): 1.2B Privately Held
SIC: 3589 7699 Water purification equipment, household type; cleaning services
HQ: Evoqua Water Technologies Llc
181 Thorn Hill Rd
Warrenton PA 15086
724 772-0044

(G-10621)
FLOOD HELIARC INC
4181 Venture Pl (43125-9207)
P.O. Box 237 (43125-0237)
PHONE.....................................614 835-3929
Robert Flood, *President*
Suzanne Flood, *Corp Secy*
EMP: 10
SQ FT: 7,000
SALES: 1.2MM Privately Held
WEB: www.floodheliarc.com
SIC: 3444 3613 3469 Sheet metalwork; switchgear & switchboard apparatus; metal stampings

(G-10622)
FRANK BRUNCKHORST COMPANY LLC
2225 Spiegel Dr (43125-9036)
PHONE.....................................614 662-5300
Alexander Morris, *Principal*
EMP: 8
SALES (est): 4.7MM Privately Held
SIC: 5142 2013 Meat, frozen: packaged; frozen meats from purchased meat

(G-10623)
FRANKLIN EQUIPMENT LLC (PA)
4141 Hamilton Square Blvd (43125-9084)
PHONE.....................................614 228-2014
Fax: 614 228-2548
Troy Gabriel, *Mng Member*
Lory Johnson, *Manager*
EMP: 24
SQ FT: 20,000
SALES (est): 45.1MM Privately Held
SIC: 5083 3524 Tractors, agricultural; lawn & garden equipment; cultivators (garden tractor equipment)

(G-10624)
GRAPHIC TS
Also Called: Industrial Graphic
532 Main St Rear Bldg (43125-1417)
PHONE.....................................614 836-2613
Fax: 614 836-3038
Al Wilkins, *Partner*
Joe Wilkins, *Partner*
EMP: 4
SQ FT: 6,500
SALES (est): 253K Privately Held
SIC: 7336 2752 Silk screen design; graphic arts & related design; commercial printing, lithographic

(G-10625)
HOME CITY ICE COMPANY
4505 S Hamilton Rd (43125-9335)
PHONE.....................................614 836-2877
Fax: 614 836-7523
Tony Bakes, *Branch Mgr*
EMP: 50
SQ FT: 12,000
SALES (corp-wide): 305.4MM Privately Held
WEB: www.homecityice.com
SIC: 5199 5999 2097 Ice, manufactured or natural; ice; manufactured ice
PA: The Home City Ice Company
6045 Bridgetown Rd Ste 1
Cincinnati OH 45248
513 574-1800

(G-10626)
INNOVTIVE CRTIVE SOLUTIONS LLC
Also Called: I C S
5835 Green Pointe Dr S B (43125-2000)
PHONE.....................................614 491-9638
Bob Pushay, *Mng Member*
EMP: 38
SALES (est): 950K Privately Held
SIC: 2759 7336 Screen printing; commercial art & graphic design

(G-10627)
IOSIL ENERGY CORPORATION
5700 Green Pointe Dr N A (43125-1082)
PHONE.....................................614 295-8680
Dr Sudheer Pimputkar, *CEO*
Dr Karthik Balakrishnan, *Senior VP*
Jim Swan, *Opers Staff*
Geoffrey Flagg, *CFO*
Lynne McLaughlin, *Manager*
EMP: 10 EST: 2010
SALES (est): 1.1MM Privately Held
SIC: 3433 Solar heaters & collectors

(G-10628)
IRONMAN METALWORKS LLC
250 Lowery Ct Ste A (43125-9346)
PHONE.....................................614 907-6629
Andrew Gussler,
EMP: 3
SALES (est): 262.2K Privately Held
SIC: 3443 Fabricated plate work (boiler shop); tanks for tank trucks, metal plate

(G-10629)
KOMAR INDUSTRIES INC (PA)
4425 Marketing Pl (43125-9556)
PHONE.....................................614 836-2366
Fax: 614 836-9870
Larry E Koenig, *President*
Debra Koenig, *Vice Pres*
Mark Koenig, *Vice Pres*
Mark Landis, *Engineer*
◆ EMP: 50
SQ FT: 58,000
SALES (est): 8.8MM Privately Held
WEB: www.komarindustries.com
SIC: 3423 3523 3531 3567 Hand & edge tools; farm machinery & equipment; construction machinery; industrial furnaces & ovens; sewage & water treatment equipment

(G-10630)
KRAFT ELECTRICAL CONTG INC
4407 Professional Pkwy (43125-9228)
PHONE.....................................614 836-9300
EMP: 36
SALES (corp-wide): 13.4MM Privately Held
SIC: 4813 3699 Telephone communication, except radio; electrical equipment & supplies
PA: Kraft Electrical Contracting, Inc.
5710 Hillside Ave
Cincinnati OH 45233
513 467-0500

(G-10631)
KUBOTA TRACTOR CORPORATION
6300 At One Kubota Way (43125-1186)
PHONE.....................................614 835-3800
Ted Pederson, *General Mgr*
Toby Anderson, *Controller*
EMP: 14
SALES (corp-wide): 14.4B Privately Held
SIC: 3531 Construction machinery
HQ: Kubota Tractor Corporation
1000 Kubota Dr
Grapevine TX 76051
310 370-3370

(G-10632)
KURTZ BROS INC
Also Called: Branch 300
2850 Rohr Rd (43125-9311)
P.O. Box 207, Westerville (43086-0207)
PHONE.....................................614 491-0868
Fax: 614 491-0878
Robert Misso, *Bookkeeper*
Bonnie Straight, *Manager*
Gretchen Anderson, *Manager*
Byron Brannon, *Manager*
Jeff Moore, *Manager*
EMP: 20
SALES (corp-wide): 41.1MM Privately Held
WEB: www.kurtz-bros.com
SIC: 1241 5261 Coal mining services; top soil
PA: Kurtz Bros., Inc.
6415 Granger Rd
Independence OH 44131
216 986-7000

(G-10633)
LOMAR ENTERPRISES INC
Also Called: Ecc Company
5905 Green Pointe Dr S G (43125-2007)
PHONE.....................................614 409-9104
Lou Onders, *President*
Mark Molnar, *Treasurer*
EMP: 15
SQ FT: 10,000
SALES: 1.8MM Privately Held
WEB: www.eccco.com
SIC: 3825 3544 Test equipment for electronic & electrical circuits; special dies, tools, jigs & fixtures

(G-10634)
MCGILL AIRFLOW LLC (DH)
1 Mission Park (43125-1149)
PHONE.....................................614 829-1200
James D McGill, *President*
John Montell, *Vice Pres*
Joe Schelbie, *Opers Mgr*
Todd Stine, *Sales Mgr*
Shiela Shallcross, *Sales Associate*
◆ EMP: 2
SQ FT: 13,000
SALES (est): 27.2MM
SALES (corp-wide): 62.8MM Privately Held
WEB: www.mcgillairflow.com
SIC: 3444 Ducts, sheet metal
HQ: United Mcgill Corporation
1 Mission Park
Groveport OH 43125
614 829-1200

(G-10635)
MCGILL CORPORATION (PA)
1 Mission Park (43125-1149)
PHONE.....................................614 829-1200
James D McGill, *Ch of Bd*
Norm Boyer, *Account Dir*
Jayne F McGill, *Admin Sec*
◆ EMP: 10
SQ FT: 13,000
SALES (est): 62.8MM Privately Held
WEB: www.themcgillcorp.com
SIC: 3564 3444 5169 Precipitators, electrostatic; air purification equipment; ducts, sheet metal; sealants

(G-10636)
METAL MAN INC
4681 Homer Ohio Ln Ste A (43125-9231)
PHONE.....................................614 830-0968
Fax: 614 830-0973
Robert Posey, *President*
Ken Gilkerson, *Vice Pres*
EMP: 6
SALES (est): 949.5K Privately Held
SIC: 3441 Fabricated structural metal

(G-10637)
NIFCO AMERICA CORPORATION
4485 S Hamilton Rd (43125-9334)
PHONE.....................................614 836-8691
Allen Hofmann, *Principal*
EMP: 250
SALES (corp-wide): 2.2B Privately Held
SIC: 3089 Automotive parts, plastic
HQ: Nifco America Corporation
8015 Dove Pkwy
Canal Winchester OH 43110
614 920-6800

(G-10638)
PARTS CHANNEL INC
5830 Green Pointe Dr S A (43125-1188)
PHONE.....................................614 497-9199
Cooper Rusty, *Manager*
▲ EMP: 11
SALES (est): 1.5MM Privately Held
SIC: 3465 Body parts, automobile: stamped metal

(G-10639)
PEERLESS LASER PROCESSORS INC
4353 Directors Blvd (43125-9504)
PHONE.....................................614 836-5790
Fax: 614 836-5824
Tim Gase, *President*
Paul Duclos, *Sales Associate*
EMP: 45
SQ FT: 35,000

SALES (est): 4.2MM
SALES (corp-wide): 16.7MM Privately Held
SIC: 3699 Laser welding, drilling & cutting equipment
PA: The Peerless Saw Company
4353 Directors Blvd
Groveport OH 43125
614 836-5790

(G-10640)
PEERLESS SAW COMPANY (PA)
4353 Directors Blvd (43125-9350)
PHONE.....................................614 836-5790
Tim Gase, *Owner*
Ken Lloyd, *Vice Pres*
Steve Hartshorn, *Sales Mgr*
Theo Trefz, *Sales Mgr*
Joe Duncan, *Sales Staff*
▲ EMP: 50 EST: 1931
SQ FT: 30,000
SALES (est): 16.7MM Privately Held
SIC: 3425 3541 Saw blades for hand or power saws; machine tools, metal cutting type

(G-10641)
PINNACLE DATA SYSTEMS INC (HQ)
Also Called: Pdsi
6600 Port Rd Ste 100 (43125-9129)
PHONE.....................................614 748-1150
Fax: 614 748-1209
John D Bair, *President*
Darren Sweet, *Business Mgr*
Timothy J Harper, *COO*
Gregory Cooper, *Pastor*
George Mehok, *Vice Pres*
▲ EMP: 148
SQ FT: 113,000
SALES (est): 21.4MM
SALES (corp-wide): 26.2B Publicly Held
WEB: www.pinnacle.com
SIC: 3575 3572 7378 7373 Computer terminals; computer terminals, monitors & components; computer auxiliary storage units; magnetic storage devices, computer; computer maintenance & repair; systems software development services; systems integration services
PA: Avnet, Inc.
2211 S 47th St
Phoenix AZ 85034
480 643-2000

(G-10642)
PLAN B TOYS LTD
4036 London Lancaster Rd (43125-9202)
PHONE.....................................614 751-6605
EMP: 3
SALES (est): 210K Privately Held
SIC: 3069 Mfg Toys And Statues

(G-10643)
SHERMCO INDUSTRIES INC
4383 Professional Pkwy (43125-9035)
PHONE.....................................614 836-8556
EMP: 4
SALES (corp-wide): 150MM Privately Held
SIC: 3999 Atomizers, toiletry
PA: Shermco Industries, Inc.
2425 E Pioneer Dr
Irving TX 75061
972 793-5523

(G-10644)
SHOCKAKHAN EXPRESS LLC
4953 Bixby Ridge Dr W (43125-1167)
PHONE.....................................614 432-3133
Tony Channakhon, *Principal*
EMP: 4
SALES (est): 547.8K Privately Held
SIC: 2655 Fiber shipping & mailing containers

(G-10645)
STABER INDUSTRIES INC
4800 Homer Ohio Ln (43125-9390)
PHONE.....................................614 836-5995
Fax: 614 836-9524
William Staber, *President*
Jill Young, *Manager*
▲ EMP: 35
SQ FT: 55,000

SALES (est): 8MM **Privately Held**
WEB: www.staber.com
SIC: 3633 3444 Household laundry equipment; sheet metalwork

(G-10646)
TIMKEN COMPANY
3782 Potomac St (43125-9472)
PHONE..................................614 836-3337
James Ferguson, *Branch Mgr*
EMP: 15
SALES (corp-wide): 2.6B **Publicly Held**
SIC: 3562 Ball & roller bearings
PA: The Timken Company
4500 Mount Pleasant St Nw
North Canton OH 44720
234 262-3000

(G-10647)
TRANE US INC
6600 Port Rd Ste 200 (43125-9129)
PHONE..................................614 497-6300
Sean Strane, *Branch Mgr*
EMP: 150 **Privately Held**
SIC: 3585 Refrigeration & heating equipment
HQ: Trane U.S. Inc.
1 Centennial Ave Ste 101
Piscataway NJ 08854
732 652-7100

(G-10648)
UNITED MCGILL CORPORATION (HQ)
1 Mission Park (43125-1100)
PHONE..................................614 829-1200
Fax: 614 445-8850
James D McGill, *President*
Vicky Oneal, *Buyer*
Kathleen Cauley, *Personnel*
Mary Dorsey, *Sales Mgr*
Derek McGill, *Sales Mgr*
▲ EMP: 30 EST: 1951
SQ FT: 13,000
SALES (est): 55.9MM
SALES (corp-wide): 62.8MM **Privately Held**
WEB: www.unitedmcgill.com
SIC: 3444 3564 5169 3567 Ducts, sheet metal; precipitators, electrostatic; air purification equipment; sealants; industrial furnaces & ovens; adhesives & sealants
PA: The Mcgill Corporation
1 Mission Park
Groveport OH 43125
614 829-1200

(G-10649)
WILLIAM R HAGUE INC
Also Called: Hague Quality Water Intl
4343 S Hamilton Rd (43125-9332)
P.O. Box 298 (43125-0298)
PHONE..................................614 836-2115
Fax: 614 836-9876
Robert Hague, *President*
Brad Bremer, *Regional Mgr*
David Hague, *Vice Pres*
Jeffrey Hague, *Vice Pres*
Stephanie Entler, *Purch Mgr*
◆ EMP: 100
SQ FT: 90,000
SALES (est): 23.4MM **Privately Held**
SIC: 3589 Water treatment equipment, industrial

(G-10650)
XEROX CORPORATION
6500 Port Rd (43125-9103)
PHONE..................................614 409-6527
Alice Schadler, *Branch Mgr*
EMP: 77
SALES (corp-wide): 10.7B **Publicly Held**
SIC: 3577 Computer peripheral equipment
PA: Xerox Corporation
201 Merritt 7
Norwalk CT 06851
203 968-3000

(G-10651)
XEROX CORPORATION C/O GENCO
6290 Opus Dr (43125-9633)
PHONE..................................503 582-6059
▲ EMP: 5

SALES (est): 854.9K **Privately Held**
SIC: 3861 Photographic equipment & supplies

Grover Hill
Paulding County

(G-10652)
FABSTAR TANKS INC
20302 Road 48 (45849-9324)
PHONE..................................419 587-3639
Mark Sinn, *President*
EMP: 18
SALES (est): 1.5MM **Privately Held**
SIC: 3443 7389 Fuel tanks (oil, gas, etc.): metal plate;

(G-10653)
R & L TRUSS INC
17985 Road 60 (45849-9400)
P.O. Box 130 (45849-0130)
PHONE..................................419 587-3440
Fax: 419 587-3617
Ron Treece, *CEO*
Larry Pressler, *President*
Neal Welch, *Manager*
EMP: 10
SQ FT: 3,360
SALES (est): 1.6MM **Privately Held**
WEB: www.rltruss.com
SIC: 2439 Trusses, wooden roof

Guysville
Athens County

(G-10654)
ROBERT ASHCRAFT
4350 Bethany Ridge Rd (45735-9564)
PHONE..................................740 667-3690
Robert Ashcraft, *Principal*
EMP: 3
SALES (est): 232.6K **Privately Held**
SIC: 2411 Logging

Gypsum
Ottawa County

(G-10655)
UNITED STATES GYPSUM COMPANY
121 S Lake St (43433)
P.O. Box 121 (43433-0121)
PHONE..................................419 734-3161
Fax: 419 732-2890
P V Savu, *Plant Mgr*
Kathy Hughes, *QC Dir*
B T Webster, *Engineer*
Tony Gable, *Human Res Mgr*
Joni Ledinsky, *Department Mgr*
EMP: 350
SALES (corp-wide): 3B **Publicly Held**
WEB: www.usg.com
SIC: 3275 Gypsum products
HQ: United States Gypsum Company Inc
550 W Adams St Ste 1300
Chicago IL 60661
312 606-4000

Hamden
Vinton County

(G-10656)
CORBETT R CAUDILL CHIPPING INC
35887 State Route 324 (45634-8824)
PHONE..................................740 596-5984
Corbett R Caudill, *President*
Myrta Caudill, *Admin Sec*
EMP: 15
SALES (est): 2.8MM **Privately Held**
SIC: 3546 4212 Hammers, portable: electric or pneumatic, chipping, etc.; local trucking, without storage

(G-10657)
SANDS HILL COAL HAULING CO INC (PA)
38701 State Route 160 (45634)
PHONE..................................740 384-4211
Alan Arthur, *President*
Diane Derrow, *Accountant*
EMP: 26 EST: 1946
SQ FT: 3,500
SALES (est): 23.9MM **Privately Held**
SIC: 1221 Strip mining, bituminous

(G-10658)
SANDS HILL MINING LLC
38701 State Route 160 (45634)
PHONE..................................740 384-4211
Marcia Nichols, *Project Leader*
Steve Garson,
Chris Walton, *Asst Sec*
EMP: 12
SALES (est): 988K **Privately Held**
SIC: 1429 Grits mining (crushed stone)

Hamilton
Butler County

(G-10659)
7 ROWE COURT PROPERTIES LLC
Also Called: Bren-Ko Patterns
7 Rowe Ct (45015-2211)
PHONE..................................513 874-7236
Fax: 513 874-8829
Randy Johnson, *President*
Debbie Johnson, *Corp Secy*
EMP: 7
SQ FT: 85,000
SALES (est): 630K **Privately Held**
SIC: 3543 Industrial patterns

(G-10660)
A & L MACHINE TOOL
3080 Darrtown Rd (45013-9331)
PHONE..................................513 863-2662
Fax: 513 863-2662
Steve Miller, *Owner*
EMP: 4
SQ FT: 1,500
SALES: 65K **Privately Held**
SIC: 3599 Machine shop, jobbing & repair

(G-10661)
ACE-TEX ENTERPRISES INC
Also Called: Hamilton Whiting Cloth
4981 Factory Dr (45014-1946)
PHONE..................................513 829-8899
Fax: 513 829-8894
Sonia Lewis, *Branch Mgr*
EMP: 14
SALES (corp-wide): 20.4MM **Privately Held**
WEB: www.ace-tex.com
SIC: 5087 2392 Cleaning & maintenance equipment & supplies; household furnishings
PA: Ace-Tex Enterprises, Inc.
7601 Central St
Detroit MI 48210
313 834-4000

(G-10662)
ADVANCED DRAINAGE SYSTEMS INC
ADS Hancor
2650 Hamilton Eaton Rd (45011-9502)
P.O. Box 718 (45012-0718)
PHONE..................................513 863-1384
Fax: 513 863-5410
Nathan Williams, *Branch Mgr*
EMP: 100
SALES (corp-wide): 1.2B **Publicly Held**
WEB: www.ads-pipe.com
SIC: 3084 Plastics pipe
PA: Advanced Drainage Systems, Inc.
4640 Trueman Blvd
Hilliard OH 43026
614 658-0050

(G-10663)
AIR ONE JET CENTER
2808 Bobmeyer Rd (45015-1308)
PHONE..................................513 867-9500

EMP: 3 EST: 2010
SALES: 130K **Privately Held**
SIC: 3721 Mfg Aircraft

(G-10664)
ALECO MACHINE LLC
233 N Martin L King Blvd (45011)
PHONE..................................513 894-6400
Bernard A Lemieux,
EMP: 3
SALES (est): 332.5K **Privately Held**
SIC: 3599 Machine shop, jobbing & repair

(G-10665)
AMERICAN QUALITY MOLDS LLC
2275 Millville Ave Ste E (45013-4256)
PHONE..................................513 276-7345
Jimmy A Hitchcock, *Mng Member*
EMP: 5
SALES (est): 719.1K **Privately Held**
SIC: 3465 Moldings or trim, automobile: stamped metal

(G-10666)
AMERICAN RUGGED ENCLOSURES (PA)
4 Standen Dr (45015-2208)
PHONE..................................513 942-3004
Fax: 513 942-2006
Raymond J Casey, *President*
Shawn Beckman, *Corp Secy*
EMP: 12
SQ FT: 13,500
SALES (est): 2.3MM **Privately Held**
WEB: www.areinc.com
SIC: 3469 Electronic enclosures, stamped or pressed metal

(G-10667)
AMERICAN TOOL WORKS INC
1691 Thall Dr (45013-5122)
PHONE..................................513 844-6363
Scott Lorance, *Manager*
EMP: 16 **Privately Held**
SIC: 3599 Machine shop, jobbing & repair
PA: American Tool Works, Inc.
160 Hancock Ave
Hamilton OH 45011

(G-10668)
AMERICAN TOOL WORKS INC (PA)
Also Called: ATW
160 Hancock Ave (45011-4351)
PHONE..................................513 844-6363
Michael Lorance, *President*
EMP: 14
SALES (est): 2MM **Privately Held**
SIC: 3599 Machine shop, jobbing & repair

(G-10669)
ANEST IWATA AIR ENGRG INC
5325 Muhlhauser Rd (45011-9349)
PHONE..................................513 755-3100
Atsuo Shiria, *President*
Tom Ferman, *Sales Mgr*
▲ EMP: 10
SALES (est): 2MM **Privately Held**
SIC: 3563 Air & gas compressors; spraying & dusting equipment; air & gas compressors including vacuum pumps

(G-10670)
ANEST IWATA USA INC
5325 Muhlhauser Rd (45011-9349)
PHONE..................................513 755-3100
Fax: 513 755-0888
Hiroki Nishida, *President*
▲ EMP: 8
SQ FT: 4,800
SALES (est): 1.5MM
SALES (corp-wide): 252.3MM **Privately Held**
WEB: www.anestiwata.com
SIC: 3479 5013 Painting, coating & hot dipping; motor vehicle supplies & new parts; automotive supplies & parts
PA: Anest Iwata Corporation
3176, Shin-Yoshidacho, Kohoku-Ku
Yokohama KNG 223-0
455 911-111

(G-10671)
ART METALS GROUP INC
3795 Symmes Rd (45015-1373)
PHONE..........................513 942-8800
Fax: 513 942-3200
Marlon Bailey, *CEO*
Robert McCoy, *CFO*
Lisa Lawson, *Human Resources*
Scott Hunter, *Manager*
▲ EMP: 60 EST: 1946
SQ FT: 40,000
SALES (est): 21.7MM **Privately Held**
SIC: 3568 Bearings, plain

(G-10672)
BARNCRAFT STORAGE BUILDINGS
2527 Millville Shandon Rd (45013-8209)
PHONE..........................513 738-5654
Dennis Donovan, *Owner*
EMP: 3
SQ FT: 1,440
SALES (est): 345.6K **Privately Held**
SIC: 3448 1542 Farm & utility buildings; agricultural building contractors

(G-10673)
BAXTER HOLDINGS INC
3370 Port Union Rd (45014-4223)
PHONE..........................513 860-3593
Fax: 513 860-3893
Robert Kelly, *CEO*
Andrew Baxter, *Sales Mgr*
Michael Cochran, *Sales Mgr*
Tom Belcher, *Technology*
EMP: 20
SQ FT: 32,000
SALES (est): 3.8MM **Privately Held**
WEB: www.baxterprecast.com
SIC: 3272 3443 Steps, prefabricated concrete; slabs, crossing: concrete; concrete products, precast; burial vaults, concrete or precast terrazzo; fabricated plate work (boiler shop)

(G-10674)
BELL BURIAL VAULT CO
804 Belle Ave (45015-1151)
PHONE..........................513 896-9044
Brian Bell, *Owner*
EMP: 5
SQ FT: 5,000
SALES: 450K **Privately Held**
SIC: 3281 3272 5087 Burial vaults, stone; burial vaults, concrete or precast terrazzo; concrete burial vaults & boxes

(G-10675)
BETHART ENTERPRISES INC (PA)
Also Called: Bethart Printing Services
531 Main St (45013-3221)
PHONE..........................513 863-6161
Fax: 513 863-8330
Richard Bethart, *President*
Gina Kimble, *Purchasing*
EMP: 14
SQ FT: 4,400
SALES (est): 1.5MM **Privately Held**
SIC: 2752 7334 Commercial printing, offset; photocopying & duplicating services

(G-10676)
BMC OF BARFIELD INC
3501 Symmes Rd (45015-1369)
PHONE..........................513 860-4455
Mike Dill, *Principal*
EMP: 8
SALES (est): 1MM **Privately Held**
SIC: 3999 Manufacturing industries

(G-10677)
BROWN DAVE PRODUCTS INC
4560 Layhigh Rd (45013-9200)
PHONE..........................513 738-1576
Fax: 513 738-0152
David Brown, *President*
EMP: 12
SQ FT: 4,000
SALES (est): 1.4MM **Privately Held**
SIC: 3944 7371 Airplane models, toy & hobby; custom computer programming services

(G-10678)
BUTLER PROCESSING INC
Also Called: Thompson Metals and Tubing
1326 Stephanie Dr (45013-6336)
P.O. Box 785 (45012-0785)
PHONE..........................513 874-1400
Kurt Robinson, *President*
Donald Ryan, *Vice Pres*
EMP: 50
SQ FT: 130,000
SALES (est): 8.2MM **Privately Held**
SIC: 3315 Steel wire & related products

(G-10679)
BUTLER TECH CAREER DEV SCHOOLS
Also Called: Southwest Ohio Computer Assn
3611 Hmlton Middletown Rd (45011-2241)
PHONE..........................513 867-1028
Mike Crumley, *Superintendent*
Donna Norris, *Asst Supt*
Chuck Adelsperger, *Administration*
Brad Pursell, *Tech/Comp Coord*
Donna Leroy, *Nurse*
EMP: 16
SALES (corp-wide): 43.6MM **Privately Held**
SIC: 8211 7372 Public combined elementary & secondary school; educational computer software
PA: Butler Technology & Career Development Schools
3603 Hmlton Middletown Rd
Hamilton OH 45011
513 868-1911

(G-10680)
CONNAUGHTON WLDG & FENCE LLC
440 Hensel Pl (45011-1702)
PHONE..........................513 867-0230
Fax: 513 867-1851
Jeanie Isaacs, *Exec Dir*
Robert Singhoffer,
David Singhoffer,
EMP: 6
SQ FT: 5,000
SALES (est): 481.5K **Privately Held**
SIC: 1799 7692 3469 Fence construction; welding repair; ornamental metal stampings

(G-10681)
CONNECTOR MANUFACTURING CO (DH)
Also Called: C M C
3501 Symmes Rd (45015-1369)
PHONE..........................513 860-4455
Fax: 513 860-3599
William J Boehm, *Ch of Bd*
Joe Klenk, *President*
Frank Privett, *Senior VP*
Alan Beck, *Vice Pres*
James Boehm, *VP Mfg*
▲ EMP: 172
SQ FT: 103,000
SALES (est): 62.7MM
SALES (corp-wide): 3.5B **Publicly Held**
WEB: www.cmclugs.com
SIC: 3643 Electric connectors
HQ: Burndy Llc
47 E Industrial Park Dr
Manchester NH 03109
603 626-3730

(G-10682)
CUSC INTERNATIONAL LTD
3 Standen Dr (45015-2209)
PHONE..........................513 881-2000
Caroline McIntosh, *CEO*
Jeff Kellerman, *Regl Sales Mgr*
Patrick Sullivan, *Sales Staff*
Agnes Parks, *Manager*
▲ EMP: 9
SALES (est): 888.2K **Privately Held**
SIC: 2299 4225 7389 Tops & top processing, manmade or other fiber; warehousing, self-storage; packaging & labeling services
HQ: Ifgl Refractories Limited
Mcleod House,
Kolkata WB 70000

(G-10683)
D B S STINLESS STL FABRICATORS
21 Standen Dr (45015-2209)
PHONE..........................513 856-9600
Fax: 513 856-9602
Nick Bauer, *General Mgr*
Russell Bowermaster, *Shareholder*
▲ EMP: 9
SQ FT: 12,000
SALES (est): 1.5MM **Privately Held**
SIC: 3444 Restaurant sheet metalwork

(G-10684)
DUBOIS CHEMICALS INC
Also Called: Eagle Chemicals
2550 Bobmeyer Rd (45015-1366)
PHONE..........................513 868-9662
Tisha Adette, *Manager*
Marcia Waddle, *Manager*
EMP: 14
SALES (corp-wide): 221.1MM **Privately Held**
SIC: 2819 Industrial inorganic chemicals
PA: Dubois Chemicals, Inc.
3630 E Kemper Rd
Cincinnati OH 45241
513 731-6350

(G-10685)
DURO DYNE MIDWEST CORP
3825 Symmes Rd (45015-1376)
PHONE..........................513 870-6000
Fax: 513 870-6005
Randall Hinden, *President*
Steve Simowitz, *Division Mgr*
William Watman, *Corp Secy*
Leo White, *Vice Pres*
▲ EMP: 290
SQ FT: 51,000
SALES (est): 40.8MM
SALES (corp-wide): 126.3MM **Privately Held**
SIC: 3585 3564 3498 3469 Air conditioning equipment, complete; ventilating fans: industrial or commercial; fabricated pipe & fittings; metal stampings; sheet metalwork; heating equipment, except electric
PA: Dyne Duro National Corp
81 Spence St
Bay Shore NY 11706
631 249-9000

(G-10686)
DYNAMIC CONTROL NORTH AMER INC (PA)
3042 Symmes Rd (45015-1331)
PHONE..........................513 860-5094
Fax: 513 860-5095
Scott Whitaker, *President*
Duane Gray, *Sales Mgr*
Beth Maranda, *Manager*
▲ EMP: 16
SQ FT: 15,000
SALES (est): 3.3MM **Privately Held**
WEB: www.dynamat.com
SIC: 3443 Baffles

(G-10687)
ELLISON TECHNOLOGIES INC
5333 Muhlhauser Rd (45011-9349)
PHONE..........................513 874-2736
Greg Hegedus, *Engineer*
Matt Spiller, *Sales Engr*
EMP: 5
SALES (corp-wide): 40.6B **Privately Held**
SIC: 3545 Machine tool attachments & accessories
HQ: Ellison Technologies, Inc.
9912 Pioneer Blvd
Santa Fe Springs CA 90670
562 949-8311

(G-10688)
ELRA INDUSTRIES INC
550 S Erie Hwy (45011-4346)
PHONE..........................513 868-6228
Fax: 513 863-6555
Eldon Smith, *President*
EMP: 8
SQ FT: 13,000
SALES: 750K **Privately Held**
WEB: www.elra.com
SIC: 3089 Injection molding of plastics

(G-10689)
EVAN RAGOUZIS CO
4 Standen Dr (45015-2208)
PHONE..........................513 242-5900
Fax: 513 242-5906
Evan Ragouzis, *Owner*
EMP: 2
SQ FT: 8,464
SALES (est): 1MM **Privately Held**
SIC: 3272 Building materials, except block or brick: concrete

(G-10690)
FAB SHOP INC
1520 Bender Ave (45011-4075)
PHONE..........................513 860-1332
Pamela Walden, *President*
Joseph Pate Jr, *President*
Annette H Pate, *Corp Secy*
Pamela Pate, *Vice Pres*
EMP: 3
SQ FT: 12,000
SALES (est): 360K **Privately Held**
SIC: 3441 Fabricated structural metal

(G-10691)
FAIRFIELD LICENSE CENTER INC
530 Wessel Dr Ste L (45014-3651)
PHONE..........................513 829-6224
Pamela Bock, *Principal*
EMP: 5
SALES (est): 482.8K **Privately Held**
SIC: 3469 Automobile license tags, stamped metal

(G-10692)
FIN PAN INC (PA)
3255 Symmes Rd (45015-1361)
P.O. Box 411 (45012-0411)
PHONE..........................513 870-9200
Fax: 513 870-9606
Elisa Schafer, *President*
Louis A Beimford, *Principal*
Ryan Schaffer, *Engineer*
Theodore Clear, *Treasurer*
Jeff Bower, *Controller*
▲ EMP: 18
SQ FT: 40,000
SALES (est): 8.5MM **Privately Held**
WEB: www.finpan.com
SIC: 3272 Concrete products, precast

(G-10693)
FUTURE FINISHES INC
40 Standen Dr (45015-2210)
PHONE..........................513 860-0020
Fax: 513 860-2112
Daniel L Brown, *President*
Alison Fossette, *Opers Staff*
Barbara Brown, *Financial Exec*
Teresa Brennan, *Office Mgr*
Ranne Pellman, *Manager*
EMP: 30
SQ FT: 25,000
SALES (est): 4MM **Privately Held**
WEB: www.futurefinishes.com
SIC: 3471 Plating & polishing

(G-10694)
G & J PEPSI-COLA BOTTLERS INC
2580 Bobmeyer Rd (45015-1394)
PHONE..........................513 896-3700
Fax: 513 896-4091
Ann Hartman, *COO*
Don Chalfant, *Branch Mgr*
Chris Witzgall, *Manager*
EMP: 145
SQ FT: 50,000
SALES (corp-wide): 490.5MM **Privately Held**
WEB: www.gjpepsi.com
SIC: 2086 Carbonated soft drinks, bottled & canned
PA: G & J Pepsi-Cola Bottlers Inc
9435 Waterstone Blvd # 390
Cincinnati OH 45249
513 785-6060

(G-10695)
G & M METAL PRODUCTS INC
1001 Fairview Ave (45015-1629)
PHONE..........................513 863-3353
Fax: 513 863-3457

Charles Garrod, *President*
Dawn Garrod, *Corp Secy*
William D Moore, *Vice Pres*
EMP: 5 **EST:** 1965
SQ FT: 6,800
SALES (est): 770.2K **Privately Held**
SIC: 3469 3499 Stamping metal for the trade; machine bases, metal

(G-10696)
G L INDUSTRIES INC
Also Called: Climax Packaging Machinery
25 Standen Dr (45015-2209)
P.O. Box 18097, Fairfield (45018-0097)
PHONE.....................................513 874-1233
Fax: 513 874-3375
William P George, *President*
Barb Rothwell, *Parts Mgr*
Jack Bunce, *Sales/Mktg Mgr*
EMP: 20
SQ FT: 18,000
SALES (est): 5.7MM **Privately Held**
WEB: www.climaxpackaging.com
SIC: 3565 7389 Packaging machinery; packaging & labeling services

(G-10697)
G R K MANUFACTURING CO INC
1200 Dayton St (45011-4220)
PHONE.....................................513 863-3131
Fax: 513 863-1670
Gary Kilday, *President*
Eileen K Kilday, *Corp Secy*
David S Kilday, *Vice Pres*
Lori E Kilday, *Vice Pres*
▲ **EMP:** 30 **EST:** 1917
SQ FT: 100,000
SALES (est): 3.9MM **Privately Held**
WEB: www.grkmfg.com
SIC: 2511 2499 2512 Wood household furniture; decorative wood & woodwork; upholstered household furniture

(G-10698)
GEMINI ADVERTISING ASSOCIATES
1637 Dixie Hwy (45011-4041)
PHONE.....................................513 896-3541
Dave R Lippert, *President*
Steve Lippert, *Vice Pres*
EMP: 65
SALES (est): 4.4MM **Privately Held**
WEB: www.hamiltoncaster.com
SIC: 3562 Casters

(G-10699)
GVS INDUSTRIES INC
Also Called: Cadillac Papers
1030 Beissinger Rd (45013-9322)
PHONE.....................................513 887-8660
Sharon Sheppard, *Office Mgr*
Donald Gillespie II, *Shareholder*
Ronald Green, *Shareholder*
EMP: 6
SALES (est): 879K **Privately Held**
SIC: 2621 3861 5113 5112 Specialty or chemically treated papers; toners, prepared photographic (not made in chemical plants); industrial & personal service paper; stationery & office supplies; printing & writing paper

(G-10700)
HACKER WOOD PRODUCTS INC
2144 Jackson Rd (45011-9534)
PHONE.....................................513 737-4462
Chris Hacker, *President*
EMP: 6
SQ FT: 2,200
SALES (est): 145K **Privately Held**
SIC: 2448 Wood pallets & skids

(G-10701)
HAMILTON BRASS & ALUM CASTINGS
706 S 8th St (45011-3753)
PHONE.....................................513 867-0400
Fax: 513 867-0512
Tom Koehler, *President*
Dale Heinzelman, *Vice Pres*
EMP: 20 **EST:** 1918
SQ FT: 25,000
SALES (est): 4.4MM **Privately Held**
WEB: www.hamilton-litestat.com
SIC: 3364 3321 Brass & bronze die-castings; gray & ductile iron foundries

(G-10702)
HAMILTON CUSTOM MOLDING INC
1365 Shuler Ave (45011-4567)
PHONE.....................................513 844-6643
Ed White, *President*
Adam White, *General Mgr*
Dorothy White, *Corp Secy*
EMP: 7
SQ FT: 20,000
SALES (est): 700K **Privately Held**
WEB: www.hamiltoncm.com
SIC: 3089 3544 Plastic containers, except foam; special dies, tools, jigs & fixtures

(G-10703)
HARTFORD STEEL SALES
6 S 2nd St Ste 214 (45011-2862)
P.O. Box 1236 (45012-1236)
PHONE.....................................513 275-1744
Scott Hartford, *Mng Member*
EMP: 1
SQ FT: 100
SALES (est): 2MM **Privately Held**
SIC: 3449 Bars, concrete reinforcing: fabricated steel

(G-10704)
IMI-IRVING MATERIALS INC
600 Augspurger Rd (45011-6913)
PHONE.....................................513 844-8444
Fax: 513 844-6333
Randy Jones, *Principal*
EMP: 3
SALES (est): 181.4K **Privately Held**
SIC: 3273 Ready-mixed concrete

(G-10705)
INNOVATIVE CONTROL SYSTEMS
5870 Fairham Rd (45011-2035)
PHONE.....................................513 894-3712
Fax: 513 422-4568
Steven Saunders, *President*
Dave Edester, *Vice Pres*
EMP: 6
SALES (est): 812.3K **Privately Held**
SIC: 3613 Control panels, electric

(G-10706)
INNOVTIVE LBLING SOLUTIONS INC
Also Called: I L S
4000 Hmlton Middletown Rd (45011-2263)
PHONE.....................................513 860-2457
Jay Dollries, *President*
Steve Wolf, *Vice Pres*
Jeanne Wolf, *Admin Sec*
▲ **EMP:** 65
SQ FT: 65,000
SALES (est): 14.2MM **Privately Held**
WEB: www.ilslabels.com
SIC: 2759 Commercial printing

(G-10707)
INTEGRATED POWER SERVICES LLC
2175a Schlichter Dr (45015-1482)
PHONE.....................................513 863-8816
Don Foley, *Manager*
EMP: 33
SQ FT: 20,500
SALES (corp-wide): 1.7B **Privately Held**
WEB: www.integratedps.com
SIC: 7694 Rebuilding motors, except automotive
HQ: Integrated Power Services Llc
   3 Independence Pt Ste 100
   Greenville SC 29615
   864 451-5600

(G-10708)
IRVING MATERIALS INC
600 Augspurger Rd (45011-6913)
PHONE.....................................513 844-8444
Randy Jones, *Branch Mgr*
EMP: 10
SALES (corp-wide): 814MM **Privately Held**
SIC: 3273 Ready-mixed concrete
PA: Irving Materials Inc
   8032 N State Road 9
   Greenfield IN 46140
   317 326-3101

(G-10709)
J N LINROSE MFG LLC
999 East Ave (45011-3831)
P.O. Box 1187 (45012-1187)
PHONE.....................................513 867-5500
Frank C Pfirman, *President*
EMP: 5
SALES (est): 1MM **Privately Held**
WEB: www.jnlinrose.com
SIC: 3444 3446 1751 Studs & joists, sheet metal; lintels light gauge steel; lightweight steel framing (metal stud) installation

(G-10710)
J R CUSTOM UNLIMITED
2620 Bobmeyer Rd (45015-1306)
PHONE.....................................513 894-9800
Fax: 513 894-9801
James Riesenberg, *President*
EMP: 10
SALES (est): 1.2MM **Privately Held**
SIC: 2499 Decorative wood & woodwork

(G-10711)
JASON INCORPORATED
Also Called: Jacksonlea
3440 Symmes Rd (45015-1359)
PHONE.....................................513 860-3400
Ron Locher, *General Mgr*
EMP: 18
SALES (corp-wide): 705.5MM **Publicly Held**
WEB: www.jasoninc.com
SIC: 3446 3471 3291 2842 Ornamental metalwork; plating & polishing; abrasive products; specialty cleaning, polishes & sanitation goods
HQ: Jason Incorporated
   411 E Wisconsin Ave
   Milwaukee WI 53202
   414 277-9300

(G-10712)
JEFF COUCHS CAMPERS LLC
Also Called: Jeff Couchs Rv Nation
2122 Hamilton Eaton Rd (45011-9557)
PHONE.....................................513 863-7000
Fax: 513 863-0192
Jeff Couch, *Owner*
EMP: 9
SALES: 950K **Privately Held**
SIC: 3792 Travel trailers & campers

(G-10713)
JUMP N SALES LLC
6745 Gilmore Rd Ste E (45011-5388)
P.O. Box 1683, West Chester (45071-1683)
PHONE.....................................513 509-7661
Dena K Barger, *CEO*
Dena K Long, *Owner*
EMP: 1
SQ FT: 3,000
SALES: 1MM **Privately Held**
SIC: 3545 Cutting tools for machine tools

(G-10714)
KAIVAC INC
401 S 3rd St (45011-3236)
PHONE.....................................513 887-4600
Bob Robinson Sr, *President*
Carlene Robinson, *Corp Secy*
Robert Toews, *CFO*
Aaron Humfleet, *Regl Sales Mgr*
Nick Wehby, *Regl Sales Mgr*
◆ **EMP:** 40
SALES (est): 8MM **Privately Held**
WEB: www.kaivac.com
SIC: 3589 Commercial cleaning equipment

(G-10715)
KATHOM MANUFACTURING CO INC
661 Williams Ave (45015-1158)
PHONE.....................................513 868-8890
Fax: 513 868-8851
Thomas R Wells, *President*
EMP: 22
SALES (est): 4.3MM **Privately Held**
WEB: www.kathom.com
SIC: 3089 3643 2821 Plastic processing; current-carrying wiring devices; plastics materials & resins

(G-10716)
KING RETAIL SOLUTIONS INC
3865 Symmes Rd (45015-1376)
PHONE.....................................513 729-5858
EMP: 10
SALES (corp-wide): 39.8MM **Privately Held**
SIC: 7336 3993 Commercial Art/Graphic Design Mfg Signs/Advertising Specialties
HQ: King Retail Solutions, Inc.
   3850 W 1st Ave
   Eugene OR 97402
   541 686-2848

(G-10717)
KUHLMANNS FABRICATION
1753 Millville Oxford Rd (45013-8931)
PHONE.....................................513 967-4617
Mark Kuhlmann, *Principal*
EMP: 3 **EST:** 2008
SALES (est): 268.7K **Privately Held**
SIC: 3842 Welders' hoods

(G-10718)
LOUS MACHINE COMPANY INC
102 Hastings Ave (45011-4708)
PHONE.....................................513 856-9199
Fax: 513 856-7068
G Danny Jackson, *President*
EMP: 10
SQ FT: 10,000
SALES (est): 1.9MM **Privately Held**
SIC: 3599 Machine shop, jobbing & repair

(G-10719)
M C L WINDOW COVERINGS INC
6741 Gilmore Rd Ste H (45011-5386)
PHONE.....................................513 868-6000
Fax: 513 779-0044
Joe Lagedrost, *Branch Mgr*
EMP: 3
SALES (corp-wide): 2.7MM **Privately Held**
SIC: 2591 5714 7359 2221 Window blinds; drapery & upholstery stores; equipment rental & leasing; upholstery, tapestry & wall covering fabrics; drapery track installation
PA: M C L Window Coverings Inc
   11815 Technology Ln
   Fishers IN 46038
   317 577-2670

(G-10720)
M L C TECHNOLOGIES INC
4 Standen Dr (45015-2208)
PHONE.....................................513 874-7792
Michael L Crompton, *President*
James Jackson,
Marty Todd,
EMP: 4
SQ FT: 6,000
SALES (est): 602.7K **Privately Held**
SIC: 3599 3089 Custom machinery; injection molding of plastics

(G-10721)
MA FLYNN ASSOCIATES LLC
Also Called: Flynn Metering
4115 Tonya Trl (45011-8535)
PHONE.....................................513 893-7873
Larry Rhodis, *General Mgr*
Marvin Flynn, *Mng Member*
Paula Rhodis, *Manager*
Diana Flynn,
EMP: 5
SQ FT: 12,000
SALES (est): 2.7MM **Privately Held**
WEB: www.flynnmeteringsystems.com
SIC: 5084 3625 Meters, consumption registering; motor starters & controllers, electric

(G-10722)
MACHINE TOOL CORPORATION
102 Hastings Ave (45011-4708)
PHONE.....................................513 863-4920
George Jackson, *President*
EMP: 9 **EST:** 1959
SQ FT: 10,800
SALES (est): 660K **Privately Held**
WEB: www.mtc2.com
SIC: 3544 3537 Dies & die holders for metal cutting, forming, die casting; tables, lift: hydraulic

GEOGRAPHIC

(G-10723)
MATANDY STEEL & METAL PDTS LLC
Also Called: Matandy Steel Sales
1200 Central Ave (45011-3825)
P.O. Box 1186 (45012-1186)
PHONE....................513 844-2277
Fax: 513 844-6120
Andrew Schuster, *President*
Aaron Higdon, *General Mgr*
Jim Hirka, *Production*
Melissa Holder, *Controller*
Matthew Pfirman, *Finance*
EMP: 100
SQ FT: 125,000
SALES (est): 116.4MM **Privately Held**
WEB: www.matandy.com
SIC: 5051 3312 3444 3399 Metals serv-
ice centers & offices; sheet or strip, steel,
cold-rolled: own hot-rolled; studs & joists,
sheet metal; nails: aluminum, brass or
other nonferrous metal or wire

(G-10724)
MEMBRANE SPECIALISTS LLC
2 Rowe Ct (45015-2211)
PHONE....................513 860-9490
Leif Nilsson, *Managing Prtnr*
Jason Butkus, *Project Mgr*
Paul Koren, *Project Mgr*
Cathy L Jacobs, *Manager*
David Pearson,
EMP: 7
SQ FT: 12,000
SALES (est): 1.9MM **Privately Held**
SIC: 3569 Filters, general line: industrial

(G-10725)
MINNICKS DRIVE-THRU
828 East Ave (45011-3808)
PHONE....................513 868-6126
Ralph Minnick, *Principal*
EMP: 3 EST: 2010
SALES (est): 188.7K **Privately Held**
SIC: 2082 Beer (alcoholic beverage)

(G-10726)
NETUREN AMERICA CORPORATION
2995 Moser Ct (45011-5430)
PHONE....................513 863-1900
Etsla Yamamura, *CEO*
Makoto Nakahara, *Principal*
Chad Johnson, *Human Res Mgr*
▲ EMP: 18
SALES (est): 3.6MM **Privately Held**
SIC: 3398 Metal heat treating

(G-10727)
NK MACHINE INC
1550 Pleasant Ave (45015-1035)
PHONE....................513 737-8035
Fax: 513 737-8045
Nick Emenaker, *President*
Betty Emenaker, *Owner*
Edward Emenaker, *Owner*
EMP: 7
SQ FT: 6,000
SALES: 1MM **Privately Held**
SIC: 3599 Machine shop, jobbing & repair

(G-10728)
OLD WEST INDUSTRIES INC (PA)
Also Called: Moser Leather Company
1405 Boyle Rd (45013-1825)
P.O. Box 13030 (45013-0030)
PHONE....................513 889-0500
James Cox, *Principal*
▲ EMP: 5
SALES (est): 559.3K **Privately Held**
WEB: www.ket-moy.com
SIC: 5941 3111 Saddlery & equestrian
equipment; leather tanning & finishing

(G-10729)
OLIVER PRODUCTS COMPANY
Also Called: Oliver-Tolas Healthcare Packg
3840 Symmes Rd (45015-1378)
PHONE....................513 860-6880
James Smith, *QC Mgr*
Tom Backs, *Engineer*
Heather Fletcher, *Branch Mgr*
Bill Daeschler, *Manager*
EMP: 19

SALES (corp-wide): 3.2B **Privately Held**
SIC: 2672 Chemically treated papers:
made from purchased materials; adhesive
papers, labels or tapes: from purchased
material
HQ: Oliver Products Company
445 6th St Nw
Grand Rapids MI 49504
616 456-7711

(G-10730)
PLAS-TANKS INDUSTRIES INC (PA)
39 Standen Dr (45015-2209)
PHONE....................513 942-3800
Fax: 513 942-3993
J Kent Covey, *President*
Connie Royse, *Vice Pres*
EMP: 39
SQ FT: 33,000
SALES (est): 9.1MM **Privately Held**
WEB: www.plastanks.com
SIC: 3089 3564 3444 3084 Tubs, plastic
(containers); blowers & fans; sheet metal-
work; plastics pipe

(G-10731)
PRODUCTION MANUFACTURING INC
870 Hanover St Bldg A (45011-3790)
PHONE....................513 892-2331
Fax: 513 892-0014
James Napier, *President*
Dale K Henderson, *Chairman*
Linda Napier, *Corp Secy*
EMP: 25
SQ FT: 75,000
SALES (est): 6.3MM **Privately Held**
SIC: 3444 Sheet metalwork

(G-10732)
QLOG CORP
33 Standen Dr (45015-2209)
PHONE....................513 874-1211
Fax: 513 874-1903
J Robert Warden, *President*
Thomas Rebel, *Vice Pres*
Andy Koeller, *Office Mgr*
Andi Maggard, *Office Mgr*
EMP: 9
SQ FT: 7,500
SALES: 2MM **Privately Held**
WEB: www.qlog.com
SIC: 8748 3679 Systems analysis or de-
sign; electronic circuits

(G-10733)
QUALITY PUBLISHING CO
Also Called: Quality Printing & Publishing
3200 Symmes Rd (45015-1357)
PHONE....................513 863-8210
Fax: 513 863-8761
Jane Johnson, *President*
David Johnson, *Vice Pres*
Diana Jackson, *Manager*
Steve Clark, *Graphic Designe*
EMP: 10 EST: 1953
SQ FT: 10,000
SALES: 1.2MM **Privately Held**
WEB: www.qualitypublishing.com
SIC: 2752 Commercial printing, offset

(G-10734)
RUBBERDUCK 4X4
1622 Smith Rd (45013-8629)
PHONE....................513 889-1735
Travis Depew, *Owner*
EMP: 6
SALES (est): 500K **Privately Held**
SIC: 3714 Motor vehicle parts & acces-
sories

(G-10735)
SCC INSTRUMENTS
4436 Hamilton Scipio Rd (45013-9129)
PHONE....................513 856-8444
Fax: 513 856-7243
William Sefton, *President*
EMP: 5
SALES (est): 580K **Privately Held**
SIC: 3625 Flow actuated electrical
switches

(G-10736)
SCHAEFER BOX & PALLET CO
11800 Paddys Run Rd (45013-9365)
PHONE....................513 738-2500
Fax: 513 738-1605
Stanley Schaefer, *CEO*
Tod Hollifield, *President*
EMP: 32
SQ FT: 45,000
SALES (est): 5.3MM **Privately Held**
WEB: www.schaeferboxandpallet.com
SIC: 2449 2448 2441 Rectangular boxes
& crates, wood; pallets, wood; nailed
wood boxes & shook

(G-10737)
SENSUS LLC
2991 Hamilton Mason Rd (45011-5355)
PHONE....................513 892-7100
Bruce Rust, *Engineer*
Dave Polan, *Marketing Staff*
Dan Wampler, *Mng Member*
▲ EMP: 12
SQ FT: 25,000
SALES (est): 2.1MM **Privately Held**
WEB: www.sensusflavors.com
SIC: 2087 Pastes, flavoring
HQ: Synergy Flavors Inc
1500 Synergy Dr
Wauconda IL 60084
847 487-1011

(G-10738)
SHAPE SUPPLY INC
700 S Erie Hwy (45011-3904)
PHONE....................513 863-6695
Fax: 513 863-6964
Eugene Lukjan, *President*
Kenzie Cain, *Managing Dir*
Carol Shape, *Office Mgr*
EMP: 4
SQ FT: 16,000
SALES: 500K **Privately Held**
SIC: 3444 5075 Pipe, sheet metal; warm
air heating equipment & supplies

(G-10739)
SIGNERY2 LLC
2571 Millville Shandon Rd (45013-8218)
PHONE....................513 738-3048
Lois Schmidt,
EMP: 3
SQ FT: 3,600
SALES (est): 210K **Privately Held**
WEB: www.schmidtsignery.com
SIC: 3993 Signs & advertising specialties

(G-10740)
SPECIALTY PLAS FABRICATIONS
Also Called: Custom Cases For Collectibles
1600 Irma Ave (45011-4454)
PHONE....................513 856-9475
Fax: 513 856-9133
Betty Brickner, *President*
▲ EMP: 7
SQ FT: 12,000
SALES: 600K **Privately Held**
WEB: www.casesforcollectibles.com
SIC: 3089 Plastic containers, except foam

(G-10741)
STAT INDUSTRIES INC
3269 Profit Dr (45014-4239)
PHONE....................513 860-4482
Fax: 513 860-4487
Robyn Kellough, *Manager*
EMP: 6
SALES (corp-wide): 930K **Privately Held**
WEB: www.statindex.com
SIC: 2675 Index cards, die-cut: made from
purchased materials
PA: Stat Industries, Inc.
137 Stone Rd
Chillicothe OH 45601
740 779-6561

(G-10742)
STONE & SULLIVAN INDUSTRIES
1299 Roundhill Dr (45013-9352)
PHONE....................513 896-1976
Ed Sullivan, *Principal*
EMP: 15

SALES (est): 640.9K **Privately Held**
SIC: 3999 Manufacturing industries

(G-10743)
SYNERGY FLAVORS (OH) LLC
Also Called: Sensus
2991 Hamilton Mason Rd (45011-5355)
PHONE....................513 892-7100
Fax: 513 892-7111
Greg Bach, *CEO*
Kevin Goodner, *Director*
EMP: 1 EST: 2011
SALES (est): 4.8MM **Privately Held**
SIC: 2087 Extracts, flavoring
HQ: Synergy Flavors Inc
1500 Synergy Dr
Wauconda IL 60084
847 487-1011

(G-10744)
TERRY ASPHALT MATERIALS INC (DH)
8600 Bilstein Blvd (45015-2204)
PHONE....................513 874-6192
Dan Koeninger, *CEO*
Dave Shaw, *Asst Supt*
Mike Haag, *Terminal Mgr*
Jim Monroe, *Terminal Mgr*
Ken Collins, *Accountant*
EMP: 25
SALES (est): 43.9MM
SALES (corp-wide): 77.1MM **Privately
Held**
SIC: 5082 2952 Road construction &
maintenance machinery; asphalt felts &
coatings
HQ: Barrett Industries Corporation
3 Becker Farm Rd Ste 307
Roseland NJ 07068
973 533-1001

(G-10745)
THERMOLOCK MFG LLC
2921 Mcbride Ct (45011-5420)
PHONE....................513 771-6555
James Doerger, *Mng Member*
EMP: 7
SALES (est): 680K **Privately Held**
SIC: 2431 Windows & window parts & trim,
wood

(G-10746)
THREE LEAF INC
3189 Princeton Rd Ste 123 (45011-5338)
PHONE....................888 308-1007
Joseph Brandabur, *CEO*
David A Ferris, *President*
Timber Smith, *Manager*
▲ EMP: 2
SALES: 1.2MM **Privately Held**
SIC: 2819 Copper compounds or salts, in-
organic

(G-10747)
THYSSENKRUPP BILSTEIN AMER INC (HQ)
8685 Bilstein Blvd (45015-2205)
PHONE....................513 881-7600
Fabian Schmahl, *President*
Hendrik Walde, *Opers Mgr*
Markus Mencher, *Opers Staff*
Ben Fisher, *Purch Mgr*
James Sagedal, *Purch Agent*
▲ EMP: 212
SQ FT: 115,000
SALES (est): 69.9MM
SALES (corp-wide): 44.2B **Privately Held**
SIC: 3714 5013 Shock absorbers, motor
vehicle; springs, shock absorbers & struts
PA: Thyssenkrupp Ag
Thyssenkrupp Allee 1
Essen 45143
201 844-5641

(G-10748)
TIPCO PUNCH INC
6 Rowe Ct (45015-2211)
PHONE....................513 874-9140
Fax: 513 874-0204
Jack Pickins, *CEO*
Scott Ellsworth, *Vice Pres*
Derrick Giffen, *Sales Staff*
Carla Wilburn, *Manager*
EMP: 30
SQ FT: 12,000

SALES (est): 5MM
SALES (corp-wide): 12.2MM **Privately
Held**
SIC: 3544 Punches, forming & stamping
HQ: Tipco Inc
1 Coventry Rd
Brampton ON L6T 4
905 791-9811

(G-10749)
TRI-MAC MFG & SVCS CO
Also Called: Tri-Mac Mfg & Serv
860 Belle Ave (45015-1151)
PHONE......................513 896-4445
William Bates, *President*
Bill Galster, *Vice Pres*
EMP: 17
SQ FT: 40,000
SALES (est): 3.4MM **Privately Held**
SIC: 3714 3554 5084 3549 Motor vehicle
parts & accessories; paper industries ma-
chinery; trucks, industrial; trailers, indus-
trial; metalworking machinery; sheet
metalwork

(G-10750)
TRI-STATE JET MFG LLC
1480 Beissinger Rd (45013-1110)
PHONE......................513 896-4538
Jeff Pierson, *Principal*
EMP: 3 EST: 2012
SALES (est): 265K **Privately Held**
SIC: 3812 Aircraft/aerospace flight instru-
ments & guidance systems

(G-10751)
TRIANGLE SIGN CO
221 N B St (45013-3195)
PHONE......................513 863-2578
Fax: 513 863-8740
Donald K Whittlesey, *Partner*
Everett Hoskins Jr, *Partner*
Tim Hoskins, *Partner*
EMP: 9 EST: 1920
SQ FT: 6,695
SALES (est): 700K **Privately Held**
SIC: 3993 7389 Neon signs; sign painting
& lettering shop

(G-10752)
UFP HAMILTON LLC
115 Distribution Dr (45014-4257)
PHONE......................513 285-7190
Fax: 513 870-9304
Ken Rewa, *Principal*
EMP: 16
SALES (est): 413.7K
SALES (corp-wide): 3.2B **Publicly Held**
SIC: 2491 Wood preserving
PA: Universal Forest Products, Inc.
2801 E Beltline Ave Ne
Grand Rapids MI 49525
616 364-6161

(G-10753)
**VENICE CORNERSTONE
NEWSPAPER**
2640 Cncnnati Brkville Rd (45014-5973)
PHONE......................513 738-7151
Lanny Leach, *Owner*
Treasa Leach, *Business Mgr*
EMP: 3
SALES (est): 172.8K **Privately Held**
SIC: 2711 Newspapers, publishing & print-
ing

(G-10754)
VINYLMAX CORPORATION
2921 Mcbride Ct (45011-5420)
PHONE......................800 847-3736
Fax: 513 772-0364
James Doerger, *CEO*
Craig Doerger, *Opers Mgr*
EMP: 90 EST: 1982
SQ FT: 100,000
SALES (est): 15.7MM **Privately Held**
WEB: www.vinylmax.com
SIC: 3089 2431 Window frames & sash,
plastic; doors & door parts & trim, wood

(G-10755)
**W & W CUSTOM FABRICATION
INC (PA)**
143 E Fairway Dr (45013-3528)
PHONE......................513 353-4617
Fax: 513 737-8281

Steven Webb, *President*
Mike Hutcheson, *Vice Pres*
Tammy Webb, *Office Mgr*
EMP: 2
SQ FT: 600
SALES: 1MM **Privately Held**
SIC: 3444 Sheet metalwork

(G-10756)
WALLOVER OIL HAMILTON INC
Also Called: National Oil Products
1000 Forest Ave (45015-1632)
P.O. Box 15097 (45015-0097)
PHONE......................513 896-6692
Fax: 513 896-6705
George Marquis, *Chairman*
Steve Napier, *Manager*
EMP: 13 EST: 1963
SQ FT: 15,000
SALES (est): 2.2MM **Privately Held**
SIC: 2992 Re-refining lubricating oils &
greases
HQ: Wallover Enterprises Inc.
21845 Drake Rd
Strongsville OH 44149
440 238-9250

(G-10757)
WATSON GRAVEL INC (PA)
2728 Hamilton Cleves Rd (45013-9452)
PHONE......................513 863-0070
Ronald E Watson, *President*
Janet L Meyers, *Corp Secy*
Michael T Watson, *Vice Pres*
Brian Bottoms, *Manager*
EMP: 37
SQ FT: 2,000
SALES (est): 15.7MM **Privately Held**
WEB: www.watsongravel.com
SIC: 1442 Gravel mining

(G-10758)
Z P ENTERPRISES INC
Also Called: Office Graphics
223 Court St (45011-2827)
P.O. Box 395 (45012-0395)
PHONE......................513 863-3393
William Pittman, *President*
Phyllis Pittman, *Corp Secy*
Norm Zins, *Vice Pres*
EMP: 7
SQ FT: 1,500
SALES (est): 1.1MM **Privately Held**
SIC: 5112 2752 Stationery & office sup-
plies; commercial printing, offset

Hamler
Henry County

(G-10759)
**CROP PRODUCTION SERVICES
INC**
8767 County Road F (43524-9726)
PHONE......................419 274-2701
Dick Heilman, *Project Mgr*
Russ Rice, *Branch Mgr*
EMP: 7
SALES (corp-wide): 13.6B **Privately Held**
WEB: www.cropproductionservices.com
SIC: 2875 Fertilizers, mixing only
HQ: Crop Production Services, Inc.
3005 Rocky Mountain Ave
Loveland CO 80538
970 685-3300

Hammondsville
Jefferson County

(G-10760)
SAM ABDALLAH
Also Called: Aquanaut Lounge
777 Hamnondsville Rd (43930)
P.O. Box 114, Stratton (43961-0114)
PHONE......................330 532-3900
Sam Abdallah, *Owner*
EMP: 30
SQ FT: 10,000
SALES (est): 2.5MM **Privately Held**
WEB: www.samabdallah.com
SIC: 2899 Fireworks; citronella oil

Hanging Rock
Lawrence County

(G-10761)
AMERICAS STYRENICS LLC
925 County Road 1a (45638-8687)
PHONE......................740 533-4017
EMP: 92
SALES (corp-wide): 531.2MM **Privately
Held**
SIC: 2821 2865 Polystyrene resins;
styrene
PA: Americas Styrenics Llc
24 Waterway Ave Ste 1200
The Woodlands TX 77380
832 616-7800

(G-10762)
WORLEYS MACHINE & FAB INC
1003 State Rr 650 (45638)
P.O. Box 604, Ironton (45638-0604)
PHONE......................740 532-3337
Fax: 740 532-3463
James Worley, *President*
Diana Worley, *Corp Secy*
EMP: 8
SALES (est): 500K **Privately Held**
SIC: 3599 7692 Machine shop, jobbing &
repair; welding repair

Hannibal
Monroe County

(G-10763)
ORMET CORPORATION
43840 State Rte 7 (43931)
PHONE......................740 483-1381
Fax: 740 483-2622
Jeffrey Marshall, *Ch of Bd*
Mike Tanchuk, *President*
Matt Powell, *Vice Pres*
Gary Mallett, *Plant Mgr*
James Burns Riley, *CFO*
▲ EMP: 1250
SQ FT: 10,000
SALES (est): 175.6MM **Privately Held**
WEB: www.ormet.com
SIC: 3334 Primary aluminum

(G-10764)
**TRIPLE J OILFIELD SERVICES
LLC**
42722 State Route 7 (43931)
PHONE......................740 483-9030
John Mata, *Principal*
EMP: 6
SALES (est): 871.2K **Privately Held**
SIC: 1389 Oil field services

Harpster
Wyandot County

(G-10765)
COONS HOMEMADE CANDIES
16451 County Highway 113 (43323-9331)
PHONE......................740 496-4141
Charles W Coons, *President*
EMP: 4
SALES (est): 212.8K **Privately Held**
SIC: 2064 5961 5441 Candy & other con-
fectionery products; food, mail order;
candy

Harrison
Hamilton County

(G-10766)
**AERO PROPULSION SUPPORT
INC**
Also Called: Aero Propulsion Support Group
108 May Dr Ste A (45030-2005)
PHONE......................513 367-9452
Fax: 513 367-7930
Allan Slattery, *President*
Rose Slattery, *Vice Pres*

EMP: 49
SQ FT: 25,000
SALES (est): 11.3MM **Privately Held**
WEB: www.aeropropulsion.com
SIC: 3511 Turbines & turbine generator
sets & parts

(G-10767)
**AIR LOGIC POWER SYSTEMS
LLC**
10100 Progress Way (45030-1295)
PHONE......................513 202-5130
David Huberfield, *CEO*
EMP: 5
SALES (corp-wide): 5.8MM **Privately
Held**
SIC: 3823 Industrial instrmnts msrmnt dis-
play/control process variable; industrial
flow & liquid measuring instruments
PA: Air Logic Power Systems, Llc
2440 W Corp Prsrv Dr # 600
Oak Creek WI 53154
414 671-3332

(G-10768)
ALLIANCE KNIFE INC
124 May Dr (45030-2024)
P.O. Box 729 (45030-0729)
PHONE......................513 367-9000
Fax: 513 367-2233
William L Keith, *President*
Sharon Keith, *Corp Secy*
Lonnie Keith, *Vice Pres*
Jackie Elmore, *Sales Associate*
Joe Daughery, *Sales Executive*
◆ EMP: 50
SALES (est): 7.4MM **Privately Held**
WEB: www.allianceknife.com
SIC: 3545 5085 3541 3423 Machine
knives, metalworking; knives, industrial;
machine tools, metal cutting type; hand &
edge tools; cutlery

(G-10769)
BELL INDUSTRIES
9843 New Haven Rd (45030-1836)
PHONE......................513 353-2355
Edward Vierling, *Owner*
EMP: 10
SQ FT: 8,600
SALES (est): 500K **Privately Held**
WEB: www.bellindustries.net
SIC: 3931 Bells (musical instruments); car-
illon bells; chimes & parts (musical instru-
ments)

(G-10770)
**CAMPBELL HAUSFELD LLC
(DH)**
Also Called: Campbell Group
100 Production Dr (45030-1477)
PHONE......................513 367-4811
Fax: 812 637-4508
Eric Tinnemeyer, *President*
Edward Andros, *Vice Pres*
Frank Cann, *Vice Pres*
Josh Davis, *Vice Pres*
Randy Smith, *Vice Pres*
▼ EMP: 112
SQ FT: 3,000
SALES (est): 158.3MM
SALES (corp-wide): 223.6B **Publicly
Held**
WEB: www.waynepumps.com
SIC: 3563 3546 3548 Air & gas compres-
sors including vacuum pumps; spraying
outfits: metals, paints & chemicals (com-
pressor); power-driven handtools; welding
apparatus
HQ: The Marmon Group Llc
181 W Madison St Ste 2600
Chicago IL 60602
312 372-9500

(G-10771)
CHICAGO DENTAL SUPPLY INC
10051 Simonson Rd Unit 9 (45030-2001)
PHONE......................800 571-5211
Paul E Myers III, *President*
▲ EMP: 7 EST: 2002
SALES (est): 560K **Privately Held**
SIC: 3843 Dental equipment & supplies

(G-10772)
CINCINNATI CRANE & HOIST LLC
10860 Paddys Run Rd (45030-9252)
P.O. Box 1072, Hamilton (45012-1072)
PHONE..................................513 202-1408
Richard Strobl, *CEO*
Joyce Cross, *Accountant*
EMP: 13
SQ FT: 36,000
SALES (est): 6MM **Privately Held**
SIC: 3536 1796 Hoists, cranes & mono-rails; installing building equipment

(G-10773)
CINCINNATI TEST SYSTEMS INC (PA)
10100 Progress Way (45030-1295)
PHONE..................................800 850-3189
Fax: 513 367-5426
Kevin Hansell, *General Mgr*
Jay Hong, *General Mgr*
Barry Welborn, *General Mgr*
Barbara A Jackson, *Principal*
Jeffrey Beebe, *Business Mgr*
EMP: 145
SQ FT: 25,000
SALES (est): 30.6MM **Privately Held**
WEB: www.cincinnati-test.com
SIC: 3823 Industrial instrmnts msrmnt display/control process variable; pressure measurement instruments, industrial; industrial flow & liquid measuring instruments

(G-10774)
COATING SYSTEMS INC
Also Called: C S I
150 Sales Ave (45030-1484)
PHONE..................................513 367-5600
Fax: 513 367-5598
Thomas W Ritter, *President*
Christopher Thomas, *General Mgr*
John Ritter, *Vice Pres*
EMP: 17
SQ FT: 20,000
SALES (est): 2.5MM **Privately Held**
WEB: www.coatingsystems.com
SIC: 3479 Painting, coating & hot dipping; coating of metals & formed products

(G-10775)
CROWN PLASTICS CO
116 May Dr (45030-2095)
PHONE..................................513 367-0238
Fax: 513 367-4004
Robert H Ellerhorst, *Ch of Bd*
Gary Ellerhorst, *President*
Gregg Ellerhorst, *Vice Pres*
Dan Dunham, *Controller*
Ken Myers, *Shareholder*
▲ **EMP:** 52
SQ FT: 56,000
SALES (est): 17MM **Privately Held**
WEB: www.crownplastics.com
SIC: 2821 3081 Plastics materials & resins; polypropylene film & sheet

(G-10776)
EDELMANN PROVISION COMPANY
Also Called: Fresh Sausage Specialists
10000 Martins Way (45030-2090)
PHONE..................................513 881-5800
James Frondorf, *President*
James Burke, *Vice Pres*
Gary Willhite, *Vice Pres*
Tony Johnson, *Inv Control Mgr*
Susan Taylor, *Manager*
EMP: 80 **EST:** 1930
SQ FT: 10,000
SALES (est): 16.3MM **Privately Held**
SIC: 2013 Sausages from purchased meat; luncheon meat from purchased meat; frankfurters from purchased meat; prepared pork products from purchased pork

(G-10777)
FASTPATCH LTD
10774 Carolina Trace Rd (45030-2729)
P.O. Box 5 (45030-0005)
PHONE..................................513 367-1838
Mike Jacobs, *President*
EMP: 10

SALES (est): 496.6K **Privately Held**
SIC: 2395 Embroidery & art needlework

(G-10778)
FEILHAUERS MACHINE SHOP INC (PA)
421 Industrial Dr (45030-2104)
PHONE..................................513 202-0545
Fax: 513 367-3702
Don Feilhauer, *President*
Jill Feilhauer, *Office Mgr*
EMP: 5 **EST:** 1979
SQ FT: 8,000
SALES (est): 933.5K **Privately Held**
WEB: www.feilhauers.com
SIC: 3599 Machine shop, jobbing & repair

(G-10779)
FRONTIER SIGNS & DISPLAYS INC
525 New Biddinger Rd (45030-1252)
P.O. Box 328 (45030-0328)
PHONE..................................513 367-0813
Fax: 513 367-5739
Jack S Wuesterfeld, *President*
Ruth Wuesterfeld, *Treasurer*
Sheri Wuesterfeld, *Sales Staff*
EMP: 7
SQ FT: 17,000
SALES (est): 965.8K **Privately Held**
SIC: 2521 2522 3993 Wood office furniture; office furniture, except wood; signs & advertising specialties

(G-10780)
GEOGRAPH INDUSTRIES INC
475 Industrial Dr (45030-2104)
PHONE..................................513 202-9200
Fax: 513 202-9299
George Freudiger, *President*
Mark Freudiger, *Vice Pres*
Vanessa Miller, *Design Engr*
George Michael Freudiger, *Treasurer*
Robin Dunn, *Accounts Exec*
EMP: 26
SQ FT: 25,000
SALES: 4MM **Privately Held**
WEB: www.geograph-ind.com
SIC: 2541 3993 2521 2522 Wood partitions & fixtures; signs & advertising specialties; cabinets, office: wood; chairs, office: padded or plain, except wood

(G-10781)
GREER & WHITEHEAD CNSTR INC
510 S State St Ste D (45030-1494)
PHONE..................................513 202-1757
Fax: 513 202-1757
Steven Whitehead, *President*
EMP: 35
SALES (est): 5.7MM **Privately Held**
SIC: 1711 1389 Mechanical contractor; building oil & gas well foundations on site

(G-10782)
HOLIDAY HOMES INC
Also Called: Holiday Hmes Rvrview Crossings
10620 Sand Run Rd (45030-9452)
PHONE..................................513 353-9777
Fax: 513 353-2521
Adam Perkins, *General Mgr*
EMP: 12
SQ FT: 1,781
SALES (corp-wide): 9.6MM **Privately Held**
SIC: 2451 6531 Mobile homes; real estate agents & managers
PA: Holiday Homes, Inc.
1252 Goshen Pike
Milford OH 45150
513 575-7697

(G-10783)
HUBERT ENTERPRISES INC
9555 Dry Fork Rd (45030-1994)
PHONE..................................513 367-8600
Bart Kohler, *President*
Laura Hawley, *HR Admin*
Vicki Rickabaugh, *Manager*
EMP: 5
SQ FT: 372,500

SALES (est): 1.2MM **Privately Held**
SIC: 5046 2761 Store equipment; store fixtures; manifold business forms

(G-10784)
HUSAC PAVING
114 S Walnut St (45030-1373)
P.O. Box 409 (45030-0409)
PHONE..................................513 200-2818
Joe Wasinger, *Owner*
EMP: 5
SALES (est): 191.2K **Privately Held**
SIC: 2951 Paving blocks

(G-10785)
ILSCO CORPORATION
Glenmoor Company Division
119 May Dr (45030-2023)
PHONE..................................513 367-9100
Fax: 513 367-5166
Russ Hensley, *Opers-Prdtn-Mfg*
Alan Merritt, *QC Dir*
EMP: 30
SQ FT: 37,068
SALES (corp-wide): 120.9MM **Privately Held**
WEB: www.ilsco.com
SIC: 3451 Screw machine products
HQ: Ilsco Corporation
4730 Madison Rd
Cincinnati OH 45227
513 533-6200

(G-10786)
JAMTEK ENTERPRISES INC
10845 State Route 128 (45030-9236)
PHONE..................................513 738-4700
Fax: 513 738-4701
Thomas Kroeger, *President*
Jerome Kroeger, *Vice Pres*
Paul Kroeger, *CFO*
▲ **EMP:** 4
SQ FT: 12,900
SALES (est): 1.2MM **Privately Held**
WEB: www.jamtek.net
SIC: 5085 5169 3566 Industrial supplies; industrial chemicals; drives, high speed industrial, except hydrostatic

(G-10787)
JTM PROVISIONS COMPANY INC
Also Called: Jtm Food Group
200 Sales Ave (45030-1485)
PHONE..................................513 367-4900
Fax: 513 367-1132
Anthony A Maas, *President*
Doug Littelmann, *Business Mgr*
Scott Bonta, *Vice Pres*
Jamie Cronen, *Vice Pres*
Jerome Maas, *Vice Pres*
EMP: 350 **EST:** 1963
SQ FT: 96,000
SALES: 154.8MM **Privately Held**
WEB: www.jtmfoodgroup.com
SIC: 2013 2051 Frozen meats from purchased meat; buns, bread type: fresh or frozen

(G-10788)
MAB FABRICATION INC
320 N State St (45030-1146)
PHONE..................................855 622-3221
James Rice, *Principal*
EMP: 4
SALES (est): 446.6K **Privately Held**
SIC: 3499 3999 Aerosol valves, metal; barber & beauty shop equipment

(G-10789)
MARTIN MARIETTA MATERIALS INC
Also Called: Martin Marietta Aggregates
170 Pilot Rd (45030)
PHONE..................................513 200-2303
Fax: 513 367-0974
Dewey Powell, *Manager*
EMP: 3
SQ FT: 1,705
SALES (corp-wide): 3.8B **Publicly Held**
WEB: www.martinmarietta.com
SIC: 1442 Construction sand & gravel
PA: Martin Marietta Materials Inc
2710 Wycliff Rd
Raleigh NC 27607
919 781-4550

(G-10790)
MCFEELYS INC
320 N State St (45030-1146)
PHONE..................................800 443-7937
Peter Putterman, *President*
EMP: 15
SALES: 7.1MM **Privately Held**
SIC: 5085 3553 Fasteners & fastening equipment; woodworking machinery

(G-10791)
MIAMI VALLEY READY MIX INC
9540 Hamilton Cleves Hwy (45030-9706)
PHONE..................................513 738-2616
Tom Norris, *Manager*
EMP: 30
SALES (corp-wide): 2.6MM **Privately Held**
SIC: 3273 Ready-mixed concrete
PA: Miami Valley Ready Mix, Inc.
7466 New Haven Rd
Harrison OH
513 738-2616

(G-10792)
NAVPAR INC
11029 State Route 128 (45030-9710)
PHONE..................................513 738-2230
Fax: 513 738-2240
Earl Keim, *President*
Jerome J Charls, *Principal*
Wendell Shallenberger, *Corp Secy*
Mike Ledars, *Vice Pres*
EMP: 3
SQ FT: 3,500
SALES (est): 485.9K **Privately Held**
SIC: 3441 Ship sections, prefabricated metal

(G-10793)
NEASE CO LLC
Also Called: Nease Performance Chemicals
10740 Paddys Run Rd (45030-9251)
PHONE..................................513 738-1255
Steve Hamilton, *Engineer*
Jennifer Titus, *Controller*
Gordon Geist, *Sales Staff*
Frank Canepa, *Branch Mgr*
EMP: 60 **Privately Held**
SIC: 2869 Glycol ethers
HQ: Nease Co. Llc
9774 Windisch Rd
West Chester OH 45069
513 587-2800

(G-10794)
PCS PHOSPHATE COMPANY INC
10818 Paddys Run Rd (45030-9252)
PHONE..................................513 738-1261
Mark Muse, *QC Mgr*
Jack Sullivan, *Manager*
Roy Brown, *Manager*
Scott Folz, *Director*
Kim Lawson, *Director*
EMP: 24
SALES (corp-wide): 4.4B **Privately Held**
WEB: www.potashcorp.com
SIC: 2819 Phosphates, except fertilizers: defluorinated & ammoniated
HQ: Pcs Phosphate Company, Inc.
1101 Skokie Blvd Ste 400
Northbrook IL 60062
847 849-4200

(G-10795)
POWEREX-IWATA AIR TECH INC
150 Production Dr (45030-1477)
PHONE..................................888 769-7979
Fax: 513 367-3125
Gary Heman, *President*
Charles Heman, *President*
Pruce Jacobs, *President*
Steve Pelicano, *Business Mgr*
Brian Thomas, *Controller*
EMP: 70
SQ FT: 75,000
SALES: 35MM
SALES (corp-wide): 223.6B **Publicly Held**
WEB: www.powerexinc.com
SIC: 3563 Air & gas compressors
HQ: The Scott Fetzer Company
28800 Clemens Rd
Westlake OH 44145
440 892-3000

(G-10796)
PREMIER INK SYSTEMS INC (PA)
10420 N State St (45030-9501)
P.O. Box 670 (45030-0670)
PHONE..................513 367-4700
Fax: 513 367-5346
Thomas Farmer, *President*
Bridget Allen, *Purchasing*
Scott Reese, *VP Sales*
Judy Fritz, *Office Mgr*
Loren Shuler, *Manager*
EMP: 15
SALES (est): 14.3MM Privately Held
WEB: www.premierink.com
SIC: 2851 2893 2899 Lacquers, varnishes, enamels & other coatings; printing ink; chemical preparations

(G-10797)
PUTTMANN INDUSTRIES INC
Also Called: Atlas Dowel & Wood Products Co
320 N State St (45030-1146)
P.O. Box 327 (45030-0327)
PHONE..................513 202-9444
Fax: 513 202-0942
Peter Puttmann, *President*
▲ EMP: 19 EST: 1951
SQ FT: 65,000
SALES (est): 3.1MM Privately Held
WEB: www.atlasdowel.com
SIC: 2499 3965 Dowels, wood; fasteners, buttons, needles & pins

(G-10798)
QUIKRETE COMPANIES INC
Also Called: Quikrete Cincinnati
5425 Kilby Rd (45030-8910)
PHONE..................513 367-6135
Fax: 513 367-1920
Russ Smiley, *General Mgr*
Richard Curl, *Sales Staff*
Brian Tillett, *Marketing Staff*
Glen Lainhart, *Manager*
Tyler Elkins, *Manager*
EMP: 40
SQ FT: 21,340 Privately Held
WEB: www.quikrete.com
SIC: 3272 3273 Dry mixture concrete; ready-mixed concrete
HQ: The Quikrete Companies Llc
3490 Piedmont Rd Ne # 1300
Atlanta GA 30305
404 634-9100

(G-10799)
R HOUSTON SON SNDBLST SPCLISTS (PA)
115 May Dr (45030-2023)
PHONE..................513 367-5252
Fax: 513 367-1181
Jeff Houston, *President*
Cindy Kidwell, *Office Mgr*
EMP: 25
SALES (est): 2.6MM Privately Held
WEB: www.rhouston.com
SIC: 3589 Sandblasting equipment

(G-10800)
R L TORBECK INDUSTRIES INC
355 Industrial Dr (45030-1483)
PHONE..................513 367-0080
Fax: 513 367-0081
Richard L Torbeck Jr, *President*
R Stephen Millbourn, *Vice Pres*
Gerald Meab, *Mfg Mgr*
Rhonda Clark, *Accountant*
John Bohnenkamp, *Sales Mgr*
EMP: 90
SQ FT: 67,000
SALES (est): 26.9MM Privately Held
WEB: www.torbeckind.com
SIC: 3441 3499 3448 3444 Fabricated structural metal; metal household articles; prefabricated metal buildings; sheet metalwork

(G-10801)
ROBERT E MOORE
Also Called: Valley Welding Service
10430 New Biddinger Rd (45030-8720)
PHONE..................513 367-0006
Robert E Moore, *Owner*
Robert Moore, *Owner*
Linda Moore, *Co-Owner*
EMP: 4 EST: 1945
SQ FT: 3,760
SALES (est): 420.1K Privately Held
SIC: 7692 Welding repair

(G-10802)
SIMPSON & SONS INC
10220 Harrison Ave (45030-1938)
PHONE..................513 367-0152
Fax: 513 367-9409
Joseph A Simpson, *President*
James Simpson, *Vice Pres*
EMP: 14
SQ FT: 10,500
SALES (est): 1.5MM Privately Held
SIC: 4789 7692 Railroad maintenance & repair services; welding repair

(G-10803)
SNYDER ELECTRONICS
5501 Lawrenceburg Rd # 100 (45030-8501)
P.O. Box 111 (45030-0111)
PHONE..................513 738-7200
William Snyder, *Owner*
◆ EMP: 5
SQ FT: 9,000
SALES (est): 210K Privately Held
SIC: 3651 Audio electronic systems

(G-10804)
SOFFSEAL INC
104 May Dr (45030-2024)
PHONE..................513 367-0028
Fax: 513 367-5506
Gary Anderson, *President*
Jackie Schaefer, *Plant Mgr*
Rose Byrd, *Purch Mgr*
Donna Anderson, *Admin Sec*
▲ EMP: 40
SQ FT: 24,000
SALES (est): 8.2MM Privately Held
WEB: www.soffseal.com
SIC: 3069 3061 3053 Rubber automotive products; mechanical rubber goods; gaskets, packing & sealing devices

(G-10805)
STELTER AND BRINCK INC
201 Sales Ave (45030-1472)
PHONE..................513 367-9300
Fax: 513 367-1524
Joseph A Brinck II, *President*
Larry Brinck, *Principal*
Henry Stelter, *Principal*
Mary B Turpen, *Principal*
Melanie Brinck, *Marketing Mgr*
EMP: 35 EST: 1940
SQ FT: 17,000
SALES (est): 9.1MM Privately Held
WEB: www.stelterbrinck.com
SIC: 3564 3567 3494 3433 Blowers & fans; industrial furnaces & ovens; valves & pipe fittings; heating equipment, except electric

(G-10806)
STOP STICK LTD
365 Industrial Dr (45030-1483)
PHONE..................513 202-5500
Andrew Morrison, *President*
Scott Trentel, *Accounts Mgr*
Louis M Groen, *Mng Member*
Ken French, *Director*
Clifford J Robson,
▲ EMP: 27
SQ FT: 10,000
SALES (est): 5.8MM Privately Held
WEB: www.stopstick.com
SIC: 3315 Nails, spikes, brads & similar items

(G-10807)
SUPERIOR STRUCTURES INC
320 N State St (45030-1146)
P.O. Box 26 (45030-0026)
PHONE..................513 942-5954
Chris Harrison, *General Mgr*
Tim Bischel, *Principal*
Brandon Vanderyt, *Office Mgr*
Charles Hatfield, *Admin Sec*
EMP: 10
SQ FT: 7,500
SALES (est): 2.2MM Privately Held
SIC: 3448 1531 Greenhouses: prefabricated metal; operative builders

(G-10808)
SUR-SEAL CORPORATION
10053 Simonson Rd (45030-2193)
PHONE..................513 574-8500
Mike Kasselmann, *Manager*
EMP: 5
SALES (corp-wide): 40MM Privately Held
SIC: 3053 Gaskets, all materials; packing, rubber
PA: Sur-Seal Corporation
6156 Wesselman Rd
Cincinnati OH 45248
513 574-8500

(G-10809)
TASI HOLDINGS INC (PA)
Also Called: Tasi Group
10100 Progress Way (45030-1295)
PHONE..................513 202-5182
David Huberfield, *CEO*
Jack Goffena, *CFO*
EMP: 23
SALES (est): 18.7MM Privately Held
SIC: 3823 3629 Industrial flow & liquid measuring instruments; electronic generation equipment

(G-10810)
TENKOTTE TOPS INC
11029 State Route 128 (45030-9710)
P.O. Box 592, Miamitown (45041-0592)
PHONE..................513 738-7300
Fax: 513 738-7300
Richard G Tenkotte, *President*
Diane Tenkotte, *Corp Secy*
EMP: 5
SQ FT: 4,300
SALES (est): 630.8K Privately Held
SIC: 2541 2434 Table or counter tops, plastic laminated; vanities, bathroom: wood

(G-10811)
WAYNE/SCOTT FETZER COMPANY
Also Called: Wayne Water Systems
101 Production Dr (45030-1477)
PHONE..................800 237-0987
Fax: 513 367-3229
Duane Johnson, *President*
Melissa Pasmore, *Mfg Spvr*
Susan Wilcox, *VP Finance*
Jim Hudson, *Human Res Dir*
Deb Dils, *Sales Staff*
▲ EMP: 200
SQ FT: 160,000
SALES (est): 71MM
SALES (corp-wide): 223.6B Publicly Held
SIC: 3561 5074 Pumps, domestic: water or sump; water purification equipment
HQ: The Scott Fetzer Company
28800 Clemens Rd
Westlake OH 44145
440 892-3000

(G-10812)
WHITEWATER PROCESSING CO
10964 Campbell Rd (45030-8902)
PHONE..................513 367-4133
Fax: 513 367-2426
Kelly Kopp, *President*
Steve Kopp, *President*
Kevin Kopp, *Vice Pres*
EMP: 100
SQ FT: 7,500
SALES (est): 13.3MM Privately Held
SIC: 2015 Turkey, slaughtered & dressed

Harrod
Allen County

(G-10813)
EARTH SAFE CHEMICAL LLC
8122 Faulkner Rd (45850-9730)
PHONE..................419 648-7801
John D Stephens,
John C Stephens,
EMP: 3
SALES (est): 401.9K Privately Held
SIC: 2899 Chemical preparations

Hartford
Trumbull County

(G-10814)
JONES PROCESSING
Hc 7 (44424)
P.O. Box 178 (44424-0178)
PHONE..................330 772-2193
Terry Jones, *President*
Sandra Jones, *Vice Pres*
EMP: 4 EST: 1964
SALES (est): 200K Privately Held
SIC: 2011 Meat packing plants

Hartville
Stark County

(G-10815)
A S NF PRODUCING INC
10539 Schlabach Ave Ne (44632-9134)
PHONE..................330 933-0622
Donna M Moyer, *Principal*
EMP: 3 EST: 2012
SALES (est): 162.7K Privately Held
SIC: 1311 Crude petroleum & natural gas

(G-10816)
AMERICRAFT STOR BUILDINGS LTD
1147 W Maple St (44632-8529)
PHONE..................330 877-6900
Scott Raymon, *President*
Bill Rayman, *Manager*
EMP: 5
SQ FT: 448
SALES (est): 228.8K Privately Held
SIC: 1521 2452 Patio & deck construction & repair; prefabricated wood buildings

(G-10817)
C AND J MACHINE INC
403 State Route 44 (44632-9202)
PHONE..................330 935-2170
Fax: 330 935-2170
Tim Wittensoldner, *President*
EMP: 5
SQ FT: 6,500
SALES: 1MM Privately Held
SIC: 3599 Machine shop, jobbing & repair

(G-10818)
C E KEGG INC (PA)
Also Called: Kegg Pipe Organ Builders
1184 Woodland St Sw (44632-8304)
PHONE..................330 877-8800
Charles E Kegg, *President*
Ellen Kegg, *Admin Sec*
EMP: 5
SQ FT: 5,000
SALES (est): 738.6K Privately Held
WEB: www.keggorgan.com
SIC: 3931 Pipes, organ

(G-10819)
CNB MACHINING AND MFG LLC
1052 Manning Rd Nw (44632-9505)
PHONE..................330 877-7920
Richard Reaven, *Principal*
EMP: 5
SALES (est): 387.9K Privately Held
SIC: 3999 Manufacturing industries

(G-10820)
DMC WELDING INCORPORATED
9975 Market Ave N (44632-8720)
PHONE..................330 877-1935
Daniel Mihalik, *President*
EMP: 3
SALES (est): 250K Privately Held
SIC: 3441 1799 Fabricated structural metal; welding on site

(G-10821)
GROW WITH ME- CREATIONS
Also Called: Grow With ME Bibs
14236 Wade Ave Ne (44632-9336)
PHONE....................800 850-1889
Fax: 330 935-0427
Diane Pullen, *Owner*
EMP: 5
SALES: 30K **Privately Held**
WEB: www.growwithme.com
SIC: 2385 2211 Bibs, waterproof: made
from purchased materials; blankets &
blanketings, cotton

(G-10822)
HARTVILLE CHOCOLATES INC
Also Called: Hartville Chocolate Factory
114 S Prospect Ave (44632-8906)
P.O. Box 1360 (44632-1360)
PHONE....................330 877-1999
Mary L Barton, *President*
EMP: 18
SQ FT: 3,200
SALES (est): 3.1MM **Privately Held**
WEB: www.hartvillechocolatefactory.com
SIC: 2066 5441 5999 Chocolate; candy;
cake decorating supplies

(G-10823)
HARTVILLE LOCKER SERVICE INC
119 Sunnyside St Sw (44632-8933)
P.O. Box 7 (44632-0007)
PHONE....................330 877-9547
James Young, *President*
Jill E Young, *Corp Secy*
EMP: 8
SQ FT: 5,500
SALES (est): 815.7K **Privately Held**
SIC: 2011 Meat packing plants

(G-10824)
HARTVILLE PLASTICS INC
322 Lake Ave Ne (44632-9683)
PHONE....................330 877-9090
Robert Andrews, *President*
EMP: 8
SALES (est): 1MM **Privately Held**
SIC: 3089 Plastic processing

(G-10825)
JERRY MOORE INC (PA)
1010 Sunnyside St Sw (44632-9094)
P.O. Box 1180 (44632-1180)
PHONE....................330 877-1155
Fax: 330 877-2612
Gerald H Moore, *President*
Robert D Moore, *Vice Pres*
John N Teeple, *Admin Sec*
EMP: 4
SQ FT: 3,000
SALES (est): 1.7MM **Privately Held**
SIC: 1311 Crude petroleum production;
natural gas production

(G-10826)
KINGSWAY ART & SIGN
1555 Andrews St Ne (44632-9018)
PHONE....................330 877-6241
Fax: 330 877-1154
Lloyd King, *President*
Mary J King, *Treasurer*
EMP: 3
SALES (est): 300.6K **Privately Held**
SIC: 3993 Signs & advertising specialties

(G-10827)
KNOWLES PRESS INC
Also Called: Hartville News
316 E Maple St (44632-8880)
P.O. Box 428 (44632-0428)
PHONE....................330 877-9345
Fax: 330 877-1364
Rosalee Haines, *President*
Patrick Haines, *Site Mgr*
Zoe Werner, *Opers Staff*
Jacquelin Vaughn, *Admin Sec*
EMP: 5
SQ FT: 2,400
SALES: 235K **Privately Held**
SIC: 2711 2752 Commercial printing &
newspaper publishing combined; litho-
graphing on metal

(G-10828)
L C F INC
Also Called: Love Chocolate Factory
114 S Prospect Ave (44632-8906)
P.O. Box 1360 (44632-1360)
PHONE....................330 877-3322
Fax: 330 877-1100
Robert M Barton, *President*
▼ EMP: 18
SQ FT: 12,000
SALES (est): 2.3MM **Privately Held**
SIC: 2066 Chocolate candy, solid

(G-10829)
LOUISVILLE MOLDED PRODUCTS
Also Called: Lmp
13122 Duquette Ave Ne (44632-8829)
PHONE....................330 877-9740
Fax: 330 877-9745
Robert Osolinski, *President*
Charles Lynn, *Vice Pres*
EMP: 6
SQ FT: 40,000
SALES (est): 660K **Privately Held**
WEB: www.lmp.com
SIC: 2821 Polyurethane resins

(G-10830)
MITCHELL PIPING LLC
1101 Sunnyside St Sw C (44632-9066)
PHONE....................330 245-0258
Scott Mitchell, *President*
EMP: 30
SALES (est): 950K **Privately Held**
SIC: 3498 Fabricated pipe & fittings

(G-10831)
QUALITY MACHINE
6788 Center St Ne (44632-9183)
PHONE....................330 877-6163
Charles Smyers, *Principal*
EMP: 3
SALES (est): 278.2K **Privately Held**
SIC: 3599 Machine shop, jobbing & repair

(G-10832)
RANDOLPH TOOL COMPANY INC
750 Wales Dr (44632-8852)
PHONE....................330 877-4923
Patrick Franze, *President*
Lisa M Franze, *Treasurer*
EMP: 12
SQ FT: 5,800
SALES (est): 2.2MM **Privately Held**
WEB: www.randolphtool.com
SIC: 3599 3423 Machine shop, jobbing &
repair; knives, agricultural or industrial

(G-10833)
SCANACON INCORPORATED
950 Wales Dr (44632-8856)
PHONE....................330 877-7600
Fax: 330 877-9831
Sven Hedman, *Ch of Bd*
Kevin Wolf, *President*
Shannon Gledhill, *Project Mgr*
Andy Ruan, *CFO*
Connie Miller, *Controller*
▲ EMP: 6
SALES (est): 1.9MM
SALES (corp-wide): 721.6K **Privately Held**
WEB: www.scanacon.com
SIC: 3565 Canning machinery, food
HQ: Scanacon Ab
Bergkallavagen 36c
Sollentuna 192 7
856 482-300

(G-10834)
SCOTT PROCESS SYSTEMS INC
Also Called: Spsi
1160 Sunnyside St Sw (44632-9098)
PHONE....................330 877-2350
Fax: 330 877-1524
Frank Diener, *Vice Pres*
Jason Kinsley, *Plant Mgr*
Donald Nauer, *Sales Staff*
Tom Kyner, *Marketing Staff*
Kevin Schaack, *Director*
▲ EMP: 240
SQ FT: 30,000

SALES (est): 97.5MM
SALES (corp-wide): 44.2MM **Privately Held**
WEB: www.scottprocess.com
SIC: 3498 Piping systems for pulp paper &
chemical industries
HQ: Industrial Piping, Inc.
212 S Tryon St Ste 1050
Charlotte NC 28281
704 588-1100

(G-10835)
TRANSEL CORPORATION
Also Called: Transel Technologies
123 E South St (45032)
PHONE....................513 897-3442
Darrell McKinney, *President*
Kimberly McKinney, *Vice Pres*
EMP: 5
SQ FT: 3,792
SALES: 500K **Privately Held**
WEB: www.transeltech.com
SIC: 5999 3663 8742 Communication
equipment; radio & TV communications
equipment; management consulting serv-
ices

(G-10836)
ALTIVIA PETROCHEMICALS LLC
1019 Haverhill Ohio (45636)
PHONE....................740 532-3420
Mark Tipton, *Manager*
EMP: 50
SALES (corp-wide): 8.9MM **Privately Held**
SIC: 2865 Phenol, alkylated & cumene
PA: Altivia Petrochemicals, Llc
1100 La St Ste 4800
Houston TX 77002
713 658-9000

(G-10837)
CUSTOM ASSEMBLY INC
2952 Road 107 (45851-9638)
PHONE....................419 622-3040
Fax: 419 622-3012
George Keysor, *President*
Steven R Plummer, *Principal*
Gus A Schlatter, *Principal*
Sharon Keysor, *Vice Pres*
Connie Krzesinski, *Office Mgr*
EMP: 50
SQ FT: 60,000
SALES (est): 9.7MM **Privately Held**
SIC: 3751 Motorcycles, bicycles & parts

(G-10838)
DRAINAGE PRODUCTS INC
100 W Main St (45851)
P.O. Box 61 (45851-0061)
PHONE....................419 622-6951
Fax: 419 622-6911
Craig A Stoller, *President*
Thomas Coy, *Corp Secy*
EMP: 25 **EST:** 1978
SALES (est): 3.9MM **Privately Held**
SIC: 3084 Plastics pipe

(G-10839)
HAVILAND CULVERT COMPANY
100 W Main (45851)
P.O. Box 97 (45851-0097)
PHONE....................419 622-6951
Russell W Stoller, *President*
Thomas A Gordon, *Corp Secy*
EMP: 7

SALES (est): 911.9K **Privately Held**
SIC: 3272 Pipe, concrete or lined with concrete

(G-10840)
HAVILAND DRAINAGE PRODUCTS CO (PA)
100 W Main St (45851)
PHONE....................419 622-4611
Russell Stoller, *President*
Todd Stoller, *Corp Secy*
EMP: 17 **EST:** 1924
SQ FT: 1,000
SALES (est): 50.8MM **Privately Held**
SIC: 3259 Drain tile, clay

(G-10841)
HAVILAND PLASTIC PRODUCTS CO
119 W Main St (45851)
P.O. Box 38 (45851-0038)
PHONE....................419 622-3110
Fax: 419 622-3111
Craig Stoller, *President*
Todd Stoller, *Corp Secy*
▼ EMP: 26
SALES (est): 8MM **Privately Held**
WEB: www.havilandplastics.com
SIC: 3089 Fittings for pipe, plastic

(G-10842)
MODERN PLASTICS RECOVERY INC
100 Main St (45851)
P.O. Box 38 (45851-0038)
PHONE....................419 622-4611
Craig Stoller, *President*
Renae Goings, *Asst Controller*
EMP: 16
SALES (est): 3.5MM **Privately Held**
SIC: 2821 Plastics materials & resins

(G-10843)
COBURN INC (PA)
636 Ashland Cnty Rd 30 A (44838)
P.O. Box 447, Ashland (44805-0447)
PHONE....................419 368-4051
Fax: 419 281-4312
Charles Zimmerman, *CEO*
Todd Zimmerman, *President*
Eric Feeman, *Warehouse Mgr*
Sharon Roose, *Purch Mgr*
John Spreng, *Sales Mgr*
EMP: 65
SQ FT: 82,000
SALES (est): 15.3MM **Privately Held**
SIC: 2631 Container, packaging &
boxboard; folding boxboard

(G-10844)
JBM TECHNOLOGIES INC
1926 State Rte 179 (44838)
P.O. Box 108 (44838-0108)
PHONE....................419 368-4362
Leslie W Jordan, *President*
EMP: 5
SQ FT: 10,000
SALES (est): 596.1K **Privately Held**
SIC: 3053 Gaskets & sealing devices; gas-
kets, all materials

(G-10845)
ATLANTIC INERTIAL SYSTEMS INC
781 Irving Wick Dr W (43056-9492)
PHONE....................740 788-3800
Deborah Barber, *General Mgr*
Larry Anderson, *Mfg Staff*
Anthony Falzone, *Engineer*
Mark Guinn, *Engineer*
Geoffrey D Ruddenow, *Engineer*
EMP: 30

▲ = Import ▼=Export
◆ =Import/Export

SALES (corp-wide): 57.2B **Publicly Held**
WEB: www.condorpacific.com
SIC: 3812 Gyroscopes
HQ: Atlantic Inertial Systems Inc.
250 Knotter Dr
Cheshire CT 06410
203 250-3500

(G-10846)
DATA IMAGE
2345 Gratiot Rd Se (43056-9743)
PHONE..................................740 763-7017
Dave Speelman, *Owner*
EMP: 30
SALES (est): 1.6MM **Privately Held**
SIC: 2759 Laser printing

(G-10847)
HARTMAN DISTRIBUTING LLC
1262 Bluejack Ln (43056-8228)
PHONE..................................740 616-7764
Troy Hartman, *CEO*
EMP: 84
SALES (est): 4.9MM **Privately Held**
SIC: 2759 Screen printing

(G-10848)
KAISER ALUMINUM FAB PDTS LLC
Also Called: Kaiser Aluminum Newark Works
600 Kaiser Dr (43056-1088)
PHONE..................................740 522-1151
Fax: 740 522-0435
Laura Wiles, *Production*
Larry Spring, *Purch Agent*
Joe Beres, *Engineer*
Ray Plewa, *Engineer*
Simon Michael, *Controller*
EMP: 250
SALES (corp-wide): 1.3B **Publicly Held**
WEB: www.kaisertwd.com
SIC: 3355 3334 Rods, rolled, aluminum; primary aluminum
HQ: Kaiser Aluminum Fabricated Products, Llc
27422 Portola Pkwy # 200
Foothill Ranch CA 92610
949 614-1740

(G-10849)
KPS NAPA
441 Hopewell Dr (43056-1547)
PHONE..................................740 522-9445
Howard Warner, *Owner*
EMP: 15
SALES (est): 640K **Privately Held**
SIC: 3711 Automobile bodies, passenger car, not including engine, etc.

(G-10850)
MATTERWORKS
2135 James Pkwy (43056-4002)
PHONE..................................740 200-0071
Thomas Miller, *President*
EMP: 3 EST: 2010
SALES (est): 229.6K **Privately Held**
SIC: 2822 Ethylene-propylene rubbers, EPDM polymers

(G-10851)
POLYMER TECH & SVCS INC
Also Called: Pts
1835 James Pkwy (43056-1092)
PHONE..................................740 929-5500
Fax: 740 929-5501
Sharad Thakkar, *President*
Scott Ritz, *Plant Mgr*
Meena Thakkar, *Accounts Mgr*
EMP: 35
SQ FT: 50,000
SALES (est): 8.7MM **Privately Held**
WEB: www.polymertechnologiesinc.com
SIC: 3089 2611 Casting of plastic; pulp mills

(G-10852)
R D HOLDER OIL CO INC
1000 Keller Dr (43056-8055)
PHONE..................................740 522-3136
EMP: 5
SALES (corp-wide): 35MM **Privately Held**
SIC: 1311 Crude petroleum & natural gas

PA: R. D. Holder Oil Co., Inc.
600 N Dayton Lakeview Rd
New Carlisle OH 45344
800 243-0432

(G-10853)
RAMP CREEK III LTD
1100 Thornwood Dr Lot 1 (43056-9501)
P.O. Box 240, Reynoldsburg (43068-0240)
PHONE..................................740 522-0660
Fax: 740 522-0702
Roberto Ditommaso, *Principal*
EMP: 6
SALES (est): 424.3K **Privately Held**
SIC: 3272 Housing components, prefabricated concrete

(G-10854)
RESINOID ENGINEERING CORP
2040 James Pkwy (43056-1031)
PHONE..................................740 928-2220
Fax: 740 929-2036
R Young, *Controller*
John Maurer, *Branch Mgr*
EMP: 20
SALES (corp-wide): 42.4MM **Privately Held**
WEB: www.resinoid.com
SIC: 3089 3714 3625 Plastic hardware & building products; motor vehicle parts & accessories; relays & industrial controls
PA: Resinoid Engineering Corp
251 O Neill Dr
Hebron OH 43025
847 673-1050

(G-10855)
SAMUEL STRAPPING SYSTEMS INC
1455 James Pkwy (43056-4007)
PHONE..................................740 522-2500
Jay Matthews, *Vice Pres*
Jay Jones, *Manager*
David Joos, *Manager*
EMP: 100
SALES (corp-wide): 1.9B **Privately Held**
WEB: www.samuelstrapping.com
SIC: 3565 3089 5085 5084 Wrapping machines; plastic processing; industrial supplies; industrial machinery & equipment; packaging materials
HQ: Samuel Strapping Systems, Inc.
1401 Davey Rd Ste 300
Woodridge IL 60517
630 783-8900

(G-10856)
SAND HOLLOW WINERY
12558 Sand Hollow Rd (43056-9789)
PHONE..................................740 323-3959
Jim Young, *Principal*
EMP: 3
SALES (est): 158.3K **Privately Held**
SIC: 2084 Wines

(G-10857)
SITE TECH (PA)
75 Central Pkwy (43056-1253)
PHONE..................................740 522-0019
Phil Jones, *Principal*
EMP: 4
SALES (est): 723.9K **Privately Held**
SIC: 3571 Electronic computers

(G-10858)
XPERION E&E USA LLC
1475 James Pkwy (43056-4007)
PHONE..................................740 788-9560
Sean Ellen, *Mng Member*
EMP: 25
SQ FT: 50,000
SALES (est): 6.9MM
SALES (corp-wide): 166.6MM **Privately Held**
SIC: 3624 Fibers, carbon & graphite
HQ: Xperion Energy & Environment Gmbh
Planckstr. 15
Herford 32052
561 585-490

Hebron
Licking County

(G-10859)
4W SERVICES
7901 Minecaster Rd (43025)
PHONE..................................614 554-5427
Donald White, *Owner*
EMP: 15
SALES: 300K **Privately Held**
SIC: 3715 8999 Semitrailers for truck tractors; artists & artists' studios

(G-10860)
ALLIED TUBE & CONDUIT CORP
250 Capital Dr (43025-9489)
PHONE..................................740 928-1018
Scott Shipley, *Branch Mgr*
EMP: 12 **Publicly Held**
WEB: www.alliedtube.com
SIC: 3644 Electric conduits & fittings
HQ: Allied Tube & Conduit Corporation
16100 Lathrop Ave
Harvey IL 60426
708 339-1610

(G-10861)
ARMORSOURCE LLC
3600 Hebron Rd (43025-9664)
PHONE..................................740 928-0070
Yoav Kapah, *CEO*
Shachar Bernhard, *Principal*
Don Blake, *Exec VP*
Donald Blake, *Exec VP*
Carl Fulmore, *Vice Pres*
▼ EMP: 20
SALES (est): 6.5MM **Privately Held**
SIC: 2821 Plastics materials & resins

(G-10862)
CLEARWATER WOOD GROUP LLC
4401 Hunts Landing Rd (43025-9493)
PHONE..................................567 644-9951
Aaron Mayes, *Mng Member*
Girard Besanceney, *Mng Member*
▲ EMP: 4 EST: 2010
SALES: 2MM **Privately Held**
SIC: 2511 Wood household furniture

(G-10863)
COVESTRO LLC
Newark Industrial Park (43025)
PHONE..................................740 929-2015
Dustin McDonald, *Production*
Duane Brumage, *Engineer*
Lora Rand, *Manager*
Norman Trowbridge, *Maintence Staff*
EMP: 150
SALES (corp-wide): 49.4B **Privately Held**
SIC: 2822 2821 Synthetic rubber; plastics materials & resins
HQ: Covestro Llc
1 Covestro Cir
Pittsburgh PA 15205
412 413-2000

(G-10864)
DAVID OGILBEE
1881 Beaver Run Rd Se (43025-9651)
PHONE..................................740 929-2638
David Ogilbee, *CEO*
EMP: 3
SALES (est): 196.2K **Privately Held**
SIC: 3715 Truck trailers

(G-10865)
FORCEONE LLC
3600 Hebron Rd (43025-9664)
PHONE..................................513 939-1018
Lewis Edward, *Plant Mgr*
Steven Plummer, *Plant Mgr*
Kurt Gembolis, *QC Dir*
Larra Stojohen, *Manager*
Dannie Dubley,
EMP: 30
SQ FT: 17,000
SALES (est): 4.8MM **Privately Held**
WEB: www.hardarmor.com
SIC: 3842 Bulletproof vests

(G-10866)
GE INFRASTRUCTURE SENSING INC
611 O Neill Dr (43025-9680)
PHONE..................................740 928-7010
Elizabeth May, *Branch Mgr*
EMP: 301
SALES (corp-wide): 123.6B **Publicly Held**
SIC: 3823 Moisture meters, industrial process type
HQ: Ge Infrastructure Sensing, Inc.
1100 Technology Park Dr # 100
Billerica MA 01821
978 437-1000

(G-10867)
GENERAL ELECTRIC COMPANY
611 O Neill Dr (43025-9659)
PHONE..................................740 928-7010
Fax: 740 928-4702
Patrick Hannon, *Engineer*
Ken Horn, *Maintence Staff*
EMP: 9
SALES (corp-wide): 123.6B **Publicly Held**
SIC: 3297 Crucibles: graphite, magnesite, chrome, silica, etc.
PA: General Electric Company
41 Farnsworth St
Boston MA 02210
617 443-3000

(G-10868)
GLUTEN-FREE EXPRESSIONS
520 E Main St (43025-9702)
PHONE..................................740 928-0338
Cyndi Baughman, *Principal*
EMP: 4
SALES (est): 183.3K **Privately Held**
SIC: 2051 Cakes, bakery: except frozen

(G-10869)
HARRY AND DAVID LLC
Also Called: Harry and David's
500 Reliance Dr (43025-9205)
PHONE..................................740 929-7100
Greg Wilson, *Senior VP*
Steve Dow, *Vice Pres*
Stephanie Nelson, *Human Res Dir*
Bryan Gandee, *Manager*
Robert Adams, *Consultant*
EMP: 125
SALES (corp-wide): 1.1B **Publicly Held**
WEB: www.bco.com
SIC: 2834 Vitamin, nutrient & hematinic preparations for human use
HQ: Harry And David, Llc
2500 S Pacific Hwy
Medford OR 97501
541 864-2500

(G-10870)
HENDRICKSON INTERNATIONAL CORP
Also Called: Hendrickson Auxiliary Axles
277 N High St (43025-8008)
PHONE..................................740 929-5600
Fax: 740 929-5601
Mike Keeler, *General Mgr*
Lisa Kirkingburg, *VP Mfg*
Bill Lewis, *Mfg Dir*
Sherrill Moore, *Opers Mgr*
Mike Blake, *Prdtn Mgr*
EMP: 78
SALES (corp-wide): 1B **Privately Held**
SIC: 3714 3493 3089 5084 Motor vehicle parts & accessories; steel springs, except wire; plastic containers, except foam; industrial machinery & equipment; truck & bus bodies
HQ: Hendrickson International Corporation
500 Park Blvd Ste 450
Itasca IL 60143
630 874-9700

(G-10871)
HOLLYS CUSTOM PRINT INC
1001 O Neill Dr (43025-9409)
P.O. Box 4454, Newark (43058-4454)
PHONE..................................740 928-2697
Fax: 740 928-8004
Steve Hollingshead, *President*
Lisa Wetzel, *Manager*
EMP: 35 EST: 1983

GEOGRAPHIC

SQ FT: 22,500
SALES (est): 3.3MM **Privately Held**
SIC: 2752 2759 Commercial printing, lithographic; commercial printing

(G-10872)
LEAR CORPORATION
Also Called: Renosol Seating
180 N High St (43025-9011)
P.O. Box 640 (43025-0640)
PHONE......................................740 928-4358
Fax: 740 928-4458
Jeff O'Sickey, *Plant Mgr*
Derek Bujak, *Materials Mgr*
Mark Dobransky, *Materials Mgr*
EMP: 50
SALES (corp-wide): 18.5B **Publicly Held**
SIC: 3714 Motor vehicle parts & accessories
PA: Lear Corporation
21557 Telegraph Rd
Southfield MI 48033
248 447-1500

(G-10873)
MCKINLEYS MEADERY LLC ◒
4412 Keller Rd (43025-9630)
PHONE......................................740 928-0229
Jarrod McKinley, *Principal*
EMP: 3 EST: 2016
SALES (est): 68.6K **Privately Held**
SIC: 2082 Malt beverages

(G-10874)
MOMENTIVE PERFORMANCE MTLS INC
611 O Neill Dr (43025-9680)
PHONE......................................740 928-7010
Jim White, *Vice Pres*
Hannon Patrick, *Opers Mgr*
Dorsey Hessler, *Opers Staff*
Mordhorst Steve, *Marketing Mgr*
Cherly Glaton, *Manager*
EMP: 195
SALES (corp-wide): 2.2B **Publicly Held**
SIC: 2869 3479 Silicones; coating of metals with silicon
HQ: Momentive Performance Materials Inc.
260 Hudson River Rd
Waterford NY 12188
518 237-3330

(G-10875)
MPW INDUSTRIAL SVCS GROUP INC (PA)
9711 Lancaster Rd (43025-9764)
PHONE......................................740 927-8790
Fax: 740 928-1077
Monte R Black, *CEO*
Jared Black, *President*
Adam Black, *General Mgr*
Gary Babaryk, *Area Mgr*
John Bergin, *Area Mgr*
EMP: 105 EST: 1972
SQ FT: 24,000
SALES (est): 228.6MM **Privately Held**
WEB: www.mpwgroup.com
SIC: 7349 8744 3589 Cleaning service, industrial or commercial; facilities support services; commercial cleaning equipment

(G-10876)
MTI ACQUISITION LLC
Also Called: Molding Technologies
85 N High St (43025)
P.O. Box 730 (43025-0730)
PHONE......................................740 929-2065
Angela Baumgartner, *CFO*
Jesse Downhour, *Mng Member*
EMP: 25
SQ FT: 55,000
SALES (est): 4.5MM **Privately Held**
WEB: www.moldingtech.com
SIC: 3089 Plastic hardware & building products

(G-10877)
MUSCLE FEAST LLC
101 Longbow Dr (43025-8024)
PHONE......................................888 734-3634
EMP: 5 **Privately Held**
SIC: 2023 Mfg Dry/Evaporated Dairy Products
PA: Muscle Feast, Llc
2447 Crestview Woods Ct
Newark OH 43025

(G-10878)
MUSCLE FEAST LLC (PA)
101 Longbow Dr (43025-8024)
PHONE......................................740 877-8808
Jonathan Sean Gillespie,
EMP: 11
SQ FT: 16,000
SALES: 2.3MM **Privately Held**
SIC: 5149 2023 Health foods; dietary supplements, dairy & non-dairy based

(G-10879)
OHIO METAL TECHNOLOGIES INC
470 John Alford Pkwy (43025-9437)
PHONE......................................740 928-8288
Toshi Hara, *President*
Chuck Shearer, *General Mgr*
Masao Segawa, *Vice Pres*
Cecilia Walters, *Safety Mgr*
Craig Councell, *Purchasing*
▲ EMP: 80
SQ FT: 20,600
SALES (est): 27.3MM **Privately Held**
WEB: www.ohiometal.net
SIC: 3462 Automotive & internal combustion engine forgings

(G-10880)
PLASTIPAK PACKAGING INC
Also Called: Constar International
610 O Neill Dr Bldg 22 (43025-9680)
PHONE......................................740 928-4435
Fax: 740 928-4483
Jerry Clark, *Plant Mgr*
Darrick Foster, *Purchasing*
Larry Drake, *QC Dir*
Brian Dunlap, *Manager*
Kim Green, *CTO*
EMP: 125
SALES (corp-wide): 36.3MM **Privately Held**
WEB: www.constarllc.com
SIC: 3089 3085 Plastic containers, except foam; plastics bottles
HQ: Plastipak Packaging, Inc.
41605 Ann Arbor Rd E
Plymouth MI 48170
734 455-3600

(G-10881)
RESINOID ENGINEERING CORP (PA)
251 O Neill Dr (43025-9680)
PHONE......................................847 673-1050
Robert C Herbst, *President*
Clarence A Herbst Jr, *Chairman*
Jana Souslin, *Production*
Joe Wiley, *Purch Agent*
Chad Morgan, *Engineer*
▲ EMP: 58 EST: 1939
SQ FT: 70,000
SALES (est): 42.4MM **Privately Held**
WEB: www.resinoid.com
SIC: 2821 3089 6514 3083 Molding compounds, plastics; injection molding of plastics; dwelling operators, except apartments; laminated plastics plate & sheet

(G-10882)
RR DONNELLEY & SONS COMPANY
Also Called: R R Donnelley
190 Milliken Dr (43025-9657)
PHONE......................................740 928-6110
Phill Annarino, *Empl Rel Mgr*
Jeff Gebhart, *Branch Mgr*
EMP: 280
SALES (corp-wide): 6.9B **Publicly Held**
SIC: 2759 Business forms: printing
PA: R. R. Donnelley & Sons Company
35 W Wacker Dr Ste 3650
Chicago IL 60601
312 326-8000

(G-10883)
S R DOOR INC (PA)
Also Called: Seal-Rite Door
1120 O Neill Dr (43025-9409)
P.O. Box 460 (43025-0460)
PHONE......................................740 927-3558
Fax: 740 927-3690
Scott A Miller, *President*
Glen Miller, *Vice Pres*
EMP: 80

SQ FT: 75,000
SALES (est): 12.6MM **Privately Held**
WEB: www.seal-ritedoor.com
SIC: 2431 3442 3211 5031 Doors, wood; windows & window parts & trim, wood; metal doors; construction glass; lumber, plywood & millwork

(G-10884)
SCHWEBEL BAKING COMPANY
121 O Neill Dr (43025-9680)
PHONE......................................330 783-2860
Fax: 740 928-4811
Alyson Winick, *Marketing Mgr*
John Phillips, *Manager*
EMP: 74
SALES (corp-wide): 170MM **Privately Held**
WEB: www.schwebels.com
SIC: 5461 2051 Bakeries; bread, cake & related products
PA: Schwebel Baking Company
965 E Midlothian Blvd
Youngstown OH 44502
330 783-2860

(G-10885)
SMARTBILL LTD
1050 O Neill Dr (43025-9409)
P.O. Box 105 (43025-0105)
PHONE......................................740 928-6909
Denise Hess, *Manager*
Sherry Obrien, *Executive*
Robin Hess,
Randy W Hess,
EMP: 17
SQ FT: 10,000
SALES (est): 4.1MM **Privately Held**
WEB: www.smartbillcorp.com
SIC: 2759 Business forms: printing

(G-10886)
STATE INDUSTRIAL PRODUCTS CORP
Also Called: State Chemical Manufacturing
383 N High St (43025-9436)
PHONE......................................740 929-5800
Kale Moberg, *Branch Mgr*
EMP: 21
SALES (corp-wide): 107.9MM **Privately Held**
SIC: 2841 5072 Soap: granulated, liquid, cake, flaked or chip; bolts, nuts & screws
PA: State Industrial Products Corporation
5915 Landerbrook Dr # 300
Cleveland OH 44124
877 747-6986

(G-10887)
SUNFIELD INC
116 Enterprise Dr (43025-9200)
PHONE......................................740 928-0404
Fax: 740 928-2002
Norio Hirotani, *President*
Chuck Curran, *Plant Mgr*
Kenny A Davis, *Safety Mgr*
Donna Estep, *Production*
Joe Boyer, *Sales Mgr*
▲ EMP: 70
SQ FT: 33,000
SALES (corp-wide): 661.3K **Privately Held**
SIC: 3469 Stamping metal for the trade
HQ: Ikeda Manufacturing Co., Ltd.
135-3, Nishishinmachi
Ota GNM 373-0
276 313-131

(G-10888)
TENCATE ADVANCED ARMOR USA INC
1051 O Neill Dr (43025-9409)
PHONE......................................740 928-0326
Terence M Keegan, *President*
Stephen Simmerer, *President*
Joe Glovier, *Vice Pres*
Dan Tuttle, *Opers Staff*
Dean Busack, *Controller*
▲ EMP: 83
SQ FT: 120,000
SALES (est): 24.8MM **Privately Held**
WEB: www.composix.com
SIC: 3229 3795 Yarn, fiberglass; tanks & tank components

HQ: Royal Ten Cate (Usa), Inc.
365 S Holland Dr
Pendergrass GA 30567
706 693-2226

(G-10889)
THK MANUFACTURING AMERICA INC
471 N High St (43025-9012)
P.O. Box 759 (43025-0759)
PHONE......................................740 928-1415
Fax: 740 928-1418
Nobuyuki Maki, *President*
Marlene McCallum, *Opers Mgr*
Andrew Lower, *Project Engr*
Clay Hooper, *Maintence Staff*
▲ EMP: 160
SQ FT: 400,000
SALES (est): 44.2MM
SALES (corp-wide): 2B **Privately Held**
WEB: www.thk.com
SIC: 3823 3469 Industrial instrmnts msrmnt display/control process variable; machine parts, stamped or pressed metal
HQ: T H K Holdings Of America Llc
200 Commerce Dr
Schaumburg IL 60173
847 310-1111

(G-10890)
TI GROUP AUTO SYSTEMS LLC
Bundy Tubing Div
3600 Hebron Rd (43025-9664)
PHONE......................................740 929-2049
Fax: 740 928-4878
Don Roberts, *Purchasing*
Dan Lilly, *Controller*
Tom Smith, *Controller*
Mark Lanancusa, *Manager*
EMP: 250
SALES (corp-wide): 1.7B **Privately Held**
WEB: www.tiautomotive.com
SIC: 3317 3714 3498 Steel pipe & tubes; motor vehicle parts & accessories; fabricated pipe & fittings
HQ: Ti Group Automotive Systems, Llc
2020 Taylor Rd
Auburn Hills MI 48326
248 296-8000

(G-10891)
TRANSCENDIA INC
Also Called: Dow Chemical
3700 Hebron Rd (43025-9665)
PHONE......................................740 929-5100
Lynn Wilkinson, *Purch Mgr*
Cindy Dyas, *Purchasing*
Teresa Johnson, *Personnel*
Andy Maynard, *Branch Mgr*
John Carmichael, *Manager*
EMP: 105
SALES (corp-wide): 421.8MM **Privately Held**
WEB: www.dow.com
SIC: 3081 Unsupported plastics film & sheet
PA: Transcendia, Inc.
9201 Belmont Ave
Franklin Park IL 60131
847 678-1800

(G-10892)
TRULITE GL ALUM SOLUTIONS LLC
160 N High St (43025-9011)
P.O. Box 220 (43025-0220)
PHONE......................................740 929-2443
Bill Bryan, *Engineer*
David Preston, *Engineer*
Sandra Souza, *Finance*
Jerry Hackler, *Branch Mgr*
EMP: 60 **Privately Held**
WEB: www.afg.com
SIC: 3211 5039 3231 Tempered glass; exterior flat glass: plate or window; products of purchased glass
PA: Trulite Glass & Aluminum Solutions, Llc
403 Westpark Ct Ste 201
Peachtree City GA 30269

(G-10893)
UNIPAC INC
2109 National Rd Sw (43025-9639)
PHONE......................................740 929-2000
Fax: 740 929-1265
David L De Ment, *President*

▲ = Import ▼=Export
◆ =Import/Export

Chris De Ment, *Treasurer*
Tricia Holtz, *Finance*
Leslie Cassell, *Sales Mgr*
Chris Dement, *Manager*
EMP: 22
SQ FT: 50,000
SALES (est): 8.6MM **Privately Held**
WEB: www.unipacinc.com
SIC: 2657 2653 Folding paperboard boxes; boxes, corrugated: made from purchased materials

(G-10894)
VIRGAIL INDUSTRIES INC
Also Called: Accufilm
145 S High St (43025-9690)
P.O. Box 277 (43025-0277)
PHONE.............................740 928-6001
Bradley Jay Smith, *President*
▲ **EMP:** 7
SQ FT: 11,200
SALES: 457.7K **Privately Held**
SIC: 2671 Packaging paper & plastics film, coated & laminated

Helena
Sandusky County

(G-10895)
FREMONT QUICK PRINT
2870 W Us Highway 6 (43435-9709)
PHONE.............................419 334-8808
Scott McConnell, *Owner*
EMP: 3
SALES: 120K **Privately Held**
SIC: 7334 2752 Photocopying & duplicating services; commercial printing, offset

(G-10896)
GLASS MIRROR AWARDS INC
703 County Road 26 (43435-9776)
PHONE.............................419 638-2221
Mark Leyerle, *President*
Laurie Leyerle, *Vice Pres*
EMP: 5
SALES (est): 600K **Privately Held**
SIC: 3999 5231 Plaques, picture, laminated; glass

Hicksville
Defiance County

(G-10897)
A & P TOOL INC
Also Called: APT Manufacturing Solutions
801 Industrial Dr (43526-1174)
P.O. Box 88 (43526-0088)
PHONE.............................419 542-6681
Fax: 419 542-8590
Anthony R Nighswander, *President*
Brent Staugler, *Purch Agent*
Travis Hughes, *Engineer*
EMP: 30
SALES (est): 8.6MM **Privately Held**
WEB: www.aptoolinc.com
SIC: 3541 3822 Machine tools, metal cutting type; building services monitoring controls, automatic

(G-10898)
ADROIT THINKING INC
Also Called: 5-Acre Mill
10860 State Route 2 (43526-9366)
PHONE.............................419 542-9363
Tim Becker, *President*
Mary Becker, *Vice Pres*
EMP: 17
SQ FT: 28,000
SALES (est): 2.3MM **Privately Held**
SIC: 2499 Decorative wood & woodwork

(G-10899)
ARC SOLUTIONS INC
605 Industrial Dr (43526-1177)
P.O. Box 264 (43526-0264)
PHONE.............................419 542-9272
Dennis Vetter, *President*
EMP: 10
SALES (est): 1.5MM **Privately Held**
WEB: www.arcsolutions.com
SIC: 7692 Welding repair

(G-10900)
AVALIGN TECHNOLOGIES INC (HQ)
801 Industrial Dr (43526-1174)
PHONE.............................419 542-7743
Forrest Whittaker, *CEO*
Kevin L Countryman, *President*
Kalli Countryman, *Vice Pres*
Brad Schlegel, *Engineer*
John Rapes, *CFO*
EMP: 12
SQ FT: 50,000
SALES (est): 13.4MM
SALES (corp-wide): 302.4MM **Privately Held**
WEB: www.nemcomed.net
SIC: 3842 3841 Splints, pneumatic & wood; surgical & medical instruments
PA: Roundtable Healthcare Partners, Lp
272 E Deerpath Ste 350
Lake Forest IL 60045
847 482-9275

(G-10901)
BATTERSHELL CABINETS
312 Defiance Ave (43526-1210)
PHONE.............................419 542-6448
Fax: 419 542-6448
John Battershell, *Owner*
EMP: 4
SALES (est): 228K **Privately Held**
SIC: 1751 2511 Cabinet & finish carpentry; wood household furniture

(G-10902)
FWT LLC
761 W High St (43526-1052)
P.O. Box 8597, Fort Worth TX (76124-0597)
PHONE.............................419 542-1420
Drew Wort, *Safety Dir*
Robert Krause, *Branch Mgr*
EMP: 9
SALES (corp-wide): 8.9B **Privately Held**
SIC: 3441 Building components, structural steel
HQ: Fwt, L.L.C.
5750 E Interstate 20
Fort Worth TX 76119
817 255-2965

(G-10903)
MST INC
Also Called: Modern Safety Techniques
11370 Breininger Rd (43526-9339)
P.O. Box 87 (43526-0087)
PHONE.............................419 542-6645
Fax: 419 542-6475
Charles Martin, *President*
James M Prickett, *Principal*
EMP: 7
SQ FT: 10,000
SALES (est): 740K **Privately Held**
WEB: www.modsafe.com
SIC: 3842 Respiratory protection equipment, personal

(G-10904)
NEMCO FOOD EQUIPMENT LTD (PA)
301 Meuse Argonne St (43526-1143)
P.O. Box 305 (43526-0305)
PHONE.............................419 542-7751
Kenny Moffatt, *Ch of Bd*
Stanley Guilliam, *President*
Jeff Fidler, *Opers Mgr*
Jarrod Phlipot, *Engineer*
Larry Stewart, *CFO*
◆ **EMP:** 75 **EST:** 1976
SQ FT: 50,000
SALES (est): 16.8MM **Privately Held**
WEB: www.nemconet.com
SIC: 3556 Food products machinery

(G-10905)
PARKER-HANNIFIN CORPORATION
Hydraulic Valve Div
373 Meuse Argonne St (43526-1182)
PHONE.............................419 542-6611
Fax: 419 518-1317
Dan Foust, *Vice Pres*
John Myslenski, *Vice Pres*
Matt Cichocki, *Opers Mgr*
Brian Clay, *Materials Mgr*

Byron Dunham, *Engineer*
EMP: 161
SALES (corp-wide): 11.3B **Publicly Held**
WEB: www.parker.com
SIC: 3492 3491 Valves, hydraulic, aircraft; industrial valves
PA: Parker-Hannifin Corporation
6035 Parkland Blvd
Cleveland OH 44124
216 896-3000

(G-10906)
STEELES 5 ACRE MILL INC
10860 State Route 2 (43526-9366)
PHONE.............................419 542-9363
Fax: 419 542-1504
Cathy Steele, *President*
EMP: 17
SALES (est): 1.7MM **Privately Held**
SIC: 2499 Decorative wood & woodwork

(G-10907)
STOETT INDUSTRIES INC
Also Called: Libart North America
600 Defiance Ave (43526-9352)
PHONE.............................419 542-0247
Jack Stover, *President*
Chris Stover, *Manager*
EMP: 24
SQ FT: 68,000
SALES: 1.4MM **Privately Held**
WEB: www.stoett.com
SIC: 3442 Screen & storm doors & windows

(G-10908)
TRI STATE DAIRY
210 Wendell Ave (43526-1405)
P.O. Box 284 (43526-0284)
PHONE.............................419 542-8788
Nelson Hershberger, *Principal*
EMP: 8
SALES (est): 989.6K **Privately Held**
SIC: 2022 Cheese, natural & processed

(G-10909)
TRIBUNE PRINTING INC
Also Called: News Tribune
147 E High St (43526-1159)
P.O. Box 303 (43526-0303)
PHONE.............................419 542-7764
Fax: 419 542-7370
Mary Ann Barth, *President*
Jan Heffelfinger, *Editor*
EMP: 9
SQ FT: 2,000
SALES (est): 589.8K **Privately Held**
WEB: www.hicksvillenewstribune.com
SIC: 2711 2752 Newspapers: publishing only, not printed on site; commercial printing, lithographic

Highland Heights
Cuyahoga County

(G-10910)
C & S ASSOCIATES INC
Also Called: National Lien Digest
729 Miner Rd (44143-2117)
P.O. Box 24101, Cleveland (44124-0101)
PHONE.............................440 461-9661
Fax: 440 461-0822
Mary B Cowan, *President*
Delores A Cowan, *President*
Cathleen M Cowan, *Principal*
Bernard J Cowan, *Exec VP*
Greg Powelson, *Vice Pres*
EMP: 50 **EST:** 1974
SQ FT: 9,000
SALES (est): 6.8MM **Privately Held**
SIC: 7322 2721 Collection agency, except real estate; periodicals: publishing only

(G-10911)
COTSWORKS LLC
749 Miner Rd (44143-2145)
PHONE.............................440 446-8800
Evan Katz, *Engineer*
Ken Applebaum, *Mng Member*
Lindy Anthony, *President*
Ilene Cesa, *Office Admin*
Charles IAMS, *Info Tech Mgr*
EMP: 36
SQ FT: 6,000

SALES (est): 8.9MM **Privately Held**
WEB: www.cotsworks.com
SIC: 3661 Fiber optics communications equipment

(G-10912)
FORKLIFTS OF AMERICAS LLC
28 Alpha Park (44143-2208)
PHONE.............................440 821-5143
Ken Jecmen,
Henry Alvarado,
Samuel Benavides,
Steve Maniaci,
Maria Moyano,
EMP: 7
SALES (est): 1.2MM **Privately Held**
SIC: 3537 7359 5063 Forklift trucks; pallet rental services; batteries

(G-10913)
GLOBAL WOOD PRODUCTS LLC
734 Alpha Dr Ste J (44143-2135)
PHONE.............................440 442-5859
EMP: 3 **EST:** 2010
SALES (est): 180K **Privately Held**
SIC: 2499 Mfg Wood Products

(G-10914)
GOOCH & HOUSEGO (OHIO) LLC
Also Called: Clevelandcrystals
676 Alpha Dr (44143-2123)
PHONE.............................216 486-6100
Gareth Jones, *CEO*
Terry Scribbins, *COO*
Jon Fowler, *Exec VP*
Andrew Boteler, *CFO*
Ken Neczypor, *CFO*
EMP: 65
SQ FT: 51,000
SALES (est): 15.3MM
SALES (corp-wide): 111.5MM **Privately Held**
WEB: www.clevelandcrystals.com
SIC: 3823 3827 Industrial instrmnts msrmnt display/control process variable; optical instruments & lenses
PA: Gooch & Housego Plc
Dowlish Ford
Ilminster TA19
146 025-6440

(G-10915)
HEICO AEROSPACE PARTS CORP (DH)
Also Called: Flight Specialties Components
375 Alpha Park (44143-2237)
PHONE.............................954 987-6101
Luis J Morell, *President*
Jeff Williams, *General Mgr*
Carlos L Macau, *Treasurer*
Elizabeth R Letendre, *Admin Sec*
EMP: 294
SQ FT: 1,500
SALES (est): 23.1MM
SALES (corp-wide): 1.3B **Publicly Held**
WEB: www.inertial.com
SIC: 3728 Aircraft parts & equipment
HQ: Heico Aerospace Corporation
3000 Taft St
Hollywood FL 33021
954 987-6101

(G-10916)
KONECRANES INC
Also Called: Crane Pro Services
740 Beta Dr Ste G (44143-2332)
PHONE.............................440 461-8400
Fax: 440 461-8776
Ron Cerny, *Manager*
Jack Recer, *Manager*
Denise Collins, *Administration*
EMP: 10
SALES (corp-wide): 2.2B **Privately Held**
WEB: www.kciusa.com
SIC: 3536 7389 Hoists, cranes & monorails; crane & aerial lift service
HQ: Konecranes, Inc.
4401 Gateway Blvd
Springfield OH 45502
937 525-5533

(G-10917)
NORMAN NOBLE INC (PA)
5507 Avion Park Dr (44143-1921)
PHONE.............................216 761-5387

Fax: 216 761-5251
Lawrence Noble, *President*
Rick Link, *General Mgr*
Chris Noble, *Vice Pres*
Dan Stefano, *Vice Pres*
Bill Loucks, *Project Dir*
EMP: 135 **EST:** 1962
SQ FT: 20,000
SALES (est): 103.5MM **Privately Held**
WEB: www.nnoble.com
SIC: 3599 Machine shop, jobbing & repair

(G-10918)
NORMAN NOBLE INC
5340 Avion Park Dr (44143-1917)
PHONE..................216 761-5387
Bryan Payne, *QC Mgr*
Dan Stefano, *Manager*
EMP: 287
SALES (corp-wide): 103.5MM **Privately Held**
WEB: www.nnoble.com
SIC: 3599 Machine shop, jobbing & repair
PA: Norman Noble, Inc.
5507 Avion Park Dr
Highland Heights OH 44143
216 761-5387

(G-10919)
PHILIPS MEDICAL SYSTEMS MR
603 Alpha Dr (44143-2114)
PHONE..................440 483-2499
Leverda Wallace, *Surgery Dir*
EMP: 223
SALES (corp-wide): 26B **Privately Held**
SIC: 3845 3674 3679 Electromedical equipment; magnetic resonance imaging device, nuclear; integrated circuits, semiconductor networks, etc.; cryogenic cooling devices for infrared detectors, masers; cores, magnetic
HQ: Philips Medical Systems Mr, Inc
450 Old Niskayuna Rd
Latham NY 12110
518 782-1122

(G-10920)
SKF USA INC (DH)
Also Called: Machined Seals
670 Alpha Dr (44143-2123)
PHONE..................440 720-1500
Jim Dwyer, *Principal*
Scott Simmonds, *Vice Pres*
Shawn Clarke, *Plant Mgr*
Jason Mais, *Project Mgr*
Alan Madsen, *Prdtn Mgr*
▲ **EMP:** 12
SQ FT: 12,000
SALES (est): 2MM
SALES (corp-wide): 7.8B **Privately Held**
WEB: www.ecosealtech.com
SIC: 3053 Gaskets & sealing devices
HQ: Skf Usa Inc.
890 Forty Foot Rd
Lansdale PA 19446
267 436-6000

(G-10921)
WG MOBILE WELDING LLC
6151 Wilson Mills Rd # 210 (44143-2153)
PHONE..................440 720-1940
Wayne Greg, *Owner*
EMP: 5
SALES (est): 160K **Privately Held**
SIC: 7692 Welding repair

Hilliard
Franklin County

(G-10922)
ADS VENTURES INC (HQ)
4640 Trueman Blvd (43026-2438)
PHONE..................614 658-0050
Joseph A Chlapaty, *Ch of Bd*
EMP: 5
SALES (est): 1.5MM
SALES (corp-wide): 1.2B **Publicly Held**
SIC: 3084 3086 Plastics pipe; plastics foam products
PA: Advanced Drainage Systems, Inc.
4640 Trueman Blvd
Hilliard OH 43026
614 658-0050

(G-10923)
ADS WORLDWIDE INC (PA)
4640 Trueman Blvd (43026-2438)
PHONE..................614 658-0050
EMP: 5 **EST:** 2015
SALES (est): 1.5MM **Privately Held**
SIC: 3086 Plastics foam products

(G-10924)
ADVANCED DRAINAGE OF OHIO INC
4640 Trueman Blvd (43026-2438)
PHONE..................614 658-0050
Franklin E Eck, *CEO*
Joseph A Chlapaty, *President*
EMP: 80
SALES (est): 5.7MM
SALES (corp-wide): 1.2B **Publicly Held**
WEB: www.ads-pipe.com
SIC: 3084 Plastics pipe
PA: Advanced Drainage Systems, Inc.
4640 Trueman Blvd
Hilliard OH 43026
614 658-0050

(G-10925)
ADVANCED DRAINAGE SYSTEMS INC (PA)
4640 Trueman Blvd (43026-2438)
PHONE..................614 658-0050
Fax: 614 658-0204
Joseph A Chlapaty, *President*
Thomas M Fussner, *Exec VP*
Robert M Klein, *Exec VP*
Ronald R Vitarelli, *Exec VP*
Scott A Cottrill, *CFO*
▼ **EMP:** 100
SQ FT: 36,000
SALES: 1.2B **Publicly Held**
WEB: www.ads-pipe.com
SIC: 3084 3086 Plastics pipe; plastics foam products

(G-10926)
ARES SPORTSWEAR LTD
3704 Lacon Rd (43026-1207)
PHONE..................614 767-1950
Fax: 614 527-3794
Kristina Reece, *Opers Staff*
Dan Girard, *Buyer*
Christopher Mills, *Natl Sales Mgr*
Shawna Smith, *Cust Mgr*
Jaclyn Miller, *Mktg Dir*
▲ **EMP:** 55
SQ FT: 50,000
SALES (est): 20MM **Privately Held**
WEB: www.areswear.com
SIC: 2261 Screen printing of cotton broadwoven fabrics

(G-10927)
ARMSTRONG WORLD INDUSTRIES INC
4241 Leap Rd Bldg A (43026-1125)
P.O. Box 580 (43026-0580)
PHONE..................614 771-9307
Fax: 614 771-9306
David G Haggerty, *Opers-Prdtn-Mfg*
Nick Strausser, *Plant Engr*
Deb Hill, *Human Res Dir*
Jackie Kauffman, *Manager*
Laurie Kulas, *Manager*
EMP: 80
SQ FT: 225,000
SALES (corp-wide): 1.2B **Publicly Held**
WEB: www.armstrong.com
SIC: 5713 3996 3251 Floor covering stores; hard surface floor coverings; brick & structural clay tile
PA: Armstrong World Industries, Inc.
2500 Columbia Ave
Lancaster PA 17603
717 397-0611

(G-10928)
ATLAS MACHINE AND SUPPLY INC
5040 Nike Dr (43026-7420)
PHONE..................614 351-1603
Greg Dyky, *Branch Mgr*
EMP: 4

SALES (corp-wide): 50.1MM **Privately Held**
WEB: www.atlasmachine.com
SIC: 3599 5084 3563 Machine shop, jobbing & repair; industrial machinery & equipment; air & gas compressors
PA: Atlas Machine And Supply, Inc.
7000 Global Dr
Louisville KY 40258
502 584-7262

(G-10929)
AXALT POWDE COATI SYSTE USA I
4130 Lyman Dr (43026-1230)
PHONE..................614 600-4104
Brian Phillippi, *Prdtn Mgr*
EMP: 11
SALES (corp-wide): 4.1B **Publicly Held**
SIC: 2851 Paints & paint additives
HQ: Axalta Powder Coating Systems Usa, Inc.
9800 Genard Rd
Houston TX 77041
800 247-3886

(G-10930)
BARNEY CORPORATION INC (PA)
Also Called: Filters.com
4089 Leap Rd (43026-1117)
P.O. Box 1270 (43026-6270)
PHONE..................614 274-9069
Fax: 614 274-9064
Marshall Barney, *President*
Virginia L Barney, *Vice Pres*
Brad Barney, *Administration*
◆ **EMP:** 7
SQ FT: 8,400
SALES (est): 1.3MM **Privately Held**
WEB: www.barneycorp.com
SIC: 3569 Filters

(G-10931)
BENZLE PORCELAIN COMPANY INC
6100 Hayden Run Rd (43026-9456)
PHONE..................614 876-2159
Curtis M Benzle, *President*
EMP: 6
SALES (est): 320K **Privately Held**
SIC: 3269 3961 Art & ornamental ware, pottery; costume jewelry, ex. precious metal & semiprecious stones

(G-10932)
BESTWAY CABINETS LLC
3525 Ridgewood Dr (43026-2455)
PHONE..................614 306-3518
Mike E Dooper, *Principal*
EMP: 4 **EST:** 2015
SALES (est): 288.6K **Privately Held**
SIC: 2434 Wood kitchen cabinets

(G-10933)
BIAGINIS DRAPERIES
3082 Alton Darby Creek Rd (43026-8337)
PHONE..................614 876-1706
Debra Biagini, *Owner*
Butch Biagini, *Co-Owner*
EMP: 3
SALES: 80K **Privately Held**
SIC: 2391 Curtains & draperies

(G-10934)
BIG BILLS TRUCKING LLC
6023 Homestead Ct (43026-7369)
PHONE..................614 850-0626
William Davis, *Mng Member*
EMP: 4
SALES: 180K **Privately Held**
SIC: 1442 7389 Construction sand & gravel;

(G-10935)
BLIND FACTORY SHOWROOM
Also Called: The Blind Factory
3670 Parkway Ln Ste M (43026-1237)
PHONE..................614 771-6549
Don Grove, *President*
Ann Grove, *Corp Secy*
Andrew Grove, *Vice Pres*
EMP: 20
SQ FT: 16,000

SALES (est): 2.2MM **Privately Held**
WEB: www.theblindfactory.com
SIC: 2591 5719 5023 Blinds vertical; vertical blinds; vertical blinds

(G-10936)
BREIBACH ASSOCIATION
Also Called: Breibach & Associates
5117 Grandon Dr (43026-1715)
PHONE..................614 876-6480
June Breibach, *Owner*
EMP: 7
SALES (est): 390K **Privately Held**
SIC: 3993 5099 Signs & advertising specialties; advertising novelties; signs, except electric

(G-10937)
C & C MARBLE & GRANITE LLC
4401 Lyman Dr Ste A (43026-2627)
PHONE..................614 873-1919
Mike Shielts, *Manager*
Jung Hwa Chang,
EMP: 10
SALES: 700K **Privately Held**
WEB: www.ccgranite.com
SIC: 1411 Granite dimension stone

(G-10938)
CITYSCAPES INTERNATIONAL INC
4200 Lyman Ct (43026-1213)
PHONE..................614 850-2540
James Cullinan, *President*
Mike Cullinan, *Finance Mgr*
Linda Gilbert, *VP Human Res*
Marcus Bryan, *Info Tech Mgr*
David Cullinan, *Director*
EMP: 22
SQ FT: 30,000
SALES: 4.6MM **Privately Held**
WEB: www.cityscapesinc.com
SIC: 3531 Construction machinery

(G-10939)
CLOVERLEAF OFFICE SLUTIONS LLC
5394 Old Creek Ln (43026-8870)
PHONE..................614 219-9050
Debbie Derenzo,
Derenzo Brian,
EMP: 3
SALES (est): 289.2K **Privately Held**
SIC: 2759 Commercial printing

(G-10940)
CME FEDERAL CREDIT UNION
4099 Trueman Blvd (43026-2492)
PHONE..................614 876-1382
Fax: 614 850-9548
Ruth Cline, *Principal*
EMP: 14
SALES (corp-wide): 8.4MM **Privately Held**
SIC: 3578 Automatic teller machines (ATM)
PA: Cme Federal Credit Union
150 E Mound St Ste 100
Columbus OH 43215
614 224-4388

(G-10941)
CNG BUSINESS GROUP
Also Called: Friday's Creations
4974 Scioto Darby Rd A (43026-1549)
PHONE..................614 771-0877
Fax: 614 771-5421
Anthony Currie, *Owner*
EMP: 3
SQ FT: 2,200
SALES: 250K **Privately Held**
SIC: 2395 Embroidery & art needlework

(G-10942)
COLORAMICS LLC
Also Called: Mayco Colors
4077 Weaver Ct S (43026-1197)
PHONE..................614 876-1171
Fax: 614 675-2054
Bob Moreni, *Marketing Staff*
Cathy Kreuz, *Manager*
Colleen Carey,
Denise Ertler, *Representative*
◆ **EMP:** 43
SQ FT: 75,000

SALES (est): 12.7MM **Privately Held**
WEB: www.maycocolors.com
SIC: 2851 Paints & paint additives

(G-10943)
CONNECT TELEVISION
4811 Northwest Pkwy (43026-1128)
PHONE..................................614 876-4402
Tamy Valkosky, *Principal*
EMP: 3
SALES (est): 176.8K **Privately Held**
SIC: 2298 Cable, fiber

(G-10944)
CRUISE QUARTERS
4013 Main St (43026-1422)
PHONE..................................614 777-6022
Steven Kirk Boganwright, *Principal*
EMP: 3 EST: 2012
SALES (est): 319.4K **Privately Held**
SIC: 3131 Quarters

(G-10945)
CUMMINS - ALLISON CORP
Also Called: Cummins-Allison
3970 Brown Park Dr Ste C (43026-1166)
PHONE..................................614 529-1940
Darcy Devore, *Manager*
Aaron Shipp, *Manager*
EMP: 3
SALES (corp-wide): 377.1MM **Privately Held**
WEB: www.gsb.com
SIC: 5046 3519 Commercial equipment; internal combustion engines
PA: Cummins - Allison Corp.
852 Feehanville Dr
Mount Prospect IL 60056
847 759-6403

(G-10946)
CUMMINS BRIDGEWAY LLC
4000 Lyman Dr (43026-1212)
PHONE..................................614 771-1000
Fax: 614 771-0716
Greg Bowl, *Branch Mgr*
EMP: 25
SALES (corp-wide): 17.5B **Publicly Held**
WEB: www.bridgewaypower.com
SIC: 5084 7538 3519 Engines & parts, diesel; diesel engine repair: automotive; internal combustion engines
HQ: Cummins Bridgeway, Llc
21810 Clessie Ct
New Hudson MI 48165
248 573-1600

(G-10947)
CUMMINS BRIDGEWAY COLUMBUS LLC
4000 Lyman Dr (43026-1212)
PHONE..................................614 771-1000
Fax: 614 771-0769
Tammy Fawley, *General Mgr*
Bill Bergner,
EMP: 60
SALES (est): 5.2MM
SALES (corp-wide): 17.5B **Publicly Held**
WEB: www.bridgewaypower.com
SIC: 5084 3519 Engines & parts, diesel; internal combustion engines
HQ: Cummins Bridgeway, Llc
21810 Clessie Ct
New Hudson MI 48165
248 573-1600

(G-10948)
DECENT HILL PUBLISHERS LLC
Also Called: Decent Hill Press
2825 Wynneleaf St (43026-8144)
PHONE..................................216 548-1255
Jude Odu,
EMP: 6
SALES (est): 310K **Privately Held**
SIC: 2731 Book music: publishing only, not printed on site

(G-10949)
GOULD GROUP LLC
4653 Trueman Blvd Ste 120 (43026-2597)
PHONE..................................740 807-4294
Brian Gould, *CEO*
Julie Gould, *COO*
EMP: 4

SALES (est): 199.8K **Privately Held**
SIC: 1711 1731 3585 4911 Plumbing, heating, air-conditioning contractors; electrical work; refrigeration & heating equipment; transmission, electric power; roofing, siding & insulation

(G-10950)
HANCOR INC (DH)
4640 Trueman Blvd (43026-2438)
PHONE..................................614 658-0050
Fax: 419 424-8302
Steven A Anderson, *President*
William E Altermatt, *Vice Pres*
Pat Ferren, *Vice Pres*
Derek Kamp, *Vice Pres*
Larry Dunson, *Plant Mgr*
◆ EMP: 330
SQ FT: 20,000
SALES (est): 173MM
SALES (corp-wide): 1.2B **Publicly Held**
SIC: 3084 3088 3089 3083 Plastics pipe; plastics plumbing fixtures; septic tanks, plastic; laminated plastics plate & sheet
HQ: Hancor Holding Corporation
401 Olive St
Findlay OH 45840
419 422-6521

(G-10951)
HIGHLIGHTS FOR CHILDREN INC
4555 Lyman Dr (43026-1282)
PHONE..................................614 486-0631
Steve Fuhrman, *General Mgr*
Kim Clements, *Manager*
EMP: 140
SALES (corp-wide): 216.4MM **Privately Held**
WEB: www.highlights.com
SIC: 2721 Magazines: publishing & printing; magazines: publishing only, not printed on site
PA: Highlights For Children, Inc.
1800 Watermark Dr
Columbus OH 43215
614 486-0631

(G-10952)
HILLIARD CAT SHACK LLC
5484 Pearson Ct (43026-7518)
PHONE..................................614 527-9711
Kimberly Mash,
EMP: 4
SALES (est): 320.3K **Privately Held**
SIC: 2329 Men's & boys' sportswear & athletic clothing

(G-10953)
INS ROBOTICS INC
3600 Parkway Ln (43026-1281)
PHONE..................................888 293-5325
Beth Harkins, *Principal*
EMP: 6
SALES (est): 665.1K **Privately Held**
SIC: 3535 Robotic conveyors

(G-10954)
INTERNATIONAL PRODUCTS (HQ)
Also Called: Ipsg / Micro Center
4119 Leap Rd (43026-1117)
PHONE..................................614 850-3000
Richard Mershad, *President*
▲ EMP: 15
SQ FT: 125,000
SALES (est): 42MM
SALES (corp-wide): 2.9B **Privately Held**
WEB: www.microcenter.com
SIC: 3571 Electronic computers; computers, digital, analog or hybrid; personal computers (microcomputers)
PA: Micro Electronics, Inc.
4119 Leap Rd
Hilliard OH 43026
614 850-3000

(G-10955)
JD POWER SYSTEMS LLC
Also Called: John Deere Authorized Dealer
4079 Lyman Dr (43026-1211)
PHONE..................................614 317-9394
Fax: 614 801-0439
Jeffrey D Mitchell, *Owner*
Norm Murphy, *CFO*
Kent Finton, *Sales Associate*

Adam Taylor, *Manager*
Jeff Leach, *Pharmacy Dir*
EMP: 12
SALES (est): 3.3MM **Privately Held**
SIC: 3621 5082 Motors & generators; construction & mining machinery

(G-10956)
JIT COMPANY INC
2180 Venus Dr (43026-8124)
PHONE..................................614 529-8010
Fax: 614 529-8122
Marcy Wu, *President*
Jom Pin Chen, *Vice Pres*
EMP: 13
SALES (est): 2.5MM **Privately Held**
SIC: 3599 Machine & other job shop work

(G-10957)
JOHNSON ENGINE & MACHINE
2899 Walcutt Rd (43026-8880)
PHONE..................................614 876-0724
Donald H Johnson, *Owner*
Carolyn Fausey, *Bookkeeper*
EMP: 7
SQ FT: 10,000
SALES (est): 590.9K **Privately Held**
SIC: 3599 7538 Machine shop, jobbing & repair; general automotive repair shops; engine rebuilding: automotive; truck engine repair, except industrial

(G-10958)
LASERFLEX CORPORATION (HQ)
3649 Parkway Ln (43026-1214)
PHONE..................................614 850-9600
Fax: 614 850-9635
Ken Kinkopf, *President*
Gene White, *Vice Pres*
Mary Beth Hagerty, *Finance Mgr*
Mike Shirley, *Sales Mgr*
Paul Trombley, *Manager*
EMP: 62
SQ FT: 75,000
SALES (est): 28.8MM
SALES (corp-wide): 2.8B **Publicly Held**
WEB:
www.customlasercuttingservices.com
SIC: 7389 7699 7692 3599 Metal cutting services; finishing services; industrial machinery & equipment repair; welding repair; machine shop, jobbing & repair; fabricated structural metal; metallizing of fabrics
PA: Ryerson Holding Corporation
227 W Monroe St Fl 27
Chicago IL 60606
312 292-5000

(G-10959)
MARBLE CLIFF LIMESTONE INC
2650 Old Dublin Rd (43026)
PHONE..................................614 488-3030
Fax: 614 488-0347
Paul D Rice, *President*
EMP: 3
SQ FT: 1,884
SALES (est): 207.6K **Privately Held**
SIC: 1411 Limestone & marble dimension stone

(G-10960)
MERRY X-RAY CHEMICAL CORP
Also Called: Baldwin
4770 Northwest Pkwy (43026-1131)
PHONE..................................614 219-2011
Fax: 614 876-2192
Eric Cole, *Manager*
EMP: 6
SALES (corp-wide): 278.8MM **Privately Held**
SIC: 6411 2899 Medical insurance claim processing, contract or fee basis; chemical supplies for foundries
PA: Merry X-Ray Chemical Corporation
4444 Viewridge Ave A
San Diego CA 92123
858 565-4472

(G-10961)
METROPOLITAN ENVMTL SVCS INC
5055 Nike Dr (43026-9692)
PHONE..................................614 771-1881
Rick Gaffey, *President*

James Aman, *Corp Secy*
Erick Zediger, *Vice Pres*
EMP: 75
SQ FT: 10,000
SALES (est): 19.9MM
SALES (corp-wide): 150MM **Privately Held**
WEB: www.metenviro.com
SIC: 3589 1799 1794 1629 Vacuum cleaners & sweepers, electric: industrial; central vacuum cleaning system installation; excavation work; dredging contractor
PA: Carylon Corporation
2500 W Arthington St
Chicago IL 60612
312 666-7700

(G-10962)
MID-OHIO PRODUCTS INC
4329 Reynolds Dr (43026-1261)
PHONE..................................614 771-2795
Fax: 614 771-9115
Richard Coleman II, *President*
Dan Niemeister, *Purchasing*
Julie Battles, *Controller*
Jim Rayner, *Sales Mgr*
▲ EMP: 56 EST: 1980
SQ FT: 16,000
SALES (est): 10.4MM **Privately Held**
WEB: www.mid-ohioproducts.com
SIC: 3544 Dies & die holders for metal cutting, forming, die casting; punches, forming & stamping; sheet metalwork

(G-10963)
MIDWEST INDUSTRIAL RUBBER INC
Also Called: Mir
4847 Northwest Pkwy (43026-1128)
PHONE..................................614 876-3110
Fax: 614 876-3072
George Binek, *Branch Mgr*
Mark Hambacker, *Manager*
Bill Carmen, *Info Tech Mgr*
Phil Harris, *Director*
EMP: 14
SALES (corp-wide): 62.4MM **Privately Held**
SIC: 5085 3535 3061 3053 Hose, belting & packing; power transmission equipment & apparatus; rubber goods, mechanical; conveyors & conveying equipment; mechanical rubber goods; gaskets, packing & sealing devices
PA: Midwest Industrial Rubber Inc
10431 Midwest Indus Dr
Saint Louis MO 63132
314 890-0016

(G-10964)
MORLAN & ASSOCIATES INC (PA)
Also Called: Flex-Core Division
4970 Scioto Darby Rd D (43026-1548)
P.O. Box 6047 (43026-6047)
PHONE..................................614 889-6152
Fax: 614 876-8538
Donald Morlan, *Ch of Bd*
Teri Shaw, *President*
Eric Whelan, *Vice Pres*
Amy McNabb, *Admin Sec*
▼ EMP: 29
SQ FT: 15,000
SALES: 10MM **Privately Held**
WEB: www.flex-core.com
SIC: 3612 Transformers, except electric

(G-10965)
OCS TELECOM LLC
4138 Weaver Ct E (43026-1299)
P.O. Box 291, Centerburg (43011-0291)
PHONE..................................740 503-5939
Jeremy Funk, *Partner*
EMP: 12 EST: 2012
SALES (est): 912.3K **Privately Held**
SIC: 3661 Telephone station equipment & parts, wire

(G-10966)
OHIO LAMINATING & BINDING INC
4364 Reynolds Dr (43026-1260)
PHONE..................................614 771-4868
Fax: 614 771-0271
Jim Ondecko, *President*

Jimmy R Ondecko, *Vice Pres*
Jan McKee, *Manager*
EMP: 40
SQ FT: 5,000
SALES (est): 3.3MM **Privately Held**
WEB: www.ohiolaminatingandbinding.com
SIC: 7389 2789 2672 Laminating service; bookbinding & related work; coated & laminated paper

(G-10967)
OHIO SEMITRONICS INC (PA)
Also Called: OSI
4242 Reynolds Dr (43026-1264)
PHONE..................................614 777-1005
Fax: 614 777-4511
Warren E Bulman, *Ch of Bd*
John D Redmyer, *Vice Ch Bd*
Robert A Shaw, *President*
John Iben, *Opers Staff*
David Baldock, *Production*
◆ EMP: 88
SQ FT: 49,000
SALES: 10.9MM **Privately Held**
WEB: www.ohiosemi.com
SIC: 3674 3679 3663 3625 Semiconductors & related devices; transducers, electrical; radio & TV communications equipment; relays & industrial controls; motors & generators; transformers, except electric

(G-10968)
OPEN TEXT INC
3671 Ridge Mill Dr (43026-7752)
PHONE..................................614 658-3588
Anik Ganguly, *Manager*
Justin Zerby, *Manager*
Terry W Weirick, *Director*
EMP: 50
SALES (corp-wide): 1.8B **Privately Held**
SIC: 7372 Prepackaged software
HQ: Open Text Inc.
　　951 Mariners Island Blvd # 7
　　San Mateo CA 94404
　　650 645-3000

(G-10969)
PHARMAFORCE INC
4150 Lyman Ct (43026-1213)
PHONE..................................614 436-2222
Michael Medors, *CFO*
EMP: 11
SALES (corp-wide): 8.4B **Privately Held**
WEB: www.pharmaforceinc.com
SIC: 2834 5122 Pharmaceutical preparations; pharmaceuticals
HQ: Pharmaforce, Inc.
　　960 Crupper Ave
　　Columbus OH 43229
　　614 436-2222

(G-10970)
PHOENIX HYDRAULIC PRESSES INC
4299 Reynolds Dr (43026-1261)
PHONE..................................614 850-8940
Fax: 614 850-9065
Charles Sherman, *President*
Cristy Gaskin, *Office Mgr*
Vicki Miller, *Administration*
EMP: 10
SQ FT: 6,000
SALES (est): 1.8MM **Privately Held**
WEB: www.phoenixhydraulic.com
SIC: 3542 Presses: hydraulic & pneumatic, mechanical & manual

(G-10971)
POWELL PRINTS LLC
3991 Main St (43026-1449)
PHONE..................................614 771-4830
Fax: 614 771-0585
Larry Powell, *Mng Member*
EMP: 4
SALES (est): 556.9K **Privately Held**
SIC: 2759 Commercial printing

(G-10972)
PPG INDUSTRIES INC
Also Called: PPG 9282
5054 Cemetery Rd (43026-1671)
PHONE..................................614 921-9228
Randy Ridgeway, *Manager*
EMP: 3

SALES (corp-wide): 14.7B **Publicly Held**
WEB: www.ppg.com
SIC: 2851 3011 Paints & allied products; tire sundries or tire repair materials, rubber
PA: Ppg Industries, Inc.
　　1 Ppg Pl
　　Pittsburgh PA 15272
　　412 434-3131

(G-10973)
PRO LIGHTING LLC
5864 Hunting Haven Dr (43026-7992)
P.O. Box 1201 (43026-6201)
PHONE..................................614 561-0089
Jeffrey J Treadway, *Principal*
EMP: 4
SALES (est): 426.7K **Privately Held**
SIC: 3648 Lighting equipment

(G-10974)
RAGE CORPORATION (PA)
3949 Lyman Dr (43026-1274)
P.O. Box 159 (43026-0159)
PHONE..................................614 771-4771
Fax: 614 771-4770
George Saliaris, *President*
Dan Saliaris, *Vice Pres*
Randy McIntyre, *Plant Engr*
Shanoon Bulina, *Controller*
▲ EMP: 68
SQ FT: 65,000
SALES (est): 18.6MM **Privately Held**
SIC: 3544 3089 Special dies, tools, jigs & fixtures; injection molding of plastics

(G-10975)
RAW REAL AND WONDERFUL LLC
4118 Anson Dr (43026-2206)
P.O. Box 504, Galloway (43119-0504)
PHONE..................................614 529-8606
Angela Zody, *Mng Member*
EMP: 10
SALES (est): 882.3K **Privately Held**
SIC: 2034 Dried & dehydrated fruits

(G-10976)
RICH PRODUCTS CORPORATION
4600 Northwest Pkwy (43026-1130)
P.O. Box 490 (43026-0490)
PHONE..................................614 771-1117
Fax: 614 771-8286
Joyce Deskins, *Opers Mgr*
John Maier, *Opers Mgr*
Jon Burns, *QC Dir*
Michael Callaway, *Manager*
Will Richards, *Manager*
EMP: 150
SALES (corp-wide): 3.2B **Privately Held**
WEB: www.richs.com
SIC: 2023 2099 2051 2045 Dry, condensed, evaporated dairy products; food preparations; bread, cake & related products; prepared flour mixes & doughs
PA: Rich Products Corporation
　　1 Robert Rich Way
　　Buffalo NY 14213
　　716 878-8000

(G-10977)
S & G MANUFACTURING GROUP LLC (PA)
Also Called: S&G Distribution
4830 Northwest Pkwy (43026-1131)
PHONE..................................614 529-0100
Bret Klisares, *President*
Thomas Anderson, *Business Mgr*
Josh Ball, *VP Opers*
Thomas Greer, *Purch Mgr*
Charles Klick, *Purch Agent*
EMP: 142
SQ FT: 105,500
SALES (est): 24.6MM **Privately Held**
WEB: www.sgmgroup.com
SIC: 3441 3444 2435 2436 Fabricated structural metal; sheet metalwork; hardwood veneer & plywood; softwood veneer & plywood; vanities, bathroom: wood

(G-10978)
SENSOTEC LLC
Also Called: Sensorwerks
3964 Brown Park Dr Ste B (43026-1163)
PHONE..................................614 481-8616
Fax: 614 486-0506
John L Priest Jr, *President*
EMP: 6
SALES: 500K **Privately Held**
WEB: www.sensorwerks.com
SIC: 3829 Pressure transducers

(G-10979)
SMALL DOG PRINTING
3972 Brown Park Dr Ste E (43026-1167)
P.O. Box 750 (43026-0750)
PHONE..................................614 777-7620
Amy Bias, *CEO*
Rebecca Dornsife, *Co-Owner*
EMP: 4
SALES (est): 430.6K **Privately Held**
WEB: www.smalldogprinting.com
SIC: 2759 Commercial printing

(G-10980)
STACEYS KITCHEN LIMITED
4350 Kerr Dr Ste B (43026-1055)
PHONE..................................614 921-1290
EMP: 4 EST: 2005
SALES (est): 140K **Privately Held**
SIC: 2099 Mfg Food Preparations

(G-10981)
STAR DYNAMICS CORPORATION (PA)
Also Called: Aeroflex Powell
4455 Reynolds Dr (43026-1261)
PHONE..................................614 334-4510
Jerry Jost, *President*
Andy Bell, *General Mgr*
Chris Fox, *General Mgr*
Julie West, *General Mgr*
Stephen Adamo, *Principal*
▲ EMP: 65
SQ FT: 20,000
SALES (est): 13.8MM **Privately Held**
WEB: www.isarinc.com
SIC: 3812 Radar systems & equipment

(G-10982)
STATE METAL HOSE INC
4171 Lyman Dr (43026-1228)
PHONE..................................614 527-4700
Ward Argust, *Principal*
EMP: 7 EST: 2007
SALES (est): 1.2MM **Privately Held**
SIC: 3492 Fluid power valves & hose fittings

(G-10983)
STENCILSMITH LLC
3001 Stouenburgh Dr (43026-8862)
P.O. Box 401 (43026-0401)
PHONE..................................614 876-4350
April Dabaie,
EMP: 4
SALES (est): 340.6K **Privately Held**
SIC: 3953 Stencils, painting & marking

(G-10984)
SUNDAY SCHOOL SOFTWARE
4369 Brickwood Dr (43026-3420)
PHONE..................................614 527-8776
Neil Mac Queen, *President*
EMP: 3
SALES (est): 205.7K **Privately Held**
WEB: www.sundaysoftware.com
SIC: 7372 8661 Prepackaged software; religious organizations

(G-10985)
TEACHERS PUBLISHING GROUP
Also Called: Essential Learning Products
4200 Parkway Ct (43026-1200)
PHONE..................................614 486-0631
Gary Meyers, *President*
Thomas Mason, *Treasurer*
EMP: 10
SQ FT: 36,000

SALES (est): 896.9K
SALES (corp-wide): 216.4MM **Privately Held**
WEB: www.elpdealer.com
SIC: 7371 2731 Custom computer programming services; books: publishing only
PA: Highlights For Children, Inc.
　　1800 Watermark Dr
　　Columbus OH 43215
　　614 486-0631

(G-10986)
TEXTILES INC
Also Called: Sales Office Rob Jordan Vp Sls
5892 Heritage Lakes Dr (43026-7617)
PHONE..................................614 529-8642
Jawad Gardner, *Executive*
EMP: 8
SALES (corp-wide): 16.6MM **Privately Held**
SIC: 2511 2599 Wood household furniture; hotel furniture
PA: Textiles, Inc.
　　23 Old Springfield Rd
　　London OH 43140
　　740 852-0782

(G-10987)
THERMOPLASTIC ACCESSORIES CORP
Also Called: T A C
3949 Lyman Dr (43026-1209)
P.O. Box 159 (43026-0159)
PHONE..................................614 771-4777
George Saliaris, *President*
Mary Lou Saliaris, *Admin Sec*
EMP: 45
SQ FT: 48,000
SALES: 3.8MM
SALES (corp-wide): 18.6MM **Privately Held**
SIC: 3089 Blow molded finished plastic products
PA: Rage Corporation
　　3949 Lyman Dr
　　Hilliard OH 43026
　　614 771-4771

(G-10988)
TOUCH LIFE CENTERS LLC
3455 Mill Run Dr Ste 310 (43026-9082)
PHONE..................................614 388-8075
Stuart Mead,
Mark Ford,
EMP: 5
SALES (est): 412K **Privately Held**
SIC: 3842 Prosthetic appliances

(G-10989)
TUBULAR TECHNIQUES INC
3025 Scioto Darby Exec Ct (43026-8990)
PHONE..................................614 529-4130
Fax: 614 529-4140
Steve Harman, *President*
Amy Pope-Harman, *Admin Sec*
EMP: 6 EST: 1972
SQ FT: 7,500
SALES (est): 2.4MM **Privately Held**
WEB: www.tubulartechniques.com
SIC: 5051 3599 Tubing, metal; tubing, flexible metallic

(G-10990)
ULTERIOR PRODUCTS LLC
2459 Scioto Harper Dr (43026)
P.O. Box 759 (43026-0759)
PHONE..................................614 519-3210
Kurt Nienberg, *President*
Doug Nienberg, *Design Engr*
EMP: 4 EST: 2013
SALES: 500K **Privately Held**
SIC: 3535 Unit handling conveying systems

(G-10991)
VANNER HOLDINGS INC
4282 Reynolds Dr (43026-1260)
PHONE..................................614 771-2718
Steven Funk, *President*
Merry H Pieper, *Principal*
Chris Collet, *Vice Pres*
Brenda Porter, *Purch Dir*
Delmer Wells, *IT/INT Sup*
◆ EMP: 55
SQ FT: 20,000

SALES (est): 12.9MM **Privately Held**
WEB: www.vanner.com
SIC: 3629 3823 3699 3648 Inverters, nonrotating: electrical; power conversion units, a.c. to d.c.: static-electric; battery chargers, rectifying or nonrotating; industrial instrmnts msrmnt display/control process variable; electrical equipment & supplies; lighting equipment; motors & generators

(G-10992)
VICART PRCSION FABRICATORS INC
Also Called: Proto Precision Fabricators
4101 Leap Rd (43026-1117)
PHONE..........................614 771-0080
Fax: 614 771-0186
Arthur Handshy, *President*
Bryan Graham, *Engineer*
Debbie L Hedrick, *Financial Exec*
Art Shandy, *Sales Executive*
Debbie Hendrick, *Manager*
EMP: 35
SQ FT: 18,000
SALES (est): 7.1MM **Privately Held**
WEB: www.protoprecision.com
SIC: 3444 Sheet metalwork

(G-10993)
WINE VAULT ENTERPRISES LLC
4907 Hawkstone Rd (43026-9749)
PHONE..........................614 850-0047
Todd McDonald, *Principal*
EMP: 3
SALES (est): 228.1K **Privately Held**
SIC: 3272 Concrete products

(G-10994)
ZURN INDUSTRIES LLC
4501 Sutphen Ct (43026-1224)
PHONE..........................814 455-0921
Pat Capretta, *Sales Staff*
Melissa Heckman, *Sales Staff*
Jen Morton, *Sales Staff*
Kristin Spinosi, *Sales Staff*
Bob Armbrewster, *Manager*
EMP: 10
SALES (corp-wide): 1.9B **Publicly Held**
WEB: www.zurn.com
SIC: 5074 3431 Plumbing & hydronic heating supplies; sinks: enameled iron, cast iron or pressed metal
HQ: Zurn Industries, Llc
1801 Pittsburgh Ave
Erie PA 16502
814 455-0921

Hillsboro
Highland County

(G-10995)
ABBOTT SIGNS (PA)
251 John St (45133-1021)
PHONE..........................937 393-6600
Randy Abbott, *Owner*
EMP: 5
SALES (est): 300K **Privately Held**
SIC: 3993 Signs, not made in custom sign painting shops

(G-10996)
B M PALLETS
5837 Dry Bone Rd (45133-8922)
PHONE..........................740 634-2659
Matthew Cinnerman, *Owner*
EMP: 4
SALES (est): 140K **Privately Held**
WEB: www.bmpallets.com
SIC: 2448 Pallets, wood & wood with metal

(G-10997)
CAMECO COMMUNICATIONS
Also Called: Highland County Press
128 S High St (45133-1443)
P.O. Box 849 (45133-0849)
PHONE..........................937 840-9490
Fax: 937 840-9492
Rory Ryan, *President*
Angie Matticks, *Vice Pres*
Rosemary Ryan, *Manager*
EMP: 7
SQ FT: 1,000

SALES (est): 250K **Privately Held**
SIC: 2711 Newspapers, publishing & printing

(G-10998)
G FORDYCE CO
210 Hobart Dr (45133-9487)
P.O. Box 309 (45133-0309)
PHONE..........................937 393-3241
Fax: 937 393-4652
Bob Wilson, *Owner*
Stan Storts, *General Mgr*
Jeff Morris, *Manager*
EMP: 6
SQ FT: 12,000
SALES (est): 200K **Privately Held**
SIC: 3554 Folding machines, paper

(G-10999)
HANSON AGGREGATES EAST LLC
Plum Run Stone Division
4281 Roush Rd (45133-9147)
PHONE..........................937 364-2311
Hanson Div, *COO*
Lee Robb, *Maint Spvr*
Dennis Mount, *Sales Mgr*
J Craig Morgan, *Manager*
Butch Farmer, *Manager*
EMP: 35
SALES (corp-wide): 16B **Privately Held**
SIC: 3281 3273 1422 Stone, quarrying & processing of own stone products; ready-mixed concrete; crushed & broken limestone
HQ: Hanson Aggregates East Llc
3131 Rdu Center Dr
Morrisville NC 27560
919 380-2500

(G-11000)
HERSHBERGER & SONS LLC
12439 Turley Ln (45133-8997)
PHONE..........................937 588-2195
Jacob Hershberger, *Mng Member*
EMP: 3
SALES: 235K **Privately Held**
SIC: 3523 Tractors, farm

(G-11001)
HIGHLAND COMPUTER FORMS INC (PA)
1025 W Main St (45133-8219)
P.O. Box 831 (45133-0831)
PHONE..........................937 393-4215
Fax: 937 393-7760
Robert D Wilson, *President*
Philip D Wilson, *Chairman*
Rob Jones, *Plant Mgr*
Rhonda Smith, *Controller*
Ashley Watson, *Sales Associate*
EMP: 56
SQ FT: 70,000
SALES (est): 28.5MM **Privately Held**
WEB: www.hcf.com
SIC: 2761 Computer forms, manifold or continuous

(G-11002)
HIGHLAND PRECISION PLATING
6940 State Route 124 (45133-9435)
P.O. Box 784 (45133-0784)
PHONE..........................937 393-9501
Fax: 937 393-6791
Allen Brotherton, *President*
EMP: 3
SQ FT: 400
SALES (est): 650K **Privately Held**
SIC: 3471 Plating & polishing

(G-11003)
HIGHLAND STONE
4281 Roush Rd (45133-9147)
PHONE..........................937 364-2311
Fax: 937 364-2509
Craig Morgan, *Principal*
EMP: 3
SALES (est): 387.7K **Privately Held**
SIC: 3272 Concrete products

(G-11004)
ILLINOIS TOOL WORKS INC
Also Called: Hobart
1495 N High St (45133-8203)
PHONE..........................937 393-4271
Jody Dean, *Plant Mgr*

Bill Zinno, *Manager*
Matthew French, *Technology*
Chad Potter, *Executive*
EMP: 241
SALES (corp-wide): 13.6B **Publicly Held**
SIC: 2672 Coated & laminated paper
PA: Illinois Tool Works Inc.
155 Harlem Ave
Glenview IL 60025
847 724-7500

(G-11005)
JD ENTERPRISES
8493 State Route 785 (45133-9554)
PHONE..........................937 764-1611
Gerald Dunham, *Owner*
EMP: 6 **EST:** 1974
SALES (est): 50K **Privately Held**
SIC: 3564 Air purification equipment

(G-11006)
JERRYS WELDING SUPPLY INC
Also Called: Jerry's Welding Supply ICN
5367 Us Highway 50 (45133-7532)
PHONE..........................937 364-1500
Gerald Bonnet, *Owner*
EMP: 5 **EST:** 1998
SALES (est): 429.1K **Privately Held**
SIC: 5084 7692 5169 Welding machinery & equipment; welding repair; oxygen

(G-11007)
MAC PRINTING COMPANY
406 N West St (45133-1088)
PHONE..........................937 393-1101
Fax: 937 393-8025
John R Mc Laughlin, *President*
Lois Mc Laughlin, *Corp Secy*
Linda Mc Laughlin, *Office Mgr*
EMP: 5
SQ FT: 3,500
SALES (est): 500K **Privately Held**
WEB: www.macprintingcompany.com
SIC: 2759 2752 Commercial printing; commercial printing, lithographic

(G-11008)
MAINES BROTHERS TIN SHOP
Also Called: Maines, Clyde Sons Tin Shop
121 S West St (45133-1355)
PHONE..........................937 393-1633
Harley Maines, *Partner*
Clyde Maines, *Partner*
Roger Maines, *Partner*
EMP: 3
SALES (est): 50K **Privately Held**
WEB: www.windsorfair.com
SIC: 1761 3444 Roofing contractor; sheet metalwork

(G-11009)
OHIO ASPHALTIC LIMESTONE CORP
8591 Mad River Rd (45133-9451)
PHONE..........................937 364-2191
Toll Free:..........................888 -
Diana Jones, *President*
William C Mason, *President*
Dianna Jones, *Vice Pres*
Amy Huebner, *Office Mgr*
Tom Mason, *Manager*
EMP: 10
SQ FT: 1,200
SALES: 3.1MM
SALES (corp-wide): 4.8MM **Privately Held**
WEB: www.ohio-asphaltic-limestone.com
SIC: 1422 Limestones, ground
PA: Miller-Mason Paving Co (Inc)
8591 Mad River Rd
Hillsboro OH
937 364-2369

(G-11010)
OHIO VALLEY TRUSS CO (PA)
6000 Us Highway 50 (45133-7546)
P.O. Box 365 (45133-0365)
PHONE..........................937 393-3995
Fax: 937 393-3918
Willard G Bohrer, *President*
Joann Bohrer, *Corp Secy*
EMP: 35
SQ FT: 12,000
SALES (est): 4.3MM **Privately Held**
SIC: 2439 Trusses, wooden roof; trusses, except roof: laminated lumber

(G-11011)
OHIO VALLEY TRUSS CO
887 1/2 W Main St (45133-7452)
P.O. Box 365 (45133-0365)
PHONE..........................937 393-3995
Willard Bohrer, *President*
EMP: 5
SQ FT: 3,000
SALES (corp-wide): 4.3MM **Privately Held**
SIC: 2439 Trusses, wooden roof
PA: Ohio Valley Truss Co
6000 Us Highway 50
Hillsboro OH 45133
937 393-3995

(G-11012)
PAS TECHNOLOGIES INC
214 Hobart Dr (45133-9487)
PHONE..........................937 840-1000
Nathanael Young, *Engineer*
Mark Greene, *Manager*
Scott Rankin, *Manager*
Scott Barrera, *Maintence Staff*
EMP: 100 **Privately Held**
WEB: www.pas-technologies.com
SIC: 3724 7699 Aircraft engines & engine parts; aircraft & heavy equipment repair services
HQ: Pas Technologies Inc.
1234 Atlantic Ave
North Kansas City MO 64116
816 556-5113

(G-11013)
ROTARY FORMS PRESS INC (PA)
835 S High St (45133-9692)
PHONE..........................937 393-3426
Fax: 937 393-8473
Jon Cassner, *President*
Brian Cassner, *Treasurer*
EMP: 50
SQ FT: 24,500
SALES: 388.7K **Privately Held**
WEB: www.rotaryformspress.com
SIC: 2761 2752 Computer forms, manifold or continuous; commercial printing, lithographic

(G-11014)
SEAL TITE LLC
120 Moore Rd (45133-8523)
PHONE..........................937 393-4268
Michael J Kelley, *CEO*
Eric Newswanger, *Opers Mgr*
Jeff Leasure, *Opers Staff*
Sherry Leasure, *Opers Staff*
Sandy Rumpke, *Human Res Mgr*
EMP: 100
SQ FT: 120,000
SALES (est): 23.9MM **Privately Held**
SIC: 3498 Fabricated pipe & fittings

(G-11015)
THROCK SUPPLY CO LLC
439 N West St (45133-1048)
PHONE..........................937 393-9276
Don D Throckmorton Jr,
Dale Throckmorton,
EMP: 4
SALES (est): 346.8K **Privately Held**
SIC: 3585 Heating & air conditioning combination units

(G-11016)
TOM HUDSON
Also Called: Hudson Drilling
6655 Us Highway 50 (45133-9193)
PHONE..........................937 393-1285
Thomas Hudson, *Owner*
EMP: 5 **EST:** 1952
SALES (est): 564.3K **Privately Held**
SIC: 1481 Test boring for nonmetallic minerals

(G-11017)
UNIT SETS INC
835 S High St (45133-9602)
PHONE..........................937 840-6123
Fax: 937 382-6005
Jon Cassner, *President*
Jon H Cassner, *President*
Brian Cassner, *Treasurer*
Beverly Chainy, *Manager*
Kathy Cassner, *Admin Sec*

EMP: 24
SQ FT: 25,000
SALES (est): 186.6K
SALES (corp-wide): 388.7K **Privately Held**
WEB: www.rotaryformspress.com
SIC: 2761 Unit sets (manifold business forms)
PA: Rotary Forms Press, Inc.
835 S High St
Hillsboro OH 45133
937 393-3426

(G-11018)
WEASTEC INCORPORATED (HQ)
1600 N High St (45133-9400)
PHONE..........................937 393-6800
Fax: 937 393-3020
Yasusuke Sugino, *President*
Kiyoshi Koide, *Chairman*
Robert Moots, *COO*
Bill Smith, *Senior VP*
Doug Ernst, *Prdtn Mgr*
▲ **EMP:** 222
SQ FT: 190,000
SALES (est): 69MM
SALES (corp-wide): 240.5MM **Privately Held**
WEB: www.weastec.com
SIC: 3714 Motor vehicle electrical equipment
PA: Toyo Denso Co., Ltd.
2-10-4, Shimbashi
Minato-Ku TKY 105-0
335 020-151

(G-11019)
WILLIAMSON SAFE INC
5631 State Route 73 (45133-9005)
PHONE..........................937 393-9919
Fax: 937 393-9586
J Edgar Williamson, *President*
Bing C Williamson, *Vice Pres*
Karl Boldman, *Purch Agent*
Katha Henson, *Accountant*
EMP: 34
SQ FT: 40,000
SALES (est): 4MM **Privately Held**
WEB: www.wsco.net
SIC: 3499 Safe deposit boxes or chests, metal; safes & vaults, metal

---

Hinckley
Medina County

(G-11020)
A-KOBAK CONTAINER COMPANY
1701 W 130th St (44233-9586)
P.O. Box 490 (44233-0490)
PHONE..........................330 225-7791
Fax: 330 225-1920
Gerald H Dolph, *President*
Edward Clark, *Vice Pres*
EMP: 15 **EST:** 1963
SQ FT: 40,000
SALES (est): 4.4MM **Privately Held**
SIC: 2653 Corrugated boxes, partitions, display items, sheets & pad; boxes, corrugated; made from purchased materials

(G-11021)
ALPINE CABINETS INC
1515 W 130th St Ste E (44233-9169)
PHONE..........................330 273-2131
Jim Artel, *President*
EMP: 4
SQ FT: 6,000
SALES (est): 460K **Privately Held**
SIC: 2434 Wood kitchen cabinets

(G-11022)
AMERICAN CUBE MOLD INC
Also Called: Acm
1515 W 130th St Ste C (44233-9169)
PHONE..........................330 558-0044
Fax: 330 558-0055
Frank J Kichurchak, *President*
Sylvia Hayes, *Treasurer*
EMP: 6
SQ FT: 3,800

SALES: 1.5MM **Privately Held**
SIC: 3544 3829 Industrial molds; testing equipment: abrasion, shearing strength, etc.

(G-11023)
CONTROLLED ACCESS INC
Also Called: Sentronic
1515 W 130th St Ste A (44233-9169)
PHONE..........................330 273-6185
Michelle Sherba, *President*
Sylvia Hayes, *Treasurer*
Debbie Mercier, *Sales Staff*
Mike Sherba, *Shareholder*
▲ **EMP:** 16
SQ FT: 10,000
SALES: 2.6MM **Privately Held**
WEB: www.controlledaccess.com
SIC: 3829 Turnstiles, equipped with counting mechanisms

(G-11024)
GREAT LAKES STAIR & MLLWK CO
1545 W 130th St Ste A1 (44233-9168)
PHONE..........................330 225-2005
Fax: 330 225-6001
Tim Noonan, *President*
Barb Noonan, *Corp Secy*
EMP: 7
SQ FT: 7,500
SALES: 1MM **Privately Held**
WEB: www.stair.com
SIC: 2431 5031 Staircases & stairs, wood; doors & windows; door frames, all materials; windows

(G-11025)
HINCKLEY WOOD PRODUCTS
1545 W 130th St (44233-9121)
PHONE..........................330 220-9999
Tim Noonan, *President*
EMP: 15
SALES (est): 1.4MM **Privately Held**
SIC: 2431 Staircases & stairs, wood

(G-11026)
JAMAR PRECISION GRINDING CO
2661 Center Rd (44233-9562)
PHONE..........................330 220-0099
John Hatala, *President*
EMP: 48
SALES (est): 7.9MM **Privately Held**
SIC: 3599 Grinding castings for the trade

(G-11027)
LIBERTY MOLD & MACHINE COMPANY
1369 Ridge Rd Ste B (44233-9297)
P.O. Box 193 (44233-0193)
PHONE..........................330 278-7825
Fax: 330 278-2609
John Babich, *President*
Joel Babich, *President*
Jim Babich, *General Mgr*
EMP: 3
SQ FT: 2,200
SALES: 600K **Privately Held**
SIC: 3544 Dies, plastics forming; forms (molds), for foundry & plastics working machinery

(G-11028)
PERFORMANCE POINT GRINDING
1669 W 130th St Ste 302 (44233-9104)
PHONE..........................330 220-0871
Aaron Vanke, *Owner*
EMP: 3
SALES: 300K **Privately Held**
SIC: 3599 Grinding castings for the trade

(G-11029)
STRICODYNARAD CORP
605 Ledge Rd (44233-9733)
PHONE..........................330 239-0005
Dave Kozman, *Manager*
EMP: 15 **EST:** 1999
SALES (est): 1.1MM **Privately Held**
WEB: www.strikodynarad.com
SIC: 3567 Industrial furnaces & ovens

(G-11030)
TARANTULA PERFORMANCE RACG LLC
Also Called: Tpr
1669 W 130th St Ste 301 (44233-9104)
PHONE..........................330 273-3456
Bryan Fredmonsky,
Jim Clopp,
Steve Fredmonsky,
◆ **EMP:** 3
SQ FT: 15,000
SALES (est): 108.9K **Privately Held**
SIC: 3751 Motorcycles, bicycles & parts

(G-11031)
TURNWOOD INDUSTRIES INC
365 State Rd (44233-9634)
PHONE..........................330 278-2421
Peter Svilar, *President*
Steve Svilar, *Vice Pres*
EMP: 26
SQ FT: 26,000
SALES (est): 1.7MM **Privately Held**
WEB: www.turnwoodinc.com
SIC: 2431 2434 Millwork; interior & ornamental woodwork & trim; wood kitchen cabinets

(G-11032)
ZS CREAM & BEAN
2706 Boston Rd (44233-9498)
PHONE..........................440 652-6369
Lawrence Zirker, *Principal*
EMP: 5
SALES (est): 419.8K **Privately Held**
SIC: 2024 Ice cream, bulk

Hiram
Portage County

(G-11033)
DURAMAX GLOBAL CORP
Also Called: Duramax Marine
17990 Great Lakes Pkwy (44234-9681)
PHONE..........................440 834-5400
Richard Spangler, *Director*
Tammy Simsa, *Director*
EMP: 90
SQ FT: 65,000
SALES (est): 4MM **Privately Held**
SIC: 3061 Mechanical rubber goods

(G-11034)
DURAMAX MARINE LLC
17990 Great Lakes Pkwy (44234-9681)
PHONE..........................440 834-5400
Fax: 440 834-4950
Richard Spangler, *President*
Richard Lockhart, *General Mgr*
Jose Ovies, *General Mgr*
Cory Waggoner, *General Mgr*
Richard Darocha, *Opers Mgr*
◆ **EMP:** 85
SQ FT: 65,000
SALES (est): 29.8MM **Privately Held**
WEB: www.duracooler.com
SIC: 3531 Marine related equipment

(G-11035)
GARYS PALLET SALES
12680 Herr Dr (44234-9724)
PHONE..........................330 569-7676
EMP: 4 **EST:** 2010
SALES (est): 170K **Privately Held**
SIC: 2448 Pallets, wood & wood with metal

(G-11036)
GREAT LAKES CHEESE CO INC (PA)
17825 Great Lakes Pkwy (44234-9677)
P.O. Box 1806 (44234-1806)
PHONE..........................440 834-2500
Gary Vanic, *President*
Marcel Dasen, *Principal*
Hans Epprecht, *Principal*
Albert Z Meyers, *Principal*
John Epprecht, *Corp Secy*
◆ **EMP:** 500
SQ FT: 218,000
SALES (est): 1.4B **Privately Held**
WEB: www.greatlakescheese.com
SIC: 5143 2022 Cheese; natural cheese

(G-11037)
SAINT-GOBAIN CERAMICS PLAS INC
Saint-Gobain Crystals
17900 Great Lakes Pkwy (44234-9681)
PHONE..........................440 834-0061
Fax: 440 534-8047
Michael West, *Purch Mgr*
Gerald O'Shea, *Engineer*
Sandy Clarke, *Cust Mgr*
Tom Penninsky, *Manager*
Mike Mayhugh, *Technical Staff*
EMP: 210
SALES (corp-wide): 185.8MM **Privately Held**
WEB: www.sgceramics.com
SIC: 2819 Industrial inorganic chemicals
HQ: Saint-Gobain Ceramics & Plastics, Inc.
750 E Swedesford Rd
Valley Forge PA 19482

Holgate
Henry County

(G-11038)
OHIO MACHINED PRODUCTS INC
503 Joe E Brown Ave (43527-9804)
PHONE..........................419 264-2400
Gregory Timmons, *President*
EMP: 14
SQ FT: 18,000
SALES (est): 2.6MM **Privately Held**
WEB: www.omp-inc.com
SIC: 3451 Screw machine products

(G-11039)
PEREZ FOODS LLC
515 Richholt St (43527-7731)
P.O. Box 65 (43527-0065)
PHONE..........................419 264-0303
James McDaniel, *Mng Member*
EMP: 8
SQ FT: 5,000
SALES: 275K **Privately Held**
SIC: 2099 Tortillas, fresh or refrigerated

(G-11040)
RETTIG FAMILY PALLETS INC
G510 County Road 14 (43527-9781)
PHONE..........................419 264-1540
Robert Rettig, *President*
EMP: 10
SQ FT: 30,000
SALES (est): 1.2MM **Privately Held**
SIC: 2448 Wood pallets & skids

(G-11041)
ROZEVINK ENGINES LLC
14316 State Route 281 (43527-9775)
PHONE..........................419 789-1159
Jonathan Rozevink, *Principal*
▼ **EMP:** 3
SALES (est): 263.2K **Privately Held**
SIC: 3519 Gas engine rebuilding

(G-11042)
WARRIOR TRIKES INC
E366 County Road 13 (43527-9704)
PHONE..........................419 264-6008
Rod Cruey, *President*
EMP: 3
SALES: 70K **Privately Held**
SIC: 3751 Motorcycles, bicycles & parts

Holland
Lucas County

(G-11043)
ADDITIVE METAL ALLOYS LTD
1421 Holloway Rd Ste B (43528-8647)
PHONE..........................800 687-6110
Richard Meklus, *Principal*
EMP: 8 **EST:** 2014
SQ FT: 1,100
SALES (est): 518.5K **Privately Held**
SIC: 3399 Powder, metal

▲ = Import ▼=Export
◆ =Import/Export

(G-11044)
ALL COUNTY PHONE DIRECTORIES
Also Called: All County Phone Directory
7056 Wexford Hill Ln (43528-9101)
P.O. Box 130 (43528-0130)
PHONE.................................419 865-2464
Jamie Toland, *Owner*
EMP: 4
SQ FT: 800
SALES: 500K **Privately Held**
SIC: 2741 Directories, telephone: publishing only, not printed on site

(G-11045)
ARCLIN
7230 Lilac Ct (43528-8248)
PHONE.................................877 689-9145
Rick Bruyea, *Manager*
EMP: 3
SALES (est): 149.6K **Privately Held**
SIC: 2891 Adhesives & sealants

(G-11046)
BOLLINGER TOOL & DIE INC
959 Hamilton Dr (43528-8211)
PHONE.................................419 866-5180
Fax: 419 475-6611
Danny N Bollinger, *President*
Anne Bollinger, *Vice Pres*
EMP: 7
SQ FT: 6,700
SALES: 950K **Privately Held**
SIC: 3544 Special dies, tools, jigs & fixtures

(G-11047)
BUNTING BEARINGS LLC (PA)
1001 Holland Park Blvd (43528-9287)
P.O. Box 729 (43528-0729)
PHONE.................................419 866-7000
Fax: 419 866-0653
Thomas Kwiatkowski, *President*
Keith Brown, *Chairman*
Dale Kucaj, *Corp Secy*
George Mugford, *COO*
Patrick F Taylor, *Vice Pres*
▲ EMP: 75
SQ FT: 94,000
SALES (est): 60.4MM **Privately Held**
SIC: 3566 3366 Speed changers, drives & gears; brass foundry

(G-11048)
CAMEO COUNTERTOPS INC (PA)
1610 Kieswetter Rd (43528-8678)
PHONE.................................419 865-6371
Brian Hudock, *President*
Tim Sorokin, *Vice Pres*
Sandy Garrett, *Sales Associate*
EMP: 9
SQ FT: 22,000
SALES (est): 3.7MM **Privately Held**
WEB: www.cameocountertops.com
SIC: 2541 5031 2821 Counter & sink tops; lumber, plywood & millwork; plastics materials & resins

(G-11049)
CREATIVE PRODUCTS INC
Also Called: CPI
1430 Kieswetter Rd (43528-9785)
PHONE.................................419 866-5501
Marvin Smith, *President*
EMP: 33
SQ FT: 26,000
SALES (est): 1.8MM **Privately Held**
SIC: 5023 5211 2541 Kitchen tools & utensils; cabinets, kitchen; counter tops; wood partitions & fixtures

(G-11050)
CUSTOM COLOR MATCH AND SPC
Also Called: Watkins Auto Body Shop
8930 Airport Hwy (43528-9604)
PHONE.................................419 868-5882
Menuel Fajardo, *Owner*
EMP: 3
SALES (est): 130K **Privately Held**
SIC: 3479 Painting, coating & hot dipping

(G-11051)
CUSTOM DESIGN & TOOL
8900 Geiser Rd (43528-9022)
PHONE.................................419 865-9773
Chuck Bolanger, *President*
EMP: 4
SQ FT: 6,719
SALES (est): 429.3K **Privately Held**
SIC: 3544 Special dies, tools, jigs & fixtures

(G-11052)
D & J DISTRIBUTING & MFG
Also Called: Exotica Fresheners Co
1302 Holloway Rd (43528-9538)
PHONE.................................419 865-2552
Oussama Elassir, *President*
Sean Alecphair, *Business Mgr*
Adnan Elassir, *Vice Pres*
Danny Elassir, *Director*
▲ EMP: 20
SQ FT: 45,000
SALES (est): 4.2MM **Privately Held**
SIC: 2842 Sanitation preparations, disinfectants & deodorants

(G-11053)
DAILY DOG
8325 Hill Ave (43528-9192)
PHONE.................................419 708-4923
Jennifer Bettinger, *Principal*
EMP: 3
SALES (est): 143.2K **Privately Held**
SIC: 2711 Newspapers, publishing & printing

(G-11054)
DESIGNETICS INC (PA)
1624 Eber Rd (43528-9776)
PHONE.................................419 866-0700
Fax: 419 866-0767
Craig Williams, *President*
Charles Barnhart, *Research*
Donald Welch, *Controller*
Brad Spraw, *Sales Dir*
Ken Dewood, *Sales Mgr*
EMP: 58
SQ FT: 20,000
SALES (est): 9MM **Privately Held**
WEB: www.designetics.com
SIC: 3559 3991 Automotive related machinery; brooms & brushes

(G-11055)
DOYLE MANUFACTURING INC
Also Called: Shamrock Molded Products
1440 Holloway Rd (43528-8608)
PHONE.................................419 865-2548
Fax: 419 865-3326
Michael A Doyle, *President*
Linda Doyle, *Corp Secy*
Carol Darrah, *Purchasing*
Keith Parker, *QC Mgr*
Marlene McCartney, *Manager*
EMP: 70
SQ FT: 100,000
SALES (est): 10.3MM **Privately Held**
WEB: www.doyleshamrock.com
SIC: 3089 3544 Injection molding of plastics; special dies, tools, jigs & fixtures

(G-11056)
DREAMSCAPE MEDIA LLC (PA)
1417 Timber Wolf Dr (43528-8302)
PHONE.................................877 983-7326
Bradley Rose, *General Mgr*
Michael Olah, *Opers Staff*
EMP: 8 EST: 2011
SALES (est): 845.2K **Privately Held**
SIC: 2731 Book publishing

(G-11057)
DRS INDUSTRIES INC
1067 Hamilton Dr (43528-8165)
PHONE.................................419 861-0334
Fax: 419 861-0338
J Peter Hottois, *President*
Tracy King, *Manager*
Lorie Watson, *Manager*
Angie Colburn, *Administration*
EMP: 65
SQ FT: 28,120
SALES (est): 28MM **Privately Held**
WEB: www.drsinc.com
SIC: 2819 3089 Aluminum compounds; injection molding of plastics

(G-11058)
DURA TEMP CORPORATION
949 S Mccord Rd (43528-8695)
PHONE.................................419 866-4348
Fax: 419 866-4656
Dave Rollins, *President*
Luc Lutters, *Sales Staff*
Erica Wilkowski, *Manager*
EMP: 13
SQ FT: 6,000
SALES (est): 3MM **Privately Held**
WEB: www.duratemp.com
SIC: 3559 3221 Glass making machinery: blowing, molding, forming, etc.; glass containers

(G-11059)
ELECTRONIC CONCEPTS ENGRG INC
Also Called: E C E
1465 Timber Wolf Dr (43528-8302)
PHONE.................................419 861-9000
Fax: 419 861-9001
Karl W Swonger Jr, *President*
Scott Nofzinger, *QC Mgr*
Rick Mills, *Engineer*
Steve Underwood, *Sales Engr*
Dan Kerry, *Manager*
EMP: 14
SQ FT: 17,900
SALES (est): 2MM **Privately Held**
WEB: www.eceinc.com
SIC: 7371 8731 3728 7373 Computer software development; electronic research; aircraft assemblies, subassemblies & parts; computer integrated systems design

(G-11060)
FINISHING MACHINE INC
707 Lost Lakes Dr (43528-8483)
PHONE.................................419 491-0197
Robert Motz, *President*
Sharon Volpe, *Sr Corp Ofcr*
Christine Motz, *Treasurer*
Lisa Cox, *Financial Exec*
Lisa Volpe, *Financial Exec*
EMP: 23
SQ FT: 12,000
SALES (est): 2.2MM **Privately Held**
WEB: www.finishingmachine.com
SIC: 3599 Machine shop, jobbing & repair

(G-11061)
FIRE NATION LTD
Also Called: Fire Nation Glassline Stud
7166 Front St (43528-8295)
P.O. Box 521 (43528-0521)
PHONE.................................419 866-6288
Fax: 419 866-6288
Matt Paskiet, *Owner*
EMP: 10
SQ FT: 4,550
SALES (est): 457.4K **Privately Held**
SIC: 3231 Art glass: made from purchased glass

(G-11062)
GENERIC SYSTEMS INC
10560 Geiser Rd (43528-8506)
PHONE.................................419 841-8460
Fax: 419 843-1420
Michael McLaughlin, *President*
James Fletcher, *Vice Pres*
EMP: 15
SQ FT: 12,000
SALES (est): 3.4MM **Privately Held**
WEB: www.genericsys.com
SIC: 3549 7373 7371 Assembly machines, including robotic; systems integration services; computer software development & applications

(G-11063)
HAMILTON MANUFACTURING CORP
1026 Hamilton Dr (43528-8210)
PHONE.................................419 867-4858
Fax: 419 867-4850
Robin Ritz, *CEO*
Steve Alt, *President*
Bonnie Osborne, *Exec VP*
Jill Snyder, *Buyer*
Bill Irwin, *Engineer*
EMP: 45 EST: 1921

SQ FT: 32,000
SALES (est): 10.2MM **Privately Held**
WEB: www.hamiltonmfg.com
SIC: 3172 8711 Coin purses; designing: ship, boat, machine & product

(G-11064)
ICO PRODUCTS LLC
6415 Angola Rd (43528-8555)
PHONE.................................419 867-3900
Chuck Ames, *Marketing Staff*
Bryan Bay, *Manager*
Ligue Zhao,
Michael Zhao,
▲ EMP: 3
SALES: 6MM **Privately Held**
WEB: www.icoproducts.com
SIC: 3089 Injection molding of plastics

(G-11065)
IMAGE GROUP INC
1255 Corporate Dr (43528-9590)
PHONE.................................419 866-3300
Fax: 419 866-3309
Brian Kingsmore, *General Mgr*
Troy Hill, *Sales Dir*
Danielle Bauhaus, *Accounts Mgr*
John Livingston, *Accounts Mgr*
Scott Loehrke, *Accounts Mgr*
EMP: 3
SALES (est): 199.8K **Privately Held**
SIC: 2261 Screen printing of cotton broadwoven fabrics

(G-11066)
IMAGE GROUP OF TOLEDO INC
1255 Corporate Dr (43528-9590)
P.O. Box 1147 (43528-1147)
PHONE.................................419 866-3300
Jon M Levine, *CEO*
Tom Herman, *Principal*
Linda Gomez, *Prdtn Mgr*
Marge Bollman, *Controller*
Judy Maiorana, *VP Sales*
◆ EMP: 44 EST: 1989
SQ FT: 29,400
SALES (est): 7.9MM **Privately Held**
WEB: www.theimagegroup.net
SIC: 2261 Screen printing of cotton broadwoven fabrics

(G-11067)
JEFFREY A CLARK
Also Called: Bad Brush Design
148 N King Rd (43528-8768)
PHONE.................................419 866-8775
Jeffrey A Clark, *Owner*
EMP: 5 EST: 1990
SQ FT: 2,800
SALES: 180K **Privately Held**
WEB: www.badbrush.com
SIC: 7336 3993 Commercial art & graphic design; signs & advertising specialties

(G-11068)
JOHNSON CONTRLS BTRY GROUP INC
10300 Industrial St (43528-9791)
PHONE.................................419 865-6155
Fax: 419 865-6155
Aaron Byrne, *Opers-Prdtn-Mfg*
John Feindt, *Controller*
Kiri Ort, *Executive*
EMP: 600 **Privately Held**
SIC: 3691 Batteries, rechargeable
HQ: Johnson Controls Battery Group Inc.
5757 N Green Bay Ave
Milwaukee WI 53209
414 524-1200

(G-11069)
KERN-LIEBERS TEXAS INC
1510 Albon Rd (43528-8684)
PHONE.................................419 865-2437
Hannes Stein, *CEO*
Jose Castellanos, *Controller*
EMP: 30 EST: 1988
SALES: 67.8MM **Privately Held**
SIC: 3495 Wire springs

(G-11070)
KERN-LIEBERS USA INC (HQ)
1510 Albon Rd (43528-9159)
P.O. Box 396 (43528-0396)
PHONE.................................419 865-2437
Fax: 419 865-2738

Hans Jocheim Steim, *Ch of Bd*
Lothar Bauerle, *President*
Scott Sevits, *Engineer*
Gert Wagner, *Treasurer*
Craig Trares, *Controller*
▲ **EMP:** 60 **EST:** 1977
SQ FT: 40,000
SALES (est): 19.5MM
SALES (corp-wide): 702.8MM **Privately Held**
SIC: 3495 3493 Mechanical springs, precision; steel springs, except wire
PA: Hugo Kern Und Liebers Gmbh & Co.
Kg Platinen- Und Federnfabrik
Dr.-Kurt-Steim-Str. 35
Schramberg 78713
742 251-10

(G-11071)
MATHESON TRI-GAS INC
1720 Trade Rd (43528-8202)
PHONE......................................419 865-8881
Fax: 419 865-7194
Wayne McConndll, *Plant Mgr*
Craig Morton, *Manager*
Greg Alexander, *Manager*
EMP: 16
SQ FT: 18,120
SALES (corp-wide): 5.4B **Privately Held**
WEB: www.airliquide.com
SIC: 2813 5084 Industrial gases; nitrogen; oxygen, compressed or liquefied; argon; welding machinery & equipment; safety equipment
HQ: Matheson Tri-Gas, Inc.
150 Allen Rd Ste 302
Basking Ridge NJ 07920
908 991-9200

(G-11072)
MESTEK INC
American Warming & Vent Div
7301 International Dr (43528-9412)
PHONE......................................419 288-2703
Fax: 419 865-1375
Richard McKnight, *Exec VP*
M Almaguer, *Vice Pres*
Phil Larosa, *Vice Pres*
R Lichtenwald, *Vice Pres*
E Shepler, *Vice Pres*
EMP: 61
SQ FT: 18,000
SALES (corp-wide): 482.1MM **Privately Held**
SIC: 3822 3444 3442 Air flow controllers, air conditioning & refrigeration; sheet metalwork; metal doors, sash & trim
PA: Mestek, Inc.
260 N Elm St
Westfield MA 01085
413 568-9571

(G-11073)
NATIONAL COMPRESSOR SVCS LLC
10349 Industrial St (43528-9791)
P.O. Box 760 (43528-0760)
PHONE......................................419 865-3126
Brenda Sevenski, *Purch Mgr*
Ann Jeffries, *Office Mgr*
Erik E Babcock, *Mng Member*
Bill Rost, *Manager*
EMP: 46
SQ FT: 60,000
SALES: 8MM **Privately Held**
SIC: 3563 Air & gas compressors including vacuum pumps

(G-11074)
NATIONAL ILLMINATION SIGN CORP
6525 Angola Rd (43528-9651)
P.O. Box 563 (43528-0563)
PHONE......................................419 866-1666
Fax: 419 866-5731
George L Jeakle, *President*
Neil Jeakle, *Vice Pres*
Cindy Studebaker, *Admin Mgr*
EMP: 9
SQ FT: 18,200
SALES: 1MM **Privately Held**
SIC: 3993 Electric signs

(G-11075)
OTTAWA RUBBER COMPANY (PA)
1600 Commerce Rd (43528-8689)
P.O. Box 553 (43528-0553)
PHONE......................................419 865-1378
Fax: 419 865-8249
Mike Bugert, *President*
James H Bugert, *Plant Mgr*
Chuck Bodi, *Treasurer*
Jeff Bretz, *Sales Staff*
Lori Heldt, *Office Mgr*
EMP: 17 **EST:** 1945
SQ FT: 12,000
SALES (est): 10.5MM **Privately Held**
WEB: www.ottawarubber.com
SIC: 3061 Mechanical rubber goods

(G-11076)
PATRIOT PRODUCTS INC
Also Called: Patriot Mobility
1133 Corporate Dr Ste B (43528-7405)
P.O. Box 850 (43528-0850)
PHONE......................................419 865-9712
Fax: 419 865-9721
Steven Grudzien, *President*
Trish Crandall, *Opers Mgr*
Ryan Wright, *Officer*
EMP: 15
SALES (est): 1.7MM **Privately Held**
SIC: 3841 Surgical & medical instruments

(G-11077)
PATTERSON COLBURNE (PA)
1100 S Hlland Sylvania Rd (43528)
PHONE......................................419 866-5544
Tony Colbourne, *Owner*
EMP: 6
SALES (est): 1.3MM **Privately Held**
WEB: www.rapatterson.com
SIC: 8721 7372 Accounting services, except auditing; prepackaged software

(G-11078)
PRECISION CUTOFF LLC
7400 Airport Hwy (43528-9545)
P.O. Box 1040 (43528-1040)
PHONE......................................419 866-8000
Duane Glase, *Purch Agent*
Jim Cannaley, *Mng Member*
EMP: 120
SQ FT: 150,000
SALES: 10MM **Privately Held**
WEB: www.woodsage.com
SIC: 3498 Tube fabricating (contract bending & shaping)

(G-11079)
PRINCIPLED DYNAMICS INC
6920 Hall St (43528-9485)
PHONE......................................419 351-6303
Gene Gunderson, *Principal*
Michael W Holmes, *Principal*
Robert E Holmes, *Principal*
James Swartz, *Principal*
Patricia Earl, *Vice Pres*
EMP: 9 **EST:** 2012
SALES (est): 1.2MM **Privately Held**
SIC: 2834 Pharmaceutical preparations

(G-11080)
RENNCO AUTOMATION SYSTEMS INC
971 Hamilton Dr (43528-8211)
PHONE......................................419 861-2340
Fax: 419 861-2342
Mike E Owens, *President*
Dave Miklos, *Vice Pres*
Dirk Albring, *Engineer*
Josh Kreager, *Program Mgr*
David Breese, *Director*
EMP: 30
SQ FT: 15,000
SALES (est): 8MM **Privately Held**
SIC: 3569 Robots, assembly line: industrial & commercial

(G-11081)
RG MOLD
8385 Water Park Dr (43528-7849)
PHONE......................................419 868-9390
Ramsey Ganoom, *Owner*
Lisa Ganoom, *Manager*
EMP: 3

SALES: 275K **Privately Held**
SIC: 3089 Automotive parts, plastic

(G-11082)
RNM HOLDINGS INC
1810 Eber Rd Ste C (43528-7898)
PHONE......................................419 867-8712
Matthew Milton, *President*
EMP: 20
SQ FT: 15,000
SALES (corp-wide): 38.3MM **Privately Held**
SIC: 5084 3536 Cranes, industrial; hoists; hoists, cranes & monorails; cranes, industrial plant; cranes, overhead traveling; cranes & monorail systems
PA: Rnm Holdings, Inc.
550 Conover Dr
Franklin OH 45005
937 704-9900

(G-11083)
SCHENA COMPANY LTD
Also Called: Midwest Granite & Stone
7710 Hill Ave Ste B (43528-7607)
PHONE......................................419 868-5207
Fax: 419 868-5850
Don Schena, *President*
David Schena, *Vice Pres*
EMP: 5
SQ FT: 8,000
SALES: 450K **Privately Held**
WEB: www.midwestgraniteandstone.com
SIC: 3281 Granite, cut & shaped

(G-11084)
SCHINDLER ELEVATOR CORPORATION
1530 Timber Wolf Dr (43528-9161)
P.O. Box 960 (43528-0960)
PHONE......................................419 861-5900
Fax: 419 867-5901
Don Mette, *Facilities Mgr*
Dennis Meyer, *Warehouse Mgr*
Brian Robbins, *Human Resources*
Mark Kershner, *Manager*
David Tenhoeve, *Analyst*
EMP: 26
SALES (corp-wide): 9.5B **Privately Held**
WEB: www.us.schindler.com
SIC: 3534 7699 Elevators & equipment; escalators, passenger & freight; elevators: inspection, service & repair
HQ: Schindler Elevator Corporation
20 Whippany Rd
Morristown NJ 07960
973 397-6500

(G-11085)
SELCO INDUSTRIES INC
1590 Albon Rd Ste 1 (43528-9410)
PHONE......................................419 861-0336
Ruby Hill, *CEO*
Seldon Hill, *President*
Keonda Banks, *Manager*
Sharon Taylor, *Administration*
EMP: 190
SQ FT: 17,000
SALES (est): 29.3MM **Privately Held**
SIC: 2678 Papeteries & writing paper sets

(G-11086)
SOLAR CON INC
7134 Railroad St (43528-9539)
P.O. Box 176 (43528-0176)
PHONE......................................419 865-5877
Fax: 419 865-9449
Donald Wells, *Ch of Bd*
Suzanna Wells, *Treasurer*
J Patrick Dooley Jr, *Marketing Staff*
Shannon Caswell, *Systems Mgr*
EMP: 45
SQ FT: 26,725
SALES (est): 6.3MM **Privately Held**
WEB: www.solarcon.com
SIC: 3679 3663 Antennas, receiving; radio & TV communications equipment

(G-11087)
SPONSELLER GROUP INC (PA)
1600 Timber Wolf Dr (43528-8303)
PHONE......................................419 861-3000
Fax: 419 861-3004
Keith Sponseller, *President*
Harold P Sponseller, *Chairman*
Kevin R Nevius, *Vice Pres*

David Nowak, *Vice Pres*
Joe Jackson, *Project Mgr*
EMP: 44
SQ FT: 8,900
SALES (est): 8.7MM **Privately Held**
SIC: 8711 3599 Consulting engineer; machine shop, jobbing & repair

(G-11088)
TEKNI-PLEX INC
Also Called: Global Technology Center
1445 Timber Wolf Dr (43528-8302)
PHONE......................................419 491-2407
Paul J Young, *CEO*
Phil Bourgeois, *Vice Pres*
Edward McKinley, *Director*
EMP: 21 **EST:** 1967
SALES (est): 4.6MM
SALES (corp-wide): 1.1B **Privately Held**
SIC: 2679 7389 2672 Egg cartons, molded pulp: made from purchased material; packaging & labeling services; cloth lined paper: made from purchased paper
PA: Tekni-Plex, Inc.
460 E Swedesford Rd # 3000
Wayne PA 19087
484 690-1520

(G-11089)
TMB ENTERPRISES LLC
Also Called: Haas Jordan Company
6509 Angola Rd (43528-9651)
PHONE......................................419 243-2189
Todd Blackmar, *President*
David F Waltz, *President*
Thomas A Waltz, *Vice Pres*
Jeffrey Cohen, *Treasurer*
EMP: 10 **EST:** 1899
SQ FT: 25,000
SALES (est): 1.6MM **Privately Held**
WEB: www.haas-jordan.com
SIC: 3999 Umbrellas, canes & parts

(G-11090)
TOLEDO TRANSDUCERS INC
Also Called: Toledo Integrated Systems
6834 Spring Valley Dr # 3 (43528-7864)
PHONE......................................419 724-4170
Fax: 419 867-4180
Mark Storer, *President*
Gene Gautz, *Vice Pres*
John Everson, *Engineer*
Randall W Seed, *Treasurer*
Lyn Espino, *Asst Controller*
EMP: 40 **EST:** 1976
SQ FT: 16,000
SALES (est): 10.5MM **Privately Held**
WEB: www.toledointegratedsystems.com
SIC: 3823 3829 3625 3613 Industrial instrmnts msrmnt display/control process variable; measuring & controlling devices; relays & industrial controls; switchgear & switchboard apparatus

(G-11091)
TRANE COMPANY
Also Called: Ingersoll Rand
1001 Hamilton Dr (43528-8210)
PHONE......................................419 491-2278
Dennis Goldsmith, *Branch Mgr*
EMP: 12 **Privately Held**
SIC: 3585 Heating equipment, complete
HQ: The Trane Company
3600 Pammel Creek Rd
La Crosse WI 54601
608 787-2000

(G-11092)
TRONAIR INC (DH)
1740 Eber Rd Ste E (43528-9138)
PHONE......................................419 866-6301
Fax: 419 867-0634
Harley Kaplan, *CEO*
Mark Iddon, *President*
Patrick Caligiuri, *General Mgr*
Dawn Deshetler, *General Mgr*
Jeffrey Lee, *Corp Secy*
◆ **EMP:** 100
SQ FT: 80,000
SALES: 35MM
SALES (corp-wide): 7.4B **Privately Held**
WEB: www.tronair.com
SIC: 3728 Aircraft parts & equipment

HQ: Tronair Parent, Inc.
1740 Eber Rd Ste E
Holland OH 43528
419 866-6301

(G-11093)
TRONAIR PARENT INC (HQ)
1740 Eber Rd Ste E (43528-9138)
PHONE....................................419 866-6301
Harley Kaplan, *CEO*
Jeffrey Lee, *Corp Secy*
EMP: 0
SQ FT: 110,000
SALES (est): 6MM
SALES (corp-wide): 7.4B **Privately Held**
SIC: 6719 3728 Investment holding com-
panies, except banks; aircraft parts &
equipment
PA: Golden Gate Capital Lp
1 Embarcadero Ctr # 3900
San Francisco CA 94111
415 983-2700

(G-11094)
TURBINE STANDARD LTD (PA)
10550 Industrial St (43528-7732)
PHONE....................................419 865-0355
David R Corwin, *Partner*
Patty Kops, *Partner*
Cheri Lehnertz, *Mktg Coord*
Dave Campbell, *Manager*
Julia Ruger, *Manager*
▲ EMP: 17
SALES (est): 4.1MM **Privately Held**
WEB: www.turbinestandard.com
SIC: 3724 Aircraft engines & engine parts

(G-11095)
VINYL DESIGN CORPORATION
7856 Hill Ave (43528-9181)
PHONE....................................419 283-4009
Fax: 419 865-4453
Patrick J Trompeter, *President*
Joe Shoots, *General Mgr*
EMP: 29
SQ FT: 36,000
SALES (est): 5.8MM **Privately Held**
WEB: www.vinyldesigncorp.com
SIC: 3089 5033 2452 Windows, plastic;
siding, except wood; prefabricated wood
buildings

(G-11096)
WETTLE CORPORATION
952 Holland Park Blvd (43528-9279)
PHONE....................................419 865-6923
Heather Wettle, *Principal*
EMP: 4
SALES (est): 471.1K **Privately Held**
SIC: 3993 Signs & advertising specialties

(G-11097)
WOODSAGE CORPORATION
7400 Airport Hwy (43528-9545)
PHONE....................................419 476-3553
Curtis Bowers, *Branch Mgr*
EMP: 70
SALES (corp-wide): 3.1MM **Privately
Held**
SIC: 3498 Tube fabricating (contract bend-
ing & shaping)
PA: Woodsage Corporation
7400 Airport Hwy
Holland OH 43528
419 866-8000

(G-11098)
WOODSAGE LLC
7400 Airport Hwy (43528-9545)
P.O. Box 1040 (43528-1040)
PHONE....................................419 866-8000
Daniel Brown, *CEO*
Curtis Bowers, *Vice Pres*
Mick Bryan, *Vice Pres*
EMP: 110
SQ FT: 150,000
SALES (est): 150K **Privately Held**
SIC: 3317 Steel pipe & tubes

Holmesville
Holmes County

(G-11099)
ACTION COUPLING & EQP INC
8248 County Road 245 (44633-9724)
P.O. Box 99 (44633-0099)
PHONE....................................330 279-4242
Fax: 330 279-4208
Scott Eliot, *President*
Mike Franks, *Purchasing*
Jean Elliot, *Accounts Mgr*
▲ EMP: 80
SQ FT: 75,000
SALES (est): 18.1MM **Privately Held**
WEB: www.actiongolfcarts.com
SIC: 3569 5087 3429 Firefighting appara-
tus & related equipment; firefighting
equipment; manufactured hardware (gen-
eral)

(G-11100)
CLASSIC METALS LTD
7051 State Route 83 (44633-9603)
PHONE....................................330 763-1162
Fax: 330 674-7052
John E Yoder, *Principal*
EMP: 5 EST: 2008
SALES (est): 547.2K **Privately Held**
SIC: 2952 Roofing materials

(G-11101)
H I SMITH OIL & GAS INC
8255 County Road 192 (44633)
PHONE....................................330 279-2361
Kenny Jacobs, *President*
Tammy Haubenschield, *Corp Secy*
EMP: 3
SALES: 210K **Privately Held**
SIC: 1311 Crude petroleum production;
natural gas production

(G-11102)
**HEARTLAND STAIRWAYS INC
(PA)**
8230 County Road 245 (44633)
PHONE....................................330 279-2554
Roy Hostewtler, *President*
Delon Shetler, *Vice Pres*
Brad Rippel, *Natl Sales Mgr*
EMP: 11
SQ FT: 17,000
SALES: 1.7MM **Privately Held**
SIC: 3534 Elevators & moving stairways

(G-11103)
HEARTLAND STAIRWAYS INC
Township Road 245 (44633)
PHONE....................................330 279-2554
Fax: 330 695-9905
EMP: 8
SALES: 1MM **Privately Held**
SIC: 3534 Mfg Elevators/Escalators

(G-11104)
HOLMES STAIR PARTS LTD
8614 Township Road 561 (44633-9706)
PHONE....................................330 279-2797
Ben R Hershberger, *Owner*
Arlyn Hershberger,
EMP: 20
SALES (est): 3.9MM **Privately Held**
SIC: 3534 Elevators & moving stairways

(G-11105)
HOLMES SUPPLY CORP
7571 State Route 83 (44633-9633)
PHONE....................................330 279-2634
Steve Schlabach, *President*
EMP: 9
SALES (est): 1.2MM **Privately Held**
SIC: 3299 2951 1442 Sand lime products;
asphalt paving mixtures & blocks; con-
struction sand & gravel

(G-11106)
HOLMES WHEEL SHOP INC
Also Called: American Stirrup
7969 County Road 189 (44633-9756)
P.O. Box 56 (44633-0056)
PHONE....................................330 279-2891
Fax: 330 279-3605
Ronald Clark, *President*

Paul Stutzman, *Vice Pres*
▲ EMP: 20
SQ FT: 32,000
SALES (est): 2.4MM **Privately Held**
SIC: 2499 3199 Spools, reels & pulleys:
wood; stirrups, wood or metal

(G-11107)
IAC HOLMESVILLE LLC
8281 County Road 245 (44633)
PHONE....................................330 279-4505
Robert S Miller, *President*
Tim Brown, *Purch Agent*
EMP: 14
SALES (est): 2.4MM **Privately Held**
WEB: www.iaaawards.com
SIC: 3089 Automotive parts, plastic
HQ: International Automotive Components
Group North America, Inc.
28333 Telegraph Rd
Southfield MI 48034
248 455-7000

(G-11108)
INTERNATIONAL AUTOMOTIVE
8281 County Road 245 (44633-9724)
P.O. Box 115 (44633-0115)
PHONE....................................330 279-6557
Kim Landall, *Principal*
EMP: 10
SALES (est): 1.3MM **Privately Held**
SIC: 3069 Hard rubber products

(G-11109)
MILLER LOGGING INC
8373 State Route 83 (44633-9726)
P.O. Box 86 (44633-0086)
PHONE....................................330 279-4721
Fax: 330 279-3865
Roy A Miller Jr, *President*
Levi Miller, *Corp Secy*
Barbara Miller, *Vice Pres*
EMP: 28
SALES: 1.7MM **Privately Held**
SIC: 2421 1629 2411 Wood chips, pro-
duced at mill; land clearing contractor;
logging

(G-11110)
ROTO SOLUTIONS INC
8300 County Rd 189 (44633)
P.O. Box 100 (44633-0100)
PHONE....................................330 279-2424
Richard Cook, *President*
Ralph Kirkpatrick, *Vice Pres*
Mark Scheibe, *Vice Pres*
EMP: 100
SALES (est): 11.6MM **Privately Held**
WEB: www.rotosolutions.com
SIC: 3089 Blow molded finished plastic
products; injection molded finished plastic
products; extruded finished plastic prod-
ucts

(G-11111)
RPI OF INDIANA INC
8339 County Road 245 (44633-9724)
P.O. Box 38 (44633-0038)
PHONE....................................330 279-2421
Adrienne Cooper, *CEO*
Mike McVicker, *President*
Michael Littwin, *Controller*
Carl Kennedy, *Sales Executive*
Renee Sipes, *Office Mgr*
EMP: 31
SQ FT: 20,000
SALES (est): 6.7MM **Privately Held**
WEB: www.rpicontainers.com
SIC: 3443 Dumpsters, garbage

(G-11112)
SOMMERS FOODS INC
Also Called: Sommers Noodles
6399 State Route 83 (44633-9636)
P.O. Box 710, Sugarcreek (44681-0710)
PHONE....................................888 906-7452
Carma Miller, *CEO*
Oscar Monroy, *COO*
EMP: 4
SQ FT: 6,000
SALES (est): 309.7K **Privately Held**
SIC: 2098 Noodles (e.g. egg, plain &
water), dry

Homer
Licking County

(G-11113)
OHIO STATE PALLET CORP
2175 Broehm Rd (43027)
PHONE....................................614 332-3961
Teresa Salyers, *Principal*
EMP: 4
SALES (est): 339.3K **Privately Held**
SIC: 2448 Pallets, wood & wood with metal

Homerville
Medina County

(G-11114)
PRINT MARKETING INC
11820 Black River Schl Rd (44235-9716)
PHONE....................................330 625-1500
Fax: 330 625-1515
Robert Rodman, *President*
▲ EMP: 20
SQ FT: 1,854
SALES: 5.5MM **Privately Held**
SIC: 2752 Commercial printing, offset

Homeworth
Columbiana County

(G-11115)
**BUCKMAN MACHINE WORKS
INC**
24841 Georgetown Rd (44634-9522)
PHONE....................................330 525-7665
Dale L Buckman, *President*
Marylou Buckman, *Vice Pres*
EMP: 5
SALES: 100K **Privately Held**
WEB: www.ohiodrill.com
SIC: 3011 Tires & inner tubes

(G-11116)
**HOMEWORTH FABRICATIONS &
MCHS**
23094 Georgetown Rd (44634)
P.O. Box 127 (44634-0127)
PHONE....................................330 525-5459
Ronald D Matz, *President*
Rocco Vizzuso, *Vice Pres*
Keri Steede, *Data Proc Dir*
EMP: 11
SQ FT: 3,000
SALES (est): 750K **Privately Held**
SIC: 3823 3544 Industrial instrmnts
msrmnt display/control process variable;
jigs & fixtures

(G-11117)
OHIO DRILL & TOOL CO (PA)
Also Called: Homeworth Sales Service Div
23255 Georgetown Rd (44634)
P.O. Box 154 (44634-0154)
PHONE....................................330 525-7717
Fax: 330 525-5432
George Sanor, *Ch of Bd*
Connie Hallman, *President*
Dale Buckman, *General Mgr*
Daniel Matz, *Vice Pres*
Joe Shopfer, *Sls & Mktg Exec*
EMP: 20
SQ FT: 5,000
SALES (est): 13.8MM **Privately Held**
SIC: 5085 5261 3546 3545 Industrial
tools; lawn & garden equipment; power-
driven handtools; machine tool acces-
sories

Hopedale
Harrison County

(G-11118)
HOPEDALE MINING LLC
86900 Sinfield Rd (43976)
P.O. Box 415 (43976-0415)
PHONE....................................740 937-2225

GEOGRAPHIC

David G Zatezalo,
EMP: 40
SALES (est): 5.9MM **Privately Held**
SIC: 1081 Metal mining services

Hopewell
Muskingum County

(G-11119)
J & M CONSTRUCTION LLP
8780 Hopewell National Rd (43746-9791)
PHONE..................................740 454-8986
Fax: 740 454-8983
Jonathan Mast, *Managing Prtnr*
Ervin Zook, *Partner*
EMP: 5
SALES (est): 673.1K **Privately Held**
SIC: 3089 Prefabricated plastic buildings

Houston
Shelby County

(G-11120)
BLUE WOLFE AIR SYSTEMS INC
5611 Houston Rd (45333-9729)
PHONE..................................937 295-3632
Janice E Wolfe, *Principal*
EMP: 4
SALES (est): 330.6K **Privately Held**
SIC: 3822 Pressure controllers, air-conditioning system type

(G-11121)
GLAZIER PATTERN & COACH
3720 Loramie Wash Rd (45333-9714)
PHONE..................................937 492-7355
Steve R Glazier, *Owner*
EMP: 3
SALES: 130K **Privately Held**
WEB: www.gpcw.com
SIC: 3543 Industrial patterns

Howard
Knox County

(G-11122)
BAM FUEL INC
21191 Floralwood Dr (43028-9649)
PHONE..................................740 397-6674
Beth A Mickley, *Principal*
EMP: 3
SALES (est): 317.2K **Privately Held**
SIC: 2869 Fuels

(G-11123)
KACY STAIRS
Also Called: Kacy Architectural Millwork
19762 Nunda Rd (43028-9657)
PHONE..................................740 599-5201
Fax: 740 599-5229
Kevin Noble, *President*
Dave Noble, *Treasurer*
Linda Noble, *Bookkeeper*
EMP: 11
SQ FT: 10,000
SALES (est): 1.3MM **Privately Held**
SIC: 2431 Staircases & stairs, wood

(G-11124)
PREMIER SILICA LLC
Also Called: Millwood Plant
26900 Coshocton Rd (43028-9216)
PHONE..................................740 599-7773
Fax: 740 599-5134
Steven Bell, *Manager*
EMP: 30
SALES (corp-wide): 3.8B **Publicly Held**
SIC: 3295 1446 1442 Minerals, ground or
treated; industrial sand; construction sand
& gravel
HQ: Premier Silica Llc
5205 N O Connor Blvd # 200
Irving TX 75039
972 444-9001

(G-11125)
YODER MANUFACTURING
7679 Flack Rd (43028-9740)
PHONE..................................740 504-5028
Noah E Yoder, *Principal*
EMP: 3 **EST:** 2001
SALES (est): 223.3K **Privately Held**
SIC: 3999 Manufacturing industries

Hubbard
Trumbull County

(G-11126)
B W ELECTRICAL & MAINT SVC
6204 Yungstown Hubbard Rd
(44425-1317)
P.O. Box 297 (44425-0297)
PHONE..................................330 534-7870
Bruce Wylie, *President*
EMP: 4
SQ FT: 625
SALES (est): 478.6K **Privately Held**
SIC: 7694 Electric motor repair

(G-11127)
BAKER HUGHES C/O TANGOE INC
8008 Truck World Blvd (44425-3210)
PHONE..................................304 884-6442
EMP: 3
SALES (est): 230.1K **Privately Held**
SIC: 3533 Oil & gas field machinery

(G-11128)
BALL AROSOL SPECIALTY CONT INC
644 Myon St (44425)
PHONE..................................330 534-9273
Gary Lohr, *Engineer*
Amy Braden, *Persnl Dir*
Bernie Grilli, *Manager*
Jim Boker, *IT/INT Sup*
Sarah Harkelich, *Director*
EMP: 129
SALES (corp-wide): 9B **Publicly Held**
SIC: 3411 Food & beverage containers
HQ: Ball Aerosol And Specialty Container Inc.
9308 W 108th Cir
Westminster CO 80021
303 469-5511

(G-11129)
BALL CORPORATION
644 Myron St (44425-1466)
PHONE..................................330 534-7418
Frank Candiotti, *Production*
Steve Hersher, *Production*
John Havalo, *Controller*
Amy Braden, *Persnl Dir*
Michael Maiella, *Manager*
EMP: 19
SALES (est): 3.5MM **Privately Held**
SIC: 3411 5199 Metal cans; food & beverage containers; packaging materials

(G-11130)
ELLWOOD ENGINEERED CASTINGS CO
7158 Hubbard Masury Rd (44425-9756)
PHONE..................................330 568-3000
Fax: 330 534-1660
David E Barensfeld, *CEO*
Kevin Handerhan, *President*
Jack Staiger, *General Mgr*
Susan A Apel, *Vice Pres*
Lyda Force, *Vice Pres*
◆ **EMP:** 135
SALES (est): 39.6MM
SALES (corp-wide): 774.9MM **Privately Held**
WEB: www.ellwoodgroup.com
SIC: 3321 3369 3322 Gray iron ingot
molds, cast; nonferrous foundries; malleable iron foundries
PA: Ellwood Group, Inc.
600 Commercial Ave
Ellwood City PA 16117
724 752-3680

(G-11131)
INDEPENDENCE 2 LLC
Also Called: I2
623 W Liberty St (44425-1750)
P.O. Box 40 (44425-0040)
PHONE..................................800 414-0545
Ronald P Baldine, *Managing Prtnr*
Bonnie L Buchanan, *Partner*
Nick Ingoedue, *Partner*
▲ **EMP:** 10
SQ FT: 10,000
SALES (est): 2MM **Privately Held**
SIC: 3429 Door locks, bolts & checks

(G-11132)
JAMES J FAIRBANKS COMPANY INC
7342 Hubbard Bedford Rd (44425-9736)
PHONE..................................330 534-1374
James J Fairbanks, *President*
EMP: 3
SALES (est): 172.3K **Privately Held**
SIC: 8611 3999 Manufacturers' institute;
barber & beauty shop equipment

(G-11133)
KILAR MANUFACTURING INC
2616 N Main St (44425-3246)
PHONE..................................330 534-8961
Marilyn Kilar, *President*
EMP: 30
SQ FT: 12,000
SALES (est): 4.7MM **Privately Held**
SIC: 3713 3714 Car carrier bodies; motor
vehicle parts & accessories

(G-11134)
MAGEROS CANDIES
132 N Main St (44425-1654)
PHONE..................................330 534-1146
Manuel Mageros, *Owner*
Pasciala Boukis, *Owner*
Helen Magereros, *Owner*
EMP: 5
SQ FT: 1,800
SALES (est): 267.4K **Privately Held**
WEB: www.clevelandwedding.com
SIC: 2066 Chocolate & cocoa products

(G-11135)
NANOLOGIX INC
843 N Main St (44425-1128)
PHONE..................................330 534-0800
Fax: 330 534-0826
Bret Barnhizer, *President*
Allen Dana, *Vice Pres*
Sergey Gazenko, *Vice Pres*
William Lewis, *VP Sls/Mktg*
Carol Surrena, *Manager*
EMP: 9
SQ FT: 5,000
SALES: 24K **Privately Held**
WEB: www.nanologixinc.com
SIC: 3829 Testing equipment: abrasion,
shearing strength, etc.

(G-11136)
OHIO STEEL SHEET & PLATE INC
7845 Chestnut Ridge Rd (44425-9702)
P.O. Box 1146, Warren (44482-1146)
PHONE..................................800 827-2401
Fax: 330 534-3204
John Rebhan, *President*
Mike Link, *Vice Pres*
Eric Rebhan, *Vice Pres*
Paul Musante, *Engineer*
Marie Cline, *Accounts Exec*
EMP: 45
SQ FT: 320,000
SALES (est): 12.9MM **Privately Held**
WEB: www.ohiosteelplate.com
SIC: 3312 5051 3444 Sheet or strip,
steel, hot-rolled; plate, steel; metals service centers & offices; sheet metalwork

(G-11137)
OMEGA LOGGING INC (PA)
2550 State Line Rd (44425-9749)
P.O. Box 524, West Middlesex PA (16159-0524)
PHONE..................................330 534-0378
Richard G Conti, *President*
Paul Chovan, *President*
Priscilla Iliss, *Corp Secy*

EMP: 4
SALES (est): 5MM **Privately Held**
WEB: www.omega-inc.biz
SIC: 2411 2421 Logging; sawmills & planing mills, general

(G-11138)
PROGRESSIVE PRINTING SERVICES
264 W Liberty St Frnt (44425-1778)
PHONE..................................330 534-8501
David Pettola, *President*
EMP: 5 **EST:** 1992
SALES (est): 567.8K **Privately Held**
SIC: 2752 Commercial printing, lithographic

(G-11139)
PSK STEEL CORP
2960 Gale Dr (44425-1099)
P.O. Box 308 (44425-0308)
PHONE..................................330 759-1251
Fax: 330 759-8599
Henry Kinast, *Ch of Bd*
Jerry Kinast, *President*
Steven R Anderson, *Vice Pres*
Sharon Goist, *Manager*
Patricia Lybrick, *Manager*
▲ **EMP:** 40
SQ FT: 70,000
SALES (est): 8.9MM **Privately Held**
WEB: www.psksteel.com
SIC: 3544 Special dies & tools; industrial
molds

(G-11140)
TAYLOR - WINFIELD CORPORATION (PA)
Also Called: Denton & Anderson Mktg Div
3200 Innovation Pl (44425)
PHONE..................................330 259-8500
Fax: 330 448-3538
John A Anderson II, *Ch of Bd*
Roger Bacon, *President*
Robert Kornack, *General Mgr*
Frank Stein, *Vice Pres*
Dan Baker, *Purchasing*
▼ **EMP:** 90
SQ FT: 45,000
SALES (est): 20.3MM **Privately Held**
WEB: www.coil-joining.com
SIC: 3548 3542 3567 Welding apparatus;
machine tools, metal forming type; robots
for metal forming: pressing, extruding,
etc.; induction heating equipment

(G-11141)
WILLIAMS MACHINE CO INC
461 N Main St (44425-1422)
P.O. Box 310 (44425-0310)
PHONE..................................330 534-3058
Fax: 330 534-4839
EMP: 6
SQ FT: 6,500
SALES: 300K **Privately Held**
SIC: 3599 Machine Shop

(G-11142)
WISE ENTERPRISES INC
1911 Wick Campbell Rd (44425-2868)
PHONE..................................330 568-7095
Fax: 330 568-7221
Ted Wise, *President*
Kathy Lesnak, *Treasurer*
Kathy Miller, *Admin Sec*
EMP: 4
SQ FT: 3,200
SALES: 275K **Privately Held**
SIC: 3599 Machine shop, jobbing & repair

(G-11143)
YOUNGSTOWN-KENWORTH INC (PA)
Also Called: All-Line Truck Sales
7255 Hubbard Masury Rd (44425-9757)
PHONE..................................330 534-9761
Fax: 330 534-2966
Tomiel Mikes, *President*
Geraldine Mikes, *Principal*
Randall R Fiest, *Vice Pres*
EMP: 35
SQ FT: 14,900

▲ = Import ▼ =Export
◆ =Import/Export

SALES (est): 8.4MM Privately Held
WEB: www.youngstownkenworth.com
SIC: 5013 5012 7538 3713 Truck parts & accessories; trucks, commercial; general automotive repair shops; truck & bus bodies; industrial trucks & tractors

Huber Heights
Montgomery County

(G-11144)
CONTINENTAL FAN MFG
6274 Executive Blvd (45424-1424)
PHONE..................................937 233-5524
Fax: 937 233-5534
Ken Grimes, *Principal*
Jud Alexander, *Manager*
EMP: 3
SALES (est): 220.1K Privately Held
SIC: 3999 Manufacturing industries

(G-11145)
EIGHTY SIX INC
8823 Salon Cir (45424-1581)
PHONE..................................800 760-0722
Jonathan Annarino, *CEO*
Nitin Gautam, *COO*
Nick Hartwig, *Vice Pres*
EMP: 3
SALES (est): 172.8K Privately Held
SIC: 7371 7372 Computer software systems analysis & design, custom; computer software development & applications; application computer software

(G-11146)
ENGINETICS CORPORATION (DH)
Also Called: Enginetics Aero Space
7700 New Carlisle Pike (45424-1570)
PHONE..................................937 878-3800
Fax: 937 754-3297
Dale Pelfrey, *CEO*
Patrice Lallement, *General Mgr*
Don Hainley, *Vice Pres*
Stan Matthews, *Vice Pres*
Shane Williams, *QC Mgr*
EMP: 131
SQ FT: 57,000
SALES (est): 23.1MM
SALES (corp-wide): 751.5MM Publicly Held
WEB: www.enginetics.com
SIC: 3724 3728 3812 3519 Aircraft engines & engine parts; aircraft parts & equipment; search & navigation equipment; jet propulsion engines
HQ: Mpe Aeroengines, Inc.
7700 New Carlisle Pike
Huber Heights OH 45424
937 878-3800

(G-11147)
FISHER TESTERS LLC
5079 Kerridge Rd (45424)
PHONE..................................937 416-6554
James A Fisher,
EMP: 4
SALES (corp-wide): 200K Privately Held
SIC: 3825 Instruments to measure electricity
PA: Fisher Testers, Llc
324 E Schantz Ave
Oakwood OH 45409
937 416-6554

(G-11148)
HESS ADVANCED TECHNOLOGY INC
7415 Chambersburg Rd (45424-3921)
P.O. Box 17669, Dayton (45417-0669)
PHONE..................................937 268-4377
Fax: 937 263-5258
Fred Edmonds, *CEO*
Delilah Stevens, *President*
EMP: 1
SQ FT: 38,000
SALES (est): 2MM Privately Held
SIC: 2851 Shellac (protective coating)

(G-11149)
INTEGRITY INDUSTRIAL EQP INC
7401 Bridgewater Rd (45424-2406)
PHONE..................................937 238-9275
Jeffrey Smith, *President*
EMP: 3
SQ FT: 8,000
SALES (est): 168.1K Privately Held
SIC: 3537 Forklift trucks

(G-11150)
MPE AEROENGINES INC (HQ)
Also Called: Enginetics
7700 New Carlisle Pike (45424-1512)
PHONE..................................937 878-3800
Dale Pelfrey, *CEO*
EMP: 5
SALES (est): 23.1MM
SALES (corp-wide): 751.5MM Publicly Held
SIC: 3365 Aerospace castings, aluminum
PA: Standex International Corporation
11 Keewaydin Dr
Salem NH 03079
603 893-9701

(G-11151)
PVS PLASTICS TECHNOLOGY CORP
6290 Executive Blvd (45424-1424)
PHONE..................................937 233-4376
Fax: 937 233-4378
Juerden Frank, *President*
Scott Newton, *Opers Mgr*
Chad Terrill, *Prdtn Mgr*
Tony Rockus, *Manager*
▲ EMP: 20
SQ FT: 25,000
SALES (est): 4.4MM
SALES (corp-wide): 54.5MM Privately Held
WEB: www.pvs-plastics.net
SIC: 3089 Injection molding of plastics
PA: Pvs - Kunststofftechnik Gmbh & Co. Kg
Salzstr. 20
Niedernhall 74676
794 091-260

(G-11152)
UPDIKE SUPPLY COMPANY (PA)
Also Called: Machine Tools Supply
8241 Expansion Way (45424-6381)
PHONE..................................937 482-4000
Steve Short, *President*
Shane Hannan, *Principal*
Jeff Butts, *Exec VP*
Rob Johnson, *Vice Pres*
Trixi Myers, *CFO*
EMP: 36
SALES (est): 7.7MM Privately Held
SIC: 3541 Machine tools, metal cutting type

Hudson
Summit County

(G-11153)
ABOUT AND DOGS LLC
7600 Olde Eight Rd (44236-1057)
PHONE..................................440 263-8989
Derek Ruff, *Mng Member*
EMP: 4
SALES: 250K Privately Held
SIC: 2047 Dog & cat food

(G-11154)
ADVANCED MATERIALS PRODUCTS
Also Called: Adma Products
1890 Georgetown Rd (44236-4058)
PHONE..................................330 650-4000
Vladimir Moxson, *President*
Sophia Moxson, *Vice Pres*
▲ EMP: 6
SQ FT: 20,000
SALES (est): 1.1MM Privately Held
WEB: www.admaproducts.com
SIC: 3339 Titanium metal, sponge & granules

(G-11155)
ALTERA CORPORATION
591 Boston Mills Rd # 600 (44236-1195)
PHONE..................................330 650-5200
Fax: 330 650-5209
Donald Kautzman, *Branch Mgr*
EMP: 4
SALES (corp-wide): 59.3B Publicly Held
SIC: 3559 Semiconductor manufacturing machinery
HQ: Altera Corporation
101 Innovation Dr
San Jose CA 95134
408 544-7000

(G-11156)
AMERICAN FIREWORKS COMPANY INC
7041 Darrow Rd (44236-2254)
P.O. Box 394 (44236-0394)
PHONE..................................330 650-1776
Fax: 330 653-9030
Nancy Sorgi, *President*
Katie Duvernay, *Office Mgr*
John Sorgi, *Manager*
▲ EMP: 10 EST: 1902
SQ FT: 10,000
SALES (est): 2.4MM Privately Held
SIC: 2899 Chemical preparations

(G-11157)
AMERICAN ULTRA SPECIALTIES INC
6855 Industrial Pkwy (44236-1158)
PHONE..................................330 656-5000
Fax: 330 656-9742
Christi Yacinski, *President*
Michaela M Stofey, *Corp Secy*
Martin Yacinski, *Vice Pres*
John Ningard Sr, *Shareholder*
Albert Sivillo, *Shareholder*
EMP: 18
SQ FT: 37,500
SALES (est): 5MM Privately Held
SIC: 2992 5172 Re-refining lubricating oils & greases; lubricating oils & greases

(G-11158)
AMF BRUNS AMERICA LP
Also Called: AMF Bruns of America
1797 Georgetown Rd (44236-4192)
PHONE..................................877 506-3770
EMP: 4
SQ FT: 54,450
SALES (est): 345.8K Privately Held
SIC: 3443 Pressurizers or auxiliary equipment, nuclear: metal plate

(G-11159)
ASHLAND INC VALVOLINE INSTANT
1691 Georgetown Rd Unit C (44236-4091)
PHONE..................................330 653-3926
EMP: 3
SALES (est): 290.7K Privately Held
SIC: 2752 Commercial printing, lithographic

(G-11160)
BEDFORD ANODIZING CO (PA)
82 Aurora St (44236-2945)
PHONE..................................330 650-6052
Fax: 330 468-3426
Thomas E De Weese, *President*
Thomas Deweese, *President*
EMP: 47 EST: 1978
SQ FT: 125,000
SALES (est): 18.4MM Privately Held
SIC: 3471 Anodizing (plating) of metals or formed products

(G-11161)
BERRY CO (PA)
571 Boston Mills Rd # 300 (44236-5507)
PHONE..................................877 742-3779
EMP: 11
SALES (est): 18.6MM Privately Held
SIC: 2741 Miscellaneous Publishing

(G-11162)
CAMBRIDGE MFG JEWELERS
Also Called: Cambridge Jewelers
76 Maple Dr Ste 1 (44236-3029)
PHONE..................................330 528-0207
Fax: 330 528-0207

O William Koke, *President*
EMP: 5
SQ FT: 1,800
SALES (est): 576.7K Privately Held
SIC: 3911 5094 5944 Jewelry apparel; jewelry; jewelry, precious stones & precious metals

(G-11163)
CLAFLIN COMPANY INC
5270 Hudson Dr (44236-3738)
PHONE..................................330 650-0582
Fax: 330 928-7237
James C Claflin, *President*
Howard Claflin, *President*
EMP: 8
SQ FT: 10,000
SALES (est): 670K Privately Held
SIC: 3089 Plastic processing

(G-11164)
CLEARSONIC MANUFACTURING INC
1223 Norton Rd (44236-4403)
PHONE..................................330 650-1420
Brian Smith, *President*
Chris Marari, *Marketing Staff*
Karen Smith, *Office Mgr*
Mike Connelly, *Manager*
▲ EMP: 8
SQ FT: 8,100
SALES (est): 1.4MM Privately Held
SIC: 3089 Panels, building: plastic

(G-11165)
COMET TECHNOLOGIES USA INC
Also Called: Yxlon International
5675 Hudson Indus Pkwy (44236-5012)
PHONE..................................234 284-7849
Ray Kramer, *General Mgr*
Jason Robbins, *Business Mgr*
Robert Jardim, *Vice Pres*
EMP: 15
SALES (corp-wide): 328.1MM Privately Held
SIC: 3844 X-ray apparatus & tubes
HQ: Comet Technologies Usa Inc.
100 Trap Falls Road Ext
Shelton CT 06484
203 447-3200

(G-11166)
COSO MEDIA LLC
5603 Darrow Rd Ste 500 (44236-5039)
PHONE..................................330 904-5889
Matthew Dewees, *President*
Bernard Dewees, *Principal*
EMP: 4 EST: 2011
SQ FT: 1,146
SALES (est): 330K Privately Held
SIC: 7371 2759 Computer software development; commercial printing

(G-11167)
CURTIS CHEMICAL INC
6020 Ogilby Dr (44236-3946)
P.O. Box 460 (44236-0460)
PHONE..................................330 656-2514
Ron G Frew, *President*
EMP: 8
SQ FT: 35,000
SALES (est): 1MM Privately Held
SIC: 2819 Industrial inorganic chemicals

(G-11168)
DELUXE CORPORATION
10030 Phillipp Pkwy (44236)
PHONE..................................330 342-1500
Robin Lebine, *Principal*
EMP: 200
SALES (corp-wide): 1.8B Publicly Held
WEB: www.dlx.com
SIC: 2782 Blankbooks & looseleaf binders
PA: Deluxe Corporation
3680 Victoria St N
Shoreview MN 55126
651 483-7111

(G-11169)
DESIGN MAGNETICS LTD
7941 Valley View Rd (44236-1250)
PHONE..................................234 380-5500
Margaret Obrien, *President*
EMP: 3

GEOGRAPHIC

SALES (est): 187.5K **Privately Held**
SIC: 3429 Hangers, wall hardware

(G-11170)
ENVIRONMENTAL WALL SYSTEMS
77 Milford Dr Ste 283 (44236-2782)
P.O. Box 1388 (44236-0888)
PHONE..............................440 542-6600
EMP: 4
SQ FT: 46,000
SALES (est): 530K **Privately Held**
SIC: 2542 Mfg Movable Walls (Non Wood)

(G-11171)
FLUID POWER INC
Also Called: Guardian Mfg.
1300 Hudson Gate Dr (44236-4401)
PHONE..............................330 653-5107
Fax: 330 656-1790
Matt Davis, *President*
Matthew Davis, *Exec VP*
Henry Walton, *Design Engr*
Karen Voytek, *Office Mgr*
Gene Lameraux, *Manager*
EMP: 12 **EST:** 1949
SQ FT: 12,000
SALES (est): 1.9MM **Privately Held**
WEB: www.fluidpowerohio.com
SIC: 3728 Oxygen systems, aircraft

(G-11172)
GEO SPECIALTY CHEMICAL
2685 Blue Heron Dr (44236-1868)
PHONE..............................330 650-0237
Martin Gregor, *Manager*
EMP: 3
SALES (est): 188.8K **Privately Held**
SIC: 2869 Industrial organic chemicals

(G-11173)
GLC BIOTECHNOLOGY INC
7925 Megan Meadow Dr (44236-4536)
PHONE..............................440 349-2193
Baochuan Guo, *President*
EMP: 4
SALES (est): 498.5K **Privately Held**
SIC: 3829 Medical diagnostic systems, nuclear

(G-11174)
GLOBAL DESIGN FACTORY LLC
1227 Norton Rd 3b (44236-4403)
PHONE..............................330 322-8775
Valerie Miller, *President*
EMP: 3
SQ FT: 900
SALES (est): 449.5K **Privately Held**
SIC: 2521 Wood office furniture

(G-11175)
GRACE METALS LTD
685 Ashbrooke Way (44236-1280)
P.O. Box 712 (44236-0712)
PHONE..............................234 380-1433
Kristin Douglas, *President*
EMP: 5 **EST:** 2013
SALES: 10MM **Privately Held**
SIC: 3312 Stainless steel

(G-11176)
GRAPHIX JUNCTION
5170 Hudson Dr Ste B (44236-3797)
PHONE..............................234 284-8392
Cathy Andrade, *Owner*
EMP: 5 **EST:** 2010
SALES (est): 250K **Privately Held**
SIC: 7389 2759 2395 Apparel pressing
service; screen printing; art goods for embroidering, stamped: purchased materials

(G-11177)
HALIFAX INDUSTRIES INC
2060 Garden Ln (44236-1320)
PHONE..............................216 990-8951
Fax: 216 581-3898
William J Dodson, *President*
Gerald W Dodson, *Office Mgr*
EMP: 5
SQ FT: 8,000
SALES: 350K **Privately Held**
SIC: 3559 Frame straighteners, automobile
(garage equipment)

(G-11178)
HANDCRAFTED JEWELRY INC
Also Called: Jewelry Art
116 N Main St (44236-2827)
PHONE..............................330 650-9011
Fax: 330 650-1027
Georgianna Bojtos, *President*
Barbara Johnson, *Vice Pres*
EMP: 7 **EST:** 1977
SQ FT: 1,000
SALES: 500K **Privately Held**
WEB: www.handcraftedjewelry.com
SIC: 5944 5947 7699 2759 Jewelry, precious stones & precious metals; silverware; gift shop; customizing services; engraving

(G-11179)
HUDSON ACCESS GROUP II
2460 Bramfield Way (44236-4939)
PHONE..............................330 283-6214
Thomas Mendoza, *Owner*
EMP: 1
SQ FT: 1,100
SALES: 1.4MM **Privately Held**
SIC: 3651 5731 Household audio & video
equipment; radio, television & electronic
stores

(G-11180)
HUDSON EXTRUSIONS INC
1255 Norton Rd (44236-4403)
P.O. Box 255 (44236-0255)
PHONE..............................330 653-6015
Fax: 330 653-6551
Marylin Hansen, *President*
Donald Morgan, *Marketing Staff*
Melanie Chaplin, *Manager*
Dale Johnson, *Manager*
Kenny Lin, *Manager*
EMP: 35 **EST:** 1956
SQ FT: 33,000
SALES (est): 8MM **Privately Held**
WEB: www.hudsonextrusions.com
SIC: 3089 Extruded finished plastic products

(G-11181)
IMPRINTS
77 Maple Dr (44236-3037)
PHONE..............................330 650-0467
William Stemple, *Owner*
EMP: 10
SQ FT: 1,100
SALES (est): 510K **Privately Held**
SIC: 2791 Typesetting

(G-11182)
INTERNTNAL PRECISION CAST SUPS
1570 Terex Rd (44236-4069)
PHONE..............................330 342-0407
Diane Gray, *Accounts Mgr*
Charlotte Joseph, *Director*
EMP: 5
SQ FT: 50,000
SALES (est): 1.1MM **Privately Held**
SIC: 3324 Aerospace investment castings,
ferrous; commercial investment castings,
ferrous

(G-11183)
ISOTOPX INC
194 Atterbury Blvd (44236-1644)
PHONE..............................508 337-8467
Zenon Palancz, *Principal*
Jeremy Inglis, *Vice Pres*
Mark Yardley, *Treasurer*
Laurie Lischer, *Manager*
EMP: 3
SALES: 950K **Privately Held**
SIC: 3826 Analytical instruments

(G-11184)
J R MACHINING INC
5170 Hudson Dr Ste G (44236-3797)
PHONE..............................330 528-3406
Mark Pasuit, *CEO*
Daniel Pasuit, *President*
Dolores Pasuit, *Admin Sec*
▼ **EMP:** 3
SQ FT: 3,000
SALES (est): 429.7K **Privately Held**
SIC: 3469 Machine parts, stamped or
pressed metal

(G-11185)
JAMES O EMERT JR
7920 Princewood Dr (44236-1576)
PHONE..............................330 650-6990
James O Emert, *Principal*
EMP: 4
SALES (est): 414.5K **Privately Held**
SIC: 3317 Steel pipe & tubes

(G-11186)
JAMES SORGI
7041 Darrow Rd (44236-2254)
PHONE..............................330 653-5180
James Sorgi, *Owner*
▲ **EMP:** 5 **EST:** 1998
SALES (est): 426.6K **Privately Held**
SIC: 2899 Fireworks

(G-11187)
KOBELCO STEWART BOLLING INC
1600 Terex Rd (44236-4086)
PHONE..............................330 655-3111
Fax: 330 656-9724
Atsushi Shigeno, *President*
Mitch Asada, *General Mgr*
Ivan Lozano, *Business Mgr*
Scott Morgan, *Opers Mgr*
Robert Deily, *Purch Agent*
▲ **EMP:** 94
SQ FT: 270,000
SALES (est): 41.6MM
SALES (corp-wide): 15.5B **Privately Held**
WEB: www.ksbiusa.com
SIC: 3559 Rubber working machinery, including tires
HQ: Kobe Steel Usa Holdings Inc.
535 Madison Ave Fl 5
New York NY 10022
212 751-9400

(G-11188)
LOCAL INSIGHT YELLOW PAGES INC
100 Executive Pkwy (44236-1630)
P.O. Box 2502 (44236-0002)
PHONE..............................330 650-7100
EMP: 175 **EST:** 1984
SALES (est): 21.4MM **Privately Held**
SIC: 2741 Misc Publishing
PA: Berry
100 Executive Pkwy
Hudson OH 44236
330 650-7100

(G-11189)
NCRX OPTICAL SOLUTIONS INC (PA)
105 Executive Pkwy # 401 (44236-1692)
P.O. Box 38004, Pittsburgh PA (15238-8004)
PHONE..............................330 239-5353
John Traina, *CEO*
Patrick Cook, *President*
Ed McCall, *COO*
EMP: 14
SALES (est): 1.8MM **Privately Held**
SIC: 3827 Optical test & inspection equipment

(G-11190)
OILS BY NATURE INCORPORATED
5712 Abbyshire Dr 1a (44236-2678)
PHONE..............................330 468-8897
Marilyn Salvucci, *President*
Scott C Anderson, *Vice Pres*
◆ **EMP:** 5
SQ FT: 6,000
SALES (est): 917.7K **Privately Held**
WEB: www.oilsbynature.com
SIC: 2844 Cosmetic preparations

(G-11191)
OPTI VISION INC (PA)
5697 Darrow Rd (44236-4013)
P.O. Box 995 (44236-5995)
PHONE..............................330 650-0919
Fax: 330 656-3151
Pamela Mumick, *President*
EMP: 5
SQ FT: 2,790

SALES (est): 915.2K **Privately Held**
SIC: 5995 3851 Eyeglasses, prescription;
ophthalmic goods; eyeglasses, lenses &
frames

(G-11192)
OUCHLESS LURES INC
305 Kilbourne Dr (44236-3423)
PHONE..............................330 653-3867
Lee V Iken, *Principal*
EMP: 4
SALES (est): 277.6K **Privately Held**
SIC: 3949 Lures, fishing: artificial

(G-11193)
PATIENT FOCUS SYSTEMS
1140 Terex Rd (44236-3771)
PHONE..............................330 655-7222
Pete Spitalieri, *Owner*
Joanne Leonard, *Vice Pres*
EMP: 3
SALES (est): 180K **Privately Held**
SIC: 7372 7371 Application computer software; custom computer programming
services

(G-11194)
PRINTERS DEVIL INC
77 Maple Dr (44236-3037)
PHONE..............................330 650-1218
Fax: 330 650-1625
William Stemple, *President*
EMP: 14
SQ FT: 800
SALES: 1MM **Privately Held**
WEB: www.printersdevil.com
SIC: 2752 7334 Commercial printing, offset; photocopying & duplicating services

(G-11195)
RAMCO SPECIALTIES INC
5445 Hudson Indus Pkwy (44236-3777)
PHONE..............................330 653-5135
Fax: 330 655-2443
Richard A Malson II, *President*
James A Merlitti, *Principal*
Ron Hoover, *Controller*
Narayana Surapaneni, *Marketing Staff*
▲ **EMP:** 95
SQ FT: 120,000
SALES (est): 28.8MM **Privately Held**
WEB: www.ramconut.com
SIC: 3965 3452 3714 Fasteners; nuts,
metal; motor vehicle parts & accessories

(G-11196)
REZKEM CHEMICALS LLC
77 Milford Dr Ste 258 (44236-2785)
PHONE..............................330 653-9104
Eric Gorze, *President*
▲ **EMP:** 11 **EST:** 2011
SALES (est): 1.8MM **Privately Held**
SIC: 2869 Laboratory chemicals, organic

(G-11197)
ROPER LOCKBOX LLC
7600 Olde Eight Rd (44236-1057)
PHONE..............................330 656-5148
John Evans, *President*
Joann Riddles, *Vice Pres*
EMP: 5 **EST:** 1997
SQ FT: 1,700
SALES (est): 640.3K **Privately Held**
WEB: www.roperlock.com
SIC: 3469 5099 Boxes, stamped metal;
locks & lock sets

(G-11198)
SHERWIN-WILLIAMS COMPANY
5860 Darrow Rd (44236-3864)
PHONE..............................330 528-0124
Fax: 330 656-2988
Mindy Malone, *Manager*
EMP: 6
SALES (corp-wide): 11.8B **Publicly Held**
WEB: www.sherwin.com
SIC: 5231 2851 Paint & painting supplies;
wallcoverings; paints & allied products;
varnishes; lacquer: bases, dopes, thinner
PA: The Sherwin-Williams Company
101 W Prospect Ave # 1020
Cleveland OH 44115
216 566-2000

(G-11199)
SINTERED METAL INDUSTRIES INC
Also Called: Simet
1890 Georgetown Rd (44236-4058)
PHONE.....................................330 650-4000
Vladimir Moxson, *President*
Sophia Moxson, *Vice Pres*
Cathy Tonkin, *Admin Mgr*
EMP: 10
SALES (est): 1.3MM **Privately Held**
SIC: 3441 3568 Fabricated structural metal; bearings, bushings & blocks

(G-11200)
SNS NANO FIBER TECHNOLOGY LLC
5633 Hudson Indus Pkwy (44236-5012)
PHONE.....................................330 655-0030
Kaylee Yodor, *Project Mgr*
Laura M Frazier, *Mng Member*
Darrell Reneker, *Technical Staff*
EMP: 9 EST: 2005
SALES (est): 799.2K **Privately Held**
SIC: 7379 3325 ; alloy steel castings, except investment

(G-11201)
SPECIALTY METALS PROCESSING
837 Seasons Rd (44224-1027)
PHONE.....................................330 656-2767
Fax: 330 656-1644
Michael Miniea, *President*
Edward Nosek, *CFO*
▲ EMP: 46
SQ FT: 170,000
SALES (est): 11.6MM **Privately Held**
SIC: 3541 Machine tools, metal cutting type

(G-11202)
STANDING ROCK DESIGNERY
Also Called: Standing Rock Gallery
5194 Darrow Rd (44236-4004)
PHONE.....................................330 650-9089
Fax: 330 650-9089
Kaye McFarland, *Partner*
John Herring, *Partner*
Earl McFarland, *Partner*
EMP: 5
SALES (est): 280K **Privately Held**
SIC: 3231 5231 Stained glass: made from purchased glass; glass, leaded or stained

(G-11203)
SUMMIT RESOURCES GROUP INC
7476 Whitemarsh Way (44236-1289)
PHONE.....................................330 653-3992
Fax: 330 653-3993
E Dennis Matecun Jr, *Vice Pres*
Tammy Matecun, *Vice Pres*
EMP: 3
SALES (est): 586.8K **Privately Held**
SIC: 3324 5051 Steel investment foundries; metals service centers & offices

(G-11204)
THOMPSON ASSOC HUDSON OHIO
Also Called: Handkerchief House, The
5771 Sunset Dr (44236-3836)
P.O. Box 268 (44236-0268)
PHONE.....................................330 655-2142
Fax: 330 342-0562
Helen D Thompson, *President*
Pat Smith, *Principal*
Judith Maupin, *Vice Pres*
EMP: 5 EST: 1962
SALES (est): 398K **Privately Held**
SIC: 2395 Embroidery & art needlework

(G-11205)
TRU-HAR PRODUCTS
7946 Darrow Rd Unit 334 (44236-1314)
P.O. Box 1394 (44236-0894)
PHONE.....................................330 338-6826
John T Faulkner, *Office Mgr*
EMP: 5
SALES (est): 377.1K **Privately Held**
SIC: 3399 Metal fasteners

(G-11206)
UNIVERSAL DRECT FLFLLMENT CORP
5581 Hudson Indus Pkwy (44236-5019)
PHONE.....................................330 650-5000
Jared Florian, *President*
▲ EMP: 140
SQ FT: 78,000
SALES (est): 60.7MM
SALES (corp-wide): 61.3MM **Privately Held**
WEB: www.artandartifact.com
SIC: 5961 2741 2396 Catalog & mail-order houses; miscellaneous publishing; automotive & apparel trimmings
PA: Universal Screen Arts, Inc.
5581 Hudson Indus Pkwy
Hudson OH 44236
330 650-5000

(G-11207)
WBC GROUP LLC (PA)
Also Called: Meyerpt
6333 Hudson Crossing Pkwy (44236-4346)
PHONE.....................................866 528-2144
Ron Harrington, *CEO*
Elizabeth Cross, *Treasurer*
Aaron Carino, *Accounts Mgr*
Andrea Scala, *Director*
Madeline Gomolka, *Analyst*
▲ EMP: 106
SQ FT: 50,000
SALES (est): 117.5MM **Privately Held**
WEB: www.indemed.com
SIC: 5122 5047 3843 Vitamins & minerals; pharmaceuticals; medical & hospital equipment; dental equipment & supplies

(G-11208)
WESTERN RESERVE DISTILLERS LLC
6549 Thornbrook Cir (44236-3552)
PHONE.....................................330 671-0347
Ann Thomas,
Kevin Thomas,
EMP: 7 EST: 2014
SALES (est): 210.5K **Privately Held**
SIC: 2085 Distilled & blended liquors

(G-11209)
WESTERN RESERVE PRINTING
218 N Main St (44236-2826)
PHONE.....................................330 650-9800
Michelle Scourfield, *Principal*
EMP: 4
SALES (est): 302K **Privately Held**
SIC: 2759 Commercial printing

(G-11210)
WOLTERS KLUWER CLINICAL DRUG
1100 Terex Rd (44236-3771)
PHONE.....................................330 650-6506
Fax: 330 656-4307
Denise Basow, *President*
David A Del Toro, *Vice Pres*
Ginger Stein, *Project Mgr*
Gerald Stralko, *Engineer*
Michael Metz, *CFO*
EMP: 65
SQ FT: 24,000
SALES (est): 12.5MM
SALES (corp-wide): 4.5B **Privately Held**
SIC: 2731 2791 7379 Books: publishing only; typesetting, computer controlled; computer related maintenance services
HQ: Wolters Kluwer Health, Inc.
2001 Market St Lbby 1
Philadelphia PA 19103
215 521-8300

(G-11211)
YXLON
5675 Hudson Indus Pkwy (44236-5012)
PHONE.....................................234 284-7862
Chris Warren, *Principal*
Ragnar Vaga, *Regl Sales Mgr*
EMP: 3
SALES (est): 180K **Privately Held**
SIC: 3844 X-ray apparatus & tubes

Huntsville
Logan County

(G-11212)
DUFF QUARRY INC (PA)
9042 State Route 117 (43324-9617)
P.O. Box 305 (43324-0305)
PHONE.....................................937 686-2811
James E Duff, *President*
Scott Duff, *Vice Pres*
Sandy Duff, *Admin Sec*
EMP: 15
SQ FT: 26,000
SALES (est): 2.2MM **Privately Held**
SIC: 1422 Crushed & broken limestone

(G-11213)
FIRE SAFETY SERVICES INC
6228 Township Road 95 (43324-9673)
PHONE.....................................937 686-2000
Fax: 937 686-6425
Steven Spath, *President*
Kay Spath, *Corp Secy*
Marcus Taylor, *Vice Pres*
EMP: 18
SQ FT: 6,400
SALES (est): 5.9MM **Privately Held**
WEB: www.fssohio.com
SIC: 5099 5012 5087 3999 Fire extinguishers; fireproof clothing; fire trucks; firefighting equipment; fire extinguishers, portable; fire extinguisher servicing

(G-11214)
GADGETS MANUFACTURING CO
9366 State Route 117 (43324-9617)
PHONE.....................................937 686-5371
Bill Page, *Owner*
EMP: 4
SALES (est): 220K **Privately Held**
SIC: 5731 3651 Antennas, satellite dish; household audio & video equipment

(G-11215)
RETENTION KNOB SUPPLY & MFG CO
4905 State Route 274 W (43324-9643)
P.O. Box 61, Bellefontaine (43311-0061)
PHONE.....................................937 686-4125
Fax: 937 686-4125
Thomas E Christen, *President*
Charles Townsend, *Vice Pres*
Wilbor Mummey, *Mfg Mgr*
Susie White, *Controller*
Carrie Christen, *Admin Sec*
EMP: 10
SQ FT: 100,000
SALES (est): 1.3MM **Privately Held**
SIC: 3545 Machine tool attachments & accessories

Huron
Erie County

(G-11216)
ARTHUR CORPORATION
1305 Huron Avery Rd (44839-2429)
PHONE.....................................419 433-7202
Fax: 419 433-7088
Charles Hensel, *President*
Mark Svancara, *Vice Pres*
EMP: 65 EST: 1981
SQ FT: 65,000
SALES (est): 24.2MM **Privately Held**
SIC: 3089 3083 Thermoformed finished plastic products; laminated plastics plate & sheet

(G-11217)
ASSEMBLY WORKS INC
Also Called: Assembly Works Matrix Automtn
1705 Sawmill Pkwy (44839-2232)
PHONE.....................................419 433-5010
Fax: 419 433-5588
William E Kaman, *President*
Julie Smart, *Admin Sec*
EMP: 8 EST: 1998
SQ FT: 10,200

SALES (est): 996.5K **Privately Held**
SIC: 3613 Panelboards & distribution boards, electric

(G-11218)
CANTELLI BLOCK AND BRICK INC (PA)
1001 Sawmill Pkwy (44839-2297)
PHONE.....................................419 433-0102
Fax: 419 433-0103
Raymond J Cantelli, *President*
Anita Cantelli, *Co-President*
Adriana Cantelli, *Corp Secy*
Ray A Cantelli, *Vice Pres*
Jackie Worley, *Sls & Mktg Exec*
EMP: 23 EST: 1923
SQ FT: 43,580
SALES: 2.8MM **Privately Held**
SIC: 3271 Blocks, concrete or cinder: standard

(G-11219)
CENTRAL OHIO PAPER & PACKG INC (PA)
Also Called: Breckenridge Paper & Packaging
2350 University Dr E (44839-9173)
PHONE.....................................419 621-9239
Fax: 419 621-9919
Edward Pettegrew Jr, *President*
Bob Matthews, *Sales Staff*
Hope Nottke, *Office Mgr*
EMP: 15
SQ FT: 12,000
SALES (est): 5.1MM **Privately Held**
WEB: www.breckpack.com
SIC: 2671 Paper coated or laminated for packaging

(G-11220)
DENTON ATD INC (PA)
900 Denton Dr (44839-8922)
PHONE.....................................567 265-5200
David C Stein, *President*
Robert A Denton, *Chairman*
Micheal Beebe, *Vice Pres*
Shawn Rice, *Draft/Design*
Tommy Vara, *Draft/Design*
EMP: 46
SQ FT: 16,000
SALES (est): 6MM **Privately Held**
WEB: www.dentonatd.com
SIC: 3999 3821 3829 Mannequins; calibration tapes for physical testing machines; measuring & controlling devices

(G-11221)
GDM MAILBOX COMPANY LLC
Also Called: Direct Mailbox
912 University Dr S (44839-9172)
PHONE.....................................419 433-3022
Carol Dunkle, *Manager*
Glen Peterman,
Karen Peterman,
EMP: 4
SQ FT: 18,000
SALES (est): 800K **Privately Held**
WEB: www.directmailbox.com
SIC: 3444 Mail (post office) collection or storage boxes, sheet metal

(G-11222)
GEOCORP INC
9010 River Rd (44839-9523)
PHONE.....................................419 433-1101
Fax: 419 433-1102
George Conrad, *President*
Niel Fleetwood, *Human Res Mgr*
Jim Oehme, *Manager*
Vicki Novak, *Director*
EMP: 46
SQ FT: 6,000
SALES (est): 12.6MM **Privately Held**
WEB: www.geocorpinc.com
SIC: 3823 Thermocouples, industrial process type

(G-11223)
HEALTHCARE BENEFITS INC
1212 Cleveland Rd W (44839-1410)
P.O. Box 326 (44839-0326)
PHONE.....................................419 433-4499
Joan Norton, *CEO*
Ed Norton, *President*
EMP: 5
SQ FT: 20,000

SALES: 100K **Privately Held**
SIC: **1542** 3732 Hospital construction; lifeboats, building & repairing

(G-11224)
HURON CEMENT PRODUCTS COMPANY (PA)
Also Called: H & C Building Supplies
617 Main St (44839-2593)
PHONE....................................419 433-4161
Fax: 419 433-4690
John Caporini, *President*
Peggy Day, *Vice Pres*
Lauren Jones, *Controller*
Vince Thompson, *Admin Asst*
EMP: 38
SQ FT: 37,800
SALES (est): 8.7MM **Privately Held**
SIC: **5211** 5032 3273 3546 Cement; sand & gravel; cement; gravel; ready-mixed concrete; power-driven handtools; concrete products; cement, hydraulic

(G-11225)
HURON HOMETOWN NEWS
304 Williams St (44839-1648)
PHONE....................................419 433-1401
John Schaffner, *Principal*
EMP: 3
SALES (est): 117.8K **Privately Held**
SIC: **2711** Newspapers, publishing & printing

(G-11226)
HURON LIME INC
100 Meeker St (44839-1713)
P.O. Box 451 (44839-0451)
PHONE....................................419 433-2141
Fax: 419 433-3479
Edward Gordon, *President*
Christopher Kitts, *General Mgr*
Jerome Osborne, *Chairman*
Nancy J Case, *Vice Pres*
Kristene Mollison, *Manager*
EMP: 30 EST: 1966
SQ FT: 10,000
SALES (est): 18.5MM **Privately Held**
WEB: www.huronlime.com
SIC: **3274** Quicklime

(G-11227)
HYBRID TRAILER CO LLC
912 University Dr S (44839-9172)
PHONE....................................419 433-3022
Glenn Peterman,
EMP: 5 EST: 2010
SALES (est): 341.3K **Privately Held**
SIC: **3792** Travel trailers & campers

(G-11228)
INTERNATIONAL AUTOMOTIVE
Also Called: Automotive Industries Division
1608 Sawmill Pkwy (44839-2200)
PHONE....................................419 433-5653
Robert S Miller, *President*
Scott Womack, *Plant Mgr*
Dean Tran, *Engineer*
Brian Holm, *Executive*
Jeff McCarthy, *Maintence Staff*
EMP: 700 **Privately Held**
WEB: www.iaaawards.com
SIC: **3089** 3714 3429 3229 Injection molded finished plastic products; motor vehicle parts & accessories; manufactured hardware (general); pressed & blown glass
HQ: International Automotive Components Group North America, Inc.
28333 Telegraph Rd
Southfield MI 48034
248 455-7000

(G-11229)
JCK INDUSTRIES
730 River Rd (44839-2623)
P.O. Box 486 (44839-0486)
PHONE....................................419 433-6277
Jack Kenning, *President*
EMP: 30
SALES (est): 3MM **Privately Held**
SIC: **3312** Blast furnaces & steel mills

(G-11230)
KEVIN G RYBA INC
3727 Perkins Ave (44839-1058)
PHONE....................................419 627-2010

Kevin G Ryba, *President*
EMP: 3 EST: 1995
SALES (est): 200K **Privately Held**
SIC: **2064** Candy & other confectionery products

(G-11231)
LABEL AID INC
608 Rye Beach Rd (44839-2064)
PHONE....................................419 433-2888
Fax: 419 433-2279
Darlene Crooks, *President*
Carl S Hanson, *Vice Pres*
Lucille Hanson, *Treasurer*
Amy Saville, *Sales Staff*
Heather Feeney, *Admin Sec*
▲ EMP: 15
SQ FT: 40,000
SALES: 3.5MM **Privately Held**
WEB: www.labelaidinc.com
SIC: **2679** Tags & labels, paper

(G-11232)
LAKEWAY MFG INC (PA)
730 River Rd (44839-2623)
P.O. Box 486 (44839-0486)
PHONE....................................419 433-3030
Fax: 419 433-6888
Jack Kenning, *President*
Barbara K Straka, *Corp Secy*
Greg Daniel, *Mfg Staff*
Kathy Weaver, *Purchasing*
EMP: 25
SALES (est): 3.6MM **Privately Held**
SIC: **3567** 3255 3446 3433 Industrial furnaces & ovens; clay refractories; architectural metalwork; heating equipment, except electric; steel foundries; cold finishing of steel shapes

(G-11233)
LATANICK EQUIPMENT INC
720 River Rd (44839-2623)
PHONE....................................419 433-2200
Fax: 419 433-6261
Richard D Poorman, *President*
Richard Decker, *Vice Pres*
Pam Neill, *Draft/Design*
Judy Poorman, *Manager*
Vera Conley, *Admin Sec*
EMP: 20
SQ FT: 32,000
SALES (est): 4.1MM **Privately Held**
WEB: www.latanickequipment.com
SIC: **8711** 3599 Designing: ship, boat, machine & product; custom machinery

(G-11234)
MUDBROOK GOLF CENTER
1609 Mudbrook Rd (44839-8905)
PHONE....................................419 433-2945
Fax: 419 433-0132
EMP: 6
SALES (est): 260K **Privately Held**
SIC: **3949** Mfg Sporting/Athletic Goods

(G-11235)
N2Y LLC
Also Called: Djc Holdings
909 University Dr S (44839-9172)
P.O. Box 550 (44839-0550)
PHONE....................................419 433-9800
Fax: 419 433-9810
Jacquelyn Clark, *President*
David Clark, *Principal*
Michael Clark, *Principal*
Don Wostmann, *Principal*
Mike Iacobucci, *Editor*
EMP: 20
SQ FT: 16,800
SALES: 3MM **Privately Held**
WEB: www.news-2-you.com
SIC: **3999** Education aids, devices & supplies

(G-11236)
ODYSSEY PRESS INC
913 Superior Dr (44839-1454)
PHONE....................................614 410-0356
Fax: 614 436-4365
David L Trotter, *President*
Mark Bober, *Vice Pres*
EMP: 15
SQ FT: 10,000

SALES (est): 1.5MM **Privately Held**
WEB: www.odysseypress.com
SIC: **2752** 2759 Commercial printing, offset; letterpress printing

(G-11237)
PLASTIC WORKS INC (PA)
10502 Mudbrook Rd (44839-9372)
P.O. Box 369 (44839-0369)
PHONE....................................419 433-6576
Martin Kvarne, *President*
EMP: 2
SALES (est): 1.1MM **Privately Held**
SIC: **3081** 3089 Packing materials, plastic sheet; plastic processing

(G-11238)
PPG ARCHITECTURAL FINISHES INC
Glidden Professional Paint Ctr
300 Sprowl Rd (44839-2636)
PHONE....................................419 433-5664
Fax: 419 433-2276
Mike Powell, *Human Res Mgr*
William Radjewski, *Branch Mgr*
Michael Herlihy, *Admin Sec*
EMP: 230
SALES (corp-wide): 14.7B **Publicly Held**
WEB: www.gliddenpaint.com
SIC: **2891** Adhesives
HQ: Ppg Architectural Finishes, Inc.
1 Ppg Pl
Pittsburgh PA 15272
412 434-3131

(G-11239)
PPG INDUSTRIES
400 Sprowl Rd (44839-2638)
PHONE....................................419 433-0567
EMP: 3
SALES (est): 199.8K **Privately Held**
SIC: **3999** Atomizers, toiletry

(G-11240)
PRECISION MACHINING CORP
9307 Wikel Rd (44839-9140)
PHONE....................................419 433-3520
Fax: 419 433-9678
James Ebert, *President*
EMP: 4
SQ FT: 4,400
SALES (est): 423.4K **Privately Held**
SIC: **3599** Machine shop, jobbing & repair; custom machinery

(G-11241)
ROSWELL INC
9808 Barrows Rd (44839-9796)
PHONE....................................419 433-4709
Fax: 419 433-0539
John Delamater, *President*
EMP: 5
SQ FT: 6,500
SALES (est): 855.7K **Privately Held**
WEB: www.roswellinc.com
SIC: **3089** Plastic containers, except foam

Iberia
Morrow County

(G-11242)
COREWORTH HOLDINGS LLC
8402 County Rd (43325)
P.O. Box 205 (43325-0205)
PHONE....................................419 468-7100
Rodney Whited, *Partner*
Randy Harper, *Partner*
Rich Kozlowski,
EMP: 4
SALES (est): 326.2K **Privately Held**
SIC: **3469** Machine parts, stamped or pressed metal

(G-11243)
GLEN-GERY CORPORATION
County Rd 9 (43325)
P.O. Box 207 (43325-0207)
PHONE....................................419 468-5002
Fax: 419 468-5205
George Robinson, *Manager*
EMP: 50 **Privately Held**
WEB: www.glengerybrick.com

SIC: **3251** 3255 Structural brick & blocks; clay refractories
HQ: Glen-Gery Corporation
1166 Spring St
Reading PA 19610
610 374-4011

(G-11244)
IBERIA MACHINE SHOP INC
8402 County Rd 30 (43325)
P.O. Box 205 (43325-0205)
PHONE....................................419 468-7100
Fax: 419 468-8748
Rodney L Whited, *President*
EMP: 4 EST: 1969
SQ FT: 6,000
SALES (est): 569.4K **Privately Held**
SIC: **3599** Machine shop, jobbing & repair

Independence
Cuyahoga County

(G-11245)
ACCEL PERFORMANCE GROUP LLC (DH)
6100 Oak Tree Blvd # 200 (44131-6914)
PHONE....................................216 658-6413
Robert Tobey, *CEO*
Robert Romanelli, *President*
Bob Bruegging, *Vice Pres*
Michael Gretchko, *Engineer*
Andrew Mazzarella, *CFO*
◆ EMP: 180
SQ FT: 200,000
SALES (est): 56MM
SALES (corp-wide): 87.7MM **Privately Held**
WEB: www.mrgasket.com
SIC: **3714** 5013 3053 Motor vehicle parts & accessories; automotive supplies & parts; gaskets, packing & sealing devices
HQ: Msdp Group Llc
1350 Pullman Dr Dr14
El Paso TX 79936
915 857-5200

(G-11246)
AGILE GLOBAL SOLUTIONS INC
5755 Granger Rd Ste 610 (44131-1458)
PHONE....................................916 655-7745
EMP: 23
SALES (corp-wide): 6.7MM **Privately Held**
SIC: **7372** Business oriented computer software
PA: Agile Global Solutions, Inc.
13405 Folsom Blvd Ste 515
Folsom CA 95630
916 293-3431

(G-11247)
ALCAN PRIMARY PRODUCTS CORP
6055 Rockside Woods Blvd (44131-2301)
PHONE....................................440 460-3300
Yvon Danjou, *President*
Eileen Burns Lerum, *Vice Pres*
Donald P Seberger, *Vice Pres*
Pamela Schneider, *Treasurer*
Timothy J Guerra, *Asst Sec*
◆ EMP: 1398
SALES (est): 125.9MM
SALES (corp-wide): 33.7B **Privately Held**
SIC: **3334** Primary aluminum
HQ: Alcan Corporation
6060 Parkland Blvd
Cleveland OH 44124
440 460-3307

(G-11248)
AMARR COMPANY
Also Called: Amarr Garage Doors
800 Resource Dr Ste 3 (44131-1875)
PHONE....................................216 573-7100
Luke Andress, *Branch Mgr*
David Dutton, *Manager*
Chris Pastula, *Manager*
EMP: 3

SALES (corp-wide): 7.8B Privately Held
WEB: www.amarr.com
SIC: 2431 3442 5211 Garage doors, overhead: wood; garage doors, overhead:
metal; garage doors, sale & installation
HQ: Amarr Company
165 Carriage Ct
Winston Salem NC 27105
336 744-5100

(G-11249)
AVTRON INC
7900 E Pleasant Valley Rd (44131-5529)
PHONE.....................................216 642-1230
Fax: 216 642-1230
John Brock, President
Edward Meyer, Engineer
Owen Patton, Engineer
Ann Williams, CFO
EMP: 39
SALES (est): 8.6MM Privately Held
SIC: 3629 Electrical industrial apparatus

(G-11250)
BASF CATALYSTS LLC
Also Called: BASF Battery Materials
8001 E Pleasant Valley Rd (44131-5526)
PHONE.....................................216 867-1047
Fax: 216 867-1088
Ralph Wise, Site Mgr
EMP: 20
SALES (corp-wide): 60.8B Privately Held
SIC: 2819 Catalysts, chemical
HQ: Basf Catalysts Llc
25 Middlesex Tpke
Iselin NJ 08830
732 205-5000

(G-11251)
BASF CORPORATION
Also Called: Novolyte Technologies
8001 E Pleasant Vly (44131-5526)
PHONE.....................................216 867-1040
Richard Watkins, Branch Mgr
EMP: 20
SALES (corp-wide): 60.8B Privately Held
SIC: 2621 Specialty or chemically treated
papers
HQ: Basf Corporation
100 Park Ave
Florham Park NJ 07932
973 245-6000

(G-11252)
DIGICOM INC
6916 Daisy Ave (44131-3380)
PHONE.....................................216 642-3838
Frank J Prucha Jr, Principal
Melissa Lapor, Principal
Nancy Prucha, Principal
EMP: 7
SALES (est): 432K Privately Held
SIC: 2711 2732 Commercial printing &
newspaper publishing combined; pam-
phlets: printing only, not published on site

(G-11253)
DUNHAM MACHINE INC
1311 E Schaaf Rd Bldg A (44131-1347)
PHONE.....................................216 398-4500
Fax: 216 398-4500
Ted Pawelec, President
EMP: 9
SQ FT: 7,500
SALES (est): 1.4MM Privately Held
WEB: www.dunhammachine.com
SIC: 3599 Machine shop, jobbing & repair

(G-11254)
EMC CORPORATION
Also Called: Emc2
6480 Rcksde Wds Blvd S # 330
(44131-2222)
PHONE.....................................216 606-2000
Fax: 216 573-0872
Peter Bell, District Mgr
Tom Weldon, Manager
David Boje, Manager
Mitchell Breen, Manager
Karl Federmann, Manager
EMP: 39
SALES (corp-wide): 67.1B Publicly Held
WEB: www.emc.com
SIC: 3572 7372 Computer storage de-
vices; prepackaged software

HQ: Emc Corporation
176 South St
Hopkinton MA 01748
508 435-1000

(G-11255)
GOODRICH CORPORATION
Also Called: Goodrich Landing Gear Division
6225 Oak Tree Blvd (44131-2509)
PHONE.....................................216 429-4018
Fax: 216 429-4643
Michael File, General Mgr
Jake Pink, Engineer
Carl Patterson, VP Finance
Theresa Scott, Accountant
Diane Dillman, Cust Mgr
EMP: 500
SQ FT: 27,772
SALES (corp-wide): 57.2B Publicly Held
WEB: www.bfgoodrich.com
SIC: 3728 Alighting (landing gear) assem-
blies, aircraft
HQ: Goodrich Corporation
2730 W Tyvola Rd
Charlotte NC 28217
704 423-7000

(G-11256)
GRAFTECH HOLDINGS INC
6100 Oak Tree Blvd # 300 (44131-6970)
PHONE.....................................216 676-2000
Joel L Hawthorne, CEO
Erick R Asmussen, Vice Pres
John D Moran, Vice Pres
EMP: 930
SALES (est): 569.1K
SALES (corp-wide): 14.9B Privately Held
SIC: 1499 3624 Graphite mining; carbon &
graphite products
HQ: Graftech International Ltd.
6100 Oak Tree Blvd # 300
Independence OH 44131

(G-11257)
**GRAFTECH INTERNATIONAL
LTD (HQ)**
6100 Oak Tree Blvd # 300 (44131-6970)
PHONE.....................................216 676-2000
J Peter Gordon, Ch of Bd
Jeffrey C Dutton, President
Bill Williams, Safety Dir
Jonathan Taylor, Engineer
Michael Capp, Project Engr
◆ EMP: 21
SALES: 437.9MM
SALES (corp-wide): 14.9B Privately Held
WEB: www.graftech.com
SIC: 3624 Carbon & graphite products
PA: Brookfield Asset Management Inc
181 Bay St Suite 300
Toronto ON M5J 2
416 363-9491

(G-11258)
**GRAFTECH INTL HOLDINGS INC
(DH)**
Also Called: UCAR Carbon
6100 Oak Tree Blvd # 300 (44131-6970)
PHONE.....................................216 676-2000
Fax: 216 676-2291
Joel Hawthorne, CEO
Mark Sullivan, Vice Pres
Yissel Hilton, Parts Mgr
Grisez Greg, Purch Agent
Janis Mizerak, Buyer
◆ EMP: 197
SQ FT: 10,000
SALES (est): 236.7MM
SALES (corp-wide): 14.9B Privately Held
SIC: 3624 Carbon & graphite products;
electrodes, thermal & electrolytic uses:
carbon, graphite

(G-11259)
**HONEYWELL INTERNATIONAL
INC**
950 Keynote Cir Ste 90 (44131-1885)
PHONE.....................................216 459-6048
Jim Rosen, General Mgr
Dan Stankey, CFO
Sam Davis, Consultant
Jon Mansco, Senior Mgr
EMP: 657

SALES (corp-wide): 39.3B Publicly Held
WEB: www.honeywell.com
SIC: 3724 Aircraft engines & engine parts;
turbines, aircraft type
PA: Honeywell International Inc.
115 Tabor Rd
Morris Plains NJ 07950
973 455-2000

(G-11260)
**INDY EQP INDPNDENCE
RECYCL INC**
6220 E Schaaf Rd (44131-1332)
PHONE.....................................216 524-0999
Victor Digeronimo, President
Shannon Carlisle, VP Mktg
Ronald Brocco, Office Mgr
Robert Digeronimo, Director
Robert Digeranimo, Admin Sec
▲ EMP: 250
SQ FT: 15,000
SALES: 250MM Privately Held
SIC: 3531 Construction machinery

(G-11261)
JENCO MANUFACTURING INC
7682 Valley Vista Rd (44131-6643)
PHONE.....................................216 898-9682
Fax: 216 898-1594
Andrew Jendre, President
Peter Jendre, Vice Pres
Tina Froment, Mfg Staff
Denise Jendre, Treasurer
Evelyn Jendre, Admin Sec
EMP: 24
SALES (est): 3MM Privately Held
WEB: www.jencomanufacturing.com
SIC: 3452 Rivets, metal

(G-11262)
JOY GLOBAL INC
981 Keynote Cir Ste 8 (44131-1842)
PHONE.....................................216 503-5029
Edward L Doheny, Branch Mgr
Mark Merhar, Manager
Mark Verdova, Senior Mgr
EMP: 8
SALES (corp-wide): 15.9B Privately Held
SIC: 3532 Mining machinery
HQ: Joy Global Inc.
100 E Wisconsin Ave # 2780
Milwaukee WI 53202
414 319-8500

(G-11263)
KOHUT ENTERPRISES INC
Also Called: Mel-Ba Manufacturing
5281 Butternut Ridge Dr (44131-4688)
PHONE.....................................440 366-6666
Fax: 440 365-2384
Kenneth M Kohut, President
EMP: 6
SQ FT: 23,000
SALES: 800K Privately Held
WEB: www.mel-ba.com
SIC: 3451 Screw machine products

(G-11264)
KRONOS INCORPORATED
6100 Oak Tree Blvd # 410 (44131-6948)
PHONE.....................................216 867-5609
Fax: 216 524-0640
Dianne Maupin, Sales & Mktg St
Carol Nowakowski, Senior Mgr
EMP: 4
SALES (corp-wide): 1.3B Privately Held
WEB: www.kronos.com
SIC: 7372 Prepackaged software
HQ: Kronos Incorporated
297 Billerica Rd
Chelmsford MA 01824
978 250-9800

(G-11265)
**LIQUID DEVELOPMENT
COMPANY (PA)**
Also Called: L D C
5708 E Schaaf Rd (44131-1308)
PHONE.....................................216 641-9366
Fax: 216 641-6416
Doug Hutchinson, President
Beldon Hutchinson, Vice Pres
Lynn Hutchinson, Treasurer
Dawn Hutchinson, Admin Sec
▲ EMP: 9 EST: 1978
SQ FT: 18,000

SALES (est): 1.1MM Privately Held
WEB: www.ldcu.com
SIC: 2899 3559 Chemical preparations;
electroplating machinery & equipment

(G-11266)
**MAGNESIUM TECHNOLOGIES
CORP (DH)**
Also Called: Rossborough
4807 Rockside Rd Ste 400 (44131-2159)
PHONE.....................................330 659-3003
David J Kruse, President
Paul Uguccioni, Vice Pres
Timothy A Andel, Controller
James Wilson, Admin Sec
EMP: 3
SQ FT: 6,000
SALES (est): 4.5MM
SALES (corp-wide): 1.1B Privately Held
WEB: www.mgtechcorp.com
SIC: 2899 Metal treating compounds
HQ: Opta Minerals Inc
407 Parkside Dr
Waterdown ON L0R 2
905 689-7361

(G-11267)
MAXON CORPORATION
950 Keynote Cir Ste 113 (44131-1880)
PHONE.....................................216 459-6056
Joseph Pomykala, Manager
EMP: 3
SALES (corp-wide): 39.3B Publicly Held
WEB: www.maxoncorp.com
SIC: 3823 Combustion control instruments
HQ: Maxon Corporation
201 E 18th St
Muncie IN 47302
765 284-3304

(G-11268)
NIDEC MOTOR CORPORATION
Also Called: Nidec Avtron
7555 E Pleasant Valley Rd (44131-5562)
PHONE.....................................216 642-1230
Bill Merkel, Vice Pres
Taylor Ittu, Buyer
John Kasunich, Engineer
Bill Trende, Regl Sales Mgr
Jake Lindquist, Branch Mgr
EMP: 150
SALES (corp-wide): 10B Privately Held
SIC: 3823 3829 Industrial instrmnts
msrmnt display/control process variable;
aircraft & motor vehicle measurement
equipment
HQ: Nidec Motor Corporation
8050 West Florissant Ave
Saint Louis MO 63136

(G-11269)
POLYMER ADDITIVES INC (HQ)
Also Called: Valtris Specialty Chemicals
7500 E Pleasant Valley Rd (44131-5536)
PHONE.....................................216 875-7200
Paul Angus, CEO
Kaval Patel, President
Bob Knighton, General Mgr
Gaurav Golechna, Vice Pres
Matthew Gullen, Vice Pres
EMP: 50 EST: 2014
SALES (est): 210MM Privately Held
SIC: 5169 2899 Chemicals & allied prod-
ucts; chemical preparations; fire retardant
chemicals
PA: Polymer Additives Holdings, Inc.
7500 E Pleasant Valley Rd
Independence OH 44131
216 875-7200

(G-11270)
**POLYMER ADDITIVES
HOLDINGS INC (PA)**
7500 E Pleasant Valley Rd (44131-5536)
PHONE.....................................216 875-7200
Anthony A Tamer, Mng Member
EMP: 3
SALES (est): 210MM Privately Held
SIC: 5169 2899 Chemicals & allied prod-
ucts; chemical preparations; fire retardant
chemicals

(G-11271)
PRECISION METALFORMING ASSN (PA)
6363 Oak Tree Blvd (44131-2556)
PHONE..................216 241-1482
Fax: 216 901-9190
Jody Fledderman, *Vice Ch Bd*
William E Gaskin, *President*
Andy Flando, *Publisher*
Daniel E Ellashek, *Vice Pres*
Greg Landgraf, *Vice Pres*
▲ EMP: 41 EST: 1942
SQ FT: 20,000
SALES: 4.6MM **Privately Held**
SIC: 8611 2731 Trade associations; book publishing

(G-11272)
RHINOSYSTEMS INC
Also Called: Navage
800 Resource Dr Ste 12 (44131-1875)
PHONE..................216 351-6262
Martin Hoke, *President*
Odette Kunath, *Manager*
EMP: 10 EST: 2007
SQ FT: 9,000
SALES (est): 438.3K **Privately Held**
SIC: 3841 Inhalation therapy equipment

(G-11273)
SANGRAF INTERNATIONAL INC
6140 W Creek Rd Ste 206 (44131-6832)
PHONE..................216 543-3288
Xiu Qin Hou, *Principal*
Lesley Inderrieden, *Business Mgr*
Dan Ilkay, *General Counsel*
▲ EMP: 11 EST: 2012
SALES (est): 1.8MM
SALES (corp-wide): 24.5MM **Privately Held**
SIC: 3624 Electrodes, thermal & electrolytic uses: carbon, graphite
PA: Henan Sanli Carbon Products Co., Ltd
North Side Of Xiaotun Village, Baiquan Town, Xijiao Development
Xinxiang 45363
373 626-5112

(G-11274)
SARINGER SHEET METAL INC
4654 Crestwood Dr (44131-5255)
PHONE..................216 447-9755
Fax: 216 267-5003
Robert Saringer, *President*
Ethel Saringer, *Corp Secy*
EMP: 20
SQ FT: 9,000
SALES: 2MM **Privately Held**
SIC: 3444 1761 Ducts, sheet metal; sheet metalwork

(G-11275)
SKILLSOFT CORPORATION
6645 Acres Dr (44131-4962)
PHONE..................216 524-5200
Joe Garrison, *Branch Mgr*
EMP: 66 **Privately Held**
SIC: 7372 Educational computer software
HQ: Skillsoft Corporation
107 Northeastern Blvd
Nashua NH 03062
603 821-3715

(G-11276)
SYMANTEC CORPORATION
6100 Oak Tree Blvd (44131-2544)
PHONE..................216 643-6700
EMP: 70
SALES (corp-wide): 3.6B **Publicly Held**
SIC: 7372 Prepackaged software
PA: Symantec Corporation
350 Ellis St
Mountain View CA 94043
650 527-8000

(G-11277)
THYSSENKRUPP MATERIALS NA INC
6050 Oak Tree Blvd # 110 (44131-6928)
PHONE..................216 883-8100
Rob Hanzie, *Regional Mgr*
Dave Vassar, *Regional Mgr*
Bryan Dascani, *Plant Mgr*
Todd Angelo, *Accounts Mgr*
E M Habart, *Marketing Staff*

EMP: 87
SQ FT: 65,000
SALES (corp-wide): 44.2B **Privately Held**
SIC: 5051 3341 Metals service centers & offices; secondary nonferrous metals
HQ: Thyssenkrupp Materials Na, Inc.
22355 W 11 Mile Rd
Southfield MI 48033
248 233-5600

(G-11278)
TITANIUM INDUSTRIES INC
200 Ventura Cir (44131-1048)
PHONE..................216 661-4610
John Spafford, *Regional Mgr*
Jerry Young, *QC Mgr*
Mauricio Tanaka, *Sales Mgr*
Mark Zaremba, *Director*
EMP: 9 **Privately Held**
SIC: 3356 Titanium
PA: Titanium Industries, Inc.
18 Green Pond Rd Ste 1
Rockaway NJ 07866

(G-11279)
UNIFIRST CORPORATION
1450 E Granger Rd (44131-1207)
PHONE..................216 658-6900
Randy Thorton, *Principal*
EMP: 78
SALES (corp-wide): 1.4B **Publicly Held**
SIC: 2326 Men's & boys' work clothing
PA: Unifirst Corporation
68 Jonspin Rd
Wilmington MA 01887
978 658-8888

(G-11280)
UNITED COMPUTER GROUP INC
Also Called: U C G
7100 E Pleasant Valley Rd # 250 (44131-5556)
PHONE..................216 520-1333
Fax: 440 717-7662
James A Kandrac, *President*
Pamela Kandrac, *Vice Pres*
Michael D Powall, *Vice Pres*
EMP: 8
SQ FT: 3,200
SALES (est): 1.1MM **Privately Held**
SIC: 7372 5045 Prepackaged software; computers, peripherals & software

(G-11281)
USER FRIENDLY PHONE BOOK LLC
2 Summit Park Dr Ste 105 (44131-2558)
PHONE..................216 674-6500
Ron Swierz, *Sales Associate*
Jack Nelson, *Branch Mgr*
EMP: 45
SALES (corp-wide): 78.5MM **Privately Held**
WEB: www.ufpb.net
SIC: 2741 Directories, telephone: publishing & printing
PA: User Friendly Phone Book, Llc
10200 Grogans Mill Rd # 440
The Woodlands TX 77380
281 465-5400

(G-11282)
VIASAT INC
5990 W Creek Rd Ste 1 (44131-2181)
PHONE..................216 706-7800
Fax: 216 706-7801
Russel Fuerst, *Vice Pres*
Greg Zaker, *Senior Engr*
Chandrasekar Raj, *Program Mgr*
William Thesling III, *CTO*
Jeanne Warman, *Officer*
EMP: 62
SQ FT: 11,000
SALES (est): 8.4MM
SALES (corp-wide): 1.4B **Publicly Held**
WEB: www.eccincorp.com
SIC: 3661 Telephone & telegraph apparatus
PA: Viasat, Inc.
6155 El Camino Real
Carlsbad CA 92009
760 476-2200

(G-11283)
WEED INSTRUMENT COMPANY INC
Also Called: Furnace Parts
6133 Rockside Rd Ste 300 (44131-2243)
PHONE..................216 676-5005
Fax: 216 676-5557
EMP: 30
SALES (corp-wide): 1.1B **Privately Held**
SIC: 3823 Industrial instrmnts msrmnt display/control process variable
HQ: Weed Instrument Company, Inc.
707 Jeffrey Way
Round Rock TX 78665
512 434-2900

(G-11284)
WESTMOUNT TECHNOLOGY INC
Also Called: Wmt
6100 Oak Tree Blvd (44131-2544)
PHONE..................216 328-2011
Sowmia Mahesh, *CEO*
Timothy Luberger, *Director*
EMP: 5
SQ FT: 600
SALES (est): 226.8K **Privately Held**
SIC: 7371 7373 7372 7379 Custom computer programming services; office computer automation systems integration; business oriented computer software;

(G-11285)
WHOLESALE SUPPLIES PLUS INC
7820 E Pleasant Valley Rd (44131-5531)
PHONE..................440 526-6556
Fax: 440 526-6597
Deborah May, *President*
David May, *Vice Pres*
▼ EMP: 45
SALES (est): 8.9MM **Privately Held**
WEB: www.wholesalesuppliesplus.com
SIC: 3999 Candles

Indian Spgs
Butler County

(G-11286)
SPR MACHINE INC
2130 Tuley Rd (45015-1333)
PHONE..................513 737-8040
Fax: 513 737-8041
Scott Roth, *President*
Robert Carringer, *Business Mgr*
Scott Pater, *Treasurer*
Rasmus Saile, *Admin Sec*
EMP: 5
SALES (est): 566.4K **Privately Held**
SIC: 3469 Machine parts, stamped or pressed metal

Irondale
Jefferson County

(G-11287)
C A JOSEPH CO
C A Joseph Machine Shop
170 Broadway St (43932)
PHONE..................330 532-4646
Nancy Joseph, *Vice Pres*
Joe Smithbower, *Manager*
EMP: 14
SALES (corp-wide): 4.1MM **Privately Held**
WEB: www.cajoseph.com
SIC: 3599 3444 3443 3441 Machine shop, jobbing & repair; sheet metalwork; fabricated plate work (boiler shop); fabricated structural metal
PA: C. A. Joseph Co.
13712 Old Frdericktown Rd
East Liverpool OH 43920
330 385-6869

Ironton
Lawrence County

(G-11288)
ALLEN ENTERPRISES INC
Also Called: Tri-State Wilbert Vault Co
2900 S 9th St (45638)
PHONE..................740 532-5913
Fax: 740 532-1080
Douglas M Allen, *Ch of Bd*
Ronald Keener, *Corp Secy*
Gretchen A Allen, *Director*
EMP: 8 EST: 1928
SQ FT: 22,000
SALES: 1.2MM **Privately Held**
SIC: 5087 5039 3272 Concrete burial vaults & boxes; septic tanks; septic tanks, concrete

(G-11289)
ARROW COAL GROVE INC
300 Marion Pike (45638-2957)
PHONE..................740 532-6143
Ron Brammer, *President*
EMP: 10
SALES (est): 850K **Privately Held**
SIC: 1542 3273 1794 Commercial & office building contractors; ready-mixed concrete; excavation work

(G-11290)
ARTHURS REFRIGERATION
2156 State Route 93 (45638-8176)
P.O. Box 272 (45638-0272)
PHONE..................740 532-0206
Chris Arthur, *Owner*
EMP: 3
SALES (est): 387.6K **Privately Held**
SIC: 3585 5064 Refrigeration & heating equipment; refrigerators & freezers

(G-11291)
CRABRO PRINTING INC
314 Chestnut St (45638-1902)
P.O. Box 670 (45638-0670)
PHONE..................740 533-3404
Steven G Cragar, *President*
Carl Brose, *Vice Pres*
EMP: 4
SALES (est): 405.7K **Privately Held**
SIC: 2759 Commercial printing

(G-11292)
DOW CHEMICAL COMPANY
925 County Road 1a (45638-8687)
PHONE..................740 533-4000
Fax: 740 533-4232
Maggie Stamper, *Purchasing*
Tom Hudson, *Human Res Dir*
Tom Hutson, *Human Res Mgr*
Earl Shippe, *Branch Mgr*
John Void, *Branch Mgr*
EMP: 175
SALES (corp-wide): 48.1B **Publicly Held**
WEB: www.dow.com
SIC: 3086 2821 Plastics foam products; plastics materials & resins
PA: The Dow Chemical Company
2030 Dow Ctr
Midland MI 48674
989 636-1000

(G-11293)
G BIG INC
Also Called: Pickett Concrete
300 Marion Pike (45638-2957)
PHONE..................740 532-9123
Ronald Jenkins, *Branch Mgr*
EMP: 6
SALES (corp-wide): 2.2MM **Privately Held**
WEB: www.gbig.com
SIC: 3273 Ready-mixed concrete
PA: G Big Inc
441 Rockwood Ave
Chesapeake OH 45619
740 867-5758

(G-11294)
IRONTON PUBLICATIONS INC
Also Called: Ironton Tribune The
2903 S 5th St (45638-2866)
P.O. Box 647 (45638-0647)
PHONE..................................740 532-1441
Fax: 740 532-1506
David Evans, *Manager*
James B Boone Jr, *Director*
EMP: 508
SQ FT: 12,000
SALES (est): 17.1MM
SALES (corp-wide): 109.9MM **Privately Held**
WEB: www.irontontribune.com
SIC: 2711 Newspapers, publishing & printing
PA: Boone Newspapers, Inc.
1060 Fairfax Park Ste 3
Tuscaloosa AL 35406
205 330-4100

(G-11295)
JANELL INC
1014 S 2nd St (45638-1984)
PHONE..................................740 532-9111
Fax: 740 532-8300
Bob Cleary, *Owner*
EMP: 4
SALES (est): 326.1K **Privately Held**
SIC: 3272 Concrete products

(G-11296)
LIEBERT CORPORATION
Also Called: Vertiv
3040 S 9th St (45638-2895)
PHONE..................................740 547-5100
Fax: 740 533-9354
Bob Walters, *General Mgr*
Carlos Morris, *Design Engr*
Marty Scott, *Human Res Mgr*
EMP: 300
SALES (corp-wide): 15.2B **Privately Held**
WEB: www.liebert.com
SIC: 3823 Industrial instrmnts msrmnt display/control process variable
HQ: Liebert Corporation
1050 Dearborn Dr
Columbus OH 43085
614 888-0246

(G-11297)
MODULAR SECURITY SYSTEMS INC
Also Called: Mssi
1804 N 2nd St (45638-1048)
P.O. Box 284 (45638-0284)
PHONE..................................740 532-7822
Robert Rhett Slagel, *CEO*
David Slagel, *President*
David Johnson, *Business Mgr*
Kevin Harrison, *Vice Pres*
Tim Hopkins, *QC Mgr*
▼ EMP: 5
SQ FT: 1,000
SALES (est): 1.5MM **Privately Held**
WEB: www.modularsecuritysystems.com
SIC: 3699 5065 Security control equipment & systems; security control equipment & systems

(G-11298)
PREMERE PRECAST PRODUCTS
317 Hecla St (45638-1370)
PHONE..................................740 533-3333
Evyian Terry, *Principal*
EMP: 12 EST: 2008
SALES (est): 1.4MM **Privately Held**
SIC: 3272 Precast terrazo or concrete products

(G-11299)
PRINTING EXPRESS INC
1229 S 3rd St (45638-2028)
P.O. Box 831 (45638-0831)
PHONE..................................740 532-7003
Fax: 740 532-6050
Mary Beth Nenni, *President*
Jennifer L Mays, *Vice Pres*
EMP: 7
SQ FT: 1,100
SALES: 700K **Privately Held**
SIC: 2752 Commercial printing, offset

(G-11300)
RIVER CITIES VAULT INC
2901 S 11th St (45638-2822)
P.O. Box 4425 (45638-4425)
PHONE..................................740 237-0010
Jim Morgan, *President*
Sherri Morgan, *Vice Pres*
EMP: 10
SALES (est): 750K **Privately Held**
SIC: 3272 Burial vaults, concrete or precast terrazzo

(G-11301)
ROACH WOOD PRODUCTS & PLAS INC
25 Township Road 328 (45638-8171)
PHONE..................................740 532-4855
Fax: 740 533-3585
Bruce Roach Sr, *CEO*
Bruce Roach Jr, *President*
Bicki Roach, *Manager*
EMP: 8
SQ FT: 10,700
SALES (est): 1.2MM **Privately Held**
SIC: 3082 Unsupported plastics profile shapes

(G-11302)
SWIFT MANUFACTURING CO INC
700 Lorain St (45638-1088)
PHONE..................................740 237-4405
Michael Moore, *President*
Zachary Moore, *Vice Pres*
Stacey Moore, *Office Mgr*
EMP: 6
SALES (est): 764.1K **Privately Held**
WEB: www.swiftmfg.net
SIC: 3339 Primary nonferrous metals

(G-11303)
UNDISCOVERED RADIO NETWORK
621 S 6th St (45638-1828)
PHONE..................................740 533-1032
Colleen Griffiths, *President*
EMP: 3
SALES (est): 292.7K **Privately Held**
SIC: 3651 Audio electronic systems

(G-11304)
WELLS GROUP LLC
487 Gallia Pike (45638-8080)
PHONE..................................740 532-9240
Kimberly Cole, *Branch Mgr*
EMP: 10
SALES (corp-wide): 30.3MM **Privately Held**
SIC: 3273 Ready-mixed concrete
PA: The Wells Group Llc
611 W Main St
West Liberty KY 41472
606 743-3485

(G-11305)
WHEELER EMBROIDERY
Also Called: Cjt's
1007 N 2nd St (45638-1235)
PHONE..................................740 550-9751
Joshua Wheeler, *Principal*
EMP: 4
SALES (est): 398.6K **Privately Held**
SIC: 3999 Manufacturing industries

Jackson
Jackson County

(G-11306)
A E RUSTON ELECTRIC LLC
121 N David Ave (45640-1112)
PHONE..................................740 286-3022
Alfred T Ruston, *Mng Member*
EMP: 5 EST: 1922
SQ FT: 15,000
SALES (est): 967.1K **Privately Held**
SIC: 7694 3599 Electric motor repair; machine shop, jobbing & repair

(G-11307)
A K READY MIX LLC
441 Dixon Run Rd (45640-8038)
PHONE..................................740 286-8900

Robert E Stewart,
EMP: 12
SALES (est): 1.2MM **Privately Held**
SIC: 3272 Concrete products

(G-11308)
ACM OHIO LLC
1 Acy Ave Ste D (45640-9563)
PHONE..................................740 286-2187
EMP: 3
SALES (est): 161.1K **Privately Held**
SIC: 2711 Newspapers, publishing & printing

(G-11309)
ALUCHEM OF JACKSON INC
14782 Beaver Pike (45640-9661)
PHONE..................................740 286-2455
Fax: 740 286-2004
Ronald P Zapletal, *President*
Edward L Butera, *Vice Pres*
Ronald L Bell, *Treasurer*
EMP: 50
SALES (est): 6.1MM **Privately Held**
SIC: 1481 Nonmetallic mineral services

(G-11310)
BEITING FARMS
5941 State Route 327 (45640-9449)
P.O. Box 273 (45640-0273)
PHONE..................................740 384-5127
Otto Beiting, *Owner*
EMP: 3 EST: 1974
SALES (est): 173K **Privately Held**
SIC: 2421 0116 0115 0111 Building & structural materials, wood; soybeans; corn; wheat

(G-11311)
BELLISIO FOODS INC
100 E Broadway St (45640-1347)
P.O. Box 550 (45640-0550)
PHONE..................................740 286-5505
Charlie Milliken, *Vice Pres*
Brad Canter, *Project Mgr*
Nikki Carpenter, *Purchasing*
Jeff Wilson, *Branch Mgr*
Dave Maynard, *Manager*
EMP: 1100
SALES (corp-wide): 11.8B **Privately Held**
SIC: 2038 2033 Dinners, frozen & packaged; spaghetti & other pasta sauce: packaged in cans, jars, etc.
HQ: Bellisio Foods, Inc
1201 Harmon Pl Ste 302
Minneapolis MN 55403
218 723-5555

(G-11312)
BRENMAR CONSTRUCTION INC
900 Morton St (45640-1089)
PHONE..................................740 286-2151
Fax: 740 286-6150
Todd Ghearing, *President*
Andy Graham, *Corp Secy*
Tim Ousley, *Vice Pres*
EMP: 60
SQ FT: 5,000
SALES: 8MM **Privately Held**
WEB: www.brenmarconstruction.com
SIC: 1542 3312 Nonresidential construction; structural shapes & pilings, steel

(G-11313)
BROWN PUBLISHING CO INC (PA)
1 Acy Ave Ste D (45640-9563)
P.O. Box 270 (45640-0270)
PHONE..................................740 286-2187
Fax: 740 286-5854
Roy Brown, *President*
EMP: 9 EST: 1925
SQ FT: 5,250
SALES (est): 1.4MM **Privately Held**
SIC: 2711 Newspapers: publishing only, not printed on site

(G-11314)
FOR EVERY HOME
Also Called: James Logan Logging
10381 Chillicothe Pike (45640-8743)
PHONE..................................740 710-1253
Kelly Logan, *Principal*
EMP: 3
SALES (est): 225.7K **Privately Held**
SIC: 2411 Logging

(G-11315)
HIGGINS BUILDING MTLS NO 2 LLC
2000 Acy Ave (45640-2506)
PHONE..................................740 395-5410
David Higgins, *Mng Member*
EMP: 3
SALES (est): 215.7K **Privately Held**
SIC: 3444 Siding, sheet metal

(G-11316)
JACKSON MONUMENT INC
14 Fairmount St (45640-1409)
PHONE..................................740 288-0428
Fax: 740 288-0428
Stan Louis, *President*
Darryl Radliff, *Principal*
EMP: 8
SALES (est): 760.3K **Privately Held**
SIC: 3272 5999 Monuments, concrete; monuments, finished to custom order

(G-11317)
JALCO INDUSTRIES INC
330 Athens St (45640-9433)
P.O. Box 947 (45640-0947)
PHONE..................................740 286-3808
Randal L Ridge, *President*
Susan R Ridge, *Treasurer*
EMP: 10
SQ FT: 10,000
SALES (est): 1MM **Privately Held**
SIC: 3281 5032 Building stone products; concrete building products

(G-11318)
LANTZ LUMBER & SAW SHOP
637 Industry Dr (45640-8737)
PHONE..................................740 286-5658
James Lantz, *Principal*
EMP: 3
SALES (est): 209.8K **Privately Held**
SIC: 2421 Sawmills & planing mills, general

(G-11319)
MARTIN BLOCK COMPANY
290 Twin Oaks Dr (45640-8608)
PHONE..................................740 286-7507
Fax: 740 286-5038
Richard L Coriell, *President*
Donna Trace, *Office Mgr*
EMP: 5 EST: 1946
SQ FT: 12,800
SALES (est): 610K **Privately Held**
SIC: 3271 5211 Blocks, concrete or cinder: standard; lumber & other building materials

(G-11320)
MASCO CABINETRY LLC
Also Called: Merillat Cabinets
960 E Main St (45640-2139)
P.O. Box 625 (45640-0625)
PHONE..................................740 286-5033
Fax: 740 286-6033
Stan Lemmon, *QC Dir*
Ron Gordon, *Persnl Mgr*
Tony Meade, *Persnl Mgr*
John Lewis, *Branch Mgr*
EMP: 455
SQ FT: 104,000
SALES (corp-wide): 7.3B **Publicly Held**
SIC: 2434 Wood kitchen cabinets
HQ: Masco Cabinetry Llc
4600 Arrowhead Dr
Ann Arbor MI 48105
734 205-4600

(G-11321)
MONTGOMERY MCH & FABRICATION
206 Watts Blevins Rd (45640-9768)
P.O. Box 247 (45640-0247)
PHONE..................................740 286-2863
Fax: 740 286-2868
Carry E Montgomery, *President*
Bobbi D Montgomery, *Vice Pres*
Jason Montgomery, *Vice Pres*
Mary Montgomery, *Vice Pres*
EMP: 35
SQ FT: 20,000
SALES (est): 5.7MM **Privately Held**
WEB: www.montgomerymachineshop.com
SIC: 3599 Machine shop, jobbing & repair

(G-11322)
MOUNTAINEER MINING CORP
885 Sternberger Rd (45640-9601)
PHONE....................................740 418-1817
Jason Adkins, *President*
EMP: 4
SALES (est): 194.2K **Privately Held**
SIC: 3535 Conveyors & conveying equipment

(G-11323)
OSCO INDUSTRIES INC
165 Athens St (45640-1306)
P.O. Box 327 (45640-0327)
PHONE....................................740 286-5004
Fax: 740 286-5311
W Burke, *Vice Pres*
John Burke, *Purchasing*
Rich Doty, *QC Dir*
Charles Cooper, *Engineer*
Keith Denny, *Branch Mgr*
EMP: 125
SALES (corp-wide): 97.3MM **Privately Held**
WEB: www.oscoind.com
SIC: 3321 3322 Gray iron castings; malleable iron foundries
PA: Osco Industries, Inc.
    734 11th St
    Portsmouth OH 45662
    740 354-3183

(G-11324)
PACIFIC MANUFACTURING TENN INC
555 Smith Ln (45640)
PHONE....................................513 900-7862
Hisaichi Seko, *President*
EMP: 20 EST: 2014
SQ FT: 189,000
SALES (est): 1.4MM **Privately Held**
SIC: 3469 Ornamental metal stampings

(G-11325)
STEVENS AUTO PARTS & TOWNG
2848 Big Rock Rd (45640-8798)
PHONE....................................740 988-2260
Fax: 740 988-5028
David Stevens, *President*
EMP: 3
SALES (est): 207K **Privately Held**
SIC: 5531 5015 7549 3546 Automotive parts; automotive parts & supplies, used; towing service, automotive; saws & sawing equipment; plumbing & heating supplies; sewer cleaning & rodding

(G-11326)
SUMMERS ORGANIZATION LLC
Also Called: Premium Wood & Garden Products
345 E Main St Ste H (45640-1789)
PHONE....................................740 286-1322
Nick Summers,
Janet Stockmeister,
EMP: 20
SALES (est): 1.5MM **Privately Held**
SIC: 2873 Fertilizers: natural (organic), except compost

(G-11327)
SUPERIOR HARDWOODS OF OHIO
78 Jackson Hill Rd (45640-9301)
P.O. Box 166 (45640-0166)
PHONE....................................740 384-6862
Ammet Tonway, *Owner*
EMP: 70
SALES (est): 4MM **Privately Held**
SIC: 2411 2421 Timber, cut at logging camp; sawmills & planing mills, general

(G-11328)
TELEGRAM
920 Veterans Dr Unit C (45640-2175)
P.O. Box 667 (45640-0667)
PHONE....................................740 286-3604
Fax: 740 286-0167
Jerry Mossbarger, *General Mgr*
EMP: 17
SALES (est): 487.6K **Privately Held**
WEB: www.thetelegram.com
SIC: 2711 Newspapers: publishing only, not printed on site

(G-11329)
TIM CRABTREE
Also Called: Tim's Woodshop
117 Athens St (45640-1306)
PHONE....................................740 286-4535
Tim Crabtree, *Owner*
EMP: 5
SALES (est): 566K **Privately Held**
WEB: www.timswoodshop.com
SIC: 2541 Display fixtures, wood

(G-11330)
TIMES JOURNAL
1 Acy Ave Ste D (45640-9563)
P.O. Box 270 (45640-0270)
PHONE....................................740 286-2187
Norman Diliiland, *President*
Jim Mingus, *President*
Jackie Denuit, *Editor*
Amanda Montgomery, *Accounts Exec*
EMP: 19
SALES (est): 716.8K **Privately Held**
WEB: www.timesjournal.com
SIC: 2711 Newspapers

(G-11331)
TOW PATH READY MIX
1668 Kessinger School Rd (45640-9127)
PHONE....................................740 286-2131
Fax: 740 286-0649
Lonnie Lemaster, *Branch Mgr*
EMP: 10 **Privately Held**
SIC: 3273 Ready-mixed concrete
PA: Tow Path Ready Mix
    12360 State Route 104
    Lucasville OH 45648

(G-11332)
VALUE ADDED BUSINESS SVCS CO (PA)
120 Twin Oaks Dr (45640-9506)
PHONE....................................614 854-9755
Craig Lund, *President*
Diane Hill, *General Mgr*
Ann Lund, *Treasurer*
EMP: 6 EST: 1997
SALES (est): 4.1MM **Privately Held**
WEB: www.valueaddedbiz.com
SIC: 2759 8742 5112 Commercial printing; management consulting services; stationery & office supplies

(G-11333)
WILLIAMS JOHN F OIL FIELD SVCS
20669 Coshocton Co Rd 6 (45640)
P.O. Box 443, Coshocton (43812-0443)
PHONE....................................740 622-7692
John F Williams, *President*
EMP: 4
SALES (est): 503.1K **Privately Held**
SIC: 1389 Oil field services; gas field services

(G-11334)
WINTERS PRODUCTS INC
Also Called: Winters Concrete
109 Athens St (45640-1306)
PHONE....................................740 286-4149
David R Michael, *President*
EMP: 10 EST: 1955
SQ FT: 800
SALES (est): 680K **Privately Held**
SIC: 3273 Ready-mixed concrete

(G-11335)
ZIP LASER SYSTEMS INC
Also Called: Zip Systems of Jackson
345 E Main St Ste H (45640-1789)
PHONE....................................740 286-6613
Fax: 740 286-7181
Nick Summers, *President*
Janet Stockmeister, *Admin Sec*
EMP: 4
SQ FT: 3,000
SALES (est): 530.4K **Privately Held**
SIC: 2752 7334 Commercial printing, lithographic; photocopying & duplicating services

---

Jackson Center
Shelby County

(G-11336)
A G PARTS INC
Also Called: Quality Parts
500 N Linden St (45334)
P.O. Box 757 (45334-0757)
PHONE....................................937 596-6448
Fax: 937 596-6107
Charles Cole, *President*
Tony Nimeyer, *Vice Pres*
EMP: 16
SALES (est): 2.1MM **Privately Held**
WEB: www.agparts.com
SIC: 3714 Motor vehicle parts & accessories

(G-11337)
AIRSTREAM INC (HQ)
419 W Pike St (45334-9728)
P.O. Box 629 (45334-0629)
PHONE....................................937 596-6111
Fax: 937 596-6802
Lawrence J Huttle, *Ch of Bd*
Peter B Orthwein, *Ch of Bd*
Robert Wheeler, *President*
Chris Burch, *General Mgr*
Rick March, *General Mgr*
◆ EMP: 350
SQ FT: 286,000
SALES (est): 94.2MM
SALES (corp-wide): 4.5B **Publicly Held**
WEB: www.airstream.com
SIC: 3716 3792 3714 3713 Motor homes; travel trailers & campers; motor vehicle parts & accessories; truck & bus bodies; motor vehicles & car bodies
PA: Thor Industries, Inc.
    601 E Beardsley Ave
    Elkhart IN 46514
    574 970-7460

(G-11338)
CREATIVE PLASTICS INTL
18163 Snider Rd (45334-9734)
PHONE....................................937 596-6769
Fax: 937 596-6265
Gerald B Wurm, *President*
Keith Korn, *Vice Pres*
Randolph Korn, *Vice Pres*
Richard Wurm, *Vice Pres*
Valerie Sanderson, *Treasurer*
EMP: 17
SQ FT: 40,000
SALES (est): 3MM **Privately Held**
SIC: 3089 Thermoformed finished plastic products

(G-11339)
DESIGN ORIGINAL INC
402 Jackson St (45334-5057)
P.O. Box 727 (45334-0727)
PHONE....................................937 596-5121
Fax: 937 596-5193
Frank E Pusey, *President*
Glenn A Pusey, *Vice Pres*
EMP: 16
SQ FT: 25,000
SALES (est): 3.9MM **Privately Held**
WEB: www.design-original.com
SIC: 5136 5137 2396 2395 Sportswear, men's & boys'; men's & boys' outerwear; shirts, men's & boys'; sweaters, men's & boys'; sportswear, women's & children's; coats: women's, children's & infants'; hats: women's, children's & infants'; sweaters, women's & children's; automotive & apparel trimmings; pleating & stitching

(G-11340)
ELDORADO NATIONAL KANSAS INC
419 W Pike St (45334-9728)
PHONE....................................937 596-6849
Andrew Imanse, *CEO*
EMP: 3 **Publicly Held**
SIC: 3711 Buses, all types, assembly of
HQ: Eldorado National (Kansas), Inc.
    1655 Wall St
    Salina KS 67401
    785 827-1033

(G-11341)
EMI CORP (PA)
Also Called: E M I Plastic Equipment
801 W Pike St (45334-6037)
P.O. Box 590 (45334-0590)
PHONE....................................937 596-5511
Fax: 216 535-4809
James E Andraitis, *President*
Bill Bruce, *Vice Pres*
Brad Wren, *Vice Pres*
Larry Stephens, *Plant Mgr*
Deb Hereld, *Purch Dir*
▲ EMP: 85 EST: 1980
SQ FT: 80,000
SALES (est): 16.3MM **Privately Held**
WEB: www.emiplastics.com
SIC: 3544 5084 Special dies, tools, jigs & fixtures; industrial machinery & equipment

(G-11342)
LACAL EQUIPMENT INC
901 W Pike St (45334-6024)
P.O. Box 757 (45334-0757)
PHONE....................................800 543-6161
Fax: 937 596-5433
Roger Dietrich, *President*
Tom Homan, *President*
Tony Niemeyer, *Principal*
Charles M Cole, *Vice Pres*
Roger Detrick, *Vice Pres*
EMP: 30
SQ FT: 14,000
SALES (est): 7.7MM
SALES (corp-wide): 96MM **Privately Held**
WEB: www.lacal.com
SIC: 3714 Motor vehicle parts & accessories
PA: Jmac Inc.
    200 W Nationwide Blvd # 1
    Columbus OH 43215
    614 436-2418

(G-11343)
MASTER SWAGING INC
210 Washington St (45334)
P.O. Box 550 (45334-0550)
PHONE....................................937 596-6171
Fax: 937 596-6170
Daniel Gilroy, *President*
Cindy Gilroy, *Principal*
Chris Burch, *Purch Mgr*
Pam Neal, *Purchasing*
EMP: 6
SQ FT: 26,000
SALES (est): 590K **Privately Held**
WEB: www.masterswaging.com
SIC: 3728 3599 Aircraft assemblies, subassemblies & parts; machine shop, jobbing & repair

(G-11344)
PLASTIPAK PACKAGING INC
18015 State Route 65 (45334-9434)
P.O. Box 789 (45334-0789)
PHONE....................................937 596-6142
Fax: 937 596-6268
Bruce Rinehart, *Project Mgr*
Roger Gibson, *Prdtn Mgr*
Hank Zimpfer, *Prdtn Mgr*
Preston Knasel, *Safety Mgr*
Tim Moore, *Safety Mgr*
EMP: 500
SALES (corp-wide): 36.3MM **Privately Held**
WEB: www.plastipak.com
SIC: 3085 2671 Plastics bottles; packaging paper & plastics film, coated & laminated
HQ: Plastipak Packaging, Inc.
    41605 Ann Arbor Rd E
    Plymouth MI 48170
    734 455-3600

(G-11345)
PLASTIPAK PACKAGING INC
300 Washington St (45334)
PHONE....................................937 596-5166
William P Young, *Branch Mgr*
EMP: 123
SALES (corp-wide): 36.3MM **Privately Held**
WEB: www.plastipak.com
SIC: 3089 Blow molded finished plastic products

HQ: Plastipak Packaging, Inc.
41605 Ann Arbor Rd E
Plymouth MI 48170
734 455-3600

(G-11346)
PRECISION DETAILS INC
104 Washington St (45334-1101)
P.O. Box 696 (45334-0696)
PHONE..............................937 596-0068
Fax: 937 295-3906
Jeff Winemiller, *President*
Tony Herring, *General Mgr*
Katie Winemiller, *Vice Pres*
EMP: 15
SQ FT: 4,500
SALES (est): 1.3MM **Privately Held**
SIC: 3544 Special dies, tools, jigs & fixtures

(G-11347)
PRODEVA INC
100 Jerry Dr (45334-5075)
P.O. Box 729 (45334-0729)
PHONE..............................937 596-6713
Fax: 937 596-5145
Steve Bunke, *Vice Pres*
Shirley Bunke, *Treasurer*
Frederick Bunke, *Admin Sec*
EMP: 12
SQ FT: 21,000
SALES (est): 1MM **Privately Held**
WEB: www.prodeva.com
SIC: 3599 3559 Machine shop, jobbing & repair; recycling machinery

(G-11348)
STEVEN YANT
Also Called: Yant Beef Jerky
103 Jerry Dr (45334-5075)
P.O. Box 67 (45334-0067)
PHONE..............................937 596-0497
Steven Yant, *Owner*
Bryan Brown, *Manager*
EMP: 3
SALES: 130K **Privately Held**
SIC: 2013 Sausages & other prepared meats

(G-11349)
THOR INDUSTRIES INC
419 W Pike St (45334-9728)
PHONE..............................937 596-6111
Fax: 937 596-6092
Chris Lawrence, *Finance*
Emily Boothe, *Mktg Dir*
Steven Hileman, *Manager*
Robert Annetta, *Prgrmr*
Penny Meyers, *General Counsel*
EMP: 21
SALES (corp-wide): 4.5B **Publicly Held**
SIC: 3799 3711 Recreational vehicles; buses, all types, assembly of
PA: Thor Industries, Inc.
601 E Beardsley Ave
Elkhart IN 46514
574 970-7460

Jamestown
Greene County

(G-11350)
BROWN PRECISION MACHINE
13 S Buckles Ave (45335-1581)
PHONE..............................937 675-6585
EMP: 5
SQ FT: 5,500
SALES: 300K **Privately Held**
SIC: 3599 Job Machine Shop

(G-11351)
CAESARCREEK PALLETS LTD
4392 Shawnee Trl (45335-1227)
PHONE..............................937 675-3391
Fax: 937 675-3391
Larry Payton, *Principal*
Clarence Payton, *Principal*
Steve Payton, *Principal*
Julie Spahr, *Exec Dir*
EMP: 14
SQ FT: 6,000
SALES: 1.5MM **Privately Held**
SIC: 2448 Pallets, wood

(G-11352)
MIKES WELDING
5589 Old Us Route 35 E (45335-9588)
P.O. Box 221 (45335-0221)
PHONE..............................937 675-6587
Michael Brown, *Owner*
EMP: 3
SALES (est): 251.9K **Privately Held**
SIC: 7692 3441 Welding repair; fabricated structural metal

(G-11353)
TWIST INC (PA)
47 S Limestone St (45335-9501)
P.O. Box 177 (45335-0177)
PHONE..............................937 675-9581
Fax: 937 675-6781
Joe W Wright, *President*
Dan Coots, *Plant Mgr*
Karl Downing, *Purch Agent*
Richard Tracy, *Purchasing*
Tiffany Combs, *Human Resources*
▲ EMP: 110
SQ FT: 50,000
SALES (est): 50.2MM **Privately Held**
SIC: 3495 3542 3469 3471 Mechanical springs, precision; machine tools, metal forming type; metal stampings; electroplating & plating

(G-11354)
TWIST INC
5100 Waynesville (45335)
PHONE..............................937 675-9581
J Smith, *Branch Mgr*
EMP: 30
SALES (corp-wide): 50.2MM **Privately Held**
SIC: 3495 3542 3469 Mechanical springs, precision; machine tools, metal forming type; metal stampings
PA: Twist Inc.
47 S Limestone St
Jamestown OH 45335
937 675-9581

Jefferson
Ashtabula County

(G-11355)
ADA SOLUTIONS INC
901 Ftville Richmond Rd E (44047)
PHONE..............................440 576-0423
David Chase, *President*
EMP: 20
SALES (est): 2MM **Privately Held**
SIC: 2821 Molding compounds, plastics

(G-11356)
ALTERA POLYMERS LLC
222 S Sycamore St (44047-1434)
PHONE..............................864 973-7000
Barry Rhodes, *Mng Member*
EMP: 9 EST: 2011
SALES (est): 1.2MM **Privately Held**
SIC: 2821 Elastomers, nonvulcanizable (plastics)

(G-11357)
BRAKERS PUBLISHING & PRTG SVC
166 W Cedar St (44047-1331)
P.O. Box 489 (44047-0489)
PHONE..............................440 576-0136
Katherine Kermetz, *Owner*
EMP: 5
SALES (est): 261.1K **Privately Held**
SIC: 7379 2759 Computer related services; commercial printing

(G-11358)
CENTERRA CO-OP
135 E Walnut St (44047-1121)
PHONE..............................800 362-9598
Fax: 440 576-4012
Jim Reader, *Manager*
EMP: 28
SALES (corp-wide): 174.6MM **Privately Held**
SIC: 5172 5261 2048 5191 Gases, liquefied petroleum (propane); fertilizer; bird food, prepared; farm supplies

PA: Centerra Co-Op
813 Clark Ave
Ashland OH 44805
419 281-2153

(G-11359)
CHUCK MEADORS PLASTICS CO
150 S Cucumber St (44047-1439)
PHONE..............................440 813-4466
Chuck Meadors, *President*
EMP: 10
SALES (est): 881.2K **Privately Held**
SIC: 3089 Hardware, plastic

(G-11360)
CLARENCE TUSSEL JR
141 E Jefferson St (44047-1186)
P.O. Box 126 (44047-0126)
PHONE..............................440 576-3415
Clarence Tussel Jr, *Owner*
EMP: 1
SQ FT: 2,500
SALES: 1.3MM **Privately Held**
SIC: 1382 1381 Geological exploration, oil & gas field; drilling oil & gas wells

(G-11361)
INTERLOCK INDUSTRIES INC
Also Called: Metal Sales Manufacturing
352 E Erie St (44047-1406)
PHONE..............................440 576-9070
Tim Wols, *Manager*
EMP: 35
SALES (corp-wide): 336.9MM **Privately Held**
WEB: www.metalsales.us.com
SIC: 3444 Roof deck, sheet metal
PA: Interlock Industries, Inc.
545 S 3rd St Ste 310
Louisville KY 40202
502 569-2007

(G-11362)
K CUPCAKES
222 Elliott Ave (44047-1230)
PHONE..............................440 576-3464
Amanda Kish, *Principal*
EMP: 4 EST: 2013
SALES (est): 198K **Privately Held**
SIC: 2051 Bread, cake & related products

(G-11363)
KARLCO OILFIELD SERVICES INC
141 E Jefferson St (44047-1113)
P.O. Box 126 (44047-0126)
PHONE..............................440 576-3415
Clarence Tussel Jr, *President*
EMP: 11
SQ FT: 3,000
SALES (est): 1.1MM **Privately Held**
SIC: 1389 Servicing oil & gas wells

(G-11364)
KEN FORGING INC
1049 Griggs Rd (44047-8772)
P.O. Box 277 (44047-0277)
PHONE..............................440 993-8091
Fax: 440 992-0360
Richard Kovach, *President*
Ken Kovach, *Vice Pres*
Chris Dewey, *QC Mgr*
Paula Johnson, *Sales Mgr*
Senthia Fleischer, *Sales Associate*
EMP: 115 EST: 1970
SQ FT: 150,000
SALES (est): 38.4MM **Privately Held**
WEB: www.kenforging.com
SIC: 3462 3544 Iron & steel forgings; special dies & tools

(G-11365)
KING LUMINAIRE COMPANY INC (HQ)
Also Called: Stresscrete
1153 State Route 46 N (44047-8748)
P.O. Box 266 (44047-0266)
PHONE..............................440 576-9073
Fax: 440 576-9348
Greg Button, *President*
Dan Craddock, *Project Mgr*
Jessica Detweiler, *Accountant*
Keri Jahn, *Financial Exec*
Todd Estes, *Regl Sales Mgr*

▲ EMP: 45
SQ FT: 18,000
SALES (est): 21.1MM
SALES (corp-wide): 60.2MM **Privately Held**
WEB: www.kingluminaire.com
SIC: 3646 Ornamental lighting fixtures, commercial
PA: Stress-Crete Holdings Inc
840 Walker's Line Suite 7
Burlington ON L7N 2
905 632-9301

(G-11366)
LAKE ERIE SHIP REPAIR
1459 State Route 46 S (44047-9505)
PHONE..............................440 624-0025
Joseph Craine, *Mng Member*
Justin Gee,
EMP: 18
SQ FT: 4,000
SALES: 4.2MM **Privately Held**
SIC: 3731 3441 Shipbuilding & repairing; fabricated structural metal

(G-11367)
METAL SALES MANUFACTURING CORP
352 E Erie St (44047-1406)
PHONE..............................440 576-9070
Fax: 440 576-9242
Tim Wolfe, *Sales Mgr*
Tim Wols, *Sales Executive*
Bill Mako, *Manager*
Wynn Wessell, *Manager*
EMP: 35
SQ FT: 33,000
SALES (corp-wide): 336.9MM **Privately Held**
SIC: 3444 3449 3441 2952 Siding, sheet metal; miscellaneous metalwork; fabricated structural metal; asphalt felts & coatings
HQ: Metal Sales Manufacturing Corporation
545 S 3rd St Ste 200
Louisville KY 40202
502 855-4300

(G-11368)
NEXT DIMENSION COMPONENTS INC
223 S Spruce St (44047-8321)
PHONE..............................440 576-0194
Rhine Blake, *CEO*
EMP: 17 EST: 2007
SALES (est): 3.1MM **Privately Held**
SIC: 3272 Concrete window & door components, sills & frames

(G-11369)
PRESRITE CORPORATION
322 S Cucumber St (44047-1423)
P.O. Box 550 (44047-0550)
PHONE..............................440 576-0015
Fax: 440 576-9057
Roy Stainfield, *General Mgr*
Ron Isenberg, *QC Dir*
EMP: 115
SALES (corp-wide): 95.3MM **Privately Held**
WEB: www.presrite.com
SIC: 3462 Iron & steel forgings
PA: Presrite Corporation
3665 E 78th St
Cleveland OH 44105
216 441-5990

(G-11370)
SHOOTING RANGE SUPPLY LLC
735 Fairway St (44047-8568)
P.O. Box 269, Andover (44003-0269)
PHONE..............................440 576-7711
Fax: 614 319-7711
Julie Cole, *Mng Member*
Martin Cole,
EMP: 4
SQ FT: 800
SALES (est): 429.2K **Privately Held**
WEB: www.perfectrubbermulch.com
SIC: 3949 Sporting & athletic goods

(G-11371)
SMOKIN TS SMOKEHOUSE
1550 Stnhpe Kllggsvlle (44047-8473)
PHONE..............................440 577-1117
Todd Neczeporenko, *Owner*

EMP: 3 **EST:** 1993
SALES: 750K **Privately Held**
SIC: 2011 Meat packing plants

(G-11372)
STRESS-CRETE COMPANY
Also Called: King Luminaire
1153 State Route 46 N (44047-8748)
P.O. Box 266 (44047-0266)
PHONE............................440 576-9073
Jim Fultz, *Branch Mgr*
EMP: 17
SALES (corp-wide): 60.2MM **Privately Held**
WEB: www.stresscrete.com
SIC: 3646 Commercial indusl & institutional electric lighting fixtures
HQ: Stress-Crete Limited
840 Walker's Line Suite 7
Burlington ON L7N 2
905 827-6901

(G-11373)
THE GAZETTE PRINTING CO INC (PA)
Also Called: Tribune , The
46 W Jefferson St (44047-1028)
P.O. Box 166 (44047-0166)
PHONE............................440 576-9125
Fax: 440 576-2735
Jeffrey Lampson, *President*
John E Lampson, *Publisher*
Stacy Millburg, *Editor*
Marilyn Lampson, *Admin Sec*
EMP: 62
SQ FT: 8,600
SALES (est): 12.1MM **Privately Held**
WEB: www.gazetteprinting.com
SIC: 2752 Commercial printing, offset

(G-11374)
TMD WEK NORTH LLC
Also Called: Wek Industries
1085 Jffrsn Eagleville Rd (44047-1267)
PHONE............................440 576-6940
Fax: 440 576-6950
William Hylan, *CFO*
Kimberly Schaefer, *Exec Sec*
EMP: 116 **EST:** 2014
SQ FT: 112,500
SALES (est): 17.9MM
SALES (corp-wide): 426.5MM **Privately Held**
SIC: 3089 Blow molded finished plastic products
PA: Toledo Molding & Die, Inc.
1429 Coining Dr
Toledo OH 43612
419 470-3950

(G-11375)
TOD THIN BRUSHES INC
1152 State Route 46 N (44047-8748)
PHONE............................440 576-6859
Fax: 440 576-0326
Michael R Oliver, *President*
Mildred Oliver, *President*
Michael Oliver, *Prdtn Mgr*
EMP: 10
SQ FT: 2,500
SALES (est): 1.7MM **Privately Held**
WEB: www.todthinbrushes.com
SIC: 3991 Brushes, household or industrial

(G-11376)
WORTHINGTON CYLINDER CORP
863 State Route 307 E (44047-9668)
PHONE............................440 576-5847
Fax: 440 576-1527
Jim Engelmann, *Project Mgr*
Brian Carroll, *Opers Staff*
Jim Williams, *Production*
Jacob Sakosd, *Purchasing*
Shelly Degennaro, *Human Resources*
EMP: 187
SALES (corp-wide): 2.8B **Publicly Held**
SIC: 3443 Cylinders, pressure: metal plate
HQ: Worthington Cylinder Corporation
200 W Old Wlson Bridge Rd
Worthington OH 43085
614 840-3210

(G-11377)
ZEHRCO-GIANCOLA COMPOSITES INC
382 E Erie St (44047-1406)
PHONE............................440 576-9941
James H Nevins, *Branch Mgr*
EMP: 5
SALES (corp-wide): 31.9MM **Privately Held**
SIC: 3089 Injection molding of plastics
PA: Zehrco-Giancola Composites, Inc.
1501 W 47th St
Ashtabula OH 44004
440 994-6317

Jeffersonville
Fayette County

(G-11378)
BUNGE NORTH AMERICA FOUNDATION
12574 State Route 41 (43128-9542)
PHONE............................740 426-6332
Drew Walker, *Manager*
EMP: 7 **Privately Held**
WEB: www.bungemarion.com
SIC: 2075 Soybean protein concentrates & isolates
HQ: Bunge North America Foundation
11720 Borman Dr
Saint Louis MO 63146
314 872-3030

(G-11379)
E R B ENTERPRISES INC
Also Called: Rocky Mountain Chocolate
8205 Factory Shops Blvd (43128-9602)
PHONE............................740 948-9174
Nalynn Hall, *Manager*
EMP: 5
SALES (corp-wide): 1.5MM **Privately Held**
SIC: 5441 2066 2064 Candy; chocolate & cocoa products; candy & other confectionery products
PA: E. R. B. Enterprises, Inc.
1500 Polaris Pkwy # 2022
Columbus OH 43240
239 567-0585

(G-11380)
GOLD TOE MORETZ HOLDINGS CORP
8512 Factory Shops Blvd (43128-9605)
PHONE............................740 948-0004
EMP: 4
SALES (corp-wide): 2.9B **Privately Held**
SIC: 3142 5311 Slipper socks, made from purchased socks; department stores, discount
HQ: Gold Toe Moretz Holdings Corp.
2121 Heilig Rd
Salisbury NC 28146
828 464-0751

(G-11381)
KEYNES BROTHERS INC
12574 State Route 41 (43128-9542)
PHONE............................740 426-6332
Bill Keynes, *President*
Jim Schneider, *Manager*
EMP: 4
SALES (est): 243.5K **Privately Held**
SIC: 3523 Elevators, farm

(G-11382)
TFO TECH CO LTD
Also Called: T F O
221 State St (43128-1090)
PHONE............................740 426-6381
Fax: 740 426-6511
Yoshio Saisharo, *President*
Curtis A Loveland, *Principal*
Katsumasa Toya, *Chairman*
Kanji Endo, *Exec VP*
Jon Cox, *Manager*
▲ **EMP:** 140
SQ FT: 70,000

SALES (est): 26MM
SALES (corp-wide): 35.4MM **Privately Held**
WEB: www.tfotech.com
SIC: 3462 3465 3714 Automotive forgings, ferrous: crankshaft, engine, axle, etc.; automotive stampings; motor vehicle parts & accessories
PA: Tfo Corporation
2-16-4, Akabane
Kita-Ku TKY 115-0
364 544-651

Jeromesville
Ashland County

(G-11383)
BARTTER & SONS
1761 Township Road 85 (44840-9651)
PHONE............................419 651-0374
Dave Bartter, *Principal*
Jody Bartter, *Office Mgr*
EMP: 3
SALES (est): 170K **Privately Held**
SIC: 3423 Plumbers' hand tools

(G-11384)
HEFFELFINGERS MEATS INC
469 County Road 30a (44840-9733)
PHONE............................419 368-7131
Fax: 419 368-3180
Rick Heffelfinger, *President*
Gloria Heffelfinger, *Corp Secy*
Steve Heffelfinger, *Vice Pres*
EMP: 20 **EST:** 1963
SALES (est): 1.8MM **Privately Held**
SIC: 2011 Meat packing plants; beef products from beef slaughtered on site; pork products from pork slaughtered on site; veal from meat slaughtered on site

---

Jerusalem
Monroe County

(G-11385)
PROFIT ENERGY COMPANY INC
36829 Township Road 2067 (43747-9713)
PHONE............................740 472-1018
Carl F Rousenberg III, *President*
L L Rousenberg, *Treasurer*
EMP: 4
SALES (est): 500K **Privately Held**
SIC: 1311 Crude petroleum production; natural gas production

Jewett
Harrison County

(G-11386)
MARKWEST UTICA EMG LLC
46700 Giacobbi Rd (43986-9553)
PHONE............................740 942-4810
Frank M Semple, *Branch Mgr*
EMP: 6
SALES (corp-wide): 2.5B **Publicly Held**
SIC: 1321 Natural gas liquids
HQ: Markwest Utica Emg, L.L.C.
1515 Arapahoe St
Denver CO 80202
303 925-9200

Johnstown
Licking County

(G-11387)
ALL PRO ALUM CYLINDER HEADS
5370 Jhnstown Alxndria Rd (43031-9575)
P.O. Box 424 (43031-0424)
PHONE............................740 967-7761
Fax: 740 967-9404
Robert P Williams, *President*
Susie Williams, *Corp Secy*
EMP: 4

SALES (est): 528.6K **Privately Held**
SIC: 3714 Cylinder heads, motor vehicle

(G-11388)
ALLIANCE CARPET CUSHION CO
143 Commerce Blvd (43031-9610)
PHONE............................740 966-5001
Fax: 740 966-5010
Keith Anders, *Manager*
Leisha Curtis, *Executive*
EMP: 60
SALES (corp-wide): 8.9B **Publicly Held**
SIC: 2282 2273 Carpet yarn: twisting, winding or spooling; carpets & rugs
HQ: Alliance Carpet Cushion Co
180 Church St
Torrington CT 06790
860 489-4273

(G-11389)
APEKS LLC
Also Called: Apeks Super Critical
150 Commerce Blvd (43031-9011)
PHONE............................740 809-1160
Andy Joseph, *President*
Kristen Joseph, *Finance*
Nick Yerico, *Manager*
EMP: 20
SQ FT: 10,000
SALES (est): 1.7MM **Privately Held**
SIC: 3542 Mechanical (pneumatic or hydraulic) metal forming machines

(G-11390)
ATRIUM CORP
188 Commerce Blvd (43031-9011)
PHONE............................740 966-8200
Fax: 740 966-8201
Russell Pyne, *Managing Prtnr*
David Hirsh, *Principal*
Mike Cornwell, *Exec VP*
EMP: 6
SALES (est): 898.2K **Privately Held**
SIC: 2759 5099 Screen printing; durable goods

(G-11391)
BIGMAR INC
9711 Sportsman Club Rd (43031-9141)
PHONE............................740 966-5800
John Tramontana, *CEO*
John Tramontata, *CEO*
Cynthia R May, *President*
Bernard Kramer, *COO*
Massimo Pedrani, *Exec VP*
EMP: 50
SQ FT: 8,600
SALES (est): 3.7MM **Privately Held**
SIC: 2834 8111 Pharmaceutical preparations; legal services

(G-11392)
BSM COLUMBUS LLP
389 Kyber Run Cir (43031-9616)
PHONE............................740 755-2380
Toby Baker, *Managing Prtnr*
Shannon Baker, *Managing Dir*
EMP: 3
SALES (est): 109.4K **Privately Held**
SIC: 3599 Custom machinery

(G-11393)
BUCKEYE READY-MIX LLC
7720 Jhnstown Alxndria Rd (43031-9340)
PHONE............................740 967-4801
Larry Randles, *Vice Pres*
EMP: 6
SALES (corp-wide): 42.4MM **Privately Held**
SIC: 3273 Ready-mixed concrete
PA: Buckeye Ready-Mix, Llc
7657 Taylor Rd Sw
Reynoldsburg OH 43068
614 575-2132

(G-11394)
BUD CORP
158 Commerce Blvd (43031-9011)
PHONE............................740 967-9992
Kelton Brown, *Principal*
EMP: 8
SALES (est): 1MM **Privately Held**
SIC: 1542 3444 5084 Nonresidential construction; sheet metalwork; materials handling machinery

(G-11395)
CHAM COR INDUSTRIES INC
117 W Coshocton St (43031-1108)
PHONE................................740 967-9015
Fax: 740 967-6830
Michael Chambers, *CEO*
Gary H Chambers Jr, *President*
Michael Bailey, *Vice Pres*
EMP: 8
SQ FT: 6,000
SALES (est): 630K **Privately Held**
WEB: www.techtirerepairs.com
SIC: 2754 Job printing, gravure

(G-11396)
CHARLES RAY EVANS
Also Called: Penny Fab
451 E Coshocton St Ste B (43031-9010)
PHONE................................740 967-3669
Fax: 740 967-5171
Charles Ray Evans, *Owner*
James Pyznik, *Manager*
EMP: 12
SQ FT: 50,000
SALES (est): 1.5MM **Privately Held**
WEB: www.pennyfab.com
SIC: 3441 Fabricated structural metal

(G-11397)
CRC METAL PRODUCTS
29 Greenscapes Ct (43031-8007)
PHONE................................740 966-0475
Gary Pittman, *President*
EMP: 5
SALES (est): 210K **Privately Held**
WEB: www.crcmetalproducts.com
SIC: 3444 Sheet metalwork

(G-11398)
FLEETWOOD CUSTOM
COUNTERTOPS (PA)
Also Called: Fleetwood Craftsman
15710 Center Village Rd (43031-9264)
PHONE................................740 965-9833
James L Jacobus, *President*
Keith Gray, *Finance Mgr*
EMP: 15
SQ FT: 16,000
SALES (est): 1.7MM **Privately Held**
SIC: 2511 2541 2434 Wood household
    furniture; wood partitions & fixtures; wood
    kitchen cabinets

(G-11399)
GM LOGGING
204 Cole Dr (43031-1085)
PHONE................................740 501-0819
Randy McFadden, *Principal*
EMP: 3 EST: 2010
SALES (est): 202.9K **Privately Held**
SIC: 2411 Logging

(G-11400)
HBK STONEWORKS
9292 Jhnstown Alxndria Rd (43031-9327)
PHONE................................740 817-2244
Ben Keller, *Manager*
EMP: 3
SALES (est): 229.8K **Privately Held**
SIC: 3281 Granite, cut & shaped

(G-11401)
HERALD HOUSE
3121 S County Line Rd (43031-9204)
PHONE................................740 967-8044
Damita Brammer, *Principal*
EMP: 3
SALES (est): 102.7K **Privately Held**
SIC: 2711 Newspapers, publishing & print-
    ing

(G-11402)
MUNSON MACHINE COMPANY
INC
80 E College Ave (43031-1204)
P.O. Box 304 (43031-0304)
PHONE................................740 967-6867
Fax: 740 967-6867
Todd Thacker, *President*
Leroy Thacker, *Admin Sec*
EMP: 7
SQ FT: 4,500
SALES: 250K **Privately Held**
SIC: 3599 Machine & other job shop work

(G-11403)
PRO-HOE UTILITY LLC
2945 Johnstown Utica Rd (43031-9394)
PHONE................................740 892-4765
Richard Arques, *Owner*
EMP: 3
SALES (est): 277.7K **Privately Held**
SIC: 1711 3531 4214 Plumbing, heating,
    air-conditioning contractors; plows: con-
    struction, excavating & grading; local
    trucking with storage

(G-11404)
SONOCO PRODUCTS COMPANY
8865 Smiths Mill Rd N (43031)
PHONE................................740 927-2525
Theresa Biel, *General Mgr*
EMP: 92
SALES (corp-wide): 4.7B **Publicly Held**
SIC: 2631 Paperboard mills
PA: Sonoco Products Company
    1 N 2nd St
    Hartsville SC 29550
    843 383-7000

(G-11405)
STAR PIZZA BOX
495 E Coshocton St (43031-9588)
PHONE................................740 967-1105
Alex Shoemaker, *Principal*
EMP: 50
SALES (est): 6.2MM **Privately Held**
SIC: 2657 Folding paperboard boxes

(G-11406)
STEEL CEILINGS INC
451 E Coshocton St Ste A (43031-9010)
PHONE................................740 967-1063
Fax: 740 967-1478
Grant Snowden, *President*
Evevly Bricker, *Manager*
▲ EMP: 24
SALES (est): 5.4MM **Privately Held**
SIC: 3324 Steel investment foundries

(G-11407)
TECHNICAL RUBBER COMPANY
INC (PA)
Also Called: Tech International
200 E Coshocton St (43031-1083)
P.O. Box 486 (43031-0486)
PHONE................................740 967-9015
Fax: 740 967-3583
Micheal Chambers, *CEO*
Dan Layne, *President*
Diane Kirkpatrick, *General Mgr*
Robert Overs, *COO*
Bob Overs, *Exec VP*
◆ EMP: 270
SQ FT: 10,000
SALES (est): 112.9MM **Privately Held**
WEB: www.techtirerepairs.com
SIC: 3011 5014 2891 Tire sundries or tire
    repair materials, rubber; tire & tube repair
    materials; sealing compounds, synthetic
    rubber or plastic

(G-11408)
TRI-TECH LABORATORIES INC
Also Called: K D C
8825 Smiths Mill Rd N (43031)
PHONE................................740 927-2817
Pierre Prudhomme, *President*
EMP: 85
SALES (est): 28.9MM **Privately Held**
SIC: 2834 Pharmaceutical preparations

(G-11409)
TRUFLEX RUBBER PRODUCTS
CO
Also Called: Pang Rubber Company
200 E Coshocton St (43031-1096)
PHONE................................740 967-9015
Pauline Chambers Yost, *President*
Mike Chambers, *COO*
George Bishop, *Exec VP*
Cheryl Poulton, *Vice Pres*
Robert Overs, *Treasurer*
EMP: 225
SQ FT: 75,000
SALES (est): 12.2MM **Privately Held**
SIC: 3011 3069 Tire & inner tube materials
    & related products; air-supported rubber
    structures

(G-11410)
WILLMAC ENTERPRISES INC
12200 Johnstown Utica Rd (43031-9562)
P.O. Box 541 (43031-0541)
PHONE................................740 967-1979
Fax: 740 967-3327
Linda Williamson, *President*
Larry E Williamson, *Admin Sec*
EMP: 4
SQ FT: 2,500
SALES (est): 250K **Privately Held**
SIC: 3599 Machine shop, jobbing & repair

Junction City
Perry County

(G-11411)
R C POLING COMPANY INC
2105 Clay Rd (43748-9770)
PHONE................................740 939-0023
Richard C Poling, *President*
Catherine Poling, *Vice Pres*
EMP: 3 EST: 1980
SQ FT: 800
SALES (est): 1.8MM **Privately Held**
SIC: 1311 Crude petroleum production;
    natural gas production

Kalida
Putnam County

(G-11412)
B-K TOOL & DESIGN INC
480 W Main St (45853)
P.O. Box 416 (45853-0416)
PHONE................................419 532-3890
Fax: 419 532-3889
Bob Kahle, *President*
Donna Horstman, *General Mgr*
Kevin M Kahle, *Vice Pres*
Scott Hoffman, *Project Mgr*
Jerry Schmenk, *Project Mgr*
EMP: 80
SQ FT: 12,000
SALES (est): 24.9MM **Privately Held**
SIC: 3312 Tool & die steel

(G-11413)
K & L READY MIX INC
105 S 6th St (45853)
P.O. Box 300 (45853-0300)
PHONE................................419 532-3585
Fax: 419 532-3558
Ron Kahle Jr, *Vice Pres*
EMP: 19
SALES (corp-wide): 8.4MM **Privately
Held**
WEB: www.kandlreadymix.com
SIC: 3273 3271 Ready-mixed concrete;
    concrete block & brick
PA: K & L Ready Mix Inc
    10391 State Route 15
    Ottawa OH 45875
    419 523-4376

(G-11414)
KALIDA MANUFACTURING INC
801 Ottawa St (45853)
P.O. Box 390 (45853-0390)
PHONE................................419 532-2026
Fax: 419 532-2027
Bruce R Henke, *President*
Tim Inoue, *President*
Sho Akimoto, *Vice Pres*
Ken Landwehr, *Facilities Mgr*
Bob Fish, *Production*
▲ EMP: 250
SQ FT: 300,000
SALES (est): 74.6MM
SALES (corp-wide): 219.4MM **Privately
Held**
WEB: www.kth.net
SIC: 3714 Motor vehicle parts & acces-
    sories
PA: Kth Parts Industries, Inc.
    1111 State Route 235 N
    Saint Paris OH 43072
    937 663-5941

(G-11415)
NICANA CONSULTING INC
801 Oak Pkwy (45853)
P.O. Box 52 (45853-0052)
PHONE................................419 615-9703
Christopher Fortman, *Principal*
Jeffrey Krouse, *Principal*
William Romes, *Principal*
EMP: 4
SALES (est): 145.3K **Privately Held**
SIC: 3484 Small arms

(G-11416)
REMLINGER MANUFACTURING
CO INC
16394 Us 224 (45853)
P.O. Box 299 (45853-0299)
PHONE................................419 532-3647
Fax: 419 532-2244
Mildred C Remlinger, *Ch of Bd*
John Remlinger, *President*
Tom Heitmeyer, *Plant Mgr*
Mark Warnecke, *Manager*
Roger Westbeld, *Manager*
▲ EMP: 32
SQ FT: 52,000
SALES: 13.3MM **Privately Held**
SIC: 3523 Farm machinery & equipment;
    harrows: disc, spring, tine, etc.

(G-11417)
SARKA BROS MACHINING INC
607 Ottawa St (45853)
P.O. Box 316 (45853-0316)
PHONE................................419 532-2393
Fax: 419 532-2405
Bob Allen, *President*
Terry Burnett, *Vice Pres*
EMP: 8
SQ FT: 24,000
SALES (est): 1.4MM **Privately Held**
SIC: 3556 Food products machinery

(G-11418)
UNVERFERTH MFG CO INC (PA)
601 S Broad St (45853)
P.O. Box 357 (45853-0357)
PHONE................................419 532-3121
Fax: 419 532-2468
R Steven Unverferth, *President*
Richard A Unverferth, *Chairman*
Daniel Fanger, *Vice Pres*
Karl Kahle, *Vice Pres*
Gladys Unverferth, *Vice Pres*
◆ EMP: 249 EST: 1948
SQ FT: 828,501
SALES (est): 164MM **Privately Held**
WEB: www.unverferth.com
SIC: 3523 Farm machinery & equipment

Kelleys Island
Erie County

(G-11419)
KELLEYS ISLAND WINE CO
418 Woodford Rd (43438)
P.O. Box 747 (43438-0747)
PHONE................................419 746-2678
Kirt Zettler, *President*
Roberta Zettler, *Corp Secy*
EMP: 8
SQ FT: 7,000
SALES (est): 853.8K **Privately Held**
WEB: www.kelleysislandwine.com
SIC: 2084 5921 Wines; wine

Kensington
Columbiana County

(G-11420)
BRIAR HILL FURNITURE
7061 Bane Rd Ne (44427-9662)
PHONE................................330 223-2109
Kenneth Yoder, *Partner*
Arthur Horst, *Partner*
EMP: 3
SALES (est): 240.6K **Privately Held**
SIC: 2511 Wood household furniture

(G-11421)
WILLIAM S MILLER INC
11250 Montgomery Rd (44427-9702)
P.O. Box 145, Hanoverton (44423-0145)
PHONE.....................................330 223-1794
William Miller, *CEO*
George Miller, *President*
Jane Todd, *Corp Secy*
David W Miller, *Vice Pres*
EMP: 9
SALES (est): 1.9MM **Privately Held**
SIC: 1311 Crude petroleum production

Kent
Portage County

(G-11422)
ACCURATE PLASTICS LLC
4430 Crystal Pkwy (44240-8006)
PHONE.....................................330 346-0048
John Satina, *Principal*
EMP: 11
SALES (est): 1.6MM **Privately Held**
SIC: 3089 Plastic processing

(G-11423)
ACTION SUPER ABRASIVE PDTS INC
945 Greenbriar Pkwy (44240-6478)
PHONE.....................................330 673-7333
Fax: 330 725-5541
Joseph Haag, *President*
Dan Noonan, *Vice Pres*
Monica Hughes, *Purchasing*
EMP: 20
SQ FT: 27,000
SALES: 2.7MM **Privately Held**
WEB: www.actionsuper.com
SIC: 3291 Wheels, grinding: artificial

(G-11424)
AILES MILLWORK INC
1520 Enterprise Way (44240-7547)
PHONE.....................................330 678-4300
Fax: 330 678-4301
Patrick Ailes, *President*
Margaret Ailes, *Corp Secy*
Ryan Ailes, *Vice Pres*
Linda Gooden, *Controller*
EMP: 18 EST: 1975
SQ FT: 13,000
SALES (est): 2.4MM **Privately Held**
WEB: www.ailesmillwork.com
SIC: 2431 2434 Millwork; wood kitchen cabinets

(G-11425)
AKRON CRATE AND PALLET LLC
1545 Mogadore Rd (44240-7540)
PHONE.....................................330 524-8955
Matthew Breiding, *President*
EMP: 4
SALES (est): 411.5K **Privately Held**
SIC: 2448 Pallets, wood & wood with metal

(G-11426)
ALLEN DRAIN SERVICE INC
1008 Mogadore Rd (44240-7598)
PHONE.....................................330 253-4206
Fax: 330 673-4666
Bernie Noble, *President*
Michael A Noble, *Vice Pres*
Karen Shipley, *Treasurer*
EMP: 3
SALES (est): 457.2K **Privately Held**
SIC: 2842 Drain pipe solvents or cleaners; deodorants, nonpersonal

(G-11427)
ALLOY EXTRUSION COMPANY
4211 Karg Indl Pkwy (44240)
PHONE.....................................330 677-4946
Fax: 330 677-4950
James Anthony, *President*
Linda Thomas, *Accountant*
Jackie Waltz, *Manager*
EMP: 20
SQ FT: 30,000
SALES (est): 4.8MM **Privately Held**
SIC: 3061 8742 Mechanical rubber goods; industrial consultant

(G-11428)
AMETEK FLORCARE SPECIALTY MTRS
100 E Erie St Ste 200 (44240-2660)
PHONE.....................................330 677-3786
David Egbert, *Vice Pres*
Kris Diehl, *Engineer*
David Pusker, *Project Engr*
Ginny Blevins, *Accountant*
Tim Michalk, *VP Human Res*
EMP: 10
SALES (est): 1.6MM **Privately Held**
SIC: 3621 Motors & generators; motors, electric

(G-11429)
AMETEK TECHNICAL & INDUS PDTS (HQ)
Also Called: Ametek Electromechanical Group
100 E Erie St Ste 130 (44240-3587)
PHONE.....................................330 677-3754
Fax: 330 677-3306
Todd Schlegel, *General Mgr*
Matt French, *Vice Pres*
Dan Kirtz, *Opers Mgr*
Peter Smith, *CFO*
William D Burke, *Treasurer*
EMP: 65 EST: 2009
SALES (est): 94.7MM
SALES (corp-wide): 3.8B **Publicly Held**
SIC: 3621 5063 3566 Motors, electric; motors, electric; speed changers, drives & gears
PA: Ametek, Inc.
1100 Cassatt Rd
Berwyn PA 19312
610 647-2121

(G-11430)
AMREX INC
431 W Elm St (44240-3717)
P.O. Box 456 (44240-0008)
PHONE.....................................330 678-7050
Harold Carlson, *CEO*
David Carlson, *President*
EMP: 3
SALES (est): 165.4K **Privately Held**
SIC: 3089 Synthetic resin finished products

(G-11431)
AREA WIDE PROTECTIVE INC (HQ)
Also Called: Awp
826 Overholt Rd (44240-7530)
PHONE.....................................330 644-0655
John P Sypek, *President*
Ron Brotherton, *Vice Pres*
Rusty Parrish, *Vice Pres*
Howard Blevins, *Opers Mgr*
Art Simms, *Facilities Mgr*
EMP: 45 EST: 1991
SALES: 117.3MM
SALES (corp-wide): 139.7MM **Privately Held**
SIC: 3669 Pedestrian traffic control equipment; traffic signals, electric
PA: Awp, Inc.
826 Overholt Rd
Kent OH 44240
330 644-0655

(G-11432)
BANG PRINTING OF OHIO INC
3765 Sunnybrook Rd (44240-7443)
PHONE.....................................800 678-1222
Tom Campion, *Principal*
EMP: 13
SALES (est): 2.3MM **Privately Held**
SIC: 2752 Commercial printing, lithographic

(G-11433)
BECKWITH ORCHARDS INC
1617 Lake Rockwell Rd (44240-3019)
PHONE.....................................330 673-6433
Charles Beckwith, *President*
Marilyn Beckwith, *Vice Pres*
EMP: 12
SQ FT: 1,824
SALES (est): 1.4MM **Privately Held**
WEB: www.beckwithorchards.com
SIC: 2099 5431 5947 Cider, nonalcoholic; fruit stands or markets; gift shop

(G-11434)
BEEMER MACHINE COMPANY INC
1530 Enterprise Way (44240-7547)
PHONE.....................................330 678-3822
Fax: 330 678-3822
Edward Burch, *President*
Terry Johnson, *Manager*
EMP: 8
SALES (est): 1.2MM **Privately Held**
SIC: 3599 Machine shop, jobbing & repair

(G-11435)
BERRY PLAS TECHNICAL SVCS INC
4175 Karg Industrial Pkwy (44240-6425)
PHONE.....................................330 995-3459
▼ EMP: 17
SALES (est): 3.3MM
SALES (corp-wide): 6.4B **Publicly Held**
SIC: 3089 Bottle caps, molded plastic
HQ: Berry Plastics Corporation
101 Oakley St
Evansville IN 47710
812 424-2904

(G-11436)
BOYCE MACHINE INC
3609 Mogadore Rd (44240-7431)
PHONE.....................................330 678-3210
Fax: 330 678-3220
Shelby C Boyce, *President*
Patricia Boyce, *Corp Secy*
Isabelle Gngler, *Human Res Mgr*
EMP: 9
SQ FT: 5,400
SALES (est): 1MM **Privately Held**
SIC: 3599 Machine shop, jobbing & repair

(G-11437)
C G C SYSTEMS INC
4763 Sherman Rd (44240-7054)
PHONE.....................................330 678-3261
Fax: 330 678-5288
David Rose, *President*
John F Szwejk, *Vice Pres*
Betty Duncan, *Treasurer*
Joseph Bystricky Jr, *Asst Treas*
Daniel Holliday, *Admin Sec*
EMP: 4
SALES: 400K **Privately Held**
WEB: www.ccgsystems.com
SIC: 3444 Sheet metalwork

(G-11438)
CITY OF KENT
Also Called: Kent Parks Recreation
497 Middlebury Rd (44240-3409)
PHONE.....................................330 673-8897
John Idone, *Director*
EMP: 10
SQ FT: 1,440 **Privately Held**
SIC: 2531 7349 Picnic tables or benches, park; building maintenance services
PA: City Of Kent
325 S Depeyster St
Kent OH 44240
330 676-4189

(G-11439)
COLONIAL MACHINE COMPANY INC
1041 Mogadore Rd (44240-7534)
P.O. Box 650 (44240-0012)
PHONE.....................................330 673-5859
Fax: 330 673-6687
Roy Metcalf, *CEO*
James Rankin, *President*
Chris Reardon, *Chief Engr*
Matt Metcalf, *VP Finance*
Eric Stevens, *VP Sales*
EMP: 71
SQ FT: 35,000
SALES (est): 11.8MM **Privately Held**
WEB: www.colonial-machine.com
SIC: 3544 Special dies & tools; industrial molds

(G-11440)
COLONIAL PATTERNS INC
920 Overholt Rd (44240-7550)
PHONE.....................................330 673-6475
Fax: 330 673-7577
Martin A Meluch, *President*
Valent Meluch, *Corp Secy*
Suzi Hallett, *Manager*
▲ EMP: 30
SQ FT: 4,800
SALES (est): 4.5MM **Privately Held**
WEB: www.colonialpatt.com
SIC: 3543 3544 Industrial patterns; special dies, tools, jigs & fixtures

(G-11441)
COPEN MACHINE INC
501 Dodge St (44240-3709)
PHONE.....................................330 678-4598
Fax: 330 678-5981
Terry D Copen, *President*
Travis Copen, *General Mgr*
EMP: 13
SQ FT: 13,000
SALES: 1.3MM **Privately Held**
SIC: 3599 Machine shop, jobbing & repair

(G-11442)
CUSTOMER SERVICE SYSTEMS INC
Also Called: Cssi & Quality Printing
1250 W Main St Ste A (44240-1979)
PHONE.....................................330 677-2877
Fax: 330 677-2874
Carla Casky, *President*
EMP: 5
SALES (est): 447K **Privately Held**
WEB: www.matriximpact.com
SIC: 2759 2796 2791 2752 Commercial printing; platemaking services; typesetting; commercial printing, lithographic

(G-11443)
D & J PRINTING INC
Also Called: Hess Print Solutions
3765 Sunnybrook Rd (44240-7443)
PHONE.....................................330 678-5868
Douglas Mann, *Branch Mgr*
EMP: 90
SALES (corp-wide): 85.8MM **Privately Held**
SIC: 2752 Commercial printing, lithographic
PA: D. & J. Printing, Inc.
3323 Oak St
Brainerd MN 56401
218 829-2877

(G-11444)
D B HESS COMPANY (HQ)
Also Called: Hess Print Solutions
3765 Sunnybrook Rd (44240-7443)
PHONE.....................................330 678-5868
Douglas L Mann, *President*
Bob Castillo, *Vice Pres*
Douglas Holzschuh, *Vice Pres*
Greg Kelsey, *Vice Pres*
James E Sula, *Vice Pres*
▲ EMP: 25
SQ FT: 350,000
SALES (est): 5.1MM
SALES (corp-wide): 583MM **Privately Held**
WEB: www.dbhess.com
SIC: 2759 2789 Commercial printing; bookbinding & related work
PA: Wellspring Capital Management Llc
390 Park Ave Fl 5
New York NY 10022
212 318-9800

(G-11445)
D B HESS COMPANY
Also Called: Hess Print Solutions
3765 Sunnybrook Rd (44240-7443)
PHONE.....................................330 676-2006
Robert Duncan, *Vice Pres*
Greg Kelsey, *Vice Pres*
Mike Manley, *Vice Pres*
Louis Papay, *Vice Pres*
Joe Meinike, *Manager*
EMP: 4
SALES (corp-wide): 583MM **Privately Held**
WEB: www.pressofohio.com
SIC: 2732 2741 2789 2759 Book printing; catalogs: publishing & printing; bookbinding & related work; commercial printing
HQ: The D B Hess Company
3765 Sunnybrook Rd
Kent OH 44240
330 678-5868

(G-11446)
DAVEY KENT INC
Also Called: Davey Drill
200 W Williams St (44240-3797)
P.O. Box 400 (44240-0007)
PHONE...................................330 673-5400
Fax: 330 673-9178
J Thomas Myers II, *CEO*
Tom Myers, *President*
Chris Cooler, *Principal*
David Myers, *Vice Pres*
Brian Marzi, *Sales Mgr*
▲ EMP: 20
SQ FT: 50,000
SALES (est): 7.2MM **Privately Held**
WEB: www.daveykent.com
SIC: 3532 Drills & drilling equipment, min-
ing (except oil & gas)

(G-11447)
DE-LUX MOLD & MACHINE INC
6523 Pleasant Ave (44240)
P.O. Box 11163, Brady Lake (44211-1163)
PHONE...................................330 678-1030
Fax: 330 678-6644
Bruce Smith, *President*
Bettymarie Smith, *Corp Secy*
Christopher Haag, *Vice Pres*
EMP: 9
SQ FT: 4,200
SALES (est): 997.5K **Privately Held**
WEB: www.de-lux.com
SIC: 3544 Forms (molds), for foundry &
plastics working machinery

(G-11448)
DENNIS CORSO CO INC
266 Martinel Dr Ste A (44240-4321)
PHONE...................................330 673-2411
Dennis Corso, *President*
EMP: 5
SQ FT: 5,000
SALES: 500K **Privately Held**
SIC: 3548 1799 Welding apparatus; weld-
ing on site

(G-11449)
DIPTECH SYSTEMS INC (PA)
4485 Crystal Pkwy Ste 100 (44240-8016)
P.O. Box 39 (44240-0001)
PHONE...................................330 673-4400
Tom Doland, *President*
Mark Baskin, *Vice Pres*
Jeff Charlton, *Vice Pres*
Bill Mars, *Vice Pres*
William T Mars, *Vice Pres*
EMP: 3
SALES (est): 3.5MM **Privately Held**
WEB: www.diptechsystems.com
SIC: 3559 Fiber optics strand coating ma-
chinery

(G-11450)
**DON WARTKO CONSTRUCTION
CO (PA)**
Also Called: Design Concrete Surfaces
975 Tallmadge Rd (44240-6474)
PHONE...................................330 673-5252
Fax: 330 673-5501
Thomas Wartko, *President*
David Wartko, *Vice Pres*
Mike Wartko, *Vice Pres*
Ron Wartko, *Vice Pres*
Doris Wartko, *Admin Sec*
EMP: 60
SQ FT: 15,000
SALES (est): 18.4MM **Privately Held**
SIC: 1623 1794 3732 Oil & gas line &
compressor station construction; sewer
line construction; water main construction;
excavation work; boat building & repairing

(G-11451)
DPM ORTHODONTICS INC
1519 Enterprise Way Ste H (44240-7524)
PHONE...................................330 673-0334
Fax: 330 673-0335
David J Marko, *President*
EMP: 6
SALES (est): 952.4K **Privately Held**
SIC: 3842 Orthopedic appliances

(G-11452)
EAST END WELDING COMPANY
357 Tallmadge Rd (44240-7201)
PHONE...................................330 677-6000

Fax: 330 677-6006
John E Susong, *President*
Fred Dietz, *Project Mgr*
John Marcolini, *Project Mgr*
Nate Molnar, *Project Mgr*
Tim Carr, *CFO*
▲ EMP: 120
SQ FT: 146,500
SALES (est): 33.1MM **Privately Held**
SIC: 3599 7692 Custom machinery; weld-
ing repair

(G-11453)
ECOPONICS GROUP LLC
964 Kevin Dr (44240-2036)
PHONE...................................330 819-1233
Joshua Myers,
EMP: 3
SALES (est): 79.6K **Privately Held**
SIC: 8999 1542 2452 7389 Earth science
services; greenhouse construction; pan-
els & sections, prefabricated, wood;

(G-11454)
ELBEX CORPORATION
300 Martinel Dr (44240-4369)
PHONE...................................330 673-3233
Fax: 330 673-3235
Edward L Bittle, *President*
Julie Pawlus, *Prdtn Mgr*
Lora Lie Jones, *Purch Mgr*
John Morgan, *Personnel*
Peggy Streacher, *Accounts Mgr*
EMP: 90
SALES (est): 28.7MM **Privately Held**
WEB: www.elbex-us.com
SIC: 3061 Mechanical rubber goods

(G-11455)
**EMERGENCY PRODUCTS & RES
INC**
Also Called: Epr
890 W Main St (44240-2284)
PHONE...................................330 673-5003
Jerold Ramsey, *President*
Jason Thompson, *General Mgr*
Jim Doherty, *Vice Pres*
David Gravell, *Opers Staff*
▲ EMP: 6
SQ FT: 350,000
SALES (est): 830.3K **Privately Held**
WEB: www.epandr.com
SIC: 2448 Wood pallets & skids

(G-11456)
ENTERPRISE PLASTICS INC
1500 Enterprise Way (44240-7547)
PHONE...................................330 346-0496
Martin Mulch, *President*
Debbie Carpenter, *Manager*
Valente Muluch, *Admin Sec*
▲ EMP: 20
SQ FT: 10,000
SALES (est): 4.1MM **Privately Held**
SIC: 3544 Forms (molds), for foundry &
plastics working machinery

(G-11457)
**EUCLID VIDARO
MANUFACTURING CO (PA)**
Also Called: Euclid Vidaro Mfg. Co.
333 Martinel Dr (44240-4370)
P.O. Box 550 (44240-0010)
PHONE...................................330 673-7413
Fax: 330 673-0228
Charles Rosenblatt, *President*
Edward Davis, *Vice Pres*
Howard Fleischmann, *Vice Pres*
Rosemarie Einholz, *Manager*
▲ EMP: 80 EST: 1870
SQ FT: 29,000
SALES (est): 12MM **Privately Held**
WEB: www.euclidgarment.com
SIC: 2326 Men's & boys' work clothing

(G-11458)
FAITHFUL MOLD POLISHING EX
4485 Crystal Pkwy (44240-8013)
PHONE...................................330 678-8006
Houa Voe, *Owner*
EMP: 3
SALES: 40K **Privately Held**
SIC: 3471 Polishing, metals or formed
products

(G-11459)
FRIENDS SERVICE CO INC
948 Cherry St (44240-7522)
PHONE...................................800 427-1704
Kenneth J Schroeder, *Branch Mgr*
EMP: 7
SALES (corp-wide): 30MM **Privately
Held**
SIC: 5112 5021 5044 5087 Stationery &
office supplies; furniture; office equip-
ment; service establishment equipment;
commercial printing, lithographic
PA: Friends Service Co., Inc.
2300 Bright Rd
Findlay OH 45840
419 427-1704

(G-11460)
FROGS IN BLOOM
1112 Delores Ave (44240-2178)
PHONE...................................330 678-9508
Paulette Thurman, *Owner*
EMP: 3
SALES (est): 151.5K **Privately Held**
SIC: 2771 Greeting cards

(G-11461)
FURUKAWA ROCK DRILL
805 Lake St (44240-2740)
PHONE...................................330 673-5821
Larry Wittensoldner, *Owner*
Tim Carroll, *Regl Sales Mgr*
Alan Stone, *Regl Sales Mgr*
▲ EMP: 3
SALES (est): 383.7K **Privately Held**
SIC: 3532 Drills (portable), rock

(G-11462)
**FURUKAWA ROCK DRILL USA
CO LTD (PA)**
Also Called: Frd
711 Lake St (44240-2738)
PHONE...................................330 673-5826
Jeff Krame, *Principal*
Bill Sagaser, *Purch Dir*
Jeff Krane, *Branch Mgr*
▼ EMP: 20
SQ FT: 27,181
SALES (est): 3.1MM **Privately Held**
WEB: www.kenttool.com
SIC: 3545 3594 3546 3423 Tools & ac-
cessories for machine tools; fluid power
pumps & motors; power-driven handtools;
hand & edge tools

(G-11463)
GOUGLER INDUSTRIES INC (HQ)
Also Called: Furukawa Rock Drill
705 Lake St (44240-2733)
PHONE...................................330 673-5826
Jeff Crane, *CEO*
Joe Burger, *Research*
Jorge Gutierrez, *Sales Mgr*
Caroline Brichford, *Director*
Shoji Iguchi, *Director*
◆ EMP: 15
SQ FT: 240,000
SALES: 8.8MM
SALES (corp-wide): 1.3B **Privately Held**
WEB: www.gougler.com
SIC: 3533 3599 3546 Drilling tools for
gas, oil or water wells; machine shop, job-
bing & repair; power-driven handtools
PA: Furukawa Co., Ltd.
2-2-3, Marunouchi
Chiyoda-Ku TKY 100-0
332 126-570

(G-11464)
GUYS BREWING GEAR
1325 Chelton Dr (44240-3264)
PHONE...................................330 554-9362
EMP: 3
SALES (est): 90K **Privately Held**
SIC: 2082 Malt beverages

(G-11465)
**GWEN ROSENBERG
ENTERPRISES LLC**
175 E Erie St Ste 201 (44240-3595)
PHONE...................................330 678-1893
Gwen Rosenberg, *Mng Member*
EMP: 5

SALES (est): 180K **Privately Held**
SIC: 2064 5441 Candy bars, including
chocolate covered bars; popcorn, including caramel corn

(G-11466)
H & S STEEL TREATING INC
Also Called: Peterson Heat Treating
4142 Mogadore Rd (44240-7263)
PHONE...................................330 678-5245
Fax: 330 678-1015
William Sullivan, *President*
EMP: 10 EST: 1984
SQ FT: 14,000
SALES (est): 870K **Privately Held**
SIC: 3398 Metal heat treating

(G-11467)
**H W FAIRWAY INTERNATIONAL
INC**
716 N Mantua St (44240-2320)
P.O. Box 782 (44240-0016)
PHONE...................................330 678-2540
Lee J Strange, *President*
Kevin Clark, *Plant Mgr*
Alice Kandes, *Treasurer*
Virginia Floyd, *Persnl Mgr*
Charles Zuehmker, *Admin Sec*
EMP: 27 EST: 1940
SQ FT: 22,000
SALES (est): 4.1MM **Privately Held**
WEB: www.hwfairway.com
SIC: 3699 3823 3621 Laser systems &
equipment; industrial instrmnts msrmnt
display/control process variable; starters,
for motors

(G-11468)
HALL CREATIONS
705 Silver Meadows Blvd (44240-1919)
PHONE...................................330 357-2428
Tralisha Hall, *Principal*
EMP: 4
SALES (est): 210K **Privately Held**
SIC: 5193 0181 5999 3231 Artificial flow-
ers; dried flowers; florists' greens & flow-
ers; artificial flowers; novelties, glass:
fruit, foliage, flowers, animals, etc.

(G-11469)
HAPCO INC
Also Called: Tarpco
390 Portage Blvd (44240-7283)
PHONE...................................330 678-9353
Charles George, *CEO*
Chuck George, *CEO*
Bernard Carpenter, *President*
John A Daily, *Principal*
Carlos Alvarez, *Sales Mgr*
◆ EMP: 11
SQ FT: 23,000
SALES (est): 2.5MM **Privately Held**
WEB: www.hapcoinc.com
SIC: 3545 5049 Machine tool accessories;
precision tools

(G-11470)
HONEY GOLD COMPANY
Also Called: My Little Red Wagon
152 E Main St (44240-2525)
PHONE...................................330 688-5502
Fax: 330 688-4578
Karl Stevens, *President*
Michelle Schar, *President*
Michelle Sahr, *Sales Staff*
EMP: 9
SQ FT: 3,000
SALES (est): 1.9MM **Privately Held**
WEB: www.mylittleredwagon.com
SIC: 2844 Cosmetic preparations

(G-11471)
HUGO SAND COMPANY
7055 State Route 43 (44240-6198)
PHONE...................................216 570-1212
Dorothy Strohm, *President*
Scott R Terhune, *Vice Pres*
Sythnia Terhune, *Vice Pres*
EMP: 7
SQ FT: 400
SALES (est): 680K **Privately Held**
SIC: 1442 Construction sand mining;
gravel mining

(G-11472)
J B MANUFACTURING INC
4465 Crystal Pkwy (44240-8005)
PHONE..................................330 676-9744
Fax: 330 676-9745
John L Anderson, *President*
EMP: 32
SQ FT: 36,000
SALES (est): 5.8MM **Privately Held**
WEB: www.taclatch.com
SIC: 3599 Machine shop, jobbing & repair

(G-11473)
J S MANUFACTURING LLC
4631 Mogadore Rd (44240-7249)
PHONE..................................330 815-2136
Debbie J Mills, *Principal*
EMP: 3
SALES (est): 191.1K **Privately Held**
SIC: 3999 Manufacturing industries

(G-11474)
JOS-TECH INC
852 W Main St (44240-2216)
P.O. Box 952 (44240-0019)
PHONE..................................330 678-3260
Bradford Joslyn, *President*
David Fox, *Vice Pres*
Jeanine Carrillo, *Manager*
Caroline Mueller, *Admin Sec*
EMP: 25
SALES (est): 7.4MM **Privately Held**
WEB: www.jos-tech.com
SIC: 3089 Plastic processing

(G-11475)
KENT ADHESIVE PRODUCTS CO
Also Called: K A P C O
1000 Cherry St (44240-7501)
P.O. Box 626 (44240-0011)
PHONE..................................330 678-1626
Fax: 330 678-3922
Edward Small, *President*
Jenifer Codrea, *Vice Pres*
Philip M Zavracky, *Vice Pres*
Nate Foltz, *Purch Mgr*
Michelle Houser, *Mktg Coord*
▼ EMP: 80 EST: 1974
SQ FT: 100,000
SALES (est): 38.4MM **Privately Held**
WEB: www.kapco.com
SIC: 2679 2672 2675 7389 Paper products, converted; adhesive papers, labels or tapes: from purchased material; tape, pressure sensitive: made from purchased materials; die-cut paper & board; laminating service; tape slitting

(G-11476)
KENT AUTOMATION INC
449 Dodge St (44240-3707)
PHONE..................................330 678-6343
Fax: 330 678-4770
Dennis Lyell, *President*
Gary Lyell, *Vice Pres*
EMP: 15
SQ FT: 12,000
SALES (est): 5.1MM **Privately Held**
SIC: 3599 Machine & other job shop work

(G-11477)
KENT DISPLAYS INC (PA)
Also Called: Improv Electronics
343 Portage Blvd (44240-9200)
PHONE..................................330 673-8784
Albert M Green PHD, *CEO*
Joel Domino, *President*
Taesun Cha, *Vice Pres*
J W Doane, *Vice Pres*
Bill Emanuele, *Mfg Mgr*
▲ EMP: 105
SQ FT: 42,000
SALES (est): 21.5MM **Privately Held**
WEB: www.kentdisplays.com
SIC: 3679 Liquid crystal displays (LCD)

(G-11478)
KENT ELASTOMER PRODUCTS INC (HQ)
1500 Saint Clair Ave (44240-4364)
P.O. Box 668 (44240-0012)
PHONE..................................330 673-1011
Bob Oborn, *President*
Anne Tennyson, *Sales Staff*
Lee Morrison, *Marketing Staff*
Tim Garner, *Director*

Lee Ann Corp, *Administration*
▲ EMP: 150
SQ FT: 42,000
SALES (est): 29.5MM
SALES (corp-wide): 374.1MM **Privately Held**
WEB: www.kentelastomer.com
SIC: 3052 Rubber & plastics hose & beltings
PA: Meridian Industries, Inc.
735 N Water St Ste 630
Milwaukee WI 53202
414 224-0610

(G-11479)
KENT INFORMATION SERVICES INC
6185 2nd Ave (44240-2991)
PHONE..................................330 672-2110
John H Graves, *President*
John Graves, *President*
EMP: 6
SALES (est): 380K **Privately Held**
SIC: 2721 8721 Periodicals; accounting, auditing & bookkeeping

(G-11480)
KENT MOLD AND MANUFACTURING CO
1190 W Main St (44240-1942)
PHONE..................................330 673-3469
Fax: 330 673-9699
Paul Ferder, *President*
Henry Trivelli, *Corp Secy*
Darlene Karg, *Purchasing*
EMP: 40 EST: 1944
SQ FT: 35,000
SALES (est): 8.1MM **Privately Held**
WEB: www.kentmold.com
SIC: 3544 Industrial molds

(G-11481)
KENT STATE UNIVERSITY
Kent State University Press
307 Lwry Hall Terrance Dr (44242-0001)
P.O. Box 5190
PHONE..................................330 672-7913
Fax: 330 672-3104
Susan L Cash, *Marketing Mgr*
Will Underwood, *Director*
EMP: 10
SALES (corp-wide): 474.6MM **Privately Held**
WEB: www.kentliv.kent.edu
SIC: 2731 8221 Book publishing; university
PA: Kent State University
1500 Horning Rd
Kent OH 44242
330 672-3000

(G-11482)
KENT STATE UNIVERSITY
Also Called: Daily Kent Stater
205 Frlanklin Hall (44242-0001)
P.O. Box 5190
PHONE..................................330 672-2586
Laurie Cantor, *General Mgr*
Vince Slomsky, *Asst Director*
EMP: 3
SALES (corp-wide): 474.6MM **Privately Held**
WEB: www.kentliv.kent.edu
SIC: 2711 8221 Newspapers, publishing & printing; university
PA: Kent State University
1500 Horning Rd
Kent OH 44242
330 672-3000

(G-11483)
KORKAN GRANITE CO INC
4561 Crystal Pkwy (44240-8022)
PHONE..................................330 677-1883
Fax: 330 677-1885
Robert H Korkan, *President*
Andrea M Korkan, *Vice Pres*
EMP: 10
SQ FT: 4,000
SALES (est): 1.5MM **Privately Held**
WEB: www.korkangranite.com
SIC: 3281 Cut stone & stone products

(G-11484)
LAMONT ENTERPRISES INC
Also Called: Riverside Wine and Imports
911 N Mantua St (44240-2323)
PHONE..................................330 677-4400
Fax: 330 677-4345
Robert Morrison, *President*
EMP: 5
SQ FT: 2,500
SALES (est): 409.6K **Privately Held**
WEB: www.riverside-wine.com
SIC: 2084 5921 Wines; wine

(G-11485)
LAND OLAKES INC
2001 Mogadore Rd (44240-7296)
PHONE..................................330 678-1578
Fax: 330 678-2950
Steve Sehafer, *Opers-Prdtn-Mfg*
Keith Springer, *Manager*
EMP: 177
SALES (corp-wide): 14.9B **Privately Held**
WEB: www.landolakes.com
SIC: 2021 Creamery butter
PA: Land O'lakes, Inc.
4001 Lexington Ave N
Arden Hills MN 55126
651 375-2222

(G-11486)
MAC LTT INC
Also Called: Mac Liquid Tank Trailer
1400 Fairchild Ave (44240-1818)
PHONE..................................330 474-3795
Jim Maiorana, *President*
Carol McNutt, *General Mgr*
Ken Grosswiler, *Plant Mgr*
Lori Picicco, *Transportation*
Ed Mansell, *Engineer*
EMP: 143
SALES (est): 101.4MM
SALES (corp-wide): 149.4MM **Privately Held**
SIC: 3569 Assembly machines, non-metalworking
PA: Mac Trailer Manufacturing, Inc.
14599 Commerce St Ne
Alliance OH 44601
330 823-9900

(G-11487)
MASTERS PRCISION MACHINING INC
4465 Crystal Pkwy (44240-8005)
PHONE..................................330 419-1933
Kenneth Rice, *President*
Charlotte Rice, *CFO*
EMP: 10 EST: 2014
SALES (est): 508K **Privately Held**
SIC: 3541 Numerically controlled metal cutting machine tools

(G-11488)
MERIDIAN INDUSTRIES INC
Also Called: Kent Elastomer Products
1500 Saint Clair Ave (44240-4364)
P.O. Box 668 (44240-0012)
PHONE..................................330 673-1011
Vann Epp Murray, *President*
Murray V Epp, *Project Mgr*
Robert Oborn, *Mfg Staff*
EMP: 60
SALES (corp-wide): 374.1MM **Privately Held**
WEB: www.meridiancompanies.com
SIC: 3069 3842 3083 3082 Tubing, rubber; surgical appliances & supplies; laminated plastics plate & sheet; unsupported plastics profile shapes; mechanical rubber goods
PA: Meridian Industries, Inc.
735 N Water St Ste 630
Milwaukee WI 53202
414 224-0610

(G-11489)
METAL-MAX INC
1540 Enterprise Way (44240-7547)
PHONE..................................330 673-9926
Richard La Mancusa, *President*
EMP: 8
SQ FT: 5,000
SALES: 900K **Privately Held**
SIC: 3444 Sheet metalwork

(G-11490)
MICHAEL KAUFMAN COMPANIES INC (PA)
Also Called: Educational Equipment
845 Overholt Rd (44240-7529)
P.O. Box 154 (44240-0003)
PHONE..................................330 673-4881
Fax: 330 673-4915
Michael Kaufman, *President*
John T Waller, *Principal*
◆ EMP: 10 EST: 1934
SQ FT: 60,000
SALES (est): 2.1MM **Privately Held**
SIC: 3281 2599 2493 2541 Blackboards, slate; boards: planning, display, notice; bulletin boards, cork; store & office display cases & fixtures; display fixtures, wood

(G-11491)
MICHAEL KAUFMAN COMPANIES INC
Also Called: Educational Equipment
845 Overholt Rd (44240-7529)
P.O. Box 154 (44240-0003)
PHONE..................................330 673-4881
Michael Kaufman, *President*
EMP: 10
SALES (corp-wide): 2.1MM **Privately Held**
SIC: 3281 2599 2493 2541 Blackboards, slate; boards: planning, display, notice; bulletin boards, cork; store & office display cases & fixtures; display fixtures, wood
PA: Michael Kaufman Companies, Inc.
845 Overholt Rd
Kent OH 44240
330 673-4881

(G-11492)
MIKE B CRAWFORD
Also Called: Advanced Display Systems
606 Mogadore Rd (44240-7533)
PHONE..................................330 673-7944
Fax: 330 673-3036
Mike Crawford, *Owner*
EMP: 3
SQ FT: 3,200
SALES: 200K **Privately Held**
SIC: 3993 5999 7532 2759 Signs & advertising specialties; decals; truck painting & lettering; screen printing; commercial printing, lithographic

(G-11493)
MILLER BEARING COMPANY INC
420 Portage Blvd (44240-7285)
PHONE..................................330 678-8844
Fax: 330 678-1765
Donald A Miller, *President*
Julie Miller, *Corp Secy*
EMP: 28
SQ FT: 75,000
SALES (est): 3.3MM **Privately Held**
WEB: www.millerbearing.com
SIC: 3562 Ball bearings & parts

(G-11494)
MOLD SURFACE TEXTURES
Also Called: MST
4485 Crystal Pkwy Ste 300 (44240-8016)
PHONE..................................330 678-8590
Joe Gendron, *President*
Kevin Gasaway, *Treasurer*
Sue Gasaway, *Office Mgr*
Aaron Pendergast, *Admin Sec*
EMP: 6
SALES (est): 1.4MM **Privately Held**
SIC: 2821 Molding compounds, plastics

(G-11495)
MRF MACHINE AND HYDRAULICS INC
912 Lock St (44240-2433)
PHONE..................................330 673-0135
Fax: 330 678-0135
Michael R Ferry, *President*
Nick Ferry, *General Mgr*
Christopher Ferry, *Corp Secy*
Paul Ferry, *Vice Pres*
EMP: 10
SQ FT: 4,500

SALES: 1.4MM **Privately Held**
WEB: www.mrfmachine.com
SIC: 3593 Fluid power cylinders & actuators; fluid power cylinders, hydraulic or pneumatic

(G-11496)
NEWELL BRANDS INC
212 Progress Blvd (44240-8015)
PHONE....................................330 733-1184
Amy Smith, *Branch Mgr*
EMP: 9
SALES (corp-wide): 13.2B **Publicly Held**
SIC: 3069 Medical & laboratory rubber sundries & related products
PA: Newell Brands Inc.
221 River St
Hoboken NJ 07030
201 610-6600

(G-11497)
NORTHCOAST WOODCRAFT INC
4259 Karg Industrial Pkwy (44240-6470)
PHONE....................................330 677-1189
Sandra Whited, *President*
EMP: 8
SALES (est): 1.6MM **Privately Held**
SIC: 3553 Cabinet makers' machinery

(G-11498)
P S P INC
Also Called: Petry Power Systems
7337 Westview Rd (44240-5911)
PHONE....................................330 283-5635
Robert V Petry, *President*
EMP: 50
SALES: 3MM **Privately Held**
SIC: 2869 Fuels

(G-11499)
PARKER-HANNIFIN CORPORATION
Also Called: Fluid System Connectors Div
838 Overholt Rd (44240-7500)
PHONE....................................330 673-2700
Fax: 330 673-0922
Russ Kalis, *Branch Mgr*
EMP: 90
SALES (corp-wide): 11.3B **Publicly Held**
WEB: www.parker.com
SIC: 3089 Fittings for pipe, plastic
PA: Parker-Hannifin Corporation
6035 Parkland Blvd
Cleveland OH 44124
216 896-3000

(G-11500)
PEGASUS PRODUCTS COMPANY INC
315 Gougler Ave (44240-2405)
PHONE....................................330 677-1123
Fax: 330 677-4130
EMP: 4
SQ FT: 24,000
SALES (est): 280K **Privately Held**
SIC: 2599 Mfg Furniture/Fixtures

(G-11501)
PODNAR PLASTICS INC
343 Portage Blvd Unit 3 (44240-9200)
PHONE....................................330 673-2255
Scott Podnar, *President*
EMP: 50
SALES (corp-wide): 4.8MM **Privately Held**
WEB: www.rez-tech.com
SIC: 3089 Molding primary plastic
PA: Podnar Plastics, Inc.
1510 Mogadore Rd
Kent OH 44240
330 673-2255

(G-11502)
PODNAR PLASTICS INC (PA)
1510 Mogadore Rd (44240-7599)
PHONE....................................330 673-2255
Fax: 330 673-2273
Jack Podnar, *President*
Craig Podnar, *Vice Pres*
Scott Podnar, *Vice Pres*
EMP: 21 **EST:** 1977
SQ FT: 38,000

SALES: 4.8MM **Privately Held**
WEB: www.rez-tech.com
SIC: 3089 Injection molding of plastics; blow molded finished plastic products

(G-11503)
POLYMERICS INC
1540 Saint Clair Ave (44240-4364)
PHONE....................................330 677-1131
Fax: 330 677-0999
Glen Peters, *Research*
Tony Bisesi, *Controller*
Kim Marquis, *Finance Mgr*
EMP: 21
SQ FT: 26,458
SALES (corp-wide): 15.3MM **Privately Held**
WEB: www.polymericsinc.com
SIC: 2899 2821 Chemical preparations; plastics materials & resins
PA: Polymerics, Inc.
2828 2nd St
Cuyahoga Falls OH 44221
330 434-6665

(G-11504)
POPPED
175 E Erie St Ste 201 (44240-3595)
PHONE....................................330 678-1893
Gwen Rosenberg, *Owner*
EMP: 10 **EST:** 2011
SALES (est): 738.2K **Privately Held**
SIC: 2064 7389 Candy & other confectionery products;

(G-11505)
POST PRODUCTS INC
1600 Franklin Ave (44240-4308)
P.O. Box 777 (44240-0015)
PHONE....................................330 678-0048
Fax: 330 678-4767
Jay McElravy, *President*
Nancy McElravy, *Corp Secy*
EMP: 7
SQ FT: 6,000
SALES (est): 1MM **Privately Held**
WEB: www.postproducts.com
SIC: 3599 Machine shop, jobbing & repair

(G-11506)
PRESS OF OHIO INC
Also Called: Hess Print Solutions
3765 Sunnybrook Rd (44240-7443)
PHONE....................................330 678-5868
Fax: 330 678-8684
Doug Mann, *President*
EMP: 28
SALES (est): 4.4MM **Privately Held**
SIC: 2759 Commercial printing

(G-11507)
PRIMAL SCREEN INC
Also Called: Alpha Strike
1021 Mason Ave (44240-2718)
PHONE....................................330 677-1766
Fax: 330 677-4299
Terry Tasker, *President*
Tom Diroll, *Corp Secy*
Andrew Diroll, *Manager*
Joe Kubesheski, *Director*
EMP: 20
SQ FT: 10,000
SALES (est): 1.5MM **Privately Held**
WEB: www.primalscreen.net
SIC: 2759 Screen printing

(G-11508)
PROTO MACHINE & MFG INC
2190 State Route 59 (44240-7142)
PHONE....................................330 677-1700
Fax: 330 677-1166
Edward L Dias, *President*
Polly Dias, *Office Mgr*
Shelly Morgan, *Administration*
EMP: 15
SQ FT: 10,000
SALES (est): 2MM **Privately Held**
WEB: www.protomachine.com
SIC: 3599 Machine shop, jobbing & repair

(G-11509)
PYRAMID MOLD INC
Also Called: Pyramid Mold & Machine Company
222 Martinel Dr (44240-4321)
P.O. Box 634 (44240-0011)
PHONE....................................330 673-5200
Fax: 330 673-3923
Joan Siciliano, *President*
Adolph Siciliano, *President*
Martin Cannistra, *Sr Project Mgr*
EMP: 15
SQ FT: 10,000
SALES (est): 2.2MM **Privately Held**
WEB: www.pyramidmold-machine.com
SIC: 3544 Industrial molds

(G-11510)
QUANTUM JEWELRY DIST
4631 Mogadore Rd (44240-7249)
PHONE....................................330 678-2222
Tammy Palmer, *President*
James Palmer, *Vice Pres*
EMP: 20
SQ FT: 8,000
SALES (est): 2MM **Privately Held**
SIC: 3914 Pewter ware

(G-11511)
QUICK SERVICE WELDING & MCH CO
117 E Summit St (44240-3556)
PHONE....................................330 673-3818
Fax: 330 673-4178
Frank S Bowen, *President*
Wilma Bowen, *Corp Secy*
James M Bowen, *Vice Pres*
EMP: 11 **EST:** 1919
SQ FT: 11,200
SALES (est): 1MM **Privately Held**
SIC: 7692 3599 Welding repair; machine shop, jobbing & repair

(G-11512)
RASCHKE ENGRAVING INC
Also Called: Buckeye Engraving
4485 Crystal Pkwy Ste 200 (44240-8016)
PHONE....................................330 677-5544
Fax: 330 677-3936
Steve Broadbent, *President*
George Botzman, *Vice Pres*
EMP: 7 **EST:** 1975
SQ FT: 4,000
SALES (est): 625.7K **Privately Held**
SIC: 7389 3953 Engraving service; marking devices

(G-11513)
RECORD PUBLISHING CO (HQ)
Also Called: Stow Sentry
1050 W Main St (44240-2006)
P.O. Box 5199 (44240-5199)
PHONE....................................330 541-9400
Fax: 330 296-2698
David Dix, *President*
Gordon C Dix, *Treasurer*
Shirley Mars, *Manager*
Christine Patronik-Holder, *Manager*
Andrew Dix, *Director*
EMP: 80 **EST:** 1931
SQ FT: 10,000
SALES (est): 10.4MM
SALES (corp-wide): 567.1MM **Privately Held**
WEB: www.recordpub.com
SIC: 2711 Newspapers, publishing & printing
PA: Wooster Republican Printing Co
212 E Liberty St
Wooster OH
330 264-3511

(G-11514)
REDUCTION ENGINEERING INC (PA)
Also Called: Accu Grind
235 Progress Blvd (44240-8055)
PHONE....................................330 677-2225
Fax: 330 677-4048
Robert Sly, *President*
Paul Merich, *Top Exec*
John Bell, *Regl Sales Mgr*
◆ **EMP:** 35
SQ FT: 15,000

SALES (est): 18MM **Privately Held**
WEB: www.reductionengineering.com
SIC: 5084 3532 Industrial machinery & equipment; pulverizing machinery & equipment; crushing, pulverizing & screening equipment; pellet mills (mining machinery)

(G-11515)
REZ-TECH CORPORATION
1510 Mogadore Rd (44240-7531)
PHONE....................................330 673-4009
Jack Podnar, *CEO*
Jeanette M Podnar, *Corp Secy*
Craig Podnar, *Exec VP*
Scott Podnar, *Vice Pres*
▲ **EMP:** 47 **EST:** 1981
SQ FT: 38,000
SALES: 5.2MM **Privately Held**
SIC: 3089 Blow molded finished plastic products

(G-11516)
RHOADS PRINTING CENTER INC (PA)
Also Called: Copy Print
302 N Water St (44240-2423)
PHONE....................................330 678-2042
Fax: 330 678-8416
Richard M Rhoads, *President*
Jill Rhoads, *Admin Sec*
EMP: 6 **EST:** 1971
SQ FT: 8,000
SALES (est): 782.7K **Privately Held**
SIC: 2752 7334 Commercial printing, offset; photocopying & duplicating services

(G-11517)
RIVERSIDE SAND & GRAVEL CO
69 Middlebury Rd (44240-5181)
P.O. Box 324, Tallmadge (44278-0324)
PHONE....................................330 673-2021
Albert H Acken Jr, *President*
EMP: 3
SALES (est): 210K **Privately Held**
SIC: 1442 3241 2952 Construction sand & gravel; gravel mining; masonry cement; asphalt felts & coatings

(G-11518)
ROBERT LONG MANUFACTURING INC
4192 Karg Industrial Pkwy (44240-6400)
PHONE....................................330 678-0911
Fax: 330 678-2858
Robert Long, *President*
Doug Atkins, *Vice Pres*
EMP: 8
SQ FT: 7,200
SALES: 1.5MM **Privately Held**
SIC: 3599 Machine shop, jobbing & repair

(G-11519)
RON-AL MOLD & MACHINE INC
1057 Mason Ave (44240-2718)
PHONE....................................330 673-7919
Fax: 330 673-7330
Ronald Siciliano, *President*
Alan Siciliano, *Treasurer*
Rebecca Gonzalez, *Office Mgr*
Rosalee Hodge, *Office Mgr*
EMP: 12
SQ FT: 2,500
SALES (est): 1.2MM **Privately Held**
WEB: www.ronalmold.com
SIC: 3544 Industrial molds

(G-11520)
ROTOLINE USA LLC
4429 Crystal Pkwy Ste B (44240-8014)
PHONE....................................330 677-3223
Alain Stpierre, *General Mgr*
EMP: 6
SALES (est): 824.2K **Privately Held**
SIC: 3524 Rototillers (garden machinery)

(G-11521)
RUB-R-ROAD INC
431 W Elm St (44240-3717)
P.O. Box 456 (44240-0008)
PHONE....................................330 678-7050
Fax: 330 678-7054
David Carlson, *President*
Kenneth Banks, *Corp Secy*
EMP: 3 **EST:** 1950
SQ FT: 8,000

SALES (est): 475.8K **Privately Held**
WEB: www.rub-r-road.com
SIC: **3069** Latex, foamed

(G-11522)
SCHNELLER LLC (HQ)
Also Called: Veritas
6019 Powdermill Rd (44240-7109)
PHONE...................................330 676-7183
Fax: 330 673-6374
Eric Custis, *Plant Mgr*
Chris Bryant, *Project Mgr*
Mark Tennant, *Project Mgr*
Nick Voorhees, *Project Mgr*
Jim Flanders, *Technical Mgr*
◆ EMP: 112
SQ FT: 125,000
SALES (est): 93.3MM
SALES (corp-wide): 3.1B **Publicly Held**
WEB: www.schneller.com
SIC: **2295** Resin or plastic coated fabrics;
laminating of fabrics
PA: Transdigm Group Incorporated
1301 E 9th St Ste 3000
Cleveland OH 44114
216 706-2960

(G-11523)
SCHNELLER LLC
Polyplastex International
6019 Powdermill Rd (44240-7109)
PHONE...................................330 673-1299
Tom Spseisser, *Manager*
EMP: 75
SALES (corp-wide): 3.1B **Publicly Held**
WEB: www.schneller.com
SIC: **3083 8731 3728** Laminated plastic
sheets; commercial physical research;
aircraft parts & equipment
HQ: Schneller Llc
6019 Powdermill Rd
Kent OH 44240
330 676-7183

(G-11524)
SCOTT MOLDERS INCORPORATED
7180 State Route 43 (44240-5940)
P.O. Box 645 (44240-0012)
PHONE...................................330 673-5777
Fax: 330 673-7036
Scott Yahner, *President*
EMP: 70
SQ FT: 23,000
SALES (est): 9.4MM **Privately Held**
SIC: **3089 2821** Thermoformed finished
plastic products; plastics materials &
resins

(G-11525)
SEAL MASTER CORPORATION
Also Called: Sealmaster
340 Martinel Dr (44240)
PHONE...................................330 673-8410
Sherri Waller, *Sales Mgr*
Edward Bittle, *Branch Mgr*
EMP: 45
SALES (corp-wide): 11.9MM **Privately
Held**
WEB: www.sealmasterseals.com
SIC: **2951** Asphalt paving mixtures &
blocks
PA: Seal Master Corporation
368 Martinel Dr
Kent OH 44240
330 673-8410

(G-11526)
SELECT MACHINE CO INC
4125 Karg Industrial Pkwy (44240-6425)
PHONE...................................330 678-7676
Fax: 330 678-7773
Bill Sagaser, *President*
William Sagaser, *Corp Secy*
Douglas Beavers, *Vice Pres*
EMP: 10
SQ FT: 7,000
SALES (est): 1.3MM **Privately Held**
SIC: **3544 3599** Special dies, tools, jigs &
fixtures; machine shop, jobbing & repair

(G-11527)
SHELLY MATERIALS INC
1181 Cherry St (44240)
PHONE...................................330 673-3646
Dennis Krohn, *Manager*

EMP: 4
SALES (corp-wide): 28.6B **Privately Held**
SIC: **1422 1442 2951 4492** Crushed &
broken limestone; construction sand &
gravel; concrete, asphaltic (not from refineries); tugboat service
HQ: Shelly Materials, Inc.
80 Park Dr
Thornville OH 43076
740 246-6315

(G-11528)
SMITHERS-OASIS COMPANY (PA)
295 S Water St Ste 201 (44240-3591)
PHONE...................................330 945-5100
Fax: 330 945-5120
Charles F Walton, *CEO*
Robin M Kilbride, *President*
James Stull, *Treasurer*
Jeanie Melvin, *Manager*
Becky Sklenka, *Executive Asst*
▼ EMP: 15
SQ FT: 7,500
SALES (est): 50.5MM **Privately Held**
WEB: www.smithersoasis.com
SIC: **3086** Plastics foam products

(G-11529)
SMITHERS-OASIS COMPANY
Also Called: Smithers-Oasis North America
919 Marvin St (44240-2436)
P.O. Box 118 (44240-0002)
PHONE...................................330 673-5831
Fax: 330 686-0007
Charles Walton, *President*
Robert Willis, *General Mgr*
Bob Williams, *VP Opers*
Robert Williams, *Branch Mgr*
Richard Gilbert, *Director*
EMP: 11
SALES (corp-wide): 50.5MM **Privately
Held**
WEB: www.smithersoasis.com
SIC: **3086** Plastics foam products
PA: Smithers-Oasis Company
295 S Water St Ste 201
Kent OH 44240
330 945-5100

(G-11530)
SORBOTHANE INC (PA)
2144 State Route 59 (44240-7142)
PHONE...................................330 678-9444
David Church, *President*
Robert Whitlinger, *Principal*
James Forsyth, *Plant Mgr*
David Breakfield, *Engineer*
Bill Youmell, *VP Finance*
EMP: 20
SQ FT: 60,000
SALES (est): 2.7MM **Privately Held**
WEB: www.sorbothane.com
SIC: **3069 3545 3296 2821** Molded rub-
ber products; machine tool accessories;
mineral wool; plastics materials & resins

(G-11531)
SPORTSGUARD LABORATORIES INC
821 W Main St (44240-2215)
PHONE...................................330 673-3932
Fax: 330 673-1096
Dan Brett, *President*
EMP: 3
SQ FT: 1,500
SALES (est): 290K **Privately Held**
WEB: www.sportsguard.com
SIC: **3843** Dental equipment & supplies

(G-11532)
STAR OF WEST MILLING COMPANY
162 N Water St (44240-2419)
P.O. Box 250 (44240-0005)
PHONE...................................330 673-2941
Steve Michael, *Branch Mgr*
Ron Dawson, *Director*
EMP: 20
SALES (corp-wide): 380.1MM **Privately
Held**
SIC: **2041** Flour
PA: Star Of The West Milling Company
121 E Tuscola St
Frankenmuth MI 48734
330 673-2941

(G-11533)
STEINERT INDUSTRIES INC
1507 Franklin Ave (44240-3770)
PHONE...................................330 678-0028
Fax: 330 678-8238
John J Steinert, *President*
Laura Cheges, *Treasurer*
EMP: 15 EST: 1976
SQ FT: 11,000
SALES: 1MM **Privately Held**
WEB: www.steinertindustries.com
SIC: **3559 3599** Glass making machinery:
blowing, molding, forming, etc.; machine
shop, jobbing & repair

(G-11534)
SUNNY BROOK PRESSED CON CO
3586 Sunnybrook Rd (44240-7448)
PHONE...................................330 673-7667
Fax: 330 677-3103
Joseph F Repasky Jr, *President*
EMP: 9
SALES (est): 2MM **Privately Held**
WEB:
www.sunnybrookpressedconcrete.com
SIC: **3271** Architectural concrete: block,
split, fluted, screen, etc.

(G-11535)
TARPCO INC
390 Portage Blvd (44240-7283)
PHONE...................................330 677-8277
Fax: 330 678-8282
Chuck George, *President*
Harold A Neidlinger, *President*
Michael R Harrison, *Vice Pres*
Paul Sabol, *Marketing Staff*
EMP: 18 EST: 1938
SQ FT: 6,500
SALES (est): 1.3MM **Privately Held**
WEB: www.tarpco.com
SIC: **2394 7359 3537** Tarpaulins, fabric:
made from purchased materials; tent &
tarpaulin rental; industrial trucks & trac-
tors

(G-11536)
TECHNIDRILL SYSTEMS INC
429 Portage Blvd (44240-7286)
PHONE...................................330 678-9980
Fax: 330 678-9981
Jim Kent, *President*
H Calhoun, *Corp Secy*
Pat Kent, *Office Mgr*
EMP: 36
SQ FT: 23,000
SALES (est): 7.1MM **Privately Held**
WEB: www.technidrillsystems.com
SIC: **3541 3546 3545** Drilling & boring
machines; power-driven handtools; ma-
chine tool accessories

(G-11537)
TMAC MACHINE INC
924 Overholt Rd (44240-7551)
PHONE...................................330 673-0621
Fax: 330 673-9292
Ray Thompson, *President*
EMP: 7
SQ FT: 10,400
SALES: 350K **Privately Held**
SIC: **3599 3069** Machine shop, jobbing &
repair; platens, except printers': solid or
covered rubber

(G-11538)
TREE CITY MOLD & MACHINE CO
6752 State Route 43 (44240-6197)
PHONE...................................330 673-9807
Fax: 330 673-8605
Robert M Zalewski, *President*
Terry Zalewski, *Corp Secy*
EMP: 6 EST: 1955
SQ FT: 12,000
SALES: 1MM **Privately Held**
SIC: **3544** Industrial molds

(G-11539)
TRI CHEM INC
7285 State Route 43 Ste C (44240-5960)
PHONE...................................330 677-1213
Tim Harteis, *President*
John Frisby, *Executive*

▲ EMP: 3
SALES (est): 460K **Privately Held**
WEB: www.colorpigmentsdyes.com
SIC: **5084 5945 2865** Paint spray equip-
ment, industrial; hobby, toy & game
shops; color pigments, organic

(G-11540)
U S DEVELOPMENT CORP
900 W Main St (44240-2285)
PHONE...................................570 966-5990
Brad Wertman, *Manager*
EMP: 30
SALES (corp-wide): 10.2MM **Privately
Held**
WEB: www.rotomold.net
SIC: **3089 3949** Plastic processing; sport-
ing & athletic goods
PA: U S Development Corp
900 W Main St
Kent OH 44240
330 673-6900

(G-11541)
U S DEVELOPMENT CORP (PA)
Also Called: Akro-Plastics
900 W Main St (44240-2285)
PHONE...................................330 673-6900
Fax: 330 673-4940
Jerold Ramsey, *President*
Darrell Laney, *Plant Mgr*
David Meier, *Prdtn Mgr*
Steve Pickrel, *Sales Executive*
EMP: 50
SQ FT: 185,000
SALES (est): 10.2MM **Privately Held**
WEB: www.rotomold.net
SIC: **3089 6512** Molding primary plastic;
commercial & industrial building operation

(G-11542)
WEISS MOTORS
101 E Crain Ave (44240-2457)
PHONE...................................330 678-5585
Fax: 330 678-3660
Robert Knapp, *Owner*
EMP: 3
SALES: 260K **Privately Held**
SIC: **3711 7532** Automobile assembly, in-
cluding specialty automobiles; top & body
repair & paint shops

Kenton
Hardin County

(G-11543)
A & P WOOD PRODUCTS INC
15790 State Route 31 (43326-9016)
PHONE...................................419 673-1196
Walter Allsup, *President*
Debbie Allsup, *Corp Secy*
Kenneth Allsup, *Vice Pres*
EMP: 3
SALES: 1MM **Privately Held**
SIC: **2411** Logging camps & contractors

(G-11544)
ATMOSPHERE ANNEALING LLC
1501 Raff Rd Sw (43326)
PHONE...................................330 478-0314
Saminathan Ramaswamy, *Manager*
EMP: 65
SALES (corp-wide): 41MM **Privately
Held**
SIC: **3398** Annealing of metal
HQ: Atmosphere Annealing, Llc
209 W Mount Hope Ave # 2
Lansing MI 48910
517 485-5090

(G-11545)
BAKELITE N SUMITOMO AMER INC
13717 Us Highway 68 (43326-9302)
PHONE...................................419 675-1282
Kurt Sandy, *Branch Mgr*
EMP: 3
SALES (corp-wide): 1.7B **Privately Held**
SIC: **3089** Plastic containers, except foam
HQ: Sumitomo Bakelite North America, Inc
46820 Magellan Dr Ste C
Novi MI 48377
248 313-7000

(G-11546)
DUREZ CORPORATION
13717 State Route 68 (43326-9302)
PHONE....................................567 295-6400
Bill Bazell, *Manager*
EMP: 150
SQ FT: 25,000
SALES (corp-wide): 1.7B **Privately Held**
WEB: www.durez.com
SIC: 2891 2295 2821 Adhesives, plastic;
resin or plastic coated fabrics; plastics
materials & resins
HQ: Durez Corporation
46820 Magellan Dr Ste C
Novi MI 48377
248 313-7000

(G-11547)
GOLDEN GIANT INC
Also Called: Golden Giants Building System
13300 S Vision Dr (43326-9599)
P.O. Box 389 (43326-0389)
PHONE....................................419 674-4038
Fax: 419 673-1384
Gene A Good, *CEO*
Wright McCullough, *Principal*
Paul N McKinley, *Principal*
Sharon J Good, *Corp Secy*
Chris Richards, *Vice Pres*
EMP: 35
SQ FT: 80,000
SALES (est): 11.1MM **Privately Held**
WEB: www.goldengiant.com
SIC: 3448 Buildings, portable: prefabri-
cated metal; prefabricated metal compo-
nents

(G-11548)
GOLDEN GRAPHICS LTD
314 W Franklin St (43326-1702)
P.O. Box 208 (43326-0208)
PHONE....................................419 673-6260
Fax: 419 675-3133
Thomas G Carrig, *Principal*
Michael Carrig,
EMP: 10
SQ FT: 8,000
SALES (est): 1.6MM **Privately Held**
WEB: www.golden-graphics.com
SIC: 2752 7335 7336 2789 Commercial
printing, offset; commercial photography;
graphic arts & related design; bookbind-
ing & related work; commercial printing

(G-11549)
**HARDIN COUNTY PUBLISHING
CO (HQ)**
Also Called: Kenton Times, The
201 E Columbus St (43326-1583)
P.O. Box 230 (43326-0230)
PHONE....................................419 674-4066
Fax: 419 673-1125
Jeff Barnes, *President*
Jim Taylor, *Plant Mgr*
EMP: 36 EST: 1953
SQ FT: 9,600
SALES (est): 3.3MM
SALES (corp-wide): 8MM **Privately Held**
SIC: 2711 Job printing & newspaper pub-
lishing combined
PA: Ray Barnes Newspaper Inc
201 E Columbus St 207
Kenton OH 43326
419 674-4066

(G-11550)
HENSEL READY MIX INC (PA)
9925 County Road 265 (43326-9773)
PHONE....................................419 675-1808
Fax: 419 674-4687
Rodney Hensel, *President*
Linda Hensel, *Vice Pres*
Jeff Bailey, *Marketing Staff*
Roger Stone, *Manager*
Laura Young, *Manager*
EMP: 10 EST: 1963
SQ FT: 5,000
SALES (est): 1.7MM **Privately Held**
WEB: www.t3hw00t.com
SIC: 3273 Ready-mixed concrete

(G-11551)
**INTERNATIONAL PAPER
COMPANY**
808 Fontaine St (43326-2160)
PHONE....................................419 675-2534
EMP: 6
SALES (corp-wide): 21B **Publicly Held**
SIC: 2621 Paper mills
PA: International Paper Company
6400 Poplar Ave
Memphis TN 38197
901 419-9000

(G-11552)
**INTERNATIONAL PAPER
COMPANY**
808 Fontaine St (43326-2160)
PHONE....................................800 422-4657
Nancy Rampage, *Personnel Exec*
Al Kayler, *Branch Mgr*
EMP: 143
SALES (corp-wide): 21B **Publicly Held**
WEB: www.internationalpaper.com
SIC: 2656 Paper cups, plates, dishes &
utensils
PA: International Paper Company
6400 Poplar Ave
Memphis TN 38197
901 419-9000

(G-11553)
**INTERNATIONAL PAPER
COMPANY**
1300 S Main St (43326-2298)
PHONE....................................419 673-0711
Jayma Davis, *Purchasing*
Heather Fleece, *Purchasing*
Dave Kretchmer, *Human Res Dir*
Ted Riggs, *Branch Mgr*
Benjamin Herman, *Manager*
EMP: 375
SALES (corp-wide): 21B **Publicly Held**
WEB: www.internationalpaper.com
SIC: 2656 2621 Cups, paper: made from
purchased material; paper mills
PA: International Paper Company
6400 Poplar Ave
Memphis TN 38197
901 419-9000

(G-11554)
**KENTON IRON PRODUCTS INC
(PA)**
347 Vine St (43326-1253)
P.O. Box P.O Box 105-347 (43326)
PHONE....................................419 674-4178
Fax: 419 673-1901
Jerry Harmeyer, *President*
Michael Heyne, *Corp Secy*
Jessica Ulmer, *Safety Dir*
Mark Brown, *Supervisor*
EMP: 35
SQ FT: 70,000
SALES (est): 11.6MM **Privately Held**
WEB: www.kentoniron.com
SIC: 3321 3322 Gray iron ingot molds,
cast; malleable iron foundries

(G-11555)
KENTON IRON PRODUCTS INC
13917 N Vision Dr (43326-9592)
P.O. Box 105 (43326-0105)
PHONE....................................419 674-4178
Terry Ulmer, *Branch Mgr*
Michele Delong, *Admin Asst*
Gary Wurtsbaugh, *Maintence Staff*
EMP: 40
SALES (corp-wide): 11.6MM **Privately
Held**
WEB: www.kentoniron.com
SIC: 3321 Gray iron ingot molds, cast
PA: Kenton Iron Products, Inc.
347 Vine St
Kenton OH 43326
419 674-4178

(G-11556)
MCCULLOUGH INDUSTRIES INC
13047 County Road 175 (43326-9022)
P.O. Box 222 (43326-0222)
PHONE....................................800 245-9490
Fax: 419 673-8176
Stephen McCullough, *CEO*
Dustin McCullough, *Sales Mgr*
Cathy Rogers, *Sales Staff*

Donna Morrison, *Sales Executive*
Bob Osbun, *Manager*
EMP: 25 EST: 1969
SQ FT: 75,000
SALES (est): 8MM **Privately Held**
SIC: 3537 Industrial trucks & tractors; hop-
pers, end dump

(G-11557)
MCRILL SERVICE LLC
5304 Us Highway 68 (43326-9220)
PHONE....................................419 408-3113
Gary McRill,
Tammy McRill,
EMP: 5
SALES: 322K **Privately Held**
WEB: www.mcrillservice.com
SIC: 3545 Drilling machine attachments &
accessories

(G-11558)
**MID OHIO WOOD RECYCLING
INC**
16289 State Route 31 (43326-8819)
PHONE....................................419 673-8470
Leo Smithberger, *Owner*
Carla Smithberger, *Vice Pres*
EMP: 8
SQ FT: 30,000
SALES: 650K **Privately Held**
SIC: 2448 Wood pallets & skids

(G-11559)
MOLDMAKERS INC
13608 Us Highway 68 (43326-9302)
P.O. Box 372 (43326-0372)
PHONE....................................419 673-0902
Fax: 419 675-3279
Gene R Longbrake, *President*
Shari K Longbrake, *Treasurer*
Merrill Kaufman, *Supervisor*
Kim Kaufman, *Admin Sec*
EMP: 10
SQ FT: 12,000
SALES (est): 1.1MM **Privately Held**
WEB: www.moldmakersinc.com
SIC: 3544 3089 Special dies & tools; in-
jection molding of plastics

(G-11560)
MORTON BUILDINGS INC
14483 State Route 31 (43326-9055)
PHONE....................................419 673-0741
Fax: 419 673-0870
James Stephens, *General Mgr*
P Dean Brim, *Opers-Prdtn-Mfg*
Mike Buxton, *Engineer*
Dean Brim, *Manager*
EMP: 20
SALES (corp-wide): 499.4MM **Privately
Held**
WEB: www.mortonbuildings.com
SIC: 3448 Farm & utility buildings
PA: Morton Buildings, Inc.
252 W Adams St
Morton IL 61550
800 447-7436

(G-11561)
MORTON BUILDINGS INC
Also Called: Morton Buildings Plant
14483 State Route 31 (43326-9055)
P.O. Box 223 (43326-0223)
PHONE....................................419 675-2311
Fax: 419 675-2012
Paul Hudson, *General Mgr*
Mike Morrison, *Vice Pres*
Karen Baker, *Plant Mgr*
Jim Stevens, *Plant Mgr*
Mike Richardson, *Production*
EMP: 70
SALES (corp-wide): 499.4MM **Privately
Held**
SIC: 3448 5039 2452 Farm & utility build-
ings; prefabricated structures; prefabri-
cated wood buildings
PA: Morton Buildings, Inc.
252 W Adams St
Morton IL 61550
800 447-7436

(G-11562)
NALCON READY MIX INC
12484 State Route 701 (43326-9225)
P.O. Box 120, Findlay (45839-0120)
PHONE....................................419 422-4341

Matthew R Pfirsch, *President*
Chris Beeman, *VP Finance*
EMP: 5
SALES (est): 366.8K
SALES (corp-wide): 4B **Privately Held**
WEB: www.natlime.com
SIC: 3273 Ready-mixed concrete
PA: The National Lime And Stone Company
551 Lake Cascade Pkwy
Findlay OH 45840
419 422-4341

(G-11563)
OCCIDENTAL CHEMICAL DUREZ
13717 Us Highway 68 (43326-9590)
PHONE....................................419 675-5300
Fax: 419 675-5396
Bill Bazell, *Principal*
Connie Stewart, *Manager*
▲ EMP: 9
SALES (est): 1.1MM **Privately Held**
SIC: 2819 Industrial inorganic chemicals

(G-11564)
PRECISION STRIP INC
190 Bales Rd (43326)
PHONE....................................419 674-4186
Burce Keifer, *Plant Mgr*
Don Bornhorst, *Branch Mgr*
EMP: 180
SALES (corp-wide): 8.6B **Publicly Held**
WEB: www.precision-strip.com
SIC: 3316 3341 Cold finishing of steel
shapes; secondary nonferrous metals
HQ: Precision Strip Inc.
86 S Ohio St
Minster OH 45865
419 628-2343

(G-11565)
RADIO HOSPITAL
30 N Main St (43326-1552)
PHONE....................................419 679-1103
David Pearson, *Branch Mgr*
EMP: 5
SALES (corp-wide): 1.4MM **Privately
Held**
SIC: 3663 Cellular radio telephone
PA: Radio Hospital
2308 Harding Hwy
Lima OH 45804
419 225-9202

(G-11566)
**RAY BARNES NEWSPAPER INC
(PA)**
Also Called: Kenton Times
201 E Columbus St 207 (43326-1583)
P.O. Box 230 (43326-0230)
PHONE....................................419 674-4066
Charles Barnes, *President*
Kendrick Jesionowski, *Editor*
Jeff Barnes, *Vice Pres*
Judith K Barnes, *Treasurer*
EMP: 4
SQ FT: 5,600
SALES (est): 8MM **Privately Held**
WEB: www.kentontimes.com
SIC: 2711 Job printing & newspaper pub-
lishing combined

(G-11567)
ROBINSON FIN MACHINES INC
13670 Us Highway 68 (43326-9302)
PHONE....................................419 674-4152
Fax: 419 674-4154
Ruth A Haushalter, *President*
David Haushalter, *Vice Pres*
Sheryl Haushalter, *Vice Pres*
Mark Haushalter, *Controller*
Shannon Barnes, *Info Tech Mgr*
▲ EMP: 46
SQ FT: 27,000
SALES (est): 11.6MM **Privately Held**
WEB: www.robfin.com
SIC: 3444 Sheet metalwork

(G-11568)
SCIOTO SIGN CO INC
6047 Us Highway 68 (43326-9218)
PHONE....................................419 673-1261
Fax: 419 675-3298
Sandra A Pruden, *Ch of Bd*
Shawn Moore, *President*
Tim Roby, *Plant Mgr*
Michael Hunt, *Sales Staff*

Tim Kohli, *Marketing Staff*
EMP: 30 **EST:** 1897
SQ FT: 52,500
SALES (est): 4.8MM **Privately Held**
WEB: www.sciotosigns.com
SIC: 3993 Signs, not made in custom sign
painting shops; advertising novelties

(G-11569)
SPECIALTY PALLET ENTPS LLC
18031 State Route 309 (43326-9541)
PHONE..............................419 673-0247
Russ Cahill, *Principal*
EMP: 4
SALES (est): 496.2K **Privately Held**
SIC: 2448 Wood pallets & skids

(G-11570)
SPECIALTY STEEL SOLUTIONS
14574 State Route 292 (43326-9063)
PHONE..............................567 674-0011
Jonathan Diem, *Principal*
EMP: 4
SALES (est): 510.7K **Privately Held**
SIC: 3441 Fabricated structural metal

(G-11571)
SUPERIOR MACHINE TOOL INC
13606 Us Highway 68 (43326-9302)
PHONE..............................419 675-2363
Fax: 419 673-1505
Bill Clum, *President*
Richard L Rapp, *President*
Cheri Newland, *Manager*
EMP: 10
SQ FT: 7,200
SALES: 650K **Privately Held**
SIC: 3599 Machine shop, jobbing & repair

Kettering
Montgomery County

(G-11572)
ACCO BRANDS CORPORATION
4751 Hempstead Station Dr (45429-5165)
PHONE..............................937 495-5723
Boris Elisman, *President*
Jeffrey Brown, *Manager*
EMP: 22
SALES (corp-wide): 1.5B **Publicly Held**
SIC: 2782 Looseleaf binders & devices;
paper ruling
PA: Acco Brands Corporation
4 Corporate Dr
Lake Zurich IL 60047
847 541-9500

(G-11573)
ACCO BRANDS USA LLC
4751 Hempstead Station Dr (45429-5165)
PHONE..............................937 495-6323
EMP: 1264
SALES (corp-wide): 1.5B **Publicly Held**
SIC: 3089 Injection molding of plastics
HQ: Acco Brands Usa Llc
4 Corporate Dr
Lake Zurich IL 60047
800 222-6462

(G-11574)
ADISCO INC
2000 Composite Dr (45420-1493)
P.O. Box 25, East Hampton CT (06424-0025)
PHONE..............................937 296-5070
Richard Koczera, *President*
Joann Brown, *Corp Secy*
David Miller, *Finance Dir*
EMP: 14
SQ FT: 10,000
SALES: 1.2MM **Privately Held**
WEB: www.adisco.com
SIC: 3599 Machine & other job shop work

(G-11575)
AMCO PRODUCTS INC
4800 Hempstead Station Dr (45429-5155)
P.O. Box 62609 (45429)
PHONE..............................937 433-7982
Fax: 937 433-7965
Joseph M Raby, *CEO*
Ronald J Raby, *President*
Karla Simmons, *Vice Pres*

EMP: 10 **EST:** 1966
SQ FT: 58,600
SALES (est): 1MM **Privately Held**
SIC: 3451 Screw machine products

(G-11576)
BWI NORTH AMERICA INC
Ahg - Global Ride Dynamics
3100 Research Blvd (45420-4022)
PHONE..............................937 455-5190
Thomas P Gold, *Branch Mgr*
Jeffrey Duckro, *Consultant*
EMP: 130
SALES (corp-wide): 34.6B **Privately Held**
SIC: 3714 Motor vehicle parts & accessories
HQ: Bwi North America Inc.
3100 Res Blvd Ste 240
Kettering OH 45420
253 253-1130

(G-11577)
BWI NORTH AMERICA INC (DH)
Also Called: Bwi Group
3100 Res Blvd Ste 240 (45420)
PHONE..............................937 253-1130
Zhong Wang, *President*
David Barta, *Engineer*
Jeff Walters, *Design Engr*
Josie Wolfe, *HR Admin*
Lori Wood, *Department Mgr*
▲ **EMP:** 20
SQ FT: 60,000
SALES: 42.7MM
SALES (corp-wide): 34.6B **Privately Held**
SIC: 3714 5511 Motor vehicle parts & accessories; new & used car dealers
HQ: Beijing West Industries Co., Ltd.
No.85 Pu An Road, Doudian Town,
Fangshan District
Beijing 10004
105 753-7300

(G-11578)
COMPOSITE TECHNICAL SVCS LLC
Also Called: CTS
2000 Composite Dr (45420-1493)
PHONE..............................937 660-3783
Charlene Kneer, *Office Mgr*
Enrico Ferri,
EMP: 5
SQ FT: 1,580
SALES (est): 520K **Privately Held**
SIC: 2821 Polyethylene resins; epoxy resins

(G-11579)
EASTMAN KODAK COMPANY
3100 Research Blvd # 250 (45420-4019)
PHONE..............................937 259-3000
Bonnie Saravullo, *Branch Mgr*
Woody Kessell, *Analyst*
Bonnie J Saravullo, *Contract Law*
EMP: 20
SALES (corp-wide): 1.8B **Publicly Held**
SIC: 3355 Aluminum rolling & drawing
PA: Eastman Kodak Company
343 State St
Rochester NY 14650
585 724-4000

(G-11580)
GREENE FUEL PLAZA INC
3151 E Dorothy Ln (45420-3819)
PHONE..............................937 532-4826
Jagtar Singh, *Principal*
EMP: 3
SALES (est): 208.7K **Privately Held**
SIC: 2869 Fuels

(G-11581)
INFINITY TRICHOLOGY CENTER
5250 Far Hills Ave (45429-2382)
PHONE..............................937 281-0555
Nancy Bellard, *Vice Pres*
EMP: 4
SALES (est): 270.5K **Privately Held**
SIC: 3845 Laser systems & equipment, medical

(G-11582)
LION HELMET MOLDING
2000 Composite Dr (45420-1493)
PHONE..............................937 297-0760
Courtney Biser, *Manager*

EMP: 3
SALES (est): 175.5K **Privately Held**
SIC: 3089 Molding primary plastic

(G-11583)
NANOSPERSE LLC
2000 Composite Dr (45420-1493)
PHONE..............................937 296-5030
Susan Robitaille, *Development*
Arthur Fritts,
▼ **EMP:** 9
SQ FT: 10,000
SALES: 1.4MM **Privately Held**
WEB: www.nanosperse.com
SIC: 2821 3087 2891 2851 Plastics materials & resins; epoxy resins; custom compound purchased resins; epoxy adhesives; epoxy coatings

(G-11584)
NANOTECHLABS INC (PA)
Also Called: Buckeye Composites
2000 Composite Dr (45420-1493)
PHONE..............................937 297-9518
Jessica Ravine, *CEO*
Richard Czerw, *Principal*
Melanie Bowser, *Engineer*
EMP: 13
SALES (est): 1.5MM **Privately Held**
SIC: 3955 Carbon paper & inked ribbons

(G-11585)
RESONETICS LLC
Also Called: Mound Laser Photonics Center
2941 College Dr (45420-1172)
PHONE..............................937 865-4070
Tom Burns, *CEO*
Kevin Hartke, *CTO*
EMP: 63
SALES (corp-wide): 28.4MM **Privately Held**
SIC: 3699 3841 Laser systems & equipment; medical instruments & equipment, blood & bone work
PA: Resonetics, Llc
44 Simon St Ste 103
Nashua NH 03060
603 886-6772

(G-11586)
SMW MANUFACTURING
Also Called: Smw Supplier Village
2555 Woodman Dr (45420-1487)
PHONE..............................937 781-4945
Robert Dunford, *CEO*
▲ **EMP:** 4 **EST:** 2013
SQ FT: 25,000
SALES (est): 330K **Privately Held**
SIC: 3452 Bolts, nuts, rivets & washers

(G-11587)
TENNECO AUTOMOTIVE OPER CO INC
2555 Woodman Dr (45420-1487)
PHONE..............................937 781-4940
Mike Andreatta, *Branch Mgr*
EMP: 60
SQ FT: 18,000
SALES (corp-wide): 8.6B **Publicly Held**
WEB: www.tenneco-automotive.com
SIC: 3714 Motor vehicle engines & parts; shock absorbers, motor vehicle
HQ: Tenneco Automotive Operating Company, Inc.
500 N Field Dr
Lake Forest IL 60045
847 482-5000

(G-11588)
WESTROCK MWV LLC
Also Called: Meadwestvaco
4751 Hempstead Station Dr (45429-5165)
PHONE..............................937 495-6323
Ronnie Hise, *General Mgr*
Peter Duquette, *Vice Pres*
Keith McGoldrick, *Purchasing*
Jen Bondick, *Marketing Mgr*
Neil McLachlan, *Branch Mgr*
EMP: 240
SALES (corp-wide): 14.1B **Publicly Held**
WEB: www.meadwestvaco.com
SIC: 2631 Paperboard mills
HQ: Westrock Mwv, Llc
501 S 5th St
Richmond VA 23219
804 444-1000

Kettlersville
Shelby County

(G-11589)
ROETTGER HARDWOOD INC
17066 Kettlersville Rd (45336)
P.O. Box 68 (45336-0068)
PHONE..............................937 693-6811
Fax: 937 693-6811
Viola Roettger, *President*
Renee Roettger, *Business Mgr*
EMP: 12
SQ FT: 74,000
SALES: 1MM **Privately Held**
SIC: 2431 2434 Millwork; wood kitchen cabinets

Kidron
Wayne County

(G-11590)
GERBER FARM DIVISION INC
5889 Kidron Rd (44636)
PHONE..............................800 362-7381
John R Metzger, *President*
EMP: 7
SALES (est): 720.1K **Privately Held**
SIC: 2015 Chicken, processed: fresh

(G-11591)
GERBER WOOD PRODUCTS INC
6075 Kidron Rd (44636)
P.O. Box 250 (44636-0250)
PHONE..............................330 857-3901
Fax: 330 857-9009
Steve Gerber, *President*
Jerry Staples, *Plant Mgr*
Wes Sprunger, *Opers Mgr*
Carl Reinhardt, *Admin Mgr*
Eldon Gerber, *Admin Sec*
EMP: 9
SALES (est): 1MM **Privately Held**
WEB: www.gerberwood.com
SIC: 3993 3999 Advertising novelties; plaques, picture, laminated

Killbuck
Holmes County

(G-11592)
BAKERWELL INC (PA)
10420 County Road 620 (44637-9728)
P.O. Box 425 (44637-0425)
PHONE..............................330 276-2161
Fax: 330 276-2287
W Rex Baker, *President*
Robert K Baker, *CFO*
Robert Baker, *Controller*
Laura Sabine, *Office Mgr*
Dustin Baker, *Manager*
EMP: 21
SQ FT: 126,000
SALES: 5.8MM **Privately Held**
SIC: 1311 1389 Crude petroleum & natural gas; servicing oil & gas wells

(G-11593)
BAKERWELL SERVICE RIGS INC (HQ)
10420 County Road 620 (44637-9728)
P.O. Box 425 (44637-0425)
PHONE..............................330 276-2161
W Rex Baker, *President*
Jeffrey Baker, *Corp Secy*
Andrew Baker, *Vice Pres*
EMP: 18
SALES (est): 1.3MM
SALES (corp-wide): 5.8MM **Privately Held**
SIC: 1381 Service well drilling
PA: Bakerwell, Inc.
10420 County Road 620
Killbuck OH 44637
330 276-2161

(G-11594)
DANIELS AMISH COLLECTION LLC
100 Straits Ln (44637-9549)
PHONE...................................330 276-0110
Christopher Karman, *Branch Mgr*
EMP: 120
SALES (corp-wide): 20MM **Privately Held**
SIC: 2519 Fiberglass furniture, household: padded or plain
PA: Daniel's Amish Collection, Llc
9190 Massillon Rd
Dundee OH 44624
330 359-0400

(G-11595)
JH WOODWORKING LLC
11259 Township Road 71 (44637-9444)
PHONE...................................330 276-7600
Joni Hostetler, *Principal*
EMP: 4 EST: 2011
SALES (est): 441.6K **Privately Held**
SIC: 2431 Millwork

(G-11596)
KILLBUCK OILFIELD SERVICES
9277 Township Road 92 (44637-9707)
PHONE...................................330 276-6706
Paul R Baker, *Partner*
Robert P Baker, *Partner*
Roger Baker, *Partner*
EMP: 4
SALES: 96.5K **Privately Held**
SIC: 1389 Oil field services; gas field services

(G-11597)
PINNACLE DRILLING LLC
10420 County Road 620 (44637-9728)
PHONE...................................330 276-1096
ROC Baker,
Rex Baker,
EMP: 16
SALES: 2MM
SALES (corp-wide): 5.8MM **Privately Held**
SIC: 1381 Drilling oil & gas wells
PA: Bakerwell, Inc.
10420 County Road 620
Killbuck OH 44637
330 276-2161

(G-11598)
PRIDE OF HILLS MFG INC
110 Straits Ln (44637-9549)
PHONE...................................800 345-1744
EMP: 31
SALES (corp-wide): 30.5MM **Privately Held**
SIC: 3533 Oil & gas field machinery
PA: Pride Of The Hills Manufacturing, Inc.
8275 State Route 514
Big Prairie OH 44611
330 567-3108

(G-11599)
SHREINER SOLE CO INC
1 Taylor Dr (44637)
P.O. Box 347 (44637-0347)
PHONE...................................330 276-6135
Fax: 330 276-1605
David Shreiner, *President*
Scott Wagers, *COO*
Katrina Geog, *Services*
▲ EMP: 10
SQ FT: 56,750
SALES: 500K **Privately Held**
WEB: www.shreinerco.com
SIC: 3069 3061 Soles, boot or shoe: rubber, composition or fiber; mechanical rubber goods

(G-11600)
SPERRY RICE MANUFACTURING LLC
1088 N Main St (44637-9504)
PHONE...................................330 276-2801
Bernice Tippon, *Cust Mgr*
Darrell Detzler, *Branch Mgr*
Tim Morris, *Manager*
EMP: 16

SALES (corp-wide): 1.2MM **Privately Held**
WEB: www.sperryrice.com
SIC: 3052 Rubber & plastics hose & beltings
PA: Sperry Rice Manufacturing Llc
9146 Us Highway 52
Brookville IN 47012
812 936-3500

(G-11601)
WILSON CABINET CO
Straits Industrial Park (44637)
P.O. Box 305 (44637-0305)
PHONE...................................330 276-8711
Fax: 330 276-5655
Carl De Maria, *President*
Rebecca Stover, *Corp Secy*
Ken Rock, *Mfg Staff*
EMP: 35 EST: 1950
SQ FT: 75,000
SALES: 3.5MM **Privately Held**
WEB: www.wilsoncabinet.com
SIC: 2434 Wood kitchen cabinets; vanities, bathroom: wood

(G-11602)
WILSONS COUNTRY CREATIONS
13248 County Road 6 (44637-9434)
PHONE...................................330 377-4190
Fax: 330 377-5010
Tom Wilson, *Owner*
EMP: 13
SQ FT: 3,500
SALES (est): 1.4MM **Privately Held**
WEB: www.wilsonscc.com
SIC: 5199 5261 3272 Statuary; lawn ornaments; concrete products

Kimbolton
Guernsey County

(G-11603)
SIMONDS INTERNATIONAL LLC
76000 Old Twenty One Rd (43749-9610)
PHONE...................................978 424-0100
John Fogle, *Branch Mgr*
EMP: 47
SALES (corp-wide): 45.3MM **Privately Held**
WEB: www.simondsinternational.com
SIC: 3423 5251 Hand & edge tools; tools
HQ: Simonds International L.L.C.
135 Intervale Rd
Fitchburg MA 01420
978 343-3731

Kingsville
Ashtabula County

(G-11604)
HYDRANT HAT LLC
5759 S Wright St (44048-5804)
PHONE...................................440 224-1007
David Laugen,
EMP: 3
SALES (est): 214.5K **Privately Held**
WEB: www.hydrant-hat.com
SIC: 3089 Plastic containers, except foam

(G-11605)
LYONS
5231 State Route 193 (44048-7713)
P.O. Box 554 (44048-0554)
PHONE...................................440 224-0676
Elijah Lyons, *Owner*
EMP: 6
SALES (est): 422.4K **Privately Held**
SIC: 3715 Truck trailers

(G-11606)
NELSON SAND & GRAVEL INC
5720 State Route 193 (44048-9715)
P.O. Box 466 (44048-0466)
PHONE...................................440 224-0198
Fax: 440 224-0044
Thomas Nelson, *President*
Donna J Nelson, *Corp Secy*
EMP: 10
SQ FT: 6,000

SALES (est): 985.6K **Privately Held**
SIC: 1442 Common sand mining; gravel mining

(G-11607)
R W SIDLEY INC
3062 E Center St (44068)
PHONE...................................440 224-2664
Fax: 440 224-2667
Robert Buescher, *President*
EMP: 15
SALES (est): 1.1MM **Privately Held**
SIC: 3272 Concrete products

Kinsman
Trumbull County

(G-11608)
BAYLOFF STMPED PDTS KNSMAN INC
8091 State Route 5 (44428-9628)
PHONE...................................330 876-4511
Fax: 330 876-4632
Richard Bayer, *President*
Rufus S Day Jr, *Principal*
Dixon Morgan, *Principal*
M E Newcomer, *Principal*
Dan Moore, *Vice Pres*
EMP: 80 EST: 1948
SQ FT: 115,000
SALES (est): 15.4MM **Privately Held**
SIC: 3469 7692 3444 3315 Metal stampings; welding repair; sheet metalwork; steel wire & related products

(G-11609)
HANDLE LIGHT INC
5533 State Route 7 (44428-9751)
PHONE...................................330 772-8901
Daniel Bozzo, *President*
EMP: 9
SALES (est): 929.6K **Privately Held**
WEB: www.handlelight.com
SIC: 3559 Automotive maintenance equipment

(G-11610)
MCGILL SEPTIC TANK CO
8913 State St (44428-9706)
PHONE...................................330 876-2171
Fax: 330 876-0393
Charles McGill, *President*
James McElhinny, *Vice Pres*
EMP: 30
SQ FT: 10,000
SALES (est): 3.3MM **Privately Held**
SIC: 3272 2531 Concrete products, precast; public building & related furniture

(G-11611)
SELECT ENTERPRISES INC
6345 State Route 7 (44428-9755)
PHONE...................................724 588-4141
Rosemary Weaver, *Principal*
▼ EMP: 13 EST: 2008
SALES (est): 1.8MM **Privately Held**
SIC: 2421 Sawmills & planing mills, general

(G-11612)
STRATTON CREEK WOOD WORKS LLC
5915 Burnett East Rd (44428-9757)
PHONE...................................330 876-0005
Bill Sandrock,
Kathy Marie,
EMP: 11
SALES (est): 1.5MM **Privately Held**
WEB: www.strattoncreek.com
SIC: 2431 Millwork

Kirtland
Lake County

(G-11613)
ENDURA PLASTICS INC
7955 Euclid Chardon Rd (44094-9014)
PHONE...................................440 951-4466
Fax: 440 256-3053
Mark Di Lillo, *President*

Susan Thomas, *Buyer*
Mary Kenny, *QC Mgr*
Don Kitchen, *Engineer*
Rick Bissell, *Marketing Staff*
EMP: 85 EST: 1961
SQ FT: 26,000
SALES (est): 14.5MM **Privately Held**
WEB: www.endura.com
SIC: 3089 3544 Injection molded finished plastic products; special dies, tools, jigs & fixtures

(G-11614)
EZSHRED LLC (PA)
7621 Euclid Chardon Rd (44094-8740)
P.O. Box 8, Chesterland (44026-0008)
PHONE...................................440 256-7640
Ronald Ray,
EMP: 5
SALES (est): 603.7K **Privately Held**
SIC: 5734 7371 7372 Computer software & accessories; computer software development & applications; publishers' computer software

(G-11615)
OUTDOOR SUPPLY
7899 Euclid Chardon Rd (44094-9536)
PHONE...................................440 256-3338
Fax: 440 256-3313
David P Dicillo, *President*
Michael Dicillo, *Vice Pres*
Matthew Dicillo, *Treasurer*
EMP: 3 EST: 2002
SALES (est): 357.2K **Privately Held**
WEB: www.outdoorsupply.com
SIC: 3272 Stone, cast concrete

(G-11616)
SPEC MASK OHIO LLC
7899 Euclid Chardon Rd (44094-9536)
PHONE...................................440 522-3055
Thomas Dicillo, *Principal*
Teresa Dicillo, *Principal*
EMP: 3 EST: 2010
SALES (est): 222K **Privately Held**
SIC: 2992 Lubricating oils & greases

(G-11617)
STEWART ACQUISITION LLC
Also Called: Endura Plastics
7955 Euclid Chardon Rd (44094-9014)
PHONE...................................800 376-4466
James Stewart, *President*
EMP: 30
SALES (corp-wide): 11.7MM **Privately Held**
SIC: 3089 Injection molding of plastics
PA: Stewart Acquisition Llc
2146 Enterprise Pkwy
Twinsburg OH 44087
330 963-0322

(G-11618)
VILLAGE OUTDOORS
7875 Euclid Chardon Rd (44094)
PHONE...................................440 256-1172
Anne Difranco, *Owner*
EMP: 5
SALES (est): 703.3K **Privately Held**
SIC: 3524 Lawn & garden equipment

(G-11619)
WHOLESALE CHANNEL LETTERS
8603 Euclid Chardon Rd (44094-9586)
PHONE...................................440 256-3200
Dale Heigley, *Owner*
EMP: 8
SALES (est): 665.5K **Privately Held**
WEB: www.wholesalesignsuperstore.com
SIC: 3993 Electric signs

Kitts Hill
Lawrence County

(G-11620)
DAVID ADKINS LOGGING
1260 Township Road 256 (45645-8885)
PHONE...................................740 533-0297
Fax: 740 533-0253
David A Adkins, *Admin Sec*
EMP: 6

SALES (est): 476K **Privately Held**
SIC: 2411 Logging camps & contractors

(G-11621)
MILLWRGHT WLDG FBRICATION SVCS
1590 County Road 105 (45645-8632)
PHONE................................740 533-1510
Mike Moore, *President*
Stephen H Thompson, *Vice Pres*
EMP: 11
SALES (est): 443.1K **Privately Held**
SIC: 7692 Welding repair

La Rue
Marion County

(G-11622)
POWERMOUNT SYSTEMS INC
1602 Larue Marseilles Rd (43332-8928)
PHONE................................740 499-4330
Ronald Abbott, *Principal*
EMP: 10
SALES (est): 1MM **Privately Held**
SIC: 3355 Extrusion ingot, aluminum: made in rolling mills

(G-11623)
VICTORY STORE FIXTURES INC
3153 Winnemac Pike S (43332-8818)
PHONE................................740 499-3494
Karen Lightner, *President*
John C Lightner, *Vice Pres*
EMP: 16
SQ FT: 1,200
SALES (est): 1.3MM **Privately Held**
SIC: 3083 Plastic finished products, laminated

Lagrange
Lorain County

(G-11624)
COLONIAL CABINETS INC
337 S Center St (44050-9014)
P.O. Box 62 (44050-0062)
PHONE................................440 355-9663
Fax: 440 355-9676
Jerry Duelley, *President*
Barry Ickes, *Vice Pres*
Kenneth Sooy, *Treasurer*
Rose Cornell, *Office Mgr*
EMP: 13
SQ FT: 10,000
SALES: 900K **Privately Held**
SIC: 2434 Wood kitchen cabinets

(G-11625)
FREAK-N-FRIES INC
204 Taylor Blvd (44050-9304)
PHONE................................440 453-1877
Rob Dirne, *President*
EMP: 3
SALES (est): 218.3K **Privately Held**
SIC: 2015 Sausage, poultry

(G-11626)
GREY HAWK GOLF CLUB
665 U S Grant St (44050-8508)
PHONE................................440 355-4844
Fax: 440 355-3428
David De Benadetto, *Owner*
EMP: 50
SALES (est): 2.9MM **Privately Held**
WEB: www.greyhawkgolf.com
SIC: 3949 Shafts, golf club

(G-11627)
INSERVCO INC (DH)
Also Called: Staci Lagrange
110 Commerce Dr (44050-9491)
P.O. Box 106 (44050-0106)
PHONE................................847 855-9600
Jere Simonson, *Corp Secy*
Greg Hebson, *Vice Pres*
Mike Nargi, *Vice Pres*
Dennis Sudnick, *Safety Mgr*
Patty Copp, *Manager*
▲ EMP: 71
SQ FT: 26,300

SALES (est): 19.1MM **Privately Held**
WEB: www.inservco.com
SIC: 3679 Electronic circuits
HQ: Staci Corp.
110 Commerce Dr
Lagrange OH 44050
440 355-5102

(G-11628)
JEHM TECHNOLOGIES INC
612 N Center St Ste 201 (44050-9000)
P.O. Box 657 (44050-0657)
PHONE................................440 355-5558
Jeff Pufnock, *Principal*
EMP: 5
SALES (est): 327.7K **Privately Held**
SIC: 7372 Prepackaged software

(G-11629)
KECK ENGINEERING INC
39610 Whitney Rd (44050-9753)
PHONE................................440 355-9855
Reinhard Keck, *President*
EMP: 7 EST: 1966
SALES (est): 506.7K **Privately Held**
WEB: www.keckengineering.com
SIC: 3599 Machine shop, jobbing & repair

(G-11630)
LA GRANGE ELEC ASSEMBLIES CO
349 S Center St (44050-9014)
P.O. Box 555 (44050-0555)
PHONE................................440 355-5388
W Robin Mc Clain, *President*
Richard M Mc Clain, *Vice Pres*
Don Tolbert, *Plant Mgr*
Sally Tolbert, *Manager*
EMP: 13
SQ FT: 40,000
SALES (est): 2.3MM **Privately Held**
WEB: www.lagrangeelectrical.com
SIC: 3679 Harness assemblies for electronic use: wire or cable; power supplies, all types: static

(G-11631)
M C INDUSTRIES INC
111 Commerce Dr (44050-9491)
P.O. Box 116 (44050-0116)
PHONE................................440 355-4040
Fax: 440 355-4030
Dave Mick, *President*
Karen Mick, *Vice Pres*
Sunnie Polen, *Office Mgr*
EMP: 15
SQ FT: 10,000
SALES (est): 1.7MM **Privately Held**
SIC: 3452 Bolts, nuts, rivets & washers

(G-11632)
MADER MACHINE CO INC
Also Called: Mader Dampers
422 Commerce Dr E (44050-9316)
PHONE................................440 355-4505
Fax: 440 355-6582
Lon Zeager, *President*
Nancy Zeager, *Corp Secy*
Lon James Zeager, *Vice Pres*
Brendan Moran, *Opers Mgr*
Blaine Frayser, *Sales Mgr*
EMP: 32 EST: 1963
SQ FT: 45,000
SALES (est): 10.4MM **Privately Held**
SIC: 3822 Damper operators: pneumatic, thermostatic, electric; controls, combination limit & fan

(G-11633)
MICRON MANUFACTURING INC
186 Commerce Dr (44050-8926)
PHONE................................440 355-4200
Fax: 440 355-4246
Mark A Zupan, *President*
Anne Zupan, *Vice Pres*
Scott Slosier, *Opers Mgr*
Sue Gessner, *Purch Dir*
Kim Truxall, *Accounting Mgr*
EMP: 60
SQ FT: 50,000
SALES (est): 15.8MM **Privately Held**
WEB: www.micmfg.com
SIC: 3541 Machine tools, metal cutting type

(G-11634)
NEW AGE DESIGN & TOOL INC
162 Commerce Dr (44050-8926)
PHONE................................440 355-5400
Fax: 440 355-5403
Glen Allen, *President*
Donald Youngblood, *Corp Secy*
EMP: 15
SQ FT: 10,000
SALES: 1.9MM **Privately Held**
SIC: 3312 Tool & die steel

(G-11635)
PANEL MASTER LLC
191 Commerce Dr (44050-8926)
PHONE................................440 355-4442
Fax: 440 355-4444
Sherri Haun, *Purchasing*
Dave Terlop, *Engineer*
Cheryl Watts, *Finance Mgr*
Ridley Watts, *Mng Member*
EMP: 30
SQ FT: 24,000
SALES (est): 6.9MM **Privately Held**
WEB: www.panelmaster.com
SIC: 3613 3625 Control panels, electric; relays & industrial controls

(G-11636)
QUALITY METAL PRODUCTS INC
210 Commerce Dr (44050-9492)
PHONE................................440 355-6165
Fax: 440 355-6172
Mark Duplata, *President*
Robert Yunker, *President*
Mark Duplaga, *Vice Pres*
Kathleen Norton Fox, *Services*
EMP: 5
SQ FT: 5,000
SALES (est): 624.5K **Privately Held**
SIC: 3599 3469 Machine shop, jobbing & repair; metal stampings

(G-11637)
SLADE GARDNER
233 Commerce Dr Unit B (44050-9227)
P.O. Box 595 (44050-0595)
PHONE................................440 355-8015
Mark Pinto, *Owner*
EMP: 3
SALES (est): 412.4K **Privately Held**
SIC: 3542 7692 Machine tools, metal forming type; welding repair

(G-11638)
STACI CORP (DH)
Also Called: Vexos
110 Commerce Dr (44050-9491)
P.O. Box 106 (44050-0106)
PHONE................................440 355-5102
David M Buckley, *CEO*
Jim Thirkill, *President*
Greg Hebson, *Senior VP*
Keith Mallery, *Vice Pres*
Joe Shero, *Vice Pres*
▲ EMP: 18
SQ FT: 7,688
SALES (est): 160.1MM **Privately Held**
WEB: www.stacicorp.com
SIC: 3672 Circuit boards, television & radio printed
HQ: Vexos, Inc.
110 Commerce Dr
Lagrange OH 44050
646 843-0710

(G-11639)
TRIMLINE DIE CORPORATION
421 Commerce Dr E (44050-9316)
P.O. Box 66 (44050-0066)
PHONE................................440 355-6900
Fax: 440 355-6935
Dave Gido, *President*
Mike W Wentlink, *Manager*
EMP: 20
SQ FT: 10,000
SALES (est): 4.3MM **Privately Held**
WEB: www.trimlinedie.com
SIC: 3544 Special dies & tools

(G-11640)
TRUE TURN INDUSTRIES
233 Commerce Dr Unit D (44050-9227)
PHONE................................440 355-6256
Joe Maloney, *Owner*

EMP: 3
SALES: 500K **Privately Held**
SIC: 3469 Machine parts, stamped or pressed metal

(G-11641)
VIRGILS KITCHENS INC
100 Public Sq (44050-9841)
P.O. Box 625 (44050-0625)
PHONE................................440 355-5058
Fax: 440 355-5060
James Rader, *President*
Barb Rader, *Corp Secy*
Virgil Rader, *Vice Pres*
EMP: 9 EST: 1961
SQ FT: 5,000
SALES (est): 236.5K **Privately Held**
SIC: 2434 5712 Wood kitchen cabinets; cabinet work, custom; cabinets, except custom made: kitchen

Lake Milton
Mahoning County

(G-11642)
DISCIPLE TOOL & MACHINE
189 Se River Rd (44429-9613)
PHONE................................330 503-7879
John E Lorent, *Owner*
EMP: 5
SALES (est): 344.9K **Privately Held**
SIC: 3544 Special dies, tools, jigs & fixtures

Lake Waynoka
Brown County

(G-11643)
KAYLEE RYAN PUBLISHING LLC
133 Horse Shoe Dr (45171-8134)
P.O. Box 541046, Cincinnati (45254-1046)
PHONE................................937 446-3926
Jessica Roquet, *Principal*
EMP: 4
SALES (est): 136K **Privately Held**
SIC: 2741 Miscellaneous publishing

Lakemore
Summit County

(G-11644)
FOUR GENERATIONS INC
Also Called: Ideal Baking Co
1320 Main St (44250-9805)
PHONE................................330 784-2243
Greg Godar, *President*
EMP: 7 EST: 1920
SQ FT: 10,000
SALES (est): 605K **Privately Held**
WEB: www.idealbakeryequipment.com
SIC: 2052 Bakery products, dry

(G-11645)
ROBAN INC
1319 Main St (44250-9803)
P.O. Box 526 (44250-0526)
PHONE................................330 794-1059
Karen Medzi, *President*
Barbara George, *Treasurer*
EMP: 9
SQ FT: 7,000
SALES: 1MM **Privately Held**
WEB: www.robansignage.com
SIC: 2796 7336 3479 Engraving platemaking services; silk screen design; etching on metals; etching, photochemical

▲ = Import ▼=Export
◆ =Import/Export

Lakeside
Ottawa County

(G-11646)
CUSTOM CANVAS & BOAT REPAIR
Also Called: Custom Canvas & Upholstery
29 S Bridge Rd (43440-9483)
PHONE.................................419 732-3314
Fax: 419 732-3314
Shawn Harrison, *President*
Von Ellis, *Vice Pres*
David Walter, *Treasurer*
Carol Ellis, *Admin Sec*
EMP: 11
SQ FT: 4,800
SALES: 500K **Privately Held**
SIC: 2394 Liners & covers, fabric: made from purchased materials

Lakeside Marblehead
Ottawa County

(G-11647)
BIRO MANUFACTURING COMPANY (PA)
1114 W Main St (43440-2099)
PHONE.................................419 798-4451
Fax: 419 798-9106
Richard C Biro, *President*
Carl G Biro, *Principal*
Michael J Biro, *Vice Pres*
Robert S Biro, *Vice Pres*
Bill Lacure, *Plant Mgr*
◆ EMP: 57 EST: 1986
SQ FT: 76,000
SALES (est): 17.1MM **Privately Held**
SIC: 3556 Food products machinery; choppers, commercial, food; poultry processing machinery; grinders, commercial, food

(G-11648)
FINE PRINT LLC
508 Oak Ave (43440-1744)
PHONE.................................419 702-7087
Beverly Bartczak, *Owner*
EMP: 4
SALES (est): 384K **Privately Held**
SIC: 2752 Commercial printing, lithographic

Lakeview
Logan County

(G-11649)
DRAIN PRODUCTS LLC (PA)
13051 County Road 301 (43331-9502)
PHONE.................................419 230-4549
Jonathan Myers, *Owner*
EMP: 4
SQ FT: 20,000
SALES: 600K **Privately Held**
SIC: 5162 3084 Plastics materials & basic shapes; plastics pipe

(G-11650)
UNITED TOOL AND MACHINE INC
490 S Main St (43331-9460)
P.O. Box 307 (43331-0307)
PHONE.................................937 843-5603
Fax: 937 843-6896
Claude Heintz, *President*
Sylvia Heintz, *Treasurer*
Chris Shrader, *Admin Sec*
EMP: 13 EST: 1973
SQ FT: 41,000
SALES (est): 1.2MM **Privately Held**
WEB: www.united-tm.com
SIC: 3469 Metal stampings; machine parts, stamped or pressed metal

Lakeville
Holmes County

(G-11651)
INTERDEN INDUSTRIES INC
2377 County Road 175 (44638-9610)
PHONE.................................419 368-9011
Fax: 419 368-9011
Terra Studer, *President*
Boett Grogen, *Vice Pres*
EMP: 5
SALES: 280K **Privately Held**
SIC: 1381 1389 Drilling oil & gas wells; oil & gas wells: building, repairing & dismantling

Lakewood
Cuyahoga County

(G-11652)
717 INC
Also Called: 717 Ink
13000 Athens Ave Ste 110 (44107-6256)
PHONE.................................440 925-0402
Joseph Haddad, *President*
EMP: 7
SALES: 150K **Privately Held**
SIC: 2262 Finishing plants, manmade fiber & silk fabrics

(G-11653)
ABC LETTERING & EMBROIDERY
13727 Madison Ave (44107-4744)
PHONE.................................216 321-8338
Fax: 216 321-8838
Michael J Martin, *Owner*
EMP: 5
SALES: 150K **Privately Held**
SIC: 2396 Screen printing on fabric articles

(G-11654)
ADVANCED ENERGY TECH LLC
11709 Madison Ave (44107-5230)
PHONE.................................216 676-2259
Joel Hawthorne, *CEO*
EMP: 20
SALES (est): 821.6K
SALES (corp-wide): 14.9B **Privately Held**
SIC: 3624 Carbon & graphite products; electrodes, thermal & electrolytic uses: carbon, graphite
HQ: Graftech International Holdings Inc.
6100 Oak Tree Blvd # 300
Independence OH 44131
216 676-2000

(G-11655)
ALLENBAUGH FOODS LLC
14305 Bayes Ave (44107-6011)
PHONE.................................216 952-3984
Craig Allenbaugh, *Principal*
EMP: 3
SALES (est): 252.9K **Privately Held**
SIC: 2099 Food preparations

(G-11656)
AMPLIFIED SOLAR INC
1453 Wayne Ave (44107-3422)
PHONE.................................216 236-4225
Justin Walker, *President*
EMP: 4
SALES (est): 265.3K **Privately Held**
SIC: 3629 Electrical industrial apparatus

(G-11657)
BENSAN JEWELERS INC
Also Called: Broestl & Wallis Fine Jewelers
14410 Madison Ave (44107-4513)
PHONE.................................216 221-1434
Daniel D Wallis, *President*
Jeffery Broestl, *Admin Sec*
EMP: 7
SQ FT: 2,106
SALES (est): 940.7K **Privately Held**
WEB: www.broestlwallis.com
SIC: 5944 3911 7631 Jewelry stores; jewelry apparel; jewelry repair services

(G-11658)
BLUE COTTAGE BAKERY LLC
15612 Lake Ave (44107-1222)
PHONE.................................216 221-9733
Carole Rojas, *Principal*
EMP: 4
SALES (est): 166.2K **Privately Held**
SIC: 2051 Bread, cake & related products

(G-11659)
CAHILL SERVICES INC
13000 Athens Ave Ste 104e (44107-6256)
P.O. Box 811132, Cleveland (44181-1132)
PHONE.................................216 410-5595
Christine M Cahill, *Principal*
EMP: 4
SALES (est): 440.7K **Privately Held**
SIC: 2851 Removers & cleaners

(G-11660)
COLOSSAL CUPCAKES
1060 Abbieshire Ave (44107-1238)
PHONE.................................216 322-7656
Kelly Kandah, *Manager*
EMP: 4
SALES (est): 191.4K **Privately Held**
SIC: 2051 Bread, cake & related products

(G-11661)
CURRY COPY CENTER OF LAKEWOOD
14528 Detroit Ave (44107-4317)
PHONE.................................216 521-5775
Fax: 216 521-5880
Dennis Little, *President*
EMP: 3
SQ FT: 900
SALES: 220K **Privately Held**
SIC: 2752 7334 Commercial printing, offset; photocopying & duplicating services

(G-11662)
DISCOUNT COMPUTER PARTS
Also Called: Cpu Satellite Systems
16500 Detroit Ave (44107-3628)
PHONE.................................216 228-4949
Fax: 216 228-5040
Candace Lutian, *Vice Pres*
Patricia Lutian, *Vice Pres*
Bob Lutian, *Manager*
Sera Wilczy, *Manager*
EMP: 6
SALES: 500K **Privately Held**
WEB: www.budgetcables.com
SIC: 3575 5045 Computer terminals, monitors & components; computers, peripherals & software

(G-11663)
FENIX MAGNETICS INC
1360 W Clifton Blvd (44107-3365)
PHONE.................................415 308-0134
Douglas Kirkpatrick, *CEO*
David Matthiesen, *Chief Engr*
Joshua Silber, *Treasurer*
EMP: 3
SQ FT: 1,000
SALES (est): 137.9K **Privately Held**
SIC: 3499 8731 Magnets, permanent: metallic; commercial physical research; energy research

(G-11664)
FERRY CAP & SET SCREW COMPANY (DH)
13300 Bramley Ave (44107-6248)
PHONE.................................216 649-7400
Joseph Mc Auliffe, *President*
Gerald O Mullin, *Corp Secy*
Daniel Baatz, *Draft/Design*
Donald E Johnson, *VP Sales*
Brock Massullo, *Sales Mgr*
▲ EMP: 175
SQ FT: 130,000
SALES (est): 88.8MM **Privately Held**
WEB: www.ferrycap.com
SIC: 3452 Bolts, nuts, rivets & washers; bolts, metal; nuts, metal; screws, metal
HQ: Fastentech, Inc.
8500 Normandale Lake Blvd
Minneapolis MN 55437
952 921-2090

(G-11665)
GLASS FABRICATORS INC
2160 Halstead Ave (44107-6244)
P.O. Box 347251, Cleveland (44134-7251)
PHONE.................................216 529-1919
Fax: 216 529-1922
EMP: 5
SQ FT: 28,000
SALES: 1MM **Privately Held**
SIC: 3211 Fabricates Glass

(G-11666)
HARBRO LLC
18615 Detroit Ave Ste 203 (44107-3221)
PHONE.................................810 229-4755
Fax: 810 227-1659
Mark Hartwell,
Lisa Hartwell,
Marla Hartwell,
Mike Hartwell,
Greg Heslin,
EMP: 6
SQ FT: 100,000
SALES (est): 560K **Privately Held**
WEB: www.harbrollc.com
SIC: 2752 Playing cards, lithographed

(G-11667)
HAWTHORNE WIRE LTD
13000 Athens Ave Ste 101 (44107-6233)
PHONE.................................216 712-4747
Christopher Whiting, *President*
Suzanne Sorige, *Accountant*
EMP: 13 EST: 2005
SALES (est): 2MM **Privately Held**
SIC: 3315 Wire & fabricated wire products

(G-11668)
HAWTHORNE WIRE SERVICES LTD
13000 Athens Ave Ste 101 (44107-6233)
PHONE.................................216 712-4747
Christopher Whiting, *Principal*
EMP: 5
SALES (est): 909.6K **Privately Held**
SIC: 3315 Steel wire & related products

(G-11669)
INITIALLY YOURS
15028 Madison Ave (44107-4014)
PHONE.................................216 228-4478
Gary Galauner, *Owner*
Richard Ebert, *Co-Owner*
Andy Hess, *Co-Owner*
EMP: 3
SALES: 60K **Privately Held**
WEB: www.initiallyyoursengravers.com
SIC: 5999 2395 Trophies & plaques; decorative & novelty stitching, for the trade

(G-11670)
JOE THE PRINTER GUY LLC
1590 Parkwood Rd (44107-4739)
PHONE.................................216 651-3880
Joseph E McHugh, *Principal*
EMP: 6 EST: 2008
SALES (est): 748.8K **Privately Held**
SIC: 2752 Commercial printing, lithographic

(G-11671)
LAKE ERIE INDUSTRIES LLC
13000 Athens Ave Ste 101 (44107-6233)
P.O. Box 771392 (44107-0057)
PHONE.................................216 255-1867
Hugh J Campbell,
▲ EMP: 4
SALES: 750K **Privately Held**
SIC: 3451 Screw machine products

(G-11672)
LAKEWOOD OBSERVER INC
14900 Detroit Ave Ste 205 (44107-3922)
PHONE.................................216 712-7070
Jim O'Bryan, *Principal*
EMP: 7
SALES (est): 363.1K **Privately Held**
SIC: 2711 Newspapers, publishing & printing

(G-11673)
MADISON PRESS INC
1381 Summit Ave (44107-2495)
PHONE.................................216 521-3789
Alton Willcox, *President*

GEOGRAPHIC

Frank Underwood, *Admin Sec*
Dawn Auzle, *Administration*
EMP: 4
SQ FT: 1,500
SALES (est): 386.2K **Privately Held**
WEB: www.madisonpress.net
SIC: 2759 Letterpress printing

(G-11674)
MALLEYS CANDIES (PA)
Also Called: Malley's Chocolates
1685 Victoria Ave (44107-4054)
PHONE...............................216 362-8700
Fax: 216 265-2989
William Malley, *President*
Mike Malley, *Principal*
Daniel Malley, *Vice Pres*
William McConnville, *Vice Pres*
Elisa Bender, *Manager*
▲ **EMP:** 93
SQ FT: 60,000
SALES (est): 55.8MM **Privately Held**
WEB: www.malleys.com
SIC: 5441 5451 2064 2068 Candy; nuts;
ice cream (packaged); candy bars, includ-
ing chocolate covered bars; chocolate
candy, except solid chocolate; nuts: dried,
dehydrated, salted or roasted; ice cream
& ice milk; chocolate & cocoa products

(G-11675)
MCGAW TECHNOLOGY INC
17439 Lake Ave (44107-1147)
P.O. Box 26268, Cleveland (44126-0268)
PHONE...............................216 521-3490
Mike McGraw, *President*
EMP: 3
SALES (est): 500K **Privately Held**
WEB: www.mcgawtech.com
SIC: 7372 Prepackaged software

(G-11676)
NORTON INDUSTRIES INC
1366 W 117th St (44107-3011)
PHONE...............................888 357-2345
Fax: 216 228-9065
Jack E Norton, *President*
Karen Norton, *Corp Secy*
Mary P Norton, *Vice Pres*
Alan Rhea, *Vice Pres*
Jackie Norton, *Manager*
EMP: 15
SQ FT: 30,000
SALES (est): 3.6MM **Privately Held**
WEB: www.nortonceilings.com
SIC: 3646 2541 Ceiling systems, lumi-
nous; store fixtures, wood; display fix-
tures, wood

(G-11677)
PROCOMSOL LTD
13001 Athens Ave Ste 220 (44107-6246)
PHONE...............................216 221-1550
Jeffrey A Dobos, *Principal*
Irena Wasylyk, *Sales Staff*
EMP: 5
SALES (est): 910.6K **Privately Held**
SIC: 3661 3695 Modems; computer soft-
ware tape & disks: blank, rigid & floppy

(G-11678)
RAD-CON INC (PA)
Also Called: Entec International Systems
13001 Athens Ave Ste 300 (44107-6246)
PHONE...............................440 871-5720
Fax: 440 871-2948
David R Blackman, *President*
Christopher Messina, *President*
Michael McDonald, *Vice Pres*
Sean McGreer, *Vice Pres*
Christopher J Messina, *Vice Pres*
EMP: 26
SQ FT: 6,000
SALES: 10MM **Privately Held**
WEB: www.rad-con.com
SIC: 8711 3567 Engineering services; in-
dustrial furnaces & ovens

(G-11679)
SENTRY PROTECTION LLC
Also Called: Sentry Protection Products
16927 Detroit Ave Ste 3 (44107-3642)
PHONE...............................216 228-3200
James Ryan, *Mng Member*
▼ **EMP:** 5 **EST:** 1998
SQ FT: 1,500

SALES (est): 959.2K **Privately Held**
WEB: www.sentrypro.com
SIC: 3089 Molding primary plastic

(G-11680)
TODD SMITH PRODUCTS
Also Called: Smith, Todd Products
13001 Athens Ave Ste 203 (44107-6245)
PHONE...............................216 529-0525
Todd Smith, *Owner*
▲ **EMP:** 4
SQ FT: 6,000
SALES (est): 325.4K **Privately Held**
SIC: 3089 3944 Plastic processing;
games, toys & children's vehicles

(G-11681)
VOLL HOCKEY INC
11820 Edgewater Dr # 418 (44107-1798)
P.O. Box 418 (44107-0418)
PHONE...............................216 521-4625
Gregory Voloshen, *President*
Ann Miholovic, *Manager*
EMP: 3
SQ FT: 250
SALES: 10K **Privately Held**
SIC: 3949 Sporting & athletic goods

(G-11682)
WONDERFUL FAILURE LLC
2140 Bunts Rd (44107-6151)
PHONE...............................440 666-0919
Raymonad Harris,
Anthony Grimaldi,
Devin Lumley,
EMP: 3
SALES (est): 94.7K **Privately Held**
SIC: 7372 7389 Home entertainment com-
puter software;

Lancaster
Fairfield County

(G-11683)
ACCURATE MECHANICAL INC
2257 W Fair Ave (43130-8821)
EMP: 40
SALES (corp-wide): 14.8MM **Privately Held**
SIC: 5074 5063 3499 1711 Heating
equipment (hydronic); electrical supplies;
aerosol valves, metal; septic system construction
PA: Accurate Mechanical, Inc.
3001 River Rd
Chillicothe OH
740 775-5005

(G-11684)
AMERICAN NDT INCORPORATED
671 E Walnut St (43130-3947)
PHONE...............................740 687-1321
Fax: 740 687-5276
C A Covington Jr, *President*
Joe Marie, *General Mgr*
Joseph S Donchess, *Principal*
M G Wood, *Principal*
J R Grace, *Vice Pres*
EMP: 18
SQ FT: 5,000
SALES (est): 3.8MM **Privately Held**
WEB: www.americanndtinc.com
SIC: 3829 Measuring & controlling devices

(G-11685)
AMERICAN PENNEKAMP MFG INC
1495 Longwood Dr Ne (43130-1373)
PHONE...............................740 687-0096
Fax: 740 687-0725
Robert Muckensturm, *Manager*
EMP: 3
SALES (corp-wide): 1.8MM **Privately Held**
SIC: 3496 Conveyor belts
PA: American Pennekamp Mfg, Inc
2502 Shelburn Rd
Millville NJ
856 327-5290

(G-11686)
ANCHI INC
Also Called: Anchor Hocking
1115 W 5th Ave (43130-2938)
PHONE...............................740 653-2527
Mark R Eichhorn, *CEO*
Kenny Hall, *Opers Staff*
Steve Chovan, *Controller*
Dan Bender, *VP Human Res*
Mike Ghere, *Manager*
◆ **EMP:** 1500
SALES (est): 154.9MM
SALES (corp-wide): 526.1MM **Privately Held**
SIC: 3231 Products of purchased glass
HQ: Anchor Hocking, Llc
519 N Pierce Ave
Lancaster OH 43130
740 681-6478

(G-11687)
ANCHOR HOCKING LLC (HQ)
Also Called: Anchor Hocking Company, The
519 N Pierce Ave (43130-2969)
PHONE...............................740 681-6478
Fax: 740 687-2977
Mark Eichhorn, *President*
John McDonough, *Vice Chairman*
Bert Filice, *Senior VP*
Joe Sundberg, *Senior VP*
Greg Stark, *Plant Mgr*
◆ **EMP:** 1200
SALES (est): 362.5MM
SALES (corp-wide): 526.1MM **Privately Held**
WEB: www.anchor.com
SIC: 3229 3089 3411 3221 Tableware,
glass or glass ceramic; cooking utensils,
glass or glass ceramic; cups, plastic, ex-
cept foam; plates, plastic; bottle caps,
molded plastic; metal cans; glass contain-
ers
PA: Everyware Global, Inc.
519 N Pierce Ave
Lancaster OH 43130
740 687-2500

(G-11688)
ANCHOR HOCKING CONSMR GL CORP
1115 W 5th Ave (43130-2900)
PHONE...............................740 653-2527
Mark Eichorn, *President*
Tim Riddle, *Info Tech Mgr*
Ronald Moneypenny, *Technician*
EMP: 7
SALES (est): 1.5MM **Privately Held**
SIC: 3229 Glassware, art or decorative

(G-11689)
ANCHOR HOCKING CORPORATION
1115 W 5th Ave (43130-2900)
PHONE...............................740 681-6461
Fax: 740 681-6040
Mark Eichorn, *Principal*
Jason Shepard, *Safety Mgr*
Clarence R Davenpot, *Treasurer*
William T Alldredge, *VP Finance*
Stacy Sherwood, *Manager*
◆ **EMP:** 64
SALES (est): 18MM **Privately Held**
SIC: 3211 Building glass, flat

(G-11690)
B & T WELDING AND MACHINE CO
423 S Mount Pleasant Ave (43130-3913)
P.O. Box 987 (43130-0987)
PHONE...............................740 687-1908
Fax: 740 687-9116
Alvin R Brown, *President*
Scott Brown, *General Mgr*
Patricia Brown, *Vice Pres*
Darlene Baker, *Treasurer*
EMP: 6
SQ FT: 8,500
SALES (est): 733.2K **Privately Held**
SIC: 3599 Machine shop, jobbing & repair

(G-11691)
BAINTER MACHINING COMPANY (PA)
1230 Rainbow Dr Ne (43130-1137)
PHONE...............................740 653-2422

Fax: 740 756-7015
Daniel A Bainter, *President*
Reda L Bainter, *Corp Secy*
EMP: 9
SQ FT: 2,000
SALES: 600K **Privately Held**
SIC: 3444 3599 Sheet metalwork; ma-
chine shop, jobbing & repair

(G-11692)
BROOKE PRINTERS INC
Also Called: First Impressions Printing
358 Lincoln Ave Ste C (43130-3747)
PHONE...............................614 235-6800
Gary N Brooke, *President*
EMP: 3
SQ FT: 1,800
SALES: 250K **Privately Held**
SIC: 2752 7334 Commercial printing, off-
set; photocopying & duplicating services

(G-11693)
BUCKEYE READY-MIX LLC
Fairfield Concrete
1750 Logan Langster Rd (43130-9001)
PHONE...............................740 654-4423
Dick Dalrymple, *Plant Mgr*
Jerry Culp, *Manager*
EMP: 15
SALES (corp-wide): 42.4MM **Privately Held**
WEB: www.buckeyereadymix.com
SIC: 3273 Ready-mixed concrete
PA: Buckeye Ready-Mix, Llc
7657 Taylor Rd Sw
Reynoldsburg OH 43068
614 575-2132

(G-11694)
C J KRAFT ENTERPRISES INC
Also Called: Bay Packing
301 S Maple St (43130-4406)
PHONE...............................740 653-9606
Fax: 740 653-9515
Kathleen Kraft, *President*
David Kraft, *Vice Pres*
Karen Kraft, *Admin Sec*
EMP: 21
SQ FT: 2,000
SALES (est): 1.7MM **Privately Held**
SIC: 5411 2011 5148 Grocery stores;
meat packing plants; fruits, fresh; vegeta-
bles, fresh

(G-11695)
CAMERON INTERNATIONAL CORP
471 Quarry Rd Se (43130-8272)
PHONE...............................740 654-4260
EMP: 8 **Privately Held**
SIC: 3533 Oil & gas field machinery
HQ: Cameron International Corporation
4646 W Sam Houston Pkwy N
Houston TX 77041

(G-11696)
CARELESS HEART ENTERPRISES (PA)
600 N Columbus St (43130-2535)
PHONE...............................740 654-9999
Mason Reta, *Principal*
EMP: 7
SALES (est): 528K **Privately Held**
SIC: 3949 Skateboards

(G-11697)
CITY OF LANCASTER
Also Called: Lancaster Municipal Gas
1424 Campground Rd (43130-9503)
PHONE...............................740 687-6670
Fax: 740 653-5708
Michael R Pettit, *Superintendent*
Bill Burrows, *Superintendent*
Cheryl K Lott, *Controller*
Jeff Gerken, *Manager*
Mike Courtney, *Director*
EMP: 25 **Privately Held**
WEB: www.ci.lancaster.oh.us
SIC: 1311 4924 Crude petroleum & natu-
ral gas; natural gas distribution
PA: City Of Lancaster
104 E Main St
Lancaster OH 43130
740 687-6617

▲ = Import ▼=Export
◆ =Import/Export

(G-11698)
COMPLETE FILTER MEDIA LLC
1000 Mcgrery Rd Se (43130-7854)
PHONE................................740 438-0929
Mike Beier,
EMP: 45
SALES (est): 1.7MM Privately Held
SIC: 3564 Filters, air: furnaces, air condi-
tioning equipment, etc.

(G-11699)
CONSOLIDATED GRAPHICS INC
Also Called: Cyril-Scott Company The
3950 Lancaster New Lxngtn (43130-7899)
PHONE................................740 654-2112
Chad Stephenson, President
Kitty Vanatta, Human Res Mgr
EMP: 155
SALES (corp-wide): 6.9B Publicly Held
SIC: 2759 Commercial printing
HQ: Consolidated Graphics, Inc.
5858 Westheimer Rd # 200
Houston TX 77057
713 787-0977

(G-11700)
CRISTS MACHINING INC
Also Called: CMI
1910 Hamburg Rd Sw (43130-8904)
PHONE................................740 653-0041
Arthur Crist, President
Pamala Crist, Treasurer
EMP: 3
SQ FT: 2,000
SALES: 120K Privately Held
SIC: 3599 Machine shop, jobbing & repair

(G-11701)
**CROWN CLOSURES
MACHINERY**
1765 W Fair Ave (43130-2325)
PHONE................................740 681-6593
Fax: 740 681-6527
John Conway, CEO
Sheila Heath, Human Res Mgr
Amanda Marutz, Officer
▲ EMP: 40
SALES (est): 6.4MM
SALES (corp-wide): 8.2B Publicly Held
WEB: www.crownholdings.net
SIC: 3565 Packaging machinery
PA: Crown Holdings Inc.
1 Crown Way
Philadelphia PA 19154
215 698-5100

(G-11702)
CROWN CORK & SEAL USA INC
940 Mill Park Dr (43130-9576)
PHONE................................740 681-3000
Fax: 740 681-3001
Ed Schott, Manager
Shane Clemons, Network Tech
Linda R Miller, Executive
Kim Graves, Administration
EMP: 90
SALES (corp-wide): 8.2B Publicly Held
WEB: www.crowncork.com
SIC: 3089 3466 3411 Closures, plastic;
closures, stamped metal; jar tops &
crowns, stamped metal; metal cans
HQ: Crown Cork & Seal Usa, Inc.
1 Crown Way
Philadelphia PA 19154
215 698-5100

(G-11703)
CROWN CORK & SEAL USA INC
1765 W Fair Ave (43130-2325)
PHONE................................740 681-6593
Shelia Heath, Branch Mgr
EMP: 35
SALES (corp-wide): 8.2B Publicly Held
WEB: www.crowncork.com
SIC: 3411 Metal cans
HQ: Crown Cork & Seal Usa, Inc.
1 Crown Way
Philadelphia PA 19154
215 698-5100

(G-11704)
D K MANUFACTURING
2118 Commerce St (43130-9363)
PHONE................................740 654-5566
Daniel Keifer, President
Ginny King, Human Res Dir

Art Bentley, Manager
EMP: 90
SALES (est): 14.9MM Privately Held
SIC: 3089 Injection molded finished plastic
products

(G-11705)
**DEVAULT MACHINE & MOULD
CO LLC**
Also Called: General Machine and Mould Co
2294 Commerce St (43130-9363)
P.O. Box 785 (43130-0785)
PHONE................................740 654-5925
Fax: 740 654-4032
Terris E Devault, Mng Member
EMP: 7 EST: 1966
SQ FT: 5,000
SALES (est): 1.1MM Privately Held
WEB: www.genmach.com
SIC: 3599 Machine & other job shop work

(G-11706)
DIAMOND ELECTRONICS INC
Also Called: Honeywell
1858 Cedar Hill Rd (43130-4178)
PHONE................................740 652-9222
Fax: 740 756-4237
George K Broady, Ch of Bd
Patrick Muroni, Managing Dir
JP Ashooh, Vice Pres
John Cannon, Vice Pres
Andy Chapman, Vice Pres
EMP: 118
SQ FT: 72,000
SALES (est): 9.8MM Privately Held
SIC: 3663 Television closed circuit equip-
ment

(G-11707)
DIAMOND POWER INTL INC
Also Called: Diamond Electronics
2530 E Main St (43130-8490)
PHONE................................740 687-4001
Fax: 740 687-4201
Karyo Arizumi, General Mgr
Ron Burris, Manager
EMP: 13
SALES (corp-wide): 1.5B Publicly Held
WEB: www.diamondpower.com
SIC: 3823 Industrial instrmnts msrmnt dis-
play/control process variable
HQ: Diamond Power International, Inc.
2600 E Main St
Lancaster OH 43130
740 687-6500

(G-11708)
DIAMOND POWER INTL INC (DH)
Also Called: Diamond Power Specialty
2600 E Main St (43130-9366)
P.O. Box 415 (43130-0415)
PHONE................................740 687-6500
Fax: 740 687-4229
Eileen M Competti, President
Ron Burris, Project Mgr
Garfield Bryant, Facilities Mgr
James Vines, Purch Mgr
Margaret Coussa, Senior Buyer
◆ EMP: 277
SALES (est): 133.6MM
SALES (corp-wide): 1.5B Publicly Held
WEB: www.diamondpower.com
SIC: 3564 Blowers & fans
HQ: The Babcock & Wilcox Company
20 S Van Buren Ave
Barberton OH 44203
330 753-4511

(G-11709)
DITTMAR SALES AND SERVICE
132 W 6th Ave (43130-2505)
PHONE................................740 653-7933
Fax: 740 653-7602
Thomas F Daubenmire, Owner
EMP: 5
SQ FT: 7,600
SALES: 900K Privately Held
SIC: 3261 5251 5261 3432 Flush tanks,
vitreous china; drinking fountains, vitreous
china; chainsaws; nurseries & garden
centers; plumbing fixture fittings & trim

(G-11710)
**DK MANUFACTURING
LANCASTER INC**
2118 Commerce St (43130-9363)
PHONE................................740 654-5566
Daniel Keifer, President
Sharon Adaire, Finance
Art Bantley, Manager
Jim Greenley, Manager
EMP: 85
SALES (est): 10.4MM
SALES (corp-wide): 24.3MM Privately
Held
SIC: 3089 Injection molded finished plastic
products
PA: Dak Enterprises, Inc.
18062 Timber Trails Rd
Marysville OH 43040
740 828-3291

(G-11711)
EVERYWARE GLOBAL INC (PA)
Also Called: Oneida Group, The
519 N Pierce Ave (43130-2927)
PHONE................................740 687-2500
Patrick Lockwood-Taylor, CEO
Daniel J Collin, Ch of Bd
Thomas J Baldwin, Vice Ch Bd
Erika Schoenberger, Principal
Anthony Reisig, Senior VP
EMP: 59
SALES (est): 526.1MM Privately Held
SIC: 3469 3089 Kitchen fixtures & equip-
ment, porcelain enameled; plastic
kitchenware, tableware & houseware

(G-11712)
**FABRICATED PACKAGING MTLS
INC**
296 Quarry Rd Se (43130)
PHONE................................740 681-1750
Fax: 740 687-3671
Dale Statter, Manager
EMP: 5
SALES (corp-wide): 5.6MM Privately
Held
SIC: 3086 Packaging & shipping materials,
foamed plastic
PA: Fabricated Packaging Materials, Inc.
2109 Commerce St
Lancaster OH 43130
740 654-3492

(G-11713)
**FABRICATED PACKAGING MTLS
INC (PA)**
Also Called: F P M
2109 Commerce St (43130-9363)
PHONE................................740 654-3492
Jeff Gross, President
Dale Stalter, Treasurer
Linda Osborne, Controller
Jennifer Godby, Office Mgr
EMP: 13
SALES: 5.6MM Privately Held
SIC: 3086 Packaging & shipping materials,
foamed plastic

(G-11714)
**FAIRFIELD SCREW PRODUCTS
CO**
505 Slocum St (43130-2952)
PHONE................................740 653-7627
Fax: 740 653-7628
Sheryl A Nutter, President
Dennis R Monnett, Vice Pres
Russell E King III, Admin Sec
EMP: 5 EST: 1945
SQ FT: 7,200
SALES: 367.1K Privately Held
SIC: 3451 Screw machine products

(G-11715)
FAIRFIELD WOODWORKS LTD
1612 E Main St (43130-3472)
PHONE................................740 689-1953
Fax: 740 689-1983
Ron Smith, President
Ben Smith, Vice Pres
Jed Smith, Vice Pres
EMP: 7
SQ FT: 5,000

SALES: 500K Privately Held
SIC: 2434 2431 Wood kitchen cabinets;
moldings & baseboards, ornamental &
trim

(G-11716)
FEDEX CORPORATION
1612 N Memorial Dr (43130-1631)
PHONE................................740 687-0334
Fax: 740 687-0297
EMP: 4
SALES (corp-wide): 47.4B Publicly Held
SIC: 2752 Lithographic Commercial Print-
ing
PA: Fedex Corporation
942 Shady Grove Rd S
Memphis TN 38120
901 818-7500

(G-11717)
FUNCTIONAL IMAGING LTD
2368 Pine Crest Dr (43130-7731)
PHONE................................740 689-2466
Theresa Spiers, Partner
Carla Conkey, Partner
EMP: 3
SALES (est): 253.2K Privately Held
SIC: 2759 3299 Thermography; images,
small: gypsum, clay or papier mache

(G-11718)
GANNETT CO INC
Also Called: Lancaster Eagle Gazette
138 W Chestnut St (43130-4308)
P.O. Box 848 (43130-0848)
PHONE................................740 654-1321
Fax: 740 681-4456
Rick Zabrak, Branch Mgr
EMP: 50
SALES (corp-wide): 3B Publicly Held
WEB: www.gannett.com
SIC: 2711 Newspapers: publishing only,
not printed on site
PA: Gannett Co., Inc.
7950 Jones Branch Dr
Mc Lean VA 22102
703 854-6000

(G-11719)
GHP II LLC (DH)
Also Called: Anchor Hocking Indus GL Div
1115 W 5th Ave (43130-2938)
PHONE................................740 687-2500
Fax: 800 848-0082
Mark Eichorn, CEO
Mark Hedstrom, CFO
Larry Reed, Supervisor
George Hamilton,
▼ EMP: 200 EST: 1905
SQ FT: 41,900
SALES (est): 148MM
SALES (corp-wide): 526.1MM Privately
Held
WEB: www.anchorhocking.com
SIC: 3229 3089 3411 3221 Tableware,
glass or glass ceramic; cooking utensils,
glass or glass ceramic; cups, plastic, ex-
cept foam; plates, plastic; bottle caps,
molded plastic; bowl covers, plastic; metal
cans; glass containers
HQ: Anchor Hocking, Llc
519 N Pierce Ave
Lancaster OH 43130
740 681-6478

(G-11720)
GHP II LLC
2893 W Fair Ave (43130-8993)
P.O. Box 600 (43130-0600)
PHONE................................740 681-6825
Fax: 740 681-6842
Tom Gilligan, Manager
EMP: 280
SQ FT: 1,300,000
SALES (corp-wide): 526.1MM Privately
Held
WEB: www.anchorhocking.com
SIC: 5023 3231 China; glassware; prod-
ucts of purchased glass
HQ: Ghp Ii, Llc
1115 W 5th Ave
Lancaster OH 43130
740 687-2500

GEOGRAPHIC

(G-11721)
GLASFLOSS INDUSTRIES INC (PA)
2168 Commerce St (43130-9363)
P.O. Box 789, Desoto TX (75123-0789)
PHONE...............................740 687-1100
Fax: 740 687-1145
Scott Lange, *President*
Cheryl Thompson, *Principal*
Donald Kingston, *Vice Pres*
Janet Peterson, *Purchasing*
Bob Burnette, *Sales Mgr*
EMP: 250 EST: 1956
SALES (est): 45MM **Privately Held**
WEB: www.glasflossindustries.com
SIC: 3564 Filters, air: furnaces, air condi-
tioning equipment, etc.

(G-11722)
HANGER PRSTHETCS & ORTHO INC
111 N Ewing St (43130-3364)
PHONE...............................740 654-1884
Curt Hoellrich, *Manager*
Kurt Hoellrich, *Manager*
EMP: 4
SALES (corp-wide): 460MM **Publicly Held**
SIC: 5999 3842 Orthopedic & prosthesis
applications; prosthetic appliances
HQ: Hanger Prosthetics & Orthotics, Inc.
10910 Domain Dr Ste 300
Austin TX 78758
512 777-3800

(G-11723)
INCESSANT SOFTWARE INC
8577 Ohio Wesleyan Ct Nw (43130-9329)
PHONE...............................614 206-2211
Al Pruden, *President*
EMP: 9
SALES (est): 670K **Privately Held**
WEB: www.incessant.com
SIC: 7372 Prepackaged software

(G-11724)
JOHNSON TOOL DISTRIBUTORS
1059 Rockmill Rd Nw (43130-9517)
PHONE...............................740 653-6959
Fax: 740 756-9203
Gary Johnson, *Owner*
Molly Hines, *Manager*
EMP: 5
SQ FT: 7,000
SALES: 142K **Privately Held**
SIC: 3524 5083 Lawn & garden equip-
ment; lawn & garden machinery & equip-
ment

(G-11725)
LANCASTER WEST SIDE COAL CO (PA)
700 Van Buren Ave (43130-2339)
PHONE...............................740 862-4713
Jerry H Fahrer, *President*
Mary K Cann, *Vice Pres*
Bruce Fahrer, *Treasurer*
William Cann, *Admin Sec*
EMP: 12 EST: 1925
SQ FT: 1,600
SALES (est): 1.2MM **Privately Held**
SIC: 3273 5211 5032 Ready-mixed con-
crete; lumber & other building materials;
brick, stone & related material

(G-11726)
LITHCHEM INTL TOXCO INC
265 Quarry Rd Se (43130-8271)
PHONE...............................740 653-6290
Fax: 740 653-6373
Ed Green, *Principal*
EMP: 3
SALES (est): 340K **Privately Held**
SIC: 3691 Storage batteries

(G-11727)
MARGO TOOL TECHNOLOGY INC
2616 Setter Ct Nw (43130-9151)
PHONE...............................740 653-8115
Fax: 740 653-6255
John Porter, *President*
Jeff Ellis, *Corp Secy*
Gus Spohn, *Project Engr*
EMP: 10

SQ FT: 7,500
SALES (est): 1.8MM **Privately Held**
SIC: 3599 Custom machinery

(G-11728)
MEMAC INDUSTRIES INC
324 Quarry Rd Se (43130-8055)
P.O. Box 231 (43130-0231)
PHONE...............................740 653-4815
Fax: 740 653-5291
Carol L Figgins-Clarke, *President*
Danny Clarke, *Vice Pres*
EMP: 8
SQ FT: 5,900
SALES (est): 1.2MM **Privately Held**
WEB: www.memacindustries.com
SIC: 3599 Machine shop, jobbing & repair

(G-11729)
MID-WEST FABRICATING CO
Also Called: Rock Mill Division
3115 W Fair Ave (43130-9568)
PHONE...............................740 681-4411
Fax: 740 681-4433
Chad Shuttleworth, *Branch Mgr*
Lonnie White, *Manager*
EMP: 9
SALES (corp-wide): 28.3MM **Privately Held**
WEB: www.midwestfab.com
SIC: 3714 3452 Tie rods, motor vehicle;
bolts, metal
PA: Mid-West Fabricating Co.
313 N Johns St
Amanda OH 43102
740 969-4411

(G-11730)
MINUTMAN PRESS FRFELD CNTY LLC
135 N Columbus St (43130-3704)
PHONE...............................740 689-1992
Fax: 740 689-1993
Pam O'Connor, *Human Resources*
Dan O'Connor,
Dan Oconnor,
EMP: 3
SQ FT: 1,400
SALES (est): 362.7K **Privately Held**
SIC: 2752 Commercial printing, litho-
graphic

(G-11731)
MONDI AKROSIL LLC
3165 Wilson Rd (43130-8144)
PHONE...............................740 653-4102
Shawn Someday, *General Mgr*
Spencer Malcolm, *Plant Mgr*
Kristen Watters, *HR Admin*
Alyson Cupp, *Manager*
EMP: 120 **Privately Held**
SIC: 2679 Paper products, converted
HQ: Mondi Akrosil, Llc
7201 108th St
Pleasant Prairie WI 53158
262 947-3371

(G-11732)
NAUMAN COMMUNICATIONS INC
Also Called: Nauman Outdoor Advertising Co
743 S Columbus St (43130-4663)
P.O. Box 726 (43130-0726)
PHONE...............................740 654-0084
Fax: 740 654-6988
Jay Nauman, *CEO*
Jim Harmon, *Accounts Exec*
EMP: 6
SQ FT: 800
SALES (est): 644.9K **Privately Held**
WEB: www.naumanoutdoor.com
SIC: 3993 Signs & advertising specialties

(G-11733)
NEIL R SCHOLL INC
54 Snoke Hill Rd Ne (43130-9315)
PHONE...............................740 653-6593
Neil R Scholl, *President*
Betty Scholl, *Vice Pres*
Richard Scholl, *Chief Engr*
EMP: 10
SQ FT: 2,000
SALES (est): 929.7K **Privately Held**
SIC: 3599 5084 Custom machinery; indus-
trial machinery & equipment

(G-11734)
NORTH END PRESS INCORPORATED
235 S Columbus St (43130-4315)
PHONE...............................740 653-6514
Fax: 740 653-7080
Richard Benadum, *President*
Brad A Benadum, *Vice Pres*
Greg Benadum, *Vice Pres*
EMP: 20 EST: 1933
SQ FT: 55,000
SALES (est): 1.2MM **Privately Held**
SIC: 2789 Bookbinding & related work

(G-11735)
NORWESCO INC
3111 Wilson Rd (43130-8144)
PHONE...............................740 654-6402
Fax: 740 654-6724
Darrin Dittman, *Manager*
EMP: 20
SQ FT: 15,000
SALES (corp-wide): 49MM **Privately Held**
WEB: www.ncmmolding.com
SIC: 3089 Plastic & fiberglass tanks
PA: Norwesco, Inc.
4365 Steiner St
Saint Bonifacius MN 55375
952 446-1945

(G-11736)
OHIO MATTRESS
1408 Ety Rd Nw (43130-7745)
PHONE...............................740 739-8219
Lee Winters, *Principal*
EMP: 6 EST: 2012
SALES (est): 893.2K **Privately Held**
SIC: 2515 Mattresses & foundations

(G-11737)
ONE-WRITE COMPANY
3750 Lancaster New Lexing (43130-9314)
PHONE...............................740 654-2128
Fax: 740 654-2260
Norman Boyd, *President*
Charlie Staten, *Foreman/Supr*
Debbie Brown, *Manager*
Gene Hennessy, *Manager*
▼ EMP: 28
SALES (est): 4.3MM **Privately Held**
WEB: www.onewriteco.com
SIC: 2752 Commercial printing, offset

(G-11738)
PHILLIPS AWNING CO
2052 W Fair Ave (43130-9672)
PHONE...............................740 653-2433
Patricia Probasco, *Owner*
EMP: 3
SQ FT: 1,800
SALES (est): 240K **Privately Held**
SIC: 5211 2394 3444 Jalousies; awnings,
fabric: made from purchased materials;
sheet metalwork

(G-11739)
PHOENIX/ELECTROTEK LLC
890 Mill Park Dr (43130-2572)
PHONE...............................740 681-1412
Meredith Englehart, *Sales Engr*
Cindy Webb, *Office Mgr*
Duane Astrauskas, *Mng Member*
EMP: 25
SALES: 1.7MM
SALES (corp-wide): 2.5MM **Privately Held**
SIC: 2298 Ropes & fiber cables
PA: Phoenix/Edt Inc
1080 Meyerside Dr
Mississauga ON L5T 1
905 678-9400

(G-11740)
PRECISION CNC LLC
1858 Cedar Hill Rd (43130-4178)
PHONE...............................740 689-9009
Bonnie Brehm, *Manager*
Sarah Richardson, *Manager*
Paul Davis, *Executive Asst*
Nathan Hawkins,
EMP: 28
SQ FT: 10,000
SALES (est): 2.7MM **Privately Held**
WEB: www.metalforce.net
SIC: 3549 Metalworking machinery

(G-11741)
PRO-KLEEN INDUSTRIAL SVCS INC
Also Called: Porta-Kleen
1030 Mill Park Dr (43130-9576)
PHONE...............................740 689-1886
Fax: 740 689-1778
Monte Black, *Ch of Bd*
Chad Littrell, *Sales Dir*
Fran Borelli, *Asst Director*
EMP: 45
SALES (est): 8.3MM **Privately Held**
WEB: www.portakleen.com
SIC: 7359 7699 5963 3088 Portable toi-
let rental; septic tank cleaning service;
bottled water delivery; tubs (bath, shower
& laundry), plastic

(G-11742)
PROFESSIONAL SCREEN PRINTING
731 N Pierce Ave (43130-2416)
PHONE...............................740 687-0760
Fax: 740 687-6276
Jeff Uhl, *President*
John Uhl,
EMP: 8
SQ FT: 3,000
SALES (est): 800K **Privately Held**
WEB: www.promotionalproducts-promo-
tionalitems.co
SIC: 7336 2752 Silk screen design; com-
mercial printing, lithographic

(G-11743)
Q2POWER TECHNOLOGIES INC (PA)
1858 Cedar Hill Rd (43130-4178)
PHONE...............................740 415-2073
Christopher Nelson, *CEO*
Kevin Bolin, *Ch of Bd*
Arthur R Batson, *President*
Gerald Fly, *Vice Pres*
Eric Schacht, *Vice Pres*
EMP: 5
SQ FT: 2,500
SALES: 20K **Publicly Held**
SIC: 2842 Specialty cleaning, polishes &
sanitation goods; disinfectants, household
or industrial plant

(G-11744)
R J SILVIA
1235 E Walnut St (43130-4064)
PHONE...............................740 400-4066
Robert Sylvia, *Partner*
Jenna Sylvia, *Partner*
Roberta Sylvia, *Partner*
EMP: 3
SALES (est): 146.3K **Privately Held**
SIC: 3575 Computer terminals, monitors &
components

(G-11745)
RESIDENTIAL ELECTRONIC SVCS
3155 Lancstr Kirkrsvll Nw (43130-8599)
PHONE...............................740 681-9150
Fax: 740 653-7423
Daniel Miller, *President*
EMP: 3 EST: 1998
SALES: 25K **Privately Held**
SIC: 3699 Security devices

(G-11746)
RETRIEV TECHNOLOGIES INC
265 Quarry Rd Se (43130-8271)
PHONE...............................740 653-6290
Ed Green, *Branch Mgr*
Johnny Glassburn, *Manager*
EMP: 100
SALES (corp-wide): 49.9MM **Privately Held**
SIC: 3691 Batteries, rechargeable
PA: Retriev Technologies Incorporated
125 E Commercial St Ste A
Anaheim CA 92801
714 738-8516

(G-11747)
ROBERT ALTEN INC
449 S Ewing St (43130-9400)
P.O. Box 731 (43130-0731)
PHONE...............................740 653-2640
Fax: 740 653-7932

Jan C Alten, *President*
Chris Alten, *General Mgr*
Mary Ann Alten, *Vice Pres*
EMP: 5 **EST:** 1933
SQ FT: 3,000
SALES: 450K **Privately Held**
SIC: 3599 7692 Machine shop, jobbing & repair; welding repair

(G-11748)
ROCKBRIDGE OUTFITTERS
Also Called: Ohio Valley Trading and Exch
2805 Clmbus Lncster Rd Nw (43130-8663)
PHONE......................740 654-1956
Jason Thomason, *President*
EMP: 7
SALES (est): 399.3K **Privately Held**
SIC: 3949 Camping equipment & supplies

(G-11749)
ROCKSIDE WINERY & VINEYARDS LL
2363 Lncster Newark Rd Ne (43130-8200)
PHONE......................740 687-4414
EMP: 4
SALES (est): 306K **Privately Held**
SIC: 2084 Wines, brandy & brandy spirits

(G-11750)
SHELLY COMPANY
Also Called: Shelly Materials
3232 Lgan Lancaster Rd Se (43130-9007)
PHONE......................740 687-4420
Tony Marks, *Manager*
EMP: 14
SALES (corp-wide): 28.6B **Privately Held**
SIC: 1442 Construction sand mining; gravel mining
HQ: Shelly Company
80 Park Dr
Thornville OH 43076
740 246-6315

(G-11751)
SHERIDAN ONE STOP CARRYOUT
1510 Sheridan Dr (43130-1303)
PHONE......................740 687-1300
Eric Molzan, *Owner*
EMP: 7 **EST:** 1981
SALES (est): 394.3K **Privately Held**
SIC: 1311 Crude petroleum & natural gas

(G-11752)
SILVER EXPRESSIONS
1635 River Valley Cir S # 5078 (43130-5712)
PHONE......................740 687-0144
Diane Rosenberger, *Principal*
EMP: 4
SALES (est): 315.2K **Privately Held**
SIC: 3423 Jewelers' hand tools

(G-11753)
SMITH RN SHEET METAL SHOP INC
1312 Campground Rd (43130-9503)
PHONE......................740 653-5011
Fax: 740 653-5009
Patrick Smith, *President*
Sue Smith, *Treasurer*
Doug Franke, *Manager*
Mary Jo Smith, *Admin Sec*
EMP: 25
SQ FT: 1,800
SALES: 3MM **Privately Held**
SIC: 3444 Sheet metalwork

(G-11754)
SOUTHSTERN MACHINING FIELD SVC (PA)
500 Lincoln Ave (43130-4243)
PHONE......................740 689-1147
Fax: 740 689-1148
John Treitmaier, *President*
EMP: 37
SQ FT: 6,500
SALES (est): 5.3MM **Privately Held**
WEB: www.semohio.com
SIC: 3599 Custom machinery

(G-11755)
SRI OHIO INC
1061 Mill Park Dr (43130-9577)
PHONE......................740 653-5800

Bonnita Heston, *Principal*
Matt Tilden, *Business Mgr*
Lisa Jones, *Executive*
▲ **EMP:** 51
SALES (est): 12.6MM **Privately Held**
SIC: 2759 Screen printing

(G-11756)
STELLAR INDUSTRIAL TECH CO
Also Called: Stellar I T Co
1918 York Town Ct (43130-1242)
PHONE......................740 654-7052
Fax: 740 654-7053
Michael Vawter, *President*
Carolyn Vawter, *Vice Pres*
EMP: 4
SQ FT: 1,500
SALES: 300K **Privately Held**
SIC: 8742 4953 3694 Industrial consultant; liquid waste, collection & disposal; distributors, motor vehicle engine

(G-11757)
TOXCO INC
265 Quarry Rd Se (43130-8271)
PHONE......................740 653-6290
Ed Green, *Branch Mgr*
EMP: 71
SALES (corp-wide): 19.5MM **Privately Held**
WEB: www.toxco.com
SIC: 3691 Batteries, rechargeable
PA: Toxco, Inc.
125 E Commercial St Ste A
Anaheim CA 92801
714 738-8516

(G-11758)
TREEHOUSE PRIVATE BRANDS INC
Also Called: Ralston Food
3775 Lanc New Lex Rd Se (43130-9314)
PHONE......................740 654-8880
Fax: 740 681-3216
Alex Ichite, *Opers Mgr*
Kevin Rotsching, *Safety Mgr*
David Dupler, *Purchasing*
Don Eiferd, *QC Dir*
Fred Mendell, *Senior Engr*
EMP: 350
SALES (corp-wide): 6.1B **Publicly Held**
SIC: 2043 Cereal breakfast foods
HQ: Treehouse Private Brands, Inc.
800 Market St Ste 2600
Saint Louis MO 63101
314 877-7300

(G-11759)
TREEHOUSE PRIVATE BRANDS INC
276 Bremen Rd (43130-7873)
PHONE......................740 654-8880
Gary Rodkin, *CEO*
Jennifer Spires, *Manager*
EMP: 8
SALES (corp-wide): 6.1B **Publicly Held**
SIC: 2043 Cereal breakfast foods
HQ: Treehouse Private Brands, Inc.
800 Market St Ste 2600
Saint Louis MO 63101
314 877-7300

(G-11760)
US CORRUGATED INC
1290 Campground Rd (43130-9503)
PHONE......................740 681-1600
Rick Morgan, *General Mgr*
EMP: 107
SQ FT: 314,000
SALES (corp-wide): 36.8MM **Privately Held**
SIC: 2653 Corrugated & solid fiber boxes
PA: Kapstone Container Corporation
95 W Beau St
Washington PA 15301
724 345-2050

(G-11761)
VIC MAR MANUFACTURING INC
Also Called: S&S Manufacturing
730 Lawrence St (43130-9401)
PHONE......................740 687-5434
Fax: 740 687-5331
Stephen R Shumaker, *President*
Lawrence H Smith, *Vice Pres*
EMP: 5

SQ FT: 4,600
SALES: 300K **Privately Held**
SIC: 3599 Machine shop, jobbing & repair

(G-11762)
WIZARD PUBLICATIONS INC
Also Called: Hawaii Revealed
1979 Wilshire Ln Nw (43130-7957)
P.O. Box 991, Lihue HI (96766-0991)
PHONE......................808 821-1214
Andrew Doughty, *President*
EMP: 10
SALES (est): 9.1K **Privately Held**
SIC: 2741 Miscellaneous publishing

(G-11763)
ZEBCO INDUSTRIES INC
211 N Columbus St (43130-3006)
PHONE......................740 654-4510
Fax: 740 654-7130
Kevin Stalter, *President*
Jill Stalter, *Vice Pres*
Madonna Christy, *Admin Sec*
Marcy Roberts, *Admin Sec*
EMP: 19
SQ FT: 128,000
SALES (est): 3.6MM **Privately Held**
WEB: www.zebcoindustries.com
SIC: 3086 5113 2671 Packaging & shipping materials, foamed plastic; industrial & personal service paper; packaging paper & plastics film, coated & laminated

---

Langsville
Meigs County

(G-11764)
DUFF FARM
30762 Old Dexter Rd (45741-9554)
PHONE......................740 742-2182
Robin Duff, *Owner*
EMP: 3
SALES (est): 133.7K **Privately Held**
SIC: 3949 Hooks, fishing

Latham
Pike County

(G-11765)
LATHAM LIMESTONE LLC
6424 State Route 124 (45646-9703)
PHONE......................740 493-2677
Brett Coark, *Office Mgr*
Gerald Lee, *Manager*
Dennis Garrison,
EMP: 8
SQ FT: 500
SALES (est): 555.5K **Privately Held**
SIC: 1422 Limestones, ground

(G-11766)
LATHAM LUMBER & PALLET CO INC
9445 Street Rte 124 (45646)
P.O. Box 147 (45646-0147)
PHONE......................740 493-2707
Fax: 740 493-2287
Karen Chandler, *President*
EMP: 15
SQ FT: 12,000
SALES: 4MM **Privately Held**
SIC: 2499 Mulch, wood & bark

Latty
Paulding County

(G-11767)
AL-CO PRODUCTS INC
485 2nd St (45855)
P.O. Box 74 (45855-0074)
PHONE......................419 399-3867
Fax: 419 399-4702
Russell W Stoller, *President*
Trent Stoller, *Corp Secy*
John F Kohler, *Vice Pres*
Kevin Albright, *Purchasing*
Fredrick Schubert, *Sales Mgr*
EMP: 13

SQ FT: 11,000
SALES (est): 1.5MM
SALES (corp-wide): 50.8MM **Privately Held**
WEB: www.al-coproducts.com
SIC: 3281 3949 2821 2434 Marble, building: cut & shaped; sporting & athletic goods; plastics materials & resins; wood kitchen cabinets
PA: Haviland Drainage Products Co.
100 W Main St
Haviland OH 45851
419 622-4611

Laura
Miami County

(G-11768)
PRESTONS REPAIR & WELDING
11611 State Route 571 (45337-9836)
P.O. Box M (45337-0808)
PHONE......................937 947-1883
Kevin Mote, *President*
EMP: 3
SQ FT: 4,800
SALES (est): 289.6K **Privately Held**
SIC: 7538 7692 General automotive repair shops; automotive welding

---

Laurelville
Hocking County

(G-11769)
C & L ERECTORS & RIGGERS INC
16412 Thompson Ridge Rd (43135-9238)
P.O. Box 98 (43135-0098)
PHONE......................740 332-7185
Fax: 740 332-1038
Chris Riddle, *President*
Craig Riddle, *Vice Pres*
Dale W Riddle, *Shareholder*
EMP: 20
SQ FT: 1,500
SALES (est): 1.8MM **Privately Held**
SIC: 1629 2411 Land clearing contractor; logging; wood chips, produced in the field

(G-11770)
KING CONVEYOR LLC
21397 State Route 180 (43135-9307)
P.O. Box 2455, Brookfield WI (53008-2455)
PHONE......................740 332-6200
Tom Furness, *President*
Randy Ogg, *General Mgr*
Bill Campbell, *Vice Pres*
Vanessa Ogg, *Office Admin*
EMP: 13 **EST:** 2010
SQ FT: 20,000
SALES: 550K
SALES (corp-wide): 1.9MM **Privately Held**
SIC: 3535 Conveyors & conveying equipment
PA: Hilmot Holdings, Inc.
11925 W Carmen Ave
Milwaukee WI 53225
262 544-9960

(G-11771)
OHIO ENERGY ASSETS INC
16276 Long Run Rd (43135-9544)
P.O. Box 377 (43135-0377)
PHONE......................740 332-9511
Fax: 740 332-6296
Nancy Melville, *President*
EMP: 2
SQ FT: 2,400
SALES (est): 1MM **Privately Held**
SIC: 3533 Oil & gas field machinery

(G-11772)
T & D THOMPSON INC
Also Called: Hocking Hills Hardwoods
15952 State Route 56 E (43135-9741)
P.O. Box 88 (43135-0088)
PHONE......................740 332-8515
Fax: 740 332-9663
Terry L Thompson, *President*
David R Thompson, *Vice Pres*
EMP: 50

G E O G R A P H I C

SQ FT: 50,000
SALES (est): 6.9MM Privately Held
WEB: www.hockinghillshardwoods.com
SIC: 2448 2449 2431 2426 Pallets,
wood; wood containers; millwork; hardwood dimension & flooring mills; sawmills
& planing mills, general

Lebanon
Warren County

(G-11773)
**A A A PROFESSIONAL HTG &
COOLG**
535 N Broadway St (45036-1736)
PHONE..............................513 933-0564
Fax: 513 228-0863
Mitch Underwood, *President*
Chris Smith, *Vice Pres*
EMP: 5
SALES (est): 519.2K Privately Held
SIC: 1711 3444 Heating & air conditioning
contractors; ducts, sheet metal

(G-11774)
ADDISONMCKEE INC (PA)
1637 Kingsview Dr (45036-8395)
PHONE..............................513 228-7000
Jim Sabine, *CEO*
Lonnie McGrew, *Vice Pres*
Mike Burnett, *VP Mfg*
Claud Lessard, *CFO*
Nancy A McKee,
▲ EMP: 142
SQ FT: 78,000
SALES: 8MM Privately Held
WEB: www.addisonmckee.com
SIC: 3542 3599 5084 3549 Bending ma-
chines; machine shop, jobbing & repair;
industrial machinery & equipment; metal-
working machinery; rolling mill machinery;
special dies, tools, jigs & fixtures

(G-11775)
**ADVANCED MED INTERFACES
LLC**
950 Mulford Rd (45036-9146)
PHONE..............................937 361-8385
Shawn Grubb, *CEO*
Michale Lakes, *President*
EMP: 3
SALES (est): 201.5K Privately Held
SIC: 3841 7389 Inhalators, surgical &
medical;

(G-11776)
**ADVICS MANUFACTURING OHIO
INC**
1650 Kingsview Dr (45036-8390)
PHONE..............................513 934-0023
Fax: 513 932-9073
Atsuo Matsumoto, *CEO*
Geoffrey J Hearsum, *President*
Dave Bolton, *Vice Pres*
Ron Lipps, *Vice Pres*
Hiro Nakanishi, *Vice Pres*
▲ EMP: 625
SQ FT: 323,000
SALES (est): 201MM
SALES (corp-wide): 27.7B Privately Held
WEB: www.advics-ohio.com
SIC: 3714 Motor vehicle brake systems &
parts
HQ: Advics North America, Inc.
1650 Kingsview Dr
Lebanon OH 45036
513 696-5450

(G-11777)
AEROSERV
603 Norgal Dr Ste B (45036-9382)
PHONE..............................513 932-9227
Steve Michael, *President*
Miranda Paytes, *Info Tech Mgr*
EMP: 10
SQ FT: 14,000
SALES (est): 1MM Privately Held
WEB: www.aeroserv.com
SIC: 3599 Machine shop, jobbing & repair

(G-11778)
ALLEN FIELDS ASSOC INC
3525 Grant Ave Ste D (45036-6431)
PHONE..............................513 228-1010
Fax: 513 228-1011
Raymond Watson, *Owner*
EMP: 6
SALES (est): 728.4K Privately Held
SIC: 3699 5063 Electrical equipment &
supplies; electrical apparatus & equip-
ment

(G-11779)
AMA FUEL SERVICES LLC
3053 Hart Rd (45036-9123)
PHONE..............................513 836-3800
Danielle Bingman,
EMP: 5
SQ FT: 9,000
SALES (est): 672.7K Privately Held
SIC: 2869 Fuels

(G-11780)
**ARCHITECTURAL DOOR
SYSTEMS LLC**
2810 Highland Ave (45036)
PHONE..............................513 808-9900
Richard Beckman, *President*
Charles Beckman, *Vice Pres*
EMP: 5
SALES (est): 310K Privately Held
SIC: 2431 3429 Door frames, wood; man-
ufactured hardware (general)

(G-11781)
ARI PHOENIX INC (PA)
4119 Binion Way (45036-9336)
PHONE..............................513 229-3750
Gareth Hudson, *CEO*
James Mock, *CFO*
EMP: 27
SALES (est): 15.7MM Privately Held
SIC: 3536 3564 Hoists; exhaust fans: in-
dustrial or commercial

(G-11782)
AWS INDUSTRIES INC
Also Called: Tomak Precision
2600 Henkle Dr (45036-8026)
PHONE..............................513 932-7941
Fax: 513 421-1853
Alvin W Schaeper, *President*
Siobhan Kelly, *General Mgr*
A J Schaeper, *General Mgr*
Wilson Gabbard, *Vice Pres*
Pam Johnson, *Office Mgr*
EMP: 45 EST: 1953
SQ FT: 20,000
SALES (est): 10.3MM Privately Held
WEB: www.tomak.com
SIC: 3728 3841 Aircraft parts & equip-
ment; surgical & medical instruments

(G-11783)
**BENNERS CUSTOM
WOODWORKING (PA)**
1004 W Main St (45036-9512)
PHONE..............................513 932-9159
Michael Benner, *President*
EMP: 5
SQ FT: 3,700
SALES (est): 995.7K Privately Held
SIC: 2511 Wood household furniture

(G-11784)
**BIG CHIEF MANUFACTURING
LTD**
250 Harmon Ave (45036-8800)
PHONE..............................513 934-3888
James Howe Jr, *Partner*
Mike Heald, *Plant Mgr*
David G Van Horn, *CFO*
▲ EMP: 25
SQ FT: 20,000
SALES (est): 1.8MM
**SALES (corp-wide): 8.2MM Privately
Held**
SIC: 3545 Machine tool accessories
PA: Big Chief, Inc.
5150 Big Chief Dr
Cincinnati OH 45227
513 271-7411

(G-11785)
C T CHEMICALS INC
4110 Columbia Rd (45036-9588)
PHONE..............................513 336-6160
Fax: 513 336-6160
Gregory Lalonde, *President*
Robert Bokon, *Vice Pres*
Greg Leary, *Sls & Mktg Exec*
EMP: 5
SQ FT: 97,000
SALES (est): 842.6K Privately Held
SIC: 2819 Industrial inorganic chemicals

(G-11786)
CADILLAC PRODUCTS INC
265 S West St (45036-2152)
PHONE..............................248 813-8255
Jeff Yezzi, *Branch Mgr*
EMP: 20
**SALES (corp-wide): 182.3MM Privately
Held**
SIC: 3714 Motor vehicle parts & acces-
sories
PA: Cadillac Products Inc
5800 Crooks Rd Ste 100
Troy MI 48098
248 813-8200

(G-11787)
**CARL E OEDER SONS SAND &
GRAV**
1000 Mason Morrow Rd (45036-9271)
PHONE..............................513 494-1555
Carl Edward Oeder, *President*
David Oeder, *Vice Pres*
Diane Browning, *Treasurer*
Verna Rae Oeder, *Admin Sec*
EMP: 30 EST: 1955
SQ FT: 23,600
SALES (est): 2.1MM Privately Held
WEB: www.oeder.com
SIC: 1442 4212 7538 Sand mining; gravel
mining; dump truck haulage; truck engine
repair, except industrial

(G-11788)
CCTM INC
838 Carson Dr (45036-1316)
PHONE..............................513 934-3533
Fax: 513 934-3190
Dan Collins, *President*
Gregory Collins, *Vice Pres*
Jeff Boldman, *Foreman/Supr*
Connie Collins, *Admin Sec*
EMP: 5
SQ FT: 7,500
SALES (est): 507.4K Privately Held
WEB: www.cctmath.org
SIC: 3544 7389 3499 3599 Special dies,
tools, jigs & fixtures; metal slitting &
shearing; automobile seat frames, metal;
machine shop, jobbing & repair

(G-11789)
COLONIAL WOODCRAFT INC
Also Called: River Bend Chair Co
1004 W Main St (45036-9512)
PHONE..............................513 779-8088
Fax: 513 777-8859
Kenneth Shannon, *President*
Ruth Shannon, *Vice Pres*
Kathy Wimmer, *Office Mgr*
EMP: 11
SQ FT: 9,000
SALES: 500K Privately Held
SIC: 2511 Chairs, household, except up-
holstered: wood

(G-11790)
CONNOR ELECTRIC INC
605 N Liberty Keuter Rd (45036-9755)
PHONE..............................513 932-5798
Warren Conner, *President*
Donna Conner, *Admin Sec*
EMP: 3
SALES (est): 240K Privately Held
SIC: 3531 1731 Construction machinery;
electrical work

(G-11791)
**CONTEMPRARY IMAGE
LABELING INC**
2034 Mckinley Blvd (45036-6425)
PHONE..............................513 583-5699
Doug Weideman, *Principal*

Kurt Wiedeman, *Vice Pres*
EMP: 6
SQ FT: 18,000
SALES (est): 965.6K Privately Held
SIC: 2759 Labels & seals: printing

(G-11792)
CVC LIMITED 1 LLC
568 S Liberty Keuter Rd (45036-9337)
PHONE..............................740 605-3853
Carl Cardi,
EMP: 5
SALES (est): 340.1K Privately Held
SIC: 3629 Electronic generation equipment

(G-11793)
D & E MACHINE CO
962 S Us Route 42 (45036-7918)
PHONE..............................513 932-2184
Fax: 513 932-1104
Kent P Coomer, *President*
Tim Wilkerson, *Opers Mgr*
Kimberly A Coomer, *Treasurer*
Cristen Anders, *Accounts Mgr*
EMP: 9
SQ FT: 12,000
SALES: 1.6MM Privately Held
WEB: www.demachine.com
SIC: 3599 Machine shop, jobbing & repair

(G-11794)
DAVIDSON JEWELERS INC
726 E Main St (45036-1900)
PHONE..............................513 932-3936
John Davidson, *Owner*
Mary Davidson, *Co-Owner*
EMP: 3
SQ FT: 800
SALES (est): 180K Privately Held
SIC: 5944 3911 7631 Jewelry, precious
stones & precious metals; jewelry, pre-
cious metal; jewelry repair services

(G-11795)
E-BEAM SERVICES INC
2775 Henkle Dr Unit B (45036-8256)
PHONE..............................513 933-0031
Fax: 513 933-0542
Dave Keenan, *Branch Mgr*
Jennifer Griggs, *Technical Staff*
EMP: 20
SQ FT: 129,116
SALES (corp-wide): 5MM Privately Held
WEB: www.e-beamservices.com
SIC: 3699 Electronic training devices
PA: E-Beam Services, Inc.
270 Duffy Ave Ste H
Hicksville NY 11801
516 622-1422

(G-11796)
ECOLAB INC
726 E Main St Ste F (45036-1900)
PHONE..............................513 932-0830
Dan Elam, *District Mgr*
Debbie McCurry, *Manager*
EMP: 8
SALES (corp-wide): 13.1B Publicly Held
WEB: www.ecolab.com
SIC: 2842 Sanitation preparations, disin-
fectants & deodorants
PA: Ecolab Inc.
1 Ecolab Pl
Saint Paul MN 55102
800 232-6522

(G-11797)
**ENGINRED PLSTIC
COMPONENTS INC**
315 S West St (45036-2182)
PHONE..............................513 228-0298
Wanda Boyle, *Branch Mgr*
EMP: 128 Privately Held
SIC: 3089 Injection molding of plastics
PA: Engineered Plastic Components, Inc
1408 Zimmerman Dr
Grinnell IA 50112

(G-11798)
ERNST ENTERPRISES INC
4250 Columbia Rd (45036-9589)
PHONE..............................513 874-8300
Fax: 513 398-1897
Robert Himes, *Manager*
EMP: 50
SQ FT: 2,822

SALES (corp-wide): 191MM **Privately Held**
WEB: www.ernstconcrete.com
SIC: 3273 Ready-mixed concrete
PA: Ernst Enterprises, Inc.
   3361 Successful Way
   Dayton OH 45414
   937 233-5555

(G-11799)
FAIRBORN SERVICES INC
3816 Welden Dr (45036-8815)
PHONE.................................513 492-9422
Bill McBrayer, *President*
EMP: 18
SALES (est): 5.5MM **Privately Held**
SIC: 3537 Truck trailers, used in plants, docks, terminals, etc.

(G-11800)
FLINT GROUP US LLC
Also Called: Flint Group Global Packaging
2675 Henkle Dr (45036-8027)
PHONE.................................513 934-6500
Fax: 513 746-1048
Greg Bowers, *Buyer*
Philip Ernest, *Chief Mktg Ofcr*
Michael Hackett, *Branch Mgr*
Joshua Maxwell, *Supervisor*
EMP: 5
SALES (corp-wide): 3.8B **Privately Held**
WEB: www.flintink.com
SIC: 2893 Printing ink
PA: Flint Group Us Llc
   14909 N Beck Rd
   Plymouth MI 48170
   734 781-4600

(G-11801)
GEORGE MANUFACTURING INC
160 Harmon Ave (45036-9511)
PHONE.................................513 932-1067
Fax: 513 934-3519
Erin George, *President*
Dan George, *Shareholder*
EMP: 28
SQ FT: 60,000
SALES (est): 4.1MM **Privately Held**
WEB: www.georgemfg.com
SIC: 3312 3479 3444 Pipes & tubes; painting, coating & hot dipping; sheet metalwork

(G-11802)
GEORGE STEEL FABRICATING INC
1207 S Us Route 42 (45036-8198)
PHONE.................................513 932-2887
Fax: 513 932-2059
John George, *President*
Brad Frost, *Corp Secy*
Kevin Nickell, *Vice Pres*
Blake Berryman, *Project Mgr*
Vince Young, *Safety Mgr*
EMP: 35
SQ FT: 32,100
SALES (est): 7.9MM **Privately Held**
WEB: www.georgesteel.com
SIC: 7692 3441 3599 Welding repair; fabricated structural metal; machine shop, jobbing & repair

(G-11803)
GEYGAN ENTERPRISES INC
Also Called: Minuteman Press
101 Dave Ave Ste E (45036-2293)
PHONE.................................513 932-4222
Fax: 513 932-0950
Michael Geygan, *President*
Lisa Wilson, *Vice Pres*
EMP: 12
SALES: 1.2MM **Privately Held**
WEB: www.mmpressleb.com
SIC: 2752 7334 2759 5999 Commercial printing, lithographic; photocopying & duplicating services; labels & seals: printing; invitations: printing; rubber stamps; typesetting; manifold business forms

(G-11804)
GMI COMPANIES INC (PA)
Also Called: Ghent Manufacturing
2999 Henkle Dr (45036-9260)
PHONE.................................513 932-3445
John Rouse, *General Mgr*
George L Leasure, *Chairman*

Mark Leasure, *Vice Pres*
Jeff Nahrup, *Warehouse Mgr*
Tom Septer, *Purchasing*
▲ **EMP:** 130
SQ FT: 101,000
SALES (est): 22.9MM **Privately Held**
WEB: www.ghent.com
SIC: 2531 2493 2599 2541 Blackboards, wood; bulletin boards, wood; bulletin boards, cork; boards: planning, display, notice; showcases, except refrigerated: wood; panel systems & partitions (freestanding), office: wood; panel systems & partitions, office: except wood

(G-11805)
GOLDEN TURTLE CHOCOLATE FCTRY
120 S Broadway St Ste 1 (45036-1729)
P.O. Box 647 (45036-0647)
PHONE.................................513 932-1990
Fax: 513 932-1990
Joy Kossouji, *Owner*
Ted Kossouji, *Partner*
EMP: 6
SQ FT: 3,000
SALES: 200K **Privately Held**
WEB:
www.goldenturtlechocolatefactory.com
SIC: 2066 5441 5947 Chocolate; candy, nut & confectionery stores; gifts & novelties

(G-11806)
GREEN BAY PACKAGING INC
Cincinnati Division
760 Kingsview Dr (45036-9554)
PHONE.................................513 228-5560
Fax: 513 489-1152
Dwayne Owens, *Production*
Paul Hasemeyer, *Controller*
Michel Hughes, *Controller*
Cecelia Auxter, *Accounting Mgr*
Thomas Fullove, *Human Res Dir*
EMP: 71
SQ FT: 103,000
SALES (corp-wide): 896.8MM **Privately Held**
WEB: www.gbp.com
SIC: 2653 3412 Boxes, corrugated: made from purchased materials; metal barrels, drums & pails
PA: Green Bay Packaging Inc.
   1700 N Webster Ave
   Green Bay WI 54302
   920 433-5111

(G-11807)
HEAT AND SENSOR TECH LLC
Also Called: Heat & Sensor
627 Norgal Dr (45036-9275)
PHONE.................................513 228-0481
Fax: 513 228-0482
Gary Shackleford, *General Mgr*
Adam Montgomery, *QC Mgr*
Gary Shackeford, *Mng Member*
Michelle Shackeford,
▲ **EMP:** 53
SQ FT: 12,000
SALES: 3.7MM **Privately Held**
WEB: www.heatandsensortech.com
SIC: 3567 Heating units & devices, industrial: electric

(G-11808)
HESS TECHNOLOGIES INC
Also Called: Rotex Silver Recovery Co
200 Harmon Ave (45036-8800)
PHONE.................................513 228-0909
Paul Hess, *President*
Bernadine Hess, *Corp Secy*
EMP: 4
SQ FT: 29,000
SALES: 165K **Privately Held**
WEB: www.rotexsilver.com
SIC: 3559 Silver recovery equipment

(G-11809)
INX INTERNATIONAL INK CO
350 Homan Rd (45036-1181)
PHONE.................................513 282-2920
Fax: 513 769-0615
Randy Robinson, *Manager*
EMP: 12
SALES (corp-wide): 1.3B **Privately Held**
SIC: 2893 Printing ink

HQ: Inx International Ink Co
   150 N Martingale Rd # 700
   Schaumburg IL 60173
   630 382-1800

(G-11810)
JIT PACKAGING CINCINNATI INC (PA)
Also Called: J I T
1550 Kingsview Dr (45036-8389)
PHONE.................................513 933-0250
Jeff Jones, *President*
Dave Jones, *Principal*
Gary Buchman, *QC Mgr*
Stefana Popoviciu, *Controller*
Mike Hughes, *Executive*
EMP: 24
SALES (est): 9.9MM **Privately Held**
WEB: www.jitpackaging.net
SIC: 2631 Container, packaging & boxboard

(G-11811)
KANDO OF CINCINNATI INC
Also Called: Franklin Brazing Met Treating
2025 Mckinley Blvd (45036-8075)
PHONE.................................513 459-7782
Fax: 513 459-7662
Timothy Mathile, *CEO*
Blake Michaels, *President*
Larry Synder, *Director*
EMP: 50
SQ FT: 53,000
SALES (est): 9.9MM **Privately Held**
WEB: www.franklinbrazing.com
SIC: 3398 Brazing (hardening) of metal

(G-11812)
KIRBYS AUTO & TRUCK REPAIR
Also Called: Warren Welding and Fabrication
875 Columbus Ave (45036-1692)
PHONE.................................513 934-3999
Fax: 513 934-3225
Glen Kirby, *President*
Jennifer Kirby, *Treasurer*
EMP: 8
SQ FT: 12,510
SALES: 650K **Privately Held**
SIC: 7538 7692 General automotive repair shops; welding repair

(G-11813)
LEBANON ELECTRIC MOTOR SVC LLC
602 E Main St (45036-1916)
P.O. Box 156 (45036-0156)
PHONE.................................513 932-2889
Fax: 513 932-6845
Tom Carter, *Owner*
EMP: 3
SQ FT: 3,000
SALES (est): 280K **Privately Held**
SIC: 5063 7694 5999 Motors, electric; electric motor repair; motors, electric

(G-11814)
MAGNET TECHNOLOGY INC
1599 Kingsview Dr (45036-9573)
PHONE.................................513 932-4416
Fax: 513 932-4502
Larry Mosteller, *President*
▲ **EMP:** 6 **EST:** 1977
SALES (est): 2MM **Privately Held**
WEB: www.flexiblemagnets.com
SIC: 3695 Magnetic tape

(G-11815)
MANE INC (DH)
Also Called: Mane Calafornia
2501 Henkle Dr (45036-7794)
PHONE.................................513 248-9876
Jean Mane, *Ch of Bd*
Ken Hunter, *President*
Stacie Bennison, *Corp Secy*
Brad Kelley, *COO*
Jill Fleury, *Vice Pres*
◆ **EMP:** 70 **EST:** 1998
SQ FT: 70,000
SALES (est): 103.2MM **Privately Held**
SIC: 2087 2099 Flavoring extracts & syrups; food preparations
HQ: Mane Usa Inc.
   60 Demarest Dr
   Wayne NJ 07470
   973 633-5533

(G-11816)
MANE INC
1093 Mane Way (45036-8049)
PHONE.................................513 248-9876
EMP: 70 **Privately Held**
SIC: 2087 Mfg Flavor Extracts/Syrup
HQ: Mane, Inc.
   2501 Henkle Dr
   Lebanon OH 45036
   513 248-9876

(G-11817)
MIX-MASTERS INC
Also Called: Jbs Industries
2550 Henkle Dr (45036-7793)
PHONE.................................513 228-2800
Fax: 513 228-2810
Scott Baeten, *President*
Mike Scott, *General Mgr*
John T Hufford, *Vice Pres*
Laurie Baeten, *CFO*
Erica Luncan, *Accountant*
EMP: 17 **EST:** 2000
SQ FT: 18,000
SALES (est): 4.4MM **Privately Held**
SIC: 2841 2842 Soap & other detergents; polishing preparations & related products

(G-11818)
NEWMAN SANITARY GASKET COMPANY
964 W Main St (45036-9173)
P.O. Box 222 (45036-0222)
PHONE.................................513 932-7379
Fax: 513 932-4493
David William Newman, *President*
Thomas Moore, *Vice Pres*
Justin Todd, *Plant Mgr*
Robin Chittum, *Purchasing*
Sheryl Lee, *Controller*
EMP: 41
SQ FT: 38,000
SALES (est): 6MM **Privately Held**
WEB: www.newmangasket.com
SIC: 3053 Gaskets, all materials

(G-11819)
NIBCO INC
2800 Henkle Dr (45036-8894)
PHONE.................................513 228-1426
Chris Mason, *Branch Mgr*
EMP: 47
SALES (corp-wide): 500MM **Privately Held**
SIC: 3088 Plastics plumbing fixtures
PA: Nibco Inc.
   1516 Middlebury St
   Elkhart IN 46516
   574 295-3000

(G-11820)
OEDER CARL E SONS SAND & GRAV
1000 Mason Mrrow Mlgrv Rd (45036-9271)
PHONE.................................513 494-1238
Carl E Oeder, *President*
EMP: 35
SALES (est): 3.5MM **Privately Held**
SIC: 4213 1442 Trucking, except local; construction sand & gravel

(G-11821)
OHIO FLAME HARDENING COMPANY (PA)
4110 Columbia Rd (45036-9588)
PHONE.................................513 336-6160
Robert Bokon, *President*
EMP: 7
SQ FT: 65,000
SALES (est): 1.4MM **Privately Held**
SIC: 3398 Brazing (hardening) of metal

(G-11822)
OIL ETC INC
Also Called: Pennzoil 10 Min Oil Change
804 Cherry Hill Ln (45036-8285)
PHONE.................................513 933-8280
Stephen Beason, *President*
Mike Bradley, *Vice Pres*
Richard P Pennington, *Manager*
EMP: 6
SALES (est): 83K **Privately Held**
SIC: 2992 Lubricating oils & greases

(G-11823)
ON-POWER INC
3525 Grant Ave Ste A (45036-6431)
PHONE....................................513 228-2100
Fax: 513 228-0111
Larry D Davis, *President*
Joe Back, *Purchasing*
Tim Quackenbush, *Electrical Engi*
Tom Mergy, *CFO*
Mark Meineke, *Info Tech Mgr*
EMP: 32
SALES: 8MM **Privately Held**
WEB: www.onpowerinc.com
SIC: 3511 8711 Gas turbines, mechanical drive; consulting engineer

(G-11824)
OPW ENGINEERED SYSTEMS INC
2726 Henkle Dr (45036-8209)
PHONE....................................888 771-9438
Fax: 513 932-9845
Robert B Nicholson III, *CEO*
Tim Warning, *President*
Mike Krauser, *Vice Pres*
Rick Johnson, *Human Res Mgr*
Bill Burns, *Regl Sales Mgr*
▲ **EMP:** 60
SALES (est): 18.4MM
SALES (corp-wide): 6.7B **Publicly Held**
WEB: www.opw-es.com
SIC: 3494 3825 3625 3568 Valves & pipe fittings; instruments to measure electricity; relays & industrial controls; power transmission equipment; conveyors & conveying equipment
HQ: Opw Fluid Transfer Group
4304 Nw Mattox Rd
Kansas City MO 64150
816 741-6600

(G-11825)
OVERLY HAUTZ MOTOR BASE CO
Also Called: Overly Hautz Company
215 S West St (45036-2152)
P.O. Box 837 (45036-0837)
PHONE....................................513 932-0025
Fax: 513 932-1688
Thomas Copanas, *President*
Edward Bees, *Vice Pres*
Pete Gough, *Plant Mgr*
Andre Vestavik, *Purchasing*
Clara Mendez, *Finance*
▲ **EMP:** 50
SQ FT: 27,000
SALES (est): 10.2MM **Privately Held**
WEB: www.overlyhautz.com
SIC: 3699 Electrical equipment & supplies

(G-11826)
PAX CORRUGATED PRODUCTS INC
Also Called: P A X
1899 Kingsview Dr (45036-8397)
PHONE....................................513 932-9855
Fax: 513 932-1226
Stan Bernard, *CEO*
James E Cory II, *President*
Jeff Neubecker, *Opers Mgr*
Phil Perry, *Engineer*
Kern Z McKee III, *Accounts Mgr*
EMP: 100
SQ FT: 119,457
SALES: 25.8MM **Privately Held**
WEB: www.paxbox.com
SIC: 2653 Corrugated & solid fiber boxes

(G-11827)
PIONEER PRECISION TOOL INC
5100 Bunnell Hill Rd (45036-9052)
PHONE....................................513 932-8805
Glenn Johnson, *President*
Cyndi Johnson, *Vice Pres*
EMP: 3
SALES (est): 219.4K **Privately Held**
SIC: 3544 Special dies & tools

(G-11828)
PKG TECHNOLOGIES INC
212 N Broadway St Ste 7 (45036-2736)
P.O. Box 267, Ashburn VA (20146-0267)
PHONE....................................513 967-2783
David Wallace, *CEO*

Mihkael Denola, *Ch of Bd*
Mary Schaefer, *CFO*
Paul Denola, *Treasurer*
David Rossow, *Info Tech Mgr*
EMP: 4 **EST:** 2008
SALES: 596.1K **Privately Held**
SIC: 7372 Prepackaged software

(G-11829)
PRESS FOR LESS PRINTING FIRM I
1836 Stubbs Mill Rd (45036-9654)
PHONE....................................931 912-4606
EMP: 4 **EST:** 2008
SALES (est): 320K **Privately Held**
SIC: 2752 Lithographic Commercial Printing

(G-11830)
QUAD/GRAPHICS INC
760 Fujitec Dr (45036)
PHONE....................................513 932-1064
Mike Lehky, *Branch Mgr*
EMP: 509
SALES (corp-wide): 4.3B **Publicly Held**
SIC: 2752 2754 3823 2721 Commercial printing, lithographic; commercial printing, gravure; controllers for process variables, all types; magazines: publishing & printing
PA: Quad/Graphics Inc.
N61w23044 Harrys Way
Sussex WI 53089
414 566-6000

(G-11831)
RACEWAY BEVERAGE LLC
11 S Broadway St (45036-1769)
PHONE....................................513 932-2214
James P Smith Jr, *Principal*
EMP: 3 **EST:** 2008
SALES (est): 142.1K **Privately Held**
SIC: 3644 Raceways

(G-11832)
RED LION NURSERY INC
3505 N State Route 741 (45036-9783)
P.O. Box 67, Franklin (45005-0067)
PHONE....................................937 704-9840
Dennis Myers, *President*
EMP: 5
SALES (est): 30.9K **Privately Held**
SIC: 2499 Saddle trees, wood

(G-11833)
RF LINX INC
2142 Greentree Rd (45036-8129)
PHONE....................................513 777-2774
Fax: 513 779-2632
Joe Janning, *President*
Linda Badovick, *Controller*
▲ **EMP:** 6
SQ FT: 5,000
SALES (est): 966.3K **Privately Held**
SIC: 3663 Amplifiers, RF power & IF

(G-11834)
ROYCE CO
2340 Lebanon Rd (45036-9681)
PHONE....................................513 933-0344
Fax: 513 932-8339
Royce Burton, *Owner*
EMP: 3
SQ FT: 4,000
SALES: 140K **Privately Held**
SIC: 3599 Machine shop, jobbing & repair

(G-11835)
RPMI PACKAGING INC
3899 S Us Route 42 (45036-9530)
P.O. Box 105, Mason (45040-0105)
PHONE....................................513 398-4040
Fax: 513 398-3535
Robert Hillerich, *President*
Jane Ribarsky, *Accountant*
Terry Christman, *Sales Executive*
Keith Goodhart, *Sales Executive*
Donald Hillerich, *Sales Executive*
EMP: 10
SALES (est): 1.4MM **Privately Held**
WEB: www.rpmipackaging.com
SIC: 3565 Packaging machinery

(G-11836)
SARDINIA CONCRETE COMPANY
1622 Mason Morrow Rd (45036)
PHONE....................................513 248-0090
Fax: 513 336-7346
EMP: 13
SALES (corp-wide): 10.7MM **Privately Held**
SIC: 3273 Ready-mixed concrete
PA: Sardinia Concrete Company
911 Us Route 50
Milford OH 45150
513 248-0090

(G-11837)
SCHMIDT PROGRESSIVE LLC
Also Called: Food Furniture
360 Harmon Ave (45036-8801)
P.O. Box 380 (45036-0380)
PHONE....................................513 934-2600
Joe Pardy, *General Mgr*
Don Blades, *Vice Pres*
Mike Stouder, *Prdtn Mgr*
Ron Adler, *Natl Sales Mgr*
Cindy Dixon, *Sales Associate*
EMP: 20
SQ FT: 55,000
SALES: 2.2MM **Privately Held**
WEB: www.schmidtprogressive.com
SIC: 3089 Fiberglass doors

(G-11838)
SCHNEDER ELC BLDNGS AMRCAS INC
1770 Masn Mrrw Millgrv Rd (45036-9688)
PHONE....................................513 398-9800
James C Mocas, *Project Mgr*
Bill Korn, *Branch Mgr*
Larry Mueller, *Branch Mgr*
EMP: 80
SALES (corp-wide): 241K **Privately Held**
SIC: 1731 3822 Electrical work; auto controls regulating residntl & coml environmt & applncs
HQ: Schneider Electric Buildings Americas, Inc.
1650 W Crosby Rd
Carrollton TX 75006
972 323-1111

(G-11839)
SIEMENS INDUSTRY INC
4170 Columbia Rd (45036-9588)
PHONE....................................513 336-2267
Fax: 513 494-5120
EMP: 87
SALES (corp-wide): 96B **Privately Held**
SIC: 3822 Mfg Environmntl Controls
HQ: Siemens Industry, Inc.
1000 Deerfield Pkwy
Buffalo Grove IL 60089
847 215-1000

(G-11840)
SIGNERY
1002 W Main St Apt D (45036-8267)
PHONE....................................513 932-1938
Fax: 513 932-0567
Richard Freed, *Owner*
EMP: 3
SQ FT: 1,444
SALES (est): 185.7K **Privately Held**
SIC: 7389 3993 Sign painting & lettering shop; signs & advertising specialties

(G-11841)
SOFTWARE SOLUTIONS INC (PA)
420 E Main St (45036-2234)
PHONE....................................513 932-6667
Fax: 513 932-4058
John Rettig, *President*
Laura Brown, *Vice Pres*
Rick Fortman, *Vice Pres*
Linda Jones, *Opers Staff*
Dave Christensen, *QC Mgr*
EMP: 29
SQ FT: 12,200
SALES (est): 8MM **Privately Held**
WEB: www.elocalgovernment.com
SIC: 5045 7372 7373 Computers, peripherals & software; disk drives; application computer software; computer integrated systems design

(G-11842)
STC INTERNATIONAL CO LTD (PA)
1499 Shaker Run Blvd (45036-4041)
PHONE....................................561 308-6002
Frank Ferguson, *President*
EMP: 8
SALES (est): 1.9MM **Privately Held**
SIC: 3541 3545 2821 Machine tools, metal cutting type; machine tool accessories; plastics materials & resins

(G-11843)
TELEMPU N HAYASHI AMER CORP
1500 Kingsview Dr (45036-8389)
PHONE....................................513 932-9319
Mohsin Yaqoob, *Marketing Mgr*
Harry Okamoto, *Director*
EMP: 6
SALES (corp-wide): 1.7B **Privately Held**
SIC: 2396 Automotive trimmings, fabric
HQ: Hayashi Telempu North America Corporation
14328 Genoa Ct
Plymouth MI 48170
734 456-5221

(G-11844)
TOTAL MAINTENANCE MANAGEMENT
320 Harmon Ave (45036-8801)
PHONE....................................513 228-2345
Thomas Koerner, *President*
EMP: 6
SQ FT: 14,700
SALES (est): 1.4MM **Privately Held**
SIC: 7694 Electric motor repair

(G-11845)
TRIM PARTS INC
2175 Deerfield Rd (45036-6422)
PHONE....................................513 934-0815
Fax: 513 934-0816
Carl Chadwell, *President*
Charles Pray, *Plant Mgr*
Alex Tainsh, *Office Mgr*
Jill Threm, *Office Mgr*
Connie Pendley, *Manager*
▲ **EMP:** 35
SQ FT: 55,000
SALES (est): 7.7MM
SALES (corp-wide): 7.2MM **Privately Held**
WEB: www.trimparts.com
SIC: 3714 3544 3429 Motor vehicle parts & accessories; special dies, tools, jigs & fixtures; manufactured hardware (general)
PA: Restoration Parts Unlimited, Inc.
2175 Deerfield Rd
Lebanon OH 45036
513 934-0815

(G-11846)
TURTLECREEK TOWNSHIP
670 N Rte 123 (45036-7016)
PHONE....................................513 932-4080
Steven Flint, *Chief*
EMP: 16 **Privately Held**
SIC: 9199 3621 General government administration; ; generating apparatus & parts, electrical
PA: Turtlecreek Township
670 N State Route 123
Lebanon OH 45036
513 932-4902

(G-11847)
UGN INC
201 Exploration Dr (45036)
PHONE....................................513 360-3500
Peter Anthony, *President*
EMP: 160
SALES (corp-wide): 2.1B **Privately Held**
SIC: 3714 Motor vehicle parts & accessories
HQ: Ugn, Inc.
18410 Crossing Dr Ste C
Tinley Park IL 60487
773 437-2400

(G-11848)
VISTECH MFG SOLUTIONS LLC
265 S West St (45036-2152)
PHONE....................................513 933-9300

Dylan Roundtree, *Plant Mgr*
Steve Campbell, *Plant Mgr*
Michael Gonzalez, *Plant Mgr*
Alex Ramirez, *Plant Mgr*
Terence McLaughlin, *VP Finance*
EMP: 10
SALES (corp-wide): 14MM **Privately Held**
SIC: 3565 Packaging machinery
PA: Vistech Manufacturing Solutions, Llc
1156 Scenic Dr Ste 120
Modesto CA 95350
209 544-9333

(G-11849)
WRAY PRECISION PRODUCTS INC
3650 Turtlecreek Rd (45036-9685)
PHONE.................................513 228-5000
Fax: 513 336-8650
Steven Dorgan, *President*
EMP: 7
SQ FT: 12,000
SALES: 286K **Privately Held**
SIC: 3599 Machine shop, jobbing & repair

Leesburg
Highland County

(G-11850)
CANDLE-LITE COMPANY LLC
250 Eastern Ave (45135-9783)
P.O. Box 385 (45135-0385)
PHONE.................................937 780-2711
Fax: 937 780-9571
Wayne Donie, *Vice Pres*
Tim Glasgo, *Engineer*
Richard Leonard, *Manager*
Douglas McKay, *Manager*
Jeremy Streitenberger, *Info Tech Mgr*
EMP: 50
SQ FT: 900,000
SALES (corp-wide): 262.6MM **Privately Held**
WEB: www.lancastercolony.com
SIC: 3999 Candles
HQ: Candle-Lite Company, Llc
10521 Millington Ct Ste B
Blue Ash OH 45242
513 563-1113

(G-11851)
CREATIVE FAB & WELDING LLC
Also Called: Valley Trailers
9691 Stafford Rd (45135-9464)
PHONE.................................937 780-5000
Milton Wiggers, *Prdtn Mgr*
Cameron Dyck, *Mng Member*
Jeremy Dyck, *Manager*
EMP: 22
SQ FT: 800
SALES (est): 2.2MM **Privately Held**
SIC: 3441 7692 Fabricated structural metal; welding repair

(G-11852)
JAYRON FABRICATION LLC
13140 New Martinsburg Rd (45135-9623)
PHONE.................................740 335-3184
James Gingerich, *Mng Member*
EMP: 5
SALES: 590K **Privately Held**
SIC: 3441 7699 Fabricated structural metal; agricultural equipment repair services

(G-11853)
JR KENNEL MFG
12196 Wilmington Ave (45135-9453)
PHONE.................................937 780-6104
John Russell, *Owner*
EMP: 5
SALES: 300K **Privately Held**
SIC: 2679 Adding machine rolls, paper: made from purchased material

(G-11854)
LEESBURG MODERN SALES INC
12607 Monroe Rd (45135)
P.O. Box 346 (45135-0346)
PHONE.................................937 780-2613
Fax: 937 780-6276

Janet Dove, *President*
EMP: 3
SQ FT: 7,200
SALES (est): 375.5K **Privately Held**
WEB: www.fivestarproducts.com
SIC: 2891 2842 Sealing compounds, synthetic rubber or plastic; adhesives; degreasing solvent

(G-11855)
MASON COMPANY LLC
260 Depot Ln (45135-8438)
P.O. Box 365 (45135-0365)
PHONE.................................937 780-2321
Fax: 937 780-6336
Greg Taylor, *CEO*
Elaine Schmidt, *General Mgr*
Ked Sturgill, *Safety Dir*
Jeff Ballman, *Plant Mgr*
Gary Silvis, *Engineer*
EMP: 44
SQ FT: 35,000
SALES (est): 13.4MM **Privately Held**
SIC: 3496 Cages, wire

(G-11856)
PRIEST MILLWRIGHT SERVICE
101 Miller St (45135-0377)
P.O. Box 169 (45135-0169)
PHONE.................................937 780-3405
Fax: 937 780-3405
Forrest Priest, *Owner*
EMP: 8
SQ FT: 3,000
SALES (est): 728.7K **Privately Held**
SIC: 3444 Sheet metalwork

Leetonia
Columbiana County

(G-11857)
2828 CLINTON INC (PA)
Also Called: Cleveland Vibrator Company
600 Cherry Fork Ave (44431-1279)
PHONE.................................216 241-7157
Fax: 216 241-3480
Michael Valore, *CEO*
Jeffrey Chokel, *Ch of Bd*
Craig Macklin, *Vice Pres*
Glen Roberts, *Vice Pres*
Eddie Colon, *Opers Mgr*
▲ **EMP:** 27 **EST:** 1922
SALES: 5.7MM **Privately Held**
WEB: www.clevelandvibrator.com
SIC: 3532 Mining machinery

(G-11858)
BUCKEYE FBRICATORS OF LEETONIA
38009 Butcher Rd (44431-9746)
PHONE.................................330 427-0330
Fax: 330 427-0343
Frank Grimes, *President*
EMP: 4
SQ FT: 4,950
SALES (est): 410K **Privately Held**
WEB: www.buckeyemachine.com
SIC: 3441 Fabricated structural metal

(G-11859)
DEIBEL MANUFACTURING LLC
41659 Esterly Dr (44431-9676)
PHONE.................................330 482-3351
Andrew C Deibel, *Mng Member*
Jane M Deibel,
EMP: 6
SALES: 500K **Privately Held**
SIC: 3443 Fabricated plate work (boiler shop)

(G-11860)
GAM
142 Chestnut St (44431-1001)
PHONE.................................330 427-6470
Richard Gurlea, *Owner*
▼ **EMP:** 3
SALES (est): 200K **Privately Held**
SIC: 3559 3462 Special industry machinery; iron & steel forgings

(G-11861)
LEETONIA TOOL COMPANY
142 Main St (44431-1181)
PHONE.................................330 427-6944
Fax: 330 427-6128
Robert L Holt, *President*
Dennis J Holt, *Vice Pres*
J W Holt, *Treasurer*
EMP: 12
SQ FT: 25,000
SALES: 450K **Privately Held**
SIC: 3429 Builders' hardware; marine hardware

(G-11862)
MAIN STREET MACHINE INC
88 W Main St (44431)
P.O. Box 86 (44431-0086)
PHONE.................................330 427-9828
Fax: 330 427-9829
Andrew McCoy, *President*
Mark Butler, *Vice Pres*
EMP: 5
SQ FT: 1,800
SALES (est): 583.8K **Privately Held**
SIC: 3599 Machine shop, jobbing & repair

(G-11863)
PENNEX ALUMINUM
1 Commerce Ave (44431-8720)
PHONE.................................330 427-6704
Thomas Hutchinson, *Principal*
Jack Woods, *Plant Mgr*
EMP: 100
SALES (est): 4.2MM **Privately Held**
SIC: 2819 Aluminum compounds

(G-11864)
QUAKER CITY SEPTIC TANKS LLC
290 E High St (44431-9653)
PHONE.................................330 427-2239
Fax: 330 427-2762
Jeff Foust, *Mng Member*
EMP: 8
SQ FT: 4,000
SALES (est): 1.7MM **Privately Held**
SIC: 3272 Septic tanks, concrete

(G-11865)
STAINLESS MACHINE ENGINEERING
5275 Woodville Rd (44431-9622)
PHONE.................................330 501-1992
Ken Baun, *President*
EMP: 4
SALES (est): 220K **Privately Held**
WEB: www.stainlessmachine-engineering.com
SIC: 3599 5719 Machine shop, jobbing & repair; metalware

(G-11866)
SUPER SHEET METAL
40811 Bonesville Schl Rd (44431-8623)
PHONE.................................330 482-9045
Wilma J Bolton, *Owner*
Tom Bolton, *Co-Owner*
EMP: 3
SQ FT: 3,000
SALES: 200K **Privately Held**
SIC: 3444 Sheet metalwork

Leipsic
Putnam County

(G-11867)
CRABAR/GBF INC (HQ)
Also Called: Crabar/Gbf Inc.
68 Vine St (45856-1488)
PHONE.................................419 943-2141
Keith Walters, *CEO*
Marshall Griffen, *CFO*
EMP: 51 **EST:** 2002
SALES (est): 132.2MM
SALES (corp-wide): 568.9MM **Publicly Held**
SIC: 2752 Business form & card printing, lithographic
PA: Ennis, Inc.
2441 Presidential Pkwy
Midlothian TX 76065
972 775-9801

(G-11868)
CRABAR/GBF INC
Also Called: Crabar Business Systems
68 Vine St (45856-1488)
P.O. Box 66 (45856-0066)
PHONE.................................419 943-2141
Roger Hermiller, *Manager*
Mike Schuetz, *Data Proc Staff*
EMP: 9
SALES (corp-wide): 568.9MM **Publicly Held**
SIC: 2759 2791 2761 2752 Business forms: printing; typesetting; manifold business forms; commercial printing, lithographic; packaging paper & plastics film, coated & laminated; automotive & apparel trimmings
HQ: Crabar/Gbf, Inc.
68 Vine St
Leipsic OH 45856
419 943-2141

(G-11869)
DILLER METALS INC
507 S Eastom St (45856-1300)
PHONE.................................419 943-3364
Pete Diller, *President*
EMP: 6
SALES (est): 1.5MM **Privately Held**
SIC: 3443 Metal parts

(G-11870)
IAMS COMPANY
3700 State Route 65 (45856-9231)
P.O. Box 87 (45856-0087)
PHONE.................................419 943-4267
Fax: 419 943-4270
Margie Quillen, *Human Res Dir*
Greg Wolking, *Manager*
Bob Straley, *Manager*
Amy Thornton, *Manager*
Euka Korea, *Director*
EMP: 140
SALES (corp-wide): 35B **Privately Held**
WEB: www.iams.com
SIC: 2047 Dog food
HQ: The Iams Company
8700 S Masn Montgomery Rd
Mason OH 45040
800 675-3849

(G-11871)
LAUREATE MACHINE & AUTOMTN LLC
100 Laureate Dr (45856-8710)
P.O. Box 55 (45856-0055)
PHONE.................................419 615-4601
John Mullett, *Mng Member*
▲ **EMP:** 5
SQ FT: 11,000
SALES (est): 650K **Privately Held**
SIC: 3569 Liquid automation machinery & equipment

(G-11872)
MICKENS INC
Also Called: Leipsic Messenger Newspaper
117 E Main St (45856-1428)
PHONE.................................419 943-2590
Keith Mickens, *Branch Mgr*
EMP: 5
SALES (corp-wide): 559K **Privately Held**
WEB: www.mickens.com
SIC: 2711 Newspapers
PA: Mickens Inc
107 East St Ste 1
Liberty Center OH 43532
419 533-2401

(G-11873)
PRECISION LASER & FORMING
6500 Road 5 (45856-9763)
PHONE.................................419 943-4350
Fax: 419 943-4351
Thomas Koenig, *CEO*
Howard Hermiller, *Treasurer*
Matthew Michel, *Shareholder*
EMP: 13
SQ FT: 17,000
SALES (est): 1.4MM **Privately Held**
SIC: 3312 Blast furnaces & steel mills

(G-11874)
PRETIUM PACKAGING LLC
Also Called: Patricks
150 S Werner St (45856-1363)
PHONE................................419 943-3733
EMP: 145 Privately Held
SIC: 3089 Plastic containers, except foam
HQ: Pretium Packaging, L.L.C.
15450 S Outer Forty Dr St Ste 120
Chesterfield MO 63017
314 727-8200

(G-11875)
PRO-TEC COATING COMPANY INC
5500 Pro-Tec Pkwy (45856-8215)
PHONE................................419 943-1211
Fax: 419 943-1101
Richard E Veitch, President
Robert M Stanton, Principal
Brent Rosebrook, Vice Pres
Eric Franks, Controller
Shannon Sharteli, Human Res Dir
▲ EMP: 230
SQ FT: 725,000
SALES (est): 66.4MM Privately Held
WEB: www.proteccoating.com
SIC: 3479 Galvanizing of iron, steel or end-formed products

(G-11876)
RUHE SALES INC (PA)
5450 State Route 109 (45856-9438)
PHONE................................419 943-3357
Fax: 419 943-3971
Marilyn Ruhe, President
Robert G Ruhe, Vice Pres
EMP: 10
SQ FT: 10,000
SALES (est): 765.1K Privately Held
SIC: 0721 3721 4581 4512 Crop dusting services; aircraft; airports, flying fields & services; air transportation, scheduled

(G-11877)
SUMMIT ETHANOL LLC
Also Called: Poet Biorefining-Leipsic
3875 State Rd 65 (45856)
PHONE................................419 943-7447
Jeff Lautt, CEO
Mark Borer, General Mgr
Daniel Loveland, CFO
EMP: 40
SALES (est): 12MM
SALES (corp-wide): 4.3B Privately Held
SIC: 2869 Ethyl alcohol, ethanol; ethanolamines
PA: Poet, Llc
4615 N Lewis Ave
Sioux Falls SD 57104
605 965-2200

(G-11878)
WAGNER FARMS & SAWMILL LLC
13201 Road X (45856-9295)
PHONE................................419 653-4126
Fax: 419 653-4127
Jeffrey Wagner, Partner
Martin Wagner, Partner
Michael Wagner, Partner
Steven Wagner, Partner
Thomas Wagner, Partner
EMP: 13
SALES (est): 1.2MM Privately Held
WEB: www.wagnerfarms.com
SIC: 2421 0191 2426 Sawmills & planing mills, general; general farms, primarily crop; hardwood dimension & flooring mills

(G-11879)
WARD CONSTRUCTION CO (PA)
385 Oak St (45856-1358)
PHONE................................419 943-2450
Fax: 419 943-2440
Arnold W Rosebrock, President
Patricia A Newell, Corp Secy
Barry A Rosebrock, Vice Pres
Daniel A Rosebrock, Vice Pres
EMP: 17
SALES: 7.5MM Privately Held
SIC: 1611 4212 1442 1771 General contractor, highway & street construction; local trucking, without storage; sand mining; gravel mining; concrete work

---

Lewis Center
Delaware County

(G-11880)
ABRASIVE TECHNOLOGY INC (PA)
8400 Green Meadows Dr N (43035-9453)
P.O. Box 545 (43035-0545)
PHONE................................740 548-4100
Fax: 740 548-6249
Loyal M Peterman Jr, President
Philip Teng, General Mgr
Daryl L Peterman, Principal
Ian Watkins, Site Mgr
Don Dorr, QA Dir
▲ EMP: 200 EST: 1971
SQ FT: 100,000
SALES (est): 98MM Privately Held
WEB: www.abrasive-tech.com
SIC: 3291 Abrasive stones, except grinding stones: ground or whole; abrasive wheels & grindstones, not artificial

(G-11881)
ABRASIVE TECHNOLOGY LAPIDARY
Also Called: Crystalite
8400 Green Meadows Dr N (43035-9453)
P.O. Box 545 (43035-0545)
PHONE................................740 548-4855
Loyal M Peterman, President
EMP: 200
SQ FT: 50,000
SALES (est): 14MM Privately Held
WEB: www.crystalite.com
SIC: 3545 Diamond cutting tools for turning, boring, burnishing, etc.

(G-11882)
ABSOLUTE IMPRESSIONS INC (PA)
281 Enterprise Dr (43035-9418)
PHONE................................614 840-0599
Keith Hamilton, President
Phil Harris, General Mgr
Jeff Vigar, Vice Pres
Teri Stuckey, Marketing Staff
EMP: 8
SQ FT: 15,000
SALES (est): 1.2MM Privately Held
WEB: www.absoluteimpressions.com
SIC: 2395 Embroidery products, except schiffli machine

(G-11883)
AIR WAVES INC
7750 Green Meadows Dr A (43035-8381)
PHONE................................740 548-1200
Fax: 740 548-1212
Robert Grawe, Ch of Bd
Kevin Simpson, President
Chris Mullin, Vice Pres
Jodi Richards, Accountant
Joseph Flores, Human Resources
◆ EMP: 250 EST: 1981
SQ FT: 110,000
SALES (est): 70.2MM Privately Held
WEB: www.airwavesinc.com
SIC: 2752 2261 2396 Transfers, decalcomania or dry: lithographed; screen printing of cotton broadwoven fabrics; automotive & apparel trimmings

(G-11884)
ATS OHIO INC
Also Called: Automation Tooling Systems
425 Enterprise Dr (43035-9424)
PHONE................................614 888-2344
Anthony Caputo, CEO
Jeff Brennan, General Mgr
Carl Galloway, Vice Pres
Jerry Lepley, Prdtn Mgr
Rich Snodgrass, Project Engr
▼ EMP: 125
SQ FT: 99,000
SALES (est): 17.3MM
SALES (corp-wide): 750.9MM Privately Held
WEB: www.ats-ohio.com
SIC: 3563 Robots for industrial spraying, painting, etc.

PA: Ats Automation Tooling Systems Inc
730 Fountain St Suite 2b
Cambridge ON N3H 4
519 653-4483

(G-11885)
ATS SYSTEMS OREGON INC
425 Enterprise Dr (43035-9424)
PHONE................................541 738-0932
Anthony Caputo, CEO
Maria Perrella, President
Mike Larkin, Purch Mgr
Sam Haines, Engineer
Michael Forgt, Design Engr
▲ EMP: 300
SQ FT: 85,000
SALES (est): 100.1MM
SALES (corp-wide): 750.9MM Privately Held
SIC: 3569 5084 Robots, assembly line: industrial & commercial; industrial machinery & equipment
PA: Ats Automation Tooling Systems Inc
730 Fountain St Suite 2b
Cambridge ON N3H 4
519 653-4483

(G-11886)
AUNTIES ATTIC
1550 Lewis Center Rd G (43035-8232)
PHONE................................740 548-5059
Sherry Clay, Owner
EMP: 35
SQ FT: 3,500
SALES (est): 1.5MM Privately Held
SIC: 2392 5199 Comforters & quilts: made from purchased materials; tablecloths & table settings; towels, dishcloths & dust cloths; gifts & novelties

(G-11887)
AUTOMATION TOOLING SYSTEMS (HQ)
Also Called: Ats Ohio
425 Enterprise Dr (43035-9424)
PHONE................................614 781-8063
Wayne Uhl, General Mgr
Joe Moreno, Principal
Dawn Martinski, Senior VP
Linda Snashall, Purchasing
Douglas Anderson, Engineer
◆ EMP: 140
SQ FT: 150,000
SALES (est): 439.3MM
SALES (corp-wide): 750.9MM Privately Held
SIC: 3569 Assembly machines, non-metalworking; robots, assembly line: industrial & commercial
PA: Ats Automation Tooling Systems Inc
730 Fountain St Suite 2b
Cambridge ON N3H 4
519 653-4483

(G-11888)
AVURE TECHNOLOGIES INC
8270 Green Meadows Dr N (43035-9450)
PHONE................................614 891-2732
Joakim Brangel, Project Mgr
Melanie Harter, Branch Mgr
EMP: 20
SALES (corp-wide): 1.3B Publicly Held
SIC: 3823 Industrial process control instruments
HQ: Avure Technologies Incorporated
1830 Airport Exchange Blv
Erlanger KY 41018
614 255-6633

(G-11889)
BAY INDUSTRIES INCORPORATED
3390 Woodstone Dr (43035-8325)
PHONE................................740 549-2305
Bill Doellman, Principal
EMP: 3
SALES (corp-wide): 364.2MM Privately Held
SIC: 3999 Atomizers, toiletry
HQ: Bay Industries Incorporated
2929 Walker Dr
Green Bay WI 54311
920 406-4000

(G-11890)
BLACK BOX CORPORATION
Also Called: Black Box Columbus
255 Enterprise Dr (43035-9418)
P.O. Box 327 (43035-0327)
PHONE................................614 825-7400
Jessica Kwaczala, Buyer
Mike Jennings, Engineer
Mel Dent, Branch Mgr
Joseph Bash, Branch Mgr
John Kuczkowski, Technology
EMP: 23
SALES (corp-wide): 912.6MM Publicly Held
SIC: 3577 3679 3661 Computer peripheral equipment; electronic switches; modems
PA: Black Box Corporation
1000 Park Dr
Lawrence PA 15055
724 746-5500

(G-11891)
BREAKING BREAD PIZZA COMPANY
9042 Cotter St (43035-7101)
PHONE................................614 754-4777
Thomas Dumit, President
Micheal Scott, Vice Pres
William York, Vice Pres
EMP: 35
SALES (est): 4MM Privately Held
SIC: 2051 Bread, cake & related products

(G-11892)
BTC INC
8595 Columbus Pike 158 (43035-9614)
PHONE................................740 549-2722
Sheldon Lambert, Principal
Jerold S Cook, Principal
Kathy King, Manager
EMP: 26
SALES (est): 5.3MM Privately Held
SIC: 3812 Search & navigation equipment

(G-11893)
CONSUMERS NEWS SERVICES INC (HQ)
Also Called: This Week
7801 N Central Dr (43035-9407)
PHONE................................740 888-6000
Fax: 614 888-6001
Floyd V Jones, President
Felicia Balch, Human Res Dir
Staci Perkins, Mktg Dir
Doug Dixon, Adv Dir
EMP: 150
SALES (est): 15.1MM
SALES (corp-wide): 648.7MM Privately Held
SIC: 2711 Newspapers
PA: The Dispatch Printing Company
62 E Broad St
Columbus OH 43215
614 461-5000

(G-11894)
DICKMAN DIRECTORIES INC
6145 Columbus Pike (43035-9008)
PHONE................................740 548-6130
Toll Free:................................877 -
Fax: 740 548-2217
William L Michel, President
Gerry Michel, Corp Secy
EMP: 6
SQ FT: 5,000
SALES (est): 594.8K Privately Held
SIC: 2741 Directories: publishing & printing

(G-11895)
DISPATCH PRINTING COMPANY
Also Called: Columbus Dispatch
7801 N Central Dr (43035-9407)
PHONE................................740 548-5331
Fax: 740 888-6406
Don Patton, Branch Mgr
EMP: 238
SALES (corp-wide): 648.7MM Privately Held
SIC: 2711 4833 Commercial printing & newspaper publishing combined; television broadcasting stations

PA: The Dispatch Printing Company
62 E Broad St
Columbus OH 43215
614 461-5000

(G-11896)
DURACORP LLC
Also Called: Solut
7787 Graphics Way (43035-8000)
PHONE.................................740 549-3336
Bill Shepard, *CEO*
Scott Rechel, *President*
Jason Kauffman, *Vice Pres*
Erik O Neil, *Vice Pres*
Sam Thomsen, *Vice Pres*
EMP: 25
SALES: 16.7MM **Privately Held**
SIC: 2621 Packaging paper

(G-11897)
EOI INC
Also Called: Medwurx
8377 C Gree Meado Dr N St (43035)
PHONE.................................740 201-3300
Fax: 740 201-3309
Suzi Reichenbach, *CEO*
Randy Reichenbach, *Vice Pres*
Dianne Risch, *CFO*
Muhamad Shehada, *Manager*
▼ **EMP:** 16
SQ FT: 18,000
SALES (est): 8.2MM **Privately Held**
SIC: 5712 5021 5047 3841 Furniture
stores; office & public building furniture;
medical equipment & supplies; hospital
equipment & furniture; instruments, surgi-
cal & medical; diagnostic apparatus, med-
ical; electromedical equipment

(G-11898)
FISCHER-BACKUS CORP
8919 Whitney Dr (43035-7105)
PHONE.................................740 362-2100
Fax: 740 363-0860
Tony Carstens, *CEO*
Dee Gale, *QC Mgr*
EMP: 13
SALES (est): 2.7MM **Privately Held**
SIC: 3679 Harness assemblies for elec-
tronic use: wire or cable

(G-11899)
GRANDVIEW MATERIALS INC
8598 Cotter St (43035-7137)
PHONE.................................614 488-6998
Jonathan Qian, *President*
Jordan Metzker, *Opers Staff*
▲ **EMP:** 4
SALES: 3MM **Privately Held**
WEB: www.grandviewmaterials.com
SIC: 3341 Secondary nonferrous metals

(G-11900)
INDUSTRIAL SOLUTIONS INC
Also Called: I S I
8333 Green Meadows Dr N A
(43035-8497)
PHONE.................................614 431-8118
Fax: 614 431-8843
James D Cooke, *President*
Susan Cooke, *Vice Pres*
Tom Howard, *Opers Mgr*
Scott Cooke, *Finance Dir*
EMP: 21
SALES (est): 4.8MM **Privately Held**
SIC: 3613 Panelboards & distribution
boards, electric

(G-11901)
INPOWER LLC
8311 Green Meadows Dr N (43035-9451)
P.O. Box 2520, Westerville (43086-2520)
PHONE.................................740 548-0965
Greg Woeste, *QC Mgr*
John Melvin, *Engineer*
Robert Ladow, *Natl Sales Mgr*
Chuck Bennett, *VP Mktg*
Karen Sullivan, *Marketing Mgr*
EMP: 15
SQ FT: 14,000
SALES: 59MM **Privately Held**
WEB: www.inpowerdirect.com
SIC: 3559 Electronic component making
machinery

(G-11902)
INTERNATIONAL NOODLE COMPANY
341 Enterprise Dr (43035-9418)
PHONE.................................614 888-0665
Fax: 614 888-0665
Ridge Cheung, *President*
Jerry Cheung, *Vice Pres*
Nathan Cheung, *Manager*
Ning Ho Cheung, *Admin Sec*
▲ **EMP:** 15
SQ FT: 12,000
SALES (est): 2.1MM **Privately Held**
SIC: 2098 Noodles (e.g. egg, plain &
water), dry

(G-11903)
KEITH CHRISSINGER
Also Called: Chrissinger Co
2101 Tucker Trl (43035-8082)
PHONE.................................740 549-0683
Keith Chrissinger, *Owner*
Karen Chrissinger, *Office Mgr*
EMP: 3 **EST:** 1959
SALES (est): 234.9K **Privately Held**
SIC: 3585 Heating & air conditioning com-
bination units

(G-11904)
LAPEL PINS UNLIMITED LLC
5649 Ketch St (43035-8233)
PHONE.................................614 562-3218
Dean M Kuhn, *Principal*
EMP: 3
SALES (est): 250.2K **Privately Held**
SIC: 3452 Pins

(G-11905)
LESCO INC
729-731 Carle Ave (43035)
PHONE.................................740 549-2141
Ted Vonderwell, *Branch Mgr*
EMP: 3
SALES (corp-wide): 26.6B **Publicly Held**
WEB: www.lesco.com
SIC: 2875 Fertilizers, mixing only
HQ: Lesco, Inc.
1385 E 36th St
Cleveland OH 44114
216 706-9250

(G-11906)
LUMENOMICS INC
Also Called: Inside Outfitters
8333 Green Meadows Dr N (43035-8496)
PHONE.................................614 798-3500
Carlee Swihart, *Vice Pres*
EMP: 46
SALES (corp-wide): 5.4MM **Privately
Held**
SIC: 5023 2591 2221 2211 Draperies;
venetian blinds; vertical blinds; window
covering parts & accessories; drapery
hardware & blinds & shades; window
shades; draperies & drapery fabrics, manmade fiber & silk; draperies & drapery
fabrics, cotton; shades, canvas: made
from purchased materials
PA: Lumenomics, Inc.
2819 62nd Ave Sw
Seattle WA 98116
206 327-9037

(G-11907)
MICROCOM CORPORATION
8220 Green Meadows Dr N (43035-9450)
PHONE.................................740 548-6262
Fax: 740 548-6556
Steven Wolfe, *CEO*
James R Larson, *CEO*
Oriana D'Amico, *Exec VP*
David Dezse, *Vice Pres*
John Collins, *Warehouse Mgr*
▲ **EMP:** 24
SQ FT: 29,000
SALES (est): 7.2MM **Privately Held**
WEB: www.microcomcorp.com
SIC: 3577 5111 5112 3953 Printers, com-
puter; bar code (magnetic ink) printers;
printing & writing paper; inked ribbons;
marking devices

(G-11908)
MIDWEST ENERGY EMISSIONS CORP
670 Enterprise Dr Ste D (43035-9441)
PHONE.................................614 505-6115
Christopher Greenberg, *Ch of Bd*
Richard Macpherson, *President*
John Pavlish, *Senior VP*
James Trettel, *Vice Pres*
Richard H Gross, *CFO*
EMP: 17
SALES: 32.3MM **Privately Held**
SIC: 3822 Auto controls regulating residntl
& coml environmt & applncs

(G-11909)
PELTON ENVIRONMENTAL PDTS INC
8638 Cotter St (43035-7136)
PHONE.................................440 838-1221
Patrice Pelton, *President*
Edward Pelton, *Vice Pres*
Art Kimpton, *Sales Engr*
Dan Miller, *Sales Engr*
Jim Pelton, *Sales Engr*
EMP: 8
SALES: 920K **Privately Held**
WEB: www.peltonenv.com
SIC: 5074 3589 Water purification equip-
ment; sewage & water treatment equip-
ment

(G-11910)
PINK CORNER OFFICE INC
8595 Columbus Pike (43035-9614)
PHONE.................................614 547-9350
Mary Young, *CEO*
EMP: 3 **EST:** 2012
SQ FT: 3,000
SALES (est): 224.5K **Privately Held**
SIC: 2721 Magazines: publishing only, not
printed on site

(G-11911)
POWERWASH OF OHIO
8029 Cranes Crossing Dr (43035-8633)
PHONE.................................614 260-2756
Leo Santillo, *Owner*
EMP: 3
SALES (est): 83K **Privately Held**
SIC: 3589 Car washing machinery

(G-11912)
QUINTUS TECHNOLOGIES LLC
8270 Green Meadows Dr N (43035-9450)
PHONE.................................614 891-2732
Corey O'Donnell, *Manager*
EMP: 23
SALES (est): 3.1MM **Privately Held**
SIC: 7699 7389 3443 Industrial equip-
ment services; industrial & commercial
equipment inspection service; industrial
vessels, tanks & containers

(G-11913)
READY MADE RC LLC
7719 Graphics Way Ste F (43035-9667)
PHONE.................................740 936-4500
Timothy J Stanfield, *President*
▲ **EMP:** 4
SQ FT: 2,400
SALES (est): 220K **Privately Held**
SIC: 5945 3944 Children's toys & games,
except dolls; airplane models, toy &
hobby; automobile & truck models, toy &
hobby

(G-11914)
RETAIL MANAGEMENT PRODUCTS
Also Called: Rxscan
8851 Whitney Dr (43035-7107)
PHONE.................................740 548-1725
Max J Peoples, *Partner*
Bill Peoples, *Partner*
Harold Lynch, *Engineer*
William Brunken, *CFO*
William Peoples, *CFO*
EMP: 15
SALES (est): 1.7MM **Privately Held**
WEB: www.rxscan.com
SIC: 7372 Business oriented computer
software

(G-11915)
ROYAL SPA COLUMBUS
9022 Cotter St (43035-7101)
PHONE.................................614 529-8569
Fax: 614 529-8589
Dan Wilson, *Principal*
EMP: 4
SALES (est): 208K **Privately Held**
SIC: 3949 5091 5999 Water sports equip-
ment; hot tubs; hot tub & spa chemicals,
equipment & supplies

(G-11916)
RUBBERTEC INDUSTRIAL PDTS CO
Elledge Gasket
7580 Commerce Ct (43035-9702)
PHONE.................................740 657-3345
Mark Knore, *Manager*
Jeff Severe, *Manager*
EMP: 8
SALES (corp-wide): 6.6MM **Privately
Held**
SIC: 3053 Gaskets, packing & sealing de-
vices
PA: Rubbertec Industrial Products Com-
pany
7580 Commerce Ct
Lewis Center OH 43035
740 657-3345

(G-11917)
SHALLOW LAKE CORP
Also Called: Minuteman Press
8958 Cotter St (43035-7103)
PHONE.................................614 883-6350
Fax: 614 883-6349
Mark Werner, *President*
EMP: 3
SQ FT: 1,200
SALES (est): 364.5K **Privately Held**
SIC: 2752 Commercial printing, litho-
graphic

(G-11918)
SIGNMASTER INC
758 Radio Dr (43035-7112)
PHONE.................................614 777-0670
Sandy Beatner, *President*
Cassandra Gilson, *Marketing Staff*
EMP: 5 **EST:** 1997
SALES (est): 400K **Privately Held**
SIC: 3993 Signs & advertising specialties

(G-11919)
SKY VAULT LTD
1398 Royal Oak Dr (43035-8760)
PHONE.................................740 549-0623
Joshua Paul Nourse, *Principal*
EMP: 3
SALES (est): 217K **Privately Held**
SIC: 3272 Burial vaults, concrete or pre-
cast terrazzo

(G-11920)
SOLID LIGHT COMPANY INC
Also Called: Airwaves
7750 Green Meadows Dr A (43035-8380)
PHONE.................................740 548-1219
Stan Peterson, *Ch of Bd*
Brian Peterson, *President*
Tracy Lytle, *Opers Mgr*
EMP: 28
SQ FT: 12,000
SALES (est): 3.5MM **Privately Held**
WEB: www.solidlightco.com
SIC: 3552 Silk screens for textile industry

(G-11921)
STREAMLINE PRINTING
650 Radio Dr (43035-7111)
P.O. Box 607 (43035-0607)
PHONE.................................740 549-0330
Fax: 740 549-0331
Todd Ichida, *Principal*
EMP: 6
SALES (est): 537.3K **Privately Held**
SIC: 2752 Commercial printing, litho-
graphic

(G-11922)
SUN COMMUNITIES INC
5277 Columbus Pike (43035-9710)
PHONE.................................740 548-1942
EMP: 3

SQ FT: 7,942
SALES (corp-wide): 471.6MM **Publicly Held**
SIC: 6798 2451 Real Estate Investment Trust & Mobile Homes
PA: Sun Communities, Inc.
27777 Franklin Rd Ste 200
Southfield MI 48034
248 208-2500

(G-11923)
TARA ACQUISITION GROUP
Also Called: V-Seal Concrete Sealer
9042 Cotter St (43035-7101)
PHONE..............................614 754-4777
William York, *President*
EMP: 10
SALES (est): 980K **Privately Held**
SIC: 2891 Sealants

(G-11924)
TEC LINE INC
8020 Strawberry Hill Rd (43035-7030)
PHONE..............................740 881-5948
Richard Edgar, *President*
EMP: 4
SALES (est): 792K **Privately Held**
SIC: 2819 Industrial inorganic chemicals

(G-11925)
TESA INC
544 Enterprise Dr Ste A (43035-9704)
PHONE..............................614 847-8200
John Truitt, *President*
Becky Rowland, *Sales Staff*
EMP: 7 EST: 1973
SALES (est): 1MM **Privately Held**
SIC: 3612 5063 Distribution transformers, electric; electrical apparatus & equipment

(G-11926)
TITANIUM LACROSSE LLC
2671 Coltsbridge Dr (43035-8754)
PHONE..............................614 562-8082
Andrew J Auld, *CEO*
EMP: 12
SALES (est): 1.5MM **Privately Held**
SIC: 3356 Titanium

(G-11927)
TRACEWELL SYSTEMS INC (PA)
567 Enterprise Dr (43035-9431)
PHONE..............................614 846-6175
Fax: 614 846-2903
Larry Tracewell, *President*
Doug Hill, *Exec VP*
Matt Tracewell, *Exec VP*
Betty Tracewell, *Vice Pres*
David Angelo, *Engineer*
EMP: 61
SQ FT: 10,000
SALES (est): 29.3MM **Privately Held**
WEB: www.tracewellsystems.com
SIC: 3572 3571 3728 Computer storage devices; electronic computers; aircraft parts & equipment

(G-11928)
WORLDWIDE MACHINE TOOL LLC
9000 Cotter St (43035-7101)
PHONE..............................614 496-9414
Bill Garbe, *President*
◆ EMP: 3
SALES (est): 625.8K **Privately Held**
SIC: 3545 Machine tool accessories

(G-11929)
XIGENT AUTOMATION SYSTEMS INC
8303 Green Meadows Dr N (43035-9451)
PHONE..............................740 548-3700
Joe Moreno, *President*
David Braden, *Design Engr*
Brian Bleichrodt, *CFO*
David Hirth, *Admin Sec*
EMP: 90
SQ FT: 78,000
SALES (est): 25.5MM **Privately Held**
WEB: www.xasinc.com
SIC: 3569 Robots, assembly line: industrial & commercial

(G-11930)
ZSHOT INC
746 Carle Ave (43035-8363)
PHONE..............................800 385-8581
Wallace Lau, *President*
EMP: 3
SALES (est): 406.6K **Privately Held**
SIC: 3484 Small arms; rifles or rifle parts, 30 mm. & below; machine guns or machine gun parts, 30 mm. & below; machine guns & grenade launchers

Lewisburg
Preble County

(G-11931)
ANDERSON PALLET & PACKG INC
Also Called: Anderson Pallet Service
210 Western Ave (45338-9584)
P.O. Box 669 (45338-0669)
PHONE..............................937 962-2614
Fax: 937 962-4783
Ross Anderson, *President*
Marc Anderson, *Vice Pres*
Grace Anderson, *Treasurer*
EMP: 25
SQ FT: 10,000
SALES (est): 3MM **Privately Held**
SIC: 2448 Pallets, wood

(G-11932)
D M TOOL & PLASTICS INC (PA)
4140 Us Route 40 E (45338-9506)
P.O. Box 309, Brookville (45309-0309)
PHONE..............................937 962-4140
Fax: 937 962-4160
Dennis Meyer, *President*
Bill Meyer, *Vice Pres*
Pat Meyer, *Treasurer*
Robert Meyer, *Sales Executive*
Michelle Meyer, *Office Mgr*
EMP: 18
SQ FT: 35,000
SALES (est): 4.2MM **Privately Held**
WEB: www.bulldogtools.com
SIC: 3089 3599 Injection molding of plastics; machine shop, jobbing & repair

(G-11933)
FETZER MACHINING CO INC
5192 Pyrmont Rd (45338-8759)
PHONE..............................937 962-4019
Don Fetzer, *President*
Linda Joy Fetzer, *Vice Pres*
EMP: 4
SQ FT: 1,728
SALES (est): 410.4K **Privately Held**
SIC: 3599 Machine shop, jobbing & repair

(G-11934)
HEALTHY LIVING
4248 New Market Banta Rd (45338-7739)
PHONE..............................937 962-4705
Thomas Apple, *Owner*
Pam Apple, *Co-Owner*
EMP: 3
SALES (est): 205.4K **Privately Held**
SIC: 2023 Dietary supplements, dairy & non-dairy based

(G-11935)
IAMS COMPANY
6571 State Route 503 N (45338-6713)
P.O. Box 862 (45338-0862)
PHONE..............................937 962-2624
Fax: 937 415-8873
Steve Steinberger, *Purchasing*
Ambre Long, *Human Res Dir*
Kurt Petry, *Manager*
EMP: 90
SQ FT: 35,000
SALES (corp-wide): 35B **Privately Held**
WEB: www.iams.com
SIC: 2047 5199 Dog food; pet supplies
HQ: The Iams Company
8700 S Masn Montgomery Rd
Mason OH 45040
800 675-3849

(G-11936)
LEWISBURG CONTAINER COMPANY (DH)
275 W Clay St (45338-8107)
P.O. Box 39 (45338-0039)
PHONE..............................937 962-2681
Fax: 937 962-4504
Anthony Pratt, *President*
Davis Kyles, *Corp Secy*
Chris Prater, *Plant Mgr*
David Wiser, *CFO*
Walter Locker, *Controller*
▲ EMP: 235
SQ FT: 384,000
SALES (est): 52.2MM
SALES (corp-wide): 1.7B **Privately Held**
WEB: www.lpgdesign.com
SIC: 2653 Boxes, corrugated: made from purchased materials; display items, corrugated: made from purchased materials
HQ: Pratt Properties, Inc.
1800 Sarasot Bus Pkwy Ne
Conyers GA 30013
770 918-5678

(G-11937)
MANCO INC
6531 State Route 503 N (45338-6713)
PHONE..............................937 962-2661
Dwight Armstrong, *President*
EMP: 4
SALES (est): 320.5K **Privately Held**
WEB: www.akey.com
SIC: 2048 5499 Bone meal, prepared as animal feed; health & dietetic food stores

(G-11938)
PARKER-HANNIFIN CORPORATION
Also Called: Tube Fitting
700 W Cumberland St (45338-8903)
PHONE..............................937 962-5301
Fax: 937 962-4965
Bill Rammel, *Engineer*
William Bowman, *Branch Mgr*
EMP: 150
SALES (corp-wide): 11.3B **Publicly Held**
WEB: www.parker.com
SIC: 3494 Pipe fittings
PA: Parker-Hannifin Corporation
6035 Parkland Blvd
Cleveland OH 44124
216 896-3000

(G-11939)
PARKER-HANNIFIN CORPORATION
Also Called: Tube Fittings Division
704 W Cumberland St (45338-8903)
PHONE..............................937 962-5566
Fax: 937 962-4505
Jeff Beier, *Plant Mgr*
William Bowman, *Branch Mgr*
Tom Reeves, *Executive*
EMP: 200
SALES (corp-wide): 11.3B **Publicly Held**
WEB: www.parker.com
SIC: 3492 Hose & tube fittings & assemblies, hydraulic/pneumatic
PA: Parker-Hannifin Corporation
6035 Parkland Blvd
Cleveland OH 44124
216 896-3000

(G-11940)
PROVIMI NORTH AMERICA INC
6531 State Route 503 N (45338-6713)
PHONE..............................937 770-2400
Dwight Armstrong, *President*
Dave Norby, *Exec VP*
Charles Shininger, *Senior VP*
Terrence Quinlan, *Vice Pres*
Dan Brouse, *Plant Mgr*
EMP: 55
SALES (corp-wide): 107.1B **Privately Held**
SIC: 2048 Prepared feeds
HQ: Provimi North America, Inc.
10 Collective Way
Brookville OH 45309
937 770-2400

(G-11941)
ROYAL CANIN USA INC
6574 State Route 503 N (45338-8764)
PHONE..............................937 962-7352
EMP: 3
SALES (corp-wide): 35B **Privately Held**
SIC: 0752 2047 Animal specialty services; dog food
HQ: Royal Canin U.S.A., Inc.
500 Fountain Lakes Blvd # 100
Saint Charles MO 63301
636 724-1692

(G-11942)
WYSONG STONE CO
5897 State Route 503 N (45338-6733)
P.O. Box 159 (45338-0159)
PHONE..............................937 962-2559
Fax: 937 962-2842
John D Wysong, *Corp Secy*
Carroll Wysong, *Vice Pres*
EMP: 13 EST: 1965
SQ FT: 1,500
SALES (est): 1MM **Privately Held**
SIC: 1422 Crushed & broken limestone

Lewistown
Logan County

(G-11943)
BLOOM CENTER BIODIESEL LLC
4974 Township Road 79 (43333-9739)
PHONE..............................937 585-6412
Tanya Knief, *Office Mgr*
Timothy Knief,
EMP: 4
SQ FT: 18,000
SALES: 150K **Privately Held**
SIC: 2911 Diesel fuels

(G-11944)
INDUSTRIAL FARM TANK INC
10676 Township Road 80 (43333-9767)
PHONE..............................937 843-2972
Fax: 937 843-2088
Pyllis Yazel, *CEO*
Roger Overbey, *Vice Pres*
EMP: 25
SQ FT: 10,000
SALES (est): 3.3MM **Privately Held**
SIC: 3089 3443 Molding primary plastic; farm storage tanks, metal plate

(G-11945)
KNIEF FARMS A PARTNERSHIP
10532 County Road 13 (43333-9740)
PHONE..............................937 585-4810
Jerry Knief, *Partner*
Kevin Knief, *Partner*
Kyle Knief, *Partner*
EMP: 3
SALES (est): 336.9K **Privately Held**
SIC: 3523 Driers (farm): grain, hay & seed

(G-11946)
MID-STATES PACKAGING INC
12163 State Route 274 (43333-9707)
P.O. Box 126 (43333-0126)
PHONE..............................937 843-3243
Jeffrey C Davidson, *President*
Larry Winner, *Vice Pres*
Bill Frost, *Plant Mgr*
Cathy Nicely, *Manager*
Rich Draper, *Supervisor*
EMP: 35
SQ FT: 40,000
SALES (est): 7.5MM **Privately Held**
SIC: 2679 Hats, paper novelties: made from purchased paper

Lewisville
Monroe County

(G-11947)
BOLON TIMBER LLC
45436 Smithberger Rd (43754-9605)
PHONE..............................740 567-4102
Bill Bolon, *Mng Member*
Becky Bolon,

▲ = Import ▼ = Export
◆ = Import/Export

EMP: 5
SALES: 400K **Privately Held**
SIC: 2411 Logging camps & contractors

(G-11948)
GERALD CHRISTMAN
Also Called: Christman Quarry
47278 Swazey Rd (43754-9410)
PHONE...................................740 838-2475
Fax: 740 838-2545
Gerald Christman, *Owner*
EMP: 5 EST: 1949
SQ FT: 1,000
SALES: 597K **Privately Held**
SIC: 1411 1422 Limestone, dimension-quarrying; crushed & broken limestone

---

Lexington
Richland County

(G-11949)
CONTACT INDUSTRIES INC
25 Industrial Dr (44904-1372)
P.O. Box 3086, Mansfield (44904-0086)
PHONE...................................419 884-9788
Fax: 419 884-9767
James Arnholt, *President*
Jack Arnholt, *General Mgr*
E R Mc Intyre, *Vice Pres*
EMP: 36
SQ FT: 12,000
SALES (est): 5.4MM **Privately Held**
WEB: www.contactind.com
SIC: 3625 3825 3612 Switches, electronic applications; instruments to measure electricity; transformers, except electric

(G-11950)
ENGINEERED FILMS DIVISION (HQ)
230 Industrial Dr (44904-1346)
PHONE...................................419 884-8150
David A Frecka, *CEO*
David J Rehfeldt, *COO*
Dan Niss, *Vice Pres*
Jody Bozeman, *Buyer*
Ryan Courtright, *Financial Analy*
▲ EMP: 2
SQ FT: 44,000
SALES (est): 34.3MM **Privately Held**
WEB: www.nextgenfilms.com
SIC: 2673 2671 Plastic & pliofilm bags; plastic film, coated or laminated for packaging

(G-11951)
NEXT GENERATION FILMS INC (PA)
230 Industrial Dr (44904-1346)
PHONE...................................419 884-8150
Fax: 419 884-8162
David A Frecka, *CEO*
Dan Niss, *President*
Brian Ellis, *Plant Mgr*
Jason Frecka, *Plant Mgr*
David Bubar, *CFO*
▲ EMP: 165
SALES (est): 50.7MM **Privately Held**
SIC: 2673 2671 3089 Plastic & pliofilm bags; plastic film, coated or laminated for packaging; floor coverings, plastic

(G-11952)
SMH MANUFACTURING INC
Also Called: Deca Manufacturing
300 S Mill St (44904-8519)
P.O. Box 3269 (44904-0269)
PHONE...................................419 884-0071
Mark Huffman, *President*
Scott Huffman, *Vice Pres*
EMP: 11
SALES (est): 957.5K **Privately Held**
SIC: 3643 3714 3679 Current-carrying wiring devices; booster (jump-start) cables, automotive; harness assemblies for electronic use: wire or cable

(G-11953)
STONERIDGE INC
Also Called: Hi-Stat A Stoneridge Co
345 S Mill St (44904-9573)
PHONE...................................419 884-1219
Tom Morell, *Plant Mgr*

EMP: 700
SALES (corp-wide): 695.9MM **Publicly Held**
WEB: www.stoneridge.com
SIC: 3714 Motor vehicle electrical equipment
PA: Stoneridge, Inc.
39675 Mackenzie Dr # 400
Novi MI 48377
248 489-9300

(G-11954)
SUPPORT SVC LLC
Also Called: Support Service
25 Walnut St Rear (44904-1260)
PHONE...................................419 617-0660
William Purcell, *Owner*
David Johnson, *Vice Pres*
Robert Purcell III, *CFO*
EMP: 7
SQ FT: 450,000
SALES (est): 1MM **Privately Held**
SIC: 5531 7539 7536 8711 Automotive & home supply stores; alternators & generators, rebuilding & repair; machine shop, automotive; tune-up service, automotive; automotive springs, rebuilding & repair; automotive glass replacement shops; engineering services; nonferrous die-castings except aluminum

---

Liberty Center
Henry County

(G-11955)
MICKENS INC (PA)
Also Called: Deshler Flag
107 East St Ste 1 (43532-9423)
P.O. Box 6 (43532-0006)
PHONE...................................419 533-2401
Donald Mickens, *President*
Susan Mickens, *Vice Pres*
EMP: 5
SQ FT: 2,000
SALES (est): 559K **Privately Held**
WEB: www.mickens.com
SIC: 2711 Newspapers: publishing only, not printed on site

(G-11956)
TRIPLE DIAMOND PLASTICS LLC
405 N Pleasantview Dr (43532-9376)
P.O. Box 1967, Nokomis FL (34274-1967)
PHONE...................................419 533-0085
Fax: 419 533-0087
N Berry Taylor, *CEO*
Michael Wheeler, *Vice Pres*
Megan Taylor, *QC Mgr*
Kristine Taylor, *CFO*
Kevin Knight, *Financial Exec*
EMP: 75
SQ FT: 40,000
SALES: 11MM **Privately Held**
SIC: 3089 Boxes, plastic; pallets, plastic

Liberty Township
Butler County

(G-11957)
ADVANCED OEM SOLUTIONS LLC
6655 Woodsedge Dr (45044-9018)
PHONE...................................513 846-5755
Gavin Dao, *CEO*
EMP: 2
SQ FT: 3,146
SALES: 3MM **Privately Held**
SIC: 3829 Ultrasonic testing equipment

(G-11958)
BOATFUN SPORTS INC
Also Called: FUNSPORTS BRANDS
6548 Westminster Ct (45044-8793)
PHONE...................................513 379-0506
Albert F Buchweitz III, *President*
Stephanie Buchweitz, *Treasurer*
EMP: 3
SQ FT: 400

SALES: 121.4K **Privately Held**
SIC: 3949 Basketball equipment & supplies, general

(G-11959)
COX NEWSPAPERS LLC
Also Called: Western Star Newspaper
200 Harmon Ave (45044)
PHONE...................................513 696-4500
Fax: 513 932-5065
Thomas Barr, *Principal*
Alicia Rosso, *Manager*
EMP: 25
SALES (corp-wide): 32.4B **Privately Held**
WEB: www.coxnewspapers.com
SIC: 2711 Newspapers
HQ: Cox Newspapers, Inc.
6205 Peachtree Dunwoody
Atlanta GA 30328

(G-11960)
COX NEWSPAPERS LLC
Also Called: Hamilton Journalnews
7320 Yankee Rd (45044-9168)
PHONE...................................513 863-8200
EMP: 60
SALES (corp-wide): 32.4B **Privately Held**
SIC: 2711 Newspapers
HQ: Cox Newspapers, Inc.
6205 Peachtree Dunwoody
Atlanta GA 30328

(G-11961)
FLEXTRONICS INTERNATIONAL USA
6224 Windham Ct (45044-8659)
PHONE...................................513 755-2500
EMP: 535
SALES (corp-wide): 24.4B **Privately Held**
SIC: 3672 Printed circuit boards
HQ: Flextronics International Usa, Inc.
6201 America Center Dr
San Jose CA 95002

(G-11962)
GO CALENDARS
7100 Foundry Row (45069-7538)
PHONE...................................513 755-1555
EMP: 4
SALES (est): 119.3K **Privately Held**
SIC: 5943 5112 2752 Office forms & supplies; stationery & office supplies; calendar & card printing, lithographic

(G-11963)
HAMILTON JOURNAL NEWS INC
7320 Yankee Rd (45044-9168)
PHONE...................................513 863-8200
Fax: 513 896-9489
Anne Hoffman, *President*
Dan Hudson, *Technician*
EMP: 75
SALES (est): 3MM **Privately Held**
SIC: 2711 Newspapers, publishing & printing

(G-11964)
HAMPTON PUBLISHING COMPANY
7739 Derbyshire Ct (45044-9028)
PHONE...................................513 777-9543
Mike McNeil, *President*
Angie Fallon, *Mktg Dir*
Barbara McNeil, *Director*
EMP: 5
SALES (est): 517.6K **Privately Held**
SIC: 2741 Maps: publishing & printing

(G-11965)
PULSE JOURNAL
7320 Yankee Rd (45044-9168)
PHONE...................................513 829-7900
Ann Hoffman, *Principal*
EMP: 25
SALES (est): 941.5K **Privately Held**
SIC: 2711 Newspapers, publishing & printing

(G-11966)
QUEST SOLUTIONS GROUP LLC
8046 Green Lake Dr (45044-9474)
PHONE...................................513 703-4520
Larry Thomas,
P Diana Thomas,

EMP: 6
SALES (est): 555.5K **Privately Held**
SIC: 2891 Adhesives & sealants

(G-11967)
SCHNEIDER ELECTRIC USA INC
5425 Longhunter Chase Dr (45044-9817)
PHONE...................................513 755-5503
Alan Turner, *Branch Mgr*
Mark Turner, *Consultant*
EMP: 152
SALES (corp-wide): 241K **Privately Held**
SIC: 3613 Switchgear & switchboard apparatus
HQ: Schneider Electric Usa, Inc.
800 Federal St
Andover MA 01810
978 975-9600

(G-11968)
SHUR CLEAN USA LLC
7568 Wyandot Ln Unit 3 (45044-9609)
P.O. Box 8406, West Chester (45069-8406)
PHONE...................................513 341-5486
David Kling,
EMP: 4 EST: 2011
SQ FT: 5,000
SALES (est): 307.2K **Privately Held**
SIC: 1799 2842 3471 Exterior cleaning, including sandblasting; steam cleaning of building exteriors; specialty cleaning preparations; cleaning, polishing & finishing; cleaning & descaling metal products; decontaminating & cleaning of missile or satellite parts

(G-11969)
TITAN METAL FABRICATORS
Also Called: Sales Engineering Dept
7835 Kyles Station Rd (45044-9404)
PHONE...................................513 755-3394
Larry Haubner, *Business Mgr*
EMP: 10
SALES (corp-wide): 36.3MM **Privately Held**
SIC: 3499 Aerosol valves, metal
PA: Titan Metal Fabricators, Inc.
352 Balboa Cir
Camarillo CA 93012
805 487-5050

Liberty Twp
Butler County

(G-11970)
APOSTROPHE APPS LLC
4452 Millikin Rd (45011-2309)
PHONE...................................513 608-4399
Mark Seremet,
EMP: 3
SALES (est): 149.1K **Privately Held**
SIC: 7372 7389 Application computer software;

(G-11971)
ARC BLINDS INC
4889 Mercedes Dr (45011-2429)
PHONE...................................513 889-4864
Dan Tichenor, *Principal*
EMP: 4 EST: 2012
SALES (est): 513.1K **Privately Held**
SIC: 2591 Window blinds

(G-11972)
COFFING CORPORATION (PA)
5336 Lesourdsville Rd (45011-9740)
PHONE...................................513 919-2813
Fax: 513 779-7323
Chris Coffing, *President*
Jerry Stretch, *Controller*
Kenny Wilson, *CIO*
EMP: 21
SQ FT: 5,000
SALES (est): 3.8MM **Privately Held**
SIC: 7372 Prepackaged software

(G-11973)
D M L STEEL TECH
6974 Zenith Ct (45011-7207)
PHONE...................................513 737-9911
Suguna Bommaraju, *Partner*
Rama Bommaraju, *Partner*

EMP: 13
SALES (est): 1.3MM **Privately Held**
SIC: 3315 8748 Steel wire & related products; business consulting

(G-11974)
DALACO MATERIALS LLC
4805 Hamilton Middltwn (45011-2686)
PHONE..................................513 893-5483
Fax: 513 893-5484
Randy Ledford, *Manager*
Dallas Myers,
EMP: 15
SQ FT: 120,000
SALES (est): 3.1MM **Privately Held**
SIC: 3272 Concrete products

(G-11975)
KENNETH SHANNON
5438 Kyles Station Rd (45011-9741)
PHONE..................................513 777-8888
Kenneth Shannon, *Principal*
EMP: 3
SALES (est): 180K **Privately Held**
SIC: 2512 Upholstered household furniture

(G-11976)
KUWATCH PRINTING LLC
Also Called: Corporate Printing
7163 Ashview Ln (45011-8723)
PHONE..................................513 759-5850
Kurt Kuwatch,
EMP: 4
SQ FT: 6,500
SALES: 500K **Privately Held**
WEB: www.corp-print.com
SIC: 2752 Commercial printing, lithographic

(G-11977)
OE PLASTICS LLC
7070 Lindley Way (45011-9166)
PHONE..................................513 847-8101
Matt Crossin,
EMP: 3
SALES (est): 193.4K **Privately Held**
SIC: 3089 Air mattresses, plastic

(G-11978)
R&D SOFTWARE SERVICES INC
4648 Mesa Pl (45011-7235)
P.O. Box 249, West Chester (45071-0249)
PHONE..................................513 755-8851
Ronald Gregory, *President*
EMP: 5
SALES: 160K **Privately Held**
WEB: www.rdssi.com
SIC: 7372 Prepackaged software

Lima
Allen County

(G-11979)
3 BROTHERS TORCHING INC
4915 Dutch Hollow Rd (45807-9703)
PHONE..................................419 339-9985
Donnie Gipson, *Mng Member*
EMP: 3
SALES (est): 291.7K **Privately Held**
SIC: 3541 Machine tools, metal cutting type

(G-11980)
ACCUBUILT INC (PA)
2550 Cent Point Pkwy (45804)
PHONE..................................419 224-3910
Gregory J Corona, *President*
Ronald Reagan, *Principal*
Tim Keiber, *Opers Staff*
Kevin Grady, *CFO*
EMP: 216
SQ FT: 168,000
SALES: 81.3MM **Privately Held**
SIC: 3711 Hearses (motor vehicles), assembly of

(G-11981)
ACCUBUILT INC
Also Called: Eureeka
2550 Central Point Pkwy (45804-3890)
PHONE..................................419 224-3910
Rob Hubbard, *CEO*
Ed McDonald, *VP Sls/Mktg*

EMP: 119
SQ FT: 168,000
SALES (est): 17.2MM
SALES (corp-wide): 81.3MM **Privately Held**
SIC: 3711 Hearses (motor vehicles), assembly of
PA: Accubuilt, Inc.
2550 Cent Point Pkwy
Lima OH 45804
419 224-3910

(G-11982)
AFFORDABLE MED SCRUBS LLC (PA)
Also Called: AMS Uniforms
2190 Allentown Rd (45805-1706)
PHONE..................................419 222-1088
Ted Ralston, *President*
▲ **EMP:** 40
SQ FT: 15,000
SALES (est): 12.7MM **Privately Held**
WEB: www.affordablemedscrubs.com
SIC: 2326 Medical & hospital uniforms, men's

(G-11983)
AIRGAS USA LLC
1590 Mcclain Rd (45804-1974)
PHONE..................................419 228-2828
Jason Morsow, *Manager*
EMP: 16
SALES (corp-wide): 163.9MM **Privately Held**
WEB: www.us.linde-gas.com
SIC: 2813 5084 Argon; welding machinery & equipment
HQ: Airgas Usa, Llc
259 N Radnor Chester Rd # 100
Radnor PA 19087
610 687-5253

(G-11984)
AIRWAVE COMMUNICATIONS CONS
Also Called: Cell 4less
1209 Allentown Rd (45805-2432)
P.O. Box 5216 (45802-5216)
PHONE..................................419 331-1526
Dominic Sementelli, *President*
Jeff Lunguy, *Exec VP*
EMP: 5
SQ FT: 2,700
SALES (est): 900K **Privately Held**
SIC: 4813 4812 3577 7371 Local & long distance telephone communications; voice telephone communications; radio pager (beeper) communication services; computer peripheral equipment; computer software systems analysis & design, custom

(G-11985)
AKZO NOBEL CHEMICALS LLC
1747 Fort Amanda Rd (45804-1864)
PHONE..................................419 229-0088
Kathy Scott, *Manager*
Ron Wilson, *Manager*
EMP: 4
SALES (corp-wide): 15.9B **Privately Held**
WEB: www.akzo-nobel.com
SIC: 2869 2899 Industrial organic chemicals; chemical preparations
HQ: Akzo Nobel Chemicals Llc
525 W Van Buren St # 1600
Chicago IL 60607
312 544-7000

(G-11986)
ALLEN COUNTY FABRICATION INC
Also Called: A C F
999 Industry Ave (45804-4171)
PHONE..................................419 227-7447
Fax: 419 227-7599
Kevin E Hall, *President*
Ronald M Kennedy, *President*
Patricia Kennedy, *Treasurer*
Billie Neal, *Manager*
Margie Egan, *Administration*
EMP: 20
SQ FT: 16,800
SALES (est): 3.8MM **Privately Held**
WEB: www.allencountyfab.com
SIC: 3444 Sheet metalwork

(G-11987)
ALPHA BUS FORMS & PRTG LLC
4330 East Rd (45807-1535)
PHONE..................................419 999-5138
Kris Griss, *Manager*
Karen E Burgoon,
Pam Baker,
Phillip Kleman,
Karen McElroy,
EMP: 3
SQ FT: 6,000
SALES (est): 285.3K **Privately Held**
WEB: www.alphaprintingforms.com
SIC: 2759 Business forms: printing

(G-11988)
AMERICAN BOTTLING COMPANY
Also Called: 7 Up Bottling Co
2350 Central Point Pkwy (45804-3806)
PHONE..................................419 229-7777
Fax: 419 224-2082
Mike Hoenie, *Manager*
EMP: 26
SALES (corp-wide): 6.4B **Publicly Held**
WEB: www.cs-americas.com
SIC: 2086 Bottled & canned soft drinks
HQ: The American Bottling Company
5301 Legacy Dr
Plano TX 75024

(G-11989)
AMERICAN TRIM LLC
Also Called: Superior Metal Products
999 W Grand Ave (45801-3427)
PHONE..................................419 996-4703
Dustin Halleck, *Engineer*
Brian Bishop, *Electrical Engi*
Randy Fosnaugh, *Branch Mgr*
EMP: 3
SALES (corp-wide): 460MM **Privately Held**
SIC: 3469 Metal stampings; porcelain enameled products & utensils; ornamental metal stampings
HQ: American Trim, L.L.C.
1005 W Grand Ave
Lima OH 45801

(G-11990)
AMERICAN TRIM LLC
651 N Baxter St (45801-3953)
PHONE..................................419 996-4729
Gary Fosnaugh, *Branch Mgr*
Chris Hunt, *Maintence Staff*
EMP: 100
SALES (corp-wide): 460MM **Privately Held**
SIC: 3469 Metal stampings; porcelain enameled products & utensils; ornamental metal stampings
HQ: American Trim, L.L.C.
1005 W Grand Ave
Lima OH 45801

(G-11991)
AMERICAN TRIM LLC
625 Victory Ave (45801-3952)
PHONE..................................419 996-4703
Randy Fosnaugh, *Manager*
Steve Hatkevich, *Director*
EMP: 73
SALES (corp-wide): 460MM **Privately Held**
SIC: 3469 Metal stampings; porcelain enameled products & utensils; ornamental metal stampings
HQ: American Trim, L.L.C.
1005 W Grand Ave
Lima OH 45801

(G-11992)
AMERICAN TRIM LLC (HQ)
1005 W Grand Ave (45801-3429)
PHONE..................................419 228-1145
Fax: 419 221-4884
Jeffrey A Hawk, *CEO*
Marcelo Gonzalez, *General Mgr*
Leo J Hawk, *Chairman*
Rick Pfeifer, *Vice Pres*
Jerry Handrich, *Project Mgr*
▲ **EMP:** 50
SQ FT: 15,000

SALES (est): 256MM
SALES (corp-wide): 460MM **Privately Held**
SIC: 3469 Metal stampings; porcelain enameled products & utensils; ornamental metal stampings
PA: Superior Metal Products, Inc.
1005 W Grand Ave
Lima OH 45801
419 228-1145

(G-11993)
AREA WIDE PROTECTIVE INC
413 Flanders Ave (45801-4117)
PHONE..................................419 221-2997
EMP: 3
SALES (corp-wide): 139.7MM **Privately Held**
SIC: 3669 Pedestrian traffic control equipment
HQ: Area Wide Protective, Inc.
826 Overholt Rd
Kent OH 44240
330 644-0655

(G-11994)
ARTS ROLLOFFS & REFUSE INC
108 Cheshire Cir (45804-3316)
P.O. Box 2039, Cridersville (45806-0039)
PHONE..................................419 991-3730
Arthor Recker, *President*
EMP: 3
SALES (est): 414.4K **Privately Held**
SIC: 3713 Garbage, refuse truck bodies

(G-11995)
ASHLAND LLC
1220 S Metcalf St (45804-1171)
PHONE..................................419 998-8728
Charley Gaspereppi, *Manager*
EMP: 40
SALES (corp-wide): 4.9B **Publicly Held**
WEB: www.ispcorp.com
SIC: 2899 Chemical preparations
HQ: Ashland Llc
50 E Rivercenter Blvd # 1600
Covington KY 41011
859 815-3333

(G-11996)
BRANDON SCREEN PRINTING
326 S West St (45801-4844)
PHONE..................................419 229-9837
Fax: 419 224-3595
Robert L Liddle, *Owner*
Tiffany Liddle, *Office Mgr*
EMP: 10
SQ FT: 12,000
SALES: 1MM **Privately Held**
SIC: 2396 3993 2752 Screen printing on fabric articles; signs & advertising specialties; commercial printing, lithographic

(G-11997)
BRINKMAN LLC
Also Called: American Paint Recyclers
1524 Adak Ave (45805-3905)
PHONE..................................419 204-5934
Jeremy Brinkman, *Mng Member*
Joshua Brinkman,
EMP: 10 EST: 2007
SALES (est): 220K **Privately Held**
SIC: 2851 5812 7359 Paints & paint additives; pizzeria, independent; equipment rental & leasing

(G-11998)
BRP MANUFACTURING COMPANY
Also Called: Buckeye Rubber Products
637 N Jackson St (45801-4125)
PHONE..................................800 858-0482
Fax: 419 222-5010
Kendall House, *President*
Steve Pendergast, *Vice Pres*
Matt Henderson, *Controller*
Jim Ward, *Sales Mgr*
Donovan Lonsway, *Manager*
◆ **EMP:** 44 EST: 1997
SQ FT: 190,000

SALES (est): 10.8MM **Privately Held**
WEB: www.brpmfg.com
SIC: 3069 3061 2822 Sheeting, rubber or rubberized fabric; friction tape, rubber; mechanical rubber goods; synthetic rubber

(G-11999)
CAMERON PACKAGING INC
250 E Hanthorn Rd (45804-2344)
PHONE.............................419 222-9404
Fax: 419 222-9802
Michael Cameron, *CEO*
Grant Morgenstern, *President*
Bridget Cribben, *Treasurer*
Diane Cameron, *Admin Sec*
▲ **EMP:** 9
SQ FT: 56,000
SALES (est): 1.7MM **Privately Held**
WEB: www.cameronpackaging.com
SIC: 2653 Corrugated & solid fiber boxes

(G-12000)
COCA-COLA BOTTLING CO CNSLD
201 N Shore Dr (45801-4822)
P.O. Box 268, Findlay (45839-0268)
PHONE.............................419 422-3743
Fax: 419 422-9532
John Iafolla, *Branch Mgr*
EMP: 9
SALES (corp-wide): 3.1B **Publicly Held**
WEB: www.colasic.net
SIC: 2086 Bottled & canned soft drinks
PA: Coca-Cola Bottling Co. Consolidated
4100 Coca Cola Plz # 100
Charlotte NC 28211
704 557-4400

(G-12001)
COCA-COLA BOTTLING CO CNSLD
201 N Shore Dr (45801-4822)
PHONE.............................419 229-2000
Fax: 419 228-6102
Greg Walker, *Manager*
EMP: 43
SQ FT: 5,000
SALES (corp-wide): 3.1B **Publicly Held**
WEB: www.colasic.net
SIC: 2086 Bottled & canned soft drinks
PA: Coca-Cola Bottling Co. Consolidated
4100 Coca Cola Plz # 100
Charlotte NC 28211
704 557-4400

(G-12002)
CSS PUBLISHING CO INC
5450 N Dixie Hwy (45807-9559)
PHONE.............................419 227-1818
Wesley T Runk, *President*
Patti Furr, *Vice Pres*
Elen Shockey, *Treasurer*
David Runk, *VP Sales*
Alanna Pugsley, *Marketing Staff*
EMP: 30
SQ FT: 50,000
SALES (est): 2.6MM **Privately Held**
WEB: www.csspub.com
SIC: 2731 5192 Book publishing; books

(G-12003)
CUSTOM BLAST & COAT INC
1511 S Dixie Hwy (45804-1844)
PHONE.............................419 225-6024
G J Gossard, *President*
Bruce Dukeman, *Admin Sec*
EMP: 8
SALES (est): 1MM **Privately Held**
SIC: 3312 Blast furnace & related products

(G-12004)
DANA DRIVESHAFT MFG LLC
Also Called: Dana Driveshaft Products
777 Bible Rd (45801-2025)
PHONE.............................419 222-9708
Larry Kuphal, *Facilities Mgr*
Nick Fasone, *Branch Mgr*
Steve Grose, *Manager*
Dan Sommers, *Manager*
Paul Suber, *Manager*
EMP: 118
SALES (corp-wide): 5.8B **Publicly Held**
SIC: 3714 Motor vehicle parts & accessories

HQ: Dana Driveshaft Manufacturing, Llc
3939 Technology Dr
Maumee OH 43537
419 887-3000

(G-12005)
DR PEPPER/SEVEN UP INC
2350 Central Point Pkwy (45804-3806)
PHONE.............................419 229-7777
Marvin Lehman, *Principal*
Kevin Perry, *Manager*
EMP: 68
SALES (corp-wide): 6.4B **Publicly Held**
SIC: 2086 Bottled & canned soft drinks
HQ: Dr Pepper/Seven Up, Inc.
5301 Legacy Dr Fl 1
Plano TX 75024
972 673-7000

(G-12006)
DYNACO USA INC
1075 Prosperity Rd (45801-3127)
PHONE.............................419 227-3000
Deb Kruger, *Branch Mgr*
EMP: 3
SALES (corp-wide): 7.8B **Privately Held**
SIC: 3442 Rolling doors for industrial buildings or warehouses, metal
HQ: Dynaco Usa, Inc.
935 Campus Dr
Mundelein IL 60060
847 562-4910

(G-12007)
E L FRUEH INC
Also Called: Longmeier Printing & Advg
232 N Union St (45801-4452)
PHONE.............................419 222-9741
Fax: 419 222-5196
Micheal Frueh, *President*
Jim Lewis, *Purchasing*
John Parkins, *Web Dvlpr*
EMP: 14
SQ FT: 27,750
SALES (est): 2.5MM **Privately Held**
WEB: www.longmeier.com
SIC: 2752 2789 7331 2791 Letters, circular or form: lithographed; binding only: books, pamphlets, magazines, etc.; direct mail advertising services; typesetting; commercial printing; automotive & apparel trimmings

(G-12008)
E S INDUSTRIES INC (PA)
110 Brookview Ct (45801-2070)
PHONE.............................419 643-2625
Charles L Dale, *President*
EMP: 7
SALES (est): 6.9MM **Privately Held**
SIC: 3535 3556 4221 Conveyors & conveying equipment; food products machinery; grain elevator, storage only

(G-12009)
ELWERS FENCE
Also Called: Elwer Fence
367 Fraunfelter Rd N (45807-9409)
PHONE.............................419 221-2511
David E Elwer, *President*
EMP: 5
SALES (est): 250K **Privately Held**
SIC: 3446 Fences, gates, posts & flagpoles

(G-12010)
ERIE CERAMIC ARTS COMPANY LLC
1005 W Grand Ave (45801-3429)
PHONE.............................419 228-1145
Rick Pfeifer,
Jeffrey Hawk,
Leo J Hawk,
Dana Morgan,
EMP: 5 **EST:** 1946
SQ FT: 200,000
SALES (est): 825K
SALES (corp-wide): 460MM **Privately Held**
SIC: 3479 Enameling, including porcelain, of metal products
PA: Superior Metal Products, Inc.
1005 W Grand Ave
Lima OH 45801
419 228-1145

(G-12011)
ERNST ENTERPRISES INC
Also Called: Ernst Ready Mix Division
377 S Central Ave (45804-1301)
PHONE.............................419 222-2015
Fax: 419 227-6120
Edward Bryam, *Manager*
EMP: 17
SALES (corp-wide): 191MM **Privately Held**
WEB: www.ernstconcrete.com
SIC: 5211 3275 Concrete & cinder block; gypsum products
PA: Ernst Enterprises, Inc.
3361 Successful Way
Dayton OH 45414
937 233-5555

(G-12012)
F3 DEFENSE SYSTEMS LLC
1601 S Dixie Hwy (45804-1842)
P.O. Box 344, Ellenton FL (34222-0344)
PHONE.............................419 982-2020
Shefali Vibhakar, *Partner*
EMP: 9 **EST:** 2013
SQ FT: 24,600
SALES (est): 619.3K **Privately Held**
SIC: 3599 Machine & other job shop work; machine shop, jobbing & repair

(G-12013)
FMH ELECTRIC INC
Also Called: Mac Electric
1240 Fairgreen Ave (45805-4432)
PHONE.............................419 782-0671
Nancy Hartung, *President*
F Michael Hartung, *Vice Pres*
EMP: 12
SQ FT: 6,400
SALES (est): 1.2MM **Privately Held**
SIC: 7694 7699 5063 Electric motor repair; compressor repair; pumps & pumping equipment repair; motors, electric

(G-12014)
FORD MOTOR COMPANY
1155 Bible Rd (45801-3193)
PHONE.............................419 226-7000
Fax: 419 226-7338
Colleen Stein, *Purch Mgr*
Marcus Lyons, *QC Mgr*
Rick Froning, *Engineer*
Jim Hare, *Engineer*
Bart Moser, *Engineer*
EMP: 1949
SQ FT: 2,424,360
SALES (corp-wide): 151.8B **Publicly Held**
WEB: www.ford.com
SIC: 3714 3519 Motor vehicle engines & parts; internal combustion engines
PA: Ford Motor Company
1 American Rd
Dearborn MI 48126
313 322-3000

(G-12015)
FORT AMANDA SPECIALTIES LLC
1747 Fort Amanda Rd (45804-1864)
PHONE.............................419 229-0088
Tom Keating, *General Mgr*
Ross Recker, *Project Mgr*
Bouke Ankone, *Opers Mgr*
Mike Murray, *Opers Mgr*
Lisa Goodin, *Engineer*
▲ **EMP:** 85
SALES (est): 38.1MM
SALES (corp-wide): 15.9B **Privately Held**
WEB: www.fortamanda.com
SIC: 2899 Chemical preparations
PA: Akzo Nobel N.V.
Christian Neefestraat 2
Amsterdam
889 697-555

(G-12016)
FULTZ SIGN CO INC
3350 Slabtown Rd (45801-2212)
PHONE.............................419 225-6000
Fax: 419 225-6000
Chris Fultz, *President*
Evelyn Fultz, *Vice Pres*
EMP: 4
SQ FT: 1,492

SALES (est): 399.1K **Privately Held**
SIC: 3993 Signs & advertising specialties

(G-12017)
GASDORF TOOL AND MCH CO INC
445 N Mcdonel St (45801-4266)
P.O. Box 1194 (45802-1194)
PHONE.............................419 227-0103
Fax: 419 227-5984
Richard R Rapp, *President*
Dave Prinsen, *General Mgr*
Lynn Krohn, *Corp Secy*
Chris Rode, *Plant Engr*
Shannon Rapp, *Office Mgr*
EMP: 30 **EST:** 1953
SQ FT: 20,000
SALES (est): 5.1MM **Privately Held**
SIC: 3599 3544 Custom machinery; special dies & tools; jigs & fixtures; industrial molds

(G-12018)
GENERAL DYNAMICS LAND
Also Called: General Dynamics Lima Army Tan
1161 Buckeye Rd (45804-1825)
PHONE.............................419 221-7000
Fax: 419 221-7026
John Grothouse, *Engineer*
Tom Heckman, *Engineer*
Dominic Inkrott, *Engineer*
Joe Mueller, *Engineer*
Craig Otto, *Engineer*
EMP: 400
SALES (corp-wide): 31.3B **Publicly Held**
WEB: www.gdls.com
SIC: 3795 Tanks, military, including factory rebuilding
HQ: General Dynamics Land Systems Inc.
38500 Mound Rd
Sterling Heights MI 48310
586 825-4000

(G-12019)
GREATER OHIO ETHANOL LLC (PA)
7227 Harding Hwy (45801-8719)
PHONE.............................567 940-9500
Gregory A Kruger, *Mng Member*
Michelle Grapner, *Admin Asst*
James Blair,
EMP: 8
SQ FT: 3,000
SALES (est): 559K **Privately Held**
WEB: www.go-ethanol.com
SIC: 2869 Ethyl alcohol, ethanol

(G-12020)
GROSS & SONS CUSTOM MILLWORK
1219 Grant St (45801-3735)
PHONE.............................419 227-0214
Fax: 419 227-0214
James H Gross, *Partner*
Louise Gross, *Treasurer*
EMP: 6
SQ FT: 8,000
SALES (est): 800.8K **Privately Held**
SIC: 2431 Millwork

(G-12021)
GUARDIAN LIMA LLC
2485 Houx Pkwy (45804-3901)
PHONE.............................567 940-9500
Don Dales, *CEO*
Chris Kaufman, *Maintence Staff*
EMP: 34
SALES (est): 13.1MM
SALES (corp-wide): 21.9MM **Privately Held**
SIC: 2869 Ethyl alcohol, ethanol
PA: Guardian Energy, Llc
4745 380th Ave
Janesville MN 56048
507 234-5000

(G-12022)
HCF OF BOWLING GREEN INC
1100 Shawnee Rd (45805-3583)
PHONE.............................419 999-2010
EMP: 3
SALES (est): 116.1K **Privately Held**
SIC: 2673 Bags: plastic, laminated & coated

GEOGRAPHIC

(G-12023)
HEAT TREATING TECHNOLOGIES
1799 E 4th St (45804-2713)
PHONE.................................419 224-8324
Fax: 419 229-3299
Chester L Walthall, *CEO*
Richard W Deibel, *President*
Matt Arlington, *Manager*
Mike Schoenleben, *Manager*
Judith Walthall, *Admin Sec*
EMP: 23
SQ FT: 33,000
SALES (est): 4.9MM **Privately Held**
WEB: www.httlima.com
SIC: 3398 Metal heat treating

(G-12024)
HIGH TECH METAL PRODUCTS LLC
2300 Central Point Pkwy (45804-3806)
PHONE.................................419 227-9414
Fax: 419 227-2554
Jerry Neuman, *Owner*
Carmon Gehrlich, *Manager*
Judy Stark, *Manager*
EMP: 8
SQ FT: 25,000
SALES (est): 660K **Privately Held**
SIC: 3599 Machine shop, jobbing & repair

(G-12025)
HILL-ROM HOLDINGS INC
1273 N Cole St (45801-3413)
PHONE.................................937 604-6019
EMP: 3
SALES (corp-wide): 2.6B **Publicly Held**
SIC: 3841 Surgical & medical instruments
PA: Hill-Rom Holdings, Inc.
    2 Prudential Plz Ste 4100
    Chicago IL 60601
    312 819-7200

(G-12026)
IHEARTCOMMUNICATIONS INC
Also Called: Clear Channel
667 W Market St (45801-4603)
PHONE.................................419 223-2060
Kim Field, *General Mgr*
Matt Bell, *Sales Executive*
John Bell, *Executive*
Robin Palmer, *Executive*
EMP: 65
SALES (corp-wide): 6.2B **Publicly Held**
SIC: 4832 2711 Radio broadcasting stations; newspapers
HQ: Iheartcommunications, Inc.
    200 E Basse Rd
    San Antonio TX 78209
    210 822-2828

(G-12027)
INEOS LLC (PA)
1900 Fort Amanda Rd (45804-1827)
P.O. Box 628 (45802-0628)
PHONE.................................419 226-1200
Dennis Seith, *President*
Tracey Maag, *COO*
Patrick Kiser, *Safety Mgr*
Baron Wair, *Buyer*
Bradley Crossen, *Engineer*
▲ EMP: 66
SALES (est): 36MM **Privately Held**
SIC: 2821 Plastics materials & resins

(G-12028)
INEOS AMERICAS LLC
1900 Fort Amanda Rd (45804-1827)
P.O. Box 628 (45802-0628)
PHONE.................................419 226-1200
Ulises Cruz, *Regional Mgr*
Mike Hazel, *Mfg Mgr*
Gerry Zajac, *Research*
Sandi Feltz, *Electrical Engi*
Elaine Schield, *Controller*
EMP: 300
SALES (corp-wide): 40B **Privately Held**
WEB: www.ineostechnologies.com
SIC: 2869 2873 2819 2813 Industrial organic chemicals; nitrogenous fertilizers; industrial inorganic chemicals; industrial gases

HQ: Ineos Americas Llc
    2600 S Shore Blvd Ste 500
    League City TX 77573
    281 535-6600

(G-12029)
INEOS USA LLC
1900 Fort Amanda Rd (45804-1827)
P.O. Box 628 (45802-0628)
PHONE.................................419 226-1200
Cheri Zuber, *Branch Mgr*
EMP: 89
SALES (corp-wide): 40B **Privately Held**
SIC: 2821 Plastics materials & resins
HQ: Ineos Usa Llc
    2600 S Shore Blvd Ste 500
    League City TX 77573
    281 535-6600

(G-12030)
INNOVATIVE PACKAGING LLC
1150 N Cable Rd Ste B (45805-1436)
PHONE.................................419 222-6071
Mike Baker, *Mng Member*
Drew Fields,
Brian Hanneman, *Assistant*
EMP: 15
SQ FT: 27,000
SALES (est): 4.7MM **Privately Held**
SIC: 2653 Corrugated & solid fiber boxes

(G-12031)
ISP LIMA LLC
12220 S Metcalf St (45804)
PHONE.................................419 998-8700
Sunil Kumar,
EMP: 36
SALES (est): 8.4MM
SALES (corp-wide): 124.7MM **Privately Held**
SIC: 2911 Petroleum refining
HQ: Isp Chemicals Llc
    455 N Main St
    Calvert City KY 42029
    270 395-4165

(G-12032)
J M HAMILTON GROUP INC
Also Called: Metal Coating Company
1700 Elida Rd (45805-1511)
PHONE.................................419 229-4010
Fax: 419 229-4020
Howell D Glover Jr, *President*
Marie L Glover, *Principal*
James I Hunt, *Principal*
John H Romey, *Principal*
Linda Musselman, *Business Mgr*
EMP: 18
SQ FT: 25,000
SALES (est): 2.6MM **Privately Held**
WEB: www.metalcoatingcompany.com
SIC: 3479 3559 3471 Painting, coating & hot dipping; glass making machinery: blowing, molding, forming, etc.; plating & polishing

(G-12033)
J&D BECK CO INC
Also Called: Imageries
325 W High St (45801-4701)
PHONE.................................419 224-0027
Toll Free:.........................877 -
Fax: 419 224-0029
David Beck, *President*
Julie Kirk, *Corp Secy*
EMP: 5
SALES (est): 541.5K **Privately Held**
SIC: 2396 Screen printing on fabric articles

(G-12034)
JOINT SYSTEMS MFG CTR
1155 Buckeye Rd Bldg 147 (45804-1815)
PHONE.................................419 221-9580
▲ EMP: 3
SALES (est): 240.5K **Privately Held**
SIC: 3795 Tanks & tank components

(G-12035)
KENNEDY GRAPHICS INC (PA)
1640 N Main St (45801-2825)
PHONE.................................419 223-9825
Fax: 419 222-7103
Mary Sprague-Mccourt, *President*
EMP: 5
SALES (est): 607.3K **Privately Held**
SIC: 2752 Commercial printing, offset

(G-12036)
KW SERVICES LLC
1864 Mccullough St (45801-3059)
PHONE.................................419 228-1325
Fax: 419 222-6653
Kermit Caudill Jr, *General Mgr*
EMP: 6
SALES (corp-wide): 87.7MM **Privately Held**
WEB: www.koontz-wagner.com
SIC: 7694 Electric motor repair
PA: Kw Services, Llc
    3801 Voorde Dr Ste B
    South Bend IN 46628
    574 232-2051

(G-12037)
LEADAR ROLL INC (PA)
893 Shawnee Rd (45805-3437)
PHONE.................................419 227-2200
Gary Stanklus, *President*
Darlene Stanklus, *Corp Secy*
Steve Hull, *Vice Pres*
Rob Monnin, *Controller*
▲ EMP: 25
SQ FT: 12,000
SALES (est): 5.1MM **Privately Held**
SIC: 3547 Rolling mill machinery

(G-12038)
LEE A WILLIAMS JR
205 W Elm St (45804-4811)
P.O. Box 267 (45802-0267)
PHONE.................................419 225-6751
Lee A Wiliams Jr, *Owner*
EMP: 3
SALES (est): 206.1K **Privately Held**
SIC: 1311 Crude petroleum & natural gas production

(G-12039)
LIMA ARMATURE WORKS INC
Also Called: Double Eagle
142 E Pearl St (45804-4149)
PHONE.................................419 222-4010
Fax: 419 224-4749
James W Smith, *Ch of Bd*
Rick Smith, *President*
Margaret E Smith, *Corp Secy*
EMP: 7 EST: 1927
SQ FT: 41,000
SALES (est): 1.5MM **Privately Held**
WEB: www.limaarmature.com
SIC: 7694 5063 Electric motor repair; motors, electric; motor controls, starters & relays: electric; transformers & transmission equipment; electrical supplies

(G-12040)
LIMA EQUIPMENT CO
895 Shawnee Rd (45805-3437)
P.O. Box 943 (45802-0943)
PHONE.................................419 222-4181
Fax: 419 222-4181
James Gideon, *President*
Angie Mox, *Office Mgr*
▲ EMP: 5
SQ FT: 20,000
SALES: 400K **Privately Held**
SIC: 3548 5063 5085 Welding & cutting apparatus & accessories; generators; industrial supplies

(G-12041)
LIMA PALLET COMPANY INC
1470 Neubrecht Rd (45801-3122)
PHONE.................................419 229-5736
Fax: 419 229-5736
Tracie Sanchez, *President*
Kelly Sarno, *Vice Pres*
Brian Cunningham, *Marketing Staff*
Micah French, *Manager*
Matt Hefner, *Administration*
EMP: 21
SQ FT: 25,000
SALES (est): 3.5MM **Privately Held**
WEB: www.limapallet.com
SIC: 2448 2441 Pallets, wood; nailed wood boxes & shook

(G-12042)
LIMA REFINING COMPANY (HQ)
1150 S Metcalf St (45804-1145)
P.O. Box 4505 (45802-4505)
PHONE.................................419 226-2300
William Kalsse, *CEO*

Gregory King, *President*
Todd Neu, *Senior VP*
Dylan Luth, *Research*
Kara Bihn, *Engineer*
▲ EMP: 277
SALES (est): 173.5MM
SALES (corp-wide): 9.5B **Privately Held**
WEB: www.premcor.com
SIC: 2911 Petroleum refining
PA: Husky Energy Inc
    707 8 Ave Sw
    Calgary AB T2P 1
    403 298-6111

(G-12043)
LIMA REFINING COMPANY
1150 S Metcalf St (45804-1145)
P.O. Box 4505 (45802-4505)
PHONE.................................419 226-2300
Patty Chapman, *Branch Mgr*
EMP: 60
SALES (corp-wide): 9.5B **Privately Held**
WEB: www.premcor.com
SIC: 2911 Petroleum refining
HQ: Lima Refining Company
    1150 S Metcalf St
    Lima OH 45804
    419 226-2300

(G-12044)
LIMA SANDBLASTING & PNTG CO
4310 East Rd (45807-1535)
P.O. Box 3037 (45807-0037)
PHONE.................................419 331-2939
Larry Smith, *President*
Laura Smith, *Vice Pres*
EMP: 5
SQ FT: 17,000
SALES (est): 646.9K **Privately Held**
SIC: 3471 3479 Sand blasting of metal parts; painting of metal products

(G-12045)
LIMA SHEET METAL MACHINE & MFG
1001 Bowman Rd (45804-3409)
PHONE.................................419 229-1161
Fax: 419 229-8538
Michael R Emerick, *President*
Ann Emerick, *Corp Secy*
Thomas Emerick, *Exec VP*
Steve Emerick, *Engineer*
EMP: 31 EST: 1974
SQ FT: 26,250
SALES (est): 6.6MM **Privately Held**
WEB: www.limasheetmetal.com
SIC: 3589 3599 7349 7692 Commercial cooking & foodwarming equipment; machine shop, jobbing & repair; building maintenance, except repairs; welding repair; food products machinery; sheet metalwork

(G-12046)
LIMA SPORTING GOODS INC
1404 Allentown Rd (45805-2204)
PHONE.................................419 222-1036
Fax: 419 222-8885
David Kirian, *President*
EMP: 20
SQ FT: 12,900
SALES: 2.9MM **Privately Held**
SIC: 5941 2759 Sporting goods & bicycle shops; team sports equipment; screen printing

(G-12047)
LINDE LLC
961 Industry Ave (45804-4171)
PHONE.................................419 227-9585
Carl Frommer, *Branch Mgr*
EMP: 23
SALES (corp-wide): 17.9B **Privately Held**
SIC: 2813 Industrial gases
HQ: Linde Llc
    200 Somerset Corporate Bl
    Bridgewater NJ 08807
    908 464-8100

(G-12048)
LINDE LLC
1680 Buckeye Rd (45804-1826)
PHONE.................................419 221-5043
Stuart Emmons, *Branch Mgr*
EMP: 22

▲ = Import ▼=Export
◆ =Import/Export

SALES (corp-wide): 17.9B **Privately Held**
SIC: 2813 Industrial gases
HQ: Linde Llc
200 Somerset Corporate Bl
Bridgewater NJ 08807
908 464-8100

(G-12049)
LONGS CUSTOM DOORS
229 S Greenlawn Ave (45807-1339)
PHONE..................................419 339-2331
Darrell Long, *Owner*
EMP: 4
SALES (est): 475K **Privately Held**
SIC: 2431 Doors & door parts & trim, wood

(G-12050)
MAC ELECTRIC INC
1240 Fairgreen Ave (45805-4432)
PHONE..................................419 782-0671
Fax: 419 229-7952
Michael Hartung, *President*
Nancy Hartung, *Vice Pres*
EMP: 9
SQ FT: 6,500
SALES: 748.7K **Privately Held**
SIC: 7694 Electric motor repair

(G-12051)
MARTIN PRINTING CO
400 N Main St (45801-4315)
PHONE..................................419 224-9176
Margaret Whitlatch, *Owner*
EMP: 3
SQ FT: 2,000
SALES (est): 245.1K **Privately Held**
SIC: 2759 2752 Letterpress printing; commercial printing, offset

(G-12052)
ME SIGNS INC
Also Called: Fastsigns
2155 Elida Rd (45805-1518)
PHONE..................................419 222-7446
Mark E Engle, *President*
EMP: 5
SALES: 650K **Privately Held**
SIC: 3993 Signs & advertising specialties

(G-12053)
MENARD INC
2614 N Eastown Rd (45807-1601)
PHONE..................................419 998-4348
Timothy Bart, *Manager*
Steve Martino, *Manager*
Mark Schoch, *Manager*
Jennie Lapoint, *Technology*
EMP: 50
SALES (corp-wide): 15.5B **Privately Held**
WEB: www.menards.com
SIC: 2431 Millwork
PA: Menard, Inc.
5101 Menard Dr
Eau Claire WI 54703
715 876-5911

(G-12054)
METOKOTE CORPORATION (HQ)
Also Called: Ppg-Metokote
1340 Neubrecht Rd (45801-3120)
PHONE..................................419 996-7800
Fax: 419 224-1043
Jeffrey J Oravitz, *President*
▲ **EMP:** 445
SQ FT: 30,000
SALES (est): 688.1MM
SALES (corp-wide): 14.7B **Publicly Held**
WEB: www.metokote.com
SIC: 3479 Painting, coating & hot dipping
PA: Ppg Industries, Inc.
1 Ppg Pl
Pittsburgh PA 15272
412 434-3131

(G-12055)
METOKOTE CORPORATION
Also Called: Plant 25
1340 Neubrecht Rd (45801-3120)
PHONE..................................419 227-1100
Jim Bender, *Principal*
Jim Burke, *Info Tech Dir*
Kolanthia Edmondson, *Info Tech Dir*
Jim Kreig, *Info Tech Dir*
Jeff Mesmer, *Info Tech Dir*
EMP: 59

SALES (corp-wide): 14.7B **Publicly Held**
SIC: 3479 Painting, coating & hot dipping
HQ: Metokote Corporation
1340 Neubrecht Rd
Lima OH 45801
419 996-7800

(G-12056)
METOKOTE CORPORATION
1340 Neubrecht Rd (45801-3120)
PHONE..................................319 232-6994
Chad Dirks, *Manager*
EMP: 60
SALES (corp-wide): 14.7B **Publicly Held**
WEB: www.metokote.com
SIC: 3479 Coating of metals with plastic or resins
HQ: Metokote Corporation
1340 Neubrecht Rd
Lima OH 45801
419 996-7800

(G-12057)
METOKOTE CORPORATION
1340 Neubrecht Rd (45801-3120)
PHONE..................................419 221-2754
Fax: 419 861-1984
Jay Binder, *Manager*
EMP: 120
SQ FT: 118,500
SALES (corp-wide): 14.7B **Publicly Held**
WEB: www.metokote.com
SIC: 3479 3471 Coating of metals with plastic or resins; plating & polishing
HQ: Metokote Corporation
1340 Neubrecht Rd
Lima OH 45801
419 996-7800

(G-12058)
METOKOTE CORPORATION
1340 Neubrecht Rd (45801-3120)
PHONE..................................419 996-7800
Lewis Phillipson, *Manager*
EMP: 7
SALES (corp-wide): 14.7B **Publicly Held**
WEB: www.metokote.com
SIC: 1081 Metal mining services
HQ: Metokote Corporation
1340 Neubrecht Rd
Lima OH 45801
419 996-7800

(G-12059)
MODERN INK TECHNOLOGY LLC
Also Called: Organic Coating Products
1005 W Grand Ave (45801-3429)
PHONE..................................419 738-9664
Dana Morgan,
EMP: 11
SQ FT: 12,000
SALES (est): 925.2K
SALES (corp-wide): 460MM **Privately Held**
SIC: 3952 Ink, drawing: black & colored
HQ: American Trim, L.L.C.
1005 W Grand Ave
Lima OH 45801

(G-12060)
MOTION INDUSTRIES INC
Also Called: Paragon Service & Supply Div
3945 Stewart Rd (45801-1337)
PHONE..................................419 224-1988
Dan Clark, *Branch Mgr*
EMP: 13
SALES (corp-wide): 15.3B **Publicly Held**
SIC: 3549 Coiling machinery
HQ: Motion Industries, Inc.
1605 Alton Rd
Birmingham AL 35210
205 956-1122

(G-12061)
MURPHY TRACTOR & EQP CO INC
Also Called: John Deere Authorized Dealer
3550 Saint Johns Rd (45804-4017)
PHONE..................................419 221-3666
Chris Cron, *Branch Mgr*
EMP: 8

SALES (corp-wide): 176.9MM **Privately Held**
SIC: 3531 5082 Construction machinery; construction & mining machinery
HQ: Murphy Tractor & Equipment Co., Inc.
5375 N Deere Rd
Park City KS 67219
855 246-9124

(G-12062)
NATIONAL LIME AND STONE CO
1314 Findlay Rd (45801-3106)
PHONE..................................419 228-3434
Fax: 419 223-0791
Debbie Montooth, *Human Res Dir*
Joe Watson, *Sales Executive*
Nick Morris, *Manager*
EMP: 22
SQ FT: 1,200
SALES (corp-wide): 4B **Privately Held**
WEB: www.natlime.com
SIC: 1422 Crushed & broken limestone
PA: The National Lime And Stone Company
551 Lake Cascade Pkwy
Findlay OH 45840
419 422-4341

(G-12063)
NEWS GAZETTE PRINTING COMPANY
Also Called: Ngp Printing Professional
324 W Market St (45801-4714)
P.O. Box 1017 (45802-1017)
PHONE..................................419 227-2527
Fax: 419 222-2303
Dan Mills, *President*
James Honegger, *Vice Pres*
Peter Paulik, *Vice Pres*
Dorothy Johnson, *Manager*
EMP: 11
SQ FT: 2,800
SALES (est): 1.5MM **Privately Held**
WEB: www.ngpco.com
SIC: 2759 Letterpress printing

(G-12064)
NWC HUD CORP II
1404 N West St (45801-2828)
PHONE..................................419 228-8400
EMP: 5
SALES (est): 19.2K **Privately Held**
SIC: 3021 Rubber & plastics footwear

(G-12065)
P-AMERICAS LLC
1750 Greely Chapel Rd (45804-4122)
PHONE..................................419 227-3541
Rob Rosser, *Manager*
EMP: 25
SALES (corp-wide): 62.8B **Publicly Held**
SIC: 5149 2086 Soft drinks; bottled & canned soft drinks
HQ: P-Americas Llc
1 Pepsi Way
Somers NY

(G-12066)
PCS NITROGEN INC
Also Called: Arcadian Ohio
1900 Fort Amanda Rd (45804-1827)
P.O. Box 628 (45802-0628)
PHONE..................................419 226-1200
Chuck Treloar, *Manager*
EMP: 370
SALES (corp-wide): 4.4B **Privately Held**
SIC: 2873 Nitrogen solutions (fertilizer)
HQ: Pcs Nitrogen, Inc.
1101 Skokie Blvd Ste 400
Northbrook IL 60062
847 849-4200

(G-12067)
PCS NITROGEN OHIO LP
2200 Fort Amanda Rd (45804-1801)
P.O. Box 628 (45802-0628)
PHONE..................................419 879-8989
Jochen Tilk, *President*
Wayne Brownlee, *CFO*
EMP: 3
SALES (est): 1.7MM
SALES (corp-wide): 4.4B **Privately Held**
SIC: 2873 Nitrogenous fertilizers

PA: Potash Corporation Of Saskatchewan Inc
122 1st Ave S Suite 500
Saskatoon SK S7K 7
306 933-8500

(G-12068)
PERFECTION BAKERIES INC
1278 W Robb Ave (45801-2406)
PHONE..................................419 221-2359
Fax: 419 225-6344
Carol Moyer, *Principal*
EMP: 58
SALES (corp-wide): 567MM **Privately Held**
SIC: 2051 Bakery: wholesale or wholesale/retail combined
PA: Perfection Bakeries, Inc.
350 Pearl St
Fort Wayne IN 46802
260 424-8245

(G-12069)
PF POLYMERS LLC
Also Called: Planet Friendly Polymers
1200 E Kibby St (45804-3163)
PHONE..................................567 712-7046
Kelly Compton, *Office Mgr*
Craig O Connor,
EMP: 35
SALES (est): 2.8MM
SALES (corp-wide): 5.4MM **Privately Held**
SIC: 2821 Polymethyl methacrylate resins (plexiglass)
PA: J. Terence Thompson
19833 Ltrsburg Pike Ste 5
Hagerstown MD 21742
301 671-2500

(G-12070)
PGW AUTO GLASS LLC
Also Called: PPG Industries
2599 Ft Shawnee Ind Dr (45804-2365)
PHONE..................................419 993-2421
Mark Hemans, *Manager*
EMP: 50
SALES (corp-wide): 457.8MM **Privately Held**
SIC: 5013 7536 3229 Automobile glass; automotive glass replacement shops; pressed & blown glass
HQ: Pgw Auto Glass, Llc
1 Ppg Pl Fl 6
Pittsburgh PA 15272
412 434-4058

(G-12071)
PRAXAIR INC
961 Industry Ave (45804-4171)
PHONE..................................419 422-1353
Terry Peyton, *Opers-Prdtn-Mfg*
EMP: 4
SALES (corp-wide): 10.5B **Publicly Held**
SIC: 2813 Industrial gases
PA: Praxair, Inc.
10 Riverview Dr
Danbury CT 06810
203 837-2000

(G-12072)
PRAXAIR DISTRIBUTION INC
961 Industry Ave (45804-4171)
PHONE..................................419 422-1353
Fax: 419 626-3830
Barrow Turner, *Manager*
EMP: 4
SALES (corp-wide): 10.5B **Publicly Held**
SIC: 2813 5084 5999 Carbon dioxide; dry ice, carbon dioxide (solid); oxygen, compressed or liquefied; welding machinery & equipment; welding supplies
HQ: Praxair Distribution, Inc.
10 Riverview Dr
Danbury CT 06810
203 837-2000

(G-12073)
PRAXAIR DISTRIBUTION INC
961 Industry Ave (45804-4171)
PHONE..................................419 221-0517
Tyler Benjamin, *Branch Mgr*
EMP: 3

SALES (corp-wide): 10.5B **Publicly Held**
SIC: 2813 5084 Industrial gases; carbon dioxide; dry ice, carbon dioxide (solid); oxygen, compressed or liquefied; welding machinery & equipment
HQ: Praxair Distribution, Inc.
　　10 Riverview Dr
　　Danbury CT 06810
　　203 837-2000

(G-12074)
PRECISION WOOD & METAL CO
3960 E Bluelick Rd　(45801-1555)
PHONE..............................419 221-1512
Fax: 419 221-1711
Leo Robert Schneider, *Owner*
EMP: 4
SALES: 89K **Privately Held**
SIC: 3312 Tool & die steel

(G-12075)
PROCTER & GAMBLE MFG CO
3875 Reservoir Rd　(45801-3310)
P.O. Box 1900　(45802-1900)
PHONE..............................419 226-5500
Fax: 419 226-5754
Thomas Sciranka, *Safety Dir*
Bruce Hoffman, *Project Mgr*
Louis Thompson, *Engineer*
Rick Simon, *Human Res Mgr*
J G Boney, *Branch Mgr*
EMP: 250
SALES (corp-wide): 65.3B **Publicly Held**
SIC: 2842 2841 Fabric softeners; soap & other detergents
HQ: The Procter & Gamble Manufacturing Company
　　1 Procter And Gamble Plz
　　Cincinnati OH 45202
　　513 983-1100

(G-12076)
PROFORMA SYSTEMS ADVANTAGE
1207 Findlay Rd　(45801-3103)
PHONE..............................419 224-8747
Robert McPheron, *President*
Michelle McPheron, *Vice Pres*
Cathy Richard, *Admin Sec*
EMP: 6
SALES (est): 727.4K **Privately Held**
SIC: 2759 Commercial printing; calendars: printing

(G-12077)
PUNCH COMPONENTS INC
505 N Cable Rd　(45805-2132)
PHONE..............................419 224-1242
Kevin Perry, *Plant Mgr*
EMP: 30
SQ FT: 50,000
SALES (est): 2MM
SALES (corp-wide): 2K **Privately Held**
WEB: www.punchinternational.com
SIC: 3663 3827 Television broadcasting & communications equipment; optical instruments & lenses
PA: Iep Invest Nv
　　Noorderlaan 139
　　Antwerpen
　　572 267-20

(G-12078)
QUALITOR INC (PA)
1840 Mccullough St　(45801-3059)
PHONE..............................248 204-8600
Gary Cohen, *CEO*
Scott Gibaratz, *CFO*
Lyndsay Smock, *Manager*
▲ EMP: 6
SQ FT: 2,500
SALES (est): 191MM **Privately Held**
WEB: www.qualitorinc.com
SIC: 3714 5013 Motor vehicle engines & parts; motor vehicle brake systems & parts; air brakes, motor vehicle; wipers, windshield, motor vehicle; motor vehicle supplies & new parts

(G-12079)
QUICK AS A WINK PRINTING CO
321 W High St　(45801-4701)
PHONE..............................419 224-9786
Fax: 419 222-5942
David S Beck, *President*
Julie Kirk, *Business Mgr*

Deb Gerding, *Purchasing*
Connie Kruse, *Sales Staff*
Andrew Beck, *Manager*
EMP: 18
SQ FT: 5,000
SALES (est): 1.7MM **Privately Held**
SIC: 2752 2791 7389 5099 Commercial printing, offset; typesetting; sign painting & lettering shop; rubber stamps; marking devices; commercial printing

(G-12080)
RANDALL BEARINGS INC (PA)
1046 S Greenlawn Ave　(45804-1100)
P.O. Box 1258　(45802-1258)
PHONE..............................419 223-1075
Fax: 419 228-0200
Kent Morgan, *President*
Jeff Hager, *Vice Pres*
Pat Ridenour, *Plant Mgr*
Jennifer Rode, *Purch Dir*
Doug Hamilton, *Engineer*
▲ EMP: 78
SQ FT: 117,400
SALES (est): 14MM **Privately Held**
WEB: www.randallbearings.com
SIC: 3568 3624 3366 Bearings, bushings & blocks; carbon & graphite products; copper foundries

(G-12081)
RESOURCE RECYCLING INC
1596 Neubrecht Rd　(45801-3124)
PHONE..............................419 222-2702
Micah Hollinger, *President*
EMP: 15
SALES: 4.2MM **Privately Held**
SIC: 4953 3999 4214 Recycling, waste materials; custom pulverizing & grinding of plastic materials; local trucking with storage

(G-12082)
REVENUE MANAGEMENT GROUP LLC
2348 Baton Rouge　(45805-1167)
P.O. Box 747　(45802-0747)
PHONE..............................419 993-2200
Ned Kaning, *Mng Member*
Scott G Koenig,
EMP: 3 EST: 2000
SALES (est): 176.7K **Privately Held**
WEB: www.easypmts.com
SIC: 2754 Invitations: gravure printing

(G-12083)
REX MANUFACTURING CO
Also Called: Rex Auto Seat Covers
805 S Cable Rd　(45805-3467)
P.O. Box 1294　(45802-1294)
PHONE..............................419 224-5751
Fax: 419 224-5751
James M Rex, *Owner*
EMP: 5 EST: 1930
SQ FT: 4,500
SALES (est): 383.3K **Privately Held**
SIC: 5013 5531 2399 2394 Automotive supplies & parts; automotive accessories; seat covers, automobile; convertible tops, canvas or boat: from purchased materials

(G-12084)
RIGHTWAY FOOD SERVICE
3255 Saint Johns Rd　(45804-4022)
PHONE..............................419 223-4075
Jason Dorsten, *General Mgr*
Ronald Williams, *Purchasing*
EMP: 3
SALES (est): 270K **Privately Held**
SIC: 5046 2599 2499 Restaurant equipment & supplies; restaurant furniture, wood or metal; food handling & processing products, wood

(G-12085)
RMT HOLDINGS INC
1025 Findlay Rd　(45801-3171)
P.O. Box 5183　(45802-5183)
PHONE..............................419 221-1168
Fax: 419 221-0659
Richard Toth, *President*
Cathi Toth, *Vice Pres*
Michelle Smith, *Controller*
Brenda Adams, *Office Mgr*
Steven A Romey,
EMP: 15

SQ FT: 15,000
SALES (est): 2.5MM **Privately Held**
SIC: 2789 Paper cutting

(G-12086)
RUDA PRINT & GRAPHICS
4129 Elida Rd　(45807-1549)
PHONE..............................419 331-7832
Fax: 419 331-2329
Jason Sumner, *Owner*
EMP: 4
SALES: 400K **Privately Held**
SIC: 2752 Commercial printing, lithographic

(G-12087)
RUDOLPH FOODS COMPANY INC (PA)
6575 Bellefontaine Rd　(45804-4415)
P.O. Box 509　(45802-0509)
PHONE..............................909 383-7463
Fax: 419 648-4087
James Rudolph, *CEO*
Richard Rudolph, *President*
Philip Rudolph, *Corp Secy*
Barbara Snyder, *Vice Pres*
Gary Burns, *Plant Mgr*
◆ EMP: 160
SQ FT: 110,000
SALES (est): 128.7MM **Privately Held**
SIC: 2096 2099 Pork rinds; food preparations

(G-12088)
SCHWANS HOME SERVICE INC
2545 Saint Johns Rd　(45804-4004)
PHONE..............................419 222-9977
Fax: 419 221-2391
Mark Cornwell, *Branch Mgr*
EMP: 25
SALES (corp-wide): 4.8B **Privately Held**
SIC: 5963 2024 2037 Food services, direct sales; ice cream, packaged: molded, on sticks, etc.; fruit juice concentrates, frozen
HQ: Schwan's Home Service, Inc.
　　115 W College Dr
　　Marshall MN 56258
　　507 532-3274

(G-12089)
SEWER RODDING EQUIPMENT CO
Also Called: Sreco Flexible
3434 S Dixie Hwy　(45804-3756)
PHONE..............................419 991-2065
Fax: 419 999-2300
Larry Drain, *Manager*
EMP: 30
SALES (corp-wide): 17.6MM **Privately Held**
SIC: 5032 3546 3423 Sewer pipe, clay; power-driven handtools; hand & edge tools
PA: Sewer Rodding Equipment Co Inc
　　3217 Carter Ave
　　Marina Del Rey CA 90292
　　310 301-9009

(G-12090)
SHELLY MATERIALS INC
600 N Sugar St　(45801-4184)
PHONE..............................419 229-2741
Lyle Snyder, *Manager*
EMP: 5
SALES (corp-wide): 28.6B **Privately Held**
SIC: 2951 Asphalt paving mixtures & blocks
HQ: Shelly Materials, Inc.
　　80 Park Dr
　　Thornville OH 43076
　　740 246-6315

(G-12091)
SIGN PRO OF LIMA
404 Brower Rd　(45801-2502)
PHONE..............................419 222-7767
Fax: 419 222-6565
Michelle Sterling, *Manager*
George Davis, *Manager*
EMP: 5
SQ FT: 1,700
SALES (est): 340K **Privately Held**
WEB: www.signproimaging.com
SIC: 3993 Signs & advertising specialties

(G-12092)
SIGN SOURCE USA INC
1700 S Dixie Hwy　(45804-1834)
P.O. Box 776　(45802-0776)
PHONE..............................419 224-1130
Fax: 419 224-1138
Jeff Pisel, *President*
Sompahkoun Southibounnorath, *Vice Pres*
Grant Pisel, *Production*
Karen Hoblein, *Admin Sec*
EMP: 55
SALES (est): 25MM **Privately Held**
WEB: www.signsourceusa.com
SIC: 5085 3993 Signmaker equipment & supplies; signs & advertising specialties

(G-12093)
SNOW PRINTING CO INC
1000 W Grand Ave Frnt　(45801-3498)
PHONE..............................419 229-7669
Fax: 419 229-3986
Donald L Kohl, *President*
Joyce Kohl, *Corp Secy*
Daniel Kohl, *Vice Pres*
EMP: 10
SQ FT: 4,200
SALES (est): 980K **Privately Held**
SIC: 2752 2759 Commercial printing, offset; letterpress printing

(G-12094)
SPALLINGER MILLWRIGHT SVC CO
Also Called: Spall Autoc Syste / US Millwr
1155 E Hanthorn Rd　(45804-3929)
PHONE..............................419 225-5830
Fax: 419 225-8466
Scott Spallinger, *President*
Debbie Earl, *Manager*
EMP: 85
SQ FT: 80,000
SALES (est): 31.7MM **Privately Held**
WEB: www.spallinger.com
SIC: 3446 1796 Stairs, staircases, stair treads: prefabricated metal; railings, prefabricated metal; machinery installation

(G-12095)
SPECIALIZED PHARMACEUTICALS
799 S Main St　(45804-1519)
PHONE..............................419 371-2081
EMP: 4 EST: 2012
SALES (est): 325.7K **Privately Held**
SIC: 5912 2834 Drug stores & proprietary stores; pharmaceutical preparations

(G-12096)
STAR SPANGLED SPECTACULAR INC
4230 Elida Rd　(45807-1550)
PHONE..............................419 879-3502
Kurt Neeper, *Principal*
EMP: 4
SALES: 121.6K **Privately Held**
SIC: 2836 Culture media

(G-12097)
SUEVER STONE COMPANY (PA)
706 E Main St　(45807-1071)
PHONE..............................419 331-1945
Fax: 419 647-4054
Neil Lause, *President*
Glen Lause, *Vice Pres*
Eileen Lause, *Treasurer*
Sharon Speakman, *Admin Sec*
EMP: 15
SQ FT: 10,000
SALES: 3MM **Privately Held**
SIC: 1422 1611 Crushed & broken limestone; surfacing & paving

(G-12098)
SUPERIOR FORGE & STEEL CORP (PA)
1820 Mcclain Rd　(45804-1978)
PHONE..............................419 222-4412
Fax: 419 222-0257
James C Markovitz, *CEO*
Ken Wheeler, *QA Dir*
Paul Haney, *Engineer*
Jeff Mason, *Engineer*
Anthony Bartley, *Treasurer*
◆ EMP: 100
SQ FT: 350,000

SALES (est): 24.7MM **Privately Held**
WEB: www.qrolls.com
SIC: 3312 3316 Sheet or strip, steel, cold-rolled; own hot-rolled; cold finishing of steel shapes

(G-12099)
SUPERIOR METAL PRODUCTS INC (PA)
Also Called: American Trim
1005 W Grand Ave (45801-3400)
PHONE.............................419 228-1145
Fax: 419 224-0466
Leo Hawk, *CEO*
Jeffrey A Hawk, *CEO*
Richard Pfeifer, *President*
Gary Fosnaugh, *Plant Mgr*
Carl Lewis, *Production*
◆ **EMP:** 50 **EST:** 1958
SQ FT: 15,000
SALES (est): 460MM **Privately Held**
SIC: 3469 3429 Metal stampings; porcelain enameled products & utensils; ornamental metal stampings; manufactured hardware (general)

(G-12100)
T J ELLIS ENTERPRISES INC
1505 Neubrecht Rd (45801-3123)
PHONE.............................419 224-1969
Johnnie Small, *Manager*
EMP: 5
SALES (corp-wide): 4.5MM **Privately Held**
SIC: 2411 Logging
PA: T J Ellis Enterprises Inc
1505 Neubrecht Rd
Lima OH 45801
419 999-5026

(G-12101)
TAMBLINGSON INC
Also Called: Signs Now
1942 Elida Rd (45805-1515)
PHONE.............................419 221-3437
Glen Tamblingson, *President*
EMP: 3
SALES (est): 130.6K **Privately Held**
SIC: 3993 Signs & advertising specialties

(G-12102)
TANNER INDUSTRIES INC
8070 Harding Hwy (45801-8714)
PHONE.............................419 221-1576
EMP: 10
SALES (corp-wide): 166.3MM **Privately Held**
SIC: 3999 Atomizers, toiletry
PA: Tanner Industries, Inc.
735 Davisville Rd Ste 3
Southampton PA 18966
215 322-1238

(G-12103)
TERRY & JACK NEON SIGN CO
225 S Collins Ave (45804-3001)
PHONE.............................419 229-0674
Fax: 419 228-3712
Jack L Pisel Jr, *President*
Patricia Woods, *Corp Secy*
Robert Balyeat, *Counsel*
Eric Binkley, *Sr Corp Ofcr*
Mike Strange, *Vice Pres*
EMP: 26 **EST:** 1947
SQ FT: 40,000
SALES (est): 2.1MM **Privately Held**
SIC: 3993 Electric signs

(G-12104)
THAPA INDUSTRIES
1324 W Elm St (45805-2665)
PHONE.............................419 234-3498
Prem Thapa, *Owner*
Mohan Thapa, *Co-Owner*
EMP: 3
SALES (est): 76.5K **Privately Held**
SIC: 3999 Manufacturing industries

(G-12105)
TRINITY HIGHWAY PRODUCTS LLC
425 E O Connor Ave (45801)
PHONE.............................419 227-1296
Fax: 419 227-1296
Sherri Braun, *Human Resources*
Susan Henline, *Office Mgr*

Keith Hamburg, *Branch Mgr*
John Hickman, *Manager*
EMP: 21
SALES (corp-wide): 4.5B **Publicly Held**
SIC: 3743 Railroad equipment
HQ: Trinity Highway Products, Llc.
2525 N Stemmons Fwy
Dallas TX 75207
214 631-4420

(G-12106)
TURNER VAULT
1488 Elida Rd (45805-1548)
PHONE.............................419 223-6861
Steve Turner, *President*
EMP: 5
SALES (est): 435.5K **Privately Held**
SIC: 3272 3271 Burial vaults, concrete or precast terrazzo; brick, concrete

(G-12107)
TYSEKA
1021 Brower Rd (45801-2301)
PHONE.............................419 860-9585
Jason Dancs, *Owner*
EMP: 5
SALES (est): 232.1K **Privately Held**
SIC: 3231 Cut & engraved glassware: made from purchased glass

(G-12108)
UNITED STATES DEPT OF ARMY
Also Called: Lima Army Tank Plant
1155 Buckeye Rd (45804-1815)
PHONE.............................419 221-9500
Fax: 419 221-9633
Ted Epple, *Branch Mgr*
John Dowling, *Systems Mgr*
EMP: 75 **Publicly Held**
SIC: 3795 9711 Tanks & tank components; tanks, military, including factory rebuilding; Army;
HQ: United States Department Of The Army
1400 Defense Pentagon
Washington DC 20310
703 695-1717

(G-12109)
VINNIES DRIVE THRU
864 W North St (45801-3925)
PHONE.............................419 225-5272
James Faircloth, *Principal*
EMP: 4
SALES (est): 350.6K **Privately Held**
SIC: 2086 Bottled & canned soft drinks

(G-12110)
W T INC
Also Called: Midwest Plastics
606 N Jackson St (45801-4126)
P.O. Box 1687 (45802-1687)
PHONE.............................419 224-6942
Fax: 419 224-6942
William M Taflinger, *President*
Rebecca Taflinger, *Vice Pres*
William S Talfinger, *Treasurer*
Bill Taflinger, *Manager*
Stephen C Talfinger, *Admin Sec*
▼ **EMP:** 11
SQ FT: 7,500
SALES (est): 1.9MM **Privately Held**
SIC: 3088 Toilet fixtures, plastic

(G-12111)
WAHLIES CSTM CFT DRAPERY UPHL
605 W Kibby St (45804-1018)
PHONE.............................419 229-1731
Tim Marshall, *President*
Carol Marshall, *Manager*
EMP: 5
SQ FT: 1,000
SALES: 350K **Privately Held**
SIC: 7641 2391 5712 Reupholstery; draperies, plastic & textile: from purchased materials; furniture stores

(G-12112)
WHEMCO-OHIO FOUNDRY INC
1600 Mcclain Rd (45804-1979)
PHONE.............................419 222-2111
Fax: 419 222-2318
Charles R Novelli, *President*
John Hirbar, *Managing Dir*
Michael P Nakon, *Principal*
Anthony J Poli, *Principal*

Robert J Peterson, *Vice Pres*
EMP: 140
SALES (est): 31.7MM
SALES (corp-wide): 564.1MM **Privately Held**
WEB: www.whemco.com
SIC: 3321 3325 3322 Gray & ductile iron foundries; steel foundries; malleable iron foundries
HQ: Whemco Inc.
5 Hot Metal St Ste 300
Pittsburgh PA 15203
412 390-2700

(G-12113)
YANKEE CANDLE COMPANY INC
2400 Elida Rd (45805-1299)
PHONE.............................419 223-0073
EMP: 3
SALES (corp-wide): 13.2B **Publicly Held**
SIC: 3999 Candles
HQ: The Yankee Candle Company Inc
16 Yankee Candle Way
South Deerfield MA 01373
413 665-8306

Lima
Auglaize County

(G-12114)
ALPLA INC
3320 Fort Shwnee Indus Dr (45806-1843)
PHONE.............................419 991-9484
Keith Wagner, *Principal*
▲ **EMP:** 17
SALES (est): 4.4MM **Privately Held**
SIC: 3085 Plastics bottles
HQ: Alpla - Werke Lehner Gmbh & Co Kg
Daimlerstr. 4-6
Markdorf 88677
754 450-80

(G-12115)
PRECISION THRMPLSTC COMPONTS
Also Called: P T C
3765 Saint Johns Rd (45806-2629)
P.O. Box 1296 (45802-1296)
PHONE.............................419 227-4500
Fax: 419 227-1292
Randy E Carter, *President*
Brian Schumacher, *Engineer*
Dave Ewing, *Manager*
◆ **EMP:** 100
SQ FT: 62,000
SALES: 13MM **Privately Held**
WEB: www.ptclima.com
SIC: 3089 Plastic processing; injection molded finished plastic products; extruded finished plastic products

Lisbon
Columbiana County

(G-12116)
AMERICAN BUILT CUSTOM PALLETS
42120 Glasgow Rd (44432-9665)
PHONE.............................330 532-4780
EMP: 4
SALES (est): 180K **Privately Held**
SIC: 2448 Pallets, wood & wood with metal

(G-12117)
AMERICAN CLIMBER & MCH CORP
38294 Industrial Park Rd (44432-8325)
P.O. Box 471 (44432-0471)
PHONE.............................330 420-0019
Fax: 330 424-7218
Louis Horvath Sr, *President*
Peter Horvath, *Admin Sec*
EMP: 5
SQ FT: 5,000
SALES (est): 560.1K **Privately Held**
SIC: 3536 Hoists

(G-12118)
COLUMBUS MCKINNON CORPORATION
Chester Hoist
7573 State Route 45 (44432-8382)
PHONE.............................330 424-7248
Fax: 330 424-3126
Bob Burkey, *General Mgr*
Gino Savarino, *General Mgr*
Robert Meyers, *Vice Pres*
Chris Mull, *Plant Mgr*
Joe Runyon, *Sales Staff*
EMP: 57
SALES (corp-wide): 597.1MM **Publicly Held**
WEB: www.cmworks.com
SIC: 3536 3713 3568 3496 Hoists, cranes & monorails; truck & bus bodies; power transmission equipment; miscellaneous fabricated wire products
PA: Columbus Mckinnon Corporation
205 Crosspoint Pkwy
Getzville NY 14068
716 689-5400

(G-12119)
D W DICKEY AND SON INC (PA)
Also Called: D W Dickey
7896 Dickey Dr (44432-9391)
P.O. Box 189 (44432-0189)
PHONE.............................330 424-1441
Fax: 330 424-7607
Gary Neville, *President*
Timothy Dickey, *President*
David Dickey, *Vice Pres*
Janet Blosser, *Admin Sec*
EMP: 44
SALES (est): 64.4MM **Privately Held**
SIC: 5169 3273 5172 Explosives; ready-mixed concrete; fuel oil

(G-12120)
GRANT STREET PALLET INC
39196 Grant St (44432-9781)
P.O. Box 268 (44432-0268)
PHONE.............................330 424-0355
Kenneth Miller, *President*
EMP: 8
SALES: 1MM **Privately Held**
SIC: 2448 Wood pallets & skids

(G-12121)
HEIM SHEET METAL INC
525 E Chestnut St (44432-1319)
PHONE.............................330 424-7820
Fax: 330 424-0322
David Belaney, *President*
Melinda Belaney, *Corp Secy*
EMP: 6 **EST:** 1928
SQ FT: 11,100
SALES: 516K **Privately Held**
SIC: 3499 Ladder assemblies, combination workstand: metal

(G-12122)
HOUSING & EMRGNCY LGSTCS PLNNR
36905 State Route 30 (44432-9413)
PHONE.............................209 201-7511
Janice Regalo, *
EMP: 20
SALES (est): 685.2K **Privately Held**
SIC: 3999 Manufacturing industries

(G-12123)
J & A MACHINE
8362 Thomas Rd (44432-9475)
PHONE.............................330 424-5235
Fax: 330 424-9028
EMP: 4
SQ FT: 12,000
SALES (est): 370K **Privately Held**
SIC: 4212 7692 5082 7389 Local Trucking Operator Welding Repair Whol Construction/Mining Equipment Business Services

(G-12124)
J I T PALLETS INC
39196 Grant St (44432-9781)
P.O. Box 268 (44432-0268)
PHONE.............................330 424-0355
Kenneth Miller, *President*
EMP: 3

GEOGRAPHIC

SALES (est): 183.4K **Privately Held**
SIC: 2448 Wood pallets & skids

(G-12125)
J P INDUSTRIAL PRODUCTS INC (PA)
Also Called: JP Industrial
11988 State Route 45 (44432-8625)
PHONE..............................330 424-1110
Fax: 330 424-1199
James E Pastore, *President*
Kurt Kessler, *Opers Staff*
Rebecca Brown, *Manager*
Cory Kempf, *Maintence Staff*
▲ EMP: 8
SQ FT: 5,000
SALES (est): 12MM **Privately Held**
WEB: www.jpindustrial.com
SIC: 2821 Plastics materials & resins

(G-12126)
J P INDUSTRIAL PRODUCTS INC
Hc 518 (44432)
PHONE..............................330 424-3388
Beccy Brown, *Manager*
EMP: 22
SALES (corp-wide): 12MM **Privately Held**
WEB: www.jpindustrial.com
SIC: 3086 Padding, foamed plastic
PA: J. P. Industrial Products, Inc.
    11988 State Route 45
    Lisbon OH 44432
    330 424-1110

(G-12127)
LISBON HOIST INC
321 S Beaver St (44432)
P.O. Box 462 (44432-0462)
PHONE..............................330 424-7283
Fax: 330 424-7445
Michael Burlingame, *President*
Connie Burlingame, *Finance Mgr*
EMP: 18
SQ FT: 35,000
SALES (est): 2.2MM **Privately Held**
WEB: www.lisbonhoist.com
SIC: 3536 Hoists, cranes & monorails; hoists

(G-12128)
LISBON PATTERN LIMITED
7629 State Route 45 (44432-9394)
P.O. Box 506 (44432-0506)
PHONE..............................330 424-7676
Fax: 330 424-0193
David Tolson, *Owner*
Kenneith Lovett, *Owner*
EMP: 5
SALES (est): 484.4K **Privately Held**
SIC: 3543 Industrial patterns

(G-12129)
OGDEN NEWSPAPERS OHIO INC (HQ)
Also Called: Morning Journal
308 Maple St (44432-1205)
PHONE..............................330 424-9541
Fax: 440 424-0048
Larry Dorschner, *Publisher*
Beth Bentley, *Purch Agent*
Beth Todd, *Controller*
Brenda Kidder, *Persnl Mgr*
Heidi Grimm, *Director*
EMP: 29 EST: 1852
SQ FT: 13,000
SALES (est): 2.5MM
SALES (corp-wide): 617.1MM **Privately Held**
WEB: www.morningjournalnews.com
SIC: 2711 Job printing & newspaper publishing combined
PA: The Ogden Newspapers Inc
    1500 Main St
    Wheeling WV 26003
    304 233-0100

(G-12130)
OHIO PET FOODS INC (PA)
38251 Indl Pk Rd (44432)
PHONE..............................330 424-1431
Fax: 330 424-1108
Jim Golladay, *President*
Matthew Golladay, *Vice Pres*
Don Grimm, *Production*
Travis Golladay, *Treasurer*

◆ EMP: 37 EST: 1978
SQ FT: 50,000
SALES (est): 7.3MM **Privately Held**
WEB: www.ohiopetfoods.com
SIC: 2048 2047 Feeds, specialty: mice, guinea pig, etc.; dog food

(G-12131)
PAPER SERVICE INC
12022 Leslie Rd (44432-9531)
PHONE..............................330 227-3546
Fax: 330 385-6775
Randy Barnard, *President*
Dean Barnard, *Vice Pres*
EMP: 17 EST: 1968
SQ FT: 20,000
SALES (est): 3.3MM **Privately Held**
SIC: 2679 Paperboard products, converted

(G-12132)
PAUL E CEKOVICH
Also Called: Pallet Man The
9403 Black Rd (44432-9685)
PHONE..............................330 424-3213
Paul E Cekovich, *Principal*
EMP: 3 EST: 2012
SALES (est): 212K **Privately Held**
SIC: 2448 Pallets, wood & wood with metal

(G-12133)
R L CRAIG INC
6496 State Route 45 (44432-8357)
PHONE..............................330 424-1525
Fax: 330 424-0763
Richard L Craig, *President*
Katheryn A Craig, *Vice Pres*
John Glenn, *Electrical Engi*
EMP: 13
SQ FT: 7,600
SALES (est): 3.2MM **Privately Held**
WEB: www.rlcraig.com
SIC: 3599 Machine shop, jobbing & repair

(G-12134)
VANCE ADAMS
Also Called: Frontiers Unlimited
123 E Lincoln Way (44432-1405)
PHONE..............................330 424-9670
Vance A Adams, *Owner*
EMP: 3
SQ FT: 950
SALES (est): 185.2K **Privately Held**
SIC: 5941 3827 Camping equipment; binoculars

(G-12135)
WELDING IMPROVEMENT COMPANY
10070 Stookesberry Rd (44432-8639)
PHONE..............................330 424-9666
Fax: 330 424-5352
Tina Strong, *President*
Scott Strong, *Vice Pres*
Julie Chuck, *Purch Mgr*
John Anderson, *CFO*
Karen Hall, *Controller*
EMP: 8
SALES (est): 2MM **Privately Held**
SIC: 3441 Fabricated structural metal

(G-12136)
WRIGHT BUFFING WHEEL COMPANY
300 S Market St (44432-1236)
PHONE..............................330 424-7887
Fax: 330 424-9743
Kent Brennemen, *President*
Frederick L Brenneman, *President*
Linda Brenneman, *Admin Sec*
EMP: 4
SQ FT: 6,000
SALES (est): 270K **Privately Held**
WEB: www.wrightbuffingwheel.com
SIC: 7389 3291 3545 Grinding, precision: commercial or industrial; buffing or polishing wheels, abrasive or nonabrasive; machine tool accessories

(G-12137)
ARTISTIC COMPOSITE & MOLD CO
9225 Stone Rd (44253-9789)
PHONE..............................330 352-6632
Bryan Whittenberger, *President*
Nicole Whittenberger, *Vice Pres*
EMP: 4
SQ FT: 4,000
SALES (est): 276.5K **Privately Held**
SIC: 3356 2655 Welding rods; cans, composite: foil-fiber & other: from purchased fiber

(G-12138)
MEDINA FOODS INC
Also Called: Gold Rush Jerky
9706 Crow Rd (44253-9549)
PHONE..............................330 725-1390
Fax: 330 725-3920
Abdalla Nimer, *President*
Cathy Fobes, *Vice Pres*
EMP: 45
SQ FT: 50,000
SALES (est): 8.4MM **Privately Held**
WEB: www.medinafoods.com
SIC: 2015 Variety meats (fresh edible organs), poultry

(G-12139)
PARKN MANUFACTURING LLC
8035 Norwalk Rd Ste 107 (44253-9135)
PHONE..............................330 723-8172
Willard Robert Scandlon, *CEO*
Bob Scandlon,
EMP: 12
SQ FT: 10,000
SALES: 4.5MM **Privately Held**
SIC: 3541 Machine tool replacement & repair parts, metal cutting types

(G-12140)
SHARPER TOOLING
9473 Smith Rd (44253-9737)
PHONE..............................330 667-2960
Brad O'Donnell, *Owner*
EMP: 4
SQ FT: 7,500
SALES (est): 132K **Privately Held**
SIC: 3545 Machine tool accessories

(G-12141)
7 UP OF MARIETTA INC
871 State Route 618 (45742-5377)
PHONE..............................740 423-9230
Fax: 740 423-9206
Bruce Freeman, *Manager*
Robert Deeds, *Manager*
Lisa Pettit, *Admin Sec*
EMP: 30
SALES (est): 2MM **Privately Held**
SIC: 2086 Bottled & canned soft drinks

(G-12142)
AMERICAN BOTTLING COMPANY
871 State Route 618 (45742-5377)
PHONE..............................740 423-9230
Robert Deeds, *Principal*
EMP: 70
SALES (corp-wide): 6.4B **Publicly Held**
WEB: www.cs-americas.com
SIC: 2086 Bottled & canned soft drinks
HQ: The American Bottling Company
    5301 Legacy Dr
    Plano TX 75024

(G-12143)
BAKERS PRINT SHOP
23 Wood Dr (45742-9711)
PHONE..............................740 423-1717
Blanche Baker, *Principal*
EMP: 3 EST: 2012

SALES (est): 100K **Privately Held**
SIC: 5999 2711 Alarm signal systems; commercial printing & newspaper publishing combined

(G-12144)
CHEMOURS COMPANY FC LLC
Also Called: Du Pont E I De Nemours and Co
251 Arrowhead Rd (45742-5394)
P.O. Box 452 (45742-0452)
PHONE..............................740 989-5202
Larry Hawkins, *Plant Mgr*
Barry Pifer, *Manager*
Jim Slate, *Manager*
Donald Rymer, *Associate*
EMP: 82
SALES (corp-wide): 5.4B **Publicly Held**
WEB: www.dupont.com
SIC: 2911 Petroleum refining
HQ: The Chemours Company Fc Llc
    1007 Market St
    Wilmington DE 19898
    302 774-1000

(G-12145)
AMERISOURCEBERGEN CORPORATION
6305 Lasalle Dr (43137-9280)
PHONE..............................614 497-3665
Frank Dicenso, *Director*
EMP: 100
SALES (corp-wide): 146.8B **Publicly Held**
SIC: 2834 5122 Pharmaceutical preparations; pharmaceuticals; druggists' sundries
PA: Amerisourcebergen Corporation
    1300 Morris Dr Ste 100
    Chesterbrook PA 19087
    610 727-7000

(G-12146)
CITY OF COLUMBUS
Also Called: Compost Facility
7000 State Route 104 (43137-9712)
PHONE..............................614 645-3152
John Hoff, *Branch Mgr*
EMP: 23 **Privately Held**
WEB: www.cityofcolumbus.org
SIC: 2875 9511 Compost; air, water & solid waste management;
PA: City Of Columbus
    90 W Broad St Rm B33
    Columbus OH 43215
    614 645-7671

(G-12147)
J P SAND & GRAVEL COMPANY
Also Called: Marble Cliff Block & Bldrs Sup
5911 Lockbourne Rd (43137-9256)
P.O. Box 2 (43137-0002)
PHONE..............................614 497-0083
Fax: 614 497-1138
Herbert Hartshorn, *Ch of Bd*
Richard A Roberts, *President*
Mike Craiglow, *Vice Pres*
Joann Roberts, *Treasurer*
EMP: 28 EST: 1925
SQ FT: 6,200
SALES (est): 3MM **Privately Held**
SIC: 3271 1442 Blocks, concrete or cinder: standard; construction sand mining; gravel mining

(G-12148)
LOCKBOURNE AG CENTER INC
10 Commerce St (43137)
P.O. Box 11 (43137-0011)
PHONE..............................614 491-0635
Fax: 614 492-9438
Kenneth R Gregory, *President*
Vicky Gregory, *Treasurer*
EMP: 4
SQ FT: 20,000
SALES (est): 512.6K **Privately Held**
SIC: 3199 Feed bags for horses

(G-12149)
LUXOTTICA RETAIL N AMER INC
Also Called: Luxottica Optical Mfg
2150 Bixby Rd (43137-9273)
PHONE..............................614 409-9381
Chip Sexton, *Branch Mgr*
Bob Blankenship, *Manager*
EMP: 102 **Privately Held**
SIC: 3851 Ophthalmic goods
HQ: Luxottica Retail North America Inc.
4000 Luxottica Pl
Mason OH 45040
513 765-6000

(G-12150)
NATIONAL LIME AND STONE CO
5911 Lockbourne Rd (43137-9256)
PHONE..............................614 497-0083
Martin Cudoc, *Plant Mgr*
Richard Roberts, *Branch Mgr*
EMP: 25
SQ FT: 4,032
SALES (corp-wide): 4B **Privately Held**
WEB: www.natlime.com
SIC: 3271 1442 Blocks, concrete or cinder: standard; construction sand mining; gravel mining
PA: The National Lime And Stone Company
551 Lake Cascade Pkwy
Findlay OH 45840
419 422-4341

(G-12151)
RUEDE CABINET COMPANY
7171 State Route 104 (43137-9712)
PHONE..............................614 875-8717
Fax: 614 875-2772
Larry Ruede, *President*
EMP: 3 **EST:** 1965
SQ FT: 20,000
SALES: 100K **Privately Held**
WEB: www.ruedeinc.com
SIC: 2434 Wood kitchen cabinets; vanities; bathroom: wood

(G-12152)
VSP LAB COLUMBUS
2605 Rohr Rd (43137-9281)
PHONE..............................614 409-8900
Ed Morris, *Principal*
EMP: 23
SALES (est): 4.5MM **Privately Held**
SIC: 3827 Optical instruments & lenses

(G-12153)
WHIRLPOOL CORPORATION
6241 Shook Rd (43137-9306)
PHONE..............................614 409-4340
EMP: 175
SALES (corp-wide): 20.7B **Publicly Held**
SIC: 3633 3585 3632 Household laundry equipment; household laundry machines, including coin-operated; laundry dryers, household or coin-operated; washing machines, household: including coin-operated; air conditioning units, complete: domestic or industrial; refrigerators, mechanical & absorption: household; freezers, home & farm
PA: Whirlpool Corporation
2000 N M 63
Benton Harbor MI 49022
269 923-5000

Lodi
Medina County

(G-12154)
ABC PLASTICS INC
140 West Dr (44254-1062)
PHONE..............................330 948-3322
Fax: 330 948-2447
Barbara Lohmier, *President*
Ricki Mervis, *Controller*
Russ Porter, *Sales Mgr*
EMP: 40
SQ FT: 66,000
SALES (est): 6.9MM **Privately Held**
SIC: 3089 Injection molded finished plastic products

(G-12155)
ADVANCE BRONZE INC (PA)
139 Ohio St (44254-1047)
P.O. Box 280 (44254-0280)
PHONE..............................330 948-1231
Fax: 330 641-0570
David Del Propost, *President*
David Delpropost, *General Mgr*
John Wenneman, *Vice Pres*
Brett Fehrenbach, *Engineer*
Vincent J Del Propost, *Treasurer*
▲ **EMP:** 60
SQ FT: 150,000
SALES (est): 11.1MM **Privately Held**
WEB: www.advancebronze.com
SIC: 3568 3366 Power transmission equipment; bushings & bearings

(G-12156)
ALLOY FABRICATORS INC
700 Wooster St (44254-1340)
PHONE..............................330 948-3535
Fax: 330 948-0000
Lance Yurich, *President*
Dan Dietrick, *General Mgr*
Doug Dowen, *Engineer*
Shelly Aux, *Accounts Mgr*
Edward Fere, *Manager*
EMP: 21
SQ FT: 15,000
SALES (est): 4.3MM **Privately Held**
WEB: www.alloyfab.net
SIC: 3444 Sheet metalwork

(G-12157)
ARTISTIC FOODS INCORPORATED
355 Elyria St (44254-1067)
PHONE..............................330 401-1313
Nicole Whittenberger, *Principal*
EMP: 3
SALES (est): 156.1K **Privately Held**
SIC: 2099 Food preparations

(G-12158)
BUCKEYE POLYMERS INC (PA)
104 Lee St (44254-1056)
PHONE..............................330 948-3007
Fax: 330 948-2037
Jeffery Fisher, *President*
Todd Young, *Controller*
Yvon Carudel, *Accounts Mgr*
David McLellan, *Manager*
Teresa Weyburne, *Manager*
▲ **EMP:** 37
SQ FT: 35,000
SALES (est): 9.9MM **Privately Held**
WEB: www.buckeyepolymers.com
SIC: 2821 2824 Molding compounds, plastics; polyethylene resins; acrylonitrile fibers

(G-12159)
CROPKING INCORPORATED
134 West Dr (44254-1062)
PHONE..............................330 302-4203
Paul Brentlinger, *President*
Marilyn Brentlinger, *Corp Secy*
Tammy Tector, *Accounts Mgr*
Nancy Greer, *Manager*
◆ **EMP:** 16
SQ FT: 40,000
SALES (est): 4MM **Privately Held**
WEB: www.cropking.com
SIC: 3448 3999 Greenhouses: prefabricated metal; hydroponic equipment

(G-12160)
FASTFEED CORP
124 S Academy St (44254-1345)
PHONE..............................330 948-7333
Dan Reed, *President*
EMP: 6
SALES (est): 1.1MM **Privately Held**
SIC: 3441 Fabricated structural metal

(G-12161)
FEINKOST INGREDIENT CO U S A
Also Called: Feinkost Ingredients
103 Billman St (44254-1029)
PHONE..............................330 948-3006
Fax: 330 948-3016
Mark Sandridge, *President*
EMP: 5

SALES: 150K **Privately Held**
SIC: 2099 Emulsifiers, food

(G-12162)
HERALD LOOMS
118 Lee St (44254-1056)
PHONE..............................330 948-1080
Alan Anderson, *Principal*
EMP: 3
SALES (est): 120.7K **Privately Held**
SIC: 2711 Newspapers, publishing & printing

(G-12163)
L C I INC
101 West Dr (44254-1061)
P.O. Box 205 (44254-0205)
PHONE..............................330 948-1922
Fax: 330 948-2143
Elias A Sutton Jr, *President*
Diana L Sutton, *Corp Secy*
EMP: 3
SQ FT: 16,000
SALES (est): 450K **Privately Held**
SIC: 3469 3599 Stamping metal for the trade; machine shop, jobbing & repair

(G-12164)
LODI FOUNDRY CO INC
106 Billman St (44254-1030)
P.O. Box 185 (44254-0185)
PHONE..............................330 948-1516
Fax: 330 948-2112
EMP: 24
SQ FT: 14,000
SALES: 1.2MM **Privately Held**
SIC: 3365 Aluminum Foundry

(G-12165)
LOWELL MARCUM
Also Called: Marcum Machine Shop
328 Bank St (44254-1006)
P.O. Box 337 (44254-0337)
PHONE..............................330 948-2353
Lowell Marcum, *Owner*
EMP: 5
SALES (est): 410.6K **Privately Held**
SIC: 3599 Machine shop, jobbing & repair

(G-12166)
MAGNACO INDUSTRIES INC (PA)
140 West Dr (44254-1062)
PHONE..............................216 961-3636
Ken Geith, *President*
Magdalaine Geith, *Treasurer*
EMP: 20
SQ FT: 43,000
SALES: 1,000K **Privately Held**
SIC: 3714 7389 Motor vehicle parts & accessories; packaging & labeling services

(G-12167)
OAK FRONT INC
Also Called: Bent Nail Millwork
830 Bank St (44254-1028)
P.O. Box 217 (44254-0217)
PHONE..............................330 948-4500
Fax: 330 948-5000
David Fetherolf, *Vice Pres*
EMP: 5
SQ FT: 8,000
SALES (est): 694.8K **Privately Held**
SIC: 2431 Millwork

(G-12168)
PIONEER MACHINE INC
104 S Prospect St (44254-1313)
PHONE..............................330 948-6500
Don Gray, *President*
Sherry Gray, *Vice Pres*
EMP: 6
SQ FT: 8,400
SALES (est): 560K **Privately Held**
SIC: 3441 3599 Fabricated structural metal; machine shop, jobbing & repair

(G-12169)
SHILLING TRANSPORT
9718 Avon Lake Rd (44254-9639)
PHONE..............................330 948-1105
Gary Frank, *President*
EMP: 7
SALES: 420K **Privately Held**
SIC: 3715 Truck trailers

(G-12170)
STEPHEN ANDREWS INC
Also Called: Camelot Printing
7634 Lafayette Rd (44254-9607)
PHONE..............................330 725-2672
Fax: 330 725-2608
Stephen Andrews, *President*
EMP: 7
SQ FT: 1,700
SALES (est): 874.3K **Privately Held**
SIC: 2759 2752 Commercial printing; commercial printing, lithographic; commercial printing, offset

---

Logan
Hocking County

(G-12171)
AMANDA MANUFACTURING
1120 C I C Dr (43138-9153)
P.O. Box 1027 (43138-4027)
PHONE..............................740 385-6893
Fax: 740 385-5445
Donald E Gruschow, *President*
Sandra Zwayer, *Manager*
Bill Skillman, *Bd of Directors*
▲ **EMP:** 110
SQ FT: 139,000
SALES (est): 29.7MM
SALES (corp-wide): 70.8MM **Privately Held**
WEB: www.amandabentbolt.com
SIC: 3496 3452 Miscellaneous fabricated wire products; bolts, nuts, rivets & washers
PA: Deshler Group, Inc.
34450 Industrial Rd
Livonia MI 48150
734 525-9100

(G-12172)
CLAY LOGAN PRODUCTS COMPANY
Also Called: LOGAN FOUNDRY & MACHINE
201 S Walnut St (43138-1376)
P.O. Box 698 (43138-0698)
PHONE..............................740 385-2184
Fax: 740 385-0758
Richard H Brandt, *Ch of Bd*
William R Brandt, *President*
William Heft, *Vice Pres*
Bill Heft, *Manager*
Donald Hoobler, *Director*
EMP: 80
SQ FT: 266,000
SALES: 18.5MM **Privately Held**
WEB: www.claypipe.com
SIC: 3952 3259 Palettes, artists'; clay sewer & drainage pipe & tile

(G-12173)
COLUMBUS WASHBOARD COMPANY LTD
14 Gallagher Ave (43138-1666)
PHONE..............................740 380-3828
Fax: 740 380-1528
Jacqueline M Barnett,
Bevan Barnett,
Joyce Gerstner,
Larry Gerstner,
James Martin,
▲ **EMP:** 13
SQ FT: 15,000
SALES: 500K **Privately Held**
SIC: 2499 Washboards, wood & part wood
PA: Carbolic Soap Company Ltd
Peills Court Yard
Keston

(G-12174)
GABRIEL LOGAN LLC (PA)
1689 E Front St (43138-9290)
PHONE..............................740 380-6809
Fax: 740 380-6698
Troy L Gabriel, *CEO*
Tom Richardson, *Exec VP*
Brandon Rogers, *Design Engr*
Darcy Bamgartner, *Controller*
Misty Wilfing, *Marketing Staff*
▲ **EMP:** 61
SQ FT: 300,000

SALES (est): 9.6MM **Privately Held**
WEB: www.gabriellogan.com
SIC: **2541** Display fixtures, wood;
pedestals & statuary, wood; store & office
display cases & fixtures

(G-12175)
GENERAL ELECTRIC COMPANY
Hc 93 Box N (43138)
PHONE.................................740 385-2114
Fax: 740 385-2523
John Davis, *Manager*
Michael Wilhite, *Manager*
EMP: 100
SALES (corp-wide): 123.6B **Publicly
Held**
SIC: **3231** 3229 Products of purchased
glass; pressed & blown glass
PA: General Electric Company
41 Farnsworth St
Boston MA 02210
617 443-3000

(G-12176)
HOCKING HILLS ENERGY &
WELL SE
32919 Logan Horns Mill Rd (43138-8497)
PHONE.................................740 385-6690
David Poling, *Mng Member*
EMP: 7
SALES: 3.5MM **Privately Held**
SIC: **1382** 1381 Geophysical exploration,
oil & gas field; drilling oil & gas wells

(G-12177)
HOCKING VALLEY CONCRETE
INC (PA)
35255 Hocking Dr (43138-9482)
PHONE.................................740 385-2165
Fax: 740 385-2166
William Vaughn, *President*
David Vaughn, *Vice Pres*
Mark Vaughn, *Vice Pres*
Tim Persons, *Finance Mgr*
Doug Dicken, *Sales Associate*
EMP: 12 EST: 1956
SQ FT: 2,000
SALES (est): 2.7MM **Privately Held**
SIC: **3273** 1442 Ready-mixed concrete;
construction sand mining; gravel mining

(G-12178)
HOCKING VALLEY CONCRETE
INC
35255 Hocking Dr (43138-9482)
PHONE.................................740 385-2165
William Laughn, *Manager*
EMP: 8
SALES (corp-wide): 2.7MM **Privately
Held**
SIC: **3273** Ready-mixed concrete
PA: Hocking Valley Concrete, Inc.
35255 Hocking Dr
Logan OH 43138
740 385-2165

(G-12179)
HOFFMANS COUNTRY MARKET
685 E Front St (43138-1719)
Rural Route 10350 Webb (43138)
PHONE.................................740 216-0115
Crystal Hoffman, *Partner*
EMP: 5
SQ FT: 1,269
SALES (est): 193.7K **Privately Held**
SIC: **2051** Bakery: wholesale or whole-
sale/retail combined

(G-12180)
JUDITH C ZELL
21313 State Route 93 S (43138-7508)
PHONE.................................740 385-0386
Edward Zell, *President*
Judith Zell, *Owner*
EMP: 3
SALES: 300K **Privately Held**
SIC: **3993** 2499 Signs & advertising spe-
cialties; decorative wood & woodwork

(G-12181)
KEYNES BROS INC (PA)
1 W Front St (43138-1825)
P.O. Box 628 (43138-0628)
PHONE.................................740 385-6824
Fax: 740 385-9076

William W Keynes, *President*
William W Keynes Jr, *Corp Secy*
Charles H Keynes, *Vice Pres*
Jeffrey Rose, *Human Res Mgr*
Dave Remley, *Sales Mgr*
EMP: 37 EST: 1869
SQ FT: 13,145
SALES: 43.7MM **Privately Held**
WEB: www.keynesbros.com
SIC: **2041** 5191 Flour mills, cereal (except
rice); feed

(G-12182)
KILBARGER CONSTRUCTION
INC
Also Called: C & L Supply
450 Gallagher Ave (43138-1893)
P.O. Box 946 (43138-0946)
PHONE.................................740 385-5531
Fax: 740 385-7254
Edward Kilbarger, *CEO*
Anthony Kilbarger, *Vice Pres*
James E Kilbarger, *Vice Pres*
Daniel Stohs, *Opers Mgr*
Dave Sterling, *CFO*
EMP: 120
SQ FT: 2,500
SALES (est): 25.8MM **Privately Held**
WEB: www.kilbarger.com
SIC: **1381** Drilling oil & gas wells

(G-12183)
KILBARGER INVESTMENTS INC
Also Called: Kilbarger Investment Co
450 Gallagher Ave (43138-1893)
P.O. Box 946 (43138-0946)
PHONE.................................740 385-6019
Edward F Kilbarger, *President*
Anthony Kilbarger, *Vice Pres*
James E Kilbarger, *Vice Pres*
Ann Kilbarger, *Admin Sec*
EMP: 4
SQ FT: 2,500
SALES (est): 594.4K **Privately Held**
SIC: **1311** Crude petroleum production;
natural gas production

(G-12184)
LOGAN COATINGS LLC
2255 E Front St (43138-8637)
P.O. Box 459, Waynesfield (45896-0459)
PHONE.................................740 380-0047
James M Johnson, *Principal*
EMP: 9
SALES (est): 1.1MM **Privately Held**
SIC: **3479** Coating of metals & formed
products

(G-12185)
LOGAN SCREEN PRINTING
Also Called: Logan Screen Printing & EMB
119 W Main St (43138-1605)
PHONE.................................740 385-3303
Bob Schrader, *Owner*
EMP: 5
SQ FT: 3,200
SALES (est): 398.1K **Privately Held**
WEB: www.loganscreenprinting.com
SIC: **2759** 2396 2395 Commercial print-
ing; automotive & apparel trimmings;
pleating & stitching

(G-12186)
LOGAN WELDING INC
37062 Hocking Dr (43138-9465)
PHONE.................................740 385-9651
Fax: 740 380-3223
Mark E Brandon, *President*
Dan Brandon, *Vice Pres*
Juanita Brandon, *Admin Sec*
EMP: 6
SQ FT: 5,100
SALES (est): 729.7K **Privately Held**
SIC: **7692** Welding repair

(G-12187)
OAK DALE DRILLING INC
149 Ruth Ave (43138-1851)
PHONE.................................740 385-5888
Dale Tucker, *President*
Teddy Tucker, *Treasurer*
EMP: 5
SALES (est): 347.2K **Privately Held**
SIC: **1381** Directional drilling oil & gas
wells

(G-12188)
OSBURN ASSOCIATES INC (PA)
9383 Vanatta Rd (43138-8719)
P.O. Box 912 (43138-0912)
PHONE.................................740 385-5732
Fax: 740 385-8016
Charles A Gerken, *Principal*
Jeff Osburn, *Vice Pres*
Cheryl Donahue, *Sales Staff*
Harry Osburn, *Director*
Donna Osburn, *Director*
▲ EMP: 16
SQ FT: 39,360
SALES (est): 8.9MM **Privately Held**
WEB: www.osburnassociates.com
SIC: **3089** 5063 Fittings for pipe, plastic;
boxes & fittings, electrical

(G-12189)
PATTONS TRUCK & HEAVY EQP
SVC
Also Called: K & K Auto & Truck Parts
35640 Hocking Dr (43138-9467)
P.O. Box 963 (43138-0963)
PHONE.................................740 385-4067
Fax: 740 385-6597
Paul Patton, *President*
EMP: 16
SQ FT: 3,400
SALES (est): 2.3MM **Privately Held**
SIC: **3599** 7538 5531 Machine shop, job-
bing & repair; general automotive repair
shops; automotive & home supply stores

(G-12190)
PAUL A GRIM INC
15104 State Route 328 (43138-9445)
PHONE.................................740 385-9637
Paul A Grim, *President*
Joyce Grim, *Admin Sec*
EMP: 5
SQ FT: 7,200
SALES: 500K **Privately Held**
SIC: **1381** Drilling oil & gas wells

(G-12191)
QUALITY CONCEPTS TELECOM
19485 Harble Rd (43138-9772)
PHONE.................................740 385-2003
Chris Warren, *Office Mgr*
Richard J Warren,
EMP: 20
SQ FT: 1,400
SALES (est): 2.4MM **Privately Held**
SIC: **3452** Bolts, nuts, rivets & washers

(G-12192)
RALPH ROBINSON INC
Also Called: Oil Enterprises
700 Ohio Ave (43138-8469)
P.O. Box 84 (43138-0084)
PHONE.................................740 385-2747
Fax: 740 385-1897
Michael Robinson, *President*
EMP: 6 EST: 1962
SQ FT: 4,700
SALES (est): 756.7K **Privately Held**
SIC: **1389** 5084 Oil & gas wells: building,
repairing & dismantling; oil refining ma-
chinery, equipment & supplies

(G-12193)
SIGNS UNLIMITED (PA)
Also Called: Advent Designs
21313 State Route 93 S (43138-7508)
PHONE.................................614 836-7446
Fax: 614 836-7457
Judy Zell, *CEO*
Ed Zell, *President*
Zelepsky Joel, *COO*
Ken Ross, *Manager*
EMP: 8
SQ FT: 20,000
SALES: 250K **Privately Held**
WEB: www.adventdesigns.com
SIC: **3993** Signs & advertising specialties

(G-12194)
SMEAD MANUFACTURING
COMPANY
851 Smead Rd (43138-9500)
PHONE.................................740 385-5601
Fax: 740 385-9554
Sandy Byrd, *Manager*
Ron Rutter, *Manager*

EMP: 175
SALES (corp-wide): 317MM **Privately
Held**
SIC: **2675** Folders, filing, die-cut: made
from purchased materials
PA: Smead Manufacturing Company Inc
600 Smead Blvd
Hastings MN 55033
651 437-4111

(G-12195)
SOUTHEASTERN NATURAL GAS
CO
35200 Hocking Dr (43138-9451)
P.O. Box 1956, Buckeye Lake (43008-
1956)
PHONE.................................740 385-8583
Chuck Stewart, *Manager*
EMP: 5
SALES (est): 360.8K **Privately Held**
SIC: **1311** Natural gas production

(G-12196)
TYJEN INC (PA)
Also Called: Slater's Builders Supplies
35255 Hocking Dr (43138-9482)
PHONE.................................740 380-3215
Mark Vaughn, *President*
David Vaughn, *Vice Pres*
EMP: 3 EST: 1931
SQ FT: 2,000
SALES (est): 2.8MM **Privately Held**
SIC: **3271** 5211 Blocks, concrete or cin-
der: standard; lumber & other building
materials

(G-12197)
WRIGHTS WELL SERVICE
37940 Scout Rd (43138-8832)
PHONE.................................740 380-9602
Ken Wright, *Owner*
EMP: 6
SALES (est): 204.5K **Privately Held**
SIC: **1389** Servicing oil & gas wells

London
Madison County

(G-12198)
ADVANCED DRAINAGE
SYSTEMS INC
288 Lafayette St (43140-9069)
PHONE.................................740 852-9554
Fax: 740 852-0687
Barry Trimble, *Manager*
EMP: 30
SALES (corp-wide): 1.2B **Publicly Held**
WEB: www.ads-pipe.com
SIC: **3084** Plastics pipe
PA: Advanced Drainage Systems, Inc.
4640 Trueman Blvd
Hilliard OH 43026
614 658-0050

(G-12199)
ADVANCED DRAINAGE
SYSTEMS INC
Also Called: ADS
400 E High St (43140-9501)
PHONE.................................740 852-2980
Fax: 740 852-3092
Kerry Smith, *Safety Mgr*
Robert Sensabaugh, *Branch Mgr*
Robert Slicker, *Manager*
EMP: 52
SALES (corp-wide): 1.2B **Publicly Held**
WEB: www.ads-pipe.com
SIC: **3084** Plastics pipe
PA: Advanced Drainage Systems, Inc.
4640 Trueman Blvd
Hilliard OH 43026
614 658-0050

(G-12200)
ARMALY LLC
Also Called: Armaly Brands
110 W 1st St (43140-1484)
PHONE.................................740 852-3621
Annmarie Armaly, *Treasurer*
▼ EMP: 40

SALES (est): 8.4MM **Privately Held**
SIC: 3089 5199 3086 Floor coverings, plastic; sponges (animal); plastics foam products
PA: Armaly Sponge Company
1900 Easy St
Commerce Township MI 48390
248 669-2100

(G-12201)
BODYCOTE IMT INC
443 E High St (43140-9501)
PHONE..................................740 852-5000
Fax: 740 852-5014
Chris Gattie, *Manager*
Jim Harbert, *Director*
EMP: 27
SALES (corp-wide): 739.3MM **Privately Held**
SIC: 3398 3269 Metal heat treating; pottery household articles, except kitchen articles
HQ: Bodycote Imt, Inc.
155 River St
Andover MA 01810
978 470-0876

(G-12202)
BODYCOTE THERMAL PROC INC
Also Called: Bodycote Kolsterising
443 E High St (43140-9501)
PHONE..................................740 852-4955
Doug Ridgeway, *General Mgr*
EMP: 7
SALES (corp-wide): 739.3MM **Privately Held**
SIC: 3398 Metal heat treating
HQ: Bodycote Thermal Processing, Inc.
12700 Park Central Dr # 700
Dallas TX 75251
214 904-2420

(G-12203)
CENTRAL OHIO PRINTING CORP
Also Called: Madison Press
55 W High St (43140-1074)
PHONE..................................740 852-1616
Fax: 740 852-1620
Donald Hartley, *President*
Linda Marx, *Publisher*
William Armstrong, *Advt Staff*
EMP: 55 EST: 1961
SQ FT: 20,000
SALES (est): 2.7MM **Privately Held**
WEB: www.madison-press.com
SIC: 2711 2752 Newspapers, publishing & printing; commercial printing, lithographic
PA: Walls Newspapers Inc
525 Office Park Dr
Mountain Brk AL 35223
205 870-1684

(G-12204)
CHURCH & DWIGHT CO INC
Also Called: Arm & Hammer
110 W 1st St (43140-1484)
PHONE..................................740 852-3621
Neil Parrish, *Opers Mgr*
Richard Newberry, *Purch Mgr*
Sandra Wood, *Supervisor*
EMP: 70
SALES (corp-wide): 3.4B **Publicly Held**
WEB: www.churchdwight.com
SIC: 2812 Sodium bicarbonate
PA: Church & Dwight Co., Inc.
500 Charles Ewing Blvd
Ewing NJ 08628
609 806-1200

(G-12205)
COLUMBUS MESSENGER COMPANY
Also Called: Madison Messenger
78 S Main St (43140-1212)
PHONE..................................740 852-0809
Fax: 740 852-0814
Jim Durban, *Manager*
EMP: 4
SALES (corp-wide): 1.9MM **Privately Held**
SIC: 2711 Newspapers
PA: The Columbus Messenger Company
3500 Sullivant Ave
Columbus OH 43204
614 272-5422

(G-12206)
CONVEYORS LTD
Also Called: Versa Conveyors
475 E High St (43140-9303)
P.O. Box 899 (43140-0899)
PHONE..................................740 490-0300
Randall Petitt, *Vice Pres*
Eugene Noble, *Research*
Andrew Petitt,
▲ EMP: 135
SALES (est): 15.5MM **Privately Held**
WEB: www.conveyors.com
SIC: 3535 Conveyors & conveying equipment

(G-12207)
CREAMER METAL PRODUCTS INC (PA)
77 S Madison Rd (43140-1444)
P.O. Box 587 (43140-0587)
PHONE..................................740 852-1752
Fax: 614 852-1797
Karen C Peters, *President*
Robert Snyder, *Vice Pres*
Rob Conley, *Purchasing*
Frank Spilker, *CFO*
EMP: 30 EST: 1945
SQ FT: 31,000
SALES: 1B **Privately Held**
WEB: www.creamermetal.com
SIC: 3523 Farm machinery & equipment

(G-12208)
DEER CREEK HONEY FARMS LTD
551 E High St (43140-9304)
PHONE..................................740 852-0899
Fax: 740 852-4530
Christopher L Dunham, *Partner*
Lee T Dunham, *Partner*
Mark L Dunham, *Partner*
EMP: 8 EST: 1938
SQ FT: 22,000
SALES (est): 1MM **Privately Held**
SIC: 2099 0279 Honey, strained & bottled; apiary (bee & honey farm)

(G-12209)
DIGIONYX LLC
8420 Opossum Run Rd (43140-9437)
PHONE..................................614 594-9897
Timothy Fleming,
Harold Goings,
EMP: 5
SALES (est): 141.8K **Privately Held**
SIC: 7372 7389 Prepackaged software;

(G-12210)
GARY I TEACH JR
4855 Rsdale Mlford Ctr Rd (43140)
PHONE..................................614 582-7483
Gary L Teach, *Principal*
EMP: 4
SALES (est): 437K **Privately Held**
SIC: 2672 Coated & laminated paper

(G-12211)
GRA-MAG TRUCK INTR SYSTEMS LLC (DH)
470 E High St (43140-9303)
PHONE..................................740 490-1000
Fax: 614 801-9857
Coleen Uhrg, *Human Resources*
Rick Chefer, *Mng Member*
▲ EMP: 30
SQ FT: 60,000
SALES (est): 8.6MM
SALES (corp-wide): 36.4B **Privately Held**
WEB: www.gramag.com
SIC: 2531 Seats, automobile
HQ: Magna Seating Of America, Inc.
39600 Lewis Dr Ste 216
Novi MI 48377
248 553-8094

(G-12212)
INTELLIGRATED PRODUCTS LLC
475 E High St (43140-9303)
P.O. Box 899 (43140-0899)
PHONE..................................740 490-0300
Fax: 740 490-0282
Chris Cole, *CEO*
Brad Bijonowski, *COO*
Frank Pellegrino, *Vice Pres*

John Grigsby, *Opers Staff*
Doug Westerman, *Opers Staff*
▲ EMP: 33
SQ FT: 210,000
SALES (est): 10.2MM **Privately Held**
SIC: 3535 Conveyors & conveying equipment

(G-12213)
JOHN C STARR
Also Called: Starr Trophy & Awards
15 S Main St (43140-1243)
P.O. Box 615 (43140-0615)
PHONE..................................740 852-5592
John C Starr, *Owner*
EMP: 3
SQ FT: 2,400
SALES (est): 269.4K **Privately Held**
SIC: 5999 5947 7389 2759 Trophies & plaques; gift shop; engraving service; imprinting

(G-12214)
KMAK GROUP LLC
480 E High St (43140-9303)
P.O. Box 496 (43140-0496)
PHONE..................................937 308-1023
Kevin Henry, *President*
EMP: 11
SQ FT: 15,000
SALES (est): 1.7MM **Privately Held**
SIC: 2448 Cargo containers, wood & wood with metal

(G-12215)
NISSEN CHEMITEC AMERICA INC
350 E High St (43140-9773)
PHONE..................................740 852-3200
Shawn Hendrix, *President*
Shinya Kawakami, *President*
Richard Hendrix, *Senior VP*
Kunihiko Nagura, *Vice Pres*
Damion Manns, *Plant Mgr*
▲ EMP: 230
SQ FT: 155,000
SALES (est): 48MM
SALES (corp-wide): 246.4MM **Privately Held**
WEB: www.londonind.com
SIC: 3089 Injection molding of plastics
PA: Nissen Chemitec Corporation
2-4-34, Nishiharacho
Niihama EHM 792-0
897 334-171

(G-12216)
O CONNOR OFFICE PDTS & PRTG
60 W High St (43140-1075)
PHONE..................................740 852-2209
Gary Feliks, *Owner*
EMP: 8
SQ FT: 3,200
SALES (est): 560K **Privately Held**
SIC: 5943 2752 Office forms & supplies; commercial printing, offset

(G-12217)
OAKVALE FARM CHEESE INC
1283 State Route 29 Ne (43140-9545)
PHONE..................................740 857-1230
Dale King, *President*
Randall Finke, *Vice Pres*
Elizabeth Finke, *Treasurer*
Jean King, *Admin Sec*
EMP: 5
SALES (est): 384.5K **Privately Held**
SIC: 2022 Cheese, natural & processed

(G-12218)
OHIO PROCESSORS INC
244 E 1st St (43140-1478)
P.O. Box 594 (43140-0594)
PHONE..................................740 852-9243
Fax: 740 488-2536
Ronald Potts, *Purchasing*
Douglas Smith, *Sales Executive*
Doug Smith, *Branch Mgr*
EMP: 20
SALES (corp-wide): 43.5MM **Privately Held**
SIC: 2099 Food preparations

HQ: Ohio Processors Inc
2200 Cardigan Ave
Columbus OH 43215
740 852-9243

(G-12219)
STANLEY ELECTRIC US CO INC (HQ)
420 E High St (43140-9799)
PHONE..................................740 852-5200
Fax: 740 852-5201
Shinomiya Masahiro, *President*
Brian Boldman, *Plant Mgr*
Debbie Rotman, *Purchasing*
Cody Smucker, *QA Dir*
Matt Connolly, *Draft/Design*
▲ EMP: 277
SQ FT: 733,000
SALES: 40MM
SALES (corp-wide): 3.4B **Privately Held**
WEB: www.stanleyus.com
SIC: 3647 3694 3089 Automotive lighting fixtures; automotive electrical equipment; injection molding of plastics
PA: Stanley Electric Co.,Ltd.
2-9-13, Nakameguro
Meguro-Ku TKY 153-0
368 662-222

(G-12220)
TEXTILES INC (PA)
Also Called: Jordan Young International
23 Old Springfield Rd (43140-2033)
PHONE..................................740 852-0782
Phillip Jordan, *President*
Catherine Jordan, *Vice Pres*
Rob Jordan, *Vice Pres*
▲ EMP: 6
SQ FT: 4,000
SALES (est): 16.6MM **Privately Held**
SIC: 2511 Wood household furniture

(G-12221)
UNDER HILL WATER WELL
1789 Itawamba Trl (43140-8737)
PHONE..................................740 852-0858
Timothy Underhill, *Principal*
EMP: 3
SALES (est): 368.7K **Privately Held**
SIC: 3533 Drilling tools for gas, oil or water wells

(G-12222)
UNITED LANDMARK LLC
131 S Walnut St (43140-1423)
PHONE..................................740 852-2062
Joe Henry, *Manager*
Michael Bay, *Manager*
Clayton Cook, *Manager*
EMP: 3
SALES (est): 140K **Privately Held**
SIC: 1321 Casing-head butane & propane production

(G-12223)
WHITE TIGER INC
Also Called: White Tiger Graphics
131 S Oak St (43140-1446)
PHONE..................................740 852-4873
Fax: 614 852-0543
George Peyton, *President*
Brad Johnson, *Sales Executive*
EMP: 14
SQ FT: 6,000
SALES (est): 1.3MM **Privately Held**
SIC: 7336 2752 5199 Graphic arts & related design; silk screen design; commercial printing, offset; advertising specialties

(G-12224)
WILSON PRTG GRAPHICS OF LONDON (PA)
158 S Main St (43140-1439)
PHONE..................................740 852-5934
Tim Wilson, *President*
Barbara Clark, *Admin Sec*
EMP: 5
SQ FT: 4,800
SALES (est): 533.3K **Privately Held**
SIC: 2752 Commercial printing, lithographic

Londonderry
Ross County

(G-12225)
ALBRIGHT SAW COMPANY INC
Also Called: Albright Supply Company
33535 Us Highway 50 (45647-9715)
PHONE.................................740 887-2107
EMP: 3
SALES (est): 226.2K **Privately Held**
SIC: 3524 5261 Mfg Lawn/Garden Equipment Ret Nursery/Garden Supplies

(G-12226)
CLARK MACHINE SERVICE
33926 Us Highway 50 (45647-9704)
P.O. Box 203 (45647-0203)
PHONE.................................740 887-2396
Fax: 740 887-2400
Barry L Clark, *Owner*
Patty Clark, *Bookkeeper*
EMP: 3
SQ FT: 3,696
SALES (est): 267.1K **Privately Held**
SIC: 3599 Machine shop, jobbing & repair

(G-12227)
DON PUCKETT LUMBER INC
31263 Beech Grove Rd (45647-8942)
PHONE.................................740 887-4191
Fax: 740 887-2539
Tim Puckett, *President*
Jeff Puckett, *Vice Pres*
EMP: 17
SALES (est): 1.4MM **Privately Held**
SIC: 2421 Sawmills & planing mills, general

Long Bottom
Meigs County

(G-12228)
AGE GRAPHICS LLC (PA)
52231 State Route 248 (45743-9744)
PHONE.................................740 989-0006
Jim Bushong,
EMP: 10 EST: 1997
SALES (est): 1.7MM **Privately Held**
WEB: www.agegraphics.com
SIC: 3577 Graphic displays, except graphic terminals

Lorain
Lorain County

(G-12229)
A CLASS COATINGS INC
4481 Oakhill Blvd (44053-1959)
PHONE.................................440 960-6869
Lee Bolber, *President*
Tess Bolber, *Office Mgr*
EMP: 12
SQ FT: 20,000
SALES (est): 810K **Privately Held**
SIC: 3479 Coating of metals & formed products; aluminum coating of metal products

(G-12230)
A-1 WELDING & FABRICATING INC
1005 E 32nd St (44055-1598)
PHONE.................................440 233-8474
Fax: 440 233-5591
Daniel F Balko, *President*
Wayne Balko, *Vice Pres*
Rosy Harris, *Manager*
Holly Herbert, *Admin Sec*
EMP: 12
SQ FT: 60,000
SALES (est): 2.7MM **Privately Held**
SIC: 3443 3312 Weldments; structural shapes & pilings, steel

(G-12231)
ALPHA PRINT SPECIALTIES
3330 Oberlin Ave (44053-2754)
P.O. Box 596, Amherst (44001-0596)
PHONE.................................440 282-1150
Fax: 440 960-2335
Juan Colon, *Owner*
EMP: 4
SQ FT: 1,500
SALES: 150K **Privately Held**
WEB: www.softwarespecialties.com
SIC: 2752 Commercial printing, lithographic

(G-12232)
AMERICAN METAL CHEMICAL CORP
Also Called: Amcor Marine
200 E 9th St (44052-1903)
PHONE.................................440 244-1800
Fax: 440 244-1804
Debbie Smith, *Branch Mgr*
EMP: 5
SALES (corp-wide): 14.3MM **Privately Held**
SIC: 2899 Fluxes: brazing, soldering, galvanizing & welding
PA: American Metal Chemical Corporation
835 W Smith Rd
Medina OH 44256
330 725-4501

(G-12233)
ATLANTIC INVESTMENT
6117 Antler Xing (44053-1879)
PHONE.................................440 567-5054
Jose Moquete, *Principal*
EMP: 4
SQ FT: 2,450
SALES: 144K **Privately Held**
SIC: 2099 Food preparations

(G-12234)
BODNAR PRINTING CO INC
3480 Colorado Ave (44052-2818)
PHONE.................................440 277-8295
Fax: 440 277-9345
Ralph Woodward, *President*
Bonnie Woodward, *Corp Secy*
EMP: 12 EST: 1948
SQ FT: 5,000
SALES (est): 2.3MM **Privately Held**
WEB: www.bodnarprinting.com
SIC: 2752 Commercial printing, lithographic

(G-12235)
BUSES INTERNATIONAL
702 N Ridge Rd E (44055-3018)
PHONE.................................440 233-4091
Fax: 440 233-4580
Todd Rainey, *COO*
Tom Szychowicz, *Director*
Norman Beetler, *Director*
EMP: 12
SALES: 441.7K **Privately Held**
WEB: www.busesinternational.org
SIC: 8661 3711 8011 Christian & Reformed Church; bus & other specialty vehicle assembly; medical centers

(G-12236)
CAMACO LLC
Also Called: Camaco Lorain
3400 River Indus Pk Rd (44052-2900)
PHONE.................................440 288-4444
Fax: 440 288-4440
Ruby Srivastava, *Buyer*
Siegbert Plewa, *Engineer*
Bruce Price, *Engineer*
Thomas Rockwell, *CFO*
Tom Koutsou, *Controller*
EMP: 560
SALES (corp-wide): 552.7MM **Privately Held**
WEB: www.camaco.com
SIC: 3499 Automobile seat frames, metal
HQ: Camaco, Llc
37000 W 12 Mile Rd
Farmington Hills MI 48331
248 442-6800

(G-12237)
CASE PLATING INC
736 Idaho Ave (44052-3354)
PHONE.................................440 288-8304
Fax: 440 288-8307
Bonnie Pickett, *President*
EMP: 4
SQ FT: 12,000
SALES: 300K **Privately Held**
SIC: 3471 Plating of metals or formed products

(G-12238)
CLEVELAND RECLAIM INDS INC
Also Called: Turtle Plastics
7400 Industrial Pkwy Dr (44053-2064)
PHONE.................................440 282-4917
Fax: 440 282-8822
Thomas Norton, *President*
Michele Norton, *Vice Pres*
Charles Norton, *CFO*
Kristin Saez, *Sales Staff*
Liz Priess,
EMP: 10 EST: 1982
SQ FT: 15,000
SALES (est): 2.1MM **Privately Held**
WEB: www.turtleplastics.com
SIC: 3089 Floor coverings, plastic; plastic processing

(G-12239)
CONSUMERACQ INC (PA)
2509 N Ridge Rd E (44055-3772)
P.O. Box 823 (44055-0823)
PHONE.................................440 277-9305
Jeffrey Riddell, *President*
Jacqueline Riddell, *Admin Sec*
EMP: 18
SQ FT: 4,000
SALES (est): 10.9MM **Privately Held**
SIC: 3273 5211 Ready-mixed concrete; lumber & other building materials

(G-12240)
CONSUMERS BUILDERS SUPPLY CO (PA)
2509 N Ridge Rd E (44055-3772)
P.O. Box 824 (44052-0824)
PHONE.................................440 277-9306
Fax: 440 211-6317
Jeffrey Riddell, *President*
Linda Mollison, *Controller*
Jacqueline Riddell, *Admin Sec*
EMP: 20
SALES (est): 1.9MM **Privately Held**
WEB: www.consumersbbuilderssupply.com
SIC: 3273 5211 Ready-mixed concrete; lumber & other building materials

(G-12241)
CUSTOM MOLDED FOAM PRODUCTS
1821 Iowa Ave (44052-3359)
PHONE.................................440 288-8951
Richard Persico, *Principal*
EMP: 5 EST: 2011
SALES (est): 512K **Privately Held**
SIC: 3089 Molding primary plastic

(G-12242)
CUSTOM SINK TOP MFG
Also Called: C S T Geometric Forms
302 W 12th St (44052-3406)
PHONE.................................440 245-6220
Fax: 440 245-3676
Greg Luca, *Principal*
EMP: 11
SALES (est): 1.2MM **Privately Held**
SIC: 5031 2599 Structural assemblies, prefabricated: wood; factory furniture & fixtures; cabinets, factory

(G-12243)
DAYTON HEIDELBERG DISTRG CO
5901 Baumhart Rd (44053-2012)
PHONE.................................440 989-1027
EMP: 164
SALES (corp-wide): 390.5MM **Privately Held**
SIC: 2082 Beer (alcoholic beverage)
PA: Dayton Heidelberg Distributing Co.
3601 Dryden Rd
Moraine OH 45439
937 222-8692

(G-12244)
EMERSON ELECTRIC CO
1509 Iowa Ave (44052-3379)
PHONE.................................440 288-1122
Andy Schacht, *Vice Pres*
Eli Martinez, *Program Mgr*
Stacey Hardwick, *Manager*
George Plaza, *Sr Software Eng*
EMP: 21
SALES (corp-wide): 14.5B **Publicly Held**
SIC: 3823 Industrial instrmnts msrmnt display/control process variable
PA: Emerson Electric Co.
8000 West Florissant Ave
Saint Louis MO 63136
314 553-2000

(G-12245)
ERDIE INDUSTRIES INC
1205 Colorado Ave (44052-3313)
PHONE.................................440 288-0166
Jason Erdie, *President*
Jeffrey Erdie, *Vice Pres*
Jeff Hendrea, *Production*
EMP: 40
SQ FT: 50,000
SALES (est): 9.5MM **Privately Held**
WEB: www.erdiepaper.com
SIC: 2655 Fiber cans, drums & similar products; tubes, fiber or paper: made from purchased material; cores, fiber: made from purchased material; cans, fiber: made from purchased material

(G-12246)
EXOCHEM CORPORATION
Also Called: Energy Products
2421 E 28th St (44055-2198)
PHONE.................................440 277-6116
Randy Miraldi, *President*
Lois Miraldi, *Corp Secy*
John L Hammer, *Vice Pres*
EMP: 55
SQ FT: 4,000
SALES (est): 5.5MM **Privately Held**
WEB: www.exochem.com
SIC: 3543 Foundry cores

(G-12247)
EXOCHEM CORPORATION (PA)
2421 E 28th St (44055-2198)
PHONE.................................800 807-7464
Fax: 440 277-1615
Randall Miraldi, *President*
Melissa Wicker, *General Mgr*
Lois Miraldi, *Corp Secy*
Timothy Jenkins, *Exec VP*
Kathleen Roark, *Exec VP*
▲ EMP: 37 EST: 1968
SQ FT: 21,000
SALES (est): 11.5MM **Privately Held**
SIC: 3299 Insulsleeves (foundry materials)

(G-12248)
H P NIELSEN INC
Also Called: Nielsen Jewelers
753 Broadway (44052-1805)
PHONE.................................440 244-4255
Fax: 440 244-5040
Carl G Nielsen, *President*
Krystina Nielsen, *Vice Pres*
EMP: 6 EST: 1877
SQ FT: 2,600
SALES (est): 762.4K **Privately Held**
SIC: 5944 3911 7631 Jewelry, precious stones & precious metals; jewelry, precious metal; jewelry repair services

(G-12249)
HPC MANUFACTURING INC
7405 Industrial Pkwy Dr (44053-2064)
PHONE.................................440 322-8334
Robert Drake, *CEO*
Celeste Kangas, *Manager*
EMP: 3
SQ FT: 20,000
SALES (est): 580.9K **Privately Held**
SIC: 3561 Pumps & pumping equipment

(G-12250)
JOURNAL BKR
1657 Broadway (44052-3439)
PHONE.................................440 245-6901
Fax: 440 245-5637
Jeff Subrook, *Publisher*
EMP: 3 EST: 2011

SALES (est): 106.1K **Privately Held**
SIC: 2711 Newspapers, publishing & printing

(G-12251)
JOURNAL REGISTER COMPANY
Also Called: Morning Journal
1657 Broadway (44052-3439)
PHONE..............................440 245-6901
April Grasso, *Editor*
Beth Todd, *Controller*
Jeff Sudbrook, *Manager*
Jackie Sigman, *Technology*
Wilburn Gould, *Assoc Prof*
EMP: 115
SALES (corp-wide): 745.5MM **Privately Held**
SIC: 2711 5994 Newspapers, publishing & printing; newsstand
PA: Journal Register Company
5 Hanover Sq Fl 25
New York NY 10004
212 257-7212

(G-12252)
KTS-MET BAR PRODUCTS INC
967 G St (44052-3329)
PHONE..............................440 288-9308
Fax: 440 288-9815
Delvis Kerns, *President*
EMP: 9
SQ FT: 8,500
SALES (est): 1.4MM **Privately Held**
SIC: 3451 Screw machine products

(G-12253)
KUHN FABRICATING INC
1637 E 28th St (44055-1701)
PHONE..............................440 277-4182
Fax: 440 277-1798
Lewis Kuhn, *President*
Rosemary Kuhn, *Vice Pres*
EMP: 6 EST: 1958
SQ FT: 18,000
SALES (est): 1MM **Privately Held**
SIC: 3444 Sheet metal specialties, not stamped

(G-12254)
LAKE SCREEN PRINTING INC
1924 Broadway (44052-3682)
PHONE..............................440 244-5707
Fax: 440 244-5482
Ben Zientarski Jr, *President*
Annette Zientarski, *Corp Secy*
Rachelle Gulyas, *Vice Pres*
Teresa Zientakski, *Vice Pres*
Teresa Zientarski, *Vice Pres*
EMP: 8
SQ FT: 10,000
SALES (est): 1MM **Privately Held**
WEB: www.lakescreen.com
SIC: 2759 Commercial printing; screen printing

(G-12255)
LEVIT JEWELERS INC
4274 Oberlin Ave (44053-2925)
PHONE..............................440 985-1685
Rob M Levit, *President*
Katrina Levit, *Vice Pres*
EMP: 4
SALES (est): 367.1K **Privately Held**
WEB: www.levitjewelers.com
SIC: 3911 Jewelry, precious metal

(G-12256)
LORAIN COUNTY AUTO SYSTEMS INC (HQ)
Also Called: Lcas
7470 Industrial Pkwy Dr (44053-2070)
PHONE..............................440 960-7470
Fax: 440 960-1878
Arvind Pradhan, *CEO*
Tom Rockwell, *CFO*
Francois Rome, *Human Res Mgr*
Pam Cooper, *Administration*
▲ EMP: 50
SQ FT: 36,000
SALES: 194.2MM
SALES (corp-wide): 552.7MM **Privately Held**
WEB: www.lcas.com
SIC: 3714 Motor vehicle engines & parts

PA: P & C Group I, Inc.
37000 W 12 Mile Rd
Farmington Hills MI 48331
248 442-6800

(G-12257)
LORAIN JOURNAL
1657 Broadway (44052-3489)
PHONE..............................440 245-6900
Jeff Sudbrook, *President*
EMP: 4 EST: 2012
SALES (est): 199.7K **Privately Held**
SIC: 2711 Newspapers, publishing & printing

(G-12258)
LORAIN PRINTING COMPANY
1310 Colorado Ave (44052-3322)
PHONE..............................440 288-6000
Fax: 440 288-4222
Brian Koethe, *CEO*
Edwin Koethe II, *Ch of Bd*
Jon Koethe, *President*
Chades Billingsley, *Production*
Joe Krall, *Production*
EMP: 40 EST: 1905
SQ FT: 31,000
SALES (est): 3.6MM **Privately Held**
SIC: 2752 Commercial printing, lithographic

(G-12259)
MARIOTTI PRINTING CO LLC
513 E 28th St (44055-1396)
PHONE..............................440 245-4120
Fax: 440 245-7487
L Walters, *Purchasing*
Martin Mariotti, *Mng Member*
Eileen Mariotti,
EMP: 6
SQ FT: 15,000
SALES (est): 578.2K **Privately Held**
WEB: www.mariottiprinting.com
SIC: 2752 2759 Commercial printing, offset; letterpress printing

(G-12260)
MATERION BRUSH INC
7375 Industrial Pkwy (44053-4800)
PHONE..............................440 960-5660
Fax: 440 960-5668
James Lippert, *Engineer*
Stacy Bonitz, *Controller*
Bill Bishop, *Manager*
Curt Hawke, *Manager*
EMP: 21
SALES (corp-wide): 969.2MM **Publicly Held**
WEB: www.brushwellman.com
SIC: 2821 5051 Plastics materials & resins; metals service centers & offices
HQ: Materion Brush Inc.
6070 Parkland Blvd Ste 1
Mayfield Heights OH 44124
216 486-4200

(G-12261)
NATIONAL BRONZE AND METALS
5311 W River Rd (44055-3735)
PHONE..............................440 277-1226
Michael Greathead, *President*
Norman M Lazarus, *Exec VP*
Jeff Fulton, *Purch Mgr*
Stephanie Dadante, *QC Mgr*
Tim Nielsens, *Sales Staff*
▲ EMP: 27
SALES (est): 14.1MM **Privately Held**
SIC: 5051 3366 3341 Metals service centers & offices; copper; copper foundries; secondary nonferrous metals
PA: Metchem Anstalt
Feger Treuunternehmen Reg.
Vaduz
237 454-5

(G-12262)
NORLAB INC
Also Called: Norlab Dyes
7465 Industrial Pkwy Dr (44053-2079)
P.O. Box 380, Amherst (44001-0380)
PHONE..............................440 282-5265
Fax: 440 282-5498
John Azok, *President*
Cliff Azok, *Vice Pres*
EMP: 5

SQ FT: 10,000
SALES (est): 957.9K
SALES (corp-wide): 17.5B **Privately Held**
WEB: www.norlabdyes.com
SIC: 2865 Dyes & pigments
HQ: Bio-Medical Applications Of Missouri, Inc.
920 Winter St
Waltham MA 02451
781 699-4404

(G-12263)
NORTH CAST ORTHTICS PRSTHETICS (PA)
6100 S Broadway Ste 104 (44053-3875)
PHONE..............................440 233-4314
Fax: 440 233-7526
Jeffrey J Yakovich, *President*
Kathleen Yakovich, *Vice Pres*
Craig Williams,
EMP: 15
SQ FT: 5,000
SALES (est): 2MM **Privately Held**
SIC: 3842 Braces, orthopedic; limbs, artificial

(G-12264)
NOVEX PRODUCTS INCORPORATED
2707 Toledo Ave Ste A (44055-1465)
PHONE..............................440 244-3330
Fax: 440 244-3331
Peyman Pakdel, *President*
▲ EMP: 30
SQ FT: 30,000
SALES (est): 6.5MM **Privately Held**
SIC: 2676 Towels, napkins & tissue paper products

(G-12265)
OKEEFE CASTING CO
2401 E 28th St (44055-2197)
PHONE..............................440 277-5427
Fax: 440 277-0011
Patrick O'Keefe, *Owner*
Lawrence O'Keefe, *Owner*
EMP: 5
SQ FT: 1,200
SALES (est): 360K **Privately Held**
WEB: www.okeefecasting.com
SIC: 3365 3366 Aluminum & aluminum-based alloy castings; castings (except die): bronze; castings (except die)

(G-12266)
PC CAMPANA INC (PA)
6155 Park Square Dr Ste 1 (44053-4145)
PHONE..............................440 246-6500
David Campana, *President*
Michael Marsico, *COO*
Robert M Campana, *CFO*
Sandra Loucka, *Controller*
▲ EMP: 35
SQ FT: 250,000
SALES (est): 21.1MM **Privately Held**
WEB: www.pccampana.com
SIC: 3325 Steel foundries

(G-12267)
PERKINS MOTOR SERVICE LTD (PA)
Also Called: Standard Welding & Lift Truck
1864 E 28th St (44055-1804)
PHONE..............................440 277-1256
Fax: 440 277-0970
Thomas L Shumaker,
EMP: 18
SQ FT: 10,200
SALES (est): 8.3MM **Privately Held**
SIC: 5013 5531 7692 7539 Truck parts & accessories; automotive supplies & parts; truck equipment & parts; automotive parts; automotive welding; radiator repair shop, automotive; brake repair, automotive; automotive springs, rebuilding & repair; hydraulic equipment repair

(G-12268)
PRIME INDUSTRIES INC
1817 Iowa Ave (44052-3359)
PHONE..............................440 288-3626
Fax: 440 288-3655
Richard Persico, *President*
Joseph Persico Jr, *Vice Pres*
Mary S Persico, *Manager*

Jennifer George, *Webmaster*
EMP: 35
SQ FT: 53,000
SALES (est): 5.3MM **Privately Held**
WEB: www.primeindustries.net
SIC: 3086 3544 2821 2671 Plastics foam products; special dies, tools, jigs & fixtures; plastics materials & resins; packaging paper & plastics film, coated & laminated

(G-12269)
QUALITY SECURITY DOOR & MFG CO (PA)
1925 Broadway (44052-3626)
PHONE..............................440 246-0770
Fax: 440 246-9447
Barbara Jacobs, *President*
Robert Jacobs, *Corp Secy*
EMP: 6
SQ FT: 25,000
SALES (est): 511.7K **Privately Held**
WEB: www.qualitysecuritydoor.com
SIC: 3442 3446 Metal doors, sash & trim; storm doors or windows, metal; gates, ornamental metal; railings, prefabricated metal

(G-12270)
RACEWAY PETROLEUM INC
3040 Oberlin Ave (44052-4563)
PHONE..............................440 989-2660
Fax: 440 989-2669
Imran Nazir, *Principal*
EMP: 7
SALES (est): 879.5K **Privately Held**
SIC: 3644 Raceways

(G-12271)
REPUBLIC ENGINEERED PRODUCTS
Also Called: Republic Steel
1807 E 28th St (44055-1803)
PHONE..............................440 277-2000
Michael Dougan, *Supervisor*
Mark Plato, *Maintence Staff*
EMP: 34
SALES (est): 5.7MM **Privately Held**
SIC: 3312 Bars, iron: made in steel mills

(G-12272)
REPUBLIC STEEL INC
1807 E 28th St (44055-1803)
PHONE..............................440 277-2000
Joseph Lapinsky, *Branch Mgr*
Richard Wildman, *Manager*
Gregg Kruth, *Technology*
Jon Sosnowski, *IT/INT Sup*
EMP: 40
SALES (corp-wide): 1.4B **Privately Held**
SIC: 3312 Blast furnaces & steel mills
HQ: Republic Steel Inc.
2633 8th St Ne
Canton OH 44704
330 438-5435

(G-12273)
ROCKWELL METALS COMPANY LLC
3709 W Erie Ave (44053-1237)
PHONE..............................440 242-2420
Julie Haggard, *Vice Pres*
Chris Harrington, *Mng Member*
▲ EMP: 10
SQ FT: 54,000
SALES: 21MM **Privately Held**
SIC: 3444 5051 Sheet metalwork; sheets, metal

(G-12274)
SENTINEL MANAGEMENT INC
Also Called: Semco Carbon
3000 Leavitt Rd Ste 1 (44052-4167)
PHONE..............................440 821-7372
Vincent L Thompson, *President*
Nancy Thompson, *Corp Secy*
Matt Thompson, *Vice Pres*
Jake Twydell, *Foreman/Supr*
Frank Blatnik, *Production*
EMP: 28
SALES: 7MM **Privately Held**
SIC: 3624 Carbon & graphite products

(G-12275)
SHERWIN-WILLIAMS COMPANY
2280 Coper Foster Pk Rd W (44053-3610)
PHONE..440 282-2310
Jameson Maag, *Manager*
Mary Cotila, *Manager*
EMP: 4
SALES (corp-wide): 11.8B **Publicly Held**
SIC: 5231 2851 Paint & painting supplies;
paints & allied products
PA: The Sherwin-Williams Company
101 W Prospect Ave # 1020
Cleveland OH 44115
216 566-2000

(G-12276)
SKY RIDERS INC
3736 Dallas Ave (44055-2354)
PHONE..440 310-6819
Charles Brown, *CEO*
EMP: 4
SALES (est): 196.3K **Privately Held**
SIC: 3721 Aircraft

(G-12277)
SKYLIFT INC
3000 Leavitt Rd Ste 6 (44052-4166)
PHONE..440 960-2100
George Wojnowski, *President*
Pat Campana, *Vice Pres*
Nicholas Jarmoszuk, *Vice Pres*
Dave Schmidt, *Engineer*
Andrew Jarmoszuk, *VP Sales*
EMP: 8
SQ FT: 6,000
SALES (est): 2.2MM **Privately Held**
WEB: www.skyliftus.com
SIC: 3537 Cranes, industrial truck

(G-12278)
SLUTZKERS QUICKPRINT CENTER
Also Called: Quick Print
721 Broadway (44052-1805)
PHONE..440 244-0330
Fax: 440 245-2721
Roger Slutzker, *President*
Jane Slutzker, *Vice Pres*
EMP: 4
SQ FT: 2,000
SALES: 150K **Privately Held**
SIC: 2752 2789 2759 Commercial print-
ing, offset; bookbinding & related work;
commercial printing

(G-12279)
SOO NYEO WON INC
1146 E St (44052-2268)
PHONE..562 569-8390
Gl Kim, *President*
EMP: 3
SALES (est): 152.7K **Privately Held**
SIC: 2035 Soy sauce

(G-12280)
STAINWOOD PRODUCTS
2803 Toledo Ave (44055-1445)
PHONE..440 244-1352
William Hoag, *Ch of Bd*
Michael Hoag, *Vice Pres*
Richard Hoag, *Vice Pres*
Thomas Hoag, *Vice Pres*
EMP: 13
SQ FT: 14,000
SALES: 1.1MM
SALES (corp-wide): 74.2MM **Privately Held**
WEB: www.stainwood.com
SIC: 2431 Millwork
PA: Nilco, Llc
1221 W Maple St Ste 100
Hartville OH 44632
888 248-5151

(G-12281)
STEIN INC
1807 E 28th St (44055-1803)
P.O. Box 1 (44052-0001)
PHONE..440 277-6148
Fax: 440 277-4901
Bill Riddle, *Manager*
Ed Sovacool, *Manager*
EMP: 100

SALES (corp-wide): 83.3MM **Privately Held**
WEB: www.stein.com
SIC: 3399 5051 Iron ore recovery from
open hearth slag; metals service centers
& offices
PA: Stein, Inc.
1929 E Royalton Rd Ste C
Cleveland OH 44147
440 526-9301

(G-12282)
SUPERPRINTER INC
1925 N Ridge Rd E (44055-3344)
PHONE..440 277-0787
Fax: 440 240-0007
Michael Potts, *President*
EMP: 3
SALES (est): 300K **Privately Held**
SIC: 2752 Commercial printing, offset

(G-12283)
SUPERPRINTER LTD
1901 N Ridge Rd E (44055-3344)
PHONE..440 277-0787
Fax: 440 277-0787
Michael Potts, *Partner*
Karen Potts, *Partner*
EMP: 3
SQ FT: 2,000
SALES: 200K **Privately Held**
SIC: 2752 Commercial printing, offset

(G-12284)
SWOCAT DESIGN INC
Also Called: Shoreway Sports
4325 Oberlin Ave Uppr (44053-2958)
PHONE..440 282-4700
Fax: 440 282-4708
Jim Swope, *President*
Gay Swope, *Corp Secy*
EMP: 5
SQ FT: 910
SALES (est): 1MM **Privately Held**
WEB: www.shorewaysports.com
SIC: 5136 5137 2396 5699 Shirts, men's
& boys'; women's & children's outerwear;
screen printing on fabric articles; sports
apparel

(G-12285)
SYSCO GUEST SUPPLY LLC
7395 Lorain Indus Pkwy (44052)
PHONE..440 960-2515
Randy Strickland, *Buyer*
Jeff Dubois, *Manager*
Cecilia Colon, *Manager*
EMP: 18
SALES (corp-wide): 50.3B **Publicly Held**
SIC: 5122 2844 5131 5139 Drugs, pro-
prietaries & sundries; toilet preparations;
piece goods & notions; footwear
HQ: Sysco Guest Supply, Llc
300 Davidson Ave
Somerset NJ 08873
732 537-2297

(G-12286)
TERMINAL READY-MIX INC
524 Colorado Ave (44052-2198)
PHONE..440 288-0181
Fax: 440 288-3142
Theresa Pelton, *President*
John Falbo, *Vice Pres*
Russ Rosso, *Plant Mgr*
Pete Falbo, *Treasurer*
Diane Gale, *Admin Sec*
▲ EMP: 45 EST: 1954
SQ FT: 1,000
SALES (est): 9.6MM **Privately Held**
WEB: www.falboconstruction.com
SIC: 3273 1611 Ready-mixed concrete;
highway & street paving contractor

(G-12287)
UNITED STATES STEEL CORP
Lorain Pipe Mill
2199 E 28th St (44055-1932)
PHONE..440 240-2500
Amir R Shayan, *QA Dir*
Neal Weaver, *Electrical Engi*
Sarah Casalla, *Manager*
Sam Lutz, *Administration*
EMP: 550
SALES (corp-wide): 10.2B **Publicly Held**
SIC: 3312 Blast furnaces & steel mills

PA: United States Steel Corp
600 Grant St Ste 468
Pittsburgh PA 15219
412 433-1121

(G-12288)
V & A PROCESS INC
2345 E 28th St (44055-2003)
PHONE..440 288-8137
Fax: 440 288-2323
Albert Di Luciano, *President*
Marie Diluciano, *Vice Pres*
Gilbert Rothman, *Vice Pres*
Alice Wiegand, *Office Mgr*
EMP: 11
SALES (est): 1.1MM **Privately Held**
WEB: www.vandaprocess.com
SIC: 3083 Thermoplastic laminates: rods,
tubes, plates & sheet

(G-12289)
VARCO LP
1807 E 28th St (44055-1803)
PHONE..440 277-8696
Randy Hamilton, *Branch Mgr*
Peggy Roblin, *Admin Asst*
EMP: 35
SALES (corp-wide): 7.2B **Publicly Held**
WEB: www.tuboscope.com
SIC: 1389 Running, cutting & pulling cas-
ings, tubes & rods
HQ: Varco, L.P.
2835 Holmes Rd
Houston TX 77051
713 799-5272

(G-12290)
VERTIV CO
1510 Kansas Ave (44052-3364)
PHONE..440 288-1122
Dave Smith, *Opers Mgr*
EMP: 9
SALES (corp-wide): 15.2B **Privately Held**
SIC: 3661 3644 7629 Telephone & tele-
graph apparatus; noncurrent-carrying
wiring services; telecommunication equip-
ment repair (except telephones)
HQ: Vertiv Co.
1050 Dearborn Dr
Columbus OH 43085
614 888-0246

(G-12291)
VISUAL EXPRESSIONS SIGN CO
901 Broadway (44052-1949)
PHONE..440 245-6660
Fax: 440 245-6660
Thomas Ott, *President*
Brian Bartlebaugh, *Vice Pres*
EMP: 6
SQ FT: 600
SALES (est): 523.9K **Privately Held**
SIC: 3993 Signs & advertising specialties

(G-12292)
WEST ERIE FUEL
4935 W Erie Ave (44053-1333)
PHONE..440 282-3493
EMP: 3 EST: 2013
SALES (est): 195.8K **Privately Held**
SIC: 2869 Fuels

(G-12293)
WS THERMAL PROCESS TECH INC
8301 W Erie Ave (44053-2090)
PHONE..440 385-6829
Fax: 440 365-9452
Joachin G Wunning, *President*
Lee Rabe, *Vice Pres*
Steve Mickey, *Engineer*
H Tuttle, *VP Finance*
EMP: 9
SALES (est): 1.3MM **Privately Held**
SIC: 3433 Gas burners, industrial

Lore City
Guernsey County

(G-12294)
SABRE ENERGY CORPORATION
175 Main St Nw (43755-9798)
P.O. Box 113 (43755-0113)
PHONE..740 685-8266
Fax: 740 685-8428
Mike Rawlings, *Vice Pres*
EMP: 3
SQ FT: 1,200
SALES (est): 369.2K **Privately Held**
SIC: 8742 1381 Public utilities consultant;
drilling oil & gas wells

Loudonville
Ashland County

(G-12295)
ACTIVEWARES
431 E Haskell St (44842-1312)
PHONE..419 994-5932
Jack A Campbell, *Owner*
EMP: 3
SALES (est): 145.3K **Privately Held**
SIC: 5699 5136 5091 2396 Sports ap-
parel; sportswear, men's & boys'; sporting
& recreation goods; screen printing on
fabric articles

(G-12296)
ARDENT MILLS LLC
Also Called: Conagra Foods
945 Mill Rd (44842-9564)
P.O. Box 90 (44842-0090)
PHONE..419 994-4181
Fax: 419 994-5475
Kermit Borchert, *Branch Mgr*
EMP: 12
SALES (corp-wide): 30.3B **Publicly Held**
WEB: www.conagra.com
SIC: 2041 5149 Flour mills, cereal (except
rice); flour
HQ: Ardent Mills Llc
1875 Lawrence St Ste 1400
Denver CO 80202
800 851-9618

(G-12297)
EASTERN GRAPHIC ARTS
214 N Jefferson St (44842-1316)
P.O. Box 477 (44842-0477)
PHONE..419 994-5815
Carla Goudy, *Owner*
EMP: 3
SALES (est): 233.1K **Privately Held**
SIC: 2759 Commercial printing

(G-12298)
HOCHSTETLER MILLING LLC
552 State Route 95 (44842-9611)
PHONE..419 368-0004
Fax: 419 994-4831
Levi Hochstetler,
EMP: 22
SQ FT: 13,000
SALES (est): 1.8MM **Privately Held**
SIC: 7389 2452 Log & lumber broker; log
cabins, prefabricated, wood

(G-12299)
MOHICAN LOG HOMES INC
Also Called: H&H Custom Homes
2441 State Route 60 (44842-9673)
PHONE..419 994-4088
Levi Hostetler, *President*
EMP: 3
SALES (est): 230.7K **Privately Held**
SIC: 1521 1522 2452 New construction,
single-family houses; residential construc-
tion; log cabins, prefabricated, wood;
modular homes, prefabricated, wood

(G-12300)
MOHICAN STEEL FABRICATORS INC
521 N Spring St (44842-1037)
PHONE..419 994-4802
Richard Gash, *President*

Barbara Gash, *Corp Secy*
EMP: 3
SALES (est): 241.7K **Privately Held**
SIC: 3441 Fabricated structural metal

(G-12301)
OAKBRIDGE TIMBER FRAMING
9001 Township Road 461 (44842-9701)
P.O. Box 89 (44842-0089)
PHONE....................................419 994-1052
Johnny Miller, *Owner*
EMP: 6 **Privately Held**
SIC: 2411 Timber, cut at logging camp
PA: Oakbridge Timber Framing
20857 Earnest Rd
Howard OH 43028

(G-12302)
OHIO BIOSYSTEMS COOP INC
135 N Market St (44842-1216)
P.O. Box 381, Nashville (44661-0381)
PHONE....................................419 980-7663
Glenn Chipner, *President*
EMP: 7
SALES: 500K **Privately Held**
SIC: 2869 Industrial organic chemicals

(G-12303)
R D THOMPSON PAPER PDTS CO INC
1 Madison St (44842-9786)
P.O. Box 88 (44842-0088)
PHONE....................................419 994-3614
Fax: 419 994-4456
Thomas Thompson, *President*
EMP: 35 **EST:** 1953
SQ FT: 25,000
SALES (est): 6.8MM **Privately Held**
WEB: www.rdthompsonpaper.com
SIC: 2675 Manila folders

(G-12304)
ROWTAC INC
16125 Township Road 458 (44842-9732)
PHONE....................................419 994-4777
Frank Nestich, *President*
Aaron Nestich, *Vice Pres*
Annette Nestich, *Admin Sec*
EMP: 5
SALES: 350K **Privately Held**
SIC: 3599 Machine shop, jobbing & repair

(G-12305)
TEA HILLS GOURMET CHICKEN PDTS
269 Township Road 2450 (44842-9624)
PHONE....................................419 685-1689
Cara Tipton, *Owner*
EMP: 5
SALES (est): 180.6K **Privately Held**
SIC: 2013 Sausages & other prepared meats

(G-12306)
TRUAX PRINTING INC
425 E Haskell St (44842-1312)
PHONE....................................419 994-4166
Bruce Truax, *Ch of Bd*
Tom Truax, *President*
Zack Truax, *Vice Pres*
Dan Truax, *Vice Pres*
Jay Hollinger, *Safety Dir*
EMP: 45 **EST:** 1966
SQ FT: 56,000
SALES (est): 5.7MM **Privately Held**
WEB: www.truaxprinting.com
SIC: 2711 Commercial printing & newspaper publishing combined

(G-12307)
YOUNG SAND & GRAVEL CO INC
689 State Route 39 (44842-9512)
P.O. Box 117 (44842-0117)
PHONE....................................419 994-3040
Fax: 419 994-3065
Myron Oswalt, *President*
EMP: 14 **EST:** 1946
SQ FT: 2,400
SALES: 780K **Privately Held**
SIC: 1442 Construction sand & gravel

Louisville
Stark County

(G-12308)
ALLEGHENY LUDLUM LLC
Also Called: ATI Allegheny Ludlum
1500 W Main St (44641-2325)
PHONE....................................330 875-2244
Tony Denoy, *Plant Mgr*
Gerry Campbell, *Persnl Mgr*
Tony Denoi, *Manager*
Dominic Backowski, *Manager*
William Stevens, *Manager*
EMP: 26 **Publicly Held**
WEB: www.alleghenyludlum.com
SIC: 3312 3471 3398 3316 Stainless steel; plating & polishing; metal heat treating; cold finishing of steel shapes
HQ: Allegheny Ludlum, Llc
1000 Six Ppg Pl
Pittsburgh PA 15222
412 394-2800

(G-12309)
BAKED & MORE LLC
5194 California Ave (44641-9038)
PHONE....................................330 324-4981
Michelle Noble, *Principal*
EMP: 4
SALES (est): 88.6K **Privately Held**
SIC: 2051 Cakes, bakery: except frozen

(G-12310)
BIERY CHEESE CO (PA)
6544 Paris Ave (44641-9544)
PHONE....................................330 875-3381
Fax: 330 875-5896
Dennis Biery, *President*
Benjamin Biery, *Vice Pres*
Roger Foulk, *Transptn Dir*
Mitchell Colly, *Plant Mgr*
Steve Buso, *Warehouse Mgr*
▲ **EMP:** 250
SQ FT: 110,000
SALES (est): 85.4MM **Privately Held**
WEB: www.bierycheese.com
SIC: 2022 Cheese, natural & processed

(G-12311)
BRADLEY ENTERPRISES INC (PA)
Also Called: Family Fun
3750 Beck Ave (44641-9455)
PHONE....................................330 875-1444
Scott Cook, *President*
Pamela Halgreen, *Corp Secy*
Terry McKimm, *Vice Pres*
EMP: 6 **EST:** 1958
SQ FT: 1,500
SALES (est): 6.9MM **Privately Held**
SIC: 3949 5091 Swimming pools, except plastic; swimming pools, equipment & supplies

(G-12312)
H & H QUICK MACHINE INC
7816 Edison St (44641-8325)
PHONE....................................330 935-0944
Fax: 330 935-0945
Martin Hustead, *President*
Anthony Hustead, *Vice Pres*
EMP: 10 **EST:** 1997
SALES (est): 300K **Privately Held**
SIC: 3599 Machine shop, jobbing & repair

(G-12313)
H-P PRODUCTS INC
2000 W Main St (44641-2344)
PHONE....................................330 875-7193
Kevin Metzger, *Export Mgr*
Jim Smith, *Engineer*
Linda Pafe, *Human Res Mgr*
Richard Wilklow, *Personnel Exec*
Paul Bishop, *Branch Mgr*
EMP: 50
SQ FT: 24,000
SALES (corp-wide): 54.3MM **Privately Held**
WEB: www.metflo.com
SIC: 3498 3635 Tube fabricating (contract bending & shaping); household vacuum cleaners

PA: H-P Products, Inc.
512 W Gorgas St
Louisville OH 44641
330 875-5556

(G-12314)
HERITAGE GROUP INC
303 S Chapel St (44641-1612)
PHONE....................................330 875-5566
John M Falk, *Branch Mgr*
EMP: 30
SALES (corp-wide): 27.1MM **Privately Held**
SIC: 2951 Asphalt & asphaltic paving mixtures (not from refineries)
PA: Heritage Group Inc
5400 W 86th St
Indianapolis IN 46268
317 872-6010

(G-12315)
HOPPEL FABRICATION SPECIALTIES
9481 Columbus Rd Ste 1 (44641-8546)
PHONE....................................330 823-5700
Steffon Hoppel, *President*
Sheryl Hoppel, *Vice Pres*
Renee Heilman, *Treasurer*
EMP: 10 **EST:** 1987
SALES (est): 1MM **Privately Held**
SIC: 3549 Wiredrawing & fabricating machinery & equipment, ex. die

(G-12316)
INK INC
200 S Bauman Ct (44641-1602)
P.O. Box 223 (44641-0223)
PHONE....................................330 875-4789
Fax: 330 875-4721
Bruce Leone, *President*
Jennifer Leone, *Vice Pres*
Dave Norris, *Prdtn Mgr*
EMP: 6
SALES (est): 1MM **Privately Held**
WEB: www.planetink.com
SIC: 2752 Commercial printing, lithographic

(G-12317)
J & L SPECIALTY STEEL INC
4055 Beck Ave (44641-9458)
P.O. Box 3920 (44641-3920)
PHONE....................................330 875-6200
Fax: 330 875-6437
Victor Fusco, *Principal*
EMP: 7
SALES (est): 804.7K **Privately Held**
SIC: 3441 Fabricated structural metal

(G-12318)
LOUISVILLE HERALD INC
308 S Mill St (44641-1643)
P.O. Box 170 (44641-0170)
PHONE....................................330 875-5610
Fax: 330 875-4475
Frank Clapper, *President*
Shirley Clapper, *Advt Staff*
Paula Fether, *MIS Dir*
EMP: 5
SQ FT: 2,800
SALES (est): 441.6K **Privately Held**
WEB: www.louisvilleherald.com
SIC: 2711 Newspapers: publishing only, not printed on site

(G-12319)
MIDLAKE PRODUCTS & MFG CO
819 N Nickelplate St (44641-2455)
PHONE....................................330 875-4202
Fax: 330 875-8479
Jeffrey Rich, *President*
Greg Duplin, *Vice Pres*
Ken Grosswiller, *VP Opers*
Jane Pukys, *CFO*
Sue Kase, *Accountant*
EMP: 60
SQ FT: 28,000
SALES (est): 13.4MM **Privately Held**
WEB: www.midlake.com
SIC: 3429 Manufactured hardware (general)

(G-12320)
NALCO COMPANY LLC
3934 Jeffries Cir (44641-7923)
PHONE....................................432 528-5214

Joe Delaney, *Branch Mgr*
EMP: 18
SALES (corp-wide): 13.1B **Publicly Held**
SIC: 3559 Chemical machinery & equipment
HQ: Nalco Company Llc
1601 W Diehl Rd
Naperville IL 60563
630 305-1000

(G-12321)
OHIO GENERATOR REMANUFACTURING
134 N Chapel St (44641-1205)
PHONE....................................330 875-6677
Fax: 330 875-6688
Thomas Eliopoulos, *President*
EMP: 5 **EST:** 1979
SQ FT: 20,000
SALES (est): 758.6K **Privately Held**
WEB: www.ohiogen.com
SIC: 3694 3621 Alternators, automotive; generators, automotive & aircraft; starters, for motors

(G-12322)
OHIO ROLL GRINDING INC
5165 Louisville St (44641-8630)
P.O. Box 7099, Canton (44705-0099)
PHONE....................................330 453-1884
Fax: 330 453-2904
James P Robinson, *President*
Catherine Robinson, *Treasurer*
EMP: 26
SQ FT: 14,000
SALES (est): 4.3MM **Privately Held**
SIC: 3599 3471 Machine shop, jobbing & repair; plating & polishing

(G-12323)
OTC SERVICES INC
1776 Constitution Ave (44641-1362)
P.O. Box 188 (44641-0188)
PHONE....................................330 871-2444
Robert Ganser Jr, *President*
William Bruner, *General Mgr*
Karen Kosko, *Corp Secy*
Valerie Dinarda, *Sales Executive*
Jeffrey Sands, *Manager*
▲ **EMP:** 80 **EST:** 2012
SQ FT: 98,000
SALES (est): 22MM **Privately Held**
SIC: 3612 Transformers, except electric

(G-12324)
PERFORMANCE TECHNOLOGIES LLC
3690 Tulane Ave (44641-7960)
PHONE....................................330 875-1216
Andy Connolly, *Branch Mgr*
EMP: 7
SALES (corp-wide): 1.1B **Privately Held**
SIC: 1389 Pumping of oil & gas wells
HQ: Performance Technologies Llc
3715 S Radio Rd
El Reno OK 73036

(G-12325)
SABRECAT BAT COMPANY INC
1616 W Main St (44641-2322)
PHONE....................................330 327-1532
Rob Roberts, *President*
EMP: 3
SALES: 100K **Privately Held**
SIC: 3949 Baseball equipment & supplies, general

(G-12326)
SALCO MACHINE INC
3822 Victory Ave (44641-8601)
PHONE....................................330 456-8281
Fax: 330 456-8446
Annette Rosenverg, *President*
John Saliol, *Vice Pres*
Susanna Saliola, *Treasurer*
EMP: 11
SQ FT: 8,900
SALES (est): 1.8MM **Privately Held**
WEB: www.salcomachine.com
SIC: 3599 Machine shop, jobbing & repair

(G-12327)
SGB USA INC
1776 Constitution Ave (44641-1362)
P.O. Box 188, Golden CO (80402-0188)
PHONE....................................720 897-7090

Kerwin Stretch, *Director*
▲ **EMP:** 3
SQ FT: 12,500
SALES (est): 48.8K **Privately Held**
SIC: 3612 Autotransformers, electric
(power transformers)
HQ: Starkstrom - Geratebau Gesellschaft
Mit Beschrankter Haftung
Ohmstr. 10
Regensburg 93055
941 784-10

(G-12328)
SHERWOOD RTM CORP
4043 Beck Ave (44641-9458)
P.O. Box 211 (44641-0211)
PHONE........................330 875-7151
Ronald Brookes, *President*
Gregory Brookes, *Sales Staff*
EMP: 6
SQ FT: 15,000
SALES (est): 1.3MM **Privately Held**
WEB: www.sherwoodcorp.com
SIC: 2821 3543 Plastics materials &
resins; industrial patterns

(G-12329)
SMITH P K WOODCARVING LLC
2021 A Riverside Drv Stea (44641)
PHONE........................513 271-7077
Philip K Smith, *Mng Member*
EMP: 3
SQ FT: 3,000
SALES (est): 269.7K **Privately Held**
WEB: www.pksmithwoodcarving.com
SIC: 2499 Carved & turned wood

(G-12330)
SOUTHWEST ELECTRIC CO
609 Enterprise Cir (44641-7947)
P.O. Box 82639, Oklahoma City OK
(73148-0639)
PHONE........................330 875-7000
Fax: 330 875-7736
John Saylor, *Manager*
EMP: 13
SALES (corp-wide): 103.7MM **Privately
Held**
SIC: 7694 Motor repair services
PA: Southwest Electric Co.
6503 Se 74th St
Oklahoma City OK 73135
800 364-4445

(G-12331)
TRILOGY PLASTICS INC
900 N Chapel St (44641-1002)
PHONE........................330 875-1789
Stephen Osborn, *President*
▲ **EMP:** 5
SALES (est): 507.1K **Privately Held**
SIC: 3089 Plastic processing

(G-12332)
**UNIWALL MANUFACTURING CO
(HQ)**
3750 Beck Ave (44641-9455)
PHONE........................330 875-1444
Fax: 330 875-8074
Scott Cook, *President*
Pamala Hellgren, *Corp Secy*
Terry McKimm, *Vice Pres*
EMP: 10
SQ FT: 4,500
SALES (est): 1.5MM
SALES (corp-wide): 6.9MM **Privately
Held**
SIC: 3949 Swimming pools, except plastic
PA: Bradley Enterprises Inc
3750 Beck Ave
Louisville OH 44641
330 875-1444

(G-12333)
VACUFLO FACTORY
512 W Gorgas St (44641-1332)
PHONE........................330 875-2450
Fax: 330 875-7584
Paul Bishop, *Principal*
Anna Vogt, *Manager*
EMP: 3
SALES (est): 231.8K **Privately Held**
SIC: 2241 Braids, textile

(G-12334)
**WASHITA VALLEY
ENTERPRISES INC**
3707 Tulane Ave Bldg 9 (44641-7949)
P.O. Box 409 (44641-0409)
PHONE........................330 510-1568
Tiffany Midgett, *President*
EMP: 24
SALES (corp-wide): 48MM **Privately
Held**
SIC: 1389 Oil consultants
PA: Washita Valley Enterprises, Inc.
1705 Se 59th St
Oklahoma City OK 73129
405 670-5338

(G-12335)
XPRESS PRINT INC
Also Called: Xpress Print & Bus Systems
6424 Easton St (44641-9054)
PHONE........................330 494-7246
William Mullen, *President*
M Dianne Mullen, *Vice Pres*
Chris Sutton, *Purchasing*
Chuck Pinkerton, *Sales Mgr*
EMP: 14
SALES (est): 1.3MM **Privately Held**
SIC: 2752 5044 Commercial printing, off-
set; duplicating machines

Loveland
Clermont County

(G-12336)
ABM DRIVES INC
394 Wards Corner Rd # 110 (45140-8300)
PHONE........................513 576-1300
Gabriel Venzin, *President*
Bettina Place, *Admin Sec*
▲ **EMP:** 3
SQ FT: 2,300
SALES (est): 646.4K
SALES (corp-wide): 368.4K **Privately
Held**
WEB: www.abm-drives.com
SIC: 3621 Motors, electric
HQ: Abm Greiffenberger Antriebstechnik
Gmbh
Friedenfelser Str. 24
Marktredwitz 95615
923 167-0

(G-12337)
ALCON INC (PA)
6522 Snider Rd (45140-9587)
PHONE........................513 722-1037
Fax: 513 722-1036
C G Sorflaten, *President*
EMP: 20
SQ FT: 15,000
SALES (est): 4.3MM **Privately Held**
SIC: 3643 Connectors & terminals for elec-
trical devices

(G-12338)
**AMANO CINCINNATI
INCORPORATED**
130 Commerce Dr (45140-7726)
PHONE........................513 697-9000
Fax: 513 241-9549
Kash Gokli, *Vice Pres*
Rick Wright, *Materials Mgr*
Rommy Viltrakis, *Purchasing*
John Gutapfel, *Supervisor*
Mike Ciorda, *Maintence Staff*
EMP: 70
SQ FT: 52,200
SALES (corp-wide): 1B **Privately Held**
SIC: 3559 3873 3829 3625 Parking facil-
ity equipment & supplies; watches,
clocks, watchcases & parts; measuring &
controlling devices; relays & industrial
controls
HQ: Amano Cincinnati Incorporated
140 Harrison Ave
Roseland NJ 07068
973 403-1900

(G-12339)
AMP ELECTRIC VEHICLES INC
100 Commerce Dr (45140-7726)
PHONE........................513 360-4704
Stephen S Burns, *CEO*

Martin J Rucidlo, *President*
Chuck Strasser, *Buyer*
Elliot Bokeno, *Engineer*
Ryan Doll, *Engineer*
EMP: 18 **EST:** 2007
SALES (est): 2MM **Publicly Held**
SIC: 3711 3714 Motor vehicles & car bod-
ies; motor vehicle parts & accessories
PA: Workhorse Group Inc.
100 Commerce Dr
Loveland OH 45140

(G-12340)
BASEBALL CARD CORNER
1812 Arrowhead Trl (45140-8517)
PHONE........................513 677-0464
EMP: 3
SALES (est): 140K **Privately Held**
SIC: 5947 3949 Ret Gifts/Novelties Mfg
Sporting/Athletic Goods

(G-12341)
BAY ISLAND COMPANY INC
Also Called: Point Five Golf Co
585 Ibold Rd (45140-6901)
PHONE........................513 248-0356
Duane Peterson, *President*
Dale Peterson, *Vice Pres*
Willis Peterson, *Vice Pres*
EMP: 3
SALES (est): 75K **Privately Held**
SIC: 3949 1629 Golf equipment; golf
course construction

(G-12342)
BECK FLAVORS INC (PA)
1301 Mattec Dr (45140-7300)
PHONE........................513 889-1268
Robert Sloane, *President*
Charley Beck, *Vice Pres*
EMP: 3 **EST:** 2010
SALES (est): 654.5K **Privately Held**
SIC: 2087 Extracts, flavoring

(G-12343)
BINTZLER INC
9570 S State Route 48 (45140-9619)
PHONE........................513 677-1164
Fax: 513 984-9789
John Bintzler, *President*
Douglas Bintzler, *Exec VP*
EMP: 11
SQ FT: 6,000
SALES (est): 1MM **Privately Held**
WEB: www.bintzlerinc.com
SIC: 3542 Machine tools, metal forming
type

(G-12344)
BRENTMOOR HAMS LLC
10367 Brentmoor Dr (45140-4804)
PHONE........................513 677-0813
Richard Neuenschwander, *Principal*
EMP: 6
SALES (est): 599.6K **Privately Held**
SIC: 2013 Prepared pork products from
purchased pork

(G-12345)
BROGAN MACHINE SHOP
501 Lovelnd Madera Rd # 2 (45140-2740)
PHONE........................513 683-9054
Fax: 513 683-9053
Richard J Brogan, *President*
Joan Brogan, *Corp Secy*
EMP: 4
SQ FT: 2,500
SALES (est): 260K **Privately Held**
SIC: 3599 2431 Machine shop, jobbing &
repair; millwork

(G-12346)
COLD JET LLC (PA)
455 Wards Corner Rd # 100 (45140-9033)
PHONE........................513 831-3211
Fax: 513 831-1209
Eugene L Cooke III, *CEO*
Scott Gatje, *COO*
Edward Uwu, *Accountant*
Jamie Churchill, *Marketing Staff*
◆ **EMP:** 97
SQ FT: 40,000
SALES: 44.6MM **Privately Held**
WEB: www.coldjet.com
SIC: 3559 Chemical machinery & equip-
ment

(G-12347)
**CREATIVE COMMERCIAL
FINISHING**
1298 State Route 28 Ste B (45140-8817)
PHONE........................513 722-9393
Fax: 513 722-9394
Robert Hattersley, *Owner*
EMP: 5
SQ FT: 12,000
SALES: 700K **Privately Held**
SIC: 2269 2899 2851 Chemical coating or
treating of narrow fabrics; chemical
preparations; paints & allied products

(G-12348)
**DEXPORT TOOL
MANUFACTURING CO**
855 Carpenter Rd (45140-8102)
PHONE........................513 625-1600
Fax: 513 625-1626
Elizabeth Hite, *President*
Richard Hite, *Vice Pres*
John Lanoue, *Shareholder*
EMP: 4
SALES (est): 473K **Privately Held**
WEB: www.dexport-tool.com
SIC: 3541 5085 Machine tools, metal cut-
ting type; industrial supplies

(G-12349)
**FISCHER GLOBAL
ENTERPRISES LLC**
Also Called: Periflo/Px Pumps USA
155 Commerce Dr (45140-7727)
PHONE........................513 583-4900
Fax: 513 583-4819
Phil Douglas,
Ken Fischer,
▲ **EMP:** 25
SALES (est): 3MM **Privately Held**
WEB: www.fpv.com
SIC: 3561 Industrial pumps & parts

(G-12350)
FLOWSERVE CORPORATION
422 Wards Corner Rd F (45140-6965)
PHONE........................513 874-6990
Fax: 513 874-1512
Brad Harrellson, *General Mgr*
Brad Harrellson, *Manager*
EMP: 6
SALES (corp-wide): 3.9B **Publicly Held**
SIC: 3561 Pumps & pumping equipment
PA: Flowserve Corporation
5215 N Oconnor Blvd Connor
Irving TX 75039
972 443-6500

(G-12351)
GARYS CLASSIC GUITARS
6692 Sandy Shores Dr (45140-5851)
PHONE........................513 891-0555
Gary S Dick, *Owner*
EMP: 4
SALES (est): 200K **Privately Held**
WEB: www.garysguitars.com
SIC: 3931 7389 Guitars & parts, electric &
nonelectric;

(G-12352)
**GEOTECH PATTERN & MOLD
INC**
272 E Kemper Rd (45140-8601)
P.O. Box 276 (45140-0276)
PHONE........................513 683-2600
Fax: 513 683-2601
Jonathan D Ledford, *President*
Frank Schilling, *Opers-Prdtn-Mfg*
Frank Diedrichs, *Admin Sec*
EMP: 9
SQ FT: 9,000
SALES (est): 2MM **Privately Held**
WEB: www.geotech-pattern.com
SIC: 3543 Industrial patterns

(G-12353)
GL NAUSE CO INC
1971 Phoenix Dr (45140-9241)
PHONE........................513 722-9500
Fax: 513 722-0819
Gregory L Nause, *President*
Mark Rosselot, *General Mgr*
Jeff Brewsaugh, *Sales Staff*
Jodie K Nause, *Admin Sec*
Jodie Nause, *Admin Sec*

EMP: 25
SQ FT: 30,000
SALES (est): 5.7MM **Privately Held**
WEB: www.glnause.com
SIC: 3441 3443 1791 7699 Fabricated structural metal; fabricated plate work (boiler shop); structural steel erection; industrial equipment services; industrial machinery & equipment repair; architectural metalwork; sheet metalwork

(G-12354)
GREENLIGHT OPTICS LLC
8940 Glendale Milford Rd (45140-8908)
PHONE....................................513 247-9777
Carol Barett, *Office Mgr*
Todd Rutherford,
Michael Okeefe,
Bill Phillips,
EMP: 20
SQ FT: 8,000
SALES (est): 7.5MM **Privately Held**
SIC: 3827 3089 Optical instruments & lenses; lenses, except optical: plastic

(G-12355)
GREGORY AUTO SERVICE
Also Called: Dragon Racing Service
224 Beech Rd (45140-8827)
PHONE....................................513 248-0423
Nicholas Gregory, *Partner*
David Gregory, *Partner*
EMP: 4
SALES (est): 300K **Privately Held**
SIC: 7538 3714 General automotive repair shops; motor vehicle engines & parts

(G-12356)
HAECO INC (PA)
6504 Snider Rd (45140-9228)
PHONE....................................513 722-1030
Fax: 513 722-1032
Jerry Henline, *President*
Doug Forkner, *Sales Mgr*
Darrell Dick, *Manager*
Brandon Reitiger, *IT/INT Sup*
Brandon Rediger, *Executive*
▲ EMP: 12
SQ FT: 7,200
SALES (est): 1.7MM **Privately Held**
WEB: www.haeco.us
SIC: 3559 Pack-up assemblies, wheel overhaul

(G-12357)
HEALTHPRO BRANDS INC
12044 Millstone Ct (45140-6295)
P.O. Box 867, Mason (45040-0867)
PHONE....................................513 492-7512
Todd Wichmann, *CEO*
Mark Winterhalter, *CFO*
Margaret Combs, *Controller*
Peggy Combs, *Manager*
Durk Jager, *Shareholder*
▼ EMP: 5
SQ FT: 2,000
SALES (est): 1MM **Privately Held**
WEB: www.healthprobrands.com
SIC: 3523 Cleaning machines for fruits, grains & vegetables

(G-12358)
HERITAGE TOOL
6225 N Shadow Hill Way (45140-9187)
PHONE....................................513 753-7300
Mark J Myers, *Owner*
EMP: 12
SALES (est): 515.7K **Privately Held**
SIC: 3599 3751 Machine shop, jobbing & repair; motorcycles & related parts

(G-12359)
I D X MEDICAL LTD
101 Southbend Ct (45140-7134)
PHONE....................................513 583-9081
Warren Williamson, *President*
EMP: 3
SALES (est): 257.9K **Privately Held**
SIC: 3841 Surgical & medical instruments

(G-12360)
INNERWOOD & COMPANY
688 Elizabeth Ln (45140-9172)
PHONE....................................513 677-2229
Janine V Melink-Hueber, *CEO*
J V Melink-Hueber, *Principal*

EMP: 17
SALES: 2MM **Privately Held**
WEB: www.innerwood.com
SIC: 2517 2521 Wood television & radio cabinets; wood office filing cabinets & bookcases

(G-12361)
INTELLIGENT SIGNAL TECH
Also Called: Ist International
6318 Dustywind Ln (45140-7730)
PHONE....................................614 530-4784
Fax: 513 891-1892
Sheldyn K Armstrong, *President*
Matthew Bolton, *CFO*
EMP: 8
SQ FT: 2,500
SALES (est): 1MM **Privately Held**
WEB: www.intelligentsignals.com
SIC: 3669 Traffic signals, electric

(G-12362)
INTERNATIONAL PAPER COMPANY
6283 Tri Ridge Blvd (45140-8318)
PHONE....................................513 248-6365
EMP: 4
SALES (corp-wide): 21B **Publicly Held**
SIC: 2621 Paper mills
PA: International Paper Company
6400 Poplar Ave
Memphis TN 38197
901 419-9000

(G-12363)
INTERNATIONAL PAPER COMPANY
6283 Tri Ridge Blvd (45140-8318)
PHONE....................................513 248-6000
EMP: 4
SALES (corp-wide): 21B **Publicly Held**
SIC: 2621 Paper mills
PA: International Paper Company
6400 Poplar Ave
Memphis TN 38197
901 419-9000

(G-12364)
JACO INC
Also Called: Cincinnati Stair
1451 State Route 28 Ste D (45140-8442)
PHONE....................................513 722-3947
Marc Tirey, *President*
EMP: 3
SQ FT: 5,000
SALES (est): 100K **Privately Held**
WEB: www.cincinnatistair.com
SIC: 2431 Staircases & stairs, wood

(G-12365)
KBC SERVICES
9993 Union Cemetery Rd (45140-7187)
PHONE....................................513 693-3743
Kevin Brown, *Principal*
EMP: 10
SALES (est): 311.3K **Privately Held**
SIC: 1389 8742 Construction, repair & dismantling services; construction project management consultant

(G-12366)
KESSLER STUDIOS INC
273 E Broadway St (45140-3121)
PHONE....................................513 683-7500
Bob Kessler, *President*
Cindy Kessler, *Vice Pres*
EMP: 3 EST: 1981
SALES (est): 170K **Privately Held**
WEB: www.kesslerstudios.com
SIC: 3231 Stained glass: made from purchased glass

(G-12367)
KMGRAFX INC
Also Called: Asi Sign Systems
394 Wards Corner Rd # 100 (45140-8339)
PHONE....................................513 248-4100
Fax: 513 248-4101
Kimberly Moscarino, *President*
Heather Knox, *Project Mgr*
Kenneth Knarr, *Treasurer*
Lisa Hartman, *Manager*
EMP: 8
SQ FT: 2,700

SALES (est): 1.3MM **Privately Held**
WEB: www.kmgrafx.com
SIC: 3993 Signs & advertising specialties

(G-12368)
KYS WELDING & FABRICATION
154 Shoemaker Dr (45140-7786)
PHONE....................................513 702-9081
KY Nguyen, *Owner*
EMP: 3
SALES (est): 63.5K **Privately Held**
SIC: 7692 Welding repair

(G-12369)
L & I NATURAL RESOURCES INC
10369 Cones Rd (45140-7211)
PHONE....................................513 683-2045
Alvin Walker, *President*
Marjorie Walker, *Corp Secy*
Jerry Walker, *Vice Pres*
EMP: 5
SQ FT: 1,000
SALES (est): 341.7K **Privately Held**
SIC: 1442 Sand mining; gravel mining

(G-12370)
LANDEN DESKTOP PUBG CTR INC
Also Called: Landen Digital Publishing
8976 Columbia Rd (45140-1114)
P.O. Box 468 (45140-0468)
PHONE....................................513 683-5181
Fax: 513 683-0263
Martha Hines, *President*
Linda G Dorn, *Principal*
Frances E Hober, *Principal*
EMP: 6
SQ FT: 5,000
SALES (est): 715.2K **Privately Held**
WEB: www.landendigital.com
SIC: 2759 2752 2791 7338 Commercial printing; commercial printing, lithographic; typesetting; secretarial & court reporting

(G-12371)
LIFO ENTERPRISES INC
Also Called: Fontova Mexican Foods
810 Carrington Pl Apt 206 (45140-8693)
P.O. Box 236 (45140-0236)
PHONE....................................513 225-8801
Pevro Fontova, *President*
EMP: 3 EST: 1981
SALES (est): 480K **Privately Held**
SIC: 2032 7389 Mexican foods: packaged in cans, jars, etc.;

(G-12372)
MACPRO INC
Also Called: Machine Products
1456 Fay Rd Unit B (45140-9771)
PHONE....................................513 575-3000
Fax: 513 575-3222
D Wayne Hughes, *President*
David Hughes, *Vice Pres*
Julie Silvey, *Manager*
EMP: 10 EST: 1967
SQ FT: 20,000
SALES: 1MM **Privately Held**
WEB: www.macpro.com
SIC: 3599 Machine shop, jobbing & repair

(G-12373)
MAULL TOOL & DIE SUPPLY LLC
216 Timber Trl (45140-8813)
PHONE....................................513 646-4229
Charlie Maull, *Mng Member*
EMP: 2
SALES: 5MM **Privately Held**
SIC: 3312 Tool & die steel

(G-12374)
MICHAELS PRE-CAST CON PDTS
1917 Adams Rd (45140-7236)
PHONE....................................513 683-1292
Fax: 513 683-3537
Vernon Michael, *President*
Mary Jane Micheal, *Corp Secy*
Donald Michael, *Vice Pres*
Vernon Jim Michael, *Vice Pres*
EMP: 10
SQ FT: 5,000

SALES (est): 1.2MM **Privately Held**
SIC: 5032 5999 3446 3272 Concrete building products; concrete products, precast; architectural metalwork; concrete products; public building & related furniture; wood household furniture

(G-12375)
NEPTUNE AQUATIC SYSTEMS INC
6641 Smith Rd (45140-6508)
PHONE....................................513 575-2989
Jeffrey Quint, *President*
EMP: 4
SALES (est): 343.2K **Privately Held**
SIC: 3841 Surgical & medical instruments

(G-12376)
PAUL MIRACLE
Also Called: Air Shop, The
6749 Oakland Rd (45140-9455)
PHONE....................................513 575-3113
Paul Miracle, *Owner*
EMP: 5
SQ FT: 1,440
SALES: 370K **Privately Held**
SIC: 3442 Metal doors, sash & trim

(G-12377)
PHOENIX INDUSTRIES & APPARATUS
6466 Snider Rd Apt C (45140-9542)
PHONE....................................513 722-1085
Fax: 513 722-1535
Sheri L Nause, *President*
Carl D Nause, *Vice Pres*
EMP: 15
SQ FT: 8,550
SALES: 1.4MM **Privately Held**
WEB: www.phoenixdottank.com
SIC: 7692 Welding repair

(G-12378)
POWDER ALLOY CORPORATION
101 Northeast Dr (45140-7145)
PHONE....................................513 984-4016
Fax: 513 984-4017
E Stephen Payne, *President*
Darlene Payne, *Vice Pres*
Kimberly R Gatto, *CFO*
Larry Nurre, *Accounts Mgr*
Scott Ostholthoff, *Manager*
▲ EMP: 40
SQ FT: 20,000
SALES (est): 11.7MM **Privately Held**
WEB: www.powderalloy.com
SIC: 3399 Powder, metal

(G-12379)
R & W PRINTING COMPANY
1394 Stella Dr (45140-8714)
PHONE....................................513 575-0131
Fax: 513 575-0131
Steve Poole, *President*
EMP: 3 EST: 1969
SALES (est): 230K **Privately Held**
SIC: 2752 2791 Commercial printing, offset; typesetting

(G-12380)
R G C INC
Also Called: Donisi Mirror Company
507 Loveland Madeira Rd (45140-2713)
PHONE....................................513 683-3110
Fax: 513 683-3225
Thomas G Crawford, *President*
Ken Crawford, *General Mgr*
Tom Crawford, *Sales Staff*
Bill Ward, *Office Mgr*
EMP: 10
SQ FT: 30,000
SALES: 1.6MM **Privately Held**
WEB: www.donisimirror.com
SIC: 3231 3229 Products of purchased glass; mirrored glass; furniture tops, glass: cut, beveled or polished; pressed & blown glass

(G-12381)
ROBERDS CONVERTING CO INC
113 Northeast Dr (45140-7145)
PHONE....................................513 683-6667
James J Achberger, *President*
Mike Scherder, *General Mgr*

GEOGRAPHIC

John M Achberger, *Vice Pres*
Will Achberger, *Vice Pres*
Philip Weinrich, *Accounts Mgr*
EMP: 38
SQ FT: 72,000
SALES (est): 14.9MM **Privately Held**
WEB: www.robertsconverting.com
SIC: 2679 Paperboard products, converted

(G-12382)
ROZZI COMPANY INC (PA)
118 Karl Brown Way (45140-2902)
P.O. Box 5 (45140-0005)
PHONE.................................513 683-0620
Fax: 513 683-2043
Joseph Rozzi, *President*
Arthur Rozzi, *Treasurer*
Nancy Rozzi, *Admin Sec*
▲ **EMP:** 33
SQ FT: 5,000
SALES (est): 5.4MM **Privately Held**
SIC: 2899 Chemical preparations

(G-12383)
SAFE-GRAIN INC (PA)
417 Wards Corner Rd Ste B (45140-9083)
PHONE.................................513 398-2500
Fax: 513 398-2536
Scott Chant, *President*
Lauren Pieper, *Manager*
EMP: 7
SALES (est): 3.4MM **Privately Held**
SIC: 3829 1731 Temperature sensors, except industrial process & aircraft; electronic controls installation

(G-12384)
SCRIP-SAFE SECURITY PRODUCTS
Also Called: Scrip-Safe International
136 Commerce Dr (45140-7726)
PHONE.................................513 697-7789
Fax: 513 697-7891
Joseph E Orndorff, *President*
Bill Varney, *Production*
Joanne Orndorff, *CFO*
Steven Black, *Sales Dir*
Kevin Hickey, *Sales Dir*
▼ **EMP:** 20
SQ FT: 15,000
SALES (est): 5MM **Privately Held**
WEB: www.scrip-safe.com
SIC: 2752 7389 Commercial printing, offset; printing broker

(G-12385)
SFL ENTERPRISES INC
10017 Somerset Dr (45140-1875)
PHONE.................................513 239-6822
Steven Ling, *Owner*
EMP: 3
SALES (est): 302.3K **Privately Held**
SIC: 3842 Welders' hoods

(G-12386)
SHAWCOR INC
Also Called: Dsg-Canusa
173 Commerce Dr (45140-7727)
P.O. Box 498830, Cincinnati (45249-8830)
PHONE.................................513 683-7800
Jim Raussen, *Sales Staff*
EMP: 40
SALES (corp-wide): 1.3B **Privately Held**
SIC: 3317 Steel pipe & tubes
HQ: Shawcor Inc.
　　3838 N Sam Houston Pkwy E # 300
　　Houston TX 77032
　　281 886-2350

(G-12387)
SIGNODE INDUSTRIAL GROUP LLC
Also Called: Angleboard
396 Wards Corner Rd # 100 (45140-9060)
PHONE.................................513 248-2990
Shane Harrisson, *Manager*
EMP: 20 **Privately Held**
SIC: 2679 2671 Paper products, converted; packaging paper & plastics film, coated & laminated
HQ: Signode Industrial Group Llc
　　3650 W Lake Ave
　　Glenview IL 60026
　　847 724-7500

(G-12388)
SIRRUS INC
422 Wards Corner Rd (45140-6964)
PHONE.................................513 448-0308
Jeff Uhrig, *CEO*
Kousay Said, *Senior VP*
Jeff Sullivan, *Senior VP*
Debra Savage, *Office Mgr*
Jessica Dicerbo, *Manager*
▲ **EMP:** 34
SALES (est): 8.5MM **Privately Held**
SIC: 2891 Adhesives & sealants

(G-12389)
SST CONVEYOR COMPONENTS INC
185 Commerce Dr (45140-7727)
PHONE.................................513 583-5500
Winfield Scott, *President*
Thomas C Hamm, *Principal*
Joe Schuetz, *CFO*
Tim Reed, *Manager*
▲ **EMP:** 20
SALES (est): 5.3MM **Privately Held**
SIC: 3535 Conveyors & conveying equipment

(G-12390)
SST PRECISION MANUFACTURING
154 Commerce Dr (45140-7726)
PHONE.................................513 583-5500
Winfield Scott, *President*
Joe Schuetz, *CFO*
Glen Stidham, *Sales Mgr*
Pam Catron, *Info Tech Mgr*
EMP: 10
SALES (est): 1.4MM **Privately Held**
SIC: 3599 7699 Crankshafts & camshafts, machining; industrial tool grinding

(G-12391)
SUN & SOIL LLC
1357 State Route 28 (45140-8426)
PHONE.................................513 575-5900
Sam McLamb, *Vice Pres*
Karl Scheidler,
EMP: 3
SALES: 230K **Privately Held**
SIC: 2899 Chemical preparations

(G-12392)
SUPPLY DYNAMICS LLC
6279 Tr Rdge Blvd Ste 310 (45140)
PHONE.................................513 965-2000
Fax: 513 965-2001
Trevor Stansbury, *President*
Geoffrey Wu, *Manager*
Bryan Atwood, *Software Dev*
Bob Hales, *Director*
Mark Creamer, *Admin Asst*
EMP: 16
SALES (est): 963.3K
SALES (corp-wide): 2.4MM **Privately Held**
WEB: www.supplydynamics.com
SIC: 5051 3544 3541 2836 Iron & steel (ferrous) products; copper sheets, plates, bars, rods, pipes, etc.; aluminum bars, rods, ingots, sheets, pipes, plates, etc.; foundry products; special dies, tools, jigs & fixtures; machine tools, metal cutting type; biological products, except diagnostic; sawmills & planing mills, general
PA: O'neal Industries, Inc
　　2311 Highland Ave S # 200
　　Birmingham AL 35205
　　205 721-2880

(G-12393)
T&T WELDING
1469 State Route 28 (45140-8778)
P.O. Box 115 (45140-0115)
PHONE.................................513 615-1156
Fax: 513 722-8329
Tom Polltt, *Owner*
EMP: 3
SALES (est): 324K **Privately Held**
SIC: 7692 Welding repair

(G-12394)
THREADED IMAGE
10035 Dallasburg Rd (45140-6651)
PHONE.................................513 683-9069
Charlotte Melcho, *Owner*

EMP: 3
SALES: 75K **Privately Held**
SIC: 2395 Embroidery & art needlework

(G-12395)
TRANSDUCERS DIRECT LLC
112 Lakeview Ct (45140-7745)
PHONE.................................513 583-7597
Connie Clark, *Principal*
EMP: 3
SALES (est): 311.5K **Privately Held**
SIC: 3674 Ultra-violet sensors, solid state

(G-12396)
VACCA INC (PA)
9501 Union Cemetery Rd # 100 (45140-9686)
PHONE.................................513 697-0270
Giampaolo Vacca, *CEO*
Lawrence Weber, *President*
EMP: 4
SALES (est): 384.7K **Privately Held**
WEB: www.vaccainc.com
SIC: 3999 Heating pads, nonelectric

(G-12397)
VALVE RELATED CONTROLS INC
Also Called: Vrc
143 Commerce Dr (45140-7727)
PHONE.................................513 677-8724
Fax: 513 677-8731
Fred Tasch, *CEO*
Ed Lester, *President*
Jason Lester, *Design Engr*
▲ **EMP:** 12
SQ FT: 12,000
SALES (est): 2.1MM **Privately Held**
WEB: www.vrc-usa.com
SIC: 3625 5084 Relays & industrial controls; positioning controls, electric; industrial electrical relays & switches; industrial machinery & equipment

(G-12398)
VENUS TRADING LLC
10965 Rednor Ct (45140-7763)
PHONE.................................513 374-0066
Vinit Trivedi, *Partner*
▼ **EMP:** 5
SALES (est): 246.7K **Privately Held**
SIC: 3479 Coating of metals & formed products

(G-12399)
WASHING SYSTEMS LLC
167 Commerce Dr (45140-7727)
PHONE.................................800 272-1974
Dean Lewis, *Division Mgr*
Greg Brodrick, *VP Opers*
Bryon Ohmart, *Project Mgr*
Phil Newman, *Materials Mgr*
Leah Boyd, *Safety Mgr*
▼ **EMP:** 110
SALES: 90MM **Privately Held**
WEB: www.washingsystems.com
SIC: 5169 2841 Detergents; industrial chemicals; soap & other detergents

(G-12400)
WIRENET INC
250 E Kemper Rd (45140-8601)
PHONE.................................513 774-7759
Fax: 513 774-7795
Kenneth Cowan, *President*
Mark Davis, *Bookkeeper*
EMP: 15
SQ FT: 5,000
SALES (est): 1.5MM **Privately Held**
WEB: www.wirenet.com
SIC: 1623 8742 3663 3441 Transmitting tower (telecommunication) construction; management consulting services; radio & TV communications equipment; fabricated structural metal

(G-12401)
WORKHORSE GROUP INC (PA)
100 Commerce Dr (45140-7726)
PHONE.................................513 297-3640
Stephen S Burns, *CEO*
Raymond J Chess, *Ch of Bd*
Martin J Rucidlo, *President*
Julio C Rodriguez, *CFO*
EMP: 18
SQ FT: 30,000

SALES: 6.4MM **Publicly Held**
SIC: 3711 3714 Motor vehicles & car bodies; motor vehicle parts & accessories

---

Lowell
Washington County

(G-12402)
J & J LOGGING
7100 Highland Ridge Rd (45744-7605)
PHONE.................................740 896-2827
John Seevers, *Principal*
EMP: 3
SALES (est): 273.9K **Privately Held**
SIC: 2411 Logging

(G-12403)
OAKWOOD FURNITURE INC
10105 State Route 60 (45744-7272)
PHONE.................................740 896-3162
Fax: 740 896-3188
Robert Huck, *President*
Rhonda Huck, *Vice Pres*
EMP: 4
SQ FT: 3,500
SALES: 235K **Privately Held**
SIC: 2434 5712 5211 1751 Wood kitchen cabinets; furniture stores; cabinets, kitchen; cabinet & finish carpentry

---

Lowellville
Mahoning County

(G-12404)
ALUMINUM COLOR INDUSTRIES INC (PA)
369 W Wood St (44436-1039)
P.O. Box 206 (44436-0206)
PHONE.................................330 536-6295
Fax: 330 536-8086
Trude Stoeckel-Spinosa, *President*
Tom Kozusko, *Production*
Tina Spinosa, *Treasurer*
John Frejik, *Manager*
Lorna Willard, *Admin Sec*
EMP: 24 **EST:** 1953
SQ FT: 30,000
SALES (est): 6.9MM **Privately Held**
SIC: 3442 3471 3444 Moldings & trim, except automobile: metal; finishing, metals or formed products; sheet metalwork

(G-12405)
ARS RECYCLING SYSTEMS LLC
Also Called: Advanced Recycling Systems,
4000 Mccartney Rd (44436-9413)
PHONE.................................330 536-8210
Fax: 330 534-9249
Gus G Lyras, *President*
Elio Mussullo, *Vice Pres*
Victor Pallotta, *Vice Pres*
Tony Nackino, *Engineer*
Samuel Snyder, *Engineer*
EMP: 14
SQ FT: 25,000
SALES (est): 3.5MM **Privately Held**
WEB: www.arsrecycling.com
SIC: 7699 3559 Welding equipment repair; recycling machinery

(G-12406)
CROWES CABINETS INC
725 S Hubbard Rd (44436-9754)
PHONE.................................330 536-2545
Paul Crowe, *President*
Tim Crowe, *General Mgr*
Roberta Crowe, *Vice Pres*
David Smith, *Project Mgr*
EMP: 9
SQ FT: 6,000
SALES (est): 1MM **Privately Held**
WEB: www.crowescabinets.com
SIC: 2431 Millwork

(G-12407)
FALCON FOUNDRY COMPANY
96 6th St (44436-1264)
P.O. Box 301 (44436-0301)
PHONE.................................330 536-6221
Fax: 330 536-6371
Gary S Slaven, *President*

▲ = Import ▼ =Export
◆ =Import/Export

John Lopatta, *Principal*
William R Lopatta, *Exec VP*
Skip Slaven, *Exec VP*
Leon Slaven, *Vice Pres*
◆ **EMP:** 90
SQ FT: 175,000
SALES (est): 27MM **Privately Held**
WEB: www.falconfoundry.com
SIC: 3366 Castings (except die): copper &
copper-base alloy; castings (except die):
bronze

(G-12408)
GARLAND WELDING CO INC
804 E Liberty St (44436-1266)
PHONE................................330 536-6506
Fax: 330 536-6691
Rose Del Signore, *President*
Vincent Del Signore, *Principal*
Ralph Signore, *Vice Pres*
Joanne Del Signore, *Admin Sec*
Nick Del Signore, *Admin Sec*
EMP: 12
SQ FT: 6,880
SALES (est): 2.4MM **Privately Held**
WEB: www.garlandwelding.com
SIC: 3441 7692 Fabricated structural
metal; welding repair

(G-12409)
GENNARO PAVERS
6065 Arrel Smith Rd (44436-9545)
PHONE................................330 536-6825
Fax: 330 536-6838
David Gennaro, *President*
Ray Gennaro, *Vice Pres*
EMP: 6
SALES (est): 640K **Privately Held**
SIC: 1771 3271 Concrete work; paving
blocks, concrete

(G-12410)
LYCO CORPORATION
Also Called: Pilorusso Construction Div
1089 N Hubbard Rd (44436-9737)
PHONE................................330 534-3330
Fax: 330 534-9249
Patsy Pilorusso, *President*
Elio Massullo, *Owner*
W C Pilorusso, *Vice Pres*
Mike Pallotto, *Treasurer*
EMP: 20 EST: 1947
SQ FT: 25,000
SALES (est): 4.1MM **Privately Held**
WEB: www.lyco-mfg.com
SIC: 7699 3441 Welding equipment repair;
fabricated structural metal

(G-12411)
RAVANA INDUSTRIES INC
6170 Center Rd (44436-9521)
P.O. Box 152 (44436-0152)
PHONE................................330 536-4015
Fax: 330 536-6745
Danette J St Vencent, *CEO*
William St Vincent, *President*
EMP: 8
SALES (est): 860K **Privately Held**
WEB: www.ridingtheelephant.blogs.for-
tune.cnn.co
SIC: 3541 3363 Machine tool replacement
& repair parts, metal cutting types; alu-
minum die-castings

(G-12412)
RC OUTSOURCING LLC
102 E Water St (44436-1117)
PHONE................................330 536-8500
Raymond Carlson,
EMP: 3 EST: 2015
SQ FT: 4,500
SALES (est): 164K **Privately Held**
SIC: 2834 Pharmaceutical preparations

(G-12413)
SAFEWAY CONTACT LENS INC
1212 Bedford Rd (44436-8705)
PHONE................................330 536-6469
Fax: 330 726-3782
John A Kizar, *President*
Mariruth Stewart, *Treasurer*
EMP: 6 EST: 1960
SQ FT: 1,832
SALES (est): 793.2K **Privately Held**
SIC: 3851 Contact lenses

(G-12414)
**WELDING EQUIPMENT REPAIR
CO**
142 E Water St (44436-1117)
P.O. Box 143 (44436-0143)
PHONE................................330 536-2125
Merle Holloway, *President*
EMP: 5
SQ FT: 2,000
SALES (est): 385.1K **Privately Held**
SIC: 7692 Welding repair

Lower Salem
Washington County

(G-12415)
BLAIR LOGGING
30530 Lebanon Rd (45745-9733)
PHONE................................740 934-2730
Ronald Blair, *Owner*
EMP: 6
SALES: 150K **Privately Held**
SIC: 2411 Logging camps & contractors

(G-12416)
WARNER VESS INC
12 Warner Second St (45745-8844)
PHONE................................740 585-2481
Ronald Vess, *President*
EMP: 4
SALES (est): 240K **Privately Held**
SIC: 3541 Machine tool replacement & re-
pair parts, metal cutting types

Lucasville
Scioto County

(G-12417)
C & D COUNTERS
359b Back St (45648-7710)
P.O. Box 1131 (45648-1131)
PHONE................................740 259-5529
Darrell Spriggs, *President*
EMP: 3
SALES (est): 296K **Privately Held**
SIC: 2541 Counter & sink tops

(G-12418)
COX INC
Also Called: Cox Precast
11201 State Route 104 (45648-7512)
PHONE................................740 858-4400
Forest Arbaugh, *President*
Keith Gallimore, *Office Mgr*
EMP: 12
SALES (est): 619.4K **Privately Held**
SIC: 3272 Concrete products, precast

(G-12419)
E A COX INC
11201 State Route 104 (45648-7512)
P.O. Box 819 (45648-0819)
PHONE................................740 858-4400
Fax: 740 259-2885
Forrest Arbaugh, *President*
EMP: 8
SALES (est): 1.2MM **Privately Held**
SIC: 3272 Septic tanks, concrete; manhole
covers or frames, concrete; tanks, con-
crete

(G-12420)
**FALCON FAB AND FINISHES
LLC**
Also Called: Falcon Fabrication
3368 Piketon Rd (45648-8767)
P.O. Box 285, Minford (45653-0285)
PHONE................................740 820-4458
Deron M Brisker, *President*
EMP: 3
SALES: 80K **Privately Held**
SIC: 3312 3449 3315 3496 Wire prod-
ucts, steel or iron; hot-rolled iron & steel
products; bars, concrete reinforcing: fabri-
cated steel; wire & fabricated wire prod-
ucts; miscellaneous fabricated wire
products

(G-12421)
**LAWRENCE PALLETS &
SOLUTIONS**
620 Owensville Rd (45648-8476)
PHONE................................740 259-4283
EMP: 4 EST: 2006
SALES (est): 250K **Privately Held**
SIC: 2448 Mfg Wood Pallets/Skids

(G-12422)
MITCHELL WELDING LLC
11761 State Route 104 (45648-8583)
PHONE................................740 259-2211
James Richard Mitchell, *Partner*
Timothy T Mitchell, *Partner*
EMP: 3
SALES (est): 223.5K **Privately Held**
SIC: 7692 Welding repair

(G-12423)
NEWTONS PAINT & BODY
768 Fairground Rd (45648-8363)
PHONE................................740 352-9334
Michael Newton, *Owner*
EMP: 7
SQ FT: 20,000
SALES: 1.3MM **Privately Held**
SIC: 7532 3479 Paint shop, automotive;
painting of metal products

(G-12424)
RAY L LUTE LL
494 Coldicott Hill Rd (45648-9595)
PHONE................................740 372-7703
Ray L Lute II, *Owner*
EMP: 3
SALES (est): 228.2K **Privately Held**
SIC: 2411 0811 Logging; timber tracts

(G-12425)
TOW PATH READY MIX (PA)
Also Called: Tow Path Materials
12360 State Route 104 (45648-8201)
PHONE................................740 259-3222
Fax: 740 259-0659
Mark Salisbury, *Owner*
EMP: 4
SALES (est): 1.4MM **Privately Held**
SIC: 3273 Ready-mixed concrete

Ludlow Falls
Miami County

(G-12426)
FENNER ENTERPRISES INC
Also Called: Fenner Sand & Gravel
7131 Fenner Rd (45339-9765)
PHONE................................937 698-7048
Tom Wagner, *President*
EMP: 5
SQ FT: 800
SALES (est): 350K **Privately Held**
SIC: 1442 Sand mining; gravel mining

(G-12427)
MARMAX MACHINE CO
Also Called: Meiring Precision
2425 S State Route 48 (45339-9792)
P.O. Box 99 (45339-0099)
PHONE................................937 698-9900
David M Shepherd, *Owner*
EMP: 7
SQ FT: 7,200
SALES (est): 291.3K **Privately Held**
SIC: 3599 Machine shop, jobbing & repair

(G-12428)
STULL WOODWORKS
7925 Fenner Rd (45339-9746)
PHONE................................937 698-8181
Brian Stull, *President*
Sandy Stull, *Vice Pres*
EMP: 6
SALES: 900K **Privately Held**
WEB: www.stullwoodworks.com
SIC: 2431 Woodwork, interior & ornamen-
tal

(G-12429)
WALL POLISHING LLC
1953 S State Route 48 (45339-8760)
PHONE................................937 698-1330
Kenneth Wall, *Principal*

EMP: 3
SALES (est): 227.9K **Privately Held**
SIC: 3471 Polishing, metals or formed
products

Lyons
Fulton County

(G-12430)
AEROTECH STYLING INC
14181 County Road 10 2 (43533-9709)
PHONE................................419 923-6970
Fax: 419 923-6970
Bently Shaw, *President*
Todd Shaw, *Vice Pres*
EMP: 5
SQ FT: 11,700
SALES: 330K **Privately Held**
WEB: www.aerotechstyling.com
SIC: 3714 7532 Motor vehicle parts & ac-
cessories; customizing services, non-fac-
tory basis

(G-12431)
B W GRINDING CO
Also Called: Bw Supply Co.
15048 County Road 10 3 (43533-9713)
P.O. Box 307 (43533-0307)
PHONE................................419 923-1376
Fax: 419 923-1381
Martin Welch, *President*
Robert Welch, *Vice Pres*
Rick Rozewicki, *Manager*
EMP: 35
SQ FT: 30,000
SALES (est): 16.2MM **Privately Held**
WEB: www.bwsupplyco.com
SIC: 5085 3324 Industrial supplies; com-
mercial investment castings, ferrous

(G-12432)
MCS MFG LLC
15210 County Road 10 3 (43533-9713)
PHONE................................419 923-7535
Aaron R Call, *Principal*
EMP: 4 EST: 2008
SALES (est): 326.7K **Privately Held**
SIC: 3999 Manufacturing industries

Macedonia
Summit County

(G-12433)
AGS CUSTOM GRAPHICS INC
Also Called: A G S Ohio
8107 Bavaria Dr E (44056-2252)
PHONE................................330 963-7770
Fax: 330 349-4771
John Green, *President*
Mark Edgar, *Co-CEO*
Chuck Straka, *VP Opers*
Laura Williams, *Project Mgr*
Stephan Kolakowski, *Production*
EMP: 74
SQ FT: 70,000
SALES: 18.3MM
SALES (corp-wide): 6.9B **Publicly Held**
WEB: www.automatedgraphic.com
SIC: 2752 2721 7375 2791 Commercial
printing, offset; periodicals; information re-
trieval services; typesetting; bookbinding
& related work; commercial printing
HQ: Automated Graphic Systems, Llc
4590 Graphics Dr
White Plains MD 20695
301 843-1800

(G-12434)
ALPHABET SOUP INC
981 Cessna Dr (44056-1105)
PHONE................................330 467-4418
Wanda Glowacki, *President*
Robert Glowacki, *Vice Pres*
Robert Scott, *Vice Pres*
EMP: 3
SALES: 100K **Privately Held**
SIC: 2395 Embroidery & art needlework

(G-12435)
AMERICAN LIGHT METALS LLC
Also Called: Empire Die Casting Company
635 Highland Rd E (44056-2109)
PHONE.................................330 467-0750
Fax: 330 908-3065
Robert Spiegle, *Controller*
Yogen Rahangdale, *Mng Member*
Robert A Hopkins,
▲ EMP: 210 EST: 2013
SQ FT: 200,000
SALES: 34MM **Privately Held**
SIC: 3363 3364 Aluminum die-castings;
zinc & zinc-base alloy die-castings
HQ: Srs Die Casting Holdings, Llc
635 Highland Rd E
Macedonia OH 44056
330 467-0750

(G-12436)
BANCEQUITY PETROLEUM CORP
8821 Freeway Dr (44056-1506)
P.O. Box 670490, Northfield (44067-0490)
PHONE.................................330 468-5935
Thomas J Fischietto, *President*
Brenda S Eilbeck, *Director*
EMP: 4 EST: 1983
SALES (est): 484.5K **Privately Held**
SIC: 1381 Drilling oil & gas wells

(G-12437)
BILZ VIBRATION TECHNOLOGY INC
895 Highland Rd E Ste F (44056-2128)
P.O. Box 241305, Cleveland (44124-8305)
PHONE.................................330 468-2459
Marc A Brower, *President*
Bill Granchi, *Vice Pres*
William Granchi, *Vice Pres*
▲ EMP: 15
SQ FT: 8,000
SALES: 1.3MM **Privately Held**
SIC: 5084 3829 Machinists' precision
measuring tools; vibration meters, analyz-
ers & calibrators

(G-12438)
BLACKBURN HUBCAPS & WHEELS LLC
1001 Paster Ct (44056-9401)
PHONE.................................330 467-0236
Fax: 330 467-0443
James Blackburn,
Torrey Blackburn,
EMP: 8
SALES (est): 2MM **Privately Held**
WEB: www.hubcaps-n-wheels.com
SIC: 3465 Hub caps, automobile: stamped
metal

(G-12439)
BUDGET MOLDERS SUPPLY INC
8303 Corporate Park Dr (44056-2300)
PHONE.................................216 367-7050
Fax: 216 467-0016
Ed Kuchar Sr, *President*
Ed Kuchar Jr, *Vice Pres*
Raymond A Kuchar, *Vice Pres*
Francis E Kuchar, *Treasurer*
Jeff Hauff, *Manager*
EMP: 25
SALES (est): 3.6MM **Privately Held**
WEB: www.budgetmolders.com
SIC: 3559 Plastics working machinery

(G-12440)
CHAMPION WIN CO CLEVELAND LLC
9011 Freeway Dr Ste 1 (44056-1524)
PHONE.................................440 899-2562
Chris Maple, *President*
Renee Lewis, *Manager*
◆ EMP: 45
SALES (est): 5MM **Privately Held**
SIC: 3081 3442 Vinyl film & sheet; storm
doors or windows, metal

(G-12441)
CHAMPION WINDOW CO OF AKRON
Also Called: Champion Windows
9011 Freeway Dr Ste 1 (44056-1524)
PHONE.................................330 474-3024

Fax: 330 678-8234
Frank Rizzo, *President*
EMP: 30
SALES (est): 4MM **Privately Held**
SIC: 3089 Window frames & sash, plastic

(G-12442)
COBRA PLASTICS INC
1244 Highland Rd E (44056-2308)
PHONE.................................330 425-3669
Kent Houser, *President*
George Sehringer, *Corp Secy*
Carolyn Myers, *Controller*
Mike Cornett, *Human Res Mgr*
Victor Gullatta, *Supervisor*
◆ EMP: 100
SQ FT: 95,000
SALES (est): 25.9MM **Privately Held**
WEB: www.cobraplastics.com
SIC: 3089 Molding primary plastic

(G-12443)
CONNELLY INDUSTRIES LLC
9651 N Bedford Rd (44056-1007)
PHONE.................................330 468-0675
M K Connelly, *Principal*
EMP: 3
SALES (est): 149.3K **Privately Held**
SIC: 3999 Manufacturing industries

(G-12444)
DESIGN MOLDED PLASTICS INC
8220 Bavaria Rd (44056)
PHONE.................................330 963-4400
Fax: 330 963-4300
Jay Honsaker, *President*
Diane Hanson, *Corp Secy*
Mark Furlong, *Safety Mgr*
Sue Kahley, *Purch Agent*
Greg Ans, *Engineer*
EMP: 132 EST: 2014
SALES (est): 28.6MM **Privately Held**
SIC: 3089 Injection molded finished plastic
products

(G-12445)
DIEMASTER TOOL & MOLD INC
895 Highland Rd E 5 (44056-2128)
PHONE.................................330 467-4281
Fax: 330 467-6452
Paul Badovick, *President*
Dorothy Badovick, *Corp Secy*
Donald Andrasik, *Vice Pres*
EMP: 12 EST: 1966
SQ FT: 7,200
SALES (est): 1.4MM **Privately Held**
SIC: 3544 Forms (molds), for foundry &
plastics working machinery

(G-12446)
DON BASCH JEWELERS INC
8210 Mcidonia Comm Blvd36
(44056-1861)
PHONE.................................330 467-2116
Don Basch, *President*
Denise Basch, *Admin Sec*
EMP: 13
SALES (est): 2.1MM **Privately Held**
WEB: www.donbaschjewelers.com
SIC: 3911 7631 Jewelry, precious metal;
watch, clock & jewelry repair

(G-12447)
ELITE MFG SOLUTIONS LLC
7792 Capital Blvd Ste 6 (44056-2132)
PHONE.................................330 612-7434
Dean O'Malley, *Partner*
EMP: 5
SALES (est): 668.9K **Privately Held**
SIC: 3549 Metalworking machinery

(G-12448)
ETS SCHAEFER LLC
8050 Highland Pointe Pkwy (44056-2147)
PHONE.................................330 468-6600
Fax: 330 468-6610
Terrance J Hogan, *CEO*
Hugh Storms, *Engineer*
Michael Hobey, *CFO*
EMP: 40
SQ FT: 73,000

SALES (est): 11.5MM
SALES (corp-wide): 1.1B **Publicly Held**
WEB: www.etsschaefer.com
SIC: 3297 3433 2221 Nonclay refracto-
ries; heating equipment, except electric;
broadwoven fabric mills, manmade
HQ: Real Alloy Holding, Inc.
3700 Park East Dr Ste 300
Beachwood OH 44122
216 755-8800

(G-12449)
FERROLUX METALS CO OHIO LLC
8055a Hghland Pointe Pkwy (44056-2147)
PHONE.................................216 671-6161
Mark Nester, *General Mgr*
Eduardo Gonzalez,
EMP: 9
SQ FT: 250,000
SALES (est): 1.2MM
SALES (corp-wide): 65.1MM **Privately
Held**
WEB: www.ferragon.com
SIC: 3316 Cold finishing of steel shapes
PA: Ferragon Corporation
11103 Memphis Ave
Cleveland OH 44144
216 671-6161

(G-12450)
FINAL FINISH CORP
596 Highland Rd E (44056-2108)
PHONE.................................440 439-3303
William R Griffith, *President*
Gisele Griffith, *Vice Pres*
Deena Weber, *Marketing Mgr*
Julie Doskocil, *Office Mgr*
EMP: 5
SQ FT: 11,700
SALES (est): 220K **Privately Held**
SIC: 3479 Painting of metal products

(G-12451)
FORTERRA PIPE & PRECAST LLC
7925 Empire Pkwy (44056-2144)
PHONE.................................330 467-7890
Scott Bundrant, *Vice Pres*
Michael Pepper, *Vice Pres*
Grafton Redfern, *VP Sales*
Gary Erickson, *Sales Staff*
Sherri Karpinski, *Office Mgr*
EMP: 8
SALES (corp-wide): 141.7MM **Publicly
Held**
SIC: 3272 Culvert pipe, concrete
HQ: Forterra Pipe & Precast, Llc
511 E John Carpenter Fwy
Irving TX 75062
469 458-7973

(G-12452)
FUNCTIONAL PRODUCTS INC
8282 Bavaria Dr E (44056-2248)
PHONE.................................330 963-3060
David Devore, *President*
Diane Costas, *Vice Pres*
Jeff Plumley, *Plant Mgr*
Kathy Monda, *QC Mgr*
Jan Bialous, *Sales Staff*
▲ EMP: 20
SQ FT: 24,000
SALES (est): 6.2MM **Privately Held**
WEB: www.functionalproducts.com
SIC: 2992 Lubricating oils & greases

(G-12453)
G & G HEADER DIE INC
1200 Saybrook Dr (44056-2408)
PHONE.................................330 468-3458
George Giles, *President*
Candice Giles, *Vice Pres*
EMP: 6
SQ FT: 3,000
SALES: 320K **Privately Held**
SIC: 3544 Special dies, tools, jigs & fix-
tures

(G-12454)
G W STEFFEN BOOKBINDERS INC
8212 Bavaria Dr E (44056-2248)
PHONE.................................330 963-0300
William Turoczy, *President*

Elizabeth L Turoczy, *Corp Secy*
EMP: 50 EST: 1904
SQ FT: 45,000
SALES (est): 6.1MM **Privately Held**
WEB: www.steffenbookbinders.com
SIC: 2789 Bookbinding & related work

(G-12455)
GASPAR SERVICES LLC
Also Called: Akland Printing
9009 Freeway Dr 4 (44056-1523)
PHONE.................................330 467-8292
Gregory Apanasewicz,
EMP: 6
SQ FT: 4,200
SALES (est): 923.2K **Privately Held**
SIC: 2752 Commercial printing, offset

(G-12456)
GREAT DAY IMPROVEMENTS LLC (HQ)
Also Called: Patio Enclosures
700 Highland Rd E (44056-2160)
PHONE.................................330 468-0700
Fax: 330 467-4297
Steve White, *CEO*
Craig Cox, *President*
Tom Edger, *General Mgr*
Brian Hejmanowski, *General Mgr*
Robert Knecht, *General Mgr*
EMP: 5
SALES (est): 45.7MM **Privately Held**
SIC: 3231 3448 3444 5712 Products of
purchased glass; prefabricated metal
buildings; sunrooms, prefabricated metal;
sheet metalwork; outdoor & garden furni-
ture; window furnishings

(G-12457)
HANSON AGGREGATES EAST LLC
7925 Empire Pkwy (44056-2144)
PHONE.................................330 467-7890
Geoff Richardson, *Manager*
EMP: 25
SALES (corp-wide): 16B **Privately Held**
SIC: 3272 Concrete products used to facili-
tate drainage
HQ: Hanson Aggregates East Llc
3131 Rdu Center Dr
Morrisville NC 27560
919 380-2500

(G-12458)
IER FUJIKURA INC (PA)
Also Called: I E R Industries
8271 Bavaria Dr E (44056-2259)
PHONE.................................330 425-7121
John Elsley, *President*
Athur E Lange, *President*
Carol Braunschweig, *Principal*
Dave Twarek, *Production*
Sara Hammond, *Purch Agent*
▲ EMP: 128
SQ FT: 60,000
SALES (est): 35.3MM **Privately Held**
WEB: www.ierindustries.com
SIC: 3069 3061 3053 2821 Molded rub-
ber products; mechanical rubber goods;
gaskets, packing & sealing devices; plas-
tics materials & resins

(G-12459)
INOVENT ENGINEERING INC
8877 Freeway Dr (44056-1506)
P.O. Box 560314 (44056-0314)
PHONE.................................330 468-0005
P Clark Hungerford Jr, *President*
Ron Fenn, *Vice Pres*
Jim Eucker, *Shareholder*
EMP: 8
SQ FT: 7,000
SALES: 537K **Privately Held**
WEB: www.inoventengineering.com
SIC: 8711 3599 Professional engineer;
custom machinery

(G-12460)
INSIGHTFUEL LLC
Also Called: Afv
1333 Highland Rd E Ste P (44056-2445)
PHONE.................................330 998-7380
Kevin Dickey, *General Mgr*
Jeffrey King,
EMP: 15
SQ FT: 16,500

SALES: 5.5MM **Privately Held**
SIC: 2869 Industrial organic chemicals

(G-12461)
J & D BERDINE SIGNS INC
746 E Aurora Rd Ste 3 (44056-2733)
PHONE..................................330 468-0556
Joseph V Berdine II, *President*
Debbie Berdine, *Manager*
EMP: 4
SALES (est): 365.5K **Privately Held**
SIC: 3993 Signs & advertising specialties

(G-12462)
JAMES THOMAS SHIVELEY
Also Called: Innovative Industries
585 Highland Rd E (44056-2107)
P.O. Box 41205, Cleveland (44141-0205)
PHONE..................................330 468-2601
Fax: 330 468-2602
James Thomas Shiveley, *President*
Curtis Schrack, *Engineer*
EMP: 4
SQ FT: 30,000
SALES: 125K **Privately Held**
WEB: www.innovativeindustries.com
SIC: 3567 Heating units & devices, industrial: electric

(G-12463)
JAY DEE SERVICE CORPORATION
Also Called: Bearing & Transm Sup Co Div
1320 Highland Rd E (44056-2310)
P.O. Box 560185 (44056-0185)
PHONE..................................330 425-1546
Fax: 330 425-1646
John Zimmerman Sr, *CEO*
Constance A Zimmerman, *President*
Julia Hall, *Principal*
Alfred Palay, *Principal*
Julia Zimmerman, *Principal*
▲ EMP: 8
SQ FT: 13,000
SALES: 28MM **Privately Held**
WEB: www.bearingtrans.com
SIC: 5084 3562 Industrial machinery & equipment; ball bearings & parts

(G-12464)
JOHNSTON-MOREHOUSE-DICKEY CO
1290 Highland Rd E (44056-2308)
PHONE..................................330 405-6050
Tony Blaknik, *Branch Mgr*
EMP: 5
SALES (corp-wide): 34.3MM **Privately Held**
SIC: 2299 3089 5039 Narrow woven fabrics: linen, jute, hemp & ramie; plastic hardware & building products; netting, plastic; soil erosion control fabrics
PA: Johnston-Morehouse-Dickey Co Inc
5401 Progress Blvd
Bethel Park PA 15102
412 833-7100

(G-12465)
JOSLYN MANUFACTURING COMPANY
9400 Valley View Rd (44056-2060)
PHONE..................................330 467-8111
Fax: 330 467-6574
Bret Joslyn, *President*
Charles B Joslyn, *Principal*
Brain Joslyn, *Vice Pres*
Joanne Ispan, *QC Mgr*
Hollis Woods-Williams, *QC Mgr*
▲ EMP: 25 EST: 1946
SQ FT: 105,000
SALES (est): 6.2MM **Privately Held**
WEB: www.joslyn-mfg.com
SIC: 3089 Plastic processing

(G-12466)
KIMPTON PRINTING & SPC CO
Also Called: Kimpton Prtg & Specialities
400 Highland Rd E (44056-2133)
PHONE..................................330 467-1640
Fax: 330 467-9263
Dale Kimpton, *President*
Don Kimpton, *Vice Pres*
Helen Kimpton, *Vice Pres*
EMP: 10
SQ FT: 2,400

SALES (est): 1.6MM **Privately Held**
WEB: www.kimptonprinting.com
SIC: 2752 7336 Commercial printing, offset; silk screen design

(G-12467)
M & M CERTIFIED WELDING INC
556 Highland Rd E Ste 3 (44056-2162)
PHONE..................................330 467-1729
Fax: 330 467-1728
Matthew B McCann, *President*
EMP: 10
SQ FT: 16,000
SALES (est): 2.2MM **Privately Held**
WEB: www.mmcertifiedwelding.com
SIC: 3443 1799 Weldments; welding on site

(G-12468)
PARKER-HANNIFIN CORPORATION
1390 Highland Rd E (44056-2310)
PHONE..................................330 963-0601
EMP: 120
SALES (corp-wide): 11.3B **Publicly Held**
SIC: 3594 Fluid power pumps & motors
PA: Parker-Hannifin Corporation
6035 Parkland Blvd
Cleveland OH 44124
216 896-3000

(G-12469)
PARKER-HANNIFIN CORPORATION
Human Motion & Ctrl Bus Unit
1390 Highland Rd E (44056-2310)
PHONE..................................216 896-3000
Achilleas Dorotheou, *Manager*
Edgar Wilson, *Manager*
EMP: 12
SALES (corp-wide): 11.3B **Publicly Held**
SIC: 3594 Fluid power pumps & motors; fluid power pumps; fluid power motors
PA: Parker-Hannifin Corporation
6035 Parkland Blvd
Cleveland OH 44124
216 896-3000

(G-12470)
PEI LIQUIDATION COMPANY (PA)
700 Highland Rd E (44056-2160)
PHONE..................................330 467-4267
Fax: 330 468-0816
Robert J Schneider, *Ch of Bd*
Donald M Levy, *Principal*
Gerald J Fox, *Exec VP*
Jim Potts, *Plant Mgr*
Bob Boger, *Mfg Staff*
▲ EMP: 152
SQ FT: 240,295
SALES (est): 16.9MM **Privately Held**
WEB: www.patioenc.com
SIC: 3231 3448 3444 5712 Products of purchased glass; prefabricated metal buildings; sunrooms, prefabricated metal; sheet metalwork; outdoor & garden furniture; window furnishings

(G-12471)
PEI LIQUIDATION COMPANY
720 Highland Rd E (44056-2160)
PHONE..................................615 781-5020
Brad Codd, *Manager*
EMP: 20
SALES (corp-wide): 16.9MM **Privately Held**
WEB: www.patioenc.com
SIC: 3448 6794 5712 5719 Prefabricated metal buildings; sunrooms, prefabricated metal; franchises, selling or licensing; outdoor & garden furniture; window furnishings; patio & deck construction & repair; sheet metalwork
PA: Pei Liquidation Company
700 Highland Rd E
Macedonia OH 44056
330 467-4267

(G-12472)
PLASTIC MATERIALS INC (PA)
775 Highland Rd E (44056-2111)
PHONE..................................330 468-5706
William Speaks, *Principal*
EMP: 24

SALES (est): 12.3MM **Privately Held**
SIC: 3089 Air mattresses, plastic

(G-12473)
PLASTIC MATERIALS INC
Also Called: PMI
775 Highland Rd E (44056-2111)
PHONE..................................330 468-0184
Fax: 330 633-6361
EMP: 33
SALES (corp-wide): 12.3MM **Privately Held**
SIC: 3089 Air mattresses, plastic
PA: Plastic Materials Inc
775 Highland Rd E
Macedonia OH 44056
330 468-5706

(G-12474)
PLASTIC PROCESS EQUIPMENT INC (PA)
Also Called: Ppe
8303 Corporate Park Dr (44056-2300)
PHONE..................................216 367-7000
Fax: 216 367-7022
Edward Kuchar, *President*
Ray Kuchar, *Senior VP*
Frances Kuchar, *Vice Pres*
Henry G Roethel, *Engineer*
Gary Croy, *Sales Mgr*
◆ EMP: 20
SALES (est): 7.8MM **Privately Held**
SIC: 3559 5085 5084 Plastics working machinery; industrial supplies; industrial machinery & equipment

(G-12475)
PLATING RESOURCES SUPPLY
573 Highland Rd E Ste 7 (44056-2158)
PHONE..................................330 908-3949
David Kroger, *Owner*
EMP: 3
SALES (est): 134.3K **Privately Held**
SIC: 3471 Plating & polishing

(G-12476)
PRECISION REPLACEMENT LLC
9009 Freeway Dr Unit 7 (44056-1523)
PHONE..................................330 908-0410
Joseph D Lukes, *Principal*
Michael Tecca, *Mfg Mgr*
Dan Auvio, *Marketing Staff*
EMP: 6
SQ FT: 5,500
SALES (est): 2MM **Privately Held**
SIC: 3565 5999 Vacuum packaging machinery; electronic parts & equipment

(G-12477)
PRO QUIP INC
850 Highland Rd E (44056-2190)
PHONE..................................330 468-1850
Fax: 330 467-3724
Harry J Abraham, *CEO*
George Braun, *Principal*
Brian Abraham, *Vice Pres*
David Grutzmacher, *Vice Pres*
Dave Grutzmacher, *Sls & Mktg Exec*
▲ EMP: 55 EST: 1969
SQ FT: 26,000
SALES (est): 20.5MM **Privately Held**
WEB: www.proquipinc.com
SIC: 3559 Refinery, chemical processing & similar machinery

(G-12478)
PROGRESSIVE MACHINE DIE INC
8406 Bavaria Dr E (44056-2275)
PHONE..................................330 405-6600
Fax: 330 405-6604
Julius Feitl, *President*
James Podojil, *Plant Mgr*
EMP: 40 EST: 1963
SQ FT: 70,000
SALES (est): 7.1MM **Privately Held**
WEB: www.pmd-inc.com
SIC: 3429 3544 3469 Manufactured hardware (general); special dies, tools, jigs & fixtures; metal stampings

(G-12479)
RALPH A FELICE INC
Also Called: Far Associates
1532 Newport Dr (44056-1970)
PHONE..................................330 468-0482
Ralph A Felice, *President*
EMP: 4
SALES (est): 521.3K **Privately Held**
WEB: www.pyrometry.com
SIC: 3823 Pyrometers, industrial process type

(G-12480)
REINECKERS BAKERY LTD
Also Called: Reinecker Party Center & Catrg
8575 Freeway Dr (44056-1534)
PHONE..................................330 467-2221
Fax: 330 468-3579
Caroline Davis, *Partner*
Heidi Reinecker, *Partner*
Richard Reinecker, *Partner*
EMP: 3 EST: 1959
SALES: 200K **Privately Held**
SIC: 2051 5812 Bakery: wholesale or wholesale/retail combined; caterers

(G-12481)
SC FIRE PROTECTION LTD
Also Called: S C Fastening Systems
8531 Freeway Dr (44056-1534)
PHONE..................................330 468-3300
Chuck Domonkos, *CEO*
Scott Filips, *President*
▲ EMP: 7
SALES: 680K **Privately Held**
SIC: 2899 Fire extinguisher charges

(G-12482)
SILVERCOTE LLC
9600b Valley View Rd (44056)
PHONE..................................330 748-8500
Jodi Shankweiler, *Branch Mgr*
EMP: 9
SALES (corp-wide): 31MM **Privately Held**
SIC: 3296 Insulation: rock wool, slag & silica minerals
PA: Silvercote, Llc
25 Logue Ct
Greenville SC 29615
864 469-9716

(G-12483)
SOURCE3MEDIA INC
9085 Freeway Dr (44056-1508)
PHONE..................................330 467-9003
Fax: 330 467-1419
Gary Began, *President*
Loren Miranda, *Accountant*
Ronald S Marshek, *Director*
Jerry Parkins, *Representative*
◆ EMP: 35
SQ FT: 17,000
SALES (est): 8MM **Privately Held**
WEB: www.hudsonpr.com
SIC: 2752 Commercial printing, offset

(G-12484)
SPECIALTY MAGNETICS LLC
440 Highland Rd E (44056-2106)
PHONE..................................330 468-8834
Shawn Grill, *Mng Member*
Jeff Glen, *Mng Member*
▲ EMP: 3
SQ FT: 800
SALES (est): 486.4K **Privately Held**
SIC: 3499 Magnets, permanent: metallic

(G-12485)
SPEEDWAY LLC
Also Called: Speedway Superamerica 1848
757 E Aurora Rd (44056)
PHONE..................................330 468-3320
Jerry Kurinsky, *Branch Mgr*
EMP: 14 **Publicly Held**
WEB: www.speedwaynet.com
SIC: 1311 Crude petroleum production
HQ: Speedway Llc
500 Speedway Dr
Enon OH 45323
937 864-3000

(G-12486)
SR PRODUCTS
1380 Highland Rd E (44056-2310)
PHONE..................................330 998-6500

Steve Harnish, *President*
Stephen Duke, *CFO*
EMP: 5
SALES (est): 763.8K **Privately Held**
SIC: 2952 Asphalt felts & coatings

(G-12487)
SRS DIE CASTING HOLDINGS LLC (HQ)
635 Highland Rd E (44056-2109)
PHONE.................................330 467-0750
Yogen Rahangdale,
EMP: 2
SALES (est): 34MM **Privately Held**
SIC: 3363 3364 Aluminum die-castings; zinc & zinc-base alloy die-castings
PA: Srs Light Metals Inc.
635 Highland Rd E
Macedonia OH 44056
330 467-0750

(G-12488)
SRS LIGHT METALS INC (PA)
635 Highland Rd E (44056-2109)
PHONE.................................330 467-0750
Yogen Rahangdale,
EMP: 2 **EST:** 2013
SALES (est): 34MM **Privately Held**
SIC: 3363 3364 Aluminum die-castings; zinc & zinc-base alloy die-castings

(G-12489)
STANDARD SIGNS INCORPORATED (PA)
Also Called: Lumacurve Airfield Signs
9115 Freeway Dr (44056-1543)
PHONE.................................330 467-2030
Fax: 330 467-2076
John A Messner, *President*
Dave Benson, *Project Mgr*
Craig Fussner, *Opers Staff*
Dan Scholz, *Engineer*
Liz Humpage, *Marketing Staff*
EMP: 19 **EST:** 1936
SQ FT: 27,000
SALES (est): 3.4MM **Privately Held**
WEB: www.standardsigns.com
SIC: 3993 Signs, not made in custom sign painting shops

(G-12490)
STANEK E F AND ASSOC INC
Also Called: Stanek Windows
700 Highland Rd E (44056-2160)
PHONE.................................216 341-7700
Fax: 216 341-0060
Mark Davis, *President*
Mike Graham, *Sr Corp Ofcr*
Jerry Donatelli, *Exec VP*
Wien Coew, *Vice Pres*
Ron Stanek, *Vice Pres*
EMP: 120
SQ FT: 35,000
SALES (est): 18.3MM **Privately Held**
WEB: www.stanekwindows.com
SIC: 3089 Windows, plastic; window frames & sash, plastic

(G-12491)
SUNLESS INC (HQ)
8909 Freeway Dr Ste A (44056-1574)
PHONE.................................440 836-0199
Peter Van Niekerk, *CEO*
Jared Bordovsky, *Asst Controller*
Chelsea Greer, *Sales Mgr*
Ben Brown, *Info Tech Mgr*
Lisa Staberg, *Executive*
▲ **EMP:** 120
SQ FT: 68,000
SALES (est): 34MM
SALES (corp-wide): 3.6B **Privately Held**
WEB: www.sunlessinc.com
SIC: 3648 Sun tanning equipment, incl. tanning beds
PA: Riverside Partners L.L.C.
45 Rockefeller Plz # 400
New York NY 10111
212 265-6575

(G-12492)
SUPERFINISHERS INC
380 Highland Rd E (44056-2139)
PHONE.................................330 467-2125
Frank Bucar, *President*
EMP: 7 **EST:** 1958
SQ FT: 5,000

SALES: 700K **Privately Held**
SIC: 3471 3599 Finishing, metals or formed products; machine shop, jobbing & repair

(G-12493)
SYSTEMS PACK INC
649 Highland Rd E (44056-2109)
PHONE.................................330 467-5729
Fax: 216 468-2299
Ray Attwell, *President*
Denny Kay, *VP Sales*
John Hood, *Sales Mgr*
Cindi Laing, *Consultant*
EMP: 30 **EST:** 1977
SQ FT: 62,131
SALES (est): 15.2MM **Privately Held**
WEB: www.systemspackinc.com
SIC: 5199 7389 5113 2653 Packaging materials; packaging & labeling services; shipping supplies; corrugated & solid fiber boxes

(G-12494)
TIN WIZARD HEATING AND COOLING
8853 Robinwood Ter (44056-2719)
PHONE.................................330 468-7884
James Plush, *Principal*
EMP: 3
SALES (est): 21.4K **Privately Held**
SIC: 3356 Tin

(G-12495)
WILLARD MACHINE & WELDING INC
556 Highland Rd E Ste 3 (44056-2162)
PHONE.................................330 467-0642
Margaret Willard, *President*
George C Willard, *Vice Pres*
EMP: 10
SQ FT: 9,600
SALES (est): 843.4K **Privately Held**
SIC: 3713 7532 Specialty motor vehicle bodies; top & body repair & paint shops

---

Madison
Lake County

(G-12496)
BUCKEYE ALUMINUM FOUNDRY INC (PA)
457 N Lake St (44057-3139)
PHONE.................................440 428-7180
Peter Otterman Sr, *President*
Peter Otterman Jr, *Vice Pres*
EMP: 3 **EST:** 1973
SALES (est): 2MM **Privately Held**
WEB: www.buckeyealuminum.com
SIC: 3363 Aluminum die-castings

(G-12497)
CASHEN INC
Also Called: Cashen Builders Supply
1225 Dock Rd (44057-2209)
PHONE.................................440 428-1148
Andrew Cashen, *President*
EMP: 3 **EST:** 1940
SQ FT: 600
SALES: 400K **Privately Held**
WEB: www.cashen.com
SIC: 3272 5211 Concrete products; masonry materials & supplies

(G-12498)
CENTER MASS AMMO LLC
6642 Middle Ridge Rd (44057-2904)
PHONE.................................440 796-6207
Christopher Sanford, *CEO*
Jason Bosworth, *Co-Owner*
Scott Graham, *Co-Owner*
EMP: 3
SALES (est): 184K **Privately Held**
SIC: 3483 3482 Ammunition loading & assembling plant; small arms ammunition; cartridge cases for ammunition, 30 mm. & below

(G-12499)
CHALET DEBONNE VINEYARDS INC
7840 Doty Rd (44057-9511)
PHONE.................................440 466-3485
Fax: 440 466-6753
Anthony Paul Debevc, *President*
Tony J Debevc, *Vice Pres*
Beth Debevc, *Admin Sec*
EMP: 12
SQ FT: 14,000
SALES (est): 1.8MM **Privately Held**
SIC: 2084 Wines

(G-12500)
CHEM MASTERS
300 Edwards St (44057-3112)
PHONE.................................440 428-2105
Daniel Schodowski, *Principal*
Hank Vavrik, *Personnel Exec*
EMP: 9
SALES (est): 1.8MM **Privately Held**
SIC: 2819 Industrial inorganic chemicals

(G-12501)
CHEMMASTERS INC
300 Edwards St (44057-3112)
PHONE.................................440 428-2105
Daniel Schodowski, *President*
John Fauth, *General Mgr*
Greg Myers, *Vice Pres*
Brenda Carr, *Safety Mgr*
John Kirk, *Technical Mgr*
▲ **EMP:** 20
SQ FT: 25,000
SALES (est): 7.3MM **Privately Held**
WEB: www.chemmasters.net
SIC: 2899 2891 5169 Concrete curing & hardening compounds; sealants; chemicals & allied products

(G-12502)
COUNTY OF LAKE
Also Called: Waste Water Treatment Plant
7815 Cashen Rd (44057-1651)
PHONE.................................440 428-1794
Fax: 440 428-6450
Terry Rascke, *Manager*
EMP: 10
SQ FT: 650 **Privately Held**
WEB: www.lakecountyohio.gov
SIC: 3589 Water treatment equipment, industrial
PA: County Of Lake
8 N State St Ste 215
Painesville OH 44077
440 350-2500

(G-12503)
D & L MANUFACTURING
2715 Bennett Rd (44057-2657)
PHONE.................................440 428-1627
Richard W Kuehnle, *President*
Elizabeth Kuehnle, *Corp Secy*
EMP: 5 **EST:** 1973
SQ FT: 1,200
SALES (est): 380K **Privately Held**
SIC: 3469 Stamping metal for the trade

(G-12504)
DEE LEE MACHINE INC
3921 Townline Rd (44057-3326)
PHONE.................................440 259-2245
Dale Broadwater, *President*
Sally Broadwater, *Vice Pres*
EMP: 3
SQ FT: 1,876
SALES (est): 500K **Privately Held**
SIC: 3599 Machine shop, jobbing & repair

(G-12505)
EAE LOGISTICS COMPANY LLC
5907 S Ridge Rd (44057-9741)
PHONE.................................440 417-4788
Daniel T Larned,
EMP: 3
SALES: 500K **Privately Held**
SIC: 3542 4491 4731 7389 Presses: forming, stamping, punching, sizing (machine tools); marine cargo handling; freight transportation arrangement;

(G-12506)
EMPIRE POWER SYSTEMS CO
6211 Shore Dr (44057-1945)
P.O. Box 1893, Mentor (44061-1893)
PHONE.................................440 796-4401
Ronald Lapham, *Principal*
EMP: 4
SALES (est): 450K **Privately Held**
SIC: 3643 3613 3694 3679 Power line cable; switchgear & switchboard apparatus; battery cable wiring sets for internal combustion engines; harness assemblies for electronic use: wire or cable

(G-12507)
INTERNATIONAL PAPER COMPANY
3200 County Line Rd (44057-9731)
PHONE.................................440 428-5116
EMP: 3
SALES (corp-wide): 21B **Publicly Held**
SIC: 2621 Paper mills
PA: International Paper Company
6400 Poplar Ave
Memphis TN 38197
901 419-9000

(G-12508)
KG TOOL COMPANY
5640 Middle Ridge Rd (44057-2814)
PHONE.................................440 428-8633
Fax: 440 428-8532
Greg Giecerich, *Principal*
EMP: 4
SALES (est): 370K **Privately Held**
SIC: 3544 Special dies, tools, jigs & fixtures

(G-12509)
MADISON MANUFACTURING LLC
444 Oak Hollow Dr (44057-7204)
PHONE.................................440 428-4630
Craig Winkleman, *Principal*
EMP: 3
SALES (est): 215.2K **Privately Held**
SIC: 3679 Rheostats, for electronic end products

(G-12510)
MARSCH MACHINE PRODUCTS
16107 Moseley Rd (44057-9407)
PHONE.................................440 298-3932
Marlene Marsch, *Owner*
EMP: 3
SQ FT: 1,438
SALES (est): 167.2K **Privately Held**
SIC: 3599 Machine & other job shop work

(G-12511)
PUMPHREY MACHINE CORP
7240 N Ridge Rd (44057-2629)
P.O. Box 477 (44057-0477)
PHONE.................................440 417-0481
Fax: 440 417-0482
Herbert Pumphrey, *President*
EMP: 9
SQ FT: 9,000
SALES (est): 1.4MM **Privately Held**
SIC: 3599 Machine shop, jobbing & repair

(G-12512)
TOPKOTE INC
404 N Lake St (44057-3151)
PHONE.................................440 428-0525
Shane Slattman, *Principal*
EMP: 9
SALES (est): 720K **Privately Held**
SIC: 3399 Silver powder

(G-12513)
UNIVERSAL SCIENTIFIC INC
6210 Campbell Dr (44057-2003)
PHONE.................................440 428-1777
Fax: 440 428-8650
Thomas W Heckman, *President*
Phoebe Heckman, *Corp Secy*
EMP: 8
SQ FT: 2,500
SALES (est): 1.4MM **Privately Held**
WEB: www.universalscientific.com
SIC: 3821 Laboratory apparatus & furniture

▲ = Import ▼=Export
◆ =Import/Export

(G-12514)
ZERO-D PRODUCTS INC (PA)
Also Called: Akron Jewelry Rubber
7183 Lake Rd (44057-1508)
PHONE..........................440 417-1843
William W Mull, *President*
James R Dillhoefer, *Corp Secy*
Robert J Beausoleil, *Vice Pres*
EMP: 5
SALES (est): 745.6K Privately Held
WEB: www.zerodproducts.com
SIC: 3915 Jewelers' findings & materials

Magnolia
Stark County

(G-12515)
**BINDER OIL FIELD
CONSTRUCTION**
5100 Battlesburg St Se (44643-9760)
P.O. Box 485 (44643-0485)
PHONE..........................330 484-3680
Robert Kemp, *President*
EMP: 4
SALES: 200K Privately Held
SIC: 1389 Oil & gas wells: building, repair-
ing & dismantling

(G-12516)
**MAGNOLIA MACHINE & REPAIR
INC**
3315 Magnolia Rd Nw (44643-9528)
PHONE..........................330 866-4200
Daniel Fedeli, *President*
EMP: 5
SQ FT: 3,000
SALES (est): 430K Privately Held
SIC: 3599 Machine shop, jobbing & repair

(G-12517)
OLDE WOOD LTD
7557 Willowdale St (44643-9718)
PHONE..........................330 866-1441
Fax: 330 863-9181
Thomas Sancic, *CEO*
Jeff Dewees, *Controller*
Kris Young, *Sales Dir*
Kinsey Douglass, *Mktg Coord*
Chris Young, *Manager*
EMP: 35
SQ FT: 70,000
SALES (est): 7MM Privately Held
SIC: 3272 Building materials, except block
or brick: concrete

(G-12518)
**PHOENIX ASPHALT COMPANY
INC**
18025 Imperial Rd (44643)
PHONE..........................330 339-4935
James R Demuth, *President*
Mary Yonally, *Admin Asst*
EMP: 6 EST: 2002
SALES (est): 203.2K Privately Held
SIC: 1442 5032 Construction sand &
gravel; sand, construction

(G-12519)
SMITH SMITH & DEYARMAN
9260 Bachelor Rd Nw (44643-9564)
P.O. Box 406 (44643-0406)
PHONE..........................330 866-5521
D Michael Smith, *Partner*
Charles Deyarman, *Partner*
EMP: 3
SALES (est): 209.1K Privately Held
SIC: 1381 Drilling oil & gas wells

Maineville
Warren County

(G-12520)
**ABCO BAR & TUBE CUTTING
SVC**
7685 S State Route 48 # 1 (45039-8802)
PHONE..........................513 697-9487
Fax: 513 573-9067
Kris Martin, *President*
Jason Martin, *Vice Pres*

Nathan Huff, *VP Opers*
Amanda Martin, *Office Mgr*
Christine Bowles, *Director*
EMP: 30
SQ FT: 40,000
SALES (est): 7.5MM Privately Held
WEB: www.abcomachining.com
SIC: 3451 3452 3599 Screw machine
products; bolts, nuts, rivets & washers;
machine & other job shop work; machine
shop, jobbing & repair

(G-12521)
**CONTINGNCY PRCRMENTS
GROUP LLC**
Also Called: Real Tactical Gear
2800 Millbank Row (45039-9711)
PHONE..........................513 204-9590
William Cornett, *CEO*
Irina Khusainova-Cornett, *Principal*
EMP: 4
SALES (est): 208.3K Privately Held
SIC: 7382 7381 2311 Protective devices,
security; detective & armored car serv-
ices; military uniforms, men's & youths':
purchased materials; policemen's uni-
forms: made from purchased materials

(G-12522)
ELIZABETHS CLOSET
8847 Dover Dr (45039-9738)
PHONE..........................513 646-5025
Liz Cook, *Owner*
EMP: 3
SALES: 92K Privately Held
SIC: 5632 5812 2032 Costume jewelry;
American restaurant; Mexican foods:
packaged in cans, jars, etc.

(G-12523)
ELKEN CO
2905 Afton Valley Ct (45039-8847)
PHONE..........................513 459-7207
Kenneth Lippert, *President*
Elaine Lippert, *Vice Pres*
John Lippert, *Treasurer*
EMP: 5
SALES (est): 626.3K Privately Held
WEB: www.clearviewbinders.com
SIC: 2782 2396 Blankbooks & looseleaf
binders; bindings, cap & hat: made from
purchased materials

(G-12524)
FABACRAFT INC
Also Called: Fabacraft Co
201 Grandin Rd (45039-9762)
PHONE..........................513 677-0500
Fax: 513 677-0552
Edward F Bavis, *Ch of Bd*
William Sieber, *President*
Dolly Mattingly, *Corp Secy*
Michael Brown, *Vice Pres*
David McCartt, *Purch Mgr*
EMP: 35 EST: 1958
SQ FT: 44,000
SALES (est): 7.4MM Privately Held
WEB: www.bavis.com
SIC: 3535 Conveyors & conveying equip-
ment

(G-12525)
JMR ENTERPRISES LLC
Also Called: Robinson Ordnance
7808 Hyatts Ln (45039-7285)
PHONE..........................937 618-1736
Joseph Robinson, *Agent*
EMP: 3
SALES (est): 167K Privately Held
SIC: 5961 3484 3482 Catalog sales; guns
(firearms) or gun parts, 30 mm. & below;
small arms ammunition

(G-12526)
KROGER CO
2900 W Us Hwy 22 3 Unit 1 (45039)
PHONE..........................513 683-4001
Fax: 513 677-6362
Amanda Keechle, *Office Mgr*
Bob Oaters, *Manager*
EMP: 80

SALES (corp-wide): 115.3B Publicly
Held
WEB: www.kroger.com
SIC: 5411 5992 5912 2052 Supermarkets, chain; florists; drug stores & proprietary stores; cookies & crackers; bread,
cake & related products
PA: The Kroger Co
1014 Vine St Ste 1000
Cincinnati OH 45202
513 762-4000

(G-12527)
LAUGHING STAR MONTESSORY
8725 Davis Rd (45039-8329)
PHONE..........................513 683-5682
Susan Barker, *President*
EMP: 3
SALES (est): 260.4K Privately Held
WEB: www.laughingstarmontessori.com
SIC: 2759 Commercial printing

(G-12528)
MARKET READY
1129 Avalon Dr (45039-9131)
PHONE..........................513 289-9231
Dan H Letzler, *Owner*
EMP: 5
SALES (est): 429.6K Privately Held
SIC: 3273 Ready-mixed concrete

(G-12529)
**MIDWEST METALS & SUPPLY
LLC**
952 Hamlin Dr (45039-9814)
PHONE..........................513 489-1666
Greg Wichmann, *Mng Member*
Jeff Wichmann,
EMP: 4
SQ FT: 8,000
SALES (est): 470.1K Privately Held
SIC: 3499 Barricades, metal

(G-12530)
NAIL SECRET
3187 Wstn Row Rd Ste 105 (45039)
PHONE..........................513 459-3373
Stacey Chau, *Owner*
EMP: 3
SALES (est): 115.3K Privately Held
SIC: 3999 Fingernails, artificial

(G-12531)
POLYGROUP INC
2808 Millbank Row (45039-9711)
PHONE..........................877 476-5972
Paul Jackson, *President*
▲ EMP: 50
SALES (est): 5.5MM Privately Held
SIC: 2821 Plastics materials & resins

(G-12532)
SVM AMERICA LTD
1004 River Forest Dr (45039-7717)
PHONE..........................937 218-7591
Timothy Homan,
EMP: 50
SALES (est): 3.1MM Privately Held
SIC: 3711 Cars, armored, assembly of

(G-12533)
UTV HITCHWORKS LLC
1295 W Us Highway 22 & 3 (45039-8218)
PHONE..........................513 615-8568
Mark Altemeier,
EMP: 4 EST: 2011
SALES (est): 532.7K Privately Held
SIC: 3714 Motor vehicle electrical equip-
ment

Malinta
Henry County

(G-12534)
**GILSON SCREEN
INCORPORATED**
8-810 K 2 Rd (43535)
P.O. Box 99 (43535-0199)
PHONE..........................419 256-7711
Fax: 419 256-7005
David A Cody, *President*
Steven J Roby, *Vice Pres*
Trent Smith, *Vice Pres*

Richard Franz, *Site Mgr*
James A Cody, *Treasurer*
EMP: 42 EST: 1961
SQ FT: 30,000
SALES (est): 9.9MM Privately Held
WEB: www.globalgilson.com
SIC: 3829 3444 Testing equipment: abra-
sion, shearing strength, etc.; sheet metal-
work

(G-12535)
JAD MACHINE COMPANY INC
10620 County Road J (43535-9713)
PHONE..........................419 256-6332
Fax: 419 256-6785
Jim Hastedt, *President*
Diane Hastedt, *Corp Secy*
Dough Dietrich, *Manager*
EMP: 12
SQ FT: 12,000
SALES (est): 1MM Privately Held
WEB: www.jadmachine.com
SIC: 3451 Screw machine products

Malta
Morgan County

(G-12536)
EZ GROUT CORPORATION INC
Also Called: Ezg Manufacturing
1833 N Riverview Rd (43758-9303)
PHONE..........................740 962-2024
Damian Lang, *Owner*
EMP: 40 EST: 2007
SALES (est): 13MM Privately Held
SIC: 5082 3499 3549 Masonry equipment
& supplies; chests, fire or burglary resis-
tive: metal; wiredrawing & fabricating ma-
chinery & equipment, ex. die

(G-12537)
J VALTIER GAS AND OIL CO INC
10416 State Route 37 (43758-9417)
PHONE..........................740 342-2839
Fax: 740 342-1913
Joseph N Altier Jr, *President*
EMP: 5
SALES (est): 501.5K Privately Held
SIC: 1381 1389 Directional drilling oil &
gas wells; servicing oil & gas wells

(G-12538)
WOLFE CREEK FARMS
Also Called: Wilson Well Service
433 Wilson Dr (43758-9286)
PHONE..........................740 962-4563
Jerry R Wilson, *Owner*
Alan Wilson, *Partner*
Azcal Wilson, *Partner*
Mark Wilson, *Partner*
EMP: 4
SALES (est): 283.4K Privately Held
SIC: 1389 0115 0116 0212 Oil field serv-
ices; gas field services; corn; soybeans;
beef cattle except feedlots; hogs

Malvern
Carroll County

(G-12539)
**CAMBRIDGE MILL PRODUCTS
INC**
6005 Alliance Rd Nw (44644-9439)
P.O. Box 490 (44644-0490)
PHONE..........................330 863-1121
Fax: 330 863-2043
Charles Lebeau III, *President*
Jerry W Morris II, *Vice Pres*
Pam Stich, *Accountant*
EMP: 7
SQ FT: 2,400
SALES (est): 1.9MM Privately Held
WEB: www.cambridgemillproducts.com
SIC: 2992 Oils & greases, blending & com-
pounding; re-refining lubricating oils &
greases

G E O G R A P H I C

(G-12540)
CEDAR OUTDOOR FURNITURE INC
8229 Old Canal Ln Nw (44644-9706)
PHONE..................................330 863-2580
Gary Pearce, *President*
Elizabeth Pearce, *Admin Sec*
EMP: 5
SQ FT: 9,400
SALES: 250K **Privately Held**
WEB: www.cedaroutdoor.com
SIC: 2511 Wood lawn & garden furniture; porch furniture & swings: wood

(G-12541)
COLFOR MANUFACTURING INC (DH)
3255 Alliance Rd Nw (44644-9756)
PHONE..................................330 863-0404
David C Dauch, *Chairman*
Thomas J Szymanski, *COO*
Richard F Dauch, *Exec VP*
Michael K Simonte, *Exec VP*
Alberto Satine, *Senior VP*
▲ EMP: 363
SALES (est): 135MM
SALES (corp-wide): 3.9B **Publicly Held**
SIC: 3462 3599 3463 Iron & steel forgings; machine shop, jobbing & repair; nonferrous forgings
HQ: American Axle & Manufacturing, Inc.
1 Dauch Dr
Detroit MI 48211
313 758-3600

(G-12542)
DUNN S TANK SERVICE INC
6036 Alliance Rd Nw (44644-9445)
PHONE..................................330 863-2200
EMP: 3 EST: 2012
SALES (est): 130K **Privately Held**
SIC: 1382 Oil/Gas Exploration Services

(G-12543)
ELASTON COMPANY
448 E Mohawk Dr (44644-9510)
PHONE..................................330 863-2865
Fax: 330 863-2867
Theodore J Dettling, *President*
Ted Dettling Jr, *Vice Pres*
Marlyn Dettling, *Treasurer*
EMP: 10
SALES: 850K **Privately Held**
SIC: 2891 Adhesives & sealants; adhesives

(G-12544)
FOR CALL INC
3255 Alliance Rd Nw (44644-9756)
PHONE..................................330 863-0404
Inacio Moriguchi, *President*
Michael Kisher, *Finance*
Bob Nappi, *Persnl Mgr*
Susan Chiuco, *Manager*
Kelli Betar, *Executive Asst*
EMP: 500 EST: 1967
SALES (est): 32.8MM **Privately Held**
SIC: 3462 Iron & steel forgings

(G-12545)
GBS CORP
Also Called: GBS Filing Solutions
224 Morges Rd (44644-9736)
P.O. Box 308 (44644-0308)
PHONE..................................330 863-1828
Patrick Lieser, *Vice Pres*
Tom Pignotti, *Vice Pres*
Debbie Bugh, *Human Res Dir*
Michele Benson, *Branch Mgr*
Ryan Hamsher, *CTO*
EMP: 116
SALES (corp-wide): 171.7MM **Privately Held**
SIC: 2675 2752 2672 2761 Folders, filing, die-cut: made from purchased materials; business forms, lithographed; adhesive papers, labels or tapes: from purchased material; manifold business forms
PA: Gbs Corp.
7233 Freedom Ave Nw
North Canton OH 44720
330 494-5330

(G-12546)
GORDONS GRAPHICS INC
123 S Reed Ave (44644-9496)
P.O. Box 586 (44644-0586)
PHONE..................................330 863-2322
Brad Lewis, *President*
Jerry Hinton, *Corp Secy*
EMP: 7
SQ FT: 1,500
SALES (est): 325K **Privately Held**
SIC: 2752 2759 5734 5943 Commercial printing, offset; engraving; computer & software stores; office forms & supplies

(G-12547)
MECHANICAL ELASTOMERICS INC
Also Called: MEI
3266 Coral Rd Nw (44644-9467)
P.O. Box 588 (44644-0588)
PHONE..................................330 863-1014
Jonathan Walters, *President*
Dale Olbon, *General Mgr*
Rex Kempton, *QC Dir*
Meg Walters, *Treasurer*
EMP: 5
SQ FT: 1,932
SALES (est): 649.8K **Privately Held**
SIC: 3052 Rubber & plastics hose & beltings

(G-12548)
PERFECT PRODUCTS COMPANY
Also Called: Aurora Balloon Company
265 Morges Rd (44644-9753)
PHONE..................................330 863-1466
Fax: 330 863-2988
William D Allen, *Ch of Bd*
Douglas Kerr Sr, *President*
Angel Leary, *Sales Staff*
Tammy Pole, *Manager*
EMP: 25
SQ FT: 36,000
SALES (est): 3.7MM **Privately Held**
SIC: 3069 Balloons, advertising & toy: rubber

Manchester
Adams County

(G-12549)
HEADWATERS INCORPORATED
745 Us Route 52 (45144-8450)
PHONE..................................989 671-1500
Sam Jackson, *Manager*
EMP: 18
SALES (corp-wide): 974.8MM **Publicly Held**
SIC: 3272 Siding, precast stone
PA: Headwaters Incorporated
10701 S River Front Pkwy # 300
South Jordan UT 84095
801 984-9400

(G-12550)
MOYER VINEYARDS INC
Also Called: Moyer Winery & Restaurant
3859 Us Highway 52 (45144-8338)
P.O. Box 235 (45144-0235)
PHONE..................................937 549-2957
Fax: 937 549-2957
Carol White, *President*
EMP: 22
SQ FT: 5,000
SALES (est): 2.9MM **Privately Held**
SIC: 2084 5812 Wines, brandy & brandy spirits; restaurant, family: independent

(G-12551)
PETERSON RADIO INC
9711 Us Highway 52 (45144-9577)
PHONE..................................937 549-3731
Neil Peterson, *President*
EMP: 3
SQ FT: 8,000
SALES (est): 703.3K **Privately Held**
SIC: 5064 7622 3663 Radios; radio repair & installation; radio broadcasting & communications equipment

(G-12552)
VANCES DEPARTMENT STORE (PA)
Also Called: Vance's Wonder Store
37 E 2nd St (45144-1301)
P.O. Box 326 (45144-0326)
PHONE..................................937 549-2188
David A Scott, *Owner*
EMP: 6
SQ FT: 5,000
SALES (est): 1.6MM **Privately Held**
SIC: 5651 5661 5211 2541 Family clothing stores; shoe stores; lumber & other building materials; cabinets, except refrigerated: show, display, etc.: wood

(G-12553)
VANCES DEPARTMENT STORE
Also Called: Adams County Lumber
600 Washington St (45144-1362)
PHONE..................................937 549-3033
Fax: 937 549-3248
Gregory B Scott, *Principal*
EMP: 11
SALES (corp-wide): 1.6MM **Privately Held**
SIC: 5651 5661 5211 2541 Family clothing stores; shoe stores; lumber & other building materials; cabinets, except refrigerated: show, display, etc.: wood
PA: Vance's Department Store
37 E 2nd St
Manchester OH 45144
937 549-2188

Mansfield
Richland County

(G-12554)
A L CALLAHAN DOOR SALES
35 Industrial Dr (44904-1372)
PHONE..................................419 884-3667
Fax: 419 884-0899
Don Callahan, *Owner*
EMP: 7
SQ FT: 3,000
SALES (est): 1.1MM **Privately Held**
SIC: 5211 7699 3699 Door & window products; garage door repair; door opening & closing devices, electrical

(G-12555)
AARONYX PUBLISHING
Also Called: Aaronyx Design
1924 Springmill Rd (44903-8908)
PHONE..................................419 747-2400
Michael Holloway, *Owner*
EMP: 4
SALES: 90K **Privately Held**
WEB: www.aaronyx.com
SIC: 2741 Miscellaneous publishing

(G-12556)
AK MANSFIELD
913 Bowman St (44903-4109)
PHONE..................................419 755-3011
Randy Hartman, *Principal*
Steven Sorvold, *Vice Pres*
Mark Black, *Engineer*
Barbara Eckhardt, *Engineer*
Kevin Sainiak, *Electrical Engi*
EMP: 350
SALES (est): 9.3MM **Privately Held**
SIC: 3999 Bleaching & dyeing of sponges

(G-12557)
AK STEEL CORPORATION
Also Called: Mansfield Operations
913 Bowman St (44903-4109)
P.O. Box 247 (44901-0247)
PHONE..................................419 755-3011
Larry Turowski, *QC Dir*
John Smith, *Chief Engr*
Bradley Tilton, *Engineer*
Ben L Bishop, *VP Sales*
Robert J Pasquarelli, *Branch Mgr*
EMP: 500
SALES (corp-wide): 5.8B **Publicly Held**
WEB: www.ketnar.org
SIC: 3312 Blast furnaces & steel mills

HQ: Ak Steel Corporation
9227 Centre Pointe Dr
West Chester OH 45069
513 425-4200

(G-12558)
AMAROQ INC
Also Called: Guetle Die & Stamping
648 N Trimble Rd (44906-2002)
PHONE..................................419 747-2110
Fax: 419 747-6300
Rt Mong, *President*
Jerry Bartman, *Manager*
EMP: 7
SQ FT: 8,000
SALES (est): 1MM **Privately Held**
SIC: 3469 3544 Metal stampings; special dies, tools, jigs & fixtures

(G-12559)
AMERASCREW INC
653 Lida St (44903-1242)
P.O. Box 1407 (44901-1407)
PHONE..................................419 522-2232
John R Keith, *President*
EMP: 21
SQ FT: 37,000
SALES (est): 4.5MM **Privately Held**
WEB: www.amerascrew.com
SIC: 3451 Screw machine products

(G-12560)
AMERICAN BOTTLING COMPANY
1115 National Pkwy (44906-1910)
PHONE..................................419 529-6773
Ralph Haller, *Manager*
Tony Gurges, *Manager*
EMP: 20
SALES (corp-wide): 6.4B **Publicly Held**
WEB: www.cs-americas.com
SIC: 2086 Soft drinks: packaged in cans, bottles, etc.
HQ: The American Bottling Company
5301 Legacy Dr
Plano TX 75024

(G-12561)
AMERICAN TOOL & MFG CO
Also Called: American Tool & Manufacturing
211 Newman St (44902-1461)
P.O. Box 1242 (44901-1242)
PHONE..................................419 522-2452
Fax: 419 522-5744
Myron Brenner, *President*
EMP: 14
SQ FT: 40,000
SALES (est): 1.2MM **Privately Held**
WEB: www.americantoolmfg.com
SIC: 3469 Metal stampings

(G-12562)
AMERICAS BEST SIDING CO
1395 W Longview Ave (44906-1802)
PHONE..................................419 589-5900
Darlow C Bartram, *Owner*
Beth Horfey, *Manager*
EMP: 5
SQ FT: 5,000
SALES (est): 610.5K **Privately Held**
SIC: 3444 Metal flooring & siding

(G-12563)
AS AMERICA INC
Also Called: American Standard Brands
41 Cairns Rd (44903-8992)
PHONE..................................615 873-2410
Sheryl Myers, *Branch Mgr*
EMP: 3
SALES (corp-wide): 16.1B **Privately Held**
SIC: 3261 3432 Vitreous plumbing fixtures; plumbing fixture fittings & trim
HQ: As America, Inc.
1 Centennial Ave Ste 101
Piscataway NJ 08854
732 980-3000

(G-12564)
AUTOMATIC PARTS
433 Springmill St (44903-7008)
P.O. Box 1505 (44901-1505)
PHONE..................................419 524-5841
Fax: 419 526-2727
Robert H Wittmer, *President*
David A Wittmer, *Vice Pres*
John Call, *Engineer*

Justin Constable, *Manager*
EMP: 20
SQ FT: 17,000
SALES (est): 3.2MM **Privately Held**
WEB: www.automaticparts.com
SIC: 3541 Machine tool replacement & repair parts, metal cutting types

(G-12565)
BAY WORLD INTERNATIONAL INC
395 Reed St (44903-1084)
PHONE................................419 525-2222
Fax: 419 522-8768
Jon P Ralph, *CEO*
Jay Ralph, *Vice Pres*
EMP: 40
SQ FT: 30,000
SALES (est): 6.1MM **Privately Held**
WEB: www.bayworldmfg.com
SIC: 2431 Window frames, wood

(G-12566)
BEER COMMUNICATIONS INC
1717 Mccarrick Pkwy (44903-6533)
PHONE................................419 756-6882
Fax: 419 756-7512
Edward L Beer, *President*
EMP: 7
SALES (est): 561.7K **Privately Held**
SIC: 7311 2791 Advertising agencies; typesetting

(G-12567)
BLEVINS METAL FABRICATION INC
Also Called: Blevins Fabrication
288 Illinois Ave S (44905-2827)
PHONE................................419 522-6082
Fax: 419 522-6092
Lloyd T Blevins, *President*
Jeff Schad, *CFO*
Karen Smith, *Manager*
EMP: 25 EST: 1997
SQ FT: 13,000
SALES (est): 4.7MM **Privately Held**
SIC: 7692 3446 3444 3443 Welding repair; architectural metalwork; sheet metalwork; fabricated plate work (boiler shop); fabricated structural metal

(G-12568)
BRANDTS CUSTOM MACHINING LLC
1183 Stewart Rd N (44905-1551)
PHONE................................419 566-3192
Benjamin Brandt, *Principal*
EMP: 7
SALES (est): 540.4K **Privately Held**
SIC: 3599 Custom machinery

(G-12569)
BREITINGER COMPANY
595 Oakenwaldt St (44905-1900)
PHONE................................419 526-4255
Fax: 419 526-1398
Milo Breitinger, *President*
Richard Bayer, *QC Mgr*
Breitinger Kim, *CFO*
Kim Breitinger, *Manager*
Nikki Williams, *Admin Asst*
EMP: 120
SQ FT: 106,000
SALES (est): 33.5MM **Privately Held**
WEB: www.breitingercompany.com
SIC: 3441 3469 7692 3444 Fabricated structural metal; metal stampings; welding repair; sheet metalwork; fabricated plate work (boiler shop)

(G-12570)
BROST FOUNDRY COMPANY
198 Wayne St (44902-1433)
PHONE................................419 522-1133
Fax: 419 522-6030
Malcolm Flinn, *Vice Pres*
Chuck Horvath, *Manager*
EMP: 15
SALES (corp-wide): 5.3MM **Privately Held**
WEB: www.brostfoundry.com
SIC: 3366 Copper foundries; brass foundry

PA: Brost Foundry Company (Inc)
2934 E 55th St
Cleveland OH 44127
216 641-1131

(G-12571)
BUCKEYE VAULT SERVICE INC
Also Called: Buckeye Delivery
2253 Stiving Rd (44903-8900)
P.O. Box 1261 (44901-1261)
PHONE................................419 747-1976
Fax: 419 747-6141
Don Neighbors, *President*
Jill Neighbors, *Corp Secy*
Douglas Neighbors, *Vice Pres*
EMP: 7
SALES (est): 1.2MM **Privately Held**
SIC: 3272 Burial vaults, concrete or precast terrazzo

(G-12572)
BUNTING BEARINGS LLC
153 E 5th St (44902-1407)
P.O. Box 1053 (44901-1053)
PHONE................................419 522-3323
Fax: 419 522-6011
Michael Lee, *QC Dir*
Denise Cole, *Sales Staff*
Kim J Keogh, *Branch Mgr*
EMP: 47
SQ FT: 68,000
SALES (corp-wide): 60.4MM **Privately Held**
SIC: 3366 3568 3369 3356 Bushings & bearings, bronze (nonmachined); power transmission equipment; nonferrous foundries; nonferrous rolling & drawing
PA: Bunting Bearings, Llc
1001 Holland Park Blvd
Holland OH 43528
419 866-7000

(G-12573)
C & G ASSOCIATES INC
3130 Hastings Newville Rd (44903-7740)
P.O. Box 3954 (44907-3954)
PHONE................................419 756-6583
Paul M Cocanour, *President*
EMP: 4
SQ FT: 3,200
SALES (est): 300K **Privately Held**
WEB: www.cg-associates.org
SIC: 2381 Fabric dress & work gloves

(G-12574)
CAPITAL PROSTHETIC &
271 Cline Ave Ste 3 (44907-1042)
PHONE................................567 560-2051
Fax: 740 397-8145
Lisa Crawford, *Branch Mgr*
EMP: 3
SALES (corp-wide): 2.9MM **Privately Held**
SIC: 3842 Limbs, artificial; braces, orthopedic
PA: Capital Prosthetic And Orthotic Center, Inc.
4678 Larwell Dr
Columbus OH 43220
614 451-0446

(G-12575)
CAROUSEL MAGIC LLC
44 W 4th St (44902-1206)
PHONE................................419 522-6456
Fax: 419 526-4561
Sherrell Anderson, *Human Res Dir*
Sherell Anderson,
Pauline Anderson,
Andrea Clark,
Ross Clark,
EMP: 4
SQ FT: 16,000
SALES: 300K **Privately Held**
WEB: www.carouselmagic.com
SIC: 3599 7699 Carousels (merry-go-rounds); antique repair & restoration, except furniture, automobiles

(G-12576)
CAROUSEL WORKS INC
1285 Pollock Pkwy (44905-1374)
PHONE................................419 522-7558
Fax: 419 524-9603
Art Ritchie, *President*
Daniel Jones, *Vice Pres*

Kate Blakely, *Treasurer*
Marilyn Ritchie, *Treasurer*
Ryan D Jones, *Admin Sec*
EMP: 23
SQ FT: 25,000
SALES: 2.1MM **Privately Held**
WEB: www.carouselworks.com
SIC: 3599 Carousels (merry-go-rounds)

(G-12577)
CASE-MAUL MANUFACTURING CO
30 Harker St (44903-1395)
PHONE................................419 524-1061
Fax: 419 524-1547
Craig Case, *President*
Sandra Collins, *Corp Secy*
Sandra Long, *Treasurer*
Helen Witschi, *Office Mgr*
Debbie Johnson, *Manager*
▲ **EMP:** 10 EST: 1953
SQ FT: 18,000
SALES (est): 1.6MM **Privately Held**
WEB: www.case-maulmfg.com
SIC: 3599 7692 Machine shop, jobbing & repair; welding repair

(G-12578)
CEMENT PRODUCTS INC
389 Park Ave E (44905-2896)
PHONE................................419 524-4342
Toll Free:........................877 -
Fax: 419 522-2069
David Schmitz, *President*
Brock Kisor, *General Mgr*
Douglas Schmitz, *Vice Pres*
Daniel Schmitz, *Treasurer*
Dwight Schmitz, *Admin Sec*
EMP: 26 EST: 1916
SQ FT: 82,778
SALES (est): 4.2MM **Privately Held**
WEB: www.cementproducts.com
SIC: 3271 3273 3272 Blocks, concrete or cinder: standard; ready-mixed concrete; concrete products

(G-12579)
CHILD EVNGELISM FELLOWSHIP INC
Also Called: Ashland R Crawford Knox
827 Lexington Ave (44907-1920)
P.O. Box 67 (44901-0067)
PHONE................................419 756-7799
Dale Baer, *Manager*
EMP: 41
SALES (corp-wide): 28.6MM **Privately Held**
SIC: 2752 Commercial printing, lithographic
PA: Child Evangelism Fellowship Incorporated
17482 Highway M
Warrenton MO 63383
636 456-4321

(G-12580)
CITY OF MANSFIELD
2010 S Lexngtn Sprngml Rd (44904)
PHONE................................419 884-3310
Llydia Ride, *Branch Mgr*
EMP: 12 **Privately Held**
WEB: www.metrich.com
SIC: 3569 Filters & strainers, pipeline
PA: City Of Mansfield
30 N Diamond St
Mansfield OH 44902
419 755-9626

(G-12581)
CLEANING LADY INC
190 Stewart Rd N (44905-2639)
PHONE................................419 589-5566
Fax: 419 589-5572
Suzanne Stewart, *Principal*
John Stewart, *Vice Pres*
EMP: 15
SQ FT: 7,360
SALES (est): 473.9K **Privately Held**
SIC: 7349 5169 2841 Janitorial service, contract basis; detergents; detergents, synthetic organic or inorganic alkaline

(G-12582)
COCA-COLA COMPANY
100 Industrial Pkwy (44903-8999)
PHONE................................419 522-2653

Fax: 419 522-2090
Mike Dewalt, *Manager*
EMP: 45
SALES (corp-wide): 41.8B **Publicly Held**
WEB: www.colasic.net
SIC: 2086 Bottled & canned soft drinks
PA: The Coca-Cola Company
1 Coca Cola Plz Nw
Atlanta GA 30313
404 676-2121

(G-12583)
COMMERCIAL CUTNG GRAPHICS LLC
208 Central Ave (44905-2410)
PHONE................................419 526-4800
Fax: 419 526-5328
Barbara Lindsay, *President*
Chuck Johnson, *Design Engr*
Matt Patrick, *Manager*
Matt Seifert, *Manager*
Jeffrey A Burkhart,
EMP: 62
SQ FT: 45,000
SALES (est): 15.2MM **Privately Held**
WEB: www.commercialcutting.com
SIC: 2675 Die-cut paper & board

(G-12584)
CONTAINERCRAFT INC
144 Plymouth St (44904-1124)
PHONE................................419 884-2414
Fax: 419 884-3486
Charles Marcum, *President*
Jay Brokaw, *Plant Mgr*
Darrell Baker, *Sales Staff*
EMP: 10 EST: 1976
SQ FT: 27,000
SALES (est): 5MM **Privately Held**
SIC: 2653 Corrugated & solid fiber boxes

(G-12585)
CORNS QUALITY WOODWORKING LLC
1525 Chew Rd (44903-9231)
PHONE................................419 589-4899
Jeff Corns, *Principal*
EMP: 4
SALES (est): 240K **Privately Held**
SIC: 2431 Millwork

(G-12586)
CORPAD COMPANY INC
555 Park Ave E (44905-2871)
P.O. Box 1492 (44901-1492)
PHONE................................419 522-7818
Fax: 419 522-1703
Larry Fulmer, *General Mgr*
Dane Arlen Bonecutter, *Principal*
Jacob Beard, *Sales Mgr*
EMP: 55
SQ FT: 97,500
SALES (est): 16.4MM **Privately Held**
SIC: 2631 Paperboard mills

(G-12587)
CRANE PLUMBING LLC
Also Called: Crane Plumbing Products
41 Cairns Rd (44903-8992)
PHONE................................419 522-4211
Dick Matthes, *Engineer*
Jim Japczyk, *CFO*
Kevin Oak, *Mng Member*
EMP: 20
SALES (corp-wide): 136.8MM **Privately Held**
WEB: www.sanymetal.com
SIC: 3261 3431 3281 2541 Plumbing fixtures, vitreous china; metal sanitary ware; cut stone & stone products; wood partitions & fixtures; wood kitchen cabinets
PA: Crane Plumbing Llc
41 Cairns Rd
Mansfield OH 44903
419 522-4211

(G-12588)
CRANE PLUMBING LLC (PA)
41 Cairns Rd (44903-8992)
PHONE................................419 522-4211
Kevin Oak, *CEO*
Ken Sapp, *Sales Mgr*
Reed Beither, *Manager*
Tracy Dawes, *Administration*
Jim Japczyk,
◆ **EMP:** 15,

SQ FT: 6,000
SALES (est): 136.8MM **Privately Held**
WEB: www.sanymetal.com
SIC: 3261 3431 3088 Bathroom accessories/fittings, vitreous china or earthenware; metal sanitary ware; bathtubs: enameled iron, cast iron or pressed metal; shower stalls, metal; sinks: enameled iron, cast iron or pressed metal; shower stalls, fiberglass & plastic

(G-12589)
CRANE PLUMBING LLC
41 Cairns Rd (44903-8992)
PHONE.................................419 522-0321
Reed Beidler, *Owner*
Marc Nagley, *Manager*
EMP: 200
SALES (corp-wide): 136.8MM **Privately Held**
WEB: www.sanymetal.com
SIC: 3261 3264 Bathroom accessories/fittings, vitreous china or earthenware; porcelain electrical supplies
PA: Crane Plumbing Llc
    41 Cairns Rd
    Mansfield OH 44903
    419 522-4211

(G-12590)
CSM HORVATH LEDGEBROOK
Also Called: Rost Boundry
198 Wayne St (44902-1433)
PHONE.................................419 522-1133
Chuck Horvath, *President*
EMP: 4
SALES (est): 404.3K **Privately Held**
SIC: 3363 Aluminum die-castings

(G-12591)
D & S CRTIVE CMMUNICATIONS INC (PA)
Also Called: Black River Display Group
140 Park Ave E (44902-1830)
P.O. Box 876 (44901-0876)
PHONE.................................419 524-6699
Terry Neff, *President*
Julie Campbell, *Editor*
Rick Schroeder, *Project Mgr*
David Whitaker, *Project Mgr*
Steve Winters, *Safety Mgr*
EMP: 65
SQ FT: 74,000
SALES: 120MM **Privately Held**
WEB: www.ds-creative.com
SIC: 7311 2752 2791 2789 Advertising agencies; commercial printing, lithographic; typesetting; bookbinding & related work

(G-12592)
DALLAS DESIGN & TECHNOLOGY INC
184 Industrial Dr (44904-1339)
P.O. Box 3043 (44904-0043)
PHONE.................................419 884-9750
Fax: 419 884-9755
Mark Stevens, *President*
Eric Fadale, *Manager*
EMP: 9
SQ FT: 8,500
SALES: 2MM **Privately Held**
WEB: www.dallasdesigntech.com
SIC: 3549 Assembly machines, including robotic

(G-12593)
DAVIES SINCE 1900
Also Called: Davies Interiors
913 S Main St (44907-2037)
PHONE.................................419 756-4212
Fax: 419 756-4212
David J Davies, *Owner*
EMP: 3
SQ FT: 8,000
SALES: 500K **Privately Held**
SIC: 5713 1721 2273 1743 Floor covering stores; interior commercial painting contractor; carpets & rugs; marble installation, interior

(G-12594)
DECA MANUFACTURING CO INC
300 S Mill St (44904-8519)
P.O. Box 3269 (44904-0269)
PHONE.................................419 884-0071
Fax: 419 884-3887
Hansford R Williams, *President*
Carolyn Williams, *Corp Secy*
Karen M Cashell, *Vice Pres*
EMP: 100
SQ FT: 33,000
SALES (est): 17.3MM **Privately Held**
WEB: www.decamfgcables.com
SIC: 3679 3544 3672 Harness assemblies for electronic use: wire or cable; industrial molds; printed circuit boards

(G-12595)
DND EMULSIONS INC
270 Park Ave E (44902-1849)
PHONE.................................419 525-4988
Delbert Dawson, *President*
Dave Scott, *Marketing Mgr*
EMP: 5
SQ FT: 2,940
SALES (est): 497.1K **Privately Held**
SIC: 2869 2952 2992 Industrial organic chemicals; coating compounds, tar; cutting oils, blending: made from purchased materials

(G-12596)
DR PEPPER SNAPPLE GROUP
1115 National Pkwy (44906-1910)
PHONE.................................419 529-6773
Fax: 419 529-8931
Ralph Haller, *Manager*
EMP: 7
SALES (est): 284K **Privately Held**
SIC: 2086 Soft drinks: packaged in cans, bottles, etc.

(G-12597)
DTE INC
110 Baird Pkwy (44903-7909)
PHONE.................................419 522-3428
Fax: 419 522-3568
Rob Nelson, *CEO*
Dean Russell, *President*
Roger Nelson, *General Mgr*
Burke Melching, *Vice Pres*
EMP: 30
SQ FT: 45,000
SALES (est): 3.8MM **Privately Held**
WEB: www.dteinc.com
SIC: 7629 3661 Telephone set repair; telephone & telegraph apparatus

(G-12598)
EDGE PLASTICS INC (PA)
449 Newman St (44902-1123)
PHONE.................................419 522-6696
Fax: 419 522-2596
Shelley Fisher, *President*
Jim Gondek, *Managing Dir*
Jody Bozeman, *Purchasing*
Ron Pore, *Manager*
Julie Vogt, *Manager*
▲ EMP: 150
SQ FT: 146,000
SALES (est): 58.7MM **Privately Held**
SIC: 3089 Injection molded finished plastic products

(G-12599)
ELTOOL CORPORATION
1400 Park Ave E (44905-2989)
PHONE.................................513 723-1772
Edward Crotty, *President*
Vicky Young, *Office Mgr*
EMP: 7
SALES (est): 551.5K **Privately Held**
WEB: www.eltool.com
SIC: 8742 3599 5084 Marketing consulting services; machine shop, jobbing & repair; industrial machinery & equipment

(G-12600)
ENERGY TECHNOLOGIES INC
Also Called: E T I
219 Park Ave E (44902-1845)
PHONE.................................419 522-4444
Paul C Madden, *President*
P D Madden, *General Mgr*
Travis Browning, *Engineer*

Lou Grazaini, *Design Engr*
Neil Yoder, *Design Engr*
EMP: 80
SQ FT: 30,000
SALES (est): 16.8MM **Privately Held**
WEB: www.ruggedsystems.com
SIC: 3629 3625 3621 Electronic generation equipment; relays & industrial controls; motors & generators

(G-12601)
ENGINEERED FILMS DIVISION
Also Called: Next Generation Films
215 Industrial Dr (44904-1347)
PHONE.................................419 884-8150
Sherry Barlar, *General Mgr*
David J Rehfeldt, *CFO*
Neil Winslow, *VP Human Res*
David Frecka, *Manager*
Jason Poth, *Info Tech Mgr*
EMP: 15 **Privately Held**
WEB: www.nextgenfilms.com
SIC: 2671 Packaging paper & plastics film, coated & laminated
HQ: Engineered Films Division, Inc
    230 Industrial Dr
    Lexington OH 44904
    419 884-8150

(G-12602)
FAMILY VALUES MAGAZINE
3027 Fox Rd (44904-9707)
P.O. Box 9012 (44904-9012)
PHONE.................................419 566-1102
Shane Hostetler, *Principal*
EMP: 5
SALES (est): 292.1K **Privately Held**
SIC: 2721 Periodicals

(G-12603)
FIVE HANDICAP INC (PA)
Also Called: Mansfield Graphics
127 N Walnut St (44902-1221)
P.O. Box 7 (44901-0007)
PHONE.................................419 525-2511
Fax: 419 525-2941
Chuck B McCartney, *President*
EMP: 15 EST: 1929
SQ FT: 20,000
SALES (est): 2.2MM **Privately Held**
WEB: www.mansfieldgraphics.com
SIC: 3479 Etching on metals

(G-12604)
FIVES ST CORP
1485 Lexington Ave (44907-2629)
PHONE.................................419 522-1080
Daniel Balcer, *President*
EMP: 10
SALES (corp-wide): 5.8MM **Privately Held**
SIC: 3537 Skids, metal
HQ: Fives St. Corp.
    1485 Lexington Ave
    Mansfield OH 44907
    419 522-1080

(G-12605)
FIVES ST CORP (DH)
1485 Lexington Ave (44907-2629)
PHONE.................................419 522-1080
Daniel Balcer, *President*
Etienne Debettignies, *CFO*
Bernadette Fincke, *Manager*
▲ EMP: 14
SALES (est): 3.3MM
SALES (corp-wide): 5.8MM **Privately Held**
SIC: 3537 Skids, metal
HQ: Fives Stein
    A 108 112
    Maisons Alfort 94700
    145 186-500

(G-12606)
FORBES REHAB SERVICES INC (PA)
49 Illinois Ave S (44905-2824)
PHONE.................................419 589-7688
Paul Forbes, *President*
EMP: 5
SQ FT: 2,400
SALES (est): 902.3K **Privately Held**
WEB: www.frs-solutions.com
SIC: 3842 Technical aids for the handicapped

(G-12607)
FORREST MACHINE PDTS CO LTD
Also Called: Forrest Scrw Machine
139 Illinois Ave S (44905-2825)
P.O. Box 3648 (44907-0648)
PHONE.................................419 589-3774
Cyd McCready, *Principal*
Steven Coffey, *Mfg Mgr*
Joseph Scali, *Manager*
Mark Whitaker, *Manager*
Brett Dewees,
EMP: 22
SALES: 950K **Privately Held**
SIC: 3549 3451 Metalworking machinery; screw machine products

(G-12608)
FRIEND ENGRG & MCH CO INC
67 Illinois Ave S (44905-2824)
PHONE.................................419 589-5066
Fax: 419 589-6917
David Friend, *President*
Beth Friend, *Corp Secy*
EMP: 3
SQ FT: 10,000
SALES (est): 450K **Privately Held**
SIC: 3599 Custom machinery

(G-12609)
GANNETT CO INC
News Journal
70 W 4th St (44903-1676)
P.O. Box 25 (44901-0025)
PHONE.................................419 522-3311
Fax: 419 522-2672
Tom Brennen, *Principal*
Jim Bottorff, *Mfg Staff*
Jay Hollon, *Controller*
Nickolas Monico, *Loan Officer*
EMP: 165
SALES (corp-wide): 3B **Publicly Held**
WEB: www.gannett.com
SIC: 2711 Newspapers
PA: Gannett Co., Inc.
    7950 Jones Branch Dr
    Mc Lean VA 22102
    703 854-6000

(G-12610)
GANNETT CO INC
Also Called: Bucyrus Telegraph-Forum
70 W 4th St (44903-1676)
PHONE.................................419 562-3333
Tom Brennan, *Manager*
Anthony Concheo, *Manager*
EMP: 6
SALES (corp-wide): 3B **Publicly Held**
WEB: www.gannett.com
SIC: 2711 Newspapers, publishing & printing
PA: Gannett Co., Inc.
    7950 Jones Branch Dr
    Mc Lean VA 22102
    703 854-6000

(G-12611)
GANNETT PUBLISHING SVCS LLC
70 W 4th St (44903-1676)
PHONE.................................419 522-3311
Fax: 419 522-6177
EMP: 74
SALES (corp-wide): 10.4MM **Privately Held**
SIC: 2711 Commercial printing & newspaper publishing combined
PA: Gannett Publishing Services, Llc
    7950 Jones Branch Dr
    Mc Lean VA 22107
    703 854-6000

(G-12612)
GENERAL TECHNOLOGIES INC
855 W Longview Ave (44906-2131)
P.O. Box 1726 (44901-1726)
PHONE.................................419 747-1800
Susan L Moran, *Principal*
Margaret Marlow, *Vice Pres*
Dave Marlow, *VP Mfg*
Stanley Marlow, *Manager*
▲ EMP: 20 EST: 1957
SQ FT: 40,000

SALES: 5MM Privately Held
WEB: www.general-technologies.com
SIC: 3469 7692 3444 3443 Metal stampings; welding repair; sheet metalwork; fabricated plate work (boiler shop)

(G-12613)
GLOBAL OILFIELD SERVICES LLC
Also Called: Gofs
3401 State Route 13 (44904-9394)
PHONE................................419 756-8027
Jim Jackson, *President*
Annette Jones, *Admin Sec*
EMP: 3
SALES (est): 288K Privately Held
SIC: 1389 5082 1623 Oil field services; oil field equipment; oil & gas line & compressor station construction

(G-12614)
GORMAN-RUPP COMPANY (PA)
600 S Airport Rd (44903-7831)
P.O. Box 1217 (44901-1217)
PHONE................................419 755-1011
Fax: 419 755-1251
James C Gorman, *Ch of Bd*
Jeffrey S Gorman, *President*
Doug Renner, *General Mgr*
John Amundsen, *District Mgr*
Mike Retter, *District Mgr*
EMP: 277 EST: 1933
SALES: 382MM Publicly Held
WEB: www.gormanrupp.com
SIC: 3561 3594 Pumps & pumping equipment; industrial pumps & parts; pumps, oil well & field; pumps, domestic: water or sump; fluid power pumps & motors

(G-12615)
GORMAN-RUPP COMPANY
Ipt Pumps Division
305 Bowman St (44903-1689)
P.O. Box 1217 (44901-1217)
PHONE................................419 755-1011
Fax: 419 755-1287
Scott King, *Mfg Dir*
James Robinette, *Engineer*
Wayne Knabel, *CFO*
Wayne L Knabe, *Treasurer*
Angie Morehead, *Controller*
EMP: 500
SALES (corp-wide): 382MM Publicly Held
WEB: www.gormanrupp.com
SIC: 3561 Pumps & pumping equipment
PA: Gorman-Rupp Company
    600 S Airport Rd
    Mansfield OH 44903
    419 755-1011

(G-12616)
GORMAN-RUPP COMPANY
Also Called: Warehouse
100 Rump Rd (44903)
P.O. Box 1217 (44901-1217)
PHONE................................419 755-1245
Fax: 419 755-1525
Jeffrey Gorman, *President*
Jake Jakubick, *Marketing Staff*
EMP: 8
SALES (corp-wide): 382MM Publicly Held
WEB: www.gormanrupp.com
SIC: 5084 3561 Pumps & pumping equipment; pumps & pumping equipment
PA: Gorman-Rupp Company
    600 S Airport Rd
    Mansfield OH 44903
    419 755-1011

(G-12617)
GORMAN-RUPP COMPANY
100 Rupp Rd (44903-6512)
PHONE................................419 755-1011
Judith Sorine, *Principal*
EMP: 3
SALES (corp-wide): 382MM Publicly Held
SIC: 3594 Fluid power pumps & motors
PA: Gorman-Rupp Company
    600 S Airport Rd
    Mansfield OH 44903
    419 755-1011

(G-12618)
GOYAL INDUSTRIES INC
382 Park Ave E (44905-2843)
PHONE................................419 522-7099
Fax: 419 522-7111
Prakash R Goyal, *President*
▲ EMP: 21
SQ FT: 18,000
SALES (est): 3.3MM Privately Held
SIC: 3599 3441 Machine shop, jobbing & repair; fabricated structural metal

(G-12619)
GRAPHIC PAPER
Also Called: Warehousingconverting
1111 N Main St (44903-9718)
PHONE................................419 526-4123
Wayne Penrod, *Owner*
EMP: 50
SALES (est): 4.6MM Privately Held
SIC: 2679 Paper products, converted

(G-12620)
GRASAN EQUIPMENT COMPANY INC
440 S Illinois Ave (44907-1809)
PHONE................................419 526-4440
Fax: 419 524-2176
Marian L Eilenfeld, *President*
Edward Eilenfeld Jr, *Vice Pres*
Chuck Ferguson, *Engineer*
Aaron Niswander, *Engineer*
Rod Scheidler, *Design Engr*
▼ EMP: 65 EST: 1970
SQ FT: 62,000
SALES (est): 20.2MM Privately Held
WEB: www.grasan.com
SIC: 4953 3532 3559 3535 Recycling, waste materials; crushers, stationary; rock crushing machinery, stationary; screeners, stationary; recycling machinery; conveyors & conveying equipment; construction machinery

(G-12621)
GRAYWACKE ENGINEERING INC
300 S Mill St (44904-8519)
PHONE................................419 884-7014
Scott Huffman, *President*
Mark Huffman, *Vice Pres*
EMP: 15
SQ FT: 14,000
SALES (est): 3.2MM Privately Held
WEB: www.graywacke.net
SIC: 3691 Batteries, rechargeable

(G-12622)
HAYFORD TECHNOLOGIES
Also Called: Milark Industries
500 S Airport Rd (44903)
PHONE................................419 524-7627
Matt Breitinger, *President*
Brooke Breitinger,
Mary Breitinger,
Trisha Breitinger,
EMP: 99
SALES (est): 2.8MM Privately Held
SIC: 3465 3469 Automotive stampings; metal stampings; perforated metal, stamped

(G-12623)
HERGATT MACHINE INC
2530 Pavonia Rd (44903-7807)
PHONE................................419 589-2931
Fax: 419 589-4116
Neil N Hergatt, *President*
Becky Hergatt, *Corp Secy*
EMP: 8
SQ FT: 4,000
SALES: 600K Privately Held
SIC: 3599 Machine shop, jobbing & repair

(G-12624)
HESS INDUSTRIES LTD
108 Sawyer Pkwy (44903-6514)
PHONE................................419 525-4000
Mark A Hess, *President*
Pamela Hess, *Vice Pres*
EMP: 10
SQ FT: 12,000
SALES: 1MM Privately Held
WEB: www.hessindltd.com
SIC: 3544 Special dies, tools, jigs & fixtures

(G-12625)
HIGHPOINT FIREARMS
Also Called: Hi-Point Firearms
1015 Springmill St (44906-1571)
PHONE................................419 747-9444
Fax: 419 747-1081
Tom Deeb, *President*
Shirley Deeb, *Admin Sec*
EMP: 28
SQ FT: 24,000
SALES (est): 4.5MM Privately Held
SIC: 3484 5941 Guns (firearms) or gun parts, 30 mm. & below; sporting goods & bicycle shops

(G-12626)
HYUNDAI IDEAL ELECTRIC CO
Also Called: Ideal Electric Company
330 E 1st St (44902-7756)
PHONE................................419 520-3314
Fax: 419 522-9386
Justin Lim, *President*
Nick Smollen, *General Mgr*
Jim Lehman, *Project Mgr*
Gary Zellner, *Project Mgr*
David Jones, *Purch Mgr*
◆ EMP: 208
SQ FT: 650,000
SALES: 70MM
SALES (corp-wide): 22.1B Privately Held
WEB: www.hhi.co.kr
SIC: 3621 3613 3625 Generators & sets, electric; motors, electric; switchgear & switchgear accessories; relays & industrial controls
PA: Hyundai Heavy Industries Co., Ltd.
    1000 Bangeojinsunhwando-Ro, Dong-Gu
    Ulsan 44032
    522 022-114

(G-12627)
JOAN B MAILLOUX
Also Called: J B'S Crafts & Things
2273 Lakewood Dr (44905-1729)
PHONE................................361 992-5311
Joan Mailloux, *Owner*
EMP: 3
SALES: 80K Privately Held
SIC: 2395 7389 Embroidery & art needlework;

(G-12628)
JOHN L GARBER MATERIALS CORP
2745 Gass Rd (44904-8715)
PHONE................................419 884-1567
Fax: 419 884-1663
John L Garber, *President*
Matthew Garber, *Vice Pres*
Donna West, *Admin Sec*
EMP: 13
SQ FT: 500
SALES (est): 979.3K Privately Held
SIC: 1442 Gravel mining

(G-12629)
JONES POTATO CHIP CO (PA)
823 Bowman St (44903-4107)
PHONE................................419 529-9424
Fax: 419 529-6789
Robert Jones, *President*
Charles K Hellinger, *Principal*
Frederick W Jones, *Principal*
Darryl Jones, *Vice Pres*
Rick Bartram, *Prdtn Mgr*
EMP: 46
SQ FT: 50,000
SALES (est): 8.8MM Privately Held
WEB: www.joneschips.com
SIC: 2096 5145 Potato chips & other potato-based snacks; potato chips

(G-12630)
JOTCO INC
1400 Park Ave E (44905-2989)
PHONE................................513 721-4943
Fax: 513 721-8974
John Young, *President*
Vicki Young, *Admin Sec*
EMP: 6
SQ FT: 100,000

SALES (est): 691.1K Privately Held
WEB: www.jotco-inc.com
SIC: 3471 8711 3599 Finishing, metals or formed products; engineering services; machine & other job shop work

(G-12631)
KA MOLDED PRODUCTS
40 Eagle Dr (44904-1369)
PHONE................................419 884-3375
Kevin Kleer, *President*
EMP: 8
SALES (est): 1MM Privately Held
SIC: 3089 Injection molded finished plastic products

(G-12632)
KARMA METAL PRODUCTS INC
556 Caldwell Ave (44905-1401)
PHONE................................419 524-4371
Fax: 419 524-4790
Thomas Taska, *President*
Ron Kocher, *Vice Pres*
April Sevits, *Purch Agent*
Judy Taska, *Treasurer*
EMP: 10
SQ FT: 6,800
SALES (est): 1.4MM Privately Held
WEB: www.karmametalproducts.com
SIC: 3451 3545 Screw machine products; measuring tools & machines, machinists' metalworking type

(G-12633)
KLOPFENSTEIN ART EQUIPMENT
25 Walnut St (44904-1260)
P.O. Box 9057 (44904-9057)
PHONE................................419 884-2900
Jeffrey Penny, *President*
Stanley Butler, *Vice Pres*
EMP: 4
SQ FT: 14,000
SALES (est): 476.9K Privately Held
WEB: www.artpaper.us
SIC: 3269 Art & ornamental ware, pottery

(G-12634)
KOKOSING MATERIALS INC
215 Oak St (44907-1439)
PHONE................................419 522-2715
Bill Burgett, *Branch Mgr*
EMP: 10
SALES (corp-wide): 18.1MM Privately Held
SIC: 2951 Asphalt & asphaltic paving mixtures (not from refineries)
PA: Kokosing Materials, Inc.
    17531 Waterford Rd
    Fredericktown OH 43019
    740 694-9585

(G-12635)
LENNOX MACHINE INC
Also Called: Lennox Machine Shop
1471 Sprang Pkwy (44903-6531)
P.O. Box 1643 (44901-1643)
PHONE................................419 525-1020
Fax: 419 525-1955
Terry L Eighinger, *President*
David Eighinger, *Vice Pres*
EMP: 11
SALES (est): 1.7MM Privately Held
SIC: 3599 Machine shop, jobbing & repair

(G-12636)
LESCH BTRY & PWR SOLUTION LLC
2744 Lexington Ave (44904-1429)
PHONE................................419 884-0219
Tom Lesch, *Manager*
Brian Lesch,
Sandra Lesch,
EMP: 4
SALES (est): 514.2K Privately Held
SIC: 3621 7389 Storage battery chargers, motor & engine generator type; business services

(G-12637)
LONG VIEW STEEL CORP
1555 W Longview Ave (44906-1806)
P.O. Box 2839 (44906-0839)
PHONE................................419 747-1108
Fax: 419 747-1110
David Jacko, *President*

EMP: 12
SALES (est): 3.4MM **Privately Held**
WEB: www.longviewsteel.com
SIC: 3312 Blast furnaces & steel mills

(G-12638)
M GRAFIX LLC
384 Gatewood Dr Apt 2 (44907-2349)
PHONE....................................419 528-8665
Maurice Byrd,
EMP: 14
SALES: 34K **Privately Held**
WEB: www.mgrafix.net
SIC: 7374 2741 Computer graphics serv-
ice; shopping news: publishing & printing

(G-12639)
MAJOR METALS COMPANY
844 Kochheiser Rd (44904-8637)
PHONE....................................419 886-4600
Fax: 419 886-4670
Jeffrey C Mason, *President*
Wayne Riffe, *Vice Pres*
Jason Dials, *Sales Mgr*
Tim Rinehart, *Sales Executive*
Ania Pitchco, *Manager*
EMP: 30
SQ FT: 60,000
SALES (est): 13.7MM **Privately Held**
WEB: www.majormetalscompany.com
SIC: 3312 5051 3317 Plate, sheet & strip,
except coated products; iron or steel flat
products; steel pipe & tubes

(G-12640)
MANAIRCO INC
28 Industrial Pkwy (44903-8999)
P.O. Box 111 (44901-0111)
PHONE....................................419 524-2121
Fax: 419 525-4790
James C Gorman, *Ch of Bd*
Gayle Gorman Freeman, *President*
Jeff Koontz, *General Mgr*
Marjorie Gorman, *Corp Secy*
Joel Beinbrech, *Vice Pres*
EMP: 9 EST: 1953
SQ FT: 14,000
SALES (est): 1.4MM **Privately Held**
WEB: www.manairco.com
SIC: 3648 3645 Airport lighting fixtures:
runway approach, taxi or ramp; residential
lighting fixtures

(G-12641)
**MANSFIELD BRICK & SUPPLY
CO (PA)**
320 N Diamond St (44902-1008)
P.O. Box 1273 (44901-1273)
PHONE....................................419 526-1191
Toll Free:...888 -
Fax: 419 526-1470
Mike Anderson, *President*
Jane Anderson, *Corp Secy*
EMP: 8
SQ FT: 3,500
SALES (est): 1.4MM **Privately Held**
SIC: 5211 5032 3272 Brick; brick, except
refractory; concrete products, precast

(G-12642)
**MANSFIELD IMAGING CENTER
LLC**
536 S Trimble Rd Ste A (44906-3418)
PHONE....................................419 756-8899
Michael R Viau,
EMP: 12
SALES (est): 1.3MM **Privately Held**
SIC: 3826 Magnetic resonance imaging
apparatus

(G-12643)
MANSFIELD INDUSTRIES INC
1776 Harrington Mem Rd (44903-8996)
PHONE....................................419 524-1300
Otis M Cummins, *Chairman*
Greg Beal, *Mfg Mgr*
Jeff Habegger, *Engineer*
Nick Sir, *Project Engr*
EMP: 29
SALES (est): 5.7MM **Privately Held**
WEB: www.mansfieldindustries.com
SIC: 3469 Metal stampings

(G-12644)
**MANSFIELD SCREW MCH PDTS
CO**
145 Industrial Dr (44904-1392)
PHONE....................................419 884-1511
Fax: 419 884-0680
Richard D Witchey Jr, *Ch of Bd*
Richard Witchey III, *President*
Steve Witchey, *Vice Pres*
Ken Tomecko, *Plant Mgr*
Ted Brissell, *Draft/Design*
EMP: 65 EST: 1945
SQ FT: 35,000
SALES (est): 11.6MM **Privately Held**
SIC: 3451 3541 Screw machine products;
machine tools, metal cutting type

(G-12645)
MCDANIEL PRODUCTS INC
Also Called: Automatic Parts
433 Springmill St (44907-7008)
P.O. Box 1505 (44901-1505)
PHONE....................................419 524-5841
Justin Constable, *Branch Mgr*
EMP: 31 **Privately Held**
SIC: 3451 Screw machine products
PA: Mcdaniel Products, Inc.
1775 Liberty Ave
Vermilion OH 44089

(G-12646)
MERRICO INC
541 Grant St (44903-1215)
P.O. Box 156 (44901-0156)
PHONE....................................419 525-2711
Fax: 419 525-1612
Sandy Powers, *President*
EMP: 4
SQ FT: 15,000
SALES (est): 520K **Privately Held**
WEB: www.merrico.com
SIC: 3644 3069 Insulators & insulation
materials, electrical; hard rubber &
molded rubber products

(G-12647)
MID OHIO TROPHY & AWARDS
131 W Cook Rd (44907-2403)
PHONE....................................419 756-2266
Fax: 419 756-2266
Charlotte Brown, *Owner*
Darrel Brown, *Vice Pres*
EMP: 3
SALES (est): 232.1K **Privately Held**
SIC: 3499 5999 Trophies, metal, except
silver; trophies & plaques

(G-12648)
**MIDWEST AIRCRAFT
PRODUCTS CO**
Also Called: Mapco
125 S Mill St (44904-9571)
PHONE....................................419 884-2164
Jerry Miller, *Owner*
▼ EMP: 17
SQ FT: 25,000
SALES (est): 3.4MM **Privately Held**
WEB: www.midwestaircraft.com
SIC: 3728 Aircraft parts & equipment

(G-12649)
**MINNICH MANUFACTURING CO
INC**
1444 State Route 42 (44903-9509)
P.O. Box 367 (44901-0367)
PHONE....................................419 903-0010
Fax: 419 903-0110
James R Minnich, *President*
Lynn Beck, *Purch Mgr*
Jeff McDaniel, *Research*
Troy Kingan, *Engineer*
Rob Minnich, *Sales Staff*
▲ EMP: 25
SQ FT: 43,000
SALES (est): 9.2MM **Privately Held**
WEB: www.minnich-mfg.com
SIC: 3531 Vibrators for concrete construc-
tion

(G-12650)
MK METAL PRODUCTS INC (PA)
Also Called: Mavericks Stainless
90 Sawyer Pkwy (44903-6514)
P.O. Box 878 (44901-0878)
PHONE....................................419 756-3644

Fax: 419 756-9881
Richard L Kemp, *CEO*
J Douglas Drusbal, *Principal*
David Cole, *Vice Pres*
James P Barrett, *Treasurer*
EMP: 35
SQ FT: 39,000
SALES (est): 6.6MM **Privately Held**
WEB: www.mkmetalproducts.com
SIC: 3449 Miscellaneous metalwork

(G-12651)
**MODERN BUILDERS SUPPLY
INC**
85 Smith Ave (44905-2854)
PHONE....................................419 526-0002
Rich Graham, *Manager*
EMP: 12
SALES (corp-wide): 437.3MM **Privately
Held**
WEB: www.polaristechnologies.com
SIC: 5032 3089 5033 5031 Brick, stone
& related material; doors, folding: plastic
or plastic coated fabric; windows, plastic;
roofing, asphalt & sheet metal; kitchen
cabinets
PA: Modern Builders Supply, Inc.
302 Mcclurg Rd
Youngstown OH 44512
330 729-2690

(G-12652)
MORITZ CONCRETE INC
362 N Trimble Rd (44906-2541)
P.O. Box 1342 (44901-1342)
PHONE....................................419 529-3232
Fax: 419 529-6853
Martin F Moritz Jr, *President*
Peter Moritz, *Assistant VP*
James Moritz, *Vice Pres*
Robert Moritz, *Treasurer*
Joe Moritz, *Admin Sec*
EMP: 47
SQ FT: 260,000
SALES (est): 7.5MM **Privately Held**
WEB: www.moritzconcrete.com
SIC: 3273 Ready-mixed concrete

(G-12653)
MORITZ INTERNATIONAL INC
665 N Main St (44902-4201)
PHONE....................................419 526-5222
Fax: 419 526-9500
Frank Moritz, *President*
Thomas R Moritz, *Vice Pres*
Lisa Moritz, *Manager*
EMP: 37
SQ FT: 50,000
SALES (est): 9.7MM **Privately Held**
WEB: www.moritzinternational.com
SIC: 3715 Truck trailers

(G-12654)
MR ELECTRIC
24 Bell St (44906)
P.O. Box 572, Bellville (44813-0572)
PHONE....................................419 289-7474
Tom Lamp, *Owner*
EMP: 5
SALES (est): 379.2K **Privately Held**
SIC: 5063 3699 1731 Generators; electri-
cal equipment & supplies; electrical work

(G-12655)
**NATIONAL PATENT ANALYTICAL
SYS**
2090 Harrington Mem Rd (44903-8051)
P.O. Box 1435 (44901-1435)
PHONE....................................419 526-6727
Fax: 419 526-9446
John Fusco, *President*
Cliff Broeden, *Exec VP*
Daniel Fusco, *Vice Pres*
Dave Radomski, *Engineer*
Debbie Russman, *Administration*
EMP: 31
SQ FT: 2,000
SALES (est): 6.4MM **Privately Held**
WEB: www.npas.com
SIC: 3829 Breathalyzers

(G-12656)
**NEWMAN TECHNOLOGY INC
(HQ)**
100 Cairns Rd (44903-8990)
PHONE....................................419 525-1856
Fax: 419 524-1965
Shigeyuki Handa, *President*
Yukihisa Murata, *Exec VP*
Dick Pacelli, *Senior VP*
Stephen Rourke, *Senior VP*
Timothy Dougherty, *Opers Staff*
▲ EMP: 232
SQ FT: 450,000
SALES (est): 219MM
SALES (corp-wide): 18.2MM **Privately
Held**
WEB: www.newmantech.com
SIC: 3714 3751 Motor vehicle parts & ac-
cessories; mufflers (exhaust), motor vehi-
cle; motorcycle accessories
PA: Sankei Giken Co.,Ltd.
1024-10, Niihori
Kawaguchi STM 334-0
482 959-460

(G-12657)
**NEWSPAPER NETWORK
CENTRAL OH**
70 W 4th St (44903-1676)
PHONE....................................419 524-3545
Tom Brennan, *Principal*
EMP: 8
SALES (est): 555.4K **Privately Held**
WEB: www.nncogannett.com
SIC: 2711 Newspapers, publishing & print-
ing

(G-12658)
NEXT GENERATION BAG INC
230 Industrial Dr (44904-1346)
PHONE....................................419 884-1327
Fax: 419 884-1375
John D Frecka, *CEO*
David Rehfeldt, *Financial Exec*
Michael Helinski, *Sales Mgr*
EMP: 350
SALES (est): 24.1MM **Privately Held**
SIC: 2673 Plastic & pliofilm bags

(G-12659)
NORMANT CANDY CO
Also Called: Normant's Salt Water Taffy
1821 Mock Rd (44904-9302)
PHONE....................................419 886-4214
Richard Normant, *Owner*
EMP: 18
SALES (est): 1.4MM **Privately Held**
SIC: 2064 5441 Candy & other confec-
tionery products; candy

(G-12660)
OGS TOOL & MANUFACTURING
3520 N Main St (44903-9735)
PHONE....................................419 524-6200
Fax: 419 524-6202
Scott Miller, *Owner*
EMP: 5
SQ FT: 4,000
SALES (est): 240K **Privately Held**
SIC: 3544 Special dies, tools, jigs & fix-
tures

(G-12661)
**OHIO ELECTRIC MOTOR SVC
LLC**
311 E 3rd St (44902-1511)
PHONE....................................419 525-2225
Mike Moshier, *Branch Mgr*
EMP: 4
SALES (corp-wide): 1.7MM **Privately
Held**
SIC: 7699 7694 5063 3699 Pumps &
pumping equipment repair; electric motor
repair; electrical supplies; electrical equip-
ment & supplies
PA: Ohio Electric Motor Service, Llc
1909 E Livingston Ave
Columbus OH 43209
614 444-1451

(G-12662)
**OHIO VALLEY MANUFACTURING
INC**
1501 Harrington Mem Rd (44903-8995)
PHONE....................................419 522-5818

Fax: 419 522-1050
Michael C Fanello, *President*
John Fanello, *President*
Jeff Fanello, *Vice Pres*
Steven Fanello, *Vice Pres*
Jim Day, *Plant Mgr*
EMP: 80
SQ FT: 75,000
SALES (est): 28.8MM **Privately Held**
WEB: www.ohiovalleymfg.com
SIC: 3469 3399 Stamping metal for the
trade; flakes, metal

(G-12663)
**OHIO VLY STMPNG-
ASSEMBLIES INC**
500 Newman St (44902-1122)
PHONE..............................419 522-0983
Todd J Flagel, *Principal*
Bob Ganfield, *Engineer*
EMP: 30
SALES (est): 4.3MM **Privately Held**
SIC: 3297 Nonclay refractories

(G-12664)
OMEGA TEK INC
649 Old Mill Run Rd (44906-3474)
P.O. Box 185, Shelby (44875-0185)
PHONE..............................419 756-9580
Fax: 419 756-9580
James C Hudson, *President*
Marguerite Hudson, *Vice Pres*
EMP: 6
SALES: 500K **Privately Held**
SIC: 3625 Control circuit relays, industrial

(G-12665)
OUR DETERGENT INC
Also Called: D.B.G. Cleaners
101 Knight Pkwy (44903-6548)
PHONE..............................419 589-5571
Suzanne Stewart, *President*
James C Stewart, *Principal*
John C Stewart, *Vice Pres*
EMP: 3
SQ FT: 6,000
SALES (est): 350K **Privately Held**
SIC: 2841 Detergents, synthetic organic or
inorganic alkaline

(G-12666)
P C R RESTORATIONS INC
Also Called: Lehr Awning Co
933 W Longview Ave (44906-2133)
PHONE..............................419 747-7957
Fax: 419 747-8427
Phillip E Russell, *President*
Debbie Russell, *Vice Pres*
Kelly Messer, *Admin Sec*
EMP: 16
SQ FT: 11,000
SALES (est): 1.9MM **Privately Held**
WEB: www.pcr-lehrawning.com
SIC: 2394 3089 2221 5999 Canvas
awnings & canopies; awnings, fiberglass
& plastic combination; upholstery, tapes-
try & wall covering fabrics; awnings

(G-12667)
PRECISION SWITCHING INC
2090 Harrington Mem Rd (44903-8051)
P.O. Box 1435 (44901-1435)
PHONE..............................800 800-8143
John Fusco, *President*
Daniel Fusco, *Vice Pres*
Tim Blair, *Purchasing*
Mike Blair, *Systems Mgr*
EMP: 7
SQ FT: 10,000
SALES (est): 943.5K **Privately Held**
SIC: 3613 3677 3672 3625 Switchgear &
switchboard apparatus; electronic coils,
transformers & other inductors; printed
circuit boards; relays & industrial controls;
transformers, except electric

(G-12668)
PREMIER OFFICE
Also Called: Clean Jeans Laundry Room
225 Ashland Rd (44905-2401)
PHONE..............................419 329-9692
Debbie Feeney, *Manager*
EMP: 8
SALES (est): 215.6K **Privately Held**
SIC: 7215 3648 Laundry, coin-operated;
sun tanning equipment, incl. tanning beds

(G-12669)
R M DAVIS INC
Also Called: Mall Compan, The
517 Walfield Dr (44904-1649)
PHONE..............................419 756-6719
Fax: 419 529-9170
Richard Byus, *President*
Wendy Laidlaw, *Vice Pres*
Dora Byus, *Admin Sec*
Amanda Neuts, *Admin Asst*
EMP: 3
SQ FT: 4,900
SALES: 275K **Privately Held**
SIC: 3993 1799 Electric signs; sign instal-
lation & maintenance

(G-12670)
R M INDUSTRIES INC
95 Ohio Brass Rd (44902-1029)
PHONE..............................419 529-8970
Fax: 419 529-8345
Robert Mc Coy, *President*
Linda S Mc Coy, *Corp Secy*
EMP: 5
SQ FT: 11,000
SALES (est): 461.6K **Privately Held**
SIC: 3999 Education aids, devices & sup-
plies

(G-12671)
**RICHLAND NEWHOPE
INDUSTRIES (PA)**
150 E 4th St (44902-1520)
P.O. Box 916 (44901-0916)
PHONE..............................419 774-4400
Fax: 419 774-4409
Greg Young, *Prdtn Mgr*
Mike Bradley, *Manager*
Elizabeth Prather, *Exec Dir*
Dave Keinath, *Director*
Marsha Madden, *Executive*
EMP: 250
SQ FT: 63,000
SALES: 3.3MM **Privately Held**
SIC: 0782 2448 7349 8331 Lawn & gar-
den services; wood pallets & skids; build-
ing maintenance services; job training &
vocational rehabilitation services; packag-
ing & labeling services

(G-12672)
**RICHLAND SCREW MCH PDTS
INC**
531 Grant St (44903-1213)
P.O. Box 696 (44901-0696)
PHONE..............................419 524-1272
Fax: 419 524-5699
Randall L Schoenman, *President*
Rochelle Ashbrook, *Manager*
EMP: 21
SQ FT: 15,000
SALES (est): 3.7MM **Privately Held**
WEB: www.richlandscrewmachine.com
SIC: 3451 Screw machine products

(G-12673)
**RURAL FARM DISTRIBUTORS
CO**
2690 Bowman Street Rd (44903-7429)
PHONE..............................419 747-6807
Robin Sheer, *Manager*
EMP: 3
SALES (corp-wide): 3.3MM **Privately
Held**
WEB: www.rfd.com
SIC: 2875 5191 Fertilizers, mixing only;
farm supplies
PA: Rural Farm Distributors, Co.
2680 Olivesburg Rd
Mansfield OH

(G-12674)
**RUSSELL T BUNDY
ASSOCIATES INC**
Also Called: Pan-Glo
1711 N Main St (44903-8111)
PHONE..............................419 526-4454
Fax: 419 526-6776
William Matzke, *Manager*
EMP: 30
SALES (corp-wide): 64MM **Privately
Held**
SIC: 3479 Pan glazing

PA: Russell T. Bundy Associates, Inc.
417 E Water St Ste 1
Urbana OH 43078
937 652-2151

(G-12675)
S & S MACHINING LTD
76 Atenway St (44902-1025)
PHONE..............................419 524-9525
Cliff Shindeldecker, *Partner*
Rhonda Shindeldecker, *Partner*
EMP: 10
SQ FT: 7,000
SALES: 600K **Privately Held**
SIC: 3451 Screw machine products

(G-12676)
SASH FOAM WORKS INC
555 Park Ave E (44905-2871)
P.O. Box 1494 (44901-1494)
PHONE..............................419 522-4074
Gary Haverfield, *President*
EMP: 3
SALES (est): 342.6K **Privately Held**
SIC: 3086 Plastics foam products

(G-12677)
SHELLY FISHER
Also Called: P P C Greatstuff Co
449 Newman St (44902-1123)
PHONE..............................419 522-6696
Shelley Fisher, *Principal*
EMP: 100
SALES (est): 7.4MM **Privately Held**
SIC: 3089 Injection molding of plastics

(G-12678)
SIR STEAK MACHINERY INC
40 Baird Pkwy (44903-7908)
PHONE..............................419 526-9181
Fax: 419 526-9760
James Munroe, *President*
Michael J Biro, *Vice Pres*
Richard C Biro, *Vice Pres*
Dean Schlichting, *Treasurer*
Barbara Burkhardt, *Office Mgr*
EMP: 20
SQ FT: 37,500
SALES (est): 3.8MM
SALES (corp-wide): 17.1MM **Privately
Held**
WEB: www.birosaw.com
SIC: 3549 Metalworking machinery
PA: The Biro Manufacturing Company
1114 W Main St
Lakeside Marblehead OH 43440
419 798-4451

(G-12679)
SKYBOX INVESTMENTS INC
Also Called: Brasspack Packing Supply
1275 Pollock Pkwy (44905-1374)
P.O. Box 1567 (44901-1567)
PHONE..............................419 525-6013
James Miller, *CEO*
Marc Miller, *Corp Secy*
Marty Rice, *Vice Pres*
Rodney Robertson, *Vice Pres*
Joseph R Murach, *CFO*
EMP: 45
SQ FT: 60,000
SALES (est): 10MM **Privately Held**
SIC: 2653 Boxes, corrugated: made from
purchased materials

(G-12680)
SKYBOX PACKAGING LLC
Also Called: Mr Box
1275 Pollock Pkwy (44905-1374)
P.O. Box 1567 (44901-1567)
PHONE..............................419 525-7209
Fax: 419 525-7210
Marc Miller, *President*
Rodney Robertson, *Vice Pres*
John Olin, *Finance Mgr*
James D Miller, *Administration*
EMP: 71
SALES (est): 17.5MM
SALES (corp-wide): 302.5MM **Privately
Held**
SIC: 3086 5199 Packaging & shipping ma-
terials, foamed plastic; packaging materi-
als

PA: Atlantic Packaging Products Ltd
111 Progress Ave
Scarborough ON M1P 2
416 298-8101

(G-12681)
SNYDER MACHINE CO INC
256 N Diamond St (44902-1006)
PHONE..............................419 526-1527
Fax: 419 526-1527
Joseph E Greene, *CEO*
Joseph A Greene, *President*
Joy Greene, *Corp Secy*
EMP: 5 **EST:** 1960
SQ FT: 9,000
SALES: 500K **Privately Held**
SIC: 3599 Machine shop, jobbing & repair

(G-12682)
SOLSYS INC
96 Vanderbilt Rd (44904-8603)
PHONE..............................419 886-4683
Jeffrey C Mason, *President*
EMP: 7
SALES (est): 754.8K **Privately Held**
SIC: 3572 Computer storage devices

(G-12683)
STEIN INC
1490 Old Bowman St (44903-8805)
PHONE..............................419 747-2611
EMP: 17 **EST:** 2010
SALES (est): 1.2MM **Privately Held**
SIC: 2431 Millwork

(G-12684)
STERLING COLLECTABLES INC
862 Pugh Rd (44903-8755)
PHONE..............................419 892-5708
Kelly Spencer, *President*
EMP: 6 **EST:** 2011
SALES (est): 263.5K **Privately Held**
SIC: 3999 5199 Christmas tree orna-
ments, except electrical & glass; Christ-
mas novelties; Christmas trees, including
artificial

(G-12685)
STRASSELLS MACHINE INC
1015 Springmill St (44906-1571)
PHONE..............................419 747-1088
Fax: 419 747-1088
Michael Strassell, *President*
Kimberly Strassell, *Vice Pres*
EMP: 10
SQ FT: 1,600
SALES (est): 1.7MM **Privately Held**
SIC: 3599 Machine shop, jobbing & repair

(G-12686)
SUGAR SHACK
4703 Flowers Rd (44903-7780)
PHONE..............................419 961-4016
EMP: 4 **EST:** 2015
SALES (est): 161.7K **Privately Held**
SIC: 2051 Cakes, pies & pastries

(G-12687)
SUMMERS ACQUISITION CORP
10 W Piper Rd (44903-8116)
PHONE..............................419 526-5800
Bill Atkins, *Branch Mgr*
EMP: 5
SALES (corp-wide): 2.5B **Privately Held**
WEB: www.summersrubber.com
SIC: 5085 3429 3052 Rubber goods, me-
chanical; manufactured hardware (gen-
eral); rubber & plastics hose & beltings
HQ: Summers Acquisition Corporation
12555 Berea Rd
Cleveland OH 44111
216 941-7700

(G-12688)
**SYSTEMS JAY LLC NANOGATE
(PA)**
Also Called: Broshco Fabricated Products
150 Longview Ave E (44903-4206)
PHONE..............................419 524-3778
Fax: 419 526-3239
Rick R Taylor, *President*
R G Taylor, *Principal*
Dave Benick, *Exec VP*
Paul Shatlock, *Vice Pres*
Josh Taylor, *Vice Pres*
▲ **EMP:** 194

(PA)=Parent Co (HQ)=Headquarters (DH)=Div Headquarters
✪ = New Business established in last 2 years

SQ FT: 125,000
SALES (est): 222.8MM **Privately Held**
WEB: www.jayindinc.com
SIC: **2531** 3089 Seats, automobile; injection molding of plastics

(G-12689)
SYSTEMS JAY LLC NANOGATE
Rohr Manufacturing Div
1555 W Longview Ave (44906-1806)
PHONE..................................419 747-1096
EMP: 50
SALES (corp-wide): 222.8MM **Privately Held**
WEB: www.jayindinc.com
SIC: **3312** Tubes, steel & iron
PA: Jay Nanogate Systems Llc
150 Longview Ave E
Mansfield OH 44903
419 524-3778

(G-12690)
SYSTEMS JAY LLC NANOGATE
Crestline Paint
515 Newman St (44902-1160)
PHONE..................................419 522-7745
Fax: 419 522-5936
Paul Boggs, *Vice Pres*
Steve Kunz, *Branch Mgr*
Rhonda Dean, *MIS Mgr*
EMP: 130
SALES (corp-wide): 222.8MM **Privately Held**
WEB: www.jayindinc.com
SIC: **3714** Motor vehicle parts & accessories
PA: Jay Nanogate Systems Llc
150 Longview Ave E
Mansfield OH 44903
419 524-3778

(G-12691)
SYSTEMS JAY LLC NANOGATE
Broscho Fabricated Products
1595 W Longview Ave (44906-1806)
PHONE..................................419 747-4161
John Vidonish, *Maint Spvr*
Dick Young, *Mfg Staff*
Carlos Sanjur, *QC Dir*
Bruce Souder, *Engineer*
Kay Zartman, *Human Resources*
EMP: 400
SALES (corp-wide): 222.8MM **Privately Held**
WEB: www.jayindinc.com
SIC: **3499** 7692 Automobile seat frames, metal; welding repair
PA: Jay Nanogate Systems Llc
150 Longview Ave E
Mansfield OH 44903
419 524-3778

(G-12692)
SYSTEMS JAY LLC NANOGATE
Also Called: Broshco Fabricated Products
1595 W Longview Ave (44906-1806)
PHONE..................................419 747-4161
Fax: 419 747-2652
Dick Young, *Manager*
Erv Howard, *Manager*
Tom Miller, *Manager*
Carlos Sanjur, *Manager*
EMP: 480
SALES (corp-wide): 222.8MM **Privately Held**
WEB: www.jayindinc.com
SIC: **3499** Automobile seat frames, metal
PA: Jay Nanogate Systems Llc
150 Longview Ave E
Mansfield OH 44903
419 524-3778

(G-12693)
TAYLOR METAL PRODUCTS CO
700 Springmill St (44903-1199)
PHONE..................................419 522-3471
Fax: 419 525-2948
Richard G Taylor, *President*
Helen F Taylor, *Vice Pres*
Gary Purvis, *Safety Mgr*
Larry Huffman, *Engineer*
Wes Linton, *Engineer*
▲ EMP: 155 EST: 1923
SQ FT: 160,000

SALES (est): 36.6MM **Privately Held**
WEB: www.tmpind.com
SIC: **3469** 3465 Metal stampings; automotive stampings

(G-12694)
TE CONNECTIVITY CORPORATION
Cii Technologies Hartman Pdts
175 N Diamond St (44902-1004)
PHONE..................................419 521-9500
Michael Hartge, *Engineer*
Dennis Ridgeway, *Sls & Mktg Exec*
Joseph Murach, *Controller*
Kathy Castor, *Branch Mgr*
EMP: 235
SALES (corp-wide): 12.2B **Privately Held**
WEB: www.raychem.com
SIC: **3613** 3625 3812 3769 Power switching equipment; control panels, electric; relays, for electronic use; search & navigation equipment; guided missile & space vehicle parts & auxiliary equipment
HQ: Te Connectivity Corporation
1050 Westlakes Dr
Berwyn PA 19312
610 893-9800

(G-12695)
THE MANSFIELD STRL & ERCT CO (PA)
Also Called: Mansfield Fabricated Products
429 Park Ave E (44905-2844)
P.O. Box 427 (44901-0427)
PHONE..................................419 522-5911
Fax: 419 525-4948
Richard Gash, *President*
Barbara Gash, *Corp Secy*
Ken Carroll, *Plant Mgr*
Tanya Smith, *Manager*
EMP: 16 EST: 1924
SQ FT: 60,000
SALES (est): 4.3MM **Privately Held**
SIC: **3441** 5051 Fabricated structural metal; metals service centers & offices

(G-12696)
THE MANSFIELD STRL & ERCT CO
Also Called: Mansfield Fabricated Products
817 Belmont Ave (44906-2022)
PHONE..................................419 747-6571
Fax: 419 747-1815
Bill Kent, *Manager*
EMP: 16
SALES (corp-wide): 4.3MM **Privately Held**
SIC: **3441** Fabricated structural metal
PA: Mansfield Structural And Erecting Company, The (Inc)
429 Park Ave E
Mansfield OH 44905
419 522-5911

(G-12697)
THERM-O-DISC INCORPORATED (DH)
1320 S Main St (44907-5500)
PHONE..................................419 525-8500
Fax: 419 525-8282
Charles C G, *CEO*
Scott Klonowski, *Vice Pres*
Martin Leslie, *Vice Pres*
Steve Motter, *Vice Pres*
Matt Grist, *Plant Mgr*
▲ EMP: 900 EST: 1945
SQ FT: 333,400
SALES (est): 512.1MM
SALES (corp-wide): 14.5B **Publicly Held**
WEB: www.thermodisc.com
SIC: **3822** 3823 Built-in thermostats, filled system & bimetal types; industrial instrmnts msrmnt display/control process variable

(G-12698)
THORNTON POWDER COATINGS INC
2300 N Main St (44903-6703)
P.O. Box 1119 (44901-1119)
PHONE..................................419 522-7183
Fax: 419 522-7384
James Thornton, *President*
Dawn Thornton, *Vice Pres*
EMP: 15

SQ FT: 20,000
SALES (est): 2MM **Privately Held**
SIC: **3479** Coating of metals & formed products

(G-12699)
TRI R TOOLING INC
220 Piper Rd (44905-1370)
PHONE..................................419 522-8665
Fax: 419 522-8665
Robert John, *President*
Rudy John, *Vice Pres*
Renee John, *Treasurer*
EMP: 12
SQ FT: 6,500
SALES (est): 1.6MM **Privately Held**
WEB: www.trirtooling.com
SIC: **3599** Machine & other job shop work

(G-12700)
TRIDICO SILK SCREEN & SIGN CO
162 N Diamond St (44902-1326)
PHONE..................................419 526-1695
Fax: 419 524-7446
Michael T Tridico, *Owner*
EMP: 3
SQ FT: 25,000
SALES (est): 170K **Privately Held**
SIC: **3993** 7336 5198 Signs & advertising specialties; silk screen design; stain

(G-12701)
VIDONISH STUDIOS
Also Called: Vidonish Stained Glass Studio
20 E Main St (44904-1223)
PHONE..................................419 884-1119
Cherri Vidonish, *Partner*
Bill Vidonish, *Partner*
EMP: 4
SQ FT: 1,700
SALES: 220K **Privately Held**
SIC: **3231** Stained glass: made from purchased glass

(G-12702)
WALTER GRAPHICS INC
850 Oak St (44907-1452)
P.O. Box 3781 (44907-0781)
PHONE..................................419 522-5261
Fax: 419 522-5261
Herbert F Walter, *President*
Susan Walter, *Corp Secy*
Phillip Walter, *Vice Pres*
EMP: 3
SQ FT: 5,000
SALES (est): 381K **Privately Held**
SIC: **2752** Commercial printing, offset

(G-12703)
WARREN RUPP INC
800 N Main St (44902-4209)
P.O. Box 1568 (44901-1568)
PHONE..................................419 524-8388
Fax: 419 522-7867
Scott Aiello, *President*
John Carter, *President*
Dan Johnston, *Vice Pres*
Mark McCourt, *Vice Pres*
Jim Baumikirchner, *Buyer*
▲ EMP: 224
SQ FT: 80,000
SALES (est): 68.1MM
SALES (corp-wide): 2.1B **Publicly Held**
WEB: www.warrenrupp.com
SIC: **3561** Pumps & pumping equipment
PA: Idex Corporation
1925 W Field Ct Ste 200
Lake Forest IL 60045
847 498-7070

(G-12704)
WEISS INDUSTRIES INC
Also Called: Weiss Metallurgical Services
2480 N Main St (44903-8555)
P.O. Box 157 (44901-0157)
PHONE..................................419 526-2480
Fax: 419 526-1158
Rudolph Weiss, *President*
Robert Nikolaus, *Principal*
Maria Weiss, *Principal*
Paul Jamieson, *Opers Mgr*
Tim Cramer, *Engineer*
EMP: 30
SQ FT: 40,000

SALES: 5MM **Privately Held**
WEB: www.weissind.com
SIC: **3469** 3398 3544 Metal stampings; metal heat treating; special dies & tools

(G-12705)
WESTINGHOUSE A BRAKE TECH CORP
472 Rembrandt St (44902-7015)
PHONE..................................419 526-5323
EMP: 96
SALES (corp-wide): 2.9B **Publicly Held**
SIC: **3743** Brakes, air & vacuum: railway
PA: Westinghouse Air Brake Technologies Corporation
1001 Airbrake Ave
Wilmerding PA 15148
412 825-1000

Mantua
Portage County

(G-12706)
AETNA PLASTICS CORP
Also Called: Vanguard Fabrication Division
4466 Orchard Rd (44255-9049)
PHONE..................................330 274-2855
James Bailey, *Manager*
EMP: 5
SALES (corp-wide): 16.2MM **Privately Held**
WEB: www.aetnaplastics.com
SIC: **3272** 3089 3443 7389 Panels & sections, prefabricated concrete; ducting, plastic; tanks, standard or custom fabricated: metal plate; metal cutting services; plastics pipe; laminated plastics plate & sheet
PA: Aetna Plastics Corp.
9075 Bank St
Cleveland OH 44125
330 762-1901

(G-12707)
ASSOCIATED ASSOCIATES INC
Also Called: Associated Ready Mix Concrete
9551 Elliman Rd (44255-9440)
P.O. Box 670538, Northfield (44067-0538)
PHONE..................................330 626-3300
Fax: 330 626-2711
Harold Joslin, *President*
Sandra Riha, *Admin Sec*
EMP: 20
SQ FT: 2,700
SALES (est): 2.9MM **Privately Held**
SIC: **3273** 5211 Ready-mixed concrete; masonry materials & supplies

(G-12708)
CREATIVE PROCESSING INC
17540 Rapids Rd (44255)
P.O. Box 708, Burton (44021-0708)
PHONE..................................440 834-4070
Daniel Piscura Jr, *President*
Freida Piscura, *Admin Sec*
EMP: 12
SQ FT: 10,000
SALES (est): 1.9MM **Privately Held**
SIC: **3599** Machine shop, jobbing & repair

(G-12709)
DESIGN FABRICATORS OF MANTUA
10612 Main St (44255-9636)
PHONE..................................330 274-5353
Fax: 330 274-0055
Paul Janson, *President*
Cindy Janson, *Corp Secy*
EMP: 4
SQ FT: 6,800
SALES (est): 850K **Privately Held**
SIC: **3559** Chemical machinery & equipment

(G-12710)
GALLAGHER LUMBER CO
10272 Vaughn Rd (44255-9745)
P.O. Box 698 (44255-0698)
PHONE..................................330 274-2333
Lel Gallagher, *Owner*
Terry Gallagher, *Owner*
EMP: 3

▲ = Import ▼=Export
◆ =Import/Export

SALES (est): 252.4K Privately Held
SIC: 2448 Pallets, wood

(G-12711)
GOODELL FARMS
5212 Goodell Rd (44255-9746)
PHONE..............................330 274-2161
Jay Goodell, *Partner*
EMP: 5
SALES (est): 339.6K Privately Held
SIC: 0241 0134 2099 Dairy farms; Irish potatoes; maple syrup

(G-12712)
HYDRA AIR EQUIPMENT INC
9222 State Route 44 (44255-9709)
P.O. Box 1324, Kent (44240-0025)
PHONE..............................330 274-2222
Fax: 330 677-0940
Dennis Marn, *President*
Ann Marn, *Vice Pres*
Shirley Stanley, *Treasurer*
EMP: 4
SQ FT: 6,000
SALES: 190K Privately Held
SIC: 3545 5084 Machine tool attachments & accessories; hydraulic systems equipment & supplies

(G-12713)
INDUSTRIAL CONNECTIONS INC
11730 Timber Point Trl (44255-9694)
PHONE..............................330 274-2155
Wendy Carlton, *President*
▼ EMP: 7
SQ FT: 7,000
SALES (est): 3.2MM Privately Held
SIC: 5084 3492 Hydraulic systems equipment & supplies; power plant machinery; hose & tube fittings & assemblies, hydraulic/pneumatic

(G-12714)
LAKESIDE SAND & GRAVEL INC
3498 Frost Rd (44255-9136)
PHONE..............................330 274-2569
Fax: 330 274-3569
Larry Kotkowski, *President*
Ronald Kotkowski, *Corp Secy*
William Ulla, *Engineer*
EMP: 25
SQ FT: 4,200
SALES: 1.6MM Privately Held
SIC: 1442 Construction sand mining; gravel mining

(G-12715)
MANTALINE CORPORATION
Also Called: Transportation Group
4754 E High St (44255-9201)
PHONE..............................330 274-2264
Fax: 330 995-3773
Bryan Fink, *Manager*
Jeff Watson, *Manager*
EMP: 75
SALES (corp-wide): 31.6MM Privately Held
WEB: www.mantaline.com
SIC: 5169 3061 Synthetic rubber; mechanical rubber goods
PA: Mantaline Corporation
4754 E High St
Mantua OH 44255
330 274-2264

(G-12716)
MAR-ZANE INC
9551 Elliman Rd (44255-9440)
PHONE..............................330 626-2079
Jeff Parks, *Superintendent*
Mike Cline, *Controller*
EMP: 3
SALES (corp-wide): 301.4MM Privately Held
SIC: 2951 1611 Asphalt paving mixtures & blocks; surfacing & paving
HQ: Mar-Zane, Inc.
3570 S River Rd
Zanesville OH 43701
740 453-0721

(G-12717)
MERIDIENNE INTERNATIONAL INC
Also Called: Atlantic Water Gardens
4494 Orchard St (44255-9049)
PHONE..............................330 274-8317
William Lynne, *President*
Bachir Soueidan, *Vice Pres*
Jeff Weemhoff, *Vice Pres*
◆ EMP: 7
SQ FT: 15,000
SALES: 2.5MM Privately Held
SIC: 3842 3083 Whirlpool baths, hydrotherapy equipment; laminated plastics plate & sheet

(G-12718)
O K BRUGMANN JR & SONS INC
4083 Mennonite Rd (44255-9413)
PHONE..............................330 274-2106
Fax: 330 274-0031
Oscar Brugmann Jr, *President*
Mark Brugmann, *Principal*
Gail Brugmann, *Vice Pres*
EMP: 12
SALES (est): 2MM Privately Held
SIC: 5032 5211 3273 3272 Concrete & cinder building products; concrete & cinder block; ready-mixed concrete; concrete products

(G-12719)
OSCAR BRUGMANN SAND & GRAVEL
3828 Dudley Rd (44255-9426)
PHONE..............................330 274-8224
Fax: 330 274-8404
Roy Brugmann, *President*
Olga Van Auken, *Admin Sec*
Joan Martin, *Asst Sec*
EMP: 14
SQ FT: 1,000
SALES (est): 2.8MM Privately Held
SIC: 1442 Construction sand mining; gravel mining

(G-12720)
P & S WELDING CO
11611 Mantua Center Rd (44255-9447)
P.O. Box 842 (44255-0842)
PHONE..............................330 274-2850
Fax: 330 274-0146
Victor Grimm, *President*
EMP: 3
SQ FT: 3,200
SALES (est): 331K Privately Held
SIC: 3089 1799 Plastic processing; welding on site

(G-12721)
SHELLY MATERIALS INC
3943 Beck Rd (44255-9471)
PHONE..............................330 274-0802
Bruce Ahrens, *Branch Mgr*
EMP: 4
SALES (corp-wide): 28.6B Privately Held
SIC: 1422 Crushed & broken limestone
HQ: Shelly Materials, Inc.
80 Park Dr
Thornville OH 43076
740 246-6315

(G-12722)
SINGLETON REELS INC
11783 Timber Point Trl (44255-9694)
PHONE..............................330 274-2961
Fax: 330 274-0323
Scott Hamilton, *President*
Kelly Brode, *Office Mgr*
Murry Miller, *Manager*
Jerome Garro, *Info Tech Dir*
Rob Garro, *Director*
EMP: 20
SQ FT: 28,000
SALES (est): 5.6MM Privately Held
WEB: www.singletonreels.com
SIC: 2499 Reels, plywood

(G-12723)
STAMM CONTRACTING CO INC
4566 Orchard St (44255-9701)
P.O. Box 450 (44255-0450)
PHONE..............................330 274-8230
Fax: 330 274-3520
Hal Stamm, *President*

Elva Novotny, *Corp Secy*
Quinn Novotny, *Exec VP*
Paul Stamm, *Vice Pres*
Jason Hielman, *Purch Agent*
EMP: 40 EST: 1913
SQ FT: 1,500
SALES (est): 5.9MM Privately Held
WEB: www.stammcontracting.com
SIC: 3273 1541 1542 5211 Ready-mixed concrete; industrial buildings & warehouses; commercial & office building contractors; lumber & other building materials; brick, stone & related material; concrete work

(G-12724)
VICTORY ATHLETICS INC
10702 Second St (44255-9374)
PHONE..............................330 274-2854
Butch Schultz, *President*
Tammy Schultz, *Vice Pres*
EMP: 3
SALES (est): 230.2K Privately Held
WEB: www.victoryathleticsinc.com
SIC: 3949 Sporting & athletic goods

(G-12725)
VISUAL ART GRAPHIC SERVICES
5244 Goodell Rd (44255-9746)
PHONE..............................330 274-2775
George South, *President*
EMP: 30
SQ FT: 35,000
SALES (est): 3MM Privately Held
WEB: www.evisualarts.com
SIC: 2752 7336 Commercial printing, lithographic; commercial art & graphic design

---

Maple Heights
Cuyahoga County

(G-12726)
A-1 MANUFACTURING CORP
5446 Dunham Rd (44137-3653)
PHONE..............................216 475-6084
Fax: 216 475-6085
Robert Hill, *President*
Don Dillon, *Prdtn Mgr*
Marlene Hill, *Treasurer*
EMP: 9
SQ FT: 20,000
SALES (est): 1.5MM Privately Held
SIC: 3469 Metal stampings

(G-12727)
BARNES SERVICES LLC
20677 Centuryway Rd (44137-3116)
PHONE..............................440 319-2088
Leon Barnes, *Principal*
EMP: 6
SALES (est): 149.9K Privately Held
SIC: 1389 Construction, repair & dismantling services

(G-12728)
BOGGS GRAPHIC EQUIPMENT LLC
14901 Broadway Ave (44137-1107)
P.O. Box 544, Newbury (44065-0544)
PHONE..............................440 564-9675
Christopher Boggs, *Vice Pres*
Jack L Boggs,
▼ EMP: 9
SALES (est): 1.7MM Privately Held
WEB: www.boggsgraphics.com
SIC: 3555 3565 Printing trades machinery; printing presses; bookbinding machinery; collating machines for printing & bookbinding; packaging machinery

(G-12729)
BROWN-CAMPBELL COMPANY
Also Called: Brown-Campbell Steel
14400 Industrial Ave S (44137-3253)
PHONE..............................216 332-0101
Fax: 216 332-0303
Raymond Gualtier, *Manager*
EMP: 10
SQ FT: 12,000

SALES (corp-wide): 63.7MM Privately Held
WEB: www.brown-campbell.com
SIC: 3446 Gratings, open steel flooring
PA: Brown-Campbell Company
11800 Investment Dr
Shelby Township MI 48315
586 884-2180

(G-12730)
CHARLES SVEC INC (PA)
Also Called: Rock Lite
5470 Dunham Rd (44137-3690)
PHONE..............................216 662-5200
Fax: 216 662-5666
Michael Svec, *President*
Dean Svec, *Corp Secy*
Thann Peacock, *Plant Supt*
John Sanuk, *Sales Mgr*
Keith Chipchase, *Office Mgr*
EMP: 20
SQ FT: 25,000
SALES (est): 2.3MM Privately Held
SIC: 3271 3272 Concrete block & brick; concrete products

(G-12731)
CLIFTON STEEL COMPANY (PA)
16500 Rockside Rd (44137-4324)
PHONE..............................216 662-6111
Fax: 216 662-6107
Herbert C Neides, *President*
Howard Feldenkris, *Vice Pres*
Bruce Goodman, *Vice Pres*
Janis Kowalski, *Controller*
Pamela Neides, *Human Res Mgr*
▲ EMP: 89
SQ FT: 160,000
SALES (est): 56.7MM Privately Held
WEB: www.cliftonsteel.com
SIC: 5051 3441 3443 3398 Metals service centers & offices; structural shapes, iron or steel; fabricated structural metal; metal parts; metal heat treating

(G-12732)
DEWITT INC
Also Called: Non-Ferrous Heat Treating
14450 Industrial Ave N (44137-3249)
PHONE..............................216 662-0800
Fax: 216 662-4762
John Whittaker, *President*
Joe Frankhauser, *Treasurer*
EMP: 8
SQ FT: 10,000
SALES: 580K Privately Held
SIC: 3398 Metal heat treating

(G-12733)
DR Z AMPS INC
Also Called: Dr Z Amplification
17011 Broadway Ave (44137-3407)
PHONE..............................216 475-1444
Michael D Zaite, *President*
EMP: 10
SQ FT: 3,500
SALES: 2MM Privately Held
WEB: www.drzamps.com
SIC: 3651 Amplifiers: radio, public address or musical instrument

(G-12734)
ELG INC
Also Called: Leafguard
14600 Industrial Ave S (44137-3267)
PHONE..............................216 518-0476
Brad Beldon, *President*
EMP: 14
SALES (est): 158.2K
SALES (corp-wide): 53MM Privately Held
SIC: 3444 Gutters, sheet metal
HQ: Beldon Roofing & Remodeling Co, Inc
5039 West Ave
San Antonio TX 78213
210 341-3100

(G-12735)
OCTAPHARMA PLASMA INC
5398 Northfield Rd (44137-3100)
PHONE..............................216 518-0322
EMP: 5
SALES (corp-wide): 1.4B Privately Held
SIC: 2836 Plasmas

HQ: Octapharma Plasma, Inc.
10644 Westlake Dr
Charlotte NC 28273
704 654-4600

(G-12736)
OHIO MAGNETICS INC
5400 Dunham Rd (44137-3653)
PHONE.................................216 662-8484
Fax: 216 662-2911
Thomas J Pozda, *CEO*
Randy L Greely, *Ch of Bd*
John Wohlgemuth, *Manager*
▲ EMP: 36
SQ FT: 140,000
SALES (est): 8.7MM
SALES (corp-wide): 230.1MM **Privately Held**
WEB: www.ohiomagnetics.com
SIC: 3499 3559 3669 3625 Magnets, permanent: metallic; separation equipment, magnetic; metal detectors; relays & industrial controls; motors & generators; conveyors & conveying equipment
HQ: Peerless-Winsmith, Inc.
5200 Upper Metro Pl # 110
Dublin OH 43017
614 526-7000

(G-12737)
OR-TEC INC
14500 Industrial Ave S (44137-3255)
PHONE.................................216 475-5225
Ciaran O-Mezia, *President*
David Marriott, *General Mgr*
▲ EMP: 9
SALES (est): 1.5MM **Privately Held**
SIC: 3589 Sewage & water treatment equipment

(G-12738)
R AND D INCORPORATED
16645 Granite Rd (44137-4301)
PHONE.................................216 581-6328
Fax: 330 832-5080
Mary Lou Jester, *Ch of Bd*
Kerry Keyes, *President*
D Bemiller, *Sales Staff*
EMP: 27
SQ FT: 20,000
SALES (est): 6.1MM **Privately Held**
SIC: 2653 2652 Boxes, corrugated: made from purchased materials; setup paperboard boxes

(G-12739)
RACELITE SOUTH COAST INC
16518 Broadway Ave (44137-2602)
P.O. Box 370076 (44137-9076)
PHONE.................................216 581-4600
Fax: 216 663-7095
James Sima, *President*
Maryann Sima, *Admin Sec*
EMP: 10 EST: 1967
SQ FT: 5,000
SALES (est): 720K **Privately Held**
SIC: 3429 3732 3469 3312 Marine hardware; boat building & repairing; metal stampings; blast furnaces & steel mills

(G-12740)
SALON STYLING CONCEPTS LTD
Also Called: One Styling
20900 Libby Rd (44137-2929)
PHONE.................................216 539-0437
Eun Joo Park, *President*
Allison Roller, *Manager*
▲ EMP: 20 EST: 2011
SALES (est): 1.3MM **Privately Held**
SIC: 3999 Hair curlers, designed for beauty parlors

(G-12741)
SUNTWIST CORP
5461 Dunham Rd (44137-3644)
PHONE.................................800 935-3534
▲ EMP: 46
SQ FT: 38,000
SALES (est): 4.9MM **Privately Held**
SIC: 2759 Commercial Printing, Nec

(G-12742)
UNITED METAL FABRICATORS INC
14301 Industrial Ave S (44137-3252)
PHONE.................................216 662-2000
Fax: 216 662-4744
James A Martis, *Ch of Bd*
Stephen B Martis, *President*
Roald Amundson, *Info Tech Mgr*
EMP: 30
SQ FT: 16,500
SALES (est): 7.1MM **Privately Held**
WEB: www.unitedmetalfabricators.com
SIC: 3498 Tube fabricating (contract bending & shaping)

(G-12743)
US CORRUGATED OF MASSILLON
16645 Granite Rd (44137-4301)
PHONE.................................216 663-3344
Charles Messina, *CEO*
Marybeth Black, *Sales Staff*
Joe Dalpra, *Marketing Staff*
EMP: 17
SALES (est): 3.7MM **Privately Held**
SIC: 2653 Corrugated & solid fiber boxes

Marblehead
Ottawa County

(G-12744)
FERGUSONS CUT GLASS WORKS
5890 East Harbor Rd (43440-9612)
PHONE.................................419 734-0808
Cary Ferguson, *President*
Jackie Ferguson, *Vice Pres*
EMP: 5
SQ FT: 10,000
SALES (est): 516.2K **Privately Held**
SIC: 3231 Leaded glass; furniture tops, glass: cut, beveled or polished; mirrored glass; decorated glassware: chipped, engraved, etched, etc.

(G-12745)
JPB LURES MANUFACTURING LLC
7516 E Bayshore Rd Lot 25 (43440-9300)
P.O. Box 21, Lakeside Marblehead (43440-0021)
PHONE.................................419 734-9488
Jim Kiser, *Mng Member*
Paul Bormuth, *Mng Member*
EMP: 5 EST: 1999
SALES (est): 450K **Privately Held**
SIC: 3949 7389 Lures, fishing: artificial;

(G-12746)
REEF RUNNER TACKLE CO INC
102 Cherry St (43440-2209)
P.O. Box 450 (43440-0450)
PHONE.................................419 798-9125
Scott Stecher, *President*
Elizabeth Stecher, *Corp Secy*
EMP: 6
SALES (est): 300K **Privately Held**
WEB: www.reefrunner.com
SIC: 3949 Lures, fishing: artificial

Marengo
Morrow County

(G-12747)
CHAMPION MANUFACTURING INC
4025 Bennington Way (43334-9536)
P.O. Box 2003, Westerville (43086-2003)
PHONE.................................419 253-7930
Fax: 419 253-7931
Mike Mills, *President*
Dave Rose, *Director*
Bob Bayt, *Officer*
EMP: 4
SALES (est): 543.5K **Privately Held**
WEB: www.champion-mfg.com
SIC: 3069 Floor coverings, rubber

(G-12748)
CLEAR RUN LUMBER CO
2830 State Route 229 (43440-9456)
PHONE.................................740 747-2665
Millard Fisher, *Owner*
EMP: 3
SALES (est): 190.8K **Privately Held**
SIC: 2421 Sawmills & planing mills, general

(G-12749)
D & L MACHINING LLC
4621 Township Road 21 (43334-9706)
PHONE.................................419 253-1351
Don M Blair, *Principal*
EMP: 3
SALES (est): 369.5K **Privately Held**
SIC: 3599 Machine shop, jobbing & repair

(G-12750)
FISHBURN TANK TRUCK SERVICE
5012 State Route 229 (43334-9634)
P.O. Box 278 (43334-0278)
PHONE.................................419 253-6031
Jack Fishburn, *Owner*
EMP: 60
SALES (est): 2.1MM **Privately Held**
SIC: 1389 Haulage, oil field

(G-12751)
HENSEL READY MIX
4050 Bennington Way (43334-9535)
PHONE.................................419 253-9200
EMP: 3
SALES (est): 22.1K **Privately Held**
SIC: 3273 5211 Ready-mixed concrete; concrete & cinder block

(G-12752)
MARENGO FABRICATED STEEL LTD (PA)
1089 County Road 26 (43334-9643)
P.O. Box 179 (43334-0179)
PHONE.................................419 253-2119
Fax: 419 253-2119
Rick Howell, *Partner*
Robert C Howell, *Partner*
Bob Howell, *General Ptnr*
Dave Lovell, *Engineer*
Michelle Mounts, *Office Mgr*
EMP: 17
SQ FT: 60,000
SALES (est): 3.2MM **Privately Held**
SIC: 3713 Tank truck bodies; dump truck bodies

(G-12753)
SAUNDERS TRUCKING LCC
4747 State Route 229 (43334-9636)
P.O. Box 125 (43334-0125)
PHONE.................................419 210-0551
Ted Saunders, *Mng Member*
Diane Saunders, *Mng Member*
EMP: 5
SALES (est): 689.5K **Privately Held**
SIC: 3537 Truck trailers, used in plants, docks, terminals, etc.

(G-12754)
SELECT LOGGING
5739 Township Road 21 (43334-9710)
PHONE.................................419 564-0361
Jason Pauley, *Principal*
EMP: 3 EST: 2010
SALES (est): 219.2K **Privately Held**
SIC: 2411 Logging

(G-12755)
SIGN SMITH LLC
2760 County Road 26 (43334-9666)
PHONE.................................614 519-9144
Michael Shawn Smith, *Principal*
EMP: 7
SALES (est): 827.2K **Privately Held**
SIC: 3993 Signs & advertising specialties

Maria Stein
Mercer County

(G-12756)
3WAY MACHINE AND TOOL COMPANY
2411 Cssella Montezuma Rd (45860-9797)
PHONE.................................419 925-7222
David L Moorman, *President*
Lily Heart, *Vice Pres*
Dave Pottkotter, *Admin Sec*
EMP: 6
SQ FT: 3,500
SALES: 450K **Privately Held**
SIC: 3599 Machine shop, jobbing & repair

(G-12757)
BERGMAN TOOL & MACHINE CO
8066 Industrial Dr (45860-9546)
PHONE.................................419 925-4963
Ted Bergman, *President*
John Bergman, *Vice Pres*
Angie Wynk, *Manager*
EMP: 8
SQ FT: 8,000
SALES: 830K **Privately Held**
SIC: 3599 Machine shop, jobbing & repair

(G-12758)
M S WELDING
1729 Hartings Rd (45860-8711)
PHONE.................................419 925-4141
Leonard R Holdheide, *Co-Owner*
Marilyn Holdheide, *Co-Owner*
EMP: 9
SALES (est): 438.4K **Privately Held**
SIC: 7692 Welding repair

(G-12759)
MANCO MANUFACTURING CO
2411 Rolfes Rd (45860-9708)
PHONE.................................419 925-4152
Fax: 419 925-4122
Nancy Nieberding, *President*
Patrick R Nieberding, *Vice Pres*
Eric Nieberding, *Treasurer*
EMP: 8 EST: 1974
SQ FT: 14,000
SALES (est): 860K **Privately Held**
SIC: 3443 Tanks, standard or custom fabricated: metal plate

(G-12760)
PETERMANN
8037 Marion Dr (45860-8707)
PHONE.................................419 925-5404
Wayne Sucharda, *Principal*
EMP: 3
SALES (est): 232.9K **Privately Held**
SIC: 3711 Buses, all types, assembly of

(G-12761)
UNIQUE COVERS
8758 State Route 119 (45860-9521)
PHONE.................................419 925-9600
Patricia Unrast, *Owner*
EMP: 4
SALES (est): 271.9K **Privately Held**
SIC: 2679 Book covers, paper

Marietta
Washington County

(G-12762)
ARNOLDS REPAIR SHOP
101 Simpson St (45750-6759)
PHONE.................................740 373-5313
Gary J Arnold, *Partner*
Ivan F Arnold, *Partner*
Richard P Arnold, *Partner*
EMP: 3 EST: 1948
SQ FT: 2,400
SALES (est): 270K **Privately Held**
SIC: 3599 7692 Machine shop, jobbing & repair; welding repair

---

▲ = Import ▼ =Export
◆ =Import/Export

(G-12763)
ARTEX OIL COMPANY
2337 State Route 821 (45750-5362)
PHONE................................740 373-3313
Arthur Rupe, *CEO*
Jerry James, *President*
Gene Huck, *Vice Pres*
Casey Fritz, *Safety Mgr*
Debra Smith, *Accountant*
EMP: 20 EST: 1995
SALES (est): 3.9MM **Privately Held**
WEB: www.artexoil.com
SIC: 1381 Drilling oil & gas wells

(G-12764)
ASPHALT MATERIALS INC
505 River Ln (45750-8481)
PHONE................................740 373-3040
Fax: 740 373-6051
Josh Gregory, *Plant Mgr*
EMP: 4
SALES (corp-wide): 314.9MM **Privately Held**
SIC: 2951 Asphalt paving mixtures & blocks
PA: Asphalt Materials, Inc.
5400 W 86th St
Indianapolis IN 46268
317 872-6010

(G-12765)
ASPHALT MATERIALS INC
13925 State Route 7 (45750-8244)
PHONE................................740 374-5100
Fax: 740 374-5912
Josh Gregory, *Plant Mgr*
EMP: 10
SALES (corp-wide): 314.9MM **Privately Held**
SIC: 2951 Paving mixtures
PA: Asphalt Materials, Inc.
5400 W 86th St
Indianapolis IN 46268
317 872-6010

(G-12766)
BALDWIN B AA DESIGN
256 Front St (45750-2908)
P.O. Box 542 (45750-0542)
PHONE................................740 374-5844
Fax: 740 374-5844
Anthony A Baldwin, *Owner*
Rebecca Baldwin, *Co-Owner*
EMP: 4
SALES: 225K **Privately Held**
SIC: 3911 Jewelry, precious metal

(G-12767)
BOB LANES WELDING INC
545 Rummer Rd (45750-6710)
PHONE................................740 373-3567
Fax: 740 373-3426
Robert Lane, *President*
Sandra Lane, *Corp Secy*
EMP: 12
SQ FT: 6,700
SALES: 750K **Privately Held**
SIC: 1799 1623 7692 3444 Welding on site; pipe laying construction; welding repair; sheet metalwork; metal heat treating

(G-12768)
BROUGHTON FOODS COMPANY (HQ)
1701 Greene St (45750)
PHONE................................740 373-4121
Fax: 740 373-2861
Michelle Biehl, *General Mgr*
Michael McCullum, *Principal*
David Broughton, *Manager*
Dee Andris, *Info Tech Mgr*
EMP: 160 EST: 1910
SQ FT: 8,000
SALES (est): 58.6MM **Publicly Held**
SIC: 2026 2024 5451 Cottage cheese; half & half; milk processing (pasteurizing, homogenizing, bottling); yogurt; ice cream, packaged: molded, on sticks, etc.; dairy products stores

(G-12769)
C L W INC
1201 Gilman Ave (45750-9499)
PHONE................................740 374-8443
Fax: 740 374-3793
David Armstrong, *President*

Frederick L Burge, *Corp Secy*
EMP: 9
SQ FT: 7,500
SALES (est): 840K **Privately Held**
SIC: 3444 Concrete forms, sheet metal

(G-12770)
CARON PRODUCTS AND SVCS INC
27640 State Route 7 (45750-5146)
P.O. Box 715 (45750-0715)
PHONE................................740 373-6809
Fax: 740 374-3760
Jessica Fenton, *General Mgr*
Jon F Bergen, *Principal*
Bob Beckelman, *Principal*
Sue Eckberg, *Principal*
Spencer Krigsman, *Principal*
▲ **EMP:** 22
SQ FT: 12,000
SALES (est): 5.7MM **Privately Held**
WEB: www.caronproducts.com
SIC: 3823 3821 Temperature instruments: industrial process type; laboratory apparatus, except heating & measuring

(G-12771)
CARPER WELL SERVICE INC
30745 State Route 7 (45750-5177)
P.O. Box 273, Reno (45773-0273)
PHONE................................740 374-2567
Fax: 740 374-2610
Millard E Carper, *President*
Ryan Carper, *Treasurer*
Becky Whidkle, *Manager*
EMP: 10
SQ FT: 3,500
SALES (est): 792K **Privately Held**
SIC: 1389 Construction, repair & dismantling services

(G-12772)
CC INVESTORS MANAGEMENT CO LLC
30765 State Route 7 (45750-5177)
PHONE................................740 374-8129
Claudia Martin, *General Mgr*
Mark Hugh, *Engineer*
Michael D Rosenbaum, *Mktg Dir*
David Scott Farrar, *Mng Member*
Carl Hauptmann, *Director*
EMP: 2
SQ FT: 1,000
SALES: 8MM **Privately Held**
SIC: 3497 Foil containers for bakery goods & frozen foods

(G-12773)
CERTIFIED PRESSURE TESTING LLC (PA)
27515 State Route 7 (45750-5144)
P.O. Box 1437, Kalkaska MI (49646-1437)
PHONE................................740 374-2071
Jason Corser, *Principal*
Tanya Tinker, *Manager*
EMP: 8
SALES (est): 4.4MM **Privately Held**
SIC: 3829 Anamometers

(G-12774)
CITY OF MARIETTA
Also Called: Water Treatment Plant
2000 4th St (45750)
PHONE................................740 374-6864
Fax: 740 376-2002
Jaime Emerick, *Facilities Mgr*
Jeff Kephart, *Manager*
David Sands, *Director*
EMP: 40 **Privately Held**
SIC: 3589 9111 Water treatment equipment, industrial; mayors' offices
PA: City Of Marietta
301 Putnam St Frnt Frnt
Marietta OH 45750
740 373-0473

(G-12775)
COIL SPECIALTY CHEMICALS LLC
2375 Glendale Rd (45750-8038)
PHONE................................740 236-2407
Robert Coil, *Mng Member*
EMP: 8
SQ FT: 5,000

SALES (est): 1.4MM **Privately Held**
SIC: 2869 Glycerin

(G-12776)
COMMUNITY ACTION PROGRAM CORP
Also Called: Community Action Wic Hlth Svc
696 Wayne St (45750-3265)
PHONE................................740 374-8501
Fax: 740 374-3555
Kathleen Boersma, *Director*
EMP: 10
SALES (corp-wide): 9.9MM **Privately Held**
WEB: www.wmcap.org
SIC: 8399 8093 8011 2241 Community action agency; family planning & birth control clinics; offices & clinics of medical doctors; wicking
PA: Community Action Program Corp
218 Putnam St
Marietta OH 45750
740 373-3745

(G-12777)
CYTEC INDUSTRIES INC
1405 Greene St (45750-9807)
P.O. Box 388 (45750-0388)
PHONE................................740 374-7171
Gene Kunkle, *Plt & Fclts Mgr*
J R Boersma, *Engineer*
M Oliver, *Persnl Mgr*
Mike Mau, *Manager*
EMP: 3
SALES (corp-wide): 135.3MM **Privately Held**
SIC: 2899 Chemical preparations
HQ: Cytec Industries Inc.
5 Garret Mountain Plz
Woodland Park NJ 07424
973 357-3100

(G-12778)
DIMEX LLC
28305 State Route 7 (45750-5151)
PHONE................................740 374-3100
Fax: 740 374-2700
David Wesel, *CEO*
Melissa Jarvis, *Safety Dir*
Darren Bolen, *Safety Mgr*
Kathy Biehl, *Engineer*
William Dopp, *CFO*
◆ **EMP:** 120
SQ FT: 224,000
SALES (est): 50.7MM
SALES (corp-wide): 402.1MM **Privately Held**
WEB: www.dimexcorp.com
SIC: 3089 Extruded finished plastic products
PA: Grey Mountain Partners, Llc
1470 Walnut St Ste 400
Boulder CO 80302
303 449-5692

(G-12779)
DIRECTIONAL ONE SVCS INC USA
2163a-1 Gwb Complex (45750)
PHONE................................740 371-5031
Kevin Onishenko, *CEO*
Paul Cunningham, *Office Mgr*
EMP: 6
SALES (est): 565.4K **Privately Held**
SIC: 1381 Directional drilling oil & gas wells

(G-12780)
DISCOUNT SIGNS AWNINGS
114 Greene St (45750-3127)
PHONE................................740 373-3556
Penny Weeks, *Principal*
EMP: 5
SALES (est): 546.5K **Privately Held**
SIC: 3993 Signs & advertising specialties

(G-12781)
DOAK LASER
2801 Waterford Rd (45750-6910)
PHONE................................740 374-0090
Bill Doak, *Principal*
EMP: 4
SALES (est): 313.2K **Privately Held**
SIC: 3479 Etching & engraving

(G-12782)
EAGLE FIREWORKS CO (PA)
26400 State Route 7 (45750-5111)
PHONE................................740 373-3357
Fred Wells, *Owner*
▲ **EMP:** 5
SALES (est): 609.3K **Privately Held**
WEB: www.wvfireworks.net
SIC: 5999 2899 Fireworks; fireworks

(G-12783)
ELPRO SERVICES INC
210 Mill Creek Rd (45750-1394)
PHONE................................740 568-9900
Sylvain Riendeau, *President*
Andrea Bischof, *Vice Pres*
Philip Archambault, *Accounts Mgr*
Sarah Houck, *Accounts Mgr*
Brenda Earley, *Sales Staff*
EMP: 4
SQ FT: 1,200
SALES (est): 862.8K **Privately Held**
WEB: www.elpro.us
SIC: 3823 Industrial instrmnts msrmnt display/control process variable
PA: Elpro-Buchs Ag
Langaulistrasse 45
Buchs SG
815 520-808

(G-12784)
FLEXMAG INDUSTRIES INC (DH)
107 Industry Rd (45750-9355)
PHONE................................740 373-3492
Fax: 740 374-5068
Tim Wilson, *President*
Chris Weihl, *Plant Engr*
Sharon Webb, *Controller*
Ferris Arnold, *CTO*
▲ **EMP:** 100
SQ FT: 84,619
SALES (est): 18MM
SALES (corp-wide): 978.3MM **Publicly Held**
WEB: www.arnoldmagnetics.com
SIC: 3499 Magnets, permanent: metallic
HQ: Arnold Magnetic Technologies Corporation
770 Linden Ave
Rochester NY 14625
585 385-9010

(G-12785)
GHOSTBLIND INDUSTRIES INC
2347a State Route 821 (45750-5362)
P.O. Box 644 (45750-0644)
PHONE................................740 374-6766
Kevin Pottmeyer, *CEO*
▲ **EMP:** 6 EST: 2008
SQ FT: 7,500
SALES (est): 1.7MM **Privately Held**
SIC: 5091 3949 Hunting equipment & supplies; hunting equipment

(G-12786)
GILLARD CONSTRUCTION INC
Also Called: Cypress Valley Log Homes
1308 Greene St (45750-9809)
PHONE................................740 376-9744
Fax: 740 376-0744
John Gillard, *President*
Debra Gillard, *Vice Pres*
Jill Wright, *Treasurer*
Kelly Gillard, *Admin Sec*
EMP: 16
SALES: 2MM **Privately Held**
WEB: www.cypressvalleyloghomes.com
SIC: 1521 2434 5211 2452 Single-family housing construction; wood kitchen cabinets; cabinets, kitchen; log cabins, prefabricated, wood

(G-12787)
GRIMM SCIENTIFIC INDUSTRIES
1403 Pike St (45750-5106)
P.O. Box 2143 (45750-7143)
PHONE................................740 374-3412
Fax: 740 374-5745
Joseph E Grimm, *President*
Edmund Dutton, *Vice Pres*
Skip Vosler, *Vice Pres*
Walt Brothers, *Treasurer*
Tammy Williamson, *Human Resources*
EMP: 10
SQ FT: 5,000

SALES: 750K **Privately Held**
WEB: www.grimmscientific.com
SIC: **3841** Physiotherapy equipment, electrical

(G-12788)
HAESSLY LUMBER SALES CO
(PA)
25 Sheets Run Rd (45750-5186)
PHONE..................................740 373-6681
Norman E Haessly Jr, *President*
Mark Haessly, *Vice Pres*
Steve Haessly, *Vice Pres*
Julie Haessly, *Treasurer*
Jim Tidd, *Manager*
EMP: 55 EST: 1941
SQ FT: 160
SALES (est): 8.5MM **Privately Held**
SIC: **2421** 2449 2448 2435 Lumber: rough, sawed or planed; wood containers; wood pallets & skids; hardwood veneer & plywood; hardwood dimension & flooring mills; logging

(G-12789)
HARDMAGIC
125 Frederick St (45750-3407)
PHONE..................................415 390-6232
Matt Hackney, *Owner*
EMP: 12
SQ FT: 4,000
SALES: 726.5K **Privately Held**
SIC: **7336** 7372 Commercial art & graphic design; publishers' computer software

(G-12790)
HI-VAC CORPORATION
27895 State Route 7 (45750)
PHONE..................................740 374-2306
Philip Coerper, *Branch Mgr*
EMP: 7
SALES (corp-wide): 20.2MM **Privately Held**
SIC: **3589** Vacuum cleaners & sweepers, electric: industrial
PA: Hi-Vac Corporation
117 Industry Rd
Marietta OH 45750
740 374-2306

(G-12791)
HUNTER EUREKA PIPELINE LLC
125 Putnam St (45750-2936)
PHONE..................................740 374-2940
EMP: 10
SALES (est): 1.4MM
SALES (corp-wide): 154.1MM **Publicly Held**
SIC: **1311** Crude petroleum & natural gas; crude petroleum & natural gas production
PA: Blue Ridge Mountain Resources, Inc.
909 Lake Carolyn Pkwy # 600
Irving TX 75039
832 369-6986

(G-12792)
HYDE BROTHERS PRTG &
MKTG LLC (PA)
101 Rathbone Rd (45750-1437)
PHONE..................................740 373-2054
Richard Kulick, *President*
Steve Flaughers, *Vice Pres*
EMP: 4
SALES (est): 540.2K **Privately Held**
SIC: **2759** Promotional printing

(G-12793)
INLAND HARDWOOD
CORPORATION
Also Called: Inland Wood Products
25 Sheets Run Rd (45750-5186)
PHONE..................................740 373-7187
Fax: 740 373-6009
Norman E Haessly Jr, *President*
Thomas Becker, *General Mgr*
Mark Haessly, *Vice Pres*
Tom Braker, *Opers Mgr*
Steve Haessly, *Treasurer*
EMP: 72
SALES (est): 8.5MM **Privately Held**
SIC: **2448** Pallets, wood
PA: Haessly Lumber Sales Co.
25 Sheets Run Rd
Marietta OH 45750
740 373-6681

(G-12794)
JAMES ENGINEERING INC
Also Called: Artex Oil Company
2163 State Route 821 (45750-5462)
PHONE..................................740 373-9521
Fax: 740 373-2750
Jerry James, *President*
Rhonda James, *Corp Secy*
EMP: 5
SQ FT: 2,000
SALES (est): 380K **Privately Held**
SIC: **8711** 1389 Consulting engineer; oil field services

(G-12795)
JMIKE LLC
110 Windy Pt (45750-9371)
PHONE..................................740 525-1734
Brenda Jones,
EMP: 4 EST: 2011
SALES (est): 172.3K **Privately Held**
SIC: **2086** Carbonated beverages, nonalcoholic: bottled & canned

(G-12796)
KEITO GAS INC
101 Wheelbarrow Run Rd (45750-5248)
P.O. Box 256, Reno (45773-0256)
PHONE..................................740 374-5463
EMP: 4
SALES (est): 267.8K **Privately Held**
SIC: **1381** Drilling oil & gas wells

(G-12797)
KETELI TEAMWEAR LLC
111 Putnam St (45750-2924)
PHONE..................................740 373-7969
Brian Ketelsen, *Owner*
EMP: 3
SALES (est): 230.5K **Privately Held**
SIC: **2759** Commercial printing

(G-12798)
KROGER CO
40 Acme St (45750-3306)
PHONE..................................740 374-2523
Fax: 740 374-5353
Stan Ness, *Manager*
Stan Neff, *Manager*
EMP: 100
SALES (corp-wide): 115.3B **Publicly Held**
WEB: www.kroger.com
SIC: **5411** 5992 5912 5812 Supermarkets, chain; florists; drug stores & proprietary stores; eating places; cookies & crackers; bread, cake & related products
PA: The Kroger Co
1014 Vine St Ste 1000
Cincinnati OH 45202
513 762-4000

(G-12799)
LOKEN OIL FIELD SERVICES
LLC
2190 Olinn Rd (45750-6525)
PHONE..................................740 749-3495
Curtis L Loken, *Principal*
EMP: 3 EST: 2009
SALES (est): 127.1K **Privately Held**
SIC: **1389** Oil field services

(G-12800)
LONGYEAR COMPANY
1010 Greene St (45750-2409)
PHONE..................................740 373-2190
EMP: 35
SALES (corp-wide): 735.1MM **Privately Held**
SIC: **1481** Test boring for nonmetallic minerals
HQ: Longyear Company
10808 S River Front Pkwy
South Jordan UT 84095
801 972-6430

(G-12801)
MAGNUM MAGNETICS
CORPORATION (PA)
Also Called: Magnum Inks & Coatings
801 Masonic Park Rd (45750-9357)
PHONE..................................740 373-7770
Fax: 740 373-2880
Allen Love, *President*
Bruce Dean, *General Mgr*

Joe Stout, *General Mgr*
Tom Love, *Vice Pres*
Doug Rummer, *Prdtn Mgr*
▼ EMP: 160
SQ FT: 30,000
SALES (est): 30.3MM **Privately Held**
WEB: www.magnummagnetics.com
SIC: **3499** Magnets, permanent: metallic

(G-12802)
MARIETTA ERAMET INC
16705 State Route 7 (45750-8519)
P.O. Box 299 (45750-0299)
PHONE..................................740 374-1000
Frank Vallera, *Engineer*
Michel Masci, *CFO*
Marc Blanquart, *CFO*
Jay Arnold, *Human Res Mgr*
Dean Douglass, *Department Mgr*
▲ EMP: 205
SALES (est): 112.4MM
SALES (corp-wide): 618.6MM **Privately Held**
WEB: www.emspecialproducts.com
SIC: **3313** Ferroalloys
HQ: Eramet Holding Manganese
Tour Maine Montparnasse
Paris 75015
145 384-242

(G-12803)
MARIETTA RESOURCES
CORPORATION
704 Pike St (45750-3501)
PHONE..................................740 373-6305
Lynn Foster, *President*
EMP: 10
SALES (est): 970K **Privately Held**
SIC: **1311** Crude petroleum production; natural gas production

(G-12804)
MARTYS PRINT SHOP
307 3rd St (45750-2902)
PHONE..................................740 373-3454
Fax: 740 373-3454
Marty Margolis, *Owner*
EMP: 3
SQ FT: 1,700
SALES (est): 327K **Privately Held**
SIC: **2752** Commercial printing, offset

(G-12805)
MASTER MAGNETICS INC
Also Called: Magnetic Source
108 Industry Rd (45750-9355)
PHONE..................................740 373-0909
Fax: 740 373-0970
Dewayne Collins, *Branch Mgr*
EMP: 12
SALES (corp-wide): 15.5MM **Privately Held**
WEB: www.magnetsource.com
SIC: **3357** Magnet wire, nonferrous
PA: Master Magnetics, Inc.
747 S Gilbert St
Castle Rock CO 80104
303 688-3966

(G-12806)
MC ALARNEY POOL SPAS AND
BILLD
Also Called: McAlarney Pols Spas Billd More
908 Pike St (45750-3505)
PHONE..................................740 373-6698
Fax: 740 373-7724
Cheryl McAlarney, *President*
Wayne Mc Alarney, *Exec VP*
EMP: 25 EST: 1975
SQ FT: 6,500
SALES: 1.2MM **Privately Held**
WEB: www.mcalarney.com
SIC: **5091** 3949 Swimming pools, equipment & supplies; spa equipment & supplies; billiard equipment & supplies; sporting & athletic goods

(G-12807)
MICHAEL BRADLEY
APPARATUS LLC
116 Industry Rd (45750-9355)
PHONE..................................740 374-6255
Brad Webb, *Sales Staff*
Kristi Potts, *Office Mgr*
Kristi Baker, *Manager*

Kevin Joyce, *Manager*
Michael D Beardmore,
EMP: 10
SQ FT: 10,000
SALES (est): 3.9MM **Privately Held**
SIC: **3621** 7629 Motors & generators; electrical repair shops

(G-12808)
MIDWAY MACHINING INC
1060 Gravel Bank Rd (45750-8370)
PHONE..................................740 373-8976
Fax: 740 373-7240
Robert L Casto, *President*
Katherine E Murphy, *Corp Secy*
Gary Hendershot, *Vice Pres*
Katherine Casto, *Manager*
Brooke Proffitt, *Admin Sec*
EMP: 11
SQ FT: 3,000
SALES (est): 1.8MM **Privately Held**
WEB: www.midwaymachininginc.net
SIC: **3599** Machine shop, jobbing & repair

(G-12809)
MORRIS PAVING
1470 Killwell Run Rd (45750-7480)
PHONE..................................740 373-2457
Mike Moore, *President*
EMP: 16
SQ FT: 300
SALES (est): 1.7MM **Privately Held**
SIC: **2951** 1771 Asphalt & asphaltic paving mixtures (not from refineries); blacktop (asphalt) work

(G-12810)
NEW MULCH IN A BOTTLE
LIMITED
140 Gross St Ste 116 (45750-2031)
PHONE..................................724 290-2341
Russell Coffin,
EMP: 4
SALES (est): 282.5K **Privately Held**
SIC: **2869** Carbon disulfide

(G-12811)
OHIO VALLEY ALLOY SERVICES
INC
100 Westview Ave (45750-9403)
PHONE..................................740 373-1900
Fax: 740 373-1943
Randall Henthorn, *President*
Richard J Henthorn Jr, *Treasurer*
Laura Fischer, *Manager*
▲ EMP: 20
SQ FT: 2,500
SALES (est): 4.3MM **Privately Held**
SIC: **3312** 4225 3341 Blast furnaces & steel mills; general warehousing; secondary nonferrous metals

(G-12812)
OHIO VALLEY SPECIALTY
COMPANY
115 Industry Rd (45750-9355)
PHONE..................................740 373-2276
Fax: 740 373-9910
Larry G Hawkins, *President*
Frank D Mendicino, *Vice Pres*
John Schafer, *Prdtn Mgr*
Art Mendicino, *Manager*
EMP: 12
SQ FT: 7,000
SALES (est): 2.4MM **Privately Held**
WEB: www.ovsc.com
SIC: **3339** Silicon, pure

(G-12813)
PARDSON INC
Also Called: Bird Watcher's Digest
149 Acme St (45750-3402)
P.O. Box 110 (45750-0110)
PHONE..................................740 373-5285
Fax: 740 373-8443
William Thompson III, *President*
Andy Thompson, *President*
Jim Cirigliano, *Editor*
Elsa Thompson, *Treasurer*
Ann Kerenyi, *Controller*
EMP: 13
SQ FT: 3,400

SALES: 1.3MM **Privately Held**
SIC: 2721 2731 5961 Magazines: publishing only, not printed on site; book publishing; mail order house

(G-12814)
PAWNEE MAINTENANCE INC
111 3rd St (45750-3107)
P.O. Box 269 (45750-0269)
PHONE..................740 373-6861
Fax: 740 373-6832
Ted R Szabo, *President*
Judy Pierpont, *Manager*
EMP: 60
SQ FT: 3,000
SALES (est): 5.5MM **Privately Held**
WEB: www.pawnee.com
SIC: 1541 3272 Industrial buildings & warehouses; concrete products

(G-12815)
PEN-ANN CORPORATION
Also Called: Hyde Brothers Printing Co
101 Rathbone Rd (45750-1437)
P.O. Box 586 (45750-0586)
PHONE..................740 373-2054
Fax: 740 373-8440
Lewis Camp, *President*
David McCullough, *Corp Secy*
Joan Hushion, *Vice Pres*
EMP: 9 **EST:** 1991
SQ FT: 5,000
SALES (est): 1.4MM **Privately Held**
WEB: www.hydebrothersprinting.com
SIC: 2752 Commercial printing, lithographic

(G-12816)
PIONEER PIPE INC
Also Called: Pioneer Pipe Fabricating
2021 Hanna Rd (45750-8255)
PHONE..................740 376-2400
Fax: 740 373-8964
David M Archer, *President*
Matthew Hilverding, *Corp Secy*
Arlene M Archer, *Vice Pres*
Karl Robinson, *Vice Pres*
Larry Silvus, *Transptn Dir*
▲ **EMP:** 275
SQ FT: 24,800
SALES (est): 153.8MM **Privately Held**
WEB: www.pioneerpipeinc.com
SIC: 3498 1711 3443 3441 Pipe sections fabricated from purchased pipe; pipe fittings, fabricated from purchased pipe; plumbing contractors; warm air heating & air conditioning contractor; mechanical contractor; fabricated plate work (boiler shop); fabricated structural metal; blast furnaces & steel mills

(G-12817)
PITNEY BOWES INC
111 Marshall Rd (45750-1160)
PHONE..................740 374-5535
Marcia Pawloski, *Branch Mgr*
EMP: 60
SALES (corp-wide): 3.4B **Publicly Held**
SIC: 3579 7359 Postage meters; business machine & electronic equipment rental services
PA: Pitney Bowes Inc.
3001 Summer St Ste 3
Stamford CT 06905
203 356-5000

(G-12818)
PRAXAIR INC
2034 Blue Knob Rd (45750)
PHONE..................740 374-5525
Chip Green, *Manager*
EMP: 12
SALES (corp-wide): 10.5B **Publicly Held**
SIC: 2813 Industrial gases
PA: Praxair, Inc.
10 Riverview Dr
Danbury CT 06810
203 837-2000

(G-12819)
PREMIER PRINTING SOLUTIONS
115 Pineview Cir (45750-9433)
PHONE..................740 374-2836
Max Huck, *Owner*
EMP: 4 **EST:** 2001

SALES (est): 319.5K **Privately Held**
SIC: 2752 Commercial printing, lithographic

(G-12820)
PRESSMARK INC
641 State Route 821 Ste A (45750-8042)
P.O. Box 931, Cornelius NC (28031-0931)
PHONE..................740 373-6005
Richard F Cataldo, *President*
Dona Cernus, *Manager*
Barbara Cataldo, *Admin Sec*
EMP: 5
SQ FT: 3,500
SALES (est): 650.3K **Privately Held**
WEB: www.pressmarkprinting.com
SIC: 2752 Commercial printing, offset

(G-12821)
PROFUSION INDUSTRIES LLC
700 Bf Goodrich Rd (45750-7849)
P.O. Box 657 (45750-0657)
PHONE..................740 374-6400
Dave Everly, *Opers Mgr*
Nick Garst, *Research*
Jon Golden, *Branch Mgr*
Bill Kenworthy, *CIO*
EMP: 92
SALES (corp-wide): 27.2MM **Privately Held**
SIC: 3081 Unsupported plastics film & sheet
PA: Profusion Industries, Llc
822 Kumho Dr Ste 202
Fairlawn OH 44333
800 938-2858

(G-12822)
RAMPP COMPANY (PA)
20445 State Route 550 Ofc (45750-6900)
P.O. Box 608 (45750-0608)
PHONE..................740 373-7886
Fax: 740 373-0624
Mark E Fulton, *President*
Charles D Fogle, *Principal*
David Fox, *Principal*
Charles Hall, *Principal*
Martin J Ramp, *Principal*
EMP: 45 **EST:** 1950
SQ FT: 50,000
SALES (est): 9.9MM **Privately Held**
WEB: www.ramppco.com
SIC: 3533 3443 3425 Drilling tools for gas, oil or water wells; crane hooks, laminated plate; alloy steel castings, except investment

(G-12823)
RENT-A-CENTER INC
243 Captain D Seeley Mia (45750-3508)
PHONE..................740 373-1342
Mike Morgan, *Manager*
EMP: 5
SALES (corp-wide): 2.9B **Publicly Held**
WEB: www.rentacenter.com
SIC: 3699 Appliance cords for household electrical equipment
PA: Rent-A-Center, Inc.
5501 Headquarters Dr
Plano TX 75024
972 801-1100

(G-12824)
RICHARDSON PRINTING CORP (PA)
Also Called: Zip Center, The-Division
201 Acme St (45750-3404)
P.O. Box 663 (45750-0663)
PHONE..................740 373-5362
Fax: 740 373-8713
Dennis E Valentine, *President*
Candace Schwab, *Manager*
Robert Richardson Jr, *Shareholder*
Charles E Schwab, *Admin Sec*
▲ **EMP:** 60 **EST:** 1944
SQ FT: 100,000
SALES (est): 8.5MM **Privately Held**
WEB: www.rpcprint.com
SIC: 2752 7389 Commercial printing, lithographic; commercial printing, offset; photo-offset printing; mailing & messenger services

(G-12825)
ROCKBOTTOM OIL & GAS
Also Called: Gibson, Jo K
1 Court House Ln Ste 3 (45750-2900)
PHONE..................740 374-2478
Charles Kiser, *Partner*
EMP: 3
SALES (est): 216.6K **Privately Held**
SIC: 1381 Drilling oil & gas wells

(G-12826)
ROSSI PASTA FACTORY INC
106 Front St (45750-3123)
P.O. Box 930 (45750-0930)
PHONE..................740 376-2065
Fax: 740 373-5310
Frank Christy, *Ch of Bd*
John Hammat, *President*
Brandy Dibert, *Sales Dir*
Brian Hausman, *Manager*
EMP: 15
SQ FT: 8,000
SALES (est): 1.8MM **Privately Held**
WEB: www.rossipasta.com
SIC: 2099 5499 Pasta, uncooked: packaged with other ingredients; gourmet food stores

(G-12827)
SEWAH STUDIOS INC
190 Mill Creek Rd (45750-1381)
P.O. Box 298 (45750-0298)
PHONE..................740 373-2087
Fax: 740 373-3733
Bradford Smith, *President*
David Smith, *Vice Pres*
EMP: 15 **EST:** 1927
SQ FT: 6,000
SALES (est): 1.3MM **Privately Held**
WEB: www.sewahstudios.com
SIC: 3446 Architectural metalwork

(G-12828)
SHELLY AND SANDS INC
Hc 7 Box S (45750)
P.O. Box 1 (45750-0001)
PHONE..................740 373-6495
Roger Thomas, *Manager*
EMP: 10
SALES (corp-wide): 301.4MM **Privately Held**
WEB: www.shellyandsands.com
SIC: 2951 Asphalt & asphaltic paving mixtures (not from refineries)
PA: Shelly And Sands, Inc.
3570 S River Rd
Zanesville OH 43701
740 453-0721

(G-12829)
SILICON PROCESSORS INC
1988 Masonic Park Rd (45750-5402)
PHONE..................740 373-2252
W Trent Elliott, *President*
David Downing, *CFO*
EMP: 6
SALES (est): 950K **Privately Held**
SIC: 3339 Silicon refining (primary, over 99% pure)

(G-12830)
SILVESCO INC
2985 State Route 26 (45750-7586)
P.O. Box 161 (45750-0161)
PHONE..................740 373-6661
Fax: 740 373-4995
Rodney Paxton, *President*
Michele Paxton, *Vice Pres*
Marika Akers, *Recruiter*
EMP: 10 **EST:** 1964
SQ FT: 11,800
SALES (est): 1.3MM **Privately Held**
SIC: 2448 2449 Pallets, wood; rectangular boxes & crates, wood

(G-12831)
SKUTTLE MFG CO
Also Called: Skuttle Indoor Air Qulty Pdts
101 Margaret St (45750-9052)
PHONE..................740 373-9169
Fax: 740 373-9565
Davis Powers, *President*
Debby Romick, *Corp Secy*
Mike Ward, *Plant Mgr*
John Hinton, *Purchasing*
Earl Lewis Jr, *Engineer*

▲ **EMP:** 14 **EST:** 1917
SQ FT: 96,500
SALES: 3.5MM **Privately Held**
WEB: www.skuttle.com
SIC: 3634 3564 3822 Humidifiers, electric: household; filters, air: furnaces, air conditioning equipment, etc.; auto controls regulating residntl & coml environmt & applncs

(G-12832)
SMITH BROTHERS ERECTION INC
101 Industry Rd (45750-9355)
PHONE..................740 373-3575
Robert A Gribben Jr, *President*
Robert A Gribben III, *Director*
EMP: 45 **EST:** 2011
SALES: 1.2MM **Privately Held**
SIC: 1791 3449 Structural steel erection; bars, concrete reinforcing: fabricated steel

(G-12833)
SOLVAY SPCLTY POLYMERS USA LLC
17005 State Route 7 (45750-8248)
P.O. Box 446 (45750-0446)
PHONE..................740 373-9242
Craig Wade, *Buyer*
Vincent Nedeff, *QA Dir*
Wally Kandell, *Branch Mgr*
EMP: 20
SALES (corp-wide): 135.3MM **Privately Held**
WEB: www.solvayadvancedpolymers.com
SIC: 3089 Plastic processing
HQ: Solvay Specialty Polymers Usa, L.L.C.
4500 Mcginnis Ferry Rd
Alpharetta GA 30005
770 772-8200

(G-12834)
SOMERVILLE MANUFACTURING INC
15 Townhall Rd (45750-5374)
PHONE..................740 336-7847
Steve Somerville, *President*
Peggy Somerville, *Vice Pres*
EMP: 20
SALES (est): 4.4MM **Privately Held**
SIC: 3441 3444 7692 Fabricated structural metal; sheet metalwork; welding repair

(G-12835)
STEVENS OIL & GAS LLC
110 Lynch Church Rd (45750-7545)
PHONE..................740 374-4542
Matthew Stevens, *Principal*
EMP: 7
SALES (est): 621.5K **Privately Held**
SIC: 1389 Oil & gas field services

(G-12836)
STEVES VANS & ACCESSORIES LLC
Also Called: Marietta Mobility
221 Pike St (45750-3320)
PHONE..................740 374-3154
Fax: 740 374-9713
Stephen K Hesson,
EMP: 9
SQ FT: 3,700
SALES (est): 3.4MM **Privately Held**
SIC: 5511 7532 5531 5999 Vans, new & used; van conversion; automotive accessories; technical aids for the handicapped; recreational vehicle parts & accessories; wheelchair lifts

(G-12837)
STONEBRIDGE OILFIELD SVCS LLC
406 Colegate Dr (45750-9252)
P.O. Box 60 (45750-0060)
PHONE..................740 373-6134
Eddy Biehl, *Manager*
EMP: 55
SALES (est): 3.8MM **Privately Held**
SIC: 1389 Oil field services

(G-12838)
STRATAGRAPH NE INC
116 Ellsworth Ave (45750-8607)
P.O. Box 59, Reno (45773-0059)
PHONE...............................740 373-3091
Fax: 740 373-3091
Walt Teer, *President*
EMP: 32
SQ FT: 2,400
SALES: 700K **Privately Held**
SIC: 1389 1381 Oil field services; drilling oil & gas wells

(G-12839)
SUMMERS ACQUISITION CORP
Also Called: Summers Rubber Co Branch 06
100 Tennis Center Dr (45750-8802)
PHONE...............................740 373-0303
Fax: 740 373-8574
Bruce Mullen, *General Mgr*
Mel Shipley, *Branch Mgr*
EMP: 4
SALES (corp-wide): 2.5B **Privately Held**
WEB: www.summersrubber.com
SIC: 3052 3492 Rubber hose; hose & tube fittings & assemblies, hydraulic/pneumatic
HQ: Summers Acquisition Corporation
12555 Berea Rd
Cleveland OH 44111
216 941-7700

(G-12840)
TERRA SONIC INTERNATIONAL LLC
27825 State Route 7 (45750-9060)
PHONE...............................740 374-6608
Jim Walker, *Business Mgr*
Kim Satterfield, *Controller*
John Walsh, *Mng Member*
Sharen Savinkoff, *Manager*
James Savinkoff, *Supervisor*
◆ **EMP:** 22 **EST:** 1998
SQ FT: 600,000
SALES (est): 6.9MM **Privately Held**
SIC: 3533 1623 7353 Oil & gas field machinery; oil & gas drilling rigs & equipment; oil & gas pipeline construction; oil field equipment, rental or leasing

(G-12841)
THERMO FISHER SCIENTIFIC
401 Mill Creek Rd (45750-4304)
P.O. Box 649 (45750-0649)
PHONE...............................740 373-4763
David Leister, *Opers Staff*
Carrie Conley, *Purch Agent*
Jamie Keefer, *Branch Mgr*
Tom Kuhn, *Manager*
Gordon Shields, *Software Dev*
EMP: 592
SQ FT: 287
SALES (corp-wide): 18.2B **Publicly Held**
WEB: www.thermo.com
SIC: 3821 Freezers, laboratory
HQ: Thermo Fisher Scientific (Ashville) Llc
28 Schenck Pkwy Ste 400
Asheville NC 28803
828 658-2711

(G-12842)
TOP DRILLING CORPORATION (PA)
107 Lancaster St 301 (45750-2734)
PHONE...............................304 477-3333
Doug Haught, *President*
Robin J Cook, *Director*
EMP: 15
SQ FT: 1,000
SALES (est): 2.7MM **Privately Held**
WEB: www.topdrilling.com
SIC: 1381 Directional drilling oil & gas wells

(G-12843)
TRADEMARK SOLUTIONS
2167 State Route 821 B (45750-1196)
P.O. Box 243 (45750-0243)
PHONE...............................740 374-9779
Joan E Zoller, *Owner*
EMP: 3
SALES (est): 529.1K **Privately Held**
SIC: 2395 Embroidery products, except schiffli machine

(G-12844)
TRIAD ENERGY CORPORATION
125 Putnam St (45750-2936)
PHONE...............................740 374-2940
Kean Weaver, *President*
James R Bryden, *Vice Pres*
Brent Powell, *Safety Mgr*
Kim Arnold, *Human Res Mgr*
EMP: 26
SALES (est): 3.3MM **Privately Held**
SIC: 2992 1382 Lubricating oils & greases; oil & gas exploration services

(G-12845)
TRIAD HUNTER LLC (HQ)
125 Putnam St (45750-2936)
PHONE...............................740 374-2940
Richard S Farrell, *Senior VP*
James W Denny III, *Vice Pres*
Mike Horan, *Vice Pres*
Sam Miracle, *Project Mgr*
Rodney Boron, *Opers Staff*
EMP: 15
SALES (est): 40.4MM
SALES (corp-wide): 154.1MM **Publicly Held**
SIC: 1311 Crude petroleum & natural gas
PA: Blue Ridge Mountain Resources, Inc.
909 Lake Carolyn Pkwy # 600
Irving TX 75039
832 369-6986

(G-12846)
TRIAD HUNTER LLC
125 Putnam St (45750-2936)
PHONE...............................740 374-2940
Kimberly R Arnold, *Branch Mgr*
EMP: 9
SALES (corp-wide): 154.1MM **Publicly Held**
SIC: 1311 Crude petroleum & natural gas
HQ: Triad Hunter, Llc
125 Putnam St
Marietta OH 45750

(G-12847)
UNITED CHART PROCESSORS INC
1461 Masonic Park Rd (45750-5393)
PHONE...............................740 373-5801
David Graham, *President*
Barbara Graham, *Vice Pres*
Dave Medley, *Supervisor*
EMP: 8
SALES (est): 881.5K **Privately Held**
SIC: 1389 Gas field services

(G-12848)
VIKING FABRICATORS INC
2021 Hanna Rd (45750-8255)
PHONE...............................740 374-5246
Fax: 740 374-5232
David M Archer, *President*
James S Huggins, *Principal*
Matthew Hilverding, *Corp Secy*
Arlene M Archer, *Vice Pres*
EMP: 25
SQ FT: 20,000
SALES (est): 5.1MM **Privately Held**
SIC: 3441 7692 3446 3443 Fabricated structural metal; welding repair; architectural metalwork; fabricated plate work (boiler shop)

(G-12849)
VIKING INTL RESOURCES CO INC
Also Called: Virco
125 Putnam St (45750-2936)
PHONE...............................304 628-3878
Fax: 740 373-9511
Thomas G Palmer, *President*
John Albrecht, *Manager*
EMP: 5
SQ FT: 1,200
SALES (est): 1.1MM
SALES (corp-wide): 154.1MM **Publicly Held**
WEB: www.vircoinc.net
SIC: 1311 Crude petroleum & natural gas production
HQ: Triad Hunter, Llc
125 Putnam St
Marietta OH 45750

(G-12850)
WINSTON OIL CO INC
1 Court House Ln Ste 3 (45750-2900)
P.O. Box 754 (45750-0754)
PHONE...............................740 373-9664
Deborah Cunningham, *Principal*
EMP: 7
SALES (est): 647K **Privately Held**
SIC: 3569 Gas producers, generators & other gas related equipment

(G-12851)
YOUTHTOPIA LLC
Also Called: Youthtopia Beverages
110 Windy Pt (45750-9371)
PHONE...............................740 525-1734
Brenda Jones,
Ron Fuqua,
EMP: 4
SALES: 350K **Privately Held**
SIC: 2086 Carbonated beverages, nonalcoholic: bottled & canned

(G-12852)
ZIDE SPORT SHOP OF OHIO INC
Also Called: Zide Screen Printing
118 Industry Rd (45750-9355)
PHONE...............................740 373-8199
Fax: 740 374-3406
Randy Schneeberger, *Manager*
EMP: 14
SALES (corp-wide): 6.6MM **Privately Held**
SIC: 2396 Screen printing on fabric articles
PA: Zide Sport Shop Of Ohio, Inc.
253 2nd St
Marietta OH 45750
740 373-6446

Marion
Marion County

(G-12853)
ALIN MACHINING COMPANY INC
875 E Mark St (43302-2748)
PHONE...............................740 223-0200
Ryan Dballinger, *Branch Mgr*
EMP: 43
SALES (corp-wide): 80.5MM **Privately Held**
SIC: 3511 Turbines & turbine generator sets
PA: Alin Machining Company, Inc.
3131 W Soffel Ave
Melrose Park IL 60160
708 681-1043

(G-12854)
AMBASSADOR STEEL CORPORATION
850 Barks Rd W (43302-7270)
PHONE...............................740 382-9969
Richard Kripps, *Plant Mgr*
Paul Klautsch, *Sales Staff*
Gene Baker, *Manager*
EMP: 12
SALES (corp-wide): 16.2B **Publicly Held**
WEB: www.ambassadorsteel.com
SIC: 3441 5051 Fabricated structural metal; bars, metal
HQ: Ambassador Steel Corporation
1340 S Grandstaff Dr
Auburn IN 46706
260 925-5440

(G-12855)
ARCELORMITTAL TUBULAR
686 W Fairground St (43302-1706)
PHONE...............................740 382-3979
Jerome Granboulan, *CEO*
Bhikam Agarwal, *Exec VP*
Verne Sizemore, *Engineer*
Mark Bryer, *CFO*
Tim Abbott, *VP Sales*
▲ **EMP:** 100
SQ FT: 410,000
SALES (est): 21.9MM **Privately Held**
WEB: www.dofascomarion.com
SIC: 3317 Steel pipe & tubes
HQ: Arcelormittal Tubular Products Luxembourg Sa
Boulevard D'avranches 24-26
Luxembourg

(G-12856)
ARCELORMITTAL USA LLC
686 W Fairground St (43302-1706)
PHONE...............................740 375-2299
Bernard Buchanan, *General Mgr*
Carl Spitzer, *Safety Mgr*
George J Cavender, *Buyer*
Jay Varhola, *Engineer*
Dan J Hughes, *Sales Associate*
EMP: 14 **Privately Held**
SIC: 3449 Bars, concrete reinforcing: fabricated steel
HQ: Arcelormittal Usa Llc
1 S Dearborn St Ste 1800
Chicago IL 60603
312 346-0300

(G-12857)
BERT RADEBAUGH
Also Called: American Quality Door
1544 Marion Marysville Rd (43302-7332)
PHONE...............................740 382-8134
Fax: 740 382-4067
Bert Radebaugh, *Owner*
EMP: 3
SALES: 350K **Privately Held**
SIC: 5031 1751 7699 5211 Doors & windows; window & door installation & erection; door & window repair; door & window products; door opening & closing devices, electrical

(G-12858)
BUCKEYE READY-MIX LLC
627 Likens Rd (43302-8653)
PHONE...............................740 387-8846
Kevin McCoy, *Manager*
EMP: 10
SALES (corp-wide): 42.4MM **Privately Held**
WEB: www.buckeyereadymix.com
SIC: 3273 Ready-mixed concrete
PA: Buckeye Ready-Mix, Llc
7657 Taylor Rd Sw
Reynoldsburg OH 43068
614 575-2132

(G-12859)
BUNGE NORTH AMERICA FOUNDATION
751 E Farming St (43302-3113)
P.O. Box 1805 (43301-1805)
PHONE...............................740 383-1181
EMP: 63 **Privately Held**
SIC: 2075 Soybean Oil Mill
HQ: Bunge North America Foundation
11720 Borman Dr
Saint Louis MO 63146
314 872-3030

(G-12860)
BUZZ N SHUTTLE SERVICE
333 Executive Dr Apt I (43302-6351)
PHONE...............................740 223-0567
EMP: 3 **EST:** 2000
SALES (est): 170K **Privately Held**
SIC: 3532 Mfg Mining Machinery

(G-12861)
CARL GRAPHICS COMPANY
Also Called: Carl Graphics Printing
600 Bellefontaine Ave (43302-6196)
PHONE...............................740 382-6583
Fax: 740 382-2393
Carl Wade, *President*
EMP: 4 **EST:** 1955
SQ FT: 5,000
SALES: 402.5K **Privately Held**
WEB: www.carlgraphics.com
SIC: 2752 Commercial printing, offset

(G-12862)
CENTRAL MACHINERY COMPANY LLC
Also Called: Denmac Metalworks
1339 E Fairground Rd (43302-8873)
PHONE...............................740 387-1289
Fax: 740 383-3751
Rod Galbreath, *President*
EMP: 17 **EST:** 2001
SQ FT: 25,000

SALES (est): 4.2MM **Privately Held**
SIC: 3544 Subpresses, metalworking;
punches, forming & stamping

(G-12863)
COUNTRY CATERERS INC (PA)
Also Called: Riverside Homemade Ice Cream
409 Mrion Cardington Rd W (43302-7313)
PHONE...................................740 389-1013
Fax: 740 389-1013
Rob Lill, *President*
Vickie Lill, *Vice Pres*
EMP: 4
SQ FT: 2,000
SALES (est): 296.1K **Privately Held**
WEB: www.countrycaterers.net
SIC: 5812 2024 Caterers; ice cream, bulk

(G-12864)
CREATIVE DOCUMENTS SOLUTIONS
1629 Marion Waldo Rd (43302-7425)
PHONE...................................740 389-4252
Lorraine Corbin, *Principal*
EMP: 6
SALES (est): 1MM **Privately Held**
SIC: 2759 Commercial printing

(G-12865)
FOLKS CREATIVE PRINTERS INC
101 E George St (43302-2304)
PHONE...................................740 383-6326
Fax: 740 382-5628
Trudi E Maish, *Ch of Bd*
James L Saiter, *President*
Dixon Ericson, *Manager*
Linda M Maish, *Admin Sec*
Chris Dickson, *Admin Asst*
EMP: 27 EST: 1922
SALES (est): 3.6MM **Privately Held**
WEB: www.folksprinting.com
SIC: 2752 3993 2789 2759 Commercial
printing, offset; signs & advertising spe-
cialties; bookbinding & related work; com-
mercial printing

(G-12866)
GANNETT CO INC
Also Called: Marion Star
163 E Center St (43302-3813)
PHONE...................................419 521-7341
Fax: 740 375-5111
Tom Brennan, *Editor*
Linda Millisor, *Sales & Mktg St*
Aalok Kharel, *Manager*
Lou Phillips, *Manager*
Karie Sargent, *Manager*
EMP: 41
SALES (corp-wide): 3B **Publicly Held**
WEB: www.gannett.com
SIC: 2711 Newspapers: publishing only,
not printed on site
PA: Gannett Co., Inc.
7950 Jones Branch Dr
Mc Lean VA 22102
703 854-6000

(G-12867)
GENERAL MACHINE & SAW COMPANY
305 Davis St (43302)
PHONE...................................740 375-5730
Don Miracle, *Mfg Spvr*
Matt Murphy, *Branch Mgr*
EMP: 21
SALES (corp-wide): 16.9MM **Privately Held**
SIC: 3317 Steel pipe & tubes
PA: General Machine & Saw Company
740 W Center St
Marion OH 43302
740 382-1104

(G-12868)
GEYER TRANSPORT & MFG
1443 N Main St (43302-1551)
PHONE...................................740 382-9008
Steve Ritchey, *President*
EMP: 18
SALES (est): 1.3MM **Privately Held**
SIC: 3799 1799 Trailer hitches; welding on
site

(G-12869)
GRAPHIC PACKAGING INTL INC
1171 W Center St (43302-3465)
PHONE...................................740 387-6543
Bill Campagna, *Manager*
Haza Eddauod, *Manager*
Sharon Young, *Director*
EMP: 150
SQ FT: 100,000 **Publicly Held**
SIC: 2657 Folding paperboard boxes
HQ: Graphic Packaging International, Inc.
1500 Riveredge Pkwy # 100
Atlanta GA 30328
770 240-7200

(G-12870)
GRINDEL SALES CORP
1645 Cascade Dr (43302-8509)
PHONE...................................740 382-1528
Fax: 740 383-1780
Steve Sandridge, *President*
Kim Murray, *Office Mgr*
Cheryll Sandridge, *Admin Sec*
EMP: 5
SQ FT: 5,000
SALES (est): 470K **Privately Held**
WEB: www.pistolammo.com
SIC: 3482 Small arms ammunition; car-
tridge cases for ammunition, 30 mm. &
below

(G-12871)
HANGER PRSTHETCS & ORTHO INC
1136 Independence Ave (43302-6318)
PHONE...................................419 522-0055
Fax: 419 525-0442
Bill Neu, *Manager*
EMP: 3
SALES (corp-wide): 460MM **Publicly Held**
SIC: 8071 3842 5999 Medical laborato-
ries; limbs, artificial; orthopedic & prosthe-
sis applications
HQ: Hanger Prosthetics & Orthotics, Inc.
10910 Domain Dr Ste 300
Austin TX 78758
512 777-3800

(G-12872)
HANGER PRSTHETCS & ORTHO INC
1136 Independence Ave (43302-6318)
PHONE...................................740 383-2163
Tim Riedlinger, *Manager*
EMP: 3
SALES (corp-wide): 460MM **Publicly Held**
SIC: 3842 5999 Limbs, artificial; orthope-
dic & prosthesis applications
HQ: Hanger Prosthetics & Orthotics, Inc.
10910 Domain Dr Ste 300
Austin TX 78758
512 777-3800

(G-12873)
HARSCO CORPORATION
Also Called: Patent Construction Systems
3477 Harding Hwy E (43302-8534)
PHONE...................................740 387-1150
Don Broadwater, *Branch Mgr*
Ray Fredricks, *Manager*
EMP: 24
SALES (corp-wide): 1.4B **Publicly Held**
SIC: 3537 3536 3535 3531 Industrial
trucks & tractors; hoists, cranes & mono-
rails; conveyors & conveying equipment;
construction machinery; architectural met-
alwork
PA: Harsco Corporation
350 Poplar Church Rd
Camp Hill PA 17011
717 763-7064

(G-12874)
HIGHWAY SAFETY CORP
473 W Fairground St (43302-1701)
PHONE...................................740 387-6991
Fax: 740 375-0029
Marnie Sniezko, *Purch Dir*
Larry Ross, *Sales Staff*
Jim Chick, *Manager*
EMP: 15

SALES (corp-wide): 59.3MM **Privately Held**
SIC: 3444 3479 Guard rails, highway;
sheet metal; galvanizing of iron, steel or
end-formed products
PA: Highway Safety Corp.
239 Commerce St Ste C
Glastonbury CT 06033
860 659-4330

(G-12875)
HILDRETH MFG LLC
1657 Cascade Dr (43302-8509)
P.O. Box 905 (43301-0905)
PHONE...................................740 375-5832
Fax: 740 375-4950
Gerald Hildreth, *Vice Pres*
Eric Perini, *Maint Spvr*
Theresa Tebee, *Accountant*
Susan Flone, *Manager*
Terry Hildreth,
EMP: 25
SALES (est): 9.3MM **Privately Held**
WEB: www.hildrethmfg.com
SIC: 3331 Blocks, copper

(G-12876)
HPM NORTH AMERICA CORP
1193 Pole Lane Rd (43302-8524)
PHONE...................................740 382-5600
John Beary, *Sales Mgr*
Randy Clements, *Manager*
▲ EMP: 20
SALES (est): 5.1MM
SALES (corp-wide): 57.6MM **Privately Held**
SIC: 3542 Die casting machines; pressing
machines
PA: Guangdong Yizumi Precision Machin-
ery Co., Ltd.
No.22,Ke Yuan 3 Road, Hi-Tech Area,
Ronggui, Shunde
Foshan 52830
757 292-6216

(G-12877)
INTERNATIONAL PAPER COMPANY
1600 Cascade Dr (43302-8509)
PHONE...................................740 383-4061
Ron Iden, *Principal*
Steve Tullis, *Sales Executive*
EMP: 163
SALES (corp-wide): 21B **Publicly Held**
SIC: 2631 Paperboard mills
PA: International Paper Company
6400 Poplar Ave
Memphis TN 38197
901 419-9000

(G-12878)
KA WANNER INC
Also Called: Robotworx
370 W Fairground St (43302-1728)
PHONE...................................740 251-4636
Fax: 740 383-3939
Keith Wanner, *President*
Tonya Diaz, *Opers Mgr*
Jason Oldfield, *Draft/Design*
Stacey Wanner, *Accountant*
Steve Dillon, *Sales Associate*
EMP: 30
SQ FT: 75,000
SALES (est): 11.7MM **Privately Held**
WEB: www.robotsforwelding.com
SIC: 3535 Robotic conveyors

(G-12879)
LAIPPLYS PRTG MKTG SLTIONS INC
270 E Center St (43302-4124)
P.O. Box 777 (43301-0777)
PHONE...................................740 387-9282
Fax: 740 382-1557
Ronald E Laipply, *President*
Effie Laipply, *Corp Secy*
Jacque Laipply, *Vice Pres*
EMP: 9
SQ FT: 5,000
SALES (est): 1.5MM **Privately Held**
WEB: www.laipplyqprint.com
SIC: 2789 7336 7311 Bookbinding & re-
lated work; graphic arts & related design;
direct mail advertising services

(G-12880)
LOBO AWRDS SCREEN PRTG GRAPHIX
627 Bellefontaine Ave (43302-6101)
PHONE...................................740 972-9087
Jeff Roberts, *Owner*
EMP: 3
SALES: 50K **Privately Held**
SIC: 2752 Commercial printing, litho-
graphic

(G-12881)
MARCY INDUSTRIES COMPANY LLC
1836 Likens Rd (43302-8652)
PHONE...................................740 387-1213
Craig Taylor, *Principal*
EMP: 30 EST: 2012
SALES (est): 240K **Privately Held**
SIC: 3999 Atomizers, toiletry

(G-12882)
MARION ETHANOL LLC
Also Called: Poet Borefining- Marion 22200
1660 Hillman Ford Rd (43302-9475)
PHONE...................................740 383-4400
Jeff Lautt, *CEO*
Cliff Brannon, *General Mgr*
Joe Bouza, *Marketing Mgr*
Jeff Broin,
Daniel R McDonald,
EMP: 40
SALES (est): 12MM
SALES (corp-wide): 4.3B **Privately Held**
SIC: 2869 Ethyl alcohol, ethanol
PA: Poet, Llc
4615 N Lewis Ave
Sioux Falls SD 57104
605 965-2200

(G-12883)
MARION INDUSTRIES INC
999 Kellogg Pkwy (43302-1791)
PHONE...................................740 223-0075
Rick Charville, *CEO*
James R Conway, *Ch of Bd*
Jerome Curtis, *President*
Louis Scutellaro, *Sr Corp Ofcr*
Gerald Lehrke, *Vice Pres*
EMP: 753
SQ FT: 144,000
SALES (est): 228.8MM
SALES (corp-wide): 575.1MM **Privately Held**
WEB: www.egreeninc.com
SIC: 3714 Motor vehicle wheels & parts
PA: Ernie Green Industries, Inc.
2030 Dividend Dr
Columbus OH 43228
614 291-1423

(G-12884)
MID OHIO PACKAGING LLC
Also Called: Mopac
2135 Innovation Dr (43302-8261)
PHONE...................................740 383-9200
Fax: 740 387-4725
Tim Tootle, *General Mgr*
Jim McFarland, *General Mgr*
Jeff Gorsuch, *Controller*
Margie Napper, *Info Tech Mgr*
Jack Schwarz,
EMP: 30
SQ FT: 78,000
SALES (est): 6.6MM
SALES (corp-wide): 248.2MM **Privately Held**
WEB: www.mopac-ssp.com
SIC: 2653 Boxes, corrugated: made from
purchased materials; sheets, solid fiber:
made from purchased materials
HQ: Schwarz Partners Packaging, Llc
3600 Woodview Trce # 300
Indianapolis IN 46268
317 290-1140

(G-12885)
MILLS COMPANY (HQ)
3007 Harding Hwy E 4n (43302-8370)
PHONE...................................740 375-0770
Fax: 740 375-0880
Donald H Mullett, *Ch of Bd*
Greg Geishidle, *Plant Mgr*
John Kleczka, *Admin Sec*
▲ EMP: 25 EST: 1921

SALES (est): 10.4MM
SALES (corp-wide): 184.3MM **Privately Held**
WEB: www.mills-co.com
SIC: 2542 Partitions for floor attachment, prefabricated: except wood
PA: Bradley Corporation
W142n9101 Fountain Blvd
Menomonee Falls WI 53051
262 251-6000

(G-12886)
MISSION INDUSTRIAL GROUP LLC
Also Called: Drum Runner
3602 Harding Hwy E (43302-8534)
PHONE.............................740 387-2287
Fax: 740 387-2272
Mark Snow,
Richard Hempy,
EMP: 10
SQ FT: 17,000
SALES: 500K **Privately Held**
WEB: www.drumrunner.com
SIC: 3599 Machine & other job shop work

(G-12887)
MURPHY INDUSTRIES INC
1650 Cascade Dr (43302-8509)
PHONE.............................740 387-7890
Fax: 614 387-0007
Theodore J Murphy Sr, *CEO*
Theodore J Murphy Jr, *President*
Michael J Murphy, *Vice Pres*
Paul Murphy, *Vice Pres*
Brian Decker, *Controller*
▲ **EMP:** 35
SQ FT: 25,000
SALES (est): 6.8MM **Privately Held**
WEB: www.murphyind.com
SIC: 3315 3357 Cable, steel: insulated or armored; nonferrous wiredrawing & insulating

(G-12888)
NACHURS ALPINE SOLUTIONS CORP (HQ)
421 Leader St (43302-2225)
PHONE.............................740 382-5701
Fax: 614 383-2615
Jeffrey Barnes, *CEO*
Bob Hopp, *Vice Pres*
Robert Hopp, *Vice Pres*
Reiny Packull, *Vice Pres*
David Rose, *Vice Pres*
◆ **EMP:** 25
SALES (est): 39.5MM
SALES (corp-wide): 117.6MM **Privately Held**
WEB: www.nachurs.com
SIC: 2875 2869 2819 Fertilizers, mixing only; industrial organic chemicals; industrial inorganic chemicals
PA: Trans-Resources, Inc.
17780 Collins Ave
Sunny Isles Beach FL 33160
305 933-8301

(G-12889)
NATIONAL LIME AND STONE CO
700 Likens Rd (43302-8601)
P.O. Box 144 (43301-0144)
PHONE.............................740 387-3485
Fax: 614 422-3952
Scott Silver, *Manager*
EMP: 20
SALES (corp-wide): 4B **Privately Held**
WEB: www.natlime.com
SIC: 1422 5999 Crushed & broken limestone; rock & stone specimens
PA: The National Lime And Stone Company
551 Lake Cascade Pkwy
Findlay OH 45840
419 422-4341

(G-12890)
NEWSAFE TRANSPORT SERVICE INC
979 Pole Lane Rd (43302-8524)
P.O. Box 749 (43301-0749)
PHONE.............................740 387-1679
Rachpal Sangh, *Owner*
EMP: 11
SQ FT: 400

SALES (est): 2.7MM **Privately Held**
SIC: 3537 Trucks: freight, baggage, etc.: industrial, except mining

(G-12891)
OHIO GALVANIZING CORP
467 W Fairground St (43302-1701)
PHONE.............................740 387-6474
Fax: 740 382-8101
W Patric Gregory, *CEO*
Robert J West, *CFO*
Linda Newel, *Admin Sec*
EMP: 50
SQ FT: 57,000
SALES: 10.6MM **Privately Held**
WEB: www.ohgalv.com
SIC: 3479 Galvanizing of iron, steel or end-formed products

(G-12892)
OVERHEAD DOOR CORPORATION
Todco
1332 E Fairground Rd (43302-8505)
PHONE.............................740 383-6376
Daniel C Rengert, *President*
Charles Lindsey, *Purchasing*
Colin Quibell, *Purchasing*
Fred Kellogg, *Engineer*
Margaret Roush, *Finance Other*
EMP: 100
SALES (corp-wide): 3.1B **Privately Held**
WEB: www.overheaddoor.com
SIC: 3442 2431 3441 Garage doors, overhead: metal; doors, wood; fabricated structural metal
HQ: Overhead Door Corporation
2501 S State Hwy 121 Ste
Lewisville TX 75067
469 549-7100

(G-12893)
PROMO COSTUMES INC
381 W Center St (43302-3651)
P.O. Box 37 (43301-0037)
PHONE.............................740 383-5176
Fax: 740 382-0026
Lyn Giles, *Vice Pres*
Daniel Giles, *Vice Pres*
Zach Wheeler, *Sales Staff*
EMP: 19
SALES: 750K **Privately Held**
WEB: www.promocostumes.com
SIC: 2389 7299 Costumes; costume rental

(G-12894)
R ANTHONY ENTERPRISES LLC
2626 Whetstone River Rd S (43302-8937)
PHONE.............................419 341-0961
Rocco Piacentino, *Mng Member*
EMP: 10
SQ FT: 10,000
SALES: 1MM **Privately Held**
SIC: 1389 Construction, repair & dismantling services

(G-12895)
RI ALTO MFG INC
1632 Cascade Dr (43302-8509)
PHONE.............................740 914-4230
Fax: 740 499-2089
Rick Mattix, *President*
Maryann Mattix, *Corp Secy*
Sam Hawkins, *Vice Pres*
EMP: 19
SQ FT: 9,000
SALES (est): 4MM **Privately Held**
WEB: www.rialtomfg.com
SIC: 3599 7692 Machine shop, jobbing & repair; welding repair

(G-12896)
ROY I KAUFMAN INC
1672 Marion Uppr Sndsk Rd (43302-1531)
PHONE.............................740 382-0643
Fax: 614 383-4120
Beth Kaufman, *Treasurer*
Terry Weber, *Office Mgr*
Martin T Kaufman II, *Director*
EMP: 8 **EST:** 1956
SQ FT: 12,000
SALES: 1.6MM **Privately Held**
SIC: 3496 Woven wire products

(G-12897)
SAKAMURA USA INC
970 Kellogg Pkwy (43302-1783)
PHONE.............................740 223-7777
Takayuki Nakano, *President*
Jun Kobayashi, *Vice Pres*
Nathan Conley, *Purchasing*
Naomi Taniguchi, *Treasurer*
▲ **EMP:** 14
SQ FT: 10,000
SALES (est): 3MM
SALES (corp-wide): 63.4MM **Privately Held**
WEB: www.sakamura.net
SIC: 3542 Forging machinery & hammers
PA: Sakamura Machine Co.,Ltd.
46, Tominoshiro, Shimotsuya, Kumiya-macho
Kuse-Gun KYO 613-0
774 437-000

(G-12898)
SCOTT SYSTEMS INTERNATIONAL
Also Called: Robotworx
370 W Fairground St (43302-1728)
PHONE.............................740 383-8383
Stacey McGill, *Principal*
Christopher Pappas, *Project Mgr*
Greg Chiles, *CFO*
Candi Sherman, *Sales Staff*
Mike Black, *Manager*
EMP: 4
SALES (est): 200.8K **Privately Held**
SIC: 3549 8742 Assembly machines, including robotic; automation & robotics consultant

(G-12899)
SEMCO
1025 Pole Lane Rd (43302-8524)
P.O. Box 561 (43301-0561)
PHONE.............................800 848-5764
Fax: 740 387-6127
Bob Diersing, *Principal*
J Douglass Schrim, *Principal*
Leonard Furman, *Chairman*
Randy Furman, *Vice Pres*
Shelby Furman, *Vice Pres*
▲ **EMP:** 60
SQ FT: 40,000
SALES (est): 14.1MM **Privately Held**
WEB: www.semcotips.com
SIC: 3599 3366 Machine shop, jobbing & repair; copper foundries

(G-12900)
SIKA CORPORATION
1550 Cascade Dr (43302)
PHONE.............................740 375-3020
EMP: 5
SALES (corp-wide): 5.4B **Privately Held**
SIC: 2899 5169 3566 Chemical preparations; chemicals & allied products; speed changers, drives & gears
HQ: Sika Corporation
201 Polito Ave
Lyndhurst NJ 07071
201 933-8800

(G-12901)
SIKA CORPORATION
1682 Mrn Williamsprt Rd E (43302-8694)
PHONE.............................740 387-9224
Fax: 740 382-6454
Todd Petrie, *VP Opers*
Ray Gear, *Purch Mgr*
Scott Joehlin, *Engineer*
Jim Hendley, *Accounts Mgr*
Doug White, *Branch Mgr*
EMP: 62
SALES (corp-wide): 5.4B **Privately Held**
WEB: www.sikacorp.com
SIC: 2899 5169 3566 Concrete curing & hardening compounds; concrete additives; speed changers, drives & gears
HQ: Sika Corporation
201 Polito Ave
Lyndhurst NJ 07071
201 933-8800

(G-12902)
SIMCOTE INC
Also Called: Simcote of Ohio Division
250 N Greenwood St (43302-3177)
PHONE.............................740 382-5000

Fax: 614 383-1167
Art Tofte, *Branch Mgr*
EMP: 26
SALES (corp-wide): 18MM **Privately Held**
WEB: www.simcote.com
SIC: 3479 3449 Painting, coating & hot dipping; miscellaneous metalwork
PA: Simcote, Inc.
1645 Red Rock Rd
Saint Paul MN 55119
651 735-9660

(G-12903)
STEAM TURB ALTE RESO
Also Called: Star
116 Latourette St (43302-3429)
P.O. Box 862 (43301-0862)
PHONE.............................740 387-5535
Sue B Flaherty, *Ch of Bd*
Tammy Flaherty, *President*
Ken Kubinski, *Vice Pres*
Donna Macgregor Rambin, *Vice Pres*
Judy Miller, *Manager*
EMP: 45
SQ FT: 12,000
SALES (est): 10.3MM **Privately Held**
WEB: www.starturbine.com
SIC: 3511 Steam turbines

(G-12904)
STORAD LABEL CO
126 Blaine Ave (43302-3612)
P.O. Box 493 (43301-0493)
PHONE.............................740 382-6440
Fax: 614 383-3241
Bob Hord, *President*
Ann Hord, *Vice Pres*
EMP: 13 **EST:** 1966
SQ FT: 7,000
SALES (est): 1.5MM **Privately Held**
WEB: www.storadlabel.com
SIC: 2672 Labels (unprinted), gummed: made from purchased materials; tape, pressure sensitive: made from purchased materials

(G-12905)
TA DIE FOR GOURMET CUPCAKES
2094 Harding Hwy E (43302-8527)
PHONE.............................740 751-4586
Missy Meddins,
EMP: 4
SALES (est): 299.9K **Privately Held**
SIC: 2051 Bakery: wholesale or wholesale/retail combined

(G-12906)
TMS INTERNATIONAL CORPORATION
Also Called: International Mill Service
912 Cheney Ave (43302-6208)
PHONE.............................740 223-0091
Fax: 740 387-2543
George Post, *General Mgr*
EMP: 12 **Privately Held**
WEB: www.envirosources.com
SIC: 3295 Slag, crushed or ground
HQ: Tms International Holding Corporation
12 Monongahela Ave
Glassport PA 15045
412 678-6141

(G-12907)
TODD W GOINGS
Also Called: Carousel Carvings
360 Summit St (43302-5228)
PHONE.............................740 389-5842
Todd W Goings, *Owner*
EMP: 3
SALES: 200K **Privately Held**
WEB: www.carouselsandcarvings.com
SIC: 7641 7299 5812 2499 Antique furniture repair & restoration; banquet hall facilities; caterers; carved & turned wood

(G-12908)
TREE FREE RESOURCES LLC
Also Called: Tfr Printing
175 Park Blvd (43302-3534)
PHONE.............................740 751-4844
Dale G Haddad,
EMP: 12
SALES (est): 1.6MM **Privately Held**
SIC: 2759 Commercial printing

▲ = Import ▼=Export
◆ =Import/Export

(G-12909)
TRI COUNTY QUALITY WTR SYSTEMS
659 N Main St (43302-2332)
PHONE......................................740 751-4764
Jessica Bosh, *General Mgr*
EMP: 5
SALES (est): 319.5K **Privately Held**
SIC: 3589 Water filters & softeners, household type

(G-12910)
US YACHIYO INC
1177 Kellogg Pkwy (43302-1779)
PHONE......................................740 223-3134
Hiroshi Sasamoto, *President*
Kazuyoshi Itai, *Vice Pres*
Ray Sanders, *Opers Mgr*
Troy Nichols, *Manager*
Kazuhiro Asabuki, *Director*
▲ EMP: 232
SQ FT: 125,000
SALES (est): 159.3MM
SALES (corp-wide): 124.7B **Privately Held**
SIC: 3795 Tanks & tank components
HQ: Yachiyo Of America Inc.
2285 Walcutt Rd
Columbus OH 43228
614 876-3220

(G-12911)
WARREN ZACHMAN CONTRACTING
5005 Marion Edison Rd (43302-8979)
PHONE......................................740 389-4503
H Warren Zachman, *President*
David Schrote, *Vice Pres*
M Joyce Zachman, *Treasurer*
EMP: 3
SALES: 93K **Privately Held**
SIC: 3523 Farm machinery & equipment

(G-12912)
WATER POLL CONTROL
1810 Marion Agosta Rd (43302-9576)
PHONE......................................740 383-4446
Mark Fieldman, *Superintendent*
EMP: 30
SALES (est): 2.1MM **Privately Held**
SIC: 3589 Water treatment equipment, industrial

(G-12913)
WHIRLPOOL CORPORATION
1300 Marion Agosta Rd (43302-9577)
P.O. Box 1808 (43301-1808)
PHONE......................................740 383-7122
Fax: 740 383-7656
Brian Gahr, *President*
Stan Kenneth, *Vice Pres*
David Strzalka, *Mfg Dir*
Barbara Klee, *Safety Dir*
Bruce Alexander, *Plant Mgr*
EMP: 250
SALES (corp-wide): 20.7B **Publicly Held**
WEB: www.whirlpoolcorp.com
SIC: 3633 5064 3632 Laundry dryers, household or coin-operated; washing machines; household refrigerators & freezers
PA: Whirlpool Corporation
2000 N M 63
Benton Harbor MI 49022
269 923-5000

(G-12914)
WILLIAMS LEATHER PRODUCTS INC
Also Called: McKinley Leather
1476 Likens Rd Ste 104 (43302-8788)
PHONE......................................740 223-1604
Derek Williams, *President*
EMP: 6
SQ FT: 8,000
SALES (est): 1.4MM **Privately Held**
WEB: www.mckinleyleather.com
SIC: 3172 Personal leather goods

(G-12915)
WILSON BOHANNAN COMPANY
Also Called: W B
621 Buckeye St (43302-6121)
P.O. Box 504 (43301-0504)
PHONE......................................740 382-3639
Fax: 740 383-1653

Howard Smith, *President*
Josiah Bindley, *Principal*
G B Knapp, *Principal*
E J Schoenlaub, *Principal*
Pamela Smith, *Corp Secy*
EMP: 65 EST: 1860
SQ FT: 40,000
SALES (est): 21.2MM **Privately Held**
WEB: www.padlocks.com
SIC: 3429 Padlocks

(G-12916)
WYANDOT INC
135 Wyandot Ave (43302-1538)
PHONE......................................740 383-4031
Fax: 614 382-5584
Nick R Chilton, *CEO*
Rex Parrott, *President*
Jon Clunk, *Area Mgr*
Wayne Cook, *Area Mgr*
Clyde Ebert, *Area Mgr*
▲ EMP: 350 EST: 1936
SQ FT: 250,000
SALES (est): 111.4MM **Privately Held**
WEB: www.wyandotsnacks.com
SIC: 2096 Corn chips & other corn-based snacks

Marshallville
Wayne County

(G-12917)
D & R SUPPLY INC
18228 Fulton Rd (44645-9716)
PHONE......................................330 855-3781
Lindsey Schmitt, *President*
Jane Lavis, *Manager*
EMP: 3 EST: 1955
SALES (est): 407.6K **Privately Held**
WEB: www.drsupply.com
SIC: 2951 Asphalt & asphaltic paving mixtures (not from refineries)

(G-12918)
MARSHALLVILLE PACKING CO INC
50 E Market St (44645-9468)
P.O. Box 276 (44645-0276)
PHONE......................................330 855-2871
Frank T Tucker, *President*
Jeannette Tucker, *Corp Secy*
EMP: 29 EST: 1960
SQ FT: 35,000
SALES (est): 1.9MM **Privately Held**
SIC: 5421 5147 2013 2011 Meat markets, including freezer provisioners; meats, fresh; sausages & other prepared meats; meat packing plants

(G-12919)
NANCYS DRAPERIES
57 S Main St (44645-9773)
P.O. Box 305 (44645-0305)
PHONE......................................330 855-7751
Fax: 330 855-7855
Nancy Yoder, *Owner*
EMP: 12
SALES (est): 1MM **Privately Held**
SIC: 2211 5714 1799 Draperies & drapery fabrics, cotton; draperies; drapery track installation

(G-12920)
RUPP CONSTRUCTION INC
18228 Fulton Rd (44645-9716)
PHONE......................................330 855-2781
Fax: 330 855-4745
Gary Radabaugh, *President*
Dorothea Radabaugh, *Corp Secy*
Jane Davis, *Manager*
EMP: 10
SQ FT: 20,000
SALES (est): 1.5MM **Privately Held**
WEB: www.ruppconstruction.com
SIC: 1442 Construction sand & gravel

Martins Ferry
Belmont County

(G-12921)
ARROWSTRIP INC
1st & Locust St S (43935)
P.O. Box 37 (43935-0037)
PHONE......................................740 633-2609
W Quay Mull II, *Ch of Bd*
Pete Mysliwic, *President*
Gary A Butler, *Exec VP*
Lisa M Leach, *Vice Pres*
EMP: 21
SQ FT: 25,000
SALES (est): 5.2MM **Privately Held**
WEB: www.arrowstrip.com
SIC: 3312 Iron & steel: galvanized, pipes, plates, sheets, etc.

(G-12922)
BLENDZALL INC
310 S 1st St (43935-1774)
PHONE......................................740 633-1333
Fax: 740 633-5032
Larry Eagle, *President*
Linda Parsons, *Vice Pres*
Larry A Egle, *Plant Mgr*
James Parsons, *Treasurer*
EMP: 5
SQ FT: 3,500
SALES (est): 750.5K **Privately Held**
WEB: www.blendzall.com
SIC: 2992 Oils & greases, blending & compounding

(G-12923)
CRUMMITT & SON VAULT CORP (PA)
329 N 2nd St (43935-2514)
P.O. Box 277 (43935-0277)
PHONE......................................304 281-2420
Fax: 740 633-1942
Michael Crummitt Jr, *President*
EMP: 9 EST: 1947
SQ FT: 10,000
SALES: 1.2MM **Privately Held**
SIC: 3272 Burial vaults, concrete or precast terrazzo

(G-12924)
EASTERN OHIO NEWSPAPERS INC
200 S 4th St (43935-1312)
PHONE......................................740 633-1131
G O Nutting, *President*
EMP: 7
SALES (est): 405.3K **Privately Held**
SIC: 2711 Newspapers

(G-12925)
LESCO INC
100 Picoma Rd (43935-9700)
PHONE......................................740 633-6366
Fax: 740 633-6958
Brian Menue, *Technical Mgr*
Frank Damato, *Manager*
Alice Burns, *Director*
EMP: 10
SALES (corp-wide): 26.6B **Publicly Held**
WEB: www.lesco.com
SIC: 5191 2875 Limestone, agricultural; seeds: field, garden & flower; fertilizers, mixing only
HQ: Lesco, Inc.
1385 E 36th St
Cleveland OH 44114
216 706-9250

(G-12926)
ULTIMATE SIGNS AND GRAPHICS
904 Indiana St (43935-2039)
PHONE......................................740 633-8928
Fax: 740 633-2844
Jeff Rehberg, *Owner*
EMP: 3
SALES (est): 131K **Privately Held**
SIC: 3993 Signs & advertising specialties

(G-12927)
UNITED DAIRY INC (PA)
Also Called: United Quality Chekd Dairy
300 N 5th St (43935-1647)
P.O. Box 280 (43935-0280)
PHONE......................................740 633-1451
Fax: 740 633-6759
Joseph L Carson, *President*
John Duty, *General Mgr*
Joseph M Carson Jr, *Chairman*
George Wood, *Corp Secy*
Gary Cowell, *Vice Pres*
EMP: 200 EST: 1903
SQ FT: 20,000
SALES (est): 203.4MM **Privately Held**
WEB: www.uniteddairy.com
SIC: 2026 2024 Milk processing (pasteurizing, homogenizing, bottling); ice cream, bulk

(G-12928)
WILSON BLACKTOP CORPORATION
915 Carlisle St Rear (43935-1511)
PHONE......................................740 635-3566
Fax: 740 635-1805
Dale M Wilson, *President*
Janice L Wilson, *Corp Secy*
Mark E Wilson, *Vice Pres*
EMP: 20
SQ FT: 1,000
SALES (est): 4MM **Privately Held**
SIC: 2951 1611 1771 Asphalt & asphaltic paving mixtures (not from refineries); highway & street paving contractor; blacktop (asphalt) work; driveway contractor

---

Martinsburg
Knox County

(G-12929)
COVER UP BUILDING SYSTEMS
101 N Market St (43037)
P.O. Box 133 (43037-0133)
PHONE......................................740 668-8985
Stephen Kidwell, *Owner*
EMP: 3
SALES (est): 247.3K **Privately Held**
SIC: 3448 Prefabricated metal buildings

Martinsville
Clinton County

(G-12930)
WILLIAM OEDER READY MIX INC
8807 State Route 134 (45146-9533)
PHONE......................................513 899-3901
William Oeder, *President*
Robert Oeder, *Vice Pres*
Ronald Oeder, *Vice Pres*
Alma Oeder, *Treasurer*
Jo Ann Parker, *Admin Sec*
EMP: 20 EST: 1939
SQ FT: 3,000
SALES (est): 1.7MM **Privately Held**
SIC: 3273 Ready-mixed concrete

Marysville
Union County

(G-12931)
ALPHA CONTAINER CO INC
16789 Square Dr (43040-9496)
PHONE......................................937 644-5511
Fax: 937 644-0295
Fred L McClellan Sr, *President*
Fred L Mc Clellan Sr, *President*
Chris McClellan, *Vice Pres*
▲ EMP: 12
SQ FT: 40,000
SALES (est): 3.7MM **Privately Held**
WEB: www.alphacontainer.net
SIC: 2653 Corrugated & solid fiber boxes

GEOGRAPHIC

(G-12932)
AVS OIL RECOVERY LLC
13311 Industrial Pkwy (43040-9589)
PHONE...................................937 645-4600
Karen Sullivan, *VP Sales*
Ross Youngs, *VP Sales*
Chad Hummell, *Sales Staff*
Ross O Youngs,
EMP: 5
SALES: 950K **Privately Held**
SIC: 3599 Industrial machinery

(G-12933)
BAR1 MOTORSPORTS
1757 Creekview Dr (43040-8556)
PHONE...................................614 284-3732
Brian J Alder, *Owner*
EMP: 10
SALES (est): 723.3K **Privately Held**
SIC: 7694 Motor repair services

(G-12934)
BUCKEYE DIAMOND LOGISTICS INC
21963 Northwest Pkwy (43040-9147)
PHONE...................................937 644-2194
Kenneth La Chey, *Branch Mgr*
EMP: 6
SALES (corp-wide): 33.3MM **Privately Held**
WEB: www.buckeyegroup.com
SIC: 3081 Packing materials, plastic sheet
PA: Buckeye Diamond Logistics, Inc.
15 Sprague Rd
South Charleston OH 45368
937 462-8361

(G-12935)
BUCKEYE READY-MIX LLC
838 N Main St (43040-9701)
P.O. Box 31, Reynoldsburg (43068-0031)
PHONE...................................937 642-2951
Fax: 937 575-1307
Larry Randels, *Vice Pres*
EMP: 30
SQ FT: 3,000
SALES (corp-wide): 42.4MM **Privately Held**
WEB: www.buckeyereadymix.com
SIC: 3273 Ready-mixed concrete
PA: Buckeye Ready-Mix, Llc
7657 Taylor Rd Sw
Reynoldsburg OH 43068
614 575-2132

(G-12936)
CONNOLLY CONSTRUCTION CO INC
179 Emmaus Rd (43040-5524)
P.O. Box 271 (43040-0271)
PHONE...................................937 644-8831
Phillip F Connolly, *President*
John Eufinger, *Treasurer*
Steve Drake, *Accountant*
Bonnie Spurling, *Receptionist*
EMP: 5
SQ FT: 2,244
SALES (est): 774.3K **Privately Held**
WEB: www.connollyconstruction.com
SIC: 1623 1521 1411 Sewer line construction; new construction, single-family houses; dimension stone

(G-12937)
CONTITECH USA INC
Also Called: Continental Contitech
13601 Industrial Pkwy (43040-8890)
PHONE...................................937 644-8900
E Hites, *Purchasing*
Ken Kontely, *Enginr/R&D Mgr*
Al Phillips, *Human Res Mgr*
Dave Royer, *Data Proc Mgr*
EMP: 37
SALES (corp-wide): 42.8B **Privately Held**
WEB: www.veyance.com
SIC: 3496 Conveyor belts
HQ: Contitech Usa, Inc.
703 S Clvland Mssillon Rd
Fairlawn OH 44333
330 664-7000

(G-12938)
CONTRACT BUILDING COMPONENTS
Also Called: C B C
14540 Industrial Pkwy (43040-9595)
PHONE...................................937 644-0739
Steven Yoder, *Vice Pres*
Jeff Coulter, *Manager*
EMP: 20
SALES (est): 2.9MM **Privately Held**
SIC: 2439 Structural wood members

(G-12939)
COPY SOURCE INC
105 S Main St (43040-1551)
PHONE...................................937 642-7140
Fax: 937 642-7141
Joan Izzard, *CEO*
EMP: 3
SQ FT: 8,680
SALES (est): 315.5K **Privately Held**
SIC: 2759 2741 Commercial printing; miscellaneous publishing

(G-12940)
D C RAMEY PIANO CO
17768 Woodview Dr (43040-9711)
PHONE...................................708 602-3961
David Ramey Jr, *Owner*
EMP: 3
SALES: 300K **Privately Held**
WEB: www.dcramey.com
SIC: 3931 Keyboards, piano or organ

(G-12941)
DAK ENTERPRISES INC (PA)
18062 Timber Trails Rd (43040-9021)
P.O. Box 409, Frazeysburg (43822-0409)
PHONE...................................740 828-3291
Daniel Keifer, *President*
EMP: 10
SALES (est): 24.3MM **Privately Held**
SIC: 3089 Injection molded finished plastic products

(G-12942)
ENGINEERED MFG & EQP CO
Also Called: E M E C
11611 Industrial Pkwy (43040-9522)
PHONE...................................937 642-7776
Fax: 937 642-7983
Raymond A Grigorenko, *President*
Thomas Walter, *General Mgr*
Leslie Grigorenko, *Vice Pres*
EMP: 8
SQ FT: 9,000
SALES: 1MM **Privately Held**
SIC: 3544 3699 Special dies, tools, jigs & fixtures; electrical equipment & supplies

(G-12943)
FILE 13 INC
232 N Main St Ste K (43040-1160)
P.O. Box 626 (43040-0626)
PHONE...................................937 642-4855
Mark Ropp, *Principal*
EMP: 12
SALES (est): 1.8MM **Privately Held**
SIC: 3559 Tire shredding machinery

(G-12944)
FRANKES WOOD PRODUCTS LLC
825 Collins Ave (43040-1330)
PHONE...................................937 642-0706
Fax: 937 642-3528
William Franke, *President*
Judy Franke, *Office Mgr*
Christopher S Franke, *Shareholder*
Kevin Franke, *Shareholder*
Michelle R Franke, *Shareholder*
EMP: 37
SQ FT: 93,800
SALES (est): 7MM **Privately Held**
SIC: 2448 2449 2493 3061 Cargo containers, wood; shipping cases & drums, wood; wirebound & plywood; fiberboard, other vegetable pulp; mechanical rubber goods; rubber scrap; marketing consulting services

(G-12945)
GRAPHIC STITCH INC
169 Grove St Rm A (43040-1342)
PHONE...................................937 642-6707
Fax: 937 642-5118
Todd M Hoge, *President*
EMP: 9
SQ FT: 2,800
SALES (est): 833.6K **Privately Held**
WEB: www.graphicstitch.com
SIC: 2395 2759 Embroidery & art needlework; commercial printing

(G-12946)
GREENVILLE TECHNIOLOGY INC
15000 Industrial Pkwy (43040-9547)
PHONE...................................937 642-6744
EMP: 5 EST: 2015
SALES (est): 360K **Privately Held**
SIC: 3089 Automotive parts, plastic

(G-12947)
HANGER PRSTHETCS & ORTHO INC
Also Called: Hanger Orthopedic
211 Stocksdale Dr Ste C (43040-5507)
PHONE...................................740 369-2424
Steve Williams, *Manager*
EMP: 3
SALES (corp-wide): 460MM **Publicly Held**
SIC: 3842 Prosthetic appliances
HQ: Hanger Prosthetics & Orthotics, Inc.
10910 Domain Dr Ste 300
Austin TX 78758
512 777-3800

(G-12948)
HONDA ENGINEERING N AMER INC
24000 Honda Pkwy (43040-9251)
PHONE...................................937 642-5000
Akira Takeshita, *President*
Bob Brizendine, *Division Mgr*
Melissa Martinez, *Research*
Ken Pyo, *Chief Engr*
John Andreas, *Engineer*
▲ EMP: 350
SALES (est): 176.6MM
SALES (corp-wide): 124.7B **Privately Held**
SIC: 3544 Special dies & tools; industrial molds
HQ: Honda Engineering Co.,Ltd.
6-1, Hagadai, Hagamachi
Haga-Gun TCG 321-3
286 775-511

(G-12949)
HONDA ENGINEERING NA INC
24000 Honda Pkwy (43040-9251)
PHONE...................................937 707-5357
Greg Dejaynes, *Webmaster*
Deb Benston, *Program Dir*
EMP: 7
SALES (est): 218.9K
SALES (corp-wide): 124.7B **Privately Held**
SIC: 3544 Special dies & tools
HQ: Honda Engineering Co.,Ltd.
6-1, Hagadai, Hagamachi
Haga-Gun TCG 321-3
286 775-511

(G-12950)
HONDA OF AMERICA MFG INC (HQ)
Also Called: Marysville Auto Plant
24000 Honda Pkwy (43040-9251)
PHONE...................................937 642-5000
Fax: 937 644-6575
Tomomi Kosaka, *CEO*
Akio Hamada, *President*
Mike Fischer, *Division Mgr*
Gen Tsujii, *General Mgr*
Satoshi Aoki, *Managing Dir*
◆ EMP: 750
SQ FT: 2,235,000
SALES: 3.6B
SALES (corp-wide): 124.7B **Privately Held**
WEB: www.hondamfg.com
SIC: 3711 Automobile assembly, including specialty automobiles
PA: Honda Motor Co., Ltd.
2-1-1, Minamiaoyama
Minato-Ku TKY 107-0
334 231-111

(G-12951)
HONDA OF AMERICA MFG INC
Also Called: Honda Support Office
19900 State Route 739 (43040-9256)
PHONE...................................937 644-0724
Nobu Hashimoto, *Purchasing*
EMP: 200
SALES (corp-wide): 124.7B **Privately Held**
SIC: 3714 3711 3465 8742 Motor vehicle parts & accessories; motor vehicles & car bodies; automotive stampings; training & development consultant
HQ: Honda Of America Mfg., Inc.
24000 Honda Pkwy
Marysville OH 43040
937 642-5000

(G-12952)
HONDA OF AMERICA MFG INC
25000 Honda Pkwy (43040-9190)
PHONE...................................937 642-5000
Jim Schmidt, *Maintence Staff*
EMP: 500
SALES (corp-wide): 124.7B **Privately Held**
SIC: 3711 Automobile assembly, including specialty automobiles
HQ: Honda Of America Mfg., Inc.
24000 Honda Pkwy
Marysville OH 43040
937 642-5000

(G-12953)
HYPONEX CORPORATION (DH)
Also Called: Scotts- Hyponex
14111 Scottslawn Rd (43040-7800)
PHONE...................................937 644-0011
James Hagedorn, *President*
David M Brockman, *Exec VP*
Christopher Nagel, *Exec VP*
David C Evans, *CFO*
David M Aronowitz, *Admin Sec*
EMP: 100 EST: 1980
SQ FT: 73,000
SALES (est): 488.5MM
SALES (corp-wide): 2.8B **Publicly Held**
SIC: 2873 2875 Fertilizers: natural (organic), except compost; plant foods, mixed: from plants making nitrog. fertilizers; fertilizers, mixing only; potting soil, mixed
HQ: The Scotts Company Llc
14111 Scottslawn Rd
Marysville OH 43040
937 644-3729

(G-12954)
INFRARED IMAGING SYSTEMS INC
22718 Holycross Epps Rd (43040-9144)
PHONE...................................614 989-1148
James W Sharpe, *CEO*
Dale Siegel, *President*
Greg Miller, *Vice Pres*
Michael Schlesinger, *CFO*
Robert L Crane PHD, *Officer*
EMP: 4
SQ FT: 1,200
SALES (est): 330K **Privately Held**
SIC: 3823 Infrared instruments, industrial process type

(G-12955)
KREIS SAWMILL
728 N Main St (43040-1146)
PHONE...................................937 537-1248
EMP: 3
SALES (est): 159.3K **Privately Held**
SIC: 2421 Sawmills & planing mills, general

(G-12956)
MAGNETIC SCREW MACHINE PDTS
23241 State Route 37 (43040-9749)
PHONE...................................937 348-2807
Fax: 937 348-2800
Bryan Bayes, *President*
EMP: 7
SQ FT: 16,000
SALES (est): 1MM **Privately Held**
SIC: 3451 Screw machine products

(G-12957)
MARYSVILLE NEWSPAPER INC (PA)
Also Called: Richwood Gazette
207 N Main St (43040-1161)
P.O. Box 226 (43040-0226)
PHONE..................................937 644-9211
Fax: 937 644-9211
Daniel Behrens, *President*
Karlyn Byers, *Publisher*
Kevin Behrens, *Principal*
Tim Miller, *Editor*
Marie Woodford, *Adv Mgr*
EMP: 30
SQ FT: 10,000
SALES (est): 2.7MM **Privately Held**
WEB: www.marysvillejt.com
SIC: 2711 2731 Newspapers, publishing & printing; books: publishing & printing

(G-12958)
MARYSVILLE PRINTING COMPANY
127 S Main St (43040-1551)
PHONE..................................937 644-4959
Fax: 937 642-9779
William S Lithgo, *Owner*
EMP: 3
SQ FT: 3,600
SALES (est): 379.7K **Privately Held**
SIC: 2752 2759 Commercial printing, offset; commercial printing

(G-12959)
MARYSVILLE STEEL INC
323 E 8th St (43040)
P.O. Box 383 (43040-0383)
PHONE..................................937 642-5971
Fax: 937 642-1529
Steven J Clayman, *CEO*
Sheryl Blum, *Admin Asst*
EMP: 31
SQ FT: 50,000
SALES (est): 10.6MM **Privately Held**
SIC: 3441 1791 5039 Fabricated structural metal; structural steel erection; joists

(G-12960)
MCDANNALD WELDING & MACHINING
11879 State Route 736 (43040-9516)
PHONE..................................937 644-0300
Keith E McDannald, *President*
Susan McDannald, *Vice Pres*
EMP: 4
SALES: 275K **Privately Held**
SIC: 7692 3599 1799 1542 Welding repair; machine shop, jobbing & repair; welding on site; design & erection, combined: non-residential

(G-12961)
NKC OF AMERICA INC
24000 Honda Pkwy Gate E (43040)
PHONE..................................937 642-4033
Frederick Sheward, *Manager*
EMP: 5
SALES (corp-wide): 399.9MM **Privately Held**
WEB: www.nkcusa.com
SIC: 3535 Belt conveyor systems, general industrial use
HQ: Nkc Of America, Inc.
1584 E Brooks Rd
Memphis TN 38116
901 396-6334

(G-12962)
PARKER-HANNIFIN CORPORATION
Hydraulic Pump Division
14249 Industrial Pkwy (43040-9504)
PHONE..................................937 644-3915
Fax: 937 644-4533
Ken Theiss, *Branch Mgr*
Andrew Cailteux, *Manager*
EMP: 230
SALES (corp-wide): 11.3B **Publicly Held**
WEB: www.parker.com
SIC: 3594 3491 3679 Pumps, hydraulic power transfer; industrial valves; electronic circuits

PA: Parker-Hannifin Corporation
6035 Parkland Blvd
Cleveland OH 44124
216 896-3000

(G-12963)
PRECISION COATINGS SYSTEMS
948 Columbus Ave (43040-9501)
PHONE..................................937 642-4727
Fax: 937 644-3206
Fred Myers Jr, *President*
Mark Myers, *Vice Pres*
Sherry Myers, *Vice Pres*
Wendy Myers, *Vice Pres*
Graig Bartlett, *Plant Mgr*
EMP: 30
SQ FT: 26,000
SALES (est): 2.4MM **Privately Held**
WEB: www.precisioncoatingsystems.com
SIC: 3479 7532 7549 7514 Painting of metal products; paint shop, automotive; collision shops, automotive; towing services; rent-a-car service

(G-12964)
QUANTUM TECHONOLOGY & SERVICES
648 Clymer Rd (43040-9827)
PHONE..................................937 642-2929
Fred Myers, *Principal*
EMP: 6
SALES (est): 1MM **Privately Held**
SIC: 3572 Computer storage devices

(G-12965)
RAY LEWIS & SON INCORPORATED
916 Delaware Ave (43040-1726)
P.O. Box 399 (43040-0399)
PHONE..................................937 644-4015
Robert Lewis, *President*
Nancy Lewis, *Corp Secy*
Bruce Valentino, *CFO*
Duane Hammer, *Sales Staff*
Terry Glassburn, *Supervisor*
EMP: 40
SQ FT: 75,000
SALES (est): 7.1MM **Privately Held**
WEB: www.raylewisandson.com
SIC: 3364 3369 Zinc & zinc-base alloy die-castings; nonferrous foundries

(G-12966)
ROD MCLELLAN COMPANY
14111 Scottslawn Rd (43040-7800)
PHONE..................................513 644-0011
Mark West, *Principal*
EMP: 5
SALES (est): 556.9K **Privately Held**
SIC: 2875 Fertilizers, mixing only

(G-12967)
SCOTTS COMPANY LLC (HQ)
Also Called: Scotts Miracle-Gro Products
14111 Scottslawn Rd (43040-7801)
P.O. Box 388 (43040-0388)
PHONE..................................937 644-3729
Fax: 937 644-7557
James Hagedorn, *CEO*
Ryan McClendon, *General Mgr*
David Sanborn, *Managing Dir*
Christiane Schmenk, *Managing Dir*
Mike Lukemire, *Exec VP*
◆ EMP: 650
SALES (est): 2B
SALES (corp-wide): 2.8B **Publicly Held**
WEB: www.scottscompany.com
SIC: 2873 2874 2879 0782 Fertilizers: natural (organic), except compost; phosphates; fungicides, herbicides, insecticides, agricultural or household; lawn services; mulch, wood & bark; lawn & garden equipment; lawnmowers, residential: hand or power
PA: The Scotts Miracle-Gro Company
14111 Scottslawn Rd
Marysville OH 43040
937 644-0011

(G-12968)
SCOTTS MIRACLE-GRO COMPANY (PA)
Also Called: Scotts, The
14111 Scottslawn Rd (43040-7801)
PHONE..................................937 644-0011
James Hagedorn, *Ch of Bd*
Michael C Lukemire, *President*
Ivan C Smith, *Exec VP*
Denise S Stump, *Exec VP*
Thomas R Coleman, *CFO*
◆ EMP: 277
SALES: 2.8B **Publicly Held**
WEB: www.scotts.com
SIC: 3542 0782 7342 Machine tools, metal forming type; lawn & garden services; pest control services

(G-12969)
SCOTTS MIRACLE-GRO COMPANY
Also Called: East Chemical Plant
14101 Industrial Pkwy (43040-9591)
PHONE..................................937 578-5065
Mike Henkel, *Branch Mgr*
EMP: 29
SALES (corp-wide): 2.8B **Publicly Held**
SIC: 2873 2879 Fertilizers: natural (organic), except compost; fungicides, herbicides

PA: The Scotts Miracle-Gro Company
14111 Scottslawn Rd
Marysville OH 43040
937 644-0011

(G-12970)
SCOTTS MIRACLE-GRO PRODUCTS
14111 Scottslawn Rd (43040-7801)
PHONE..................................937 644-0011
John Kenlon, *President*
Paul Duval, *Senior VP*
Jean H Mordo, *CFO*
Patrick Norton, *CFO*
EMP: 45
SQ FT: 10,000
SALES (est): 5MM
SALES (corp-wide): 2.8B **Publicly Held**
SIC: 2873 3432 Nitrogenous fertilizers; plumbing fixture fittings & trim
PA: The Scotts Miracle-Gro Company
14111 Scottslawn Rd
Marysville OH 43040
937 644-0011

(G-12971)
SMG GROWING MEDIA INC (HQ)
14111 Scottslawn Rd (43040-7800)
PHONE..................................937 644-0011
EMP: 5
SALES (est): 19.6MM
SALES (corp-wide): 2.8B **Publicly Held**
SIC: 3524 5083 Lawn & garden equipment; farm & garden machinery
PA: The Scotts Miracle-Gro Company
14111 Scottslawn Rd
Marysville OH 43040
937 644-0011

(G-12972)
ST MARYS CEMENT INC (US)
14531 Industrial Pkwy (43040-9596)
PHONE..................................937 642-4573
John Coolidge, *Manager*
EMP: 3 **Privately Held**
SIC: 3241 Cement, hydraulic
HQ: St. Marys Cement Inc. (U.S.)
9333 Dearborn St
Detroit MI 48209
313 842-4600

(G-12973)
STRAIGHT 72 INC
Also Called: MAI Manufacturing
20078 State Route 4 (43040-9723)
PHONE..................................740 943-5730
Chris Vogelsang, *President*
John Haller, *General Mgr*
Linda Wolf, *Vice Pres*
Mike Thomas, *QC Mgr*
Veda Kirt, *Accountant*
EMP: 60
SALES (est): 7.6MM **Privately Held**
SIC: 8711 3544 Acoustical engineering; special dies, tools, jigs & fixtures

(G-12974)
SUMITOMO ELC WIRG SYSTEMS INC
14800 Industrial Pkwy (43040-7507)
PHONE..................................937 642-7579
EMP: 33
SALES (corp-wide): 25B **Privately Held**
SIC: 3714 5063 3694 Automotive wiring harness sets; wire & cable; engine electrical equipment
HQ: Sumitomo Electric Wiring Systems, Inc.
1018 Ashley St
Bowling Green KY 42103
270 782-7397

(G-12975)
TOOL TECHNOLOGIES VAN DYKE
639 Clymer Rd (43040-9502)
P.O. Box 256, Milford Center (43045-0256)
PHONE..................................937 349-4900
Steven Vand Yke, *Owner*
Angela Robinson, *Opers Staff*
EMP: 10
SQ FT: 5,000
SALES (est): 930K **Privately Held**
WEB: www.tooltechohio.com
SIC: 3829 3544 Measuring & controlling devices; special dies, tools, jigs & fixtures

(G-12976)
TRIPLE ARROW INDUSTRIES INC
Also Called: Arch Polymers
13311 Industrial Pkwy (43040-9589)
PHONE..................................614 437-5588
Howard WEI, *President*
George Wu, *Vice Pres*
EMP: 7 EST: 2010
SALES (est): 1.6MM **Privately Held**
SIC: 2821 5093 Plastics materials & resins; metal scrap & waste materials; nonferrous metals scrap

(G-12977)
Z LINE KITCHEN AND BATH LLC (PA)
Also Called: Range Hood Store, The
916 Delaware Ave (43040-1726)
PHONE..................................614 777-5004
Andy Zuro,
EMP: 8
SQ FT: 12,500
SALES: 6.5MM **Privately Held**
SIC: 3444 5722 Hoods, range: sheet metal; gas ranges; electric ranges

Mason
Warren County

(G-12978)
AAK KINGS MILLS LLC
5250 Courseview Dr (45040-2370)
PHONE..................................513 598-4460
James M Kaiser, *Principal*
EMP: 3
SALES (est): 150.3K **Privately Held**
SIC: 2711 Newspapers, publishing & printing

(G-12979)
AERO FULFILLMENT SERVICES CORP (PA)
3900 Aero Dr (45040-8840)
PHONE..................................800 225-7145
Fax: 513 459-3950
Jon T Gimpel, *Ch of Bd*
Brenda Conaway, *VP Finance*
Marianne Morisson, *VP Finance*
Jeremy Shubert, *CTO*
Doug Striker, *Business Dir*
EMP: 100
SQ FT: 125,000
SALES: 23MM **Privately Held**
WEB: www.aerofulfillment.com
SIC: 4225 7374 7331 2759 General warehousing; data processing service; mailing service; commercial printing

(G-12980)
AKOS PROMOTIONS INC
668 Reading Rd Ste C (45040-1583)
P.O. Box 78 (45040-0078)
PHONE..................................513 398-6324
Christine Smith, *President*
EMP: 3
SQ FT: 2,500
SALES (est): 460K **Privately Held**
WEB: www.akospromo.com
SIC: 5199 2759 Advertising specialties;
commercial printing

(G-12981)
ANDRE CORPORATION
4600 N Masn Montgomery Rd
(45040-9176)
PHONE..................................574 293-0207
David Andre, *President*
EMP: 50
SQ FT: 50,000
SALES (est): 15.6MM **Privately Held**
WEB: www.andrecorp.com
SIC: 3452 3469 5085 Washers, metal;
stamping metal for the trade; fasteners,
industrial: nuts, bolts, screws, etc.

(G-12982)
ARMOR CONSOLIDATED INC
(PA)
Also Called: Armor Group, The
4600 N Masn Montgomery Rd
(45040-9176)
PHONE..................................513 923-5260
David K Schmitt, *CEO*
Katherine D Schmitt, *Chairman*
Peggy Nolan, *Controller*
Dave Moushey, *Sales Dir*
Derek Wardwell, *Mktg Coord*
▲ EMP: 102
SALES: 60MM **Privately Held**
WEB: www.cinind.com
SIC: 3441 3446 3444 3443 Fabricated
structural metal; architectural metalwork;
sheet metalwork; fabricated plate work
(boiler shop)

(G-12983)
ARMOR METAL GROUP MASON
INC (HQ)
Also Called: Armormetal
4600 N Masn Montgomery Rd
(45040-9176)
PHONE..................................513 769-0700
Fax: 513 923-5645
David K Schmitt, *CEO*
Frank Ahaus, *President*
Jeffrey G Stagnaro, *Principal*
Peggy Nolan, *Controller*
Dave Moses, *Regl Sales Mgr*
▲ EMP: 200
SALES (est): 58.8MM **Privately Held**
SIC: 3441 3446 3444 3443 Fabricated
structural metal; architectural metalwork;
sheet metalwork; fabricated plate work
(boiler shop)

(G-12984)
ASHLEY F WARD INC (PA)
Also Called: Precision Tek Manufacturing
7490 Easy St (45040-9423)
PHONE..................................513 398-1414
Fax: 513 398-1125
Bill Ward, *Ch of Bd*
William H Ward, *Ch of Bd*
Terry Bien, *President*
Michael Evans, *General Mgr*
Brian Scalf, *Vice Pres*
▲ EMP: 116
SQ FT: 150,000
SALES (est): 51.7MM **Privately Held**
WEB: www.ashleyward.com
SIC: 3451 Screw machine products

(G-12985)
ATRICURE INC (PA)
7555 Innovation Way (45040-9695)
PHONE..................................513 755-4100
Fax: 513 755-4567
Richard M Johnston, *Ch of Bd*
Michael H Carrel, *President*
Douglas J Seith, *COO*
Vinayak Doraiswamy, *Senior VP*
Andrew L Lux, *Senior VP*
EMP: 249 EST: 2000

SQ FT: 92,000
SALES: 155.1MM **Publicly Held**
WEB: www.atricure.com
SIC: 3841 Surgical instruments & appara-
tus; clamps, surgical

(G-12986)
BASCO MANUFACTURING
COMPANY (PA)
Also Called: Basco Shower Enclosures
7201 Snider Rd (45040-9601)
PHONE..................................513 573-1900
Fax: 513 229-3434
George W Rohde Jr, *President*
G William Rohde Sr, *Chairman*
Don Gamble, *Exec VP*
Cindy Goodwin, *Vice Pres*
Steve Lotz, *Vice Pres*
◆ EMP: 174 EST: 1946
SQ FT: 80,000
SALES (est): 27.6MM **Privately Held**
WEB: www.bascoshowerdoor.com
SIC: 3231 Doors, glass: made from pur-
chased glass; mirrored glass

(G-12987)
BEARCAT CONSTRUCTION INC
4457 Bethany Rd (45040-8128)
PHONE..................................513 314-0867
Mike Gates, *Owner*
Irwin Vanwinkle, *General Mgr*
EMP: 4
SALES: 150K **Privately Held**
SIC: 1389 1522 Building oil & gas well
foundations on site; residential construc-
tion

(G-12988)
BEAUMONT MACHINE LLC
7697 Innovation Way (45040-9605)
PHONE..................................513 701-0421
Fax: 513 248-3652
Barry Ramsay, *General Mgr*
Ramish Malhotra,
Cathy Didday, *Administration*
EMP: 15
SQ FT: 21,000
SALES (est): 4MM **Privately Held**
WEB: www.beaumontmachine.com
SIC: 3823 7699 Industrial process meas-
urement equipment; precision instrument
repair

(G-12989)
BEELINE PURCHASING LLC
4454 N Mallard Cv (45040-9041)
PHONE..................................513 703-3733
Cathleen Holden, *President*
Kevin Holden, *Principal*
EMP: 3 EST: 2010
SALES (est): 214.1K **Privately Held**
SIC: 5999 5047 3842 Alarm & safety
equipment stores; auction rooms (general
merchandise); industrial safety devices:
first aid kits & masks; personal safety
equipment

(G-12990)
CARDEN DOOR COMPANY LLC
1224 Castle Dr (45040-9433)
PHONE..................................513 459-2233
John Jackson, *Council Mbr*
Bruce Carden,
EMP: 7
SQ FT: 10,000
SALES (est): 760K **Privately Held**
SIC: 2431 Doors & door parts & trim,
wood; doors, combination screen-storm,
wood

(G-12991)
CARTER MANUFACTURING CO
INC
4220 State Route 42 (45040-1931)
PHONE..................................513 398-7303
Fax: 513 398-6231
Chris Carter, *President*
David Bullock, *Foreman/Supr*
Gordon Stewart, *Purchasing*
Kathy Valandingham, *Accounting Mgr*
EMP: 26

SALES (est): 605K **Privately Held**
WEB: www.cartermanufacturing.com
SIC: 3544 7692 3541 Dies & die holders
for metal cutting, forming, die casting; jigs
& fixtures; welding repair; machine tools,
metal cutting type

(G-12992)
CARTER SCOTT-BROWNE
4220 State Route 42 (45040-1931)
PHONE..................................513 398-3970
Christopher Carter, *President*
Don Bullock, *Vice Pres*
EMP: 25
SALES (est): 1.7MM **Privately Held**
SIC: 3312 Tool & die steel

(G-12993)
CENGAGE LEARNING INC
770 Broadway (45040)
PHONE..................................513 234-5967
EMP: 143
SALES (corp-wide): 141.3MM **Privately**
Held
SIC: 2731 Text Book Publishing
PA: Cengage Learning Inc
20 Channel Ctr St
Boston MA 02210
203 965-8600

(G-12994)
CINCINNATI INDUSTRIAL MCHY
INC
4600 N Masn Montgomery Rd
(45040-9176)
PHONE..................................513 923-5600
Joshua Donay, *President*
David Meinking, *Vice Pres*
Peggy Nolan, *CFO*
Shawn Fields, *Sales Staff*
Paul Mullen, *Manager*
EMP: 200
SQ FT: 200,000
SALES (est): 23.5MM **Privately Held**
SIC: 3441 Fabricated structural metal
HQ: Armor Metal Group Mason, Inc.
4600 N Masn Montgomery Rd
Mason OH 45040
513 769-0700

(G-12995)
CINCINNATI WINDOW SHADE
INC
Also Called: Blinds Plus and More
5633 Tylersville Rd Ste 1 (45040-2533)
PHONE..................................513 398-8510
Tom Louden, *Branch Mgr*
EMP: 3
SALES (corp-wide): 4.4MM **Privately**
Held
SIC: 5023 5719 2591 Window furnish-
ings; window shades; venetian blinds;
vertical blinds; window shades; venetian
blinds; vertical blinds; window shades; ve-
netian blinds; blinds vertical
PA: Cincinnati Window Shade, Inc.
3004 Harris Ave
Cincinnati OH 45212
513 631-7200

(G-12996)
CINCOM SYSTEMS INC
4605 Duke Dr (45040-9410)
PHONE..................................513 459-1470
Thomas M Nies, *Branch Mgr*
EMP: 200
SALES (corp-wide): 129MM **Privately**
Held
SIC: 7372 Business oriented computer
software
PA: Cincom Systems, Inc.
55 Merchant St Ste 100
Cincinnati OH 45246
513 612-2300

(G-12997)
CINTAS CORPORATION
6847 Cintas Blvd Ste 120 (45040-9101)
PHONE..................................513 336-6300
Belinda Snell, *Manager*
EMP: 10
SALES (corp-wide): 4.9B **Publicly Held**
WEB: www.cintas-corp.com
SIC: 2326 Work uniforms

PA: Cintas Corporation
6800 Cintas Blvd
Cincinnati OH 45262
513 459-1200

(G-12998)
CLOPAY BUILDING PDTS CO INC
(DH)
Also Called: Ideal Door
8585 Duke Blvd (45040-3100)
PHONE..................................513 770-4800
Fax: 513 770-3863
Gene Colleran, *President*
Alan Leist, *President*
Dan Beckley, *Vice Pres*
Daniel F Beckley, *Vice Pres*
Alan R Leist, *Vice Pres*
◆ EMP: 36
SQ FT: 35,000
SALES (est): 214.4MM
SALES (corp-wide): 1.9B **Publicly Held**
SIC: 2431 3442 2436 Garage doors,
overhead: wood; garage doors, overhead:
metal; plywood, softwood
HQ: Clopay Corporation
8585 Duke Blvd
Mason OH 45040
800 282-2260

(G-12999)
CLOPAY CORPORATION (HQ)
8585 Duke Blvd (45040-3100)
PHONE..................................800 282-2260
Gary Abyad, *President*
Eugene Colleran, *Senior VP*
Ellen Shoemaker, *Senior VP*
Vivek Jain, *Vice Pres*
John Palazzolo, *Vice Pres*
▲ EMP: 231
SQ FT: 130,587
SALES (est): 984.8MM
SALES (corp-wide): 1.9B **Publicly Held**
WEB: www.clopay.com
SIC: 3081 3442 2431 1796 Plastic film &
sheet; garage doors, overhead: metal;
garage doors, overhead: wood; doors,
wood; power generating equipment instal-
lation
PA: Griffon Corporation
712 5th Ave Fl 18
New York NY 10019
212 957-5000

(G-13000)
CLOPAY PLASTIC PRODUCTS
CO INC (DH)
8585 Duke Blvd (45040-3100)
PHONE..................................513 770-4800
Alan H Koblin, *President*
Tor Chamberlain, *Engineer*
John Henwood, *Engineer*
David Toppen, *Engineer*
Tom Givens, *Treasurer*
◆ EMP: 100
SQ FT: 35,000
SALES (est): 96MM
SALES (corp-wide): 1.9B **Publicly Held**
SIC: 3081 Plastic film & sheet
HQ: Clopay Corporation
8585 Duke Blvd
Mason OH 45040
800 282-2260

(G-13001)
CLOROX COMPANY
5181 Natorp Blvd Ste 610 (45040-5909)
PHONE..................................513 445-1840
Gina Kelly, *Manager*
EMP: 19
SALES (corp-wide): 5.7B **Publicly Held**
WEB: www.clorox.com
SIC: 2842 2812 Laundry cleaning prepa-
rations; chlorine, compressed or liquefied
PA: The Clorox Company
1221 Broadway Ste 1300
Oakland CA 94612
510 271-7000

(G-13002)
CM PAULA COMPANY (PA)
Also Called: Geocentral
6049 Hi Tek Ct (45040-2603)
PHONE..................................513 759-7473
Fax: 513 336-3119
Charles W Mc Cullough, *Ch of Bd*
Greg Ionna, *President*

▲ = Import ▼=Export
◆ =Import/Export

William Creager II, *Exec VP*
Monika Brandrup-Thomas, *Vice Pres*
Bill Ash, *CFO*
◆ **EMP:** 25 EST: 1958
SQ FT: 56,000
SALES (est): 12.9MM **Privately Held**
WEB: www.upwithpaper.com
SIC: 3089 2678 2499 3999 Novelties, plastic; stationery: made from purchased materials; decorative wood & woodwork; bric-a-brac

(G-13003)
CMC ELECTRONICS CINCINN
7500 Innovation Way (45040-9695)
PHONE.....................513 573-6316
Alan Scalf, *Engineer*
EMP: 3 EST: 2015
SALES (est): 226.8K **Privately Held**
SIC: 3679 Electronic components

(G-13004)
CNC INDEXING FEEDING TECH LLC (PA)
7944 Innovation Way Ste B (45040-9396)
PHONE.....................513 770-4200
Steven Smith, *President*
Marc Tanzilli, *Controller*
Jamie Schwarz,
EMP: 7
SALES (est): 933.3K **Privately Held**
SIC: 3545 Machine tool accessories

(G-13005)
COMPOSITE CONCEPTS INC
615 Bunker Ln (45040-2044)
PHONE.....................440 247-3844
Dan Tomalin, *President*
Gary Meader, *Vice Pres*
EMP: 3
SALES (est): 313K **Privately Held**
SIC: 3357 Nonferrous wiredrawing & insulating

(G-13006)
CONAGRA BRANDS INC
7308 Central Parke Blvd (45040-6802)
PHONE.....................513 229-0305
David Booth, *VP Sales*
Roland Rubio, *Branch Mgr*
EMP: 120
SALES (corp-wide): 11.6B **Publicly Held**
SIC: 2099 Food preparations
PA: Conagra Brands, Inc.
222 Merchandise Mart Plz
Chicago IL 60654
312 549-5000

(G-13007)
CUSTOM FOUNTAINS INC
4300 State Route 42 (45040-1933)
PHONE.....................513 398-1447
Fax: 513 398-5141
Frank Bravard, *President*
Charlene Bravard, *Vice Pres*
EMP: 10
SALES (est): 740K **Privately Held**
WEB: www.golfcoursefountains.com
SIC: 3299 5199 5261 Fountains, plaster of paris; statuary; fountains, outdoor

(G-13008)
DEERFIELD MANUFACTURING INC
Also Called: Ice Industries Deerfield
320 N Mason Montgomery Rd (45040-7528)
PHONE.....................513 398-2010
Fax: 513 398-2014
Howard Ice, *President*
Paul Bishop, *COO*
Jeff Boger, *Exec VP*
Wayne Schechter, *Engineer*
Brent Fairchild, *Manager*
EMP: 24 EST: 1946
SQ FT: 80,000
SALES (est): 15.2MM
SALES (corp-wide): 100MM **Privately Held**
WEB: www.iceindustries.com
SIC: 3469 Metal stampings
PA: Ice Industries, Inc.
3810 Herr Rd
Sylvania OH 43560
419 842-3612

(G-13009)
DEERFIELD MEDICAL IMAGING LLC
9311 S Masn Montgomery Rd (45040)
PHONE.....................513 271-5717
Diane Bebout, *CFO*
Linda Stamper,
Michael D Ames, *Radiology*
Joseph E Bernstein, *Radiology*
M Patricia Braeuning, *Radiology*
EMP: 3
SQ FT: 1,332
SALES (est): 375.2K **Privately Held**
SIC: 3845 CAT scanner (Computerized Axial Tomography) apparatus

(G-13010)
DOVER CORPORATION
Also Called: Opw Fluid Transfer Group
4680 Parkway Dr Ste 203 (45040-8296)
PHONE.....................513 696-1790
Fax: 513 204-5770
David Crouse, *Branch Mgr*
EMP: 9
SALES (corp-wide): 6.7B **Publicly Held**
SIC: 3531 3542 3565 Construction machinery; machine tools, metal forming type; packaging machinery
PA: Dover Corporation
3005 Highland Pkwy # 200
Downers Grove IL 60515
630 541-1540

(G-13011)
DOWN-LITE INTERNATIONAL INC (PA)
Also Called: Downlite
8153 Duke Blvd (45040-8104)
PHONE.....................513 229-3696
Fax: 513 229-6300
James P Lape, *CEO*
Frank Corella, *General Mgr*
Bob Altbaier, *Vice Pres*
Chad Altbaier, *Vice Pres*
Robert Altbaier, *Vice Pres*
◆ **EMP:** 230
SQ FT: 20,000
SALES (est): 95.5MM **Privately Held**
WEB: www.downbuyingguide.com
SIC: 2392 5719 Pillows, bed: made from purchased materials; comforters & quilts: made from purchased materials; bedding (sheets, blankets, spreads & pillows)

(G-13012)
EBSCO INDUSTRIES INC
1111 Western Row Rd (45040-1365)
PHONE.....................513 398-2149
Randy Sams, *Controller*
Rob Cordes, *Sales Mgr*
EMP: 15
SQ FT: 27,140
SALES (corp-wide): 1.8B **Privately Held**
WEB: www.ebscoind.com
SIC: 3949 Fishing tackle, general
PA: Ebsco Industries, Inc.
5724 Highway 280 E
Birmingham AL 35242
205 991-6600

(G-13013)
ELLISON GROUP INC (PA)
8118 Corp Way Ste 201 (45040)
PHONE.....................513 770-4900
C Michael Ellison, *President*
Kevin Michael, *CFO*
EMP: 15
SALES (est): 54.1MM **Privately Held**
SIC: 3479 Painting, coating & hot dipping

(G-13014)
ELLISON SRFC TECH - MEXICO LLC
8093 Columbia Rd Ste 201 (45040-9560)
PHONE.....................513 770-4900
Michael Ellison, *President*
Kevin Michael, *CFO*
EMP: 330
SQ FT: 13,000
SALES: 47MM **Privately Held**
SIC: 3398 Metal heat treating

(G-13015)
ELLISON SURFACE TECH - W LLC (HQ)
8093 Columbia Rd Ste 201 (45040-9560)
PHONE.....................513 770-4900
C Michael Ellison, *President*
EMP: 6
SALES (est): 2.6MM
SALES (corp-wide): 54.1MM **Privately Held**
SIC: 3479 Painting, coating & hot dipping
PA: The Ellison Group Inc
8118 Corp Way Ste 201
Mason OH 45040
513 770-4900

(G-13016)
ELLISON SURFACE TECH INC (HQ)
8118 Corp Way Ste 201 (45040)
PHONE.....................513 770-4922
C Michael Ellison, *President*
Tim Perkins, *Vice Pres*
David Terkosky, *Vice Pres*
Andy McCort, *QC Mgr*
Don Dunaway, *Engineer*
EMP: 15
SQ FT: 27,000
SALES: 50MM
SALES (corp-wide): 54.1MM **Privately Held**
WEB: www.ellisonsurfacetech.com
SIC: 3479 Painting, coating & hot dipping
PA: The Ellison Group Inc
8118 Corp Way Ste 201
Mason OH 45040
513 770-4900

(G-13017)
ENGSTROM MANUFACTURING INC
4503b State Route 42 (45040)
PHONE.....................513 573-0010
Steve Engstrom, *President*
Joe Tako, *Corp Secy*
Jack Horstman, *Vice Pres*
Dave Tenny, *Vice Pres*
EMP: 14
SALES: 780K **Privately Held**
WEB: www.engstromprecision.com
SIC: 3452 3451 Screws, metal; screw machine products

(G-13018)
EPIC TECHNOLOGIES LLC
4240 Irwin Simpson Rd (45040-9859)
PHONE.....................513 683-5455
Kenneth Schubeler, *Vice Pres*
Paul Tarashuk, *QC Dir*
Cameron Mc Gillivary, *VP Sls/Mktg*
Edward Bisig, *Controller*
Ken Briggs, *Persnl Mgr*
EMP: 100
SALES (corp-wide): 1.3B **Privately Held**
SIC: 3577 3679 Computer peripheral equipment; electronic circuits
HQ: Epic Technologies, Llc
9340 Owensmouth Ave
Chatsworth CA 91311
818 734-6500

(G-13019)
FAG BEARINGS CORPORATION
4035 N Ascot Pl (45040-1850)
PHONE.....................513 398-1139
EMP: 200
SALES (corp-wide): 56.1B **Privately Held**
SIC: 3562 Ball & roller bearings
HQ: Fag Bearings Llc
200 Park Ave
Danbury CT 06810

(G-13020)
FANUC AMERICA CORPORATION
7700 Innovation Way (45040-9696)
PHONE.....................513 754-2400
Fax: 513 754-2440
Keith Gerhardt, *District Mgr*
Eric Cahall, *Engineer*
Mark Jones, *Engineer*
Todd Payne, *Engineer*
Chris Weaver, *Engineer*
EMP: 35
SQ FT: 40,000
SALES (corp-wide): 5.3B **Privately Held**
WEB: www.fanucrobotics.com
SIC: 3559 3548 3569 Metal finishing equipment for plating, etc.; electric welding equipment; robots, assembly line: industrial & commercial
HQ: Fanuc America Corporation
3900 W Hamlin Rd
Rochester Hills MI 48309
248 377-7000

(G-13021)
FEDEX OFFICE & PRINT SVCS INC
8463 S Mason Montgomery R (45040-4023)
PHONE.....................513 754-1482
Fax: 513 754-1751
Eric Logel, *Branch Mgr*
EMP: 5
SALES (corp-wide): 50.3B **Publicly Held**
WEB: www.kinkos.com
SIC: 2752 Commercial printing, lithographic
HQ: Fedex Office And Print Services, Inc.
7900 Legacy Rd
Plano TX 75024
214 550-7000

(G-13022)
FORTE INDUS EQP SYSTEMS INC
Also Called: Forte Industries
6037 Commerce Ct (45040-8819)
PHONE.....................513 398-2800
Eugene A Forte, *President*
Michael Howes, *Vice Pres*
Mark Miller, *Vice Pres*
Charlie Rizzo, *Vice Pres*
Jerry Vink, *Vice Pres*
EMP: 32
SQ FT: 16,000
SALES (est): 25.2MM **Privately Held**
WEB: www.forte-industries.com
SIC: 5084 8711 3537 Materials handling machinery; consulting engineer; industrial trucks & tractors
HQ: Swisslog Holding Ag
Webereiweg 3
Buchs AG
628 379-537

(G-13023)
FRITO-LAY NORTH AMERICA INC
5181 Natorp Blvd Ste 400 (45040-2184)
PHONE.....................513 229-3000
Chuck Shields, *Branch Mgr*
EMP: 160
SALES (corp-wide): 62.8B **Publicly Held**
SIC: 2096 Potato chips & similar snacks
HQ: Frito-Lay North America, Inc.
7701 Legacy Dr
Plano TX 75024

(G-13024)
FUJITEC AMERICA INC (HQ)
7258 Innovation Way (45040-8015)
PHONE.....................513 755-6100
Fax: 513 933-5539
Takakazu Uchiyama, *CEO*
Katsuji Okuda, *President*
Kirk Feuerback, *Vice Pres*
Masashi Tsuchihata, *Vice Pres*
Bill Kerr, *Facilities Mgr*
▲ **EMP:** 200
SQ FT: 300,000
SALES (est): 199.3MM
SALES (corp-wide): 1.5B **Privately Held**
WEB: www.fujiteceurope.com
SIC: 3534 Elevators & equipment; escalators, passenger & freight; walkways, moving
PA: Fujitec Co., Ltd.
591-1, Miyatacho
Hikone SGA 522-0
749 307-111

(G-13025)
GATESAIR INC (DH)
5300 Kings Island Dr (45040-2353)
PHONE.....................513 459-3400
Phil Argyris, *President*
Bryant Burke, *Vice Pres*
Joseph Mack, *Vice Pres*
Mark Thompson, *Prdtn Mgr*

Daniel Vale, *QC Mgr*
EMP: 35
SQ FT: 30,000
SALES (est): 9.3MM
SALES (corp-wide): 6.2B **Privately Held**
SIC: 1731 3663 7371 Communications specialization; radio & TV communications equipment; computer software development & applications
HQ: Imagine Communications Corp.
　　3001 Dallas Pkwy Ste 300
　　Frisco TX 75034
　　469 803-4900

(G-13026)
GENERAL MILLS INC
5181 Natorp Blvd Ste 540　(45040-2183)
PHONE..............................513 770-0558
Peter Baruk, *Branch Mgr*
EMP: 55
SALES (corp-wide): 16.5B **Publicly Held**
WEB: www.generalmills.com
SIC: 5141 2041 Food brokers; flour mixes
PA: General Mills, Inc.
　　1 General Mills Blvd
　　Minneapolis MN 55426
　　763 764-7600

(G-13027)
GEORGIA-PACIFIC LLC
5181 Natorp Blvd Ste 520　(45040-5907)
PHONE..............................513 336-4200
James Hannan, *Branch Mgr*
EMP: 12
SALES (corp-wide): 27.3B **Privately Held**
SIC: 2676 Sanitary paper products
HQ: Georgia-Pacific Llc
　　133 Peachtree St Ne # 4810
　　Atlanta GA 30303
　　404 652-4000

(G-13028)
GLASSLIGHT CANDLES LLC
8706 Charleston Ridge Dr　(45040-8032)
PHONE..............................443 509-5505
Carri Brown, *Principal*
EMP: 3
SALES (est): 179.3K **Privately Held**
SIC: 3999 Candles

(G-13029)
GLOBAL LASER TEK
7697 Innovation Way # 700　(45040-9605)
PHONE..............................513 701-0452
Dan Polto, *Director*
EMP: 29 **EST:** 2014
SALES (est): 2.3MM
SALES (corp-wide): 4.1MM **Privately Held**
SIC: 3699 Laser systems & equipment
PA: Global Specialty Machines Llc
　　7697 Innovation Way # 700
　　Mason OH 45040
　　513 701-0452

(G-13030)
GLOBAL SPECIALTY MACHINES LLC (PA)
7697 Innovation Way # 700　(45040-9605)
PHONE..............................513 701-0452
Ramesh Malhotra, *Mng Member*
Dan Polto, *Mng Member*
▲ **EMP:** 11
SQ FT: 3,000
SALES (est): 4.1MM **Privately Held**
SIC: 3541 Electron-discharge metal cutting machine tools

(G-13031)
GLOBAL TRADE NETWORK INC
7697 Innovation Way # 200　(45040-9619)
PHONE..............................513 701-0411
Fax: 513 573-9919
Ramesh Malhotra, *President*
Leslie Boehm, *Accountant*
Denise Frost, *Manager*
◆ **EMP:** 3
SQ FT: 2,400
SALES (est): 979.2K **Privately Held**
SIC: 3545 3599 Machine tool attachments & accessories; custom machinery

(G-13032)
GRAHAM PACKAGING CO EUROPE LLC
1225 Castle Dr　(45040-9672)
PHONE..............................513 398-5000
Fax: 513 398-9289
Kevin Grosser, *COO*
Rick Blevins, *Engineer*
Glenn Opalski, *Engineer*
Faye Allen, *Benefits Mgr*
Lee Banks, *Branch Mgr*
EMP: 125 **Privately Held**
WEB: www.liquidcontainer.com
SIC: 3089 Buckets, plastic
HQ: Graham Packaging Company Europe Llc
　　2401 Pleasant Valley Rd # 2
　　York PA 17402

(G-13033)
HAAG-STREIT HOLDING US INC (HQ)
3535 Kings Mills Rd　(45040-2303)
PHONE..............................513 336-7255
Dennis Imwalle, *President*
David R Edenfield, *Vice Pres*
EMP: 20
SALES (est): 50.3MM **Privately Held**
SIC: 5047 3841 Surgical equipment & supplies; surgical & medical instruments; ophthalmic instruments & apparatus
PA: Haag-Streit Holding Ag
　　Gartenstadtstrasse 10
　　KOniz BE
　　319 780-100

(G-13034)
HANDS ON INTERNATIONAL LLC
8541 Charleston Ridge Dr　(45040-7995)
PHONE..............................513 502-9000
Micheal Proctor, *Accounting Mgr*
Glyn Bryson, *Business Dir*
Fessel Khan,
Julie Khan,
▲ **EMP:** 7
SALES (est): 275K **Privately Held**
SIC: 5136 2326 7389 Work clothing, men's & boys'; work apparel, except uniforms;

(G-13035)
HARRIS BROADCAST COMMUNICATION
5300 Kings Island Dr　(45040-2353)
PHONE..............................513 459-3400
Jeremy Wenfinger, *General Mgr*
Sal Mendez, *Principal*
Chris Parsons, *VP Opers*
Bob Jennett, *Opers Mgr*
Keyur Parikh, *Prdtn Mgr*
EMP: 46
SALES (est): 7.8MM **Privately Held**
SIC: 3663 Mfg Radio/Tv Communication Equipment

(G-13036)
HARRIS HAWK
306 W Main St　(45040-1622)
PHONE..............................800 459-4295
Frank Batsche, *President*
Frank Geers, *Principal*
EMP: 5
SALES: 1MM **Privately Held**
WEB: www.harrishawk.com
SIC: 5199 2752 8999 Advertising specialties; commercial printing, offset; communication services

(G-13037)
HI-TEK MANUFACTURING INC
Also Called: System EDM of Ohio
6050 Hi Tek Ct　(45040-2602)
PHONE..............................513 459-1094
Fax: 513 459-9882
Cletis Jackson, *President*
Scott Stang, *Plant Mgr*
Craig Enderle, *QA Dir*
George Carrington, *QC Mgr*
Ricardo Hinojosa, *Engineer*
EMP: 180
SQ FT: 71,000

SALES (est): 74.4MM **Privately Held**
WEB: www.hitekmfg.com
SIC: 3599 7692 3724 3714 Machine shop, jobbing & repair; welding repair; aircraft engines & engine parts; motor vehicle parts & accessories; special dies, tools, jigs & fixtures

(G-13038)
IAMS COMPANY (HQ)
8700 S Masn Montgomery Rd　(45040-9760)
PHONE..............................800 675-3849
AG Losley, *CEO*
Brian Robson, *CFO*
Carol Esch, *Manager*
B J Hennig, *Manager*
Terrence J Macewen, *Director*
▲ **EMP:** 300
SQ FT: 50,000
SALES (est): 212.4MM
SALES (corp-wide): 35B **Privately Held**
WEB: www.iams.com
SIC: 2047 2048 Dog food; cat food; prepared feeds
PA: Mars, Incorporated
　　6885 Elm St
　　Mc Lean VA 22101
　　703 821-4900

(G-13039)
IBIZA HOLDINGS INC
7901 Innovation Way　(45040-9498)
PHONE..............................513 701-7300
Chris Cole, *CEO*
EMP: 50
SALES (est): 3.7MM **Privately Held**
SIC: 3535 Conveyors & conveying equipment

(G-13040)
ICE INDUSTRIES INC
320 N Mason Montgomery Rd　(45040-7528)
PHONE..............................513 398-2010
Ken Kneip, *Controller*
Jene Swick, *Branch Mgr*
EMP: 3
SALES (corp-wide): 100MM **Privately Held**
SIC: 3469 Metal stampings
PA: Ice Industries, Inc.
　　3810 Herr Rd
　　Sylvania OH 43560
　　419 842-3612

(G-13041)
IMAGINE COMMUNICATIONS CORP
Also Called: Harris Broadcast
5300 Kings Island Dr # 101　(45040-2353)
PHONE..............................513 459-3400
Fax: 513 459-3890
P Harris Morris, *CEO*
Rich Lohmueller, *Principal*
Geoff Mendenhall, *Vice Pres*
David Danielsons, *Engineer*
Mary Harnet, *Manager*
EMP: 75
SQ FT: 17,000
SALES (corp-wide): 6.2B **Privately Held**
SIC: 3663 Radio broadcasting & communications equipment; television broadcasting & communications equipment
HQ: Imagine Communications Corp.
　　3001 Dallas Pkwy Ste 300
　　Frisco TX 75034
　　469 803-4900

(G-13042)
INTELLIGRATED INC (HQ)
7901 Innovation Way　(45040-9498)
PHONE..............................866 936-7300
Fax: 513 701-7320
Chris Cole, *CEO*
Jim McCarthy, *President*
Tony Dinello, *Business Mgr*
Jim Sharp, *Exec VP*
Jim McDonald, *Senior VP*
▲ **EMP:** 29 **EST:** 2001
SALES (est): 20.3MM
SALES (corp-wide): 39.3B **Publicly Held**
SIC: 3535 Conveyors & conveying equipment

PA: Honeywell International Inc.
　　115 Tabor Rd
　　Morris Plains NJ 07950
　　973 455-2000

(G-13043)
INTELLIGRATED HEADQUARTERS LLC
7901 Innovation Way　(45040-9498)
PHONE..............................866 936-7300
EMP: 7 **EST:** 2014
SALES (est): 457.7K
SALES (corp-wide): 39.3B **Publicly Held**
SIC: 3535 Conveyors & conveying equipment
HQ: Intelligrated Systems, Inc.
　　7901 Innovation Way
　　Mason OH 45040
　　866 936-7300

(G-13044)
INTELLIGRATED SUB HOLDINGS INC (PA)
7901 Innovation Way　(45040-9498)
PHONE..............................513 701-7300
Chris Cole, *CEO*
Derek Nemeth, *Credit Mgr*
EMP: 23
SQ FT: 250,000
SALES (est): 7.8MM **Privately Held**
SIC: 3535 Conveyors & conveying equipment

(G-13045)
INTELLIGRATED SYSTEMS INC (HQ)
7901 Innovation Way　(45040-9498)
PHONE..............................866 936-7300
Chris Cole, *CEO*
Jim McCarthy, *President*
Gregory Cronin, *Exec VP*
Jim Sharp, *Exec VP*
John Cullen, *Senior VP*
EMP: 800 **EST:** 1996
SQ FT: 390,000
SALES: 800MM
SALES (corp-wide): 39.3B **Publicly Held**
SIC: 3535 5084 7371 Conveyors & conveying equipment; industrial machinery & equipment; computer software development
PA: Honeywell International Inc.
　　115 Tabor Rd
　　Morris Plains NJ 07950
　　973 455-2000

(G-13046)
INTELLIGRATED SYSTEMS LLC
7901 Innovation Way　(45040-9498)
PHONE..............................513 701-7300
Chris Cole, *CEO*
Jim McCarthy, *President*
Amy Ball, *General Mgr*
James Sharp, *Exec VP*
Jim McKnight, *Senior VP*
EMP: 2300
SQ FT: 260,000
SALES (est): 228.8MM
SALES (corp-wide): 39.3B **Publicly Held**
SIC: 3535 5084 7371 Conveyors & conveying equipment; materials handling machinery; computer software development
HQ: Intelligrated Systems, Inc.
　　7901 Innovation Way
　　Mason OH 45040
　　866 936-7300

(G-13047)
INTELLIGRATED SYSTEMS OHIO LLC (DH)
7901 Innovation Way　(45040-9498)
P.O. Box 60843, Charlotte NC　(28260)
PHONE..............................513 701-7300
Jim McCarthy, *President*
Stephen Ackerman, *Exec VP*
Chuck Waddle, *Exec VP*
Stephen Causey, *Vice Pres*
Wes Goode, *Vice Pres*
◆ **EMP:** 600 **EST:** 2010
SQ FT: 332,000

SALES (est): 216.1MM
SALES (corp-wide): 39.3B **Publicly Held**
WEB: www.fkilogistex.com
SIC: 3535 5084 3537 Conveyors & conveying equipment; industrial machinery & equipment; palletizers & depalletizers
HQ: Intelligrated Systems, Inc.
7901 Innovation Way
Mason OH 45040
866 936-7300

(G-13048)
INTERSTATE CONTRACTORS LLC
Also Called: Ic Roofing
762 Reading Rd G (45040-1362)
PHONE.................................513 372-5393
Joel Presar, *Vice Pres*
Young Chon Jung,
Jiah Jung,
EMP: 40
SALES (est): 2.8MM **Privately Held**
SIC: 8611 3444 Business associations; metal roofing & roof drainage equipment

(G-13049)
JERSEY WEST DRILLING INC
6715 Irwin Simpson Rd (45040-9717)
PHONE.................................513 398-0774
Carol Caprioni, *President*
Michael Caprioni, *Vice Pres*
EMP: 3
SQ FT: 1,800
SALES (est): 360K **Privately Held**
SIC: 1381 Drilling water intake wells

(G-13050)
JETOPTERA INC
3092 Crooked Tree Dr (45040-7955)
P.O. Box 537 (45040-0537)
PHONE.................................516 456-7609
Denis Dancanet, *CEO*
Andrei Evulet, *Chief Engr*
Simina Farcasiu, *CFO*
EMP: 3 **EST:** 2015
SALES (est): 129.6K **Privately Held**
SIC: 3721 Research & development on aircraft by the manufacturer

(G-13051)
K & K PRECISION INC
5001 N Masn Montgomery Rd (45040-9148)
PHONE.................................513 336-0032
Fax: 513 336-0035
David J Kappes, *President*
Larry G Hixson, *Vice Pres*
Jay Kappa, *Office Mgr*
Melinda Kappes, *Admin Sec*
EMP: 21 **EST:** 1991
SALES (est): 4.7MM **Privately Held**
WEB: www.kkprecision.com
SIC: 3599 Machine shop, jobbing & repair

(G-13052)
KADANT BLACK CLAWSON INC (HQ)
7312 Central Parke Blvd (45040-6802)
PHONE.................................513 229-8100
Jonathan W Painter, *President*
Thomas M Obrie, *President*
Thomas M Brien, *Exec VP*
Tom Golden, *Opers Staff*
Neale Fetterly, *Engineer*
▲ **EMP:** 75
SQ FT: 26,000
SALES (est): 38.6MM
SALES (corp-wide): 414.1MM **Publicly Held**
WEB: www.kadantbc.com
SIC: 3554 Paper industries machinery
PA: Kadant Inc.
1 Technology Park Dr # 210
Westford MA 01886
978 776-2000

(G-13053)
KLOSTERMAN BAKING CO
1130 Reading Rd (45040-9156)
PHONE.................................513 398-2707
Fax: 513 398-4838
Chip Klosterman, *President*
Brandon Hoehn, *Manager*
Brandon Holem, *Manager*
EMP: 19
SQ FT: 60,000

SALES (corp-wide): 209.5MM **Privately Held**
SIC: 2051 4225 Bread, cake & related products; general warehousing
PA: Klosterman Baking Co.
4760 Paddock Rd
Cincinnati OH 45229
513 242-5667

(G-13054)
L-3 CMMNCATIONS NOVA ENGRG INC
4393 Digital Way (45040-7604)
P.O. Box 16850, Salt Lake City UT (84116-0850)
PHONE.................................877 282-1168
Fax: 513 642-3300
Mark Fischer, *President*
Andrea West, *Accountant*
EMP: 150
SQ FT: 80,000
SALES (est): 10.1MM
SALES (corp-wide): 10.5B **Publicly Held**
WEB: www.l-3com.com
SIC: 8711 3663 Electrical or electronic engineering; carrier equipment, radio communications
PA: L3 Technologies, Inc.
600 3rd Ave Fl 34
New York NY 10016
212 697-1111

(G-13055)
L-3 COMMUNICATIONS CINCINNATI (HQ)
7500 Innovation Way (45040-9695)
PHONE.................................513 573-6100
Fax: 513 573-6290
Russ Walker, *CEO*
Patrick J Sweeney, *Chairman*
Dale E Lhmann, *VP Admin*
Doug Becker, *Vice Pres*
Mark Dapore, *Vice Pres*
EMP: 600
SQ FT: 230,000
SALES (est): 132.6MM
SALES (corp-wide): 10.5B **Publicly Held**
WEB: www.cinele.com
SIC: 3812 3769 3823 Detection apparatus: electronic/magnetic field, light/heat; missile guidance systems & equipment; guided missile & space vehicle parts & auxiliary equipment; infrared instruments, industrial process type
PA: L3 Technologies, Inc.
600 3rd Ave Fl 34
New York NY 10016
212 697-1111

(G-13056)
M C SYSTEMS INC
4455 Bethany Rd Unit C (45040-9688)
PHONE.................................513 336-6007
Mark Chrostowski, *President*
Drew Chrostowski, *Vice Pres*
EMP: 4
SALES (est): 423.7K **Privately Held**
SIC: 3577 7699 Bar code (magnetic ink) printers; repair services

(G-13057)
MAD POTTER LLC
6680b Tri Way Dr (45040)
PHONE.................................513 770-5585
Kehra Woofolf, *Owner*
EMP: 5
SALES (est): 362.9K **Privately Held**
SIC: 3269 Pottery products

(G-13058)
MAKINO INC (HQ)
7680 Innovation Way (45040-9695)
P.O. Box 8003 (45040-8003)
PHONE.................................513 573-7200
Fax: 513 583-7360
Donald Lane, *President*
Thomas Clark, *President*
Robert Henry, *President*
Bart Andrews, *Regional Mgr*
Bob Henry, *Vice Pres*
▲ **EMP:** 356 **EST:** 1887
SQ FT: 320,000

SALES (est): 210.6MM **Privately Held**
WEB: www.moldmakermag.com
SIC: 3541 Machine tools, metal cutting type
PA: Makino Milling Machine Co., Ltd.
2-3-19, Nakane
Meguro-Ku TKY 152-0
337 171-151

(G-13059)
MAMMAS MANDEL
7952 Hedgewood Cir (45040-6008)
PHONE.................................513 827-2457
Howard Pinsky, *Principal*
EMP: 3 **EST:** 2011
SALES (est): 169.5K **Privately Held**
SIC: 2053 Cakes, bakery: frozen

(G-13060)
MARTIN MARIETTA MATERIALS INC
4900 Parkway Dr (45040-8430)
PHONE.................................513 701-1120
Michael Hunt, *Principal*
Tom Lombardi, *Sales Staff*
EMP: 10
SALES (corp-wide): 3.8B **Publicly Held**
SIC: 1423 Crushed & broken granite
PA: Martin Marietta Materials Inc
2710 Wycliff Rd
Raleigh NC 27607
919 781-4550

(G-13061)
MAUSER USA LLC
1229 Castle Dr (45040-9672)
P.O. Box 350 (45040-0350)
PHONE.................................513 398-1300
Steve Haunert, *Plant Mgr*
EMP: 90
SALES (corp-wide): 6.6B **Privately Held**
SIC: 3412 Drums, shipping: metal
HQ: Mauser Usa, Llc
2 Tower Center Blvd 20-1
East Brunswick NJ 08816
732 353-7100

(G-13062)
MICROSOFT CORPORATION
4605 Duke Dr Ste 800 (45040-7627)
PHONE.................................513 339-2800
Jack Lapan, *Branch Mgr*
EMP: 54
SALES (corp-wide): 85.3B **Publicly Held**
WEB: www.microsoft.com
SIC: 7372 Prepackaged software
PA: Microsoft Corporation
1 Microsoft Way
Redmond WA 98052
425 882-8080

(G-13063)
MILLER AND SLAY WDWKG LLC
8284 Winters Ln (45040-9100)
PHONE.................................513 265-3816
Jon Miller, *Principal*
EMP: 3
SALES (est): 224.1K **Privately Held**
SIC: 2431 Millwork

(G-13064)
MILLINIUM 3 INC (PA)
Also Called: Pavetech International
4660 Duke Dr Ste 390 (45040-8466)
PHONE.................................513 770-3122
Robert Ricaud, *President*
Jamey Deeter, *Finance Mgr*
EMP: 8
SQ FT: 3,007
SALES (est): 1MM **Privately Held**
SIC: 3272 Concrete products

(G-13065)
MITSUBISHI ELC AUTO AMER INC (DH)
4773 Bethany Rd (45040-8344)
PHONE.................................513 573-6614
Fax: 513 398-1121
Takeo Sasaki, *President*
Richard Krieger, *President*
Troy Fultz, *Opers Staff*
Tom Wylie, *Purch Mgr*
Mike Newkirk, *Buyer*
◆ **EMP:** 422
SQ FT: 220,000

SALES (est): 226MM
SALES (corp-wide): 37.5B **Privately Held**
SIC: 3694 3651 3714 Motors, starting: automotive & aircraft; alternators, automotive; household audio & video equipment; motor vehicle parts & accessories
HQ: Mitsubishi Electric Us Holdings, Inc.
5900 Katella Ave Ste A
Cypress CA 90630
714 220-2500

(G-13066)
MORSE ENTERPRISES INC
Also Called: AlphaGraphics Cincinnati
6678 Tri Way Dr (45040-2605)
PHONE.................................513 229-3600
Fax: 513 204-6900
Cinda Morse, *Principal*
Steven Morse, *Principal*
EMP: 7 **EST:** 2013
SQ FT: 3,200
SALES (est): 480K **Privately Held**
SIC: 2759 7334 2752 7336 Commercial printing; photocopying & duplicating services; commercial printing, offset; business form & card printing, lithographic; commercial art & graphic design; pamphlets: printing & binding, not published on site

(G-13067)
NORITAKE CO INC
4990 Alliance Dr (45040-4516)
PHONE.................................513 234-0770
Nori Kambayashi, *Branch Mgr*
EMP: 30
SALES (corp-wide): 936.9MM **Privately Held**
WEB: www.noritake.com
SIC: 3291 Synthetic abrasives
HQ: Noritake Co., Inc.
15-22 Fair Lawn Ave
Fair Lawn NJ 07410
201 796-2222

(G-13068)
NORWICH OVERSEAS INC (HQ)
8700 S Masn Montgomery Rd (45040-9760)
PHONE.................................513 983-1100
Mark Collar, *President*
Sanford H Argabrite, *Treasurer*
J Douglas Gerstle, *Treasurer*
James F Prevost, *Treasurer*
Roger C Stewart, *Treasurer*
▲ **EMP:** 10
SALES (est): 4.8MM
SALES (corp-wide): 259.8MM **Privately Held**
SIC: 2834 Pharmaceutical preparations
PA: Warner Chilcott Pharmaceuticals Inc.
1 Procter And Gamble Plz
Cincinnati OH 45202
513 983-1100

(G-13069)
O C TANNER COMPANY
Also Called: O.c Tanner Recognition
8569 S Mason Montgomery R (45040-9806)
PHONE.................................513 583-1100
Debbie Phipps, *Manager*
EMP: 5
SALES (corp-wide): 344.1MM **Privately Held**
WEB: www.octanner.com
SIC: 3911 Pins (jewelry), precious metal
PA: O. C. Tanner Company
1930 S State St
Salt Lake City UT 84115
801 486-2430

(G-13070)
OAKLEY DIE & MOLD CO
Also Called: O D M
7595 Innovation Way (45040-9052)
PHONE.................................513 754-8500
Fax: 513 754-8501
Ernest Petrinowitsch, *CEO*
Harry Petrinowitsch, *President*
Peggy Braun, *Admin Sec*
▲ **EMP:** 35 **EST:** 1948
SQ FT: 80,950

SALES (est): 6.6MM **Privately Held**
WEB: www.odm.com
SIC: 3599 3544 3545 Machine shop, jobbing & repair; industrial molds; tools & accessories for machine tools

(G-13071)
OSG USA INC
3611 Socialvl Fstr Rd # 102 (45040-7361)
PHONE.....................................513 755-3360
Rick Jones, *Branch Mgr*
EMP: 6
SALES (corp-wide): 1B **Privately Held**
WEB: www.osgtool.com
SIC: 3544 Special dies, tools, jigs & fix-
tures
HQ: Osg Usa, Inc.
676 E Fullerton Ave
Glendale Heights IL 60139
630 790-1400

(G-13072)
PHANTOM SOUND
104 Reading Rd (45040-1634)
PHONE.....................................513 759-4477
Fax: 513 759-5544
Howard Mc Gurdy, *Owner*
Carla Johnson, *Technical Mgr*
◆ EMP: 12
SALES: 810K **Privately Held**
WEB: www.phantomsound.com
SIC: 3651 5731 Speaker systems; radio,
television & electronic stores

(G-13073)
**PILOT PRODUCTION
SOLUTIONS LLC**
Also Called: Pps
6253 Crooked Creek Dr (45040-2443)
PHONE.....................................513 602-1467
Michael Ullom,
EMP: 3
SALES (est): 229.1K **Privately Held**
SIC: 2672 7389 Coated & laminated
paper;

(G-13074)
PORTION PAC INC (DH)
7325 Snider Rd (45040-9193)
PHONE.....................................513 398-0400
Fax: 513 459-5300
Jeffrey Berger, *President*
Pete Jack, *President*
Susan Al, *General Mgr*
Arthur C Jack, *Managing Dir*
Timothy E Hoberg, *Principal*
▼ EMP: 400
SQ FT: 100,000
SALES (est): 167MM
SALES (corp-wide): 26.4B **Publicly Held**
WEB: www.portionpac.com
SIC: 2033 2035 Catsup: packaged in
cans, jars, etc.; jams, including imitation:
packaged in cans, jars, etc.; jellies, edi-
ble, including imitation: in cans, jars, etc.;
marmalade: packaged in cans, jars, etc.;
seasonings & sauces, except tomato &
dry; mustard, prepared (wet); horserad-
ish, prepared; dressings, salad: raw &
cooked (except dry mixes)
HQ: Kraft Heinz Foods Company
1 Ppg Pl Ste 3200
Pittsburgh PA 15222
412 456-5700

(G-13075)
PRATT INDUSTRIES USA INC
Also Called: Pratt Displays
4700 Duke Dr Ste 140 (45040-9507)
PHONE.....................................513 770-0851
Dave Connors, *Manager*
Debbie Richey, *Manager*
EMP: 66
SALES (corp-wide): 1.7B **Privately Held**
SIC: 2653 Display items, corrugated: made
from purchased materials
PA: Pratt Industries (U.S.A.), Inc.
1800 Sarasota Busin Ste C
Conyers GA 30013
770 918-5678

(G-13076)
**PRECISION QUINCY SHELTERS
INC**
4600 N Masn Montgomery Rd
(45040-9176)
PHONE.....................................888 312-5442
Frank Ferguson, *President*
EMP: 300
SQ FT: 315,000
SALES (est): 15.1MM **Privately Held**
SIC: 3441 Fabricated structural metal

(G-13077)
PRESTIGE FIREWORKS LLC
222 Van Buren Dr (45040-2138)
PHONE.....................................513 492-7726
Kevin Shew, *President*
Martin Schaefer, *Vice Pres*
EMP: 19
SALES: 250K **Privately Held**
WEB: www.prestigefireworks.com
SIC: 2899 Fireworks

(G-13078)
PROCTER & GAMBLE COMPANY
8700 Mason Montgomery Rd (45040-9760)
P.O. Box 8006 (45040-8006)
PHONE.....................................513 622-1000
Fax: 513 622-0406
Jim Brogan, *Vice Pres*
Mary Haver, *Project Mgr*
Murthy Jayanthi, *Project Mgr*
Anne Gentile, *Facilities Mgr*
Michelle Hare, *Buyer*
EMP: 165
SALES (corp-wide): 65.3B **Publicly Held**
WEB: www.pg.com
SIC: 2844 Toilet preparations
PA: The Procter & Gamble Company
1 Procter And Gamble Plz
Cincinnati OH 45202
513 983-1100

(G-13079)
R-K ELECTRONICS INC
7405 Industrial Row Dr (45040-1301)
PHONE.....................................513 204-6060
Fax: 513 204-6061
John L Keller, *President*
Carolyn R Keller, *Exec VP*
Nancy Wilson, *Purchasing*
Rebekah Erck, *Manager*
Oscar Shelley, *Systs Prg Mgr*
▲ EMP: 14
SQ FT: 11,200
SALES (est): 3.2MM **Privately Held**
WEB: www.rke.com
SIC: 3625 3672 Relays & industrial con-
trols; control circuit relays, industrial; tim-
ing devices, electronic; wiring boards

(G-13080)
**RELIANCE MEDICAL PRODUCTS
INC (DH)**
3535 Kings Mills Rd (45040-2303)
PHONE.....................................513 398-3937
Fax: 513 398-0256
Ernest Cavin, *President*
Russ Stearns, *Assistant VP*
Mark Pabst, *Safety Mgr*
Thomas Stadtmiller, *Production*
Steve Lawhorn, *Purchasing*
◆ EMP: 85
SQ FT: 100,000
SALES (est): 16.6MM **Privately Held**
SIC: 3841 Surgical & medical instruments

(G-13081)
REMTEC CORP
6049 Hi Tek Ct (45040-2603)
PHONE.....................................513 860-4299
Fax: 513 860-4587
Teri Campbell, *Principal*
EMP: 4
SALES (est): 945.9K **Privately Held**
SIC: 3569 Assembly machines, non-metal-
working

(G-13082)
REMTEC ENGINEERING
Also Called: Mbs Acquisition
6049 Hi Tek Ct (45040-2603)
PHONE.....................................513 860-4299
Keith Rosnell, *CEO*
Steven Mustain, *Engineer*

EMP: 45
SQ FT: 25,000
SALES (est): 8.2MM **Privately Held**
WEB: www.remtecautomation.com
SIC: 3569 5084 Assembly machines, non-
metalworking; robots, assembly line: in-
dustrial & commercial; robots, industrial

(G-13083)
**RHINESTAHL CORPORATION
(PA)**
Also Called: Rhinestahl AMG
7687 Innovation Way (45040-9695)
PHONE.....................................513 229-5300
Fax: 513 489-3899
Dieter Moeller, *President*
Janice Clarke, *General Mgr*
Scott Crislip, *Vice Pres*
Chris Hanna, *Vice Pres*
Dave Rettenmaier, *Vice Pres*
EMP: 72
SQ FT: 120,000
SALES (est): 36.7MM **Privately Held**
SIC: 3523 Turf & grounds equipment

(G-13084)
RHINESTAHL CORPORATION
7687 Innovation Way (45040-9695)
PHONE.....................................513 229-5300
Tom Hohnston, *Branch Mgr*
EMP: 25
SALES (corp-wide): 36.7MM **Privately
Held**
SIC: 3544 Special dies, tools, jigs & fix-
tures
PA: Rhinestahl Corporation
7687 Innovation Way
Mason OH 45040
513 229-5300

(G-13085)
**SARA WOOD
PHARMACEUTICALS LLC ◑**
4518 Margaret Ct (45040-2922)
PHONE.....................................513 833-5502
Keith Kociba, *CEO*
Thomas Docherty, *COO*
Mina Pathel, *Officer*
Eileen Rogers, *Officer*
David Schultenover, *Officer*
EMP: 8 EST: 2016
SALES (est): 374K **Privately Held**
SIC: 2834 Solutions, pharmaceutical

(G-13086)
SCICOMPRO - LLC
4861 Hampton Pond Ln (45040-5698)
PHONE.....................................513 680-8686
Kurt W Weingand,
EMP: 3
SALES (est): 195.8K **Privately Held**
SIC: 2834 Veterinary pharmaceutical
preparations

(G-13087)
SEAPINE SOFTWARE INC (HQ)
6960 Cintas Blvd (45040-8922)
PHONE.....................................513 754-1655
Richard Riccetti, *President*
Paula Rome, *President*
Mark Mason, *General Mgr*
Ashley Agar, *Business Mgr*
Bill Anastasia, *Business Mgr*
EMP: 50
SQ FT: 36,000
SALES (est): 18.1MM **Privately Held**
WEB: www.seapine.net
SIC: 7372 7371 Prepackaged software;
operating systems computer software;
business oriented computer software; ap-
plication computer software; custom com-
puter programming services

(G-13088)
SPEAR USA INC (PA)
5510 Courseview Dr (45040-2366)
PHONE.....................................513 459-1100
Fax: 513 229-3646
Richard Spear, *CEO*
Randall Spear, *President*
Bob Kramer, *Purchasing*
Lonnie Wagers, *Purchasing*
Tom Faugno, *Sls & Mktg Exec*
EMP: 125
SQ FT: 80,000

SALES (est): 90.1MM **Privately Held**
SIC: 2759 Screen printing

(G-13089)
**SPECIAL MACHINED
COMPONENTS**
7626 Easy St (45040-9424)
PHONE.....................................513 459-1113
Fax: 513 459-1134
Larry Johnson, *Owner*
EMP: 9
SQ FT: 12,000
SALES (est): 751.8K **Privately Held**
SIC: 3599 Machine shop, jobbing & repair

(G-13090)
**STAR COMBUSTION SYSTEMS
LLC**
6506 Castle Dr (45040-9413)
P.O. Box 636 (45040-0636)
PHONE.....................................513 282-0810
Tom Ballman, *Project Mgr*
Tim Daugherty, *Opers Staff*
Andrew Greve, *Engineer*
Andrew J Kemppainen, *Mng Member*
Kim Walsh, *Admin Asst*
EMP: 3
SQ FT: 3,000
SALES (est): 590.1K **Privately Held**
SIC: 3823 Combustion control instruments

(G-13091)
STARBUCKS CORPORATION
6300 Kings Island Dr (45040-9665)
PHONE.....................................513 754-5700
Sara Maine, *Principal*
EMP: 8
SALES (corp-wide): 21.3B **Publicly Held**
SIC: 3421 Table & food cutlery, including
butchers'
PA: Starbucks Corporation
2401 Utah Ave S
Seattle WA 98134
206 447-1575

(G-13092)
**SUPERIOR LABEL SYSTEMS
INC (HQ)**
Also Called: Superior Machine Systems
7500 Industrial Row Dr (45040-1307)
PHONE.....................................513 336-0825
Fax: 513 459-2400
Kenneth Kidd, *Ch of Bd*
Thomas Braig, *Vice Pres*
Erin Hernes, *Human Res Mgr*
Pat Linder, *Info Tech Mgr*
EMP: 275
SQ FT: 30,000
SALES (est): 30.4MM
SALES (corp-wide): 774MM **Privately
Held**
SIC: 3565 2759 3993 3577 Labeling ma-
chines, industrial; flexographic printing;
signs & advertising specialties; computer
peripheral equipment; coated & laminated
paper; packaging paper & plastics film,
coated & laminated
PA: W/S Packaging Group, Inc.
2571 S Hemlock Rd
Green Bay WI 54229
920 866-6300

(G-13093)
**SYNERGY HEALTH NORTH
AMER INC**
7086 Industrial Row Dr (45040-1363)
PHONE.....................................513 398-6406
Mike Vell, *Manager*
EMP: 75
SALES (corp-wide): 8.3MM **Privately
Held**
SIC: 3841 7213 Surgical & medical instru-
ments; linen supply
HQ: Synergy Health North America, Inc.
3903 Northdale Blvd 100e
Tampa FL 33624
813 891-9550

(G-13094)
TELEDYNE INSTRUMENTS INC
Also Called: Teledyne Tekmar
4736 Scialville Foster Rd (45040-8265)
PHONE.....................................513 229-7000
Robert Mehrabian, *CEO*
Martin Motz, *Electrical Engi*

Melanie Dahlberg, *Manager*
Tammy Rellar, *Manager*
EMP: 25
SALES (corp-wide): 2.1B **Publicly Held**
SIC: 5049 3826 3829 3821 Laboratory equipment, except medical or dental; analytical instruments; environmental testing equipment; measuring & controlling devices; laboratory apparatus & furniture
HQ: Teledyne Instruments, Inc.
16830 Chestnut St
City Of Industry CA 91748
626 934-1500

(G-13095)
TELEDYNE TEKMAR COMPANY (HQ)
Also Called: Tekmar-Dohrmann
4736 Scialville Foster Rd (45040-8265)
PHONE...................................513 229-7000
Fax: 513 229-7050
Robert Mehrabian, *Ch of Bd*
Ron Uchtman, *Opers Mgr*
Cindy Cancel, *Purchasing*
Roger Bardsley, *Research*
Stephen Proffitt, *Research*
EMP: 25
SQ FT: 40,000
SALES (est): 41.2MM
SALES (corp-wide): 2.1B **Publicly Held**
WEB: www.teledynetekmar.com
SIC: 5049 3826 3829 3821 Laboratory equipment, except medical or dental; analytical instruments; environmental testing equipment; measuring & controlling devices; laboratory apparatus & furniture
PA: Teledyne Technologies Inc
1049 Camino Dos Rios
Thousand Oaks CA 91360
805 373-4545

(G-13096)
TENNESSEE COATINGS INC (HQ)
Also Called: Ellison Surfc Technologies-Tn
8093 Columbia Rd Ste 201 (45040-9560)
P.O. Box 749, Wartburg TN (37887-0749)
PHONE...................................513 770-4900
C Michael Ellison, *CEO*
EMP: 15
SALES (est): 1.5MM
SALES (corp-wide): 54.1MM **Privately Held**
SIC: 3479 Coating of metals & formed products
PA: The Ellison Group Inc
8118 Corp Way Ste 201
Mason OH 45040
513 770-4900

(G-13097)
TERRENE LABS
5939 Deerfield Blvd (45040-2671)
PHONE...................................404 408-2241
Piyush Sing, *CEO*
EMP: 6
SALES (est): 117.2K **Privately Held**
SIC: 7372 Prepackaged software

(G-13098)
THE DANNON COMPANY INC
7577 Central Parke Blvd (45040-6810)
PHONE...................................513 229-0092
George Denmen, *Manager*
EMP: 390
SALES (corp-wide): 685.2MM **Privately Held**
WEB: www.dannon.com
SIC: 2024 Yogurt desserts, frozen
HQ: The Dannon Company Inc
100 Hillside Ave Fl 3
White Plains NY 10603
914 872-8400

(G-13099)
TO SCALE SOFTWARE LLC
Also Called: Stack Constructyion Technology
6398 Thornberry Ct (45040-7816)
PHONE...................................513 253-0053
Phillip Ogilby, *Mng Member*
Jane Baysore, *Manager*
EMP: 35
SALES: 2.5MM **Privately Held**
SIC: 7372 Prepackaged software

(G-13100)
VELOCITY CONCEPT DEV GROUP LLC (PA)
4393 Digital Way (45040-7604)
PHONE...................................513 204-2100
John D Speridakos, *EMP:* 8
SALES (est): 4MM **Privately Held**
SIC: 3999 Atomizers, toiletry

(G-13101)
VIGILANT DEFENSE
Also Called: Vigilant Technology Solutions
9378 S Masn Montgomery Rd (45040-8827)
PHONE...................................513 214-1635
Chris Nyhuis, *Owner*
Katherine Nyhuis, *CFO*
EMP: 40 EST: 2010
SALES (est): 4.7MM **Privately Held**
SIC: 3699 Security devices

(G-13102)
W/S PACKAGING GROUP INC
7500 Industrial Row Dr (45040-1307)
PHONE...................................513 459-2400
Fax: 513 459-8815
Mark Lutz, *Vice Pres*
James L Casey, *Vice Pres*
Karen Naze, *Vice Pres*
Randy Barlow, *Project Mgr*
Tom Nelson, *Project Mgr*
EMP: 150
SALES (corp-wide): 774MM **Privately Held**
WEB: www.wspackaging.com
SIC: 2679 3565 Labels, paper: made from purchased material; packaging machinery
PA: W/S Packaging Group, Inc.
2571 S Hemlock Rd
Green Bay WI 54229
920 866-6300

(G-13103)
WITT INDUSTRIES INC (HQ)
Also Called: Witt Products
4600 N Masn Montgomery Rd (45040-9176)
PHONE...................................513 871-5700
Fax: 513 871-0347
Tim Harris, *President*
Rick Royse, *Purch Agent*
William Acra, *Sales Mgr*
Patty Richardson, *Cust Mgr*
Ron Curnayn, *CTO*
▼ **EMP:** 100
SQ FT: 71,500
SALES (est): 21.1MM **Privately Held**
WEB: www.witt.com
SIC: 3479 3469 3441 3412 Galvanizing of iron, steel or end-formed products; garbage cans, stamped & pressed metal; fabricated structural metal; metal barrels, drums & pails; metal cans; blast furnaces & steel mills

---

Massillon
Stark County

(G-13104)
3-D SERVICE LTD (PA)
Also Called: Magnetech
800 Nave Rd Se (44646-9476)
PHONE...................................330 830-3500
Fax: 330 830-3510
Bernie Dewees, *President*
Gordon Mayer, *Controller*
Lori Oberlin, *Asst Controller*
Tracy Tucker, *Human Res Mgr*
Trisha Abbruzzi, *Manager*
▲ **EMP:** 120
SQ FT: 85,000
SALES (est): 7.9MM **Privately Held**
WEB: www.3-dservice.com
SIC: 7694 7699 Electric motor repair; industrial equipment services

(G-13105)
A & R MACHINE CO INC
13212 Vega St Sw (44647-9200)
PHONE...................................330 832-4631
Fax: 330 832-6198
Rollin Shriner, *President*

Patsy Shriner, *Vice Pres*
Kathleen L Shriner, *Admin Sec*
EMP: 6
SQ FT: 10,000
SALES: 350K **Privately Held**
SIC: 3599 Custom machinery

(G-13106)
ABP INDUCTION LLC
607 1st St Sw (44646-6729)
PHONE...................................330 830-6252
Todd Alley, *Branch Mgr*
David Grider, *Manager*
EMP: 10
SALES (corp-wide): 8.2MM **Privately Held**
SIC: 3567 Industrial furnaces & ovens
PA: Abp Induction, Llc
1440 13th Ave
Union Grove WI 53182
262 317-5300

(G-13107)
AMERICAN WINDOW PDTS OF OHIO
1200 Cleveland St Sw D (44647-7956)
PHONE...................................330 830-0274
Fax: 330 830-0276
Roger Warnick, *General Mgr*
EMP: 10
SQ FT: 20,000
SALES (est): 1.4MM **Privately Held**
SIC: 3442 Casements, aluminum

(G-13108)
ANOINTED DESIGN & TECHNOLOGIES
1766 Huron Rd Se (44646-8362)
PHONE...................................330 826-1493
Greg Streator, *Principal*
EMP: 4
SALES (est): 10K **Privately Held**
SIC: 3325 Steel foundries

(G-13109)
APPLIED INNOVATIONS
1245 Cleveland St Sw (44647-7955)
PHONE...................................330 837-5694
Scott Brown, *Owner*
EMP: 6
SALES (est): 330K **Privately Held**
SIC: 3312 Tool & die steel

(G-13110)
ARE ACCESSORIES LLC
Also Called: Are
400 Nave Rd Se (44646-8898)
P.O. Box 1100 (44648-1100)
PHONE...................................330 830-7800
Terry Seikel, *CEO*
Todd Hoffman, *President*
Jason Warren, *General Mgr*
Ron Bostard, *Regional Mgr*
Robert Glasgow, *Safety Dir*
▲ **EMP:** 750
SQ FT: 240,000
SALES (est): 206.3MM
SALES (corp-wide): 64.7MM **Privately Held**
SIC: 3713 Truck bodies & parts
PA: Tectum Holdings Inc
5400 S State Rd
Ann Arbor MI 48108
734 677-0444

(G-13111)
ARE INC (PA)
400 Nave Rd Sw (44646)
P.O. Box 1100 (44648-1100)
PHONE...................................330 830-7800
Fax: 330 830-4545
Ralph Gatti, *President*
Bill Andrea, *Vice Pres*
Aden Miller, *Vice Pres*
Todd Roberson, *Vice Pres*
Richard Schmeltzer, *Plant Mgr*
EMP: 393
SQ FT: 236,000
SALES: 107MM **Privately Held**
WEB: www.4are.com
SIC: 3713 3714 3792 5013 Truck bodies & parts; motor vehicle body components & frame; travel trailers & campers; motor vehicle supplies & new parts

(G-13112)
ARE INC
400 Nave Rd Se (44646-8898)
P.O. Box 1100 (44648-1100)
PHONE...................................330 830-7800
Lisa Hartong, *Human Res Mgr*
Rick Smeltzer, *Branch Mgr*
Bruce Beadle, *Information Mgr*
EMP: 125
SALES (corp-wide): 107MM **Privately Held**
WEB: www.4are.com
SIC: 3479 3792 3713 Painting, coating & hot dipping; travel trailers & campers; truck & bus bodies
PA: A.R.E. Inc.
400 Nave Rd Sw
Massillon OH 44646
330 830-7800

(G-13113)
BAIRD CABINET SHOP INC
Also Called: Baird Furniture Repair
2330 Tiffin Cir Se (44646-7457)
PHONE...................................330 837-9075
Burt Baird, *President*
EMP: 5
SQ FT: 5,000
SALES (est): 300K **Privately Held**
SIC: 7641 2434 Reupholstery & furniture repair; wood kitchen cabinets

(G-13114)
BATES PRINTING INC
150 23rd St Se (44646-7046)
PHONE...................................330 833-5830
Fax: 330 833-5838
Dan Bates, *President*
John Bates, *President*
Daniel Bates, *Vice Pres*
EMP: 10
SQ FT: 3,000
SALES: 800K **Privately Held**
WEB: www.batesprinting.com
SIC: 2752 2759 Commercial printing, offset; commercial printing

(G-13115)
BRINKLEY TECHNOLOGY GROUP LLC
Also Called: Hercules Engine Components
2770 Erie St S (44646-7943)
PHONE...................................330 830-2498
Douglas Brinkley, *President*
EMP: 17 EST: 2015
SQ FT: 34,000
SALES (est): 1.2MM **Privately Held**
SIC: 3599 3519 3621 3694 Oil filters, internal combustion engine, except automotive; governors, diesel engine; diesel engine rebuilding; storage battery chargers, motor & engine generator type; distributors, motor vehicle engine

(G-13116)
C MASSOUH PRINTING CO INC
Also Called: C Massouh Printing Services
9589 Portage St Nw (44646-9074)
PHONE...................................330 832-6334
Carl Massouh, *President*
Cheryl Massouh, *Admin Sec*
EMP: 3
SALES: 700K **Privately Held**
SIC: 7389 2752 Printing broker; commercial printing, lithographic

(G-13117)
C N C WHOLESALE
1300 Erie St S (44646-7906)
PHONE...................................330 832-9525
Sally Clendenin, *Partner*
John Braime, *Partner*
Mark Crider, *Partner*
EMP: 4
SALES (est): 300.6K **Privately Held**
SIC: 3011 Automobile tires, pneumatic

(G-13118)
C-N-D INDUSTRIES INC
Also Called: Cnd Machine
359 State Ave Nw (44647-4269)
PHONE...................................330 478-8811
Clyde Shetler, *President*
Don Rossbach, *CFO*
Karen Hawelo, *Manager*
EMP: 42

SQ FT: 28,000
SALES (est): 8.6MM **Privately Held**
WEB: www.cndinc.com
SIC: **3441** 3599 7692 3444 Fabricated structural metal; machine shop, jobbing & repair; welding repair; sheet metalwork

(G-13119)
CARBONLESS ON DEMANDCOM
332 Erie St S (44646-6740)
PHONE.................................330 837-8611
David Mathis, *Owner*
EMP: 19
SALES: 3MM **Privately Held**
SIC: **2752** Business form & card printing, lithographic

(G-13120)
COLD HEADED FAS ASSEMBLIES INC
1875 Harsh Ave Se (44646-7182)
P.O. Box 547 (44648-0547)
PHONE.................................330 833-0800
Oscar Lee, *President*
Scott Moyer, *Opers Mgr*
Nick Koumoutzis, *Manager*
Gwen Hemperly, *Admin Sec*
▲ EMP: 12
SQ FT: 30,000
SALES: 1.8MM **Privately Held**
WEB: www.coldheaded.us
SIC: **3452** 3599 Bolts, nuts, rivets & washers; machine shop, jobbing & repair

(G-13121)
COPLEY OHIO NEWSPAPERS INC
Also Called: Independent, The
729 Lincoln Way E (44646-6829)
PHONE.................................330 833-2631
Kevin Coffey, *Principal*
EMP: 70
SQ FT: 9,221
SALES (corp-wide): 1.2B **Publicly Held**
WEB: www.timesreporter.com
SIC: **2711** 2752 Newspapers, publishing & printing; commercial printing, lithographic
HQ: Copley Ohio Newspapers Inc
　　500 Market Ave S
　　Canton OH 44702
　　585 598-0030

(G-13122)
CORRCHOICE INC (HQ)
777 3rd St Nw (44647-4203)
P.O. Box 934 (44648-0934)
PHONE.................................330 833-5705
Fax: 330 833-5717
Geoffrey Jollay, *Ch of Bd*
Geoffrey A Jollay, *President*
Daniel J Gunseft, *Principal*
John Clifford, *Vice Pres*
Chris Krumm, *VP Mfg*
▲ EMP: 80
SALES (est): 59.9MM
SALES (corp-wide): 3.3B **Publicly Held**
SIC: **2679** Paperboard products, converted
PA: Greif, Inc.
　　425 Winter Rd
　　Delaware OH 43015
　　740 549-6000

(G-13123)
CROWN CORK & SEAL USA INC
700 16th St Se (44646-7152)
P.O. Box 642 (44648-0642)
PHONE.................................330 833-1011
Art Boske, *VP Mfg*
Svetlana Khoundal, *QC Mgr*
Trevor Price, *Engineer*
James Skinner, *Engineer*
Bernard Baumann, *Manager*
EMP: 300
SALES (corp-wide): 8.2B **Publicly Held**
WEB: www.crowncork.com
SIC: **3411** Aluminum cans
HQ: Crown Cork & Seal Usa, Inc.
　　1 Crown Way
　　Philadelphia PA 19154
　　215 698-5100

(G-13124)
DAVID A AND MARY A MATHIS
Also Called: D & M Printing
332 Erie St S (44646-6740)
PHONE.................................330 837-8611

David A Mathis, *Owner*
Mary A Mathis, *Co-Owner*
EMP: 6
SALES (est): 490K **Privately Held**
SIC: **2752** Commercial printing, lithographic

(G-13125)
DOVER ATWOOD CORP
1875 Harsh Ave Se Ste 1 (44646-7182)
PHONE.................................330 809-0630
John Levengood, *President*
EMP: 4
SALES (est): 527.3K **Privately Held**
SIC: **1389** Oil field services; gas field services

(G-13126)
DRAIME ENTERPRISES INC
1300 Erie St S Unit C (44646-7997)
PHONE.................................330 837-2254
Fax: 330 830-0841
John E Draime, *President*
David Draime, *Treasurer*
EMP: 5 EST: 1970
SALES (est): 420K **Privately Held**
SIC: **3519** Internal combustion engines

(G-13127)
DW HERCULES LLC
Also Called: Hercules Engine Components
2770 Erie St S (44646-7943)
P.O. Box 451 (44648-0451)
PHONE.................................330 830-2498
Doug Brinkley, *President*
Kim Zapf, *Accounting Mgr*
Jack Dienes,
Bruce Weick,
▲ EMP: 40
SQ FT: 22,000
SALES (est): 7.5MM **Privately Held**
WEB: www.herculesengine.com
SIC: **3519** 5999 Parts & accessories, internal combustion engines; engine & motor equipment & supplies

(G-13128)
EARTHWALK ORTHOTIC
500 Vista Ave Se (44646-7949)
P.O. Box 1196 (44648-1196)
PHONE.................................330 837-6569
Brigham Wilson, *President*
EMP: 16
SQ FT: 9,000
SALES: 1,000K **Privately Held**
SIC: **3842** Orthopedic appliances

(G-13129)
ELECTRA - CORD INC
1320 Sanders Ave Sw (44647-7631)
P.O. Box 875 (44648-0875)
PHONE.................................330 832-8124
Fax: 330 832-5905
Michael Hutsell, *CEO*
Randall A Hutsell, *President*
Linda K Pratt, *Purch Mgr*
▲ EMP: 75
SQ FT: 33,000
SALES (est): 13.5MM **Privately Held**
SIC: **3699** 3357 Extension cords; nonferrous wiredrawing & insulating

(G-13130)
ENGRAVERS GALLERY & SIGN CO
10 Lincoln Way E (44646-6632)
PHONE.................................330 830-1271
Bonnie Fall, *Owner*
EMP: 6
SQ FT: 1,600
SALES: 250K **Privately Held**
SIC: **3993** 7389 Letters for signs, metal; engraving service

(G-13131)
FIBERCORR MILLS LLC
670 17th St Nw (44647-5343)
P.O. Box 453 (44648-0453)
PHONE.................................330 837-5151
Scott Shew, *Vice Pres*
Scott Sanders, *Purch Agent*
Ralph Reisinger, *CFO*
David Shew, *Financial Exec*
Allan Lynch, *Cust Mgr*
▲ EMP: 77
SQ FT: 87,500

SALES (est): 30.1MM **Privately Held**
WEB: www.fibercorr.com
SIC: **2679** 2631 Paper products, converted; paperboard mills

(G-13132)
FIMCO SERVICES LLC
11771 Barrs Rd Sw (44647-9273)
PHONE.................................330 830-1413
Randy Neff, *Principal*
EMP: 21
SALES (corp-wide): 4.4MM **Privately Held**
SIC: **3589** Vacuum cleaners & sweepers, electric: industrial
PA: Fimco Services, Llc
　　945 Manufacturers Rd
　　Dayton TN 37321
　　423 775-5004

(G-13133)
FRANKS CASING
607 1st St Sw (44646-6729)
PHONE.................................330 236-4264
Brandon Veberica, *General Mgr*
EMP: 5
SALES (est): 353.8K **Privately Held**
SIC: **1389** Cementing oil & gas well casings

(G-13134)
FRESENIUS USA INC
2474 Lincoln Way E (44646-5085)
PHONE.................................330 837-2575
Mark Fawcett, *Branch Mgr*
EMP: 40
SALES (corp-wide): 17.5B **Privately Held**
SIC: **2834** Intravenous solutions
HQ: Fresenius Usa, Inc.
　　4040 Nelson Ave
　　Concord CA 94520
　　925 288-4218

(G-13135)
FRESH MARK INC (PA)
Also Called: Superior's Brand Meats
1888 Southway St Se (44646)
P.O. Box 571 (44648-0571)
PHONE.................................330 834-3669
Fax: 330 430-5658
Neil Genshaft, *CEO*
David Cochenour, *President*
Tim Cranor, *President*
Richard Foster, *General Mgr*
Bernie Mueller, *General Mgr*
◆ EMP: 500 EST: 1932
SQ FT: 80,000
SALES (est): 521.3MM **Privately Held**
WEB: www.freshmark.com
SIC: **2013** 5147 2011 Prepared beef products from purchased beef; prepared pork products from purchased pork; sausages & related products, from purchased meat; meats & meat products; meat packing plants

(G-13136)
FRESH MARK INC
Also Called: Fresh Mark Sugardale
1888 Southway St Sw (44646-9429)
P.O. Box 571 (44648-0571)
PHONE.................................330 832-7491
Fax: 330 830-3174
Tim Craner, *President*
Shirley Kale, *General Mgr*
Bob Goode, *Superintendent*
Scott Bowers, *COO*
Stacy Green, *Trustee*
EMP: 350
SALES (corp-wide): 521.3MM **Privately Held**
WEB: www.freshmark.com
SIC: **5147** 2013 Meats & meat products; sausages & other prepared meats
PA: Fresh Mark, Inc.
　　1888 Southway St Se
　　Massillon OH 44646
　　330 834-3669

(G-13137)
GAMEDAY VISION
1147 Oberlin Ave Sw (44647-7665)
PHONE.................................330 830-4550
Krista Simcic, *President*
EMP: 10

SALES (est): 665.5K **Privately Held**
SIC: **3577** Printers & plotters

(G-13138)
GARY LAWRENCE ENTERPRISES INC
Also Called: Lawrence Machine
21 Charles Ave Sw (44646-6621)
P.O. Box 727 (44648-0727)
PHONE.................................330 833-7181
Fax: 330 833-0703
Gary Lawrence, *President*
Michelle Diebel, *Manager*
Eric Lawrence, *Manager*
EMP: 10
SQ FT: 15,000
SALES (est): 1.4MM **Privately Held**
WEB: www.lawrencemachineinc.com
SIC: **3993** Signs & advertising specialties

(G-13139)
GERSTENSLAGER CONSTRUCTION
Also Called: Gerstenslager Hardwood Pdts
343 16th St Se (44646-7177)
PHONE.................................330 832-3604
Mike Gerstenslager, *Owner*
Myron F Gerstenslager Jr, *Owner*
EMP: 6
SQ FT: 12,000
SALES (est): 330K **Privately Held**
SIC: **2431** Millwork

(G-13140)
GOLD N KRISP CHIPS & PRETZELS
1900 Erie Ave Nw (44646-4050)
PHONE.................................330 832-8395
Odell Gainey, *President*
Doug Roudebush, *Manager*
EMP: 5
SQ FT: 2,400
SALES (est): 657.4K **Privately Held**
SIC: **2096** Potato chips & other potato-based snacks

(G-13141)
GQI INC
2650 Richville Dr Sw # 105 (44646-8397)
PHONE.................................330 830-9805
Axel Dannoritzer, *President*
Richard Hassel, *Vice Pres*
Susan Frantz, *Manager*
EMP: 4
SALES (est): 449.3K **Privately Held**
SIC: **3841** Surgical instruments & apparatus

(G-13142)
GREGS EAGLE TIRE CO INC
3425 Lincoln Way E (44646-3762)
PHONE.................................330 837-1983
Greg Lawley, *President*
EMP: 4
SQ FT: 792
SALES (est): 571.8K **Privately Held**
SIC: **5531** 3011 Automotive tires; tires & inner tubes

(G-13143)
GREIF INC
787 Warmington Rd Se (44646-8830)
P.O. Box 675 (44648-0675)
PHONE.................................330 879-2936
Jack Eschliman, *Plant Engr*
Brian Dum, *Credit Mgr*
Jamie Cutcher, *Human Resources*
Matt Sullivan, *Manager*
Greg Cox, *Maintence Staff*
EMP: 110
SALES (corp-wide): 3.3B **Publicly Held**
WEB: www.greif.com
SIC: **2621** Fine paper
PA: Greif, Inc.
　　425 Winter Rd
　　Delaware OH 43015
　　740 549-6000

(G-13144)
GREIF PACKAGING LLC
787 Warmington Rd Sw (44646)
P.O. Box 675 (44648-0675)
PHONE.................................330 879-2101
Chip Shew, *Manager*
EMP: 110

▲ = Import ▼ =Export
◆ =Import/Export

SALES (corp-wide): 3.3B **Publicly Held**
SIC: **2611** Pulp manufactured from waste or recycled paper
HQ: Greif Packaging Llc
366 Greif Pkwy
Delaware OH 43015
740 549-6000

(G-13145)
H P E INC
2025 Harsh Ave Se (44646-7127)
PHONE...........................330 833-3161
Fax: 330 833-3162
Robert Boley, *President*
Robert N Boley, *President*
Sandra Boley, *Treasurer*
EMP: 12
SQ FT: 12,000
SALES: 790K **Privately Held**
SIC: **3533** 3569 3547 3494 Oil & gas field machinery; gas separators (machinery); gas producers, generators & other gas related equipment; rolling mill machinery; valves & pipe fittings; fabricated plate work (boiler shop)

(G-13146)
HEINZ FOREIGN INVESTMENT CO (HQ)
1301 Oberlin Ave Sw (44647-7669)
P.O. Box 15222, Pittsburgh PA (15237-0222)
PHONE...........................330 837-8331
Bernardo Hees, *CEO*
EMP: 5
SALES (est): 25.5MM
SALES (corp-wide): 26.4B **Publicly Held**
SIC: **2037** Frozen fruits & vegetables
PA: The Kraft Heinz Company
200 E Randolph St # 7600
Chicago IL 60601
412 456-5700

(G-13147)
HENDRICKS VACUUM FORMING INC (PA)
3500 17th St Sw (44647-9700)
PHONE...........................330 837-2040
Fax: 330 837-6629
Donald G Hendricks, *President*
Rob Hendricks, *Vice Pres*
Quinton Wratchford, *Plant Supt*
Bonnie Hendricks, *Bookkeeper*
Terry Casebeer, *Sales Associate*
EMP: 20 EST: 1978
SQ FT: 40,000
SALES (est): 2.1MM **Privately Held**
WEB: www.hvfi.com
SIC: **3993** Signs & advertising specialties

(G-13148)
HENDRICKS VACUUM FORMING INC
Also Called: Massillon Machine & Die
3536 17th St Sw (44647-9211)
PHONE...........................330 833-8913
Gary Burkholder, *Branch Mgr*
EMP: 7
SALES (corp-wide): 2.1MM **Privately Held**
WEB: www.hvfi.com
SIC: **3542** Die casting machines
PA: Hendricks Vacuum Forming, Inc.
3500 17th St Sw
Massillon OH 44647
330 837-2040

(G-13149)
HIBBETT SPORTING GOODS INC
2010 Lincoln Way E Ste 1 (44646-7085)
PHONE...........................330 837-9272
Gary Meisemer, *Branch Mgr*
EMP: 8
SALES (corp-wide): 913.4MM **Publicly Held**
WEB: www.hibbett.com
SIC: **3949** Sporting & athletic goods
HQ: Hibbett Sporting Goods, Inc.
2700 Milan Ct
Birmingham AL 35211
205 942-4292

(G-13150)
HJ HEINZ COMPANY LP
Also Called: Heinz Frozen Foods
1301 Oberlin Ave Sw (44647-7669)
PHONE...........................330 837-8331
Allan Briggs, *Managing Prtnr*
Deanna Smith, *Warehouse Mgr*
Sherry Amos, *Manager*
Robert Ferguson, *Manager*
Mike Parks, *Manager*
▲ EMP: 600
SALES (est): 60.4MM
SALES (corp-wide): 26.4B **Publicly Held**
SIC: **2037** Frozen fruits & vegetables
HQ: Kraft Heinz Foods Company
1 Ppg Pl Ste 3200
Pittsburgh PA 15222
412 456-5700

(G-13151)
HK ENGINE COMPONENTS LLC (HQ)
800 Nave Rd Se (44646-9476)
PHONE...........................330 830-3500
J Cullen Burdette, *President*
Mark Krcmaric, *Controller*
James I Depew, *Admin Sec*
▲ EMP: 2
SALES (est): 8.8MM
SALES (corp-wide): 301.9MM **Privately Held**
SIC: **3519** Governors, diesel engine
PA: National Railway Equipment Co.
1100 Shawnee St
Mount Vernon IL 62864
618 242-6590

(G-13152)
HUTH READY MIX & SUPPLY CO
Also Called: Huth Ready-Mix & Supply Co
501 5th St Nw (44647-5473)
P.O. Box 524 (44648-0524)
PHONE...........................330 833-4191
Fax: 330 833-4199
Roger L Huth, *President*
Donna Dunlap, *Bookkeeper*
Alice H Huth, *Admin Sec*
EMP: 15
SQ FT: 3,000
SALES (est): 2.9MM **Privately Held**
SIC: **3273** 5211 Ready-mixed concrete; brick; concrete & cinder block

(G-13153)
HYDRO-DYNE INC
225 Wetmore Ave Se (44646-6788)
P.O. Box 318 (44648-0318)
PHONE...........................330 832-5076
Fax: 330 832-8163
Rose Ann Dare, *President*
Lynn Neel, *Vice Pres*
Jean Holiday, *Manager*
Craig McMillen, *Manager*
Sherri McMillen, *Manager*
▲ EMP: 30
SQ FT: 130,000
SALES (est): 8.2MM **Privately Held**
WEB: www.hydrodyneinc.com
SIC: **3585** 8711 Evaporative condensers, heat transfer equipment; engineering services

(G-13154)
HYDRO-THRIFT CORPORATION
Also Called: Hydrothrift
1301 Sanders Ave Sw (44647-7632)
P.O. Box 1037 (44648-1037)
PHONE...........................330 837-5141
Fax: 330 837-0558
T K Heston, *President*
Matt Sands, *Project Engr*
Paul Heston, *Treasurer*
Ronald Lair, *Sales Mgr*
Jim Huntsberger, *Manager*
▼ EMP: 23 EST: 1973
SQ FT: 27,000
SALES (est): 5.3MM **Privately Held**
WEB: www.hydrothrift.com
SIC: **3585** 3443 Refrigeration & heating equipment; air conditioning equipment, complete; heat exchangers, condensers & components

(G-13155)
IDENTITEK SYSTEMS INC
Also Called: Adams Signs
1100 Industrial Ave Sw (44647-7608)
P.O. Box 347 (44648-0347)
PHONE...........................330 832-9844
Fax: 330 832-6999
Joseph Pugliese, *President*
EMP: 53
SQ FT: 70,000
SALES (est): 8.4MM **Privately Held**
WEB: www.adamsigns.com
SIC: **1799** 3993 Sign installation & maintenance; signs & advertising specialties; electric signs

(G-13156)
INDEPENDENT PROTECTION SYSTEMS
2510 Upland Ave Sw (44647-7270)
P.O. Box 214 (44648-0214)
PHONE...........................330 832-7992
Randall P Ross, *Owner*
EMP: 5 EST: 1975
SALES (est): 302.9K **Privately Held**
SIC: **1731** 2381 Fire detection & burglar alarm systems specialization; glove linings, except fur

(G-13157)
INTEGRITY CRANE SERVICES LTD
2100 Venture Cir Se (44646-8633)
PHONE...........................330 479-2003
Fax: 330 834-2150
Kyle A Wenger, *President*
Sandy Yorksimer, *Manager*
EMP: 9
SQ FT: 10,000
SALES: 3MM **Privately Held**
SIC: **3599** Custom machinery

(G-13158)
J L R PRODUCTS INC
1212 Oberlin Ave Sw (44647-7668)
PHONE...........................330 832-9557
Matthew Radocaj, *President*
EMP: 15
SALES: 1.6MM **Privately Held**
SIC: **3429** 3568 Pulleys metal; pulleys, power transmission

(G-13159)
JACODAR INC
1212 Oberlin Ave Sw (44647-7668)
PHONE...........................330 832-9557
Fax: 330 832-3225
Matthew Radocaj, *President*
EMP: 10
SQ FT: 24,000
SALES: 770.8K
SALES (corp-wide): 590.9K **Privately Held**
SIC: **3452** Bolts, metal
PA: Ojim, Inc.
1212 Oberlin Ave Sw
Massillon OH 44647
330 832-9557

(G-13160)
JOSEPH KNAPP
Also Called: Knapp Enterprises
151 Lennox Ave Sw (44646-3807)
PHONE...........................330 832-3515
Fax: 330 832-3515
Joseph Knapp, *Owner*
EMP: 11
SQ FT: 15,000
SALES (est): 776K **Privately Held**
SIC: **2599** 7213 5046 Restaurant furniture, wood or metal; table cover supply; restaurant equipment & supplies

(G-13161)
KENDEL WELDING & FABRICATION
1700 Navarre Rd Se (44646)
PHONE...........................330 834-2429
Bettina M Kendel, *President*
Donald R Kendel, *Vice Pres*
EMP: 8 EST: 1999
SALES (est): 839.3K **Privately Held**
SIC: **7692** Welding repair

(G-13162)
KENMORE CONSTRUCTION CO INC
Also Called: American Sand & Gravel Div
9500 Forty Corners Rd Nw (44647-9309)
PHONE...........................330 832-8888
Chris Scala, *Manager*
EMP: 48
SALES (corp-wide): 93MM **Privately Held**
WEB: www.kenmorecompanies.com
SIC: **1611** 1442 General contractor, highway & street construction; construction sand & gravel
PA: Kenmore Construction Co., Inc.
700 Home Ave
Akron OH 44310
330 762-8936

(G-13163)
KENNEWEGS WOOD PRODUCTS
973 Vindell Ave Nw (44647-5273)
PHONE...........................330 832-1540
John Kenneweg, *Owner*
Brenda Kenneweg, *Co-Owner*
EMP: 3
SALES (est): 210K **Privately Held**
SIC: **5712** 2499 Custom made furniture, except cabinets; wood products

(G-13164)
KING MACHINE AND TOOL CO
1237 Sanders Ave Sw (44647-7684)
PHONE...........................330 833-7217
Fax: 330 833-2761
William Kapper, *President*
Tracy Kapper, *Vice Pres*
Kelly Kapper, *Treasurer*
Judith A Kapper, *Admin Sec*
▲ EMP: 18 EST: 1949
SQ FT: 22,000
SALES (est): 4.3MM **Privately Held**
WEB: www.kmtco.com
SIC: **3544** Dies & die holders for metal cutting, forming, die casting

(G-13165)
KRAFT HEINZ COMPANY
Also Called: Kraft Heinz Company
1301 Oberlin Ave Sw (44647-7669)
PHONE...........................330 837-8331
Jolene Mutiglu, *Human Res Dir*
Ken Stiffler, *Manager*
EMP: 700
SQ FT: 1,196
SALES (corp-wide): 26.4B **Publicly Held**
SIC: **2033** 2099 Tomato sauce: packaged in cans, jars, etc.; food preparations
PA: The Kraft Heinz Company
200 E Randolph St # 7600
Chicago IL 60601
412 456-5700

(G-13166)
LAND OLAKES INC
8485 Navarre Rd Sw (44646-8814)
PHONE...........................330 879-2158
Fax: 330 879-5804
Gary Hauenstin, *Manager*
EMP: 41
SALES (corp-wide): 14.9B **Privately Held**
WEB: www.landolakes.com
SIC: **2048** 5191 2047 Livestock feeds; animal feeds; dog & cat food
PA: Land O'lakes, Inc.
4001 Lexington Ave N
Arden Hills MN 55126
651 375-2222

(G-13167)
LLC RING MASTERS
240 6th St Nw (44647-5413)
PHONE...........................330 832-1511
Fax: 330 830-7506
Jeffrey Headlee,
Randy Hunt,
Tony Lee,
John Nelson,
EMP: 34
SQ FT: 51,000
SALES: 3.5MM **Privately Held**
WEB: www.ring-masters.net
SIC: **3316** Cold finishing of steel shapes

(G-13168)
LTG POLYMERS LIMITED
7612 Onyx Ave Nw (44646-9206)
PHONE............................330 854-5609
Howard Galberach, *Principal*
EMP: 3 EST: 2010
SALES (est): 233K **Privately Held**
SIC: 2821 Plastics materials & resins

(G-13169)
M T METALS LLC
240 6th St Nw (44647-5413)
PHONE............................330 809-6465
Doug Kriner, *Owner*
EMP: 2 EST: 2015
SQ FT: 10,000
SALES: 1MM **Privately Held**
SIC: 3443 Fabricated plate work (boiler shop)

(G-13170)
MAGNETECH INDUSTRIAL SVCS INC
800 Nave Rd Se (44646-9476)
PHONE............................330 830-3500
Mike Rice, *Branch Mgr*
Bill Muncy, *Manager*
David Tharp, *Manager*
EMP: 120
SALES (corp-wide): 695.9MM **Publicly Held**
SIC: 7694 7699 Electric motor repair; industrial equipment services
HQ: Magnetech Industrial Services, Inc.
  800 Nave Rd Se
  Massillon OH 44646
  330 830-3500

(G-13171)
MAINTENANCE AND REPAIR FABG CO
427 Harding Ave Nw (44646-3295)
PHONE............................330 478-1149
James A Paulus, *President*
Jackie Paulus, *Admin Sec*
EMP: 5
SQ FT: 8,580
SALES (est): 157.8K **Privately Held**
SIC: 7692 Welding repair

(G-13172)
MARTIN PALLET INC
Also Called: M P I Logistics
1414 Industrial Ave Sw (44647-7663)
PHONE............................330 832-5309
Fax: 330 832-1210
Richard D Miller, *President*
Judith A Miller, *Vice Pres*
EMP: 21
SQ FT: 16,500
SALES (est): 4.2MM **Privately Held**
WEB: www.martinpallet.com
SIC: 2448 7699 Pallets, wood; pallet repair

(G-13173)
MASSILLON ASPHALT CO
1833 Riverside Dr Nw (44647-9300)
PHONE............................330 833-6330
Fax: 330 833-7218
Dave Aventino, *Manager*
Bruce Bickle, *Manager*
EMP: 3
SALES (corp-wide): 620.4K **Privately Held**
SIC: 1771 2951 Blacktop (asphalt) work; asphalt paving mixtures & blocks
PA: Massillon Asphalt Co
  5947 Whipple Ave Nw
  Canton OH 44720
  330 494-5472

(G-13174)
MASSILLON METAPHYSICS
912 Amherst Rd Ne (44646-4568)
P.O. Box 1305 (44648-1305)
PHONE............................330 837-1653
Lena Fain, *Principal*
EMP: 4
SALES (est): 147.8K **Privately Held**
SIC: 1499 Gemstone & industrial diamond mining

(G-13175)
MASSILLON-CLEVELAND-AKRON SIGN (PA)
Also Called: MCA Industries
681 1st St Sw (44646-6729)
PHONE............................330 833-3165
Samuel Mollet, *President*
Sam Mollet, *President*
Gary Hoyt, *COO*
Brian Mollet, *VP Mfg*
EMP: 130
SQ FT: 210,000
SALES (est): 18.6MM **Privately Held**
WEB: www.mcapop.com
SIC: 3993 Signs & advertising specialties

(G-13176)
MATCH MOLD & MACHINE INC
1100 Nova Dr Se (44646-8867)
PHONE............................330 830-5503
Timothy V Lidderdale, *President*
Thomas Knipfer, *Vice Pres*
Ruth Lidderdale, *Treasurer*
EMP: 40
SALES (est): 3.7MM **Privately Held**
SIC: 3544 Forms (molds), for foundry & plastics working machinery

(G-13177)
MATRIX SYS AUTO FINISHES LLC
600 Nova Dr Se (44646-8884)
PHONE............................248 668-8135
W Kent Gardner, *President*
Sean Hook, *Director*
EMP: 100
SQ FT: 26,000
SALES (est): 41.2MM
SALES (corp-wide): 173.2MM **Privately Held**
WEB: www.matrixsystem.com
SIC: 5198 2851 Paints; paints & allied products
PA: Quest Specialty Chemicals, Inc.
  225 Sven Farms Dr Ste 204
  Charleston SC 29492
  800 966-7580

(G-13178)
MEL WACKER SIGN INC
13076 Barrs Rd Sw (44647-9746)
PHONE............................330 832-1726
Fax: 330 832-1666
Bonnie Maier, *President*
Melville Maier, *Vice Pres*
Rod Maier, *Vice Pres*
EMP: 6
SALES (est): 806.8K **Privately Held**
WEB: www.wackersigns.com
SIC: 3993 1799 5999 Signs, not made in custom sign painting shops; sign installation & maintenance; flags

(G-13179)
MELANDA INC
Also Called: Express Lube
2646 Lincoln Way Nw (44646-5119)
PHONE............................330 833-0517
Louis Brio, *President*
Larry Grim, *Manager*
EMP: 9
SQ FT: 4,000
SALES: 300K **Privately Held**
SIC: 2992 Lubricating oils

(G-13180)
MIDWESTERN INDUSTRIES INC (PA)
915 Oberlin Ave Sw (44647-7661)
P.O. Box 810 (44648-0810)
PHONE............................330 837-4203
Fax: 330 837-4210
W A Blackwell, *Principal*
Laverne J Riesbeck, *Principal*
Mary E Riesbeck, *Principal*
David Weaver, *Vice Pres*
William J Crone, *Vice Pres*
▼ EMP: 104
SQ FT: 148,000

SALES: 19MM **Privately Held**
WEB: www.midwesternind.com
SIC: 3559 3496 3564 3443 Screening equipment, electric; mesh, made from purchased wire; screening, woven wire; made from purchased wire; blowers & fans; fabricated plate work (boiler shop); steel wire & related products

(G-13181)
MOMENTS TO REMEMBER USA LLC
1250 Sanders Ave Sw (44647-7683)
PHONE............................330 830-0839
Nancy Schmidt, *Partner*
Karl Schmidt, *Partner*
Jen Wetvel, *Administration*
EMP: 7
SALES (est): 1MM **Privately Held**
WEB: www.momentsusa.com
SIC: 3993 7313 7331 3555 Signs & advertising specialties; electronic media advertising representatives; printed media advertising representatives; direct mail advertising services; mats, advertising & newspaper

(G-13182)
MONOVISION MACHINE
125 Walnut Rd Se (44646-7934)
PHONE............................330 833-2146
Glen Marthy, *Principal*
EMP: 7
SALES (est): 795.2K **Privately Held**
SIC: 3599 Industrial machinery

(G-13183)
MUSAIR OHIO
128 North Ave Ne (44646-5526)
PHONE............................330 455-2800
Williams Slater, *President*
EMP: 7
SALES (est): 389.4K **Privately Held**
SIC: 7389 3663 3669 Music & broadcasting services; television closed circuit equipment; intercommunication systems, electric

(G-13184)
NFM/WELDING ENGINEERS INC (PA)
Also Called: N F M
577 Oberlin Ave Sw (44647-7820)
PHONE............................330 837-3868
Fax: 330 837-2230
Philip A Roberson, *President*
Ronald Pribich, *Senior VP*
John Roberson, *Vice Pres*
Paul Roberson, *Vice Pres*
Scott Swallen, *Vice Pres*
▲ EMP: 140
SQ FT: 150,000
SALES (est): 43.2MM **Privately Held**
WEB: www.nfmwe.com
SIC: 3599 Machine shop, jobbing & repair

(G-13185)
OHIO METALIZING LLC
2519 Erie St S (44646-7918)
P.O. Box 1182 (44648-1182)
PHONE............................330 830-1092
George Pribich,
EMP: 5
SQ FT: 17,000
SALES (est): 573.2K
SALES (corp-wide): 43.2MM **Privately Held**
SIC: 2295 3599 3471 Metallizing of fabrics; machine & other job shop work; plating & polishing
PA: Nfm/Welding Engineers, Inc.
  577 Oberlin Ave Sw
  Massillon OH 44647
  330 837-3868

(G-13186)
OHIO PACKAGING (DH)
777 3rd St Nw (44647-4203)
PHONE............................330 833-2884
Geoffrey Jolley, *Safety Mgr*
Kathy Cozel, *Controller*
Kathy Cozzo, *Financial Exec*
Cindy Fulz, *Human Res Mgr*
Gil Soley, *Manager*
▲ EMP: 20 EST: 1964
SQ FT: 1,800

SALES (est): 14.1MM
SALES (corp-wide): 3.3B **Publicly Held**
SIC: 2679 5199 Paperboard products, converted; packaging materials
HQ: Corrchoice, Inc.
  777 3rd St Nw
  Massillon OH 44647
  330 833-5705

(G-13187)
OJIM INC (PA)
1212 Oberlin Ave Sw (44647-7668)
PHONE............................330 832-9557
Mijo Radocaj, *Ch of Bd*
Matt Radocaj, *President*
EMP: 15
SQ FT: 39,500
SALES: 590.9K **Privately Held**
SIC: 3599 Machine shop, jobbing & repair

(G-13188)
OMNI DIE CASTING INC
1100 Nova Dr Se (44646-8867)
PHONE............................330 830-5500
Fax: 330 830-5505
Timothy Lidderdale, *President*
Derek Lidderdale, *Vice Pres*
Darin Jacobs, *Project Mgr*
Dan Swab, *Purch Agent*
▼ EMP: 30 EST: 1958
SQ FT: 10,000
SALES (est): 7.6MM **Privately Held**
SIC: 3363 Aluminum die-castings

(G-13189)
OMNI USA INC
1100 Nova Dr Se (44646-8867)
PHONE............................330 830-5500
Timothy V Lidderdale, *President*
Theodore Buss, *Treasurer*
EMP: 100
SALES (est): 14.8MM **Privately Held**
SIC: 3364 Zinc & zinc-base alloy die-castings

(G-13190)
OSTER SAND AND GRAVEL INC
Also Called: Oster Enterprises
1955 Riverside Dr Nw (44647-9300)
PHONE............................330 833-2649
Bruce Bickel, *Manager*
EMP: 8
SALES (corp-wide): 3.5MM **Privately Held**
SIC: 1442 1422 Construction sand & gravel; crushed & broken limestone
PA: Oster Sand And Gravel, Inc.
  5947 Whipple Ave Nw
  Canton OH 44720
  330 494-5472

(G-13191)
P-AMERICAS LLC
Also Called: Pepsico
815 Oberlin Ave Sw (44647-7876)
PHONE............................330 837-4224
Fax: 330 879-3510
Jenny Plummet, *Manager*
EMP: 123
SALES (corp-wide): 62.8B **Publicly Held**
SIC: 2086 Carbonated soft drinks, bottled & canned
HQ: P-Americas Llc
  1 Pepsi Way
  Somers NY

(G-13192)
PACE MOLD & MACHINE LLC
8225 Navarre Rd Sw (44646-8813)
P.O. Box 6, Navarre (44662-0006)
PHONE............................330 879-1777
Fax: 330 879-1778
Patrick Nolan,
Marilyn Hurst, *Admin Sec*
Leonard Buckner,
EMP: 6 EST: 1977
SQ FT: 14,000
SALES (est): 793.4K **Privately Held**
SIC: 3544 2821 3089 Forms (molds), for foundry & plastics working machinery; molding compounds, plastics; injection molding of plastics; molding primary plastic

(G-13193)
PER-TECH INC
113 Erie St S (44646-6649)
PHONE................................330 833-8824
Fax: 330 833-5004
Robert Phillips, *Vice Pres*
Chris Scott, *Manager*
Randall Hutsell, *Admin Sec*
Rex Kick, *Technician*
EMP: 28
SQ FT: 90,000
SALES: 2MM **Privately Held**
SIC: 3679 3694 Harness assemblies for
electronic use: wire or cable; engine elec-
trical equipment

(G-13194)
**PLASTIC FORMING COMPANY
INC**
201 Vista Ave Se (44646-7938)
PHONE................................330 830-5167
Fax: 330 830-5169
Mike Warth, *Manager*
David Norcia, *Manager*
Robinson Talanna, *CTO*
EMP: 25
SALES (corp-wide): 7.4MM **Privately
Held**
WEB: www.plasticformingcompany.com
SIC: 3089 3086 3161 Blow molded fin-
ished plastic products; plastics foam prod-
ucts; luggage
PA: The Plastic Forming Company Inc
20 S Bradley Rd
Woodbridge CT 06525
203 397-1338

(G-13195)
POLYMER PACKAGING INC (PA)
Also Called: Polymer Protective Packaging
8333 Navarre Rd Se (44646-9652)
PHONE................................330 832-2000
Larry L Lanham, *CEO*
Ronald Reagan, *President*
Jerrod Vance, *Regional Mgr*
William D Lanham, *Exec VP*
Chris Thomazin, *Vice Pres*
▲ EMP: 65
SQ FT: 36,000
SALES (est): 58.1MM **Privately Held**
WEB: www.polymerpkg.com
SIC: 5113 5162 2621 2821 Paper &
products, wrapping or coarse; plastics
products; wrapping & packaging papers;
plastics materials & resins

(G-13196)
POLYONE CORPORATION
1675 Navarre Rd Se (44646-9607)
PHONE................................330 834-3812
Steve Strover, *Manager*
EMP: 75 **Publicly Held**
WEB: www.polyone.com
SIC: 2821 Plastics materials & resins
PA: Polyone Corporation
33587 Walker Rd
Avon Lake OH 44012

(G-13197)
**PREMIER BUILDING SOLUTIONS
INC (PA)**
480 Nova Dr Se (44646-9597)
PHONE................................330 244-2907
Derek J Miller, *President*
Rebecca J Miller, *Vice Pres*
Eli Saba, *Credit Mgr*
Dj Nichols, *Accounts Mgr*
Gary Caviness, *Manager*
◆ EMP: 75
SALES (est): 20.1MM **Privately Held**
SIC: 2891 Adhesives

(G-13198)
R W SCREW PRODUCTS INC
999 Oberlin Ave Sw (44647-7698)
P.O. Box 310 (44648-0310)
PHONE................................330 837-9211
Fax: 330 837-9223
James Woolley, *CEO*
Larry Longworth, *President*
Jeff Grace, *Draft/Design*
Diane Wooley, *Treasurer*
Tim Longworth, *Human Res Dir*
EMP: 240 EST: 1948
SQ FT: 180,000

SALES (est): 58.1MM **Privately Held**
SIC: 3451 Screw machine products

(G-13199)
REPUBLIC STEEL INC
401 Rose Ave Se (44646-6870)
PHONE................................330 837-7024
Fax: 330 837-7051
K W Hazard, *Branch Mgr*
James Stevens, *Manager*
EMP: 16
SALES (corp-wide): 1.4B **Privately Held**
SIC: 3316 Cold finishing of steel shapes
HQ: Republic Steel Inc.
2633 8th St Ne
Canton OH 44704
330 438-5435

(G-13200)
SCASSA ASPHALT INC
4167 Beaumont Ave Nw (44647-9556)
PHONE................................330 830-2039
Nicholas Scassa, *President*
EMP: 10
SALES (est): 1.2MM **Privately Held**
SIC: 1389 Construction, repair & disman-
tling services

(G-13201)
SHEARERS FOODS LLC (PA)
100 Lincoln Way E (44646-6634)
PHONE................................330 834-4030
C J Fraleigh, *CEO*
Christopher Fraleigh, *CEO*
John Stephenson, *Top Exec*
Dan Kessler, *Business Mgr*
Erik Nadig, *Business Mgr*
◆ EMP: 700 EST: 1980
SQ FT: 200,000
SALES: 198.5MM **Privately Held**
SIC: 2096 5145 Potato chips & similar
snacks; snack foods

(G-13202)
SNACK ALLIANCE INC (HQ)
100 Lincoln Way E (44646-6634)
P.O. Box 70, Hermiston OR (97838-0070)
PHONE................................330 767-3426
Robert Shearer, *CEO*
Scott Smith, *President*
Thomas Shearer, *Exec VP*
Fredric Kohmann, *CFO*
Elaine Price, *Controller*
◆ EMP: 23
SALES (est): 130MM
SALES (corp-wide): 198.5MM **Privately
Held**
SIC: 2096 Potato chips & similar snacks
PA: Shearer's Foods, Llc
100 Lincoln Way E
Massillon OH 44646
330 834-4030

(G-13203)
**STANDARDS TESTING LABS INC
(PA)**
1845 Harsh Ave Se (44646-7123)
P.O. Box 758 (44648-0758)
PHONE................................330 833-8548
Fax: 330 833-7902
Anthony E Efremoff, *President*
Darryl Fuller, *President*
Cheryl Schnuth, *General Mgr*
Tina Wood, *Purch Mgr*
Jason Sumney, *Draft/Design*
▲ EMP: 48
SQ FT: 84,000
SALES (est): 9.8MM **Privately Held**
WEB: www.stllabs.com
SIC: 3829 8734 8071 Testing equipment:
abrasion, shearing strength, etc.; product
testing laboratory, safety or performance;
automobile proving & testing ground;
medical laboratories

(G-13204)
STERILITE CORPORATION
4495 Sterilite St Se (44646-7400)
PHONE................................330 830-2204
Fax: 330 830-2744
Mike Simmons, *Human Res Dir*
Dennis Forges, *Manager*
Dennis Forgues, *Manager*
Rich Mayer, *Maintence Staff*
EMP: 355

SALES (corp-wide): 259.9MM **Privately
Held**
WEB: www.sterilite.com
SIC: 3089 Plastic kitchenware, tableware &
houseware; plastic containers, except
foam
PA: Sterilite Corporation
30 Scales Ln
Townsend MA 01469
978 597-1000

(G-13205)
TIGER SAND & GRAVEL LLC
411 Oberlin Ave Sw (44647-7826)
PHONE................................330 833-6325
David M Dipietro, *Mng Member*
Leenn Cush, *Manager*
Steven P Dipeitro,
EMP: 10
SALES (est): 1.8MM **Privately Held**
SIC: 1442 Construction sand & gravel

(G-13206)
TORTILLERIA EL MAIZAL LLP
1895 Greentree Pl Se (44646-8181)
PHONE................................330 209-9344
Dawn Mora, *Principal*
EMP: 3
SALES (est): 118.6K **Privately Held**
SIC: 2099 Tortillas, fresh or refrigerated

(G-13207)
TOWER INDUSTRIES LTD
2101 9th St Sw (44647-7651)
PHONE................................330 837-2216
Fax: 330 837-2642
Melody Bowman, *Consultant*
Todd Werstler,
Robert Werstler,
EMP: 43
SQ FT: 15,000
SALES (est): 10MM **Privately Held**
SIC: 3088 Plastics plumbing fixtures

(G-13208)
U S CHEMICAL & PLASTICS
600 Nova Dr Se (44646-8884)
PHONE................................740 254-4311
John Nelson, *Plant Mgr*
Bob Exner, *Purch Dir*
Tom Schroeter, *Plant Engr*
Mike Akers, *Manager*
EMP: 5
SALES (est): 571.5K **Privately Held**
SIC: 2899 Chemical preparations

(G-13209)
VALSPAR CORPORATION
Valspar Automotive
600 Nova Dr Se (44646-8884)
P.O. Box 709 (44648-0709)
PHONE................................330 830-6000
Thomas M Perry, *President*
John Franken, *Vice Pres*
Bill Powell, *Human Res Dir*
Wade Bowman, *Sales Staff*
Dennis Brownn, *Manager*
EMP: 192
SQ FT: 139,645
SALES (corp-wide): 4.1B **Publicly Held**
WEB: www.alcoind.com
SIC: 2851 3087 2842 2891 Paints &
paint additives; epoxy coatings; custom
compound purchased resins; stain re-
movers; adhesives & sealants
PA: The Valspar Corporation
1101 S 3rd St
Minneapolis MN 55415
612 851-7000

(G-13210)
VEHICLE SYSTEMS INC
Also Called: V S I
7130 Lutz Ave Nw (44646-9343)
PHONE................................330 854-0535
Ervin Van Denberg, *President*
Vivian Vandenberg, *Corp Secy*
Scott Vandenberg, *Vice Pres*
EMP: 7
SALES (est): 1.5MM **Privately Held**
WEB: www.vehiclesys.com
SIC: 3714 8742 8731 Motor vehicle brake
systems & parts; management consulting
services; commercial physical research

(G-13211)
WASHINGTON PRODUCTS INC
1875 Harsh Ave Ste 1 (44648-7182)
P.O. Box 644 (44648-0644)
PHONE................................330 837-5101
Fax: 330 837-5401
John A Boring, *President*
Rose Butterman, *Manager*
EMP: 11
SQ FT: 30,000
SALES (est): 2MM **Privately Held**
SIC: 3469 3443 3647 3429 Metal stamp-
ings; kitchen fixtures & equipment: metal,
except cast aluminum; fabricated plate
work (boiler shop); automotive lighting fix-
tures; manufactured hardware (general);
sanitary food containers

(G-13212)
YANKE BIONICS INC
2400 Wales Ave Nw (44646-0804)
PHONE................................330 833-0955
Steven Simko, *Branch Mgr*
EMP: 5
SALES (corp-wide): 10.5MM **Privately
Held**
SIC: 3842 Orthopedic appliances
PA: Yanke Bionics Inc
303 W Exchange St
Akron OH 44302
330 762-6411

Masury
Trumbull County

(G-13213)
BULL MOOSE TUBE COMPANY
1433 Standard Ave (44438-1558)
P.O. Box 67 (44438-0067)
PHONE................................330 448-4878
Teri Rowles, *Vice Pres*
Dave Thompson, *Manager*
EMP: 8 **Privately Held**
WEB: www.bullmoosetube.com
SIC: 3317 Steel pipe & tubes
HQ: Bull Moose Tube Company
1819 Clarkson Rd Ste 100
Chesterfield MO 63017
636 537-1249

(G-13214)
**CUSTOM CNTRWGHT PLATE
PROC INC**
7799 Locust St (44438-1567)
P.O. Box 594, Cortland (44410-0594)
PHONE................................330 448-2347
Timothy Gearhart, *President*
EMP: 5
SQ FT: 22,000
SALES (est): 450K **Privately Held**
SIC: 2796 Platemaking services

(G-13215)
PIPELINES INC
7800 Addison Rd (44438-1207)
PHONE................................330 448-0000
Nicholas Tepsic, *Controller*
William Bilske, *Manager*
EMP: 6
SALES (corp-wide): 25.3MM **Privately
Held**
WEB: www.corp.enbridge.com
SIC: 3494 1794 Line strainers, for use in
piping systems; excavation work
PA: Pipelines, Inc.
16363 Saint Clair Ave
East Liverpool OH 43920
330 386-3646

(G-13216)
ROEMER INDUSTRIES INC
1555 Masury Rd (44438-1702)
PHONE................................330 448-2000
Fax: 330 448-8161
Joseph L O'Toole, *President*
Carolyn Shultz, *Vice Pres*
Vicki Cornell, *Accounts Mgr*
Faith Otoole, *Admin Sec*
EMP: 71
SQ FT: 52,000

SALES (est): 9.7MM **Privately Held**
WEB: www.roemerind.com
SIC: 3479 3469 3993 3613 Name plates: engraved, etched, etc.; metal stampings; signs & advertising specialties; switchgear & switchboard apparatus; coated & laminated paper

(G-13217)
T N T TECHNOLOGIES INC
7848 Locust St (44438-1533)
PHONE................................330 448-4744
Thomas Caldwell, *President*
Deb Sok, *Office Mgr*
EMP: 3
SQ FT: 7,500
SALES (est): 358.2K **Privately Held**
SIC: 3599 Machine shop, jobbing & repair; custom machinery

(G-13218)
WESTERN RESERVE METALS INC
7775 Addison Rd (44438-1208)
P.O. Box 126 (44438-0126)
PHONE................................330 448-4092
Fax: 330 448-4365
Tod Theodore, *President*
EMP: 22 **EST:** 1972
SQ FT: 24,000
SALES (est): 7.7MM **Privately Held**
SIC: 5051 3312 3316 Metals service centers & offices; blast furnaces & steel mills; cold finishing of steel shapes

---

Maumee
Lucas County

(G-13219)
ADVANCED DSTRBTED GNRATION LLC
1331 Conant St Ste 107 (43537-4214)
PHONE................................419 530-3792
John Witte, *President*
EMP: 3
SALES (est): 108.3K **Privately Held**
SIC: 3674 Semiconductors & related devices

(G-13220)
AFFYMETRIX INC
434 W Dussel Dr (43537-1685)
PHONE................................419 887-1233
Ken Kreh, *Opers Mgr*
Kristin Yakimow, *Branch Mgr*
EMP: 12
SALES (corp-wide): 18.2B **Publicly Held**
SIC: 3826 Analytical instruments
HQ: Affymetrix, Inc.
3450 Central Expy
Santa Clara CA 95051
408 731-5000

(G-13221)
ALTON PRODUCTS INC
425 W Sophia St (43537-1845)
P.O. Box 1115 (43537-8115)
PHONE................................419 893-0201
Fax: 419 893-9352
Marcia Janicki, *President*
Joseph M Albright, *Vice Pres*
Dave Hamilton, *Mfg Staff*
Karen S Prala, *Treasurer*
Cindy Albright, *Admin Sec*
EMP: 13 **EST:** 1949
SQ FT: 21,000
SALES (est): 1.2MM **Privately Held**
SIC: 3599 Machine shop, jobbing & repair

(G-13222)
AMERICAN FRAME CORPORATION
400 Tomahawk Dr (43537-1695)
PHONE................................419 893-5595
Fax: 419 893-3553
Ronald J Mickel, *President*
Michael Cromly, *Vice Pres*
Larry Haddad, *Vice Pres*
Kevin Wiley, *Plant Mgr*
Dana Dunbar, *Treasurer*
▲ **EMP:** 75
SQ FT: 33,000

SALES (est): 8.7MM **Privately Held**
WEB: www.americanframe.com
SIC: 7699 5961 5023 3444 Picture framing, custom; mail order house; home furnishings; sheet metalwork

(G-13223)
AMERICAN HEART ASSOCIATION INC
4331 Keystone Dr Ste D (43537-8797)
PHONE................................419 740-6180
Fax: 419 740-6182
Christine Colvin, *Branch Mgr*
EMP: 12
SALES (corp-wide): 780.2MM **Privately Held**
SIC: 8399 2721 Health systems agency; periodicals
PA: American Heart Association, Inc.
7272 Greenville Ave
Dallas TX 75231
214 373-6300

(G-13224)
ANDERSONS INC (PA)
1947 Briarfield Blvd (43537-1690)
P.O. Box 119 (43537-0119)
PHONE................................419 893-5050
Fax: 419 891-6672
Michael J Anderson, *Ch of Bd*
Patrick E Bowe, *President*
Naran U Burchinow, *Senior VP*
Charles Brown, *Vice Pres*
Art Depompei, *Vice Pres*
EMP: 150
SQ FT: 245,000
SALES: 3.9B **Publicly Held**
WEB: www.andersonsinc.com
SIC: 5153 0723 5191 2874 Grain & field beans; grains; grain elevators; crop preparation services for market; cash grain crops market preparation services; farm supplies; fertilizers & agricultural chemicals; seeds & bulbs; phosphatic fertilizers; plant foods, mixed: from plants making phosphatic fertilizer; railroad car repair; rental of railroad cars

(G-13225)
ANDERSONS INC
Also Called: Fabrication Division
415 Illinois Ave (43537-1705)
P.O. Box 119 (43537-0119)
PHONE................................419 891-2930
Fax: 419 891-6650
Rob Gieryng, *General Mgr*
Joseph Christen, *Engineer*
Colleen Kander, *Regl Sales Mgr*
Andrea Gay, *Sales Staff*
Michael Andersons, *Branch Mgr*
EMP: 36
SALES (corp-wide): 3.9B **Publicly Held**
WEB: www.andersonsinc.com
SIC: 3599 Machine shop, jobbing & repair
PA: The Andersons Inc
1947 Briarfield Blvd
Maumee OH 43537
419 893-5050

(G-13226)
ANDERSONS LAWN FERT DIV INC
Also Called: Farm Centers
480 W Dussel Dr Ste A (43537-1639)
P.O. Box 119 (43537-0119)
PHONE................................419 893-5050
Mike Anderson, *President*
Tom Wagoner, *Vice Pres*
Sandra Alexander, *Treasurer*
EMP: 12
SALES (est): 1.8MM
SALES (corp-wide): 3.9B **Publicly Held**
WEB: www.andersonsinc.com
SIC: 2899 5399 5191 Chemical preparations; country general stores; fertilizers & agricultural chemicals
PA: The Andersons Inc
1947 Briarfield Blvd
Maumee OH 43537
419 893-5050

(G-13227)
APPLIED ENERGY TECH INC
Also Called: A E T
1720 Indian Wood Cir E (43537-4041)
PHONE................................419 537-9052

Terence Seikel, *Ch of Bd*
Craig Winn, *President*
Aaron Faust, *Vice Pres*
John Harberts, *Vice Pres*
Lori Pierson, *CFO*
EMP: 26
SQ FT: 16,100
SALES (est): 9.5MM **Privately Held**
SIC: 3441 Fabricated structural metal

(G-13228)
B & B PRINTING GRAPHICS INC
1689 Lance Pointe Rd (43537-1603)
PHONE................................419 893-7068
Fax: 419 893-4820
Beth Stewart, *President*
Barney Stewart, *Vice Pres*
EMP: 10
SQ FT: 6,000
SALES (est): 1.6MM **Privately Held**
WEB: www.printinggraphics.com
SIC: 2752 Commercial printing, offset

(G-13229)
BARNES GROUP INC
Associated Spring Raymond
370 W Dussel Dr Ste A (43537-1604)
PHONE................................419 891-9292
Fax: 419 891-9192
Peter Korczynski, *Opers Mgr*
Erica Denton, *Purch Mgr*
Tracy Allison, *Controller*
EMP: 26
SALES (corp-wide): 1.2B **Publicly Held**
WEB: www.barnesgroupinc.com
SIC: 5072 3495 Hardware; wire springs
PA: Barnes Group Inc.
123 Main St
Bristol CT 06010
860 583-7070

(G-13230)
BARTON-CAREY MEDICAL PRODUCTS (PA)
1331 Conant St Ste 102 (43537-1665)
P.O. Box 421, Perrysburg (43552-0421)
PHONE................................419 887-1285
Fax: 419 874-0888
John H Mays, *President*
Freddie Hudak, *Controller*
EMP: 28
SALES (est): 2.4MM **Privately Held**
WEB: www.bartoncarey.com
SIC: 3842 2339 2326 Clothing, fire resistant & protective; women's & misses' outerwear; men's & boys' work clothing

(G-13231)
BAY CONTROLS LLC
6528 Weatherfield Ct (43537-9468)
PHONE................................419 891-4390
Fax: 419 891-4399
Amy Otis, *General Mgr*
Gary Ruff, *Senior Engr*
Mike Bavis, *CFO*
Wendy Beitzel, *Accounting Mgr*
Michael Davis, *Accounting Mgr*
▼ **EMP:** 30
SQ FT: 12,000
SALES (est): 5.9MM
SALES (corp-wide): 532.8K **Privately Held**
WEB: www.baycontrols.com
SIC: 3625 Industrial controls: push button, selector switches, pilot
PA: Entelco Corporation
6528 Weatherfield Ct
Maumee OH 43537
419 872-4620

(G-13232)
BPREX CLOSURES LLC
Also Called: Research & Development
1695 Indian Cir Ste 116 (43537)
PHONE................................812 424-2904
Michael Wenerd, *Plt & Fclts Mgr*
Lila Edwards, *Purchasing*
EMP: 100
SALES (corp-wide): 6.4B **Publicly Held**
SIC: 3089 Bottle caps, molded plastic
HQ: Bprex Closures, Llc
101 Oakley St
Evansville IN 47710
812 424-2904

(G-13233)
CGS SIGNS LLC
Also Called: Cgs Imaging
385 Osage St (43537-1637)
PHONE................................419 897-3000
Fax: 419 893-4316
Paul Juhasz, *Marketing Staff*
Chuck Stranc,
Carol Stranc,
▲ **EMP:** 14
SQ FT: 14,000
SALES (est): 2MM **Privately Held**
WEB: www.cgssigns.net
SIC: 3993 Signs & advertising specialties

(G-13234)
CHAMPION OPCO LLC
6214 Monclova Rd (43537-9761)
PHONE................................419 740-5193
EMP: 80
SALES (corp-wide): 516.7MM **Privately Held**
SIC: 3089 Window frames & sash, plastic
PA: Champion Opco, Llc
12121 Champion Way
Cincinnati OH 45241
513 924-4858

(G-13235)
CUMMINS BRIDGEWAY TOLEDO LLC
801 Illinois Ave (43537-1713)
PHONE................................419 893-8711
Fax: 419 893-5362
Holly Roesch,
EMP: 19
SALES (est): 4.2MM
SALES (corp-wide): 17.5B **Publicly Held**
WEB: www.bridgewaypower.com
SIC: 5084 3519 Engines & parts, diesel; internal combustion engines
HQ: Cummins Bridgeway, Llc
21810 Clessie Ct
New Hudson MI 48165
248 573-1600

(G-13236)
DAN K WILLIAMS INC
1350 Ford St (43537-1733)
P.O. Box 147 (43537-0147)
PHONE................................419 893-3251
Dan K Williams, *President*
EMP: 22
SALES (est): 3.8MM **Privately Held**
SIC: 3273 Ready-mixed concrete

(G-13237)
DANA AUTO SYSTEMS GROUP LLC (DH)
3939 Technology Dr (43537-9194)
PHONE................................419 887-3000
Rick Harman,
◆ **EMP:** 61
SALES (est): 328.2MM
SALES (corp-wide): 5.8B **Publicly Held**
SIC: 3714 Motor vehicle parts & accessories
HQ: Dana Limited
3939 Technology Dr
Maumee OH 43537
630 697-3783

(G-13238)
DANA BRAZIL HOLDINGS I LLC (DH)
3939 Technology Dr (43537-9194)
PHONE................................419 887-3000
Roger Wood, *CEO*
EMP: 5
SALES (est): 573.1K
SALES (corp-wide): 5.8B **Publicly Held**
SIC: 3714 Motor vehicle parts & accessories
HQ: Dana World Trade Corp
3939 Technology Dr
Maumee OH 43537
419 887-3000

(G-13239)
DANA COMMERCIAL VHCL MFG LLC (DH)
Also Called: Dana Commercial Vehicle Pdts
3939 Technology Dr (43537-9194)
PHONE................................419 887-3000
Susan Herring, *General Mgr*

Ron Parks, *Vice Pres*
Mike Morrison, *Mfg Staff*
Barry Hirsch, *Purch Mgr*
Diana Patton, *Purchasing*
◆ **EMP:** 61
SALES (est): 42.1MM
SALES (corp-wide): 5.8B **Publicly Held**
SIC: 3714 Motor vehicle parts & accessories
HQ: Dana Commercial Vehicle Products, Llc
    3939 Technology Dr
    Maumee OH 43537
    419 887-3000

(G-13240)
DANA COMMERCIAL VHCL PDTS LLC (DH)
3939 Technology Dr (43537-9194)
PHONE...................................419 887-3000
Latanian Goodwin, *Superintendent*
Marvin Franklin, *Vice Pres*
◆ **EMP:** 131
SALES (est): 80.3MM
SALES (corp-wide): 5.8B **Publicly Held**
SIC: 3714 Motor vehicle parts & accessories
HQ: Dana Heavy Vehicle Systems Group, Llc
    3939 Technology Dr
    Maumee OH 43537
    419 887-3000

(G-13241)
DANA DRIVESHAFT MFG LLC (DH)
Also Called: Dana Driveshaft Products
3939 Technology Dr (43537-9194)
PHONE...................................419 887-3000
Eric Bogerson, *Finance Dir*
Margot Hoffman,
▲ **EMP:** 50
SALES (est): 40.1MM
SALES (corp-wide): 5.8B **Publicly Held**
SIC: 3714 Motor vehicle parts & accessories
HQ: Dana Driveshaft Products, Llc
    3939 Technology Dr
    Maumee OH 43537
    419 887-3000

(G-13242)
DANA DRIVESHAFT PRODUCTS LLC (DH)
3939 Technology Dr (43537-9194)
PHONE...................................419 887-3000
Rod Filcek,
▲ **EMP:** 49
SALES (est): 45.2MM
SALES (corp-wide): 5.8B **Publicly Held**
SIC: 3714 Motor vehicle parts & accessories
HQ: Dana Automotive Systems Group, Llc
    3939 Technology Dr
    Maumee OH 43537
    419 887-3000

(G-13243)
DANA GLOBAL PRODUCTS INC
3939 Technology Dr (43537-9194)
PHONE...................................419 887-3000
EMP: 4
SALES (corp-wide): 5.8B **Publicly Held**
SIC: 3714 Motor vehicle parts & accessories
HQ: Dana Global Products, Inc.
    3939 Technology Dr
    Maumee OH 43537
    419 887-3000

(G-13244)
DANA GLOBAL PRODUCTS INC (DH)
3939 Technology Dr (43537-9194)
P.O. Box 1000 (43537-7000)
PHONE...................................419 887-3000
Rodney R Filcek, *President*
Jeffrey S Bowen, *Vice Pres*
Lillian Etzkorn, *Treasurer*
Marc S Levin, *Admin Sec*
◆ **EMP:** 7
SALES (est): 3.6MM
SALES (corp-wide): 5.8B **Publicly Held**
SIC: 3714 Motor vehicle parts & accessories

HQ: Dana Limited
    3939 Technology Dr
    Maumee OH 43537
    630 697-3783

(G-13245)
DANA HEAVY VEHICLE SYSTEMS (DH)
Also Called: Dana Heavy Vhcl Systems Group
3939 Technology Dr (43537-9194)
PHONE...................................419 887-3000
Nick Stanage, *Mng Member*
◆ **EMP:** 31
SALES (est): 191.4MM
SALES (corp-wide): 5.8B **Publicly Held**
SIC: 3714 Motor vehicle parts & accessories
HQ: Dana Limited
    3939 Technology Dr
    Maumee OH 43537
    630 697-3783

(G-13246)
DANA INCORPORATED (PA)
3939 Technology Dr (43537-9194)
P.O. Box 1000 (43537-7000)
PHONE...................................419 887-3000
Keith E Wandell, *Ch of Bd*
James K Kamsickas, *President*
Dwayne E Matthews, *President*
Robert D Pyle, *President*
Mark E Wallace, *President*
EMP: 300
SALES: 5.8B **Publicly Held**
SIC: 3714 3053 3593 3492 Motor vehicle parts & accessories; motor vehicle transmissions, drive assemblies & parts; axles, motor vehicle; clutches, motor vehicle; gaskets & sealing devices; fluid power cylinders, hydraulic or pneumatic; control valves, fluid power: hydraulic & pneumatic

(G-13247)
DANA LIGHT AXLE MFG LLC (DH)
Also Called: Dana Light Axle Products
3939 Technology Dr (43537-9194)
P.O. Box B1000 (43537)
PHONE...................................419 887-3000
Thomas Stone, *Mng Member*
Mike Worland, *Technology*
▲ **EMP:** 13
SALES: 130MM
SALES (corp-wide): 5.8B **Publicly Held**
SIC: 3714 Motor vehicle parts & accessories
HQ: Dana Light Axle Products, Llc
    2100 W State Blvd
    Fort Wayne IN 46808
    260 483-7174

(G-13248)
DANA LIMITED
Also Called: Dana Information Technology
580 Longbow Dr (43537-1759)
PHONE...................................419 482-2000
Fax: 419 535-4439
Al Henderson, *Manager*
Lynn Crawford, *Manager*
Luciano Satine, *Manager*
Shelbey Carter, *Technology*
Gurjeet Singh, *Technology*
EMP: 100
SALES (corp-wide): 5.8B **Publicly Held**
WEB: www.intelligentcooling.com
SIC: 3714 Motor vehicle parts & accessories
HQ: Dana Limited
    3939 Technology Dr
    Maumee OH 43537
    630 697-3783

(G-13249)
DANA LIMITED (HQ)
3939 Technology Dr (43537-9194)
P.O. Box 1000 (43537-7000)
PHONE...................................630 697-3783
James Sweetnam, *President*
John Devine, *Chairman*
Marc S Levin, *Senior VP*
Bob Silcek, *Vice Pres*
Dean Wilson, *Vice Pres*
▲ **EMP:** 500

SALES (est): 5.4B
SALES (corp-wide): 5.8B **Publicly Held**
WEB: www.intelligentcooling.com
SIC: 3714 3053 3593 3492 Motor vehicle parts & accessories; gaskets & sealing devices; fluid power cylinders, hydraulic or pneumatic; control valves, fluid power: hydraulic & pneumatic
PA: Dana Incorporated
    3939 Technology Dr
    Maumee OH 43537
    419 887-3000

(G-13250)
DANA OFF HIGHWAY PRODUCTS LLC (DH)
3939 Technology Dr (43537-9194)
P.O. Box 1000 (43537-7000)
PHONE...................................419 887-3000
Nick Stanage, *President*
◆ **EMP:** 50
SALES (est): 35.7MM
SALES (corp-wide): 5.8B **Publicly Held**
SIC: 3714 Motor vehicle parts & accessories
HQ: Dana Heavy Vehicle Systems Group, Llc
    3939 Technology Dr
    Maumee OH 43537
    419 887-3000

(G-13251)
DANA SEALING MANUFACTURING LLC (DH)
Also Called: Dana Sealing Products
3939 Technology Dr (43537-9194)
PHONE...................................419 887-3000
Rod Filcek,
Ralf Goettel,
▲ **EMP:** 78
SALES (est): 57.8MM
SALES (corp-wide): 5.8B **Publicly Held**
SIC: 3714 Motor vehicle parts & accessories
HQ: Dana Sealing Products, Llc
    3939 Technology Dr
    Maumee OH 43537
    419 887-3000

(G-13252)
DANA SEALING PRODUCTS LLC (DH)
3939 Technology Dr (43537-9194)
P.O. Box 1000 (43537-7000)
PHONE...................................419 887-3000
Jeffery Clarke, *Controller*
Rod Filcek, *Representative*
Ralf Goettel,
EMP: 40
SALES (est): 97.1MM
SALES (corp-wide): 5.8B **Publicly Held**
SIC: 3714 Motor vehicle parts & accessories
HQ: Dana Automotive Systems Group, Llc
    3939 Technology Dr
    Maumee OH 43537
    419 887-3000

(G-13253)
DANA STRUCTURAL PRODUCTS LLC (DH)
3939 Technology Dr (43537-9194)
PHONE...................................419 887-3000
Gilberto Ceretti,
EMP: 3
SALES (est): 837.7K
SALES (corp-wide): 5.8B **Publicly Held**
SIC: 3714 Motor vehicle parts & accessories
HQ: Dana Automotive Systems Group, Llc
    3939 Technology Dr
    Maumee OH 43537
    419 887-3000

(G-13254)
DANA THERMAL PRODUCTS LLC (DH)
3939 Technology Dr (43537-9194)
PHONE...................................419 887-3000
Ralf Goettel,
▲ **EMP:** 17
SALES (est): 8.1MM
SALES (corp-wide): 5.8B **Publicly Held**
SIC: 3714 Motor vehicle parts & accessories

HQ: Dana Automotive Systems Group, Llc
    3939 Technology Dr
    Maumee OH 43537
    419 887-3000

(G-13255)
DANA WORLD TRADE CORP (DH)
3939 Technology Dr (43537-9194)
PHONE...................................419 887-3000
Kenneth A Hiltz, *CFO*
EMP: 4
SALES (est): 3.9MM
SALES (corp-wide): 5.8B **Publicly Held**
SIC: 3714 Motor vehicle parts & accessories
HQ: Dana Limited
    3939 Technology Dr
    Maumee OH 43537
    630 697-3783

(G-13256)
DENTSPLY INTERNATIONAL INC
Ransom & Randolph
3535 Briarfield Blvd (43537-9383)
PHONE...................................419 865-9497
Fax: 419 893-4988
Marti Hunyor, *Sls & Mktg Exec*
Scott Todd, *Sales Executive*
Dan Nixon, *Branch Mgr*
Casey Wolfe, *Manager*
EMP: 72
SALES (corp-wide): 3.7B **Publicly Held**
SIC: 3843 3844 2821 3915 Dental equipment & supplies; impression material, dental; denture materials; teeth, artificial (not made in dental laboratories); X-ray apparatus & tubes; beta-ray irradiation equipment; radiographic X-ray apparatus & tubes; molding compounds, plastics; jewelers' castings
PA: Dentsply Sirona Inc.
    221 W Philadelphia St
    York PA 17401
    717 845-7511

(G-13257)
DENTSPLY SIRONA INC
520 Illinois Ave (43537-1708)
PHONE...................................419 893-5672
M Smith, *Division Mgr*
Garyn Livecchi, *General Mgr*
Warren Clark, *Controller*
S Waters, *Sales Staff*
EMP: 50
SQ FT: 4,000
SALES (corp-wide): 3.7B **Publicly Held**
WEB: www.dentsply.com
SIC: 3843 Teeth, artificial (not made in dental laboratories)
PA: Dentsply Sirona Inc.
    221 W Philadelphia St
    York PA 17401
    717 845-7511

(G-13258)
EATON-AEROQUIP INC
1660 Indian Wood Cir (43537-4004)
PHONE...................................419 891-7775
Howard Selland, *President*
Chad Achenbach, *Purchasing*
Susan Groom, *Engineer*
Lennard McMinn, *Technology*
EMP: 90 **Privately Held**
SIC: 8711 3594 3593 3561 Professional engineer; fluid power pumps & motors; fluid power cylinders & actuators; pumps & pumping equipment; fluid power valves & hose fittings; rubber & plastics hose & beltings
HQ: Eaton-Aeroquip Llc.
    1000 Eaton Blvd
    Cleveland OH 44122
    216 523-5000

(G-13259)
FRIPRO ENERGY LLC
7008 Garden Rd (43537-1010)
PHONE...................................419 865-0002
Thomas E Fairbairin, *CEO*
Terrence J Sherman, *President*
James O'Brien, *Production*
EMP: 3
SQ FT: 43,560

SALES (est): 160K **Privately Held**
SIC: 8731 3671 Energy research; electron
beam (beta ray) generator tubes

(G-13260)
FYPON LTD
1750 Indian Wood Cir (43537-4049)
P.O. Box 301, Archbold (43502-0301)
PHONE................................800 446-3040
Merle G Beck, *President*
Jack Folland, *Credit Mgr*
Mike Kasubski, *Accountant*
Sterling Feeser, *Human Res Dir*
Deb Beck, *Sales Associate*
▲ EMP: 200
SQ FT: 150,000
SALES (est): 28.4MM
SALES (corp-wide): 72.3MM **Privately
Held**
SIC: 3089 Plastic hardware & building
products
HQ: Simonton Holdings, Inc.
520 Lake Cook Rd
Deerfield IL 60015
304 428-8261

(G-13261)
GOMECH LTD
355 Tomahawk Dr Unit 2 (43537-1756)
P.O. Box 371, Bowling Green (43402-0371)
PHONE................................419 419-4446
Francis Lanciaux,
EMP: 3
SALES (est): 329.4K **Privately Held**
SIC: 3444 Sheet metalwork

(G-13262)
**GREAT LAKES ENGRAVING
CORP**
Also Called: Great Lakes Reprographic
1736 Henthorne Dr (43537-1350)
PHONE................................419 867-1607
Fax: 419 248-1096
Jack P Kerin, *President*
Jill Weiser, *Vice Pres*
EMP: 4
SQ FT: 7,500
SALES (est): 523.8K **Privately Held**
WEB: www.greatlakesengraving.net
SIC: 7334 2752 Photocopying & duplicat-
ing services; commercial printing, litho-
graphic

(G-13263)
HALL-TOLEDO INC
525 W Sophia St (43537-1881)
PHONE................................419 893-4334
Andrew F Boesel, *President*
Tresa Duffy, *Purchasing*
EMP: 10
SQ FT: 5,000
SALES (est): 1.2MM **Privately Held**
SIC: 3546 3714 Power-driven handtools;
motor vehicle parts & accessories
PA: Michabo Inc
525 W Sophia St
Maumee OH 43537

(G-13264)
**HAMMILL MANUFACTURING CO
(PA)**
Also Called: Impact Cutoff Div
360 Tomahawk Dr (43537-1612)
P.O. Box 1450 (43537-8450)
PHONE................................419 476-0789
Fax: 419 470-3600
John Hammill, *Ch of Bd*
John E Hamill Jr, *President*
Brian Lewandowski, *General Mgr*
Brian Burns, *Exec VP*
Robert Doubler, *Exec VP*
EMP: 100 EST: 1955
SQ FT: 80,000
SALES (est): 27.6MM **Privately Held**
WEB: www.hammillmfg.com
SIC: 3842 3545 Implants, surgical;
chucks; drill, lathe or magnetic (machine
tool accessories)

(G-13265)
**HELM INSTRUMENT COMPANY
INC**
361 W Dussel Dr (43537-1649)
PHONE................................419 893-4356
Fax: 419 893-1371

Richard T Wilhelm, *President*
Mary L Tice, *Vice Pres*
Michael Wilhelm, *Vice Pres*
Thomas Wilhelm, *Vice Pres*
Ned Phillips, *Buyer*
EMP: 34 EST: 1962
SQ FT: 12,500
SALES (est): 7.4MM **Privately Held**
WEB: www.helminstrument.com
SIC: 3829 3825 3823 3822 Measuring &
controlling devices; instruments to meas-
ure electricity; industrial instrmnts msrmnt
display/control process variable; auto
controls regulating residntl & coml envi-
ronmt & applncs; relays & industrial con-
trols

(G-13266)
**HENRY-GRIFFITTS LIMITED
(HQ)**
Also Called: About Golf
352 Tomahawk Dr (43537-1612)
PHONE................................419 482-9095
Bill Bales, *CEO*
Paul Hill, *Controller*
▲ EMP: 9
SALES (est): 3.7MM
SALES (corp-wide): 4.8MM **Privately
Held**
SIC: 3999 Atomizers, toiletry
PA: Aboutgolf, Limited
352 Tomahawk Dr
Maumee OH 43537
419 482-9095

(G-13267)
ICGC THE ANDERSONS INC
1947 Briarfield Blvd (43537-9803)
PHONE................................419 893-5050
Pat Bowe, *President*
EMP: 3
SALES (est): 134.6K **Privately Held**
SIC: 2873 Fertilizers: natural (organic), ex-
cept compost

(G-13268)
**ISHOS BROS FUEL VENTURES
INC**
1289 Conant St (43537-1607)
PHONE................................586 634-0187
Michael Isho, *Owner*
EMP: 4
SALES (est): 331.3K **Privately Held**
SIC: 2869 Fuels

(G-13269)
J-M DESIGNS LLC
128 W Wayne St (43537-2151)
PHONE................................419 794-2114
Mary Ellen Gedert,
Francis R Gedert,
Mary Gedert,
EMP: 5
SQ FT: 4,500
SALES (est): 486K **Privately Held**
SIC: 5949 5099 2759 Sewing & needle-
work; signs, except electric; screen print-
ing

(G-13270)
JAZZ TEXTILE IMPRESSIONS
1425 Holland Rd (43537-1617)
P.O. Box 6778, Toledo (43612-0778)
PHONE................................419 242-5940
Daniel Burke, *President*
EMP: 5
SALES (est): 420K **Privately Held**
WEB: www.jazztextiles.com
SIC: 2759 Screen printing

(G-13271)
**JOHNS MANVILLE
CORPORATION**
1020 Ford St (43537-1820)
PHONE................................419 467-8189
EMP: 224
SALES (corp-wide): 223.6B **Publicly
Held**
WEB: www.jm.com
SIC: 3296 Fiberglass insulation
HQ: Johns Manville Corporation
717 17th St Ste 800
Denver CO 80202
303 978-2000

(G-13272)
JOSTENS INC
3455 Briarfield Blvd F (43537-8933)
PHONE................................419 794-7343
Jason Miller, *Manager*
EMP: 4
SALES (corp-wide): 13.2B **Publicly Held**
SIC: 3911 Rings, finger: precious metal
HQ: Jostens, Inc.
3601 Minnesota Dr Ste 400
Minneapolis MN 55435
952 830-3300

(G-13273)
KUHLMAN CORPORATION (PA)
Also Called: Kuhlman Construction Products
1845 Indian Wood Cir (43537-4072)
P.O. Box 714, Toledo (43697-0714)
PHONE................................419 897-6000
Fax: 419 897-6061
Timothy L Goligoski, *President*
Kenneth Kuhlman, *Vice Pres*
Larry Matuszak, *Purchasing*
Terry Schaefer, *CFO*
Vernon J Nagel, *Treasurer*
EMP: 32 EST: 1901
SQ FT: 18,000
SALES: 55.6MM **Privately Held**
WEB: www.kuhlman-corp.com
SIC: 4226 5032 3273 Special warehous-
ing & storage; brick, stone & related ma-
terial; brick, except refractory; building
blocks; sewer pipe, clay; ready-mixed
concrete

(G-13274)
LAFARGE NORTH AMERICA INC
1645 Indian Wood Cir # 201 (43537-4409)
PHONE................................419 897-7656
Fax: 419 897-7659
Keith Deighton, *Vice Pres*
Larry Papenfuss, *Manager*
EMP: 14
SQ FT: 2,088
SALES (corp-wide): 26.6B **Privately Held**
WEB: www.lafargenorthamerica.com
SIC: 3241 Cement, hydraulic
HQ: Lafarge North America Inc.
8700 W Bryn Mawr Ave Ll
Chicago IL 60631
703 480-3600

(G-13275)
LARRYS WATER CONDITIONING
Also Called: Lwc
720 Illinois Ave Ste I (43537-1750)
PHONE................................419 887-0290
Teresa Gallo, *Manager*
Larry Kohlenberg,
Sandra Kohlenberg,
EMP: 3
SQ FT: 2,400
SALES (est): 360K **Privately Held**
SIC: 3589 Water treatment equipment, in-
dustrial

(G-13276)
LINE DRIVE SPORTZ-LCRC LLC
2901 Key St Ste 1 (43537-2421)
PHONE................................419 794-7150
Elizabeth Beck,
James Hanna,
EMP: 6
SALES (est): 655.6K **Privately Held**
SIC: 3949 Sporting & athletic goods

(G-13277)
**MAGNESIUM PRODUCTS
GROUP INC**
Also Called: M P G
3928 Azalea Cir (43537-9191)
PHONE................................310 971-5799
Bradley A Hirou, *President*
Steve Hubble, *COO*
Ronald W Banks, *Exec VP*
EMP: 6
SALES (est): 307.1K **Privately Held**
WEB: www.mpg-mfg.com
SIC: 3441 Fabricated structural metal

(G-13278)
**MAUMEE ASSEMBLY &
STAMPING LLC**
920 Illinois Ave (43537-1716)
PHONE................................419 304-2887

Stanley Chlebowski, *CEO*
Jack Sculfort, *COO*
Phil Caron, *VP Opers*
Joseph W Weiss, *Controller*
Pam Geha, *Manager*
EMP: 100
SALES (est): 23.4MM **Privately Held**
SIC: 3469 Metal stampings

(G-13279)
MAUMEE HOSE & FITTING INC
Also Called: Maumee Hose & Belting Co
720 Illinois Ave Ste H (43537-1750)
PHONE................................419 893-7252
Fax: 419 893-4744
James C Walsh, *President*
Karen Walsh, *Vice Pres*
EMP: 7
SQ FT: 10,000
SALES (est): 1.8MM **Privately Held**
WEB: www.maumeehose.com
SIC: 5085 3429 Industrial supplies; hose,
belting & packing; industrial fittings;
clamps, couplings, nozzles & other metal
hose fittings

(G-13280)
MAUMEE QUICK PRINT INC
219 Conant St (43537-3355)
PHONE................................419 893-4321
Fax: 419 893-3615
Peggy Masters, *President*
Jennifer Starr, *Vice Pres*
EMP: 5
SQ FT: 1,400
SALES (est): 150K **Privately Held**
SIC: 2752 Commercial printing, offset

(G-13281)
**METAL FORMING & COINING
CORP (PA)**
Also Called: MFC
1007 Illinois Ave (43537-1752)
PHONE................................419 897-9530
Fax: 419 893-6828
Thomas Wienrich, *President*
Tim Cripsey, *General Mgr*
Paul Kessler, *Exec VP*
John Knapp, *Safety Dir*
Mike Hooven, *Plant Mgr*
EMP: 100 EST: 1953
SQ FT: 103,000
SALES (est): 26.9MM **Privately Held**
WEB: www.mfccorp.com
SIC: 3462 Iron & steel forgings

(G-13282)
MICHABO INC (PA)
525 W Sophia St (43537-1847)
PHONE................................419 893-4334
Milton C Boesel Jr, *President*
Andrew Boesel, *Vice Pres*
EMP: 1
SQ FT: 5,000
SALES (est): 1.2MM **Privately Held**
SIC: 3546 Power-driven handtools

(G-13283)
**MIDWEST TRMNALS TLEDO
INTL INC (PA)**
383 W Dussel Dr (43537-1632)
PHONE................................419 897-6868
Fax: 419 897-6869
Alexander Johnson, *President*
Fred Deichert, *CFO*
Brent Gerken, *Treasurer*
Lauri A Hiatt, *Financial Analy*
▲ EMP: 3
SALES (est): 19.2MM **Privately Held**
SIC: 2952 Asphalt felts & coatings

(G-13284)
MIRROR
Also Called: Community Mirror, The
113 W Wayne St (43537-2150)
PHONE................................419 893-8135
Fax: 419 893-6397
Michael Mc Carthy, *Owner*
Mike McCarthy, *Publisher*
McCarthy Mike, *COO*
Carol McCarthy, *Persnl Dir*
Andy Rower, *Personnel Exec*
EMP: 20
SQ FT: 5,000

▲ = Import ▼=Export
◆ =Import/Export

SALES (est): 1.1MM **Privately Held**
SIC: 2711 Newspapers, publishing & printing

(G-13285)
MIRROR PUBLISHING CO INC
Also Called: Mirror, The
113 W Wayne St (43537-2150)
PHONE..................................419 893-8135
Michael McCarthy, *President*
EMP: 20
SQ FT: 3,000
SALES (est): 1MM **Privately Held**
SIC: 2711 Newspapers: publishing only, not printed on site

(G-13286)
MITCHS WELDING & HITCHES
802 Kingsbury St (43537-1826)
PHONE..................................419 893-3117
Fax: 419 893-3990
James Mitchell, *President*
EMP: 8
SQ FT: 5,000
SALES (est): 775K **Privately Held**
SIC: 3537 5561 Industrial trucks & tractors; recreational vehicle parts & accessories

(G-13287)
OLDCASTLE BUILDINGENVELOPE INC
1789 Indian Wood Cir (43537-4096)
PHONE..................................419 887-1228
Ashley Zale, *Branch Mgr*
EMP: 9
SALES (corp-wide): 28.6B **Privately Held**
WEB: www.oldcastleglass.com
SIC: 3231 5231 Tempered glass: made from purchased glass; insulating glass: made from purchased glass; glass
HQ: Oldcastle Buildingenvelope, Inc.
5005 Lndn B Jnsn Fwy 10 Ste 1050
Dallas TX 75244
214 273-3400

(G-13288)
PRO-PAK INDUSTRIES INC (PA)
1125 Ford St (43537-1703)
P.O. Box 1176 (43537-8176)
PHONE..................................419 729-0751
Leo Deiger, *President*
Charles M Deiger, *Corp Secy*
Anthony Deiger, *Vice Pres*
Randy Deiger, *Vice Pres*
Toni Villolovos, *Vice Pres*
EMP: 110 EST: 1948
SALES (est): 22.7MM **Privately Held**
SIC: 2653 Boxes, corrugated: made from purchased materials

(G-13289)
PROTEL SYSTEMS AND SVCS LLC
1298 Conant St Ste 504 (43537-1608)
PHONE..................................419 893-2440
Fax: 419 913-0528
Denny R McBroom, *Branch Mgr*
EMP: 5 **Privately Held**
SIC: 7372 Prepackaged software
PA: Protel Systems And Services Llc
3453 Chapel Dr
Toledo OH 43615

(G-13290)
S E JOHNSON COMPANIES INC (DH)
1360 Ford St (43537-1733)
PHONE..................................419 893-8731
John T Bearss, *CEO*
Donald Weber, *Vice Pres*
Mark W Karchner, *CFO*
Terry J Moore, *Treasurer*
Joanne Jones, *MIS Staff*
EMP: 19 EST: 1924
SQ FT: 34,000
SALES (est): 77.2MM
SALES (corp-wide): 28.6B **Privately Held**
WEB: www.sejohnson.com
SIC: 1611 1622 2951 1411 General contractor; highway & street construction; bridge construction; asphalt & asphaltic paving mixtures (not from refineries); limestone, dimension-quarrying

HQ: Shelly Company
80 Park Dr
Thornville OH 43076
740 246-6315

(G-13291)
SENATOR INTERNATIONAL INC (PA)
Also Called: Allermuir
4111 N Jerome Rd (43537-7100)
PHONE..................................419 887-5806
Mark Brettschneider, *President*
Jeff Rogers, *Controller*
Paul Hoelzle, *Accountant*
Keith Cooper, *Sales Mgr*
Sharon Kachenmeister, *Sales Mgr*
▲ EMP: 38
SALES (est): 9.4MM **Privately Held**
SIC: 2511 Wood household furniture

(G-13292)
SERVICE SPRING CORP (PA)
1703 Toll Gate Dr (43537-1673)
PHONE..................................419 838-6081
Fax: 419 838-6071
Michael McAlear, *CEO*
Clarence J Veigel, *Principal*
Evelyn F Veigel, *Principal*
Dan Susor, *Safety Mgr*
Jeff Reau, *Engineer*
▼ EMP: 87 EST: 1962
SQ FT: 98,000
SALES (est): 21.8MM **Privately Held**
WEB: www.sscorp.com
SIC: 3493 Steel springs, except wire

(G-13293)
SIMPLEX TIME RECORDER LLC
Also Called: Simplex Time Recorder 584
3661 Brrfeld Blvd Ste 101 (43537)
PHONE..................................419 861-0661
Darry Greenleaf, *Sales/Mktg Mgr*
EMP: 60 **Privately Held**
WEB: www.comtec-alaska.com
SIC: 5065 3494 Electronic parts; valves & pipe fittings
HQ: Simplex Time Recorder Llc
50 Technology Dr
Westminster MA 01441
978 731-2500

(G-13294)
SIMPLEXGRINNELL LP
3661 Brrfeld Blvd Ste 101 (43537)
PHONE..................................419 861-0662
Fax: 419 861-0603
Christopher Bonacci, *District Mgr*
Kurt Hagley, *Opers Mgr*
Jim Ravaf, *Manager*
Jason Mack, *Manager*
EMP: 50 **Privately Held**
WEB: www.simplexgrinnell.com
SIC: 3669 Emergency alarms
HQ: Simplexgrinnell Lp
4700 Exchange Ct
Boca Raton FL 33431
561 988-7200

(G-13295)
SKR ENTERPRISES LLC
Also Called: Always Promoting Co.
127 W Wayne St (43537-2150)
PHONE..................................419 891-1112
Scott Stearns, *Sales Staff*
Scott Sterns,
Kevin Sterns,
EMP: 3
SALES: 700K **Privately Held**
WEB: www.alwayspromoting.com
SIC: 3999 Advertising display products

(G-13296)
SOCCER CENTRE OWNERS LTD
1620 Market Place Dr (43537-4318)
PHONE..................................419 893-5425
Brant Smith, *Principal*
EMP: 30 EST: 2012
SQ FT: 300,000
SALES (est): 802.3K **Privately Held**
SIC: 3949 7999 Pads: football, basketball, soccer, lacrosse, etc.; indoor court clubs

(G-13297)
SPARTAN CHEMICAL COMPANY INC (PA)
1110 Spartan Dr (43537-1725)
PHONE..................................419 897-5551
Fax: 419 897-9862
Stephen H Swigart, *CEO*
John Swigart, *President*
Kenneth G Ford, *Vice Pres*
James R Lenardson, *Vice Pres*
Jim Lenardson, *Vice Pres*
◆ EMP: 40 EST: 1956
SQ FT: 450,000
SALES (est): 88.5MM **Privately Held**
WEB: www.spartanchemical.com
SIC: 2842 Specialty cleaning, polishes & sanitation goods; floor waxes; disinfectants, household or industrial plant

(G-13298)
STONECO INC
Also Called: Shelley Company
1360 Ford St (43537-1733)
PHONE..................................419 893-7645
Fax: 419 891-3014
Lee Wehner, *Manager*
Mark Parran, *Manager*
EMP: 15
SALES (corp-wide): 28.6B **Privately Held**
WEB: www.stoneco.net
SIC: 1422 5032 Crushed & broken limestone; stone, crushed or broken
HQ: Stoneco, Inc.
1700 Fostoria Ave Ste 200
Findlay OH 45840
419 422-8854

(G-13299)
SUN CHEMICAL CORPORATION
Ink & Plates
1380 Ford St (43537-1733)
PHONE..................................419 891-3514
Fax: 419 891-3529
Sara Bokesch, *Human Resources*
Wes Lucas, *Manager*
EMP: 80
SQ FT: 68,000
SALES (corp-wide): 6.7B **Privately Held**
WEB: www.sunchemical.com
SIC: 2893 Printing ink
HQ: Sun Chemical Corporation
35 Waterview Blvd Ste 100
Parsippany NJ 07054
973 404-6000

(G-13300)
SURFACE COMBUSTION INC (PA)
1700 Indian Wood Cir (43537-4067)
P.O. Box 428 (43537-0428)
PHONE..................................419 891-7150
Fax: 419 891-7151
William J Bernard Jr, *President*
Lori Lingle, *President*
Alex Kominek, *Superintendent*
Randy Behnfeldt, *Regional Mgr*
W Moseley, *Exec VP*
▲ EMP: 110
SQ FT: 36,000
SALES (est): 23.8MM **Privately Held**
WEB: www.surfacecombustion.com
SIC: 3567 Industrial furnaces & ovens

(G-13301)
THERMA-TRU CORP (HQ)
1750 Indian Wood Cir # 100 (43537-4079)
PHONE..................................419 891-7400
Fax: 419 891-7411
Brett Finley, *President*
Patrick Pelham, *District Mgr*
Jeffrey Grizzard, *Business Mgr*
Mark Edick, *Vice Pres*
Manny Francione, *Vice Pres*
▲ EMP: 50
SQ FT: 10,000
SALES (est): 581.5MM
SALES (corp-wide): 4.9B **Publicly Held**
WEB: www.thermatru.com
SIC: 3442 Metal doors
PA: Fortune Brands Home & Security, Inc.
520 Lake Cook Rd
Deerfield IL 60015
847 484-4400

(G-13302)
TILT-OR-LIFT INC (PA)
124 E Dudley St (43537-3366)
P.O. Box 8728 (43537-8728)
PHONE..................................419 893-6944
Fax: 419 893-5714
Dennis Rober, *President*
Roz Rober, *Admin Sec*
EMP: 6
SQ FT: 1,400
SALES: 1MM **Privately Held**
SIC: 3537 5084 Lift trucks, industrial: fork, platform, straddle, etc.; industrial machinery & equipment

(G-13303)
TOP NOTCH FLEET SERVICES LLC
801 Wall St (43537-3567)
PHONE..................................419 260-4057
Tom J Laurie, *Mng Member*
EMP: 5
SALES: 297.2K **Privately Held**
SIC: 7692 7549 7538 Automotive welding; road service, automotive; general truck repair

(G-13304)
TUPPAS SOFTWARE CORPORATION
1690 Woodlands Dr (43537-4045)
PHONE..................................419 897-7902
Paul Tupciauskas, *CEO*
EMP: 200
SALES (est): 12.7MM **Privately Held**
WEB: www.tuppas.com
SIC: 3829 Medical diagnostic systems, nuclear

(G-13305)
TWENTY SECOND CNTURY FOODS LLC
Also Called: Petit Gourmet
6546 Weatherfield Ct C (43537-9252)
PHONE..................................419 866-6343
Jason E Dzierwa, *Principal*
EMP: 3
SALES (est): 110K **Privately Held**
SIC: 2099 Food preparations

(G-13306)
US COEXCELL INC
400 W Dussel Dr Ste C (43537-1636)
PHONE..................................419 897-9110
Fax: 419 897-9112
Robert Huebner, *President*
Harley Cramer, *Vice Pres*
Mark Wotell, *VP Sales*
Chris Master, *Manager*
Gail Sherman, *Manager*
▲ EMP: 39
SQ FT: 40,000
SALES (est): 9.1MM **Privately Held**
WEB: www.uscoxl.com
SIC: 3089 Plastic containers, except foam

(G-13307)
VICKERS INTERNATIONAL INC
3000 Strayer Rd (43537-9529)
PHONE..................................419 867-2200
Darryl F Allen, *President*
James Oathout, *Vice Pres*
Gary J Findling, *Treasurer*
EMP: 20
SQ FT: 21,000
SALES (est): 1.8MM **Privately Held**
SIC: 3561 3594 3491 Pumps & pumping equipment; motors, pneumatic; motors: hydraulic, fluid power or air; industrial valves
HQ: Eaton Corporation
1000 Eaton Blvd
Cleveland OH 44122
216 523-5000

(G-13308)
WELLINGTON INDUSTRIES
Also Called: Wellington Maumee
920 Illinois Ave (43537-1716)
P.O. Box 672355, Detroit MI (48267-2355)
PHONE..................................734 942-1060
Marvin Tyghem, *Principal*
EMP: 75

SALES (est): 3.4MM
SALES (corp-wide): 84.1MM **Privately Held**
SIC: 3469 Metal stampings
PA: Wellington Industries, Inc.
39555 S I 94 Servce Dr
Belleville MI 48111
734 942-1060

(G-13309)
WILLIAMS CONCRETE INC
1350 Ford St (43537-1733)
PHONE.................................419 893-3251
Fax: 419 893-2929
Mark Williams, *President*
Terry Schaefer, *VP Finance*
Jason Wampler, *Manager*
EMP: 14
SALES: 2.8MM
SALES (corp-wide): 55.6MM **Privately Held**
WEB: www.kuhlman-corp.com
SIC: 3273 Ready-mixed concrete
PA: Kuhlman Corporation
1845 Indian Wood Cir
Maumee OH 43537
419 897-6000

(G-13310)
Y Z ENTERPRISES INC
Also Called: Almondina Brand Biscuits
1930 Indian Wood Cir # 100 (43537-4001)
PHONE.................................419 893-8777
Fax: 419 893-8825
Yuval N Zaliouk, *CEO*
Jack Hunter, *Vice Pres*
Tamar Markham, *Vice Pres*
Christopher Moody, *Vice Pres*
Susan M Zaliouk, *Treasurer*
EMP: 20
SQ FT: 12,500
SALES (est): 4.7MM **Privately Held**
WEB: www.zaliouk.com
SIC: 2052 Cookies

Mayfield Heights
Cuyahoga County

(G-13311)
BECK ALUMINUM ALLOYS LTD
6150 Parkland Blvd (44124-4103)
PHONE.................................216 861-4455
Edward G Cowan, *President*
Michael N Poling, *Vice Pres*
Bryan C Beck, *Treasurer*
Thomas Kish, *Manager*
Scott W Beck, *Admin Sec*
EMP: 63
SQ FT: 82,000
SALES (est): 21.3MM
SALES (corp-wide): 81.5MM **Privately Held**
WEB: www.beckalloys.com
SIC: 3341 Secondary nonferrous metals
PA: Beck Aluminum Corporation
6150 Parkland Blvd # 260
Mayfield Heights OH 44124
216 861-4455

(G-13312)
DATATRAK INTERNATIONAL INC
5900 Landerbrook Dr # 170 (44124-4085)
PHONE.................................440 443-0082
Fax: 440 442-3482
Alex Tabatabai, *Ch of Bd*
James R Ward, *President*
Marc J Shlaes, *Vice Pres*
Niki Kutac, *Project Mgr*
Osman Muhammad, *Project Mgr*
EMP: 47
SQ FT: 4,300
SALES: 9.9MM **Privately Held**
WEB: www.datatrak.net
SIC: 7374 7372 Data processing & preparation; prepackaged software

(G-13313)
FERRO CORPORATION (PA)
6060 Parkland Blvd # 250 (44124-4225)
PHONE.................................216 875-5600
Fax: 216 566-1464
Peter T Thomas, *Ch of Bd*

Mark H Duesenberg, *Vice Pres*
Benjamin J Schlater, *CFO*
◆ EMP: 90
SALES: 1.1B **Publicly Held**
WEB: www.ferro.com
SIC: 3479 2816 2851 3399 Coating of metals & formed products; color pigments; enamels; plastics base paints & varnishes; paste, metal; plastics materials & resins; carbohydrate plastics; proprietary drug products

(G-13314)
FERRO INTERNATIONAL SVCS INC
6060 Parkland Blvd # 250 (44124-4225)
PHONE.................................216 875-5600
EMP: 5
SALES (est): 382.4K
SALES (corp-wide): 1.1B **Publicly Held**
WEB: www.ferro.com
SIC: 2816 Color pigments
PA: Ferro Corporation
6060 Parkland Blvd # 250
Mayfield Heights OH 44124
216 875-5600

(G-13315)
GANEDEN BIOTECH INC
5800 Landerbrook Dr # 300 (44124-6509)
PHONE.................................440 229-5200
Andrew Lefkowitz, *CEO*
Abby Valencic, *Business Mgr*
Michael Bush, *Vice Pres*
David Kelier, *Vice Pres*
Xiali Liu, *Engineer*
EMP: 21
SQ FT: 8,000
SALES (est): 6.3MM **Privately Held**
SIC: 2099 Noodles, uncooked: packaged with other ingredients

(G-13316)
HANGER PRSTHETCS & ORTHO INC
6001 Landerhaven Dr Ste A (44124-4190)
PHONE.................................440 605-0232
Fax: 440 381-5179
EMP: 7
SALES (corp-wide): 460MM **Publicly Held**
SIC: 3842 Limbs, artificial
HQ: Hanger Prosthetics & Orthotics, Inc.
10910 Domain Dr Ste 300
Austin TX 78758
512 777-3800

(G-13317)
MATERION BRUSH INC (HQ)
6070 Parkland Blvd Ste 1 (44124-4191)
PHONE.................................216 486-4200
Fax: 216 481-2523
Tony Ong, *Managing Dir*
B R Harman, *Principal*
E A Levine, *Principal*
Michael C Hasychak, *Corp Secy*
Mark J Asany, *Vice Pres*
▲ EMP: 100 EST: 1931
SALES (est): 285.3MM
SALES (corp-wide): 969.2MM **Publicly Held**
WEB: www.brushwellman.com
SIC: 3351 3356 3264 3339 Copper & copper alloy sheet, strip, plate & products; strip, copper & copper alloy; plates, copper & copper alloy; tubing, copper & copper alloy; nickel & nickel alloy pipe, plates, sheets, etc.; porcelain parts for electrical devices, molded; beryllium metal; secondary precious metals; semiconductors & related devices
PA: Materion Corporation
6070 Parkland Blvd Ste 1
Mayfield Heights OH 44124
216 486-4200

(G-13318)
MATERION CORPORATION (PA)
6070 Parkland Blvd Ste 1 (44124-4191)
PHONE.................................216 486-4200
Richard J Hipple, *Ch of Bd*
Jugal Vijayvargiya, *President*
Gregory R Chemnitz, *Vice Pres*
Joseph P Kelley, *CFO*
◆ EMP: 150
SQ FT: 79,130

SALES: 969.2MM **Publicly Held**
SIC: 3339 3351 3356 3341 Beryllium metal; copper & copper alloy sheet, strip, plate & products; nickel & nickel alloy pipe, plates, sheets, etc.; secondary precious metals; semiconductors & related devices

(G-13319)
NATURAL BEAUTY HC EXPRESS
6809 Mayfield Rd Apt 550 (44124-2262)
PHONE.................................440 459-1776
Stacey Carlton, *Manager*
EMP: 7 EST: 2010
SALES (est): 210.3K **Privately Held**
SIC: 3999 Furniture, barber & beauty shop

(G-13320)
ONX HOLDINGS LLC (HQ)
5910 Landerbrook Dr # 250 (44124-6505)
PHONE.................................800 559-2497
Mike Cox, *President*
Robb Warwick, *Chairman*
Rosalind Lehman, *Exec VP*
Brian Pavlak, *Vice Pres*
Rick Rudolph, *Vice Pres*
EMP: 8 EST: 2011
SALES (est): 89.1MM
SALES (corp-wide): 3.8B **Privately Held**
SIC: 7379 7372 Computer related consulting services; business oriented computer software
PA: Marlin Equity Partners, Llc
338 Pier Ave
Hermosa Beach CA 90254
310 364-0100

(G-13321)
PRIEST SERVICES INC (PA)
1127 Linda St 5885 (44124)
P.O. Box 16307, Rocky River (44116-0307)
PHONE.................................440 333-1123
Fax: 440 333-0070
Howard E Priest, *Ch of Bd*
Homer S Taft, *President*
Donald W Farley, *Principal*
Carol Kuehnle, *Principal*
Judy Oneacre, *Principal*
EMP: 8 EST: 1950
SQ FT: 40,000
SALES (est): 2.6MM **Privately Held**
WEB: www.floorprep.com
SIC: 3275 2891 2851 Gypsum products; adhesives & sealants; paints & allied products

(G-13322)
TMW SYSTEMS INC (HQ)
6085 Parkland Blvd (44124-4184)
PHONE.................................216 831-6606
Fax: 216 831-3606
David Wangler, *President*
Rod Strata, *COO*
Timothy Leonard, *Exec VP*
David Mook, *Exec VP*
Jeffrey Ritter, *Exec VP*
EMP: 125
SQ FT: 32,500
SALES (est): 94.3MM
SALES (corp-wide): 2.3B **Publicly Held**
WEB: www.bulktrucker.com
SIC: 7372 Business oriented computer software
PA: Trimble Inc.
935 Stewart Dr
Sunnyvale CA 94085
408 481-8000

(G-13323)
TRUE NORTH ENERGY LLC
Also Called: Truenorth Energy
6411 Mayfield Rd (44124-3214)
PHONE.................................440 442-0060
EMP: 29
SALES (corp-wide): 281.5MM **Privately Held**
SIC: 5541 1382 Gasoline service stations; oil & gas exploration services
PA: True North Energy, Llc
10346 Brecksville Rd
Brecksville OH 44141
877 245-9336

Mayfield Village
Cuyahoga County

(G-13324)
PREFORMED LINE PRODUCTS CO (PA)
660 Beta Dr (44143-2398)
P.O. Box 91129, Cleveland (44101-3129)
PHONE.................................440 461-5200
Fax: 440 442-8816
Robert G Ruhlman, *Ch of Bd*
Bob Hazenfield, *President*
Jennifer Ruple, *Editor*
Jean Reilly, *COO*
Dennis F McKenna, *Exec VP*
EMP: 246 EST: 1947
SALES: 336.6MM **Publicly Held**
WEB: www.preformed.com
SIC: 3644 3661 Pole line hardware; fiber optics communications equipment

(G-13325)
PROFORMA ADVANTAGE
640 Som Center Rd (44143-2311)
PHONE.................................440 781-5255
David Littlefield, *President*
EMP: 5 EST: 2011
SALES (est): 373K **Privately Held**
SIC: 2759 Commercial printing

(G-13326)
QUALITY ELECTRODYNAMICS LLC
6655 Beta Dr Ste 100 (44143-2380)
PHONE.................................440 638-5106
Hiroyuki Fujita, *CEO*
Michael P Esposito Jr, *Chairman*
Albert B Ratner, *Chairman*
Nholas Castrilla, *Plant Mgr*
John Schellenberg, *Opers Staff*
EMP: 115
SALES (est): 24MM **Privately Held**
SIC: 3841 Surgical & medical instruments

(G-13327)
SURGICAL THEATER LLC (PA)
781 Beta Dr Ste A (44143-2360)
PHONE.................................216 452-2177
Mordechai Avifar, *CEO*
Guy Gary, *Vice Pres*
Guy Geri, *Vice Pres*
Jon Beltrone, *Sales Dir*
Alon Geri, *CTO*
▼ EMP: 9
SQ FT: 5,000
SALES (est): 4.3MM **Privately Held**
SIC: 3841 Surgical & medical instruments

Mc Arthur
Vinton County

(G-13328)
APPALACHIA WOOD INC (PA)
Also Called: McArthur Lumber and Post
31310 State Route 93 (45651-8924)
PHONE.................................740 596-2551
Fax: 740 596-2555
Richard Jakmas, *President*
Bob Marlowe, *Vice Pres*
Larry Murdoch, *Manager*
Colleen Thomas, *Manager*
EMP: 10 EST: 1951
SQ FT: 150,000
SALES: 3.6MM **Privately Held**
WEB: www.mcarthurlumberandpost.com
SIC: 2491 2421 5031 2411 Wood preserving; sawmills & planing mills, general; lumber: rough, dressed & finished; logging

(G-13329)
AUSTIN POWDER COMPANY
Also Called: Red Diamond Plant
430 Powder Plant Rd (45651)
P.O. Box 317 (45651-0317)
PHONE.................................740 596-5286
Fax: 740 596-4050
Curt Prater, *VP Opers*
Nick Rupert, *Purchasing*
John Capers, *Technical Mgr*

Maria Moreno, *Plant Engr*
Keith Mills, *Manager*
EMP: 225
SALES (corp-wide): 504.2MM **Privately Held**
SIC: 2892 Explosives
HQ: Austin Powder Company
25800 Science Park Dr # 300
Cleveland OH 44122
216 464-2400

(G-13330)
CROWNOVER LUMBER CO INC (PA)
501 Fairview Ave (45651)
P.O. Box 301 (45651-0301)
PHONE..............................740 596-5229
Fax: 740 596-3219
Lundy Crownover, *President*
Cheryl Crownover, *Personnel*
EMP: 60
SQ FT: 2,000
SALES: 9MM **Privately Held**
WEB: www.crownoverlumber.com
SIC: 2421 2426 Sawmills & planing mills, general; hardwood dimension & flooring mills

(G-13331)
ERICKSON-HUFF TOOL AND DIE
61698 Locker Plant Rd (45651-8622)
PHONE..............................740 596-4036
Fax: 740 596-0425
Frank Erickson, *President*
David Huff, *Vice Pres*
EMP: 5
SQ FT: 3,200
SALES (est): 200K **Privately Held**
WEB: www.ehtool.com
SIC: 3544 Industrial molds; special dies & tools

(G-13332)
NIMCO INC
Also Called: LP Propane Gas
33711 State Route 93 (45651-1280)
PHONE..............................740 596-4477
Alfred Robertson, *President*
EMP: 4 EST: 1987
SALES (est): 263.1K **Privately Held**
WEB: www.nimco.com
SIC: 1321 Propane (natural) production

(G-13333)
SUPERIOR HARDWOODS OF OHIO
62581 Us Highway 50 (45651-8414)
P.O. Box 320 (45651-0320)
PHONE..............................740 596-2561
Emmett Conway Jr, *President*
John Cline, *General Mgr*
Adam Conway, *Vice Pres*
Wes Davidson, *Purch Mgr*
EMP: 32 EST: 1979
SQ FT: 11,000
SALES (est): 3.5MM **Privately Held**
WEB: www.superior-hardwoods.com
SIC: 2421 2426 Sawmills & planing mills, general; hardwood dimension & flooring mills

---

Mc Clure
Henry County

(G-13334)
C DCAP MODEM LINE
232 S East St (43534-9900)
PHONE..............................419 748-7409
Barry Connly, *Principal*
EMP: 3
SALES (est): 154.9K **Privately Held**
SIC: 3661 Modems

(G-13335)
M & R REDI MIX INC
L207 County Road 1c (43534-9769)
P.O. Box 53038, Pettisville (43553-0038)
PHONE..............................419 748-8442
Scott Bergman, *Director*
EMP: 5
SQ FT: 2,400
SALES (corp-wide): 3MM **Privately Held**
SIC: 3273 Ready-mixed concrete

PA: M & R Redi Mix Inc
521 Commercial St
Pettisville OH 43553
419 445-7771

Mc Comb
Hancock County

(G-13336)
CONSOLIDATED BISCUIT COMPANY
312 Rader Rd (45858-9751)
PHONE..............................419 293-2911
Derrick Presley, *Manager*
EMP: 15
SQ FT: 136,806
SALES (est): 2MM **Privately Held**
WEB: www.consolidatedcreditservices.com
SIC: 2052 Biscuits, dry

(G-13337)
CRUSHPROOF TUBING CO
100 North St (45858)
P.O. Box 668 (45858-0668)
PHONE..............................419 293-2111
Fax: 419 293-2609
Vance M Kramer Jr, *President*
Todd Grayson, *Sales Mgr*
Barbara Farquharson, *Manager*
Richard Hollington, *Admin Sec*
EMP: 35 EST: 1950
SQ FT: 28,000
SALES: 5.7MM **Privately Held**
WEB: www.crushproof.com
SIC: 3069 Tubes, hard rubber

(G-13338)
HEARTHSIDE FOOD SOLUTIONS LLC
Also Called: Consolidated Biscuit Company
312 Rader Rd (45858-9751)
PHONE..............................419 293-2911
Brian Gower, *Project Mgr*
Bob Branham, *Safety Mgr*
Robert Avery, *Warehouse Mgr*
Jack Johnson, *Human Res Mgr*
Rudy Lomeli, *Human Res Mgr*
EMP: 2500
SALES (corp-wide): 2.3B **Privately Held**
SIC: 2052 Cookies; crackers, dry
PA: Hearthside Food Solutions, Llc
3250 Lacey Rd Ste 200
Downers Grove IL 60515
630 967-3600

(G-13339)
K & L READY MIX INC
5511 State Route 613 (45858-9345)
PHONE..............................419 293-2937
Fax: 419 293-1080
Gary Langhals, *Director*
EMP: 10
SALES (corp-wide): 8.4MM **Privately Held**
WEB: www.kandlreadymix.com
SIC: 3273 Ready-mixed concrete
PA: K & L Ready Mix Inc
10391 State Route 15
Ottawa OH 45875
419 523-4376

Mc Cutchenville
Wyandot County

(G-13340)
BUCKYS MACHINE AND FAB LTD
8376 S County Road 47 (44844-9620)
PHONE..............................419 981-5050
Daniel L Buckingham,
EMP: 7
SQ FT: 5,500
SALES: 200K **Privately Held**
SIC: 3599 Machine shop, jobbing & repair

Mc Dermott
Scioto County

(G-13341)
DALE LUTE LOGGING
2696 Henley Deemer Rd (45652-9061)
PHONE..............................740 352-1779
Dale F Lute, *Owner*
EMP: 5
SALES: 150K **Privately Held**
SIC: 4789 3537 Cargo loading & unloading services; platforms, stands, tables, pallets & similar equipment

(G-13342)
J M MEAT PROCESSING
360 S Zuefle Dr (45652-8938)
PHONE..............................740 259-3030
Jerry Montavon, *Administration*
EMP: 3
SALES (est): 178.3K **Privately Held**
SIC: 2011 Meat packing plants

(G-13343)
S & S PALLETT
1974 Henley Deemer Rd (45652-9063)
PHONE..............................740 372-0238
Kimberly Shope, *Owner*
EMP: 4
SALES: 500K **Privately Held**
SIC: 2448 Pallets, wood

(G-13344)
TAYLOR LUMBER WORLDWIDE INC
18253 State Route 73 (45652-8925)
P.O. Box 279 (45652-0279)
PHONE..............................740 259-6222
Fax: 740 259-6543
Edward Robbins, *President*
Greg Lute, *Vice Pres*
Art Robbins, *VP Opers*
Chris Bailey, *CFO*
Shery Spriggs, *CFO*
◆ **EMP:** 132 EST: 1882
SQ FT: 290
SALES (est): 26.1MM **Privately Held**
WEB: www.taylorlumberinc.com
SIC: 2421 Sawmills & planing mills, general

(G-13345)
WALLER BROTHERS STONE COMPANY
744 Mcdermott Rushtown Rd (45652)
PHONE..............................740 858-1948
Fax: 740 259-2308
Frank L Waller, *President*
Connie Scott, *Mng Dir*
Lowell M Shope, *Vice Pres*
David Ballengee, *Plant Mgr*
EMP: 45
SQ FT: 5,175
SALES: 6.5MM **Privately Held**
SIC: 3281 3821 2511 Stone, quarrying & processing of own stone products; building stone products; laboratory apparatus & furniture; wood household furniture

---

Mc Donald
Trumbull County

(G-13346)
AMROD BRIDGE & IRON LLC
105 Ohio Ave (44437-1900)
P.O. Box 749, Youngstown (44501-0749)
PHONE..............................330 530-8230
Jonathan M Dorma, *Mng Member*
Joe Telleni, *Manager*
Alex Benyo,
Brian Benyo,
EMP: 24
SALES (est): 5.1MM **Privately Held**
SIC: 3441 Fabricated structural metal

(G-13347)
MCDONALD STEEL CORPORATION
100 Ohio Ave (44437-1954)
P.O. Box 416 (44437-0416)
PHONE..............................330 530-9118
Fax: 330 530-8181
Tim Egnot, *President*
Daniel B Roth, *Chairman*
William K Clark, *VP Opers*
Joe Jenyk, *Engineer*
Michael J Havalo, *CFO*
▲ **EMP:** 105
SQ FT: 680,000
SALES: 21.1MM **Privately Held**
WEB: www.mcdonaldsteel.com
SIC: 3312 Bars & bar shapes, steel, hot-rolled

(G-13348)
STEEL & ALLOY UTILITY PDTS INC
110 Ohio Ave (44437-1900)
PHONE..............................330 530-2220
Nathan Gallo, *President*
Nick Gallo, *Vice Pres*
Nick Steelalloy, *Vice Pres*
▼ **EMP:** 50 EST: 1946
SQ FT: 60,000
SALES (est): 16.5MM **Privately Held**
SIC: 3569 3443 3444 3441 Assembly machines, non-metalworking; fabricated plate work (boiler shop); sheet metalwork; fabricated structural metal

---

McConnelsville
Morgan County

(G-13349)
EAGLES CLUB
407 W Riverside Dr (43756-1274)
PHONE..............................740 962-6490
John Rex, *President*
Jeck Ciurtis, *President*
Gary Woodard, *Admin Sec*
EMP: 8
SALES (est): 394.7K **Privately Held**
SIC: 2082 8641 Beer (alcoholic beverage); civic social & fraternal associations

(G-13350)
FOLLOW RIVER DESIGNS LLC
4330 E Hppole Ridge Rd Ne (43756-9505)
PHONE..............................614 325-9954
Karla Voyten, *Owner*
Jennifer Ponchak, *Owner*
EMP: 4 EST: 2006
SALES (est): 686.3K **Privately Held**
SIC: 3822 Auto controls regulating residntl & coml environmt & applncs

(G-13351)
HANN BOX WORKS
Also Called: Hann Construction
4678 N State Route 60 Nw (43756-9317)
P.O. Box 400, Malta (43758-0400)
PHONE..............................740 962-3752
Darl Hann, *Owner*
Mitchell Downing, *Manager*
EMP: 25
SALES (est): 1.2MM **Privately Held**
WEB: www.hannmfg.com
SIC: 2449 2448 Wood containers; wood pallets & skids

(G-13352)
HANN MANUFACTURING INC
4678 N State Route 60 Nw (43756-9317)
P.O. Box 400, Malta (43758-0400)
PHONE..............................740 962-3752
Fax: 740 962-4877
Darl Hann, *President*
Toni Eckert, *Financial Exec*
Cory Hann, *Sales Executive*
Michele Downing, *Office Mgr*
Andrea Spears, *Office Mgr*
EMP: 26
SQ FT: 30,000
SALES (est): 4.6MM **Privately Held**
SIC: 2531 2448 2441 Public building & related furniture; wood pallets & skids; nailed wood boxes & shook

---

GEOGRAPHIC

(G-13353)
MAHLE INDUSTRIES INCORPORATED
5130 N State Route 60 Nw (43756-9021)
PHONE..........................740 962-2040
John Carpenter, *Research*
John Feather, *Branch Mgr*
Chuck Furr, *Manager*
EMP: 115 **Privately Held**
WEB: www.glacier-vandervell.com
SIC: 3714 Camshafts, motor vehicle
HQ: Mahle Industries, Incorporated
  23030 Mahle Dr
  Farmington Hills MI 48335
  248 305-8200

(G-13354)
MIBA BEARINGS US LLC
5037 N State Route 60 Nw (43756-9218)
PHONE..........................740 962-4242
F Peter Mitterbauer, *Ch of Bd*
Ted Mc Mc Connell, *Plant Mgr*
Dave Ciacci, *Research*
Travis Dozer, *Engineer*
Joe Kovalcsik, *Design Engr*
▲ EMP: 300
SQ FT: 182,000
SALES (est): 100.4MM
SALES (corp-wide): 760.1MM **Privately Held**
SIC: 3799 Automobile trailer chassis
PA: Mitterbauer Beteiligungs-Aktienge-
  sellschaft.
  Dr. Mitterbauer-StraBe 3
  Laakirchen 4663
  761 325-41

(G-13355)
MIBA SINTER USA LLC
5045 N State Route 60 Nw (43756-9640)
PHONE..........................740 962-4242
Peter Chudoba, *Managing Dir*
Roman Bukovy, *QC Mgr*
Bruno Kalischko, *QC Mgr*
Marilyn Wampleman, *QC Mgr*
Shawn Light, *Engineer*
▲ EMP: 10
SALES: 27.2MM
SALES (corp-wide): 760.1MM **Privately Held**
SIC: 3312 Sinter, iron
PA: Mitterbauer Beteiligungs-Aktienge-
  sellschaft.
  Dr. Mitterbauer-StraBe 3
  Laakirchen 4663
  761 325-41

(G-13356)
MORGAN COUNTY PUBLISHING CO
Also Called: Morgan County Herald
89 W Main St (43756-1264)
P.O. Box 268 (43756-0268)
PHONE..........................740 962-3377
Fax: 740 962-6861
Jack Barnes, *President*
Mark Faulhaber, *Editor*
Don Keller, *Editor*
EMP: 9 EST: 1964
SQ FT: 5,000
SALES (est): 694.9K **Privately Held**
WEB: www.mchnews.com
SIC: 2711 Newspapers

Mechanicsburg
Champaign County

(G-13357)
INFINITY PLUS
7213 Brigner Rd (43044-9554)
PHONE..........................937 828-1350
Donald P Greider, *Owner*
EMP: 4 EST: 1969
SQ FT: 7,500
SALES: 50K **Privately Held**
SIC: 3433 3825 Solar heaters & collec-
  tors; test equipment for electronic & elec-
  trical circuits

(G-13358)
MECHANICSBURG SAND & GRAVEL
5734 State Route 4 (43044-9748)
PHONE..........................937 834-2606
Fax: 937 834-3951
James Cushman, *President*
Ruth Wibright, *Corp Secy*
EMP: 12 EST: 1957
SQ FT: 3,400
SALES (est): 1MM **Privately Held**
SIC: 1442 Construction sand mining;
  gravel mining

Mechanicstown
Carroll County

(G-13359)
KINGS WELDING AND FABG INC
5259 Bane Rd Ne (44651-9020)
PHONE..........................330 738-3592
Fax: 330 738-2008
Glen Richard King Sr, *President*
Diane Garrett, *Corp Secy*
Ray Wilson, *Project Mgr*
EMP: 45
SQ FT: 9,500
SALES (est): 6.3MM **Privately Held**
SIC: 3599 7692 3498 3441 Machine
  shop, jobbing & repair; welding repair;
  fabricated pipe & fittings; fabricated struc-
  tural metal

(G-13360)
MILLER & SON LOGGING
8521 Clover Rd Ne (44651-9041)
PHONE..........................330 738-2031
Ruth Miller, *Principal*
EMP: 3
SALES (est): 231.5K **Privately Held**
SIC: 2411 Logging

Medina
Medina County

(G-13361)
3M COMPANY
1030 Lake Rd (44256-2450)
PHONE..........................330 725-1444
Ty Silberhorn, *Business Mgr*
Maurice Jefferson, *Engineer*
Greg Peters, *Engineer*
Joe Petrie, *Sls & Mktg Exec*
Jillian Skaar, *Human Res Mgr*
EMP: 100
SALES (corp-wide): 30.1B **Publicly Held**
WEB: www.mmm.com
SIC: 2672 Coated & laminated paper
PA: 3m Company
  3m Center Bldg 22011w02
  Saint Paul MN 55144
  651 733-1110

(G-13362)
7D MARKETING INC
345 N State Rd (44256-1405)
PHONE..........................330 721-8822
Fax: 330 721-8833
Patrick Spoerndle, *President*
Greg Macek, *Manager*
EMP: 12
SQ FT: 60,000
SALES (est): 1.7MM **Privately Held**
SIC: 2541 2431 Store & office display
  cases & fixtures; millwork

(G-13363)
ADVANCED CHEM SOLUTIONS INC (PA)
1114 N Court St 196 (44256-1579)
PHONE..........................330 283-5157
Gerry Groudle, *President*
David Fidel, *Vice Pres*
EMP: 4 EST: 2001
SQ FT: 12,000
SALES: 3.5MM **Privately Held**
WEB:
www.advancedchemicalsolutions.com
SIC: 2899 Chemical preparations; metal
  treating compounds

(G-13364)
AI ROOT COMPANY (PA)
Also Called: West Liberty Commons
623 W Liberty St (44256-2225)
P.O. Box 706 (44258-0706)
PHONE..........................330 723-4359
Fax: 330 725-5624
John A Root, *Ch of Bd*
Dawnlee Sweitzer, *General Mgr*
Brad I Root, *Senior VP*
Kathy Summers, *Prdtn Mgr*
Jane Martin, *Purch Agent*
▲ EMP: 190
SQ FT: 182,000
SALES (est): 42.1MM **Privately Held**
WEB: www.beeculture.com
SIC: 3999 3085 Candles; plastics bottles

(G-13365)
AI ROOT COMPANY
Also Called: Root Candles
234 S State Rd (44256-2697)
PHONE..........................330 725-6677
Brad Root, *President*
Chris Novick, *IT/INT Sup*
EMP: 150
SALES (corp-wide): 42.1MM **Privately Held**
WEB: www.beeculture.com
SIC: 3999 3085 Candles; plastics bottles
PA: The A I Root Company
  623 W Liberty St
  Medina OH 44256
  330 723-4359

(G-13366)
ALCHEM CORPORATION
525 W Liberty St (44256-2223)
PHONE..........................330 725-2436
Fax: 330 722-2272
B George Buskin, *President*
Mary Djordjevic, *Engineer*
Ashley Thomas, *Engineer*
▲ EMP: 8
SQ FT: 28,000
SALES (est): 1.6MM **Privately Held**
WEB: www.alcheminc.com
SIC: 2819 Industrial inorganic chemicals

(G-13367)
ALLFASTENERS USA LLC (HQ)
959 Laker Rd (44256)
PHONE..........................440 232-6060
Russell Macgregor, *Purchasing*
Bruce Carmichael, *Sales Mgr*
Lincoln Cottle, *Mng Member*
Jason Cottle, *Manager*
Michael Strange,
▲ EMP: 15 EST: 2008
SALES (est): 4.8MM
SALES (corp-wide): 1.4MM **Privately Held**
SIC: 3429 Builders' hardware
PA: Allfasteners Corporation Pty Ltd
  78-84 Logistics St
  Keilor Park VIC 3042
  180 025-5349

(G-13368)
AMERI-CAL CORPORATION
1001 Lake Rd (44256-2760)
PHONE..........................330 725-7735
Fax: 330 725-3579
Jay D Vigneault, *President*
Cindy Stuart, *Manager*
Jacqueline Avigneault, *Manager*
Jay Vigneaul, *Info Tech Dir*
▲ EMP: 13
SQ FT: 15,000
SALES (est): 4MM **Privately Held**
WEB: www.americalcorp.com
SIC: 2672 Adhesive papers, labels or
  tapes: from purchased material; tape,
  pressure sensitive: made from purchased
  materials

(G-13369)
AMERICAN METAL CHEMICAL CORP (PA)
Also Called: Amcor
835 W Smith Rd (44256-2424)
PHONE..........................330 725-4501
Fax: 216 723-0487
Erin Fauber, *President*
Margaret Fauber, *Exec VP*
Ted Fauber, *Treasurer*

Kathy Dany, *Controller*
Brad Ptack, *Sales Engr*
◆ EMP: 37
SQ FT: 60,000
SALES (est): 14.3MM **Privately Held**
SIC: 2899 Fluxes: brazing, soldering, gal-
  vanizing & welding

(G-13370)
ANCHOR LAMINA AMERICA INC
445 W Liberty St (44256-2273)
PHONE..........................330 952-1595
EMP: 31
SALES (corp-wide): 2B **Privately Held**
SIC: 3545 Machine tool accessories
HQ: Anchor Lamina America, Inc.
  39830 Grand River Ave B-2
  Novi MI 48375
  248 489-9122

(G-13371)
APEX SPECIALTY CO INC
620 E Smith Rd Ste E7 (44256-3650)
PHONE..........................330 725-6663
David Shmidtke, *President*
EMP: 7 EST: 1956
SQ FT: 3,000
SALES (est): 774.2K **Privately Held**
SIC: 3599 Machine shop, jobbing & repair

(G-13372)
APPC PLUMBING CO
3247 Pearl Rd (44256-7645)
PHONE..........................330 722-7754
Eric Scroeter,
EMP: 5
SALES (est): 527.8K **Privately Held**
SIC: 3241 Masonry cement

(G-13373)
ARCHITECTURAL DAYLIGHTING LLC
Also Called: Archday
879 S Progress Dr Ste C (44256-3926)
PHONE..........................330 460-5000
Ken Palak, *General Mgr*
Victoria Tifft, *Mng Member*
EMP: 5
SQ FT: 8,000
SALES (est): 510K **Privately Held**
SIC: 3444 Skylights, sheet metal

(G-13374)
AXON MEDICAL LLC
1484 Medina Rd Ste 117 (44256-5378)
Drawer 784 Medina (44256)
PHONE..........................216 276-0262
Christopher Hardin, *Principal*
Joel Hawley, *Principal*
EMP: 20
SALES: 1.3MM **Privately Held**
SIC: 3841 3842 5047 Surgical & medical
  instruments; surgical appliances & sup-
  plies; abdominal supporters, braces &
  trusses; braces, orthopedic; instruments,
  surgical & medical

(G-13375)
B & B BINDERY INC
4381 Pine Lake Dr (44256-7641)
PHONE..........................330 722-5430
EMP: 6
SQ FT: 8,000
SALES: 500K **Privately Held**
SIC: 2789 Bookbinding

(G-13376)
B C COMPOSITES CORPORATION
777 W Smith Rd (44256-3501)
PHONE..........................330 262-3070
Fax: 330 722-4883
Mark McConnell, *President*
EMP: 11
SQ FT: 50,000
SALES: 1.3MM
SALES (corp-wide): 8.4MM **Privately Held**
WEB: www.bccomposites.com
SIC: 3499 Metal ladders
PA: Bc Investment Corporation
  1505 E Bowman St
  Wooster OH 44691
  330 262-3070

(G-13377)
BIL-JAC FOODS INC (PA)
3337 Medina Rd (44256-9631)
PHONE....................................330 722-7888
Fax: 330 722-7999
Robert Kelly, *President*
Bonnie Phillip, *General Mgr*
William Kelly, *Chairman*
James Kelly, *Vice Pres*
Lynn Bingham, *Engineer*
EMP: 25
SQ FT: 6,000
SALES (est): 22.3MM **Privately Held**
WEB: www.biljac.com
SIC: 2047 Dog food; cat food

(G-13378)
BLEACHTECH LLC
4231 Weymouth Rd (44256-7203)
PHONE....................................330 421-2134
Timothy Maegly,
Richard Immerman,
EMP: 65
SALES (est): 666.1K **Privately Held**
SIC: 3589 Sewage & water treatment
equipment

(G-13379)
BOND CHEMICALS INC
1154 W Smith Rd (44256-2443)
PHONE....................................330 725-5935
Fax: 330 723-1333
Thomas Goslee Jr, *President*
Carol Goslee, *Vice Pres*
Evan Goslee, *Sales Engr*
EMP: 16 EST: 1960
SQ FT: 24,000
SALES (est): 2.7MM **Privately Held**
WEB: www.bondchemicals.com
SIC: 2899 2819 Water treating com-
pounds; corrosion preventive lubricant;
rust resisting compounds; industrial inor-
ganic chemicals

(G-13380)
BONDED CHEMICALS INC
909 W Smith Rd (44256-2446)
PHONE....................................330 723-4570
Rich Ferrebee, *Warehouse Mgr*
EMP: 5
SALES (corp-wide): 122.2MM **Privately
Held**
SIC: 2869 Laboratory chemicals, organic
HQ: Bonded Chemicals, Inc.
2645 Charter St
Columbus OH 43228
614 777-9240

(G-13381)
**BPR-RICO ELC TRCK SPCALIST
INC**
691 W Liberty St (44256-2225)
PHONE....................................330 723-4050
Dave Mueller, *President*
EMP: 75
SALES (est): 6.8MM
SALES (corp-wide): 36.8MM **Privately
Held**
WEB: www.bpr-rico.com
SIC: 3537 Lift trucks, industrial: fork, plat-
form, straddle, etc.
PA: Bpr-Rico Equipment, Inc.
691 W Liberty St
Medina OH 44256
330 723-4050

(G-13382)
**BPR-RICO MANUFACTURING
INC**
Also Called: Bpr/Rico
691 W Liberty St (44256-2225)
PHONE....................................330 723-4050
Dave Mueller, *CEO*
Steve Shuck, *President*
Sandy Mueller, *Corp Secy*
Kent Stelmasczuk, *CFO*
▲ EMP: 100
SQ FT: 175,000
SALES: 30MM
SALES (corp-wide): 36.8MM **Privately
Held**
SIC: 3537 Lift trucks, industrial: fork, plat-
form, straddle, etc.

PA: Bpr-Rico Equipment, Inc.
691 W Liberty St
Medina OH 44256
330 723-4050

(G-13383)
**BUCKBUILT MANUFACTURING
CO**
7007 Wooster Pike (44256-8861)
PHONE....................................330 764-3363
Dana Buchholzer, *President*
EMP: 18
SALES (est): 729.7K **Privately Held**
SIC: 3999 Manufacturing industries

(G-13384)
BUG-BARRIER SCREEN CORP
Also Called: Arch Angle Window and Door
6979 Wooster Pike (44256-8860)
PHONE....................................330 723-2551
Fax: 330 723-2439
Curtis D Weaver, *President*
Sharren A Weaver, *Vice Pres*
EMP: 6
SQ FT: 2,700
SALES: 340K **Privately Held**
WEB: www.bugbarrierscreen.com
SIC: 3442 3714 3354 Screens, window,
metal; winter fronts, motor vehicle; alu-
minum extruded products

(G-13385)
**CARLISLE BRAKE & FRICTION
INC**
920 Lake Rd (44256-2453)
PHONE....................................330 725-4941
Chris Koch, *President*
Justine Moen, *Buyer*
Justin Bracey, *Engineer*
Michelle Cope, *Engineer*
Joshua Cordova, *Engineer*
EMP: 46
SALES (corp-wide): 3.6B **Publicly Held**
SIC: 3751 Brakes, friction clutch & other:
bicycle
HQ: Carlisle Brake & Friction, Inc.
6180 Cochran Rd
Solon OH 44139
440 528-4000

(G-13386)
**CHICK MASTER INCUBATOR
COMPANY (PA)**
945 Lafayette Rd (44256-3510)
P.O. Box 704 (44258-0704)
PHONE....................................330 722-5591
Fax: 330 723-0233
Robert Holzer, *CEO*
Brian Keiser, *COO*
Chad Daniels, *Vice Pres*
Michael Hurd, *Vice Pres*
Alan Shandler, *Vice Pres*
◆ EMP: 118
SQ FT: 100,000
SALES (est): 24.9MM **Privately Held**
WEB: www.chickmaster.com
SIC: 3523 1711 Incubators & brooders,
farm; plumbing, heating, air-conditioning
contractors

(G-13387)
CHRONICLE TELEGRAM
885 W Liberty St (44256-1312)
PHONE....................................330 725-4166
George Hudnutt, *Owner*
EMP: 3
SALES (est): 116.4K **Privately Held**
SIC: 2711 Newspapers

(G-13388)
CLASSIC EVOLUTION INC
910 Lake Rd (44256-2453)
P.O. Box 86, Brunswick (44212-0086)
PHONE....................................216 440-0559
Brian Ridzy, *President*
Shawn Ritchie, *Vice Pres*
EMP: 3 EST: 2015
SQ FT: 60,000
SALES (est): 216.9K **Privately Held**
SIC: 3471 Plating & polishing

(G-13389)
CLETRONICS INC
2262 Port Centre Dr (44256-5994)
PHONE....................................330 239-2002

Fax: 330 722-3040
David Sands, *President*
Steve Garfield, *Vice Pres*
Ed Wurgler, *Prdtn Mgr*
Vasu Navalpakkam, *Chief Engr*
▼ EMP: 19
SQ FT: 12,500
SALES: 2.4MM **Privately Held**
WEB: www.cletronics.com
SIC: 3677 Transformers power supply,
electronic type

(G-13390)
**COMMERCIAL GRINDING
SERVICES**
Also Called: Cgs
1155 Industrial Pkwy # 1 (44256-2492)
P.O. Box 1121 (44258-1121)
PHONE....................................330 273-5040
Fax: 216 241-6129
Kevin T Butas, *President*
Steve Bruns, *General Mgr*
Joseph Crookston, *Sales Staff*
Renzo Canellia, *Manager*
EMP: 20
SQ FT: 3,600
SALES (est): 1.4MM **Privately Held**
WEB: www.cgstool.com
SIC: 7699 3541 3545 Knife, saw & tool
sharpening & repair; machine tools, metal
cutting type; end mills

(G-13391)
CONCORD DESIGN INC
3382 S Weymouth Rd (44256-9227)
PHONE....................................330 722-5133
Gerald Smith, *President*
Dina Smith, *Treasurer*
EMP: 3
SQ FT: 800
SALES: 33.2K **Privately Held**
SIC: 3544 Special dies & tools; jigs & fix-
tures

(G-13392)
CONTROLS INC
5204 Portside Dr (44256-5966)
P.O. Box 368, Sharon Center (44274-0368)
PHONE....................................330 239-4345
Fax: 330 239-2845
Robert Cowen, *President*
Scott Izzo, *Vice Pres*
Becky McNamara, *Manager*
EMP: 25
SALES: 1.8MM **Privately Held**
WEB: www.controlsinc.com
SIC: 3625 7389 1731 Control equipment,
electric; industrial controls: push button,
selector switches, pilot; design services;
electronic controls installation

(G-13393)
CONVIBER INC
Also Called: Heintz Conveying Belt Service
1066 Industrial Pkwy (44256-2449)
PHONE....................................330 723-6006
Rich Serrena, *Manager*
EMP: 10
SALES (corp-wide): 15.3MM **Privately
Held**
WEB: www.conviber.com
SIC: 7699 3559 Rubber product repair;
rubber working machinery, including tires
PA: Conviber, Inc.
644 Garfield St
Springdale PA 15144
724 274-6300

(G-13394)
**CORRPRO COMPANIES INC
(DH)**
1055 W Smith Rd (44256-2444)
PHONE....................................330 723-5082
David H Kroon, *President*
Gehring George, *Exec VP*
Dorwin Hawn, *Exec VP*
Grady Joiner, *Exec VP*
Barry W Schadeck, *Exec VP*
▼ EMP: 50
SQ FT: 8,000
SALES (est): 169.4MM
SALES (corp-wide): 1.2B **Publicly Held**
WEB: www.corrpro.com
SIC: 3699 8711 Electrical equipment &
supplies; engineering services

HQ: Insituform Technologies, Llc
17988 Edison Ave
Chesterfield MO 63005
636 530-8000

(G-13395)
CORRPRO COMPANIES INC
Also Called: Corrpro Waterworks
1055 W Smith Rd (44256-2444)
PHONE....................................330 725-6681
Fax: 330 722-7654
Angie Pedraza, *Sales Executive*
George Giannakos, *Branch Mgr*
EMP: 15
SALES (corp-wide): 1.2B **Publicly Held**
WEB: www.corrpro.com
SIC: 3699 8711 Electrical equipment &
supplies; engineering services
HQ: Corrpro Companies, Inc.
1055 W Smith Rd
Medina OH 44256
330 723-5082

(G-13396)
CORRPRO COMPANIES INTL INC
1055 W Smith Rd (44256-2444)
PHONE....................................330 723-5082
EMP: 4 EST: 2013
SALES (est): 316.5K
SALES (corp-wide): 1.2B **Publicly Held**
SIC: 3699 Electrical equipment & supplies
HQ: Insituform Technologies, Llc
17988 Edison Ave
Chesterfield MO 63005
636 530-8000

(G-13397)
COUNTY OF MEDINA
Also Called: Medina County Recorders
144 N Broadway St Ste 117 (44256-1928)
PHONE....................................330 723-3641
Colleen Swedyk, *Principal*
EMP: 13 **Privately Held**
WEB: www.mcbmrdd.org
SIC: 3825 Recorders, oscillographic
PA: County Of Medina
144 N Brdwy St Rm 201
Medina OH 44256
330 722-9208

(G-13398)
CREATIVE CONCEPTS
620 E Smith Rd Ste W1 (44256-3648)
PHONE....................................216 513-6463
Ryan Fairbanks, *Owner*
EMP: 3
SALES (est): 277.9K **Privately Held**
SIC: 3444 2426 Concrete forms, sheet
metal; dimension, hardwood

(G-13399)
D O TECHNOLOGIES INC
667 Lafayette Rd (44256-3700)
PHONE....................................330 725-4561
Fax: 330 725-1601
Douglas R Piskac, *President*
Douglas Piskac, *President*
EMP: 10
SQ FT: 14,700
SALES (est): 800K **Privately Held**
SIC: 3599 Machine shop, jobbing & repair

(G-13400)
DAIRY FARMERS AMERICA INC
1035 Medina Rd Ste 300 (44256-5398)
PHONE....................................330 670-7800
Glenn Wallace, *Chief*
Sam Stone, *Exec VP*
EMP: 30
SALES (corp-wide): 13.8B **Privately Held**
WEB: www.dfamilk.com
SIC: 2022 2026 2021 0211 Cheese, nat-
ural & processed; fluid milk; creamery
butter; beef cattle feedlots
PA: Dairy Farmers Of America, Inc.
10220 N Ambassador Dr
Kansas City MO 64153
816 801-6455

(G-13401)
DEBANDALE PRINTING INC
Also Called: Minuteman Press
2785 Sharon Copley Rd (44256-9718)
PHONE....................................330 725-5122
Dale Heufner, *President*
EMP: 4

SQ FT: 1,100
SALES (est): 300K **Privately Held**
SIC: 2752 2759 2791 2789 Commercial printing, lithographic; screen printing; engraving; typesetting; bookbinding & related work

(G-13402)
DIE GUYS INC
5238 Portside Dr (44256-5966)
PHONE..............................330 948-1984
Fax: 330 239-4897
John Andreae, *President*
Ron Erhard, *Prdtn Mgr*
Jeri Potts, *Treasurer*
Luke Darling, *Admin Sec*
EMP: 24 **EST:** 2000
SQ FT: 14,000
SALES: 2.7MM **Privately Held**
WEB: www.dieguys.com
SIC: 3544 Dies, steel rule

(G-13403)
DIVERSIFIED TECHNOLOGY INC
650 W Smith Rd Ste 10 (44256-3717)
PHONE..............................330 722-4995
Fax: 330 722-0549
William F Musal, *President*
EMP: 3
SQ FT: 5,500
SALES: 400K **Privately Held**
SIC: 2992 Lubricating oils

(G-13404)
DRS MILBURN-MEDINA INC
Also Called: Milburn Eye Center
409 N Court St (44256-1869)
PHONE..............................330 725-4680
T M Milburn, *President*
Timothy Michael Milburn, *President*
EMP: 9
SALES (est): 1MM **Privately Held**
SIC: 3641 Electrotherapeutic lamp units

(G-13405)
ENI USA R & M CO INC
Also Called: ENI USA R & M CO. INC.
740 S Progress Dr (44256-1368)
PHONE..............................330 723-6457
Joe Krisky, *Vice Pres*
EMP: 10
SQ FT: 6,000
SALES (corp-wide): 36.1B **Privately Held**
WEB: www.americanagip.com
SIC: 2992 5172 Lubricating oils & greases; petroleum products
HQ: Eni Usa R & M Co. Inc.
485 Madison Av Fl 6
New York NY 10022
646 264-2100

(G-13406)
ERIE COPPER WORKS INC
230 N State Rd (44256-1404)
P.O. Box 309 (44258-0309)
PHONE..............................330 725-5590
Fax: 330 723-0267
David A Surgeon, *President*
David Berg, *Vice Pres*
James Tober, *VP Opers*
Pam Cunningham, *Manager*
EMP: 4
SQ FT: 2,200
SALES (est): 736.1K **Privately Held**
SIC: 3643 Current-carrying wiring devices

(G-13407)
ERODETECH INC
4986 Gateway Dr (44256-8637)
P.O. Box 1643 (44258-1643)
PHONE..............................330 725-9181
Fred Wolk, *President*
EMP: 6
SALES (est): 298.4K **Privately Held**
SIC: 1389 Testing, measuring, surveying & analysis services

(G-13408)
FACULTATIEVE TECH AMERICAS INC
Also Called: Incinerator Specialists
940 Lake Rd (44256-2453)
PHONE..............................330 723-6339
Fax: 330 723-5841
Henri Keizer, *CEO*
▲ **EMP:** 27

SALES (est): 6.5MM **Privately Held**
SIC: 3567 Fuel-fired furnaces & ovens; incinerators, metal: domestic or commercial

(G-13409)
FALCON INDUSTRIES INC (PA)
180 Commerce Dr (44256-3949)
PHONE..............................330 723-0099
Fax: 330 723-5399
J Don Fitzgerald, *CEO*
Steve Sogor, *Plant Mgr*
Brian Fitzgerald, *Director*
EMP: 27
SQ FT: 24,000
SALES (est): 11.5MM **Privately Held**
WEB: www.falconindustries.com
SIC: 3541 3535 3444 3423 Machine tools, metal cutting type; conveyors & conveying equipment; sheet metalwork; hand & edge tools

(G-13410)
FIRE-DEX LLC
780 S Progress Dr (44256-1368)
PHONE..............................330 723-0000
Brett Jaffe, *CEO*
Joe Luic, *Buyer*
Dave Liana, *Finance Dir*
Dee Ocallaghan, *Accounting Mgr*
Tony Moore, *Regl Sales Mgr*
▲ **EMP:** 100
SQ FT: 28,000
SALES (est): 26.7MM **Privately Held**
WEB: www.firedex.com
SIC: 2389 Uniforms & vestments

(G-13411)
FORGING EQP SOLUTIONS INC
1486 Medina Rd Ste 209 (44256-5384)
PHONE..............................330 239-2222
Jeff Jones, *President*
Dianne Koscianski, *Admin Asst*
EMP: 4
SQ FT: 1,000
SALES (est): 652K **Privately Held**
SIC: 3462 Iron & steel forgings

(G-13412)
FOUNDATIONS WORLDWIDE INC (PA)
5216 Portside Dr (44256-5966)
PHONE..............................330 722-5033
Joseph A Lawlor, *President*
Chris Krauth, *Vice Pres*
Lisa Vanadia, *Vice Pres*
Mandy Balyer, *QA Dir*
Alan Lytle, *Engineer*
◆ **EMP:** 33
SQ FT: 60,000
SALES: 18MM **Privately Held**
WEB: www.shamrock-industries.com
SIC: 5999 2511 3944 Children's furniture; children's wood furniture; strollers, baby (vehicle); walkers, baby (vehicle); structural toy sets; scooters, children's

(G-13413)
FRICTION PRODUCTS CO
Also Called: Hawk Performance
920 Lake Rd (44256-2453)
PHONE..............................330 725-4941
Fax: 330 725-1643
Chris Disantis, *CEO*
Ronald E Weinberg, *Chairman*
Don Brown, *Vice Pres*
Thomas A Gilbride, *Vice Pres*
Nick Aloi, *Engineer*
◆ **EMP:** 266
SQ FT: 176,000
SALES (est): 106.7MM
SALES (corp-wide): 3.6B **Publicly Held**
WEB: www.hawkperformance.com
SIC: 3728 3714 Aircraft landing assemblies & brakes; motor vehicle brake systems & parts
HQ: Carlisle Brake & Friction, Inc.
6180 Cochran Rd
Solon OH 44139
440 528-4000

(G-13414)
GASKO FABRICATED PRODUCTS LLC (HQ)
4049 Ridge Rd (44256-8618)
PHONE..............................330 239-1781
Fax: 330 239-1768

Randy Guernsey, *President*
Gregory Nemecek, *President*
Ed Bosken, *Vice Pres*
Susan Sponsler, *Director*
EMP: 32
SQ FT: 12,000
SALES: 6.5MM
SALES (corp-wide): 8.5MM **Privately Held**
WEB: www.gasko.com
SIC: 3053 Gaskets & sealing devices; gaskets, all materials
PA: Cornerstone Industrial Holdings Inc
100 Park Pl
Chagrin Falls OH 44022
440 893-9144

(G-13415)
GAZETTE EDITORIAL DEPARTMENT
885 W Liberty St (44256-1396)
PHONE..............................330 725-6220
George Hudnutt, *Owner*
Barbara Webb, *Manager*
EMP: 4 **EST:** 1832
SALES (est): 165.4K **Privately Held**
SIC: 2711 Newspapers

(G-13416)
GENERAL PACKAGING PRODUCTS
1030 Industrial Pkwy (44256-2449)
PHONE..............................330 725-7731
Fax: 330 725-0093
David L Shafer, *President*
Robert C Berg, *Vice Pres*
Judy Thomas, *Office Mgr*
EMP: 24 **EST:** 1969
SQ FT: 55,000
SALES: 5MM **Privately Held**
WEB: www.genpkg.com
SIC: 2653 Boxes, corrugated: made from purchased materials; boxes, solid fiber: made from purchased materials

(G-13417)
GLAXOSMITHKLINE LLC
6250 Highland Meadows Dr (44256-6528)
PHONE..............................330 241-4447
EMP: 26
SALES (corp-wide): 34.3B **Privately Held**
SIC: 2834 Pharmaceutical preparations
HQ: Glaxosmithkline Llc
5 Crescent Dr
Philadelphia PA 19112
215 751-4000

(G-13418)
GLORIOUS CUPCAKES
3132 Sterling Lake Dr (44256-6241)
PHONE..............................216 544-2325
EMP: 4 **EST:** 2014
SALES (est): 156.7K **Privately Held**
SIC: 2051 Bread, cake & related products

(G-13419)
HAWTHORNE BOLT WORKS CORP
355 Lake Rd Ste A (44256-3557)
PHONE..............................330 723-0555
Nick Gentile, *President*
EMP: 4
SALES (est): 528.4K **Privately Held**
SIC: 3429 Manufactured hardware (general)

(G-13420)
HEINTZ MANUFACTURERS INC
Also Called: Conviber
1066 Industrial Pkwy (44256-2449)
P.O. Box 301, Springdale PA (15144-0301)
PHONE..............................724 274-6300
Fax: 330 723-7101
Frank Pucciarelli, *President*
Kenneth Gangl, *President*
Kirk Gangl, *Vice Pres*
◆ **EMP:** 3 **EST:** 1918
SALES (est): 395.5K **Privately Held**
SIC: 7699 3559 Rubber product repair; rubber working machinery, including tires

(G-13421)
HERAEUS ELECTRO-NITE CO LLC
585 N State Rd (44256-1400)
PHONE..............................330 725-1419
EMP: 6 **Privately Held**
WEB: www.electro-nite.com
SIC: 3829 3674 Thermocouples; semiconductors & related devices
HQ: Heraeus Electro-Nite Co., Llc
541 S Industrial Dr
Hartland WI 53029
215 944-9000

(G-13422)
HOWDEN NORTH AMERICA INC
935 Heritage Dr (44256-2404)
PHONE..............................330 721-7374
Edward Biesiada, *Branch Mgr*
EMP: 22
SALES (corp-wide): 3.6B **Publicly Held**
SIC: 3441 Fabricated structural metal
HQ: Howden North America Inc.
2475 George Urban Blvd # 120
Depew NY 14043
803 741-2700

(G-13423)
HOWDEN NORTH AMERICA INC
411 Independence Dr (44256-2406)
PHONE..............................330 723-0492
Fax: 330 723-7727
Cal Robertson, *Vice Pres*
Scott Burdett, *Manager*
EMP: 30
SQ FT: 2,662
SALES (corp-wide): 3.6B **Publicly Held**
SIC: 3564 Blowing fans: industrial or commercial
HQ: Howden North America Inc.
2475 George Urban Blvd # 120
Depew NY 14043
803 741-2700

(G-13424)
HUDSON PRINTING OF MEDINA LLC
2425 Medina Rd Ste 206 (44256-5381)
PHONE..............................330 591-4800
Steve Vojvodich, *Principal*
Byron Nemeth, *Master*
EMP: 4
SALES (est): 250K **Privately Held**
SIC: 2752 Commercial printing, lithographic

(G-13425)
ICANDI GRAPHICS LLC
650 W Smith Rd Ste 3 (44256-2397)
PHONE..............................330 723-8337
Fax: 330 241-5610
Benjamin D Schmid, *Owner*
EMP: 4
SALES (est): 458.6K **Privately Held**
SIC: 2752 Commercial printing, lithographic

(G-13426)
INNOVATION SALES LLC
784 Medina Rd Ste 103 (44256-9634)
PHONE..............................330 239-0400
Frank Mastromatteo, *Opers Staff*
Pamela Blackburn, *Manager*
EMP: 7
SALES (est): 407.4K **Privately Held**
SIC: 3291 Abrasive metal & steel products

(G-13427)
INTERACTIVE ENGINEERING CORP
884 Medina Rd (44256-9615)
PHONE..............................330 239-6888
Ming Zhang, *President*
EMP: 25 **EST:** 1995
SQ FT: 200,000
SALES (est): 3.3MM **Privately Held**
SIC: 8748 3672 Systems analysis & engineering consulting services; printed circuit boards

(G-13428)
J R GOSLEE CO
1154 W Smith Rd (44256-2443)
PHONE..............................330 723-4904
Carol Goslee, *President*

▲ = Import ▼=Export
◆ =Import/Export

Tom Goslee Jr, *Vice Pres*
EMP: 10 **EST:** 1928
SQ FT: 1,164
SALES (est): 674.1K **Privately Held**
SIC: 3295 Clay, ground or otherwise treated

(G-13429)
JACOBSON MFG LLC (DH)
Also Called: Minuteman Distribution
941 Lake Rd 955 (44256-2453)
PHONE..................................330 725-8853
Robert S Kaminski, *CEO*
Matt Kerschner, *Principal*
David Kaminski, *COO*
Mary Spitzer, *Store Mgr*
Amro Hassan, *Prdtn Mgr*
◆ **EMP:** 146
SALES (est): 57.6MM **Privately Held**
WEB: www.jacobsonmfg.com
SIC: 3452 Bolts, nuts, rivets & washers
HQ: Continental/Midland, Llc
    24000 S Western Ave
    Park Forest IL 60466
    708 747-1200

(G-13430)
JROLL LLC
Also Called: Sushi On The Roll
985 Boardman Aly (44256-1599)
PHONE..................................330 661-0600
Kenneth Oppenheimer,
Jon Roller,
EMP: 12
SQ FT: 3,000
SALES: 990K **Privately Held**
SIC: 2048 5146 Fish food; fish & seafoods

(G-13431)
KATHYS KRAFTS AND KOLLECTIBLES
3303 Hamilton Rd (44256-7633)
PHONE..................................423 787-3709
Kathy Hayes, *Principal*
EMP: 3 **EST:** 2013
SALES (est): 164.4K **Privately Held**
SIC: 2022 Processed cheese

(G-13432)
KELLEY BROTHERS ROOFING INC
6867 Wooster Pike (44256-8859)
PHONE..................................330 273-3700
Mark Overholt, *President*
Sherry Overholt, *Vice Pres*
Mark Scott, *Engineer*
EMP: 15
SQ FT: 12,000
SALES (est): 1.5MM **Privately Held**
WEB: www.tigergeneral.com
SIC: 5012 7538 3533 5082 Commercial vehicles; general automotive repair shops; drill rigs; oil field equipment

(G-13433)
KELLY FOODS CORPORATION (PA)
3337 Medina Rd (44256-9631)
PHONE..................................330 722-8855
Robert Kelly, *President*
Jim Kelly, *Corp Secy*
Joann Sanford, *CFO*
▼ **EMP:** 22
SALES (est): 14.9MM **Privately Held**
WEB: www.kellyfoodscorp.com
SIC: 2048 2047 Dry pet food (except dog & cat); dog & cat food

(G-13434)
KOKSING MATERIAL INC
310 N State Rd (44256-1406)
PHONE..................................330 721-2775
Fax: 330 721-0824
Steve Easterday, *Principal*
Bill Reel, *Manager*
EMP: 4
SALES (est): 332.9K **Privately Held**
SIC: 2951 Asphalt paving mixtures & blocks

(G-13435)
KURTS AUTO PARTS LLC
4093 Watercourse Dr (44256-7895)
PHONE..................................330 723-0166
Fax: 330 769-5900

Kurt Morse, *President*
EMP: 3
SALES (est): 240K **Privately Held**
SIC: 3714 Motor vehicle parts & accessories

(G-13436)
LOUIS LEASING LLC
950 Lake Rd (44256-2453)
PHONE..................................440 243-3810
Louis Palombo,
▲ **EMP:** 25
SQ FT: 20,000
SALES (est): 3.7MM **Privately Held**
SIC: 3549 Metalworking machinery

(G-13437)
LSQ MANUFACTURING INC
1140 Industrial Pkwy (44256-2486)
PHONE..................................330 725-4905
Richard L Rauckhorst III, *President*
Richard L Rauckhorst III, *President*
Judith L Coffman, *Vice Pres*
Marianne Clevidence, *Manager*
EMP: 10 **EST:** 1946
SQ FT: 8,000
SALES: 1MM **Privately Held**
WEB: www.arthurproducts.com
SIC: 3494 3563 3432 Valves & pipe fittings; air & gas compressors; plumbing fixture fittings & trim

(G-13438)
LUXX ULTRA-TECH INC
7334 Lonesome Pine Trl (44256-7133)
PHONE..................................330 483-6051
Mary Matejka, *President*
Rudolph Matejka, *Principal*
Cathy Johnson, *Vice Pres*
EMP: 5
SQ FT: 5,500
SALES: 1.5MM **Privately Held**
SIC: 3069 Molded rubber products

(G-13439)
MANSFIELD PAINT CO INC
525 W Liberty St (44256-2223)
PHONE..................................330 725-2436
Fax: 330 725-8354
George Bufkin, *CEO*
Tom Tuckerman, *Manager*
EMP: 12
SQ FT: 24,000
SALES (est): 2.4MM **Privately Held**
SIC: 2851 Paints: oil or alkyd vehicle or water thinned; lacquer: bases, dopes, thinner; enamels

(G-13440)
MATRIX PLASTICS CO INC
171 Granger Rd Unit 156 (44256-7308)
PHONE..................................330 666-7730
Joan Mann, *Principal*
EMP: 5
SALES (est): 602K **Privately Held**
SIC: 3089 Plastics products

(G-13441)
MCJAK CANDY COMPANY LLC
1087 Branch Rd (44256-8900)
PHONE..................................330 722-3531
Fax: 330 723-4293
Emily Everett, *Senior Mgr*
Larry Johns,
Francine Johns,
▲ **EMP:** 44
SQ FT: 27,000
SALES: 3MM **Privately Held**
WEB: www.mcjakcandy.com
SIC: 2064 Candy & other confectionery products

(G-13442)
MEDINA LIGHTING INC
3983 Pearl Rd (44256-9036)
PHONE..................................330 721-1441
Lisa M Powers, *Principal*
EMP: 3
SALES (est): 335.6K **Privately Held**
SIC: 3648 Lighting equipment

(G-13443)
MEDINA PLATING CORP
940 Lafayette Rd (44256-3504)
PHONE..................................330 725-4155
Fax: 330 722-7737

Shawn Ritchie, *President*
Susan Kohanski, *Corp Secy*
Ron Dorfeld, *Info Tech Dir*
EMP: 28 **EST:** 1962
SQ FT: 10,000
SALES: 7MM **Privately Held**
WEB: www.medinaplating.com
SIC: 3471 Electroplating of metals or formed products

(G-13444)
MEDINA SIGNS POST INC
411 W Smith Rd (44256-2354)
PHONE..................................330 723-2484
Fax: 330 723-7446
David A Sterrett, *President*
Carol Sterrett, *Vice Pres*
EMP: 5
SQ FT: 6,000
SALES: 414.5K **Privately Held**
SIC: 3993 7389 Neon signs; sign painting & lettering shop

(G-13445)
MEDINA SUPPLY COMPANY (DH)
230 E Smith Rd (44256-3616)
PHONE..................................330 723-3681
Fax: 330 723-3681
Jerry A Schwab, *President*
David Schwab, *Vice Pres*
David Scheck, *Plant Mgr*
Mary Lynn Schwab, *Treasurer*
Rich Brady, *Sales Mgr*
EMP: 20 **EST:** 1974
SQ FT: 2,000
SALES (est): 39.2MM
SALES (corp-wide): 28.6B **Privately Held**
SIC: 1442 3273 3281 5211 Construction sand & gravel; ready-mixed concrete; cut stone & stone products; brick; concrete & cinder block
HQ: Schwab Industries, Inc.
    2301 Progress St
    Dover OH 44622
    330 364-4411

(G-13446)
MEDINVENT LLC
1133 Medina Rd Ste 500 (44256-5914)
PHONE..................................330 247-0921
William John Flickinger,
Steven F Isenberg MD,
EMP: 4
SQ FT: 200
SALES (est): 646.2K **Privately Held**
SIC: 3841 3845 Surgical & medical instruments; respiratory analysis equipment, electromedical

(G-13447)
METAL MERCHANTS USA INC
445 W Liberty St (44256-2273)
P.O. Box 302 (44258-0302)
PHONE..................................330 723-3228
Fax: 440 722-2413
Jerry Moody, *Principal*
EMP: 7
SALES (est): 759.8K **Privately Held**
SIC: 3356 Nonferrous rolling & drawing

(G-13448)
MOLDING MACHINE SERVICES INC (PA)
734 N Progress Dr (44256)
PHONE..................................330 461-2270
William Waite, *President*
Ross Sharratt, *Vice Pres*
EMP: 7 **EST:** 2007
SALES: 650.6K **Privately Held**
SIC: 1796 3541 Machinery installation; machine tool replacement & repair parts, metal cutting types

(G-13449)
MONTVIEW CORPORATION
Also Called: Repro Depot
404 W Liberty St (44256-2222)
PHONE..................................330 723-3409
Fax: 330 725-6375
Diane Korfhage, *President*
EMP: 2
SQ FT: 3,200

SALES: 1.1MM **Privately Held**
SIC: 2752 7334 2791 2789 Commercial printing, offset; photocopying & duplicating services; typesetting; bookbinding & related work

(G-13450)
NORTHSTAR PUBLISHING
437 Lafayette Rd Ste 310 (44256-2398)
P.O. Box 1166 (44258-1166)
PHONE..................................330 721-9126
Fax: 330 723-6598
Rodney Auth, *President*
Judy Cehelnik, *Opers Mgr*
Al Holappa, *Accounts Exec*
EMP: 7
SQ FT: 500
SALES: 1MM **Privately Held**
WEB: www.camp-business.com
SIC: 2731 Books: publishing & printing

(G-13451)
OCCIDENTAL CHEMICAL CORP
3984 Dogleg Trl (44256-7208)
PHONE..................................330 764-3441
Roger Hirl, *President*
EMP: 35
SALES (corp-wide): 10.4B **Publicly Held**
WEB: www.oxychem.com
SIC: 2812 Alkalies & chlorine
HQ: Occidental Chemical Corporation
    5005 Lyndon B Johnson Fwy # 2200
    Dallas TX 75244
    972 404-3800

(G-13452)
OFFICE MAGIC INC (PA)
Also Called: Electrocoat
2290 Wilbur Rd (44256-8496)
PHONE..................................510 782-6100
Craig Codding, *President*
Joel Codding, *Manager*
EMP: 14
SALES (est): 1.6MM **Privately Held**
SIC: 3479 2522 7641 2519 Painting, coating & hot dipping; office desks & tables: except wood; reupholstery; fiberglass & plastic furniture

(G-13453)
OLIVE TAP (PA)
30 Public Sq (44256-2203)
PHONE..................................330 721-6500
John Petrocelloy, *Owner*
EMP: 1
SALES (est): 20.8MM **Privately Held**
SIC: 2079 Olive oil

(G-13454)
ORTHOTIC AND PROSTHETICS SVC
132 Highland Dr (44256)
PHONE..................................330 723-6679
Fax: 330 722-7727
Justin Proctor, *President*
EMP: 5
SALES (est): 607.5K **Privately Held**
SIC: 3842 Orthopedic appliances

(G-13455)
OVATION POLYMER TECHNOLOGY AND
Also Called: Optem
1030 W Smith Rd (44256-2445)
PHONE..................................330 723-5686
Asis Banerjie, *President*
Delbert Henderson, *COO*
Abby Kamleh, *Manager*
▲ **EMP:** 23
SQ FT: 55,000
SALES (est): 2MM **Privately Held**
WEB: www.opteminc.com
SIC: 2821 Plastics materials & resins

(G-13456)
OWENS CORNING SALES LLC
890 W Smith Rd (44256-2484)
PHONE..................................330 764-7800
Fax: 330 723-1660
Jerry Moore, *Manager*
Mark Brendel, *Senior Mgr*
EMP: 125
SALES (corp-wide): 5.6B **Publicly Held**
WEB: www.owenscorning.com
SIC: 2952 Asphalt felts & coatings

GEOGRAPHIC

HQ: Owens Corning Sales, Llc
1 Owens Corning Pkwy
Toledo OH 43659
419 248-8000

(G-13457)
PACKAGING SPECIALTIES INC
300 Lake Rd (44256-2459)
PHONE....................................330 723-6000
Fax: 330 725-8180
Robert Syme, *Ch of Bd*
James Munson, *President*
Joe Lorenz, *General Mgr*
Tony Canterbury, *Warehouse Mgr*
Ron Mulhollen, *Purch Agent*
▲ EMP: 50 EST: 1959
SQ FT: 59,000
SALES (est): 10.6MM Privately Held
WEB: www.packspec.com
SIC: 3412 3411 Metal barrels, drums &
pails; metal cans
PA: Syme Inc
300 Lake Rd
Medina OH 44256
330 723-6000

(G-13458)
PLASTI-KEMM INC
Also Called: Plastic-Kemm
2805 Stony Hill Rd (44256-8693)
PHONE....................................330 239-1555
Joseph Kemmerling, *President*
EMP: 5
SALES (est): 340K Privately Held
SIC: 2821 Plastics materials & resins

(G-13459)
PLASTI-KOTE CO INC (HQ)
Also Called: Valspar
1000 Lake Rd (44256-3598)
PHONE....................................330 725-4511
Fax: 330 723-3674
Richard Rompala, *Ch of Bd*
Michael Brandt, *General Mgr*
Debbie Miller, *Purch Agent*
Tim Korkowski, *Accounting Mgr*
Chris Wolfe, *Sales Dir*
▲ EMP: 110 EST: 1989
SQ FT: 145,000
SALES (est): 40.1MM
SALES (corp-wide): 4.1B Publicly Held
SIC: 2813 2992 2851 Industrial gases; lu-
bricating oils & greases; paints & allied
products
PA: The Valspar Corporation
1101 S 3rd St
Minneapolis MN 55415
612 851-7000

(G-13460)
**PLASTICS CONVERTING
SOLUTIONS**
5341 River Styx Rd (44256-8725)
P.O. Box 88 (44258-0088)
PHONE....................................330 722-2537
Victor R Balest, *Principal*
EMP: 3
SALES (est): 346.3K Privately Held
SIC: 3089 Plastics products

(G-13461)
PLASTIPAK PACKAGING INC
850 W Smith Rd (44256-2425)
PHONE....................................330 725-0205
Fax: 330 723-7019
Richard Dasch, *Engineer*
Larry Downey, *Engineer*
Robert Jedreski, *Manager*
Larry Booth, *Manager*
Chris Evans, *Manager*
EMP: 200
SQ FT: 60,000
SALES (corp-wide): 36.3MM Privately
Held
WEB: www.plastipak.com
SIC: 3085 Plastics bottles
HQ: Plastipak Packaging, Inc.
41605 Ann Arbor Rd E
Plymouth MI 48170
734 455-3600

(G-13462)
**PLATE ENGRAVING
CORPORATION**
2324 Sharon Copley Rd (44256-9773)
PHONE....................................330 239-2155

Fax: 330 239-2608
James Michael Brobeck, *President*
Malissa Nutter, *General Mgr*
Von Brobeck, *Vice Pres*
EMP: 12
SQ FT: 4,018
SALES (est): 1.2MM Privately Held
WEB: www.plate-engraving.com
SIC: 2796 3089 Engraving on copper,
steel, wood or rubber: printing plates; en-
graving of plastic

(G-13463)
**PROFORMA STEINBACHER &
ASSOC**
3745 Medina Rd Ste A (44256-9510)
PHONE....................................330 241-5370
Larry Steinbacher, *Principal*
EMP: 3 EST: 2007
SALES (est): 301.6K Privately Held
SIC: 2759 Commercial printing

(G-13464)
PROGRESSIVE MOLDING TECH
5234 Portside Dr (44256-5966)
PHONE....................................330 220-7030
Laird Daubenspeck, *CEO*
EMP: 8
SQ FT: 8,900
SALES (est): 1.5MM Privately Held
SIC: 3089 Injection molding of plastics

(G-13465)
QPMR INC
Also Called: Quality Plastic Machine Repair
7599 Hidden Acres Dr (44256-8813)
PHONE....................................330 723-1739
Fax: 330 723-5753
Jennifer Shurratt, *President*
EMP: 13
SALES (est): 760K Privately Held
SIC: 7699 3599 Industrial machinery &
equipment repair; machine shop, jobbing
& repair

(G-13466)
**QUALITY TOOLING SYSTEMS
INC**
650 W Smith Rd Ste 4 (44256-2397)
PHONE....................................330 722-5025
Fax: 330 722-7296
Robert Kacic, *Owner*
Joe Schuld, *Engrg Mgr*
EMP: 11
SQ FT: 12,000
SALES (est): 1.6MM Privately Held
SIC: 3544 Special dies, tools, jigs & fix-
tures

(G-13467)
**REPUBLIC POWDERED METALS
INC (HQ)**
2628 Pearl Rd (44256-9099)
P.O. Box 777 (44256-0777)
PHONE....................................330 225-3192
Fax: 330 225-8743
Thomas Sullivan, *Ch of Bd*
Frank C Sullivan, *President*
Michel Nolis, *Managing Dir*
Tony Clapperton, *Regional Mgr*
Ken Armstrong, *Vice Pres*
◆ EMP: 61
SQ FT: 20,000
SALES (est): 1.4B
SALES (corp-wide): 4.8B Publicly Held
SIC: 2851 2891 3069 2899 Paints & al-
lied products; adhesives & sealants; roof-
ing, membrane rubber; waterproofing
compounds; dyes & pigments; specialty
cleaning preparations
PA: Rpm International Inc.
2628 Pearl Rd
Medina OH 44256
330 273-5090

(G-13468)
ROBERT GOREY
Also Called: Gorey Construction
6811 Stone Rd (44256-8991)
PHONE....................................330 725-7272
Robert Gorey, *Owner*
EMP: 3

SALES (est): 280K Privately Held
SIC: 2951 1623 Concrete, asphaltic (not
from refineries); sewer line construction;
water main construction

(G-13469)
ROBERTS CABINETRY LLC
1718 Melody Ln (44256-9221)
PHONE....................................330 421-4374
Robert Kathe, *Principal*
EMP: 3 EST: 2012
SALES (est): 278.2K Privately Held
SIC: 2434 Wood kitchen cabinets

(G-13470)
**RPM CONSUMER HOLDING
COMPANY (HQ)**
2628 Pearl Rd (44256-7623)
P.O. Box 777 (44258-0777)
PHONE....................................330 273-5090
Frank C Sullivan, *President*
Ron Rice, *President*
John Kramer, *Vice Pres*
G Paul, *Vice Pres*
Ronald A Rice, *Vice Pres*
EMP: 6
SALES (est): 14.9MM
SALES (corp-wide): 4.8B Publicly Held
SIC: 2851 2891 3089 3952 Paints & al-
lied products; enamels; lacquer: bases,
dopes; adhesives; cement, except
linoleum & tile; kits, plastic; brushes,
air, artists'; games, toys & children's vehi-
cles
PA: Rpm International Inc.
2628 Pearl Rd
Medina OH 44256
330 273-5090

(G-13471)
RPM INTERNATIONAL INC (PA)
2628 Pearl Rd (44256-7623)
P.O. Box 777 (44258-0777)
PHONE....................................330 273-5090
Frank C Sullivan, *Ch of Bd*
Ronald A Rice, *President*
Robert Krug, *Area Mgr*
John J McLaughlin, *Senior VP*
Janeen B Kastner, *Vice Pres*
◆ EMP: 61 EST: 1947
SALES: 4.8B Publicly Held
WEB: www.rpminc.com
SIC: 2851 2891 3069 2899 Paints & al-
lied products; lacquers, varnishes, enam-
els & other coatings; lacquer: bases,
dopes, thinner; varnishes; adhesives &
sealants; sealants; adhesives; roofing,
membrane rubber; waterproofing com-
pounds; concrete curing & hardening
compounds; corrosion preventive lubricant; dyes & pigments; specialty cleaning
preparations

(G-13472)
S&V INDUSTRIES INC (PA)
5054 Paramount Dr (44256-5363)
PHONE....................................330 666-1986
Fax: 330 253-7573
Senthil Sundarapandian, *President*
Senthil Kumar Sundarapandian, *President*
Joan Owens, *Vice Pres*
Fallon Juma, *CFO*
Karen Peel, *Manager*
▲ EMP: 4
SQ FT: 1,618
SALES (est): 9MM Privately Held
WEB: www.svindustries.com
SIC: 5049 3089 3312 Engineers' equip-
ment & supplies; casting of plastic; forg-
ings, iron & steel

(G-13473)
SAFESMART USA
959 Lake Rd (44256-2453)
PHONE....................................404 703-1008
Mick Strange, *CEO*
EMP: 3
SALES (est): 138.9K Privately Held
SIC: 3531 Construction machinery

(G-13474)
**SANDRIDGE FOOD
CORPORATION (PA)**
Also Called: Sandridge Gourmet Salads
133 Commerce Dr (44256-1333)
PHONE....................................330 725-2348

Fax: 330 722-3998
Mark D Sandridge, *CEO*
William G Frantz, *President*
Frank Sidari, *President*
Jordan Sandridge, *General Mgr*
Gene Gorniak, *Business Mgr*
▲ EMP: 5
SQ FT: 130,000
SALES (est): 112.3MM Privately Held
WEB: www.sandridge.com
SIC: 2099 Salads, fresh or refrigerated

(G-13475)
**SANDRIDGE FOOD
CORPORATION**
Also Called: Sandridge Gourmet Salads
133 Commerce Dr (44256-1333)
PHONE....................................330 725-8883
Barry Pioski, *Manager*
EMP: 225
SALES (corp-wide): 112.3MM Privately
Held
WEB: www.sandridge.com
SIC: 2099 5141 Salads, fresh or refriger-
ated; groceries, general line
PA: Sandridge Food Corporation
133 Commerce Dr
Medina OH 44256
330 725-2348

(G-13476)
SCIS AEROSPACE LLC
1179 Alexandria Ln (44256-3262)
PHONE....................................216 533-8533
Robert Boyd, *President*
Brian Jaskiewicz, *Vice Pres*
James Ralph, *Treasurer*
Jeffrey Jaskiewicz, *Admin Sec*
EMP: 4
SALES (est): 149.8K Privately Held
SIC: 3724 3728 Research & development
on aircraft engines & parts; military air-
craft equipment & armament; research &
dev by manuf., aircraft parts & auxiliary
equip

(G-13477)
SEALY MATTRESS COMPANY
1070 Lake Rd (44256-2450)
PHONE....................................330 725-4146
Fax: 330 722-2307
Mike Kindall, *Safety Mgr*
Donna Warholic, *Buyer*
Thomas Fries, *Engineer*
Lisa Nowak, *Engineer*
Jackie Foster, *Controller*
EMP: 180
SQ FT: 143,000
SALES (corp-wide): 3.1B Publicly Held
SIC: 2515 Mattresses, containing felt, foam
rubber, urethane, etc.; box springs, as-
sembled
HQ: Sealy Mattress Company
1 Office Parkway Rd
Trinity NC 27370
336 861-3500

(G-13478)
SEALY MATTRESS MFG CO INC
1070 Lake Rd (44256-2450)
PHONE....................................800 697-3259
Vicky Avans, *Manager*
EMP: 100
SALES (corp-wide): 3.1B Publicly Held
SIC: 2515 Mattresses, innerspring or box
spring
HQ: Sealy Mattress Manufacturing Com-
pany, Inc.
1 Office Parkway Rd
Trinity NC 27370
336 861-3500

(G-13479)
SHARK SOLAR LLC
4386 Belmont Ct (44256-7486)
PHONE....................................216 630-7395
Jeffrey Burns, *Principal*
EMP: 5
SALES (est): 185.7K Privately Held
SIC: 1711 3433 Solar energy contractor;
solar heaters & collectors

(G-13480)
SHELLY MATERIALS INC
300 N State Rd (44256-1406)
PHONE....................................330 722-2190

▲ = Import ▼=Export
◆ =Import/Export

EMP: 4
SALES (corp-wide): 23.7B **Privately Held**
SIC: 1422 Crushed/Broken Limestone
HQ: Shelly Materials, Inc.
80 Park Dr
Thornville OH 43076
740 246-6315

(G-13481)
SINFUL SWEETS LLC
3862 Turnberry Dr (44256-6885)
PHONE.................................330 721-0916
Judi Campobenedetto, *Principal*
EMP: 4
SALES (est): 228K **Privately Held**
SIC: 2051 Cakes, bakery: except frozen

(G-13482)
STANDARD WELDING & STEEL PDTS
260 S State Rd (44256-2474)
P.O. Box 297 (44258-0297)
PHONE.................................330 273-2777
Fax: 330 723-0399
Charles Coleman, *CEO*
Christopher Coleman, *President*
Charles F Coleman, *President*
Jayne Coleman, *Corp Secy*
Jack Colman, *Vice Pres*
EMP: 18 EST: 1939
SQ FT: 30,000
SALES (est): 4.1MM **Privately Held**
WEB: www.stdwelding.com
SIC: 3443 Fabricated plate work (boiler shop)

(G-13483)
STANDOUT STICKERS INC
4930 Chippewa Rd Unit A (44256-8824)
PHONE.................................877 449-7703
Jeffrey Nemecek, *CEO*
Katie Drabik, *Accounts Mgr*
Josh Hippley, *Marketing Staff*
Evan Leake, *Art Dir*
EMP: 6
SALES: 650.6K **Privately Held**
SIC: 2759 Commercial printing

(G-13484)
STRAIGHT RAZOR DESIGNES
23 Public Sq Ste L1 (44256-2274)
PHONE.................................330 598-1414
Don Addlean, *Owner*
EMP: 3
SALES (est): 240.1K **Privately Held**
SIC: 3199 Razor strops

(G-13485)
SUPRO SPRING & WIRE FORMS INC
6440 Norwalk Rd Ste N (44256-7154)
PHONE.................................330 722-5628
Fax: 330 725-5628
Kevin Provagna, *President*
James Gensert, *Vice Pres*
Eileen Paul, *Personnel Exec*
All Meinke, *Manager*
▲ EMP: 35
SQ FT: 12,000
SALES: 5MM **Privately Held**
WEB: www.suprospring.com
SIC: 3495 Wire springs

(G-13486)
SYME INC (PA)
300 Lake Rd (44256-2459)
PHONE.................................330 723-6000
Robert P Syme, *CEO*
Jim L Munson, *President*
Joseph Hyclak, *Controller*
EMP: 21
SQ FT: 58,000
SALES (est): 10.6MM **Privately Held**
WEB: www.syme.com
SIC: 3412 Metal barrels, drums & pails

(G-13487)
THERMO VENT MANUFACTURING INC
Also Called: Therm-O-Vent
1213 Medina Rd (44256-8135)
PHONE.................................330 239-0239
Stephen Boesch, *President*
Charles R Boesch, *Vice Pres*
Jeffery W Boesch, *Vice Pres*

Tony Kava, *Vice Pres*
Nancy Vacha, *Administration*
▲ EMP: 11
SQ FT: 6,800
SALES (est): 1.1MM **Privately Held**
SIC: 3444 3564 Ventilators, sheet metal; blowers & fans

(G-13488)
THOMAS ROSS ASSOCIATES INC
303 N Broadway St (44256-1930)
PHONE.................................330 723-1110
Fax: 330 725-1319
Thomas Ross, *President*
Melody A Ross, *Project Mgr*
Melody Ross, *Office Mgr*
Jason Vasil, *Comp Tech*
EMP: 8
SALES (est): 150K **Privately Held**
SIC: 3571 1731 7378 5045 Electronic computers; computer installation; computer & data processing equipment repair/maintenance; computers; computer software; accounting machines using machine readable programs

(G-13489)
TIGER GENERAL LLC
6867 Wooster Pike (44256-8859)
PHONE.................................330 239-4949
Mark Overholt, *President*
John Loeper, *General Mgr*
Mickey Manack, *Vice Pres*
Sherry Overholt, *Vice Pres*
Mark Scott, *Engrg Mgr*
EMP: 70
SQ FT: 18,000
SALES (est): 14.2MM **Privately Held**
SIC: 3533 5511 Oil & gas drilling rigs & equipment; oil field machinery & equipment; trucks, tractors & trailers: new & used

(G-13490)
TRAILER ONE INC
6378 Norwalk Rd (44256-9455)
PHONE.................................330 723-7474
Kenneth Smith, *President*
Bradley Thomas, *Vice Pres*
Chris Shuster, *Office Mgr*
Kristin Organ, *Admin Asst*
EMP: 6
SQ FT: 250
SALES: 7.8MM **Privately Held**
WEB: www.trailerone.com
SIC: 5511 3715 7359 Trucks, tractors & trailers: new & used; truck trailers; equipment rental & leasing

(G-13491)
TROGDON PUBLISHING INC
Also Called: Ohio Standard Bread
5164 Normandy Park Dr # 100 (44256-5901)
PHONE.................................330 721-7678
Bruce Trogdon, *President*
Raymond Leroy, *Vice Pres*
Mike Trogdon, *Manager*
EMP: 42
SQ FT: 6,200
SALES: 4.5MM **Privately Held**
WEB: www.tradingpostnewspapers.com
SIC: 2741 2711 Guides: publishing & printing; newspapers

(G-13492)
UNISAND INCORPORATED
1097 Industrial Pkwy (44256-2448)
PHONE.................................330 722-0222
Fax: 330 722-2019
David W Bullock, *President*
Douglas Bullock, *Vice Pres*
Todd Seefeldt, *Plant Mgr*
Jeanne Hejny, *Manager*
▲ EMP: 26
SQ FT: 3,000
SALES (est): 4.1MM **Privately Held**
WEB: www.unisand.com
SIC: 3291 Abrasive wheels & grindstones, not artificial

(G-13493)
UNITED SPORT APPAREL
229 Harding St Ste B (44256-1288)
PHONE.................................330 722-0818

Fax: 330 723-0689
David A Bricker, *Owner*
EMP: 10
SQ FT: 6,000
SALES (est): 1MM **Privately Held**
WEB: www.unitedsportapparel.com
SIC: 2759 2395 Screen printing; embroidery products, except schiffli machine

(G-13494)
UNITED TUBE CORPORATION
960 Lake Rd (44256-2453)
PHONE.................................330 725-4196
Frank J Sadowski, *President*
Harvey O Yoder, *Principal*
Angelina Chaplain, *Vice Pres*
David Collins, *Plant Mgr*
Jack Bretz, *VP Sales*
EMP: 54 EST: 1945
SALES (est): 13.2MM **Privately Held**
SIC: 3317 Tubes, wrought: welded or lock joint; welded pipe & tubes

(G-13495)
VALVOLE AMERICA LLC
2550 Medina Rd (44256-8144)
PHONE.................................330 464-8872
Steven H Huzyak, *General Mgr*
EMP: 5 EST: 2015
SQ FT: 7,600
SALES (est): 616.7K **Privately Held**
SIC: 3492 Valves, hydraulic, aircraft

(G-13496)
W G MACHINE TOOL SERVICE CO
7735 Spieth Rd (44256-8914)
PHONE.................................330 723-3428
EMP: 9
SQ FT: 10,000
SALES (est): 978.8K **Privately Held**
SIC: 3542 Rebuilds Machine Tools

(G-13497)
WOODBINE PRODUCTS COMPANY
Also Called: Powrkleen
915 W Smith Rd (44256-2446)
PHONE.................................330 725-0165
Fax: 330 723-5463
Phillip Navratil, *President*
Stephen A Kuzyk Jr, *Corp Secy*
Dennis Vehr, *Pastor*
▲ EMP: 14 EST: 1961
SQ FT: 20,000
SALES (est): 4.2MM **Privately Held**
WEB: www.powrklean.com
SIC: 2842 2844 Cleaning or polishing preparations; toilet preparations

(G-13498)
X-TREME FINISHES INC
Also Called: Line-X of Akron/Medina
387 Medina Rd Ste 1000 (44256-9681)
PHONE.................................330 474-0614
Tawny R Zajc, *Principal*
EMP: 10 EST: 2013
SALES (est): 131.3K **Privately Held**
SIC: 3479 2851 1752 7549 Etching & engraving; epoxy coatings; polyurethane coatings; access flooring system installation; undercoating/rustproofing cars; exterior cleaning, including sandblasting

Medway
Clark County

(G-13499)
AERO COMPOSITES INC
3400 Spangler Rd (45341-9752)
P.O. Box 404 (45341-0404)
PHONE.................................937 849-0244
David Patko, *President*
Patricia Ann Scully, *President*
Dave Scully, *Vice Pres*
EMP: 4
SQ FT: 6,000
SALES (est): 350K **Privately Held**
WEB: www.aerocomposites.com
SIC: 3721 8711 Aircraft; consulting engineer

(G-13500)
MONS MEG CARTRIDGES INC
20 E Aspen Rd (45341-1302)
PHONE.................................937 849-9646
Jim Leonard, *President*
EMP: 3
SALES: 50K **Privately Held**
SIC: 3482 Cartridge cases for ammunition, 30 mm. & below

(G-13501)
PROTOFAB MANUFACTURING INC
8 University Rd (45341-1260)
PHONE.................................937 849-4983
EMP: 5
SALES (est): 27.1K **Privately Held**
SIC: 3552 Mfg Industrial Machinery

(G-13502)
WAYNE CONCRETE COMPANY
223 Western Dr (45341-9521)
PHONE.................................937 545-9919
Wayne Gibson, *Owner*
EMP: 10
SALES: 258K **Privately Held**
SIC: 1442 Construction sand & gravel

Mentor
Lake County

(G-13503)
1 888 U PITCH IT
7176 Fillmore Ct (44060-4816)
PHONE.................................440 796-9028
Frank A Jurkoshek Jr, *Principal*
EMP: 4
SALES (est): 449.1K **Privately Held**
SIC: 3089 Garbage containers, plastic

(G-13504)
ABSOLUTE GRINDING CO INC
7007 Spinach Dr (44060-4959)
PHONE.................................440 974-4030
Fax: 440 974-4030
Rob Murnyack, *President*
EMP: 11
SQ FT: 8,100
SALES: 752.2K **Privately Held**
WEB: www.absolutegrinding.com
SIC: 3544 Special dies & tools

(G-13505)
ACCU-TECH MFG & SUPPORT
8875 East Ave (44060-4305)
PHONE.................................440 205-8882
Fax: 440 205-8884
Jeff Moore, *President*
Ron Curtiss, *Vice Pres*
EMP: 10
SQ FT: 6,500
SALES: 500K **Privately Held**
SIC: 3599 Machine & other job shop work

(G-13506)
ACCURATE TECH INC
7230 Industrial Park Blvd (44060-5316)
PHONE.................................440 951-9153
Fax: 440 951-5123
Micheal Karcic Jr, *President*
Glen Yamamoto, *Business Mgr*
EMP: 6
SQ FT: 3,000
SALES: 550K **Privately Held**
SIC: 3599 Machine shop, jobbing & repair

(G-13507)
ACHILLES RUNNING SHOP LLC (PA)
7439 Mentor Ave (44060-5405)
PHONE.................................440 942-2059
Kristen K Mendeszoon, *President*
Pat McCloskey, *Manager*
Mark Mendesvoon,
EMP: 8
SALES: 800K **Privately Held**
SIC: 3949 Track & field athletic equipment

(G-13508)
ACO POLYMER PRODUCTS INC (DH)
Also Called: Quartz
9470 Pinecone Dr (44060-1863)
PHONE..................................440 285-7000
Fax: 440 285-7005
Derek Humphries, *President*
Jeff Lipp, *Area Mgr*
Brian Parent, *Opers Mgr*
Karen Ferguson, *Opers Staff*
Larry Hunt, *Production*
◆ EMP: 50 EST: 1978
SQ FT: 30,000
SALES (est): 29.4MM
SALES (corp-wide): 702.1MM **Privately Held**
WEB: www.acousa.com
SIC: 3272 3089 3312 Concrete products, precast; plastic & fiberglass tanks; stainless steel
HQ: Severin Ahlmann Holding Gmbh
    Am Ahlmannkai
    Budelsdorf
    433 135-40

(G-13509)
ACTIVITIES PRESS INC
Also Called: AP Direct
7181 Industrial Park Blvd (44060-5327)
PHONE..................................440 953-1200
Fax: 440 951-2110
Graydon Bullard, *President*
Leroy Bridges, *Vice Pres*
Linda Bridges, *Treasurer*
Dale Piccirillo, *Sales Staff*
Don Porvasnik, *Sales Staff*
▲ EMP: 28
SQ FT: 24,000
SALES (est): 4.8MM **Privately Held**
WEB: www.activitiespress.com
SIC: 2752 2791 2789 Commercial printing, offset; typesetting; bookbinding & related work

(G-13510)
ADVANCED PNEUMATICS INC
Also Called: Advanced F.M.e Products
9413 Hamilton Dr (44060-8709)
PHONE..................................440 953-0700
Fax: 440 953-3131
Thomas Nalfi, *President*
EMP: 5
SQ FT: 1,200
SALES (est): 993.6K **Privately Held**
WEB: www.advancedpneumatics.com
SIC: 3568 Power transmission equipment

(G-13511)
AIR POWER DYNAMICS LLC
7350 Corporate Blvd (44060-4856)
PHONE..................................440 701-2100
Fax: 440 701-2120
Edward F Crawford, *CEO*
Stan Beaty, *Manager*
William Sopko, *Manager*
Boya Belasic,
EMP: 200
SQ FT: 73,000
SALES (est): 36.1MM **Privately Held**
WEB: www.beechtechnology.com
SIC: 3543 Industrial patterns

(G-13512)
AIR TECHNICAL INDUSTRIES INC
7501 Clover Ave (44060-5297)
P.O. Box 149 (44061-0149)
PHONE..................................440 951-5191
Fax: 440 951-5191
Pero Novak, *CEO*
Cyndi McCloud, *General Mgr*
Vida Novak, *Vice Pres*
Nick Oriti, *Foreman/Supr*
Ann Novak, *Pub Rel Mgr*
◆ EMP: 40 EST: 1964
SQ FT: 80,000
SALES (est): 12.5MM **Privately Held**
WEB: www.airtechnical.com
SIC: 3537 3569 3536 3421 Stacking machines, automatic; robots, assembly line: industrial & commercial; hoists, cranes & monorails; cutlery; bulk handling conveyor systems

(G-13513)
AIR TOOL SERVICE COMPANY (PA)
7722 Metric Dr (44060-4862)
PHONE..................................440 701-1021
Rick J Sabath, *President*
Henry Brueggeman, *Principal*
Betty J Gerhard, *Principal*
James Becker, *Vice Pres*
Greg Visser, *Finance Mgr*
EMP: 14 EST: 1956
SQ FT: 30,000
SALES (est): 1.7MM **Privately Held**
WEB: www.atsco.com
SIC: 3494 3546 Valves & pipe fittings; power-driven handtools

(G-13514)
AJ FLUID POWER SALES & SUP INC
Also Called: Safe Air Valve Co.
8766 Tyler Blvd (44060-4329)
PHONE..................................440 255-7960
Adam Jenkins, *President*
EMP: 5
SQ FT: 4,000
SALES (est): 789.9K **Privately Held**
WEB: www.safeairvalve.com
SIC: 7699 3492 Valve repair, industrial; control valves, fluid power: hydraulic & pneumatic

(G-13515)
AL CHEM SPECIALTIES LLC
Also Called: ACS
7284 Justin Way (44060-4881)
PHONE..................................440 255-2826
Nancy Dubin, *Office Mgr*
Mark Chambers,
EMP: 1
SALES (est): 2MM **Privately Held**
SIC: 1099 Aluminum & beryllium ores mining

(G-13516)
ALAMARRA INC
8788 Tyler Blvd (44060-4328)
PHONE..................................800 336-3007
Lawrence Boros, *President*
Markay Boros, *CFO*
EMP: 3
SALES (est): 338.5K **Privately Held**
WEB: www.alamarra.com
SIC: 2045 Prepared flour mixes & doughs

(G-13517)
ALIEN PRODUCTS LLC
7123 Industrial Park Blvd (44060-5313)
PHONE..................................440 946-9100
Angelo Pariza Jr, *President*
Tracey Horton, *Manager*
EMP: 20
SALES (est): 4.1MM **Privately Held**
SIC: 3541 3542 Machine tools, metal cutting type; machine tools, metal forming type

(G-13518)
ALL - FLO PUMP COMPANY
7750 Tyler Blvd (44060-4802)
PHONE..................................440 354-1700
Robert Brizes, *President*
Keith Osborn, *VP Mfg*
Frank Stroud, *Finance Mgr*
Paul McGarry, *Sales Staff*
Steve Weirich, *Technology*
▲ EMP: 22
SALES (est): 3.9MM **Privately Held**
WEB: www.allflo.com
SIC: 3594 3561 Fluid power pumps; pumps & pumping equipment

(G-13519)
ALL STATE GL BLOCK FCTRY INC
8781 East Ave (44060-4303)
PHONE..................................440 205-8410
Fax: 440 205-8410
Vince Tassone, *President*
Vince Tasone, *President*
EMP: 8
SQ FT: 3,000
SALES (est): 720K **Privately Held**
SIC: 1793 5231 3229 Glass & glazing work; glass; blocks & bricks, glass

(G-13520)
AMERICAN POLYMER STANDARDS
8680 Tyler Blvd (44060-4348)
P.O. Box 901 (44061-0901)
PHONE..................................440 255-2211
Fax: 440 255-8397
John E Armonas, *President*
Courntey Cassidy, *Office Mgr*
Eric Johnson, *Manager*
EMP: 5
SQ FT: 5,600
SALES (est): 587.4K **Privately Held**
WEB: www.ampolymer.com
SIC: 8734 2821 Testing laboratories; plastics materials & resins

(G-13521)
ANGSTROM AUTOMOTIVE GROUP LLC
8229 Tyler Blvd (44060-4218)
PHONE..................................440 255-6700
EMP: 7 **Privately Held**
SIC: 3714 Axle housings & shafts, motor vehicle
PA: Angstrom Automotive Group, Llc
    26980 Trolley Indus Dr
    Taylor MI 48180

(G-13522)
ANGSTROM PRECISION METALS LLC
8229 Tyler Blvd (44060-4218)
PHONE..................................440 255-6700
Nagesh K Palakurthi, *CEO*
Mario Manocchio, *President*
David Berg, *General Mgr*
Sandy Bradford, *COO*
▲ EMP: 60
SALES (est): 12.1MM **Privately Held**
SIC: 3545 Precision tools, machinists'
PA: Angstrom Automotive Group, Llc
    26980 Trolley Indus Dr
    Taylor MI 48180

(G-13523)
ANODIZING SPECIALISTS INC
7547 Tyler Blvd (44060-4869)
PHONE..................................440 951-0257
Fax: 440 951-0257
David J Pecjak, *President*
Michael T Pecjak, *Vice Pres*
EMP: 18 EST: 1977
SQ FT: 11,000
SALES (est): 1.5MM **Privately Held**
WEB: www.anodizingspecialists.com
SIC: 3471 Finishing, metals or formed products; anodizing (plating) of metals or formed products

(G-13524)
APOLLO MANUFACTURING CO LLC
7911 Enterprise Dr (44060-5311)
PHONE..................................440 951-9972
Fax: 440 951-8773
Draga Marusic, *Vice Pres*
Christine Hawk, *Purchasing*
Andrea Myers, *Accountant*
Allen Sandy, *Mng Member*
Helen Mausser, *Manager*
EMP: 30
SQ FT: 25,000
SALES (est): 7.6MM **Privately Held**
WEB: www.apollo-mfg.com
SIC: 3545 Precision tools, machinists'

(G-13525)
APOLLO PLASTICS INC
7555 Tyler Blvd Ste 11 (44060-4866)
PHONE..................................440 951-7774
Stanley Skrbis, *President*
Maria Skrbis, *Corp Secy*
Dineen Tyler, *Office Mgr*
EMP: 10
SQ FT: 8,000
SALES (est): 484K **Privately Held**
WEB: www.apolloplastics.net
SIC: 3544 3089 Special dies, tools, jigs & fixtures; plastic processing

(G-13526)
AREM CO
Also Called: Jaytee Division
8200 Tyler Blvd Ste L (44060-4216)
PHONE..................................440 974-6740
Fax: 440 974-6740
Bob Myotte, *President*
Becky Uyesugi, *Vice Pres*
Jack Kurant, *Admin Sec*
EMP: 14
SALES (est): 3.2MM **Privately Held**
WEB: www.arema.net
SIC: 3498 3949 3354 3471 Fabricated pipe & fittings; sporting & athletic goods; aluminum extruded products; plating & polishing; tubing, copper & copper alloy

(G-13527)
ASTER ELEMENTS INC
7657 Saint Clair Ave (44060-5235)
PHONE..................................440 942-2799
Joe Lopez, *CEO*
Dennis Goetze, *Business Mgr*
EMP: 22
SQ FT: 30,000
SALES (est): 5.3MM **Privately Held**
SIC: 3441 Fabricated structural metal

(G-13528)
ATS MACHINE & TOOL CO INC
7750 Division Dr (44060-4860)
PHONE..................................440 255-1120
Fax: 440 255-1122
Robert E Dutko, *President*
Denise Dutko, *Vice Pres*
Paul Motiejunas, *Plant Mgr*
EMP: 12
SQ FT: 15,000
SALES: 2MM **Privately Held**
WEB: www.atsmachine.com
SIC: 3599 Machine shop, jobbing & repair

(G-13529)
AUTOMATION METROLOGY INTL LLC (PA)
8808 Tyler Blvd (44060-4361)
PHONE..................................440 354-6436
Fax: 440 639-9983
David Denman,
▼ EMP: 5
SQ FT: 5,000
SALES (est): 1.9MM **Privately Held**
WEB: www.auto-met.com
SIC: 5084 3823 3699 Measuring & testing equipment, electrical; industrial process measurement equipment; digital displays of process variables; laser systems & equipment

(G-13530)
AVERY DENNISON CORPORATION
7100 Lindsay Dr (44060-4923)
PHONE..................................440 358-2828
Fax: 440 639-2801
Frederick Buse, *Branch Mgr*
Mark Baierl, *Manager*
EMP: 115
SALES (corp-wide): 6B **Publicly Held**
SIC: 2672 Adhesive backed films, foams & foils
PA: Avery Dennison Corporation
    207 N Goode Ave Fl 6
    Glendale CA 91203
    626 304-2000

(G-13531)
AVERY DENNISON CORPORATION
7236 Justin Way (44060-4881)
PHONE..................................440 266-2500
Rob Dibble, *Branch Mgr*
EMP: 115
SALES (corp-wide): 6B **Publicly Held**
SIC: 2672 Adhesive backed films, foams & foils
PA: Avery Dennison Corporation
    207 N Goode Ave Fl 6
    Glendale CA 91203
    626 304-2000

▲ = Import ▼=Export
◆ =Import/Export

GEOGRAPHIC

(G-13532)
AVERY DENNISON CORPORATION
7070 Spinach Dr Bldg 19 (44060-4958)
PHONE.....................440 358-2930
EMP: 115
SALES (corp-wide): 6B **Publicly Held**
SIC: 2672 Adhesive backed films, foams & foils
PA: Avery Dennison Corporation
207 N Goode Ave Fl 6
Glendale CA 91203
626 304-2000

(G-13533)
B & G MACHINE COMPANY INC
7205 Commerce Dr (44060-5307)
PHONE.....................440 946-8787
Donald Kuchenbecker, President
Paul Augustine, Purchasing
EMP: 4 EST: 1954
SQ FT: 25,000
SALES (est): 280K **Privately Held**
SIC: 3599 Machine shop, jobbing & repair

(G-13534)
B N MACHINE INC
8853 East Ave (44060-4305)
PHONE.....................440 255-5200
Fax: 440 255-5266
Bill Nicholl, President
EMP: 4
SQ FT: 4,000
SALES (est): 403.7K **Privately Held**
WEB: www.bnmachine.com
SIC: 3599 Machine shop, jobbing & repair

(G-13535)
BILL WYATT INC
Also Called: Wyatt Printing
8857 Lake Shore Blvd (44060-1521)
PHONE.....................330 535-1113
Fax: 330 535-1132
Bill Wyatt, President
EMP: 7
SQ FT: 10,000
SALES (est): 570K **Privately Held**
WEB: www.oneguyandadog.com
SIC: 2752 2791 2789 Commercial printing, offset; typesetting; bookbinding & related work

(G-13536)
BLEIL CHAN
Also Called: Bleil Manufacturing Company
9451 Jackson St (44060-4513)
PHONE.....................440 352-6012
Fax: 440 352-6256
Chan Bleil, President
Mary Ann Bleil, Treasurer
EMP: 5
SQ FT: 2,000
SALES: 300K **Privately Held**
SIC: 3599 Machine shop, jobbing & repair

(G-13537)
BOBS GRINDING INC
7564 Tyler Blvd Ste D (44060-4870)
PHONE.....................440 946-6179
Fax: 440 946-7799
Robert Murnyack, President
EMP: 4
SALES: 160K **Privately Held**
SIC: 3599 Machine shop, jobbing & repair; grinding castings for the trade

(G-13538)
BRUMALL MFG COROPORATION
7850 Division Dr (44060-4874)
PHONE.....................440 974-2622
Fax: 440 974-2622
Rod Brumberg, President
Wanda Brumberg, Corp Secy
Yvonne Brumberg, Vice Pres
▲ EMP: 40
SQ FT: 25,000
SALES (est): 7.2MM **Privately Held**
WEB: www.brumall.com
SIC: 3643 Connectors & terminals for electrical devices

(G-13539)
BURTON INDUSTRIES INC
7875 Division Dr (44060-4877)
PHONE.....................440 974-1700
Fax: 440 974-1700
Drew Burton, Engineer
Chris Burton Jr, Branch Mgr
EMP: 15
SALES (corp-wide): 23.6MM **Privately Held**
WEB: www.burtonind.com
SIC: 3599 Machine shop, jobbing & repair
PA: Burton Industries, Inc.
9821 Cedar Falls Rd
Hazelhurst WI 54531
715 356-5767

(G-13540)
BUYERS PRODUCTS COMPANY (PA)
9049 Tyler Blvd (44060-4800)
PHONE.....................440 974-8888
Fax: 440 974-0165
James Kleinman, President
Dave Durst, General Mgr
Aaron Gayheart, General Mgr
Jeff Mueller, Vice Pres
Mark Saltzman, Vice Pres
▲ EMP: 150
SQ FT: 172,000
SALES (est): 98.5MM **Privately Held**
WEB: www.buyersproducts.com
SIC: 5013 3714 Truck parts & accessories; motor vehicle parts & accessories

(G-13541)
BUYERS PRODUCTS COMPANY
8120 Tyler Blvd (44060-4852)
PHONE.....................440 974-8888
James Kleinman, Branch Mgr
EMP: 5
SALES (corp-wide): 98.5MM **Privately Held**
SIC: 3465 Body parts, automobile: stamped metal
PA: Buyers Products Company
9049 Tyler Blvd
Mentor OH 44060
440 974-8888

(G-13542)
BUYERS PRODUCTS COMPANY
7700 Tyler Blvd (44060-4802)
PHONE.....................440 974-8888
Fax: 440 974-8888
James Kleinman, Branch Mgr
EMP: 5
SALES (corp-wide): 98.5MM **Privately Held**
SIC: 5013 3714 Truck parts & accessories; motor vehicle parts & accessories
PA: Buyers Products Company
9049 Tyler Blvd
Mentor OH 44060
440 974-8888

(G-13543)
CHEMSULTANTS INTERNATIONAL INC (PA)
9079 Tyler Blvd (44060-1868)
P.O. Box 1118 (44061-1118)
PHONE.....................440 974-3080
Fax: 440 352-8572
Joe Mausar, Business Mgr
Judith Muny, Corp Secy
Keith Muny, Vice Pres
Brian Koski, Opers Mgr
Mark Van Ness, Prdtn Mgr
EMP: 9
SQ FT: 10,000
SALES (est): 4.2MM **Privately Held**
SIC: 3821 8734 8742 Laboratory apparatus & furniture; product testing laboratory, safety or performance; industry specialist consultants

(G-13544)
CLARK RBR PLASTIC INTL SLS INC (PA)
8888 East Ave (44060-4306)
P.O. Box 299 (44061-0299)
PHONE.....................440 953-9514
Fax: 440 255-9793
Gregory Clark, President
James T Clark II, Vice Pres
Patty Clark, Purchasing
Ed Phillips, VP Finance
EMP: 75
SQ FT: 16,000
SALES (est): 23.6MM **Privately Held**
WEB: www.clarkrandp.com
SIC: 3061 3069 3089 Mechanical rubber goods; molded rubber products; extruded finished plastic products

(G-13545)
CLEVELAND CARBIDE TOOL CO
7755 Division Dr (44060-4861)
PHONE.....................440 974-1155
John Halick, President
Barbara Halick, Vice Pres
EMP: 4 EST: 1941
SQ FT: 5,000
SALES: 400K **Privately Held**
SIC: 3545 Cutting tools for machine tools; milling cutters

(G-13546)
CLEVELAND SPECIALTY INSPTN SVC
8562 East Ave (44060-4302)
PHONE.....................440 578-1046
Fax: 440 974-6828
James Popovic, President
EMP: 13
SQ FT: 3,200
SALES (est): 920K **Privately Held**
WEB: www.clevelandspecialty.com
SIC: 7389 3545 Inspection & testing services; threading tools (machine tool accessories); gauges (machine tool accessories)

(G-13547)
CLIMAX METAL PRODUCTS COMPANY
8141 Tyler Blvd (44060-4855)
PHONE.....................440 943-8898
Fax: 440 585-5762
Jerry Wheaton, CEO
Gerald R Wheaton, President
L G Knecht, Principal
John T White, Principal
Edward C Bartlett, COO
▲ EMP: 65 EST: 1946
SQ FT: 25,000
SALES (est): 16.2MM
SALES (corp-wide): 597.4MM **Publicly Held**
WEB: www.climaxmetal.com
SIC: 3366 3568 Bushings & bearings; couplings, shaft: rigid, flexible, universal joint, etc.; collars, shaft (power transmission equipment)
PA: Rbc Bearings Incorporated
102 Willenbrock Rd Bldg B
Oxford CT 06478
203 267-7001

(G-13548)
COASTAL DIAMOND INCORPORATED
7255 Industrial Park Blvd A (44060-5331)
PHONE.....................440 946-7171
Fax: 440 946-3181
Art Bastulli, President
Kathleen Potts, Corp Secy
Jody Kamenshy, Vice Pres
EMP: 9
SQ FT: 7,500
SALES (est): 1MM **Privately Held**
WEB: www.coastaldiamond.com
SIC: 3291 5085 Abrasive products; industrial supplies

(G-13549)
COBB INDUSTRIES INC
7605 Saint Clair Ave (44060-5235)
PHONE.....................440 946-4695
Fax: 440 946-3380
Lawrence Rokosky, President
Marcia Rokosky, Vice Pres
EMP: 4
SQ FT: 4,000
SALES: 500K **Privately Held**
SIC: 3544 Special dies, tools, jigs & fixtures

(G-13550)
COMMERCIAL DOCK & DOOR INC
7653 Saint Clair Ave (44060-5235)
PHONE.....................440 951-1210
Allen A Kovar, President
Raymond M Strumbly, Vice Pres
Tom Liebhardt, CFO
EMP: 22
SALES (est): 3.9MM **Privately Held**
SIC: 3448 Docks: prefabricated metal

(G-13551)
COMPETETIVE CARBIDE INC
Also Called: Competitive Carbide
9332 Pinecone Dr (44060-1861)
PHONE.....................440 350-9393
Fax: 440 350-9394
Tom Cirino, President
Charlie Novak, General Mgr
Erik Hennie, Engineer
Deloris Morrison, Design Engr
Ralph Lehman, Sales Engr
▲ EMP: 40
SQ FT: 10,000
SALES (est): 7.5MM **Privately Held**
WEB: www.competitivecarbide.com
SIC: 3541 Machine tools, metal cutting type

(G-13552)
CORE MANUFACTURING LLC
8878 East Ave (44060-4306)
PHONE.....................440 946-8002
Richard Stark, Director
David Sukenik, Director
Theodore Wolf, Director
EMP: 9
SALES (est): 1.4MM **Privately Held**
SIC: 3452 Bolts, nuts, rivets & washers

(G-13553)
CORE-TECH INC
7850 Enterprise Dr (44060-5310)
PHONE.....................440 946-8324
Fax: 440 946-8325
Jim Corbett, President
Gary Uterhark, Engineer
Greg Castillo, Sales Executive
Paul Lynch, Manager
Deneen Tyler, Manager
EMP: 5
SQ FT: 14,000
SALES (est): 1MM **Privately Held**
WEB: www.core-tech-inc.com
SIC: 3599 Machine shop, jobbing & repair

(G-13554)
CR SUPPLY LLC
7661 Ohio St (44060-4848)
PHONE.....................440 759-5408
Robert Hemly, Mng Member
EMP: 1 EST: 2015
SQ FT: 2,500
SALES: 1MM **Privately Held**
SIC: 3545 Cutting tools for machine tools

(G-13555)
CRESCENT METAL PRODUCTS INC (PA)
Also Called: Cres Cor
5925 Heisley Rd (44060-1833)
PHONE.....................440 350-1100
Fax: 440 358-7140
Clifford D Baggott, Principal
Rio Degennaro, Vice Pres
Chad Fisher, Electrical Engi
Gregory D Baggott, Treasurer
Marie Nemanic, Manager
▲ EMP: 171 EST: 1947
SALES (est): 33.6MM **Privately Held**
WEB: www.crescor.com
SIC: 3556 3567 3537 2542 Food products machinery; industrial furnaces & ovens; industrial trucks & tractors; partitions & fixtures, except wood

(G-13556)
CREST PRODUCTS INC
Also Called: Crest Aluminum Products
8287 Tyler Blvd (44060-4218)
PHONE.....................440 942-5770
Fax: 440 255-1577
John M Allin, President
Timothy Antos, Vice Pres

Peter Antos, *Treasurer*
Nancy Worden, *Admin Sec*
EMP: 18 **EST:** 1966
SQ FT: 41,500
SALES (est): 4.3MM **Privately Held**
WEB: www.crestproducts.com
SIC: 3444 7389 Awnings, sheet metal;
metal slitting & shearing

(G-13557)
D & L OVERHEAD DOOR CO LTD
9118 Tyler Blvd (44060-1881)
P.O. Box 1298 (44061-1298)
PHONE..........................440 255-9720
Fax: 440 255-1136
Edward Fitzgerald, *Partner*
Mark Hendricks, *Branch Mgr*
EMP: 4
SALES (est): 565.2K **Privately Held**
SIC: 2431 Garage doors, overhead: wood

(G-13558)
DANAHER CORPORATION
7171 Industrial Park Blvd (44060-5351)
PHONE..........................440 995-3025
Mary Niederer, *Principal*
EMP: 173
SALES (corp-wide): 16.8B **Publicly Held**
SIC: 3823 Water quality monitoring & control systems
PA: Danaher Corporation
2200 Penn Ave Nw Ste 800w
Washington DC 20037
202 828-0850

(G-13559)
DAVENPORT SERVICE GROUP INC
7561 Tyler Blvd Ste 9 (44060-4867)
PHONE..........................440 487-9353
Bart Davenport, *President*
Jennifer Davenport, *Treasurer*
EMP: 2
SALES: 1MM **Privately Held**
SIC: 7692 Welding repair

(G-13560)
DEEPWOOD ROLL TOOLING
7591 Tyler Blvd Ste 3 (44060-4873)
PHONE..........................440 946-5640
Fax: 440 946-5640
Lee Spotts, *Owner*
Keith Roberts, *Manager*
EMP: 4
SQ FT: 1,800
SALES (est): 240K **Privately Held**
SIC: 3544 Special dies & tools

(G-13561)
DMI PRODUCTS INC
7177 Industrial Park Blvd (44060-5327)
PHONE..........................440 951-1828
Mark Van, *Branch Mgr*
EMP: 5
SALES (corp-wide): 1.1MM **Privately Held**
SIC: 5087 5046 3999 Restaurant supplies; commercial cooking & food service equipment; barber & beauty shop equipment
PA: Dmi Products, Inc.
7177 Industrial Park Blvd
Mentor OH 44060
440 975-8645

(G-13562)
DMI PRODUCTS INC (PA)
7177 Industrial Park Blvd (44060-5327)
PHONE..........................440 975-8645
Joe Bondi, *President*
Sam Steinhouse, *Exec VP*
Denise Bangasser, *Vice Pres*
Mark Bangasser, *Vice Pres*
Ilona Emmerth, *Shareholder*
▲ **EMP:** 10
SQ FT: 4,800
SALES (est): 1.1MM **Privately Held**
WEB: www.dmiparts.com
SIC: 3433 Burners, furnaces, boilers & stokers; gas infrared heating units

(G-13563)
DOVER CORPORATION
7201 Industrial Park Blvd (44060-5315)
PHONE..........................440 951-6600
Theodore Caldwell, *Branch Mgr*

EMP: 5
SALES (corp-wide): 6.7B **Publicly Held**
SIC: 3592 Pistons & piston rings
PA: Dover Corporation
3005 Highland Pkwy # 200
Downers Grove IL 60515
630 541-1540

(G-13564)
DRILLEX INC (PA)
Also Called: Fairway Pines Golf Course
8100 Deepwood Blvd (44060-7704)
PHONE..........................440 255-7500
Fax: 440 255-8079
Edward Tresger, *President*
Mary Tresger, *Manager*
EMP: 8
SQ FT: 1,000
SALES (est): 974.4K **Privately Held**
WEB: www.drillex.com
SIC: 1311 1381 7992 Crude petroleum & natural gas; drilling oil & gas wells; public golf courses

(G-13565)
DRUMMOND DOLOMITE INC
Also Called: Drummond Dolomite Quarry
7954 Reynolds Rd (44060-5334)
P.O. Box 658 (44061-0658)
PHONE..........................440 942-7000
Jerome T Osborne, *President*
Harold T Larned, *Vice Pres*
Ilda Hayden, *Admin Sec*
EMP: 10
SALES (est): 740K **Privately Held**
SIC: 1422 Dolomite, crushed & broken-quarrying

(G-13566)
DRYCAL INC
7355 Production Dr (44060-4858)
PHONE..........................440 974-1999
Fax: 440 974-7159
Margus Sweigard, *President*
Lembit Sweigard, *Vice Pres*
EMP: 8
SQ FT: 14,500
SALES (est): 900K **Privately Held**
WEB: www.drycal.com
SIC: 2759 Screen printing

(G-13567)
DYNA-FLEX INC
7300 Industrial Park Blvd (44060-5318)
PHONE..........................440 946-9424
Fax: 440 946-4620
James D'Amico, *President*
Bob Ritchie, *General Mgr*
Michael Damico, *Managing Dir*
Barbara D'Amico, *Vice Pres*
Jim Ritchie, *Engineer*
▲ **EMP:** 10
SALES (est): 1MM **Privately Held**
WEB: www.flexinc.com
SIC: 3492 Hose & tube couplings, hydraulic/pneumatic

(G-13568)
DYNAMIC SPECIALTIES INC
7471 Tyler Blvd Ste E (44060-5413)
PHONE..........................440 946-2838
Fax: 440 946-2838
Charles Heinrich, *CEO*
Dorothy Heinrich, *Admin Sec*
EMP: 3
SQ FT: 3,500
SALES: 100K **Privately Held**
SIC: 7692 Welding repair

(G-13569)
EASTERN SLIPCOVER COMPANY INC
6399 Cumberland Dr (44060-2465)
PHONE..........................440 951-2310
John E Bolden, *President*
Pat Bolden, *Vice Pres*
EMP: 5
SQ FT: 1,300
SALES (est): 447.3K **Privately Held**
SIC: 2392 Slipcovers: made of fabric, plastic etc.

(G-13570)
EASY BOARD INC
8621 Station St (44060-4336)
PHONE..........................440 205-8836

Sean Meaney, *President*
EMP: 5
SQ FT: 4,000
SALES: 400K **Privately Held**
WEB: www.easyboardinc.com
SIC: 2542 Office & store showcases & display fixtures

(G-13571)
ELLEN L ELLSWORTH
9930 Johnnycake Ridge Rd 4b
(44060-6752)
PHONE..........................440 352-8031
Fax: 440 352-7671
Ellen L Ellsworth, *Owner*
EMP: 5
SALES (est): 481.3K **Privately Held**
SIC: 3841 Optometers

(G-13572)
EMBROIDERED ID INC
Also Called: Embroidered Identity
7845 Hidden Hollow Dr (44060-7316)
PHONE..........................440 974-8113
Jacklyn Fatica, *President*
Diana Palmer, *Vice Pres*
EMP: 3
SQ FT: 1,200
SALES: 500K **Privately Held**
SIC: 5131 5949 2395 Sewing accessories; sewing, needlework & piece goods; embroidery products, except schiffli machine

(G-13573)
ENTERPRISE C N C INC
9280 Pineneedle Dr (44060-1824)
PHONE..........................440 354-3868
Fax: 440 354-3868
Ivan Katic, *President*
Michael Katic, *Vice Pres*
Slavko Katic, *Treasurer*
Chris Weinkamer, *Admin Sec*
EMP: 4
SQ FT: 5,000
SALES: 150K **Privately Held**
SIC: 3599 Machine shop, jobbing & repair

(G-13574)
ENTERPRISE WELDING & FABG INC
6257 Heisley Rd (44060-1887)
PHONE..........................440 354-4128
Fax: 440 354-4431
Ivan Katic, *President*
Chris Weinkamer, *General Mgr*
Albert R Amigoni, *Principal*
Ben Beller, *Purchasing*
Philip Carlon, *Engineer*
EMP: 170 **EST:** 1975
SQ FT: 100,000
SALES (est): 45.7MM **Privately Held**
WEB: www.enterprisewelding.com
SIC: 3444 Sheet metalwork

(G-13575)
EVENT INC
Also Called: Progage
7555 Tyler Blvd Ste 6 (44060-4866)
PHONE..........................440 951-4477
Fax: 440 951-1326
Edward Vadakin, *President*
Paul Paliobeis, *Engineer*
EMP: 13
SQ FT: 14,000
SALES (est): 2.3MM **Privately Held**
WEB: www.progage.com
SIC: 3544 Jigs & fixtures

(G-13576)
EYE LIGHTING INTL N AMER INC
9150 Hendricks Rd (44060-2146)
PHONE..........................440 350-7000
Tsuneo Kobayashi, *CEO*
Tatsuyuki Kawajiri, *CEO*
Tom Salpietra, *President*
Christine Dibley, *Regional Mgr*
Christina Calaway, *Business Mgr*
▲ **EMP:** 170
SQ FT: 100,000

SALES (est): 29.4MM
SALES (corp-wide): 497.4MM **Privately Held**
WEB: www.eyelighting.com
SIC: 3229 3641 Pressed & blown glass; electric lamps & parts for generalized applications
PA: Iwasaki Electric Co.,Ltd.
1-4-16, Nihombashibakurocho
Chuo-Ku TKY 103-0
358 478-611

(G-13577)
EYE LIGHTNING INTERNATIONAL
8150 Hendricks Rd (44060)
PHONE..........................440 354-2938
Fax: 440 350-7001
Tom Salpietra, *President*
Philip Drone, *Engineer*
Anne Gates, *VP Finance*
Barbara Baranauskas, *Finance Mgr*
Suzanne Beatrice, *Human Res Dir*
▲ **EMP:** 58
SALES (est): 14.2MM **Privately Held**
SIC: 3641 Electric lamps

(G-13578)
FISCHER SPECIAL TOOLING CORP
7219 Commerce Dr (44060-5307)
PHONE..........................440 951-8411
Kevin Johnson, *President*
Shirley Johnson, *Corp Secy*
EMP: 14 **EST:** 1957
SQ FT: 5,000
SALES (est): 2.8MM **Privately Held**
WEB: www.fischerspecialtooling.com
SIC: 3541 3544 3545 Machine tools, metal cutting: exotic (explosive, etc.); drilling machine tools (metal cutting); reaming machines; special dies, tools, jigs & fixtures; machine tool accessories

(G-13579)
FMT REPAIR SERVICE CO
6374 Dawson Blvd (44060-3648)
PHONE..........................330 347-7374
Fax: 330 939-0222
Steve Shearer, *President*
Tom Warnick, *Vice Pres*
EMP: 3
SALES (est): 329.6K **Privately Held**
SIC: 3549 7699 1796 Wiredrawing & fabricating machinery & equipment, ex. die; mechanical instrument repair; installing building equipment

(G-13580)
FORMASTERS CORPORATION
5959 Pinecone Dr (44060-1866)
PHONE..........................440 639-9206
Fax: 440 639-9206
John J Ferguson, *President*
Pamela Ferguson, *Plant Mgr*
Annette Blashinsky, *Office Mgr*
EMP: 12
SQ FT: 10,500
SALES (est): 2.9MM **Privately Held**
SIC: 3469 3449 Metal stampings; custom roll formed products

(G-13581)
FOUNDRY SUPPORT OPERATION
7849 Enterprise Dr (44060-5309)
PHONE..........................440 951-4142
Joshua Corvett, *Principal*
EMP: 15
SALES (est): 1MM **Privately Held**
SIC: 3471 Finishing, metals or formed products

(G-13582)
FRANTZ MEDICAL DEVELOPMENT LTD (PA)
7740 Metric Dr (44060-4862)
PHONE..........................212 308-4860
Fax: 440 255-6975
Mark G Frantz, *President*
J Paul Hanson, *Vice Pres*
Stephanie Harrington, *Vice Pres*
Jeffrey Dunlop, *CFO*
Marc Penn, *Director*
EMP: 8

▲ = Import ▼=Export
◆ =Import/Export

SQ FT: 3,750
SALES (est): 13.1MM **Privately Held**
WEB: www.frantz.com
SIC: 3841 3089 Surgical & medical instruments; injection molding of plastics

(G-13583)
FRANTZ MEDICAL DEVELOPMENT LTD
7740 Metric Dr (44060-4862)
PHONE.................................440 205-9026
Paul Hanson, *Exec VP*
Joe Lasher, *Opers-Prdtn-Mfg*
Jason Lisy, *Engineer*
EMP: 75
SQ FT: 3,000
SALES (corp-wide): 13.1MM **Privately Held**
WEB: www.frantz.com
SIC: 3841 3561 Surgical & medical instruments; pumps & pumping equipment
PA: Frantz Medical Development Ltd.
7740 Metric Dr
Mentor OH 44060
212 308-4860

(G-13584)
FREDON CORPORATION
8990 Tyler Blvd (44060-5368)
P.O. Box 600 (44061-0600)
PHONE.................................440 951-5200
Fax: 440 951-5200
Roger J Sustar, *CEO*
Alyson Scott, *President*
Richard Ditto, *Vice Pres*
Chris Sustar, *Vice Pres*
Arthur Hollis, *Manager*
▼ **EMP:** 80
SQ FT: 70,000
SALES (est): 16.2MM **Privately Held**
WEB: www.fredon.com
SIC: 3599 3541 Custom machinery; grinding machines, metalworking

(G-13585)
FREPEG INDUSTRIES INC
8624 East Ave (44060-4365)
PHONE.................................440 255-8595
Fax: 440 205-0433
Fred Stout, *President*
Peggy Stout, *Vice Pres*
EMP: 15
SQ FT: 8,000
SALES (est): 1.5MM **Privately Held**
SIC: 3469 Metal stampings

(G-13586)
FROYO TWIST
7267 Center St (44060-4907)
PHONE.................................440 974-1001
Ed Sammon, *Principal*
EMP: 5 **EST:** 2011
SALES (est): 312.5K **Privately Held**
SIC: 2024 Ice cream, bulk

(G-13587)
FULTON SIGN & DECAL INC
7144 Industrial Park Blvd (44060-5314)
PHONE.................................440 951-1515
Fax: 440 951-2727
Charles Fulton, *President*
Gary Fulton, *General Mgr*
Gertrude Fulton, *Vice Pres*
Robert B Fulton, *Treasurer*
EMP: 6 **EST:** 1969
SQ FT: 5,000
SALES (est): 500K **Privately Held**
SIC: 2759 Screen printing

(G-13588)
G & T MANUFACTURING CO
6085 Pinecone Dr (44060-1866)
PHONE.................................440 639-7777
Fax: 440 639-7770
Gerald Cutts, *President*
Thomas B Cutts, *President*
Pat Caticchio, *Principal*
Beverly Cutts, *Corp Secy*
Thomas Keptner, *Accountant*
EMP: 19
SQ FT: 6,200
SALES (est): 3.1MM **Privately Held**
WEB: www.gtmanufacturingco.com
SIC: 3531 3537 Aerial work platforms: hydraulic/elec. truck/carrier mounted; industrial trucks & tractors

(G-13589)
G T M ASSOCIATES INC
7112 Industrial Park Blvd (44060-5314)
PHONE.................................440 951-0006
Antone Mutter, *President*
EMP: 4
SALES (est): 340K **Privately Held**
WEB: www.gtmassociates.com
SIC: 3599 Machine shop, jobbing & repair

(G-13590)
GDJ INC
Also Called: Technology Explortation Pdts
7585 Tyler Blvd (44060-4869)
PHONE.................................440 975-0258
Jack Gilbert, *President*
Deborah Gilbert, *Vice Pres*
EMP: 6
SQ FT: 6,500
SALES (est): 660K **Privately Held**
SIC: 3821 Laboratory equipment: fume hoods, distillation racks, etc.

(G-13591)
GENERAL GLASS & SCREEN INC
6095 Pinecone Dr (44060-1866)
PHONE.................................440 350-9033
Stephen Rostar, *President*
Heidi Rostar, *Vice Pres*
EMP: 4
SQ FT: 3,900
SALES (est): 625.6K **Privately Held**
SIC: 5231 3231 Glass; products of purchased glass

(G-13592)
GENESIS QUALITY PRINTING INC
7250 Commerce Dr Ste G (44060-5332)
P.O. Box 5157, Eastlake (44095-0157)
PHONE.................................440 975-5700
Fax: 440 975-5701
Edward Dulzer, *President*
EMP: 3
SQ FT: 1,700
SALES (est): 260.8K **Privately Held**
SIC: 2759 2791 2752 Commercial printing; typesetting; commercial printing, lithographic

(G-13593)
GLO-QUARTZ ELECTRIC HEATER CO
7084 Maple St (44060-4932)
P.O. Box 358 (44061-0358)
PHONE.................................440 255-9701
Fax: 440 255-7852
George T Strokes, *President*
Nancy L Strokes, *Corp Secy*
Thomas M Strokes, *Exec VP*
Jeffrey Payne, *Plant Mgr*
EMP: 25 **EST:** 1952
SQ FT: 22,000
SALES (est): 5.9MM **Privately Held**
SIC: 3567 3823 3634 3433 Heating units & devices, industrial: electric; electric instrmnts msrmnt display/control process variable; electric housewares & fans; heating equipment, except electric

(G-13594)
GLOBAL MANUFACTURING TECH LLC
8671 Tyler Blvd Unit F (44060-4347)
PHONE.................................440 205-1001
Jeffrey T Rose,
Kenny Anderson,
EMP: 5
SQ FT: 6,000
SALES: 234K **Privately Held**
SIC: 3469 Machine parts, stamped or pressed metal

(G-13595)
GOAL MEDICAL LLC
7555 Tyler Blvd (44060-4866)
PHONE.................................541 654-5951
Scott Cottrell, *President*
EMP: 25 **EST:** 2013
SQ FT: 5,000
SALES (est): 1.3MM **Privately Held**
SIC: 3841 Surgical & medical instruments

(G-13596)
GREAT LAKES POWER PRODUCTS INC (PA)
Also Called: John Deere Authorized Dealer
7455 Tyler Blvd (44060-8389)
PHONE.................................440 951-5111
Fax: 216 953-1052
Harry Allen Jr, *CEO*
Harry L Allen Jr, *Ch of Bd*
Richard J Pennza, *President*
David Bell, *Vice Pres*
Sam Profio, *Vice Pres*
▲ **EMP:** 60
SQ FT: 55,000
SALES (est): 33.7MM **Privately Held**
WEB: www.glpowerlift.com
SIC: 5085 5084 3566 Power transmission equipment & apparatus; materials handling machinery; speed changers (power transmission equipment), except auto

(G-13597)
GTD MACHINE INC
7875 Enterprise Dr (44060-5309)
P.O. Box 106, Madison (44057-0106)
PHONE.................................440 812-6877
Fax: 440 951-5158
Timothy G Repko, *President*
Diana Repko, *Corp Secy*
EMP: 5
SQ FT: 12,000
SALES (est): 350K **Privately Held**
SIC: 3451 Screw machine products

(G-13598)
HABCO TOOL AND DEV CO INC
7725 Metric Dr (44060-4863)
PHONE.................................440 946-5546
Fax: 440 255-8122
Steven Sanders, *President*
Ron Giannetti, *Exec VP*
James Patchin, *Plant Mgr*
Kathy Fulmer, *Purchasing*
Cathy Fulmer, *Manager*
EMP: 46 **EST:** 1955
SQ FT: 24,000
SALES: 3MM **Privately Held**
WEB: www.habcotool.com
SIC: 3599 7692 Machine shop, jobbing & repair; welding repair

(G-13599)
HALF PRICE BKS REC MGZINES INC
9383 Mentor Ave (44060-6413)
PHONE.................................440 255-2581
Kerry West, *Branch Mgr*
EMP: 17
SALES (corp-wide): 250.9MM **Privately Held**
SIC: 2721 5932 Magazines: publishing & printing; book stores, secondhand
PA: Half Price Books, Records, Magazines, Incorporated
5803 E Northwest Hwy
Dallas TX 75231
214 379-8000

(G-13600)
HEATSTAR
7547 Mentor Ave Ste 304 (44060-5432)
PHONE.................................440 701-1031
EMP: 3
SALES (est): 192.5K **Privately Held**
SIC: 3471 Finishing, metals or formed products

(G-13601)
HI TEK MOLD
7777 Saint Clair Ave (44060-5237)
PHONE.................................440 942-4090
EMP: 7
SQ FT: 7,500
SALES (est): 370K **Privately Held**
SIC: 3089 Mfg Plastic Injection Molds

(G-13602)
HIGHLAND PRODUCTS CORP
9331 Mercantile Dr (44060-4523)
PHONE.................................440 352-4777
Mark Erickson, *President*
Jeanne Wojciechowicz, *Corp Secy*
EMP: 10
SQ FT: 11,000

SALES (est): 1MM **Privately Held**
SIC: 3599 Machine & other job shop work

(G-13603)
HOB ENTERPRISES LLC
Also Called: House of Blinds and More
8255 Mentor Ave (44060-5730)
PHONE.................................440 290-8861
Brian Ross, *Branch Mgr*
EMP: 5
SALES (corp-wide): 13.7MM **Privately Held**
WEB: www.everythingforwindows.com
SIC: 5719 2591 Window furnishings; venetian blinds; window shades; mini blinds; window shades
PA: Hob Enterprises, Llc
21472 Bridge St
Southfield MI 48033
248 357-4710

(G-13604)
HOLLOW BORING INC
7832 Enterprise Dr (44060-5310)
P.O. Box 58 (44061-0058)
PHONE.................................440 951-2929
Fax: 440 951-2929
Joseph Cerne, *President*
EMP: 4
SQ FT: 3,000
SALES (est): 458.2K **Privately Held**
SIC: 3599 Machine shop, jobbing & repair

(G-13605)
HYPROLAP FINISHING CO
9300 Pinecone Dr (44060-1861)
PHONE.................................440 352-0270
Elmer Guiher, *President*
Beverly Guiher, *Treasurer*
Jennifer Bothwell, *CIO*
EMP: 5
SQ FT: 7,000
SALES (est): 600K **Privately Held**
SIC: 3599 Machine shop, jobbing & repair

(G-13606)
INDUSTRIAL QUARTZ CORP
7552 Saint Clair Ave D (44060-5201)
PHONE.................................440 942-0909
Fax: 440 942-0909
Richard Intihar, *President*
Susan Pedaci, *Sales Staff*
Bob Intihar, *Sales Executive*
Sue Kozlowski, *Office Mgr*
EMP: 19
SQ FT: 10,000
SALES: 3.6MM **Privately Held**
SIC: 3295 3769 3677 3498 Minerals, ground or treated; guided missile & space vehicle parts & auxiliary equipment; electronic coils, transformers & other inductors; fabricated pipe & fittings

(G-13607)
INDUSTRIAL SYSTEMS & SOLUTIONS
Also Called: ISS
8812 Tyler Blvd (44060-4361)
PHONE.................................440 205-1658
David Kelley, *President*
Dawn Hoban, *CFO*
EMP: 3
SQ FT: 2,200
SALES: 100K **Privately Held**
WEB: www.industrialss.com
SIC: 3694 Distributors, motor vehicle engine

(G-13608)
INDUSTRIAL THERMOSET PLAS INC
Also Called: I.T. Plastics
7675 Jenther Dr (44060-4872)
PHONE.................................440 975-0411
Fax: 440 354-9355
Jack Schriner, *President*
EMP: 10
SQ FT: 8,000
SALES (est): 1.2MM **Privately Held**
WEB: www.itplastics.com
SIC: 3479 Coating of metals with plastic or resins

GEOGRAPHIC

(G-13609)
INTEGRATED MED SOLUTIONS INC
7124 Industrial Park Blvd (44060-5314)
PHONE...................................440 269-6984
Mike Watts, *President*
Lee Dwyer, *Principal*
Larry Kopniske, *Purch Agent*
Gus Deangelo, *CFO*
Joe Eisenbart, *Sales Engr*
EMP: 60
SALES (est): 10MM **Privately Held**
WEB: www.astromodel.com
SIC: 3841 3842 Surgical & medical instruments; surgical appliances & supplies

(G-13610)
INTERNATIONAL HYDRAULICS INC
Also Called: Ihi Connectors R
7700 Saint Clair Ave (44060-5238)
PHONE...................................440 951-1781
Fax: 440 951-7186
Charles Ridley, *President*
Paul Ridley, *Business Mgr*
Lori Silvis, *QC Mgr*
David Hiltner, *Engineer*
Nancy Plickert, *HR Admin*
▲ EMP: 50
SQ FT: 62,000
SALES (est): 10.9MM **Privately Held**
WEB: www.ihiconnectors.com
SIC: 3643 Current-carrying wiring devices; electric connectors; connectors & terminals for electrical devices

(G-13611)
INTERPAK INC
Also Called: Roto Mold
7278 Justin Way (44060-4881)
PHONE...................................440 974-8999
Fax: 440 974-3383
Mark Shaw, *President*
Fred Razavi, *General Mgr*
Tad Heyman, *Vice Pres*
Elaine Crompton, *Controller*
Mark Eubank, *Sales Mgr*
▼ EMP: 43
SQ FT: 65,000
SALES (est): 6.4MM **Privately Held**
WEB: www.rotomold.com
SIC: 3089 Molding primary plastic

(G-13612)
ISOMEDIX INC
5960 Heisley Rd (44060-1834)
PHONE...................................440 354-2600
▲ EMP: 13
SALES (est): 3MM
SALES (corp-wide): 2.2B **Privately Held**
WEB: www.steris.com
SIC: 3842 Surgical appliances & supplies
HQ: Steris Corporation
5960 Heisley Rd
Mentor OH 44060
440 354-2600

(G-13613)
J & C GROUP INC OF OHIO
6781 Hopkins Rd (44060-4311)
PHONE...................................440 205-9658
James J Smolik, *President*
Christine Smolik, *Shareholder*
▲ EMP: 22
SQ FT: 13,000
SALES (est): 4.1MM **Privately Held**
SIC: 3679 Electronic circuits

(G-13614)
J & L MANAGEMENT CORPORATION
Also Called: Kramer Printing
8634 Station St (44060-4316)
PHONE...................................440 205-1199
Fax: 440 205-1188
Leonard Kramer, *Partner*
Gerald Kramer, *Partner*
Sarah Kramer, *Sales Staff*
EMP: 6
SQ FT: 7,000
SALES (est): 630K **Privately Held**
SIC: 2752 2732 Commercial printing, lithographic; book printing

(G-13615)
J & M CUTTING TOOLS INC
9401 Hamilton Dr (44060-8709)
PHONE...................................440 622-3900
Fax: 440 354-2325
Michael Cunningham, *President*
Joanne Cunningham, *Corp Secy*
EMP: 8
SQ FT: 3,200
SALES (est): 790K **Privately Held**
WEB: www.jmcuttingtools.com
SIC: 3451 Screw machine products

(G-13616)
J & P PRODUCTS INC
Also Called: Specialties Unlimited
8865 East Ave (44060-4305)
PHONE...................................440 974-2830
Fax: 440 951-4570
Paul Jonke, *President*
Dennis Jonke, *Admin Sec*
EMP: 34
SQ FT: 18,000
SALES (est): 5.3MM **Privately Held**
WEB: www.specialtiesunlimited.net
SIC: 3599 Machine shop, jobbing & repair

(G-13617)
JACK G WALKER
Also Called: Walker Printing Co
9517 Jackson St (44060-4515)
PHONE...................................440 352-4222
Fax: 440 357-0211
Jack Walker, *Owner*
Mike Walker, *Vice Pres*
Heather Vonspeegle, *Marketing Staff*
▲ EMP: 18
SQ FT: 3,500
SALES (est): 1.3MM **Privately Held**
SIC: 2752 2791 2789 2759 Commercial printing, lithographic; typesetting; bookbinding & related work; commercial printing

(G-13618)
JADE PRODUCTS INC
9309 Mercantile Dr (44060-4523)
PHONE...................................440 352-1700
Fax: 440 352-9034
John Erickson, *President*
EMP: 17
SQ FT: 5,500
SALES (est): 2.8MM **Privately Held**
SIC: 3599 Machine & other job shop work

(G-13619)
JJ SLEEVES INC
6850 Patterson Dr (44060-4331)
PHONE...................................440 205-1055
Allen Beach, *Sales Mgr*
EMP: 8
SALES: 800K **Privately Held**
WEB: www.advancedsleeve.com
SIC: 3599 Machine shop, jobbing & repair

(G-13620)
JOHN D OIL AND GAS COMPANY
7001 Center St (44060-4933)
P.O. Box 5069 (44061-5069)
PHONE...................................440 255-6325
Richard M Osborne, *Ch of Bd*
Timothy P Reilly, *President*
Gregory J Osbourne, *COO*
William Sochor, *Research*
Carolyn Coatoam, *CFO*
EMP: 7
SALES (est): 1.8MM **Privately Held**
SIC: 1382 1311 4225 Oil & gas exploration services; crude petroleum & natural gas production; warehousing, self-storage

(G-13621)
JOHNSTON MANUFACTURING INC
Also Called: J M C Rollmasters
7611 Saint Clair Ave (44060-5235)
PHONE...................................440 269-1420
Fax: 440 269-1410
Dennis Johnston, *President*
Marsha Johnston, *Corp Secy*
Bruce Weber, *Engineer*
EMP: 8
SQ FT: 8,500

SALES (est): 1.5MM **Privately Held**
SIC: 3544 Special dies & tools

(G-13622)
KAEPER MACHINE INC
8680 Twinbrook Rd (44060-4341)
PHONE...................................440 974-1010
Kye Hwang, *President*
Jinu Hwang, *Vice Pres*
EMP: 8 EST: 1998
SALES (est): 2.9MM **Privately Held**
SIC: 3545 Machine tool accessories

(G-13623)
KITCHEN & BATH FACTORY INC
7170 Hawthorne Dr (44060-4631)
PHONE...................................440 510-8111
Fax: 440 946-4560
Louis Hundza, *President*
EMP: 3
SALES (est): 278.3K **Privately Held**
SIC: 2541 Counter & sink tops

(G-13624)
KSI DISTRIBUTION INC (PA)
8724 Tyler Blvd (44060-4350)
PHONE...................................440 256-2500
Lynn Keegan, *Principal*
James P Keegan, *Principal*
EMP: 3
SALES (est): 407.6K **Privately Held**
SIC: 3465 Body parts, automobile: stamped metal

(G-13625)
L B WEISS CONSTRUCTION INC
Also Called: Weiss Construction & Sewer
8677 Twinbrook Rd (44060-4340)
PHONE...................................440 205-1774
L Weiss, *President*
Lavele Weiss, *President*
Shirley Weiss, *Admin Sec*
EMP: 4
SQ FT: 3,600
SALES (est): 600.5K **Privately Held**
SIC: 3272 Sewer pipe, concrete

(G-13626)
L J MANUFACTURING INC
9436 Mercantile Dr (44060-1889)
PHONE...................................440 352-1979
Fax: 440 352-0777
Michael Ball, *President*
Darlene Ball, *Admin Sec*
EMP: 8
SQ FT: 10,000
SALES (est): 810K **Privately Held**
WEB: www.ljmfg.com
SIC: 3599 Machine shop, jobbing & repair

(G-13627)
LAKE COUNTY PLATING CORP
7790 Division Dr (44060-4860)
PHONE...................................440 255-8835
Fax: 440 255-8841
Charles H Dowling, *President*
Janet Dowling, *Vice Pres*
EMP: 10 EST: 1958
SQ FT: 20,000
SALES (est): 660K **Privately Held**
WEB: www.lakecountyplating.com
SIC: 3471 Plating of metals or formed products

(G-13628)
LAKE PUBLISHING INC
Also Called: Callender Group, The
9853 Johnnycake Ridge Rd # 107 (44060-6700)
PHONE...................................440 299-8500
James S Callender Jr, *Principal*
Heidi Callender, *Officer*
Sarah Gunnoe, *Assistant*
EMP: 7 EST: 2009
SQ FT: 1,100
SALES (est): 387.6K **Privately Held**
SIC: 2741 8748 Miscellaneous publishing; business consulting

(G-13629)
LANKO INDUSTRIES INC
7301 Industrial Park Blvd (44060-5317)
PHONE...................................440 269-1641
Fax: 440 975-0471
John Lanphier, *President*
George Hickey, *Branch Mgr*

Shannon Myers, *Manager*
Susan Lanphier, *Admin Sec*
EMP: 8
SQ FT: 9,000
SALES (est): 770K **Privately Held**
SIC: 3544 Wire drawing & straightening dies

(G-13630)
LASERDEALER INC
9323 Hamilton Dr (44060-4559)
PHONE...................................440 357-8419
R Burns, *Principal*
EMP: 3
SALES (est): 122.8K **Privately Held**
WEB: www.laserdealer.com
SIC: 3479 Name plates: engraved, etched, etc.

(G-13631)
LIBRA INDUSTRIES INC (PA)
7770 Division Dr (44060-4860)
PHONE...................................440 974-7770
Fax: 440 974-7770
Rod Howell, *CEO*
Albert Catani, *COO*
Basil May, *Purch Mgr*
Job Bonilla, *Sales Engr*
Terry Frederick, *Manager*
EMP: 120 EST: 1980
SQ FT: 52,000
SALES (est): 41.5MM **Privately Held**
WEB: www.libraind.com
SIC: 3699 Electrical equipment & supplies

(G-13632)
LIBRA INDUSTRIES INC
7715 Metric Dr (44060-4863)
PHONE...................................440 974-7770
Ron Rehberger, *Mfg Mgr*
EMP: 40
SALES (corp-wide): 41.5MM **Privately Held**
WEB: www.libraind.com
SIC: 3672 Printed circuit boards
PA: Libra Industries, Inc.
7770 Division Dr
Mentor OH 44060
440 974-7770

(G-13633)
LIDS CORPORATION
7850 Mentor Ave Ste 542 (44060-5520)
PHONE...................................440 974-9127
Erick Marpecei, *Manager*
EMP: 3
SALES (corp-wide): 2.8B **Publicly Held**
WEB: www.hatworld.com
SIC: 2353 Hats & caps
HQ: Lids Corporation
7555 Woodland Dr
Indianapolis IN 46278

(G-13634)
LINCOLN ELECTRIC HOLDINGS INC
Mentor Mfg Fcilty Div
6500 Heisley Rd (44060-1805)
PHONE...................................440 255-7696
Fax: 440 974-6969
Jeff Iannini, *Plant Mgr*
Pat Dimassa, *QC Dir*
Bill Cooper, *Engineer*
Herb Matthews, *Engineer*
Jeremy Addis, *Plant Engr*
EMP: 540
SALES (corp-wide): 2.2B **Publicly Held**
WEB: www.lincolnelectric.com
SIC: 3548 Welding wire, bare & coated
PA: Lincoln Electric Holdings, Inc.
22801 Saint Clair Ave
Cleveland OH 44117
216 481-8100

(G-13635)
LINTERN CORPORATION (PA)
8685 Station St (44060-4336)
P.O. Box 90 (44061-0090)
PHONE...................................440 255-9333
Fax: 440 255-9333
Richard K Lintern, *President*
Ray Ohler, *Vice Pres*
Beixiong Zhang, *Vice Pres*
James Lynch, *Purch Dir*
Louann Zook, *Purch Agent*
▲ EMP: 35

SQ FT: 22,500
SALES: 7.1MM Privately Held
WEB: www.lintern.com
SIC: 3585 3714 3648 Air conditioning
units, complete: domestic or industrial;
heaters, motor vehicle; filters: oil, fuel &
air, motor vehicle; lanterns: electric, gas,
carbide, kerosene or gasoline

(G-13636)
**LOECY PRECISION
MANUFACTURING**
9180 Hilo Farm Dr (44060-7935)
PHONE....................................440 358-0551
Fax: 440 358-0552
Steve Loecy, President
Terry Princic, Office Mgr
EMP: 14
SQ FT: 15,000
SALES (est): 2MM Privately Held
WEB: www.loecyprecision.com
SIC: 3599 Machine shop, jobbing & repair

(G-13637)
LUMINAUD INC
8688 Tyler Blvd (44060-4348)
PHONE....................................440 255-9082
Fax: 440 255-2250
Thomas Lennox, President
Dorothy Lennox, Vice Pres
EMP: 7
SQ FT: 5,000
SALES (est): 1.1MM Privately Held
SIC: 3842 Prosthetic appliances

(G-13638)
M & S ACQUISTION CO LLC
Also Called: Miltronics & Skye
9470 Pinecone Dr (44060-1863)
PHONE....................................440 951-8700
Marty Cole, Plant Mgr
David Fox, Manager
William Stuart,
EMP: 20
SQ FT: 33,000
SALES (est): 2.1MM
SALES (corp-wide): 26.4MM Privately
Held
WEB: www.trust-tech.com
SIC: 3841 3842 Surgical & medical instru-
ments; surgical appliances & supplies
PA: Kilroy Company
34929 Curtis Blvd Ste 104
Eastlake OH 44095
440 951-8700

(G-13639)
M P MACHINE INC
8743 East Ave (44060-4303)
PHONE....................................440 255-8355
Fax: 440 255-0978
Bennie Barbera, President
Cettina Barbera, Admin Sec
EMP: 3
SQ FT: 4,000
SALES (est): 411.1K Privately Held
SIC: 3599 Machine shop, jobbing & repair

(G-13640)
**MAC DHUI PROBE OF AMERICA
INC**
7867 Enterprise Dr 9 (44060-5309)
PHONE....................................440 942-5597
Raymond Janasek, President
EMP: 3 EST: 1980
SQ FT: 1,200
SALES (est): 180K Privately Held
SIC: 3841 Probes, surgical

(G-13641)
MACEK INDUSTRIES
8830 Tyler Blvd (44060-4361)
PHONE....................................440 205-8711
James Macek, Owner
EMP: 4
SQ FT: 2,000
SALES: 450K Privately Held
SIC: 3544 Special dies, tools, jigs & fix-
tures

(G-13642)
MAG MACHINE INC
7243 Industrial Park Blvd (44060-5315)
PHONE....................................440 946-3381
Michael R Spehar, President
EMP: 4

SQ FT: 1,640
SALES (est): 467.8K Privately Held
SIC: 3599 Machine shop, jobbing & repair

(G-13643)
MAG-NIF INC
8820 East Ave (44060-4390)
P.O. Box 720 (44061-0720)
PHONE....................................440 946-4308
Fax: 440 946-4308
William W Knox Jr, Ch of Bd
Dennis Delaat, Vice Pres
Jay Knox, Vice Pres
Don Rapposelli, Purch Agent
Jim Weiss, Treasurer
▲ EMP: 100
SQ FT: 180,000
SALES: 18.7MM Privately Held
WEB: www.magnif.com
SIC: 3944 3089 Banks, toy; puzzles; injec-
tion molding of plastics

(G-13644)
MALISH CORPORATION (PA)
7333 Corporate Blvd (44060-4857)
PHONE....................................440 951-5356
Jeffery J Malish, President
Ken Shary, President
Gordon Overs, COO
Fred Lombardi, Vice Pres
Jerry Schemm, Project Mgr
◆ EMP: 115 EST: 1948
SQ FT: 82,000
SALES: 23.5MM Privately Held
WEB: www.malish.com
SIC: 3991 3089 Brushes, household or in-
dustrial; extruded finished plastic products

(G-13645)
MALONE SPECIALTY INC
8900 East Ave (44060-4306)
PHONE....................................440 255-4200
Fax: 440 255-0458
Donald L Malone, CEO
Steven Malone, President
▲ EMP: 12
SQ FT: 10,000
SALES (est): 4.1MM Privately Held
WEB: www.malonespecialtyinc.com
SIC: 5013 3492 Truck parts & acces-
sories; hose & tube fittings & assemblies,
hydraulic/pneumatic

(G-13646)
**MARTIN & MARIANNE TOOLS
INC**
9335 Kathleen Dr (44060-4479)
PHONE....................................440 255-5107
Martin Sherman, President
EMP: 6
SALES (est): 656.2K Privately Held
SIC: 3541 Drilling machine tools (metal
cutting)

(G-13647)
**MASTER CARBIDE TOOLS
COMPANY**
Also Called: Mastertech Diamond Products
Co
9423 Mercantile Dr (44060-4524)
PHONE....................................440 352-1112
Fax: 440 352-1113
Thomas Frakes, President
Cynthia Frakes, Vice Pres
EMP: 16 EST: 1946
SQ FT: 5,000
SALES (est): 1.5MM Privately Held
WEB: www.mastertechdiamond.com
SIC: 3545 Machine tool accessories

(G-13648)
MATRIX TOOL & MACHINE INC
7870 Division Dr (44060-4874)
PHONE....................................440 255-0300
Fax: 440 255-0300
Richard Wilson, President
George Maust, Vice Pres
Alan Bockmuller, Admin Sec
EMP: 24
SQ FT: 20,000
SALES (est): 3.8MM Privately Held
SIC: 3599 3545 Custom machinery; ma-
chine tool accessories

(G-13649)
MC SIGN COMPANY (PA)
8959 Tyler Blvd (44060-2184)
PHONE....................................440 209-6200
Fax: 440 992-8882
Tim Eippert, President
James Peake, Sales Staff
Jeff Puffenbarger, Manager
Jim Mueller, CTO
Mary Dieter, Admin Asst
▲ EMP: 130 EST: 1995
SALES (est): 41.2MM Privately Held
WEB: www.mcsign.com
SIC: 3993 2752 7336 Signs & advertising
specialties; commercial printing, litho-
graphic; commercial art & graphic design

(G-13650)
**MEDALLION LIGHTING
CORPORATION**
Also Called: Complements Lighting
8710 East Ave (44060-4304)
P.O. Box 51 (44061-0051)
PHONE....................................440 255-8383
Fax: 440 255-6981
William A Knuff, President
Kenneth Maclean, COO
Michael Lynch, Plant Mgr
Scott Spaulding, Sales Dir
Greg Swan, Information Mgr
◆ EMP: 40 EST: 1982
SQ FT: 50,000
SALES (est): 7.4MM Privately Held
WEB: www.medallionlighting.com
SIC: 3645 3641 2514 Table lamps; floor
lamps; wall lamps; electric lamps; metal
household furniture

(G-13651)
**MENTOR GLASS SUPPLIES AND
REPR**
8985 Osborne Dr (44060-4326)
PHONE....................................440 255-9444
David Reed, President
Robert Reed, Vice Pres
EMP: 3
SQ FT: 2,000
SALES (est): 268.8K Privately Held
SIC: 3211 7536 1793 Insulating glass,
sealed units; automotive glass replace-
ment shops; glass & glazing work

(G-13652)
**MENTOR SIGNS & GRAPHICS
INC**
Also Called: Soulsby, John
7522a Tyler Blvd Ste A (44060-5450)
PHONE....................................440 951-7446
John Soulsby, President
Josh McDainel, Sales Staff
EMP: 4
SQ FT: 2,600
SALES: 180K Privately Held
SIC: 3993 Signs & advertising specialties

(G-13653)
METAL CRAFT DOCKS INC
6989 Lindsay Dr (44060-4928)
PHONE....................................440 286-7135
Fax: 440 286-7134
Dave Bender, President
Etta Berskie, Manager
EMP: 5 EST: 1935
SQ FT: 15,000
SALES (est): 804.3K Privately Held
WEB: www.metalcraftdocks.com
SIC: 3448 3446 Docks: prefabricated
metal; architectural metalwork

(G-13654)
METAL SEAL PRECISION LTD
8687 Tyler Blvd (44060-4346)
PHONE....................................440 205-0016
John L Habe IV, President
Allan B Pirnat, Vice Pres
Michael Bobbitt, QC Mgr
Dan Gibson, Engineer
Dale Umbel, Engineer
▼ EMP: 200
SQ FT: 158,000
SALES (est): 46.4MM Privately Held
SIC: 3448 Prefabricated metal components

(G-13655)
MICRO LABORATORIES INC
7158 Industrial Park Blvd (44060-5314)
PHONE....................................440 918-0001
Keith Kokal, President
EMP: 6
SQ FT: 1,500
SALES (est): 670K Privately Held
SIC: 3829 8734 Measuring & controlling
devices; testing laboratories

(G-13656)
**MILL ROSE LABORATORIES
INC**
7310 Corp Blvd (44060)
PHONE....................................440 974-6730
Fax: 440 255-5061
Paul M Miller, President
Thom Olmstead, General Mgr
Stephen W Kovalcheck Jr, CFO
Vince Ponna, Controller
Lawrence W Miller, Admin Sec
▲ EMP: 40
SQ FT: 59,000
SALES (est): 6.3MM
SALES (corp-wide): 32.4MM Privately
Held
WEB: www.millrose.com
SIC: 3991 5047 Brooms & brushes; med-
ical equipment & supplies
PA: The Mill-Rose Company
7995 Tyler Blvd
Mentor OH 44060
440 255-9171

(G-13657)
MILL-ROSE COMPANY (PA)
7995 Tyler Blvd (44060-4896)
PHONE....................................440 255-9171
Fax: 440 255-5039
Paul M Miller, President
Gregory Miller, General Mgr
Lawrence W Miller, Vice Pres
Barbara Tokar, Manager
Diane Miller, Admin Sec
▲ EMP: 160
SQ FT: 61,000
SALES (est): 32.4MM Privately Held
WEB: www.millrose.com
SIC: 3841 5085 3991 3624 Surgical in-
struments & apparatus; industrial sup-
plies; brushes, industrial; brushes,
household or industrial; carbon & graphite
products; abrasive products

(G-13658)
MINUTEMAN PRESS
7450 Mentor Ave (44060-5406)
PHONE....................................440 946-3311
Fax: 440 946-6491
Steven Shaeffer, Owner
Elizabeth Adamic, Manager
EMP: 4
SQ FT: 1,400
SALES (est): 409.2K Privately Held
SIC: 2752 Commercial printing, litho-
graphic

(G-13659)
MOLD MASTERS INTL INC
7500 Clover Ave (44060-5296)
PHONE....................................440 953-0220
Fax: 440 953-1016
Jim Allen, CEO
George Goodrich, President
Ron Kern, Principal
Vic Sirotek, Principal
Robert Soltis, Vice Pres
EMP: 170
SQ FT: 54,000
SALES (est): 35.8MM Privately Held
WEB: www.moldmastersintl.com
SIC: 3324 2842 Steel investment
foundries; specialty cleaning, polishes &
sanitation goods

(G-13660)
**MONODE MARKING PRODUCTS
INC (PA)**
Also Called: Waldorf Marking Devices Div
9200 Tyler Blvd (44060-1882)
PHONE....................................440 975-8802
Fax: 440 975-1364
Tom Mackey, President
Bill Vickery, General Mgr

Christine Lillstrung, *Plant Mgr*
Tom Rempe, *Purch Agent*
Les Szakallas, *Engineer*
EMP: 45
SQ FT: 15,000
SALES (est): 8.6MM **Privately Held**
SIC: 3542 5084 Marking machines; printing trades machinery, equipment & supplies

(G-13661)
MONODE STEEL STAMP INC
7620 Tyler Blvd (44060-4853)
PHONE..................................440 975-8802
Chris Lillstrung, *Manager*
EMP: 15
SALES (corp-wide): 1.8MM **Privately Held**
WEB: www.monode.com
SIC: 3542 3469 Marking machines; metal stampings
PA: Monode Steel Stamp, Inc
149 High St
New London OH 44851
419 929-3501

(G-13662)
MSD PRODUCTS INC
7842 Enterprise Dr (44060-5310)
PHONE..................................440 946-0040
Mark Davis, *President*
EMP: 4
SQ FT: 3,000
SALES: 300K **Privately Held**
SIC: 3469 Machine parts, stamped or pressed metal

(G-13663)
MUM INDUSTRIES INC
7750 Tyler Blvd (44060-4802)
P.O. Box 1870 (44061-1870)
PHONE..................................440 269-4966
Jim Cooney, *President*
Keith Osborn, *Exec VP*
Chris Brizes, *Vice Pres*
Tricia Stokes, *Project Mgr*
Tom Stanish, *Materials Mgr*
▲ **EMP:** 32
SQ FT: 15,000
SALES (est): 8.1MM **Privately Held**
WEB: www.mumindustries.com
SIC: 2821 Plasticizer/additive based plastic materials

(G-13664)
N C TOOL & DIE COMPANY
Also Called: NC Tool
9435 Pineneedle Dr (44060-1827)
PHONE..................................440 354-4152
Fax: 440 354-4152
Nikola Cvijanovic, *President*
Frank Cvijanovic, *Vice Pres*
Anthony Cvijanovic, *VP Sls/Mktg*
Ivanica Cvijanovic, *Treasurer*
Renee Leburton, *Office Mgr*
EMP: 15 **EST:** 1979
SQ FT: 11,000
SALES (est): 1.6MM **Privately Held**
WEB: www.nctool.com
SIC: 3599 Machine shop, jobbing & repair

(G-13665)
NHVS INTERNATIONAL INC
7600 Tyler Blvd (44060-4853)
PHONE..................................440 527-8610
Sherry Richcreek, *CEO*
Heather Richcreek, *Plant Mgr*
Kelly Cameron, *Controller*
EMP: 325
SQ FT: 100,000
SALES (est): 28.6MM **Privately Held**
SIC: 3812 Acceleration indicators & systems components, aerospace

(G-13666)
NICHOLS MANUFACTURING INC
8980 Osborne Dr (44060-4326)
PHONE..................................440 255-0188
Michael Nichols, *President*
Tiffany Aquila, *Vice Pres*
Melissa Buhas, *Manager*
EMP: 15
SQ FT: 13,500
SALES (est): 1.6MM **Privately Held**
SIC: 3599 Machine shop, jobbing & repair

(G-13667)
NIFTECH INC
Also Called: Niftech Precision Race Pdts
5565 Wilson Dr (44060-1555)
PHONE..................................440 257-6018
Fax: 440 257-4281
Julie Knaus, *President*
Raymond Knaus, *Vice Pres*
EMP: 10
SALES: 200K **Privately Held**
SIC: 3699 Electrical equipment & supplies

(G-13668)
NORTH COAST MEDI-TEK INC
8603 East Ave (44060-4366)
PHONE..................................440 974-0106
Fax: 440 974-0106
Teri Sokolowski, *President*
Robert Sokolowski, *Vice Pres*
EMP: 11
SQ FT: 6,600
SALES (est): 1.6MM **Privately Held**
SIC: 3841 Surgical & medical instruments

(G-13669)
NORTHCOAST VALVE AND GATE INC
9437 Mercantile Dr (44060-4524)
PHONE..................................440 392-9910
Anthony Fistek, *President*
EMP: 8
SALES (est): 1.4MM **Privately Held**
SIC: 3494 Valves & pipe fittings

(G-13670)
O H TECHNOLOGIES INC
9300 Progress Pkwy (44060-1859)
P.O. Box 5039 (44061-5039)
PHONE..................................440 354-8780
Dwight Bowden, *President*
EMP: 3
SQ FT: 5,000
SALES (est): 511.8K **Privately Held**
WEB: www.ohtech.com
SIC: 3825 Instruments to measure electricity

(G-13671)
OE EXCHANGE LLC (PA)
8200 Tyler Blvd (44060-4252)
PHONE..................................440 266-1639
Don Boston, *Marketing Staff*
Peter L Mooney, *Vice Pres*
EMP: 9
SALES (est): 1.2MM **Privately Held**
SIC: 3714 Wheels, motor vehicle

(G-13672)
OMEGA MACHINE & TOOL INC
7590 Jenther Dr (44060-4872)
PHONE..................................440 946-6846
Fax: 440 946-6846
Dolf Litschel, *President*
Ema Litschel, *Vice Pres*
EMP: 10
SQ FT: 9,000
SALES: 1MM **Privately Held**
SIC: 3599 Machine shop, jobbing & repair

(G-13673)
ORBIS CORPORATION
9050 Tyler Blvd (44060-1897)
PHONE..................................440 974-3857
Laura Stevens, *Human Res Dir*
David Skinner, *Sales Engr*
Kim Cantwell, *Manager*
Dwayne Hughes, *Manager*
EMP: 120
SALES (corp-wide): 1.8B **Privately Held**
WEB: www.orbiscorporation.com
SIC: 3089 Synthetic resin finished products
HQ: Orbis Corporation
1055 Corporate Center Dr
Oconomowoc WI 53066
262 560-5000

(G-13674)
ORDNANCE CLEANING SYSTEMS LLC
7895 Division Dr (44060-4877)
PHONE..................................440 205-0677
Jeffrey Allenby,
EMP: 5
SQ FT: 14,000

SALES (est): 175K **Privately Held**
SIC: 3489 Ordnance & accessories

(G-13675)
OSAIR INC (PA)
7001 Center St (44060-4933)
P.O. Box 1020 (44061-1020)
PHONE..................................440 974-6500
Fax: 440 974-0844
Richard Osborne, *President*
Jon Magnusson, *Vice Pres*
Donald Whickman, *Controller*
EMP: 9
SQ FT: 4,000
SALES (est): 11.2MM **Privately Held**
SIC: 2813 1381 Industrial gases; nitrogen; drilling oil & gas wells

(G-13676)
OSAIR INC
8649 East Ave (44060-4366)
PHONE..................................440 255-8238
Fax: 440 255-0954
John Magnusson, *Manager*
EMP: 3
SALES (corp-wide): 11.2MM **Privately Held**
SIC: 3569 Separators for steam, gas, vapor or air (machinery)
PA: Osair, Inc.
7001 Center St
Mentor OH 44060
440 974-6500

(G-13677)
OSBORNE INC (PA)
7954 Reynolds Rd (44060-5334)
P.O. Box 658 (44061-0658)
PHONE..................................440 942-7000
Fax: 440 942-7000
Jerome T Osborne, *Principal*
William Mackey, *Treasurer*
J Fitzgerald, *Director*
▲ **EMP:** 25
SQ FT: 4,500
SALES (est): 15.4MM **Privately Held**
SIC: 5211 3273 3271 Lumber & other building materials; ready-mixed concrete; blocks, concrete or cinder: standard

(G-13678)
PAKO INC
7615 Jenther Dr (44060-4872)
PHONE..................................440 946-8030
Fax: 440 946-0570
Paul Kosir, *President*
Bronko Leban, *Project Mgr*
Don Chesnes, *Purch Dir*
Adam Perusek, *Purch Mgr*
David Osenar, *Engineer*
EMP: 246
SQ FT: 142,000
SALES (est): 80.6MM **Privately Held**
WEB: www.pako.com
SIC: 3728 3714 Aircraft parts & equipment; motor vehicle parts & accessories

(G-13679)
PANELBLOC INC
8665 Tyler Blvd (44060-4346)
PHONE..................................440 974-8877
Fax: 440 974-8877
Betty Gotliebowski, *President*
Raymond Gotliebowski Jr, *Exec VP*
EMP: 5
SQ FT: 7,800
SALES: 400K **Privately Held**
WEB: www.panelbloc.com
SIC: 3433 Gas infrared heating units

(G-13680)
PARKER PRECISION INC
8950 Tyler Blvd (44060-2185)
PHONE..................................440 951-6501
Reeve J Parker, *President*
Maria Parker, *Vice Pres*
EMP: 9
SQ FT: 12,000
SALES (est): 2.2MM **Privately Held**
WEB: www.parkerprecision.com
SIC: 3599 Machine shop, jobbing & repair

(G-13681)
PARKER-HANNIFIN CORPORATION
Also Called: Gas Turbine Fuel Systems
8940 Tyler Blvd (44060-2185)
PHONE..................................440 266-2300
Fax: 440 205-7899
Louise Watson, *Safety Mgr*
Andrew McClelland, *Engineer*
George Stevenson, *Engineer*
Michael Teter, *Project Engr*
Jeff Melzak, *Design Engr*
EMP: 50
SALES (corp-wide): 11.3B **Publicly Held**
WEB: www.parker.com
SIC: 3594 Fluid power pumps
PA: Parker-Hannifin Corporation
6035 Parkland Blvd
Cleveland OH 44124
216 896-3000

(G-13682)
PARKER-HANNIFIN CORPORATION
Gas Turbine Fuel Systems Div
8940 Tyler Blvd (44060-2185)
PHONE..................................440 205-8230
Michael Frederick, *Engineer*
Jeremy Rotz, *Engineer*
Dennis Rice, *Controller*
Less Conner, *Manager*
Ron Bylicki, *Manager*
EMP: 168
SALES (corp-wide): 11.3B **Publicly Held**
WEB: www.parker.com
SIC: 3728 Aircraft parts & equipment
PA: Parker-Hannifin Corporation
6035 Parkland Blvd
Cleveland OH 44124
216 896-3000

(G-13683)
PCC AIRFOILS LLC
8607 Tyler Blvd (44060-4222)
PHONE..................................440 255-9770
Fax: 440 255-3733
Armand Lauzon, *General Mgr*
Brian Grover, *Mfg Mgr*
Brian Watkins, *Materials Mgr*
Richard Kreske, *Enginr/R&D Mgr*
Scotty Richmond, *Human Res Mgr*
EMP: 108
SQ FT: 55,000
SALES (corp-wide): 223.6B **Publicly Held**
WEB: www.pccairfoils.com
SIC: 3369 3324 3724 Castings, except die-castings, precision; steel investment foundries; airfoils, aircraft engine
HQ: Pcc Airfoils Llc
3401 Entp Pkwy Ste 200
Cleveland OH 44122
216 831-3590

(G-13684)
PELOTON MANUFACTURING CORP
Also Called: SSC Controls Company
8909 East Ave (44060-4305)
PHONE..................................440 205-1600
James E Moll, *President*
Brent Moll, *Vice Pres*
▲ **EMP:** 15
SQ FT: 8,500
SALES: 5MM **Privately Held**
WEB: www.ssccontrols.com
SIC: 3625 8742 Relays & industrial controls; marketing consulting services

(G-13685)
PERFORMANCE SUPERABRASIVES LLC
Also Called: Coastal Diamond
7255 Industrial Park Blvd A (44060-5331)
PHONE..................................440 946-7171
Scott Kaplan, *Mng Member*
Tim Rash,
EMP: 9
SQ FT: 5,200
SALES (est): 680.2K **Privately Held**
SIC: 3291 3545 Wheels, grinding: artificial; wheel turning equipment, diamond point or other

(G-13686)
**PHILIPS MEDICAL SYSTEMS
CLEVEL**
Also Called: Picker Health Care Products
8020 Tyler Blvd (44060-4825)
PHONE...................................440 473-3001
Arlene Burnside, *General Mgr*
Cheryl Jackson, *Accountant*
Leverda Wallace, *Surgery Dir*
EMP: 50
SALES (corp-wide): 26B **Privately Held**
SIC: 3841 Surgical & medical instruments
HQ: Philips Medical Systems (Cleveland),
     Inc.
     595 Miner Rd
     Cleveland OH 44143
     440 247-2652

(G-13687)
**PILOT-RUN STAMPING
COMPANY**
8209 Tyler Blvd (44060-4298)
PHONE...................................440 255-8821
Fax: 440 255-2919
Anthony Mitalski, *President*
Jim Tracy, *President*
Marvin Davison, *Vice Pres*
Lawrence Johnson, *Vice Pres*
Judy Kelce, *Manager*
EMP: 26 **EST:** 1966
SQ FT: 14,000
SALES (est): 4.7MM **Privately Held**
SIC: 3469 3316 Metal stampings; cold fin-
    ishing of steel shapes

(G-13688)
PLASTICS MENTOR LLC
6160 Brownstone Ct (44060-2168)
PHONE...................................440 352-1357
Roger R Rhoads, *Principal*
EMP: 3
SALES (est): 199.2K **Privately Held**
SIC: 3089 Plastics products

(G-13689)
**PLATING PROCESS SYSTEMS
INC**
7561 Tyler Blvd Ste 5 (44060-4867)
P.O. Box 808 (44061-0808)
PHONE...................................440 951-9667
Fax: 440 951-9077
John Salyards, *President*
Rosalie Salyards, *Corp Secy*
Louis Gianelos, *Vice Pres*
Mat Shario, *Office Mgr*
▼**EMP:** 9
SQ FT: 9,880
SALES: 2.5MM **Privately Held**
WEB: www.platingprocess.com
SIC: 2899 Plating compounds

(G-13690)
**PMI OPERATING COMPANY INC
(HQ)**
Also Called: Performnce Mtorsports Intl Inc
7201 Industrial Park Blvd (44060-5315)
PHONE...................................440 951-6600
Fax: 440 951-6600
Brian Reese, *President*
Ted Caldwell, *Vice Pres*
Josh Vogel, *CFO*
▲**EMP:** 290 **EST:** 1980
SQ FT: 150,000
SALES: 70MM
SALES (corp-wide): 193.2MM **Privately
Held**
WEB: www.wiseco.com
SIC: 3592 3714 Pistons & piston rings;
    motor vehicle parts & accessories
PA: Kinderhook Industries, Llc
     521 5th Ave Fl 34
     New York NY 10175
     212 201-6780

(G-13691)
POLYCHEM CORPORATION (PA)
6277 Heisley Rd (44060-1899)
PHONE...................................440 357-1500
Fax: 440 352-9553
Brian Jeckering, *CEO*
Jim Cantelmi, *Vice Pres*
Mihai Cojocaru, *Vice Pres*
Dan Quick, *Plant Mgr*
Pat McWilliams, *Opers Staff*
▲**EMP:** 180

SQ FT: 165,000
SALES (est): 153.7MM **Privately Held**
SIC: 2671 Plastic film, coated or laminated
    for packaging

(G-13692)
POLYCHEM CORPORATION
7214 Justin Way (44060-4881)
PHONE...................................440 357-1500
EMP: 5
SALES (corp-wide): 153.7MM **Privately
Held**
SIC: 2671 Plastic film, coated or laminated
    for packaging
PA: Polychem Corporation
     6277 Heisley Rd
     Mentor OH 44060
     440 357-1500

(G-13693)
POLYMER CONCEPTS INC
7555 Tyler Blvd Ste 1 (44060-4866)
PHONE...................................440 953-9605
Fax: 440 953-9602
Chris Callsen, *President*
▼**EMP:** 7
SQ FT: 6,000
SALES (est): 1.4MM **Privately Held**
WEB: www.polymerconcept.com
SIC: 2821 Polyurethane resins

(G-13694)
**PPG ARCHITECTURAL FINISHES
INC**
Also Called: Glidden Professional Paint Ctr
7444 Mentor Ave (44060-5406)
PHONE...................................440 942-7708
Fax: 440 942-1554
Scott Koeth, *Manager*
EMP: 4
SALES (corp-wide): 14.7B **Publicly Held**
WEB: www.gliddenpaint.com
SIC: 2891 Adhesives
HQ: Ppg Architectural Finishes, Inc.
     1 Ppg Pl
     Pittsburgh PA 15272
     412 434-3131

(G-13695)
PRECISION DIE MASTERS
8724 East Ave (44060-4304)
P.O. Box 263 (44061-0263)
PHONE...................................440 255-1204
Fax: 440 255-1204
Frank E Carmichael, *President*
EMP: 16
SQ FT: 16,000
SALES (est): 1.2MM **Privately Held**
SIC: 3544 Special dies & tools

(G-13696)
PRECISION WOODWORK LTD
6385 Mentor Park Blvd (44060-3721)
PHONE...................................440 257-3002
Fax: 440 257-3111
Patrick D Foss, *Partner*
Linda J Foss, *Partner*
EMP: 3
SQ FT: 1,500
SALES: 450K **Privately Held**
WEB: www.precisionwoodwork.com
SIC: 2434 Wood kitchen cabinets

(G-13697)
PRO MOLD DESIGN INC
9853 Johnnycake Ridge Rd # 308
(44060-6792)
PHONE...................................440 352-1212
Ronald Kowalski, *President*
Russ Kowalski, *Vice Pres*
EMP: 3
SALES: 125K **Privately Held**
SIC: 2821 Molding compounds, plastics

(G-13698)
PROFAC INC
Also Called: Merritt Woodwork
7198 Industrial Park Blvd (44060-5328)
PHONE...................................440 942-0205
Fax: 440 942-0205
G Michael Merritt, *CEO*
Tony Aoun, *President*
James Myers, *Managing Dir*
Janet E Bowden, *Principal*
Harold M Chattman, *Principal*
▲**EMP:** 135

SQ FT: 90,000
SALES (est): 32.3MM **Privately Held**
WEB: www.merrittwoodwork.com
SIC: 2541 Wood partitions & fixtures

(G-13699)
PROFICIENT MACHINING CO
7522 Tyler Blvd Unit B-G (44060-5450)
PHONE...................................440 942-4942
Fax: 440 942-4942
Kenneth Putman, *President*
Kyle Faasse, *General Mgr*
Carol Putman, *Corp Secy*
Kenneth Putman Jr, *Exec VP*
Don Bennington, *Opers Mgr*
EMP: 22
SQ FT: 15,000
SALES (est): 4.5MM **Privately Held**
WEB: www.proficientmachining.com
SIC: 3599 Machine shop, jobbing & repair

(G-13700)
PROFICIENT PLASTICS INC
7777 Saint Clair Ave (44060-5237)
P.O. Box 5053 (44061-5053)
PHONE...................................440 205-9700
Robert W Wisen, *President*
Joe Wesley, *Plant Mgr*
Missy McGonnell, *Office Mgr*
EMP: 10
SQ FT: 1,500
SALES (est): 1.9MM **Privately Held**
SIC: 2821 Plastics materials & resins

(G-13701)
**PROGRESSIVE POWDER
COATING INC**
7742 Tyler Blvd (44060-4802)
PHONE...................................440 974-3478
Fax: 440 974-1778
Mark Saltzman, *President*
John Sikora, *General Mgr*
Thomas Gries, *Vice Pres*
Sandy Schneider, *Manager*
EMP: 25
SQ FT: 24,024
SALES (est): 3.8MM **Privately Held**
SIC: 3479 Coating of metals & formed
    products

(G-13702)
PROLINE SCREENWEAR
8586 East Ave (44060-4302)
PHONE...................................440 205-3700
Fax: 440 205-3701
David Juka, *Principal*
EMP: 3
SALES (est): 307.3K **Privately Held**
SIC: 2759 Screen printing

(G-13703)
PROVIDENCE GROUP INC
Also Called: Sheet Metal Products Company
5950 Pinecone Dr (44060-1865)
PHONE...................................440 350-4615
Jim Saxa, *President*
Jerry Richardson, *Plant Mgr*
EMP: 20
SQ FT: 18,000
SALES (corp-wide): 8.6MM **Privately
Held**
WEB: www.smpohio.com
SIC: 3822 3444 Air conditioning & refriger-
    ation controls; sheet metalwork
PA: The Providence Group Inc
     9290 Metcalf Rd
     Willoughby OH
     440 247-4340

(G-13704)
PYROMATICS CORP (PA)
9321 Pineneedle Dr (44060-1825)
PHONE...................................440 352-3500
Fax: 440 951-8728
Andre Ezis, *CEO*
Cyndi St Julian, *CFO*
Sandy Cook, *Sales Mgr*
Sandra Meadows, *Marketing Staff*
Tia Scott, *Manager*
EMP: 10
SQ FT: 27,000
SALES (est): 1.2MM **Privately Held**
WEB: www.pyromatics.com
SIC: 3221 3231 3297 Glass containers;
    products of purchased glass; nonclay re-
    fractories

(G-13705)
QUADREL INC
Also Called: Quadrel Labeling Systems
7670 Jenther Dr (44060-4872)
PHONE...................................440 602-4700
Fax: 440 602-4701
Lon Deckard, *President*
Charles Wepler, *Vice Pres*
Mike Feltovich, *Materials Mgr*
Tom Roberts, *Controller*
Joseph P Rouse, *Admin Sec*
◆**EMP:** 43
SQ FT: 3,842
SALES (est): 14.5MM **Privately Held**
WEB: www.quadrel.com
SIC: 3565 Labeling machines, industrial

(G-13706)
QUALITY COMPONENTS INC
8825 East Ave (44060-4305)
P.O. Box 956 (44061-0956)
PHONE...................................440 255-0606
William Dennison Sr, *President*
Tina Joynt, *Sales Mgr*
EMP: 15
SQ FT: 10,000
SALES (est): 2.9MM
SALES (corp-wide): 500.1MM **Publicly
Held**
WEB: www.qccompany.com
SIC: 7699 3548 Welding equipment repair;
    welding & cutting apparatus & acces-
    sories
HQ: Stratos International, Inc.
     299 Johnson Ave Sw
     Waseca MN

(G-13707)
**QUALITY DESIGN MACHINING
INC**
9349 Hamilton Dr (44060-4559)
PHONE...................................440 352-7290
Robert Fletcher, *President*
EMP: 8
SQ FT: 5,000
SALES: 574.5K **Privately Held**
SIC: 3599 Amusement park equipment

(G-13708)
**QUALITY MACHINE SYSTEMS
LLC**
7875 Enterprise Dr (44060-5309)
PHONE...................................440 223-2217
Paul Kinczel, *Partner*
Steve Vucic, *Partner*
St Jepan Vucic,
EMP: 8
SQ FT: 10,000
SALES (est): 974.1K **Privately Held**
WEB: www.qualitymachineairtools.com
SIC: 3599 Machine shop, jobbing & repair

(G-13709)
**QUALITY QUARTZ OF AMERICA
INC**
9362 Hamilton Dr (44060-4558)
PHONE...................................440 352-2851
Fax: 440 974-3755
Carmella Petruziello, *Owner*
Mike Petruziello, *Opers Mgr*
Ray Petruziello, *Mfg Staff*
Ray Woodcock, *QC Mgr*
Lou Ruscitto, *Mktg Dir*
EMP: 3
SQ FT: 11,130
SALES (est): 320K **Privately Held**
WEB: www.qualityquartz.com
SIC: 3679 Quartz crystals, for electronic
    application

(G-13710)
QUALTEK ELECTRONICS CORP
7610 Jenther Dr (44060-4872)
PHONE...................................440 951-3300
Fax: 440 951-3300
John Hallums, *President*
Twila Loft, *Regl Sales Mgr*
Didier Sansoni, *Regl Sales Mgr*
▲**EMP:** 120
SQ FT: 20,000

GEOGRAPHIC

SALES (est): 23.3MM **Privately Held**
WEB: www.qualtekusa.com
SIC: 3634 3643 3577 3612 Electric housewares & fans; current-carrying wiring devices; power outlets & sockets; computer peripheral equipment; transformers, except electric; blowers & fans; miscellaneous fabricated wire products

(G-13711)
R C PACKAGING SYSTEMS
6277 Heisley Rd (44060-1858)
PHONE.................................248 684-6363
Vaughan B Nesbit, *President*
Rose Gross, *Manager*
▲ EMP: 15
SQ FT: 12,000
SALES (est): 2.9MM **Privately Held**
WEB: www.rcpackaging.com
SIC: 2298 Twine, cord & cordage

(G-13712)
R J K ENTERPRISES INC
Also Called: Niftech
5565 Wilson Dr (44060-1555)
PHONE.................................440 257-6018
Raymond Knaus, *President*
Ellen Cook, *Vice Pres*
Julie Knaus, *Vice Pres*
Karen Knaus, *Admin Asst*
EMP: 10
SQ FT: 1,500
SALES: 1MM **Privately Held**
WEB: www.niftech.com
SIC: 7389 3599 Design, commercial & industrial; custom machinery

(G-13713)
R S MANUFACTURING INC
8878 East Ave (44060-4306)
PHONE.................................440 946-8002
Fax: 440 946-7842
Richard Stark Sr, *President*
Richard Stark Jr, *Vice Pres*
Dee Haskett, *MIS Dir*
David Stark, *Shareholder*
Dee Ann Stark, *Shareholder*
EMP: 15
SQ FT: 4,800
SALES: 400K **Privately Held**
SIC: 3452 Bolts, metal; nuts, metal; screws, metal; washers

(G-13714)
R T & T MACHINING CO INC
8195 Tyler Blvd Ste 56 (44060-4854)
PHONE.................................440 974-8479
Fax: 440 255-5439
F Paul Thompson, *President*
Ellen Thompson, *Vice Pres*
EMP: 14
SQ FT: 12,000
SALES: 1MM **Privately Held**
SIC: 3451 3599 3545 3544 Screw machine products; machine shop, jobbing & repair; machine tool accessories; special dies, tools, jigs & fixtures

(G-13715)
RKI INC (PA)
Also Called: Roll-Kraft
8901 Tyler Blvd (44060-2184)
PHONE.................................888 953-9400
George C Gehrisch Jr, *President*
Sanjay Singh, *President*
Dennis M Langer, *Exec VP*
Chuck Summerhill, *Vice Pres*
Steve Young, *VP Opers*
EMP: 121 **EST:** 1964
SQ FT: 100,000
SALES (est): 22.2MM **Privately Held**
WEB: www.roll-kraft.com
SIC: 3547 Rolling mill machinery; primary rolling mill equipment; secondary rolling mill equipment

(G-13716)
RLR INDUSTRIES INC
Also Called: Rainbow Plastics
8677 Tyler Blvd Unit B (44060-4346)
PHONE.................................440 951-9501
Fax: 440 974-1903
Richard Rodgers Jr, *President*
Patty Zuber, *Human Res Mgr*
EMP: 38 **EST:** 1978
SQ FT: 25,000

SALES: 2.2MM **Privately Held**
SIC: 3089 Thermoformed finished plastic products

(G-13717)
ROYAL PLASTICS INC
9410 Pineneedle Dr (44060-1880)
PHONE.................................440 352-1357
Fax: 440 352-6681
Gary Connell, *President*
Gary Mc Connell, *President*
Song Crawford, *Vice Pres*
Patricia Garner, *Vice Pres*
Bruce Usnik, *Vice Pres*
▲ EMP: 225
SQ FT: 135,000
SALES (est): 60.9MM **Privately Held**
SIC: 3089 3643 Injection molding of plastics; current-carrying wiring devices

(G-13718)
S T TOOL & DESIGN INC
9452 Mercantile Dr (44060-1889)
PHONE.................................440 357-1250
John Fifa, *General Mgr*
Tony Sisa, *Manager*
EMP: 14
SQ FT: 6,000
SALES (est): 2.5MM **Privately Held**
SIC: 3599 Machine shop, jobbing & repair

(G-13719)
SEMPER QUALITY INDUSTRY INC
Also Called: Mc Cartney Industries
9411 Mercantile Dr (44060-4524)
PHONE.................................440 352-8111
Fax: 440 352-3880
Dale B McCartney, *President*
Duane McCartney, *Vice Pres*
EMP: 8
SQ FT: 12,000
SALES: 750K **Privately Held**
WEB: www.semperquality.com
SIC: 1721 3479 Industrial painting; coating of metals & formed products

(G-13720)
SENTINEL CONSUMER PRODUCTS INC (PA)
7750 Tyler Blvd (44060-4802)
PHONE.................................801 825-5671
Fax: 440 974-0249
Michael S Klein, *President*
EMP: 80
SQ FT: 53,000
SALES (est): 20.5MM **Privately Held**
WEB: www.sentinelconsumer.com
SIC: 3842 3131 2844 First aid, snake bite & burn kits; dressings, surgical; swabs, sanitary cotton; inner soles, leather; toilet preparations

(G-13721)
SGM CO INC
9000 Tyler Blvd (44060-1897)
PHONE.................................440 255-1190
Patrick L Gerboth, *CEO*
Laura L Gerboth, *President*
Maurine Vauvaet, *Purchasing*
Marya Lecjaks, *Sales Staff*
Marya Teal, *Manager*
EMP: 40
SQ FT: 45,000
SALES (est): 6.4MM **Privately Held**
SIC: 3433 Heating equipment, except electric

(G-13722)
SHEET METAL PRODUCTS CO INC
5950 Pinecone Dr (44060-1865)
PHONE.................................440 392-9000
Fax: 440 392-0000
Joseph J Mahovlic, *CEO*
James F Saxa, *President*
Steven H Sneiderman, *Principal*
Jev Vaidean, *Purch Dir*
Andy Greiner, *QC Mgr*
EMP: 25

SALES (est): 7.1MM
SALES (corp-wide): 8.6MM **Privately Held**
WEB: www.sheetmetalproductsco.com
SIC: 3444 3429 Sheet metalwork; manufactured hardware (general)
PA: The Providence Group Inc
9290 Metcalf Rd
Willoughby OH
440 247-4340

(G-13723)
SIGNS N STUFF INC
9354 Mentor Ave Ste 4 (44060-6467)
PHONE.................................440 974-3151
Fax: 440 974-3151
William Budziak, *President*
Cynthia Budziak, *Vice Pres*
EMP: 5
SALES (est): 452.9K **Privately Held**
SIC: 3993 Signs & advertising specialties

(G-13724)
SKRIBS TOOL AND DIE INC
Also Called: Apollo Plastic
7555 Tyler Blvd Ste 11 (44060-4866)
PHONE.................................440 951-7774
Stanley Skrbis, *President*
Maria Skrbis, *Corp Secy*
Stanley Skrbis Jr, *Vice Pres*
EMP: 28 **EST:** 1973
SQ FT: 24,000
SALES (est): 3.5MM **Privately Held**
SIC: 3544 3089 Forms (molds), for foundry & plastics working machinery; injection molding of plastics

(G-13725)
SMP WELDING LLC
8171 Tyler Blvd (44060-4826)
PHONE.................................440 205-9353
Fax: 440 255-7273
Patrick Studnicka, *Financial Exec*
Renee Patti, *Sales Mgr*
Debi Morris, *Manager*
EMP: 12
SQ FT: 10,000
SALES (est): 4.5MM **Privately Held**
SIC: 7692 Welding repair

(G-13726)
SP ACQUISITIONS LLC
Also Called: Star Precision Products
6989 Lindsay Dr (44060-4928)
PHONE.................................440 205-0143
Fax: 440 266-7701
Anne M McNeely, *CFO*
Sue Kacsala, *Finance Mgr*
Gina Mitchell, *Bookkeeper*
Anne McNeeley, *Human Res Mgr*
Mike Cervar, *Director*
EMP: 35
SQ FT: 45,000
SALES (est): 7.6MM **Privately Held**
WEB: www.starprecision.net
SIC: 3599 5049 Machine shop, jobbing & repair; precision tools

(G-13727)
SPANG & COMPANY
Spang Power Electronic
9305 Progress Pkwy (44060-1855)
PHONE.................................440 350-6108
Robert Smith, *President*
EMP: 31
SALES (corp-wide): 106.8MM **Privately Held**
SIC: 3699 3625 3674 3566 Electron linear accelerators; control equipment, electric; controls for adjustable speed drives; semiconductors & related devices; speed changers, drives & gears
PA: Spang & Company
110 Delta Dr
Pittsburgh PA 15238
412 963-9363

(G-13728)
SPORTSMASTER
9140 Lake Shore Blvd (44060-1637)
PHONE.................................440 257-3900
Ronald Micchia DDS, *Owner*
EMP: 13
SQ FT: 1,800
SALES (est): 821.5K **Privately Held**
SIC: 2891 Adhesives & sealants

(G-13729)
STAM INC
7350 Production Dr (44060-4859)
P.O. Box 951108, Cleveland (44193-0005)
PHONE.................................440 974-2500
Kent Marvin, *President*
H James Sheedy, *Principal*
David Baumgardner, *Buyer*
Brendan Anderson, *CFO*
EMP: 45
SQ FT: 28,000
SALES (est): 10.6MM **Privately Held**
WEB: www.staminc.com
SIC: 3498 Tube fabricating (contract bending & shaping)

(G-13730)
STANDARD REGISTER INC
7200 Justin Way (44060-4881)
PHONE.................................440 974-1611
James Larson, *Manager*
EMP: 7
SQ FT: 10,000
SALES (corp-wide): 4.6B **Privately Held**
WEB: www.stdreg.com
SIC: 2761 Manifold business forms
HQ: Standard Register, Inc.
600 Albany St
Dayton OH 45417
937 221-1000

(G-13731)
STERIS CORPORATION
9260 Progress Pkwy (44060-1854)
PHONE.................................440 352-8724
Fax: 440 352-8724
Tom Olson, *Production*
Pete Adams, *Engineer*
Paul Brazeau, *Engineer*
Lance Bellows, *Senior Engr*
Ron Tusai, *Senior Engr*
EMP: 200
SALES (corp-wide): 2.2B **Privately Held**
WEB: www.steris.com
SIC: 3842 Belts: surgical, sanitary & corrective
HQ: Steris Corporation
5960 Heisley Rd
Mentor OH 44060
440 354-2600

(G-13732)
STERIS CORPORATION
Also Called: Research & Development II
5900 Heisley Rd (44060-1834)
PHONE.................................440 354-2600
EMP: 5
SALES (corp-wide): 2.2B **Privately Held**
SIC: 3842 Surgical appliances & supplies
HQ: Steris Corporation
5960 Heisley Rd
Mentor OH 44060
440 354-2600

(G-13733)
STERIS CORPORATION (HQ)
5960 Heisley Rd (44060-1834)
PHONE.................................440 354-2600
Fax: 440 354-7043
Walter M Rosebrough Jr, *President*
Robert E Moss, *President*
Jack Bedell, *Vice Pres*
Dan Carestio, *Vice Pres*
Mark Fraser, *Plant Mgr*
◆ EMP: 843
SALES: 1.8B
SALES (corp-wide): 2.2B **Privately Held**
WEB: www.steris.com
SIC: 3841 3842 3845 Surgical & medical instruments; diagnostic apparatus, medical; sterilizers, hospital & surgical; endoscopic equipment, electromedical
PA: Steris Plc
Chancery House
Leicester LEICS LE5 1
116 276-8636

(G-13734)
STERIS CORPORATION
6100 Heisley Rd (44060-1838)
PHONE.................................440 354-2600
Rick Lee, *Business Mgr*
Jan Miller, *Vice Pres*
CPS, *Manager*
EMP: 126

SALES (corp-wide): 2.2B **Privately Held**
WEB: www.steris.com
SIC: **3842** Surgical appliances & supplies
HQ: Steris Corporation
5960 Heisley Rd
Mentor OH 44060
440 354-2600

(G-13735)
STERIS CORPORATION
Also Called: Steris University
5914 Heisley Rd (44060-1834)
PHONE..................................440 354-2600
EMP: 3
SALES (corp-wide): 2.2B **Privately Held**
WEB: www.steris.com
SIC: **3842** Surgical appliances & supplies
HQ: Steris Corporation
5960 Heisley Rd
Mentor OH 44060
440 354-2600

(G-13736)
STERIS CORPORATION
6515 Hopkins Rd (44060-4307)
PHONE..................................440 354-2600
Scott Wittler, *Engineer*
Toby Duff, *Project Engr*
Jeff Kiessel, *Sales Staff*
Les Vinney, *Manager*
Toby Soots, *Manager*
EMP: 100
SALES (corp-wide): 2.2B **Privately Held**
WEB: www.steris.com
SIC: **3842** Sterilizers, hospital & surgical;
surgical appliances & supplies
HQ: Steris Corporation
5960 Heisley Rd
Mentor OH 44060
440 354-2600

(G-13737)
STERIS CORPORATION
9325 Pinecone Dr (44060-1862)
P.O. Box 75044, Cleveland (44101-2199)
PHONE..................................440 354-2600
Maryann Clomera, *Director*
EMP: 7
SALES (corp-wide): 2.2B **Privately Held**
WEB: www.steris.com
SIC: **3842** Surgical appliances & supplies
HQ: Steris Corporation
5960 Heisley Rd
Mentor OH 44060
440 354-2600

(G-13738)
STRATEGIC TECHNOLOGY ENTP
5960 Heisley Rd (44060-1834)
PHONE..................................440 354-2600
Gerry Reis, *President*
Les Binney, *President*
Ken Barnes, *Manager*
EMP: 20
SALES (est): 1.7MM **Privately Held**
SIC: **3821** Clinical laboratory instruments,
except medical & dental

(G-13739)
STROUSE INDUSTRIES INC
8090 Danbury Ct (44060-2421)
PHONE..................................440 257-2520
Fax: 440 257-2341
Joseph Strouse, *President*
Judy Strouse, *Treasurer*
EMP: 4
SALES (est): 481.1K **Privately Held**
SIC: **3541** Machine tools, metal cutting
type

(G-13740)
SULECKI PRECISION PRODUCTS
8785 East Ave (44060-4303)
PHONE..................................440 255-5454
Fax: 440 255-5531
Daniel Sulecki, *President*
David Sulecki, *Corp Secy*
John Sulecki, *Vice Pres*
Ed Sulecki, *Purch Dir*
EMP: 10
SQ FT: 4,500

SALES (est): 1.4MM **Privately Held**
SIC: **3599** 3544 3444 3441 Machine
shop, jobbing & repair; special dies, tools,
jigs & fixtures; sheet metalwork; fabricated structural metal

(G-13741)
SUNBRIGHT USA INC
8909 East Ave (44060-4305)
PHONE..................................440 205-0600
James E Moll, *President*
Bob Wilson, *Buyer*
Jay Santamaria, *Mktg Dir*
Jan Myers, *Administration*
▲ EMP: 3
SALES (est): 377.1K **Privately Held**
SIC: **3999** Combs, except hard rubber

(G-13742)
SUTTERLIN MACHINE & TOOL CO
9445 Pineneedle Dr (44060-1827)
PHONE..................................440 357-0817
Fax: 440 357-0427
Claude Sutterlin, *President*
Ben Sutterlin, *Engineer*
Ray Elersich, *Sales Staff*
Jim Lucha, *Manager*
EMP: 17 EST: 1966
SQ FT: 6,000
SALES (est): 2.9MM **Privately Held**
WEB: www.sutterlinmachine.com
SIC: **3544** Special dies & tools

(G-13743)
TECMARK CORPORATION (PA)
7745 Metric Dr (44060-4863)
PHONE..................................440 205-7600
Walter Swick, *CEO*
Ron Sayles, *President*
Sean Swick, *President*
Chuck Stein, *Vice Pres*
Matthew Duncan, *Engineer*
▲ EMP: 60 EST: 1999
SQ FT: 23,000
SALES (est): 10.2MM **Privately Held**
WEB: www.tecmarkcorp.com
SIC: **3629** 3823 3643 Electronic genera-
tion equipment; industrial instrmnts
msrmnt display/control process variable;
current-carrying wiring devices

(G-13744)
TECMARK CORPORATION
Also Called: North Shore Safety
7335 Production Dr (44060-4858)
PHONE..................................440 205-9188
Fax: 440 205-9187
EMP: 25
SALES (corp-wide): 10.2MM **Privately
Held**
SIC: **3822** Appliance regulators
PA: Tecmark Corporation
7745 Metric Dr
Mentor OH 44060
440 205-7600

(G-13745)
TERSUS PHARMACEUTICALS
5966 Heisley Rd (44060-1886)
PHONE..................................440 951-2451
Jeffrey A Green, *Principal*
Brian Seifert, *CFO*
Beverly Vitaz, *Manager*
EMP: 10
SALES (est): 480K **Privately Held**
SIC: **2834** Pharmaceutical preparations

(G-13746)
THERMOTION CORP
Also Called: Thermotion-Madison
6520 Hopkins Rd (44060-4308)
PHONE..................................440 639-8325
Fax: 440 639-8365
Gary Swanson, *President*
Tara Webster, *Bookkeeper*
Phillip Cebelar, *Manager*
EMP: 15
SALES (est): 2.7MM **Privately Held**
WEB: www.thermotion.com
SIC: **3625** Actuators, industrial

(G-13747)
TIMOTHY ALLEN JEWELERS INC
8925 Mentor Ave Ste D (44060-6350)
PHONE..................................440 974-8885

Fax: 440 974-2048
Timothy Allen Sobonya, *President*
Michelle Sobonya, *Vice Pres*
EMP: 5
SQ FT: 2,072
SALES: 400K **Privately Held**
WEB: www.timothyallenjewelers.com
SIC: **3911** 5944 Jewelry apparel; jewelry
stores

(G-13748)
TOM RICHARDS INC
Also Called: Process Technology
7010 Lindsay Dr (44060-4921)
PHONE..................................440 974-1300
Fax: 440 974-1300
Jody Richards, *President*
Laurie Hinton, *Buyer*
Chuck Schulkins, *QA Dir*
Robert Galloway, *QC Mgr*
Howard Base, *Engineer*
▲ EMP: 150
SQ FT: 72,000
SALES (est): 49.5MM **Privately Held**
WEB: www.process-technology.com
SIC: **3559** Metal finishing equipment for
plating, etc.; semiconductor manufactur-
ing machinery

(G-13749)
TOPS INC
Also Called: Tops Auto Interiors
7564 Tyler Blvd Ste A (44060-4870)
PHONE..................................440 954-9451
Fax: 440 954-9137
Frank Frazza, *President*
Theodora Farinacci, *Bookkeeper*
EMP: 5
SALES (est): 502K **Privately Held**
SIC: **2299** 7641 7542 Tops, combing &
converting; upholstery work; carwashes

(G-13750)
TOTAL MANUFACTURING CO INC
7777 Saint Clair Ave (44060-5237)
P.O. Box 5053 (44061-5053)
PHONE..................................440 205-9700
Fax: 440 946-2420
Robert W Wisen, *President*
Greg Wisen, *Opers Mgr*
EMP: 22
SALES (est): 4.5MM **Privately Held**
SIC: **3599** Machine shop, jobbing & repair

(G-13751)
TOTAL PLASTICS INC
7895 Division Dr (44060-4877)
PHONE..................................440 205-9700
Fax: 440 205-9800
Bob Wisen, *Principal*
EMP: 5
SALES (est): 457.1K **Privately Held**
SIC: **2819** Industrial inorganic chemicals

(G-13752)
TQ MANUFACTURING COMPANY INC
7345 Production Dr (44060-4858)
PHONE..................................440 255-9000
James Klopp, *President*
Thomas Cooper, *General Mgr*
Todd Penkowski, *Vice Pres*
EMP: 11
SQ FT: 10,000
SALES (est): 1.5MM **Privately Held**
WEB: www.tqmfg.com
SIC: **3599** Machine shop, jobbing & repair

(G-13753)
TRAILER COMPONENT MFG INC
8120 Tyler Blvd (44060-4852)
PHONE..................................440 255-2888
Fax: 440 255-1888
James Kleinman, *President*
Thomas Gries, *Vice Pres*
Mark Saltzman, *Treasurer*
Violeta Sikora, *Manager*
Ken Pobuda, *Director*
▲ EMP: 30
SQ FT: 42,000
SALES (est): 8.4MM **Privately Held**
SIC: **3714** 3599 3537 Motor vehicle parts
& accessories; machine & other job shop
work; industrial trucks & tractors

(G-13754)
TRANSCON INC
8824 Twinbrook Rd (44061-4391)
P.O. Box 29 (44061-0029)
PHONE..................................440 255-7600
Fax: 440 255-7600
John J Musial, *President*
J Robert Malloy, *Principal*
D Rusk, *Principal*
Mary E Shalala, *Principal*
Evanne Makarra, *Manager*
◆ EMP: 20 EST: 1959
SQ FT: 45,000
SALES (est): 5.8MM **Privately Held**
WEB: www.transconinc.com
SIC: **3535** Conveyors & conveying equip-
ment

(G-13755)
TRANSFER EXPRESS INC
7650 Tyler Blvd (44060-4853)
PHONE..................................440 918-1900
Fax: 440 918-1920
Ted Stahl, *President*
Jason Ziga, *General Mgr*
Kristen Jancigar, *Business Mgr*
Paul Fultz, *Senior Buyer*
Matt Cook, *CFO*
◆ EMP: 65
SQ FT: 85,000
SALES: 14.6MM
SALES (corp-wide): 30.4MM **Privately
Held**
WEB: www.txpress.com
SIC: **2759** 2752 Screen printing; transfers,
decalcomania or dry; lithographed
HQ: Stahl's Inc.
6353 E 14 Mile Rd
Sterling Heights MI 48312
800 478-2457

(G-13756)
TYLER HAVER INC (DH)
Also Called: W S Tyler
8570 Tyler Blvd (44060-4232)
PHONE..................................440 974-1047
Fax: 440 974-0921
Randy A Bakeberg, *President*
Bill Conway, *Opers Mgr*
Jared Lane, *Engineer*
Judy Osgood, *Controller*
Tracy Stein, *Human Res Dir*
▲ EMP: 50
SQ FT: 65,000
SALES (est): 11MM
SALES (corp-wide): 491MM **Privately
Held**
SIC: **3496** Miscellaneous fabricated wire
products
HQ: Tylinter, Inc.
8570 Tyler Blvd
Mentor OH 44060
800 321-6188

(G-13757)
TYLER HAVER INC
W S Tyler
8570 Tyler Blvd (44060-4232)
PHONE..................................800 255-1259
Judy Osgood, *Vice Pres*
John Sarrecchia, *Prdtn Mgr*
Kevin Deighan, *Manager*
EMP: 60
SALES (corp-wide): 491MM **Privately
Held**
SIC: **3569** Sifting & screening machines
HQ: Tyler Haver Inc
8570 Tyler Blvd
Mentor OH 44060
440 974-1047

(G-13758)
ULTRA IMPRESSIONS INC
Also Called: PIP Printing
7533 Tyler Blvd Ste D (44060-5415)
PHONE..................................440 951-4777
Fax: 440 255-8097
Wayne G Reese, *President*
James E Reese, *Vice Pres*
EMP: 5
SQ FT: 2,600
SALES (est): 857.2K **Privately Held**
SIC: **2752** Commercial printing, offset

(G-13759)
UNIQUE PACKAGING & PRINTING
9086 Goldfinch Ct (44060-1810)
P.O. Box 417, Grand River (44045-0417)
PHONE.....................................440 785-6730
Fax: 440 974-0350
Robert F Bradach, *President*
Madeline Bradach, *Vice Pres*
EMP: 10
SQ FT: 20,000
SALES (est): 100K **Privately Held**
SIC: 7389 3991 Packaging & labeling
　services; brooms & brushes

(G-13760)
UNITED STATES ENDOSCOPY
6091 Heisley Rd (44060-1835)
PHONE.....................................440 639-4494
EMP: 3
SALES (corp-wide): 2.2B **Privately Held**
SIC: 3841 Surgical instruments & apparatus
HQ: United States Endoscopy Group, Inc.
　5976 Heisley Rd
　Mentor OH 44060
　440 639-4494

(G-13761)
UNITED STATES ENDOSCOPY (DH)
Also Called: US Endoscopy
5976 Heisley Rd (44060-1873)
PHONE.....................................440 639-4494
Fax: 440 639-4495
Tony Siracusa, *CEO*
Kenneth Turley, *Regional Mgr*
Dan Croteau, *Exec VP*
Frank Buchy, *Vice Pres*
Gulam Kahn, *Vice Pres*
▲ **EMP:** 15
SQ FT: 30,000
SALES (est): 65.2MM
SALES (corp-wide): 2.2B **Privately Held**
WEB: www.usendoscopy.com
SIC: 3841 Surgical instruments & apparatus
HQ: Steris Corporation
　5960 Heisley Rd
　Mentor OH 44060
　440 354-2600

(G-13762)
UNIVERSAL PLASTICS INC
9081 Agard Ct (44060-4426)
PHONE.....................................440 942-7510
Fax: 440 942-7510
William Brunelle, *President*
Brian Novogurski, *General Mgr*
Beverly Brunelle, *Vice Pres*
Barry Friedman, *Vice Pres*
EMP: 31 EST: 1982
SQ FT: 30,000
SALES (est): 4.9MM **Privately Held**
SIC: 3082 3052 Tubes, unsupported plastic; plastic hose

(G-13763)
US POWDER COATING INC
8665 Tyler Blvd (44060-4346)
PHONE.....................................440 255-3090
Ray Gotliewbowski, *Principal*
EMP: 4
SALES (est): 320K **Privately Held**
SIC: 3499 Friction material, made from powdered metal

(G-13764)
V K C INC
Also Called: Fab Form
7667 Jenther Dr (44060-4872)
PHONE.....................................440 951-9634
Joseph Chmielewski, *President*
Lori Bastian, *Exec VP*
Raymond Gotliebowski, *VP Opers*
Chad Gotliebowski, *Sales Dir*
Ryan Rowland, *Sales Staff*
EMP: 19
SQ FT: 10,000
SALES (est): 4.7MM **Privately Held**
SIC: 3469 Stamping metal for the trade

(G-13765)
VAST MOLD & TOOL CO INC
7154 Industrial Park Blvd (44060-5314)
PHONE.....................................440 942-7585
Vincent Romano, *President*
EMP: 5
SQ FT: 8,000
SALES: 600K **Privately Held**
SIC: 3089 Molding primary plastic

(G-13766)
VECTOR INTERNATIONAL CORP
Also Called: Vector Screenprinting & EMB
7404 Tyler Blvd (44060-5402)
PHONE.....................................440 942-2002
Fax: 440 942-2012
Doug Anderson, *President*
Michele Silvis, *Manager*
EMP: 8
SQ FT: 6,000
SALES (est): 500K **Privately Held**
WEB: www.vectorproimage.com
SIC: 2396 2395 Screen printing on fabric articles; embroidery & art needlework

(G-13767)
VICON FABRICATING COMPANY LTD
7200 Justin Way (44060-4881)
PHONE.....................................440 205-6700
Fax: 440 974-8285
Robert S Seidemann, *CEO*
Jeffrey Conforte, *President*
Penny Smith, *Finance Other*
Joseph Geitz, *Manager*
Michael Conforte, *Executive*
EMP: 35 EST: 1965
SQ FT: 40,000
SALES (est): 8.9MM **Privately Held**
WEB: www.viconfab.com
SIC: 3441 3398 Fabricated structural metal; metal heat treating

(G-13768)
VOLK OPTICAL INC
7893 Enterprise Dr (44060-5309)
PHONE.....................................440 942-6161
Fax: 440 942-2257
Jyoti Gupta, *President*
Terry Cooper, *Regional Mgr*
Arlinda Vaughn, *Regional Mgr*
Steve Cech, *Vice Pres*
John Strobel, *Vice Pres*
▲ **EMP:** 70 EST: 1974
SQ FT: 18,000
SALES (est): 12.6MM
SALES (corp-wide): 1.1B **Privately Held**
SIC: 8011 3851 3827 Offices & clinics of medical doctors; lenses, ophthalmic; optical instruments & lenses
HQ: Halma Holdings Inc.
　11500 Northlake Dr # 306
　Cincinnati OH 45249
　513 772-5501

(G-13769)
WILSON OPTICAL LABORATORY INC
Also Called: North American Coating Labs
9450 Pineneedle Dr (44060-1828)
PHONE.....................................440 357-7000
John H Wilson, *CEO*
Brian Wilson, *President*
Lori Grabowy, *Marketing Staff*
EMP: 50
SQ FT: 30,000
SALES (est): 8.5MM **Privately Held**
WEB: www.nacl.com
SIC: 3851 3827 3229 Lens coating, ophthalmic; optical instruments & lenses; pressed & blown glass

(G-13770)
WINES FOR YOU
7344 Mentor Ave (44060-7543)
PHONE.....................................440 946-1420
Debbie Iacofano, *Principal*
EMP: 4
SALES (est): 239K **Privately Held**
SIC: 2084 Wines

(G-13771)
WIRE SHOP INC
5959 Pinecone Dr (44060-1866)
PHONE.....................................440 354-6842
John Ferguson, *President*
Howard Pindale, *Vice Pres*
Annette Blashinsky, *Manager*
EMP: 20
SQ FT: 20,000
SALES (est): 3.6MM **Privately Held**
WEB: www.thewireshop.com
SIC: 3544 3599 Special dies & tools; machine & other job shop work

(G-13772)
WOOD SPECIALISTS
9485 Pinecone Dr (44060-1864)
PHONE.....................................440 639-9797
Fax: 440 639-0133
Ken Demarchi, *Owner*
EMP: 4 EST: 1977
SQ FT: 7,000
SALES (est): 430K **Privately Held**
SIC: 2541 2653 Wood partitions & fixtures; cabinets, lockers & shelving; counters or counter display cases, wood; corrugated boxes, partitions, display items, sheets & pad

---

Mentor On The Lake
Lake County

(G-13773)
AQUA PENNSYLVANIA INC
Also Called: Aqua Ohio
7748 Twilight Dr (44060-2629)
PHONE.....................................440 257-6190
Bill Bowers, *Branch Mgr*
EMP: 6
SALES (corp-wide): 819.8MM **Publicly Held**
SIC: 5499 4941 3589 Water: distilled mineral or spring; water supply; water treatment equipment, industrial
HQ: Aqua Pennsylvania, Inc.
　762 W Lancaster Ave
　Bryn Mawr PA 19010
　610 525-1400

(G-13774)
MENTOR INC
Also Called: Action Door
5983 Andrews Rd (44060-2819)
PHONE.....................................440 255-1250
Fax: 440 209-8343
Shelly Mastanuono, *CEO*
Michael Whittwer, *President*
Dino Mastanuono, *Vice Pres*
▲ **EMP:** 9
SALES (est): 1.6MM **Privately Held**
WEB: www.mentor.net
SIC: 3732 Dories, building & repairing

Mesopotamia
Trumbull County

(G-13775)
INNOVATIVE INTEGRATIONS INC
Also Called: I3
7877 Girdle Rd (44439)
P.O. Box 222 (44439-0222)
PHONE.....................................216 533-5353
Matthew Toddy, *President*
EMP: 3
SALES (est): 287.4K **Privately Held**
SIC: 3625 7373 7389 Relays, for electronic use; office computer automation systems integration; systems software development services;

Metamora
Fulton County

(G-13776)
PARKER-HANNIFIN CORPORATION
Hydraulic Filter Division
16810 Fulton County Rd 2 (43540)
PHONE.....................................419 644-4311
Fax: 419 644-6205
Jack Atkinson, *Principal*
Tom Brooks, *Principal*
D Crooks, *Principal*
Al Zingaro, *Principal*
Dan Sekerak, *Plant Mgr*
EMP: 150
SALES (corp-wide): 11.3B **Publicly Held**
WEB: www.parker.com
SIC: 3542 Presses: hydraulic & pneumatic, mechanical & manual
PA: Parker-Hannifin Corporation
　6035 Parkland Blvd
　Cleveland OH 44124
　216 896-3000

Miamisburg
Montgomery County

(G-13777)
3 DIPS
33 S Main St (45342-2830)
PHONE.....................................937 247-5914
Connie L Grubbs, *Principal*
EMP: 4
SALES (est): 299.2K **Privately Held**
SIC: 2024 Ice cream, bulk

(G-13778)
A & T ORNAMENTAL IRON COMPANY
415 E Sycamore St (45342-2331)
PHONE.....................................937 859-6006
Fax: 937 859-6021
Terry L Wagerman, *Owner*
EMP: 4
SALES (est): 368.4K **Privately Held**
SIC: 3446 Railings, prefabricated metal; gates, ornamental metal

(G-13779)
A-1 SPRINKLER COMPANY INC
2383 Northpointe Dr (45342-2989)
PHONE.....................................937 859-6198
Fax: 937 859-0651
Bill Hausmann, *CEO*
Tara Lawson, *Controller*
Kime Faine-Shaffer, *Office Mgr*
Erin Chambers, *Comp Tech*
Nick Hudgens, *Comp Tech*
EMP: 68
SQ FT: 15,000
SALES (est): 9.6MM **Privately Held**
WEB: www.spkr.com
SIC: 3569 5087 Firefighting apparatus & related equipment; firefighting equipment

(G-13780)
ADVANCED INDUSTRIAL MEASUREMNT
2580 Kohnle Dr (45342-3669)
P.O. Box 341118, Beavercreek (45434-1118)
PHONE.....................................937 320-4930
David A Delph, *President*
▲ **EMP:** 21
SALES (est): 3.9MM **Privately Held**
SIC: 3829 Measuring & controlling devices

(G-13781)
ALDRICH CHEMICAL
Also Called: Sigma-Aldrich
3858 Benner Rd (45342-4304)
PHONE.....................................937 859-1808
Fax: 937 859-4878
Paul Ripplinger, *Vice Pres*
Brett Eshbauth, *Safety Mgr*
Tom Fahey, *Mfg Staff*
Tisha Micer, *Purch Agent*
Phil Darragh, *Research*
EMP: 70
SQ FT: 30,000
SALES (corp-wide): 15.8B **Privately Held**
SIC: 2819 5084 2899 2869 Isotopes, radioactive; chemical process equipment; chemical preparations; industrial organic chemicals
HQ: Aldrich Chemical
　3050 Spruce St
　Saint Louis MO 63103
　314 771-5765

(G-13782)
ALEGRE INC
Also Called: Alegre Global Supply Solutions
3101 W Tech Blvd (45342-0819)
PHONE..........................937 885-6786
Fax: 937 885-6787
Lilly Phillips, *President*
Kevin Hyde, *General Mgr*
Don Phillips, *Vice Pres*
Roger McNutt, *Opers Staff*
Saith Green, *Accountant*
▲ EMP: 14
SQ FT: 24,000
SALES (est): 2.8MM Privately Held
SIC: 4225 5013 3714 General warehousing & storage; automotive supplies & parts; motor vehicle engines & parts

(G-13783)
ANDERSON PUBLISHING CO (PA)
9443 Springboro Pike (45342-4425)
PHONE..........................513 474-9305
John L Mason, *Ch of Bd*
Dale Hartig, *President*
John Qualls, *Vice Pres*
Bill Bruden, *Production*
Diane Perry, *CFO*
EMP: 84 EST: 1887
SQ FT: 22,000
SALES (est): 5.6MM Privately Held
WEB: www.andersonpublishing.com
SIC: 2731 2741 Books: publishing only; pamphlets: publishing only, not printed on site; textbooks: publishing only, not printed on site; miscellaneous publishing; technical papers: publishing only, not printed on site

(G-13784)
APPLEHEART
2240 E Central Ave (45342-7601)
PHONE..........................937 384-0430
Tom Robbins, *President*
EMP: 6
SQ FT: 4,500
SALES: 380K Privately Held
WEB: www.tomrobbins.com
SIC: 5699 2759 2395 Uniforms & work clothing; commercial printing; embroidery products, except schiffli machine

(G-13785)
BELL VAULT & MONUMENT WORKS
1019 S Main St (45342-3148)
PHONE..........................937 866-2444
Timothy Bell, *President*
Greg Bell, *Corp Secy*
EMP: 24 EST: 1928
SQ FT: 17,000
SALES (est): 4.1MM Privately Held
SIC: 3272 5999 7261 3281 Burial vaults, concrete or precast terrazzo; monuments, finished to custom order; gravestones, finished; funeral service & crematories; cut stone & stone products; public building & related furniture

(G-13786)
BRAINERD INDUSTRIES INC (PA)
680 Precision Ct (45342-6138)
PHONE..........................937 228-0488
Gregory W Fritz, *President*
Rhonda Reynolds, *Vice Pres*
EMP: 50 EST: 1997
SQ FT: 72,000
SALES (est): 9.6MM Privately Held
WEB: www.brainerdindustries.com
SIC: 3469 3993 3442 Metal stampings; name plates: except engraved, etched, etc.: metal; metal doors, sash & trim

(G-13787)
BROWN CNC MACHINERY INC
433 E Maple Ave (45342-2343)
PHONE..........................937 865-9191
Fax: 937 865-9192
Mike Brown, *President*
Steve Brown, *Exec VP*
Gary Alcorn, *Engineer*
Don Lamb, *Manager*
EMP: 28
SQ FT: 20,000

SALES (est): 4.6MM Privately Held
SIC: 3599 Machine shop, jobbing & repair

(G-13788)
C B & S SPOUTING INC
4609 Slders Hm Mmsburg Rd
(45342-1127)
PHONE..........................937 866-1600
Penny Bullock, *President*
EMP: 3
SALES (est): 250K Privately Held
SIC: 3089 Spouting, plastic & glass fiber reinforced

(G-13789)
CARLTON-BATES COMPANY
Cbc Connect
4900 Lyons Rd Unit B (45342-6417)
PHONE..........................937 384-0426
Fax: 937 384-0495
Tara Trissel, *Buyer*
Tara Larison, *Purchasing*
Ben Albu, *Manager*
EMP: 6 Publicly Held
WEB: www.carlton-bates.com
SIC: 3714 Automotive wiring harness sets
HQ: Carlton-Bates Company
3600 W 69th St
Little Rock AR 72209
501 562-9100

(G-13790)
CB MANUFACTURING & SLS CO INC (PA)
4455 Infirmary Rd (45342-1299)
PHONE..........................937 866-5986
Fax: 937 866-6844
Charles S Biehn Jr, *CEO*
Richard Porter, *President*
Donald M Cain, *Vice Pres*
Roger Adams, *Plant Mgr*
Angie Matheney, *Purch Agent*
▲ EMP: 67
SQ FT: 90,000
SALES (est): 41.4MM Privately Held
WEB: www.cbmfg.com
SIC: 5085 3423 Knives, industrial; knives, agricultural or industrial

(G-13791)
CERTIFIED TOOL & GRINDING INC
Also Called: Ctg
4455 Infirmary Rd (45342-1233)
PHONE..........................937 865-5934
Charles Biehn, *President*
Rich Porter, *General Mgr*
Joseph Biehn, *Vice Pres*
Bob Miller, *Sales Staff*
Matt Smith, *Manager*
▲ EMP: 7 EST: 1972
SALES (est): 1.1MM
SALES (corp-wide): 2.4MM Privately Held
WEB: www.certifiedindustrialservices.com
SIC: 3545 Cutting tools for machine tools; tools & accessories for machine tools
PA: Certified Heat Treating, Inc
4475 Infirmary Rd
Dayton OH 45449
937 866-0245

(G-13792)
CHRISTIAN BLUE PAGES (PA)
521 Byers Rd Ste 102 (45342-5379)
PHONE..........................937 847-2583
Darrel Geis, *President*
Ruth Reed, *VP Opers*
Brian Hegyi, *Sales Dir*
Gary Abston, *Accounts Mgr*
Ron Auble, *Accounts Exec*
EMP: 10
SALES (est): 713.4K Privately Held
WEB: www.cbpgs.com
SIC: 2741 Directories, telephone: publishing only, not printed on site

(G-13793)
CONNECTIVE DESIGN INCORPORATED
Also Called: C D I
3010 S Tech Blvd (45342-4860)
PHONE..........................937 746-8252
Danya A Chandler, *President*
Mike Chandler, *Vice Pres*

EMP: 11
SQ FT: 8,500
SALES (est): 2.5MM Privately Held
WEB: www.cdinc.us
SIC: 3678 3714 3679 Electronic connectors; automotive wiring harness sets; harness assemblies for electronic use: wire or cable

(G-13794)
COX NEWSPAPERS LLC
Also Called: Miamisburg News
230 S 2nd St (45342-2925)
P.O. Box 108 (45343-0108)
PHONE..........................937 866-3331
Fax: 937 866-6011
Donald J Miller, *President*
EMP: 10
SALES (corp-wide): 32.4B Privately Held
WEB: www.coxnewspapers.com
SIC: 2711 Newspapers, publishing & printing
HQ: Cox Newspapers, Inc.
6205 Peachtree Dunwoody
Atlanta GA 30328

(G-13795)
CUSTOMFORMED PRODUCTS INC
Also Called: Custom Formed Products
645 Precision Ct (45342-6138)
PHONE..........................937 388-0480
Michael Schindler, *President*
Mike Shindler, *Officer*
EMP: 15
SQ FT: 15,000
SALES (est): 2.3MM Privately Held
SIC: 2789 3469 3544 Paper cutting; metal stampings; dies, steel rule

(G-13796)
D+H USA CORPORATION
8555 Gander Creek Dr (45342-5436)
PHONE..........................937 435-2335
Connie Bruce, *Manager*
EMP: 9
SALES (corp-wide): 1.2B Privately Held
WEB: www.harlandfinancialsolutions.com
SIC: 7372 7389 Prepackaged software; personal service agents, brokers & bureaus
HQ: D+H Usa Corporation
605 Crescent Executive Ct # 600
Lake Mary FL 32746
407 804-6600

(G-13797)
DAY-TEC TOOL & MFG INC
4900 Lyons Rd Unit A (45342-6417)
PHONE..........................937 847-0022
Fax: 937 847-0033
Gerald Whitehead, *President*
Dana Whitehead, *President*
Joseph Baylogh, *Vice Pres*
Jack Meyers, *Sales Mgr*
Jana McNeal, *Office Mgr*
EMP: 12
SQ FT: 15,000
SALES: 2MM Privately Held
WEB: www.dtma.org
SIC: 3559 Robots, molding & forming plastics

(G-13798)
DAYTON SUPERIOR CORPORATION (HQ)
1125 Byers Rd (45342-5765)
PHONE..........................937 866-0711
Fax: 937 866-1558
James McRickard, *CEO*
Lutz Richter, *CEO*
Eric R Zimmerman, *Principal*
Kevin Walsh, *Business Mgr*
Randy Brown, *Senior VP*
▲ EMP: 115
SALES: 353MM
SALES (corp-wide): 1.7B Privately Held
WEB: www.daytonsuperior.com
SIC: 3315 3452 3462 3089 Steel wire & related products; dowel pins, metal; construction or mining equipment forgings, ferrous; plastic hardware & building products; chemical preparations

PA: Odyssey Investment Partners Llc
590 Madison Ave Fl 39
New York NY 10022
212 351-7900

(G-13799)
DAYTON SYSTEMS GROUP INC
3003 S Tech Blvd (45342-4864)
PHONE..........................937 885-5665
Henry C Bachmann, *President*
Brad Bachmann, *COO*
Steve Cook, *Vice Pres*
Dale Conley, *Research*
Cook Jason, *Manager*
EMP: 55
SQ FT: 23,000
SALES (est): 11.6MM Privately Held
WEB: www.dsgtech.com
SIC: 3565 Canning machinery, food

(G-13800)
DAYTRONIC CORPORATION (HQ)
2566 Kohnle Dr (45342-3669)
PHONE..........................937 866-3300
Robert Hart, *President*
Joanne Wos, *Controller*
EMP: 10 EST: 1954
SQ FT: 5,000
SALES (est): 1.1MM Privately Held
WEB: www.daytronic.com
SIC: 3829 Measuring & controlling devices

(G-13801)
DIGITAL CONTROLS CORPORATION (PA)
444 Alexandersville Rd (45342-3658)
PHONE..........................513 746-8118
Fax: 937 384-0842
Michael Denny, *CEO*
Chatles Landreville, *Senior VP*
Dan Rang, *Vice Pres*
Bob Arney, *Treasurer*
Theresa Gebhardt, *Human Res Dir*
EMP: 52 EST: 1969
SQ FT: 24,000
SALES (est): 9.1MM Privately Held
WEB: www.digital-controls.com
SIC: 7379 7372 5045 8742 Computer related maintenance services; prepackaged software; computers, peripherals & software; management consulting services

(G-13802)
DOUBLE DIPPIN INC
949 Blanche Dr (45342-2027)
PHONE..........................937 847-2572
Don Smith, *Principal*
EMP: 4
SALES (est): 299.2K Privately Held
SIC: 2024 Ice cream & ice milk

(G-13803)
EAGLE MFG SOLUTIONS LLC
2585 Belvo Rd (45342-3911)
PHONE..........................937 865-0366
Rich Treppa, *General Mgr*
Dave Batner, *Mng Member*
Scott Lovelace, *Mng Member*
EMP: 12
SALES (est): 2.6MM Privately Held
SIC: 3599 Machine shop, jobbing & repair

(G-13804)
ELECTRIPACK INC
2064 Byers Rd (45342-1167)
PHONE..........................937 433-2602
Fax: 937 433-2604
Jeanne Wright, *CEO*
Garth Shadoan, *Manager*
◆ EMP: 40
SQ FT: 20,000
SALES: 7MM Privately Held
WEB: www.electripack.com
SIC: 3694 Harness wiring sets, internal combustion engines

(G-13805)
ESKO-GRAPHICS INC (DH)
Also Called: Eskoartwork
8535 Gander Creek Dr (45342-5436)
PHONE..........................937 454-1721
Kurt Demeuleneere, *CEO*
Jill Gehrhardt, *President*
Mark Quinlan, *President*
Tony Wiley, *President*

GEOGRAPHIC

Gary Evers, *Vice Pres*
▲ **EMP:** 70
SQ FT: 27,000
SALES (est) 118.2MM
SALES (corp-wide): 130.3K **Privately Held**
SIC: 5084 7372 Printing trades machinery, equipment & supplies; prepackaged software
HQ: Esko-Graphics Bvba
Kortrijksesteenweg 1095
Gent 9051
921 692-11

(G-13806)
EVENFLO COMPANY INC (HQ)
225 Byers Rd (45342-3614)
PHONE..................937 415-3300
Jon Chamberlain, *CEO*
Andy Antil, *Vice Pres*
Peter Banat, *Vice Pres*
Erick Lara, *Buyer*
Jason Riehle, *QC Mgr*
◆ **EMP:** 150
SQ FT: 1,250,000
SALES (est): 296.3MM
SALES (corp-wide): 896.7MM **Privately Held**
WEB: www.evenflo.com
SIC: 3944 2519 Games, toys & children's vehicles; child restraint seats, automotive; fiberglass & plastic furniture
PA: Goodbaby International Holdings Limited
Rm 2001 20/F Two Chinachem Exchange Sq
North Point HK
280 603-38

(G-13807)
EXCELITAS TECHNOLOGIES CORP
1100 Vanguard Blvd (45342-0312)
PHONE..................937 865-4621
Olivia Romstad, *General Mgr*
John Martin, *Vice Pres*
Steven Cornett, *Electrical Engi*
Doug Benner, *Branch Mgr*
Steven Damian, *Program Mgr*
EMP: 120 **Privately Held**
SIC: 3829 3489 Thermometers & temperature sensors; ordnance & accessories
HQ: Excelitas Technologies Corp.
200 West St
Waltham MA 02451

(G-13808)
EXLINE MANUFACTURING CO INC
4352 Slders Hm Mmsburg Rd (45342-1122)
PHONE..................937 866-1515
James Exline III, *President*
James Albert Exline III, *President*
EMP: 3 **EST:** 1949
SQ FT: 21,500
SALES (est): 290K **Privately Held**
SIC: 3429 3469 3599 Manufactured hardware (general); stamping metal for the trade; machine shop, jobbing & repair

(G-13809)
FLORIDA TILE INC
Florida Tile 79
2105 Lyons Rd (45342-4463)
PHONE..................937 293-5151
Michelle Clary, *Manager*
EMP: 6
SQ FT: 2,000
SALES (corp-wide): 144.6MM **Privately Held**
WEB: www.floridatile.com
SIC: 3253 Wall tile, ceramic
PA: Florida Tile, Inc.
998 Governors Ln Ste 300
Lexington KY 40513
859 219-5200

(G-13810)
FOXTRONIX INC
2240 E Central Ave Ste 4 (45342-3683)
PHONE..................937 866-2112
Christopher Sweeney, *Owner*
EMP: 5
SQ FT: 2,200

SALES (est): 1.7MM **Privately Held**
WEB: www.foxtronix.com
SIC: 5065 3069 Electronic parts & equipment; hard rubber & molded rubber products

(G-13811)
FREEDOM ASPHALT SEALANT & LINE
1241 Stephens St (45342-1745)
PHONE..................937 416-1053
Larry West, *Principal*
EMP: 3
SALES (est): 149.6K **Privately Held**
SIC: 2891 Sealants

(G-13812)
GAYSTON CORPORATION
721 Richard St (45342-1840)
P.O. Box 523 (45343-0523)
PHONE..................937 743-6050
Fax: 859 746-1239
Mark W Stone, *Ch of Bd*
Willard W Deey, *Vice Pres*
Willard W Dewey, *Vice Pres*
J G Heitz, *Vice Pres*
Connie G Hinkel, *Vice Pres*
▲ **EMP:** 200
SQ FT: 280,000
SALES (est): 59.7MM **Privately Held**
WEB: www.gayston.com
SIC: 3443 3999 3949 2813 Nuclear reactors, military or industrial; military insignia; baseball, softball & cricket sports equipment; oxygen, compressed or liquefied

(G-13813)
GERALD ROSE
Also Called: Rose Grinding & Mfg Co
9600 Byers Rd (45342-4340)
PHONE..................937 866-6339
Fax: 937 866-6167
Gerald L Rose, *Owner*
EMP: 4
SQ FT: 4,000
SALES (est): 566.7K **Privately Held**
SIC: 3599 Machine shop, jobbing & repair

(G-13814)
HAMMELMANN CORPORATION (HQ)
436 Southpointe Dr (45342-6459)
PHONE..................937 859-8777
Fax: 937 859-9188
Kathy Miller, *General Mgr*
Stephen Laviers, *Regional Mgr*
Peter Englehardt, *Corp Secy*
Gisela Hammelmann, *Vice Pres*
Michael Goecke, *Vice Pres*
▲ **EMP:** 17
SQ FT: 10,000
SALES (est): 26.3MM
SALES (corp-wide): 83.7MM **Privately Held**
WEB: www.hammelmann.com
SIC: 5084 3443 Pumps & pumping equipment; fabricated plate work (boiler shop)

(G-13815)
HARTZELL MANUFACTURING CO INC
2533 Technical Dr (45342-6108)
PHONE..................937 859-5955
Fax: 937 859-5954
David Vickroy, *President*
Nancy Boles, *Principal*
Roy Gibson, *Principal*
Fred Issenmann, *Principal*
Alan Pummill, *Principal*
EMP: 48
SQ FT: 35,000
SALES (est): 8.9MM **Privately Held**
WEB: www.hartzellmfg.com
SIC: 3444 3479 3471 Sheet metalwork; coating of metals & formed products; plating & polishing

(G-13816)
HEARTLAND PUBLICATIONS LLC (HQ)
Also Called: Civitas Media
4500 Lyons Rd (45342-6447)
PHONE..................860 664-1075
Michael Bush, *President*
Brian Garner, *Editor*

Bob Bertz, *CFO*
Kathy Venturino, *Accounting Mgr*
EMP: 11
SALES (est): 9.7MM
SALES (corp-wide): 1.4B **Privately Held**
WEB: www.heartlandpublications.com
SIC: 2759 Publication printing
PA: Civitas Media, Llc
130 Harbour Place Dr # 300
Davidson NC 28036
704 897-6020

(G-13817)
HILLTOP BASIC RESOURCES INC
Also Called: Riverbend Sand Rock and Gravel
4710 Soldiers Home W (45342)
PHONE..................937 859-3616
Fax: 937 859-8295
Mike Oliver, *Manager*
EMP: 15
SALES (corp-wide): 135MM **Privately Held**
WEB: www.hilltopbasicresources.com
SIC: 5032 1442 Gravel; sand, construction; construction sand & gravel
PA: Hilltop Basic Resources, Inc.
1 W 4th St Ste 1100
Cincinnati OH 45202
513 651-5000

(G-13818)
HOOVEN - DAYTON CORP (PA)
Also Called: H D C
511 Byers Rd (45342-5337)
PHONE..................937 233-4473
Fax: 937 233-9382
Christopher Che, *President*
Mindy App, *General Mgr*
Al Abolofia, *Senior VP*
Evan Arrindell, *Vice Pres*
Jack Miller, *Vice Pres*
EMP: 73
SQ FT: 40,000
SALES (est): 22MM **Privately Held**
WEB: www.hoovendayton.com
SIC: 2679 2672 2671 2759 Tags & labels, paper; tape, pressure sensitive: made from purchased materials; packaging paper & plastics film, coated & laminated; labels & seals: printing

(G-13819)
INNOMARK COMMUNICATIONS LLC
3005 W Tech Blvd (45342-0824)
PHONE..................513 285-1040
EMP: 238
SALES (corp-wide): 126.2MM **Privately Held**
SIC: 2759 Commercial printing
PA: Innomark Communications Llc
3233 S Tech Blvd
Miamisburg OH 45342
937 427-6100

(G-13820)
INVOTEC ENGINEERING INC
10909 Industry Ln (45342-0818)
PHONE..................937 886-3232
Fax: 937 886-2131
John C Hanna, *President*
Daryl R Greywitt, *Vice Pres*
Mark Goode, *Mfg Mgr*
Karen Brunke, *Engineer*
Mark Hopkins, *Engineer*
EMP: 60
SQ FT: 63,000
SALES (est): 13.6MM **Privately Held**
WEB: www.invotec.com
SIC: 8711 3599 Machine tool design; custom machinery

(G-13821)
JATRODIESEL INC
845 N Main St (45342-1871)
PHONE..................937 847-8050
Rajesh Mosali, *President*
Rahul Bobbili, *Vice Pres*
Sharath Bobbili, *Engineer*
Sabrina Pennington, *Accounting Mgr*
▼ **EMP:** 17

SALES: 4.5MM **Privately Held**
WEB: www.jatrodiesel.com
SIC: 2869 3519 Industrial organic chemicals; diesel engine rebuilding

(G-13822)
JOHNSON ENERGY COMPANY
Also Called: Jec Forest & Paper Related Co
1 Prestige Pl Ste 270 (45342-6146)
P.O. Box 9035, Dayton (45409-9035)
PHONE..................937 435-5401
Fax: 937 435-5402
Michael D Johnson, *President*
Frank V Surico, *Vice Pres*
EMP: 3 **EST:** 1978
SQ FT: 1,800
SALES: 42.5MM **Privately Held**
SIC: 5052 2671 Coal & other minerals & ores; plastic film, coated or laminated for packaging

(G-13823)
JOHNSON MACHINING SERVICES LLC
4505 Infirmary Rd (45342-1235)
PHONE..................937 866-4744
Tom Johnson, *Mng Member*
Robert Mason,
EMP: 7
SQ FT: 2,500
SALES (est): 983.7K **Privately Held**
SIC: 3599 3499 8711 Machine & other job shop work; machine bases, metal; mechanical engineering

(G-13824)
KINGSCOTE CHEMICALS INC
Also Called: Kingscote-Formulabs
3334 S Tech Blvd (45342-0823)
PHONE..................937 886-9100
Fax: 937 886-9300
Robert Ciulla, *President*
EMP: 4
SALES: 900K **Privately Held**
WEB: www.kingscotechemicals.com
SIC: 2865 Dyes, synthetic organic

(G-13825)
LEXISNEXIS GROUP (DH)
9443 Springboro Pike (45342-5490)
PHONE..................937 865-6800
Kurt Sanford, *CEO*
Doug Kaplan, *CEO*
Michael Lamb, *President*
Billy Last, *Managing Dir*
Mike Pilmer, *Managing Dir*
EMP: 148
SALES (est): 652.2MM
SALES (corp-wide): 8.4B **Privately Held**
SIC: 7375 2741 Data base information retrieval; miscellaneous publishing
HQ: Relx Inc.
230 Park Ave Ste 700
New York NY 10169
212 309-8100

(G-13826)
LIQUID LOGIC LLC
720 Mound Rd Ste 250 (45342-3204)
P.O. Box 4 (45343-0004)
PHONE..................937 865-3068
Bill Merten, *CEO*
David Steuart, *Executive*
EMP: 3 **EST:** 2001
SALES (est): 168.7K **Privately Held**
WEB: www.liquidlogicdispensers.com
SIC: 3841 Surgical & medical instruments

(G-13827)
MATTHEW BENDER & COMPANY INC
9443 Springboro Pike (45342-4425)
PHONE..................518 487-3000
George Bearse, *Vice Pres*
Stephanie Singer, *Vice Pres*
Randall Baumgarte, *Engineer*
Arthur V Dohre III, *Engineer*
Ian Dumbauld, *Engineer*
EMP: 240
SALES (corp-wide): 8.4B **Privately Held**
SIC: 2721 2731 Periodicals; book publishing
HQ: Matthew Bender & Company, Inc.
744 Broad St Fl 8
Newark NJ 07102
518 487-3000

(G-13828)
MAX DAETWYLER CORP
2133 Lyons Rd (45344-4463)
PHONE...................................937 428-1781
Fax: 937 439-1592
Peter Daetwyler, *President*
Donna Aker, *Admin Asst*
EMP: 12 Privately Held
SIC: 3599 Electrical discharge machining (EDM)
HQ: Max Daetwyler Corp.
13420 Reese Blvd W
Huntersville NC 28078
704 875-1200

(G-13829)
MDI OF OHIO INC
Also Called: Dempsey Industries
802 N 4th St (45342-1812)
PHONE...................................937 866-2345
Fax: 937 866-9621
John E Dempsey, *President*
Duane Estes, *Opers Mgr*
Gary Taspoe, *Engineer*
Brenda Hill, *Manager*
EMP: 34
SALES (est): 7MM
SALES (corp-wide): 13.6MM Privately Held
SIC: 3089 Injection molded finished plastic products; injection molding of plastics
PA: Molded Devices, Inc.
740 W Knox Rd
Tempe AZ 85284
800 852-1472

(G-13830)
METAL SHREDDERS INC
5101 Farmersville W (45342)
P.O. Box 244, Dayton (45449)
PHONE...................................937 866-0777
Fax: 937 866-7420
Ken Cohen, *President*
Wilbur Cohen, *Chairman*
EMP: 30
SQ FT: 8,000
SALES (est): 3.5MM Privately Held
WEB: www.metalshredders.com
SIC: 7389 3341 Metal slitting & shearing; secondary nonferrous metals

(G-13831)
MIAMI VALLEY COUNTERS & SPC
8515 Dyton Cincinnati Pike (45342-3168)
PHONE...................................937 865-0562
Fax: 937 859-0248
Ron James, *President*
Robert Dennis, *Vice Pres*
EMP: 6
SQ FT: 2,987
SALES (est): 805.1K Privately Held
SIC: 2541 Counter & sink tops

(G-13832)
MIAMI VALLEY PRECISION INC
456 Alexandersville Rd (45342-3658)
PHONE...................................937 866-1804
Fax: 937 866-1806
Michael Smith, *President*
Brian Smith, *Vice Pres*
Christine Smith, *Treasurer*
EMP: 22
SQ FT: 16,000
SALES (est): 3.5MM Privately Held
SIC: 3599 Machine shop, jobbing & repair

(G-13833)
MIAMI-CAST INC
901 N Main St (45342-1873)
PHONE...................................937 866-2951
George Deckebach, *President*
C Thomas Koehler, *Vice Pres*
Charles Koehler, *Treasurer*
EMP: 26
SQ FT: 20,000
SALES (est): 5.6MM Privately Held
WEB: www.miami-cast.com
SIC: 3321 Gray iron castings

(G-13834)
MIAMISBURG COATING
925 N Main St (45342-1873)
PHONE...................................937 866-1323
Fax: 937 866-5723
William Sizemore, *Partner*

Opal Sizemore, *Partner*
EMP: 10
SQ FT: 15,000
SALES (est): 1.1MM Privately Held
SIC: 3479 Coating of metals & formed products

(G-13835)
MIDWEST FASTENERS INC
450 Richard St (45342-1863)
PHONE...................................937 866-0463
Fax: 937 866-4174
Thomas Hartmann, *President*
Robert Fairbank, *Corp Secy*
Brian Waterhouse, *Vice Pres*
Gloria Ramsey, *Purch Agent*
George Bratz, *Engineer*
▲ EMP: 85
SQ FT: 46,000
SALES (est): 18.6MM Privately Held
WEB: www.midwestfasteners.com
SIC: 3548 Electric welding equipment

(G-13836)
MIL-MAR CENTURY CORPORATION
8641 Washington Church Rd (45342-4470)
PHONE...................................937 275-4860
Trib Tewari, *President*
Jon Angier, *Project Mgr*
Beth Corwin, *Controller*
Aaron Pelfrey, *Manager*
Bob Wehmeier, *Manager*
▲ EMP: 15
SALES (est): 2.3MM Privately Held
SIC: 3599 Machine shop, jobbing & repair

(G-13837)
MILLER PUBLISHING COMPANY
230 S 2nd St (45342-2925)
P.O. Box 1085 (45343-1085)
PHONE...................................937 866-3331
Donald J Miller, *Principal*
EMP: 3
SALES (est): 303.1K Privately Held
SIC: 2721 Periodicals

(G-13838)
MOUND PRINTING COMPANY INC
Also Called: Promotional Spring
2455 Belvo Rd (45342-3909)
PHONE...................................937 866-2872
Fax: 937 866-6551
Wade Riggs, *President*
Dennis Riggs, *General Mgr*
Frances Riggs, *Vice Pres*
Wayne Funk, *Accounts Exec*
Dave Weide, *Accounts Exec*
EMP: 25
SQ FT: 30,000
SALES (est): 5.2MM Privately Held
WEB: www.goldenbooks.com
SIC: 2759 Commercial printing

(G-13839)
NAUTILUS HYOSUNG AMERICA INC
2076 Byers Rd (45342-1167)
PHONE...................................937 203-4900
Justin Kim, *Director*
Kay Jinn, *Admin Asst*
EMP: 3
SALES (est): 289.9K Privately Held
SIC: 3612 Power transformers, electric

(G-13840)
NEWPAGE ENERGY SERVICES LLC
8540 Gander Creek Dr (45342-5439)
PHONE...................................877 855-7243
Debra Graham, *Engng Exec*
Linda Sheffield, *Marketing Staff*
George F Martin,
▼ EMP: 6000
SALES (est): 228.8MM Privately Held
SIC: 2672 2621 2611 Coated & laminated paper; paper mills; uncoated paper; pulp mills

(G-13841)
NEWPAGE GROUP INC (HQ)
8540 Gander Creek Dr (45342-5439)
PHONE...................................937 242-9500
George F Martin, *President*

Chan W Galbato, *Chairman*
James C Tyrone, *Exec VP*
Daniel A Clark, *Senior VP*
Douglas K Cooper, *Senior VP*
EMP: 36
SALES (est): 3.1B
SALES (corp-wide): 39.9B Publicly Held
SIC: 2671 Packaging paper & plastics film, coated & laminated
PA: Cerberus Capital Management, L.P.
875 3rd Ave
New York NY 10022
212 891-2100

(G-13842)
NEWPAGE HOLDING CORPORATION
8540 Gander Creek Dr (45342-5439)
PHONE...................................877 855-7243
Fax: 937 242-9109
George F Martin, *President*
James C Tyrone, *Exec VP*
Daniel A Clark, *Senior VP*
Laszlo M Lukacs, *Senior VP*
Douglas K Cooper, *Vice Pres*
EMP: 6000
SALES (est): 680.4MM
SALES (corp-wide): 39.9B Publicly Held
SIC: 2621 2672 2611 Fine paper; coated & laminated paper; pulp mills
HQ: Newpage Group Inc.
8540 Gander Creek Dr
Miamisburg OH 45342
937 242-9500

(G-13843)
NEWS DEMOCRAT
4500 Lyons Rd (45342-6447)
PHONE...................................937 378-6161
EMP: 4
SALES (est): 204.5K Privately Held
SIC: 2711 Newspapers, publishing & printing

(G-13844)
OCM LLC (HQ)
Also Called: Ohio Community Media
4500 Lyons Rd (45342-6447)
PHONE...................................937 247-2700
Roy Brown, *CEO*
EMP: 42
SALES (est): 137MM
SALES (corp-wide): 1.4B Privately Held
SIC: 2711 Newspapers
PA: Civitas Media, Llc
130 Harbour Place Dr # 300
Davidson NC 28036
704 897-6020

(G-13845)
OEM CORPORATION
3660 Benner Rd (45342-4368)
PHONE...................................937 859-7492
Fax: 937 859-7594
Randy Shupert, *President*
Gautam Sharda, *Sales Associate*
▼ EMP: 14
SQ FT: 38,000
SALES: 3MM Privately Held
WEB: www.oem-corp.com
SIC: 3564 Blowers & fans

(G-13846)
OHIO GRAVURE TECHNOLOGIES INC
1241 Byers Rd (45342-5770)
PHONE...................................937 439-1582
Eric Serenius, *President*
Doug Jones, *Engineer*
Kent Seibel, *Sales Staff*
Chris Winter, *Senior Mgr*
Donna Aker, *Admin Asst*
▲ EMP: 30
SALES: 5MM Privately Held
SIC: 2754 Commercial printing, gravure
HQ: Heliograph Holding Gmbh
Konrad-Zuse-Bogen 18
Krailling 82152
897 859-6179

(G-13847)
ONEIL & ASSOCIATES INC (PA)
495 Byers Rd (45342-3798)
PHONE...................................937 865-0800
Fax: 937 865-5858
Bob Heilman, *President*

Ralph E Heyman, *Principal*
Gerald D Rapp, *Principal*
Howard N Thiele Jr, *Principal*
John Staten, *Chairman*
EMP: 200 EST: 1947
SQ FT: 75,000
SALES (est): 48.9MM Privately Held
WEB: www.oneil.com
SIC: 2741 8999 7336 Technical manuals: publishing only, not printed on site; technical manual preparation; commercial art & illustration

(G-13848)
PRINTING SERVICE COMPANY
3233 S Tech Blvd (45342-0843)
PHONE...................................937 425-6100
Fax: 937 425-6110
William Fair, *President*
Gary Boens, *Exec VP*
Jeff Ross, *Vice Pres*
Mindy Brown, *Purch Agent*
Paul Molyneaux, *Treasurer*
EMP: 70
SQ FT: 40,000
SALES (est): 14.5MM Privately Held
SIC: 2752 Commercial printing, offset; color lithography

(G-13849)
PROJECT ENGINEERING COMPANY
3010 S Tech Blvd (45342-4860)
PHONE...................................937 743-9114
John L Michael, *President*
Trey Michael, *General Mgr*
Kristy Michael, *Finance Mgr*
EMP: 12
SQ FT: 8,000
SALES (est): 2MM Privately Held
WEB: www.projectengineeringcompany.com
SIC: 3469 Machine parts, stamped or pressed metal

(G-13850)
QUALITY CHANNEL LETTERS
1115 N 11th St (45342-1931)
PHONE...................................859 866-6500
John M Wells, *Owner*
EMP: 3
SQ FT: 3,000
SALES (est): 170K Privately Held
SIC: 3993 Electric signs

(G-13851)
RELX INC
Also Called: Lexis Nexis
9443 Springboro Pike (45342-4425)
PHONE...................................937 865-6800
Fax: 937 865-1555
Kim Saldana, *Sls & Mktg Exec*
Michael Weber, *Branch Mgr*
Clemens Ceipek, *Manager*
Dean Marker, *Manager*
Becky Whitaker, *Executive Asst*
EMP: 49
SALES (corp-wide): 8.4B Privately Held
WEB: www.lexis-nexis.com
SIC: 2721 2731 7389 7999 Trade journals: publishing only, not printed on site; books: publishing only; trade show arrangement; exposition operation
HQ: Relx Inc.
230 Park Ave Ste 700
New York NY 10169
212 309-8100

(G-13852)
RELX INC
4700 Lyons Rd (45342-6453)
PHONE...................................937 865-6800
Joyce Hull, *Engineer*
Chris Koogler, *Engineer*
Edward Lewis, *Engineer*
Pat McElhany, *Engineer*
Bill Wheeler, *Manager*
EMP: 15
SALES (corp-wide): 8.4B Privately Held
WEB: www.lexis-nexis.com
SIC: 2721 Periodicals
HQ: Relx Inc.
230 Park Ave Ste 700
New York NY 10169
212 309-8100

(G-13853)
RELX INC
Also Called: Lexisnexis
9333 Springboro Pike (45342-4424)
PHONE....................................937 865-6800
Joyce Hull, *Engineer*
Doug Kaplan, *Branch Mgr*
David Arndt, *Technology*
Gerald Manino, *IT/INT Sup*
Alice Kaltenmark, *Director*
EMP: 128
SALES (corp-wide): 8.4B **Privately Held**
WEB: www.lexis-nexis.com
SIC: 2731 Books: publishing only
HQ: Relx Inc.
    230 Park Ave Ste 700
    New York NY 10169
    212 309-8100

(G-13854)
RENEGADE MATERIALS CORPORATION
3363 S Tech Blvd (45342-0826)
PHONE....................................508 579-7888
Robert Gray, *President*
Susan Robitaille, *General Mgr*
Ron Garcia, *Opers Mgr*
Eric Collins, *CFO*
Laura Gray, *Sales Staff*
▲ EMP: 22
SQ FT: 25,000
SALES (est): 4.2MM **Privately Held**
SIC: 3081 2891 2821 Plastic film & sheet; epoxy adhesives; epoxy resins; polyimides (skybond, kaplon); nylon resins

(G-13855)
RETALIX INC
2490 Technical Dr (45342-6136)
PHONE....................................937 384-2277
Barry Shake, *CEO*
Barry Shaked, *President*
Shelly Mandich, *Opers Mgr*
Eli Spirer, *Mfg Staff*
Tabitha Barrett, *Purchasing*
EMP: 155
SQ FT: 72,000
SALES (est): 11MM
SALES (corp-wide): 6.5B **Publicly Held**
SIC: 5734 7372 Software, business & non-game; prepackaged software
HQ: Ncr Global Ltd
    9/27 Dafna
    Raanana 43662
    747 756-677

(G-13856)
RUMFORD PAPER COMPANY
8540 Gander Creek Dr (45342-5439)
PHONE....................................937 242-9230
George F Martin, *President*
EMP: 5
SALES (est): 477.7K **Privately Held**
SIC: 3554 Paper industries machinery

(G-13857)
SEELAUS INSTRUMENT CO
422 Alexandersville Rd (45342-3658)
PHONE....................................513 733-8222
Hank Seelaus, *President*
Beth Seelaus, *Vice Pres*
EMP: 5
SQ FT: 1,500
SALES: 2.5MM **Privately Held**
SIC: 3823 Industrial process measurement equipment

(G-13858)
SGI MATRIX LLC (PA)
1041 Byers Rd (45342-5487)
PHONE....................................937 438-9033
Bruce Rogoff, *CEO*
James Young, *President*
John Gorretta, *Vice Pres*
Steven J Koranda, *Vice Pres*
Jeffrey S Young, *Vice Pres*
EMP: 68 EST: 1977
SQ FT: 12,000
SALES (est): 32.5MM **Privately Held**
WEB: www.matrixsys.com
SIC: 8711 7373 3873 Engineering services; computer integrated systems design; watches, clocks, watchcases & parts

(G-13859)
SIGNATURE TECHNOLOGIES INC (DH)
Also Called: Com-Net Software Specialists
3728 Benner Rd (45342-4302)
PHONE....................................937 859-6323
Fax: 937 859-7511
Elie Geva, *President*
David Michaels, *COO*
Stephen Rohrig, *VP Opers*
Todd Lucius, *Accounts Exec*
Doug Cook, *Sales Engr*
EMP: 40
SQ FT: 25,000
SALES (est): 20.9MM
SALES (corp-wide): 1.2B **Privately Held**
WEB: www.comnetsoftware.com
SIC: 3669 3674 3577 Transportation signaling devices; semiconductors & related devices; computer peripheral equipment
HQ: Sita Information Networking Computing Uk Limited
    1 London Gate
    Hayes MIDDX UB3 1
    800 026-0256

(G-13860)
SILVER TOOL INC
2440 Cross Pointe Dr (45342-3584)
PHONE....................................937 865-0012
Fax: 937 865-0031
Marty Gebhardt, *Principal*
EMP: 40
SALES (corp-wide): 5.2MM **Privately Held**
WEB: www.silvertool.com
SIC: 3599 3545 3559 Machine shop, jobbing & repair; gauges (machine tool accessories); precision measuring tools; metal finishing equipment for plating, etc.
PA: Silver Tool, Inc.
    2440 Crosspointe Dr
    Miamisburg OH
    937 865-0067

(G-13861)
SIMPLEX TIME RECORDER LLC
8899 Gander Creek Dr (45342-5432)
PHONE....................................937 291-0355
Fax: 937 291-9371
Krissy McCrudden, *Branch Mgr*
EMP: 53 **Privately Held**
SIC: 3579 Time clocks & time recording devices
HQ: Simplex Time Recorder Llc
    50 Technology Dr
    Westminster MA 01441
    978 731-2500

(G-13862)
SOURCELINK OHIO LLC
3303 W Tech Blvd (45342-0817)
PHONE....................................937 885-8000
Fax: 937 885-8015
Don Landrum, *CEO*
Jim Wisnionski, *President*
Mike Dolan, *COO*
Karen Clear, *Vice Pres*
Darryl K Myers, *Prdtn Mgr*
EMP: 120
SQ FT: 140,000
SALES (est): 26.5MM
SALES (corp-wide): 113.1MM **Privately Held**
SIC: 7331 7374 2752 Direct mail advertising services; data processing service; commercial printing, lithographic
PA: Sourcelink Acquisition, Llc
    500 Park Blvd Ste 1425
    Itasca IL 60143
    866 947-6872

(G-13863)
STACO ENERGY PRODUCTS CO (HQ)
1229 Byers Rd (45342-5770)
PHONE....................................937 253-1191
Fax: 937 253-1723
Cary M Maguire, *Ch of Bd*
Jim Clark, *President*
Jeff Hoffman, *Principal*
Richard K Hoesterey, *Principal*
Jerry Combs, *Vice Pres*
◆ EMP: 6 EST: 1944
SQ FT: 120,000

SALES: 15MM
SALES (corp-wide): 45.7MM **Privately Held**
SIC: 3677 3612 3999 Electronic coils, transformers & other inductors; generator voltage regulators; military insignia
PA: Components Corporation Of America
    5950 Berkshire Ln # 1500
    Dallas TX 75225
    214 969-0166

(G-13864)
STAR CITY ART CO
421 S 9th St (45342-3340)
PHONE....................................937 865-9792
Andrew Huesman, *Owner*
EMP: 15
SALES (est): 770K **Privately Held**
SIC: 3577 Graphic displays, except graphic terminals

(G-13865)
STEINER EOPTICS INC (PA)
Also Called: Sensor Technology Systems
3475 Newmark Dr (45342-5426)
PHONE....................................937 426-2341
Alan Page, *General Mgr*
Doris Byerly Anderson, *Office Mgr*
Stan Babb, *Manager*
Doris Keith, *Info Tech Mgr*
EMP: 80
SQ FT: 10,000
SALES (est): 13.9MM **Privately Held**
SIC: 8731 3851 Electronic research; ophthalmic goods

(G-13866)
SYNAGRO MIDWEST INC
4515 Infirmary Rd (45342-1235)
PHONE....................................937 384-0669
Jim Rosendall, *Vice Pres*
EMP: 10
SALES (est): 2.4MM
SALES (corp-wide): 208MM **Privately Held**
SIC: 4953 2873 Recycling, waste materials; nitrogenous fertilizers
HQ: Synagro Technologies, Inc.
    435 Williams Ct Ste 100
    Baltimore MD 21220
    800 370-0035

(G-13867)
TECH PRODUCTS CORPORATION (DH)
2215 Lyons Rd (45342-4465)
PHONE....................................937 438-1100
Fax: 937 438-2190
Dan Rork, *President*
Greg Kiefer, *General Mgr*
Hugh E Wall Jr, *Principal*
Peirce Wood, *Principal*
A M Zimmerman, *Principal*
EMP: 29
SQ FT: 25,000
SALES (est): 5.6MM
SALES (corp-wide): 7.8B **Privately Held**
WEB: www.tpcdayton.com
SIC: 3625 5084 3829 3651 Noise control equipment; noise control equipment; measuring & controlling devices; household audio & video equipment
HQ: Fabreeka International Holdings, Inc.
    1023 Turnpike St
    Stoughton MA 02072
    781 341-3655

(G-13868)
TECHNICOTE INC (PA)
222 Mound Ave (45342-2996)
P.O. Box 188 (45343-0188)
PHONE....................................800 358-4448
Fax: 937 859-9096
Doug O'Connell, *President*
Doug Oconnell, *General Mgr*
Dorothy L Chapman, *Principal*
Peggy Curtiss, *Principal*
Michael A Ogline, *Principal*
◆ EMP: 46
SQ FT: 35,000

SALES (est): 84.6MM **Privately Held**
WEB: www.technicote.com
SIC: 2672 Adhesive papers, labels or tapes: from purchased material; labels (unprinted), gummed: made from purchased materials

(G-13869)
TECHNICOTE WESTFIELD INC
222 Mound Ave (45342-2996)
PHONE....................................937 859-4448
Dirk Desanzo, *President*
Douglas Garwood, *Corp Secy*
John L Mc Cormick, *Vice Pres*
John Petel, *Vice Pres*
Steve Strassner, *Manager*
EMP: 60
SQ FT: 35,000
SALES (est): 6.5MM **Privately Held**
SIC: 2672 Adhesive papers, labels or tapes: from purchased material

(G-13870)
TERADATA CORPORATION (PA)
10000 Innovation Dr (45342-4927)
PHONE....................................866 548-8348
Victor L Lund, *CEO*
James M Ringler, *Ch of Bd*
Robert Fair, *COO*
Dan Harrington, *Exec VP*
Daniel Harrington, *Exec VP*
EMP: 277
SALES: 2.3B **Publicly Held**
WEB: www.teradata.com
SIC: 3571 3572 7372 7371 Electronic computers; mainframe computers; minicomputers; personal computers (microcomputers); computer storage devices; disk drives, computer; prepackaged software; application computer software; software programming applications

(G-13871)
TERADATA OPERATIONS INC
2461 Rosina Dr (45342-6431)
PHONE....................................937 866-0032
EMP: 3
SALES (corp-wide): 2.3B **Publicly Held**
SIC: 3571 Electronic computers
HQ: Teradata Operations, Inc.
    10000 Innovation Dr
    Miamisburg OH 45342
    937 242-4030

(G-13872)
TERADATA OPERATIONS INC (HQ)
10000 Innovation Dr (45342-4927)
PHONE....................................937 242-4030
John Emanuel, *President*
Tom Knupp, *Engineer*
Emily Dell, *Human Res Dir*
Jeanne Pierce, *Human Res Dir*
Patrick Vogelaar, *Marketing Staff*
EMP: 100
SALES (est): 434.8MM
SALES (corp-wide): 2.3B **Publicly Held**
SIC: 3571 Electronic computers
PA: Teradata Corporation
    10000 Innovation Dr
    Miamisburg OH 45342
    866 548-8348

(G-13873)
UNCLE JESTERS FINE FOODS LLC
2564 Kohnle Dr (45342-3669)
P.O. Box 751953, Dayton (45475-1953)
PHONE....................................937 550-1025
Jeffrey Stevenson, *President*
EMP: 4 EST: 2010
SQ FT: 5,000
SALES (est): 352K **Privately Held**
SIC: 2033 5141 2035 5149 Barbecue sauce: packaged in cans, jars, etc.; jams, jellies & preserves: packaged in cans, jars, etc.; groceries, general line; pickles, sauces & salad dressings; seasonings, sauces & extracts

(G-13874)
VENTARI CORPORATION
8641 Washington Church Rd (45342-4470)
PHONE....................................937 278-4269
Trib Tawari, *President*
Bob Pelfrey, *General Mgr*

▲ = Import ▼=Export
◆ =Import/Export

Jim Donaldson, *Purchasing*
EMP: 25
SALES (est): 2.3MM **Privately Held**
SIC: 3449 Miscellaneous metalwork

(G-13875)
VERSO CORPORATION
Also Called: Verso Paper
8540 Gander Creek Dr (45342-5439)
PHONE..................................901 369-4105
Beverly Childs, *Transptn Dir*
Daniel McCoy, *Sales Engr*
Rhonda Hubbard, *Sales Associate*
Ruth Taylor, *Sales Associate*
Tanya Pipo, *Marketing Mgr*
EMP: 58
SALES (corp-wide): 3.1B **Publicly Held**
SIC: 2621 2653 2656 2631 Paper mills;
printing paper; text paper; bristols; boxes,
corrugated: made from purchased materi-
als; food containers (liquid tight), including
milk cartons; cartons, milk: made from
purchased material; container, packaging
& boxboard; container board; packaging
board; pulp mills
PA: Verso Corporation
6775 Lenox Center Ct # 400
Memphis TN 38115
901 369-4100

(G-13876)
**VERSO PAPER HOLDING LLC
(HQ)**
8540 Gander Creek Dr (45342-5439)
PHONE..................................877 855-7243
Mike Jackson, *CEO*
Mark A Angelson, *Chairman*
James C Tyrone, *Exec VP*
J Mark Lukacs, *Senior VP*
Barry Nelson, *Senior VP*
◆ **EMP:** 380
SALES (est): 837MM
SALES (corp-wide): 3.1B **Publicly Held**
SIC: 2621 2611 Fine paper; uncoated
paper; pulp manufactured from waste or
recycled paper
PA: Verso Corporation
6775 Lenox Center Ct # 400
Memphis TN 38115
901 369-4100

(G-13877)
WALTER GRINDERS INC
510 Earl Blvd (45342-6411)
PHONE..................................937 859-1975
Joe Szenay, *Principal*
EMP: 4
SALES (est): 338.4K **Privately Held**
SIC: 3541 Crankshaft regrinding machines

(G-13878)
WARREN FIRE EQUIPMENT INC
2240 E Central Ave (45342-7601)
PHONE..................................937 866-8918
Robert Keefer, *Branch Mgr*
EMP: 5
SALES (corp-wide): 4MM **Privately Held**
WEB: www.warrenfireequip.com
SIC: 5087 5012 7389 3569 Firefighting
equipment; automobiles & other motor ve-
hicles; fire extinguisher servicing; firefight-
ing apparatus & related equipment
PA: Warren Fire Equipment, Inc.
6880 Tod Ave Sw
Warren OH 44481
330 824-3523

(G-13879)
WAXCO INTERNATIONAL INC
Also Called: Dacraft
727 Dayton Oxford Rd (45342)
P.O. Box 147 (45343-0147)
PHONE..................................937 746-4845
Roger Wax, *President*
Bill Wax, *Vice Pres*
EMP: 10
SALES (est): 1.8MM **Privately Held**
SIC: 3355 1521 5211 1761 Structural
shapes, rolled, aluminum; general remod-
eling, single-family houses; door & win-
dow products; siding contractor

(G-13880)
WILLIAMS PRECISION TOOL INC
6855 Gillen Ln (45342-1507)
PHONE..................................937 384-0608

EMP: 12
SALES (est): 870K **Privately Held**
SIC: 3599 Mfg Industrial Machinery

(G-13881)
WINCO STAMPING INC
650 Precision Ct (45342-6138)
PHONE..................................937 859-5522
Bryan Dull, *Manager*
EMP: 8
SALES (corp-wide): 9.8MM **Privately
Held**
WEB: www.wincostamping.com
SIC: 3469 Stamping metal for the trade
PA: Winco Stamping, Inc.
W156n9277 Tipp St
Menomonee Falls WI 53051
262 251-5900

(G-13882)
X-SPINE SYSTEMS INC
452 Alexandersville Rd (45342-3658)
PHONE..................................937 847-8400
David L Kirschman, *President*
Daniel Abromowitz, *Vice Pres*
Eric Linder, *Vice Pres*
Eric Badders, *QA Dir*
Jeremy Chaney, *QC Mgr*
EMP: 70
SQ FT: 24,000
SALES (est): 16.5MM **Publicly Held**
WEB: www.x-spine.com
SIC: 3842 Surgical appliances & supplies
PA: Xtant Medical Holdings, Inc.
664 Cruiser Ln
Belgrade MT 59714

(G-13883)
YASKAWA AMERICA INC
Motoman Robotics Division
100 Automation Way (45342-4962)
PHONE..................................937 847-6200
Fax: 937 847-6277
Steve Barhorst, *Division Pres*
Jennifer Henry, *Purch Agent*
Jon Olis, *Engineer*
John Teserovitch, *Electrical Engi*
Roger Christian, *VP Sls/Mktg*
EMP: 180
SQ FT: 304,815
SALES (corp-wide): 3.5B **Privately Held**
WEB: www.motoman.com
SIC: 3569 Robots, assembly line: industrial
& commercial
HQ: Yaskawa America, Inc.
2121 Norman Dr
Waukegan IL 60085
847 887-7000

Miamitown
Hamilton County

(G-13884)
**BICKERS METAL PRODUCTS
INC**
5825 State Rte128 (45041)
P.O. Box 648 (45041-0648)
PHONE..................................513 353-4000
Fax: 513 353-4090
Robert C Graff, *President*
Roger Coffaro, *Vice Pres*
Charles Coffaro, *Shareholder*
EMP: 40 EST: 1964
SQ FT: 30,000
SALES (est): 10.8MM **Privately Held**
SIC: 3441 3444 Fabricated structural
metal; sheet metalwork

(G-13885)
BROTHERS TOOL AND MFG LTD
8300 Harrison Ave (45041)
P.O. Box 89 (45041-0089)
PHONE..................................513 353-9700
Grant Schutte, *Partner*
John Schutte, *Partner*
EMP: 12
SQ FT: 6,000
SALES (est): 1.2MM **Privately Held**
WEB: www.brotherstool.net
SIC: 3544 Special dies, tools, jigs & fix-
tures

(G-13886)
CHARGER PRESS INC
6088 Rte128 (45041)
P.O. Box 117 (45041-0117)
PHONE..................................513 542-3113
Fax: 513 542-3138
Gerald J Laake, *President*
EMP: 18 EST: 1956
SALES (est): 1.8MM **Privately Held**
SIC: 2752 Commercial printing, offset

(G-13887)
**GATEWAY CONCRETE FORMING
SVCS**
5938 Hamilton Cleves Rd (45041)
P.O. Box 130 (45041-0130)
PHONE..................................513 353-2000
Fax: 513 353-2002
Robert Bilz, *President*
Tim Hughey, *President*
Brandon Erfman, *Vice Pres*
Jean C Hughey, *Treasurer*
J Robert Hughey, *Shareholder*
EMP: 75
SQ FT: 3,000
SALES (est): 7.9MM **Privately Held**
WEB: www.gatewaybuildingproducts.com
SIC: 1771 3449 3496 3429 Concrete
work; bars, concrete reinforcing; fabri-
cated steel; miscellaneous fabricated wire
products; manufactured hardware (gen-
eral)

(G-13888)
JACP INC (PA)
5928 Hamilton Cleves Rd (45041)
P.O. Box 230 (45041-0230)
PHONE..................................513 353-3660
Michael Baltes, *President*
EMP: 4
SQ FT: 25,000
SALES (est): 890K **Privately Held**
WEB: www.jacp.com
SIC: 3541 3443 3564 Grinding machines,
metalworking; buffing & polishing ma-
chines; tanks for tank trucks, metal plate;
dust or fume collecting equipment, indus-
trial

(G-13889)
MACLEOD INC
5928 Hamilton Cleves Rd (45041)
PHONE..................................513 771-9560
Robert J Wallace, *President*
EMP: 5
SQ FT: 22,000
SALES (est): 445K **Privately Held**
WEB: www.macleod.com
SIC: 3443 Tanks for tank trucks, metal
plate
PA: Jacp Inc
5928 Hamilton Cleves Rd
Miamitown OH 45041

(G-13890)
**MODERN SHEET METAL WORKS
INC**
6037 State Rte 128 (45041)
P.O. Box 445 (45041-0445)
PHONE..................................513 353-3666
Fax: 513 353-4334
Dorothy Johnson, *President*
Cynthia Freppon, *Vice Pres*
Pamela Rosenacher, *Treasurer*
William Freppon, *Manager*
EMP: 25 EST: 1936
SQ FT: 16,000
SALES (est): 5.5MM **Privately Held**
WEB: www.modernsheetmetal.com
SIC: 3443 Tanks, standard or custom fabri-
cated: metal plate

(G-13891)
RHINO ROBOTICS LTD
5928 State Rte 128 (45041)
P.O. Box 230 (45041-0230)
PHONE..................................513 353-9772
Robert Wallace, *President*
Colleen Grace, *Manager*
EMP: 4
SQ FT: 25,000
SALES (est): 390K **Privately Held**
SIC: 3535 5084 Robotic conveyors; indus-
trial machinery & equipment

(G-13892)
SEILKOP INDUSTRIES INC
A-G Tool & Die Company
5927 State Route 128 (45041)
P.O. Box 250 (45041-0250)
PHONE..................................513 353-3090
Fax: 513 353-3095
Ken Seilkop, *Owner*
Richard Gentry, *Purchasing*
George Meister, *Engineer*
Jim Mundstock, *Engineer*
John Mason, *Sales Engr*
EMP: 40
SQ FT: 19,000
SALES (corp-wide): 24.1MM **Privately
Held**
WEB: www.epcorfoundry.com
SIC: 3312 3544 Tool & die steel; special
dies, tools, jigs & fixtures
PA: Seilkop Industries, Inc.
425 W North Bend Rd
Cincinnati OH 45216
513 761-1035

(G-13893)
U S ELECTRICAL TOOL INC
5928 Hamilton Cleves Rd (45041)
PHONE..................................513 353-3660
Robert J Wallace, *President*
Michael G Baltes, *Corp Secy*
Roger Henthorn, *Vice Pres*
EMP: 10
SQ FT: 25,000
SALES (est): 890K **Privately Held**
WEB: www.uselectricaltool.com
SIC: 3541 5084 Grinding machines, met-
alworking; buffing & polishing machines;
industrial machinery & equipment
PA: Jacp Inc
5928 Hamilton Cleves Rd
Miamitown OH 45041

Miamiville
Clermont County

(G-13894)
IRVINE WOOD RECOVERY INC
110 Glendale Milford Rd (45147)
P.O. Box 110 (45147-0110)
PHONE..................................513 831-0060
Fax: 513 831-3637
Les Irvine, *President*
EMP: 40
SQ FT: 15,000
SALES (est): 7.1MM **Privately Held**
SIC: 2499 Mulch, wood & bark

(G-13895)
LINDE LLC
Boc Gases
State Road 126160 St State Ro (45147)
P.O. Box 21 (45147-0021)
PHONE..................................513 831-4742
John L Seibert, *Manager*
EMP: 23
SALES (corp-wide): 17.9B **Privately Held**
SIC: 2813 Industrial gases
HQ: Linde Llc
200 Somerset Corporate Bl
Bridgewater NJ 08807
908 464-8100

Middle Point
Van Wert County

(G-13896)
ADDITIVE TECHNOLOGY INC
Also Called: Adtec
404 W Railroad St (45863-9779)
P.O. Box 221 (45863-0221)
PHONE..................................419 968-2777
John Sheeran, *President*
H Daniel Sheeran, *Vice Pres*
▲ **EMP:** 4
SQ FT: 15,000
SALES (est): 609.5K **Privately Held**
SIC: 2892 Explosives

(G-13897)
AMERICAN PAINT RECYCLERS LLC
4664 Mddle Pint Wetzel Rd (45863-9536)
PHONE....................................888 978-6558
Jeremy Brinkman, *Principal*
EMP: 4
SALES (est): 156.7K **Privately Held**
SIC: 2851 Paints & paint additives

(G-13898)
B & B WELDING
6647 Middle Pt Wetzel Rd (45863-9635)
PHONE....................................419 968-2743
Larry Black, *Owner*
EMP: 3 EST: 1992
SALES (est): 101K **Privately Held**
SIC: 7692 Welding repair

(G-13899)
TRAVELING & RECYCLE WOOD PDTS
Also Called: T&R Wood Products
19590 Bellis Rd (45863-9721)
P.O. Box 143 (45863-0143)
PHONE....................................419 968-2649
Fax: 419 968-2693
Eddy Miller, *President*
Scott Miller, *Vice Pres*
EMP: 12
SQ FT: 13,680
SALES (est): 1.2MM **Privately Held**
SIC: 2441 2448 2449 Boxes, wood;
cases, wood; pallets, wood; wood containers

Middlebranch
Stark County

(G-13900)
ESSROC CEMENT CORP
8282 Middlebranch Ave Ne (44652-9006)
P.O. Box 234 (44652-0234)
PHONE....................................330 499-9100
Dale Lewis, *Branch Mgr*
EMP: 18
SALES (corp-wide): 16B **Privately Held**
WEB: www.essroc.com
SIC: 3241 Cement, hydraulic
HQ: Essroc Cement Corp.
3251 Bath Pike
Nazareth PA 18064
610 837-6725

(G-13901)
KARG FIBERGLASS INC
2831 Diamond St (44652)
P.O. Box 35 (44652-0035)
PHONE....................................330 494-2611
Fax: 330 494-5274
George L Karg, *President*
EMP: 4
SQ FT: 7,000
SALES: 380K **Privately Held**
WEB: www.kargfiberglass.com
SIC: 3714 Motor vehicle body components
& frame

Middleburg Heights
Cuyahoga County

(G-13902)
ASSOCIATED SOFTWARE CONS INC
Also Called: A S C
7251 Engle Rd Ste 300 (44130-3400)
PHONE....................................440 826-1010
Fax: 440 826-1140
Tim Liston, *President*
John H Liston, *Corp Secy*
Danny Liggett, *Project Mgr*
Drew Bechler, *Purch Agent*
Dave Stricklen, *Manager*
EMP: 43
SQ FT: 7,500
SALES (est): 5.1MM **Privately Held**
WEB: www.asconline.com
SIC: 7371 7372 Computer software systems analysis & design, custom; prepackaged software

(G-13903)
BARRETTE OUTDOOR LIVING INC (DH)
7830 Freeway Cir (44130-6307)
PHONE....................................440 891-0790
Fax: 440 891-5267
Jean Desautels, *President*
Peter Fickinger, *General Mgr*
Neil W Gurney, *Principal*
James M Moore, *Principal*
Danny West, *Plant Mgr*
◆ EMP: 277
SQ FT: 600,000
SALES (est): 430.7MM
SALES (corp-wide): 93.2K **Privately Held**
WEB: www.usfenceonline.com
SIC: 3315 Fence gates posts & fittings:
steel
HQ: Entreprises Barrette Ltee, Les
583 Ch Du Grand-Bernier N
Saint-Jean-Sur-Richelieu QC J3B 8
450 357-7000

(G-13904)
CLEVELAND DIE & MFG CO (PA)
20303 1st Ave (44130-2433)
PHONE....................................440 243-3404
Juan Chahda, *President*
Liliana Chahda, *Vice Pres*
Stela Mimis, *Purch Mgr*
David George, *Engrg Mgr*
Oderet Behri, *Manager*
▲ EMP: 85
SQ FT: 165,000
SALES (est): 38.6MM **Privately Held**
WEB: www.clevelanddie.com
SIC: 3469 3544 Metal stampings; special
dies, tools, jigs & fixtures

(G-13905)
DUBOSE ENERGY FASTENERS & MACH
18737 Sheldon Rd (44130-2472)
PHONE....................................216 362-1700
Carl Rogers, *CEO*
Martin Kossick, *President*
Richard Rogers, *Vice Pres*
Melanie Creeger, *Accounting Mgr*
EMP: 18
SALES (est): 2.4MM **Privately Held**
SIC: 3965 Fasteners

(G-13906)
IEC INFRARED SYSTEMS LLC
7803 Freeway Cir (44130-6308)
PHONE....................................440 234-8000
Randall Lavoy, *Design Engr*
Arthur Stachowicz, *Electrical Engi*
Matthew Tuskan, *Accounts Mgr*
Richard Pettegrew, *Mng Member*
EMP: 22
SALES (est): 2.3MM **Privately Held**
SIC: 7389 3826 Design services; infrared
analytical instruments

(G-13907)
NOVA MACHINE PRODUCTS INC (HQ)
18001 Sheldon Rd (44130-2465)
PHONE....................................216 267-3200
David Linton, *CEO*
Martin R Benante, *Ch of Bd*
Timothy A Davis, *General Mgr*
Tad Gray, *General Mgr*
Butch Siracusa, *Project Mgr*
▲ EMP: 115
SALES (est): 30.3MM
SALES (corp-wide): 2.1B **Publicly Held**
SIC: 3452 3429 3369 3356 Bolts, metal;
washers; nuts, metal; lock washers; manufactured hardware (general); nonferrous
foundries; nonferrous rolling & drawing
PA: Curtiss-Wright Corporation
13925 Balntyn Corp Pl
Charlotte NC 28277
704 869-4600

(G-13908)
SOLUTION INDUSTRIES LLC
17830 Englewood Dr Ste 11 (44130-3485)
PHONE....................................440 816-9500
John Radel, *President*
EMP: 43

SALES (est): 5.3MM **Privately Held**
SIC: 3965 Fasteners, buttons, needles &
pins

(G-13909)
VERANTIS CORPORATION (HQ)
7251 Engle Rd Ste 300 (44130-3400)
PHONE....................................440 243-0700
William Jackson, *Senior VP*
Jeffrey Edwards, *Production*
Josh Sheppard, *Finance*
▼ EMP: 30
SALES (est): 15.7MM **Privately Held**
SIC: 3564 5075 Air purification equipment;
blowers & fans; air pollution control equipment & supplies
PA: Tanglewood Investments Inc.
5051 Westheimer Rd # 300
Houston TX 77056
713 629-5525

(G-13910)
WILLIAMS EXECUTIVE ENTPS INC ●
Also Called: Minuteman Press
6886 Pearl Rd Ste A (44130-3618)
PHONE....................................440 887-1000
Christopher Williams, *President*
EMP: 3 EST: 2016
SALES (est): 115.1K **Privately Held**
SIC: 2752 Commercial printing, lithographic

Middlefield
Geauga County

(G-13911)
A & M PALLET SHOP INC
14550 Madison Rd (44062-9499)
P.O. Box 765 (44062-0765)
PHONE....................................440 632-1941
Fax: 440 632-1823
Andy A Miller, *President*
EMP: 11
SQ FT: 4,200
SALES (est): 1.1MM **Privately Held**
SIC: 2448 Pallets, wood

(G-13912)
ADVANCING ECO-AGRICULTURE LLC
4551 Parks West Rd (44062-9345)
P.O. Box 683 (44062-0683)
PHONE....................................800 495-6603
Jason Hobson, *CEO*
P Van Den Bossche, *Chairman*
Philippe Van Den Bossche, *Chairman*
Ed Perkins, *Finance Dir*
John Kempf,
EMP: 5 EST: 2008
SALES (est): 1.4MM **Privately Held**
SIC: 2873 8748 Fertilizers: natural (organic), except compost; agricultural consultant

(G-13913)
AIRWOLF AEROSPACE LLC
15369 Madison Rd (44062-8404)
PHONE....................................440 632-1687
John Kochy, *Managing Prtnr*
EMP: 5
SALES (est): 471.9K **Privately Held**
SIC: 3728 Research & dev by manuf., aircraft parts & auxiliary equip

(G-13914)
AMERICAN PLASTIC TECH INC (PA)
Also Called: A P T
15229 S State Ave (44062-9468)
P.O. Box 37 (44062-0037)
PHONE....................................440 632-5203
Fax: 440 632-1848
Joseph A Bergen, *President*
Duncan M Simpson Jr, *Senior VP*
Steve Byler, *Warehouse Mgr*
Edd Hiksman, *CFO*
Mary Elwood, *Accountant*
▲ EMP: 70
SQ FT: 178,000

SALES (est): 33.8MM **Privately Held**
WEB: www.sajar.com
SIC: 3089 3559 Injection molding of plastics; plastics working machinery

(G-13915)
ARROWHEAD PALLETS LLC
7851 Parkman Mespo Rd (44062-9328)
PHONE....................................440 693-4241
Fax: 440 693-4658
Ervin C Byler,
EMP: 16
SALES (est): 129.7K **Privately Held**
SIC: 2448 Wood pallets & skids

(G-13916)
BASETEK LLC (PA)
14975 White Rd (44062-9216)
PHONE....................................877 712-2273
Pam Kistner, *Business Mgr*
Scott Sapita, *Mng Member*
Juspim Sli, *Manager*
Timothy E Marklay,
EMP: 16
SALES: 5MM **Privately Held**
SIC: 3531 5032 Construction machinery;
concrete & cinder block

(G-13917)
BENTRONIX CORP
14999 Madison Rd (44062-8403)
P.O. Box 1297 (44062-1297)
PHONE....................................440 632-0606
Fax: 440 632-0605
Ludmilla Benins, *President*
Peter Benins, *Vice Pres*
Brian Lanstrum, *Vice Pres*
EMP: 7
SQ FT: 2,500
SALES: 600K **Privately Held**
SIC: 3613 7629 Control panels, electric;
electronic equipment repair

(G-13918)
BRADFORD NEAL MACHINERY INC
14503 Old State Rd (44062-9703)
P.O. Box 1237 (44062-1237)
PHONE....................................440 632-1393
Fax: 440 632-1458
James Skinner, *President*
Ruth Skinner, *Corp Secy*
EMP: 3
SQ FT: 6,000
SALES (est): 471.8K **Privately Held**
WEB: www.bradfordneal.com
SIC: 3559 7699 Plastics working machinery; robots, molding & forming plastics; industrial machinery & equipment repair

(G-13919)
BUCKEYE CHOCOLATE CO
15010 Brkshire Indus Pkwy (44062-9390)
PHONE....................................440 564-8086
Eric Hart, *Principal*
EMP: 13
SALES (est): 1.8MM **Privately Held**
SIC: 2064 Candy & other confectionery
products

(G-13920)
CARTER-JONES LUMBER COMPANY
14601 Kinsman Rd (44062-9245)
PHONE....................................440 834-8164
Fax: 440 834-4925
Lenny Barciskoi, *Manager*
EMP: 15
SALES (corp-wide): 1.2B **Privately Held**
SIC: 2452 5074 5211 Prefabricated buildings, wood; plumbing & hydronic heating
supplies; lumber products
HQ: The Carter-Jones Lumber Company
601 Tallmadge Rd
Kent OH 44240
330 673-6100

(G-13921)
CHEM TECHNOLOGIES LTD
14875 Bonner Dr (44062-8493)
PHONE....................................440 632-9311
Fax: 440 632-9578
S James Schill, *Principal*
Randall Vancura, *COO*
Kevin Cohill, *Vice Pres*
Angela Pruitt, *Buyer*

Kim Boyd, *QC Mgr*
EMP: 30
SQ FT: 120,000
SALES (est): 13.8MM **Privately Held**
WEB: www.chemtechnologiesltd.com
SIC: 2819 2899 Industrial inorganic chemicals; chemical preparations

(G-13922)
CHEROKEE HARDWOODS INC (PA)
Also Called: Amish Heritg WD Floors & Furn
16741 Newcomb Rd (44062-8248)
PHONE..................................440 632-0322
Fax: 440 834-1924
Wallace D Byler, *President*
Bill W Byler, *Vice Pres*
EMP: 10 EST: 1997
SQ FT: 12,500
SALES (est): 813.9K **Privately Held**
SIC: 2421 2426 Sawmills & planing mills, general; hardwood dimension & flooring mills

(G-13923)
CHIPMUNK LOGGING & LUMBER LLC
15750 Chipmunk Ln (44062-7204)
PHONE..................................440 834-4660
Jacob Detweiler, *Owner*
EMP: 3
SALES (est): 290.7K **Privately Held**
SIC: 2411 Logging

(G-13924)
COMPANY FRONT AWARDS
12653 Madison Rd (44062-9749)
PHONE..................................440 636-5493
Fax: 440 636-5578
Alan Byrne, *Partner*
EMP: 3
SQ FT: 2,800
SALES: 150K **Privately Held**
SIC: 3499 2499 Trophies, metal, except silver; trophy bases, wood

(G-13925)
CREATION INDUSTRIES LLC
15236 Shedd Rd (44062-9222)
PHONE..................................440 554-6286
Alba Whiteside, *Principal*
EMP: 3 EST: 2009
SALES (est): 266.6K **Privately Held**
SIC: 3999 Manufacturing industries

(G-13926)
CROSSCREEK PALLET CO
14530 Madison Rd (44062-9499)
PHONE..................................440 632-1940
Michael Yoder, *Owner*
EMP: 3
SALES (est): 394.7K **Privately Held**
SIC: 2448 Pallets, wood & wood with metal

(G-13927)
CUSTOM PALET MANUFACTURING
9291 N Girdle Rd (44062-9531)
PHONE..................................440 693-4603
Lester Mullet, *Owner*
EMP: 7
SALES (est): 585.3K **Privately Held**
SIC: 2448 Wood pallets & skids

(G-13928)
D MARTONE INDUSTRIES INC
Also Called: Jaco Products
15060 Madison Rd (44062-9450)
PHONE..................................440 632-5800
Fax: 440 632-0012
Frank Defino, *President*
David B Cathcart, *Principal*
Samuel R Martillotta, *Principal*
Mark Strumbly, *Plant Mgr*
Melanie Gotham, *Director*
EMP: 30
SQ FT: 38,000
SALES (est): 5.2MM **Privately Held**
WEB: www.jacoproducts.com
SIC: 3089 Injection molded finished plastic products
PA: A.J.D. Holding Co.
2181 Enterprise Pkwy
Twinsburg OH 44087

(G-13929)
D P PRODUCTS INC
14790 Brkshire Ind Pkwy (44062)
PHONE..................................440 834-9663
Fax: 440 834-9664
Ken Ashba, *Principal*
EMP: 3
SALES (est): 195.6K **Privately Held**
SIC: 2448 Wood pallets & skids

(G-13930)
D T KOTHERA INC
Also Called: Liberty Fabricating & Steel
15422 Georgia Rd (44062-9011)
P.O. Box 1048 (44062-1048)
PHONE..................................440 632-1651
Fax: 440 632-1383
Dave Kothera, *President*
EMP: 4
SQ FT: 9,600
SALES (est): 750K **Privately Held**
SIC: 5051 3441 Metals service centers & offices; fabricated structural metal

(G-13931)
DRUMMOND CORP
14990 Brkshire Indus Pkwy (44062)
P.O. Box 389, Burton (44021-0389)
PHONE..................................440 834-9660
Fax: 440 834-9661
Paul Spangler Sr, *President*
Joan Spangler, *Vice Pres*
Paul Spangler Jr, *Vice Pres*
Eric Hammonds, *Sales Mgr*
EMP: 15
SQ FT: 10,000
SALES (est): 2.3MM **Privately Held**
WEB: www.drummondcorp.com
SIC: 3089 Plastic processing

(G-13932)
DYNAMIC TOOL DIE
14925 White Rd (44062-9216)
PHONE..................................440 834-0007
David Mance, *Owner*
EMP: 3 EST: 1998
SALES: 100K **Privately Held**
SIC: 3544 Special dies & tools

(G-13933)
E & L SPRING SHOP
16035 Nauvoo Rd (44062-9766)
PHONE..................................440 632-1439
Ervin Byler, *President*
William Byler, *Partner*
Walter Miller, *Vice Pres*
EMP: 3
SALES (est): 335.3K **Privately Held**
SIC: 3493 Leaf springs: automobile, locomotive, etc.

(G-13934)
FISHER PALLET
8496 Bundysburg Rd (44062-9303)
PHONE..................................440 632-0863
Daniel Fisher Jr, *Owner*
EMP: 3
SQ FT: 3,148
SALES (est): 174K **Privately Held**
SIC: 2448 Pallets, wood & wood with metal

(G-13935)
FLAMBEAU INC
15981 Valplast St (44062-9399)
PHONE..................................440 632-3752
Marc Mason, *VP Mfg*
Zack Radnour, *Marketing Staff*
Mary Ann Parker, *Branch Mgr*
Terry Fishel, *Director*
EMP: 40
SALES (corp-wide): 342.8MM **Privately Held**
SIC: 3089 Plastic containers, except foam
HQ: Flambeau, Inc.
801 Lynn Ave
Baraboo WI 53913
800 352-6266

(G-13936)
FLAMBEAU INC
Ornamates By Flambeau
15981 Valplast St (44062-9399)
P.O. Box 97 (44062-0097)
PHONE..................................440 632-1631
Bill Flint, *President*
Carolyn Corley, *Mfg Spvr*

Cleo Bailey, *Maint Spvr*
Kurt Mulhauser, *Engineer*
Curt Mulhouser, *Engineer*
EMP: 97
SALES (corp-wide): 342.8MM **Privately Held**
SIC: 3089 Casting of plastic
HQ: Flambeau, Inc.
801 Lynn Ave
Baraboo WI 53913
800 352-6266

(G-13937)
GOLD KEY PROCESSING INC
14910 Madison Rd (44062-8403)
PHONE..................................440 632-0901
Fax: 440 632-0929
Tracy Garrison, *President*
Randy Simpson, *COO*
Don Picard, *Vice Pres*
Doug Thomas, *Buyer*
Cynthia Chill, *Accountant*
▲ **EMP:** 170
SQ FT: 160,000
SALES (est): 82.8MM
SALES (corp-wide): 1.2B **Privately Held**
WEB: www.goldkeyltd.com
SIC: 3069 2891 Reclaimed rubber & specialty rubber compounds; adhesives & sealants
HQ: Hexpol Holding Inc.
14330 Kinsman Rd
Burton OH 44021
440 834-4644

(G-13938)
H & H TREE SERVICE LLC
15530 Old State Rd (44062-8208)
P.O. Box 179 (44062-0179)
PHONE..................................440 632-0551
Kimberly Heiss, *President*
EMP: 3
SQ FT: 6,000
SALES (est): 185.1K **Privately Held**
SIC: 2411 Timber, cut at logging camp

(G-13939)
HANS ROTHENBUHLER & SON INC
15815 Nauvoo Rd (44062-8501)
PHONE..................................440 632-6000
John Rothenbuhler, *President*
Joyce Filla, *General Mgr*
Ann Rothenbuhler, *Controller*
Gary Schoenwald, *Marketing Staff*
EMP: 40
SALES (est): 12.3MM **Privately Held**
SIC: 2022 5451 5143 2023 Natural cheese; dairy products stores; dairy products, except dried or canned; dry, condensed, evaporated dairy products

(G-13940)
HARDWOOD FLRG & PANELING INC
Also Called: Sheoga Hardwood Flrg Paneling
15320 Burton Windsor Rd (44062-9785)
P.O. Box 248 (44062-0248)
PHONE..................................440 834-1710
Fax: 440 834-9310
Pete C Miller, *President*
Steve Trudick, *Chairman*
Larry Yoder, *Corp Secy*
Barbara Titus, *CFO*
▼ **EMP:** 72
SQ FT: 135,000
SALES (est): 16.4MM **Privately Held**
WEB: www.sheogaflooring.com
SIC: 2426 Flooring, hardwood; lumber, hardwood dimension

(G-13941)
HAUSER SERVICES LLC
Also Called: Hauser Landscaping
15668 Old State Rd (44062-8488)
P.O. Box 1161 (44062-1161)
PHONE..................................440 632-5126
Monique Hauser, *Mng Member*
Dave Hauser, *Manager*
EMP: 20
SQ FT: 10,000
SALES: 2.6MM **Privately Held**
SIC: 2499 0781 Mulch, wood & bark; landscape services

(G-13942)
HERBERT WOOD PRODUCTS INC
15089 White Rd (44062-9216)
PHONE..................................440 834-1410
Bryan Herbert, *President*
EMP: 3
SQ FT: 5,000
SALES (est): 295.1K **Privately Held**
SIC: 1541 2499 Renovation, remodeling & repairs: industrial buildings; decorative wood & woodwork

(G-13943)
J D L HARDWOODS
9024 N Girdle Rd (44062-9604)
PHONE..................................440 272-5630
Joe Miller, *Partner*
Dan Miller, *Partner*
Levi Yoder, *Partner*
EMP: 4
SQ FT: 4,120
SALES (est): 339.5K **Privately Held**
SIC: 2448 5211 Pallets, wood; lumber products

(G-13944)
J K PLASTICS CO
14135 Madison Rd (44062-9763)
PHONE..................................440 632-1482
Fax: 440 632-1482
John Krupa, *Owner*
Paul Billings, *Systems Mgr*
EMP: 6
SQ FT: 8,400
SALES (est): 621.3K **Privately Held**
WEB: www.jkplastics.com
SIC: 3089 3635 Injection molding of plastics; household vacuum cleaners

(G-13945)
J S COMPANY
16351 Nauvoo Rd (44062-9769)
PHONE..................................440 632-0052
Jones Sputzman, *Owner*
EMP: 3
SALES (est): 132K **Privately Held**
SIC: 3599 Machine shop, jobbing & repair

(G-13946)
J S STAIRS
16118 Old State Rd (44062-8205)
PHONE..................................440 632-5680
John Stutzman, *Owner*
EMP: 4
SALES: 300K **Privately Held**
SIC: 3446 Stairs, staircases, stair treads: prefabricated metal

(G-13947)
JOBAP ASSEMBLY INC
16090 Industrial Pkwy # 9 (44062-6302)
PHONE..................................440 632-5393
Fax: 440 632-5405
Rebecca Portman, *President*
Jeannine Reeves, *General Mgr*
Judith Mellenger, *Treasurer*
▲ **EMP:** 16
SQ FT: 6,000
SALES (est): 3.1MM **Privately Held**
SIC: 3699 1731 Electrical equipment & supplies; electrical work

(G-13948)
JOHNSONITE INC
Also Called: Johnsonite Rubber Flooring
16035 Industrial Pkwy (44062-9386)
P.O. Box 880 (44062-0880)
PHONE..................................440 632-3441
Jeff Buttitta, *President*
Tom Dowling, *CFO*
▲ **EMP:** 500
SALES (est): 71MM
SALES (corp-wide): 537K **Privately Held**
SIC: 3086 Carpet & rug cushions, foamed plastic
HQ: Tarkett
Tour Initiale
Puteaux
141 204-040

(G-13949)
KRAFTMAID TRUCKING INC (PA)
16052 Industrial Pkwy (44062-9382)
P.O. Box 1055 (44062-1055)
PHONE..............................440 632-2531
Tom Chieffe, *President*
Richard Moodie, *COO*
Sandy Allen, *Vice Pres*
Bob Hawthorne, *Plant Mgr*
Paul Graham, *Engineer*
EMP: 100
SQ FT: 12,000
SALES (est): 16.7MM **Privately Held**
SIC: 4813 2517 Telephone communication, except radio; wood television & radio cabinets

(G-13950)
LA ROSE PAVING CO INC
16590 Nauvoo Rd (44062-9408)
PHONE..............................440 632-0330
Toll Free:........................888 -
Fax: 440 632-0484
Linda Rose, *President*
Jim Rose, *Vice Pres*
EMP: 8
SALES: 500K **Privately Held**
SIC: 2951 Paving blocks

(G-13951)
M A MILLER
16790 Pioneer Rd (44062-8716)
PHONE..............................440 636-5697
Mark Miller, *Owner*
Barbara Miller, *Co-Owner*
EMP: 4
SALES (est): 260K **Privately Held**
SIC: 2434 Wood kitchen cabinets

(G-13952)
MAINE RUBBER PREFORMS LLC
16090 Industrial Pkwy # 1 (44062-6300)
PHONE..............................216 210-2094
Wesley L Hellegers, *Partner*
EMP: 3
SALES (est): 358.3K **Privately Held**
SIC: 3069 Custom compounding of rubber materials

(G-13953)
MARSH VALLEY FOREST PDTS LTD
14141 Old State Rd (44062-9740)
PHONE..............................440 632-1889
Mervin P Miller, *President*
Pete Miller, *General Ptnr*
EMP: 7
SQ FT: 16,000
SALES (est): 1.2MM **Privately Held**
SIC: 2426 5211 Flooring, hardwood; lumber products

(G-13954)
MASCO CABINETRY LLC
15535 S State Ave (44062)
PHONE..............................440 632-2547
Mike Newton, *Manager*
EMP: 601
SALES (corp-wide): 7.3B **Publicly Held**
SIC: 2517 Radio cabinets & cases, wood
HQ: Masco Cabinetry Llc
4600 Arrowhead Dr
Ann Arbor MI 48105
734 205-4600

(G-13955)
MASCO CBINETRY MIDDLEFIELD LLC (DH)
15535 S State Ave (44062)
P.O. Box 1055 (44062-1055)
PHONE..............................440 632-5333
Fax: 440 632-0726
Keith Scherzer, *President*
Eugene A Gargaro, *Vice Pres*
Andrew Rattray, *Vice Pres*
Michelle Weaver, *Purch Mgr*
Warren Arthur, *Purchasing*
◆ **EMP:** 2533
SALES (est): 487.2MM
SALES (corp-wide): 7.3B **Publicly Held**
WEB: www.kraftmaid.com
SIC: 2434 Wood kitchen cabinets; vanities; bathroom: wood

HQ: Masco Cabinetry Llc
4600 Arrowhead Dr
Ann Arbor MI 48105
734 205-4600

(G-13956)
MASCO CBINETRY MIDDLEFIELD LLC
16052 Industrial Pkwy (44062-9382)
P.O. Box 1055 (44062-1055)
PHONE..............................440 632-5058
Keith Scherzer, *Branch Mgr*
EMP: 100
SALES (corp-wide): 7.3B **Publicly Held**
SIC: 2511 2434 Wood household furniture; wood kitchen cabinets
HQ: Masco Cabinetry Middlefield Llc
15535 S State Ave
Middlefield OH 44062
440 632-5333

(G-13957)
MERCURY PLASTICS INC
15760 Madison Rd (44062-8408)
P.O. Box 989 (44062-0989)
PHONE..............................440 632-5281
Fax: 440 632-5606
William Rowley Sr, *Ch of Bd*
William Rowley Jr, *President*
Bob Yunk, *General Mgr*
Mark Baker, *Corp Secy*
Chuck Hayes, *Plant Mgr*
▲ **EMP:** 225 **EST:** 1964
SQ FT: 130,000
SALES (est): 53MM **Privately Held**
SIC: 3089 Extruded finished plastic products

(G-13958)
MESPO WOODWORKING
4421 Donley Rd (44062-9549)
PHONE..............................440 693-4041
Jacob Miller, *Owner*
EMP: 3 **EST:** 1997
SALES (est): 200K **Privately Held**
SIC: 2541 Cabinets, except refrigerated: show, display, etc.: wood

(G-13959)
MIDDLEFIELD GLASS INCORPORATED
17447 Kinsman Rd (44062-9433)
P.O. Box 1266 (44062-1266)
PHONE..............................440 632-5699
Fax: 440 632-5703
Michael Lyons, *President*
Carol Lyons, *President*
EMP: 20
SQ FT: 9,000
SALES (est): 1.8MM **Privately Held**
WEB: www.middlefieldglass.com
SIC: 3231 5231 Stained glass: made from purchased glass; glass, leaded or stained

(G-13960)
MIDDLEFIELD MIX INC
15815 Nauvoo Rd (44062-8501)
PHONE..............................440 632-0157
John Rothenbuhler, *President*
EMP: 15
SQ FT: 1,364
SALES (est): 2.3MM **Privately Held**
SIC: 2022 Natural cheese

(G-13961)
MIDDLEFIELD PALLET INC
15940 Burton Windsor Rd (44062-9791)
PHONE..............................440 632-0553
Fax: 440 632-0505
Robert J Troyer, *President*
John A Yoder, *Exec VP*
Nick Hall, *Sales Mgr*
EMP: 42
SQ FT: 30,000
SALES (est): 7.8MM **Privately Held**
WEB: www.middlefieldpallet.com
SIC: 2448 Wood pallets & skids

(G-13962)
MIDDLEFIELD PLASTICS INC
15235 Burton Windsor Rd (44062-9784)
P.O. Box 708 (44062-0708)
PHONE..............................440 834-4638
Fax: 440 834-1247
John D Fisher, *President*
Edward Minick, *Vice Pres*

Dan Fisher, *Manager*
Sam Fisher, *Manager*
EMP: 45
SQ FT: 44,000
SALES (est): 11MM **Privately Held**
WEB: www.middlefieldplastics.com
SIC: 3089 3053 Extruded finished plastic products; gaskets, packing & sealing devices

(G-13963)
MIDDLEFIELD SIGN CO
14895 N State Ave Unit G (44062-9724)
P.O. Box 490 (44062-0490)
PHONE..............................440 632-0708
Larry Lasich, *Owner*
EMP: 3
SALES (est): 140K **Privately Held**
SIC: 3993 7336 7335 Signs & advertising specialties; commercial art & graphic design; commercial photography

(G-13964)
MIDDLFELD ORIGINAL CHEESE COOP
Also Called: Das Deutsch Cheese
16942 Kinsman Rd (44062-9484)
P.O. Box 237 (44062-0237)
PHONE..............................440 632-5567
Fax: 440 632-0892
Eli D L Miller, *President*
Nevin R Byler, *Vice Pres*
Sharon Klima, *Bookkeeper*
EMP: 20
SQ FT: 12,000
SALES (est): 2.6MM **Privately Held**
SIC: 2022 Natural cheese; processed cheese

(G-13965)
MILLER LOGGING
5327 Parks West Rd (44062-9352)
PHONE..............................440 693-4001
Eli P Miller, *Principal*
EMP: 3
SALES (est): 315.4K **Privately Held**
SIC: 2411 Logging camps & contractors

(G-13966)
MILLERS LINIMENTS LLC
17150 Bundysburg Rd (44062-9247)
PHONE..............................440 548-5800
Albert Miller, *Principal*
EMP: 3
SALES (est): 224.7K **Privately Held**
SIC: 2834 Liniments

(G-13967)
MK ENTERPRISES INC
11162 Industrial Pkwy (44062)
PHONE..............................440 632-0121
Fax: 440 632-1121
Mark W Frieling, *President*
Rodney W Hurd, *Vice Pres*
Kimberly H Frieling, *Treasurer*
Greg Shipman, *Sales Mgr*
Kristie Mullinex, *Director*
EMP: 30
SQ FT: 6,000
SALES (est): 5.4MM **Privately Held**
WEB: www.mkenter.com
SIC: 3679 Harness assemblies for electronic use: wire or cable

(G-13968)
MOLTEN MTAL EQP INNVATIONS LLC
Also Called: Mmei
15510 Old State Rd (44062-8208)
PHONE..............................440 632-9119
Fax: 440 632-9187
Paul Cooper, *President*
Kevin Doherty, *Treasurer*
▲ **EMP:** 28
SALES (est): 8.4MM **Privately Held**
SIC: 3561 Industrial pumps & parts

(G-13969)
MULTI-WING AMERICA INC
15030 Brkshire Indus Pkwy (44062-9390)
P.O. Box 425, Burton (44021-0425)
PHONE..............................440 834-9400
Fax: 440 834-0449
Jim Crowley, *President*
Terese Crowley, *Corp Secy*
Bill Crowley, *Vice Pres*

John Crowley, *Vice Pres*
Jerry Harris, *Vice Pres*
▲ **EMP:** 45
SQ FT: 27,500
SALES (est): 13.6MM **Privately Held**
WEB: www.mw-america.com
SIC: 3564 Exhaust fans: industrial or commercial

(G-13970)
MVP PLASTICS INC (PA)
15005 Enterprise Way (44062-9369)
PHONE..............................330 872-4451
Darrell McNair, *President*
Joe Hardy, *QC Mgr*
Ed Kalbfell, *QC Mgr*
Sharon Verner, *Controller*
Shon Dionne, *Director*
EMP: 10
SQ FT: 5,000
SALES (est): 2.9MM **Privately Held**
SIC: 3089 Plastic processing

(G-13971)
MYERS INDUSTRIES INC
Also Called: Dillen Products
15150 Madison Rd (44062-9495)
P.O. Box 738 (44062-0738)
PHONE..............................440 632-1006
Fax: 440 632-1882
Joe Rothbrust, *Purch Mgr*
Dexter Chumley, *Manager*
EMP: 40
SALES (corp-wide): 558MM **Publicly Held**
WEB: www.myersind.com
SIC: 3089 3423 Injection molded finished plastic products; hand & edge tools
PA: Myers Industries, Inc.
1293 S Main St
Akron OH 44301
330 253-5592

(G-13972)
MYERS INDUSTRIES INC
Dillen Products
15150 Madison Rd (44062-9495)
P.O. Box 738 (44062-0738)
PHONE..............................440 632-0230
Dexter Chumley, *Manager*
Joe Rothbrust, *Manager*
EMP: 90
SALES (corp-wide): 558MM **Publicly Held**
WEB: www.myersind.com
SIC: 0781 3423 Horticulture services; hand & edge tools
PA: Myers Industries, Inc.
1293 S Main St
Akron OH 44301
330 253-5592

(G-13973)
NAUVOD MACHINE CO
16254 Nauvoo Rd (44062-9731)
PHONE..............................440 632-1990
Lester Byler, *Principal*
EMP: 3 **EST:** 2008
SALES (est): 281.9K **Privately Held**
SIC: 3599 Machine & other job shop work

(G-13974)
NAUVOO CUSTOM WOODWORKING
17231 Nauvoo Rd (44062-8416)
PHONE..............................440 632-9502
EMP: 4
SALES (est): 542.2K **Privately Held**
SIC: 2431 Millwork

(G-13975)
NEFF-PERKINS COMPANY
16080 Industrial Pkwy (44062-9382)
PHONE..............................440 632-1658
Sherri Davis, *Engineer*
Tammy Moodt, *Human Res Dir*
Robert Elly, *Branch Mgr*
EMP: 170
SQ FT: 12,800
SALES (corp-wide): 36.4MM **Privately Held**
WEB: www.neffp.com
SIC: 3069 3061 3053 Molded rubber products; mechanical rubber goods; gaskets, packing & sealing devices

PA: Neff-Perkins Company
16080 Industrial Pkwy
Middlefield OH 44062
440 632-1658

(G-13976)
NORMANDY PRODUCTS COMPANY
16125 Industrial Pkwy (44062-9393)
P.O. Box 52 (44062-0052)
PHONE....................440 632-5050
Fax: 440 632-1055
Carl Arysiak, *Principal*
Diane Donaldson, *Office Mgr*
EMP: 60
SQ FT: 64,000
SALES (corp-wide): 12.5MM **Privately Held**
WEB: www.normandyproducts.com
SIC: 3082 3498 Tubes, unsupported plastic; fabricated pipe & fittings
HQ: Normandy Products Company
1150 Freeport Rd
Pittsburgh PA 15238
412 826-1825

(G-13977)
NORSTAR ALUMINUM MOLDS INC
Also Called: Starwood
15986 Valplast St (44062-9399)
PHONE....................440 632-0853
Erik Adams, *Sales Staff*
Brian Gresch, *Branch Mgr*
Ravi Mehra, *Director*
EMP: 60
SALES (corp-wide): 8MM **Privately Held**
SIC: 7011 3444 Hotels & motels; sheet metalwork
PA: Norstar Aluminum Molds, Inc.
W66n622 Madison Ave
Cedarburg WI 53012
262 375-5600

(G-13978)
O A R VINYL WINDOWS & SIDING
Also Called: O A R Vinyl Window Co
12880 Clay St (44062-8733)
PHONE....................440 636-5573
Andy Bylar, *Owner*
Mary W Bylar, *Owner*
EMP: 4
SALES (est): 348.6K **Privately Held**
SIC: 3089 5211 5033 1761 Windows, plastic; siding; siding, except wood; siding contractor

(G-13979)
PARKS WEST PALLET LLC
4566 Parks West Rd (44062-9345)
PHONE....................440 693-4651
Joe Bricker,
Rebecca Bricker,
EMP: 4
SQ FT: 2,348
SALES (est): 300K **Privately Held**
SIC: 2448 Pallets, wood

(G-13980)
PCKD ENTERPRISES INC
Also Called: Molten Metals
15510 Old State Rd (44062-8208)
PHONE....................440 632-9119
Fax: 440 632-9817
Paul Cooper, *President*
Mark Andes, *Principal*
Sarah Mikash, *Principal*
Vince Fontana, *Engineer*
Kevin Doherty, *Treasurer*
EMP: 22
SQ FT: 16,000
SALES (est): 4.1MM **Privately Held**
WEB: www.mmei-inc.com
SIC: 3561 Industrial pumps & parts

(G-13981)
PERFORMA LA MAR PRINTING INC
15912 W High St (44062)
PHONE....................440 632-9800
Fax: 440 632-5799
David Chase, *President*
Kathy McClure, *President*
Lamar McClure, *Vice Pres*

EMP: 8
SALES (est): 700K **Privately Held**
SIC: 2752 2791 Offset & photolithographic printing; typesetting

(G-13982)
PLASTIC EXTRUSION TECHNOLOGIES
15229 S State Ave (44062-9468)
P.O. Box 92 (44062-0092)
PHONE....................440 632-5611
Fax: 440 632-5647
William E Spencer, *President*
Diane Spencer, *Admin Sec*
▼ EMP: 25
SQ FT: 38,500
SALES (est): 10MM **Privately Held**
SIC: 3089 Extruded finished plastic products

(G-13983)
PLEASANT VALLEY WDWKG LLC
13424 Clay St (44062-8741)
PHONE....................440 636-5860
Lester L Mullet Jr, *Mng Member*
Andy M Byler,
EMP: 5
SALES (est): 599K **Privately Held**
SIC: 2431 2434 Interior & ornamental woodwork & trim; wood kitchen cabinets

(G-13984)
POLYCHEM DISPERSIONS INC
16066 Industrial Pkwy (44062-9382)
PHONE....................800 545-3530
Fax: 440 632-5102
William Nichols, *CEO*
Anthony Vanni, *President*
Jeff Nichols, *Director*
EMP: 45 EST: 1981
SQ FT: 30,000
SALES (est): 13.9MM **Privately Held**
WEB: www.dispersions.com
SIC: 2869 Industrial organic chemicals

(G-13985)
RESOURCE MTL HDLG & RECYCL INC (PA)
14970 Brkshire Indus Pkwy (44062-9390)
PHONE....................440 834-0727
Josh Jones, *President*
Stacey Cremers, *COO*
▼ EMP: 20
SQ FT: 50,000
SALES (est): 7.6MM **Privately Held**
SIC: 5099 3089 Containers: glass, metal or plastic; plastic containers, except foam

(G-13986)
SAJAR PLASTICS INC
15285 S State Ave (44062-9468)
P.O. Box 37 (44062-0037)
PHONE....................440 632-5203
L Nowak, *CEO*
Scott Simpson, *President*
Duncan M Simpson Jr, *Senior VP*
Ed Ytsna, *Controller*
EMP: 100
SQ FT: 178,000
SALES (est): 13.2MM
SALES (corp-wide): 33.8MM **Privately Held**
WEB: www.sajarplastics.com
SIC: 3089 Injection molding of plastics
PA: American Plastic Technologies, Inc.
15229 S State Ave
Middlefield OH 44062
440 632-5203

(G-13987)
SCHNIDER PALLET LLC
9782 Bundysburg Rd (44062-9362)
PHONE....................440 632-5346
Fred Schnider,
EMP: 9
SALES (est): 530K **Privately Held**
SIC: 2448 Pallets, wood & wood with metal

(G-13988)
SELINICK CO
15879 Madison Rd (44062-8409)
PHONE....................440 632-1788
Merv Miller, *Owner*
EMP: 3

SQ FT: 3,600
SALES (est): 280.5K **Privately Held**
SIC: 7537 7692 Automotive transmission repair shops; welding repair

(G-13989)
SHAWNEE WOOD PRODUCTS INC
8918 Bundysburg Rd (44062-9525)
PHONE....................440 632-1771
Raymond C Miller, *President*
Michael Byler, *Vice Pres*
Douglas King, *Admin Sec*
EMP: 5
SQ FT: 6,000
SALES (est): 550.1K **Privately Held**
SIC: 2434 2431 Wood kitchen cabinets; staircases & stairs, wood

(G-13990)
SHOOTERS CHOICE LLC
15050 Berkshire Ind Pkwy (44062-9390)
PHONE....................440 834-8888
Joseph Ventimiglia, *President*
Frank Ventimiglia, *Principal*
EMP: 5
SQ FT: 13,104
SALES (est): 249.4K **Privately Held**
SIC: 2992 Lubricating oils & greases

(G-13991)
SIMON DE YOUNG CORPORATION
15010 Brkshire Indus Pkwy (44062-9390)
P.O. Box 217 (44062-0217)
PHONE....................440 834-3000
Simon D Young, *President*
Margaret D Young, *Corp Secy*
EMP: 8
SALES (est): 500K **Privately Held**
WEB: www.braidingmachinery.com
SIC: 3552 3549 Braiding machines, textile; wiredrawing & fabricating machinery & equipment, ex. die

(G-13992)
STUTZMAN BROTHERS SAWMILL
15991 Nauvoo Rd (44062-9765)
PHONE....................440 272-5179
EMP: 8 EST: 1995
SALES (est): 750K **Privately Held**
SIC: 2421 5031 Sawmill/Planing Mill Whol Lumber/Plywood/Millwork

(G-13993)
SUBURBAN COMMUNICATIONS INC
Also Called: Good News
14905 N State Ave (44062-9747)
P.O. Box 95 (44062-0095)
PHONE....................440 632-0130
Fax: 440 632-0877
Thomas Henry, *President*
Don Cimorell, *Chairman*
Neil Belcher, *Vice Pres*
Gayle Moore, *Prdtn Mgr*
EMP: 30 EST: 1979
SALES (est): 1.5MM **Privately Held**
WEB: www.good-news.com
SIC: 2721 2741 Magazines: publishing only, not printed on site; miscellaneous publishing

(G-13994)
SUGARBUSH CREEK FARM
13034 Madison Rd (44062-9753)
PHONE....................440 636-5371
Pam Cermak, *Owner*
EMP: 3
SALES (est): 130K **Privately Held**
SIC: 2099 Maple syrup

(G-13995)
TIMBER PRODUCTS INC
8652 Parkman Mespo Rd (44062-9334)
PHONE....................440 693-4098
George A Chittle Jr, *President*
George Chittle III, *Corp Secy*
John Rowland, *Vice Pres*
EMP: 4
SQ FT: 7,500
SALES (est): 340K **Privately Held**
SIC: 2448 Pallets, wood; skids, wood

(G-13996)
TROY INNOVATIVE INSTRS INC
15111 White Rd (44062-9216)
P.O. Box 1328 (44062-1328)
PHONE....................440 834-9567
Fax: 330 527-3299
Thomas Cseplo, *President*
August Deangelo, *Principal*
Randall Hampton, *Principal*
Brett Crawford, *VP Sales*
Carol Cseplo, *Admin Sec*
EMP: 40
SQ FT: 12,000
SALES (est): 6.8MM **Privately Held**
SIC: 3841 Surgical & medical instruments

(G-13997)
TROYMILL MANUFACTURING INC (PA)
Also Called: Troymill Wood Products
17055 Kinsman Rd (44062-9485)
P.O. Box 306 (44062-0306)
PHONE....................440 632-5580
Fax: 440 632-0402
Marvin Schaefer, *President*
Crist Miller, *General Mgr*
Brian Schaefer, *Principal*
Keith Grinberg, *COO*
Steven Belman, *Vice Pres*
EMP: 12
SQ FT: 19,500
SALES (est): 14.5MM **Privately Held**
SIC: 5031 2448 Lumber, plywood & millwork; wood pallets & skids

(G-13998)
TRUMBULL COUNTY HARDWOODS
9446 Bundysburg Rd (44062-9300)
PHONE....................440 632-0555
Fax: 440 632-1599
John Betweiler, *Partner*
Rudy Detweiler, *Partner*
Yvonne May, *Office Mgr*
EMP: 23
SQ FT: 600
SALES (est): 5.2MM **Privately Held**
WEB: www.tchardwoods.com
SIC: 2421 2426 Sawmills & planing mills, general; hardwood dimension & flooring mills

(G-13999)
ULTIMATE PALLET & TRUCKING LLC
4774 Parks West Rd (44062-9347)
PHONE....................440 693-4090
David Miller, *Principal*
EMP: 4
SALES (est): 280K **Privately Held**
SIC: 2448 Wood pallets & skids

(G-14000)
UNIVERSAL POLYMER & RUBBER LTD (PA)
15730 Madison Rd (44062-8408)
P.O. Box 767 (44062-0767)
PHONE....................440 632-1691
Joe Colebank, *President*
Andrew Cavanagh, *Vice Pres*
▲ EMP: 109
SQ FT: 56,000
SALES (est): 46.5MM **Privately Held**
WEB: www.universalpolymer.com
SIC: 3069 3089 Molded rubber products; extruded finished plastic products

(G-14001)
VENTCO INC
15050 Brkshire Indus Pkwy (44062-9390)
PHONE....................440 834-8888
Fax: 440 834-3388
Joseph Ventimiglia, *President*
Frank Ventimiglia, *Vice Pres*
Sal J Ventimiglia, *Treasurer*
▼ EMP: 10
SQ FT: 15,500
SALES (est): 1.5MM **Privately Held**
WEB: www.shooters-choice.com
SIC: 2842 2992 Cleaning or polishing preparations; lubricating oils & greases

---

(G-14002)
VENTURE PLAS MIDDLEFIELD LLC
15005 Enterprise Way (44062-9369)
P.O. Box 249, Newton Falls (44444-0249)
PHONE......................................440 834-0704
J Stephen Trapp, *Principal*
Arvid Danielson, *Principal*
Gary R Flattum, *Treasurer*
◆ EMP: 40
SQ FT: 48,000
SALES (est): 2.2MM **Privately Held**
SIC: 3089 3991 Injection molding of plastics; brushes for vacuum cleaners, carpet sweepers, etc.

(G-14003)
VITAMIN LAC
17642 Tavern Rd (44062-9191)
PHONE......................................440 548-5294
Melvin Yoder, *Owner*
EMP: 11
SALES (est): 576.5K **Privately Held**
SIC: 2399 Horse & pet accessories, textile

(G-14004)
VLCHEK PLASTICS
15981 Valplast St (44062-9399)
P.O. Box 5 (44062-0005)
PHONE......................................440 632-1631
Jason Sauey, *Principal*
EMP: 3
SALES (est): 239.8K **Privately Held**
SIC: 3089 Plastics products

(G-14005)
WHITE HOUSE CHOCOLATE
14607 Kinsman Rd (44062-9245)
P.O. Box 1034, Burton (44021-1034)
PHONE......................................440 834-3133
Debbie Butler, *Owner*
EMP: 5
SALES (est): 346K **Privately Held**
SIC: 2064 Fudge (candy)

(G-14006)
WINSPEC INC
15470 Chipmunk Ln (44062-9218)
PHONE......................................440 834-9068
Fax: 440 834-1065
Gregory Klausner, *President*
Joan Klausner, *Vice Pres*
EMP: 4
SQ FT: 12,000
SALES (est): 486.9K **Privately Held**
WEB: www.winspec.com
SIC: 2211 Draperies & drapery fabrics, cotton

(G-14007)
WOODCRAFT INDUSTRIES INC
15351 S State Ave (44062-9469)
P.O. Box 250 (44062-0250)
PHONE......................................440 632-9655
Fax: 440 632-9588
Cheryl Urmson, *Site Mgr*
Bobbi Phenicie, *Purch Agent*
Dan Miller, *Manager*
EMP: 160
SALES (corp-wide): 928.1MM **Publicly Held**
SIC: 2434 2431 2426 Wood kitchen cabinets; millwork; dimension, hardwood
HQ: Woodcraft Industries, Inc.
525 Lincoln Ave Se
Saint Cloud MN 56304
320 656-2345

(G-14008)
WOODWORKS DESIGN
9005 N Girdle Rd (44062-9502)
PHONE......................................440 693-4414
Fax: 440 693-4395
Todd Armfelt, *Principal*
EMP: 7
SALES (est): 1.6MM **Privately Held**
SIC: 2499 Decorative wood & woodwork

(G-14009)
YODERS HARNESS SHOP
14698 Bundysburg Rd (44062-9775)
PHONE......................................440 632-1505
Levi J Yoder, *Owner*
Fannie J Yoder, *Co-Owner*
EMP: 3

SQ FT: 2,500
SALES: 180K **Privately Held**
SIC: 3199 5191 5948 Harness or harness parts; harness equipment; leather goods, except luggage & shoes

---

Middleport
Meigs County

(G-14010)
FACEMYER FOREST PRODUCTS INC
Hc 7 (45760)
P.O. Box 89 (45760-0089)
PHONE......................................740 992-7425
Fax: 740 992-2345
William L Facemyer, *President*
Tammy Capehart, *Admin Sec*
EMP: 15
SALES (est): 1.2MM **Privately Held**
SIC: 2421 Lumber: rough, sawed or planed

(G-14011)
QUALITY PRINT SHOP INC
255 Mill St (45760-1163)
PHONE......................................740 992-3345
Fax: 740 992-3394
Dwane Weber, *President*
EMP: 3 EST: 1993
SQ FT: 4,200
SALES: 150K **Privately Held**
SIC: 2759 Commercial printing

Middletown
Butler County

(G-14012)
ADONAI TECHNOLOGIES LLC
1223 Hook Dr (45042-1734)
PHONE......................................513 560-9020
Jerran Adkins, *President*
EMP: 3
SQ FT: 9,000
SALES (est): 125.7K **Privately Held**
SIC: 3672 Printed circuit boards

(G-14013)
AIR PRODUCTS AND CHEMICALS INC
2500 Yankee Rd (45044-7652)
PHONE......................................513 420-3663
Andrew Cummins, *Vice Pres*
Wallace Brashear, *Branch Mgr*
Bill Arthur, *Branch Mgr*
Wally Brashear, *Manager*
George Robinson, *IT/INT Sup*
EMP: 51
SALES (corp-wide): 9.5B **Publicly Held**
WEB: www.airproducts.com
SIC: 2813 Industrial gases
PA: Air Products And Chemicals, Inc.
7201 Hamilton Blvd
Allentown PA 18195
610 481-4911

(G-14014)
AK STEEL CORPORATION
801 Crawford St (45044-4537)
PHONE......................................513 425-3694
Robert Jordan, *General Mgr*
Svend Jensen, *District Mgr*
Jim Funk, *Senior Buyer*
Daniel Scherrer, *Research*
Paul Janavicius, *Engineer*
EMP: 298
SALES (corp-wide): 5.8B **Publicly Held**
SIC: 3312 Blast furnaces & steel mills
HQ: Ak Steel Corporation
9227 Centre Pointe Dr
West Chester OH 45069
513 425-4200

(G-14015)
AK STEEL CORPORATION
622 Box (45042)
PHONE......................................513 425-3593
EMP: 10
SALES (corp-wide): 5.8B **Publicly Held**
WEB: www.ketnar.org
SIC: 3312 Blast furnaces & steel mills

HQ: Ak Steel Corporation
9227 Centre Pointe Dr
West Chester OH 45069
513 425-4200

(G-14016)
AKERS PACKAGING SERVICE INC (PA)
Also Called: Akers Packaging Service Group
2820 Lefferson Rd (45044-6999)
P.O. Box 610 (45042-0610)
PHONE......................................513 422-6312
James F Akers, *Ch of Bd*
William C Akers II, *President*
David Econie, *General Mgr*
Marilyn R Akey, *Corp Secy*
Michael S Akey, *Vice Pres*
▲ EMP: 140 EST: 1963
SQ FT: 220,000
SALES (est): 73.4MM **Privately Held**
WEB: www.akers-pkg.com
SIC: 2653 Corrugated boxes, partitions, display items, sheets & pad; boxes, corrugated: made from purchased materials

(G-14017)
AKERS PACKAGING SOLUTIONS INC (PA)
Also Called: Akers Packaging Service Group
2820 Lefferson Rd (45044-6999)
P.O. Box 610 (45042-0610)
PHONE......................................513 422-6312
James F Akers, *Ch of Bd*
William C Akers, *President*
Alfred J Pedicone, *Corp Secy*
Michael Shannon Akey, *Vice Pres*
EMP: 42 EST: 2014
SALES (est): 11.9MM **Privately Held**
SIC: 2653 Corrugated & solid fiber boxes

(G-14018)
AL BRADSHAW JR
Also Called: Machine Doctors
5009 Oxford Middleton Rd (45042)
PHONE......................................513 422-8870
Al Bradshaw Jr, *Owner*
EMP: 3 EST: 1987
SALES (est): 260.2K **Privately Held**
SIC: 7694 Electric motor repair

(G-14019)
ALLIANCE PRINTING & PUBLISHING
2520 Atco Ave (45042-2517)
PHONE......................................513 422-7611
Fax: 937 423-8204
Greg Brauch, *President*
Karen Downs, *Publisher*
Mike Fakes, *Vice Pres*
Ed McConnell, *Vice Pres*
Barry Henry, *CFO*
EMP: 15
SQ FT: 20,000
SALES (est): 1.5MM **Privately Held**
WEB: www.allianceprinting.net
SIC: 2752 Commercial printing, offset

(G-14020)
AMTECO INC
5773 Elk Creek Rd (45042-9669)
P.O. Box 1458, West Chester (45071-1458)
PHONE......................................513 217-4430
Jeffrey L Myers, *President*
EMP: 3
SALES (est): 404.5K **Privately Held**
WEB: www.amtecoincorporated.com
SIC: 3821 Laboratory apparatus & furniture

(G-14021)
ARGROV BOX CO
1500 S University Blvd (45044-5968)
PHONE......................................513 217-5900
Patrick Larmon, *Principal*
Cheryl Garber, *Director*
EMP: 4
SALES (est): 341.9K **Privately Held**
SIC: 3949 Boxing equipment & supplies, general

(G-14022)
AVURE TECHNOLOGIES INC
2601 S Verity Pkwy # 13 (45044-7495)
PHONE......................................513 433-2500
Keith Cripe, *Branch Mgr*

EMP: 51
SALES (corp-wide): 1.3B **Publicly Held**
SIC: 3556 Food products machinery
HQ: Avure Technologies Incorporated
1830 Airport Exchange Blv
Erlanger KY 41018
614 255-6633

(G-14023)
BACKYARD SCOREBOARDS LLC
Also Called: Nifty Promo Products
431 Kenridge Dr (45042-4930)
PHONE......................................513 702-6561
Keith Bailey, *Sales Mgr*
Douglas Poffenderger,
EMP: 9
SQ FT: 11,000
SALES: 275K **Privately Held**
SIC: 3949 Sporting & athletic goods; team sports equipment

(G-14024)
BROWN-SINGER CO
108 Dorset Dr (45044-4948)
PHONE......................................513 422-9619
James Brown, *President*
EMP: 15 EST: 1875
SQ FT: 16,800
SALES (est): 1.8MM **Privately Held**
SIC: 3443 Fabricated plate work (boiler shop)

(G-14025)
C RC AUTOMOTIVE
460 N Verity Pkwy (45042-2129)
PHONE......................................513 422-4775
Ron Cole, *Principal*
EMP: 3
SALES (est): 169K **Privately Held**
SIC: 7539 5013 3599 Electrical services; automotive servicing equipment; machine shop, jobbing & repair

(G-14026)
CARROLL DISTRG & CNSTR SUP INC
6688 Georgetown Ln (45042-1315)
PHONE......................................513 422-3327
Steve Carroll, *President*
EMP: 5
SALES (corp-wide): 75.9MM **Privately Held**
SIC: 5082 3444 Contractors' materials; concrete forms, sheet metal
PA: Carroll Distributing & Construction Supply, Inc.
205 S Iowa Ave
Ottumwa IA 52501
641 683-1888

(G-14027)
CENTURY MOLD COMPANY INC
55 Wright Dr (45044-3287)
PHONE......................................513 539-9283
Richard Ballweg, *Inv Control Mgr*
Ron Ricotta, *Branch Mgr*
EMP: 89
SALES (corp-wide): 222.9MM **Privately Held**
WEB: www.centurymold.com
SIC: 3089 Injection molding of plastics
PA: Century Mold Company, Inc.
25 Vantage Point Dr
Rochester NY 14624
585 352-8600

(G-14028)
CHAUTAUQUA FIBERGLASS & PLASTI
2601 S Verity Pkwy (45044-7482)
PHONE......................................513 423-8840
Adam Bennett, *Principal*
EMP: 6
SALES (est): 573.5K **Privately Held**
SIC: 2221 Fiberglass fabrics
PA: Reinforced Plastic Systems
740 Main St S
Mahone Bay NS B0J 2
902 624-8383

▲ = Import ▼ =Export
◆ =Import/Export

(G-14029)
CHEMTRADE CHEMICALS US LLC
305 Richmond St (45044-4322)
PHONE..............................513 422-6319
Fax: 513 422-4617
Steve Combs, *Plant Supt*
Steve Combes, *Manager*
EMP: 4
SALES (corp-wide): 116.9MM **Privately Held**
SIC: 2819 Aluminum sulfate
HQ: Chemtrade Chemicals Us Llc
   90 E Halsey Rd
   Parsippany NJ 07054
   973 515-0900

(G-14030)
CITY OF MIDDLETOWN
Also Called: Water Treatment
805 Columbia Ave (45042-1907)
PHONE..............................513 425-7781
Fax: 513 425-7769
Scott Belcher, *Manager*
Preston Combs, *Deputy Dir*
EMP: 12 **Privately Held**
WEB: www.trentonlibrary.net
SIC: 3589 4941 Water treatment equipment, industrial; water supply
PA: City Of Middletown
   1 Donham Plz
   Middletown OH 45042
   513 425-7766

(G-14031)
COHEN BROTHERS INC (PA)
1723 Woodlawn Ave (45044-4348)
P.O. Box 957 (45044-0957)
PHONE..............................513 422-3696
Fax: 937 422-9018
Wilbur Cohen, *Ch of Bd*
Kenneth Cohen, *President*
Kyle Dean, *General Mgr*
Mose Cohen, *Principal*
Philip Cohen, *Principal*
EMP: 9 EST: 1924
SQ FT: 90,000
SALES (est): 93.8MM **Privately Held**
WEB: www.cohenbrothersinc.com
SIC: 5093 3441 3341 3312 Ferrous metal scrap & waste; nonferrous metals scrap; fabricated structural metal; secondary nonferrous metals; blast furnaces & steel mills

(G-14032)
CONTECH ENGNERED SOLUTIONS LLC
1001 Grove St (45044-5890)
PHONE..............................513 645-7000
EMP: 70 **Privately Held**
SIC: 3444 3084 3317 3441 Sheet metalwork; culverts, sheet metal; plastics pipe; steel pipe & tubes; fabricated structural metal; fabricated plate work (boiler shop)
HQ: Contech Engineered Solutions Llc
   9025 Ctr Pinte Dr Ste 400
   West Chester OH 45069
   513 645-7000

(G-14033)
CONTECH ENGNERED SOLUTIONS LLC
1001 Grove St (45044-5890)
PHONE..............................513 425-5337
Fax: 513 425-2933
Keith Wingfield, *Sales & Mktg St*
Michael S Gilligan, *Human Resources*
Jane Archer, *Office Mgr*
EMP: 10 **Privately Held**
SIC: 3443 Culverts, metal plate
HQ: Contech Engineered Solutions Llc
   9025 Ctr Pinte Dr Ste 400
   West Chester OH 45069
   513 645-7000

(G-14034)
CRANE CONSUMABLES LLC
155 Westheimer Dr (45044-3228)
PHONE..............................513 539-9980
Robert Crane, *Marketing Staff*
EMP: 5

SALES (est): 889.5K **Privately Held**
WEB: www.craneconsumables.com
SIC: 7389 2241 Packaging & labeling services; labels, woven

(G-14035)
CROWN ELECTRIC ENGRG & MFG LLC
175 Edison Dr (45044-3269)
PHONE..............................513 539-7394
Chad Shell, *Mng Member*
Donna Keller, *Admin Mgr*
Jessica Payne, *Administration*
Bruce Hack,
▲ EMP: 25
SQ FT: 48,000
SALES (est): 8.6MM **Privately Held**
WEB: www.crown-electric.com
SIC: 3643 3444 Bus bars (electrical conductors); sheet metal specialties, not stamped

(G-14036)
DAUBENMIRES PRINTING
1527 Central Ave (45044-4135)
PHONE..............................513 425-7223
Fax: 513 425-7149
Gary Daubenmire, *Owner*
EMP: 8
SQ FT: 4,000
SALES (est): 869.2K **Privately Held**
WEB: www.daubenmiresprinting.com
SIC: 2752 2791 Commercial printing, offset; typesetting

(G-14037)
DIGITAL VISUALS INC
Also Called: Dvi Retal
15 N Clinton St (45042-2003)
PHONE..............................513 420-9466
Debra S Edwards, *President*
James L Edwards, *Vice Pres*
EMP: 3
SQ FT: 5,000
SALES (est): 333.1K **Privately Held**
WEB: www.dvisuals.com
SIC: 2759 Commercial printing

(G-14038)
DMK INDUSTRIES INC
1801 Made Dr (45044-8948)
PHONE..............................513 727-4549
Fax: 513 727-4552
Dennis Kuna, *President*
Mary Beth Ferree, *Office Mgr*
EMP: 15 EST: 1996
SALES (est): 2.2MM **Privately Held**
SIC: 3369 Nonferrous foundries

(G-14039)
ELECTRO-METALLICS CO
3004 Lefferson Rd (45044-6903)
PHONE..............................513 423-8091
Fax: 513 424-4525
Hamilton Watkins, *President*
Jane M Watkins, *Corp Secy*
Robert Bryant, *Plant Mgr*
EMP: 8 EST: 1965
SQ FT: 2,500
SALES (est): 864.2K **Privately Held**
WEB: www.electrometallics.com
SIC: 3471 Electroplating of metals or formed products; plating of metals or formed products

(G-14040)
EVERTZ TECHNOLOGY SERVICE USA
2601 S Verity Pkwy # 102 (45044-7481)
PHONE..............................513 422-8400
Egon Evertz, *President*
Bob Hendrick, *General Mgr*
Janace Dewitt, *Treasurer*
Stephen Miller, *Manager*
▲ EMP: 31
SALES (est): 6.7MM **Privately Held**
WEB: www.etsusainc.net
SIC: 3325 Steel foundries

(G-14041)
FIXTURE DIMENSIONS INC
4355 Salzman Rd (45044-9741)
PHONE..............................513 360-7512
Fax: 513 539-3306
Linda F Schaffeld, *President*
Rob Hoover, *Purchasing*

▼ EMP: 30
SQ FT: 10,000
SALES (est): 5MM **Privately Held**
SIC: 2541 2431 Store & office display cases & fixtures; display fixtures, wood; millwork

(G-14042)
FLEXODIE (HQ)
1310 Hook Dr (45042-1712)
PHONE..............................513 489-0433
Fax: 513 705-9527
Donald McCaughey, *Treasurer*
Marie Litz, *Controller*
Richard Godfrey,
▲ EMP: 4
SALES (est): 724K
SALES (corp-wide): 42.9MM **Privately Held**
SIC: 3555 Printing plates
PA: Mark/Trece, Inc.
   2001 Stockton Rd
   Joppa MD 21085
   410 879-0060

(G-14043)
GRANGER PLASTIC COMPANY
1600 M A D E Indus Dr (45044)
PHONE..............................513 424-4799
Fax: 513 424-4799
James Cravens, *President*
Jeffrey T Witschey, *Principal*
Jack Cobb, *Vice Pres*
Alli Cravens, *Sales Staff*
Shawn Cravens, *Manager*
EMP: 20
SALES (est): 5MM **Privately Held**
WEB: www.rotocasting.com
SIC: 3082 Unsupported plastics profile shapes

(G-14044)
GRAPHIC PACKAGING INTL INC
Also Called: Altivity Packaging
407 Charles St (45042-2107)
PHONE..............................513 424-4200
Earl Hill, *Plant Engr*
Neil Shockey, *Controller*
Scott Lebeau, *Manager*
Nancy Horn, *Manager*
James Brown, *Supervisor*
EMP: 143 **Publicly Held**
SIC: 2631 2657 Folding boxboard; packaging board; folding paperboard boxes
HQ: Graphic Packaging International, Inc.
   1500 Riveredge Pkwy # 100
   Atlanta GA 30328
   770 240-7200

(G-14045)
HY-BLAST INC
70 Enterprise Dr (45044-8925)
P.O. Box 602 (45042-0602)
PHONE..............................513 424-0704
Fax: 513 424-5272
Robert Cunningham, *President*
Betty Jane Cunningham, *Corp Secy*
Donald Ray Cunningham, *Vice Pres*
Thomas Cunningham, *Vice Pres*
EMP: 16
SQ FT: 25,000
SALES (est): 1.2MM **Privately Held**
WEB: www.hyblastinc.com
SIC: 1799 3471 7699 Epoxy application; polishing, metals or formed products; industrial equipment cleaning

(G-14046)
HYTEK COATINGS INC
1700 S University Blvd (45044-5972)
PHONE..............................513 424-0131
Fax: 513 424-7330
James Hammer, *President*
Anne Scott, *Manager*
EMP: 5
SQ FT: 13,300
SALES: 400K **Privately Held**
SIC: 2851 Removers & cleaners; paints: oil or alkyd vehicle or water thinned

(G-14047)
INJECTION ALLOYS INCORPORATED
1700 Made Industrial Dr (45044-8937)
PHONE..............................513 422-8819
Chris Jackson, *CEO*

Manuel Franco, *CFO*
Michelle Shockley, *Controller*
▲ EMP: 10
SQ FT: 29,000
SALES: 6MM **Privately Held**
SIC: 3315 Wire & fabricated wire products
HQ: Injection Alloys Limited
   The Way
   Royston HERTS SG8 7
   156 275-0363

(G-14048)
INLINE LABEL COMPANY
4720 Emerald Way (45044-8962)
PHONE..............................513 217-5662
Fax: 513 217-5663
David S Heckler, *President*
EMP: 14 EST: 1997
SALES (est): 3MM **Privately Held**
SIC: 2679 Labels, paper: made from purchased material

(G-14049)
INTERNATIONAL PAPER COMPANY
912 Nelbar St (45042-2529)
PHONE..............................800 473-0830
John Tirlo, *Human Res Mgr*
EMP: 160
SALES (corp-wide): 21B **Publicly Held**
SIC: 2621 Paper mills
PA: International Paper Company
   6400 Poplar Ave
   Memphis TN 38197
   901 419-9000

(G-14050)
INTERSCOPE MANUFACTURING INC
2901 Carmody Blvd (45042-1761)
PHONE..............................513 423-8866
Fax: 513 423-5065
John Michael Brill, *CEO*
Robert Conrad, *General Mgr*
◆ EMP: 50
SQ FT: 175,000
SALES (est): 6.6MM **Privately Held**
WEB: www.interscopemfg.com
SIC: 3599 7389 Custom machinery; repossession service

(G-14051)
JACK C KEIR INC
Also Called: Keir Educational Resources
4785 Emerald Way Ste A (45044-8112)
PHONE..............................513 422-4860
Fax: 513 422-8719
John Keir, *CEO*
Henrietta Nye, *President*
Jeff Nye, *Corp Secy*
Debra S Klamo, *Opers Staff*
Aileen Crass, *Accounts Mgr*
EMP: 16
SQ FT: 5,000
SALES (est): 1.7MM **Privately Held**
WEB: www.keirsuccess.com
SIC: 2731 7372 Books: publishing only; prepackaged software

(G-14052)
JOHN H HOSKING INC
Also Called: Diamond Aluminum Co
4665 Emerald Way (45044-8966)
PHONE..............................513 821-1080
Fax: 513 821-0121
James Hodde Jr, *President*
EMP: 6
SQ FT: 6,725
SALES: 900K **Privately Held**
WEB: www.diamond-aluminum.com
SIC: 3498 Fabricated pipe & fittings

(G-14053)
LAYNE HEAVY CIVIL INC
6451 Germantown Rd (45042-1352)
PHONE..............................513 424-7287
Fax: 513 424-7820
Ron Alexander, *Branch Mgr*
Michael Wiley, *Manager*
EMP: 20
SALES (corp-wide): 601.9MM **Publicly Held**
WEB: www.ranneymethod.com
SIC: 1781 3589 5251 Water well drilling; water treatment equipment, industrial; pumps & pumping equipment

HQ: Layne Heavy Civil, Inc.
    4520 N State Road 37
    Orleans IN 47452
    812 865-3232

(G-14054)
LIM SERVICES LLC
Also Called: Locke Industrial Maint Svcs
3351 Cincinnati Dayton Rd (45044-8955)
PHONE..................................513 217-0801
Beau Hoy, *Branch Mgr*
David Locke, *Admin Mgr*
EMP: 10
SQ FT: 2,200
SALES (est): 560K **Privately Held**
SIC: 1799 7699 3498 1721 Welding on
site; boiler & heating repair services; fab-
ricated pipe & fittings; residential painting

(G-14055)
**LOW BOBS DISCOUNT
TOBACCO**
408 S Breiel Blvd (45044-5110)
PHONE..................................513 727-1430
Fax: 513 727-1430
Larry Bell, *President*
EMP: 3
SALES: 840K **Privately Held**
SIC: 2111 Cigarettes

(G-14056)
LOXCREEN COMPANY INC
100 Westheimer Dr (45044-3242)
PHONE..................................513 539-2255
Fax: 513 539-2288
Carrie Taylor, *Manager*
EMP: 10
SALES (corp-wide): 253.6MM **Privately
Held**
WEB: www.loxcreen.com
SIC: 5051 5031 3354 3442 Aluminum
bars, rods, ingots, sheets, pipes, plates,
etc.; doors; aluminum extruded products;
screens, window, metal
HQ: The Loxcreen Company Inc
    1630 Old Dunbar Rd
    West Columbia SC 29172
    803 822-1600

(G-14057)
M-D BUILDING PRODUCTS INC
100 Westheimer Dr (45044-3242)
PHONE..................................513 539-2255
Carrie Taylor-Lane, *Principal*
EMP: 288
SALES (corp-wide): 253.6MM **Privately
Held**
SIC: 3442 Weather strip, metal
PA: M-D Building Products, Inc.
    4041 N Santa Fe Ave
    Oklahoma City OK 73118
    405 528-4411

(G-14058)
**MAGELLAN AROSPC
MIDDLETOWN INC (HQ)**
2320 Wedekind Dr (45042-2390)
PHONE..................................513 422-2751
Fax: 513 422-0812
James S Butyniec, *CEO*
Robert Howiler, *Materials Mgr*
Brian Latz, *Mfg Staff*
Susan Glenn, *Buyer*
Joshuah Upton, *Engineer*
EMP: 100
SALES (est): 17.7MM
SALES (corp-wide): 715.3MM **Privately
Held**
WEB: www.aeroncainc.com
SIC: 3724 3728 Aircraft engines & engine
parts; aircraft body assemblies & parts
PA: Magellan Aerospace Corporation
    3160 Derry Rd E
    Mississauga ON L4T 1
    905 677-1889

(G-14059)
**MANUFACTURERS EQUIPMENT
CO**
Also Called: Meco
35 Enterprise Dr (45044-8928)
PHONE..................................513 424-3573
Adam W Miller, *President*
Frank B Carraher, *Vice Pres*
David Andrews, *Project Mgr*

Joseph Mahlmeister, *Human Res Dir*
Bryan Sicking, *Sales Mgr*
▲ EMP: 13
SQ FT: 16,000
SALES: 2.6MM **Privately Held**
WEB: www.mecoservices.com
SIC: 3496 3535 Wire chain; belt conveyor
systems, general industrial use; bucket
type conveyor systems

(G-14060)
MATHESON TRI-GAS INC
Also Called: AK Steel Door 360
1801 Crawford St (45044-4572)
PHONE..................................513 727-9638
Fax: 513 727-9640
John Green, *Branch Mgr*
Don Pierce, *Manager*
EMP: 21
SALES (corp-wide): 5.4B **Privately Held**
SIC: 2813 5084 Industrial gases; nitrogen;
oxygen, compressed or liquefied; argon;
welding machinery & equipment; safety
equipment
HQ: Matheson Tri-Gas, Inc.
    150 Allen Rd Ste 302
    Basking Ridge NJ 07920
    908 991-9200

(G-14061)
MECCO INC
2100 S Main St (45044-7345)
PHONE..................................513 422-3651
Fax: 513 422-8746
David T Morgan, *President*
Charles E Morgan, *Vice Pres*
Bill Perry, *Vice Pres*
Ron Price, *Vice Pres*
Stephen Rains, *Treasurer*
EMP: 45 EST: 1956
SQ FT: 2,000
SALES (est): 4.7MM **Privately Held**
WEB: www.meccoconcrete.com
SIC: 3273 1442 Ready-mixed concrete;
construction sand mining; gravel mining

(G-14062)
**MIDDLETOWN LICENSE
AGENCY INC**
3232 Roosevelt Blvd (45044-6424)
PHONE..................................513 422-7225
Cristy Gamble, *President*
EMP: 12
SALES (est): 900K **Privately Held**
WEB: www.middletownlicenseagency.com
SIC: 3469 Automobile license tags,
stamped metal

(G-14063)
MIDDLETOWN PHARMACY INC
4421 Roosevelt Blvd Ste H (45044-9024)
PHONE..................................513 705-6252
Raef Hamaed, *President*
EMP: 9
SALES (est): 1.5MM **Privately Held**
SIC: 2834 Pharmaceutical preparations

(G-14064)
**MIDDLETOWN TUBE WORKS
INC**
2201 Trine St (45044-5766)
PHONE..................................513 727-0080
Fax: 513 727-1879
Angela Phillips, *President*
Scott Gilbert, *Opers Mgr*
Chris Lange, *Opers Staff*
Kevin Hart, *Purch Mgr*
Kathy Young, *Purch Agent*
EMP: 80
SQ FT: 230,000
SALES (est): 23MM
SALES (corp-wide): 25.9MM **Privately
Held**
WEB: www.middletowntube.com
SIC: 3312 Tubes, steel & iron
PA: Phillips Mfg. And Tower Co.
    5578 State Route 61 N
    Shelby OH 44875
    419 347-1720

(G-14065)
MTR MARTCO LLC
3350 Yankee Rd (45044-8927)
PHONE..................................513 424-5307
Raymond McIntosh, *President*
Ottie Craycraft, *Foreman/Supr*

Dan Miller, *Engineer*
Randy Yoder, *Controller*
Ron Bradford, *Sales Staff*
▼ EMP: 55
SQ FT: 60,000
SALES (est): 16.9MM **Privately Held**
WEB: www.mtrmartco.com
SIC: 3554 3312 Paper industries machin-
ery; stainless steel

(G-14066)
MUELLER GAS PRODUCTS
1800 Clayton Ave (45042-2200)
PHONE..................................513 424-5311
Doug Murdock, *Owner*
Tim Cole, *Opers Mgr*
Sabrina Bowman, *Human Resources*
Angie Wilmath, *Manager*
EMP: 10
SALES (est): 7.4MM **Privately Held**
SIC: 3714 Manifolds, motor vehicle

(G-14067)
N-STOCK BOX INC
1500 S University Blvd (45044-5968)
PHONE..................................513 423-0319
Fax: 513 423-7943
Jeff Pennington, *President*
Lori Combs, *Vice Pres*
Jon Combs, *Human Res Mgr*
Jed Brubaker, *VP Sales*
Matthew Janosik, *Sales Staff*
EMP: 40
SQ FT: 70,000
SALES (est): 10.9MM **Privately Held**
WEB: www.n-stockbox.com
SIC: 2653 Boxes, corrugated: made from
purchased materials

(G-14068)
**NATURAL BEAUTY PRODUCTS
INC**
Also Called: Decaplus
50 S Main St (45044-4060)
P.O. Box 1566 (45042-7383)
PHONE..................................513 420-9400
Fax: 513 420-9220
Kenneth Alsop, *President*
David Haddix, *Vice Pres*
Marcelina Cornwall, *Engineer*
James Webb, *Treasurer*
Michelle Randall, *Admin Sec*
EMP: 10
SALES (est): 911.4K **Privately Held**
WEB: www.deccaplus.com
SIC: 5999 2844 Hair care products; hair
preparations, including shampoos

(G-14069)
NCI BUILDING SYSTEMS INC
2400 Yankee Rd (45044-8301)
PHONE..................................937 584-3300
John Wallace, *General Mgr*
Michael Thornburg, *QC Mgr*
Darren Valentine, *Sales Mgr*
Donnie Snow, *Accounts Mgr*
Duane Appel, *Manager*
EMP: 164
SALES (corp-wide): 1.6B **Publicly Held**
SIC: 3448 Prefabricated metal buildings
PA: Nci Building Systems, Inc.
    10943 N Sam Huston Pkwy W
    Houston TX 77064
    281 897-7788

(G-14070)
NEW CENTURY SALES LLC
2905 Lopane Ave (45044-6063)
PHONE..................................513 422-3631
Tony Dicristoforo, *Principal*
EMP: 4
SALES (est): 340.9K **Privately Held**
SIC: 2741 Miscellaneous publishing

(G-14071)
**PAC WORLDWIDE
CORPORATION**
Png Envelope
3131 Cincinnati Dayton Rd (45044-8965)
PHONE..................................513 217-3200
Carter Miller, *Manager*
Jeff Brooks, *Manager*
EMP: 20 **Privately Held**
SIC: 2677 Envelopes

HQ: Pac Worldwide Corporation
    15435 Ne 92nd St
    Redmond WA 98052
    425 202-4015

(G-14072)
**PAC WORLDWIDE
CORPORATION**
Also Called: Pac Manufacturing
3131 Cincinnati Dayton Rd (45044-8965)
PHONE..................................800 610-9367
Fax: 513 933-9744
Bruce Johnson, *Manager*
EMP: 77 **Privately Held**
SIC: 5112 2677 Envelopes; envelopes
HQ: Pac Worldwide Corporation
    15435 Ne 92nd St
    Redmond WA 98052
    425 202-4015

(G-14073)
**PACKAGING CORPORATION
AMERICA**
Also Called: Pca/Middletown 353
1824 Baltimore St (45044-5902)
P.O. Box 127 (45042-0127)
PHONE..................................513 424-3542
Minnie Griffin, *Vice Pres*
Howard Lanier, *Safety Mgr*
Joe Burley, *Sales Staff*
Robert Garland, *Sales Staff*
Michael Kennedy, *Sales Staff*
EMP: 100
SQ FT: 200,000
SALES (corp-wide): 5.7B **Publicly Held**
WEB: www.packagingcorp.com
SIC: 2653 Corrugated & solid fiber boxes
PA: Packaging Corporation Of America
    1955 W Field Ct
    Lake Forest IL 60045
    847 482-3000

(G-14074)
PHONAK LLC
2951 Cincinnati Dayton Rd (45044-9313)
PHONE..................................513 420-4568
EMP: 3
SALES (corp-wide): 2B **Privately Held**
SIC: 3842 Hearing aids
HQ: Phonak, Llc
    4520 Weaver Pkwy Ste 1
    Warrenville IL 60555
    630 821-5000

(G-14075)
PILOT CHEMICAL CORP
3439 Yankee Rd (45044-8931)
PHONE..................................513 424-9700
Richard Caskey, *Vice Pres*
Jeff Russell, *Branch Mgr*
Ken Gregor, *Executive*
EMP: 50
SQ FT: 25,000
SALES (corp-wide): 81.9MM **Privately
Held**
WEB: www.pilotchemical.com
SIC: 2841 2842 Soap & other detergents;
specialty cleaning, polishes & sanitation
goods
HQ: Pilot Chemical Corp.
    2744 E Kemper Rd
    Cincinnati OH 45241
    513 326-0600

(G-14076)
PIXSLAP INC
1634 Central Ave (45044-4191)
PHONE..................................937 559-2671
Adam Ali, *CEO*
EMP: 5
SQ FT: 2,500
SALES (est): 250K **Privately Held**
SIC: 2741 7311 7319 7371 Miscella-
neous publishing; ; advertising agencies;
media buying service; custom computer
programming services

(G-14077)
PPG INDUSTRIES INC
Also Called: PPG 4335
4480 Marie Dr (45044-6248)
PHONE..................................513 424-1241
Brian Wright, *Branch Mgr*
James Freeland, *Manager*
EMP: 24

SALES (corp-wide): 14.7B **Publicly Held**
WEB: www.ppg.com
SIC: 2851 Paints & allied products
PA: Ppg Industries, Inc.
1 Ppg Pl
Pittsburgh PA 15272
412 434-3131

(G-14078)
PROGRESSIVE RIBBON INC (PA)
1533 Central Ave (45044-4135)
PHONE.................................513 705-9319
Darryl Bowen, *President*
Dan Bush, *Vice Pres*
Jack Little, *Controller*
Dave Chable, *Finance Mgr*
Don Scheetz, *Sales Mgr*
EMP: 20
SQ FT: 20,000
SALES (est): 4.8MM **Privately Held**
SIC: 3955 Ribbons, inked: typewriter, adding machine, register, etc.

(G-14079)
PROPIPE TECHNOLOGIES INC
1800 Clayton Ave (45042-2200)
PHONE.................................513 424-5311
John Blount, *President*
Angie Wilmath, *Human Resources*
John Nugent, *Sales Mgr*
EMP: 43
SQ FT: 52,500
SALES (est): 6.7MM
SALES (corp-wide): 2B **Publicly Held**
WEB: www.muellerbrass.com
SIC: 3498 Manifolds, pipe: fabricated from purchased pipe
HQ: Mueller Brass Co.
8285 Tournament Dr # 150
Memphis TN 38125
901 753-3200

(G-14080)
QUAKER CHEMICAL CORPORATION (HQ)
3431 Yankee Rd (45044-8931)
PHONE.................................513 422-9600
Michael F Barry, *President*
John Hufnal, *Business Mgr*
D Jeffry Benoliel, *Corp Secy*
Patrick J Piccioni, *Vice Pres*
Sean Tolbert, *Mfg Dir*
▲ EMP: 60
SALES (est): 16MM
SALES (corp-wide): 746.6MM **Publicly Held**
WEB: www.quakerchem.com
SIC: 2992 2899 Lubricating oils & greases; chemical preparations
PA: Quaker Chemical Corporation
901 E Hector St
Conshohocken PA 19428
610 832-4000

(G-14081)
REBILTCO INC
8775 Thomas Rd (45042-1233)
PHONE.................................513 424-2024
Fax: 513 424-4878
Larry Eckhardt, *President*
EMP: 6
SQ FT: 25,000
SALES (est): 967.6K **Privately Held**
SIC: 3554 Paper industries machinery; corrugating machines, paper

(G-14082)
SHADETREE MACHINE
5994 Kalbfleisch Rd (45042-8937)
PHONE.................................513 727-8771
John Bridges, *Owner*
EMP: 4
SALES (est): 210K **Privately Held**
WEB: www.shadetreemachine.com
SIC: 3549 Wiredrawing & fabricating machinery & equipment, ex. die

(G-14083)
SHEPHERD CHEMICAL COMPANY
Also Called: Shepherd Middletown Co
3444 Yankee Rd (45044-8931)
PHONE.................................513 424-7276
Fax: 513 424-8156

Bayard Pelsor, *Branch Mgr*
Mark Anderson, *Manager*
Ron Kraeft, *Maintence Staff*
EMP: 15
SQ FT: 945
SALES (corp-wide): 58.2MM **Privately Held**
SIC: 2819 Metal salts & compounds, except sodium, potassium, aluminum
PA: The Shepherd Chemical Company
4900 Beech St
Norwood OH 45212
513 731-1110

(G-14084)
SPURLINO MATERIALS LLC (PA)
4000 Oxford State Rd (45044-8973)
PHONE.................................513 705-0111
Fax: 513 422-6678
Jim Spurlino, *President*
Gary Thomas, *Marketing Staff*
EMP: 50
SQ FT: 10,000
SALES (est): 27MM **Privately Held**
WEB: www.spurlino.net
SIC: 3273 Ready-mixed concrete

(G-14085)
START PRINTING
3140 Cincinnati Dayton Rd (45044-8921)
PHONE.................................513 424-2121
Teresa Lytle, *Principal*
EMP: 4
SALES (est): 472.5K **Privately Held**
SIC: 2752 Commercial printing, lithographic

(G-14086)
SUNCOKE ENERGY NC
Also Called: Mto Suncoke
3353 Yankee Rd (45044-8927)
PHONE.................................513 727-5571
Frederick Fritz A Henderson, *CEO*
Terry Harris, *Manager*
David O'Brien, *Manager*
Kris Singleton, *Manager*
EMP: 40
SALES (est): 5.4MM **Privately Held**
SIC: 1241 Coal mining services

(G-14087)
TEMPLE INLAND
912 Nelbar St (45042-2529)
PHONE.................................513 425-0830
Fax: 513 425-0830
Kent Kimmel, *Personnel Exec*
EMP: 6
SALES (est): 527.1K **Privately Held**
SIC: 2653 Corrugated & solid fiber boxes

(G-14088)
THOMPSON DISTRIBUTING CO INC
3227 Seneca St (45044-7755)
PHONE.................................513 422-9011
Clark L Thompson, *President*
EMP: 3
SALES (est): 169K **Privately Held**
SIC: 3582 Drycleaning equipment & machinery, commercial

(G-14089)
TOMSON STEEL COMPANY
1400 Made Industrial Dr (45044-8936)
P.O. Box 940 (45044-0940)
PHONE.................................513 420-8600
Fax: 513 420-8610
Stephen Lutz, *President*
Larry L Knapp, *Principal*
Thomas Lutz, *Vice Pres*
Steve Reynolds, *Plant Mgr*
Jim Strok, *VP Sales*
EMP: 25
SQ FT: 94,000
SALES (est): 25.1MM **Privately Held**
WEB: www.tomsonsteel.com
SIC: 5051 3291 Metals service centers & offices; abrasive metal & steel products

(G-14090)
TRI TECHNOLOGIES INC
1300 Lafayette Ave (45044-5913)
PHONE.................................513 422-1300
Audrey M Dyer, *President*
David Dyer, *Vice Pres*
David Hirsch, *Vice Pres*

EMP: 10 EST: 1962
SQ FT: 15,000
SALES: 900K **Privately Held**
WEB: www.tritechnologies.com
SIC: 3559 Plastics working machinery

(G-14091)
UNBRIDLED BREWING COMPANY LLC
Also Called: Figleaf Brewing Company
3387 Cincinnati Dayton Rd (45044-8905)
PHONE.................................937 361-2573
Brian Yavorsky,
Andrew Allgeyer,
Tasha Brown,
Paul Jeff Fortney,
EMP: 12
SQ FT: 8,400
SALES (est): 438.8K **Privately Held**
SIC: 2082 Beer (alcoholic beverage)

(G-14092)
UNITED LUBRICANTS CORPORATION
3431 Yankee Rd (45044-8931)
PHONE.................................513 422-9600
Fax: 513 705-1150
Michael F Barry, *President*
D Jeffry Benoliel, *Corp Secy*
Craig E Bush, *Vice Pres*
Patrick J Piccioni, *Vice Pres*
Sean Tolbert, *Mfg Dir*
EMP: 60 EST: 1974
SQ FT: 12,000
SALES (est): 9.8MM
SALES (corp-wide): 746.6MM **Publicly Held**
WEB: www.unitedlubricants.com
SIC: 2992 2899 Lubricating oils & greases; cutting oils, blending: made from purchased materials; chemical preparations; rust resisting compounds; water treating compounds
PA: Quaker Chemical Corporation
901 E Hector St
Conshohocken PA 19428
610 832-4000

(G-14093)
VAIL RUBBER WORKS INC
Also Called: Midwest Service
605 Clark St (45042-2117)
PHONE.................................513 705-2060
Bruce Barger, *Project Mgr*
Henry Lykins, *Project Mgr*
Donald Bown, *Branch Mgr*
EMP: 18
SALES (corp-wide): 17.6MM **Privately Held**
WEB: www.vailrubber.com
SIC: 3554 Paper industries machinery
PA: Vail Rubber Works, Inc.
521 Langley Ave
Saint Joseph MI 49085
877 350-0441

(G-14094)
VANDERPOOL MOTOR SPORTS
6315 Howe Rd (45042-1657)
PHONE.................................513 424-2166
Daniel Vanderpool, *Owner*
EMP: 5
SALES (est): 304.8K **Privately Held**
SIC: 3714 Motor vehicle engines & parts

(G-14095)
WATSON GRAVEL INC
2100 S Main St (45044-7345)
PHONE.................................513 422-3781
Ron Price, *Manager*
EMP: 20
SALES (corp-wide): 15.7MM **Privately Held**
SIC: 1442 Gravel mining
PA: Watson Gravel, Inc.
2728 Hamilton Cleves Rd
Hamilton OH 45013
513 863-0070

(G-14096)
WAUSAU PAPER CORP
Also Called: Wausau Mosinee Paper
700 Columbia Ave (45042-1931)
PHONE.................................513 217-3623
Dick Early, *Vice Pres*
Raymond Lighthart, *Vice Pres*

Jim McDonnell, *Vice Pres*
John Wells, *VP Opers*
Melissa Wells, *Purchasing*
EMP: 200
SALES (corp-wide): 13.2B **Privately Held**
SIC: 2621 Paper mills
HQ: Wausau Paper Corp.
100 Paper Pl
Kronenwetter WI 54455
715 693-4470

(G-14097)
WAUSAU PPR TOWEL & TISSUE LLC
700 Columbia Ave (45042-1931)
PHONE.................................513 424-2999
Daniel Olvley, *Div Sub Head*
Pat Bradley, *Manager*
EMP: 220
SALES (corp-wide): 13.2B **Privately Held**
SIC: 2621 2676 Towels, tissues & napkins: paper & stock; sanitary paper products
HQ: Wausau Paper Towel & Tissue Llc
1150 Industry Rd
Harrodsburg KY 40330
859 734-0538

(G-14098)
WHITT MACHINE INC
806 Central Ave (45044-1718)
PHONE.................................513 423-7624
Fax: 513 423-7634
Dean Whitt, *President*
Wendy Whitt, *Vice Pres*
Angie Snarski, *Treasurer*
EMP: 15
SQ FT: 35,000
SALES: 1.2MM **Privately Held**
SIC: 3599 7692 Machine shop, jobbing & repair; welding repair

(G-14099)
WIKOFF COLOR CORPORATION
1330 Hook Dr (45042-1712)
PHONE.................................513 423-0727
Fax: 513 423-0729
Bill Dishman, *Sales/Mktg Mgr*
Graham Skinner, *Manager*
Janice Kolker, *Info Tech Dir*
EMP: 9
SQ FT: 3,600
SALES (corp-wide): 152.7MM **Privately Held**
WEB: www.wikoff.com
SIC: 2893 Printing ink
PA: Wikoff Color Corporation
1886 Merritt Rd
Fort Mill SC 29715
803 548-2210

(G-14100)
WORTHINGTON STEEL COMPANY
1501 Made Dr (45044-8938)
PHONE.................................513 702-0130
Tim Glaab, *Branch Mgr*
EMP: 4
SALES (corp-wide): 2.8B **Publicly Held**
SIC: 5051 3444 Steel; sheet metalwork
HQ: The Worthington Steel Company
200 W Old Wilson Bridge Rd
Worthington OH 43085
614 438-3210

Middletown
Warren County

(G-14101)
BARRETT PAVING MATERIALS INC
3751 Commerce Dr (45005-5234)
PHONE.................................513 271-6200
Fax: 937 279-3205
Jerry Bushelman, *Division Mgr*
Rod Russell, *Regional Mgr*
Tony Strete, *Financial Exec*
Janice Misch, *Human Res Mgr*
Missy Herrmann, *Human Resources*
EMP: 200

SALES (corp-wide): 77.1MM **Privately Held**
WEB: www.barrettpaving.com
SIC: 5032 2951 1771 1611 Asphalt mixture; asphalt paving mixtures & blocks; driveway, parking lot & blacktop contractors; surfacing & paving; construction sand & gravel
HQ: Barrett Paving Materials Inc.
3 Becker Farm Rd Ste 307
Roseland NJ 07068
973 533-1001

(G-14102)
NL MFG & DISTRIBUTION SYS IN
6107 Market Ave (45005-5238)
PHONE..................................513 422-5216
Tom Frederick, *Principal*
▲ **EMP:** 8
SALES (est): 1.1MM **Privately Held**
SIC: 3999 Manufacturing industries

Midvale
Tuscarawas County

(G-14103)
ALTERNTIVE SPPORT APPRATUS LLC
5609 Gundy Dr (44653)
P.O. Box 556 (44653-0556)
PHONE..................................740 922-2727
Erica Wright, *Info Tech Mgr*
Mark Natoli,
Cheryl Price,
Kurt Shelley,
EMP: 3
SQ FT: 10,000
SALES (est): 538.9K **Privately Held**
WEB: www.asap911.com
SIC: 3713 Ambulance bodies

(G-14104)
AMERICAN BOTTLING COMPANY
Also Called: 7 Up Bottling Co
Old Rte 250 (44653)
P.O. Box 535 (44653-0535)
PHONE..................................740 922-5253
Nick Kazocoff, *Manager*
EMP: 35
SALES (corp-wide): 6.4B **Publicly Held**
WEB: www.cs-americas.com
SIC: 2086 Bottled & canned soft drinks
HQ: The American Bottling Company
5301 Legacy Dr
Plano TX 75024

(G-14105)
AMKO SERVICE COMPANY (HQ)
Also Called: Dover Cryogenics
3211 Brightwood Rd (44653)
P.O. Box 280 (44653-0280)
PHONE..................................330 364-8857
Darren Nippard, *President*
Duane R Yant, *Principal*
Tim Johnson, *Purch Mgr*
Gordon Wheating, *Purchasing*
Andrew Lee, *Manager*
▲ **EMP:** 50 **EST:** 1965
SALES (est): 7.9MM
SALES (corp-wide): 10.5B **Publicly Held**
SIC: 7699 3443 7629 Tank repair & cleaning services; cryogenic tanks, for liquids & gases; electrical repair shops
PA: Praxair, Inc.
10 Riverview Dr
Danbury CT 06810
203 837-2000

(G-14106)
DOVER CONVEYOR INC
3323 Brightwood Rd (44653)
P.O. Box 300 (44653-0300)
PHONE..................................740 922-9390
Joseph Coniglio, *President*
Tim Frank, *Project Engr*
Cheryl Coniglio, *Controller*
EMP: 25
SQ FT: 40,000

SALES (est): 6.6MM **Privately Held**
WEB: www.doverconveyor.com
SIC: 3535 3441 3532 Conveyors & conveying equipment; fabricated structural metal; cages, mine shaft

(G-14107)
FIBA TECHNOLOGIES INC
Also Called: Amko Service Company
3211 Brightwood Rd (44653)
P.O. Box 280 (44653-0280)
PHONE..................................330 602-7300
David Ohl, *Branch Mgr*
EMP: 55
SALES (corp-wide): 77.5MM **Privately Held**
SIC: 3443 Cryogenic tanks, for liquids & gases
PA: Fiba Technologies, Inc.
53 Ayer Rd
Littleton MA 01460
508 887-7100

(G-14108)
HYDRAULIC SPECIALISTS INC
5655 Gundy Dr (44653)
P.O. Box 500 (44653-0500)
PHONE..................................740 922-3343
Dale Burkholder, *President*
Laraine Burkholder, *Corp Secy*
EMP: 25
SQ FT: 15,000
SALES (est): 3.7MM **Privately Held**
SIC: 3443 7699 3593 Industrial vessels, tanks & containers; hydraulic equipment repair; fluid power cylinders & actuators

(G-14109)
MAINTENANCE REPAIR SUPPLY INC
Also Called: Convertapax
5539 Gundy Dr (44653)
P.O. Box 540 (44653-0540)
PHONE..................................740 922-3006
Fax: 740 922-5716
Brad Mathias, *President*
Kenny Weber, *Sales Executive*
Dawn Burney, *Office Mgr*
▲ **EMP:** 20
SQ FT: 48,000
SALES (est): 6.7MM **Privately Held**
WEB: www.m-r-sinc.com
SIC: 5085 2821 5084 Industrial supplies; polyesters; plastic products machinery

---

Milan
Erie County

(G-14110)
CERTAINTEED CORPORATION
11519 Us Highway 250 N (44846-9708)
PHONE..................................419 499-2581
Fax: 419 499-4074
C Rentz, *Purchasing*
Pat Lewis, *Human Res Dir*
Mark Bayley, *Sales Mgr*
Mark Hyde, *Manager*
EMP: 247
SALES (corp-wide): 185.8MM **Privately Held**
WEB: www.certainteed.net
SIC: 2952 Asphalt felts & coatings
HQ: Certainteed Corporation
20 Moores Rd
Malvern PA 19355
610 893-5000

(G-14111)
EDISON SOLAR INC
3809 State Route 113 E (44846-9430)
PHONE..................................419 499-0000
David Miller, *President*
EMP: 10
SALES (est): 1.5MM **Privately Held**
SIC: 3585 1711 Heating equipment, complete; solar energy contractor

(G-14112)
HEMCO INC
Also Called: Bay Manufacturing
1413 State Route 113 E (44846-9527)
P.O. Box 1250 (44846-1250)
PHONE..................................419 499-4602

Fax: 419 499-4603
Michael J Mc Guire, *President*
Joyce Mc Guire, *Corp Secy*
Cheryl Graziani, *Purchasing*
▲ **EMP:** 4
SQ FT: 20,000
SALES (est): 621.9K **Privately Held**
WEB: www.baymfg.com
SIC: 3519 Outboard motors; parts & accessories, internal combustion engines

(G-14113)
JASON INCORPORATED
Janesville-Sackner Group
12406 Us Rte 250 (44846)
P.O. Box 349, Norwalk (44857-0349)
PHONE..................................419 668-4474
Fax: 419 668-6401
David Cataldi, *CEO*
James Schultz, *Principal*
Joel Mersereau, *Purchasing*
Duane Beal, *Controller*
Kevin Dow, *Manager*
EMP: 53
SQ FT: 2,000
SALES (corp-wide): 705.5MM **Publicly Held**
WEB: www.jasoninc.com
SIC: 3086 Insulation or cushioning material, foamed plastic
HQ: Jason Incorporated
411 E Wisconsin Ave
Milwaukee WI 53202
414 277-9300

(G-14114)
JOHNS MANVILLE CORPORATION
49 Lockwood Rd (44846-9734)
PHONE..................................419 499-1400
Brian Keyser, *General Mgr*
EMP: 75
SALES (corp-wide): 223.6B **Publicly Held**
SIC: 2952 Asphalt felts & coatings
HQ: Johns Manville Corporation
717 17th St Ste 800
Denver CO 80202
303 978-2000

(G-14115)
PULLMAN COMPANY
Also Called: Tenneco
33 Lockwood Rd (44846-9734)
PHONE..................................419 499-2541
Pat Payne, *Production*
James Adkins, *Engineer*
James La Salle, *Engineer*
Robert Maracic, *Engineer*
Tim Mcllrath, *Design Engr*
EMP: 50
SALES (corp-wide): 8.6B **Publicly Held**
WEB: www.tenneco-automotive.com
SIC: 3714 Shock absorbers, motor vehicle
HQ: The Pullman Company
1 International Dr
Monroe MI 48161
734 243-8000

(G-14116)
SCHLESSMAN SEED CO (PA)
11513 Us Highway 250 N (44846-9708)
PHONE..................................419 499-2572
Fax: 419 499-2574
Daryl Deering, *Ch of Bd*
Vicki Zorn, *Plant Mgr*
David Schlessman, *CFO*
Dave Herzer, *Treasurer*
Mark Skaggs, *Controller*
EMP: 25 **EST:** 1915
SQ FT: 100,000
SALES (est): 21.3MM **Privately Held**
WEB: www.schlessman-seed.com
SIC: 5191 2075 0723 0116 Seeds: field, garden & flower; soybean oil mills; crop preparation services for market; soybeans; corn; wheat

(G-14117)
TRADITIONAL MARBLE & GRAN LTD
10105 Us Highway 250 N (44846-9570)
PHONE..................................419 625-3966
Albert T Gasparini, *President*
Deanna Adams, *Admin Asst*
▲ **EMP:** 12

SQ FT: 12,000
SALES (est): 1.4MM **Privately Held**
WEB: www.traditionalmarblengranite.com
SIC: 3281 Cut stone & stone products

Milford
Clermont County

(G-14118)
3M COMPANY
910 Lila Ave (45150-1631)
PHONE..................................513 248-1749
Cindy Lamping, *Purch Dir*
Beth Gramza, *Branch Mgr*
Ed Weaver, *Associate*
EMP: 324
SALES (corp-wide): 30.1B **Publicly Held**
SIC: 3841 Surgical instruments & apparatus
PA: 3m Company
3m Center Bldg 22011w02
Saint Paul MN 55144
651 733-1110

(G-14119)
AB PLASTICS INC
1287 Us Route 50 (45150-9688)
PHONE..................................513 576-6333
Fax: 513 576-8733
Robert Basile, *President*
Kimberlee Basile, *Controller*
Kim Basille, *Admin Sec*
EMP: 9
SQ FT: 5,000
SALES (est): 1.9MM **Privately Held**
WEB: www.ab-plastics.com
SIC: 3089 Plastic & fiberglass tanks; ducting, plastic; plastic hardware & building products

(G-14120)
AMERICAN INSULATION TECH LLC
6071 Branch Hill Guinea P (45150-1567)
PHONE..................................513 733-4248
Jerome Napier, *Mng Member*
EMP: 12
SALES (est): 796.2K **Privately Held**
SIC: 3296 3081 Fiberglass insulation; film base, cellulose acetate or nitrocellulose plastic

(G-14121)
APPLIED SYSTEMS INC
Also Called: Ivans Insurance Solutions
100 Techne Center Dr # 125 (45150-2780)
PHONE..................................513 943-0000
EMP: 20
SALES (corp-wide): 248MM **Privately Held**
SIC: 7371 7372 Computer software development & applications; prepackaged software
PA: Applied Systems, Inc.
200 Applied Pkwy
University Park IL 60484
708 534-5575

(G-14122)
ARCHITECTURAL ART GLASS STUDIO
5 Water St (45150-1133)
PHONE..................................513 731-7336
Richard Dunkin, *Owner*
EMP: 5
SQ FT: 3,700
SALES (est): 240.3K **Privately Held**
WEB: www.architecturalartglass.net
SIC: 7699 3231 Customizing services; stained glass: made from purchased glass

(G-14123)
B & D MACHINISTS INC
1350 Us Route 50 (45150-9205)
PHONE..................................513 831-8588
Fax: 513 831-8699
Tonson Boone Jr, *President*
Velma Boone, *Corp Secy*
Gary W Boone, *Vice Pres*
Steven Boone, *Vice Pres*
EMP: 11
SQ FT: 16,000

▲ = Import ▼ = Export
◆ = Import/Export

SALES: 1.2MM **Privately Held**
SIC: 3599 Machine shop, jobbing & repair

(G-14124)
BEARING PRECIOUS SEED (PA)
1369 Woodville Pike B (45150-2260)
PHONE.................................513 575-1706
Fax: 513 575-1791
William Duttry, *President*
Stephen Zeinner, *Director*
▼ **EMP:** 6
SALES (est): 2MM **Privately Held**
SIC: 2731 Books: publishing & printing

(G-14125)
BECK STUDIOS INC
1001 Tech Dr (45150-9780)
PHONE.................................513 831-6650
Fax: 513 831-6681
Dan L Ilhardt, *President*
Luann Schott, *General Mgr*
Matthew Mullen, *Vice Pres*
Cathie Haverkamp, *Admin Sec*
Luann Schatt, *Admin Asst*
EMP: 20
SQ FT: 9,000
SALES: 4.9MM **Privately Held**
WEB: www.beckstudios.com
SIC: 1799 3999 Rigging, theatrical; stage hardware & equipment, except lighting; theatrical scenery

(G-14126)
BKHN INC
Also Called: Buckhorn
55 W Techne Center Dr (45150-8901)
PHONE.................................513 831-4402
Bill Tonachio, *General Mgr*
Greg Stodnick, *Treasurer*
Milton I Wiskind, *Admin Sec*
EMP: 68
SQ FT: 29,000
SALES (est): 9.3MM
SALES (corp-wide): 558MM **Publicly Held**
WEB: www.buckhorninc.com
SIC: 3089 Plastic containers, except foam
HQ: Buckhorn Inc.
55 W Techne Center Dr A
Milford OH 45150
513 831-4402

(G-14127)
BREWER COMPANY (PA)
Also Called: Brewercote
1354 Us Route 50 (45150-9205)
PHONE.................................800 394-0017
Fax: 513 576-1414
Pinckney W Brewer, *President*
Michael T Dooley, *Vice Pres*
Gail Menzel, *Hum Res Coord*
Thomas P Matlock, *VP Sales*
Dan Massman, *Sales Mgr*
▲ **EMP:** 8
SQ FT: 8,000
SALES: 50MM **Privately Held**
WEB: www.thebrewerco.com
SIC: 2952 0782 2951 Coating compounds, tar; roofing materials; seeding services, lawn; turf installation services, except artificial; asphalt paving mixtures & blocks

(G-14128)
BUCKHORN INC (HQ)
55 W Techne Center Dr A (45150-9779)
PHONE.................................513 831-4402
Fax: 513 831-5474
Kirk Pinto, *District Mgr*
Joel Grant, *Senior VP*
Clyde C Allen, *Opers Staff*
Matt Gerstner, *Opers Staff*
Bill Snyder, *QA Dir*
◆ **EMP:** 37
SQ FT: 19,000
SALES (est): 101.4MM
SALES (corp-wide): 558MM **Publicly Held**
WEB: www.buckhorninc.com
SIC: 3089 Plastic containers, except foam
PA: Myers Industries, Inc.
1293 S Main St
Akron OH 44301
330 253-5592

(G-14129)
BUCKHORN MATERIAL HDLG GROUP
Also Called: Nestier
55 W Techne Center Dr A (45150-9779)
PHONE.................................513 831-4402
Bill Tonachio, *President*
Greg Stodnick, *Treasurer*
Tom Weber, *Controller*
Milt Wiskind, *Admin Sec*
▼ **EMP:** 68
SQ FT: 29,000
SALES (est): 17.2MM
SALES (corp-wide): 558MM **Publicly Held**
SIC: 3089 Plastic containers, except foam
PA: Myers Industries, Inc.
1293 S Main St
Akron OH 44301
330 253-5592

(G-14130)
CINCY SAFE COMPANY
1607 State Route 131 (45150-2667)
PHONE.................................513 900-9152
Fax: 513 793-5227
Gary Krug, *President*
EMP: 20
SQ FT: 12,400
SALES (est): 3.2MM **Privately Held**
SIC: 3499 Safes & vaults, metal

(G-14131)
COMBINED INDUSTRIAL SOLUTIONS
944 Klondyke Rd (45150-9683)
PHONE.................................513 659-3091
Dwayne Dixie, *Owner*
EMP: 5
SALES: 300K **Privately Held**
SIC: 3599 Industrial machinery

(G-14132)
COMCO MACHINERY INC
Also Called: Comco Machnry
910 Lila Ave (45150-1631)
PHONE.................................513 248-8000
Fax: 513 248-8406
Mark L Herrmann, *President*
John Schultz, *Vice Pres*
Otto Kircher, *QC Dir*
Shari Hobek, *Personnel Exec*
Tim Beitz, *Prgrmr*
EMP: 170
SQ FT: 70,000
SALES: 5MM **Privately Held**
SIC: 3555 3554 Printing trades machinery; paper industries machinery

(G-14133)
CONTROL WORKS INC
400 Techne Center Dr # 104 (45150-2746)
PHONE.................................513 831-9959
Fax: 513 831-3549
Douglas Strief, *President*
Catherine Strief, *Corp Secy*
EMP: 40
SQ FT: 20,000
SALES (est): 5.1MM **Privately Held**
WEB: www.controlworksinc.com
SIC: 3613 3823 3699 3625 Control panels, electric; industrial instrmnts msrmnt display/control process variable; electrical equipment & supplies; relays & industrial controls

(G-14134)
CONVEYOR TECHNOLOGIES LTD
501 Techne Center Dr B (45150-2772)
PHONE.................................513 248-0663
Charles Mitchell, *President*
Tim Mitchell, *Vice Pres*
Tony Mitchell, *Vice Pres*
William Sutter, *Info Tech Dir*
EMP: 8
SQ FT: 7,000
SALES (est): 1.5MM **Privately Held**
WEB: www.conveyortechltd.com
SIC: 3535 Conveyors & conveying equipment

(G-14135)
CUSTOM BUILT CRATES INC
1700 Victory Park Dr (45150-1812)
PHONE.................................513 248-4422
Glen Brandenburg, *President*
Eric Douglas Bradenburg, *Vice Pres*
Bobbie Bradenburg, *Office Mgr*
Nathan Utter, *Business Dir*
EMP: 20
SALES (est): 4.5MM **Privately Held**
SIC: 4213 2449 7389 Trucking, except local; rectangular boxes & crates, wood;

(G-14136)
DEX-CUT TOOLS
71 Powhatton Dr (45150-1661)
P.O. Box 441 (45150-0441)
PHONE.................................513 248-9898
Craig Benhase, *Principal*
EMP: 7
SALES (est): 787.8K **Privately Held**
SIC: 3599 Machine shop, jobbing & repair

(G-14137)
DIGIMAX SIGNS
759 Us Route 50 (45150-9510)
PHONE.................................513 576-0747
Rick Seissiger, *President*
EMP: 3
SALES (est): 318.6K **Privately Held**
WEB: www.digimaxsigns.com
SIC: 3993 Signs & advertising specialties

(G-14138)
DOWNING DISPLAYS INC (PA)
550 Techne Center Dr (45150-2763)
PHONE.................................513 248-9800
Fax: 513 248-2605
Michael J Scherer, *President*
Catherine H Downing, *Principal*
Wesley Jacobs, *Vice Pres*
Peter O Toole, *Vice Pres*
Greg Ward, *Vice Pres*
▲ **EMP:** 65 **EST:** 1967
SQ FT: 110,000
SALES (est): 18.8MM **Privately Held**
WEB: www.downingdisplays.com
SIC: 3993 Signs & advertising specialties

(G-14139)
EPS WASTEWATER LLC
601 Brooklyn Ave Ste B (45150-1447)
PHONE.................................859 689-4300
Tim Fitzgerald, *Managing Prtnr*
Glenn Harbold, *General Mgr*
EMP: 8
SALES (est): 1.6MM **Privately Held**
SIC: 3589 Water treatment equipment, industrial

(G-14140)
EVOQUA WATER TECHNOLOGIES LLC
Also Called: U S Filter/Envirex
2002 Ford Cir Ste F (45150-2748)
P.O. Box 1604, Waukesha WI (53187-1604)
PHONE.................................262 521-8352
Ernest Downs, *Manager*
EMP: 8
SALES (corp-wide): 1.2B **Privately Held**
SIC: 3589 Sewage & water treatment equipment; water treatment equipment, industrial; sewage treatment equipment
HQ: Evoqua Water Technologies Llc
181 Thorn Hill Rd
Warrendale PA 15086
724 772-0044

(G-14141)
FLUID CONSERVATION SYSTEMS (DH)
Also Called: Fcs
502 Techne Center Dr B (45150-8780)
PHONE.................................513 831-9335
Fax: 513 831-9336
Andrew Richardson, *Ch of Bd*
Neal Summers, *President*
Deborah Savage, *Controller*
Teresa Fischer, *Manager*
Julie Platton, *Admin Asst*
EMP: 11
SQ FT: 4,500

SALES (est): 1.1MM
SALES (corp-wide): 1.1B **Privately Held**
WEB: www.fluidconservation.com
SIC: 3599 7389 3812 Water leak detectors; inspection & testing services; search & navigation equipment
HQ: Halma Holdings Inc.
11500 Northlake Dr # 306
Cincinnati OH 45249
513 772-5501

(G-14142)
FOUNTAIN SPECIALISTS INC
226 Main St (45150-1124)
PHONE.................................513 831-5717
Fax: 513 831-0096
Lois Sedacca, *President*
Mark Sedacca, *Vice Pres*
EMP: 8 **EST:** 1960
SQ FT: 5,000
SALES (est): 710K **Privately Held**
SIC: 5261 3272 3499 3089 Fountains, outdoor; fountains, concrete; fountains (except drinking), metal; plastic processing; lighting, lamps & accessories; pumps & pumping equipment

(G-14143)
GANNETT STLLITE INFO NTWRK INC
Also Called: Enquirer, The
200 Techne Center Dr # 206 (45150-2790)
PHONE.................................513 576-1800
EMP: 4
SALES (corp-wide): 3B **Publicly Held**
WEB: www.usatoday.com
SIC: 2711 Newspapers
HQ: Gannett Satellite Information Network, Llc
7950 Jones Branch Dr
Mc Lean VA 22102
703 854-6000

(G-14144)
GOLDEN SIGNS AND LIGHTING LLC
120-150 Olympic Rd (45150)
PHONE.................................513 248-0895
Harold Golden, *Owner*
EMP: 3
SALES (est): 284.3K **Privately Held**
SIC: 3993 Signs & advertising specialties

(G-14145)
GOOD BEANS COFFEE ROASTERS LLC
1381 Cottonwood Dr (45150-2455)
PHONE.................................513 310-9516
Chris Bean, *Principal*
EMP: 3 **EST:** 2015
SALES (est): 123.1K **Privately Held**
SIC: 2095 Roasted coffee

(G-14146)
GORDON BERNARD CO INC
22 Whitney Dr (45150-9781)
PHONE.................................513 248-7600
Robert Sherman Jr, *President*
EMP: 45
SQ FT: 25,000
SALES (est): 5.1MM **Privately Held**
SIC: 5199 2752 2741 Calendars; commercial printing, lithographic; miscellaneous publishing

(G-14147)
GORDON BERNARD COMPANY LLC
22 Whitney Dr (45150-9781)
PHONE.................................513 248-7600
Fax: 513 248-7606
Leon Lovette, *Regional Mgr*
Bo Sherman, *Vice Pres*
Tom Compton, *Finance Mgr*
Clair Pardue, *Bookkeeper*
Kathy Kluska, *Human Res Dir*
EMP: 50
SALES (est): 7.7MM **Privately Held**
WEB: www.gordonbernard.com
SIC: 2752 7371 2759 2741 Commercial printing, lithographic; calendar & card printing, lithographic; custom computer programming services; commercial printing; miscellaneous publishing

(G-14148)
GREGG MACMILLAN
Also Called: Macmillan Graphics
2002 Ford Cir Ste A (45150-2748)
PHONE..................................513 248-2121
Fax: 513 248-5141
Gregg J Macmillan, CEO
Gregg Macmillan, Owner
EMP: 8
SQ FT: 4,000
SALES (est): 494.7K Privately Held
WEB: www.macgra.com
SIC: 2752 7336 Commercial printing, litho-
graphic; graphic arts & related design

(G-14149)
H & H OF MILFORD OHIO LLC
1194 Wintercrest Cir (45150-2600)
PHONE..................................513 576-9004
Mark Hartwell, President
▲ EMP: 5
SQ FT: 10,000
SALES: 1.2MM Privately Held
SIC: 5092 3949 Playing cards; sporting &
athletic goods

(G-14150)
HASON USA CORP
1262 Us Highway 50 (45150-9767)
PHONE..................................513 248-0287
Dennis Blain, Principal
Michael O'Keefe, Controller
EMP: 25 EST: 2014
SALES (est): 6.4MM Privately Held
SIC: 3443 Tanks, standard or custom fabri-
cated: metal plate

(G-14151)
HYDRO SYSTEMS COMPANY
401 Milford Pkwy (45150-1298)
PHONE..................................513 271-8800
Joe Stamter, Manager
EMP: 5
SALES (corp-wide): 6.7B Publicly Held
SIC: 3586 Measuring & dispensing pumps
HQ: Hydro Systems Company
3798 Round Bottom Rd
Cincinnati OH 45244

(G-14152)
**INTELLIGENT BIOMETRIC
CONTROLS**
601 Brooklyn Ave Ste A (45150-1447)
PHONE..................................513 239-6322
Scott Bosley, President
Dan Falk, Principal
Daniel Falk, Vice Pres
EMP: 7
SALES (est): 560K Privately Held
SIC: 3699 Security control equipment &
systems

(G-14153)
**INTERNATIONAL PAPER
COMPANY**
5806 Jeb Stuart Dr (45150-2117)
P.O. Box 788 (45150-0788)
PHONE..................................877 447-2737
EMP: 277
SALES (corp-wide): 21B Publicly Held
WEB: www.internationalpaper.com
SIC: 2621 Paper mills
PA: International Paper Company
6400 Poplar Ave
Memphis TN 38197
901 419-9000

(G-14154)
INTERPLEX MEDICAL LLC
25 Whitney Dr Ste 114 (45150-8400)
PHONE..................................513 248-5120
Fax: 513 248-5124
Craig Berky, General Mgr
Karen G Granik, Mng Member
EMP: 24
SALES (est): 4.4MM Privately Held
WEB: www.interplexmedical.com
SIC: 3842 Grafts, artificial: for surgery

(G-14155)
JAMES G MOREHOUSE
Also Called: Morehouse Welding
4814a Woodlawn Dr (45150-9735)
PHONE..................................513 752-2236
Fax: 513 752-3769

James Morehouse, Owner
EMP: 5
SQ FT: 1,200
SALES (est): 258.5K Privately Held
SIC: 7692 Welding repair

(G-14156)
JEFF PENDERGRASS
Also Called: Titan Chemical
6037 Mill Row Ct (45150-2258)
PHONE..................................513 575-1226
Jeff Pendergrass, Owner
EMP: 3
SALES: 52.7K Privately Held
SIC: 2899 5087 5169 5999 Chemical
preparations; carpet & rug cleaning equip-
ment & supplies, commercial; detergents
& soaps, except specialty cleaning; clean-
ing equipment & supplies;

(G-14157)
JOURNEY SYSTEMS LLC (PA)
25 Whitney Dr Ste 100 (45150-8400)
PHONE..................................513 831-6200
John L Whittley, CEO
Nancy Whittley, Manager
Justin Heard, Technology
Richard Graham,
Nancy C Whittley,
EMP: 14
SQ FT: 9,875
SALES (est): 1.3MM Privately Held
SIC: 3571 5045 5734 Electronic comput-
ers; computers, peripherals & software;
computer software; computer & software
stores; computer software & accessories

(G-14158)
**KANAWHA SCALES & SYSTEMS
INC**
26 Whitney Dr (45150-9783)
PHONE..................................513 576-0700
James Bradbury, President
EMP: 19
SALES (corp-wide): 51.1MM Privately
Held
SIC: 5046 7699 3822 3596 Scales, ex-
cept laboratory; scale repair service; auto
controls regulating residntl & coml envi-
ronmt & applncs; scales & balances, ex-
cept laboratory
PA: Kanawha Scales & Systems, Inc.
111 Jacobson Dr
Poca WV 25159
304 755-8321

(G-14159)
LORE INC
5526 Garrett Dr (45150-2824)
PHONE..................................513 969-8481
Igor Haheu, Principal
EMP: 3
SALES (est): 86.7K Privately Held
SIC: 2711 Newspapers

(G-14160)
**MARTIN BAUDER
WOODWORKING LLC**
1498 Binning Rd (45150-9113)
PHONE..................................513 735-0659
Martin Bauder, Principal
EMP: 4
SALES (est): 246.6K Privately Held
SIC: 2431 Millwork

(G-14161)
MELINK CORPORATION (PA)
5140 River Valley Rd (45150-9108)
PHONE..................................513 685-0958
Fax: 513 965-7350
Stephen K Melink, President
Donna Jones, Vice Pres
Luci Feie, Marketing Mgr
Jennifer Sivak, Marketing Staff
Amanda Ford, Officer
EMP: 12
SQ FT: 36,000
SALES (est): 19.7MM Privately Held
WEB: www.melinkcorp.com
SIC: 8711 8748 3822 Heating & ventila-
tion engineering; energy conservation
consultant; appliance controls except air-
conditioning & refrigeration

(G-14162)
MILFORD PRINTERS (PA)
317 Main St (45150-1125)
P.O. Box 674 (45150-0674)
PHONE..................................513 831-6630
Fax: 513 248-4023
Robert M Heichel, Owner
Jenny Grosse, General Mgr
Ron Woodruff, General Mgr
Randy Mosley, Prdtn Mgr
EMP: 20
SQ FT: 8,000
SALES (est): 2.3MM Privately Held
WEB: www.milfordprinters.com
SIC: 2752 Commercial printing, offset; lith-
ographing on metal

(G-14163)
MILFORD PRINTERS
18 Locust St (45150-1024)
PHONE..................................513 831-6630
Ron Woodruff, Manager
EMP: 3
SALES (corp-wide): 2.3MM Privately
Held
WEB: www.milfordprinters.com
SIC: 2752 Commercial printing, offset
PA: Milford Printers
317 Main St
Milford OH 45150
513 831-6630

(G-14164)
**MOTOR SYSTEMS
INCORPORATED**
Also Called: MSI
460 Milford Pkwy (45150-9104)
PHONE..................................513 576-1725
Fax: 513 576-1915
Fred Daniel Freshley, President
Kevin Salm, President
Bev Walsh, Sales Staff
John Albrecht, Technology
EMP: 32
SQ FT: 16,000
SALES (est): 9.9MM Privately Held
WEB: www.motorsystems.com
SIC: 3569 Robots, assembly line: industrial
& commercial

(G-14165)
**OVERHOFF TECHNOLOGY
CORP**
1160 Us Route 50 (45150-9517)
P.O. Box 182 (45150-0182)
PHONE..................................513 248-2400
Fax: 513 248-2402
Robert Goldstein, President
Jim Campbell, Controller
EMP: 14
SQ FT: 8,000
SALES (est): 3MM Privately Held
WEB: www.overhoff.com
SIC: 3829 3823 Nuclear instrument mod-
ules; controllers for process variables, all
types
PA: U.S. Nuclear Corp.
7051 Eton Ave
Canoga Park CA 91303
818 296-0746

(G-14166)
**PARKER-HANNIFIN
CORPORATION**
Also Called: Electromechanical North Amer
50 W Techne Center Dr H (45150-8403)
PHONE..................................513 831-2340
Kenneth Sweet, Branch Mgr
Burleigh Bailey, Manager
EMP: 75
SALES (corp-wide): 11.3B Publicly Held
WEB: www.parker.com
SIC: 3577 7371 3575 3571 Computer
peripheral equipment; computer software
development; computer terminals; elec-
tronic computers
PA: Parker-Hannifin Corporation
6035 Parkland Blvd
Cleveland OH 44124
216 896-3000

(G-14167)
PPG INDUSTRIES INC
Also Called: P P G
500 Techne Center Dr (45150-2763)
PHONE..................................513 576-0360
Greg Wagner, Manager
Angie Maly, Manager
EMP: 50
SALES (corp-wide): 14.7B Publicly Held
WEB: www.ppg.com
SIC: 2851 Shellac (protective coating)
PA: Ppg Industries, Inc.
1 Ppg Pl
Pittsburgh PA 15272
412 434-3131

(G-14168)
PPG INDUSTRIES INC
500 Techne Center Dr (45150-2763)
PHONE..................................513 576-3100
Eckhardt Pohl, Branch Mgr
David Kuhns, Manager
EMP: 24
SALES (corp-wide): 14.7B Publicly Held
WEB: www.ppg.com
SIC: 2851 Paints & allied products
PA: Ppg Industries, Inc.
1 Ppg Pl
Pittsburgh PA 15272
412 434-3131

(G-14169)
**REDI ROCK STRUCTURES OKI
LLC**
1050 Round Bottom Rd (45150-9740)
PHONE..................................513 965-9221
Kenny Swanson, Sales Staff
Josh Turton, Sales Staff
Tim Turton, Mng Member
EMP: 6
SALES (est): 490K Privately Held
SIC: 3272 Floor slabs & tiles, precast con-
crete

(G-14170)
**REMINGTON ENGRG
MACHINING INC**
5105 River Valley Rd (45150-9117)
PHONE..................................513 965-8999
Dan Mallaley, President
Colin Stith, General Mgr
Valerie Mallaley, Corp Secy
Flo Flinders, Accountant
EMP: 6 EST: 1996
SQ FT: 2,500
SALES (est): 907.6K
SALES (corp-wide): 44.6MM Privately
Held
WEB: www.remingtonengineering.com
SIC: 3599 Machine & other job shop work
PA: Cold Jet, Llc
455 Wards Corner Rd # 100
Loveland OH 45140
513 831-3211

(G-14171)
S & S PALLETS
1536 Pointe Dr (45150-2695)
PHONE..................................513 967-7432
EMP: 4 EST: 2010
SALES (est): 386.2K Privately Held
SIC: 2448 Pallets, wood & wood with metal

(G-14172)
**SARDINIA CONCRETE
COMPANY (PA)**
911 Us Route 50 (45150-9703)
PHONE..................................513 248-0090
Fax: 513 248-1872
James Fraley, Managing Prtnr
Charlie T Stone, Vice Pres
Chad Kelley, QC Mgr
Chad Kelly, Engineer
Jerry Ziegelmeyer, Controller
EMP: 40
SQ FT: 12,500
SALES (est): 10.7MM Privately Held
SIC: 3273 Ready-mixed concrete

(G-14173)
SCHENCK PROCESS LLC
1000 Ford Cir Ste B (45150-2732)
PHONE..................................513 576-9200
Mike Brand, Engineer
Graham Cooper, Branch Mgr

EMP: 10 Privately Held
SIC: 3535 3564 5084 Pneumatic tube
conveyor systems; dust or fume collecting
equipment, industrial; pneumatic tools &
equipment
HQ: Schenck Process Llc
7901 Nw 107th Ter
Kansas City MO 64153
816 891-9300

(G-14174)
SIGN GRAPHICS & DESIGN
420 Main St Unit A (45150-1170)
PHONE....................................513 576-1639
Fax: 513 831-8134
K Scot Conover, Owner
EMP: 4
SALES (est): 170K Privately Held
WEB: www.signgraphics-design.com
SIC: 3993 Signs & advertising specialties

(G-14175)
STEPP SEWING SERVICE
927 State Route 28 Unit B (45150-1948)
PHONE....................................513 248-0822
Chris Stepp, Owner
EMP: 6
SQ FT: 1,200
SALES: 150K Privately Held
SIC: 2395 5651 Embroidery & art needle-
work; unisex clothing stores

(G-14176)
TACTICAL ENVMTL SYSTEMS INC
Also Called: T E S
1156 Us Route 50 (45150-9517)
PHONE....................................513 831-2663
Fax: 513 831-2675
Dillard Pegg Jr, President
Randel West, Vice Pres
Lynn West, Controller
Ronald Billiter, Manager
Melissa Wenczkowski, Manager
EMP: 4
SALES (est): 1.2MM Privately Held
WEB: www.tacticalsys.com
SIC: 3585 5075 Air conditioning equip-
ment, complete; air conditioning & ventila-
tion equipment & supplies

(G-14177)
TATA AMERICA INTL CORP
Also Called: Tata Consultancy Services
1000 Summit Dr Unit 1 (45150-2724)
PHONE....................................513 677-6500
Sumanta Roy, Regional Mgr
Vikas Gupta, Manager
Brian Purvis, Manager
Khizar Mahamad, Project Leader
Megha Lohana, Network Analyst
EMP: 300
SALES (corp-wide): 1.9B Privately Held
SIC: 7372 7373 7371 Prepackaged soft-
ware; computer integrated systems de-
sign; custom computer programming
services
HQ: Tata America International Corporation
101 Park Ave Rm 2603
New York NY 10178
212 557-8038

(G-14178)
TOOMEY INC
Also Called: Toomey Natural Foods
914 Lila Ave (45150-1631)
PHONE....................................513 831-4771
Mimi Toomey, President
J Patrick Toomey, President
EMP: 6
SQ FT: 2,400
SALES (est): 550K Privately Held
WEB: www.toomeynaturalfoods.com
SIC: 2023 Dietary supplements, dairy &
non-dairy based

(G-14179)
TRI-TECH MACHINING LLC
1885 Seven Lands Dr (45150-2668)
PHONE....................................513 575-3959
Timothy Crawford,
EMP: 5
SQ FT: 4,000

SALES: 275K Privately Held
SIC: 3821 1731 Laboratory equipment:
fume hoods, distillation racks, etc.; sound
equipment specialization

(G-14180)
TRIUMPH SIGNS & CONSULTING INC
480 Milford Pkwy (45150-9104)
PHONE....................................513 576-8090
William Downey, President
Nicolelynn Hyrne, Project Mgr
Sheri S Iker, Controller
EMP: 39
SALES (est): 5.9MM Privately Held
SIC: 3993 Signs & advertising specialties

Milford Center
Union County

(G-14181)
CROP PRODUCTION SERVICES INC
9972 State Route 38 (43045-9760)
PHONE....................................614 873-4253
Fax: 614 873-1849
Jason Hess, Principal
EMP: 6
SALES (corp-wide): 13.6B Privately Held
SIC: 5261 5191 2875 Fertilizer; fertilizers
& agricultural chemicals; fertilizers, mixing
only
HQ: Crop Production Services, Inc.
3005 Rocky Mountain Ave
Loveland CO 80538
970 685-3300

Millbury
Wood County

(G-14182)
AMERICAN RACE CARS
29724 Pemberville Rd (43447-9740)
PHONE....................................419 836-5070
Mark Horton, Partner
Travis Colangelo, Partner
EMP: 5
SALES (est): 514.9K Privately Held
SIC: 3711 Chassis, motor vehicle

(G-14183)
CUSTOM GL SLTONS MILLBURY CORP
Also Called: Guardian Millbury
24145 W Moline Martin Rd (43447-9568)
PHONE....................................419 855-7706
Michael Morrison, President
EMP: 225
SQ FT: 25,000
SALES (est): 28.5MM
SALES (corp-wide): 27.3B Privately Held
SIC: 3211 3231 Plate glass, polished &
rough; tempered glass; insulating glass,
sealed units; products of purchased glass
HQ: Custom Glass Solutions Corp.
2300 Harmon Rd
Auburn Hills MI 48326
248 340-1800

(G-14184)
LAKE TOWNSHIP TRUSTEES
3800 Ayers Rd (43447-9745)
PHONE....................................419 836-1143
Dan McLargin, Manager
Dave Miesmer, Supervisor
EMP: 9 Privately Held
WEB: www.laketwp.com
SIC: 9111 7997 3531 City & town man-
agers' offices; baseball club, except pro-
fessional & semi-professional; road
construction & maintenance machinery
PA: Lake Township Trustees
27975 Cummings Rd
Millbury OH 43447

(G-14185)
LEVISON ENTERPRISES LLC
Also Called: Epi Global
4470 Moline Martin Rd (43447-9201)
PHONE....................................419 838-7365

David Levison, President
David Feltner, Project Engr
Charlene Hudson, Controller
EMP: 20
SQ FT: 14,000
SALES (est): 4.3MM Privately Held
SIC: 3672 Printed circuit boards

(G-14186)
SPECTRA GROUP LIMITED INC
Also Called: Sgl
27800 Lemoyne Rd Ste J (43447-9683)
PHONE....................................419 837-9783
Fax: 419 837-6816
Douglas C Neckers, Ch of Bd
Oleg Greiwich, President
Alex Mejiritski, President
Maria M Small, Mktg Dir
Cindy Kneel, Manager
EMP: 7
SQ FT: 5,680
SALES (est): 1.7MM Privately Held
WEB: www.sglinc.com
SIC: 2899 Chemical preparations

Millersburg
Holmes County

(G-14187)
77 COACH SUPPLY LTD
7426 County Road 77 (44654-9279)
PHONE....................................330 674-1454
Fax: 330 359-5946
Atlee Kaufman,
EMP: 26
SALES (est): 3MM Privately Held
SIC: 5099 2499 Wood & wood by-prod-
ucts; decorative wood & woodwork

(G-14188)
A & M KILN DRY LTD
3570 County Road 135 (44654-9239)
PHONE....................................330 473-8634
Abe Raber, President
Daniel A Raber, Vice Pres
EMP: 3
SALES (est): 374.8K Privately Held
SIC: 3559 Kilns

(G-14189)
A & M WOODWORKING
6440 State Route 515 (44654-8854)
PHONE....................................330 893-1331
Andrew Yoder, Principal
EMP: 3
SALES (est): 208K Privately Held
SIC: 2431 Millwork

(G-14190)
AFFORDABLE BARN CO LTD
Also Called: Southern Wholesale
4260 Township Road 617 (44654-7913)
PHONE....................................330 674-3001
Robert Yoder, Manager
Japheth Yoder,
Gabriel Schlabach,
EMP: 14 EST: 2012
SALES: 2.7MM Privately Held
SIC: 3448 Buildings, portable: prefabri-
cated metal

(G-14191)
AL YODER CONSTRUCTION COMPANY
Also Called: Fairview Log Homes
3375 County Road 160 (44654-8366)
P.O. Box 275, Winesburg (44690-0275)
PHONE....................................330 359-5726
Alvin A Yoder, President
Ruth Yoder, Corp Secy
Sarah Troyer, Admin Sec
EMP: 6
SALES: 1.2MM Privately Held
SIC: 1521 2452 New construction, single-
family houses; log cabins, prefabricated,
wood

(G-14192)
AMISH COUNTRY ESSENTIALS LLC
1817 State Route 83 # 353 (44654-9446)
PHONE....................................330 674-3088
Tracy Cultice,

Shane Cultice,
▼ EMP: 3
SQ FT: 2,100
SALES: 129K Privately Held
SIC: 2844 2841 2834 Face creams or lo-
tions; shampoos, rinses, conditioners:
hair; soap: granulated, liquid, cake, flaked
or chip; lip balms

(G-14193)
AMISH WEDDING FOODS INC
316 S Mad Anthony St (44654-1388)
PHONE....................................330 674-9199
Fax: 330 674-9115
John R Troyer, President
Luke Stutzman, Manager
EMP: 40
SALES (est): 7.1MM Privately Held
SIC: 2022 2099 2013 Cheese, natural &
processed; noodles, uncooked: packaged
with other ingredients; beef, dried: from
purchased meat

(G-14194)
ANDY A RABER
Also Called: A & M Hardwoods
3497 County Road 135 (44654-9284)
PHONE....................................330 893-0400
Andy A Raber, Owner
EMP: 9
SALES (est): 740.9K Privately Held
SIC: 2421 Sawmills & planing mills, gen-
eral

(G-14195)
B AND L SALES INC (PA)
3149 State Rte Ste 39 (44654)
P.O. Box 172, Walnut Creek (44687-0172)
PHONE....................................330 279-2007
Ben Mast, President
EMP: 4
SALES (est): 563.7K Privately Held
SIC: 2273 Floor coverings: paper, grass,
reed, coir, sisal, jute, etc.

(G-14196)
BANDS COMPANY INC
164 E Jackson St (44654-1235)
P.O. Box 328 (44654-0328)
PHONE....................................330 674-0446
Michael Brown, President
Brent Smith, Vice Pres
Susan Hager, Treasurer
Ann Brown, Admin Sec
EMP: 8
SQ FT: 3,000
SALES (est): 895.5K Privately Held
SIC: 1382 Oil & gas exploration services

(G-14197)
BARKMAN PRODUCTS LLC
2550 Township Road 121 (44654-8909)
PHONE....................................330 893-2520
Albert Barkman, Principal
EMP: 3 EST: 2008
SALES (est): 271.4K Privately Held
SIC: 2499 Decorative wood & woodwork

(G-14198)
BEECHVALE LAMINATING
7241 Township Road 572 (44654-9160)
PHONE....................................330 674-2804
Jonas Hochstetler, Owner
EMP: 11
SALES (est): 840.9K Privately Held
SIC: 2431 Millwork

(G-14199)
BENT WOOD SOLUTIONS LLC
7426 County Road 77 (44654-9279)
PHONE....................................330 674-1454
Atlee N Kaufman, Principal
EMP: 4
SALES (est): 589.5K Privately Held
SIC: 1542 3553 Commercial & office build-
ing contractors; woodworking machinery

(G-14200)
BERLIN CUSTOM LEATHER LTD
5085 Township Road 353 (44654-8715)
PHONE....................................330 674-3768
EMP: 3
SALES (est): 404.9K Privately Held
SIC: 3199 Leather goods

(G-14201)
BERLIN TRUCK CAPS LTD
Also Called: Berlin Parts
4560 State Route 39 (44654-9600)
PHONE..............................330 893-2811
Fax: 330 893-3296
Wayne Beachy Jr, *Partner*
James Beachy, *Partner*
EMP: 10
SQ FT: 12,000
SALES: 800K **Privately Held**
SIC: 5199 3792 Tarpaulins; pickup covers, canopies or caps

(G-14202)
BERLIN WOODWORKING
4575 Township Road 366 (44654-9102)
PHONE..............................330 893-3234
Gary Troyer, *Principal*
EMP: 4
SALES (est): 349.4K **Privately Held**
SIC: 2431 Millwork

(G-14203)
BROTY ENTERPRISES INC (PA)
Also Called: Thoughts That Count
88 W Jackson St (44654-1302)
PHONE..............................330 674-6900
Victoria Curren, *President*
Kelly Curren, *Vice Pres*
EMP: 3
SQ FT: 5,000
SALES (est): 443.5K **Privately Held**
SIC: 5947 2411 Gift shop; logging

(G-14204)
BUCKEYE PALLETT
3463 County Road 160 (44654-8369)
PHONE..............................330 359-5919
Merlin Miller, *Principal*
EMP: 4 EST: 2008
SALES (est): 397.1K **Privately Held**
SIC: 2448 Wood pallets & skids

(G-14205)
BUCKEYE SEATING LLC
6960 County Road 672 (44654-8350)
P.O. Box 128, Berlin (44610-0128)
PHONE..............................330 473-2379
Emanuel Weaver, *Mng Member*
EMP: 8
SALES (est): 710K **Privately Held**
SIC: 2399 Seat covers, automobile

(G-14206)
BUCKEYE WELDING
2507 Township Road 110 (44654-9085)
PHONE..............................330 674-0944
Alvin Wengerd, *Principal*
EMP: 5
SALES (est): 292.2K **Privately Held**
SIC: 7692 Welding repair

(G-14207)
BUNKER HILL CHEESE CO INC
Also Called: Heinis Cheese Chalet
6005 County Road 77 (44654-9045)
PHONE..............................330 893-2131
Fax: 330 893-2079
Peter Dauwalder, *President*
Heath Fouts, *Managing Prtnr*
P H C Dauwalder, *Principal*
T D Gindlesberger, *Principal*
Lisa Troyer, *Exec VP*
EMP: 60 EST: 1935
SQ FT: 80,000
SALES (est): 12.4MM **Privately Held**
SIC: 2022 5451 5812 Natural cheese; cheese; snack shop

(G-14208)
BURKHOLDER BUGGY SHOP
7400 County Road 77 (44654-9279)
PHONE..............................330 674-5891
EMP: 3
SALES (est): 200K **Privately Held**
SIC: 3799 Mfg Transportation Equipment

(G-14209)
BUSY BEE LUMBER
5965 Township Road 355 (44654-8880)
P.O. Box 16, Berlin (44610-0016)
PHONE..............................330 674-1305
Alvin Miller, *Owner*
EMP: 6

SALES (est): 382.9K **Privately Held**
SIC: 2411 Logging

(G-14210)
CANAL DOVER FURNITURE LLC
8211 Township Road 652 (44654-8341)
PHONE..............................330 359-5375
Fax: 330 359-5362
Karen Yoder, *General Mgr*
Dan Mast, *Mng Member*
Firman Miller, *Representative*
▼ EMP: 60
SQ FT: 60,000
SALES: 7.6MM **Privately Held**
SIC: 2511 Dining room furniture: wood

(G-14211)
CARTER-JONES LUMBER COMPANY
6139 State Route 39 (44654-8845)
PHONE..............................330 674-9060
EMP: 104
SALES (corp-wide): 1.2B **Privately Held**
SIC: 5031 5211 2439 2434 Lumber, plywood & millwork; lumber & other building materials; structural wood members; wood kitchen cabinets; millwork; hardwood dimension & flooring mills
HQ: The Carter-Jones Lumber Company
601 Tallmadge Rd
Kent OH 44240
330 673-6100

(G-14212)
DOVETAIL DIMENSIONS
6534 Township Road 603 (44654-7010)
PHONE..............................330 674-9533
Timon Miller, *Partner*
David Miller, *Partner*
EMP: 4
SALES (est): 416.9K **Privately Held**
SIC: 2541 Cabinets, lockers & shelving

(G-14213)
EDUCATIONAL ELECTRONICS INC
Also Called: Artsinheaven.com
101 Lakeview Dr Apt 28 (44654-6800)
PHONE..............................234 301-9077
Fax: 330 253-5529
Ed Bedford, *CEO*
Kathleen Bedford, *Admin Sec*
EMP: 5
SALES: 240K **Privately Held**
WEB: artsinheaven.com
SIC: 3679 Electronic circuits

(G-14214)
EUROCASE ARCHITECTURAL CABINET
7488 State Route 241 (44654-8383)
PHONE..............................330 674-0681
Garrett M Roach, *Mng Member*
Klev Moan, *Manager*
EMP: 15
SALES (est): 1.1MM **Privately Held**
SIC: 3469 Architectural panels or parts, porcelain enameled

(G-14215)
FEIKERT SAND & GRAVEL CO INC
Also Called: Feikert Concrete
6971 County Road 189 (44654-9186)
PHONE..............................330 674-0038
Fax: 330 674-5782
Lynn Feikert, *President*
James Feikert, *Vice Pres*
Steve Feikert, *Safety Mgr*
John T Feikert, *Treasurer*
Sheila Feikert, *Financial Exec*
EMP: 20
SQ FT: 6,000
SALES (est): 4MM **Privately Held**
SIC: 1442 3273 1422 Common sand mining; ready-mixed concrete; crushed & broken limestone

(G-14216)
G & H DRILLING INC
Also Called: Land & Shore Drilling
5550 County Road 314 (44654-9713)
P.O. Box 149 (44654-0149)
PHONE..............................330 674-4868

Fax: 330 674-4713
Brian Galford, *President*
Teri Norman, *Manager*
EMP: 20
SQ FT: 300
SALES (est): 2.7MM **Privately Held**
SIC: 1381 Drilling oil & gas wells

(G-14217)
GALION-GODWIN TRUCK BDY CO LLC
Also Called: Galion Dump Bodies
7415 Peabody Kent Rd (44654)
P.O. Box 208, Winesburg (44690-0208)
PHONE..............................330 359-5495
Fax: 330 359-5660
James P Godwin,
EMP: 64
SALES (est): 14.2MM **Privately Held**
WEB: www.galion-godwin.com
SIC: 3536 3713 5531 3711 Hoists, cranes & monorails; truck & bus bodies; truck equipment & parts; motor vehicles & car bodies; fabricated structural metal; sheet metalwork

(G-14218)
GRAPHIC PUBLICATIONS INC
Also Called: Bargain Hunter
7368 County Road 623 (44654-9256)
P.O. Box 358 (44654-0358)
PHONE..............................330 674-2300
Fax: 330 674-2461
Michael Mast, *President*
Paul Money, *Editor*
Cynthia Reiheld, *Business Mgr*
Frances Mast, *Corp Secy*
Devlin Stermer, *Credit Mgr*
EMP: 45
SQ FT: 12,000
SALES (est): 6.6MM **Privately Held**
WEB: www.gpubs.com
SIC: 2721 7336 Periodicals: publishing only; graphic arts & related design

(G-14219)
GUGGISBERG CHEESE INC (PA)
Also Called: Chalet In The Valley
5060 State Route 557 (44654-9266)
PHONE..............................330 893-2550
Fax: 330 893-3240
Richard Guggisberg, *President*
Glenn Meier, *General Mgr*
Cynthia Mellor, *Principal*
Paul A Miller, *Principal*
Rosanne Parrot, *Principal*
EMP: 50
SQ FT: 10,000
SALES (est): 11.2MM **Privately Held**
WEB: www.guggisberg.com
SIC: 2022 5812 5961 5451 Natural cheese; eating places; cheese, mail order; cheese

(G-14220)
HEARTLAND STAIRWAY LTD
7080 Township Road 601 (44654-8892)
PHONE..............................330 279-2554
Roy Hochstetler, *Partner*
Emanuel Hochstetler, *Partner*
Mark Wengerd, *Partner*
EMP: 4
SALES (est): 280K **Privately Held**
SIC: 2431 Staircases & stairs, wood

(G-14221)
HERSHBERGER LAWN STRUCTURES
Also Called: Play Mor
8990 State Route 39 (44654-9791)
PHONE..............................330 674-3900
Fax: 330 674-5559
Paul Hershberger, *Partner*
Amos Stoltzfus Jr, *Partner*
EMP: 17
SQ FT: 21,000
SALES (est): 2.2MM **Privately Held**
WEB: www.playmorswingsets.com
SIC: 3944 5941 5091 Structural toy sets; playground equipment; sporting & recreation goods

(G-14222)
HERSHEY MACHINE
5502 State Route 557 (44654-9488)
PHONE..............................330 674-2718

Atlee Hershberger, *Owner*
EMP: 4 EST: 1996
SALES (est): 340K **Privately Held**
SIC: 3443 Tanks, standard or custom fabricated: metal plate

(G-14223)
HERSHY WAY LTD
5918 County Road 201 (44654-9294)
PHONE..............................330 893-2809
Fax: 330 893-4139
Aden Hershberger, *Partner*
Jay Hershberger, *Partner*
Steven Hershberger, *Partner*
EMP: 7
SALES (est): 773.3K **Privately Held**
WEB: www.hershyway.com
SIC: 2519 3523 Lawn furniture, except wood, metal, stone or concrete; cattle feeding, handling & watering equipment

(G-14224)
HIDDEN VIEW WOODWORKING
7826 State Route 241 (44654-8820)
P.O. Box 113, Mount Hope (44660-0113)
PHONE..............................330 674-5196
Norman Yutzy, *Owner*
EMP: 3
SALES: 200K **Privately Held**
SIC: 2511 Wood household furniture

(G-14225)
HILLSIDE WOOD LTD
8413 Township Road 652 (44654-8343)
PHONE..............................330 359-5991
Fax: 330 359-5997
Aden Troyer, *Manager*
EMP: 20
SALES: 3MM **Privately Held**
SIC: 2426 Chair seats, hardwood

(G-14226)
HOCHSTETLER WOOD
Also Called: H W Chair Co
6791 County Road 77 (44654-7901)
PHONE..............................330 893-2384
Eli Hochstetler, *Partner*
David Hochstetler, *Partner*
Ivan Hochstetler, *Partner*
Mark Hochstetler, *Partner*
Wayne Hochstetler, *Partner*
EMP: 16
SQ FT: 35,500
SALES (est): 2.1MM **Privately Held**
SIC: 2426 2511 Hardwood dimension & flooring mills; chairs, bentwood

(G-14227)
HOCHSTETLER WOOD LTD
6791 County Road 77 (44654-7901)
PHONE..............................330 893-1601
Eli Hochstetler, *President*
Judas Hochstetler, *Admin Sec*
EMP: 17
SALES (est): 2MM **Privately Held**
SIC: 2511 Wood household furniture

(G-14228)
HOLMES BY PRODUCTS CO
3175 Township Road 411 (44654-9176)
PHONE..............................330 893-2322
Fax: 330 893-2321
Abe Miller, *President*
Brian Miller, *Vice Pres*
Mary Miller, *Treasurer*
▲ EMP: 50
SQ FT: 15,000
SALES (est): 7.7MM **Privately Held**
SIC: 2048 Bone meal, prepared as animal feed

(G-14229)
HOLMES CHEESE CO
9444 State Route 39 (44654-9764)
PHONE..............................330 674-6451
Fax: 330 674-6673
Robert J Ramseyer, *President*
Walter P Ramseyer, *Vice Pres*
▲ EMP: 35
SQ FT: 42,000
SALES (est): 10.9MM **Privately Held**
WEB: www.holmescheese.com
SIC: 2022 Natural cheese; whey, raw or liquid

▲ = Import　▼=Export
◆ =Import/Export

(G-14230)
HOLMES COUNTY HUB INC
Also Called: Daily Record, The
25 N Clay St (44654-1117)
P.O. Box 151 (44654-0151)
PHONE...................................330 674-1811
Fax: 330 674-3780
V Dix, *Publisher*
Cindy Hinkle, *Manager*
EMP: 9
SALES (est): 230K **Privately Held**
WEB: www.the-daily-record.com
SIC: 2711 Newspapers

(G-14231)
HOLMES LUMBER & BLDG CTR INC
Also Called: Holmes Lumber & Supply
6139 Hc 39 (44654)
PHONE...................................330 674-9060
Fax: 330 674-0265
Paul Miller, *President*
Eric Wiedemann, *Store Mgr*
D Tim Yoder, *Credit Mgr*
Randy Smith, *Sales Staff*
Dan Broderick, *Manager*
EMP: 150 **EST:** 1952
SQ FT: 16,000
SALES (est): 729.8K **Privately Held**
WEB: www.holmeslumber.com
SIC: 5031 5211 2439 2434 Lumber, plywood & millwork; lumber & other building materials; structural wood members; wood kitchen cabinets; millwork; hardwood dimension & flooring mills

(G-14232)
HOPEWOOD INC
8087 Township Road 652 (44654-8898)
PHONE...................................330 359-5656
Fax: 330 359-5268
Ronald Clark, *President*
Fred Raber, *Purch Agent*
Marie Beachy, *Admin Asst*
EMP: 20
SALES (est): 1.5MM **Privately Held**
WEB: www.hopewoodinc.com
SIC: 2512 2511 Upholstered household furniture; wood household furniture

(G-14233)
HRH DOOR CORP
Also Called: Wayne-Dalton
4577 Tr 634 (44654)
P.O. Box 266, Green (44232-0266)
PHONE...................................330 896-2175
Tom Weston, *Principal*
EMP: 34
SALES (corp-wide): 665.2MM **Privately Held**
SIC: 3442 Metal doors, sash & trim
PA: Hrh Door Corp.
1 Door Dr
Mount Hope OH 44660
850 208-3400

(G-14234)
J & R WOODWORKING
4925 Private Road 386 (44654)
PHONE...................................330 893-0713
Joe Troyer, *Owner*
EMP: 7
SALES (est): 695.4K **Privately Held**
SIC: 2499 Decorative wood & woodwork

(G-14235)
JLM LOGGING LLC
3334 County Road 160 (44654-8390)
PHONE...................................330 340-4863
Junior Miller, *Principal*
EMP: 3
SALES (est): 205.1K **Privately Held**
SIC: 2411 Logging

(G-14236)
KAUFMAN MULCH INC
Also Called: Kaufman Trucking
3988 County Road 135 (44654-9217)
PHONE...................................330 893-3676
Fax: 330 893-3686
Larry Kaufman, *President*
Kim Kaufman, *Vice Pres*
Nelson Burkholder, *Manager*
EMP: 4

SALES (est): 519.3K **Privately Held**
SIC: 2499 2421 Mulch, wood & bark; sawmills & planing mills, general

(G-14237)
KENT SPORTING GOODS CO INC
Also Called: J Sport
374 Railroad St (44654-1718)
PHONE...................................330 674-2233
Laurie Vaughn, *Manager*
EMP: 40
SALES (corp-wide): 135.6MM **Privately Held**
SIC: 3069 Life jackets, inflatable: rubberized fabric
PA: Kent Sporting Goods Company, Inc.
433 Park Ave
New London OH 44851
419 929-7021

(G-14238)
LAB ELECTRONICS INC
5640 Township Road 353 (44654-8759)
PHONE...................................330 674-9818
Lawrence Lamp, *President*
William Baker, *Principal*
EMP: 8
SQ FT: 200
SALES (est): 603.4K **Privately Held**
SIC: 3571 Electronic computers

(G-14239)
LAMAR D STEINER
Also Called: D & K Designs
6815 State Route 39 (44654-9796)
PHONE...................................330 466-1479
Lamar Steiner, *Owner*
EMP: 4
SQ FT: 1,000
SALES (est): 139.8K **Privately Held**
SIC: 2759 Screen printing

(G-14240)
LBC CLAY CO LLC
4501 Township Road 307 (44654-9656)
PHONE...................................330 674-0674
Larry L Clark, *Principal*
EMP: 8 **EST:** 2010
SALES (est): 765.8K **Privately Held**
SIC: 3251 Brick & structural clay tile

(G-14241)
LITTLE COTTAGE COMPANY
4070 State Route 39 (44654)
PHONE...................................330 893-4212
EMP: 7
SALES (est): 917.4K **Privately Held**
SIC: 2426 Carvings, furniture: wood

(G-14242)
LLC BOWMAN LEATHER
6705 Private Road 387 (44654-8249)
PHONE...................................330 893-1954
Dan Bowman,
EMP: 7
SALES (est): 552K **Privately Held**
SIC: 3199 5699 Leather goods; leather garments

(G-14243)
M H WOODWORKING LLC
Also Called: Buckeye Rocker
2789 County Rd Ste 600 (44654)
PHONE...................................330 893-3929
Mose V Hershberger,
EMP: 8
SALES (est): 1MM **Privately Held**
SIC: 2431 Millwork

(G-14244)
MAC OIL FIELD SERVICE INC
7861 Township Road 306 (44654-9666)
P.O. Box 211 (44654-0211)
PHONE...................................330 674-7371
Robert G Mc Vicker Jr, *President*
Patricia Mc Vicker, *Vice Pres*
EMP: 15
SQ FT: 1,376
SALES (est): 2.9MM **Privately Held**
SIC: 1389 4212 Oil field services; liquid haulage, local

(G-14245)
MAPLE HILL WOODWORKING
2726 Trl 128 (44654)
PHONE...................................330 674-2500
Mark Miller, *Principal*
EMP: 4 **EST:** 2008
SALES (est): 291.3K **Privately Held**
SIC: 2431 Millwork

(G-14246)
MIDFLOW SERVICES LLC
812 S Washington St (44654-1398)
PHONE...................................330 674-2399
EMP: 23
SALES (corp-wide): 3.5MM **Privately Held**
SIC: 3533 Oil & gas field machinery
PA: Midflow Services, Llc
10774 Township Road 506
Shreve OH 44676
330 567-3108

(G-14247)
MILLER LUMBER CO INC
7101 State Route 39 (44654-8828)
PHONE...................................330 674-0273
Fax: 330 674-0375
Myron Miller, *President*
Scott Miller, *Treasurer*
EMP: 22 **EST:** 1949
SQ FT: 5,000
SALES: 5.5MM **Privately Held**
WEB: www.millerlumberco.com
SIC: 2421 Kiln drying of lumber; planing mills

(G-14248)
MILLERS STORAGE BARNS LLC
4230 State Route 39 (44654-9682)
PHONE...................................330 893-3293
Fax: 330 893-9603
Eric Kuhns, *General Mgr*
Owen Miller, *Mng Member*
Linda Kuhns,
Marlin Kuhns,
EMP: 23
SQ FT: 15,928
SALES (est): 5MM **Privately Held**
WEB: www.millersstoragebuildings.com
SIC: 2452 Farm buildings, prefabricated or portable: wood

(G-14249)
MILLERSBURG ICE CO
25 S Grant St (44654-1322)
PHONE...................................330 674-3016
Lewis Ritchey, *President*
Phillip Ritchey, *Treasurer*
EMP: 20 **EST:** 1936
SQ FT: 18,000
SALES (est): 2.6MM **Privately Held**
SIC: 2097 5921 Manufactured ice; beer (packaged); wine

(G-14250)
MOUNT HOPE PLANING
Also Called: Mhp Flooring
7598 Tr652 (44654)
PHONE...................................330 359-0538
John Miller Jr, *Owner*
EMP: 16
SQ FT: 36,000
SALES (est): 2.7MM **Privately Held**
SIC: 2431 1771 Millwork; flooring contractor

(G-14251)
MT EATON PALLET LTD
4761 County Road 207 (44654-9055)
PHONE...................................330 893-2986
Fax: 330 893-3530
Dwain Schlabach, *Partner*
Roman Raber, *Plant Mgr*
EMP: 40
SQ FT: 12,000
SALES (est): 6MM **Privately Held**
SIC: 2448 Pallets, wood & wood with metal

(G-14252)
MULTI PRODUCTS COMPANY
7188 State Route 39 (44654-9204)
P.O. Box 1597, Gainesville TX (76241-1597)
PHONE...................................330 674-5981

Fax: 330 674-2125
Jeff Berlin, *CEO*
William T Baker, *President*
Bud Doty, *Corp Secy*
Greg Guthrie, *Vice Pres*
Heather Sprang, *Controller*
▲ **EMP:** 42
SQ FT: 30,000
SALES (est): 12.5MM **Privately Held**
SIC: 3533 5084 Oil field machinery & equipment; industrial machinery & equipment

(G-14253)
NATIONAL MORTGAGE WEEKLEY
1817 State Route 83 (44654-9445)
PHONE...................................330 674-2887
Bill Leclair, *President*
EMP: 6
SALES (est): 320K **Privately Held**
SIC: 2721 Periodicals: publishing only

(G-14254)
NJM FURNITURE OUTLET INC
6899 County Road 672 (44654-8349)
PHONE...................................330 893-3514
James Kandell, *Principal*
EMP: 10
SALES (est): 627.5K **Privately Held**
SIC: 2512 Upholstered household furniture

(G-14255)
PLAINS PRECUT LTD
4917 County Road 207 (44654-8221)
PHONE...................................330 893-3300
Abe Weaver, *Principal*
EMP: 4
SALES (est): 378.7K **Privately Held**
SIC: 2448 Wood pallets & skids

(G-14256)
PRECISION GEOPHYSICAL INC (PA)
2695 State Route 83 (44654-9455)
PHONE...................................330 674-2198
Fax: 330 674-1729
Steven Mc Crossin, *President*
EMP: 32
SALES (est): 4.8MM **Privately Held**
WEB: www.precisiongeophysical.com
SIC: 1382 Oil & gas exploration services

(G-14257)
R & B ENTERPRISES USA INC
1868 County Road 150 (44654-8922)
PHONE...................................330 674-2227
Fax: 330 674-9539
Roger Patterson, *President*
EMP: 3
SALES: 700K **Privately Held**
SIC: 1389 1794 Roustabout service; excavation work

(G-14258)
REXAM PLC
Rexam Prescription Products
5091 County Road 120 (44654-9231)
PHONE...................................330 893-2451
Paul Arsenault, *Manager*
EMP: 10
SALES (corp-wide): 9B **Publicly Held**
SIC: 3085 Plastics bottles
HQ: Rexam Limited
Rexam, Rexam Limited
Luton BEDS LU1 3
207 227-4100

(G-14259)
RIDGEVIEW SHEET METAL
4772 Township Road 352 (44654-9099)
PHONE...................................330 674-3768
EMP: 3 **EST:** 2013
SALES (est): 206.9K **Privately Held**
SIC: 3444 Sheet metalwork

(G-14260)
RIGHT FIT ERGONOMICS LLC
4613 Township Road 305 (44654-8521)
PHONE...................................330 674-0977
Chad Croskey, *Vice Pres*
William Shrimplin,
EMP: 3
SALES: 75K **Privately Held**
SIC: 2522 Office furniture, except wood

(G-14261)
SALTILLO CORPORATION (PA)
2143 Township Road 112 (44654-9410)
PHONE..........................330 674-6722
Fax: 330 674-6726
Leona Hershberger, *President*
Fanie Herb Miller, *Corp Secy*
David H Hershberger, *Vice Pres*
Paul Jones, *Manager*
Jane Anderson, *Consultant*
▲ EMP: 8
SALES: 2.2MM **Privately Held**
WEB: www.saltillo.com
SIC: 3669 Intercommunication systems, electric

(G-14262)
SCHLABACH WOODWORKS LTD
6678 State Route 241 (44654-8826)
PHONE..........................330 674-7488
David Schlabach, *Owner*
EMP: 20
SALES (est): 2.8MM **Privately Held**
SIC: 3996 Hard surface floor coverings

(G-14263)
SIMPLE PRODUCTS LLC
Also Called: Design Farm
10336 Township Road 262 (44654-8746)
P.O. Box 94 (44654-0094)
PHONE..........................330 674-2448
Michael Jaeb, *Principal*
EMP: 3
SALES (est): 154.7K **Privately Held**
SIC: 2099 Syrups

(G-14264)
STAR BRITE EXPRESS CAR WA
887 S Washington St (44654-1707)
PHONE..........................330 674-0062
Rodney J Starr, *Principal*
EMP: 9
SALES (est): 543.8K **Privately Held**
SIC: 2741 Miscellaneous publishing

(G-14265)
STUTZMAN MANUFACTURING LTD
7727 Township Road 604 (44654-8352)
PHONE..........................330 674-4359
Bert L Stutzman, *Mng Member*
EMP: 6
SALES (est): 1MM **Privately Held**
SIC: 3542 7389 Nail heading machines;

(G-14266)
SWARTZ WOODWORKING
7136 Township Road 654 (44654-8367)
PHONE..........................330 359-6359
Paul Swartz, *Principal*
EMP: 4
SALES (est): 327.5K **Privately Held**
SIC: 2431 Millwork

(G-14267)
TECH TOOL INC
2901 County Road 150 (44654-8510)
PHONE..........................330 674-1176
Fax: 330 674-1176
David M Kauffman, *President*
Elizabeth Kauffman, *Corp Secy*
Kim Kauffman, *Manager*
▲ EMP: 10
SQ FT: 4,800
SALES: 900K **Privately Held**
SIC: 3533 3498 3494 Oil & gas field machinery; fabricated pipe & fittings; valves & pipe fittings

(G-14268)
TGS INTERNATIONAL INC
4464 State Route 39 (44654-9677)
P.O. Box 355, Berlin (44610-0355)
PHONE..........................330 893-2428
Paul Weaver, *Vice Pres*
Roman Mullet, *Treasurer*
David Troyer, *Exec Dir*
EMP: 20
SALES: 2.6MM
SALES (corp-wide): 111.1MM **Privately Held**
SIC: 4731 2731 Freight forwarding; book publishing

PA: Christian Aid Ministries
4464 State Route 39
Millersburg OH 44654
330 893-2428

(G-14269)
TH MANUFACTURING INC
4674 County Road 120 (44654-9280)
PHONE..........................330 893-3572
Fax: 330 893-3592
Jeff Tomski, *President*
Donald Troyer, *Manager*
EMP: 9
SQ FT: 60,000
SALES (est): 880K **Privately Held**
SIC: 3543 Industrial patterns

(G-14270)
TMARZETTI COMPANY
Inn Maid Products Div
7445 County Road 68 (44654)
P.O. Box 27 (44654-0027)
PHONE..........................330 674-2993
Theodore Zuercher, *Manager*
EMP: 14
SQ FT: 35,000
SALES (corp-wide): 1.1B **Publicly Held**
SIC: 2098 Noodles (e.g. egg, plain & water), dry
HQ: T.Marzetti Company
380 Polaris Pkwy Ste 400
Westerville OH 43082
614 846-2232

(G-14271)
TOPE PRINTING INC
1056 S Washington St (44654-9438)
PHONE..........................330 674-4993
Fax: 330 674-2613
John C Tope, *President*
Vanessa Tope, *Corp Secy*
Andrew P Tope, *Vice Pres*
EMP: 7 EST: 1974
SQ FT: 6,000
SALES: 530.9K **Privately Held**
SIC: 2752 2759 Commercial printing, offset; letterpress printing

(G-14272)
TRICO ENTERPRISES LLC
6430 Township Road 348 (44654-9754)
PHONE..........................330 674-1157
Darryl Chajon,
Ed Miller,
EMP: 31 EST: 2012
SALES (est): 4.8MM **Privately Held**
SIC: 3553 Woodworking machinery

(G-14273)
TRICO ENTERPRISES LLC
6430 Tr 348 (44654)
PHONE..........................330 674-1157
Joe Miller, *Sales Associate*
Ed Miller,
EMP: 22
SQ FT: 20,000
SALES (est): 3.2MM **Privately Held**
SIC: 3553 Sawmill machines

(G-14274)
TROYER CHEESE INC
Also Called: Amish Wedding Foods
6597 County Road 625 (44654-9071)
PHONE..........................330 893-2479
Fax: 330 893-2375
James Troyer, *President*
Jonas A Troyer, *Chairman*
Aaron Yoder, *Purch Mgr*
Charlotte Kawczk, *Human Res Mgr*
Larry Lukens, *Sales Staff*
EMP: 45
SQ FT: 59,500
SALES (est): 23.7MM **Privately Held**
WEB: www.troyercheese.com
SIC: 5149 5143 5147 2032 Specialty food items; cheese; meats, cured or smoked; ethnic foods: canned, jarred, etc.

(G-14275)
UNIVERSAL WELL SERVICES INC
11 S Washington St (44654-1341)
PHONE..........................330 264-1109
Fax: 330 263-4872
Matt Teichmer, *District Mgr*
Lisa Seibert, *Financial Exec*

Rick Sloan, *Manager*
Tom Funk, *Manager*
EMP: 24
SALES (corp-wide): 915.8MM **Publicly Held**
WEB: www.univwell.com
SIC: 1389 Hydraulic fracturing wells; cementing oil & gas well casings
HQ: Universal Well Services, Inc.
13549 S Mosiertown Rd
Meadville PA 16335
814 337-1983

(G-14276)
V & W WOODCRAFT
5071 Township Road 353 (44654-8715)
PHONE..........................330 674-0073
Vernon Weaver, *Principal*
EMP: 3
SALES: 110K **Privately Held**
SIC: 2431 Woodwork, interior & ornamental

(G-14277)
VALLEYVIEW WOOD TURNING CO
8260 Township Road 652 (44654-8341)
PHONE..........................330 763-0407
Ervin Hershberger, *Owner*
Leon Hershberger, *Manager*
EMP: 18
SQ FT: 15,000
SALES: 2.2MM **Privately Held**
SIC: 2426 Stock, chair, hardwood: turned, shaped or carved

(G-14278)
VINYL TECH STORAGE BARN
5930 State Route 39 (44654-8331)
PHONE..........................330 674-5670
Eugene Miller, *Owner*
EMP: 4
SALES (est): 1MM **Privately Held**
SIC: 3448 Farm & utility buildings

(G-14279)
W H PATTEN DRILLING CO INC
6336 County Road 207 (44654-9153)
P.O. Box 10 (44654-0010)
PHONE..........................330 674-3046
Fax: 330 674-3248
William H Patten III, *President*
William H Patten Jr, *Shareholder*
Kim Mathie, *Admin Sec*
EMP: 8 EST: 1940
SQ FT: 1,200
SALES: 600K **Privately Held**
SIC: 1311 Crude petroleum & natural gas

(G-14280)
WALNUT CREEK CART SHOP
3309 State Route 39 (44654-8848)
PHONE..........................330 893-1097
Clyde Yoder, *Owner*
EMP: 3
SALES: 7K **Privately Held**
SIC: 3799 Carriages, horse drawn

(G-14281)
WALNUT CREEK PLANING LTD
5778 State Route 515 (44654-8807)
PHONE..........................330 893-3244
Fax: 330 893-2468
Dwight Kratzer, *President*
Charles Kratzer, *General Mgr*
Marie Miller, *General Mgr*
Brad Smith, *General Mgr*
Ken Kratzer, *Vice Pres*
▲ EMP: 100
SQ FT: 90,000
SALES: 30MM **Privately Held**
WEB: www.walnutcreekplaning.com
SIC: 5211 2421 2499 2426 Millwork & lumber; planing mills; decorative wood & woodwork; hardwood dimension & flooring mills

(G-14282)
WASTE PARCHMENT INC
4510 Township Road 307 (44654-9656)
PHONE..........................330 674-6868
Fax: 330 674-5057
Robert Smith, *President*
Cheri Mainwaring, *Manager*
Elaine Smith, *Admin Sec*
EMP: 30

SQ FT: 80,000
SALES: 1MM **Privately Held**
SIC: 4953 2611 Recycling, waste materials; pulp mills

(G-14283)
WASTEQUIP MANUFACTURING CO LLC
930 Massillon Rd (44654-8200)
PHONE..........................330 674-1119
Larry Mohler, *Manager*
EMP: 49
SALES (corp-wide): 562.6MM **Privately Held**
WEB: www.rayfo.com
SIC: 3443 Dumpsters, garbage
HQ: Wastequip Manufacturing Company Llc
1901 Roxborough Rd # 300
Charlotte NC 28211

(G-14284)
WEEKLY BROTHERS CNTY LINE FAR
1533 Township Road 110 (44654-9616)
PHONE..........................330 674-4195
Paul Weekley, *Principal*
EMP: 4
SALES (est): 222.2K **Privately Held**
SIC: 2711 Newspapers

(G-14285)
WENGERD CABINETS
6605 Township Road 362 (44654-8248)
PHONE..........................330 231-0879
Roy Wengerd, *Principal*
EMP: 4
SALES (est): 291.4K **Privately Held**
SIC: 2434 Wood kitchen cabinets

(G-14286)
WILKSHIRE DRY CLEANERS LLC
5660 County Road 203 (44654-8275)
PHONE..........................330 674-7696
Ryan Torrence, *Mng Member*
EMP: 5
SALES (est): 337.4K **Privately Held**
SIC: 2842 Drycleaning preparations

(G-14287)
WOOD WORKS
9210 Township Road 304 (44654-8523)
PHONE..........................330 674-0333
Don Hubener, *Owner*
EMP: 3
SALES (est): 200.7K **Privately Held**
SIC: 2599 Bar furniture

(G-14288)
YODER LUMBER CO INC (PA)
4515 Township Road 367 (44654-8885)
PHONE..........................330 893-3121
Fax: 330 893-3031
Eli J Yoder, *President*
Robert Mapes, *President*
Ken Grate, *Corp Secy*
Melvin Yoder, *Vice Pres*
Roy Yoder, *Vice Pres*
▼ EMP: 55 EST: 1947
SQ FT: 15,000
SALES (est): 30.3MM **Privately Held**
WEB: www.yoderlumber.com
SIC: 2421 2448 2499 2431 Lumber: rough, sawed or planed; pallets, wood; mulch, wood & bark; millwork; hardwood dimension & flooring mills

(G-14289)
YODER LUMBER CO INC
7100 County Road 407 (44654-9628)
PHONE..........................330 674-1435
Fax: 330 674-1445
Mel Yoder, *Manager*
EMP: 50
SALES (corp-wide): 30.3MM **Privately Held**
WEB: www.yoderlumber.com
SIC: 2421 2448 Sawmills & planing mills, general; wood pallets & skids
PA: Yoder Lumber Co., Inc.
4515 Township Road 367
Millersburg OH 44654
330 893-3121

(G-14290)
YODERS NYLON HALTER SHOP
7682 Township Road 652 (44654-8337)
PHONE....................330 893-3479
Daniel O Yoder, *Owner*
EMP: 3
SALES (est): 100K **Privately Held**
SIC: 2221 Nylon broadwoven fabrics

(G-14291)
YODERS WOODWORKING
2249 Township Road 112 (44654-8226)
PHONE....................888 818-0568
Phillip L Yoder, *Owner*
EMP: 6
SQ FT: 6,000
SALES: 865.6K **Privately Held**
SIC: 2511 Bed frames, except water bed
frames: wood

(G-14292)
YUTZY WOODWORKING LTD
6995 Township Road 654 (44654-8815)
PHONE....................330 359-6166
Fax: 330 359-7166
Dennis Yutzy, *Owner*
▲ EMP: 230
SALES (est): 21.8MM **Privately Held**
SIC: 2431 Millwork

Millersport
Fairfield County

(G-14293)
GRAVEL DOCTOR OF OHIO LLC
Also Called: Gravel Doctor of Ohio, The
2985 Canal Dr (43046-8044)
PHONE....................844 472-8353
EMP: 3 EST: 2014
SALES (est): 218.2K **Privately Held**
SIC: 1442 Construction sand & gravel

(G-14294)
HEFTY HOIST INC
Also Called: Aqua Marine Supply
2397a Refugee Rd Ne (43046-9748)
P.O. Box 44 (43046-0044)
PHONE....................740 467-2515
Fax: 740 467-2519
Chet Hauck, *President*
Jason Moore, *Purch Mgr*
▲ EMP: 20
SQ FT: 14,000
SALES (est): 3MM **Privately Held**
SIC: 3566 Reduction gears & gear units for
turbines, except automotive

(G-14295)
JACOBSON MFG LLC
Also Called: Minuteman Distribution
2140 Refugee Rd Ne (43046-9748)
PHONE....................740 467-3199
Michael Kaehler, *Opers Mgr*
Rawlyn Cook, *Accountant*
Dale Wellman, *Manager*
Frank Bennett, *Manager*
Steve Elrad, *Info Tech Mgr*
EMP: 4 **Privately Held**
WEB: www.jacobsonmfg.com
SIC: 3452 Bolts, nuts, rivets & washers;
bolts, metal
HQ: Jacobson Mfg., Llc
941 Lake Rd 955
Medina OH 44256
330 725-8853

(G-14296)
PHANTOM FIREWORKS
10442 Outville Rd (43046)
PHONE....................740 927-6943
Fax: 740 927-0248
Howard Allison, *Owner*
EMP: 25 EST: 1990
SALES (est): 2.4MM **Privately Held**
SIC: 2899 Fireworks

(G-14297)
PHANTOM FIREWORKS INC
10442 Outville Rd (43046)
PHONE....................740 927-6943
Howard Allison, *Owner*
EMP: 25

SALES (corp-wide): 23.2MM **Privately
Held**
SIC: 2899 Chemical preparations
PA: Phantom Fireworks Inc
555 Martin L King Jr Blvd
Youngstown OH 44502
330 746-1064

(G-14298)
SEE YA THERE INC
Also Called: See Ya There Vacation and Trvl
12710 W Bank Dr Ne (43046-9738)
PHONE....................614 856-9037
John J Allen, *President*
Michael Hatem, *Vice Pres*
George Lindsey, *Treasurer*
EMP: 7
SQ FT: 800
SALES (est): 400K **Privately Held**
WEB: www.seeyathere.com
SIC: 2741 Newsletter publishing

(G-14299)
WELDON ICE CREAM COMPANY
2887 Canal Dr (43046-9701)
PHONE....................740 467-2400
David Pierce, *Principal*
EMP: 8
SQ FT: 10,800
SALES (est): 400K **Privately Held**
WEB: www.weldons.com
SIC: 2024 Ice cream & frozen desserts

Millersville
Sandusky County

(G-14300)
CARMEUSE LIME INC
Also Called: Carmeuse Lime & Stone
3964 County Road 41 (43435-9619)
PHONE....................419 638-2511
Fax: 419 638-2311
Tim Haubert, *Purchasing*
Mike Klenda, *Branch Mgr*
Brent Sandberg, *Manager*
EMP: 37 **Privately Held**
SIC: 3281 Limestone, cut & shaped
HQ: Carmeuse Lime, Inc.
11 Stanwix St Fl 21
Pittsburgh PA 15222
412 995-5500

Mineral City
Tuscarawas County

(G-14301)
HILLTOP ENERGY INC
6978 Lindentree Rd Ne (44656-8973)
P.O. Box 395 (44656-0395)
PHONE....................330 859-2108
Fax: 330 859-2432
Roger Hambleton, *Plant Mgr*
Brandy Caterley, *Director*
EMP: 22
SQ FT: 3,200
SALES (corp-wide): 68.1MM **Privately
Held**
SIC: 2892 2819 Explosives; industrial inor-
ganic chemicals
HQ: Hilltop Energy, Inc.
7896 Dickey Dr
Lisbon OH 44432
330 424-1441

Mineral Ridge
Trumbull County

(G-14302)
ALSTEEL FABRICATORS INC
3500 Union St (44440-9007)
P.O. Box 14395, Youngstown (44514-7395)
PHONE....................330 652-4344
Fax: 330 652-4345
Richard Mc Vey, *President*
Cathy Duck, *Manager*
EMP: 13
SQ FT: 9,600

SALES (est): 1.7MM **Privately Held**
SIC: 3441 Fabricated structural metal

(G-14303)
BADURIK BUTCHER BLOCK
3761 Main St (44440-9550)
PHONE....................330 652-2333
Steve Badurik, *Principal*
EMP: 4
SALES (est): 342.3K **Privately Held**
SIC: 3421 Table & food cutlery, including
butchers'

(G-14304)
FBR INDUSTRIES INC
1336 Seaborn St Ste 7 (44440-9006)
PHONE....................330 701-7425
Stephen Fbrown, *Principal*
EMP: 3
SALES (est): 343.6K **Privately Held**
SIC: 3999 Manufacturing industries

(G-14305)
J & K POWDER COATING
1336 Seaborn St (44440-9006)
PHONE....................330 540-6145
Jeffrey A Christy, *Principal*
EMP: 6
SALES (est): 498.3K **Privately Held**
SIC: 3399 Powder, metal

(G-14306)
J & W CANVAS COMPANY
1386 Church St (44440-9532)
PHONE....................330 652-7678
Timothy J McNeil, *Owner*
EMP: 4
SQ FT: 1,600
SALES: 250K **Privately Held**
SIC: 7699 2394 Tent repair shop; canvas
& related products

(G-14307)
L B FOSTER COMPANY
Also Called: Relay Rail Div.
1193 Salt Springs Rd (44440-9318)
PHONE....................330 652-1461
Fax: 330 652-7494
Scott Calahoun, *Manager*
EMP: 25
SQ FT: 3,000
SALES (corp-wide): 483.5MM **Publicly
Held**
WEB: www.lbfoster.com
SIC: 1799 3743 Coating of metal struc-
tures at construction site; railroad equip-
ment
PA: L. B. Foster Company
415 Holiday Dr Ste 1
Pittsburgh PA 15220
412 928-3400

(G-14308)
MASHEEN SPECIALTIES
3519 Union St (44440-9008)
PHONE....................330 652-7535
EMP: 20
SALES (est): 1.7MM **Privately Held**
SIC: 3541 Die sinking machines

(G-14309)
P & S ENERGY INC
3729 Union St (44440-9004)
P.O. Box 523 (44440-0523)
PHONE....................330 652-2525
Martin Solomon, *President*
Ben Z Post, *Corp Secy*
Howard Solomon, *Vice Pres*
EMP: 3
SQ FT: 4,500
SALES (est): 270K **Privately Held**
SIC: 1311 1381 Crude petroleum & natu-
ral gas; drilling oil & gas wells

(G-14310)
**RX INSTITUTIONAL SERVICES
LLC**
3379 Main St Ste A (44440-9735)
PHONE....................330 505-1979
Fax: 330 505-4178
Ronald T McDermott, *Principal*
EMP: 7
SALES (est): 868.7K **Privately Held**
SIC: 2834 Pharmaceutical preparations

(G-14311)
**SPECIALTY PIPE & TUBE INC
(HQ)**
3600 Union St (44440-9000)
P.O. Box 516 (44440-0516)
PHONE....................330 505-8262
Fax: 330 505-8260
Steven J Baroff, *President*
Pat Aldridge, *Manager*
Dale Janus, *Director*
◆ EMP: 19
SQ FT: 18,600
SALES (est): 10.1MM
SALES (corp-wide): 138.5MM **Publicly
Held**
WEB: www.specialtypipe.com
SIC: 3317 Welded pipe & tubes; tubes,
wrought: welded or lock joint
PA: Synalloy Corporation
4510 Cox Rd Ste 201
Glen Allen VA 23060
864 585-3605

(G-14312)
**THE MAHONING VALLEY SANI
DST**
1181 Ohltown Mcdonald Rd (44440-9322)
P.O. Box 4119, Youngstown (44515-0119)
PHONE....................330 799-6315
Jack Vaughn, *President*
Thomas Holloway, *Chief Engr*
Marty Kielbasa, *Engineer*
Alan Tatalovich, *Treasurer*
David Tabak, *Human Res Dir*
EMP: 53
SALES (est): 11.5MM **Privately Held**
SIC: 3589 Water treatment equipment, in-
dustrial

(G-14313)
TOMCO INDUSTRIES
1660 E County Line Rd (44440-9404)
PHONE....................330 652-7531
Fax: 330 652-7557
Lloyd Tompkins Jr, *President*
EMP: 5
SALES: 600K **Privately Held**
SIC: 3544 Extrusion dies; industrial molds

(G-14314)
VALLEY CONTAINERS INC
3515 Union St (44440-9007)
PHONE....................330 544-2244
Fax: 330 544-5430
Steve Hershfeldt, *President*
Brad Hershfeldt, *Vice Pres*
EMP: 14
SQ FT: 15,000
SALES (est): 2.7MM **Privately Held**
SIC: 2653 Corrugated boxes, partitions,
display items, sheets & pad

(G-14315)
WHOLE SOLUTIONS
1217 Salt Springs Rd (44440-9331)
PHONE....................330 652-1725
Jeffrey Hattendorf, *Principal*
Kathy Budd, *Manager*
Doug Norton, *Agent*
EMP: 3
SALES (est): 373.9K **Privately Held**
SIC: 3541 Drilling & boring machines

Minerva
Stark County

(G-14316)
ALLIANCE PUBLISHING CO INC
Also Called: Minerva Leader
177 Curry St (44657-1817)
P.O. Box 30 (44657-0030)
PHONE....................330 868-5222
Fax: 330 868-3273
Kimberly Lewis, *Manager*
Lynn Bond, *Manager*
Sarah Reed, *Manager*
EMP: 12
SALES (corp-wide): 567.1MM **Privately
Held**
WEB: www.alliancelink.com
SIC: 2711 Newspapers, publishing & print-
ing

(PA)=Parent Co (HQ)=Headquarters (DH)=Div Headquarters
✪ = New Business established in last 2 years

2017 Harris Ohio
Industrial Directory

581

GEOGRAPHIC

HQ: Alliance Publishing Co Inc
　　40 S Linden Ave
　　Alliance OH 44601
　　330 453-1304

(G-14317)
B & H MACHINE INC
15001 Lincoln St Se (44657-8900)
P.O. Box 96 (44657-0096)
PHONE..................................330 868-6425
Fax: 330 868-4699
J Timothy Bush, *President*
Ron Wilhelm, *Engineer*
Ron Wilhelm, *Engineer*
Thomas Williams, *Engineer*
Christine Logan, *Accounting Mgr*
EMP: 36 **EST:** 1951
SQ FT: 70,000
SALES (est): 7.9MM **Privately Held**
WEB: www.bhcylinders.com
SIC: 3593 3599 Fluid power cylinders, hydraulic or pneumatic; machine shop, jobbing & repair

(G-14318)
CARAUSTAR INDUSTRIAL AND CON
Also Called: Minerva Tube Plant
460 Knox Ct (44657-1528)
PHONE..................................330 868-4111
Steve Lacher, *Manager*
EMP: 35
SQ FT: 45,000
SALES (corp-wide): 1.5B **Privately Held**
SIC: 2655 Tubes, fiber or paper: made from purchased material; cores, fiber: made from purchased material
HQ: Caraustar Industrial And Consumer Products Group Inc
　　2031 Carolina Place Dr
　　Fort Mill SC 29708
　　803 548-5100

(G-14319)
COLFOR MANUFACTURING INC
Also Called: Minerva Operations
461 Knox Ct (44657-1530)
PHONE..................................330 863-0404
Kevin Romano, *Plant Mgr*
Rich Varagliotti, *Plant Mgr*
John Staley, *Purchasing*
Dave Bush, *QC Dir*
Robert Nappi, *Human Res Dir*
EMP: 150
SALES (corp-wide): 3.9B **Publicly Held**
SIC: 3462 Iron & steel forgings
HQ: Colfor Manufacturing, Inc.
　　3255 Alliance Rd Nw
　　Malvern OH 44644

(G-14320)
DUTCHCRAFT TRUSS COMPONENT INC
2212 Fox Ave Se (44657-9146)
PHONE..................................330 862-2220
Reginald Stoltzfus, *Principal*
Jennette Stolzfus, *Principal*
EMP: 16
SALES (est): 2.3MM **Privately Held**
SIC: 2439 Structural wood members

(G-14321)
ERVIN LEE LOGGING
8555 Stump Rd (44657-9002)
PHONE..................................330 771-0039
Ervin Lee, *Administration*
EMP: 3
SALES (est): 147.9K **Privately Held**
SIC: 2411 Logging

(G-14322)
GENERAL COLOR INVESTMENTS INC
Also Called: Plastic Color Division
250 Bridge St (44657-1509)
P.O. Box 7 (44657-0007)
PHONE..................................330 868-4161
Fax: 330 868-5880
Holly Gartner, *President*
Keith W Gartner, *Vice Pres*
Sharee Swank, *Purchasing*
Doug Nightengale, *QC Mgr*
EMP: 100 **EST:** 1938
SQ FT: 142,800

SALES (est): 26.5MM **Privately Held**
WEB: www.generalcolor.com
SIC: 2816 3087 Color pigments; custom compound purchased resins

(G-14323)
HARBISONWALKER INTL INC
1316 Alliance Rd Nw (44657-9767)
P.O. Box 240 (44657-0240)
PHONE..................................330 868-4141
Fax: 330 868-5233
Jan Smith, *Branch Mgr*
EMP: 12
SALES (corp-wide): 923MM **Privately Held**
WEB: www.hwr.com
SIC: 3255 Clay refractories
HQ: Harbisonwalker International, Inc.
　　1305 Cherrington Pkwy # 100
　　Moon Township PA 15108
　　412 375-6600

(G-14324)
HARN VAULT SERVICE INC (PA)
422 East St (44657-1429)
PHONE..................................330 832-1995
Karen Harn, *President*
EMP: 12
SQ FT: 4,872
SALES (est): 1.5MM **Privately Held**
SIC: 3272 Burial vaults, concrete or precast terrazzo

(G-14325)
HOFFEE JOHN
Also Called: Lion's Den Sport Shop
207 N Market St (44657-1615)
PHONE..................................330 868-3553
John Hoffee, *Owner*
Rita Hoffee, *Co-Owner*
EMP: 5
SQ FT: 2,500
SALES (est): 240K **Privately Held**
SIC: 5941 2759 Sporting goods & bicycle shops; screen printing

(G-14326)
IMPERIAL ALUM - MINERVA LLC
217 Roosevelt St (44657-1541)
PHONE..................................330 868-7765
Fax: 330 868-4308
Mike Chenoweth, *Vice Pres*
David Riddell, *Vice Pres*
Gary Grim, *Plant Supt*
David Goss, *CFO*
Greg Donay, *Sales Staff*
EMP: 55
SALES (est): 12.7MM **Privately Held**
SIC: 3334 5093 Slabs (primary), aluminum; scrap & waste materials

(G-14327)
KEPCOR INC
Also Called: Ssi Tiles
215 Bridge St (44657-1508)
P.O. Box 119 (44657-0119)
PHONE..................................330 868-6434
Fax: 330 868-6437
Robert B Keplinger, *President*
Connie Keplinger, *Vice Pres*
EMP: 10
SQ FT: 121,500
SALES (est): 700K **Privately Held**
SIC: 3253 3251 Ceramic wall & floor tile; brick & structural clay tile

(G-14328)
KMI PROCESSING LLC (PA)
15383 Lisbon St Ne (44657-9191)
PHONE..................................330 862-2185
Randy Kuttler,
EMP: 7
SALES (est): 2.7MM **Privately Held**
SIC: 3541 Sawing & cutoff machines (metalworking machinery)

(G-14329)
KMI PROCESSING LLC
15441 Lisbon St Ne (44657-9191)
PHONE..................................330 862-2185
EMP: 19
SALES (corp-wide): 2.7MM **Privately Held**
SIC: 3541 Sawing & cutoff machines (metalworking machinery)

PA: Kmi Processing, Llc
　　15383 Lisbon St Ne
　　Minerva OH 44657
　　330 862-2185

(G-14330)
KOUNTRY PRIDE ENTERPRISES
10167 Malibu Rd Ne (44657-9750)
PHONE..................................330 868-3345
Corwin W Stahler, *Partner*
Marian Stahler, *Partner*
EMP: 3
SALES (est): 260K **Privately Held**
SIC: 2448 Wood pallets & skids

(G-14331)
MACHINE DYNAMICS & ENGRG INC
Also Called: Energy Transfer
9312 Arrow Rd Nw (44657-8742)
PHONE..................................330 868-5603
Fax: 330 627-2025
Kenneth Barkan II, *President*
Andrew Powell, *Purchasing*
Kevin Pasiuk, *Engineer*
Paul D Barkan, *Treasurer*
EMP: 75
SQ FT: 240,000
SALES (est): 19.7MM **Privately Held**
WEB: www.machinedynamics.com
SIC: 3498 Tube fabricating (contract bending & shaping); coils, pipe: fabricated from purchased pipe

(G-14332)
MCDANIEL ENVELOPE CO INC
1400 Union Ave Se (44657-9171)
P.O. Box 355, Damascus (44619-0355)
PHONE..................................330 868-5929
James H Pidgeon, *President*
Barry Pidgeon, *Vice Pres*
Michael J Pidgeon, *Admin Sec*
EMP: 17 **EST:** 1973
SALES (est): 2MM **Privately Held**
SIC: 2759 Envelopes: printing

(G-14333)
MCGUIRE MACHINE LLC
1400 Union Ave Se (44657-9171)
PHONE..................................330 868-3072
Patrick McGuire, *Partner*
Kimberly McGuire, *Partner*
EMP: 5
SALES (est): 762.2K **Privately Held**
SIC: 3599 7699 Machine shop, jobbing & repair; industrial machinery & equipment repair

(G-14334)
MINERVA DAIRY INC
Also Called: Minerva Maid
430 Radloff Ave (44657-1400)
P.O. Box 60 (44657-0060)
PHONE..................................330 868-4196
Fax: 330 868-7947
Phillip Muller, *President*
Venae Watts, *Corp Secy*
Adam Muller, *Vice Pres*
Matt Smith, *Engineer*
Diana Lanzer, *Director*
EMP: 65 **EST:** 1970
SQ FT: 53,000
SALES (est): 25.4MM **Privately Held**
WEB: www.minervacheese.com
SIC: 2023 2021 2022 Dry, condensed, evaporated dairy products; creamery butter; processed cheese

(G-14335)
MINERVA WELDING AND FABG INC
22133 Us Route 30 (44657-9401)
P.O. Box 369 (44657-0369)
PHONE..................................330 868-7731
Fax: 330 868-3377
James A Gram, *President*
Mike Gasper, *Project Mgr*
Stephen J Gram, *Treasurer*
Daniel E Gram, *Admin Sec*
Margie Wilson, *Admin Asst*
EMP: 40 **EST:** 1949
SQ FT: 10,000

SALES (est): 18.7MM **Privately Held**
WEB: www.minweld.com
SIC: 5084 3599 Industrial machinery & equipment; machine shop, jobbing & repair

(G-14336)
MONARCH PRODUCTS CO
105 Short St (44657-1698)
P.O. Box 118 (44657-0118)
PHONE..................................330 868-7717
Fax: 330 868-6661
Gene Mercarelli, *Vice Pres*
Gene Mercorelli, *Facilities Mgr*
EMP: 26
SQ FT: 16,000
SALES (est): 3.8MM **Privately Held**
SIC: 3544 Special dies & tools; jigs & fixtures

(G-14337)
PCC AIRFOILS LLC
3860 Union Ave Se (44657-8944)
PHONE..................................330 868-6441
Fax: 330 868-7309
Ken Buck, *Vice Pres*
Scott Bush, *Opers Mgr*
Randall Evans, *Prdtn Mgr*
Todd Kestranek, *Facilities Mgr*
Tammy Crowl, *Purchasing*
EMP: 214
SQ FT: 300,000
SALES (corp-wide): 223.6B **Publicly Held**
WEB: www.pccairfoils.com
SIC: 3369 3324 Nonferrous foundries; steel investment foundries
HQ: Pcc Airfoils Llc
　　3401 Entp Pkwy Ste 200
　　Cleveland OH 44122
　　216 831-3590

(G-14338)
PRECISION CASTPARTS CORP
3860 Union Ave Se (44657-8901)
PHONE..................................330 868-7376
Steve Lohmeyer, *Engineer*
John Jerse, *Manager*
EMP: 8
SALES (est): 1.2MM **Privately Held**
SIC: 7372 Application computer software

(G-14339)
REGAL METAL PRODUCTS CO (PA)
3615 Union Ave Se (44657-8972)
P.O. Box 207 (44657-0207)
PHONE..................................330 868-6343
Fax: 330 868-6648
J Ted Tomak Sr, *President*
Ted Tomak, *Vice Pres*
Charlie Walker, *Plant Mgr*
Jenny Ford, *Manager*
EMP: 44 **EST:** 1965
SQ FT: 125,000
SALES (est): 7.6MM **Privately Held**
SIC: 3469 3544 Stamping metal for the trade; special dies, tools, jigs & fixtures

(G-14340)
REGAL METAL PRODUCTS CO
162 Arbor Rd (44657)
P.O. Box 207 (44657-0207)
PHONE..................................330 868-6343
Fax: 330 868-3538
John Theodore, *Vice Pres*
EMP: 17
SALES (corp-wide): 7.6MM **Privately Held**
SIC: 3469 3544 Metal stampings; special dies & tools
PA: Regal Metal Products Co.
　　3615 Union Ave Se
　　Minerva OH 44657
　　330 868-6343

(G-14341)
RESCAR INDUSTRIES INC
700 Murray Ave (44657-1705)
PHONE..................................630 963-1114
Barb Thomas, *Branch Mgr*
EMP: 19
SALES (corp-wide): 313.9MM **Privately Held**
SIC: 3743 Railroad car rebuilding

PA: Rescar Industries, Inc.
1101 31st St Ste 250
Downers Grove IL 60515
630 963-1114

(G-14342)
SHANEWAY INC (PA)
1032 Brush Rd Ne (44657-9755)
P.O. Box 357, Tallmadge (44278-0357)
PHONE..................................330 868-2220
Paul A Weick, *CEO*
Judith A Miller, *President*
Sam Keller, *Vice Pres*
Jerry Shane, *Vice Pres*
Judy Bell, *Treasurer*
EMP: 5
SQ FT: 800
SALES (est): 570.3K **Privately Held**
SIC: 3341 4953 7361 Recovery & refining of nonferrous metals; recycling, waste materials; labor contractors (employment agency)

(G-14343)
SUMMITVILLE TILES INC
1310 Alliance Rd Nw (44657-9767)
P.O. Box 283 (44657-0283)
PHONE..................................330 868-6771
Fax: 330 868-4470
James A Miller, *Manager*
EMP: 130
SALES (corp-wide): 34MM **Privately Held**
WEB: www.summitville.com
SIC: 3253 Floor tile, ceramic; wall tile, ceramic
PA: Summitville Tiles, Inc
15364 State Rte 644
Summitville OH 43962
330 223-1511

(G-14344)
SUMMITVILLE TILES INC
Also Called: Summitville Lab
81 Arbor Rd Ne (44657-8755)
P.O. Box 90 (44657-0090)
PHONE..................................330 868-6463
Fax: 330 868-5638
Joseph Dutt, *Manager*
EMP: 23
SALES (corp-wide): 34MM **Privately Held**
WEB: www.summitville.com
SIC: 2891 3255 2899 Epoxy adhesives; clay refractories; chemical preparations
PA: Summitville Tiles, Inc
15364 State Rte 644
Summitville OH 43962
330 223-1511

(G-14345)
WESTMONT INC
3035 Union Ave Ne (44657-8667)
PHONE..................................330 862-3080
Fax: 330 862-3080
Michael Zawaski, *President*
EMP: 8
SQ FT: 5,000
SALES (est): 1.2MM **Privately Held**
WEB: www.westmontinc.com
SIC: 3824 Mechanical & electromechanical counters & devices

Minford
Scioto County

(G-14346)
SWARTZ AUDIE
Also Called: Swartz Race Cars
527 Flower Ison Rd (45653-7900)
PHONE..................................740 820-2341
Fax: 740 820-4123
Audie Swartz, *Owner*
Tammy Swartz, *Admin Sec*
EMP: 3
SALES (est): 286.8K **Privately Held**
SIC: 3799 Off-road automobiles, except recreational vehicles

Mingo Junction
Jefferson County

(G-14347)
CHOICE BRANDS
2680 Commercial Ave (43938-1613)
P.O. Box 2399, Steubenville (43953-0399)
PHONE..................................740 598-4121
Fax: 740 598-4618
Michael Bellas, *Principal*
EMP: 8
SALES (est): 739.5K **Privately Held**
SIC: 2082 Beer (alcoholic beverage)

(G-14348)
EASTERN AUTOMATED PIPING
424 State St (43938-1053)
P.O. Box 249 (43938-0249)
PHONE..................................740 535-8184
Ron Kleineke, *Owner*
EMP: 6
SALES (est): 1MM **Privately Held**
SIC: 3499 3312 1711 1623 Fabricated metal products; blast furnaces & steel mills; plumbing, heating, air-conditioning contractors; pipeline construction

Minster
Auglaize County

(G-14349)
ALBERT FREYTAG INC
306 Executive Dr (45865)
P.O. Box 5 (45865-0005)
PHONE..................................419 628-2018
Fax: 419 628-3771
William Freytag, *President*
Joseph Freytag, *Vice Pres*
Kelli Francis, *Engineer*
Dorothy Weaver, *Controller*
EMP: 25 **EST:** 1943
SQ FT: 1,200
SALES (est): 6.7MM **Privately Held**
SIC: 3441 1741 Fabricated structural metal; masonry & other stonework

(G-14350)
BENDCO MACHINE & TOOL CO INC
283 W 1st St (45865-1251)
P.O. Box 6 (45865-0006)
PHONE..................................419 628-3802
Fax: 419 628-3145
Kenneth C Wolaver, *President*
Norman E Tidwell, *Corp Secy*
Brian Schwieterman, *Project Engr*
Pamela Thomas, *CFO*
Norman E Tidwll, *Treasurer*
EMP: 13
SQ FT: 19,500
SALES (est): 825K **Privately Held**
WEB: www.bendcomachine.com
SIC: 3542 3547 Bending machines; rolling mill machinery

(G-14351)
DUCO TOOL & DIE INC
19 S Main St (45865-1349)
PHONE..................................419 628-2031
Fax: 419 628-3709
Dale J Dues, *President*
Margaret Dues, *Corp Secy*
EMP: 10
SQ FT: 10,000
SALES (est): 1.3MM **Privately Held**
WEB: www.ducotoolanddie.com
SIC: 3544 7692 Special dies & tools; welding repair

(G-14352)
EGYPT STRUCTURAL STEEL PROC
480 Osterloh Rd (45865-9750)
P.O. Box 124 (45865-0124)
PHONE..................................419 628-2375
Fax: 419 628-3414
Kenneth Osterloh, *President*
Doris Osterloh, *Vice Pres*
EMP: 40
SQ FT: 36,360

SALES (est): 3.9MM **Privately Held**
SIC: 3441 3312 Fabricated structural metal; blast furnaces & steel mills

(G-14353)
GB IMAGE MACHINE INCORPORATED (PA)
179 N Ohio St (45865-1072)
P.O. Box 181 (45865-0181)
PHONE..................................419 628-4150
Fax: 419 628-4922
Lynn Bergman, *President*
Jerry Bergman, *Vice Pres*
EMP: 5
SQ FT: 12,000
SALES (est): 300K **Privately Held**
SIC: 3599 Machine shop, jobbing & repair

(G-14354)
GLOBUS PRINTING & PACKG CO INC (PA)
1 Executive Pkwy (45865-1274)
P.O. Box 114 (45865-0114)
PHONE..................................419 628-2381
Fax: 419 628-3105
Dennis Schmiesing, *President*
Tim Schmiesing, *Corp Secy*
Mike Grunner, *Controller*
Tom Kasle, *Sales Staff*
Dick Harrod, *Sales Executive*
EMP: 70 **EST:** 1957
SQ FT: 100,000
SALES (est): 15.8MM **Privately Held**
WEB: www.globusprinting.com
SIC: 2752 Commercial printing, lithographic

(G-14355)
HORIZON PUBLICATIONS INC
Also Called: Community Post
326 N Main St Ste 200 (45865)
P.O. Box 155 (45865-0155)
PHONE..................................419 628-2369
Fax: 419 628-4712
Deb Zwez, *Manager*
EMP: 4
SALES (corp-wide): 71.4MM **Privately Held**
WEB: www.malvern-online.com
SIC: 2711 Newspapers
PA: Horizon Publications, Inc.
1120 N Carbon St Ste 100
Marion IL 62959
618 993-1711

(G-14356)
KARD WELDING INC
Also Called: Kard Bridge Products
480 Osterloh Rd (45865-9750)
P.O. Box 124 (45865-0124)
PHONE..................................419 628-2598
Fax: 419 628-3114
Doris Osterloh, *President*
Ken Osterloh, *Owner*
Kenneth H Osterloh, *Vice Pres*
Jason Osterloh, *Data Proc Staff*
EMP: 20
SQ FT: 36,360
SALES (est): 5.6MM **Privately Held**
SIC: 3499 3443 Machine bases, metal; fabricated plate work (boiler shop)

(G-14357)
MACHINE CONCEPTS INC
2167 State Route 66 (45865-9401)
P.O. Box 127 (45865-0127)
PHONE..................................419 628-3498
Fax: 419 628-2794
John Eiting, *President*
David Kahlig, *Plant Mgr*
Randy May, *Draft/Design*
Chad Wray, *Engineer*
Janet Bruns, *Manager*
▲ **EMP:** 32
SQ FT: 30,000
SALES (est): 9.2MM **Privately Held**
WEB: www.machineconcepts.com
SIC: 3542 Machine tools, metal forming type

(G-14358)
MARK ONE MANUFACTURING LTD
351 Industrial Dr Ste 9 (45865-1258)
PHONE..................................419 628-4405
Doug Larger, *President*

Renee Rosengarden, *Office Mgr*
EMP: 4
SALES (est): 331.7K **Privately Held**
SIC: 3443 Plate work for the metalworking trade

(G-14359)
POST PRINTING CO (PA)
205 W 4th St (45865-1062)
P.O. Box 101 (45865-0101)
PHONE..................................859 254-7714
Fax: 419 628-4040
Tim Thompson, *President*
Glenn Thompson II, *Vice Pres*
Dan Schmiesing, *Plant Mgr*
Gary Nosek, *Accountant*
Lucy Homan, *Accounts Exec*
EMP: 54 **EST:** 1896
SQ FT: 14,400
SALES (est): 12.5MM **Privately Held**
WEB: www.postprinting.com
SIC: 2759 2752 Letterpress printing; commercial printing, offset

(G-14360)
PROGRESS TOOL & STAMPING INC
Also Called: Progress Tool Co
207 Southgate Dr (45865)
P.O. Box 53 (45865-0053)
PHONE..................................419 628-2384
Fax: 419 628-3708
Lee H Westerheide, *President*
Jeff Johnston, *Design Engr*
EMP: 20
SQ FT: 22,000
SALES (est): 3.4MM **Privately Held**
SIC: 3544 3469 Special dies & tools; jigs & fixtures; metal stampings

(G-14361)
SECURCOM INC
307 W 1st St (45865-1210)
P.O. Box 116 (45865-0116)
PHONE..................................419 628-1049
Fax: 419 628-2015
Bill Bergman, *President*
James R Shenk, *Principal*
Tanya Prenger, *Sales Mgr*
Marlene Hoying, *Admin Sec*
EMP: 22 **EST:** 1997
SALES (est): 3.6MM **Privately Held**
WEB: www.securcom.com
SIC: 5999 7382 3699 5065 Telephone & communication equipment; security systems services; security control equipment & systems; communication equipment

(G-14362)
SUNRISE COOPERATIVE INC
Also Called: Minster Farmers
292 W 4th St (45865-1024)
P.O. Box 100 (45865-0100)
PHONE..................................419 628-4705
Mike Bensman, *Branch Mgr*
EMP: 11
SALES (corp-wide): 46.5MM **Privately Held**
SIC: 5191 5153 5172 2041 Farm supplies; grain elevators; grains; field beans; engine fuels & oils; flour & other grain mill products
PA: Sunrise Cooperative, Inc.
2025 W State St Ste A
Fremont OH 43420
419 332-6468

(G-14363)
THE DANNON COMPANY INC
216 Southgate Dr (45865)
P.O. Box 122 (45865-0122)
PHONE..................................419 628-3861
Fax: 419 628-4008
Larry McCartney, *Facilities Mgr*
Dane Thrush, *Production*
Diane Wright, *Hum Res Coord*
Didier Menu, *Manager*
Greg Burnette, *Manager*
EMP: 390
SALES (corp-wide): 685.2MM **Privately Held**
WEB: www.dannon.com
SIC: 2024 Yogurt desserts, frozen

HQ: The Dannon Company Inc
100 Hillside Ave Fl 3
White Plains NY 10603
914 872-8400

(G-14364)
THIEMAN MACHINE
5395 State Route 119 (45865-9404)
PHONE..................................419 628-2474
Fax: 419 628-2474
Ken Thieman, *President*
EMP: 3
SALES (est): 428.8K **Privately Held**
SIC: 3599 Machine shop, jobbing & repair

(G-14365)
TRADEMARK DESIGNS INC
17 Jackson St (45865-1144)
P.O. Box 217 (45865-0217)
PHONE..................................419 628-3897
Fax: 419 628-2497
Mark Nolan, *President*
Jerry Henkaline, *Corp Secy*
Barbara Starr, *Vice Pres*
Beau Williams, *Accounts Mgr*
EMP: 20
SQ FT: 3,700
SALES: 2.8MM **Privately Held**
SIC: 3999 Identification plates

Mogadore
Portage County

(G-14366)
AKRON CULTURED MARBLE PDTS LLC
3992 Mogadore Rd (44260-1303)
PHONE..................................330 628-6757
Chris Stiffler,
EMP: 3
SALES: 200K **Privately Held**
SIC: 3281 Cut stone & stone products

(G-14367)
AMERIMOLD INC
595a Waterloo Rd Ste A (44260-8710)
PHONE..................................330 628-2190
Fax: 330 628-2856
Bill Wensel, *President*
EMP: 6
SQ FT: 2,000
SALES: 550K **Privately Held**
WEB: www.amerimold.com
SIC: 3544 3599 Industrial molds; machine
shop, jobbing & repair

(G-14368)
ARCONIC INC
Also Called: Alcoa
3340 Gilchrist Rd (44260-1254)
PHONE..................................330 835-6000
Kevin Matske, *Manager*
EMP: 135
SALES (corp-wide): 12.3B **Publicly Held**
SIC: 3353 Aluminum sheet & strip
PA: Arconic Inc.
390 Park Ave
New York NY 10022
212 836-2758

(G-14369)
BICO AKRON INC
Also Called: Bico Steel Service Centers
3100 Gilchrist Rd (44260-1246)
PHONE..................................330 794-1716
Fax: 330 733-7189
Thomas Fiocca, *President*
Marilyn L Tuzzio, *Principal*
Michael Ensminger, *Vice Pres*
Chad Kovitk, *Controller*
▲ EMP: 65
SQ FT: 90,000
SALES (est): 48.2MM
SALES (corp-wide): 61.6MM **Privately Held**
SIC: 5051 3443 Steel; fabricated plate
work (boiler shop)
HQ: Bico Michigan, Inc.
O-99 Steele St Nw
Grand Rapids MI 49534
616 453-2400

(G-14370)
CORNWELL QUALITY TOOLS COMPANY
200 N Cleveland Ave (44260-1205)
PHONE..................................330 628-2627
Fax: 330 628-8496
Bill Nobley, *Branch Mgr*
Dianna Stump, *Executive*
EMP: 75
SQ FT: 3,000
SALES (corp-wide): 151.2MM **Privately Held**
WEB: www.cornwelltools.com
SIC: 3423 5085 Hand & edge tools; industrial supplies
PA: The Cornwell Quality Tools Company
667 Seville Rd
Wadsworth OH 44281
330 336-3506

(G-14371)
COUNTRYSIDE PUMPING INC
1496 Martin Rd (44260-1558)
PHONE..................................330 628-0058
Melissa Rufener, *President*
Mary J Roth, *Corp Secy*
EMP: 3
SALES: 50.4K **Privately Held**
SIC: 1389 Oil field services; gas field services

(G-14372)
CREATIVE ELEMENTS STUDIO
1717 Trares Rd (44260-9349)
PHONE..................................330 606-2068
EMP: 3
SALES (est): 196.8K **Privately Held**
SIC: 2819 Mfg Industrial Inorganic Chemicals

(G-14373)
DUMAS MEATS INC
857 Randolph Rd (44260-9343)
P.O. Box 54 (44260-0054)
PHONE..................................330 628-3438
Fax: 330 628-3438
Dave Duma, *President*
Beverley Duma, *Treasurer*
EMP: 8
SQ FT: 3,000
SALES (est): 770.7K **Privately Held**
WEB: www.dumameatsfarmmarket.com
SIC: 5421 2013 Freezer provisioners,
meat; meat markets, including freezer
provisioners; sausages & other prepared
meats

(G-14374)
ENDURANCE MANUFACTURING INC
213 Randolph Rd (44260-1341)
PHONE..................................330 628-2600
Thomas J Turkalj, *Principal*
EMP: 5
SALES (est): 473.4K **Privately Held**
SIC: 2813 Industrial gases

(G-14375)
EXTRUDED SILICON PRODUCTS INC
3300 Gilchrist Rd (44260-1254)
PHONE..................................330 733-0101
Joseph E Foreman, *President*
EMP: 48
SALES (est): 7MM **Privately Held**
SIC: 3061 Mechanical rubber goods

(G-14376)
GEORGIA-PACIFIC LLC
3265 Gilchrist Rd (44260-1247)
PHONE..................................330 794-4444
Fax: 330 794-8667
Chad Kalka, *Production*
Tony Baldacci, *Sales Staff*
Charles Brown, *Mktg Coord*
Craig McNeil, *Manager*
EMP: 150
SALES (corp-wide): 27.3B **Privately Held**
WEB: www.gp.com
SIC: 2621 Paper mills
HQ: Georgia-Pacific Llc
133 Peachtree St Ne # 4810
Atlanta GA 30303
404 652-4000

(G-14377)
HUNTERS MANUFACTURING CO INC (PA)
Also Called: Tenpoint Crossbow Technologies
1325 Waterloo Rd (44260-9608)
PHONE..................................330 628-9245
Fax: 330 628-0999
Richard L Bednar, *CEO*
George R Gardner, *President*
Steve Hays, *Purch Mgr*
Dick Gardner, *Engineer*
Joanna Rolenz, *CFO*
▲ EMP: 30
SALES (est): 8MM **Privately Held**
WEB: www.tenpointcrossbows.com
SIC: 3949 Crossbows; arrows, archery

(G-14378)
JANORPOT LLC
3175 Gilchrist Rd (44260-1245)
PHONE..................................330 564-0232
Fax: 330 564-0239
Norm Belliveau, *President*
Ron Vandiver, *Vice Pres*
Rob Gumpf, *Sales Mgr*
Kimberly Pratt, *Accounts Mgr*
Ann Saccone, *Office Mgr*
▲ EMP: 35
SQ FT: 40,000
SALES (est): 9.2MM **Privately Held**
WEB: www.janorpot.com
SIC: 3089 Flower pots, plastic

(G-14379)
KENT ELASTOMER PRODUCTS INC
3890 Mogadore Indus Pkwy (44260-1223)
PHONE..................................800 331-4762
Murrey Vanepp, *Principal*
EMP: 6
SALES (corp-wide): 374.1MM **Privately Held**
SIC: 3052 Rubber & plastics hose & beltings
HQ: Kent Elastomer Products, Inc.
1500 Saint Clair Ave
Kent OH 44240
330 673-1011

(G-14380)
LABEL PRINT TECHNOLOGIES LLC
3380 Gilchrist Rd (44260-1254)
PHONE..................................800 475-4030
Dennis Corrado,
▲ EMP: 15
SALES (est): 4.1MM **Privately Held**
SIC: 2754 Labels: gravure printing

(G-14381)
MOORE WELL SERVICES INC
246 N Cleveland Ave (44260-1205)
PHONE..................................330 650-4443
Fax: 330 650-0105
Jeff Moore, *President*
Jeita Moore, *Vice Pres*
EMP: 21
SQ FT: 8,000
SALES (est): 4.9MM **Privately Held**
SIC: 1381 Drilling oil & gas wells

(G-14382)
OMNOVA SOLUTIONS INC
Gencorp Specialty Polmers
165 S Cleveland Ave (44260-1593)
PHONE..................................330 628-6550
Fax: 330 628-6501
Marvin Zima, *President*
Richard Garrett, *Plant Mgr*
Gerald Miller, *Project Mgr*
Duane Clarke, *Mfg Staff*
Lou Franceschelli, *Purchasing*
EMP: 150
SALES (corp-wide): 759.9MM **Publicly Held**
WEB: www.omnova.com
SIC: 2824 3087 Organic fibers, noncellulosic; custom compound purchased resins
PA: Omnova Solutions Inc.
25435 Harvard Rd
Beachwood OH 44122
216 682-7000

(G-14383)
RUBBERMAID INCORPORATED
3200 Gilchrist Rd (44260-1248)
PHONE..................................330 733-7771
Joe Soldano, *Plant Mgr*
John Bias, *Manager*
Matt Blake, *Manager*
EMP: 182
SALES (corp-wide): 13.2B **Publicly Held**
WEB: www.rubbermaid.com
SIC: 3089 Planters, plastic; plastic kitchenware, tableware & houseware
HQ: Rubbermaid Incorporated
3 Glenlake Pkwy
Atlanta GA 30328
770 418-7000

(G-14384)
SAM AMERICAS INC
3555 Gilchrist Rd (44260-1240)
P.O. Box 8 (44260-0008)
PHONE..................................330 628-1118
Kaz Nakai, *CEO*
Kenji Saito, *President*
Jay Theiss, *Vice Pres*
Sean Ellis, *Opers Mgr*
Jim Gilmore, *Warehouse Mgr*
EMP: 33
SQ FT: 60,000
SALES (est): 6.8MM
SALES (corp-wide): 836.5MM **Privately Held**
SIC: 3369 Castings, except die-castings, precision
PA: Shinagawa Refractories Co.,Ltd.
2-2-1, Otemachi
Chiyoda-Ku TKY 100-0
362 651-600

(G-14385)
SHINAGAWA ADVANCED MATERIALS A
3555 Gilchrist Rd (44260-1240)
P.O. Box 8 (44260-0008)
PHONE..................................330 628-1118
K G Keiji Saito, *President*
Jay Theiss, *Plant Mgr*
◆ EMP: 28
SQ FT: 28,800
SALES (est): 5.5MM **Privately Held**
WEB: www.fmpinc.net
SIC: 3399 Metal powders, pastes & flakes

(G-14386)
SUMMIT MACHINE LTD
3991 Mogadore Rd (44260-1367)
PHONE..................................330 628-2663
Fax: 330 628-1468
Clement Knapp, *General Mgr*
Kim Downey, *Manager*
Jim Burns,
▲ EMP: 20
SQ FT: 23,000
SALES (est): 4.4MM **Privately Held**
WEB: www.summitmachine.com
SIC: 3451 Screw machine products

(G-14387)
VERTEX INC
3956 Mogadore Indus Pkwy (44260-1201)
PHONE..................................330 628-6230
Fax: 330 628-6231
Ronald Mayfield, *President*
Salvatore Brugnano, *Chairman*
James Westhoff, *Corp Secy*
Mike Ferarra, *Vice Pres*
▲ EMP: 30
SQ FT: 20,000
SALES (est): 8.2MM **Privately Held**
SIC: 3069 3061 3053 Valves, hard rubber; mechanical rubber goods; gaskets, packing & sealing devices

---

Monclova
Lucas County

(G-14388)
ADVANCED LITHO SYSTEMS
4429 Weckerly Rd (43542-9483)
PHONE..................................419 865-2652
Marty McClanahan, *Owner*
EMP: 4

▲ = Import ▼=Export
◆ =Import/Export

SALES (est): 240K **Privately Held**
WEB: www.advancedlithosystems.com
SIC: 3861 Printing equipment, photographic

Monroe
Butler County

(G-14389)
ADIDAS NORTH AMERICA INC
937 Premium Outlets Dr (45050-1843)
PHONE..................................513 360-2979
EMP: 4
SALES (corp-wide): 20.4B **Privately Held**
SIC: 2329 Athletic (warmup, sweat & jogging) suits: men's & boys'
HQ: Adidas North America, Inc.
5055 N Greeley Ave
Portland OR 97217
971 234-2300

(G-14390)
ADVANCED GROUND SYSTEMS
441 Breaden Dr (45050-1490)
PHONE..................................513 402-7226
Roy Stone, *Manager*
EMP: 18
SALES (corp-wide): 23.7MM **Privately Held**
SIC: 3724 Aircraft engines & engine parts
HQ: Advanced Ground Systems Engineering Llc
10805 Painter Ave
Santa Fe Springs CA 90670
562 906-9300

(G-14391)
AM RETAIL GROUP INC
628 Premium Outlets Dr (45050-1836)
PHONE..................................513 539-7837
EMP: 3
SALES (corp-wide): 2.3B **Publicly Held**
SIC: 3199 Leather garments
HQ: Am Retail Group, Inc.
7401 Boone Ave N
Brooklyn Park MN 55428
763 391-4000

(G-14392)
ARKAY INDUSTRIES INC (PA)
240 American Way (45050-1202)
PHONE..................................513 360-0390
Kevin Kuhnash, *President*
John Kuhnash, *Exec VP*
Steve Jones, *Vice Pres*
Janet Rosser, *Accountant*
Jody Carter, *Human Res Dir*
EMP: 25
SQ FT: 19,000
SALES (est): 31.5MM **Privately Held**
SIC: 3089 3086 Injection molding of plastics; plastic processing; plastics foam products

(G-14393)
ARKAY PLASTICS ALABAMA INC (HQ)
220 American Way (45050-1202)
PHONE..................................513 360-0390
Fax: 513 539-8904
Kevin John Kuhnash, *CEO*
John Kuhnash, *CEO*
Arthur R Kuhnash, *Ch of Bd*
Chris Smith, *General Mgr*
Jeff Testerman, *General Mgr*
EMP: 15
SALES (est): 23.5MM
SALES (corp-wide): 31.5MM **Privately Held**
SIC: 3089 Injection molding of plastics
PA: Arkay Industries, Inc.
240 American Way
Monroe OH 45050
513 360-0390

(G-14394)
BITS & CHIPS MACHINING COMPANY
730 Lebanon St (45050-1439)
PHONE..................................513 539-0800
Kimberly A Ludwig, *President*
EMP: 8
SQ FT: 6,000

SALES (est): 1.9MM **Privately Held**
SIC: 3599 Machine & other job shop work

(G-14395)
CHROME DEPOSIT CORPORATION
341 Lawton Ave (45050-1215)
PHONE..................................513 539-8486
Fax: 513 539-8013
Mark Kidd, *Human Resources*
Vikas Kapil, *Chief Mktg Ofcr*
Dan Zimmerman, *Manager*
Tonya Chapman, *Manager*
Edward Schultz, *Supervisor*
EMP: 27
SALES (corp-wide): 23.7MM **Privately Held**
WEB: www.cdcportage.com
SIC: 3471 Chromium plating of metals or formed products
PA: Chrome Deposit Corporation
6640 Melton Rd
Portage IN 46368
219 763-1571

(G-14396)
CHROME DEPOSIT CORPORATION
341 Lawton Ave (45050-1215)
PHONE..................................513 539-8486
EMP: 40
SALES (corp-wide): 24.7MM **Privately Held**
SIC: 3471 Plating And Polishing
PA: Chrome Deposit Corporation
6640 Melton Rd
Portage IN 46368
219 763-1571

(G-14397)
CIPTED CORP
301 Lawton Ave (45050-1215)
PHONE..................................412 829-2120
Victor Tedesco, *President*
Ann Einsporn, *Bookkeeper*
EMP: 75
SALES (est): 4.8MM **Privately Held**
SIC: 3713 5012 Truck bodies (motor vehicles); trucks, noncommercial

(G-14398)
COACH INC
849 Premium Outlets Dr (45050-1841)
PHONE..................................513 539-8087
EMP: 15
SALES (corp-wide): 4.4B **Publicly Held**
SIC: 3171 Women's handbags & purses
PA: Coach, Inc.
10 Hudson Yards
New York NY 10001
212 594-1850

(G-14399)
DECEUNINCK NORTH AMERICA LLC (PA)
351 N Garver Rd (45050-1233)
PHONE..................................513 539-5466
Filip Geeraert, *President*
Roy Frost, *Managing Dir*
Scott Sheffield, *Vice Pres*
Heather Slaton, *Safety Dir*
Richard Harnis, *Purchasing*
▲ **EMP:** 269 **EST:** 1969
SALES (est): 125MM **Privately Held**
WEB: www.daytech.com
SIC: 3082 Unsupported plastics profile shapes

(G-14400)
DIXIE MACHINERY INC
Also Called: Dixitech Cnc
845 Todhunter Rd (45050-1032)
P.O. Box 1019, Mason (45040-6019)
PHONE..................................513 360-0091
Richard Patrick, *President*
EMP: 12
SQ FT: 23,000
SALES (est): 3.5MM **Privately Held**
WEB: www.dixiemachineryinc.com
SIC: 3541 Machine tools, metal cutting type

(G-14401)
FLEETCHEM LLC
651 N Garver Rd (45050-1207)
PHONE..................................513 539-1111
Angela Lovejoy, *Controller*
Tj Blakemor, *Branch Mgr*
EMP: 10
SALES (corp-wide): 1.1MM **Privately Held**
WEB: www.fleetchem.com
SIC: 2045 Blended flour: from purchased flour
PA: Fleetchem, Llc
1222 Brassie Ave Ste 19
Flossmoor IL 60422
708 957-5311

(G-14402)
GARDNER METAL CRAFT INC
490 S Main St (45050-1415)
P.O. Box 176 (45050-0176)
PHONE..................................513 539-4538
Fax: 513 539-4511
Jack Blevins, *President*
Gail Blevins, *Vice Pres*
EMP: 5
SQ FT: 8,000
SALES (est): 807.7K **Privately Held**
WEB: www.gardnermetalcraft.net
SIC: 3441 Fabricated structural metal

(G-14403)
GLASS COATINGS & CONCEPTS LLC
300 Lawton Ave (45050-1216)
PHONE..................................513 539-5300
Fax: 513 539-5177
Jeff Nixon,
▲ **EMP:** 25
SALES (est): 6.1MM
SALES (corp-wide): 34.4MM **Privately Held**
WEB: www.gcconcepts.com
SIC: 2893 Printing ink
PA: The Shepherd Color Company
4539 Dues Dr
West Chester OH 45246
513 874-0714

(G-14404)
HI TECH TOOL CORPORATION
415 Breaden Dr Ste 1 (45050-2479)
PHONE..................................513 346-4061
James Gregory, *Ch of Bd*
Kelly Thompson, *Exec VP*
EMP: 5
SALES (est): 613.3K **Privately Held**
SIC: 3545 Cutting tools for machine tools

(G-14405)
HONEY CELL INC MID WEST
6480 Hamilton Lebanon Rd (45044-9285)
PHONE..................................513 360-0280
Rick Gillette, *General Mgr*
EMP: 27
SQ FT: 40,000
SALES (est): 5.4MM **Privately Held**
SIC: 2621 Paper mills
PA: Honey Cell, Inc.
850 Union Ave
Bridgeport CT 06607

(G-14406)
JOURNEY ELECTRONICS CORP
902 N Garver Rd (45050-1241)
PHONE..................................513 539-9836
Michael Gorden, *President*
Jeremy Ackerman, *Accounting Mgr*
EMP: 7
SQ FT: 3,000
SALES: 400K
SALES (corp-wide): 544.6K **Privately Held**
WEB: www.gorden.org
SIC: 3672 3823 Printed circuit boards; industrial process control instruments
PA: Gorden Inc.
201 Inspiration Blvd # 400
Reading PA 19607
610 644-4476

(G-14407)
KERRY FLAVOR SYSTEMS US LLC
Also Called: Kerry Ingredients & Flavours
1055 Reed Dr (45050-1725)
PHONE..................................513 539-7373
David Moats, *Vice Pres*
Robert Jennings, *Safety Mgr*
EMP: 28 **Privately Held**
WEB: www.cargill.com
SIC: 2869 2819 Flavors or flavoring materials, synthetic; industrial inorganic chemicals
PA: Kerry Flavor Systems Us, Llc
10261 Chester Rd
Cincinnati OH 45215

(G-14408)
KLW PLASTICS INC
930 Deneen Ave (45050-1210)
PHONE..................................678 674-2990
Mike Legeza, *Branch Mgr*
EMP: 8
SALES (corp-wide): 824MM **Privately Held**
SIC: 3089 Plastic containers, except foam
HQ: Klw Plastics, Inc.
980 Deneen Ave
Monroe OH 45050
513 539-2673

(G-14409)
KLW PLASTICS INC (DH)
980 Deneen Ave (45050-1210)
PHONE..................................513 539-2673
Kenneth M Roessler, *President*
Russ Neuman, *Opers Staff*
Don Pearson, *CFO*
Kristen Evans, *Sales Staff*
Kathleen Jay, *Marketing Staff*
EMP: 6
SQ FT: 37,000
SALES (est): 8.6MM
SALES (corp-wide): 824MM **Privately Held**
WEB: www.klwplastics.com
SIC: 3089 5099 Blow molded finished plastic products; containers: glass, metal or plastic
HQ: Bway Corporation
8607 Roberts Dr Ste 250
Atlanta GA 30350
770 645-4800

(G-14410)
LEVI STRAUSS & CO
211 Premium Outlets Dr (45050-1829)
PHONE..................................513 539-7822
EMP: 19
SALES (corp-wide): 4.5B **Privately Held**
SIC: 2325 Jeans: men's, youths' & boys'
PA: Levi Strauss & Co.
1155 Battery St
San Francisco CA 94111
415 501-6000

(G-14411)
ORORA NORTH AMERICA
Also Called: Landsberg Cincinnati Div 1017
930 Deneen Ave (45050-1210)
PHONE..................................513 539-8274
Bob Firenze, *Manager*
EMP: 5
SALES (corp-wide): 2.8B **Privately Held**
SIC: 5113 2653 Paper & products, wrapping or coarse; boxes, corrugated: made from purchased materials
HQ: Orora Packaging Solutions
6600 Valley View St
Buena Park CA 90620
714 562-6000

(G-14412)
R & L SOFTWARE LLC (PA)
Also Called: Marz Direct
421 Breaden Dr Ste 3 (45050-1575)
PHONE..................................513 847-4942
Robert Casto, *President*
Lawanna Casto,
EMP: 9
SQ FT: 2,500
SALES (est): 1.3MM **Privately Held**
SIC: 7373 7372 Computer system selling services; prepackaged software

(G-14413)
SNYDER CONCRETE
PRODUCTS INC
Also Called: Snyder Brick and Block
233 Senate Dr (45050-1716)
PHONE..................................513 539-7686
Fax: 513 539-8215
Lee Snyder, *Manager*
EMP: 12
SQ FT: 37,984
SALES (corp-wide): 13.3MM **Privately Held**
WEB: www.snyderonline.com
SIC: 5999 5211 3272 Concrete products, pre-cast; brick; concrete products, precast
PA: Snyder Concrete Products, Inc.
2301 W Dorothy Ln
Moraine OH 45439
937 885-5176

(G-14414)
STERLING PAPER COMPANY
INC
960 Deneen Ave (45050-1210)
PHONE..................................513 242-3678
Fax: 937 224-8588
Robert Rosenfeld, *President*
EMP: 15
SALES (est): 1.4MM **Privately Held**
SIC: 2671 Paper coated or laminated for packaging

(G-14415)
STEWARTS MACHINING INC
960 Holman Dr (45050-1077)
PHONE..................................513 422-5000
Fax: 513 422-5017
Karen Stewart, *President*
Kenneth Stewart, *Vice Pres*
EMP: 5
SQ FT: 4,000
SALES (est): 390K **Privately Held**
SIC: 3599 Machine shop, jobbing & repair

(G-14416)
TEREX UTILITIES INC
Also Called: Cincinnati Division
920 Deneen Ave (45050-1210)
PHONE..................................513 539-9770
Fax: 513 539-6971
Steve Harris, *Vice Pres*
Ron Schmittou, *Regl Sales Mgr*
Rick Girffis, *Branch Mgr*
Ruedi Vancoppenolle, *Manager*
Stephen Watkin, *Supervisor*
EMP: 53
SALES (corp-wide): 4.4B **Publicly Held**
WEB: www.craneamerica.com
SIC: 3531 7629 3536 Cranes; electrical repair shops; hoists, cranes & monorails
HQ: Terex Utilities, Inc.
12805 Sw 77th Pl
Tigard OR 97223
503 620-0611

(G-14417)
VALVSYS LLC
421 Breaden Dr Ste 15 (45050-1575)
PHONE..................................513 539-1234
Fax: 513 539-2176
Brad Frank, *President*
Lak Frank,
▲ EMP: 8 EST: 2000
SQ FT: 1,200
SALES (est): 1.1MM **Privately Held**
WEB: www.valvsys.com
SIC: 2812 Alkalies

(G-14418)
VINYL BUILDING PRODUCTS
LLC
351 N Garver Rd (45050-1233)
PHONE..................................513 539-4444
Ralph Weiss, *President*
Bruce Jones, *Controller*
EMP: 265
SALES (est): 15MM **Privately Held**
WEB: www.tkvbp.com
SIC: 3081 Unsupported plastics film & sheet; vinyl film & sheet

(G-14419)
WAFFLE HOUSE INC
1225 Hamilton Lebanon Rd (45050-1705)
PHONE..................................513 539-8372

Fax: 513 539-8372
Rob Helton, *Branch Mgr*
EMP: 19
SALES (corp-wide): 752.9MM **Privately Held**
SIC: 2096 5145 Potato chips & similar snacks; snack foods
PA: Waffle House, Inc.
5986 Financial Dr
Norcross GA 30071
770 729-5700

(G-14420)
WORTHINGTON INDUSTRIES
INC
Worthington Steel
350 Lawton Ave (45050-1216)
PHONE..................................513 539-9291
John Lawhorn, *Purchasing*
Rusty Alward, *QC Dir*
Daniel Kay, *Engineer*
Dustin Lawson, *Engineer*
David Kleimeyer, *Sales/Mktg Mgr*
EMP: 165
SQ FT: 120,000
SALES (corp-wide): 2.8B **Publicly Held**
WEB: www.worthingtonindustries.com
SIC: 3325 5051 3471 3441 Steel foundries; metals service centers & offices; plating & polishing; fabricated structural metal; blast furnaces & steel mills
PA: Worthington Industries, Inc.
200 W Old Wlson Bridge Rd
Worthington OH 43085
614 438-3210

(G-14421)
XEROX CORPORATION
6500 Hamilton Lebanon Rd (45044-9702)
PHONE..................................513 539-4858
Greg Bafaoyga, *Manager*
William Detcher, *Manager*
EMP: 84
SALES (corp-wide): 10.7B **Publicly Held**
SIC: 3577 Computer peripheral equipment
PA: Xerox Corporation
201 Merritt 7
Norwalk CT 06851
203 968-3000

(G-14422)
XEROX CORPORATION
6490 Hamilton Lebanon Rd (45044-9285)
PHONE..................................513 539-4808
Jerry Cook, *Manager*
EMP: 5
SALES (corp-wide): 10.7B **Publicly Held**
SIC: 3577 Computer peripheral equipment
PA: Xerox Corporation
201 Merritt 7
Norwalk CT 06851
203 968-3000

Monroeville
Huron County

(G-14423)
2ND ROE LLC
12014 Thomas Rd (44847-9692)
PHONE..................................419 499-3031
Cheryl Roe, *Principal*
EMP: 3 EST: 2011
SALES (est): 178.7K **Privately Held**
SIC: 2048 Poultry feeds

(G-14424)
ALBRIGHT MACHINE
4296 Us Highway 20 W (44847-9758)
P.O. Box 514 (44847-0514)
PHONE..................................419 483-1088
Terry Albright, *Owner*
EMP: 3
SQ FT: 6,000
SALES (est): 283.7K **Privately Held**
SIC: 3599 Custom machinery

(G-14425)
BORES MANUFACTURING CO
INC
Also Called: Bores, J F Mfg
300 Sandusky St (44847)
P.O. Box 216 (44847-0216)
PHONE..................................419 465-2606

Fax: 419 465-2470
Kevin Bores, *President*
Shirley Bores, *Vice Pres*
EMP: 12
SQ FT: 9,200
SALES (est): 1.9MM **Privately Held**
WEB: www.boresmfg.com
SIC: 3714 3713 Motor vehicle parts & accessories; truck & bus bodies

(G-14426)
HBE MACHINE
1100 State Route 61 N (44847-9202)
PHONE..................................419 668-9426
Fax: 419 663-2301
Thomas R Hedrick, *President*
EMP: 6
SQ FT: 10,000
SALES (est): 885.6K **Privately Held**
SIC: 3599 Machine shop, jobbing & repair

(G-14427)
NARI INC
Also Called: Lorain Quickprint
5190 State Route 99 N (44847-9426)
PHONE..................................440 960-2280
Richard Gfell, *President*
EMP: 4
SQ FT: 1,800
SALES (est): 230K **Privately Held**
WEB: www.lorainquickprint.com
SIC: 2752 2791 2789 Commercial printing, offset; typesetting; bookbinding & related work

(G-14428)
SCOTTRODS LLC
2512 Higbee Rd (44847-9617)
PHONE..................................419 499-2705
Scott Leber,
EMP: 7
SALES (est): 280K **Privately Held**
SIC: 3229 7389 3711 Glass fiber products; ; automobile bodies, passenger car, not including engine, etc.

(G-14429)
SMS TECHNOLOGIES INC
3531 Everingin Rd (44847-9726)
PHONE..................................419 465-4175
Fax: 419 465-2873
Stanley Schug, *President*
Nickie Schug, *Vice Pres*
Scott Sowders, *Engineer*
EMP: 10
SALES (est): 1.5MM **Privately Held**
WEB: www.smstechnologies.com
SIC: 3646 Commercial indusl & institutional electric lighting fixtures

(G-14430)
VENTURE PACKAGING INC
311 Monroe St (44847-9406)
PHONE..................................419 465-2534
Fax: 419 465-2534
Ira Boots, *President*
James Kratochuil, *Vice Pres*
John Rathbun, *Vice Pres*
Tom Thompson, *QC Dir*
Kirk Klodnick, *Controller*
EMP: 360 EST: 1976
SQ FT: 112,000
SALES (est): 47.1MM
SALES (corp-wide): 6.4B **Publicly Held**
WEB: www.6sens.com
SIC: 3089 Injection molded finished plastic products
HQ: Berry Plastics Corporation
101 Oakley St
Evansville IN 47710
812 424-2904

(G-14431)
VENTURE PACKAGING
MIDWEST INC
311 Monroe St (44847-9406)
PHONE..................................419 465-2534
Kurt Klodnick, *Principal*
Jennifer Watson, *Human Res Dir*
EMP: 9
SALES (est): 1MM
SALES (corp-wide): 6.4B **Publicly Held**
SIC: 3089 Bottle caps, molded plastic

HQ: Berry Plastics Corporation
101 Oakley St
Evansville IN 47710
812 424-2904

Montgomery
Hamilton County

(G-14432)
HAUTE CHOCOLATE INC
9424 Shelly Ln (45242-7610)
PHONE..................................513 793-9999
Fax: 513 793-9900
Lisa Holmes, *President*
John Holmes, *Managing Dir*
Linda Obrian, *Manager*
EMP: 4
SQ FT: 2,000
SALES (est): 280K **Privately Held**
SIC: 2066 5441 Chocolate & cocoa products; candy

(G-14433)
KEMPF SURGICAL APPLIANCES
INC
10567 Montgomery Rd (45242-4451)
PHONE..................................513 984-5758
Fax: 513 984-1178
Steven Kempf, *President*
Susan Kempf, *Treasurer*
Kathy Myers, *Manager*
EMP: 22
SALES (est): 3MM **Privately Held**
SIC: 5999 5047 7352 3842 Hospital equipment & supplies; hospital equipment & supplies; medical equipment rental; surgical appliances & supplies

(G-14434)
O & P OPTIONS LLC
10547 Montgomery Rd # 600 (45242-4418)
PHONE..................................513 791-7767
Douglas B Van Atta,
EMP: 3
SALES (est): 247.3K **Privately Held**
SIC: 3842 Prosthetic appliances; braces, orthopedic

(G-14435)
OFFICE BSED ANSTHESIA SVCS
LLC
10296 Gentlewind Dr (45242-5813)
PHONE..................................513 582-5170
Brian Kasson, *President*
EMP: 3
SALES (est): 238.5K **Privately Held**
SIC: 3841 Surgical & medical instruments

(G-14436)
WISE CONSUMER PRODUCTS
COMPANY
7972 Shelldale Way (45242-6431)
PHONE..................................513 484-6530
Willam S Wise, *CEO*
Pamela S Wise, *Vice Pres*
EMP: 2 EST: 2001
SALES: 1.5MM **Privately Held**
SIC: 2842 Cleaning or polishing preparations

Montpelier
Williams County

(G-14437)
20/20 CUSTOM MOLDED PLAST
14620 Selwyn Dr (43543-9237)
PHONE..................................419 485-2020
Fax: 419 485-1619
Ron Ernsberger, *President*
Toby Ernsberger, *Purchasing*
Rod Eckley, *QC Mgr*
Chad Adams, *Controller*
Betsy Cuff, *Office Mgr*
EMP: 100 EST: 2000
SQ FT: 40,000
SALES (est): 57.3MM **Privately Held**
WEB: www.2020cmp.com
SIC: 2821 Molding compounds, plastics

▲ = Import ▼=Export
◆ =Import/Export

(G-14438)
ADVANCE REPORTER (PA)
Also Called: Williams County Publishing
115 Broad St (43543-1325)
PHONE..................................419 485-4851
Fax: 419 924-2382
Forrest R Church, *Owner*
Monica Smith, *Editor*
Casey Church, *Co-Owner*
EMP: 3
SALES (est): 609K **Privately Held**
SIC: 2711 5994 Newspapers, publishing & printing; news dealers & newsstands

(G-14439)
BULLSEYE MACHINES LLC
13121 County Road 1250 (43543-9641)
PHONE..................................419 485-5951
Harry Croft,
EMP: 3
SALES (est): 319.8K **Privately Held**
SIC: 3599 Machine shop, jobbing & repair

(G-14440)
CHASE BRASS AND COPPER CO LLC (DH)
14212 Selwyn Dr (43543-9595)
PHONE..................................419 485-3193
Fax: 419 485-5945
Devin Denner, *President*
Daniel Goehler, *President*
James Palmour, *President*
Dan Borkowski, *Business Mgr*
Peter Santoro, *Vice Pres*
◆ EMP: 304
SQ FT: 129,000
SALES (est): 91.9MM
SALES (corp-wide): 1.3B **Publicly Held**
WEB: www.chasebrass.com
SIC: 3351 Brass rolling & drawing
HQ: Global Brass And Copper, Inc.
305 Lewis And Clark Blvd
East Alton IL 62024
502 873-3000

(G-14441)
CK TECHNOLOGIES LLC (HQ)
1701 Magda Dr (43543-9368)
PHONE..................................419 485-1110
Mark Miller, *CEO*
Eric Martz, *Plant Mgr*
Jeremie Thiel, *Plant Mgr*
Bob Houston, *Facilities Mgr*
Ramiro Flores, *Opers Staff*
▲ EMP: 250
SQ FT: 164,000
SALES (est): 165.1MM
SALES (corp-wide): 358.8MM **Privately Held**
WEB: www.cktech.biz
SIC: 3089 3999 Plastic containers, except foam; injection molding of plastics; atomizers, toiletry
PA: Cascade Engineering, Inc.
3400 Innovation Ct Se
Grand Rapids MI 49512
616 975-4800

(G-14442)
D-FLITE MFG LLC
705 Shawanoe St (43543-9679)
PHONE..................................419 485-3081
Lisa Keough,
EMP: 4 EST: 2008
SALES (est): 341.3K **Privately Held**
SIC: 3334 Primary aluminum

(G-14443)
DECO PLAS PROPERTIES LLC
700 Randolph St (43543-1464)
PHONE..................................419 485-0632
Mike Avina, *QC Mgr*
Michael Kreps,
John Simon,
EMP: 50
SALES: 10MM **Privately Held**
SIC: 2851 Paints & allied products

(G-14444)
DYCO MANUFACTURING INC
12708 State Route 576 (43543-9242)
PHONE..................................419 485-5525
Fax: 419 485-8628
Alan M Dye, *President*
Wes Dye, *Vice Pres*
Ronald L Whetro, *Controller*

Crystal Tyre, *Admin Sec*
EMP: 14
SALES (est): 1.3MM **Privately Held**
WEB: www.chwchospital.com
SIC: 3469 3544 Stamping metal for the trade; special dies & tools

(G-14445)
ENGELS MACHINING LLC
13299 State Route 107 (43543-9102)
P.O. Box 73 (43543-0073)
PHONE..................................419 485-1500
James Engels, *Owner*
EMP: 4
SQ FT: 5,000
SALES (est): 445.4K **Privately Held**
WEB: www.engelsmachining.com
SIC: 3451 3931 Screw machine products; musical instruments

(G-14446)
ENGINEERING COATINGS LLC
1826 Magda Dr (43543-9374)
PHONE..................................419 485-0077
Tim Bricker, *Mng Member*
EMP: 3
SALES (est): 139K **Privately Held**
SIC: 3471 Plating of metals or formed products

(G-14447)
KIMBLE MACHINES INC
124 S Jonesville St (43543-1337)
PHONE..................................419 485-8449
Fax: 419 485-8449
Robert J Kimble, *President*
Margaret Kimble, *Corp Secy*
EMP: 14
SQ FT: 8,200
SALES (est): 2.1MM **Privately Held**
WEB: www.kimblemachines.com
SIC: 3599 Custom machinery

(G-14448)
MARTIN SPROCKET & GEAR INC
350 S Airport Rd (43543-9329)
PHONE..................................419 485-5515
Fax: 419 485-3565
Jeff Page, *Sales Mgr*
Thomas H Kurtz, *Branch Mgr*
EMP: 75
SALES (corp-wide): 403.8MM **Privately Held**
SIC: 3566 3537 3535 3462 Gears, power transmission, except automotive; industrial trucks & tractors; conveyors & conveying equipment; iron & steel forgings; hand & edge tools; sprockets (power transmission equipment)
PA: Martin Sprocket & Gear, Inc.
3100 Sprocket Dr
Arlington TX 76015
817 258-3000

(G-14449)
MOORE INDUSTRIES INC
1317 Henricks Dr (43543-1951)
P.O. Box 316 (43543-0316)
PHONE..................................419 485-5572
Michael Moore, *President*
Rebecca Moore, *Vice Pres*
Rachel Gendron, *Manager*
Heather Green, *Manager*
▲ EMP: 65
SQ FT: 40,000
SALES (est): 17.1MM **Privately Held**
WEB: www.mooreindustries.com
SIC: 3089 Molding primary plastic

(G-14450)
POWERS AND SONS LLC (DH)
1613 Magda Dr (43543-9359)
PHONE..................................419 485-3151
Fax: 419 485-5490
Doug Link, *COO*
Morris Hendricks, *COO*
Sandy Howard, *Mfg Mgr*
Dennis Wasnich, *QC Mgr*
Cheree Lee, *Engineer*
▲ EMP: 220
SQ FT: 200,000

SALES (est): 62.8MM
SALES (corp-wide): 2.9B **Privately Held**
WEB: www.powersandsonsllc.com
SIC: 3714 Motor vehicle parts & accessories
HQ: Wanxiang (Usa) Holdings Corporation
88 Airport Rd Ste 100
Elgin IL 60123
847 622-8838

(G-14451)
RANTEK PRODUCTS LLC
1826 Magda Dr Ste A (43543-9366)
PHONE..................................419 485-2421
Sherri Derr, *Office Mgr*
Randy Wyman,
EMP: 6 EST: 2001
SALES (est): 904.1K **Privately Held**
SIC: 3199 Harness or harness parts

(G-14452)
RASSINI CHASSIS SYSTEMS LLC
1812 Magda Dr (43543-9373)
PHONE..................................419 485-1524
Jose Resendiz, *Plant Mgr*
Tammy Burroughs, *Human Res Mgr*
Robert Anderson, *Mng Member*
Pam Vandermoon,
EMP: 60
SQ FT: 100,000
SALES (est): 40.1MM
SALES (corp-wide): 745.6MM **Privately Held**
SIC: 3493 Coiled flat springs
HQ: Sanluis Rassini, S.A. De C.V.
Monte Pelvoux No. 220, Piso 8
Ciudad De Mexico CDMX 11000
555 520-9037

(G-14453)
RAYMONDS TOOL & GAUGE LLC
6726 County Road N30 (43543-9773)
P.O. Box 106 (43543-0106)
PHONE..................................419 485-8340
Fax: 419 485-3448
Steve Raymond, *Mng Member*
Melissa Raymond,
EMP: 5
SQ FT: 3,600
SALES (est): 570K **Privately Held**
SIC: 3544 Special dies, tools, jigs & fixtures

(G-14454)
RICHMOND MACHINE CO
1528 Travis Dr (43543-9524)
PHONE..................................419 485-5740
Fax: 419 485-4719
Lee Richmond, *President*
Robert Richmond, *Vice Pres*
EMP: 32 EST: 1965
SQ FT: 60,000
SALES (est): 7.1MM **Privately Held**
SIC: 3599 3535 Custom machinery; conveyors & conveying equipment

(G-14455)
TOMAHAWK TOOL SUPPLY
1604 Magda Dr (43543-9206)
PHONE..................................419 485-8737
Jeff Thomas, *President*
EMP: 9
SALES (est): 750K **Privately Held**
WEB: www.tomahawktoolservice.com
SIC: 3544 Special dies & tools

(G-14456)
VILLAGE REPORTER
115 Broad St (43543-1325)
PHONE..................................419 485-4851
Forrest Church, *Principal*
EMP: 4
SALES (est): 204.5K **Privately Held**
SIC: 2711 Newspapers, publishing & printing

(G-14457)
W C HELLER & CO INC
Also Called: Heller Sports Center
201 W Wabash St (43543-1840)
PHONE..................................419 485-3176
Fax: 419 485-8694
Robert L Heller, *President*
Andrew Heller, *Vice Pres*

Patricia Heller, *Treasurer*
EMP: 12 EST: 1891
SQ FT: 25,500
SALES (est): 1.3MM **Privately Held**
WEB: www.wcheller.com
SIC: 2531 School furniture; library furniture

(G-14458)
WINZELER STAMPING CO
129 W Wabash St (43543-1881)
PHONE..................................419 485-3147
Fax: 419 485-5700
Don Brenner, *QC Dir*
Mike Winzeler, *Branch Mgr*
Dean Skiles, *Manager*
Conrad Dick, *Executive*
EMP: 80
SALES (corp-wide): 32MM **Privately Held**
WEB: www.winzelerstamping.com
SIC: 3429 3492 3469 Clamps & couplings, hose; fluid power valves & hose fittings; metal stampings
PA: Winzeler Stamping Co.
129 W Wabash St
Montpelier OH 43543
419 485-3147

Montville
Geauga County

(G-14459)
5S INC
9755 Plank Rd (44064-9712)
P.O. Box 188 (44064-0188)
PHONE..................................440 968-0212
Tom Sparks, *President*
EMP: 7
SALES (est): 787.3K **Privately Held**
SIC: 3599 Machine shop, jobbing & repair

(G-14460)
NT MACHINE INC
Also Called: Nt Machine Inorp
10080 Clay St (44064-9738)
PHONE..................................440 968-3506
Nicholas Saris Jr, *President*
Darlene Sparks, *Corp Secy*
Tom Sparks, *Vice Pres*
EMP: 3
SALES (est): 358.1K **Privately Held**
SIC: 3599 Machine & other job shop work

(G-14461)
RAY TOWNSEND
Also Called: Townsend Machinery
9168 Clay St (44064-9700)
PHONE..................................440 968-3617
Ray Townsend, *Owner*
EMP: 5
SQ FT: 35,000
SALES (est): 435.9K **Privately Held**
WEB: www.townsendmachinery.com
SIC: 3599 7692 Machine shop, jobbing & repair; welding repair

---

Moraine
Montgomery County

(G-14462)
3JD INC
Also Called: Stone Center of Dayton
2823 Northlawn Ave (45439-1645)
PHONE..................................513 324-9655
Jerry Berkemeyer, *Principal*
EMP: 15
SALES (est): 1.5MM **Privately Held**
SIC: 2541 Counter & sink tops

(G-14463)
ACCUPHASE METAL TREATING LLC
2490 Arbor Blvd (45439-1780)
PHONE..................................937 610-5934
Randy Benson,
Christopher Panetta,
EMP: 4
SQ FT: 500
SALES (est): 495K **Privately Held**
SIC: 3398 Metal heat treating

GEOGRA

(G-14464)
ACUTEMP THERMAL SYSTEMS
2900 Dryden Rd (45439-1618)
PHONE.................................937 312-0114
Marshall Griffin, *CFO*
EMP: 12
SALES (est): 2.3MM **Privately Held**
SIC: 3822 Temperature controls, automatic

(G-14465)
ANGELS LANDING INC
Also Called: Compass
3430 S Dixie Dr Ste 301 (45439-2316)
PHONE.................................513 687-3681
John Riedl, *Principal*
Dan Jackson, *CFO*
Mark Jovanovic, *Asst Broker*
Scott Hustis, *Associate*
▲ EMP: 6
SQ FT: 2,000
SALES (est): 631K **Privately Held**
SIC: 2514 Juvenile furniture, household:
metal

(G-14466)
ANTHONY DECORATIVE FABRICS AND
Also Called: Anthony's Fabric
2701 Lance Dr (45409-1519)
PHONE.................................937 299-4637
Fax: 937 298-6218
Marion Scrimenti, *President*
Charlene Scrimenti, *Corp Secy*
EMP: 3 EST: 1977
SQ FT: 6,000
SALES (est): 503.4K **Privately Held**
SIC: 5131 2391 Drapery material, woven;
curtains, window: made from purchased
materials

(G-14467)
BAYARD INC
2621 Dryden Rd Ste 300 (45439-1600)
PHONE.................................937 293-1415
John P Koize, *Principal*
Beth Paciorek, *Sales Staff*
EMP: 5
SALES (corp-wide): 220MM **Privately Held**
SIC: 2759 Publication printing
HQ: Bayard, Inc.
　1 Montauk Ave Ste 200
　New London CT 06320
　860 437-3012

(G-14468)
BDS PACKAGING INC
3155 Elbee Rd Ste 201 (45439-2046)
PHONE.................................937 643-0530
Fax: 937 643-0866
Wendell T Bryant, *President*
Jeff Sloneker, *Vice Pres*
Mildred Clarke, *Supervisor*
EMP: 58
SQ FT: 78,264
SALES (est): 11.6MM **Privately Held**
WEB: www.bdspackaging.com
SIC: 2653 3993 7389 Boxes, corrugated:
made from purchased materials; displays
& cutouts, window & lobby; packaging &
labeling services

(G-14469)
BERRY INVESTMENTS INC
3055 Kettering Blvd # 418 (45439-1989)
PHONE.................................937 293-0398
Fax: 937 293-9193
John W Berry Sr, *CEO*
William T Lincoln, *President*
EMP: 6
SQ FT: 2,500
SALES (est): 1.1MM **Privately Held**
WEB: www.berryinvestments.com
SIC: 5091 3679 Sporting & recreation
goods; microwave components

(G-14470)
BRONT MACHINING INC
2601 W Dorothy Ln (45439-1831)
PHONE.................................937 228-4551
Fax: 937 228-4516
Gary Warlaumont, *President*
Tim Logan, *Vice Pres*
Brian Warlaumont, *Vice Pres*
Susan Rue, *Office Mgr*
EMP: 20

SQ FT: 25,000
SALES: 4MM **Privately Held**
SIC: 3451 3599 Screw machine products;
machine shop, jobbing & repair

(G-14471)
C A T-WOOD METAL WORKS INC
2701 Lance Dr (45409-1519)
PHONE.................................937 866-4917
Fax: 937 866-4957
Richard Wood, *President*
Gary Catron, *Vice Pres*
Debbie Myers, *Manager*
EMP: 25
SQ FT: 11,000
SALES (est): 3.5MM **Privately Held**
SIC: 3599 Machine shop, jobbing & repair

(G-14472)
CLIPPER MAGAZINE LLC
2360 W Dorothy Ln Ste 101 (45439-1861)
PHONE.................................937 534-0470
Bob Levine, *Principal*
EMP: 3 **Privately Held**
SIC: 2754 2721 Coupons: gravure print-
ing; periodicals
HQ: Clipper Magazine, Llc
　3708 Hempland Rd
　Mountville PA 17554
　717 569-5100

(G-14473)
CSAFE LLC
2900 Dryden Rd (45439-1618)
PHONE.................................937 312-0114
Brian Kohr,
Dana Lloyd, *Admin Asst*
▲ EMP: 8
SALES (est): 1.8MM **Privately Held**
SIC: 3585 Refrigeration & heating equip-
ment

(G-14474)
DADDY KATZ LLC
3250 Kettering Blvd (45439-1926)
PHONE.................................937 296-0347
William Winger Jr, *Principal*
EMP: 7
SALES (est): 852.6K **Privately Held**
SIC: 3089 Automotive parts, plastic

(G-14475)
DAPSCO
3110 Kettering Blvd (45439-1972)
PHONE.................................937 294-5331
Fax: 937 293-9591
Richard Schwartz, *Principal*
Bruce Anderson, *CPA*
EMP: 14
SALES (est): 2.8MM **Privately Held**
SIC: 3571 Electronic computers

(G-14476)
DAYTON AIR CONTROL PDTS LLC
2785 Lance Dr (45409-1519)
PHONE.................................937 254-4441
Robin Haviland, *President*
EMP: 3
SQ FT: 6,000
SALES (est): 459.7K **Privately Held**
SIC: 3491 3714 Industrial valves; motor
vehicle parts & accessories

(G-14477)
DAYTON BRICK COMPANY INC
Also Called: D & M Welding
2300 Arbor Blvd (45439-1724)
PHONE.................................937 293-4189
Fax: 937 293-5404
Jeffrey McCarroll, *President*
Jeffrey Mc Carroll, *President*
Brian Mc Carroll, *Corp Secy*
Justin McCarroll, *Opers Mgr*
Tona Potter, *Office Mgr*
EMP: 15
SQ FT: 15,000
SALES (est): 2.2MM **Privately Held**
SIC: 7692 Welding repair

(G-14478)
DEUER DEVELOPMENTS INC
Also Called: Tuf-Tug Products Div
3434 Encrete Ln (45439-1946)
PHONE.................................937 299-1213
Joseph F Deuer Jr, *President*

Louise Deuer, *Treasurer*
▲ EMP: 18
SQ FT: 27,000
SALES (est): 3.4MM **Privately Held**
WEB: www.tuf-tug.com
SIC: 3544 7539 Special dies, tools, jigs &
fixtures; machine shop, automotive

(G-14479)
DMAX LTD (DH)
3100 Dryden Rd (45439-1622)
PHONE.................................937 425-9700
Fax: 937 425-9775
Debbie Fisher, *Safety Mgr*
Matthew Swart, *QC Mgr*
Rowdy Hiler, *Engineer*
Raymond Johnson, *Engineer*
Sunil Mathew, *Engineer*
◆ EMP: 100
SQ FT: 700,000
SALES (est): 127.1MM
SALES (corp-wide): 166.3MM **Publicly Held**
WEB: www.dmax-ltd.com
SIC: 3519 Engines, diesel & semi-diesel or
dual-fuel

(G-14480)
DOUBLEDAY ACQUISITIONS LLC
Also Called: Acutemp
2900 Dryden Rd (45439-1618)
PHONE.................................937 242-6768
Brian Kohr, *CEO*
Nadine Siqueland, *Vice Pres*
Patrick Schafer, *CFO*
Rick Davis, *Marketing Staff*
Linda Raisch, *Marketing Staff*
▲ EMP: 110
SQ FT: 30,000
SALES (est): 29.5MM **Privately Held**
WEB: www.acutemp.com
SIC: 3823 Temperature instruments: indus-
trial process type

(G-14481)
E-ONE ELECTRIC
2754 Viking Ln (45439-1720)
PHONE.................................937 296-4420
David J Sauer, *Principal*
EMP: 4
SALES (est): 332.2K **Privately Held**
SIC: 3699 Electrical equipment & supplies

(G-14482)
EAGLE WRIGHT INNOVATIONS INC
2591 Lance Dr (45409-1513)
PHONE.................................937 640-8093
Fax: 937 640-8097
Mary F Catanzaro, *President*
Ronald Catanzaro, *President*
EMP: 5
SQ FT: 12,600
SALES (est): 696.8K **Privately Held**
WEB: www.eaglewright.com
SIC: 2621 5045 Printing paper; computer
peripheral equipment; disk drives

(G-14483)
EICOM CORPORATION
3249 Dryden Rd (45439-1423)
PHONE.................................937 294-5692
Fax: 937 294-1433
Lisa S Pierce, *Principal*
Cheldon Rose, *Sales Mgr*
EMP: 34
SALES (est): 11.5MM **Privately Held**
SIC: 3568 Couplings, shaft: rigid, flexible,
universal joint, etc.

(G-14484)
ENTING WATER CONDITIONING INC (PA)
Also Called: Superior Water Conditioning Co
3211 Dryden Rd Frnt Frnt (45439-1400)
PHONE.................................937 294-5100
Mel Entingh, *CEO*
Dan Entingh, *President*
Yvonne Albert, *Purch Mgr*
Amber Entingh, *Purchasing*
Karen Entingh, *Treasurer*
▲ EMP: 31
SQ FT: 43,440

SALES (est): 3.2MM **Privately Held**
WEB: www.enting.com
SIC: 3589 5999 5074 Water filters & softeners, household type; water purification
equipment, household type; water treatment equipment, industrial; water purification equipment; water purification
equipment; water softeners

(G-14485)
ERNST METAL TECHNOLOGIES LLC
2920 Kreitzer Rd (45439-1644)
PHONE.................................937 434-3133
Neil Cordonnier, *President*
Tom Huelsman, *Production*
Dana Fultz, *Purchasing*
Jolene Calladine, *Treasurer*
Joanne Calladine, *Controller*
▲ EMP: 44
SALES (est): 20.1MM
SALES (corp-wide): 664.2K **Privately Held**
SIC: 3469 3312 Stamping metal for the
trade; tool & die steel & alloys
HQ: Ernst Umformtechnik Gmbh
　Am Wiesenbach 1
　Oberkirch 77704
　780 540-60

(G-14486)
F & G TOOL AND DIE CO (PA)
3024 Dryden Rd (45439-1690)
PHONE.................................937 294-1405
Fax: 937 294-3862
Jeff Johnson, *President*
Gary M Fischer, *President*
John Grady, *VP Mfg*
Tony Dauby, *Plant Engr*
Ed Scharer, *CFO*
EMP: 50 EST: 1948
SQ FT: 60,000
SALES (est): 10.7MM **Privately Held**
SIC: 3544 3599 Special dies, tools, jigs &
fixtures; custom machinery

(G-14487)
FALCON TOOL & MACHINE INC
2795 Lance Dr (45409-1519)
PHONE.................................937 534-9999
Don Voehringer, *President*
John Noble, *Treasurer*
Mark Metter, *Admin Sec*
EMP: 7
SQ FT: 7,000
SALES (est): 500K **Privately Held**
SIC: 3541 3599 Machine tools, metal cut-
ting type; machine shop, jobbing & repair

(G-14488)
FORGELINE INC
3522 Kettering Blvd Ste B (45439-2035)
PHONE.................................937 299-0298
David Schardt, *President*
Steven Schardt, *Sales Mgr*
EMP: 10
SQ FT: 5,600
SALES (est): 1.6MM **Privately Held**
WEB: www.forgeline.com
SIC: 3714 Wheels, motor vehicle

(G-14489)
G L T INC
2691 Lance Dr (45409-1515)
PHONE.................................937 395-4817
Patrick Haley, *President*
Kevin Knight, *Vice Pres*
▲ EMP: 20
SQ FT: 30,000
SALES (est): 2.5MM **Privately Held**
WEB: www.glt.com
SIC: 3599 Machine shop, jobbing & repair

(G-14490)
GARDA CL TECHNICAL SVCS INC
2690 Lance Dr (45409-1527)
PHONE.................................937 294-4099
Steve Fosnot, *Branch Mgr*
EMP: 34
SALES (corp-wide): 3B **Privately Held**
SIC: 7381 3578 4513 Armored car serv-
ices; coin counters; air courier services

HQ: Garda CI Technical Services, Inc.
700 S Federal Hwy Ste 300
Boca Raton FL 33432
561 939-7000

(G-14491)
GLOBAL GAUGE CORPORATION
3200 Kettering Blvd (45439-1926)
PHONE..............................937 222-0797
Tim McCormick, *Principal*
Brad Bernard, *Engineer*
Tom Fairchild, *Engineer*
Paul Tung, *Treasurer*
Mike Welch, *Sales Executive*
EMP: 18
SQ FT: 45,000
SALES: 4.3MM **Privately Held**
WEB: www.globalgauge.com
SIC: 3829 Gauging instruments, thickness
ultrasonic

(G-14492)
HAMILTON ANIMAL PRODUCTS LLC
2425 W Dorothy Ln (45439-1827)
PHONE..............................937 293-9994
Patricia Weimer, *CFO*
William Sherk,
▲ **EMP:** 20
SQ FT: 85,000
SALES (est): 3MM
SALES (corp-wide): 21MM **Privately Held**
WEB: www.hamiltonproducts.com
SIC: 3199 Harness or harness parts; dog
furnishings: collars, leashes, muzzles,
etc.: leather
PA: Miraclecorp Products
2425 W Dorothy Ln
Moraine OH 45439
937 293-9994

(G-14493)
HARCO INDUSTRIES INC
3535 Kettering Blvd (45439-2014)
PHONE..............................937 832-9697
Larry G Harris, *President*
Tina L Harris, *Vice Pres*
Dennis Snyder, *Controller*
Tom McNulty, *Manager*
▲ **EMP:** 15
SQ FT: 300,000
SALES (est): 2.9MM **Privately Held**
SIC: 3714 8748 Motor vehicle parts & acces-
sories; motor vehicle brake systems &
parts; motor vehicle engines & parts;
business consulting

(G-14494)
HARCO MANUFACTURING GROUP LLC (PA)
3535 Kettering Blvd (45439-2014)
PHONE..............................937 528-5000
Fax: 937 528-5091
Mike Howard, *Purch Dir*
Jim Helpling, *Engineer*
Dennis Snider, *Controller*
Kathy Weaver, *Office Mgr*
Tom McNulty, *Manager*
▲ **EMP:** 150
SQ FT: 300,000
SALES (est): 45.7MM **Privately Held**
SIC: 3714 Motor vehicle brake systems &
parts

(G-14495)
HARCO MANUFACTURING GROUP LLC
3535 Kettering Blvd 200 (45439-2014)
PHONE..............................937 528-5000
Tom Mc Nulty, *Branch Mgr*
EMP: 150
SALES (corp-wide): 45.7MM **Privately Held**
SIC: 3714 Motor vehicle brake systems &
parts
PA: Harco Manufacturing Group, Llc
3535 Kettering Blvd
Moraine OH 45439
937 528-5000

(G-14496)
HESLER MACHINE TOOL
2651 E River Rd (45439-1533)
PHONE..............................937 299-3833

Fax: 937 299-0066
Terry Hesler, *Owner*
Vicky Hesler, *Co-Owner*
EMP: 5
SQ FT: 8,000
SALES: 300K **Privately Held**
SIC: 3541 3599 Machine tools, metal cut-
ting type; machine shop, jobbing & repair

(G-14497)
JENA TOOL INC
5219 Springboro Pike (45439-2970)
PHONE..............................937 296-1122
Fax: 937 296-0842
George J Derr, *Chairman*
Eric Kleinschmidt, *Vice Pres*
Thomas Derr, *Engineer*
Craig Johnson, *Engineer*
Shaun Lowry, *Sales Executive*
EMP: 74
SQ FT: 45,000
SALES (est): 13.3MM **Privately Held**
SIC: 3544 Special dies, tools, jigs & fix-
tures

(G-14498)
JONES OLD RUSTIC SIGN
Also Called: Jones Signs
2758 Viking Ln (45439-1720)
PHONE..............................937 643-1695
Fax: 937 643-1666
Lorna Jones, *President*
Kenneth Jones, *Corp Secy*
EMP: 40
SQ FT: 9,000
SALES: 1.2MM **Privately Held**
SIC: 3993 Signs & advertising specialties

(G-14499)
KRAMER GRAPHICS INC
2408 W Dorothy Ln (45439-1828)
PHONE..............................937 296-9600
Fax: 937 296-7496
John Kramer Jr, *President*
David Vermette, *General Mgr*
Mary Lou Kramer, *Chairman*
Kelley Kramer, *Vice Pres*
Diane Schell, *Bookkeeper*
▲ **EMP:** 50
SALES (est): 10.1MM **Privately Held**
WEB: www.kramergraphics.com
SIC: 2759 Commercial printing

(G-14500)
L M BERRY AND COMPANY (PA)
3170 Kettering Blvd (45439-1924)
PHONE..............................937 296-2121
Fax: 937 296-2011
Daniel J Graham, *President*
Jack Mullins, *Engng Exec*
Carol Betts, *Sls & Mktg Exec*
Ron Huist, *Controller*
Jim Bowles, *Persnl Mgr*
EMP: 650
SQ FT: 141,000
SALES (est): 65.4MM **Privately Held**
WEB: www.lmberry.com
SIC: 7311 2741 Advertising agencies; mis-
cellaneous publishing

(G-14501)
L&H THREADED RODS CORP
3050 Dryden Rd (45439-1620)
PHONE..............................937 294-6666
Fax: 937 294-6667
John C Gray, *President*
Rob Herrmann, *QA Dir*
Jeff Schroder, *CFO*
Joe Young, *Sales Staff*
Sharon Thompson, *Office Mgr*
▲ **EMP:** 125
SQ FT: 45,000
SALES (est): 24.6MM
SALES (corp-wide): 52.5MM **Privately Held**
WEB: www.lhrods.com
SIC: 3312 Rods, iron & steel: made in steel
mills
PA: Gray America Corp.
3050 Dryden Rd
Moraine OH 45439
937 293-9313

(G-14502)
LASTAR INC (DH)
3555 Kettering Blvd (45439-2014)
PHONE..............................937 224-0639
Fax: 937 496-4030
John Selldorf, *CEO*
Sam Little, *Purch Dir*
Elizabeth Baugh, *Asst Controller*
Denise Scarpelli, *Marketing Mgr*
Larry Brown, *Manager*
▲ **EMP:** 60
SQ FT: 120,000
SALES (est): 108.9MM
SALES (corp-wide): 21.1MM **Privately Held**
WEB: www.lastar.com
SIC: 3678 Electronic connectors
HQ: Legrand France
128 Av Du Mal De Lattre De Tassigny
Limoges 87000
555 067-474

(G-14503)
LEGRAND NORTH AMERICA LLC
Also Called: C2g
3555 Kettering Blvd (45439-2014)
PHONE..............................937 224-0639
Andrea McDermott, *Project Mgr*
April Mick, *Buyer*
Matthew Rathbun, *Sales Dir*
Pete Zeller, *Sales Staff*
Everett Poffenberger, *Manager*
EMP: 420
SALES (corp-wide): 21.1MM **Privately Held**
SIC: 1731 5063 5045 3643 Communica-
tions specialization; cable conduit; com-
puter peripheral equipment;
current-carrying wiring devices; nonfer-
rous wiredrawing & insulating
HQ: Legrand North America, Llc
60 Woodlawn St
West Hartford CT 06110
860 233-6251

(G-14504)
MAR-CON TOOL COMPANY
2301 Arbor Blvd (45439-1788)
PHONE..............................937 299-2244
Fax: 937 299-9310
Gene A Hamrick, *President*
Rodney Byrnes, *General Mgr*
Jeff Hamrick, *Vice Pres*
Jim Hamrick, *Vice Pres*
Jeffrey Hecht, *Sls & Mktg Exec*
EMP: 25 EST: 1959
SQ FT: 15,500
SALES (est): 4.5MM **Privately Held**
WEB: www.marcontool.com
SIC: 3599 Machine shop, jobbing & repair

(G-14505)
METALLURGICAL SERVICE INC
2221 Arbor Blvd (45439-1575)
PHONE..............................937 294-2681
Fax: 937 294-8913
William R Miller, *Ch of Bd*
Larry Cartwright, *General Mgr*
Alice L Miller, *Corp Secy*
Robert Miller, *Vice Pres*
Thomas Miller, *Vice Pres*
EMP: 50
SQ FT: 45,000
SALES (est): 9.1MM
SALES (corp-wide): 27.3MM **Privately Held**
WEB: www.millerconsolidated.com
SIC: 3398 Metal heat treating
PA: Miller Consolidated Industries Inc
2221 Arbor Blvd
Moraine OH 45439
937 294-2681

(G-14506)
METRO FLEX INC
3304 Encrete Ln (45439-1944)
PHONE..............................937 299-5360
Fax: 937 299-5380
Scot Terry, *CEO*
Charleston Cline, *Admin Sec*
EMP: 8
SALES (est): 680K **Privately Held**
SIC: 2759 Commercial printing

(G-14507)
MILLER CONSOLIDATED INDUSTRIES (PA)
2221 Arbor Blvd (45439-1521)
PHONE..............................937 294-2681
Fax: 937 296-7986
Larry Cartwright, *General Mgr*
Nick Miller, *Plant Mgr*
Tom Miller, *CFO*
Carl Black, *Sales Mgr*
Kelly Henderson, *Director*
EMP: 49
SQ FT: 55,000
SALES (est): 27.3MM **Privately Held**
WEB: www.millerconsolidated.com
SIC: 3398 5051 Metal heat treating; steel

(G-14508)
MILLWORK FABRICATORS INC
3176 Kettering Blvd (45439-1924)
PHONE..............................937 299-5452
Fax: 937 299-3254
Dennis D Williams, *President*
EMP: 4
SQ FT: 5,000
SALES (est): 491K
SALES (corp-wide): 16MM **Privately Held**
WEB: www.wilconcorp.com
SIC: 2431 Millwork
PA: Wil Con Corporation
3176 Kettering Blvd
Moraine OH 45439
937 299-9920

(G-14509)
MIRACLECORP PRODUCTS (PA)
2425 W Dorothy Ln (45439-1827)
PHONE..............................937 293-9994
Fax: 937 293-9995
William M Sherk Jr, *President*
Debbie Wietzel, *Sales Mgr*
Susie Lovy, *Mktg Dir*
Ron Castonguay, *Marketing Staff*
Lori Lindsey, *Manager*
◆ **EMP:** 55
SQ FT: 11,500
SALES: 21MM **Privately Held**
WEB: www.miraclecorp.com
SIC: 3999 0752 5999 Pet supplies; ani-
mal specialty services; pet supplies

(G-14510)
NEW DIMENSION METALS CORP
3050 Dryden Rd (45439-1620)
PHONE..............................937 299-2233
Fax: 937 299-6667
John Gray, *President*
Randall Fox, *Exec VP*
Phil Huston, *Materials Mgr*
Daniel Wilson, *QC Dir*
Jeff Schroder, *CFO*
▲ **EMP:** 40
SQ FT: 110,000
SALES (est): 23.7MM
SALES (corp-wide): 52.5MM **Privately Held**
WEB: www.grayamerica.com
SIC: 3316 Bars, steel, cold finished, from
purchased hot-rolled
PA: Gray America Corp.
3050 Dryden Rd
Moraine OH 45439
937 293-9313

(G-14511)
PARKER TRIAD STORE
2402 Springboro Pike (45439)
PHONE..............................937 293-4080
Doug Whitman, *CEO*
Brandon Hook, *Manager*
EMP: 99
SALES (est): 5.5MM **Privately Held**
SIC: 3511 Hydraulic turbines

(G-14512)
PERFORMNCE PLYMR SOLUTIONS INC
Also Called: Proof Research Acd
2711 Lance Dr (45409-1519)
PHONE..............................937 298-3713
Fax: 937 298-6615
Larry Murphy, *CEO*
David B Curliss, *President*
Jason Lincoln, *Vice Pres*

GEOGRAPHIC

Zach McHale, *Program Mgr*
EMP: 14
SQ FT: 25,000
SALES: 1.5MM **Privately Held**
WEB: www.p2si.com
SIC: 8733 8731 8711 2821 Scientific research agency; commercial research laboratory; mechanical engineering; plastics materials & resins
PA: Proof Research, Inc.
　　10 Western Village Ln
　　Columbia Falls MT 59912

(G-14513)
PJL ENTERPRISE INC (DH)
Also Called: Peter LI Education Group
3055 Kettering Blvd # 100 (45439-1989)
PHONE......................937 293-1415
Fax: 937 292-1310
Peter J LI, *President*
Pamela Gibson, *Vice Pres*
Cullen Schippe, *Vice Pres*
Mary Parr, *Human Res Dir*
Maureen Christensen, *Accounts Mgr*
EMP: 65 **EST:** 1971
SQ FT: 17,500
SALES (est): 9.3MM
SALES (corp-wide): 220MM **Privately Held**
SIC: 2721 Magazines: publishing only, not printed on site
HQ: Bayard, Inc.
　　1 Montauk Ave Ste 200
　　New London CT 06320
　　860 437-3012

(G-14514)
PJL ENTERPRISE INC
2019 Springboro W (45439-1665)
PHONE......................937 293-1415
Peter LI, *President*
EMP: 25
SALES (corp-wide): 220MM **Privately Held**
SIC: 2721 Magazines: publishing only, not printed on site
HQ: Pjl Enterprise, Inc.
　　3055 Kettering Blvd # 100
　　Moraine OH 45439
　　937 293-1415

(G-14515)
PLACECRETE INC
2475 Arbor Blvd (45439-1776)
PHONE......................937 298-2121
Donald L Phlipot, *President*
Fred Cook, *Vice Pres*
EMP: 15
SQ FT: 17,000
SALES: 3MM **Privately Held**
SIC: 3273 Ready-mixed concrete

(G-14516)
POLAR INC
2297 N Moraine Dr (45439-1507)
P.O. Box 2995, Elkhart IN (46515-2995)
PHONE......................937 297-0911
Robert J Crawford, *President*
Shaery Eilon, *Accounting Mgr*
▼ **EMP:** 10
SQ FT: 3,000
SALES (est): 2.1MM **Privately Held**
WEB: www.polarcompanies.com
SIC: 5169 5172 2841 Chemicals & allied products; petroleum products; soap & other detergents

(G-14517)
PRINTING EXPRESS
3350 Kettering Blvd (45439-2011)
P.O. Box 456, Springboro (45066-0456)
PHONE......................937 276-7794
James Armstrong, *Owner*
EMP: 6
SALES (est): 576.8K **Privately Held**
SIC: 2752 Commercial printing, lithographic

(G-14518)
PRO FAB WELDING SERVICE LLC (PA)
2765 Lance Dr (45409-1519)
PHONE......................937 272-2142
Stephen Brandenburg, *Mng Member*
EMP: 3
SQ FT: 5,500

SALES (est): 479.9K **Privately Held**
SIC: 7692 Welding repair

(G-14519)
PRODUCTION CONTROL UNITS INC
2280 W Dorothy Ln (45439-1892)
PHONE......................937 299-5594
Fax: 937 299-3843
Thomas Hoge, *President*
Jeff King, *Prdtn Mgr*
Jeff Elrod, *Mfg Mgr*
James Bowman, *Production*
William Sims, *Engineer*
▼ **EMP:** 100 **EST:** 1946
SQ FT: 58,000
SALES: 15MM **Privately Held**
WEB: www.sterlingpcu.com
SIC: 3829 3823 Measuring & controlling devices; industrial process control instruments

(G-14520)
PRODUCTION TURNING LLC
2490 Arbor Blvd Unit A (45439-1780)
PHONE......................937 424-0034
Fax: 937 424-0059
Basil Morrison, *President*
Bob Kirk, *General Mgr*
Michael Turner, *Vice Pres*
EMP: 8
SALES (est): 1MM **Privately Held**
WEB: www.productionturning.com
SIC: 3714 Motor vehicle wheels & parts

(G-14521)
RACK PROCESSING COMPANY INC (PA)
2350 Arbor Blvd (45439-1760)
PHONE......................937 294-1911
Fax: 937 294-7153
Craig Coy, *President*
Kevyn Coy, *Vice Pres*
Dave Girouard, *Controller*
Jo-Ann Spears, *Human Res Mgr*
Keith Chadd, *Sales Mgr*
EMP: 50 **EST:** 1948
SQ FT: 24,000
SALES: 21MM **Privately Held**
WEB: www.rackprocessing.com
SIC: 2542 3471 Partitions & fixtures, except wood; plating & polishing

(G-14522)
RACK PROCESSING COMPANY INC
Also Called: Pique Stripping Division
2350 Arbor Blvd (45439-1760)
PHONE......................937 294-1911
Fax: 937 773-0726
Dan Grammer, *Branch Mgr*
EMP: 45
SALES (corp-wide): 21MM **Privately Held**
WEB: www.rackprocessing.com
SIC: 3471 3479 2542 Plating & polishing; coating of metals with plastic or resins; racks, merchandise display or storage; except wood
PA: Rack Processing Company, Inc.
　　2350 Arbor Blvd
　　Moraine OH 45439
　　937 294-1911

(G-14523)
RACO CUTTING INC (PA)
2230 E River Rd (45439-1519)
PHONE......................937 293-1228
Fax: 937 293-1228
Paul Etter, *President*
Mike Etter, *Treasurer*
Steve Etter, *Admin Sec*
EMP: 4
SQ FT: 5,000
SALES (est): 570.3K **Privately Held**
SIC: 3316 Cold finishing of steel shapes

(G-14524)
S & J PRECISION INC
2015 Dryden Rd (45439-1741)
P.O. Box 562, Miamisburg (45343-0562)
PHONE......................937 296-0068
Forest Freeze, *President*
Judy Freeze, *Corp Secy*
EMP: 4

SALES: 300K **Privately Held**
SIC: 3312 Tool & die steel & alloys

(G-14525)
SANTOS INDUSTRIAL LTD (PA)
Also Called: Bimac
3034 Dryden Rd (45439-1620)
PHONE......................937 299-7333
Fax: 937 299-7367
Roberto Santos, *President*
Dan Bizzarro, *Opers-Prdtn-Mfg*
Sue Jordan, *Bookkeeper*
EMP: 42 **EST:** 1958
SQ FT: 33,280
SALES (est): 7.2MM **Privately Held**
WEB: www.bimac.com
SIC: 3325 Alloy steel castings, except investment

(G-14526)
SANTOS INDUSTRIAL LTD
Also Called: Bimac Machine
2960 Springboro W (45439-1764)
PHONE......................937 299-7333
Bill Jordan, *Manager*
EMP: 3
SQ FT: 10,200
SALES (corp-wide): 7.2MM **Privately Held**
WEB: www.bimac.com
SIC: 3599 Machine & other job shop work
PA: Santos Industrial Ltd
　　3034 Dryden Rd
　　Moraine OH 45439
　　937 299-7333

(G-14527)
SCOTTISSUE LLC
3275 Dryden Rd (45439-1461)
PHONE......................937 293-2139
Fax: 937 293-9188
Steve Ford, *President*
Dave Kling, *Human Res Dir*
Brian Gompers, *Sales Associate*
Bill Walkup, *Sales Executive*
EMP: 21
SALES (est): 4.7MM **Privately Held**
SIC: 2842 Sanitation preparations, disinfectants & deodorants

(G-14528)
SNYDER CONCRETE PRODUCTS INC (PA)
Also Called: Snyder Brick and Block
2301 W Dorothy Ln (45439-1825)
PHONE......................937 885-5176
Lee E Snyder, *CEO*
Mark Snyder, *Vice Pres*
Julie Flory, *Treasurer*
▲ **EMP:** 25
SQ FT: 50,000
SALES (est): 13.3MM **Privately Held**
WEB: www.snyderonline.com
SIC: 5032 3271 3272 Brick, except refractory; concrete & cinder building products; blocks, concrete or cinder: standard; concrete products

(G-14529)
SODERBERG INC
Also Called: Walman Optical
1851 Ebert Ave (45439-2008)
PHONE......................937 298-0223
Fax: 937 298-4845
Kim Davidson, *Branch Mgr*
EMP: 15
SALES (corp-wide): 287.9MM **Privately Held**
WEB: www.soseyes.com
SIC: 3851 Eyeglasses, lenses & frames
HQ: Soderberg, Inc
　　230 Eva St
　　Saint Paul MN 55107
　　651 291-1400

(G-14530)
SOLAR INTEGRATED RESOURCES LLC ◆
4501 Kettering Blvd (45439-2137)
PHONE......................937 608-4498
Mark Wiley, *Mng Member*
EMP: 3 **EST:** 2016
SALES: 500K **Privately Held**
SIC: 3674 Photovoltaic devices, solid state

(G-14531)
SOUTHPAW ENTERPRISES INC
2350 Dryden Rd (45439-1736)
P.O. Box 1047, Dayton (45401-1047)
PHONE......................937 252-7676
Frank Howard, *President*
Alex Moore, *VP Opers*
Linda Allen, *Purch Mgr*
Mark Hamilton, *Engineer*
Paul Lauzau, *CFO*
▼ **EMP:** 34 **EST:** 1975
SQ FT: 37,500
SALES (est): 7.2MM **Privately Held**
WEB: www.southpawenterprises.com
SIC: 3842 Technical aids for the handicapped

(G-14532)
SPIRIT SOLUTIONS INC
2400 E River Rd (45439-1530)
PHONE......................937 431-8041
Randy Lane, *President*
Ron Cope, *Controller*
EMP: 3
SALES (est): 220K **Privately Held**
SIC: 3826 Infrared analytical instruments

(G-14533)
SUMMIT FINISHING TECHNOLOGIES
2490 Arbor Blvd Unit B (45439-1780)
PHONE......................937 424-5512
Robert Bauer, *CEO*
Christopher Panetta, *President*
EMP: 5
SALES (est): 200K **Privately Held**
SIC: 2796 Electrotype plates

(G-14534)
TAILORED SYSTEMS INC
Also Called: Vibrodyne Division
2853 Springboro W (45439-2045)
PHONE......................937 299-3900
Fax: 937 299-1107
Joseph Riess, *President*
Ron Logan, *Corp Secy*
John Riess, *Vice Pres*
Karen Berry, *Treasurer*
EMP: 7
SQ FT: 12,000
SALES: 800K **Privately Held**
WEB: www.vibrodyne.com
SIC: 3541 3599 Deburring machines; machine shop, jobbing & repair

(G-14535)
TKO MFG SERVICES INC
2360 W Dorothy Ln Ste 111 (45439-1861)
P.O. Box 2246, Dayton (45401-2246)
PHONE......................937 299-1637
Fax: 937 298-7835
Gary Keithley, *President*
Agripina Boettcher, *Vice Pres*
John Whaley, *Plant Supt*
EMP: 22
SQ FT: 10,000
SALES (est): 2.5MM **Privately Held**
SIC: 3714 7389 Motor vehicle parts & accessories; packaging & labeling services

(G-14536)
VAGABOND CREATIONS INC
2560 Lance Dr (45409-1581)
PHONE......................937 298-1124
Fax: 937 298-1124
George F Stanley Jr, *President*
Dan McKnight, *Counsel*
Matt Powers, *Controller*
Ed Mora, *Sales Staff*
Marion Barga, *Manager*
EMP: 6 **EST:** 1955
SQ FT: 20,700
SALES (est): 605.1K **Privately Held**
WEB: www.vagabondcreations.net
SIC: 2759 2771 Stationery: printing; greeting cards

Moreland Hills
Cuyahoga County

(G-14537)
BOWS BARRETTES & BAUBLES
4180 Chagrin River Rd (44022-1111)
PHONE..................................440 247-2697
Cherrie Miller, *Owner*
EMP: 10
SALES (est): 300K **Privately Held**
SIC: 2353 Hats, trimmed: women's, misses' & children's

(G-14538)
PRECISION POLYMER CASTING LLC
140 Greentree Rd (44022-2424)
PHONE..................................440 343-0461
Terry Capuano, *Principal*
EMP: 7
SALES (est): 950K **Privately Held**
SIC: 3325 Alloy steel castings, except investment

Morral
Marion County

(G-14539)
CONAGRA BRANDS INC
Golden Valley Microwave Foods
2970 County Highway 74 (43337-9206)
PHONE..................................740 465-3912
William Harris, *Branch Mgr*
EMP: 13
SALES (corp-wide): 11.6B **Publicly Held**
WEB: www.conagra.com
SIC: 2099 Food preparations
PA: Conagra Brands, Inc.
222 Merchandise Mart Plz
Chicago IL 60654
312 549-5000

(G-14540)
J-LENCO INC (PA)
664 N High St (43337)
P.O. Box 346, La Rue (43332-0346)
PHONE..................................740 499-2260
Fax: 614 499-2631
Edward P Murphy, *President*
Thomas A Frericks, *Principal*
Nancy Murphy, *Corp Secy*
Judy Vangeloff, *Safety Mgr*
Stephanie Forry, *Financial Exec*
▲ **EMP:** 51
SALES (est): 7.4MM **Privately Held**
WEB: www.jlenco.com
SIC: 3543 Industrial patterns

Morristown
Belmont County

(G-14541)
BUCKEYE BRAKE MANUFACTURING
40168 National Rd W (43759)
P.O. Box 676, Saint Clairsville (43950-0676)
PHONE..................................740 782-1379
Greg Beckett, *President*
EMP: 10 EST: 1996
SALES: 500K **Privately Held**
SIC: 3714 Motor vehicle brake systems & parts

Morrow
Warren County

(G-14542)
ACTION MACHINE & MANUFACTURING
6788 E Us Highway 22 & 3 (45152-9713)
PHONE..................................513 899-3889
Fax: 513 899-2286
Delores Nadine Hartman, *President*
Nick Hartman, *Corp Secy*

Daryl Hartman, *Vice Pres*
EMP: 4 EST: 1963
SQ FT: 14,000
SALES (est): 469.5K **Privately Held**
SIC: 3599 Machine shop, jobbing & repair

(G-14543)
ARETE INNOVATIVE SOLUTIONS LLC
3050 Shawhan Rd (45152-8360)
PHONE..................................513 503-2712
William Herman,
EMP: 5
SALES (est): 178.7K **Privately Held**
SIC: 3499 3544 3511 3563 Welding tips, heat resistant: metal; special dies, tools, jigs & fixtures; turbines & turbine generator sets; air & gas compressors; oil & gas drilling rigs & equipment

(G-14544)
BROWN CONSTRUCTION & PAVING
4755 Stubbs Mills Rd (45152-9604)
PHONE..................................513 494-0095
Fax: 513 899-4486
Clint Brown, *Owner*
EMP: 8
SQ FT: 2,576
SALES (est): 993.4K **Privately Held**
SIC: 2951 Asphalt paving mixtures & blocks

(G-14545)
CHRISTMAS RANCH LLC
3205 S Waynesville Rd (45152-8222)
PHONE..................................513 505-3865
Debbie Fuchs, *Owner*
Michael Fuchs, *Owner*
EMP: 22
SALES (est): 2.5MM **Privately Held**
SIC: 3699 5999 Christmas tree lighting sets, electric; Christmas lights & decorations

(G-14546)
GRAVEL-TECH
4005 E Fster Mineville Rd (45152-8502)
PHONE..................................513 703-3672
Michael Engel, *Principal*
EMP: 3 EST: 2007
SALES (est): 177.9K **Privately Held**
SIC: 1442 Construction sand & gravel

(G-14547)
H E LONG COMPANY
3910 Anderson Rd (45152-7117)
P.O. Box 197 (45152-0197)
PHONE..................................513 899-2610
Fax: 513 899-4094
Michael E Long, *President*
Richard Long, *Vice Pres*
EMP: 10
SALES (est): 1.3MM **Privately Held**
WEB: www.helongco.com
SIC: 3545 5084 Shaping tools (machine tool accessories); metalworking tools (such as drills, taps, dies, files)

(G-14548)
ISAACS JR FLOYD THOMAS
Also Called: 4 Him Sales
3480 E Us Highway 22 & 3 (45152-8237)
PHONE..................................513 899-2342
Floyd Isaacs Jr, *Mng Member*
EMP: 10
SALES: 500K **Privately Held**
SIC: 5561 3792 Camper & travel trailer dealers; tent-type camping trailers

(G-14549)
MORROW GRAVEL COMPANY INC
Also Called: Valley Asphalt
4850 Stubbs Mills Rd (45152-8340)
PHONE..................................513 899-2000
Fax: 513 899-2000
Rick Dostal, *Manager*
EMP: 14
SALES (corp-wide): 32.5MM **Privately Held**
SIC: 1442 Gravel mining

PA: Morrow Gravel Company Inc
11641 Mosteller Rd Ste 2
Cincinnati OH 45241
513 771-0820

(G-14550)
OZONE SYSTEMS SVCS GROUP INC
6687 State Route 132 (45152-8143)
PHONE..................................513 899-4131
Ataur C Rehman, *President*
EMP: 3 EST: 1999
SALES: 1MM **Privately Held**
SIC: 8711 3441 7349 Consulting engineer; fabricated structural metal; chemical cleaning services

(G-14551)
STEPHEN R LILLEY
Also Called: Lilleys Fabrication and Design
2900 S Waynesville Rd (45152-9619)
PHONE..................................513 899-4400
Stephen R Lilley, *Owner*
EMP: 4
SQ FT: 5,000
SALES: 300K **Privately Held**
SIC: 3299 2541 Moldings, architectural: plaster of paris; store & office display cases & fixtures

(G-14552)
VALLEY ASPHALT CORPORATION
Also Called: Morrow Gravel
4850 Stubbs Mills Rd (45152-8340)
PHONE..................................513 381-0652
Fax: 513 899-2021
Bob Stayton, *Plant Mgr*
Bob Ftayton, *Manager*
EMP: 8
SALES (corp-wide): 109.5MM **Privately Held**
SIC: 2951 Asphalt paving mixtures & blocks
PA: Valley Asphalt Corporation
11641 Mosteller Rd
Cincinnati OH 45241
513 771-0820

(G-14553)
VALLEY MACHINE TOOL CO INC
9773 Morrow Cozaddale Rd (45152-8589)
PHONE..................................513 899-2737
Fax: 513 899-2390
Larry R Wilson, *President*
Douglas Wilson, *Corp Secy*
Ralph Wilson, *Vice Pres*
Charlotte Lyttle, *Office Mgr*
Roger J Wilson, *Manager*
EMP: 40
SQ FT: 11,000
SALES (est): 6.5MM **Privately Held**
SIC: 3599 7692 Machine shop, jobbing & repair; welding repair

Mount Cory
Hancock County

(G-14554)
SNAPS INC
2557 Township Road 35 (45868-9701)
PHONE..................................419 477-5100
Fax: 419 477-5125
Nancy Ruppright, *President*
Gary Ruppright, *Vice Pres*
EMP: 6
SALES: 100K **Privately Held**
SIC: 2389 Theatrical costumes

Mount Eaton
Wayne County

(G-14555)
FLEX TECHNOLOGIES INC
Also Called: Mount Eaton Division
16183 E Main St (44659)
P.O. Box 223 (44659-0223)
PHONE..................................330 359-5415
Fax: 330 359-5416
Judy Stine, *Plant Mgr*

Diann Sherrets, *Plt & Fclts Mgr*
Jim Eichel, *Manager*
Will Beavers, *Manager*
EMP: 80
SALES (corp-wide): 57.8MM **Privately Held**
WEB: www.flextechnologies.com
SIC: 3089 3714 3694 3564 Plastic processing; motor vehicle parts & accessories; engine electrical equipment; blowers & fans
PA: Flex Technologies, Inc.
5479 Gundy Dr
Midvale OH 44653
740 922-5992

(G-14556)
QUALITY BLOCK & SUPPLY INC (DH)
Rr 250 (44659)
PHONE..................................330 364-4411
Jerry A Schwab, *President*
David Schwab, *Vice Pres*
Donna Schwab, *Admin Sec*
EMP: 27
SQ FT: 4,000
SALES (est): 2MM
SALES (corp-wide): 28.6B **Privately Held**
SIC: 3271 3273 5032 Blocks, concrete or cinder: standard; ready-mixed concrete; concrete & cinder block
HQ: Schwab Industries, Inc.
2301 Progress St
Dover OH 44622
330 364-4411

Mount Gilead
Morrow County

(G-14557)
CONSOLIDATED GAS COOP INC
5255 State Route 95 (43338-9763)
PHONE..................................419 946-6600
Nancy Salyer, *CFO*
Dave Edwards, *Manager*
EMP: 6
SALES (est): 656.3K **Privately Held**
SIC: 1321 Propane (natural) production

(G-14558)
EDCO PRODUCING
869 Meadow Dr (43338-1069)
P.O. Box 329 (43338-0329)
PHONE..................................419 947-2515
Alan Jones, *President*
Eric Brown, *Vice Pres*
Carol Studer, *Office Mgr*
Wanda Jones, *Admin Sec*
EMP: 3
SQ FT: 3,000
SALES (est): 337.9K **Privately Held**
SIC: 1311 Natural gas production

(G-14559)
FETTERS AND SON SIGN COMPANY
4305 State Route 314 (43338-9556)
P.O. Box 2967, Westerville (43086-2967)
PHONE..................................614 299-6947
Fax: 614 299-5972
Edward L Fetters, *President*
Donald Fetters, *Vice Pres*
Dubbie Cellar, *Admin Sec*
EMP: 4 EST: 1973
SQ FT: 5,409
SALES (est): 511.3K **Privately Held**
SIC: 7699 3993 Plastics products repair; neon signs

(G-14560)
GERICH FIBERGLASS INC
7004 Us Highway 42 (43338-9638)
PHONE..................................419 362-4591
Fax: 419 362-4811
Anton J Gerich, *President*
Lila S Gerich, *Vice Pres*
Kim Gerich, *Accountant*
Joseph Gerich, *Personnel*
EMP: 30
SQ FT: 20,000

GEOGRAPHIC

SALES: 1.5MM **Privately Held**
WEB: www.fibrecore.com
SIC: **3714** 3713 3715 3792 Motor vehicle body components & frame; bus bodies (motor vehicles); trailer bodies; travel trailers & campers

(G-14561)
HARTMAN PRINTING CO
425 W Marion St (43338-1386)
PHONE...................................419 946-2854
Fax: 419 947-9777
Steve Hartman, *Owner*
Karen Hartman, *Co-Owner*
EMP: 4
SQ FT: 5,000
SALES (est): 260K **Privately Held**
WEB: www.hartmanprinting.com
SIC: **2752** Commercial printing, lithographic

(G-14562)
HIRT PUBLISHING CO INC
Also Called: Marrow County Sentinel
245 Neal Ave Ste A (43338-9372)
P.O. Box 149 (43338-0149)
PHONE...................................419 946-3010
Spring Rodriguez, *Accounting Dir*
Vicki Taylor, *Manager*
Becky Jones, *Administration*
EMP: 25
SALES (corp-wide): 5.4MM **Privately Held**
SIC: **2711** 5999 Newspapers; rubber stamps
PA: Hirt Publishing Co, Inc
　　224 E Main St
　　Ottawa OH 45875
　　419 523-5709

(G-14563)
LILLY INDUSTRIES INC (PA)
Also Called: Lightning Bolt Fastners
6437 County Road 20 (43338-9624)
PHONE...................................419 946-7908
Fax: 419 946-6420
Phil Lilly, *President*
Alvin Lilly, *Vice Pres*
Sandy Chalfant, *Manager*
EMP: 20
SQ FT: 8,000
SALES (est): 2.7MM **Privately Held**
SIC: **3441** Fabricated structural metal

(G-14564)
MARROW COUNTY SENTINEL
245 Neal Ave Ste A (43338-9372)
PHONE...................................419 946-3010
EMP: 4
SALES (est): 182.5K **Privately Held**
SIC: **2711** Newspapers

(G-14565)
POP A TOP CRUISE THRU
157 S Main St (43338-1409)
PHONE...................................419 947-5855
Nikki Farson, *Owner*
EMP: 3
SALES (est): 188.8K **Privately Held**
SIC: **2082** Beer (alcoholic beverage)

(G-14566)
R M WOOD CO
5795 County Road 30 (43338-9701)
PHONE...................................419 845-2661
Roy Murphey, *Administration*
EMP: 5
SALES (est): 279.8K **Privately Held**
SIC: **2421** 2499 Sawmills & planing mills, general; wood products

(G-14567)
SHOPPERS COMPASS
114 Iberia St (43338-1263)
P.O. Box 109 (43338-0109)
PHONE...................................419 947-9234
Fax: 419 947-1030
James Walsh, *Partner*
EMP: 3
SALES (est): 211.5K **Privately Held**
SIC: **2741** Guides: publishing only, not printed on site; shopping news: publishing only, not printed on site

(G-14568)
SIGN CITY INC
5357 State Route 95 (43338-9764)
PHONE...................................614 486-6700
Ron Moody, *President*
EMP: 4
SALES (est): 380.2K **Privately Held**
SIC: **7336** 3993 Commercial art & graphic design; letters for signs, metal

(G-14569)
SNYDER FABRICATION LLC
6145 County Road 30 (43338-9705)
PHONE...................................419 946-6616
Terri Snyder,
Robert T Snyder,
EMP: 5
SQ FT: 1,800
SALES (est): 1MM **Privately Held**
WEB: www.snyderfab.com
SIC: **3599** Machine shop, jobbing & repair

Mount Hope
Holmes County

(G-14570)
ERVIN YODER
Also Called: Mount Hope Harness & Shoe
7700 County Rd 77 (44660)
P.O. Box 32 (44660-0032)
PHONE...................................330 359-5862
Ervin S Yoder, *Owner*
EMP: 3
SALES (est): 302.7K **Privately Held**
SIC: **5661** 3199 Shoe stores; harness or harness parts

(G-14571)
GMI HOLDINGS INC (DH)
Also Called: Genie Company, The
1 Door Dr (44660)
P.O. Box 67 (44660-0067)
PHONE...................................330 821-5360
Fax: 330 821-1927
Mike Kridel, *President*
Carl Adrien, *Principal*
Craig Smith, *Vice Pres*
Diana Lukasewicz, *Controller*
Linda Campbell, *Finance*
▲ EMP: 350
SQ FT: 230,000
SALES (est): 106.7MM
SALES (est): 3.1B **Privately Held**
WEB: www.geniecompany.com
SIC: **3699** 3635 Door opening & closing devices, electrical; household vacuum cleaners
HQ: Overhead Door Corporation
　　2501 S State Hwy 121 Ste
　　Lewisville TX 75067
　　469 549-7100

(G-14572)
HRH DOOR CORP (PA)
Also Called: Wayne Dalton
1 Door Dr (44660)
PHONE...................................850 208-3400
Fax: 330 674-4983
Willis Mullet, *CEO*
Thomas B Bennett III, *President*
Jose E Gonzalez, *General Mgr*
Theresa Labute, *General Mgr*
E E Muller, *Principal*
◆ EMP: 650
SQ FT: 1,000,000
SALES (est): 665.2MM **Privately Held**
WEB: www.waynedalton.com
SIC: **3442** 2431 Garage doors, overhead: metal; garage doors, overhead: wood

(G-14573)
OVERHEAD DOOR CORPORATION
1 Door Dr (44660)
P.O. Box 67 (44660-0067)
PHONE...................................330 674-7015
EMP: 97
SALES (corp-wide): 3.1B **Privately Held**
SIC: **3442** Garage doors, overhead: metal
HQ: Overhead Door Corporation
　　2501 S State Hwy 121 Ste
　　Lewisville TX 75067
　　469 549-7100

(G-14574)
OVERHEAD DOOR CORPORATION
4576 County Rd 160 (44660)
PHONE...................................330 674-7015
Kim Brown, *Director*
EMP: 93
SALES (corp-wide): 3.1B **Privately Held**
SIC: **3442** Garage doors, overhead: metal
HQ: Overhead Door Corporation
　　2501 S State Hwy 121 Ste
　　Lewisville TX 75067
　　469 549-7100

Mount Orab
Brown County

(G-14575)
ATW OHIO LLC
200 Front St (45154-8964)
PHONE...................................937 444-4295
EMP: 150
SALES (est): 7.7MM **Privately Held**
SIC: **3715** Truck trailers; trailer bodies; truck trailer chassis

(G-14576)
CINCINNATI DOWEL & WD PDTS CO
135 Oak St (45154-9090)
PHONE...................................937 444-2502
Fax: 937 444-4095
William Streight, *President*
Christopher Pizzuto, *Purchasing*
Eric A Frey, *Sales/Mktg Mgr*
Bethany Spires, *Credit Mgr*
Melissa Hacker, *Admin Mgr*
◆ EMP: 25 EST: 1925
SQ FT: 2,400
SALES (est): 3.5MM **Privately Held**
WEB: www.cincinnatidowel.com
SIC: **2499** Dowels, wood; carved & turned wood

(G-14577)
CINDOCO WOOD PRODUCTS CO
Also Called: Craftwood
410 Mount Clifton Dr (45154-9353)
PHONE...................................937 444-2504
Melissa Hacker, *President*
EMP: 6
SALES (est): 174.6K **Privately Held**
SIC: **5099** 2431 Wood & wood by-products; millwork

(G-14578)
CLERMONT SUN PUBLISHING CO
Also Called: Brown County Press
219 S High St (45154-9039)
PHONE...................................937 444-3441
Fax: 937 444-2652
Tony Adams, *Marketing Staff*
Steve Large, *Manager*
Anthony Adams, *Manager*
Eunice Ott, *Manager*
EMP: 4
SALES (corp-wide): 3.4MM **Privately Held**
WEB: www.clermontsun.com
SIC: **2711** Newspapers, publishing & printing
PA: Clermont Sun Publishing Company (Inc)
　　465 E Main St
　　Batavia OH
　　513 732-2511

(G-14579)
HAWKLINE NEVADA LLC
200 Front St (45154-8964)
PHONE...................................937 444-4295
Fax: 937 444-0888
Anthony Danna, *Manager*
Candy Smith, *Executive*
John Burgess,
Larry Danna,
▲ EMP: 50
SQ FT: 150,000

WEB: www.gohawkline.com
SIC: **3523** 3799 Cabs, tractors & agricultural machinery; trailers & trailer equipment

(G-14580)
HIGHLAND TECHNOLOGIES LLC
630 Harwood Rd (45154-8797)
PHONE...................................513 739-3510
Lester E McFarland, *Principal*
EMP: 4
SALES: 250K **Privately Held**
SIC: **3999** Manufacturing industries

(G-14581)
HIRONS MEMORIAL WORKS INC
14950 Us Highway 68 (45154-9701)
PHONE...................................937 444-2917
Fax: 937 444-2646
Ronald Hirons, *President*
Jane Hirons, *Corp Secy*
John Hirons, *Vice Pres*
EMP: 5
SQ FT: 10,000
SALES (est): 723.4K **Privately Held**
WEB: www.hironsmemorials.com
SIC: **5999** 5084 3589 Monuments & tombstones; industrial machinery & equipment; sandblasting equipment

(G-14582)
LUXUS PRODUCTS LLC
Also Called: Luxus Arms
222 Homan Way (45154-8269)
P.O. Box 11 (45154-0011)
PHONE...................................937 444-6500
Clay Barker, *Principal*
EMP: 6
SALES (est): 400K **Privately Held**
SIC: **2491** Structural lumber & timber, treated wood

(G-14583)
MILACRON PLAS TECH GROUP LLC
418 W Main St (45154-9596)
PHONE...................................937 444-2532
Fax: 937 536-2927
James Kinzie, *General Mgr*
Tom Page, *Opers Staff*
Daryl Smith, *Buyer*
Bryan Davis, *Engineer*
Dick Colwell, *Manager*
EMP: 183
SALES (corp-wide): 1.1B **Publicly Held**
SIC: **3544** Forms (molds), for foundry & plastics working machinery
HQ: Milacron Plastics Technologies Group Llc
　　4165 Half Acre Rd
　　Batavia OH 45103
　　513 536-2000

(G-14584)
NORTH HIGH MARATHON
570 N High St (45154-7902)
PHONE...................................937 444-1894
Imad Shattya, *Owner*
EMP: 4
SALES (est): 229.5K **Privately Held**
SIC: **3443** Fuel tanks (oil, gas, etc.): metal plate

(G-14585)
PRECISION WELDING & MFG
101 Day Rd (45154-8924)
P.O. Box 369 (45154-0369)
PHONE...................................937 444-6925
Fax: 937 444-7622
Dan Fisher, *President*
Barb Wooten, *Manager*
EMP: 18
SQ FT: 20,000
SALES (est): 1.1MM **Privately Held**
WEB: www.danfisher.com
SIC: **3441** Fabricated structural metal

(G-14586)
PRO-TECH MANUFACTURING INC
14944 Hillcrest Rd (45154-8513)
PHONE...................................937 444-6484
Patrick Gregory, *President*
Jeff Roades, *Vice Pres*
EMP: 10

SQ FT: 9,000
SALES (est): 1.4MM **Privately Held**
SIC: 3599 Machine shop, jobbing & repair

(G-14587)
WEDCO LLC
Also Called: Bardwell Winery
716 N High St (45154-8349)
P.O. Box 391 (45154-0391)
PHONE..............................513 309-0781
Roy R Weddle, *Mng Member*
EMP: 6
SALES: 130K **Privately Held**
SIC: 6531 2082 5182 Real estate brokers
& agents; brewers' grain; wine

(G-14588)
WORTHINGTON INDUSTRIES INC
351 Apple St (45154-8565)
PHONE..............................937 556-6111
John P McConnell, *Manager*
EMP: 23
SALES (corp-wide): 2.8B **Publicly Held**
SIC: 2899 Fluxes: brazing, soldering, galvanizing & welding
PA: Worthington Industries, Inc.
200 W Old Wilson Bridge Rd
Worthington OH 43085
614 438-3210

(G-14589)
X-MIL INC
220 Homan Way (45154-8269)
P.O. Box 452 (45154-0452)
PHONE..............................937 444-1323
Fax: 513 735-6991
Steven E Seibert, *President*
Erica Carpenter, *General Mgr*
Joel Scott Dalton, *Vice Pres*
Steve Dalton, *Info Tech Mgr*
Angie Kreidler, *Admin Sec*
EMP: 20
SALES (est): 1.2MM **Privately Held**
WEB: www.x-mil.com
SIC: 3599 Machine shop, jobbing & repair

Mount Perry
Perry County

(G-14590)
B & D COMMISSARY LLC
5705 State Route 204 Ne (43760)
PHONE..............................740 743-3890
Fax: 740 743-3895
William Dugas, *Partner*
David Dugas, *Partner*
EMP: 30
SALES (est): 3.2MM **Privately Held**
SIC: 2045 Pizza doughs, prepared: from
purchased flour

(G-14591)
KNOX ENERGY INC
930 Mount Perry Rd (43760)
PHONE..............................740 787-1391
EMP: 7
SALES (corp-wide): 2.4MM **Privately Held**
SIC: 2911 Oils, fuel
PA: Knox Energy, Inc.
11872 Worthington Rd Nw
Pataskala OH 43062
740 927-6731

(G-14592)
MT PERRY FOODS INC
5705 State Route 204 Ne (43760-9733)
P.O. Box 159, Glenford (43739-0159)
PHONE..............................740 743-3890
Reg Martin, *President*
Jon Largent, *General Mgr*
B Kay, *Office Mgr*
Tom Weiss, *Manager*
Ron Pratt, *Maintence Staff*
EMP: 75 **EST:** 2000
SALES (est): 15.6MM **Privately Held**
WEB: www.perrycountyohiocofc.com
SIC: 2499 Food handling & processing
products, wood

(G-14593)
PRECISION GEOPHYSICAL INC
4700 Rucker Rd (43760-9613)
PHONE..............................740 849-3044
Don Wiliford, *Manager*
EMP: 10
SALES (corp-wide): 4.8MM **Privately Held**
WEB: www.precisiongeophysical.com
SIC: 1382 Oil & gas exploration services
PA: Precision Geophysical Inc
2695 State Route 83
Millersburg OH 44654
330 674-2198

(G-14594)
S & S SPRING SHOP
1755 Mount Perry Rd (43760-9641)
PHONE..............................800 619-4652
Fax: 740 787-9814
Fred Bates, *Owner*
Gary Smith, *Owner*
James D Smith, *Partner*
EMP: 4
SQ FT: 2,400
SALES (est): 169.3K **Privately Held**
SIC: 7692 0721 Welding repair; planting
services

(G-14595)
SMITH SPRINGS INC
1755 Mount Perry Rd (43760-9641)
PHONE..............................800 619-4652
Gary B Smith, *President*
Roxy R Smith, *Vice Pres*
Teha Hutchinson, *Admin Sec*
EMP: 4
SALES (est): 345.1K **Privately Held**
SIC: 7692 7539 Welding repair; automotive repair shops

Mount Sterling
Madison County

(G-14596)
BLESCO SERVICES
8905 Mckendree Rd (43143-9120)
PHONE..............................614 871-4900
EMP: 3
SALES (est): 260.6K **Privately Held**
SIC: 3444 Sheet metalwork

(G-14597)
CROP PRODUCTION SERVICES INC
249 Chestnut St (43143-9722)
PHONE..............................740 869-3369
Scott Riddle, *Site Mgr*
Doug Penwell, *Manager*
EMP: 15
SALES (corp-wide): 13.6B **Privately Held**
WEB: www.cropproductionservices.com
SIC: 2875 Fertilizers, mixing only
HQ: Crop Production Services, Inc.
3005 Rocky Mountain Ave
Loveland CO 80538
970 685-3300

(G-14598)
FURNISS CORPORATION LTD
15812 State Route 56 W (43143-9532)
P.O. Box 128 (43143-0128)
PHONE..............................614 871-1470
Andy Furniss, *Managing Prtnr*
Elizabeth Furniss, *General Mgr*
EMP: 19 **EST:** 1997
SQ FT: 27,000
SALES (est): 3.2MM **Privately Held**
WEB: www.furnisscorp.com
SIC: 3845 Electromedical equipment; electromedical apparatus

(G-14599)
KEIHIN THERMAL TECH AMER INC
10500 Oday Harrison Rd (43143-9474)
PHONE..............................740 869-3000
Tatsuhiko Arai, *President*
Scott Mortimer, *General Mgr*
Scott Amortimer, *Vice Pres*
Robert Feltz, *Safety Mgr*
Steve Shonk, *Purchasing*
◆ **EMP:** 475

SALES (est): 110MM **Privately Held**
SIC: 5013 3714 Automotive engines & engine parts; motor vehicle engines & parts

(G-14600)
LANDSCAPE GROUP LLC
15740 Scioto Darby Rd (43143-9036)
PHONE..............................614 302-4537
Greg Whaley,
EMP: 3
SALES (est): 219.4K **Privately Held**
SIC: 3523 Grounds mowing equipment

(G-14601)
OHIO WILLOW WOOD COMPANY
Also Called: Willowwood
15441 Scioto Darby Rd (43143-9036)
P.O. Box 130 (43143-0130)
PHONE..............................740 869-3377
Fax: 740 869-4374
Ryan Arbogast, *President*
C Joseph Arbogast, *Exec VP*
Jim Capper, *Exec VP*
Robert E Arbogast, *Vice Pres*
Mitchell Neff, *Facilities Dir*
▲ **EMP:** 185 **EST:** 1907
SQ FT: 90,000
SALES (est): 30MM **Privately Held**
WEB: www.owwco.com
SIC: 3842 Prosthetic appliances

(G-14602)
SHOWA ALUMINUM CORP AMERICA
10500 Oday Harrison Rd (43143-9474)
PHONE..............................740 869-3333
Ken Gakasuki, *President*
Rodney Riley, *General Mgr*
David White, *Purch Agent*
Drew Schultz, *Engineer*
Scott Mortimer, *Controller*
◆ **EMP:** 476
SQ FT: 210,000
SALES (est): 37.4MM
SALES (corp-wide): 6.3B **Privately Held**
WEB: www.sdk.co.jp
SIC: 3714 Motor vehicle parts & accessories; motor vehicle electrical equipment; air conditioner parts, motor vehicle
PA: Showa Denko K.K.
1-13-9, Shibadaimon
Minato-Ku TKY 105-0
354 703-235

(G-14603)
SHOWA ALUMINUM CORP AMERICA (HQ)
10500 Oday Harrison Rd (43143-9474)
PHONE..............................740 869-3333
Fumihiko Ohmi, *President*
Bruce R Henke, *Principal*
Shotic Japan, *Principal*
Lonnie Caupp, *Electrical Engi*
Jerry Reber, *Human Res Mgr*
▲ **EMP:** 15
SALES (est): 5.1MM
SALES (corp-wide): 6.3B **Privately Held**
SIC: 3463 Aluminum forgings
PA: Showa Denko K.K.
1-13-9, Shibadaimon
Minato-Ku TKY 105-0
354 703-235

(G-14604)
STEPHENS PIPE & STEEL LLC
10732 Schadel Ln (43143-9731)
P.O. Box 237 (43143-0237)
PHONE..............................740 869-2257
Rick Redman, *Principal*
Don Bowsher, *Manager*
Russ Brasher, *Info Tech Mgr*
EMP: 150
SALES (corp-wide): 2.9B **Privately Held**
WEB: www.stephenspipeandsteel.com
SIC: 3315 3523 3496 3494 Chain link fencing; farm machinery & equipment; miscellaneous fabricated wire products; valves & pipe fittings; architectural metalwork
HQ: Stephens Pipe & Steel, Llc
2224 E Highway 619
Russell Springs KY 42642
270 866-3331

Mount Vernon
Knox County

(G-14605)
AMG INDUSTRIES LLC
200 Commerce Dr (43050-4699)
PHONE..............................740 397-4044
Fax: 740 397-3092
David J McElroy, *President*
Michael Pingstock, *President*
James McElroy, *COO*
Dennis McElroy, *Exec VP*
Mike Miller, *Vice Pres*
EMP: 100
SQ FT: 120,000
SALES (est): 38.7MM
SALES (corp-wide): 192.8MM **Privately Held**
WEB: www.amgindustries.com
SIC: 3465 Automotive stampings
PA: Reserve Group Management Company
3560 W Market St Ste 300
Fairlawn OH 44333
330 665-6706

(G-14606)
ARIEL CORPORATION
8585 Blackjack Road Ext (43050-2782)
PHONE..............................740 397-0311
EMP: 10
SALES (corp-wide): 114.7MM **Privately Held**
SIC: 3563 Air & gas compressors including vacuum pumps
PA: Ariel Corporation
35 Blackjack Road Ext
Mount Vernon OH 43050
740 397-0311

(G-14607)
ARIEL CORPORATION
35 Blackjack Road Ext (43050-9482)
PHONE..............................740 397-0311
Karen Buchwald Wright, *President*
Kirk E Townsend, *Director*
EMP: 14
SALES (corp-wide): 114.7MM **Privately Held**
SIC: 3563 Air & gas compressors
PA: Ariel Corporation
35 Blackjack Road Ext
Mount Vernon OH 43050
740 397-0311

(G-14608)
ARISTOCRAT INDUSTRIES INC
7555 Sharp Rd (43050-9412)
PHONE..............................740 694-2752
Fax: 740 393-2200
Robert Peters, *President*
Cecelia McClelland, *Manager*
EMP: 11
SQ FT: 15,000
SALES (est): 1.3MM **Privately Held**
WEB: www.aristocrat.com
SIC: 2493 Reconstituted wood products;
bulletin boards, wood; bulletin boards,
cork

(G-14609)
BENCHMARK CABINETS
17239 Sycamore Rd (43050-8527)
PHONE..............................740 397-4615
Wesley Crum, *Owner*
EMP: 22
SALES (est): 834.1K **Privately Held**
SIC: 2434 Wood kitchen cabinets

(G-14610)
C-H TOOL & DIE
Also Called: Ch Tool & Die
711 N Sandusky St (43050-1034)
P.O. Box 889 (43050-0889)
PHONE..............................740 397-7214
David Davison, *Owner*
EMP: 5
SQ FT: 10,000
SALES (est): 422.3K **Privately Held**
WEB: www.ch4d.com
SIC: 3423 3544 Tools or equipment for
use with sporting arms; special dies &
tools

(G-14611)
CAMERON INTERNATIONAL CORP
Also Called: Cooper Energy Services
8043 Columbus Rd (43050-9358)
PHONE..................................740 397-4888
Barry Thompson, *Principal*
EMP: 5 **Privately Held**
SIC: 3519 Internal combustion engines
HQ: Cameron International Corporation
4646 W Sam Houston Pkwy N
Houston TX 77041

(G-14612)
CAPITAL CITY OIL INC
Also Called: American Energy Pdts Inc Ind
375 Columbus Rd (43050-4427)
PHONE..................................740 397-4483
Roy Bailey, *President*
EMP: 6
SALES (est): 750K **Privately Held**
SIC: 2911 4953 Oils, fuel; refuse systems

(G-14613)
CENTRAL OHIO FABRICATORS LLC
105 Progress Dr (43050-4772)
PHONE..................................740 393-3892
Fax: 740 393-3205
Jewel Jacobs, *Manager*
Barry Jacobs,
EMP: 50
SQ FT: 22,000
SALES (est): 9.4MM **Privately Held**
SIC: 3441 Fabricated structural metal

(G-14614)
CENTRAL OHIO MAT COMPANY
1025 Harcourt Rd Ste 500 (43050-4465)
P.O. Box 1226 (43050-8226)
PHONE..................................740 627-7261
Arthur Schad, *Principal*
EMP: 3
SALES (est): 196.2K **Privately Held**
SIC: 2515 Mattresses & foundations

(G-14615)
CITY OF MOUNT VERNON
Also Called: Water & Waste Water Dept.
1550 Old Delaware Rd (43050-8631)
PHONE..................................740 393-9508
Judie Scott, *Administration*
EMP: 8 **Privately Held**
WEB: www.mountvernonohio.org
SIC: 2899 Water treating compounds
PA: City Of Mount Vernon
40 Public Sq Ste 206
Mount Vernon OH 43050
740 393-9520

(G-14616)
CLIFFS HIGH PERFORMANCE
20579 Berry Rd (43050-9226)
PHONE..................................740 397-2921
Cliff Ruggles, *Owner*
EMP: 3
SALES (est): 223.4K **Privately Held**
SIC: 3462 Automotive & internal combustion engine forgings

(G-14617)
CLYDE FERENBAUGH
Allen Rd (43050)
PHONE..................................740 397-0287
Clyde Ferenbaugh, *Principal*
EMP: 3 **EST:** 2001
SALES (est): 166.9K **Privately Held**
SIC: 2421 Box lumber

(G-14618)
DANDY PRODUCTS INC
1095 Harcourt Rd Ste C (43050-4476)
PHONE..................................800 591-2284
Dan Cleveland, *Branch Mgr*
EMP: 5 **Privately Held**
WEB: www.dandyproducts.com
SIC: 3531 Construction machinery
PA: Dandy Products Inc

Dublin OH 43016

(G-14619)
DIVERSIFIED PRODUCTS & SVCS
1250 Vernonview Dr (43050-1447)
PHONE..................................740 393-6202
Louis Ohara, *Director*
EMP: 118
SALES (est): 6.6MM **Privately Held**
SIC: 5199 2541 2511 Packaging materials; wood partitions & fixtures; wood household furniture

(G-14620)
DOWN HOME
Also Called: Down Home Leather
9 N Main St (43050-3203)
PHONE..................................740 393-1186
Laurel Lee Wagoner, *Owner*
Duke Wagoner, *Sales Mgr*
EMP: 8
SQ FT: 5,000
SALES (est): 300K **Privately Held**
WEB: www.downhomeleather.com
SIC: 5947 3172 Gift shop; personal leather goods

(G-14621)
ENERGY MACHINE INC
100 Commerce Dr (43050-4641)
PHONE..................................740 397-1155
Fax: 740 392-7744
Heather McCracken, *Project Mgr*
Brian Meiers, *Executive*
Karen Buchwald Wright,
▲ **EMP:** 50
SQ FT: 60,000
SALES (est): 6.5MM **Privately Held**
WEB: www.energy-machine.com
SIC: 3599 Machine shop, jobbing & repair; crankshafts & camshafts, machining

(G-14622)
FAMOUS INDUSTRIES INC
Also Called: Heating & Cooling Products
325 Commerce Dr (43050-4643)
PHONE..................................740 397-8842
Don Smith, *General Mgr*
N M Greenberger, *Principal*
Harold J Rothwell, *Principal*
H A Sullivan, *Principal*
Donnie Hyatt, *Plant Mgr*
EMP: 160 **Privately Held**
WEB: www.jfgoodco.com
SIC: 3444 3585 3312 Sheet metalwork; refrigeration & heating equipment; blast furnaces & steel mills
HQ: Famous Industries, Inc.
2620 Ridgewood Rd Ste 200
Akron OH 44313
330 535-1811

(G-14623)
INTERNATIONAL PAPER COMPANY
8800 Granville Rd (43050-9192)
PHONE..................................740 397-5215
Mark Smith, *Branch Mgr*
Kathy Baird, *Manager*
Doug Wheeler, *Manager*
EMP: 180
SALES (corp-wide): 21B **Publicly Held**
WEB: www.internationalpaper.com
SIC: 2653 Boxes, corrugated: made from purchased materials
PA: International Paper Company
6400 Poplar Ave
Memphis TN 38197
901 419-9000

(G-14624)
J B KEPPLE SHEET METAL
1010 Vernonview Dr (43050-1451)
PHONE..................................740 393-2971
Michael Kepple, *Owner*
EMP: 3
SALES (est): 250K **Privately Held**
SIC: 3444 3496 3443 3429 Sheet metalwork; miscellaneous fabricated wire products; fabricated plate work (boiler shop); manufactured hardware (general)

(G-14625)
JELD-WEN INC
Also Called: Jeld-Wen Windows
1201 Newark Rd (43050-4728)
PHONE..................................740 397-1144
Leona Williamson, *Purch Mgr*
Brad Hunter, *Manager*
EMP: 345
SALES (corp-wide): 22.5B **Publicly Held**
WEB: www.jeld-wen.com
SIC: 2431 Millwork
HQ: Jeld-Wen, Inc.
440 S Church St Ste 400
Charlotte NC 28202
800 535-3936

(G-14626)
JELD-WEN INC
335 Commerce Dr (43050-4643)
PHONE..................................740 397-3403
Fax: 740 397-7442
Ted Schnormeier, *Branch Mgr*
EMP: 20
SALES (corp-wide): 22.5B **Publicly Held**
WEB: www.jeld-wen.com
SIC: 2431 Millwork
HQ: Jeld-Wen, Inc.
440 S Church St Ste 400
Charlotte NC 28202
800 535-3936

(G-14627)
KNOX MACHINE & TOOL
250 Columbus Rd (43050-4428)
PHONE..................................740 392-3133
Fax: 740 392-3290
Korby Bricker, *President*
Trent Hauke, *Corp Secy*
EMP: 9 **EST:** 1994
SALES (est): 1MM **Privately Held**
SIC: 3599 Machine shop, jobbing & repair

(G-14628)
LANES WELDING & REPAIR
9180 Kinney Rd (43050-9333)
PHONE..................................740 397-2525
Frank H Lane, *Owner*
EMP: 3
SQ FT: 2,400
SALES (est): 121.6K **Privately Held**
SIC: 7692 Welding repair

(G-14629)
LONGRIDERS TRUCKING COMPANY
7 Delano St (43050-4503)
P.O. Box 4006, Newark (43058-4006)
PHONE..................................740 975-7863
Debra Smith, *Principal*
Larry Green,
EMP: 5
SALES: 67K **Privately Held**
SIC: 3715 Truck trailers

(G-14630)
MEDIA MATRIX LLC
13252 Wooster Rd (43050-9726)
PHONE..................................888 833-8681
William H Brumfield,
EMP: 3 **EST:** 2014
SALES (est): 238.6K **Privately Held**
SIC: 3677 Filtration devices, electronic

(G-14631)
MOHAWK MANUFACTURING INC
306 E Gambier St (43050-3514)
PHONE..................................860 632-2345
Walter Nacey, *President*
EMP: 8
SALES (est): 490K **Privately Held**
SIC: 3799 Horse trailers, except fifth-wheel type

(G-14632)
MOUNT VERNON PACKAGING INC
135 Progress Dr (43050-4772)
P.O. Box 950 (43050-0950)
PHONE..................................740 397-3221
Fax: 740 393-2002
Donald Nuce, *President*
Margo Nuce, *Vice Pres*
EMP: 10

(G-14633)
MT VERNON CY WASTEWATER TRTMNT
3 Cougar Dr Unit 3 (43050-3866)
PHONE..................................740 393-9502
Mathias Orndorf, *Director*
Judi Scott, *Administration*
EMP: 12
SALES (est): 1.7MM **Privately Held**
SIC: 3589 Water treatment equipment, industrial

(G-14634)
NOVOLEX HOLDINGS INC
Also Called: Packaging Div
101 Commerce Dr (43050-4646)
PHONE..................................740 397-2555
Fax: 740 392-9453
Andy Frazee, *Production*
Phil Penwell, *Executive*
EMP: 78
SALES (corp-wide): 2.2B **Publicly Held**
WEB: www.burrowspaper.com
SIC: 2621 2672 2671 Tissue paper; coated & laminated paper; waxed paper: made from purchased material
HQ: Novolex Holdings, Inc.
101 E Carolina Ave
Hartsville SC 29550
843 857-4800

(G-14635)
OWENS CORNING SALES LLC
100 Blackjack Road Ext (43050-9194)
PHONE..................................614 399-3915
Bob Demory, *Manager*
EMP: 54
SALES (corp-wide): 5.6B **Publicly Held**
WEB: www.owenscorning.com
SIC: 2621 3296 Building paper, insulation; mineral wool
HQ: Owens Corning Sales, Llc
1 Owens Corning Pkwy
Toledo OH 43659
419 248-8000

(G-14636)
PAGE ONE GROUP
10 E Vine St Ste C (43050-3244)
PHONE..................................740 397-4240
Fax: 740 397-0906
Jana Burson, *Partner*
EMP: 7
SQ FT: 800
SALES: 516K **Privately Held**
SIC: 2752 8742 Commercial printing, offset; marketing consulting services

(G-14637)
PERFORMACE DIESEL INC
16901 Mcvay Rd (43050)
PHONE..................................740 392-3693
Stephen Harsany, *President*
Angel Harsany, *Treasurer*
EMP: 10
SQ FT: 7,000
SALES: 530K **Privately Held**
SIC: 3519 Diesel engine rebuilding

(G-14638)
POTEMKIN INDUSTRIES INC (PA)
8043 Columbus Rd (43050-9358)
PHONE..................................740 397-4888
Fax: 740 397-8529
Horst Krajenski, *President*
Debbie Hamilton, *Vice Pres*
Rachel Lamb, *Production*
Jim Wells, *Engineer*
Mike Radermacher, *Project Engr*
EMP: 30 **EST:** 1980
SQ FT: 14,000
SALES (est): 4.8MM **Privately Held**
WEB: www.potemkinindustries.com
SIC: 3563 Air & gas compressors including vacuum pumps

(G-14639)
PRINTING ARTS PRESS
8028 Newark Rd (43050-8155)
P.O. Box 431 (43050-0431)
PHONE..................................740 397-6106

Fax: 740 397-6832
Robert Vogt, *Principal*
Theresa Kauser, *Accounts Mgr*
Charles Gherman, *Manager*
Rhonda Gherman, *Exec Dir*
Katrina Burke, *Administration*
EMP: 10
SQ FT: 15,000
SALES (est): 1.6MM **Privately Held**
WEB: www.printingartspress.com
SIC: 2752 2791 Commercial printing, offset; typesetting

(G-14640)
PROGRESSIVE
COMMUNICATIONS
Also Called: Mount Vernon News
18 E Vine St (43050-3226)
P.O. Box 791 (43050-0791)
PHONE....................740 397-5333
Fax: 740 397-1321
Kay H Culbertson, *President*
Fred Main, *General Mgr*
Bill Davis, *Editor*
Joe Huddleston, *Editor*
Michelle L Hartman, *Vice Pres*
EMP: 65
SQ FT: 30,000
SALES (est): 5.1MM **Privately Held**
SIC: 2711 2752 2791 Commercial printing & newspaper publishing combined; job printing & newspaper publishing combined; commercial printing, offset; typesetting

(G-14641)
REPLEX MIRROR COMPANY
Also Called: Replex Plastics
11 Mount Vernon Ave (43050-4163)
PHONE....................740 397-5535
Fax: 740 397-5548
Mark Schuetz, *President*
Karen Batten, *Safety Dir*
Laurie Fosher, *Controller*
Blumensheid Tammy, *Accountant*
Alicia Nicholson, *Cust Svc Mgr*
EMP: 21
SQ FT: 100,000
SALES (est): 7.8MM **Privately Held**
WEB: www.replex.com
SIC: 3089 Thermoformed finished plastic products

(G-14642)
ROBERT COLEMAN
Also Called: Patient Medicines
15850 Carson Rd (43050-7520)
PHONE....................740 393-4336
Robert Coleman, *Owner*
EMP: 3
SQ FT: 3,000
SALES (est): 166.4K **Privately Held**
SIC: 3229 Pressed & blown glass

(G-14643)
SANOH AMERICA INC
7905 Industrial Park Dr (43050-2776)
PHONE....................740 392-9200
Eric Carroll, *Principal*
Barbara Biffath, *Administration*
Clay Hooper, *Maintence Staff*
EMP: 220
SALES (corp-wide): 1.1B **Privately Held**
WEB: www.sanoh-america.com
SIC: 7539 3714 Automotive repair shops; motor vehicle parts & accessories
HQ: Sanoh America, Inc.
1849 Industrial Dr
Findlay OH 45840
419 425-2600

(G-14644)
SANT SAND & GRAVEL CO
14220 Parrott Ext (43050-4500)
P.O. Box 750 (43050-0750)
PHONE....................740 397-0000
Fax: 740 397-0862
EMP: 8 EST: 1959
SQ FT: 2,000
SALES: 366.8K
SALES (corp-wide): 28.7MM **Privately Held**
SIC: 1442 Sand & Gravel Mining

PA: United Precast Inc.
400 Howard St
Mount Vernon OH 43050
740 393-1121

(G-14645)
SELECTIVE MED COMPONENTS
INC
504 Harcourt Rd Ste 3 (43050-3945)
PHONE....................740 397-7838
Fax: 740 397-6112
Richard Fisher III, *President*
Peggy Fingering, *Personnel Exec*
Glen Geboard, *Manager*
EMP: 30
SQ FT: 6,000
SALES (est): 3.7MM **Privately Held**
WEB: www.selectivemed.com
SIC: 3823 Electrodes used in industrial process measurement

(G-14646)
SHAMROCK PLASTICS INC
633 Howard St (43050-3709)
PHONE....................740 392-5555
Fax: 740 392-3555
Tom Ruffner, *President*
Debbie Ruffner, *Manager*
EMP: 10
SALES (est): 1.8MM **Privately Held**
WEB: www.shamrockplasticsinc.com
SIC: 2796 3083 Platemaking services; laminated plastic sheets

(G-14647)
SHELLENBARGER EXCAVATING
& LOG
9260 Fairview Rd (43050-9307)
PHONE....................740 397-9949
Francis Shellenbarger, *Principal*
EMP: 3
SALES (est): 217K **Privately Held**
SIC: 2411 Logging camps & contractors

(G-14648)
SIEMENS ENERGY INC
105 N Sandusky St (43050-2447)
PHONE....................740 393-8897
EMP: 252
SALES (corp-wide): 89.6B **Privately Held**
SIC: 1629 1731 3511 Power plant construction; energy management controls; turbines & turbine generator sets
HQ: Siemens Energy, Inc.
4400 N Alafaya Trl
Orlando FL 32826
407 736-2000

(G-14649)
SIEMENS ENERGY INC
607 W Chestnut St (43050-2335)
PHONE....................740 393-8464
EMP: 8
SALES (corp-wide): 89.6B **Privately Held**
SIC: 3661 Telephones & telephone apparatus
HQ: Siemens Energy, Inc.
4400 N Alafaya Trl
Orlando FL 32826
407 736-2000

(G-14650)
SIGNLINE GRAPHICS &
LETTERING
114 Clinton Rd (43050-8601)
P.O. Box 254 (43050-0254)
PHONE....................740 397-5806
Charles Blubaugh, *President*
Candi L Blubaugh, *Vice Pres*
EMP: 4
SQ FT: 1,400
SALES: 200K **Privately Held**
WEB: www.signline1.com
SIC: 3993 Signs & advertising specialties

(G-14651)
SMARTCOPY INC (PA)
Also Called: Blue Fox Group, The
50 Parrott St Ste A (43050-4568)
PHONE....................740 392-6162
Fax: 740 392-6162
Michael Hajjar, *President*
David Williams, *Service Mgr*
Susan Nicholson, *Admin Sec*
EMP: 9

SQ FT: 20,000
SALES (est): 1.2MM **Privately Held**
SIC: 8999 3861 Art related services; processing equipment, photographic

(G-14652)
STATE-MATE COMPANY
Also Called: Pro Forma All Print Source
1558 Coshocton Ave (43050-5416)
PHONE....................740 392-9487
Fax: 740 599-9480
Joseph F Bobo, *President*
Delores Bobo, *Treasurer*
EMP: 3
SQ FT: 2,500
SALES: 250K **Privately Held**
SIC: 2759 2752 Business forms: printing; advertising posters, lithographed

(G-14653)
UPPER CUT
444 Columbus Rd Ste F (43050-4461)
PHONE....................740 397-0330
Connie Lemon, *Principal*
EMP: 4 EST: 2005
SALES (est): 329.8K **Privately Held**
SIC: 3131 Uppers

(G-14654)
VER-MAC INDUSTRIES INC
100 Progress Dr (43050-4700)
PHONE....................740 397-6511
Fax: 740 393-2708
Dennis McElroy, *President*
William D Heichel, *Principal*
Mitch Durbin, *Vice Pres*
Dave Bickers, *Prdtn Mgr*
Doug Beckley, *Mfg Staff*
▲ **EMP:** 40
SQ FT: 26,000
SALES (est): 7.6MM **Privately Held**
WEB: www.ver-macindustries.com
SIC: 3599 3496 3449 Machine shop, jobbing & repair; air intake filters, internal combustion engine, except auto; miscellaneous fabricated wire products; miscellaneous metalwork

(G-14655)
WEYERHAEUSER CO
CONTAINEERBOAR
8800 Granville Rd (43050-9192)
PHONE....................740 397-5215
Larry Tignor, *Principal*
EMP: 10 EST: 2009
SALES (est): 1MM **Privately Held**
SIC: 2653 Corrugated & solid fiber boxes

(G-14656)
WOLFF HOUSE ART PAPERS
INC
133 S Main St (43050-3323)
PHONE....................740 501-3766
Jess Gabric, *President*
Thomas Wise, *Principal*
Dixie Gabric, *Vice Pres*
EMP: 3
SQ FT: 3,640
SALES: 120K **Privately Held**
SIC: 2679 Wallpaper

Mount Victory
Hardin County

(G-14657)
OHIO FRESH EGGS LLC
20449 County Road 245 (43340-9710)
P.O. Box 118 (43340-0118)
PHONE....................937 354-2233
Brian Kinter, *Manager*
EMP: 30
SALES (corp-wide): 123.5MM **Privately Held**
SIC: 5144 2015 0252 Eggs; poultry slaughtering & processing; chicken eggs
PA: Ohio Fresh Eggs, Llc
11212 Croton Rd
Croton OH 43013
740 893-7200

(G-14658)
RAVENWORKS DEER SKIN
34477 Shertzer Rd (43340-9615)
P.O. Box 6 (43340-0006)
PHONE....................937 354-5151
Charles Harris, *Partner*
Nina Harris, *Partner*
EMP: 6
SALES (est): 628.6K **Privately Held**
SIC: 3171 3172 Women's handbags & purses; personal leather goods

(G-14659)
ROEHLERS MACHINE
PRODUCTS
117 Taylor St E (43340-8811)
P.O. Box 366 (43340-0366)
PHONE....................937 354-4401
Fax: 937 354-4402
Scott Roehler, *Owner*
EMP: 3
SQ FT: 5,500
SALES: 300K **Privately Held**
SIC: 3451 3545 3452 Screw machine products; machine tool accessories; bolts, nuts, rivets & washers

---

Munroe Falls
Summit County

(G-14660)
HARDCOATING TECHNOLOGIES
LTD
103 S Main St (44262-1637)
PHONE....................330 686-2136
James Haag, *President*
EMP: 20
SQ FT: 10,000
SALES (est): 2.4MM **Privately Held**
WEB: www.hardcoatingtech.com
SIC: 3479 Painting, coating & hot dipping

(G-14661)
KYOCERA SGS PRECISION
TOOLS (PA)
55 S Main St (44262-1635)
P.O. Box 187 (44262-0187)
PHONE....................330 688-6667
Fax: 330 686-4111
Thomas Haag, *President*
Ernest Garza, *Regional Mgr*
Jacob Rak, *Mfg Staff*
Sara Yakubik, *Purch Agent*
Denise Jimenez, *Research*
EMP: 50 EST: 1961
SQ FT: 45,000
SALES: 78.5MM **Privately Held**
WEB: www.sgstool.com
SIC: 3545 5084 Cutting tools for machine tools; industrial machinery & equipment

(G-14662)
LEHNER SCREW MACHINE LLC
71 S River Rd (44262-1654)
PHONE....................330 688-6616
Fax: 330 688-6627
Thomas Bader, *President*
John Bader, *Vice Pres*
EMP: 21
SQ FT: 10,524
SALES: 680K **Privately Held**
WEB: www.lehnerscrewmachine.com
SIC: 3451 3599 Screw machine products; machine shop, jobbing & repair

(G-14663)
LEM INCORPORATED
71 S River Rd (44262-1654)
PHONE....................330 535-6422
Anne Mc Gaughey, *President*
EMP: 4
SQ FT: 3,200
SALES (est): 509.7K **Privately Held**
SIC: 3599 Machine shop, jobbing & repair

(G-14664)
M S B MACHINE INC
36 Castle Dr (44262-1602)
PHONE....................330 686-7740
Jim Burkart, *President*
EMP: 6
SQ FT: 3,880

SALES (est): 639.2K **Privately Held**
SIC: 3599 Machine shop, jobbing & repair

(G-14665)
SONOCO PRODUCTS COMPANY
59 N Main St (44262-1064)
P.O. Box 217 (44262-0217)
PHONE................................330 688-8247
Fax: 330 688-2534
S Glenn, *Plant Mgr*
C Duncan, *Mfg Staff*
Colleen Hudson, *Purchasing*
John Parman, *Manager*
EMP: 110
SALES (corp-wide): 4.7B **Publicly Held**
WEB: www.sonoco.com
SIC: 2631 2655 Paperboard mills; fiber
cans, drums & similar products
PA: Sonoco Products Company
1 N 2nd St
Hartsville SC 29550
843 383-7000

(G-14666)
SUPERIOR MOLD & DIE CO
449 N Main St (44262-1007)
PHONE................................330 688-8251
Fax: 330 688-8253
Richard Yamokoski, *President*
Jeffery Yamokoski, *Owner*
Gale Young, *Vice Pres*
EMP: 40
SQ FT: 43,000
SALES (est): 6.1MM **Privately Held**
SIC: 3544 3599 Industrial molds; machine
shop, jobbing & repair

(G-14667)
VADOSE SYN FUELS INC
323 S Main St (44262-1658)
PHONE................................330 564-0545
Sheri A Peters, *Principal*
EMP: 7
SALES (est): 889.9K **Privately Held**
SIC: 2869 Fuels

(G-14668)
WESCO MACHINE INC
99 Rustic Ter (44262-1532)
PHONE................................330 688-6973
De Etta Connelly, *President*
Ronald Connelly, *Vice Pres*
EMP: 17
SQ FT: 10,000
SALES (est): 2.2MM **Privately Held**
SIC: 3599 3559 Machine shop, jobbing &
repair; plastics working machinery

Napoleon
Henry County

(G-14669)
**ADVANCED DRAINAGE
SYSTEMS INC**
1075 Independence Dr (43545-9717)
PHONE................................419 599-9565
Fax: 419 592-2638
Janet Packard, *Personnel*
Jason Hartland, *Manager*
Marie Busch, *MIS Dir*
EMP: 30
SQ FT: 14,000
SALES (corp-wide): 1.2B **Publicly Held**
WEB: www.ads-pipe.com
SIC: 3084 3083 Plastics pipe; laminated
plastics plate & sheet
PA: Advanced Drainage Systems, Inc.
4640 Trueman Blvd
Hilliard OH 43026
614 658-0050

(G-14670)
**AMCOR RIGID PLASTICS USA
LLC**
12993 State Route 110 (43545-5899)
PHONE................................419 592-1998
Fax: 419 592-0940
Ray Behm, *Manager*
EMP: 33 **Privately Held**
WEB: www.slpcamericas.com
SIC: 3089 Plastic containers, except foam

HQ: Amcor Rigid Plastics Usa, Llc
10521 M 52
Manchester MI 48158

(G-14671)
AUTOMATIC FEED CO (PA)
Also Called: Automatic Feed Company
476 E Riverview Ave (43545-1899)
PHONE................................419 592-0050
Fax: 419 592-8950
William L Beck, *Principal*
Peter Beck, *Vice Pres*
Jon Knepley, *Project Mgr*
Barb Vannewhouse, *Purchasing*
Jeff Gerken, *Engineer*
▲ EMP: 94 EST: 1949
SQ FT: 160,000
SALES (est): 22MM **Privately Held**
WEB: www.automaticfeed.com
SIC: 3549 Cutting-up lines

(G-14672)
AVINA SPECIALTIES INC
116 W Washington St (43545-1740)
PHONE................................419 592-5646
Fax: 419 599-4740
Nicholas Avina, *President*
Susan Avina, *Vice Pres*
EMP: 5
SALES (est): 400K **Privately Held**
SIC: 2395 Embroidery & art needlework

(G-14673)
B & B MOLDED PRODUCTS INC
600 Fillmore St (43545-1651)
P.O. Box 213 (43545-0213)
PHONE................................419 592-8700
Fax: 419 592-6350
Donald V Gillett, *President*
Bryan Perry, *QC Mgr*
Lin Rogers, *Manager*
Ty Whitacre, *Business Dir*
▲ EMP: 40
SQ FT: 55,000
SALES (est): 7.9MM **Privately Held**
WEB: www.bbmolded.com
SIC: 3089 Injection molded finished plastic
products

(G-14674)
CAMPBELL SOUP COMPANY
110 E Maumee Ave (43545)
P.O. Box 311 (43545-0311)
PHONE................................419 592-1010
Fax: 419 599-6748
Dale Morrison, *Principal*
T Richard, *Opers Mgr*
Dan L Ginter, *Purch Dir*
Robert Brown, *Asst Mgr*
Steve Wright, *Network Enginr*
EMP: 100
SALES (corp-wide): 7.9B **Publicly Held**
WEB: www.campbellsoups.com
SIC: 5461 2033 Bakeries; canned fruits &
specialties
PA: Campbell Soup Company
1 Campbell Pl
Camden NJ 08103
856 342-4800

(G-14675)
CARSON INDUSTRIES LLC
1675 Industrial Dr (43545-9734)
PHONE................................419 592-2309
Rich Gordinier, *Principal*
Bob Youngs, *Plant Mgr*
Mike Tunell, *Mfg Mgr*
Andres Peterson, *Purch Agent*
Theresa Ginter, *Human Res Mgr*
EMP: 5
SALES (est): 465.6K **Privately Held**
SIC: 3089 Plastic processing

(G-14676)
CUSTAR STONE CO
9072 County Road 424 (43545-9732)
PHONE................................419 669-4327
Fax: 419 669-4327
Brent Gerken, *President*
Jon Myers, *Corp Secy*
Mike Gerken, *Vice Pres*
John Mengerink, *Manager*
Julian Gerken, *Shareholder*
EMP: 11
SQ FT: 3,000

SALES (est): 910K **Privately Held**
SIC: 3281 Stone, quarrying & processing
of own stone products

(G-14677)
DEFIANCE STAMPING CO
800 Independence Dr (43545-9192)
PHONE................................419 782-5781
Fax: 419 782-0004
Tony Stuart, *President*
Brian Callan, *Principal*
Michael Figy, *QC Mgr*
Greg Yeager, *QC Mgr*
Vince Baker, *Engineer*
▲ EMP: 65 EST: 1927
SQ FT: 60,000
SALES (est): 20.9MM **Privately Held**
WEB: www.defiancestamping.com
SIC: 3465 Automotive stampings

(G-14678)
**GILSON MACHINE & TOOL CO
INC**
529 Freedom Dr (43545-5945)
PHONE................................419 592-2911
Fax: 419 599-1078
William E Gilson Jr, *President*
Glen Gilson, *Corp Secy*
EMP: 20 EST: 1946
SQ FT: 11,000
SALES (est): 3MM **Privately Held**
WEB: www.gilsonmachine.com
SIC: 3599 7692 3549 3544 Machine
shop, jobbing & repair; welding repair;
metalworking machinery; special dies,
tools, jigs & fixtures; fabricated structural
metal

(G-14679)
GRAEBENER GROUP TECH LTD
476 E Riverview Ave (43545-1855)
PHONE................................419 591-7033
Richard Marando, *President*
Krista Gerkens, *Controller*
▲ EMP: 2
SQ FT: 10,000
SALES: 1MM **Privately Held**
SIC: 3547 Pipe & tube mills

(G-14680)
**HIGH PRODUCTION
TECHNOLOGY LLC (HQ)**
476 E Riverview Ave (43545-1855)
PHONE................................419 591-7000
Fax: 419 599-1511
Krista Gerken, *Controller*
Marlowe Witt,
EMP: 15 EST: 1997
SQ FT: 6,000
SALES: 3MM
SALES (corp-wide): 22MM **Privately
Held**
WEB: www.hiprotech.com
SIC: 3542 3441 Presses: hydraulic &
pneumatic, mechanical & manual; fabri-
cated structural metal
PA: Automatic Feed Co.
476 E Riverview Ave
Napoleon OH 43545
419 592-0050

(G-14681)
**HIGH PRODUCTION
TECHNOLOGY LLC**
13068 County Road R (43545-5964)
PHONE................................419 599-1511
Marlow Witt, *Branch Mgr*
EMP: 8
SALES (corp-wide): 22MM **Privately
Held**
WEB: www.hiprotech.com
SIC: 3542 Machine tools, metal forming
type
HQ: High Production Technology, Llc
476 E Riverview Ave
Napoleon OH 43545
419 591-7000

(G-14682)
HOLGATE METAL FAB INC
555 Independence Dr (43545-9656)
PHONE................................419 599-2000
Jeff Spangler, *President*
Denise Spangler, *Vice Pres*
Don Grimm, *Engineer*

Randy Elling, *Sales Engr*
EMP: 15
SQ FT: 16,000
SALES (est): 3.5MM **Privately Held**
WEB: www.holgatemetalfab.com
SIC: 1711 1761 3444 3441 Boiler main-
tenance contractor; sheet metalwork;
sheet metalwork; fabricated structural
metal; blast furnaces & steel mills

(G-14683)
HP2G LLC
2611 Scott St Napoleon (43545)
PHONE................................419 906-1525
Sheila Kay, *Vice Pres*
Jen Rodgers, *Controller*
Douglas Pelmear,
John Rahm, *Associate*
EMP: 30
SALES: 950K **Privately Held**
SIC: 3714 Motor vehicle parts & acces-
sories

(G-14684)
INNOVATIVE TOOL & DIE INC
1700 Industrial Dr (43545-9282)
PHONE................................419 599-0492
Fax: 419 599-0493
Loren Sonnenberg, *President*
Larry Huber, *Corp Secy*
EMP: 8
SQ FT: 5,000
SALES (est): 1.1MM **Privately Held**
SIC: 3544 3599 Special dies & tools; ma-
chine & other job shop work

(G-14685)
**ISOFOTON NORTH AMERICA
INC**
800 Independence Dr (43545-9192)
PHONE................................419 591-4330
Michael A Peck, *President*
Joseph M Garton, *Vice Pres*
▲ EMP: 10
SQ FT: 185,000
SALES (est): 1.1MM **Privately Held**
SIC: 3674 Solar cells

(G-14686)
**JACKSON DELUXE CLEANERS
LTD (PA)**
522 Hobson St (43545-1802)
PHONE................................419 592-2826
Fax: 419 512-7989
Robert Jackson, *Owner*
EMP: 7
SQ FT: 2,500
SALES: 350K **Privately Held**
SIC: 7216 2842 Drycleaning plants, ex-
cept rugs; rug, upholstery, or dry cleaning
detergents or spotters

(G-14687)
KOESTER CORPORATION (PA)
813 N Perry St (43545-1521)
PHONE................................419 599-0291
Michael Koester, *President*
John F Kaduk, *Principal*
Carol A Koester, *Principal*
Wm C Koester, *Principal*
Cindy Wendell, *Accounts Mgr*
EMP: 60
SQ FT: 40,000
SALES: 15.1MM **Privately Held**
WEB: www.koester-corp.com
SIC: 3569 3823 3613 Lubricating equip-
ment; pressure measurement instru-
ments, industrial; control panels, electric

(G-14688)
**LEADER ENGNRNG-
FABRICATION INC (PA)**
695 Independence Dr (43545-9191)
P.O. Box 670 (43545-0670)
PHONE................................419 592-0008
Fax: 419 592-0340
Charles Leader, *President*
John Cichocki Jr, *Vice Pres*
Tony Koppenhofer, *Agent*
Calvin Leader, *Shareholder*
Truus Leader, *Shareholder*
EMP: 3
SQ FT: 23,800

SALES: 8.2MM **Privately Held**
WEB:
www.leaderengineeringfabrication.com
SIC: 3599 Machine & other job shop work

(G-14689)
MARY JAMES INC
1025 Clairmont Ave (43545-1240)
PHONE...............................419 599-2941
James E Lammy Sr, *Principal*
EMP: 20
SALES (est): 1.3MM **Privately Held**
SIC: 2211 Apparel & outerwear fabrics,
cotton

(G-14690)
MUSTANG PRINTING
Also Called: Turkeyfoot Printing
119 W Washington St (43545-1739)
P.O. Box 413, Wauseon (43567-0413)
PHONE...............................419 592-2746
Fax: 419 591-1442
Jerry Dehnbostel, *President*
Bev Griteman, *Manager*
EMP: 10
SQ FT: 4,800
SALES (est): 989.5K
SALES (corp-wide): 1MM **Privately Held**
SIC: 2752 Commercial printing, offset
HQ: Mustang Corporation
229 N Fulton St
Wauseon OH
419 335-9070

(G-14691)
NAPOLEON INC
Also Called: Northwest Signal
595 E Riverview Ave (43545-1865)
PHONE...............................419 592-5055
Fax: 419 592-9778
Christopher Cullis, *President*
Peggy Woods, *Office Mgr*
EMP: 40 EST: 1852
SQ FT: 7,200
SALES (est): 2.5MM **Privately Held**
WEB: www.northwestsignal.net
SIC: 2711 Newspapers: publishing only,
not printed on site

(G-14692)
OLDCASTLE PRECAST INC
1675 Industrial Dr (43545-9734)
PHONE...............................419 592-2309
Aleta McGinnis, *Manager*
Jeff Taylor, *Maintence Staff*
EMP: 35
SALES (corp-wide): 28.6B **Privately Held**
WEB: www.oldcastle-precast.com
SIC: 3089 Boxes, plastic
HQ: Oldcastle Precast, Inc.
1002 15th Sw Ste 110
Auburn WA 98001
253 833-2777

(G-14693)
PULLMAN COMPANY
Also Called: Tenneco
11800 County Road 424 (43545-5778)
PHONE...............................419 592-2055
Joseph Angi, *Mfg Mgr*
Leonard Coleman, *Opers Staff*
Tim Kohart, *QC Dir*
Marty Cantwell, *Engineer*
Vernon Stacey, *Engineer*
EMP: 204
SQ FT: 220,000
SALES (corp-wide): 8.6B **Publicly Held**
WEB: www.tenneco-automotive.com
SIC: 3714 Motor vehicle parts & acces-
sories
HQ: The Pullman Company
1 International Dr
Monroe MI 48161
734 243-8000

(G-14694)
R S V WLDG FBRCATION
MACHINING
M063 County Road 12 (43545-9366)
P.O. Box 430 (43545-0430)
PHONE...............................419 592-0993
Ralph F Vocke, *President*
Randy Vocke, *Vice Pres*
Steve Vocke, *Admin Sec*
EMP: 10
SQ FT: 10,400

SALES: 750K **Privately Held**
WEB: www.rsvwelding.com
SIC: 3441 7692 Fabricated structural
metal; welding repair

(G-14695)
RAILTECH BOUTET INC
25 Interstate Dr (43545-8700)
P.O. Box 69 (43545-0069)
PHONE...............................419 592-5050
Fax: 419 599-3630
Alex Hellcamp, *General Mgr*
Oliver Dolder, *Principal*
Marv Huber, *Accountant*
▲ EMP: 53
SQ FT: 60,000
SALES (est): 13MM **Privately Held**
SIC: 2899 Chemical preparations
HQ: Delachaux Sa
Immeuble West Plaza
Colombes 92700
146 520-519

(G-14696)
RAILTECH MATWELD INC
15 Interstate Dr (43545)
PHONE...............................419 592-5050
Oliver Dolder, *President*
EMP: 5 **Privately Held**
SIC: 2899 Chemical preparations
HQ: Railtech Matweld, Inc.
25 Interstate Dr
Napoleon OH 43545

(G-14697)
RAILTECH MATWELD INC (DH)
25 Interstate Dr (43545-8700)
P.O. Box 69 (43545-0069)
PHONE...............................419 591-3770
Oliver Dolder, *CEO*
Gregory B Minter, *President*
Pallavi Raj, *Exec Sec*
EMP: 18
SALES (est): 1.7MM **Privately Held**
SIC: 2899 Chemical preparations
HQ: Railtech International
Zone Industrielle
Raismes 59590
327 222-626

(G-14698)
SCOTT PORT-A-FOLD INC
5963 State Route 110 (43545-9332)
PHONE...............................419 748-8880
Fax: 419 446-2974
James Lammy Jr, *President*
James E Lammy Jr, *President*
Don Fisher, *Office Mgr*
▲ EMP: 30
SQ FT: 45,000
SALES: 1MM **Privately Held**
SIC: 3086 3531 Plastics foam products;
construction machinery

(G-14699)
SILGAN CAN COMPANY
12773 State Route 110 (43545-5898)
P.O. Box 311 (43545-0311)
PHONE...............................419 592-1010
Fax: 419 599-6666
Marcus Leong, *QC Mgr*
Martin Nezick, *Engineer*
Steve Wright, *Manager*
EMP: 13
SQ FT: 78,000
SALES (corp-wide): 3.6B **Publicly Held**
SIC: 2032 Canned specialties
HQ: Silgan Can Company
21800 Oxnard St Ste 600
Woodland Hills CA 91367
818 348-3700

(G-14700)
TOY & SPORT TRENDS INC
Also Called: Scott Port-A-Fold
5963 State Route 110 (43545-9332)
PHONE...............................419 748-8880
James E Lammy Jr, *President*
Don Fisher, *Purchasing*
Diane Smucker, *Admin Sec*
EMP: 20
SQ FT: 45,000

SALES: 1.5MM **Privately Held**
SIC: 5091 5092 3949 3086 Sporting &
recreation goods; toys & hobby goods &
supplies; sporting & athletic goods; plastics foam products

(G-14701)
UNITED AUTO WORKER AFL CIO
Also Called: Napoleon Products Co
410 Fillmore St (43545-1614)
PHONE...............................419 592-0434
EMP: 15
SALES (est): 1.1MM **Privately Held**
SIC: 3451 Mfg Screw Machine Products

(G-14702)
ZELCOR GROUP LLC
L902 State Route 108 (43545-5741)
P.O. Box 737 (43545-0737)
PHONE...............................419 592-0803
Donald C Cordes,
EMP: 4
SALES: 650K **Privately Held**
SIC: 3449 Bars, concrete reinforcing: fabri-
cated steel

Nashport
Muskingum County

(G-14703)
B D P SERVICES INC
Also Called: Sports Art
8255 Blackrun Rd (43830-9774)
PHONE...............................740 828-9685
Fax: 740 828-1009
Stephen Baum, *President*
Vince Paul, *Corp Secy*
Chad Lemley, *Office Mgr*
EMP: 60
SQ FT: 28,000
SALES (est): 4.5MM **Privately Held**
WEB: www.sportsart-online.com
SIC: 2396 2395 Screen printing on fabric
articles; embroidery products, except
schiffli machine

(G-14704)
BROCKS CHIMNEY
4620 Gorsuch Rd (43830-9738)
PHONE...............................740 819-2489
Dean Brocklehurst, *Principal*
EMP: 3 EST: 2008
SALES (est): 252.2K **Privately Held**
SIC: 3281 Flagstones

(G-14705)
HANBY FARMS INC
10790 Newark Rd (43830-9066)
P.O. Box 97 (43830-0097)
PHONE...............................740 763-3554
Fax: 740 828-3621
Ralph F Hanby, *President*
David R Hanby, *President*
Ron Seitez, *Plant Mgr*
Doug Hanby, *CFO*
Carol Hanby, *Admin Sec*
EMP: 34
SQ FT: 10,000
SALES (est): 7.8MM **Privately Held**
SIC: 2048 5153 5191 Livestock feeds;
corn; soybeans; fertilizer & fertilizer mate-
rials

(G-14706)
PETE EMMERT CO
5580 Pleasant Valley Rd (43830-9570)
PHONE...............................740 455-3924
Peter Emmert, *Owner*
EMP: 5
SALES (est): 412.5K **Privately Held**
SIC: 2431 Interior & ornamental woodwork
& trim

(G-14707)
RJ DRILLING COMPANY INC
5755 Licking Valley Rd Se (43830-2500)
PHONE...............................740 763-3991
Ronald F Moran, *President*
EMP: 3
SALES (est): 183.3K **Privately Held**
SIC: 1381 Drilling oil & gas wells

Navarre
Stark County

(G-14708)
ALFRED NICKLES BAKERY INC
(PA)
26 Main St N (44662-1158)
PHONE...............................330 879-5635
David A Gardner, *President*
Mark Sponseller, *Senior VP*
Matthew Boxrucker, *Vice Pres*
Ernest Brideweser, *Vice Pres*
Christian Gardner, *Vice Pres*
▲ EMP: 500 EST: 1909
SQ FT: 110,000
SALES: 205MM **Privately Held**
WEB: www.nicklesbakery.com
SIC: 2051 Bread, all types (white, wheat,
rye, etc): fresh or frozen

(G-14709)
B & S TRANSPORT INC (PA)
11325 Lawndell Rd Sw (44662-8804)
P.O. Box 2678, North Canton (44720-0678)
PHONE...............................330 767-4319
Fax: 330 767-3741
Ronald Harris, *President*
Irvin Jackson, *Vice Pres*
EMP: 9 EST: 1977
SQ FT: 6,000
SALES (est): 3.2MM **Privately Held**
SIC: 3011 5014 5052 5045 Tires & inner
tubes; tires & tubes; coal & other minerals
& ores; computers, peripherals & soft-
ware; books, periodicals & newspapers;
book publishing

(G-14710)
BETHLEHEM FIRE AND RESCUE
INC
34 Main St S (44662-1141)
PHONE...............................330 879-5800
Stan Josefczyk, *Principal*
EMP: 3
SALES: 261.2K **Privately Held**
SIC: 3711 Fire department vehicles (motor
vehicles), assembly of

(G-14711)
CENTRAL ALLIED
ENTERPRISES INC
Also Called: Massillon Washed Gravel Co
6331 Blough Ave Sw (44662-8506)
P.O. Box 80718, Canton (44708-0718)
PHONE...............................330 879-2132
Fax: 330 879-1313
Jerry Orn, *Div Sub Head*
Gary Miller, *Branch Mgr*
EMP: 8
SQ FT: 2,056
SALES (corp-wide): 54.5MM **Privately
Held**
SIC: 1442 Construction sand mining;
gravel mining
PA: Central Allied Enterprises, Inc.
1243 Raff Rd Sw
Canton OH 44710
330 477-6751

(G-14712)
FAR CORNER
13189 Mount Eaton St Sw (44662-9476)
P.O. Box 92, Brewster (44613-0092)
PHONE...............................330 767-3734
Cheryl Hintz, *Owner*
EMP: 6
SALES (est): 452.6K **Privately Held**
WEB: www.farcorner-online.com
SIC: 2752 Commercial printing, litho-
graphic

(G-14713)
GREEN ACRES FURNITURE LTD
7412 Massillon Rd Sw (44662-9318)
PHONE...............................330 359-6251
Paul Swartzentruber, *Principal*
EMP: 12
SQ FT: 7,200
SALES (est): 1.4MM **Privately Held**
WEB: www.greenacresfurniture.com
SIC: 5712 2511 Furniture stores; wood
household furniture

(G-14714)
GREIF INC
9420 Warmington St Sw (44662-9670)
P.O. Box 675 (44662-0675)
PHONE................................330 879-2101
Chip Shew, *Branch Mgr*
EMP: 100
SALES (corp-wide): 3.3B **Publicly Held**
WEB: www.greif.com
SIC: 2679 Paper products, converted
PA: Greif, Inc.
　425 Winter Rd
　Delaware OH 43015
　740 549-6000

(G-14715)
H & K FABRICATING
13415 Baughman St Sw (44662-9631)
PHONE................................330 767-4279
Rick Studer, *Owner*
EMP: 3 EST: 1995
SALES: 200K **Privately Held**
SIC: 7692 Welding repair

(G-14716)
IMAGINE THIS RENOVATIONS
4220 Alabama Ave Sw (44662-9618)
PHONE................................330 833-6739
Scott Miller, *Principal*
Eric Baker, *Manager*
EMP: 8
SALES (est): 524K **Privately Held**
SIC: 2759 Commercial printing

(G-14717)
L N BRUT MANUFACTURING CO
4680 Alabama Ave Sw (44662-8708)
PHONE................................330 833-9045
Fax: 330 833-6513
Lynn Neiss, *President*
Dolores J Schmidt, *Corp Secy*
EMP: 8
SQ FT: 11,000
SALES (est): 600K **Privately Held**
SIC: 3589 Sandblasting equipment

(G-14718)
L N S PALLETS
6144 Smith Rd Sw (44662-8107)
PHONE................................330 936-7507
EMP: 4
SALES (est): 315.3K **Privately Held**
SIC: 2448 Pallets, wood & wood with metal

(G-14719)
MILLER WELDMASTER CORPORATION (PA)
4220 Alabama Ave Sw (44662-9618)
PHONE................................330 833-6739
Scott Miller, *Owner*
◆ EMP: 91 EST: 1973
SQ FT: 20,000
SALES: 15MM **Privately Held**
WEB: www.weldmaster.com
SIC: 3548 Welding & cutting apparatus & accessories

(G-14720)
MYSTA EQUIPMENT CO
6434 Werstler Ave Sw (44662-9140)
PHONE................................330 879-5353
Stanley Josefczyk, *Owner*
EMP: 6
SALES: 175K **Privately Held**
SIC: 3599 Machine & other job shop work

(G-14721)
NAVARRE INDUSTRIES INC
10384 Navarre Rd Sw (44662-9462)
PHONE................................330 767-3003
Fax: 330 767-3481
Paul Miller, *President*
Gregory Miller, *Vice Pres*
Ron Heavner, *Plant Mgr*
Tina L Derrow, *QC Mgr*
Sue Thompson, *Controller*
EMP: 25
SQ FT: 45,000
SALES (est): 6.3MM **Privately Held**
WEB: www.navarreindustries.com
SIC: 3354 Aluminum extruded products

(G-14722)
NAVARRE TRAILER SALES INC
Also Called: Haul, Mark Sales/Service/Parts
4633 Erie Ave Sw (44662-9666)
PHONE................................330 879-2406
Fax: 330 879-2632
Dina Jones, *President*
EMP: 3
SQ FT: 20,000
SALES: 1MM **Privately Held**
SIC: 5599 3715 Utility trailers; truck trailers

(G-14723)
OWENS CORNING
9318 Erie Ave Sw (44662-9448)
PHONE................................419 248-8000
EMP: 6
SALES (corp-wide): 5.6B **Publicly Held**
SIC: 3296 Mineral wool
PA: Owens Corning
　1 Owens Corning Pkwy
　Toledo OH 43659
　419 248-8000

(G-14724)
PREMIER PALLET & RECYCLING
11361 Lawndell Rd Sw (44662-8804)
P.O. Box 31, Brewster (44613-0031)
PHONE................................330 767-2221
Pete Grove, *President*
Leslie Grove, *Financial Exec*
EMP: 17 EST: 2004
SALES (est): 2.4MM **Privately Held**
SIC: 2448 Wood pallets & skids

(G-14725)
RADIANT ARTS INC
8215 Mona St Sw (44662-9708)
PHONE................................330 879-0013
James Foltz, *President*
EMP: 3
SALES (est): 18.5K **Privately Held**
SIC: 3231 Stained glass: made from purchased glass

(G-14726)
RC INDUSTRIES INC
Also Called: Mid's Spaghetti Sauce
12 Oakbrook St Sw (44662-8502)
P.O. Box 5 (44662-0005)
PHONE................................330 879-5486
Fax: 330 879-2939
Steve Cress, *CEO*
Scott Ricketts, *President*
EMP: 25 EST: 1964
SQ FT: 10,000
SALES (est): 6.1MM **Privately Held**
SIC: 2033 2035 Spaghetti & other pasta sauce: packaged in cans, jars, etc.; pickles, sauces & salad dressings

(G-14727)
RUEGG MFG LLC
13955 Elton St Sw (44662-9663)
PHONE................................330 418-5617
Bill Ruegg, *Owner*
EMP: 5
SALES: 300K **Privately Held**
SIC: 3643 Power line cable

(G-14728)
TERYDON INC
7260 Erie Ave Sw (44662-8807)
PHONE................................330 879-2448
Terry Gromes Sr, *President*
Elizabeth Gromes, *Accounts Mgr*
EMP: 12
SQ FT: 800
SALES: 1.5MM **Privately Held**
SIC: 3599 8711 Custom machinery; machine tool design

Negley
Columbiana County

(G-14729)
CUSTOM COILS
51305 Carmel Achor Rd (44441-9708)
PHONE................................330 426-3797
Allen Mackall,
EMP: 4

SALES (est): 573.4K **Privately Held**
SIC: 3567 Induction heating equipment

(G-14730)
MAGNECO/METREL INC
51365 State Route 154 (44441-9728)
P.O. Box 176 (44441-0176)
PHONE................................330 426-9468
Fax: 330 426-2727
Steve Young, *Vice Pres*
Judy Gibson, *Purchasing*
Paul Painter, *Branch Mgr*
Pam Crawford, *Intl Dir*
EMP: 38
SALES (corp-wide): 65.8MM **Privately Held**
WEB: www.magneco-metrel.com
SIC: 3255 3297 Clay refractories; nonclay refractories
PA: Magneco/Metrel, Inc.
　223 W Interstate Rd
　Addison IL 60101
　630 543-6660

(G-14731)
MELT INC
51621 Darlington Rd (44441-9701)
PHONE................................330 426-3545
Ellen Beagle, *Principal*
EMP: 5
SALES (est): 491.5K **Privately Held**
SIC: 2448 Wood pallets & skids

(G-14732)
STATE LINE RESOURCES INC
51545 State Route 154 (44441-9728)
P.O. Box 419 (44441-0419)
PHONE................................330 426-9611
Fax: 330 426-2728
Charles H Muse Jr, *President*
James Muse, *Vice Pres*
Albert Muse, *Treasurer*
EMP: 7
SALES: 1.5MM **Privately Held**
SIC: 1455 1241 Kaolin & ball clay; coal mining services

(G-14733)
X L SAND AND GRAVEL CO INC
9289 Jackman Rd (44441)
P.O. Box 255 (44441-0255)
PHONE................................330 426-9876
Fax: 330 426-2525
Raymond Lansberry, *President*
James Lansberry, *Treasurer*
EMP: 15
SQ FT: 1,000
SALES (est): 2.3MM **Privately Held**
SIC: 1442 Common sand mining; gravel mining

Nelsonville
Athens County

(G-14734)
GEORGIA BOOT LLC
39 E Canal St (45764-1247)
PHONE................................740 753-1951
Gerald M Cohn, *CEO*
Thomas R Morrison, *President*
Jim McDonald, *CFO*
Ken Furlong, *Controller*
Kevin Lyle, *Controller*
EMP: 100
SALES (est): 23.6MM
SALES (corp-wide): 269.3MM **Publicly Held**
WEB: www.durangoboot.com
SIC: 5139 3144 3143 3021 Shoes; women's footwear, except athletic; men's footwear, except athletic; rubber & plastics footwear
HQ: Ej Footwear Llc
　381 Riverside Dr Ste 300
　Franklin TN

(G-14735)
QUICK LOADZ DELIVERY SYS LLC
185 W Canal St (45764-1144)
PHONE................................888 304-3946
Steve Karem, *Sales Mgr*
Sean Jones,

Judy Vogelsang, *Administration*
EMP: 4 EST: 2014
SALES (est): 522.5K **Privately Held**
SIC: 3715 Trailer bodies

(G-14736)
ROCKY BRANDS INC (PA)
39 E Canal St (45764-1247)
PHONE................................740 753-1951
Mike Brooks, *CEO*
Gary Adam, *President*
Jason Brooks, *President*
Richard Simms, *President*
David Dixon, *Opers Staff*
▲ EMP: 277
SQ FT: 25,000
SALES: 269.3MM **Publicly Held**
WEB: www.rockybrands.com
SIC: 3143 3144 2329 2331 Men's footwear, except athletic; women's footwear, except athletic; men's & boys' sportswear & athletic clothing; women's & misses' blouses & shirts; women's & misses' accessories; men's miscellaneous accessories

(G-14737)
ROCKY BRANDS INC
39 E Canal St (45764-1247)
PHONE................................740 753-1951
Becky Steenrod, *Branch Mgr*
EMP: 60
SALES (corp-wide): 269.3MM **Publicly Held**
SIC: 3143 Men's footwear, except athletic
PA: Rocky Brands, Inc.
　39 E Canal St
　Nelsonville OH 45764
　740 753-1951

(G-14738)
ROCKY BRANDS INC
45 E Canal St (45764-1247)
PHONE................................740 753-9100
Fax: 740 753-4024
Michael Brooks, *President*
EMP: 530
SALES (corp-wide): 269.3MM **Publicly Held**
SIC: 3143 Men's footwear, except athletic; boots, dress or casual: men's
PA: Rocky Brands, Inc.
　39 E Canal St
　Nelsonville OH 45764
　740 753-1951

(G-14739)
SHOT-FORCE PRO LLC
13580 Kimberley Rd (45764-9511)
PHONE................................740 753-3927
Stephen Davis,
EMP: 4
SALES (est): 145.3K **Privately Held**
SIC: 3462 7389 Armor plate, forged iron or steel;

(G-14740)
STARR MACHINE INC
226 Sylvania Ave (45764)
PHONE................................740 753-0009
Fax: 740 753-0184
Brian Kasler, *President*
Mindi Lanser, *Manager*
EMP: 24
SQ FT: 34,000
SALES (est): 3.4MM **Privately Held**
WEB: www.starrmachine.com
SIC: 3599 Machine & other job shop work

(G-14741)
T & M MACHINE PRODUCTS INC
14265 State Route 691 (45764-9428)
PHONE................................740 753-2960
Fax: 740 753-2511
Darrow M Tolliver, *President*
Darrow G Tolliver Jr, *Vice Pres*
EMP: 5
SQ FT: 11,000
SALES (est): 340K **Privately Held**
SIC: 3599 Machine shop, jobbing & repair

2017 Harris Ohio
Industrial Directory

▲ = Import ▼=Export
◆ =Import/Export

(G-14742)
TAT PUMPS INC
Also Called: Tat Engineering
398 Poplar St (45764-1425)
P.O. Box 268, Logan (43138-0268)
PHONE...................................740 385-0008
Fax: 740 753-2355
Kay Your, *President*
Robert Your, *Vice Pres*
EMP: 5 EST: 1998
SQ FT: 8,000
SALES: 150K **Privately Held**
WEB: www.tatpumps.com
SIC: 3561 Pumps, oil well & field

Nevada
Wyandot County

(G-14743)
STIGER PRE CAST INC
17793 State Highway 231 (44849-9710)
PHONE...................................740 482-2313
Fax: 740 482-2895
Jim Riedlinger, *President*
Cathy Scheffler, *Corp Secy*
Eva Mae Riedlinger, *Vice Pres*
EMP: 8
SQ FT: 2,200
SALES (est): 1.2MM **Privately Held**
SIC: 3272 3271 Septic tanks, concrete;
steps, prefabricated concrete; blocks,
concrete or cinder: standard

New Albany
Franklin County

(G-14744)
614 CUPCAKES LLC
4045 Chelsea Grn W (43054-6027)
PHONE...................................614 245-8800
Dawn Freeman,
EMP: 4
SALES (est): 384.4K **Privately Held**
SIC: 2051 Bread, cake & related products

(G-14745)
ANOMATIC CORPORATION (DH)
8880 Innovation Campus Ct (43054-6651)
PHONE...................................740 522-2203
Fax: 740 522-3339
William B Rusch, *President*
Pete McCallin, *President*
Don Perry, *Exec VP*
Julie Drew, *Vice Pres*
Peter McCallin, *Vice Pres*
◆ EMP: 277 EST: 1974
SQ FT: 65,000
SALES (est): 118.5MM
SALES (corp-wide): 420MM **Privately Held**
WEB: www.anomatic.com
SIC: 3471 3469 2396 Anodizing (plating)
of metals or formed products; metal
stampings; automotive & apparel trim-
mings
HQ: Thyssen'sche Handelsgesellschaft Mit
Beschrankter Haftung
Dohne 54
Mulheim An Der Ruhr
208 992-180

(G-14746)
ARCHITECTURAL BUSSTRUT CORP
4311 Brompton Ct (43054-8982)
PHONE...................................614 933-8695
Ellen Robinson, *Sales Associate*
EMP: 9 **Privately Held**
SIC: 3648 5063 Lighting fixtures, except
electric: residential; lighting fixtures
PA: Architectural Busstrut Corp.
921 Eastwind Dr
Westerville OH 43081

(G-14747)
AUTOMATIC TIMING & CONTRLS INC (PA)
Also Called: Automatic Timing & Contrls Div
7795 Walton Pkwy Ste 175 (43054-0002)
P.O. Box 305, Newell WV (26050-0305)
PHONE...................................614 888-8855
Arnold B Siemer, *President*
Thomas Villano, *Vice Pres*
Roger D Bailey, *CFO*
Henry Phillips, *Controller*
Russell Gertmenian, *Admin Sec*
EMP: 68
SQ FT: 5,500
SALES (est): 18.3MM **Privately Held**
WEB: www.automatictiming.com
SIC: 3625 3824 3823 Relays & industrial
controls; timing devices, electronic; re-
lays, for electronic use; fluid meters &
counting devices; counters, revolution;
tachometer, centrifugal; temperature in-
struments: industrial process type

(G-14748)
AVERY DENNISON CORPORATION
7795 Walton Pkwy Ste 370 (43054-8246)
PHONE...................................614 418-7740
EMP: 115
SALES (corp-wide): 6.3B **Publicly Held**
SIC: 2672 Mfg Coated/Laminated Paper
PA: Avery Dennison Corporation
207 N Goode Ave Fl 6
Glendale CA 91203
626 304-2000

(G-14749)
BLACK RADISH CREAMERY LTD
7064 Cunningham Dr (43054-9063)
PHONE...................................614 323-6016
John Reese, *Principal*
EMP: 6
SALES (est): 510.9K **Privately Held**
SIC: 2021 Creamery butter

(G-14750)
BOB EVANS FARMS INC (PA)
8111 Smiths Mill Rd (43054-1183)
PHONE...................................614 491-2225
Fax: 614 497-4393
Mike Townsley, *CEO*
Douglas N Benham, *Ch of Bd*
George Furman, *Business Mgr*
Colin M Daly, *Exec VP*
Richard D Hall, *Exec VP*
EMP: 325 EST: 1948
SALES: 1.3B **Publicly Held**
WEB: www.bobevans.com
SIC: 5812 2011 2099 2035 Restaurant,
family: chain; sausages from meat
slaughtered on site; salads, fresh or re-
frigerated; pickles, sauces & salad dress-
ings

(G-14751)
BOCCHI LABORATIES OHIO LLC
9200 Smiths Mill Rd N (43054-6703)
PHONE...................................661 673-8500
Joe Pender, *CEO*
Patrick Kelley, *CFO*
EMP: 300
SQ FT: 125,000
SALES (est): 8.1MM **Privately Held**
SIC: 2844 Toilet preparations

(G-14752)
BUCKEYE PREP REPORT MAGAZINE
Also Called: Buckeye Prep Magazine
8599 Swisher Creek Xing (43054-8385)
PHONE...................................614 855-6977
Richard Crockett, *Partner*
Robert Taylor, *Partner*
EMP: 3
SALES (est): 153K **Privately Held**
SIC: 2721 Periodicals

(G-14753)
COMMERCIAL VEHICLE GROUP INC (PA)
Also Called: Cvg
7800 Walton Pkwy (43054-8233)
PHONE...................................614 289-5360

Fax: 614 289-5361
Richard A Snell, *Ch of Bd*
Patrick E Miller, *President*
C Timothy Trenary, *CFO*
EMP: 1850
SALES: 662.1MM **Publicly Held**
WEB: www.commercialvehiclegroup.com
SIC: 3714 3231 Motor vehicle parts & ac-
cessories; windshield wiper systems,
motor vehicle; motor vehicle body compo-
nents & frame; wipers, windshield, motor
vehicle; mirrors, truck & automobile:
made from purchased glass

(G-14754)
CONTRACTOR TOOLS ONLINE LLC
Uknown (43054)
P.O. Box 942 (43054-0942)
PHONE...................................614 264-9392
Paul Proffitt, *Co-Venturer*
Brian Swalwell, *Co-Venturer*
EMP: 3
SALES (est): 136.3K **Privately Held**
SIC: 7372 7374 Business oriented com-
puter software; optical scanning data
service

(G-14755)
CUSTOM AUTOMATION TECHNOLOGIES
1267 Bayboro Dr (43054-9411)
PHONE...................................614 939-4228
Daniel D Hoehnen, *President*
Sally Hoehnen, *Vice Pres*
EMP: 3
SALES (est): 429.9K **Privately Held**
WEB: www.customautomationtech.com
SIC: 5999 3651 Audio-visual equipment &
supplies; home entertainment equipment,
electronic

(G-14756)
CUSTOM METAL PRODUCTS INC
Also Called: Do All Sheet Metal
5037 Babbitt Rd (43054-8301)
P.O. Box 119 (43054-0119)
PHONE...................................614 855-2263
Sheri Brock, *President*
Darrell Brock, *Corp Secy*
Carolyn Clark, *Controller*
Jana Cottrill, *Human Res Mgr*
EMP: 10
SQ FT: 24,000
SALES (est): 907.9K **Privately Held**
WEB: www.do-all-precision.com
SIC: 3444 Metal housings, enclosures,
casings & other containers

(G-14757)
DESCO CORPORATION (PA)
7795 Walton Pkwy Ste 175 (43054-0002)
PHONE...................................614 888-8855
Fax: 614 888-3779
Arnold B Siemer, *President*
Mc Connell A Coakwell, *Principal*
James M Smith, *Principal*
Thomas Villano, *Vice Pres*
Joy Ferguson, *Project Mgr*
EMP: 9
SQ FT: 5,500
SALES (est): 210.3MM **Privately Held**
WEB: www.descocapitalpartners.com
SIC: 3442 3825 3643 3531 Window &
door frames; metal doors; instruments to
measure electricity; current-carrying
wiring devices; construction machinery;
manufactured hardware (general)

(G-14758)
FAITH GUIDING CAFE LLC
Also Called: Renegade Candle Company
5195 Hampsted Vlg Ctr Way (43054-8331)
PHONE...................................614 245-8451
William Lavanier, *President*
Kathy Lavan, *Mng Member*
▲ EMP: 10 EST: 2010
SALES: 400K **Privately Held**
SIC: 3999 8742 Candles; general man-
agement consultant

(G-14759)
FLEXCART LLC
5868 Kitzmiller Rd (43054-8576)
PHONE...................................614 348-2517
Edward Guirlinger, *President*

James Marable, *Exec VP*
EMP: 5 EST: 2012
SQ FT: 4,200
SALES: 4MM **Privately Held**
SIC: 3589 Janitors' carts

(G-14760)
GIBBS E & ASSOCIATES LLC
7386 Hampstd Sq S (43054-8741)
PHONE...................................614 939-1672
Edwards Gibbs, *Mng Member*
EMP: 7
SALES (est): 468.1K **Privately Held**
SIC: 7319 2253 Advertising; T-shirts &
tops, knit

(G-14761)
INNOVATIVE APPS LTD
8000 Walton Pkwy Ste 208 (43054-7073)
PHONE...................................330 687-2888
Kevin Ly,
EMP: 3
SALES (est): 71.1K **Privately Held**
SIC: 7372 Prepackaged software

(G-14762)
ISOCHEM INCORPORATED
7721 Sutton Pl (43054-8757)
PHONE...................................614 775-9328
Kevin E Klingerman, *President*
EMP: 5
SALES (est): 601K **Privately Held**
SIC: 2821 Plastics materials & resins

(G-14763)
JANOVA LLC
7570 N Goodrich Sq (43054-8983)
PHONE...................................614 638-6785
Jeffrey Lusenhop, *CEO*
Brian Lusenhop, *Vice Pres*
Kelly Di Cesare, *Human Resources*
Brian Steel, *VP Sales*
EMP: 19
SALES (est): 1.1MM **Privately Held**
SIC: 7372 Application computer software;
business oriented computer software

(G-14764)
JEYES US HOLDINGS INC
8860 Smiths Mill Rd # 500 (43054-6653)
PHONE...................................614 984-2896
Richard Nihei, *CFO*
EMP: 500
SALES (est): 48.3MM **Privately Held**
SIC: 2842 Cleaning or polishing prepara-
tions

(G-14765)
MUELLER ELECTRIC COMPANY INC
7795 Walton Pkwy Ste 175 (43054-0002)
PHONE...................................614 888-8855
Rodger Bailey, *CEO*
EMP: 30
SALES: 6.2MM **Privately Held**
SIC: 3679 3678 3825 Harness assem-
blies for electronic use: wire or cable;
electronic connectors; test equipment for
electronic & electric measurement

(G-14766)
NATIONAL SEATING COMPANY
Also Called: C V G
7800 Walton Pkwy (43054-8233)
PHONE...................................219 872-7295
Fax: 614 985-1842
Mervin Dunn, *President*
Milt Kniss, *Vice Pres*
Bill Stimel, *Opers Mgr*
Jeremy Mosley, *QC Mgr*
Ashley Dittoe, *Marketing Staff*
▲ EMP: 66
SALES (est): 99.3MM
SALES (corp-wide): 662.1MM **Publicly Held**
SIC: 2392 Chair covers & pads: made from
purchased materials
PA: Commercial Vehicle Group, Inc.
7800 Walton Pkwy
New Albany OH 43054
614 289-5360

(G-14767)
NOW SOFTWARE INC
3720 Head Of Pond Rd (43054-8992)
PHONE...................................614 783-4517

John Wallace Click, *Principal*
Amy Barnhardt, *Manager*
EMP: 5
SALES (est): 418.5K **Privately Held**
SIC: 7372 Prepackaged software

(G-14768)
PEN PAL LLC
5868 Kitzmiller Rd (43054-8576)
PHONE..................................614 348-2517
Edward G Guirlinger, *Mng Member*
EMP: 3
SQ FT: 4,200
SALES: 1MM **Privately Held**
SIC: 3952 Pencil holders

(G-14769)
PINKY & THUMB LLC
Also Called: Project Aloha
5216 Sugar Run Dr (43054-9471)
PHONE..................................614 939-5216
Michael Paz, *Principal*
EMP: 4
SALES: 100K **Privately Held**
SIC: 2396 Screen printing on fabric articles

(G-14770)
PWI INC
Also Called: Privacyware
5195 Hampsted Vlg Ctr Way (43054-8331)
PHONE..................................732 212-8110
Gregory Salvato, *CEO*
EMP: 15
SALES (est): 1MM **Privately Held**
WEB: www.pwicorp.com
SIC: 7372 7371 8742 Prepackaged software; software programming applications; corporation organizing

(G-14771)
RAYS WHISTLE STOP
5264 Settlement Dr (43054-9493)
PHONE..................................740 965-2085
Raymond Radabaugh, *Principal*
EMP: 3
SALES (est): 192.2K **Privately Held**
SIC: 3999 Whistles

(G-14772)
SAMUEL CLARK (PA)
Also Called: Do All Sheet Metal
5037 Babbitt Rd (43054-8301)
P.O. Box 119 (43054-0119)
PHONE..................................614 855-2263
Fax: 614 855-7161
Samuel Clark, *Owner*
Darrell Brock, *Purch Mgr*
Carolyn Clark, *Controller*
Dan Clark, *Sales Mgr*
Sherry Mechling, *Manager*
EMP: 18
SQ FT: 77,000
SALES: 1MM **Privately Held**
SIC: 3444 Housings for business machines, sheet metal

(G-14773)
TRIM SYSTEMS OPERATING CORP (HQ)
Also Called: Cvg Trim Systems
7800 Walton Pkwy (43054-8233)
PHONE..................................614 289-5360
Gerald L Armstrong, *President*
Pom Kim, *Manager*
Paul Miller, *Director*
▲ **EMP:** 80
SALES (est): 137.7MM
SALES (corp-wide): 662.1MM **Publicly Held**
SIC: 3714 Motor vehicle parts & accessories
PA: Commercial Vehicle Group, Inc.
7800 Walton Pkwy
New Albany OH 43054
614 289-5360

(G-14774)
TRIM SYSTEMS OPERATING CORP
7800 Walton Pkwy (43054-8233)
PHONE..................................614 289-5360
Margaret Adkins, *Human Res Dir*
Russ Jansen, *Manager*
Kim Berridge, *Manager*
EMP: 240

SALES (corp-wide): 662.1MM **Publicly Held**
SIC: 2295 3713 3429 3083 Laminating of fabrics; truck & bus bodies; manufactured hardware (general); laminated plastics plate & sheet; public building & related furniture
HQ: Trim Systems Operating Corp.
7800 Walton Pkwy
New Albany OH 43054
614 289-5360

(G-14775)
VENTURE THERAPEUTICS INC
10739 Johnstown Rd (43054-9752)
PHONE..................................614 430-3300
Peter Stoelzle, *CEO*
Michael Medors, *CFO*
EMP: 5
SALES (est): 621.4K **Privately Held**
SIC: 2834 Pharmaceutical preparations

New Bavaria
Henry County

(G-14776)
VERHOFF ALFALFA MILLS INC
1577 Henry Y (43548)
P.O. Box 233
PHONE..................................419 653-4161
Fax: 419 523-5715
Larry A Mansfield, *Treasurer*
Darwin Verhoff, *Branch Mgr*
EMP: 3
SALES (corp-wide): 6.1MM **Privately Held**
SIC: 2048 Alfalfa or alfalfa meal, prepared as animal feed
PA: Verhoff Alfalfa Mills, Inc.
1188 Sugar Mill Dr
Ottawa OH 45875
419 523-4767

New Bloomington
Marion County

(G-14777)
DIA ENTERPRISES INC
731 Decliff Rd N (43341-9533)
PHONE..................................740 802-7075
Doug Greenwood, *General Mgr*
Ike Greenwood,
EMP: 3
SALES: 100K **Privately Held**
SIC: 2421 Sawmills & planing mills, general

New Boston
Scioto County

(G-14778)
A & M REFRACTORIES INC
202 West Ave (45662-4946)
PHONE..................................740 456-8020
Fax: 740 353-4507
Michael Cartee, *President*
Richard Bobst, *Vice Pres*
EMP: 20
SQ FT: 60,000
SALES (est): 2.2MM **Privately Held**
SIC: 3297 Nonclay refractories

(G-14779)
BEAUTY SYSTEMS GROUP LLC
3606 Rhodes Ave (45662-4935)
PHONE..................................740 456-5434
Hollie Hale, *Branch Mgr*
EMP: 4
SALES (corp-wide): 3.9B **Publicly Held**
SIC: 5087 3999 Beauty salon & barber shop equipment & supplies; barber & beauty shop equipment
HQ: Beauty Systems Group Llc
3001 Colorado Blvd
Denton TX 76210
940 297-2000

New Bremen
Auglaize County

(G-14780)
AUGLAIZE ERIE MACHINE COMPANY
07148 Quellhorst Rd (45869-9632)
P.O. Box 72 (45869-0072)
PHONE..................................419 629-2068
Fax: 419 629-3306
Tom W Slife, *President*
Elaine Slife, *Corp Secy*
Jeremy Homan, *Admin Sec*
EMP: 25
SQ FT: 7,500
SALES (est): 5.2MM **Privately Held**
WEB: www.aemcnc.com
SIC: 3599 Machine shop, jobbing & repair

(G-14781)
CISCO SYSTEMS INC
130 S Washington St (45869-1249)
PHONE..................................419 977-2404
Timothy Roth, *Engineer*
Aimee Bucher, *Analyst*
EMP: 656
SALES (corp-wide): 49.2B **Publicly Held**
SIC: 3577 Computer peripheral equipment
PA: Cisco Systems, Inc.
170 W Tasman Dr
San Jose CA 95134
408 526-4000

(G-14782)
CROWN CREDIT COMPANY
44 S Washington St (45869-1247)
P.O. Box 640352, Cincinnati (45264-0352)
PHONE..................................419 629-2311
James Dicke III, *President*
Julie Ahlers, *Exec Dir*
Kathy A Doseck, *Admin Sec*
Bradley Smith, *Admin Sec*
EMP: 17
SQ FT: 2,492
SALES: 4.5MM
SALES (corp-wide): 5.5B **Privately Held**
SIC: 3537 Lift trucks, industrial: fork, platform, straddle, etc.
PA: Crown Equipment Corporation
44 S Washington St
New Bremen OH 45869
419 629-2311

(G-14783)
CROWN EQUIPMENT CORPORATION
Also Called: Crown Lift Trucks
120 W Monroe St (45869-1149)
PHONE..................................419 629-9201
Mike Kovach, *Engineer*
Dave Besser, *Branch Mgr*
Maria Schwieterman, *Manager*
James F Dicke III, *Director*
Warren Webster II, *Director*
EMP: 4
SALES (corp-wide): 5.5B **Privately Held**
SIC: 3537 Lift trucks, industrial: fork, platform, straddle, etc.
PA: Crown Equipment Corporation
44 S Washington St
New Bremen OH 45869
419 629-2311

(G-14784)
CROWN EQUIPMENT CORPORATION
Also Called: Crown Lift Trucks
624 W Monroe St (45869-1351)
PHONE..................................419 629-2311
David Obringer, *Branch Mgr*
EMP: 65
SALES (corp-wide): 5.5B **Privately Held**
SIC: 3537 Lift trucks, industrial: fork, platform, straddle, etc.
PA: Crown Equipment Corporation
44 S Washington St
New Bremen OH 45869
419 629-2311

(G-14785)
CROWN EQUIPMENT CORPORATION
40 S Washington St (45869-1247)
PHONE..................................419 629-2311
EMP: 65
SALES (corp-wide): 1.3B **Privately Held**
SIC: 5084 3537 Whol Industrial Equipment Mfg Industrial Trucks/Tractors
PA: Crown Equipment Corporation
44 S Washington St
New Bremen OH 45869
419 629-2311

(G-14786)
CROWN EQUIPMENT CORPORATION
Also Called: Crown Lift Trucks
510 W Monroe St (45869-1300)
PHONE..................................419 629-2311
James F Dicke II, *Branch Mgr*
Kim Klopfleisch, *Commissioner*
Dan Bohman, *Supervisor*
Deb Brackman, *Admin Mgr*
Deb Homan, *Admin Mgr*
EMP: 62
SALES (corp-wide): 5.5B **Privately Held**
SIC: 3537 Lift trucks, industrial: fork, platform, straddle, etc.
PA: Crown Equipment Corporation
44 S Washington St
New Bremen OH 45869
419 629-2311

(G-14787)
FASTENAL COMPANY
575 W Monroe St (45869-1323)
PHONE..................................419 629-3024
Mark Suseland, *Branch Mgr*
EMP: 3
SALES (corp-wide): 3.9B **Publicly Held**
SIC: 5085 3429 Fasteners & fastening equipment; manufactured hardware (general)
PA: Fastenal Company
2001 Theurer Blvd
Winona MN 55987
507 454-5374

(G-14788)
KINNINGER PROD WLDG CO INC
710 Kuenzel Dr (45869-9699)
P.O. Box 33 (45869-0033)
PHONE..................................419 629-3491
Fax: 419 629-3902
Kevin Thobe, *President*
Donna Thobe, *Treasurer*
Cheryl Thobe, *Admin Sec*
EMP: 53
SQ FT: 54,000
SALES (est): 9.8MM **Privately Held**
WEB: www.kinningerwelding.com
SIC: 3544 Welding positioners (jigs)

(G-14789)
MARKETING ESSENTIALS LLC
18 N Washington St (45869-1113)
PHONE..................................419 629-0080
Patricia Cisco,
EMP: 13
SALES (est): 292.1K **Privately Held**
SIC: 8743 2741 2721 2711 Public relations & publicity; ; magazines: publishing only, not printed on site; magazines: publishing & printing; newspapers: publishing only, not printed on site

(G-14790)
NEW BREMEN MACHINE & TOOL CO
705 Kuenzel Dr (45869-8600)
PHONE..................................419 629-3295
Fax: 419 629-2599
Joan Leffel, *CEO*
Jay Bergman, *Vice Pres*
Randy Bergman, *Vice Pres*
Robert Roth, *Vice Pres*
Mark Cisco, *CPA*
EMP: 25 **EST:** 1928
SQ FT: 45,000
SALES (est): 5.7MM **Privately Held**
WEB: www.newbremenmachine.com
SIC: 3469 3544 Metal stampings; special dies & tools

(G-14791)
NUPCO INC
06561 County Road 66a (45869-9615)
PHONE................................419 629-2259
Fax: 419 629-3381
Luke Wilker, *President*
Virginia Dickie, *Vice Pres*
EMP: 6 **EST:** 1946
SQ FT: 3,750
SALES (est): 670.5K **Privately Held**
SIC: 3084 Plastics pipe

(G-14792)
PRECISION REFLEX INC
710 Streine Dr (45869-8608)
P.O. Box 95 (45869-0095)
PHONE................................419 629-2603
Fax: 419 629-2173
N David Dunlap, *President*
Mary Dunlap, *Corp Secy*
Shawn Schneider, *Opers Mgr*
EMP: 12
SQ FT: 2,100
SALES: 1MM **Privately Held**
WEB: www.pri-mounts.com
SIC: 3599 2796 7692 Machine shop, job-
bing & repair; engraving on copper, steel,
wood or rubber: printing plates; welding
repair

(G-14793)
SAFEWAY PACKAGING INC (PA)
300 White Mountain Dr (45869-8621)
PHONE................................419 629-3200
Kevin Manor, *President*
Nicole Brewer, *General Mgr*
Doug Stemen, *General Mgr*
Ralph Stoner, *Vice Pres*
Nick Prenger, *Engineer*
EMP: 67
SQ FT: 100,000
SALES (est): 23.7MM **Privately Held**
WEB: www.safewaypkg.com
SIC: 2653 2673 2671 2631 Corrugated
boxes, partitions, display items, sheets &
pad; bags: plastic, laminated & coated;
packaging paper & plastics film, coated &
laminated; paperboard mills

(G-14794)
SUNRISE COOPERATIVE INC
Also Called: Auglaize Farmers
435 S Herman St (45869-8602)
PHONE................................419 629-2338
Robert Heitkamp, *Manager*
EMP: 6
SALES (corp-wide): 46.5MM **Privately
Held**
SIC: 2048 Prepared feeds
PA: Sunrise Cooperative, Inc.
2025 W State St Ste A
Fremont OH 43420
419 332-6468

(G-14795)
**THIEMAN QUALITY METAL FAB
INC**
05140 Dicke Rd (45869-9750)
P.O. Box 45 (45869-0045)
PHONE................................419 629-2612
Fax: 419 629-3720
Doug Broering, *Human Resources*
Tim Rasawehr, *Prgrmr*
Linda Holdren, *Director*
EMP: 80
SQ FT: 90,000
SALES: 14MM **Privately Held**
WEB: www.thieman.com
SIC: 3499 Machine bases, metal

(G-14796)
**VISIONMARK NAMEPLATE CO
LLC**
100 White Mountain Dr (45869-8626)
P.O. Box 280, New Knoxville (45871-0280)
PHONE................................419 977-3131
Jerry Merges, *President*
Mark Nolan, *Vice Pres*
Tonia Gates, *Manager*
EMP: 27 **EST:** 2014
SQ FT: 20,000
SALES (est): 1.8MM **Privately Held**
SIC: 3479 Name plates: engraved, etched,
etc.

New Carlisle
Clark County

(G-14797)
**BEACH MFG PLASTIC MOLDING
DIV**
7816 W National Rd (45344)
PHONE................................937 882-6400
Theodore Beach, *President*
EMP: 75
SALES (est): 6.3MM **Privately Held**
SIC: 3089 Molding primary plastic

(G-14798)
**CARLISLE PLASTICS COMPANY
INC**
320 Ohio St (45344-1630)
P.O. Box 146 (45344-0146)
PHONE................................937 845-9411
Fax: 937 845-9413
Cynthia A Thomas, *President*
Howard M Clay, *President*
Shannan Stewart, *General Mgr*
Cynthia Group, *VP Opers*
James Thomas, *Admin Sec*
EMP: 7
SQ FT: 12,000
SALES (est): 450K **Privately Held**
WEB: www.carlisleplastics.com
SIC: 3479 Hot dip coating of metals or
formed products

(G-14799)
**CUSTOM THREADING SYSTEMS
LLC**
Also Called: A Plus Machining & Tooling
1833 N Dayton Lakeview Rd (45344-9501)
PHONE................................937 846-1405
James E Payne,
Denise Berkshire,
EMP: 7
SALES (est): 866K **Privately Held**
SIC: 3554 Paper industries machinery

(G-14800)
CUSTOM WAY WELDING INC
2217 N Dayton Lakeview Rd (45344-9578)
PHONE................................937 845-9469
Fax: 937 845-1964
Brian Bonham, *President*
Renae Fahr, *Manager*
Amy Bonham, *Admin Sec*
EMP: 11
SQ FT: 12,052
SALES: 3.3MM **Privately Held**
SIC: 1799 7692 5599 Ornamental metal
work; welding repair; utility trailers

(G-14801)
G KEENER & CO
2936 Liberty Rd (45344-8511)
PHONE................................937 846-1210
Gary Keener, *President*
Andrea Keener, *Vice Pres*
EMP: 4
SALES (est): 100K **Privately Held**
WEB: www.gkeenerco.com
SIC: 2519 Lawn & garden furniture, except
wood & metal

(G-14802)
HTCI CO
12170 Milton Carlisle Rd (45344-9701)
P.O. Box 486 (45344-0486)
PHONE................................937 845-1204
Kevin King, *President*
Deborah Jenkins, *Corp Secy*
Raymond Franks, *Exec VP*
Ryan Storey, *Engineer*
EMP: 18
SALES: 2MM **Privately Held**
WEB: www.htc-inc.com
SIC: 3365 Aerospace castings, aluminum

(G-14803)
INDIAN CREEK DISTILLERY
7095 Staley Rd (45344-9416)
PHONE................................937 846-1443
Julianne Staley, *Principal*
EMP: 5

SALES (est): 294.4K **Privately Held**
SIC: 2085 Distillers' dried grains & solubles
& alcohol

(G-14804)
**KAFFENBARGER TRUCK EQP
CO (PA)**
10100 Ballentine Pike (45344-9534)
PHONE................................937 845-3804
Fax: 937 857-9068
Larry Kaffenbarger, *President*
Edward W Dunn, *Principal*
Everett L Kaffenbarger, *Principal*
Timothy Schuler, *Controller*
Denise Miller, *Accountant*
EMP: 110 **EST:** 1961
SQ FT: 30,000
SALES (est): 33.4MM **Privately Held**
WEB: www.kaffenbarger.com
SIC: 3713 5013 Truck bodies (motor vehi-
cles); truck parts & accessories

(G-14805)
**KRAM PRECISION MACHINING
INC**
1751 Dalton Dr (45344-2309)
PHONE................................937 849-1301
Greg Flory, *President*
Douglas Flory, *Treasurer*
▲ **EMP:** 6
SQ FT: 6,000
SALES: 500K **Privately Held**
SIC: 3599 Machine shop, jobbing & repair

(G-14806)
MAD RIVER STEEL LTD
Also Called: Mad River Steel Company
2141 N Dayton Lakeview Rd (45344-9578)
P.O. Box 411 (45344-0411)
PHONE................................937 845-4046
Fax: 937 845-4048
John Bobo, *President*
EMP: 8
SQ FT: 10,200
SALES (est): 1.1MM **Privately Held**
SIC: 3441 Building components, structural
steel

(G-14807)
**MAJESTIC ENGINEERING & TL
LLC**
107 W Washington St (45344-1844)
PHONE................................937 845-1079
Brad Hornback, *Managing Prtnr*
Mike Notestine, *Managing Prtnr*
EMP: 4
SQ FT: 2,500
SALES: 275K **Privately Held**
SIC: 8711 3599 Engineering services; ma-
chine & other job shop work

(G-14808)
**NCT TECHNOLOGIES GROUP
INC (PA)**
7867 W National Rd (45344-8268)
P.O. Box 37 (45344-0037)
PHONE................................937 882-6800
Andrew Flora, *President*
Curtis Flora, *Vice Pres*
Mark Mangen, *Prdtn Mgr*
EMP: 25
SQ FT: 7,500
SALES (est): 5.4MM **Privately Held**
WEB: www.newcarlisletool.com
SIC: 3441 Fabricated structural metal

(G-14809)
NEO TECH
123 S Main St (45344-1952)
PHONE................................937 845-0999
Ted Buskirk, *Owner*
EMP: 3
SALES (est): 211.3K **Privately Held**
SIC: 2813 Neon

(G-14810)
NUMERICS UNLIMITED INC
1700 Dalton Dr (45344-2307)
PHONE................................937 849-0100
Fax: 937 849-4285
Wayne Atkins, *President*
Derick Simmons, *Opers Mgr*
Richard Rice, *Engineer*
Wendy Minnich, *Manager*
EMP: 22

SQ FT: 15,000
SALES (est): 4.6MM **Privately Held**
WEB: www.numericsunlimited.com
SIC: 3544 Industrial molds

(G-14811)
**PATTON ALUMINUM PRODUCTS
INC**
65 Quick Rd (45344-9253)
PHONE................................937 845-9404
Fax: 937 845-9424
Edward E Patton, *President*
Angie King, *Opers Mgr*
Steve Bacon, *Sales Staff*
Dave Patton, *Manager*
EMP: 17
SQ FT: 14,000
SALES (est): 2.5MM **Privately Held**
WEB: www.pattonaluminum.com
SIC: 3354 3448 Shapes, extruded alu-
minum; screen enclosures; sunrooms,
prefabricated metal

(G-14812)
PFI PRECISION INC
Also Called: Pfi Precision Machining
2011 N Dayton Lakeview Rd (45344-9550)
PHONE................................937 845-3563
Fax: 937 845-0475
Thomas Janek, *President*
Greg Macpherson, *Engineer*
Gregory Janek, *Manager*
Ralph Thieman, *Manager*
▲ **EMP:** 29
SQ FT: 26,300
SALES (est): 6.4MM **Privately Held**
WEB: www.pfiprecision.com
SIC: 3451 3545 Screw machine products;
precision tools, machinists'

(G-14813)
TAYLOR TOOL & DIE INC
306 N Main St (45344-1839)
PHONE................................937 845-1491
Fax: 937 845-9961
Michael L Taylor, *President*
Jim Elrod, *Vice Pres*
Vern Young, *Admin Sec*
EMP: 7 **EST:** 1982
SQ FT: 3,900
SALES (est): 670K **Privately Held**
SIC: 3544 Special dies & tools

(G-14814)
TETRA MOLD & TOOL INC
51 Quick Rd (45344-9294)
PHONE................................937 845-1651
Fax: 937 845-2261
Brent Hughes, *President*
Arleen Hughes, *Vice Pres*
Ronald L Hughes, *Vice Pres*
Carrie Yates, *Accountant*
Sarah Miller, *Manager*
EMP: 25
SQ FT: 10,000
SALES (est): 6.4MM **Privately Held**
WEB: www.tetramold.com
SIC: 3089 3544 3714 Injection molding of
plastics; special dies, tools, jigs & fixtures;
motor vehicle parts & accessories

(G-14815)
TIG WOOD & DIE INC
1760 Dalton Dr (45344-2307)
PHONE................................937 849-6741
Fax: 937 849-6875
Richard Levally, *President*
Betty Levally, *Vice Pres*
EMP: 19
SQ FT: 12,000
SALES: 1.3MM **Privately Held**
SIC: 3544 5051 Paper cutting dies; dies,
steel rule; stampings, metal

New Concord
Muskingum County

(G-14816)
**CAMPTON ELECTRIC SALES &
SVC**
11615 Norfield Rd (43762-9756)
PHONE................................740 826-4429
Clara Campton, *Partner*

John Campton, *Partner*
Richard Campton, *General Ptnr*
EMP: 3
SALES (est) 310K **Privately Held**
SIC: 5063 7694 Motors, electric; electric motor repair

(G-14817)
CARBONLESS & CUT SHEET FORMS
1948 John Glenn Hwy (43762-9485)
PHONE..................................740 826-1700
Jason Killiany, *President*
David A Killainy, *President*
EMP: 18
SQ FT: 6,000
SALES: 500K **Privately Held**
SIC: 2759 5722 Commercial printing; vacuum cleaners

(G-14818)
FABRI-FORM COMPANY (DH)
200 S Friendship Dr (43762-9641)
PHONE..................................740 826-5000
Fax: 740 826-5001
Jack Slinger, *CEO*
John W Knight, *Ch of Bd*
Paul Baker, *President*
Thomas A Brown, *Principal*
Edward V Cain, *Principal*
EMP: 70 EST: 1944
SQ FT: 50,000
SALES (est): 27.7MM
SALES (corp-wide): 34.7MM **Privately Held**
WEB: www.fabri-form.com
SIC: 3089 Thermoformed finished plastic products
HQ: The Pendaform Company
200 S Friendship Dr
New Concord OH 43762
740 826-5000

(G-14819)
PENDAFORM COMPANY (HQ)
200 S Friendship Dr (43762-9641)
PHONE..................................740 826-5000
John Brown, *CEO*
David Kruger, *President*
Ron Smith, *Engineer*
Eric Wright, *Engineer*
John Hamilton, *Design Engr*
EMP: 30 EST: 2013
SALES (est): 205.4MM
SALES (corp-wide): 34.7MM **Privately Held**
SIC: 3089 Thermoformed finished plastic products

(G-14820)
PENDAFORM COMPANY
200 S Friendship Dr (43762-9641)
PHONE..................................740 826-5000
EMP: 200
SALES (corp-wide): 477.9MM **Privately Held**
SIC: 3089 Mfg Plastic Products
PA: The Pendaform Company
200 S Friendship Dr
New Concord OH 43762
740 826-5000

(G-14821)
ROBERT BARR
Also Called: Big Sky Petroleum
1245 Friendship Dr (43762-1023)
PHONE..................................740 826-7325
Robert Barr, *Principal*
EMP: 12
SALES: 1.2MM **Privately Held**
WEB: www.robertbarr.com
SIC: 1311 5812 Crude petroleum production; natural gas production; restaurant, family: independent

(G-14822)
TK GAS SERVICES INC
2303 John Glenn Hwy (43762-9310)
PHONE..................................740 826-0303
Ted Korte, *President*
Jill Pattison, *Corp Secy*
EMP: 50
SQ FT: 4,000
SALES (est): 6.6MM **Privately Held**
SIC: 1389 Oil field services

(G-14823)
CLINTON MACHINE CO INC
6270 Van Buren Rd (44216-9743)
PHONE..................................330 882-6743
Fax: 330 882-6749
Joe Podnar, *CEO*
Delores C Gregory, *Principal*
John D Judge, *Principal*
▲ **EMP:** 3
SALES (est): 746.3K **Privately Held**
WEB: www.clintalum.com
SIC: 3365 Machinery castings, aluminum

(G-14824)
G & J EXTRUSIONS INC
1580 Turkeyfoot Lake Rd (44203-4852)
P.O. Box 275, Hessel MI (49745-0275)
PHONE..................................330 753-0162
Garry Dumbauld, *President*
Julie Dumbauld, *Vice Pres*
EMP: 6
SQ FT: 10,000
SALES (est): 661.3K **Privately Held**
WEB: www.gjextrude.com
SIC: 3089 Extruded finished plastic products

(G-14825)
J MCCAMAN ENTERPRISES INC
Also Called: J M Machinery
3032 Franks Rd (44216-9327)
P.O. Box 378, Wadsworth (44282-0378)
PHONE..................................330 825-2401
Fax: 330 825-0569
Michael L Dyer, *President*
Jacqueline McCaman, *Vice Pres*
Jason Breth, *Sales Mgr*
EMP: 15
SQ FT: 2,500
SALES (est): 2.4MM **Privately Held**
WEB: www.jmktm.com
SIC: 3559 5084 Plastics working machinery; rubber working machinery, including tires; industrial machinery & equipment

(G-14826)
JCI JONES CHEMICALS INC
2500 Vanderhoof Rd (44203-4650)
PHONE..................................330 825-2531
Barry Allshouse, *Safety Mgr*
Lisa Glover, *Office Mgr*
Dan Casmey, *Manager*
EMP: 15
SQ FT: 22,848
SALES (corp-wide): 134.4MM **Privately Held**
WEB: www.jcichem.com
SIC: 2812 8734 Chlorine, compressed or liquefied; testing laboratories
PA: Jci Jones Chemicals, Inc.
1765 Ringling Blvd
Sarasota FL 34236
941 330-1537

(G-14827)
OHIO PLASTICS & SAFETY PDTS
6140 Manchester Rd (44319-4615)
P.O. Box 593, Columbia Station (44028-0593)
PHONE..................................330 882-6764
Fax: 330 882-4850
Leanne Keith, *President*
Lesa Taylor, *Buyer*
EMP: 5
SQ FT: 3,850
SALES (est): 478.7K **Privately Held**
SIC: 3993 Signs & advertising specialties

(G-14828)
OHIO PLASTICS BELTING CO
6140 Manchester Rd (44319-4615)
P.O. Box 593, Columbia Station (44028-0593)
PHONE..................................330 882-6764
John David Satink, *Owner*
John G David, *Co-Owner*
Le-Anne Keith, *Co-Owner*
EMP: 6

SALES (est): 500K **Privately Held**
WEB: www.ohiothane.com
SIC: 2824 Nylon fibers

(G-14829)
PHILLIPS MCH & STAMPING CORP
5290 S Main St (44319-4997)
PHONE..................................330 882-6714
Fax: 330 882-6716
Wilda Phillips, *President*
Shawn Phillips, *General Mgr*
Craig Phillips, *Vice Pres*
Judy Simms, *Purch Mgr*
Beau Phillips, *Sls & Mktg Exec*
EMP: 8
SQ FT: 16,000
SALES (est): 1.3MM **Privately Held**
SIC: 3469 3544 Metal stampings; special dies & tools

(G-14830)
PRISTINE EXTERIORS
5925 Renninger Rd (44319-4833)
PHONE..................................330 957-5664
Jerry Largent, *Owner*
EMP: 3 EST: 2015
SALES (est): 73.7K **Privately Held**
SIC: 2381 Dyeing gloves, woven or knit: for the trade

(G-14831)
RUBBER ASSOCIATES INC
1522 Turkeyfoot Lake Rd (44203-4898)
PHONE..................................330 745-2186
Fax: 330 745-6788
Eugene Fiocca, *President*
Joseph Machek, *Division Mgr*
Kris Fiocca, *Exec VP*
Kip Fiocca, *Human Res Mgr*
Shirley Graver, *MIS Mgr*
▲ **EMP:** 100 EST: 1952
SQ FT: 76,000
SALES (est): 16.3MM **Privately Held**
WEB: www.rubberassociates.com
SIC: 3069 Molded rubber products

(G-14832)
SPEEDWAY LLC
Also Called: Speedway Superamerica 3672
5211 Manchester Rd (44319-3913)
PHONE..................................330 644-2730
Judy Hankison, *Manager*
EMP: 5 **Publicly Held**
WEB: www.speedwaynet.com
SIC: 1311 Crude petroleum production
HQ: Speedway Llc
500 Speedway Dr
Enon OH 45323
937 864-3000

(G-14833)
BETHEL ENGINEERING AND EQP INC (PA)
13830 Mcbeth Rd (45870)
P.O. Box 67 (45870-0067)
PHONE..................................419 568-1100
Fax: 419 568-1807
David Whitaker, *President*
Kevin Connor, *Project Engr*
Tim Murphy, *VP Sls/Mktg*
Kathy Whitaker, *Treasurer*
Jenny Lowe, *Manager*
EMP: 34
SQ FT: 51,000
SALES: 5.6MM **Privately Held**
WEB: www.bethelengr.com
SIC: 3559 3441 Paint making machinery; fabricated structural metal

(G-14834)
BETHEL ENGINEERING AND EQP INC
13830 Mcbeth Rd (45870)
P.O. Box 67 (45870-0067)
PHONE..................................419 568-7976
David Whitaker, *Branch Mgr*
EMP: 20 **Privately Held**
WEB: www.bethelengr.com
SIC: 3559 Paint making machinery

PA: Bethel Engineering And Equipment, Inc.
13830 Mcbeth Rd
New Hampshire OH 45870

(G-14835)
NEW HOLLAND ENGINEERING INC
43 E Front St (43145-9662)
P.O. Box 125 (43145-0125)
PHONE..................................740 495-5200
Fax: 740 495-1122
John Berker, *President*
Beverly Berker, *Vice Pres*
Randy Smith, *Foreman/Supr*
EMP: 7
SQ FT: 7,000
SALES (est): 900K **Privately Held**
WEB: www.gutterhangers.net
SIC: 3469 3541 Metal stampings; machine tools, metal cutting type

(G-14836)
HOGE LUMBER COMPANY (PA)
Also Called: Hoge Brush
701 S Main St State (45871)
PHONE..................................419 753-2263
Fax: 419 753-2611
John H Hoge, *President*
Jack R Hoge, *Exec VP*
Clark T Froning, *Vice Pres*
Bruce L Hoge, *Vice Pres*
▲ **EMP:** 35 EST: 1904
SQ FT: 400,000
SALES (est): 6.8MM **Privately Held**
WEB: www.hoge.com
SIC: 3448 1521 2521 Prefabricated metal buildings; new construction, single-family houses; cabinets, office: wood

(G-14837)
HOGE LUMBER COMPANY
Hoge Brush Co
202 E South St (45871)
P.O. Box 189 (45871-0189)
PHONE..................................419 753-2351
Fax: 419 753-2893
Dave Zwiep, *Manager*
EMP: 10
SQ FT: 80
SALES (corp-wide): 6.8MM **Privately Held**
WEB: www.hoge.com
SIC: 3991 Brooms & brushes
PA: Hoge Lumber Company
701 S Main St State
New Knoxville OH 45871
419 753-2263

(G-14838)
MODERN AG SUPPLY INC
302 S Main St (45871)
P.O. Box 249 (45871-0249)
PHONE..................................419 753-3484
Jack Leffel, *President*
EMP: 3
SALES (est): 320K **Privately Held**
SIC: 2879 Chemicals, agricultural

(G-14839)
A-BUCK MANUFACTURING INC
12251 Eagle Rd (45345-9122)
PHONE..................................937 687-3738
EMP: 3
SALES (est): 147.4K **Privately Held**
SIC: 3999 Mfg Misc Products

(G-14840)
B & B GEAR & MACHINE CO INC
440 W Main St (45345-1426)
PHONE..........................937 687-1771
Fax: 937 687-1320
Kevin Brinson, *President*
Jennifer Brinson, *Owner*
EMP: 12
SQ FT: 15,000
SALES (est): 3.7MM **Privately Held**
SIC: 3566 3599 Gears, power transmission, except automotive; machine shop, jobbing & repair

(G-14841)
DIXIE FLYER & PRINTING CO
424 Rosetta St (45345-1520)
PHONE..........................937 687-0088
Fax: 937 227-3466
Roger Salyer, *Principal*
EMP: 4
SALES (est): 240K **Privately Held**
SIC: 2752 Commercial printing, lithographic

(G-14842)
H DUANE LEIS ACQUISITIONS
Also Called: Micro Tool Service
443 S Diamond Mill Rd (45345)
PHONE..........................937 835-5621
Fax: 937 835-5476
H Duane Leis, *President*
Duane Leis, *Vice Pres*
EMP: 20
SALES: 3MM **Privately Held**
SIC: 3545 Cutting tools for machine tools

(G-14843)
MARTIN WELDING LLC (PA)
1472 W Main St (45345-9772)
PHONE..........................937 687-3602
Mike Martin,
EMP: 10
SALES (est): 872.2K **Privately Held**
SIC: 7692 Welding repair

(G-14844)
MCINTOSH MACHINE
11 S Church St (45345-1213)
P.O. Box 164 (45345-0164)
PHONE..........................937 687-3936
Terry McIntosh, *Owner*
EMP: 5
SQ FT: 3,000
SALES (est): 210K **Privately Held**
SIC: 7692 5571 5013 3599 Welding repair; motorcycle parts & accessories; motorcycle parts; machine & other job shop work

---

New Lexington
Perry County

(G-14845)
C S A ENTERPRISES
Also Called: Tla Designs
932 S Main St (43764-1552)
PHONE..........................740 342-9367
Corlyn Speake Altier, *Owner*
EMP: 5
SALES: 100K **Privately Held**
SIC: 8721 2221 Billing & bookkeeping service; wall covering fabrics, manmade fiber & silk

(G-14846)
COOPER-STANDARD AUTOMOTIVE INC
2378 State Route 345 Ne (43764)
PHONE..........................740 342-3523
Gary Smith, *Personnel*
Mr B Dickens, *Branch Mgr*
EMP: 352
SQ FT: 80,000
SALES (corp-wide): 3.4B **Publicly Held**
WEB: www.cooperstandard.com
SIC: 3714 3443 Motor vehicle brake systems & parts; fuel systems & parts, motor vehicle; heat exchangers, condensers & components

HQ: Cooper-Standard Automotive Inc.
39550 Orchard Hill Pl
Novi MI 48375
248 596-5900

(G-14847)
DNL OIL CORP
Also Called: Dusty's Salvage & Supply
7913 State Route 37 E (43764-9512)
PHONE..........................740 342-4970
Fax: 740 342-4399
N L Altier Jr, *President*
EMP: 7
SQ FT: 4,230
SALES (est): 800.6K **Privately Held**
SIC: 1381 5211 Drilling oil & gas wells; lumber & other building materials

(G-14848)
LORI HOLDING CO (PA)
Also Called: Siemer Distributing
1400 Commerce Dr (43764-9500)
PHONE..........................740 342-3230
Fax: 740 342-9813
Joseph A Siemer III, *President*
Dolores Siemer, *Admin Sec*
EMP: 30
SALES (est): 10.4MM **Privately Held**
SIC: 5147 5143 5199 5142 Meats, fresh; cheese; ice, manufactured or natural; packaged frozen goods; manufactured ice

(G-14849)
LUDOWICI ROOF TILE INC
4757 Tile Plant Rd Se (43764-9630)
P.O. Box 69 (43764-0069)
PHONE..........................740 342-1995
Fax: 740 342-0025
Herve Gastinel, *President*
Guillaume Latil, *Vice Pres*
Kyle Riggle, *Project Mgr*
Shelby Stevenson, *Project Mgr*
Jonathan Gothard, *Design Engr*
▲ EMP: 80
SQ FT: 100,000
SALES (est): 14.3MM
SALES (corp-wide): 6.8MM **Privately Held**
WEB: www.ludowici.com
SIC: 3259 Roofing tile, clay
HQ: Terreal
13 17
Suresnes 92150
149 972-030

(G-14850)
OXFORD MINING COMPANY INC
Also Called: Tunnell Hill Reclamation
2500 Township Rd 205 (43764)
PHONE..........................740 342-7666
Jeff Williams, *Superintendent*
EMP: 58
SALES (corp-wide): 1.4B **Publicly Held**
SIC: 1221 Strip mining, bituminous
HQ: Oxford Mining Company, Inc.
544 Chestnut St
Coshocton OH 43812
740 622-6302

(G-14851)
PERRY COUNTY TRIBUNE
Also Called: Tribune Shopping News, The
399 Lincoln Park Dr Ste A (43764-1078)
P.O. Box 312 (43764-0312)
PHONE..........................740 342-4121
Fax: 740 342-4131
Deb Hutmire, *General Mgr*
EMP: 10
SALES (est): 438.3K **Privately Held**
SIC: 2711 6512 Newspapers; property operation, retail establishment

(G-14852)
R & D HILLTOP LUMBER INC
2126 State Route 93 Se (43764-9666)
PHONE..........................740 342-3051
Fax: 740 342-5405
Russell Howdyshell, *President*
Polly Howdyshell, *Vice Pres*
EMP: 23
SQ FT: 8,000
SALES (est): 3.3MM **Privately Held**
SIC: 2421 Sawmills & planing mills, general

(G-14853)
R CARNEY THOMAS
Also Called: T C Woodworking
1600 Commerce Dr (43764-9562)
PHONE..........................740 342-3388
Thomas Carney, *Owner*
EMP: 5
SQ FT: 13,000
SALES (est): 287.9K **Privately Held**
SIC: 1751 2521 2434 2431 Cabinet building & installation; cabinets, office: wood; wood kitchen cabinets; millwork

(G-14854)
SOUTHEASTERN SHAFTING MFG
402 W Broadway St (43764-1007)
P.O. Box 168 (43764-0168)
PHONE..........................740 342-4629
Fax: 740 342-4565
Scott Jones Sr, *President*
Jones Teresa, *Financial Exec*
Theresa M Jones, *Admin Sec*
EMP: 18
SALES (est): 2.1MM **Privately Held**
WEB: www.seshafting.com
SIC: 3568 3599 Collars, shaft (power transmission equipment); machine shop, jobbing & repair

(G-14855)
STAR ENGINEERING INC
701 Madison St (43764-1086)
P.O. Box 71 (43764-0071)
PHONE..........................740 342-3514
Fax: 740 342-2343
Bill Mooney, *CEO*
Christopher Mooney, *President*
William J Mooney, *President*
Daniel P Mooney, *Vice Pres*
John Mooney, *Vice Pres*
EMP: 35 EST: 1941
SQ FT: 36,000
SALES (est): 9.7MM **Privately Held**
WEB: www.starengineering.com
SIC: 3567 Ceramic kilns & furnaces

(G-14856)
SURVEYING CANNON LAND
7945 Township Road 114 Ne (43764-9608)
PHONE..........................740 342-2835
Fax: 740 342-5009
Kevin Cannon, *Owner*
EMP: 3
SALES (est): 158.5K **Privately Held**
SIC: 1389 Oil field services

(G-14857)
T & R NOODLES LLC
11400 State Route 37 E (43764-9655)
PHONE..........................614 537-4710
Joseph Metz, *COO*
Donald Metz, *CFO*
Donna Metz, *Chief Mktg Ofcr*
Andrew Metz, *Security Dir*
EMP: 4
SQ FT: 900
SALES (est): 240K **Privately Held**
SIC: 2098 Noodles (e.g. egg, plain & water), dry

New London
Huron County

(G-14858)
APPLIED AUTOMATION ENTERPRISE
24 Cedar St (44851-1218)
PHONE..........................419 929-2428
Fax: 419 929-8109
Timothy Hedrick, *President*
Vaughn Lucal, *Treasurer*
Jennifer Pabst, *Manager*
Stephan Pabst, *Admin Sec*
EMP: 11
SQ FT: 15,000
SALES (est): 1.8MM **Privately Held**
WEB: www.automationent.com
SIC: 3541 Chucking machines, automatic

(G-14859)
FITCHVILLE EAST CORP
Also Called: Fitchville East Storage
1732 Us Highway 250 S (44851-9372)
PHONE..........................419 929-1510
Gene Rieske, *President*
Leonard Leach, *Vice Pres*
Lewis Rieske, *Manager*
EMP: 22
SALES (est): 1.3MM **Privately Held**
SIC: 3799 Trailers & trailer equipment

(G-14860)
KENT SPORTING GOODS CO INC (PA)
433 Park Ave (44851-1314)
PHONE..........................419 929-7021
Fax: 419 929-1769
Robert Archer, *CEO*
J Robert Tipton, *President*
Marlene Sipp, *Vice Pres*
Wayne Walters, *Vice Pres*
Brian C Zaletel, *Vice Pres*
▲ EMP: 100
SQ FT: 25,000
SALES (est): 135.6MM **Privately Held**
SIC: 3949 Water sports equipment

(G-14861)
MONODE MARKING PRODUCTS INC
Also Called: Waldorf Marking Devices
149 High St (44851-1118)
PHONE..........................419 929-0346
Fax: 419 929-8806
Thomas Mackey, *President*
EMP: 10
SALES (corp-wide): 8.6MM **Privately Held**
SIC: 3542 3953 Marking machines; marking devices
PA: Monode Marking Products, Inc.
9200 Tyler Blvd
Mentor OH 44060
440 975-8802

(G-14862)
MONODE STEEL STAMP INC (PA)
149 High St (44851-1118)
PHONE..........................419 929-3501
Thomas Mackey, *President*
William Vickery, *Vice Pres*
EMP: 2
SQ FT: 3,000
SALES: 1.8MM **Privately Held**
WEB: www.monode.com
SIC: 3542 3469 3953 Marking machines; metal stampings; marking devices

(G-14863)
NEW LONDON FOUNDRY INC
80 Walnut St (44851-1240)
P.O. Box 227 (44851-0227)
PHONE..........................419 929-2073
Fax: 419 929-0213
Keith Gregory, *President*
Dorothy Gregory, *Corp Secy*
EMP: 15 EST: 1949
SQ FT: 21,000
SALES (est): 2.4MM **Privately Held**
SIC: 3365 3369 Aluminum & aluminum-based alloy castings; nonferrous foundries

(G-14864)
ROERIG MACHINE
27348 State Route 511 (44851-9667)
PHONE..........................440 647-4718
William Roerig, *Partner*
Ron Roerig, *Partner*
EMP: 6
SALES: 200K **Privately Held**
SIC: 3599 Machine shop, jobbing & repair

(G-14865)
SDG NEWS GROUP INC
Also Called: Firelands Farmer, The
43 E Main St (44851-1213)
P.O. Box 146 (44851-0146)
PHONE..........................419 929-3411
Fax: 419 929-8210
Scott Glove, *President*
Scott Gove, *President*
EMP: 10

SALES (est): 458.7K **Privately Held**
SIC: 2711 2752 Newspapers; commercial printing, lithographic

(G-14866)
SEWLINE PRODUCTS INC
30 S Railroad St (44851-1243)
PHONE....................................419 929-1114
Fax: 419 929-2404
Duane E Mills, *President*
Alana Mills, *Admin Sec*
EMP: 12
SQ FT: 30,980
SALES: 350K **Privately Held**
SIC: 2392 2399 Blankets, comforters & beddings; infant carriers

(G-14867)
THOMAS CREATIVE APPAREL INC
1 Harmony Pl (44851-1248)
PHONE....................................419 929-1506
Fax: 419 929-0122
Vickie Hall, *President*
EMP: 35
SQ FT: 14,000
SALES (est): 3.7MM **Privately Held**
WEB: www.thomasrobes.com
SIC: 2384 2389 2353 Robes & dressing gowns; lodge costumes; hats, caps & millinery

(G-14868)
TIERRA-DERCO INTERNATIONAL LLC
40 S Main St (44851-1138)
PHONE....................................419 929-2240
Heath White, *Manager*
EMP: 7
SALES (corp-wide): 6MM **Privately Held**
SIC: 3524 Lawn & garden equipment
PA: Tierra-Derco International, Llc
1000 S Saint Charles St
Jasper IN 47546
812 482-1644

New Madison
Darke County

(G-14869)
FLORIDA PRODUCTION ENGRG INC
Ernie Green Industries
1855 State Route 121 N (45346-9716)
PHONE....................................937 996-4361
Fax: 937 996-4714
Jeramy Elliot, *Safety Mgr*
John Dorsten, *QC Dir*
Eric Opicka, *Enginr/R&D Mgr*
EMP: 90
SALES (corp-wide): 575.1MM **Privately Held**
SIC: 3465 3714 3429 Moldings or trim, automobile: stamped metal; motor vehicle parts & accessories; manufactured hardware (general)
HQ: Florida Production Engineering, Inc.
2 E Tower Cir
Ormond Beach FL 32174
386 677-2566

(G-14870)
LUDY GREENHOUSE MFG CORP (PA)
122 Railroad St (45346-5016)
P.O. Box 141 (45346-0141)
PHONE....................................800 255-5839
Fax: 937 996-8031
Stephan A Scantland, *President*
Deborah Scantland, *Vice Pres*
Brian Munchel, *Engineer*
Becky Yount, *Regl Sales Mgr*
EMP: 58
SQ FT: 2,500
SALES (est): 20.7MM **Privately Held**
SIC: 1542 3448 Greenhouse construction; greenhouses: prefabricated metal

New Marshfield
Athens County

(G-14871)
DIESEL FLTRTION SPCIALISTS LLC
Also Called: Timothy A. Lyons
5475 Ste Rte 681 (45766)
P.O. Box 312, Albany (45710-0312)
PHONE....................................740 698-0255
Timothy A Lyons,
EMP: 3 EST: 2014
SALES (est): 165.7K **Privately Held**
SIC: 1389 Bailing, cleaning, swabbing & treating of wells

(G-14872)
SCHARENBERG SHEET METAL
2261 Scott Rd (45766-9502)
PHONE....................................740 664-2431
William Scharenberg, *Owner*
EMP: 4
SALES (est): 362.9K **Privately Held**
SIC: 3444 1711 Ducts, sheet metal; ventilation & duct work contractor; warm air heating & air conditioning contractor

New Matamoras
Washington County

(G-14873)
CREIGHTON SPORTS CENTER INC (PA)
205 Broadway Ave (45767-1193)
P.O. Box 400 (45767-0400)
PHONE....................................740 865-2521
Bill Creighton, *President*
Pam Creighton, *Corp Secy*
Chris Creighton, *Vice Pres*
EMP: 7
SQ FT: 2,400
SALES (est): 733K **Privately Held**
SIC: 3949 Sporting & athletic goods

New Middletown
Mahoning County

(G-14874)
CC IRONWORKS LLC
10613 Main St (44442-8762)
PHONE....................................330 542-0500
Robert Pacella,
EMP: 3
SALES: 100K **Privately Held**
SIC: 3599 Industrial machinery

(G-14875)
COLUMBIA MIDSTREAM GROUP LLC
10846 Stateline Rd (44442-9727)
PHONE....................................330 542-1095
Scott Singer,
EMP: 18
SALES (est): 12.6MM
SALES (corp-wide): 9.2B **Privately Held**
SIC: 1311 Natural gas production
HQ: Columbia Pipeline Group, Inc.
5151 San Felipe St
Houston TX 77056
713 386-3701

(G-14876)
CONTROL SYSTEM MANUFACTURING
10725 Struthers Rd (44442-9704)
PHONE....................................330 542-0000
Fax: 330 542-0001
Rex Cyrus, *Owner*
Cindy Cyrus, *Financial Exec*
EMP: 50
SQ FT: 7,500
SALES (est): 7.4MM **Privately Held**
WEB: www.controlsystemmfg.com
SIC: 3699 Electrical equipment & supplies

(G-14877)
HITCH-HIKER MFG INC
10065 Rapp Rd (44442-9753)
PHONE....................................330 542-3052
Fax: 330 542-0304
Jeffrey Swartz, *President*
Holly Swartz, *Vice Pres*
EMP: 11
SQ FT: 38,000
SALES (est): 1.9MM **Privately Held**
WEB: www.hitch-hikermfg.com
SIC: 3799 Trailers & trailer equipment

(G-14878)
PARAGON PLASTICS
5551 E Calla Rd (44442-9768)
P.O. Box 22 (44442-0022)
PHONE....................................330 542-9825
Michelle Rothrauff, *Principal*
EMP: 8
SALES (est): 1MM **Privately Held**
SIC: 3089 Plastic processing

New Paris
Preble County

(G-14879)
DYNAMIC PLASTICS INC
Also Called: H & H Sailcraft
8207 H W Rd (45347-9241)
PHONE....................................937 437-7261
Fax: 937 437-6629
Paul Hemker, *President*
Heide Hemker, *Admin Sec*
EMP: 8
SQ FT: 20,000
SALES: 500K **Privately Held**
WEB: www.dynamicplastics.com
SIC: 3089 3732 3531 5551 Plastic processing; sailboats, building & repairing; construction machinery; boat dealers

(G-14880)
H & S PRECISION SCREW PDTS INC
8205 H W Rd (45347)
PHONE....................................937 437-0316
Fax: 937 437-2533
Jerry J Winkle, *President*
Carolyn Winkle, *Manager*
EMP: 20
SQ FT: 10,000
SALES (est): 3.5MM **Privately Held**
SIC: 3451 Screw machine products

(G-14881)
RUTHIE ANN INC
Also Called: Admaster Supply
313 New Paris Ave (45347-1324)
PHONE....................................800 231-3567
Pat Brennan, *President*
Ruthann Brennan, *Vice Pres*
▲ EMP: 18
SQ FT: 47,000
SALES (est): 1.4MM **Privately Held**
WEB: www.admasterline.com
SIC: 3993 2759 Advertising novelties; screen printing

New Philadelphia
Tuscarawas County

(G-14882)
ADVANCED INNOVATION & MFG INC
326 Pearl Ave Ne (44663-3918)
PHONE....................................330 308-6360
Frank J Michal, *President*
Bobie Stein, *Info Tech Mgr*
EMP: 4
SALES (est): 220K **Privately Held**
SIC: 3489 Ordnance & accessories

(G-14883)
ALLEN GREEN ENTERPRISES LLC
Also Called: UPS
513 Mill Ave Se (44663-3864)
PHONE....................................330 339-0200
Fax: 330 339-0300

Allen Green, *Mng Member*
EMP: 4
SALES: 300K **Privately Held**
SIC: 7389 3555 Mailing & messenger services; mailbox rental & related service; printing presses

(G-14884)
AQUABLUE INC
1776 Tech Park Dr Ne (44663-9410)
P.O. Box 446 (44663-0446)
PHONE....................................330 343-0220
Don Whittingham, *President*
EMP: 8
SALES: 1.9MM **Privately Held**
SIC: 2899 5169 Water treating compounds; chemicals & allied products

(G-14885)
ATLAS AMERICA INC
1026a Cookson Ave Se (44663-9500)
PHONE....................................330 339-3155
Fax: 330 339-5825
Rich Weber, *President*
EMP: 20
SALES (est): 1.6MM **Privately Held**
SIC: 1382 Oil & gas exploration services

(G-14886)
BROWN WOOD PRODUCTS COMPANY
7783 Crooked Run Rd Sw (44663-6411)
PHONE....................................330 339-8000
Todd Dennison, *Manager*
EMP: 8
SALES (corp-wide): 3.2MM **Privately Held**
SIC: 2499 Decorative wood & woodwork
PA: Brown Wood Products Company
7040 N Lawndale Ave
Lincolnwood IL 60712
847 673-4780

(G-14887)
BULK CARRIER TRNSP EQP CO
2743 Brightwood Rd Se (44663-6773)
PHONE....................................330 339-3333
Fax: 330 339-6606
Richard S Hartrick, *President*
Jim Everett, *Exec VP*
Marcia Hartrick, *Vice Pres*
Nick Pace, *CFO*
EMP: 26
SALES (est): 4.9MM **Privately Held**
WEB: www.bcte.com
SIC: 5012 2519 Trailers for trucks, new & used; household furniture, except wood or metal: upholstered

(G-14888)
C & A LAND AND ENERGY LLC
1243 Monroe St Nw (44663-4139)
PHONE....................................606 434-1420
William C Abel, *Mng Member*
EMP: 2 EST: 2013
SALES: 1MM **Privately Held**
SIC: 1382 Oil & gas exploration services

(G-14889)
CADO DOOR & DESIGN INC
Also Called: Cado Woodworking
5964 Main St Se (44663-8859)
PHONE....................................330 343-4288
Brian Cadele, *President*
EMP: 3
SALES: 400K **Privately Held**
WEB: www.cadomotus.com
SIC: 2499 Decorative wood & woodwork

(G-14890)
CASTINGS USA INC
2061 Brightwood Rd Se (44663-7724)
P.O. Box 202, Midvale (44653-0202)
PHONE....................................330 339-3611
Gregory M Dean, *President*
Terry Yahard, *Admin Sec*
EMP: 7 EST: 1974
SQ FT: 8,000
SALES (est): 690K **Privately Held**
WEB: www.reymondproducts.com
SIC: 3321 3325 Gray & ductile iron foundries; steel foundries

▲ = Import ▼ =Export
◆ =Import/Export

(G-14891)
CLICK BURIAL VAULT AND MFG CO
1118 Lakeview Rd Nw (44663-1331)
PHONE..................................330 343-1143
Timothy Halter, *President*
EMP: 3 **EST:** 1927
SQ FT: 3,024
SALES: 300K **Privately Held**
SIC: 3272 Burial vaults, concrete or precast terrazzo; septic tanks, concrete

(G-14892)
COPLEY OHIO NEWSPAPERS INC
Also Called: Times Reporter/Midwest Offset
629 Wabash Ave Nw (44663-4145)
P.O. Box 667 (44663-0667)
PHONE..................................330 364-5577
Fax: 330 364-1364
Kevin Kampman, *Publisher*
Mike Starn, *Publisher*
Gene Cush, *Manager*
Travis Fisher, *Manager*
Mike Gorfich, *Manager*
EMP: 245
SALES (corp-wide): 1.2B **Publicly Held**
WEB: www.timesreporter.com
SIC: 2711 2752 7313 2791 Newspapers, publishing & printing; commercial printing, offset; newspaper advertising representative; typesetting; bookbinding & related work
HQ: Copley Ohio Newspapers Inc
500 Market Ave S
Canton OH 44702
585 598-0030

(G-14893)
COSHOCTON INDUSTRIES INC
Also Called: Universal Machine Division
1040 Commercial Ave Se (44663-2355)
PHONE..................................330 339-4744
Fax: 330 364-8986
Jim Harrison, *Branch Mgr*
EMP: 4
SALES (corp-wide): 2.1MM **Privately Held**
WEB: www.jnindustries.com
SIC: 3599 Machine shop, jobbing & repair
PA: Coshocton Industries, Inc.
605 N 15th St
Coshocton OH 43812
740 622-4734

(G-14894)
DENNEY PLASTICS MACHINING LLC
149 Stonecreek Rd Nw (44663-6902)
PHONE..................................330 308-5300
Nicole Denney,
David Denney,
EMP: 12
SALES (est): 1.4MM **Privately Held**
SIC: 2821 Thermoplastic materials

(G-14895)
DOVER FABRICATION AND BURN INC (HQ)
1106 Commercial Ave Se (44663-2355)
PHONE..................................330 339-1057
Robert Sensel, *President*
EMP: 4 **EST:** 2012
SALES (est): 1MM
SALES (corp-wide): 12.3MM **Privately Held**
SIC: 1799 7692 7353 Welding on site; welding repair; oil well drilling equipment, rental or leasing
PA: Dover Hydraulics, Inc.
2996 Progress St
Dover OH 44622
330 364-1617

(G-14896)
EDWARDS AUGER MINING INC
1010 Hummel Valley Rd Sw (44663-7508)
PHONE..................................330 339-7318
Jim L Edwards, *President*
EMP: 3
SALES (est): 280K **Privately Held**
SIC: 1221 Auger mining, bituminous

(G-14897)
ELLIS LAUNDRY & LINEN SUPPLY
213 8th Street Ext Sw (44663-2088)
PHONE..................................330 339-4941
Katherine Ellis, *President*
Jerry Ellis, *Admin Sec*
EMP: 6
SALES (est): 200K **Privately Held**
SIC: 3582 Ironers, commercial laundry & drycleaning

(G-14898)
FENTON BROS ELECTRIC CO
Also Called: Fenton's Festival of Lights
235 Ray Ave Ne (44663-2813)
P.O. Box 996 (44663-0996)
PHONE..................................330 343-0093
Fax: 330 343-6874
Tom Fenton, *President*
Dennis Fenton, *Vice Pres*
Brian Fenton, *Treasurer*
Warren Toland, *Human Res Dir*
Dale E Fenton, *Shareholder*
EMP: 30 **EST:** 1947
SQ FT: 37,000
SALES (est): 23.4MM **Privately Held**
WEB: www.fentonbros.com
SIC: 5063 7694 Electrical supplies; electric motor repair

(G-14899)
FIRST STOP SIGNS AND DECALS
138 E High Ave (44663-2540)
PHONE..................................330 343-1859
Todd Kinsey, *Owner*
Todd Kensey, *Owner*
EMP: 3
SQ FT: 8,250
SALES (est): 140K **Privately Held**
SIC: 3993 5999 2759 Signs & advertising specialties; decals; screen printing

(G-14900)
GE BETZ INC
Also Called: GE Water & Process Tech
2118 Reiser Ave Se (44663-3332)
PHONE..................................330 339-2292
Gregg Sensbach, *Production*
Tom Johnston, *Branch Mgr*
Walt Sheehan, *Executive*
EMP: 50
SALES (corp-wide): 123.6B **Publicly Held**
SIC: 2899 Chemical preparations
HQ: Ge Betz, Inc.
4636 Somerton Rd
Trevose PA 19053
215 355-3300

(G-14901)
GRADALL INDUSTRIES INC (HQ)
406 Mill Ave Sw (44663-3835)
PHONE..................................330 339-2211
Fax: 330 339-5224
Michael Haberman, *President*
Daniel Kaltenbaugh, *Vice Pres*
Joseph H Keller, *Vice Pres*
Damon Gould, *Facilities Mgr*
Jason Garner, *Controller*
◆ **EMP:** 207 **EST:** 1992
SQ FT: 429,320
SALES (est): 102.6MM
SALES (corp-wide): 844.7MM **Publicly Held**
WEB: www.gradall.com
SIC: 3537 3531 Industrial trucks & tractors; construction machinery
PA: Alamo Group Inc.
1627 E Walnut St
Seguin TX 78155
830 379-1480

(G-14902)
HYDRAULIC PARTS STORE INC
145 1st Dr Ne (44663-2663)
P.O. Box 808 (44663-0808)
PHONE..................................330 364-6667
Fax: 330 364-1601
Robert M Henning Sr, *President*
Jason Newburn, *Finance Mgr*
EMP: 30
SQ FT: 25,000

SALES (est): 14.6MM **Privately Held**
SIC: 5084 3594 3593 3492 Hydraulic systems equipment & supplies; fluid power pumps & motors; fluid power cylinders & actuators; fluid power valves & hose fittings

(G-14903)
IMAGE ARMOR LLC
220 1st Dr Ne (44663-2804)
PHONE..................................877 673-4377
Bryan Walker, *CEO*
Karen Carbauth, *Manager*
◆ **EMP:** 5
SQ FT: 3,000
SALES: 850K **Privately Held**
SIC: 2869 Accelerators, rubber processing: cyclic or acyclic

(G-14904)
J & D MINING INC
3497 University Dr Ne (44663-6711)
PHONE..................................330 339-4935
Fax: 330 866-4511
John R Demuth, *President*
James R Demuth, *Vice Pres*
EMP: 38
SQ FT: 1,000
SALES (est): 4.8MM **Privately Held**
SIC: 1221 Bituminous coal surface mining

(G-14905)
KAY ZEE INC
1279 Crestview Ave Sw (44663-9642)
P.O. Box 95 (44663-0095)
PHONE..................................330 339-1268
Fax: 330 339-4324
John Stratton, *President*
Kathryn Stratton, *Vice Pres*
EMP: 7
SALES (est): 831.5K **Privately Held**
WEB: www.kay-zee.com
SIC: 3861 Lens shades, camera

(G-14906)
KIMBLE CUSTOM CHASSIS COMPANY
Also Called: Kimble Manufacturing Company
1951 Reiser Ave Se (44663-3348)
PHONE..................................877 546-2537
James C Cahill, *President*
Philip Keegan, *Vice Pres*
Jim Moberg, *Vice Pres*
Gregory Stohler, *Vice Pres*
Amie Guy, *CFO*
▲ **EMP:** 100
SQ FT: 100,000
SALES (est): 25MM
SALES (corp-wide): 238.3MM **Privately Held**
SIC: 3713 Truck bodies & parts
PA: Hines Corporation
1218 E Pontaluna Rd Ste B
Norton Shores MI 49456
231 799-6240

(G-14907)
KIMBLE MIXER COMPANY
Also Called: Hines Specialty Vehicle Group
1951 Reiser Ave Se (44663-3348)
PHONE..................................330 308-6700
Fax: 330 339-0055
James C Cahill, *President*
Philip Keegan, *President*
Jim Moberg, *Vice Pres*
Dave Hanson, *Purch Agent*
Paul Morehead, *Engineer*
▲ **EMP:** 75
SQ FT: 100,000
SALES (est): 29.1MM
SALES (corp-wide): 238.3MM **Privately Held**
WEB: www.kimblemixer.com
SIC: 3713 Cement mixer bodies
PA: Hines Corporation
1218 E Pontaluna Rd Ste B
Norton Shores MI 49456
231 799-6240

(G-14908)
LAUREN INTERNATIONAL LTD (PA)
Also Called: Lauren Manufacturing
2228 Reiser Ave Se (44663-3334)
PHONE..................................330 339-3373
Fax: 330 339-1515

Kevin E Gray, *President*
Pamela Blackwell, *Research*
Pam Brindley, *Research*
Aaron Kochman, *Research*
Eric Alander, *Engineer*
◆ **EMP:** 200 **EST:** 1965
SQ FT: 160,000
SALES (est): 172.9MM **Privately Held**
WEB: www.laureninternational.com
SIC: 3069 Molded rubber products

(G-14909)
LAUREN MANUFACTURING LLC
2228 Reiser Ave Se (44663-3334)
PHONE..................................330 339-3373
Kevin E Gray, *CEO*
Dale Foland, *Ch of Bd*
Lisa Huntsman, *President*
Chuck Laney, *President*
Jim Hummel, *Vice Pres*
▲ **EMP:** 288
SQ FT: 160,000
SALES (est): 48.2MM
SALES (corp-wide): 172.9MM **Privately Held**
WEB: www.lauren.com
SIC: 3069 3061 Molded rubber products; mechanical rubber goods
PA: Lauren International, Ltd.
2228 Reiser Ave Se
New Philadelphia OH 44663
330 339-3373

(G-14910)
MANSFIELD JOURNAL CO
Also Called: Times Reporter
629 Wabash Ave Nw (44663-4145)
P.O. Box 667 (44663-0667)
PHONE..................................330 364-8641
Fax: 330 364-8449
Richard Farrell, *Division Mgr*
Brent Kettlewell, *Controller*
Candice Grimm, *Loan Officer*
EMP: 1 **EST:** 1930
SQ FT: 65,000
SALES (est): 3.9MM
SALES (corp-wide): 745.5MM **Privately Held**
SIC: 2711 2752 Newspapers, publishing & printing; commercial printing, offset
PA: Journal Register Company
5 Hanover Sq Fl 25
New York NY 10004
212 257-7212

(G-14911)
MARATHON MFG & SUP CO
5165 Main St Ne (44663-8802)
P.O. Box 701 (44663-0701)
PHONE..................................330 343-2656
Emory Brumit, *President*
Peggy Brumit, *Treasurer*
EMP: 60
SALES (est): 5MM **Privately Held**
SIC: 5199 3953 Advertising specialties; screens, textile printing

(G-14912)
MARSH INDUSTRIES INC
Marsh Chalk Board Co Div
1117 Bowers Ave Nw (44663-4129)
P.O. Box 1000 (44663-5100)
PHONE..................................330 308-8667
Marilynn Doll, *Marketing Mgr*
Brian Marsh, *Manager*
Dan Ledsome, *Manager*
EMP: 32
SALES (corp-wide): 14.2MM **Privately Held**
WEB: www.marsh-ind.com
SIC: 2431 5211 5943 3281 Millwork; planing mill products & lumber; school supplies; cut stone & stone products; office furniture, except wood; wood kitchen cabinets
PA: Marsh Industries, Inc.
2301 E High Ave
New Philadelphia OH 44663
330 308-5515

(G-14913)
MERIDIAN MACHINE INC
702 Steele Hill Rd Nw (44663-6512)
PHONE..................................330 308-0296
Michael A Cargnel, *President*
David Miller, *Vice Pres*

Laurie Miller, *Treasurer*
Jill Cargnel, *Office Mgr*
EMP: 3
SALES (est): 262.4K **Privately Held**
SIC: 3599 5162 Machine & other job shop
　work; plastics basic shapes

(G-14914)
MID-AMERICA PACKAGING LLC
(PA)
2127 Reiser Ave Se (44663-3331)
PHONE................................330 963-4199
Fax: 330 425-2772
James V Livingston, *CEO*
Dave Tallarico, *Plant Mgr*
Mark Van Dame,
▲ **EMP:** 175
SQ FT: 300,000
SALES (est): 85.6MM **Privately Held**
WEB: www.twinbag.com
SIC: 2674 Bags: uncoated paper & multi-
　wall

(G-14915)
MILLER PRODUCTS INC
Also Called: Beech Engineering & Mfg
642 Wabash Ave Nw (44663-4146)
P.O. Box 947 (44663-0947)
PHONE................................330 308-5934
Fax: 330 308-5222
Naomi Downend, *General Mgr*
EMP: 35
SALES (corp-wide): 32.3MM **Privately
Held**
SIC: 3537 3535 Industrial trucks & trac-
　tors; conveyors & conveying equipment
PA: Miller Products, Inc.
　450 Courtney Rd
　Sebring OH 44672
　330 938-2134

(G-14916)
MILLER STUDIO INC
734 Fair Ave Nw (44663-1589)
P.O. Box 997 (44663-0997)
PHONE................................330 339-1100
Fax: 330 339-4379
Jeff Miller, *President*
John A Basiletti, *Vice Pres*
George Kail, *Purch Mgr*
Tina Schlemmer, *Human Res Mgr*
Mark Gazdik, *Natl Sales Mgr*
▲ **EMP:** 60 **EST:** 1934
SALES (est): 8.9MM
SALES (corp-wide): 32.3MM **Privately
Held**
WEB: www.miller-studio.com
SIC: 3299 2672 3452 3429 Plaques:
　clay, plaster or papier mache; adhesive
　papers, labels or tapes: from purchased
　material; bolts, nuts, rivets & washers;
　manufactured hardware (general)
PA: Miller Products, Inc.
　450 Courtney Rd
　Sebring OH 44672
　330 938-2134

(G-14917)
**MPS MANUFACTURING
COMPANY LLC**
326 Pearl Ave Ne (44663-3918)
PHONE................................330 343-1435
Mike Stein,
Jeff Powers,
EMP: 6
SALES (est): 950.6K **Privately Held**
SIC: 3069 Molded rubber products

(G-14918)
NATIONAL LIME AND STONE CO
2942 Brightwood Rd Se (44663-7728)
PHONE................................330 339-2144
David Weber, *Branch Mgr*
EMP: 3
SALES (est): 4B **Privately Held**
WEB: www.natlime.com
SIC: 1499 1442 3273 1423 Asphalt (na-
　tive); sand mining; gravel mining;
　ready-mixed concrete; crushed & broken
　granite
PA: The National Lime And Stone Company
　551 Lake Cascade Pkwy
　Findlay OH 45840
　419 422-4341

(G-14919)
OAKTREE WIRELINE LLC
1825 E High Ave (44663-3280)
Rural Route 83 Bay Vw, Akron (44319)
PHONE................................330 352-7250
Tim Canter,
Sean Casey,
Dan Krawczyk,
Mark Miller,
Gary Reese,
EMP: 9
SQ FT: 3,000
SALES (est): 378.6K **Privately Held**
SIC: 1389 Well logging

(G-14920)
OHIO VALLEY SAND LLC
513 Mill Ave Se (44663-3864)
PHONE................................740 661-4240
Mark Ogg, *Owner*
EMP: 3 **EST:** 2013
SALES (est): 135.6K **Privately Held**
SIC: 1442 Construction sand & gravel

(G-14921)
**PARAMONT MACHINE
COMPANY LLC**
963 Commercial Ave Se (44663-2355)
PHONE................................330 339-3489
Fax: 330 339-2790
Thomas Garrett, *CEO*
Greg Rees, *General Mgr*
Michael Goldberg, *Vice Pres*
Scott Stephens, *Treasurer*
EMP: 35
SQ FT: 11,000
SALES (est): 4.8MM
SALES (corp-wide): 923.9MM **Privately
Held**
WEB: www.paramontmachinecompany.com
SIC: 3599 3451 3053 Machine shop, job-
　bing & repair; screw machine products;
　gaskets, packing & sealing devices
HQ: Total Plastics Resources Llc
　2810 N Burdick St Ste A
　Kalamazoo MI 49004
　269 344-0009

(G-14922)
PERFORMANCE ADDITIVES
906 Cookson Ave Se (44663-6859)
PHONE................................330 365-9256
Daniel Flynn, *Principal*
◆ **EMP:** 5
SALES (est): 340K **Privately Held**
SIC: 3069 Rubber automotive products

(G-14923)
REYMOND PRODUCTS INTL INC
2066 Brightwood Rd Se (44663-7724)
P.O. Box 202, Midvale (44653-0202)
PHONE................................330 339-3583
Greg Dean, *President*
Robert Schatz, *Purchasing*
Jonathon Baker, *Engineer*
Greg Camp, *Sales Staff*
Mark Milburn, *Sales Staff*
▲ **EMP:** 20
SQ FT: 15,000
SALES (est): 3.7MM **Privately Held**
SIC: 3599 3544 Machine shop, jobbing &
　repair; special dies, tools, jigs & fixtures

(G-14924)
RICH INDUSTRIES INC
2384 Brightwood Rd Se (44663-6772)
PHONE................................330 339-4113
Rita Contini, *Corp Secy*
William Arnold, *Vice Pres*
Anthony Contini, *Vice Pres*
Scott Trammell, *Vice Pres*
Jeffrey Contini, *CFO*
▲ **EMP:** 50
SQ FT: 28,000
SALES (est): 10.2MM **Privately Held**
WEB: www.richindustriesinc.com
SIC: 2389 2393 2326 Disposable gar-
　ments & accessories; textile bags; men's
　& boys' work clothing

(G-14925)
RICHMONDS WOODWORKS INC
1115 Oak Shadows Dr Ne (44663-7078)
PHONE................................330 343-8184
EMP: 15

SALES (est): 880K **Privately Held**
SIC: 2511 Mfg Wood Household Furniture

(G-14926)
ROBERT H SHACKELFORD (PA)
Also Called: Quick Print Center
147 Ashwood Ln Ne (44663-2841)
PHONE................................330 364-2221
Fax: 330 343-0804
Robert H Shackelford, *Owner*
EMP: 5 **EST:** 1977
SQ FT: 2,000
SALES: 500K **Privately Held**
WEB: www.quickprint-center.com
SIC: 2752 2796 2789 2759 Commercial
　printing, offset; platemaking services;
　bookbinding & related work; commercial
　printing

(G-14927)
S S T ENTERPRISES INC
Also Called: Marathon Manufacturing
5165 Main St Ne (44663-8802)
P.O. Box 701 (44663-0701)
PHONE................................330 343-2656
Fax: 330 343-2166
Emery B Brumit, *President*
Peggy Brumit, *Corp Secy*
▲ **EMP:** 85
SALES (est): 6.9MM **Privately Held**
SIC: 2396 Screen printing on fabric articles

(G-14928)
SPEEDWAY LLC
Also Called: Speedway Superamerica 6246
1260 W High Ave (44663-6943)
PHONE................................330 339-7770
Joy Cladwell, *Manager*
EMP: 8 **Publicly Held**
WEB: www.speedwaynet.com
SIC: 1311 Crude petroleum production
HQ: Speedway Llc
　500 Speedway Dr
　Enon OH 45323
　937 864-3000

(G-14929)
**STATE ELECTRIC SUPPLY
COMPANY**
201 Stonecreek Rd Nw (44663-6902)
PHONE................................330 308-0659
Ned Morton, *General Mgr*
EMP: 12
SALES (corp-wide): 502MM **Privately
Held**
SIC: 3699 Electrical equipment & supplies
HQ: State Electric Supply Company
　2010 2nd Ave
　Huntington WV 25703
　304 523-7491

(G-14930)
STICK-IT GRAPHICS LLC
3161 Egypt Rd Ne (44663-7055)
PHONE................................330 407-0142
Curtis Edward, *Owner*
Curtis Seward, *Principal*
EMP: 3
SALES (est): 193.2K **Privately Held**
SIC: 7336 2752 Commercial art & graphic
　design; commercial printing, lithographic;
　commercial printing, offset

(G-14931)
SWANSON INDUSTRIES INC
Also Called: Morgantown Mch Hydraulics
Ohio
464 Robinson Dr Se (44663-3336)
PHONE................................304 284-5199
Fax: 330 339-8068
Denny Goltz, *Sales Staff*
Sam Police, *Branch Mgr*
EMP: 52
SALES (corp-wide): 2.5B **Privately Held**
SIC: 3561 7699 5084 3594 Pumps &
　pumping equipment; hydraulic equipment
　repair; hydraulic systems equipment &
　supplies; fluid power pumps & motors
HQ: Swanson Industries, Inc.
　2608 Smithtown Rd
　Morgantown WV 26508
　304 292-0021

(G-14932)
T-TOP SHOPPE
138 E High Ave (44663-2540)
PHONE................................330 343-3481
Fax: 330 343-2051
Todd A Kensey, *Owner*
EMP: 5
SALES (est): 210K **Privately Held**
SIC: 5699 3993 Sports apparel; signs &
　advertising specialties

(G-14933)
TGS INDUSTRIES INC (DH)
406 Mill Ave Sw (44663-3835)
PHONE................................330 339-2211
Barry L Phillips, *President*
Leigh B Trevor, *Principal*
James C Cahill, *Vice Pres*
Joseph H Keller Jr, *Vice Pres*
Michael Popovich, *Vice Pres*
▼ **EMP:** 22
SQ FT: 430,000
SALES (est): 5.6MM
SALES (corp-wide): 844.7MM **Publicly
Held**
SIC: 3531 Excavators: cable, clamshell,
　crane, derrick, dragline, etc.
HQ: Gradall Industries, Inc.
　406 Mill Ave Sw
　New Philadelphia OH 44663
　330 339-2211

(G-14934)
TIMKEN COMPANY
1957 E High Ave (44663-3240)
PHONE................................330 339-1151
Fax: 330 339-3444
Steve Barnes, *Plant Mgr*
John Carr, *Opers-Prdtn-Mfg*
Harry West, *Purchasing*
Ben Carlisle, *Engineer*
Craig Wilcoxon, *Electrical Engi*
EMP: 115
SALES (corp-wide): 2.6B **Publicly Held**
SIC: 3562 Ball & roller bearings
PA: The Timken Company
　4500 Mount Pleasant St Nw
　North Canton OH 44720
　234 262-3000

(G-14935)
TOLLOTI PIPE LLC
102 Barnhill Rd Se (44663-8864)
P.O. Box 129, Uhrichsville (44683-0129)
PHONE................................330 364-6627
Kyle Miller, *Principal*
EMP: 12
SALES (est): 1.8MM **Privately Held**
SIC: 3084 Plastics pipe

(G-14936)
TOLLOTI PLASTIC PIPE INC (PA)
102 Barnhill Rd Se (44663-8864)
P.O. Box 40 (44663-0040)
PHONE................................330 364-6627
Fax: 330 364-1392
Theodore Tolloti, *President*
John Tolloti, *President*
Doris Tolloti, *Corp Secy*
EMP: 38
SQ FT: 5,000
SALES (est): 3.8MM **Privately Held**
SIC: 3084 Plastics pipe

(G-14937)
TRISTATE TUBULAR INC
2713 Stonecreek Rd Sw (44663-6930)
P.O. Box 508, Dover (44622-0508)
PHONE................................330 339-5240
Emory Brumit, *President*
Greg Kimble, *Vice Pres*
Lisa Clum, *Manager*
EMP: 8
SQ FT: 1,200
SALES (est): 1.4MM **Privately Held**
SIC: 3498 Fabricated pipe & fittings

(G-14938)
**UNDER PRESSURE SYSTEMS
INC**
322 North Ave Ne (44663-2714)
PHONE................................330 602-4466
Cynthia J Valentine, *President*
Shawn Smith, *Marketing Staff*
EMP: 9
SQ FT: 10,000

SALES (est): 2.6MM **Privately Held**
SIC: 3589 Water treatment equipment, industrial

(G-14939)
WELL SERVICE GROUP INC
1490 Truss Rd Sw (44663-7530)
PHONE..................................330 308-0880
Bil Woessner, *General Mgr*
Jeff Atkinson, *Manager*
EMP: 13
SALES (est): 1.9MM **Privately Held**
SIC: 1381 Service well drilling

New Richmond
Clermont County

(G-14940)
B & S BLACKTOP CO
1704 Lndale Nchlsville Rd (45157)
PHONE..................................513 797-5759
Steve Brock, *Owner*
EMP: 4
SALES (est): 300K **Privately Held**
SIC: 2951 3271 Paving blocks; paving blocks, concrete

(G-14941)
LIVINGSTON & COMPANY LTD
1103 Ten Mile Rd (45157-9156)
PHONE..................................513 553-6430
James Livingston, *President*
William Jacobs, *Treasurer*
Barbara Livingston, *Admin Sec*
EMP: 4
SALES: 4MM **Privately Held**
SIC: 3441 Fabricated structural metal

(G-14942)
MASTER DISPOSERS INC
Also Called: Market-Master
2128 Idlett Hill Rd (45157-8658)
PHONE..................................513 553-2289
Mary Grogan, *President*
Rich J Grogan, *Vice Pres*
Durk Van Wagner, *Sales Mgr*
Nancy McElroy, *Admin Sec*
EMP: 10 EST: 1960
SQ FT: 8,000
SALES (est): 1MM **Privately Held**
WEB: www.masterdisposers.com
SIC: 3589 Garbage disposers & compactors, commercial

(G-14943)
MIDWEST PLASTIC SYSTEMS INC
100 Front St (45157-1403)
PHONE..................................513 553-4380
Dale Werle, *Branch Mgr*
EMP: 4
SALES (corp-wide): 1.2MM **Privately Held**
SIC: 3089 Plastic containers, except foam
PA: Midwest Plastic Systems Inc
326 1/2 N Main St
Piqua OH 45356
513 553-2900

(G-14944)
RAPID SIGNS & MORE INC
Also Called: Rapid Signs & Sportswear
1044 Old Us Highway 52 (45157-9773)
PHONE..................................513 553-4040
Fax: 513 553-3761
William R Gilpin, *President*
Deborah Gilpin, *Admin Sec*
EMP: 4
SALES (est): 424.7K **Privately Held**
SIC: 3993 7336 2261 Signs & advertising specialties; art design services; printing of cotton broadwoven fabrics

(G-14945)
RELIABLE FUR CO
2541 State Route 222 (45157-8604)
PHONE..................................513 288-5093
Kent Hoverman,
EMP: 7
SALES (est): 420K **Privately Held**
SIC: 3999 2371 Furs; fur finishers & liners for the fur goods trade

New Riegel
Seneca County

(G-14946)
FRITO-LAY NORTH AMERICA INC
6661 State Route 587 (44853-9750)
PHONE..................................419 595-2338
F L Holding, *Owner*
EMP: 20
SALES (corp-wide): 62.8B **Publicly Held**
WEB: www.fritolay.com
SIC: 2096 Potato chips & similar snacks
HQ: Frito-Lay North America, Inc.
7701 Legacy Dr
Plano TX 75024

(G-14947)
NEW RIEGEL CAFE INC
Also Called: Boes, Wilbert J
14 N Perry St (44853-9776)
P.O. Box 237 (44853-0237)
PHONE..................................419 595-2255
Fax: 419 595-3047
Wilbert J Boes, *President*
Hildegarde Boes, *Principal*
Tom Boes, *Vice Pres*
Richard Boes, *Admin Sec*
EMP: 32
SQ FT: 4,500
SALES (est): 1.3MM **Privately Held**
SIC: 5812 2011 Barbecue restaurant; meat packing plants

(G-14948)
SCHREINER MANUFACTURING
1997 Township Road 66 (44853-9728)
PHONE..................................419 937-0300
Brandan Schreiner, *Principal*
EMP: 3 EST: 2012
SALES (est): 147.2K **Privately Held**
SIC: 3999 Barber & beauty shop equipment

New Springfield
Mahoning County

(G-14949)
B V MFG INC
13426 Woodworth Rd (44443-9789)
P.O. Box 176 (44443-0176)
PHONE..................................330 549-5331
Fax: 330 549-5141
Robert Maine, *President*
EMP: 18
SQ FT: 6,200
SALES (est): 2.3MM **Privately Held**
SIC: 3544 Extrusion dies; special dies & tools

(G-14950)
D & D MINING CO INC
3379 E Garfield Rd (44443-9743)
PHONE..................................330 549-3127
Fax: 330 549-3970
Donald Thompson, *President*
David Thompson, *Vice Pres*
EMP: 10
SQ FT: 1,000
SALES (est): 799.3K **Privately Held**
SIC: 1221 Strip mining, bituminous

(G-14951)
MANTAPART
1161 E Garfield Rd Unit 2 (44443-8709)
P.O. Box 2206 (44443-2206)
PHONE..................................330 549-2389
Tim Meehan, *Owner*
EMP: 3 EST: 1971
SQ FT: 5,000
SALES (est): 263.3K **Privately Held**
WEB: www.mantapart.com
SIC: 3519 5013 5961 Parts & accessories, internal combustion engines; automotive engines & engine parts; cards, mail order

(G-14952)
THOMPSON BROTHERS MINING CO
3379 E Garfield Rd (44443-9743)
PHONE..................................330 549-3979
Don Thompson, *President*
Dave Thompson, *Vice Pres*
EMP: 10
SQ FT: 1,000
SALES (est): 770K **Privately Held**
SIC: 1221 Strip mining, bituminous

(G-14953)
TRINITY DOOR SYSTEMS
13886 Woodworth Rd (44443-8725)
PHONE..................................877 603-2018
Bill Warden, *President*
EMP: 3
SALES (est): 240K **Privately Held**
SIC: 3699 1796 1793 Door opening & closing devices, electrical; installing building equipment; glass & glazing work

New Vienna
Clinton County

(G-14954)
ALLEN TOOL CO INC
300 S 2nd St (45159-9083)
P.O. Box 311 (45159-0311)
PHONE..................................937 987-2037
David Allen, *President*
Bill Allen, *Vice Pres*
Shirley Allen, *Treasurer*
EMP: 4
SQ FT: 2,500
SALES (est): 260K **Privately Held**
SIC: 3544 Special dies & tools

(G-14955)
HUHTAMAKI INC
Also Called: Huhtamaki Plastics
5566 New Vienna Rd (45159-9533)
PHONE..................................937 987-3078
Kathy Howard, *Purchasing*
Dan Curliss, *Technical Mgr*
Howard Liming, *Branch Mgr*
Kelly Bolin, *Maintence Staff*
EMP: 350
SALES (corp-wide): 2.9B **Privately Held**
SIC: 3089 Plastic containers, except foam
HQ: Huhtamaki, Inc.
9201 Packaging Dr
De Soto KS 66018
913 583-3025

(G-14956)
OHIO VLY LIGHTNING PROTECTION
520 Leeka Rd (45159-9052)
PHONE..................................937 987-0245
Fax: 937 987-0248
Lucia Riley, *President*
EMP: 4
SQ FT: 1,500
SALES (est): 330K **Privately Held**
WEB: www.lightning-systems.com
SIC: 3643 Lightning protection equipment

(G-14957)
WELLS MANUFACTURING CO LLC
280 W Main St (45159)
P.O. Box 325 (45159-0325)
PHONE..................................937 987-2481
Fax: 937 987-2819
Grant Douglas, *President*
Glenn Douglas, *Vice Pres*
Ted Waln, *Purchasing*
EMP: 10
SQ FT: 100,000
SALES: 3.5MM **Privately Held**
SIC: 3944 Games, toys & children's vehicles

New Washington
Crawford County

(G-14958)
C E WHITE CO (HQ)
417 N Kibler St (44854-9426)
P.O. Box 308 (44854-0308)
PHONE..................................419 492-2157
Fax: 419 492-2544
Tony Everett, *President*
Bob Knapp, *President*
Bill Loshbough, *Sales Mgr*
Jerry Hiler, *Director*
Danny Maxwell, *Executive*
▲ EMP: 53 EST: 1937
SQ FT: 65,000
SALES (est): 15MM
SALES (corp-wide): 832MM **Privately Held**
WEB: www.cewhite.com
SIC: 2531 Seats, miscellaneous public conveyances
PA: Hickory Springs Manufacturing Company
235 2nd Ave Nw
Hickory NC 28601
828 328-2201

(G-14959)
CREST BENDING INC
108 John St (44854-9702)
P.O. Box 458 (44854-0458)
PHONE..................................419 492-2108
Fax: 419 492-2546
Robert E Studer, *President*
EMP: 45 EST: 1966
SQ FT: 50,000
SALES (est): 9.2MM **Privately Held**
WEB: www.crestbending.com
SIC: 3312 7692 3498 3317 Tubes, steel & iron; welding repair; fabricated pipe & fittings; steel pipe & tubes

(G-14960)
HERALD INC
625 S Kibler St (44854-9541)
P.O. Box 367 (44854-0367)
PHONE..................................419 492-2133
Fax: 419 492-2128
Suzanne Stump, *CEO*
Dave Binkley, *Opers Staff*
Carol Aurand, *Human Res Mgr*
Robert Tarr, *Sales Dir*
Bonnie Ackerman, *Assoc Editor*
EMP: 35
SALES (est): 8.7MM **Privately Held**
SIC: 2752 Commercial printing, lithographic

(G-14961)
MANSFIELD BRASS & ALUM CORP
Also Called: Mansfield Castings
636 S Center St (44854-9417)
PHONE..................................419 492-2154
Fax: 419 492-2775
James R Bierly, *Ch of Bd*
Lynn Bierly-Edmonds, *President*
Bob Laser, *Sales Mgr*
EMP: 55 EST: 1892
SQ FT: 85,000
SALES (est): 12.5MM **Privately Held**
WEB: www.mansfield-castings.com
SIC: 3365 Aluminum foundries

(G-14962)
NEW MANSFIELD BRASS & ALUM CO
636 S Center St (44854-9711)
PHONE..................................419 492-2166
Russell Nelson, *President*
EMP: 30
SALES (est): 4.6MM **Privately Held**
SIC: 3365 Aluminum foundries

(G-14963)
OHIO FOAM CORPORATION
529 S Kibler St (44854-9524)
P.O. Box 61, Bucyrus (44820-0061)
PHONE..................................419 492-2151
Fax: 419 492-2152
Rob Alderich, *Division Mgr*
Diane Swartzmiller, *Principal*

Terri Lady, *Administration*
EMP: 10
SQ FT: 15,000
SALES (corp-wide): 13MM **Privately Held**
WEB: www.ohiofoam.com
SIC: 3069 2821 Foam rubber; plastics materials & resins
PA: Ohio Foam Corporation
　　820 Plymouth St
　　Bucyrus OH 44820
　　419 563-0399

(G-14964)
SHEEP & FARM LIFE INC
Also Called: Shepherd, The
5696 Johnston Rd (44854-9736)
PHONE......................................419 492-2364
Ken Kark, *President*
Guy Flora, *Vice Pres*
Kathy Kark, *Treasurer*
Pat Flora, *Admin Sec*
EMP: 4
SALES (est): 280K **Privately Held**
SIC: 2721 Magazines: publishing only, not printed on site

(G-14965)
STUMPS CONVERTING INC
742 W Mansfield St (44854-9403)
PHONE......................................419 492-2542
Fax: 419 492-1400
Suzanne Stump, *President*
Dave Q Stump, *Vice Pres*
EMP: 10
SALES: 500K **Privately Held**
WEB: www.stumpsconverting.com
SIC: 2679 5149 Paper products, converted; syrups, except for fountain use

(G-14966)
WURMS WOODWORKING COMPANY
Also Called: Gr Golf
725 W Mansfield St (44854-9403)
P.O. Box 275 (44854-0275)
PHONE......................................419 492-2184
Fax: 419 492-2531
Gerald B Wurm, *President*
Richard Wurm, *Vice Pres*
Valerie Sanderson, *Treasurer*
Mary Wurm, *Admin Sec*
EMP: 36 **EST:** 1947
SQ FT: 60,000
SALES (est): 6MM **Privately Held**
WEB: www.wurmsproducts.com
SIC: 2499 2531 3082 3083 Furniture inlays (veneers); vehicle furniture; unsupported plastics profile shapes; laminated plastics plate & sheet; wood kitchen cabinets

---

New Waterford
Columbiana County

(G-14967)
AMERICAN PIONEER MANUFACTURING
3672 Silliman St (44445-9658)
PHONE......................................330 457-1400
EMP: 3
SALES (est): 160K **Privately Held**
SIC: 3999 Mfg Misc Products

(G-14968)
AMRON LLC
Also Called: Amron Testing
47287 State Route 558 (44445-9628)
PHONE......................................330 457-8570
Ronald Allen Hodge, *Owner*
Krista Cutter, *Manager*
EMP: 3
SALES (est): 80.5K **Privately Held**
SIC: 8734 3829 Product testing laboratory, safety or performance; ultrasonic testing equipment

(G-14969)
CENTURY CONTAINER LLC (HQ)
5331 State Route 7 (44445-9787)
PHONE......................................330 457-2367
Mark Brothers, *President*

EMP: 42
SALES (est): 16.8MM
SALES (corp-wide): 92.9MM **Privately Held**
SIC: 3089 Plastic containers, except foam
PA: Thorworks Industries, Inc.
　　2520 Campbell St
　　Sandusky OH 44870
　　419 626-4375

(G-14970)
DYNAMIC LEASING LTD
3790 State Route 7 (44445-9784)
PHONE......................................330 892-0164
Scott McCrea, *President*
EMP: 3 **EST:** 1998
SQ FT: 10,000
SALES (est): 391.3K
SALES (corp-wide): 7.2MM **Privately Held**
SIC: 3533 Oil & gas drilling rigs & equipment
PA: Dynamic Structures, Inc.
　　3790 State Route 7 Ste B
　　New Waterford OH 44445
　　330 892-0164

(G-14971)
GILLAM MACHINE COMPANY
1888 Macklin Rd (44445-9776)
PHONE......................................330 457-2557
Fax: 330 457-0419
Earon Gillam, *Owner*
EMP: 3
SALES (est): 178.4K **Privately Held**
SIC: 3599 Machine shop, jobbing & repair

(G-14972)
MAJESTIC MANUFACTURING INC
4536 State Route 7 (44445-9785)
P.O. Box 128 (44445-0128)
PHONE......................................330 457-2447
Fax: 330 457-7490
Paul Kudler, *President*
Jeff Kudler, *Vice Pres*
Rick Steed, *Purch Agent*
Vincent Kudler, *Treasurer*
Candy Hawkins, *Executive*
▲ **EMP:** 45
SQ FT: 68,000
SALES (est): 7.2MM **Privately Held**
WEB: www.majesticrides.com
SIC: 3599 5087 Carnival machines & equipment, amusement park; carnival & amusement park equipment

(G-14973)
REISER MANUFACTURING
4571 Millrock Rd (44445-9627)
PHONE......................................330 846-8003
Lori Reiser, *Principal*
EMP: 3
SALES (est): 279.5K **Privately Held**
SIC: 3999 Manufacturing industries

(G-14974)
STEELCON INC
47287 State Route 558 (44445-9628)
PHONE......................................330 457-2419
Chuck Ferrell, *President*
EMP: 14
SALES (est): 5.3MM **Privately Held**
SIC: 3449 Bars, concrete reinforcing: fabricated steel

(G-14975)
STEELCON LLC
47287 State Route 558 (44445-9628)
PHONE......................................330 457-4003
Ronald Allen Hodge,
EMP: 5
SALES (est): 544.1K **Privately Held**
SIC: 3441 Fabricated structural metal; building components, structural steel

(G-14976)
WILLOUGHBY MANUFACTURING INC
47415 Heck Rd (44445-9729)
PHONE......................................330 402-8217
EMP: 3
SALES (est): 219.1K **Privately Held**
SIC: 3999 Manufacturing industries

New Weston
Darke County

(G-14977)
FRED WINNER
Also Called: Winner Welding Fabricating
7860 Cohn Rd (45348-9715)
PHONE......................................419 582-2421
Fred Winner, *Owner*
EMP: 8
SQ FT: 10,000
SALES: 750K **Privately Held**
SIC: 3443 3444 7692 Weldments; sheet metalwork; welding repair

---

Newark
Licking County

(G-14978)
ACTION ENTERPRISE
Also Called: Action Signs
416 W Main St (43055-4168)
PHONE......................................740 522-1678
Fax: 740 522-1678
Robert B Rickard, *Owner*
EMP: 3
SALES (est): 184.8K **Privately Held**
SIC: 3993 Signs & advertising specialties

(G-14979)
ACUITY BRANDS LIGHTING INC
Also Called: ACUITY BRANDS LIGHTING, INC.
214 Oakwood Ave (43055-6716)
PHONE......................................740 349-4343
John Harvey, *Vice Pres*
Kim Lombardi, *Vice Pres*
Steve Hummel, *Plant Mgr*
Robert Taylor, *Human Res Dir*
Keith Keller, *VP Sales*
EMP: 500
SALES (corp-wide): 3.2B **Publicly Held**
SIC: 3646 3648 3645 3612 Commercial indusl & institutional electric lighting fixtures; lighting equipment; residential lighting fixtures; transformers, except electric; aluminum foundries
HQ: Acuity Brands Lighting, Inc.
　　1 Acuity Way
　　Conyers GA 30012
　　800 922-9641

(G-14980)
ACUITY BRANDS LIGHTING INC
Also Called: Hollphane
465 Mckinley Ave (43055-6735)
PHONE......................................740 349-4409
EMP: 150
SALES (corp-wide): 2.7B **Publicly Held**
SIC: 3646 3645 3641 Mfg Commercial Lighting Fixtures Mfg Residential Lighting Fixtures Mfg Electric Lamps
HQ: Acuity Brands Lighting, Inc.
　　1 Acuity Way
　　Conyers GA 30012
　　800 922-9641

(G-14981)
AMERICAN VENEER EDGEBANDING
1700 James Pkwy (43056-4027)
PHONE......................................740 928-0266
Fax: 740 928-0271
Germany Heigtz, *Principal*
Andrew Lenkei, *Sales Mgr*
▲ **EMP:** 6
SQ FT: 30,000
SALES (est): 945.3K **Privately Held**
WEB: www.avec-usa.com
SIC: 2435 2436 Veneer stock, hardwood; veneer stock, softwood

(G-14982)
AMPACET CORPORATION
1855 James Pkwy (43056-1092)
PHONE......................................740 929-5521
Tim King, *Purchasing*
Jim Edge, *Branch Mgr*
EMP: 150

SALES (corp-wide): 626.1MM **Privately Held**
WEB: www.ampacet.com
SIC: 2869 2816 Industrial organic chemicals; inorganic pigments
PA: Ampacet Corporation
　　660 White Plains Rd # 360
　　Tarrytown NY 10591
　　914 631-6600

(G-14983)
ARBORIS LLC
1780 Tamarack Rd (43055-1359)
PHONE......................................740 522-9350
Tom Lindow, *Branch Mgr*
EMP: 34
SALES (corp-wide): 8.6MM **Privately Held**
WEB: www.arboris-us.com
SIC: 2819 Chemicals, high purity: refined from technical grade
PA: Arboris, Llc
　　1101 W Lathrop Ave
　　Savannah GA 31415
　　912 238-6355

(G-14984)
ASHCRAFT MACHINE & SUPPLY INC
185 Wilson St (43055-4099)
PHONE......................................740 349-8110
Fax: 740 345-2776
Larry G Ashcraft, *President*
Jerry Ashcraft, *Vice Pres*
Mike Ashcraft, *Vice Pres*
John Balser, *Purchasing*
John Balster, *Manager*
EMP: 12 **EST:** 1949
SQ FT: 15,000
SALES (est): 1.2MM **Privately Held**
WEB: www.ashcraftmachine.com
SIC: 3599 Machine shop, jobbing & repair

(G-14985)
BOEING COMPANY
801 Irving Wick Dr W (43056-1199)
PHONE......................................740 788-4000
Fax: 740 788-6414
Brian McGuire, *Vice Pres*
Anthony J Panella, *Project Dir*
Tony Hensley, *QC Mgr*
Jeremy Addy, *Engineer*
Daryl Dickerson, *Engineer*
EMP: 700
SALES (corp-wide): 94.5B **Publicly Held**
SIC: 3761 4581 Guided missiles & space vehicles; airports, flying fields & services
PA: The Boeing Company
　　100 N Riverside Plz
　　Chicago IL 60606
　　312 544-2000

(G-14986)
BOEING COMPANY
801 Irving Wick Dr W (43056-1199)
PHONE......................................740 788-4000
Daniel Acassidy, *Branch Mgr*
Dan Cassidy, *MIS Mgr*
EMP: 25
SALES (corp-wide): 94.5B **Publicly Held**
SIC: 7629 3812 Electrical repair shops; search & navigation equipment
PA: The Boeing Company
　　100 N Riverside Plz
　　Chicago IL 60606
　　312 544-2000

(G-14987)
BOEING COMPANY
801 Irving Wick Dr W (43056-1199)
PHONE......................................740 788-5805
Charles Dutch, *Manager*
J D Dickey, *Commissioner*
Ed Weir, *Commissioner*
EMP: 600
SALES (corp-wide): 94.5B **Publicly Held**
SIC: 3812 Search & navigation equipment
PA: The Boeing Company
　　100 N Riverside Plz
　　Chicago IL 60606
　　312 544-2000

(G-14988)
BOWERSTON SHALE COMPANY
1329 Seven Hills Rd (43055-8964)
PHONE......................................740 763-3921

Fax: 740 763-2949
William Milliken, *Chairman*
Beth Hillyer, *Manager*
Mark Willard, *Officer*
EMP: 35
SQ FT: 100,000
SALES (corp-wide): 36.8MM **Privately Held**
SIC: 3251 Brick clay: common face, glazed, vitrified or hollow; paving brick, clay
PA: Bowerston Shale Company (Inc)
515 Main St
Bowerston OH 44695
740 269-2921

(G-14989)
BURDENS MACHINE & WELDING
94 S 5th St (43055-5302)
P.O. Box 177 (43058-0177)
PHONE............................740 345-9246
Fax: 740 345-9247
Donald Burden Sr, *President*
Robert Burden, *Corp Secy*
Darrell Burden, *Vice Pres*
Donald Burden Jr, *Vice Pres*
EMP: 26
SQ FT: 4,400
SALES: 1.9MM **Privately Held**
SIC: 1799 3599 Welding on site; machine shop, jobbing & repair

(G-14990)
BURGIE BRAUEREI INC
860 Village Pkwy (43055-2851)
PHONE............................740 344-1620
Robert Burgie, *Principal*
EMP: 3
SALES (est): 187K **Privately Held**
SIC: 2082 Malt beverages

(G-14991)
CAPITAL PROSTHETIC &
Also Called: Capital Prsthetic Orthotic Ctr
55 S Terrace Ave (43055-1355)
PHONE............................740 522-3331
Fax: 740 522-1233
Lisa Craford, *Manager*
EMP: 6
SALES (corp-wide): 2.9MM **Privately Held**
SIC: 5999 3842 Orthopedic & prosthesis applications; limbs, artificial
PA: Capital Prosthetic And Orthotic Center, Inc.
4678 Larwell Dr
Columbus OH 43220
614 451-0446

(G-14992)
CBS PHARMACY
955 N 21st St (43055-2921)
PHONE............................740 366-9082
Rod Arn, *Principal*
EMP: 3
SALES (est): 173.5K **Privately Held**
SIC: 2834 Pharmaceutical preparations

(G-14993)
CITY OF NEWARK
Also Called: Newark Water Plant
164 Waterworks Rd (43055-6057)
PHONE............................740 349-6765
Fax: 740 349-6799
Steve Rhodes, *Manager*
EMP: 16 **Privately Held**
SIC: 3561 Pumps, domestic: water or sump
PA: City Of Newark
40 W Main St
Newark OH 43055
740 670-7512

(G-14994)
COLUMBUS ROOF TRUSSES INC
Also Called: Central Ohio Bldg Components
400 Marne Dr (43055-8817)
PHONE............................740 763-3000
Bill Walker, *Branch Mgr*
EMP: 10
SALES (corp-wide): 4.1MM **Privately Held**
SIC: 2439 Trusses, wooden roof; trusses, except roof: laminated lumber

PA: Columbus Roof Trusses, Inc.
2525 Fisher Rd
Columbus OH 43204
614 272-6464

(G-14995)
COMP-U-CHEM INC
195 Dayton Rd Ne (43055-8879)
PHONE............................740 345-3332
Warren G Knorr, *President*
EMP: 5
SALES: 750K **Privately Held**
WEB: www.comp-u-chem.com
SIC: 3589 1711 Sewage & water treatment equipment; plumbing, heating, air-conditioning contractors

(G-14996)
CONTOUR FORMING INC
215 Oakwood Ave (43055-6751)
P.O. Box 727 (43058-0727)
PHONE............................740 345-9777
Fax: 740 345-7968
Terrie Lee Hill, *President*
Garrie Hill, *VP Mfg*
Tracie Hill, *VP Sales*
Tammy Winters, *Admin Sec*
EMP: 24 **EST:** 1955
SQ FT: 100,000
SALES (est): 5.2MM **Privately Held**
SIC: 3315 3356 3469 3444 Steel wire & related products; nonferrous rolling & drawing; metal stampings; sheet metalwork

(G-14997)
CP INDUSTRIES INC
Also Called: Pilot Chemical
11047 Lambs Ln (43055-9779)
PHONE............................740 763-2886
Kent Pitcher, *President*
Brian Pitcher, *Corp Secy*
Jeff Pitcher, *Vice Pres*
Martin Solomon, *Vice Pres*
▲ **EMP:** 12
SALES (est): 970K **Privately Held**
SIC: 2891 Adhesives & sealants; adhesives

(G-14998)
CRAIN-THARP PRINTING INC
Also Called: A Printed Impression
11 W Main St (43055-5503)
PHONE............................740 345-9823
Fax: 740 345-0613
Donna Corbett, *President*
Cheryl Tharp, *Corp Secy*
EMP: 3
SQ FT: 1,800
SALES: 185K **Privately Held**
SIC: 2752 Commercial printing, offset

(G-14999)
DENNIS LAVENDER
Also Called: Western Star Rail Services
200 Maholm St (43055-3832)
PHONE............................740 344-3336
Dennis Lavender, *Owner*
Brenda Lavender, *Manager*
EMP: 5
SALES: 300K **Privately Held**
SIC: 3743 Railroad equipment

(G-15000)
DOUG SMITH
Also Called: Roger's Quick Print
55 W Church St (43055-5013)
PHONE............................740 345-1398
Fax: 740 345-4739
Doug Smith, *Owner*
EMP: 4
SQ FT: 3,300
SALES: 120K **Privately Held**
SIC: 2752 7334 2759 Commercial printing, offset; photocopying & duplicating services; invitations: printing

(G-15001)
EAGLE MACHINE AND WELDING INC
18 W Walnut St (43055-5408)
PHONE............................740 345-5210
Wade Ranck, *President*
Janet Ranck, *Treasurer*
Kristie E Ranck, *Admin Sec*
EMP: 3

SALES: 150K **Privately Held**
WEB: www.eaglemw.com
SIC: 3599 7692 Machine & other job shop work; welding repair

(G-15002)
ELKHEAD GAS & OIL CO
12163 Marne Rd (43055-8810)
PHONE............................740 763-3966
Fax: 740 763-2937
Maurice Dale Chapin, *President*
James Chapin, *Corp Secy*
Michael Chapin, *Vice Pres*
EMP: 6 **EST:** 1964
SQ FT: 1,000
SALES (est): 745.7K **Privately Held**
SIC: 1382 1311 Oil & gas exploration services; crude petroleum production; natural gas production

(G-15003)
ENZYME INDUSTRIES OF THE U S A
2090 James Pkwy (43056-1031)
P.O. Box 2242 (43056-0242)
PHONE............................740 929-4975
Fax: 740 929-4836
Thomas G Gregg, *President*
Robert T Gregg, *Vice Pres*
Carol Gregg, *Treasurer*
EMP: 4
SQ FT: 3,750
SALES: 400K **Privately Held**
SIC: 2869 Enzymes

(G-15004)
EQUIPMENT GUYS INC
185 Westgate Dr (43055-9313)
PHONE............................614 871-9220
Fax: 614 871-9271
Matthew A Purdy, *President*
Becky Twaddell, *Cust Mgr*
Zoe Klein, *Marketing Staff*
Don Sharrock, *Manager*
Shari L Purdy, *Incorporator*
EMP: 11
SALES (est): 1.1MM **Privately Held**
SIC: 3949 5084 Dumbbells & other weightlifting equipment; industrial machinery & equipment

(G-15005)
ES MANUFACTURING INC
55 Builders Dr (43055-1343)
PHONE............................888 331-3443
Kenneth Walls, *President*
Rick Ault, *Plant Mgr*
EMP: 4
SQ FT: 13,000
SALES (est): 391.5K **Privately Held**
SIC: 2869 Methyl alcohol, synthetic methanol

(G-15006)
FAMILY MEDICAL CLINIC & LASER
44 S 29th St (43055-2564)
PHONE............................740 345-2767
EMP: 5
SALES (est): 556.8K **Privately Held**
SIC: 2834 Mfg Pharmaceutical Preparations

(G-15007)
FLINT RIDGE ENERGY
Also Called: Arrowhead Energy
581 Country Club Dr Ste B (43055-2164)
PHONE............................740 344-1351
Gary W Sitler, *President*
Judson K Byrd, *Vice Pres*
Patricia Hixson, *Controller*
EMP: 3
SALES (est): 372.1K **Privately Held**
SIC: 1382 Oil & gas exploration services

(G-15008)
FRANKLIN FRAMES AND CYCLES
7179 Reform Rd (43055-9120)
PHONE............................740 763-3838
Fax: 740 763-3838
John Trumbull, *Owner*
EMP: 3

SALES (est): 232K **Privately Held**
SIC: 3751 3498 3444 Frames, motorcycle & bicycle; fabricated pipe & fittings; sheet metalwork

(G-15009)
GANNETT CO INC
Newark Advocate
22 N 1st St (43055-5608)
PHONE............................740 345-4053
Fax: 740 328-8580
Jason Mann, *Editor*
Carl Lovern, *Vice Pres*
Leslie Myers, *Human Resources*
Melissa Nichols, *Sales Staff*
Karie Sargent, *Sales Staff*
EMP: 135
SALES (corp-wide): 3B **Publicly Held**
WEB: www.gannett.com
SIC: 2711 Newspapers, publishing & printing
PA: Gannett Co., Inc.
7950 Jones Branch Dr
Mc Lean VA 22102
703 854-6000

(G-15010)
GANNETT CO INC
Also Called: Newspaper Network Central Ohio
2 N 1st St (43055-5608)
PHONE............................740 349-1100
Mandy Shugars, *Editor*
Gale Betz, *Manager*
EMP: 19
SALES (corp-wide): 3B **Publicly Held**
WEB: www.gannett.com
SIC: 2711 Newspapers: publishing only, not printed on site
PA: Gannett Co., Inc.
7950 Jones Branch Dr
Mc Lean VA 22102
703 854-6000

(G-15011)
GARNER INDUSTRIES INC
767 Country Club Dr (43055-1605)
PHONE............................740 349-0238
Daniel Garner, *President*
EMP: 4
SALES (est): 487.6K **Privately Held**
SIC: 3599 Machine shop, jobbing & repair

(G-15012)
GARY KRINN
Also Called: Signs Now
951 Buckeye Ave Ste D (43055-2594)
PHONE............................740 344-3695
Fax: 740 344-3690
Gary Krinn, *Owner*
EMP: 3
SALES (corp-wide): 511.7K **Privately Held**
SIC: 3993 Signs & advertising specialties
PA: Gary Krinn
1204 E Powell Rd
Lewis Center OH

(G-15013)
GEMCO MACHINE & TOOL INC
88 Decrow Ave (43055-3870)
PHONE............................740 344-3111
Fax: 740 344-3110
Steve Hays, *President*
Faye Hays, *Admin Sec*
EMP: 10
SQ FT: 8,500
SALES (est): 900K **Privately Held**
SIC: 3599 Machine shop, jobbing & repair

(G-15014)
GOLF GALAXY GOLFWORKS INC
4820 Jacksontown Rd (43056-9377)
P.O. Box 3008 (43058-3008)
PHONE............................740 328-4193
Fax: 740 328-4213
Mark McCormick, *CEO*
Richard C Nordvoid, *Principal*
Mark Wilson, *Vice Pres*
Pete Calloway, *Research*
Jerry Datz, *CFO*
▲ **EMP:** 150 **EST:** 1974
SQ FT: 80,000

SALES (est): 77.4MM
SALES (corp-wide): 7.9B **Publicly Held**
WEB: www.golfworks.com
SIC: 5091 2731 3949 5941 Golf & skiing equipment & supplies; books: publishing only; golf equipment; shafts, golf club; golf, tennis & ski shops
HQ: Golf Galaxy, Inc.
345 Court St
Coraopolis PA 15108

(G-15015)
GRANVILLE MILLING CO
Also Called: Granville Milling Drive-Thru
145 N Cedar St (43055-6705)
PHONE.............................740 345-1305
Trent Smith, *Manager*
EMP: 6
SALES (corp-wide): 7.7MM **Privately Held**
WEB: www.granvillemilling.com
SIC: 2048 5191 Prepared feeds; animal feeds
PA: Granville Milling Co.
400 S Main St
Granville OH 43023
740 587-0221

(G-15016)
H & A DRILLING
4780 Tavener Rd (43056-9086)
PHONE.............................740 763-2575
Albert Bevard, *Owner*
EMP: 3
SALES (est): 170K **Privately Held**
SIC: 1381 Drilling oil & gas wells

(G-15017)
H & N INSTRUMENTS INC
219 N Westmoor Ave (43055-1837)
P.O. Box 4338 (43058-4338)
PHONE.............................740 344-4351
Fax: 740 344-7958
Gary M Nishioka, *President*
Charles K Holloway, *Vice Pres*
EMP: 5
SQ FT: 4,000
SALES: 450K **Privately Held**
SIC: 8731 3821 Commercial physical research; industrial laboratory, except testing; computer (hardware) development; chemical laboratory apparatus; physics laboratory apparatus; time interval measuring equipment, electric (lab type)

(G-15018)
HOLOPHANE CORPORATION
Also Called: Unique Solutions
515 Mckinley Ave (43055-6737)
PHONE.............................740 349-4194
Richard Peterson, *Manager*
EMP: 10
SALES (corp-wide): 2.7B **Publicly Held**
SIC: 3646 Commercial indusl & institutional electric lighting fixtures
HQ: Holophane Corporation
3825 Columbus Rd Bldg A
Granville OH 43023
866 759-1577

(G-15019)
HOPE TIMBER & MARKETING GROUP (PA)
Also Called: Wood Recovery
141 Union St (43055-3976)
P.O. Box 502, Granville (43023-0502)
PHONE.............................740 344-1788
Fax: 614 344-9361
Thomas J Harvey, *President*
Deborah L Harvey, *Chairman*
Michelle Wright, *Office Mgr*
Carol Busenberry, *Manager*
EMP: 18
SQ FT: 40,000
SALES (est): 2.1MM **Privately Held**
SIC: 2499 2448 Mulch or sawdust products, wood; pallets, wood

(G-15020)
HOPE TIMBER MULCH INC
141 Union St (43055-3976)
P.O. Box 502, Granville (43023-0502)
PHONE.............................740 344-1788
Thomas Harvey, *President*
Timothy Harvey, *General Mgr*
Deborah L Harvey, *Exec VP*

EMP: 6
SQ FT: 20,000
SALES (est): 674.9K **Privately Held**
SIC: 2499 Mulch or sawdust products, wood

(G-15021)
HOPE TIMBER PALLET RECYCL INC
141 Union St (43055-3976)
P.O. Box 502, Granville (43023-0502)
PHONE.............................740 344-1788
Fax: 740 344-9361
Thomas J Harvey, *President*
EMP: 22
SALES (est): 3.5MM **Privately Held**
SIC: 2448 4953 Wood pallets & skids; recycling, waste materials

(G-15022)
I G BRENNER INC
Also Called: Brenner International
32 E North St (43055-5823)
PHONE.............................740 345-8845
Robert M Fitzgerald, *President*
Jennifer Fitzgerald, *Admin Sec*
EMP: 10 **EST:** 1950
SQ FT: 12,000
SALES (est): 880K **Privately Held**
WEB: www.igbint.com
SIC: 3559 Plastics working machinery

(G-15023)
INTERNATIONAL PAPER COMPANY
1851 Tamarack Rd (43055-1350)
PHONE.............................740 522-3123
Fax: 740 522-4770
Bill Hartshorn, *General Mgr*
Belinda Hughes, *Executive*
Jeff Lee, *Maintence Staff*
EMP: 70
SALES (corp-wide): 21B **Publicly Held**
WEB: www.internationalpaper.com
SIC: 2653 Boxes, corrugated: made from purchased materials
PA: International Paper Company
6400 Poplar Ave
Memphis TN 38197
901 419-9000

(G-15024)
JETT INDUSTRIES INC
180 Grant St (43055-3845)
PHONE.............................740 344-4140
Fax: 740 344-4142
Jodi E Priest, *President*
Timothy W Priest, *Vice Pres*
EMP: 4
SQ FT: 4,500
SALES (est): 380K **Privately Held**
SIC: 3599 5084 Machine shop, jobbing & repair; machine tools & accessories

(G-15025)
JOSEPH SCARBERRY
Also Called: Paper People
1038 Idlewilde Ave (43055-2438)
PHONE.............................740 522-1551
Fax: 740 522-1538
Joseph Scarberry, *Owner*
EMP: 3
SQ FT: 1,700
SALES (est): 165K **Privately Held**
WEB: www.paperpeople.com
SIC: 2752 Commercial printing, offset; lithographing on metal

(G-15026)
KATHY EDIE
Also Called: Kam Services
2737 Licking Valley Rd (43055-9105)
PHONE.............................740 763-4887
Kathy Edie, *Owner*
EMP: 3
SALES (est): 115K **Privately Held**
SIC: 3271 Blocks, concrete: landscape or retaining wall

(G-15027)
KLARITY MEDICAL PRODUCTS LLC
1987 Coffman Rd (43055-1361)
PHONE.............................740 788-8107
Peter Larson, *President*

Susan Larson, *Vice Pres*
EMP: 10
SALES (est): 1.6MM **Privately Held**
SIC: 3841 Surgical & medical instruments

(G-15028)
KRAJEWSKI CORP (PA)
Also Called: Universal Veneer Sales
1776 Tamarack Rd (43055-1359)
PHONE.............................740 522-1147
Klaus Krajewski, *President*
Patty Showalter, *COO*
Rhonda Hrabak, *Manager*
◆ **EMP:** 186
SQ FT: 75,000
SALES (est): 19.5MM **Privately Held**
SIC: 2411 Veneer logs

(G-15029)
L & T COLLINS INC
Also Called: Minuteman of Heath
44 S 4th St (43055-5436)
PHONE.............................740 345-4494
Timothy M Collins, *President*
Laura Collins, *CFO*
EMP: 6
SQ FT: 12,500
SALES: 470K **Privately Held**
SIC: 2752 Commercial printing, lithographic

(G-15030)
LIBIDO EDGE LABS LLC
26 E Stevens St (43055-5923)
P.O. Box 253 (43058-0253)
PHONE.............................740 344-1401
Tammy Miller, *Managing Dir*
Tammy Creel, *Mng Member*
Ruth Moran,
EMP: 5 **EST:** 2006
SQ FT: 4,000
SALES: 427.5K **Privately Held**
SIC: 2834 Vitamin preparations

(G-15031)
M & H SCREEN PRINTING
1486 Hebron Rd (43056-1035)
PHONE.............................740 522-1957
Douglas Moore, *Partner*
Stan Hall, *Partner*
Laurie Moore, *Partner*
EMP: 6
SQ FT: 4,000
SALES: 280K **Privately Held**
SIC: 2396 Screen printing on fabric articles

(G-15032)
M & R PHILLIPS ENTERPRISES
Also Called: Serappers Gallery
6242 Jacksontown Rd (43056-8303)
PHONE.............................740 323-0580
Mary Phillips, *President*
Rick Phillips, *Corp Secy*
EMP: 10
SALES (est): 680K **Privately Held**
SIC: 2782 Scrapbooks, albums & diaries

(G-15033)
MID OHIO WOOD PRODUCTS INC
535 Franklin Ave (43056-1610)
PHONE.............................740 323-0427
Fax: 740 323-0657
Jay Parkinson, *President*
Nancy Parkinson, *Corp Secy*
Tom Parkinson, *Sales Staff*
EMP: 33
SQ FT: 16,000
SALES (est): 4.1MM **Privately Held**
SIC: 2448 2426 Pallets, wood; skids, wood; hardwood dimension & flooring mills

(G-15034)
MINI-MIX INC
746 Maple Grove Ave (43055-3863)
PHONE.............................740 345-3186
Bernard Holton, *President*
Lorene Holton, *Corp Secy*
EMP: 6
SQ FT: 4,900
SALES: 550K **Privately Held**
SIC: 3273 Ready-mixed concrete

(G-15035)
MODERN WELDING CO OHIO INC
1 Modern Way (43055-3921)
P.O. Box 4430 (43058-4430)
PHONE.............................740 344-9425
John W Jones, *President*
Doug Routher, *General Mgr*
Bob Weidner, *COO*
James M Ruth, *Exec VP*
Jerry Waller, *Vice Pres*
EMP: 30
SQ FT: 52,000
SALES (est): 8.1MM
SALES (corp-wide): 99.4MM **Privately Held**
WEB: www.modweldco.net
SIC: 3443 5051 Tanks, lined: metal plate; metals service centers & offices
PA: Modern Welding Company, Inc.
2880 New Hartford Rd
Owensboro KY 42303
270 685-4400

(G-15036)
NATIONAL GAS & OIL COMPANY (PA)
1500 Granville Rd (43055-1500)
P.O. Box 4970 (43058-4970)
PHONE.............................740 344-2102
William H Sullivan Jr, *Ch of Bd*
Patrick J Mc Gonagle, *President*
Todd Ware, *Vice Pres*
EMP: 2
SQ FT: 20,000
SALES (est): 72.4MM **Privately Held**
SIC: 4922 4924 1311 Natural gas transmission; natural gas distribution; natural gas production

(G-15037)
NATIONAL GAS & OIL CORPORATION (HQ)
Also Called: Permian Oil & Gas Division
1500 Granville Rd (43055-1500)
P.O. Box 4970 (43058-4970)
PHONE.............................740 344-2102
Fax: 740 344-2054
William Sullivan Jr, *Ch of Bd*
Patrick J Mc Gonagle, *President*
Gordon M King, *Vice Pres*
Todd P Ware, *Vice Pres*
EMP: 36
SQ FT: 10,000
SALES: 37.1MM
SALES (corp-wide): 72.4MM **Privately Held**
WEB: www.theenergycoop.com
SIC: 4922 4924 4932 4911 Natural gas transmission; natural gas distribution; gas & other services combined; electric services; industrial gases
PA: National Gas & Oil Company Inc
1500 Granville Rd
Newark OH 43055
740 344-2102

(G-15038)
NEW WORLD ENERGY RESOURCES (PA)
1500 Granville Rd (43055-1536)
PHONE.............................740 344-4087
John Manczak, *CEO*
EMP: 13
SALES (est): 34.7MM **Privately Held**
SIC: 1382 Geological exploration, oil & gas field

(G-15039)
NGO DEVELOPMENT CORPORATION (HQ)
Also Called: National Production
1500 Granville Rd (43055-1536)
P.O. Box 4970 (43058-4970)
PHONE.............................740 344-3790
Dave Potter, *President*
Daniel S Mc Vey, *COO*
Todd P Ware, *CFO*
▲ **EMP:** 13 **EST:** 1975
SALES (est): 4.9MM
SALES (corp-wide): 34.7MM **Privately Held**
SIC: 4922 1381 Pipelines, natural gas; directional drilling oil & gas wells

PA: New World Energy Resources Inc
1500 Granville Rd
Newark OH 43055
740 344-4087

(G-15040)
NORTHEL USA LLC
5772 Bear Hollow Rd Se (43056-9464)
PHONE....................................740 973-0309
Cem Yalcin, *CEO*
Gursel Inceoglu, *President*
EMP: 4 EST: 2015
SALES (est): 137K **Privately Held**
SIC: 4911 3511 ; turbines & turbine generator set units, complete

(G-15041)
OHIO PLASTICS COMPANY
3933 Price Rd Ne (43055-9507)
PHONE....................................740 828-3291
Allen L Handlan, *President*
Abraham Godinez, *Sales Mgr*
William C Kraner, *Director*
EMP: 4 EST: 1938
SQ FT: 10,000
SALES (est): 537.3K **Privately Held**
SIC: 3089 Injection molded finished plastic products

(G-15042)
OHIO RIVER VALLEY CABINET
4 Waterworks Rd (43055-6060)
PHONE....................................740 975-8846
Bob Bachmann, *Owner*
EMP: 6
SALES (est): 240K **Privately Held**
SIC: 2434 Wood kitchen cabinets

(G-15043)
OWENS CORNING SALES LLC
400 Case Ave (43055-5805)
P.O. Box 3012 (43058-3012)
PHONE....................................740 328-2300
Fax: 740 328-2509
Mark Wiseman, *Purchasing*
Katty Cobb, *Human Resources*
Fred Ramquist, *Branch Mgr*
EMP: 148
SALES (corp-wide): 5.6B **Publicly Held**
WEB: www.owenscorning.com
SIC: 3296 Mineral wool
HQ: Owens Corning Sales, Llc
1 Owens Corning Pkwy
Toledo OH 43659
419 248-8000

(G-15044)
PACKAGING CORPORATION AMERICA
Also Called: PCA/Newark 365
205 S 21st St (43055-3879)
P.O. Box 4610 (43058-4610)
PHONE....................................740 344-1126
Mark Donnelly, *Plant Mgr*
Max Kackstetter, *Safety Mgr*
Scott Kiefer, *Safety Mgr*
Scott Robinson, *Sls & Mktg Exec*
Connie Nutter, *Controller*
EMP: 100
SALES (corp-wide): 5.7B **Publicly Held**
WEB: www.packagingcorp.com
SIC: 2653 Corrugated & solid fiber boxes
PA: Packaging Corporation Of America
1955 W Field Ct
Lake Forest IL 60045
847 482-3000

(G-15045)
PENICK GAS & OIL
1504 Blue Jay Rd (43056-1767)
PHONE....................................740 323-3040
EMP: 5 EST: 1939
SALES (est): 326.5K **Privately Held**
SIC: 1311 Crude petroleum production; natural gas production

(G-15046)
PLUS PUBLICATIONS INC
Also Called: Independent Restaurateur
57 S 3rd St (43055-5433)
P.O. Box 917 (43058-0917)
PHONE....................................740 345-5542
Fax: 740 345-5557
James T Young, *Owner*
EMP: 5

SALES (est): 270K **Privately Held**
SIC: 2721 Magazines: publishing only, not printed on site

(G-15047)
POWER CORP SIGN PRODUCTS INC
632 Swansea Rd (43055-1526)
PHONE....................................740 344-0468
Jeff Jones, *President*
EMP: 3
SQ FT: 10,000
SALES (est): 286.7K **Privately Held**
SIC: 3993 Signs & advertising specialties

(G-15048)
PRESTON
42 Sandalwood Dr (43055-9233)
PHONE....................................740 788-8208
Judith Preston, *Principal*
EMP: 12
SALES (est): 2.1MM **Privately Held**
SIC: 3545 Collars (machine tool accessories)

(G-15049)
PUGHS DESIGNER JEWELERS INC
44 S 2nd St (43055-5432)
PHONE....................................740 344-9259
Fax: 740 345-9267
Kevin Pugh, *President*
Sandi Johnson, *Associate*
Marilyn Krebs, *Associate*
EMP: 8
SQ FT: 2,500
SALES: 900K **Privately Held**
WEB: www.diamondstodiefor.com
SIC: 5944 3961 7389 7631 Jewelry stores; costume jewelry; appraisers, except real estate; jewelry repair services

(G-15050)
QUANTUM
400 Case Ave (43055-5805)
PHONE....................................740 328-2548
EMP: 3
SALES (est): 165.3K **Privately Held**
SIC: 3572 Computer storage devices

(G-15051)
RYANS NEWARK LEADER EX PRTG
Also Called: Leader Printing
56 Westgate Dr (43055-9313)
P.O. Box 4902 (43058-4902)
PHONE....................................740 522-2149
Fax: 740 522-6926
Andrew T Ryan, *President*
Gary Ryan, *Treasurer*
Sherri Griffith, *Graphic Designe*
Terre Shoenfelt, *Graphic Designe*
EMP: 10 EST: 1895
SQ FT: 9,600
SALES (est): 1.1MM **Privately Held**
WEB: www.leaderprinting1895.com
SIC: 2752 2791 2789 2759 Commercial printing, offset; typesetting; bookbinding & related work; commercial printing

(G-15052)
SENTINEL USA INC
Also Called: Sentinel Utility Services
1285 Granville Rd (43055-2130)
PHONE....................................740 345-6412
Fax: 740 345-9438
Daniel Colby, *President*
EMP: 12
SQ FT: 2,400
SALES (est): 711.3K
SALES (corp-wide): 8.8MM **Privately Held**
WEB: www.sentinelusa.com
SIC: 2741 7371 Maps: publishing & printing; custom computer programming services
PA: Irth Solutions, Inc.
5009 Horizons Dr Ste 100
Columbus OH 43220
614 459-2328

(G-15053)
SHELLY MATERIALS INC
6824 Mount Vernon Rd (43055-9625)
PHONE....................................740 745-5965

Fax: 740 745-1029
Wayne Spray, *Manager*
EMP: 5
SALES (corp-wide): 28.6B **Privately Held**
SIC: 1442 Construction sand & gravel
HQ: Shelly Materials, Inc.
80 Park Dr
Thornville OH 43076
740 246-6315

(G-15054)
SPECTRUM ADHESIVES INC
11047 Lambs Ln (43055-9779)
PHONE....................................740 763-2886
Kent Pitcher, *Branch Mgr*
EMP: 13
SALES (corp-wide): 5.8MM **Privately Held**
SIC: 2891 Glue
PA: Spectrum Adhesives, Inc.
5611 Universal Dr
Memphis TN 38118
901 795-1943

(G-15055)
SPENCER-WALKER PRESS INC (PA)
1433 Amesbury Ln (43055-1894)
PHONE....................................740 344-6110
Fax: 740 224-1375
David B Sinclair, *President*
Ted Rowe, *Purchasing*
EMP: 12
SQ FT: 16,000
SALES: 1.5MM **Privately Held**
SIC: 2752 2791 2789 2759 Commercial printing, offset; typesetting; bookbinding & related work; commercial printing; die-cut paper & board

(G-15056)
SPENCER-WALKER PRESS INC
Also Called: Print Shop, The
44 S 4th St (43055-5436)
PHONE....................................740 345-4494
Fax: 740 345-2423
David Sinclair, *Owner*
EMP: 3
SALES (corp-wide): 1.5MM **Privately Held**
SIC: 2759 Commercial printing
PA: Spencer-Walker Press Inc
1433 Amesbury Ln
Newark OH 43055
740 344-6110

(G-15057)
STEPHEN R WHITE
Also Called: Carat Patch, The
800 Hebron Rd (43056-1443)
PHONE....................................740 522-1512
Stephen R White, *Owner*
EMP: 3
SALES (est): 170K **Privately Held**
WEB: www.srwesq.com
SIC: 5944 3911 Jewelry, precious stones & precious metals; jewelry apparel

(G-15058)
STONEWORKD
1050 Harris Ave (43055-2429)
PHONE....................................740 920-4099
Erin Denner, *Office Mgr*
Ericeh Horvath,
EMP: 10
SALES (est): 850K **Privately Held**
SIC: 3559 Stone working machinery

(G-15059)
STRATEGIC MATERIALS INC
101 S Arch St (43055-6202)
P.O. Box 816 (43058-0816)
PHONE....................................740 349-9523
Michael Back, *Manager*
EMP: 6 **Privately Held**
SIC: 3231 Products of purchased glass
HQ: Strategic Materials, Inc.
16365 Park Ten Pl Ste 200
Houston TX 77084
281 647-2700

(G-15060)
SUGARTREE SQUARE MERCANTILE
5541 Grumms Ln Ne (43055-9755)
PHONE....................................740 345-3882

Shirley Simms, *Partner*
EMP: 3
SALES (est): 236.1K **Privately Held**
SIC: 3795 Tanks & tank components

(G-15061)
SUMMIT CUSTOM CABINETS
10430 Hoover Rd Ne (43055-9751)
PHONE....................................740 345-1734
Fax: 740 345-1497
Bill Guisinger, *Owner*
Scott Thomas, *Owner*
EMP: 3 EST: 1998
SALES (est): 180K **Privately Held**
SIC: 1751 2541 2434 Cabinet & finish carpentry; table or counter tops, plastic laminated; wood kitchen cabinets

(G-15062)
TECH WEAR EMBROIDERY COMPANY
738 W Main St (43055-2512)
PHONE....................................740 344-1276
Chris McInturf, *President*
EMP: 5
SALES (est): 225.7K **Privately Held**
WEB: www.embroideryshop.net
SIC: 2395 Embroidery & art needlework

(G-15063)
TECTUM INC
105 S 6th St (43055-4908)
P.O. Box 3002 (43058-3002)
PHONE....................................740 345-9691
Fax: 740 349-9305
Michael Massaro, *President*
Wayne Chester, *Exec VP*
Linda Young, *Purchasing*
Ken Fitzrovich, *Sls & Mktg Exec*
Diane Austin, *Accountant*
▼ EMP: 120
SQ FT: 100,000
SALES: 12.9MM **Privately Held**
WEB: www.tectum.com
SIC: 2493 3444 3296 Fiberboard, other vegetable pulp; sheet metalwork; mineral wool

(G-15064)
TRAFFIC CNTRL SGNLS SIGNS & MA
Also Called: City of Newark
1195 E Main St (43055-8869)
PHONE....................................740 670-7763
Gary Snavely, *Director*
EMP: 7 EST: 2007
SALES (est): 792.5K **Privately Held**
SIC: 3993 Signs & advertising specialties

(G-15065)
UNIVERSAL PRODUCTION CORP
1776 Tamarack Rd (43055-1359)
PHONE....................................740 522-1147
Klaus Krajewski, *President*
Robert Baldwin, *CFO*
▼ EMP: 200
SQ FT: 98,000
SALES (est): 19.5MM **Privately Held**
SIC: 2431 Mantels, wood

(G-15066)
WYETH-SCOTT COMPANY
85 Dayton Rd Ne (43055-8814)
P.O. Box 888 (43058-0888)
PHONE....................................740 345-4528
Fax: 740 345-0123
Amy L Kent, *President*
◆ EMP: 3
SQ FT: 7,692
SALES: 595K **Privately Held**
WEB: www.wyeth-scott.com
SIC: 3546 3531 Power-driven handtools; winches

Newburgh Heights
Cuyahoga County

(G-15067)
ALCOA INC
1600 Harvard Ave (44105-3092)
PHONE....................................216 641-3600
John Roggenburk, *General Mgr*

Victor Marquez, *Vice Pres*
Charles D McLane Jr, *Vice Pres*
Clifford Shotton, *Engineer*
Ray Mitchell, *Human Res Mgr*
EMP: 1200
SALES (corp-wide): 12.3B **Publicly Held**
SIC: 3463 Aluminum forgings
PA: Arconic Inc.
　　390 Park Ave
　　New York NY 10022
　　212 836-2758

(G-15068)
ALCOA INC
1616 Harvard Ave (44105-3040)
PHONE..............................608 363-5214
Andrew Martin, *Engineer*
Natalie Schilling, *VP Human Res*
Jennifer Heilman, *Marketing Staff*
Raluca Pascu, *Marketing Staff*
Victor Marquez, *Branch Mgr*
EMP: 20
SALES (corp-wide): 12.3B **Publicly Held**
SIC: 3334 3353 1099 Primary aluminum;
　aluminum sheet & strip; coils, sheet alu-
　minum; plates, aluminum; foil, aluminum;
　bauxite mining
PA: Arconic Inc.
　　390 Park Ave
　　New York NY 10022
　　212 836-2758

(G-15069)
ARCONIC INC
Also Called: Alcoa
1600 Harvard Ave (44105-3040)
PHONE..............................216 641-3600
Fax: 216 641-5283
Jeffrey Matz, *Production*
Stephen J Makosey, *Engineer*
Gerard Maniscalco, *Engineer*
Ray Mitchell, *Human Res Mgr*
Thomas Mataloni, *Sales Staff*
EMP: 1200
SALES (corp-wide): 12.3B **Publicly Held**
SIC: 3463 3321 Aluminum forgings; gray
　& ductile iron foundries
PA: Arconic Inc.
　　390 Park Ave
　　New York NY 10022
　　212 836-2758

(G-15070)
H GOODMAN INC
Also Called: White Dove Mattress
3201 Harvard Ave (44105-3060)
PHONE..............................216 341-0200
Fax: 216 341-3399
Bruce Goodman, *President*
Henry J Goodman, *Chairman*
Bill Dippel, *Vice Pres*
Annette Thomas, *Accountant*
▲ **EMP:** 90
SQ FT: 270,000
SALES (est): 11.8MM **Privately Held**
WEB: www.whitedoveusa.com
SIC: 2515 2512 Mattresses & bedsprings;
　mattresses, innerspring or box spring; box
　springs, assembled; upholstered house-
　hold furniture

(G-15071)
HARVARD METAL TREATING INC
2819 Harvard Ave (44105-3047)
PHONE..............................216 271-4424
Fax: 216 271-6215
John Zawada, *President*
Joseph Thomas, *Corp Secy*
EMP: 7 **EST:** 1971
SQ FT: 20,000
SALES (est): 570K **Privately Held**
SIC: 3398 Metal heat treating

(G-15072)
HOWMET ALUMINUM CASTING INC (HQ)
Also Called: Sigma Div
1600 Harvard Ave (44105-3040)
PHONE..............................216 641-4340
Raymond B Mitchell, *President*
Janet Duderstadt, *General Counsel*
EMP: 50
SQ FT: 10,000

SALES (est): 43.8MM
SALES (corp-wide): 12.3B **Publicly Held**
SIC: 3365 Aluminum & aluminum-based
　alloy castings
PA: Arconic Inc.
　　390 Park Ave
　　New York NY 10022
　　212 836-2758

(G-15073)
HOWMET CASTINGS & SERVICES INC (DH)
1616 Harvard Ave (44105-3040)
PHONE..............................216 641-4400
Eric M Brzostek, *President*
Natalie Schilling, *Vice Pres*
Christi Hall, *Human Res Mgr*
EMP: 277 **EST:** 2004
SALES (est): 531.2MM
SALES (corp-wide): 12.3B **Publicly Held**
SIC: 3324 Commercial investment cast-
　ings, ferrous
HQ: Howmet Corporation
　　1616 Harvard Ave
　　Newburgh Heights OH 44105
　　800 242-9898

(G-15074)
HOWMET CORPORATION (DH)
Also Called: Alcoa Power & Propulsion
1616 Harvard Ave (44105-3040)
PHONE..............................800 242-9898
David L Squier, *President*
Marklin Lasker, *Senior VP*
James R Stanley, *Senior VP*
Roland A Paul, *Vice Pres*
B Dennis Albrechtsen, *VP Mfg*
◆ **EMP:** 30
SQ FT: 10,000
SALES (est): 1.7B
SALES (corp-wide): 12.3B **Publicly Held**
WEB: www.alcoa.com
SIC: 3324 3542 5051 3479 Commercial
　investment castings, ferrous; machine
　tools, metal forming type; ferroalloys; in-
　gots; coating of metals & formed products
HQ: Howmet Holdings Corporation
　　1 Misco Dr
　　Whitehall MI 49461
　　231 894-5686

(G-15075)
HUNT PRODUCTS INC
3982 E 42nd St (44105-3165)
PHONE..............................440 667-2457
Fax: 216 281-1128
Jo Ann Hunt, *President*
Laura Hunt, *Vice Pres*
Albert Styer, *Manager*
Sandra Jones, *Receptionist*
EMP: 35 **EST:** 1970
SQ FT: 30,000
SALES (est): 2.4MM **Privately Held**
SIC: 7389 3544 3053 2675 Packaging &
　labeling services; special dies, tools, jigs
　& fixtures; gaskets, packing & sealing de-
　vices; die-cut paper & board; packaging
　paper & plastics film, coated & laminated;
　automotive & apparel trimmings

(G-15076)
MCGEAN-ROHCO INC
2910 Harvard Ave (44105-3010)
PHONE..............................216 441-4900
Dick Whitney, *VP Sales*
Kerry May, *Branch Mgr*
Rita Tormento, *Manager*
John Gherlein, *Admin Sec*
EMP: 60
SQ FT: 350,000
SALES (corp-wide): 62.8MM **Privately
Held**
WEB: www.mcgean.com
SIC: 2899 2819 3471 2842 Chemical
　preparations; industrial inorganic chemi-
　cals; plating & polishing; specialty clean-
　ing, polishes & sanitation goods
PA: Mcgean-Rohco, Inc.
　　2910 Harvard Ave
　　Newburgh Heights OH 44105
　　216 441-4900

(G-15077)
PARK-OHIO INDUSTRIES INC
Also Called: Ohio Crankshaft Div
3800 Harvard Ave (44105-3208)
PHONE..............................216 341-2300
Fax: 216 883-7553
Felix Parorick, *Principal*
Ron Galla, *Dir Ops-Prd-Mfg*
Dave Johnson, *QC Dir*
Lee Demastry, *Personnel*
Gerry Stadler, *Marketing Staff*
EMP: 150
SQ FT: 427,000
SALES (corp-wide): 1.2B **Publicly Held**
WEB: www.pkoh.com.cn
SIC: 3714 Camshafts, motor vehicle
HQ: Park-Ohio Industries, Inc.
　　6065 Parkland Blvd Ste 1
　　Cleveland OH 44124
　　440 947-2000

(G-15078)
PQ CORPORATION
5200 Harvard Ave (44105-4855)
PHONE..............................216 341-2578
EMP: 3
SALES (est): 177.6K **Privately Held**
SIC: 2819 Industrial inorganic chemicals

(G-15079)
SAMCO TECHNOLOGIES INC
1600 Harvard Ave (44105-3040)
PHONE..............................216 641-5288
Jim Batter, *Manager*
EMP: 6
SALES (corp-wide): 9MM **Privately Held**
WEB: www.samcotech.com
SIC: 3589 4941 Water treatment equip-
　ment, industrial; water supply
PA: Samco Technologies, Inc.
　　1 River Rock Dr
　　Buffalo NY 14207
　　716 743-9000

(G-15080)
WESTERN RSERVE WTR SYSTEMS INC
4133 E 49th St (44105-3267)
PHONE..............................216 341-9797
Fax: 216 441-6149
Joe Hooley, *CEO*
Michael D Eiermann, *President*
Alan Lauvray, *Project Mgr*
Greg Molnar, *Project Mgr*
Bill Kovacs, *Engineer*
◆ **EMP:** 70
SQ FT: 10,000
SALES: 12.5MM **Privately Held**
WEB: www.westernreservewater.com
SIC: 3589 Water treatment equipment, in-
　dustrial

(G-15081)
WHITE DOVE MATTRESS LTD
3201 Harvard Ave (44105-3060)
PHONE..............................216 341-0200
Gary Eddy, *VP Opers*
Rich Morando, *Opers Mgr*
Karen Morchak, *Purch Mgr*
Rebecca Scott, *QC Mgr*
Arlene Turocy, *Controller*
▲ **EMP:** 48
SALES (est): 11.1MM **Privately Held**
SIC: 2515 Mattresses & bedsprings

Newbury
Geauga County

(G-15082)
BOGGS RECYCLING INC
12355 Kinsman Rd Unit J (44065-9620)
P.O. Box 576, Burton (44021-0576)
PHONE..............................800 837-8101
Kimberly Boggs, *President*
Christopher A Boggs, *Principal*
EMP: 8
SQ FT: 10,000
SALES (est): 840K **Privately Held**
SIC: 3334 Primary aluminum

(G-15083)
CHESTERLAND CABINET COMPANY
10389 Kinsman Rd (44065-9701)
P.O. Box 69 (44065-0069)
PHONE..............................440 564-1157
Fax: 440 729-7834
Joe Mazzurco, *President*
Madeline Mazzurco, *Vice Pres*
EMP: 3
SQ FT: 1,500
SALES: 100K **Privately Held**
SIC: 2434 1751 Wood kitchen cabinets;
　cabinet & finish carpentry

(G-15084)
CLEVELAND RUBBER PRODUCTS LLC
Also Called: Geauga Machine and Tool
9988 Kinsman Rd (44065)
P.O. Box 258 (44065-0258)
PHONE..............................440 564-7100
Jim McConnell, *Vice Pres*
Todd Zeitz,
EMP: 5
SQ FT: 3,000
SALES: 280K **Privately Held**
WEB: www.clevelandrubber.com
SIC: 3069 Molded rubber products

(G-15085)
COUNTRY MOLDING
12375 Kinsman Rd (44065-9684)
PHONE..............................440 564-5235
EMP: 3
SALES (est): 144.2K **Privately Held**
SIC: 3089 Molding primary plastic

(G-15086)
COUNTY WIDE WELDING LLC
14999 Cross Creek Pkwy (44065-9788)
PHONE..............................440 564-1333
Fax: 440 564-1345
David Smith,
EMP: 3
SQ FT: 5,000
SALES: 300K **Privately Held**
SIC: 7692 Welding repair

(G-15087)
CREATIVE MOLD AND MACHINE INC
10385 Kinsman Rd (44065-9701)
P.O. Box 323 (44065-0323)
PHONE..............................440 338-5146
Fax: 440 338-1647
Ray Lyons, *President*
Greg Davis, *Vice Pres*
Mishal Dedeck, *Vice Pres*
Kimberly Simcak, *Accountant*
EMP: 25
SQ FT: 39,000
SALES (est): 4.8MM **Privately Held**
SIC: 7692 3599 Welding repair; machine
　shop, jobbing & repair

(G-15088)
DEM MANUFACTURING LLC
10357 Kinsman Rd (44065-9701)
P.O. Box 220 (44065-0220)
PHONE..............................440 564-7160
▲ **EMP:** 10
SALES (est): 1.3MM **Privately Held**
SIC: 3999 Manufacturing Industries, Nec,
　Nsk

(G-15089)
EEI ACQUISITION CORP
Also Called: Engineered Endeavors
10975 Kinsman Rd (44065-9787)
PHONE..............................440 564-5484
Patrick Deloney, *President*
Pat Tyrell, *Business Mgr*
Terry Mills, *Opers Mgr*
Boris Fayman, *Engineer*
Gerry Truax, *CFO*
EMP: 45 **EST:** 2010
SALES (est): 10MM **Privately Held**
SIC: 3663 Mobile communication equip-
　ment

▲ = Import ▼=Export
◆ =Import/Export

(G-15090)
FAIRMOUNT WATER SOLUTIONS LLC
10975 Kinsman Rd (44065-9787)
PHONE.................................440 285-3132
Dana Cooper, *General Mgr*
Jenniffer D Deckard,
EMP: 4
SALES (est): 271.7K
SALES (corp-wide): 535MM **Publicly Held**
SIC: 1446 Foundry sand mining
HQ: Fairmount Santrol Inc.
8834 Mayfield Rd Ste A
Chesterland OH 44026
440 214-3200

(G-15091)
GEAUGA CONCRETE INC
10509 Kinsman Rd (44065-9803)
P.O. Box 249, Grand River (44045-0249)
PHONE.................................440 338-4915
Fax: 440 564-7693
Hal Larned, *President*
Don Sustar, *Business Mgr*
EMP: 10
SALES (est): 1.4MM
SALES (corp-wide): 3.5MM **Privately Held**
WEB: www.osdocks.com
SIC: 3273 Ready-mixed concrete
PA: Osborne Concrete & Stone Co.
1 Williams St
Grand River OH 44045
440 357-5562

(G-15092)
GEAUGA FEED AND GRAIN SUPPLY
11030 Kinsman Rd (44065-9744)
P.O. Box 654 (44065-0654)
PHONE.................................440 564-5000
Kevin Oreilly, *Owner*
EMP: 5 EST: 2002
SALES (est): 613.8K **Privately Held**
SIC: 5153 2048 Grains; livestock feeds

(G-15093)
GREEN VISION MATERIALS INC
11220 Kinsman Rd (44065-9676)
PHONE.................................440 564-5500
Beau Gibney, *Owner*
EMP: 15
SALES (est): 2.1MM **Privately Held**
SIC: 4953 3271 Refuse systems; blocks, concrete: landscape or retaining wall

(G-15094)
HAUETER CONSTRUCTION CO
Haueter Sand & Gravel Division
15349 Ravenna Rd (44065)
PHONE.................................440 834-8220
Tom Bevington, *Manager*
EMP: 8
SALES (corp-wide): 2.2MM **Privately Held**
SIC: 1442 Gravel mining
PA: Haueter Construction Co
Grant Street Ext
Chardon OH
440 286-9482

(G-15095)
HOSTAR INTERNATIONAL INC (PA)
15000 Cross Creek Pkwy (44065-9726)
PHONE.................................440 564-5362
Fax: 440 564-5389
Claudia Berg, *President*
Todd Bush, *President*
Ron Vitale, *Exec VP*
Dolores Lapalio, *Vice Pres*
Andy McCabe, *Vice Pres*
EMP: 11
SALES (est): 3.3MM **Privately Held**
WEB: www.hostar.com
SIC: 3535 Unit handling conveying systems

(G-15096)
HOSTAR INTERNATIONAL INC
15000 Cross Creek Pkwy (44065-9726)
PHONE.................................440 564-5362
Todd Bush, *Vice Pres*
Claudia Borg, *Manager*

Claudia Berg, *Manager*
EMP: 12
SALES (corp-wide): 3.3MM **Privately Held**
WEB: www.hostar.com
SIC: 3535 Conveyors & conveying equipment
PA: Hostar International, Inc.
15000 Cross Creek Pkwy
Newbury OH 44065
440 564-5362

(G-15097)
JAC CONSTRUCTION OHIO LLC
14985 Cross Creek Pkwy (44065-9788)
PHONE.................................440 564-5005
Richard Fletcher,
EMP: 3
SALES: 500K **Privately Held**
SIC: 1381 1731 Directional drilling oil & gas wells; fiber optic cable installation

(G-15098)
KINETICO INCORPORATED
Also Called: Kinetico Engineered Systems
11015 Kinsman Rd (44065-9787)
P.O. Box 127 (44065-0127)
PHONE.................................440 564-7167
Fax: 440 338-8694
Chris Hanson, *Vice Pres*
Keith Tompkins, *Plant Mgr*
Wayne Heberand, *Buyer*
Dan McArdle, *Buyer*
Tom Menard, *Engineer*
EMP: 30
SQ FT: 2,400
SALES (corp-wide): 457.2MM **Privately Held**
WEB: www.kinetico.com
SIC: 3589 Water treatment equipment, industrial
HQ: Kinetico Incorporated
10845 Kinsman Rd
Newbury OH 44065
440 564-9111

(G-15099)
L & N OLDE CAR CO
Also Called: Newbury Sandblasting & Pntg
9992 Kinsman Rd (44065)
P.O. Box 378 (44065-0378)
PHONE.................................440 564-7204
Nelson Peterson, *President*
Pamela Peterson, *Corp Secy*
EMP: 7
SQ FT: 25,000
SALES (est): 805K **Privately Held**
SIC: 3471 7532 Sand blasting of metal parts; paint shop, automotive

(G-15100)
NEWBURY WOODWORKS
10958 Kinsman Rd Unit 2 (44065-8602)
PHONE.................................440 564-5273
Aloysius Hoenigman Jr, *Owner*
EMP: 7
SQ FT: 8,000
SALES (est): 490K **Privately Held**
SIC: 5712 2499 Furniture stores; decorative wood & woodwork

(G-15101)
OREILLY EQUIPMENT LLC
14555 Ravenna Rd (44065-9513)
PHONE.................................440 564-1234
Bill Splitler, *Parts Mgr*
Mikaela Klein, *Marketing Staff*
Paul Oreilly, *Manager*
Jeffery M O'Reilly,
EMP: 6
SQ FT: 6,000
SALES (est): 2.5MM **Privately Held**
WEB: www.oreillyequipment.com
SIC: 5599 3714 Utility trailers; ice scrapers & window brushes, motor vehicle

(G-15102)
R W SIDLEY INCORPORATED
10688 Kinsman Rd (44065-9761)
PHONE.................................440 564-2221
Fax: 440 564-9357
Dan Craver, *Branch Mgr*
Dave Fox, *Manager*
Robert Roberti, *Director*
EMP: 21

SALES (corp-wide): 143.8MM **Privately Held**
WEB: www.rwsidleyinc.com
SIC: 3273 3272 3271 1442 Ready-mixed concrete; concrete products; concrete block & brick; construction sand & gravel
PA: R. W. Sidley Incorporated
436 Casement Ave
Painesville OH 44077
440 352-9343

(G-15103)
RALSTON INSTRUMENTS LLC
15035 Cross Creek Pkwy (44065-9726)
P.O. Box 340, Novelty (44072-0340)
PHONE.................................440 564-1430
Douglas Ralston, *CEO*
Corey Ralston,
EMP: 20
SALES (est): 3.7MM **Privately Held**
WEB: www.ralstoninst.com
SIC: 3829 Measuring & controlling devices

(G-15104)
S J K METALWORKING INC
Also Called: S K Industries
14940 Cross Creek Pkwy (44065-9788)
P.O. Box 267 (44065-0267)
PHONE.................................440 564-7877
Fax: 440 564-9020
Katherina Kekedy, *President*
Steven Kekedy, *Vice Pres*
EMP: 4
SQ FT: 8,000
SALES (est): 482.7K **Privately Held**
SIC: 3599 Machine shop, jobbing & repair

(G-15105)
STEVEN DOUGLAS CORP
10420 Kinsman Rd (44065-9724)
PHONE.................................440 564-5200
Fax: 440 564-5205
Stephen Belliveau, *President*
Tim Mocz, *General Mgr*
Paul Belliveau, *Exec VP*
John Blake, *Engineer*
Greg Merrill, *Sales Mgr*
EMP: 22 EST: 1998
SQ FT: 27,000
SALES (est): 7.7MM **Privately Held**
WEB: www.s-d-c.com
SIC: 3569 Assembly machines, non-metalworking

(G-15106)
WATER STAR INC
12369 Kinsman Rd Bldg K (44065-9620)
P.O. Box 710, Parkman (44080-0710)
PHONE.................................440 564-1001
Marilyn Niksa, *President*
Andrew Niksa, *Vice Pres*
▲ EMP: 5 EST: 2002
SQ FT: 5,000
SALES (est): 1.4MM
SALES (corp-wide): 808.5MM **Publicly Held**
WEB: www.waterstarinc.com
SIC: 3356 Titanium
PA: Tennant Company
701 Lilac Dr N
Minneapolis MN 55422
763 540-1200

Newcomerstown
Tuscarawas County

(G-15107)
31 INC
Also Called: Extra Seal
100 Enterprise Dr (43832-9242)
P.O. Box 278 (43832-0278)
PHONE.................................740 498-8324
Fax: 740 498-8325
Charles Muhs, *President*
Robert Hendry, *Vice Pres*
Melissa Smith, *Safety Mgr*
Barbara Simms, *Opers Staff*
Tim Lint, *Manager*
◆ EMP: 100 EST: 1961
SQ FT: 130,000
SALES (est): 19.1MM **Privately Held**
WEB: www.31inc.com
SIC: 3011 3714 Tire sundries or tire repair materials, rubber; tire valve cores

(G-15108)
ACCURATE PRODUCTS COMPANY
98 Elizabeth St (43832-1432)
P.O. Box 106 (43832-0106)
PHONE.................................740 498-7202
Fax: 740 498-7507
Clark H Smith, *President*
R Clark Smith, *Vice Pres*
Annette Parks, *Manager*
EMP: 6 EST: 1946
SALES (est): 600K **Privately Held**
SIC: 3366 Castings (except die): brass; castings (except die): bronze

(G-15109)
BOLTARON INC
Also Called: Empire Plastics
1 General St (43832-1230)
PHONE.................................740 498-5900
Fax: 740 498-5448
Lawrence J Schorr, *CEO*
Kevin Asti, *VP Opers*
John Shade, *Opers Mgr*
Curtis Stogner, *Research*
Jay Coventry, *Engineer*
▲ EMP: 100
SQ FT: 175,000
SALES (est): 43.5MM **Privately Held**
WEB: www.empireplastics.com
SIC: 3081 2891 Film base, cellulose acetate or nitrocellulose plastic; adhesives & sealants

(G-15110)
BUCKEYE BOP LLC
Also Called: Buckeye Blow Out Preventer
401 Enterprise Dr (43832-9239)
PHONE.................................740 498-9898
EMP: 3
SALES (est): 250.6K **Privately Held**
SIC: 3564 3592 5719 Blowers & fans; valves; brushes

(G-15111)
CLAY LBC CO
59260 County Road 9 (43832-9702)
PHONE.................................740 492-5055
Chad Clark, *CEO*
EMP: 5
SALES (est): 198.8K **Privately Held**
SIC: 1442 Construction sand & gravel

(G-15112)
ECHO DRILLING INC (PA)
11 Crestview Mnr (43832-9654)
PHONE.................................740 498-8560
Kenneth E Ebersbach, *President*
Virgil Ebersbach, *Admin Sec*
EMP: 3
SQ FT: 100
SALES (est): 1.3MM **Privately Held**
SIC: 5172 1389 Crude oil; oil field services

(G-15113)
GENERAL ELECTRIC COMPANY
700 Newport St (43832-1298)
PHONE.................................740 498-5151
Fax: 614 498-5151
Charlene Begley, *Vice Pres*
Harold Riffle, *Purchasing*
Mary Hykes, *Personnel*
Rod Rumar, *Manager*
John Anderson, *Manager*
EMP: 25
SALES (corp-wide): 123.6B **Publicly Held**
SIC: 3621 3677 Coils, for electric motors or generators; electronic coils, transformers & other inductors
PA: General Electric Company
41 Farnsworth St
Boston MA 02210
617 443-3000

(G-15114)
H3D TOOL CORPORATION
Also Called: High Definition Tooling
295 Enterprise Dr (43832-8954)
P.O. Box 314 (43832-0314)
PHONE.................................740 498-5181
Fax: 740 498-5454
Gary Dyer, *President*
Chris Dyer, *Vice Pres*
Bill Ludwig, *Engineer*
Bob Arick, *Sales Dir*

EMP: 9
SALES (est): 2MM **Privately Held**
SIC: 3545 5085 Diamond cutting tools for turning, boring, burnishing, etc.; industrial supplies

(G-15115)
HERCO INC
295 Enterprise Dr (43832-8954)
P.O. Box 314 (43832-0314)
PHONE...740 498-5181
Fax: 614 498-5454
Gary Dyer, *President*
Chris Dyer, *Vice Pres*
James P Edsall, *Mfg Dir*
Jim Conlon, *Production*
EMP: 40
SQ FT: 20,000
SALES (est): 6MM **Privately Held**
WEB: www.herco.net
SIC: 3545 Cutting tools for machine tools

(G-15116)
INFINITY OILFIELD SERVICES LLC
311 Adena Dr (43832-9445)
P.O. Box 610 (43832-0610)
PHONE...570 567-7027
Linda McCauley, *Principal*
EMP: 4
SALES (est): 238.4K **Privately Held**
SIC: 1389 Oil field services

(G-15117)
KURZ-KASCH INC
Kurz-Kasch Newcomerstown Div
199 E State St (43832-1468)
PHONE...740 498-8343
John Taylor, *Chairman*
Richard Norris, *Vice Pres*
Diane Powell, *Purchasing*
Jeff Smith, *Branch Mgr*
EMP: 175
SALES (corp-wide): 764.1MM **Privately Held**
WEB: www.kurz-kasch.com
SIC: 3089 Molding primary plastic
HQ: Kurz-Kasch, Inc.
   199 E State St
   Newcomerstown OH 43832
   740 498-8343

(G-15118)
KURZ-KASCH INC (HQ)
199 E State St (43832-1468)
PHONE...740 498-8343
Fax: 614 498-6776
George E Kochanowski, *CEO*
Chad Merkel, *CEO*
Julie Nay, *Opers Mgr*
Jerry Thone, *Engineer*
Carl Risch, *Design Engr*
▲ EMP: 105 EST: 1916
SQ FT: 6,000
SALES: 16MM
SALES (corp-wide): 764.1MM **Privately Held**
WEB: www.kurz-kasch.com
SIC: 3089 3677 Thermoformed finished plastic products; injection molded finished plastic products; electronic coils, transformers & other inductors
PA: Monomoy Capital Partners, L.P.
   142 W 57th St Fl 17
   New York NY 10019
   212 699-4000

(G-15119)
KURZKASCH INC WILM DIV
199 E State St (43832-1468)
PHONE...740 498-8345
Fax: 937 299-0990
Julie Nay, *Principal*
▲ EMP: 17 EST: 2011
SALES (est): 3.1MM **Privately Held**
SIC: 3089 Plastics products

(G-15120)
OAK POINTE STAIR SYSTEMS INC
96 New Pace Rd (43832-1287)
PHONE...740 498-9820
Fax: 740 498-9821
Bernard Booth, *President*
EMP: 20

SALES (est): 3.5MM **Privately Held**
WEB: www.oakpointestair.com
SIC: 2431 Staircases, stairs & railings

(G-15121)
PACEMAKER PLASTIC COMPANY INC
126 New Pace Rd (43832-1200)
PHONE...740 498-4181
Fax: 740 498-4184
Frank J Stark, *President*
William Mc Garrity, *Vice Pres*
EMP: 45
SQ FT: 120,000
SALES (est): 4.1MM **Privately Held**
SIC: 3086 Insulation or cushioning material, foamed plastic; packaging & shipping materials, foamed plastic

(G-15122)
RAINBOW HILLS VINEYARDS INC
Also Called: Raindow Hills Vineyards
26349 Township Road 251 (43832-9631)
PHONE...740 545-9305
Leland Wyse, *President*
Glenna Wyse, *Vice Pres*
EMP: 3
SALES (est): 226.1K **Privately Held**
SIC: 2084 Wines

(G-15123)
SHAW PALLETS & SPECIALTIES
12269 Lick Brown Rd (43832)
PHONE...740 498-7892
Kenneth Shaw, *President*
Rhea Shaw, *Vice Pres*
EMP: 4
SQ FT: 1,440
SALES (est): 320K **Privately Held**
WEB: www.shawpallet.com
SIC: 2448 Wood pallets & skids

(G-15124)
SHAW WILBERT VAULTS LLC
Also Called: Wilbert Shaw Valts
12269 Lick Run Rd (43832-9145)
PHONE...740 498-7438
Kenneth Shaw, *Mng Member*
EMP: 5
SALES (est): 519.5K **Privately Held**
SIC: 5087 3272 Concrete burial vaults & boxes; burial vaults, concrete or precast terrazzo

(G-15125)
THE JEFFERSONIAN
Also Called: Necomerstown News
140 W Main St (43832-1041)
P.O. Box 30 (43832-0030)
PHONE...740 498-7117
Ray Boots, *Manager*
Ray Booth, *Manager*
EMP: 5
SALES (corp-wide): 567.1MM **Privately Held**
WEB: www.daily-jeff.com
SIC: 2711 7313 Newspapers; newspaper advertising representative
HQ: The Jeffersonian
   831 Wheeling Ave
   Cambridge OH
   740 439-3531

Newport
Washington County

(G-15126)
CARLTON OIL CORP
961 Greene St (45768-5057)
PHONE...740 473-2629
Danny W Thompson, *Ch of Bd*
Janet Thompson, *President*
EMP: 8
SQ FT: 900
SALES: 1.5MM **Privately Held**
SIC: 1311 Crude petroleum production; natural gas production

(G-15127)
THREE H LUMBER
176 Dana Rd (45768)
PHONE...740 473-2515

Mack Haessly, *Partner*
Kenneth Haessly, *Partner*
EMP: 8
SALES (est): 822.5K **Privately Held**
SIC: 2421 5031 7389 Lumber: rough, sawed or planed; lumber: rough, dressed & finished;

Newton Falls
Trumbull County

(G-15128)
AMERICAN MOLDED PLASTICS INC
3876 Newton Fls Bailey Rd (44444-9746)
P.O. Box 434 (44444-0434)
PHONE...330 872-3838
Fax: 330 872-3325
Ray Allen, *President*
Bertha Allen, *Vice Pres*
Joe Allen, *Finance Mgr*
EMP: 10
SQ FT: 6,000
SALES (est): 1.5MM **Privately Held**
WEB: www.americanmoldedplastic.com
SIC: 3089 Injection molding of plastics

(G-15129)
BAR PROCESSING CORPORATION
1000 Windham Rd (44444-9586)
P.O. Box 280 (44444-0280)
PHONE...330 872-0914
Fax: 330 872-0231
Scott Griffin, *QC Dir*
Myrna Staats, *Human Res Dir*
Jack Starkey, *Sales Dir*
Jack Stacky, *Manager*
Rich Scheidly, *Maintence Staff*
EMP: 100
SALES (corp-wide): 36.3MM **Privately Held**
SIC: 3471 3316 Finishing, metals or formed products; polishing, metals or formed products; cold finishing of steel shapes
HQ: Bar Processing Corporation
   26601 W Huron River Dr
   Flat Rock MI 48134
   734 782-4454

(G-15130)
CARTER WOODCRAFT CENTER
3747 State Route 5 (44444-9566)
PHONE...330 872-6474
Dale Webber, *Principal*
EMP: 3
SALES (est): 166.4K **Privately Held**
SIC: 2435 Panels, hardwood plywood

(G-15131)
CRISSMAN TOOL & MACHINE INC
3877 Hallock Sook Rd (44444-8716)
PHONE...330 872-1412
Lionel Crissman, *President*
Sally Stacy, *Office Mgr*
Scott Crissman, *Admin Sec*
EMP: 3
SQ FT: 5,000
SALES (est): 220K **Privately Held**
SIC: 3599 Machine shop, jobbing & repair

(G-15132)
DIP IT GOOD FOODS INC
325 S Milton Blvd (44444-1732)
Rural Route 5189taylo (44444)
PHONE...330 219-3137
Robert D Giuliano, *President*
EMP: 5
SALES (est): 50K **Privately Held**
SIC: 2026 7389 Dips, sour cream based;

(G-15133)
GUYS BARBEQUE INC
Also Called: Guy's Award Winning Barbeque
4498 W Oakland St Sw (44444-9535)
P.O. Box 431 (44444-0431)
PHONE...330 872-7256
Ira Hughes, *President*
Lyn Hughes, *Principal*
EMP: 9 EST: 2001

SALES (est): 500K **Privately Held**
WEB: www.guysbbq.com
SIC: 2033 Barbecue sauce: packaged in cans, jars, etc.

(G-15134)
KENS HIS & HERS SHOP INC
Also Called: Positive Images
8 W Broad St (44444-1605)
PHONE...330 872-3190
Fax: 330 872-7712
Doug Cochran, *President*
Dawn Cochran, *Vice Pres*
EMP: 6
SQ FT: 5,200
SALES (est): 825.8K **Privately Held**
SIC: 2759 2395 Screen printing; embroidery & art needlework

(G-15135)
LUXAIRE CUSHION CO
2410 S Center St (44444-9408)
P.O. Box 156 (44444-0156)
PHONE...330 872-0995
Fax: 330 872-7227
Alan E Rathbun Jr, *President*
Steve Fackelman, *Vice Pres*
Julie Miller, *Shareholder*
EMP: 10 EST: 1946
SQ FT: 55,000
SALES (est): 1.2MM **Privately Held**
WEB: www.luxairecushion.com
SIC: 2393 Cushions, except spring & carpet: purchased materials

(G-15136)
MATRIX MEASURING SYSTEM
3877 Hallock Sook Rd (44444-8716)
PHONE...330 718-2804
Fax: 330 782-6030
Scott Crissman, *Owner*
EMP: 5
SALES: 100K **Privately Held**
SIC: 3829 7629 7389 Measuring & controlling devices; business machine repair, electric;

(G-15137)
NEWTON FALLS PRINTING
27 E Broad St (44444-1604)
PHONE...330 872-3532
Fax: 330 872-3532
Robert Staunton, *Owner*
EMP: 3
SQ FT: 4,275
SALES: 300K **Privately Held**
SIC: 2759 2752 Commercial printing; commercial printing, lithographic

(G-15138)
QUALITY SWITCH INC
715 Arlington Blvd (44444-8765)
P.O. Box 250 (44444-0250)
PHONE...330 872-5707
Russell Sewell, *President*
Jeremy Sewell, *Vice Pres*
Rick Sewell, *Vice Pres*
Larry Dix, *Plant Mgr*
Shannon Lawson, *Manager*
EMP: 29
SQ FT: 31,200
SALES (est): 5.5MM **Privately Held**
WEB: www.qualityswitch.com
SIC: 3679 Electronic switches

(G-15139)
S & S WLDG FABG MACHINING INC
2587 Miller Graber Rd (44444-9724)
PHONE...330 392-7878
Fax: 330 872-4024
R Saxton, *CEO*
Jonathan Saxton, *President*
Steven Saxton, *Administration*
EMP: 25
SALES (est): 3.2MM **Privately Held**
WEB: www.sandsweb.com
SIC: 3315 Welded steel wire fabric

(G-15140)
TRANSCO RAILWAY PRODUCTS INC
2310 S Center St (44444-9406)
PHONE...330 872-0934
Fax: 330 872-1432
Kevin Fedder, *Purch Mgr*

▲ = Import ▼=Export
◆ =Import/Export

Stephanie Tresino, *Human Res Dir*
Robert Ewing, *Manager*
EMP: 60
SQ FT: 100,000
SALES (corp-wide): 109.8MM **Privately Held**
SIC: 3441 3743 Fabricated structural metal; railroad equipment
HQ: Transco Railway Products Inc.
200 N La Salle St # 1550
Chicago IL 60601
312 427-2818

(G-15141)
VENTURE PLASTICS INC (PA)
Also Called: V P
4000 Warren Rd (44444)
P.O. Box 249 (44444-0249)
PHONE...................................330 872-5774
Fax: 330 872-3597
Kenneth M Groff, *CEO*
J Stephen Trapp, *President*
Dave Banfield, *General Mgr*
Stephen Trapp, *General Mgr*
David S Dennison, *Principal*
▲ **EMP:** 115
SQ FT: 60,000
SALES (est): 38MM **Privately Held**
WEB: www.ventureplastics.com
SIC: 3089 Injection molding of plastics

Ney
Defiance County

(G-15142)
JANET SULLIVAN
Also Called: Real Products Manufacturing
3480 State Route 15 (43549-9713)
PHONE...................................419 658-2333
Janet Sullivan, *Owner*
EMP: 4
SQ FT: 9,000
SALES (est): 400K **Privately Held**
SIC: 2851 Removers & cleaners

(G-15143)
RUSSELL E COY
Also Called: C & C Special Machine
2543 Flickinger Rd (43549-9730)
PHONE...................................419 658-2366
Fax: 419 658-2366
Russell E Coy, *Owner*
Cindra Coy, *Principal*
EMP: 4
SALES: 300K **Privately Held**
SIC: 3569 Filters

Niles
Trumbull County

(G-15144)
AUNTIE ANNES
5555 Youngstown Warren Rd # 637
(44446-4830)
PHONE...................................330 652-1939
Fax: 330 652-1939
Debra Barbara, *Manager*
EMP: 3
SALES (est): 86.6K **Privately Held**
SIC: 5461 5999 2051 5812 Pretzels; miscellaneous retail stores; bread, cake & related products; eating places

(G-15145)
BRT EXTRUSIONS INC
Also Called: Building Rlationships Together
1818 N Main St Unit 1 (44446-1285)
P.O. Box 309 (44446-0309)
PHONE...................................330 544-0177
Roy Smith, *President*
William Fusco, *Vice Pres*
Rick Russo, *Credit Mgr*
Frank Harris, *Sales Mgr*
EMP: 220
SQ FT: 92,000
SALES (est): 53.3MM **Privately Held**
WEB: www.brtextrusions.com
SIC: 3354 Aluminum extruded products

(G-15146)
CHIEFFOS FROZEN FOODS INC
406 S Main St (44446-1454)
PHONE...................................330 652-1222
Fax: 330 652-6448
Richard Yannucci, *President*
EMP: 8
SQ FT: 7,200
SALES: 760K **Privately Held**
WEB: www.chieffopasta.com
SIC: 2098 Macaroni & spaghetti

(G-15147)
CLEVELAND STEEL CONTAINER CORP
412 Mason St (44446-2349)
PHONE...................................330 544-2271
Fax: 330 544-4727
Chistopher Page, *Owner*
Derek Shepherd, *Safety Mgr*
EMP: 50
SALES (corp-wide): 147.3MM **Privately Held**
SIC: 3412 Barrels, shipping: metal; drums, shipping: metal; milk (fluid) shipping containers, metal; pails, shipping: metal
PA: Cleveland Steel Container Corporation
30310 Emerald Valley Pkwy
Solon OH 44139
440 349-8000

(G-15148)
CONDO INC
49 W Federal St (44446-5122)
PHONE...................................330 505-0485
John Condoleon, *Principal*
EMP: 3
SALES (est): 116.6K **Privately Held**
SIC: 3451 Screw machine products

(G-15149)
DINESOL PLASTICS INC
195 E Park Ave (44446-2352)
P.O. Box 470 (44446-0470)
PHONE...................................330 544-7171
Fax: 330 544-9632
Kenneth Fibus, *President*
David Tyo, *General Mgr*
Robert Hendricks Jr, *Vice Pres*
Kenneth Leonard, *Vice Pres*
Randy Fredrick, *QC Dir*
▲ **EMP:** 125 **EST:** 1976
SQ FT: 120,000
SALES: 86.3MM **Privately Held**
WEB: www.dinesol.com
SIC: 3089 Injection molding of plastics

(G-15150)
DURSO BAKERY INC
212 S Cedar Ave (44446-2308)
P.O. Box 605 (44446-0605)
PHONE...................................330 652-4741
Dominic D' Urso, *President*
Anthony D'Urso, *Shareholder*
Tony D'Urso, *Admin Sec*
EMP: 18
SQ FT: 7,000
SALES: 1.5MM **Privately Held**
SIC: 2051 Bakery: wholesale or wholesale/retail combined

(G-15151)
ENGINE MACHINE SERVICE INC
865 Summit Ave Unit 2 (44446-3661)
PHONE...................................330 505-1804
Fax: 330 505-1733
Randall Gains, *President*
Paul Gains, *Corp Secy*
EMP: 4
SQ FT: 400
SALES: 210K **Privately Held**
WEB: www.enginemachineservice.com
SIC: 3599 7539 Air intake filters, internal combustion engine, except auto; machine shop, automotive

(G-15152)
FAULL & SON LLC
515 Holford Ave (44446-1796)
P.O. Box 627 (44446-0627)
PHONE...................................330 652-4341
Fax: 330 652-4342
James K Faull, *Principal*
Ted Faull,
EMP: 10 **EST:** 1949
SQ FT: 16,000

SALES (est): 330K **Privately Held**
WEB: www.faullandson.com
SIC: 3469 3544 3498 3429 Stamping metal for the trade; special dies & tools; fabricated pipe & fittings; manufactured hardware (general)

(G-15153)
FRAME DEPOT INC
1043 Youngstown Warren Rd (44446-4620)
PHONE...................................330 652-7865
Robert Fowler, *President*
Jill Fowler, *Vice Pres*
Joe Fowler, *Vice Pres*
EMP: 5
SALES (est): 356.3K **Privately Held**
SIC: 7699 2499 7999 Picture framing, custom; picture & mirror frames, wood; arts & crafts instruction

(G-15154)
GENERAL ELECTRIC COMPANY
403 N Main St (44446-5130)
PHONE...................................330 297-0861
Fax: 330 297-7957
John Gritti, *Opers Mgr*
Jianwu LI, *Engineer*
Brian Sweiers, *Engineer*
Claude Yee, *Engineer*
Kent Snyder, *Manager*
EMP: 600
SALES (corp-wide): 123.6B **Publicly Held**
SIC: 3641 Electric lamps
PA: General Electric Company
41 Farnsworth St
Boston MA 02210
617 443-3000

(G-15155)
GENERAL ELECTRIC COMPANY
403 N Main St (44446-5130)
PHONE...................................330 373-1400
Fax: 330 393-5370
Joseph Connolly, *Mfg Staff*
William Stredney, *Purchasing*
David Martin, *Branch Mgr*
Kimberly Hamilton, *Clerk*
EMP: 600
SALES (corp-wide): 123.6B **Publicly Held**
SIC: 3641 3648 3229 Lamps, sealed beam; lighting equipment; pressed & blown glass
PA: General Electric Company
41 Farnsworth St
Boston MA 02210
617 443-3000

(G-15156)
GLENWOOD ERECTORS INC
905 Summit Ave (44446-3612)
PHONE...................................330 652-9616
Fax: 330 652-9615
Linda L Trunick, *President*
Michael E Trunick, *Vice Pres*
EMP: 7
SQ FT: 4,000
SALES (est): 1.1MM **Privately Held**
SIC: 3441 Fabricated structural metal

(G-15157)
HAMILTON RTI INC
1000 Warren Ave (44446-1168)
PHONE...................................330 652-9951
Allyn E Mathews, *Principal*
EMP: 5
SALES (est): 444.1K
SALES (corp-wide): 12.3B **Publicly Held**
SIC: 3339 Titanium metal, sponge & granules
HQ: Rti International Metals, Inc.
5th Fl 1550 Crplis Hts Rd
Coraopolis PA 15108
412 893-0026

(G-15158)
HOWLAND MACHINE CORP
947 Summit Ave (44446-3612)
PHONE...................................330 544-4029
Fax: 330 544-4324
Bruce V Dewey, *President*
Carl Ford, *General Mgr*
Becky Daley, *Manager*
EMP: 20

SQ FT: 22,000
SALES (est): 3.9MM **Privately Held**
WEB: www.howland-machine.com
SIC: 3469 Machine parts, stamped or pressed metal

(G-15159)
INDUCTION SERVICES INC
1713 N Main St (44446-1249)
PHONE...................................330 652-4494
Fax: 330 652-0340
Merle N Money, *President*
Brian Money, *Corp Secy*
Nora Money, *Purchasing*
Brant Delahunty, *Manager*
EMP: 7
SQ FT: 11,000
SALES: 750K **Privately Held**
SIC: 3567 Induction heating equipment

(G-15160)
INTER-POWER CORPORATION
1713 N Main St (44446-1249)
PHONE...................................330 652-4494
Merle Money, *President*
EMP: 8 **Privately Held**
WEB: www.interpwr.com
SIC: 3567 Induction heating equipment
PA: Inter-Power Corporation
3578 Van Dyke Rd
Almont MI 48003

(G-15161)
INTERNATIONAL TECHNICAL
Also Called: Itps
852 Ann Ave (44446-2924)
P.O. Box 111 (44446-0111)
PHONE...................................330 505-1218
Samuel H Berkowitz, *CEO*
Richard L Goodman, *President*
▲ **EMP:** 23
SQ FT: 5,000
SALES (est): 5.5MM **Privately Held**
WEB: www.itps-inc.com
SIC: 2821 Plastics materials & resins

(G-15162)
IRONICS INC
750 S Main St (44446-1372)
P.O. Box 292 (44446-0292)
PHONE...................................330 652-0583
Fax: 330 652-2534
Pete Tominey Jr, *President*
Mary Jane Tominey, *Shareholder*
EMP: 9
SQ FT: 10,000
SALES (est): 1.5MM **Privately Held**
WEB: www.ironics.com
SIC: 2816 3295 Iron oxide pigments (ochers, siennas, umbers); blast furnace slag

(G-15163)
J A MCMAHON INCORPORATED
649 Grant St (44446-2331)
PHONE...................................330 652-2588
Fax: 330 652-2451
J A McMahon, *President*
Debbie Chufo, *Manager*
EMP: 26
SQ FT: 32,000
SALES: 11.6MM **Privately Held**
WEB: www.jamcmahon.com
SIC: 3441 Fabricated structural metal

(G-15164)
JET STREAM INTERNATIONAL INC
931 Summit Ave Unit 3 (44446-3662)
PHONE...................................330 505-9988
Fax: 330 505-9959
Edgar B Rumble Jr, *President*
John Isbill, *Vice Pres*
▲ **EMP:** 45 **EST:** 2000
SQ FT: 70,000
SALES (est): 7.7MM **Privately Held**
WEB: www.jetstr.com
SIC: 3469 3272 Metal stampings; concrete stuctural support & building material

(G-15165)
JOHN MANEELY COMPANY
Also Called: Wheatland Tube Company
1800 Hunter Ave (44446-1671)
PHONE...................................724 342-6851
Mark Bahrey, *Branch Mgr*

GEOGRAPHIC

EMP: 35
SALES (corp-wide): 637.5MM **Privately Held**
SIC: 3498 3317 3312 Pipe sections fabricated from purchased pipe; steel pipe & tubes; blast furnaces & steel mills
HQ: Wheatland Tube, Llc
　227 W Monroe St Ste 2600
　Chicago IL 60606
　312 275-1600

(G-15166)
KROK PRINTING INC
414 W Federal St (44446-1805)
P.O. Box 91 (44446-0091)
PHONE..............................330 652-8198
Richard Krok, *President*
EMP: 3
SQ FT: 1,000
SALES: 70K **Privately Held**
SIC: 2752 2759 Commercial printing, offset; letterpress printing

(G-15167)
KRONER PUBLICATIONS INC (PA)
1123 W Park Ave (44446-1188)
P.O. Box 150 (44446-0150)
PHONE..............................330 544-5500
John Kroner Jr, *President*
Nick Poorbaugh, *General Mgr*
EMP: 30
SALES: 540K **Privately Held**
SIC: 2711 Commercial printing & newspaper publishing combined

(G-15168)
METAL PRODUCTS COMPANY (PA)
Also Called: Stamtex Metal Stampings
112 Erie St (44446-2320)
PHONE..............................330 652-2558
Fax: 330 652-7369
Philip Frankle, *President*
Patty Camps, *General Mgr*
Jay Rossi, *Accounts Mgr*
Russell Caddes, *Sales Associate*
Gerald Dungan, *Data Proc Staff*
EMP: 40 **EST:** 1921
SQ FT: 50,000
SALES (est): 7.3MM **Privately Held**
WEB: www.stamtexmp.com
SIC: 3465 Automotive stampings

(G-15169)
METAL PRODUCTS COMPANY
Also Called: Stamtex
1818 N Main St Unit 4 (44446-1285)
PHONE..............................330 652-6201
Philip Frankel, *President*
Bob Oatridge, *Executive*
EMP: 20
SALES (corp-wide): 7.2MM **Privately Held**
WEB: www.stamtexmp.com
SIC: 3469 Metal stampings
PA: The Metal Products Company
　112 Erie St
　Niles OH 44446
　330 652-2558

(G-15170)
MICHAELS STORES INC
Also Called: Michaels 9837
5555 Youngstown Warren Rd # 914 (44446-4804)
PHONE..............................330 505-1168
Fax: 330 505-1179
Paul Rockenfelder, *Branch Mgr*
EMP: 35
SALES (corp-wide): 5.2B **Publicly Held**
WEB: www.michaels.com
SIC: 3944 5945 Craft & hobby kits & sets; hobby, toy & game shops
HQ: Michaels Stores, Inc.
　8000 Bent Branch Dr
　Irving TX 75063
　972 409-1300

(G-15171)
NILES MANUFACTURING & FINSHG
465 Walnut St (44446-2374)
PHONE..............................330 544-0402
Fax: 330 544-8018

Robert Hendricks, *President*
Richard Handricks, *Opers Mgr*
Beth Hall, *CFO*
Nancy Skaggs, *Manager*
EMP: 110
SQ FT: 150,000
SALES (est): 24.9MM **Privately Held**
WEB: www.nilesmfg.com
SIC: 3469 3479 3471 3444 Metal stampings; coating of metals & formed products; plating & polishing; sheet metalwork

(G-15172)
NILES ROLL SERVICE INC (PA)
704 Warren Ave (44446-1643)
PHONE..............................330 544-0026
Timothy L Boggs, *President*
Beverly Boggs, *Corp Secy*
Mithc Collins, *VP Opers*
EMP: 11
SQ FT: 4,964
SALES (est): 1MM **Privately Held**
SIC: 3069 Roll coverings, rubber

(G-15173)
PHILLIPS MANUFACTURING CO
504 Walnut St (44446-2961)
PHONE..............................330 652-4335
Fax: 330 652-5981
Robert Beach, *Purchasing*
Brian Biggins, *Human Res Dir*
Steve Dalrymple, *Branch Mgr*
Roy Rantilla, *Manager*
Kathy Bauge, *Director*
EMP: 90
SALES (corp-wide): 54.4MM **Privately Held**
WEB: www.phillipsmfg.com
SIC: 3442 3444 3541 Metal doors, sash & trim; sheet metalwork; machine tools, metal cutting type
PA: Phillips Manufacturing Co.
　4949 S 30th St
　Omaha NE 68107
　402 339-3800

(G-15174)
PIERCE-SPAFFORD METALS CO INC
1000 Warren Ave (44446-1168)
PHONE..............................800 421-3778
John W Spafford, *Principal*
EMP: 3
SALES (est): 180K **Privately Held**
SIC: 3724 Aircraft engines & engine parts

(G-15175)
PLUGGERS INC
1617 Warren Ave (44446-1170)
P.O. Box 474, Columbiana (44408-0474)
PHONE..............................330 383-7692
Orville Nicholas, *Vice Pres*
EMP: 5
SALES (est): 343.2K **Privately Held**
WEB: www.pluggers.com
SIC: 1389 Well plugging & abandoning, oil & gas

(G-15176)
RMI TITANIUM COMPANY LLC (DH)
Also Called: Rti Niles
1000 Warren Ave (44446-1168)
PHONE..............................330 652-9952
Dawn S Hickton, *President*
Timothy Rupert, *President*
John H Odle, *Exec VP*
Stephen R Giangiordano, *Senior VP*
William Hull, *Senior VP*
▼ **EMP:** 20
SQ FT: 677,605
SALES (est): 153.7MM
SALES (corp-wide): 12.3B **Publicly Held**
WEB: www.rti-intl.com
SIC: 3399 3356 1741 3533 Powder, metal; titanium; masonry & other stonework; oil & gas drilling rigs & equipment
HQ: Rti International Metals, Inc.
　5th Fl 1550 Crplis Hts Rd
　Coraopolis PA 15108
　412 893-0026

(G-15177)
RTI ALLOYS
1000 Warren Ave (44446-1168)
PHONE..............................330 652-9952
Frank Marino, *Manager*
Robert G Helwig, *Administration*
EMP: 8
SALES (est): 1.1MM **Privately Held**
SIC: 3312 Blast furnaces & steel mills

(G-15178)
RTI FINANCE CORP
Also Called: Rti Niles
1000 Warren Ave (44446-1168)
PHONE..............................330 652-9952
Dawne S Hickton, *CEO*
EMP: 5
SALES (est): 1MM
SALES (corp-wide): 12.3B **Publicly Held**
SIC: 3339 Primary nonferrous metals
HQ: Rti International Metals, Inc.
　5th Fl 1550 Crplis Hts Rd
　Coraopolis PA 15108
　412 893-0026

(G-15179)
RTI INTERNATIONAL METALS INC
2000 Warren Ave (44446-1148)
PHONE..............................330 544-9470
Kenneth Roach, *Manager*
Bryan Palmer, *Technology*
Roy Rohrabaugh, *Lab Dir*
EMP: 5
SALES (corp-wide): 12.3B **Publicly Held**
SIC: 3441 Fabricated structural metal
HQ: Rti International Metals, Inc.
　5th Fl 1550 Crplis Hts Rd
　Coraopolis PA 15108
　412 893-0026

(G-15180)
RTI INTERNATIONAL METALS INC
Also Called: Rti Niles
1000 Warren Ave (44446-1168)
P.O. Box 269 (44446-0269)
PHONE..............................330 544-7633
Fax: 330 544-7876
Diane S Seman, *Principal*
Michael Wellham, *COO*
Blane Salvador, *Plant Mgr*
Eldon Wyatt, *Safety Mgr*
Mark Diehl, *Production*
EMP: 42
SALES (corp-wide): 12.3B **Publicly Held**
SIC: 3356 Titanium & titanium alloy: rolling, drawing or extruding
HQ: Rti International Metals, Inc.
　5th Fl 1550 Crplis Hts Rd
　Coraopolis PA 15108
　412 893-0026

(G-15181)
RTI INTERNATIONAL METALS INC
Rti Hermitage
1000 Warren Ave (44446-1168)
PHONE..............................330 652-9955
Fax: 330 544-7701
Karl Haff, *Engineer*
Larry Jancay, *Engineer*
Chuck Prachick, *Engineer*
Paul Mandell, *Branch Mgr*
Larry Restivo, *Technology*
EMP: 9
SALES (corp-wide): 12.3B **Publicly Held**
SIC: 3356 Titanium
HQ: Rti International Metals, Inc.
　5th Fl 1550 Crplis Hts Rd
　Coraopolis PA 15108
　412 893-0026

(G-15182)
RTI NILES
1000 Warren Ave (44446-1168)
PHONE..............................330 455-4010
Ron Sloan, *Plant Mgr*
EMP: 4
SALES (est): 288.5K **Privately Held**
SIC: 2816 Inorganic pigments

(G-15183)
RYMAN GRINDERS INC
704 Warren Ave (44446-1643)
PHONE..............................330 652-5080
Fax: 330 652-6644
Timothy L Boggs, *President*
Tim L Boggs, *President*
EMP: 19 **EST:** 1996
SALES (est): 2.6MM **Privately Held**
SIC: 3531 Grinders, stone: portable

(G-15184)
S AND K PAINTING
1346 Clark St (44446-3446)
PHONE..............................330 505-1910
Stephen Hrosar, *President*
EMP: 4
SALES (est): 440.2K **Privately Held**
SIC: 2752 Commercial printing, lithographic

(G-15185)
TIMKEN COMPANY
1819 N Main St (44446-1251)
P.O. Box 477905, Broadview Heights (44147-7905)
PHONE..............................234 262-3000
Fax: 330 652-1207
Richard Hill, *Manager*
EMP: 100
SALES (corp-wide): 2.6B **Publicly Held**
SIC: 3562 Ball & roller bearings; ball bearings & parts
PA: The Timken Company
　4500 Mount Pleasant St Nw
　North Canton OH 44720
　234 262-3000

(G-15186)
TRAICHAL CONSTRUCTION COMPANY (PA)
Also Called: Warren Door
332 Plant St (44446-1895)
P.O. Box 70 (44446-0070)
PHONE..............................800 255-3667
Fax: 330 652-6899
Edward Traichal, *President*
Nick Gorcheff, *Vice Pres*
Vince Roberts, *Purchasing*
Mike Lisko, *Controller*
Alfonso Roberts, *VP Sales*
EMP: 26
SQ FT: 15,000
SALES: 5MM **Privately Held**
WEB: www.plantia.com
SIC: 3442 1751 5199 5031 Metal doors; rolling doors for industrial buildings or warehouses, metal; window & door installation & erection; advertising specialties; doors & windows

(G-15187)
VALLEY GRAPHICS
1494 Salt Springs Rd (44446-1348)
PHONE..............................330 652-0484
James S Fentules, *Owner*
EMP: 4
SALES: 210K **Privately Held**
WEB: www.valley-services.com
SIC: 2752 Color lithography

(G-15188)
WARREN DOOR
Also Called: Traichal Construction
332 Plant St (44446-1844)
P.O. Box 70 (44446-0070)
PHONE..............................330 652-6346
Warren Door, *Principal*
EMP: 35
SALES (est): 2MM
SALES (corp-wide): 5MM **Privately Held**
SIC: 3442 Metal doors
PA: The Traichal Construction Company
　332 Plant St
　Niles OH 44446
　800 255-3667

(G-15189)
WEST & BARKER INC
950 Summit Ave (44446-3693)
PHONE..............................330 652-9923
Fax: 330 652-9991
Samuel M Barker III, *President*
Suzanne Leone, *Treasurer*
June Barker, *Admin Sec*
EMP: 25 **EST:** 1971

SQ FT: 106,000
SALES (est): 5MM **Privately Held**
WEB: www.westandbarker.com
SIC: **3089** 2396 3069 3714 Plastic hardware & building products; automotive & apparel trimmings; thread, rubber; motor vehicle parts & accessories

(G-15190)
YAR CORPORATION
406 S Main St (44446-1454)
PHONE..................330 652-1222
Richard A Yannucci, *President*
EMP: 7
SALES: 800K **Privately Held**
SIC: **2098** Macaroni & spaghetti

North Baltimore
Wood County

(G-15191)
AUTOMATED BLDG COMPONENTS INC (PA)
2359 Grant Rd (45872-9662)
PHONE..................419 257-2152
Fax: 419 257-2779
Harold L McCarty, *CEO*
Marshal McCarty, *President*
John Gilpin, *CFO*
Jerry Reisgraf, *Info Tech Dir*
Jennifer Buckingham, *Shareholder*
EMP: 30
SQ FT: 10,000
SALES (est): 22.3MM **Privately Held**
WEB: www.abctruss.com
SIC: **2421** 2439 2541 2435 Building & structural materials, wood; trusses, wooden roof; wood partitions & fixtures; hardwood veneer & plywood; millwork

(G-15192)
CONTINENTAL STRL PLAS INC
Also Called: CSP North Baltimore
100 S Poe Rd (45872-9551)
PHONE..................419 257-2231
Gary Dickson, *Branch Mgr*
EMP: 234
SALES (corp-wide): 6.7B **Privately Held**
WEB: www.cs-plastics.com
SIC: **3089** 3714 Plastic processing; motor vehicle parts & accessories
HQ: Continental Structural Plastics, Inc.
255 Rex Blvd
Auburn Hills MI 48326
248 237-7800

(G-15193)
KEYSTONE FOODS LLC
Equity Group-Ohio Div
2208 Grant Rd (45872-9663)
P.O. Box 307 (45872-0307)
PHONE..................419 257-2341
Ken Shafer, *QC Dir*
Hank Goebel, *Persnl Mgr*
Ginger Mills, *Personnel*
Steven Alberts, *Manager*
Jeff Bryant, *Director*
EMP: 250
SQ FT: 60,000 **Privately Held**
WEB: www.keystonefoods.com
SIC: **2013** Sausages & other prepared meats
HQ: Keystone Foods Llc
905 Airport Rd Ste 400
West Chester PA 19380
610 667-6700

(G-15194)
MABAR PRINTING SERVICE
400 N Tarr St (45872-1157)
PHONE..................419 257-3659
Fax: 419 257-3768
Eric Mays, *Owner*
EMP: 3 EST: 1960
SALES: 90K **Privately Held**
SIC: **2752** Commercial printing, lithographic

(G-15195)
MID-WOOD INC
Also Called: True Value
101 E State St (45872-1358)
PHONE..................419 257-3331

Fax: 419 257-3218
Joe Smith, *Manager*
Scott Barnhisel, *Manager*
EMP: 10
SALES (corp-wide): 80MM **Privately Held**
SIC: **5153** 5261 5251 5531 Grains; fertilizer; hardware; automotive tires; prepared feeds; lawn & garden services
PA: Mid-Wood, Inc.
12965 Defiance Pike
Cygnet OH
419 352-5231

(G-15196)
POLYONE CORPORATION
733 E Water St (45872-1434)
PHONE..................573 468-6513
Eric F Mall, *Manager*
EMP: 15 **Publicly Held**
WEB: www.polyone.com
SIC: **3087** Custom compound purchased resins
PA: Polyone Corporation
33587 Walker Rd
Avon Lake OH 44012

(G-15197)
POLYONE CORPORATION
733 E Water St (45872-1434)
P.O. Box 247 (45872-0247)
PHONE..................440 930-1000
Pete Jacob, *Vice Pres*
Peter Jacobs, *Plant Mgr*
Pete Laughlin, *Purchasing*
Brent Cassata, *VP Sales*
Mike Brandenburg, *Sales Staff*
EMP: 80 **Publicly Held**
WEB: www.polyone.com
SIC: **2821** 5169 3087 Vinyl resins; synthetic resins, rubber & plastic materials; custom compound purchased resins
PA: Polyone Corporation
33587 Walker Rd
Avon Lake OH 44012

(G-15198)
S M C ALUMINUM FOUNDRY INC
100 Peters St (45872-1200)
PHONE..................419 257-2175
Fax: 419 257-3979
James Adkins, *President*
EMP: 14
SQ FT: 2,894
SALES (est): 1.1MM **Privately Held**
SIC: **3365** Machinery castings, aluminum

(G-15199)
TRUCK STOP EMBROIDERY (PA)
12906 Deshler Rd (45872-9650)
PHONE..................419 257-2860
Phillip Johnson, *Principal*
EMP: 5
SALES (est): 1.5MM **Privately Held**
SIC: **3552** Embroidery machines

(G-15200)
TRUCK STOP EMBROIDERY
Also Called: Innovative Stiching
12906 Deshler Rd (45872-9650)
PHONE..................419 257-2860
Jen Fackler, *Manager*
EMP: 5
SALES (corp-wide): 1.5MM **Privately Held**
SIC: **2395** Embroidery products, except schiffli machine
PA: Truck Stop Embroidery
12906 Deshler Rd
North Baltimore OH 45872
419 257-2860

North Bend
Hamilton County

(G-15201)
AGRIUM US INC
10743 Brower Rd (45052-9761)
P.O. Box 158 (45052-0158)
PHONE..................513 941-4100
Fax: 513 941-3910
Bob Mendenhall, *Branch Mgr*
EMP: 68

SALES (corp-wide): 13.6B **Privately Held**
SIC: **2873** Nitrogenous fertilizers
HQ: Agrium U.S. Inc.
3005 Rocky Mountain Ave
Loveland CO 80538
970 685-3300

(G-15202)
BALECO INTERNATIONAL INC
3200 State Line Rd (45052-9731)
P.O. Box 11331, Cincinnati (45211-0331)
PHONE..................513 353-3000
Fax: 513 353-1090
Martin T Hammersmith, *President*
Jeffrey Hammersmith, *Vice Pres*
Todd E Hammersmith, *CFO*
▲ EMP: 20
SQ FT: 72,000
SALES (est): 11.9MM **Privately Held**
SIC: **5091** 3589 Swimming pools, equipment & supplies; swimming pool filter & water conditioning systems

(G-15203)
CHEMOURS COMPANY FC LLC
11215 Brower Rd (45052-9755)
PHONE..................513 941-4121
Robert Ellis, *Purchasing*
John Ferguson, *Branch Mgr*
Henry Sparks, *Maintence Staff*
EMP: 19
SALES (corp-wide): 5.4B **Publicly Held**
WEB: www.dupont.com
SIC: **2819** Sulfuric acid, oleum
HQ: The Chemours Company Fc Llc
1007 Market St
Wilmington DE 19898
302 774-1000

(G-15204)
CROP PRODUCTION SERVICES INC
10743 Brower Rd (45052-9761)
PHONE..................513 941-4100
Robert Mendenhall, *Sales Staff*
Bill Chokran, *Manager*
EMP: 30
SALES (corp-wide): 13.6B **Privately Held**
WEB: www.cropproductionservices.com
SIC: **2873** 2875 2819 Nitrogenous fertilizers; fertilizers, mixing only; industrial inorganic chemicals
HQ: Crop Production Services, Inc.
3005 Rocky Mountain Ave
Loveland CO 80538
970 685-3300

(G-15205)
IMPACT SPORTS WEAR INC
Also Called: Impact Promotions
99 Saint Annes Ave (45052-9655)
PHONE..................513 922-7406
David J Becker, *President*
EMP: 3
SQ FT: 800
SALES (est): 250K **Privately Held**
SIC: **3552** 5137 5136 Silk screens for textile industry; uniforms, women's & children's; uniforms, men's & boys'

(G-15206)
MARTIN MARIETTA MATERIALS INC
Martin Marietta Aggregates
10905 Us 50 (45052)
PHONE..................513 353-1400
Bernie Jelen, *Branch Mgr*
EMP: 55
SALES (corp-wide): 3.8B **Publicly Held**
WEB: www.martinmarietta.com
SIC: **1422** Crushed & broken limestone
PA: Martin Marietta Materials Inc
2710 Wycliff Rd
Raleigh NC 27607
919 781-4550

(G-15207)
RACK DRAFT SERVICE INC
11109 Guard Ln (45052-9413)
PHONE..................513 353-5520
James M Rack, *President*
Jimmy Rack, *Vice Pres*
Melissa Seal, *Treasurer*
EMP: 11
SQ FT: 3,000

SALES (est): 1.8MM **Privately Held**
SIC: **3585** Beer dispensing equipment

(G-15208)
STEEL SERVICES INC
Also Called: Marky Welding
3150 State Line Rd (45052-9731)
PHONE..................513 353-4173
Jeff Wernke, *President*
John Wernke, *Corp Secy*
EMP: 3
SALES (est): 310K **Privately Held**
WEB: www.wernkesteel.com
SIC: **3441** Expansion joints (structural shapes), iron or steel

(G-15209)
SUPER SIGNS INC
9890 Mount Nebo Rd (45052-9480)
PHONE..................480 968-2200
Fax: 513 941-9615
Sammy Boner, *President*
Barb Huhey, *Marketing Staff*
Joe Mazzei, *Manager*
EMP: 36
SQ FT: 1,500
SALES: 1MM **Privately Held**
WEB: www.supersigns.com
SIC: **3993** Signs & advertising specialties

(G-15210)
WERNKE WLDG & STL ERECTION CO
3150 State Line Rd (45052-9731)
PHONE..................513 353-4173
Fax: 513 353-3306
Jeff Wernke, *President*
James Wernke, *Chairman*
John Wernke, *Corp Secy*
Jerry Wernke, *Vice Pres*
EMP: 14
SQ FT: 4,800
SALES (est): 1.8MM **Privately Held**
SIC: **1791** 3441 Iron work, structural; fabricated structural metal

---

North Benton
Portage County

(G-15211)
ALLIANCE DRILLING INC
20388 N Benton West Rd (44449-9636)
PHONE..................330 584-2781
EMP: 10
SALES (est): 940K **Privately Held**
SIC: **3541** Drilling

(G-15212)
BELOIT FUEL LLC
9379 First East St (44449)
PHONE..................330 584-1915
Charles R Pierce, *Principal*
EMP: 7
SALES (est): 873K **Privately Held**
SIC: **2869** Fuels

(G-15213)
PAUL J TATULINSKI LTD
1595 W Main St (44449)
P.O. Box 382 (44449-0382)
PHONE..................330 584-8251
Paul J Tatulinski, *President*
EMP: 10
SQ FT: 4,704
SALES: 700K **Privately Held**
SIC: **3053** Gaskets, all materials

(G-15214)
THEISS UAV SOLUTIONS LLC
10881 Johnson Rd (44449-9652)
P.O. Box 1086, Salem (44460-8086)
PHONE..................330 584-2070
Chad Kapper, *President*
Shawn Theiss, *General Mgr*
Richard Theiss, *Prdtn Mgr*
EMP: 8
SQ FT: 4,600
SALES (est): 960.1K
SALES (corp-wide): 172.9MM **Privately Held**
WEB: www.theissaviation.com
SIC: **3721** 7363 Aircraft; pilot service, aviation

PA: Lauren International, Ltd.
2228 Reiser Ave Se
New Philadelphia OH 44663
330 339-3373

North Bloomfield
Trumbull County

(G-15215)
C DCAP MODEM LINE
8829 State Route 45 (44450-9800)
PHONE...................................440 685-4302
EMP: 3
SALES (est): 156.2K **Privately Held**
SIC: 3661 Mfg Telephone/Telegraph Apparatus

(G-15216)
DELUCA VINEYARDS
8954 State Route 45 (44450-9777)
PHONE...................................440 685-4242
Randy Deluca, *Partner*
Joe Deluca, *Partner*
EMP: 4
SQ FT: 1,765
SALES (est): 98.7K **Privately Held**
SIC: 0172 2084 Grapes; wines

North Canton
Stark County

(G-15217)
A SCHULMAN INC
8562 Port Jackson Ave Nw (44720-5467)
PHONE...................................330 498-4840
A Maghes, *Branch Mgr*
EMP: 50
SALES (corp-wide): 2.5B **Publicly Held**
SIC: 3089 Coloring & finishing of plastic products
PA: A. Schulman, Inc.
3637 Ridgewood Rd
Fairlawn OH 44333
330 666-3751

(G-15218)
A STUCKI COMPANY
7376 Whipple Ave Nw (44720-7140)
PHONE...................................412 424-0560
EMP: 5
SALES (corp-wide): 23.7MM **Privately Held**
SIC: 3743 Railroad equipment
PA: A. Stucki Company
360 Wright Brothers Dr
Coraopolis PA 15108
412 424-0560

(G-15219)
AMISH LIGHTS CANDLES
8748 Woodlore Cir Nw (44720-4695)
PHONE...................................330 546-3900
Tracy Oconnor, *Administration*
EMP: 3
SALES (est): 195.3K **Privately Held**
SIC: 3999 Candles

(G-15220)
ASC INDUSTRIES INC
2100 International Pkwy (44720-1373)
PHONE...................................330 899-0340
William Blackerby, *CEO*
Yinghua LI, *VP Engrg*
Sorin Hodea, *Engineer*
◆ **EMP:** 24
SQ FT: 200,000
SALES (est): 97.2MM **Privately Held**
WEB: www.asc-ind.com
SIC: 3714 Water pump, motor vehicle
HQ: United Components, Llc
1900 W Field Ct
Lake Forest IL 60045
812 867-4516

(G-15221)
B2 INCORPORATED (PA)
Also Called: B-Squared Prtg Mktg Solutions
8324c Cleveland Ave Nw (44720-4820)
PHONE...................................330 244-9510
Fax: 330 899-9922
Brent Belles, *CEO*

Kara Fitzwater, *Manager*
EMP: 9
SALES (est): 868.7K **Privately Held**
SIC: 2752 Commercial printing, lithographic

(G-15222)
BALL CORPORATION
3075 Brookline Rd (44720-1526)
PHONE...................................330 244-2313
EMP: 7
SALES (corp-wide): 9B **Publicly Held**
SIC: 3411 Food & beverage containers
PA: Ball Corporation
10 Longs Peak Dr
Broomfield CO 80021
303 469-3131

(G-15223)
CANTON CUT STONE CO
6570 Promway Ave Nw (44720-7314)
PHONE...................................330 456-8408
Fax: 330 456-0635
Dick Nicely, *President*
Ronald Gasper, *General Mgr*
▲ **EMP:** 4 **EST:** 1953
SQ FT: 3,000
SALES (est): 390K **Privately Held**
WEB: www.cantoncutstone.com
SIC: 3281 5032 Stone, quarrying & processing of own stone products; stone, crushed or broken

(G-15224)
CANTON ELEVATOR INC
2575 Greensburg Rd (44720-1419)
PHONE...................................330 833-3600
Fax: 330 833-0229
Robert A Kazar, *CEO*
Michael J Paschke, *President*
Rod Digman, *Purchasing*
Frank Dangelo, *Engineer*
Bob Kasar, *Human Res Dir*
▲ **EMP:** 75
SQ FT: 80,000
SALES (est): 18.8MM **Privately Held**
WEB: www.cantonelevator.com
SIC: 3534 3537 Elevators & moving stairways; industrial trucks & tractors

(G-15225)
CUSTER PRODUCTS LIMITED
4101 Shuffel St Nw # 100 (44720-6900)
P.O. Box 2997, Canton (44720-0997)
PHONE...................................330 490-3158
Fax: 330 497-9736
Bradley Custer, *President*
▲ **EMP:** 15
SQ FT: 12,500
SALES (est): 3.6MM **Privately Held**
WEB: www.custerproducts.com
SIC: 3714 5013 5072 Motor vehicle parts & accessories; motor vehicle supplies & new parts; hardware

(G-15226)
DANSIZEN PRINTING CO INC
4525 Aultman Ave Nw (44720-8235)
PHONE...................................330 966-4962
Fax: 330 966-5969
James Dansizen, *President*
Beverly Danizen, *Finance Other*
EMP: 4
SALES: 175K **Privately Held**
SIC: 2752 Commercial printing, lithographic

(G-15227)
DIEBOLD INCORPORATED
5995 Mayfair Rd (44720-1597)
PHONE...................................330 490-4000
Fax: 330 497-4555
Diane Pellegrene, *Principal*
Natalie Gainer, *Vice Pres*
Roy E Hathaway, *Engineer*
Lee Neutzling, *Marketing Staff*
Dawn Brown, *Manager*
EMP: 59
SALES (corp-wide): 3.3B **Publicly Held**
WEB: www.diebold.com
SIC: 3578 Automatic teller machines (ATM)
PA: Diebold Nixdorf, Incorporated
5995 Mayfair Rd
North Canton OH 44720
330 490-4000

(G-15228)
DIEBOLD NIXDORF INCORPORATED (PA)
5995 Mayfair Rd (44720-1550)
P.O. Box 3077 (44720-8077)
PHONE...................................330 490-4000
Fax: 330 490-4679
Andreas W Mattes, *CEO*
Henry D G Wallace, *Ch of Bd*
Jacob Trimmer, *Business Mgr*
Juergen Wunram, *COO*
James L M Chen, *Exec VP*
EMP: 900 **EST:** 1859
SALES: 3.3B **Publicly Held**
WEB: www.diebold.com
SIC: 3578 3699 3499 Automatic teller machines (ATM); banking machines; security control equipment & systems; safes & vaults, metal; safe deposit boxes or chests, metal

(G-15229)
FAIRWAY CARTS PARTS & MORE LLC
6944 Wales Ave Nw (44720-6333)
PHONE...................................234 209-9008
Timothy Doug Schuller, *President*
EMP: 4
SALES (est): 607.1K **Privately Held**
SIC: 3537 4789 4212 Trucks, tractors, loaders, carriers & similar equipment; cargo loading & unloading services; local trucking, without storage

(G-15230)
FANNIE MAY CNFCTONS BRANDS INC
5353 Lauby Rd (44720-1572)
PHONE...................................330 494-0833
Terry Michell, *President*
Gina Miller, *General Mgr*
Calvin Reynolds, *Plant Mgr*
Vince Grishaber, *Opers Mgr*
Ken Wannemacher, *Warehouse Mgr*
EMP: 800
SALES: 90MM
SALES (corp-wide): 1.1B **Publicly Held**
SIC: 5441 2066 Candy; chocolate bars, solid
HQ: Fannie May Confections Brands, Inc.
2457 W North Ave
Melrose Park IL 60160
773 693-9100

(G-15231)
FIVES BRONX INC
Also Called: Bronx Taylor Wilson
8817 Pleasantwood Ave Nw (44720-4759)
PHONE...................................330 277-1366
Richard Jeschelnig, *President*
Jeffrey T Knoll, *Principal*
Mike Pollard, *Vice Pres*
Brian Lombardi, *VP Opers*
Andrejs Maskancevs, *Buyer*
◆ **EMP:** 70 **EST:** 1988
SQ FT: 10,000
SALES (est): 21.1MM
SALES (corp-wide): 5.8MM **Privately Held**
WEB: www.btwcorp.com
SIC: 3547 Finishing equipment, rolling mill
HQ: Fives
27 Au 29
Paris 75009
145 237-575

(G-15232)
FLUID AUTOMATION INC
8400 Port Jackson Ave Nw (44720-5464)
PHONE...................................248 912-1970
Lance H Daby, *President*
Beverly Daby, *Corp Secy*
Leon L Daby, *Vice Pres*
Amber Daby, *Manager*
EMP: 25 **EST:** 1974
SQ FT: 16,000
SALES (est): 3.8MM **Privately Held**
WEB: www.fluidautomation.com
SIC: 3561 3569 Industrial pumps & parts; liquid automation machinery & equipment

(G-15233)
GBS CORP (PA)
Also Called: GBS Computer Solutions
7233 Freedom Ave Nw (44720-7123)
P.O. Box 2340, Canton (44720-0340)
PHONE...................................330 494-5330
Fax: 330 497-6943
Eugene Calpria, *CEO*
Jeff Fusco, *President*
Steve Hoy, *Managing Dir*
James R Carey, *Exec VP*
Jackie Davison, *Vice Pres*
▲ **EMP:** 150 **EST:** 1971
SQ FT: 115,000
SALES (est): 171.7MM **Privately Held**
WEB: www.gbscorp.com
SIC: 5045 5112 2675 2672 Computers, peripherals & software; business forms; folders, filing, die-cut: made from purchased materials; labels (unprinted), gummed: made from purchased materials; tape, pressure sensitive: made from purchased materials; manifold business forms; commercial printing

(G-15234)
GLASCRAFT INC
8400 Port Jackson Ave Nw (44720-5464)
PHONE...................................330 966-3000
Morris Wheeler, *President*
Byron Bradley, *Vice Pres*
Rob Pawlak, *Controller*
Michael Keegan, *Sales Mgr*
Karl Loomb, *Manager*
EMP: 65 **EST:** 1959
SQ FT: 51,200
SALES (est): 7.4MM
SALES (corp-wide): 1.3B **Publicly Held**
WEB: www.glascraft.com
SIC: 3563 Spraying outfits: metals, paints & chemicals (compressor)
PA: Graco Inc.
88 11th Ave Ne
Minneapolis MN 55413
612 623-6000

(G-15235)
GRACO OHIO INC (HQ)
Also Called: Liquid Control
8400 Port Jackson Ave Nw (44720-5464)
PHONE...................................330 494-1313
Fax: 330 494-5383
William C Schiltz, *Ch of Bd*
Kenneth Jacobs, *President*
Ronald W Dougherty, *Principal*
Charles John, *Purch Mgr*
Hank Gonzalez, *Purch Agent*
▲ **EMP:** 100
SQ FT: 73,000
SALES (est): 26.3MM
SALES (corp-wide): 1.3B **Publicly Held**
WEB: www.dispensit.com
SIC: 3824 3586 5251 Predetermining counters; measuring & dispensing pumps; pumps & pumping equipment
PA: Graco Inc.
88 11th Ave Ne
Minneapolis MN 55413
612 623-6000

(G-15236)
GRADY MCCAULEY INCORPORATED
Also Called: LSI Graphic Solutions Plus
9260 Pleasantwood Ave Nw (44720-9006)
PHONE...................................330 494-9444
Fax: 330 494-9991
David McCauley, *President*
Scott Ready, *Vice Pres*
Dave Lashchuk, *VP Mfg*
Rick McFarren, *Mfg Dir*
Brian Baughman, *Safety Mgr*
EMP: 100
SQ FT: 212,000
SALES (est): 19.6MM
SALES (corp-wide): 322.2MM **Publicly Held**
WEB: www.gradymccauley.com
SIC: 3993 2759 Signs & advertising specialties; screen printing
PA: Lsi Industries Inc.
10000 Alliance Rd
Blue Ash OH 45242
513 793-3200

(G-15237)
HAINES & COMPANY INC (PA)
Also Called: Criss Cross Directories
8050 Freedom Ave Nw (44720-6985)
P.O. Box 2117 (44720-0117)
PHONE....................................330 494-9111
Fax: 330 497-5507
William K Haines Jr, *Ch of Bd*
Leonard W Haines, *Principal*
Harriet E Jones, *Principal*
Lori Hohman, *Prdtn Mgr*
Delores Ball, *Treasurer*
▲ EMP: 130 EST: 1932
SQ FT: 20,000
SALES (est): 34MM **Privately Held**
WEB: www.haines.com
SIC: 2741 7331 2752 2759 Directories:
publishing & printing; mailing list compil-
ers; commercial printing, lithographic;
commercial printing

(G-15238)
HAINES CRISS CROSS (PA)
8050 Freedom Ave Nw (44720-6912)
PHONE....................................330 494-9111
John Segherd, *Principal*
EMP: 4
SALES (est): 509.9K **Privately Held**
SIC: 2741 Miscellaneous publishing

(G-15239)
HARRY LONDON CANDIES INC (DH)
Also Called: Harry London Chocolates
5353 Lauby Rd (44720-1572)
PHONE....................................330 494-0833
Fax: 330 499-6902
Terry Michell, *President*
Bill Rohm, *Vice Pres*
Ed Seibolt, *Vice Pres*
Ken Bourquin, *Facilities Mgr*
Matthew J Anderson, *CFO*
▲ EMP: 111
SQ FT: 200,000
SALES (est): 41.7MM
SALES (corp-wide): 1.1B **Publicly Held**
WEB: www.londoncandies.com
SIC: 2066 5441 Chocolate & cocoa prod-
ucts; candy
HQ: Fannie May Confections Brands, Inc.
2457 W North Ave
Melrose Park IL 60160
773 693-9100

(G-15240)
HOME QUARTERS NORTH CANTO
717 S Main St (44720-3009)
PHONE....................................330 806-5336
Rebecca Canto, *Principal*
EMP: 3
SALES (est): 163.8K **Privately Held**
SIC: 3131 Quarters

(G-15241)
HSM WIRE INTERNATIONAL INC
820 S Valley Blvd Nw (44720-2770)
P.O. Box 2153 (44720-0153)
PHONE....................................330 244-8501
Hal Marker, *Principal*
EMP: 5
SALES (est): 213.6K **Privately Held**
SIC: 3315 Fencing made in wiredrawing
plants

(G-15242)
IN THE MIX DJ SERVICE
5437 Portage St Nw (44720-6861)
PHONE....................................330 704-2833
Wayne Elliott, *Principal*
EMP: 4
SALES (est): 324.6K **Privately Held**
SIC: 3273 Ready-mixed concrete

(G-15243)
ISLAND CASTINGS INC
4321 Strausser St Nw (44720-7144)
PHONE....................................231 733-1053
Richard Lynham, *President*
Craig Klinkner, *Manager*
Susan Jackson, *Admin Mgr*
EMP: 75

SALES (est): 7.9MM
SALES (corp-wide): 14.2MM **Privately Held**
WEB: www.harbor-castings.com
SIC: 3324 3325 Steel investment
foundries; steel foundries
PA: Harbor Castings, Inc.
2508 Bailey Rd
Cuyahoga Falls OH 44221
330 499-7178

(G-15244)
JANE VALENTINE
Also Called: Colors
912 Woodside Ave Se (44720-3768)
PHONE....................................330 452-3154
Jane Valentine, *Owner*
EMP: 3
SALES (est): 120K **Privately Held**
SIC: 2395 Embroidery products, except
schiffli machine

(G-15245)
KIRK KEY INTERLOCK COMPANY LLC
9048 Meridian Cir Nw (44720-8387)
PHONE....................................330 833-8223
Fax: 330 833-1528
Scott Life, *President*
Tom Baer, *Production*
James G Owens, *Mng Member*
Christopher Smith, *Manager*
James R Fink,
▲ EMP: 47
SQ FT: 26,000
SALES (est): 14MM
SALES (corp-wide): 1.1B **Privately Held**
WEB: www.kirkkey.com
SIC: 3429 5063 Keys, locks & related
hardware; electrical apparatus & equip-
ment
PA: Halma Public Limited Company
Misbourne Court
Amersham BUCKS HP7 0
149 472-1111

(G-15246)
LETS GOLF DAILY INC
3199 Whitewood St Nw (44720-8362)
PHONE....................................330 966-3373
EMP: 3 EST: 2011
SALES (est): 113.4K **Privately Held**
SIC: 2711 Newspapers, publishing & print-
ing

(G-15247)
LT ENTERPRISES OF OHIO LLC
334 Orchard Ave Ne (44720-2556)
PHONE....................................330 526-6908
Dawn Tyburk, *CFO*
John D Larke, *Mng Member*
Nil Tyburk,
▲ EMP: 24
SQ FT: 10,000
SALES (est): 3.1MM **Privately Held**
SIC: 3444 Sheet metalwork

(G-15248)
LYNN TRUCK PARTS & SERVICE
2690 Missenden St Nw (44720-8218)
PHONE....................................330 966-1470
Fax: 330 833-9741
Lynn Hetrick, *President*
Melanie Hetrick, *Vice Pres*
EMP: 2
SQ FT: 10,000
SALES: 1MM **Privately Held**
WEB: www.lynntruckparts.com
SIC: 3714 Motor vehicle parts & acces-
sories

(G-15249)
MICROPLEX INC
7568 Whipple Ave Nw (44720-6922)
PHONE....................................330 498-0600
Fax: 330 498-0433
Valerie Walters, *President*
Peter Dankowski, *Vice Pres*
John Walters, *Vice Pres*
Jo A Schwenning, *Purch Agent*
Elsie Osowski, *Purchasing*
EMP: 30
SQ FT: 12,000

SALES (est): 6.2MM **Privately Held**
WEB: www.microplex.com
SIC: 3496 3679 5045 Cable, uninsulated
wire: made from purchased wire; harness
assemblies for electronic use: wire or
cable; computer peripheral equipment

(G-15250)
MOHLER LUMBER COMPANY
4214 Portage St Nw (44720-7399)
PHONE....................................330 499-5461
Fax: 330 499-0007
Jennifer Hamilton, *Ch of Bd*
Richard Rohrer, *Ch of Bd*
Willidam Leed, *President*
Gary Leed, *Corp Secy*
Jed Rohrer, *Vice Pres*
EMP: 20 EST: 1911
SQ FT: 8,320
SALES: 2.2MM **Privately Held**
SIC: 2435 5211 2421 2426 Hardwood
veneer & plywood; millwork & lumber;
sawmills & planing mills, general; hard-
wood dimension & flooring mills

(G-15251)
MOTION MOBILITY & DESIGN INC
6490 Promler St Nw (44720-7625)
PHONE....................................330 244-9723
Fax: 330 244-9730
Paul V Pettini, *President*
Martin Giles, *General Mgr*
Steve Williams, *Vice Pres*
Daniel Freday, *CIO*
EMP: 11
SQ FT: 12,000
SALES (est): 2.3MM **Privately Held**
WEB: www.motionmobility.com
SIC: 3842 Braces, elastic

(G-15252)
MRO BUILT INC
6410 Promway Ave Nw (44720-7622)
PHONE....................................330 526-0555
Alfred Olivieri, *President*
Dean Olivieri, *Vice Pres*
Virginia Olivieri, *Treasurer*
Timothy Feller, *Admin Sec*
EMP: 75 EST: 1977
SQ FT: 55,000
SALES (est): 13.1MM
SALES (corp-wide): 87.5MM **Privately Held**
WEB: www.fredolivieri.com
SIC: 2599 2542 2434 Cabinets, factory;
partitions & fixtures, except wood; wood
kitchen cabinets
PA: Fred Olivieri Construction Company
6315 Promway Ave Nw
North Canton OH 44720
330 494-1007

(G-15253)
MYERS CONTROLLED POWER LLC (HQ)
219 E Maple St 100-200e (44720-2586)
PHONE....................................330 834-3200
James Owens, *President*
Gary Coury, *Managing Dir*
Shirley Lawrence, *Comptroller*
Jack Hastings, *Natl Sales Mgr*
Kathleen Michaels, *Sales Staff*
▲ EMP: 105
SALES (est): 32.4MM
SALES (corp-wide): 110.6MM **Privately Held**
SIC: 3613 Switchgear & switchboard appa-
ratus
PA: Myers Power Products, Inc.
2950 E Philadelphia St
Ontario CA 91761
909 923-1800

(G-15254)
NAVIGATOR CONSTRUCTION LLC
Also Called: Cabinet 2 Countertops
7530 Tim Ave Nw Ste B (44720-6960)
PHONE....................................330 244-0221
Kurt Bonk, *Mng Member*
EMP: 3
SALES (est): 391.7K **Privately Held**
SIC: 2434 Wood kitchen cabinets

(G-15255)
NEW RIVER EQUIPMENT CORP
7793 Pittsburg Ave Nw (44720-7947)
PHONE....................................330 669-0040
EMP: 3
SALES: 800K **Privately Held**
SIC: 3531 Mfg Construction Machinery At-
tachments

(G-15256)
PAARLO PLASTICS INC
7720 Tim Ave Nw (44720-6955)
P.O. Box 2556, Canton (44720-0556)
PHONE....................................330 494-3798
Fax: 330 494-2493
James D Park, *President*
Joe Sheridan, *QA Dir*
Heather Oyler, *Engineer*
Cindy Hawk, *Accounting Dir*
▲ EMP: 65
SQ FT: 80,000
SALES (est): 13.8MM **Privately Held**
WEB: www.paarloplastics.com
SIC: 3089 Blow molded finished plastic
products

(G-15257)
PATENTHEALTH LLC
8000 Freedom Ave Nw (44720-6912)
PHONE....................................330 208-1111
Michael Moorhead, *Vice Pres*
Laura Rogers, *Vice Pres*
Dean Petersen, *CFO*
Darla Miller, *Marketing Mgr*
Melissa Borland, *Marketing Staff*
EMP: 5
SQ FT: 5,000
SALES (est): 2MM
SALES (corp-wide): 63.2MM **Privately Held**
WEB: www.patenthealth.com
SIC: 2834 2833 Pharmaceutical prepara-
tions; medicinals & botanicals
PA: Arthur Middleton Capital Holdings, Inc.
8000 Freedom Ave Nw
North Canton OH 44720
330 966-9000

(G-15258)
PAUL STIPKOVICH
Also Called: Franklin Graphics
515 Browning Ave Nw (44720-2341)
PHONE....................................330 499-7391
Fax: 330 455-2100
Paul Stipkovich, *Owner*
EMP: 3 EST: 1973
SQ FT: 3,500
SALES (est): 243.8K **Privately Held**
SIC: 2752 Commercial printing, offset

(G-15259)
PORTAGE ELECTRIC PRODUCTS INC
Also Called: Pepi
7700 Freedom Ave Nw (44720-6906)
P.O. Box 2170, Canton (44720-0170)
PHONE....................................330 499-2727
Fax: 330 499-1853
Brandon Wehl, *Ch of Bd*
Robert E Mylett, *Principal*
W Donald Reader, *Principal*
Edward J Zink, *Principal*
Omar R Givler, *Senior VP*
▲ EMP: 220 EST: 1963
SQ FT: 11,000
SALES (est): 41.7MM **Privately Held**
WEB: www.pepiusa.com
SIC: 3822 3829 Appliance controls except
air-conditioning & refrigeration; measuring
& controlling devices

(G-15260)
R R R DEVELOPMENT CO (PA)
8817 Pleasantwood Ave Nw (44720-4759)
PHONE....................................330 966-8855
Fax: 330 966-8008
Ronald Dillard, *President*
Gene Emerick, *President*
Robert Irwin, *President*
Thomas Dillard, *Vice Pres*
Bob Irwin, *Vice Pres*
▲ EMP: 80
SQ FT: 60,000

GEOGRAPHIC

SALES (est): 16.2MM **Privately Held**
WEB: www.rrrdev.com
SIC: 3559 Rubber working machinery, including tires

(G-15261)
RESTLESS NOGGINS MFG LLC
334 Orchard Ave Ne (44720-2556)
P.O. Box 2995 (44720-0995)
PHONE...................................330 526-6908
Dawn Tyburk, *Principal*
EMP: 3
SALES (est): 195.2K **Privately Held**
SIC: 3999 Manufacturing industries

(G-15262)
RHINO RUBBER LLC (PA)
7054 Meadowlands Ave Nw (44720-8813)
PHONE...................................877 744-6603
Tim Ryan, *President*
▲ EMP: 15
SALES (est): 4.7MM **Privately Held**
SIC: 3089 3559 5014 Tires, plastic; rubber working machinery, including tires; tires & tubes

(G-15263)
SECO MACHINE INC
7376 Whipple Ave Nw (44720-7140)
PHONE...................................330 499-2150
Fax: 330 499-9430
Mary Seccombe, *President*
Richard Seccombe, *General Mgr*
Delano F Rossio, *Treasurer*
Annette M Rossio, *Admin Sec*
EMP: 30
SALES (est): 6.8MM **Privately Held**
WEB: www.secomachine.com
SIC: 3545 Precision tools, machinists'

(G-15264)
SHERWIN-WILLIAMS COMPANY
6483 Dressler Rd Nw (44720-7637)
PHONE...................................330 253-6625
EMP: 4
SALES (corp-wide): 11.3B **Publicly Held**
SIC: 5231 2851 Ret Paint/Glass/Wallpaper Mfg Paints/Allied Products
PA: The Sherwin-Williams Company
101 W Prospect Ave # 1020
Cleveland OH 44115
216 566-2000

(G-15265)
SIGN A RAMA
Also Called: Sign-A-Rama
435 Applegrove St Nw (44720-1617)
PHONE...................................330 499-4653
Fax: 330 305-9364
Jeff Cyfrod, *Owner*
EMP: 3
SALES (est): 196K **Privately Held**
WEB: www.lsti.net
SIC: 3993 Signs & advertising specialties

(G-15266)
SPECIALTY HOSE CORPORATION (PA)
7800 Freedom Ave Nw (44720-6908)
PHONE...................................330 497-9650
Fax: 330 497-0415
Michael L Helfer, *President*
H L Helfer, *General Mgr*
Marjorie Onslow, *Treasurer*
Robert Howard, *Natl Sales Mgr*
EMP: 13 EST: 1977
SQ FT: 10,000
SALES: 1.4MM **Privately Held**
SIC: 3599 Hose, flexible metallic

(G-15267)
STANDARD ENGINEERING GROUP INC
3516 Highland Park Nw (44720-4532)
PHONE...................................330 494-4300
Fax: 330 494-4303
Ronald Schlemmer, *President*
William Simmons, *Vice Pres*
Denny Marlatt, *Manager*
▲ EMP: 5
SQ FT: 15,000
SALES (est): 2.3MM **Privately Held**
SIC: 3542 Machine tools, metal forming type

(G-15268)
STARK AIRWAYS
5430 Lauby Rd Bldg 27 (44720-1576)
PHONE...................................330 526-6416
Tom Landis, *Opers Staff*
Ton Lambis, *Manager*
EMP: 3
SALES (est): 300.3K **Privately Held**
SIC: 3721 Aircraft

(G-15269)
STARK INDUSTRIAL LLC
5103 Stoneham Rd (44720-1540)
P.O. Box 3030 (44720-8030)
PHONE...................................330 493-9773
Beth Miller, *Purch Agent*
Drew Prine, *Technical Mgr*
Ed Ginther, *Engineer*
Jonathan Wilkof, *Design Engr*
Rosetta Wilkof, *CFO*
▼ EMP: 40
SQ FT: 25,000
SALES (est): 24.2MM **Privately Held**
WEB: www.starkindustrial.com
SIC: 5085 3545 Industrial supplies; machine tool accessories

(G-15270)
SUNCOLOR CORPORATION
1325 Irondale Cir Ne (44720-2157)
PHONE...................................330 499-7010
David Smetana, *President*
EMP: 3
SALES (est): 409.6K **Privately Held**
SIC: 2851 Paints & paint additives

(G-15271)
THE NATIONAL LIME AND STONE CO
5377 Lauby Rd Ste 201 (44720-1529)
PHONE...................................330 455-5722
Dave Weber, *Principal*
Ken Dinwiddie, *Sales Dir*
EMP: 5
SALES (corp-wide): 4B **Privately Held**
WEB: www.natlime.com
SIC: 1422 Crushed & broken limestone
PA: The National Lime And Stone Company
551 Lake Cascade Pkwy
Findlay OH 45840
419 422-4341

(G-15272)
THERMTROL CORPORATION (PA)
8914 Pleasantwood Ave Nw (44720-4762)
PHONE...................................330 497-4148
Fax: 330 497-4189
Mark Jeffries Sr, *President*
Mark A Jeffries Jr, *Exec VP*
John Komer, *Senior VP*
Dan Curren, *Vice Pres*
David Lett, *Finance Dir*
◆ EMP: 30
SQ FT: 40,550
SALES: 22MM **Privately Held**
WEB: www.thermtrol.com
SIC: 3679 3822 Harness assemblies for electronic use: wire or cable; thermostats & other environmental sensors

(G-15273)
TIMKEN COMPANY (PA)
4500 Mount Pleasant St Nw (44720-5450)
P.O. Box 6929, Canton (44706-0929)
PHONE...................................234 262-3000
Fax: 330 471-7032
John M Timken Jr, *Ch of Bd*
Richard G Kyle, *President*
William R Burkhart, *Exec VP*
Christopher A Coughlin, *Exec VP*
Philip D Fracassa, *CFO*
◆ EMP: 4800 EST: 1899
SALES: 2.6B **Publicly Held**
SIC: 3562 Ball & roller bearings; roller bearings & parts

(G-15274)
TIMKEN COMPANY
4500 Mount Pleasant St Nw (44720-5450)
PHONE...................................234 262-3000
Donald Beebee, *Branch Mgr*
EMP: 6
SALES (corp-wide): 2.6B **Publicly Held**
SIC: 3562 Ball & roller bearings

PA: The Timken Company
4500 Mount Pleasant St Nw
North Canton OH 44720
234 262-3000

(G-15275)
TIMKEN RECEIVABLES CORPORATION
4500 Mount Pleasant St Nw (44720-5450)
PHONE...................................234 262-3000
Glenn Eisenberg, *President*
EMP: 5
SALES (est): 546.9K
SALES (corp-wide): 2.6B **Publicly Held**
SIC: 3312 Blast furnaces & steel mills
PA: The Timken Company
4500 Mount Pleasant St Nw
North Canton OH 44720
234 262-3000

(G-15276)
TMSI LLC
9073 Pleasantwood Ave Nw (44720-4763)
P.O. Box 5414, Akron (44334-0414)
PHONE...................................888 867-4872
Gerald R Potts, *President*
◆ EMP: 14
SQ FT: 24,000
SALES (est): 8.4MM
SALES (corp-wide): 141.1MM **Privately Held**
WEB: www.tmsi-usa.com
SIC: 5013 3825 Testing equipment, electrical: automotive; instruments to measure electricity
PA: Mesnac Co., Ltd.
No.43, Zhengzhou Road, Sifang District
Qingdao 26604
532 840-1299

(G-15277)
TRI - FLEX OF OHIO INC (PA)
2701 Applegrove St Nw (44720-6213)
PHONE...................................330 705-7084
Paul Lili, *President*
EMP: 10 EST: 2011
SALES (est): 1.8MM **Privately Held**
SIC: 3365 Machinery castings, aluminum

(G-15278)
TRISTAN RUBBER MOLDING INC (PA)
7255 Whipple Ave Nw (44720-7137)
PHONE...................................330 499-4055
Fax: 330 499-4750
Peter Fritz, *President*
Larry W Ball, *Principal*
Christina Fritz, *Treasurer*
Susan Pellikan, *Controller*
EMP: 28
SQ FT: 20,000
SALES (est): 8.6MM **Privately Held**
SIC: 3069 Molded rubber products

(G-15279)
UNITED TECHNOLOGIES CORP
6051 W Airport Dr (44720)
PHONE...................................330 784-5477
EMP: 268
SALES (corp-wide): 57.2B **Publicly Held**
SIC: 3585 Refrigeration & heating equipment
PA: United Technologies Corporation
10 Farm Springs Rd
Farmington CT 06032
860 728-7000

(G-15280)
UPL INTERNATIONAL INC
Also Called: Universal Plastics
7661 Freedom Ave Nw (44720-6903)
PHONE...................................330 433-2860
Fax: 330 645-0064
Jeffrey Scarpitti, *President*
Wade Scarpitti, *President*
Julie Holland, *Purch Agent*
Karen Scarpitti, *Controller*
EMP: 20 EST: 1976
SQ FT: 18,000
SALES (est): 4.5MM **Privately Held**
WEB: www.universalplasticsmachine.com
SIC: 3089 5162 Plastic processing; plastics products

(G-15281)
VEGA TECHNOLOGY GROUP LLC
412 Sheraton Dr Nw (44720-2225)
PHONE...................................216 772-1434
Kevin D Busto, *Owner*
EMP: 3
SALES (est): 199.3K **Privately Held**
SIC: 3674 Semiconductors & related devices

(G-15282)
VILLERS ENTERPRISES LIMITED (PA)
Also Called: Simxperience
3146 Brumbaugh St Nw (44720-7940)
PHONE...................................330 818-9838
Bernard L Villers Jr, *Mng Member*
Bernard Villers Sr,
EMP: 3
SQ FT: 2,500
SALES (est): 605.8K **Privately Held**
SIC: 3699 Automotive driving simulators (training aids), electronic

(G-15283)
W3 ULTRASONICS LLC
5288 Huckleberry St Nw (44720-6876)
PHONE...................................330 284-3667
Scott Miller, *President*
EMP: 4
SQ FT: 5,000
SALES (est): 257.2K **Privately Held**
SIC: 3589 Commercial cleaning equipment

(G-15284)
WILLIAMS PARTNERS LP
7235 Whipple Ave Nw (44720-7137)
PHONE...................................330 966-3674
Travis Bonine, *Branch Mgr*
Kelly Coney, *Admin Asst*
EMP: 221
SALES (corp-wide): 7.4B **Publicly Held**
SIC: 1311 Natural gas production
PA: Williams Partners L.P.
1 Williams Ctr
Tulsa OK 74172
918 573-2000

North Fairfield
Huron County

(G-15285)
FLY RACE FUELS LLC
1905 Maple Ridge Rd (44855-9653)
PHONE...................................419 744-9402
Brenda Ooten, *Principal*
EMP: 3
SALES (est): 187.3K **Privately Held**
SIC: 2869 Fuels

North Georgetown
Columbiana County

(G-15286)
ANTRAM FIRE EQUIPMENT
27970 Winona Rd (44665)
P.O. Box 74 (44665-0074)
PHONE...................................330 525-7171
Paul Antram, *Owner*
EMP: 3
SQ FT: 4,040
SALES (est): 221.6K **Privately Held**
SIC: 5087 7389 Firefighting equipment; fire extinguisher servicing; fire department vehicles (motor vehicles), assembly of

---

North Jackson
Mahoning County

(G-15287)
BCI AND V INVESTMENTS INC
11675 Mahoning Ave (44451-9688)
P.O. Box 698 (44451-0698)
PHONE...................................330 538-0660
Harold Bartels, *President*

Randy Vegso, *Vice Pres*
EMP: 55
SQ FT: 26,000
SALES (est): 8.2MM **Privately Held**
SIC: 2821 3356 Vinyl resins; nonferrous rolling & drawing

(G-15288)
BLUE RIBBON TRAILERS LTD
12800 Leonard Pkwy (44451-8611)
PHONE....................330 538-4114
Clint Leonard, *President*
Scott Dyke, *Purch Mgr*
EMP: 21
SALES (est): 4.3MM **Privately Held**
WEB: www.blueribbontrailers.com
SIC: 3799 Trailers & trailer equipment

(G-15289)
CANFIELD MANUFACTURING CO INC
Also Called: Wilson Specialties
489 Rosemont Rd (44451-9717)
PHONE....................330 533-3333
Fax: 330 533-2704
M J Stewart, *CEO*
Mary Mc Mahon, *Office Mgr*
EMP: 7 EST: 1800
SQ FT: 20,000
SALES (est): 420K **Privately Held**
SIC: 2426 2499 Lumber, hardwood dimension; handles, wood

(G-15290)
EXTRUDEX ALUMINUM INC
12051 Mahoning Ave (44451-9617)
P.O. Box 697 (44451-0697)
PHONE....................330 538-4444
Fax: 330 538-4450
Andrew Gucciardi, *President*
Brian Carder, *General Mgr*
Stuart Craig, *Plant Mgr*
Dick Gargasz, *Controller*
Todd Perren, *Accounting Dir*
▲ **EMP:** 120
SQ FT: 110,000
SALES (est): 35.7MM
SALES (corp-wide): 875.5K **Privately Held**
WEB: www.extrudexohio.com
SIC: 3354 Aluminum extruded products
PA: Extrudex Aluminum Corp
411 Chrislea Rd
Woodbridge ON L4L 8
416 745-4444

(G-15291)
HEATHER CREEK FOODS LLC
12485 Commissioner Dr (44451-9628)
PHONE....................330 792-8654
EMP: 40
SQ FT: 20,500
SALES: 15MM **Privately Held**
SIC: 2099 Mfg Food Preparations

(G-15292)
INNOVAR SYSTEMS LIMITED
12155 Commissioner Dr (44451-9640)
P.O. Box 486 (44451-0486)
PHONE....................330 538-3942
John Frano, *CEO*
Paul Graff, *President*
Kim Hoffman, *Manager*
EMP: 11
SQ FT: 15,000
SALES (est): 2.9MM
SALES (corp-wide): 4MM **Privately Held**
SIC: 3699 Laser welding, drilling & cutting equipment
PA: Radix Holdings Llc
12155 Commissioner Dr
North Jackson OH 44451
330 538-2268

(G-15293)
LEARNING EGG LLC
Also Called: Learning Egg, The
9332 Silica Rd (44451-9670)
PHONE....................330 207-8663
Elijah Stambaugh,
EMP: 4
SQ FT: 1,000
SALES (est): 238.4K **Privately Held**
SIC: 7372 Educational computer software

(G-15294)
LIBERTY STEEL PRESSED PDTS LLC
11650 Mahoning Ave (44451-9688)
PHONE....................330 538-2236
EMP: 3
SALES (est): 131.3K **Privately Held**
SIC: 3399 Primary metal products

(G-15295)
NORTH JCKSON SPECIALTY STL LLC
Also Called: Universal Stainless
2058 S Bailey Rd (44451-9639)
PHONE....................330 538-9621
EMP: 23
SALES (corp-wide): 7.9MM **Privately Held**
SIC: 3312 Stainless steel
PA: North Jackson Specialty Steel, Llc
600 Mayer St
Bridgeville PA 15017
412 257-7600

(G-15296)
PATRIOT SPECIAL METALS INC
2058 S Bailey Rd (44451-9639)
PHONE....................330 538-9621
▲ **EMP:** 6
SALES (est): 1MM **Privately Held**
SIC: 3356 Nonferrous rolling & drawing

(G-15297)
PMC SYSTEMS LIMITED
12155 Commissioner Dr (44451-9640)
P.O. Box 486 (44451-0486)
PHONE....................330 538-2268
John Frano, *President*
Randy G Yakubek, *President*
Paul Graff, *Vice Pres*
Kim Hoffman, *Manager*
EMP: 30
SQ FT: 3,000
SALES (est): 5.7MM **Privately Held**
SIC: 3625 8711 Electric controls & control accessories, industrial; electrical or electronic engineering

(G-15298)
SOVEREIGN CIRCUITS INC
12080 Debartolo Dr (44451-9642)
P.O. Box 216 (44451-0216)
PHONE....................330 538-3900
Fax: 330 538-3820
Robert Buss, *Principal*
EMP: 10
SALES (est): 1.1MM **Privately Held**
SIC: 3679 Electronic circuits

(G-15299)
STAMPED STEEL PRODUCTS INC
151 S Bailey Rd (44451-9636)
P.O. Box 5224, Poland (44514-0224)
PHONE....................330 538-3951
Fax: 330 538-3952
William Robinson Jr, *President*
Micheal D Geiger, *Corp Secy*
Michela Geiger, *Admin Sec*
EMP: 11 EST: 2001
SQ FT: 59,000
SALES: 4.3MM **Privately Held**
SIC: 3469 5051 Metal stampings; stampings, metal

(G-15300)
VIASYSTEMS TECH CORP LLC
12080 Debartolo Dr (44451-9642)
P.O. Box 216 (44451-0216)
PHONE....................330 538-3900
Fax: 330 538-2434
Tony Mrvelj, *Manager*
EMP: 118
SALES (corp-wide): 2.5B **Publicly Held**
WEB: www.sovereign-circuits.com
SIC: 3672 Printed circuit boards
HQ: Viasystems Technologies Corp, Llc
520 Maryville Centre Dr
Saint Louis MO 63141
314 719-1845

(G-15301)
VINYL PROFILES ACQUISITION LLC
11675 Mahoning Ave (44451-9688)
P.O. Box 698 (44451-0698)
PHONE....................330 538-0660
Fax: 330 538-0671
Randy Vegso, *President*
Jack Cappabianca, *Marketing Staff*
EMP: 29
SALES (est): 7.5MM **Privately Held**
SIC: 2821 Plastics materials & resins

(G-15302)
VINYLTECH INC
11635 Mahoning Ave (44451-9688)
P.O. Box 127 (44451-0127)
PHONE....................330 538-0369
Fax: 330 538-0459
Rick Amato, *President*
Mike Buchanan, *Vice Pres*
EMP: 30
SALES (est): 4.4MM **Privately Held**
SIC: 3544 Forms (molds), for foundry & plastics working machinery

North Kingsville
Ashtabula County

(G-15303)
BUHI IMPORTS
3210 E Center St (44068)
P.O. Box 420 (44068-0420)
PHONE....................440 224-0013
Paul Buhite, *General Mgr*
Gemma Buhite, *Vice Pres*
▲ **EMP:** 4
SALES (est): 291.9K **Privately Held**
SIC: 5199 2499 5945 Baskets; reed, rattan, wicker & willow ware, except furniture; hobby, toy & game shops

(G-15304)
PREMIX INC (DH)
Also Called: Molded Parts Division
3365 E Center St (44068)
P.O. Box 281 (44068-0281)
PHONE....................440 224-2181
Fax: 440 224-2766
Thomas J Meola, *President*
David Marple, *General Mgr*
Mike Morehouse, *General Mgr*
Marc Imbrogno, *Business Mgr*
Mark Sjostrom, *Opers Staff*
▼ **EMP:** 197 EST: 1959
SQ FT: 300,000
SALES (est): 116.4MM
SALES (corp-wide): 2.5B **Publicly Held**
WEB: www.premix.com
SIC: 3089 2821 Thermoformed finished plastic products; injection molding of plastics; plastic kitchenware, tableware & houseware; plastics materials & resins

North Lawrence
Stark County

(G-15305)
AAA PLASTICS AND PALLETS LTD
13943 Sousa St (44666-9739)
PHONE....................330 844-2556
Dan A Hargrove, *Principal*
EMP: 8 EST: 2008
SALES (est): 1MM **Privately Held**
SIC: 2448 Pallets, wood & wood with metal

(G-15306)
KELBLYS RIFLE RANGE INC
7222 Dalton Fox Lake Rd (44666-9543)
PHONE....................330 683-0070
Fax: 330 682-7349
George Kelbly Sr, *President*
Karen Kelbly, *Corp Secy*
George Kelbly Jr, *Vice Pres*
James Kelbly, *Vice Pres*
EMP: 8

SALES (est): 1.6MM **Privately Held**
WEB: www.kelbly.com
SIC: 3484 7999 Rifles or rifle parts, 30 mm. & below; shooting range operation

(G-15307)
US TUBULAR PRODUCTS INC
Also Called: Benmit Division
14852 Lincoln Way W (44666)
P.O. Box 494, Dalton (44618-0494)
PHONE....................330 832-1734
Fax: 330 832-8284
Jeffrey J Cunningham, *President*
Connye Cunningham, *Corp Secy*
Brian Cunningham, *Vice Pres*
Jennifer Woodruff, *CFO*
EMP: 60 EST: 1973
SQ FT: 100,000
SALES (est): 11.3MM **Privately Held**
SIC: 8734 3498 Hydrostatic testing laboratory; tube fabricating (contract bending & shaping)

North Lewisburg
Champaign County

(G-15308)
PREHISTORIC ANTIQUITIES
7045 State Route 245 (43060-9720)
P.O. Box 100, Winchester (45697-0100)
PHONE....................937 747-2225
Bill Ballinger, *President*
Linda Ballinger, *Vice Pres*
EMP: 3
SALES (est): 140K **Privately Held**
SIC: 2721 Magazines: publishing & printing

(G-15309)
WORTHNGTON STELPAC SYSTEMS LLC
5256 Burton Rd (43060-7000)
PHONE....................937 747-2370
Paul Mc, *Branch Mgr*
EMP: 6
SALES (corp-wide): 2.8B **Publicly Held**
SIC: 3441 Fabricated structural metal
HQ: Worthington Steelpac Systems, Llc
1205 Dearborn Dr
Columbus OH 43085
614 438-3205

North Lima
Mahoning County

(G-15310)
BERLIN INDUSTRIES INC (HQ)
Also Called: Berlin Inds Protector Pdts
131 W South Range Rd (44452-9578)
P.O. Box 128 (44452-0128)
PHONE....................330 549-2100
Fax: 330 549-2024
Scott Gorley, *President*
EMP: 12
SQ FT: 35,000
SALES (est): 5MM
SALES (corp-wide): 1.1B **Privately Held**
SIC: 2834 5047 Veterinary pharmaceutical preparations; veterinarians' equipment & supplies
PA: Kobayashi Pharmaceutical Co., Ltd.
4-4-10, Doshomachi, Chuo-Ku
Osaka OSK 541-0
662 311-144

(G-15311)
BIRD EQUIPMENT LLC
Also Called: Specialty Fab
11950 South Ave (44452-9744)
PHONE....................330 549-1004
Fax: 330 549-2004
Joe Colletti, *President*
Brian Dwyer, *Vice Pres*
Bill Lawry, *Vice Pres*
Ron Lipscomb, *Sales Staff*
Ronald Jackson, *Manager*
EMP: 28
SQ FT: 49,500
SALES: 2.6MM
SALES (corp-wide): 210.3MM **Privately Held**
SIC: 3441 Fabricated structural metal

GEOGRAPHIC

PA: Desco Corporation
7795 Walton Pkwy Ste 175
New Albany OH 43054
614 888-8855

(G-15312)
COBRA MOTORCYCLES MFG
11511 Springfield Rd (44452-9755)
PHONE................................330 207-3844
Fax: 330 549-9605
Bud Maimone, *President*
▲ EMP: 25
SALES (est): 3.2MM **Privately Held**
WEB: www.cobramotorcycle.com
SIC: 3751 Motorcycles & related parts

(G-15313)
COMMERCIAL MINERALS INC
10900 South Ave (44452-9792)
P.O. Box 217 (44452-0217)
PHONE................................330 549-2165
Fax: 330 549-0618
Thomas Mackall, *President*
Melanie Dunn, *Treasurer*
EMP: 6 EST: 1981
SQ FT: 6,000
SALES (est): 443.6K **Privately Held**
SIC: 1221 Bituminous coal surface mining

(G-15314)
CULTURED MARBLE INC
11331 South Ave (44452-9772)
P.O. Box 284 (44452-0284)
PHONE................................330 549-2282
Fax: 330 549-5110
Todd Worsencroft, *President*
David Worsencroft, *President*
Arthur D Worsencroft, *Corp Secy*
EMP: 8
SQ FT: 12,000
SALES: 400K **Privately Held**
SIC: 3299 3088 Synthetic stones, for gem
stones & industrial use; plastics plumbing
fixtures

(G-15315)
DUO-CORP
280 Miley Rd (44452-8581)
P.O. Box 313 (44452-0313)
PHONE................................330 549-2149
Fax: 330 549-0316
William G Kinkade, *CEO*
Bradley W Kinkade, *President*
Stephen De Capua, *CFO*
Stephen Decapua, *CFO*
Diane Kinkade, *Admin Sec*
EMP: 30
SQ FT: 70,000
SALES (est): 5.3MM **Privately Held**
WEB: www.duo-corp.com
SIC: 3089 3442 Windows, plastic; screen
& storm doors & windows

(G-15316)
EXPERT OUTFITTERS
9074 Market St (44452-9557)
PHONE................................330 965-9620
Ronald Oldland, *Owner*
EMP: 4
SALES: 1.5MM **Privately Held**
WEB: www.expertoutfitters.com
SIC: 3489 Guns or gun parts, over 30 mm.

(G-15317)
HUNTER LIFT LTD
11233 South Ave (44452-9731)
PHONE................................330 549-3347
Fax: 330 549-3424
Douglas R Verenski, *Principal*
Tim Brookbank, *Chief Engr*
Nick Craciun, *Sales Staff*
Shelly Inn, *Manager*
EMP: 15
SQ FT: 50,000
SALES (est): 398.1K **Privately Held**
WEB: www.hunterlift.com
SIC: 3537 Lift trucks, industrial: fork, plat-
form, straddle, etc.

(G-15318)
KTSDI LLC
801 E Middletown Rd (44452-9761)
PHONE................................330 783-2000
Ken Timmings, *Principal*
Bryon Gotham, *Accountant*
Duke Siddle, *Manager*

EMP: 7
SALES (est): 460K **Privately Held**
SIC: 8748 3714 Business consulting; axle
housings & shafts, motor vehicle

(G-15319)
L AND S EXPRESS FUEL
CENTER
10125 Market St (44452-9556)
PHONE................................330 549-9566
Lee Padula, *Principal*
EMP: 4
SALES (est): 431.7K **Privately Held**
SIC: 2869 Fuels

(G-15320)
LATELIER CUSTOM
WOODWORKING
11905 Woodworth Rd (44452-9794)
PHONE................................234 759-3359
Fax: 330 549-2029
EMP: 5
SALES (est): 675K **Privately Held**
SIC: 2521 2512 2431 Mfg Custom Wood-
workings

(G-15321)
PRINT FACTORY PLL
Also Called: Poland Print Shop
11471 South Ave (44452-9772)
P.O. Box 312 (44452-0312)
PHONE................................330 549-9640
Fax: 330 549-9642
John Primm, *Partner*
Doris Primm, *Partner*
EMP: 7
SALES (est): 100K **Privately Held**
SIC: 2752 Commercial printing, litho-
graphic

(G-15322)
R A M PLASTICS CO INC
11401 South Ave (44452)
P.O. Box 402 (44452-0402)
PHONE................................330 549-3107
Fax: 330 549-9910
Richard Mallory, *President*
EMP: 35
SQ FT: 20,000
SALES (est): 5.1MM **Privately Held**
SIC: 3089 Injection molded finished plastic
products

(G-15323)
STERLING MINING
CORPORATION (HQ)
10900 South Ave (44452-9792)
P.O. Box 217 (44452-0217)
PHONE................................330 549-2165
W Thomas Mackall, *President*
Denise Mackall, *Treasurer*
Melanie Dunn, *Controller*
EMP: 12
SQ FT: 6,000
SALES (est): 18MM
SALES (corp-wide): 126.2MM **Privately**
Held
SIC: 1222 Bituminous coal-underground
mining
PA: The East Fairfield Coal Co
10900 South Ave
North Lima OH
330 549-2165

North Olmsted
Cuyahoga County

(G-15324)
ABSORBCORE LLC
30275 Lorain Rd (44070-3925)
PHONE................................440 614-0457
Charles Flury,
EMP: 3
SALES (est): 307.8K **Privately Held**
SIC: 2273 Mats & matting

(G-15325)
ADVANSTAR COMMUNICATIONS
INC
Also Called: Advanstar Art Group
24950 Country Club Blvd # 200
(44070-5342)
PHONE................................440 243-8100
Teresa McNulty, *Editor*
Steve Hermer, *Nat'l Sales Mgr*
Georgiann Decenzo, *VP Mktg*
Lenore Mason, *Marketing Staff*
Debbie Rustic, *Office Mgr*
EMP: 18
SALES (corp-wide): 1B **Privately Held**
WEB: www.advanstar.com
SIC: 2721 Magazines: publishing only, not
printed on site
HQ: Advanstar Communications Inc.
2501 Colorado Ave Ste 280
Santa Monica CA 90404
310 857-7500

(G-15326)
ANAHEIM MANUFACTURING
COMPANY
Also Called: Waste King
25300 Al Moen Dr (44070-5619)
P.O. Box 4146, Anaheim CA (92803-4146)
PHONE................................800 767-6293
Steve Lattman, *President*
Robert A Schneider, *Vice Pres*
Barbara Arsenault, *Manager*
▲ EMP: 50
SALES (est): 9MM
SALES (corp-wide): 4.9B **Publicly Held**
WEB: www.anaheimmfg.com
SIC: 3639 Garbage disposal units, house-
hold
HQ: Moen Incorporated
25300 Al Moen Dr
North Olmsted OH 44070
440 962-2000

(G-15327)
AVAIL VAPOR LLC
26429 Grt Nthrn Shop Ctr (44070-4372)
PHONE................................440 716-6027
EMP: 3
SALES (corp-wide): 70.1MM **Privately**
Held
SIC: 2111 Cigarettes
PA: Avail Vapor, Llc
820 Southlake Blvd
North Chesterfield VA 23236
804 419-2180

(G-15328)
BTA OF MOTORCARS INC
27500 Lorain Rd (44070-4038)
PHONE................................440 716-1000
Gary Tamerlano, *Principal*
EMP: 8
SALES (est): 815.7K **Privately Held**
SIC: 3479 Painting of metal products

(G-15329)
DEL HOLDASH
29891 Westminster Dr (44070-5083)
PHONE................................440 427-0611
Del Holdash, *Principal*
EMP: 3
SALES (est): 213.2K **Privately Held**
SIC: 2421 Sawmills & planing mills, gen-
eral

(G-15330)
DYNAMIC CONTROL NORTH
AMER INC
31335 Industrial Pkwy # 2 (44070-4764)
PHONE................................440 979-0657
Fax: 440 979-1028
Donald Calhoun, *Manager*
EMP: 5
SALES (corp-wide): 3.6MM **Privately**
Held
WEB: www.dynamat.com
SIC: 3842 Surgical appliances & supplies
PA: Dynamic Control Of North America, Inc.
3042 Symmes Rd
Hamilton OH 45015
513 860-5094

(G-15331)
E T & K INC
Also Called: American Speedy Printing
23545 Lorain Rd (44070-2219)
PHONE................................440 777-7375
Edward Scully, *President*
Theresa Scully, *Treasurer*
Ana Boggs, *Sales Staff*
EMP: 3
SQ FT: 1,600
SALES: 310K **Privately Held**
SIC: 2752 Commercial printing, offset

(G-15332)
EMTA INC
Also Called: Joe D'S Printing
28875 Lorain Rd (44070-4043)
PHONE................................440 734-6464
Fax: 440 734-6465
Joe Delamielleure, *President*
Ron Dale, *Corp Secy*
Timothy Smith, *Vice Pres*
Ronald Deyo, *Treasurer*
EMP: 3
SQ FT: 1,200
SALES: 140K **Privately Held**
SIC: 2759 2791 2752 Commercial print-
ing; typesetting; commercial printing, lith-
ographic

(G-15333)
EW PUBLISHING COMPANY
Also Called: Fastsigns
24181 Lorain Rd (44070-2163)
PHONE................................440 887-0131
Fax: 440 979-0325
Paul Girgash, *Owner*
EMP: 3
SQ FT: 4,500
SALES (est): 367.7K **Privately Held**
SIC: 3993 Signs & advertising specialties

(G-15334)
FORM-A-TOP PRODUCTS INC
25044 Chase Dr (44070-1217)
PHONE................................440 779-9452
Richard Drozdz, *President*
Harriet Drozdz, *Vice Pres*
EMP: 9 EST: 1952
SQ FT: 10,000
SALES (est): 753K **Privately Held**
SIC: 2541 Table or counter tops, plastic
laminated

(G-15335)
FRAGAPANE BAKERIES INC
(PA)
Also Called: Fragapane Bakery & Deli
28625 Lorain Rd (44070-4009)
PHONE................................440 779-6050
Fax: 440 779-6262
John Fragapane, *President*
Nick Fragapane, *Vice Pres*
Victoria Fragapane, *Treasurer*
Rose Fragapane, *Admin Sec*
EMP: 8 EST: 1971
SQ FT: 4,000
SALES (est): 1.9MM **Privately Held**
SIC: 5411 5461 2051 Delicatessens; bak-
eries; bread, cake & related products

(G-15336)
FRESENIUS USA INC
Also Called: Fresenius Medical Care
25050 Country Club Blvd # 250
(44070-5356)
PHONE................................440 734-7474
Tim Martin, *Branch Mgr*
Martin Timothy, *Manager*
EMP: 40
SALES (corp-wide): 17.5B **Privately Held**
WEB: www.fresenius.org
SIC: 2834 Intravenous solutions
HQ: Fresenius Usa, Inc.
4040 Nelson Ave
Concord CA 94520
925 288-4218

(G-15337)
GC CONTROLS INC
Also Called: Eurotherm
3926 Pine Cir (44070-1766)
P.O. Box 450799, Westlake (44145-0617)
PHONE................................440 779-4777
Fax: 440 779-9097
Bob Roberts, *President*

Joanne Albers, *Treasurer*
Jim Trait, *Sales Mgr*
Gary Albers, *Director*
EMP: 7
SALES (est): 791.4K **Privately Held**
SIC: 3625 Industrial controls: push button, selector switches, pilot

(G-15338)
HEADS & THREADS INTL LLC
289070 Lorain Rd Ste 101 (44070)
PHONE................................216 433-1660
Robin Campion, *Manager*
EMP: 15
SALES (corp-wide): 21.3MM **Privately Held**
WEB: www.handt.com
SIC: 3965 5072 Fasteners; staples
PA: Heads & Threads Intl Llc
 1212 Dolton Dr Ste 302
 Dallas TX 75207
 630 868-2300

(G-15339)
HILO TECH INC
31532 Lorain Rd (44070-4733)
PHONE................................440 979-1155
Fax: 440 979-1156
Gerald Potchatek, *President*
Debbie Heck, *Corp Secy*
EMP: 3
SALES (est): 388.7K **Privately Held**
SIC: 1796 3589 Machinery installation; car washing machinery

(G-15340)
KELLY PRINTS LLC
Also Called: Minuteman Press
24112 Lorain Rd (44070-2116)
PHONE................................440 356-6361
William Loyd Kelly,
EMP: 4
SALES (est): 575.4K **Privately Held**
SIC: 2752 Commercial printing, lithographic

(G-15341)
LIDS CORPORATION
577 Great Nthrn Mall 102 (44070)
PHONE................................440 779-4998
James Topham, *Partner*
Wil Arndt, *Principal*
Howard Donaldson, *Vice Pres*
Sang Mah, *Vice Pres*
Abby Rivers, *VP Opers*
EMP: 10
SALES (corp-wide): 2.8B **Publicly Held**
WEB: www.hatworld.com
SIC: 2353 Hats, caps & millinery
HQ: Lids Corporation
 7555 Woodland Dr
 Indianapolis IN 46278

(G-15342)
P C POWER INC
23792 Lorain Rd Ste 300 (44070-2225)
PHONE................................440 779-4080
Fax: 440 779-1718
Arthur Bibbs, *President*
EMP: 4
SQ FT: 1,000
SALES: 500K **Privately Held**
SIC: 7378 3643 Computer maintenance & repair; electric connectors

(G-15343)
Q MUSIC USA LLC
Also Called: Music Systems
5730 Great Northern Blvd E1 (44070-5626)
P.O. Box 60474, Fort Myers FL (33906-6474)
PHONE................................239 995-5888
Frans Kox, *Technical Staff*
Allison Kox,
EMP: 4
SALES (est): 279.6K **Privately Held**
WEB: www.quebbie.com
SIC: 3651 Music distribution apparatus

(G-15344)
SCREEN IMAGES INC
6122 Croton Dr (44070-4430)
PHONE................................440 779-7356
Karl Kullik, *President*
Carol Guncer, *Manager*
EMP: 3

SQ FT: 500
SALES (est): 170K **Privately Held**
SIC: 3993 Signs & advertising specialties

(G-15345)
SERVO SYSTEMS INC
31375 Lorain Rd (44070-4730)
P.O. Box 45552, Westlake (44145-0552)
PHONE................................440 779-2780
Fax: 440 871-7756
Peter Ganczarski, *President*
EMP: 4
SQ FT: 2,000
SALES (est): 827.9K **Privately Held**
WEB: www.servo-systems.com
SIC: 5063 3678 Motor controls, starters & relays: electric; electronic connectors

(G-15346)
SMILE BRANDS INC
Also Called: Bright Now Dental
25102 Brookpark Rd (44070-6414)
PHONE................................440 471-6133
Diane Ulichney, *Branch Mgr*
EMP: 6
SALES (corp-wide): 627.6MM **Privately Held**
SIC: 3843 Dental equipment & supplies
HQ: Smile Brands Inc.
 100 Spectrum Center Dr
 Irvine CA 92618
 714 668-1300

(G-15347)
SPECIAL MTLS RES & TECH INC
Also Called: Specmat
27390 Lusandra Cir (44070-1747)
PHONE................................440 777-4024
Maria Faur, *CEO*
EMP: 3
SQ FT: 3,000
SALES (est): 265.1K **Privately Held**
SIC: 8741 3674 8732 Management services; semiconductors & related devices; research services, except laboratory

(G-15348)
THERM-ALL INC (PA)
31387 Industrial Pkwy (44070-4764)
PHONE................................440 779-9494
Fax: 440 734-5282
Robert Smigel, *President*
Ann Sliwa, *Principal*
Jared Welsh, *District Mgr*
Tim Chambers, *Opers Mgr*
Richard Sobiech, *CFO*
EMP: 20
SQ FT: 56,000
SALES (est): 19MM **Privately Held**
WEB: www.columnsentry.com
SIC: 3211 Building glass, flat; plate & sheet glass

(G-15349)
THRIFTY PRINT
Also Called: Scott Enterprises
5168 Hampton Dr (44070-3085)
PHONE................................440 360-7826
Raymond Nicholls, *Owner*
Madonna Nicholls, *Manager*
EMP: 3
SALES (est): 150K **Privately Held**
SIC: 2752 Commercial printing, lithographic

(G-15350)
US VIDEO
23551 Westchester Dr (44070-1431)
PHONE................................440 734-6463
Shailesh Shah,
EMP: 3
SALES: 80K **Privately Held**
SIC: 7841 3695 Video tape rental; video recording tape, blank

(G-15351)
WESTERN RESERVE FURNITURE CO
Also Called: William F Kelly
29701 Wellington Dr (44070-5063)
PHONE................................440 235-6216
William Kelly, *Owner*
EMP: 3
SALES: 128K **Privately Held**
SIC: 1752 2511 Floor laying & floor work; wood household furniture

(G-15352)
WHISKEY FOX CORPORATION
Also Called: Csqp Quick Printing
26824 Lorain Rd (44070-3209)
PHONE................................440 779-6767
Fax: 440 779-9184
William McKay, *President*
EMP: 11
SALES (est): 870K **Privately Held**
SIC: 2752 Commercial printing, offset

(G-15353)
YOST & SON INC
5502 Barton Rd (44070-3836)
PHONE................................440 779-8025
Diana Yost, *President*
Marie Glasby, *Vice Pres*
EMP: 5
SALES: 1.1MM **Privately Held**
SIC: 3559 Chemical machinery & equipment

North Ridgeville
Lorain County

(G-15354)
8888 BUTLER INVESTMENTS INC
8888 Riverwood Dr (44039-6311)
PHONE................................440 748-0810
Fax: 440 946-5993
Larry D Butler, *President*
Bradley A Butler, *Vice Pres*
EMP: 9 **EST:** 1960
SQ FT: 10,000
SALES (est): 1.2MM **Privately Held**
WEB: www.jlcapital.com
SIC: 3728 3599 Aircraft parts & equipment; machine shop, jobbing & repair

(G-15355)
AEROWAVE INC
37190 Sugar Ridge Rd (44039-3630)
PHONE................................440 731-8464
Bob Avon, *CEO*
EMP: 7
SALES: 700K **Privately Held**
SIC: 3548 Welding apparatus

(G-15356)
ALANOD WESTLAKE METAL IND INC
36696 Sugar Ridge Rd (44039-3832)
PHONE................................440 327-8184
Fax: 440 327-0814
John R Johnston Jr, *President*
Franke Lee, *President*
James Gula, *Vice Pres*
Patrick Records, *Sales Mgr*
Chris Volk, *Manager*
◆ **EMP:** 21
SQ FT: 80,000
SALES: 50MM
SALES (corp-wide): 134.4MM **Privately Held**
WEB: www.westlakemetals.com
SIC: 5051 3354 Aluminum bars, rods, ingots, sheets, pipes, plates, etc.; aluminum extruded products
PA: Alanod Gmbh & Co. Kg
 Egerstr. 12
 Ennepetal 58256
 233 398-6500

(G-15357)
ALL AROUND GARAGE DOOR INC
33434 Liberty Pkwy (44039-2670)
PHONE................................440 759-5079
Steve Mazur, *President*
Kathleen Mazur, *Director*
EMP: 4
SQ FT: 2,500
SALES: 308K **Privately Held**
SIC: 3442 3089 2431 Garage doors, overhead: metal; fences, gates & accessories: plastic; garage doors, overhead: wood

(G-15358)
AVI FOOD SYSTEMS INC
4937 Mills Indus Pkwy (44039-1968)
PHONE................................440 327-1944
Fax: 440 327-2073
Scott Matthews, *Principal*
Craig Herrin, *Site Mgr*
Don Cirino, *Manager*
EMP: 39
SALES (corp-wide): 659.4MM **Privately Held**
WEB: www.avifoodsystems.com
SIC: 3581 Automatic vending machines
PA: Avi Food Systems, Inc.
 2590 Elm Rd Ne
 Warren OH 44483
 330 372-6000

(G-15359)
BECKETT AIR INCORPORATED (PA)
Also Called: PM Motor Fan Blade Company
37850 Taylor Pkwy (44039-3600)
P.O. Box 1236, Elyria (44036-1236)
PHONE................................440 327-9999
Fax: 440 327-3569
Michael Hashem, *President*
Scribner L Fauver, *Principal*
Tim Tuttle, *Engineer*
John D Beckett, *Treasurer*
Adam Franczak, *Sales Staff*
▲ **EMP:** 100
SALES (est): 30.1MM **Privately Held**
WEB: www.beckettair.com
SIC: 3433 3585 3564 Heating equipment, except electric; refrigeration & heating equipment; blowers & fans

(G-15360)
BECKETT GAS INC (PA)
38000 Taylor Pkwy (44039-3645)
P.O. Box 4037, Elyria (44036-4037)
PHONE................................440 327-3141
John D Beckett, *Ch of Bd*
Morrison J Carter, *President*
Kevin A Beckett, *Corp Secy*
Dennis Zemanek, *Mfg Spvr*
Jeff Craycraft, *Purch Mgr*
◆ **EMP:** 165
SQ FT: 140,000
SALES: 39.1MM **Privately Held**
SIC: 3433 Burners, furnaces, boilers & stokers

(G-15361)
BIOTHANE COATED WEBBING CORP
34655 Mills Rd (44039-1843)
PHONE................................440 327-0485
Fax: 440 327-3666
Frank Boron, *President*
Craig Tennant, *COO*
Robert Krebs, *Purchasing*
Robert Opalko, *Research*
Rick Case, *Treasurer*
▲ **EMP:** 35 **EST:** 1976
SQ FT: 25,000
SALES (est): 8.7MM **Privately Held**
WEB: www.bioplastics.us
SIC: 2295 3083 2821 Coated fabrics, not rubberized; laminated plastics plate & sheet; plastics materials & resins

(G-15362)
BRACEMART LLC
36097 Westminister Ave (44039-4537)
PHONE................................440 353-2830
Aaron Dibucci, *President*
William Hagy, *Principal*
EMP: 3 **EST:** 2015
SALES (est): 173.9K **Privately Held**
SIC: 3842 3949 Braces, orthopedic; supports: abdominal, ankle, arch, kneecap, etc.; sporting & athletic goods; exercise equipment

(G-15363)
BRUCK MANUFACTURING CO INC
33471 Liberty Pkwy (44039-3298)
PHONE................................440 327-6619
Fax: 440 327-6371
George Bruck Jr, *CEO*
Kevin Bruck, *President*
George Bruck III, *Corp Secy*

EMP: 5 EST: 1957
SQ FT: 6,500
SALES: 300K **Privately Held**
SIC: 3599 3544 Machine shop, jobbing &
repair; special dies, tools, jigs & fixtures

(G-15364)
CONTOUR TOOL INC
38830 Taylor Pkwy (44035-6254)
PHONE....................................440 365-7333
Paul Reichlin, *President*
R Stephen Laux, *Principal*
Yvonne D Reichlin, *Vice Pres*
Sue Mims, *Admin Asst*
EMP: 35
SQ FT: 11,000
SALES (est): 6.4MM **Privately Held**
WEB: www.contourtool.com
SIC: 3545 3544 Machine tool accessories;
special dies & tools

(G-15365)
CUPCAKE DIVAZ
5480 Autumn Ln (44039-1177)
PHONE....................................216 509-3850
Gina King, *Principal*
EMP: 4
SALES (est): 217.4K **Privately Held**
SIC: 2051 Bread, cake & related products

(G-15366)
CUPCAKE WISHES
34340 Bainbridge Rd (44039-4101)
PHONE....................................440 315-3856
Holly Kennedy, *Principal*
EMP: 4
SALES (est): 240.3K **Privately Held**
SIC: 2051 Bread, cake & related products

(G-15367)
**CUSTOM NEON & COMMERCIAL
SIGNS**
7820 Maddock Rd (44039-3714)
PHONE....................................440 327-0225
Orison Fields, *Owner*
EMP: 3
SALES (est): 150K **Privately Held**
SIC: 1799 3993 Sign installation & mainte-
nance; signs & advertising specialties

(G-15368)
CUYAHOGA VENDING CO INC
Also Called: Cuyahoga Group, The
39405 Taylor Pkwy (44035-6264)
PHONE....................................440 353-9595
EMP: 40
SALES (corp-wide): 10.9MM **Privately
Held**
SIC: 7359 2099 Vending machine rental;
food preparations
PA: Cuyahoga Vending Co., Inc.
14250 Industrial Ave S # 104
Maple Heights OH 44137
216 663-1457

(G-15369)
DIRECT IMAGE SIGNS INC
7820 Maddock Rd (44039-3714)
PHONE....................................440 327-5575
Brett Smith, *President*
EMP: 3
SALES (est): 210K **Privately Held**
SIC: 3993 Signs & advertising specialties

(G-15370)
DRECO INC
7887 Root Rd (44039-4013)
P.O. Box 39328 (44039-0328)
PHONE....................................440 327-6021
Fax: 440 327-9922
Christopher A Draudt, *President*
Russell Draudt, *President*
H T Ammerman, *Principal*
Harold F Ellsworth, *Principal*
Johanna S Rolfe, *Principal*
▲ EMP: 130 EST: 1932
SQ FT: 135,000
SALES (est): 19.9MM **Privately Held**
SIC: 3089 Injection molded finished plastic
products

(G-15371)
ECHOGRAPHICS INC
9454 Grist Mill Dr (44039-9702)
P.O. Box 742, Berea (44017-0742)
PHONE....................................440 846-2330

Fax: 440 846-2332
James Fogleson, *President*
Linda Fogleson, *Corp Secy*
▲ EMP: 3
SQ FT: 2,000
SALES (est): 466.6K **Privately Held**
WEB: www.echographics.com
SIC: 2752 2759 5199 7336 Commercial
printing, offset; business forms: printing;
screen printing; advertising specialties;
commercial art & graphic design

(G-15372)
FATE INDUSTRIES INC
36682 Sugar Ridge Rd (44039-3832)
PHONE....................................440 327-1770
Fax: 440 327-7626
Rick Fate, *President*
Julie Fate, *Admin Sec*
EMP: 8
SQ FT: 2,800
SALES (est): 760K **Privately Held**
SIC: 3599 Machine shop, jobbing & repair

(G-15373)
**FEDERAL BARCODE LABEL
SYSTEMS**
33438 Liberty Pkwy (44039-2670)
PHONE....................................440 748-8060
Fax: 440 748-2258
James K Jenkins, *President*
James Jenkins Jr, *Vice Pres*
EMP: 5
SQ FT: 5,200
SALES: 330K **Privately Held**
WEB: www.federalbarcode.com
SIC: 2679 2759 5045 Tags & labels,
paper; labels & seals: printing; computer
software

(G-15374)
FINE WOOD DESIGN INC
35535 Center Ridge Rd (44039-3019)
PHONE....................................440 327-0751
Uwe Neumann, *Principal*
EMP: 5
SALES (est): 659.3K **Privately Held**
SIC: 2434 5712 Wood kitchen cabinets;
customized furniture & cabinets

(G-15375)
FROHOCK-STEWART INC
39400 Taylor Pkwy (44035-6263)
PHONE....................................440 329-6000
Gerald B Blouch, *President*
▲ EMP: 40 EST: 1954
SALES (est): 3.3MM
SALES (corp-wide): 1B **Publicly Held**
WEB: www.invacare.com
SIC: 3842 Surgical appliances & supplies
PA: Invacare Corporation
1 Invacare Way
Elyria OH 44035
440 329-6000

(G-15376)
GLAXOSMITHKLINE LLC
37381 Stone Creek Dr (44039-1243)
PHONE....................................440 552-2895
EMP: 26
SALES (corp-wide): 34.3B **Privately Held**
SIC: 2834 Pharmaceutical preparations
HQ: Glaxosmithkline Llc
5 Crescent Dr
Philadelphia PA 19112
215 751-4000

(G-15377)
**GOLD STAR MET FABG & REPR
INC**
4940 Mills Indus Pkwy (44039-1954)
PHONE....................................440 353-3233
Fax: 440 353-3955
Mark A Galinas, *President*
Barb Seith, *Manager*
EMP: 17
SQ FT: 17,170
SALES (est): 3.7MM **Privately Held**
SIC: 3441 Fabricated structural metal

(G-15378)
**HEIL ENGNEERED PROCESS
EQP INC**
37000 Center Ridge Rd (44039-2804)
PHONE....................................440 327-6051

Kyle Hankinson, *President*
James Hark, *Controller*
EMP: 13
SALES (est): 573.4K **Privately Held**
SIC: 3559 Chemical machinery & equip-
ment

(G-15379)
HOISTECH LLC
5131 Mills Indus Pkwy (44039-1957)
PHONE....................................440 327-5379
Ray Mack,
EMP: 6
SALES (est): 588.8K **Privately Held**
SIC: 3949 Sporting & athletic goods

(G-15380)
IMPACT INDUSTRIES INC
5120 Mills Indus Pkwy (44039-1958)
PHONE....................................440 327-2360
Fax: 440 327-2465
William Nestor, *President*
Leslie Nestor, *Vice Pres*
EMP: 41
SQ FT: 25,000
SALES (est): 6.3MM **Privately Held**
WEB: www.impactindustries.com
SIC: 3469 3544 Stamping metal for the
trade; special dies & tools; jigs & fixtures

(G-15381)
INVACARE CORPORATION
Also Called: Invacare Hme
38683 Taylor Pkwy (44035-6200)
PHONE....................................440 329-6000
Diane Ostang, *Research*
David Thompson, *Electrical Engi*
Brad Kushner, *Branch Mgr*
Steven Wilder, *Program Mgr*
Charlene Powe, *Director*
EMP: 14
SALES (corp-wide): 1B **Publicly Held**
WEB: www.invacare.com
SIC: 3842 Surgical appliances & supplies
PA: Invacare Corporation
1 Invacare Way
Elyria OH 44035
440 329-6000

(G-15382)
INVACARE CORPORATION (TW)
39400 Taylor Pkwy (44035-6270)
PHONE....................................440 329-6000
Fax: 440 329-6270
A Malachi Mixon III, *President*
Mary Whitesel, *Manager*
◆ EMP: 45
SALES (est): 1.6B **Privately Held**
SIC: 3842 Surgical appliances & supplies

(G-15383)
JBC TECHNOLOGIES INC
7887 Bliss Pkwy (44039-3475)
PHONE....................................440 327-4522
Joe Bliss, *CEO*
▲ EMP: 55
SALES (est): 14.1MM **Privately Held**
WEB: www.jbc-tech.com
SIC: 3423 Cutting dies, except metal cut-
ting

(G-15384)
**KALT MANUFACTURING
COMPANY**
36700 Sugar Ridge Rd (44039-3800)
PHONE....................................440 327-2102
Fax: 440 327-6171
Joseph W Kalt, *President*
William E Kalt, *Principal*
John Lowstetter, *Prdtn Mgr*
Daryl Bishop, *Purchasing*
Edwin Lipowski, *Engineer*
▲ EMP: 54
SQ FT: 60,000
SALES (est): 14.3MM **Privately Held**
WEB: www.kaltmfg.com
SIC: 3544 3545 3549 3599 Special dies,
tools, jigs & fixtures; machine tool acces-
sories; metalworking machinery; machine
shop, jobbing & repair

(G-15385)
KITCHEN WORKS INC
34425 Lorain Rd Ste 5 (44039-4492)
PHONE....................................440 353-0939
Fax: 440 353-0939

Dan Vaneck, *President*
Lisa Stoltz, *Vice Pres*
Jose Cendelero, *Treasurer*
EMP: 4
SQ FT: 7,500
SALES: 320K **Privately Held**
SIC: 2434 1751 1799 1521 Wood kitchen
cabinets; cabinet building & installation;
kitchen & bathroom remodeling; general
remodeling, single-family houses

(G-15386)
LAKE ERIE MACHINE
5165 Mills Indus Pkwy (44039-1957)
PHONE....................................440 353-9191
Jeff Reed, *Owner*
EMP: 4
SALES (est): 361.5K **Privately Held**
SIC: 3599 Machine shop, jobbing & repair

(G-15387)
LEAR MANUFACTURING INC
7855 Race Rd (44039-3615)
PHONE....................................440 327-4545
Fax: 440 327-1442
Bonnie Lear, *President*
John Lear, *Corp Secy*
Greg Lear, *Opers Mgr*
EMP: 5
SQ FT: 2,688
SALES (est): 756K **Privately Held**
SIC: 3451 3545 Screw machine products;
machine tool attachments & accessories

(G-15388)
**LORAIN COUNTY METRO PK
DST**
6195 Otten Rd (44039-1117)
PHONE....................................440 327-3626
Tim Fairweather, *Branch Mgr*
EMP: 5
SQ FT: 1,836
SALES (corp-wide): 46K **Privately Held**
SIC: 2531 Public building & related furni-
ture
PA: Lorain County Metropolitan Park Dis-
trict
12882 Diagonal Rd
Lagrange OH 44050
440 458-5121

(G-15389)
**LORAIN RULED DIE PRODUCTS
INC**
6287 Lear Nagle Rd Ste 4 (44039-3369)
PHONE....................................440 281-8607
Roger Galippo, *President*
EMP: 6
SQ FT: 2,800
SALES (est): 750K **Privately Held**
SIC: 3544 Dies, steel rule

(G-15390)
MAXIMUM GRAPHIX INC
33426 Liberty Pkwy (44039-2670)
PHONE....................................440 353-3301
Gregory Comwell, *President*
Kimberly Cromwell, *Vice Pres*
EMP: 5
SQ FT: 2,200
SALES: 300K **Privately Held**
SIC: 2752 7336 Commercial printing, off-
set; commercial art & graphic design

(G-15391)
**NORLAKE MANUFACTURING
COMPANY**
39301 Taylor Pkwy (44035-6272)
P.O. Box 215, Elyria (44036-0215)
PHONE....................................440 353-3200
Fax: 440 353-3232
James Markus, *President*
Daryl Jackson, *Vice Pres*
Kenneth Sroka, *Prdtn Mgr*
Eric Richardson, *Engineer*
Tj Sulkowski, *Electrical Engi*
▼ EMP: 90 EST: 1963
SQ FT: 50,000
SALES (est): 36.2MM **Privately Held**
WEB: www.norlakemfg.com
SIC: 3677 3714 3612 Transformers
power supply, electronic type; motor vehi-
cle parts & accessories; transformers, ex-
cept electric

▲ = Import ▼=Export
◆ =Import/Export

(G-15392)
NORTH EAST TECHNOLOGIES INC
5127 Mills Indus Pkwy (44039-1957)
PHONE..............................440 327-9278
Harry Salverson, *President*
EMP: 5 **EST:** 1995
SQ FT: 2,500
SALES (est): 703.4K **Privately Held**
SIC: 3541 Gear cutting & finishing machines

(G-15393)
P M MOTOR COMPANY
Also Called: P M Motor -Fan Blade Company
37850 Taylor Pkwy (44039-3643)
PHONE..............................440 327-9999
Michael Macken, *President*
Catherine E Macken, *Corp Secy*
Joan B Macken, *Vice Pres*
EMP: 14 **EST:** 1952
SQ FT: 10,000
SALES (est): 1.6MM **Privately Held**
WEB: www.pmfan.com
SIC: 3469 Machine parts, stamped or pressed metal

(G-15394)
PLEXTRUSIONS INC
38870 Taylor Pkwy (44035-6254)
PHONE..............................330 668-2587
Eve Gribble, *Principal*
EMP: 9
SALES (est): 1.3MM **Privately Held**
SIC: 3083 Thermoplastic laminates: rods, tubes, plates & sheet

(G-15395)
POLARX ORNAMENTS LLC
35490 Lorain Rd (44039-4461)
PHONE..............................866 298-0433
Laura Bunevich, *Accounting Mgr*
John Norris,
Jay Butterworth,
Michael Mahoney,
EMP: 12
SALES (est): 600K **Privately Held**
SIC: 3961 5199 Ornaments, costume, except precious metal & gems; gifts & novelties

(G-15396)
PROTECTIVE INDUSTRIAL POLYMERS
7875 Bliss Pkwy (44039-3475)
PHONE..............................440 327-0015
Patrick Scudder, *President*
Don Batke, *Opers Mgr*
Craig Scudder, *Finance Dir*
Jason Tobias, *Manager*
Sean Walsh, *Manager*
EMP: 10
SALES (est): 699K **Privately Held**
SIC: 1771 2515 2822 8741 Flooring contractor; mattresses, containing felt, foam rubber, urethane, etc.; ethylene-propylene rubbers, EPDM polymers; construction management

(G-15397)
PURITAS METAL PRODUCTS INC
7720 Race Rd (44039-3614)
PHONE..............................440 353-1917
Fax: 440 353-1918
Richard Cook, *CEO*
Todd Whitney, *Opers Mgr*
Sandra West, *Office Mgr*
Jennifer Lear, *Manager*
EMP: 15
SQ FT: 15,000
SALES (est): 2.4MM **Privately Held**
WEB: www.puritasmetal.com
SIC: 3599 Ties, form: metal

(G-15398)
QUALITY COMPOUND MFG
5212 Mills Indus Pkwy (44039-1960)
PHONE..............................440 353-0150
Jeff Hopkins, *Mng Member*
EMP: 5
SALES (est): 519K **Privately Held**
SIC: 3999 Manufacturing industries

(G-15399)
RAVEN CONCEALMENT SYSTEMS LLC
7889 Root Rd (44039-4013)
PHONE..............................440 508-9000
John Chapman, *CEO*
Kelly Laurence, *General Mgr*
Vicky Sawyer, *General Mgr*
John K Famlacher, *Principal*
Dotson Burton, *Principal*
EMP: 8
SALES (est): 291.7K **Privately Held**
SIC: 5399 3949 3089 Army-Navy goods; cases, gun & rod (sporting equipment); injection molding of plastics

(G-15400)
RETAYS WELDING COMPANY
7650 Race Rd (44039-3612)
PHONE..............................440 327-4100
Fax: 440 327-4304
Allen Retay, *President*
Marilyn Hoskinson, *Admin Sec*
EMP: 25 **EST:** 1973
SQ FT: 28,000
SALES (est): 1.8MM **Privately Held**
SIC: 3443 3441 Fabricated plate work (boiler shop); fabricated structural metal

(G-15401)
RHENIUM ALLOYS INC (PA)
38683 Taylor Pkwy (44035-6200)
P.O. Box 245, Elyria (44036-0245)
PHONE..............................440 365-7388
Fax: 440 366-9831
Mike Prokop, *President*
Todd Leonhardt, *Vice Pres*
Randall Mohr, *Buyer*
Carol Pilan, *Sls & Mktg Exec*
William McVicker, *Controller*
▲ **EMP:** 60 **EST:** 1994
SQ FT: 35,500
SALES (est): 13.5MM **Privately Held**
WEB: www.rhenium.com
SIC: 3313 3356 3498 3339 Electrometallurgical products; tungsten, basic shapes; fabricated pipe & fittings; primary nonferrous metals; chemical preparations; ferroalloy ores, except vanadium

(G-15402)
RW BECKETT CORPORATION (PA)
38251 Center Ridge Rd (44039-2895)
P.O. Box 1289, Elyria (44036-1289)
PHONE..............................440 327-1060
Fax: 440 327-1064
John D Beckett, *Ch of Bd*
John Beckett, *Ch of Bd*
Kevin D Beckett, *Ch of Bd*
Adam Friedrick, *Plant Supt*
Rick Roth, *Foreman/Supr*
◆ **EMP:** 193 **EST:** 1937
SQ FT: 40,000
SALES (est): 31.6MM **Privately Held**
WEB: www.lovingmonday.com
SIC: 3433 Oil burners, domestic or industrial

(G-15403)
SAVANNA TOOL AND MANUFACTURING
34395 Mills Rd (44039-2060)
PHONE..............................440 327-8330
Fax: 440 327-5482
Stephen Santa, *President*
Phil Santa, *Vice Pres*
EMP: 5
SQ FT: 5,000
SALES: 500K **Privately Held**
SIC: 3599 Machine shop, jobbing & repair

(G-15404)
TANGO ECHO BRAVO MFG INC
4915 Mills Indus Pkwy (44039-1953)
PHONE..............................440 937-3800
Timothy E Bennett, *President*
EMP: 6
SQ FT: 2,800
SALES (est): 575.6K **Privately Held**
SIC: 3999 Barber & beauty shop equipment

(G-15405)
THE METAL MARKER MFG CO
6225 Lear Nagle Rd (44039-3223)
PHONE..............................440 327-2300
Fax: 440 327-2830
William Primrose, *President*
Robin Dunbar, *Accountant*
Mike Solarz, *VP Sales*
Dave Odonnell, *Sales Mgr*
Bill Primrose, *Info Tech Mgr*
EMP: 13
SQ FT: 16,000
SALES (est): 1.2MM **Privately Held**
WEB: www.metalmarkermfg.com
SIC: 3953 Marking devices

(G-15406)
TOOL & DIE SYSTEMS INC
38900 Taylor Indus Pkwy (44039)
PHONE..............................440 327-5800
Fax: 440 327-4777
Leonard Sikora, *President*
William T Flickinger, *Vice Pres*
Frank Greszler, *Manager*
EMP: 28 **EST:** 1976
SQ FT: 60,000
SALES (est): 5.9MM **Privately Held**
WEB: www.tooldiesystems.com
SIC: 3444 3469 3599 3479 Sheet metalwork; metal stampings; machine shop, jobbing & repair; painting of metal products

(G-15407)
UNIVERSITY ACCESSORIES INC
Also Called: Avetec Products Group
5152 Mills Indus Pkwy (44039-1958)
PHONE..............................440 327-4151
Douglas J Cook, *President*
Justin Simon, *Warehouse Mgr*
Moe Jemiola, *Purch Mgr*
Alice Linn, *Treasurer*
▲ **EMP:** 5
SQ FT: 5,500
SALES (est): 2.5MM **Privately Held**
WEB: www.usecure.com
SIC: 5065 3577 Electronic parts & equipment; computer peripheral equipment

(G-15408)
US REFRACTORY PRODUCTS LLC
7660 Race Rd (44039-3612)
PHONE..............................440 386-4580
William Drake, *Vice Pres*
Gary M Demarco, *Mng Member*
▲ **EMP:** 25
SQ FT: 30,000
SALES (est): 5MM **Privately Held**
SIC: 3297 Nonclay refractories

North Royalton
Cuyahoga County

(G-15409)
ANDREW TOOL CO INC
12146 York Rd Unit 2 (44133-3678)
PHONE..............................440 237-4340
Fax: 440 237-0323
Kevin Yeo, *President*
Alice Yeo, *Treasurer*
EMP: 3
SQ FT: 3,400
SALES (est): 371.4K **Privately Held**
SIC: 3599 Machine shop, jobbing & repair

(G-15410)
AXEL AUSTIN LLC
10147 Royalton Rd Ste I (44133-4462)
PHONE..............................440 237-1610
▼ **EMP:** 3 **EST:** 2012
SQ FT: 1,200
SALES (est): 330K **Privately Held**
SIC: 3625 Mfg Relays/Industrial Controls

(G-15411)
BEST EQUIPMENT CO INC
12359 Abbey Rd Ste A (44133-2642)
PHONE..............................440 237-3515
Mike Dahlman, *Mng Member*
EMP: 22

SALES (corp-wide): 24MM **Privately Held**
SIC: 3589 Sewer cleaning equipment, power
PA: Best Equipment Co Inc
5550 Poindexter Dr
Indianapolis IN 46235
317 823-3050

(G-15412)
BSK INDUSTRIES INC (PA)
10143 Royalton Rd Ste C (44133-4463)
P.O. Box 33697 (44133-0697)
PHONE..............................440 230-9299
Stephen Kisan, *President*
EMP: 4
SALES (est): 1.1MM **Privately Held**
WEB: www.bskindustries.com
SIC: 3823 8711 Industrial process control instruments; consulting engineer

(G-15413)
CARDINAL PRODUCTS INC
11929 Abbey Rd Ste D (44133-2664)
PHONE..............................440 237-8280
Janet Stanley, *President*
EMP: 8
SQ FT: 10,000
SALES (est): 950K **Privately Held**
SIC: 3089 Molding primary plastic

(G-15414)
CHARLES V SNIDER & ASSOC INC
10139 Royalton Rd Ste K (44133-4473)
PHONE..............................440 877-9151
Fax: 440 877-9159
Charles V Snider, *President*
David McKendry, *Vice Pres*
Judy Nair, *Office Mgr*
John Kane, *Representative*
EMP: 10
SQ FT: 3,200
SALES (est): 1.3MM **Privately Held**
WEB: www.cvsniderlaw.com
SIC: 3949 Playground equipment

(G-15415)
CPMG
12955 York Delta Dr Ste G (44133-3550)
PHONE..............................440 263-2780
Michael W Johns, *Owner*
EMP: 5
SALES (est): 347.3K **Privately Held**
SIC: 3499 Fabricated metal products

(G-15416)
D J METRO MOLD & DIE INC
9841 York Alpha Dr Ste J (44133-3554)
PHONE..............................440 237-1130
Fax: 440 237-1130
David Metro, *President*
EMP: 5
SALES (est): 524.1K **Privately Held**
SIC: 3544 3089 Special dies & tools; injection molding of plastics

(G-15417)
DENTAL SEALANTS
7029 Royalton Rd (44133-4874)
PHONE..............................440 582-3466
EMP: 3
SALES (est): 149.7K **Privately Held**
SIC: 2891 Sealants

(G-15418)
EAGLE PRECISION PRODUCTS LLC
13800 Progress Pkwy Ste J (44133-4354)
PHONE..............................440 582-9393
Joshua Reger, *Vice Pres*
Bruce Reger, *Mng Member*
EMP: 9
SQ FT: 18,000
SALES: 2MM **Privately Held**
WEB: www.eagleprecisionproducts.com
SIC: 3469 3544 Stamping metal for the trade; special dies & tools

(G-15419)
FGM MEDIA INC
13981 Stoney Creek Dr (44133-4114)
P.O. Box 33411 (44133-0411)
PHONE..............................440 376-0487
Frank Malec, *President*

Paulette Holland, *Admin Sec*
EMP: 5
SALES (est): 400K **Privately Held**
WEB: www.fgmmedia.com
SIC: 2741 7371 Technical manual & paper publishing; custom computer programming services;

(G-15420)
GARDELLA JEWELRY LLC
Also Called: Earth Dreams Jewelry
7432 Julia Dr (44133-3715)
PHONE........................440 877-9261
Jacqueline Magyar, *COO*
David Magyar, *CFO*
EMP: 6 **EST:** 2011
SALES (est): 551.1K **Privately Held**
SIC: 3961 7389 Jewelry apparel, non-precious metals; business services

(G-15421)
GLOBAL SIGNS AND GRAPHICS INC
10147 Royalton Rd Ste M (44133-4466)
PHONE........................440 230-2100
Kirk Miller, *President*
Stacey Miller, *Office Mgr*
Sheila Mangano, *Executive Asst*
EMP: 5
SALES (est): 717.1K **Privately Held**
WEB: www.go4globalgraphics.com
SIC: 3993 Signs & advertising specialties

(G-15422)
GRABER METAL WORKS INC
9664 Akins Rd Ste 1 (44133-4595)
PHONE........................440 237-8422
Fax: 440 237-0135
Steve M Graber Sr, *President*
Michael R Horvath, *Vice Pres*
Katherine Graber, *Treasurer*
Richard Graber, *Office Mgr*
EMP: 30 **EST:** 1965
SQ FT: 25,000
SALES (est): 3MM **Privately Held**
WEB: www.grabermetal.com
SIC: 3599 5051 3446 3444 Machine shop, jobbing & repair; tubing, flexible metallic; metals service centers & offices; architectural metalwork; sheet metalwork; fabricated plate work (boiler shop); fabricated structural metal

(G-15423)
H & D STEEL SERVICE INC
Also Called: H & D Steel Service Center
9960 York Alpha Dr (44133-3588)
PHONE........................440 237-3390
Fax: 440 237-4540
Raymond Gary Schreiber, *Ch of Bd*
Joseph Bubba, *President*
Joseph A Cachat, *Principal*
R M Jones, *Principal*
R G Schreiber, *Principal*
▲ **EMP:** 50
SQ FT: 125,000
SALES (est): 54.4MM **Privately Held**
WEB: www.hdsteel.com
SIC: 5051 3541 5085 Iron or steel flat products; sheets, metal; tubing, metal; bars, metal; home workshop machine tools, metalworking; industrial tools

(G-15424)
HAWK ENGINE & MACHINE
12166 York Rd Unit 1 (44133-3689)
PHONE........................440 582-0900
Terry R Hawk, *President*
Denise Hawk, *Admin Sec*
EMP: 3
SQ FT: 3,200
SALES (est): 200K **Privately Held**
SIC: 3599 2431 Machine & other job shop work; millwork

(G-15425)
HIGHSCHOOLBALL INC
10143 Royalton Rd (44133-4470)
P.O. Box 123, Hinckley (44233-0123)
PHONE........................844 472-2551
Matthew Zelinski, *President*
EMP: 3 **EST:** 2015
SQ FT: 1,200
SALES (est): 117.3K **Privately Held**
SIC: 2711 Newspapers, publishing & printing

(G-15426)
INDUCTION TOOLING INC
12510 York Delta Dr (44133-3543)
PHONE........................440 237-0711
Fax: 440 237-7009
William Stuehr, *President*
John Gadus, *Engineer*
Sherry Stuehr, *Human Res Dir*
David Lynch, *Mktg Dir*
Lisa Drabish, *Office Mgr*
EMP: 20
SQ FT: 25,000
SALES (est): 4.8MM **Privately Held**
WEB: www.inductiontooling.com
SIC: 3567 Induction heating equipment

(G-15427)
INDUSTRIAL PARTS DEPOT LLC
Also Called: I P D
11266 Royalton Rd (44133-4474)
PHONE........................440 237-9164
Fax: 440 237-6344
Jeff Guiliano, *Branch Mgr*
EMP: 6
SALES (corp-wide): 74.6MM **Privately Held**
SIC: 3519 5084 Parts & accessories, internal combustion engines; engines & parts, diesel
HQ: Industrial Parts Depot, Llc
23231 Normandie Ave
Torrance CA 90501
310 530-1900

(G-15428)
JAGUAR MEDICAL SUPPLIES INC
12955 York Delta Dr Ste G (44133-3550)
PHONE........................440 263-2780
Michael Johns, *President*
EMP: 3
SALES (est): 116.7K **Privately Held**
SIC: 3499 Machine bases, metal

(G-15429)
KADER PRINTING LLC
12822 Heritage Trl (44133-3665)
PHONE........................440 668-1579
EMP: 4
SALES (est): 489K **Privately Held**
SIC: 2752 Commercial printing, lithographic

(G-15430)
KENT CORPORATION
9601 York Alpha Dr (44133-3503)
PHONE........................440 582-3400
Dean Costello, *CEO*
David Tsai, *President*
Sawyer Jeremiah, *COO*
Pat Resco, *Controller*
Patricia Gresko, *Accounting Mgr*
▲ **EMP:** 31
SQ FT: 22,000
SALES (est): 9.3MM **Privately Held**
WEB: www.kenttesgo.com
SIC: 3549 Coiling machinery

(G-15431)
KRIST KRENZ MACHINE INC
9801 York Alpha Dr (44133-3507)
PHONE........................440 237-1800
Fax: 440 237-0509
Richard Krenz Jr, *President*
Alfred Krist, *Vice Pres*
Adam Krenz, *Treasurer*
Nellie Keller, *Manager*
Paul Krenz, *Admin Sec*
EMP: 65
SQ FT: 35,000
SALES (est): 9.4MM **Privately Held**
WEB: www.krenzkristmachine.com
SIC: 3451 Screw machine products

(G-15432)
LASZERAY TECHNOLOGY LLC
12315 York Delta Dr (44133-3544)
PHONE........................440 582-8430
Fax: 440 582-9536
Greg Clark, *CEO*
Steve Patton, *Vice Pres*
Amely Wallace, *Manager*
▲ **EMP:** 81 **EST:** 1997
SQ FT: 60,000

SALES (est): 26.7MM **Privately Held**
WEB: www.laszeray.com
SIC: 3089 3544 Injection molding of plastics; special dies, tools, jigs & fixtures

(G-15433)
LOZINAK & SONS INC
8695 York Rd (44133-1506)
PHONE........................440 877-1819
Jerry Liveneck, *President*
EMP: 3
SALES (est): 286.8K **Privately Held**
SIC: 3241 Masonry cement

(G-15434)
LUNAR TOOL & MOLD INC
9860 York Alpha Dr (44133-3586)
PHONE........................440 237-2141
Fax: 440 237-8606
Friedrich Hoffman Jr, *President*
Frank Zimmer, *Manager*
EMP: 19 **EST:** 1965
SQ FT: 20,000
SALES (est): 2.8MM **Privately Held**
WEB: www.lunarmold.com
SIC: 3544 7692 Special dies & tools; industrial molds; welding repair

(G-15435)
MAY CONVEYOR INC
9981 York Theta Dr (44133-3545)
PHONE........................440 237-8012
Leonard May, *President*
Matias Dost, *Vice Pres*
▲ **EMP:** 15
SQ FT: 55,000
SALES (est): 2MM **Privately Held**
WEB: www.mayconveyor.com
SIC: 3496 Conveyor belts

(G-15436)
MDF TOOL CORPORATION
10166 Royalton Rd (44133-4427)
PHONE........................440 237-2277
Fax: 440 237-6590
John Bunjevac, *CEO*
Larry Jackson, *President*
Mark Geiger, *Engineer*
Jason Panaro, *Engineer*
Tracy Grega, *Controller*
EMP: 18
SQ FT: 8,000
SALES (est): 2.9MM **Privately Held**
WEB: www.mdftool.com
SIC: 3544 3545 Special dies & tools; machine tool accessories

(G-15437)
NEXT GERENATION CRIMPING
Also Called: N G C
9880 York Alpha Dr (44133-3508)
PHONE........................440 237-6300
Fax: 440 237-0143
Fred Krist, *Partner*
EMP: 8
SALES (est): 953.7K **Privately Held**
SIC: 3432 Plumbing fixture fittings & trim

(G-15438)
NU-TOOL INDUSTRIES INC
9920 York Alpha Dr (44133-3510)
PHONE........................440 237-9240
Fax: 440 237-9240
Bruce Thompson, *President*
Richard Kuper, *Vice Pres*
Daniel Worthington, *Vice Pres*
EMP: 14
SQ FT: 8,000
SALES: 2.4MM **Privately Held**
WEB: www.nutoolind.com
SIC: 3542 Die casting & extruding machines

(G-15439)
OAK INDUSTRIAL INC
12955 York Delta Dr Ste G (44133-3550)
PHONE........................440 263-2780
Michael Johns, *CEO*
Russ Karla, *COO*
EMP: 7
SQ FT: 5,000
SALES: 500K **Privately Held**
SIC: 3599 Machine & other job shop work

(G-15440)
OIL SKIMMERS INC
12800 York Rd Ste G (44133-3682)
P.O. Box 33092 (44133-0092)
PHONE........................440 237-4600
Fax: 440 582-2759
William R Townsend, *President*
Jim Petrucci, *Vice Pres*
Craig Riley, *Purch Mgr*
Jeff Mann, *Engineer*
Jim Hebert, *Sales Mgr*
EMP: 22
SQ FT: 100,000
SALES (est): 6.2MM **Privately Held**
WEB: www.oilskim.com
SIC: 3569 3564 3553 3443 Filters; blowers & fans; oil & gas field machinery; fabricated plate work (boiler shop); filters, air & oil

(G-15441)
PALLET GUYS
12720 N Star Dr (44133-5945)
PHONE........................440 897-3001
Josh Wentz, *Principal*
EMP: 4 **EST:** 2010
SALES (est): 295.8K **Privately Held**
SIC: 2448 Pallets, wood & wood with metal

(G-15442)
PARMA INTERNATIONAL INC
13927 Progress Pkwy (44133-4394)
PHONE........................440 237-8650
Fax: 440 237-6333
Michael S Macdowell, *President*
Haydee Cooke, *Principal*
Giuseppe Franza, *Purchasing*
Mark Mathis, *Art Dir*
▲ **EMP:** 45
SQ FT: 17,000
SALES (est): 5.9MM **Privately Held**
WEB: www.parmapse.com
SIC: 3944 Automobile & truck models, toy & hobby

(G-15443)
PART RITE INC
12855 York Delta Dr (44133-3539)
PHONE........................216 362-4100
Fax: 440 237-2310
Daniel W Mihovk, *President*
Sharon C Mihovk, *Corp Secy*
EMP: 3 **EST:** 1964
SQ FT: 5,000
SALES (est): 346.7K **Privately Held**
SIC: 3599 3544 Machine shop, jobbing & repair; special dies, tools, jigs & fixtures

(G-15444)
PAUL POPOV
Also Called: Product Machine Company
13800 Progress Pkwy Ste A (44133-4354)
PHONE........................440 582-6677
Fax: 440 582-6680
Paul Popov, *Owner*
EMP: 3
SALES (est): 250K **Privately Held**
SIC: 3599 Machine shop, jobbing & repair

(G-15445)
PRECISE TUBE FORMING INC
9591 York Alpha Dr Ste 7 (44133-3555)
P.O. Box 425, East Palestine (44413-0425)
PHONE........................440 237-3956
EMP: 7 **EST:** 1996
SQ FT: 6,000
SALES (est): 830K **Privately Held**
SIC: 3498 Mfg Fabricated Pipe/Fittings Specialzies In Assembling

(G-15446)
ROYAL WIRE PRODUCTS INC (PA)
13450 York Delta Dr (44133-3584)
PHONE........................440 237-8787
Fax: 440 237-9330
William F Peshina, *President*
William Nelson, *Vice Pres*
Paige Peshina, *Vice Pres*
Victor Grima, *Plant Mgr*
Tom Merrill, *Safety Mgr*
▲ **EMP:** 60
SQ FT: 35,000

SALES: 19MM **Privately Held**
SIC: 3496 Miscellaneous fabricated wire products; cages, wire; woven wire products; grilles & grillework, woven wire

(G-15447)
ROYALTON ARCHTCTRAL FBRICATION
13155 York Delta Dr (44133-3522)
PHONE.................................440 582-0400
Fax: 440 582-0402
Stefan Winkler, *President*
EMP: 13
SQ FT: 10,000
SALES (est): 1.6MM **Privately Held**
WEB: www.rafpanels.com
SIC: 3444 3446 Sheet metalwork; architectural metalwork

(G-15448)
ROYALTON FOOD SERVICE EQP CO
9981 York Theta Dr (44133-3545)
PHONE.................................440 237-0806
Leonhard May, *President*
Hannelore May, *Corp Secy*
Brian Moore, *Foreman/Supr*
Dan Mytnick, *Purch Agent*
Pat Patton, *Controller*
EMP: 20
SQ FT: 40,000
SALES (est): 3.7MM **Privately Held**
SIC: 3556 3631 Food products machinery; household cooking equipment

(G-15449)
ROYALTON MANUFACTURING INC
12777 Abbey Rd Ste E (44133-2630)
P.O. Box 33190, Cleveland (44133-0190)
PHONE.................................440 237-2233
Fax: 440 237-4727
Kenneth Wesner, *President*
William Calfee, *Vice Pres*
Judith Wesner, *Treasurer*
Bruce Holzheimer, *Office Mgr*
EMP: 18
SQ FT: 12,000
SALES (est): 2.5MM **Privately Held**
SIC: 3599 Machine shop, jobbing & repair

(G-15450)
ROYALTON RECORDER
13737 State Rd (44133-3907)
PHONE.................................440 237-2235
Maria Magmelli, *President*
EMP: 5
SALES (est): 292.7K **Privately Held**
SIC: 2711 Newspapers

(G-15451)
S & D ARCHITECTURAL METALS
12955 York Delta Dr (44133-3534)
PHONE.................................440 582-2560
Cynthia Blessing, *President*
Keith Blessing, *Vice Pres*
EMP: 7
SALES (est): 756.8K **Privately Held**
SIC: 3444 Sheet metalwork

(G-15452)
SPA POOL COVERS INC
7806 Royalton Rd (44133-4708)
PHONE.................................440 235-9981
Fax: 440 235-9982
Rudy J Martinez, *President*
Gail A Martinez, *Vice Pres*
Theresa L Jedlinsky, *Admin Sec*
EMP: 5
SQ FT: 1,000
SALES: 150K **Privately Held**
SIC: 3423 1799 Leaf skimmers or swimming pool rakes; swimming pool construction

(G-15453)
SYLVAN FORGE INC
7420 James Dr (44133-3703)
PHONE.................................440 237-3626
Mike Mason, *President*
Eric Blackmore, *Vice Pres*
EMP: 7
SALES (est): 587.3K **Privately Held**
SIC: 2431 Woodwork, interior & ornamental

(G-15454)
SYMBOL TOOL & DIE INC
11000 Industrial First Av (44133-2678)
PHONE.................................440 582-5989
Fax: 440 582-8777
Jon Ardelian, *President*
EMP: 6
SQ FT: 4,000
SALES (est): 774.1K **Privately Held**
SIC: 3544 Special dies, tools, jigs & fixtures

(G-15455)
SYSTEMATIC MACHINE CORP
12955 York Delta Dr Ste F (44133-3550)
PHONE.................................440 877-9884
Richard Locker, *President*
EMP: 3
SQ FT: 5,200
SALES: 228K **Privately Held**
SIC: 3541 Machine tools, metal cutting type

(G-15456)
TRAVELERS VACATION GUIDE
10143 Royalton Rd (44133-4470)
PHONE.................................440 582-4949
Pam Voigt, *President*
EMP: 7
SQ FT: 1,400
SALES (est): 526.5K **Privately Held**
SIC: 2711 Newspapers: publishing only, not printed on site

(G-15457)
TRIAXIS MACHINE & TOOL LLC
11941 Abbey Rd Ste H (44133-2663)
PHONE.................................440 230-0303
Mark Timura, *General Mgr*
Ray Timura, *Mng Member*
Douglas Timura, *Director*
EMP: 5
SALES: 800K **Privately Held**
SIC: 5251 3089 7389 3599 Tools; injection molding of plastics; grinding, precision: commercial or industrial; chemical milling job shop; electrical discharge machining (EDM); blades, aircraft propeller: metal or wood

(G-15458)
VALLEY TOOL & DIE INC
Also Called: Valco Division
10020 York Theta Dr (44133-3581)
PHONE.................................440 237-0160
Fax: 440 237-0089
Adolf Eisenloeffel, *President*
James Homady, *General Mgr*
Helmut Eisenloeffel, *Principal*
Ernst Peters, *Principal*
Phillip S Eisenloeffel, *Vice Pres*
EMP: 65 **EST:** 1968
SQ FT: 54,000
SALES (est): 12.9MM **Privately Held**
WEB: www.valcocleve.com
SIC: 3465 3451 3452 3542 Automotive stampings; screw machine products; bolts, nuts, rivets & washers; machine tools, metal forming type; metal stampings; special dies & tools

(G-15459)
WESTGATE MACHINE CO INC
10665 Knights Way (44133-1998)
PHONE.................................216 889-9745
Fax: 216 267-6233
Terry Macho, *President*
Michael Macho, *Vice Pres*
Larry Oster, *Treasurer*
Cindy De Groot, *CPA*
Carolyn Macho, *Admin Sec*
EMP: 5
SQ FT: 1,600
SALES: 300K **Privately Held**
SIC: 3599 Machine shop, jobbing & repair

(G-15460)
WHITE MACHINE INC
9621 York Alpha Dr Side (44133-3594)
PHONE.................................440 237-3282
Fax: 440 237-2410
Larry White, *President*
Ronald White, *Exec VP*
Ruth White, *Vice Pres*
Robert Lee, *Mfg Dir*
Marita Castle, *Finance Mgr*

EMP: 8 **EST:** 1971
SQ FT: 7,600
SALES: 700K **Privately Held**
SIC: 3599 3728 3544 Machine shop, jobbing & repair; aircraft parts & equipment; special dies, tools, jigs & fixtures

(G-15461)
ZIEGLER ENGINEERING INC
9840 York Alpha Dr Ste F (44133-3553)
PHONE.................................440 582-8515
Fax: 440 292-3948
Ed Ziegler, *President*
EMP: 5
SQ FT: 5,400
SALES: 600K **Privately Held**
SIC: 3441 Fabricated structural metal

Northfield
Summit County

(G-15462)
BULK HANDLING EQUIPMENT CO
28 W Aurora Rd (44067-2073)
P.O. Box 670855 (44067-0855)
PHONE.................................330 468-5703
Joseph Stakes, *President*
Joanne Stakes, *Vice Pres*
Brian Stakes, *Engineer*
Mary Anne Stakes, *Admin Sec*
EMP: 7
SALES (est): 855.8K **Privately Held**
WEB: www.bulkhand.com
SIC: 3535 Bulk handling conveyor systems

(G-15463)
COLUMBIA STEEL AND WIRE INC
30 W Aurora Rd (44067-2004)
PHONE.................................330 468-2709
Fax: 330 468-2710
Marty Koppleman, *President*
Betty Koppleman, *Vice Pres*
EMP: 4
SQ FT: 8,000
SALES: 3.8MM **Privately Held**
WEB: www.columbiasteelandwire.com
SIC: 3316 5051 Bars, steel, cold finished, from purchased hot-rolled; steel

(G-15464)
CONNELL LIMITED PARTNERSHIP
Danly Die Set
154 E Aurora Rd Pmb 186 (44067-2053)
PHONE.................................877 534-8986
Dave Lowum, *President*
Jordon Owen, *COO*
John Dedic, *Marketing Mgr*
John Siggeman, *CTO*
Michael Kellogg, *Director*
EMP: 60
SALES (corp-wide): 500MM **Privately Held**
WEB: www.connell-lp.com
SIC: 3544 3542 3568 3366 Die sets for metal stamping (presses); die springs; punches, forming & stamping; forms (molds), for foundry & plastics working machinery; presses: hydraulic & pneumatic, mechanical & manual; bearings, bushings & blocks; bushings & bearings; bushings & bearings, bronze (nonmachined); spring washers, metal; cams (machine tool accessories)
PA: Connell Limited Partnership
1 International Pl Fl 31
Boston MA 02110
617 737-2700

(G-15465)
E Z ROUT INC
102 E Aurora Rd (44067-2019)
PHONE.................................330 467-4814
Keith Johnson, *President*
EMP: 3 **EST:** 1991
SALES (est): 307.9K **Privately Held**
SIC: 3423 Edge tools for woodworking: augers, bits, gimlets, etc.

(G-15466)
GENERAL DIE CASTERS INC
6212 Akron Peninsula Rd (44067)
PHONE.................................330 467-6700
Tom Lenin, *Branch Mgr*
EMP: 98
SQ FT: 45,136
SALES (corp-wide): 32.6MM **Privately Held**
WEB: www.generaldie.com
SIC: 3363 3364 Aluminum die-castings; zinc & zinc-base alloy die-castings
PA: General Die Casters, Inc.
2150 Highland Rd
Twinsburg OH 44087
330 678-2528

(G-15467)
IN GOOD HLTH & ANIMAL WELLNESS
9425 Olde 8 Rd Ste 4 (44067-1944)
PHONE.................................330 908-1234
Fax: 330 908-1242
Susan Glassner, *Owner*
EMP: 3
SALES (est): 141.8K **Privately Held**
SIC: 2047 3199 Dog & cat food; dog furnishings: collars, leashes, muzzles, etc.: leather

(G-15468)
MOSBRO MACHINE AND TOOL INC
8135 Crystal Creek Rd (44067-1802)
PHONE.................................330 467-0913
Neal J Moss, *President*
Kenneth S Moss, *Vice Pres*
EMP: 3
SQ FT: 8,000
SALES: 150K **Privately Held**
SIC: 3544 3559 Special dies, tools, jigs & fixtures; foundry machinery & equipment

(G-15469)
PARKSIDE & EATON ESTATE
8689 Parkside Dr (44067-1889)
PHONE.................................330 467-2995
William J Weigand, *Principal*
EMP: 3
SALES (est): 230K **Privately Held**
SIC: 3625 Motor controls & accessories

(G-15470)
PROGRESSIVE FOLDING BINDING CO
Also Called: Progressive Book Binding Co
8082 Augusta Ln (44067-1171)
PHONE.................................216 621-1893
Fax: 216 621-4434
EMP: 5 **EST:** 1944
SQ FT: 10,692
SALES (est): 420K **Privately Held**
SIC: 2789 Bookbinding/Related Work

(G-15471)
SENTRY GRAPHICS INC
114 Hiram College Dr (44067-2415)
PHONE.................................440 735-0850
Thomas Uridel, *President*
David Uridel, *Vice Pres*
EMP: 8
SQ FT: 7,200
SALES: 1MM **Privately Held**
SIC: 2752 5112 Commercial printing, offset; business forms; stationers, commercial; envelopes

(G-15472)
SMARTRONIX INC
416 Apple Hill Dr (44067-1107)
PHONE.................................216 378-3300
Fax: 216 378-2280
Gyorgy M Kovacs, *President*
Austin Hobbs, *Engineer*
Marnee McGlndy, *Office Mgr*
Justin Raley, *Sr Ntwrk Engine*
Greg Turpin, *Admin Asst*
EMP: 12
SQ FT: 4,500

SALES: 1MM **Privately Held**
WEB: www.cablawonline.com
SIC: 3571 5045 7373 7378 Electronic computers; computers, peripherals & software; systems integration services; computer peripheral equipment repair & maintenance

(G-15473)
SUMMIT AEROSPACE PRODUCTS
159 Ballantrae Dr (44067-2481)
PHONE...........................330 612-7341
Henry Prusinski, *Principal*
EMP: 3
SALES (est): 311K **Privately Held**
SIC: 3721 Aircraft

(G-15474)
TERMINAL EQUIPMENT INDUSTRIES
64 Privet Ln (44067-2883)
PHONE...........................330 468-0322
Fax: 440 468-0318
Ernest Pugh, *President*
Priscilla Pugh, *Treasurer*
EMP: 6
SQ FT: 1,100
SALES (est): 669.1K **Privately Held**
SIC: 3542 Machine tools, metal forming type

(G-15475)
TERRA COAT LLC
500 W Aurora Rd Ste 140 (44067-2164)
PHONE...........................216 254-8157
Dennis M Trusnik, *Principal*
EMP: 3
SALES (est): 345.9K **Privately Held**
SIC: 3479 Metal coating & allied service

Northwood
Wood County

(G-15476)
ANALYTIC STRESS RELIEVING INC
Also Called: Western Stress
6944 Mcnerney Dr (43619-1079)
PHONE...........................804 271-7198
George Walle, *Sales Mgr*
Martin Kellie, *Branch Mgr*
EMP: 7
SALES (corp-wide): 249.9MM **Privately Held**
SIC: 3398 5084 Metal heat treating; metalworking machinery
PA: Analytic Stress Relieving, Inc.
    3118 W Pinhook Rd Ste 202
    Lafayette LA 70508
    337 237-8790

(G-15477)
AUTO-TRONIC CONTROL CO
240 W Andrus Rd (43619-1206)
PHONE...........................419 666-5100
Harold M Kowalka, *President*
Kenneth Kowalka, *Vice Pres*
Sharon A Kowalka, *Treasurer*
Thomas Balyat, *Admin Sec*
EMP: 15 **EST:** 1946
SQ FT: 28,000
SALES (est): 3.3MM **Privately Held**
WEB: www.auto-tronic.com
SIC: 3613 Control panels, electric

(G-15478)
BERGMAN SAFETY SPANNER CO INC
3002 Woodville Rd Ste B (43619-1469)
PHONE...........................419 691-1462
Fax: 419 693-4606
Virginia Schlicher, *President*
Edythe Pocse, *Corp Secy*
Wayne F Bergman, *Vice Pres*
Beth Woodruff, *Manager*
EMP: 5
SQ FT: 1,198
SALES (est): 930.5K **Privately Held**
SIC: 3423 Wrenches, hand tools

(G-15479)
CONDOS AND TREES LLC
2674 Woodville Rd (43619-1446)
PHONE...........................419 691-2287
Donna McClellan, *Principal*
EMP: 3 **EST:** 2011
SALES (est): 251.2K **Privately Held**
SIC: 3999 Pet supplies

(G-15480)
ENK TENOFOUR LLC
6964 Mcnerney Dr (43619-1079)
PHONE...........................419 661-1465
Ron Flazingski,
▲ **EMP:** 9 **EST:** 2012
SALES (est): 1MM **Privately Held**
SIC: 3443 Cylinders, pressure: metal plate

(G-15481)
FAB STEEL CO INC
240 W Andrus Rd (43619-1206)
PHONE...........................419 666-5100
Harold M Kowalka, *President*
Sharon A Kowalka, *Vice Pres*
Thomas Balyat, *Admin Sec*
EMP: 14
SQ FT: 13,000
SALES: 546.7K **Privately Held**
WEB: www.fab-steel.com
SIC: 3444 Metal housings, enclosures, casings & other containers

(G-15482)
HIRZEL CANNING COMPANY (PA)
Also Called: Dei Fratelli
411 Lemoyne Rd (43619-1699)
PHONE...........................419 693-0531
Fax: 419 693-4859
Karl A Hirzel Jr, *President*
Lou Kozma, *General Mgr*
Emily Neuenschwander, *QA Dir*
Michael Rudin, *QC Mgr*
William J Hirzel, *Treasurer*
▲ **EMP:** 25 **EST:** 1947
SQ FT: 250,000
SALES (est): 24MM **Privately Held**
WEB: www.hirzel.com
SIC: 2033 8611 2034 Tomato products: packaged in cans, jars, etc.; tomato juice: packaged in cans, jars, etc.; tomato paste: packaged in cans, jars, etc.; tomato purees: packaged in cans, jars, etc.; business associations; dehydrated fruits, vegetables, soups

(G-15483)
HOT GRAPHIC SERVICES INC
2595 Tracy Rd (43619-1004)
P.O. Box 307, Toledo (43697-0307)
PHONE...........................419 242-7000
Gregory D Shapiro, *President*
Flora I Shapiro, *Chairman*
Norman Shapiro, *Corp Secy*
Myron Shapiro, *Vice Pres*
Grace Schumacher, *Controller*
EMP: 30 **EST:** 1976
SQ FT: 11,000
SALES (est): 5.2MM **Privately Held**
WEB: www.h-o-tgraphics.com
SIC: 2791 2752 Photocomposition, for the printing trade; commercial printing, offset

(G-15484)
MAGNA EXTERIORS AMERICA INC
Also Called: Norplas Industries
7825 Caple Blvd (43619-1078)
PHONE...........................419 662-3256
WEI Chua, *QC Mgr*
Chris Orchard, *Controller*
EMP: 600
SALES (corp-wide): 36.4B **Privately Held**
SIC: 3544 Special dies, tools, jigs & fixtures
HQ: Magna Exteriors Of America, Inc.
    750 Tower Dr
    Troy MI 48098
    248 631-1100

(G-15485)
NORPLAS INDUSTRIES INC (DH)
Also Called: Magna
7825 Caple Blvd (43619-1070)
PHONE...........................419 662-3317

Fax: 419 662-3201
Donald J Walker, *CEO*
Ray Beil, *General Mgr*
Graham Burrow, *Vice Pres*
Corey Honisko, *Foreman/Supr*
Greg Garrow, *Engineer*
◆ **EMP:** 270
SQ FT: 450,000
SALES (est): 372.1MM
SALES (corp-wide): 36.4B **Privately Held**
SIC: 3469 Metal stampings
HQ: Magna Exteriors Of America, Inc.
    750 Tower Dr
    Troy MI 48098
    248 631-1100

(G-15486)
OAKLEY INDUSTRIES SUB ASSEMBLY
6317 Fairfield Dr (43619-7508)
PHONE...........................419 661-8888
Fax: 419 666-0144
Dick Schmeltz, *President*
EMP: 50
SALES (corp-wide): 148.5MM **Privately Held**
SIC: 3714 Motor vehicle body components & frame
PA: Oakley Industries Sub Assembly Division, Inc.
    4333 Matthew
    Flint MI 48507
    810 720-4444

(G-15487)
PERFECT PACKAGING
6959 Wales Rd (43619-1015)
PHONE...........................419 662-1700
Dan Klasen, *Manager*
EMP: 3
SALES (est): 196.9K **Privately Held**
SIC: 2671 Packaging paper & plastics film, coated & laminated

(G-15488)
PILKINGTON NORTH AMERICA INC
2401 E Broadway St (43619-1318)
PHONE...........................800 547-9280
Fax: 419 247-4472
Robert Bobel, *Project Mgr*
Rodney Baker, *Research*
David Wagner, *Senior Engr*
Jennifer Wolfe, *Senior Engr*
Stephen Weidner, *VP Sls/Mktg*
EMP: 125
SALES (corp-wide): 5.3B **Privately Held**
WEB: www.low-eglass.com
SIC: 3211 Flat glass
HQ: Pilkington North America, Inc.
    811 Madison Ave Fl 1
    Toledo OH 43604
    419 247-4955

(G-15489)
ROYAL TOOL AND MACHINE LLC
5740 Woodville Rd (43619-2398)
PHONE...........................419 836-7781
Marco Vallera, *Mng Member*
Rose Schnitker, *Admin Sec*
EMP: 5
SQ FT: 10,000
SALES: 250K **Privately Held**
SIC: 3599 Machine shop, jobbing & repair

(G-15490)
TL INDUSTRIES INC (PA)
2541 Tracy Rd (43619-1097)
PHONE...........................419 666-8144
Fax: 419 666-6534
Richard Blausey, *President*
Joseph Young, *Vice Pres*
Theodore Stetschulte, *Vice Pres*
Paul Rodgers, *Prdtn Mgr*
Keith Kogler, *Purch Agent*
EMP: 105
SQ FT: 36,000
SALES (est): 41.9MM **Privately Held**
SIC: 8711 3444 3629 3679 Engineering services; sheet metalwork; battery chargers, rectifying or nonrotating; loads, electronic

(G-15491)
TOLEDO METAL FINISHING INC
Also Called: Toledo Deburring Co
7880 Caple Blvd (43619-1099)
PHONE...........................419 661-1422
Fax: 419 661-1424
Robert E Van Schoick Jr, *President*
EMP: 8
SQ FT: 18,000
SALES (est): 1MM **Privately Held**
SIC: 3471 Finishing, metals or formed products

(G-15492)
TRI COUNTY WHEEL AND RIM LTD
6943 Wales Rd Ste A (43619-1073)
PHONE...........................419 666-1760
EMP: 4 **EST:** 2012
SALES (est): 419.9K **Privately Held**
SIC: 3715 Truck trailers

(G-15493)
TURNER VAULT CO
2121 Tracy Rd (43619-1324)
PHONE...........................419 537-1133
Steven Turner, *President*
EMP: 30
SALES (est): 5MM **Privately Held**
SIC: 3272 Burial vaults, concrete or precast terrazzo

(G-15494)
WC SALES INC
Also Called: Whitney Company
5732 Woodville Rd Ste C (43619-2300)
P.O. Box 218, Williston (43468-0218)
PHONE...........................419 836-2300
David Whitney, *CEO*
EMP: 5
SALES (est): 798.9K **Privately Held**
WEB: www.greasetrapsales.com
SIC: 3599 5074 Machine & other job shop work; plumbing & hydronic heating supplies

(G-15495)
WESCO DISTRIBUTION INC
6519 Fairfield Dr (43619-7507)
PHONE...........................419 666-1670
EMP: 28 **Publicly Held**
SIC: 5085 3699 Industrial supplies; electrical equipment & supplies
HQ: Wesco Distribution, Inc.
    225 W Station Square Dr # 700
    Pittsburgh PA 15219
    412 454-2200

(G-15496)
WHITAKER FINISHING LLC
2707 Tracy Rd (43619-1050)
PHONE...........................419 666-7746
Fax: 419 666-4649
Greg Heminger, *President*
Jeffrey E Cooley,
Scott Helmke,
Scott Hilty,
▲ **EMP:** 30
SALES (est): 4MM **Privately Held**
SIC: 3471 Plating & polishing

(G-15497)
WHITAKER SURFACE SYSTEMS
2707 Tracy Rd (43619-1050)
PHONE...........................419 874-1211
Scott Helmke, *Plant Mgr*
Scott Hilty, *Opers Mgr*
James Gagnet, *Controller*
Dave Duncan, *Human Res Mgr*
Greg Heminger, *Mng Member*
EMP: 20
SALES (est): 2.5MM **Privately Held**
SIC: 3471 Plating & polishing

(G-15498)
XENOTRONIX/TLI INC
2541 Tracy Rd (43619-1004)
PHONE...........................407 331-4793
Joseph Young, *President*
Ted Stezshulte, *General Mgr*
Theodore Stechshulte, *Vice Pres*
Theodore Stetschulte, *Vice Pres*
Tom Harrison, *Director*
▲ **EMP:** 3

SALES (est): 311.4K
SALES (corp-wide): 41.9MM **Privately Held**
WEB: www.xenotronix.com
SIC: 3629 Battery chargers, rectifying or nonrotating
PA: T.L. Industries, Inc.
2541 Tracy Rd
Northwood OH 43619
419 666-8144

(G-15499)
YANFENG US AUTOMOTIVE
Also Called: Johnson Contrls Authorized Dlr
7560 Arbor Dr (43619-7500)
PHONE....................419 662-4905
Fax: 419 662-4977
Jeffrey Peterson, *Engineer*
Justin Shupp, *Manager*
EMP: 96
SALES (corp-wide): 55MM **Privately Held**
SIC: 2531 5075 Public building & related furniture; warm air heating & air conditioning
HQ: Yanfeng Us Automotive Interior Systems I Llc
45000 Helm St
Plymouth MI 48170
414 524-1200

Norton
Summit County

(G-15500)
ACCENT MANUFACTURING INC (PA)
Also Called: Accent Showroom & Design Ctr
1026 Gardner Blvd (44203-6670)
PHONE....................330 724-7704
Fax: 330 724-7717
Timothy Bush, *CEO*
Tim Bush, *President*
Betty Bush, *Corp Secy*
Anthony Piatko, *Sales Mgr*
Tom Baum, *Manager*
EMP: 18
SQ FT: 12,500
SALES (est): 1.6MM **Privately Held**
WEB: www.accentmanufacturing.com
SIC: 3281 1751 3433 3431 Cut stone & stone products; table tops, marble; bathroom fixtures, cut stone; cabinet building & installation; heating equipment, except electric; metal sanitary ware; vitreous plumbing fixtures; wood partitions & fixtures

(G-15501)
ACE READY MIX COMPANY INC
3826 Summit Rd (44203-5380)
PHONE....................330 745-8125
Albert C Perren Jr, *President*
Cliff Perren, *Vice Pres*
Skip Perren, *Treasurer*
Rhonda Regan, *Admin Sec*
EMP: 5
SQ FT: 5,100
SALES: 750K **Privately Held**
SIC: 3273 Ready-mixed concrete

(G-15502)
ACE READY MIX CONCRETE CO INC
3826 Summit Rd (44203-5380)
PHONE....................330 745-8125
Clifford Perren, *Vice Pres*
EMP: 10
SALES (est): 870.3K **Privately Held**
SIC: 3273 Ready-mixed concrete

(G-15503)
ACTION SPORTS APPAREL INC
3070 Wadsworth Rd (44203-5265)
PHONE....................330 848-9300
Fax: 330 848-9302
Thomas Gough, *President*
EMP: 3
SQ FT: 4,500

SALES: 460K **Privately Held**
WEB: www.seisports.com
SIC: 2396 5091 2395 Fabric printing & stamping; bowling equipment; pleating & stitching

(G-15504)
AKRON INDUSTRIAL MOTOR SERVICE
3041 Barber Rd (44203-1094)
PHONE....................330 753-7624
Fax: 330 753-7610
Tim Lance, *President*
Louis Ratener, *Vice Pres*
EMP: 4
SQ FT: 10,000
SALES: 750K **Privately Held**
SIC: 5063 7694 Motors, electric; electric motor repair

(G-15505)
ALBERTS SCREEN PRINT INC
Also Called: Albert Screenprint
3704 Summit Rd (44203-5378)
P.O. Box 1041 (44203-9441)
PHONE....................330 753-7559
Fax: 330 753-1612
Margaret Falkenstein, *CEO*
Albert Falkenstein Sr, *Ch of Bd*
Albert S Falkenstein, *President*
David Hughes, *General Mgr*
Patrick Finn, *Mfg Dir*
▲ EMP: 115 EST: 1962
SQ FT: 103,000
SALES (est): 21.5MM **Privately Held**
WEB: www.albertinc.com
SIC: 2759 3993 2752 Screen printing; signs & advertising specialties; commercial printing, lithographic

(G-15506)
ALLEN MORGAN TRUCKING & REPAIR
Also Called: Pro Street Chassis Shop
4162 Greenwich Rd (44203-5434)
PHONE....................330 336-5192
Al Morgan, *President*
Deborah Morgan, *Corp Secy*
EMP: 3
SQ FT: 4,000
SALES: 200K **Privately Held**
SIC: 3711 3354 Chassis, motor vehicle; aluminum rod & bar

(G-15507)
BUCKEYE FIELD MACHINING INC
Also Called: Tech Group
2131 Wadsworth Rd Ste 500 (44203-5317)
PHONE....................330 336-7036
Ben Riley, *President*
Pauline Riley, *Manager*
EMP: 3
SALES: 140K **Privately Held**
SIC: 3599 Machine shop, jobbing & repair

(G-15508)
COMPASS SYSTEMS & SALES LLC
5185 New Haven Cir (44203-4672)
PHONE....................330 733-2111
Fax: 330 733-2161
Robert S Sherrod, *President*
Mark Rubin, *Vice Pres*
Brenda Pavlantos, *Treasurer*
Phil Hart, *Admin Sec*
Joyce Zickefoose, *Administration*
▼ EMP: 56
SQ FT: 43,500
SALES (est): 16.6MM **Privately Held**
SIC: 3542 0724 Mechanical (pneumatic or hydraulic) metal forming machines; cotton ginning

(G-15509)
CUSTOM FAB
5281 S Hametown Rd (44203-6159)
PHONE....................330 825-3586
Charles Gilbertson, *Owner*
EMP: 3
SQ FT: 1,472
SALES: 125K **Privately Held**
SIC: 3714 Motor vehicle engines & parts

(G-15510)
E L STONE COMPANY
Also Called: Stonecote
2998 Eastern Rd (44203-3902)
P.O. Box 1012 (44203-9412)
PHONE....................330 825-4565
Fax: 330 825-7952
Mark Micire, *President*
Elma Micire, *Vice Pres*
Jerry Baughman, *Purch Dir*
EMP: 50 EST: 1955
SQ FT: 135,000
SALES: 3.5MM **Privately Held**
WEB: www.elstonecoinc.com
SIC: 3479 3471 Aluminum coating of metal products; plating & polishing

(G-15511)
ETKO MACHINE INC
2796 Barber Rd (44203-1002)
P.O. Box 710, Barberton (44203-0710)
PHONE....................330 745-4033
Fax: 330 745-5780
Julius J Koroshazi, *President*
Etelka Koroshazi, *Corp Secy*
George J Koroshazi, *Vice Pres*
EMP: 9
SQ FT: 4,000
SALES (est): 1.4MM **Privately Held**
WEB: www.etko.com
SIC: 3599 Machine shop, jobbing & repair

(G-15512)
FISHER SAND & GRAVEL INC
Also Called: Flesher Sand & Gravel
3322 Clark Mill Rd (44203-1028)
PHONE....................330 745-9239
James Fisher, *President*
EMP: 7 EST: 1968
SQ FT: 3,888
SALES: 500K **Privately Held**
SIC: 1442 Construction sand & gravel

(G-15513)
ICP ADHESIVES AND SEALANTS INC
Also Called: Fomo Products
2775 Barber Rd (44203-1001)
P.O. Box 1078 (44203-9478)
PHONE....................330 753-4585
Stefan Gantenbein, *President*
George Onacila, *Sales Staff*
EMP: 1
SALES (est): 1.9MM
SALES (corp-wide): 73.2MM **Privately Held**
SIC: 3086 2891 2821 Plastics foam products; adhesives & sealants; plastics materials & resins
PA: Innovative Chemical Products Group, Llc
150 Dascomb Rd
Andover MA

(G-15514)
INDEPENDENT DIGITAL CONSULTING
2081 Wadsworth Rd (44203-5305)
P.O. Box 697, Akron (44309-0697)
PHONE....................330 753-0777
Fax: 330 753-0772
Thomas H Schurr, *President*
Emily J Schurr, *Corp Secy*
Stephanie Bolinger, *Purchasing*
Jeff Rummer, *Software Engr*
Nathan Schurr, *Shareholder*
EMP: 4
SQ FT: 4,200
SALES: 500K **Privately Held**
WEB: www.idconline.com
SIC: 8711 3625 Consulting engineer; designing: ship, boat, machine & product; relays & industrial controls

(G-15515)
J E DOYLE COMPANY
Also Called: Doyle Systems
5186 New Haven Cir (44203-4671)
PHONE....................330 564-0743
Joseph M Lynch, *President*
▲ EMP: 23
SQ FT: 10,000
SALES (est): 4MM **Privately Held**
WEB: www.doylesystems.com
SIC: 3554 Paper industries machinery

(G-15516)
JJC PLASTICS LTD
4021 Deerspring Ct (44203-5481)
PHONE....................330 334-3637
Michael Primovero, *President*
Barbara K Primovero, *Vice Pres*
EMP: 3
SALES (est): 415.4K **Privately Held**
SIC: 2821 Plastics materials & resins

(G-15517)
LASER HORIZONS
1879 Caroline Ave (44203-1401)
PHONE....................330 208-0575
Joseph Maier, *Partner*
June Maier, *Partner*
Denise Sautters, *Partner*
Dennis Sautters, *Partner*
EMP: 3 EST: 1998
SALES (est): 229.8K **Privately Held**
WEB: www.laserhorizons.com
SIC: 2823 Cuprammonium fibers

(G-15518)
MULCH MAKERS OF OHIO INC
3307 Clark Mill Rd (44203-1027)
PHONE....................330 753-3090
Fax: 330 753-3093
Keith Luck, *CEO*
Barbara Luck, *President*
EMP: 3
SALES (est): 408.4K **Privately Held**
WEB: www.mulchmakers.biz
SIC: 2499 Mulch, wood & bark

(G-15519)
NVISION TECHNOLOGY INC
2769 Pinegate Dr (44203-3963)
PHONE....................412 254-4668
Nicholas Vitalbo, *President*
EMP: 5
SALES (est): 327.9K **Privately Held**
SIC: 8748 3826 7371 Systems analysis & engineering consulting services; laser scientific & engineering instruments; computer software systems analysis & design, custom

(G-15520)
PACKAGING MATERIALS SVCS LLC
Also Called: PMS
3960 Summit Rd (44203-1052)
P.O. Box 13491, Akron (44334-8891)
PHONE....................330 745-9722
Greg Bobonik, *President*
EMP: 14
SALES: 5MM **Privately Held**
SIC: 2441 Boxes, wood

(G-15521)
SPARTON ENTERPRISES INC
3717 Clark Mill Rd (44203-1035)
PHONE....................330 745-6088
Fax: 330 745-5862
James E Little Jr, *President*
Andy Little, *Vice Pres*
Mike Littel, *Finance*
▲ EMP: 25
SQ FT: 110,000
SALES (est): 5.7MM **Privately Held**
WEB: www.spartonenterprises.com
SIC: 3069 Reclaimed rubber (reworked by manufacturing processes)

(G-15522)
STARPOINT EXTRUSIONS LLC
3985 Eastern Rd C (44203-6215)
PHONE....................330 825-2373
Greg Bilek, *Mng Member*
EMP: 25
SALES: 5MM **Privately Held**
SIC: 3069 Hard rubber & molded rubber products

(G-15523)
WAGNER MACHINE INC
5151 Wooster Rd W (44203-6261)
PHONE....................330 706-0700
Michael Wagner, *President*
Courtney Wagner, *Admin Sec*
▲ EMP: 35
SQ FT: 20,000

SALES (est): 7.4MM Privately Held
WEB: www.wagnermachine.com
SIC: 3599 Machine shop, jobbing & repair

Norwalk
Huron County

(G-15524)
ACCU-FEED ENGINEERING
50 Newton St (44857-1224)
P.O. Box 404 (44857-0404)
PHONE...............................419 668-7990
Fax: 419 663-5601
Jim Tracht, Owner
Peggy Englert, Office Mgr
EMP: 9
SQ FT: 14,000
SALES (est): 1.1MM Privately Held
WEB: www.accu-feed.com
SIC: 3825 Meters: electric, pocket, portable, panelboard, etc.

(G-15525)
AMERICRAFT CARTON INC
209 Republic St (44857-1157)
PHONE...............................419 668-1006
Dwight Henry, Site Mgr
Darrin Carlson, Manager
EMP: 40
SALES (corp-wide): 195.7MM Privately Held
WEB: www.americraft.com
SIC: 2657 Food containers, folding: made from purchased material; paperboard backs for blister or skin packages
PA: Americraft Carton, Inc.
7400 State Line Rd # 206
Prairie Village KS 66208
913 387-3700

(G-15526)
ARMETON US CO
205 Republic St (44857-1157)
P.O. Box 234 (44857-0234)
PHONE...............................419 554-1866
Primoz Seljak, Manager
EMP: 7
SALES (est): 580.5K
SALES (corp-wide): 29MM Privately Held
SIC: 3089 5084 Billfold inserts, plastic; machine tools & metalworking machinery
HQ: Armeton Engineering B.V.
Strawinskylaan 3127 8e Verdiepin
Amsterdam
885 609-950

(G-15527)
BENNETT ELECTRIC INC
211 Republic St (44857-1157)
PHONE...............................800 874-5405
Fax: 419 668-1960
Daniel L Stewart, President
Jean Stewart, Corp Secy
Charles Avarello, Vice Pres
Benjamin Jones, Sales Staff
Terry Roberts, Sales Staff
EMP: 14 EST: 1925
SQ FT: 15,000
SALES (est): 8.8MM Privately Held
WEB: www.bennett-electric.com
SIC: 5063 7694 Motors, electric; electric motor repair

(G-15528)
BROOKER BROS FORGING CO INC
102 Jefferson St (44857-1969)
P.O. Box 498 (44857-0498)
PHONE...............................419 668-2535
Fax: 419 663-1149
Rickard E Brooker, President
EMP: 20 EST: 1946
SQ FT: 16,000
SALES (est): 3.6MM Privately Held
WEB: www.brookerbros.com
SIC: 3462 Iron & steel forgings

(G-15529)
CASE-MAUL CLAMPS INC
69 Northwest St (44857-1213)
P.O. Box 605 (44857-0605)
PHONE...............................419 668-6563
Fax: 419 663-4015
James R Maul, President
Dr Peggy Maul, Vice Pres
▲ EMP: 17
SALES (est): 2.9MM Privately Held
WEB: www.case-maulclamps.com
SIC: 3429 Clamps, metal

(G-15530)
CHAMPION DIRECTORIES INC
Also Called: Championpages
100 Old State Rd S (44857-2228)
P.O. Box 22 (44857-0022)
PHONE...............................419 668-1280
Fax: 419 663-0574
P D Meadows, President
Lois Meadows, Corp Secy
EMP: 19
SQ FT: 4,800
SALES (est): 2.1MM Privately Held
WEB: www.championdirectories.com
SIC: 2741 Directories, telephone: publishing only, not printed on site

(G-15531)
CUSTOM METAL WORKS INC (PA)
193 State Route 18 (44857-9203)
PHONE...............................419 668-7831
Fax: 419 660-9023
Lawrence A Skinn, President
Andy Skinn, Vice Pres
Bradley Skinn, Vice Pres
L Andrew Skinn, Vice Pres
Cynthia Skinn, Treasurer
EMP: 14 EST: 1981
SQ FT: 19,400
SALES (est): 2.4MM Privately Held
SIC: 7699 3599 3429 Industrial machinery & equipment repair; machine shop, jobbing & repair; manufactured hardware (general)

(G-15532)
DAN-MAR COMPANY INC
Also Called: Danmarco
200 Bluegrass Dr E (44857-1169)
PHONE...............................419 660-8830
Fax: 419 433-5726
James D Heckelman, President
Margaret Heckelman, Vice Pres
Nancy Ritz, Opers Staff
Cheryl Randleman, Purch Mgr
Nancy Heckelman, Treasurer
EMP: 26
SQ FT: 50,000
SALES (est): 2.4MM Privately Held
WEB: www.danmarco.com
SIC: 3674 3629 Solid state electronic devices; blasting machines, electrical

(G-15533)
DAVID PRICE METAL SERVICES INC
360 Eastpark Dr (44857-9500)
PHONE...............................419 668-3358
Christopher C Price, President
Faith A Price, Corp Secy
David Smith, Vice Pres
Nicholas Caudill, Foreman/Supr
Krista Smith, Opers Staff
▲ EMP: 130
SQ FT: 100,000
SALES (est): 59.4MM Privately Held
WEB: www.dpms-inc.com
SIC: 3599 Machine shop, jobbing & repair

(G-15534)
DS EXPRESS CARRIERS INC (PA)
203 Republic St (44857-1157)
PHONE...............................419 433-6200
Daniela Stankic, President
EMP: 6
SALES (est): 2.3MM Privately Held
SIC: 4213 3669 8742 3715 Trucking, except local; transportation signaling devices; transportation consultant; semitrailers for missile transportation; rocket transportation casings; freight transportation arrangement

(G-15535)
DURABLE CORPORATION
Also Called: D C
75 N Pleasant St (44857-1218)
P.O. Box 290 (44857-0290)
PHONE...............................419 668-8138
Fax: 419 668-8068
Jon M Anderson, CEO
Tom Secor, President
Michael Croskey, Plant Mgr
Hilary Alexander, Accounting Mgr
Phillis Hales, Human Res Dir
◆ EMP: 60
SQ FT: 3,000
SALES (est): 12.3MM Privately Held
WEB: www.durablecorp.com
SIC: 3069 2273 5013 Mats or matting, rubber; molded rubber products; rubber automotive products; mats & matting; bumpers

(G-15536)
DURAMAX MARINE INDUSTRIES
53 Saint Marys St (44857-1841)
PHONE...............................419 668-3728
Tom Rice, Principal
EMP: 3
SALES (est): 302.9K Privately Held
SIC: 3999 Manufacturing industries

(G-15537)
EXTOL OF OHIO INC (PA)
208 Republic St (44857-1185)
PHONE...............................419 668-2072
Fax: 419 663-1992
Robin L Degraff, President
Brian Eisenhauer, Plant Mgr
Margie Simon, Treasurer
Mergie Simon, Treasurer
Maureen Ringle, Human Resources
▼ EMP: 35
SQ FT: 45,000
SALES (est): 7.4MM Privately Held
WEB: www.norwalkohio.com
SIC: 3296 Insulation: rock wool, slag & silica minerals

(G-15538)
EXTOL OF OHIO INC
208 Republic St (44857-1185)
PHONE...............................419 668-2072
Robin L Degraff, President
Brian Eisenhower, Vice Pres
Margie Simon, Treasurer
Maureen Ringle, Payroll Mgr
Robert Baldwin, Admin Sec
EMP: 35
SQ FT: 45,000
SALES (est): 7.4MM Privately Held
WEB: www.extolohio.com
SIC: 3086 Plastics foam products
PA: Extol Of Ohio, Inc.
208 Republic St
Norwalk OH 44857
419 668-2072

(G-15539)
FABRIWELD CORPORATION
360 Eastpark Dr (44857-9500)
PHONE...............................419 668-3358
Fax: 419 663-3010
Christopher C Price, President
David C Price, Chairman
Faith A Price, Corp Secy
David Smith, Vice Pres
Karen Krupp, Executive Asst
EMP: 9
SQ FT: 8,400
SALES (est): 1.1MM Privately Held
WEB: www.fabriweldcorp.com
SIC: 3542 3625 3613 3549 Machine tools, metal forming type; presses: hydraulic & pneumatic, mechanical & manual; relays & industrial controls; switchgear & switchboard apparatus; metalworking machinery

(G-15540)
FAIR PUBLISHING HOUSE INC
15 Schauss Ave (44857-1851)
P.O. Box 350 (44857-0350)
PHONE...............................419 668-3746
Kevin F Doyle, President
Fred Waugh, Counsel
Charles Doyle, Vice Pres
Leonard Zilko, Controller

Walter R Trinkaus, Agent
EMP: 27
SQ FT: 25,000
SALES (est): 3.7MM
SALES (corp-wide): 3.9MM Privately Held
SIC: 2759 3993 2752 2396 Imprinting; signs & advertising specialties; commercial printing, lithographic; automotive & apparel trimmings
PA: Rotary Printing Company
15 Schauss Ave
Norwalk OH 44857
419 668-4821

(G-15541)
FIRELANDS FAS-PRINT LLC
59 Benedict Ave (44857-2127)
PHONE...............................419 668-3045
Fax: 419 663-0265
Sandra Reitzelar,
Michael Reitzelar,
EMP: 3
SQ FT: 2,600
SALES (est): 208K Privately Held
SIC: 2759 Commercial printing

(G-15542)
GYRUS ACMI LP
93 N Pleasant St (44857-1218)
PHONE...............................419 668-8201
Tom Motta, General Mgr
EMP: 190
SQ FT: 55,000
SALES (corp-wide): 6.8B Privately Held
WEB: www.circoncorp.com
SIC: 3841 3845 Surgical & medical instruments; electromedical equipment
HQ: Gyrus Acmi, L.P.
9600 Louisiana Ave N
Minneapolis MN 55445
763 416-3000

(G-15543)
HART ADVERTISING INC
6975 E Seminary St (44857)
P.O. Box 499 (44857-0499)
PHONE...............................419 668-1194
Fax: 419 663-2787
W Taylor Hart, President
Gay Hart-Sanders, Corp Secy
Mark Ackerman, Sales Staff
EMP: 12
SALES (est): 1.2MM Privately Held
SIC: 7312 3993 Billboard advertising; signs & advertising specialties

(G-15544)
HEN HOUSE INC
Also Called: Ditz Designs
100 Northwest St (44857-1273)
P.O. Box 586 (44857-0586)
PHONE...............................419 663-3377
Fax: 419 668-0376
Robert Ludwig, President
Jon Ditz, Treasurer
Lynn Grant, Manager
Joyce Ditz, Bd of Directors
Melissa Hipp, Executive Asst
▲ EMP: 35
SQ FT: 37,000
SALES (est): 3.5MM Privately Held
WEB: www.ditzdesigns.com
SIC: 2511 Stools, household: wood

(G-15545)
HERALD REFLECTOR INC (PA)
Also Called: Norwalk Reflector
61 E Monroe St (44857-1532)
P.O. Box 71 (44857-0071)
PHONE...............................419 668-3771
Fax: 419 668-2424
David Rau, President
Joanne Didion, District Mgr
Richard Russell, Business Mgr
Alice Rau, Treasurer
John Ringenberg, Sales Staff
EMP: 50 EST: 1829
SQ FT: 10,000
SALES (est): 4.1MM Privately Held
WEB: www.goreflector.com
SIC: 2711 Newspapers, publishing & printing

▲ = Import ▼=Export
◆ =Import/Export

(G-15546)
HUG MANUFACTURING CORPORATION
2858 Arcade Rd (44857-9525)
P.O. Box 667 (44857-0667)
PHONE................................419 668-5086
Fax: 419 668-6913
John Hug, *President*
EMP: 3
SQ FT: 3,375
SALES: 300K **Privately Held**
WEB: www.truckstriper.com
SIC: 3531 5084 Road construction & maintenance machinery; industrial machinery & equipment

(G-15547)
INTELLIWORKS HT
61 Saint Marys St (44857-1841)
P.O. Box 899 (44857-0899)
PHONE................................419 660-9050
Fax: 419 660-9091
Dave Nunez, *Principal*
Tim Bechtler, *Sales Mgr*
Dan Gulley, *Sales Engr*
Tim Johnson, *Sales Engr*
Philip Kirk, *Sales Engr*
EMP: 6
SALES (est): 1.2MM **Privately Held**
SIC: 3559 Sewing machines & attachments, industrial

(G-15548)
KUHLMAN INSTRUMENT COMPANY
54 Summit St (44857-2134)
P.O. Box 468 (44857-0468)
PHONE................................419 668-9533
Fax: 419 668-2179
Mark Lacy, *CEO*
Ernest Tuller, *Vice Pres*
EMP: 6
SQ FT: 5,000
SALES (est): 927.1K **Privately Held**
WEB: www.kuhlmaninstrument.com
SIC: 3823 Industrial instrmnts msrmnt display/control process variable

(G-15549)
LASER IMAGES INC
28 W Main St (44857-1440)
P.O. Box 524 (44857-0524)
PHONE................................419 668-8348
Fax: 419 668-8434
Ilene Tracht, *President*
Lindy Clouse, *Purchasing*
EMP: 4
SQ FT: 3,200
SALES (est): 639.3K **Privately Held**
WEB: www.drc-mn.com
SIC: 2752 Commercial printing, offset

(G-15550)
LESCH BOAT COVER CANVAS CO LLC
43 1/2 Saint Marys St (44857-1809)
PHONE................................419 668-6374
Fax: 419 663-7075
Daniel Lesch, *Owner*
EMP: 4
SQ FT: 3,000
SALES (est): 405.6K **Privately Held**
SIC: 2394 2396 Tarpaulins, fabric: made from purchased materials; convertible tops, canvas or boat: from purchased materials; automotive trimmings, fabric

(G-15551)
MAPLE CITY RUBBER COMPANY
Also Called: Tuf-Tex
55 Newton St (44857-1298)
P.O. Box 587 (44857-0587)
PHONE................................419 668-8261
Fax: 419 668-1275
Michael Kilbane, *President*
Paul Bennett, *COO*
Jim Prater, *Plant Mgr*
Jim Pratter, *Site Mgr*
Trisha Cross, *Purch Mgr*
▲ EMP: 44 EST: 1915
SQ FT: 104,000

SALES: 5.2MM **Privately Held**
WEB: www.maplecityrubber.com
SIC: 3069 Balloons, advertising & toy: rubber

(G-15552)
MOTO-ELECTRIC INC
262 Cleveland Rd (44857-9024)
PHONE................................419 668-7894
Fax: 419 663-2783
Nicholas McCall, *President*
Teresa Chandler, *Manager*
EMP: 8
SQ FT: 8,000
SALES: 1.4MM **Privately Held**
WEB: www.motoelectric.com
SIC: 7694 5063 Electric motor repair; motors, electric

(G-15553)
NEW HORIZONS BAKING COMPANY (PA)
211 Woodlawn Ave (44857-2276)
PHONE................................419 668-8226
Fax: 419 663-6537
Ronald Jones, *President*
Trina Bediako, *Vice Pres*
Robert Creighton, *Vice Pres*
Mark Duke, *Vice Pres*
Mike Porter, *Vice Pres*
EMP: 220
SQ FT: 4,526
SALES: 94MM **Privately Held**
SIC: 2051 Buns, bread type: fresh or frozen; breads, rolls & buns

(G-15554)
NORWALK CONCRETE INDS INC (PA)
80 Commerce Dr (44857-9003)
P.O. Box 563 (44857-0563)
PHONE................................419 668-8167
Fax: 419 663-0627
John A Lendrum, *President*
Terry Boose, *General Mgr*
Jeffrey S Malcolm, *Vice Pres*
Shane Horner, *Plant Mgr*
Dennis Weisenberger, *Plant Mgr*
▲ EMP: 40 EST: 1906
SALES (est): 13.7MM **Privately Held**
WEB: www.nciprecast.com
SIC: 3272 Concrete products, precast

(G-15555)
NORWALK CONCRETE INDS INC
80 Commerce Dr (44857-9003)
PHONE................................419 668-8167
John Lendrum, *Branch Mgr*
EMP: 50
SALES (corp-wide): 13.7MM **Privately Held**
WEB: www.nciprecast.com
SIC: 3272 Concrete products, precast
PA: Norwalk Concrete Industries, Inc.
80 Commerce Dr
Norwalk OH 44857
419 668-8167

(G-15556)
NORWALK CUSTOM ORDER FURN LLC
Also Called: Norwalk Furniture
100 Furniture Pkwy (44857-9587)
PHONE................................419 744-3200
Michael Kenney, *President*
Bill Gerken, *Vice Chairman*
William R Gerken, *Vice Chairman*
Scott Nutter, *Purch Mgr*
Sheila Buckingham, *Marketing Mgr*
EMP: 200
SQ FT: 450,000
SALES: 2.6MM **Privately Held**
SIC: 2519 Household furniture, except wood or metal: upholstered

(G-15557)
NORWALK PRECAST MOLDS INC
205 Industrial Pkwy (44857-3105)
P.O. Box 293 (44857-0293)
PHONE................................419 668-1639
Fax: 419 668-9156
Jan Graves, *President*
Gregory D Graves, *President*
Jennifer Jenne, *Administration*

EMP: 20
SQ FT: 75,000
SALES (est): 3.5MM **Privately Held**
WEB: www.norwalkprecastmolds.com
SIC: 3544 Industrial molds

(G-15558)
NORWALK WASTEWATER EQP CO
Also Called: Norweco
220 Republic St (44857-1156)
P.O. Box 410 (44857-0410)
PHONE................................419 668-4471
Fax: 419 663-5440
Jan Graves, *Ch of Bd*
Gregory Graves, *President*
Michele Graves, *Corp Secy*
Jennifer Jenne, *Vice Pres*
Susan Wilson, *Human Res Mgr*
◆ EMP: 50 EST: 1906
SQ FT: 70,000
SALES (est): 23.8MM **Privately Held**
WEB: www.norweco.com
SIC: 3589 Water treatment equipment, industrial

(G-15559)
POLYONE CORPORATION
80 Northwest St (44857-1239)
PHONE................................419 668-4844
Bob Mc Elsresh, *Plant Mgr*
Gary Weaver, *Purchasing*
Steve Schneider, *Sales Staff*
Marc Rasor, *Manager*
Mike Miller, *Business Dir*
EMP: 126 **Publicly Held**
WEB: www.polyone.com
SIC: 2865 3087 2851 2816 Dyes & pigments; custom compound purchased resins; paints & allied products; inorganic pigments
PA: Polyone Corporation
33587 Walker Rd
Avon Lake OH 44012

(G-15560)
R & C LORTCHER LLC
1384 Ridge Rd (44857-9147)
PHONE................................419 663-1531
Ronald Lortcher, *Principal*
EMP: 3
SALES (est): 143.6K **Privately Held**
SIC: 2711 Newspapers

(G-15561)
R & D EQUIPMENT INC
206 Republic St (44857-1185)
PHONE................................419 668-8439
Fax: 419 668-0447
George Gilbert, *President*
Chuck Plumb, *Vice Pres*
▲ EMP: 13 EST: 1977
SQ FT: 18,000
SALES (est): 2.9MM **Privately Held**
WEB: www.rdequipment.com
SIC: 3555 Printing trades machinery

(G-15562)
RESEARCH METRICS LLC
4832 Plank Rd (44857-9792)
P.O. Box 809 (44857-0809)
PHONE................................419 464-3333
Robert Bleile, *Mng Member*
EMP: 4
SQ FT: 200
SALES (est): 145.1K **Privately Held**
SIC: 7372 Business oriented computer software

(G-15563)
ROTARY PRINTING COMPANY (PA)
Also Called: Fair Publishing
15 Schauss Ave (44857-1851)
P.O. Box 350 (44857-0350)
PHONE................................419 668-4821
Fax: 419 663-3247
Kevin F Doyle, *President*
Gayle Steinger, *Accountant*
EMP: 2
SQ FT: 25,000
SALES (est): 3.9MM **Privately Held**
SIC: 5112 2759 Business forms; letterpress printing; embossing on paper

(G-15564)
SOLID DIMENSIONS INC
Also Called: Solid Dimensions Line
720 Townline Road 151 (44857-9535)
PHONE................................419 663-1134
Fax: 419 663-6907
Tim Parcher, *President*
Darla Parcher, *Vice Pres*
▲ EMP: 9
SALES: 900K **Privately Held**
WEB: www.soliddimensions.com
SIC: 2499 Engraved wood products; novelties, wood fiber; trophy bases, wood

(G-15565)
VERTEX REFINING OH LLC
4376 State Route 601 (44857-9128)
PHONE................................419 668-8373
EMP: 47
SALES (est): 661.8K
SALES (corp-wide): 98MM **Publicly Held**
SIC: 2911 Petroleum refining
PA: Vertex Energy, Inc.
1331 Gemini St Ste 250
Houston TX 77058
866 660-8156

(G-15566)
WHEELER SHEET METAL INC
4640 Plank Rd (44857-9792)
PHONE................................419 668-0481
Fax: 419 663-0482
Deloris Wheeler, *President*
Delores Wheeler, *Vice Pres*
Wilma Collier, *Corp Secy*
EMP: 5
SQ FT: 14,000
SALES (est): 705.3K **Privately Held**
SIC: 1711 3444 Warm air heating & air conditioning contractor; ventilation & duct work contractor; sheet metalwork

(G-15567)
WILLIAM DAUCH CONCRETE COMPANY (PA)
84 Cleveland Rd (44857-9020)
P.O. Box 204 (44857-0204)
PHONE................................419 668-4458
William Dauch, *President*
Mona E Dauch, *Corp Secy*
David Burkholder, *Controller*
Monica McDonald, *Human Resources*
Duane Graffice, *Sales Staff*
EMP: 15 EST: 1966
SQ FT: 2,000
SALES (est): 19.1MM **Privately Held**
WEB: www.dauchconcrete.com
SIC: 5032 3273 3272 3271 Brick, stone & related material; ready-mixed concrete; concrete products; concrete block & brick

(G-15568)
WOODEN HORSE CORPORATION
819 Dublin Rd (44857-9746)
PHONE................................419 663-1472
Sandy Lovato, *President*
Frank Lovato Jr, *Vice Pres*
EMP: 3
SALES: 350K **Privately Held**
SIC: 3949 Exercise equipment

Norwich
Muskingum County

(G-15569)
LUMI-LITE CANDLE COMPANY
Also Called: Lumi Craft
102 Sundale Rd (43767-9717)
P.O. Box 97 (43767-0097)
PHONE................................740 872-3248
Fax: 740 872-4023
George Pappas, *President*
William W Wilson, *Chairman*
Tina Bales, *Vice Pres*
Pete Pappas, *Vice Pres*
Shannon Yawkey, *Purchasing*
▲ EMP: 100
SQ FT: 50,000
SALES (est): 12.3MM **Privately Held**
SIC: 3999 Candles

Norwood
Hamilton County

(G-15570)
AUTORENTALSYSTEMSCOM LLC
1776 Mentor Ave Ste 427 (45212-3586)
PHONE................................513 334-1040
Laura Tierney, *Sales Mgr*
Chris Irwin,
Bryon Tierney,
EMP: 3
SQ FT: 482
SALES (est): 85.8K **Privately Held**
SIC: 7372 Business oriented computer software

(G-15571)
BLT INC
Also Called: Uptown Graphics
2834 Highland Ave (45212-2410)
PHONE................................513 631-5050
Fax: 513 458-6111
Ronald Bush, *President*
Luigi Lavalle, *Vice Pres*
EMP: 13
SQ FT: 8,000
SALES (est): 1.6MM **Privately Held**
WEB: www.q-c-p.com
SIC: 2752 3083 2791 Commercial printing, offset; plastic finished products, laminated; typesetting

(G-15572)
EMD MILLIPORE CORPORATION
2909 Highland Ave (45212-2411)
PHONE................................513 631-0445
Michael Mulligan, *Vice Pres*
Bob Wileczek, *Prdtn Mgr*
Rob Highley, *Safety Mgr*
Lisa Morris, *Purch Mgr*
Kevin Drews, *Purch Agent*
EMP: 150
SQ FT: 100,000
SALES (corp-wide): 15.8B **Privately Held**
WEB: www.emdchemicals.com
SIC: 8731 3295 2899 2842 Commercial physical research; minerals, ground or treated; chemical preparations; specialty cleaning, polishes & sanitation goods; biological products, except diagnostic
HQ: Emd Millipore Corporation
290 Concord Rd
Billerica MA 01821
781 533-6000

(G-15573)
PALLET SPECS PLUS LLC
1701 Mills Ave (45212-2825)
P.O. Box 15236, Cincinnati (45215-0236)
PHONE................................513 351-3200
Scott M Senter, *President*
Jason Catron, *COO*
EMP: 10
SQ FT: 20,000
SALES: 500K **Privately Held**
SIC: 2448 Pallets, wood

(G-15574)
SHEPHERD CHEMICAL COMPANY
2803 Highland Ave (45212)
PHONE................................513 731-1110
Thomas Shepherd, *CEO*
EMP: 15
SALES (corp-wide): 58.2MM **Privately Held**
SIC: 2819 Metal salts & compounds, except sodium, potassium, aluminum
PA: The Shepherd Chemical Company
4900 Beech St
Norwood OH 45212
513 731-1110

Nova
Ashland County

(G-15575)
AMP-TECH INC
910 County Road 40 (44859-9723)
PHONE................................419 652-3444
Dana White, *Principal*
EMP: 3
SALES (est): 444.6K **Privately Held**
SIC: 3599 Industrial machinery

(G-15576)
AMPTECH MACHINING & WELDING
910 County Road 40 (44859-9723)
PHONE................................419 652-3444
Fax: 419 652-3445
Dana White, *Owner*
EMP: 9
SALES (est): 285.5K **Privately Held**
WEB: www.amptechwelding.com
SIC: 7692 Welding repair

(G-15577)
DANA WHITE MACHINING WLDG INC
910 County Road 40 (44859-9723)
PHONE................................419 652-3444
Fax: 419 652-3441
Dana White, *President*
Tammy White, *Admin Sec*
EMP: 6
SQ FT: 1,000
SALES (est): 510K **Privately Held**
SIC: 3599 Machine shop, jobbing & repair

(G-15578)
GRAPHITE SALES INC
220 Township Road 791 (44859-9703)
PHONE................................419 652-3388
Fax: 419 652-3985
Bob Archer, *Safety Dir*
Susan Hales, *Office Mgr*
Thomas Hoffman, *Branch Mgr*
EMP: 38
SALES (corp-wide): 17.9MM **Privately Held**
WEB: www.graphitesales.com
SIC: 2819 3624 Industrial inorganic chemicals; carbon & graphite products
PA: Graphite Sales, Inc.
16710 W Park Circle Dr
Chagrin Falls OH 44023
440 543-8221

(G-15579)
PATTERSON & SONS INC
10 Township Road 1031 (44859-9721)
PHONE................................419 281-0897
Fax: 419 289-1102
Nick H Crow, *President*
Nick Crow, *President*
Jean Crow, *Vice Pres*
Mathew Miller, *Treasurer*
EMP: 10 EST: 1945
SQ FT: 30,000
SALES (est): 1.4MM **Privately Held**
SIC: 3444 Sheet metalwork

(G-15580)
ULTRABUILT PLAY SYSTEMS INC
1114 Us Highway 224 (44859-9773)
P.O. Box 11 (44859-0011)
PHONE................................419 652-2294
Fax: 419 652-2295
Stephen Bennet, *President*
EMP: 10
SQ FT: 6,200
SALES (est): 1MM **Privately Held**
SIC: 3949 2541 Playground equipment; display fixtures, wood

Novelty
Geauga County

(G-15581)
ARROW FABRICATING CO
7355 Calley Ln (44072-9585)
PHONE................................216 641-0490
Fax: 216 641-0807
Ramesh Gavhane, *President*
Gaye Gavhane, *Corp Secy*
Frank B Greifenstein, *Plant Mgr*
EMP: 30
SQ FT: 40,000
SALES (est): 5.5MM **Privately Held**
SIC: 3441 Fabricated structural metal

(G-15582)
ASM INTERNATIONAL
9639 Kinsman Rd (44073-0002)
PHONE................................440 338-5151
Fax: 440 338-4634
Thomas Dudley, *CEO*
William Mahoney, *Managing Dir*
Steve Lampman, *Editor*
Patty Conti, *Production*
Veronica Becker, *Controller*
▲ EMP: 80 EST: 1913
SQ FT: 55,000
SALES: 12.8MM **Privately Held**
WEB: www.aeromat.com
SIC: 2731 2721 7389 7999 Books: publishing only; periodicals: publishing only; advertising, promotional & trade show services; promoters of shows & exhibitions; trade show arrangement; exhibition operation

(G-15583)
NORAMAR COMPANY INC
8501 Kinsman Rd (44072-9640)
P.O. Box 771, Chagrin Falls (44022-0771)
PHONE................................440 338-5740
Fax: 440 247-3879
Norm Tomiello, *President*
Marilyn Tomiello, *Corp Secy*
EMP: 7
SALES (est): 1MM **Privately Held**
WEB: www.noramar.com
SIC: 3823 Industrial instrmnts msrmnt display/control process variable

(G-15584)
WHITE CO DAVID
10161 Music St (44072-9622)
PHONE................................440 247-2920
EMP: 3 EST: 2015
SALES (est): 162.8K **Privately Held**
SIC: 3089 Mfg Plastic Products

(G-15585)
WINANS MANUFACTURING CO INC
7861 Kinsman Rd (44072-9519)
PHONE................................440 338-8599
Catherine Winans, *President*
William Winans, *Corp Secy*
EMP: 3
SALES (est): 200K **Privately Held**
SIC: 3599 Machine shop, jobbing & repair

Oak Harbor
Ottawa County

(G-15586)
AYLING AND REICHERT CO CONSENT
411 S Railroad St (43449-1053)
P.O. Box 389 (43449-0389)
PHONE................................419 898-2471
Robert G Wilson, *President*
Evelyn Wilson, *Vice Pres*
Kelly Polkin, *Materials Mgr*
Kathy Roosan, *Manager*
EMP: 35 EST: 1926
SQ FT: 23,000
SALES (est): 7.3MM **Privately Held**
SIC: 3469 3561 3443 Metal stampings; industrial pumps & parts; floating covers, metal plate

(G-15587)
C NELSON MANUFACTURING CO
265 N Lake Winds Pkwy (43449-9012)
PHONE................................419 898-3305
Fax: 419 898-4098
Kelley Smith, *President*
Chuck Benner, *Engineer*
Tammy Almendinger, *Sales Mgr*
George Dunlap, *Sales Staff*
▼ EMP: 36
SQ FT: 1,200
SALES: 5MM **Privately Held**
WEB: www.cnelson.com
SIC: 3585 Refrigeration & heating equipment

(G-15588)
DAVIS FABRICATORS INC
15765 W State Route 2 (43449-9488)
PHONE................................419 898-5297
Fax: 419 898-5703
Todd Davis, *CEO*
Walter Davis, *President*
Sandra Davis, *Vice Pres*
EMP: 20
SQ FT: 25,000
SALES (est): 3.7MM **Privately Held**
WEB: www.davisfabricators.com
SIC: 3441 Fabricated structural metal

(G-15589)
ESPERIA HOLDINGS LLC (PA)
Also Called: S T A
8035 W Lake Winds Dr (43449-8903)
PHONE................................714 249-7888
Dennis M Liebman,
Anthony L Hunter,
EMP: 0 EST: 2015
SALES (est): 19.9MM **Privately Held**
SIC: 6719 2671 5084 Investment holding companies, except banks; packaging paper & plastics film, coated & laminated; processing & packaging equipment

(G-15590)
FIRSTENERGY CORP
5501 N State Route 2 (43449-9752)
PHONE................................419 321-7114
Anthony J Alexander, *President*
Angie Ayres, *General Mgr*
Vernon Patton, *Safety Dir*
Alex Garza, *Opers Mgr*
Scott Gluth, *Opers Mgr*
EMP: 47
SALES (est): 9.8MM **Privately Held**
SIC: 3443 Nuclear reactors, military or industrial

(G-15591)
FORMETAL INC
220 Houghton St Ste 36 (43449-1123)
P.O. Box 416 (43449-0416)
PHONE................................419 898-2211
Fax: 419 898-4387
William L Briggs, *CEO*
Patrick A Briggs, *President*
Stanley A Simon, *Admin Sec*
Eileen M Hasselbach, *Asst Sec*
EMP: 10
SQ FT: 52,000
SALES (est): 730K **Privately Held**
WEB: www.formetal.com
SIC: 3316 3469 Cold finishing of steel shapes; metal stampings

(G-15592)
NORTHERN MANUFACTURING CO INC
150 N Lake Winds Pkwy (43449-8921)
PHONE................................419 898-2821
Fax: 419 898-4470
Quintin R Smith, *President*
Harry Bethel, *Principal*
Joe Bodner, *Principal*
Paul Schmitt, *Principal*
Kevin Rodenhauser, *COO*
▲ EMP: 145 EST: 1951
SQ FT: 120,000
SALES (est): 71.7MM **Privately Held**
WEB: www.versagage.com
SIC: 3441 Fabricated structural metal

▲ = Import ▼ =Export
◆ =Import/Export

(G-15593)
PRIESMAN PRINTERY
218 W Water St (43449-1334)
P.O. Box 233 (43449-0233)
PHONE................................419 898-2526
Fax: 419 898-2726
James Priesman, *Owner*
EMP: 4
SQ FT: 3,640
SALES (est): 240K **Privately Held**
WEB: www.priesmanprintery.com
SIC: 2752 Commercial printing, offset

Oak Hill
Jackson County

(G-15594)
ART SAYLOR LOGGING
343 Slab Hill Rd (45656-9638)
PHONE................................740 682-6188
Fax: 740 682-7146
Art Saylor, *Owner*
EMP: 10
SALES: 1MM **Privately Held**
SIC: 2411 Logging

(G-15595)
DENVER ADKINS
Also Called: Adkins & Sons
642 Phillip Kuhn Rd (45656-9645)
PHONE................................740 682-3123
Denver Adkins, *Partner*
EMP: 12
SALES (est): 820K **Privately Held**
SIC: 2411 Logging camps & contractors;
timber, cut at logging camp

(G-15596)
H & H INDUSTRIES INC
5400 State Route 93 (45656-9361)
PHONE................................740 682-7721
Noah Hickman, *President*
Ken Daniels, *General Mgr*
Lisa Hickman, *Admin Sec*
EMP: 9
SALES (est): 1.9MM **Privately Held**
SIC: 3011 Retreading materials, tire

(G-15597)
HARBISONWALKER INTL INC
1627 Pyro Rd (45656-9311)
PHONE................................740 682-7711
Fax: 740 682-7715
John Crooks, *Plant Mgr*
Jay Broadway, *Sales Mgr*
John Carboy, *Branch Mgr*
EMP: 60
SALES (corp-wide): 923MM **Privately
Held**
SIC: 3255 3297 Clay refractories; nonclay
refractories
HQ: Harbisonwalker International, Inc.
1305 Cherrington Pkwy # 100
Moon Township PA 15108
412 375-6600

(G-15598)
**JACKSON MACHINE &
FABRICATION**
6679 State Route 93 (45656-9301)
PHONE................................740 682-3994
John H Shriver, *Owner*
EMP: 5
SALES (est): 351.7K **Privately Held**
SIC: 1799 3599 Welding on site; machine
shop, jobbing & repair

(G-15599)
KCS CLEANING SERVICE
7550 State Route 93 (45656-9359)
PHONE................................740 418-5479
Kathleen Strickland, *Principal*
EMP: 10
SALES: 85K **Privately Held**
SIC: 2842 Specialty cleaning, polishes &
sanitation goods

(G-15600)
**L&L EXCAVATING & LAND
CLEARING**
56 Jim Reese Rd (45656-9656)
PHONE................................740 682-7823
Larry E Strickland, *Principal*
EMP: 4
SALES (est): 421.2K **Privately Held**
SIC: 1629 2411 5082 Land clearing con-
tractor; logging; timber, cut at logging
camp; logging & forestry machinery &
equipment

(G-15601)
MICHAEL D STRICKLAND
Also Called: Mike Strickland Logging
2730 Hickory Grove Rd (45656-8986)
PHONE................................740 682-6902
EMP: 3
SALES (est): 180K **Privately Held**
SIC: 2411 Logging

(G-15602)
NOCK AND SON COMPANY
4138 Monroe Hollow Rd (45656-8995)
PHONE................................740 682-7741
Hayden Hammond, *Opers-Prdtn-Mfg*
Ronald E Muffley, *Engineer*
EMP: 15
SALES (corp-wide): 35.2MM **Privately
Held**
WEB: www.nockandson.com
SIC: 3255 Clay refractories
PA: The Nock And Son Company
27320 W Oviatt Rd
Cleveland OH 44140
440 871-5525

(G-15603)
**OAK HILL FOUNDRY & MCH
WORKS**
333 S Front St (45656-1322)
P.O. Box 297 (45656-0297)
PHONE................................740 682-7746
Fax: 740 682-6000
Frank Wasch, *President*
William C Rowland, *Vice Pres*
George S Wasch, *Admin Sec*
EMP: 37
SQ FT: 65,000
SALES (est): 5.4MM **Privately Held**
SIC: 3321 Gray & ductile iron foundries;
gray iron castings; ductile iron castings

(G-15604)
PLIBRICO COMPANY LLC
454 County Road 33 (45656-8900)
PHONE................................740 682-7755
Patrick Barry, *CEO*
EMP: 31
SALES (corp-wide): 35MM **Privately
Held**
SIC: 3297 Brick refractories
PA: Plibrico Company, Llc
1010 N Hooker St Ste 101
Chicago IL 60642
312 337-9000

(G-15605)
RESCO PRODUCTS INC
Cedar Heights Clay Division
3542 State Route 93 (45656-8548)
P.O. Box 295 (45656-0295)
PHONE................................740 682-7794
Fax: 740 682-6438
Howard Carter, *Purchasing*
Ron Stowers, *Sales Mgr*
Linda Simpson, *Manager*
Angie Smith, *Director*
EMP: 35
SALES (corp-wide): 192.1MM **Privately
Held**
SIC: 3255 3297 3251 Ladle brick, clay;
nonclay refractories; brick & structural
clay tile
PA: Resco Products, Inc.
1 Robinson Plz Ste 300
Pittsburgh PA 15205
412 494-4491

(G-15606)
**ROMAR METAL FABRICATING
INC**
201 Zane Oak Rd (45656-9742)
PHONE................................740 682-7731
Fax: 740 682-7042
Wayne R Newsom, *President*
Robert H Newsom, *President*
EMP: 6
SQ FT: 3,700
SALES: 1MM **Privately Held**
SIC: 3441 7692 3444 Fabricated struc-
tural metal; welding repair; sheet metal-
work

Oakwood
Montgomery County

(G-15607)
FACIAL SENSATION PRODUCTS
12 Beverly Pl (45419-3401)
P.O. Box 9191, Dayton (45409-9191)
PHONE................................937 293-2280
Karl Stein, *Owner*
EMP: 4
SALES (est): 256.3K **Privately Held**
SIC: 2844 Toilet preparations

(G-15608)
LEE OIL & GAS INC
326 Spirea Dr (45419-3541)
PHONE................................937 223-8891
Richard Akers, *President*
James Adcock, *Vice Pres*
John H Thoma, *Vice Pres*
EMP: 3
SALES (est): 250K **Privately Held**
SIC: 1381 Drilling oil & gas wells

(G-15609)
MEDICAL SOFT INC
1800 Southwood Ln W (45419-1378)
PHONE................................937 293-2575
M M Hall, *Owner*
Bruce Hall, *Owner*
EMP: 3 EST: 1990
SALES (est): 271.2K **Privately Held**
SIC: 3695 Computer software tape &
disks: blank, rigid & floppy

(G-15610)
OBSIDIAN BIODENT
260 Ridgewood Ave (45409-2218)
PHONE................................937 938-9244
Sean Cahill, *Principal*
EMP: 4
SALES (est): 351.6K **Privately Held**
SIC: 3843 Dental equipment & supplies

(G-15611)
TRANSIMAGE INC
314 Spirea Dr (45419-3541)
PHONE................................937 293-0261
Mark Roll, *President*
Carol Ackerman, *Corp Secy*
EMP: 4
SQ FT: 6,000
SALES: 500K **Privately Held**
WEB: www.transimageinc.com
SIC: 3861 7384 Photographic paper &
cloth, all types; photofinish laboratories

(G-15612)
TRIGON INDUSTRIES INC
1616 Delaine Ave (45419-3209)
PHONE................................937 299-1350
Fax: 937 298-6872
Charles J Blank Jr, *President*
EMP: 5
SALES: 500K **Privately Held**
SIC: 2842 Industrial plant disinfectants or
deodorants

Oakwood
Paulding County

(G-15613)
**ACME MACHINE TECHNOLOGY
LLC**
115 Main St (45873)
P.O. Box 70 (45873-0070)
PHONE................................419 594-3349
David Dangler, *Mng Member*
EMP: 3 EST: 2008
SQ FT: 120
SALES: 400K **Privately Held**
SIC: 3599 Machine shop, jobbing & repair

(G-15614)
ANDREWS FARMS INC
12878 Road 209 (45873-9128)
PHONE................................419 594-2111
Edward Andrews, *President*
Eugene Andrews, *Vice Pres*
Julie R Andrews, *Treasurer*
EMP: 6
SALES: 800K **Privately Held**
WEB: www.andrewsfarms.com
SIC: 3523 Driers (farm): grain, hay & seed

(G-15615)
COOPER HATCHERY INC (PA)
Also Called: Cooper Farms
22348 Road 140 (45873)
PHONE................................419 594-3325
Fax: 419 594-3372
James R Cooper, *President*
Gary A Cooper, *COO*
Neil Diller, *Vice Pres*
Karl Koenig, *Facilities Dir*
Dale Hart, *Opers Staff*
EMP: 225 EST: 1934
SQ FT: 47,000
SALES (est): 256.7MM **Privately Held**
WEB: www.cooperfarm.com
SIC: 0254 0253 2015 5153 Poultry
hatcheries; turkey farm; turkey,
processed; grains; prepared feeds

(G-15616)
END SEPARATION LLC
12742 Road 191 (45873-9136)
PHONE................................419 438-0879
Christopher Pessefall, *Mng Member*
EMP: 4
SALES: 400K **Privately Held**
SIC: 3523 Loaders, farm type: manure,
general utility

(G-15617)
**MANSFIELD WELDING
SERVICES LLC**
20027 State Route 613 (45873-9437)
PHONE................................419 594-2738
Randy Mansfield,
Jan Mansfield,
EMP: 7
SALES (est): 791.4K **Privately Held**
SIC: 3499 1799 Machine bases, metal;
welding on site

(G-15618)
**ROBERTS MANUFACTURING CO
INC**
24338 Road 148 (45873-9115)
PHONE................................419 594-2712
Fax: 419 594-2900
Brian Bauer, *President*
Brian Miller, *Corp Secy*
Charles Louis Behrens, *Vice Pres*
Chuck Behrens, *Vice Pres*
Bob Ward, *Engineer*
▲ EMP: 50
SQ FT: 15,000
SALES: 4.5MM **Privately Held**
SIC: 3599 Machine shop, jobbing & repair

(G-15619)
STONECO INC
13762 Road 179 (45873-9012)
PHONE................................419 393-2555
Fax: 419 393-2455
Rick Welch, *Superintendent*
Dale Mathew, *Sales Mgr*
Scott Rychener, *Sales Staff*
EMP: 25
SALES (corp-wide): 28.6B **Privately Held**
WEB: www.stoneco.net
SIC: 1422 2951 Crushed & broken lime-
stone; asphalt paving mixtures & blocks
HQ: Stoneco, Inc.
1700 Fostoria Ave Ste 200
Findlay OH 45840
419 422-8854

(G-15620)
TOOLING CONNECTION INC
N Ste 12603 Hc 66 (45873)
P.O. Box 238 (45873-0238)
PHONE................................419 594-3339
Fax: 419 594-2000
Klee Dangler, *President*
David Dangler, *Engineer*

GEOGRAPHIC

Todd Dangler, *Sales Mgr*
EMP: 9
SQ FT: 12,000
SALES (est): 610K **Privately Held**
SIC: 3541 3544 Machine tools, metal cutting type; special dies & tools

Oakwood Village
Cuyahoga County

(G-15621)
AGMET METALS INC
7800 Medusa Rd (44146-5549)
PHONE.................................440 439-7400
Dana J Cassidy, *CEO*
Timothy A Andel, *CFO*
Fred Warren, *Info Tech Mgr*
EMP: 22
SALES (est): 4.8MM **Privately Held**
SIC: 3559 Recycling machinery

(G-15622)
AIRGAS USA LLC
21610 Alexander Rd (44146-5509)
PHONE.................................440 232-6397
Christopher Williams, *Director*
EMP: 3
SALES (corp-wide): 163.9MM **Privately Held**
SIC: 5169 5084 5085 2813 Industrial gases; gases, compressed & liquefied; carbon dioxide; dry ice; welding machinery & equipment; safety equipment; welding supplies; industrial gases; carbon dioxide; nitrous oxide; dry ice, carbon dioxide (solid); industrial inorganic chemicals; calcium carbide
HQ: Airgas Usa, Llc
　　259 N Radnor Chester Rd # 100
　　Radnor PA 19087
　　610 687-5253

(G-15623)
CROWN EQUIPMENT CORPORATION
Also Called: Crown Lift Trucks
26400 Broadway Ave Ste B (44146-6538)
PHONE.................................440 232-7772
Chuck Rammel, *Branch Mgr*
EMP: 23
SALES (corp-wide): 5.5B **Privately Held**
SIC: 3537 Lift trucks, industrial: fork, platform, straddle, etc.
PA: Crown Equipment Corporation
　　44 S Washington St
　　New Bremen OH 45869
　　419 629-2311

(G-15624)
GOOD NUTRITION LLC
Also Called: Good Greens
7710 First Pl (44146-6717)
P.O. Box 201727, Cleveland (44120-8112)
PHONE.................................216 534-6617
John Huff, *CEO*
Bill Ross, *Chairman*
Natalie Alesci, *Treasurer*
EMP: 10
SQ FT: 3,000
SALES: 5MM **Privately Held**
SIC: 2064 Granola & muesli, bars & clusters

(G-15625)
GROUNDHOGS 2000 LLC
6070 Richmond Rd (44146-2564)
PHONE.................................440 653-1647
Troy H Hauff,
EMP: 6
SALES: 180K **Privately Held**
SIC: 1381 1623 7389 Drilling oil & gas wells; drilling water intake wells; service well drilling; water, sewer & utility lines; oil & gas line & compressor station construction; communication line & transmission tower construction; water & sewer line construction;

(G-15626)
OAKWOOD LABORATORIES LLC (PA)
7670 First Pl Ste A (44146-6721)
PHONE.................................440 359-0000

Fax: 440 359-0001
Edward C Smith, *Ch of Bd*
Larry Johnson, *President*
Mark T Smith, *President*
Michael Lanzilotti, *Vice Pres*
Bc Thanoo, *Vice Pres*
EMP: 20 **EST:** 1997
SQ FT: 15,000
SALES (est): 9.1MM **Privately Held**
SIC: 2834 Pharmaceutical preparations

(G-15627)
SHARPYS FOOD SYSTEMS LLC
26245 Broadway Ave (44146-6523)
PHONE.................................440 232-9601
Rajesh R Nair, *President*
Leah Acton, *Business Mgr*
Leela Nair, *Director*
EMP: 7
SQ FT: 13,600
SALES: 250K **Privately Held**
SIC: 2099 Food preparations

(G-15628)
SWIFT FILTERS INC (PA)
24040 Forbes Rd (44146-5650)
PHONE.................................440 735-0995
Edwin C Swift Jr, *President*
Edwin Swift, *General Mgr*
Charles C Swift, *Vice Pres*
Mat Fleischer, *Plant Mgr*
George Belletti, *Opers Staff*
EMP: 38
SQ FT: 6,000
SALES: 6.9MM **Privately Held**
WEB: www.swiftfilters.com
SIC: 3569 5075 Filters; air filters

(G-15629)
THERMO EBERLINE LLC
Also Called: Thermo Fisher Scientific
1 Thermo Fisher Way (44146-6536)
PHONE.................................440 703-1400
Adam Grose, *Vice Pres*
Gary Magyar, *Branch Mgr*
EMP: 122
SALES (corp-wide): 18.2B **Publicly Held**
SIC: 3829 Measuring & controlling devices
HQ: Thermo Eberline Llc
　　27 Forge Pkwy
　　Franklin MA 02038
　　508 553-1582

(G-15630)
THERMO FISHER SCIENTIFIC INC
Also Called: Remel Products
1 Thermo Fisher Way (44146-6536)
PHONE.................................800 871-8909
Harold Liepert, *Project Leader*
EMP: 150
SALES (corp-wide): 18.2B **Publicly Held**
SIC: 5047 3841 2835 Diagnostic equipment, medical; surgical & medical instruments; in vitro & in vivo diagnostic substances
PA: Thermo Fisher Scientific Inc.
　　168 3rd Ave
　　Waltham MA 02451
　　781 622-1000

(G-15631)
VIEWRAY INCORPORATED
2 Thermo Fisher Way (44146-6536)
PHONE.................................440 703-3210
Chris A Raanes, *President*
Bela Vajko, *Managing Dir*
Peter Sullivan, *Exec VP*
Robert Bea, *Senior VP*
John Patrick, *Senior VP*
▲ **EMP:** 70
SALES: 22.2MM **Privately Held**
SIC: 3845 5047 Electromedical equipment; therapy equipment

(G-15632)
WEBER TOOL & MFG INC
7761 First Pl (44146-6705)
PHONE.................................440 786-0221
Fax: 440 786-1555
Emery Teller, *President*
EMP: 4 **EST:** 1963
SQ FT: 6,000
SALES (est): 350K **Privately Held**
SIC: 3599 Machine shop, jobbing & repair

(G-15633)
WELDON PUMP ACQUITION LLC
640 Golden Oak Pkwy (44146-6504)
PHONE.................................440 232-2282
Fax: 440 232-0606
Jeffrey Kelly, *President*
Jim Craig, *Prdtn Mgr*
Jerry Heintz, *Production*
Jennifer Kelly, *Comptroller*
John Dematteis, *Manager*
EMP: 28
SQ FT: 16,000
SALES (est): 2.3MM **Privately Held**
SIC: 3694 3728 3795 9661 Distributors, motor vehicle engine; research & dev by manuf., aircraft parts & auxiliary equip; tanks & tank components; space research & technology

Oberlin
Lorain County

(G-15634)
ARGES
275 N Pleasant St (44074-1124)
PHONE.................................440 574-1305
Daniel Solorzano, *CEO*
Daniel Bulhosa Solorzano, *CEO*
Andrew Moran, *Chief Engr*
EMP: 3
SALES (est): 71.1K **Privately Held**
SIC: 7372 4581 8731 Prepackaged software; airport control tower operation, except government; commercial physical research

(G-15635)
BIG PRODUCTIONS INC
45300b Us Highway 20 (44074-9262)
PHONE.................................440 775-0015
Fax: 440 835-8034
Joanne Douglas, *President*
EMP: 6
SQ FT: 7,000
SALES: 573.9K **Privately Held**
WEB: www.bigproductionsinc.com
SIC: 2299 Jute & flax textile products

(G-15636)
CHAOS MATRIX LTD
44451 Kipton Nickle Plate (44074-9519)
PHONE.................................614 638-4748
David Clark,
Karrie Pontius,
EMP: 4
SALES (est): 225.6K **Privately Held**
WEB: www.chaosmatrix.com
SIC: 3571 Electronic computers

(G-15637)
EAST OBERLIN CABINETS
13184 Hale Rd (44074-9741)
PHONE.................................440 775-1166
Fax: 440 775-2800
Dennis Luttrell, *Owner*
EMP: 7
SALES (est): 662.5K **Privately Held**
SIC: 2434 2511 Wood kitchen cabinets; vanities, bathroom: wood; silverware chests: wood; desks, household: wood

(G-15638)
ENERGY DEVELOPMENTS INC
43550 Oberlin Elyria Rd (44074-9591)
PHONE.................................440 774-6816
EMP: 4
SALES (est): 410K **Privately Held**
SIC: 3612 Mfg Transformers

(G-15639)
FORMED METAL PRODUCTS INC
185 Oberlin Rd (44074-1226)
P.O. Box 261, Lagrange (44050-0261)
PHONE.................................440 775-0819
Fax: 440 323-5532
David Ebosh, *President*
Mike Ebosh, *Exec VP*
Brian Ebosh, *Plant Mgr*
Joy Ebosh, *Admin Sec*
Joy Paxton, *Admin Sec*
EMP: 15 **EST:** 1953
SQ FT: 12,500

SALES (est): 2.6MM **Privately Held**
SIC: 3469 3643 3545 3493 Metal stampings; current-carrying wiring devices; machine tool accessories; steel springs, except wire

(G-15640)
GAZETTE PUBLISHING COMPANY (PA)
Also Called: Bellevue Gazette
42 S Main St (44074-1627)
PHONE.................................419 483-4190
Fax: 419 483-3737
Rick Miller, *President*
Thomas R Smith, *President*
Donald Reiderman, *Vice Pres*
Kathy Nageotte, *Office Mgr*
Gaylord Miller, *Manager*
EMP: 45
SQ FT: 6,000
SALES (est): 8.2MM **Privately Held**
WEB: www.theoberlinnews.com
SIC: 2711 2791 2752 Newspapers, publishing & printing; typesetting; commercial printing, lithographic

(G-15641)
GIBSON BROS INC
Also Called: Gibson Bakery
23 W College St (44074-1543)
PHONE.................................440 774-2401
Allyn Gibson, *President*
David Gibson, *Treasurer*
Melba Gibson, *Admin Sec*
EMP: 23 **EST:** 1885
SQ FT: 3,010
SALES (est): 2.2MM **Privately Held**
WEB: www.gibsonbros.com
SIC: 5411 2051 2064 2024 Grocery stores, independent; bakery: wholesale or wholesale/retail combined; candy & other confectionery products; ice cream & ice milk

(G-15642)
GREENFIELD SOLAR INC
126 Artino St (44074-1206)
P.O. Box 37 (44074-0037)
PHONE.................................216 535-9200
Neil Sater, *President*
Terry Zahuranec, *Engineer*
EMP: 30
SALES (est): 3.8MM **Privately Held**
SIC: 5211 3674 Solar heating equipment; semiconductors & related devices

(G-15643)
HAMCO MANUFACTURING INC
48882 State Route 511 (44074-9496)
PHONE.................................440 774-1637
Fax: 440 774-1637
Maurice R Hand, *President*
David Hand, *Vice Pres*
EMP: 4 **EST:** 1963
SQ FT: 4,000
SALES: 300K **Privately Held**
SIC: 3451 Screw machine products

(G-15644)
HYDRO TUBE ENTERPRISES INC (PA)
137 Artino St (44074-1265)
PHONE.................................440 774-1022
Fax: 440 774-1482
Mike Prokop, *President*
Richard Cooks, *Vice Pres*
Thomas E Hamel, *Vice Pres*
Tim Althaus, *VP Opers*
Richard Cook, *VP Opers*
▲ **EMP:** 70 **EST:** 1922
SQ FT: 67,000
SALES (est): 21.7MM **Privately Held**
WEB: www.hydrotube.com
SIC: 3498 Tube fabricating (contract bending & shaping)

(G-15645)
MOLD SOLUTIONS
55 S Main St Ste 131 (44074-1626)
PHONE.................................800 948-4947
Charles Bodey, *Principal*
EMP: 4
SALES (est): 360.4K **Privately Held**
SIC: 3544 Industrial molds

(G-15646)
NANOTECH INNOVATIONS LLC
132 Artino St (44074-1206)
PHONE....................................440 926-4888
Dennis Flood,
▼ EMP: 4
SQ FT: 2,000
SALES (est): 260K Privately Held
SIC: 3821 Laboratory equipment: fume
hoods, distillation racks, etc.

(G-15647)
RR DONNELLEY & SONS COMPANY
Also Called: R & S Label
450 Sterns Rd (44074-1209)
PHONE....................................440 774-2101
Jake Martin, Manager
Diana Hill, Manager
EMP: 50
SQ FT: 23,141
SALES (corp-wide): 6.9B Publicly Held
WEB: www.moore.com
SIC: 2761 2752 2759 2672 Manifold
business forms; continuous forms, office
& business; commercial printing, litho-
graphic; promotional printing, lithographic;
tickets, lithographed; tags, lithographed;
letterpress printing; promotional printing;
schedule, ticket & tag printing & engraving; tags: printing; coated & laminated
paper
PA: R. R. Donnelley & Sons Company
35 W Wacker Dr Ste 3650
Chicago IL 60601
312 326-8000

(G-15648)
SWITZER PERFORMANCE ENGRG
Also Called: Switzer Performance Innovation
235 Artino St (44074-1207)
P.O. Box 66 (44074-0066)
PHONE....................................440 774-4219
Tymme Switzer, President
▲ EMP: 11
SALES (est): 1.6MM Privately Held
SIC: 3714 Motor vehicle engines & parts

(G-15649)
WORLD COLOR (USA) CORP
235 Artino St (44074-1207)
PHONE....................................847 230-1547
Tony Levatino, Principal
Arthur Noe, Purch Dir
EMP: 6
SALES (est): 383.3K
SALES (corp-wide): 4.3B Publicly Held
SIC: 2754 Commercial printing, gravure
PA: Quad/Graphics Inc.
N61w23044 Harrys Way
Sussex WI 53089
414 566-6000

Obetz
Franklin County

(G-15650)
CAPITOL CITY MFG CO INC
3881 Groveport Rd (43207-5126)
PHONE....................................614 491-1192
Matthew Peters, President
EMP: 4
SQ FT: 5,000
SALES: 500K Privately Held
SIC: 3452 Bolts, nuts, rivets & washers

(G-15651)
CAPITOL CITY TRAILERS INC
3960 Groveport Rd (43207-5127)
PHONE....................................614 491-2616
Fax: 614 491-2665
Buck Stewart, President
Scott Brown, Vice Pres
Dante Holland, Vice Pres
Tim Stewart, Vice Pres
Mark Woloveck, VP Sales
EMP: 58
SQ FT: 20,000
SALES (est): 10.8MM Privately Held
WEB: www.capitolcitytrailers.net
SIC: 7539 3792 Trailer repair; travel trail-
ers & campers

(G-15652)
CENTRAL ALUMINUM COMPANY LLC
2045 Broehm Rd (43207-5206)
PHONE....................................614 491-5700
Fax: 614 491-8478
Lee Grove, General Mgr
Kory Brockman, CFO
Jeannie Dawson, Accounts Mgr
EMP: 50
SQ FT: 94,000
SALES (est): 17.9MM Privately Held
WEB: www.centralaluminum.com
SIC: 3354 3479 Aluminum extruded prod-
ucts; painting, coating & hot dipping
PA: Gdic Group, Llc
1300 E 9th St Fl 20
Cleveland OH 44114

(G-15653)
CHERYL & CO
4465 Industrial Center Dr (43207-4589)
PHONE....................................614 776-1500
Jodi Dixon, Branch Mgr
Kevin Rooney, Manager
EMP: 80
SALES (corp-wide): 1.1B Publicly Held
WEB: www.cherylandco.com
SIC: 2052 2066 Cookies & crackers;
chocolate & cocoa products
HQ: Cheryl & Co.
646 Mccorkle Blvd
Westerville OH 43082
614 776-1500

(G-15654)
CONTINENTAL CARBONIC PDTS INC
4852 Frusta Dr (43207-4581)
PHONE....................................614 491-4327
Rick Dehner, Branch Mgr
EMP: 3
SALES (corp-wide): 5.4B Privately Held
SIC: 2813 Dry ice, carbon dioxide (solid)
HQ: Continental Carbonic Products, Inc.
3985 E Harrison Ave
Decatur IL 62526
217 428-2068

(G-15655)
MASONS SAND AND GRAVEL CO
2385 Rathmell Rd (43207-4835)
PHONE....................................614 491-3611
Fax: 614 409-9632
George C Smith, President
Jo Hanson, Manager
EMP: 9 EST: 1951
SQ FT: 3,000
SALES (est): 972.4K Privately Held
SIC: 1442 Construction sand mining;
gravel mining

(G-15656)
MICHAEL R KELLY
Also Called: Kelly Printing
1657 Victor Ave (43207-4364)
PHONE....................................614 491-1745
Fax: 614 491-0324
Michael Kelly, Principal
Terri Kelly, Controller
EMP: 5
SQ FT: 2,000
SALES: 300K Privately Held
SIC: 2752 Lithographing on metal; com-
mercial printing, offset

(G-15657)
NATIONAL BEVERAGE CORP
Also Called: Shasta Beverges
4685 Groveport Rd (43207-5216)
PHONE....................................614 491-5415
Fax: 614 497-1569
Monte Hale, Manager
EMP: 50
SALES (corp-wide): 704.7MM Publicly
Held
WEB: www.natbev.com
SIC: 2086 Soft drinks: packaged in cans,
bottles, etc.
PA: National Beverage Corp.
8100 Sw 10th St Ste 4000
Plantation FL 33324
954 581-0922

(G-15658)
PRODUCTION PLUS CORP
Also Called: Magic Rack
2490 Mcgaw Rd (43207-4513)
PHONE....................................614 492-8811
Fax: 614 492-8812
Dan Davitz, President
Tammy Davitz, Vice Pres
Nancy Topping, Admin Sec
EMP: 9
SQ FT: 5,000
SALES (est): 1.1MM Privately Held
WEB: www.magicrack.com
SIC: 3496 Miscellaneous fabricated wire
products

(G-15659)
SHASTA BEVERAGES INC
Also Called: National Beverage
4685 Groveport Rd (43207-5295)
PHONE....................................614 491-5415
Monty Hale, Manager
EMP: 30
SALES (corp-wide): 704.7MM Publicly
Held
SIC: 2086 Soft drinks: packaged in cans,
bottles, etc.
HQ: Shasta Beverages, Inc.
26901 Indl Blvd
Hayward CA 94545
954 581-0922

Ohio City
Van Wert County

(G-15660)
BAKER BUILT PRODUCTS INC
Also Called: Foot Wings
11877 Walnut Grove Ch Rd (45874-9244)
PHONE....................................419 965-2646
Fax: 419 965-2646
John A Baker Sr, President
Bruce L Baker, President
Barbara Baker, Corp Secy
John Baker, Vice Pres
EMP: 3 EST: 1974
SQ FT: 3,600
SALES (est): 500K Privately Held
WEB: www.bakerbuilt.com
SIC: 2851 7692 3523 Polyurethane coat-
ings; welding repair; farm machinery &
equipment

(G-15661)
ELKHART PLASTICS
Also Called: Elkham Plastics
106 S Ball Rd (45874-9182)
PHONE....................................419 965-2103
Jack Welter, Branch Mgr
EMP: 25
SALES (corp-wide): 142.9MM Privately
Held
SIC: 3089 Plastic & fiberglass tanks
PA: Elkhart Plastics
3300 N Kenmore St
South Bend IN 46628
574 232-8066

Okeana
Butler County

(G-15662)
AC SHINERS INC
5747 Jenkins Rd (45053-9688)
PHONE....................................513 738-1573
Fax: 513 738-1135
William Schoultheis, President
Arthur Schoultheis, General Mgr
Joseph Schoultheis, Corp Secy
EMP: 4
SQ FT: 3,500
SALES: 125K Privately Held
WEB: www.acshiners.com
SIC: 3949 Lures, fishing: artificial

(G-15663)
CHRISNIK INC
7461 Cncnnati Brkville Rd (45053-9780)
P.O. Box 516, Ross (45061-0516)
PHONE....................................513 738-2920
Fax: 513 738-2920

(G-15664)
CUSTOM FABRICATION BY FISHER
100 Weaver Rd (45053-9711)
PHONE....................................513 738-4600
Rodney Fisher, Principal
EMP: 7
SALES (est): 822.2K Privately Held
SIC: 3499 Novelties & giftware, including
trophies

(G-15665)
D & E ELECTRIC INC
7055 Okana Drewersburg Rd
(45053-9651)
PHONE....................................513 738-1172
Fax: 513 738-1171
Douglas E Fritz, President
Edward H Fritz, Vice Pres
EMP: 15
SALES: 2MM Privately Held
SIC: 1731 3643 Electrical work; current-
carrying wiring devices

(G-15666)
WAGERS INC
2464 California Rd (45053-9618)
PHONE....................................513 825-6300
Jim Wagers, President
EMP: 6
SALES (est): 540K Privately Held
WEB: www.wagers.com
SIC: 2899 Ink or writing fluids

(G-15667)
WHITMAN CORPORATION
2530 Joyce Ln (45053-9746)
PHONE....................................513 541-3223
Toll Free:....................................888 -
Fax: 513 541-4082
James Erhardt, President
Susan Erhardt, Treasurer
Charles Brown, Admin Sec
EMP: 6
SQ FT: 8,016
SALES: 500K Privately Held
WEB: www.taxidermist.net
SIC: 3161 3199 Cases, carrying; saddles
or parts

(G-15668)
ZAENKERT SURVEYING ESSENTIALS
7461a Cncnnati Brkvlle Rd (45053-9780)
PHONE....................................513 738-2917
Fax: 513 738-5817
Robert Zaenkert, President
Michelle Zaenkert, Vice Pres
EMP: 8
SQ FT: 2,100
SALES (est): 1.1MM Privately Held
SIC: 2499 5049 5211 Surveyors' stakes,
wood; surveyors' instruments; lumber &
other building materials

Robert Zaenkert, President
EMP: 6
SQ FT: 10,000
SALES: 300K Privately Held
SIC: 3423 5072 Masons' hand tools; hard-
ware

Okolona
Henry County

(G-15669)
REPUBLIC MILLS INC
Also Called: Hudson Feeds
888 School St (43545-9246)
P.O. Box 50146 (43550-3146)
PHONE....................................419 758-3511
William H Koon II, President
Richard Lange, General Mgr
Becky Hardy, Principal
Sandy Wagner, Principal
Ronald Wingfield, Corp Secy
▼ EMP: 14
SQ FT: 30,000
SALES (est): 2.3MM Privately Held
WEB: www.republicmills.com
SIC: 2048 5191 Livestock feeds; feed

Old Fort
Seneca County

(G-15670)
CHURCH & DWIGHT CO INC
2501 E County Rd 34 (44861)
P.O. Box 122 (44861-0122)
PHONE....................419 992-4244
Fax: 419 992-4413
Michael Ziebold, *Purchasing*
Matthew Burr, *QC Dir*
Bruce Neeley, *Branch Mgr*
B Scott, *Director*
EMP: 14
SALES (corp-wide): 3.4B **Publicly Held**
WEB: www.churchdwight.com
SIC: 2812 Sodium bicarbonate
PA: Church & Dwight Co., Inc.
500 Charles Ewing Blvd
Ewing NJ 08628
609 806-1200

Old Washington
Guernsey County

(G-15671)
HERSHBERGERS DUTCH MARKET LLP
Also Called: Dutch Barn Builders
228 Old National Rd (43768)
PHONE....................740 489-5322
James Hershberger, *Partner*
Iva Hershberger, *Partner*
EMP: 22
SQ FT: 8,400
SALES (est): 1.1MM **Privately Held**
SIC: 5251 5411 5499 2452 Hardware; grocery stores; dried fruit; spices & herbs; prefabricated buildings, wood

Olmsted Falls
Cuyahoga County

(G-15672)
ADAMS AUTOMATIC INC
26070 N Depot St (44138-1647)
P.O. Box 38156 (44138-0156)
PHONE....................440 235-4416
Fax: 440 235-7655
Edward Bond, *President*
Eric Dales, *President*
Adria Bond, *Vice Pres*
Cathy Bollek, *Manager*
EMP: 10 EST: 1952
SQ FT: 7,200
SALES: 1.1MM **Privately Held**
WEB: www.adamsautomatic.com
SIC: 3451 Screw machine products

(G-15673)
AMERIPRINT
8119 Columbia Rd (44138-2023)
PHONE....................440 235-6094
Anthoney Giancaterino, *Principal*
EMP: 3
SALES (est): 180K **Privately Held**
SIC: 2759 Commercial printing

(G-15674)
BLUE RIDGE PAPER PRODUCTS INC
Also Called: Dairy Pak Div
7920 Mapleway Dr (44138-1626)
PHONE....................440 235-7200
Fax: 440 235-7299
Charles Grotsky, *Plant Mgr*
Bill Krivonak, *Controller*
Dave Lewallen, *Branch Mgr*
EMP: 200
SQ FT: 161,146 **Privately Held**
WEB: www.blueridgepaper.com
SIC: 2621 Fine paper; kraft paper
HQ: Blue Ridge Paper Products Inc.
41 Main St
Canton NC 28716
828 454-0676

(G-15675)
EVERGREEN PACKAGING INC
Also Called: Olmsted Falls Plant
7920 Mapleway Dr (44138-1626)
PHONE....................440 235-7200
William Shroka, *Safety Dir*
Marlene Smith, *Plant Mgr*
Greg Jones, *Branch Mgr*
Nick Smith, *Maintence Staff*
Richard Stewart, *Maintence Staff*
EMP: 5 **Privately Held**
SIC: 2621 5199 Paper mills; packaging materials
HQ: Evergreen Packaging Inc.
5350 Poplar Ave Ste 600
Memphis TN 38119
901 821-5350

(G-15676)
TAYJUS PERSONALIZED WOODWORKS
Also Called: Tayjus Woodworks
25366 Tyndall Falls Dr (44138-2768)
PHONE....................440 427-9145
Amy Taseff, *Owner*
EMP: 3
SALES (est): 166.3K **Privately Held**
SIC: 2499 Decorative wood & woodwork

(G-15677)
THERMAFAB ALLOY INC
25367 Water St (44138-2015)
PHONE....................216 861-0540
George M Donnelly, *CEO*
Gilbert Sherman, *COO*
Daniel P Conway, *CFO*
Lynda Savage, *Administration*
EMP: 35 EST: 1930
SQ FT: 58,000
SALES (est): 4.9MM **Privately Held**
WEB: www.tfaballoy.com
SIC: 3087 Custom compound purchased resins

Olmsted Twp
Cuyahoga County

(G-15678)
AMERICAN WIRE & CABLE COMPANY (PA)
7951 Bronson Rd (44138-1088)
PHONE....................440 235-1140
Fax: 440 235-3330
Richard M McClain, *President*
Gary Gilliland, *Div Sub Head*
Kim R McClain, *Vice Pres*
Doug McClain, *Personnel Exec*
Walter McClain, *Sales Mgr*
▲ EMP: 30 EST: 1955
SQ FT: 80,000
SALES (est): 24.4MM **Privately Held**
WEB: www.americanwireandcable.com
SIC: 3357 3351 3315 Nonferrous wire-drawing & insulating; wire, copper & copper alloy; steel wire & related products

(G-15679)
LA DUA INC
24481 Barrett Rd (44138-1309)
PHONE....................440 243-9600
Fax: 440 529-1330
Albert Kishman, *President*
Audry Kishman, *Chairman*
Kim Neuendorf, *Vice Pres*
Kimber L Neuendorf, *Vice Pres*
EMP: 6
SQ FT: 2,400
SALES (est): 497.6K **Privately Held**
WEB: www.laduainc.com
SIC: 7336 2791 Commercial art & graphic design; typesetting

(G-15680)
LIBER LIMITED LLC
7162 Windwood Way (44138-1167)
PHONE....................440 427-0647
David C Liber, *President*
EMP: 5
SALES: 1.2MM **Privately Held**
SIC: 3465 5531 Body parts, automobile: stamped metal; automotive parts

(G-15681)
NEBULATRONICS INC
24542 Nobottom Rd (44138-1540)
PHONE....................440 243-2370
Kenneth Rados, *President*
Steve Harris, *Vice Pres*
Mike Panfil, *Vice Pres*
EMP: 26
SQ FT: 5,000
SALES (est): 3MM **Privately Held**
SIC: 3825 3829 Transducers for volts, amperes, watts, vars, frequency, etc.; measuring & controlling devices

(G-15682)
OLMSTED ICE INC
8134 Bronson Rd (44138-1033)
PHONE....................440 235-8411
Fax: 440 235-3487
Norman Dickson, *President*
Tom Dickson, *Vice Pres*
Ted Dickson, *Treasurer*
Tony Dickson, *Admin Sec*
EMP: 20
SQ FT: 3,000
SALES (est): 2.5MM **Privately Held**
WEB: www.olmstedice.com
SIC: 2097 Manufactured ice

(G-15683)
SSO INC
27064 Dogwood Ln (44138-3253)
PHONE....................440 235-3500
Senad Osmic, *President*
EMP: 15
SALES (est): 1MM **Privately Held**
WEB: www.sso.net
SIC: 3554 Sandpaper manufacturing machines

Ontario
Richland County

(G-15684)
ADDED TOUCH DECORATING GALLERY
1162 Cobblefield Dr (44903-8257)
PHONE....................419 747-3146
Lorretta Compton, *Owner*
Lori Mc Clintock, *Manager*
EMP: 3
SQ FT: 3,150
SALES (est): 238.8K **Privately Held**
SIC: 3263 7389 Semivitreous table & kitchenware; kitchenware; lighting, lamps & accessories; window furnishings; pictures & mirrors; interior designer

(G-15685)
CNB LLC
Also Called: Minuteman Press
84 Briggs Dr (44906-3829)
PHONE....................419 528-3109
Bonnie Brody, *Mng Member*
Mark Cooper, *Manager*
Mark A Cooper,
EMP: 3
SQ FT: 1,300
SALES (est): 25K **Privately Held**
SIC: 2752 Commercial printing, lithographic

(G-15686)
COLE TOOL & DIE COMPANY
Also Called: Oil Tooling and Stamping
466 State Route 314 N (44903-6555)
P.O. Box 150 (44862-0150)
PHONE....................419 522-1272
Fax: 419 522-5506
Alan D Cole, *CEO*
Dave Harmon, *President*
David Harmon, *COO*
Darren Nihizer, *Opers Staff*
Mark Besenti, *Engineer*
EMP: 40 EST: 1953
SQ FT: 28,000
SALES (est): 11.6MM **Privately Held**
SIC: 3544 3469 3465 Special dies & tools; metal stampings; automotive stampings

(G-15687)
EMERSON PROCESS MANAGEMENT
Also Called: Shafer
2500 Park Ave W (44906-1235)
PHONE....................419 529-4311
Barbara Schwartz, *Controller*
Mike McQuade, *VP Sales*
Dale Opperman, *Regl Sales Mgr*
John Kurtz, *Manager*
Denise McQuade, *Info Tech Mgr*
EMP: 35
SALES (corp-wide): 14.5B **Publicly Held**
SIC: 3593 3594 Fluid power actuators, hydraulic or pneumatic; fluid power pumps & motors
HQ: Emerson Process Management Valve Automation, Inc.
8000 West Florissant Ave
Saint Louis MO 63136
314 553-2000

(G-15688)
HEMPY WATER CONDITIONING INC
4148b Park Ave W (44903-8589)
PHONE....................419 529-4002
Dan Casher, *Owner*
EMP: 6
SALES (corp-wide): 2.3MM **Privately Held**
SIC: 3589 Water treatment equipment, industrial
PA: Hempy Water Conditioning Inc
505 Smith St
Forest OH 45843
419 273-2531

(G-15689)
MAR-ZANE INC
1300 W 4th St (44906-1828)
P.O. Box 1321, Mansfield (44901-1321)
PHONE....................419 529-2086
Herb Jarsar, *Manager*
EMP: 3
SALES (corp-wide): 301.4MM **Privately Held**
SIC: 1499 Asphalt (native) mining
HQ: Mar-Zane, Inc.
3570 S River Rd
Zanesville OH 43701
740 453-0721

(G-15690)
MYPRO APPAREL LLC
Also Called: My Pro Apparel
325 Shelby Ontario Rd (44906-1027)
PHONE....................419 462-9464
Aaron Brown, *Principal*
EMP: 3
SALES (est): 202.6K **Privately Held**
SIC: 5621 2326 5699 Ready-to-wear apparel, women's; work apparel, except uniforms; sports apparel; customized clothing & apparel

(G-15691)
ONTARIO MECHANICAL LLC
2880 Park Ave W (44906-1026)
PHONE....................419 529-2578
Kenneth Earhart, *Mng Member*
Margaret Pauley, *Info Tech Mgr*
EMP: 30
SALES (est): 6.8MM **Privately Held**
SIC: 3449 1761 1791 Custom roll formed products; sheet metalwork; structural steel erection

(G-15692)
OXYRASE INC
3000 Park Ave W (44906-1050)
P.O. Box 1345, Mansfield (44901-1345)
PHONE....................419 589-8800
Fax: 419 589-9919
James Copeland, *Ch of Bd*
Casey Zace, *President*
Jeff Little, *QC Mgr*
Lisa Stewart, *Marketing Mgr*
Diana Freer, *Manager*
EMP: 10
SQ FT: 7,000
SALES: 1MM **Privately Held**
WEB: www.oxyrase.com
SIC: 2869 Enzymes

▲ = Import ▼=Export
◆ =Import/Export

(G-15693)
P R MACHINE WORKS INC
1825 Nussbaum Pkwy (44906-2360)
PHONE..................................419 529-5748
Fax: 419 529-9052
Mark Romanchuk, *President*
Mark J Romanchuk, *President*
Jerry Schwall, *Vice Pres*
Jeff Berrier, *Maint Spvr*
Steve Fensch, *Engineer*
▲ EMP: 75
SQ FT: 14,100
SALES: 9.5MM **Privately Held**
WEB: www.prmachineworks.com
SIC: 3599 1531 Machine shop, jobbing & repair;

(G-15694)
POLY GREEN TECHNOLOGIES LLC
1237 W 4th St (44906-1825)
PHONE..................................419 529-9909
Jeffrey Schultheis,
EMP: 5
SALES (est): 330K **Privately Held**
SIC: 2821 Plastics materials & resins

(G-15695)
STUMBO PUBLISHING CO
Also Called: Tribune Courier
347 Allen Dr (44906-1001)
P.O. Box 127 (44862-0127)
PHONE..................................419 529-2847
Fax: 419 529-2847
Frank Stumbo, *President*
Jenna Wolford, *Production*
Betty Stumbo, *Treasurer*
Kim Knapp, *Sales Staff*
James Hellinger, *Director*
EMP: 3 EST: 1961
SQ FT: 800
SALES (est): 359.6K **Privately Held**
WEB: www.tribunecourier.com
SIC: 2791 2711 Typesetting; newspapers

(G-15696)
UNISPORT INC
Also Called: Johnny Johnson Sports
2254 Stumbo Rd (44906-3804)
PHONE..................................419 529-4727
Fax: 419 529-6812
H Kim Baird, *President*
Todd Baird, *Vice Pres*
EMP: 10
SALES: 1.5MM **Privately Held**
SIC: 5136 5137 5699 2759 Sportswear, men's & boys'; sportswear, women's & children's; sports apparel; screen printing; embroidery products, except schiffli machine

(G-15697)
WHITE MULE COMPANY
2420 W 4th St (44906-1207)
PHONE..................................740 382-9008
Steve Ritchey, *President*
Georgia Jordon, *Office Mgr*
Debby Ritchey, *Admin Sec*
EMP: 21
SQ FT: 15,000
SALES (est): 4.2MM **Privately Held**
WEB: www.whitemuleproductions.com
SIC: 3714 1791 Trailer hitches, motor vehicle; iron work, structural

---

Oregon
Lucas County

(G-15698)
A & L INDUSTRIES
Also Called: A & L Inds Machining & Repr
2054 Grange St (43616-4442)
PHONE..................................419 698-3733
Fax: 419 698-3733
Allen Hoar Jr, *Owner*
EMP: 30
SALES (est): 2.8MM **Privately Held**
SIC: 3599 Machine shop, jobbing & repair

(G-15699)
ABC APPLIANCE INC
3012 Navarre Ave (43616-3308)
PHONE..................................419 693-4414
Fax: 419 693-4142
J R Pruss, *Manager*
EMP: 30
SALES (corp-wide): 371.8MM **Privately Held**
WEB: www.abcwarehouse.com
SIC: 3639 5722 5731 5065 Major kitchen appliances, except refrigerators & stoves; vacuum cleaners; high fidelity stereo equipment; telephone equipment; photo-copy machines
PA: Abc Appliance, Inc.
1 W Silverdome Indus Park
Pontiac MI 48342
248 335-4222

(G-15700)
ACUREN INSPECTION INC
205 N Lallendorf Rd Ste B (43616-5501)
PHONE..................................419 698-5040
EMP: 3
SALES (corp-wide): 513MM **Privately Held**
SIC: 3829 Measuring & controlling devices
HQ: Acuren Inspection, Inc.
30 Main St Ste 402
Danbury CT 06810
203 702-8740

(G-15701)
AECOM ENERGY & CNSTR INC
Also Called: Washington Group
4001 Cedar Point Rd (43616-1310)
P.O. Box 696, Toledo (43697-0696)
PHONE..................................419 698-6277
EMP: 125
SALES (corp-wide): 17.4B **Publicly Held**
WEB: www.wgint.com
SIC: 1542 2911 Nonresidential construction; petroleum refining
HQ: Aecom Energy & Construction, Inc.
6200 S Quebec St
Greenwood Village CO 80111
303 694-2770

(G-15702)
ASPHALT MATERIALS INC
940 N Wynn Rd (43616-1428)
PHONE..................................419 693-0626
Fax: 419 693-1069
Chris Arman, *Manager*
Alexander Nikolov, *Manager*
EMP: 13
SQ FT: 5,600
SALES (corp-wide): 314.9MM **Privately Held**
SIC: 1499 Asphalt (native) mining
PA: Asphalt Materials, Inc.
5400 W 86th St
Indianapolis IN 46268
317 872-6010

(G-15703)
AUTONEUM NORTH AMERICA INC
Also Called: Rieter Automotive-Oregon Plant
645 N Lallendorf Rd (43616-1334)
PHONE..................................419 693-0511
Ivan Pickering, *Personnel*
Gordon Shaw, *Branch Mgr*
EMP: 350
SQ FT: 150,000
SALES (corp-wide): 2.1B **Privately Held**
WEB: www.rieter.com
SIC: 3625 3714 3444 3296 Relays & industrial controls; motor vehicle parts & accessories; sheet metalwork; mineral wool; nonwoven fabrics
HQ: Autoneum North America, Inc.
29293 Haggerty Rd
Novi MI 48377
248 848-0100

(G-15704)
BRANAM ORAL HEALTH TECH INC (PA)
3140 Dustin Rd (43616-4341)
PHONE..................................248 670-0040
Michael J Janness, *President*
EMP: 4
SQ FT: 5,000
SALES (est): 599.6K **Privately Held**
SIC: 3843 Abrasive points, wheels & disks, dental

(G-15705)
CITGO PETROLEUM CORPORATION
1840 Otter Creek Rd (43616-1212)
PHONE..................................419 698-8055
Pete Krivas, *Manager*
EMP: 5 **Privately Held**
WEB: www.citgo.com
SIC: 2911 Petroleum refining
HQ: Citgo Petroleum Corporation
1293 Eldridge Pkwy
Houston TX 77077
832 486-4000

(G-15706)
COULTON CHEMICAL
1400 Otter Creek Rd (43616-1241)
PHONE..................................419 698-8181
Fax: 419 698-5233
D S Abbott, *Principal*
EMP: 4
SALES (est): 299.6K **Privately Held**
SIC: 2819 Industrial inorganic chemicals

(G-15707)
CTS SIGNS & SALES
1030 Cresceus Rd (43616-3123)
PHONE..................................419 407-5534
Charles Baptista, *Owner*
EMP: 3
SALES (est): 153.6K **Privately Held**
SIC: 3993 Signs & advertising specialties

(G-15708)
ENT PHYSICIANS INC (PA)
1050 Isaac Streets Dr # 137 (43616-8203)
PHONE..................................419 698-4505
Fax: 419 698-3806
Vijay Adappa MD, *President*
Gary Coleman MD, *Principal*
EMP: 16
SALES (est): 1.6MM **Privately Held**
WEB: www.entphysiciansinc.com
SIC: 3842 Hearing aids

(G-15709)
FOUTY & COMPANY INC
5003 Bayshore Rd (43616-4478)
P.O. Box 167544 (43616-7544)
PHONE..................................419 693-0017
Fax: 419 693-5802
Marion L Fouty, *Ch of Bd*
Ken Fouty, *President*
Ken Poupard, *Accounts Mgr*
Gary Fouty, *Administration*
▲ EMP: 8
SQ FT: 20,000
SALES (est): 4.6MM **Privately Held**
WEB: www.foutywaterjet.com
SIC: 5085 3053 Rubber goods, mechanical; gaskets, all materials

(G-15710)
MR EMBLEM INC
3209 Navarre Ave (43616-3311)
PHONE..................................419 697-1888
Fax: 419 697-4226
Pat Slygh, *CEO*
Scott Slygh, *Business Mgr*
Edna Simmons, *Bookkeeper*
EMP: 7
SQ FT: 3,600
SALES: 950K **Privately Held**
WEB: www.mremblem.com
SIC: 2395 2396 5199 Embroidery & art needlework; screen printing on fabric articles; advertising specialties

(G-15711)
NISSEN LUMBER & COAL CO INC (PA)
5700 Navarre Ave (43616-3546)
PHONE..................................419 836-8035
Fax: 419 836-4007
Jerry Nissen, *President*
Alan Nissen, *Vice Pres*
Eugene Nissen, *Treasurer*
Dennis Nissen, *Admin Sec*
EMP: 5 EST: 1933
SQ FT: 1,200
SALES (est): 3.5MM **Privately Held**
SIC: 3273 5211 Ready-mixed concrete; sand & gravel; concrete & cinder block

(G-15712)
NORFOLK SOUTHERN CORPORATION
3830 Corduroy Rd (43616-1810)
PHONE..................................419 697-5070
James Swider, *Manager*
EMP: 20
SALES (corp-wide): 9.8B **Publicly Held**
WEB: www.nscorp.com
SIC: 3743 4789 Railroad car rebuilding; railroad car repair
PA: Norfolk Southern Corporation
3 Commercial Pl Ste 1a
Norfolk VA 23510
757 629-2680

(G-15713)
PRAXAIR INC
3742 Cedar Point Rd (43616-1305)
PHONE..................................419 698-8005
Bill Engberg, *Manager*
EMP: 8
SALES (corp-wide): 10.5B **Publicly Held**
SIC: 2813 Industrial gases
PA: Praxair, Inc.
10 Riverview Dr
Danbury CT 06810
203 837-2000

(G-15714)
R-MED INC
Also Called: Endoglobe
3465 Navarre Ave (43616-3427)
P.O. Box 167636 (43616-7636)
PHONE..................................419 693-7481
Fax: 419 693-7044
Erol Riza, *President*
James Wilson, *Branch Mgr*
Burak Riza, *Manager*
▲ EMP: 7
SQ FT: 2,500
SALES (est): 972.1K **Privately Held**
SIC: 3841 Surgical & medical instruments

(G-15715)
RBM ENVIRONMENTAL AND CNSTR
4526 Bayshore Rd (43616-1035)
PHONE..................................419 693-5840
Fax: 419 693-8746
Bob J Petty, *President*
Mike S Petty, *Vice Pres*
EMP: 40
SALES (est): 4.9MM **Privately Held**
SIC: 1794 7699 7692 3498 Excavation work; tank & boiler cleaning service; welding repair; fabricated pipe & fittings; fabricated structural metal

(G-15716)
SNOWS WOOD SHOP INC (PA)
7220 Brown Rd (43616-5805)
PHONE..................................419 836-3805
Fax: 419 836-6036
Vernon Snow, *President*
Minda Snow, *Corp Secy*
Kurt Snow, *Vice Pres*
EMP: 22
SQ FT: 10,380
SALES (est): 2.3MM **Privately Held**
SIC: 2434 1751 Wood kitchen cabinets; cabinet & finish carpentry

(G-15717)
STANDARD OIL COMPANY
4001 Cedar Point Rd (43616-1310)
P.O. Box 696, Toledo (43697-0696)
PHONE..................................419 698-6200
Terri Harlan, *Manager*
EMP: 50
SALES (corp-wide): 183B **Privately Held**
WEB: www.crystal-enterprise.com
SIC: 2911 5541 Petroleum refining; gasoline service stations
HQ: The Standard Oil Company
4101 Winfield Rd Ste 100
Warrenville IL 60555
630 836-5000

(G-15718)
STANDARD OIL COMPANY
Also Called: Pipeline Dept
4151 Cedar Point Rd (43616-1312)
PHONE..................................419 691-2460
Dennis Lahey, *Manager*

EMP: 5
SALES (corp-wide): 183B **Privately Held**
WEB: www.crystal-enterprise.com
SIC: **1382** 1389 Oil & gas exploration
services; gas field services
HQ: The Standard Oil Company
　4101 Winfield Rd Ste 100
　Warrenville IL 60555
　630 836-5000

(G-15719)
SWANSON ORTHOTIC &
PROSTHETIC
Also Called: Novacare Prosthetics Orthotics
3048 Navarre Ave (43616-3308)
PHONE...........................419 690-0026
Vern Swanson, *Principal*
John Duggan, *Principal*
Robert Ortenzio, *Principal*
Scott Romberger, *Principal*
Michael Tarvin, *Principal*
EMP: 5
SALES (est): 357.6K **Privately Held**
SIC: **3842** Limbs, artificial

(G-15720)
TOLEDO ALFALFA MILLS INC
861 S Stadium Rd (43616-5898)
PHONE...........................419 836-3705
Fax: 419 836-3705
Kathryn Lumbrezes, *President*
Gary Lumbrezer, *Vice Pres*
Becky Lumbrezer-Box, *Admin Sec*
EMP: 8
SQ FT: 6,000
SALES: 758.2K **Privately Held**
SIC: **2048** Alfalfa or alfalfa meal, prepared
as animal feed

(G-15721)
VORLAGE SPECIAL TOOL
205 Utah St (43605-2243)
PHONE...........................419 697-1201
Donald F Arnold, *Principal*
EMP: 3
SALES (est): 223.1K **Privately Held**
SIC: **3599** Machine shop, jobbing & repair

Oregonia
Warren County

(G-15722)
PROCTER & GAMBLE COMPANY
600 S Waynesville Rd (45054-9405)
PHONE...........................513 934-3406
C C Grabowski-Flaherty, *Manager*
EMP: 150
SALES (corp-wide): 65.3B **Publicly Held**
WEB: www.pg.com
SIC: **2676** Towels, napkins & tissue paper
products
PA: The Procter & Gamble Company
　1 Procter And Gamble Plz
　Cincinnati OH 45202
　513 983-1100

Orient
Pickaway County

(G-15723)
KMJ LEASING LTD
Also Called: B & B Industries
7001 Harrisburg Pike (43146-9468)
PHONE...........................614 871-3883
Kenneth A Harwood,
Mary A Harwood,
EMP: 38 EST: 1971
SQ FT: 5,000
SALES (est): 6.6MM **Privately Held**
WEB: www.bandbindustriesinc.com
SIC: **4213** 3799 Contract haulers; golf
carts, powered

(G-15724)
SPECIALTEE SPORTSWEAR &
DESIGN
9819 Us Highway 62 (43146-9175)
PHONE...........................614 877-0976
Randy Hill, *Mng Member*
EMP: 5

SALES (est): 559.5K **Privately Held**
SIC: **2759** 5199 Screen printing; advertising specialties

(G-15725)
TONNS FABRICATION
7767 Harrisburg London Rd (43146-9416)
PHONE...........................614 989-5097
Michael Tonn, *Principal*
EMP: 3
SALES (est): 249.4K **Privately Held**
SIC: **3443** Tanks, standard or custom fabri-
cated: metal plate

(G-15726)
WONDER WELD INC
6127 Harrisburg Pike (43146-9409)
PHONE...........................614 875-1447
Doris Jean, *President*
Timothy Albaugh, *Vice Pres*
EMP: 4
SQ FT: 17,000
SALES (est): 520.4K **Privately Held**
WEB: www.wonderweld.com
SIC: **7692** 3677 3548 Welding repair;
electronic coils, transformers & other in-
ductors; welding apparatus

Orrville
Wayne County

(G-15727)
ACCURATE ELECTRONICS INC
169 S Main St (44667-1801)
P.O. Box 900 (44667-0900)
PHONE...........................330 682-7015
Jeffrey Evans, *CEO*
EMP: 250
SQ FT: 6,000
SALES (est): 16.9MM
SALES (corp-wide): 63.8MM **Privately**
Held
WEB: www.willburt.com
SIC: **3679** 3621 3812 3672 Electronic cir-
cuits; generators & sets, electric; search
& navigation equipment; printed circuit
boards; radio & TV communications
equipment; current-carrying wiring de-
vices
PA: The Will-Burt Company
　169 S Main St
　Orrville OH 44667
　330 682-7015

(G-15728)
ADVANCED CHEM SOLUTIONS
INC
150 Allen Ave (44667-9021)
PHONE...........................216 692-3005
Gerry Groudle, *Branch Mgr*
EMP: 5
SALES (corp-wide): 3.5MM **Privately**
Held
SIC: **2899** Chemical preparations
PA: Advanced Chemical Solutions Inc.
　1114 N Court St 196
　Medina OH 44256
　330 283-5157

(G-15729)
BEKAERT CORPORATION
Also Called: Contours
322 E Pine St (44667-1853)
PHONE...........................330 683-5060
Otto Simmerman, *Principal*
Rod Ady, *Opers Mgr*
Bill Pennel, *Purchasing*
EMP: 190
SQ FT: 260,000
SALES (corp-wide): 451MM **Privately**
Held
WEB: www.bekaert.com
SIC: **3315** 3316 3398 3479 Wire & fabri-
cated wire products; fencing made in
wiredrawing plants; cold-rolled strip or
wire; wire, flat, cold-rolled strip: not made
in hot-rolled mills; metal heat treating;
coating of metals & formed products
HQ: Bekaert Corporation
　1395 S Marietta Pkwy Se 500-100
　Marietta GA 30067
　770 421-8520

(G-15730)
BEKAERT CORPORATION
510 Collins Blvd (44667-9796)
PHONE...........................330 683-5060
Otto Simmerman, *Principal*
EMP: 15
SALES (corp-wide): 451MM **Privately**
Held
SIC: **3315** Wire & fabricated wire products;
fencing made in wiredrawing plants
HQ: Bekaert Corporation
　1395 S Marietta Pkwy Se 500-100
　Marietta GA 30067
　770 421-8520

(G-15731)
BIG HEART PET BRANDS
1 Strawberry Ln (44667-1241)
P.O. Box 80, Pittsburgh PA (15230-0080)
PHONE...........................412 222-2200
Richard Thompson, *Manager*
EMP: 107
SALES (corp-wide): 7.8B **Publicly Held**
SIC: **2047** Dog & cat food
HQ: Big Heart Pet Brands
　1 Maritime Plz Fl 2
　San Francisco CA 94111
　415 247-3000

(G-15732)
BUCKEYE COUNTERS
10207 Ely Rd (44667-9510)
PHONE...........................330 682-0902
David A Miller, *Principal*
EMP: 3
SALES (est): 262.9K **Privately Held**
SIC: **3131** Counters

(G-15733)
CASKEYS INC
Also Called: Caskey's Recreation
14847 Fosnight Rd (44667-9716)
PHONE...........................330 683-0249
Fax: 330 683-4900
Jonathan Caskey, *President*
Donald Caskey, *Vice Pres*
Sandra Caskey, *Treasurer*
Beulah Caskey, *Admin Sec*
Bonnie Good, *Administration*
EMP: 4
SALES: 300K **Privately Held**
SIC: **3599** 7033 Machine shop, jobbing &
repair; campgrounds

(G-15734)
DALTON WOOD PRODUCTS INC
101 N Swinehart Rd (44667-9532)
PHONE...........................330 682-0727
Fax: 330 682-0720
Robert Swartzentruber, *Manager*
EMP: 5
SALES: 475K **Privately Held**
SIC: **2499** Laundry products, wood

(G-15735)
DUTCH CNTRY APPLE
DMPLINGS INC
229 W Market St (44667-1848)
P.O. Box 603 (44667-0603)
PHONE...........................330 683-0646
Fax: 330 683-4630
Andrew Hamsher, *President*
Creg Rohr, *General Mgr*
EMP: 70
SQ FT: 12,000
SALES: 8.8MM **Privately Held**
SIC: **2051** Cakes, pies & pastries

(G-15736)
FERRO CORPORATION
1560 N Main St (44667-9170)
P.O. Box 602 (44667-0602)
PHONE...........................330 682-8015
Fax: 330 682-2293
Kenneth Ackerman, *Branch Mgr*
EMP: 19
SALES (corp-wide): 1.1B **Publicly Held**
WEB: www.ferro.com
SIC: **2865** Cyclic crudes & intermediates
PA: Ferro Corporation
　6060 Parkland Blvd # 250
　Mayfield Heights OH 44124
　216 875-5600

(G-15737)
FOLGER COFFEE COMPANY
(HQ)
Also Called: Folgers
1 Strawberry Ln (44667-1241)
PHONE...........................800 937-9745
Fax: 513 983-4905
Susan E Arnold, *President*
Alan G Lafley, *President*
J M Smucker, *Principal*
D R Walker, *President*
Joseph H Etter, *Senior VP*
▲ EMP: 15 EST: 1850
SQ FT: 1,600,000
SALES (est): 217.1MM
SALES (corp-wide): 7.8B **Publicly Held**
SIC: **2095** Roasted coffee; instant coffee;
coffee, ground: mixed with grain or
chicory; freeze-dried coffee
PA: The J M Smucker Company
　1 Strawberry Ln
　Orrville OH 44667
　330 682-3000

(G-15738)
GRAND UNIFICATION PRESS
INC
2380 Wayne St (44667-9626)
PHONE...........................330 683-1187
Tim Brenneman, *President*
EMP: 4
SALES (est): 202.6K **Privately Held**
WEB: www.grandupress.com
SIC: **2731** Book publishing

(G-15739)
HEARTLAND EDUCATION
COMMUNITY
200 N Main St (44667-1640)
P.O. Box 280 (44667-0280)
PHONE...........................330 684-3034
Carol Ubelhart, *Principal*
EMP: 14
SALES: 439.4K **Privately Held**
SIC: **2711** Newspapers, publishing & print-
ing

(G-15740)
HEAT EXCHANGE APPLIED
TECH
150b Allen Ave (44667)
PHONE...........................330 682-4328
Fax: 330 682-4329
Bharat Patel, *President*
EMP: 10
SQ FT: 19,000
SALES (est): 2.1MM **Privately Held**
WEB: www.heat-voss.com
SIC: **3585** Heating equipment, complete

(G-15741)
INTERNATIONAL MULTIFOODS
CORP (HQ)
Also Called: J M Smucker
1 Strawberry Ln (44667-1241)
P.O. Box 280 (44667-0280)
PHONE...........................330 682-3000
Gary Costley PHD, *CEO*
Dan C Swander, *President*
Frank W Bonvino, *Senior VP*
Ralph P Hargrow, *Vice Pres*
Dennis R Johnson, *Vice Pres*
◆ EMP: 5 EST: 2000
SQ FT: 20,000
SALES (est): 192.4MM
SALES (corp-wide): 7.8B **Publicly Held**
WEB: www.multifoods.com
SIC: **5145** 5149 5143 2048 Candy; snack
foods; chewing gum; coffee, green or
roasted; tea bagging; baking supplies;
pizza supplies; cheese; livestock feeds;
pizza dough, prepared; flour; flour mixes
PA: The J M Smucker Company
　1 Strawberry Ln
　Orrville OH 44667
　330 682-3000

(G-15742)
J M SMUCKER COMPANY (PA)
1 Strawberry Ln (44667-1298)
PHONE...........................330 682-3000
Fax: 330 684-3428
Richard K Smucker, *Ch of Bd*
Mark T Smucker, *President*
Jeannette L Knudsen, *Senior VP*

▲ = Import ▼=Export
◆ =Import/Export

Jill R Penrose, *Senior VP*
Rob Fox, *Vice Pres*
◆ **EMP:** 750 **EST:** 1897
SALES: 7.8B **Publicly Held**
WEB: www.smuckers.com
SIC: 2099 2033 2023 2087 Syrups; frosting, ready-to-use; sandwiches, assembled & packaged: for wholesale market; peanut butter; jams, jellies & preserves: packaged in cans, jars, etc.; jellies, edible, including imitation: in cans, jars, etc.; vegetable juices: packaged in cans, jars, etc.; fruit juices: packaged in cans, jars, etc.; canned milk, whole; beverage bases, concentrates, syrups, powders & mixes; pickles, sauces & salad dressings

(G-15743)
JLG INDUSTRIES INC
2927 Paradise St (44667-9628)
PHONE..............................330 684-0132
EMP: 122
SALES (corp-wide): 6.2B **Publicly Held**
SIC: 3531 Construction machinery
HQ: Jlg Industries, Inc.
   1 J L G Dr
   Mc Connellsburg PA 17233
   717 485-5161

(G-15744)
JLG INDUSTRIES INC
600 E Chestnut St (44667-1951)
PHONE..............................330 684-0200
Wade Jones, *Branch Mgr*
Paul D Ballard, *Director*
EMP: 125
SALES (corp-wide): 6.2B **Publicly Held**
WEB: www.jlg.com
SIC: 3531 Construction machinery
HQ: Jlg Industries, Inc.
   1 J L G Dr
   Mc Connellsburg PA 17233
   717 485-5161

(G-15745)
LEHMAN & SONS
3328 S Kohler Rd (44667-9604)
PHONE..............................330 857-7404
Albert Lehman, *Owner*
EMP: 6 **EST:** 1969
SALES: 1.5MM **Privately Held**
SIC: 2431 Exterior & ornamental woodwork & trim

(G-15746)
LETTER GRAPHICS SIGN CO INC
400 W Market St (44667-1823)
P.O. Box 613 (44667-0613)
PHONE..............................330 683-3903
Fax: 330 684-2704
Jim R Webster, *CEO*
Frank Wessels, *President*
Chris Butdorf, *Finance*
EMP: 8
SQ FT: 1,500
SALES (est): 1.2MM **Privately Held**
SIC: 3993 Electric signs

(G-15747)
MONARCH PLASTIC INC
516 Jefferson Ave (44667-1811)
PHONE..............................330 683-0822
Fax: 330 684-2601
Larry R Caskey, *President*
Debra Caskey, *Vice Pres*
EMP: 12
SQ FT: 10,000
SALES (est): 1.1MM **Privately Held**
SIC: 3711 3714 Automobile bodies, passenger car, not including engine, etc.; motor vehicle parts & accessories

(G-15748)
MOOG INC
1701 N Main St (44667-9172)
PHONE..............................330 682-0010
James King, *Principal*
Judy Murdock, *Editor*
Allen Ruef, *Sales Staff*
EMP: 63
SALES (corp-wide): 2.4B **Publicly Held**
SIC: 3625 Actuators, industrial

PA: Moog Inc.
   400 Jamison Rd Plant26
   Elma NY 14059
   716 652-2000

(G-15749)
MYRON D BUDD
Also Called: Orrcast Aluminum Foundry
480 S Crown Hill Rd (44667-9553)
P.O. Box 277 (44667-0277)
PHONE..............................330 682-5866
Mary Budd, *Owner*
EMP: 3 **EST:** 1952
SQ FT: 3,000
SALES (est): 268.4K **Privately Held**
SIC: 3365 Aluminum foundries

(G-15750)
NATIONAL PATTERN MFG CO
1318 N Main St (44667-9761)
P.O. Box 58 (44667-0058)
PHONE..............................330 682-6871
Fax: 330 683-9421
Anthony J Yonto, *President*
Anthony A Nicholas, *President*
Karen Schmalzer, *Finance Mgr*
Robert C Nicholas, *Admin Sec*
EMP: 10
SQ FT: 3,000
SALES (est): 1.6MM
SALES (corp-wide): 57.2MM **Privately Held**
WEB: www.qcfoundry.com
SIC: 3544 3543 Dies, plastics forming; foundry patternmaking
PA: Quality Castings Company
   1200 N Main St
   Orrville OH 44667
   330 682-6871

(G-15751)
NUCOR BRIGHT BAR ORVILLE LLC
555 Collins Blvd (44667-9796)
PHONE..............................330 682-5555
David A Sumoski, *President*
EMP: 19
SALES (est): 1MM
SALES (corp-wide): 16.2B **Publicly Held**
SIC: 3316 Bars, steel, cold finished, from purchased hot-rolled
PA: Nucor Corporation
   1915 Rexford Rd Ste 400
   Charlotte NC 28211
   704 366-7000

(G-15752)
ORRVILLE PRINTING CO INC
1645 N Main St (44667-9171)
PHONE..............................330 682-5066
Fax: 330 682-6388
Eric Badertscher, *President*
Ron Badertscher, *President*
Brittany Armentrout, *District Mgr*
EMP: 8
SALES (est): 500K **Privately Held**
SIC: 2752 2791 2789 Commercial printing, offset; typesetting; bookbinding & related work

(G-15753)
ORRVILLE TRUCKING & GRADING CO (PA)
475 Orr St (44667-9764)
P.O. Box 220 (44667-0220)
PHONE..............................330 682-4010
Fax: 330 682-4457
Auvil Richmond, *President*
Tim Fnyter, *General Mgr*
John H Wilson, *Treasurer*
EMP: 50
SQ FT: 15,000
SALES (est): 7.5MM **Privately Held**
SIC: 3273 3272 5031 Ready-mixed concrete; concrete products; building materials, exterior; building materials, interior

(G-15754)
ORRVILON INC
1400 Dairy Ln (44667-2505)
PHONE..............................330 684-9400
K P Singh, *President*
Alan Soler, *Exec VP*
Michael Joyce, *Project Mgr*
Frank Bongrazio, *CFO*
Julie Keesee, *Office Mgr*

▲ **EMP:** 110 **EST:** 2009
SQ FT: 350,000
SALES (est): 51MM
SALES (corp-wide): 348.3MM **Privately Held**
SIC: 3354 3442 Aluminum extruded products; metal doors
PA: Holtec International
   1001 N Us Highway 1
   Jupiter FL 33477
   561 745-7772

(G-15755)
PURINA MILLS LLC
635 Collins Blvd (44667-9796)
PHONE..............................330 682-1951
Fax: 330 682-4606
Curly Elliot, *Plant Mgr*
Ken Fchwarzrock, *Manager*
EMP: 9
SALES (corp-wide): 14.9B **Privately Held**
WEB: www.purina-mills.com
SIC: 2048 Feed premixes
HQ: Purina Mills, Llc
   555 Maryvle Univ Dr 200
   Saint Louis MO 63141
   877 454-7094

(G-15756)
QUALITY CASTINGS COMPANY (PA)
1200 N Main St (44667-1017)
P.O. Box 58 (44667-0058)
PHONE..............................330 682-6871
Fax: 330 683-3153
Di CK Nicholas, *CEO*
Richard Nicholas, *Ch of Bd*
David Yonto, *President*
F L Strauss, *Principal*
Anthony A Nicholas, *Vice Pres*
EMP: 290 **EST:** 1927
SALES (est): 57.2MM **Privately Held**
WEB: www.qcfoundry.com
SIC: 3321 Gray iron castings; ductile iron castings

(G-15757)
REFRACTORY COATING TECH INC
Also Called: Refcotec
542 Collins Blvd (44667-9796)
PHONE..............................330 683-2200
Fax: 330 683-8200
William Dewood, *President*
Timothy P Sheehan, *Vice Pres*
Brad Anderson, *Sales Staff*
Collin Dewood, *Sales Staff*
Matt Dewood, *Sales Staff*
EMP: 25
SQ FT: 23,400
SALES (est): 5MM **Privately Held**
WEB: www.refcotec.com
SIC: 3297 Heat resistant mixtures

(G-15758)
RICELAND DRY KILN
1287 S Kansas Rd (44667-9566)
PHONE..............................330 683-9151
Dan Miller, *Principal*
EMP: 3
SALES (est): 283.1K **Privately Held**
SIC: 3559 Kilns

(G-15759)
ROCK DECOR COMPANY
2877 Kidron Rd (44667-9603)
P.O. Box 148, Apple Creek (44606-0148)
PHONE..............................330 857-7625
Gary Miller, *Owner*
EMP: 5
SALES (est): 590.5K **Privately Held**
SIC: 3272 Stone, cast concrete

(G-15760)
ROGER HOOVER
571 Kidron Rd (44667-9203)
PHONE..............................330 857-1815
Roger Hoover, *Principal*
EMP: 3
SALES (est): 249.4K **Privately Held**
SIC: 2851 Removers & cleaners

(G-15761)
S & S PANEL
3314 S Kohler Rd (44667-9604)
PHONE..............................330 412-6735
Philip Schrock, *Owner*
EMP: 5
SALES (est): 291.7K **Privately Held**
SIC: 2431 Millwork; panel work, wood

(G-15762)
SCHANTZ ORGAN COMPANY (PA)
626 S Walnut St (44667-2238)
P.O. Box 156 (44667-0156)
PHONE..............................330 682-6065
Fax: 330 683-2274
Victor B Schantz, *President*
Jeff Dexter, *Vice Pres*
Eric Gastier, *Vice Pres*
Wes Hofstetler, *Safety Mgr*
Russ Forrer, *Warehouse Mgr*
EMP: 30 **EST:** 1873
SQ FT: 45,600
SALES (est): 7.2MM **Privately Held**
WEB: www.schantzorgan.com
SIC: 3931 Organs, all types: pipe, reed, hand, electronic, etc.

(G-15763)
SCOTTS MIRACLE-GRO COMPANY
1220 Schrock Rd (44667-9582)
PHONE..............................330 684-0421
Ark Dish, *Branch Mgr*
EMP: 70
SALES (corp-wide): 2.8B **Publicly Held**
SIC: 2873 Nitrogenous fertilizers
PA: The Scotts Miracle-Gro Company
   14111 Scottslawn Rd
   Marysville OH 43040
   937 644-0011

(G-15764)
SMITHFOODS INC (PA)
1381 Dairy Ln (44667-2503)
P.O. Box 87 (44667-0087)
PHONE..............................330 683-8710
Stephen Schmid, *President*
Daniel Brimm, *Principal*
EMP: 5
SALES (est): 66.9MM **Privately Held**
SIC: 2026 2024 Milk processing (pasteurizing, homogenizing, bottling); ice cream, bulk

(G-15765)
SMITHFOODS ORRVILLE INC
230 N Vine St (44667-1644)
P.O. Box 638 (44667-0638)
PHONE..............................330 684-6502
Daniel Brimm, *President*
EMP: 200
SALES (est): 4.5MM
SALES (corp-wide): 66.9MM **Privately Held**
SIC: 2023 Dry, condensed, evaporated dairy products
PA: Smithfoods Inc.
   1381 Dairy Ln
   Orrville OH 44667
   330 683-8710

(G-15766)
SMUCKER INTERNATIONAL INC (HQ)
Also Called: Smucker Latin America Inc
1 Strawberry Ln (44667-1241)
PHONE..............................330 682-3000
Richard Smucker, *CEO*
Tim Smucker, *Ch of Bd*
Robert Ferguson, *Senior VP*
Vince Byrd, *Vice Pres*
John Stangel, *Opers Mgr*
▼ **EMP:** 4
SALES (est): 447.4K
SALES (corp-wide): 7.8B **Publicly Held**
WEB: www.smuckers.com
SIC: 2033 2099 2086 Canned fruits & specialties; syrups; bottled & canned soft drinks
PA: The J M Smucker Company
   1 Strawberry Ln
   Orrville OH 44667
   330 682-3000

(G-15767)
SMUCKER NATURAL FOODS INC
Strawberry Ln (44667)
PHONE..............................330 682-3000
H Wagstaff, *Branch Mgr*
EMP: 44
SALES (corp-wide): 7.8B **Publicly Held**
WEB: www.knudsenjuices.com
SIC: 2086 Bottled & canned soft drinks
HQ: Smucker Natural Foods, Inc.
　　37 Speedway Ave
　　Chico CA 95928
　　530 899-5000

(G-15768)
SPECIALTY PALLET & DESIGN LTD
2600 Kidron Rd (44667-9645)
PHONE..............................330 857-0257
Shawn Loft,
Dan Andrews,
David Gruttle,
EMP: 30
SALES (est): 5.5MM **Privately Held**
SIC: 2448 Pallets, wood & wood with metal

(G-15769)
WILL-BURT ADVNCED CMPSITES INC
356 Collins Blvd (44667)
PHONE..............................330 684-5286
Vicki Oravec, *Principal*
Greg Much,
EMP: 15
SALES (est): 1.7MM
SALES (corp-wide): 63.8MM **Privately Held**
SIC: 3448 Prefabricated metal buildings
PA: The Will-Burt Company
　　169 S Main St
　　Orrville OH 44667
　　330 682-7015

(G-15770)
WILL-BURT COMPANY (PA)
169 S Main St (44667-1801)
P.O. Box 900 (44667-0900)
PHONE..............................330 682-7015
Fax: 330 684-1190
Jeffrey Evans, *President*
Scott Carter, *General Mgr*
Diane Pellegrene, *General Mgr*
Phil Tryon, *General Mgr*
Eric Dubendorfer, *Business Mgr*
▲ EMP: 275 EST: 1918
SQ FT: 170,000
SALES: 63.8MM **Privately Held**
WEB: www.willburt.com
SIC: 3599 5039 3443 3449 Machine shop, jobbing & repair; prefabricated structures; fabricated plate work (boiler shop); miscellaneous metalwork; lighting equipment; sheet metalwork

(G-15771)
WILL-BURT COMPANY
150 Allen Ave (44667-9021)
PHONE..............................330 683-9991
John Yurkschatt, *General Mgr*
EMP: 4
SALES (corp-wide): 63.8MM **Privately Held**
SIC: 3599 Machine shop, jobbing & repair
PA: The Will-Burt Company
　　169 S Main St
　　Orrville OH 44667
　　330 682-7015

(G-15772)
WILL-BURT COMPANY
401 Collins Blvd (44667-9752)
P.O. Box 900 (44667-0900)
PHONE..............................330 682-7015
Vicki Oravec, *Purch Agent*
Mike Ohlsen, *Engineer*
Andrew Wasson, *Engineer*
Daniel Wesman, *Design Engr*
Deborah Malta, *Human Res Dir*
EMP: 39

SALES (corp-wide): 63.8MM **Privately Held**
WEB: www.willburt.com
SIC: 3443 3449 3599 5039 Fabricated plate work (boiler shop); miscellaneous metalwork; machine shop, jobbing & repair; prefabricated structures
PA: The Will-Burt Company
　　169 S Main St
　　Orrville OH 44667
　　330 682-7015

(G-15773)
XL PATTERN SHOP INC
242 N Kansas Rd (44667-9638)
PHONE..............................330 682-2981
Fax: 330 682-0382
Gary Snyder, *President*
Rico Warfel, *General Mgr*
EMP: 5
SALES: 300K **Privately Held**
WEB: www.xlpatternshop.com
SIC: 3543 Industrial patterns

Orwell
Ashtabula County

(G-15774)
CT HYDRAULICS INC
Also Called: Cooper
243 Staley Rd Ste A (44076-8381)
P.O. Box 339, Wheatland PA (16161-0339)
PHONE..............................440 437-2101
Kyle Klaric, *Managing Dir*
▲ EMP: 19
SALES (est): 4.8MM **Privately Held**
SIC: 3429 Manufactured hardware (general)

(G-15775)
FASCO MACHINE PRODUCTS INC
554 E Main St (44076)
P.O. Box 187 (44076-0187)
PHONE..............................440 437-6242
Fax: 440 437-6700
Richard Fularz, *President*
EMP: 3
SQ FT: 2,400
SALES: 340.4K **Privately Held**
WEB: www.fascomachine.com
SIC: 3599 Machine shop, jobbing & repair

(G-15776)
HERITAGE SLEEP PRODUCTS LLC
243 Staley Rd (44076-8380)
P.O. Box 459 (44076-0459)
PHONE..............................440 437-4425
Eli Schnucker, *Mng Member*
EMP: 26 EST: 2015
SALES (est): 2.5MM **Privately Held**
SIC: 2515 Mattresses & bedsprings

(G-15777)
KENNAMETAL INC
180 Penniman Rd (44076-9500)
PHONE..............................440 437-5131
Fax: 440 437-4256
Denny Bell, *Opers Staff*
William Enstrom, *Purchasing*
William Anderson, *Engineer*
David Orth, *Manager*
EMP: 126
SALES (corp-wide): 2.1B **Publicly Held**
WEB: www.kennametal.com
SIC: 3545 Machine tool accessories
PA: Kennametal Inc.
　　600 Grant St Ste 5100
　　Pittsburgh PA 15219
　　412 248-8200

(G-15778)
MASCO CBINETRY MIDDLEFIELD LLC
Also Called: Kraftmaid Cabinetry
150 Grand Valley Ave (44076-9419)
P.O. Box 1055, Middlefield (44062-1055)
PHONE..............................440 437-8537
Fax: 440 437-8534
Deborah Keene, *Human Res Mgr*
Paul Schamrock, *Manager*
James Glass, *Programmer Anys*

EMP: 500
SALES (corp-wide): 7.3B **Publicly Held**
SIC: 2431 2434 Doors, wood; wood kitchen cabinets
HQ: Masco Cabinetry Middlefield Llc
　　15535 S State Ave
　　Middlefield OH 44062
　　440 632-5333

(G-15779)
TEP BEDDING GRP INC
Also Called: Therapedic Mattress
161 Grand Valley Ave (44076-9420)
PHONE..............................440 437-7700
Fax: 440 437-7617
Scott Rogers, *Principal*
Michael J Teitelbaum, *Principal*
EMP: 20 EST: 2004
SALES (est): 2.4MM **Privately Held**
SIC: 2515 Mattresses & bedsprings

(G-15780)
WECALL INC
64 Penniman Rd (44076-9557)
P.O. Box 39 (44076-0039)
PHONE..............................440 437-8202
Fax: 440 437-8208
Paul David Doherty, *President*
Bernard Doherty, *Vice Pres*
Helen Doherty, *Vice Pres*
EMP: 9
SQ FT: 7,400
SALES (est): 1.4MM **Privately Held**
WEB: www.wecallinc.com
SIC: 3429 3452 Metal fasteners; bolts, nuts, rivets & washers

(G-15781)
WELDED TUBES INC (PA)
135 Penniman Rd (44076-9535)
PHONE..............................216 378-2092
Robert C Lewis Jr, *Ch of Bd*
Lewis L Guarnieri, *Principal*
George W Secrest, *Principal*
Charles A Young, *Principal*
Joe Frandanisa, *COO*
▲ EMP: 2 EST: 1958
SQ FT: 400
SALES (est): 17.8MM **Privately Held**
WEB: www.weldedtubes.com
SIC: 3317 Tubes, wrought: welded or lock joint

(G-15782)
WELDED TUBES INC
Also Called: WELDED TUBES,INC.
135 Penniman Rd (44076-9535)
PHONE..............................440 437-5144
Larry N Lamphier, *Vice Pres*
Tom Spence, *Sales Staff*
Jim Everson, *Director*
EMP: 10
SQ FT: 100,000
SALES (corp-wide): 17.8MM **Privately Held**
WEB: www.weldedtubes.com
SIC: 3317 3498 Steel pipe & tubes; fabricated pipe & fittings
PA: Welded Tubes, Inc.
　　135 Penniman Rd
　　Orwell OH 44076
　　216 378-2092

(G-15783)
WOODCRAFT INDUSTRIES INC
131 Grand Valley Ave (44076-9420)
P.O. Box 128 (44076-0128)
PHONE..............................440 437-7811
Fax: 440 437-7821
Brain Richie, *Branch Mgr*
EMP: 100
SALES (corp-wide): 928.1MM **Publicly Held**
SIC: 2434 2426 2431 Wood kitchen cabinets; dimension, hardwood; millwork
HQ: Woodcraft Industries, Inc.
　　525 Lincoln Ave Se
　　Saint Cloud MN 56304
　　320 656-2345

(G-15784)
Y&B LOGGING
3647 Montgomery Rd (44076-9742)
PHONE..............................440 437-1053
Urie Yoder, *Principal*
EMP: 3

SALES (est): 132.3K **Privately Held**
SIC: 2411 Logging

Osgood
Darke County

(G-15785)
DYNAMIC WELD CORPORATION
242 N St (45351)
P.O. Box 127 (45351-0127)
PHONE..............................419 582-2900
Fax: 419 582-2105
Harry Heitkamp, *President*
Greg Heitkamp, *Engineer*
Sue Heitkamp, *Finance Mgr*
Lois Poeppelman, *Manager*
EMP: 44
SQ FT: 35,000
SALES (est): 11.8MM **Privately Held**
WEB: www.dynamicweld.com
SIC: 3444 7692 Sheet metalwork; welding repair

Ostrander
Delaware County

(G-15786)
ENVIRNMNTAL PRTCTIVE CTNGS LLC
5999 Houseman Rd (43061)
P.O. Box 8 (43061-0008)
PHONE..............................740 363-6180
Brian Parish, *General Mgr*
Robert W Stone, *Mng Member*
EMP: 4
SQ FT: 4,500
SALES (est): 351K **Privately Held**
SIC: 2851 2899 Paints & allied products; chemical preparations

(G-15787)
K L M MANUFACTURING COMPANY
56 Houston St (43061-9618)
PHONE..............................740 666-5171
Fax: 740 666-1516
K Leroy Moore, *President*
Bill Ewing, *Executive*
EMP: 6
SQ FT: 5,000
SALES: 270K **Privately Held**
WEB: www.klmmfg.com
SIC: 3541 Machine tools, metal cutting type

(G-15788)
LIBERTY DIE CAST MOLDS INC
57 2nd St (43061-9441)
P.O. Box 2 (43061-0002)
PHONE..............................740 666-7492
Fax: 614 666-1304
Kenny L Nicol, *President*
Jack Fryman, *Corp Secy*
Duane C Glick, *Vice Pres*
EMP: 15
SQ FT: 6,544
SALES: 1.7MM **Privately Held**
WEB: www.libertydiecastmolds.com
SIC: 3544 Industrial molds

(G-15789)
SHELLY MATERIALS INC
8328 Watkins Rd (43061-9311)
PHONE..............................740 666-5841
Keith Siler, *Vice Pres*
EMP: 25
SALES (corp-wide): 28.6B **Privately Held**
SIC: 2951 1611 3274 1422 Asphalt & asphaltic paving mixtures (not from refineries); surfacing & paving; lime; crushed & broken limestone
HQ: Shelly Materials, Inc.
　　80 Park Dr
　　Thornville OH 43076
　　740 246-6315

Ottawa
Putnam County

(G-15790)
BROOKHILL CENTER INDUSTRIES
7989 State Route 108 (45875-9678)
PHONE............................419 876-3932
Fax: 419 876-3931
Bill Unterbink, *President*
Terry Leopold, *Superintendent*
EMP: 115
SQ FT: 16,000
SALES: 595.1K **Privately Held**
SIC: 8331 2448 Sheltered workshop; wood pallets & skids

(G-15791)
CUSTOM WOODWORKING INC
214 S Main St (45875-9416)
PHONE............................419 456-3330
Fax: 419 456-3330
Jerry Hovest, *President*
EMP: 9
SALES (est): 1MM **Privately Held**
SIC: 2434 Wood kitchen cabinets

(G-15792)
D 4 INDUSTRIES INC
685 Woodland Dr (45875-8627)
PHONE............................419 523-9555
Jim Bibler, *President*
EMP: 9
SALES (est): 670K **Privately Held**
SIC: 3599 Machine shop, jobbing & repair

(G-15793)
DRAINAGE PIPE & FITTING
450 Tile Company St (45875-9217)
PHONE............................419 538-6337
Floyd Tony Meyer, *Principal*
Crystal Solano, *Principal*
EMP: 8 EST: 2012
SALES: 300K **Privately Held**
SIC: 3494 Pipe fittings

(G-15794)
HIRT PUBLISHING CO INC (PA)
Also Called: Putnam County Sentinel
224 E Main St (45875-1944)
P.O. Box 149 (45875-0149)
PHONE............................419 523-5709
Tim Garry, *President*
Steven Coburn-Griffis, *Editor*
Gary L Hirt, *Chairman*
Karen L Hirt, *Corp Secy*
Brian Hirt, *Vice Pres*
EMP: 4
SQ FT: 1,800
SALES (est): 5.4MM **Privately Held**
SIC: 2711 Newspapers, publishing & printing

(G-15795)
HIRT PUBLISHING CO INC
Also Called: Putnam County Sentinel
224 E Main St (45875-1944)
P.O. Box 149 (45875-0149)
PHONE............................419 523-5709
Fax: 419 523-3512
Patricia Ferrell, *Editor*
Dianne Wright, *Editor*
Don Hemple, *Manager*
Jeanne Oehler, *Info Tech Dir*
EMP: 11
SALES (corp-wide): 5.4MM **Privately Held**
SIC: 2711 Newspapers
PA: Hirt Publishing Co, Inc
224 E Main St
Ottawa OH 45875
419 523-5709

(G-15796)
HIRZEL CANNING COMPANY
Ottawa Foods, Div of
325 E Williamstown Rd (45875-1802)
PHONE............................419 523-3225
Fax: 419 523-6145
Karl E Hirzel, *Plant Mgr*
EMP: 18

SALES (corp-wide): 22.9MM **Privately Held**
WEB: www.hirzel.com
SIC: 2033 Tomato products: packaged in cans, jars, etc.; tomato juice: packaged in cans, jars, etc.; tomato paste: packaged in cans, jars, etc.; tomato purees: packaged in cans, jars, etc.
PA: Hirzel Canning Company
411 Lemoyne Rd
Northwood OH 43619
419 693-0531

(G-15797)
JB MACHINING CONCEPTS LLC
995 Sugar Mill Dr (45875-8526)
PHONE............................419 523-0096
Alexander Blankemeyer, *Engineer*
John Blankemeyer,
EMP: 8 EST: 2007
SQ FT: 18,000
SALES: 885.2K **Privately Held**
SIC: 3646 3645 Commercial indusl & institutional electric lighting fixtures; residential lighting fixtures

(G-15798)
K & L READY MIX INC (PA)
10391 State Route 15 (45875-8641)
P.O. Box 325 (45875-0325)
PHONE............................419 523-4376
Fax: 419 523-6205
Ron Kahle Jr, *President*
John Miller, *Director*
Chris Kahle, *Admin Sec*
EMP: 19
SQ FT: 12,000
SALES (est): 8.4MM **Privately Held**
WEB: www.kandlreadymix.com
SIC: 3273 Ready-mixed concrete

(G-15799)
KAHLE TECHNOLOGIES INC
1204 E 3rd St (45875-2022)
P.O. Box 127 (45875-0127)
PHONE............................419 523-3951
Jameson Kahle, *President*
John Kahle II, *Vice Pres*
Robert Kahle, *Treasurer*
Randal Kahle, *Admin Sec*
EMP: 3
SQ FT: 2,400
SALES (est): 527.7K **Privately Held**
SIC: 3625 Relays & industrial controls

(G-15800)
MC ELWAIN INDUSTRIES INC
17941 Road L (45875-9455)
PHONE............................419 532-3126
Richard Mc Elwain, *President*
Millie Mc Elwain, *Corp Secy*
EMP: 8
SALES (est): 1.3MM **Privately Held**
SIC: 7692 Welding repair

(G-15801)
MIKES MILL SHOP INC
14768 Road J (45875-9441)
PHONE............................419 538-6091
Michael Huffman, *President*
EMP: 3
SALES (est): 233.7K **Privately Held**
SIC: 1521 2499 General remodeling, single-family houses; decorative wood & woodwork

(G-15802)
NELSON MANUFACTURING COMPANY
6448 State Route 224 (45875-9789)
PHONE............................419 523-5321
Fax: 419 523-6247
Anthony Niese, *President*
Chad Stall, *Vice Pres*
Patricia Taylor, *Treasurer*
Tony Niese, *Sales Executive*
Amy Niese, *Admin Sec*
▼ EMP: 83 EST: 1947
SQ FT: 46,000
SALES: 17.6MM **Privately Held**
WEB: www.nelsontrailer.com
SIC: 3715 7539 Semitrailers for truck tractors; trailer repair

(G-15803)
PALPAC INDUSTRIES INC
610 N Agner St (45875-1533)
P.O. Box 109 (45875-0109)
PHONE............................419 523-3230
Fax: 419 523-4859
Danny E Meyer, *President*
Mike Meyer, *Treasurer*
EMP: 18
SQ FT: 62,000
SALES: 1.3MM **Privately Held**
SIC: 3089 3086 Molding primary plastic; plastics foam products

(G-15804)
PHANTASM DESIGNS
112 W Main St (45875-1722)
PHONE............................419 538-6737
Fax: 419 523-4866
Don Huber, *Owner*
Holly Huber, *Co-Owner*
EMP: 9
SALES (est): 744.2K **Privately Held**
WEB: www.phantasmdesigns.com
SIC: 2262 2261 2395 7336 Screen printing: manmade fiber & silk broadwoven fabrics; screen printing of cotton broadwoven fabrics; embroidery & art needlework; emblems, embroidered; graphic arts & related design; silk screen design

(G-15805)
POWER HOUSE ELECTRIC SUP LLC
823 N Locust St (45875-1216)
PHONE............................419 523-6614
Fax: 419 523-6618
Clifford J Schroeder, *President*
Doris Warnimont, *Office Mgr*
Tony Maag, *General Counsel*
Andrew Schroeder,
EMP: 4
SALES: 3.8MM **Privately Held**
SIC: 3612 Transformers, except electric

(G-15806)
R K INDUSTRIES INC
725 N Locust St (45875-1466)
P.O. Box 306 (45875-0306)
PHONE............................419 523-5001
Fax: 419 523-5187
Ann Woodyard, *President*
Joe Maag, *Vice Pres*
Dennis Siefker, *VP Mfg*
Barry Woodyard, *Manager*
Kimberly French, *Admin Sec*
▲ EMP: 85
SQ FT: 45,000
SALES (est): 8.8MM **Privately Held**
WEB: www.rkindustries.org
SIC: 7692 3465 Automotive welding; automotive stampings

(G-15807)
SCRAPBOOK GALLERY
7919 Road 13g (45875-9622)
PHONE............................419 523-4419
Lisa Gerdeman, *Owner*
EMP: 5
SQ FT: 1,300
SALES: 100K **Privately Held**
SIC: 2782 Scrapbooks

(G-15808)
SILGAN PLASTICS LLC
690 Woodland Dr (45875-8627)
P.O. Box 29 (45875-0029)
PHONE............................419 523-3737
Russ Zervais, *President*
John Tadena, *Safety Mgr*
Michael Schneeg, *Purch Mgr*
Bob Martin, *Senior Engr*
Rhonda Pester, *Manager*
EMP: 200
SALES (corp-wide): 3.6B **Publicly Held**
WEB: www.silganplastics.com
SIC: 3085 Plastics bottles
HQ: Silgan Plastics Llc
14515 North Outer 40 Rd # 210
Chesterfield MO 63017
800 274-5426

(G-15809)
STEEL TECHNOLOGIES LLC
740 E Williamstown Rd (45875-1873)
PHONE............................419 523-5199

John Watkins, *Human Res Dir*
Rick Furber, *Manager*
Gail Creamer, *Manager*
EMP: 50 **Privately Held**
WEB: www.steeltechnologies.com
SIC: 3312 Sheet or strip, steel, cold-rolled: own hot-rolled
HQ: Steel Technologies Llc
700 N Hurstbourne Pkwy
Louisville KY 40222
502 245-2110

(G-15810)
STERLING INDUSTRIES INC
740 E Main St (45875-2029)
PHONE............................419 523-3788
Fax: 419 523-9539
Marilyn Kulhman, *President*
Keith Kuhlman, *Vice Pres*
EMP: 10
SQ FT: 9,600
SALES (est): 1.1MM **Privately Held**
SIC: 2441 2448 Boxes, wood; pallets, wood

(G-15811)
STOEPFEL DRILLING CO
12245 State Route 115 (45875-9488)
PHONE............................419 532-3307
Fax: 419 532-2275
John H Stoepfel Jr, *Partner*
Roger Winkle, *Partner*
EMP: 7
SQ FT: 6,000
SALES (est): 515.6K **Privately Held**
SIC: 1481 1781 Mine & quarry services; nonmetallic minerals; water well drilling

(G-15812)
TACTICAL REVOLUTION LLC
10436 Country Acres Dr # 7 (45875-9400)
P.O. Box 651, Kalida (45853-0651)
PHONE............................419 348-9526
William Romes,
EMP: 3
SALES (est): 158.2K **Privately Held**
SIC: 2389 Apparel & accessories

(G-15813)
VERHOFF ALFALFA MILLS INC (PA)
Also Called: ALFA GREEN SUPREME
1188 Sugar Mill Dr (45875-8518)
PHONE............................419 523-4767
Fax: 419 653-4162
Constance A Verhoff, *President*
Judith Fullenkamp, *Corp Secy*
Donald Verhoff, *Vice Pres*
▼ EMP: 7 EST: 1940
SQ FT: 500
SALES: 6.1MM **Privately Held**
SIC: 0723 2048 Crop preparation services for market; alfalfa or alfalfa meal, prepared as animal feed

(G-15814)
WARREN PRINTING & OFF PDTS INC
250 E Main St (45875-1944)
P.O. Box 229 (45875-0229)
PHONE............................419 523-3635
Fax: 419 523-3243
Robert E Warren Jr, *President*
EMP: 10
SALES (est): 1.4MM **Privately Held**
SIC: 2752 2759 5943 2679 Commercial printing, lithographic; flexographic printing; office forms & supplies; tags & labels, paper

(G-15815)
WHIRLPOOL CORPORATION
677 Woodland Dr (45875-8627)
PHONE............................419 523-5100
Glenn Kaufman, *Engineer*
Douglas Recker, *Engineer*
Al Inkrott, *Branch Mgr*
EMP: 175

GEOGRAPHIC

SALES (corp-wide): 20.7B **Publicly Held**
SIC: 3633 3632 3639 Household laundry machines, including coin-operated; washing machines, household: including coin-operated; laundry dryers, household or coin-operated; refrigerators, mechanical & absorption: household; freezers, home & farm; dishwashing machines, household; garbage disposal units, household; trash compactors, household
PA: Whirlpool Corporation
2000 N M 63
Benton Harbor MI 49022
269 923-5000

Ottawa Hills
Lucas County

(G-15816)
INTEGRATED SENSORS LLC
2403 Evergreen Rd (43606-2323)
PHONE.................................419 536-3212
Peter Friedman, *Mng Member*
EMP: 9
SALES: 500K **Privately Held**
WEB: www.isensors.net
SIC: 3674 Radiation sensors

(G-15817)
PHOENIX PARTNERS LLC
Also Called: Clevland Valve & Gauge Co
3464 Brookside Rd (43606-2609)
PHONE.................................734 654-2201
James Rorick, *CEO*
EMP: 40
SALES (est): 3.9MM **Privately Held**
SIC: 3491 Industrial valves

(G-15818)
PRECISION PALLET INC
3919 W Bancroft St (43606-2534)
PHONE.................................419 381-8191
Fax: 419 381-9401
Linwood Miller, *President*
EMP: 4
SQ FT: 5,000
SALES: 555K **Privately Held**
SIC: 2448 Pallets, wood

(G-15819)
SACKS BRUCE & ASSOCIATES
4959 Damascus Dr (43615-2151)
PHONE.................................419 537-0623
Bruce Sacks, *Owner*
EMP: 4
SALES (est): 474.1K **Privately Held**
SIC: 2329 Men's & boys' clothing

(G-15820)
TIDEWATER PRODUCTS INC
4520 Brookside Rd (43615-2206)
P.O. Box 23181, Toledo (43623-0181)
PHONE.................................419 534-9870
Steven Karakas, *President*
EMP: 3
SALES (est): 398.3K **Privately Held**
SIC: 2899 Water treating compounds

Ottoville
Putnam County

(G-15821)
GLOBAL PRECISION PARTS INC
111 Progressive Dr (45876)
P.O. Box 579 (45876-0579)
PHONE.................................419 453-0010
Randy Mueller, *President*
Shaun Beiswanger, *Manager*
Scott Grothouse, *Agent*
EMP: 95
SQ FT: 62,500
SALES (est): 17.8MM **Privately Held**
WEB: www.acmemachine.net
SIC: 3451 3484 Screw machine products; small arms; guns (firearms) or gun parts, 30 mm. & below

(G-15822)
H & M MACHINE SHOP INC
290 State Route 189 (45876)
P.O. Box 207 (45876-0207)
PHONE.................................419 453-3414
Fax: 419 453-3896
Todd Horstman, *President*
Roger A Horstman, *Corp Secy*
Diane Horstman, *Vice Pres*
EMP: 16
SQ FT: 50,000
SALES: 2MM **Privately Held**
SIC: 3599 Machine shop, jobbing & repair

(G-15823)
J L WANNEMACHER SALES & SVC
26992 Us 224 W (45876)
PHONE.................................419 453-3445
James P Wannemacher, *President*
Ruth Wannemacher, *Corp Secy*
Lisa Wannemacher, *Vice Pres*
EMP: 14 EST: 1867
SQ FT: 10,000
SALES (est): 4MM **Privately Held**
SIC: 5083 7699 2452 Farm & garden machinery; farm machinery repair; modular homes, prefabricated, wood

(G-15824)
M & W TRAILERS INC
525 E Main St (45876)
P.O. Box 519 (45876-0519)
PHONE.................................419 453-3331
Fax: 419 453-3336
Kenneth Markward, *President*
Elmer A Markward, *Principal*
Elenor Wannemacher, *Principal*
Lavern S Wannemacher, *Principal*
Thomas Markward, *Vice Pres*
EMP: 10
SQ FT: 10,000
SALES: 2MM **Privately Held**
SIC: 7539 3715 5012 7538 Trailer repair; truck trailers; trailers for trucks, new & used; general truck repair

(G-15825)
PROGRESSIVE STAMPING INC
200 Progressive Dr (45876)
P.O. Box 549 (45876-0549)
PHONE.................................419 453-1111
Fax: 419 453-2323
Lloyd Miller, *President*
Bob Christi, *Plant Mgr*
◆ EMP: 250
SALES (est): 68.1MM **Privately Held**
SIC: 3465 Automotive stampings
PA: Midway Products Group, Inc.
1 Lyman E Hoyt Dr
Monroe MI 48161

Otway
Scioto County

(G-15826)
BLANKENSHIP LOGGING LLC
433 Curtis Smith Rd (45657-8936)
PHONE.................................740 372-3833
Harold Blankenship, *Owner*
Harold L Blankenship Jr,
EMP: 6
SALES (est): 400K **Privately Held**
SIC: 2411 Logging camps & contractors

(G-15827)
BLANKENSHIP LUMBER INC
5356 State Route 348 (45657-8937)
PHONE.................................740 372-0191
Harold Blandkenship, *Principal*
EMP: 3
SALES (est): 266.5K **Privately Held**
SIC: 2421 Sawmills & planing mills, general

(G-15828)
BROWN FOREST PRODUCTS
652 State Route 348 (45657-8973)
PHONE.................................937 544-1515
Thomas Brown, *Owner*
EMP: 5

SALES: 500K **Privately Held**
SIC: 2411 Logging; pulpwood contractors engaged in cutting

(G-15829)
COX WOOD PRODUCT INC
5715 State Route 348 (45657-8938)
PHONE.................................740 372-4735
Shelby Kratzer, *President*
Eric Kratzer, *Vice Pres*
EMP: 10
SALES (est): 500K **Privately Held**
SIC: 2448 5211 Pallets, wood; planing mill products & lumber

(G-15830)
GARY BROWN FARM & SAWMILL
3575 State Route 348 (45657-8966)
PHONE.................................740 372-5022
Gary Brown, *Owner*
Cathy Brown, *Co-Owner*
EMP: 4
SALES (est): 220K **Privately Held**
SIC: 2421 Sawmills & planing mills, general

(G-15831)
POWELL LOGGING
7593 State Route 348 (45657-9078)
PHONE.................................740 372-6131
Russell Powell, *Principal*
EMP: 3
SALES (est): 177.7K **Privately Held**
SIC: 2411 Logging

Overpeck
Butler County

(G-15832)
MIAMI MACHINE CORPORATION
4251 Riverside Dr (45055)
P.O. Box 145 (45055-0145)
PHONE.................................513 863-6707
Fax: 513 863-8009
Michael T Mc Neil, *President*
Katie Mc Neil, *Vice Pres*
Becky Hedges, *Manager*
▲ EMP: 17
SQ FT: 55,000
SALES (est): 4.5MM **Privately Held**
WEB: www.miamimachine.com
SIC: 3554 Paper mill machinery: plating, slitting, waxing, etc.

Owensville
Clermont County

(G-15833)
R & M GRINDING INC
5080 State Rd 132 (45160)
PHONE.................................513 732-3330
Roger Gadzinski, *President*
Michael Gadzinski, *President*
Mike Gadzinski, *Vice Pres*
EMP: 4
SQ FT: 9,000
SALES (est): 675K **Privately Held**
SIC: 3599 7699 Machine shop, jobbing & repair; knife, saw & tool sharpening & repair

Oxford
Butler County

(G-15834)
CITY OF OXFORD
Also Called: Maintenance Building
945 Collins Run Rd (45056)
PHONE.................................513 523-8412
Fax: 513 524-1146
Eric Keebler, *Manager*
EMP: 16 **Privately Held**
WEB: www.cityofoxford.org
SIC: 3531 Road construction & maintenance machinery

PA: City Of Oxford
101 E High St Ste 1
Oxford OH 45056
513 524-5200

(G-15835)
COX NEWSPAPERS LLC
Also Called: Oxford Press
30 W Park Pl Uppr Uppr (45056-2658)
PHONE.................................513 523-4139
Fax: 513 523-1935
EMP: 7 **Publicly Held**
SIC: 2711 Newspapers-Publishing/Printing
HQ: Cox Newspapers, Inc.
6205 Pchtree Dnwody Rd Ne
Atlanta GA 30328
678 645-0000

(G-15836)
GALLAGHER WOOD & CRAFTS
2715 Scott Rd (45056-9154)
PHONE.................................513 523-2748
Shawn Gallagher, *President*
EMP: 3
SALES (est): 227K **Privately Held**
SIC: 3732 Tenders (small motor craft), building & repairing

(G-15837)
HYQ TECHNOLOGIES LLC
Also Called: Hyq Teq
2897 Miamiview Ct Apt A (45056-8004)
PHONE.................................513 225-6911
Michael Lang, *Principal*
Robert Setlock, *Principal*
EMP: 4
SALES (est): 206.5K **Privately Held**
SIC: 3711 3443 3441 3663 Cars, armored; assembly of; housings, pressure; fabricated structural metal; ; fire detection systems, electric

(G-15838)
IRVING MATERIALS INC
6601 Ringwood Rd (45056-9047)
P.O. Box 15 (45056-0015)
PHONE.................................513 523-7127
Eddie G Moster, *Administration*
EMP: 11
SALES (corp-wide): 814MM **Privately Held**
SIC: 3273 Ready-mixed concrete
PA: Irving Materials Inc
8032 N State Road 9
Greenfield IN 46140
317 326-3101

(G-15839)
LETTERMAN PRINTING INC
316 S College Ave (45056-2225)
PHONE.................................513 523-1111
Fax: 513 523-0305
Jon C Rupel, *President*
Rhonda Rupel, *Admin Sec*
EMP: 8
SQ FT: 1,500
SALES (est): 765.2K **Privately Held**
SIC: 2752 2759 Commercial printing, offset; commercial printing

(G-15840)
MOONSHINE SCREEN PRINTING INC
23 N College Ave (45056-1108)
PHONE.................................513 523-7775
Fax: 513 523-7740
John Brosier, *President*
EMP: 13
SQ FT: 7,500
SALES (est): 600K **Privately Held**
WEB: www.moonshinescreenprinting.com
SIC: 2759 3993 Screen printing; neon signs

(G-15841)
MORNING SUN TECHNOLOGIES INC
7191 Morning Sun Rd (45056-8846)
PHONE.................................513 461-1417
Harold Elliot, *Principal*
EMP: 3
SALES (est): 155.6K **Privately Held**
SIC: 1221 Bituminous coal & lignite-surface mining

(G-15842)
RELEVIUM LABS INC (PA)
4663 Katie Ln Ste O (45056-9525)
PHONE...................................614 568-7000
Brent Reider, *President*
EMP: 3 EST: 2015
SALES (est): 647.3K **Privately Held**
SIC: 3845 5047 5999 Electromedical
equipment; electromedical apparatus;
electro-medical equipment; medical appa-
ratus & supplies

(G-15843)
SCHNEIDER ELECTRIC USA INC
5735 College Corner Pike (45056-9715)
PHONE...................................513 523-4171
Anna Pavlova, *President*
Pat Mc Donald, *Div Sub Head*
Marc Bochirol, *Senior VP*
Steve Halsey, *Vice Pres*
Doug Taylor, *Vice Pres*
EMP: 500
SALES (corp-wide): 241K **Privately Held**
WEB: www.squared.com
SIC: 3643 3699 3677 3612 Bus bars
(electrical conductors); electrical equip-
ment & supplies; electronic coils, trans-
formers & other inductors; transformers,
except electric; nonferrous wiredrawing &
insulating
HQ: Schneider Electric Usa, Inc.
800 Federal St
Andover MA 01810
978 975-9600

(G-15844)
TOM FUCITO INC
21 Lynn Ave (45056-1598)
PHONE...................................513 273-2092
Joe Engelhard, *Branch Mgr*
EMP: 25
SALES (corp-wide): 1.2MM **Privately
Held**
SIC: 3421 Table & food cutlery, including
butchers'
PA: Tom Fucito Inc
2111 Beechmont Ave
Cincinnati OH 45230
513 347-1111

(G-15845)
WATER SYSTEMS SERVICES
4164 Miami Western Dr (45056-9033)
P.O. Box 588 (45056-0588)
PHONE...................................513 523-6766
Dave Judy, *President*
EMP: 4
SALES: 250K **Privately Held**
SIC: 3589 1711 Water filters & softeners,
household type; plumbing, heating, air-
conditioning contractors

(G-15846)
WILD BERRY INCENSE INC
Also Called: Wild Berry Incense Factory
5475 College Corner Pike (45056-1010)
PHONE...................................513 523-8583
Fax: 513 523-8992
Mark Biales, *President*
Roger Atkin, *Vice Pres*
Kim Windland, *Sales Staff*
Shane Curtis, *Technology*
▲ EMP: 19
SQ FT: 20,000
SALES (est): 4.2MM **Privately Held**
WEB: www.wildberryincense.com
SIC: 2899 5947 Incense; novelties

```
┌─────────────────────────┐
│      Painesville        │
│      Lake County        │
└─────────────────────────┘
```

(G-15847)
**ACCURATE METAL MACHINING
INC**
882 Callendar Blvd (44077-1218)
PHONE...................................440 350-8225
John Racic, *President*
Gabriel Loiczly, *Vice Pres*
Thomas Loiczly, *Vice Pres*
Rick Schulz, *QC Mgr*
Steve Frazier, *Engineer*
EMP: 171 EST: 1976
SQ FT: 15,000

SALES (est): 33.4MM **Privately Held**
WEB: www.accuratemetalmachining.com
SIC: 3599 Machine shop, jobbing & repair

(G-15848)
ALPHA OMEGA DEV & MCH CO
Also Called: Accesories Tools
10395 Squires Ct (44077-2040)
PHONE...................................440 352-9915
Tibor Korosi, *Owner*
EMP: 3
SQ FT: 1,100
SALES: 100K **Privately Held**
SIC: 3599 Custom machinery

(G-15849)
ALTANA
830 E Erie St (44077-4453)
P.O. Box 747 (44077-0747)
PHONE...................................440 954-7600
Ameo Anthony, *President*
EMP: 3
SALES (est): 138.8K **Privately Held**
SIC: 3399 Primary metal products

(G-15850)
**AMERICAN FOAM PRODUCTS
INC**
753 Liberty St (44077-3623)
PHONE...................................440 352-3434
Fax: 440 352-0134
Charles Luck, *President*
Kelly Grimes, *Administration*
EMP: 30 EST: 1977
SQ FT: 36,000
SALES (est): 6.1MM **Privately Held**
WEB: www.americanfoamproducts.com
SIC: 3086 Packaging & shipping materials,
foamed plastic; insulation or cushioning
material, foamed plastic

(G-15851)
**AMERICAN ROLL FORMED
PDTS CORP (HQ)**
Also Called: Arf
141 W Walnut Ave (44077-2925)
PHONE...................................440 352-0753
Fax: 440 352-1959
Rob Touzalin, *President*
Dave Simmons, *Plant Mgr*
Ken Obermiyer, *Project Mgr*
Robert Pattison, *QC Mgr*
Jeff Laturell, *CFO*
EMP: 105 EST: 1960
SQ FT: 70,000
SALES (est): 28.7MM
SALES (corp-wide): 62.6MM **Privately
Held**
WEB: www.arfpcorp.com
SIC: 3498 3449 Fabricated pipe & fittings;
custom roll formed products
PA: Hynes Industries, Inc.
3805 Hericks Rd
Youngstown OH 44515
330 799-3221

(G-15852)
**ASBEKA CUSTOM PRODUCTS
LLC**
11288 Saint Andrews Way (44077-9332)
PHONE...................................440 352-0839
Harold Arrowsmith, *President*
John Arrowsmith, *Sales Mgr*
Bonnie Moore, *Office Mgr*
Harold F Arrowsmith Jr, *Admin Sec*
EMP: 10
SQ FT: 20,000
SALES (est): 750K **Privately Held**
WEB: www.asbeka.com
SIC: 3821 Laboratory apparatus & furniture

(G-15853)
ATRA METAL SPINNING INC
572 S Saint Clair St (44077-3637)
P.O. Box 731 (44077-0731)
PHONE...................................440 354-9525
Fax: 440 354-9525
Carl Dixon, *President*
James Dixon, *Corp Secy*
Greg Shirk, *Vice Pres*
EMP: 10
SQ FT: 22,000
SALES (est): 1.2MM **Privately Held**
SIC: 3469 Spinning metal for the trade;
stamping metal for the trade

(G-15854)
AUTOSYTE
829 Callendar Blvd (44077-1218)
PHONE...................................440 858-3226
Richard Rose, *Owner*
EMP: 5
SALES (est): 454.2K **Privately Held**
SIC: 3679 Electronic components

(G-15855)
**AVERY DENNISON
CORPORATION**
670 Hardy Rd (44077-4573)
PHONE...................................440 358-3466
Fax: 440 639-3402
Linda E Chandler, *Branch Mgr*
EMP: 36
SALES (corp-wide): 6B **Publicly Held**
SIC: 3081 Unsupported plastics film &
sheet
PA: Avery Dennison Corporation
207 N Goode Ave Fl 6
Glendale CA 91203
626 304-2000

(G-15856)
**AVERY DENNISON
CORPORATION**
7600 Auburn Rd Bldg 18 (44077-9608)
PHONE...................................440 358-4691
Fax: 440 639-7492
Aimee Trusso, *Human Res Mgr*
Martina Mclssac, *Manager*
Joe Chubb, *Network Analyst*
Terry Markushic, *Director*
EMP: 115
SALES (corp-wide): 6B **Publicly Held**
WEB: www.avery.com
SIC: 2672 2679 Adhesive papers, labels
or tapes: from purchased material; build-
ing, insulating & packaging paper
PA: Avery Dennison Corporation
207 N Goode Ave Fl 6
Glendale CA 91203
626 304-2000

(G-15857)
**AVERY DENNISON
CORPORATION**
Avery Dennison Graphic Div
250 Chester St (44077-4129)
PHONE...................................440 358-3700
Fax: 440 358-3026
Larry Bright, *Research*
Dale Smith, *Engineer*
Erica Getzendiner, *Human Resources*
Steven Giuliano, *Sales Staff*
Harold Houston, *Marketing Staff*
EMP: 300
SALES (corp-wide): 6B **Publicly Held**
WEB: www.avery.com
SIC: 2672 2891 Coated & laminated
paper; adhesives & sealants
PA: Avery Dennison Corporation
207 N Goode Ave Fl 6
Glendale CA 91203
626 304-2000

(G-15858)
**AVERY DENNISON
CORPORATION**
250 Chester St (44077-4129)
PHONE...................................800 282-8379
EMP: 4
SALES (corp-wide): 6B **Publicly Held**
SIC: 2672 Coated & laminated paper
PA: Avery Dennison Corporation
207 N Goode Ave Fl 6
Glendale CA 91203
626 304-2000

(G-15859)
**AVERY DENNISON
CORPORATION**
250 Chester St Bldg 11 (44077-4129)
PHONE...................................440 358-3408
David Neff, *Plt & Fclts Mgr*
Cynthia Bellian, *Marketing Mgr*
Tony Hume, *Manager*
Robert H Costantini, *Manager*
EMP: 100
SALES (corp-wide): 6B **Publicly Held**
WEB: www.avery.com
SIC: 2672 3081 Coated & laminated
paper; unsupported plastics film & sheet

PA: Avery Dennison Corporation
207 N Goode Ave Fl 6
Glendale CA 91203
626 304-2000

(G-15860)
**B B BRADLEY COMPANY INC
(PA)**
7755 Crile Rd (44077-9702)
PHONE...................................440 354-2005
Fax: 440 354-0425
Bruce Beaty, *President*
Fernando M Vargas, *Human Res Mgr*
EMP: 40
SALES (est): 5.1MM **Privately Held**
WEB: www.bbbradley.com
SIC: 3086 Packaging & shipping materials,
foamed plastic

(G-15861)
BEASLEY FIBERGLASS INC
799 Lakeshore Blvd (44077-1125)
PHONE...................................440 357-6644
Benjamin Beasley, *President*
Claudia Beasley, *Admin Sec*
EMP: 3
SQ FT: 4,500
SALES (est): 328.8K **Privately Held**
WEB: www.beasleycomposites.com
SIC: 3714 3751 Motor vehicle body com-
ponents & frame; motorcycles & related
parts

(G-15862)
**BRUCE HIGH PERFORMANCE
TRAN**
1 High Tech Ave (44077-3701)
PHONE...................................440 357-8964
Laurie Dibiase, *Principal*
EMP: 21 EST: 2013
SALES (est): 4.3MM **Privately Held**
SIC: 3715 Truck trailers

(G-15863)
CASCADE UNLIMITED LLC
2510 Hale Rd (44077-4926)
PHONE...................................440 352-7995
Dieter Billig,
EMP: 6
SALES (est): 231.7K **Privately Held**
SIC: 3599 Machine shop, jobbing & repair

(G-15864)
CHAS J STEVEN INC
Also Called: Fastsigns
7251 S Meadow Dr (44077-2232)
PHONE...................................440 954-9191
Fax: 440 954-9192
Charles Steven, *President*
Barbara Steven, *General Mgr*
EMP: 6
SQ FT: 2,000
SALES: 150K **Privately Held**
SIC: 3993 Signs & advertising specialties

(G-15865)
**COE MANUFACTURING
COMPANY (DH)**
Also Called: Automated Systems Div
70 W Erie St Ste 150 (44077-3279)
P.O. Box 520 (44077-0520)
PHONE...................................440 352-9381
Fax: 440 352-1487
Shawn Casey, *CEO*
John Kucharik, *President*
Lucy P Coe Et Al, *Principal*
Harry P Coe, *Principal*
Walt Halun, *Purchasing*
EMP: 100
SQ FT: 300,000
SALES (est): 34.3MM **Privately Held**
WEB: www.coemfg.com
SIC: 3553 3531 Woodworking machinery;
presses for making particleboard, hard-
board, plywood, etc.; sawmill machines;
veneer mill machines; construction ma-
chinery
HQ: Three Cities Research, Inc.
37 W 20th St Ste 908
New York NY 10011
212 838-9660

(G-15866)
CONCORD PAVING CO
500a Lakeshore Blvd (44077-1122)
PHONE..................................440 354-8580
Kit D Conley, *President*
Kit Conley, *Owner*
Janet Conley, *Corp Secy*
EMP: 8
SALES (est): 1.1MM **Privately Held**
SIC: 2951 Asphalt paving blocks (not from
refineries)

(G-15867)
CONCORD ROAD EQUIPMENT MFG INC
348 Chester St (44077-4154)
P.O. Box 772 (44077-0772)
PHONE..................................440 357-5344
Fax: 440 357-1942
Glen Warfield, *President*
Jeffrey Warfield, *Vice Pres*
EMP: 30 EST: 1975
SALES (est): 11.6MM **Privately Held**
WEB: www.concordroadequipment.com
SIC: 3531 Road construction & mainte-
nance machinery

(G-15868)
CONNECTORS UNLIMITED INC (PA)
1359 W Jackson St (44077-1341)
PHONE..................................440 357-1161
Martin Ignasiak, *President*
Ralph Victor, *Treasurer*
Don Barber, *Admin Sec*
▲ EMP: 23
SALES (est): 2.1MM **Privately Held**
WEB: www.connectorsunlimited.com
SIC: 3357 3678 Nonferrous wiredrawing &
insulating; electronic connectors

(G-15869)
CONTROL MEASUREMENT INC
1400 Mentor Ave Ste 5 (44077-1803)
PHONE..................................440 639-0020
Steve J Kovach, *President*
EMP: 3
SQ FT: 1,400
SALES (est): 409.1K **Privately Held**
WEB: www.controlmeasurement.com
SIC: 3829 Measuring & controlling devices

(G-15870)
CORA CUPCAKES
95 Park Rd (44077-5012)
PHONE..................................440 227-7145
Wendy Savot, *Principal*
EMP: 4
SALES (est): 311.7K **Privately Held**
SIC: 2051 Bread, cake & related products

(G-15871)
COUNTERTOP XPRESS
381 Fountain Ave (44077-1209)
PHONE..................................440 358-0500
Joe Trunkely, *Principal*
EMP: 5
SALES (est): 496.2K **Privately Held**
SIC: 2541 Counter & sink tops

(G-15872)
CUSTOM DESIGN CABINETS & TOPS
Also Called: Custom Design Kitchen & Bath
379 Fountain Ave (44077-1209)
PHONE..................................440 639-9900
George Lehtonen, *President*
Kaarina Lehtonen, *Vice Pres*
EMP: 8
SQ FT: 11,000
SALES (est): 950K **Privately Held**
SIC: 5031 2541 Kitchen cabinets; cabi-
nets, except refrigerated: show, display,
etc.: wood; sink tops, plastic laminated;
table or counter tops, plastic laminated

(G-15873)
DE NORA HOLDINGS US INC (DH)
7590 Discovery Ln (44077-9190)
PHONE..................................440 710-5300
Paolo Dellacha, *President*
Angelo Ferrari, *Treasurer*
Silvia Bertini, *Admin Sec*
Charlotte Valencic, *Asst Sec*

EMP: 370
SALES (est): 9.9MM **Privately Held**
SIC: 3589 Water purification equipment,
household type; water treatment equipment, industrial

(G-15874)
DE NORA NORTH AMERICA INC (DH)
7590 Discovery Ln (44077-9190)
PHONE..................................440 357-4000
Lucieno Iacopeti, *CEO*
Ken Branchick, *Manager*
▲ EMP: 12
SQ FT: 70,000
SALES (est): 1.9MM **Privately Held**
SIC: 3479 Coating electrodes
HQ: Oronzio De Nora International B.V.
Prins Bernhardplein 200
Amsterdam 1097
205 214-777

(G-15875)
DE NORA TECH INC (DH)
7590 Discovery Ln (44077-9190)
PHONE..................................440 710-5300
Paolo Dellacha, *CEO*
Takashi Oishi, *General Mgr*
Charlotte Valencic, *General Mgr*
Frank J McGorty, *COO*
Kenneth Branchick, *Plant Mgr*
◆ EMP: 80 EST: 1982
SQ FT: 20,000
SALES (est): 38MM **Privately Held**
WEB: www.eltechsystems.com
SIC: 3624 3589 7359 Electrodes, thermal
& electrolytic uses: carbon, graphite;
sewage & water treatment equipment;
equipment rental & leasing
HQ: Industrie De Nora Spa
Via Leonardo Bistolfi 35
Milano MI 20134
022 129-1

(G-15876)
ECKART AMERICA CORPORATION (DH)
Also Called: Eckart Aluminum
830 E Erie St (44077-4453)
P.O. Box 747 (44077-0747)
PHONE..................................440 954-7600
Fax: 440 354-6224
Anthony J Ameo Jr, *President*
Sher Andre, *Opers Mgr*
Barbara Petersen, *Plant Engr*
Thomas Meola, *CFO*
Peggy Knesebeck, *Controller*
◆ EMP: 100
SALES (est): 42.6MM **Privately Held**
SIC: 3399 2893 2816 Powder, metal;
printing ink; inorganic pigments

(G-15877)
ECM BIOFILMS INC
1 Victoria Pl Ste 304 (44077-3406)
PHONE..................................440 350-1400
Robert Sinclair, *President*
Timothy Gooding, *Admin Sec*
EMP: 4 EST: 1998
SQ FT: 1,200
SALES (est): 866.4K **Privately Held**
WEB: www.ecmbiofilms.com
SIC: 2824 Organic fibers, noncellulosic

(G-15878)
EXECUTIVE WINGS INC
13550 Carter Rd (44077-9171)
PHONE..................................440 254-1812
Michael Toman, *Owner*
EMP: 8 EST: 2001
SALES (est): 513.4K **Privately Held**
SIC: 3721 Aircraft

(G-15879)
EXTRUDEX LIMITED PARTNERSHIP (PA)
310 Figgie Dr (44077-3028)
PHONE..................................440 352-7101
Fax: 440 352-3146
Tod Oliva, *Partner*
George Humphrey, *General Ptnr*
Sharyl Brennan, *CFO*
Wendy White, *Human Res Mgr*
EMP: 35
SQ FT: 27,120

SALES (est): 4.3MM **Privately Held**
WEB: www.extrudex.net
SIC: 3089 3524 3431 Extruded finished
plastic products; lawn & garden equipment; metal sanitary ware

(G-15880)
FARETEC INC
1610 W Jackson St Unit 6 (44077-1388)
PHONE..................................440 350-9510
Fax: 440 350-9520
Tod C R Sackett, *President*
Constance Sackett, *Treasurer*
Lee Sackett, *Sales Staff*
Dr George Sackett, *Admin Sec*
▲ EMP: 10
SQ FT: 7,000
SALES (est): 1.8MM **Privately Held**
WEB: www.faretec.com
SIC: 3842 5047 Braces, orthopedic;
splints, pneumatic & wood; medical
equipment & supplies

(G-15881)
FIRST FRANCIS COMPANY INC (HQ)
Also Called: Federal Hose Manufacturing
25 Florence Ave (44077-1103)
PHONE..................................440 352-8927
Ron George, *President*
Jim McLain, *Vice Pres*
Beverly Gladson, *Opers Staff*
John Lally, *Controller*
Debbie Middleton, *Accounting Mgr*
EMP: 28
SALES (est): 2.2MM
SALES (corp-wide): 6.6MM **Publicly Held**
WEB: www.federalhose.com
SIC: 5085 3599 3444 3429 Industrial
supplies; hose, flexible metallic; sheet
metalwork; manufactured hardware (gen-
eral)
PA: Hickok Incorporated
10514 Dupont Ave
Cleveland OH 44108
216 541-8060

(G-15882)
FIVES LANDIS CORP
Also Called: Citco Diamond & Cbn Products
7605 Discovery Ln (44077-9396)
PHONE..................................440 709-0700
Fax: 440 709-0710
Michael Sweeney, *Vice Pres*
S A Sitler, *Engineer*
Thomas W Toaddy, *Persnl Mgr*
EMP: 75
SQ FT: 7,000
SALES (corp-wide): 5.8MM **Privately Held**
SIC: 3541 Grinding machines, metalwork-
ing
HQ: Fives Landis Corp.
16778 Halfway Blvd
Hagerstown MD 21740
301 797-3400

(G-15883)
GENESIS LAMP CORP
375 N Saint Clair St (44077-4053)
PHONE..................................440 354-0095
Fax: 440 354-0624
Edward C Zukowski, *President*
Margaret Zukowski, *Corp Secy*
Frank Laszlo, *Engineer*
Donna Williams, *Admin Sec*
▲ EMP: 15
SQ FT: 6,400
SALES (est): 3.5MM **Privately Held**
WEB: www.genesislamp.com
SIC: 3646 3648 Commercial indusl & insti-
tutional electric lighting fixtures; lighting
equipment

(G-15884)
GRAND-ROCK COMPANY INC
395 Fountain Ave (44077-1209)
PHONE..................................440 639-2000
Fax: 440 639-2010
William H Stoneman, *President*
Bill Fischer, *Engineer*
Gerard Arth, *CFO*
Irvin Foster, *Regl Sales Mgr*
Larry Spyke, *Marketing Mgr*
▲ EMP: 50
SQ FT: 52,000

SALES (est): 13.8MM **Privately Held**
SIC: 3714 3621 2531 Motor vehicle parts
& accessories; motors & generators; public building & related furniture

(G-15885)
GREAT LAKES GLASSWERKS INC
360 W Prospect St (44077-3258)
PHONE..................................440 358-0460
Fax: 440 358-0462
Richard Chaykowsky, *President*
Julie Patterson, *Vice Pres*
John Wolfe, *Treasurer*
▲ EMP: 7
SQ FT: 10,000
SALES: 1MM **Privately Held**
WEB: www.glglasswerks.com
SIC: 3299 Tubing for electrical purposes,
quartz

(G-15886)
GUYER PRECISION INC
280 W Prospect St (44077-3256)
PHONE..................................440 354-8024
Thomas Guyer, *President*
Melissa Ferrara, *General Mgr*
Nick Edgington, *Opers Spvr*
Ian Skinner, *QC Mgr*
Jay Johnson, *Regl Sales Mgr*
EMP: 11
SQ FT: 12,500
SALES (est): 2.5MM **Privately Held**
SIC: 3599 Machine shop, jobbing & repair

(G-15887)
HARDY INDUSTRIAL TECH LLC
Also Called: H I T
679 Hardy Rd (44077-4574)
PHONE..................................440 350-6300
Eric Lofquist, *CEO*
Scott Forster, *Vice Pres*
▲ EMP: 67
SALES (est): 13.9MM
SALES (corp-wide): 60.7MM **Privately Held**
SIC: 2869 Fuels
PA: Magnus International Group, Inc.
16533 Chillicothe Rd
Chagrin Falls OH 44023
216 592-8355

(G-15888)
HIGH TECH PRFMCE TRLRS INC
1 High Tech Ave (44077-3701)
PHONE..................................440 357-8964
Fax: 440 357-8572
Bruce C Hanusosky, *President*
Robert Manley, *General Mgr*
Judy Hanusosky, *Exec VP*
Caity Hanusosky, *Director*
Steve Lewis, *Director*
EMP: 65
SQ FT: 84,000
SALES (est): 11.4MM **Privately Held**
SIC: 3715 Truck trailers

(G-15889)
IMAX INDUSTRIES INC
117 W Walnut Ave (44077-2925)
PHONE..................................440 639-0242
Mike Miller, *President*
EMP: 10
SALES (est): 2.4MM **Privately Held**
WEB: www.imaxindustries.com
SIC: 8711 3548 Engineering services;
welding apparatus

(G-15890)
INJECTION MOLDING SPECIALIST
251 W Prospect St (44077-3257)
PHONE..................................440 639-7896
Lee Albers, *Owner*
EMP: 5
SQ FT: 4,500
SALES: 120K **Privately Held**
SIC: 3089 Injection molding of plastics

(G-15891)
INTERNATIONAL CNTR ARTFCIAL OR
Also Called: ICAOT
10 W Erie St Ste 200 (44077-3270)
PHONE..................................440 358-1102

▲ = Import ▼=Export
◆ =Import/Export

Paul S Malcheski, *President*
EMP: 3
SALES: 149K **Privately Held**
SIC: 2752 8299 Publication printing, lithographic; educational services

(G-15892)
ISK AMERICAS INCORPORATED (HQ)
7474 Auburn Rd (44077-9703)
PHONE..........................440 357-4600
Fax: 440 357-4610
Fujio Tamara, *Ch of Bd*
Marvin Hosokawa, *Managing Dir*
F O Hicks, *Vice Pres*
R C Andrews, *Admin Sec*
EMP: 36
SQ FT: 4,400
SALES: 14.2MM
SALES (corp-wide): 879.4MM **Privately Held**
WEB: www.woodguard.com
SIC: 2816 2491 Titanium dioxide, anatase or rutile (pigments); wood preserving
PA: Ishihara Sangyo Kaisha, Ltd.
1-3-15, Edobori, Nishi-Ku
Osaka OSK 550-0
664 441-451

(G-15893)
J & H CORPORATION
Also Called: US Mold Machine Tool Company
444 Newell St (44077-1254)
PHONE..........................440 357-5982
Jeff Hughes, *President*
Doug Hughes, *Corp Secy*
Dan Hobson, *Design Engr*
EMP: 8
SQ FT: 10,000
SALES (est): 630K **Privately Held**
WEB: www.superiormfgcorp.com
SIC: 3544 Industrial molds

(G-15894)
KEENEY SAND & STONE INC
13320 Girdled Rd (44077-8715)
PHONE..........................440 254-4582
Dennis Keeney, *President*
Kim Keeney, *General Mgr*
Kevin Keeney, *Superintendent*
Kathy Keeney, *Admin Sec*
EMP: 4
SQ FT: 1,332
SALES (est): 630.5K **Privately Held**
SIC: 1442 Sand mining; gravel mining

(G-15895)
KELCO HARDWOOD FLOORS INC
10137 Johnnycake Ridge Rd (44077-2163)
P.O. Box 1421 (44077-7332)
PHONE..........................440 354-0974
David Kelly, *Owner*
Weeberly Kelly, *Vice Pres*
EMP: 4 **EST:** 1994
SALES (est): 302.2K **Privately Held**
SIC: 2426 Flooring, hardwood

(G-15896)
L B L LITHOGRAPHERS INC (PA)
Also Called: L B L Printing
365 W Prospect St (44077-3259)
PHONE..........................440 350-0106
Fax: 440 352-1861
Lawrence Gidley, *CEO*
Brian Gidley, *President*
Lois Gidley, *Treasurer*
Alaina Maloney, *Manager*
EMP: 7
SQ FT: 4,500
SALES (est): 1.1MM **Privately Held**
WEB: www.lblprinting.com
SIC: 2752 Commercial printing, lithographic

(G-15897)
LAKE COUNTY AUTO RECYCLERS
427 Newell St (44077-1253)
PHONE..........................440 428-2886
Joseph Woitella Sr, *Owner*
EMP: 5 **EST:** 1974
SQ FT: 2,000

SALES (est): 430.6K **Privately Held**
SIC: 5093 3341 Ferrous metal scrap & waste; automotive wrecking for scrap; secondary nonferrous metals

(G-15898)
LUBRIZOL CORPORATION
Also Called: Lubrizol Production Plant
155 Freedom Rd (44077-1234)
PHONE..........................440 357-7064
Fax: 440 347-1595
Tanya Travis, *General Mgr*
Rich E Lorentz, *Plant Mgr*
Michael Gallagher, *Engineer*
Sarah Kipp, *Sls & Mktg Exec*
Albert Murphy, *Sales Executive*
EMP: 44
SQ FT: 1,524
SALES (corp-wide): 223.6B **Publicly Held**
WEB: www.lubrizol.com
SIC: 2899 2992 Chemical preparations; rust arresting compounds, animal or vegetable oil base
HQ: The Lubrizol Corporation
29400 Lakeland Blvd
Wickliffe OH 44092
440 943-4200

(G-15899)
MADISON TOOL & DIE INC
147 Elevator Ave (44077-3609)
PHONE..........................440 354-8642
Fax: 440 354-8642
C L Graniteo, *President*
Chris B Graniteo, *Vice Pres*
EMP: 4 **EST:** 1973
SQ FT: 5,500
SALES (est): 446.4K **Privately Held**
SIC: 3599 Machine shop, jobbing & repair

(G-15900)
MATPLUS LTD
76 Burton St (44077-3011)
PHONE..........................440 352-7201
Jeffrey M Bednar, *President*
Nicole Cooke, *Accounts Mgr*
Holly Fulmer, *Info Tech Mgr*
▲ **EMP:** 8
SALES (est): 1.3MM **Privately Held**
SIC: 3842 Orthopedic appliances

(G-15901)
MCNEIL INDUSTRIES INC
835 Richmond Rd (44077-1143)
PHONE..........................440 951-7756
Fax: 440 721-0401
Randall J McNeil, *President*
Justin McNeil, *COO*
Robert Madden, *Vice Pres*
Michael Congin, *Mfg Spvr*
Jim Cammereta, *Engineer*
▲ **EMP:** 30
SQ FT: 18,000
SALES (est): 8.4MM **Privately Held**
WEB: www.mcneilindustries.com
SIC: 3366 5085 Bushings & bearings; seals, industrial

(G-15902)
MORTON SALT INC
570 Headlands Rd (44077)
P.O. Box 428, Grand River (44045-0428)
PHONE..........................440 354-9901
Fax: 440 639-4281
Vivian Horvath, *Facilities Mgr*
Jimmy Jacquez, *Engineer*
Jon Wade, *Engineer*
Paul Shank, *Branch Mgr*
Jim Kiswicki, *Executive*
EMP: 15
SALES (corp-wide): 3.6B **Privately Held**
SIC: 2899 Packers' salt
HQ: Morton Salt, Inc.
444 W Lake St Ste 3000
Chicago IL 60606

(G-15903)
NEL-ACK SHEET METAL INC
546 Hoyt St Ste 18 (44077-3674)
PHONE..........................440 357-7844
Fax: 440 357-1730
A William Nelson, *President*
EMP: 3
SALES (est): 260K **Privately Held**
SIC: 3444 Sheet metalwork

(G-15904)
NOVA CHEMICALS INC
786 Hardy Rd (44077-4524)
PHONE..........................440 352-3381
Paul Pollo, *Branch Mgr*
EMP: 56 **Privately Held**
SIC: 2821 Polystyrene resins
HQ: Nova Chemicals Inc.
400 Frankfort Rd
Monaca PA 15061
412 490-4560

(G-15905)
OBRON ATLANTIC CORPORATION
Also Called: Eckart America
830 E Erie St (44077-4453)
P.O. Box 747 (44077-0747)
PHONE..........................440 954-7600
Anthony Ameo, *President*
Mark Wallace, *CFO*
Peter Olley, *VP Sales*
Andy Panozzo, *Marketing Staff*
EMP: 60
SALES (est): 3.9MM **Privately Held**
WEB: www.eckart.net
SIC: 2816 3399 Metallic & mineral pigments; powder, metal
HQ: Eckart America Corporation
830 E Erie St
Painesville OH 44077
440 954-7600

(G-15906)
OHIO ASSOCIATED ENTPS LLC (PA)
97 Corwin Dr (44077-1802)
P.O. Box 110 (44077-0110)
PHONE..........................440 354-2106
Fax: 440 354-0687
John Hartman, *President*
Craig Levstek, *Mfg Spvr*
Bob Bruner, *Research*
Alan Roath, *Senior Engr*
Kim Calio, *Human Res Dir*
▲ **EMP:** 20
SQ FT: 123,000
SALES (est): 37.3MM **Privately Held**
WEB: www.meritec.com
SIC: 3678 Electronic connectors

(G-15907)
OHIO ASSOCIATED ENTPS LLC
Also Called: Omnitec
1359 W Jackson St (44077-1341)
P.O. Box 110 (44077-0110)
PHONE..........................440 354-3148
Fax: 440 354-5692
James T Walch, *Branch Mgr*
EMP: 125
SQ FT: 25,000
SALES (corp-wide): 37.3MM **Privately Held**
WEB: www.meritec.com
SIC: 3643 Electric connectors; connectors & terminals for electrical devices
PA: Ohio Associated Enterprises Llc
97 Corwin Dr
Painesville OH 44077
440 354-2106

(G-15908)
OHIO ASSOCIATED ENTPS LLC
Also Called: Meritech
72 Corwin Dr (44077-1802)
PHONE..........................440 354-3148
Fax: 440 354-0509
John Hartman, *President*
Tom Wirsing, *Engineer*
Barb Reckart, *Marketing Staff*
John T Venaleck, *Branch Mgr*
EMP: 50
SALES (corp-wide): 37.3MM **Privately Held**
WEB: www.meritec.com
SIC: 3678 3544 3469 3357 Electronic connectors; special dies, tools, jigs & fixtures; metal stampings; communication wire
PA: Ohio Associated Enterprises Llc
97 Corwin Dr
Painesville OH 44077
440 354-2106

(G-15909)
PANAMA JEWELERS LLC
Also Called: Aero Refining
7250 Brakeman Rd (44077-9326)
PHONE..........................440 376-6987
Jabra Deir,
EMP: 5 **EST:** 2010
SALES (est): 225.5K **Privately Held**
SIC: 5944 3341 Jewelry stores; gold smelting & refining (secondary)

(G-15910)
PENCA DESIGN GROUP LTD
1325 Yale Pl (44077-5492)
PHONE..........................440 210-4422
Patricia Penca, *Manager*
EMP: 3
SQ FT: 500
SALES (est): 214.2K **Privately Held**
SIC: 7311 2759 7389 3993 Advertising agencies; advertising consultant; advertising literature: printing; advertising, promotional & trade show services; advertising artwork; commercial art & graphic design; art design services; graphic arts & related design; graphic displays, except graphic terminals

(G-15911)
PET PROCESSORS LLC
1350 Bacon Rd (44077-4781)
PHONE..........................440 354-4321
Fax: 440 354-2031
Ken Noble, *Purchasing*
Juliana Levi, *Engineer*
Renee Keener, *Human Resources*
Gary Laughlin, *Sales Dir*
Ken Berlin, *Accounts Mgr*
◆ **EMP:** 77
SQ FT: 350,000
SALES (est): 19.8MM
SALES (corp-wide): 22.8MM **Privately Held**
WEB: www.petuk.com
SIC: 2821 Polyesters
PA: Diefenthal Holdings, Llc
1750 South Ln Ste 1
Mandeville LA 70471
985 867-1801

(G-15912)
PRESSURE TECHNOLOGY OHIO INC
7996 Auburn Rd (44077-9701)
P.O. Box 1534, Horsham PA (19044-6534)
PHONE..........................215 628-1975
David Bowles, *President*
EMP: 20
SALES (est): 3.5MM **Privately Held**
WEB: www.pressuretechnology.com
SIC: 3398 Metal heat treating

(G-15913)
R W SIDLEY INCORPORATED (PA)
436 Casement Ave (44077-3817)
P.O. Box 150 (44077-0150)
PHONE..........................440 352-9343
Fax: 440 352-3822
Robert C Sidley, *Ch of Bd*
Robert J Buescher, *President*
Iola Black, *Principal*
R H Bostick, *Principal*
S S Bostwick, *Principal*
▲ **EMP:** 30
SQ FT: 10,000
SALES (est): 143.8MM **Privately Held**
WEB: www.rwsidleyinc.com
SIC: 1771 3299 Concrete work; blocks & brick, sand lime

(G-15914)
R W SIDLEY INCORPORATED
Mining & Materials Division
436 Casement Ave (44077-3817)
P.O. Box 150 (44077-0150)
PHONE..........................440 352-9343
Bob Buscher, *President*
EMP: 30
SALES (corp-wide): 143.8MM **Privately Held**
WEB: www.rwsidleyinc.com
SIC: 1422 Cement rock, crushed & broken-quarrying

PA: R. W. Sidley Incorporated
436 Casement Ave
Painesville OH 44077
440 352-9343

(G-15915)
RAILING CRAFTERS LTD
632 Argonne Dr (44077-4304)
PHONE....................................440 506-9336
Ken Kotnik, *Owner*
EMP: 3
SALES: 50K **Privately Held**
SIC: 3441 Fabricated structural metal

(G-15916)
RAPID BLANKET RESTORER CORP
188 N State St (44077-3940)
P.O. Box 674, Chesterland (44026-0674)
PHONE....................................330 821-6326
Walter Tornstrom, *President*
EMP: 4
SQ FT: 1,200
SALES (est): 678.2K **Privately Held**
SIC: 2819 8748 Chemicals, reagent grade: refined from technical grade; business consulting

(G-15917)
REGAL INDUSTRIES INC
857 Richmond Rd (44077-1143)
PHONE....................................440 352-9600
Fax: 440 352-9682
Richard Lutzke, *President*
Kristin Lutzke V Pres-Cfo, *CFO*
EMP: 3
SQ FT: 3,000
SALES (est): 1.8MM **Privately Held**
WEB: www.regal-industries.com
SIC: 3568 3821 3559 Power transmission equipment; crushing & grinding apparatus, laboratory; chemical machinery & equipment

(G-15918)
RHINO GEAR MANUFACTURING INC
428 N Saint Clair St (44077-4106)
PHONE....................................440 639-1125
Richard Reinholz, *President*
Deborah Reinhols, *Office Mgr*
EMP: 5
SALES: 400K **Privately Held**
SIC: 3566 Speed changers, drives & gears

(G-15919)
ROPAMA INC
Also Called: Roco Industries
380 W Prospect St (44077-3258)
PHONE....................................440 358-1304
Fax: 440 358-1305
Ron Mahoney, *President*
Pat Mahoney, *Vice Pres*
EMP: 15
SALES (est): 1MM **Privately Held**
SIC: 3398 Metal heat treating

(G-15920)
RUFF NEON & LIGHTING MAINT INC
295 W Prospect St (44077-3257)
PHONE....................................440 350-6267
Fax: 440 350-6277
Thomas A Ruff, *President*
EMP: 10 **EST:** 1991
SALES (est): 800K **Privately Held**
SIC: 3993 Neon signs

(G-15921)
SPECTRUM BRANDS INC
447 Lexington Ave (44077)
PHONE....................................440 357-2600
David Lundstedt, *President*
Scott Harris, *Safety Dir*
EMP: 13
SALES (corp-wide): 5.2B **Publicly Held**
SIC: 3714 Motor vehicle parts & accessories
HQ: Spectrum Brands, Inc.
3001 Deming Way
Middleton WI 53562
608 275-3340

(G-15922)
STAFAST PRODUCTS INC (PA)
Also Called: Stafast West
505 Lakeshore Blvd (44077-1197)
PHONE....................................440 357-5546
Fax: 440 357-7137
Donald S Selle, *President*
Elmer T Elbrecht, *Principal*
John G Roberts, *Principal*
Joan Selle, *Corp Secy*
Stephen Selle, *Production*
▲ **EMP:** 40
SQ FT: 20,600
SALES (est): 25.7MM **Privately Held**
WEB: www.stafast.com
SIC: 5085 3452 Fasteners, industrial: nuts, bolts, screws, etc.; bolts, nuts, rivets & washers

(G-15923)
STP PRODUCTS MANUFACTURING CO
477 Lexington Ave (44077-3001)
PHONE....................................440 352-6176
Karen Wood, *Principal*
Dan Feruf, *Plant Mgr*
Alfred Fross, *Accounting Mgr*
▲ **EMP:** 80
SALES (est): 20.2MM
SALES (corp-wide): 5.2B **Publicly Held**
WEB: www.clorox.com
SIC: 2911 Oils, fuel
HQ: Spectrum Brands, Inc.
3001 Deming Way
Middleton WI 53562
608 275-3340

(G-15924)
T & T MACHINE INC
892 Callendar Blvd (44077-1218)
PHONE....................................440 354-0605
Fax: 440 354-0856
Tony Padovic, *President*
EMP: 14 **EST:** 1993
SQ FT: 13,000
SALES: 1.5MM **Privately Held**
WEB: www.terrymgt.com
SIC: 3599 Machine shop, jobbing & repair

(G-15925)
TECHNICAL GLASS PRODUCTS INC (PA)
881 Callendar Blvd (44077-1218)
PHONE....................................440 639-6399
Fax: 440 639-1292
Jim Horvath, *President*
Halle Ricciardo, *Corp Secy*
Robert Singer, *Vice Pres*
▲ **EMP:** 12
SQ FT: 10,500
SALES: 6MM **Privately Held**
WEB: www.technicalglass.com
SIC: 3559 Glass making machinery: blowing, molding, forming, etc.

(G-15926)
TEKRAFT INDUSTRIES INC
244 Latimore St (44077-3903)
PHONE....................................440 352-8321
Fax: 440 352-8321
Terrence Tekavec, *President*
Tim Tekavec, *VP Mfg*
Victor Tekavec, *Shareholder*
EMP: 8
SQ FT: 3,500
SALES (est): 250K **Privately Held**
SIC: 3599 Machine shop, jobbing & repair

(G-15927)
TENEX TOOL CO
546 Hoyt St Ste 2 (44077-3674)
PHONE....................................440 354-5979
Jim Kenesky, *President*
Patricia Kenesky, *Vice Pres*
EMP: 6
SQ FT: 1,200
SALES: 180K **Privately Held**
SIC: 3599 Machine shop, jobbing & repair

(G-15928)
TESSA PRECISION PRODUCT INC
850 Callendar Blvd (44077-1218)
PHONE....................................440 392-3470
Fax: 440 392-3477

Paul Battaglia, *President*
Erika Battaglia, *Vice Pres*
Don Cimino, *Manager*
Ron Hartman, *Manager*
EMP: 36
SQ FT: 25,000
SALES (est): 7.6MM **Privately Held**
WEB: www.tessaprecision.com
SIC: 3599 Machine shop, jobbing & repair

(G-15929)
THE MAX
759 Lakeshore Blvd (44077-1176)
PHONE....................................440 357-0036
Ray Minger, *Owner*
Connie Maxey, *Principal*
EMP: 4
SALES (est): 412.5K **Privately Held**
SIC: 2211 Print cloths, cotton

(G-15930)
THIRION BROTHERS EQP CO LLC
Also Called: Tbec
340 W Prospect St (44077-3258)
PHONE....................................440 357-8004
David Thirion, *Principal*
EMP: 6
SQ FT: 1,015
SALES (est): 646.4K **Privately Held**
SIC: 3694 7699 5082 Distributors, motor vehicle engine; pumps & pumping equipment repair; general construction machinery & equipment

(G-15931)
TRANSDIGM INC
Aero Fluid Products
313 Gillett St (44077-2918)
PHONE....................................440 352-6182
Paula Wheeler, *President*
Jen Woodworth, *Buyer*
Alex Santucci, *QA Dir*
Erich Hahn, *Sales Engr*
Jennifer Griffin, *Manager*
EMP: 31
SALES (corp-wide): 3.1B **Publicly Held**
WEB: www.electromotion.com
SIC: 3561 Pumps & pumping equipment
HQ: Transdigm, Inc.
4223 Monticello Blvd
Cleveland OH 44121
216 706-2939

(G-15932)
TRANSDIGM INC
Also Called: Aero Fluid Products
313 Gillett St (44077-2918)
PHONE....................................440 352-6182
Rodger Jones, *Branch Mgr*
EMP: 98
SALES (corp-wide): 2.7B **Publicly Held**
SIC: 3728 Aircraft parts & equipment
HQ: Aerocontrolex Group, Inc.
4223 Monticello Blvd
Cleveland OH 44121
440 352-6182

(G-15933)
TRISON TOOL INC
69 Burton St (44077-3010)
P.O. Box 2166 (44077-7166)
PHONE....................................440 352-1055
Nick Trivisonno, *President*
EMP: 3
SQ FT: 144
SALES (est): 240K **Privately Held**
SIC: 3545 Cutting tools for machine tools

(G-15934)
TURBO-MOLD INC
440 Blackbrook Rd (44077-1219)
PHONE....................................440 352-2530
Fax: 440 352-2530
George Tirak, *President*
Greg Tirak, *Vice Pres*
EMP: 3 **EST:** 1967
SQ FT: 3,000
SALES: 135K **Privately Held**
SIC: 3544 Industrial molds

(G-15935)
TWIN RVERS TECH - PNSVILLE LLC
Also Called: Twin Rivers Technologies Mfg
679 Hardy Rd (44077-4574)
PHONE....................................440 350-6300
Chris Schneider, *Sales Dir*
Paul J Angelico, *Mng Member*
EMP: 70
SALES (est): 11.2MM **Privately Held**
WEB: www.twinrivertechnologies.com
SIC: 2869 Industrial organic chemicals

(G-15936)
VAL-CON INC
7201 Hermitage Rd (44077-9718)
PHONE....................................440 357-1898
Richard Vertocnik, *President*
Jonell Vertocnik, *Vice Pres*
EMP: 7
SALES: 750K **Privately Held**
SIC: 3825 Energy measuring equipment, electrical

(G-15937)
VISION PRESS INC
1634 W Jackson St (44077-1312)
P.O. Box 1308 (44077-8308)
PHONE....................................440 357-6362
Fax: 440 352-9911
Douglas Advey, *President*
Ronald Advey, *Vice Pres*
EMP: 6
SALES: 750K **Privately Held**
SIC: 2759 Commercial printing

(G-15938)
WEAVER MEATS INC
380 Fountain Ave (44077-1207)
PHONE....................................440 639-1954
Mike Weaver, *President*
Roy Schwartz, *Principal*
David Weaver, *Vice Pres*
EMP: 16 **EST:** 1981
SQ FT: 8,600
SALES: 2.1MM **Privately Held**
WEB: www.weavermeats.com
SIC: 2013 Beef, dried: from purchased meat

(G-15939)
WESTERN RESERVE LUBRICANTS
13981 Leroy Center Rd (44077-9782)
PHONE....................................440 951-5700
EMP: 3
SALES (est): 252.9K **Privately Held**
SIC: 2992 Lubricating oils

(G-15940)
WHOLESALE PRINTERS LTD
195 N Doan Ave (44077-1445)
PHONE....................................440 354-5788
Elizabeth Kincaid, *Principal*
EMP: 4
SALES (est): 496.3K **Privately Held**
SIC: 2752 Commercial printing, lithographic

(G-15941)
WILLIAM WEBER
Also Called: Accurate Fabricating
411 N State St (44077-4142)
PHONE....................................440 350-9397
William Weber, *Owner*
EMP: 6
SALES: 150K **Privately Held**
WEB: www.accuratefabricating.com
SIC: 3599 3444 Machine & other job shop work; sheet metalwork

(G-15942)
WILLOW WATER TREATMENT INC
7855 Jennings Dr (44077-9383)
PHONE....................................440 254-6313
Fax: 440 254-4845
Stephen Hall, *President*
EMP: 3
SALES (est): 240K **Privately Held**
SIC: 3589 Water treatment equipment, industrial

(G-15943)
XPONET INC
Also Called: Mold Tech
20 Elberta Rd (44077-1231)
PHONE..............................440 354-6617
Fax: 440 357-1248
Ralph Victor, *Ch of Bd*
Don Barber, *President*
John Webster, *Engineer*
Ted Mars, *Info Tech Mgr*
Anna Manley, *Officer*
EMP: 50
SQ FT: 25,000
SALES (est): 8.3MM **Privately Held**
WEB: www.moldtech.com
SIC: 3357 3678 3643 3577 Communication wire; electronic connectors; current-carrying wiring devices; computer peripheral equipment

(G-15944)
YOKOHAMA INDS AMRICAS OHIO INC
474 Newell St (44077-1254)
P.O. Box 388 (44077-0388)
PHONE..............................440 352-3321
Fax: 440 352-6975
Yosahisa Makabayopshi, *President*
Don Patt, *Exec VP*
Brad Edelman, *Plant Mgr*
Walter Mason, *Opers Staff*
Larry Tremaglio, *Treasurer*
▲ EMP: 92
SQ FT: 132,000
SALES (est): 17.7MM
SALES (corp-wide): 5.3B **Privately Held**
WEB: www.sasrubber.com
SIC: 3069 Molded rubber products; rubber automotive products
HQ: Yokohama Corporation Of North America
1500 Indiana St
Salem VA 24153
540 389-5426

(G-15945)
YOKOHAMA TIRE CORPORATION
Also Called: S A S Rubber
474 Newell St (44077-1254)
PHONE..............................440 352-3321
Donald A Patt, *Principal*
Pat Fleming, *Purchasing*
EMP: 132
SQ FT: 50,000
SALES (corp-wide): 5.3B **Privately Held**
WEB: www.yrc.co.jp
SIC: 3061 Mechanical rubber goods
PA: Yokohama Rubber Company, Limited, The
5-36-11, Shimbashi
Minato-Ku TKY 105-0
354 004-520

(G-15946)
YOUR DAILY MOTIVATION YDM FITN
6631 Vrooman Rd (44077-8841)
PHONE..............................440 954-1038
Thomas Salvatore, *Principal*
EMP: 4
SALES (est): 229.1K **Privately Held**
SIC: 2711 Newspapers, publishing & printing

Pandora
Putnam County

(G-15947)
ADVANCED DRAINAGE SYSTEMS INC
501 Basinger Rd (45877-8772)
PHONE..............................419 384-3140
Ryan Felt, *Branch Mgr*
EMP: 14
SALES (corp-wide): 1.2B **Publicly Held**
SIC: 3089 Plastic hardware & building products
PA: Advanced Drainage Systems, Inc.
4640 Trueman Blvd
Hilliard OH 43026
614 658-0050

(G-15948)
UNARCO MATERIAL HANDLING INC
407 E Washington St (45877-8770)
P.O. Box 266 (45877-0266)
PHONE..............................419 384-3211
Jerry Hight, *Engineer*
Bruce Ontrop, *Manager*
Todd Kiene, *Maintence Staff*
EMP: 4
SALES (est): 4.3B **Privately Held**
WEB: www.unarcorack.com
SIC: 2542 5084 Racks, merchandise display or storage: except wood; industrial machinery & equipment
HQ: Unarco Material Handling, Inc.
701 16th Ave E
Springfield TN 37172
615 384-3531

Paris
Stark County

(G-15949)
CAR-NATION INC
1216 Fox Ave Se (44669-9794)
PHONE..............................330 862-9001
Doug Hosterman, *President*
Cheryl Vandergrift, *Manager*
EMP: 4
SQ FT: 1,000
SALES: 300K **Privately Held**
SIC: 3589 Car washing machinery

Parkman
Geauga County

(G-15950)
C N C PRECISION MACHINE INC
18360 Industrial Cir (44080)
PHONE..............................440 548-3880
Alex Szkoe, *President*
EMP: 63
SALES (est): 12.7MM **Privately Held**
WEB: www.cncprecisionmachine.com
SIC: 3599 Machine shop, jobbing & repair

(G-15951)
DAN SHROCK CEMENT
9344 Pritchard Rd (44080)
PHONE..............................440 548-2498
Dan Shrock, *Principal*
EMP: 3
SALES (est): 157.5K **Privately Held**
SIC: 1771 3273 5211 Concrete work; ready-mixed concrete; cement

(G-15952)
MONTVILLE PLASTICS & RBR LLC
Also Called: Iron Horse Engineering
15567 Main Market Rd (44080)
P.O. Box 527 (44080-0527)
PHONE..............................440 548-3211
Fax: 440 548-2198
Jay Roberts, *Partner*
Tracy Roberts, *Vice Pres*
Russ Nidy, *CFO*
EMP: 55
SQ FT: 50,000
SALES (est): 4.9MM **Privately Held**
SIC: 3089 Extruded finished plastic products

(G-15953)
REVONOC INC
18125 Madison Rd (44080)
PHONE..............................440 548-3491
Ernest Conover III, *Principal*
EMP: 3
SQ FT: 3,500
SALES (est): 180.5K **Privately Held**
WEB: www.conoverworkshops.com
SIC: 8249 8999 2499 Vocational schools; technical manual preparation; decorative wood & woodwork

Parma
Cuyahoga County

(G-15954)
AMAC ENTERPRISES INC (PA)
5909 W 130th St (44130-1040)
PHONE..............................216 362-1880
Fax: 216 362-0812
George Chimples, *Ch of Bd*
Constantine Chimples, *President*
Thomas Chimples, *Vice Pres*
Bryan Goldberg, *Plant Mgr*
Rick Forrest, *Mfg Staff*
EMP: 112 EST: 1951
SQ FT: 190,000
SALES (est): 18MM **Privately Held**
WEB: www.amacent.com
SIC: 3398 3471 Metal heat treating; finishing, metals or formed products

(G-15955)
COWGILL PRINTING CO
4427 Brookpark Rd (44134-1163)
P.O. Box 34193, Cleveland (44134-0893)
PHONE..............................216 741-2076
Fax: 216 741-3045
Jeff Cowgill, *President*
EMP: 4 EST: 1926
SQ FT: 8,000
SALES: 575K **Privately Held**
WEB: www.cowgillprinting.com
SIC: 2752 Commercial printing, lithographic

(G-15956)
DYNAMIC TEMPERATURE SUPS LLC
Also Called: Dts
12448 Plaza Dr (44130-1057)
PHONE..............................216 767-5799
Fax: 216 767-5797
Gary Kloock,
▲ EMP: 3 EST: 2010
SALES: 1.5MM **Privately Held**
SIC: 3823 Industrial instrmnts msrmnt display/control process variable

(G-15957)
ELECTRA SOUND INC (PA)
Also Called: Electrasound TV & Appl Svc
5260 Commerce Pkwy W (44130-1271)
PHONE..............................216 433-9600
Robert C Masa Jr, *CEO*
Charles C Masa, *President*
Patricia Masa, *Vice Pres*
Charles Masa, *CFO*
Ancy Reschke, *Mktg Dir*
EMP: 70
SQ FT: 28,000
SALES (est): 31MM **Privately Held**
WEB: www.electrasound.com
SIC: 3694 7622 5065 5731 Automotive electrical equipment; television repair shop; radio repair shop; video repair; sound equipment, electronic; sound equipment, automotive

(G-15958)
FOURJAYS INC
Also Called: Minuteman Press
5341 Broadview Rd (44134-1628)
PHONE..............................216 741-8258
Gary Blevins, *President*
EMP: 4 EST: 2007
SQ FT: 1,800
SALES (est): 200K **Privately Held**
SIC: 2752 Commercial printing, lithographic

(G-15959)
GMR FURNITURE SERVICES LTD
Also Called: PDQ Installation Co
7403 Dorothy Ave (44129-3604)
PHONE..............................216 244-5072
Eric Liss,
EMP: 18
SALES (est): 1.6MM **Privately Held**
SIC: 2542 Partitions & fixtures, except wood

(G-15960)
GRAFTECH ADVANCED GRAPHITE
12300 Snow Rd (44130-1001)
PHONE..............................216 676-2259
Joel Hawthorne, *CEO*
EMP: 20
SALES (est): 816.8K
SALES (corp-wide): 14.9B **Privately Held**
SIC: 3624 Carbon & graphite products; electrodes, thermal & electrolytic uses: carbon, graphite
HQ: Graftech International Holdings Inc.
6100 Oak Tree Blvd # 300
Independence OH 44131
216 676-2000

(G-15961)
GRAFTECH INTL HOLDINGS INC
12300 Snow Rd (44130-1001)
PHONE..............................330 239-3023
EMP: 132
SALES (corp-wide): 14.9B **Privately Held**
SIC: 3624 Carbon & graphite products; electrodes, thermal & electrolytic uses: carbon, graphite
HQ: Graftech International Holdings Inc.
6100 Oak Tree Blvd # 300
Independence OH 44131
216 676-2000

(G-15962)
HILLMAN GROUP INC
Needa Parts
12400 Plaza Dr (44130-1057)
PHONE..............................800 800-4900
EMP: 3
SALES (corp-wide): 399.2MM **Privately Held**
SIC: 3429 5162 Keys & key blanks; plastics materials
HQ: The Hillman Group Inc
8990 S Kyrene Rd
Tempe AZ 85284
800 800-4900

(G-15963)
NORTH AMRCN SSTNABLE ENRGY LTD
Also Called: Renewable Energy
1360 Grant Dr (44134-5327)
PHONE..............................440 539-7133
Michael Pasela,
EMP: 4
SALES (est): 260K **Privately Held**
SIC: 3433 Heating equipment, except electric

(G-15964)
OSG-STERLING DIE INC
12502 Plaza Dr (44130-1045)
PHONE..............................216 267-1300
Fax: 216 267-3356
Denise L Lucas, *Principal*
Tak Kojima, *Exec VP*
Richard Girardot, *Vice Pres*
Jeff Tennant, *Vice Pres*
▲ EMP: 70
SALES (est): 14.6MM
SALES (corp-wide): 1B **Privately Held**
WEB: www.sterlingdie.com
SIC: 3545 Machine tool accessories
HQ: Osg Usa, Inc.
676 E Fullerton Ave
Glendale Heights IL 60139
630 790-1400

(G-15965)
PAULIN INDUSTRIES INC
12400 Plaza Dr (44130-1057)
PHONE..............................216 433-7633
Fax: 216 433-7622
Richard Paulin, *President*
Bill Davis, *Principal*
Kimberley Gardina, *Sales Associate*
Tim Weatherbie, *Info Tech Mgr*
Brenda Campbell, *Admin Asst*
▲ EMP: 23
SQ FT: 800
SALES (est): 10.6MM
SALES (corp-wide): 179.3MM **Privately Held**
WEB: www.hpaulin.com
SIC: 5072 3452 Hardware; bolts, nuts, rivets & washers

PA: Hillman Group Canada Ulc, The
55 Milne Ave
Scarborough ON M1L 4
416 694-3351

Pataskala
Licking County

(G-15966)
ALBIN SALES INC
81 Brandon Dr (43062-8291)
PHONE......................................740 927-7210
Frederick D Albin, *President*
Sheley Albin, *Vice Pres*
EMP: 2 **EST:** 2001
SALES: 7MM **Privately Held**
SIC: 3585 8611 Heating & air conditioning
combination units; manufacturers' insti-
tute

(G-15967)
AMERICAN POWER HOIST INC
63 E Mill St (43062-8203)
PHONE......................................740 964-2035
Thomas Jones, *President*
EMP: 5
SALES (est): 630K **Privately Held**
SIC: 3536 Boat lifts

(G-15968)
ASH MACHINE CORPORATION
10795 Morse Rd Sw (43062-9757)
PHONE......................................740 927-0506
Fax: 740 927-1667
Bob Dodel, *President*
Tim Kiger, *Vice Pres*
Thomas Dodel, *Treasurer*
Lucia Dodel, *Admin Sec*
EMP: 8
SQ FT: 8,000
SALES (est): 876.3K **Privately Held**
SIC: 3599 Machine shop, jobbing & repair

(G-15969)
DLWOODWORKING
9330 Hollow Rd Sw (43062-9134)
PHONE......................................740 927-2693
EMP: 4 **EST:** 2013
SALES (est): 197.2K **Privately Held**
SIC: 2431 Millwork

(G-15970)
EXCELSIOR PRINTING CO
1014 Putnam Rd Sw (43062-9754)
PHONE......................................740 927-2934
Fax: 614 443-2775
David Fannon, *President*
Melissa Fannon, *Vice Pres*
Mike Tinapple, *Information Mgr*
EMP: 9
SQ FT: 8,200
SALES (est): 1.3MM **Privately Held**
WEB: www.xlcr.com
SIC: 2752 Commercial printing, litho-
graphic

(G-15971)
GRAYSON GRAPHICS INC
Also Called: Sir Speedy
910 Villas Dr (43062-8043)
PHONE......................................740 927-7080
Michael Grayson, *President*
Linda Wood, *Manager*
EMP: 6
SQ FT: 2,400
SALES (est): 600K **Privately Held**
SIC: 2752 Commercial printing, litho-
graphic

(G-15972)
INNOVATIVE LAB SERVICES LLC
7123 National Rd Sw Rear (43062-8610)
PHONE......................................614 554-6446
James Miller, *Business Mgr*
Alan Miller,
EMP: 4 **EST:** 2015
SQ FT: 4,000
SALES (est): 162.8K **Privately Held**
SIC: 3826 Spectroscopic & other optical
properties measuring equipment; spec-
trometers; liquid chromatographic instru-
ments

(G-15973)
KARS OHIO LLC
6359 Summit Rd Sw (43062-8763)
P.O. Box 34, Summit Station (43073-0034)
PHONE......................................614 655-1099
Lisa Keyser Vega,
EMP: 8
SALES (est): 904K **Privately Held**
SIC: 2851 3479 1721 1629 Undercoat-
ings, paint; painting of metal products; in-
dustrial painting; blasting contractor,
except building demolition; tank repair &
cleaning services

(G-15974)
KNOX ENERGY INC (PA)
11872 Worthington Rd Nw (43062-9770)
P.O. Box 705, New Albany (43054-0705)
PHONE......................................740 927-6731
Fax: 740 964-1742
Mark Jordan, *President*
Michael Cole, *CFO*
EMP: 17
SALES (est): 2.4MM **Privately Held**
SIC: 2911 Oils, fuel

(G-15975)
OHIO STEEL INDUSTRIES INC
Also Called: Structural Steel Fabrication
13792 Broad St Sw (43062-9189)
P.O. Box 197, Summit Station (43073-
0197)
PHONE......................................740 927-9500
Fax: 740 927-8187
Joe Leggett, *General Mgr*
Robert Eaton, *Vice Pres*
Linda Strohschein, *Engineer*
Robet Eaton, *Branch Mgr*
Jim Welton, *Manager*
EMP: 50
SQ FT: 200,000
SALES (corp-wide): 21.6MM **Privately
Held**
WEB: www.ohiosteel.com
SIC: 3441 Fabricated structural metal
PA: Ohio Steel Industries, Inc.
2575 Ferris Rd
Columbus OH 43224
614 471-4800

(G-15976)
OWENS CORNING
1 Corning Pkwy (43062)
PHONE......................................740 964-1727
Ireland Erick, *Branch Mgr*
EMP: 130
SALES (corp-wide): 5.6B **Publicly Held**
SIC: 3296 Fiberglass insulation
PA: Owens Corning
1 Owens Corning Pkwy
Toledo OH 43659
419 248-8000

(G-15977)
PATASKALA POST
Also Called: Heartland Communications Div
190 E Broad St Ste 2 (43062-7106)
P.O. Box 722 (43062-0722)
PHONE......................................740 964-6226
Fax: 740 964-6226
Randall Almendinger, *Owner*
EMP: 10
SALES (est): 330K **Privately Held**
SIC: 2711 Newspapers

(G-15978)
**PROGRAMMABLE CONTROL
SERVICE**
Also Called: P C S
6900 Blacks Rd Sw (43062-9512)
PHONE......................................740 927-0744
Phil Fraley, *President*
Kathleen Napier, *Vice Pres*
EMP: 12
SALES (est): 1.1MM **Privately Held**
WEB: www.programmablecontrol.com
SIC: 3569 5084 7378 Robots, assembly
line: industrial & commercial; robots, in-
dustrial; computer maintenance & repair

(G-15979)
**REDHAWK ENERGY SYSTEMS
LLC**
10340 Palmer Rd Sw (43062-9449)
P.O. Box 36, Etna (43018-0036)
PHONE......................................740 927-8244
Jeff Donaldson, *Warehouse Mgr*
Thomas J Ulrich,
Arthur J Ulrich,
James J Ulrich,
John Ulrich,
EMP: 6
SQ FT: 5,000
SALES: 1.1MM **Privately Held**
SIC: 3674 Solar cells

(G-15980)
RIGHTER PLUMBING
1451 Galway Bnd N (43062-7099)
PHONE......................................614 604-7197
John Righter, *General Ptnr*
EMP: 5
SALES (est): 510.6K **Privately Held**
SIC: 3088 Plastics plumbing fixtures

(G-15981)
RONA ENTERPRISES INC
30 W Broad St (43062-8180)
P.O. Box 1498 (43062-1498)
PHONE......................................740 927-9971
Ronald A Thomas, *President*
Trisha Kilcoyne, *Manager*
EMP: 9
SQ FT: 1,500
SALES (est): 1.1MM **Privately Held**
WEB: www.ronahomes.com
SIC: 2452 6531 Prefabricated wood build-
ings; real estate agents & managers

(G-15982)
RYDER ENGRAVING INC
1029 Hazelton Etna Rd Sw (43062-8528)
PHONE......................................740 927-7193
Fax: 740 927-9341
Jill Gosnell, *President*
Chris Dusnell, *Admin Sec*
Chris Gosnell, *Admin Sec*
EMP: 6
SALES (est): 675.9K **Privately Held**
WEB: www.ryderengraving.com
SIC: 3479 7389 Name plates: engraved,
etched, etc.; engraving service

(G-15983)
SCIOTO READY MIX LLC
6214 Taylor Rd Sw (43062-8885)
PHONE......................................740 924-9273
Rick Baldini, *Controller*
Steve W Edmund,
Steve Edmond,
EMP: 60 **EST:** 2005
SALES (est): 12MM **Privately Held**
SIC: 5211 3273 Cement; ready-mixed
concrete

(G-15984)
**SCREEN MACHINE INDUSTRIES
LLC**
10685 Columbus Pkwy (43062-7421)
PHONE......................................740 927-3464
Steve Cohen, *President*
Mark McGuire, *Accountant*
EMP: 4 **EST:** 2013
SALES (est): 469.8K **Privately Held**
SIC: 3531 5084 Construction machinery;
industrial machinery & equipment

(G-15985)
SMI HOLDINGS INC (PA)
Also Called: Screen Machine
10685 Columbus Pkwy (43062-7421)
P.O. Box 423 (43062-0423)
PHONE......................................740 927-3464
Fax: 740 927-8818
Steven Cohen, *President*
Bernard Cohen, *Chairman*
La June Cohen, *Corp Secy*
Douglas Cohen, *Vice Pres*
Brad Thompson, *Purch Agent*
◆ **EMP:** 54 **EST:** 1966
SALES (est): 20.7MM **Privately Held**
WEB: www.screenmach.com
SIC: 3532 Mining machinery

(G-15986)
SMI HOLDINGS INC
Also Called: Screen Machine
10685 Columbus Exp Park E (43062)
PHONE......................................740 927-3464
Laverne Pabian, *Branch Mgr*
Tom Pandolfi, *Director*
EMP: 15
SALES (corp-wide): 20.7MM **Privately
Held**
WEB: www.screenmach.com
SIC: 2752 Offset & photolithographic print-
ing
PA: Smi Holdings, Inc.
10685 Columbus Pkwy
Pataskala OH 43062
740 927-3464

(G-15987)
**TRANSPORTATION OHIO
DEPARTMENT**
Also Called: Pataskala License Bureau
318 S Township Rd (43062-7700)
PHONE......................................740 927-2285
Dottie Schirtzinger, *Manager*
EMP: 5 **Privately Held**
SIC: 3469 9621 Automobile license tags,
stamped metal;
HQ: Ohio Department Of Transportation
1980 W Broad St
Columbus OH 43223
614 466-7170

(G-15988)
TRI-CO INDUSTRIES
13804 Refugee Rd Sw (43062-9422)
PHONE......................................740 927-1928
Bob Byers, *Owner*
Robert Byers, *Owner*
EMP: 4
SQ FT: 1,000
SALES (est): 180K **Privately Held**
SIC: 2599 2541 Cabinets, factory; table or
counter tops, plastic laminated

(G-15989)
**VAMPIRE OPTICAL COATINGS
INC**
Also Called: Voci
63 E Mill St Unit B (43062-8203)
P.O. Box 240, Kirkersville (43033-0240)
PHONE......................................740 919-4596
Tom V Faris Jr, *President*
Thuy Nguyen, *Principal*
▲ **EMP:** 5
SQ FT: 16,000
SALES (est): 1MM **Privately Held**
WEB: www.v-coat.com
SIC: 3827 Optical test & inspection equip-
ment

(G-15990)
WHIT S FROZEN CUSTARD
564 E Broad St (43062-7570)
PHONE......................................740 927-0025
Sandy Kapton, *Branch Mgr*
EMP: 4
SALES (est): 261.6K **Privately Held**
SIC: 2024 Ice cream, bulk

(G-15991)
**WOODCRAFT FLOOR & ROOF
TRUSSES**
1076 Mink St Sw (43062-9727)
PHONE......................................740 927-9015
Marvin Douglas Lewis, *President*
Cindy Hewitt, *Administration*
EMP: 9
SQ FT: 10,000
SALES (est): 849.2K **Privately Held**
SIC: 2439 Trusses, except roof: laminated
lumber; trusses, wooden roof

(G-15992)
**WOODCRAFT MANUFACTURING
CO**
1076 Mink St Sw (43062-9727)
PHONE......................................740 927-6609
Fax: 740 927-6609
Marvin Douglas Lewis, *President*
Jeffrey D Lewis, *Vice Pres*
Kevin Lewis, *Treasurer*
Angie Lewis, *Admin Sec*
EMP: 50
SQ FT: 4,000

▲ = Import ▼=Export
◆ =Import/Export

SALES (est): 6.1MM **Privately Held**
SIC: 2431 5031 2439 2426 Staircases & stairs, wood; lumber, plywood & millwork; structural wood members; hardwood dimension & flooring mills

Patriot
Gallia County

(G-15993)
CHESTER F HALE
Also Called: Hale Logging
60 Dry Ridge Rd (45658-9250)
PHONE..................................740 379-2437
Chester F Hale, *Principal*
EMP: 3
SALES (est): 150K **Privately Held**
SIC: 2411 Logging camps & contractors

(G-15994)
CRISENBERY LOGGING LLC
7818 Lincoln Pike (45658-8914)
PHONE..................................740 256-1439
Joshua Crisenbery, *Principal*
EMP: 3
SALES (est): 125.4K **Privately Held**
SIC: 2411 Logging

(G-15995)
INGLES LOGGING
19094 State Route 141 (45658-9132)
PHONE..................................740 379-2909
Richard Ingles, *Owner*
EMP: 3
SALES: 120K **Privately Held**
SIC: 2411 5411 Logging; grocery stores

(G-15996)
INGLES LOGGING
17748 State Route 141 (45658-9206)
PHONE..................................740 379-2760
John Ingles, *Owner*
EMP: 4
SALES (est): 303.1K **Privately Held**
SIC: 2411 1794 Logging camps & contractors; excavation work

(G-15997)
PATRIOTIC BUILDINGS LLC
1753 Patriot Rd (45658-7504)
PHONE..................................740 853-3970
Allen Hershberger, *Manager*
Denver McMillion,
Denver Mc Million,
EMP: 4
SALES: 100K **Privately Held**
SIC: 2449 Food containers, wood: wirebound

Paulding
Paulding County

(G-15998)
A PLUS PROPANE LLC
8622 Us Route 127 (45879-9406)
PHONE..................................419 399-4445
Jim Stoller, *Principal*
EMP: 4
SALES (est): 327.9K **Privately Held**
SIC: 1321 Propane (natural) production

(G-15999)
ALEX PRODUCTS INC
810 W Gasser Rd (45879-8770)
PHONE..................................419 399-4500
Fax: 419 399-9023
Dave Dondeylon, *Manager*
Jade Crossland, *Executive*
EMP: 110
SALES (corp-wide): 110.3MM **Privately Held**
WEB: www.alexproducts.com
SIC: 3499 5013 3714 Automobile seat frames, metal; automotive supplies & parts; motor vehicle parts & accessories
PA: Alex Products, Inc.
   19911 County Rd T
   Ridgeville Corners OH 43555
   419 267-5240

(G-16000)
BAUGHMAN TILE COMPANY
8516 Road 137 (45879-9753)
PHONE..................................800 837-3160
Fax: 419 399-4641
Gene A Baughman, *President*
Mary A Baughman, *Corp Secy*
Brad Baughman, *Exec VP*
Eric Baughman, *Vice Pres*
Scott Kemler, *Purchasing*
EMP: 100 EST: 1883
SQ FT: 100,000
SALES (est): 30.6MM **Privately Held**
WEB: www.baughmantile.com
SIC: 3084 3259 Plastics pipe; clay sewer & drainage pipe & tile

(G-16001)
BLUE CREEK RENEWABLES LLC
7909 Broughton Pike (45879-9639)
PHONE..................................419 576-7855
Tom Sinn,
Howard Proctor,
EMP: 3
SALES (est): 139.5K **Privately Held**
SIC: 3999 Manufacturing industries

(G-16002)
BRUNE PRINTING CO
310 W Perry St (45879-1454)
P.O. Box 232 (45879-0232)
PHONE..................................419 399-2756
Fax: 419 399-2310
Mark Brant, *CEO*
EMP: 5 EST: 1920
SQ FT: 3,000
SALES: 65K **Privately Held**
SIC: 2759 Commercial printing

(G-16003)
DELPHOS HERALD INC
Paulding Progress
113 S Williams St (45879-1429)
P.O. Box 180 (45879-0180)
PHONE..................................419 399-4015
Fax: 419 399-4030
Doug Nutter, *Manager*
EMP: 7
SQ FT: 7,000
SALES (corp-wide): 1.1MM **Privately Held**
WEB: www.delphosherald.com
SIC: 2711 Newspapers, publishing & printing
PA: Herald Delphos Inc
   405 N Main St
   Delphos OH 45833
   419 695-0015

(G-16004)
HANSON AGGREGATES MIDWEST INC
11450 Road 180 (45879-8836)
P.O. Box 32 (45879-0032)
PHONE..................................419 399-4846
Mike Ryan, *Sales Mgr*
Bruce Rowley, *Manager*
Greg Hughes, *Manager*
EMP: 7
SALES (corp-wide): 16B **Privately Held**
SIC: 1422 5032 Crushed & broken limestone; limestone
HQ: Hanson Aggregates Midwest Llc
   207 Old Harrods Creek Rd
   Louisville KY 40223
   502 244-7550

(G-16005)
HERBERT E ORR COMPANY
335 W Wall St (45879-1163)
P.O. Box 209 (45879-0209)
PHONE..................................419 399-4866
Fax: 419 399-3862
Greg Johnson, *President*
Michael Murnane, *QC Mgr*
Shawn Hull, *Engineer*
Steven Mayer, *Engineer*
Ken Metzger, *Admin Sec*
EMP: 125
SQ FT: 48,000
SALES (est): 46.1MM **Privately Held**
WEB: www.heorr.com
SIC: 5013 3479 Wheels, motor vehicle; painting of metal products

(G-16006)
INNOVATIVE ASSEMBLY SVCS LLC
715 N Elm St (45879-1006)
P.O. Box 301 (45879-0301)
PHONE..................................419 399-3886
Fax: 419 399-2186
Phillip Hall, *Mng Member*
EMP: 17
SALES (est): 2.4MM **Privately Held**
SIC: 3569 Assembly machines, non-metalworking

(G-16007)
INSOURCE TECH INC
12124 Road 111 (45879-9000)
PHONE..................................419 399-3600
Roger Manz, *Principal*
Ken Manz, *Principal*
EMP: 15
SQ FT: 11,500
SALES: 7.6MM **Privately Held**
SIC: 3585 Heating & air conditioning combination units

(G-16008)
INSOURCE TECHNOLOGIES INC
12124 Road 111 (45879-9000)
PHONE..................................419 399-3600
Fax: 419 399-3602
Kenneth Manz, *President*
Roger Manz, *Vice Pres*
Ray Stoller, *Production*
Tony Manz, *Engineer*
Larry Manz, *Sales Mgr*
▲ EMP: 170
SQ FT: 11,500
SALES: 26.6MM **Privately Held**
WEB: www.insource-tech.com
SIC: 3699 Electrical equipment & supplies

(G-16009)
LAFARGE NORTH AMERICA INC
11435 County Rd 176 (45879-8834)
P.O. Box 160 (45879-0160)
PHONE..................................419 399-4861
Fax: 419 399-2459
Mark Wilson, *Purchasing*
Jennifer Harman, *QC Dir*
Geoff Fehr, *Manager*
Tim Weible, *Manager*
Kim Musch, *Admin Asst*
EMP: 105
SALES (corp-wide): 26.6B **Privately Held**
WEB: www.lafargenorthamerica.com
SIC: 3241 Cement, hydraulic
HQ: Lafarge North America Inc.
   8700 W Bryn Mawr Ave Ll
   Chicago IL 60631
   703 480-3600

(G-16010)
OHIO MIRROR TECHNOLOGIES INC (PA)
114 W Jackson St (45879-1264)
P.O. Box 223 (45879-0223)
PHONE..................................419 399-5903
Dennis R Krick, *President*
Tom Krick, *Treasurer*
EMP: 14
SQ FT: 2,700
SALES: 800K **Privately Held**
SIC: 3231 Products of purchased glass

(G-16011)
OHIO MIRROR TECHNOLOGIES INC
384 W Wall St (45879-1162)
PHONE..................................419 399-5903
Thomas Krick, *Manager*
EMP: 11
SALES (corp-wide): 800K **Privately Held**
SIC: 3231 Products of purchased glass
PA: Ohio Mirror Technologies Inc
   114 W Jackson St
   Paulding OH 45879
   419 399-5903

(G-16012)
P C WORKSHOP INC
900 W Caroline St (45879-1381)
P.O. Box 390 (45879-0390)
PHONE..................................419 399-4805
Fax: 419 399-3897
Megan Sierra, *CEO*
Brenda Miller, *Director*
EMP: 100
SALES: 424.2K **Privately Held**
WEB: www.pcworkshop.com
SIC: 7389 3711 Document & office record destruction; automobile assembly, including specialty automobiles

(G-16013)
POLYONE CORPORATION
Also Called: Spartech Plastics
925 W Gasser Rd (45879-8765)
P.O. Box 420 (45879-0420)
PHONE..................................419 399-4050
Julie A McAlindon, *Manager*
Cathy Newman, *Manager*
EMP: 114 **Publicly Held**
WEB: www.spartech.com
SIC: 3081 3089 3083 Unsupported plastics film & sheet; extruded finished plastic products; laminated plastics plate & sheet
PA: Polyone Corporation
   33587 Walker Rd
   Avon Lake OH 44012

(G-16014)
THOMPSON STEEL COMPANY INC
815 W Gasser Rd (45879-8765)
PHONE..................................419 399-4803
Fax: 419 399-4157
Douglas Fiske, *Branch Mgr*
EMP: 53
SQ FT: 400,000
SALES (corp-wide): 93.9MM **Privately Held**
WEB: www.thompsonsteelco.com
SIC: 3316 3398 Cold finishing of steel shapes; metal heat treating
PA: Thompson Steel Company, Inc.
   120 Royall St Ste 2
   Canton MA 02021
   781 828-8800

Payne
Paulding County

(G-16015)
GORDON TOOL INC
1301 State Route 49 (45880-9727)
PHONE..................................419 263-3151
Fax: 419 263-2604
William J Gordon, *President*
Lori Gordon, *Treasurer*
EMP: 15
SQ FT: 15,625
SALES (est): 1.4MM **Privately Held**
SIC: 5251 3544 Tools; special dies, tools, jigs & fixtures

(G-16016)
MARANATHA INDUSTRIES INC
102 S Main St (45880)
P.O. Box 209 (45880-0209)
PHONE..................................419 263-2013
Fax: 419 263-2893
Peggy Lee, *President*
Kevin Lee, *Vice Pres*
▲ EMP: 21
SQ FT: 6,700
SALES (est): 3.2MM **Privately Held**
SIC: 3663 Radio broadcasting & communications equipment

(G-16017)
TAYLOR PRODUCTS INC
230 Laura St (45880)
PHONE..................................419 263-2313
Fax: 419 263-2661
Denise Reed, *Principal*
EMP: 22
SALES (corp-wide): 5.4MM **Privately Held**
SIC: 3231 Products of purchased glass
PA: Taylor Products Inc
   66 Kingsboro Ave
   Gloversville NY 12078
   518 773-9312

(G-16018)
TAYLOR PRODUCTS INC
Also Called: Taylor Made Glass Systems
407 N Maple St (45880-9021)
PHONE..................................419 263-2313
Brian Castleman, *Plant Mgr*
Ryan Carper, *Engineer*
Brian Lichty, *Engineer*
Mark Preuss, *Engineer*
Mat Redinger, *Engineer*
EMP: 42
SALES (corp-wide): 5.4MM **Privately
Held**
SIC: 3231 3211 Products of purchased
glass; flat glass
PA: Taylor Products Inc
66 Kingsboro Ave
Gloversville NY 12078
518 773-9312

(G-16019)
WILDCAT CREEK FARMS INC
Also Called: Wildcat Creek Popcorn
4633 Road 94 (45880-9124)
PHONE..................................419 263-2549
Fax: 419 263-6614
Don Benschneider, *President*
Marge Yenser, *Corp Secy*
Dave Yenser, *Vice Pres*
Catherine Drake, *Accountant*
EMP: 15
SQ FT: 4,320
SALES (est): 1.6MM **Privately Held**
WEB: www.wildcatcreekpopcorn.com
SIC: 2099 0111 0119 0115 Popcorn,
packaged: except already popped; wheat;
popcorn farm; corn; soybeans

Peebles
Adams County

(G-16020)
G P MANUFACTURING INC
376 Buckeye St (45660-1114)
P.O. Box 265 (45660-0265)
PHONE..................................937 544-3190
Richard Puckett, *President*
George Puckett, *Vice Pres*
EMP: 6
SQ FT: 7,500
SALES (est): 250K **Privately Held**
SIC: 3537 Containers (metal), air cargo

(G-16021)
**HANSON AGGREGATES EAST
LLC**
Plum Run Stone Division
848 Plum Run Rd (45660-9706)
PHONE..................................937 587-2671
Fax: 937 587-2674
Karrion Bragg, *Office Mgr*
Terry Lauderback, *Manager*
Terry Louderback, *Manager*
EMP: 50
SALES (corp-wide): 16B **Privately Held**
SIC: 1422 3274 3273 Crushed & broken
limestone; lime; ready-mixed concrete
HQ: Hanson Aggregates East Llc
3131 Rdu Center Dr
Morrisville NC 27560
919 380-2500

(G-16022)
J MCCOY LUMBER CO LTD (PA)
6 N Main St (45660-1243)
P.O. Box 306 (45660-0306)
PHONE..................................937 587-3423
Fax: 937 587-3931
Jack McCoy, *Owner*
Sue Burns, *Manager*
EMP: 13
SQ FT: 2,400
SALES (est): 7.7MM **Privately Held**
SIC: 5031 2426 2431 Lumber, plywood &
millwork; dimension, hardwood; moldings,
wood: unfinished & prefinished

(G-16023)
**PEEBLES MESSENGER
NEWSPAPER**
58 S Main St (45660-1189)
PHONE..................................937 587-1451
Pamela Syroney, *Owner*

EMP: 8
SALES (est): 329.3K **Privately Held**
SIC: 2711 Newspapers: publishing only,
not printed on site

(G-16024)
RYAN DEVELOPMENT CORP
1 Ryan Rd (45660)
P.O. Box 336 (45660-0336)
PHONE..................................937 587-2266
Fax: 937 587-2879
G William Ryan, *President*
W Mark Ryan, *Vice Pres*
EMP: 20
SQ FT: 20,000
SALES (est): 2.3MM **Privately Held**
SIC: 3089 Extruded finished plastic prod-
ucts

(G-16025)
SOUTHERN OHIO LUMBER LLC
11855 State Route 73 (45660-9556)
P.O. Box 145, Worthington (43085-0145)
PHONE..................................614 436-4472
Chuck Mainous, *President*
Steve Bro, *Manager*
Kelby Moore, *Manager*
EMP: 30
SQ FT: 25,000
SALES (est): 4MM **Privately Held**
SIC: 2448 Pallets, wood

Pemberville
Wood County

(G-16026)
COUNTYLINE CO-OP INC (PA)
425 E Front St (43450-7039)
P.O. Box C (43450-0430)
PHONE..................................419 287-3241
Fax: 419 287-3243
Donald Kline, *President*
Robert Rahrig, *General Mgr*
Robert Schroder, *Vice Pres*
Chris Chalfin, *Treasurer*
Thomas Sieving, *Admin Sec*
EMP: 10 EST: 1916
SQ FT: 10,000
SALES (est): 16.2MM **Privately Held**
SIC: 5153 5191 2875 2041 Grains; farm
supplies; fertilizers, mixing only; flour &
other grain mill products

(G-16027)
HERCULES ACQUISITION CORP
Also Called: Hercules Stamping Co
850 W Front St (43450-9703)
P.O. Box F (43450-0433)
PHONE..................................419 287-3223
Fax: 419 287-3898
James Akers, *Ch of Bd*
Wes Walters, *President*
James Gale, *President*
Jan Blausey, *Manager*
EMP: 30
SQ FT: 30,000
SALES (est): 4MM **Privately Held**
SIC: 3465 3469 Automotive stampings;
metal stampings

(G-16028)
HIRZEL CANNING COMPANY
Pemberville Foods
115 Columbus St (43450-7029)
P.O. Box D (43450-0431)
PHONE..................................419 287-3288
Fax: 419 287-3880
Joseph Hirzel, *Manager*
Heidi Kopeck, *CIO*
EMP: 30
SALES (corp-wide): 24MM **Privately
Held**
WEB: www.hirzel.com
SIC: 2033 Tomato products: packaged in
cans, jars, etc.
PA: Hirzel Canning Company
411 Lemoyne Rd
Northwood OH 43619
419 693-0531

(G-16029)
**JONES INDUSTRIAL SERVICE
LLC**
17221 Eisenhour Rd (43450-9667)
PHONE..................................419 287-4553
John Dibling,
EMP: 4 EST: 1954
SQ FT: 576
SALES (est): 800.4K **Privately Held**
WEB: www.jonesindustrialservice.com
SIC: 3545 5084 Gauges (machine tool ac-
cessories); industrial machinery & equip-
ment

(G-16030)
ROMARC ENTERPRISES INC
18784 Luckey Rd (43450-9830)
P.O. Box 34 (43450-0034)
PHONE..................................419 287-4837
Roger Mullholand, *President*
EMP: 4
SALES (est): 250K **Privately Held**
SIC: 3544 3312 Special dies, tools, jigs &
fixtures; special dies & tools; tool & die
steel & alloys

(G-16031)
**UNIVERSAL METAL PRODUCTS
INC**
850 W Front St (43450-9703)
P.O. Box F (43450-0433)
PHONE..................................419 287-3223
Gordon Daugherty, *President*
Cindy Hutchison, *Human Res Mgr*
Kevin Rossman, *Sales Engr*
John Vitale, *Manager*
EMP: 35
SALES (corp-wide): 60MM **Privately
Held**
WEB: www.ump-inc.com
SIC: 3469 Metal stampings
PA: Universal Metal Products, Inc.
29980 Lakeland Blvd
Wickliffe OH 44092
440 943-3040

Peninsula
Summit County

(G-16032)
A & C WELDING INC
80 Cuyhoga Fls Indus Pkwy (44264-9568)
PHONE..................................330 762-4777
Fax: 330 762-8562
Carl Lamancusa, *President*
Michael Lamancusa, *Vice Pres*
Carl Erney, *Purch Agent*
Chad Moles, *Engineer*
Timothy Gorbach, *Treasurer*
EMP: 25
SALES (est): 5.9MM **Privately Held**
SIC: 3444 7692 Sheet metalwork; welding
repair

(G-16033)
AD SOURCE INC
1816 Main St (44264-9601)
PHONE..................................330 468-2934
Barney Barnhar, *Owner*
EMP: 6
SALES (est): 499.9K **Privately Held**
SIC: 2759 Directories, telephone: printing

(G-16034)
ANSCO MACHINE COMPANY
60 Cuyhoga Fls Indus Pkwy (44264-9568)
PHONE..................................330 929-8181
Fax: 330 929-7474
Michael D Sterling, *President*
Jon Sterling, *Plant Mgr*
▲ EMP: 45
SQ FT: 48,000
SALES (est): 12.6MM **Privately Held**
WEB: www.ansco-machine.com
SIC: 3599 Machine shop, jobbing & repair

(G-16035)
CENTER FOR INQUIRY INC
6413 Riverview Rd (44264-9624)
PHONE..................................330 671-7192
Bill Stalker, *Principal*
EMP: 3

SALES (est): 188.6K **Privately Held**
SIC: 2721 Periodicals

(G-16036)
DIMENSIONAL WORKS OF ART
2355 Main St (44264-9666)
PHONE..................................330 657-2681
Carol Adams, *Owner*
EMP: 4
SALES: 25K **Privately Held**
SIC: 8999 3911 Artist; jewelry, precious
metal

(G-16037)
EAGLE ELASTOMER INC
70 Cuyhoga Fls Indus Pkwy (44264-9568)
P.O. Box 939, Cuyahoga Falls (44223-
0939)
PHONE..................................330 923-7070
Fax: 330 923-4005
Neil X Mc Hale, *Ch of Bd*
Regan Mc Hale, *President*
Gene H McKenna, *Principal*
Vertina Ashling, *Vice Pres*
Charlie Christie, *QC Mgr*
EMP: 45
SQ FT: 26,000
SALES (est): 13.3MM **Privately Held**
WEB: www.eagleelastomer.com
SIC: 3069 2821 Tubing, rubber; rubber
tape; rapping, rubber; plastics materials &
resins

(G-16038)
LEDOW COMPANY INC
3011 Oak Hill Rd (44264-9670)
PHONE..................................330 657-2837
Fax: 330 376-2412
Leon Downing, *President*
Sharon Milhoan, *Accountant*
Beverly Downing, *Admin Sec*
EMP: 3 EST: 1978
SQ FT: 10,000
SALES: 350K **Privately Held**
WEB: www.ledow.com
SIC: 3535 Conveyors & conveying equip-
ment

(G-16039)
PENINSULA HARDWOODS INC
1710 Mill St W (44264-9701)
P.O. Box 157 (44264-0157)
PHONE..................................330 657-2701
Fax: 330 657-2940
James Montaquila, *President*
Autumn Wagner, *Admin Sec*
EMP: 8 EST: 1952
SQ FT: 6,400
SALES (est): 921.1K **Privately Held**
SIC: 2431 Millwork

(G-16040)
PENINSULA PUBLISHING LLC
Also Called: Plastics Machinery Magazine
6138 Riverview Rd Ste B (44264-9651)
PHONE..................................330 524-3359
Ja Lewellenc, *CEO*
Kathy Hayes, *Editor*
James Parada, *Prdtn Mgr*
Astra Hudson, *Manager*
Tony Eagan,
EMP: 9
SALES (est): 307.2K **Privately Held**
SIC: 2721 Magazines: publishing & printing

(G-16041)
PILOT PLASTICS INC
200 Cyhoga Fls Indus Pkwy (44264-9572)
PHONE..................................330 920-1718
Fax: 330 920-9672
Ted Jendrisak, *President*
Nikolas P Andreef, *Principal*
EMP: 25
SALES (est): 5.8MM **Privately Held**
SIC: 3089 Molding primary plastic

(G-16042)
STILLWELL EQUIPMENT CO INC
Also Called: Stillwell D L Equipment Rental
5398 Akron Cleveland Rd (44264-9516)
PHONE..................................330 650-1029
Fax: 330 650-1086
Donald L Stillwell, *President*
Ken Appleby, *Research*
Loretta Stillwell, *Treasurer*
Toni Musgrave, *Sales Mgr*

▲ = Import ▼=Export
◆ =Import/Export

EMP: 8
SQ FT: 1,100
SALES (est): 2MM Privately Held
WEB: www.stillwelleqpmt.com
SIC: 3531 7353 Construction machinery;
heavy construction equipment rental

(G-16043)
TERRY LUMBER AND SUPPLY CO
1710 Mill St W (44264-9701)
P.O. Box 216 (44264-0216)
PHONE..................................330 659-6800
Judy Lahoski, Corp Secy
James Montaquila, Vice Pres
James Montaquila, Vice Pres
John Lahoski, Manager
EMP: 11
SQ FT: 20,000
SALES (est): 1.6MM Privately Held
SIC: 5251 5211 2448 2449 Hardware;
lumber & other building materials; pallets,
wood; rectangular boxes & crates, wood

(G-16044)
WCCV FLOOR COVERINGS INC (PA)
4535 State Rd (44264-9799)
PHONE..................................330 688-0114
Fax: 330 688-5812
John F Martin, President
EMP: 23
SALES (est): 14MM Privately Held
SIC: 5713 3253 Carpets; ceramic wall &
floor tile

(G-16045)
WHOLECYCLE INC
Also Called: State 8 Motorcycle & Atv
100 Cyhoga Fls Indus Pkwy (44264-9569)
PHONE..................................330 929-8123
Fax: 330 929-8310
R Kirk Compton, President
Brett H Huff, Business Mgr
Gar Compton, Corp Secy
Paul Compton, Vice Pres
Joe Martin, Parts Mgr
▼ EMP: 40
SQ FT: 25,000
SALES (est): 13.9MM Privately Held
SIC: 5012 5571 3799 Motorcycles; motor-
cycles; all terrain vehicles (ATV)

Pepper Pike
Cuyahoga County

(G-16046)
FULL CIRCLE TECHNOLOGIES LLC
33199 Fairmount Blvd (44124-4823)
PHONE..................................216 650-0007
Hari Chandra, CEO
EMP: 3
SALES (est): 266.5K Privately Held
SIC: 2951 Asphalt & asphaltic paving mix-
tures (not from refineries)

Perry
Lake County

(G-16047)
ALL WRIGHT ENTERPRISES LLC
Fidanza Performance
4285 Main St (44081-9635)
PHONE..................................440 259-5656
Jeffrey Jenkins, President
EMP: 9
SALES (corp-wide): 1.2MM Privately
Held
SIC: 5013 3714 Clutches; wheels, motor
vehicle; gears, motor vehicle
PA: All Wright Enterprises, Llc
5 Bisbee Ct Ste 109-313
Santa Fe NM 87508
440 259-5656

(G-16048)
DIVERSIFIED FITTINGS INC
3450 Blackmore Rd (44081-9534)
P.O. Box 69 (44081-0069)
PHONE..................................440 259-0093
Fax: 440 259-5831
William C Cogar, President
Doreen Cogar, Treasurer
▲ EMP: 10
SQ FT: 3,500
SALES (est): 1.9MM Privately Held
SIC: 3599 Machine & other job shop work

(G-16049)
DOGLOK INC
3512 River Rd (44081-8603)
PHONE..................................440 223-1836
EMP: 3 EST: 2010
SALES (est): 237K Privately Held
SIC: 3089 Fences, gates & accessories:
plastic

(G-16050)
GREAT LAKES POWER SERVICE CO
Also Called: John Deere Authorized Dealer
3691 Shepard Rd (44081-9694)
PHONE..................................440 259-0025
Fax: 440 259-0098
Harry Allen, Owner
EMP: 10
SALES (corp-wide): 13.7MM Privately
Held
SIC: 3699 5082 Laser welding, drilling &
cutting equipment; construction & mining
machinery
PA: Great Lakes Power Service Co.
7455 Tyler Blvd
Mentor OH 44060
440 951-5111

(G-16051)
JOINING METALS INC
3314 Blackmore Rd (44081-9320)
PHONE..................................440 259-1790
Fax: 440 259-1791
Jeff Beckwith, President
EMP: 12
SALES (est): 2.1MM Privately Held
SIC: 3444 Sheet metalwork

(G-16052)
LEES MACHINERY
4089 N Ridge Rd (44081-9755)
PHONE..................................440 259-2222
Fax: 440 259-1092
Lee Zinn, Owner
Mike Zinn, Co-Owner
EMP: 3
SQ FT: 10,000
SALES (est): 1MM Privately Held
SIC: 5084 3599 3541 7699 Machine
tools & accessories; machine shop, job-
bing & repair; machine tools, metal cutting
type; industrial machinery & equipment
repair

(G-16053)
M M I SERVICES INC
3235 Elizabeth Dr Unit 34 (44081-9102)
PHONE..................................440 259-2939
Fax: 440 259-2393
Michael D'Aquila, President
Mark Logan, Engineer
EMP: 19
SQ FT: 8,000
SALES (est): 4.2MM Privately Held
SIC: 3446 1799 Stairs, staircases, stair
treads: prefabricated metal; railings, pre-
fabricated metal; welding on site

(G-16054)
MACDIVITT RUBBER COMPANY LLC
3291 Center Rd (44081-9589)
P.O. Box 129 (44081-0129)
PHONE..................................440 259-5937
Fax: 440 259-5941
Bob McDivitt, President
Joe Vizer, Prdtn Mgr
Jackie Bernot, Accounts Mgr
Bonnie Pekarcik, Manager
EMP: 20
SQ FT: 20,000

SALES (est): 3.7MM Privately Held
WEB: www.macdivittrubber.com
SIC: 3061 3069 Mechanical rubber goods;
molded rubber products

(G-16055)
OHIO ELASTOMERS
3470 Blackmore Rd (44081-9534)
PHONE..................................440 354-9750
William H Jaques, Owner
EMP: 4
SALES (est): 469.6K Privately Held
SIC: 3061 8731 Mechanical rubber goods;
commercial physical research

(G-16056)
PRECISION CONVEYOR TECHNOLOGY
Also Called: Pct Industries
3785 Lane Rd Ext (44081-9549)
PHONE..................................440 352-3601
Fax: 440 352-6123
Robert J Eder, President
Jeffery Smeker, President
Carol Eder, Admin Sec
EMP: 15
SQ FT: 15,000
SALES (est): 3.2MM Privately Held
WEB: www.precisionconveyor.com
SIC: 3535 3586 Conveyors & conveying
equipment; measuring & dispensing
pumps

(G-16057)
SIVON MFR CO
Also Called: Sivon Manufacturing Company
3131 Perry Park Rd (44081-9582)
PHONE..................................440 259-5505
Fax: 440 259-4602
Charlotte Kieffer, President
Alta L Lahner, Vice Pres
Ronald Kieffer, Enginr/R&D Mgr
Bonnie Kieffer Judd, Admin Sec
EMP: 3 EST: 1931
SQ FT: 7,500
SALES (est): 360K Privately Held
WEB: www.sivonmfg.com
SIC: 3567 3599 3544 Heating units & de-
vices, industrial: electric; machine shop,
jobbing & repair; special dies, tools, jigs &
fixtures

(G-16058)
SOUTH SHORE CONTROLS INC
4485 N Ridge Rd (44081-9760)
PHONE..................................440 259-2500
Rick Stark, President
Bob Weber, General Mgr
George Strekal, Vice Pres
Mike Shaffer, Plant Mgr
Jason McKinney, Project Mgr
EMP: 45
SQ FT: 22,000
SALES: 7MM Privately Held
WEB: www.southshorecontrols.com
SIC: 3549 5084 Metalworking machinery;
instruments & control equipment

(G-16059)
TCE INTERNATIONAL LTD
Also Called: Cutting Edge , The
4843 N Ridge Rd (44081-9767)
PHONE..................................800 962-2376
Fax: 440 259-2580
Joseph J Fellows, President
Angie Scheff, COO
Deborah J Fellows, Vice Pres
Dan Kade, Executive
Erica Looney, Executive
▼ EMP: 15
SQ FT: 20,000
SALES (est): 2MM Privately Held
WEB: www.cuttingedgeinc.com
SIC: 3479 3993 2752 2671 Etching & en-
graving; signs & advertising specialties;
commercial printing, lithographic; packag-
ing paper & plastics film, coated & lami-
nated

Perrysburg
Wood County

(G-16060)
7 LITTLE CUPCAKES
1021 Sandusky St Ste C (43551-3120)
PHONE..................................419 252-0858
Erin Liedigk, Principal
EMP: 3
SALES (est): 96.8K Privately Held
SIC: 2051 Bread, cake & related products

(G-16061)
ADR FUEL INC
353 Elm St (43551-2177)
PHONE..................................419 872-2178
Glen Hefflinger, Principal
EMP: 3
SALES (est): 198.9K Privately Held
SIC: 2869 Fuels

(G-16062)
ALL OHIO READY MIX CONCRETE
622 Eckel Rd (43551-1202)
PHONE..................................419 841-3838
Rick Stanley, Principal
Frank Mihalik, Vice Pres
Christie Bush, Controller
Jack Wagner, Manager
EMP: 6
SALES (est): 788.2K Privately Held
SIC: 3271 Concrete block & brick

(G-16063)
AMERICAN STEEL TREATING INC
525 W 6th St (43551-1554)
PHONE..................................419 662-5500
Roy Waits, Branch Mgr
EMP: 20
SALES (corp-wide): 10MM Privately
Held
SIC: 3398 Metal heat treating
PA: American Steel Treating, Inc.
525 W 6th St
Perrysburg OH 43551
419 874-2044

(G-16064)
AMERICAN STEEL TREATING INC (PA)
525 W 6th St (43551-1554)
PHONE..................................419 874-2044
Roy Waits, CEO
Jeff Blanker, President
Barbara Hilbert, Accountant
Susan Sears, Accountant
Jerry Ricker, Human Res Mgr
EMP: 40
SALES: 10MM Privately Held
WEB: www.americansteeltreating.com
SIC: 3398 Metal heat treating

(G-16065)
AMPP INCORPORATED
28271 Cedar Park Blvd # 5 (43551-4883)
PHONE..................................419 666-4747
Fax: 419 666-6821
Daniel A Worline, Principal
Jennifer Vance, Purch Dir
▲ EMP: 200
SQ FT: 53,000
SALES: 20.5MM
SALES (corp-wide): 41.9MM Privately
Held
WEB: www.ampp-inc.com
SIC: 3444 Sheet metalwork
PA: T.L. Industries, Inc.
2541 Tracy Rd
Northwood OH 43619
419 666-8144

(G-16066)
ARTISTIC MEMORIALS LTD
12551 Jefferson St (43551-1906)
PHONE..................................419 873-0433
Jeff Pettit, President
EMP: 5
SALES (est): 576.9K Privately Held
SIC: 3281 5999 Monument or burial stone,
cut & shaped; monuments & tombstones

(G-16067)
B & B BOX COMPANY INC
26490 Southpoint Rd (43551-1370)
PHONE....................................419 872-5600
Fax: 419 872-5700
Gregory B Hammer, *President*
Paula Peterson, *Manager*
EMP: 18
SQ FT: 32,500
SALES (est): 2.2MM Privately Held
WEB: www.b-n-bbox.com
SIC: 2653 Boxes, corrugated: made from
purchased materials

(G-16068)
**BOTTOMLINE INK
CORPORATION**
7829 Ponderosa Rd (43551-4854)
PHONE....................................419 897-8000
Mike Davison, *President*
Nicholas J Cron, *Principal*
Marry Nagy, *Accounts Mgr*
Ann Gajewski, *Manager*
▲ EMP: 29
SQ FT: 58,000
SALES (est): 5.6MM Privately Held
WEB: www.bottomlineink.com
SIC: 2752 Commercial printing, litho-
graphic

(G-16069)
**BPREX HALTHCARE
BROOKVILLE INC (DH)**
Also Called: Rexam Closure Systems
1899 N Wilkinson Way (43551-1685)
PHONE....................................847 541-9700
Steve Wirrig, *CEO*
Ron Riemer, *Executive*
▲ EMP: 135
SALES (est): 202.9MM
SALES (corp-wide): 6.4B Publicly Held
SIC: 3089 Caps, plastic; closures, plastic
HQ: Berry Plastics Corporation
101 Oakley St
Evansville IN 47710
812 424-2904

(G-16070)
BUDERER DRUG COMPANY INC
26611 Dixie Hwy Ste 119 (43551-1749)
PHONE....................................419 873-2800
Matthew Buderer, *Branch Mgr*
EMP: 13
SALES (corp-wide): 9.8MM Privately
Held
SIC: 5122 2834 Drugs & drug propri-
etaries; animal medicines; proprietary
(patent) medicines; proprietary drug prod-
ucts
PA: Buderer Drug Company, Inc.
633 Hancock St
Sandusky OH 44870
419 627-2800

(G-16071)
**BULK MOLDING COMPOUNDS
INC**
Also Called: BMC
12600 Eckel Rd (43551-1204)
PHONE....................................419 874-7941
Mark Asmus, *Facilities Mgr*
Jack Staples, *Maint Spvr*
Ron Cash, *QC Mgr*
John Slupecki, *QC Mgr*
Jeff Danielson, *Research*
EMP: 59
SALES (corp-wide): 2.5B Publicly Held
WEB: www.bulkmolding.com
SIC: 3083 2834 3842 3841 Thermoplas-
tic laminates: rods, tubes, plates & sheet;
pharmaceutical preparations; surgical ap-
pliances & supplies; surgical & medical in-
struments; ophthalmic goods; chemical
preparations
HQ: Bulk Molding Compounds, Inc.
1600 Powis Ct
West Chicago IL 60185
630 377-1065

(G-16072)
BUTT KICKN CREAMERY INC
26583 Carronade Dr (43551-6370)
PHONE....................................419 482-6610
Jerry A Benford, *Principal*
EMP: 3

SALES (est): 171.3K Privately Held
SIC: 2021 Creamery butter

(G-16073)
CAMELA NITSCHKE RIBBONRY
119 Louisiana Ave (43551-1458)
PHONE....................................419 872-0073
Camela Nitschke, *Owner*
EMP: 5
SQ FT: 3,960
SALES (est): 246K Privately Held
WEB: www.ribbonry.com
SIC: 5949 2396 Notions, including trim;
ribbons & bows, cut & sewed

(G-16074)
CAMEO INC
995 3rd St (43551-4355)
PHONE....................................419 661-9611
Fax: 419 661-9607
E Lee Ison, *President*
Brandon Ison, *Vice Pres*
Robert Fedynich, *Marketing Staff*
▲ EMP: 40
SALES (est): 5.8MM Privately Held
WEB: www.cameopaxit.com
SIC: 2844 Toilet preparations; shampoos,
rinses, conditioners: hair; mouthwashes;
lipsticks

(G-16075)
CARDINAL AGGREGATE
8026 Fremont Pike (43551-9733)
PHONE....................................419 872-4380
Mark Murray, *CEO*
Philip Bisel, *VP Opers*
Phil Eisel, *Manager*
Debbie Madson, *Manager*
EMP: 13
SALES (est): 1.5MM Privately Held
SIC: 3281 Stone, quarrying & processing
of own stone products

(G-16076)
CENTOR INC (HQ)
Also Called: Rexam Prescription Pdts Inc
1899 N Wilkinson Way (43551-1685)
PHONE....................................800 321-3391
Paul Arsenault, *President*
EMP: 12
SALES (est): 8MM
SALES (corp-wide): 1.5B Privately Held
SIC: 2631 Container, packaging &
boxboard
PA: Gerresheimer Ag
Klaus-Bungert-Str. 4
Dusseldorf 40468
211 618-100

(G-16077)
**CHAMPION WINDOW CO OF
TOLEDO**
7546 Ponderosa Rd Ste A (43551-5637)
PHONE....................................419 841-0154
Fax: 419 843-8073
Toby Tokes, *President*
Ed Levine, *President*
EMP: 40
SQ FT: 8,500
SALES (est): 6.6MM Privately Held
SIC: 5211 3444 3442 3231 Doors, storm:
wood or metal; windows, storm: wood or
metal; sheet metalwork; metal doors,
sash & trim; products of purchased glass

(G-16078)
CONTAINMENT SOLUTIONS INC
103 Secor Woods Ln (43551-2749)
PHONE....................................419 874-8765
Jack Bushmeyer, *Branch Mgr*
EMP: 128 Privately Held
WEB: www.containmentsolutions.com
SIC: 3443 Fabricated plate work (boiler
shop)
HQ: Containment Solutions, Inc.
333 N Rivershire Dr # 190
Conroe TX 77304

(G-16079)
COOL SEAL USA LLC
232 J St (43551-4416)
PHONE....................................419 666-1111
Tim Wisnewski, *CFO*
Taber Hinkle, *Manager*
EMP: 16

SALES (est): 5.3MM Privately Held
SIC: 3081 3083 Packing materials, plastic
sheet; laminated plastics plate & sheet

(G-16080)
CUPCAKES FOR A CURE
26595 Woodmont Dr (43551-7222)
PHONE....................................419 764-1719
Madison Cano, *Principal*
EMP: 5
SALES (est): 226.9K Privately Held
SIC: 2051 Bread, cake & related products

(G-16081)
**CUTTING EDGE COUNTERTOPS
INC**
1300 Flagship Dr (43551-1375)
PHONE....................................419 873-9500
Fax: 419 873-9600
Brad Burns, *President*
Jon Cousino, *Principal*
Rob Loughridge, *Principal*
Jeff Erickson, *COO*
Brian Burns, *Vice Pres*
▼ EMP: 32
SQ FT: 24,000
SALES (est): 6.1MM Privately Held
WEB: www.cectops.com
SIC: 3281 1743 Granite, cut & shaped;
marble installation, interior

(G-16082)
DANA COMPANIES LLC (HQ)
900 Ws Boundary Ste 8a (43551)
PHONE....................................419 931-9086
Michael L Debacker, *President*
Doris Brown, *Vice Pres*
Bricy Stringham,
◆ EMP: 3 EST: 1904
SALES (est): 2.1MM
SALES (corp-wide): 42.2MM Privately
Held
WEB: www.dana.com
SIC: 3751 8741 Motor scooters & parts; fi-
nancial management for business
PA: Enstar Holdings (Us) Inc.
150 2nd Ave N Fl 3
Saint Petersburg FL 33701
727 217-2900

(G-16083)
DELAFOIL PENNSYLVANIA INC
1775 Progress Dr (43551-2014)
PHONE....................................610 327-9565
James Cash, *President*
P Burke, *Exec VP*
EMP: 70
SQ FT: 35,000
SALES (est): 5.3MM Privately Held
SIC: 3444 3469 Sheet metalwork; metal
stampings

(G-16084)
DIE CAST TOOL LLC
26437 Southpoint Rd (43551-1371)
PHONE....................................419 874-1211
Jim Karl, *Purch Mgr*
Jim Gagnet, *Controller*
Tony Gagnet, *Mng Member*
EMP: 19
SQ FT: 23,000
SALES (est): 3.5MM Privately Held
SIC: 3544 Dies, plastics forming

(G-16085)
**DILLIN ENGINEERED SYSTEMS
CORP**
8030 Broadstone Rd (43551-4856)
PHONE....................................419 666-6789
David A Smith, *President*
Robin Vogel, *Draft/Design*
Chic Coleman, *Engineer*
Kathy McCormick, *Finance*
Chris Mc Ilroy, *Manager*
EMP: 50
SQ FT: 40,000
SALES (est): 10.9MM Privately Held
SIC: 8711 3535 Mechanical engineering;
conveyors & conveying equipment

(G-16086)
DYNALITE CORP
26040a Glenwood Rd Ste A (43551-4870)
PHONE....................................419 873-1706
Denny Emch, *President*
EMP: 8

SALES (est): 987.8K Privately Held
SIC: 3691 Storage batteries

(G-16087)
**EAGLE ENGINEERING WTR
TECH LLC**
10211 White Oak Dr (43551-9422)
PHONE....................................419 345-4688
Vera Hamrick, *CEO*
Charles D Hamrick, *President*
EMP: 4 EST: 2014
SALES: 750K Privately Held
SIC: 3589 Service industry machinery

(G-16088)
**ELECTRICAL CONTROL DESIGN
INC**
25571 Fort Meigs Rd Ste D (43551-2078)
PHONE....................................419 443-9290
Frank Smith, *President*
EMP: 4
SALES: 200K Privately Held
SIC: 3625 Electric controls & control ac-
cessories, industrial

(G-16089)
ELECTRONIC SOLUTIONS INC
28271 Cedar Park Blvd (43551-4883)
PHONE....................................419 666-4700
Joseph Young, *President*
Theodore Stechschulte, *President*
EMP: 11
SQ FT: 10,000
SALES (est): 5MM
SALES (corp-wide): 41.9MM Privately
Held
SIC: 3679 Loads, electronic
PA: T.L. Industries, Inc.
2541 Tracy Rd
Northwood OH 43619
419 666-8144

(G-16090)
**EMHART GLASS
MANUFACTURING INC**
1899 N Wilkinson Way (43551-1685)
PHONE....................................567 336-7733
Jared Burke, *Manager*
EMP: 78
SALES (corp-wide): 2.3B Privately Held
SIC: 3559 Glass making machinery: blow-
ing, molding, forming, etc.
HQ: Emhart Glass Manufacturing Inc.
123 Great Pond Dr
Windsor CT 06095
860 298-7340

(G-16091)
**EMHART GLASS
MANUFACTURING INC**
7401 Fremont Pike 6 (43551-9432)
PHONE....................................567 336-8784
Terry Wolfe, *Manager*
EMP: 5
SALES (corp-wide): 2.3B Privately Held
SIC: 3559 Glass making machinery: blow-
ing, molding, forming, etc.
HQ: Emhart Glass Manufacturing Inc.
123 Great Pond Dr
Windsor CT 06095
860 298-7340

(G-16092)
ENCOMPASS AUTOMATION &
622 Eckel Rd (43551-1202)
P.O. Box 2912, Toledo (43606-0912)
PHONE....................................419 873-0000
Fax: 419 872-2612
Tony Beall, *Design Engr*
Carter Stewart, *Design Engr*
Mark Weihs,
John Cheney,
Dan McCauley,
EMP: 10
SQ FT: 3,200
SALES (est): 1.9MM Privately Held
WEB: www.eaetech.com
SIC: 3823 Industrial instrmnts msrmnt dis-
play/control process variable

(G-16093)
EPRAD INC
28271 Cedar Park Blvd # 1 (43551-3846)
PHONE....................................419 666-3266
Fax: 419 666-8109

Ham-HI Lee, *President*
Theodore Steschulte, *Vice Pres*
Joseph L Young, *Vice Pres*
EMP: 8
SQ FT: 2,000
SALES (est): 660K **Privately Held**
WEB: www.eprad.com
SIC: 3861 3651 Motion picture apparatus & equipment; sound recording & reproducing equipment, motion picture; household audio & video equipment

(G-16094)
FCA US LLC
Toledo Machining Plant
8000 Chrysler Dr (43551-4813)
PHONE............................419 661-3500
Fax: 419 661-3393
David Arndt, *Principal*
William Cayson, *Engineer*
Mark Laws, *Engineer*
John Hornyak, *Plant Engr*
Tanya Young, *Director*
EMP: 1600
SALES (corp-wide): 118.7B **Privately Held**
SIC: 3714 Motor vehicle transmissions, drive assemblies & parts
HQ: Fca Us Llc
1000 Chrysler Dr
Auburn Hills MI 48326
800 334-9200

(G-16095)
FIRST FILTER LLC
620 1st St Ampoint (43551)
PHONE............................419 666-5260
Bob Righi, *Vice Pres*
Chris Righi, *Vice Pres*
Larry Walton, *Manager*
EMP: 3
SALES (est): 448.9K **Privately Held**
SIC: 3564 Filters, air: furnaces, air conditioning equipment, etc.

(G-16096)
FIRST SOLAR INC
Also Called: First Solar Electric
28101 Cedar Park Blvd (43551-4871)
P.O. Box 1032, Toledo (43697-1032)
PHONE............................419 661-1478
Lora Prew, *Vice Pres*
Glenn McConnell, *Project Mgr*
Karen Owen, *Project Mgr*
Marc Barlett, *Engineer*
Weston Gerwin, *Engineer*
EMP: 277
SALES (corp-wide): 2.9B **Publicly Held**
WEB: www.firstsolar.com
SIC: 3674 3433 Semiconductors & related devices; heating equipment, except electric
PA: First Solar, Inc.
350 W Washington St # 600
Tempe AZ 85281
602 414-9300

(G-16097)
FRAM GROUP OPERATIONS LLC
Also Called: Honeywell
28399 Cedar Park Blvd (43551-4864)
P.O. Box 981729, El Paso TX (79998-1729)
PHONE............................419 661-6700
Jerry Bolser, *Principal*
Lee Bennet, *VP Opers*
Lee Bennett, *Branch Mgr*
James Romer, *Planning Mgr*
Steven Powell, *Manager*
EMP: 100 **Privately Held**
WEB: www.honeywell.com
SIC: 3714 3694 8734 8731 Motor vehicle engines & parts; filters: oil, fuel & air, motor vehicle; spark plugs for internal combustion engines; testing laboratories; commercial physical research
HQ: Fram Group Operations Llc
1900 W Field Ct
Lake Forest IL 60045

(G-16098)
FRAZIER MACHINE AND PROD INC
26489 Southpoint Rd (43551-1371)
PHONE............................419 661-1656
Fax: 419 874-1201

Boyd M Frazier Jr, *CEO*
Jeffrey B Frazier, *President*
James Lazzaro, *General Mgr*
EMP: 23 **EST:** 1971
SQ FT: 18,000
SALES (est): 4.3MM **Privately Held**
SIC: 3599 3541 Machine shop, jobbing & repair; machine tools, metal cutting type

(G-16099)
FRESH PRODUCTS LLC
30600 Oregon Rd (43551-4544)
PHONE............................419 531-9741
Fax: 419 531-8472
Douglas S Brown, *CEO*
Doug Brown, *President*
Robert B Brown, *President*
Raymond Darr, *CTO*
◆ **EMP:** 55 **EST:** 1971
SQ FT: 48,000
SALES (est): 19.1MM **Privately Held**
WEB: www.freshproducts.com
SIC: 2842 Deodorants, nonpersonal

(G-16100)
FROZEN SPECIALTIES INC (PA)
Also Called: FSI
8600 S Wilkinson Way G (43551-2598)
P.O. Box 930 (43552-0930)
PHONE............................419 445-9015
Daniel Bender, *CEO*
Gary Swartzbeck, *CFO*
Patrick Koralewski, *VP Mktg*
Lori Hamilton, *Marketing Staff*
Sherry Larue, *Administration*
▼ **EMP:** 25
SALES (est): 29.5MM **Privately Held**
WEB: www.frozenspecialties.com
SIC: 2038 Pizza, frozen

(G-16101)
GEORGE BINIKER WOODEN PALLETS
28961 Oregon Rd (43551-4510)
PHONE............................419 666-3185
Craig Biniker, *President*
EMP: 12
SALES (est): 750K **Privately Held**
SIC: 2448 7699 Pallets, wood; pallet repair

(G-16102)
GLASSLINE CORPORATION (PA)
Also Called: Secure Pak
28905 Glenwood Rd (43551-3020)
P.O. Box 147 (43552-0147)
PHONE............................419 666-9712
Fax: 419 666-8072
Tom S Ziems, *President*
Mark Opfer, *President*
Don Antonevich, *Division Mgr*
Don Antonovich, *Division Mgr*
Brad Borkosky, *General Mgr*
◆ **EMP:** 40
SQ FT: 90,125
SALES (est): 19.6MM **Privately Held**
WEB: www.secure-pak.com
SIC: 3545 3565 3535 3541 Diamond dressing & wheel crushing attachments; bottling machinery: filling, capping, labeling; bag opening, filling & closing machines; carton packing machines; conveyors & conveying equipment; machine tools, metal cutting type

(G-16103)
GLASSTECH INC (PA)
995 4th St (43551-4321)
PHONE............................419 661-9500
Fax: 419 661-9616
Mark D Christman, *President*
Eric Fintel, *Senior VP*
Tom Noe, *Vice Pres*
Ken Wetmore, *Vice Pres*
Mark Musselman, *Plant Mgr*
▲ **EMP:** 112
SQ FT: 80,000
SALES (est): 25.9MM **Privately Held**
WEB: www.glasstech.com
SIC: 3211 3229 3231 Tempered glass; structural glass; glass tubes & tubing; tubing, glass; glass sheet, bent: made from purchased glass

(G-16104)
GRACE IMAGING LLC
28400 Cedar Park Blvd C (43551-4921)
PHONE............................419 874-2127
Robert Petrie, *Mng Member*
EMP: 3
SALES (est): 500K **Privately Held**
SIC: 2269 Labels, cotton: printed

(G-16105)
GREENWAY HOME PRODUCTS INC
1270 Flagship Dr (43551-1381)
PHONE............................419 874-6770
Fax: 419 662-8183
Douglas Greenway, *President*
Amanda Gashel Dillon, *Principal*
Ralph E Jocke, *Principal*
Patricia A Walker, *Principal*
Michael Callen, *Vice Pres*
◆ **EMP:** 12
SALES (est): 1.7MM **Privately Held**
SIC: 5023 2511 Home furnishings; wood household furniture

(G-16106)
HIAB USA INC (HQ)
12233 Williams Rd (43551-6802)
PHONE............................419 482-6000
Roland Sunden, *President*
Lennart Brelin, *President*
David Gardner, *Managing Dir*
Robert Nichols, *Plant Mgr*
Russ Parisi, *Opers Staff*
◆ **EMP:** 70
SQ FT: 56,000
SALES (est): 78.1MM
SALES (corp-wide): 4B **Privately Held**
SIC: 5084 3536 Cranes, industrial; hoists; cranes, industrial plant; hoists
PA: Cargotec Oyj
Porkkalankatu 5
Helsinki 00180
207 774-000

(G-16107)
HINKLE MANUFACTURING INC
348 5th St (43551-4922)
P.O. Box 60210, Rossford (43460-0210)
PHONE............................419 666-5550
Fax: 419 666-5367
Taber H Hinkle, *CEO*
Robert Hinkle, *COO*
Burt Jamieson, *Vice Pres*
Joe Graden, *Purch Agent*
Tom Kaltz, *Engineer*
EMP: 96 **EST:** 1963
SQ FT: 88,000
SALES (est): 41.8MM **Privately Held**
WEB: www.hinklemfg.com
SIC: 3086 2653 Packaging & shipping materials, foamed plastic; corrugated boxes, partitions, display items, sheets & pad

(G-16108)
HOLLAND SPRINGFIELD JOURNAL
117 E 2nd St (43551-2102)
PHONE............................419 874-2528
John B Welch, *Principal*
EMP: 3
SALES (est): 124.5K **Privately Held**
SIC: 2711 Newspapers, publishing & printing

(G-16109)
IMAGE INTEGRATIONS SYSTEMS (PA)
885 Commerce Dr Ste B (43551-5268)
PHONE............................419 872-0003
Bradley White, *President*
Ronald Kelley, *VP Sales*
Bob Kearney, *VP Mktg*
Brenda Armstrong, *Manager*
EMP: 11
SQ FT: 2,142
SALES (est): 3.9MM **Privately Held**
WEB: www.managedocs.com
SIC: 7374 7379 7372 7373 Data processing service; data processing consultant; prepackaged software; systems software development services

(G-16110)
IMCO CARBIDE TOOL INC (PA)
Also Called: Toledo Cutting Tools
28170 Cedar Park Blvd (43551-4872)
PHONE............................419 661-6313
Fax: 419 661-6314
Perry L Osburn, *Ch of Bd*
Matthew S Osburn, *Vice Pres*
Patrick Clewis, *Sales Staff*
Julie Whitlow, *Admin Sec*
Lesley Shawbriggs, *Admin Asst*
EMP: 78 **EST:** 1977
SQ FT: 25,000
SALES (est): 27.1MM **Privately Held**
WEB: www.imcousa.com
SIC: 3545 5084 Machine tool accessories; tools & accessories for machine tools; machine tools & accessories

(G-16111)
INDUSTRIAL HARDWOOD INC
Also Called: AAA
521 F St (43551-4313)
PHONE............................419 666-2503
Ashvin Shah, *President*
EMP: 7
SQ FT: 8,300
SALES (est): 1.1MM **Privately Held**
WEB: www.industrialhardwood.com
SIC: 2448 Pallets, wood; cargo containers, wood

(G-16112)
INNERAPPS LLC
Also Called: Identity Syncronizer
28350 Kensington Ln # 200 (43551-4174)
PHONE............................419 467-3110
Marty Rini, *COO*
James Delverne, *Exec VP*
Toby W Miller,
Deborah Gordon,
Martin Rini,
EMP: 8 **EST:** 2009
SALES (est): 663.9K **Privately Held**
SIC: 7372 Business oriented computer software

(G-16113)
JACKSON DAVID DO
1103 Village Square Dr # 101 (43551-1783)
PHONE............................419 872-3201
David Jackson Do, *Principal*
EMP: 10
SALES (est): 920K **Privately Held**
SIC: 2844 Toilet preparations

(G-16114)
JERL MACHINE INC
11140 Avenue Rd (43551-2825)
PHONE............................419 873-0270
Fax: 419 873-0276
Robert L Brossia, *CEO*
Carol Coe, *President*
Eileen Brossia, *Vice Pres*
William Peters, *Opers Mgr*
David Kessler, *Foreman/Supr*
EMP: 61
SQ FT: 76,000
SALES (est): 10.6MM **Privately Held**
WEB: www.jerl.com
SIC: 7692 3599 Welding repair; machine shop, jobbing & repair

(G-16115)
JOSHUA ENTERPRISES INC
Also Called: Joshua Label Company
12900 Eckel Junction Rd (43551-1309)
PHONE............................419 872-9699
Fax: 419 874-9699
Keith Aschliman, *President*
Robert Aschliman, *Treasurer*
EMP: 3
SQ FT: 2,000
SALES (est): 380K **Privately Held**
SIC: 2679 Labels, paper: made from purchased material

(G-16116)
JOSTENS INC
1833 Eaglecrest Rd (43551-5478)
PHONE............................419 874-5835
Steven Dufrane, *Manager*
EMP: 39

SALES (corp-wide): 13.2B **Publicly Held**
WEB: www.jostens.com
SIC: 3911 Rings, finger: precious metal
HQ: Jostens, Inc.
　　3601 Minnesota Dr Ste 400
　　Minneapolis MN 55435
　　952 830-3300

(G-16117)
KIEMLE-HANKINS COMPANY (PA)
94 H St (43551-4497)
P.O. Box 507, Toledo (43697-0507)
PHONE............................419 661-2430
Fax: 419 666-3096
Tim Martindale, *President*
Kevin Napierala, *Division Mgr*
Stephen Martindale, *Chairman*
Josh Brown, *Opers Mgr*
Daniel D'Amico, *CFO*
EMP: 50
SQ FT: 50,000
SALES (est): 17.6MM **Privately Held**
WEB: www.kiemlehankins.com
SIC: 7694 7629 3699 Electric motor repair; electrical equipment repair services; electrical equipment & supplies

(G-16118)
LAKO TOOL & MFG
7400 Ponderosa Rd (43551-4857)
P.O. Box 425 (43552-0425)
PHONE............................419 662-5256
Fax: 419 662-8225
Larry E Smith, *President*
Dario D Alvarez, *General Mgr*
Richard Hollweg, *Managing Dir*
Tony Capron, *Prdtn Mgr*
Lou Montano, *Engineer*
▲ **EMP:** 15 **EST:** 1974
SQ FT: 6,500
SALES (est): 3MM **Privately Held**
WEB: www.lakotool.com
SIC: 3544 Special dies & tools

(G-16119)
MACK INDUSTRIAL LLC
3258 Sterlingwood Ln (43551-3125)
PHONE............................800 918-9986
Scott E Charpie, *Principal*
EMP: 3
SQ FT: 30,000
SALES (est): 416.5K **Privately Held**
SIC: 3563 Air & gas compressors

(G-16120)
MARSHAS BUCKEYES LLC
25631 Fort Meigs Rd Ste E (43551-2098)
PHONE............................419 872-7666
Fax: 419 872-7667
Marsha E Smith, *Mng Member*
EMP: 22
SALES (est): 750K **Privately Held**
SIC: 2064 Candy & other confectionery products

(G-16121)
MASTER CHEMICAL CORPORATION (PA)
Also Called: Master Fluid Solutions
501 W Boundary St (43551-1200)
PHONE............................419 874-7902
Fax: 419 874-0684
Joe H Wright, *Ch of Bd*
Garret Garcia, *General Mgr*
Petr Sterba, *Managing Dir*
Michael Deel, *District Mgr*
Allen Jones, *District Mgr*
◆ **EMP:** 92 **EST:** 1951
SQ FT: 100,000
SALES (est): 102.4MM **Privately Held**
WEB: www.masterchemical.com
SIC: 2992 3559 Cutting oils, blending: made from purchased materials; oils & greases, blending & compounding; recycling machinery

(G-16122)
MILO BENNETT CORP
12922 Eckel Junction Rd (43551-1309)
P.O. Box 217 (43552-0217)
PHONE............................419 874-1492
Gerome Rollins, *President*
EMP: 4
SQ FT: 3,000

SALES (est): 370K **Privately Held**
SIC: 2752 Commercial printing, lithographic

(G-16123)
MULCH WORLD
8232 Fremont Pike (43551-9705)
PHONE............................419 873-6852
Tim Welch, *Principal*
EMP: 4
SALES (est): 311.4K **Privately Held**
SIC: 2448 5031 5261 Pallets, wood & wood with metal; pallets, wood; nurseries & garden centers

(G-16124)
NATIONWIDE CHEMICAL PRODUCTS
24851 E Broadway Rd (43551-8947)
PHONE............................419 714-7075
Joe Bassett, *Principal*
EMP: 6
SALES (est): 559.8K **Privately Held**
SIC: 2869 Laboratory chemicals, organic

(G-16125)
NEAL PUBLICATIONS INC
127 W Indiana Ave (43551-1578)
P.O. Box 451 (43552-0451)
PHONE............................419 874-4787
Fax: 419 874-1182
Dorothy J Neal, *President*
James Neal, *Admin Sec*
EMP: 5
SQ FT: 5,000
SALES (est): 370K **Privately Held**
SIC: 2731 Books: publishing only

(G-16126)
NEW WASTE CONCEPTS INC (PA)
26624 Glenwood Rd (43551-4846)
PHONE............................419 872-2190
Fax: 419 872-2602
Milton F Knight, *CEO*
Allan Wolf, *Vice Pres*
Denis Chailwick, *CFO*
Kathleen Mulinix, *Office Mgr*
EMP: 8
SALES (est): 1.9MM **Privately Held**
SIC: 2842 Sanitation preparations

(G-16127)
NORTHWEST PRINT INC
12900 Eckel Junction Rd C (43551-1309)
PHONE............................419 385-3375
Dean Warner, *President*
EMP: 5
SQ FT: 1,500
SALES (est): 300K **Privately Held**
WEB: www.northwestprint.com
SIC: 2752 Offset & photolithographic printing

(G-16128)
NORTHWOOD INDUSTRIES INC
7650 Ponderosa Rd (43551-4861)
PHONE............................419 666-2100
Fax: 419 666-2101
Kurt Miller, *President*
Ashley Woyame, *Purchasing*
Anthony Ciacelli, *Design Engr*
Laura Miller, *Controller*
Shannon White, *Office Mgr*
EMP: 18
SALES: 3.5MM **Privately Held**
SIC: 3469 3541 7699 8711 Machine parts, stamped or pressed metal; machine tools, metal cutting type; industrial equipment services; designing: ship, boat, machine & product

(G-16129)
ODYSSEY MACHINE COMPANY LTD
26675 Eckel Rd 5 (43551-1209)
PHONE............................419 455-6621
Ronald Leroux, *President*
EMP: 7
SALES (est): 1.1MM **Privately Held**
SIC: 3599 7699 Custom machinery; industrial machinery & equipment repair

(G-16130)
OHIO TABLE PAD COMPANY (PA)
Also Called: Ohio Table Pad Co Georgia Div
350 3 Meadows Dr (43551-3138)
P.O. Box 914 (43552-0914)
PHONE............................419 872-6400
Fax: 419 872-4774
Christopher P Krauser, *President*
Della B Bricker, *Principal*
N E Bricker, *Principal*
Brian Pribis, *Sls & Mktg Exec*
Jeffrey Lavoy, *Treasurer*
▲ **EMP:** 12
SQ FT: 15,000
SALES (est): 10.4MM **Privately Held**
WEB: www.otpc.com
SIC: 2299 5712 3949 2392 Felts & felt products; furniture stores; sporting & athletic goods; household furnishings

(G-16131)
OHIO TABLE PAD COMPANY
Also Called: Southern Division
350 3 Meadows Dr (43551-3138)
P.O. Box 914 (43552-0914)
PHONE............................419 872-6400
Jeanette Banner, *Division Mgr*
Chris Krauser, *Purchasing*
Don Unger, *Systems Staff*
EMP: 25
SALES (corp-wide): 10.4MM **Privately Held**
WEB: www.otpc.com
SIC: 2392 Pads & padding, table: except asbestos, felt or rattan
PA: The Ohio Table Pad Company
　　350 3 Meadows Dr
　　Perrysburg OH 43551
　　419 872-6400

(G-16132)
OHIO TABLE PAD OF INDIANA
350 3 Meadows Dr (43551-3138)
P.O. Box 914 (43552-0914)
PHONE............................419 872-6400
Stephen Krauser, *President*
Jeanette Banner, *Division Mgr*
Gary Heal, *General Mgr*
Christopher Krauser, *Vice Pres*
Jeffrey Lavoy, *Treasurer*
▲ **EMP:** 32 **EST:** 1963
SQ FT: 15,000
SALES (est): 3.4MM
SALES (corp-wide): 10.4MM **Privately Held**
SIC: 2299 Wool felts, pressed or needle loom; tow to top mills
PA: The Ohio Table Pad Company
　　350 3 Meadows Dr
　　Perrysburg OH 43551
　　419 872-6400

(G-16133)
OLDCASTLE BUILDINGENVELOPE INC
291 M St (43551-4409)
PHONE............................419 661-5079
Jeff Duty, *General Mgr*
Mike Kovacs, *Safety Dir*
Thomas Briggs, *Plant Mgr*
Kyle Wheeler, *Project Mgr*
Nigel Townsley, *Engineer*
EMP: 51
SALES (corp-wide): 28.6B **Privately Held**
WEB: www.oldcastleglass.com
SIC: 3231 5231 Tempered glass: made from purchased glass; insulating glass: made from purchased glass; glass
HQ: Oldcastle Buildingenvelope, Inc.
　　5005 Lndn B Jnsn Fwy 10 Ste 1050
　　Dallas TX 75244
　　214 273-3400

(G-16134)
ONESEAL INC (DH)
1300 3rd St (43551-4349)
PHONE............................973 599-1155
Michael Remark, *Owner*
Soren Lund, *General Mgr*
Lars Berenth, *Vice Pres*
▲ **EMP:** 3
SQ FT: 2,500

SALES: 2.5MM
SALES (corp-wide): 63.1K **Privately Held**
WEB: www.onesealusa.com
SIC: 3731 Shipbuilding & repairing
HQ: Oneseal Aps
　　Vibe Alle 2
　　Kokkedal 2980
　　491 488-00

(G-16135)
ONIX CORPORATION (PA)
27100 Oakmead Dr (43551-2670)
PHONE............................800 844-0076
Charles Verhoff, *CEO*
Richard Allen, *President*
John Halderman, *Vice Pres*
Todd Mroczkowski, *Controller*
▲ **EMP:** 7
SALES (est): 3.4MM **Privately Held**
SIC: 3433 Heating equipment, except electric

(G-16136)
ONIX CORPORATION
27100 Oakmead Dr (43551-2670)
PHONE............................800 844-0076
EMP: 30
SALES (corp-wide): 3.6MM **Privately Held**
SIC: 3714 Manufacturing Alternative Fuel Systems
PA: The Onix Corporation
　　27100 Oakmead Dr
　　Perrysburg OH 43551
　　800 844-0076

(G-16137)
OPTIMAIR LTD
Also Called: Air Compressor Exchange
29102 Glenwood Rd (43551-5644)
PHONE............................419 661-9568
EMP: 5
SALES (est): 481.3K **Privately Held**
WEB: www.optimair.com
SIC: 3563 Air & gas compressors

(G-16138)
OPTIME AIR MSP LTD
29102 Glenwood Rd (43551-5644)
PHONE............................419 661-9568
Mike Stacezek, *President*
EMP: 4
SALES (est): 390.3K **Privately Held**
SIC: 3563 Air & gas compressors

(G-16139)
OWENS-BROCKWAY GLASS CONT INC (DH)
Also Called: O-I
1 Michael Owens Way (43551-2999)
PHONE............................567 336-8449
Fax: 419 247-2216
Steve McCracken, *CEO*
Mathew Longthorne, *President*
Mr Albert P L Stroucken, *Chairman*
Jim Baehren, *Senior VP*
Steve Bramlage, *Senior VP*
◆ **EMP:** 250
SQ FT: 900,000
SALES: 6.1B
SALES (corp-wide): 6.7B **Publicly Held**
SIC: 3221 Glass containers
HQ: Owens-Brockway Packaging, Inc.
　　1 Michael Owens Way
　　Perrysburg OH 43551
　　567 336-5000

(G-16140)
OWENS-BROCKWAY PACKAGING INC (HQ)
1 Michael Owens Way (43551-2999)
PHONE............................567 336-5000
Al Stroucken, *CEO*
Ed White, *CFO*
John Reynolds, *Finance Mgr*
◆ **EMP:** 5
SQ FT: 100,000
SALES: 6.1B
SALES (corp-wide): 6.7B **Publicly Held**
WEB: www.owens-brockway.com
SIC: 3221 Glass containers
PA: Owens-Illinois, Inc.
　　1 Michael Owens Way
　　Perrysburg OH 43551
　　567 336-5000

(G-16141)
OWENS-ILLINOIS INC (PA)
1 Michael Owens Way (43551-2999)
PHONE..................................567 336-5000
Andres A Lopez, *CEO*
Miguel Alvarez, *President*
Tim Connors, *President*
Sergio B O Galindo, *President*
Vitaliano Torno, *President*
EMP: 277 **EST:** 1903
SALES: 6.7B **Publicly Held**
WEB: www.owens-brockway.com
SIC: 3221 Glass containers; food containers, glass; bottles for packing, bottling & canning: glass; medicine bottles, glass

(G-16142)
OWENS-ILLINOIS GENERAL INC (HQ)
Also Called: O-1
1 Michael Owens Way (43551-2999)
PHONE..................................567 336-5000
Al Stroucken, *CEO*
Thomas L Young, *President*
Paul Jarrell, *Senior VP*
Ed Snyder, *Senior VP*
Jim Baehren, *Vice Pres*
▲ **EMP:** 500
SQ FT: 900,000
SALES (est): 126.9K
SALES (corp-wide): 6.7B **Publicly Held**
SIC: 3221 Glass containers
PA: Owens-Illinois, Inc.
    1 Michael Owens Way
    Perrysburg OH 43551
    567 336-5000

(G-16143)
OWENS-ILLINOIS GROUP INC (HQ)
1 Michael Owens Way (43551-2999)
PHONE..................................567 336-5000
Albert P L Stroucken, *Ch of Bd*
Stephen P Bramlage Jr, *President*
James W Baehren, *Vice Pres*
Paul A Jarrell, *Vice Pres*
◆ **EMP:** 21100
SALES: 6.7B **Publicly Held**
SIC: 3221 Glass containers
PA: Owens-Illinois, Inc.
    1 Michael Owens Way
    Perrysburg OH 43551
    567 336-5000

(G-16144)
PALLET WORLD INC
8272 Fremont Pike (43551-9705)
PHONE..................................419 874-9333
Fax: 419 874-1234
Timothy Welch, *President*
Ken Welch, *Corp Secy*
Michelle Boldman, *CFO*
EMP: 26
SQ FT: 3,000
SALES (est): 6.8MM **Privately Held**
WEB: www.palletworldinc.com
SIC: 2448 Wood pallets & skids

(G-16145)
QUANEX SCREENS LLC
7597 Broadmoor Rd (43551-4875)
PHONE..................................419 662-5001
Bill Welch, *Site Mgr*
EMP: 5
SALES (corp-wide): 928.1MM **Publicly Held**
SIC: 3442 Screen & storm doors & windows
HQ: Quanex Screens Llc
    1800 West Loop S Ste 1500
    Houston TX 77027
    713 961-4600

(G-16146)
REACTIVE RESIN PRODUCTS CO
327 5th St (43551-4919)
PHONE..................................419 666-6119
Fax: 419 666-3446
Jeff Freiburger, *President*
Robert L Hinkle, *Vice Pres*
Vicki Maloy, *Manager*
Joe Leonard, *Admin Sec*
▲ **EMP:** 30
SQ FT: 150,000

SALES (est): 5MM **Privately Held**
WEB: www.rrp-mfg.com
SIC: 3565 3714 3089 Packaging machinery; motor vehicle parts & accessories; synthetic resin finished products

(G-16147)
SCHAEFER GROUP INC
Also Called: Frank W Schaefer
29102 Glenwood Rd Ste A (43551-5644)
PHONE..................................419 897-2883
Kurt Cohan, *Branch Mgr*
EMP: 5
SALES (corp-wide): 17.8MM **Privately Held**
WEB: www.theschaefergroup.com
SIC: 3312 Blast furnaces & steel mills
PA: The Schaefer Group Inc
    1300 Grange Hall Rd
    Beavercreek OH 45430
    937 253-3342

(G-16148)
SCHUETZ CONTAINER
2105 S Wilkinson Way (43551-1599)
PHONE..................................419 872-2295
Dave Bowling, *Principal*
Darin Booms, *Plant Mgr*
Keith Neubert, *Inv Control Mgr*
Tom Barrett, *Manager*
Jerry DEA, *Manager*
▲ **EMP:** 24
SALES (est): 5.5MM **Privately Held**
SIC: 2448 Cargo containers, wood & metal combination

(G-16149)
SENSOPART USA INC
28400 Cedar Park Blvd (43551-4900)
PHONE..................................419 931-7696
Daniel Simmons, *President*
Rachelle Vrabvski, *Office Mgr*
EMP: 4
SALES (est): 412.3K **Privately Held**
SIC: 3861 Cameras & related equipment

(G-16150)
SPB GLOBAL LLC
26611 Nawash Dr (43551-5463)
PHONE..................................419 931-6559
Susan Bernard, *CEO*
EMP: 4
SALES (est): 466.6K **Privately Held**
SIC: 3674 5064 5063 3613 Semiconductors & related devices; electrical appliances, television & radio; electrical apparatus & equipment; switchgear & switchboard apparatus

(G-16151)
SYSTEM PACKAGING OF GLASSLINE
28905 Glenwood Rd (43551-3020)
P.O. Box 109 (43552-0109)
PHONE..................................419 666-9712
Tom Wims, *President*
Robert Lock, *Engineer*
Chad Emch, *Electrical Engi*
EMP: 131
SALES (est): 9.6MM
SALES (corp-wide): 19.6MM **Privately Held**
WEB: www.secure-pak.com
SIC: 3565 Packaging machinery
PA: Glassline Corporation
    28905 Glenwood Rd
    Perrysburg OH 43551
    419 666-9712

(G-16152)
TARPSTOP LLC (PA)
12000 Williams Rd (43551-6809)
P.O. Box 548 (43552-0548)
PHONE..................................419 873-7867
Fax: 419 873-0548
Nick Strausbaugh, *General Mgr*
Tom Haughs, *VP Sls/Mktg*
Greg Nusbaum, *Controller*
Janet Harpest, *Human Res Mgr*
Andrew M Knepper, *Mng Member*
▲ **EMP:** 35
SALES (est): 8.6MM **Privately Held**
WEB: www.tarpstop.com
SIC: 3713 Truck & bus bodies

(G-16153)
TECH DYNAMICS INC
361 D St Ste B (43551-5645)
PHONE..................................419 666-1666
Fax: 419 666-9922
John W Zimmerman, *President*
Carolyn Fielding, *General Mgr*
David G Fielding, *Vice Pres*
Josh Fielding, *Plant Mgr*
David G Fieldin, *Treasurer*
EMP: 16
SQ FT: 18,000
SALES (est): 4.2MM **Privately Held**
WEB: www.techdynamics.com
SIC: 3441 Fabricated structural metal

(G-16154)
TECHNEGLAS INC (HQ)
2100 N Wilkinson Way (43551-1598)
PHONE..................................419 873-2000
Jeffrey T Lowry, *President*
Renee Dorr, *Purch Mgr*
Edward Grabowski, *Electrical Engi*
Jim Baney, *Sales Mgr*
Jay Armani, *Sales Executive*
▲ **EMP:** 5
SQ FT: 18,000
SALES (est): 2.6MM
SALES (corp-wide): 2B **Privately Held**
SIC: 3674 3479 Semiconductors & related devices; silicon wafers, chemically doped; coating of metals with plastic or resins
PA: Nippon Electric Glass Co., Ltd.
    2-7-1, Seiran
    Otsu SGA 520-0
    775 371-700

(G-16155)
TECHNEGLAS INC
25875 Dixie Hwy Bldg 52 (43551-1918)
PHONE..................................419 873-2000
Fax: 419 873-2020
Leyshon Townsend, *Branch Mgr*
EMP: 5
SALES (corp-wide): 2B **Privately Held**
SIC: 3229 Glass tubes & tubing
HQ: Techneglas, Inc.
    2100 N Wilkinson Way
    Perrysburg OH 43551
    419 873-2000

(G-16156)
TECHNICAL GLASS PRODUCTS INC
7460 Ponderosa Rd (43551-4857)
PHONE..................................425 396-8420
Joseph Murray, *President*
EMP: 3
SALES (est): 188.6K **Privately Held**
SIC: 3229 Scientific glassware

(G-16157)
THERMODYN CORPORATION
Sealing Resource
12265 Williams Rd Ste B (43551-6807)
PHONE..................................419 874-5100
Scott Sherwood, *Branch Mgr*
EMP: 6
SALES (corp-wide): 15MM **Privately Held**
SIC: 3053 Gaskets & sealing devices
PA: Thermodyn Corporation
    3550 Silica Rd
    Sylvania OH 43560
    419 841-7782

(G-16158)
THIRD PARTY SERVICE LTD
1205 Louisiana Ave (43552-9701)
PHONE..................................419 872-2312
Fax: 419 872-2313
Ronald L Brewer, *President*
Pamela Brewer, *Vice Pres*
EMP: 10 **EST:** 1990
SALES (est): 920K **Privately Held**
SIC: 2631 4783 4212 Specialty board; packing & crating; local trucking, without storage

(G-16159)
TIDEWATER PRODUCTS INC
12305 Williams Rd (43551-1981)
P.O. Box 23181, Toledo (43623-0181)
PHONE..................................419 873-0223
Steven Karakas, *President*
EMP: 4

SALES (est): 715.6K **Privately Held**
SIC: 2899 Water treating compounds

(G-16160)
TINY LION MUSIC GROUPS
Also Called: Groovemaster Music
144 E 5th St (43551-2235)
PHONE..................................419 874-7353
Gaylord Richardson, *Owner*
Julie Richardson, *Co-Owner*
EMP: 8
SALES (est): 331.8K **Privately Held**
WEB: www.tinymixtapes.com
SIC: 2741 7389 Miscellaneous publishing; music recording producer

(G-16161)
TMT INC
Also Called: Tmt Logistics
655 D St (43551-4908)
P.O. Box 408 (43552-0408)
PHONE..................................419 592-1041
Tony Marks, *President*
EMP: 250
SALES (est): 9.6MM **Privately Held**
SIC: 4789 3999 Railroad maintenance & repair services; dock equipment & supplies, industrial

(G-16162)
TOLEDO ELECTROMOTIVE INC
28765 White Rd (43551-3657)
PHONE..................................419 874-7751
Tony Palumbo, *President*
Jeff Mason, *Vice Pres*
EMP: 6
SALES (est): 474.4K **Privately Held**
SIC: 3625 Motor controls, electric

(G-16163)
TRS ENGINEERING LLC
26640 Lemoyne Rd (43551-9311)
PHONE..................................419 714-7034
Bob Shaw,
Kim Shaw,
Todd Shaw,
EMP: 4
SALES (est): 382.2K **Privately Held**
SIC: 3599 Machine & other job shop work

(G-16164)
UNIVERSAL HYDRAULIK USA CORP
25651 Fort Meigs Rd Ste A (43551-2076)
PHONE..................................419 873-6340
Michael Uhl, *CEO*
Ral Uhl, *CFO*
Alexander Brodt, *Manager*
EMP: 3
SQ FT: 4,500
SALES: 100K
SALES (corp-wide): 9.7MM **Privately Held**
SIC: 3443 Heat exchangers: coolers (after, inter), condensers, etc.
PA: universal Hydraulik Gmbh
    Siemensstr. 33
    Neu-Anspach 61267
    608 194-180

(G-16165)
VIRTUAL BOSS INC
517 Prairie Rose Dr (43551-5715)
PHONE..................................419 872-7686
Patrick Forester, *President*
Sping Valley, *E-Business*
EMP: 4
SALES (est): 330K **Privately Held**
SIC: 7372 Prepackaged software

(G-16166)
VISUAL ADVANTAGE LLC
13010 Five Point Rd (43551-1338)
P.O. Box 1221 (43552-1221)
PHONE..................................714 671-0988
Eric Hennan,
EMP: 3
SALES (est): 461.5K **Privately Held**
WEB: www.avisualadvantage.com
SIC: 3993 Signs & advertising specialties

(G-16167)
WALKER TOOL & MACHINE CO
7700 Ponderosa Rd (43551-4851)
PHONE..................................419 661-8000
Fax: 419 661-8004

Tarry F Beard, *President*
Larry L Beard, *Corp Secy*
EMP: 13 **EST:** 1941
SQ FT: 18,500
SALES (est): 2.2MM **Privately Held**
WEB: www.walkertm.com
SIC: 3544 Special dies & tools

(G-16168)
WELCH PUBLISHING CO (PA)
Also Called: Perrysburg Messenger-Journal
117 E 2nd St (43551-2102)
P.O. Box 267 (43552-0267)
PHONE..........................419 874-2528
Fax: 419 874-7311
Matt H Welch, *President*
John B Welch, *Vice Pres*
EMP: 20
SQ FT: 6,000
SALES (est): 2.7MM **Privately Held**
WEB: www.rossford.com
SIC: 2711 2721 7375 2752 Job printing &
newspaper publishing combined; periodi-
cals; magazines; publishing & printing; in-
formation retrieval services; commercial
printing, lithographic

(G-16169)
WHELCO INDUSTRIAL LTD (PA)
28210 Cedar Park Blvd (43551-4865)
PHONE..........................419 385-4627
Fax: 419 873-6575
Michael Farrar, *President*
Bob Wambold, *Purch Mgr*
Farrar G Richard,
EMP: 15
SQ FT: 12,000
SALES (est): 5.7MM **Privately Held**
WEB: www.whelco.com
SIC: 7694 Electric motor repair

(G-16170)
**WILLARD KELSEY SOLAR
GROUP LLC**
1775 Progress Dr (43551-2014)
PHONE..........................419 931-2001
Michael Cicak, *CEO*
Maurice Murphy, *CFO*
Bill Mulrooney, *Manager*
James Appold,
Gary T Faykosh,
▼ **EMP:** 45 **EST:** 2007
SALES (est): 8.8MM **Privately Held**
SIC: 3433 Solar heaters & collectors

(G-16171)
WOODEN CREATIONS
26730 Sheringham Rd (43551-2661)
PHONE..........................419 874-6367
Dave Grabarczyk, *Principal*
EMP: 3
SALES (est): 224.4K **Privately Held**
SIC: 2499 Wood products

(G-16172)
**WORLD WIDE MEDICAL
PHYSICS INC**
26302 Thompson Rd (43551-9355)
PHONE..........................419 266-7530
Andrew Schneider, *President*
EMP: 4 **EST:** 2011
SALES (est): 234.4K **Privately Held**
SIC: 3841 Diagnostic apparatus, medical

Perrysville
Ashland County

(G-16173)
**MANSFIELD PLUMBING PDTS
LLC (HQ)**
150 E 1st St (44864-9421)
P.O. Box 620 (44864-0620)
PHONE..........................419 938-5211
Fax: 419 938-6234
Jim Morando, *President*
Paul Stover, *VP Mfg*
Keith Hughes, *Safety Dir*
Dale Lepp, *Prdtn Mgr*
Jerry Dudte, *Mfg Spvr*
◆ **EMP:** 600
SQ FT: 700,000

SALES (est): 171.7MM **Privately Held**
SIC: 3261 3463 3088 3431 Vitreous
plumbing fixtures; plumbing fixture forgings, nonferrous; plastics plumbing fixtures; bathtubs: enameled iron, cast iron
or pressed metal; shower stalls, metal;
plumbing fixture fittings & trim; plumbing
fittings & supplies

(G-16174)
PALMER PROPERTIES LLC
Also Called: Palmer Enterprises
4688 State Route 95 (44864-9644)
PHONE..........................419 938-3114
Fax: 419 938-6814
H Scott Palmer,
EMP: 9
SALES (est): 1.2MM **Privately Held**
SIC: 1381 1623 Directional drilling oil &
gas wells; telephone & communication
line construction

(G-16175)
S & S AGGREGATES INC
Also Called: Shelly & Sands Zanesville OH
4540 State Route 39 (44864-9600)
PHONE..........................419 938-5604
Fax: 419 892-2150
Kent Ewers, *Manager*
Alden Coe, *Manager*
EMP: 12
SALES (corp-wide): 301.4MM **Privately
Held**
SIC: 1442 Construction sand mining
HQ: S & S Aggregates, Inc
      3570 S River Rd
      Zanesville OH 43701
      740 453-0721

(G-16176)
STEP2 COMPANY LLC
2 Step 2 Dr (44864)
P.O. Box 300 (44864-0300)
PHONE..........................419 938-6343
Fax: 419 938-6519
Dave Hissong, *Plant Mgr*
Robin Wachtel, *Safety Mgr*
Stacey Whitehair, *Safety Mgr*
Buster Cyrus, *Foreman/Supr*
Kevin Long, *Manager*
EMP: 270
SALES (corp-wide): 202.9MM **Privately
Held**
WEB: www.step2.com
SIC: 3089 3944 3423 Molding primary
plastic; games, toys & children's vehicles;
hand & edge tools
HQ: The Step2 Company Llc
      10010 Aurora Hudson Rd
      Streetsboro OH 44241
      866 429-5200

Petersburg
Mahoning County

(G-16177)
EAST FAIRFIELD COAL CO
13699 Youngstown Pittsbur (44454-9713)
P.O. Box 217, North Lima (44452-0217)
PHONE..........................330 542-1010
Dave Conrad, *Manager*
EMP: 20
SQ FT: 1,248
SALES (corp-wide): 126.2MM **Privately
Held**
WEB: www.eastfairfield.com
SIC: 1221 Bituminous coal & lignite-sur-
face mining
PA: The East Fairfield Coal Co
      10900 South Ave
      North Lima OH
      330 549-2165

(G-16178)
**MILSEK FURNITURE POLISH
INC**
5525 E Pine Lake Rd (44454-9711)
PHONE..........................330 542-2700
Fax: 330 542-1059
Chris Ruben, *President*
Dan Bender, *Admin Sec*
EMP: 4
SQ FT: 2,080

SALES (est): 270K **Privately Held**
SIC: 2842 Specialty cleaning, polishes &
sanitation goods

(G-16179)
YNGSTN PLASTIC FABRICATION
6820 E Garfield Rd (44454-9703)
PHONE..........................330 743-6404
William Milligan, *Principal*
EMP: 3
SALES (est): 177.6K **Privately Held**
SIC: 3089 Plastics products

(G-16180)
YPF CORPORATION
Also Called: Youngstown Plas Fabrication
6820 E Garfield Rd (44454-9703)
PHONE..........................330 743-6404
Fax: 330 743-6404
William Milligan, *President*
Kathleen Milligan, *Vice Pres*
EMP: 4
SQ FT: 5,000
SALES: 150K **Privately Held**
WEB: www.ypf.com
SIC: 3089 3544 Molding primary plastic;
special dies, tools, jigs & fixtures

Pettisville
Fulton County

(G-16181)
M & R REDI MIX INC (PA)
521 Commercial St (43553)
P.O. Box 53038 (43553-0038)
PHONE..........................419 445-7771
Kurt Nofziger, *President*
Connie Nofziger, *Vice Pres*
EMP: 20
SQ FT: 2,000
SALES (est): 3MM **Privately Held**
SIC: 3273 4212 Ready-mixed concrete;
local trucking, without storage

(G-16182)
PETTISVILLE GRAIN CO (PA)
Also Called: Pgc Feeds
18251 County Road D E (43553)
PHONE..........................419 446-2547
Fax: 419 445-0423
Neil E Rupp, *President*
Corwin D Rufenacht, *Principal*
James L Rufenacht, *Principal*
Tim Huber, *Purch Mgr*
Robert Leu, *Sales Staff*
EMP: 21
SALES (est): 10.7MM **Privately Held**
SIC: 5153 5999 2048 2041 Grain eleva-
tors; feed & farm supply; prepared feeds;
flour & other grain mill products

(G-16183)
PETTISVILLE MEATS INC
3082 Main St (43553)
P.O. Box 53148 (43553-0148)
PHONE..........................419 445-0921
Fax: 419 445-0922
Steve Mc Intosh, *President*
EMP: 11
SQ FT: 7,500
SALES: 250K **Privately Held**
SIC: 2013 4222 5421 Sausages & other
prepared meats; storage, frozen or refrig-
erated goods; meat markets, including
freezer provisioners

Phillipsburg
Montgomery County

(G-16184)
**LAWHORN MACHINE & TOOL
INC**
25 E Walnut St (45354)
P.O. Box 36 (45354-0036)
PHONE..........................937 884-5674
Fax: 937 884-7444
Elizabeth Lawhorn, *President*
Steve Quist, *General Mgr*
EMP: 5 **EST:** 1951
SQ FT: 5,600

SALES: 250K **Privately Held**
SIC: 3829 3825 Instrument board gauges,
automotive: computerized; measuring instruments & meters, electric

Pickerington
Fairfield County

(G-16185)
ABOUT TIME SOFTWARE INC
12790 Pickerington Rd (43147-9457)
PHONE..........................614 759-6295
Mark Miller, *President*
EMP: 15
SALES: 1.2MM **Privately Held**
SIC: 7372 Prepackaged software

(G-16186)
ASHTON LLC
145 W Columbus St (43147-1257)
PHONE..........................614 833-4165
David W Fisher, *Branch Mgr*
EMP: 13
SALES (corp-wide): 2.1MM **Privately
Held**
SIC: 2759 Commercial printing
PA: Ashton Llc
      309 Bethel St
      Gibsonville NC 27249
      336 447-4951

(G-16187)
BOSCO PUP CO LLC
290 Parkwood Ave (43147-2016)
PHONE..........................614 833-0349
Ward R Phillips, *Principal*
EMP: 3
SALES (est): 119.7K **Privately Held**
SIC: 3269 Pottery products

(G-16188)
CLEMENS LICENSE AGENCY
12825 Wheaton Ave (43147-8591)
PHONE..........................614 288-8007
Jennifer Clemens, *Owner*
EMP: 7
SALES (est): 492.6K **Privately Held**
WEB: www.clemensrealty.com
SIC: 3469 Automobile license tags,
stamped metal

(G-16189)
**D AND D ASP SEALCOATING
LLC**
13199 E Crosset Hill Dr (43147-8943)
PHONE..........................614 288-3597
James Davis McGee Jr,
Russell Taylor,
EMP: 4
SALES (est): 260K **Privately Held**
SIC: 2951 Asphalt paving mixtures &
blocks

(G-16190)
DELTA H TECHNOLOGIES LLC
8847 Easton Dr (43147-8871)
PHONE..........................614 561-8860
Richard Conway, *Owner*
EMP: 3
SALES: 200K **Privately Held**
SIC: 3567 Industrial furnaces & ovens

(G-16191)
ECHO MOBILE SOLUTIONS LLC
108 Leasure Dr (43147-8001)
PHONE..........................614 282-3756
Trent McMurray, *CEO*
Chis Lockhart, *Vice Pres*
EMP: 6
SALES: 1.5MM **Privately Held**
SIC: 7372 7389 Business oriented com-
puter software;

(G-16192)
**EVOQUA WATER
TECHNOLOGIES LLC**
Also Called: US Filter
1154 Hill Rd N (43147-8876)
PHONE..........................614 861-5440
Fax: 740 861-6159
Tim Swansonsn, *Manager*
EMP: 33

▲ = Import ▼=Export
◆ =Import/Export

SALES (corp-wide): 1.2B **Privately Held**
SIC: 3569 Filters
HQ: Evoqua Water Technologies Llc
181 Thorn Hill Rd
Warrendale PA 15086
724 772-0044

(G-16193)
J & A AUTO SERVICE
101 E Columbus St (43147-3100)
PHONE..............................614 837-6820
Julie Kern, *Owner*
EMP: 3
SQ FT: 3,600
SALES (est): 260K **Privately Held**
SIC: 5541 3599 Gasoline service stations;
machine shop, jobbing & repair

(G-16194)
JECH TECHNOLOGIES INC
13962 Olde Post Rd (43147-9438)
PHONE..............................740 927-3495
John Carter, *President*
Edward Cogan, *Vice Pres*
James Heidenreich, *Vice Pres*
EMP: 3
SALES: 150K **Privately Held**
WEB: www.jechtech.com
SIC: 3699 Electrical equipment & supplies

(G-16195)
JEFF KATZ (PA)
Also Called: Aquatic Lighting Systems
6265 Mamie Dr (43147-8564)
PHONE..............................614 834-0404
Jeff Katz, *Owner*
EMP: 3
SQ FT: 900
SALES (est): 626.5K **Privately Held**
SIC: 3648 Underwater lighting fixtures

(G-16196)
KIRBY ELECTRONICS INC
13056 Morrison Pl (43147-9247)
PHONE..............................614 395-8926
Fax: 614 863-1030
Michael F Kirby, *President*
Elizabeth Kirby, *Corp Secy*
EMP: 3
SQ FT: 11,600
SALES: 98.4K **Privately Held**
SIC: 3679 7629 Electronic circuits; elec-
tronic equipment repair

(G-16197)
MARBLELIFE OF CENTRAL OHIO
8440 Blacklick Eastern Rd (43147-7513)
P.O. Box 98, Reynoldsburg (43068-0098)
PHONE..............................614 837-6146
Deborah Allen, *Owner*
EMP: 5
SALES (est): 409.6K **Privately Held**
SIC: 3272 Art marble, concrete

(G-16198)
MIRION TECHNOLOGIES IST CORP
12954 Stonecreek Dr Ste C (43147-8840)
PHONE..............................614 367-2050
Fax: 614 367-2464
Daniel Messer, *Branch Mgr*
EMP: 5
SALES (corp-wide): 170.7MM **Privately Held**
SIC: 3559 Kilns
HQ: Mirion Technologies (Ist) Corporation
315 Daniel Zenker Dr # 204
Horseheads NY 14845
607 562-4300

(G-16199)
PERFECTION GLASS
139 Pickerington Ridge Dr (43147-8077)
PHONE..............................614 920-0652
Les Naylor, *President*
EMP: 7
SALES (est): 565.6K **Privately Held**
SIC: 3231 Products of purchased glass

(G-16200)
POLYSHIELD CORPORATION
8643 Chateau Dr (43147-9072)
PHONE..............................614 755-7674
Richard Allen, *CEO*

EMP: 10
SALES (est): 777.4K **Privately Held**
SIC: 2822 Ethylene-propylene rubbers,
EPDM polymers

(G-16201)
PRO COMPANIES INC
1162 Hill Rd N (43147-8657)
PHONE..............................614 738-1222
Greg Rodoski,
EMP: 4
SQ FT: 4,000
SALES (est): 176.3K **Privately Held**
SIC: 3993 5131 2396 2752 Letters for
signs, metal; flags & banners; fabric print-
ing & stamping; screen printing on fabric
articles; business form & card printing,
lithographic

(G-16202)
QUAYLE CONSULTING INC
8572 N Spring Ct (43147-9096)
PHONE..............................614 868-1363
Stanley F Quayle, *President*
◆ EMP: 2 EST: 1992
SALES: 1.8MM **Privately Held**
WEB: www.stanq.com
SIC: 8711 7389 7371 7372 Engineering
services; ; custom computer programming
services; prepackaged software; value-
added resellers, computer systems; com-
puter related consulting services

(G-16203)
RG BARRY CORPORATION (HQ)
13405 Yarmouth Rd Nw (43147)
PHONE..............................614 864-6400
Fax: 614 866-9787
Greg A Tunney, *President*
Jerry Hemphill, *President*
Yvonne E Kalucis, *Senior VP*
Thomas J Z Konecki, *Senior VP*
Lee F Smith, *Senior VP*
▲ EMP: 109 EST: 1984
SQ FT: 55,000
SALES (est): 56.7MM
SALES (corp-wide): 27.6MM **Privately Held**
WEB: www.rgbarry.com
SIC: 3143 3144 5661 5139 Men's
footwear, except athletic; women's
footwear, except athletic; shoe stores;
footwear; work apparel, except uniforms;
shirts: girls', children's & infants'
PA: Mrgb Hold Co.
382 Greenwich Ave Apt 1
Greenwich CT 06830
203 987-3500

(G-16204)
RHINO TECH SOFTWARE LLC
13938 Nantucket Ave (43147-9313)
PHONE..............................614 456-9321
Scott M Whitt, *Principal*
EMP: 5
SALES (est): 310K **Privately Held**
SIC: 7372 Prepackaged software

(G-16205)
STANDARD PROTOTYPING IDEALS
70 Cross St 100 (43147-1261)
PHONE..............................614 837-9180
Fax: 614 837-9161
George Carney,
Robert Nieves,
Don Smallwood,
EMP: 3
SALES (est): 310K **Privately Held**
SIC: 2396 Automotive & apparel trimmings

(G-16206)
SWEET PERSUASIONS LLC
9636 Circle Dr (43147-9650)
PHONE..............................614 216-9052
Melissa Lewis, *Principal*
EMP: 8
SALES (est): 782.8K **Privately Held**
SIC: 2051 Bakery: wholesale or whole-
sale/retail combined

(G-16207)
TARGET BUSINESS SERVICES
Also Called: Target Typesetting
12920 Stonecreek Dr Ste B (43147-8844)
PHONE..............................614 866-4065

Fax: 614 866-2260
Norman Hopkins, *Owner*
EMP: 12
SALES (est): 570K **Privately Held**
WEB: www.targetbusinessservices.com
SIC: 2791 7331 Typesetting; direct mail
advertising services

(G-16208)
TINY PRINTING CO
11764 Village Way Dr (43147-9622)
PHONE..............................614 920-0800
Frank Cavaughna, *Partner*
EMP: 3 EST: 2001
SALES (est): 173K **Privately Held**
WEB: www.tinyprinting.com
SIC: 2752 Commercial printing, litho-
graphic

(G-16209)
VACALON COMPANY INC
12960 Stonecreek Dr Ste D (43147-8799)
PHONE..............................614 577-1945
Bryan Frazier, *President*
Josh Andrachek, *Senior VP*
▲ EMP: 4
SQ FT: 8,000
SALES (est): 578.8K **Privately Held**
WEB: www.vacalon.com
SIC: 3843 Dental equipment & supplies

Pierpont
Ashtabula County

(G-16210)
A W TAYLOR LUMBER INCORPORATED
1114 State Route 7 S (44082-9643)
PHONE..............................440 577-1889
Fax: 440 577-1889
Allen Taylor, *President*
Maryjo Taylor, *Principal*
Angela Taylor, *Vice Pres*
EMP: 12
SALES (est): 1.5MM **Privately Held**
SIC: 2448 Wood pallets & skids

(G-16211)
COMPLETE ENERGY SERVICES INC
7338 Us Route 6 (44082-9725)
PHONE..............................440 577-1070
Gary Lauer, *Partner*
Jeff Teunisen, *Exec VP*
EMP: 11
SALES (est): 1.1MM **Privately Held**
SIC: 1389 Oil & gas field services

(G-16212)
K S W C INC
Also Called: Kodiak Springs Water Co
697 State Line Rd (44082-9728)
PHONE..............................440 577-1114
Fax: 440 577-1115
James L Bushman, *President*
Lisa Bushman, *Vice Pres*
EMP: 4
SALES: 300K **Privately Held**
WEB: www.kswc.com
SIC: 3589 5999 Water treatment equip-
ment, industrial; water purification equip-
ment, household type; water purification
equipment

(G-16213)
NATIONAL OILWELL VARCO INC
7338 N Richmond Rd (44082-9725)
PHONE..............................440 577-1225
Jerry Lower, *Owner*
EMP: 23
SALES (corp-wide): 7.2B **Publicly Held**
SIC: 3533 Oil & gas field machinery
PA: National Oilwell Varco, Inc.
7909 Parkwood Circle Dr
Houston TX 77036
713 346-7500

(G-16214)
NEAL MILLER
Also Called: Sunset Metal Roofing
6878 State Route 167 E (44082-9609)
PHONE..............................440 296-5322

Neal Miller, *Owner*
EMP: 3
SALES (est): 162.5K **Privately Held**
SIC: 3444 Metal roofing & roof drainage
equipment

Piketon
Pike County

(G-16215)
BARKER LUMBER
103 Lewis Rd (45661-9541)
PHONE..............................740 289-2424
Danny Barker, *Partner*
Gary Barker, *Partner*
EMP: 7
SALES (est): 490K **Privately Held**
SIC: 2421 Sawmills & planing mills, gen-
eral

(G-16216)
BEEKMAN LOGGING
204 Wyckoff Rd (45661-9629)
PHONE..............................740 493-2763
Gary Beekman, *Partner*
Lisa Beekman, *Partner*
EMP: 3
SALES (est): 277.7K **Privately Held**
SIC: 2411 Logging camps & contractors

(G-16217)
CENTRUS ENERGY CORP
Also Called: American Centrifuge Plant
3930 Us Rt 23 S (45661)
PHONE..............................740 897-2457
Angie Duduit, *Manager*
Christopher Harper, *Info Tech Mgr*
EMP: 200
SALES (corp-wide): 311.3MM **Publicly Held**
SIC: 1094 Uranium ore mining
PA: Centrus Energy Corp.
6901 Rockledge Dr Ste 800
Bethesda MD 20817
301 564-3200

(G-16218)
CUSTOM HITCH AND TRAILER/ OVER
Also Called: Custom Hitch & Trailer
4237 Us Highway 23 (45661-9703)
PHONE..............................740 289-3925
Fax: 740 289-8943
Della Nier, *Owner*
Jim Nier, *Co-Owner*
EMP: 7
SALES (est): 330K **Privately Held**
SIC: 3442 5531 5031 1751 Garage
doors, overhead: metal; trailer hitches,
automotive; lumber, plywood & millwork;
carpentry work

(G-16219)
DOLGENCORP LLC
Also Called: Dollar General
7095 Us Highway 23 (45661-9004)
PHONE..............................740 289-4790
Michelle Tribbey, *Branch Mgr*
EMP: 8
SALES (corp-wide): 21.9B **Publicly Held**
SIC: 5331 2851 Variety stores; removers
& cleaners
HQ: Dolgencorp, Llc
100 Mission Rdg
Goodlettsville TN 37072
615 855-4000

(G-16220)
FAMILY WOODWORKS LLC
286 Taylor Hollow Rd (45661-9686)
PHONE..............................740 289-4071
George A Barlow, *Mng Member*
EMP: 3
SALES: 300K **Privately Held**
SIC: 2499 Decorative wood & woodwork

(G-16221)
JIM NIER CONSTRUCTION INC
3877 Us Highway 23 (45661)
PHONE..............................740 289-2629
Della Nier, *Manager*
EMP: 11

SALES (corp-wide): 2.2MM **Privately Held**
SIC: 1446 1411 Industrial sand; dimension stone
PA: Jim Nier Construction, Inc.
340 Bailey Chapel Rd
Piketon OH 45661
740 289-3925

(G-16222)
JIM NIER CONSTRUCTION INC (PA)
Also Called: Jnc,
340 Bailey Chapel Rd (45661-9673)
PHONE....................................740 289-3925
Della Nier, *President*
Jim Nier, *Vice Pres*
EMP: 13
SQ FT: 7,000
SALES (est): 2.2MM **Privately Held**
SIC: 1761 3444 1542 1541 Sheet metalwork; sheet metalwork; nonresidential construction; industrial buildings & warehouses

(G-16223)
LANSING BROS SAWMILL
897 Chenoweth Fork Rd (45661-9565)
PHONE....................................937 588-4291
Lloyd Lansing, *Principal*
EMP: 3
SALES (est): 229.5K **Privately Held**
SIC: 2421 Sawmills & planing mills, general

(G-16224)
MIDWEST TIMBER & LAND CO INC
88 Jasper Rd (45661-9732)
P.O. Box 338 (45661-0338)
PHONE....................................740 493-2400
David Smith, *President*
EMP: 21
SALES (est): 4.3MM **Privately Held**
SIC: 3553 Sawmill machines

(G-16225)
OHIO VALLEY VENEER INC
Also Called: Ohio Valley Veneer Co
16523 State Route 124 (45661-9728)
Rural Route 165 (45661)
PHONE....................................740 493-2901
Ed Robbins, *Owner*
▼ EMP: 49
SALES (est): 8MM **Privately Held**
SIC: 2426 2435 2421 Lumber, hardwood dimension; hardwood veneer & plywood; sawmills & planing mills, general

(G-16226)
P H GLATFELTER COMPANY
200 Schuster Rd (45661-9687)
PHONE....................................740 289-5100
Paula Wentzell, *Project Mgr*
Robert Browm, *Branch Mgr*
Mark Percell, *Senior Mgr*
EMP: 7
SALES (corp-wide): 1.6B **Publicly Held**
SIC: 3829 Electrogamma ray loggers
PA: P. H. Glatfelter Company
96 S George St Ste 520
York PA 17401
717 225-4711

(G-16227)
PIKETON SAND & GRAVEL
3293 Us Highway 23 (45661-8120)
P.O. Box 550 (45661-0550)
PHONE....................................740 289-2316
Fax: 740 289-8010
Jeff Caudill, *Manager*
EMP: 3
SALES (est): 179.9K **Privately Held**
SIC: 1442 Construction sand & gravel

(G-16228)
SIGNS 2 GRAPHICS
746 State Route 220 (45661-9722)
PHONE....................................740 493-2049
Tim Shockey, *Owner*
EMP: 5
SALES (est): 250.8K **Privately Held**
SIC: 3993 Signs & advertising specialties

(G-16229)
WOOLDRIDGE LUMBER CO
3264 Laurel Ridge Rd (45661-9620)
PHONE....................................740 289-4912
Fax: 740 289-3920
Mick Wooldridge, *Partner*
Mick Wooldridge, *Partner*
Alva Wooldridge, *Partner*
Dora Ransey, *Admin Sec*
EMP: 60
SQ FT: 6,000
SALES (est): 6.1MM **Privately Held**
SIC: 2421 Sawmills & planing mills, general

(G-16230)
YOUR BOTTLED WATER LLC
Also Called: Sun Rush Water
705 E 2nd St (45661-8052)
PHONE....................................740 443-6079
Michael Blum, *Mng Member*
EMP: 4
SQ FT: 3,000
SALES: 270K **Privately Held**
SIC: 2086 Pasteurized & mineral waters, bottled & canned

Pioneer
Williams County

(G-16231)
ACTION PRECISION PRODUCTS INC
100 E North Ave (43554-7808)
P.O. Box 188 (43554-0188)
PHONE....................................419 737-2348
Fax: 419 737-3039
Linda Heisler, *President*
Gary Beggs, *Vice Pres*
Vonnie Beggs, *Treasurer*
EMP: 20
SQ FT: 9,000
SALES (est): 3MM **Privately Held**
SIC: 3599 Machine shop, jobbing & repair

(G-16232)
AMERICAN STEEL CARPORTS INC
200 Industrial Ave (43554-9510)
PHONE....................................419 737-1331
Primo Castillo, *Branch Mgr*
EMP: 15
SALES (corp-wide): 25.2MM **Privately Held**
SIC: 3448 Carports: prefabricated metal
PA: American Steel Carports, Inc.
457 N Brwy St
Joshua TX 76058
866 471-8761

(G-16233)
ARCELORMITTAL TAILORED BLANKS
Also Called: Powerlasers
2 Kexon Dr (43554-9200)
P.O. Box 939 (43554-0939)
PHONE....................................419 737-3180
Fax: 419 737-3181
Joe Neri, *President*
Ed Pace, *President*
Cyril Bramwell, *Vice Pres*
Denis Gionet, *Vice Pres*
John Wende, *Vice Pres*
EMP: 65
SQ FT: 167,000
SALES (est): 15.9MM **Privately Held**
WEB: www.dofasco.ca
SIC: 3465 Automotive stampings
HQ: Arcelormittal Usa Llc
1 S Dearborn St Ste 1800
Chicago IL 60603
312 346-0300

(G-16234)
HUDSON LEATHER LTD
Also Called: Hudson Leather Co
14700 State Route 15 (43554-9765)
PHONE....................................419 485-8531
Dogan J Aldemdar,
EMP: 7
SQ FT: 10,000

SALES (est): 884.8K **Privately Held**
WEB: www.hudsonleather.com
SIC: 3131 5139 5661 Footwear cut stock; boots; men's boots; women's boots

(G-16235)
N N METAL STAMPINGS INC (PA)
510 S Maple St (43554-7956)
P.O. Box 248 (43554-0248)
PHONE....................................419 737-2311
Fax: 419 737-2859
Rob Harger, *President*
Nelson Melillo, *President*
Larry Martin, *CFO*
EMP: 25 EST: 1976
SQ FT: 60,000
SALES (est): 5.3MM **Privately Held**
WEB: www.pennantcompanies.com
SIC: 3469 3544 3465 Electronic enclosures, stamped or pressed metal; special dies, tools, jigs & fixtures; automotive stampings

(G-16236)
PIONEER CUSTOM COATING LLC
255 Industrial Ave Bldg D (43554-9510)
P.O. Box 337 (43554-0337)
PHONE....................................419 737-3152
Deniss Sentle, *Mng Member*
Dennis Sentle, *Mng Member*
Merry Sentle, *Mng Member*
EMP: 9
SQ FT: 2,400
SALES (est): 670K **Privately Held**
SIC: 3479 Coating of metals & formed products

(G-16237)
PIONEER CUSTOM MOLDING INC
3 Kexon Dr (43554-9200)
P.O. Box 463 (43554-0463)
PHONE....................................419 737-3252
Fax: 419 737-3349
Terry Hendricks, *CEO*
Bill Peterson, *President*
David Roth, *Vice Pres*
EMP: 23 EST: 1997
SQ FT: 22,500
SALES (est): 2.2MM **Privately Held**
SIC: 3089 Injection molding of plastics

(G-16238)
PIONEER HOMES INC
1018 Lakeshore Dr (43554-9641)
P.O. Box 275 (43554-0275)
PHONE....................................419 737-2371
Fax: 419 737-2449
Margaret G Thorp, *President*
Dorothy Ragland, *Corp Secy*
Norman Dean Thorp, *Vice Pres*
EMP: 4
SALES (est): 379K **Privately Held**
SIC: 2439 Trusses, wooden roof

(G-16239)
PIONEER TRANSFORMER COMPANY
Also Called: Dongan Electric Mfg Co
500 Cedar St (43554-7874)
P.O. Box 158 (43554-0158)
PHONE....................................419 737-2304
Fax: 419 737-2300
Steven E Hicks, *President*
Michael Lillard, *Plant Mgr*
Carey Christenson, *Safety Mgr*
Barbara Carpenter, *Human Resources*
Gary Hicks, *Executive*
▲ EMP: 6 EST: 1957
SALES (est): 921.4K
SALES (corp-wide): 9.2MM **Privately Held**
WEB: www.dongan.com
SIC: 3612 Machine tool transformers; control transformers; signaling transformers, electric
PA: Dongan Electric Manufacturing Co Inc
34760 Garfield Rd
Fraser MI 48026
313 567-8500

(G-16240)
POWERS AND SONS LLC
Also Called: Pioneer Forge Div
101 Industrial Ave (43554)
P.O. Box 598 (43554-0598)
PHONE....................................419 737-2373
Cliff Kidder, *Opers Mgr*
Jeffrey Wilson, *Branch Mgr*
EMP: 100
SALES (corp-wide): 2.9B **Privately Held**
WEB: www.powersandsonsllc.com
SIC: 3462 3714 3463 Iron & steel forgings; motor vehicle parts & accessories; nonferrous forgings
HQ: Powers And Sons, Llc
1613 Magda Dr
Montpelier OH 43543
419 485-3151

(G-16241)
PREMIERE CON SOLUTIONS LLC
508 Cedar St (43554-7874)
P.O. Box 277 (43554-0277)
PHONE....................................419 737-9808
Douglas C Wittler, *Mng Member*
Nancy Wittler, *Manager*
Theodore P Kill,
William W Maze Jr,
EMP: 11
SALES (est): 2.3MM **Privately Held**
SIC: 3272 Concrete products

(G-16242)
PURE WATER GLOBAL INC
50 Industrial Ave (43554)
P.O. Box 567 (43554-0567)
PHONE....................................419 737-2352
EMP: 3 EST: 2008
SALES (est): 220K **Privately Held**
SIC: 3085 5085 Mfg Plastic Bottles Whol Industrial Supplies

(G-16243)
RAPID MACHINE INC
610 N State St (43554-9506)
P.O. Box 365 (43554-0365)
PHONE....................................419 737-2377
Fax: 419 737-2510
Jim F Spangler, *President*
Jennifer Wines, *Corp Secy*
Jerelyn Spangler, *Sales Mgr*
EMP: 12 EST: 1978
SQ FT: 10,000
SALES (est): 1.4MM **Privately Held**
WEB: www.spanglersuperiortool.com
SIC: 3544 3541 3469 3444 Special dies, tools, jigs & fixtures; grinding, polishing, buffing, lapping & honing machines; pointing & burring machines; metal stampings; sheet metalwork

(G-16244)
REIFEL INDUSTRIES INC
201 Ohio St (43554-7934)
PHONE....................................419 737-2138
Fax: 419 737-2578
Thomas Reifel, *President*
M Kathleen Reifel, *Corp Secy*
Louis Reifel, *Vice Pres*
Kevin Wells, *Project Mgr*
Joseph Roche, *Human Res Mgr*
▲ EMP: 65
SQ FT: 60,000
SALES (est): 9.7MM **Privately Held**
WEB: www.reifel.com
SIC: 3479 3471 Coating of metals & formed products; plating & polishing

(G-16245)
UNIVERSAL INDUSTRIAL PDTS INC
1 Coreway Dr (43554)
P.O. Box 628 (43554-0628)
PHONE....................................419 737-9584
Fax: 419 737-2130
Neil Marko, *President*
Peter Kos, *VP Mfg*
Randy Herriman, *Treasurer*
Mike Nowakowski, *Sales Mgr*
Deidre Whitman, *Info Tech Mgr*
▲ EMP: 18
SQ FT: 86,000

▲ = Import ▼=Export
◆ =Import/Export

SALES: 6.1MM **Privately Held**
WEB: www.hinge.com
SIC: 3469 Stamping metal for the trade

Piqua
Miami County

(G-16246)
AESTHETIC FINISHERS INC
1502 S Main St (45356-8319)
PHONE......................................937 778-8777
Fax: 937 778-8860
Sally Coomer, *CEO*
William Coomer III, *Vice Pres*
Deidre Baker, *Human Res Mgr*
Greg Goubeaux, *Manager*
EMP: 35
SQ FT: 72,000
SALES (est): 4.3MM **Privately Held**
WEB: www.afipowder.com
SIC: 3479 Coating of metals & formed
products

(G-16247)
ALLIED COATING CO
387 Fox Dr (45356-8252)
PHONE......................................937 615-0391
Greg Flannery, *President*
EMP: 9
SALES (corp-wide): 616.1K **Privately
Held**
WEB: www.alliedcoating.com
SIC: 3479 Etching & engraving
PA: Allied Coating Co
95 Woodhaven Ln
Troy OH

(G-16248)
**APEX ALUMINUM DIE CAST CO
INC**
8877 Sherry Dr (45356-9111)
P.O. Box 617 (45356-0617)
PHONE......................................937 773-0432
Fax: 937 773-6190
Patty Kendel, *Personnel*
Mark Zimmerman, *Incorporator*
EMP: 50
SALES (est): 12MM **Privately Held**
WEB: www.apexdiecasting.com
SIC: 3363 3369 Aluminum die-castings;
nonferrous foundries

(G-16249)
**ARKANSAS FACE VENEER CO
INC (HQ)**
1025 S Roosevelt Ave (45356-3713)
P.O. Box 919 (45356-0919)
PHONE......................................937 773-6295
Jeffery A Bannister, *CEO*
James Robert Hartzell, *Ch of Bd*
Jon Snyder, *President*
R Ward Harris III, *General Mgr*
Michael Bardo, *CFO*
▲ EMP: 20
SQ FT: 20,000
SALES (est): 3.6MM
SALES (corp-wide): 11.6MM **Privately
Held**
SIC: 2435 Veneer stock, hardwood
PA: Hartzell Industries, Inc.
1025 S Roosevelt Ave
Piqua OH 45356
937 773-6295

(G-16250)
ATLANTIS SPORTSWEAR INC
Also Called: College Issue
344 Fox Dr (45356-8298)
PHONE......................................937 773-0680
Fax: 937 773-7516
David Reardon, *President*
David Scott Reardon, *President*
Gail Reardon, *Vice Pres*
Kyle Reardon, *VP Opers*
Joe Reiber, *VP Opers*
▲ EMP: 35
SQ FT: 65,000
SALES (est): 5.7MM **Privately Held**
SIC: 2261 2395 2396 Screen printing of
cotton broadwoven fabrics; emblems, em-
broidered; automotive & apparel trim-
mings

(G-16251)
**ATLAS PRECISION MACHINING
INC**
8899 Sherry Dr (45356-9111)
PHONE......................................937 615-9585
Patrick Zimmerman, *Principal*
EMP: 3
SALES (est): 300.6K **Privately Held**
SIC: 3599 Machine shop, jobbing & repair

(G-16252)
**B & L LABELS AND PACKG CO
INC**
421 Fox Dr (45356-8237)
PHONE......................................937 773-9080
William Saddler, *President*
Lynn Saddler, *Vice Pres*
Susan Clark, *Cust Mgr*
EMP: 7
SQ FT: 7,000
SALES (est): 1.2MM **Privately Held**
WEB: www.bllabels.com
SIC: 2672 2657 Labels (unprinted),
gummed: made from purchased materi-
als; folding paperboard boxes

(G-16253)
**BORNHORST MOTOR SERVICE
INC**
Also Called: Electric Motor Service
8270 N Dixie Dr (45356-8636)
P.O. Box 110 (45356-0110)
PHONE......................................937 773-0426
Regina Owen, *President*
EMP: 8
SQ FT: 6,000
SALES (est): 1MM **Privately Held**
SIC: 7694 5063 Electric motor repair; mo-
tors, electric

(G-16254)
C A P INDUSTRIES INC
Also Called: Custom Aerosol Packaging
543 Staunton St (45356-3947)
P.O. Box 1411 (45356-1011)
PHONE......................................937 773-1824
Fax: 937 773-6009
Robert A Heckman, *President*
Mary Heckman, *Corp Secy*
Eric Heckman, *Vice Pres*
EMP: 17
SQ FT: 33,000
SALES (est): 1.7MM **Privately Held**
WEB: www.customaerosol.com
SIC: 7389 2813 5198 Packaging & label-
ing services; aerosols; paints

(G-16255)
CAMFIL USA INC
Also Called: Camfil Farr
405 Fox Dr (45356-8237)
PHONE......................................937 773-0866
Matt Caulfield, *Branch Mgr*
EMP: 3
SALES (corp-wide): 716MM **Privately
Held**
SIC: 3564 3511 Dust or fume collecting
equipment, industrial; turbines & turbine
generator sets
HQ: Camfil Usa Inc
1 N Corporate Dr
Riverdale NJ 07457
973 616-7300

(G-16256)
CRANE PUMPS & SYSTEMS INC
Also Called: Pacific Valve
420 3rd St (45356-3918)
PHONE......................................937 773-2442
Peter Kendall, *Vice Pres*
Joe Jochim, *VP Opers*
Tim Grierson, *Finance Dir*
Richard Perez, *Finance Dir*
Nancy Scanlon, *Human Res Dir*
EMP: 280
SALES (corp-wide): 2.7B **Publicly Held**
SIC: 5085 3494 Valves & fittings; valves &
pipe fittings
HQ: Crane Pumps & Systems, Inc.
420 3rd St
Piqua OH 45356
937 773-2442

(G-16257)
**CRANE PUMPS & SYSTEMS INC
(DH)**
420 3rd St (45356-3918)
PHONE......................................937 773-2442
Fax: 330 773-2238
Jim Lavish, *President*
Jeff Elmore, *Vice Pres*
Walt Erndt, *Vice Pres*
Patrick Rienks, *Vice Pres*
Lynn White, *Vice Pres*
▲ EMP: 350
SQ FT: 120,000
SALES (est): 171.8MM
SALES (corp-wide): 2.7B **Publicly Held**
WEB: www.cranepumps.com
SIC: 3561 Pumps & pumping equipment
HQ: Mcc Holdings, Inc.
4526 Res Frest Dr Ste 400
The Woodlands TX 77381
936 271-6500

(G-16258)
**D C S SPECIALTY PACKAGING
INC**
9700 Looney Rd (45356-2587)
P.O. Box 635 (45356-0635)
PHONE......................................937 615-0100
Fax: 937 615-0100
Mark Schutt, *President*
Tracy Garland, *Manager*
EMP: 10
SQ FT: 10,500
SALES (est): 1.2MM **Privately Held**
SIC: 7389 2621 Packaging & labeling
services; packaging paper

(G-16259)
DAN-LOC LLC
Also Called: Dan-Loc Express
294 Fox Dr (45356-9271)
PHONE......................................937 778-0485
Jerry Jewson, *Opers Mgr*
EMP: 4
SALES (corp-wide): 43.3MM **Privately
Held**
SIC: 3053 Gaskets, packing & sealing de-
vices
PA: Dan-Loc, Llc
725 N Drennan St
Houston TX 77003
713 356-3500

(G-16260)
DARKE PRECISION INC
291 Fox Dr (45356-9265)
P.O. Box 746, Greenville (45331-0746)
PHONE......................................937 548-2232
Fax: 937 548-3740
Harold Young, *President*
Roger Young, *Principal*
Randy Young, *Corp Secy*
EMP: 18
SQ FT: 4,800
SALES (est): 3.2MM **Privately Held**
SIC: 3544 Special dies, tools, jigs & fix-
tures

(G-16261)
DENIZEN INC
130 Fox Dr (45356-9269)
PHONE......................................937 615-9561
Fax: 937 615-9562
John H Reynolds, *President*
Nancy Steinkie, *Director*
Paula Grubb, *Administration*
▲ EMP: 12
SQ FT: 21,000
SALES (est): 3MM **Privately Held**
WEB: www.denizeninc.com
SIC: 2241 5033 Electric insulating tapes &
braids, except plastic; insulation materials

(G-16262)
DYNA VAC PLASTICS INC
921 S Downing St (45356-3823)
P.O. Box 614 (45356-0614)
PHONE......................................937 773-0092
Fax: 937 773-5793
Scott Lade, *President*
Richard Perez, *Principal*
Sandra Lade, *Corp Secy*
EMP: 6
SQ FT: 18,000
SALES: 775K **Privately Held**
SIC: 3089 Plastic processing

(G-16263)
**EAGLE PRINTING & GRAPHICS
LLC**
318 N Wayne St (45356-2230)
PHONE......................................937 773-7900
Fax: 937 773-2580
Robert Delaet, *President*
Diane Delaet, *Vice Pres*
Diane De Laet, *Manager*
EMP: 4
SALES (est): 488.4K **Privately Held**
SIC: 2752 Commercial printing, litho-
graphic

(G-16264)
FINISHERS INC
1718 Commerce Dr (45356-2602)
PHONE......................................937 773-3177
Jerry Dye, *President*
Jim Schneider, *Vice Pres*
Paula Anderson, *Office Mgr*
EMP: 5
SQ FT: 1,200
SALES (est): 370K **Privately Held**
SIC: 3471 Polishing, metals or formed
products

(G-16265)
FORREST ENTERPRISES INC
510 W Statler Rd (45356-8281)
P.O. Box 244 (45356-0244)
PHONE......................................937 773-1714
Fax: 937 773-4724
Staton C Reynolds, *President*
Curtis Reynolds, *Treasurer*
EMP: 8 EST: 1955
SQ FT: 6,500
SALES (est): 905.4K **Privately Held**
WEB: www.forrestent.net
SIC: 3949 4783 Bowling equipment & sup-
plies; packing & crating

(G-16266)
**FRENCH OIL MILL MACHINERY
CO (PA)**
Also Called: French USA
1035 W Greene St (45356-1855)
P.O. Box 920 (45356-0920)
PHONE......................................937 773-3420
Fax: 937 773-3424
Daniel P French, *CEO*
Jason P McDaniel, *COO*
Dennis D Bratton, *Treasurer*
Randall Hefelfinger, *Personnel*
Wayne Shelly, *MIS Staff*
▲ EMP: 60
SQ FT: 210,000
SALES (est): 16.5MM **Privately Held**
WEB: www.frenchoil.com
SIC: 3559 3542 3556 3554 Rubber work-
ing machinery, including tires; presses:
hydraulic & pneumatic, mechanical &
manual; presses, food: cheese, beet,
cider & sugarcane; pulp mill machinery

(G-16267)
GISCO INC
Also Called: General Industrial Supply
308 W Statler Rd (45356-9209)
P.O. Box 463 (45356-0463)
PHONE......................................937 773-7601
Fax: 937 773-4811
Jeffrey Jackson, *President*
Laura Jackson, *Vice Pres*
EMP: 5
SQ FT: 7,500
SALES: 1.2MM **Privately Held**
SIC: 3599 Machine shop, jobbing & repair

(G-16268)
HAMPSHIRE CO
9225 State Route 66 (45356-8700)
P.O. Box 1195 (45356-1195)
PHONE......................................937 773-3493
Fax: 937 773-7627
Thomas F Hampshire, *President*
Dorothy M Hampshire, *Corp Secy*
Robert Mikolajewski, *Vice Pres*
Brad Wilson, *Manager*
EMP: 50
SQ FT: 50,000

GEOGRAPHIC

SALES (est): 6.4MM **Privately Held**
WEB: www.hampshirecabinetry.com
SIC: **2434** Wood kitchen cabinets; vanities,
bathroom: wood

(G-16269)
HANGER PRSTHETCS & ORTHO INC
Also Called: Orpro Prosthetics & Orthotics
9179 N County Road 25a 2b (45356-9521)
PHONE..................................937 773-2441
Fax: 937 778-9200
Vinit Asar, *CEO*
Philip Chow, *Controller*
Carrie Melton, *Branch Mgr*
EMP: 3
SALES (corp-wide): 460MM **Publicly Held**
SIC: **3842** 5999 Prosthetic appliances; or-
thopedic appliances; orthopedic & pros-
thesis applications
HQ: Hanger Prosthetics & Orthotics, Inc.
10910 Domain Dr Ste 300
Austin TX 78758
512 777-3800

(G-16270)
HARMONY SYSTEMS AND SVC INC
1711 Commerce Dr (45356-2601)
PHONE..................................937 778-1082
Fax: 937 778-3074
Edward Adams, *CEO*
Nellie Adams, *President*
Roy Bishop, *Manager*
Hugh Wall, *General Counsel*
▲ EMP: 70
SQ FT: 110,000
SALES (est): 20.7MM **Privately Held**
WEB: www.harmonysysandsvc.com
SIC: **3089** Injection molding of plastics

(G-16271)
HARTZELL FAN INC (PA)
910 S Downing St (45356)
PHONE..................................937 773-7411
Fax: 937 773-8994
Jeff Bannister Hartzell, *CEO*
James Robert Hartzell, *Ch of Bd*
George Atkinson, *President*
Thomas Gustafson, *Vice Pres*
Ric Wallace, *Vice Pres*
◆ EMP: 145
SQ FT: 196,000
SALES (est): 45MM **Privately Held**
SIC: **3564** 3433 Blowers & fans; ventilat-
ing fans: industrial or commercial; heating
equipment, except electric

(G-16272)
HARTZELL HARDWOODS INC (PA)
1025 S Roosevelt Ave (45356-3713)
P.O. Box 919 (45356-0919)
PHONE..................................937 773-7054
Fax: 937 773-7436
Jeffery Bannister, *CEO*
James Robert Hartzell, *Ch of Bd*
Kelly Hostetter, *President*
Josiah McKamey, *Sales Associate*
Jane Osborn, *Admin Sec*
▼ EMP: 65
SQ FT: 275,000
SALES (est): 30.8MM **Privately Held**
WEB: www.hartzellhardwoods.com
SIC: **5031** 2421 2426 Lumber: rough,
dressed & finished; sawmills & planing
mills, general; hardwood dimension &
flooring mills

(G-16273)
HARTZELL INDUSTRIES INC (PA)
1025 S Roosevelt Ave (45356-3713)
P.O. Box 919 (45356-0919)
PHONE..................................937 773-6160
Fax: 937 773-6160
Jeff Bannister, *CEO*
James Robert Hartzell, *Ch of Bd*
Michael Bardo, *President*
Joe Wells, *Vice Pres*
Chris Oliss, *CFO*
EMP: 13 EST: 1964
SQ FT: 20,000

SALES (est): 11.6MM **Privately Held**
WEB: www.hartzellfan.com
SIC: **2435** 6719 Veneer stock, hardwood;
personal holding companies, except
banks

(G-16274)
HARTZELL PROPELLER INC
Also Called: Hartzell Service Center
1 Propeller Pl (45356-2656)
PHONE..................................937 778-4200
Jim Brown, *President*
Kyle Magoteaux, *Engineer*
Dan Oconnell, *Finance Mgr*
Jo Dugnulle, *Human Res Dir*
Chad Hanson, *Human Resources*
EMP: 18
SQ FT: 1,500
SALES (corp-wide): 200MM **Privately Held**
WEB: www.hartzellpropeller.com
SIC: **3728** Governors, aircraft propeller
feathering
HQ: Hartzell Propeller Inc.
1 Propeller Pl
Piqua OH 45356
937 778-4200

(G-16275)
HARTZELL PROPELLER INC (HQ)
1 Propeller Pl (45356-2656)
PHONE..................................937 778-4200
Fax: 937 778-4271
Joseph W Brown, *President*
James Brown III, *Principal*
Bob Allenbaugh, *COO*
Jj Frigge, *Exec VP*
Michael Disbrow, *Senior VP*
◆ EMP: 250
SQ FT: 175,000
SALES (est): 60.6MM
SALES (corp-wide): 200MM **Privately Held**
WEB: www.hartzellpropeller.com
SIC: **3728** Aircraft propellers & associated
equipment
PA: Tailwind Technologies Inc.
1 Propeller Pl
Piqua OH 45356
937 778-4200

(G-16276)
HOBART BROTHERS COMPANY
8585 Industry Park Dr (45356-9511)
P.O. Box 1118 (45356-1118)
PHONE..................................937 773-5869
Jim Schwepeji, *Principal*
EMP: 19
SALES (corp-wide): 13.6B **Publicly Held**
SIC: **3548** Welding apparatus
HQ: Hobart Brothers Company
101 Trade Sq E
Troy OH 45373
937 332-5439

(G-16277)
HOBART CORPORATION
Also Called: P M I Food Equipment Group
8515 Industry Park Dr (45356-9511)
P.O. Box 702 (45356-0702)
PHONE..................................937 332-2797
Larry Lyons, *Plant Mgr*
Joseph Huang, *Engineer*
Dean Ramaeker, *Manager*
Jon Shindollar, *Manager*
Bob Strouse, *Technical Staff*
EMP: 120
SALES (corp-wide): 13.6B **Publicly Held**
WEB: www.hobartcorp.com
SIC: **3589** 3556 3596 3585 Dishwashing
machines, commercial; cooking equip-
ment, commercial; commercial cooking &
foodwarming equipment; food products
machinery; weighing machines & appara-
tus; refrigeration equipment, complete;
gray & ductile iron foundries
HQ: Hobart Corporation
701 S Ridge Ave
Troy OH 45374
937 332-3000

(G-16278)
HOLE HUNTER GOLF INC
Also Called: Hole Hunter Golf Driving Range
438 S Downing St (45356-3906)
P.O. Box 731, Troy (45373-0731)
PHONE..................................937 339-5833
Fax: 937 339-6204
William S Brading, *President*
EMP: 3
SQ FT: 4,200
SALES (est): 337.9K **Privately Held**
SIC: **5941** 3949 7999 Golf goods & equip-
ment; golf equipment; golf driving range

(G-16279)
INDUSTRY PRODUCTS CO (PA)
500 W Statler Rd (45356-8281)
PHONE..................................937 778-0585
Fax: 937 778-9613
Linda Cleveland, *President*
Mike Patrick, *COO*
Tom Craft, *Mfg Dir*
Todd Guenther, *Project Mgr*
Anita Aultman, *Materials Mgr*
EMP: 366 EST: 1966
SQ FT: 335,000
SALES: 76MM **Privately Held**
WEB: www.industryproductsco.com
SIC: **7692** 3053 3714 3544 Automotive
welding; gaskets, all materials; motor ve-
hicle parts & accessories; motor vehicle
body components & frame; special dies,
tools, jigs & fixtures; unsupported plastics
film & sheet

(G-16280)
ISAIAH INDUSTRIES INC (PA)
Also Called: Classic Metal Roofing Systems
8510 Industry Park Dr (45356-8535)
P.O. Box 701 (45356-0701)
PHONE..................................937 773-9840
Fax: 937 773-9261
Donald E Miller, *CEO*
Todd Miller, *President*
Tony Helms, *Accountant*
Kelly Joseph, *Finance*
Jimmy Land, *Natl Sales Mgr*
▼ EMP: 40
SQ FT: 5,000
SALES (est): 8.7MM **Privately Held**
WEB: www.classicroof.com
SIC: **3354** 3444 2952 Aluminum extruded
products; sheet metalwork; asphalt felts &
coatings

(G-16281)
J M MOLD INC
1707 Commerce Dr (45356-2601)
P.O. Box 730 (45356-0730)
PHONE..................................937 778-0077
Fax: 937 778-1925
Kriss Scheer, *President*
Robert P Scheer, *President*
Mark Kinsella, *Controller*
Kristina Scheer,
EMP: 8 EST: 1966
SQ FT: 9,600
SALES: 1.7MM **Privately Held**
SIC: **3544** Dies & die holders for metal cut-
ting, forming, die casting; industrial molds

(G-16282)
JACKSON TUBE SERVICE INC (PA)
8210 Industry Park Dr (45356-8536)
P.O. Box 1650 (45356-4650)
PHONE..................................937 773-8550
Fax: 937 773-8806
Robert W Jackson, *CEO*
David A Hare, *Vice Pres*
Marcus Sergy, *Vice Pres*
Mathew Roop, *Buyer*
James Froning, *Engineer*
▲ EMP: 153
SQ FT: 75,000
SALES (est): 33.1MM **Privately Held**
WEB: www.jackson-tube.com
SIC: **3317** Steel pipe & tubes

(G-16283)
JERRY PULFER
Also Called: Piqua Sign
900 S Main St (45356-3858)
PHONE..................................937 778-1861
Fax: 937 773-9695
Jerry Pulfer, *Owner*

EMP: 3
SQ FT: 3,200
SALES: 200K **Privately Held**
WEB: www.piquatechnologies.com
SIC: **3993** 3953 2796 2671 Signs & advertising specialties; marking devices;
platemaking services; packaging paper &
plastics film, coated & laminated; automotive & apparel trimmings

(G-16284)
K & B STAMPING & MANUFACTURING
9676 Looney Rd (45356-9522)
P.O. Box 405 (45356-0405)
PHONE..................................937 778-8875
Manfried Kirchner, *President*
Brian Kirchner, *Vice Pres*
EMP: 5
SALES: 500K **Privately Held**
SIC: **3469** Metal stampings

(G-16285)
K B MACHINE & TOOL INC
1500 S Main St (45356-8319)
P.O. Box 426 (45356-0426)
PHONE..................................937 773-1624
Fax: 937 773-0842
Kenneth G Bricker, *President*
Miki Bricker, *Vice Pres*
Joyce K Bricker, *Admin Sec*
EMP: 9
SQ FT: 9,500
SALES (est): 1.1MM **Privately Held**
SIC: **3544** Special dies & tools

(G-16286)
LITTLE PRINTING COMPANY
Also Called: Quality Forms
4317 W Us Route 36 (45356-9334)
P.O. Box 1176 (45356-1176)
PHONE..................................937 773-4595
Fax: 937 773-2758
Tom Kinnison, *President*
Lj Bertke, *CFO*
EMP: 35
SQ FT: 54,000
SALES: 5.5MM **Privately Held**
SIC: **2761** Manifold business forms

(G-16287)
LOSTCREEK TOOL & MACHINE INC
1150 S Main St (45356-9357)
PHONE..................................937 773-6022
Fax: 937 773-6065
Steve Rowe, *President*
Michael Rowe, *President*
Shelby Rowe, *Corp Secy*
Donald Rowe, *Vice Pres*
EMP: 12
SQ FT: 15,500
SALES: 666.8K **Privately Held**
SIC: **3599** 7692 3544 Machine shop, job-
bing & repair; welding repair; special dies,
tools, jigs & fixtures

(G-16288)
LWB/ISE LP
9160 Country Club Rd (45356-8571)
PHONE..................................937 778-3828
Fax: 937 223-4198
Al Baker, *Plant Mgr*
EMP: 12
SALES (corp-wide): 1.2MM **Privately Held**
SIC: **3465** Body parts, automobile:
stamped metal
PA: Lwb-Ise Societe En Commandite
20 Rte De Windsor
Sherbrooke QC J1C 0
819 846-1044

(G-16289)
M C D PLASTICS & MANUFACTURING
Also Called: Miami Specialties
172 Robert M Davis Pkwy (45356-8338)
PHONE..................................937 778-1850
Fax: 937 778-1851
Robb Howell, *President*
EMP: 7
SQ FT: 10,000

SALES: 524.6K **Privately Held**
WEB: www.mcdplastics.com
SIC: 3599 Machine shop, jobbing & repair

(G-16290)
MAJESTIC SPORTSWEAR COMPANY
2545 Landman Mill Rd (45356-9746)
PHONE..................................937 773-1144
Mike Ivanowicz, *Owner*
EMP: 8
SALES (est): 503.9K **Privately Held**
SIC: 5137 2339 Sweaters, women's & children's; athletic clothing: women's, misses' & juniors'

(G-16291)
MEDICAL EQUIPMENT PROVIDER
102 Fox Dr (45356-9269)
PHONE..................................937 778-2190
Bryan Reed, *Manager*
EMP: 4
SALES (est): 242.9K **Privately Held**
SIC: 3845 Respiratory analysis equipment, electromedical

(G-16292)
MIAMI VALLEY POLISHING
220 Fox Dr (45356-9271)
PHONE..................................937 615-9353
Matthew Powers, *Principal*
EMP: 14
SALES (est): 2.4MM **Privately Held**
SIC: 3471 Polishing, metals or formed products

(G-16293)
MOREY WOODWORKING LLC
377 E Loy Rd (45356-9292)
PHONE..................................937 623-5280
Todd Morey, *Owner*
EMP: 4 EST: 2010
SALES (est): 431.7K **Privately Held**
SIC: 2431 Millwork

(G-16294)
NICKS PLATING CO INC
6980 Free Rd (45356-9279)
P.O. Box 337 (45356-0337)
PHONE..................................937 773-3175
Fax: 937 615-0195
Duane Penrod, *President*
EMP: 10 EST: 1973
SQ FT: 4,500
SALES: 700K **Privately Held**
SIC: 3471 Plating of metals or formed products; polishing, metals or formed products

(G-16295)
NITTO DENKO AUTO OHIO INC
1620 S Main St (45356-8320)
P.O. Box 740 (45356-0740)
PHONE..................................937 773-4820
Hideo Takasaki, *CEO*
Yukio Nagira, *Chairman*
Toru Takeuchi, *Senior VP*
Toshihiko Omote, *Vice Pres*
Yoichiro Sakuma, *Vice Pres*
▲ EMP: 200
SQ FT: 100,000
SALES: 49.7MM
SALES (corp-wide): 6.7B **Privately Held**
WEB: www.nitto.co.jp
SIC: 3053 3296 Gaskets & sealing devices; mineral wool
PA: Nitto Denko Corporation
4-20, Ofukacho, Kita-Ku
Osaka OSK 530-0
676 322-101

(G-16296)
ORR FELT COMPANY
750 S Main St (45356-3834)
P.O. Box 908 (45356-0908)
PHONE..................................937 778-0551
Fax: 937 778-9670
Dimitri M Nicholas, *CEO*
Fred Allison, *Design Engr*
Brenda Jacomet, *Personnel Exec*
Shirish Shah, *Manager*
▲ EMP: 60 EST: 1963
SQ FT: 400,000

SALES (est): 9.1MM **Privately Held**
SIC: 2231 Papermakers' felts, woven: wool, mohair or similar fibers

(G-16297)
P & R SPECIALTY INC
1835 W High St (45356-9399)
P.O. Box 741 (45356-0741)
PHONE..................................937 773-0263
Fax: 937 773-4243
Greg Blankenship, *President*
Alissa Blankenship, *Vice Pres*
Pat Kiernan, *Vice Pres*
Mike Koon, *Vice Pres*
Vincent Reidy, *Vice Pres*
▲ EMP: 35 EST: 1982
SQ FT: 47,500
SALES (est): 7MM **Privately Held**
WEB: www.prspecialty.com
SIC: 2499 3053 2675 2631 Spools, wood; gaskets, all materials; paper die-cutting; paperboard mills

(G-16298)
PALSTAR INC
9676 Looney Rd (45356-9522)
P.O. Box 1136 (45356-1136)
PHONE..................................937 773-6255
Paul Hrivnak, *President*
Donald Keffer, *Vice Pres*
Eva Hrivnak, *Treasurer*
EMP: 16
SQ FT: 4,000
SALES (est): 3.4MM **Privately Held**
WEB: www.palstar.com
SIC: 3825 Signal generators & averagers

(G-16299)
PERFECTO INDUSTRIES INC
1729 W High St (45356-9300)
PHONE..................................937 778-1900
Fax: 937 778-0059
J Heinlein, *Division Mgr*
Ralph Bateman, *Engineer*
Harvey Howard, *Branch Mgr*
EMP: 45
SALES (corp-wide): 19.6MM **Privately Held**
WEB: www.perfectoindustries.com
SIC: 3547 3549 3599 3537 Rolling mill machinery; coiling machinery; custom machinery; industrial trucks & tractors
PA: Perfecto Industries, Inc.
1567 Calkins Dr
Gaylord MI 49735
989 732-2941

(G-16300)
PIQUA CHAMPION FOUNDRY INC
918 S Main St (45356-3858)
P.O. Box 716 (45356-0716)
PHONE..................................937 773-3375
Fax: 937 773-9698
Larry W Pickering, *President*
Ken Pickering, *General Mgr*
R P Fite, *Principal*
Renate Pickering, *Vice Pres*
EMP: 25
SQ FT: 35,000
SALES (est): 4.8MM **Privately Held**
SIC: 3321 Gray & ductile iron foundries

(G-16301)
PIQUA CHOCOLATE COMPANY INC (PA)
Also Called: Winans Chocolate and Coffee
310 Spring St (45356-2334)
PHONE..................................937 773-1981
Joe Reiser, *President*
EMP: 9
SQ FT: 2,000
SALES (est): 3.5MM **Privately Held**
SIC: 5441 5947 2064 Candy; greeting cards; candy & other confectionery products

(G-16302)
PIQUA CONCRETE CORP (PA)
8395 Piqua Lockington Rd (45356-9701)
PHONE..................................937 773-0841
Fax: 937 773-6217
Henry Ernst, *President*
Richard J Hoying, *Vice Pres*
Jeff Schaffner, *Sales Mgr*
Dick Hoying, *Sales Executive*

EMP: 20
SQ FT: 2,500
SALES (est): 10.8MM **Privately Held**
WEB: www.piquaconcrete.com
SIC: 3273 Ready-mixed concrete

(G-16303)
PIQUA EMERY CUTTER & FNDRY CO
Also Called: Piqua Emery Foundry
821 S Downing St (45356)
PHONE..................................937 773-4134
Fax: 937 773-3694
Stephen Mikolajewski, *President*
Helen Mikolajewski, *Corp Secy*
Roger McLain, *Vice Pres*
David Martin, *Sales Staff*
EMP: 54 EST: 1934
SQ FT: 54,000
SALES (est): 12.7MM **Privately Held**
WEB: www.piquaemery.com
SIC: 3365 3369 3366 Aluminum & aluminum-based alloy castings; nonferrous foundries; castings (except die): bronze; castings (except die): brass

(G-16304)
PIQUA GRANITE & MARBLE CO INC (PA)
Also Called: Classic Monuments
123 N Main St (45356-2311)
P.O. Box 1197 (45356-1197)
PHONE..................................937 773-2000
Pat Obara, *President*
Steve Supinger, *Vice Pres*
EMP: 9
SQ FT: 18,000
SALES (est): 1.5MM **Privately Held**
WEB: www.hmw.com
SIC: 5999 5032 3281 Monuments, finished to custom order; granite building stone; marble, building: cut & shaped

(G-16305)
PIQUA MATERIALS INC
Also Called: Piqua Mineral Division
1750 W Statler Rd (45356-9264)
PHONE..................................937 773-4824
Fax: 937 773-0791
Brent Phillips, *Safety Mgr*
John Harris, *Branch Mgr*
EMP: 30
SQ FT: 16,808
SALES (corp-wide): 16.3MM **Privately Held**
SIC: 1422 3274 Limestones, ground; lime
PA: Piqua Materials Inc
11641 Mosteller Rd Ste 1
Cincinnati OH 45241
513 771-0820

(G-16306)
PIQUA PAPER BOX COMPANY
616 Covington Ave (45356-3205)
P.O. Box 814 (45356-0814)
PHONE..................................937 773-0313
Fax: 937 773-0142
Frank J Gleason Jr, *Ch of Bd*
Brian T Gleason, *President*
Samuel Vorhees, *Manager*
Eugene Elsass, *Admin Sec*
▲ EMP: 35
SQ FT: 85,000
SALES (est): 7.5MM **Privately Held**
SIC: 2652 Setup paperboard boxes

(G-16307)
PRECISE TOOL INC
9676 Looney Rd (45356-9522)
P.O. Box 405 (45356-0405)
PHONE..................................937 778-3441
Fax: 937 778-3461
Brian Kirchner, *President*
Theresa Kirchner, *Vice Pres*
EMP: 5
SQ FT: 10,000
SALES: 690K **Privately Held**
SIC: 3544 Special dies, tools, jigs & fixtures

(G-16308)
PROTO-MOLD PRODUCTS CO INC
1750 Commerce Dr (45356-2699)
PHONE..................................937 778-1959

Fax: 937 778-1004
Graig Flintcraft, *President*
George Reedy, *General Mgr*
Craig Flitcraft, *Vice Pres*
Jane Flitcraft, *Vice Pres*
Alan Vance, *Manager*
EMP: 25
SQ FT: 50,000
SALES (est): 6.3MM **Privately Held**
WEB: www.protomoldproducts.com
SIC: 3089 Injection molding of plastics

(G-16309)
R DUNN MOLD INC
9055 State Route 66 (45356-9727)
P.O. Box 1805 (45356-4805)
PHONE..................................937 773-3388
Fax: 937 773-3388
Robert Dunn, *President*
EMP: 3
SQ FT: 4,000
SALES: 150K **Privately Held**
SIC: 3089 3545 Injection molding of plastics; precision tools, machinists'

(G-16310)
RETTERBUSH FIBERGLASS CORP
719 Long St (45356-9262)
P.O. Box 207 (45356-0207)
PHONE..................................937 778-1936
Fax: 937 773-5642
Bryan Retterbush, *President*
Debrah Warner, *Manager*
EMP: 25
SQ FT: 32,000
SALES (est): 2.7MM **Privately Held**
WEB: www.retterbushfiberglass.com
SIC: 3089 Injection molding of plastics

(G-16311)
ROTH TRANSIT INC
8590 Industry Park Dr (45356-8535)
P.O. Box 821 (45356-0821)
PHONE..................................937 773-5051
Linda Roth, *President*
EMP: 7 EST: 1998
SQ FT: 7,200
SALES (est): 750K **Privately Held**
SIC: 3596 4212 Truck (motor vehicle) scales; local trucking, without storage

(G-16312)
RV XPRESS INC
501 East St (45356-3930)
PHONE..................................937 418-0127
Glenn McKinney, *President*
Michael T McGahan, *Principal*
EMP: 8
SALES (est): 625.3K **Privately Held**
SIC: 3799 Recreational vehicles

(G-16313)
TAILWIND TECHNOLOGIES INC (PA)
1 Propeller Pl (45356-2655)
PHONE..................................937 778-4200
James W Brown III, *President*
Joseph W Brown, *Principal*
Michael J Piscatella, *Principal*
Mike Piscatella, *Senior VP*
Matthew L Jesch, *CFO*
EMP: 22
SALES: 200MM **Privately Held**
SIC: 3356 Titanium

(G-16314)
TEMPO MANUFACTURING COMPANY
Also Called: Tempo Trophy Mfg
727 E Ash St (45356-2411)
P.O. Box 718 (45356-0718)
PHONE..................................937 773-6613
Fax: 937 773-6614
Robert Elrod, *President*
Patricia Elrod, *Vice Pres*
EMP: 8
SQ FT: 30,000
SALES (est): 710.2K **Privately Held**
SIC: 3914 Trophies

GEOGRAPHIC

(G-16315)
TK HOLDINGS INC
Also Called: T K Holdings
1401 Innovation Pkwy (45356-7524)
PHONE..................................937 778-9713
Monica Baughn, *Plant Mgr*
Monica Bauthn, *Manager*
EMP: 25 Privately Held
SIC: 2399 5013 Seat belts, automobile &
aircraft; motor vehicle supplies & new
parts
HQ: Tk Holdings Inc.
4611 Wiseman Blvd
San Antonio TX 78251
210 509-0762

(G-16316)
WRIGHTS SAW MILL
9018 Piqua Lockington Rd (45356-9741)
PHONE..................................937 773-2546
James Wright, *Principal*
EMP: 3
SALES (est): 238.1K **Privately Held**
SIC: 2421 Sawmills & planing mills, gen-
eral

Plain City
Madison County

(G-16317)
ACB THREE INC
9341 Industrial Pkwy (43064-8729)
PHONE..................................614 873-4680
Art Bafchnagel, *Principal*
EMP: 3
SALES (est): 218.4K **Privately Held**
SIC: 3559 Sewing machines & attach-
ments, industrial

(G-16318)
**ADVANCED CLEANING TECH
LLC**
Also Called: Ultimate Cloth
7533 Merchant Rd (43064-9303)
PHONE..................................614 504-5433
Christa Wiley, *Office Mgr*
Tracy J Stewart,
EMP: 3
SQ FT: 2,000
SALES (est): 351.7K **Privately Held**
SIC: 2842 Paint & wallpaper cleaners

(G-16319)
**AMERICAN APEX
CORPORATION**
8515 Rausch Dr (43064-8067)
PHONE..................................614 652-2000
Charles R Torson, *President*
Tina Adams, *Manager*
Sherry H Torson, *Admin Sec*
▲ **EMP: 13**
SQ FT: 16,000
SALES (est): 2.6MM **Privately Held**
WEB: www.americanapex.com
SIC: 3484 3489 3795 8748 Small arms;
ordnance & accessories; tanks & tank
components; specialized tank compo-
nents, military; safety training service

(G-16320)
ARCHED CASINGS INC
8490 Carters Mill Rd (43064-9116)
PHONE..................................614 873-1196
Fax: 614 873-9963
Jerry Whitmer, *President*
Don Whitmer, *Treasurer*
Aaron Beachy, *Office Mgr*
EMP: 6
SALES (est): 550K **Privately Held**
WEB: www.archedcasings.com
SIC: 3442 Molding, trim & stripping

(G-16321)
ASSOCIATED GRAPHICS INC
9021 Heritage Dr Ste I (43064-8757)
PHONE..................................614 873-1273
Fax: 614 873-6728
Adam Wright, *President*
Roger McPeek, *Vice Pres*
EMP: 10
SALES (est): 365K **Privately Held**
WEB: www.agionline.com
SIC: 2759 Commercial printing

(G-16322)
AUTOTOOL INC
7875 Corporate Blvd (43064-8045)
PHONE..................................614 733-0222
Fax: 614 733-0220
Bassam Homsi, *President*
Amy Chassin, *Purchasing*
Matthew Fry, *Design Engr*
Steve Forrest, *Electrical Engi*
Amy Chaffin, *Mktg Dir*
EMP: 38
SQ FT: 40,000
SALES (est): 10.4MM **Privately Held**
WEB: www.autotoolinc.com
SIC: 3559 Automotive related machinery

(G-16323)
BAHLER MEDICAL INC
Also Called: Venture Medical
8910 Warner Rd (43064-9467)
PHONE..................................614 873-7600
Michael Bahler, *President*
Maria Henry, *Human Resources*
EMP: 36
SALES (est): 2.9MM **Privately Held**
SIC: 3842 Implants, surgical

(G-16324)
BALMAC INC
8205 Estates Pkwy Ste N (43064-8080)
PHONE..................................614 873-8222
Mark Slebodnik, *President*
Steve Crawford, *Vice Pres*
Brad Cline, *Engineer*
EMP: 10
SQ FT: 6,000
SALES (est): 1MM **Privately Held**
WEB: www.balmacinc.com
SIC: 3829 Vibration meters, analyzers &
calibrators

(G-16325)
**BCAST STAINLESS PRODUCTS
LLC**
9000 Heritage Dr (43064-9493)
PHONE..................................614 873-3945
Lou Castelli,
▲ **EMP: 12**
SALES (est): 1MM **Privately Held**
SIC: 3312 5075 Stainless steel; furnaces,
heating: electric

(G-16326)
**BINDERY & SPC PRESSWORKS
INC**
351 W Bigelow Ave (43064-1152)
PHONE..................................614 873-4623
Fax: 614 873-4625
Dick Izzard, *President*
Betty Izzard, *Vice Pres*
Doug Izzard, *Vice Pres*
Mark Izzard, *Vice Pres*
Rodney Owens, *Manager*
EMP: 74
SQ FT: 42,000
SALES (est): 18.1MM **Privately Held**
SIC: 2791 2759 2752 2789 Typesetting;
commercial printing; commercial printing,
offset; bookbinding & related work; mail-
ing service

(G-16327)
COM-FAB INC
4657 Price Hilliards Rd (43064-8838)
PHONE..................................740 857-1107
Fax: 614 857-1757
Jim Sheehy, *President*
Virginia Smiley, *Treasurer*
Ashley Stonerock, *Manager*
EMP: 22
SQ FT: 20,000
SALES (est): 5MM **Privately Held**
WEB: www.comfab-inc.com
SIC: 3441 Fabricated structural metal

(G-16328)
COPY RIGHT OF OHIO LLC
7445 Montgomery Rd B (43064-8612)
PHONE..................................614 431-1303
James Craig Annette,
EMP: 3
SQ FT: 2,500
SALES (est): 482K **Privately Held**
SIC: 2752 Commercial printing, litho-
graphic

(G-16329)
DABAR INDUSTRIES LLC
8475 Rausch Dr (43064-8064)
PHONE..................................614 873-3949
Cliff Baseler, *President*
John Schindelar, *Controller*
EMP: 15 EST: 2015
SQ FT: 12,600
SALES (est): 1.5MM **Privately Held**
SIC: 3443 Tanks, standard or custom fabri-
cated: metal plate

(G-16330)
DAILY NEEDS ASSISTANCE
Also Called: D N A
340 W Main St (43064-1198)
PHONE..................................614 824-8340
Tamara Reed, *Director*
EMP: 12 EST: 2013
SALES (est): 166.9K **Privately Held**
SIC: 2711 Newspapers, publishing & print-
ing

(G-16331)
DARBY CREEK MILLWORK CO
10001 Plain Cy Grgesville (43064)
PHONE..................................614 873-3267
Ivan Beachy, *Owner*
EMP: 7
SQ FT: 8,000
SALES (est): 700K **Privately Held**
SIC: 2431 Millwork; door frames, wood

(G-16332)
DARBY CREEK PUBLISHING
7858 Industrial Pkwy (43064-9468)
PHONE..................................614 873-7958
John Mardeson, *President*
▲ **EMP: 10**
SALES (est): 449.2K
SALES (corp-wide): 43.9MM **Privately
Held**
SIC: 2741 Miscellaneous publishing
PA: Lerner Publishing Group, Inc.
1251 Washington Ave N
Minneapolis MN 55401
612 332-3344

(G-16333)
**DATA ANALYSIS
TECHNOLOGIES**
7715 Corporate Blvd (43064-9212)
P.O. Box 3131, Dublin (43016-0063)
PHONE..................................614 873-0710
Fax: 614 873-0810
Ronald K Mitchum, *President*
D Jane Mitchum, *CFO*
EMP: 8
SQ FT: 10,000
SALES (est): 1.5MM **Privately Held**
WEB: www.datlab.com
SIC: 8734 8748 3822 Pollution testing;
testing services; systems engineering
consultant, ex. computer or professional;
auto controls regulating residntl & coml
environmt & applncs

(G-16334)
DAVID S RODGERS ◆
8168 Business Way (43064-9224)
PHONE..................................740 490-5843
David Rodgers, *Owner*
David S Rodgers, *Principal*
EMP: 4 EST: 2016
SALES (est): 112.4K **Privately Held**
SIC: 3443 Fabricated plate work (boiler
shop)

(G-16335)
**DISTINCTIVE MARBLE & GRAN
INC**
7635 Commerce Pl (43064-9223)
PHONE..................................614 760-0003
Chris Schnetzler, *President*
Kathy Schnetzler, *Principal*
▲ **EMP: 10**
SALES (est): 970K **Privately Held**
WEB:
www.distinctivemarbleandgranite.com
SIC: 1743 3281 Marble installation, inte-
rior; curbing, granite or stone

(G-16336)
**DJ BEVERAGE INNOVATIONS
INC**
Also Called: Beertubes.com
8400 Indl Pkwy Bldg 2 (43064)
PHONE..................................614 769-1569
David J Stein, *President*
Jason M Drum, *Vice Pres*
Steve Lerner, *Business Dir*
▲ **EMP: 3**
SALES (est): 427.9K **Privately Held**
SIC: 3585 5078 Soda fountain & beverage
dispensing equipment & parts; refriger-
ated beverage dispensers

(G-16337)
DRIVETRAIN USA INC
Also Called: Cryogenic Technical Services
8445 Rausch Dr (43064-8064)
P.O. Box 3787, Dublin (43016-0406)
PHONE..................................614 733-0940
John Canfield, *President*
Glen McIntosh, *Human Res Mgr*
EMP: 10
SQ FT: 40,000
SALES (est): 1.5MM **Privately Held**
SIC: 3679 Cryogenic cooling devices for
infrared detectors, masers

(G-16338)
**EAGLE ROCK BRAND CONS
LLC**
10370 Summersweet Way (43064-6010)
PHONE..................................614 403-4802
Aimee Valentine, *CEO*
Ian Kimmel,
EMP: 3 EST: 2013
SQ FT: 200
SALES (est): 161.4K **Privately Held**
SIC: 8742 7389 2326 5699 Marketing
consulting services; textile & apparel
services; advertising, promotional & trade
show services; work apparel, except uni-
forms; customized clothing & apparel

(G-16339)
EDEN CRYOGENICS LLC
8475 Rausch Dr (43064-8064)
PHONE..................................614 873-3949
Steve L Hensley, *President*
Keith Brooks, *Manager*
Angie Dimasso, *Manager*
John Warnement, *Supervisor*
Michael Dent, *Exec Dir*
▲ **EMP: 45**
SALES (est): 11.1MM **Privately Held**
WEB: www.edencryogenics.com
SIC: 3559 Cryogenic machinery, industrial

(G-16340)
FRIESEN FAB AND EQUIPMENT
Also Called: Friesen Fab & Equipment
10030 Smith Calhoun Rd (43064-9142)
PHONE..................................614 873-4354
Fax: 614 873-5533
Cornelius Friesen, *Owner*
EMP: 4
SQ FT: 6,000
SALES (est): 371.2K **Privately Held**
WEB: www.friesenfab.com
SIC: 3524 7699 Lawn & garden mowers &
accessories; agricultural equipment repair
services

(G-16341)
FRIESEN TRANSFER LTD
9280 Iams Rd (43064-9108)
PHONE..................................614 873-5672
Klaas Friesen, *President*
EMP: 6
SALES (est): 460K **Privately Held**
SIC: 3713 0115 0111 Dump truck bodies;
corn; wheat

(G-16342)
GK PACKAGING INC (PA)
Also Called: Plain City Molding
7680 Commerce Pl (43064-9222)
PHONE..................................614 873-3900
Fax: 614 873-3901
Gene J Kuzma, *President*
Betty Jo Jerome, *Principal*
Vicki Fritchen, *Transptn Dir*
Ron Marion, *Plant Mgr*
Edward Stevenson, *Plant Mgr*

▲ EMP: 95
SQ FT: 70,000
SALES (est): 26.1MM **Privately Held**
WEB: www.gkpackaging.com
SIC: 3085 Plastics bottles

(G-16343)
GOLD METAL MACHINING INC
Also Called: Union Enterprises Division
216 W Bigelow Ave (43064-1143)
PHONE..................................614 873-5031
Fax: 740 873-4931
Kenneth J Cahill, *President*
Timothy A Goodrich, *Vice Pres*
EMP: 10 EST: 1946
SQ FT: 4,000
SALES (est): 660K **Privately Held**
SIC: 3599 Machine shop, jobbing & repair

(G-16344)
GOLF CAR COMPANY INC
8899 Memorial Dr (43064-8636)
PHONE..................................614 873-1055
William Mead, *President*
Sarah Volker, *General Mgr*
Erik Rogers, *Opers Mgr*
EMP: 12
SALES (est): 1.6MM **Privately Held**
SIC: 3949 7359 5599 Sporting & athletic
goods; stores & yards equipment rental;
golf cart, powered

(G-16345)
HALLIDAY TECHNOLOGIES INC
8525 Rausch Dr Unit B (43064-8067)
PHONE..................................614 504-4150
Don Halliday, *President*
Patricia Halliday, *Vice Pres*
Alexandra Sydney, *Vice Pres*
EMP: 4
SQ FT: 400
SALES: 1MM **Privately Held**
WEB: www.hallidaytech.com
SIC: 3829 8711 Measuring & controlling
devices; consulting engineer

(G-16346)
KBI GROUP INC
Also Called: King Mill's Woodworking
7370 Merchant Rd (43064-9301)
PHONE..................................614 873-5825
Norman King, *President*
David King, *Vice Pres*
EMP: 3
SALES: 150K **Privately Held**
SIC: 2541 1751 Counter & sink tops;
counters or counter display cases, wood;
cabinet & finish carpentry

(G-16347)
KNB TOOLS OF AMERICA INC
8440 Rausch Dr (43064-8047)
PHONE..................................614 733-0400
Toshihiko Kawanobe, *CEO*
Akira Kinoshita, *Vice Pres*
▲ EMP: 18
SALES (est): 3.2MM **Privately Held**
SIC: 3545 Cutting tools for machine tools

(G-16348)
MD SOLUTIONS INC
Also Called: M D Solutions
8225 Estates Pkwy (43064-8408)
PHONE..................................866 637-6588
Nirmal Bajoria, *Principal*
▲ EMP: 3
SALES (est): 658K **Privately Held**
SIC: 3669 3999 Traffic signals, electric; at-
omizers, toiletry

(G-16349)
MIDWEST MOLDING INC
8245 Estates Pkwy (43064-8408)
PHONE..................................614 873-1572
William Razor, *President*
EMP: 40
SQ FT: 7,800
SALES (est): 8.1MM **Privately Held**
SIC: 3089 Molding primary plastic

(G-16350)
MIDWEST QUALITY BEDDING INC
Also Called: Mattress Mart
8400 Industrial Pkwy B (43064-9231)
PHONE..................................614 504-5971

John Fogt, *Vice Pres*
EMP: 15
SALES (est): 2.5MM **Privately Held**
SIC: 2515 Mattresses & bedsprings

(G-16351)
MILLER CABINET COMPANY LLC
6217 Converse Huff Rd (43064-9185)
PHONE..................................614 873-4221
Fax: 740 873-8394
Lonnie Beachy, *Director*
Ken Wilson, *
EMP: 35
SALES (est): 4.5MM **Privately Held**
SIC: 5722 2541 2521 2511 Kitchens,
complete (sinks, cabinets, etc.); cabinets,
except refrigerated: show, display, etc.:
wood; wood office furniture; wood house-
hold furniture; wood kitchen cabinets

(G-16352)
OHIO LASER LLC
8260 Estates Pkwy (43064-8409)
PHONE..................................614 873-7030
Gregg P Simpson, *President*
Wesley Davey, *Mfg Mgr*
Christine Simpson, *HR Admin*
Matt Patrick, *Manager*
Mark Rosenberg, *Manager*
EMP: 20
SQ FT: 30,000
SALES (est): 5.4MM **Privately Held**
WEB: www.ohiolaser.com
SIC: 3499 Welding tips, heat resistant:
metal

(G-16353)
OYLAIR SPECIALTY
9029 Heritage Dr (43064-9493)
PHONE..................................614 873-3968
EMP: 6
SALES (est): 987.6K **Privately Held**
SIC: 3592 Mfg Carburetors/Pistons/Rings

(G-16354)
PHOENIX BAT COMPANY
7801 Corp Blvd Unit E (43064)
PHONE..................................614 873-7776
Charles Trudeau, *President*
▲ EMP: 4
SQ FT: 3,000
SALES (est): 475.3K **Privately Held**
WEB: www.phoenixbats.com
SIC: 3949 5941 5091 Baseball equipment
& supplies, general; baseball equipment;
sporting & recreation goods

(G-16355)
PUBLIC SAFETY CONCEPTS LLC
8495 Estates Ct (43064-8015)
PHONE..................................614 733-0200
Tom Parr, *
EMP: 6
SALES: 675K **Privately Held**
SIC: 3669 5531 Intercommunication sys-
tems, electric; automotive & home supply
stores

(G-16356)
QUILTING INC (PA)
Also Called: Mattress Mart
7600 Industrial Pkwy (43064-9468)
PHONE..................................614 504-5971
Fax: 614 873-6669
Ben Tiburzio, *President*
▲ EMP: 55
SQ FT: 85,000
SALES (est): 12.4MM **Privately Held**
WEB: www.quilting.com
SIC: 2515 Mattresses, innerspring or box
spring

(G-16357)
SCOTTS COMPANY LLC
7400 Industrial Pkwy (43064-8789)
PHONE..................................614 733-0462
Dennis Sigrist, *Manager*
EMP: 22
SALES (corp-wide): 2.8B **Publicly Held**
WEB: www.scottscompany.com
SIC: 2873 Fertilizers: natural (organic), ex-
cept compost

HQ: The Scotts Company Llc
14111 Scottslawn Rd
Marysville OH 43040
937 644-3729

(G-16358)
SIGNAFFECTS LIMITED LLC
8147 Industrial Pkwy (43064-9469)
PHONE..................................614 504-5324
Brendan Moody, *Accounts Mgr*
Paul Lyda, *Marketing Staff*
EMP: 4
SALES: 700K **Privately Held**
SIC: 3993 Electric signs

(G-16359)
SILVER THREADS INC
7710 Corporate Blvd (43064-9214)
PHONE..................................614 733-0099
Fax: 614 733-0499
Carrie Perini, *President*
Tim Perini, *Vice Pres*
Anissa Whalen, *Mktg Coord*
Marc Gould, *Marketing Staff*
Deanna Maynard, *Manager*
EMP: 20 EST: 1979
SQ FT: 6,000
SALES (est): 4MM **Privately Held**
WEB: www.silverthreadsinc.com
SIC: 2211 7389 2392 2391 Draperies &
drapery fabrics, cotton; interior designer;
household furnishings; curtains &
draperies

(G-16360)
SNAIR CO
8163 Business Way (43064-9216)
PHONE..................................614 873-7020
Masashi J Nagai, *Owner*
Hideta Nagai, *Co-Owner*
Leah Nagai, *Human Resources*
Richard Meske, *Manager*
EMP: 16 EST: 1981
SQ FT: 52,000
SALES (est): 1.1MM **Privately Held**
WEB: www.snair.net
SIC: 3542 3366 3441 3537 Die casting
machines; copper foundries; fabricated
structural metal; industrial trucks & trac-
tors; sheet metalwork; fabricated plate
work (boiler shop)

(G-16361)
SOMMERS WOOD N DOOR COMPANY
7802 Amish Pike (43064-9317)
PHONE..................................614 873-3506
Edward Sommers, *Owner*
EMP: 4
SALES: 500K **Privately Held**
WEB: www.sommerswood.com
SIC: 2431 Doors, wood

(G-16362)
UNITED ROTARY BRUSH INC
8150 Business Way (43064-9209)
PHONE..................................937 644-3515
Fax: 937 642-3552
Mark Sutherin, *Division Mgr*
Matt Rebmann, *Vice Pres*
Peter Gurney, *Mktg Dir*
Bruce Davis, *Manager*
EMP: 55
SQ FT: 63,820
SALES (corp-wide): 45MM **Privately Held**
WEB: www.united-rotary.com
SIC: 3991 Brushes, household or industrial
PA: United Rotary Brush Corporation
15607 W 100th Ter
Lenexa KS 66219
913 888-8450

(G-16363)
VELOCYS INC
7950 Corporate Blvd (43064-9230)
PHONE..................................614 733-3300
Fax: 614 733-3301
David Pummell, *CEO*
Laura Silva, *General Mgr*
Dr Paul F Schubert, *COO*
Don Kirkham, *Facilities Mgr*
Jenny Butler, *Research*
EMP: 60
SQ FT: 26,800

SALES (est): 10.5MM
SALES (corp-wide): 3MM **Privately Held**
WEB: www.velocys.com
SIC: 8731 3559 Commercial physical research; environmental research; medical
research, commercial; electronic research; refinery, chemical processing &
similar machinery
PA: Velocys Plc
115e Olympic Avenue
Abingdon OXON OX14
123 584-1700

(G-16364)
WORLD RESOURCE SOLUTONS CORP
8485 Estates Ct (43064-8015)
PHONE..................................614 733-3737
Thomas Warner, *President*
▲ EMP: 7
SQ FT: 3,750
SALES (est): 2.7MM **Privately Held**
SIC: 3089 Plastic processing

(G-16365)
YASKAWA AMERICA INC
8628 Industrial Pkwy A (43064-8069)
PHONE..................................614 733-3200
Steven Blake, *Engineer*
Jill Hoff, *Branch Mgr*
EMP: 16
SALES (corp-wide): 3.5B **Privately Held**
SIC: 3699 Electrical equipment & supplies
HQ: Yaskawa America, Inc.
2121 Norman Dr
Waukegan IL 60085
847 887-7000

(G-16366)
YODER CABINETS LTD
9996 Amish Pike (43064-9321)
PHONE..................................614 873-5186
Fax: 740 873-9986
David P Yoder Jr, *President*
EMP: 5
SALES: 520K **Privately Held**
WEB: www.yodercabinets.com
SIC: 2434 Wood kitchen cabinets; vanities,
bathroom: wood

(G-16367)
YONEZAWA USA INC
7920 Corporate Blvd A (43064-9230)
PHONE..................................614 799-2210
Shunichi Aoki, *President*
EMP: 5
SALES (est): 721.9K **Privately Held**
SIC: 3577 Computer peripheral equipment

Pleasant City
Guernsey County

(G-16368)
TIMOTHY SINFIELD
54962 Marietta Rd (43772-9601)
PHONE..................................740 685-3684
Timothy Sinfield, *Director*
EMP: 47
SALES (est): 1MM **Privately Held**
SIC: 1389 Oil & gas field services

Pleasant Hill
Miami County

(G-16369)
CD SOLUTIONS INC
100 W Monument St (45359-9669)
P.O. Box 536 (45359-0536)
PHONE..................................937 676-2376
Fax: 937 676-2478
Jerald Warner, *President*
Bonnie Warner, *Info Tech Mgr*
EMP: 8
SQ FT: 10,000
SALES (est): 570K **Privately Held**
SIC: 7374 3695 5099 Service bureau,
computer; magnetic & optical recording
media; compact discs

Pleasant Plain
Warren County

(G-16370)
DIESEL RECON SERVICE INC
2641 State Route 28 (45162-9627)
P.O. Box 329, Blanchester (45107-0329)
PHONE..........................513 625-1887
Randy Forbes, *President*
Teresa Forbes, *Vice Pres*
EMP: 4 **EST:** 1980
SQ FT: 6,000
SALES: 80K **Privately Held**
SIC: 2911 7538 Diesel fuels; general auto-motive repair shops

(G-16371)
GOODWIN FARMS
10092 State Route 132 (45162-9100)
P.O. Box 190 (45162-0190)
PHONE..........................513 877-2636
Bruce Goodwin, *Partner*
Carole Goodwin, *Partner*
EMP: 5
SALES (est): 411.4K **Privately Held**
SIC: 0115 0119 0111 3599 Corn; bean (dry field & seed) farm; wheat; machine & other job shop work

(G-16372)
HARTZ MOUNTAIN CORPORATION
Also Called: L M Animal Farms
5374 Long Spurling Rd (45162-9256)
P.O. Box 57 (45162-0057)
PHONE..........................513 877-2131
Fax: 513 877-2134
Gary Bates, *Vice Pres*
Ron Reed, *Research*
Becky Parcell, *Human Resources*
Larry Mohrfield, *Branch Mgr*
Russ Burton, *Manager*
EMP: 75
SALES (corp-wide): 6B **Privately Held**
SIC: 2047 3999 2048 Cat food; dog food; pet supplies; prepared feeds
HQ: The Hartz Mountain Corporation
400 Plaza Dr Ste 400
Secaucus NJ 07094
800 275-1414

Pleasantville
Fairfield County

(G-16373)
METALS AND ADDITIVES CORP INC
Ohio Oxide
4850 Elder Rd Ne (43148-9729)
PHONE..........................740 654-4799
Fax: 740 654-4799
Steve Rau, *Sales Staff*
Frank Jones, *Branch Mgr*
Jill Hall, *Manager*
EMP: 13
SALES (corp-wide): 16.9MM **Privately Held**
SIC: 2819 Lead compounds or salts, inor-ganic, not used in pigments
PA: Metals And Additives Corporation, Inc.
5929 Lakeside Blvd
Indianapolis IN 46278
317 290-5007

(G-16374)
OHIO OXIDE CORPORATION DEL
4850 Elder Rd Ne (43148-9729)
P.O. Box 1050, Lancaster (43130-0050)
PHONE..........................740 654-6555
Greg Stevens, *President*
David Meyers, *Admin Sec*
EMP: 13
SQ FT: 15,000
SALES (est): 1.5MM **Privately Held**
SIC: 2819 Industrial inorganic chemicals

(G-16375)
SIGNATURE BEEF LLC
5500 Canal Rd Ne (43148-9752)
PHONE..........................740 468-3579
Brad Berry,
Mary Ann Berry,
EMP: 3
SALES (est): 251.5K **Privately Held**
SIC: 2011 Corned beef from meat slaugh-tered on site

Plymouth
Huron County

(G-16376)
FIRELANDS MANUFACTURING LLC
500 Industrial Park Dr (44865)
P.O. Box 45 (44865-0045)
PHONE..........................419 687-8237
Shawn Westmeister,
EMP: 15 **EST:** 2011
SALES (est): 2.4MM **Privately Held**
SIC: 3999 3548 Barber & beauty shop equipment; welding & cutting apparatus & accessories

(G-16377)
LESAGE MACHINE INC
5269 State Route 598 (44865-9603)
PHONE..........................419 687-0131
Fax: 419 687-8100
Ronald Lesage, *President*
Rita Lesage, *Manager*
EMP: 4
SQ FT: 6,400
SALES: 500K **Privately Held**
SIC: 3599 Machine & other job shop work

(G-16378)
POWER SHELF LLC
500 Industrial Park Dr (44865)
PHONE..........................419 775-6125
Lynn K L F Westmeister,
Shawn Westmeister,
EMP: 8
SQ FT: 15,000
SALES: 500K **Privately Held**
SIC: 3644 Noncurrent-carrying wiring serv-ices

(G-16379)
SAUDER MACHINE LTD
3071 State Route 603 (44865-9769)
PHONE..........................419 896-3722
Linus H Sauder, *Partner*
Timothy L Sauder,
EMP: 3
SQ FT: 3,000
SALES: 250K **Privately Held**
SIC: 3599 Machine shop, jobbing & repair

(G-16380)
WH FETZER & SONS MFG INC
500 Donnenwirth Dr (44865-1130)
P.O. Box 45 (44865-0045)
PHONE..........................419 687-8237
Fax: 419 687-5185
EMP: 30
SQ FT: 43,800
SALES (est): 6.5MM **Privately Held**
SIC: 3312 3993 3731 3524 Blast Fur-nace-Steel Work Mfg Signs/Ad Special-ties Shipbuilding/Repairing Mfg Lawn/Garden Equip

Poland
Mahoning County

(G-16381)
ACME COMPANY
9495 Harvard Blvd (44514-3369)
PHONE..........................330 758-2313
Carmine Zarlenga Jr, *President*
Marianne Mancuso, *Manager*
Martin Suarez, *Manager*
John M Newman, *Incorporator*
EMP: 60 **EST:** 1934
SQ FT: 10,000

SALES (est): 13.3MM **Privately Held**
SIC: 5032 3423 1422 3295 Sand, con-struction; stone, crushed or broken; gravel; hand & edge tools; crushed & bro-ken limestone; minerals, ground or treated

(G-16382)
AKERS AMERICA INC
58 S Main St (44514-1978)
PHONE..........................330 757-4100
I Lundberg, *CEO*
William Bigley, *President*
Kjell Inestam, *Treasurer*
Tony Ferraro, *Admin Sec*
◆ **EMP:** 3
SQ FT: 1,200
SALES (est): 564.8K
SALES (corp-wide): 198.3MM **Privately Held**
SIC: 5051 3316 3312 Iron & steel (fer-rous) products; cold finishing of steel shapes; blast furnaces & steel mills
HQ: Akers Sweden Ab
Bruksallen 4
Akers Styckebruk 640 6
159 321-00

(G-16383)
INFINITE SYNERGY LLC
7252 Elmland Ave (44514-2617)
PHONE..........................330 892-8777
Steve Cross, *CEO*
Eric Bergman, *Webmaster*
McKenzie Crowell, *Director*
EMP: 5
SALES (est): 482.6K **Privately Held**
SIC: 7372 Application computer software

(G-16384)
POLAND CONCRETE PRODUCTS INC (PA)
70 Poland Mnr (44514-2058)
P.O. Box 5146 (44514-0146)
PHONE..........................330 757-1241
Fax: 330 757-4648
Robert Zedaker Jr, *President*
David Zedaker, *Vice Pres*
Robert Zedeker III, *Vice Pres*
EMP: 3 **EST:** 1946
SQ FT: 25,000
SALES: 3MM **Privately Held**
SIC: 3272 Concrete products, precast; septic tanks, concrete; meter boxes, con-crete; manhole covers or frames, con-crete

(G-16385)
TOP FUEL COATINGS
20 Philrose Ln (44514-3241)
PHONE..........................330 758-1166
EMP: 3
SALES (est): 158.8K **Privately Held**
SIC: 2869 Fuels

(G-16386)
UNITED STATES CONTROLS INC
8511 Foxwood Ct (44514-4302)
PHONE..........................330 758-1147
Daniel Elliot Baun, *President*
Sandy Barger, *Manager*
EMP: 8
SQ FT: 25,000
SALES (est): 1.2MM **Privately Held**
WEB: www.unitedstatescontrols.com
SIC: 3492 3625 Hose & tube fittings & as-semblies, hydraulic/pneumatic; controls for adjustable speed drives

(G-16387)
VIVO BROTHERS LLC
8420 South Ave (44514-3618)
PHONE..........................330 629-8686
Vince Vivo, *Principal*
Nick Vivo, *Vice Pres*
EMP: 10
SALES (est): 1.4MM **Privately Held**
WEB: www.vivobrothers.com
SIC: 2599 Cabinets, factory

Polk
Ashland County

(G-16388)
DEEP RESOURCES LLC
120 State Route 302 (44866-9730)
PHONE..........................419 869-7441
Debra Wollp, *Accounts Mgr*
Charles Ungurean,
Thomas Ungurean,
EMP: 17
SALES (est): 1.3MM **Privately Held**
SIC: 1382 Oil & gas exploration services

Pomeroy
Meigs County

(G-16389)
FACEMYER LUMBER CO INC (PA)
31940 Bailey Run Rd (45769-9301)
P.O. Box 227, Middleport (45760-0227)
PHONE..........................740 992-5965
Fax: 740 992-2989
Eugene Facemyer, *Ch of Bd*
Leslie Facemyer, *Corp Secy*
Dennis Facemyer Jr, *Vice Pres*
▼ **EMP:** 18
SQ FT: 1,500
SALES: 2MM **Privately Held**
SIC: 2421 2411 Custom sawmill; kiln dry-ing of lumber; veneer logs

(G-16390)
SENTINEL DAILY
109 W 2nd St (45769-1035)
PHONE..........................740 992-2155
Charlene Hoeflich, *Principal*
Margaret Lehew, *Controller*
Larry Boyer, *Manager*
Steve Lutz, *Manager*
Steve Wilson, *Manager*
EMP: 3
SALES (est): 180.2K **Privately Held**
SIC: 2711 Newspapers, publishing & print-ing

(G-16391)
SNOWVILLE CREAMERY LLC
32623 State Route 143 (45769-9695)
PHONE..........................740 698-2301
Warren Taylor, *President*
Victoria Taylor, *CFO*
EMP: 20
SALES (est): 3.4MM **Privately Held**
SIC: 2026 Milk processing (pasteurizing, homogenizing, bottling)

(G-16392)
WATSON LOGGING
39511 Sumner Rd (45769-9503)
PHONE..........................740 985-4465
Dave Watson, *Owner*
EMP: 3
SALES (est): 169.6K **Privately Held**
SIC: 2411 Logging camps & contractors

Port Clinton
Ottawa County

(G-16393)
ARES INC
818 Front St (43452)
PHONE..........................419 635-2175
Herb Roder, *President*
Ann Yamrick, *Vice Pres*
Mark Moore, *Mfg Mgr*
Drew Kertis, *Engineer*
Ann L Yamrick, *Financial Exec*
EMP: 56
SQ FT: 60,000
SALES (est): 10.4MM **Privately Held**
WEB: www.ares.com
SIC: 3443 3482 3484 3489 Fabricated plate work (boiler shop); small arms am-munition; small arms; ordnance & acces-sories; motors & generators

G
E
O
G
R
A
P
H
I
C

(G-16394)
BAY AREA PRODUCTS INC
4942 W Fremont Rd (43452-9470)
PHONE....................................419 732-2147
Fax: 419 734-9275
Chuck Heiges, *President*
Dawn Mc Nulty, *Director*
EMP: 6
SQ FT: 3,000
SALES: 175K **Privately Held**
SIC: 3949 Fishing equipment; game calls

(G-16395)
CATAWBA CANVAS COMPANY LLC
255 Se Catawba Rd (43452-2634)
PHONE....................................419 797-2050
Fax: 419 797-2050
Steve Harrison,
EMP: 3
SALES (est): 120K **Privately Held**
SIC: 2394 Canvas & related products

(G-16396)
CATAWBA ISLAND BREWING CO
2330 East Harbor Rd (43452-1517)
PHONE....................................419 960-7764
Herbert Roder, *President*
Michael J Roder, *President*
Shad Gunderson, *Treasurer*
EMP: 8
SALES (est): 586K **Privately Held**
SIC: 2085 Cocktails, alcoholic

(G-16397)
CUSTOM MARINE CANVAS TRAINING
250 Se Catawba Rd Ste C (43452-2674)
PHONE....................................419 732-8362
Roger Griffin,
Russ Griffin,
EMP: 4
SALES: 800K **Privately Held**
SIC: 2211 Canvas

(G-16398)
D & L EXCAVATING LTD
969 N Rymers Rd (43452-9437)
PHONE....................................419 271-0635
Darryl Trent, *Principal*
EMP: 6
SALES (est): 325K **Privately Held**
SIC: 3531 Buckets, excavating: clamshell, concrete, dragline, etc.

(G-16399)
FENNER DUNLOP PORT CLINTON INC
5225 W Lakeshore Rd (43452-9285)
PHONE....................................419 635-2191
David Hurd, *President*
Cassandra Pan, *President*
Ben Ficklen, *Corp Secy*
Al Bonneau, *Senior VP*
Bill Mooney, *CFO*
▲ EMP: 115
SQ FT: 200,000
SALES (est): 47.8MM
SALES (corp-wide): 743.7MM **Privately Held**
SIC: 3069 3535 Medical & laboratory rubber sundries & related products; bucket type conveyor systems
HQ: Fenner Dunlop Americas, Llc
1000 Omega Dr Ste 1400
Pittsburgh PA 15205

(G-16400)
FOWL FOOLERS LLC
2268 Nw Catawba Rd (43452-3016)
PHONE....................................419 797-2412
EMP: 4
SALES (corp-wide): 663.8K **Privately Held**
SIC: 3949 Decoys, duck & other game birds
PA: Fowl Foolers, Llc
2435 E Gill Rd
Port Clinton OH 43452
419 960-7307

(G-16401)
GREAT LAKES POPCORN COMPANY
60 Madison St (43452-1102)
PHONE....................................419 732-3080
Fax: 419 732-1794
Bill Yuhasz, *President*
EMP: 6
SQ FT: 4,000
SALES (est): 370K **Privately Held**
WEB: www.greatlakespopcorn.com
SIC: 2099 2064 5441 Popcorn, packaged: except already popped; nuts, glace; candy, nut & confectionery stores

(G-16402)
LAKECRAFT INC (PA)
1010 W Lakeshore Dr (43452-9564)
PHONE....................................419 734-2828
Fax: 419 734-3896
Samuel J Conte, *President*
Keith Conte, *Manager*
Beth Bieggert, *Administration*
EMP: 9 EST: 1940
SQ FT: 15,000
SALES (est): 1.3MM **Privately Held**
WEB: www.lakecraft.com
SIC: 3599 7692 3561 Machine shop, jobbing & repair; welding repair; pumps, domestic: water or sump

(G-16403)
LOADMASTER TRAILER COMPANY
Also Called: Loadmaster Trailers Mfg
2354 East Harbor Rd (43452-1517)
PHONE....................................419 732-3434
Fax: 419 732-2183
Gary Straw, *President*
Diane Straw, *President*
Joe Araguz, *Opers Staff*
EMP: 13
SQ FT: 12,000
SALES (est): 2.2MM **Privately Held**
WEB: www.loadmastertrailerco.com
SIC: 3799 7699 Boat trailers; nautical repair services

(G-16404)
LUC ICE INC
728 S Railroad St (43452-2063)
PHONE....................................419 734-2201
Fax: 419 734-2201
Michael Luc, *President*
Paul Luc, *Vice Pres*
EMP: 7
SQ FT: 11,000
SALES (est): 843.9K **Privately Held**
SIC: 2097 Block ice; ice cubes

(G-16405)
MARINEMAX INC
1991 Ne Catawba Rd (43452-3523)
PHONE....................................918 782-3277
Fax: 419 797-3860
Jim Conner, *Branch Mgr*
EMP: 112
SALES (corp-wide): 942MM **Publicly Held**
SIC: 5551 3732 Boat dealers; boat building & repairing
PA: Marinemax, Inc.
2600 Mccormick Dr Ste 200
Clearwater FL 33759
727 531-1700

(G-16406)
MINDERMAN MARINE PRODUCTS INC
129 Buckeye Blvd (43452-1419)
PHONE....................................419 732-2626
Fax: 419 732-2627
Stuart Ghan, *President*
Kenneth J Berger, *Vice Pres*
EMP: 7
SQ FT: 13,100
SALES (est): 530K **Privately Held**
WEB: www.mindermanmarine.com
SIC: 7699 3429 5551 Marine propeller repair; marine hardware; marine supplies & equipment

(G-16407)
NORTH COAST BUSINESS JOURNAL
205 Se Catawba Rd Ste G (43452-2669)
PHONE....................................419 734-4838
John Schaffner, *Owner*
Kristina Willoughby, *Sales Dir*
EMP: 5
SALES (est): 248.5K **Privately Held**
WEB: www.ncbj.net
SIC: 2721 Trade journals: publishing & printing

(G-16408)
OUTDOOR NEWS SERVICE
Also Called: Outdoor & News Service
127 W Perry St Ste 101 (43452-1039)
PHONE....................................419 734-5172
Rick Nemecek, *Owner*
EMP: 5
SALES (est): 168.4K **Privately Held**
SIC: 8999 2711 Editorial service; newspapers

(G-16409)
PORT CLINTON MANUFACTURING LLC
328 W Perry St (43452-1035)
P.O. Box 220 (43452-0220)
PHONE....................................419 734-2141
Fax: 419 734-5868
Daniel Stott, *President*
Jane Stott, *Vice Pres*
David Courtright, *HR Admin*
EMP: 25 EST: 1928
SQ FT: 67,000
SALES: 3.1MM **Privately Held**
WEB: www.pcmfg.net
SIC: 3451 Screw machine products

(G-16410)
QUIKSTIR INC
Also Called: Quikspray
2105 W Lakeshore Dr (43452-9485)
P.O. Box 327 (43452-0327)
PHONE....................................419 732-2601
Fax: 419 734-2628
Thomas P Mc Ritchie, *President*
Tom N McRitchie, *Vice Pres*
T Park Mc Ritchie, *Admin Sec*
EMP: 12 EST: 1954
SQ FT: 6,000
SALES (est): 1.2MM **Privately Held**
SIC: 3561 3563 3531 Pumps & pumping equipment; spraying outfits: metals, paints & chemicals (compressor); mixers: ore, plaster, slag, sand, mortar, etc.

(G-16411)
REXLES INC
Also Called: Plastiform Tool & Die
1850 W Lakeshore Dr (43452-9091)
P.O. Box 26 (43452-0026)
PHONE....................................419 732-8188
Fax: 419 732-8164
Rex Montgomery, *President*
Leslie Rister, *Corp Secy*
EMP: 6
SQ FT: 1,122
SALES (est): 220K **Privately Held**
SIC: 3089 Plastic processing

(G-16412)
SAFE 4 PEOPLE INC
4661 E Woodland Dr (43452-3142)
PHONE....................................419 797-4087
Carole Fleming, *President*
Thomas Fleming, *Vice Pres*
EMP: 5
SALES (est): 400.8K **Privately Held**
WEB: www.safe4people.com
SIC: 3999 5122 5999 Hair & hair-based products; cosmetics; cosmetics

(G-16413)
SCHAFFNER PUBLICATION INC
Also Called: Minuteman Press
3956 E Hbr Lght Lnding Dr (43452)
PHONE....................................419 732-2154
Fax: 419 734-5382
John Schaffner, *President*
Mary Alice Schaffner, *Vice Pres*
Christina Taylor, *Accounts Exec*
Bruce Dinse, *Manager*
EMP: 20

SQ FT: 4,000
SALES (est): 3.3MM **Privately Held**
WEB: www.thebeacon.net
SIC: 2752 Commercial printing, lithographic

(G-16414)
SCRAMBL-GRAM INC
Also Called: Last Word, The
5225 W Lkshore Dr Ste 340 (43452)
P.O. Box 577 (43452-0577)
PHONE....................................419 635-2321
Fax: 419 734-2868
Scott Bowers, *President*
EMP: 12
SQ FT: 5,500
SALES (est): 1.2MM **Privately Held**
WEB: www.scrambl-gram.com
SIC: 3944 5945 2741 Board games, puzzles & models, except electronic; hobby, toy & game shops; miscellaneous publishing

(G-16415)
STEVEN NICKEL
3117 E Shore Dr (43452-2748)
PHONE....................................419 732-3377
Steven Nickel, *Principal*
EMP: 3
SALES (est): 213.3K **Privately Held**
SIC: 3356 Nickel

(G-16416)
SURFACE-ALL INC
745 N Hidden Harbor Dr (43452-3744)
PHONE....................................440 428-2233
Richard Duhane, *Principal*
Clair Waid, *Vice Pres*
EMP: 3
SALES (est): 308.6K **Privately Held**
SIC: 2952 Asphalt felts & coatings

(G-16417)
TACK-ANEW INC
Also Called: Brands' Marina
451 W Lakeshore Dr (43452-9478)
PHONE....................................419 734-4212
Fax: 419 734-5854
Dalton Brand, *President*
Darrell A Brand, *President*
Elisabeth Brand, *Editor*
EMP: 26
SQ FT: 15,000
SALES: 2MM **Privately Held**
WEB: www.brandsmarina.com
SIC: 4493 3731 Marinas; shipbuilding & repairing

(G-16418)
TIMELY TOURS INC
141 Maple St Ste A (43452-1347)
PHONE....................................419 734-3751
Fax: 419 732-2736
Ralph Burnstine, *Manager*
EMP: 3
SALES (corp-wide): 402.1K **Privately Held**
SIC: 2752 Commercial printing, lithographic
PA: Timely Tours Inc
797 Ne Catawba Rd
Port Clinton OH 43452
419 797-2569

(G-16419)
WILLIAM J DUPPS
Also Called: Dupps Printing and Supply Co
126 Madison St (43452-1104)
P.O. Box 756 (43452-0756)
PHONE....................................419 734-2126
Fax: 419 732-3256
EMP: 5
SQ FT: 3,000
SALES (est): 360K **Privately Held**
SIC: 2752 5044 5021 5112 Lithographic Coml Print Office Equipment Furniture Stationery/Offc Sup Bookbinding/Related Work

Port Jefferson
Shelby County

(G-16420)
MCCRARY METAL POLISHING INC
207 Pasco Montra Rd (45360)
PHONE....................937 492-1979
Fax: 937 492-7019
James P McCrary Jr, *President*
Shirley Mc Crary, *Vice Pres*
Dru Knoop, *Office Mgr*
▲ EMP: 25
SQ FT: 4,800
SALES (est): 3.4MM Privately Held
SIC: 3471 3599 Polishing, metals or formed products; machine shop, jobbing & repair

(G-16421)
TECHNIMOLD PLUS INC
102 Wall St (45360-1105)
PHONE....................937 492-4077
Greg Jones, *President*
EMP: 3
SQ FT: 1,500
SALES (est): 250K Privately Held
SIC: 3089 Injection molding of plastics

Port Washington
Tuscarawas County

(G-16422)
BATES METAL PRODUCTS INC
403 E Mn St (43837)
P.O. Box 68 (43837-0068)
PHONE....................740 498-8371
Fax: 614 498-6315
James A Bates, *President*
Betty Bates, *Corp Secy*
Terry L Bates, *Vice Pres*
Kathy Huston, *Purch Mgr*
Justin Dichler, *Purchasing*
EMP: 60 EST: 1956
SQ FT: 106,500
SALES (est): 15.4MM Privately Held
WEB: www.batesmetal.com
SIC: 4783 2542 3993 3469 Packing & crating; racks, merchandise display or storage: except wood; signs & advertising specialties; metal stampings; automotive & apparel trimmings

(G-16423)
DESIGNER STONE CO
303 E Main St (43837-9704)
PHONE....................740 492-1300
Darren Galbraith, *President*
Dan Armstrong, *Manager*
Lisa Massner, *Admin Sec*
▲ EMP: 8
SALES (est): 1MM Privately Held
SIC: 1411 Granite dimension stone

Portage
Wood County

(G-16424)
J D HYDRAULIC INC
Rr 25 (43451)
P.O. Box 188 (43451-0188)
PHONE....................419 686-5234
Fax: 419 686-1244
James Simon, *President*
Mike Simon, *Sales Staff*
Gary Simon, *Admin Sec*
EMP: 13
SQ FT: 12,000
SALES (est): 2.2MM Privately Held
SIC: 3593 Fluid power cylinders, hydraulic or pneumatic

(G-16425)
LABORIE ENTERPRISES LLC
10892 S Dixie Hwy (43451-9798)
PHONE....................419 686-6245
Larry C Smith, *Partner*
Douglas Laborie, *Partner*
Edith Laborie, *Partner*
Ronald Laborie, *Partner*
EMP: 7
SQ FT: 10,000
SALES: 472.3K Privately Held
SIC: 5211 2431 Millwork & lumber; moldings, wood: unfinished & prefinished

(G-16426)
OGDEN HYDRAULICS LLC
396 W Main St (43451-9788)
P.O. Box 236 (43451-0236)
PHONE....................419 686-1108
Janet Abke, *Manager*
Richard Ogden, *President*
EMP: 3
SALES: 500K Privately Held
WEB: www.ogdenhydraulics.com
SIC: 3569 Bridge or gate machinery, hydraulic

(G-16427)
PALMER BROS TRANSIT MIX CON
Also Called: Precision Aggregates
12580 Greensburg Pike (43451-9755)
PHONE....................419 686-2366
Fax: 419 686-2508
Will Smelts, *Manager*
EMP: 10
SALES (corp-wide): 7MM Privately Held
SIC: 3273 5032 Ready-mixed concrete; stone, crushed or broken
PA: Palmer Bros Transit Mix Concrete Inc
12205 E Gypsy Lane Rd
Bowling Green OH 43402
419 352-4681

(G-16428)
STONECO INC
11580 S Dixie Hwy (43451-9757)
PHONE....................419 686-3311
Lee Wehner, *Manager*
EMP: 7
SALES (corp-wide): 28.6B Privately Held
WEB: www.stoneco.net
SIC: 1429 Igneous rock, crushed & broken-quarrying
HQ: Stoneco, Inc.
1700 Fostoria Ave Ste 200
Findlay OH 45840
419 422-8854

Portsmouth
Scioto County

(G-16429)
A SPECIAL TOUCH EMBROIDERY LLC
22326 State Route 73 (45663-6365)
PHONE....................740 858-2241
Fax: 740 858-9412
Travis Hoyme, *VP Sales*
Brandon Hoyme, *Marketing Staff*
Kim Hoyme,
James Hoyme,
EMP: 4
SALES: 400K Privately Held
WEB: www.s-t-e.net
SIC: 2759 Screen printing

(G-16430)
APPALACHIAN WOOD FLOORS INC
838 Campbell Ave (45662-4561)
PHONE....................740 354-4572
Fax: 740 354-6179
Jim Graf, *President*
Michael Coriell, *CFO*
Sara G Mauk, *Financial Exec*
John Walk, *Manager*
EMP: 80
SQ FT: 175,000
SALES (est): 4.4MM Privately Held
WEB: www.appalachianwoodfloors.com
SIC: 2491 Wood preserving

(G-16431)
BICKETT MACHINE AND SUPPLY INC
1411 Robinson Ave (45662-3508)
P.O. Box 698 (45662-0698)
PHONE....................740 353-5710
Fax: 740 354-2259
Frank M Coburn, *President*
Maureen Coburn, *Vice Pres*
Eric Lewis, *Manager*
EMP: 8 EST: 1948
SQ FT: 7,500
SALES (est): 1.5MM Privately Held
WEB: www.bicketts.com
SIC: 5084 3599 Welding machinery & equipment; machine shop, jobbing & repair

(G-16432)
BIG IRON GUNS INC
1712 11th St (45662-4528)
PHONE....................740 464-0852
Christopher Ponzio, *CEO*
Savanah Whitt, *Admin Sec*
EMP: 3 EST: 2015
SALES (est): 161.3K Privately Held
SIC: 3482 Small arms ammunition; shotgun ammunition: empty, blank or loaded

(G-16433)
COCA-COLA BOTTLING CO CNSLD
5050 Old Scioto Trl (45662-6461)
PHONE....................740 353-3133
Fax: 740 353-2167
Tony Burns, *Principal*
EMP: 21
SALES (corp-wide): 3.1B Publicly Held
WEB: www.colasic.net
SIC: 2086 Bottled & canned soft drinks
PA: Coca-Cola Bottling Co. Consolidated
4100 Coca Cola Plz # 100
Charlotte NC 28211
704 557-4400

(G-16434)
DELMAR E HICKS (PA)
Also Called: South Shore Gas & Oil
2310 A St (45662)
P.O. Box 1068 (45662-1068)
PHONE....................740 354-4333
Delmar E Hicks, *Owner*
EMP: 1
SALES (est): 1.6MM Privately Held
SIC: 8072 5411 1382 Dental laboratories; convenience stores; oil & gas exploration services

(G-16435)
FANTASTIC SAMS HAIR CARE SALON
4490 Gallia St (45662-5553)
PHONE....................740 456-4296
Shana Dunn, *Owner*
Dan Brisker, *Owner*
EMP: 7
SALES (est): 31.8K Privately Held
SIC: 7231 2844 Unisex hair salons; hair coloring preparations

(G-16436)
GRACIE PLUM INVESTMENTS INC
609 2nd St Unit 2 (45662-3974)
PHONE....................740 355-9029
Fax: 740 354-1170
Francesca G Hartop, *CEO*
Paul Yost, *COO*
Aaron Prose, *Vice Pres*
Casey Smith, *Opers Mgr*
Kyle Webb, *Engineer*
EMP: 27
SQ FT: 3,150
SALES: 4.3MM Privately Held
WEB: www.yostengineering.com
SIC: 7372 7374 7371 Application computer software; data processing & preparation; custom computer programming services

(G-16437)
HANGER PRSTHETCS & ORTHO INC
1611 27th St Ste 303 (45662-6932)
PHONE....................740 354-4775
Fax: 740 353-4899
David Stephens, *Manager*
Lanie Darnell, *Manager*
EMP: 4
SALES (corp-wide): 460MM Publicly Held
SIC: 8071 3842 Medical laboratories; surgical appliances & supplies
HQ: Hanger Prosthetics & Orthotics, Inc.
10910 Domain Dr Ste 300
Austin TX 78758
512 777-3800

(G-16438)
HERFF JONES INC
2470 Orizaba Ln (45662-3234)
PHONE....................740 821-3109
EMP: 3 EST: 2014
SALES (est): 268.6K Privately Held
SIC: 2752 Commercial printing, lithographic

(G-16439)
KEYSTONE PRINTING & COPY CAT
Also Called: Copy Cat Printing
842 4th St (45662-4312)
P.O. Box 174 (45662-0174)
PHONE....................740 354-6542
Fax: 740 354-2608
John Cooper, *Owner*
Stephanie Howerton, *Director*
EMP: 5
SALES (est): 347K Privately Held
SIC: 2759 2752 2791 2789 Commercial printing; commercial printing, lithographic; typesetting; bookbinding & related work

(G-16440)
KOPPERS IND INC
400 Harding Ave (45662-5419)
PHONE....................740 776-2149
Merle Klink, *Principal*
EMP: 3
SALES (est): 235.9K Privately Held
SIC: 2421 Railroad ties, sawed

(G-16441)
KOPPERS INDUSTRIES INC
6501 Pershing Ave (45662)
P.O. Box 4039 (45662-2039)
PHONE....................740 776-3238
Dick Burke, *Plant Mgr*
Phil M McDonald, *Sales Mgr*
EMP: 45
SALES (corp-wide): 18.8MM Privately Held
SIC: 3272 2421 Concrete products; sawmills & planing mills, general
PA: Koppers Industries, Inc
436 7th Ave Ste 2026
Pittsburgh PA 15219
412 227-2001

(G-16442)
KSA LIMITED PARTNERSHIP
6501 Pershing Ave (45662)
P.O. Box 4039 (45662-2039)
PHONE....................740 776-3238
Fax: 740 776-6553
Frank Anderson III, *President*
Merle Klink, *Human Res Mgr*
John Rolfe, *Manager*
Tom Lodeman, *Exec Dir*
EMP: 40
SALES (est): 4.9MM Privately Held
SIC: 3272 Ties, railroad: concrete

(G-16443)
MCGOVNEY READY MIX INC
Also Called: McGovney River Terminal
55 River Ave (45662-4712)
P.O. Box 510 (45662-0510)
PHONE....................740 353-4111
Fax: 740 354-5200
Carolyn Kegley, *President*
Debra Coburn, *Corp Secy*
David Kegley, *Vice Pres*
Rhett Hadsell, *Opers Mgr*
EMP: 20

SQ FT: 1,200
SALES (est): 3.1MM **Privately Held**
WEB: www.mcgovney.com
SIC: 3273 Ready-mixed concrete

(G-16444)
MITCHELLACE INC (PA)
830 Murray St (45662-4515)
P.O. Box 89 (45662-0089)
PHONE...................................740 354-2813
Fax: 740 353-4669
Kerry W Keating, *Ch of Bd*
Steven Keating, *President*
Ryan Bouts, *VP Opers*
Ruth Ann Carter, *Purch Dir*
Tom Keating, *Treasurer*
▲ EMP: 37 EST: 1902
SQ FT: 365,000
SALES (est): 6.6MM **Privately Held**
WEB: www.mitchellace.com
SIC: 2241 Shoe laces, except leather;
braids, textile; cotton narrow fabrics

(G-16445)
MP PRINTING & DESIGN INC
4302 Gallia St (45662-5515)
PHONE...................................740 456-2045
Eddie F Marshall, *President*
EMP: 5
SALES: 277K **Privately Held**
SIC: 2741 Miscellaneous publishing

(G-16446)
OSCO INDUSTRIES INC (PA)
Also Called: Portsmouth Division
734 11th St (45662-3407)
P.O. Box 1388 (45662-1388)
PHONE...................................740 354-3183
Fax: 740 353-1504
William J Burke, *Ch of Bd*
John M Burke, *President*
Jeffrey A Burke, *Senior VP*
Keith Denny, *Vice Pres*
Philip L Vetter, *Vice Pres*
▼ EMP: 285 EST: 1872
SQ FT: 150,000
SALES (est): 97.3MM **Privately Held**
WEB: www.oscoind.com
SIC: 3321 Gray & ductile iron foundries;
gray iron castings

(G-16447)
P&M PUBLISHING
2225 8th St (45662-4737)
P.O. Box 248 (45662-0248)
PHONE...................................740 353-3300
Aaron Bennett, *Principal*
EMP: 4
SALES (est): 303.3K **Privately Held**
SIC: 2741 Miscellaneous publishing

(G-16448)
PORTSMOUTH BLOCK INC
Also Called: Portsmouth Block & Brick
2700 Gallia St (45662-4807)
PHONE...................................740 353-4113
Fax: 740 353-4115
Glenn Coriell, *President*
Kevin Coriell, *Vice Pres*
Roddy Coriell, *Sales Mgr*
Mildred Coriell, *Admin Sec*
EMP: 11
SQ FT: 100,000
SALES (est): 1.6MM **Privately Held**
SIC: 3271 5211 Blocks, concrete or cin-
der: standard; lumber & other building
materials

(G-16449)
PREMIER KITES & DESIGNS INC
1004 Findlay St (45662-3446)
PHONE...................................888 416-0174
EMP: 5 **Privately Held**
SIC: 3944 Kites
HQ: Premier Kites & Designs Inc
5200 Lawrence Pl
Hyattsville MD 20781
301 277-3888

(G-16450)
RUSH WELDING & MACHINE INC
1657 12th St (45662-4535)
P.O. Box 208 (45662-0208)
PHONE...................................740 354-7874
Fax: 740 354-7874
Tim Rush, *President*

EMP: 3
SALES: 200K **Privately Held**
SIC: 7692 Welding repair

(G-16451)
SAVORY FOODS INC
2240 6th St (45662-4787)
P.O. Box 1604 (45662-1604)
PHONE...................................740 354-6655
Fax: 740 353-2482
James Speak, *President*
Rigel Olmos, *General Mgr*
Rick Howard, *Mfg Spvr*
Ed Thompson, *Mfg Spvr*
Patty Basham, *Office Mgr*
EMP: 58 EST: 1946
SQ FT: 40,000
SALES: 13.3MM
SALES (corp-wide): 1.6B **Privately Held**
SIC: 2096 Pork rinds
HQ: Evans Food Group Ltd.
4118 S Halsted St
Chicago IL 60609
773 254-7400

(G-16452)
SHRED DEVIL LLC
6806 6th St Ste 200 (45662)
PHONE...................................740 776-1400
John McHenry, *Mng Member*
EMP: 3
SALES (est): 169.3K **Privately Held**
SIC: 3589 Shredders, industrial & commer-
cial

(G-16453)
SIMPSON BROTHERS MACHINE WORKS
2204 Gallia St (45662-4761)
PHONE...................................740 353-6870
Fax: 740 353-6870
George Simpson, *President*
Frank Simpson, *Vice Pres*
EMP: 4 EST: 1883
SQ FT: 14,100
SALES (est): 330K **Privately Held**
SIC: 3599 Machine shop, jobbing & repair

(G-16454)
SISSEL LOGGING LLC
69 Pond Lick Rd (45663-8899)
PHONE...................................740 858-4613
Michael Sissel, *Principal*
EMP: 3
SALES (est): 213.7K **Privately Held**
SIC: 2411 Logging

(G-16455)
SNYDER PRINTING LLC
Also Called: Snyder Printing & Signs
1552 Gallia St (45662-4509)
PHONE...................................740 353-3947
Brooks Snyder, *Mng Member*
EMP: 3
SALES (est): 210K **Privately Held**
SIC: 2759 5099 Commercial printing;
signs, except electric

(G-16456)
SOLE CHOICE INC
830 Murray St (45662-4515)
P.O. Box 89 (45662-0089)
PHONE...................................740 354-2813
Nelson K Smith, *Chairman*
Bryan K Davis, *Vice Pres*
Ryan B Bouts, *CFO*
Robin Swick, *Controller*
Marc Cottle, *Shareholder*
▲ EMP: 30
SALES (est): 4.8MM **Privately Held**
SIC: 2241 Shoe laces, except leather;
braids, textile; cotton narrow fabrics

(G-16457)
TOM BARBOUR AUTO PARTS INC (PA)
915 11th St (45662-3410)
PHONE...................................740 354-4654
Fax: 740 353-0300
Josephine Keating, *President*
Michael Flannery, *Vice Pres*
EMP: 12
SQ FT: 12,000

SALES (est): 8.1MM **Privately Held**
WEB: www.barbourauto.com
SIC: 5531 3599 Automotive parts; ma-
chine shop, jobbing & repair

(G-16458)
TRI STATE COUNTERTOP SERVICE
3350 Indian Dr (45662-2409)
PHONE...................................740 354-3663
David Malone, *President*
EMP: 3
SALES: 450K **Privately Held**
SIC: 2511 Kitchen & dining room furniture

(G-16459)
YOST LABS INC
630 2nd St (45662-3902)
PHONE...................................740 876-4936
Greg Merril, *CEO*
Paul Yost, *Principal*
Lowell Morrison, *CFO*
EMP: 16
SALES (est): 707.2K **Privately Held**
SIC: 3812 Search & navigation equipment

(G-16460)
ZEBU COMPLIANCE SOLUTIONS INC
609 2nd St Unit 2 (45662-3974)
PHONE...................................740 355-9029
Francesca Hartop, *CEO*
EMP: 20 EST: 2014
SALES (est): 454.2K **Privately Held**
SIC: 7371 7372 7374 Custom computer
programming services; prepackaged soft-
ware; data processing & preparation

Powell
Delaware County

(G-16461)
ADVANCED INDUS MACHINING INC (PA)
3982 Powell Rd 218 (43065-7662)
PHONE...................................614 596-4183
Morgan Koth, *President*
EMP: 16
SQ FT: 3,600
SALES (est): 2.6MM **Privately Held**
SIC: 1629 3599 Industrial plant construc-
tion; amusement park equipment

(G-16462)
ALLERGAN INC
4321 Scioto Pkwy (43065-8056)
PHONE...................................614 623-8140
EMP: 51 **Privately Held**
SIC: 2834 Solutions, pharmaceutical
HQ: Allergan, Inc.
400 Interpace Pkwy
Parsippany NJ 07054
862 261-7000

(G-16463)
BUCKEYE VOLLEYBALL CENTER LLC
7824 Maplecreek Ct (43065-9297)
PHONE...................................614 764-1075
Steve Yates, *Principal*
EMP: 3
SALES (est): 282.9K **Privately Held**
SIC: 2273 Carpets & rugs

(G-16464)
BUILDING CTRL INTEGRATORS LLC (PA)
Also Called: B C I
383 N Liberty St (43065-8388)
PHONE...................................614 334-3300
Fax: 614 334-9004
Jim McClintock, *Regional Mgr*
Brad Lisska, *Project Mgr*
Keith North, *Project Mgr*
Nikki Lawler, *Opers Mgr*
Ken Dillingham, *Opers Staff*
EMP: 31
SQ FT: 20,000
SALES (est): 14.1MM **Privately Held**
WEB: www.bcicontrols.com
SIC: 3822 Temperature controls, automatic

(G-16465)
CANVAS SALON AND SKIN BAR
3893 Powell Rd (43065-7983)
PHONE...................................614 336-3942
Stefanie M Fox, *Principal*
EMP: 4
SALES (est): 392.2K **Privately Held**
SIC: 2211 Canvas

(G-16466)
CARDIAC ANALYTICS LLC
5683 Liberty Rd N (43065-8996)
PHONE...................................614 314-1332
Dan McFarland, *President*
EMP: 10
SALES: 100K **Privately Held**
SIC: 3845 Electromedical equipment

(G-16467)
COLUMBUS ADVANCED MFG SFTWR
Also Called: Cams
495 Village Park Dr (43065-6605)
PHONE...................................614 433-0415
Jeffrey Trevorrow, *President*
Brian Suchland, *Technology*
Denise Trevorrow, *Admin Sec*
EMP: 5
SQ FT: 1,500
SALES (est): 1.1MM **Privately Held**
WEB: www.camsnet.com
SIC: 5045 3599 7374 Computer software;
machine shop, jobbing & repair; computer
graphics service

(G-16468)
COLUMBUS OILFIELD EXPLORATION
Also Called: Columbus Oil Field Exploration
80 Grace Dr Ste G (43065-9315)
PHONE...................................614 895-9520
J Michael Murnane, *President*
Michael Blue, *Corp Secy*
Richard Wilson, *Vice Pres*
Karen Newsome, *Office Mgr*
EMP: 2
SALES: 2.4MM **Privately Held**
SIC: 1381 1382 Drilling oil & gas wells; oil
& gas exploration services

(G-16469)
CONTINENTAL GL SLS & INV GROUP
Also Called: Continental Group
315 Ashmoore Ct (43065-7486)
P.O. Box 1764 (43065-1764)
PHONE...................................614 679-1201
Sean Snyder, *Partner*
Chris Snyder, *Partner*
Mark McClain, *Vice Pres*
▲ EMP: 400
SQ FT: 100,000
SALES (est): 33.7MM **Privately Held**
SIC: 3441 7011 3211 Fabricated struc-
tural metal; hotels; structural glass

(G-16470)
CRYSTAL CARVERS INC
4040 Essex Ct (43065-7775)
PHONE...................................800 365-9782
Brad Uhl, *President*
Jennifer Uhl, *Vice Pres*
EMP: 4
SALES (est): 125K **Privately Held**
WEB: www.crystalcarversinc.com
SIC: 3423 Cutters, glass

(G-16471)
EYESCIENCE LABS LLC
493 Village Park Dr (43065-6605)
PHONE...................................614 885-7100
Jeffrey Northup, *Mng Member*
EMP: 7 EST: 2007
SQ FT: 7,000
SALES: 1.6MM **Privately Held**
SIC: 2834 Vitamin preparations

(G-16472)
GFS CHEMICALS INC (PA)
3041 Home Rd (43065-9710)
P.O. Box 245 (43065-0245)
PHONE...................................740 881-5501
Fax: 614 881-5989
J Steel Hutchinson, *President*
M Robert Pierron, *Vice Pres*

Richard Sheridan, *VP Opers*
Daniel Ewald, *QC Mgr*
Ed Reusch, *CFO*
◆ **EMP:** 20 **EST:** 1928
SQ FT: 125,000
SALES (est): 22.4MM **Privately Held**
WEB: www.gfschemicals.com
SIC: 2819 2899 2869 2812 Chemicals, reagent grade: refined from technical grade; chemical preparations; industrial organic chemicals; alkalies & chlorine

(G-16473)
HEALTHEDGE SOFTWARE INC
50 S Liberty St Ste 200 (43065-4006)
PHONE..................................614 431-3711
Nancy Riley, *Principal*
EMP: 3
SALES (est): 171.1K **Privately Held**
SIC: 7372 Prepackaged software

(G-16474)
KELLY CABINET COMPANY LLC
525 Thrush Rill Ct (43065-9781)
PHONE..................................614 563-2971
Christopher J Kelly, *Principal*
EMP: 5
SALES (est): 281.3K **Privately Held**
SIC: 2434 Wood kitchen cabinets

(G-16475)
KRAFT HOUSE NO 5
5 S Liberty St (43065-9301)
PHONE..................................614 396-9091
EMP: 4
SALES (est): 267.3K **Privately Held**
SIC: 2022 Processed cheese

(G-16476)
L E P D INDUSTRIES LTD
2292 Clairborne Dr (43065-8630)
PHONE..................................614 985-1470
Eric S Delbert, *Principal*
EMP: 3
SALES (est): 277.4K **Privately Held**
SIC: 3999 Manufacturing industries

(G-16477)
LAPCRAFT INC
195 W Olentangy St Unit A (43065-8720)
P.O. Box 389 (43065-0389)
PHONE..................................614 764-8993
Fax: 614 764-1860
Steve Ussery, *President*
Christina Ussery, *Treasurer*
EMP: 5
SQ FT: 7,500
SALES (est): 548.6K **Privately Held**
WEB: www.lapcraft.com
SIC: 3915 5085 Jewel preparing: instruments, tools, watches & jewelry; industrial supplies

(G-16478)
MICHELE MELLEN
Also Called: Jbm Enterprises
5680 Liberty Rd N (43065-9718)
PHONE..................................740 369-1422
Michelle Mellen, *Owner*
EMP: 4
SALES (est): 264.2K **Privately Held**
SIC: 3581 Automatic vending machines

(G-16479)
MILLWOOD INC
9749 Fairway Dr (43065-6947)
PHONE..................................614 717-9099
EMP: 38 **Privately Held**
SIC: 3565 Packaging machinery
PA: Millwood, Inc.
    3708 International Blvd
    Vienna OH 44473

(G-16480)
MORGAN WOOD PRODUCTS INC
9761 Fairway Dr (43065-6947)
P.O. Box 177 (43065-0177)
PHONE..................................614 336-4000
Luke Reinstetle, *President*
Dwight Reinstetle, *General Mgr*
Jannet Holbrook, *Manager*
◆ **EMP:** 12
SQ FT: 4,000
SALES: 30MM **Privately Held**
SIC: 2448 Wood pallets & skids

(G-16481)
NEW PATH INTERNATIONAL LLC
1476 Manning Pkwy Ste A (43065-7295)
PHONE..................................614 410-3974
Henry Todd, *Financial Exec*
Richard S Baum, *VP Mktg*
Damon Canfield, *Mng Member*
Aaron Carter, *Administration*
Neil Macivor,
▲ **EMP:** 50
SQ FT: 13,000
SALES (est): 8MM **Privately Held**
WEB: www.npi.com
SIC: 3639 7389 8711 Major kitchen appliances, except refrigerators & stoves; design, commercial & industrial; engineering services

(G-16482)
RANDYS COUNTERTOPS INC
3208 Home Rd (43065-9757)
PHONE..................................740 881-5831
Fax: 614 881-5981
Randolph Schirtzinger Sr, *President*
Mike Schirtzinger, *Vice Pres*
Reva Schirtzinger, *Admin Sec*
EMP: 13
SQ FT: 72,000
SALES (est): 1.5MM **Privately Held**
SIC: 2541 Counters or counter display cases, wood; sink tops, plastic laminated

(G-16483)
STELLA LOU LLC
Also Called: Coldstone Creamery
3939 Hickory Rock Dr (43065-7333)
PHONE..................................937 935-9536
Joshua Klinger, *Mng Member*
EMP: 16 **EST:** 2014
SQ FT: 1,200
SALES: 3MM **Privately Held**
SIC: 5812 2024 Ice cream stands or dairy bars; ice cream & frozen desserts

(G-16484)
SUCCESS TECHNOLOGIES INC
Also Called: Sunline Supply
324 W Case St (43065-7130)
PHONE..................................614 761-0008
Doug Kuepfer, *President*
Dori Kuepfer, *Corp Secy*
EMP: 8
SQ FT: 12,000
SALES (est): 1.3MM **Privately Held**
SIC: 2599 5099 5722 2824 Beds, not household use; tanning salon equipment & supplies; suntanning equipment & supplies; acrylic fibers

(G-16485)
SUMMIT ONLINE PRODUCTS LLC
Also Called: Massageblocks.com
3982 Powell Rd Ste 137 (43065-7662)
PHONE..................................800 326-1972
Thomas W Turner, *Mng Member*
EMP: 6
SALES: 190K **Privately Held**
SIC: 3841 Surgical & medical instruments

(G-16486)
TROGDON PUBLISHING INC
1635 Strathshire Hall Pl (43065-9436)
PHONE..................................330 620-2407
EMP: 2
SALES (est): 6.4MM **Privately Held**
SIC: 2741 Miscellaneous publishing

(G-16487)
VERTEBRATION INC
3982 Powell Rd 220 (43065-7662)
PHONE..................................614 395-3346
Richard Paul Karr, *President*
EMP: 3
SALES (est): 262.1K **Privately Held**
WEB: www.vertebration.com
SIC: 3841 Surgical & medical instruments

Powhatan Point
Belmont County

(G-16488)
COAL SERVICES INC
Also Called: Coal Services Group
155 Highway 7 S (43942-1033)
PHONE..................................740 795-5220
Don Gentry, *President*
Michael O McKown, *Principal*
Robert Moore, *Principal*
Barb Boyce, *Manager*
EMP: 90
SALES (est): 14.8MM
SALES (corp-wide): 4B **Privately Held**
WEB: www.coalservices.com
SIC: 8741 8711 1231 1222 Management services; engineering services; anthracite mining; bituminous coal-underground mining; bituminous coal & lignite-surface mining; coal mining services
HQ: The American Coal Company
    9085 Highway 34 N
    Galatia IL 62935
    618 268-6311

Proctorville
Lawrence County

(G-16489)
CANDLES BY JOYCE
343 Township Road 1233 (45669-8416)
P.O. Box 227 (45669-0227)
PHONE..................................740 886-6355
Joyce Snyder, *Owner*
EMP: 5
SALES (est): 230.1K **Privately Held**
SIC: 3999 Candles

(G-16490)
JBF REPAIR SERVICE LLC
7382 Unit B St Rt 7 (45669)
P.O. Box 9252, Huntington WV (25704-0252)
PHONE..................................740 550-0089
Phillip Wiley,
Amanda Wiley,
EMP: 4
SQ FT: 2,400
SALES (est): 175K **Privately Held**
SIC: 7549 3559 7537 7538 Trailer maintenance; automotive maintenance equipment; automotive transmission repair shops; diesel engine repair: automotive; brake repair, automotive; trailer repair

(G-16491)
ROLO SAND & GRAVEL
7165 County Road 107 (45669-8171)
PHONE..................................740 886-7407
Rob Calloway, *Owner*
EMP: 5
SALES (est): 356.7K **Privately Held**
SIC: 1442 Construction sand & gravel

(G-16492)
SPECIALTY SYSTEMS ELECTRIC LLC
1853 County Road 411 (45669-9415)
P.O. Box 677 (45669-0677)
PHONE..................................304 529-3861
John Whitfield, *Principal*
EMP: 9
SALES (est): 1.7MM **Privately Held**
SIC: 3648 Lighting fixtures, except electric: residential

(G-16493)
SUPERIOR MARINE WAYS INC
5852 County Rd 1 South Pt (45669)
P.O. Box 519 (45669-0519)
PHONE..................................740 894-6224
Dale Manns, *Manager*
EMP: 120
SALES (corp-wide): 16.3MM **Privately Held**
WEB: www.superiormarine.on.ca
SIC: 3731 7699 Barges, building & repairing; boat repair

PA: Superior Marine Ways, Inc.
    5852 County Road 1
    South Point OH 45680
    740 894-6224

(G-16494)
TRI-STATE MODEL FLYERS INC
358 Township Road 1161 (45669-8762)
PHONE..................................740 886-8429
Billy Lemley Jr, *Principal*
EMP: 84
SALES (est): 5MM **Privately Held**
SIC: 3721 Aircraft

Prospect
Marion County

(G-16495)
A S T MACHINE CO
1 N 4th St (43342-9627)
PHONE..................................740 494-2013
Leroy Zent, *Owner*
EMP: 5
SQ FT: 7,500
SALES (est): 343.1K **Privately Held**
SIC: 3599 Machine shop, jobbing & repair

(G-16496)
FLEMING CONSTRUCTION CO
Also Called: Scioto Sand & Gravel
5298 Marion Marysville Rd (43342-9342)
P.O. Box 31, Marion (43301-0031)
PHONE..................................740 494-2177
Fax: 614 494-2177
Gerald E Fleming, *President*
Sonya Fleming, *Vice Pres*
Butch Jones, *Manager*
EMP: 35
SQ FT: 2,400
SALES (est): 6.7MM **Privately Held**
SIC: 1542 1541 1623 1442 Commercial & office building, new construction; industrial buildings, new construction; sewer line construction; gravel mining; excavation & grading, building construction

(G-16497)
HERCULES INDUSTRIES INC
7194 Prospect Delaware Rd (43342-7505)
P.O. Box 197 (43342-0197)
PHONE..................................740 494-2620
Fax: 740 494-2274
Keith Popovich, *President*
Jean Meyer, *Vice Pres*
Ernie Massie, *Production*
Brandon Rowoldt, *Sales Mgr*
Jennifer Buchanan, *Manager*
▲ **EMP:** 23 **EST:** 1969
SQ FT: 18,380
SALES: 4.2MM
SALES (corp-wide): 4.9MM **Privately Held**
WEB: www.herculock.com
SIC: 3429 Manufactured hardware (general); padlocks
PA: Scientific Forming Technologies Corporation
    2545 Farmers Dr Ste 200
    Columbus OH 43235
    614 451-8330

Put In Bay
Ottawa County

(G-16498)
GIFT COVE INC
Also Called: Candy Bar
170 Delaware St (43456-6626)
P.O. Box 240 (43456-0240)
PHONE..................................419 285-2920
Linda Mahoney, *Manager*
EMP: 3
SALES (corp-wide): 2MM **Privately Held**
SIC: 2064 Fudge (candy)
PA: Gift Cove, Inc.
    156 Delaware St
    Put In Bay OH 43456
    719 510-9280

Quaker City
Guernsey County

(G-16499)
EAGLE FIREWORKS CO
21860 Bridgewater Rd (43773-9719)
PHONE..........................740 758-5649
Mindy Eagle, *Manager*
EMP: 5
SALES (corp-wide): 609.3K **Privately Held**
WEB: www.wvfireworks.net
SIC: 5999 5092 2899 Fireworks; fireworks; fireworks
PA: The Eagle Fireworks Co
26400 State Route 7
Marietta OH 45750
740 373-3357

(G-16500)
NY LOGGING & LUMBER
61285 Shannon Run Rd (43773-9552)
PHONE..........................740 679-2085
Noah E Yoder, *Principal*
EMP: 3
SALES (est): 197.3K **Privately Held**
SIC: 2411 Logging

(G-16501)
ROBBY YODER
61388 Underwood Rd (43773-9763)
PHONE..........................740 679-2776
Robby Yoder, *Principal*
EMP: 3
SALES (est): 237.6K **Privately Held**
SIC: 2411 7389 Logging;

(G-16502)
YODER LOGGING
22144 Oxford Rd (43773-9709)
PHONE..........................740 679-2635
Lester H Yoder, *Owner*
EMP: 3
SALES: 140K **Privately Held**
SIC: 2411 Logging

Quincy
Logan County

(G-16503)
F M SHEET METAL FABRICATION
13019 Shanley Rd (43343-9510)
PHONE..........................937 362-4357
Frank Williamson, *Owner*
EMP: 3
SALES (est): 158.1K **Privately Held**
SIC: 3444 Sheet metalwork

Racine
Meigs County

(G-16504)
J D DRILLING CO
107 S 3rd St (45771-9552)
P.O. Box 369 (45771-0369)
PHONE..........................740 949-2512
Fax: 740 949-2018
James E Diddle, *President*
EMP: 25
SQ FT: 6,000
SALES (est): 4MM **Privately Held**
SIC: 1381 Drilling oil & gas wells

Radnor
Delaware County

(G-16505)
CARVED STONE LLC
Also Called: Carved N Stone
3238 N Section Line Rd B7 (43066-8001)
PHONE..........................614 778-9855
Kareem Kashmiry, *President*
EMP: 3 EST: 2015

SALES (est): 242K **Privately Held**
SIC: 3479 Etching & engraving

(G-16506)
CENTRAL OHIO RTRCTABLE SCREENS
6737 Thomas Rd (43066-9618)
PHONE..........................614 868-5080
Marilyn Kulp, *President*
EMP: 5
SALES (est): 583.8K **Privately Held**
SIC: 3442 Screen doors, metal

(G-16507)
SCREENMOBILE INC
6737 Thomas Rd (43066-9618)
PHONE..........................614 868-8663
James Kulp, *President*
EMP: 6
SALES (est): 466.5K **Privately Held**
SIC: 1799 2431 7699 Screening contractor: window, door, etc.; door screens, metal covered wood; window screens, wood frame; door & window repair

(G-16508)
TIM CALVIN ACCESS CONTROLS
Also Called: Tim Calvin Enterprises
7585 Taway Rd (43066-9711)
PHONE..........................740 494-4200
Fax: 614 451-4383
Tim Calvin, *President*
Renee Calvin, *Vice Pres*
Vicki Wise, *Office Mgr*
Doug Bell, *Associate*
EMP: 8
SQ FT: 240
SALES: 900K **Privately Held**
WEB: www.calvininc.com
SIC: 3446 Architectural metalwork

Randolph
Portage County

(G-16509)
EAST MANUFACTURING CORPORATION (PA)
1871 State Rte 44 (44265)
P.O. Box 277 (44265-0277)
PHONE..........................330 325-9921
Fax: 330 325-7851
Howard D Booher, *CEO*
David De Poincy, *President*
Mark T Tate, *Corp Secy*
Robert J Bruce, *Vice Pres*
Joseph F Coletti, *Vice Pres*
▼**EMP:** 274
SQ FT: 350,000
SALES (est): 75.9MM **Privately Held**
WEB: www.eastmfg.com
SIC: 3715 5013 7539 Trailer bodies; truck parts & accessories; automotive repair shops

(G-16510)
EAST MANUFACTURING CORPORATION
3865 Waterloo Rd (44265)
PHONE..........................330 325-9921
Torie Tollman, *Manager*
EMP: 15
SALES (corp-wide): 75.9MM **Privately Held**
SIC: 3715 Trailer bodies
PA: East Manufacturing Corporation
1871 State Rte 44
Randolph OH 44265
330 325-9921

Ravenna
Portage County

(G-16511)
A C WILLIAMS CO INC (PA)
Also Called: Lake Metals
700 N Walnut St (44266-2300)
PHONE..........................330 296-6110
Dale E McCoy, *President*
Barbara Cramer, *Admin Sec*

EMP: 23 EST: 1944
SQ FT: 65,000
SALES (est): 8.1MM **Privately Held**
SIC: 3369 3321 Magnesium & magnes.-base alloy castings, exc. die-casting; gray iron castings; ductile iron castings

(G-16512)
ACCESS TO INDEPENDENCE INC
4960 S Prospect St (44266-9016)
PHONE..........................330 296-8111
Fax: 330 296-0539
Sherrie Winkler, *Senior Mgr*
Tim Spaulding, *Info Tech Dir*
Vince Pelose, *Director*
John Olson, *Director*
EMP: 4
SALES (est): 1.2MM **Privately Held**
WEB: www.accesstoindependence.com
SIC: 8399 7999 5999 5047 Community development groups; bingo hall; medical apparatus & supplies; hospital equipment & furniture; wheelchair lifts

(G-16513)
AIR CRAFT WHEELS LLC
700 N Walnut St (44266-2372)
PHONE..........................440 937-7903
Fax: 440 937-7905
Dale McCoy, *President*
EMP: 9
SALES (est): 1MM **Privately Held**
WEB: www.aircraftwheels.net
SIC: 3356 3365 3369 Magnesium; aluminum foundries; nonferrous foundries

(G-16514)
ALLEN AIRCRAFT PRODUCTS INC
312 E Lake St (44266-3428)
P.O. Box 951146, Cleveland (44193-0005)
PHONE..........................330 296-9621
Thomas Kamerer, *Buyer*
Jordan Jones, *Design Engr*
Kevin Barbeck, *Branch Mgr*
EMP: 50
SALES (corp-wide): 22MM **Privately Held**
WEB: www.allenaircraft.com
SIC: 3728 3471 Aircraft parts & equipment; plating & polishing
PA: Allen Aircraft Products, Inc.
6168 Woodbine Rd
Ravenna OH 44266
330 296-9621

(G-16515)
ALLEN AIRCRAFT PRODUCTS INC
Also Called: Metal Finishing Divison
4879 Newton Falls Rd (44266-9673)
P.O. Box 1211 (44266-1211)
PHONE..........................330 296-1531
Fax: 330 296-5532
Roger Rollison, *Branch Mgr*
Ilene Weinberg, *Manager*
EMP: 35
SALES (corp-wide): 20.8MM **Privately Held**
WEB: www.allenaircraft.com
SIC: 3471 Finishing, metals or formed products
PA: Allen Aircraft Products, Inc.
6168 Woodbine Rd
Ravenna OH 44266
330 296-9621

(G-16516)
ASTRA PRODUCTS OF OHIO LTD (PA)
7154 State Route 88 (44266-9189)
PHONE..........................330 296-0112
Brenda Pauler, *Accountant*
David Silva, *Manager*
Scott Kohl,
◆**EMP:** 100
SQ FT: 110,000
SALES (est): 22.3MM **Privately Held**
WEB: www.astraproductsltd.com
SIC: 3089 Extruded finished plastic products

(G-16517)
BECK ENERGY CORP
160 N Chestnut St (44266-2256)
P.O. Box 1070 (44266-1070)
PHONE..........................330 297-6891
Fax: 330 297-7925
Raymond Beck, *President*
EMP: 15
SQ FT: 4,000
SALES (est): 2MM **Privately Held**
SIC: 1382 Oil & gas exploration services

(G-16518)
BECK SAND & GRAVEL INC
2820 Webb Rd (44266-9459)
PHONE..........................330 626-3863
Fax: 330 626-5515
Rod Wenrich, *President*
Dan Lostoski, *Vice Pres*
EMP: 9
SQ FT: 3,200
SALES (est): 1.3MM **Privately Held**
SIC: 1442 Construction sand & gravel; gravel mining

(G-16519)
BOLLARI/DAVIS INC
5292 S Prospect St (44266-9032)
P.O. Box 609 (44266-0609)
PHONE..........................330 296-4445
Fax: 330 296-2567
David Stonestreet, *President*
EMP: 10 EST: 1958
SQ FT: 13,000
SALES (est): 1.1MM **Privately Held**
SIC: 3599 Machine shop, jobbing & repair

(G-16520)
BUILDING & CONVEYER MAINT LLC
6803 Cleveland Rd (44266-1842)
PHONE..........................303 882-0912
George Metcalf, *Mng Member*
Rebecca Metcalf,
EMP: 5 EST: 2014
SALES (est): 634.6K **Privately Held**
SIC: 3535 Conveyors & conveying equipment

(G-16521)
CIRJAK FURNITURE AND DESIGN
Also Called: Cirjak's Furntr & Design
3416 State Route 59 (44266-1350)
PHONE..........................330 296-8035
Tom Cirjak, *Owner*
EMP: 3
SQ FT: 1,200
SALES: 500K **Privately Held**
SIC: 2434 2511 1751 Wood kitchen cabinets; wood household furniture; cabinet & finish carpentry

(G-16522)
CITY OF RAVENNA
Also Called: Waste Water Plant, The
3722 Hommon Rd (44266-3543)
PHONE..........................330 296-5214
Michael Lacivita, *Manager*
Cindy Mullins, *Manager*
EMP: 9 **Privately Held**
SIC: 4952 3589 Sewerage systems; sewage treatment equipment
PA: City Of Ravenna
210 Park Way
Ravenna OH 44266
330 296-3864

(G-16523)
COLONIAL RUBBER COMPANY (PA)
706 Oakwood St (44266-2138)
P.O. Box 111 (44266-0111)
PHONE..........................330 296-2831
Fax: 330 296-7861
Dale P Fosnight, *President*
Wayne H Wise, *Corp Secy*
Wayne Slack, *VP Mfg*
Steven Fosnight, *Purchasing*
Alan D Fosnight, *Controller*
EMP: 50
SQ FT: 55,000
SALES (est): 7.7MM **Privately Held**
SIC: 3061 3069 Mechanical rubber goods; hard rubber & molded rubber products

(G-16524)
DACON INDUSTRIES CO
4839 Washington Ave (44266-9628)
PHONE...................................330 298-9491
Paula Cayton, *Principal*
EMP: 24
SALES (corp-wide): 15.4MM **Privately Held**
SIC: 3069 Hard rubber products
PA: Dacon Industries Co.
10661 N Lombard St
Portland OR 97203
503 978-0801

(G-16525)
DIE-NAMIC TOOL & DIE INC
100 Romito St Ste D (44266-2880)
PHONE...................................330 296-6923
Fax: 330 296-6924
Marie Boyce, *President*
EMP: 5 EST: 1997
SQ FT: 6,000
SALES (est): 710.8K **Privately Held**
SIC: 3544 Special dies & tools

(G-16526)
DURACOTE CORPORATION
350 N Diamond St (44266-2155)
P.O. Box 1209 (44266-1209)
PHONE...................................330 296-9600
Fax: 216 296-5102
Jack Pallay, *President*
Steven Simgel, *Controller*
Dee Baillie, *Accounts Mgr*
▼ EMP: 40 EST: 1947
SQ FT: 143,000
SALES (est): 11.4MM **Privately Held**
WEB: www.duracote.com
SIC: 3083 2295 3082 2261 Laminated
plastics plate & sheet; resin or plastic
coated fabrics; unsupported plastics pro-
file shapes; finishing plants, cotton

(G-16527)
DYNA TECH MOLDING & BETA
367 N Freedom St (44266-2444)
PHONE...................................330 296-2315
EMP: 5
SALES (est): 773.5K **Privately Held**
SIC: 2891 Mfg Adhesives/Sealants

(G-16528)
ECLIPSE BLIND SYSTEMS INC
7154 State Route 88 (44266-9189)
PHONE...................................330 296-0112
James W Watson, *President*
Dave Cline, *Plant Mgr*
Lucky Monroe, *Plant Mgr*
Mike Skidmore, *Plant Mgr*
Dennis Miller, *Purchasing*
EMP: 165
SQ FT: 110,000
SALES (est): 15.7MM **Privately Held**
SIC: 3089 7371 Extruded finished plastic
products; custom computer programming
services
HQ: Turnils (Uk) Limited
10 Fountain Crescent
Renfrew PA4 9

(G-16529)
ENDURO RUBBER COMPANY
685 S Chestnut St (44266-3068)
P.O. Box 752 (44266-0752)
PHONE...................................330 296-9603
Fax: 330 296-9604
Jerry Stuver, *President*
Luanne Stuver, *Vice Pres*
Neal A Stuver, *Treasurer*
EMP: 9 EST: 1946
SQ FT: 24,000
SALES (est): 1.3MM **Privately Held**
WEB: www.endurorubber.com
SIC: 3069 Molded rubber products

(G-16530)
G GRAFTON MACHINE & RUBBER
640 Cleveland Rd (44266-2021)
PHONE...................................330 297-1062
Fax: 330 297-6526
Montgomery Grafton, *President*
EMP: 10
SQ FT: 17,500

SALES (est): 1.3MM **Privately Held**
SIC: 3069 3069 Machine shop, jobbing &
repair; hard rubber & molded rubber products

(G-16531)
GENERAL ALUMINUM MFG COMPANY
5159 S Prospect St (44266-9031)
PHONE...................................330 297-1020
Craig Schlauch, *Branch Mgr*
EMP: 20
SALES (corp-wide): 1.2B **Publicly Held**
WEB: www.generalaluminum.com
SIC: 3365 3369 Aluminum & aluminum-
based alloy castings; nonferrous
foundries
HQ: General Aluminum Mfg. Company
6065 Parkland Blvd
Cleveland OH 44124
440 947-2000

(G-16532)
HUGO VGLSANG MASCHINENBAU GMBH
Also Called: Vogelsang Brazil Comercio E
7966 State Route 44 (44266-9781)
P.O. Box 751 (44266-0751)
PHONE...................................330 296-3820
Fax: 330 296-4113
Russell J Boring, *President*
Christian Vogeler, *Vice Pres*
Johann Kezik, *Opers Staff*
Jon Neuenschwander, *Sales Engr*
Barbara Braden, *Marketing Staff*
▲ EMP: 25
SQ FT: 30,000
SALES (est): 6.8MM
SALES (corp-wide): 86.6MM **Privately
Held**
WEB: www.vogelsangusa.com
SIC: 3561 Pumps & pumping equipment
PA: Hugo Vogelsang Maschinenbau Gmbh
Holthoge 10-14
Essen (Oldenburg) 49632
543 483-0

(G-16533)
HYTECH SILICONE PRODUCTS INC
6112 Knapp Rd (44266-8876)
PHONE...................................330 297-1888
John Roberts, *President*
EMP: 6 EST: 1987
SQ FT: 2,450
SALES (est): 220K **Privately Held**
SIC: 3069 Molded rubber products

(G-16534)
JEFF CALES CUSTOMER AVI LLC
8101 State Route 44 A (44266-8322)
PHONE...................................330 298-9479
Jeff Cales,
EMP: 3
SALES (est): 283.6K **Privately Held**
WEB: www.customaviation.com
SIC: 3728 Aircraft body assemblies & parts

(G-16535)
JOHNSON MTTHEY PRCESS TECH INC
785 N Freedom St (44266-2469)
PHONE...................................330 298-7005
EMP: 30
SALES (corp-wide): 15.5B **Privately Held**
SIC: 2819 Catalysts, chemical
HQ: Matthey Johnson Process Technolo-
gies Inc
115 Eli Whitney Blvd
Savannah GA 31408
732 223-4644

(G-16536)
KING ENERGY INC
6050 State Route 14 Lot 7 (44266-9340)
PHONE...................................330 297-5508
Robert Lindsey, *President*
EMP: 5 EST: 1992
SQ FT: 5,000
SALES (est): 100K **Privately Held**
WEB: www.playboard.com
SIC: 1381 Drilling oil & gas wells

(G-16537)
LANGSTONS ULTMATE CLG SVCS INC
3764 Summit Rd (44266-3515)
PHONE...................................330 298-9150
Blake Langston, *President*
EMP: 16 EST: 1999
SALES (est): 1.2MM **Privately Held**
SIC: 3354 7699 Aluminum extruded prod-
ucts; cleaning services

(G-16538)
LARIAT MACHINE INC
826 Cleveland Rd (44266-2029)
P.O. Box 649 (44266-0649)
PHONE...................................330 297-5765
Richard Schaak, *President*
Jeff Steese, *Vice Pres*
EMP: 6
SQ FT: 3,708
SALES (est): 100K **Privately Held**
WEB: www.lariatmachine.com
SIC: 3599 Air intake filters, internal com-
bustion engine, except auto

(G-16539)
LITE METALS COMPANY
700 N Walnut St (44266-2372)
PHONE...................................330 296-6110
Fax: 330 296-8637
Dale E Mc Coy, *President*
Barbara Cramer, *Vice Pres*
Robert Robinson, *Controller*
Nancy Green, *Human Res Mgr*
EMP: 35
SQ FT: 65,000
SALES (est): 8.1MM **Privately Held**
WEB: www.litemetals.com
SIC: 3365 3369 3356 Aluminum
foundries; nonferrous foundries; magne-
sium
PA: A C Williams Co Inc
700 N Walnut St
Ravenna OH 44266
330 296-6110

(G-16540)
MICRO MOLD CO INC
6671 Cleveland Rd (44266-1874)
PHONE...................................330 325-2373
Fax: 330 325-2356
Gary Leifheit, *President*
Jeff Power, *Vice Pres*
EMP: 9
SQ FT: 2,800
SALES: 1MM **Privately Held**
SIC: 3544 Industrial molds

(G-16541)
MILLER TOOL AND MACHINE CO
7888 Cooley Rd (44266-9752)
PHONE...................................330 297-9657
Dale Monreal, *Owner*
EMP: 3
SALES (est): 150K **Privately Held**
SIC: 3599 Machine shop, jobbing & repair

(G-16542)
MONTGOMERYS PALLET SERVICE
7937 State Route 44 (44266-9781)
PHONE...................................330 297-6677
Teresa Montgomery, *President*
William Montgomery, *Vice Pres*
EMP: 7
SALES (est): 994.8K **Privately Held**
SIC: 2448 4953 Pallets, wood & wood with
metal; refuse collection & disposal serv-
ices

(G-16543)
NETTTING TECHNOLOGIES LLC
636 S Walnut St (44266-3166)
PHONE...................................330 298-0022
Jim Ohlinger, *Principal*
EMP: 7
SALES (est): 656.3K **Privately Held**
SIC: 2269 5949 Finishing plants; needle-
work goods & supplies

(G-16544)
NICHOLS MOLD INC
222 W Lake St (44266-3651)
PHONE...................................330 297-9719

Fax: 330 297-6430
Edward Nichols, *President*
Nancy Nichols, *Corp Secy*
EMP: 5
SQ FT: 4,000
SALES (est): 500K **Privately Held**
SIC: 3544 3599 Industrial molds; machine
shop, jobbing & repair

(G-16545)
NOTEWORTHY WOODWORKING
6361 Marchinn Dr (44266-1711)
PHONE...................................330 297-0509
EMP: 4 EST: 2010
SALES (est): 230K **Privately Held**
SIC: 2431 Mfg Millwork

(G-16546)
ORGANIC ROOTS HORTICULTURE LLC
6158 State Route 303 (44266-9123)
PHONE...................................330 620-1108
Daniel Hickin, *Principal*
Matthew Hickin, *Principal*
EMP: 3
SALES (est): 304K **Privately Held**
SIC: 2824 Organic fibers, noncellulosic

(G-16547)
ORZEN EXTRUDED POLYMERS
4699 Loomis Pkwy Unit C (44266-9114)
PHONE...................................330 298-9550
Michael Orazen, *Principal*
EMP: 8 EST: 2013
SALES (est): 1.4MM **Privately Held**
SIC: 3089 Extruded finished plastic prod-
ucts

(G-16548)
PARKER-HANNIFIN CORPORATION
Parflex Div
1300 N Freedom St (44266-8405)
PHONE...................................330 296-2871
Fax: 330 296-8433
Jerry Meeks, *Plant Mgr*
Joe Sebera, *Plant Mgr*
Craig Mikin, *QC Mgr*
Ty Henry, *Engineer*
Jonathan Wilch, *Engineer*
EMP: 250
SALES (corp-wide): 11.3B **Publicly Held**
WEB: www.parker.com
SIC: 3083 Thermoplastic laminates: rods,
tubes, plates & sheet
PA: Parker-Hannifin Corporation
6035 Parkland Blvd
Cleveland OH 44124
216 896-3000

(G-16549)
PARKER-HANNIFIN CORPORATION
Energy Products Division
1300 N Freedom St (44266-8405)
PHONE...................................330 296-2871
John Jansen, *Branch Mgr*
EMP: 40
SALES (corp-wide): 11.3B **Publicly Held**
SIC: 3052 Rubber & plastics hose & belt-
ings
PA: Parker-Hannifin Corporation
6035 Parkland Blvd
Cleveland OH 44124
216 896-3000

(G-16550)
PETTIGREW PUMPING INC
4171 Sandy Lake Rd (44266-9390)
P.O. Box 809 (44266-0809)
PHONE...................................330 297-7900
Fax: 419 768-9900
Matthew Pettigrew, *Principal*
EMP: 9
SALES (est): 1.1MM **Privately Held**
SIC: 1389 Pumping of oil & gas wells

(G-16551)
QUIKRETE COMPANIES INC
Also Called: Quikrete of Cleveland
2693 Lake Rockwell Rd (44266-8041)
PHONE...................................330 296-6080
Fax: 330 296-7013
Tim Howe, *Sales Executive*
Tim Ryon, *Manager*

▲ = Import ▼=Export
◆ =Import/Export

EMP: 30
SQ FT: 48,000 **Privately Held**
WEB: www.quikrete.com
SIC: 3272 5211 3273 3241 Dry mixture concrete; masonry materials & supplies; ready-mixed concrete; cement, hydraulic
HQ: The Quikrete Companies Llc
3490 Piedmont Rd Ne # 1300
Atlanta GA 30305
404 634-9100

(G-16552)
R W MACHINE & TOOL INC
7944 State Route 44 (44266-9781)
PHONE....................................330 296-5211
Fax: 330 296-7537
Alan Wilbur, *CEO*
Mike Jenkins, *CEO*
Michael Jenkins, *President*
Karen Wilbur, *Corp Secy*
Karen Wilber, *Treasurer*
▲ **EMP:** 40
SQ FT: 17,500
SALES (est): 5.6MM **Privately Held**
WEB: www.rwmachinetool.com
SIC: 3599 Machine shop, jobbing & repair

(G-16553)
ROUTE 14 STORAGE INC
Also Called: Route 14 Storage EMB & More
7830 State Route 14 (44266-9454)
PHONE....................................330 296-0084
Fax: 330 296-1984
Anita Schmitt, *President*
EMP: 4
SALES (est): 340K **Privately Held**
SIC: 4226 5199 2395 Warehousing, self-storage; advertising specialties; embroidery products, except schiffli machine

(G-16554)
SAINT-GOBAIN PRFMCE PLAS CORP
335 N Diamond St (44266-2153)
PHONE....................................330 296-9948
Ron Bauer, *General Mgr*
Patrice Lallement, *Senior VP*
David Stresing, *Engineer*
Don Moyer, *Marketing Staff*
EMP: 130
SALES (corp-wide): 185.8MM **Privately Held**
SIC: 3089 Thermoformed finished plastic products
HQ: Saint-Gobain Performance Plastics Corporation
31500 Solon Rd
Solon OH 44139
440 836-6900

(G-16555)
SANDERS FREDRICK EXCVTG CO INC
5858 State Route 14 (44266-8745)
P.O. Box 668 (44266-0668)
PHONE....................................330 297-7980
Fred Sanders, *President*
Doris Berry, *Admin Sec*
EMP: 9
SQ FT: 3,200
SALES (est): 1.1MM **Privately Held**
SIC: 1389 1794 Oil field services; excavation work

(G-16556)
SHUR-CO LLC
1100 N Freedom St (44266-2472)
P.O. Box 827 (44266-0827)
PHONE....................................330 297-0888
Greg Graff, *Branch Mgr*
EMP: 8
SALES (corp-wide): 47.5MM **Privately Held**
WEB: www.shurco.com
SIC: 2394 5531 5199 Canvas & related products; truck equipment & parts; tarpaulins
PA: Shur-Co, Llc
2309 Shurlock St
Yankton SD 57078
605 665-6000

(G-16557)
SOBER SAND & GRAVEL CO
2898 Tallmadge Rd (44266-8212)
PHONE....................................330 325-7088

Tracy Sober, *President*
Waldo A Sober Sr, *President*
Robert Macgregor, *Vice Pres*
EMP: 3 **EST:** 1940
SALES (est): 244.9K **Privately Held**
SIC: 1442 Construction sand mining; gravel mining

(G-16558)
SPECTRUM DISPERSIONS INC
225 W Lake St (44266-3650)
P.O. Box 805 (44266-0805)
PHONE....................................330 296-0600
Fax: 330 296-3976
Gary Klemm, *President*
Gregory Klemm, *Vice Pres*
Timothy Klemm, *Treasurer*
EMP: 15
SQ FT: 70,000
SALES (est): 4.4MM **Privately Held**
SIC: 2865 2816 2851 Color pigments, organic; color pigments; paints & paint additives; lacquers, varnishes, enamels & other coatings

(G-16559)
SPORTS EXPRESS
956 E Main St (44266-3326)
PHONE....................................330 297-1112
Jim Hunt, *Owner*
EMP: 3
SQ FT: 5,200
SALES (est): 338.9K **Privately Held**
SIC: 5941 5611 5621 2759 Sporting goods & bicycle shops; clothing, sportswear, men's & boys'; women's sportswear; screen printing; sports apparel

(G-16560)
SPRINGSEAL INC
800 Enterprise Pkwy (44266-8061)
PHONE....................................330 626-0673
Mark Knapp, *President*
Robert Reddick, *Manager*
EMP: 12
SQ FT: 10,000
SALES (est): 4.1MM **Privately Held**
SIC: 3089 Thermoformed finished plastic products

(G-16561)
STA-WARM ELECTRIC COMPANY
553 N Chestnut St (44266-2217)
P.O. Box 150 (44266-0150)
PHONE....................................330 296-6461
Fax: 330 296-9243
John Snell, *President*
Brian Borthwick, *Vice Pres*
Linda Barns, *Manager*
EMP: 10 **EST:** 1920
SQ FT: 25,000
SALES (est): 1.3MM **Privately Held**
SIC: 3567 Heating units & devices, industrial: electric

(G-16562)
STAHL FARM MARKET
4560 State Route 14 (44266-8742)
PHONE....................................330 325-0640
Charlie Stahl, *Owner*
EMP: 10
SALES (est): 786.3K **Privately Held**
SIC: 2048 Stock feeds, dry

(G-16563)
STAPINS QICK CPY/PRINT CTR LLC
253 W Main St (44266-2742)
PHONE....................................330 296-0123
Fax: 330 296-1956
Kenneth Stapin, *Mng Member*
Kenneth A Stapin, *Mng Member*
EMP: 4
SQ FT: 2,800
SALES: 300K **Privately Held**
SIC: 2752 Commercial printing, lithographic

(G-16564)
T&A PALLETS INC
2849 Denny Rd (44266-9419)
PHONE....................................330 968-4743
Tony Rodriguez, *Principal*
EMP: 4 **EST:** 2009

SALES (est): 311.5K **Privately Held**
SIC: 2448 Pallets, wood & wood with metal

(G-16565)
TARPED OUT INC
4442 State Route 14 (44266-8741)
PHONE....................................330 325-7722
Marc Campitelli, *Branch Mgr*
EMP: 13
SALES (corp-wide): 562.6MM **Privately Held**
WEB: www.mountaintarp.com
SIC: 2394 Awnings, fabric: made from purchased materials; tarpaulins, fabric: made from purchased materials
HQ: Tarped Out, Inc.
1002 N 15th St
Middlesboro KY 40965
606 248-7717

(G-16566)
TOUCHSTONE WOODWORKS
7820 Cooley Rd (44266-9752)
P.O. Box 112 (44266-0112)
PHONE....................................330 297-1313
Tina Walters, *Owner*
Michelle Windhausen, *Purchasing*
EMP: 4
SALES: 300K **Privately Held**
WEB: www.touchstonewoodworks.com
SIC: 2431 Door screens, wood frame

(G-16567)
TREXLER RUBBER CO INC (PA)
503 N Diamond St (44266-2113)
P.O. Box 667 (44266-0667)
PHONE....................................330 296-9677
Fax: 330 296-2272
Jack W Schaefer, *President*
EMP: 20
SQ FT: 26,000
SALES: 2MM **Privately Held**
WEB: www.trexlerballoonwheel.com
SIC: 3069 2851 3544 Latex, foamed; polyurethane coatings; special dies, tools, jigs & fixtures

(G-16568)
TRI-WAY REBAR INC (PA)
Also Called: Clinton Supply
625 S Walnut St (44266-3167)
P.O. Box 750 (44266-0750)
PHONE....................................330 296-9662
Fax: 330 296-9802
Gerald Guy, *President*
Bradley, *Principal*
Stanley R Jarosz, *Principal*
William D Simpson, *Principal*
G Way, *Principal*
EMP: 5
SQ FT: 31,000
SALES (est): 1.5MM **Privately Held**
SIC: 3531 1791 Construction machinery; structural steel erection

(G-16569)
TRUE INDUSTRIES INC
Also Called: Cleveland Punch and Die Co
666 Pratt St (44266-3161)
P.O. Box 769 (44266-0769)
PHONE....................................330 296-4342
Fax: 330 296-6877
Dan L Brown, *President*
Roger Babb, *Vice Pres*
Jerry Spence, *Plant Mgr*
Bob Grenfell, *Controller*
Tina Fumich, *Accounting Dir*
EMP: 50
SQ FT: 70,000
SALES (est): 9.5MM **Privately Held**
WEB: www.clevelandpunch.com
SIC: 3544 Special dies, tools, jigs & fixtures

(G-16570)
W POLE CONTRACTING INC
4188 State Route 14 (44266-8739)
PHONE....................................330 325-7177
Wade Pol, *President*
Christine Pol, *Treasurer*
EMP: 10
SALES (est): 919.8K **Privately Held**
SIC: 1389 Oil field services

(G-16571)
WESTROCK CP LLC
975 N Freedom St (44266-2465)
P.O. Box 1214 (44266-1214)
PHONE....................................330 297-0841
Fax: 330 296-3855
Bill Rich, *General Mgr*
Luanne Jenkins, *Opers Staff*
Kenneth W Pittman, *Opers Staff*
Williston C Rich, *Sales Mgr*
Tim Okeefe, *Sales Staff*
EMP: 108
SALES (corp-wide): 14.1B **Publicly Held**
WEB: www.smurfit-stone.com
SIC: 2653 3412 Corrugated & solid fiber boxes; metal barrels, drums & pails
HQ: Westrock Cp, Llc
504 Thrasher St
Norcross GA 30071

(G-16572)
WESTROCK RKT COMPANY
Also Called: Rock Tenn
975 N Freedom St (44266-2465)
P.O. Box 1214 (44266-1214)
PHONE....................................330 296-5155
EMP: 8
SALES (corp-wide): 14.1B **Publicly Held**
SIC: 2653 Corrugated & solid fiber boxes
HQ: Westrock Rkt Company
504 Thrasher St
Norcross GA 30071
770 448-2193

Rawson
Hancock County

(G-16573)
DNC HYDRAULICS LLC
5219 County Road 313 (45881-9650)
PHONE....................................419 963-2800
Bill Hartman, *Prdtn Mgr*
Cody Conaway, *Sales Mgr*
Nic Conaway, *Sales Mgr*
Blaine Beilharz, *Marketing Staff*
Cody Thacker, *Marketing Staff*
EMP: 12
SALES (est): 950K **Privately Held**
SIC: 7699 3492 Industrial machinery & equipment repair; control valves, fluid power: hydraulic & pneumatic

---

Ray
Vinton County

(G-16574)
TERRY G SICKLES
2207 Boy Scout Rd (45672-9672)
PHONE....................................740 286-8880
Terry G Sickles, *Principal*
EMP: 3 **EST:** 2010
SALES (est): 222.5K **Privately Held**
SIC: 2411 Logging

Rayland
Jefferson County

(G-16575)
SHELLY AND SANDS INC
Also Called: Tri-State Asphalt Co
1731 Old State Route 7 (43943-7962)
P.O. Box 66 (43943-0066)
PHONE....................................740 859-2104
Fax: 740 859-2134
Mark Haverty, *General Mgr*
EMP: 60
SALES (corp-wide): 301.4MM **Privately Held**
WEB: www.shellyandsands.com
SIC: 2951 1542 Asphalt paving mixtures & blocks; nonresidential construction
PA: Shelly And Sands, Inc.
3570 S River Rd
Zanesville OH 43701
740 453-0721

Raymond
Union County

(G-16576)
NATURE PURE LLC (PA)
26586 State Route 739 (43067-9763)
PHONE....................................937 358-2364
Theresa Harris, *General Mgr*
Scott Colwell, *Vice Pres*
Kurt Lausecker, *Mng Member*
EMP: 23
SALES (est): 3.5MM **Privately Held**
SIC: 0252 2048 Started pullet farm; poultry feeds

Reno
Washington County

(G-16577)
MONDO POLYMER TECHNOLOGIES INC
27620 State Rte 7 (45773)
P.O. Box 250 (45773-0250)
PHONE....................................740 376-9396
Mark Mondo, *President*
Maggie Ellis, *General Mgr*
Judy Mondo, *Vice Pres*
Rick Hockenberry, *Opers Mgr*
Tony Carver, *Production*
EMP: 40
SQ FT: 3,200
SALES (est): 15.2MM **Privately Held**
WEB: www.mondopolymer.com
SIC: 4953 2822 Recycling, waste materials; synthetic rubber

(G-16578)
MUSTANG AERIAL SERVICES INC
27620 State Route 7 (45773)
P.O. Box 250 (45773-0250)
PHONE....................................740 373-9262
Mark A Mondo, *President*
Judy Mondo, *Admin Sec*
EMP: 8
SALES (est): 949.5K **Privately Held**
SIC: 3089 Plastic boats & other marine equipment

Republic
Seneca County

(G-16579)
JEB MODERN MACHINES LTD
3360 N State Route 19 (44867-9713)
PHONE....................................419 639-3937
Fax: 419 639-3940
Robert Widman, *Partner*
Eric Widman, *Partner*
James Widman, *Partner*
EMP: 3
SALES: 50K **Privately Held**
WEB: www.jebmodernmachine.com
SIC: 3541 Machine tool replacement & repair parts, metal cutting types

Reynoldsburg
Franklin County

(G-16580)
AMERICAN AIRLESS INC
7095 Americana Pkwy (43068-4118)
PHONE....................................614 552-0146
Jimmy Yang, *President*
Lonnie Wells, *General Mgr*
Charles Lee, *Director*
EMP: 50
SALES (est): 4.2MM **Privately Held**
SIC: 3011 Tire & inner tube materials & related products

(G-16581)
B B & H TOOL COMPANY
7719 Taylor Rd Sw (43068-9626)
PHONE....................................614 868-8634
Fax: 614 868-8635
Mousa Aframian, *Owner*
Shelly Aframian, *Manager*
EMP: 8
SQ FT: 8,000
SALES (est): 852.2K **Privately Held**
WEB: www.bbhtool.com
SIC: 3599 Machine shop, jobbing & repair

(G-16582)
BATH & BODY WORKS LLC (HQ)
7 Limited Pkwy E (43068-5300)
PHONE....................................614 856-6000
Fax: 614 856-6813
Nicholas Coe, *CEO*
Tony Mendoza, *President*
Mark Peters, *President*
Lori Blankenship, *District Mgr*
Mary Jackson, *District Mgr*
▲ **EMP:** 336
SALES (est): 2.8B
SALES (corp-wide): 12.5B **Publicly Held**
WEB: www.bath-and-body.com
SIC: 5999 2844 Toiletries, cosmetics & perfumes; toilet preparations
PA: L Brands, Inc.
3 Limited Pkwy
Columbus OH 43230
614 415-7000

(G-16583)
BUCKEYE READY-MIX LLC (PA)
Also Called: Buckeye Building Products
7657 Taylor Rd Sw (43068-9626)
P.O. Box 164119, Columbus (43216-4119)
PHONE....................................614 575-2132
Fax: 614 575-1449
Brandon Double, *Safety Dir*
Jeff Tyson, *Opers Mgr*
Gary Conley, *Controller*
Randy Painter, *Sales Mgr*
John Ellis, *Cust Mgr*
EMP: 50
SQ FT: 10,000
SALES (est): 42.4MM **Privately Held**
WEB: www.buckeyereadymix.com
SIC: 3273 Ready-mixed concrete

(G-16584)
COLUMBUS GRAPHICS INC
7295 Rickly St (43068-2513)
PHONE....................................614 577-9360
Fax: 614 351-1773
William Stewart III, *President*
EMP: 13
SQ FT: 8,000
SALES (est): 1.1MM **Privately Held**
SIC: 3993 Signs & advertising specialties

(G-16585)
CORNERSTONE PRINTING INC
443 Knob Ave (43068-1070)
PHONE....................................614 861-2138
Tim Kulich, *Principal*
Jill D Kulich, *Principal*
EMP: 3
SALES (est): 328.2K **Privately Held**
SIC: 2752 Commercial printing, lithographic

(G-16586)
DIMENSIONAL METALS INC (PA)
Also Called: D M I
58 Klema Dr N (43068-9691)
PHONE....................................740 927-3633
Fax: 740 927-3319
Stephen C Wissman, *CEO*
Phillip Gastaldo, *President*
Steven Gastaldo, *Vice Pres*
Shawn Walters, *Prdtn Mgr*
Brian Peck, *Purchasing*
EMP: 52
SQ FT: 34,000
SALES (est): 8.5MM **Privately Held**
WEB: www.dmimetals.com
SIC: 1761 3444 3531 Roofing, siding & sheet metal work; sheet metalwork; roofing equipment

(G-16587)
DYNALAB EMS INC
555 Lancaster Ave (43068-1128)
PHONE....................................614 866-9999
Gary James, *President*
Charles Arbuckle, *Corp Secy*
▲ **EMP:** 107
SALES: 25MM
SALES (corp-wide): 49.2MM **Privately Held**
WEB: www.dynalabems.com
SIC: 3679 Electronic circuits
PA: Dynalab, Inc.
555 Lancaster Ave
Reynoldsburg OH 43068
614 729-6127

(G-16588)
ENVIRONMENTAL CLOSURE SYSTEMS
Also Called: E C S
536 Killin Ct (43068-7100)
PHONE....................................614 759-9186
Fax: 614 759-9177
Thomas A Sisbarro, *President*
EMP: 19
SQ FT: 4,000
SALES (est): 1.2MM **Privately Held**
SIC: 3589 Commercial cleaning equipment

(G-16589)
FARBER SPECIALTY VEHICLES INC
7052 Americana Pkwy (43068-4117)
PHONE....................................614 863-6470
Fax: 614 759-2098
Ken Farber, *President*
Steve Goodyear, *Vice Pres*
Tim Detty, *Purch Mgr*
Mark Brewer, *Purchasing*
Craig Farber, *Purchasing*
▼ **EMP:** 110
SQ FT: 60,000
SALES (est): 34.3MM **Privately Held**
WEB: www.farberspecialty.com
SIC: 3711 Automobile assembly, including specialty automobiles

(G-16590)
FEDEX OFFICE & PRINT SVCS INC
2668 Brice Rd (43068-3419)
PHONE....................................614 575-0800
Greg Jackson, *Branch Mgr*
EMP: 13
SQ FT: 3,000
SALES (corp-wide): 50.3B **Publicly Held**
WEB: www.kinkos.com
SIC: 7334 2791 2789 Photocopying & duplicating services; typesetting; bookbinding & related work
HQ: Fedex Office And Print Services, Inc.
7900 Legacy Dr
Plano TX 75024
214 550-7000

(G-16591)
FRAME WAREHOUSE
7502 E Main St (43068-1208)
PHONE....................................614 861-4582
Fax: 614 861-6133
Greg Moulin, *Owner*
EMP: 6 **EST:** 1964
SQ FT: 10,000
SALES (est): 515K **Privately Held**
SIC: 2499 2752 3499 Picture & mirror frames, wood; posters, lithographed; picture frames, metal

(G-16592)
FREDRICK WELDING & MACHINING
6840 Americana Pkwy (43068-4113)
PHONE....................................614 866-9650
Fax: 614 866-9658
Fred Williams, *President*
Lillian Joyce Williams, *Corp Secy*
John Corriveau, *Vice Pres*
Tammy Corriveau, *Vice Pres*
EMP: 17 **EST:** 1973
SQ FT: 18,750
SALES (est): 2.7MM **Privately Held**
WEB: www.fredrickwelding.com
SIC: 3599 7692 Machine shop, jobbing & repair; welding repair

(G-16593)
GREGOIRE MOULIN
7502 E Main St (43068-1208)
PHONE....................................614 861-4582
Gregoire Moulin, *Owner*

EMP: 8 **EST:** 2009
SALES (est): 664.7K **Privately Held**
SIC: 2499 Wood products

(G-16594)
HERITAGE INC
Also Called: Heritage Lounge
2087 State Route 256 T (43068-8128)
PHONE....................................614 860-1185
EMP: 9
SALES (est): 700K **Privately Held**
SIC: 2253 Knit Outerwear Mill

(G-16595)
IGC SOFTWARE
Also Called: Integrity Group Consulting
6432 E Main St Ste 201 (43068-2369)
PHONE....................................614 759-9148
Brian Ferguson, *President*
Jozy Spencer, *Mktg Dir*
EMP: 10
SALES (est): 1.2MM **Privately Held**
WEB: www.igcsoftware.com
SIC: 7372 Prepackaged software

(G-16596)
OHIO STATE INSTITUTE OF FIN
Also Called: Ohio Select Imprinted Fabrics
7394 E Main St (43068-2166)
PHONE....................................614 861-8811
Fax: 614 861-0692
Eleanor J Martin, *CEO*
Robert Martin, *President*
Betsy Martin, *Vice Pres*
Fay Kamer, *Sales Staff*
EMP: 8
SQ FT: 1,600
SALES: 575K **Privately Held**
WEB: www.ohioselect.com
SIC: 2396 5199 Screen printing on fabric articles; advertising specialties

(G-16597)
PPG INDUSTRIES INC
Also Called: PPG 5538
6585 E Main St (43068-2318)
PHONE....................................614 501-7360
Larry Franc, *Branch Mgr*
EMP: 24
SALES (corp-wide): 14.7B **Publicly Held**
WEB: www.ppg.com
SIC: 2851 Paints & allied products
PA: Ppg Industries, Inc.
1 Ppg Pl
Pittsburgh PA 15272
412 434-3131

(G-16598)
PRECAST SERVICES INC
6494 Taylor Rd Sw (43068-9633)
PHONE....................................614 428-4541
Barry Copper, *Branch Mgr*
EMP: 4
SALES (corp-wide): 30MM **Privately Held**
WEB: www.precastservices.com
SIC: 1771 3272 Concrete work; concrete products, precast
PA: Precast Services, Inc.
8200 Boyle Pkwy
Twinsburg OH 44087
330 425-2880

(G-16599)
PRECISION POLYMERS INC
6919 Americana Pkwy (43068-4116)
PHONE....................................614 322-9951
Fax: 614 322-9950
Andrew Wood, *President*
EMP: 8
SQ FT: 17,500
SALES (est): 2MM **Privately Held**
WEB: www.precisionpolymers.com
SIC: 3089 Injection molding of plastics

(G-16600)
PRESERVING YOUR MEMORIES
1862 Drugan Ct Sw (43068-8181)
PHONE....................................614 861-4283
EMP: 3 **EST:** 2010
SALES (est): 170K **Privately Held**
SIC: 2491 Wood Preserving

▲ = Import ▼=Export
◆ =Import/Export

(G-16601)
PROWRITE INC
7508 Slate Ridge Blvd (43068-8188)
PHONE..................................614 864-2004
Fax: 614 864-8129
Darlena Kelley, *President*
Kelly Summers, *Vice Pres*
EMP: 4
SQ FT: 1,586
SALES (est): 662.6K **Privately Held**
WEB: www.prowrite.com
SIC: 2741 8999 Miscellaneous publishing;
technical manual & paper publishing;
technical manual preparation

(G-16602)
RES Q CLEANING SOLUTIONS INC
638 Klema Dr E (43068)
PHONE..................................740 964-9494
Chris Scott, *President*
Steve Scott, *Vice Pres*
EMP: 4
SALES (est): 240K **Privately Held**
SIC: 2841 Detergents, synthetic organic or
inorganic alkaline

(G-16603)
ROSIE S WELDING
153 S Belmar Dr (43068-9621)
PHONE..................................614 506-2475
EMP: 3
SALES (est): 36.4K **Privately Held**
SIC: 7692 Welding repair

(G-16604)
SCADATECH LLC
7384 E Main St Ste B (43068-2166)
P.O. Box 250 (43068-0250)
PHONE..................................614 552-7726
Robert Cogley, *Mng Member*
Joyce Cogley, *Mng Member*
EMP: 3
SQ FT: 1,350
SALES (est): 599.1K **Privately Held**
SIC: 3823 Industrial instrmnts msrmnt dis-
play/control process variable

(G-16605)
SMITH DAIRY PRODUCTS COMPANY
40 Cypress St Sw (43068-9672)
PHONE..................................740 927-2688
Rod Robinson, *Manager*
David Caldwell, *Executive*
EMP: 20
SALES (corp-wide): 122.9MM **Privately
Held**
WEB: www.smithdairy.com
SIC: 2026 Milk processing (pasteurizing,
homogenizing, bottling)
PA: Smithfoods Orrville Inc.
1381 Dairy Ln
Orrville OH 44667
330 683-8710

(G-16606)
SNOOK ADVERTISING AL PUBLISHER
Also Called: Snook Al Advertising/Publisher
1567 Alar Ave (43068-2601)
P.O. Box 1 (43068-0001)
PHONE..................................614 866-3333
Fax: 614 866-4849
Audrey Iles, *CEO*
Don T Iles, *Owner*
EMP: 10
SQ FT: 1,479
SALES (est): 460K **Privately Held**
SIC: 2741 Directories: publishing only, not
printed on site

(G-16607)
SPEEDWAY LLC
Also Called: Speedway Superamerica 4487
7881 E Main St (43068-1233)
PHONE..................................614 861-6397
EMP: 10 **Publicly Held**
WEB: www.speedwaynet.com
SIC: 1311 Crude petroleum production
HQ: Speedway Llc
500 Speedway Dr
Enon OH 45323
937 864-3000

(G-16608)
SWAGG PRODUCTIONS2015LLC
Also Called: Gmerecords
2003 Chalfield Ct (43068-5426)
PHONE..................................614 815-1173
Travis Maurice McDaniels,
EMP: 12 EST: 2015
SALES (est): 340.1K **Privately Held**
SIC: 2731 7819 7929 7389 Book music:
publishing & printing; sound (effects &
music production), motion picture; enter-
tainers & entertainment groups; popular
music groups or artists;

(G-16609)
TORTILLA
8134 E Broad St (43068-8037)
PHONE..................................614 557-3367
Walter Eguez, *Principal*
EMP: 3 EST: 2014
SALES (est): 216.9K **Privately Held**
SIC: 2099 Tortillas, fresh or refrigerated

(G-16610)
TS TECH USA CORPORATION (DH)
8400 E Broad St (43068-9749)
PHONE..................................614 577-1088
Fax: 614 577-1730
Kazuhiso Saito, *President*
Kazumi Morioka, *General Mgr*
Rudy Claming, *Vice Pres*
Hideo Mizusawa, *Vice Pres*
Jeff Daniels, *Opers Staff*
▲ EMP: 154
SQ FT: 244,000
SALES (est): 113.5MM
SALES (corp-wide): 3.9B **Privately Held**
WEB: www.tstna.com
SIC: 3714 Motor vehicle body components
& frame
HQ: Ts Tech Americas, Inc.
8458 E Broad St
Reynoldsburg OH 43068
614 575-4100

(G-16611)
TWO GRANDMOTHERS GOURMET KIT
9127 Firstgate Dr (43068-9596)
PHONE..................................614 746-0888
Vicky Moore, *Owner*
Ven Jackson, *Owner*
EMP: 6
SALES (est): 210K **Privately Held**
SIC: 2033 Canned fruits & specialties

Richfield
Summit County

(G-16612)
ACCESS MANUFACTURING SVCS LLC
4807 Hawkins Rd (44286-9538)
PHONE..................................330 659-9893
John Ciolkevich, *Principal*
EMP: 3
SALES (est): 119.8K **Privately Held**
SIC: 3999 Manufacturing industries

(G-16613)
AMERICAN ENVMTL GROUP LTD
3600 Brecksville Rd # 100 (44286-9668)
PHONE..................................330 659-5930
Fax: 330 659-5931
Carl Apicella, *President*
Ronald Zunker, *General Mgr*
Roy McMasters, *Superintendent*
Kevin Shull, *Superintendent*
Gerald E Hersh, *Business Mgr*
▲ EMP: 450
SALES (est): 57.6MM
SALES (corp-wide): 2.5B **Publicly Held**
WEB: www.aegl.net
SIC: 1382 Oil & gas exploration services
PA: Tetra Tech, Inc.
3475 E Foothill Blvd
Pasadena CA 91107
626 351-4664

(G-16614)
ARCELORMITTAL USA LLC
4020 Kinross Lakes Pkwy (44286-9084)
PHONE..................................330 659-9100
Terry Fedor, *General Mgr*
Mitchell Hecht, *Vice Pres*
Gordon Spelich, *Vice Pres*
Michael Cononico, *Opers Mgr*
Denise Morley, *QC Mgr*
EMP: 95 **Privately Held**
SIC: 3312 Blast furnaces & steel mills
HQ: Arcelormittal Usa Llc
1 S Dearborn St Ste 1800
Chicago IL 60603
312 346-0300

(G-16615)
BECKER SIGNS INC
4762 Black Rd (44286-9454)
PHONE..................................330 659-4504
Brian Becker, *President*
Karen J Becker, *Vice Pres*
EMP: 3
SALES: 350K **Privately Held**
WEB: www.beckersigns.com
SIC: 3993 Signs & advertising specialties

(G-16616)
BLUELEVEL TECHNOLOGIES INC
3778 Timberlake Dr (44286-9187)
PHONE..................................330 523-5215
Bob Ciulla, *Owner*
Casey Warren, *Vice Pres*
EMP: 5
SALES (est): 774.5K **Privately Held**
SIC: 3575 5085 Computer terminals, mon-
itors & components; industrial tools

(G-16617)
CENTER FOR EXCPTONAL PRACTICES
3404 Brecksville Rd (44286-9662)
PHONE..................................330 523-5240
Robyn Reis, *Principal*
EMP: 4
SALES (est): 343.6K **Privately Held**
SIC: 3821 Clinical laboratory instruments,
except medical & dental

(G-16618)
CLEVELAND COPPERSMITHING WORKS
4830 Hawkins Rd (44286-9538)
PHONE..................................330 607-3998
Leo E Engasser, *President*
Phyllis Engasser, *Vice Pres*
Mike Gill, *Vice Pres*
EMP: 3
SQ FT: 3,600
SALES (est): 360K **Privately Held**
SIC: 3498 Pipe fittings, fabricated from
purchased pipe; pipe sections fabricated
from purchased pipe; tube fabricating
(contract bending & shaping)

(G-16619)
COUNTRY MAID ICE CREAM INC
3252 W Streetsboro Rd (44286-9120)
P.O. Box 151 (44286-0151)
PHONE..................................330 659-6830
Mike Torma, *President*
Don Torma, *Corp Secy*
Steve Torma, *Vice Pres*
EMP: 3 EST: 1948
SQ FT: 1,800
SALES (est): 315.4K **Privately Held**
SIC: 2024 5812 5143 5431 Ice cream &
frozen desserts; ice cream stands or dairy
bars; ice cream & ices; fruit & vegetable
markets

(G-16620)
DENTAL CERAMICS INC
3404 Brecksville Rd (44286-9662)
PHONE..................................330 523-5240
Fax: 216 518-8225
John Lavicka, *President*
EMP: 37
SALES (est): 3.9MM **Privately Held**
WEB: www.dentalceramics.net
SIC: 8072 3843 Dental laboratories; den-
tal equipment & supplies

(G-16621)
EAGLE FAMILY FOODS GROUP LLC (PA)
4020 Kinross Lakes Pkwy (44286-9084)
PHONE..................................330 382-3725
Paul Smucker Wagstaff, *CEO*
Larry Herman, *COO*
Dan Gentile, *VP Finance*
Jeff Boyle,
EMP: 25
SALES: 200MM **Privately Held**
SIC: 2023 Condensed milk

(G-16622)
ELEMENT14 US HOLDINGS INC (DH)
4180 Highlander Pkwy (44286-9352)
PHONE..................................330 523-4280
Ralf Buehler, *President*
Joseph R Daprile, *Vice Pres*
Paul M Barlak, *Treasurer*
EMP: 3
SALES: 598MM
SALES (corp-wide): 26.2B **Publicly Held**
SIC: 5065 3429 Electronic parts & equip-
ment; nozzles, fire fighting
HQ: Premier Farnell Limited
Farnell House
Leeds LS12
870 129-8608

(G-16623)
FAWCETT CO INC
3863 Congress Pkwy (44286-9745)
PHONE..................................330 659-4187
Jack Grace, *President*
George White, *Sales Staff*
EMP: 7 EST: 1946
SQ FT: 16,000
SALES (est): 1.1MM **Privately Held**
WEB: www.fawcettco.com
SIC: 3559 7699 Paint making machinery;
industrial machinery & equipment repair

(G-16624)
FRONTIER TANK CENTER INC
3800 Congress Pkwy (44286-9745)
P.O. Box 460 (44286-0460)
PHONE..................................330 659-3888
Fax: 216 659-9410
James S Hollabaugh, *President*
Ed Vincenzi, *Finance Dir*
Erica AM, *Admin Sec*
Mary Hollabaugh, *Admin Sec*
EMP: 25
SQ FT: 25,000
SALES (est): 3.2MM **Privately Held**
WEB: www.frontiertrailer.com
SIC: 7699 5013 3714 Tank repair; trailer
parts & accessories; motor vehicle body
components & frame

(G-16625)
GAIL J SHUMAKER ORIGINALS
Also Called: Shu Shop, The
3999 Brush Rd (44286-9580)
PHONE..................................330 659-0680
Gail J Shumaker, *President*
Monna Koglin, *Bookkeeper*
Carol Ecstrand, *Office Mgr*
EMP: 3
SALES (est): 200K **Privately Held**
SIC: 3942 Dolls, except stuffed toy animals

(G-16626)
HAUL-AWAY CONTAINERS INC
3554 Brecksville Rd # 500 (44286-9157)
PHONE..................................440 546-1879
Barton F Carmichael, *President*
EMP: 4
SALES (est): 656.8K **Privately Held**
WEB: www.haul-away.net
SIC: 2655 4212 Fiber cans, drums & simi-
lar products; local trucking, without stor-
age

(G-16627)
HERSCHAL PRODUCTS INC
Also Called: H P I
3778 Timberlake Dr (44286-9187)
PHONE..................................330 659-2165
Robert Ciulla, *President*
Tracy Ciulla, *Admin Sec*
▲ EMP: 4
SQ FT: 10,000

SALES (est): 819.4K **Privately Held**
SIC: 3559 Foundry machinery & equipment

(G-16628)
ITRAN ELECTRONICS RECYCLING
4100 Congress Pkwy W (44286-9732)
PHONE...................................330 659-0801
Ryan McAllister, *Owner*
EMP: 3
SALES (est): 170K **Privately Held**
SIC: 2611 Pulp manufactured from waste or recycled paper

(G-16629)
NATIONAL POLISHING SYSTEMS INC
Also Called: NPS
5145 Brecksville Rd # 101 (44286-9250)
PHONE...................................330 659-6547
Robert Tetmayer, *President*
EMP: 28
SALES: 5.4MM **Privately Held**
SIC: 3471 Cleaning, polishing & finishing

(G-16630)
OHIO PRINTED PRODUCTS INC
3920 Congress Pkwy (44286-9745)
PHONE...................................330 659-0909
Fax: 330 659-5884
EMP: 14
SQ FT: 22,000
SALES (est): 950K **Privately Held**
SIC: 2741 Misc Publishing

(G-16631)
PAULER COMMUNICATIONS INC (PA)
Also Called: Town Planner, The
3046 Brecksville Rd Ste B (44286-9252)
PHONE...................................440 243-1229
Fax: 440 243-1299
Larry Paulozzi, *President*
Chuck Sussman, *Publisher*
Ronald Miller, *Vice Pres*
Dayle Fergusson, *Sales Staff*
Joyce Carter, *Office Mgr*
EMP: 4
SALES (est): 946.5K **Privately Held**
SIC: 2741 Miscellaneous publishing

(G-16632)
POLKA DOT PIN CUSHION INC
3807 Brecksville Rd Ste 8 (44286-9165)
PHONE...................................330 659-0233
Ronelle Rajkovich, *Principal*
EMP: 3
SALES (est): 289.9K **Privately Held**
SIC: 2393 Cushions, except spring & carpet: purchased materials

(G-16633)
PREMIER FARNELL HOLDING INC (DH)
4180 Highlander Pkwy (44286-9352)
PHONE...................................330 523-4273
Dan Hill, *President*
Tom Dietz, *General Mgr*
Kenneth Jochum, *Senior VP*
Marco Ryan, *Senior VP*
George Arteaga, *Vice Pres*
◆ EMP: 20
SQ FT: 35,000
SALES: 598MM
SALES (corp-wide): 26.2B **Publicly Held**
SIC: 5065 3429 Electronic parts & equipment; nozzles, fire fighting
HQ: Element14 Us Holdings Inc
4180 Highlander Pkwy
Richfield OH 44286
330 523-4280

(G-16634)
RAYHAVEN GROUP INC
3842 Congress Pkwy Ste A (44286-9745)
PHONE...................................330 659-3183
Robert Rickenbacker, *Manager*
EMP: 12

SALES (corp-wide): 20.8MM **Privately Held**
SIC: 5084 3448 5046 Industrial machinery & equipment; heat exchange equipment, industrial; dairy products manufacturing machinery; cream separators, except farm; prefabricated metal buildings; commercial equipment
PA: Rayhaven Group, Inc.
35901 Schoolcraft Rd
Livonia MI 48150
734 744-9260

(G-16635)
SCRIPTYPE PUBLISHING INC
Also Called: Broadview Journal, The
4300 W Streetsboro Rd (44286-9796)
PHONE...................................330 659-0303
Sue Serdinak, *President*
Suzanne Serdinak, *Publisher*
Kathleen Gaivin, *Editor*
Adam Spektor, *Editor*
Erika Milenkovich, *Accounts Exec*
EMP: 25
SQ FT: 5,708
SALES (est): 2.4MM **Privately Held**
WEB: www.scriptype.com
SIC: 2759 Publication printing; magazines: printing; newspapers: printing; periodicals: printing

(G-16636)
SEDLAK
4020 Kinross Lakes Pkwy (44286-9084)
PHONE...................................330 908-2200
Fax: 330 908-2160
Jack Bonanno, *Vice Pres*
Steve Bybyk, *Manager*
EMP: 4
SALES (est): 207.3K **Privately Held**
SIC: 3312 Blast furnaces & steel mills

(G-16637)
SENSIBLE PRODUCTS INC
3857 Brecksville Rd (44286-9634)
Rural Route 3356 (44286)
PHONE...................................330 659-4212
Fax: 330 659-2144
Philip McLean, *President*
Brittany McLean, *Vice Pres*
EMP: 9
SALES: 100K **Privately Held**
WEB: www.sensible-products.com
SIC: 3429 Nozzles, fire fighting

(G-16638)
SMC CORPORATION OF AMERICA
4160 Highlander Pkwy # 200 (44286-9082)
PHONE...................................330 659-2006
Fax: 330 659-2260
Greg Dwyer, *Marketing Staff*
Scott Chonko, *Branch Mgr*
EMP: 50
SALES (corp-wide): 4B **Privately Held**
WEB: www.smcusa.com
SIC: 3625 3492 Actuators, industrial; control valves, fluid power: hydraulic & pneumatic
HQ: Smc Corporation Of America
10100 Smc Blvd
Noblesville IN 46060
317 899-3182

(G-16639)
SNAP-ON BUSINESS SOLUTIONS (HQ)
4025 Kinross Lakes Pkwy (44286-9371)
PHONE...................................330 659-1600
Bruce Rhoades, *CEO*
Timothy Chambers, *President*
Rhett Scully, *Area Mgr*
Simon Beale, *Vice Pres*
Elliot Forsyth, *Vice Pres*
EMP: 300
SQ FT: 88,000
SALES (est): 145.8MM
SALES (corp-wide): 3.4B **Publicly Held**
WEB: www.pbs.proquest.com
SIC: 2741 Miscellaneous publishing
PA: Snap-On Incorporated
2801 80th St
Kenosha WI 53143
262 656-5200

(G-16640)
STANDARD REGISTER INC
4125 Highlander Pkwy # 230 (44286-9086)
PHONE...................................216 265-9612
Fax: 216 267-5823
Ray Taylor, *Manager*
EMP: 53
SALES (corp-wide): 4.6B **Privately Held**
WEB: www.stdreg.com
SIC: 2761 Manifold business forms
HQ: Standard Register, Inc.
600 Albany St
Dayton OH 45417
937 221-1000

(G-16641)
SWITCHBACK GROUP INC
3778 Timberlake Dr (44286-9187)
PHONE...................................330 523-5200
David Shepherd, *President*
Patti Kurnot, *Purchasing*
Tom Armour, *Engineer*
Dave Sheperd, *Manager*
Mark Shimp, *Manager*
EMP: 25
SALES (est): 8.8MM **Privately Held**
SIC: 3565 Packaging machinery

(G-16642)
TD POWER SYSTEMS (USA) INC
3380 Brecksville Rd # 300 (44286-9802)
P.O. Box 1331, Brunswick (44212-8831)
PHONE...................................330 247-5264
Victor Deleon, *Principal*
EMP: 5 EST: 2013
SQ FT: 3,000
SALES (est): 751.5K **Privately Held**
SIC: 3621 3511 3694 Power generators; turbines & turbine generator sets; alternators, automotive
PA: Td Power Systems Limited
Plot No.27, 28 & 29, Kiadb Industrial Area
Bengaluru KAR 56211

(G-16643)
TECUMSEH REDEVELOPMENT INC
4020 Kinross Lakes Pkwy (44286-9084)
PHONE...................................330 659-9100
Rodney Mott, *President*
Keith Nagel, *General Mgr*
Bruce Pole, *Vice Pres*
Robert Dalrymple, *Admin Sec*
EMP: 4
SALES (est): 326.7K **Privately Held**
SIC: 3325 3316 Steel foundries; cold finishing of steel shapes
HQ: Arcelormittal Usa Llc
1 S Dearborn St Ste 1800
Chicago IL 60603
312 346-0300

(G-16644)
VALENTINO INDUSTRIES LLC
3615 Southern Rd (44286-9554)
PHONE...................................330 523-7216
Valentino Camardo, *Principal*
EMP: 3
SALES (est): 193.7K **Privately Held**
SIC: 3999 Manufacturing industries

(G-16645)
W W WILLIAMS COMPANY LLC
Also Called: Williams Carrier Transicold
2920 Brecksville Rd B1 (44286-9395)
PHONE...................................330 659-3084
Fax: 330 659-6970
Alan Gatlin, *President*
Tom Heaton, *Manager*
Janet Gibson, *Admin Sec*
Dorian Norstrom, *Administration*
EMP: 11
SALES (corp-wide): 1.4B **Privately Held**
WEB: www.wwwilliams.com
SIC: 5084 7538 7537 3714 Industrial machinery & equipment; diesel engine repair: automotive; automotive transmission repair shops; motor vehicle engines & parts
HQ: The W W Williams Company Llc
835 Goodale Blvd
Columbus OH 43212
614 228-5000

(G-16646)
WHITEYS FOOD SYSTEMS INC
3600 Brecksville Rd Ofc (44286-9668)
PHONE...................................330 659-4070
Fax: 330 659-3459
John Bigadza, *President*
Caryl Bigadza, *Corp Secy*
EMP: 4
SQ FT: 20,240
SALES (est): 280K **Privately Held**
SIC: 2032 Chili with or without meat: packaged in cans, jars, etc.

Richmond
Jefferson County

(G-16647)
MC CONNELLS MARKET
Also Called: McConnell's Farm Market
2189 State Route 43 (43944-7980)
PHONE...................................740 765-4300
Fax: 740 765-4622
Kenneth Mc Connell, *Partner*
James Mc Connell, *Partner*
EMP: 6
SALES: 650K **Privately Held**
SIC: 2011 5421 Meat packing plants; meat markets, including freezer provisioners

(G-16648)
OVECO INDUSTRIES ELECTRICA
100 Kragel Rd Ste 4 (43944-6959)
PHONE...................................740 381-3326
Robert Whitaker, *Principal*
EMP: 3
SALES (est): 120K **Privately Held**
SIC: 3999 Manufacturing industries

(G-16649)
SIGN AMERICA INCORPORATED
3887 State Route 43 (43944-7912)
P.O. Box 396 (43944-0396)
PHONE...................................740 765-5555
Fax: 740 765-5631
Judith A Hilty, *President*
Scott Hilty Jr, *Vice Pres*
John Bray, *Admin Sec*
EMP: 40
SQ FT: 6,000
SALES (est): 9.8MM **Privately Held**
WEB: www.signamericainc.com
SIC: 5046 3993 Signs, electrical; neon signs; signs & advertising specialties

---

Richmond Dale
Ross County

(G-16650)
HOWARD & BLAKE EXCAVATING LLC
1030 Main St (45673-9713)
PHONE...................................740 701-7938
Jennifer Blake, *Partner*
EMP: 3
SALES (est): 257.3K **Privately Held**
SIC: 3531 Construction machinery

Richmond Heights
Cuyahoga County

(G-16651)
AJAMI HOLDINGS GROUP LLC
Also Called: Apex Property Management
5247 Wilson Mills Rd # 311 (44143-3016)
PHONE...................................216 396-6089
Mark A Westbrooks, *Mng Member*
Alexander Judah,
EMP: 3
SQ FT: 2,000
SALES: 200K **Privately Held**
SIC: 6719 6799 1389 6531 Investment holding companies, except banks; real estate investors, except property operators; construction, repair & dismantling services; real estate managers

(G-16652)
AVIATION CMPNENT SOLUTIONS INC
26451 Curtiss Wright Pkwy # 106 (44143-4410)
PHONE..................440 295-6590
Joe Klinehamer, *President*
Louis Buchino, *Controller*
EMP: 15
SALES (est): 3.2MM **Privately Held**
WEB: www.acs-parts.com
SIC: 3728 Aircraft parts & equipment

(G-16653)
FEDEX OFFICE & PRINT SVCS INC
5138 Wilson Mills Rd (44143-3006)
PHONE..................440 605-0191
Fax: 440 605-0193
Kevin Kidder, *Branch Mgr*
EMP: 4
SALES (corp-wide): 50.3B **Publicly Held**
SIC: 2752 Commercial printing, lithographic
HQ: Fedex Office And Print Services, Inc.
7900 Legacy Dr
Plano TX 75024
214 550-7000

(G-16654)
JC CARTER LLC
Also Called: JC Carter Nozzles
26451 Curtiss Wright Pkwy # 106 (44143-4400)
PHONE..................949 764-6465
Eric Song, *General Mgr*
Lee Rowe, *Vice Pres*
Johan Forstorp, *Controller*
John Glover,
Katherine Osuna, *Administration*
◆ EMP: 4
SALES (est): 929.4K
SALES (corp-wide): 11.7B **Privately Held**
SIC: 3559 Cryogenic machinery, industrial
HQ: Atlas Copco Mafi-Trench Company Llc
3037 Industrial Pkwy
Santa Maria CA 93455
805 352-0112

(G-16655)
MOMENTIVE PERFORMANCE MTLS INC
Also Called: Momentive Performance Mtls
24400 Highland Rd (44143-2503)
PHONE..................440 878-5705
EMP: 532
SALES (corp-wide): 2.2B **Publicly Held**
WEB: www.gewaterford.com
SIC: 2869 3479 Silicones; coating of metals with silicon
HQ: Momentive Performance Materials Inc.
260 Hudson River Rd
Waterford NY 12188
518 237-3330

(G-16656)
TRANZONIC COMPANIES (PA)
Also Called: Ccp Industries
26301 Curtiss Wright Pkwy # 200 (44143-1454)
P.O. Box 6500, Cleveland (44101-1500)
PHONE..................216 535-4300
Thomas Friedl, *CEO*
Chauck Acker, *General Mgr*
Tom Sriedl, *General Mgr*
Scott Ruderman, *District Mgr*
Greg Decapio, *Vice Pres*
◆ EMP: 150
SALES (est): 360.2MM **Privately Held**
SIC: 2676 2211 2326 2842 Sanitary paper products; napkins, sanitary: made from purchased paper; tampons, sanitary: made from purchased paper; diapers, paper (disposable): made from purchased paper; scrub cloths; work garments, except raincoats: waterproof; sanitation preparations, disinfectants & deodorants; industrial plant disinfectants or deodorants; mats & matting; napping: manmade fiber & silk broadwoven fabrics

(G-16657)
TRANZONIC COMPANIES
Also Called: Hospeco
26301 Curtiss Wright Pkwy # 200 (44143-1454)
PHONE..................216 535-4300
Vernoica Guerrero, *Plant Mgr*
Randy Story, *Plant Mgr*
Frank Gancedo, *Opers Mgr*
Virginia Eckert, *VP Sls/Mktg*
Margaret Baran, *Accounts Mgr*
EMP: 420
SALES (corp-wide): 360.2MM **Privately Held**
SIC: 2676 3581 3842 3586 Napkins, sanitary: made from purchased paper; automatic vending machines; surgical appliances & supplies; measuring & dispensing pumps; women's & children's underwear; men's & boys' underwear & nightwear
PA: The Tranzonic Companies
26301 Curtiss Wright Pkwy # 200
Richmond Heights OH 44143
216 535-4300

(G-16658)
TZ ACQUISITION CORP
26301 Curtiss Wright Pkwy (44143-4413)
PHONE..................216 535-4300
Kenneth Vuylsteke, *President*
Christopher T Cira, *CFO*
Thomas S Friedl, *CFO*
Jennis Adkins, *Manager*
Ker Werbeach, *Asst Mgr*
◆ EMP: 1100 EST: 1997
SQ FT: 22,000
SALES (est): 89.5MM **Privately Held**
SIC: 2676 2211 2326 2842 Sanitary paper products; napkins, sanitary: made from purchased paper; tampons, sanitary: made from purchased paper; diapers, paper (disposable): made from purchased paper; scrub cloths; work garments, except raincoats: waterproof; sanitation preparations, disinfectants & deodorants; industrial plant disinfectants or deodorants; napping: manmade fiber & silk broadwoven fabrics

Richwood
Union County

(G-16659)
CREATIVE FABRICATION LTD
20110 Predmore Rd (43344-9014)
PHONE..................740 262-5789
John Hughes, *Mng Member*
EMP: 7
SALES: 665K **Privately Held**
SIC: 7692 7389 Welding repair;

(G-16660)
MARYSVILLE NEWSPAPER INC
Also Called: Richwood Gazette
26 S Franklin St (43344-1132)
P.O. Box 226, Marysville (43040-0226)
PHONE..................740 943-2214
Fax: 740 943-3595
Charlene K Jolliff, *Principal*
EMP: 5
SQ FT: 3,000
SALES (corp-wide): 2.7MM **Privately Held**
WEB: www.marysvillejt.com
SIC: 2711 Newspapers: publishing only, not printed on site
PA: Marysville Newspaper Incorporated
207 N Main St
Marysville OH 43040
937 644-9111

(G-16661)
WILEY FARMS
29984 State Route 739 (43344-9770)
PHONE..................937 537-0676
David Wiley, *Owner*
Nancy Wiley, *Owner*
EMP: 4
SALES (est): 190K **Privately Held**
SIC: 3523 Driers (farm): grain, hay & seed

Ridgeville Corners
Henry County

(G-16662)
ALEX PRODUCTS INC (PA)
19911 County Rd T (43555)
P.O. Box 326 (43555-0326)
PHONE..................419 267-5240
Fax: 419 267-3815
Dave Von Deylen, *President*
Kevin Bock, *COO*
Gary Crider, *CFO*
Sharon Hancock, *Accounting Mgr*
▲ EMP: 300 EST: 1973
SQ FT: 150,000
SALES (est): 110.3MM **Privately Held**
WEB: www.alexproducts.com
SIC: 3599 Machine shop, jobbing & repair

(G-16663)
AP-ALTERNATIVES LLC
20 345 County Road X (43555)
P.O. Box 326 (43555-0326)
PHONE..................419 267-5280
David Von Deylen, *Ch of Bd*
Kristi Von Deylen, *Business Mgr*
Kimberly Long, *Controller*
Carmen Ray, *Human Res Mgr*
Joshua Von Deylen, *Sales Mgr*
EMP: 12
SQ FT: 5,000
SALES (est): 3.1MM **Privately Held**
SIC: 2531 3441 Stadium seating; fabricated structural metal

(G-16664)
AUTO-SEAT TEC LLC
19911 County Rd T (43555)
PHONE..................419 267-5240
David Vondeylen, *Mng Member*
Gerald Allgire,
EMP: 30 EST: 2013
SALES (est): 2.2MM **Privately Held**
SIC: 3714 Motor vehicle parts & accessories

(G-16665)
MAGNA INTERNATIONAL AMER INC
Also Called: Camslide South
19911 County Rd (43555)
PHONE..................905 853-3604
Phil Holjak, *Principal*
EMP: 45
SALES (corp-wide): 36.4B **Privately Held**
SIC: 2531 Seats, automobile
HQ: Magna International Of America, Inc.
750 Tower Dr 7000
Troy MI 48098
248 729-2400

Ripley
Brown County

(G-16666)
G & J PEPSI-COLA BOTTLERS INC
1111 S 2nd St (45167-1535)
P.O. Box 157 (45167-0157)
PHONE..................937 392-4937
Fax: 937 392-1456
Jim Malone, *Branch Mgr*
EMP: 55
SALES (corp-wide): 490.5MM **Privately Held**
WEB: www.gjpepsi.com
SIC: 2086 Carbonated soft drinks, bottled & canned
PA: G & J Pepsi-Cola Bottlers Inc
9435 Waterstone Blvd # 390
Cincinnati OH 45249
513 785-6060

(G-16667)
GLENRO INC
330 N Front St (45167-1016)
PHONE..................937 392-0111
EMP: 23

SALES (corp-wide): 11.4MM **Privately Held**
SIC: 3567 Heating units & devices, industrial: electric
PA: Glenro, Inc.
39 Mcbride Ave
Paterson NJ 07501
973 279-5900

(G-16668)
ODYSSEY CANVAS WORKS INC
6689 Us Highway 52 (45167-8922)
P.O. Box 280 (45167-0280)
PHONE..................937 392-4422
Fax: 937 392-4567
Bob Blom, *President*
EMP: 5
SALES: 90K **Privately Held**
SIC: 2394 Canvas & related products

(G-16669)
RIPLEY BEE
134 N Front St (45167-1110)
PHONE..................937 392-4321
Fax: 937 392-0317
Roy Brown, *President*
Morgan Ross Jr, *Managing Prtnr*
Steve Triplet, *Principal*
Judith Edgeington, *Office Mgr*
Bill Cornetet, *Manager*
EMP: 3
SQ FT: 2,000
SALES (est): 267.6K **Privately Held**
SIC: 2711 Newspapers, publishing & printing

(G-16670)
RIPLEY METALWORKS LTD
111 Waterworks Rd (45167-1456)
PHONE..................937 392-4992
Michael Walkup, *General Ptnr*
EMP: 45
SQ FT: 75,000
SALES (est): 9.8MM **Privately Held**
WEB: www.ripleymetalworks.com
SIC: 3441 Fabricated structural metal

(G-16671)
SURGICAL APPLIANCE INDS INC
1311 S 2nd St (45167)
PHONE..................937 392-4301
Brian Faught, *Manager*
Randy Bader, *Manager*
EMP: 20
SALES (corp-wide): 58.1MM **Privately Held**
SIC: 3842 Surgical appliances & supplies
PA: Surgical Appliance Industries, Inc.
3960 Rosslyn Dr
Cincinnati OH 45209
513 271-4594

Risingsun
Wood County

(G-16672)
LINEAR DYNAMICS
224 Us 23 (43457)
PHONE..................419 806-6689
Edward Martinez, *Owner*
EMP: 36
SALES (est): 2.3MM **Privately Held**
SIC: 3699 Electrical equipment & supplies

(G-16673)
WELLS INC
8176 Us Highway 23 (43457)
P.O. Box 9 (43457-0009)
PHONE..................419 457-2611
Steffen R Wellstein, *President*
EMP: 10 EST: 1967
SQ FT: 15,000
SALES (est): 1.6MM **Privately Held**
WEB: www.wells.com
SIC: 3494 Well adapters

GEOGRAPHIC

Rittman
Wayne County

(G-16674)
FASTFORMINGCOM LLC
300 Morning Star Dr (44270-9644)
PHONE..................................330 927-3277
Fax: 330 334-8191
James Reedy, *President*
EMP: 12 EST: 1999
SQ FT: 12,000
SALES: 70K **Privately Held**
WEB: www.fastforming.com
SIC: 3089 Trays, plastic; thermoformed finished plastic products

(G-16675)
IMPERIAL PLASTICS INC
80 Industrial St (44270-1508)
P.O. Box 375 (44270-0375)
PHONE..................................330 927-5065
Fax: 330 925-5890
Walter Staiger, *President*
John Klein, *Exec VP*
Eugene Staiger, *Vice Pres*
Genevieve Staiger, *Vice Pres*
Troy Cain, *Plant Mgr*
EMP: 55 EST: 1960
SQ FT: 60,000
SALES (est): 13.7MM **Privately Held**
WEB: www.ip-inc.com
SIC: 3089 Extruded finished plastic products

(G-16676)
J & O PLASTICS INC
12475 Sheets Rd (44270-9730)
PHONE..................................330 927-3169
Fax: 330 927-4203
Oscar Gross, *President*
Christine Gross, *Corp Secy*
Edgar Gross, *Vice Pres*
EMP: 50
SQ FT: 90,000
SALES (est): 11.5MM **Privately Held**
SIC: 3089 Plastic processing

(G-16677)
J SMOKIN
9797 Benner Rd (44270-9712)
PHONE..................................330 466-7087
EMP: 5
SALES (est): 527K **Privately Held**
SIC: 2448 Skids, wood & wood with metal

(G-16678)
LIZZIE MAES BIRDSEED & DG CO
11315 Steiner Rd (44270-9735)
PHONE..................................330 927-1795
Kevin Hanzie, *Principal*
Mahlon Yoder, *Principal*
EMP: 5
SALES (est): 820K **Privately Held**
SIC: 2048 Bird food, prepared

(G-16679)
LUKE ENGINEERING & MFG CORP
11 Pipestone Rd (44270-9729)
PHONE..................................330 925-3344
Fax: 330 925-3350
Pam Craig, *Manager*
EMP: 20
SALES (corp-wide): 7.1MM **Privately Held**
SIC: 3471 Plating & polishing
PA: Luke Engineering & Mfg Corp
456 South Blvd
Wadsworth OH 44281
330 335-1501

(G-16680)
MORTON SALT INC
151 Industrial Ave (44270-1593)
PHONE..................................330 925-3015
Fax: 330 927-1070
Tim Declerck, *Plant Mgr*
Robert Hileman, *Purchasing*
Eric Shirk, *QC Dir*
Chad Young, *QC Mgr*
Rick Blakeslee, *Engineer*
EMP: 150

SALES (corp-wide): 3.6B **Privately Held**
WEB: www.mortonintl.com
SIC: 5149 2899 Salt, edible; chemical preparations
HQ: Morton Salt, Inc.
444 W Lake St Ste 3000
Chicago IL 60606

(G-16681)
PFI DISPLAYS INC (PA)
Also Called: Promotional Fixtures
40 Industrial St (44270-1525)
P.O. Box 508 (44270-0508)
PHONE..................................330 925-9015
Fax: 330 925-8520
Vincent Tricomi, *Ch of Bd*
Anthony R Tricomi, *President*
Robert J Kapitan, *Principal*
Rose M Tricomi, *Principal*
James Tricomi, *Vice Pres*
EMP: 39
SQ FT: 70,000
SALES (est): 4.7MM **Privately Held**
WEB: www.pfidisplays.com
SIC: 3993 2541 2542 Signs & advertising specialties; store & office display cases & fixtures; partitions & fixtures, except wood

(G-16682)
RITTMAN INC
Also Called: Mull Iron
10 Mull Dr (44270-9777)
PHONE..................................330 927-6855
Chester Mull Jr, *President*
Robert A O'Neil, *Principal*
Richard J Wendelken, *Principal*
Beth Mull, *Corp Secy*
William Mull, *Vice Pres*
EMP: 60
SQ FT: 34,000
SALES (est): 15.8MM **Privately Held**
SIC: 3441 1791 Fabricated structural metal; structural steel erection

(G-16683)
SWISS WOODCRAFT INC
15 Industrial St (44270-1507)
PHONE..................................330 925-1807
Fax: 330 925-2807
Ken Maibach, *President*
Dave Rufener, *Vice Pres*
Sharon Stoller, *Manager*
EMP: 30
SQ FT: 45,000
SALES (est): 4.7MM **Privately Held**
WEB: www.swisswoodcraft.com
SIC: 2431 Doors, wood

Rock Creek
Ashtabula County

(G-16684)
4-SURE WIRE PRODUCTS INC
2589 Forman Rd (44084-9666)
P.O. Box 441 (44084-0441)
PHONE..................................440 563-9263
Fax: 440 563-9264
Kathy Stuart, *President*
James Stuart, *Vice Pres*
EMP: 5
SQ FT: 7,500
SALES: 500K **Privately Held**
SIC: 3496 Miscellaneous fabricated wire products

(G-16685)
REAL ALLOY SPECIALTY PRODUCTS
2639 E Water St (44084-9601)
PHONE..................................440 563-3487
Nancy Kern, *Manager*
EMP: 16
SALES (corp-wide): 1.1B **Publicly Held**
SIC: 3341 Aluminum smelting & refining (secondary)
HQ: Real Alloy Specialty Products, Inc
3700 Park East Dr Ste 300
Beachwood OH 44122
216 755-8836

(G-16686)
TRUMBULL LOCKER PLANT INC
3393 State Route 534 (44084-9776)
PHONE..................................440 474-4631
Chris Kovacic, *President*
EMP: 3
SALES (est): 260K **Privately Held**
SIC: 5421 2011 5193 Meat markets, including freezer provisioners; meat packing plants; plants, potted

(G-16687)
WELDFAB INC
Also Called: J & M Welding & Fabricating
2642 E Water St (44084-9526)
PHONE..................................440 563-3310
Joe Blaha, *President*
Mary Blaha, *Treasurer*
Graham Langford, *Executive*
EMP: 4
SQ FT: 5,000
SALES (est): 557.6K **Privately Held**
WEB: www.weldfab.com
SIC: 7692 3441 Welding repair; fabricated structural metal

Rockbridge
Hocking County

(G-16688)
ELLINGER MONUMENT INC
27841 Fairview Cmtry Rd (43149)
PHONE..................................740 385-3687
Donald Ellinger, *President*
EMP: 4
SALES: 75K **Privately Held**
SIC: 5999 3272 Monuments & tombstones; tombstones, precast terrazzo or concrete

(G-16689)
MANDI A TRIPP
12691 Ovid Rd (43149-9651)
PHONE..................................740 380-1216
Mandi Tripp, *Owner*
EMP: 5 EST: 2010
SALES (est): 346K **Privately Held**
SIC: 2431 Woodwork, interior & ornamental

(G-16690)
VORHEES LOGGING LLC
15275 Mount Olive Rd (43149-9738)
PHONE..................................740 385-0216
Todd E Vorhees, *Owner*
EMP: 3
SALES (est): 186.7K **Privately Held**
SIC: 2411 Logging

Rockford
Mercer County

(G-16691)
FREMONT COMPANY
150 Hickory St (45882-9264)
PHONE..................................419 363-2924
Fax: 419 363-2174
George Mc Cracken, *Vice Pres*
James Gibson, *Opers-Prdtn-Mfg*
Philip Reyman, *Assistant*
EMP: 40
SALES (corp-wide): 42.6MM **Privately Held**
WEB: www.fremontcompany.com
SIC: 2033 2099 2035 Canned fruits & specialties; food preparations; pickles, sauces & salad dressings
PA: The Fremont Company
802 N Front St
Fremont OH 43420
419 334-8995

(G-16692)
MERCER LANDMARK INC
450 Strable Rd (45882-9748)
PHONE..................................419 363-3391
Alvin Sell, *Branch Mgr*
EMP: 6
SALES (corp-wide): 245.7MM **Privately Held**
SIC: 2879 Agricultural chemicals

PA: Mercer Landmark, Inc.
426 W Market St
Celina OH 45822
419 628-3093

(G-16693)
TRUSS WORX LLC
12412 Frysinger Rd (45882-9520)
PHONE..................................419 363-2100
Kimberly Green, *Principal*
EMP: 5
SALES (est): 514.3K **Privately Held**
SIC: 2439 Structural wood members

(G-16694)
WORLD CONNECTIONS CORPS
10803 Erastus Durbin Rd (45882-9654)
PHONE..................................419 363-2681
Llloyd Linton, *President*
EMP: 50
SALES (est): 2.7MM **Privately Held**
SIC: 3081 Vinyl film & sheet

Rocky River
Cuyahoga County

(G-16695)
BALBO INDUSTRIES INC (PA)
Also Called: Fitness Serve
20630 Center Ridge Rd (44116-3403)
PHONE..................................440 333-0630
Fax: 440 251-3825
Joseph J Balbo, *President*
EMP: 6 EST: 1975
SALES (est): 816.9K **Privately Held**
WEB: www.fitnessserve.com
SIC: 3949 7699 5941 5091 Exercise equipment; recreational sporting equipment repair services; sporting goods & bicycle shops; sporting & recreation goods

(G-16696)
CRUISIN TIMES MAGAZINE
20545 Center Ridge Rd Ll40 (44116-3430)
PHONE..................................440 331-4615
John Shapiro, *Principal*
EMP: 8
SALES (est): 454.8K **Privately Held**
SIC: 5994 2721 Magazine stand; magazines: publishing & printing

(G-16697)
CTB CONSULTING LLC
19056 Old Detroit Rd (44116-1720)
PHONE..................................216 712-7764
Charles T Bartell,
EMP: 14
SALES (est): 701.8K **Privately Held**
SIC: 2024 2052 Ice cream & frozen desserts; cookies

(G-16698)
EXEC-U-PRINT INC
19930 Detroit Rd (44116-1837)
PHONE..................................440 333-6484
Fax: 440 333-1182
Dave Clement, *President*
Laura Joan Clement, *Corp Secy*
Joan Clement, *Vice Pres*
EMP: 5
SQ FT: 3,200
SALES (est): 622.2K **Privately Held**
SIC: 2752 Commercial printing, lithographic

(G-16699)
FINE LINE EMBROIDERY COMPANY (PA)
20525 Detroit Rd Ste 9 (44116-2444)
PHONE..................................440 331-7030
David Michael, *President*
Marilyn Michael, *Vice Pres*
EMP: 6
SALES: 1MM **Privately Held**
SIC: 2395 2759 5137 5136 Embroidery & art needlework; commercial printing; women's & children's clothing; men's & boys' clothing

(G-16700)
LORD CORPORATION
19045 Story Rd (44116-4249)
PHONE..................................440 333-5750

▲ = Import ▼=Export
◆ =Import/Export

EMP: 153
SALES (corp-wide): 848.2MM **Privately Held**
SIC: 2891 Adhesives
PA: Lord Corporation
111 Lord Dr
Cary NC 27511
919 468-5979

(G-16701)
LUCIO VANNI LLC
Also Called: Vanni Wang Couture
1545 Wooster Rd (44116-1901)
PHONE..................................440 823-6103
Vanni Wang,
EMP: 3
SALES (est): 172.4K **Privately Held**
SIC: 2337 Women's & misses' suits &
coats

(G-16702)
NEON BEACH TANNING INC
19585 Detroit Rd (44116-1809)
PHONE..................................440 333-3050
Neil Kloss, *Owner*
EMP: 4
SALES (est): 349.6K **Privately Held**
SIC: 3993 Neon signs

(G-16703)
OPAL DIAMOND LLC
20033 Detroit Rd (44116-2400)
PHONE..................................330 653-5876
William Mitchell, *President*
Michael Reilly, *Exec VP*
Henry Ng, *Vice Pres*
EMP: 7
SQ FT: 2,000
SALES (est): 200K **Privately Held**
SIC: 2875 Compost

(G-16704)
ORGANIC SPA MAGAZINE LTD
(PA)
19035 Old Detroit Rd # 201 (44116-1710)
PHONE..................................440 331-5750
Beverly Maloney-Fischba, *President*
Kelsey Lyon, *Art Dir*
EMP: 4
SALES (est): 445.2K **Privately Held**
SIC: 2721 Magazines: publishing only, not
printed on site

(G-16705)
PRIEST SERVICES INC
1127 Linda St (44116-1825)
P.O. Box 16307 (44116-0307)
PHONE..................................440 333-1123
Victor Reichle, *Production*
EMP: 17
SALES (corp-wide): 2.6MM **Privately
Held**
WEB: www.floorprep.com
SIC: 3275 Gypsum products
PA: Priest Services, Inc.
1127 Linda St 5885
Mayfield Heights OH 44124
440 333-1123

(G-16706)
PS GRAPHICS INC
20284 Orchard Grove Ave (44116-3527)
PHONE..................................440 356-9656
Nancy Vedda, *President*
Phil Vedda, *Vice Pres*
EMP: 6
SQ FT: 4,000
SALES (est): 400K **Privately Held**
WEB: www.psgraphics.com
SIC: 2759 Commercial printing

(G-16707)
RELIANCE DESIGN INC
3463 Archwood Dr (44116-3703)
PHONE..................................216 267-5450
Fax: 216 267-7906
Irene Kostakis, *President*
Alex Kostakis, *Vice Pres*
Alex Kospakis, *Engineer*
Thomas Kostakis, *Finance*
Tom Kostakis, *Manager*
EMP: 10
SQ FT: 8,000

SALES: 100K **Privately Held**
WEB: www.reliancedesigninc.com
SIC: 8711 3599 Consulting engineer; ma-
chine & other job shop work

(G-16708)
ROCKY RIVER BREWING CO
21290 Center Ridge Rd (44116-3204)
PHONE..................................440 895-2739
Fax: 440 895-9412
Gary Cintron, *Owner*
EMP: 50
SQ FT: 4,000
SALES (est): 4.8MM **Privately Held**
SIC: 2082 5813 5812 Malt beverages;
drinking places; eating places

(G-16709)
SCRATCH OFF WORKS
19537 Lake Rd (44116-1858)
PHONE..................................440 333-4302
Tony Kozak, *Owner*
Tony Kozack, *Owner*
EMP: 8
SALES: 700K **Privately Held**
SIC: 2752 Commercial printing, litho-
graphic

(G-16710)
SIDELINE TECH INC
19680 Center Ridge Rd (44116-3618)
PHONE..................................440 331-0560
John Bacan, *President*
EMP: 6
SALES (est): 42.2K **Privately Held**
SIC: 3674 Integrated circuits, semiconduc-
tor networks, etc.

(G-16711)
**SOLUS INDUS INNOVATIONS
LLC**
20782 Beaconsfield Blvd (44116-1310)
PHONE..................................440 356-1933
Jim Kullman, *Manager*
EMP: 3
SALES (corp-wide): 3.2B **Publicly Held**
SIC: 3089 Plastic processing
HQ: Solus Industrial Innovations Llc
7120 New Buffington Rd
Florence KY 41042
859 342-7900

(G-16712)
SWEET MELISSAS
19337 Detroit Rd (44116-1801)
PHONE..................................440 333-6357
Jen Graham, *General Mgr*
Raja Lalchand, *Principal*
Patrick Gerald, *Manager*
EMP: 7 **EST:** 2008
SALES (est): 999.4K **Privately Held**
SIC: 2064 Candy & other confectionery
products

(G-16713)
VITALROCK LLC
19885 Detroit Rd Ste 108 (44116-1815)
PHONE..................................888 596-8892
Ryan Brown, *Mng Member*
Chad Schron,
EMP: 4
SALES (est): 144.3K **Privately Held**
SIC: 7372 Educational computer software

Rogers
Columbiana County

(G-16714)
PAUL R LIPP & SON INC
47563 Pancake Clarkson Rd (44455-9723)
PHONE..................................330 227-9614
Fax: 330 227-2233
Gregory A Lipp, *President*
Paul R Lipp, *Vice Pres*
Lauren Lipp, *Admin Sec*
EMP: 10
SALES: 1.2MM **Privately Held**
WEB: www.prlipp.com
SIC: 1794 3273 Excavation work; ready-
mixed concrete

(G-16715)
ROGERS MILL INC (PA)
7431 Depot St (44455)
P.O. Box 297 (44455-0297)
PHONE..................................330 227-3214
Bob Black, *President*
Keith Cope, *President*
Cindy Black, *Admin Sec*
EMP: 5
SQ FT: 20,000
SALES (est): 520.9K **Privately Held**
SIC: 2048 5191 Prepared feeds; farm sup-
plies

Rome
Ashtabula County

(G-16716)
J P DENNIS MACHINE INC
4380 State Route 534 (44085-9540)
PHONE..................................440 474-0247
Fax: 440 992-1558
Jim P Dennis, *President*
EMP: 4
SQ FT: 7,200
SALES: 500K **Privately Held**
SIC: 3599 Machine shop, jobbing & repair

(G-16717)
M S C INDUSTRIES INC
5131 Ireland Rd (44085-9630)
P.O. Box 200, Montville (44064-0200)
PHONE..................................440 474-8788
John M Husek, *President*
Mary C Husek, *Admin Sec*
EMP: 6
SQ FT: 4,000
SALES (est): 600K **Privately Held**
SIC: 3545 3469 Tools & accessories for
machine tools; machine parts, stamped or
pressed metal

Rootstown
Portage County

(G-16718)
A TO Z PAPER BOX CO
4477 Tallmadge Rd (44272-9610)
P.O. Box 276 (44272-0276)
PHONE..................................330 325-8722
Douglas Eatinger, *President*
EMP: 9
SQ FT: 3,600
SALES (est): 1.5MM **Privately Held**
SIC: 2652 5113 2759 Filing boxes, paper-
board: made from purchased materials;
bags, paper & disposable plastic; com-
mercial printing

(G-16719)
ADVANTAGE CIRCUITS LTD
3512 Industry Rd (44272-9715)
PHONE..................................330 256-7768
Dawn Miller, *President*
EMP: 3
SALES (est): 351.7K **Privately Held**
WEB: www.advantagecircuits.com
SIC: 3679 Electronic circuits

(G-16720)
**CUSTOM MACHINING
SOLUTIONS LLC**
5605 Tallmadge Rd (44272-9565)
PHONE..................................330 221-1523
John Morris, *Mng Member*
Michael Morris,
EMP: 4
SALES (est): 110.4K **Privately Held**
SIC: 3531 7389 Construction machinery;

(G-16721)
EDINBURG FIXTURE & MACHINE
3101 State Route 14 (44272-9791)
PHONE..................................330 947-1700
Fax: 330 947-1708
Terri Tomazin, *President*
EMP: 15
SALES (est): 1.5MM **Privately Held**
SIC: 3599 Machine shop, jobbing & repair

(G-16722)
**GATEWAY BIOTECHNOLOGY
INC**
4209 State Route 44 D-148 (44272-9698)
PHONE..................................314 747-7199
Jianxin Bao, *Principal*
Philip Perez, *Principal*
EMP: 3
SALES (est): 134.7K **Privately Held**
SIC: 2834 Pharmaceutical preparations

(G-16723)
JET RUBBER COMPANY
4457 Tallmadge Rd (44272-9610)
PHONE..................................330 325-1821
Fax: 330 325-2876
Franklin R Brubaker, *Principal*
Karen Crooks, *Corp Secy*
Gail Tarsinos, *Vice Pres*
Sherri Zalewski, *Accountant*
Ken Beachy, *Sales Mgr*
EMP: 43 **EST:** 1954
SQ FT: 20,000
SALES (est): 8.1MM **Privately Held**
WEB: www.jetrubber.com
SIC: 3069 3053 3533 5085 Molded rub-
ber products; gaskets, packing & sealing
devices; gaskets & sealing devices; gas
field machinery & equipment; oil field ma-
chinery & equipment; rubber goods, me-
chanical

(G-16724)
MICHAEL FABRICATING INC
4003 State Route 44 (44272-9633)
PHONE..................................330 325-8636
John Micheal, *President*
EMP: 3
SALES: 500K **Privately Held**
SIC: 3444 Sheet metalwork

(G-16725)
**MINERS TRACTOR SALES INC
(PA)**
Also Called: Miner's Bishop Tractor Sales
6941 Tallmadge Rd (44272-9758)
PHONE..................................330 325-9914
Fax: 330 325-3247
Stephen Miner, *CEO*
Craig M Stephens, *President*
EMP: 11
SALES (est): 1.3MM **Privately Held**
SIC: 3537 5999 Industrial trucks & trac-
tors; farm tractors

Roseville
Muskingum County

(G-16726)
B & B CAST STONE CO INC
7790 Ransbottom Rd (43777-9506)
PHONE..................................740 697-0008
Richard E Baker, *President*
Rebecca Brydon, *Corp Secy*
Ron Brybon, *Vice Pres*
Ron Brydon, *Vice Pres*
EMP: 3
SQ FT: 5,000
SALES (est): 273.9K **Privately Held**
SIC: 3299 3272 Statuary: gypsum, clay,
papier mache, metal, etc.; concrete prod-
ucts

(G-16727)
BOYD SANITATION
5525 4th St (43777-9501)
P.O. Box 73 (43777-0073)
PHONE..................................740 697-7940
Robert Boyd, *Owner*
Robert D Boyd, *Owner*
EMP: 3
SALES (est): 156K **Privately Held**
SIC: 4953 2842 Garbage: collecting, de-
stroying & processing; specialty cleaning,
polishes & sanitation goods

(G-16728)
**CLAY BURLEY PRODUCTS CO
(PA)**
455 Gordon St (43777-1110)
P.O. Box 35 (43777-0035)
PHONE..................................740 452-3633

Fax: 740 697-0246
Peter Petratsas, *President*
Dennis Macdonald, *VP Sales*
Bobbi Bennett, *Sales Executive*
▲ EMP: 50
SQ FT: 180,000
SALES (est): 8.3MM **Privately Held**
WEB: www.burleyclay.com
SIC: 3269 5032 Stoneware pottery products; art & ornamental ware, pottery; ceramic wall & floor tile

(G-16729)
CLAY BURLEY PRODUCTS CO
451 Gordon St (43777-1110)
P.O. Box 35 (43777-0035)
PHONE..................................740 697-0221
Steve McCaan, *President*
Bobbi Bennett, *Marketing Staff*
EMP: 38
SALES (corp-wide): 8.3MM **Privately Held**
WEB: www.burleyclay.com
SIC: 3269 Stoneware pottery products
PA: Burley Clay Products Co (Inc)
455 Gordon St
Roseville OH 43777
740 452-3633

(G-16730)
COULSON CMPRSSION MSREMENT LTD
7280 Rose Hill Rd (43777-9535)
PHONE..................................740 697-0220
Loulla Anstl, *Corp Secy*
Paula Coulson, *Vice Pres*
Michael D Coulson, *Mng Member*
EMP: 13
SQ FT: 10,000
SALES (est): 2.8MM **Privately Held**
SIC: 3563 Air & gas compressors

(G-16731)
LARRY MOORE
6680 Ransbottom Rd (43777-9579)
PHONE..................................740 697-7085
Larry Moore, *Owner*
EMP: 3
SALES (est): 174K **Privately Held**
SIC: 3715 Truck trailers

(G-16732)
ROSEVILLE HARDWOOD
103 Church St (43777-1006)
PHONE..................................740 221-8712
Mike Offineer, *Partner*
EMP: 3 EST: 2013
SALES (est): 181.6K **Privately Held**
SIC: 2421 Sawmills & planing mills, general

(G-16733)
TRADEWINDS PRIN TWEAR
35 E Athens Rd (43777-1212)
PHONE..................................740 214-5005
Tom Erdico, *Owner*
Susan Erdico, *Co-Owner*
EMP: 6
SALES: 200K **Privately Held**
SIC: 2752 Commercial printing, lithographic

(G-16734)
VALLEY CLAY MINING CO
Also Called: Acco & Burley Clay Products Co
451 Gordon St (43777-1110)
P.O. Box 35 (43777-0035)
PHONE..................................740 697-0620
Steve McCann, *Partner*
Clay Graham, *Partner*
Jim Ransbottom, *Partner*
Klemm Ungemach, *Partner*
Rick Emmert, *Controller*
▲ EMP: 10
SALES (est): 825K **Privately Held**
SIC: 1459 Clays, except kaolin & ball

Rossburg
Darke County

(G-16735)
CAL-MAINE FOODS INC
3078 Washington Rd (45362-9500)
PHONE..................................937 337-9576
Fax: 937 337-6535
Leonard Kropp, *General Mgr*
Brian Clum, *Manager*
Leonard Cropp, *Manager*
EMP: 43
SALES (corp-wide): 1.5B **Publicly Held**
WEB: www.calmainefoods.com
SIC: 0252 2015 Chicken eggs; poultry slaughtering & processing
PA: Cal-Maine Foods, Inc.
3320 W Woodrow Wilson Ave
Jackson MS 39209
601 948-6813

(G-16736)
FORT RECOVERY EQUITY EXCHANGE
Also Called: S & R Egg
13243 Cochran Rd (45362-9753)
PHONE..................................937 338-8901
Fax: 937 338-8900
Lou Daniels, *Manager*
Greag Fortkamp, *Manager*
EMP: 30
SALES (est): 1.8MM **Privately Held**
SIC: 2015 Egg processing

Rossford
Wood County

(G-16737)
CALPHALON CORPORATION
3rd St & D St (43460)
P.O. Box 583, Toledo (43697-0583)
PHONE..................................419 666-8700
Jason Case, *Branch Mgr*
EMP: 20
SALES (corp-wide): 13.2B **Publicly Held**
SIC: 3365 Cooking/kitchen utensils, cast aluminum
HQ: Calphalon Corporation
3 Glenlake Pkwy
Atlanta GA 30328
770 418-7100

(G-16738)
ELECTRO PRIME ASSEMBLY INC
63 Dixie Hwy Ste 7 (43460-1264)
PHONE..................................419 476-0100
Fax: 419 666-4664
Fred Busch, *President*
Kevin Meade, *Vice Pres*
James E Wilson, *VP Mfg*
Alex Konidaris, *Opers Staff*
John Lauffer, *VP Finance*
EMP: 14
SALES: 3.5MM **Privately Held**
SIC: 3711 Automobile assembly, including specialty automobiles

(G-16739)
ELECTRO PRIME GROUP LLC
63 Dixie Hwy Ste 7 (43460-1264)
PHONE..................................419 666-5000
Don Lublin, *QC Mgr*
Kavin Meade, *Branch Mgr*
Steve Frankevic, *Manager*
EMP: 80
SALES (corp-wide): 20MM **Privately Held**
SIC: 3471 Plating & polishing
PA: Electro Prime Group Llc
4510 Lint Ave Ste B
Toledo OH 43612
419 476-0100

(G-16740)
ETCHING CONCEPTS
621 Bruns Dr (43460-1548)
PHONE..................................419 691-9086
Fax: 419 691-9086
Jim Welch, *Partner*

Carolyn Welch, *Partner*
EMP: 3
SQ FT: 1,500
SALES: 200K **Privately Held**
WEB: www.etchingconcepts.com
SIC: 3231 5199 Decorated glassware: chipped, engraved, etched, etc.; glassware, novelty

(G-16741)
HUNGER HYDRAULICS CC LTD
Also Called: Hunger Industrial Complex
63 Dixie Hwy Ste 1 (43460-1270)
P.O. Box 37 (43460-0037)
PHONE..................................419 666-4510
Walter Hunger, *President*
Armin Hunger, *General Mgr*
▲ EMP: 12
SALES (est): 2.9MM
SALES (corp-wide): 528.6K **Privately Held**
WEB: www.hunger-group.com
SIC: 3593 7699 Fluid power cylinders, hydraulic or pneumatic; hydraulic equipment repair
HQ: Walter Hunger International Gesellschaft Mit Beschrankter Haftung
Alfred-Nobel-Str. 26
Wurzburg 97080
931 900-970

(G-16742)
M C SPORTS
27171 Crossroads Pkwy (43460-1706)
PHONE..................................419 874-2990
Rick Knott, *Branch Mgr*
EMP: 15
SALES (est): 690.8K **Privately Held**
SIC: 3949 Sporting & athletic goods

(G-16743)
NAPTIME PRODUCTIONS LLC
417 Superior St Ste E (43460-1292)
PHONE..................................419 662-9521
Fax: 419 662-9540
Lisa Sattler, *Principal*
Ann Stiger, *Manager*
Kerri Brimmer,
EMP: 15
SALES (est): 1.1MM **Privately Held**
WEB: www.naptimecards.com
SIC: 2771 5947 Greeting cards; greeting cards

(G-16744)
OBR COOLING TOWERS INC
9665 S Compass Dr (43460-1740)
PHONE..................................419 243-3443
Fax: 419 244-2157
Peter Poll, *President*
Matt Pinkelman, *General Mgr*
Philip Poll, *Treasurer*
Debra Haas, *Admin Sec*
EMP: 45
SQ FT: 6,000
SALES (est): 7.7MM **Privately Held**
WEB: www.obrcoolingtowers.com
SIC: 7699 3444 Industrial equipment services; cooling towers, sheet metal

(G-16745)
PILKINGTON NORTH AMERICA INC
Also Called: Pilington Libbey-Owens-Ford Co
140 Dixie Hwy (43460-1215)
PHONE..................................419 247-3211
Fax: 419 247-3257
Dick Altman, *Opers-Prdtn-Mfg*
Dick Ashton, *Manager*
Joe Gyurasics, *Senior Mgr*
Dan Walker, *Senior Mgr*
Gary Warne, *Technology*
EMP: 360
SQ FT: 3,000,000
SALES (corp-wide): 5.3B **Privately Held**
WEB: www.low-eglass.com
SIC: 3211 3231 Float glass; products of purchased glass
HQ: Pilkington North America, Inc.
811 Madison Ave Fl 1
Toledo OH 43604
419 247-4955

(G-16746)
PRAXAIR INC
Dixie Hwy (43460)
P.O. Box 68 (43460-0068)
PHONE..................................419 666-5206
Randy Lee, *Branch Mgr*
EMP: 55
SALES (corp-wide): 10.5B **Publicly Held**
SIC: 2813 Industrial gases
PA: Praxair, Inc.
10 Riverview Dr
Danbury CT 06810
203 837-2000

(G-16747)
RADOCY INC
30652 E River Rd (43460)
P.O. Box 67 (43460-0067)
PHONE..................................419 666-4400
Fax: 419 666-8041
Thomas Bradley, *President*
Mike Bradley, *Sales Mgr*
Paul F Radocy, *Shareholder*
EMP: 15 EST: 1940
SQ FT: 18,000
SALES (est): 3.8MM **Privately Held**
WEB: www.radocy.com
SIC: 3536 3594 3566 Cranes, industrial plant; fluid power pumps & motors; speed changers, drives & gears

(G-16748)
RSW TECHNOLOGIES LLC
135 Dixie Hwy (43460-1241)
PHONE..................................419 662-8100
Russ Wumber, *Engineer*
Mark Buehrer, *Manager*
Russ Wumer,
Ben Balestra, *Technician*
▲ EMP: 17
SALES (est): 3.7MM **Privately Held**
SIC: 3823 Industrial instrmnts msrmnt display/control process variable

(G-16749)
SASHA ELECTRONICS INC
Also Called: Digital Technologies
135 Dixie Hwy (43460-1241)
PHONE..................................419 662-8100
Fax: 419 662-8200
William R Wumer Jr, *President*
▲ EMP: 19
SQ FT: 20,000
SALES (est): 1.2MM **Privately Held**
WEB: www.powermiser.com
SIC: 7629 3822 Electronic equipment repair; energy cutoff controls, residential or commercial types

(G-16750)
WELCH PUBLISHING CO
215 Osborne St (43460-1238)
PHONE..................................419 666-5344
Fax: 419 666-9212
John Welch, *Vice Pres*
EMP: 7
SQ FT: 1,167
SALES (corp-wide): 2.7MM **Privately Held**
WEB: www.rossford.com
SIC: 2711 Newspapers: publishing only, not printed on site
PA: Welch Publishing Co
117 E 2nd St
Perrysburg OH 43551
419 874-2528

Rushsylvania
Logan County

(G-16751)
DAYTON SUPERIOR CORPORATION
Also Called: Roberts Screw Products
270 Rush St (43347-2502)
PHONE..................................937 682-4015
Fax: 937 468-2113
Allan Kerns, *Branch Mgr*
EMP: 20
SALES (corp-wide): 1.7B **Privately Held**
WEB: www.daytonsuperior.com
SIC: 3429 Manufactured hardware (general)

▲ = Import ▼=Export
◆ =Import/Export

HQ: Dayton Superior Corporation
1125 Byers Rd
Miamisburg OH 45342
937 866-0711

(G-16752)
LEVANS ELECTRIC & HVAC
275 Mill St W (43347-9731)
PHONE................................937 468-2269
Fax: 937 468-2261
Le Sandy, *Principal*
EMP: 4
SALES (est): 290K **Privately Held**
SIC: 3699 Electrical equipment & supplies

Rushville
Fairfield County

(G-16753)
SOMERSET COMMERCIAL PRTG CO
9050 Pleasantville Rd Ne (43150-9658)
PHONE................................740 536-7187
Michael John Rutherford, *President*
EMP: 3 EST: 1957
SALES (est): 220K **Privately Held**
SIC: 2759 Commercial printing

Russells Point
Logan County

(G-16754)
HONDA TRANSM MFG AMER INC
6964 State Route 235 N (43348-9703)
PHONE................................937 843-5555
Yuji Takahashi, *President*
Masanori Kato, *President*
Steve Mortimer, *COO*
Gary Hand, *Vice Pres*
Jerry Cline, *Safety Dir*
▲ EMP: 1200
SQ FT: 900,000
SALES (est): 228.8MM
SALES (corp-wide): 124.7B **Privately Held**
SIC: 3714 Motor vehicle parts & accessories; wheels, motor vehicle; frames, motor vehicle; exhaust systems & parts, motor vehicle
HQ: American Honda Motor Co., Inc.
1919 Torrance Blvd
Torrance CA 90501
310 783-2000

(G-16755)
INDIAN LAKE BOAT LIFT
129 Wilgus W (43348)
P.O. Box 1145 (43348-1145)
PHONE................................937 539-2868
R Steven Snider, *Principal*
EMP: 4
SALES (est): 317.4K **Privately Held**
SIC: 3536 Boat lifts

(G-16756)
INDIAN LAKE SHOPPERS EDGE
204 1/2 Lincoln Blvd (43348-9681)
P.O. Box 38 (43348-0038)
PHONE................................937 843-6600
Fax: 937 843-2409
Art Shellenbarger, *Partner*
Miriam Shellenbarger, *Partner*
EMP: 9
SALES (est): 410K **Privately Held**
SIC: 2711 Newspapers: publishing only, not printed on site

(G-16757)
STALEY & SONS POWERWASHING LLC
6732 Wisharte (43348)
P.O. Box 161 (43348-0161)
PHONE................................937 843-2713
Lori L Staley,
Scott L Staley,
EMP: 5
SALES: 530K **Privately Held**
SIC: 3589 Commercial cleaning equipment

(G-16758)
WEST OHIO TOOL COMPANY
7311 World Class Dr (43348-9593)
P.O. Box 1457 (43348-1457)
PHONE................................937 842-6688
Fax: 937 842-6077
Kerry Buchenroth, *President*
Mike Reigelsperger, *Design Engr*
Kaci Buchenroth, *Controller*
EMP: 12
SALES (est): 2.3MM **Privately Held**
WEB: www.westohiotool.com
SIC: 3541 Machine tools, metal cutting type

(G-16759)
WORLD CLASS PLASTICS INC
7695 State Route 708 (43348-9506)
PHONE................................937 843-3003
Steven L Buchenroth, *CEO*
Mark Seeley, *President*
Dustin Buchenroth, *Business Mgr*
Mark Sealey, *Vice Pres*
Scott Wisniewski, *Vice Pres*
▲ EMP: 80
SQ FT: 42,000
SALES (est): 27.8MM **Privately Held**
WEB: www.worldclassplastics.com
SIC: 3089 Injection molding of plastics

Russia
Shelby County

(G-16760)
A & M PALLET
3860 Rangeline Rd (45363-9784)
PHONE................................937 295-3093
Fax: 937 295-2785
Andy Meyer, *Managing Prtnr*
Mike Monnin, *Partner*
EMP: 14 EST: 1984
SQ FT: 700
SALES (est): 1.8MM **Privately Held**
WEB: www.ampallet.com
SIC: 2448 Pallets, wood & wood with metal

(G-16761)
ABRASIVE SOURCE INC
211 W Main St (45363-9678)
P.O. Box 369 (45363-0369)
PHONE................................937 526-9753
Fax: 937 526-9706
Kenneth W Whetstone, *President*
Diana J Whetstone, *Vice Pres*
EMP: 10
SQ FT: 1,600
SALES (est): 1.3MM **Privately Held**
WEB: www.abrasivesource.com
SIC: 3291 Abrasive products

(G-16762)
CLOPAY BUILDING PDTS CO INC
101 N Liberty St (45363-9810)
PHONE................................937 526-4301
Steve Lanners, *Branch Mgr*
EMP: 3
SALES (corp-wide): 2B **Publicly Held**
SIC: 2431 3442 2436 Garage doors, overhead: wood; garage doors, overhead: metal; plywood, softwood
HQ: Clopay Building Products Company, Inc.
8585 Duke Blvd
Mason OH 45040
513 770-4800

(G-16763)
FRANCIS MANUFACTURING COMPANY
500 E Mn St (45363)
P.O. Box 400 (45363-0400)
PHONE................................937 526-4551
Fax: 937 526-5508
Thomas V Francis, *Ch of Bd*
William T Francis, *President*
David J Francis, *Vice Pres*
Thomas W Francis, *Vice Pres*
Christopher A Francis, *Opers Staff*
EMP: 125
SQ FT: 145,000

SALES: 25MM **Privately Held**
WEB: www.francismanufacturing.com
SIC: 3369 3365 Nonferrous foundries; aluminum foundries

(G-16764)
FRANCIS-SCHULZE CO
3880 Rangeline Rd (45363-9711)
P.O. Box 245 (45363-0245)
PHONE................................937 295-3941
Fax: 937 295-3706
Ralph Schulze, *President*
Ken Francis, *Engineer*
Rita Schulze, *Treasurer*
John Francis, *Sales Mgr*
Fred Sommer, *Sales Staff*
EMP: 45 EST: 1943
SQ FT: 50,000
SALES (est): 7.9MM **Privately Held**
WEB: www.francisschulze.com
SIC: 3442 5031 Metal doors, sash & trim; building materials, exterior

(G-16765)
L & J CABLE INC
102 Industrial Dr (45363-7501)
P.O. Box 61 (45363-0061)
PHONE................................937 526-9445
Fax: 937 526-5654
Doug Francis, *President*
Linda Francis, *Vice Pres*
Brandi Phlipot, *Office Mgr*
▲ EMP: 20
SALES (est): 3.3MM **Privately Held**
SIC: 3679 Harness assemblies for electronic use: wire or cable

(G-16766)
OREILLY PRECISION PDTS INC
560 E Main St (45363-9806)
PHONE................................937 526-4677
Jeffrey J O'Reilly, *President*
EMP: 5
SALES (est): 568K **Privately Held**
SIC: 3545 Machine tool accessories

(G-16767)
OREILLY PRECISION TOOL INC
560 E Main St (45363-9806)
PHONE................................937 526-4677
Jeffrey O'Reilly, *President*
Craig Martin, *Principal*
Shane Borchers, *Vice Pres*
EMP: 28
SALES (est): 1.5MM **Privately Held**
SIC: 3312 Tool & die steel

(G-16768)
PRODUCTION SUPPORT INC
105 Francis St (45363-9692)
P.O. Box 457 (45363-0457)
PHONE................................937 526-3897
Fax: 937 526-3843
Linda Grogean, *President*
John Grogean, *Manager*
EMP: 15
SALES (est): 1.4MM **Privately Held**
SIC: 7389 3441 Packaging & labeling services; fabricated structural metal

(G-16769)
RIGHTWAY FAB & MACHINE INC
4101 Rangeline Rd (45363-9713)
PHONE................................937 295-2200
James L McGuffey, *CEO*
Dennis McMahon, *Vice Pres*
EMP: 9
SALES: 500K **Privately Held**
SIC: 3861 Blueprint reproduction machines & equipment

(G-16770)
SAINT PARIS TOOL AND GRINDING
2270 Russia Versailles Rd (45363)
PHONE................................937 526-9800
Jeff Oreilly, *Owner*
EMP: 13
SALES (est): 825.1K **Privately Held**
SIC: 3599 Machine shop, jobbing & repair

(G-16771)
VOISARD TOOL SERVICE
2700 Russia Versailles Rd (45363-9790)
P.O. Box 276 (45363-0276)
PHONE................................937 526-5451

Fax: 937 526-9098
Eugene Voisard, *President*
Pam Voisard, *Corp Secy*
Doug Voisard, *VP Opers*
Nicki Garke, *Office Mgr*
EMP: 30
SQ FT: 25,000
SALES (est): 6.1MM **Privately Held**
WEB: www.voisardtool.com
SIC: 3544 3545 Special dies & tools; machine tool accessories

Sabina
Clinton County

(G-16772)
ACCURATE MACHINING & WELDING
764 N State Route 729 (45169-9440)
PHONE................................937 584-4518
Fax: 937 584-4518
John Meshefki, *Owner*
EMP: 5
SALES (est): 526.8K **Privately Held**
SIC: 3599 3544 3541 3548 Machine shop, jobbing & repair; special dies & tools; diamond dies, metalworking; jigs: inspection, gauging & checking; broaching machines; tapping machines; welding & cutting apparatus & accessories; resistance welders, electric; seam welding apparatus, electric; welding on site

(G-16773)
MELVIN STONE COMPANY LLC
3659 S State Route 72 (45169)
PHONE................................937 453-2032
Fax: 937 453-2033
Jerry Havens, *Principal*
EMP: 3
SALES (est): 356.9K **Privately Held**
SIC: 1429 Crushed & broken stone

(G-16774)
NEW SABINA INDUSTRIES INC (HQ)
12555 Us Highway 22 And 3 (45169-9463)
P.O. Box 8 (45169-0008)
PHONE................................937 584-2433
Fax: 937 584-2476
Kazu Kishi, *President*
Carol Engle, *Vice Pres*
Ryan Higgins, *Vice Pres*
Stuart Lohrum, *Plant Mgr*
Shawn Bowen, *Engineer*
▲ EMP: 500
SQ FT: 150,000
SALES (est): 120.1MM
SALES (corp-wide): 2B **Privately Held**
SIC: 3714 Instrument board assemblies, motor vehicle
PA: Nippon Seiki Co.,Ltd.
2-2-34, Higashizao
Nagaoka NIG 940-0
258 243-311

(G-16775)
PENNANT MOLDINGS INC
12381 Route 22 E (45169)
P.O. Box 188 (45169-0188)
PHONE................................937 584-5411
Fax: 937 584-2483
Kurt Walterhouse, *President*
Kathy Rupp, *President*
Charles E Foster, *Vice Pres*
Karen Wagoner, *Production*
Mark Thomas, *Senior Buyer*
EMP: 200 EST: 1966
SQ FT: 100,000
SALES (est): 48.4MM
SALES (corp-wide): 51.4MM **Privately Held**
WEB: www.pennantcompanies.com
SIC: 3469 3444 Metal stampings; sheet metalwork
PA: Pennant Companies
2000 Bethel Rd Ste D
Columbus OH 43220
614 451-1782

(G-16776)
PREMIER FEEDS LLC (HQ)
292 N Howard St (45169-1110)
PHONE...........................937 584-2411
Fax: 937 584-4874
Christopher V Meter, *Corp Secy*
John Heinz, *Director*
John Surber,
EMP: 7 EST: 1955
SQ FT: 60,000
SALES (est): 17.9MM
SALES (corp-wide): 17.9MM **Privately
Held**
SIC: 2048 5261 5153 2041 Prepared
feeds; fertilizer; grains; flour & other grain
mill products
PA: Sabina Farmers Exchange, Inc.
292 N Howard St
Sabina OH 45169
937 584-2411

(G-16777)
**S & R TOOL & DIE SERVICES
INC**
246 Rose Ave (45169-1200)
P.O. Box 184 (45169-0184)
PHONE...........................937 584-4691
Fax: 937 584-4114
Richard Riley, *President*
Sharon Riley, *Admin Sec*
EMP: 4
SQ FT: 3,500
SALES: 76.7K **Privately Held**
SIC: 3544 3599 Special dies, tools, jigs &
fixtures; custom machinery

Sagamore Hills
Summit County

(G-16778)
RBS CITIZENS NA
Also Called: Charter One
500 W Aurora Rd (44067-2163)
PHONE...........................330 468-1600
Fax: 330 467-0391
Sue Carbone, *Branch Mgr*
EMP: 5
SALES (corp-wide): 5.7B **Publicly Held**
SIC: 3944 Banks, toy
HQ: Citizens Bank, National Association
1 Citizens Plz Ste 1
Providence RI 02903
401 282-7000

Saint Bernard
Hamilton County

(G-16779)
**BRIGHTON TECHNOLOGIES
LLC**
Also Called: Btg Labs
5129 Kieley Pl (45217-1100)
PHONE...........................513 469-1800
Giles Dillingham, *President*
Eric Oseas, *COO*
EMP: 14
SQ FT: 14,000
SALES (est): 601.7K **Privately Held**
SIC: 3823 Industrial process control instru-
ments

Saint Clairsville
Belmont County

(G-16780)
AUSTIN POWDER COMPANY
74200 Edwards Rd (43950-9510)
PHONE...........................740 968-1555
Fax: 740 968-1566
Dave Ferri, *Manager*
EMP: 26
SALES (corp-wide): 504.2MM **Privately
Held**
SIC: 2892 Explosives
HQ: Austin Powder Company
25800 Science Park Dr # 300
Cleveland OH 44122
216 464-2400

(G-16781)
**B K FABRICATION & MACHINE
SHOP**
70300 Kagg Hill Rd (43950-9601)
PHONE...........................740 695-4164
William Kovachic, *Owner*
EMP: 4
SQ FT: 2,680
SALES (est): 137.7K **Privately Held**
SIC: 7539 3499 Machine shop, automo-
tive; fire- or burglary-resistive products

(G-16782)
BELCO WORKS INC
68425 Hammond Rd (43950-8783)
PHONE...........................740 695-0500
Fax: 740 695-5910
Sandra Elson, *Business Mgr*
Greg Arnett, *Facilities Mgr*
Giselle Wells, *Facilities Mgr*
Sally Traversa, *Finance Mgr*
Debbie Alexander, *HR Admin*
EMP: 350
SQ FT: 5,000
SALES: 2.2MM **Privately Held**
WEB: www.belcoworks.com
SIC: 8331 3993 3931 2448 Sheltered
workshop; signs & advertising specialties;
musical instruments; wood pallets & skids

(G-16783)
BELMONT COUNTY OF OHIO
Also Called: Belmon Coutn Recoder's Office
101 W Main St Ste 205 (43950-1264)
PHONE...........................740 699-2140
Mary Catherine Nixon, *Manager*
EMP: 7 **Privately Held**
WEB: www.belmontsheriff.com
SIC: 9211 3931 ; recorders (musical in-
struments)
PA: Belmont County Of Ohio
101 W Main St
Saint Clairsville OH 43950
740 695-2121

(G-16784)
CATRESS LLC
50482 National Rd E (43950-8540)
PHONE...........................740 695-0918
Robert Stewart, *Owner*
EMP: 3
SALES (est): 141.5K **Privately Held**
SIC: 1389 Gas field services

(G-16785)
**CHESAPEAKE ENERGY
CORPORATION**
156 Woodrow Ave Ste 2 (43950-1196)
PHONE...........................740 695-1623
Arnold Zack, *Branch Mgr*
EMP: 50
SALES (corp-wide): 7.8B **Publicly Held**
WEB: www.chesapeake-energy.com
SIC: 1311 Crude petroleum production;
natural gas production
PA: Chesapeake Energy Corporation
6100 N Western Ave
Oklahoma City OK 73118
405 848-8000

(G-16786)
COAL RESOURCES INC
46226 National Rd W (43950-8742)
PHONE...........................740 338-3100
Robert Murray, *Principal*
Jay C Borkenhagen, *Principal*
Lloyd Boston, *Technology*
EMP: 16
SALES (est): 3.5MM **Privately Held**
SIC: 1241 Coal mining services

(G-16787)
COLEMAN MACHINE INC
Also Called: Coleman Machine Company
49381 Firpoint Maynard Rd (43950-9660)
PHONE...........................740 695-3006
James Coleman, *President*
Kristine Melcher, *Nurse*
EMP: 5
SALES (est): 582.1K **Privately Held**
SIC: 3599 1623 5999 Machine shop, job-
bing & repair; water main construction;
farm equipment & supplies

(G-16788)
D LEWIS INC
Also Called: Bill's Counter Tops
52235 National Rd E (43950-9306)
PHONE...........................740 695-2615
Fax: 740 695-9615
David Lewis, *President*
EMP: 6
SQ FT: 5,000
SALES (est): 560K **Privately Held**
SIC: 2542 2541 2434 Cabinets: show,
display or storage: except wood; wood
partitions & fixtures; wood kitchen cabi-
nets

(G-16789)
D W TRUAX ENTERPRISE INC
Also Called: E & E Ready Rooms
52499 National Rd E (43950-9311)
PHONE...........................740 695-2596
Fax: 740 695-2596
David Truax, *President*
EMP: 3
SQ FT: 4,000
SALES: 300K **Privately Held**
SIC: 3792 Travel trailers & campers

(G-16790)
**GULFPORT ENERGY
CORPORATION**
67185 Executive Dr (43950-8494)
PHONE...........................740 251-0407
Jen Masters, *Engineer*
Cindy Gray, *Branch Mgr*
Kevin Hitt, *Consultant*
Bill Baker, *Traffic Dir*
EMP: 50
SALES (corp-wide): 385.9MM **Publicly
Held**
SIC: 1311 Crude petroleum & natural gas
production
PA: Gulfport Energy Corporation
3001 Quail Springs Pkwy
Oklahoma City OK 73134
405 848-8807

(G-16791)
**HARRISON COUNTY COAL
COMPANY (PA)**
46226 National Rd W (43950-8742)
PHONE...........................740 338-3100
Jason D Witt, *Manager*
EMP: 38
SALES (est): 33.3MM **Privately Held**
SIC: 1241 Coal mining services

(G-16792)
INTERSTATE BATTERIES INC
Also Called: Interstate Battery System Amer
44925 Lafferty Rd (43950-7736)
PHONE...........................740 968-2211
Michael Sutton, *President*
EMP: 5 **Privately Held**
SIC: 3691 5013 5063 5531 Storage bat-
teries; automotive supplies & parts; bat-
teries; batteries, automotive & truck
HQ: Interstate Batteries, Inc.
12770 Merit Dr Ste 400
Dallas TX 75251
972 991-1444

(G-16793)
**KENAMERICAN RESOURCES
INC (HQ)**
46226 National Rd W (43950-8742)
PHONE...........................740 338-3100
Bob Sandidge, *President*
Randy L Wiles, *Vice Pres*
James R Turner, *Treasurer*
James Turner Jr, *Finance Dir*
Robert E Murray, *Director*
EMP: 6
SALES (est): 48.7MM
SALES (corp-wide): 4B **Privately Held**
SIC: 1222 Bituminous coal-underground
mining
PA: Murray Energy Corporation
46226 National Rd W
Saint Clairsville OH 43950
740 338-3100

(G-16794)
LION INDUSTRIES LLC
49068 Reservoir Rd (43950-9466)
P.O. Box 455 (43950-0455)
PHONE...........................740 699-0012
David A Humphreys Jr, *Vice Pres*
Audrey Humphreys,
EMP: 20
SALES (est): 4.2MM **Privately Held**
SIC: 3443 3449 Fabricated plate work
(boiler shop); custom roll formed products

(G-16795)
MARIETTA COAL CO (PA)
67705 Friends Church Rd (43950-9500)
PHONE...........................740 695-2197
Fax: 740 695-8055
Paul Gill, *President*
George Nicolozakes, *Chairman*
John Nicolozakes, *Vice Pres*
EMP: 50 EST: 1946
SQ FT: 4,300
SALES (est): 8.2MM **Privately Held**
WEB: www.mcatee.biz
SIC: 1221 Surface mining, bituminous

(G-16796)
**MURRAY AMERICAN ENERGY
INC**
46226 National Rd W (43950-8742)
PHONE...........................740 338-3100
Robert E Murray, *President*
Robert D Moore, *Vice Pres*
Michael D Loiacono, *Treasurer*
Jason D Witt, *Admin Sec*
EMP: 2667 EST: 2013
SALES (est): 275.3K
SALES (corp-wide): 4B **Privately Held**
SIC: 1221 Bituminous coal surface mining
PA: Murray Energy Corporation
46226 National Rd W
Saint Clairsville OH 43950
740 338-3100

(G-16797)
**MURRAY ENERGY
CORPORATION (PA)**
46226 National Rd W (43950-8742)
PHONE...........................740 338-3100
Robert E Murray, *CEO*
Paul Piccolini, *Principal*
Robert D Moore, *COO*
Moore Robert D, *Exec VP*
Michael O McKwn, *Senior VP*
EMP: 4
SQ FT: 6,000
SALES (est): 4B **Privately Held**
SIC: 1222 Bituminous coal-underground
mining

(G-16798)
NOMAC DRILLING LLC
67090 Executive Dr (43950-8473)
PHONE...........................724 324-2205
Mark Hughes, *Branch Mgr*
EMP: 12
SALES (corp-wide): 1.1B **Privately Held**
SIC: 1381 Drilling oil & gas wells
HQ: Nomac Drilling, L.L.C.
3400 S Radio Rd
El Reno OK 73036
405 422-2754

(G-16799)
OFFICE PRINT N COPY
Also Called: Print-N-Copy
104 N Marietta St (43950-1218)
PHONE...........................740 695-3616
Fax: 740 695-1370
Gene Sirca, *Owner*
Helen Sirca, *Co-Owner*
EMP: 4
SQ FT: 300
SALES (est): 352.8K **Privately Held**
SIC: 2752 Commercial printing, offset

(G-16800)
OHIO HEAT TRANSFER LTD
66721 Executive Dr (43950-8474)
PHONE...........................740 695-0635
Mark E Epure, *Mng Member*
Phyliss Epure,
▲ EMP: 11

SALES: 2.8MM **Privately Held**
SIC: 3443 Heat exchangers: coolers (after, inter), condensers, etc.; air coolers, metal plate

(G-16801)
OHIO VALLEY COAL COMPANY (DH)
46226 National Rd W (43950-8742)
PHONE..................................740 926-1351
Fax: 740 926-1615
Robert E Murray, *CEO*
Ryan M Murray, *President*
John R Forrelli, *Senior VP*
Michael O McKown, *Senior VP*
Robert D Moore, *Vice Pres*
EMP: 395
SQ FT: 40,380
SALES (est): 300MM
SALES (corp-wide): 4B **Privately Held**
SIC: 1241 Bituminous coal mining services, contract basis
HQ: Ohio Valley Resources, Inc.
29325 Chagrin Blvd # 300
Beachwood OH 44122
216 765-1240

(G-16802)
OHIO VALLEY RESOURCES INC
Also Called: Ohio Valley Coal
46226 National Rd W (43950-8742)
PHONE..................................740 795-5220
Robert E Murray, *CEO*
Darrell Hamilton, *Purch Mgr*
Brent Pinkston, *Manager*
Jim Spigarelli, *Manager*
Anthony Vcelka, *Manager*
EMP: 30
SALES (corp-wide): 4B **Privately Held**
SIC: 1241 Coal mining services
HQ: Ohio Valley Resources, Inc.
29325 Chagrin Blvd # 300
Beachwood OH 44122
216 765-1240

(G-16803)
OHIO VALLEY TRANSLOADING CO
46226 National Rd W (43950-8742)
PHONE..................................740 795-4967
Fax: 740 795-5265
Robert Murray, *CEO*
Mark Hurst, *Manager*
EMP: 2566
SALES (est): 57.6MM
SALES (corp-wide): 4B **Privately Held**
SIC: 1241 Bituminous coal mining services, contract basis
HQ: Ohio Valley Resources, Inc.
29325 Chagrin Blvd # 300
Beachwood OH 44122
216 765-1240

(G-16804)
OHIO VALLEY VAPOR STATION
52171 National Rd E (43950-8397)
PHONE..................................740 449-2288
EMP: 3
SALES (est): 154.3K **Privately Held**
SIC: 5731 3634 Consumer electronic equipment; vaporizers, electric: household

(G-16805)
RAYLE COAL CO (PA)
67705 Friends Church Rd (43950-9500)
PHONE..................................740 695-2197
John Nicolozakes, *President*
George Nicolozakes, *Chairman*
EMP: 8
SQ FT: 4,300
SALES: 1.5MM **Privately Held**
SIC: 1221 4491 Surface mining, bituminous; marine cargo handling

(G-16806)
RIESBECK FOOD MARKETS INC
Also Called: Reisbeck Fd Mkts St Clirsville
104 Plaza Dr (43950-8736)
P.O. Box 707 (43950-0707)
PHONE..................................740 695-3401
Fax: 740 695-4046
Dennis Kasprowski, *Branch Mgr*
EMP: 200

SALES (corp-wide): 185.6MM **Privately Held**
SIC: 5411 5912 5421 2051 Supermarkets; drug stores & proprietary stores; meat & fish markets; bread, cake & related products
PA: Riesbeck Food Markets, Inc.
48661 National Rd W
Saint Clairsville OH 43950
740 695-7050

(G-16807)
SCREEN TECH GRAPHICS
152 Saint Patricks Aly B (43950-1581)
PHONE..................................740 695-7950
John Jenkins, *Owner*
Joe McNamara, *Manager*
EMP: 4
SALES: 500K **Privately Held**
SIC: 2759 Screen printing

(G-16808)
ST CLAIRSVILLE DAIRY QUEEN
178 E Main St (43950-1534)
PHONE..................................740 635-1800
Pat Weisal, *Principal*
Cindy Byrd, *Manager*
EMP: 2
SALES (est): 173.1K **Privately Held**
SIC: 2024 Ice cream & frozen desserts

(G-16809)
STEIN-PALMER PRINTING CO
1 Westwood Dr Unit 202 (43950-1053)
PHONE..................................740 633-3894
Fax: 740 633-2727
Thomas R Palmer, *Owner*
Melody Palmer, *Owner*
Karen Cook, *Office Mgr*
EMP: 8 **EST:** 1916
SQ FT: 2,500
SALES: 400K **Privately Held**
SIC: 2752 Commercial printing, lithographic

(G-16810)
STRATA MINE SERVICES INC
68000 Bayberry Dr Bldg 2 (43950-9132)
PHONE..................................740 695-6880
Jeff Hamrick, *Vice Pres*
Nancy Verly, *Administration*
EMP: 9
SALES (est): 831.7K **Privately Held**
SIC: 1241 Coal mining services

(G-16811)
STRATA MINE SERVICES LLC
67925 Bayberry Dr (43950-9132)
PHONE..................................740 695-0488
Peter P Irby, *Principal*
EMP: 13
SALES (est): 1MM **Privately Held**
SIC: 1241 Mine preparation services

(G-16812)
THOMAS-WILBERT VAULT CO INC
49132 Randall Dr (43950-9438)
PHONE..................................740 695-5671
Thomas D James, *Principal*
EMP: 3
SALES (est): 174.1K **Privately Held**
SIC: 3272 Burial vaults, concrete or precast terrazzo

(G-16813)
WEST RIDGE RESOURCES INC (PA)
46226 National Rd W (43950-8742)
PHONE..................................740 338-3100
Bruce Hill, *President*
Bob Putslck, *Accounts Mgr*
EMP: 5
SALES: 4.5MM **Privately Held**
SIC: 1222 Bituminous coal-underground mining

Saint Henry
Mercer County

(G-16814)
BECKMAN & GAST CO INC
282 W Kremer Hoying Rd (45883-9617)
PHONE..................................419 678-4195
William Gast, *President*
EMP: 65 **EST:** 1928
SALES (est): 2.7MM **Privately Held**
SIC: 2033 Vegetables & vegetable products in cans, jars, etc.

(G-16815)
BECKMAN & GAST COMPANY (PA)
282 W Kremer Hoying Rd (45883-9617)
P.O. Box 307 (45883-0307)
PHONE..................................419 678-4195
Fax: 419 678-3005
William C Gast, *President*
Patricia Albers, *Corp Secy*
Nicholas Gast, *Vice Pres*
Paul Moorman, *Opers Mgr*
Jane Gast, *Technology*
EMP: 15 **EST:** 1927
SQ FT: 65,000
SALES: 12MM **Privately Held**
WEB: www.beckmangast.com
SIC: 2032 2033 Beans, without meat: packaged in cans, jars, etc.; tomato products: packaged in cans, jars, etc.

(G-16816)
FUTURE POLYTECH INC
393 N Eastern Ave (45883-9501)
PHONE..................................419 763-1352
Tony Durieux, *President*
Jeff Robbins, *Plant Mgr*
Craig Dillhoff, *Prdtn Mgr*
Tracy L Nicholson, *Accountant*
Maria Anderko, *Office Mgr*
EMP: 23
SALES (est): 4.3MM **Privately Held**
SIC: 2671 Plastic film, coated or laminated for packaging

(G-16817)
HI-TECH WIRE INC
631 E Washington St (45883-9683)
PHONE..................................419 678-8376
Bill Hemmelgarn, *President*
Susan Hemmelgarn, *Vice Pres*
Kylee Ranly, *Human Res Dir*
Lisa Overlman, *Admin Sec*
EMP: 57
SQ FT: 30,000
SALES (est): 15.1MM **Privately Held**
WEB: www.hi-techwire.com
SIC: 3312 Tool & die steel & alloys

(G-16818)
HOMESTRETCH SPORTSWEAR INC
491 S Eastern Ave (45883-9585)
PHONE..................................419 678-4282
Fax: 419 678-9016
Don H Hess, *President*
Kim Hess, *Corp Secy*
Donna Hess, *Exec VP*
Kelly Hess, *Vice Pres*
EMP: 12
SQ FT: 1,920
SALES (est): 1.4MM **Privately Held**
WEB: www.homestretchsportswear.com
SIC: 2759 Screen printing

(G-16819)
ITR MANUFACTURING LLC
792 Jim Lachey Dr (45883)
PHONE..................................419 852-8574
Chris Borgerding, *President*
EMP: 10
SQ FT: 2,400
SALES: 150K **Privately Held**
SIC: 3553 Furniture makers' machinery, woodworking

(G-16820)
JACOBS & SONS LOGGING LLC
132 N Sycamore St (45883-9673)
PHONE..................................419 678-3802
Kenneth Jacobs, *Partner*

Gerald Jacobs, *Partner*
Marjorie Jacobs, *Partner*
Mark Jacobs, *Partner*
EMP: 3
SALES: 547K **Privately Held**
SIC: 2411 Logging

(G-16821)
POLY CONCEPTS LLC
712 Ash St (45883)
P.O. Box 500 (45883-0500)
PHONE..................................419 678-3300
Chris Borgerding, *Plant Mgr*
Jonathan Ranly, *Engineer*
Roger Ranly, *Mng Member*
Shirley Magoteaux,
Karen Ranly,
EMP: 5 **EST:** 2007
SALES (est): 684.9K **Privately Held**
SIC: 2519 Lawn & garden furniture, except wood & metal; lawn furniture, except wood, metal, stone or concrete

(G-16822)
ST HENRY TILE CO INC (PA)
Also Called: Richmond Builders Supply
281 W Washington St (45883-9663)
P.O. Box 318 (45883-0318)
PHONE..................................419 678-4841
Fax: 419 678-8270
Bob Homan, *President*
Robert Homan, *President*
Robert Boeckman, *Principal*
Alfred Homan, *Principal*
Raymond Kremer, *Principal*
EMP: 35 **EST:** 1960
SQ FT: 7,600
SALES: 30MM **Privately Held**
SIC: 3271 5211 3273 Concrete block & brick; masonry materials & supplies; ready-mixed concrete

(G-16823)
V H COOPER & CO INC
Cooper Processing of St Henry
1 Cooper Farm Dr (45883-9556)
PHONE..................................419 678-4853
Doris Siefring, *QC Dir*
Jack Staugler, *Human Res Dir*
Diana Kleinhenz, *Marketing Staff*
Dale Hart, *Manager*
EMP: 450
SALES (corp-wide): 316.9MM **Privately Held**
WEB: www.cooperfoods.com
SIC: 2015 2011 Turkey, processed; meat packing plants
HQ: V. H. Cooper & Co, Inc
2321 State Route 49
Fort Recovery OH 45846
419 375-4116

(G-16824)
V H COOPER & CO INC
Also Called: Cooper Farms
1 Cooper Farm Dr (45883-9556)
PHONE..................................419 678-4853
Jim Cooper, *Principal*
Marvin Lefeld, *Maintenance Dir*
Daniel J Lightle, *Safety Mgr*
Kevin Reed, *Safety Mgr*
Doris Siefring, *QC Mgr*
EMP: 46
SALES (corp-wide): 316.9MM **Privately Held**
SIC: 2011 Sausages from meat slaughtered on site
HQ: V. H. Cooper & Co, Inc
2321 State Route 49
Fort Recovery OH 45846
419 375-4116

(G-16825)
WEST OHIO TOOL & MFG LLC
Also Called: Oven Windows
3965 Lange Rd (45883-9718)
PHONE..................................419 678-4745
Christopher Brackman, *Mng Member*
EMP: 4
SALES: 700K **Privately Held**
SIC: 3541 3263 Machine tools, metal cutting type; commercial tableware or kitchen articles, fine earthenware

Saint Louisville
Licking County

(G-16826)
**C GREEN & SONS
INCORPORATED**
Also Called: 64 Metals
9020 Mount Vernon Rd (43071-9672)
PHONE....................................740 745-2998
Fax: 740 745-2903
Wayne Green, *President*
Clarence E Green, *Admin Sec*
EMP: 18
SQ FT: 32,000
SALES (est): 6.3MM **Privately Held**
SIC: 2952 3448 Siding materials; trusses
& framing: prefabricated metal

(G-16827)
KOKOSING MATERIALS INC
9134 Mount Vernon Rd (43071-9637)
PHONE....................................740 745-3341
Tom Nethers, *Principal*
EMP: 23
SALES (corp-wide): 18.1MM **Privately
Held**
SIC: 2951 Asphalt paving mixtures &
blocks
PA: Kokosing Materials, Inc.
17531 Waterford Rd
Fredericktown OH 43019
740 694-9585

(G-16828)
LOWERY INDUSTRIES
10975 Houdeshell Rd (43071-9737)
PHONE....................................740 745-5045
Fax: 740 745-5065
Jeff A Lowery, *Owner*
EMP: 3
SALES (est): 197K **Privately Held**
WEB: www.loweryindustries.com
SIC: 3469 Machine parts, stamped or
pressed metal

(G-16829)
OLEN CORPORATION
9134 Mount Vernon Rd (43071-9637)
PHONE....................................740 745-5865
Michael Miller, *Branch Mgr*
EMP: 4
SALES (corp-wide): 289.1MM **Privately
Held**
SIC: 1442 4212 Construction sand mining;
gravel mining; local trucking, without stor-
age
PA: The Olen Corporation
4755 S High St
Columbus OH 43207
614 491-1515

Saint Marys
Auglaize County

(G-16830)
AAP ST MARYS CORP
1100 Mckinley Rd (45885-1815)
PHONE....................................419 394-7840
Fax: 419 394-4776
Bruce Sakamoto, *CEO*
Mark Masuda, *President*
Randy Wendel, *President*
Jam Shen, *Engineer*
Douglas Kramer, *Treasurer*
▲ EMP: 524
SQ FT: 470,000
SALES (est): 158.5MM
SALES (corp-wide): 85.7B **Privately Held**
SIC: 3714 Wheels, motor vehicle
HQ: Hitachi Metals America, Ltd.
2 Manhattanville Rd # 301
Purchase NY 10577
914 694-9200

(G-16831)
ALLAN A IRISH
Also Called: Irish Electric Motor Service
1600 Celina Rd (45885-1214)
PHONE....................................419 394-3284
Fax: 419 394-7128

Kathryn Schneider, *Owner*
EMP: 4
SQ FT: 4,000
SALES: 700K **Privately Held**
SIC: 7694 5063 5999 Electric motor re-
pair; motors, electric; motors, electric

(G-16832)
BEHRCO INC
Also Called: Unique Awards & Signs
1865 Celina Rd (45885-1219)
PHONE....................................419 394-1612
Fax: 419 394-7698
Gerry Schetter, *President*
Tom Crast, *Corp Secy*
Julia Haehn, *Vice Pres*
EMP: 6
SQ FT: 3,000
SALES: 750K **Privately Held**
SIC: 3914 3993 5094 5046 Trophies,
plated (all metals); electric signs; trophies;
neon signs; signs, electrical; trophies &
plaques

(G-16833)
BEST INC
Hc 116 (45885)
P.O. Box 775 (45885-0775)
PHONE....................................419 394-2745
Richard Brock, *President*
Kaye Brock, *Corp Secy*
Eric Brock, *Marketing Staff*
EMP: 6
SQ FT: 12,050
SALES (est): 290K **Privately Held**
SIC: 3599 Machine shop, jobbing & repair

(G-16834)
BEST PERFORMANCE INC
14381 State Route 116 (45885-9226)
P.O. Box 238 (45885-0238)
PHONE....................................419 394-2299
Fax: 419 394-2640
Eric Brock, *President*
EMP: 6
SQ FT: 34,000
SALES (est): 800K **Privately Held**
SIC: 3599 Machine shop, jobbing & repair

(G-16835)
BRW TOOL INC
502 Scott St (45885-1862)
P.O. Box 417 (45885-0417)
PHONE....................................419 394-3371
Ray Barber, *President*
EMP: 14
SQ FT: 50,000
SALES (est): 700K **Privately Held**
WEB: www.brwtool.com
SIC: 3469 3544 Metal stampings; special
dies & tools

(G-16836)
**C O WELDING & FABRICATION
INC**
850 S Main St (45885-2553)
PHONE....................................419 394-3293
Charles E Overley, *President*
Connie Overley, *Treasurer*
EMP: 5
SQ FT: 6,000
SALES (est): 350K **Privately Held**
SIC: 7692 Welding repair

(G-16837)
CONAG INC
Also Called: Con-AG
16672 County Road 66a (45885-9212)
PHONE....................................419 394-8870
Fax: 419 394-6329
Robert Hirschfeld, *President*
John Hirschfeld, *President*
Lee Kuck, *Corp Secy*
Barbara Koenig, *Finance Mgr*
EMP: 35
SALES (est): 3.5MM **Privately Held**
WEB: www.conag.com
SIC: 1422 Limestones, ground

(G-16838)
EXPRESS TRADING PINS
105 Marbello Ct (45885-9548)
PHONE....................................419 394-2550
Jeff Steininger, *Principal*
EMP: 3

SALES (est): 177K **Privately Held**
SIC: 3452 Pins

(G-16839)
FLUIDPOWER ASSEMBLY INC
313 S Park Dr (45885-9689)
PHONE....................................419 394-7486
Fax: 419 394-7488
Ronald E Langston, *President*
Mark Langston, *Vice Pres*
Ruth Langston, *Vice Pres*
Mark Langsdon, *Sales Staff*
Eric Langston, *Admin Sec*
EMP: 6
SQ FT: 6,000
SALES (est): 580K **Privately Held**
SIC: 3542 3511 Riveting machines; tur-
bines & turbine generator sets

(G-16840)
**HORIZON OHIO PUBLICATIONS
INC (HQ)**
Also Called: Evening Leader, The
102 E Spring St (45885-2310)
PHONE....................................419 394-7414
Fax: 419 394-7202
Todd Boit, *President*
Josh Steinke, *Vice Pres*
Roland Mc Bride, *Treasurer*
Susan Topp, *Bookkeeper*
Meredith Enkoff, *Agent*
EMP: 17 EST: 1905
SQ FT: 8,000
SALES: 3.5MM
SALES (corp-wide): 71.4MM **Privately
Held**
SIC: 2711 Commercial printing & newspa-
per publishing combined
PA: Horizon Publications, Inc.
1120 N Carbon St Ste 100
Marion IL 62959
618 993-1711

(G-16841)
KNOUS TOOL & MACHINE INC
14184 State Route 116 (45885-9237)
PHONE....................................419 394-3541
Fax: 419 394-7325
Paul D Knous, *President*
Patsy Knous, *Corp Secy*
EMP: 5
SQ FT: 10,000
SALES: 400K **Privately Held**
SIC: 3599 3544 Machine & other job shop
work; special dies & tools

(G-16842)
L & S LIETTE EXPRESS
2286 Celina Rd (45885-1226)
P.O. Box 726 (45885-0726)
PHONE....................................419 394-7077
Gregory D Liette, *Principal*
EMP: 6
SQ FT: 4,910
SALES (est): 702.6K **Privately Held**
SIC: 2741 Miscellaneous publishing

(G-16843)
MIDWAY TRAILER SALES LLC
14275 Glynwood (45885)
PHONE....................................419 394-4408
Bryan Hoersten, *Manager*
Roger Miller,
EMP: 8
SALES (est): 299.2K **Privately Held**
SIC: 3799 Trailers & trailer equipment

(G-16844)
**MUROTECH OHIO
CORPORATION**
Also Called: M T O
550 Mckinley Rd (45885-1803)
P.O. Box 716 (45885-0716)
PHONE....................................419 394-6529
Fax: 419 394-6820
N Matsushima, *President*
Naonobu Kenmoku, *President*
H Taguchi, *President*
Nathan Gates, *Prdtn Mgr*
Rick Wiley, *Prdtn Mgr*
▲ EMP: 60
SQ FT: 30,000
SALES (est): 20.4MM **Privately Held**
SIC: 3465 Body parts, automobile:
stamped metal

(G-16845)
OMNI MANUFACTURING
901 Mckinley Rd (45885-1812)
PHONE....................................419 394-7424
Wayne L Freewalt, *President*
Barbara J Combs, *Corp Secy*
Charlie Kirk, *Manager*
Ron Snider, *Info Tech Mgr*
EMP: 3
SALES (est): 290K **Privately Held**
SIC: 3544 Special dies, tools, jigs & fix-
tures

(G-16846)
**OMNI MANUFACTURING INC
(PA)**
901 Mckinley Rd (45885-1812)
P.O. Box 179 (45885-0179)
PHONE....................................419 394-7424
Fax: 419 394-3437
Wayne L Freewalt, *President*
Bob Prater, *Plant Mgr*
Barbara Combs, *Treasurer*
Richard Hines, *Controller*
Dennis Hoying, *Controller*
EMP: 100
SQ FT: 190,000
SALES (est): 27.4MM **Privately Held**
WEB: www.omnimfg.com
SIC: 3469 3479 3544 Metal stampings;
coating of metals & formed products; spe-
cial dies & tools

(G-16847)
OMNI MANUFACTURING INC
220 Cleveland Ave (45885-1706)
PHONE....................................419 394-7424
Wayne Freewalt, *Manager*
Ronald Snider, *CIO*
EMP: 11
SALES (corp-wide): 27.4MM **Privately
Held**
WEB: www.omnimfg.com
SIC: 3469 3479 3544 Metal stampings;
coating of metals & formed products; spe-
cial dies & tools
PA: Omni Manufacturing, Inc.
901 Mckinley Rd
Saint Marys OH 45885
419 394-7424

(G-16848)
**PARKER-HANNIFIN
CORPORATION**
1700 E Spring St (45885-2461)
PHONE....................................419 394-9600
Fax: 419 394-4713
Donald Schaefer, *Vice Pres*
Jack Hollman, *Enginr/R&D Mgr*
Donald P Szmania, *Branch Mgr*
EMP: 150
SALES (corp-wide): 11.3B **Publicly Held**
WEB: www.parker.com
SIC: 3542 3594 3593 Machine tools,
metal forming type; fluid power pumps &
motors; fluid power cylinders & actuators
PA: Parker-Hannifin Corporation
6035 Parkland Blvd
Cleveland OH 44124
216 896-3000

(G-16849)
PRO-PET LLC
1400 Mckinley Rd (45885-1821)
P.O. Box B (45885)
PHONE....................................419 394-3374
Michael Zeneri, *VP Sales*
Brent Marquis, *Manager*
EMP: 40 **Privately Held**
SIC: 2047 2048 Dog & cat food; prepared
feeds
PA: Pro-Pet, L.L.C.
1601 Mckinley Rd
Saint Marys OH 45885

(G-16850)
PRO-PET LLC (PA)
1601 Mckinley Rd (45885-1864)
P.O. Box 369 (45885-0369)
PHONE....................................419 394-3374
Fax: 419 300-8883
W M Wright, *CEO*
Jim Wiegmann, *President*
James Flora, *COO*
J P Foster, *Vice Pres*

Darryl Lauth, *Prdtn Mgr*
◆ **EMP:** 7
SQ FT: 5,000
SALES (est): 27.6MM **Privately Held**
WEB: www.propet.com
SIC: 2047 2048 4212 7389 Cat food; dog
food; prepared feeds; animal & farm prod-
uct transportation services; packaging &
labeling services

(G-16851)
QUALITY READY MIX INC
Also Called: St Mary's Ready Mix
16672 County Road 66a (45885-9212)
PHONE.................................419 394-9097
Fax: 419 394-8870
Lee Kuck, *CFO*
Brian Hedding, *Manager*
EMP: 5
SALES (corp-wide): 5MM **Privately Held**
SIC: 3273 Ready-mixed concrete
PA: Quality Ready Mix, Inc
     16672 County Road 66a
     Saint Marys OH 45885
     419 394-8870

(G-16852)
QUALITY READY MIX INC (PA)
16672 County Road 66a (45885-9212)
PHONE.................................419 394-8870
Fax: 419 738-6010
Robert E Hirschfeld, *President*
Lee Kuck, *Corp Secy*
John Hirschfeld, *Vice Pres*
Rich Hines, *Accountant*
EMP: 10
SQ FT: 2,000
SALES (est): 5MM **Privately Held**
SIC: 3273 Ready-mixed concrete

(G-16853)
RELIABLE PRODUCTS CO INC
315 S Park Dr (45885-9689)
PHONE.................................419 394-5854
Fax: 419 394-7826
Wayne Steineman, *President*
Kristine Ranly, *Corp Secy*
EMP: 8
SQ FT: 10,000
SALES: 350K **Privately Held**
SIC: 3541 Machine tools, metal cutting
type

(G-16854)
SARAS LITTLE CUPCAKES
321 Sturgeon St (45885-2062)
PHONE.................................419 305-7914
Sara Little, *Principal*
EMP: 4
SALES (est): 159.2K **Privately Held**
SIC: 2051 Bread, cake & related products

(G-16855)
SETEX INC
1111 Mckinley Rd (45885-1816)
PHONE.................................419 394-7800
Fax: 419 394-7193
Shinichirou Shirahama, *President*
Karen Klay, *Purchasing*
Robert Bowlin, *CFO*
▲ **EMP:** 470
SQ FT: 168,000
SALES (est): 116.4MM **Privately Held**
WEB: www.tachi-s.com
SIC: 2531 Seats, automobile
HQ: Adient Us Llc
     49200 Halyard Dr
     Plymouth MI 48170
     734 254-5000

(G-16856)
ST MARYS FOUNDRY INC (PA)
405 E South St (45885-2540)
PHONE.................................419 394-3346
Fax: 419 394-8269
Angela Dine Molaskey, *CEO*
Colston L Dine, *Ch of Bd*
Mark Dine, *President*
Mark Wendel, *COO*
Ronald S Stumphauzer, *Senior VP*
EMP: 127
SQ FT: 180,000

SALES (est): 21.4MM **Privately Held**
WEB: www.stmfoundry.com
SIC: 3321 3369 3322 Gray & ductile iron
foundries; nonferrous foundries; malleable iron foundries

(G-16857)
ST MARYS IRON WORKS INC
1880 Celina Rd (45885-1218)
PHONE.................................419 300-6300
Bill Gelhaus, *President*
Dan Gelhaus, *Vice Pres*
EMP: 13
SQ FT: 35,000
SALES: 1MM **Privately Held**
SIC: 3537 3448 Engine stands & racks,
metal; prefabricated metal components

(G-16858)
TAIYO AMERICA INC (DH)
1702 E Spring St (45885-2460)
PHONE.................................419 300-8811
Matt Konishi, *President*
Tom Yamane, *Plant Mgr*
James R Weed, *Natl Sales Mgr*
Jose Martinez, *Sales Associate*
Keiko Boyd, *Administration*
▲ **EMP:** 10
SQ FT: 50,000
SALES (est): 3.7MM
SALES (corp-wide): 11.3B **Publicly Held**
SIC: 5084 3492 Industrial machinery &
equipment; fluid power valves for aircraft
HQ: Taiyo,Ltd.
     1-1-1, Kitaeguchi, Higashiyodogawa-
     Ku
     Osaka OSK 533-0
     663 401-100

Saint Paris
Champaign County

(G-16859)
BRYCE HILL INC
8801 State Route 36 (43072-9358)
PHONE.................................937 663-4152
Fax: 937 663-5682
Richard Silvers, *Sales Staff*
Bryce Hill, *Manager*
EMP: 47
SALES (corp-wide): 9.8MM **Privately
Held**
SIC: 3271 Blocks, concrete: landscape or
retaining wall
PA: Bryce Hill, Inc.
     2301 Sheridan Ave
     Springfield OH 45505
     937 325-0651

(G-16860)
C A M MACHINE INC
513 S Springfield St (43072-9410)
PHONE.................................937 663-5000
Fax: 937 663-5008
Douglas Macy, *President*
Jeff Macy, *Info Tech Dir*
EMP: 29
SALES (est): 2.5MM **Privately Held**
SIC: 3599 Machine shop, jobbing & repair

(G-16861)
CAM MACHINE INC
3833 State Route 235 N (43072-9536)
PHONE.................................937 663-0680
Doug Macy, *President*
EMP: 3
SALES (est): 158K **Privately Held**
SIC: 3599 Machine shop, jobbing & repair

(G-16862)
**KTH PARTS INDUSTRIES INC
(PA)**
1111 State Route 235 N (43072-9680)
P.O. Box 940 (43072-0940)
PHONE.................................937 663-5941
Fax: 937 663-4996
Toshio Inoue, *President*
Timothy Harrigan, *General Mgr*
Fumio Takeuchi, *Principal*
Sanichi Kanai, *Exec VP*
William Post, *Assistant VP*
▲ **EMP:** 770
SQ FT: 811,500

SALES (est): 219.4MM **Privately Held**
WEB: www.kth.net
SIC: 3714 Motor vehicle parts & acces-
sories

(G-16863)
RIGHT TRACK CORP
11124 Helltown Rd (43072-9520)
PHONE.................................937 663-0366
Lloyd Lusk, *President*
Dawn Lusk, *Office Mgr*
EMP: 3
SQ FT: 2,400
SALES (est): 408.5K **Privately Held**
SIC: 3566 Speed changers, drives & gears

(G-16864)
RUNKLES SAWMILL LLC
2534 Dialton Rd (43072-9423)
PHONE.................................937 663-0115
Fax: 937 663-0115
Steve Runkle, *Mng Member*
EMP: 7
SALES: 350K **Privately Held**
SIC: 2421 Sawmills & planing mills, gen-
eral

(G-16865)
WOODSPIRITS LIMITED INC (PA)
1920 Apple Rd (43072-9783)
P.O. Box 682 (43072-0682)
PHONE.................................937 663-5025
Fax: 937 663-0100
Barbara Bobo, *President*
EMP: 3
SALES (est): 559K **Privately Held**
WEB: www.woodspirits.com
SIC: 2841 Soap: granulated, liquid, cake,
flaked or chip

Salem
Columbiana County

(G-16866)
ABSOLUTE POLYMERS INC
Also Called: A P
2789 E State St Unit 10s (44460-9327)
PHONE.................................888 850-0455
James B Dietz, *President*
Lisa Greene, *Admin Sec*
EMP: 12
SALES (est): 2.5MM **Privately Held**
SIC: 2821 Plastics materials & resins

(G-16867)
ACCU-TEK TOOL & DIE INC
1390 Allen Rd Bldg 1 (44460-1003)
PHONE.................................330 726-1946
Fax: 330 726-1994
James A Kutchel, *President*
Gary Sebrell, *Vice Pres*
EMP: 8
SQ FT: 12,000
SALES (est): 715K **Privately Held**
SIC: 3544 3354 Special dies & tools; alu-
minum extruded products

(G-16868)
ACCURATE TOOL CO INC
1065 Salem Pkwy (44460-1062)
PHONE.................................330 332-9448
Vincent Cianciola, *President*
Timothy J Cianciola, *Vice Pres*
Jeffrey T Cianciola, *CFO*
Mary Ann Franko, *Admin Sec*
EMP: 4
SQ FT: 20,000
SALES (est): 250K **Privately Held**
SIC: 3544 3469 3493 Special dies &
tools; jigs & fixtures; stamping metal for
the trade; steel springs, except wire

(G-16869)
ADVANTAGE MACHINE SHOP
777 S Ellsworth Ave (44460-3781)
PHONE.................................330 337-8377
Fax: 330 337-8331
Vic Jones, *Owner*
EMP: 6
SALES (est): 449.2K **Privately Held**
SIC: 3599 Machine shop, jobbing & repair

(G-16870)
ALLIED RETAIL SOLUTIONS
1960 S Lincoln Ave Unit 4 (44460-4304)
PHONE.................................330 332-8141
EMP: 5 **EST:** 2010
SALES (est): 601.3K **Privately Held**
SIC: 3578 Mfg Calculating Equipment

(G-16871)
AMCAN PRODUCTIONS LTD
3735 Mccracken Rd (44460-9415)
PHONE.................................330 332-9129
Randy Strader, *CEO*
Towanna A Strader, *President*
EMP: 5
SALES: 100K **Privately Held**
SIC: 7929 3599 8711 Entertainers; ma-
chine & other job shop work; consulting
engineer

(G-16872)
APPALACHIAN TRAILER INC
5409 Newgarden Rd (44460-9520)
PHONE.................................330 277-4140
Bette Schantz, *Principal*
Rachel Ivory, *Corp Secy*
Tom Lilly, *Vice Pres*
Ashley Vingle, *Sales Staff*
EMP: 33
SALES (est): 4.2MM **Privately Held**
SIC: 3715 Truck trailers

(G-16873)
AS AMERICA INC
605 S Ellsworth Ave (44460-3743)
PHONE.................................330 337-2219
Jay Gould, *President*
EMP: 4
SALES (corp-wide): 16.1B **Privately Held**
SIC: 3261 3432 Vitreous plumbing fix-
tures; plumbing fixture fittings & trim
HQ: As America, Inc.
     1 Centennial Ave Ste 101
     Piscataway NJ 08854
     732 980-3000

(G-16874)
BARCLAY MACHINE INC
Also Called: Barclay Rolls
650 S Broadway Ave (44460-3795)
PHONE.................................330 337-9541
Fax: 330 337-0414
Jeff Cushman, *President*
John Dance, *CFO*
Mitchell Hawkins, *Manager*
Kerry Thomas, *Manager*
Barbara Bautsch, *Administration*
EMP: 16 **EST:** 1898
SALES (est): 4.1MM **Privately Held**
WEB: www.barclayrolls.com
SIC: 3542 Machine tools, metal forming
type

(G-16875)
**BAUMAN CUSTOM
WOODWORKING LLC**
13650 Green Beaver Rd (44460-9255)
PHONE.................................330 482-4330
Stuart L Bauman,
EMP: 3
SQ FT: 1,176
SALES (est): 416.5K **Privately Held**
SIC: 2541 Cabinets, except refrigerated:
show, display, etc.: wood

(G-16876)
BRASS ACCENTS INC
1693 Salem Pkwy W (44460-1082)
PHONE.................................330 332-9500
Alec Pendleton, *CEO*
Don Senne, *General Mgr*
Barry Hinchliffe, *Sales Mgr*
Tam Pendleton, *Admin Sec*
▲ **EMP:** 12
SQ FT: 8,000
SALES: 1MM **Privately Held**
WEB: www.brassaccents.com
SIC: 3429 Manufactured hardware (gen-
eral)

(G-16877)
C&C TRAILER PARK
1717 E State St (44460-3305)
PHONE.................................330 823-7733
Gene Courtney, *Owner*

EMP: 3
SALES (est): 170.5K **Privately Held**
SIC: 3792 Travel trailers & campers

(G-16878)
CARDINAL PUMPS EXCHANGERS INC (HQ)
Also Called: Unifin Chesapeake
1425 Quaker Ct (44460-1008)
PHONE.................................330 332-8558
Fax: 330 332-1560
Manny A Agostinho, *President*
Ed Shapiro, *General Mgr*
Matthew Flamini, *Vice Pres*
Jeanne R Hernandez, *Treasurer*
Manfred Schneider, *Manager*
▲ **EMP:** 16
SALES (est): 2.8MM
SALES (corp-wide): 2.9B **Publicly Held**
SIC: 3443 Fabricated plate work (boiler shop)
PA: Westinghouse Air Brake Technologies Corporation
1001 Airbrake Ave
Wilmerding PA 15148
412 825-1000

(G-16879)
CASTRUCTION COMPANY INC
1588 Salem Pkwy (44460-1071)
PHONE.................................330 332-9622
Fax: 330 332-9623
Benjamin R Brown, *President*
Shannon Brown, *Vice Pres*
Karen Michael, *Bookkeeper*
EMP: 12
SQ FT: 9,600
SALES (est): 1.8MM **Privately Held**
SIC: 3297 Cement refractories

(G-16880)
CHAPPELL-ZIMMERMAN INC
641 Olive St (44460-4219)
P.O. Box 94 (44460-0094)
PHONE.................................330 337-8711
Fax: 330 337-9155
Chris Chappell, *President*
Bonnie Adams, *Controller*
EMP: 20 **EST:** 1946
SQ FT: 2,000
SALES: 1.5MM **Privately Held**
SIC: 3273 5211 Ready-mixed concrete; lumber & other building materials; masonry materials & supplies

(G-16881)
CHURCH BUDGET MONTHLY INC
157 W Pershing St (44460-2745)
P.O. Box 420 (44460-0420)
PHONE.................................330 337-1122
Fax: 330 337-1124
James Pidgeon, *President*
EMP: 60
SALES (est): 8.7MM **Privately Held**
WEB: www.churchbudmail.com
SIC: 2677 Envelopes

(G-16882)
CHURCH-BUDGET ENVELOPE COMPANY
271 S Ellsworth Ave (44460-3071)
P.O. Box 420 (44460-0420)
PHONE.................................800 446-9780
Fax: 330 337-5990
James A Pidgeon Jr, *President*
J H Pidgeon, *Plant Mgr*
EMP: 48
SQ FT: 60,000
SALES (est): 13.8MM **Privately Held**
SIC: 2677 Envelopes

(G-16883)
CMI INDUSTRY AMERICAS INC (DH)
435 W Wilson St (44460-2767)
PHONE.................................330 332-4661
Rob Johnson, *Ch of Bd*
Patricia Simonsic, *Treasurer*
Tricia Myers, *Human Res Mgr*
▲ **EMP:** 100 **EST:** 1923
SQ FT: 250,000

SALES (est): 61.5MM **Privately Held**
SIC: 3567 Metal melting furnaces, industrial: electric; metal melting furnaces, industrial: fuel-fired

(G-16884)
COLUMBUS MCKINNON CORPORATION
Also Called: Chester Hoist
240 Pennsylvania Ave (44460-2733)
PHONE.................................330 332-5769
Gary Randles, *Production*
Jamie Jones, *Engineer*
Richard Mumford, *Engineer*
William Tutor, *Engineer*
Lambright Marty, *Human Res Mgr*
EMP: 90
SALES (corp-wide): 597.1MM **Publicly Held**
SIC: 3536 Hoists
PA: Columbus Mckinnon Corporation
205 Crosspoint Pkwy
Getzville NY 14068
716 689-5400

(G-16885)
COMPRHNSIVE BRACE LIMB CTR LLC (PA)
2235 E Pershing St (44460-3478)
PHONE.................................330 337-8333
Stephen Pollak,
Cheryl Pollak,
EMP: 3
SQ FT: 1,200
SALES (est): 631.8K **Privately Held**
SIC: 3842 Surgical appliances & supplies

(G-16886)
CRANE CO
Crane Chemical Pump
1453 Allen Rd (44460-1004)
PHONE.................................330 337-7861
Fax: 330 337-8122
Lucille Karnofel, *Buyer*
Mike Saunders, *Purchasing*
B Mitsch, *Rsch/Dvlpt Dir*
William Dunnavant, *QC Dir*
J Burns, *Personnel*
EMP: 135
SALES (corp-wide): 2.7B **Publicly Held**
WEB: www.craneco.com
SIC: 3561 Industrial pumps & parts
PA: Crane Co.
100 1st Stamford Pl # 300
Stamford CT 06902
203 363-7300

(G-16887)
CTM INTEGRATION INCORPORATED
1318 Quaker Cir (44460-1051)
P.O. Box 589 (44460-0589)
PHONE.................................330 332-1800
Fax: 330 332-2144
Thomas C Rumsey, *President*
Dan Mc Laughlin, *Exec VP*
Dan McLaughlin, *Exec VP*
Vera Sobotka, *Purchasing*
Doug Umbs, *Controller*
EMP: 36
SQ FT: 30,000
SALES (est): 10.9MM **Privately Held**
WEB: www.ctmint.com
SIC: 3565 5084 3549 Packaging machinery; industrial machinery & equipment; metalworking machinery

(G-16888)
DILCO INDUSTRIES INC
300 Benton Rd (44460-2029)
P.O. Box 859 (44460-0859)
PHONE.................................330 337-6732
Fax: 330 337-0411
Robert Dillon Jr, *President*
Kathy Dillion, *Admin Sec*
EMP: 20
SQ FT: 14,000
SALES (est): 1.6MM **Privately Held**
WEB: www.dilcoind.com
SIC: 3599 Machine shop, jobbing & repair

(G-16889)
EVERFLOW EASTERN PARTNERS LP
Also Called: Strawn Oil Field Service
29093 Salem Alliance Rd (44460-9706)
PHONE.................................330 537-3863
Richard Strawn, *Branch Mgr*
EMP: 6
SALES (corp-wide): 3.8MM **Privately Held**
SIC: 1389 Oil field services
PA: Everflow Eastern Partners, L.P.
585 W Main St
Canfield OH 44406
330 533-2692

(G-16890)
FIRESTONE SHEET METAL INC
949 S Broadway Ave (44460-3799)
PHONE.................................330 337-9551
Fax: 330 332-0735
Paul L Lippiatt, *President*
EMP: 25
SQ FT: 48,000
SALES (est): 4.3MM **Privately Held**
WEB: www.firestonesheetmetal.com
SIC: 3444 3433 Sheet metalwork; heating equipment, except electric

(G-16891)
FOERSTER INSTRUMENTS INC
Foerster Systems Div
1484 Quaker Cir (44460)
PHONE.................................330 332-9100
Dave Smith, *Branch Mgr*
EMP: 13
SALES (corp-wide): 71MM **Privately Held**
WEB: www.foerstergroup.com
SIC: 3537 Industrial trucks & tractors
HQ: Foerster Instruments Inc
140 Industry Dr
Pittsburgh PA 15275
412 788-8976

(G-16892)
FOERSTER SYSTEMS INC
1484 Quaker Cir (44460)
PHONE.................................330 332-9100
Fax: 330 332-9115
Phillip Warga, *President*
Dave Render, *Mfg Staff*
Ralph Thomas, *Manager*
Cheryl Hodnicki, *Admin Sec*
EMP: 17
SALES (est): 4.6MM
SALES (corp-wide): 71MM **Privately Held**
SIC: 3537 Forklift trucks
HQ: Foerster Instruments Inc
140 Industry Dr
Pittsburgh PA 15275
412 788-8976

(G-16893)
FRESH MARK INC
1735 S Lincoln Ave (44460-4203)
PHONE.................................330 332-8508
Carl Montalbano, *Safety Mgr*
Mark Beard, *Purch Agent*
Bryan Keefer, *Accounting Dir*
Mike Furr, *Sales Staff*
Steve Smith, *Branch Mgr*
EMP: 650
SQ FT: 125,000
SALES (corp-wide): 521.3MM **Privately Held**
WEB: www.freshmark.com
SIC: 2011 2013 Meat packing plants; sausages & other prepared meats
PA: Fresh Mark, Inc.
1888 Southway St Se
Massillon OH 44646
330 834-3669

(G-16894)
GORDON BROTHERS BTLG GROUP INC
776 N Ellsworth Ave (44460-1600)
P.O. Box 63, Lowellville (44436-0063)
PHONE.................................330 337-8754
Scott P Jones, *President*
Frank Tombo, *Principal*
Edward P Jones III, *Chairman*
Chris Wood,

EMP: 4
SALES (est): 13.1K **Privately Held**
SIC: 2086 Bottled & canned soft drinks

(G-16895)
GOTTSCHALL TOOL & DIE INC
14028 W Middletown Rd (44460-9184)
PHONE.................................330 332-1544
Fax: 330 332-0704
Danny Beegle, *President*
Robert Whinnery, *Purch Mgr*
Charles Anderson, *Treasurer*
Brad Whinnery, *Manager*
EMP: 30 **EST:** 1950
SQ FT: 24,000
SALES (est): 2.7MM **Privately Held**
SIC: 3544 3469 Special dies & tools; metal stampings

(G-16896)
GRAPHIC TOUCH INC
451 E Pershing St (44460-3028)
PHONE.................................330 337-3341
Fax: 330 337-0538
Keith Berger, *President*
Beverly Berger, *Corp Secy*
EMP: 3
SQ FT: 3,000
SALES: 158.1K **Privately Held**
SIC: 2752 2759 7336 2791 Commercial printing, offset; letterpress printing; commercial art & graphic design; typesetting

(G-16897)
GRID INDUSTRIAL HEATING INC
1108 Salem Pkwy (44460-1063)
P.O. Box 950 (44460-0950)
PHONE.................................330 332-9931
Fax: 330 332-0841
Donald Stamp, *President*
Ron Kilmer, *VP Sales*
EMP: 7
SQ FT: 20,000
SALES (est): 1MM **Privately Held**
WEB: www.gridheating.com
SIC: 3433 1711 Steam heating apparatus; plumbing, heating, air-conditioning contractors

(G-16898)
HALTEC CORPORATION
32585 N Price Rd (44460-9513)
P.O. Box 1180 (44460-8180)
PHONE.................................330 222-1501
Fax: 330 222-2302
Thomas Moyer, *President*
Edward Russell, *Chairman*
Brian Bostick, *Vice Pres*
David Caruso, *Vice Pres*
Mike Russell, *Vice Pres*
◆ **EMP:** 70
SQ FT: 65,000
SALES: 47.8MM **Privately Held**
WEB: www.haltec.com
SIC: 3714 Motor vehicle parts & accessories; tire valve cores

(G-16899)
HARRIS & COMPANY INC
980 Salem Pkwy (44460-1059)
PHONE.................................330 332-4127
Fax: 330 332-9627
David E Ritchie, *President*
Janice Ritchie, *Corp Secy*
Norman F Richie, *Vice Pres*
Michael Kiss, *Bd of Directors*
EMP: 19
SQ FT: 11,000
SALES (est): 4.6MM **Privately Held**
WEB: www.harrisco.net
SIC: 2752 2789 2759 2675 Commercial printing, lithographic; bookbinding & related work; commercial printing; die-cut paper & board; coated & laminated paper; packaging paper & plastics film, coated & laminated

(G-16900)
HAZENSTAB MACHINE INC
1575 Salem Pkwy (44460-1072)
PHONE.................................330 337-1865
Fax: 330 337-3299
James Hazenstab Jr, *President*
Jim Cox, *Manager*
▲ **EMP:** 14
SQ FT: 12,000

SALES (est): 2.1MM **Privately Held**
WEB: www.hazenstabmachine.com
SIC: 3599 Machine shop, jobbing & repair

(G-16901)
HUNT VALVE COMPANY INC
Also Called: Waeco Valve Division
1913 E State St (44460-2491)
PHONE..............................330 337-9535
Gerry Bogner, *CEO*
EMP: 50
SALES (corp-wide): 12MM **Privately Held**
WEB: www.huntvalve.com
SIC: 3491 Automatic regulating & control valves
PA: Hunt Valve Company, Inc.
1913 E State St
Salem OH 44460
330 337-9535

(G-16902)
HUNT VALVE COMPANY INC
Also Called: Union Flonetics
1913 E State St (44460-2491)
PHONE..............................330 337-9535
David Huberfield, *President*
EMP: 50
SALES (corp-wide): 12MM **Privately Held**
WEB: www.huntvalve.com
SIC: 3491 Automatic regulating & control valves
PA: Hunt Valve Company, Inc.
1913 E State St
Salem OH 44460
330 337-9535

(G-16903)
JOHN KRIZAY INC
1777 Pennsylvania Ave (44460-2781)
P.O. Box 974 (44460-0974)
PHONE..............................330 332-5607
Fax: 330 332-1573
William Stratton, *President*
Linda Horsall, *Admin Sec*
▲ **EMP:** 35
SQ FT: 12,000
SALES (est): 4.7MM **Privately Held**
SIC: 3229 Art, decorative & novelty glassware

(G-16904)
JOSEPH SABATINO
Also Called: Sabatino Cabinet
1834 Depot Rd (44460-4359)
PHONE..............................330 332-5879
Joseph Sabatino, *Owner*
EMP: 6
SQ FT: 8,500
SALES (est): 1MM **Privately Held**
SIC: 1751 2491 Carpentry work; millwork, treated wood

(G-16905)
KORFF HOLDINGS LLC
Also Called: Quaker City Casting
310 E Euclid Ave (44460-3778)
PHONE..............................330 332-1566
Fax: 330 332-5655
Geoffrey Korff, *President*
Shankra Subramanian, *Sr Corp Ofcr*
Ken Foster, *Safety Dir*
Pam Brooks, *Purchasing*
James Gagan, *CFO*
EMP: 120
SALES: 20MM **Privately Held**
WEB: www.qccast.com
SIC: 3325 3321 Steel foundries; gray & ductile iron foundries

(G-16906)
KORFF MACHINE LLC
310 E Euclid Ave (44460-3778)
PHONE..............................330 332-1566
Penelope Korff, *President*
Geoffrey Korff, *Vice Pres*
EMP: 4 **EST:** 2015
SQ FT: 20,000
SALES (est): 139.1K **Privately Held**
SIC: 3599 Machine & other job shop work

(G-16907)
L M EQUIPMENT & DESIGN INC
11000 Youngstown Salem Rd (44460-9654)
PHONE..............................330 332-9951
Dave Hrovatic, *President*
Sue Lease, *CFO*
EMP: 20
SALES (est): 700.5K **Privately Held**
WEB: www.lmequipment.com
SIC: 7699 3541 Industrial equipment services; milling machines

(G-16908)
LOWRY TOOL & DIE INC
986 Salem Pkwy (44460-1059)
PHONE..............................330 332-1722
Fax: 330 332-4681
Robert Lowry, *President*
EMP: 14
SQ FT: 10,000
SALES (est): 2.4MM **Privately Held**
WEB: www.lowrytd.com
SIC: 3544 Special dies & tools

(G-16909)
LYLE PRINTING & PUBLISHING CO (PA)
Also Called: Farm & Dairy
185 E State St (44460-2857)
P.O. Box 38 (44460-0038)
PHONE..............................330 337-3419
Scot Darling, *CEO*
Tom Darling, *President*
Gail Hettrick, *Sales Mgr*
Allison Davis, *Manager*
Janet Keene, *Manager*
EMP: 50
SQ FT: 12,500
SALES (est): 6.5MM **Privately Held**
SIC: 2721 2752 2759 Trade journals: publishing only, not printed on site; commercial printing, offset; letterpress printing

(G-16910)
LYLE PRINTING & PUBLISHING CO
193 S Howard Ave (44460-2704)
PHONE..............................330 337-7172
Mike Starr, *Branch Mgr*
EMP: 17
SALES (corp-wide): 5.9MM **Privately Held**
SIC: 2721 3555 Trade journals: publishing only, not printed on site; printing presses
PA: Lyle Printing & Publishing Co Inc
185 E State St
Salem OH 44460
330 337-3419

(G-16911)
M & W ELECTRIC MFG CO LLC
986 Salem Pkwy (44460-1059)
PHONE..............................330 332-9553
Lisa Pincombe, *Sales Executive*
Jason Miller, *Bd of Directors*
EMP: 6
SALES (est): 1MM **Privately Held**
WEB: www.mwelectricmfg.com
SIC: 3644 Electric conduits & fittings

(G-16912)
M M INDUSTRIES INC
Also Called: Vorti-Siv
36135 Salem Grange Rd (44460-9442)
P.O. Box 720 (44460-0720)
PHONE..............................330 332-5947
Fax: 330 332-1543
Barbara Maroscher, *President*
Victor Maroscher, *Vice Pres*
Kevin Penner, *Prdtn Mgr*
Britt Ortega, *Office Mgr*
Art Maroscher, *Admin Sec*
EMP: 30
SQ FT: 10,000
SALES (est): 6.6MM **Privately Held**
WEB: www.vorti-siv.com
SIC: 3559 Screening equipment, electric

(G-16913)
MAC MANUFACTURING INC
1453 Allen Rd (44460-1004)
PHONE..............................330 829-1680
David Sandor, *VP Opers*
Tony Sparks, *Sales Staff*

Brian Whitlatch, *Sales Staff*
Kenny Butler, *Sales Associate*
Kristi Rummel, *Marketing Mgr*
EMP: 104
SALES (corp-wide): 270.9MM **Privately Held**
SIC: 3715 5012 Truck trailers; trailers for trucks, new & used; truck bodies
PA: Mac Manufacturing, Inc.
14599 Commerce St Ne
Alliance OH 44601
330 823-9900

(G-16914)
METAL & WIRE PRODUCTS COMPANY (PA)
1065 Salem Pkwy (44460-1062)
PHONE..............................330 332-9448
Fax: 330 332-9404
Vincent M Cianciola, *President*
Jeffrey T Cianciola, *Vice Pres*
Timothy J Cianciola, *Vice Pres*
Kris Balsley, *Purch Agent*
Jeffrey T Ciancidla, *VP Finance*
EMP: 50
SQ FT: 62,000
SALES (est): 12.8MM **Privately Held**
SIC: 3469 3542 3544 Metal stampings; machine tools, metal forming type; special dies, tools, jigs & fixtures

(G-16915)
MIDWEST MINICRANES INC
1350 Pennsylvania Ave (44460-2737)
P.O. Box 466 (44460-0466)
PHONE..............................330 332-3700
Margaret Ann Howells, *Owner*
EMP: 3
SALES (est): 353.4K **Privately Held**
SIC: 3625 Crane & hoist controls, including metal mill

(G-16916)
MOORE MR SPECIALTY COMPANY
1050 Pennsylvania Ave (44460-2773)
P.O. Box 107 (44460-0107)
PHONE..............................330 332-1229
Fax: 330 332-0502
Robert N Moore, *President*
Martha Moore, *Treasurer*
EMP: 8
SQ FT: 5,000
SALES: 1MM **Privately Held**
SIC: 3443 Fabricated plate work (boiler shop)

(G-16917)
OGDEN NEWSPAPERS INC
Salem News
161 N Lincoln Ave (44460-2903)
P.O. Box 268 (44460-0268)
PHONE..............................330 332-4601
Fax: 330 332-1441
Beth Volosin, *Publisher*
John Celidonio, *Editor*
Nancy McCoy, *Treasurer*
Kellie Pope, *Accounts Exec*
Kevin Smith, *Manager*
EMP: 50
SALES (corp-wide): 617.1MM **Privately Held**
SIC: 2711 Newspapers: publishing only, not printed on site
PA: The Ogden Newspapers Inc
1500 Main St
Wheeling WV 26003
304 233-0100

(G-16918)
OVERHEAD DOOR OF SALEM INC
3864 Mccracken Rd (44460-9415)
PHONE..............................330 332-9530
Al Kenreigh, *President*
EMP: 3
SALES (est): 332.8K **Privately Held**
SIC: 1542 5211 3699 Garage construction; garage doors, sale & installation; door opening & closing devices, electrical

(G-16919)
PLASTIC PARTNERS LLC
1801 Newgarden Rd (44460-9514)
PHONE..............................425 765-2416

John Cote, *President*
EMP: 3 **EST:** 2012
SQ FT: 700
SALES (est): 209.8K **Privately Held**
SIC: 3559 Recycling machinery

(G-16920)
POLLOCK RESEARCH & DESIGN INC
Simmers Crane Design & Svc Co
1134 Salem Pkwy (44460-1063)
PHONE..............................330 332-3300
Fax: 330 332-3322
Peter Evans, *Vice Pres*
Mark Kastner, *Vice Pres*
Randall Gross, *Treasurer*
John Adkins, *Branch Mgr*
Randy L Stull, *Manager*
EMP: 45
SALES (corp-wide): 66.6MM **Privately Held**
SIC: 8711 7389 7353 3537 Civil engineering; mechanical engineering; structural engineering; crane & aerial lift service; heavy construction equipment rental; industrial trucks & tractors
PA: Pollock Research & Design, Inc.
11 Vanguard Dr
Reading PA 19606
610 582-7203

(G-16921)
QUAKER EXPRESS STAMPING INC
1134 Salem Pkwy (44460-1063)
PHONE..............................330 332-9266
EMP: 15
SALES (est): 671.2K **Privately Held**
SIC: 2741 Misc Publishing

(G-16922)
QUAKER MFG CORP
187 Georgetown Rd (44460-2009)
PHONE..............................330 332-4631
Fax: 330 337-3571
Alfred Dannhauser, *President*
William Shivers, *Vice Pres*
Edward Stone, *Opers Mgr*
Ron Bennett, *Purchasing*
Art Ort, *QC Mgr*
▲ **EMP:** 110 **EST:** 1962
SQ FT: 100,000
SALES (est): 37.8MM **Privately Held**
WEB: www.quakermfg.com
SIC: 3469 3544 3465 3599 Metal stampings; special dies & tools; jigs & fixtures; automotive stampings; machine & other job shop work; metal foil & leaf

(G-16923)
QUALITY FABRICATED METALS INC
14000 W Middletown Rd (44460-9184)
PHONE..............................330 332-7008
Fax: 330 332-9140
Danny Beegle, *President*
Kay Tuttle, *Manager*
EMP: 25
SQ FT: 42,000
SALES (est): 5.8MM **Privately Held**
WEB: www.gtd-qfm.com
SIC: 3469 1799 Metal stampings; welding on site

(G-16924)
REDEX INDUSTRIES INC (PA)
Also Called: Udderly Smooth
1176 Salem Pkwy (44460-1063)
P.O. Box 939 (44460-0939)
PHONE..............................330 332-9800
Fax: 330 332-1061
William C Kennedy, *President*
Margaret Kennedy, *Corp Secy*
Janet Godward, *Controller*
EMP: 17 **EST:** 1976
SQ FT: 24,000
SALES (est): 2.8MM **Privately Held**
WEB: www.uddercream.com
SIC: 2844 Face creams or lotions

GEOGRAPHIC

(G-16925)
SALEM WELDING & SUPPLY COMPANY
475 Prospect St (44460-2618)
P.O. Box 386 (44460-0386)
PHONE.................................330 332-4517
Fax: 330 332-2156
Frederick Baker Sr, *President*
Anna Baker, *Corp Secy*
Frederick Baker Jr, *Vice Pres*
Tom Baker, *Project Mgr*
Terry N Manis, *Sales Mgr*
EMP: 9 EST: 1975
SQ FT: 15,200
SALES (est): 1.8MM **Privately Held**
SIC: 7692 5084 Welding repair; welding machinery & equipment

(G-16926)
SANSCAN INC
Also Called: Instacopy
157 N Ellsworth Ave (44460-2853)
PHONE.................................330 332-9365
Jill Harmon, *President*
EMP: 4
SALES (est): 446.1K **Privately Held**
SIC: 2752 Commercial printing, lithographic

(G-16927)
SEKELY INDUSTRIES INC (PA)
240 Pennsylvania Ave (44460-2733)
PHONE.................................248 844-9201
James Sekely, *President*
John Sekely, *Vice Pres*
Earl R Miller, *Admin Sec*
▼ EMP: 162 EST: 1944
SQ FT: 100,000
SALES (est): 9.2MM **Privately Held**
WEB: www.sekely.com
SIC: 3544 Special dies & tools; jigs & fixtures

(G-16928)
SOLOMONS MINES INC
7219 Salem Unity Rd (44460-9294)
PHONE.................................330 337-0123
Fax: 330 337-0123
Jack Solomon, *President*
Shirley Solomon, *Admin Sec*
EMP: 3
SQ FT: 360
SALES (est): 609K **Privately Held**
WEB: www.solomonsmines.com
SIC: 1442 Construction sand & gravel

(G-16929)
THE LABEL TEAM INC
1251 Quaker Cir (44460-1050)
PHONE.................................330 332-1067
Fax: 330 332-1581
Dean J McDaniel, *President*
Paula McDaniel, *Vice Pres*
Karen Swetye, *Manager*
EMP: 15
SQ FT: 11,400
SALES (est): 2.4MM **Privately Held**
SIC: 2759 Commercial printing

(G-16930)
THE SALEM GOLF CLUB
1967 S Lincoln Ave (44460-4363)
PHONE.................................330 332-0346
Fax: 330 332-4652
Delores Capel, *Manager*
EMP: 2
SALES: 1.3MM **Privately Held**
SIC: 3949 Shafts, golf club

(G-16931)
TRI-FAB INC
10372 W South Range Rd (44460-9621)
P.O. Box 310 (44460-0310)
PHONE.................................330 337-3425
Samuel Lippiatt, *President*
Wes Weimer, *Engineer*
Stephen Templeton, *Sales Executive*
EMP: 32
SQ FT: 44,000
SALES (est): 4.8MM **Privately Held**
WEB: www.tri-fab.net
SIC: 3644 3441 3444 Fuse boxes, electric; junction boxes, electric; fabricated structural metal; sheet metalwork

(G-16932)
TURNER MACHINE CO
1433 Salem Pkwy (44460-1070)
PHONE.................................330 332-5821
Fax: 330 332-5871
Jacob O Kamm, *President*
Patricia Simonsic, *Treasurer*
Roy Page, *Sales Staff*
EMP: 12 EST: 1943
SALES (est): 2.2MM **Privately Held**
WEB: www.turnermachineco.com
SIC: 3599 3547 3542 Machine shop, jobbing & repair; rolling mill machinery; machine tools, metal forming type

(G-16933)
VALVECO INC
1913 E State St (44460-2422)
PHONE.................................330 337-9535
Gerald Bagner, *CEO*
Ken Meyer, *Senior VP*
Theresa Delaney, *Controller*
EMP: 100
SQ FT: 16,000
SALES (est): 6.3MM **Privately Held**
SIC: 3492 Control valves, fluid power: hydraulic & pneumatic

(G-16934)
VIC MAROSCHER
36135 Salem Grange Rd (44460-9442)
P.O. Box 720 (44460-0720)
PHONE.................................330 332-4958
Vic Maroscher, *Owner*
EMP: 10
SALES (est): 432.9K **Privately Held**
SIC: 3999 Manufacturing industries

(G-16935)
WINGS WAY DRIVE THRU INC
Also Called: Wings Way Ice
9194 Salem Warren Rd (44460-7600)
PHONE.................................330 533-2788
Fax: 330 533-7675
David Rickard, *President*
Diane Rickard, *Vice Pres*
EMP: 5
SALES (est): 790.4K **Privately Held**
SIC: 5921 2097 Beer (packaged); wine; manufactured ice

(G-16936)
WT TOOL & DIE INC
1300 Pennsylvania Ave (44460-2780)
P.O. Box 7 (44460-0007)
PHONE.................................330 332-2254
Fax: 330 332-2889
EMP: 6
SALES (est): 600K **Privately Held**
SIC: 3599 3544 Mfg Industrial Machinery Mfg Dies/Tools/Jigs/Fixtures

(G-16937)
YOU DOUGH GIRL LLC
12725 Kent Rd (44460-9135)
PHONE.................................330 207-5031
Kathy Boswell, *Mng Member*
EMP: 4
SALES (est): 219.6K **Privately Held**
SIC: 2051 Bakery: wholesale or wholesale/retail combined

Salesville
Guernsey County

(G-16938)
VELA
58560 Kennonsburg Rd (43778-9567)
PHONE.................................614 500-0150
Sarah Menkedick,
Amanda Giracca,
Simone Gorrindo,
EMP: 3
SALES (est): 102.6K **Privately Held**
SIC: 2721 7389 Periodicals;

Salineville
Columbiana County

(G-16939)
A & M LOGGING
8633 Township Road 289 (43945-7721)
PHONE.................................740 543-3171
Allen Miller, *Principal*
EMP: 3
SALES (est): 146.9K **Privately Held**
SIC: 2411 Logging

(G-16940)
COLDWELL FAMILY TREE FARM
Also Called: Ohio Woodlands
33320 Hull Rd (43945-9764)
PHONE.................................330 506-9012
Jared Coldwell, *Owner*
EMP: 3
SALES (est): 35K **Privately Held**
SIC: 6531 2411 Real estate brokers & agents; logging

(G-16941)
CREEKSIDE SPRINGS LLC
32 Washington St (43945-1078)
PHONE.................................330 679-1010
Michael Mercure, *Branch Mgr*
EMP: 25
SALES (corp-wide): 15MM **Privately Held**
WEB: www.creeksidesprings.com
SIC: 2086 Bottled & canned soft drinks
PA: Creekside Springs, Llc
    667 Merchant St
    Ambridge PA 15003
    724 266-9000

(G-16942)
J K LOGGING & CHIPWOOD COMPANY
3218 Oasis Rd Ne (43945-9420)
PHONE.................................330 738-3571
John Kruprzak, *Owner*
EMP: 3
SALES (est): 347.9K **Privately Held**
SIC: 2411 Logging camps & contractors

Sandusky
Erie County

(G-16943)
ACH LLC
Also Called: Ach Sandusky Plastics
3020 Tiffin Ave (44870-5352)
PHONE.................................419 621-5748
Andy Short, *Principal*
John Kaskewsky, *Manager*
▲ EMP: 8
SALES (est): 680K **Privately Held**
SIC: 3714 Motor vehicle parts & accessories

(G-16944)
ACME PRINTING CO INC
2143 Sherman St (44870-4714)
P.O. Box 2311 (44871-2311)
PHONE.................................419 626-4426
Fax: 419 625-4502
Dean Everson, *President*
James Kellam, *Corp Secy*
Fred Everson, *Vice Pres*
EMP: 6
SQ FT: 10,000
SALES (est): 450K **Privately Held**
SIC: 2752 2796 2759 Commercial printing, offset; embossing plates for printing; letterpress printing

(G-16945)
AHNER FABRICATING & SHTMTL INC
2001 E Perkins Ave (44870-5130)
PHONE.................................419 626-6641
Fax: 419 626-3797
Mark Ahner, *President*
Timothy Ahner, *President*
Tim Kaser, *Office Mgr*
Tracy Gilbert, *Manager*
EMP: 24

SQ FT: 7,000
SALES (est): 6.3MM **Privately Held**
WEB: www.ahner-industrial.com
SIC: 3444 3914 5049 Sheet metalwork; carving sets, stainless steel; precision tools

(G-16946)
AMERICAN QUALITY STRIPPING
1750 5th St (44870-1301)
PHONE.................................419 625-6288
Fax: 419 625-8664
Tim Finneran, *President*
Richard Finneran, *Vice Pres*
Matt Swan, *Engineer*
Don Finneran, *Sales Mgr*
Tom Link, *Sales Executive*
EMP: 30
SQ FT: 16,000
SALES (est): 4.7MM **Privately Held**
WEB: www.americanqualitystripping.com
SIC: 3471 3398 Cleaning, polishing & finishing; metal heat treating

(G-16947)
AUTOMTIVE CMPNNTS HOLDINGS LLC
3020 Tiffin Ave (44870-5352)
PHONE.................................419 627-3600
Andy Short, *QC Dir*
Craige Bulea, *Enginr/R&D Mgr*
Tom Burke, *Branch Mgr*
Rob Polinsky, *Director*
EMP: 1344
SALES (corp-wide): 151.8B **Publicly Held**
SIC: 3714 3647 3564 Motor vehicle parts & accessories; vehicular lighting equipment; blowers & fans
HQ: Automotive Components Holdings Llc
    15303 S Commerce Dr
    Dearborn MI 48120

(G-16948)
BAY ELECTRIC CO
2612 Columbus Ave (44870-5596)
PHONE.................................419 625-1046
Fax: 419 625-1458
Gary Westfall, *President*
EMP: 4
SQ FT: 4,400
SALES (est): 364.5K **Privately Held**
SIC: 7694 5063 Electric motor repair; motors, electric

(G-16949)
BLUE CHIP MACHINE & TOOL LTD
4211 Venice Rd (44870-1649)
PHONE.................................419 626-9559
John Higgins, *Vice Pres*
Brian S Fiorletta, *Mng Member*
Sherri Fischer,
Timothy C Welfle,
EMP: 5 EST: 1997
SQ FT: 10,000
SALES: 800K **Privately Held**
SIC: 3499 3599 Machine bases, metal; machine shop, jobbing & repair

(G-16950)
BUDERER DRUG CO (PA)
Also Called: Fisher Drug
633 Hancock St (44870-3603)
PHONE.................................419 626-3429
Fax: 419 626-0494
James Buderer, *Owner*
Mathew Buderer, *Vice Pres*
Joyce Buderer, *Treasurer*
EMP: 6
SALES (est): 1MM **Privately Held**
SIC: 2834 5122 5912 Medicines, capsuled or ampuled; drugs & drug proprietaries; drug stores & proprietary stores

(G-16951)
BUDERER DRUG COMPANY INC (PA)
633 Hancock St (44870-3603)
PHONE.................................419 627-2800
James Buderer, *President*
Matthew Buderer, *Vice Pres*
Suzanne Fomich, *Pharmacist*
Nancy Buderer, *Consultant*
EMP: 13 EST: 2014

SQ FT: 5,000
SALES (est): 9.8MM **Privately Held**
SIC: 5122 2834 Drugs & drug proprietaries; animal medicines; proprietary
(patent) medicines; proprietary drug products

(G-16952)
BUSCH & THIEM INC
1316 Cleveland Rd (44870-4271)
P.O. Box 1088 (44871-1088)
PHONE..............................419 625-7515
Fax: 419 625-9464
C A Busch, *President*
Sara Straley, *Bookkeeper*
Robert Castello, *Manager*
Terry Lewis, *Manager*
Cheryl Holbrook, *Data Proc Dir*
EMP: 20 EST: 1926
SQ FT: 45,000
SALES (est): 4.1MM **Privately Held**
WEB: www.buschthiem.com
SIC: 2542 3993 3496 3444 Racks, mer-
chandise display or storage: except wood;
signs & advertising specialties; miscella-
neous fabricated wire products; sheet
metalwork; steel pipe & tubes

(G-16953)
CEDAR POINT LAUNDRY
1 Cedar Point Dr (44870-5259)
PHONE..............................419 627-2274
EMP: 4
SALES (est): 130K **Privately Held**
SIC: 2842 Laundry cleaning preparations

(G-16954)
CRAWFORD RESOURCES INC
105 W Market St Ste 100 (44870-2516)
PHONE..............................419 624-8400
Fax: 419 624-0800
Dale Crawford, *President*
Elizabeth Jane Crawford, *Vice Pres*
EMP: 3
SALES (est): 385.1K **Privately Held**
SIC: 3677 Filtration devices, electronic

(G-16955)
D C FILTER & CHEMICAL INC
Also Called: Miracle Core Filters
1517 5th St (44870-3998)
PHONE..............................419 626-3967
Fax: 419 626-5013
Gary D Morey, *President*
EMP: 7
SQ FT: 60,000
SALES (est): 900K **Privately Held**
SIC: 3569 2842 Filters, general line: in-
dustrial; specialty cleaning, polishes &
sanitation goods; drycleaning prepara-
tions; industrial plant disinfectants or de-
odorants; laundry cleaning preparations

(G-16956)
DAVID BUTLER TAX SERVICE
415 Tiffin Ave (44870-2141)
PHONE..............................419 626-8086
William Butler, *Owner*
EMP: 3 EST: 1953
SALES (est): 116.5K **Privately Held**
SIC: 7291 2752 Tax return preparation
services; commercial printing, offset

(G-16957)
DECKO PRODUCTS INC
2105 Superior St (44870-1891)
PHONE..............................419 626-5757
Fax: 419 626-3135
Bill Niggemyer, *President*
Rob Simonton, *Vice Pres*
Gene Ott, *Plant Mgr*
Mary Galindo, *Purchasing*
Dave Webster, *Technical Mgr*
◆ **EMP:** 65
SQ FT: 20,000
SALES (est): 17.9MM **Privately Held**
WEB: www.decko.com
SIC: 2064 Cake ornaments, confectionery

(G-16958)
**DOUTHIT COMMUNICATIONS
INC (PA)**
Also Called: Photo Journals
520 Warren St (44870-2958)
P.O. Box 760 (44871-0760)
PHONE..............................419 625-5825

Fax: 419 625-2834
H Kenneth III, *President*
Harold K Douthit, *Chairman*
Joanne Kraine, *CFO*
EMP: 75
SQ FT: 12,000
SALES (est): 40.2MM **Privately Held**
WEB: www.autosillustrated.com
SIC: 2711 2741 Job printing & newspaper
publishing combined; miscellaneous pub-
lishing

(G-16959)
**DOUTHIT COMMUNICATIONS
INC**
Also Called: E-Narratives
165 Jackson St (44870-2505)
PHONE..............................419 621-2142
Barbara Hopkins, *General Mgr*
David Bennett, *Manager*
Jerryjames Sharkeymalloy, *Director*
EMP: 25
SALES (corp-wide): 40.2MM **Privately
Held**
WEB: www.autosillustrated.com
SIC: 2741 Miscellaneous publishing
PA: Douthit Communications, Inc.
520 Warren St
Sandusky OH 44870
419 625-5825

(G-16960)
**EDSAL SANDUSKY
CORPORATION**
117 E Washington Row (44870-2629)
PHONE..............................419 626-5465
EMP: 142
SALES (corp-wide): 53.3MM **Privately
Held**
SIC: 2522 Cabinets, office: except wood
PA: Edsal Sandusky Corporation
4815 Biloxi St
Millington TN 38053
901 872-0188

(G-16961)
ENCORE INDUSTRIES INC (PA)
Also Called: Encore Plastics
319 Howard Dr (44870-8607)
PHONE..............................419 626-8000
Fax: 419 626-8095
Timothy J Rathbun, *CEO*
Craig Rathbun, *President*
▲ **EMP:** 38
SQ FT: 250,000
SALES (est): 57.4MM **Privately Held**
WEB: www.e-encore.com
SIC: 3089 Plastic processing

(G-16962)
**ENCORE PLASTICS
CORPORATION (HQ)**
319 Howard Dr (44870-8607)
PHONE..............................419 626-8000
Timothy Rathbun, *CEO*
Donald Craig Rathbun, *President*
Willard John Rathbun, *Chairman*
Tim Rathbun, *Vice Pres*
Matt Morgan, *CFO*
▲ **EMP:** 16
SALES (est): 30.9MM
SALES (corp-wide): 57.4MM **Privately
Held**
WEB: www.encoreplasticscorporation.com
SIC: 3089 3559 3841 3411 Injection
molded finished plastic products; plastics
working machinery; surgical & medical in-
struments; metal cans
PA: Encore Industries, Inc.
319 Howard Dr
Sandusky OH 44870
419 626-8000

(G-16963)
**ENTRATECH SYSTEMS LLC
(PA)**
202 Fox Rd (44870-8363)
PHONE..............................419 433-7683
Fax: 419 433-7683
Michael Richardson, *President*
EMP: 9
SQ FT: 14,000

SALES (est): 1.3MM **Privately Held**
WEB: www.entratechsystems.com
SIC: 7539 3714 Electrical services; filters:
oil, fuel & air, motor vehicle

(G-16964)
EQUINOX ENTERPRISES LLC
Also Called: A & L Metal Processing
1920 George St (44870-1739)
P.O. Box 1367 (44871-1367)
PHONE..............................419 627-0022
Fax: 419 627-0122
Stephen Kalosis,
Anthony Clark,
EMP: 12
SQ FT: 25,000
SALES (est): 1.1MM **Privately Held**
WEB: www.almetalprocessing.com
SIC: 3471 Finishing, metals or formed
products

(G-16965)
FIRELANDS WINERY
Also Called: Mantey Vineyards
917 Bardshar Rd (44870-1507)
PHONE..............................419 625-5474
Fax: 419 625-4887
Claudio Salvador, *Principal*
EMP: 27
SALES (est): 4.6MM **Privately Held**
SIC: 2084 Wines, brandy & brandy spirits

(G-16966)
**FLAME SAFE OF NORTHERN
OHIO**
1202 Stone St (44870-3174)
PHONE..............................419 626-6204
Larry Riedy, *President*
Cherrie Riedy, *Admin Sec*
EMP: 4
SALES (est): 340K **Privately Held**
SIC: 2899 1742 Fire retardant chemicals;
plastering, drywall & insulation

(G-16967)
FLEMISH INVESTMENTS INC
Also Called: Pierre's Quickprint
1005 Cleveland Rd (44870-4035)
PHONE..............................419 625-4073
Fax: 419 625-3181
J Piere Van Raepenbusch, *President*
Anne Van Raepenbusch, *Vice Pres*
EMP: 6
SQ FT: 7,000
SALES (est): 796.9K **Privately Held**
SIC: 2752 Commercial printing, offset

(G-16968)
GARY L GAST
Also Called: Ohio Wood Fabrication
2024 Campbell St (44870-4811)
PHONE..............................419 626-5915
Fax: 419 625-6840
Gary L Gast, *Owner*
EMP: 6
SQ FT: 3,600
SALES: 425K **Privately Held**
SIC: 2541 Cabinets, except refrigerated:
show, display, etc.: wood; counter & sink
tops

(G-16969)
GEN TWO INDUSTRIES LLC
413 Industrial Pkwy (44870-5883)
PHONE..............................419 624-8803
Jennifer Findley, *Principal*
EMP: 8 EST: 2010
SALES (est): 771.1K **Privately Held**
SIC: 3999 Manufacturing industries

(G-16970)
GENERAL FABRICATIONS CORP
7777 Milan Rd (44870-9705)
P.O. Box 2461 (44871-2461)
PHONE..............................419 625-6055
Fax: 419 625-7843
Chester Boraski, *President*
Robert Garba, *General Mgr*
Kurt Livingston, *Engineer*
John Gallagher, *Sales Mgr*
Brenda Swartz, *Office Mgr*
EMP: 42 EST: 1982
SQ FT: 10,000

SALES (est): 12.1MM **Privately Held**
WEB: www.gfcfinishing.com
SIC: 3559 3563 Paint making machinery;
air & gas compressors

(G-16971)
**GUNDLACH SHEET METAL
WORKS INC (PA)**
910 Columbus Ave (44870-3594)
PHONE..............................419 626-4525
Fax: 419 626-9365
Roger M Gundlach, *President*
Terry W Gundlach, *Chairman*
Richard Hohler, *Vice Pres*
Terry Kette, *Vice Pres*
Andrew Gundluch, *Admin Sec*
EMP: 33
SQ FT: 17,000
SALES (est): 7.3MM **Privately Held**
WEB: www.gundlach-hvac.com
SIC: 1711 3444 Warm air heating & air
conditioning contractor; refrigeration con-
tractor; sheet metalwork

(G-16972)
**HULL READY MIX CONCRETE
INC**
Also Called: Hull Builders Supply
4419 Tiffin Ave (44870-9645)
P.O. Box 432, Vermilion (44089-0432)
PHONE..............................419 625-8070
Fax: 419 621-9581
Jeffery Riddell, *President*
EMP: 10 EST: 1999
SALES (est): 1MM **Privately Held**
SIC: 3273 4212 1611 7359 Ready-mixed
concrete; truck rental with drivers; high-
way & street construction; industrial truck
rental

(G-16973)
INDUSTRIAL NUT CORP
1425 Tiffin Ave (44870-2054)
PHONE..............................419 625-8543
Fax: 419 625-5517
William Springer, *President*
David Springer, *President*
John E Moffitt, *Vice Pres*
James B Springer, *Vice Pres*
John William Springer III, *Vice Pres*
▲ **EMP:** 100 EST: 1908
SQ FT: 100,000
SALES (est): 21.5MM **Privately Held**
WEB: www.industrialnut.com
SIC: 3452 Nuts, metal

(G-16974)
JAMAC INC
422 Buchanan St (44870-4700)
PHONE..............................419 625-9790
Fax: 419 625-4701
Mark Mc Gory, *President*
Elaine Mc Gory, *Vice Pres*
Blake McGory, *Facilities Mgr*
Jim McGory, *QC Mgr*
James G Mc Gory Jr, *Treasurer*
EMP: 18
SQ FT: 10,000
SALES (est): 3.9MM **Privately Held**
SIC: 2672 Labels (unprinted), gummed:
made from purchased materials

(G-16975)
**JOHN BEAN TECHNOLOGIES
CORP**
Also Called: Jbt Foodtech
1622 1st St (44870-3902)
PHONE..............................419 627-4349
William Cipiti, *Opers Mgr*
Kim Samstag, *Buyer*
Deborah Mears, *Purchasing*
Alan McCinnis, *Engineer*
Greg Stacy, *Engineer*
EMP: 260
SALES (corp-wide): 1.3B **Publicly Held**
SIC: 3556 Food products machinery
PA: John Bean Technologies Corporation
70 W Madison St Ste 4400
Chicago IL 60602
312 861-5900

(G-16976)
KELLSTONE
201 Putnam St (44870-2171)
PHONE..............................419 621-8140

Fax: 419 621-8236
Ralph Kunar, *Manager*
EMP: 4
SALES (est): 132.9K Privately Held
WEB: www.kellstone.com
SIC: 1499 Asphalt mining & bituminous stone quarrying

(G-16977)
KYKLOS BEARING INTL LLC (PA)
Also Called: K B I
2509 Hayes Ave (44870-5359)
PHONE..............................419 627-7000
George Thanopoulos, *President*
Bob Voltz, *Safety Dir*
Gene Biroth, *Plant Mgr*
Christopher Marquart, *Opers Spvr*
Bruce Rockwell, *QC Mgr*
▲ EMP: 450
SQ FT: 1,300,000
SALES (est): 149MM Privately Held
SIC: 3714 Bearings, motor vehicle

(G-16978)
LAKESHORE GRAPHIC INDUSTRIES
617 Hancock St (44870-3603)
PHONE..............................419 626-8631
Craig H Stahl, *CEO*
William E Stahl, *Chairman*
EMP: 16
SQ FT: 12,000
SALES (est): 1.8MM Privately Held
WEB: www.lakeshoregraphic.com
SIC: 2761 Manifold business forms

(G-16979)
LEWCO INC
706 Lane St (44870-3846)
PHONE..............................419 625-4014
Fax: 419 625-1247
Ronald Guerra, *President*
Gerald Guerra, *Vice Pres*
Jerry Guerra, *Vice Pres*
Mark Parker, *Mfg Dir*
Carl Guendelsberger, *Project Mgr*
◆ EMP: 104
SQ FT: 135,000
SALES (est): 45.7MM Privately Held
WEB: www.lewcoinc.com
SIC: 3535 3567 Bulk handling conveyor systems; industrial furnaces & ovens

(G-16980)
LIDS CORPORATION
Also Called: Limited
4314 Milan Rd Ste 530 (44870-7180)
PHONE..............................419 621-8742
Jordan Clark, *General Mgr*
EMP: 10
SALES (corp-wide): 2.8B Publicly Held
WEB: www.hatworld.com
SIC: 2353 Hats & caps
HQ: Lids Corporation
7555 Woodland Dr
Indianapolis IN 46278

(G-16981)
LORIS PRINTING INC
Also Called: Loris Printing & Party Center
2111 Cleveland Rd (44870-4412)
PHONE..............................419 626-6648
Fax: 419 626-4808
Joseph Loris, *President*
Kathy Loris, *Corp Secy*
EMP: 7
SALES (est): 1MM Privately Held
WEB: www.lorisprinting.net
SIC: 2759 2752 7299 Commercial printing; commercial printing, lithographic; facility rental & party planning services

(G-16982)
MAAGS AUTOMOTIVE & MACHINE
1640 Columbus Ave (44870-3542)
PHONE..............................419 626-1539
Fax: 419 626-8652
Robert Maag, *President*
EMP: 9
SQ FT: 1,500

SALES (est): 780K Privately Held
SIC: 3519 7538 7539 3714 Diesel engine rebuilding; gas engine rebuilding; engine rebuilding: automotive; diesel engine repair: automotive; automotive repair shops; motor vehicle parts & accessories; relays & industrial controls

(G-16983)
MACHINE APPLICATIONS CORP
Also Called: Mac Instruments
3410 Tiffin Ave (44870-9752)
PHONE..............................419 621-2322
Fax: 419 621-2321
James G Weit, *President*
Karen Weit, *Corp Secy*
Steve Weit, *Project Mgr*
EMP: 5
SQ FT: 1,672
SALES (est): 1MM Privately Held
WEB: www.macinstruments.com
SIC: 3823 Industrial instrmnts msrmnt display/control process variable

(G-16984)
MACK IRON WORKS COMPANY
124 Warren St (44870-2823)
PHONE..............................419 626-3712
John O Bacon, *President*
Peter P Kowalski Jr, *Vice Pres*
Robert R Rieger, *Plant Mgr*
Linda J Berardi, *Human Res Mgr*
Thomas M Hastings, *Sales Mgr*
EMP: 40 EST: 1901
SQ FT: 63,000
SALES (est): 10.9MM Privately Held
WEB: www.mackiron.com
SIC: 3446 3494 3444 3443 Architectural metalwork; stairs, staircases, stair treads: prefabricated metal; railings, bannisters, guards, etc.: made from metal pipe; fire escapes, metal; valves & pipe fittings; sheet metalwork; fabricated plate work (boiler shop)

(G-16985)
MARK ADVERTISING AGENCY INC
1600 5th St (44870-1300)
P.O. Box 413 (44871-0413)
PHONE..............................419 626-9000
Fax: 419 626-9934
Joe Wesnitzer, *CEO*
Shelly Cook, *President*
Lori Roth, *COO*
Shirley Wesnitzer, *Vice Pres*
Cody Ward, *Web Dvlpr*
EMP: 15 EST: 1965
SQ FT: 8,000
SALES (est): 2.5MM Privately Held
WEB: www.markadvertising.com
SIC: 2752 7311 Commercial printing, offset; advertising agencies

(G-16986)
MASTER LABEL COMPANY INC
1048 Cleveland Rd (44870-4034)
PHONE..............................419 625-8095
Bob Clarkson, *President*
Lee Clarkson, *Admin Sec*
EMP: 5
SQ FT: 3,500
SALES (est): 610K Privately Held
WEB: www.masterlabel.com
SIC: 2672 Labels (unprinted), gummed: made from purchased materials

(G-16987)
MCPC IMAGING AND PRINTING LLC
3911 Venice Rd (44870-8115)
PHONE..............................419 627-9872
Gina Vincent, *CEO*
Kimberly Stutsman, *Vice Pres*
Mark Tamburrino, *Vice Pres*
Paul Tamburrino Jr, *Vice Pres*
Steve Tamburrino, *Vice Pres*
EMP: 6
SALES (est): 888K Privately Held
SIC: 2759 Commercial printing

(G-16988)
MH & SON MACHINING & WLDG CO
210 W Perkins Ave Ste 10 (44870-9005)
PHONE..............................419 621-0690
Mark A Howard, *President*
Kim M Howard, *Vice Pres*
EMP: 6
SQ FT: 2,000
SALES (est): 540K Privately Held
SIC: 3599 1799 Machine shop, jobbing & repair; welding on site

(G-16989)
MIELKE FURNITURE REPAIR INC
3209 Columbus Ave (44870-5595)
PHONE..............................419 625-4572
Fax: 419 625-4572
Daniel H Mielke, *President*
Christine Mielke, *Corp Secy*
Allan R Mielke, *Vice Pres*
EMP: 8 EST: 1947
SQ FT: 2,800
SALES (est): 639.3K Privately Held
SIC: 7641 2511 Furniture refinishing; reupholstery; wood household furniture

(G-16990)
NYECO GAS INC
905 Pierce St (44870-4674)
PHONE..............................419 447-2712
Aaron Nye, *Principal*
Juve Guillen, *Manager*
EMP: 9
SALES (est): 1.2MM Privately Held
SIC: 5999 2813 Welding supplies; industrial gases; acetylene; argon

(G-16991)
OKAMOTO SANDUSKY MFG LLC
Also Called: Okamoto USA
3130 W Monroe St (44870-1811)
PHONE..............................419 626-1633
Yoshiyuki Okamoto, *President*
Daniel Lowe, *QC Mgr*
Marie Christopher, *Accounting Mgr*
Hirofumi Chiba, *Sales Staff*
Keith Kouts, *Manager*
▲ EMP: 100
SALES (est): 26.4MM Privately Held
SIC: 3069 Bibs, vulcanized rubber or rubberized fabric

(G-16992)
P & T PRODUCTS INC
472 Industrial Pkwy (44870-5883)
PHONE..............................419 621-1966
Fax: 419 621-1988
Paul Todd, *President*
Susan K Todd, *Corp Secy*
Jennifer Fildley, *Vice Pres*
EMP: 20
SQ FT: 20,000
SALES (est): 5.3MM Privately Held
WEB: www.p-tproductsinc.com
SIC: 2891 Sealants

(G-16993)
PARK PRESS DIRECT
2143 Sherman St (44870-4714)
PHONE..............................419 626-4426
Slate Kessler, *Principal*
Scott Bowlers, *Principal*
EMP: 9
SALES (est): 273.5K Privately Held
SIC: 2759 7389 Commercial printing;

(G-16994)
PEERLESS STOVE & MFG CO INC
Also Called: Peerless Prof Cooking Eqp
334 Harrison St (44870)
PHONE..............................419 625-4514
Fax: 419 625-4597
Brian R Huntley, *President*
William Bentley, *Plant Mgr*
EMP: 10
SQ FT: 40,000
SALES (est): 423.5K Privately Held
SIC: 3589 Cooking equipment, commercial

(G-16995)
PEGASUS VANS & TRAILERS INC
4003 Tiffin Ave (44870-9689)
P.O. Box 2308 (44871-2308)
PHONE..............................419 625-8953
Fax: 419 625-3149
Dean Wikel, *President*
Larry McGee, *Vice Pres*
Randy Wikel, *Vice Pres*
Paul Elli, *Info Tech Mgr*
EMP: 25
SQ FT: 50,000
SALES (est): 5.2MM Privately Held
SIC: 3715 Trailers or vans for transporting horses

(G-16996)
PELZ LETTERING INC
5003 Milan Rd (44870-5845)
PHONE..............................419 625-3567
Fax: 419 625-6697
Maryann Pelz, *President*
Kenneth Pelz, *Corp Secy*
Kevin Pelz, *Vice Pres*
EMP: 5
SQ FT: 5,000
SALES: 400K Privately Held
WEB: www.barrags.com
SIC: 2395 7299 7336 5699 Emblems, embroidered; stitching, custom; silk screen design; customized clothing & apparel; T-shirts, custom printed; finishing plants

(G-16997)
POLYNT COMPOSITES USA INC
1321 1st St (44870-3901)
PHONE..............................816 391-6000
Fax: 419 625-8210
Scott Bechtel, *Manager*
EMP: 28
SALES (corp-wide): 423.9K Privately Held
WEB: www.ccponline.com
SIC: 2821 2834 2842 2851 Plastics materials & resins; polyesters; emulsions; pharmaceutical; specialty cleaning, polishes & sanitation goods; paints & allied products
HQ: Polynt Composites Usa Inc.
99 E Cottage Ave
Carpentersville IL 60110

(G-16998)
QUANTUM SAILS
207 W Water St (44870-2529)
PHONE..............................567 283-5335
EMP: 3
SALES (est): 110.7K Privately Held
SIC: 3572 Computer storage devices

(G-16999)
R B MFG CO
Also Called: Akro-Mils
4101 Venice Rd (44870-1649)
PHONE..............................419 626-9464
Fax: 419 626-5654
Tom Roulston Sr, *Chairman*
Brenda Martin, *Vice Pres*
Pat Spate, *Facilities Mgr*
Sarah Lorcher, *Purchasing*
Jim Daw, *Manager*
▲ EMP: 18
SQ FT: 54,870
SALES (est): 4.5MM
SALES (corp-wide): 558MM Publicly Held
WEB: www.rbmfgco.com
SIC: 3537 3444 3443 2522 Industrial trucks & tractors; dollies (hand or power trucks), industrial except mining; trucks: freight, baggage, etc.: industrial, except mining; sheet metalwork; fabricated plate work (boiler shop); office furniture, except wood
PA: Myers Industries, Inc.
1293 S Main St
Akron OH 44301
330 253-5592

(G-17000)
SANDUSKY DOCK CORPORATION
2705 W Monroe St (44870-1831)
P.O. Box 899 (44871-0899)
PHONE..........................419 626-1214
Fax: 419 483-1004
Jeff Smith, *Superintendent*
EMP: 10
SALES (est): 645.1K
SALES (corp-wide): 9.8B **Publicly Held**
SIC: 1241 Coal mining services
HQ: Norfolk Southern Properties Inc
3 Commercial Pl Ste 1a
Norfolk VA 23510
757 629-2600

(G-17001)
SANDUSKY FABRICATING & SLS INC (PA)
Also Called: San-Fab Conveyor and Automtn
2000 Superior St (44870-1824)
PHONE..........................419 626-4465
Timothy H Shenigo, *President*
Mike Voegle, *General Mgr*
Greg Koutny, *Vice Pres*
Charlie Wheeler, *Engineer*
Tammy Snyder, *Manager*
EMP: 23 EST: 1954
SQ FT: 85,000
SALES (est): 4.4MM **Privately Held**
WEB: www.sanfab.com
SIC: 3535 Conveyors & conveying equipment

(G-17002)
SANDUSKY INTERNATIONAL INC
615 W Market St (44870-2413)
PHONE..........................419 626-5340
Edward R Ryan, *CEO*
Kathy Lilje, *Editor*
Nicholas Hamilton, *District Mgr*
Barbara Bohn, *Purchasing*
Warren Mehnerg, *QA Dir*
◆ **EMP:** 130 EST: 1904
SQ FT: 500,000
SALES: 22.4MM
SALES (corp-wide): 260.9MM **Privately Held**
WEB: www.sanduskyintl.com
SIC: 3325 3369 Alloy steel castings, except investment; castings, except die-castings, precision
PA: Metaltek International, Inc.
905 E Saint Paul Ave
Waukesha WI 53188
262 544-7777

(G-17003)
SANDUSKY MACHINE & TOOL INC
2223 Tiffin Ave (44870-1994)
PHONE..........................419 626-8359
Fax: 419 626-5204
Walter Schaufler, *Ch of Bd*
James Schaufler, *President*
Nora Kaufman, *Manager*
EMP: 13 EST: 1966
SQ FT: 17,600
SALES: 1MM **Privately Held**
SIC: 3599 Machine shop, jobbing & repair

(G-17004)
SANDUSKY NEWSPAPERS INC (PA)
314 W Market St (44870-2410)
PHONE..........................419 625-5500
Fax: 419 625-1137
Dudley A White Jr, *Ch of Bd*
David A Rau, *President*
Jane Righi, *Manager*
Susan E White, *Admin Sec*
EMP: 140
SQ FT: 45,000
SALES (est): 97.2MM **Privately Held**
WEB: www.sanduskyregister.com
SIC: 4832 2711 2752 Radio broadcasting stations; newspapers; commercial printing, lithographic

(G-17005)
SANDUSKY PACKAGING CORPORATION
2016 George St (44870-1797)
P.O. Box 2217 (44871-2217)
PHONE..........................419 626-8520
Fax: 419 626-8522
Richard M Longer, *President*
Herbert G Hoelzer, *Vice Pres*
Randall A Johnson, *Vice Pres*
William G McRobbie, *Vice Pres*
Lester J Norman, *Treasurer*
EMP: 49 EST: 1965
SQ FT: 75,000
SALES: 9MM **Privately Held**
WEB: www.sanduskypackaging.com
SIC: 2652 2657 Setup paperboard boxes; folding paperboard boxes

(G-17006)
SCHWAB MACHINE CO INC
3120 Venice Rd (44870-1886)
PHONE..........................419 626-0245
Fax: 419 626-2455
Robert Schwab, *President*
James McMahon, *Vice Pres*
EMP: 6 EST: 1946
SQ FT: 9,600
SALES: 800K **Privately Held**
SIC: 3599 Machine shop, jobbing & repair

(G-17007)
SCREEN PRINTING UNLIMITED
3410 Tiffin Ave (44870-9752)
PHONE..........................419 621-2335
Karen Weit, *Owner*
EMP: 3
SQ FT: 3,000
SALES: 155K **Privately Held**
WEB: www.promotionsunlimited.net
SIC: 2752 Commercial printing, lithographic

(G-17008)
SHOWCASE CAB MAR RSTORATION LL
5404 Sandy Acres Dr (44870-8626)
PHONE..........................419 626-6715
Jeffrey A Witter,
EMP: 4
SALES (est): 436.3K **Privately Held**
SIC: 2434 Wood kitchen cabinets

(G-17009)
SPOERR PRECAST CONCRETE INC
2020 Caldwell St (44870-4874)
PHONE..........................419 625-9132
Fax: 419 625-1201
William R Shank, *President*
William Shank, *President*
Robert Shank, *Vice Pres*
EMP: 13 EST: 1933
SQ FT: 18,000
SALES (est): 1.8MM **Privately Held**
WEB: www.spoerrprecast.com
SIC: 3272 Concrete products; burial vaults, concrete or precast terrazzo; wall & ceiling squares, concrete; septic tanks, concrete

(G-17010)
STEPHENS PUBLISHING CO INC
Also Called: Stephens & Associates Publr
311 W Perkins Ave (44870-4805)
P.O. Box 829 (44871-0829)
PHONE..........................419 626-5592
Fax: 419 626-9333
John Stephens, *President*
EMP: 5
SALES (est): 703.8K **Privately Held**
WEB: www.stephenspublishing.com
SIC: 2759 Advertising literature: printing

(G-17011)
SURENERGY LLC
319 Howard Dr (44870-8607)
PHONE..........................419 626-8000
Timothy Rathbun,
▲ **EMP:** 13
SALES (est): 2.3MM **Privately Held**
SIC: 3621 Windmills, electric generating

(G-17012)
THERMOCOLOR LLC (DH)
Also Called: Rhe-Tech Colors
2901 W Monroe St (44870-1810)
PHONE..........................419 626-5677
Tracy Garrison, *Principal*
Kent Walton, *Engineer*
Priscilla Frantz, *Human Resources*
Dale Reitz, *Human Resources*
Jeffery Nonekowski, *Manager*
EMP: 29
SQ FT: 30,000
SALES (est): 5.7MM
SALES (corp-wide): 1.2B **Privately Held**
SIC: 2865 Cyclic crudes & intermediates
HQ: Hexpol Holding Inc.
14330 Kinsman Rd
Burton OH 44021
440 834-4644

(G-17013)
THERMOCOLOR LLC
Also Called: Rhetech Color
2108 Superior St (44870)
PHONE..........................419 626-5677
Fax: 419 626-4806
John Levinson, *General Mgr*
Jane Call, *Controller*
Nancy Hartley, *Marketing Staff*
Jeffery Nonekowski, *Director*
EMP: 14
SALES (corp-wide): 1.2B **Privately Held**
SIC: 2865 Cyclic crudes & intermediates
HQ: Thermocolor Llc
2901 W Monroe St
Sandusky OH 44870
419 626-5677

(G-17014)
THORFOOD LLC (HQ)
Also Called: Peanut Roaster, The
2520 Campbell St (44870-5309)
P.O. Box 2218 (44871-2218)
PHONE..........................419 626-4375
John Monahan, *President*
Chris Nielsen, *CFO*
Fritz Mueller, *Controller*
David Thorson, *Mng Member*
EMP: 25
SALES (est): 7.8MM
SALES (corp-wide): 92.9MM **Privately Held**
SIC: 2068 Salted & roasted nuts & seeds
PA: Thorworks Industries, Inc.
2520 Campbell St
Sandusky OH 44870
419 626-4375

(G-17015)
THORWORKS INDUSTRIES INC (PA)
Also Called: Sealmaster
2520 Campbell St (44870-5309)
P.O. Box 2218 (44871-2218)
PHONE..........................419 626-4375
Fax: 419 626-5477
David Thorson, *President*
Chris Nielsen, *CFO*
Fritz Mueller, *Controller*
Rick Noon, *Manager*
Dave Shupe, *Director*
◆ **EMP:** 30
SQ FT: 80,000
SALES (est): 92.9MM **Privately Held**
WEB: www.sealmaster.net
SIC: 2851 3531 2952 2951 Paints & paint additives; construction machinery; asphalt felts & coatings; asphalt paving mixtures & blocks; adhesives & sealants; inorganic pigments

(G-17016)
TOFT DAIRY INC
3717 Venice Rd (44870-1640)
P.O. Box 2558 (44871-2558)
PHONE..........................419 625-4376
Fax: 419 621-2010
Eugene H Meisler, *President*
Nicholas Catri, *Principal*
Carl Meisler, *Principal*
Charles M Meisler, *Corp Secy*
Thomas E Meisler, *Vice Pres*
EMP: 52 EST: 1900
SQ FT: 94,000
SALES: 20.5MM **Privately Held**
WEB: www.toftdairy.com
SIC: 2026 2024 Milk processing (pasteurizing, homogenizing, bottling); ice cream & ice milk

(G-17017)
TUNE TOWN CAR AUDIO
2018 E Perkins Ave (44870-5129)
PHONE..........................419 627-1100
Toll Free:..........................877 -
Fax: 419 627-0099
Mark Myers, *Owner*
Kayce Berkey, *Bookkeeper*
EMP: 7
SQ FT: 4,800
SALES: 800K **Privately Held**
WEB: www.tune-town.com
SIC: 5731 3651 High fidelity stereo equipment; household audio & video equipment

(G-17018)
UNION FABRICATING & MACHINE CO
3427 Venice Rd (44870-1766)
PHONE..........................419 626-5963
Fax: 419 626-2728
Alden V Lake, *CEO*
Daniel Lake, *President*
Jeffrey Lake, *Vice Pres*
Charles Eisenhauer, *Plant Mgr*
Kelly Armbrecht, *Bookkeeper*
EMP: 7
SALES (est): 550K **Privately Held**
SIC: 3441 Fabricated structural metal

(G-17019)
US TSUBAKI POWER TRANSM LLC
Engineering Chain Div
1010 Edgewater Ave (44870-1601)
PHONE..........................419 626-4560
Fax: 419 626-5194
Myron Timmer, *Vice Pres*
Dave Zechman, *Plant Mgr*
Steve Funni, *Mfg Staff*
Ron Sennish, *Purchasing*
Vic Hostetter, *Engineer*
EMP: 180
SALES (corp-wide): 1.7B **Privately Held**
SIC: 5049 3568 3714 3462 Engineers' equipment & supplies; chain, power transmission; motor vehicle parts & accessories; iron & steel forgings
HQ: U.S. Tsubaki Power Transmission Llc
301 E Marquardt Dr
Wheeling IL 60090
847 459-9500

(G-17020)
VENTRA SANDUSKY LLC
3020 Tiffin Ave (44870-5352)
PHONE..........................419 627-3600
Douglas Cellier,
Shaun Tinnel,
▲ **EMP:** 92
SALES (est): 57.9MM
SALES (corp-wide): 3.3B **Privately Held**
SIC: 3714 3822 Motor vehicle parts & accessories; auto controls regulating residntl & coml environmt & applncs
PA: Flex-N-Gate Corporation
1306 E University Ave
Urbana IL 61802
217 384-6600

(G-17021)
WAGNER QUARRIES COMPANY
Also Called: Hanson Aggregates
4203 Milan Rd (44870-5880)
PHONE..........................419 625-8141
Fax: 419 625-7150
Chris Kinner, *Plant Mgr*
Bill Hoelzer, *Marketing Staff*
Chuck Cashan, *Manager*
Andrew Harper, *Manager*
Chuck Kashian, *Manager*
EMP: 48
SQ FT: 2,400
SALES (est): 4.5MM **Privately Held**
SIC: 1422 Crushed & broken limestone

GEOGRAPHIC

(G-17022)
WWW BOAT SERVICES INC
2218 River Ave (44870-1303)
PHONE................................419 626-0883
Fax: 419 621-0078
Ryan Kraft, *President*
Debra Kraft, *Corp Secy*
Ray Kraft, *Vice Pres*
Christie Holliday, *Manager*
EMP: 5
SALES: 142.9K **Privately Held**
SIC: 3732 5551 Boat building & repairing;
  boat dealers

Sandyville
Tuscarawas County

(G-17023)
VEGGIE VALLEY FARM LLC
3444 Dueber Rd Ne (44671)
P.O. Box 135 (44671-0135)
PHONE................................330 866-2712
Betty Frank,
Edward J Frank,
EMP: 6
SALES (est): 516.3K **Privately Held**
SIC: 2099 Ready-to-eat meals, salads &
  sandwiches

Sarahsville
Noble County

(G-17024)
BIEDENBACH LOGGING
48443 Seneca Lake Rd (43779-9732)
PHONE................................740 732-6477
John Biedenbach, *Partner*
EMP: 6
SALES (est): 559.4K **Privately Held**
SIC: 2411 1629 Logging camps & contrac-
  tors; earthmoving contractor

(G-17025)
NED A SHREVE
Also Called: Ben Logging
48398 Seneca Lake Rd (43779-9732)
PHONE................................740 732-6465
Ned A Shreve, *Owner*
EMP: 5
SALES (est): 275.2K **Privately Held**
SIC: 2411 7389 Logging; log & lumber
  broker

Sardinia
Brown County

(G-17026)
C & M TRUSS LLC
8319 Ashridge Arnheim Rd (45171-9123)
PHONE................................937 446-3400
Calvin Nissley, *Owner*
EMP: 10
SALES (est): 1.5MM **Privately Held**
SIC: 2439 Structural wood members

(G-17027)
COCA-COLA
136 Fairview Ave (45171-9354)
PHONE................................937 446-4644
EMP: 4 EST: 2011
SALES (est): 163.9K **Privately Held**
SIC: 2086 Bottled & canned soft drinks

(G-17028)
COCA-COLA COMPANY
7906 Yochum Rd (45171-8379)
PHONE................................937 446-4644
Kevin Smith, *Manager*
EMP: 18
SALES (corp-wide): 41.8B **Publicly Held**
WEB: www.colasic.net
SIC: 2086 Bottled & canned soft drinks
PA: The Coca-Cola Company
  1 Coca Cola Plz Nw
  Atlanta GA 30313
  404 676-2121

(G-17029)
**GREEN BROTHERS
ENTERPRISES**
516 Sicily Rd (45171)
P.O. Box 1 (45171-0001)
PHONE................................937 444-3323
Fax: 937 444-3323
EMP: 3
SQ FT: 15,000
SALES: 250K **Privately Held**
SIC: 2421 Sawmill/Planing Mill

(G-17030)
MANNINGS PACKING CO
100 College Ave (45171-7500)
P.O. Box 23 (45171-0023)
PHONE................................937 446-3278
Gregory Thomas Manning, *Partner*
Robert Manning, *Partner*
EMP: 8
SQ FT: 5,000
SALES (est): 866.6K **Privately Held**
SIC: 2011 Meat packing plants

(G-17031)
SARDINIA READY MIX INC (PA)
9 Oakdale Ave (45171)
P.O. Box 53 (45171-0053)
PHONE................................937 446-2523
Fax: 937 446-3780
David Taylor, *President*
Cheryl Taylor, *Corp Secy*
Charles Taylor, *Vice Pres*
Lisa Brideow, *Manager*
EMP: 3
SQ FT: 2,000
SALES (est): 2.6MM **Privately Held**
SIC: 3273 Ready-mixed concrete

(G-17032)
SARDINIA READY MIX INC
9 Oakdale Ave (45171)
P.O. Box 53 (45171-0053)
PHONE................................937 446-2523
Cheryle Taylor, *President*
EMP: 12
SALES (corp-wide): 2.6MM **Privately
Held**
SIC: 3273 Ready-mixed concrete
PA: Sardinia Ready Mix, Inc.
  9 Oakdale Ave
  Sardinia OH 45171
  937 446-2523

(G-17033)
SCOTT-RANDALL SYSTEMS INC
5815 Tracy Rd (45171-9120)
PHONE................................937 446-2293
Walter S Prather III, *President*
Janet Prather, *Vice Pres*
EMP: 15
SQ FT: 31,200
SALES (est): 1.3MM **Privately Held**
WEB: www.scott-randallsystems.com
SIC: 5084 3535 3537 Materials handling
  machinery; robotic conveyors; industrial
  trucks & tractors

(G-17034)
TRI-STATE FASTENERS LLC
2875 Gath North Rd (45171-8203)
PHONE................................937 442-1904
James Herrmann, *Mng Member*
Jayne Burke,
Mark Burke,
EMP: 3
SALES (est): 297.3K **Privately Held**
SIC: 3965 Fasteners

Sardis
Monroe County

(G-17035)
**APPALACHIAN OILFIELD SVCS
LLC**
34602 State Route 7 (43946-8704)
PHONE................................337 216-0066
Stuart Lissner,
EMP: 5 EST: 2015
SALES (est): 230.2K **Privately Held**
SIC: 1389 Oil field services

(G-17036)
MONROE WATER SYSTEM
Also Called: Monroe Water Sys Treatmnt Plnt
35100 State Route 7 (43946-8732)
P.O. Box 15, Laings (43752-0015)
PHONE................................740 472-1030
Bill Wells, *Manager*
Jim Murray, *Manager*
EMP: 4
SALES (est): 477.5K **Privately Held**
SIC: 3321 Water pipe, cast iron

Scio
Harrison County

(G-17037)
GINGERBREAD N BOWS
202 W Main St (43988)
PHONE................................740 945-1027
Jeannie Cagot, *Principal*
EMP: 5
SALES (est): 150K **Privately Held**
SIC: 3944 Craft & hobby kits & sets

(G-17038)
**SCIO LAMINATED PRODUCTS
INC**
117 Fowler Ave (43988-9779)
P.O. Box 6561, Wheeling WV (26003-
0627)
PHONE................................740 945-1321
Fax: 740 945-1321
W Quay Mull II, *Ch of Bd*
Charles J Kaiser Jr, *Principal*
Terry Call, *Vice Pres*
Michael Piazza, *VP Sales*
Wqm Industries, *Shareholder*
EMP: 28
SQ FT: 70,000
SALES (est): 2.1MM **Privately Held**
SIC: 2541 Table or counter tops, plastic
  laminated

Scottown
Lawrence County

(G-17039)
**FOUR JS BLDG COMPONENTS
LLC**
16435 State Route 217 (45678-9062)
PHONE................................740 886-6112
Jeff Ramey,
EMP: 15
SALES (est): 682.8K **Privately Held**
SIC: 1761 2439 Roofing contractor;
  trusses, wooden roof

Seaman
Adams County

(G-17040)
**ALL WAYS GREEN LAWN &
TURF LLC**
1856 Greenbrier Rd (45679-9552)
PHONE................................937 763-4766
Jeffrey Mullenix,
EMP: 7
SALES: 225K **Privately Held**
SIC: 2875 0781 Fertilizers, mixing only;
  landscape services

(G-17041)
M & L MACHINE
17400 State Route 247 (45679-9417)
P.O. Box 227 (45679-0227)
PHONE................................937 386-2604
Fax: 937 386-2739
Kathleen Mc Wain, *Owner*
EMP: 7
SQ FT: 40,000
SALES (est): 380K **Privately Held**
SIC: 3599 3728 Machine shop, jobbing &
  repair; aircraft parts & equipment

(G-17042)
RJ S MACHINE SHOP SERVICE
720 Pondlick Rd (45679-9504)
PHONE................................937 927-0137
Richard Jones, *Principal*
EMP: 3
SALES (est): 139.6K **Privately Held**
SIC: 7389 3599 ; machine shop, jobbing
  & repair

(G-17043)
SOUTHERN OHIO MATERIALS
800 Nathan Denton Rd (45679-9554)
PHONE................................937 386-3200
Nathania Shelton, *Principal*
EMP: 3
SALES (est): 242.6K **Privately Held**
SIC: 1429 Grits mining (crushed stone)

Sebring
Mahoning County

(G-17044)
CIRCLE MACHINE ROLLS INC
245 W Kentucky Ave (44672-1909)
P.O. Box 9 (44672-0009)
PHONE................................330 938-9010
Fax: 330 938-6716
Peter Kuhlmann, *President*
Ken Kuhlmann, *Vice Pres*
Brenda Reed, *Admin Sec*
▲ EMP: 27
SQ FT: 15,000
SALES (est): 5MM **Privately Held**
WEB: www.rollsbycircle.com
SIC: 3599 3547 Machine & other job shop
  work; rolling mill machinery

(G-17045)
FOUNDRY SAND SERVICE LLC
20455 Lake Park Blvd (44672-1771)
P.O. Box 262 (44672-0262)
PHONE................................330 823-6152
EMP: 3
SALES (est): 79.9K **Privately Held**
SIC: 1442 Construction sand & gravel

(G-17046)
**JF MARTT AND ASSOCIATES
INC**
501 N Johnson Rd (44672-1007)
P.O. Box 10 (44672-0010)
PHONE................................330 938-4000
Fax: 330 938-1800
Judson Martt, *President*
Frank Tluchowski, *Vice Pres*
Cheryl K Tafe, *Manager*
EMP: 15
SQ FT: 12,000
SALES (est): 3.4MM **Privately Held**
WEB: www.jfmartt.com
SIC: 7699 3599 Industrial machinery &
  equipment repair; custom machinery

(G-17047)
M PI LABEL SYSTEMS
450 Courtney Rd (44672-1339)
P.O. Box 70 (44672-0070)
PHONE................................330 938-2134
Randy Kocher, *President*
Carson Mc Neely, *President*
Donald J McDanial, *President*
Kathy Henderson, *General Mgr*
Carey Weingart, *General Mgr*
EMP: 6
SALES (est): 695.1K **Privately Held**
SIC: 2759 2754 3565 Labels & seals:
  printing; labels: gravure printing; labeling
  machines, industrial

(G-17048)
MODERN CHINA INC (PA)
550 E Ohio Ave (44672-1642)
P.O. Box 309 (44672-0309)
PHONE................................330 938-6104
Debbie Grindley, *President*
EMP: 35 EST: 1959
SQ FT: 27,000
SALES (est): 4.3MM **Privately Held**
SIC: 5947 3229 3263 Souvenirs; greeting
  cards; glassware, art or decorative; semi-
  vitreous table & kitchenware

(G-17049)
MPI LABELS OF BALTIMORE INC (HQ)
Also Called: Mpi Label Systems.
450 Courtney Rd (44672-1339)
P.O. Box 70 (44672-0070)
PHONE....................................330 938-2134
Randy L Kocher, *President*
Elvin Barnit, *President*
Carson Mc Neely, *President*
Donald McDanial, *President*
Joe Skiba, *Treasurer*
EMP: 15
SQ FT: 110,000
SALES (est): 8.3MM
SALES (corp-wide): 32.3MM **Privately Held**
SIC: 2759 2754 3565 Labels & seals: printing; labels: gravure printing; labeling machines, industrial
PA: Miller Products, Inc.
450 Courtney Rd
Sebring OH 44672
330 938-2134

(G-17050)
REFRACTORY SPECIALTIES INC
230 W California Ave (44672-1920)
PHONE....................................330 938-2101
Richard Wilk, *President*
Jim Vaughn, *Corp Secy*
Suhas Patil, *Vice Pres*
Kevin Smith, *Plant Mgr*
Sharon Rogers, *Prdtn Mgr*
▲ EMP: 49
SQ FT: 55,000
SALES (est): 10.1MM
SALES (corp-wide): 2.5B **Privately Held**
WEB: www.rsifibre.com
SIC: 3297 3296 3823 Nonclay refractories; graphite refractories: carbon bond or ceramic bond; crucibles: graphite, magnesite, chrome, silica, etc.; mineral wool; industrial instrmnts msrmnt display/control process variable
HQ: Unifrax Holding Co
55 E 52nd St Fl 35
New York NY 10055

(G-17051)
S WJ LLCRED
1100 N Johnson Rd (44672-1020)
PHONE....................................330 938-6173
Ted Hines, *Principal*
EMP: 3 EST: 2011
SALES (est): 295.3K **Privately Held**
SIC: 3672 Printed circuit boards

(G-17052)
SALEM-REPUBLIC RUBBER COMPANY
475 W California Ave (44672-1922)
P.O. Box 339 (44672-0339)
PHONE....................................330 938-2016
Fax: 330 938-9809
Drew Ney, *President*
Tammy Ulbricht, *Vice Pres*
Donald McCaughtry, *VP Mfg*
Jim Grossi, *Plant Mgr*
Dominique Nero, *Purch Agent*
▲ EMP: 47
SQ FT: 180,000
SALES (est): 10MM **Privately Held**
WEB: www.salem-republic.com
SIC: 3052 3069 Rubber hose; rubberized fabrics

(G-17053)
SEBRING FLUID POWER CORP
513 N Johnson Rd (44672-1007)
P.O. Box 6 (44672-0006)
PHONE....................................330 938-9984
Fax: 330 938-1814
Paul Mc Guire, *President*
Stan Ware, *Treasurer*
EMP: 7
SQ FT: 10,000
SALES (est): 800K **Privately Held**
SIC: 3599 3593 Machine shop, jobbing & repair; fluid power cylinders & actuators

(G-17054)
SEBRING INDUSTRIAL PLATING
Also Called: Sebring Plating
546 W Tennessee Ave (44672-1836)
P.O. Box 206 (44672-0206)
PHONE....................................330 938-6666
Fax: 330 938-9711
Richard Sickelsmith, *President*
Eric Sickelsmith, *Vice Pres*
EMP: 8
SQ FT: 10,000
SALES (est): 1.1MM **Privately Held**
SIC: 3471 Plating of metals or formed products

(G-17055)
TRUCUT INCORPORATED (PA)
1145 Allied Dr (44672-1355)
PHONE....................................330 938-9806
Fax: 330 938-9342
David Gano, *President*
Larry Grossi, *Exec VP*
Michael Geiger, *Opers Staff*
Michael Seruch, *Opers Staff*
Michael Greenamyer, *Purch Mgr*
▲ EMP: 53
SQ FT: 85,000
SALES (est): 11MM **Privately Held**
SIC: 3544 3542 3469 3613 Special dies, tools, jigs & fixtures; machine tools, metal forming type; metal stampings; control panels, electric; automotive stampings

(G-17056)
UNITED DIE & MFG CO
100 S 17th St (44672-1914)
P.O. Box 38 (44672-0038)
PHONE....................................330 938-6141
Fax: 330 938-9503
Gary Close, *President*
Dennis Close, *Corp Secy*
Don Close, *Controller*
EMP: 30
SQ FT: 40,000
SALES (est): 5.1MM **Privately Held**
WEB: www.uniteddiemfg.com
SIC: 3429 3469 Manufactured hardware (general); stamping metal for the trade

(G-17057)
VACUFORM INC
500 Courtney Rd (44672-1349)
P.O. Box 117 (44672-0117)
PHONE....................................330 938-9674
Fax: 330 938-9676
Michael Hubbs, *Vice Pres*
Bob Schmidt, *Manager*
▲ EMP: 35
SQ FT: 50,000
SALES (est): 5.3MM **Publicly Held**
WEB: www.vacuforminc.com
SIC: 3297 Nonclay refractories
HQ: Unifrax I Llc
600 Rverwalk Pkwy Ste 120
Tonawanda NY 14150

Senecaville
Guernsey County

(G-17058)
DWAYNE HALL
57501 Cherry Hill Rd (43780-9772)
PHONE....................................740 685-5270
Dwayne Hall, *Owner*
EMP: 4 EST: 2001
SALES (est): 264.4K **Privately Held**
WEB: www.dwaynehall.com
SIC: 3199 Saddles or parts

(G-17059)
PAUL YODER
13051 Deerfield Rd (43780-9406)
PHONE....................................740 439-5811
Fax: 740 439-5831
Paul Yoder, *Owner*
Levi Schwartz, *Manager*
EMP: 6
SQ FT: 6,500
SALES: 600K **Privately Held**
WEB: www.yoderbuilding.com
SIC: 2542 Cabinets: show, display or storage: except wood

Seven Hills
Cuyahoga County

(G-17060)
ART PRO GRAPHICS
7279 Summitview Dr (44131-4400)
PHONE....................................216 236-6465
Anthony Tomecko, *Owner*
EMP: 5
SALES (est): 310K **Privately Held**
SIC: 2752 Commercial printing, lithographic

(G-17061)
CLEANING BY SNDRA MSTERS TOUCH
6516 Gale Dr (44131-3131)
PHONE....................................216 524-6827
Sandra Hines, *Partner*
EMP: 11
SALES (est): 710K **Privately Held**
SIC: 7699 2842 Cleaning services; specialty cleaning preparations

(G-17062)
PREFERRED SOLUTIONS INC
7819 Broadview Rd Ste 6 (44131-6150)
PHONE....................................216 642-1200
Fax: 216 642-1200
John A Stahl, *President*
Jack Stahl, *Vice Pres*
Jack S Stahl, *Manager*
EMP: 15
SQ FT: 8,000
SALES (est): 2.8MM **Privately Held**
WEB: www.stayflex.com
SIC: 3089 Plastic processing

(G-17063)
RENT A MOM INC
4531 Hillside Rd (44131-4611)
PHONE....................................216 901-9599
Linda Delaney, *President*
EMP: 12
SALES (est): 1.3MM **Privately Held**
WEB: www.rentamominc.com
SIC: 3635 Household vacuum cleaners

(G-17064)
SEVEN HILLS REPORTER
6817 Parkgate Oval (44131-3642)
PHONE....................................216 524-9515
Timothy Fraundorf, *Principal*
EMP: 3
SALES (est): 183.4K **Privately Held**
SIC: 2711 Newspapers, publishing & printing

Seven Mile
Butler County

(G-17065)
ENCORE PRECAST LLC
416 W Ritter (45062)
P.O. Box 380 (45062-0380)
PHONE....................................513 726-5678
Fax: 513 726-5679
Charles Ehlers, *Principal*
EMP: 15
SALES (est): 2.9MM **Privately Held**
SIC: 3272 5032 5211 Septic tanks, concrete; concrete & cinder building products; concrete & cinder block

(G-17066)
OWEN & SONS
206 S Main St (45062)
P.O. Box 97 (45062-0097)
PHONE....................................513 726-5406
Thomas Owen, *Owner*
EMP: 3 EST: 1946
SALES (est): 270.6K **Privately Held**
SIC: 3548 Welding apparatus

Seville
Medina County

(G-17067)
4-B WOOD SPECIALTIES INC
Also Called: 4-B Wood Custom Cabinets
255 W Greenwich Rd (44273-8876)
PHONE....................................330 769-2188
Fax: 330 769-2850
Kurt E Grassell, *President*
Tracy Romanotto, *Manager*
EMP: 15
SQ FT: 17,000
SALES (est): 1.8MM **Privately Held**
WEB: www.4bwood.com
SIC: 2434 Wood kitchen cabinets

(G-17068)
ATLANTIC TOOL & DIE COMPANY
Also Called: Jatdco
4995 Atlantic Dr (44273-8965)
PHONE....................................330 769-4500
Frank Mehwald, *Branch Mgr*
EMP: 200
SALES (corp-wide): 147.6MM **Privately Held**
SIC: 3469 3545 3544 Metal stampings; machine tool accessories; special dies & tools
PA: Atlantic Tool & Die Company Inc
19963 Progress Dr
Strongsville OH 44149
440 238-6931

(G-17069)
BENCHMARK CRAFTSMAN INC
Also Called: Benchmark Craftsmen
4700 Greenwich Rd (44273-8848)
PHONE....................................330 975-4214
Nathan Sublett, *President*
Denise Trouten, *Controller*
Denise Trouton, *Accountant*
EMP: 30
SALES (est): 4.1MM **Privately Held**
WEB: www.benchmarkcraftsmen.com
SIC: 7389 3993 Exhibit construction by industrial contractors; displays & cutouts, window & lobby

(G-17070)
BLAIR RUBBER COMPANY
5020 Enterprise Pkwy (44273-8960)
PHONE....................................330 769-5583
Fax: 330 666-9334
David Jentzsch, *General Mgr*
Don Skraba, *Maint Spvr*
Gregg Reinmann, *QC Mgr*
Santino Desimone, *Research*
Bill Harmon, *Controller*
◆ EMP: 65
SQ FT: 50,000
SALES (est): 16.9MM
SALES (corp-wide): 42.6MM **Privately Held**
WEB: www.blairrubber.com
SIC: 3069 3535 Linings, vulcanizable rubber; belt conveyor systems, general industrial use
PA: Goldis Enterprises, Inc.
120 Hay Rd
Wilmington DE 19809
302 764-3100

(G-17071)
BLEACHTECH LLC
320 Ryan Rd (44273-9109)
PHONE....................................216 921-1980
Richard Immerman, *President*
Joseph Traylinek, *Maintenance Dir*
EMP: 25
SALES (est): 1.8MM **Privately Held**
SIC: 7349 5169 2819 Chemical cleaning services; chemicals & allied products; bleaching powder, lime bleaching compounds

(G-17072)
CENTERRA CO-OP
16 Market St (44273-8920)
PHONE....................................330 769-3469
Charles Holdren, *President*
Mike Mooney, *Credit Mgr*

GEOGRAPHIC

EMP: 20
SALES (corp-wide): 174.6MM **Privately Held**
WEB: www.tc-feed.com
SIC: 2048 Bird food, prepared
PA: Centerra Co-Op
　　813 Clark Ave
　　Ashland OH 44805
　　419 281-2153

(G-17073)
COMDESS COMPANY INC
8733 Wooster Pike Rd (44273-9363)
P.O. Box 91 (44273-0091)
PHONE..............................330 769-2094
Fax: 330 769-2199
Sam Mandich, *President*
▲ **EMP:** 15
SQ FT: 25,000
SALES (est): 2.3MM **Privately Held**
WEB: www.comdess.com
SIC: 3089 Thermoformed finished plastic
　　products

(G-17074)
DIE CAST DIVISION
5151 Greenwich Rd (44273)
PHONE..............................330 769-2013
Carl Espey, *Principal*
EMP: 3
SALES (est): 169K **Privately Held**
SIC: 3544 Special dies & tools

(G-17075)
HYLOAD INC (DH)
5020 Enterprise Pkwy (44273-8960)
PHONE..............................330 336-6604
Dave Jentzsch, *President*
Sharon Killinger, *Controller*
▼ **EMP:** 16
SQ FT: 40,000
SALES: 9MM
SALES (corp-wide): 42.6MM **Privately
Held**
WEB: www.hyload.com
SIC: 3069 2952 Roofing, membrane rub-
　　ber; asphalt felts & coatings

(G-17076)
JJ SEVILLE LLC
Also Called: Seville Bronze
22 Milton St (44273-9316)
P.O. Box 45 (44273-0045)
PHONE..............................330 769-2071
Tim Steele, *President*
Bobbi Montaquila, *Administration*
EMP: 19
SALES (est): 4.4MM
SALES (corp-wide): 511.6MM **Privately
Held**
SIC: 3351 Bronze rolling & drawing
PA: Jiangyin Mould Plastic Group Co., Ltd.
　　No.2,Changqing Rd.,Zhouzhuang
　　Town
　　Jiangyin 21442
　　510 864-0145

(G-17077)
KING DRILLING CO
24 E Main St (44273-9196)
P.O. Box 52 (44273-0052)
PHONE..............................330 769-3434
Andrew King, *President*
Peter King Jr, *Vice Pres*
EMP: 4
SQ FT: 700
SALES (est): 439.5K **Privately Held**
SIC: 1311 Crude petroleum production;
　　natural gas production

(G-17078)
MARTIN RUBBER COMPANY
5020 Panther Pkwy (44273-8960)
PHONE..............................330 336-6604
Fax: 330 336-5512
EMP: 11
SALES (est): 1.4MM **Privately Held**
SIC: 3069 3535 Mfg Fabricated Rubber
　　Products Mfg Conveyors/Equipment

Shade
Athens County

(G-17079)
**SHADE TEXT BOOK SERVICE
INC**
Also Called: Shade Winery
401 Gilkey Ridge Rd (45776-9660)
PHONE..............................740 696-1323
Neal Dix, *President*
EMP: 3 **EST:** 2002
SALES: 222K **Privately Held**
SIC: 2084 7389 Wines;

Shadyside
Belmont County

(G-17080)
**COMMERCIAL VEHICLE GROUP
INC**
60581 State Route 7 (43947-9704)
PHONE..............................740 676-6542
Mike Esten, *Plant Mgr*
Melvin Fultz, *Branch Mgr*
Ron Rose, *Executive*
EMP: 168
SALES (corp-wide): 662.1MM **Publicly
Held**
SIC: 3469 Metal stampings
PA: Commercial Vehicle Group, Inc.
　　7800 Walton Pkwy
　　New Albany OH 43054
　　614 289-5360

(G-17081)
**KNIGHT MANUFACTURING CO
INC (PA)**
399 E 40th St (43947-1206)
P.O. Box 27 (43947-0027)
PHONE..............................740 676-9532
Fax: 740 676-9550
David Knight, *President*
EMP: 10
SQ FT: 140,000
SALES (est): 2.1MM **Privately Held**
SIC: 3599 3469 Machine shop, jobbing &
　　repair; boxes: tool, lunch, mail, etc.;
　　stamped metal

(G-17082)
**KNIGHT MANUFACTURING CO
INC**
Also Called: Belmont Stamping
E 40th St (43947)
P.O. Box 98 (43947-0098)
PHONE..............................740 676-5516
David Knight, *Manager*
EMP: 6
SALES (corp-wide): 2.1MM **Privately
Held**
SIC: 3444 3469 3589 Sheet metalwork;
　　metal stampings; garbage disposers &
　　compactors, commercial
PA: Knight Manufacturing Co Inc
　　399 E 40th St
　　Shadyside OH 43947
　　740 676-9532

(G-17083)
NEW CUT TOOL AND MFG CORP
1 New Cut Rd (43947)
P.O. Box 8 (43947-0008)
PHONE..............................740 676-1666
Fax: 740 676-0949
Michael Koonce, *President*
Cynthia Badia, *Vice Pres*
EMP: 10
SQ FT: 2,700
SALES (est): 1.7MM **Privately Held**
SIC: 3599 Machine shop, jobbing & repair

Shaker Heights
Cuyahoga County

(G-17084)
**BAKER STORE EQUIPMENT
COMPANY**
23449 Laureldale Rd (44122-2106)
PHONE..............................216 475-5900
Fax: 216 581-2052
Donald Baker, *President*
EMP: 10 **EST:** 1956
SQ FT: 22,000
SALES (est): 920K **Privately Held**
SIC: 2541 Store fixtures, wood

(G-17085)
BRADLEY METAL FABRICATION
3451 Helen Rd (44122-3870)
PHONE..............................216 881-7400
Rosalyn Johnson, *Accountant*
EMP: 15 **EST:** 2011
SALES (est): 1.1MM **Privately Held**
SIC: 3339 Primary nonferrous metals

(G-17086)
CALCOL INC
23425 Bryden Rd (44122-4020)
P.O. Box 22103, Cleveland (44122-0103)
PHONE..............................216 245-6301
Norman Charles Kaplan, *Ch of Bd*
EMP: 21
SQ FT: 1,000
SALES (est): 2.3MM **Privately Held**
WEB: www.calcol.com
SIC: 2834 Pharmaceutical preparations

(G-17087)
CASENTRIC LLC
23700 Fairmount Blvd (44122-2204)
P.O. Box 21101, Cleveland (44121-0101)
PHONE..............................216 233-6300
Steven Washington, *Mng Member*
EMP: 4
SALES: 500K **Privately Held**
SIC: 7372 7379 7389 Business oriented
　　computer software; computer related con-
　　sulting services;

(G-17088)
**CELLULAR TECHNOLOGY
LIMITED**
Also Called: Ctl Analyzers
20521 Chagrin Blvd # 200 (44122-5350)
PHONE..............................216 791-5084
Fax: 216 791-8814
Barbara Staron, *Manager*
Magdelian Tary-Lehmann, *Security Dir*
Paul V Lehmann,
EMP: 40
SQ FT: 30,000
SALES (est): 5.5MM **Privately Held**
SIC: 8071 3821 Medical laboratories; clini-
　　cal laboratory instruments, except med-
　　ical & dental

(G-17089)
CTL ANALYZERS LLC (PA)
20521 Chagrin Blvd # 200 (44122-5350)
PHONE..............................216 791-5084
Paul V Lehmann PHD, *President*
George Csatary, *CFO*
Magdalana Terry-Lehmann, *Treasurer*
Barbara Staron, *Credit Staff*
EMP: 9
SALES: 5MM **Privately Held**
WEB: www.immunospot.com
SIC: 3845 Electromedical equipment

(G-17090)
**INSTITUTE MTHMTICAL
STATISTICS**
Also Called: IMS
3163 Somerset Dr (44122-3812)
P.O. Box 22718 (44122-0718)
PHONE..............................216 295-2340
Terry Steed, *President*
Shanti Gupta, *Editor*
Julia Norton, *Treasurer*
Elyse Gustasfon, *Director*
John Kolassa, *Bd of Directors*
EMP: 1
SQ FT: 500

SALES: 2MM **Privately Held**
WEB: www.imstat.org
SIC: 8699 2721 Flying club; periodicals

(G-17091)
LIGHTSTAB LTD CO
3103 Morley Rd (44122-2861)
PHONE..............................216 751-5800
Fax: 216 426-6400
Joseph R Degenfelder, *President*
Theodore Alfred,
Theodore M Alfred,
Pauline Degenfelder,
EMP: 3
SALES (est): 205.8K **Privately Held**
SIC: 2816 Inorganic pigments

(G-17092)
**MANUFACTURING FUTURES
INC (PA)**
2767 Inverness Rd (44122-2733)
PHONE..............................216 903-7993
David O'Halloran, *President*
EMP: 1
SALES: 5MM **Privately Held**
SIC: 3499 Fountains (except drinking),
　　metal

(G-17093)
PURUSHEALTH LLC
3558 Lee Rd (44120-5123)
P.O. Box 201727, Cleveland (44120-8112)
PHONE..............................800 601-0580
John Huff, *CEO*
EMP: 11 **EST:** 2011
SALES (est): 1.7MM **Privately Held**
SIC: 2099 Food preparations

(G-17094)
SHELBURNE CORP (PA)
20001 Shelburne Rd (44118-5013)
PHONE..............................216 321-9177
Edward S Young, *President*
Dave Young, *Vice Pres*
Stan Young, *Vice Pres*
EMP: 1
SALES (est): 86MM **Privately Held**
SIC: 3443 3823 3544 3769 Industrial
　　vessels, tanks & containers; heat ex-
　　changers: coolers (after, inter), con-
　　densers, etc.; temperature measurement
　　instruments, industrial; forms (molds), for
　　foundry & plastics working machinery;
　　bellows assemblies, missiles: metal

(G-17095)
SMS COMMUNICATIONS INC
Also Called: Moto Photo
20116 Chagrin Blvd (44122-4947)
PHONE..............................216 374-6686
Richard J Santich, *President*
EMP: 23
SQ FT: 2,700
SALES (est): 1.7MM **Privately Held**
SIC: 7221 7384 2759 Photographic stu-
　　dios, portrait; film developing & printing;
　　commercial printing

Shandon
Butler County

(G-17096)
CARTESSA CORPORATION
4825 Cncnnati Brkville Rd (45063-5000)
P.O. Box 190 (45063-0190)
PHONE..............................513 738-4477
Fax: 513 738-4482
Darryl Kristof, *President*
Kathleen Kristof, *Vice Pres*
Bruno Carlsson, *Research*
▼ **EMP:** 13
SQ FT: 5,000
SALES (est): 2.3MM **Privately Held**
WEB: www.cartessa.com
SIC: 3672 5065 Printed circuit boards;
　　electronic parts & equipment

(G-17097)
DIAMOND TRAILERS INC
Also Called: Diamond Heavy Haul
5045 Cncnnt Brookville Rd (45063)
P.O. Box 146 (45063-0146)
PHONE..............................513 738-4500

Fax: 513 738-4504
Tonya Engel, *President*
Steven J Engel, *President*
EMP: 28
SQ FT: 92,000
SALES (est): 5.6MM **Privately Held**
SIC: 3715 Truck trailers

(G-17098)
TRI STATE EQUIPMENT COMPANY
5009 Cncnnt Brookville Rd (45063)
P.O. Box 155 (45063-0155)
PHONE..................................513 738-7227
Kevin Hughes, *President*
David Hoppel, *Manager*
EMP: 6
SQ FT: 5,000
SALES (est): 960K **Privately Held**
SIC: 5084 7699 7359 3563 Industrial machinery & equipment; aircraft & heavy equipment repair services; equipment rental & leasing; spraying outfits: metals, paints & chemicals (compressor)

Sharon Center
Medina County

(G-17099)
AEROTORQUE CORPORATION
1441 Wolf Creek Trl (44274)
P.O. Box 305 (44274-0305)
PHONE..................................330 590-8105
David Heidenreich, *President*
Doug Herr, *General Mgr*
Karen Carson, *Manager*
Sharm Carris, *Admin Sec*
EMP: 6
SALES (est): 701.5K
SALES (corp-wide): 20.8MM **Privately Held**
SIC: 3566 Speed changers, drives & gears
PA: Ebo Group, Inc.
1441 Wolf Creek Trl
Sharon Center OH 44274
330 239-4933

(G-17100)
AMERICAN WELDQUIP INC
1375 Wolf Creek Trl (44274)
P.O. Box 397 (44274-0397)
PHONE..................................330 239-0317
Fax: 330 239-0031
Rex Carper, *President*
Don Aldridge, *Production*
Leslie Saffle, *Purch Mgr*
Rob Danbra, *Sales Mgr*
Ron Doll, *Sales Mgr*
EMP: 16
SQ FT: 10,500
SALES (est): 3.5MM **Privately Held**
WEB: www.weldquip.com
SIC: 3548 Welding apparatus

(G-17101)
ATLANTIC TOOL & DIE COMPANY
6965 Ridge Rd (44274)
P.O. Box 586 (44274-0586)
PHONE..................................330 239-3700
Dennis Motil, *Program Mgr*
Ruff Haid, *Manager*
EMP: 200
SALES (corp-wide): 147.6MM **Privately Held**
SIC: 3469 Metal stampings
PA: Atlantic Tool & Die Company Inc
19963 Progress Dr
Strongsville OH 44149
440 238-6931

(G-17102)
BEAUFORT RFD INC
1420 Wolfcreek Trl (44274)
P.O. Box 359 (44274-0359)
PHONE..................................330 239-4331
David Abbott, *President*
Doug Baxter, *Chairman*
Brian Stringer, *Vice Pres*
Dj Wilman, *Vice Pres*
Graham Robertson, *Technical Mgr*
▲ **EMP:** 17
SQ FT: 62,000

SALES: 39MM **Privately Held**
SIC: 3842 Life preservers, except cork & inflatable
HQ: Survitec Group (Usa), Inc.
1420 Wolfcreek Trl
Sharon Center OH 44274
330 239-4331

(G-17103)
CAREY COLOR INC
6835 Ridge Rd (44274)
P.O. Box 609 (44274-0609)
PHONE..................................330 239-1835
Fax: 330 239-6016
Gary Moravcik, *President*
Cheri Briggs, *Publisher*
Mark Kyner, *Vice Pres*
Russell Kotalac, *CFO*
Doug Kennedy, *Technology*
EMP: 60
SQ FT: 19,000
SALES: 8MM **Privately Held**
WEB: www.careyweb.com
SIC: 2796 Color separations for printing

(G-17104)
CELL-O-CORE CO
6935 Ridge Rd (44274)
P.O. Box 342 (44274-0342)
PHONE..................................330 239-4370
Fax: 330 239-4403
Lino Abram, *CEO*
David C Nelson, *CEO*
Craig Cook, *President*
Tom Allen, *Exec VP*
Barbara Siegel, *Manager*
▲ **EMP:** 50
SQ FT: 50,000
SALES (est): 9.7MM **Privately Held**
WEB: www.cellocore.com
SIC: 3089 Extruded finished plastic products

(G-17105)
EBO GROUP INC (PA)
Also Called: Pt Tech
1441 Wolf Creek Trl (44274)
P.O. Box 305 (44274-0305)
PHONE..................................330 239-4933
Fax: 330 239-2012
Keith Nichols, *CEO*
David Given, *Ch of Bd*
Ryan Yerkey, *COO*
Gregg Cullings, *Vice Pres*
Ralph Rogers, *Vice Pres*
EMP: 54
SQ FT: 12,200
SALES (est): 20.8MM **Privately Held**
WEB: www.pttech.com
SIC: 3568 3542 3714 3566 Clutches, except vehicular; brakes, metal forming; motor vehicle parts & accessories; speed changers, drives & gears

(G-17106)
FLAMBEAU INC
1468 Wolfe Creek Trl (44274)
PHONE..................................330 239-0202
Judy Cormican, *Credit Mgr*
Henry Boggs, *Branch Mgr*
EMP: 250
SALES (corp-wide): 342.8MM **Privately Held**
SIC: 3089 Plastic processing
HQ: Flambeau, Inc.
801 Lynn Ave
Baraboo WI 53913
800 352-6266

(G-17107)
M & G POLYMERS USA LLC
Also Called: Gruppo Mossi & Ghisolfi
6951 Ridge Rd (44274)
P.O. Box 590 (44274-0590)
PHONE..................................330 239-7400
Erica Finney, *Safety Dir*
Kent Stevens, *Production*
Gil Rogers, *Engineer*
Gianluca Ferrari, *Manager*
Stacy Mace, *Telecomm Mgr*
EMP: 20 **Privately Held**
SIC: 2819 Elements; inorganic acids, except nitric & phosphoric

HQ: M & G Polymers Usa, Llc
450 Gears Rd Ste 240
Houston TX 77067
281 873-5780

(G-17108)
PT TECH INC
1441 Wolf Creek Trl (44274)
P.O. Box 305 (44274-0305)
PHONE..................................330 239-4933
Keith Nichols, *President*
Nichole Leiser, *Publisher*
Gregg W Cullings, *Vice Pres*
Ralph Rogers, *Vice Pres*
EMP: 99
SQ FT: 45,000
SALES (est): 20.1MM
SALES (corp-wide): 20.8MM **Privately Held**
SIC: 3714 Clutches, motor vehicle
PA: Ebo Group, Inc.
1441 Wolf Creek Trl
Sharon Center OH 44274
330 239-4933

(G-17109)
SHARON MANUFACTURING INC
6867 Ridge Rd (44274)
P.O. Box 119 (44274-0119)
PHONE..................................330 239-1561
Fax: 330 239-1896
John Beres, *President*
Jeff Olson, *Plant Mgr*
Tom Klimchak, *Manager*
EMP: 20
SQ FT: 22,000
SALES (est): 4.5MM **Privately Held**
WEB: www.sharonmfg.net
SIC: 3443 3441 Metal parts; fabricated structural metal

(G-17110)
SHARON PRINTING CO INC
Also Called: Jeffrey Weaver
4983 Ridge Rd (44274)
P.O. Box 152 (44274-0152)
PHONE..................................330 239-1684
Fax: 330 239-2565
Jeffrey Weaver, *Owner*
Bobbi Klish, *Manager*
EMP: 4
SQ FT: 6,000
SALES (est): 482.4K **Privately Held**
SIC: 2752 2759 2791 Commercial printing, offset; thermography; typesetting

(G-17111)
SURVITEC GROUP (USA) INC (DH)
1420 Wolfcreek Trl (44274)
P.O. Box 359 (44274-0359)
PHONE..................................330 239-4331
David Abbott, *President*
Doug Baxter, *Chairman*
Brian Stringer, *Vice Pres*
Dj Wilman, *Vice Pres*
Gerald Chunat, *Treasurer*
▼ **EMP:** 20
SALES: 39MM **Privately Held**
SIC: 3069 Pontoons, rubber
HQ: Survitec Group Limited
Head Office, 1-5 Beaufort Road
Birkenhead CH41
238 030-2020

(G-17112)
TILT 15 INC
1440 Wolf Creek Trl (44274)
PHONE..................................330 239-4192
James Ankoviak, *President*
Neal Veon, *Technical Mgr*
Kc Corbett-Chaney, *CFO*
Michael Maske, *VP Sales*
Dan Sharpe, *VP Sales*
▲ **EMP:** 97
SALES: 14MM **Privately Held**
WEB: www.transmotionmedical.com
SIC: 3842 Surgical appliances & supplies
PA: Winco Mfg., Llc
5516 Sw 1st Ln
Ocala FL 34474

Sharonville
Hamilton County

(G-17113)
CHESTER WEST HOLDINGS INC
Also Called: West Chester Protective Gear
11500 Canal Rd (45241-1862)
PHONE..................................800 647-1900
Fax: 513 539-2827
Tim Fogarty, *CEO*
Mark J Jahnke, *President*
Ken Meyer, *President*
Robert W Fisher, *Corp Secy*
Jim Wilson, *Exec VP*
▲ **EMP:** 110
SQ FT: 200,000
SALES (est): 111.5MM **Privately Held**
SIC: 3842 2381 5136 5137 Clothing, fire resistant & protective; gloves, work: woven or knit, made from purchased materials; men's & boys' clothing; women's & children's clothing; safety equipment & supplies
PA: Wcm Holdings, Inc.
11500 Canal Rd
Cincinnati OH 45241
513 705-2100

(G-17114)
KUTOL PRODUCTS COMPANY INC
100 Partnership Way (45241-1571)
PHONE..................................513 527-5500
Fax: 513 527-5506
Joseph W Rhodenbaugh, *President*
Tom Rhodenbaugh, *Vice Pres*
Greg Nichols, *Plant Mgr*
Glenn Kolb, *Mfg Mgr*
Kelly Ihle, *Purch Mgr*
▲ **EMP:** 140 **EST:** 1912
SQ FT: 160,000
SALES (est): 48.7MM **Privately Held**
WEB: www.kutol.com
SIC: 2841 Soap & other detergents

(G-17115)
USUI INTERNATIONAL CORPORATION
88 Partnership Way (45241-1507)
PHONE..................................513 448-0410
Haruyasu Ito, *President*
EMP: 4
SALES (corp-wide): 628.4MM **Privately Held**
SIC: 3714 Connecting rods, motor vehicle engine
HQ: Usui International Corporation
44780 Helm St
Plymouth MI 48170
734 354-3626

Shawnee
Perry County

(G-17116)
NICOFIBERS INC
9702 Iron Point Rd Se (43782-9723)
PHONE..................................740 394-2491
Fax: 740 394-2496
Robert Ableidinger, *Principal*
EMP: 4
SALES (est): 266.4K **Privately Held**
SIC: 2655 2653 Fiber cans, drums & similar products; corrugated & solid fiber boxes

(G-17117)
SUPERIOR FIBERS INC
9702 Iron Point Rd Se (43782-9723)
P.O. Box 141 (43782-0141)
PHONE..................................740 394-2491
Bryan Amtower, *Plant Mgr*
Stephen E Magill, *Controller*
Robert Williams, *Director*
EMP: 434
SALES (corp-wide): 123.3MM **Privately Held**
SIC: 3089 Awnings, fiberglass & plastic combination

PA: Superior Fibers, Inc.
1333 Corporate Dr Ste 350
Irving TX 75038
972 600-9953

Sheffield Lake
Lorain County

(G-17118)
CLEARFLITE INC
5445 E Lake Rd (44054-1902)
PHONE..................................440 281-7368
Terri Zajac, *President*
EMP: 3
SQ FT: 2,500
SALES: 1MM **Privately Held**
SIC: 3564 Air purification equipment

Sheffield Village
Lorain County

(G-17119)
ADI MACHINING INC
Also Called: Advanced Design Industries
4686 French Creek Rd (44054-2716)
PHONE..................................440 277-4141
Fax: 440 277-4257
Leonard Jungbluth, *President*
Jerome R Winiasz, *Principal*
EMP: 12
SQ FT: 2,500
SALES (est): 137.7K **Privately Held**
SIC: 3599 Machine shop, jobbing & repair

(G-17120)
ADVANCED DESIGN INDUSTRIES INC
Also Called: ADI
4686 French Creek Rd (44054-2716)
PHONE..................................440 277-4141
Fax: 440 277-4257
Jerome Winiasz, *President*
R G Brooks Jr, *Principal*
Edward J Winiasz, *Principal*
Thomas Winiasz, *Corp Secy*
▲ EMP: 25
SQ FT: 27,000
SALES (est): 7.3MM **Privately Held**
SIC: 3599 3599 8711 Robots, assembly line: industrial & commercial; machine shop, jobbing & repair; designing: ship, boat, machine & product

(G-17121)
BENKO PRODUCTS INC
Also Called: Environmental Products Div
5350 Evergreen Pkwy (44054-2446)
PHONE..................................440 934-2180
Fax: 440 934-4052
John Benko, *President*
Robert Benko, *Vice Pres*
Laurie Benko, *Sales Mgr*
Eric Luckett, *Regl Sales Mgr*
Sheila Douglas, *Manager*
▼ EMP: 23
SQ FT: 30,000
SALES (est): 8.3MM **Privately Held**
WEB: www.benkoproducts.com
SIC: 3534 3567 3448 2542 Elevators & moving stairways; industrial furnaces & ovens; prefabricated metal buildings; partitions & fixtures, except wood

(G-17122)
HKM DRECT MKT CMMNICATIONS INC
Also Called: H K M Drect Mktg Cmmunica-
2931 Abbe Rd (44054-2424)
PHONE..................................440 934-3060
Fax: 440 934-3070
Joann Tomasheski, *Manager*
EMP: 20
SALES (corp-wide): 18MM **Privately Held**
WEB: www.hkmdirectmarket.com
SIC: 2759 Commercial printing

PA: Hkm Direct Market Communications, Inc.
5501 Cass Ave
Cleveland OH 44102
216 651-9500

(G-17123)
J D INDOOR COMFORT INC
Also Called: J D Indoor Comfort Duct Clg
4040 Colorado Ave (44054-2512)
PHONE..................................440 949-8758
Fax: 440 949-5426
James Sustersic, *President*
EMP: 15
SALES (est): 3.8MM **Privately Held**
WEB: www.jdindoorcomfort.com
SIC: 3585 1711 Air conditioning equipment, complete; plumbing, heating, air-conditioning contractors

(G-17124)
LAPAT SIGNS
4151 E River Rd (44054-2829)
PHONE..................................440 277-6291
Fax: 440 277-1441
Eugene Lapat, *Owner*
EMP: 3
SALES (est): 145.6K **Privately Held**
SIC: 3993 Signs & advertising specialties

(G-17125)
LECTROETCH CO
5342 Evergreen Pkwy (44054-2446)
PHONE..................................440 934-1249
Fax: 440 934-1293
David Badt, *President*
Sharon Irvin, *Manager*
Otis Mahaffey, *Shareholder*
◆ EMP: 14
SQ FT: 10,500
SALES: 1.1MM **Privately Held**
WEB: www.lectroetch.com
SIC: 3953 Figures (marking devices), metal; letters (marking devices), metal

(G-17126)
MAGNA SEATING AMERICA INC
Also Called: Techcraft Seating Systems
3637 Mallard Run (44054-2848)
PHONE..................................440 846-5680
Richard Banfield, *President*
James Butler, *Opers Mgr*
EMP: 60
SQ FT: 42,000
SALES (corp-wide): 36.4B **Privately Held**
SIC: 2531 Seats, automobile
HQ: Magna Seating Of America, Inc.
39600 Lewis Dr Ste 216
Novi MI 48377
248 553-8094

(G-17127)
METOKOTE CORPORATION
5477 Evergreen Pkwy (44054-2400)
PHONE..................................440 934-4686
Fax: 440 934-4686
Tom Elkins, *Plant Mgr*
John Carnes, *Opers-Prdtn-Mfg*
Vicki Verlato, *Human Res Dir*
Soung Vu, *Manager*
EMP: 90
SALES (corp-wide): 14.7B **Publicly Held**
WEB: www.metokote.com
SIC: 3479 3471 Coating of metals & formed products; plating & polishing
HQ: Metokote Corporation
1340 Neubrecht Rd
Lima OH 45801
419 996-7800

(G-17128)
OLDCASTLE APG MIDWEST INC
Also Called: Sheffield Oldcastle
5190 Oster Rd (44054-1566)
PHONE..................................440 949-1815
John Serdinak, *Sales Staff*
Marguerite Nank, *Office Mgr*
Jim Jergins, *Manager*
Scott Chaplin, *Manager*
Jan Norman, *Manager*
EMP: 100
SALES (corp-wide): 28.6B **Privately Held**
SIC: 3272 Concrete products

HQ: Oldcastle Apg Midwest, Inc.
901 E Troy Ave
Indianapolis IN 46203
317 786-0971

(G-17129)
ROBBINS FURNACE WORKS INC
3739 Colorado Ave (44054-2505)
PHONE..................................440 949-2292
Michael K Robbins, *President*
Jim Ford, *Project Mgr*
EMP: 11
SALES (est): 1.4MM **Privately Held**
SIC: 3567 Industrial furnaces & ovens

(G-17130)
SHEFFIELD METALS CLEVELAND LLC (PA)
Also Called: Sheffield Metals International
5467 Evergreen Pkwy (44054-2400)
PHONE..................................800 283-5262
Fax: 440 934-8506
Michael Blake, *President*
Bryan Yancy, *Project Mgr*
Jill Wilson, *Controller*
Kourtney Olter, *Sales Associate*
EMP: 10
SALES (est): 6.3MM **Privately Held**
SIC: 3353 Aluminum sheet, plate & foil

Shelby
Richland County

(G-17131)
AMTO ACQUISITION CORP
Also Called: American Tower
5085 State Route 39 W (44875-9061)
P.O. Box 29 (44875-0029)
PHONE..................................419 347-1185
Fax: 419 347-1654
Doug Schmidt, *President*
Dave Wagner, *Vice Pres*
Arwen Bover, *Office Mgr*
EMP: 11 EST: 1951
SALES (est): 2.4MM **Privately Held**
WEB: www.amertower.com
SIC: 3441 3448 Tower sections, radio & television transmission; docks: prefabricated metal

(G-17132)
ARCELORMITTAL TUBULAR
132 W Main St (44875-1475)
PHONE..................................419 347-2424
Edward Vore, *CEO*
Jim Baske, *Vice Pres*
Tim Hebauf, *Engineer*
Ray Humphrey, *Electrical Engi*
EMP: 631
SALES (est): 95.7MM **Privately Held**
SIC: 3317 3321 Steel pipe & tubes; gray & ductile iron foundries
HQ: Arcelormittal Holdings Llc
3210 Watling St
East Chicago IN 46312
219 399-1200

(G-17133)
ARCELORMITTAL USA LLC
132 W Main St (44875-1475)
PHONE..................................419 347-2424
Fax: 419 342-1437
Edward Vore, *President*
Randy Hiler, *Warehouse Mgr*
Darren Dossi, *Production*
Rhonda Gullett, *Purch Mgr*
Mark Ruffner, *Purch Mgr*
EMP: 81 **Privately Held**
SIC: 3317 Steel pipe & tubes
HQ: Arcelormittal Usa Llc
1 S Dearborn St Ste 1800
Chicago IL 60603
312 346-0300

(G-17134)
CARTON SERVICE INCORPORATED (PA)
101 First Quality Dr (44875)
PHONE..................................419 342-5010
Fax: 419 342-4804
Bob Lederer, *President*
David L Genger, *Principal*

George F Karch Jr, *Principal*
Robert W Lederer, *Principal*
R E Streeter, *Principal*
▲ EMP: 120 EST: 1926
SQ FT: 135,000
SALES (est): 63.7MM **Privately Held**
WEB: www.cartonservice.com
SIC: 2657 Folding paperboard boxes

(G-17135)
DYNAMIC MANUFACTURING
3351 State Route 39 (44875-9470)
PHONE..................................419 564-8738
Richard Young, *Owner*
EMP: 3
SQ FT: 18,000
SALES (est): 86.7K **Privately Held**
SIC: 3999 Manufacturing industries

(G-17136)
GB FABRICATION COMPANY
2510 Taylortown Rd (44875-8836)
PHONE..................................419 347-1835
Fax: 419 347-1851
Mark Brandon, *Purchasing*
Dave Groff, *Branch Mgr*
EMP: 30
SALES (corp-wide): 36.9MM **Privately Held**
WEB: www.voisard.com
SIC: 3469 3441 Metal stampings; fabricated structural metal
HQ: Gb Fabrication Company
60 Scott St
Shiloh OH 44878
419 896-3191

(G-17137)
LONDON COACH SHOP
2962 London East Rd (44875-9148)
PHONE..................................419 347-4803
Mark Weaver, *Owner*
EMP: 3
SALES (est): 259.5K **Privately Held**
SIC: 3799 Carriages, horse drawn

(G-17138)
MONARCH TRAILERS CO
3100 Plymuth Sprngmill Rd (44875-9516)
PHONE..................................419 747-2848
Carole M Walters, *President*
Monique Hypes, *Vice Pres*
EMP: 14
SQ FT: 12,000
SALES (est): 1.6MM **Privately Held**
SIC: 3715 Trailers or vans for transporting horses

(G-17139)
MTD PRODUCTS INC
Also Called: M T D Service Division
305 Mansfield Ave (44875-1884)
PHONE..................................419 342-6455
Fax: 419 342-3913
Neal Winslow, *Principal*
Karl Egner, *Maint Spvr*
Sherry Malone, *Opers Staff*
Jason Goth, *Financial Exec*
Bradford Gray, *Manager*
EMP: 250
SALES (corp-wide): 2.8B **Privately Held**
WEB: www.mtdproducts.com
SIC: 3524 Lawn & garden equipment
HQ: Mtd Products Inc
5965 Grafton Rd
Valley City OH 44280
330 225-2600

(G-17140)
PHILLIPS MFG AND TOWER CO (PA)
Also Called: Shelby Welded Tube Div
5578 State Route 61 N (44875-9564)
P.O. Box 125 (44875-0125)
PHONE..................................419 347-1720
Fax: 419 347-5231
Angela Phillip, *CEO*
Theresa Wallace, *CFO*
Ben Willman, *Sales Mgr*
EMP: 85
SQ FT: 90,000
SALES (est): 25.9MM **Privately Held**
WEB: www.shelbytube.com
SIC: 3312 3498 3317 7692 Tubes, steel & iron; fabricated pipe & fittings; steel pipe & tubes; welding repair

(G-17141)
PREMIER TANNING & NUTRITION
35 Mansfield Ave (44875-1322)
PHONE..............................419 342-6259
Jeff Tronewett, *Owner*
EMP: 6
SALES (est): 177.2K Privately Held
SIC: 7299 3111 5499 Tanning salon;
leather tanning & finishing; health & dietetic food stores

(G-17142)
SHELBY DAILY GLOBE INC
Also Called: Daily Globe
37 W Main St (44875-1238)
P.O. Box 647 (44875-0647)
PHONE..............................419 342-4276
Fax: 419 342-4246
Scott Gove, *President*
EMP: 35 EST: 1900
SQ FT: 6,000
SALES (est): 1.6MM Privately Held
SIC: 2711 Newspapers: publishing only,
not printed on site

(G-17143)
SHELBY PRINTING INC
325 S Martin Dr (44875-1761)
P.O. Box 72 (44875-0072)
PHONE..............................419 342-3171
Fax: 419 347-3114
Edward J Miller, *President*
Waye Gurney, *Vice Pres*
Darrell Porter, *Plant Mgr*
Lou Wildman, *Purchasing*
Raymond Lynch, *Treasurer*
EMP: 20
SQ FT: 8,000
SALES (est): 2MM Privately Held
SIC: 2752 Commercial printing, lithographic

(G-17144)
SUMITOMO RUBBER USA LLC
Also Called: Goodyear
31 Curtis Dr (44875-8400)
PHONE..............................419 347-1067
Fax: 419 347-2122
Mike Tracey, *Branch Mgr*
EMP: 45
SQ FT: 169,000
SALES (corp-wide): 6.8B Privately Held
WEB: www.gdtna.com
SIC: 3011 4225 5014 Automobile tires,
pneumatic; general warehousing; tires &
tubes
HQ: Sumitomo Rubber Usa, Llc
10 Sheridan Dr
Tonawanda NY 14150
716 879-8200

Sherrodsville
Carroll County

(G-17145)
ARIELS OAK INC
Also Called: Ariel's Oak
9486 Cutler Rd Ne (44675-9066)
P.O. Box 203 (44675-0203)
PHONE..............................330 343-7453
Fax: 330 364-8706
Jay A Van Natter, *President*
EMP: 25
SQ FT: 1,000
SALES (est): 2.1MM Privately Held
SIC: 2511 Wood household furniture

Sherwood
Defiance County

(G-17146)
KEITH GRIMM
100 W Pearl St (43556)
PHONE..............................419 899-2725
Keith Grimm, *Principal*
EMP: 3
SALES (est): 144.7K Privately Held
SIC: 2013 Sausages & other prepared
meats

(G-17147)
QUALITY MACHINING AND MFG INC
14168 State Route 18 (43556)
PHONE..............................419 899-2543
Dale Dreher, *President*
Amber C Yochum, *Admin Sec*
▲ EMP: 26
SQ FT: 25,000
SALES: 2MM Privately Held
SIC: 3492 Hose & tube fittings & assemblies, hydraulic/pneumatic

Shiloh
Richland County

(G-17148)
GB FABRICATION COMPANY (HQ)
60 Scott St (44878-8712)
PHONE..............................419 896-3191
EMP: 25
SALES (est): 17.5MM
SALES (corp-wide): 36.9MM Privately
Held
SIC: 3469 Metal stampings
PA: Gb Manufacturing Company
1120 E Main St
Delta OH 43515
419 822-5323

(G-17149)
HOOVER GROUP
411 Eby Rd (44878-8870)
PHONE..............................419 525-3159
Philip Hoover, *Partner*
Miriam Hoover, *Partner*
EMP: 4
SALES: 200K Privately Held
SIC: 2431 Interior & ornamental woodwork
& trim

(G-17150)
LAKESIDE CABINS LTD
7389 State Route 13 N (44878-8945)
PHONE..............................419 896-2299
Fax: 419 895-1997
Allis Zim, *Partner*
Ellis Zimmerman, *Principal*
Mary James, *Manager*
EMP: 7
SALES (est): 1MM Privately Held
SIC: 2522 Filing boxes, cabinets & cases:
except wood

(G-17151)
LEON NEWSWANGER
Also Called: Newswanger Machine
7828 Planktown North Rd (44878-8906)
PHONE..............................419 896-3336
Leon Newswanger, *Owner*
EMP: 12
SQ FT: 3,500
SALES (est): 522.5K Privately Held
SIC: 3599 1799 Machine shop, jobbing &
repair; welding on site

(G-17152)
PLYMOUTH LOCOMOTIVE SVC LLC
48 E Main St (44878-8898)
PHONE..............................419 896-2854
David A Shepherd, *Principal*
EMP: 3
SALES (est): 578.9K Privately Held
SIC: 3312 Wheels, locomotive & car: iron
& steel

(G-17153)
PLYMOUTH LOCOMOTIVE SVC LLC
8118 Shiloh Norwalk Rd (44878-9022)
PHONE..............................419 896-2854
Dennis Bailey,
David Shepherd,
EMP: 3
SALES (est): 386.5K Privately Held
WEB:
www.plymouthlocomotiveservice.com
SIC: 3743 Locomotives & parts

(G-17154)
PROLINE TRUSS
29 Free Rd (44878-8939)
PHONE..............................419 895-9980
Paul M Reiff, *Owner*
Anna Reiff, *Co-Owner*
EMP: 17
SALES (est): 1.6MM Privately Held
SIC: 2439 Trusses, wooden roof

(G-17155)
SHILOH CARRIAGE SHOP LLC
8465 Shiloh Norwalk Rd (44878-8985)
PHONE..............................419 896-3869
Earl Shark, *Partner*
Ebin Shark, *Partner*
EMP: 3 EST: 2001
SALES (est): 321.5K Privately Held
SIC: 3799 Carriages, horse drawn

Shreve
Wayne County

(G-17156)
GROWERS CHOICE LTD
5505 S Elyria Rd (44676-9567)
PHONE..............................330 262-8754
Charles R Wood, *Partner*
EMP: 6 EST: 2007
SALES (est): 641.8K Privately Held
SIC: 2499 Wood products

(G-17157)
HYPONEX CORPORATION
Also Called: Scotts- Hyponex
3875 S Elyria Rd (44676-9529)
PHONE..............................330 262-1300
Fax: 330 264-2450
Dennis Tafoya, *Branch Mgr*
EMP: 30
SALES (corp-wide): 2.8B Publicly Held
SIC: 2873 2875 Fertilizers: natural (organic), except compost; compost
HQ: Hyponex Corporation
14111 Scottslawn Rd
Marysville OH 43040
937 644-0011

(G-17158)
I CERCO INC (PA)
Also Called: Diamonite Plant
453 W Mcconkey St (44676-9769)
PHONE..............................330 567-2145
Fax: 330 567-2260
Byron Anderson, *President*
Jim Jaskowiak, *COO*
Joel Connor, *Engineer*
Richard Talbot, *Controller*
Susan English, *Finance Mgr*
▲ EMP: 157
SQ FT: 160,000
SALES (est): 58.1MM Privately Held
WEB: www.cercollc.com
SIC: 3567 Ceramic kilns & furnaces

(G-17159)
J & J PERFORMANCE INC
Also Called: J & J Performance Paintball
410 E Wood St (44676-9325)
PHONE..............................330 567-2455
Fax: 330 567-3376
Joseph West, *President*
Josh Gaumer, *Manager*
EMP: 12
SALES (est): 2.2MM Privately Held
SIC: 3499 7699 Nozzles, spray: aerosol,
paint or insecticide; gun services

(G-17160)
LENAS AMISH GRANOLA
11051 County Road 329 (44676-9417)
PHONE..............................330 600-1599
Lena Schlabach, *Principal*
EMP: 3
SALES (est): 180.1K Privately Held
SIC: 2052 Cookies & crackers

(G-17161)
MIDFLOW SERVICES LLC (PA)
10774 Township Road 506 (44676-9462)
PHONE..............................330 567-3108
Dustin Baker,
EMP: 7

SALES (est): 3.5MM Privately Held
SIC: 3533 Oil & gas field machinery

(G-17162)
RHBA ACQUISITIONS LLC
Also Called: Red Head Brass
643 Legion Dr (44676-9271)
P.O. Box 566 (44676-0566)
PHONE..............................330 567-2903
Fax: 330 567-2947
Ricardo Leon, *Plant Mgr*
Joe Carroll, *QC Dir*
Paul Runevitch, *CFO*
Rick Leon, *Human Res Dir*
Dave Hooper,
▲ EMP: 60
SQ FT: 80,000
SALES (est): 13.9MM Privately Held
WEB: www.rhbdist.net
SIC: 3569 Firefighting apparatus & related
equipment

(G-17163)
SHREVE PRINTING LLC
390 E Wood St (44676-9743)
P.O. Box 605 (44676-0605)
PHONE..............................330 567-2341
Fax: 330 567-3616
Maher Wahba,
EMP: 16
SQ FT: 10,000
SALES (est): 3.1MM Privately Held
WEB: www.gideonprinting.com
SIC: 2752 2759 Commercial printing, offset; letterpress printing

Sidney
Shelby County

(G-17164)
A & B MACHINE INC
2040 Commerce Dr (45365-9393)
P.O. Box 540 (45365-0540)
PHONE..............................937 492-8662
Fax: 937 492-1619
Marc Gilardi, *President*
Robert L Alexander, *President*
Jimmy Alexander, *Vice Pres*
Jeff Hoffman, *Purchasing*
Carol Leiss, *Manager*
EMP: 32
SQ FT: 22,500
SALES (est): 5.5MM Privately Held
WEB: www.aandbmachine.com
SIC: 3545 Precision tools, machinists'

(G-17165)
ADVANCED COMPOSITES INC (DH)
Also Called: Sidney Plant
1062 S 4th Ave (45365-8977)
PHONE..............................937 575-9800
Fax: 937 467-4367
Seiji Oshima, *President*
Yoichi Kawai, *President*
Robert Brown, *Principal*
Jared Lomax, *QC Mgr*
Marion Graham, *Personnel Exec*
▲ EMP: 220
SQ FT: 128,000
SALES (est): 70.8MM
SALES (corp-wide): 11.4B Privately Held
WEB: www.advcmp1.com
SIC: 3082 3087 Unsupported plastics profile shapes; custom compound purchased
resins
HQ: Mitsui Chemicals America, Inc.
800 Westchester Ave N607
Rye Brook NY 10573
914 253-0777

(G-17166)
ADVANCED METALS GROUP LLC
815 Oak Ave (45365-1339)
P.O. Box 609 (45365-0609)
PHONE..............................937 492-4134
Evans Beach, *General Mgr*
Bob Clements, *CFO*
EMP: 230 EST: 2015
SALES (est): 16.8MM Privately Held
SIC: 3365 3321 Aluminum foundries; cast
iron pipe & fittings

(G-17167)
AMERICAN TRIM LLC
1501 Michigan St Ste 1 (45365-3500)
PHONE......................................419 228-1145
Fax: 937 494-6265
Roger Naguit, *Vice Pres*
Timothy Hoelscher, *Opers Staff*
Cynthia Ryan, *Buyer*
Jerry Born, *Engineer*
Josh Brown, *Engineer*
EMP: 600
SALES (corp-wide): 460MM **Privately Held**
SIC: 3469 3465 Metal stampings; moldings or trim, automobile: stamped metal
HQ: American Trim, L.L.C.
1005 W Grand Ave
Lima OH 45801

(G-17168)
AMOS PRESS INC (PA)
Also Called: Coin World
911 S Vandemark Rd (45365-8974)
P.O. Box 4129 (45365-4129)
PHONE......................................937 498-2111
Fax: 937 498-0888
John O Amos, *Ch of Bd*
Bruce Boyd, *President*
William Gibbs, *Editor*
Robert Bryan, *Purch Dir*
Jane Volland, *CFO*
▲ EMP: 200
SQ FT: 90,000
SALES (est): 45.6MM **Privately Held**
SIC: 2721 2711 2796 7389 Periodicals: publishing only; newspapers, publishing & printing; platemaking services; appraisers, except real estate; miscellaneous publishing

(G-17169)
BAUMFOLDER CORPORATION
1660 Campbell Rd (45365-2480)
PHONE......................................937 492-1281
Fax: 937 492-7280
Ulrik Nygaard, *President*
Jason Muldoon, *President*
Sesha RAO, *Managing Dir*
Janice Benanzer, *Corp Secy*
Carl Fullenkamp, *Vice Pres*
▲ EMP: 100 EST: 1917
SQ FT: 125,000
SALES (est): 24.3MM
SALES (corp-wide): 2.8B **Privately Held**
WEB: www.baumfolder.com
SIC: 3554 3579 7389 Paper industries machinery; folding machines, paper; cutting machines, paper; binding machines, plastic & adhesive; packaging & labeling services
HQ: Heidelberg Americas Inc
1000 Gutenberg Dr Nw
Kennesaw GA 30144
770 419-6500

(G-17170)
CARGILL INCORPORATED
2400 Industrial Dr (45365-8952)
PHONE......................................937 498-4555
Fax: 937 498-9982
Keith Kuhlman, *Mfg Staff*
Terry Harris, *Purchasing*
Fred Silhan, *Engineer*
Shane Soloman, *Manager*
Cheryl Conidaris, *Manager*
EMP: 60
SALES (corp-wide): 107.1B **Privately Held**
WEB: www.cargill.com
SIC: 2075 2077 Soybean oil mills; animal & marine fats & oils
PA: Cargill, Incorporated
15407 Mcginty Rd W
Wayzata MN 55391
952 742-7575

(G-17171)
CARS AND PARTS MAGAZINE
911 S Vandemark Rd (45365-8974)
P.O. Box 4129 (45365-4129)
PHONE......................................937 498-0803
Bruce Boyd, *President*
EMP: 120

SALES (est): 4MM
SALES (corp-wide): 45.6MM **Privately Held**
WEB: www.carsandparts.com
SIC: 2721 5521 Magazines: publishing & printing; used car dealers
PA: Amos Press, Inc.
911 S Vandemark Rd
Sidney OH 45365
937 498-2111

(G-17172)
COMPRESSOR TECHNOLOGIES INC
Also Called: Numerics Unlimited North
211 E Russell Rd (45365-1762)
PHONE......................................937 492-3711
Fax: 937 492-4545
Wayne Adkins, *President*
Cody Adkins, *General Mgr*
Tony Young, *General Mgr*
Amanda Young, *Controller*
Jerry Barhorst, *CTO*
EMP: 49
SQ FT: 100,000
SALES (est): 7.3MM **Privately Held**
SIC: 3469 Machine parts, stamped or pressed metal

(G-17173)
CUSTOM POLISHING
559 Plum Ridge Trl (45365-1881)
PHONE......................................937 596-0430
John Kenton, *Owner*
EMP: 5 EST: 1970
SALES (est): 307.2K **Privately Held**
SIC: 3471 Polishing, metals or formed products

(G-17174)
DAMAR PRODUCTS INC (PA)
17222 State Route 47 E (45365-7242)
PHONE......................................937 492-9023
Don Alexander, *President*
Toinette Alexander, *Corp Secy*
EMP: 2
SALES: 1.6MM **Privately Held**
SIC: 2448 2441 Pallets, wood; boxes, wood; packing cases, wood: nailed or lock corner

(G-17175)
DAMAR PRODUCTS INC
516 Park St (45365-1346)
PHONE......................................937 492-9023
Fax: 937 492-3230
Don Alexander, *President*
Toinette Alexander, *Treasurer*
EMP: 12
SALES (corp-wide): 1.6MM **Privately Held**
SIC: 2448 2441 Pallets, wood; boxes, wood
PA: Damar Products Inc
17222 State Route 47 E
Sidney OH 45365
937 492-9023

(G-17176)
DERBY FABG SOLUTIONS LLC
570 Lester Ave (45365-7038)
PHONE......................................937 498-4054
Fax: 937 498-4065
Charles Couch, *QC Mgr*
Rose Houser, *Manager*
EMP: 20
SALES (corp-wide): 39.6MM **Privately Held**
WEB: www.derbyfab.com
SIC: 3296 2631 Fiberglass insulation; cardboard
HQ: Derby Fabricating Solutions, Llc
277 Industrial Dr
Cadiz KY 42211
270 522-1070

(G-17177)
DESIGN-N-WOOD LLC
3700 Michigan St (45365-7018)
PHONE......................................937 419-0479
Jason Fogt, *Owner*
Larry Fogt,
EMP: 3
SALES (est): 429.2K **Privately Held**
SIC: 2431 Millwork

(G-17178)
DETAILED MACHINING INC
2490 Ross St (45365-8834)
PHONE......................................937 492-1264
Fax: 937 492-1265
John Bertsch, *President*
Cindy Bertsch, *Manager*
EMP: 32
SQ FT: 42,000
SALES (est): 6.5MM **Privately Held**
WEB: www.detailedmachining.com
SIC: 3599 Machine shop, jobbing & repair

(G-17179)
DETROIT TECHNOLOGIES INC
1630 Ferguson Ct (45365-9398)
PHONE......................................937 492-2708
Danielle Boisbert, *Controller*
EMP: 30 **Privately Held**
WEB: www.formedfiber.com
SIC: 2396 3429 2221 Automotive trimmings, fabric; manufactured hardware (general); broadwoven fabric mills, manmade
PA: Detroit Technologies, Inc.
32500 Telg Rd Ste 207
Bingham Farms MI 48025

(G-17180)
DRT POWER SYSTEMS LLC - SIDNEY
1950 Campbell Rd (45365-2413)
PHONE......................................937 492-6121
Gary Van Gundy, *CEO*
EMP: 105
SQ FT: 115,000
SALES (est): 16.7MM **Privately Held**
SIC: 3728 Research & dev by manuf., aircraft parts & auxiliary equip

(G-17181)
DTI MOLDED PRODUCTS INC
Also Called: Conform Automotive
250 Stolle Ave (45365-8873)
PHONE......................................937 492-5008
Gary Stanis, *CFO*
EMP: 17 **Privately Held**
SIC: 3714 Motor vehicle parts & accessories
HQ: Dti Molded Products, Inc.
32500 Telg Rd Ste 207
Bingham Farms MI 48025
248 647-0400

(G-17182)
E & E MACHINE & TOOL INC
2423 Michigan St (45365-9081)
PHONE......................................937 492-3447
Fax: 937 492-2032
Debbie Egbert, *President*
Melvin Egbert, *Admin Sec*
EMP: 3
SALES (est): 270.2K **Privately Held**
SIC: 3599 Machine shop, jobbing & repair

(G-17183)
EDGEWELL PERSONAL CARE LLC
1810 Progress Way (45365-8961)
PHONE......................................937 492-1057
George Hoffman, *Plant Mgr*
Michael Metzger, *Controller*
Eric Simmons, *Branch Mgr*
Terry Ruppert, *Manager*
Tammy Stephens, *Technology*
EMP: 147
SALES (corp-wide): 2.4B **Publicly Held**
WEB: www.playtexproductsinc.com
SIC: 2844 Shaving preparations; lotions, shaving; suntan lotions & oils; hair preparations, including shampoos
HQ: Edgewell Personal Care, Llc
1350 Timberlake Mano
Chesterfield MO 63017
314 594-1900

(G-17184)
ELECTRO CONTROLS INC
1625 Ferguson Ct (45365-9398)
P.O. Box 539 (45365-0539)
PHONE......................................866 497-1717
Fax: 937 492-1351
Tim Geise, *President*
Scott Guggenbiller, *Production*
Jo E Mason, *QC Mgr*

EMP: 22
SALES (est): 4.8MM **Privately Held**
SIC: 3613 Control panels, electric

(G-17185)
ELITE ENCLOSURE COMPANY LLC
2349 Industrial Dr (45365-8100)
P.O. Box 916 (45365-0916)
PHONE......................................937 492-3548
Fax: 937 295-3582
Michael Trempe, *President*
Karen Trempe, *Corp Secy*
Sherry Pottorf, *Controller*
EMP: 35
SQ FT: 63,000
SALES (est): 6MM **Privately Held**
WEB: www.eliteenclosure.com
SIC: 3499 7389 Machine bases, metal; design, commercial & industrial
PA: Mk Trempe Corporation
2349 Industrial Dr
Sidney OH 45365
937 492-3548

(G-17186)
EMERSON CLIMATE TECH INC (DH)
1675 Campbell Rd (45365-2479)
P.O. Box 4309 (45365-4309)
PHONE......................................937 498-3011
Ed Purvis Jr, *President*
Ken Monnier, *President*
William Ragon, *President*
Mike Nipper, *Area Mgr*
Shane Angle, *Vice Pres*
◆ EMP: 1500 EST: 2006
SQ FT: 807,000
SALES (est): 1.4B
SALES (corp-wide): 14.5B **Publicly Held**
WEB: www.copeland-corp.com
SIC: 3585 Compressors for refrigeration & air conditioning equipment; condensers, refrigeration

(G-17187)
EMERSON CLIMATE TECH INC
Condensing Unit Division
756 Brooklyn Ave (45365-9401)
P.O. Box 669 (45365-0669)
PHONE......................................937 498-3011
Tom Croone, *Vice Pres*
David Kirk, *Vice Pres*
Robert E Baird, *Plant Mgr*
Lisa Schiller, *Purch Agent*
David Myszka, *Engineer*
EMP: 200
SALES (corp-wide): 14.5B **Publicly Held**
WEB: www.copeland-corp.com
SIC: 3585 Condensers, refrigeration
HQ: Emerson Climate Technologies, Inc.
1675 Campbell Rd
Sidney OH 45365
937 498-3011

(G-17188)
EMERSON CLIMATE TECH INC
Design Services Network
1351 N Vandemark Rd (45365-3501)
PHONE......................................937 498-3587
Fax: 937 493-2416
Thomas Crone, *General Mgr*
Jeff Langhals, *Engineer*
Cathy Billing, *Marketing Mgr*
Jeremy Monnin, *Program Mgr*
Keith Brown, *Manager*
EMP: 20
SALES (corp-wide): 14.5B **Publicly Held**
WEB: www.copeland-corp.com
SIC: 3585 Condensers, refrigeration; air conditioning units, complete: domestic or industrial
HQ: Emerson Climate Technologies, Inc.
1675 Campbell Rd
Sidney OH 45365
937 498-3011

(G-17189)
FABRICATION UNLIMITED LLC
4343 State Route 29 E (45365-8236)
P.O. Box 126 (45365-0126)
PHONE......................................937 492-3166
Fax: 937 492-3072
Charlene Nichols,
Darrell Nichols Sr,
EMP: 5

SQ FT: 4,300
SALES: 500K **Privately Held**
WEB: www.fabricationunlimited.com
SIC: 3444 7692 Sheet metalwork; welding
repair

(G-17190)
FRESHWAY FOODS INC (PA)
Also Called: Fresh and Limited
601 Stolle Ave (45365-8895)
PHONE..................................937 498-4664
Fax: 937 498-1529
Frank Gilardi Jr, *Ch of Bd*
Phil Gilardi, *President*
Craig Cotner, *Vice Pres*
Dan Stegall, *Transptn Dir*
Tim Redmon, *Mfg Staff*
EMP: 147
SQ FT: 90,000
SALES: 109MM **Privately Held**
SIC: 5148 2099 Vegetables, fresh; food
preparations

(G-17191)
H B PRODUCTS INC
Also Called: HB
1661 Saint Marys Rd (45365-9395)
P.O. Box 4098 (45365-4098)
PHONE..................................937 492-7031
Fax: 937 492-7023
Michael L Baker, *President*
Sheryl Bales, *Principal*
Jamie Ellis, *Vice Pres*
▲ EMP: 29
SQ FT: 53,000
SALES (est): 6.4MM **Privately Held**
WEB: www.hbproductsinc.com
SIC: 3441 3444 Fabricated structural
metal; sheet metalwork

(G-17192)
HEXA AMERICAS INC
1150 S Vandemark Rd (45365-3571)
PHONE..................................937 497-7900
Hideaki Tanaka, *President*
Takuro Miyamoto, *President*
Rachel McBride, *Manager*
John Marcum, *Admin Sec*
▲ EMP: 40
SALES (est): 9MM **Privately Held**
SIC: 2821 Protein plastics

(G-17193)
**HYDRO ALUMINUM
FAYETTEVILLE**
401 N Stolle Ave (45365-7806)
PHONE..................................937 492-9194
Fax: 937 492-6013
Eddie Smith, *Principal*
EMP: 6
SALES (est): 985.6K **Privately Held**
SIC: 3354 Aluminum extruded products

(G-17194)
IAC SIDNEY LLC
2000 Schlater Dr (45365-8904)
PHONE..................................937 492-1225
Robert S Miller, *President*
Brian K Pour, *COO*
Janis N Acosta, *Exec VP*
Dennis E Richardville, *Exec VP*
Robbie Bryan, *Senior VP*
EMP: 6
SALES (est): 1.4MM **Privately Held**
SIC: 3089 Automotive parts, plastic
HQ: International Automotive Components
Group North America, Inc.
28333 Telegraph Rd
Southfield MI 48034
248 455-7000

(G-17195)
INTERNATIONAL AUTOMOTIVE
2000 Schlater Dr (45365-8904)
PHONE..................................937 492-1225
Robert S Miller, *President*
EMP: 350 **Privately Held**
WEB: www.iaaawards.com
SIC: 2531 3714 2273 Seats, automobile;
motor vehicle parts & accessories; car-
pets & rugs
HQ: International Automotive Components
Group North America, Inc.
28333 Telegraph Rd
Southfield MI 48034
248 455-7000

(G-17196)
**IVEX PROTECTIVE PACKAGING
INC (HQ)**
456 Stolle Ave (45365-8846)
P.O. Box 4699 (45365-4699)
PHONE..................................937 498-9298
Paul Gaulin, *President*
Robert Hooper, *General Mgr*
Tom Trauscht, *Exec VP*
Leslie Hughes, *Manager*
▲ EMP: 25
SQ FT: 150,000
SALES (est): 14.3MM
SALES (corp-wide): 101.7MM **Privately
Held**
SIC: 3081 Polyethylene film
PA: Groupe Emballage Specialise S.E.C.
1805 50e Av
Lachine QC H8T 3
514 636-7951

(G-17197)
J AND L MANUFACTURING INC
9401 State Route 29 N (45365-8309)
PHONE..................................937 492-0008
Phil Robenalt, *President*
EMP: 3
SALES (est): 200K **Privately Held**
SIC: 3545 Machine tool accessories

(G-17198)
LANGSTON PALLETS
Also Called: L & H Wood Products
1650 Miami Conservancy Rd (45365-9525)
PHONE..................................937 492-8769
Fax: 937 492-5803
Craig Langston Sr, *Owner*
EMP: 4
SQ FT: 3,200
SALES (est): 170K **Privately Held**
SIC: 7699 2448 Pallet repair; pallets,
wood

(G-17199)
MASTIC HOME EXTERIORS INC
Ply Gem Siding Group
2405 Campbell Rd (45365-9529)
PHONE..................................937 497-7008
Fred Gross, *Engineer*
Jim Hall, *Finance Mgr*
Sandy Couch, *Personnel*
Bob Parker, *Branch Mgr*
Dan Mitman, *Manager*
EMP: 250
SALES (corp-wide): 1.9B **Publicly Held**
WEB: www.mastic.com
SIC: 3089 Plastic containers, except foam
HQ: Mastic Home Exteriors, Inc.
2600 Grand Blvd Ste 900
Kansas City MO 64108
816 426-8200

(G-17200)
**MECHANICAL GALV-PLATING
CORP**
933 Oak Ave (45365-1374)
P.O. Box 56 (45365-0056)
PHONE..................................937 492-3143
Fax: 937 492-6260
Tim Baker, *President*
John Garmhausen, *Corp Secy*
Susan A Baker, *Exec VP*
Rob Boller, *Vice Pres*
Russ Baker, *Controller*
▲ EMP: 45
SQ FT: 40,000
SALES (est): 5.6MM **Privately Held**
WEB: www.mechanicalgalv-plating.com
SIC: 3471 Plating of metals or formed
products

(G-17201)
METAL FINISHERS INC
2600 Fair Rd (45365-7532)
P.O. Box 963 (45365-0963)
PHONE..................................937 492-9175
Fax: 937 492-9176
Donald Stephens, *President*
Vicki Stephens, *Vice Pres*
Randall Foster, *Manager*
EMP: 16
SQ FT: 9,600
SALES (est): 1.5MM **Privately Held**
SIC: 3471 Finishing, metals or formed
products

(G-17202)
MIAMI RIVER STONE CO
1556 Miami River Rd (45365-8917)
PHONE..................................937 492-5412
Tom Milligan, *Manager*
EMP: 18
SALES (corp-wide): 3.5MM **Privately
Held**
SIC: 1422 Crushed & broken limestone
PA: Miami River Stone Co
1700 Miami River Rd
Sidney OH

(G-17203)
MIAMI VALLEY POLISHING LL
1317 Pinetree Ct (45365-3431)
PHONE..................................937 498-1634
EMP: 3
SALES (est): 148.1K **Privately Held**
SIC: 3471 Polishing, metals or formed
products

(G-17204)
**MK TREMPE CORPORATION
(PA)**
Also Called: Elite Enclosure Company
2349 Industrial Dr (45365-8100)
P.O. Box 916 (45365-0916)
PHONE..................................937 492-3548
Michael Trempe, *President*
Karen Trempe, *Corp Secy*
EMP: 32
SQ FT: 63,000
SALES (est): 6MM **Privately Held**
SIC: 3499 Aerosol valves, metal

(G-17205)
MONARCH LATHES LP
615 Oak Ave (45365-1335)
P.O. Box 4609 (45365-4609)
PHONE..................................937 492-4111
Harold Camp, *Partner*
Gary Need, *Sales Mgr*
Lisa Steinke, *Manager*
▲ EMP: 20
SQ FT: 40,000
SALES: 3.7MM **Privately Held**
SIC: 3541 Lathes, metal cutting & polishing

(G-17206)
NORCOLD INC (DH)
600 S Kuther Rd (45365-8840)
P.O. Box 180 (45365-0180)
PHONE..................................937 497-3080
Fax: 937 497-3085
Michael Harris, *CEO*
Michael Larime, *COO*
Dave Roberts, *Vice Pres*
Carmen Ismail, *Purchasing*
Keith Stickley, *Engineer*
◆ EMP: 280
SQ FT: 150,000
SALES (est): 102.8MM
SALES (corp-wide): 523.2MM **Privately
Held**
SIC: 3632 Refrigerators, mechanical & ab-
sorption: household
HQ: Thetford Corporation
7101 Jackson Rd
Ann Arbor MI 48103
734 769-6000

(G-17207)
PEERLESS FOODS INC
Also Called: Peerless Group, The
500 S Vandemark Rd (45365-8991)
P.O. Box 769 (45365-0769)
PHONE..................................937 492-4158
Fax: 937 492-3688
Robert L Zielsdorf, *CEO*
Dane A Belden, *President*
George Hoff, *Principal*
Robert F Zielsdorf, *Vice Pres*
William D Witten, *Opers Staff*
◆ EMP: 175
SQ FT: 130,000
SALES (est): 50.2MM
SALES (corp-wide): 13.6B **Publicly Held**
WEB: www.thepeerlessgroup.us
SIC: 3556 Bakery machinery; dough mix-
ing machinery
PA: Illinois Tool Works Inc.
155 Harlem Ave
Glenview IL 60025
847 724-7500

(G-17208)
PERFECTION BAKERIES INC
1900 Progress Way (45365-8961)
PHONE..................................937 492-2220
Fax: 937 497-7990
Kelly Henry, *Branch Mgr*
EMP: 57
SALES (corp-wide): 567MM **Privately
Held**
SIC: 2051 Biscuits, baked: baking powder
& raised
PA: Perfection Bakeries, Inc.
350 Pearl St
Fort Wayne IN 46802
260 424-8245

(G-17209)
**PLAYTEX MANUFACTURING
INC**
1905 Progress Way (45365-8114)
PHONE..................................937 498-4710
Lester McFarland, *Plant Mgr*
William Kinder, *Prdtn Mgr*
Pat Block, *QC Mgr*
Cindy Long, *Human Res Dir*
Daniel Synan, *Human Res Mgr*
EMP: 60
SALES (corp-wide): 2.3B **Publicly Held**
SIC: 2676 Sanitary paper products
HQ: Playtex Manufacturing, Inc.
50 N Dupont Hwy
Dover DE 19901
302 678-6000

(G-17210)
PLY GEM INDUSTRIES INC
2600 Campbell Rd (45365-8836)
PHONE..................................937 492-1111
Fax: 937 498-6088
Judith Caldwell, *Manager*
EMP: 250
SALES (corp-wide): 1.9B **Publicly Held**
SIC: 2431 Windows, wood
HQ: Ply Gem Industries, Inc.
5020 Weston Pkwy Ste 400
Cary NC 27513
919 677-3900

(G-17211)
POLYFILL LLC
960 N Vandemark Rd (45365-3508)
PHONE..................................937 493-0041
Andrew Meshew, *President*
Ralph Fearnley, *General Mgr*
Mike Clark, *Opers Staff*
Stacey Overton, *QC Mgr*
Rich Sczerowski, *Controller*
▲ EMP: 40
SQ FT: 50,000
SALES (est): 10.6MM **Privately Held**
SIC: 3089 Automotive parts, plastic

(G-17212)
PREFERRED PRINTING (PA)
3700 Michigan St (45365-7018)
PHONE..................................937 492-6961
Fax: 937 492-6942
Gil Bornhorst, *Owner*
EMP: 6
SQ FT: 2,800
SALES (est): 671.1K **Privately Held**
WEB: www.preferredprinting.net
SIC: 2752 Commercial printing, offset

(G-17213)
QUALITY STEEL FABRICATION
2339 Industrial Dr (45365-8100)
P.O. Box 905 (45365-0905)
PHONE..................................937 492-9503
Fax: 937 492-6089
Robert P Brunswick, *President*
Ted Daniel, *Vice Pres*
Gary Ellis, *Project Mgr*
EMP: 15
SQ FT: 25,000
SALES (est): 4.1MM **Privately Held**
SIC: 3441 3444 Fabricated structural
metal; sheet metalwork

(G-17214)
**REGAL TROPHY & AWARDS
COMPANY**
1269 Wapakoneta Ave (45365-1415)
PHONE..................................877 492-7531
Fax: 937 492-9328

GEOGRAPHIC

Jerry Wehrman, *President*
EMP: 4 **EST:** 1967
SQ FT: 3,400
SALES (est): 294.5K **Privately Held**
SIC: 3914 Trophies

(G-17215)
RELIABLE CASTINGS CORPORATION
1521 W Michigan Ave (45365)
P.O. Box 829 (45365-0829)
PHONE..............................937 497-5217
Fax: 937 492-1233
Shirley Branson, *Principal*
Bruce Inman, *Opers Mgr*
Tom Abney, *Opers-Prdtn-Mfg*
Mr Tom Beck, *Sales/Mktg Mgr*
David Allen, *Manager*
EMP: 90
SQ FT: 40,000
SALES (corp-wide): 38.7MM **Privately Held**
WEB: www.reliablecastings.com
SIC: 3363 3369 3365 Aluminum die-castings; nonferrous foundries; aluminum foundries
PA: Reliable Castings Corporation
3530 Spring Grove Ave
Cincinnati OH 45223
513 541-2627

(G-17216)
RING CONTAINER TECH LLC
603 Oak Ave (45365-1335)
PHONE..............................937 492-0961
Dennis W Koerner, *Vice Pres*
EMP: 40
SALES (corp-wide): 291.7MM **Privately Held**
SIC: 3085 Plastics bottles
PA: Ring Container Technologies, Llc.
1 Industrial Park
Oakland TN 38060
800 280-7464

(G-17217)
ROE TRANSPORTATION ENTPS INC
3680 W Michigan St (45365-9086)
PHONE..............................937 497-7161
Chad Roe, *Principal*
EMP: 7
SQ FT: 7,400
SALES (est): 334.5K **Privately Held**
SIC: 2875 2499 4212 4953 Potting soil, mixed; mulch or sawdust products, wood; dump truck haulage; recycling, waste materials

(G-17218)
ROSS ALUMINUM CASTINGS LLC
815 Oak Ave (45365-1317)
P.O. Box 609 (45365-0609)
PHONE..............................937 492-4134
Evan Beach, *CFO*
Robert Wyehl, *CFO*
Mike Francis, *Mng Member*
Ray Stager, *Info Tech Mgr*
Bob Clements,
▲ **EMP:** 165
SQ FT: 250,000
SALES (est): 44.2MM
SALES (corp-wide): 62.8MM **Privately Held**
WEB: www.rossal.com
SIC: 3365 3543 3369 Aluminum foundries; aluminum & aluminum-based alloy castings; machinery castings, aluminum; industrial patterns; nonferrous foundries
PA: Advanced Metals Group, L.L.C.
18 Mystic Ln
Malvern PA 19355
610 408-8006

(G-17219)
ROSS CASTING & INNOVATION LLC
Also Called: Rci
402 S Kuther Rd (45365)
P.O. Box 89 (45365-0089)
PHONE..............................937 497-4500
Fax: 937 492-3666
Sampath Ramesh, *President*

Brad Hohenstein, *Chief*
Wayne Thompson, *COO*
Robert Zangri, *CFO*
Jean Ward, *Controller*
▲ **EMP:** 350
SQ FT: 120,000
SALES: 26MM **Privately Held**
SIC: 3363 Aluminum die-castings
PA: A B I Showatech (India) Limited
Pulivalam Village & Post, Via Banavaram
Vellore TN

(G-17220)
ROTARY COMPRESSION TECH INC
Also Called: Leroi Gas Compressors
211 E Russell Rd (45365-1762)
PHONE..............................937 498-2555
Michael A Toal, *CEO*
Richard Wall, *President*
Scott Qualter, *Engineer*
Amanda Young, *Controller*
Ron Keen, *Technical Staff*
EMP: 25
SALES (est): 8.3MM **Privately Held**
SIC: 3563 Air & gas compressors

(G-17221)
SAPA EXTRUSIONS NORTH AMER LLC
401 N Stolle Ave (45365-7806)
PHONE..............................888 935-5759
Jane Johnson, *Purchasing*
Mary Hatfield, *Human Res Dir*
J D Rutt, *Human Res Mgr*
Brent Taylor, *Branch Mgr*
Jarvis Bodenmiller, *Manager*
EMP: 175
SALES (corp-wide): 6.3B **Privately Held**
WEB: www.hydroaluminumna.com
SIC: 3465 3479 Automotive stampings; painting of metal products
HQ: Sapa Extrusions North America, Llc
6250 N River Rd Ste 5000
Rosemont IL 60018
877 710-7272

(G-17222)
SCHWARZ PARTNERS PACKAGING LLC
Royal Group, The
2450 Campbell Rd (45365-7533)
PHONE..............................317 290-1140
Jim Freisthler, *Branch Mgr*
EMP: 15
SALES (corp-wide): 248.2MM **Privately Held**
WEB: www.harborpkg.com
SIC: 2653 3412 2671 Corrugated & solid fiber boxes; metal barrels, drums & pails; packaging paper & plastics film, coated & laminated
HQ: Schwarz Partners Packaging, Llc
3600 Woodview Trce # 300
Indianapolis IN 46268
317 290-1140

(G-17223)
SCSRM CONCRETE COMPANY LTD
4723 Hardin Wapakoneta Rd (45365-8056)
PHONE..............................937 533-1001
Gerald Bushelman, *Partner*
Frank Frantz,
Thomas Frantz,
EMP: 50 **EST:** 1996
SALES (est): 7.2MM **Privately Held**
SIC: 3273 Ready-mixed concrete

(G-17224)
SELMCO METAL FABRICATORS INC
1615 Ferguson Ct (45365-9398)
P.O. Box 4368 (45365-4368)
PHONE..............................937 498-1331
Fax: 937 498-9498
Tim Cotterman, *President*
Ron Jones, *Corp Secy*
Sera Cotterman, *Controller*
EMP: 18
SQ FT: 25,000
SALES (est): 3.3MM **Privately Held**
SIC: 3444 Sheet metalwork

(G-17225)
SHAFFER METAL FAB INC
2031 Commerce Dr (45365-9393)
P.O. Box 523 (45365-0523)
PHONE..............................937 492-1384
Michael R Shaffer, *Principal*
Steve McMullen, *Project Mgr*
Sheryl Scherer, *Controller*
Dan Shaffer, *VP Mktg*
EMP: 34
SQ FT: 45,000
SALES (est): 9.8MM **Privately Held**
WEB: www.shaffermetalfab.com
SIC: 3441 3444 Fabricated structural metal; sheet metalwork

(G-17226)
SIDNEY CAN & TOOL LLC
5670 Cecil Rd (45365-8075)
PHONE..............................937 492-0977
Fax: 937 492-8353
Rod Foster, *Principal*
EMP: 5
SALES (est): 343.3K **Privately Held**
SIC: 3411 Aluminum cans

(G-17227)
SIDNEY MANUFACTURING COMPANY
405 N Main Ave (45365-2345)
P.O. Box 380 (45365-0380)
PHONE..............................937 492-4154
Fax: 937 492-0919
Jon F Baker, *President*
Steven Baker, *Vice Pres*
Dan Simes, *Opers Mgr*
Tom Gross, *Engineer*
Carol Fetters, *Comptroller*
▼ **EMP:** 30
SQ FT: 125,000
SALES (est): 7.1MM **Privately Held**
WEB: www.sidneymfg.com
SIC: 3556 3444 Food products machinery; sheet metalwork

(G-17228)
SILVERADO TRUCKS & ACCESSORIES
720 Linden Ave (45365-1322)
PHONE..............................937 492-8862
Fax: 937 492-9406
Scott Dorsey, *Owner*
Eric Mueller, *Manager*
EMP: 3
SQ FT: 1,500
SALES: 150K **Privately Held**
SIC: 3713 5013 7532 4212 Truck bodies & parts; truck parts & accessories; customizing services, non-factory basis; dump truck haulage

(G-17229)
SPONSELLER GROUP INC
808 W Russell Rd Ste A (45365-9063)
PHONE..............................937 492-9949
Fax: 937 492-0049
Ken Hensworth, *Manager*
EMP: 6
SALES (corp-wide): 8.7MM **Privately Held**
SIC: 8711 3599 Consulting engineer; machine shop, jobbing & repair
PA: Sponseller Group, Inc.
1600 Timber Wolf Dr
Holland OH 43528
419 861-3000

(G-17230)
STOLLE MACHINERY COMPANY LLC
Also Called: Stolle Machinery-Sidney
2900 Campbell Rd (45365-8864)
PHONE..............................937 497-5400
Fax: 937 498-6258
Erica Paul, *Purchasing*
Greg Butcher, *Manager*
Chris McAlpine, *Manager*
Cary Monroe, *Manager*
Bill Schaaf, *Manager*
EMP: 125

SALES (corp-wide): 256.7MM **Privately Held**
WEB: www.stollemachinery.com
SIC: 3469 2759 3542 Stamping metal for the trade; commercial printing; machine tools, metal forming type
PA: Stolle Machinery Company, Llc
6949 S Potomac St
Centennial CO 80112
303 708-9044

(G-17231)
T & L WELDING LLC
211 E Russell Rd (45365-1762)
PHONE..............................937 498-9170
Lisa Whitt, *Mng Member*
EMP: 3
SALES (est): 120K **Privately Held**
SIC: 7692 Welding repair

(G-17232)
VMI LIQUIDATING INC
2309 Industrial Dr (45365-8100)
PHONE..............................937 492-3100
Fax: 800 528-3392
David Clarkson, *President*
Rick Amos, *Managing Prtnr*
John O Amos, *Chairman*
Kerry Fincik, *VP Admin*
Kari Fincik, *Vice Pres*
▲ **EMP:** 40
SQ FT: 35,000
SALES (est): 5.4MM
SALES (corp-wide): 45.6MM **Privately Held**
WEB: www.donorrecognition.com
SIC: 3993 Name plates: except engraved, etched, etc.: metal
PA: Amos Press, Inc.
911 S Vandemark Rd
Sidney OH 45365
937 498-2111

(G-17233)
WAPPOO WOOD PRODUCTS INC
Also Called: Interntnal Pckg Pallets Crates
12877 Kirkwood Rd (45365-8102)
PHONE..............................937 492-1166
Fax: 937 492-3441
Thomas G Baker, *Ch of Bd*
T Adam Baker, *President*
Gary O'Connor, *Principal*
Matthew Baker, *Office Mgr*
Timm Flinn, *Director*
EMP: 40
SQ FT: 21,800
SALES (est): 19.1MM **Privately Held**
WEB: www.wappoowood.com
SIC: 5031 2435 2436 2421 Lumber: rough, dressed & finished; hardwood veneer & plywood; softwood veneer & plywood; sawmills & planing mills, general; hardwood dimension & flooring mills

(G-17234)
WATER TREATMENT DEPT
880 E Court St (45365-2816)
PHONE..............................937 498-8180
Larry Broughton, *Superintendent*
EMP: 8
SALES (est): 565.6K **Privately Held**
SIC: 3589 Water treatment equipment, industrial

(G-17235)
WESTERN OHIO CUT STONE LTD
1130 Dingman Slagle Rd (45365-9102)
P.O. Box 419 (45365-0419)
PHONE..............................937 492-4722
Tony Strunk, *Sales Staff*
Thomas Milligan, *Mng Member*
EMP: 20
SALES: 1.9MM **Privately Held**
SIC: 3281 Cut stone & stone products

(G-17236)
WIPE OUT ENTERPRISES
6523 Dawson Rd (45365-8672)
PHONE..............................937 497-9473
Dave Waesch, *Owner*
EMP: 7
SALES (est): 842.8K **Privately Held**
WEB: www.wipeoutenterprises.com
SIC: 3599 Machine shop, jobbing & repair

GEOGRAPHIC

Silver Lake
Summit County

(G-17237)
C & C MACHINE CO
3031 S Oak Hill Rd (44224-3819)
PHONE...............................330 633-4485
Fax: 330 633-4692
Steven Cobb, *President*
Loretta Billman, *Bookkeeper*
EMP: 3 EST: 1958
SQ FT: 7,000
SALES (est): 290K Privately Held
SIC: 3599 Machine shop, jobbing & repair

Smithville
Wayne County

(G-17238)
BOVILLE INDUS COATINGS INC
7459 Leichty Rd (44677-9708)
P.O. Box 487 (44677-0487)
PHONE...............................330 669-8558
Fax: 330 669-8560
Larry Boville Sr, *President*
Larry Boville Jr, *Vice Pres*
EMP: 25
SQ FT: 30,000
SALES: 3MM Privately Held
WEB: www.boville.com
SIC: 3471 3479 Sand blasting of metal
parts; coating of metals & formed prod-
ucts; coating of metals with plastic or
resins; enameling, including porcelain, of
metal products; painting of metal products

(G-17239)
FLYING DUTCHMAN INC
6631 Egypt Rd (44677-9774)
PHONE...............................740 694-1734
Fax: 330 669-2892
James Lepley, *CEO*
Gary Lepley, *President*
Kevin Lepley, *Vice Pres*
John Waltman, *Admin Sec*
EMP: 7 EST: 1970
SQ FT: 3,600
SALES (est): 1MM Privately Held
WEB: www.flyingd.com
SIC: 3523 Silo fillers & unloaders

(G-17240)
**IFCO SYSTEMS NORTH
AMERICA INC**
179 S Gilbert Dr (44677)
PHONE...............................330 669-2726
EMP: 85 Privately Held
SIC: 2448 Mfg Wooden Pallets And Skids
HQ: Ifco Systems North America, Inc.
13100 Nw Fwy Ste 625
Houston TX 77040

(G-17241)
**MAVERICK CORP PARTNERS
LLC (PA)**
301 W Prospect St (44677-9516)
PHONE...............................330 669-2631
Regan Radzinski, *Principal*
EMP: 5
SALES (est): 6.4MM Privately Held
SIC: 3556 Food products machinery

(G-17242)
RIGGENBACH KITCHENS
790 E Main St (44677-9558)
P.O. Box 227 (44677-0227)
PHONE...............................330 669-2113
Glen Riggenbach, *Owner*
EMP: 3
SALES: 500K Privately Held
SIC: 2434 Wood kitchen cabinets

(G-17243)
**RIVERVIEW INDUS WD PDTS
INC**
179 S Gilbert Dr (44677)
PHONE...............................330 669-8509
Michael D Meenan, *President*

EMP: 10
SALES (est): 159K Privately Held
SIC: 2448 Cargo containers, wood; pallets,
wood; skids, wood

(G-17244)
S K S MANUFACTURING CORP
212 E Eberly St (44677)
P.O. Box 318 (44677-0318)
PHONE...............................330 669-9133
Fax: 330 669-9210
Allen Namen, *President*
EMP: 4
SQ FT: 8,000
SALES (est): 397.3K Privately Held
SIC: 3599 Machine shop, jobbing & repair

(G-17245)
SAIRCORP LTD
6020 N Honeytown Rd (44677-9563)
PHONE...............................330 669-9099
Larry Stanford, *CEO*
EMP: 3
SALES (est): 331.2K Privately Held
WEB: www.saircorp.com
SIC: 3812 Aircraft control instruments

(G-17246)
TYLER GRAIN & FERTILIZER CO
3388 Eby Rd (44677-9785)
PHONE...............................330 669-2341
Fax: 330 669-3933
Walter F Tyler Jr, *President*
Nick Franks, *General Mgr*
Paul Stevens, *General Mgr*
William A Tyler, *Vice Pres*
Bill Tyler, *Purch Mgr*
EMP: 10 EST: 1860
SQ FT: 18,000
SALES: 7.9MM Privately Held
SIC: 2875 5191 8748 Fertilizers, mixing
only; chemicals, agricultural; feed; seeds:
field, garden & flower; agricultural consult-
ant

Solon
Cuyahoga County

(G-17247)
ABL SCREEN PRINTING
30300 Solon Indus Pkwy (44139-4378)
P.O. Box 429, Brunswick (44212-0429)
PHONE...............................440 914-0093
Fax: 440 914-0083
Kenneth Alexiac, *President*
Lou De Marco, *Principal*
EMP: 5
SALES (est): 476.8K Privately Held
SIC: 2759 Screen printing

(G-17248)
ACLARA TECHNOLOGIES LLC
30400 Solon Rd (44139-3416)
PHONE...............................440 528-7200
Tyson Turner, *Project Mgr*
Rich Goetter, *Purch Agent*
John Bennington, *Engineer*
Justin Hennigan, *Engineer*
Derrick Aleksin, *Design Engr*
EMP: 120
SALES (corp-wide): 465MM Privately
Held
SIC: 3824 3825 3829 7371 Mechanical &
electromechanical counters & devices; in-
struments to measure electricity; measur-
ing & controlling devices; custom
computer programming services; com-
puter integrated systems design
HQ: Aclara Technologies Llc
945 Hornet Dr
Hazelwood MO 63042
314 895-6400

(G-17249)
**ADVANCED LIGHTING TECH INC
(HQ)**
7905 Cochran Rd Ste 300 (44139-5471)
PHONE...............................440 519-0500
Fax: 440 836-7030
Wayne R Hellman, *CEO*
Lalu Chandran, *General Mgr*
Sabu Krishnan, *COO*
Wayne Vespoli, *Exec VP*

Lee A Bartolomei, *Vice Pres*
▲ EMP: 82
SQ FT: 55,000
SALES (est): 209.5MM Privately Held
SIC: 3641 3645 3646 3648 Electric
lamps & parts for generalized applications; residential lighting fixtures; commercial indusl & institutional electric
lighting fixtures; lighting equipment
PA: Saratoga Lighting Holdings Llc
535 Madison Ave Fl 4
New York NY 10022
212 906-7800

(G-17250)
AIDA EMBROIDERY & PRINTING
33800 Sherbrook Park Dr (44139-2033)
PHONE...............................440 498-8981
Simon Shteyngarts, *Partner*
Aida Shteyngarts, *Partner*
EMP: 3
SALES (est): 200K Privately Held
WEB: www.aidae.com
SIC: 2395 Embroidery & art needlework

(G-17251)
ALL PREM CLEANERS INC
Also Called: All Premium Cleaners
33640 Aurora Rd (44139-3708)
PHONE...............................440 349-3649
Kishore Nandbigam, *President*
Prima Mandarn, *Vice Pres*
EMP: 5
SALES (est): 550K Privately Held
SIC: 2842 Drycleaning preparations

(G-17252)
ALL PRINT LTD
38415 Flanders Dr (44139-4669)
PHONE...............................440 349-6868
Warren Goldenberg, *Principal*
Daniel M Chessin, *Mng Member*
Deborah Chessin,
EMP: 10 EST: 1997
SQ FT: 10,000
SALES (est): 1MM Privately Held
SIC: 2752 Commercial printing, litho-
graphic

(G-17253)
ALLEN GRAPHICS INC
Also Called: Printing Partners
27100 Richmond Rd Ste 6 (44139-1030)
PHONE...............................440 349-4100
Fax: 440 498-0966
Donald J Allen, *President*
EMP: 9
SQ FT: 5,000
SALES (est): 1.4MM Privately Held
WEB: www.allen-graphics.com
SIC: 2752 2789 Commercial printing, off-
set; bookbinding & related work

(G-17254)
**ALLOY WELDING &
FABRICATING**
30340 Solon Indtl Pky B (44139-4358)
PHONE...............................440 914-0650
William Kelly, *President*
EMP: 10
SQ FT: 12,000
SALES (est): 1.8MM Privately Held
SIC: 3535 Belt conveyor systems, general
industrial use

(G-17255)
**ALLTECH MED SYSTEMS AMER
INC**
28900 Fountain Pkwy (44139-4383)
PHONE...............................440 424-2240
Mark Zou, *President*
William Joliat, *Vice Pres*
Don Russell, *Treasurer*
Sandra Ritchie, *Finance Dir*
John Duraj, *Manager*
▼ EMP: 39
SALES (est): 9.3MM Privately Held
SIC: 3845 Magnetic resonance imaging
device, nuclear

(G-17256)
AMALTECH INC
30670 Bainbridge Rd (44139-2267)
PHONE...............................440 248-7500
Farouk Altahawi, *President*
EMP: 8

SALES (est): 906.2K Privately Held
SIC: 3494 Valves & pipe fittings; pipe fittings

(G-17257)
**AMERICAN JRNL OF
DRMTPATHOLOGY**
6554 Dorset Ln (44139-6710)
PHONE...............................440 542-0041
Garry Marquiss, *Principal*
EMP: 3
SALES (est): 157.3K Privately Held
SIC: 2711 Newspapers, publishing & print-
ing

(G-17258)
**AMERICAN RUBBER PRODUCTS
CO**
30775 Solon Indus Pkwy (44139-4338)
PHONE...............................440 461-0900
Doug Kaufman, *President*
EMP: 8
SALES (est): 570K Privately Held
SIC: 3069 Molded rubber products

(G-17259)
AMRESCO LLC
6681 Cochran Rd (44139-3903)
P.O. Box 39098 (44139-0098)
PHONE...............................440 349-2805
Fax: 440 349-1182
Josephine Soukup, *Branch Mgr*
EMP: 100
SALES (corp-wide): 4.5B Publicly Held
WEB: www.amresco-inc.com
SIC: 2833 Medicinal chemicals
HQ: Amresco, Llc
28600 Fountain Pkwy
Solon OH 44139
440 349-1199

(G-17260)
ANITA PLASTICS INC
38790 Glenlivet Ct (44139-5915)
PHONE...............................216 831-5773
Chhagan Bapna, *CEO*
Chuck Bapna, *President*
Varun Bapna, *Controller*
Diwan Bapna, *Director*
▲ EMP: 3 EST: 1990
SQ FT: 300
SALES (est): 326.3K Privately Held
SIC: 2211 2221 Bags & bagging, cotton;
polyester broadwoven fabrics

(G-17261)
ARROWHEAD INDUSTRIES
33891 Canterbury Rd (44139-5618)
PHONE...............................440 349-2846
Alan Johnson, *Principal*
EMP: 3
SALES (est): 190.6K Privately Held
SIC: 3999 Manufacturing industries

(G-17262)
**ASPHALT FABRICS &
SPECIALTIES**
7710 Bond St (44139-5352)
PHONE...............................440 786-1077
Brian Reed, *President*
EMP: 7
SALES (est): 1.2MM Privately Held
SIC: 2951 Asphalt paving mixtures &
blocks

(G-17263)
B D G WRAP-TITE INC
6200 Cochran Rd (44139-3308)
PHONE...............................440 349-5400
Suresh Bafna, *CEO*
Sunil Daga, *President*
Nikhil Bafna, *Business Mgr*
Chirag Patel, *Office Mgr*
Rebecca Tousey, *Manager*
◆ EMP: 80
SQ FT: 89,000
SALES (est): 10MM Privately Held
WEB: www.jainco.com
SIC: 3069 5199 Film, rubber; leather
goods, except footwear, gloves, luggage,
belting

(G-17264)
BARDONS & OLIVER INC (PA)
5800 Harper Rd (44139-1833)
PHONE..................................440 498-5800
Fax: 440 498-5800
William Beattie, *President*
Heath Oliver, *President*
Peter Barrett, *Principal*
Jim Daffinee, *Principal*
Brett Baldi, *Vice Pres*
▲ EMP: 120
SQ FT: 94,000
SALES (est): 26.7MM **Privately Held**
WEB: www.bardonsoliver.com
SIC: 3549 3541 3547 3599 Metalworking machinery; lathes, metal cutting & polishing; finishing equipment, rolling mill; machine & other job shop work

(G-17265)
BARUDAN AMERICA INC (HQ)
30901 Carter St Frnt A (44139-4384)
PHONE..................................440 248-8770
Fax: 440 248-8770
Ted Yamaue, *Ch of Bd*
Shin Hasegawa, *President*
David Davidson, *Vice Pres*
Richard Snyder, *Vice Pres*
Robert Stone, *Vice Pres*
▲ EMP: 12
SQ FT: 34,970
SALES: 33.4MM **Privately Held**
SIC: 3552 Embroidery machines
PA: Barudan Co.,Ltd.
　906, Josuiji
　Ichinomiya AIC
　586 766-161

(G-17266)
BCS METAL PREP LLC
31000 Solon Rd (44139-3467)
PHONE..................................440 663-1100
Tom McCormic, *Controller*
Janet Hamso,
▲ EMP: 50 EST: 2001
SALES (est): 9.3MM **Privately Held**
SIC: 3316 Cold finishing of steel shapes
PA: Bluff City Steel, Llc
　1175 Harbor Ave
　Memphis TN 38113

(G-17267)
BESTEN EQUIPMENT INC
6680 Parkland Blvd (44139-4344)
PHONE..................................216 581-1166
Lynn Bisantz, *Principal*
Donald Fink, *Engineer*
EMP: 30
SALES (est): 3.8MM
SALES (corp-wide): 928.1MM **Publicly Held**
WEB: www.quanex.com
SIC: 2891 Sealants
PA: Quanex Building Products Corporation
　1800 West Loop S Ste 1500
　Houston TX 77027
　713 961-4600

(G-17268)
BIRD ELECTRONIC CORPORATION
30303 Aurora Rd (44139-2743)
PHONE..................................440 248-1200
Fax: 440 248-1200
Mark Johnson, *CEO*
Michael Fetto, *Vice Pres*
Thomas L Kuklo, *Vice Pres*
Dean Downing, *Prdtn Mgr*
Scott Martin, *Materials Mgr*
▲ EMP: 235
SQ FT: 80,000
SALES (est): 68.4MM **Privately Held**
WEB: www.bird-electronic.com
SIC: 3825 Test equipment for electronic & electric measurement
PA: Bird Technologies Group Inc.
　30303 Aurora Rd
　Solon OH 44139

(G-17269)
BIRD TECHNOLOGIES GROUP INC (PA)
30303 Aurora Rd (44139-2743)
PHONE..................................440 248-1200
Mark I Johnson, *President*

Edward J Bartos Jr, *Vice Pres*
Terrence C Grant, *Vice Pres*
Thomas L Kuklo, *Vice Pres*
Dean Downing, *Prdtn Mgr*
EMP: 8
SQ FT: 12,000
SALES (est): 94.9MM **Privately Held**
WEB: www.bird-technologies.com
SIC: 3825 3669 Test equipment for electronic & electric measurement; intercommunication systems, electric

(G-17270)
BOCK COMPANY LLC
Also Called: Bock Lighting
30901 Carter St Ste B (44139-3519)
PHONE..................................216 912-7050
Dana Zakrajsek, *Financial Exec*
Gretta Albert, *Sales Mgr*
Ezra Spero, *Mktg Dir*
▲ EMP: 6
SALES (est): 1.4MM **Privately Held**
SIC: 3646 Commercial indusl & institutional electric lighting fixtures

(G-17271)
BOWES MANUFACTURING INC
Also Called: Tungsten and Capital
30340 Solon Industrial (44139-4343)
PHONE..................................216 378-2110
Fax: 216 378-1594
Zelda Stutz, *President*
David Bornstein, *COO*
Dave Lysiak, *Sales Mgr*
Martin Ribar, *Manager*
EMP: 19
SQ FT: 30,000
SALES (est): 4MM **Privately Held**
WEB: www.bowesmfg.com
SIC: 3568 3452 3494 3429 Couplings, shaft: rigid, flexible, universal joint, etc.; bolts, metal; valves & pipe fittings; clamps & couplings, hose

(G-17272)
BPI ENERGY HOLDINGS INC
30775 Bnbridge Rd Ste 280 (44139)
PHONE..................................281 556-6200
Fax: 440 248-4240
James G Azlein, *President*
EMP: 3
SALES (est): 360K **Privately Held**
SIC: 1311 Crude petroleum & natural gas

(G-17273)
BRADLEY STONE INDUSTRIES LLC
30801 Carter St (44139-3517)
PHONE..................................440 519-3277
Fax: 440 735-0447
Bradley Disandis,
EMP: 18
SALES (est): 6.2MM **Privately Held**
SIC: 1423 Crushed & broken granite

(G-17274)
BREAKER TECHNOLOGY INC
30625 Solon Ind Pkwy (44139-4389)
PHONE..................................440 248-7168
Chris Wood, *COO*
Lauri Briner, *Marketing Staff*
EMP: 23
SALES (corp-wide): 2.9MM **Privately Held**
SIC: 3532 5084 1629 Mining machinery; hydraulic systems equipment & supplies; trenching contractor
PA: Breaker Technology, Inc.
　3453 Durahart St
　Riverside CA 92507
　951 369-0878

(G-17275)
CAD AUDIO LLC
6573 Cochran Rd Ste I (44139-3972)
PHONE..................................440 349-4900
Fax: 440 248-4902
Glenn Roop, *President*
Robert Cale, *Warehouse Mgr*
Tony Okeefe, *VP Sls/Mktg*
Bob Habel, *Sales Mgr*
John Vorndran, *Sales Mgr*
▲ EMP: 15
SALES (est): 3.2MM **Privately Held**
SIC: 3651 Microphones

(G-17276)
CARLISLE BRAKE & FRICTION INC
Also Called: Carbon Group, The
29001 Solon Rd (44139-3468)
PHONE..................................440 528-4000
Karl Messmer, *President*
EMP: 14
SALES (corp-wide): 3.6B **Publicly Held**
SIC: 3714 Motor vehicle brake systems & parts
HQ: Carlisle Brake & Friction, Inc.
　6180 Cochran Rd
　Solon OH 44139
　440 528-4000

(G-17277)
CARLISLE BRAKE & FRICTION INC (HQ)
Also Called: Cbf
6180 Cochran Rd (44139-3306)
PHONE..................................440 528-4000
Fax: 440 528-4098
Karl T Messmer, *President*
Thomas Gilbert, *VP Admin*
Matthew Jereb, *Plant Mgr*
Wes Pedersen, *QC Mgr*
Matt Murray, *Draft/Design*
▲ EMP: 239
SALES (est): 357.8MM
SALES (corp-wide): 3.6B **Publicly Held**
SIC: 3751 Brakes, friction clutch & other: bicycle
PA: Carlisle Companies Incorporated
　16430 N Scottsdale Rd # 400
　Scottsdale AZ 85254
　704 501-1100

(G-17278)
CLOPAY CORPORATION
7905 Cochran Rd Ste 500 (44139-5469)
PHONE..................................440 542-9215
Matt Laudon, *Branch Mgr*
EMP: 5
SALES (corp-wide): 1.9B **Publicly Held**
SIC: 3081 Unsupported plastics film & sheet
HQ: Clopay Corporation
　8585 Duke Blvd
　Mason OH 45040
　800 282-2260

(G-17279)
CO- AX TECHNOLOGY INC
30301 Emerald Valley Pkwy (44139-4394)
PHONE..................................440 914-9200
Fax: 440 914-9102
Gholam Hosein Varghai, *President*
Melany Verbiar, *General Mgr*
Hassan Varghai, *Vice Pres*
Randy Rager, *Senior Buyer*
Drazenka Turkalj, *Buyer*
EMP: 250
SQ FT: 22,000
SALES: 30MM **Privately Held**
WEB: www.coaxinc.com
SIC: 3672 3679 Printed circuit boards; harness assemblies for electronic use: wire or cable

(G-17280)
CUSTOM PRODUCTS CORPORATION (PA)
7100 Cochran Rd (44139-4306)
PHONE..................................440 528-7100
Fax: 440 528-0140
William J Stepanek, *President*
Timothy J Stepanek, *Exec VP*
John Stepanek, *Vice Pres*
William Stepanek Jr, *Vice Pres*
Ashley Cross, *Buyer*
▲ EMP: 78 EST: 1974
SQ FT: 82,000
SALES (est): 48MM **Privately Held**
WEB: www.customproducts.net
SIC: 5112 5131 5199 2761 Business forms; labels; packaging materials; manifold business forms; commercial printing; packaging paper & plastics film, coated & laminated

(G-17281)
D D D HAMS INC
34234 Aurora Rd (44139)
PHONE..................................440 487-9572

EMP: 3 EST: 2010
SALES (est): 183K **Privately Held**
SIC: 2013 Prepared pork products from purchased pork

(G-17282)
DANDI ENTERPRISES INC
Also Called: Dunkin' Donuts
6353 Som Center Rd (44139-2914)
PHONE..................................419 516-9070
Fax: 440 248-3551
Lonnie Weiser, *President*
EMP: 15
SALES (est): 628.5K **Privately Held**
SIC: 5461 2051 Doughnuts; doughnuts, except frozen

(G-17283)
DYNAFLOOR SYSTEMS INC
Also Called: Dyna Floor
35079 Quartermane Cir (44139-2467)
PHONE..................................330 467-6005
Fax: 330 467-4838
Jerry Torrelli, *President*
EMP: 18
SQ FT: 10,000
SALES (est): 2.1MM **Privately Held**
WEB: www.dynafloor.com
SIC: 1752 2851 Floor laying & floor work; epoxy coatings

(G-17284)
EDWARDS VACUUM LLC
7905 Cochran Rd Ste 100 (44139-5470)
PHONE..................................440 248-4453
EMP: 7
SALES (corp-wide): 11.7B **Privately Held**
SIC: 3635 Household vacuum cleaners
HQ: Edwards Vacuum Llc
　6416 Inducon Dr W
　Sanborn NY 14132
　800 848-9800

(G-17285)
EMERSON ELECTRIC CO
31100 Bainbridge Rd (44139-2229)
PHONE..................................440 248-9400
Jerry Morelli, *Sales Associate*
Michael Erickson, *Manager*
EMP: 23
SALES (corp-wide): 14.5B **Publicly Held**
WEB: www.gotoemerson.com
SIC: 3823 Industrial instrmnts msrmnt display/control process variable
PA: Emerson Electric Co.
　8000 West Florissant Ave
　Saint Louis MO 63136
　314 553-2000

(G-17286)
ENERGY FOCUS INC (PA)
32000 Aurora Rd Ste B (44139-2849)
PHONE..................................440 715-1300
Fax: 440 519-1038
Ronald D Black, *Ch of Bd*
Ted Tewksbury, *President*
Simon Cheng, *Vice Pres*
Eric Hilliard, *Vice Pres*
Tom McAuliffe, *Vice Pres*
EMP: 122
SQ FT: 75,000
SALES: 31MM **Publicly Held**
WEB: www.fiberstars.com
SIC: 3641 3648 3674 Lamps, fluorescent, electric; lamps, incandescent filament, electric; lighting equipment; light emitting diodes

(G-17287)
ERICO INC
34600 Solon Rd (44139-2631)
PHONE..................................440 248-0100
George H Vincent, *President*
Brian Hersko, *Vice Pres*
Emmy Birli, *Project Mgr*
George Nahra, *Engineer*
S Sankar, *Engineer*
◆ EMP: 27
SALES (est): 70.3MM **Privately Held**
SIC: 3644 Noncurrent-carrying wiring services

▲ = Import ▼=Export
◆ =Import/Export

(G-17288)
ERICO INTERNATIONAL CORP (HQ)
31700 Solon Rd (44139-3532)
PHONE...................................440 349-2630
Fax: 440 349-2996
Beth Wozniak, *Principal*
Alok Maskara, *President*
Peter B Korte, *Vice Pres*
Dan Lister, *Vice Pres*
Bryson Allen, *Project Mgr*
▲ EMP: 658 EST: 1903
SALES (est): 396.4MM **Privately Held**
WEB: www.erico.com
SIC: 3441 Fabricated structural metal

(G-17289)
ERICO INTERNATIONAL CORP
34600 Solon Rd (44139-2631)
PHONE...................................440 248-0100
Karen Nelson, *Marketing Mgr*
Steve Rohacz, *Branch Mgr*
EMP: 400 **Privately Held**
WEB: www.erico.com
SIC: 3441 3965 Fabricated structural
   metal; fasteners
HQ: Erico International Corporation
   31700 Solon Rd
   Solon OH 44139
   440 349-2630

(G-17290)
ETCHED METAL COMPANY
30200 Solon Indus Pkwy (44139-4311)
PHONE...................................440 248-0240
Fax: 440 248-0240
Scott Nameth, *Principal*
Mike McDivitt, *Principal*
Mark Hromi, *Engineer*
Tammy Strong, *Accountant*
Don Hunt, *Manager*
▲ EMP: 45 EST: 1928
SQ FT: 27,500
SALES (est): 5.1MM **Privately Held**
WEB: www.etched-metal.com
SIC: 3479 3613 3596 3993 Name plates:
   engraved, etched, etc.; control panels,
   electric; scales & balances, except labo-
   ratory; signs & advertising specialties;
   plating & polishing; commercial printing,
   lithographic

(G-17291)
FHI HEAT INC (PA)
31875 Solon Rd Ste 6 (44139-3565)
PHONE...................................216 456-0353
David Kim, *President*
Joseph Kim, *COO*
Michael Lee, *Vice Pres*
Michael Paull, *CFO*
Olga Garcia, *Human Resources*
▲ EMP: 5
SQ FT: 15,000
SALES (est): 2.2MM **Privately Held**
WEB: www.fhiheat.com
SIC: 3634 Hair curlers, electric

(G-17292)
FINDAWAY WORLD LLC
31999 Aurora Rd (44139-2853)
PHONE...................................440 893-0808
Mitch Kroll, *CEO*
Howard Alston, *Sales Mgr*
Andrew Goldstein, *Manager*
Jon Sustar, *Manager*
▲ EMP: 100
SALES (est): 15.4MM **Privately Held**
WEB: www.playawaydigital.com
SIC: 5999 8331 3669 5192 Audio-visual
   equipment & supplies; job training & vo-
   cational rehabilitation services; visual
   communication systems; periodicals

(G-17293)
FIRE FROM ICE VENTURES LLC
30333 Emerald Valley Pkwy (44139-4394)
PHONE...................................419 944-6705
Brain Tomazic, *Sales Mgr*
Timothy Winings,
Lynne Winings,
▲ EMP: 11
SQ FT: 13,500

SALES (est): 1.4MM
SALES (corp-wide): 8.6MM **Privately Held**
WEB: www.airserco.com
SIC: 3585 Refrigeration & heating equip-
   ment
PA: The Providence Group Inc
   9290 Metcalf Rd
   Willoughby OH
   440 247-4340

(G-17294)
FOLIO PHOTONICS LLC
6864 Cochran Rd (44139-4336)
PHONE...................................440 420-4500
Maria Anzola, *Controller*
Kenneth Singer,
EMP: 6 EST: 2012
SQ FT: 9,500
SALES (est): 146.4K **Privately Held**
SIC: 3695 Optical disks & tape, blank

(G-17295)
GEARING SOLUTIONS INC
5905 Harper Rd Ste A (44139-1865)
P.O. Box 391703 (44139-8703)
PHONE...................................440 498-9538
Fax: 440 498-9527
Merritt A Osborn, *President*
William Doyle, *Vice Pres*
Bob Morrow, *Purch Mgr*
Jim Hasman, *Engineer*
Arnold Popovitz, *Manager*
EMP: 4
SQ FT: 3,000
SALES (est): 120K **Privately Held**
SIC: 3566 8711 Speed changers, drives &
   gears; designing: ship, boat, machine &
   product

(G-17296)
GENESIS PLASTIC TECH LLC
27200 Tinkers Ct (44139-4387)
PHONE...................................440 542-0722
Jim Mayor, *Vice Pres*
Mark Urbin, *Human Resources*
Mark Urban, *Office Mgr*
Geoffrey C Hanahan,
EMP: 80
SALES (est): 16.1MM **Privately Held**
WEB: www.genesisplastic.com
SIC: 3089 Injection molding of plastics

(G-17297)
GLAVIN INDUSTRIES INC
Also Called: Glavin Specialty Co
6835 Cochran Rd Ste A (44139-3927)
P.O. Box 391316 (44139-8316)
PHONE...................................440 349-0049
Fax: 440 786-7446
Julia S Glavin, *CEO*
David H Glavin, *President*
Jody Kapsandy, *General Mgr*
EMP: 25
SQ FT: 23,000
SALES (est): 14.2MM **Privately Held**
SIC: 5084 3993 2759 Industrial machin-
   ery & equipment; signs & advertising spe-
   cialties; screen printing

(G-17298)
GLENDALE MACHINE INC
30625 Solon Industrial # 1 (44139-4390)
PHONE...................................440 248-8646
Fax: 440 248-1407
Joseph Paterniti Jr, *President*
EMP: 5 EST: 1948
SQ FT: 5,500
SALES: 400K **Privately Held**
SIC: 3544 3599 Jigs & fixtures; machine &
   other job shop work

(G-17299)
GLT FABRICATORS INC (PA)
6810 Cochran Rd (44139-3908)
PHONE...................................440 914-1122
Timothy Scott, *CEO*
EMP: 6
SALES (est): 3.5MM **Privately Held**
SIC: 3644 Insulators & insulation materials,
   electrical

(G-17300)
GRANEX INDUSTRIES INC (PA)
32400 Aurora Rd Ste 4 (44139-2800)
P.O. Box 391720 (44139-8720)
PHONE...................................440 248-4915
M Corey Obrien, *President*
G Scott Obrien, *Vice Pres*
Jeff Poprik, *Manager*
▲ EMP: 12
SALES (est): 2.1MM **Privately Held**
SIC: 3281 Curbing, granite or stone

(G-17301)
GRAPHIC PACKAGING INTL INC
Also Called: Altivity Packaging
6385 Cochran Rd (44139-3961)
PHONE...................................440 248-4370
Rich Davidson, *Safety Mgr*
Barbara Marshall, *Human Res Dir*
Mary Turk, *Branch Mgr*
EMP: 190 **Publicly Held**
SIC: 2631 2657 Folding boxboard; folding
   paperboard boxes
HQ: Graphic Packaging International, Inc.
   1500 Riveredge Pkwy # 100
   Atlanta GA 30328
   770 240-7200

(G-17302)
GRAPHICSOURCE INC
30405 Solon Rd Ste 12 (44139-3477)
PHONE...................................440 248-9200
David Scott Eichbaum, *President*
EMP: 3 EST: 1978
SQ FT: 600
SALES (est): 495K **Privately Held**
WEB: www.graphicsource.net
SIC: 2752 7336 Commercial printing, off-
   set; art design services

(G-17303)
GRAPHITE EQUIPMENT MFG CO
5577 Valley Ln (44139-1501)
PHONE...................................216 271-9500
Fax: 216 271-5566
Thomas O Mulica, *President*
Dale T Lehman, *Vice Pres*
▲ EMP: 5
SQ FT: 9,000
SALES (est): 738.8K **Privately Held**
SIC: 3561 Industrial pumps & parts

(G-17304)
GREAT LAKES TEXTILES INC (PA)
Also Called: Glt Products
6810 Cochran Rd (44139-3908)
PHONE...................................440 439-1300
Steven Wake, *President*
Joel Hammer, *Vice Pres*
Marinko Milos, *CFO*
Phil Davis, *Credit Staff*
Patti Burke, *Human Res Dir*
◆ EMP: 47
SQ FT: 117,000
SALES (est): 16.6MM **Privately Held**
WEB: www.gltproducts.com
SIC: 2821 5033 5131 5085 Polyvinyli-
   dene chloride resins; insulation materials;
   tape, textile; industrial supplies

(G-17305)
GREENES FENCE CO INC
5250 Naiman Pkwy Ste B (44139-1031)
P.O. Box 22258, Cleveland (44122-0258)
PHONE...................................216 464-3160
Fax: 216 464-3160
Larry Greenes, *President*
▲ EMP: 5
SALES (est): 1MM **Privately Held**
SIC: 2499 Fencing, wood

(G-17306)
HARDWARE EXCHANGE INC
6573 Cochran Rd Ste F (44139-3972)
PHONE...................................440 449-8006
Mark Borlin, *President*
EMP: 5
SQ FT: 7,400
SALES (est): 932.3K **Privately Held**
SIC: 3571 Electronic computers

(G-17307)
HDT EP INC
30500 Aurora Rd Ste 100 (44139-2776)
PHONE...................................216 438-6111
Sean Bond, *President*
William Calhoon, *Vice Pres*
Ed Brashear, *Prdtn Mgr*
Barry Sullivan, *CFO*
Terry Havrilla, *Sales Mgr*
EMP: 200
SQ FT: 20,000
SALES (est): 40.8K
SALES (corp-wide): 229.4MM **Privately Held**
WEB: www.nordicair.net
SIC: 3585 3564 3433 Air conditioning
   units, complete: domestic or industrial; fil-
   ters, air; furnaces; air conditioning equip-
   ment, etc.; heating equipment, except
   electric
PA: Hunter Defense Technologies, Inc.
   30500 Aurora Rd Ste 100
   Solon OH 44139
   216 438-6111

(G-17308)
HDT EXPEDITIONARY SYSTEMS INC
30500 Aurora Rd Ste 100 (44139-2776)
PHONE...................................216 438-6111
James Maurer, *President*
Mary Geiger, *Principal*
Ryan Benton, *Info Tech Mgr*
Rita Thomas, *Admin Sec*
EMP: 7
SALES (corp-wide): 229.4MM **Privately Held**
SIC: 3714 3569 Heaters, motor vehicle; fil-
   ters
HQ: Hdt Expeditionary Systems, Inc.
   30500 Aurora Rd Ste 100
   Solon OH 44139
   216 438-6111

(G-17309)
HDT EXPEDITIONARY SYSTEMS INC (HQ)
30500 Aurora Rd Ste 100 (44139-2776)
PHONE...................................216 438-6111
Sean Bond, *President*
Michelle Gawlik, *General Mgr*
Catherine Roy, *Research*
Barry Sullivan, *CFO*
Mary Geiger, *Controller*
▲ EMP: 132
SQ FT: 172,000
SALES (est): 53.3MM
SALES (corp-wide): 229.4MM **Privately Held**
WEB: www.base-x.com
SIC: 2393 2394 Canvas bags; canvas &
   related products; tents: made from pur-
   chased materials
PA: Hunter Defense Technologies, Inc.
   30500 Aurora Rd Ste 100
   Solon OH 44139
   216 438-6111

(G-17310)
HONEYWELL INTERNATIONAL INC
5935 Stephanie Ln (44139-1969)
PHONE...................................440 349-7330
EMP: 694
SALES (corp-wide): 39.3B **Publicly Held**
SIC: 3724 Aircraft engines & engine parts
PA: Honeywell International Inc.
   115 Tabor Rd
   Morris Plains NJ 07950
   973 455-2000

(G-17311)
HORIZON GLOBAL AMERICAS INC
29000 Aurora Rd Ste 2 (44139-7202)
PHONE...................................440 498-0001
EMP: 85
SALES (corp-wide): 649.2MM **Publicly Held**
SIC: 5531 3714 Automotive accessories;
   motor vehicle parts & accessories
HQ: Horizon Global Americas Inc.
   47912 Halyard Dr Ste 100
   Plymouth MI 48170
   800 632-3290

(G-17312)
HUNTER DEFENSE TECH INC (PA)
Also Called: Hdt Engineered Technologies
30500 Aurora Rd Ste 100 (44139-2776)
PHONE 216 438-6111
Sean Bond, *President*
Carl Pates, *President*
Mike Stolarz, *President*
Dilucente Anthony, *Exec VP*
Greg Miller, *Senior VP*
▼ EMP: 50
SQ FT: 26,000
SALES (est): 229.4MM **Privately Held**
SIC: 3433 3569 3822 8331 Room & wall heaters, including radiators; filters; auto controls regulating residntl & coml environmt & applncs; sheltered workshop; engineering services; assembly machines, including robotic

(G-17313)
IMPACTION CO
6100 Cochran Rd (44139-3306)
PHONE 440 349-5652
Joseph Sarakaitis, *Principal*
EMP: 5
SALES (est): 472.2K **Privately Held**
SIC: 3494 Valves & pipe fittings

(G-17314)
INDUSTRIAL METAL FINISHING
7680 Bond St (44139-5351)
PHONE 440 232-2400
Fax: 440 232-2400
Doug Whitaker, *President*
Glenn Billington, *Corp Secy*
Michael Distaulo, *Vice Pres*
Dennis J Whitaker, *Vice Pres*
EMP: 8
SQ FT: 3,800
SALES (est): 612.9K **Privately Held**
SIC: 3479 Painting, coating & hot dipping

(G-17315)
INFO-GRAPHICS INC
5960 Liberty Rd (44139-2539)
PHONE 440 498-1640
Susan Haines, *President*
Andrea Smith, *Manager*
EMP: 5
SQ FT: 1,500
SALES (est): 597.6K **Privately Held**
SIC: 5943 2752 Office forms & supplies; commercial printing, lithographic

(G-17316)
INNOCOMP
33195 Wagon Wheel Dr (44139-2368)
PHONE 440 248-5104
Jeri Lynn Hoffman, *Partner*
Robert Cecil, *Partner*
Craig Gruber, *Partner*
EMP: 7
SQ FT: 3,500
SALES (est): 590K **Privately Held**
WEB: www.innocomp.com
SIC: 3679 Voice controls

(G-17317)
INNOVATIVE RECYCLING SYSTEMS
31655 Arthur Rd (44139-4551)
PHONE 440 498-9200
Fax: 440 248-7644
Paul D Popovich, *President*
Barb Popovich, *Corp Secy*
EMP: 3
SALES (est): 340K **Privately Held**
SIC: 3559 Recycling machinery

(G-17318)
INTELLIGENT MOBILE SUPPORT INC
31320 Solon Rd Ste 17 (44139-3572)
PHONE 440 600-7343
John Steidley, *CEO*
Gina Sankey, *Project Mgr*
Francis Paez, *VP Sales*
June Getzinger, *Director*
EMP: 13
SALES (est): 970.9K **Privately Held**
SIC: 7372 Prepackaged software

(G-17319)
J & J SNACK FOODS CORP
5351 Naiman Pkwy Ste B (44139-1014)
PHONE 440 248-2084
Timothy Dorsey, *Manager*
EMP: 4
SALES (corp-wide): 992.7MM **Publicly Held**
WEB: www.jjsnack.com
SIC: 5145 2052 Snack foods; pretzels
PA: J & J Snack Foods Corp.
6000 Central Hwy
Pennsauken NJ 08109
856 665-9533

(G-17320)
JAYMAC SYSTEMS INC
34300 Sherbrook Park Dr (44139-2042)
PHONE 440 498-0810
Fred Koneval, *Principal*
Florian Koneval, *Vice Pres*
Sue Koneval, *Treasurer*
EMP: 4
SQ FT: 16,500
SALES: 750K **Privately Held**
SIC: 2752 Business forms, lithographed

(G-17321)
JEFFERSON SMURFIT CORPORATION
6385 Cochran Rd (44139-3961)
PHONE 440 248-4370
Fax: 440 248-6037
Lisa Porter, *General Mgr*
EMP: 10 EST: 2010
SALES (est): 1.4MM **Privately Held**
SIC: 2657 Folding paperboard boxes

(G-17322)
JERPBAK-BAYLESS CO
34150 Solon Rd (44139-2623)
P.O. Box 39157 (44139-0157)
PHONE 440 248-5387
Fax: 440 248-1070
J Scott Jerpbak, *President*
Gary Uterhark, *General Mgr*
Jean Hentemann, *Finance Other*
Thomas Erickson, *Director*
Bonnie Jerpbak, *Director*
EMP: 30 EST: 1944
SQ FT: 40,000
SALES (est): 6.3MM **Privately Held**
WEB: www.jerpbakbayless.com
SIC: 3599 Machine shop, jobbing & repair

(G-17323)
JOY MINING MACHINERY
Also Called: Bedford Gear
6160 Cochran Rd (44139-3306)
PHONE 440 248-7970
Fax: 440 248-7975
Ed Doheny, *President*
Edward L Doheny II, *President*
Mike Thomas, *Plant Mgr*
Jo Valahov, *Controller*
Jim Lucas, *Maintence Staff*
▲ EMP: 140
SALES (est): 55.4MM **Privately Held**
SIC: 3532 Mining machinery

(G-17324)
JTM PRODUCTS INC
Also Called: J T M
31025 Carter St (44139-3521)
PHONE 440 287-2302
Fax: 216 287-3095
Daniel Schodowski, *President*
Brian F Murphy, *Principal*
Greg Myers, *Vice Pres*
Stan Penrod, *Sales Staff*
EMP: 22
SQ FT: 75,000
SALES (est): 8.7MM **Privately Held**
SIC: 2992 2841 3053 Lubricating oils & greases; soap: granulated, liquid, cake, flaked or chip; packing: steam engines, pipe joints, air compressors, etc.

(G-17325)
KANAN ENTERPRISES INC (PA)
Also Called: King Nut Companies
31900 Solon Rd (44139-3536)
PHONE 440 248-8484
Martin Kanan, *President*
Michael Kanan, *Chairman*
Matthew Kanan, *Vice Pres*

Justin Rosenberg, *Controller*
Lynn Gordon, *Sales Executive*
◆ EMP: 160
SQ FT: 250,000
SALES (est): 96.1MM **Privately Held**
WEB: www.kingnut.com
SIC: 2068 2034 Nuts: dried, dehydrated, salted or roasted; fruits, dried or dehydrated, except freeze-dried

(G-17326)
KANAN ENTERPRISES INC
Also Called: King Nut Companies, Plant 2
6401 Davis Indus Pkwy (44139-3566)
PHONE 440 349-0719
Jim Dedario, *Warehouse Mgr*
EMP: 10
SQ FT: 84,130
SALES (corp-wide): 96.1MM **Privately Held**
WEB: www.kingnut.com
SIC: 2068 2034 Nuts: dried, dehydrated, salted or roasted; fruits, dried or dehydrated, except freeze-dried
PA: Kanan Enterprises, Inc.
31900 Solon Rd
Solon OH 44139
440 248-8484

(G-17327)
KATHERINE A STULL INC
Also Called: Crafts For Kids
7079 Navajo Trl (44139-5845)
PHONE 440 349-3977
Katherine A Stull, *President*
EMP: 4
SALES (est): 374.7K **Privately Held**
SIC: 7922 2731 Television program, including commercial producers; book publishing

(G-17328)
KEITHLEY INSTRUMENTS LLC (DH)
28775 Aurora Rd (44139-1891)
PHONE 440 248-0400
Fax: 440 248-6168
Joseph P Keithley, *President*
Linda C Rae, *COO*
Philip R Etsler, *Vice Pres*
Alan S Gaffney, *Vice Pres*
Mark A Hoersten, *Vice Pres*
▲ EMP: 165
SQ FT: 125,000
SALES (est): 106.9MM
SALES (corp-wide): 6.2B **Publicly Held**
SIC: 3825 3823 7371 Instruments to measure electricity; test equipment for electronic & electric measurement; multimeters; semiconductor test equipment; computer interface equipment for industrial process control; computer software development
HQ: Tektronix, Inc.
14150 Sw Karl Braun Dr
Beaverton OR 97005
800 833-9200

(G-17329)
KENNAMETAL INC
6865 Cochran Rd (44139-4398)
PHONE 440 349-5151
Fax: 440 349-5131
Maynard Grieves, *Mfg Dir*
Jim Recob, *Plant Mgr*
Brian Maglosky, *Opers-Prdtn-Mfg*
Thomas Quatkemeyer, *Engineer*
Sam Rosenbaum, *Engineer*
EMP: 126
SQ FT: 1,500
SALES (corp-wide): 2.1B **Publicly Held**
WEB: www.kennametal.com
SIC: 3545 3532 Tool holders; mining machinery
PA: Kennametal Inc.
600 Grant St Ste 5100
Pittsburgh PA 15219
412 248-8200

(G-17330)
MAGIC INTERFACE LTD
7295 Popham Pl (44139-5794)
PHONE 440 498-3700
Edward J Toochak, *President*
Richard J Woodland, *Vice Pres*
Eatriz Woodland, *Treasurer*

Joyce Prochak, *Admin Sec*
EMP: 7
SALES (est): 430K **Privately Held**
WEB: www.magicinterface.com
SIC: 7372 Operating systems computer software

(G-17331)
MAJESTIC TOOL AND MACHINE INC
30700 Carter St Ste C (44139-3585)
PHONE 440 248-5058
Fax: 440 786-2622
Walter Krueger, *President*
Kurt Krueger, *Vice Pres*
Todd Krueger, *Vice Pres*
EMP: 32
SQ FT: 30,000
SALES: 2.5MM **Privately Held**
SIC: 3599 7692 3544 Machine shop, jobbing & repair; welding repair; special dies, tools, jigs & fixtures

(G-17332)
MAMSYS CONSULTING SERVICES
35865 Spatterdock Ln (44139-6503)
PHONE 440 287-6824
Madhuri Kumari, *President*
Deepshikha Sharma,
Yogesh Sharma,
Charles Webb,
EMP: 2
SALES (est): 1.2MM **Privately Held**
SIC: 8748 7372 7371 7379 Business consulting; application computer software; business oriented computer software; computer software development & applications; data processing consultant;

(G-17333)
MEDICAL QUANT USA INC
Also Called: Multi Radiance Medical
6521 Davis Indus Pkwy (44139-3549)
PHONE 440 542-0761
Max Kanarsky, *President*
Galina Marqova, *CFO*
Galina Markova, *Accounting Mgr*
Todd Van Niel, *VP Sales*
Cliff Majni, *Sales Dir*
EMP: 14
SALES (est): 1.3MM **Privately Held**
SIC: 3845 Laser systems & equipment, medical

(G-17334)
MERCURY IRON & STEEL
Also Called: Misco Refractometer
6275 Cochran Rd (44139-3316)
PHONE 440 349-1500
Michael Rainer, *President*
Tosha Hudson, *Manager*
Ann Samberg, *Manager*
EMP: 14
SQ FT: 6,000
SALES (est): 2.8MM **Privately Held**
WEB: www.misco.com
SIC: 8711 3827 3443 3441 Industrial engineers; optical instruments & lenses; plate work for the metalworking trade; fabricated structural metal; refractometers, industrial process type; switchgear & switchboard apparatus

(G-17335)
MERCURY MACHINE CO
30250 Carter St (44139-3500)
PHONE 440 349-3222
Fax: 440 349-3222
Jonathon Petrenchik, *President*
Mike Stasko, *Safety Mgr*
Michael Stasko, *Manager*
Sheri Sweet, *Manager*
EMP: 67 EST: 1954
SQ FT: 10,000
SALES (est): 15.7MM **Privately Held**
WEB: www.mercurymachine.com
SIC: 3324 3544 Steel investment foundries; industrial molds

(G-17336)
MFS SUPPLY LLC (PA)
31100 Solon Rd Ste E (44139-3463)
PHONE 440 248-5300
Jay Klein, *Opers Mgr*
Michael Hajec, *Opers Staff*

Michelle Eisenberg, *Human Resources*
Taylor Branisel, *Accounts Mgr*
Joshua Grodko, *Accounts Mgr*
▲ **EMP:** 13
SALES (est): 5.6MM **Privately Held**
SIC: 2542 Postal lock boxes, mail racks & related products

(G-17337)
MI-LAR FENCE CO INC (PA)
Also Called: Greenes Fence
5250 Naiman Pkwy Ste B (44139-1031)
P.O. Box 22258, Cleveland (44122-0258)
PHONE..............................216 464-3160
Larry A Greenes, *President*
Michael Kalinich, *Vice Pres*
▲ **EMP:** 1
SQ FT: 12,000
SALES (est): 2.5MM **Privately Held**
SIC: 2499 Fencing, wood

(G-17338)
MICHAEL W HYES DESGR GOLDSMITH
Also Called: Hayes, Michael Designer
28200 Miles Rd Unit F (44139-6915)
PHONE..............................440 519-0889
Michael Hayes, *CEO*
Marcy Hayes, *Vice Pres*
EMP: 7
SALES (est): 500K **Privately Held**
SIC: 3911 5944 7631 Jewelry, precious metal; jewelry stores; jewelry repair services

(G-17339)
MOTIONSOURCE INTERNATIONAL LLC
31200 Solon Rd Ste 7 (44139-3583)
PHONE..............................440 287-7037
Charles Hautala, *Principal*
Doug Karpowicz, *Principal*
Lee Shafer, *Sales Staff*
EMP: 10 EST: 2012
SQ FT: 4,000
SALES (est): 2MM **Privately Held**
SIC: 3569 5084 5013 Lubrication equipment, industrial; pumps & pumping equipment; pumps, oil & gas

(G-17340)
MP BIOMEDICALS LLC
29525 Fountain Pkwy (44139-4351)
PHONE..............................440 337-1200
Fax: 330 337-1180
Samson Chen, *General Mgr*
Nebojsa Pesic, *Vice Pres*
Yasin Sayyad, *Vice Pres*
Elmo Bondoc, *Opers Spvr*
Rhonda Gilmartin, *Opers Staff*
EMP: 130
SALES (corp-wide): 268MM **Privately Held**
WEB: www.mpbio.com
SIC: 8731 2869 2834 8071 Biological research; enzymes; pharmaceutical preparations; medical laboratories; medical research
HQ: Mp Biomedicals, Llc
3 Hutton Centre Dr # 100
Santa Ana CA 92707
949 833-2500

(G-17341)
MULTIPLAST SYSTEMS INC
33355 Station St (44139-2961)
PHONE..............................440 349-0800
Jeff Apisdorf, *President*
Cher Miller, *Office Mgr*
EMP: 15
SALES (est): 2.9MM **Privately Held**
WEB: www.multiplastsystems.com
SIC: 2673 Bags: plastic, laminated & coated

(G-17342)
MUSTARD SEED HEALTH FD MKT INC
6025 Kruse Dr Ste 100 (44139-2378)
PHONE..............................440 519-3663
Fax: 440 519-0623
Margaret Kanfer-Nabors, *Ch of Bd*
Bill Goodwin, *Financial Exec*
Ann Vojta, *Human Res Mgr*
EMP: 35

SALES (corp-wide): 59.5MM **Privately Held**
WEB: www.mustardseedmarket.com
SIC: 5499 7299 5812 2051 Gourmet food stores; banquet hall facilities; caterers; bread, cake & related products
PA: Mustard Seed Health Food Market, Inc.
3885 Medina Rd
Akron OH 44333
330 666-7333

(G-17343)
NESTLE BRANDS COMPANY
30000 Bainbridge Rd (44139-2206)
PHONE..............................440 264-6600
Cheryl Lavine, *Principal*
EMP: 13
SALES (est): 2.3MM **Privately Held**
SIC: 2099 Food preparations

(G-17344)
NESTLE PREPARED FOODS COMPANY (DH)
30003 Bainbridge Rd (44139-2205)
P.O. Box 2178, Wilkes Barre PA (18703-2178)
PHONE..............................440 248-3600
Fax: 440 498-1754
David H Jennings, *Ch of Bd*
C Wayne Partin, *President*
James M Biggar, *Vice Pres*
Charles Werner, *Vice Pres*
Pete Reichel, *Engineer*
▲ **EMP:** 1910 EST: 1969
SQ FT: 250,000
SALES (est): 1.9B
SALES (corp-wide): 88.4B **Privately Held**
SIC: 2038 5411 2037 Dinners, frozen & packaged; soups, frozen; pizza, frozen; grocery stores; vegetables, quick frozen & cold pack, excl. potato products
HQ: The Stouffer Corporation
30003 Bainbridge Rd
Solon OH 44139
440 349-5757

(G-17345)
NESTLE PREPARED FOODS COMPANY
5750 Harper Rd (44139-1831)
PHONE..............................440 349-5757
C Wayne Partin, *President*
EMP: 68
SALES (corp-wide): 88.4B **Privately Held**
SIC: 2038 5411 2037 Frozen specialties; grocery stores; frozen fruits & vegetables
HQ: Nestle Prepared Foods Company
30003 Bainbridge Rd
Solon OH 44139
440 248-3600

(G-17346)
NESTLE R&D CENTER INC
Also Called: Nestle Prepared Foods
5750 Harper Rd (44139-1831)
PHONE..............................440 349-5757
EMP: 4
SALES (est): 103.6K **Privately Held**
SIC: 3497 3589 2064 Foil containers for bakery goods & frozen foods; coffee brewing equipment; candy & other confectionery products

(G-17347)
NESTLE USA INC
Nestle Business Services
30003 Bainbridge Rd (44139-2290)
PHONE..............................440 349-5757
Jim Triskett, *Manager*
EMP: 200
SALES (corp-wide): 88.4B **Privately Held**
WEB: www.nestleusa.com
SIC: 2023 Evaporated milk; canned milk, whole; cream substitutes
HQ: Nestle Usa, Inc.
800 N Brand Blvd
Glendale CA 91203
818 549-6000

(G-17348)
NETSHAPE TECHNOLOGIES MIM INC
31005 Solon Rd (44139-3436)
PHONE..............................440 248-5456
Fax: 440 248-5807

Dax Whitehouse, *CEO*
Ric Wrye, *COO*
Patty Burkland, *CFO*
Ammie Blueter, *Controller*
▲ **EMP:** 12
SQ FT: 27,000
SALES (est): 3.7MM
SALES (corp-wide): 171MM **Privately Held**
SIC: 3443 Metal parts
HQ: Netshape Technologies, Inc.
3620 Paoli Pike Ste 8
Floyds Knobs IN 47119
812 248-9273

(G-17349)
NETSMART TECHNOLOGIES INC
Also Called: Trend Consulting Services
30775 Bnbridge Rd Ste 200 (44139)
PHONE..............................440 942-4040
Michael Valentine, *CEO*
Brad Hudson, *Manager*
John Gohman, *Director*
Beth Harvey, *Director*
Andrew Gilson, *Sr Consultant*
EMP: 39
SALES (corp-wide): 315.9MM **Privately Held**
SIC: 7379 7372 Computer related consulting services; business oriented computer software
PA: Netsmart Technologies, Inc.
4950 College Blvd
Overland Park KS 66211
913 327-7444

(G-17350)
NOCO COMPANY
30339 Diamond Pkwy # 102 (44139-5473)
PHONE..............................216 464-8131
Fax: 216 464-8131
William K Nook, *President*
Luke Case, *Vice Pres*
Kevin Tucker, *CFO*
John Nook, *VP Sales*
▲ **EMP:** 500 EST: 1914
SQ FT: 100,000
SALES (est): 20MM **Privately Held**
WEB: www.noco-usa.com
SIC: 3694 3714 3315 2899 Battery cable wiring sets for internal combustion engines; booster (jump-start) cables, automotive; filters: oil, fuel & air, motor vehicle; steel wire & related products; chemical preparations; wire & cable; power tools & accessories

(G-17351)
NORTH PK INNOVATIONS GROUP INC
Stride Milbar Company
30333 Emerald Valley Pkwy (44139-4394)
PHONE..............................440 247-4600
Fax: 440 498-6171
Jennifer Kundrad, *Opers Mgr*
Tom Ernest, *Controller*
Molly Smith, *Human Res Mgr*
Ron Ortiz, *Manager*
EMP: 150
SQ FT: 70,000
SALES (corp-wide): 16.2MM **Privately Held**
SIC: 3423 Mechanics' hand tools
PA: North Park Innovations Group Inc.
6442 Route 242 E
Ellicottville NY 14731
716 699-2031

(G-17352)
OAKWOOD LABORATORIES LLC
27070 Miles Rd (44139-1162)
PHONE..............................440 505-2011
Gregory Hanzak, *Production*
Gonto Johns, *Research*
Jeffrey M Fehn, *CFO*
Shritin Shah, *Branch Mgr*
Rohit Jadhav, *Manager*
EMP: 17
SALES (corp-wide): 9.1MM **Privately Held**
SIC: 2834 Pharmaceutical preparations

PA: Oakwood Laboratories, L.L.C.
7670 First Pl Ste A
Oakwood Village OH 44146
440 359-0000

(G-17353)
OFFICE LINK INC
34194 Aurora Rd Ste 242 (44139-3801)
PHONE..............................440 498-1364
Karen A Massaro, *President*
EMP: 5
SALES (est): 745.3K **Privately Held**
SIC: 2865 Color lakes or toners

(G-17354)
OHIO FLOCK-COTE COMPANY INC
6810 Cochran Rd (44139-3908)
PHONE..............................440 498-3877
Steven Wake, *President*
Phil Davis, *Manager*
EMP: 3
SQ FT: 44,000
SALES (est): 370.7K **Privately Held**
SIC: 2262 Flock printing: manmade fiber & silk broadwoven fabrics

(G-17355)
OHIO LUMEX CO INC
Also Called: Ameritest
30350 Bruce Indus Pkwy (44139-3938)
PHONE..............................440 264-2500
Joseph Siperstein, *President*
Mike Neyman, *Opers Staff*
Marja Richens, *Manager*
EMP: 5
SQ FT: 4,000
SALES (est): 1.6MM **Privately Held**
WEB: www.ohiolumex.com
SIC: 3826 8734 Analytical instruments; testing laboratories

(G-17356)
OPTI MOLD INC
32400 Aurora Rd Ste 5 (44139-2841)
PHONE..............................440 248-9179
Fax: 440 248-3006
Emil Pora, *President*
Viorica Pora, *Vice Pres*
EMP: 6
SQ FT: 12,000
SALES: 275K **Privately Held**
SIC: 3089 3544 Injection molding of plastics; special dies, tools, jigs & fixtures

(G-17357)
OUTSOURCING SERVICES INC
Also Called: Packaging & Labeling Division
32503 Jefferson Dr (44139-4821)
PHONE..............................330 963-2710
Fax: 330 963-3352
David Tshantz, *President*
Mark Tsahntz, *Vice Pres*
Mark Tschantz, *Vice Pres*
EMP: 18 EST: 1995
SQ FT: 6,000
SALES (est): 1.6MM **Privately Held**
SIC: 7389 2396 Packaging & labeling services; automotive & apparel trimmings

(G-17358)
PACKAGING MATERIAL DIRECT INC
30405 Solon Rd Ste 9 (44139-3477)
PHONE..............................989 482-8400
Sunil Daga, *CEO*
Jieesheunemiy Punaniy, *President*
Heresh Vasne, *Chairman*
EMP: 5
SALES (est): 385K **Privately Held**
SIC: 2671 Plastic film, coated or laminated for packaging

(G-17359)
PDI CONSTELLATION LLC
6225 Cochran Rd (44139-3315)
PHONE..............................216 271-7344
Doug Firman,
EMP: 3
SALES (est): 103.9K **Privately Held**
SIC: 3999 Manufacturing industries

GEOGRAPHIC

(G-17360)
PDI GROUND SUPPORT SYSTEMS INC
Also Called: PDI GROUP, THE
6225 Cochran Rd (44139-3315)
PHONE..................................216 271-7344
Irwin G Haber, *Chairman*
Lou Kish, *VP Mfg*
Carrie Fetcenko, *Opers Mgr*
Pat Jeffries, *Purch Mgr*
Michael Gardner, *Marketing Mgr*
▲ EMP: 60
SQ FT: 110,000
SALES: 14.8MM **Privately Held**
WEB: www.pdi-gss.com
SIC: 3714 3715 Axle housings & shafts, motor vehicle; semitrailers for missile transportation

(G-17361)
PLAS-MAC CORP
30250 Carter St (44139-3506)
PHONE..................................440 349-3222
Fax: 440 349-2750
Jonathon Petrenchik, *President*
Marcia Splinter, *Engineer*
David Breaux, *Manager*
Anthony Kaylor, *Manager*
Rich Minkowetz, *Comp Spec*
EMP: 100
SQ FT: 33,000
SALES (est): 14.9MM **Privately Held**
WEB: www.plasmaccorp.com
SIC: 3543 3599 Foundry patternmaking; air intake filters, internal combustion engine, except auto

(G-17362)
PLYMOUTH HEALTHCARE PDTS LLC
Also Called: Loma Lux Laboratories
6521 Davis Indus Pkwy (44139-3549)
PHONE..................................440 542-0762
EMP: 10
SQ FT: 10,000
SALES (est): 915.1K **Privately Held**
SIC: 2833 Mfg Medicinal/Botanical Products

(G-17363)
PRECISION BRUSH CO
6700 Parkland Blvd (44139-4341)
PHONE..................................440 542-9600
Fax: 440 475-0834
James C Benjamin, *President*
Mike Porter, *Sales Executive*
EMP: 14
SQ FT: 11,000
SALES (est): 3.1MM **Privately Held**
WEB: www.precisionbrush.com
SIC: 3991 Brushes, household or industrial

(G-17364)
PRODUCTO DIECO CORPORATION (HQ)
30600 Aurora Rd Ste 160 (44139-2767)
PHONE..................................440 542-0000
Newman M Marsilius III, *President*
Glen Collings, *CFO*
Sandi McDonald, *Controller*
EMP: 14 EST: 1998
SQ FT: 37,000
SALES (est): 4.2MM
SALES (corp-wide): 72.7MM **Privately Held**
SIC: 3544 5085 Die sets for metal stamping (presses); bearings, bushings, wheels & gears
PA: Pmt Group, Inc.
800 Union Ave
Bridgeport CT 06607
203 367-8675

(G-17365)
PTMJ ENTERPRISES
32000 Aurora Rd (44139-2875)
P.O. Box 391437 (44139-8437)
PHONE..................................440 543-8000
Fax: 440 543-7077
Peter Joyce, *President*
Joe Miller, *Opers Staff*
Kimberly Greer, *Office Mgr*
◆ EMP: 180

SALES (est): 38.3MM **Privately Held**
WEB: www.signum-inc.com
SIC: 2541 1799 Display fixtures, wood; closet organizers, installation & design

(G-17366)
QUANEX IG SYSTEMS INC (HQ)
Also Called: Quanex Building Products
6680 Parkland Blvd (44139-4344)
PHONE..................................216 910-1519
Fax: 740 439-0121
Michael Hovan, *President*
George Wilson, *General Mgr*
Kevin Gray, *Vice Pres*
Jim Hummel, *Vice Pres*
Jeff Wycinski, *QC Mgr*
◆ EMP: 175
SQ FT: 400,000
SALES: 28.9MM
SALES (corp-wide): 928.1MM **Publicly Held**
WEB: www.superspacer.com
SIC: 3061 3053 Mechanical rubber goods; gaskets, packing & sealing devices
PA: Quanex Building Products Corporation
1800 West Loop S Ste 1500
Houston TX 77027
713 961-4600

(G-17367)
REPLACMENT PRTS SPCIALISTS INC (PA)
Also Called: RPS
30400 Solon Indus Pkwy (44139-4328)
PHONE..................................440 248-0731
Gregory Davis, *President*
Chris Davis, *Vice Pres*
EMP: 4
SALES (est): 689.1K **Privately Held**
WEB: www.rps-state.com
SIC: 3536 Hoists, cranes & monorails

(G-17368)
REPUBLIC STEEL WIRE PROC LLC
31000 Solon Rd (44139-3467)
PHONE..................................440 996-0740
Fax: 440 996-0741
Larry Braun, *General Mgr*
Jim Phillips, *General Mgr*
Brad Johnson, *Plant Mgr*
David White, *Plant Mgr*
Van Stone, *Manager*
▲ EMP: 26
SALES (est): 13MM
SALES (corp-wide): 1.4B **Privately Held**
SIC: 3315 Steel wire & related products
HQ: Republic Steel Inc.
2633 8th St Ne
Canton OH 44704
330 438-5435

(G-17369)
RLS PARTS & EQUIPMENT LLC
33595 Bnbridge Rd Ste 204 (44139)
PHONE..................................440 498-1843
Lynn M Vilcheck, *Principal*
EMP: 3
SALES (est): 1MM **Privately Held**
SIC: 3531 Asphalt plant, including gravel-mix type

(G-17370)
ROBBINS COMPANY (DH)
29100 Hall St Ste 100 (44139-3926)
PHONE..................................440 248-3303
Lok Home, *President*
Martin Eckert, *General Mgr*
Douglas Harding, *Vice Pres*
Brian Khalighi, *Vice Pres*
Gene Lockhart, *Purchasing*
◆ EMP: 150
SQ FT: 79,000
SALES (est): 163.5MM **Privately Held**
WEB: www.robbinstbm.com
SIC: 3535 3541 3531 Conveyors & conveying equipment; machine tools, metal cutting type; tunnelling machinery
HQ: Northern Heavy Industries Group Co.,Ltd.
No.16, Kaifa Avenue, Economic And Technological Development Zone
Shenyang 11014
242 580-2236

(G-17371)
ROHRER CORPORATION
Also Called: Cardpak
29601 Solon Rd (44139-3451)
PHONE..................................440 542-3100
Fax: 440 542-3399
Seth Duckworth, *Vice Pres*
Jack McGarth, *Research*
John Schieferstein, *Draft/Design*
Lynn Morrison, *Accounting Mgr*
Gayle Wellman, *Hum Res Coord*
EMP: 130
SALES (corp-wide): 130.6MM **Privately Held**
SIC: 2657 2752 Folding paperboard boxes; paperboard backs for blister or skin packages; commercial printing, lithographic
PA: Rohrer Corporation
717 Seville Rd
Wadsworth OH 44281
330 335-1541

(G-17372)
ROSEMOUNT ANALYTICAL INC
6565 Davis Industrial (44139-3559)
PHONE..................................440 914-1261
Fax: 440 914-1262
Greg Obrien, *Senior Engr*
Craig Johnson, *Sales Staff*
Jim Blue, *Marketing Mgr*
Paul Arsenault, *Products*
Pam Blasius, *Products*
EMP: 190
SALES (corp-wide): 14.5B **Publicly Held**
SIC: 3825 3829 5049 Instruments to measure electricity; measuring & controlling devices; scientific instruments
HQ: Rosemount Analytical, Inc
2400 Barranca Pkwy
Irvine CA 92606

(G-17373)
RTSI LLC
6161 Cochran Rd Ste G (44139-3324)
PHONE..................................440 542-3066
Vikki Velimesis, *General Mgr*
Donna Ross,
EMP: 7
SALES (est): 890.5K
SALES (corp-wide): 37.2MM **Privately Held**
SIC: 3451 Screw machine products
PA: Kirkwood Holding Inc.
1239 Rockside Rd
Cleveland OH 44134
216 267-6200

(G-17374)
SAGEQUEST LLC
31500 Bainbridge Rd Ste 1 (44139-2289)
PHONE..................................216 896-7243
Dennis Abrahams, *President*
Jenny Ward, *President*
David Lowman, *Exec VP*
Jonathan Durkee, *Vice Pres*
Doug Engerman, *Vice Pres*
EMP: 86
SALES (est): 14.9MM **Privately Held**
WEB: www.sage-quest.com
SIC: 3663 Mobile communication equipment
HQ: Fleetmatics Group Holdings Limited
Oyster Point
Blackrock

(G-17375)
SAINT-GOBAIN PRFMCE PLAS CORP (DH)
31500 Solon Rd (44139-3528)
PHONE..................................440 836-6900
Fax: 330 562-3933
Tom Kinisky, *President*
Josehp Grewe, *Div Sub Head*
Mark Barter, *Vice Pres*
Laurent Guillot, *CFO*
Peggy Kemp, *Manager*
▲ EMP: 200
SQ FT: 20,000
SALES (est): 1.2B
SALES (corp-wide): 185.8MM **Privately Held**
SIC: 3089 3053 Thermoformed finished plastic products; gaskets, packing & sealing devices

HQ: Saint-Gobain Abrasives, Inc.
1 New Bond St
Worcester MA 01606
508 795-5000

(G-17376)
SCHWEBEL BAKING COMPANY
Also Called: Schwebel Baking Co-Solon Bky
6250 Camp Industrial Rd (44139-2750)
PHONE..................................440 248-1500
Dave Gulau, *Plant Engr*
Grant West, *Manager*
EMP: 150
SALES (corp-wide): 170MM **Privately Held**
WEB: www.schwebels.com
SIC: 5461 5149 2051 Bakeries; groceries & related products; bread, cake & related products
PA: Schwebel Baking Company
965 E Midlothian Blvd
Youngstown OH 44502
330 783-2860

(G-17377)
SEA AIR SPC MCG AND MLD LLC
30555 Solon Indus Pkwy (44139-4329)
PHONE..................................440 248-3025
Steve Pastor, *Director*
Chip Gear,
EMP: 15
SALES: 950K **Privately Held**
SIC: 3721 Aircraft

(G-17378)
SENSICAL INC
Also Called: Unitus
31115 Aurora Rd (44139-2701)
PHONE..................................216 641-1141
John F Haas, *Ch of Bd*
Taylor Ittu, *Purch Mgr*
Ann Page, *CFO*
James Haas, *Treasurer*
Gregory Moore, *Sales Staff*
▲ EMP: 55
SQ FT: 45,000
SALES (est): 19.7MM **Privately Held**
WEB: www.sensical.net
SIC: 2759 3993 2752 2672 Commercial printing; promotional printing; poster & decal printing & engraving; signs & advertising specialties; commercial printing, lithographic; coated & laminated paper

(G-17379)
SHERWIN SOFTWARE SOLUTIONS
Also Called: Accounting Software Solutions
5380 Naiman Pkwy Ste B (44139-1032)
PHONE..................................440 498-8010
Keith Sherwin, *President*
EMP: 6
SALES (est): 570K **Privately Held**
WEB: www.erpsolutions4u.com
SIC: 7372 Prepackaged software

(G-17380)
SIGLENT TECHNOLOGIES AMER INC
6557 Cochran Rd (44139-3901)
PHONE..................................440 398-5800
Stephen Barfield, *CEO*
Steve Barfield, *General Mgr*
Ruby Wu, *Manager*
Eric Qin, *Shareholder*
EMP: 4
SQ FT: 3,000
SALES (est): 330K **Privately Held**
SIC: 3679 5085 Power supplies, all types: static; static power supply converters for electronic applications; power transmission equipment & apparatus

(G-17381)
SKIDMORE-WILHELM MFG COMPANY
Also Called: Columbia Industries
30340 Solon Industrial B (44139-4358)
PHONE..................................216 481-4774
Fax: 216 481-2427
John Obrayan, *President*
John Biel, *Engineer*
Dave Bornstein, *Executive*
John Wilhelm, *Shareholder*

2017 Harris Ohio
Industrial Directory
▲ = Import ▼=Export
◆ =Import/Export

Kathleen Wilhelm, *Shareholder*
▲ **EMP:** 28 **EST:** 1944
SQ FT: 15,000
SALES (est): 4.6MM **Privately Held**
WEB: www.skidmore-wilhelm.com
SIC: 3728 3829 3825 3593 Aircraft parts
& equipment; torsion testing equipment;
instruments to measure electricity; fluid
power cylinders & actuators; speed
changers, drives & gears; machine tool
accessories

(G-17382)
SMARTSHOPPER
ELECTRONICS INC
Also Called: Wholesale Electronics
6659 Brandamore Ct (44139-4665)
PHONE..................................440 349-5119
Richard Brindisi, *President*
Jim Easton, *President*
Gregory A Vittardi, *President*
Jack R Zeman, *CFO*
▲ **EMP:** 6
SALES (est): 660K **Privately Held**
SIC: 3629 Electronic generation equipment

(G-17383)
SOLON
38235 Mcdowell Dr (44139-4684)
PHONE..................................440 498-1798
Susan A Drucker, *Mayor*
EMP: 6
SALES (est): 677.3K **Privately Held**
SIC: 3089 Plastics products

(G-17384)
SOLON GRANITE MEMORIAL
WORKS
36050 Aurora Rd (44139-3840)
PHONE..................................440 248-6606
Fax: 440 248-2218
Edmond Dynowski Jr, *President*
Tom Dynowski, *President*
EMP: 3
SQ FT: 2,400
SALES (est): 337K **Privately Held**
SIC: 3281 5999 Monuments, cut stone
(not finishing or lettering only); monu-
ments & tombstones

(G-17385)
SPECIALIZED BUSINESS SFTWR
INC
6325 Cochran Rd Ste 1 (44139-3930)
PHONE..................................440 542-9145
Fax: 440 505-5501
Steven Wiser, *President*
Brian Dusenbury, *Project Mgr*
Ross Pollock, *Project Mgr*
Adam Engel, *Info Tech Dir*
Stuart McKinney, *Software Dev*
EMP: 20
SALES (est): 1.9MM **Privately Held**
WEB:
www.specializedbusinesssoftware.com
SIC: 7372 Prepackaged software

(G-17386)
SPEEDLINE CORPORATION (PA)
6810 Cochran Rd (44139-3908)
PHONE..................................440 914-1122
Steven Wake, *President*
Joel Hammer, *Vice Pres*
Marinko Milos, *CFO*
Greg Kelly, *Sales Staff*
Phil Davis, *Manager*
▲ **EMP:** 1
SQ FT: 34,000
SALES (est): 4.3MM **Privately Held**
WEB: www.speedlinepvc.com
SIC: 3089 Fittings for pipe, plastic

(G-17387)
STOUFFER CORPORATION (DH)
30003 Bainbridge Rd (44139-2205)
PHONE..................................440 349-5757
Fax: 440 248-6413
Peter Knox, *Principal*
George Sell, *Vice Pres*
Linda McMahon, *Project Mgr*
Jeff Ertel, *VP Human Res*
Wendy English, *Manager*
▲ **EMP:** 8
SQ FT: 124,000

SALES (est): 1.9B
SALES (corp-wide): 88.4B **Privately Held**
SIC: 2038 Dinners, frozen & packaged;
soups, frozen
HQ: Tsc Holdings, Inc.
800 N Brand Blvd
Glendale CA 91203
818 549-6000

(G-17388)
STRIDE TOOL LLC ✪
30333 Emerald Valley Pkwy (44139-4394)
PHONE..................................440 247-4600
Ron Ortiz, *CEO*
Dawn Updyke, *Buyer*
Greg Lain, *Sales Mgr*
EMP: 150 **EST:** 2016
SALES (est): 4.5MM **Privately Held**
SIC: 3423 Hand & edge tools

(G-17389)
SWAGELOK (HQ)
Also Called: Snow Metal Products Co
29500 Solon Rd (44139-3474)
PHONE..................................440 349-5657
Fax: 440 349-5657
Anthur Anton, *CEO*
William Cosgrove, *Ch of Bd*
Darren Stevenson, *Maint Spvr*
Peter Pratslavsky, *Engineer*
David Rudary, *Engineer*
▲ **EMP:** 4
SALES (est): 4.5MM
SALES (corp-wide): 1.1B **Privately Held**
SIC: 3471 3494 3492 Electroplating &
plating; valves & pipe fittings; fluid power
valves & hose fittings
PA: Swagelok Company
29500 Solon Rd
Solon OH 44139
440 248-4600

(G-17390)
SWAGELOK COMPANY (PA)
29500 Solon Rd (44139-3474)
PHONE..................................440 248-4600
Fax: 440 467-5000
Arthur F Anton, *President*
David Hester, *General Mgr*
Theresa Guillory, *Regional Mgr*
Jonathan Hudgens, *Area Mgr*
John C Cox, *Business Mgr*
◆ **EMP:** 900
SQ FT: 220,000
SALES (est): 1.1B **Privately Held**
WEB: www.swagelok.com
SIC: 3494 3491 3599 Pipe fittings; pres-
sure valves & regulators, industrial; ma-
chine shop, jobbing & repair

(G-17391)
SWAGELOK COMPANY
6100 Cochran Rd (44139-3306)
PHONE..................................440 349-5652
Kurt Miller, *Project Mgr*
Nancy Brown, *Branch Mgr*
EMP: 60
SALES (corp-wide): 1.1B **Privately Held**
WEB: www.swagelok.com
SIC: 3494 3491 3599 3498 Pipe fittings;
pressure valves & regulators, industrial;
machine shop, jobbing & repair; fabri-
cated pipe & fittings
PA: Swagelok Company
29500 Solon Rd
Solon OH 44139
440 248-4600

(G-17392)
SWAGELOK COMPANY
31400 Aurora Rd (44139-2764)
PHONE..................................440 349-5934
Fax: 440 349-5934
Jake Boland, *Sales Staff*
Sue Rooth, *Marketing Staff*
Nick Lubar, *Manager*
Linda Fall, *Manager*
Rick Roach, *Manager*
EMP: 100
SALES (corp-wide): 1.1B **Privately Held**
WEB: www.swagelok.com
SIC: 5051 3593 3498 3494 Tubing,
metal; fluid power cylinders & actuators;
fabricated pipe & fittings; valves & pipe fit-
tings; fabricated plate work (boiler shop)

PA: Swagelok Company
29500 Solon Rd
Solon OH 44139
440 248-4600

(G-17393)
SWAGELOK COMPANY
Also Called: Crawford Computer Center
6262 Cochran Rd (44139-3308)
PHONE..................................440 349-5836
Fax: 440 248-0459
Arthur Anton, *Principal*
Juliano Ritosa, *Project Mgr*
Jim Gotch, *Engineer*
Kathleen Tomlin, *HR Admin*
Chris Bryan, *Business Anlyst*
EMP: 25
SALES (corp-wide): 1.1B **Privately Held**
WEB: www.swagelok.com
SIC: 3494 3491 3599 3594 Pipe fittings;
pressure valves & regulators, industrial;
machine shop, jobbing & repair; fluid
power pumps & motors; fluid power
valves & hose fittings; heating equipment,
except electric
PA: Swagelok Company
29500 Solon Rd
Solon OH 44139
440 248-4600

(G-17394)
SWAGELOK COMPANY
32550 Old South Miles Rd (44139-2829)
PHONE..................................440 542-1250
Bruce Schneider, *Branch Mgr*
Mark Bennett, *Sr Project Mgr*
EMP: 35
SALES (corp-wide): 1.1B **Privately Held**
SIC: 3494 Pipe fittings
PA: Swagelok Company
29500 Solon Rd
Solon OH 44139
440 248-4600

(G-17395)
SWAGELOK MANUFACTURING
CO LLC
29500 Solon Rd (44139-3474)
PHONE..................................440 248-4600
Chris Gress, *Purchasing*
Kevin Cihan, *Engineer*
Jeff Kauffman, *Engineer*
Justin Soltani, *Engineer*
Greg Wittkopf, *Info Tech Dir*
▲ **EMP:** 25
SALES (est): 4.9MM **Privately Held**
SIC: 3599 Hose, flexible metallic

(G-17396)
T J DAVIES COMPANY INC
30745 Solon Rd Ste 1 (44139-3459)
PHONE..................................440 248-5510
Thomas Davies, *President*
EMP: 6
SQ FT: 5,000
SALES: 600K **Privately Held**
WEB: www.tjdavies.com
SIC: 3535 Belt conveyor systems, general
industrial use

(G-17397)
TAMERAN INC
30300 Solon Industrial Pk (44139-4382)
PHONE..................................440 349-7100
Fax: 440 349-7100
Mark Wise, *President*
David S Wise, *Vice Pres*
Scott Wise, *VP Mfg*
Kyle Schmidt, *Mfg Staff*
Dan Wilson, *Buyer*
EMP: 30 **EST:** 1975
SQ FT: 74,000
SALES (est): 5.1MM **Privately Held**
SIC: 3861 Reproduction machines &
equipment; photocopy machines; micro-
film equipment: cameras, projectors,
readers, etc.

(G-17398)
TARKETT INC (DH)
Also Called: Tarkett Delaware
30000 Aurora Rd (44139-2728)
PHONE..................................800 899-8916
Jeff Buttitta, *CEO*
Jack Lee, *President*
Pete Bruton, *Business Mgr*

Peter De Bonis, *Corp Secy*
Debbie McLaughlin, *Vice Pres*
▲ **EMP:** 99
SQ FT: 5,000
SALES (est): 688.6MM
SALES (corp-wide): 537K **Privately Held**
WEB: www.tarkettna.com
SIC: 3069 Flooring, rubber: tile or sheet
HQ: Tarkett Inc
1001 Rue Yamaska E
Farnham QC J2N 1
450 293-3173

(G-17399)
TARKETT USA INC (DH)
Also Called: Johnsonite
30000 Aurora Rd (44139-2728)
PHONE..................................440 543-8916
Fax: 440 543-7205
Jeff Fenwick, *President*
Diane Drake, *Business Mgr*
Dominic Coletta, *Senior VP*
Carmen Pastore, *Senior VP*
Joseph Zucco, *QC Mgr*
EMP: 250
SALES (est): 375MM
SALES (corp-wide): 537K **Privately Held**
SIC: 3253 Ceramic wall & floor tile
HQ: Tarkett
Tour Initiale
Puteaux
141 204-040

(G-17400)
TECHNOLOGY HOUSE THE LTD
Also Called: North Cape Manufacturing
30555 Solon Indus Pkwy (44139-4329)
PHONE..................................440 248-3025
Chip Gear, *Partner*
Pamela Gear, *Partner*
Hazel Taylor, *Facilities Mgr*
Greg Cebular, *Manager*
▲ **EMP:** 100
SQ FT: 14,000
SALES (est): 15.3MM **Privately Held**
SIC: 8711 3544 3369 Industrial engi-
neers; machine tool design; mechanical
engineering; special dies, tools, jigs & fix-
tures; nonferrous foundries

(G-17401)
TECHTRON SYSTEMS INC
29500 Fountain Pkwy (44139-4350)
PHONE..................................440 505-2990
Fax: 440 442-0737
Paul Teel Jr, *President*
Pam Teel, *Business Mgr*
George Linderman, *QC Dir*
Rosemary Wilcosky, *QC Mgr*
Bill Biscoff, *Engineer*
▲ **EMP:** 50
SQ FT: 38,000
SALES (est): 16.8MM **Privately Held**
WEB: www.techtronsys.com
SIC: 3672 Printed circuit boards

(G-17402)
TEKTRONIX INC
28775 Aurora Rd (44139-1837)
PHONE..................................440 248-0400
EMP: 26
SALES (corp-wide): 6.2B **Publicly Held**
SIC: 3825 Instruments to measure electric-
ity
HQ: Tektronix, Inc.
14150 Sw Karl Braun Dr
Beaverton OR 97005
800 833-9200

(G-17403)
TEREX MHPS CORP
29201 Aurora Rd (44139-1846)
P.O. Box 39245 (44139-0245)
PHONE..................................440 349-8235
EMP: 3
SALES (corp-wide): 2.2B **Privately Held**
SIC: 3536 Cranes, industrial plant
HQ: Terex Mhps Corp.
106 12th St Se
Waverly IA 50677
877 794-5284

(G-17404)
TEXAS TILE MANUFACTURING LLC
30000 Aurora Rd (44139-2728)
PHONE..................................713 869-5811
Gilles De Beaumont, *President*
Lee James, *Vice Pres*
Tom Dowling, *Treasurer*
Andre Burke, *Controller*
Clayton Whitehead, *VP Finance*
▲ EMP: 20
SALES (est): 3.8MM **Privately Held**
SIC: 3292 Tile, vinyl asbestos

(G-17405)
THERMACAL INC
30325 Binbridge Rd Ste 2a (44139)
PHONE..................................440 498-1005
Fax: 440 498-1062
Jerry Nickol, *President*
EMP: 5
SQ FT: 5,000
SALES (est): 721.9K **Privately Held**
WEB: www.thermacal.com
SIC: 3823 Temperature measurement in-
struments, industrial

(G-17406)
TIMEKEEPING SYSTEMS INC
30700 Bainbridge Rd Ste H (44139-6403)
PHONE..................................216 595-0890
George Markwitz, *President*
John Hoffman, *Vice Pres*
Barry Markwitz, *Vice Pres*
Guenther Thiedemann, *Opers Staff*
Dean Chriss, *Senior Engr*
EMP: 11
SALES (est): 2.3MM **Privately Held**
SIC: 7371 8711 7372 3577 Custom com-
puter programming services; engineering
services; prepackaged software; com-
puter peripheral equipment

(G-17407)
TRITON PRODUCTS LLC
30700 Carter St Ste D (44139-3585)
PHONE..................................440 248-5480
Fax: 440 248-5483
Ronald Accuardi,
Terry C Palermo,
▲ EMP: 18
SQ FT: 38,000
SALES (est): 3.7MM **Privately Held**
SIC: 3429 Hangers, wall hardware

(G-17408)
TRUSEAL TECHNOLOGIES INC (HQ)
6680 Parkland Blvd (44139-4344)
PHONE..................................216 910-1500
August J Coppola, *CEO*
Lee Burroughs, *Vice Pres*
Baratuci Jim, *Vice Pres*
David Marlar, *Vice Pres*
Joel Falck, *CFO*
◆ EMP: 35
SQ FT: 80,000
SALES (est): 27.8MM
SALES (corp-wide): 928.1MM **Publicly
Held**
WEB: www.swiggle.com
SIC: 2891 Sealants
PA: Quanex Building Products Corporation
1800 West Loop S Ste 1500
Houston TX 77027
713 961-4600

(G-17409)
TTI FLOOR CARE NORTH AMER INC (DH)
Also Called: Royal Appliance Manufacturing
7005 Cochran Rd (44139-4303)
PHONE..................................440 996-2000
Fax: 440 996-2027
Chris Gurreri, *President*
Dave Chaney, *President*
Mike Ferris, *President*
Scott Jackson, *General Mgr*
Anthony Pero, *Editor*
▲ EMP: 350
SQ FT: 450,000

SALES (est): 290.5MM
SALES (corp-wide): 5B **Privately Held**
SIC: 5072 3825 Power tools & accessories; power measuring equipment, electrical
HQ: Royal Appliance Mfg. Co.
7005 Cochran Rd
Cleveland OH 44139
440 996-2000

(G-17410)
TWINSOURCE LLC
32333 Aurora Rd Ste 50 (44139-2851)
PHONE..................................440 248-6800
Fax: 440 349-2678
Fred Tamjidi, *President*
Dave Gouttiere, *CFO*
EMP: 10
SALES (est): 2.2MM **Privately Held**
WEB: www.twinsource.net
SIC: 3822 Switches, thermostatic

(G-17411)
VALTRONIC TECHNOLOGY INC
29200 Fountain Pkwy (44139-4347)
PHONE..................................440 349-1239
Fax: 440 349-1239
Martin Zimmermann, *CEO*
Clemens J Troche, *President*
Jay Wimer, *President*
Donald Styblo, *Vice Pres*
Bob Chanda, *Mfg Mgr*
EMP: 68
SQ FT: 26,000
SALES (est): 18.8MM **Privately Held**
SIC: 3679 Harness assemblies for elec-
tronic use: wire or cable

(G-17412)
W-J INC
34180 Solon Rd (44139-2623)
P.O. Box 39157, Cleveland (44139-0157)
PHONE..................................440 248-8282
Fax: 440 248-8282
Scott Jerpbak, *President*
EMP: 5 EST: 1972
SQ FT: 28,000
SALES (est): 380K **Privately Held**
SIC: 3452 Screws, metal

(G-17413)
WATER & WASTE WATER EQP CO
32100 Solon Rd Ste 101a (44139-3584)
PHONE..................................440 542-0972
Walter Senney, *President*
Cindy Wierzchowski, *Controller*
Linda Maher, *Office Mgr*
EMP: 7
SALES (est): 1.1MM **Privately Held**
WEB: www.wwe-co.com
SIC: 3589 Sewage & water treatment
equipment

(G-17414)
WILLIAM J BERGEN & CO
Also Called: Bergen, W J & Co
32520 Arthur Rd (44139-4503)
PHONE..................................440 248-6132
Fax: 440 248-4321
William J Bergen, *Owner*
EMP: 9
SQ FT: 3,500
SALES: 1MM **Privately Held**
SIC: 5112 2752 2759 Business forms;
commercial printing, offset; lithographing
on metal; letterpress printing

(G-17415)
WORKSPEED MANAGEMENT LLC
28925 Fountain Pkwy (44139-4356)
PHONE..................................917 369-9025
Derrick Chen, *CEO*
Marcella P Mazzucca, *Chief Mktg Ofcr*
EMP: 25
SALES (est): 2.5MM **Privately Held**
WEB: www.workspeed.com
SIC: 7372 Prepackaged software

Somerset
Perry County

(G-17416)
LITZINGER LOGGING
314 S Columbus St (43783)
PHONE..................................740 743-2245
Louis Litzinger, *Principal*
EMP: 3
SALES (est): 251.4K **Privately Held**
SIC: 2411 Logging

(G-17417)
N & N OIL
6111 State Route 13 Ne (43783-9686)
P.O. Box 261 (43783-0261)
PHONE..................................740 743-2848
Amanda Noll, *Principal*
EMP: 3
SALES (est): 318.7K **Privately Held**
SIC: 3533 Oil & gas field machinery

(G-17418)
RHODES MANUFACTURING CO INC
7045 Buckeye Valley Rd Ne (43783-9709)
PHONE..................................740 743-2614
Fax: 740 743-3955
Douglas L Rhodes, *President*
Brian Rhodes, *Vice Pres*
Sam Iceman, *Office Mgr*
EMP: 20
SQ FT: 6,000
SALES: 5.4MM **Privately Held**
SIC: 3443 Industrial vessels, tanks & con-
tainers

(G-17419)
SCHMELZER INDUSTRIES INC
7970 Wesley Chapel Rd Ne (43783-9737)
P.O. Box 249 (43783-0249)
PHONE..................................740 743-2866
Fax: 740 743-2867
Jean Schmelzer, *President*
Monica Schmelzer, *COO*
EMP: 25
SQ FT: 23,700
SALES (est): 4.6MM **Privately Held**
WEB: www.siveils.com
SIC: 2221 Fiberglass fabrics

(G-17420)
VILLAGE OF SOMERSET
1672 Big Inch Rd Nw (43783-9768)
P.O. Box 10 (43783-0010)
PHONE..................................740 743-1986
Cindy Grimm, *Principal*
EMP: 4 **Privately Held**
SIC: 3589 Sewage & water treatment
equipment
PA: Village Of Somerset
100 Public Sq
Somerset OH 43783
740 743-2963

Somerton
Belmont County

(G-17421)
STUMPTOWN LBR PALLET MILLS LTD
55613 Washington St (43713-9794)
PHONE..................................740 757-2275
Jody Wilcox, *Manager*
Dennis Wilcox,
EMP: 8
SQ FT: 1,300
SALES (est): 400K **Privately Held**
SIC: 2448 Pallets, wood

South Bloomingville
Hocking County

(G-17422)
FRICKCO INC
54660 Pretty Run Rd (43152-9511)
PHONE..................................740 887-2017

Jerry Albright, *President*
EMP: 3
SALES (est): 310K **Privately Held**
SIC: 2421 Sawmills & planing mills, gen-
eral

(G-17423)
SPECIAL TOUCH MIDNIGHT PRESS
57306 N Branch Rd (43152-9521)
PHONE..................................740 596-5380
Suzanne Tschanen, *Partner*
EMP: 4
SALES (est): 250K **Privately Held**
SIC: 2759 Commercial printing

South Charleston
Clark County

(G-17424)
BUCKEYE DIAMOND LOGISTICS INC (PA)
15 Sprague Rd (45368-9644)
PHONE..................................937 462-8361
Samuel J Mc Adow Jr, *President*
Edmund Fisher, *General Mgr*
John McAdow, *Vice Pres*
Mike McAdow, *Vice Pres*
Gary Streepy, *Vice Pres*
EMP: 120
SALES (est): 33.3MM **Privately Held**
WEB: www.buckeyegroup.com
SIC: 2448 2441 Pallets, wood; boxes,
wood

(G-17425)
ENTERPRISE / AMERISEAL INC
6800 S Charleston Rd (45368-9504)
P.O. Box 88, Springfield (45501-0088)
PHONE..................................937 284-3003
Chuck Falloon, *President*
Charles Phares, *Controller*
John Rohling, *Marketing Mgr*
▲ EMP: 5
SALES (est): 631.8K **Privately Held**
SIC: 3069 5013 Rubber automotive prod-
ucts; automotive supplies

(G-17426)
JOHNS JERKY & SNACK MEATS LLC
12499 Clmbus Cncinnati Rd (45368-9307)
PHONE..................................937 207-7008
John Snook, *Mng Member*
EMP: 3 EST: 2011
SALES (est): 181.2K **Privately Held**
SIC: 2013 Snack sticks, including jerky:
from purchased meat; bologna from pur-
chased meat

(G-17427)
WOODFORD LOGISTICS
15 Sprague Rd (45368-9644)
PHONE..................................513 417-8453
Steven L Means, *Principal*
EMP: 90
SQ FT: 60,000
SALES (est): 7.2MM **Privately Held**
SIC: 2448 Wood pallets & skids

(G-17428)
YAMADA NORTH AMERICA INC
Also Called: Yotec
9000 Clmbus Cincinnati Rd (45368-9406)
P.O. Box Y (45368-0825)
PHONE..................................937 462-7111
Fax: 859 462-7466
Kiyoshi Osawa, *President*
John C Beeler, *Principal*
William Mallory, *Vice Pres*
Yoshimitsu Kobayashi, *Engineer*
Kunitoshi Sakuari, *Accounts Mgr*
▲ EMP: 350
SQ FT: 110,000
SALES (est): 156.4MM
SALES (corp-wide): 374MM **Privately
Held**
WEB: www.yna.us
SIC: 3714 3621 Motor vehicle steering
systems & parts; water pump, motor vehi-
cle; rotors, for motors

PA: Yamada Manufacturing Co., Ltd.
2-1296, Kobayashicho
Isesaki GNM 379-2
270 409-111

South Lebanon
Warren County

(G-17429)
GDW WOODWORKING LLC
120 Vista Ridge Dr (45065-8761)
PHONE..................................513 494-3041
Glenn David Williams,
EMP: 4
SALES (est): 358.6K **Privately Held**
SIC: 2431 7389 Millwork;

(G-17430)
OHIO FLEXIBLE PACKAGING CO
512 S Main St (45065-1441)
PHONE..................................513 494-1800
Fax: 513 494-1300
Larry Lehman, *President*
Juith Lehman, *Corp Secy*
Frank Remmey, *Vice Pres*
Phillip Lehman, *Prdtn Mgr*
EMP: 11
SQ FT: 10,000
SALES (est): 1.6MM **Privately Held**
WEB: www.ohioflex.com
SIC: 2759 Flexographic printing

South Point
Lawrence County

(G-17431)
ALPHA CONTROL LLC
Also Called: Alpha Control Fabg & Mfg
1042 County Road 60 (45680-7465)
P.O. Box 1036 (45680-1036)
PHONE..................................740 377-3400
Greg Joseph, *President*
EMP: 35 **EST:** 2010
SQ FT: 60,000
SALES (est): 7.5MM **Privately Held**
SIC: 3449 Bars, concrete reinforcing: fabricated steel

(G-17432)
AMERICAN BOTTLING COMPANY
2531 County Road 1 (45680-7879)
PHONE..................................740 377-4371
Rick Hannon, *Manager*
EMP: 45
SALES (corp-wide): 6.4B **Publicly Held**
WEB: www.cs-americas.com
SIC: 2086 Soft drinks: packaged in cans, bottles, etc.
HQ: The American Bottling Company
5301 Legacy Dr
Plano TX 75024

(G-17433)
BROCK BURIAL VAULT INC
1043 County Road 120 (45680-8823)
PHONE..................................740 894-5246
EMP: 3 **EST:** 1976
SQ FT: 10,000
SALES (est): 280K **Privately Held**
SIC: 3272 Mfg Burial Vaults

(G-17434)
BROUGHTON FOODS COMPANY
8099 County Road 1 (45680-7825)
PHONE..................................800 598-7545
Jonathan Christian, *Branch Mgr*
Ashley Stevenson, *Manager*
EMP: 10 **Publicly Held**
SIC: 2026 Cottage cheese
HQ: Broughton Foods Company
1701 Greene St
Marietta OH 45750
740 373-4121

(G-17435)
CABINETS INC
Also Called: Glasstastic
904 4th St E (45680-9141)
P.O. Box 636 (45680-0636)
PHONE..................................740 377-4629
Fax: 740 377-4313
John Freeman, *President*
EMP: 8 **EST:** 1957
SQ FT: 4,000
SALES (est): 774.3K **Privately Held**
SIC: 2434 Wood kitchen cabinets

(G-17436)
DOLIN SUPPLY CO
702 Solida Rd (45680-8953)
PHONE..................................304 529-4171
Marc Cocchiola, *Opers Staff*
Scott Brennen, *Accounts Exec*
Andy Griffin, *Branch Mgr*
Mark Sparks,
Chad Garrison,
EMP: 45
SQ FT: 83,000
SALES (est): 7.5MM **Publicly Held**
WEB: www.mscdirect.com
SIC: 5085 7353 7694 3496 Industrial supplies; heavy construction equipment rental; armature rewinding shops; miscellaneous fabricated wire products
PA: Msc Industrial Direct Co., Inc.
75 Maxess Rd
Melville NY 11747

(G-17437)
ENGINES INC OF OHIO
101 Commerce Dr (45680-8457)
P.O. Box 428 (45680-0428)
PHONE..................................740 377-9874
Carl C Grover, *President*
David W Sanders, *Vice Pres*
Julie Kriebel, *Safety Dir*
Dustin Stanley, *Safety Dir*
Eddy Estep, *Controller*
EMP: 65
SQ FT: 100,000
SALES (est): 14.3MM **Privately Held**
SIC: 3321 3325 3743 3532 Railroad car wheels & brake shoes, cast iron; railroad car wheels, cast steel; interurban cars & car equipment; interurban cars & car equipment; locomotives & parts; mining machinery; crushing, pulverizing & screening equipment

(G-17438)
IV J TELECOMMUNICATIONS LLC
101 Lea St (45680-9685)
PHONE..................................606 694-1762
John Johnson,
EMP: 4
SALES (est): 240.7K **Privately Held**
SIC: 3585 7699 1623 1711 Compressors for refrigeration & air conditioning equipment; miscellaneous building item repair services; oil & gas pipeline construction; heating & air conditioning contractors

(G-17439)
JENNMAR MCSWEENEY LLC
235 Commerce Dr (45680-8465)
PHONE..................................740 377-3354
Frank Calandra, *President*
Joe McSweeney, *Principal*
Sandra Blackburn, *Vice Pres*
Becky Keefer, *Accountant*
EMP: 140
SQ FT: 30,900
SALES (est): 31.7MM
SALES (corp-wide): 404.1MM **Privately Held**
SIC: 3532 3531 Bits, except oil & gas field tools, rock; auger mining equipment; blades for graders, scrapers, dozers & snow plows
PA: Calandra Frank Inc
258 Kappa Dr
Pittsburgh PA 15238
412 963-9071

(G-17440)
MCGINNIS INC (HQ)
502 2nd St E (45680-9446)
P.O. Box 534 (45680-0534)
PHONE..................................740 377-4391

Fax: 740 377-9541
Bruce D McGinnis, *CEO*
Rickey Lee Griffith, *President*
Bill Jessie, *Corp Secy*
D Dwaine Stephens, *Vice Pres*
EMP: 193 **EST:** 1971
SQ FT: 5,000
SALES (est): 48.8MM
SALES (corp-wide): 147.7MM **Privately Held**
WEB: www.mcginnisinc.com
SIC: 4491 3731 Marine cargo handling; barges, building & repairing
PA: Mcnational, Inc.
502 2nd St E
South Point OH 45680
740 377-4391

(G-17441)
MCNATIONAL INC (PA)
502 2nd St E (45680-9446)
P.O. Box 534 (45680-0534)
PHONE..................................740 377-4391
Bruce D McGinnis, *CEO*
Rick Griffith, *President*
C Barry Gipson, *Principal*
William Jessie, *Manager*
C Clayton Johnson, *Admin Sec*
EMP: 24
SQ FT: 5,000
SALES (est): 147.7MM **Privately Held**
SIC: 3731 7699 4491 Barges, building & repairing; cargo vessels, building & repairing; aircraft & heavy equipment repair services; marine cargo handling

(G-17442)
MICHAEL N WHEELER
Also Called: Phoenix Hydraulics and Contrls
1004 4th St E (45680-9129)
PHONE..................................740 377-9777
Michael N Wheeler, *Owner*
Cheryl Rowland, *Manager*
EMP: 10
SQ FT: 12,500
SALES (est): 800K **Privately Held**
WEB: www.phoenixhyd.com
SIC: 3592 Valves

(G-17443)
ORICA GROUND SUPPORT INC
101 Valley Dr (45680-1300)
P.O. Box 263, Bowerston (44695-0263)
PHONE..................................740 377-9146
EMP: 52
SALES (corp-wide): 3.9B **Privately Held**
SIC: 2821 3564 2439 Plastics materials & resins; blowers & fans; structural wood members
HQ: Orica Ground Support Inc.
150 Summer Ct
Georgetown KY 40324
502 863-6800

(G-17444)
PRECISIONS PAINT SYSTEMS LLC
5852 County Road 1 (45680-7420)
PHONE..................................740 894-6224
Michael Manns, *CEO*
EMP: 10
SALES (est): 409.5K **Privately Held**
SIC: 2851 Marine paints

(G-17445)
PYRO-CHEM CORPORATION
Also Called: Better Foam Insulation
2491 County Road 1 (45680-7879)
P.O. Box 884 (45680-0884)
PHONE..................................740 377-2244
Fax: 740 377-2283
Joseph P Smith, *President*
Gailene M Smith, *Corp Secy*
EMP: 14
SQ FT: 12,000
SALES (est): 4.5MM **Privately Held**
SIC: 2899 Fire retardant chemicals

(G-17446)
REFRIGERATION INDUSTRIES CORP
719 County Road 1 (45680-8881)
P.O. Box 617 (45680-0617)
PHONE..................................740 377-9166
Fax: 740 377-4701
John Smith, *President*

Lilly Fyffe, *Manager*
EMP: 12 **EST:** 1999
SALES (est): 2.8MM **Privately Held**
SIC: 3585 Refrigeration equipment, complete

(G-17447)
SAFE RX PHARMACIES INC
503 4th St E (45680-9110)
PHONE..................................740 377-4162
W Kent Freeman, *Principal*
EMP: 3
SALES (est): 189.3K **Privately Held**
SIC: 2834 Pharmaceutical preparations

(G-17448)
SUPERIOR MARINE WAYS INC (PA)
5852 County Road 1 (45680-7420)
P.O. Box 519 (45680-0519)
PHONE..................................740 894-6224
Robert McCune, *President*
Jeff Irby, *Vice Pres*
Matt Manns, *Vice Pres*
Michael Manns, *CFO*
Brenda McGlone, *Human Res Mgr*
EMP: 3
SQ FT: 10,000
SALES (est): 16.3MM **Privately Held**
WEB: www.superiormarine.on.ca
SIC: 3731 4492 Tugboats, building & repairing; barges, building & repairing; towing & tugboat service

South Salem
Ross County

(G-17449)
BRETT PURDUM
10989 Cropp St (45681-9784)
PHONE..................................740 626-2890
Brett Purdum, *Principal*
EMP: 6
SALES (est): 503.3K **Privately Held**
SIC: 2411 Logging

South Vienna
Clark County

(G-17450)
JOHNSONS LAMP SHOP & ANTQ CO
8518 E National Rd (45369-8772)
PHONE..................................937 568-4551
Fax: 937 568-9814
Denna L Johnson, *Owner*
EMP: 4
SQ FT: 6,500
SALES (est): 242K **Privately Held**
SIC: 5719 7629 3641 Lighting, lamps & accessories; lamp repair & mounting; lamps, fluorescent, electric; lamps, incandescent filament, electric

South Webster
Scioto County

(G-17451)
ROGER HALL
Also Called: Hall Trencher Service
429 Railroad Hollow Rd (45682-8910)
P.O. Box 507 (45682-0507)
PHONE..................................740 778-2861
Roger Hall, *CEO*
EMP: 3
SALES (est): 187.7K **Privately Held**
SIC: 1442 Construction sand & gravel

(G-17452)
WARNER HILDEBRANT
714 Bear Run Rd (45682-9024)
PHONE..................................740 286-1903
Warner O Hildebrant, *Partner*
Anthony Wayne Hildebrant, *Partner*
Louise Hilderbrant, *Partner*
EMP: 3
SALES (est): 220.5K **Privately Held**
SIC: 2411 Logging

South Zanesville
Muskingum County

(G-17453)
BAILEYS ASPHALT SEALING
2092 Newark Rd (43701-9635)
PHONE..................................740 453-9409
Sheila Mbailey, *Principal*
EMP: 10
SALES (est): 510K **Privately Held**
SIC: 1799 2951 1771 1611 Parking lot
maintenance; asphalt paving mixtures &
blocks; driveway contractor; surfacing &
paving

Southington
Trumbull County

(G-17454)
QUALITY MATCH PLATE CO
4211 State Route 534 (44470-9705)
PHONE..................................330 889-2462
Fax: 330 889-9579
James W Dittrich, *President*
Genevieve Dittrich, *Corp Secy*
Alexis Dittrich, *Treasurer*
EMP: 18
SQ FT: 6,200
SALES (est): 3.2MM **Privately Held**
WEB: www.qualitymatchplate.com
SIC: 3365 Utensils, cast aluminum

Spencer
Medina County

(G-17455)
ALTA MIRA CORPORATION
Also Called: Spencer Forge & Manufacturing
225 N Main St (44275-9759)
PHONE..................................330 648-2461
Laurence E Rich, *President*
Lee Hahner, *General Mgr*
Deborah Rich, *Corp Secy*
Debbie Rich, *Treasurer*
EMP: 86
SQ FT: 83,000
SALES (est): 18.2MM **Privately Held**
SIC: 3714 3462 Axles, motor vehicle; iron
& steel forgings

(G-17456)
JOHN BAIRD
Also Called: Temple Architectural Products
12646 Lovers Lane Rd (44275-9509)
PHONE..................................216 440-3595
John Baird, *Owner*
EMP: 4
SALES: 1MM **Privately Held**
SIC: 3444 Metal roofing & roof drainage
equipment

(G-17457)
SPENCER MANUFACTURING COMPANY
Also Called: Spencer Forge & Manufacturing
225 N Main St (44275-9759)
P.O. Box 68 (44275-0068)
PHONE..................................330 648-2461
Fax: 330 648-2380
Larry E Rich, *President*
EMP: 70 **EST:** 1954
SALES (est): 11.7MM **Privately Held**
WEB: www.spencer-forge.com
SIC: 3714 3542 Axles, motor vehicle; ma-
chine tools, metal forming type

(G-17458)
TATER TOOL & DIE INC
11145 Old Mill Rd (44275-9536)
PHONE..................................330 648-1148
John J Raida, *President*
EMP: 8
SALES (est): 697.1K **Privately Held**
SIC: 3544 Special dies & tools

Spencerville
Allen County

(G-17459)
D&M FENCING LLC
08656 Deep Cut Rd (45887-9315)
PHONE..................................419 604-0698
Matthew Wirth,
EMP: 3
SALES (est): 200K **Privately Held**
SIC: 3699 3315 5039 2411 Electric fence
chargers; chain link fencing; wire fence,
gates & accessories; rails, fence: round or
split; snow fence lath;

(G-17460)
INNOCOR FOAM TECH - ACP INC
200 E North St (45887-1065)
P.O. Box 124 (45887-0124)
PHONE..................................419 647-4172
EMP: 12
SALES (corp-wide): 1B **Privately Held**
SIC: 2515 2392 3069 Mattresses & foun-
dations; cushions & pillows; bathmats,
rubber
HQ: Innocor Foam Technologies - Acp, Inc.
200 Schulz Dr Ste 2
Red Bank NJ 07701
877 858-3855

(G-17461)
JOHN A & WILLIAM J WIECHART
Also Called: Rural Machine & Iron Works
510 N Saint Marys Rd (45887-9602)
PHONE..................................419 647-4617
Helen Wiechart, *Owner*
John A Wiechart, *Partner*
William J Wiechart, *Partner*
EMP: 5
SQ FT: 5,000
SALES (est): 552.9K **Privately Held**
SIC: 3315 3496 3446 Fence gates posts
& fittings: steel; miscellaneous fabricated
wire products; architectural metalwork

(G-17462)
N BASS BAIT CO
08780 Deep Cut Rd (45887-9315)
PHONE..................................419 647-4501
Ron Perrine, *President*
Judith Perrine, *Admin Sec*
EMP: 3
SALES (est): 230K **Privately Held**
SIC: 3949 Lures, fishing: artificial

(G-17463)
OHIO DECORATIVE PRODUCTS LLC (PA)
220 S Elizabeth St (45887-1315)
P.O. Box 126 (45887-0126)
PHONE..................................419 647-9033
Fax: 419 647-4202
Charles D Moeller, *President*
Candace Moeller, *President*
George J Bowers, *Principal*
Charles E Neuman, *Principal*
Donald L Jerwers, *Corp Secy*
◆ **EMP:** 135 **EST:** 1970
SQ FT: 5,000
SALES (est): 166.7MM **Privately Held**
SIC: 3086 3369 3471 3363 Plastics foam
products; zinc & zinc-base alloy castings,
except die-castings; plating & polishing;
aluminum die-castings

(G-17464)
RELIABLE BUFFING CO INC
Also Called: Reliable Buffing & Polishing
222 N College St (45887-1222)
PHONE..................................419 647-4432
Donald Comer, *President*
Crete Mueller, *President*
Don Comer, *Vice Pres*
Darlene Comer, *Treasurer*
EMP: 6 **EST:** 1948
SQ FT: 1,050
SALES (est): 601.2K **Privately Held**
SIC: 3471 Buffing for the trade; polishing,
metals or formed products

(G-17465)
S I DISTRIBUTING INC
Also Called: Holland Grills Distributing
13540 Spencerville Rd (45887-9525)
PHONE..................................419 647-4909
Fax: 419 394-8074
Dave Durgei, *President*
Todd Keysor, *Principal*
▲ **EMP:** 13
SQ FT: 22,000
SALES (est): 3.1MM **Privately Held**
WEB: www.sidist.com
SIC: 3523 5083 5023 Cabs, tractors &
agricultural machinery; agricultural ma-
chinery & equipment; grills, barbecue

Spring Valley
Greene County

(G-17466)
ADVANCED TELEMETRICS INTL
Also Called: A T I
2361 Darnell Dr (45370-8708)
PHONE..................................937 862-6948
Fax: 937 862-7193
Phillip Merrill, *President*
Dale Snyder, *Sales Engr*
Mike Cartmell, *Info Tech Mgr*
EMP: 11
SQ FT: 3,000
SALES (est): 750K **Privately Held**
WEB: www.atitelemetry.com
SIC: 3663 Telemetering equipment, elec-
tronic

(G-17467)
EXCELSIOR SOLUTIONS
1742 River Ridge Dr (45370-9777)
PHONE..................................937 848-2569
Timothy J Murphy, *Principal*
EMP: 3
SALES (est): 166.1K **Privately Held**
SIC: 3053 Packing materials

(G-17468)
MAX MIGHTY INC
Also Called: Advanced Wire and Cable
2434 Darnell Dr (45370-8710)
P.O. Box 98, Xenia (45385-0098)
PHONE..................................937 862-9530
Fax: 937 372-0040
Joann Merrill, *Ch of Bd*
Terry M Merrill, *President*
EMP: 12
SQ FT: 11,500
SALES: 1.7MM **Privately Held**
WEB: www.advancedwire.com
SIC: 5063 3355 Wire & cable; aluminum
wire & cable

(G-17469)
SAILORS TAILOR INC
Also Called: Bean Bag City
1480 Spg Vly Paintrs Rd (45370-9701)
PHONE..................................937 862-7781
Fax: 937 862-7701
Robert Rowland, *President*
Sandy Rowland, *Office Mgr*
Sandra Rowland, *Manager*
EMP: 9 **EST:** 1972
SQ FT: 2,400
SALES (est): 750K **Privately Held**
WEB: www.sailorstailor.com
SIC: 5961 2394 2519 5712 Catalog &
mail-order houses; furniture & furnishings,
mail order; liners & covers, fabric: made
from purchased materials; sails: made
from purchased materials; household fur-
niture, except wood or metal: upholstered;
furniture stores; marine supplies & equip-
ment; sails & equipment; textile bags

Springboro
Warren County

(G-17470)
ADVANCED ENGRG SOLUTIONS INC
Also Called: Aesi
250 Advanced Dr (45066-1802)
PHONE..................................937 743-6900
Fax: 513 743-6901
Khang Do, *President*
Thomas J Harrington, *Principal*
Marty Luers, *Plant Mgr*
Pat Croskey, *Program Mgr*
Teressa Bush, *Manager*
▲ **EMP:** 70
SQ FT: 44,000
SALES (est): 10.6MM **Privately Held**
SIC: 8711 3544 Engineering services;
special dies, tools, jigs & fixtures

(G-17471)
ADVANCED INTR SOLUTIONS INC
250 Advanced Dr (45066-1802)
PHONE..................................937 550-0065
Jeffrey S Senney, *Principal*
Teresa Bush, *Manager*
▲ **EMP:** 48
SALES (est): 6.8MM **Privately Held**
SIC: 3544 Special dies, tools, jigs & fix-
tures

(G-17472)
ALFONS HAAR INC
150 Advanced Dr (45066-1800)
PHONE..................................937 560-2031
Fax: 937 560-2032
Thomas Haar, *President*
John Dunn, *General Mgr*
Douglas Werner, *Engineer*
Bernd Haar, *Treasurer*
Kathy Fiorenza, *Controller*
▲ **EMP:** 31
SQ FT: 5,000
SALES (est): 8MM
SALES (corp-wide): 51.6MM **Privately
Held**
WEB: www.alfonshaar.com
SIC: 5084 3599 8711 Packaging machin-
ery & equipment; custom machinery; en-
gineering services
PA: Alfons Haar Maschinenbau Gmbh &
Co. Kg
Fangdieckstr. 67
Hamburg 22547
408 339-10

(G-17473)
AMERICAN EXTRUSION SVCS INC (DH)
235 Advanced Dr (45066-1803)
PHONE..................................937 743-1210
Fax: 937 743-1212
David Allison, *President*
EMP: 6
SQ FT: 15,000
SALES (est): 1.6MM
SALES (corp-wide): 1.1B **Publicly Held**
SIC: 3544 Extrusion dies
HQ: Milacron Llc
10200 Alliance Rd Ste 200
Blue Ash OH 45242
513 487-5000

(G-17474)
ASCO POWER TECHNOLOGIES LP
2715 Factory Rd (45066-7445)
PHONE..................................937 748-8884
Armand Visioli, *CEO*
EMP: 158
SALES (corp-wide): 15.2B **Privately Held**
SIC: 3699 Electrical equipment & supplies
HQ: Asco Power Technologies, L.P.
160 Park Ave
Florham Park NJ 07932

(G-17475)
BUCKEYE FABRICATING CO
245 S Pioneer Blvd (45066-1180)
PHONE..................................937 746-9822

Fax: 513 746-9823
Richard K Macaulay, *President*
Gerad Miller, *General Mgr*
Jim Siegman, *Purch Mgr*
Cheryl Schuster, *Sales Mgr*
Mary Vanbeysterveldt, *Info Tech Mgr*
▼ **EMP:** 35 **EST:** 1963
SQ FT: 20,000
SALES (est): 8.3MM **Privately Held**
WEB: www.buckeyefabricating.com
SIC: 3443 Tanks, standard or custom fabricated: metal plate

(G-17476)
CHEWRITE CO
265 S Pioneer Blvd (45066-1180)
PHONE..................................937 746-5509
Fax: 859 743-7786
Robert E Mastandrea, *President*
Dr Joseph Mastandrea, *Vice Pres*
Jim Lyons, *Controller*
Darrell Driskell, *VP Mktg*
John Hodge, *Director*
EMP: 60
SALES (est): 3.3MM **Privately Held**
SIC: 3843 2834 Denture materials; pharmaceutical preparations

(G-17477)
CROOKED HANDLE BREWING CO LLC
760 N Main St (45066-8944)
PHONE..................................937 241-5965
Jason Moore,
EMP: 7
SALES (est): 231.5K **Privately Held**
SIC: 2085 Distilled & blended liquors

(G-17478)
DAYTON AUDIO LLC
725 Pleasant Valley Dr (45066-1158)
PHONE..................................937 743-3000
Rich Taylor, *Marketing Staff*
EMP: 1
SQ FT: 10,000
SALES: 10MM
SALES (corp-wide): 35.9MM **Privately Held**
SIC: 5099 3651 Video & audio equipment; household audio & video equipment
PA: Parts Express International, Inc.
725 Pleasant Valley Dr
Springboro OH 45066
937 743-3000

(G-17479)
DIGILUBE SYSTEMS INC
216 E Mill St (45066-1614)
PHONE..................................937 748-2209
Fax: 513 748-0597
David Hamilton, *President*
John Ekes, *Manager*
EMP: 10
SQ FT: 5,000
SALES: 1.8MM **Privately Held**
WEB: www.digilube.com
SIC: 3569 2992 5084 5172 Lubricating equipment; oils & greases, blending & compounding; conveyor systems; lubricating oils & greases

(G-17480)
FEATHER LITE INNOVATIONS INC (PA)
Also Called: Tuf-N-Lite
650 Pleasant Valley Dr (45066-3026)
PHONE..................................937 743-9008
Fax: 937 743-0390
Dallas Meyers, *President*
Brent Cox, *Vice Pres*
Guy Blanton, *Manager*
Dallas Myers, *Technology*
▲ **EMP:** 20
SALES (est): 5.8MM **Privately Held**
SIC: 3444 5211 Concrete forms, sheet metal; masonry materials & supplies

(G-17481)
GENERAL DYNAMICS-OTS INC
200 S Pioneer Blvd (45066-1179)
PHONE..................................937 746-8500
Fax: 937 746-2524
Anne-Marie Stanley, *Director*
EMP: 150
SQ FT: 220,000

SALES (corp-wide): 31.3B **Publicly Held**
SIC: 3489 Ordnance & accessories
HQ: General Dynamics-Ots, Inc.
11399 16th Ct N Ste 200
Saint Petersburg FL 33716
727 578-8100

(G-17482)
GRAPHIC SYSTEMS SERVICES INC
Also Called: G S S
400 S Pioneer Blvd (45066-3001)
PHONE..................................937 746-0708
Fax: 937 746-0783
Kenneth J Green, *Ch of Bd*
Daniel L Green, *President*
James Copeland, *Corp Secy*
John Sillies, *Exec VP*
John Fillies, *Opers Mgr*
EMP: 41
SQ FT: 100,000
SALES: 6.6MM **Privately Held**
WEB: www.gsspress.com
SIC: 7699 3555 Industrial equipment services; printing presses

(G-17483)
HIGH CONCRETE GROUP LLC
95 Mound Park Dr (45066-2402)
PHONE..................................937 748-2412
Fax: 937 748-9748
B Oliver, *Vice Pres*
Rudolf Oliver, *Vice Pres*
Cheryl Gillis, *Purchasing*
Dave Schneider, *Engrg Dir*
Dennis Nemenz, *Branch Mgr*
EMP: 158
SALES (corp-wide): 381MM **Privately Held**
SIC: 3272 Concrete stuctural support & building material; wall & ceiling squares, concrete; panels & sections, prefabricated concrete
HQ: High Concrete Group Llc
125 Denver Rd
Denver PA 17517
717 336-9300

(G-17484)
JK DIGITAL PUBLISHING LLC
Also Called: Greyden Press
20 Heatherwoode Cir (45066-1500)
P.O. Box 224, Middlebranch (44652-0224)
PHONE..................................937 299-0185
Fax: 614 488-2630
Jack Graf, *CIO*
Michael Jarosz,
George R Klein,
EMP: 20
SQ FT: 7,500
SALES (est): 3.5MM **Privately Held**
WEB: www.greydenpress.com
SIC: 2752 3652 Commercial printing, lithographic; compact laser discs, prerecorded

(G-17485)
KASKELL MANUFACTURING INC
240 Hiawatha Trl (45066-3010)
PHONE..................................937 704-9700
Diane W Harris, *President*
Brian Harris, *Vice Pres*
Brent Collinsworth, *Plant Mgr*
Dave Sharp, *Manager*
EMP: 10
SQ FT: 4,500
SALES (est): 1.5MM **Privately Held**
SIC: 3545 Precision tools, machinists'

(G-17486)
KELCHNER INC (DH)
50 Advanced Dr (45066-1805)
PHONE..................................937 704-9890
Todd Kelchner, *CEO*
Troy Norvell, *President*
Jeff Kelchner, *Vice Pres*
Kevin Weckel, *Vice Pres*
Bryan Brown, *Controller*
EMP: 144 **EST:** 1948
SQ FT: 8,600
SALES: 93MM
SALES (corp-wide): 5B **Privately Held**
SIC: 1794 1389 Excavation work; mud service, oil field drilling; bailing wells

HQ: Wood Group Uk Limited
Wellheads Place
Aberdeen AB21
122 437-3366

(G-17487)
KLOSTERMAN BAKING CO INC
350 S Pioneer Blvd (45066-1181)
PHONE..................................937 743-9021
Jesse Furnas, *Assistant*
EMP: 8 **EST:** 2008
SALES (est): 788.4K **Privately Held**
SIC: 2051 Bread, cake & related products

(G-17488)
KROGER CO
725 W Central Ave (45066-1113)
PHONE..................................937 743-5900
Fax: 513 743-5906
Megan Makse, *Office Mgr*
Daniel Wiley, *Manager*
EMP: 150
SALES (corp-wide): 115.3B **Publicly Held**
WEB: www.kroger.com
SIC: 5411 2051 Supermarkets, chain; bread, cake & related products
PA: The Kroger Co
1014 Vine St Ste 1000
Cincinnati OH 45202
513 762-4000

(G-17489)
MACHINED GLASS SPECIALIST INC
245 Hiawatha Trl (45066-3011)
PHONE..................................937 743-6166
Fax: 513 743-6168
David Behm, *President*
Maurice Vines, *General Mgr*
Joe Bischak, *Comptroller*
Melanie Behm, *Admin Sec*
EMP: 16
SQ FT: 9,000
SALES (est): 1.6MM **Privately Held**
WEB: www.mgsquartz.com
SIC: 3211 5039 Flat glass; tempered glass; glass construction materials

(G-17490)
MOUND STEEL CORP
25 Mound Park Dr (45066-2410)
PHONE..................................937 748-2937
Fax: 937 748-9763
Thomas C Miller, *President*
Andy Williams, *Office Mgr*
EMP: 40
SALES (est): 7.2MM **Privately Held**
WEB: www.heartlandholdingsinc.com
SIC: 3449 Bars, concrete reinforcing: fabricated steel

(G-17491)
MOUND TECHNOLOGIES INC
25 Mound Park Dr (45066-2402)
PHONE..................................937 748-2937
Thomas Miller, *President*
John Barger, *Vice Pres*
Shelia A Campbell, *Admin Sec*
EMP: 45
SQ FT: 40,000
SALES: 20.9MM
SALES (corp-wide): 41MM **Privately Held**
WEB: www.moundtechnologies.com
SIC: 3449 Bars, concrete reinforcing: fabricated steel
PA: Heartland, Inc.
1005 N 19th St
Middlesboro KY 40965
606 248-7323

(G-17492)
NO RINSE LABORATORIES LLC
Also Called: Cleanlife Products
868 Pleasant Valley Dr (45066-1159)
PHONE..................................937 746-7357
Fax: 937 746-7621
Marsha Tuly, *Manager*
Greg Davis,
EMP: 7
SQ FT: 6,000
SALES (est): 1.3MM **Privately Held**
WEB: www.norinse.com
SIC: 2836 Veterinary biological products

(G-17493)
OVONIC ENERGY PRODUCTS INC
50 Ovonic Way (45066-1184)
PHONE..................................937 743-1001
Gary Absher, *Vice Pres*
Monique Byrd, *Finance Dir*
EMP: 125
SQ FT: 80,000
SALES (est): 13MM
SALES (corp-wide): 236.4MM **Privately Held**
WEB: www.cobasys.com
SIC: 3691 Storage batteries
HQ: Robert Bosch Battery Systems Llc
3740 S Lapeer Rd
Orion MI 48359

(G-17494)
PAPER SYSTEMS INCORPORATED (PA)
Also Called: PSI
185 S Pioneer Blvd (45066-3045)
P.O. Box 150 (45066-0150)
PHONE..................................937 746-6841
Fax: 937 746-1089
Larry Curk, *CEO*
Bob Phillips, *President*
Lee Wagoner, *President*
George Tremoulis, *Vice Pres*
Byron Cates, *Plant Mgr*
◆ **EMP:** 120
SQ FT: 90,000
SALES (est): 68.9MM **Privately Held**
WEB: www.papersystems.com
SIC: 2679 Paper products, converted; telegraph, teletype & adding machine paper

(G-17495)
PDI COMMUNICATION SYSTEMS INC (PA)
Also Called: P D I
40 Greenwood Ln (45066-3033)
PHONE..................................937 743-6010
Fax: 513 743-5664
Lou Vilardo, *Owner*
Chuck Stout, *QC Dir*
Eric Johnson, *Design Engr*
Kent Carver, *CFO*
Catherine Saettel, *Marketing Mgr*
▲ **EMP:** 60 **EST:** 1976
SQ FT: 78,000
SALES (est): 19.7MM **Privately Held**
WEB: www.pdiarm.com
SIC: 3663 3599 5047 5064 Television broadcasting & communications equipment; machine shop, jobbing & repair; hospital equipment & furniture; electrical appliances, television & radio

(G-17496)
PHYMET INC (PA)
75 N Pioneer Blvd (45066-3055)
PHONE..................................937 743-8061
Fax: 937 743-6008
Amy Minck Lachman, *President*
Kay Rathburn, *General Mgr*
Gary Dexheimer, *Sales Staff*
EMP: 17
SQ FT: 12,500
SALES (est): 1.3MM **Privately Held**
WEB: www.phymet.com
SIC: 2992 8734 Oils & greases, blending & compounding; metallurgical testing laboratory

(G-17497)
PIONEER AUTOMOTIVE TECH INC (DH)
100 S Pioneer Blvd (45066-1177)
PHONE..................................937 746-2293
Fax: 937 746-2293
Steven Moerner, *President*
Mike Honda, *Treasurer*
Shigeyoshi Okubo, *Treasurer*
Debbie Lee, *Accounting Mgr*
Amber Colon, *Sales Staff*
▲ **EMP:** 175
SQ FT: 155,000
SALES (est): 86.2MM
SALES (corp-wide): 3.8B **Privately Held**
SIC: 5013 3714 3651 Motor vehicle supplies & new parts; motor vehicle parts & accessories; household audio & video equipment

HQ: Pioneer North America, Inc.
2265 E 220th St
Long Beach CA 90810
213 746-6337

(G-17498)
PIONEER NORTH AMERICA INC
Also Called: Pioneer Automotive Tech
355 S Pioneer Blvd (45066-1182)
PHONE..............................937 746-6600
Yoshio Natsume, *Branch Mgr*
EMP: 300
SALES (corp-wide): 3.8B **Privately Held**
SIC: 3651 Sound reproducing equipment
HQ: Pioneer North America, Inc.
2265 E 220th St
Long Beach CA 90810
213 746-6337

(G-17499)
PRINTING FOR LESS
45 Tahlequah Trl (45066-1154)
PHONE..............................937 743-8268
Fax: 513 743-8276
Steve Atkinson, *Owner*
Lee Ann, *Owner*
EMP: 5
SALES (est): 240K **Privately Held**
SIC: 2752 Commercial printing, lithographic

(G-17500)
PROMATCH SOLUTIONS LLC
20 Heatherwoode Cir (45066-1500)
PHONE..............................937 299-0185
Jeffrey R Relick, *President*
Rich Culberson, *Sales Executive*
Tammy Relick, *Office Mgr*
EMP: 15
SQ FT: 11,500
SALES (est): 1.6MM **Privately Held**
SIC: 2741 7375 2789 2752 Micropublishing; information retrieval services; book-binding & related work; commercial printing, lithographic

(G-17501)
QUICK TECH BUSINESS FORMS INC
408 Sharts Dr (45066-3000)
P.O. Box 607 (45066-0607)
PHONE..............................937 743-5952
Fax: 513 753-9256
Chris Felker, *Principal*
Linda Felker, *Principal*
Jamie Witt, *Financial Exec*
Kevin Gilliam, *Manager*
EMP: 50
SALES (est): 6.2MM **Privately Held**
WEB: www.quicktechgraphics.com
SIC: 2759 3999 Financial note & certificate printing & engraving; barber & beauty shop equipment

(G-17502)
QUICK TECH GRAPHICS INC
408 Sharts Dr Frnt (45066-3021)
P.O. Box 607 (45066-0607)
PHONE..............................937 743-5952
Christopher H Felker, *President*
Linda Felker, *Principal*
David Bitner, *Manager*
Jamie Witt, *Manager*
EMP: 35
SQ FT: 15,000
SALES (est): 7MM **Privately Held**
SIC: 2761 5943 2791 2782 Manifold business forms; office forms & supplies; typesetting; blankbooks & looseleaf binders; commercial printing, lithographic

(G-17503)
R L DRAKE HOLDINGS LLC (HQ)
710 Pleasant Valley Dr (45066-1157)
PHONE..............................937 746-4556
Fax: 937 743-4507
Steve Roe, *Managing Dir*
Brian Wilkin, *Chief Engr*
Phil Hawkins, *Sales Mgr*
Bob Palle, *Mng Member*
Geoff Hinkle, *Manager*
▲ **EMP:** 13

SALES (est): 1.4MM
SALES (corp-wide): 22.5MM **Publicly Held**
SIC: 3663 Radio & TV communications equipment
PA: Blonder Tongue Laboratories, Inc.
1 Jake Brown Rd
Old Bridge NJ 08857
732 679-4000

(G-17504)
R SPORTSWEAR LLC
8068 Forest Glen Dr (45066-9145)
PHONE..............................937 748-3507
Ron Coates, *Mng Member*
EMP: 4 **EST:** 1994
SALES (est): 322.2K **Privately Held**
SIC: 2395 3552 Embroidery & art needlework; silk screens for textile industry

(G-17505)
RCT INDUSTRIES INC
Also Called: Adcura Mfg
7494 Deep Woods Ct (45066-8554)
PHONE..............................937 602-1100
Russell Thie, *President*
EMP: 10
SQ FT: 4,000
SALES (est): 500K **Privately Held**
WEB: www.adcuramfg.com
SIC: 3679 Electronic circuits

(G-17506)
ROYER TECHNOLOGIES INC
275 Hiawatha Trl (45066-3011)
PHONE..............................937 743-6114
Fax: 937 743-0072
Marshall Royer, *President*
Gregory Day, *General Mgr*
Vicky Royer, *Manager*
▲ **EMP:** 9
SQ FT: 10,000
SALES: 966.7K **Privately Held**
SIC: 3544 3545 5251 Special dies, tools, jigs & fixtures; machine tool accessories; tools

(G-17507)
SIEMENS INDUSTRY INC
10 Southfield Ct (45066-9268)
PHONE..............................937 748-1726
Jeff Rohde, *Principal*
EMP: 97
SALES (corp-wide): 89.6B **Privately Held**
SIC: 3822 Air conditioning & refrigeration controls
HQ: Siemens Industry, Inc.
1000 Deerfield Pkwy
Buffalo Grove IL 60089
847 215-1000

(G-17508)
SUNSTAR ENGRG AMERICAS INC (HQ)
85 S Pioneer Blvd (45066-3039)
PHONE..............................937 746-8575
Yoshikazu Kuwahara, *President*
Ed Robbins, *Controller*
Marsha Green, *Accountant*
▲ **EMP:** 26
SQ FT: 28,000
SALES (est): 28.7MM **Privately Held**
SIC: 3751 2891 Motorcycles & related parts; adhesives
PA: Starlecs Inc.
3-1, Asahimachi
Takatsuki OSK
726 825-552

(G-17509)
THALER MACHINE COMPANY
216 Tahlequah Trl (45066-3052)
P.O. Box 430 (45066-0430)
PHONE..............................937 550-2400
Fax: 937 865-9045
Homer Reed, *QC Mgr*
Bill Thaler, *Financial Exec*
Gregory Donson, *Manager*
EMP: 5
SALES (corp-wide): 12.8MM **Privately Held**
WEB: www.thalermachine.com
SIC: 3545 Precision measuring tools

PA: The Thaler Machine Company
216 Tahlequah Trl
Springboro OH 45066
937 550-2400

(G-17510)
TOOLING ZONE INC
285 S Pioneer Blvd (45066-1180)
PHONE..............................937 550-4180
Fax: 937 435-4229
Steven D liams, *President*
Jeniffer Guyler, *Manager*
Jane Mathews, *Manager*
EMP: 30
SQ FT: 9,000
SALES (est): 6.6MM **Privately Held**
SIC: 3544 Special dies & tools

(G-17511)
TOTAL CABLE SOLUTIONS INC
475 Victory Ln (45066-3047)
PHONE..............................513 457-7013
Charles Hoskins, *CEO*
Paul Kirk, *President*
▲ **EMP:** 9
SALES (est): 1.5MM **Privately Held**
SIC: 3679 Harness assemblies for electronic use: wire or cable

(G-17512)
TREBNICK SYSTEMS INC
Also Called: Trebnick Tags and Labels
215 S Pioneer Blvd (45066-1180)
PHONE..............................937 743-1550
Fax: 859 743-1558
Gregg Trebnick, *CEO*
Linda Trebnick, *President*
Aaron Trebnick, *Vice Pres*
John Ashby, *Production*
Brenda James, *Controller*
◆ **EMP:** 29
SQ FT: 24,480
SALES (est): 5.4MM **Privately Held**
WEB: www.trebnick.com
SIC: 2269 2752 2754 2759 Labels, cotton: printed; tags, lithographed; commercial printing, gravure; labels & seals: printing

(G-17513)
VENOM TOWING LLC
5620 Red Lion 5 Points Rd (45066-7707)
PHONE..............................937 344-6530
Diana Jones, *Principal*
EMP: 3
SALES (est): 195.2K **Privately Held**
SIC: 2836 Venoms

Springfield
Clark County

(G-17514)
ACE TRANSFER COMPANY
1017 Hometown St (45504-2000)
PHONE..............................937 398-1103
Fax: 937 398-1103
David J Shaw, *President*
EMP: 6 **EST:** 1994
SALES (est): 795.8K **Privately Held**
SIC: 2759 Screen printing

(G-17515)
AKZO NOBEL COATINGS INC
1550 Progress Rd (45505-4456)
PHONE..............................937 322-2671
Fax: 937 322-7685
Ron Cecil, *Enginr/R&D Mgr*
Mary Pavelka, *Manager*
Thomas Stubbs, *Director*
Tim Penington, *Maintence Staff*
EMP: 15
SALES (corp-wide): 15.9B **Privately Held**
WEB: www.nam.sikkens.com
SIC: 2851 Paints: oil or alkyd vehicle or water thinned
HQ: Akzo Nobel Coatings Inc.
2031 Nelson Miller Pkwy
Louisville KY 44136
502 254-0470

(G-17516)
AMCAN STAIR & RAIL LLC
20 Zischler St (45504-2853)
PHONE..............................937 781-3084
Mike Edmondson, *Principal*
EMP: 10
SALES (est): 840K **Privately Held**
SIC: 2431 Staircases, stairs & railings

(G-17517)
AOT INC
4800 Gateway Blvd (45502-8818)
PHONE..............................937 323-9669
Fax: 937 322-1000
Richard F Dauch, *CEO*
Debra Puchanan, *Finance*
Melissa Nangle, *Executive*
EMP: 21
SQ FT: 136,000
SALES (est): 5.7MM
SALES (corp-wide): 102.1MM **Privately Held**
SIC: 3559 Pack-up assemblies, wheel overhaul
HQ: Accuride Corporation
7140 Office Cir
Evansville IN 47715
812 962-5000

(G-17518)
ARCTECH FABRICATING INC (PA)
1317 Lagonda Ave (45503-4001)
P.O. Box 1447 (45501-1447)
PHONE..............................937 525-9353
Fax: 937 322-0200
Leonard McConnaghey, *CEO*
James C Roberts II, *President*
Len McConnaughey, *Vice Pres*
Kim Williams, *Buyer*
Mark Stoltz, *Engineer*
EMP: 29
SQ FT: 13,200
SALES (est): 5MM **Privately Held**
WEB: www.arctechfabricating.com
SIC: 7692 3441 Welding repair; fabricated structural metal

(G-17519)
ARMOLOY OF OHIO INC
1950 E Leffel Ln (45505-4623)
P.O. Box 996 (45501-0996)
PHONE..............................937 323-8702
Fax: 937 323-2754
Steven Neely, *President*
Ron Minerd, *QC Dir*
Cindy Ray, *Financial Exec*
EMP: 15
SQ FT: 10,000
SALES (est): 1.9MM **Privately Held**
WEB: www.armoloyofohio.com
SIC: 3479 Coating of metals & formed products

(G-17520)
B O K INC
508 W Main St (45504-2662)
PHONE..............................937 322-9588
Kenneth Klosterman, *CEO*
Chip Klosterman, *CEO*
Ken Klosterman, *CEO*
EMP: 125
SALES (est): 8.1MM
SALES (corp-wide): 209.5MM **Privately Held**
WEB: www.bok.net
SIC: 2045 Bread & bread type roll mixes: from purchased flour
PA: Klosterman Baking Co.
4760 Paddock Rd
Cincinnati OH 45229
513 242-5667

(G-17521)
BAY BUSINESS FORMS INC
1803 W Columbia St (45504-2903)
PHONE..............................937 322-3000
Fax: 937 322-9328
Robert E Troop, *CEO*
Paulette Bay, *President*
Cherrie Reed, *Office Mgr*
EMP: 11
SQ FT: 22,000

SALES (est): 1.2MM
SALES (corp-wide): 100.1MM **Privately Held**
WEB: www.baybusinessforms.net
SIC: 5112 2752 Business forms; commercial printing, offset
PA: The Shamrock Companies Inc
24090 Detroit Rd
Westlake OH 44145
440 899-9510

(G-17522)
BENJAMIN STEEL COMPANY INC
777 Benjamin Dr (45502-8846)
PHONE...................................937 233-1212
Fax: 937 233-5704
Vincent Demana, *Owner*
Nick Demana, *General Mgr*
Shawn Taylor, *Branch Mgr*
Tim Halloran, *Branch Mgr*
EMP: 40
SQ FT: 36,000
SALES (corp-wide): 86.5MM **Privately Held**
WEB: www.benjaminsteel.com
SIC: 5051 3498 3334 3317 Steel; tube fabricating (contract bending & shaping); primary aluminum; steel pipe & tubes; cold finishing of steel shapes; blast furnaces & steel mills
PA: Benjamin Steel Company, Inc.
777 Benjamin Dr
Springfield OH 45502
937 322-8600

(G-17523)
BENNETT & BENNETT INC (PA)
1318 Kenton St (45505-3206)
PHONE...................................937 324-1100
Bill Bennett, *President*
Tami Anderson, *General Mgr*
Michelle Bennett, *Treasurer*
Diane Graham, *Manager*
EMP: 11
SQ FT: 7,000
SALES (est): 1.5MM **Privately Held**
WEB: www.bennettnbennett.com
SIC: 3679 Static power supply converters for electronic applications

(G-17524)
BOX KING LLC
1125 N Bechtle Ave (45504-2009)
PHONE...................................937 322-8117
Fax: 937 322-4707
Mike Corns, *Principal*
EMP: 6 **EST:** 2009
SALES (est): 858.6K **Privately Held**
SIC: 2752 Commercial printing, lithographic

(G-17525)
BRYCE HILL INC (PA)
2301 Sheridan Ave (45505-2515)
P.O. Box 1043 (45501-1043)
PHONE...................................937 325-0651
Fax: 937 323-6231
Deborah L Hill Grimes, *President*
Andrea Treolo, *Accountant*
EMP: 2
SALES (est): 9.8MM **Privately Held**
SIC: 3271 Blocks, concrete: landscape or retaining wall

(G-17526)
CANDY PRINT SHOP
4560 Mumper Rd (45502-9230)
PHONE...................................937 390-6458
Susan Baderpscher, *Owner*
EMP: 3
SALES (est): 144.5K **Privately Held**
SIC: 2759 Bag, wrapper & seal printing & engraving

(G-17527)
CASCADE CORPORATION
2501 Sheridan Ave (45505-2519)
P.O. Box 20187, Portland OR (97294-0187)
PHONE...................................937 327-0300
Fax: 937 327-0082
Laurent Lemaire, *Vice Chairman*
Rodney Hickman, *Plant Mgr*
Paul Phillips, *Foreman/Supr*
Todd Henry, *Purch Agent*

Kevin Mercer, *Buyer*
EMP: 200
SALES (corp-wide): 19B **Privately Held**
WEB: www.cascorp.com
SIC: 3537 3713 3593 Trucks, tractors, loaders, carriers & similar equipment; truck & bus bodies; fluid power cylinders & actuators
HQ: Cascade Corporation
2201 Ne 201st Ave
Fairview OR 97024
503 669-6300

(G-17528)
CAVE TOOL & MANUFACTURING INC
20 Walnut St (45505-1145)
PHONE...................................937 324-0662
Fax: 937 324-3792
Gilbert R Cave, *President*
Carrie Cave, *Vice Pres*
EMP: 10
SQ FT: 26,000
SALES (est): 1.2MM **Privately Held**
SIC: 3599 Machine shop, jobbing & repair

(G-17529)
CENTERLINE MACHINE INC
4949 Urbana Rd (45502-8387)
PHONE...................................937 322-4887
EMP: 5
SQ FT: 2,000
SALES (est): 603.4K **Privately Held**
SIC: 3443 Mfg Fabricated Plate Work

(G-17530)
CES NATIONWIDE
567 E Leffel Ln (45504-4748)
PHONE...................................937 322-0771
John Lewis, *Principal*
Nikkie Burke, *Manager*
EMP: 7
SALES (est): 515.7K **Privately Held**
SIC: 3699 3634 5063 Electrical equipment & supplies; electric housewares & fans; electrical supplies

(G-17531)
CHAMPION COMPANY (PA)
400 Harrison St (45505-2067)
P.O. Box 967 (45501-0967)
PHONE...................................937 324-5681
Fax: 937 324-2397
Aristides Gianakopoulos, *President*
Benjamin G Devoe, *Principal*
Robert Rizer, *Opers Staff*
Bruce Harmison, *Purchasing*
Myra Starr, *Accountant*
EMP: 60 **EST:** 1878
SQ FT: 165,000
SALES (est): 12.6MM **Privately Held**
WEB: www.championspd.com
SIC: 2869 3412 Embalming fluids; metal barrels, drums & pails

(G-17532)
CHAMPION COMPANY
1100 Kenton St (45505-3136)
P.O. Box 967 (45501-0967)
PHONE...................................937 324-5681
Bob Rizer, *General Mgr*
EMP: 68
SALES (corp-wide): 12.6MM **Privately Held**
WEB: www.championspd.com
SIC: 3412 Metal barrels, drums & pails
PA: The Champion Company
400 Harrison St
Springfield OH 45505
937 324-5681

(G-17533)
COFFELT CANDY INC (PA)
6050 Urbana Rd (45502-9544)
PHONE...................................937 399-8772
Dwight W Coffelt, *President*
Betty Coffelt, *Treasurer*
Elizabeth J Coffelt, *Treasurer*
EMP: 5
SQ FT: 10,000
SALES (est): 2.8MM **Privately Held**
WEB: www.coffeltcandy.com
SIC: 5441 2064 Candy; candy & other confectionery products

(G-17534)
COLBY PROPERTIES LLC
2071 N Bechtle Ave (45504-1583)
PHONE...................................937 390-0816
Alan Cowgill, *
Julie Cowgill, *
EMP: 6
SALES (est): 565.2K **Privately Held**
SIC: 3999 Education aids, devices & supplies

(G-17535)
COMPTONS PRECISION MACHINE
Also Called: Eastern Enterprise
224 Dayton Ave (45506-1206)
P.O. Box 2614 (45501-2614)
PHONE...................................937 325-9139
Fax: 937 325-4541
EMP: 12
SQ FT: 11,000
SALES: 1MM **Privately Held**
SIC: 3599 7692 Mfg Industrial Machinery Welding Repair

(G-17536)
CORROTEC INC
1125 W North St (45504-2713)
PHONE...................................937 325-3585
Fax: 937 325-9456
David A Stratton, *CEO*
Aristides G Gianakopoulos, *President*
Walter A Wildman, *Principal*
John C Stratton, *Vice Pres*
Walt Newman, *Safety Mgr*
EMP: 35 **EST:** 1981
SQ FT: 28,500
SALES (est): 9.2MM **Privately Held**
WEB: www.corrotec.com
SIC: 3559 7699 3479 3625 Electroplating machinery & equipment; tank repair; coating of metals with plastic or resins; electric controls & control accessories, industrial

(G-17537)
CSL PLASMA INC
435 E Columbia St (45503-4214)
PHONE...................................937 325-4200
Jason Tate, *Branch Mgr*
Katie Patek, *Manager*
Tracy Young, *Manager*
EMP: 44
SALES (corp-wide): 5.9B **Privately Held**
SIC: 2836 Plasmas
HQ: Csl Plasma Inc.
900 Broken Sound Pkwy # 4
Boca Raton FL 33487
561 981-3700

(G-17538)
D L H LOCOMOTIVE WORKS
1528 Mitchell Blvd (45503-3415)
PHONE...................................937 629-0321
David L Hickinbotham, *Owner*
EMP: 6
SALES (est): 418.1K **Privately Held**
SIC: 3944 Railroad models: toy & hobby

(G-17539)
DEARTH RESOURCES INC (PA)
Also Called: Hill Bryce Concrete
2301 Sheridan Ave (45505-2515)
P.O. Box 1043 (45501-1043)
PHONE...................................937 325-0651
Debra Grimes, *Principal*
Bonnie Sowers, *Accountant*
EMP: 9
SQ FT: 20,000
SALES (est): 1.4MM **Privately Held**
WEB: www.brycehill.com
SIC: 3273 3271 5211 Ready-mixed concrete; blocks, concrete or cinder: standard; lumber & other building materials

(G-17540)
DEARTH RESOURCES INC
8801 State Route 36 (45501)
P.O. Box 1043 (45501-1043)
PHONE...................................937 663-4171
Debra Grimes, *President*
EMP: 8

SALES (corp-wide): 1.4MM **Privately Held**
WEB: www.brycehill.com
SIC: 3273 3271 Ready-mixed concrete; blocks, concrete or cinder: standard
PA: Dearth Resources, Inc.
2301 Sheridan Ave
Springfield OH 45505
937 325-0651

(G-17541)
DELILLE OXYGEN COMPANY
1101 W Columbia St (45504-2846)
PHONE...................................937 325-9595
David Smith, *Finance Mgr*
Chad Lee, *Sales Mgr*
Scott Huffman, *Sales Associate*
Mike Lee, *Manager*
EMP: 8
SALES (corp-wide): 19.8MM **Privately Held**
WEB: www.delille.com
SIC: 2813 5084 Industrial gases; welding machinery & equipment
PA: Delille Oxygen Company
772 Marion Rd
Columbus OH 43207
614 444-1177

(G-17542)
DELTA CRANE SYSTEMS INC
624 Aberfelda Dr (45504-3973)
PHONE...................................937 324-7425
Chris McCombs, *President*
Joyce McCombs, *Treasurer*
Cheryl Copes, *Controller*
EMP: 10
SQ FT: 16,600
SALES: 1MM **Privately Held**
SIC: 3536 5084 Cranes, industrial plant; materials handling machinery

(G-17543)
DEMMY SAND AND GRAVEL LLC
4324 Fairfield Pike (45502-9707)
PHONE...................................937 325-8840
Fax: 937 325-9482
Amy Demmy, *General Mgr*
Woodrow Demmy, *
EMP: 25 **EST:** 1944
SALES (est): 2.2MM **Privately Held**
SIC: 1442 0115 0119 0111 Common sand mining; gravel mining; corn; bean (dry field & seed) farm; wheat

(G-17544)
DILLON MANUFACTURING INC
2115 Progress Rd (45505-4470)
PHONE...................................937 325-8482
Fax: 937 325-8483
Joseph Shouvlin, *President*
Jeremy Hays, *Opers Mgr*
EMP: 19 **EST:** 1953
SQ FT: 15,000
SALES (est): 2.4MM **Privately Held**
WEB: www.dillonmfg.com
SIC: 3545 Chucks: drill, lathe or magnetic (machine tool accessories)

(G-17545)
DMTCO LLC
302 S Center St (45506-1604)
P.O. Box 958 (45501-0958)
PHONE...................................937 324-0061
Malcolm Lovelace, *
Duane J Newland, *
Tony A Stevens, *
EMP: 7
SQ FT: 1,100
SALES (est): 730K **Privately Held**
SIC: 3585 Refrigeration & heating equipment

(G-17546)
DOLE FRESH VEGETABLES INC
600 Benjamin Dr (45502-8860)
PHONE...................................937 525-4300
Fax: 937 525-4353
Phillip Mansour, *Maint Spvr*
Michael Locke, *Finance Mgr*
Lenny Pelifian, *Branch Mgr*
Leonard Davis, *Manager*
Michael Mendoza, *Manager*
EMP: 190

SALES (corp-wide): 10.2B **Privately Held**
SIC: 5148 2099 Fresh fruits & vegetables; food preparations
HQ: Dole Fresh Vegetables, Inc.
　2959 Salinas Hwy
　Monterey CA 93940
　831 422-8871

(G-17547)
DRAKE MONUMENT COMPANY
524 W Mccreight Ave (45504-1606)
PHONE................................937 399-7941
Linda Conley, *Partner*
Charles Thrist Jr, *Partner*
EMP: 4
SALES (est): 328.3K **Privately Held**
WEB: www.drakemonumentco.com
SIC: 5999 3281 Monuments, finished to custom order; cut stone & stone products

(G-17548)
DUPLEX MILL & MANUFACTURING CO
Also Called: Kelly Duplex
415 Sigler St (45506-1144)
P.O. Box 1266 (45501-1266)
PHONE................................937 325-5555
Fax: 937 325-0859
Eric W Wise, *President*
Frederick Wise, *Vice Pres*
EMP: 20
SQ FT: 50,000
SALES (est): 5.3MM **Privately Held**
WEB: www.dmmc.com
SIC: 3535 3531 Conveyors & conveying equipment; mixers: ore, plaster, slag, sand, mortar, etc.

(G-17549)
E & W ENTERPRISES POWELL INC (HQ)
Also Called: Muncy Co, The
2020 Progress Rd (45505-4472)
PHONE................................937 346-0800
Fax: 937 864-7637
Wayne Brumfield, *President*
Chris Wood, *Controller*
Sarah J Smith, *Human Res Dir*
▲ EMP: 80 EST: 1946
SQ FT: 60,000
SALES (est): 12.2MM
SALES (corp-wide): 96MM **Privately Held**
SIC: 3465 Automotive stampings
PA: Jmac Inc.
　200 W Nationwide Blvd # 1
　Columbus OH 43215
　614 436-2418

(G-17550)
ECHO EMR INC
2755 Columbus Rd (45503-3203)
PHONE................................937 322-4972
Fax: 937 322-6278
Ronald K Hill, *President*
Pamela Chiles, *Plant Mgr*
Bob Meyer, *Office Mgr*
▲ EMP: 15 EST: 1947
SALES (est): 1.7MM **Privately Held**
SIC: 3229 Tubing, glass

(G-17551)
ED THOMAS
Also Called: Corporate Image Makers
819 Cedar St (45504-2701)
PHONE................................937 325-4300
Ed Thomas, *Owner*
EMP: 3
SALES (est): 244K **Privately Held**
WEB: www.penceohio.com
SIC: 5112 3172 2782 2396 Stationery & office supplies; personal leather goods; blankbooks & looseleaf binders; automotive & apparel trimmings

(G-17552)
ELECTRIC EEL MFG CO INC
501 W Leffel Ln (45506-3529)
P.O. Box 419 (45501-0419)
PHONE................................937 323-4644
Fax: 937 323-3767
David Hale, *CEO*
Thomas H Hale, *Vice Pres*
Mark Speranza, *Mktg Dir*
Peggy Barnhart, *Admin Sec*
Marty Rowland, *Relations*

▲ EMP: 38 EST: 1968
SQ FT: 21,000
SALES (est): 9.1MM **Privately Held**
SIC: 3423 3589 Hand & edge tools; sewer cleaning equipment, power

(G-17553)
ERNEST INDUSTRIES INC
Also Called: Kelly-Creswell Company
1221 Groop Rd (45504-3829)
PHONE................................937 325-9851
Fax: 937 324-8992
Michael T Stute, *President*
Travis Brentlinger, *Foreman/Supr*
Jerry Preston, *Foreman/Supr*
Susan Stute, *Treasurer*
Mark Meyers, *VP Human Res*
EMP: 11
SALES (est): 3.4MM **Privately Held**
WEB: www.ernestindustries.com
SIC: 3563 Air & gas compressors

(G-17554)
ESTERLINE & SONS MFG CO LLC
6508 Old Clifton Rd (45502-8474)
PHONE................................937 265-5278
Fax: 937 265-5513
John Maurer, *Mng Member*
▲ EMP: 22 EST: 1957
SQ FT: 1,500
SALES (est): 4MM **Privately Held**
WEB: www.esterlineandsons.com
SIC: 3599 Machine shop, jobbing & repair

(G-17555)
EVER ROLL SPECIALTIES CO
3988 Lawrenceville Dr (45504-4458)
PHONE................................937 964-1302
Fax: 937 964-8400
Edwin J Kohl, *President*
I Scott Wallace, *COO*
Mike Clark, *Engineer*
▲ EMP: 50 EST: 1945
SQ FT: 43,000
SALES (est): 10.9MM **Privately Held**
WEB: www.ever-roll.com
SIC: 3498 3496 Fabricated pipe & fittings; miscellaneous fabricated wire products

(G-17556)
F H BONN CO INC
4300 Gateway Blvd (45502-8819)
PHONE................................937 323-7024
Fax: 937 323-0388
Neal Bonn, *President*
Barbara Rossler, *General Mgr*
Allan Bonn, *Corp Secy*
Darrin Bonn, *VP Mfg*
▲ EMP: 61
SQ FT: 43,000
SALES (est): 10.8MM **Privately Held**
WEB: www.fhbonn.com
SIC: 2211 Plushes & piles, broadwoven cotton: including flannels

(G-17557)
FAMILY PACKAGING INC (PA)
504 W Euclid Ave (45506-2010)
PHONE................................937 325-4106
Fax: 937 325-3338
Janet Kennedy, *President*
Paul T Miles, *Vice Pres*
Michael A Miles, *VP Prdtn*
James Miles, *Treasurer*
EMP: 6
SQ FT: 47,000
SALES: 2MM **Privately Held**
SIC: 2653 Boxes, corrugated: made from purchased materials

(G-17558)
FINK MEAT COMPANY INC
2475 Troy Rd (45504-4233)
P.O. Box 1281 (45501-1281)
PHONE................................937 390-2750
Fax: 937 390-1212
William Craig Minter, *President*
Douglas Minter, *Vice Pres*
EMP: 7
SQ FT: 8,600
SALES: 1.5MM **Privately Held**
SIC: 5147 2013 Meats, fresh; luncheon meat from purchased meat

(G-17559)
FIRE & MARINE INC
5325 Prosperity Dr (45502-9074)
PHONE................................937 323-2770
Jeffrey R Collier, *Vice Pres*
EMP: 23 EST: 2007
SALES: 1.5MM **Privately Held**
SIC: 3569 Firefighting apparatus & related equipment

(G-17560)
FLASHIONS SPORTSWEAR LTD
1002 N Bechtle Ave (45504-2008)
PHONE................................937 323-5885
Fax: 937 390-3424
Bethany Turner, *Partner*
Ronald Turner, *General Ptnr*
EMP: 9
SQ FT: 4,000
SALES (est): 802.3K **Privately Held**
WEB: www.flashions.com
SIC: 5199 2262 Advertising specialties; screen printing: manmade fiber & silk broadwoven fabrics

(G-17561)
FLUID QUIP INC (PA)
1940 S Yellow Spring St # 2 (45506-3048)
PHONE................................937 324-0352
Fax: 937 324-0048
Andy Franko, *President*
John McBlane, *Vice Pres*
Robert Patton, *Treasurer*
Sheryl Elam, *Accounts Mgr*
▲ EMP: 38
SQ FT: 50,000
SALES (est): 8.9MM **Privately Held**
WEB: www.fluidquip.com
SIC: 3554 Pulp mill machinery

(G-17562)
G & R WELDING & MACHINING
4690 E National Rd (45505-1846)
PHONE................................937 323-9353
Fax: 937 323-9353
Ralph Rybolt, *Owner*
EMP: 3
SQ FT: 9,500
SALES (est): 500K **Privately Held**
SIC: 1799 3441 Welding on site; fabricated structural metal

(G-17563)
GAIL BERNER
Also Called: Berner Screen Print
514 W Columbia St (45504-2622)
PHONE................................937 322-0314
Fax: 937 322-7872
Gail Berner, *Owner*
EMP: 3
SQ FT: 1,800
SALES: 350K **Privately Held**
WEB: www.bernerscreenprint.com
SIC: 2759 2395 5199 3993 Screen printing; embroidery products, except schiffli machine; advertising specialties; signs & advertising specialties; automotive & apparel trimmings

(G-17564)
GRAPHIC PAPER PRODUCTS CORP (HQ)
Also Called: Miller Printing Co
581 W Leffel Ln (45506-3529)
P.O. Box 1666 (45501-1666)
PHONE................................937 325-5503
Fax: 937 324-5697
Jeanne Lampe, *President*
Paul Ripplinger, *Controller*
EMP: 82 EST: 1891
SQ FT: 50,000
SALES (est): 10.7MM
SALES (corp-wide): 57.4MM **Privately Held**
WEB: www.miller-printing.com
SIC: 2754 2752 2652 2653 Job printing, gravure; commercial printing, lithographic; setup paperboard boxes; boxes, corrugated: made from purchased materials; packaging paper; miscellaneous publishing
PA: Patented Acquisition Corporation
　2490 Cross Pointe Dr
　Miamisburg OH 45342
　937 353-2299

(G-17565)
GRAPHIC PAPER PRODUCTS CORP
Barrett Brothers
581 W Leffel Ln (45506-3529)
PHONE................................937 322-7711
Fax: 937 328-2849
Julie Bennett, *Manager*
EMP: 4
SALES (corp-wide): 57.4MM **Privately Held**
SIC: 2754 2752 Directories, telephone: gravure printing, not published; commercial printing, lithographic
HQ: Graphic Paper Products Corporation
　581 W Leffel Ln
　Springfield OH 45506
　937 325-5503

(G-17566)
GRAPHIC PAPER PRODUCTS CORP
Also Called: Armstrong Printing
222 E Main St (45503-4222)
P.O. Box 166 (45501-0166)
PHONE................................937 325-3912
Carol McCoy, *General Mgr*
EMP: 5
SALES (corp-wide): 57.4MM **Privately Held**
WEB: www.miller-printing.com
SIC: 2759 Commercial printing
HQ: Graphic Paper Products Corporation
　581 W Leffel Ln
　Springfield OH 45506
　937 325-5503

(G-17567)
HAIR & NAIL IMPRESSIONS
2330 Northmoor Dr (45503-2344)
PHONE................................937 399-0221
Cathy Fent, *Owner*
EMP: 4
SALES (est): 84.3K **Privately Held**
SIC: 7231 2844 Unisex hair salons; manicure preparations

(G-17568)
HAYS FABRICATING & WELDING
633 E Leffel Ln (45505-4750)
PHONE................................937 325-0031
Fax: 937 325-0638
Clayton Hays, *President*
Richard Shaw, *Sales Mgr*
Connie Sanders, *Manager*
EMP: 27
SQ FT: 25,000
SALES (est): 7MM **Privately Held**
WEB: www.haysfab.com
SIC: 3441 3555 Fabricated structural metal; plates, metal: engravers'

(G-17569)
HDI LANDING GEAR USA INC (HQ)
663 Montgomery Ave (45506-1847)
PHONE................................513 619-1203
Michael Meshay, *President*
Donna Harvanec, *General Mgr*
William Michalski, *Treasurer*
Kevin Lewis, *Info Tech Mgr*
EMP: 150
SALES (est): 31.7MM
SALES (corp-wide): 246.3MM **Privately Held**
SIC: 3728 Alighting (landing gear) assemblies, aircraft
PA: Heroux-Devtek Inc
　1111 Rue Saint-Charles O Bureau 658
　Longueuil QC J4K 5
　450 679-3330

(G-17570)
HEAT TREATING INC (PA)
1762 W Pleasant St (45506-1128)
PHONE................................937 325-3121
Fax: 937 323-7842
Chester L Walthall, *President*
Judith A Walthall, *Corp Secy*
Keith Thue, *Vice Pres*
Michael Trimble, *Vice Pres*
Dan Antrim, *Supervisor*
EMP: 25 EST: 1959
SQ FT: 33,000

SALES (est): 3.1MM **Privately Held**
WEB: www.heattreating.com
SIC: 3398 Metal heat treating

(G-17571)
HEAT TREATING INC
1807 W Pleasant St (45506-1199)
PHONE................................937 325-3121
Chester L Walthall, *President*
Carroll Johnson, *Vice Pres*
Martin Mahoney, *Sales Staff*
EMP: 17
SALES (corp-wide): 3.1MM **Privately Held**
WEB: www.heattreating.com
SIC: 3398 Metal heat treating
PA: Heat Treating, Inc
1762 W Pleasant St
Springfield OH 45506
937 325-3121

(G-17572)
HEF USA CORPORATION (PA)
2015 Progress Rd (45505-4472)
PHONE................................937 323-2556
Fax: 937 323-5787
Kenneth Metzgar, *Principal*
Margo Metzgar, *Manager*
▲ EMP: 15
SALES (est): 3.1MM **Privately Held**
WEB: www.hefusa.net
SIC: 3826 Surface area analyzers

(G-17573)
HILLTOP BASIC RESOURCES INC
Enon Washed Sand & Gravel Div
1665 Enon Rd (45502-9102)
PHONE................................937 882-6357
Jack Blair, *Principal*
EMP: 12
SALES (corp-wide): 135MM **Privately Held**
WEB: www.hilltopbasicresources.com
SIC: 1771 1442 Concrete work; construction sand & gravel
PA: Hilltop Basic Resources, Inc.
1 W 4th St Ste 1100
Cincinnati OH 45202
513 651-5000

(G-17574)
HOLMES W & SONS PRINTING
Also Called: Holmes Printing
401 E Columbia St (45503-4214)
P.O. Box 2300 (45501-2300)
PHONE................................937 325-1509
Fax: 937 325-9555
William W Holmes, *President*
Heather Leifheit, *Marketing Staff*
Karen Miller, *Manager*
Carisa Holmes-Peters, *Admin Sec*
Karleigh Spahr, *Graphic Designe*
EMP: 14
SQ FT: 2,500
SALES (est): 1.8MM **Privately Held**
WEB: www.holmesprinting.com
SIC: 2752 Commercial printing, offset

(G-17575)
HORIZON INDUSTRIES CORP
1801 W Columbia St (45504-2903)
PHONE................................937 323-0801
Fax: 937 323-0802
John Neiswinger, *President*
Richard Koehler, *Treasurer*
EMP: 9
SQ FT: 15,000
SALES: 800K **Privately Held**
WEB: www.horizonindustriescorp.com
SIC: 3544 Special dies & tools

(G-17576)
HORNER INDUSTRIAL SERVICES INC
Also Called: Scherer Industrial Group
5330 Prosperity Dr (45502-9074)
PHONE................................937 390-6667
Fax: 937 390-7493
Mike Harper, *Manager*
Michael Harper, *Director*
EMP: 25
SALES (corp-wide): 47.3MM **Privately Held**
SIC: 5063 7694 Motors, electric; electric motor repair

PA: Horner Industrial Services, Inc.
1521 E Washington St
Indianapolis IN 46201
317 639-4261

(G-17577)
HOUSTON MACHINE PRODUCTS INC
1065 W Leffel Ln (45506-3555)
PHONE................................937 322-8022
Fax: 937 322-5737
Sandra White, *President*
EMP: 30
SQ FT: 35,000
SALES (est): 5.2MM **Privately Held**
SIC: 3599 3541 3451 Machine shop, jobbing & repair; machine tools, metal cutting type; screw machine products

(G-17578)
HUGO BOSCA COMPANY INC (PA)
Also Called: Bosca Accesories
1905 W Jefferson St (45506-1117)
P.O. Box 777 (45501-0777)
PHONE................................937 323-5523
Fax: 937 323-7063
Christopher B Bosca, *President*
Brian Janetski, *Principal*
Cathy Gainer, *COO*
D'Orsi Bosca, *Vice Pres*
Dick Rabe, *CFO*
▲ EMP: 20 EST: 1911
SQ FT: 48,000
SALES: 6MM **Privately Held**
WEB: www.boscanet.com
SIC: 3172 3171 Personal leather goods; wallets; handbags, regardless of material: men's; key cases; handbags, women's

(G-17579)
HYNES MODERN PATTERN CO INC
2141 Erie Ave (45505-4712)
PHONE................................937 322-3451
Fax: 937 322-0870
Robert L Knox, *President*
EMP: 4 EST: 1920
SQ FT: 3,000
SALES: 200K **Privately Held**
SIC: 3543 3469 Industrial patterns; patterns on metal

(G-17580)
IDEAL STEEL INC
423 York St (45505-2144)
PHONE................................937 525-9161
Fax: 937 525-9164
Sarah Coffman, *Controller*
Michele Roberts, *Accounts Mgr*
Michael Lucas, *Manager*
Elaine Duquette, *Network Enginr*
EMP: 21
SALES (corp-wide): 31.4MM **Privately Held**
WEB: www.idealsteelinc.com
SIC: 3312 Blast furnaces & steel mills
PA: Ideal Steel, Inc.
90693 Link Rd
Eugene OR 97402
541 689-0901

(G-17581)
JMS INDUSTRIES INC
Also Called: JMS Composites
3240 E National Rd (45505-1524)
P.O. Box 507 (45501-0507)
PHONE................................937 325-3502
Manjit Nagra, *CEO*
Jennifer Nagra, *Vice Pres*
Phil Cremeans, *Engineer*
Carol Haney, *Controller*
▲ EMP: 21
SQ FT: 27,000
SALES (est): 4.2MM **Privately Held**
WEB: www.glasgoplastics.com
SIC: 2821 Molding compounds, plastics

(G-17582)
JOHN R JURGENSEN CO
1780 Enon Rd (45502-9169)
PHONE................................937 293-3112
Pete Flora, *Branch Mgr*
EMP: 3

SALES (corp-wide): 117.2MM **Privately Held**
WEB: www.jrjnet.com
SIC: 1622 2951 1611 Bridge, tunnel & elevated highway; asphalt paving mixtures & blocks; surfacing & paving
HQ: John R. Jurgensen Co.
11641 Mosteller Rd
Cincinnati OH 45241
513 771-0820

(G-17583)
K K TOOL CO
115 S Center St (45502-1203)
PHONE................................937 325-1373
Fax: 937 325-5199
John Koehler, *President*
Paula Odell, *Corp Secy*
Donald Koehler, *Vice Pres*
Edward Kurt Koehler, *Vice Pres*
Kristopher Kent Koehler, *Vice Pres*
EMP: 22
SALES (est): 5.1MM **Privately Held**
SIC: 3312 Tool & die steel

(G-17584)
K WM BEACH MFG CO INC
4655 Urbana Rd (45502-9503)
PHONE................................937 399-3838
Fax: 937 399-2436
William R Beach, *CEO*
Bret L Beach, *COO*
Raymond Derrick, *Controller*
Chris Cox, *CTO*
Marc Wells, *Director*
EMP: 200 EST: 1945
SQ FT: 125,000
SALES: 32.2MM **Privately Held**
WEB: www.kwmbeach.com
SIC: 3053 3714 Gaskets, all materials; motor vehicle parts & accessories

(G-17585)
KCI HOLDING USA INC (DH)
4401 Gateway Blvd (45502-9339)
PHONE................................937 525-5533
Bernie D'Ambrosi, *Senior VP*
Guy Shumaker, *Vice Pres*
Guy Shoumaker, *CFO*
Amy Corbisier, *Treasurer*
Steve Mayes, *Treasurer*
◆ EMP: 150
SALES (est): 183.5MM
SALES (corp-wide): 2.2B **Privately Held**
SIC: 3536 Cranes, industrial plant
HQ: Konecranes Finance Oy
Koneenkatu 8
Hyvinkaa 05830
204 271-1

(G-17586)
KEYAH INTERNATIONAL TRDG LLC (PA)
4655 Urbana Rd (45502-9503)
PHONE................................937 399-3140
Bret L Beach, *President*
Jim Fritts, *General Mgr*
Deedee Hill, *Manager*
Joanna Kipp, *Director*
Brett L Beach,
▲ EMP: 20 EST: 2000
SQ FT: 30,000
SALES (est): 7.8MM **Privately Held**
WEB: www.keyahint.com
SIC: 2675 Die-cut paper & board

(G-17587)
KLOSTERMAN BAKING CO INC
508 W Main St (45504-2662)
PHONE................................937 322-9588
Fax: 937 322-6733
Lewis Banner, *Principal*
EMP: 22 EST: 2001
SALES (est): 6.1MM **Privately Held**
SIC: 2051 Bakery: wholesale or wholesale/retail combined

(G-17588)
KONECRANES INC
1600 Commerce Rd (45504-2016)
PHONE................................937 328-5123
Ashley Easter, *Manager*
EMP: 9

SALES (corp-wide): 2.2B **Privately Held**
WEB: www.kciusa.com
SIC: 3625 Crane & hoist controls, including metal mill
HQ: Konecranes, Inc.
4401 Gateway Blvd
Springfield OH 45502
937 525-5533

(G-17589)
KONECRANES INC
Also Called: Americas Components
4505 Gateway Blvd (45502-8863)
PHONE................................937 328-5100
Troy Posts, *Manager*
EMP: 50
SALES (corp-wide): 2.2B **Privately Held**
WEB: www.kciusa.com
SIC: 3536 Cranes, industrial plant
HQ: Konecranes, Inc.
4401 Gateway Blvd
Springfield OH 45502
937 525-5533

(G-17590)
KONECRANES INC (HQ)
4401 Gateway Blvd (45502-9339)
PHONE................................937 525-5533
Pekka Lundmark, *President*
Bernard D'Ambrosi Jr, *Vice Pres*
Jay Edmundson, *Vice Pres*
Keith Kings, *Vice Pres*
Steve Kosir, *Vice Pres*
◆ EMP: 279
SQ FT: 17,000
SALES: 701.7MM
SALES (corp-wide): 2.2B **Privately Held**
WEB: www.kciusa.com
SIC: 3536 Cranes, industrial plant
PA: Konecranes Abp
Koneenkatu 8
Hyvinkaa 05800
204 271-1

(G-17591)
KRAFFT AND ASSOCIATES INC
991 W Leffel Ln (45506-3537)
P.O. Box 1292 (45501-1292)
PHONE................................937 325-4671
Fax: 937 325-4672
William F Krafft, *President*
Gretchen Krafft, *Corp Secy*
Ivan Frost, *Director*
EMP: 8
SQ FT: 20,000
SALES: 903.3K **Privately Held**
SIC: 3599 Machine shop, jobbing & repair

(G-17592)
KREIDER CORP
2000 S Yellow Springs St (45506-3398)
PHONE................................937 325-8787
Fax: 937 325-6170
Aristides Gianakopoulas, *President*
John Patton, *Vice Pres*
James Gianakopoulas, *Treasurer*
Walt Wildeman, *Admin Sec*
EMP: 66 EST: 1952
SQ FT: 50,000
SALES (est): 13MM **Privately Held**
SIC: 3469 3544 Metal stampings; special dies, tools, jigs & fixtures

(G-17593)
M & H FABRICATING CO INC (PA)
717 Mound St (45505-1130)
P.O. Box 1248 (45501-1248)
PHONE................................937 325-8708
Fax: 937 325-8700
Michael C De Ramus, *President*
Kathy Chapman, *Office Mgr*
EMP: 10 EST: 1970
SQ FT: 6,000
SALES (est): 1.2MM **Privately Held**
SIC: 3441 Fabricated structural metal

(G-17594)
M & H FABRICATING CO INC
823 Mound St (45505-1132)
P.O. Box 1248 (45501-1248)
PHONE................................937 325-8708
Michael Duramus, *Manager*
EMP: 6

GEOGRAPHIC

SALES (corp-wide): 1.2MM **Privately Held**
SIC: 3443 Tanks, standard or custom fabricated: metal plate
PA: M & H Fabricating Co Inc
　717 Mound St
　Springfield OH 45505
　937 325-8708

(G-17595)
M & Y MARKETING
2651 Danbury Rd (45505-3431)
PHONE..................................937 322-3423
Karen Matthews, *Owner*
EMP: 3
SALES (est): 92K **Privately Held**
SIC: 2395 Embroidery products, except schiffli machine

(G-17596)
MACRAY CO LLC
100 W North St (45504-2547)
PHONE..................................937 325-1726
Fax: 937 325-1949
Robert Yingst, *Mng Member*
EMP: 6
SQ FT: 17,600
SALES (est): 600K **Privately Held**
SIC: 3993 1799 5099 Signs & advertising specialties; sign installation & maintenance; signs, except electric

(G-17597)
MAD RIVER FABRICATING LTD
2330 Columbus Rd (45503-3547)
P.O. Box 1204 (45501-1204)
PHONE..................................937 322-6521
David N Funk, *Principal*
Robert J Samosky, *Principal*
Allen Mills, *Engineer*
EMP: 8
SALES (est): 957.7K **Privately Held**
SIC: 3441 Fabricated structural metal

(G-17598)
MAD RIVER TOPSOIL INC
5625 Lower Valley Pike (45506-4174)
PHONE..................................937 882-6115
Richard Renner, *President*
EMP: 8
SQ FT: 8,100
SALES (est): 1.2MM **Privately Held**
SIC: 2499 5261 Mulch, wood & bark; top soil

(G-17599)
MADER ELECTR MOTOR & POWER TRA
205 E Main St (45503-4221)
P.O. Box 626 (45501-0626)
PHONE..................................937 325-5576
Fax: 937 325-7832
Bret Eric Mader, *Mng Member*
Roger Lynn, *Manager*
Cathy McManamay, *Manager*
EMP: 7
SQ FT: 20,000
SALES (est): 1.9MM **Privately Held**
SIC: 5063 7694 Motors, electric; motor controls, starters & relays: electric; electric motor repair

(G-17600)
MAI-WEAVE LLC
1800 E Pleasant St (45505-3316)
PHONE..................................937 322-1698
Christie Taylor, *Accountant*
Jeff Wright, *Sales Mgr*
Berry Handworker, *Mng Member*
Steve Wales,
▲ EMP: 75 EST: 1977
SQ FT: 67,830
SALES (est): 26MM **Privately Held**
WEB: www.maiweave.com
SIC: 3081 Packing materials, plastic sheet

(G-17601)
MAINES INC
Also Called: Maine's Sign's & Designs
1718 E Pleasant St (45505-3314)
PHONE..................................937 322-2084
Fred Maine, *President*
John Hawke Jr, *Senior VP*
Kathy Maine, *Vice Pres*
EMP: 3

SALES: 150K **Privately Held**
SIC: 3993 Signs & advertising specialties

(G-17602)
MEAD PAVING
1023 W Perrin Ave (45506-2420)
PHONE..................................937 322-7414
Rick Mead, *Mng Member*
EMP: 5
SALES (est): 928.6K **Privately Held**
SIC: 3531 Pavers

(G-17603)
METAL STAMPINGS UNLIMITED
552 W Johnny Lytle Ave (45506-2679)
PHONE..................................937 328-0206
Fax: 937 328-0208
Edward Anderson, *President*
Roger Evilsizor, *Vice Pres*
EMP: 10
SQ FT: 12,000
SALES (est): 1.1MM **Privately Held**
SIC: 3469 Metal stampings

(G-17604)
METALS USA CRBN FLAT RLLED INC
5750 Lower Valley Pike (45502-9101)
PHONE..................................937 882-6354
Ruth Workman, *Purch Mgr*
Jeff Taugh, *Manager*
David Grimm, *Manager*
EMP: 54
SALES (corp-wide): 8.6B **Publicly Held**
SIC: 5051 3312 Steel; blast furnaces & steel mills
HQ: Metals Usa Carbon Flat Rolled, Inc.
　1070 W Liberty St
　Wooster OH 44691
　330 264-8416

(G-17605)
MMH AMERICAS INC (DH)
4401 Gateway Blvd (45502-9339)
PHONE..................................414 764-6200
Tom Sothard, *President*
Ross Smith, *Vice Pres*
Joe Miller, *Project Mgr*
Bob Kotecki, *Safety Mgr*
Steve Mayes, *Treasurer*
EMP: 5
SALES (est): 135MM
SALES (corp-wide): 2.2B **Privately Held**
WEB: www.morriscranes.com
SIC: 3536 5084 6719 Hoists, cranes & monorails; cranes, overhead traveling; boat lifts; materials handling machinery; cranes, industrial; investment holding companies, except banks
HQ: Mmh Holdings, Inc.
　4401 Gateway Blvd
　Springfield OH 45502
　937 525-5533

(G-17606)
MMH HOLDINGS INC (DH)
Also Called: Morris Material Handling
4401 Gateway Blvd (45502-9339)
PHONE..................................937 525-5533
Tom Sothard, *President*
Bob Locasale, *General Mgr*
Peter A Kerrick, *Vice Pres*
Kenneth Lindstrom, *Prdtn Mgr*
Bob Kotecki, *Safety Mgr*
◆ EMP: 5
SQ FT: 10,500
SALES (est): 135MM
SALES (corp-wide): 2.2B **Privately Held**
WEB: www.morriscranes.com
SIC: 3536 5084 Hoists, cranes & monorails; cranes, overhead traveling; boat lifts; materials handling machinery; cranes, industrial
HQ: Konecranes, Inc.
　4401 Gateway Blvd
　Springfield OH 45502
　937 525-5533

(G-17607)
MORGAL MACHINE TOOL CO
Also Called: McGregor Metalworking
2100 S Yellow Springs St (45506-3369)
P.O. Box 1103 (45501-1103)
PHONE..................................937 325-5561
Fax: 937 325-1957
Daniel P Mc Gregor, *Ch of Bd*

Tom Wright, *President*
James B Mc Gregor, *President*
Dane A Belden, *Principal*
James McGregor, *Chairman*
▲ EMP: 90 EST: 1939
SQ FT: 98,000
SALES (est): 29.5MM **Privately Held**
WEB: www.morgal.com
SIC: 3469 3568 3544 3451 Metal stampings; stamping metal for the trade; power transmission equipment; special dies, tools, jigs & fixtures; screw machine products; manufactured hardware (general)

(G-17608)
MORRIS MATERIAL HANDLING INC (DH)
4401 Gateway Blvd (45502-9339)
PHONE..................................937 525-5520
Tom Sothard, *President*
Tom Berringer, *Principal*
Bernard D'Ambrosi Jr, *Vice Pres*
Keith King, *Vice Pres*
Steve Kosir, *Vice Pres*
◆ EMP: 5
SQ FT: 25,000
SALES (est): 135MM
SALES (corp-wide): 2.2B **Privately Held**
WEB: www.morriscranes.com
SIC: 3625 3443 7699 Crane & hoist controls, including metal mill; crane hooks, laminated plate; construction equipment repair
HQ: Phmh Holding Company
　315 W Forest Hill Ave
　Oak Creek WI 53154
　414 764-6200

(G-17609)
MTS ENTERPRISES LLC
1330 Perry St (45504-2347)
PHONE..................................937 324-7510
Robert M Corcoran, *President*
Michael Corcoran, *Vice Pres*
Robert Corcoran,
Karen Corcoran,
EMP: 3 EST: 2008
SALES (est): 200K **Privately Held**
SIC: 3499 Fire- or burglary-resistive products

(G-17610)
MULLER ENGINE & MACHINE CO
Also Called: Miller Engine & Machine Co
1414 S Yellow Springs St (45506-2545)
PHONE..................................937 322-1861
Fax: 937 322-5701
Ginnie Mullen, *Owner*
Todd Mullen, *General Mgr*
EMP: 7
SQ FT: 10,000
SALES (est): 780K **Privately Held**
SIC: 3511 3599 Wheels, water; machine shop, jobbing & repair

(G-17611)
NATIONAL STAIR CORP
20 Zischler St (45504-2853)
P.O. Box 1261 (45501-1261)
PHONE..................................937 325-1347
Fax: 937 325-2749
John Druckenbroad, *President*
Larry Houck, *Vice Pres*
Mike Earl, *Admin Sec*
EMP: 30
SQ FT: 11,000
SALES (est): 4.5MM **Privately Held**
SIC: 3446 Stairs, staircases, stair treads: prefabricated metal

(G-17612)
NAVISTAR INC
6125 Urbana Rd (45502-9279)
P.O. Box 600 (45501)
PHONE..................................937 390-5848
John J Pavlansky, *Mfg Dir*
Joe Leep, *Plant Mgr*
Matt Kroplin, *Opers Mgr*
Steve Davis, *Safety Mgr*
Diego Moreno, *Engineer*
EMP: 130
SALES (corp-wide): 8.1B **Publicly Held**
WEB: www.internationaldelivers.com
SIC: 3711 Truck & tractor truck assembly

HQ: Navistar, Inc.
　2701 Navistar Dr
　Lisle IL 60532
　331 332-5000

(G-17613)
NAVISTAR INC
6125 Urbana Rd (45502-9279)
PHONE..................................937 390-2800
Fax: 937 390-4501
Dave Beebe, *Principal*
Phil Bartley, *Human Res Dir*
EMP: 66
SALES (corp-wide): 8.1B **Publicly Held**
WEB: www.internationaldelivers.com
SIC: 3711 3713 3465 Truck tractors for highway use, assembly of; truck & bus bodies; automotive stampings
HQ: Navistar, Inc.
　2701 Navistar Dr
　Lisle IL 60532
　331 332-5000

(G-17614)
NAVISTAR INC
349 W County Line Rd (45502-7856)
PHONE..................................937 390-5653
Charles Moore, *Branch Mgr*
EMP: 66
SALES (corp-wide): 8.1B **Publicly Held**
WEB: www.internationaldelivers.com
SIC: 3711 3714 Truck & tractor truck assembly; chassis, motor vehicle; motor vehicle parts & accessories
HQ: Navistar, Inc.
　2701 Navistar Dr
　Lisle IL 60532
　331 332-5000

(G-17615)
NAVISTAR INC
5975 Urbana Rd (45502-9537)
PHONE..................................937 390-4774
Tom Tullis, *General Mgr*
EMP: 60
SALES (corp-wide): 8.1B **Publicly Held**
WEB: www.internationaldelivers.com
SIC: 3711 Truck & tractor truck assembly
HQ: Navistar, Inc.
　2701 Navistar Dr
　Lisle IL 60532
　331 332-5000

(G-17616)
NAVISTAR INC
4949 Urbana Rd Frnt (45502-9541)
PHONE..................................937 390-5704
Ann Hennigan, *Manager*
EMP: 30
SALES (corp-wide): 8.1B **Publicly Held**
WEB: www.internationaldelivers.com
SIC: 3711 3519 3714 Truck tractors for highway use, assembly of; diesel engine rebuilding; motor vehicle parts & accessories
HQ: Navistar, Inc.
　2701 Navistar Dr
　Lisle IL 60532
　331 332-5000

(G-17617)
NEHER BURIAL VAULT COMPANY
Also Called: Burial Vaults By Neher
1903 Saint Paris Pike (45504-1299)
PHONE..................................937 399-4494
Fax: 937 399-4511
Doreen Pinney, *President*
Gary W Pinney, *Treasurer*
Denise Sutherland, *Asst Treas*
EMP: 15 EST: 1939
SQ FT: 5,500
SALES (est): 2.2MM **Privately Held**
SIC: 3272 Burial vaults, concrete or precast terrazzo

(G-17618)
OAKES DOOR SERV
5298 Troy Rd (45502-8128)
PHONE..................................937 323-6188
Terry Oakes, *President*
EMP: 4
SALES (est): 486.8K **Privately Held**
SIC: 3699 Door opening & closing devices, electrical

(G-17619)
OHIO STAMPING & MACHINE LLC
2100 S Yellow Springs St (45506-3354)
P.O. Box 1103 (45501-1103)
PHONE................................937 322-3880
Fax: 937 322-2150
Dan McGregor, *CEO*
James McGregor, *President*
Tom Wright, *President*
James Doyle, *General Mgr*
Dwight Kent, *COO*
EMP: 120
SQ FT: 140,000
SALES (est): 20.3MM **Privately Held**
WEB: www.ohiostamping.com
SIC: 3465 Automotive stampings

(G-17620)
OS KELLY CORPORATION (DH)
318 E North St (45504-4298)
P.O. Box 1267 (45501-1267)
PHONE................................937 322-4921
Chris Hastings, *Project Engr*
Theodore Golba, *CFO*
EMP: 42
SQ FT: 110,000
SALES (est): 4.7MM
SALES (corp-wide): 189.9MM **Privately Held**
WEB: www.oskelly.com
SIC: 3321 Gray & ductile iron foundries
HQ: Steinway, Inc.
1 Steinway Pl
Long Island City NY 11105
718 721-2600

(G-17621)
P-AMERICAS LLC
Also Called: Pepsico
233 Dayton Ave (45506-1205)
PHONE................................937 328-6750
Fax: 937 323-3100
Tim Earley, *Branch Mgr*
Phillip Beach, *Manager*
Craig Howard, *Manager*
EMP: 123
SALES (corp-wide): 62.8B **Publicly Held**
SIC: 2086 Carbonated soft drinks, bottled & canned
HQ: P-Americas Llc
1 Pepsi Way
Somers NY

(G-17622)
PALMER ENGINEERED PRODUCTS INC
1310 W Main St (45504-2816)
P.O. Box 1593 (45501-1593)
PHONE................................937 322-1481
Jack F Palmer, *President*
Ken Strausbaugh, *Engineer*
▲ EMP: 3
SALES (est): 290K **Privately Held**
WEB: www.palmereng.com
SIC: 3365 Aluminum foundries

(G-17623)
PALMER KLEIN INC ✪
18 N Bechtle Ave (45504-2841)
PHONE................................937 323-6339
Jack Palmer, *President*
Matt Lis, *General Mgr*
Randy Warthman, *Purchasing*
Jim Gauldin, *Engineer*
Julie Latham, *Controller*
EMP: 6 EST: 2016
SALES (est): 275.3K **Privately Held**
SIC: 3559 Foundry machinery & equipment

(G-17624)
PALMER MFG AND SUPPLY INC
18 N Bechtle Ave (45504-2841)
P.O. Box 2579 (45501-2579)
PHONE................................937 323-6339
Fax: 937 323-2709
Jack Palmer, *President*
Marc Zerkle, *Engineer*
Ryan McGhee, *Project Engr*
Stephanie Wenning, *Design Engr*
James Palmer, *Treasurer*
◆ EMP: 25
SQ FT: 60,000
SALES (est): 7.5MM **Privately Held**
SIC: 3559 Foundry machinery & equipment

(G-17625)
PARKER TRUTEC INCORPORATED (HQ)
4700 Gateway Blvd (45502-8817)
PHONE................................937 323-8833
Fax: 937 323-9192
Keiko Satomi, *Ch of Bd*
Yutaka Satomi, *President*
Joseph Gummel, *Vice Pres*
Jay Larkin, *Human Res Mgr*
▲ EMP: 80
SQ FT: 80,000
SALES (est): 45.7MM
SALES (corp-wide): 932MM **Privately Held**
SIC: 3398 3479 Metal heat treating; painting, coating & hot dipping; rust proofing (hot dipping) of metals & formed products
PA: Nihon Parkerizing Co., Ltd.
1-15-1, Nihombashi
Chuo-Ku TKY 103-0
332 784-333

(G-17626)
PENTAFLEX INC
4981 Gateway Blvd (45502-8867)
PHONE................................937 325-5551
Fax: 937 325-2620
Dave Arndt, *President*
Ross McGregor, *Vice Pres*
Rodney Phipps, *Vice Pres*
Bob Mayberry, *Engineer*
Julie McGregor, *Treasurer*
◆ EMP: 110
SQ FT: 146,000
SALES: 32MM **Privately Held**
WEB: www.pentaflex.com
SIC: 3469 7692 Metal stampings; welding repair

(G-17627)
PHOENIX SAFETY OUTFITTERS LLC
1619 Commerce Rd (45504-2015)
P.O. Box 20445, Upper Arlington (43220-0445)
PHONE................................614 361-0544
Dennis Grogan, *General Mgr*
Steve Harting, *General Mgr*
EMP: 9
SALES (est): 2.3MM **Privately Held**
SIC: 3569 Assembly machines, non-metalworking

(G-17628)
PIECO INC
Also Called: Superior Trims Springfield Div
5225 Prosperity Dr (45502-9540)
PHONE................................937 399-5100
Bob Banghle, *Branch Mgr*
EMP: 100
SALES (corp-wide): 39.3MM **Privately Held**
WEB: www.suptrim.com
SIC: 2396 Automotive trimmings, fabric; furniture trimmings, fabric; trimming, fabric
PA: Pieco, Inc.
2151 Industrial Dr
Findlay OH 45840
419 422-5335

(G-17629)
PRATT (JET CORR) INC
Also Called: Pratt Industries USA
1515 Baker Rd (45504-4501)
PHONE................................937 390-7100
Fax: 937 390-7126
Michael Day, *General Mgr*
Sarah Castle, *General Mgr*
Mark Anderson, *Opers Mgr*
Jatin Patel, *Controller*
Jerry Blom, *Financial Exec*
EMP: 20
SALES (corp-wide): 1.7B **Privately Held**
SIC: 2653 Corrugated & solid fiber boxes
HQ: Pratt (Jet Corr), Inc.
1800 Sarasot Bus Pkwy Ne B
Conyers GA 30013
770 929-1300

(G-17630)
PRAXAIR INC
403 W Columbia St (45504-2619)
PHONE................................937 323-6408
Bruce Whaley, *Branch Mgr*
EMP: 5
SALES (corp-wide): 10.5B **Publicly Held**
SIC: 2813 Industrial gases
PA: Praxair, Inc.
10 Riverview Dr
Danbury CT 06810
203 837-2000

(G-17631)
PRESS TECHNOLOGY & MFG INC
1401 Fotler St (45504-2051)
PHONE................................937 327-0755
Fax: 937 327-0756
George Berner, *President*
Dan Berner, *Marketing Mgr*
Heidi Short, *Manager*
▲ EMP: 8
SQ FT: 30,000
SALES: 1.6MM **Privately Held**
WEB: www.presstechnology.com
SIC: 3554 Paper mill machinery: plating, slitting, waxing, etc.; pulp mill machinery

(G-17632)
R & L HYDRAULICS INC
109 Tremont City Rd (45502-9506)
PHONE................................937 399-3407
Ron Randenburg, *President*
Ryan Randenburg, *Vice Pres*
EMP: 5
SQ FT: 4,000
SALES (est): 812.3K **Privately Held**
WEB: www.r-lhydraulics.com
SIC: 7699 3594 Hydraulic equipment repair; pumps, hydraulic power transfer

(G-17633)
RAINBOW INDUSTRIES INC
Also Called: Rainbow Tarp
5975 E National Rd (45505-1854)
P.O. Box 506, South Vienna (45369-0506)
PHONE................................937 323-6493
Fax: 937 323-6495
F Vernon McCoy, *CEO*
Joe Schmid, *President*
Evelyn McCoy, *Treasurer*
▲ EMP: 7 EST: 1894
SQ FT: 6,000
SALES (est): 796.2K **Privately Held**
SIC: 2394 5999 7359 Canvas & related products; awnings, fabric: made from purchased materials; liners & covers, fabric: made from purchased materials; tents; tent & tarpaulin rental

(G-17634)
RAVEN INDUSTRIES INC
2130 Progress Rd (45505-4466)
PHONE................................937 323-4625
Fax: 937 323-4627
Daniel Sherrock, *Sales/Mktg Mgr*
EMP: 3
SQ FT: 29,000
SALES (corp-wide): 277.4MM **Publicly Held**
WEB: www.ravenind.com
SIC: 3081 3083 2671 2394 Packing materials, plastic sheet; laminated plastics plate & sheet; packaging paper & plastics film, coated & laminated; canvas & related products
PA: Raven Industries, Inc
205 E 6th St
Sioux Falls SD 57104
605 336-2750

(G-17635)
RAWAC PLATING COMPANY
125 N Bell Ave (45504-2827)
PHONE................................937 322-7491
Fax: 937 322-8658
Aristides G Gianakopoulos, *President*
Alexandra Gianakopoulos, *Treasurer*
Dave Esselstein, *Sales Mgr*
Pam Ku-Snyder, *Manager*
EMP: 33 EST: 1943
SALES (est): 2.8MM **Privately Held**
WEB: www.rawac.com
SIC: 3471 Plating of metals or formed products

(G-17636)
REED ELVIN BURL II
Also Called: Buckeye Sanitary Service
1236 Villa Rd (45503-1677)
P.O. Box 195 (45501-0195)
PHONE................................937 399-3242
Fax: 937 342-4692
Elvin Burl Reed II, *Owner*
Twyla Reed, *Treasurer*
EMP: 4
SQ FT: 1,400
SALES: 300K **Privately Held**
SIC: 7699 3272 Septic tank cleaning service; septic tanks, concrete

(G-17637)
REITER DAIRY OF AKRON INC (DH)
1961 Commerce Cir (45502-2081)
PHONE................................937 323-5777
Fax: 937 323-2420
Craig McCutcheon, *President*
Bill Riley, *General Mgr*
Stan Norris, *Plant Supt*
David Dungan, *Plant Engr*
Lisa Loughlin, *Credit Mgr*
EMP: 30 EST: 1934
SQ FT: 25,000
SALES (est): 8.9MM **Publicly Held**
SIC: 2026 Milk processing (pasteurizing, homogenizing, bottling)
HQ: Dean Holding Company
2711 N Haskell Ave
Dallas TX 75204
214 303-3400

(G-17638)
RICHARD L GIBSON
2520 Leon Ln (45502-8646)
PHONE................................937 964-1521
Richard Gibson, *Principal*
EMP: 14
SALES (est): 817.2K **Privately Held**
WEB: www.psering.com
SIC: 3069 Fabricated rubber products

(G-17639)
RITTAL CORP
3100 Upper Valley Pike (45504-4518)
PHONE................................937 399-0500
Fax: 937 390-5599
Stan Vanlandingham, *Accounts Mgr*
Jim Nichols, *VP Mktg*
Craig Taseff, *Marketing Staff*
Jerry Browning, *Manager*
Troy Miesse, *Manager*
EMP: 15
SALES (corp-wide): 2.2B **Privately Held**
WEB: www.ripac.com
SIC: 3469 Metal stampings
HQ: Rittal Corp.
425 N Martingale Rd # 400
Schaumburg IL 60173
847 240-4600

(G-17640)
RIVERROCK RECYCL CRUSHING LLC
2484 Lindair Dr (45502-9111)
PHONE................................937 325-2052
Daniel Montgomery, *CEO*
Orville Lykins, *COO*
EMP: 9
SALES (est): 1.1MM **Privately Held**
SIC: 3532 7389 1429 Cars, mining; ; basalt, crushed & broken-quarrying

(G-17641)
RIWCO CORP
2330 Columbus Rd (45503-3547)
P.O. Box 1204 (45501-1204)
PHONE................................937 322-6521
Fax: 937 322-1035
David Nelson Funk, *President*
Robert Samosky, *Vice Pres*
EMP: 16 EST: 1925
SQ FT: 40,000
SALES (est): 3MM **Privately Held**
SIC: 3441 Fabricated structural metal

(G-17642)
ROBBINS & MYERS INC
Also Called: Moyno
1895 W Jefferson St (45506-1115)
P.O. Box 1343, Dayton (45401-1343)
PHONE..............................937 327-3111
Fax: 937 327-3194
Allen Boyce, *Branch Mgr*
Norm Shearer, *Manager*
Carl Ruth, *CTO*
EMP: 300
SALES (corp-wide): 7.2B **Publicly Held**
WEB: www.robn.com
SIC: 3494 Valves & pipe fittings
HQ: Robbins & Myers, Inc.
　　10586 N Highway 75
　　Willis TX 77378
　　936 890-1064

(G-17643)
ROBBINS & MYERS INC
Also Called: Moyno
1895 W Jefferson St (45506-1115)
P.O. Box 1343, Dayton (45401-1343)
PHONE..............................937 327-3023
Norman Shearer, *Branch Mgr*
Colleen Barger, *Administration*
EMP: 200
SALES (corp-wide): 7.2B **Publicly Held**
WEB: www.robn.com
SIC: 3561 Pumps & pumping equipment
HQ: Robbins & Myers, Inc.
　　10586 N Highway 75
　　Willis TX 77378
　　936 890-1064

(G-17644)
ROBERTSON INCORPORATED
(PA)
Also Called: Tower Manufacturing Company
14 N Lowry Ave Ste 200 (45504-2678)
PHONE..............................937 323-3747
Fax: 937 323-9295
EMP: 1
SQ FT: 200,000
SALES (est): 3MM **Privately Held**
SIC: 3315 Mfg Steel Wire/Related Products

(G-17645)
ROSE CITY MANUFACTURING
INC
900 W Leffel Ln (45506-3538)
P.O. Box 1103 (45501-1103)
PHONE..............................937 325-5561
Fax: 937 324-0590
Daniel McGregor, *President*
Hugh Barnett, *Principal*
Dane A Belden, *Principal*
Grant Shearer, *Data Proc Dir*
▲ **EMP:** 60
SQ FT: 44,000
SALES (est): 8.9MM **Privately Held**
WEB: www.rosecitymfg.com
SIC: 7692 Automotive welding

(G-17646)
SAWMILL ROAD MANAGEMENT
CO LLC (PA)
1990 Kingsgate Rd Ste A (45502-8225)
PHONE..............................937 342-9071
Judy Ross, *Mng Member*
EMP: 30
SALES (est): 2.1MM **Privately Held**
SIC: 6531 2421 Buying agent, real estate; sawmills & planing mills, general

(G-17647)
SCHULERS BAKERY INC (PA)
1911 S Limestone St (45505-4045)
PHONE..............................937 323-4154
Theodore Schuler, *President*
Daniel Edward Schuler, *Corp Secy*
Larry Schuler, *Vice Pres*
Mike Peters, *Executive*
EMP: 30
SALES (est): 4.6MM **Privately Held**
SIC: 5461 2052 2051 Bakeries; cookies & crackers; bread, cake & related products

(G-17648)
SHIRTWORK
2133 Kittyhawk Ave (45503-1837)
PHONE..............................937 322-7507
Harold Pool, *Owner*

EMP: 3
SALES (est): 140K **Privately Held**
SIC: 2759 Screen printing

(G-17649)
SPEEDWAY LLC
Also Called: Speedway Superamerica 4131
2040 N Bechtle Ave (45504-1586)
PHONE..............................937 390-6651
EMP: 10 **Publicly Held**
WEB: www.speedwaynet.com
SIC: 1311 Crude petroleum production
HQ: Speedway Llc
　　500 Speedway Dr
　　Enon OH 45323
　　937 864-3000

(G-17650)
SPRADLIN BROS WELDING CO
2131 Quality Ln (45505-3625)
PHONE..............................800 219-2182
Fax: 937 325-2996
Jeffery Spradlin, *President*
Mike Spradlin, *Vice Pres*
Rhonda Spradlin, *Treasurer*
Tammi Spradlin, *Admin Sec*
EMP: 17
SQ FT: 25,500
SALES (est): 3.2MM **Privately Held**
WEB: www.spradlinbros.com
SIC: 1799 7692 3444 3443 Ornamental metal work; welding repair; sheet metalwork; fabricated plate work (boiler shop); fabricated structural metal

(G-17651)
SPRINGFIELD ENGRAVING
COMPANY
317 Canterbury Dr (45503-2603)
PHONE..............................937 390-0011
Fax: 937 390-0011
Sandra Patton, *Owner*
EMP: 3 **EST:** 1949
SALES: 100K **Privately Held**
SIC: 3555 2796 2791 2789 Typesetting machines: linotype, monotype, intertype, etc.; presses, envelope, printing; platemaking services; typesetting; bookbinding & related work; commercial printing, lithographic

(G-17652)
SPRINGFIELD METAL FINISHING
640 S Belmont Ave (45505-2326)
P.O. Box 817 (45501-0817)
PHONE..............................937 324-2353
Fax: 937 324-2432
Tim Wolfe, *President*
Vicki Wolfe, *Admin Sec*
EMP: 4
SQ FT: 4,400
SALES (est): 169.4K **Privately Held**
SIC: 3471 Electroplating of metals or formed products; plating of metals or formed products

(G-17653)
SPRINGFIELD NEWSPAPERS
INC (HQ)
Also Called: Springfield News Sun
1 S Limestone St Ste 1010 (45502-1294)
PHONE..............................937 323-5533
Fax: 937 328-0328
Ben McLaughlin, *Principal*
Karla Garrett-Harshaw, *Editor*
James Kennedy, *Chairman*
Mary Mendenhall, *Controller*
Sylvia Krupp, *Human Res Mgr*
EMP: 34 **EST:** 1904
SQ FT: 76,268
SALES (est): 4.8MM
SALES (corp-wide): 32.4B **Privately Held**
WEB: www.springfieldnewssun.com
SIC: 2711 Job printing & newspaper publishing combined
PA: Cox Enterprises, Inc.
　　6205 Pachtree Dunwoody Rd
　　Atlanta GA 30328
　　678 645-0000

(G-17654)
SPRINGFIELD PLASTICS INC
15 N Bechtle Ave (45504-2897)
PHONE..............................937 322-6071
Fax: 937 322-4580
Frederick B Becker, *President*

Doug Baker, *Engineer*
Janet Becker, *Treasurer*
Kathy Swaim, *Finance Mgr*
Bradley Baker, *Sales Mgr*
EMP: 15
SQ FT: 24,000
SALES (est): 1.6MM **Privately Held**
SIC: 3089 Injection molded finished plastic products

(G-17655)
STAHL CRANESYSTEMS INC
4401 Gateway Blvd (45502-9339)
PHONE..............................843 767-1951
EMP: 3
SALES (corp-wide): 597.1MM **Publicly Held**
SIC: 3536 Hoists, cranes & monorails
HQ: Stahl Cranesystems Inc.
　　2284 Clements Ferry Rd E
　　Charleston SC 29492

(G-17656)
STALDER SPRING WORKS INC
2345 Springfield Xenia Rd (45506-3994)
PHONE..............................937 322-6120
Fax: 937 322-2126
Damon D Kaufman, *President*
Corella Kaufman, *Corp Secy*
Dana Kaufman, *Vice Pres*
Sue Exelby, *Sls & Mktg Exec*
Dennis Kaufman, *Shareholder*
▲ **EMP:** 12 **EST:** 1945
SQ FT: 18,000
SALES (est): 2.8MM **Privately Held**
WEB: www.stalderspring.com
SIC: 3495 Mechanical springs, precision

(G-17657)
STEWART MANUFACTURING
CORP
5230 Prosperity Dr (45502-7503)
PHONE..............................937 390-3333
Fax: 937 390-7777
James S Stewart, *President*
Suzanne S Collins, *Vice Pres*
David Everhart, *Prdtn Mgr*
Eric Berg, *Maint Spvr*
Jeffrey Livingston, *Manager*
EMP: 20
SQ FT: 18,000
SALES (est): 3MM **Privately Held**
SIC: 3823 Differential pressure instruments, industrial process type

(G-17658)
SUTPHEN CORPORATION
Also Called: Chassis Division
1701 W County Line Rd (45502)
P.O. Box 2610 (45501-2610)
PHONE..............................937 969-8851
Fax: 937 969-8869
Drew Sutphen, *Opers-Prdtn-Mfg*
Ron George, *Manager*
EMP: 52
SQ FT: 31,000
SALES (corp-wide): 49.5MM **Privately Held**
WEB: www.sutpheneast.com
SIC: 3711 3714 Chassis, motor vehicle; motor vehicle parts & accessories
PA: The Sutphen Corporation
　　6450 Eiterman Rd
　　Dublin OH 43016
　　800 726-7030

(G-17659)
SWEET MANUFACTURING
COMPANY
2000 E Leffel Ln (45505-4625)
P.O. Box 1086 (45501-1086)
PHONE..............................937 325-1511
Alicia Sweet-Hupp, *President*
Chris Smith, *President*
Sam Jenkins, *Vice Pres*
Alan D Sweet, *Vice Pres*
Jodi McMurdo, *Purch Mgr*
◆ **EMP:** 40
SQ FT: 75,000
SALES (est): 16.3MM **Privately Held**
WEB: www.sweetmfg.com
SIC: 3535 3523 3534 3537 Conveyors & conveying equipment; elevators, farm; elevators & equipment; industrial trucks & tractors

(G-17660)
TAYLOR MANUFACTURING
COMPANY
1101 W Main St (45504-2899)
PHONE..............................937 322-8622
Fax: 937 322-8421
Robert B Taylor, *President*
Courtney Elliott, *Sales Mgr*
Mildred B Taylor, *Admin Sec*
EMP: 22 **EST:** 1939
SQ FT: 18,000
SALES (est): 4MM **Privately Held**
WEB: www.taylormanufacturing.com
SIC: 3728 Aircraft parts & equipment

(G-17661)
TECHNIQUES SURFACES USA
INC
2015 Progress Rd (45505-4472)
PHONE..............................937 323-2556
Alain Charlois, *President*
Kenneth Metzgar, *Director*
EMP: 7
SALES (est): 1MM **Privately Held**
SIC: 3398 Metal heat treating
PA: H.E.F. Usa Corporation
　　2015 Progress Rd
　　Springfield OH 45505

(G-17662)
TEIKURO CORPORATION
4500 Gateway Blvd (45502-8815)
PHONE..............................937 327-3955
Fax: 937 325-2046
Mike Hamell, *President*
David Thiel, *Engineer*
Robin Asterino, *Accountant*
Susan Donavan, *Human Res Mgr*
Jeanette Morris, *Sales Staff*
EMP: 95 **Privately Held**
WEB: www.teikuro.com
SIC: 3471 Plating & polishing
HQ: Teikuro Corporation
　　101 Clay St
　　San Francisco CA 94111
　　415 273-2650

(G-17663)
THOMAS TAPE AND SUPPLY
COMPANY
1713 Sheridan Ave (45505-2263)
P.O. Box 207 (45501-0207)
PHONE..............................937 325-6414
Fax: 937 325-2850
David Simonton, *President*
Dee Simonton, *Principal*
Jeanne Simonton, *Vice Pres*
EMP: 11
SQ FT: 17,500
SALES (est): 1.4MM **Privately Held**
SIC: 2672 Gummed paper: made from purchased materials

(G-17664)
TINKER OMEGA
MANUFACTURING LLC
2424 Columbus Rd (45503-3549)
P.O. Box 328 (45501-0328)
PHONE..............................937 322-2272
Ben Thomas, *VP Sales*
William F Tinker Jr, *Mng Member*
Jesse Elliott, *Manager*
Joe Yagich, *Manager*
Jonathan Tinker, *Assistant*
▲ **EMP:** 29
SQ FT: 54,000
SALES (est): 7.7MM **Privately Held**
SIC: 3555 Type casting, founding or melting machines

(G-17665)
TOMCO TOOL INC
203 S Wittenberg Ave (45506-1646)
PHONE..............................937 322-5768
Fax: 937 322-0749
Bryan Stewart, *President*
Mark Stewart, *Corp Secy*
Richard Wheeler, *Vice Pres*
Patsy Stewart, *Office Mgr*
Patfy Stewart, *Manager*
EMP: 7 **EST:** 1970
SQ FT: 18,000

▲ = Import ▼=Export
◆ =Import/Export

SALES: 270K **Privately Held**
SIC: 3545 3544 Tools & accessories for machine tools; gauges (machine tool accessories); special dies, tools, jigs & fixtures

(G-17666)
TRI CON DISTRIBUTION LLC
776 Deerfield Trl (45503-7444)
PHONE................................937 399-3312
Constance S Slagle,
Constance Slagle,
EMP: 3
SALES (est): 296.4K **Privately Held**
SIC: 2676 Napkins, paper: made from purchased paper

(G-17667)
TRI STATE PALLET INC
854 Sherman Ave (45503-4308)
PHONE................................937 323-5210
Fax: 513 746-8703
Mark See, *Branch Mgr*
EMP: 9
SALES (corp-wide): 2MM **Privately Held**
SIC: 2448 Pallets, wood
PA: Tri State Pallet, Inc.
8401 Claude Thomas Rd # 57
Franklin OH 45005
937 746-8702

(G-17668)
TURN-ALL MACHINE & GEAR CO
5499 Tremont Ln (45502-7522)
P.O. Box 448 (45501-0448)
PHONE................................937 342-8710
Fax: 937 342-8720
Carl Power, *President*
Jane Power, *Vice Pres*
Jack Williamson, *Purchasing*
EMP: 12
SALES (est): 1.8MM **Privately Held**
SIC: 3599 Machine shop, jobbing & repair

(G-17669)
U-SONICO
543 Cookston Ave (45503-2213)
PHONE................................423 348-7117
Dean Hazelton, *President*
Loretta Hazelton, *Vice Pres*
EMP: 11
SALES (est): 771.1K **Privately Held**
SIC: 3541 Ultrasonic metal cutting machine tools

(G-17670)
UNITED FIBERGLASS AMERICA INC
2145 Airpark Dr (45502-7931)
PHONE................................937 325-7305
Fax: 937 325-7380
Greg Gearhart, *President*
Jim McKay, *General Mgr*
Eric Gudger, *Sales Dir*
Shawn Schuler, *Supervisor*
EMP: 15
SQ FT: 44,000
SALES (est): 4MM **Privately Held**
WEB: www.unitedfiberglass.com
SIC: 3644 Electric conduits & fittings

(G-17671)
US PRO PAINTERS (PA)
Also Called: Deck & Fence Revivers
4504 S Yellow Springs St (45506-3850)
PHONE................................937 298-2142
Fax: 937 322-6549
Frank Weaver, *Owner*
April Weaver, *Manager*
EMP: 8
SALES (est): 187K **Privately Held**
WEB: www.deckreviver.com
SIC: 2491 Wood preserving

(G-17672)
VALCO INDUSTRIES INC
625 Burt St (45505-3266)
PHONE................................937 399-7400
Edward H Leventhal, *President*
David H Montgomery, *General Mgr*
Gary Lehning, *CFO*
Steven Queen, *Sales Engr*
Larry Huxley, *Supervisor*
EMP: 35 **EST:** 1974
SQ FT: 44,000

SALES (est): 9MM **Privately Held**
WEB: www.valco-ind.com
SIC: 3713 3441 3465 Truck cabs for motor vehicles; fabricated structural metal; body parts, automobile: stamped metal

(G-17673)
VISUAL EDUCATION ASSOCIATION
581 W Leffel Ln (45506-3529)
PHONE................................937 325-5503
Fax: 513 324-5657
Jeanne Lampe, *President*
Wendell Collins, *Purch Agent*
EMP: 3
SALES (est): 59.9K **Privately Held**
SIC: 8299 3999 2741 Educational services; manufacturing industries; miscellaneous publishing

(G-17674)
W C SIMS CO INC (PA)
3845 W National Rd (45504-3518)
P.O. Box 4 (45501-0004)
PHONE................................937 325-7035
Brad Sims, *President*
Williams C Sims, *Shareholder*
EMP: 2
SQ FT: 17,000
SALES (est): 1.5MM **Privately Held**
WEB: www.wcsims.com
SIC: 5199 2752 Advertising specialties; commercial printing, lithographic

(G-17675)
WALT MYERS
303 N Greenmount Ave (45503-4050)
PHONE................................937 325-0313
Myers Walt, *Principal*
EMP: 3
SALES (est): 160K **Privately Held**
SIC: 3599 Machine shop, jobbing & repair

(G-17676)
WEPUKO PAHNKE ENGINEERING LP
4949 Urbana Rd Rear (45502-8388)
P.O. Box 2120 (45501-2120)
PHONE................................937 390-2100
Fax: 937 390-9715
Lisa Fitz-Harris, *Partner*
M Pahnke, *Partner*
Roy Winkle, *General Mgr*
Rich Kaplan, *Business Mgr*
Solomon Islam, *Project Mgr*
▲ **EMP:** 10
SALES (est): 2.5MM **Privately Held**
WEB: www.wepuko.com
SIC: 3561 Pumps & pumping equipment

(G-17677)
WESTFIELD STEEL INC
Also Called: Remington Steel
1120 S Burnett Rd (45505-3408)
PHONE................................937 322-2414
Fax: 937 322-1654
Fritz Prine, *CEO*
Debbie Funderburg, *Treasurer*
Cynthia Austin, *Sales Associate*
EMP: 60
SALES (corp-wide): 74.4MM **Privately Held**
SIC: 5051 3714 Steel; clutches, motor vehicle
PA: Westfield Steel Inc
530 W State Road 32
Westfield IN 46074
317 896-4449

(G-17678)
WETSU GROUP INC
125 W North St (45504-2546)
P.O. Box 1985 (45501-1985)
PHONE................................937 324-9353
Fax: 937 324-9138
Charles Ingle, *President*
Kitty Henry, *General Mgr*
Bob Martineau, *General Mgr*
Jay Greenland, *Vice Pres*
Linda Rice, *Manager*
EMP: 15
SQ FT: 1,200

SALES (est): 1.4MM **Privately Held**
WEB: www.wetsugroup.com
SIC: 3679 Harness assemblies for electronic use: wire or cable

(G-17679)
WINSUPPLY INC
2187 W 1st St (45504-1928)
PHONE................................937 346-0600
EMP: 13
SALES (corp-wide): 2.7B **Privately Held**
SIC: 5722 5074 3432 1521 Air conditioning room units, self-contained; plumbing fittings & supplies; plumbing fixture fittings & trim; single-family home remodeling, additions & repairs
PA: Winsupply Inc.
3110 Kettering Blvd
Moraine OH 45439
937 294-5331

(G-17680)
WOEBER MUSTARD MFG CO
1966 Commerce Cir (45504-2012)
P.O. Box 388 (45501-0388)
PHONE................................937 323-6281
Ray Woeber, *President*
Gloria Woeber, *Corp Secy*
D I C K Woeber, *Vice Pres*
Rick Schmidt, *Vice Pres*
Richard E Woeber, *Vice Pres*
◆ **EMP:** 128 **EST:** 1905
SQ FT: 40,000
SALES (est): 40.1MM **Privately Held**
WEB: www.woebermustard.com
SIC: 2099 2035 Food preparations; mustard, prepared (wet)

(G-17681)
WOODROW CORP
105 N Thompson Ave (45504-2939)
PHONE................................937 322-7696
Jeff Clouse, *Principal*
EMP: 3
SALES (est): 364.5K **Privately Held**
SIC: 3993 Name plates: except engraved, etched, etc.: metal

(G-17682)
WOODROW MANUFACTURING CO
4300 River Rd (45502-7517)
P.O. Box 1567 (45501-1567)
PHONE................................937 399-9333
Fax: 937 399-0464
John K Woodrow, *President*
Ron Deere, *Prdtn Mgr*
Patrick T McAtee, *Treasurer*
Lou Kiernan, *Sales Mgr*
Sandy Justice, *Manager*
EMP: 40
SQ FT: 26,000
SALES (est): 5MM **Privately Held**
WEB: www.woodrowcorp.com
SIC: 7336 3479 2752 2396 Silk screen design; etching on metals; commercial printing, lithographic; automotive & apparel trimmings

(G-17683)
YOST SUPERIOR CO
300 S Center St Ste 1 (45506-1696)
P.O. Box 1487 (45501-1487)
PHONE................................937 323-7591
Fax: 937 323-5180
Bert D Barnes, *Ch of Bd*
Gary Dickerhoff, *President*
David Deerwester, *Vice Pres*
Loriane Schuyler, *Human Res Mgr*
Sarah Cosby, *Manager*
▼ **EMP:** 50
SQ FT: 47,000
SALES (est): 11.5MM **Privately Held**
WEB: www.yostsuperior.com
SIC: 3495 3496 Mechanical springs, precision; miscellaneous fabricated wire products; clips & fasteners, made from purchased wire

Sterling
Wayne County

(G-17684)
MJC ENTERPRISES INC
7820 Blough Rd (44276-9734)
P.O. Box 182, Smithville (44677-0182)
PHONE................................330 669-3744
Fax: 330 669-8565
Matt Carver, *President*
Lynn Carver, *Vice Pres*
EMP: 9
SQ FT: 1,352
SALES: 500K **Privately Held**
SIC: 2448 Wood pallets & skids

(G-17685)
STOLLER CUSTOM CABINETRY
12573 Frick Rd (44276-9722)
PHONE................................330 939-6555
Greg Stoller, *Owner*
EMP: 4
SALES: 350K **Privately Held**
WEB: www.stollercabinet.com
SIC: 2541 Cabinets, lockers & shelving

Steubenville
Jefferson County

(G-17686)
ACCESS 2 COMMUNICATIONS INC
Also Called: Bulldogsecurity
225 Technology Way (43952-7079)
PHONE................................800 561-1110
Brett Barta, *President*
Bonnie Difippo, *Opers Mgr*
Bonnie Difilippo, *Manager*
EMP: 2
SQ FT: 65,000
SALES: 10MM **Privately Held**
SIC: 3714 3699 Motor vehicle parts & accessories; security devices

(G-17687)
AMERICAN SUPERIOR LIGHTING
1506 Fernwood Rd (43953-7640)
PHONE................................740 266-2959
Mike Gill, *President*
Harold Dunlap, *Assistant*
EMP: 4
SALES: 700K **Privately Held**
SIC: 3645 Residential lighting fixtures

(G-17688)
ARM (USA) INC
1506 Fernwood Rd (43953-7640)
PHONE................................740 264-6599
Fax: 740 266-2953
Eric Bates, *Ch of Bd*
Mike Gill, *President*
◆ **EMP:** 15
SALES (est): 2.9MM **Privately Held**
WEB: www.armusa.com
SIC: 3599 Amusement park equipment

(G-17689)
BLUEFOOT INDUSTRIAL LLC
Also Called: Bluefoot Energy Services
224 N 3rd St (43952-2121)
PHONE................................740 314-5299
Clyde Larsen,
Peter Urie,
EMP: 25
SQ FT: 7,000
SALES (est): 4MM **Privately Held**
SIC: 7353 2899 7359 1623 Heavy construction equipment rental; fluxes: brazing, soldering, galvanizing & welding; industrial truck rental; oil & gas pipeline construction; crude petroleum pipelines

(G-17690)
BULLY TOOLS INC
14 Technology Way (43952-7079)
PHONE................................740 282-5834
Mark Gracy, *President*
EMP: 35

SALES (est): 2.2MM **Privately Held**
WEB: www.qpitools.com
SIC: 3545 Tools & accessories for machine tools

(G-17691)
DIETRICH VON HILDEBRAND LEGACY
1235 University Blvd (43952-1792)
PHONE..................................703 496-7821
John Crosby, *Director*
EMP: 7
SALES: 440K **Privately Held**
SIC: 2759 8299 Commercial printing; educational services

(G-17692)
DPH DISCOUNT PIN INC
30 Snug Hbr (43953-7615)
P.O. Box 2577 (43953-0577)
PHONE..................................740 264-2450
Tammy Hammer, *President*
Jim Hammer, *Vice Pres*
▲ EMP: 5
SALES: 875K **Privately Held**
WEB: www.dphcustompins.com
SIC: 3452 Pins

(G-17693)
EASTERN OHIO INVESTMENTS INC
Also Called: Auto Magic Systems
213 Braybarton Blvd (43952-2337)
PHONE..................................740 266-2228
Dennis Hasak, *General Mgr*
EMP: 4
SALES (est): 363.7K **Privately Held**
SIC: 3589 Car washing machinery

(G-17694)
EXPRESS CARE
Also Called: Ameriwood
197 Main St (43953-3780)
PHONE..................................740 266-2501
Tom Jentil, *Manager*
EMP: 15
SALES (est): 998K **Privately Held**
SIC: 2741 Miscellaneous publishing

(G-17695)
FORT STBEN BURIAL ESTATES ASSN
Also Called: Roberts Brothers
801 Canton Rd (43953-4109)
PHONE..................................740 266-6101
Fax: 740 264-0808
Kirk Roberts, *Partner*
EMP: 6
SALES: 198.9K **Privately Held**
SIC: 6553 3272 Cemeteries, real estate operation; burial vaults, concrete or precast terrazzo

(G-17696)
GENESIS STEEL CORP
6th & Adams St (43952)
P.O. Box 4667 (43952-8667)
PHONE..................................740 282-2300
Duke Rakich, *CEO*
Robert Sagrilla, *President*
EMP: 9
SALES (est): 710K **Privately Held**
SIC: 3315 Steel wire & related products

(G-17697)
HANGER PRSTHETCS & ORTHO INC
2605 Sunset Blvd Unit C (43952-1179)
PHONE..................................740 266-6400
Fax: 740 266-6407
Greg Ekoniak, *Manager*
EMP: 4
SALES (corp-wide): 460MM **Publicly Held**
SIC: 3842 5999 Prosthetic appliances; orthopedic & prosthesis applications
HQ: Hanger Prosthetics & Orthotics, Inc.
10910 Domain Dr Ste 300
Austin TX 78758
512 777-3800

(G-17698)
HESS CORPORATION
4525 Sunset Blvd (43952-3424)
PHONE..................................740 346-0581

EMP: 6
SALES (corp-wide): 4.8B **Publicly Held**
SIC: 1311 Crude petroleum production
PA: Hess Corporation
1185 Ave Of The Amer
New York NY 10036
212 997-8500

(G-17699)
HOLLYWOOD FAMILY EYE CARE
276 S Hollywood Blvd (43952-2422)
PHONE..................................740 264-1220
Maura E Stipanovich, *Principal*
EMP: 6
SALES (est): 776.5K **Privately Held**
SIC: 3851 Eyeglasses, lenses & frames

(G-17700)
J ZAMBERLAN & CO
100 Keagler Dr Bldg 4 (43953-3633)
P.O. Box 2152, Wintersville (43953-0152)
PHONE..................................740 765-9028
Joseph G Zamberlan, *President*
EMP: 3
SQ FT: 3,200
SALES: 110K **Privately Held**
SIC: 3931 Pipes, organ

(G-17701)
JEFFCO SHELTERED WORKSHOP
256 John Scott Hwy (43952-3001)
PHONE..................................740 264-4608
Fax: 740 264-1810
Mikel Michalik, *Exec Dir*
Michael Mehalik, *Exec Dir*
EMP: 20 EST: 1973
SQ FT: 15,000
SALES: 151.8K **Privately Held**
WEB: www.jcmrdd.com
SIC: 8331 8322 2511 Vocational training agency; refugee service; wood household furniture

(G-17702)
KROGER CO
264 S Hollywood Blvd (43952-2422)
PHONE..................................740 264-5057
Fax: 740 266-2896
Robert Orrico, *Manager*
EMP: 250
SALES (corp-wide): 115.3B **Publicly Held**
WEB: www.kroger.com
SIC: 5411 5912 2051 Supermarkets, chain; drug stores & proprietary stores; bread, cake & related products
PA: The Kroger Co
1014 Vine St Ste 1000
Cincinnati OH 45202
513 762-4000

(G-17703)
LT WRIGHT HANDCRAFTED KNIFE CO
130 Warren Ln Unit B (43953-3758)
PHONE..................................740 317-1404
Leonard T Wright, *President*
EMP: 10
SALES (est): 610.8K **Privately Held**
SIC: 3421 Knives: butchers', hunting, pocket, etc.

(G-17704)
MARK NELSON
Also Called: Nelson's Woodcrafts
980 Lincoln Ave (43952-3223)
PHONE..................................740 282-5334
Mark Nelson, *Owner*
Kevin Nelles, *Sales Staff*
EMP: 15 EST: 1991
SQ FT: 6,000
SALES (est): 1.7MM **Privately Held**
WEB: www.nelsonwoodcraft.com
SIC: 2499 Carved & turned wood

(G-17705)
MARTIN M HARDIN
Also Called: Williams Grgory Martin Fnrl HM
411 N 7th St (43952-1756)
PHONE..................................740 282-1234
Hardin M Martin, *Owner*
EMP: 4 EST: 2010
SALES (est): 327.8K **Privately Held**
SIC: 2869 7261 Embalming fluids; crematory

(G-17706)
NATIONAL COLLOID COMPANY
906 Adams St (43952-2709)
P.O. Box 309 (43952-5309)
PHONE..................................740 282-1171
Fax: 740 282-3874
Michael Barber Jr, *President*
Becky Panebianco, *President*
Jami Wedlake, *Manager*
Julie Zamana, *Admin Asst*
▲ EMP: 25 EST: 1938
SQ FT: 45,000
SALES (est): 11.3MM **Privately Held**
WEB: www.natcoll.com
SIC: 2869 5169 2899 2842 Industrial organic chemicals; caustic soda; calcium chloride; chemical preparations; specialty cleaning, polishes & sanitation goods; industrial inorganic chemicals; alkalies & chlorine

(G-17707)
OFF THE WALL SIGNS
1557 Cadiz Rd (43953-7631)
P.O. Box 2462 (43953-0462)
PHONE..................................740 264-7759
Fax: 740 264-7539
Matthew Mazefero, *Owner*
Tom Grady, *Manager*
EMP: 5
SQ FT: 8,000
SALES: 120K **Privately Held**
SIC: 3993 Signs & advertising specialties; electric signs

(G-17708)
OGDEN NEWSPAPERS INC
Also Called: Star Printing
401 Herald Sq (43952-2059)
PHONE..................................740 283-4711
Fax: 740 284-7355
Alex Marshall, *Publisher*
Jody Powers, *Editor*
Maggie McGinnis, *Sales Mgr*
Judy Gelestor, *Advt Staff*
Crain Bartoldeson, *Manager*
EMP: 90
SALES (corp-wide): 617.1MM **Privately Held**
SIC: 2711 Newspapers: publishing only, not printed on site
PA: The Ogden Newspapers Inc
1500 Main St
Wheeling WV 26003
304 233-0100

(G-17709)
OLIVER POOL AND SPA INC
512 Main St (43953-3742)
PHONE..................................740 264-5368
Fax: 740 264-1916
John Oliver III, *President*
EMP: 3 EST: 1967
SQ FT: 5,000
SALES: 800K **Privately Held**
SIC: 5999 7694 Swimming pools, above ground; spas & hot tubs; whirlpool baths; motors, electric; electric motor repair

(G-17710)
PUBLIC WORKS DEPT STREET DIV
238 S Lake Erie St (43952-2158)
PHONE..................................740 283-6013
Fax: 740 283-6038
Dominic Nucci, *Manager*
EMP: 23
SALES (est): 1.2MM **Privately Held**
SIC: 3991 Street sweeping brooms, hand or machine

(G-17711)
RUSSELL HUNT
Also Called: Russel Hunt Total Land Care
175 Detmar Rd (43953-7170)
P.O. Box 126 (43952-5126)
PHONE..................................740 264-1196
Russell Hunt, *Principal*
EMP: 10
SALES (est): 441.8K **Privately Held**
SIC: 0782 3524 Landscape contractors; snowblowers & throwers, residential

(G-17712)
SIGNS LIMITED LLC
356 Technology Way (43952-7079)
PHONE..................................740 282-7715
Fax: 740 266-6571
Ed Rice,
EMP: 7
SALES (est): 490K **Privately Held**
SIC: 3993 Signs & advertising specialties

(G-17713)
SPECIAL WAY 2
1592 State Route 213 (43952-7949)
PHONE..................................740 282-8281
Rick Tallant, *CEO*
EMP: 4
SALES (est): 402.1K **Privately Held**
SIC: 3669 Communications equipment

(G-17714)
STEUBENVILLE BAKERY
525 South St (43952-4808)
PHONE..................................740 282-6851
Fax: 740 282-6851
Louis Tripodi, *Owner*
EMP: 4 EST: 1937
SQ FT: 1,200
SALES (est): 100K **Privately Held**
SIC: 2051 Bakery: wholesale or wholesale/retail combined; rolls, bread type: fresh or frozen

(G-17715)
STEUBENVILLE TRUCK CENTER INC
620 South St (43952-2802)
P.O. Box 1741 (43952-7741)
PHONE..................................740 282-2711
Fax: 740 282-7707
Larry A Remp, *President*
Mary Stead, *Corp Secy*
Marney Remp, *Vice Pres*
Paul Firn, *Executive*
EMP: 25
SQ FT: 7,500
SALES (est): 5.3MM **Privately Held**
WEB: www.ohiovolvo.com
SIC: 7538 5511 7692 Truck engine repair, except industrial; trucks, tractors & trailers: new & used; welding repair

(G-17716)
SUNJOY INDUSTRIES GROUP INC (PA)
619 Slack St (43952-2821)
PHONE..................................740 283-2815
Michael Zhu, *President*
Adrienne McCarty, *Vice Pres*
Cliff Keiski, *CFO*
▲ EMP: 5
SQ FT: 4,800
SALES (est): 529.1K **Privately Held**
SIC: 3272 Furniture, garden: concrete

(G-17717)
SUNNEST SERVICE LLC
619 Slack St (43952-2821)
PHONE..................................740 283-2815
Grace Liu, *President*
▲ EMP: 25
SALES (est): 3.5MM **Privately Held**
SIC: 2514 Metal lawn & garden furniture

(G-17718)
SUPPLY INTERNATIONAL INC
Also Called: Pro Forma Supply International
602 Kingsdale Rd Ste 1 (43952-4356)
PHONE..................................740 282-8604
Thomas C Moorhead, *President*
John Ritchie, *Vice Pres*
EMP: 3
SQ FT: 1,500
SALES: 300K **Privately Held**
SIC: 5199 5112 3429 Advertising specialties; office supplies; metal fasteners

(G-17719)
TRI-STATE PUBLISHING COMPANY (PA)
Also Called: Tri-State Printing
157 N 3rd St (43952-2169)
P.O. Box 1119 (43952-6119)
PHONE..................................740 283-3686
Fax: 740 282-9351
Richard S Pflug, *President*

Dawna L McCabe, *Corp Secy*
Dawna L McCabe, *Treasurer*
Michael Davis, *Sales Mgr*
EMP: 21
SQ FT: 11,000
SALES (est): 3.3MM **Privately Held**
WEB: www.tristateprintingco.com
SIC: 2752 Commercial printing, lithographic; commercial printing, offset

(G-17720)
WEIRTON DAILY TIMES
Also Called: Herald Star Newspaper
401 Herald Sq (43952-2059)
PHONE 740 283-4711
Fax: 740 284-7355
EMP: 17
SALES (est): 1.1MM **Privately Held**
SIC: 2711 Newspapers-Publishing/Printing

Stewart
Athens County

(G-17721)
ADVANCED WEB CORPORATION
10999 E Copeland Rd (45778-9538)
PHONE 740 662-6323
Fax: 740 662-2014
Randy Copeland, *President*
Nathan Copeland, *Vice Pres*
Cheri Copeland, *Admin Asst*
EMP: 4
SQ FT: 10,000
SALES (est): 610K **Privately Held**
WEB: www.advancedwebcorporation.com
SIC: 3555 Printing presses

Stockport
Morgan County

(G-17722)
C SQUARE LUMBER PRODUCTS
1541 S Elliott Rd (43787-9315)
PHONE 740 557-3129
Carl Wolfe, *Owner*
EMP: 15
SALES: 121.4K **Privately Held**
SIC: 2431 Louver doors, wood; windows & window parts & trim, wood

(G-17723)
ROGER L BEST
Also Called: Best Logging
3080 Blind Rd (43787-9201)
PHONE 740 590-9133
Roger L Best, *Principal*
EMP: 3
SALES (est): 150K **Privately Held**
SIC: 2411 Logging

Stone Creek
Tuscarawas County

(G-17724)
M-CO WELLING
10949 Gnther Miller Rd Sw (43840-9448)
PHONE 330 897-1374
Andy Miller, *Owner*
EMP: 4 EST: 2010
SALES (est): 190K **Privately Held**
SIC: 3842 Welders' hoods

(G-17725)
OXFORD MINING INC
4371 Rice Rd Sw (43840-9478)
P.O. Box 427, Coshocton (43812-0427)
PHONE 330 339-4546
Charles Ungurean, *Principal*
Henry Sheleter, *Manager*
EMP: 3
SALES (est): 159.8K **Privately Held**
SIC: 1241 Coal mining services

(G-17726)
RICHARD A LIMBACHER
Also Called: Ral Robotics Investment Group
7148 Rocky Ridge Rd Sw (43840-9483)
PHONE 330 897-4515
Richard A Limbacher, *Owner*
EMP: 4
SQ FT: 2,000
SALES: 295K **Privately Held**
WEB: www.ralrobotics.com
SIC: 3549 Assembly machines, including robotic

Stow
Summit County

(G-17727)
A CUPCAKE A DAY LLC
115 W Liberty St (44224)
PHONE 330 389-1247
Shawna Rollheiser, *Principal*
EMP: 4
SALES (est): 230.8K **Privately Held**
SIC: 2051 Bread, cake & related products

(G-17728)
ACE PLASTICS CO
122 E Tuscarawas Ave (44224)
PHONE 330 928-7720
Fax: 330 928-9656
Peggy Lyn Assaly, *President*
Joe Vereecken, *President*
Chip Hout, *Opers-Prdtn-Mfg*
EMP: 7 EST: 1947
SQ FT: 4,000
SALES (est): 640K **Privately Held**
SIC: 3499 Novelties & giftware, including trophies; advertising specialties

(G-17729)
ADVANCED ENGRG & MFG CO INC
5026 Hudson Dr Ste D (44224-7100)
PHONE 330 686-9911
Bob Hanna, *President*
Paul Christ, *Vice Pres*
EMP: 10
SQ FT: 1,250
SALES (est): 1.1MM **Privately Held**
WEB: www.advancedengineeringmfg.com
SIC: 3599 Machine shop, jobbing & repair

(G-17730)
ANDERSON INTERNATIONAL CORP
4545 Boyce Pkwy (44224-1770)
PHONE 216 641-1112
Fax: 216 641-0709
Len Trocano, *President*
Jim Ball, *President*
Stephen C Ellis, *President*
Gary Pace, *President*
Rob Williams, *President*
▼ **EMP:** 90
SQ FT: 100,000
SALES (est): 28.7MM **Privately Held**
WEB: www.andersonintl.com
SIC: 3556 3559 Food products machinery; meat, poultry & seafood processing machinery; rubber working machinery, including tires
PA: Kembell Inc
420 Throckmorton St # 710
Fort Worth TX 76102
817 332-6104

(G-17731)
AUSTIN TAPE AND LABEL INC
3350 Cavalier Trl (44224-4906)
PHONE 330 928-7999
Fax: 330 928-8756
James Burkle Jr, *President*
Darrell K Floyd, *Vice Pres*
Jim Kelly, *Purch Mgr*
Dianne Moore, *Credit Mgr*
Jim Horan, *Manager*
EMP: 54 EST: 1976
SQ FT: 11,000

SALES (est): 11.6MM **Privately Held**
WEB: www.austintape.com
SIC: 2672 2759 2671 Tape, pressure sensitive: made from purchased materials; labels (unprinted); gummed: made from purchased materials; commercial printing; packaging paper & plastics film, coated & laminated

(G-17732)
BADIZO LLC
Also Called: Gifted Nutrition
4466 Darrow Rd Ste 3 (44224-1867)
PHONE 844 344-3833
John Hillyer, *Principal*
Michael Walker,
EMP: 5
SALES (est): 229.7K **Privately Held**
SIC: 2833 Animal based products

(G-17733)
BAKER MCMILLEN CO (PA)
Also Called: Crook Miller Company
3688 Wyoga Lake Rd (44224-4987)
PHONE 330 923-8300
Fax: 330 923-8699
William L Kimmerle, *President*
Tony Silvidi, *VP Finance*
Tim Roche, *Manager*
Marci Neal, *Executive Asst*
▲ **EMP:** 55
SQ FT: 65,000
SALES (est): 9.7MM **Privately Held**
WEB: www.baker-mcmillen.com
SIC: 2499 Carved & turned wood

(G-17734)
BAKER MCMILLEN CO
Also Called: Waddell Manufacturing Company
3688 Wyoga Lake Rd (44224-4987)
PHONE 330 923-3303
Bill Kimmerle, *Branch Mgr*
EMP: 20
SALES (corp-wide): 9.8MM **Privately Held**
WEB: www.baker-mcmillen.com
SIC: 2499 3429 2439 Handles, poles, dowels & stakes: wood; manufactured hardware (general); structural wood members
PA: Baker Mcmillen Co.
3688 Wyoga Lake Rd
Stow OH 44224
330 923-8300

(G-17735)
BEDELL-KRAUS FLEXOGRAPHIC AND
1350 Commerce Dr (44224-1737)
PHONE 330 688-4881
Fax: 330 688-3324
Anthony J Murru, *President*
EMP: 40
SQ FT: 50,000
SALES: 9.4MM **Privately Held**
WEB: www.bedellkraus.com
SIC: 3069 Reclaimed rubber & specialty rubber compounds; custom compounding of rubber materials

(G-17736)
BLAZE TECHNICAL SERVICES INC
1445 Commerce Dr (44224-1709)
PHONE 330 923-0409
Fax: 330 923-0419
Ralph Hickman, *President*
Brian Hickman, *Opers Mgr*
EMP: 25
SQ FT: 5,000
SALES (est): 5.1MM **Privately Held**
WEB: www.blazeprobes.com
SIC: 3829 Thermocouples

(G-17737)
CFC STARTEC LLC
2213 Arndale Rd (44224-1813)
P.O. Box 2213 (44224-0213)
PHONE 330 688-8316
Glenn V Tingley Jr,
Glenn Tingley,
EMP: 5
SALES (est): 456.9K **Privately Held**
SIC: 3585 7389 Refrigeration equipment, complete;

(G-17738)
CHANDLER MACHINE CO INC
Also Called: Chandler Mch & Prod Gear & Bro
4960 Hudson Dr (44224-1789)
PHONE 330 688-7615
Fax: 330 688-7984
Jeffery H Capple, *President*
EMP: 9
SQ FT: 2,400
SALES (est): 880K **Privately Held**
WEB: www.chandlermachineco.com
SIC: 3599 Machine shop, jobbing & repair

(G-17739)
CHANDLER MACHINE PROD GEAR
4960 Hudson Dr (44224-1789)
PHONE 330 688-5585
Jeffery Capple, *President*
EMP: 7 EST: 1962
SQ FT: 2,400
SALES (est): 861.9K **Privately Held**
SIC: 3599 Machine shop, jobbing & repair

(G-17740)
CLASSIC TOOL INC
4278 Hudson Dr (44224-2251)
PHONE 330 922-1933
Guilford Crocker Jr, *President*
David Crocker, *Vice Pres*
EMP: 3
SQ FT: 3,600
SALES (est): 407.3K **Privately Held**
SIC: 3544 Special dies, tools, jigs & fixtures; special dies & tools; jigs & fixtures

(G-17741)
COFFEE NEWS
4305 Cheval Cir (44224-3692)
PHONE 330 688-0952
Julie F McLain, *Principal*
EMP: 4
SALES (est): 235K **Privately Held**
SIC: 2711 Beverage stores

(G-17742)
COMPLETE NETWORK SOLUTIONS INC
3766 Fishcreek Rd Ste 287 (44224-4379)
PHONE 330 328-2596
Joel Baumgardner, *CEO*
EMP: 7
SQ FT: 1,200
SALES (est): 375.8K **Privately Held**
WEB: www.24x7cns.com
SIC: 7379 7373 3825 Computer related consulting services; local area network (LAN) systems integrator; network analyzers

(G-17743)
DONALDSON COMPANY INC
115 E Steels Corners Rd (44224-4919)
P.O. Box 1459 (44224-0459)
PHONE 330 928-4100
Dave Tallarico, *Principal*
EMP: 80
SALES (corp-wide): 2.2B **Publicly Held**
SIC: 3599 Air intake filters, internal combustion engine, except auto
PA: Donaldson Company, Inc.
1400 W 94th St
Minneapolis MN 55431
952 887-3131

(G-17744)
DUPONT PRFMCE ELASTOMERS LLC
Also Called: Plant 101
4330 Allen Rd (44224-1094)
PHONE 330 929-6934
Don Germano, *Branch Mgr*
Martha Gray, *Senior Mgr*
EMP: 130
SALES (corp-wide): 24.5B **Publicly Held**
SIC: 2822 Synthetic rubber
HQ: Dupont Performance Elastomers L.L.C.
4417 Lancaster Pike
Wilmington DE 19805

GEOGRAPHIC

(G-17745)
E I DU PONT DE NEMOURS & CO
Also Called: Dupont
4330 Allen Rd (44224-1032)
PHONE................................330 929-2961
Fax: 330 929-6961
Te Waple, *Opers Mgr*
J L Stanton, *Office Mgr*
Don Germano, *Manager*
EMP: 43
SALES (corp-wide): 24.5B **Publicly Held**
WEB: www.dupont.com
SIC: 2819 5169 8734 2899 Industrial in-
organic chemicals; synthetic rubber; test-
ing laboratories; chemical preparations;
synthetic rubber
PA: E. I. Du Pont De Nemours And Com-
pany
974 Centre Rd
Wilmington DE 19805
302 774-1000

(G-17746)
ELECTROMOTIVE INC (PA)
4880 Hudson Dr (44224-1708)
PHONE................................330 688-6494
Michael Piglia, *CEO*
Jeffrey Bissell, *CFO*
EMP: 9
SALES (est): 158.3MM **Privately Held**
WEB: www.electromotive.net
SIC: 3679 3677 Solenoids for electronic
applications; electronic coils, transformers
& other inductors

(G-17747)
EQUITY OIL & GAS FUNDS INC
(PA)
4704 Barrow Ste 1 (44224)
P.O. Box 2230 (44224-1000)
PHONE................................234 231-1004
Fax: 440 234-4260
Richard Desich, *President*
Shawn Burton, *Manager*
Linda Futrick, *Manager*
Alane King, *Admin Sec*
EMP: 3
SQ FT: 2,000
SALES: 5.6MM **Privately Held**
WEB: www.equityoil.com
SIC: 1311 Crude petroleum & natural gas

(G-17748)
ESTERLE MOLD & MACHINE CO
INC (PA)
Also Called: Plastics Division
1539 Commerce Dr (44224-1783)
PHONE................................330 686-1685
Fax: 330 686-9434
Adam Esterle, *Ch of Bd*
Richard Esterle, *President*
Carol Esterle, *Corp Secy*
Kathleen Sawyer, *Vice Pres*
Emili Grone, *Manager*
EMP: 45
SQ FT: 18,100
SALES: 9MM **Privately Held**
WEB: www.esterle.com
SIC: 3498 3599 3544 Fabricated pipe &
fittings; machine shop, jobbing & repair;
industrial molds

(G-17749)
ESTERLE MOLD & MACHINE CO
INC
1567 Commerce Dr (44224-1711)
PHONE................................330 686-1685
Richard Esterle, *Principal*
Steve Staszak, *Plant Mgr*
Michael Meloy, *Engineer*
Carol Esterle, *Treasurer*
Michael Miller, *Sales Mgr*
EMP: 11
SQ FT: 22,920
SALES (corp-wide): 8MM **Privately Held**
WEB: www.esterle.com
SIC: 3544 Special dies, tools, jigs & fix-
tures
PA: Esterle Mold & Machine Co Inc
1539 Commerce Dr
Stow OH 44224
330 686-1685

(G-17750)
EVOLUTIONS NORTH AMERICA
1699 Commerce Dr (44224-1730)
P.O. Box 2345 (44224-1200)
PHONE................................330 688-2630
Ed Spreitver, *President*
EMP: 10
SALES (est): 910K **Privately Held**
SIC: 3599 Electrical discharge machining
(EDM)

(G-17751)
FABRIC SQUARE SHOP
2091 Liberty Rd (44224-3427)
PHONE................................330 752-3044
Laura Sampsel, *Owner*
EMP: 4 EST: 2010
SALES (est): 291.3K **Privately Held**
SIC: 5949 2211 Fabric stores piece goods;
apparel & outerwear fabrics, cotton

(G-17752)
FALLS FILTRATION TECH INC
115 E Steels Corners Rd (44224-4919)
PHONE................................330 928-4100
Tom Page, *President*
Lou Scalise, *Treasurer*
EMP: 35
SALES (est): 10MM **Privately Held**
WEB: www.fallsfti.com
SIC: 3569 Filters, general line: industrial

(G-17753)
FERRY INDUSTRIES INC (PA)
Also Called: Ferry & Quintax
4445 Allen Rd Ste A (44224-1058)
PHONE................................330 920-9200
Fax: 330 920-4200
W Harry Covington Jr, *President*
Francis Routh, *Vice Pres*
Ned Brown, *Materials Mgr*
Richard Bieterman, *CFO*
Pete Barrett, *Cust Mgr*
▲ EMP: 77 EST: 1927
SQ FT: 70,000
SALES (est): 16.1MM **Privately Held**
WEB: www.ferryindustries.com
SIC: 3599 3829 Custom machinery; ma-
chine shop, jobbing & repair; measuring &
controlling devices

(G-17754)
FLEXOTECH GRAPHICS INC
(PA)
4830 Hudson Dr (44224-1708)
PHONE................................330 929-4743
Cris Apley, *President*
Lindsey Pearson, *Marketing Staff*
Greg Schals, *Property Mgr*
EMP: 12
SQ FT: 6,500
SALES (est): 1.2MM **Privately Held**
WEB: www.flexotech.com
SIC: 3555 Printing trades machinery; print-
ing plates

(G-17755)
FORMTECH ENTERPRISES INC
(PA)
3924 Clock Pointe Trl # 101 (44224-2952)
PHONE................................330 688-2171
Fax: 330 688-7290
David Turk, *President*
John Saver, *Engineer*
Terry Keck, *Accounting Mgr*
Marti Dan, *Persnl Mgr*
Ron Zieske, *Business Anlyst*
EMP: 4
SQ FT: 35,000
SALES (est): 6.7MM **Privately Held**
SIC: 3089 Extruded finished plastic prod-
ucts

(G-17756)
FRED MARVIN AND
ASSOCIATES INC
Also Called: Fred Marvin Associates
4484 Allen Rd (44224-1051)
PHONE................................330 784-9211
Fax: 330 784-1390
Jeff Mussay, *President*
▲ EMP: 6 EST: 1946
SQ FT: 7,000

SALES (est): 1MM **Privately Held**
WEB: www.pruner.com
SIC: 3421 Cutlery

(G-17757)
FRED W ALBRECHT GROCERY
CO
Also Called: Acme
4302 Allen Rd Ste 110 (44224-1070)
PHONE................................330 922-4057
Fred B Barton, *Branch Mgr*
EMP: 250
SALES (corp-wide): 339.6MM **Privately**
Held
SIC: 2834 Pills, pharmaceutical
PA: The Fred W Albrecht Grocery Company
2700 Gilchrist Rd Ste A
Akron OH 44305
330 733-2861

(G-17758)
GBS CORP
GBS Printed Products & Systems
3658 Wyoga Lake Rd (44224-4944)
PHONE................................330 929-8050
Jeff Starkey, *Vice Pres*
Ernie Saughy, *Vice Pres*
Donald Sprowls, *Plant Supt*
EMP: 48
SALES (corp-wide): 171.7MM **Privately**
Held
SIC: 5999 2759 2672 2679 Art & archi-
tectural supplies; commercial printing;
coated & laminated paper; labels, paper:
made from purchased material
PA: Gbs Corp.
7233 Freedom Ave Nw
North Canton OH 44720
330 494-5330

(G-17759)
GLEBUS ALLOYS LLC
Also Called: G Metal
883 Hampshire Rd Ste E (44224-1120)
PHONE................................330 867-9999
Michael Stefanidis, *Mng Member*
EMP: 12
SQ FT: 4,000
SALES (est): 2MM **Privately Held**
WEB: www.glebusalloys.com
SIC: 3315 Steel wire & related products

(G-17760)
GOJO INDUSTRIES INC
1366 Commerce Dr (44224-1737)
PHONE................................330 255-6525
EMP: 125
SALES (corp-wide): 305.9MM **Privately**
Held
WEB: www.gojo.com
SIC: 2842 3586 2844 Specialty cleaning,
polishes & sanitation goods; measuring &
dispensing pumps; toilet preparations
PA: Gojo Industries, Inc.
1 Gojo Plz Ste 500
Akron OH 44311
330 255-6000

(G-17761)
HAND SCREW MACHINE CO
883 Hampshire Rd Ste A (44224-1120)
PHONE................................216 475-0220
Fax: 216 475-0534
Michael Sakai, *President*
Hideo Sakai, *Principal*
Yoshiye Sakai, *Corp Secy*
EMP: 5 EST: 1948
SQ FT: 8,500
SALES (est): 450K **Privately Held**
WEB: www.strappingtoolrepair.com
SIC: 3462 Gear & chain forgings

(G-17762)
HERFF JONES LLC
4468 Berry Hl (44224-2187)
PHONE................................330 678-8138
Richard Call, *Branch Mgr*
EMP: 25
SALES (corp-wide): 1.1B **Privately Held**
SIC: 2741 Miscellaneous publishing
HQ: Herff Jones, Llc
4501 W 62nd St
Indianapolis IN 46268
800 837-4235

(G-17763)
HUDSON VILLAGE PIZZA INC
3825 Kay Dr (44224-3249)
PHONE................................330 968-4563
Fax: 330 655-5353
Frank Mc Millen, *President*
EMP: 5
SQ FT: 3,000
SALES (est): 457.3K **Privately Held**
SIC: 2038 Pizza, frozen

(G-17764)
INTEGRATED AIRCRAFT
SYSTEMS
1337 Commerce Dr Ste 9 (44224-1758)
PHONE................................330 686-2982
Fax: 330 686-1780
Bill Lipstreu, *President*
Susan Lipstreu, *Vice Pres*
EMP: 7
SALES: 1MM **Privately Held**
WEB: www.integratedaircraftsystems.com
SIC: 3492 5088 Hose & tube fittings & as-
semblies, hydraulic/pneumatic; aircraft
equipment & supplies

(G-17765)
INTEGRTED MED SYSTEMS INTL
INC
Also Called: Spectrum Surgical Instruments
4575 Hudson Dr (44224-1725)
PHONE................................800 783-9251
Eric Henning, *President*
Justin Poulin, *President*
Laura M Mather, *Vice Pres*
Joe Karaffa, *Opers Mgr*
Eric Karns, *Purch Mgr*
EMP: 30
SALES (corp-wide): 2.2B **Privately Held**
SIC: 3841 Surgical & medical instruments
HQ: Integrated Medical Systems Interna-
tional, Inc.
3316 2nd Ave N
Birmingham AL 35222
205 879-3840

(G-17766)
J & S PRODUCTS INC
778 Mccauley Rd Unit 130 (44224-1067)
PHONE................................330 686-5840
Dave Burger, *President*
EMP: 6
SALES: 300K **Privately Held**
WEB: www.jsprodinc.com
SIC: 3643 Power line cable

(G-17767)
LASPINA TOOL & DIE INC
4282 Hudson Dr (44224-2251)
PHONE................................330 923-9996
Timothy P Laspina, *Owner*
Carol Laspina, *Owner*
EMP: 18
SQ FT: 8,500
SALES (est): 1.4MM **Privately Held**
SIC: 3544 3599 Special dies & tools; ma-
chine shop, jobbing & repair

(G-17768)
LEAP PUBLISHING SERVICES
INC
4301 Darrow Rd Ste 1200a (44224-7600)
P.O. Box 2192 (44224-0192)
PHONE................................234 738-0082
Juli Cook, *Project Mgr*
Erin Tilley, *Project Mgr*
Malvine Litten, *Mng Member*
EMP: 14
SALES (est): 425.5K **Privately Held**
SIC: 2731 7389 Textbooks: publishing
only, not printed on site;

(G-17769)
LEVAN ENTERPRISES INC (PA)
Also Called: R F Cook Manufacturing Co
4585 Allen Rd (44224-1035)
PHONE................................330 923-9797
Fax: 330 923-8641
Peter H Levan, *President*
Bruce Moms, *Purchasing*
Bob Ashley, *Engineer*
Greg Rowlett, *Sales Staff*
Carolyn G Levan, *Admin Sec*
EMP: 36
SQ FT: 18,000

SALES (est): 4.4MM **Privately Held**
SIC: 3541 3542 3545 3544 Machine tools, metal cutting type; machine tools, metal forming type; precision tools, machinists'; special dies, tools, jigs & fixtures

(G-17770)
LION MOLD & MACHINE INC
4510 Darrow Rd (44224-1804)
PHONE................................330 688-4248
William Walton, *President*
EMP: 3
SQ FT: 4,000
SALES (est): 462.7K **Privately Held**
SIC: 3089 3599 Injection molding of plastics; machine shop, jobbing & repair

(G-17771)
MACTAC AMERICAS LLC
4560 Darrow Rd (44224-1898)
PHONE................................330 688-1111
Ed T Laforge, *President*
EMP: 6 EST: 2015
SQ FT: 559,400
SALES (est): 135.6M
SALES (corp-wide): 1.8B **Privately Held**
SIC: 2891 Adhesives & sealants
HQ: Lintec Usa Holding, Inc.
64 Industrial Pkwy
Woburn MA 01801
781 935-7850

(G-17772)
MASTER MARKING COMPANY INC
4830 Hudson Dr (44224-1708)
PHONE................................330 688-6797
Fax: 330 688-1627
Raymond X Heller, *President*
Steve Heller, *Vice Pres*
EMP: 12
SQ FT: 36,000
SALES (est): 1.8MM **Privately Held**
WEB: www.mastermarking.com
SIC: 3479 3953 3549 3544 Etching on metals; marking devices; metalworking machinery; special dies, tools, jigs & fixtures; platemaking services

(G-17773)
MATCO TOOLS CORPORATION 1 (HQ)
4403 Allen Rd (44224-1033)
PHONE................................330 929-4949
Fax: 330 929-3827
Timothy J Gilmore, *President*
Josh Jenkins, *District Mgr*
Mike McCaleb, *District Mgr*
David Miller, *District Mgr*
Richard Cheal, *Business Mgr*
▲ EMP: 400
SALES (est): 136.9MM
SALES (corp-wide): 6.2B **Publicly Held**
WEB: www.matcotools.com
SIC: 5251 5072 3469 3423 Hardware; hardware; metal stampings; hand & edge tools; tools & equipment, automotive
PA: Fortive Corporation
6920 Seaway Blvd
Everett WA 98203
425 446-5000

(G-17774)
MCJUNKN REDMAN
4704 Hudson Dr (44224-1706)
PHONE................................330 686-4988
Fax: 330 686-3193
Jim Kaiser, *General Mgr*
EMP: 18
SALES (est): 1.7MM **Privately Held**
SIC: 3498 Fabricated pipe & fittings

(G-17775)
MORGAN ADHESIVES COMPANY LLC (DH)
Also Called: Mactac
4560 Darrow Rd (44224-1898)
PHONE................................330 688-1111
Fax: 330 688-2540
Ed T Laforge, *President*
Clarence Chan, *General Mgr*
Ingrid V Cluyzen, *General Mgr*
Brian Kady, *General Mgr*
Monica A Rodriguez, *Purchasing*
◆ EMP: 500

SQ FT: 559,400
SALES (est): 620.5MM
SALES (corp-wide): 1.8B **Privately Held**
WEB: www.mactac.com
SIC: 2891 3565 2672 2823 Adhesives; labeling machines, industrial; adhesive papers, labels or tapes: from purchased material; cellulosic manmade fibers
HQ: Lintec Usa Holding, Inc.
64 Industrial Pkwy
Woburn MA 01801
781 935-7850

(G-17776)
MOS INTERNATIONAL INC
3213 Peterboro Dr (44224-5913)
PHONE................................330 329-0905
Jenna Myong OK Song, *President*
EMP: 18
SQ FT: 3,000
SALES: 6MM **Privately Held**
SIC: 3089 Automotive parts, plastic

(G-17777)
MRC GLOBAL (US) INC
4704 Hudson Dr (44224-1706)
PHONE................................330 686-4988
EMP: 23
SALES (corp-wide): 3B **Publicly Held**
SIC: 1311 Crude petroleum & natural gas
HQ: Mrc Global (Us) Inc.
1301 Mckinney St Ste 2300
Houston TX 77010
877 294-7574

(G-17778)
MULTI FORM MFG
4278 Hudson Dr (44224-2251)
PHONE................................330 922-1933
David S Crocker, *President*
Guilford M Crocker Jr, *Vice Pres*
Alice Crocker, *Admin Sec*
EMP: 5
SQ FT: 3,600
SALES (est): 540K **Privately Held**
SIC: 3544 Special dies, tools, jigs & fixtures

(G-17779)
NATIONAL AVIATION PRODUCTS INC (DH)
4880 Hudson Dr (44224-1708)
PHONE................................330 688-6494
Peter Piglia, *Ch of Bd*
Thomas G Knoll, *Principal*
Tom Keffler, *Controller*
Robin Hirshe, *Executive Asst*
EMP: 71
SALES (est): 14.1MM
SALES (corp-wide): 158.3MM **Privately Held**
SIC: 3599 3492 Machine & other job shop work; machine shop, jobbing & repair; control valves, fluid power: hydraulic & pneumatic
HQ: National Machine Company
4880 Hudson Dr
Stow OH 44224
330 688-6494

(G-17780)
NATIONAL MACHINE COMPANY (HQ)
Also Called: Nmg Aerospace
4880 Hudson Dr (44224-1799)
PHONE................................330 688-6494
Fax: 330 688-6952
Michael Piglia, *CEO*
Bill Anop, *President*
Brian Fakler, *President*
Tracey Bognar, *General Mgr*
Joe Pentasuglio, *General Mgr*
▲ EMP: 250
SQ FT: 80,000
SALES (est): 158.3MM **Privately Held**
SIC: 3599 3492 Machine shop, jobbing & repair; control valves, fluid power: hydraulic & pneumatic
PA: Electromotive Inc
4880 Hudson Dr
Stow OH 44224
330 688-6494

(G-17781)
NATIONAL MACHINE COMPANY
1330 Commerce Dr (44224-1737)
PHONE................................330 688-2584
Fax: 330 688-1272
Ed Jenkins, *Plant Mgr*
Joe Pentasuglio, *Plant Mgr*
Tom Huntsman, *Manager*
EMP: 20
SALES (corp-wide): 138.4MM **Privately Held**
SIC: 3545 3599 Sockets (machine tool accessories); machine shop, jobbing & repair
HQ: National Machine Company
4880 Hudson Dr
Stow OH 44224
330 688-6494

(G-17782)
NATIONAL NTWRK EMB PRFSSIONALS
3100 Surrey Hill Ln (44224-4756)
PHONE................................502 212-7500
Fax: 330 678-8988
Jennifer Cox, *President*
Arch Ritchie, *Corp Secy*
Susan Ritchie, *Vice Pres*
EMP: 3 EST: 1995
SALES (est): 161.4K **Privately Held**
SIC: 2395 Embroidery & art needlework

(G-17783)
NEOLA INC (PA)
3914 Clk Pnte Trl Ste 103 (44224)
PHONE................................330 926-0514
Fax: 330 788-5012
Richard Clapp, *President*
Paula Clapp, *Vice Pres*
Myra Wilde, *Prdtn Mgr*
Rand Becker, *Treasurer*
Melissa Chapman, *Administration*
EMP: 3
SALES (est): 1.6MM **Privately Held**
WEB: www.neola.com
SIC: 2731 8748 Pamphlets: publishing only, not printed on site; business consulting

(G-17784)
NORDEC INC
900 Hampshire Rd (44224-1113)
PHONE................................330 940-3700
Christine A Snyder, *President*
Jeffrey L Smith, *Vice Pres*
Jason D Sudbrink, *Vice Pres*
Brian Shelford, *Art Dir*
William L Snyder, *Shareholder*
EMP: 60 EST: 1962
SQ FT: 50,000
SALES (est): 9.7MM **Privately Held**
WEB: www.nordecinc.com
SIC: 2759 2675 Screen printing; decals: printing; die-cut paper & board

(G-17785)
NUCLEAR PHYSICIANS LIMITED
Also Called: Imaging Center
4161 Bridgewater Pkwy (44224-6191)
P.O. Box 452, Hudson (44236-0452)
PHONE................................330 920-3770
Anthony Passalaqua MD, *President*
Randy Rogers, *Manager*
EMP: 7
SQ FT: 2,000
SALES (est): 992.2K **Privately Held**
SIC: 3829 8071 Medical diagnostic systems, nuclear; medical laboratories

(G-17786)
OSMANS PIES INC (PA)
3678 Elm Rd (44224-3954)
PHONE................................330 607-9083
Fax: 330 655-7824
Ethel Osman, *President*
Terry Osman, *Vice Pres*
Cheryl Osman Crowe, *Admin Sec*
EMP: 20
SQ FT: 3,500
SALES (est): 600K **Privately Held**
SIC: 5461 5149 2052 2051 Bakeries; bakery products; cookies & crackers; bread, cake & related products

(G-17787)
PILAND PARTS
3215 Darrow Rd (44224-4611)
PHONE................................330 686-3083
Evan Piland, *Owner*
EMP: 4
SALES: 257.5K **Privately Held**
SIC: 2241 Fabric tapes

(G-17788)
PNEUMATIC PARTS CO
888 Hampshire Rd (44224-1165)
PHONE................................330 923-6063
Fax: 330 923-6395
Stephen Biskner, *President*
Elizabeth Biskner, *Vice Pres*
EMP: 12 EST: 1958
SQ FT: 7,000
SALES (est): 2.2MM **Privately Held**
SIC: 3532 Mining machinery

(G-17789)
POLAR PRODUCTS INC
3380 Cavalier Trl (44224-4906)
PHONE................................330 253-9973
Fax: 330 253-4233
William S Graessle, *President*
Maureen Humm, *General Mgr*
Rita Washington, *Opers Mgr*
Ryan McElroy, *Opers Staff*
Rose Graessle, *CFO*
▲ EMP: 8
SQ FT: 10,000
SALES (est): 850K **Privately Held**
SIC: 2833 8041 Medicinal chemicals; offices & clinics of chiropractors

(G-17790)
POLYSTAR INC
1676 Commerce Dr (44224-1731)
PHONE................................234 678-9020
David Kroger, *Principal*
EMP: 29
SALES (est): 7.5MM **Privately Held**
SIC: 3089 Plastic containers, except foam

(G-17791)
PREMIERE PRINTING & SIGNS INC
778 Mccauley Rd Unit 120 (44224-1067)
PHONE................................330 688-6244
Craig Evans, *President*
Cheryl Evans, *Vice Pres*
EMP: 3
SQ FT: 1,560
SALES: 240K **Privately Held**
SIC: 2759 7389 Commercial printing; sign painting & lettering shop

(G-17792)
PRINT-DIGITAL INCORPORATED
Also Called: Print Digital
4688 Darrow Rd (44224-1819)
PHONE................................330 686-5945
Marvin Weber, *President*
Eric Weber, *Vice Pres*
Harriet Weber, *Admin Sec*
EMP: 9
SQ FT: 4,500
SALES (est): 1.6MM **Privately Held**
WEB: www.digi-print.com
SIC: 2752 7334 2789 2761 Commercial printing, offset; photocopying & duplicating services; bookbinding & related work; manifold business forms

(G-17793)
PTR DAILY LLC
4501 Eastwicke Blvd (44224-2154)
PHONE................................330 673-1990
John Learner, *Principal*
EMP: 3
SALES (est): 128.5K **Privately Held**
SIC: 2711 Newspapers

(G-17794)
PURITAN SYSTEMS INC
2713 York Dr (44224-5439)
PHONE................................330 686-0527
Roger Arnold, *President*
Ann Marie, *Manager*
EMP: 28
SQ FT: 43,000

SALES (est): 2MM **Privately Held**
WEB: www.allaboutmotion.com
SIC: 3999 Custom pulverizing & grinding of plastic materials

(G-17795)
RAY COMMUNICATIONS INC
Also Called: Raytec Systems
1337 Commerce Dr Ste 11 (44224-1758)
PHONE..................................330 686-0226
Fax: 330 686-0229
Richard A Yarnell, *President*
Greg Baynes, *Opers Mgr*
EMP: 9
SQ FT: 2,400
SALES (est): 742.5K **Privately Held**
SIC: 5065 2542 5999 Communication equipment; telephone booths: except wood; telephone equipment & systems

(G-17796)
SADLER CORPORATION
4600 Hudson Dr (44224-1704)
PHONE..................................330 688-7400
Kathleen Sadler, *CEO*
Ronald L Sadler, *President*
David Hoyle, *Manager*
EMP: 7
SQ FT: 14,000
SALES (est): 300K **Privately Held**
WEB: www.sadlercorporation.com
SIC: 3469 3599 Stamping metal for the trade; machine shop, jobbing & repair

(G-17797)
SAINT-GOBAIN CERAMICS PLAS INC
Also Called: Saint-Gobain Norpro
3840 Fishcreek Rd (44224-4306)
PHONE..................................330 673-5860
EMP: 843
SALES (corp-wide): 185.8MM **Privately Held**
SIC: 2819 3679 3544 3297 Industrial inorganic chemicals; electronic crystals; special dies & tools; nonclay refractories
HQ: Saint-Gobain Ceramics & Plastics, Inc.
750 E Swedesford Rd
Valley Forge PA 19482

(G-17798)
SAINT-GOBAIN NORPRO CORP (DH)
3840 Fishcreek Rd (44224-4306)
PHONE..................................330 673-5860
Fax: 330 677-7247
Antonio Vilela, *President*
Joseph H Menendez, *Chairman*
Rob Hoffstetter, *Sales Mgr*
Nader N Khalil, *Sales Mgr*
David Gough, *Manager*
◆ EMP: 126
SALES (est): 49.9MM
SALES (corp-wide): 185.8MM **Privately Held**
WEB: www.sg-norpro.com
SIC: 3533 5211 Oil & gas field machinery; tile, ceramic
HQ: Saint-Gobain Abrasives, Inc.
1 New Bond St
Worcester MA 01606
508 795-5000

(G-17799)
SCOTT BADER INC
4280 Hudson Dr (44224-2251)
PHONE..................................330 920-4410
Fax: 330 920-4415
Nick Padfield, *President*
Chris Allan, *Plant Mgr*
Michelle Walker, *Opers Mgr*
Robert Leeson, *Engineer*
Liyaqatali Khan, *Finance*
▲ EMP: 8
SQ FT: 5,500
SALES (est): 2MM
SALES (corp-wide): 266.5MM **Privately Held**
WEB: www.scottbaderinc.com
SIC: 2821 Plastics materials & resins
HQ: Scott Bader Company Limited
Wollaston Hall
Wellingborough NORTHANTS NN29
193 366-3100

(G-17800)
SIMPLEX-IT LLC
4301 Darrow Rd Ste 1200 (44224-7600)
PHONE..................................234 380-1277
Robert L Coppedge, *Principal*
Michelle Brugmann, *Office Mgr*
EMP: 5 EST: 2007
SALES (est): 1MM **Privately Held**
SIC: 3825 7372 Network analyzers; business oriented computer software

(G-17801)
SPIRAL BRUSHES INC
1355 Commerce Dr (44224-1751)
PHONE..................................330 686-2861
Fax: 330 686-9436
Ernest R Preston III, *President*
E Preston, *Vice Pres*
Andy Mercer, *Purch Mgr*
Charles Nichols, *Sales Staff*
Richard Harala, *Manager*
▲ EMP: 30 EST: 1939
SQ FT: 25,000
SALES (est): 5.5MM **Privately Held**
WEB: www.spiralbrushes.com
SIC: 3991 Brushes, household or industrial

(G-17802)
SPIROL INTERNATIONAL CORP
Spirol Shim Division
321 Remington Rd (44224-4915)
PHONE..................................330 920-3655
Charles Kutchin, *President*
Anthony Canda, *QC Mgr*
James Camper, *Engineer*
Jessica Camburako, *Sales Engr*
David Reisinger, *Sales Engr*
EMP: 60
SQ FT: 46,000
SALES (corp-wide): 65MM **Privately Held**
SIC: 3499 Shims, metal
HQ: Spirol International Corporation
30 Rock Ave
Danielson CT 06239
860 774-8571

(G-17803)
STEEL PRODUCTS CORP AKRON
2288 Samira Rd (44224-3404)
PHONE..................................330 688-6633
Fax: 330 688-0535
William Mac Cracken, *Ch of Bd*
William E Welsh, *President*
Lou Nelson, *Vice Pres*
EMP: 22 EST: 1950
SQ FT: 100,000
SALES (est): 4.8MM **Privately Held**
WEB: www.steelprocorp.com
SIC: 3599 Machine shop, jobbing & repair

(G-17804)
STERIS CORPORATION
1469 Commerce Dr (44224-1709)
PHONE..................................330 686-4550
Wade Gossett, *Associate*
EMP: 3
SALES (corp-wide): 2.2B **Privately Held**
SIC: 3842 Surgical appliances & supplies
HQ: Steris Corporation
5960 Heisley Rd
Mentor OH 44060
440 354-2600

(G-17805)
STRUKTOL COMPANY AMERICA LLC (PA)
201 E Steels Corners Rd (44224-4921)
P.O. Box 1649 (44224-0649)
PHONE..................................330 928-5188
Fax: 330 928-8726
Gilbret Hamrick, *President*
Rita Robinette, *Business Mgr*
James Boskovitch, *Mfg Dir*
Victor Colaianni, *Buyer*
Mervin Riby, *Purchasing*
◆ EMP: 105 EST: 1977
SQ FT: 60,000
SALES (est): 30.2MM **Privately Held**
WEB: www.struktol.com
SIC: 2869 Industrial organic chemicals

(G-17806)
SUMMIT RESEARCH GROUP
4466 Darrow Rd Ste 15 (44224-1891)
PHONE..................................330 689-1778
Ron Antal, *Principal*
EMP: 3
SALES (est): 168.4K **Privately Held**
SIC: 2834 Pharmaceutical preparations

(G-17807)
SUP-R-DIE INC
1337 Commerce Dr Ste 3 (44224-1758)
PHONE..................................330 688-7600
Fax: 330 688-7601
Jamie Wells, *Manager*
EMP: 3
SALES (corp-wide): 7.7MM **Privately Held**
SIC: 3544 Special dies & tools
PA: Sup-R-Die, Inc.
10003 Memphis Ave
Cleveland OH 44144
216 252-3930

(G-17808)
THERMOFORM PRODUCTS LLC
1777 Commerce Dr (44224-1738)
PHONE..................................330 686-2050
Matthew J Ruzicka, *CEO*
James A Fladda, *COO*
EMP: 6
SALES (est): 893.4K **Privately Held**
SIC: 3089 Thermoformed finished plastic products

(G-17809)
TOTAL REPAIR EXPRESS MICH LLC
4575 Hudson Dr (44224-1725)
PHONE..................................248 690-9410
Christian Mills, *Principal*
EMP: 3 EST: 2011
SALES (est): 368.2K **Privately Held**
SIC: 3599 Machine shop, jobbing & repair

(G-17810)
TRANSMIT IDENTITY LLC
3916 Clk Pnte Trl Ste 101 (44224)
PHONE..................................330 576-4732
Catherine Licitri, *Client Mgr*
Joseph A Licitri,
EMP: 4
SALES (est): 432.4K **Privately Held**
SIC: 2621 Printing paper

(G-17811)
TRAXIUM LLC
Also Called: Printing Concepts
4246 Hudson Dr (44224-2251)
PHONE..................................330 572-8200
Fax: 330 572-8201
George Schmutz, *President*
Karen Black, *General Mgr*
Brent M Evans, *Vice Pres*
Tiffani Gerber, *Opers Mgr*
Craig Grant, *Facilities Mgr*
EMP: 49
SQ FT: 45,000
SALES (est): 6MM **Privately Held**
WEB: www.printingconcepts.com
SIC: 2759 2752 7331 2789 Letterpress printing; commercial printing, offset; direct mail advertising services; bookbinding & related work

(G-17812)
TRI-STATE TOOL & DIE INC
1396 Norton Rd (44224-1394)
PHONE..................................330 655-2536
Fax: 330 655-2208
Eric Pansegrau, *President*
▲ EMP: 5
SALES: 900K **Privately Held**
SIC: 3599 Machine shop, jobbing & repair

(G-17813)
TUFFY PAD COMPANY INC
454 Seasons Rd (44224-1020)
P.O. Box 1302 (44224-0302)
PHONE..................................330 688-0043
Fax: 330 688-4542
Joseph M Burks, *President*
Debbie Burks, *Treasurer*
Margaret Burks, *Admin Sec*
EMP: 10 EST: 1958

SQ FT: 15,000
SALES (est): 960K **Privately Held**
WEB: www.tuffypad.com
SIC: 3949 Pads: football, basketball, soccer, lacrosse, etc.; masks: hockey, baseball, football, etc.

(G-17814)
VALV-TROL COMPANY
1340 Commerce Dr (44224-1737)
P.O. Box 2259 (44224-1000)
PHONE..................................330 686-2800
Fax: 330 686-2820
Marjorie Ingram, *Ch of Bd*
Kenneth R Ingram, *President*
Richard Houck, *Vice Pres*
Amy Bigler, *Office Mgr*
EMP: 13 EST: 1947
SQ FT: 10,000
SALES: 1.2MM **Privately Held**
SIC: 3492 5084 Control valves, fluid power: hydraulic & pneumatic; industrial machinery & equipment

(G-17815)
VMI AMERICAS INC (HQ)
4670 Allen Rd (44224-1042)
PHONE..................................330 929-6800
Fax: 330 929-7254
Auke Diaster, *President*
Arthur Miller, *Production*
Rein Mulder, *Draft/Design*
Arie Kroeze, *Sls & Mktg Exec*
Frank Autz, *Manager*
▲ EMP: 47
SQ FT: 65,000
SALES (est): 7.4MM
SALES (corp-wide): 1.4B **Privately Held**
SIC: 3565 3544 Packaging machinery; special dies, tools, jigs & fixtures
PA: Tkh Group N.V.
Spinnerstraat 15
Haaksbergen 7481
535 732-900

(G-17816)
WAINO SHEET METAL INC
4198 Ellsworth Rd (44224-2204)
P.O. Box 2677 (44224-6677)
PHONE..................................330 945-4226
Sandra Waino, *Principal*
EMP: 4
SALES (est): 569.6K **Privately Held**
SIC: 3444 Sheet metalwork

(G-17817)
WOLFE GRINDING INC
4582 Allen Rd (44224-1091)
PHONE..................................330 929-6677
Fax: 330 929-6440
Larry W Wolfe, *President*
Phyllis Wolfe, *Vice Pres*
Joseph Wolfe,
EMP: 6
SQ FT: 48,750
SALES (est): 788.7K **Privately Held**
SIC: 3599 Machine shop, jobbing & repair

(G-17818)
YOUR DAILY BARGAINS
2495 Valleydale Rd (44224-1919)
PHONE..................................330 715-8324
Angela Halloran, *Principal*
EMP: 3
SALES (est): 123K **Privately Held**
SIC: 2711 Newspapers, publishing & printing

Strasburg
Tuscarawas County

(G-17819)
ALRON
805 Margo Dr Sw (44680-9792)
PHONE..................................330 477-3405
Ron Gritzam, *Partner*
Allen Knotz, *Partner*
EMP: 8
SALES (est): 520.1K **Privately Held**
SIC: 2295 Metallizing of fabrics

(G-17820)
B A MALCUIT RACING INC
Also Called: Malcuit Racing Engines
707 S Wooster Ave (44680-9702)
P.O. Box 166 (44680-0166)
PHONE..............................330 878-7111
Mark Malcuit, *President*
Brad Malcuit, *Vice Pres*
EMP: 8
SQ FT: 30,000
SALES (est): 580K **Privately Held**
SIC: 3519 3714 Internal combustion engines; motor vehicle parts & accessories

(G-17821)
BEACH CITY LUMBER LLC
5177 Austin Ln Nw (44680-9109)
PHONE..............................330 878-4097
Paul Weaver, *Owner*
EMP: 7
SQ FT: 5,000
SALES (est): 1.1MM **Privately Held**
SIC: 2421 Lumber: rough, sawed or planed

(G-17822)
CASE FARMS OF OHIO INC
Also Called: Hatchery
1225 Hensel Ave Ne (44680-9779)
PHONE..............................330 878-7118
Tom David, *Manager*
Nevin Horst, *Manager*
EMP: 11
SALES (corp-wide): 376.1MM **Privately Held**
WEB: www.casefarms.com
SIC: 2015 Poultry slaughtering & processing
HQ: Case Farms Of Ohio, Inc.
1818 County Rd 160
Winesburg OH 44690
330 359-7141

(G-17823)
GREEN RDCED EMSSONS NETWRK LLC
Also Called: Gre'n Disc
5029 Hilltop Dr Nw (44680-9069)
PHONE..............................330 340-0941
Marty Lindon,
EMP: 8
SALES (est): 425.1K **Privately Held**
SIC: 3714 Motor vehicle parts & accessories

(G-17824)
KLEEN TEST PRODUCTS CORP
216 12th St Ne (44680-9752)
PHONE..............................330 878-5586
Pete Morton, *Plant Mgr*
Bill Ahlborn, *Branch Mgr*
Phil Sibila, *Manager*
EMP: 12
SALES (corp-wide): 374.1MM **Privately Held**
SIC: 2842 Cleaning or polishing preparations
HQ: Kleen Test Products Corporation
1611 S Sunset Rd
Port Washington WI 53074
262 284-6600

(G-17825)
LEIDEN CABINET COMPANY LLC
1230 Hensel Ave Ne (44680-9779)
PHONE..............................330 878-7790
Fax: 330 878-7596
Dave Marusa, *Opers-Prdtn-Mfg*
EMP: 21
SALES (corp-wide): 23.7MM **Privately Held**
SIC: 5046 2541 Store fixtures; wood partitions & fixtures
PA: Leiden Cabinet Company, Llc
2385 Edison Blvd
Twinsburg OH 44087
330 425-8555

(G-17826)
NEWTON ASPHALT PAVING INC
8344 Central Rd Nw (44680-9115)
P.O. Box 86 (44680-0086)
PHONE..............................330 878-5648
George A Gessner, *President*
Greg Gessner, *Corp Secy*

EMP: 15
SALES (est): 2.7MM **Privately Held**
SIC: 2951 Asphalt paving mixtures & blocks

(G-17827)
OXFORD MINING COMPANY INC
7551 Reed Rd Nw (44680-8902)
P.O. Box 135 (44680-0135)
PHONE..............................330 878-5120
Chuck Ungurean, *Owner*
EMP: 5
SALES (corp-wide): 1.4B **Publicly Held**
SIC: 1241 Coal mining services
HQ: Oxford Mining Company, Inc.
544 Chestnut St
Coshocton OH 43812
740 622-6302

(G-17828)
SCHLUMBERGER LIMITED
211 Zeltman Ave Ne (44680-8983)
PHONE..............................330 878-0794
EMP: 7 **Privately Held**
SIC: 1389 Well logging
HQ: Schlumberger Limited
5599 San Felipe St Fl 17
Houston TX 77056
713 513-2000

(G-17829)
SMITH INTERNATIONAL INC
Also Called: Schlumberger Completions
211 Zeltman Ave Ne (44680-8983)
PHONE..............................570 368-2130
EMP: 12 **Privately Held**
SIC: 3533 Oil & gas field machinery
HQ: Smith International, Inc.
1310 Rankin Rd
Houston TX 77073
281 443-3370

(G-17830)
STRASBURG PROVISION INC
172 Rosanna Ave (44680-9719)
PHONE..............................330 878-1059
Rudolf M Klapper, *President*
Frank H Klapper, *Treasurer*
EMP: 25
SQ FT: 2,500
SALES (est): 1.9MM **Privately Held**
SIC: 2011 5421 2091 2013 Meat packing plants; beef products from beef slaughtered on site; pork products from pork slaughtered on site; meat & fish markets; meat markets, including freezer provisioners; canned & cured fish & seafoods; sausages & other prepared meats

(G-17831)
TREMCAR USA INC
436 12th St Ne (44680-9760)
PHONE..............................330 878-7708
William A Kyler, *President*
Jacques Tremblay, *President*
Marie Marquis, *Vice Pres*
Allan Paaren, *Vice Pres*
Daniel Tremblaym, *Vice Pres*
▲ **EMP:** 57
SQ FT: 35,000
SALES (est): 23.9MM
SALES (corp-wide): 119.2MM **Privately Held**
WEB: www.tremcarusa.com
SIC: 3713 Tank truck bodies
HQ: Tremcar Inc
790 Av Montrichard
Saint-Jean-Sur-Richelieu QC J2X 5
450 347-7822

(G-17832)
UNITED HARDWOODS LTD
5508 Hilltop Dr Nw (44680-9117)
PHONE..............................330 878-9510
Norm Shetler, *Principal*
EMP: 9
SALES (est): 1MM **Privately Held**
SIC: 2421 Custom sawmill

(G-17833)
ACCURATE FAB LLC
1760 Miller Pkwy (44241-4633)
P.O. Box 766, Aurora (44202-0766)
PHONE..............................330 562-0566
Jim Mehallis, *Sales Executive*
James Mahallis,
Scott Hollman,
EMP: 6
SALES (est): 1.4MM **Privately Held**
SIC: 3441 Ship sections, prefabricated metal

(G-17834)
AGRATRONIX LLC
10375 State Route 43 (44241-4992)
PHONE..............................330 562-2222
James Falbo, *Vice Pres*
Randy Beck, *Purch Mgr*
Trent McElhaney, *Engineer*
Dawn Decker, *Human Res Mgr*
Vicky Rickey, *Human Res Mgr*
▲ **EMP:** 30 **EST:** 2007
SALES (est): 10.9MM **Privately Held**
WEB: www.agratronix.com
SIC: 5039 3699 3446 Wire fence, gates & accessories; electric fence chargers; fences, gates, posts & flagpoles

(G-17835)
ALACRIANT INC (PA)
1760 Miller Pkwy (44241-4633)
PHONE..............................330 562-7191
James Berkes, *CEO*
Jeff Berkes, *President*
Rick Moody, *Vice Pres*
Ken Quinn, *Vice Pres*
Shawn Driscoll, *Prdtn Mgr*
EMP: 55 **EST:** 1997
SQ FT: 72,000
SALES (est): 26.7MM **Privately Held**
WEB: www.artisanindustries.com
SIC: 3499 Strapping, metal

(G-17836)
ALACRIANT INC
1760 Miller Pkwy (44241-4633)
PHONE..............................330 562-7191
EMP: 40
SALES (corp-wide): 26.7MM **Privately Held**
WEB: www.artisanindustries.com
SIC: 3499 Strapping, metal
PA: Alacriant Inc.
1760 Miller Pkwy
Streetsboro OH 44241
330 562-7191

(G-17837)
ALLEN ALLOYS
8693 State Route 14 (44241-5817)
P.O. Box 2394 (44241-0394)
PHONE..............................330 422-1814
Jeff Allen, *Owner*
EMP: 3
SALES (est): 442.6K **Privately Held**
SIC: 3312 Wheels

(G-17838)
AMERICAN HERITAGE BILLD LLC
630 Mondial Pkwy (44241-5211)
PHONE..............................330 626-3710
Joseph Pucci, *Owner*
Michael Bequette, *Controller*
Nick Abernathy, *Executive*
Garrett Walker,
◆ **EMP:** 70
SQ FT: 64,000
SALES (est): 20.5MM **Privately Held**
WEB: www.americanheritagebilliards.com
SIC: 3949 Billiard & pool equipment & supplies, general

(G-17839)
AMERICAN HERITAGE BILLIARDS
Also Called: Great Gatherings
630 Mondial Pkwy (44241-5211)
PHONE..............................330 626-3710

EMP: 4
SALES (est): 404K **Privately Held**
SIC: 3949 Sporting & athletic goods

(G-17840)
AURORA PLASTICS INC (PA)
9280 Jefferson St (44241-3966)
PHONE..............................330 422-0700
Fax: 330 995-2997
Dennis Radkowsky, *President*
Dan Odonnell, *General Mgr*
Tony Lamorte, *CFO*
Mark Abramowicz, *Sales Mgr*
Steve Harrigan, *Sales Staff*
◆ **EMP:** 70
SALES (est): 72.9MM **Privately Held**
WEB: Www.auroraplastics.com
SIC: 2821 3087 Polyvinyl chloride resins (PVC); custom compound purchased resins

(G-17841)
AUTOMATED PACKAGING SYSTEMS
10320 Philipp Pkwy (44241-4067)
PHONE..............................330 342-0205
Sandra Earl, *Principal*
EMP: 3
SALES (est): 311.8K **Privately Held**
SIC: 2295 Resin or plastic coated fabrics

(G-17842)
AUTOMATED PACKG SYSTEMS INC
600 Mondial Pkwy (44241-5211)
PHONE..............................330 626-2313
Bernard Lerner, *CEO*
EMP: 120
SQ FT: 173,000
SALES (corp-wide): 186.1MM **Privately Held**
SIC: 3081 3565 Packing materials, plastic sheet; polyethylene film; packaging machinery
PA: Automated Packaging Systems Inc.
10175 Philipp Pkwy
Streetsboro OH 44241
330 528-2000

(G-17843)
BERRY PLASTICS CORPORATION
1275 Ethan Ave (44241-4977)
PHONE..............................330 896-6700
Fax: 330 896-6702
Tawana Battle, *Human Resources*
Robert Maltarich, *Manager*
Chris Brown, *Manager*
EMP: 19
SALES (corp-wide): 6.4B **Publicly Held**
SIC: 3089 Bottle caps, molded plastic
HQ: Berry Plastics Corporation
101 Oakley St
Evansville IN 47710
812 424-2904

(G-17844)
CLEVELAND GAS SYSTEMS LLC
Also Called: Gas Tran Systems
10325 State Route 43 N (44241-4945)
PHONE..............................216 391-7780
Matthew Brinn, *President*
▼ **EMP:** 5
SQ FT: 1,500
SALES (est): 857.1K **Privately Held**
WEB: www.gastransystems.com
SIC: 3556 Food products machinery

(G-17845)
CLEVELAND STEEL CONTAINER CORP
10048 Aurora Hudson Rd (44241-1636)
PHONE..............................330 656-5600
Fax: 216 656-3332
Roger Mayle, *General Mgr*
Mike Decola, *Vice Pres*
EMP: 50
SALES (corp-wide): 147.3MM **Privately Held**
SIC: 3412 3411 Pails, shipping: metal; metal cans
PA: Cleveland Steel Container Corporation
30310 Emerald Valley Pkwy
Solon OH 44139
440 349-8000

(G-17846)
COMMERCIAL TURF PRODUCTS LTD
1777 Miller Pkwy (44241-4634)
PHONE.................................330 995-7000
Mike Sobera, *General Mgr*
Kevin Wykoff, *Plant Mgr*
Ray Smith, *QC Mgr*
Ed Zsemdik, *Controller*
EMP: 240
SQ FT: 177,000
SALES (est): 55.9MM
SALES (corp-wide): 2.8B **Privately Held**
WEB: www.mtdproducts.com
SIC: 3524 Lawn & garden equipment
HQ: Mtd Products Inc
　　5965 Grafton Rd
　　Valley City OH 44280
　　330 225-2600

(G-17847)
DAVID ROUND COMPANY INC
10200 Wellman Rd (44241-1615)
PHONE.................................330 656-1600
Bradley R Young, *President*
Dennis Wawrzyniak, *Vice Pres*
Lee Lorence, *Controller*
David Sealfon, *Sales Staff*
▲ EMP: 27 EST: 1869
SQ FT: 30,000
SALES (est): 8.6MM **Privately Held**
WEB: www.davidround.com
SIC: 3536 3531 Hoists; winches; cranes

(G-17848)
DAVIDSON CONVERTING INC
1611 Frost Rd (44241-5005)
PHONE.................................330 626-2118
Fax: 330 626-1228
James B Davidson, *President*
Venny R Davidson, *Corp Secy*
EMP: 5
SQ FT: 10,000
SALES (est): 250K **Privately Held**
SIC: 2679 Paper products, converted

(G-17849)
DAVIS MACHINE PRODUCTS INC
74 Sapphire Ln (44241-4128)
PHONE.................................440 474-0247
Fax: 440 474-9102
William G Davis, *President*
EMP: 6
SQ FT: 7,200
SALES (est): 200K **Privately Held**
SIC: 3599 Machine shop, jobbing & repair

(G-17850)
DELTA SYSTEMS INC
1734 Frost Rd (44241-5008)
P.O. Box 2459 (44241-0459)
PHONE.................................330 626-2811
Fax: 330 626-5249
Elizabeth M Barry, *President*
Mark J Fechtel, *COO*
Greg Schlechter, *Mfg Spvr*
Dianna Brown, *Opers Staff*
Steve Stonebraker, *Purch Agent*
▲ EMP: 200 EST: 1971
SQ FT: 138,000
SALES (est): 103.9MM **Privately Held**
WEB: www.deltasystemsinc.com
SIC: 3613 3625 Switchgear & switchboard
　　apparatus; relays & industrial controls

(G-17851)
DUDICK INC
1818 Miller Pkwy (44241-5067)
PHONE.................................330 562-1970
Tom Dudick, *President*
Teresa Showalter, *Business Mgr*
CC Chen, *Vice Pres*
Jeff Bailey, *Plant Mgr*
Shirley Shelly, *Safety Mgr*
EMP: 55
SALES (est): 17.5MM **Privately Held**
SIC: 2851 Lacquers, varnishes, enamels &
　　other coatings

(G-17852)
EPG INC (DH)
1780 Miller Pkwy (44241-4633)
PHONE.................................330 995-9725
Fax: 330 995-5298
Michael Orazen Jr, *President*
Smith McKee, *Vice Pres*

Michael Scanlon, *Vice Pres*
Gabriel Orazen, *CFO*
EMP: 13
SQ FT: 46,000
SALES (est): 10.6MM
SALES (corp-wide): 2.8B **Privately Held**
WEB: www.epgcando.com
SIC: 3053 3061 Gaskets, all materials;
　　mechanical rubber goods
HQ: Trelleborg Corporation
　　200 Veterans Blvd Ste 3
　　South Haven MI 49090
　　269 639-9891

(G-17853)
FORTEC LITHO CENTRAL LLC
10125 Wellman Rd (44241-1614)
PHONE.................................330 463-1265
Maria Farro, *General Mgr*
Drew C Forhan, *Principal*
EMP: 4
SALES (est): 391K **Privately Held**
SIC: 2752 Commercial printing, litho-
　　graphic

(G-17854)
FORTEC MEDICAL LITHOTRIPSY LLC
10125 Wellman Rd (44241-1614)
PHONE.................................330 656-4301
Drew Forhan, *Mng Member*
Rebecca Atkin, *Technology*
EMP: 50
SQ FT: 1,000
SALES (est): 4.7MM **Privately Held**
SIC: 3699 Laser systems & equipment

(G-17855)
GORELL ENTERPRISES INC (PA)
Also Called: Gorell Windows & Doors
10250 Philipp Pkwy (44241-4765)
PHONE.................................724 465-1800
Wayne C Gorell, *Ch of Bd*
Brian Zimmerman, *President*
Michael A Rempel, *Vice Pres*
Tyson Schwartz, *Vice Pres*
Amy Romeo, *Safety Mgr*
EMP: 360
SQ FT: 240,000
SALES (est): 16.4MM **Privately Held**
WEB: www.gorell.com
SIC: 3089 5031 Plastic hardware & build-
　　ing products; doors & windows

(G-17856)
GRAPHIC EXPRESSIONS SIGNS
8540 State Route 14 Ste D (44241-4204)
PHONE.................................330 422-7446
Ann Landgraf, *President*
EMP: 5
SALES (est): 652.3K **Privately Held**
WEB: www.gesignsnmore.com
SIC: 2752 Commercial printing, litho-
　　graphic

(G-17857)
HORSEMENS PRIDE INC
Also Called: Jolly Pats
10008 State Route 43 (44241-4940)
PHONE.................................800 232-7950
Rob Miavitz, *President*
Brenda Miavitz, *Corp Secy*
Mike Frank, *Opers Mgr*
Rudy Braydich, *Opers Staff*
Kristine Goad, *Manager*
▲ EMP: 22
SQ FT: 20,000
SALES (est): 4.9MM **Privately Held**
WEB: www.horsemenspride.com
SIC: 3089 Extruded finished plastic prod-
　　ucts

(G-17858)
INTERNATIONAL PAPER COMPANY
700 Mondial Pkwy (44241-4511)
PHONE.................................330 626-7300
Chuck Bakaitis, *Branch Mgr*
EMP: 150
SALES (corp-wide): 21B **Publicly Held**
WEB: www.tin.com
SIC: 2653 Corrugated boxes, partitions,
　　display items, sheets & pad

PA: International Paper Company
　　6400 Poplar Ave
　　Memphis TN 38197
　　901 419-9000

(G-17859)
JB PRODUCTS CO
Also Called: J B Products
10299 Wellman Rd (44241-1616)
PHONE.................................330 342-0223
Fax: 330 342-0223
Jon Beljon, *Owner*
EMP: 4
SQ FT: 4,500
SALES (est): 200K **Privately Held**
SIC: 3544 Special dies & tools

(G-17860)
JOSEPH INDUSTRIES INC
Also Called: BUCKEYE FASTENERS COM-
PANY
10039 Aurora Hudson Rd (44241-1600)
PHONE.................................330 528-0091
Fax: 330 342-3895
Patrick Finnegan, *President*
Linda Kerekes, *Corp Secy*
Dan Schiavi, *Project Mgr*
Terry Davenport, *Warehouse Mgr*
Wendy Lovejoy, *Purch Mgr*
▲ EMP: 52
SQ FT: 76,260
SALES: 10.9MM
SALES (corp-wide): 42.3MM **Privately
Held**
WEB: www.joseph.com
SIC: 3714 5084 3713 3566 Motor vehicle
　　parts & accessories; lift trucks & parts;
　　truck & bus bodies; speed changers,
　　drives & gears
PA: Fastener Industries, Inc.
　　1 Berea Commons Ste 209
　　Berea OH 44017
　　440 243-0034

(G-17861)
MICRO-PISE MSRMENT SYSTEMS LLC (HQ)
555 Mondial Pkwy (44241-4510)
P.O. Box 1869, Akron (44309-1869)
PHONE.................................330 541-9100
Fax: 330 541-9111
Steve Harris, *President*
Armand Massary, *VP Opers*
Steven Pownell, *Buyer*
Catrice Rhodes, *Buyer*
Kevin Coleman, *Investment Ofcr*
◆ EMP: 150
SALES (est): 81MM
SALES (corp-wide): 3.8B **Publicly Held**
SIC: 3559 Automotive maintenance equip-
　　ment
PA: Ametek, Inc.
　　1100 Cassatt Rd
　　Berwyn PA 19312
　　610 647-2121

(G-17862)
MICROBIOLOGICAL LABS INC
Also Called: Aspery Farms
9593 Page Rd (44241-5571)
P.O. Box 2519 (44241-0519)
PHONE.................................330 626-2264
George Aspery, *President*
Judith Hromi, *Vice Pres*
Joanne Aspery, *Admin Sec*
EMP: 4
SQ FT: 3,000
SALES (est): 371K **Privately Held**
WEB: www.microbiologicallabs.com
SIC: 8731 8734 2836 Commercial physi-
　　cal research; testing laboratories; biologi-
　　cal products, except diagnostic

(G-17863)
MM SERVICE
8936 State Route 14 (44241-5605)
PHONE.................................330 474-3098
David Phillips, *Owner*
EMP: 6
SQ FT: 10,000
SALES (est): 694.8K **Privately Held**
SIC: 3524 Lawn & garden equipment

(G-17864)
MOJONNIER USA LLC
10325 State Route 43 N (44241-4945)
PHONE.................................844 665-6664
Matt Brinn, *Manager*
EMP: 3
SALES (est): 126.3K **Privately Held**
SIC: 3556 Beverage machinery

(G-17865)
NORTHCOAST ENVIRONMENTAL LABS
10100 Wellman Rd (44241-1613)
PHONE.................................330 342-3377
Timothy Spevak, *President*
John Lawrence, *Vice Pres*
Dave Morehead, *Vice Pres*
Fred Pratt, *Vice Pres*
David Mitalski, *Lab Dir*
EMP: 8
SQ FT: 3,000
SALES (est): 1.5MM **Privately Held**
SIC: 3826 8731 Environmental testing
　　equipment; commercial physical research

(G-17866)
PERMCO INC
1500 Frost Rd (44241-5004)
P.O. Box 2068 (44241-0068)
PHONE.................................330 626-2801
Fax: 330 626-2805
Robert Gouldiez, *President*
Rick Olszewski, *Chairman*
Danny Schiavi, *Regional Mgr*
Bernie Shell, *Exec VP*
Zhang Jin, *Vice Pres*
▲ EMP: 110
SALES (est): 29.2MM
SALES (corp-wide): 12.5MM **Privately
Held**
SIC: 2869 Hydraulic fluids, synthetic base
PA: Guyan International, Inc.
　　5 Nichols Dr
　　Barboursville WV 25504
　　304 733-1029

(G-17867)
PETROX INC
10005 Ellsworth Rd (44241-1608)
PHONE.................................330 653-5526
Fax: 330 757-7924
Benjamin Cart, *President*
Mark Depew, *Vice Pres*
EMP: 10
SALES (est): 1.7MM **Privately Held**
SIC: 1389 5082 Oil field services; oil field
　　equipment

(G-17868)
PM GRAPHICS INC
10170 Philipp Pkwy (44241-4705)
PHONE.................................330 650-0861
Fax: 330 656-2225
Paul W Mc Ghee II, *President*
Christine McGhee, *Corp Secy*
Robert Davis, *CFO*
Pam Dombek, *Personnel Exec*
Cynda Brainard, *Office Admin*
EMP: 50
SQ FT: 35,000
SALES (est): 9.5MM **Privately Held**
WEB: www.pmgraphics.com
SIC: 2752 Commercial printing, offset

(G-17869)
POLYMER STEEL CORP
1818 Miller Pkwy (44241-5067)
PHONE.................................330 562-6906
Tom Dudick, *President*
EMP: 50
SALES (est): 5.2MM **Privately Held**
SIC: 3443 Tanks, lined: metal plate

(G-17870)
RB&W MANUFACTURING LLC (HQ)
10080 Wellman Rd (44241-1611)
PHONE.................................234 380-8540
Fax: 234 380-8545
Craig Cowan, *President*
▲ EMP: 10

▲ = Import ▼=Export
◆ =Import/Export

SALES (est): 3MM
SALES (corp-wide): 1.2B **Publicly Held**
SIC: 5085 3452 3469 Fasteners, industrial: nuts, bolts, screws, etc.; bolts, nuts,
rivets & washers; screws, metal; nuts,
metal; stamping metal for the trade
PA: Park-Ohio Holdings Corp.
6065 Parkland Blvd Ste 1
Cleveland OH 44124
440 947-2000

(G-17871)
READY TO HAUL COLUMBUS LLC
1240 Ethan Ave (44241-4976)
PHONE.................................614 329-5161
Don Macneill,
EMP: 10
SALES (est): 1MM **Privately Held**
SIC: 3949 Sporting & athletic goods

(G-17872)
RR DONNELLEY & SONS COMPANY
Also Called: R R Donnelley
10400 Danner Dr (44241-5070)
PHONE.................................330 562-5250
John Augustiniak, Manager
EMP: 100
SALES (corp-wide): 6.9B **Publicly Held**
WEB: www.moore.com
SIC: 2759 Screen printing
PA: R. R. Donnelley & Sons Company
35 W Wacker Dr Ste 3650
Chicago IL 60601
312 326-8000

(G-17873)
SAFEGUARD TECHNOLOGY INC
1460 Miller Pkwy (44241-4640)
PHONE.................................330 995-5200
Mervyn R Litzow, President
Glenn Gierman, Controller
Rita Rode, Human Res Mgr
Ken Angie, Sales Mgr
Connie Pederi, Sales Staff
▲ EMP: 25
SQ FT: 20,510
SALES (est): 5.6MM **Privately Held**
WEB: www.safeguard-technology.com
SIC: 3069 Stair treads, rubber

(G-17874)
SELAS HEAT TECHNOLOGY CO LLC
11012 Aurora Hudson Rd (44241-1629)
PHONE.................................216 662-8800
Christine Orteca, Branch Mgr
EMP: 4
SALES (corp-wide): 59.9MM **Privately Held**
SIC: 3433 Gas burners, industrial
HQ: Selas Heat Technology Co Llc
11012 Aurora Hudson Rd
Streetsboro OH 44241
800 523-6500

(G-17875)
SELAS HEAT TECHNOLOGY CO LLC (HQ)
11012 Aurora Hudson Rd (44241-1629)
PHONE.................................800 523-6500
David S Bovenizer, CEO
Fred Root, Controller
▲ EMP: 28
SALES (est): 22.4MM
SALES (corp-wide): 59.9MM **Privately Held**
SIC: 3433 3255 3823 3564 Heating
equipment, except electric; clay refracto-
ries; industrial instrmnts msrmnt
display/control process variable; blowers
& fans; industrial furnaces & ovens
PA: Lionheart Holdings Llc
54 Friends Ln Ste 125
Newtown PA 18940
215 283-8400

(G-17876)
SOFT-LITE LLC (HQ)
Also Called: Soft-Lite Windows
10250 Philipp Pkwy (44241-4765)
PHONE.................................330 528-3400
Fax: 877 528-3401

Roy Anderson, President
Arnold Levitt, Vice Pres
Michael Rempel, Vice Pres
Rick Robson, Vice Pres
Rich Bonney, VP Opers
EMP: 160
SQ FT: 200,000
SALES (est): 125.5MM
SALES (corp-wide): 1.2B **Privately Held**
WEB: www.softlitewindows.com
SIC: 3089 Windows, plastic
PA: Harvey Industries, Inc.
1400 Main St Fl 3
Waltham MA 02451
800 598-5400

(G-17877)
SPECTRUM MACHINE INC
1668 Frost Rd (44241-5006)
PHONE.................................330 626-3666
Fax: 330 626-3313
Kevin Lamb, President
Todd Lamb, Corp Secy
Timothy Lamb, Vice Pres
EMP: 28
SQ FT: 31,000
SALES (est): 6.1MM **Privately Held**
WEB: www.spectrummachine.com
SIC: 3545 3469 3599 Machine tool ac-
cessories; machine parts, stamped or
pressed metal; machine shop, jobbing &
repair

(G-17878)
ST LAWRENCE STEEL CORPORATION
2500 Crane Centre Dr (44241-5072)
P.O. Box 2490 (44241-0490)
PHONE.................................330 562-9000
Fax: 330 562-1100
Henry W Beechler, President
Ed Ponter, Plant Mgr
David H Harvanek, Purch Mgr
Dan Spirka, Engineer
Ken Thomas, Engineer
EMP: 34 EST: 1955
SQ FT: 60,000
SALES (est): 29.6MM **Privately Held**
WEB: www.stlawrencesteel.com
SIC: 5051 3443 3441 Steel; iron & steel
(ferrous) products; fabricated plate work
(boiler shop); fabricated structural metal

(G-17879)
STEP2 COMPANY LLC (HQ)
Also Called: Step 2
10010 Aurora Hudson Rd (44241-1619)
PHONE.................................866 429-5200
Fax: 330 528-0954
Christopher P Quinn, CEO
Lysa Liemer, Exec VP
Wayne Stock, Exec VP
Dotti Foltz, Vice Pres
Brian McDonald, Vice Pres
◆ EMP: 500
SQ FT: 400,000
SALES (est): 198.3MM
SALES (corp-wide): 202.9MM **Privately Held**
WEB: www.step2.com
SIC: 3089 3944 3423 Molding primary
plastic; games, toys & children's vehicles;
hand & edge tools
PA: Leisure Time Products, Llc
3001 N Rouse St
Pittsburg KS 66762
620 232-2400

(G-17880)
STEP2 HOLDINGS LLC
10010 Aurora Hudson Rd (44241-1619)
PHONE.................................330 656-0440
John Jack Vresics, CEO
James Schaefer, COO
Jim Smith, CFO
Dorene Francis, Credit Mgr
Jack Bresics, Mng Member
◆ EMP: 900
SALES (est): 57MM **Privately Held**
SIC: 3944 3089 Games, toys & children's
vehicles; plastic containers, except foam

(G-17881)
TELCON LLC
1677 Miller Pkwy (44241-4635)
PHONE.................................330 562-5566

Fax: 216 562-8452
Kevin Kummerlen, President
Dan Ferrara, General Mgr
EMP: 75
SQ FT: 56,000
SALES (est): 15.6MM **Privately Held**
SIC: 3599 3369 Machine shop, jobbing &
repair; nonferrous foundries

(G-17882)
TEXTRON INC
555 Mondial Pkwy (44241-4510)
PHONE.................................330 626-7800
EMP: 10
SALES (corp-wide): 12.1B **Publicly Held**
SIC: 3721 Mfg Aircraft
PA: Textron Inc.
40 Westminster St
Providence RI 02903
401 421-2800

(G-17883)
WYATT INDUSTRIES LLC
1790 Miller Pkwy (44241-4633)
PHONE.................................330 954-1790
Beverly Clemens, CEO
EMP: 6
SQ FT: 10,000
SALES (est): 273.9K **Privately Held**
SIC: 3089 Plastic processing

Strongsville
Cuyahoga County

(G-17884)
ADVANCED TECH UTILIZATION CO
12005 Prospect Rd Unit 1 (44149-2935)
P.O. Box 360461 (44136-0008)
PHONE.................................440 238-3770
Fax: 440 238-4062
Terry Yamrick, Owner
EMP: 10
SQ FT: 2,500
SALES (est): 560K **Privately Held**
SIC: 3542 5084 Rebuilt machine tools,
metal forming types; metalworking ma-
chinery

(G-17885)
ALBION INDUSTRIES INC
20246 Progress Dr (44149-3296)
PHONE.................................440 238-1955
Fax: 440 238-1956
Ralph Holstein, President
Roman T Keenen, Principal
Caroline Holstein, Corp Secy
◆ EMP: 30
SQ FT: 21,000
SALES (est): 4.3MM **Privately Held**
SIC: 2514 Frames for box springs or bed-
springs: metal

(G-17886)
ALPHAGRAPHICS 507 INC
14765 Pearl Rd (44136-5026)
PHONE.................................440 878-9700
Rob Kammer, President
Tom Breno, Manager
EMP: 6
SQ FT: 3,000
SALES (est): 855.9K **Privately Held**
SIC: 2752 Commercial printing, litho-
graphic

(G-17887)
AMERICAN WATER SERVICES INC
17449 W Sprague Rd (44136-1666)
PHONE.................................440 243-9840
Rick Meloy, Project Mgr
EMP: 7
SALES: 1.5MM **Privately Held**
SIC: 3823 4941 Water quality monitoring
& control systems; water supply

(G-17888)
AMTECH INC
Also Called: Amtech Laminating Equipment
11925 Pearl Rd Ste 207 (44136-3343)
P.O. Box 360518, Cleveland (44136-0009)
PHONE.................................440 238-2141
Fax: 440 238-4426

Paul Roache, President
Leigh Gesick, Vice Pres
Joe Marita, Vice Pres
EMP: 4
SALES (est): 932.5K **Privately Held**
SIC: 5084 7699 2759 Industrial machin-
ery & equipment; photographic equipment
repair; commercial printing

(G-17889)
ASTRO INSTRUMENTATION LLC
22740 Lunn Rd (44149-4899)
PHONE.................................440 238-2005
Fax: 440 878-4636
Sue Longley, Purch Agent
Delana McGuire, Asst Controller
Maricela Posada, Credit Staff
Jeff Hastings, Manager
Rich Smith, Manager
▲ EMP: 85 EST: 2000
SQ FT: 40,000
SALES (est): 14.6MM
SALES (corp-wide): 419.3MM **Publicly Held**
WEB: www.astroinst.com
SIC: 3826 Analytical instruments
PA: Sparton Corporation
425 N Martingale Rd
Schaumburg IL 60173
847 762-5800

(G-17890)
ATLANTIC DURANT TECHNOLOGY INC (HQ)
Also Called: Atd
19963 Progress Dr (44149-3211)
PHONE.................................440 238-6931
Frank E Mehwald, President
Joe Pace, Engineer
Jordan Tadic, Engineer
Jennifer Dumm, Human Resources
Dale Darin, Manager
▲ EMP: 1
SQ FT: 71,500
SALES (est): 5.1MM
SALES (corp-wide): 147.6MM **Privately Held**
SIC: 3469 Metal stampings
PA: Atlantic Tool & Die Company Inc
19963 Progress Dr
Strongsville OH 44149
440 238-6931

(G-17891)
ATLANTIC TOOL & DIE COMPANY (PA)
19963 Progress Dr (44149-3211)
PHONE.................................440 238-6931
Fax: 440 238-2210
Frank Mehwald, President
Matt Edmonds, President
Paul Durant, General Mgr
Russ Haid, General Mgr
Michael Spence, General Mgr
◆ EMP: 240 EST: 1947
SQ FT: 110,000
SALES (est): 147.6MM **Privately Held**
SIC: 3469 3544 Metal stampings; special
dies, tools, jigs & fixtures

(G-17892)
AUTO TECHNOLOGY COMPANY
20026 Progress Dr (44149-3214)
PHONE.................................440 572-7800
Kevin A Smith, President
Walter Senney, Vice Pres
Vicky Metzger, Accounts Mgr
Nick Johnson, Director
EMP: 15
SQ FT: 50,000
SALES (est): 4.6MM **Privately Held**
SIC: 3826 Environmental testing equip-
ment

(G-17893)
AUTOMATED MFG SOLUTIONS INC
Also Called: AMS
19706 Progress Dr (44149-3208)
PHONE.................................440 878-3711
Thomas P Setele, President
Mark Ogorzaly, Mfg Dir
Dave Minney, Engineer
Gary Gembala, Business Dir
EMP: 18
SQ FT: 8,000

SALES (est): 5.9MM **Privately Held**
WEB: www.autommfgsolutions.com
SIC: 3559 Automotive maintenance equipment

(G-17894)
AUTOWAX INC
15015 Foltz Pkwy (44149-4728)
PHONE..............................440 334-4417
Alina Baron, *CEO*
James Baron, *Vice Pres*
EMP: 6
SALES (est): 1.2MM **Privately Held**
SIC: 3711 Motor vehicles & car bodies

(G-17895)
BEARINGS MANUFACTURING COMPANY (PA)
Also Called: BMC
15157 Foltz Pkwy (44149-4730)
PHONE..............................440 846-5517
Steve Sivo, *President*
Gary Elder, *General Mgr*
Jeff Walls, *Vice Pres*
Benjamin Walls, *Prdtn Mgr*
Joletta Hannibal, *Controller*
EMP: 50
SALES (est): 11.7MM **Privately Held**
SIC: 3562 3568 Ball & roller bearings; ball bearings & parts; casters; roller bearings & parts; bearings, bushings & blocks

(G-17896)
BENCO INDUSTRIES INC
19231 Royalton Rd (44149-4944)
P.O. Box 7, Richfield (44286-0007)
PHONE..............................440 572-3555
Fax: 440 572-5338
P Douglas Hatlovic, *President*
Dolores Hatlovic, *Admin Sec*
EMP: 6
SQ FT: 15,000
SALES (est): 756.9K **Privately Held**
WEB: www.bencoindustries.com
SIC: 3479 Painting of metal products

(G-17897)
BLUE CRESCENT ENTERPRISES INC
Also Called: AlphaGraphics
19645 Progress Dr (44149-3205)
PHONE..............................440 878-9700
Fax: 440 878-9708
Saleh Afif Alafifi, *President*
EMP: 7
SQ FT: 3,800
SALES: 550K **Privately Held**
SIC: 2752 Commercial printing, lithographic

(G-17898)
BREW KETTLE INC
Also Called: Ringneck Brewing Company
8377 Pearl Rd (44136-1637)
PHONE..............................440 234-8788
Fax: 440 239-8790
Chris J McKim, *President*
EMP: 11
SQ FT: 3,500
SALES (est): 2MM **Privately Held**
SIC: 2082 5149 Malt beverages; groceries & related products

(G-17899)
CARDINAL MACHINE COMPANY
14459 Foltz Pkwy (44149-4797)
PHONE..............................440 238-7050
Fax: 440 238-7051
Richard Z Kaszei, *CEO*
Greg Kaszei, *President*
Beth Corrigan, *Office Mgr*
EMP: 15
SQ FT: 10,000
SALES: 2MM **Privately Held**
SIC: 3599 Machine shop, jobbing & repair

(G-17900)
CCL LABEL INC
Also Called: CCL Design Electronics
17700 Foltz Pkwy (44149-5536)
PHONE..............................440 878-7277
Fax: 440 878-7103
Kathleen Hall, *Vice Pres*
Bob Rotella, *Vice Pres*
Steve Hartman, *Finance Mgr*
Patrick Thomas, *Branch Mgr*

Al Bartholomew, *Manager*
EMP: 350
SALES (corp-wide): 188.4K **Privately Held**
WEB: www.avery.com
SIC: 2672 Coated & laminated paper
HQ: Ccl Label, Inc.
161 Worcester Rd Ste 504
Framingham MA 01701
508 872-4511

(G-17901)
CHEMICAL METHODS INC
20338 Progress Dr (44149-3220)
PHONE..............................216 476-8400
Daniel E Richards, *President*
John Minor, *Technology*
Dan Gaba, *Technical Staff*
EMP: 30
SQ FT: 5,000
SALES (est): 5.2MM **Privately Held**
WEB: www.chemicalmethods.com
SIC: 2842 3471 2992 2899 Cleaning or polishing preparations; plating & polishing; lubricating oils & greases; chemical preparations

(G-17902)
CLARK-RELIANCE CORPORATION (PA)
Also Called: Jerguson
16633 Foltz Pkwy (44149-5597)
PHONE..............................440 572-1500
Fax: 440 238-8828
Matthew P Figgie Jr, *Ch of Bd*
Rick Solon, *President*
Jacob Mathew, *Regional Mgr*
Peter Wang, *Regional Mgr*
Jim Karfes, *Plant Mgr*
◆ EMP: 155
SQ FT: 93,000
SALES (est): 48.1MM **Privately Held**
WEB: www.clark-reliance.com
SIC: 3823 3491 Industrial process control instruments; process control regulator valves

(G-17903)
CLARK-RELIANCE CORPORATION
Also Called: Jacoby Tarbox Co
16633 Foltz Pkwy (44149-5597)
PHONE..............................440 572-7408
Jeffrey Sawicki, *President*
Chris Fadden, *Vice Pres*
EMP: 5
SALES (corp-wide): 48.1MM **Privately Held**
WEB: www.clark-reliance.com
SIC: 3491 Industrial valves
PA: Clark-Reliance Corporation
16633 Foltz Pkwy
Strongsville OH 44149
440 572-1500

(G-17904)
CLEVELAND FINISHING INC
16979 Falmouth Dr (44136-7417)
PHONE..............................440 572-5475
Edward Eible, *President*
EMP: 3
SALES (est): 164.1K **Privately Held**
SIC: 3471 Finishing, metals or formed products

(G-17905)
COLOR PROCESS INC
13900 Prospect Rd (44149-3834)
PHONE..............................440 268-7100
Fax: 440 433-7773
Mark Ingham, *President*
Elizabeth Ingham, *Regional Mgr*
Liz Ingham, *Manager*
Jim Greiner, *Admin Sec*
EMP: 25
SQ FT: 65,000
SALES: 4.8MM **Privately Held**
WEB: www.colorprocess.com
SIC: 2759 Screen printing

(G-17906)
CONDITION MONITORING SUPPLIES
Also Called: CMS
20338 Progress Dr (44149-3220)
P.O. Box 770804, Cleveland (44107-0037)
PHONE..............................216 941-6868
Dan Richards, *Owner*
EMP: 4
SALES (est): 250.6K **Privately Held**
SIC: 3533 Oil field machinery & equipment

(G-17907)
CONSOLDTED GRNHSE SLUTIONS LLC
14800 Foltz Pkwy (44149-4725)
PHONE..............................330 844-8598
Sylvia Courtney, *Mng Member*
Rebecca Yount, *Mng Member*
John Helline,
EMP: 4
SQ FT: 4,000
SALES (est): 565.3K **Privately Held**
SIC: 1542 3448 Institutional building construction; greenhouses: prefabricated metal

(G-17908)
CRISHTRONICS LLC
15249 Sassafras Dr (44136-1781)
PHONE..............................440 572-8318
Phyllis A Crish, *Accountant*
James K Roosa, *Mng Member*
Timothy Crish, *E-Business*
EMP: 3
SALES (est): 191.1K **Privately Held**
SIC: 3674 Microcircuits, integrated (semiconductor); microprocessors

(G-17909)
CUSTOM SPEED PARTS INC
Also Called: Harland Sharp
19769 Progress Dr (44149-3207)
PHONE..............................440 238-3260
Randy Becker, *President*
Susan Becker, *Vice Pres*
Kate Kupchik, *Controller*
Sandy Cirino, *Advt Staff*
Micheal Becker, *Manager*
EMP: 15
SQ FT: 32,000
SALES (est): 3.4MM **Privately Held**
WEB: www.customspeedparts.com
SIC: 3714 Motor vehicle engines & parts

(G-17910)
CYLINDERS & VALVES INC
20811 Westwood Dr (44149-3999)
P.O. Box 360555, Cleveland (44136-0010)
PHONE..............................440 238-7343
Fax: 440 238-3812
James P Gardner III, *President*
Katherine Frederick, *Manager*
EMP: 8 EST: 1958
SQ FT: 7,500
SALES (est): 1.2MM **Privately Held**
WEB: www.cylval.com
SIC: 3594 3593 3494 Motors: hydraulic, fluid power or air; fluid power cylinders & actuators; valves & pipe fittings

(G-17911)
DONPRINT INC
Also Called: Worldmark
17700 Foltz Pkwy (44149-5536)
PHONE..............................847 573-7777
Patrick Hay, *President*
Kirsten Mahebic, *Manager*
Frank Duffin, *Admin Sec*
▲ EMP: 36
SQ FT: 20,000
SALES (est): 5.5MM
SALES (corp-wide): 188.4K **Privately Held**
WEB: www.donprint.com
SIC: 2759 Labels & seals: printing
HQ: Worldmark International Limited
4 Redwood Crescent
Glasgow G74 5
135 524-9191

(G-17912)
DOUGLAS S KUTZ
19395 Knowlton Pkwy # 103 (44149-9056)
P.O. Box 360812, Cleveland (44136-0014)
PHONE..............................440 238-8426
EMP: 3
SALES (est): 160K **Privately Held**
SIC: 3272 Mfg Concrete Products

(G-17913)
DUPLI-SYSTEMS INC
Also Called: Ohio Cut Sheet
8260 Dow Cir (44136-1762)
PHONE..............................440 234-9415
Fax: 440 234-2350
Bud Eldridge, *CEO*
Randy Eldridge, *President*
Todd Eldridge, *Exec VP*
Dave Griffith, *Vice Pres*
Laurie Scalf, *Human Res Mgr*
EMP: 125 EST: 1955
SALES (est): 23.6MM **Privately Held**
WEB: www.dupli-systems.com
SIC: 2759 2754 2782 2761 Commercial printing; business forms: gravure printing; blankbooks & looseleaf binders; manifold business forms; commercial printing, lithographic; automotive & apparel trimmings

(G-17914)
DUROX COMPANY
12312 Alameda Dr (44149-3023)
PHONE..............................440 238-5350
Fax: 216 238-5773
Fred Miller, *Sls & Mktg Exec*
Bob Gallagher, *Accounting Mgr*
Rachel De La Pena, *Human Res Mgr*
Denise Erzinger, *Director*
Steven Sabanoos, *Director*
▲ EMP: 70
SQ FT: 50,000
SALES (est): 23.1MM
SALES (corp-wide): 2.9B **Publicly Held**
WEB: www.durox.com
SIC: 3053 Gaskets & sealing devices
HQ: Standard Car Truck Company Inc
6400 Shafer Ct Ste 450
Rosemont IL 60018
847 692-6050

(G-17915)
EFFICIENT MACHINE PDTS CORP
12133 Alameda Dr (44149-3018)
PHONE..............................440 268-0205
Fax: 440 268-0215
Ted Imbrogno, *President*
Patrick McGuckin, *Vice Pres*
Paul Klonowski, *QC Mgr*
Edward Imbrogno, *Administration*
EMP: 40 EST: 1962
SQ FT: 31,000
SALES: 7MM **Privately Held**
WEB: www.efficientmachineprod.com
SIC: 3451 Screw machine products

(G-17916)
ELEGANT EMBROIDERY LLC
11053 Prospect Rd (44149-2839)
PHONE..............................440 878-0904
Peter F Sturtevant,
James Hollingsworth,
EMP: 3 EST: 2005
SQ FT: 1,000
SALES: 100K **Privately Held**
SIC: 2395 Embroidery & art needlework

(G-17917)
EMCO ELECTRIC INTERNATIONAL
19449 Progress Dr (44149-3201)
P.O. Box 361361 (44136-0023)
PHONE..............................440 878-1199
Richard Tamulewicz Jr, *President*
Michelle Tamulewicz, *Vice Pres*
Sheri Tamulewicz, *Vice Pres*
▲ EMP: 5
SQ FT: 22,000
SALES (est): 846.3K **Privately Held**
SIC: 3644 2841 Electric conduits & fittings; soap & other detergents

▲ = Import ▼ =Export
◆ =Import/Export

(G-17918)
ERNST FLOW INDUSTRIES LLC
16633 Foltz Pkwy (44149-5513)
PHONE....................................732 938-5641
Roger Ernst, *President*
John Ernst, *Vice Pres*
Diane Burd, *Purchasing*
Eugene Ernst Jr, *Treasurer*
Barbara Dayton, *Accountant*
EMP: 14 EST: 1962
SQ FT: 9,000
SALES (est): 3MM
SALES (corp-wide): 48.1MM **Privately Held**
WEB: www.tfci.com
SIC: 3823 3824 Flow instruments, industrial process type; water meters
PA: Clark-Reliance Corporation
16633 Foltz Pkwy
Strongsville OH 44149
440 572-1500

(G-17919)
EUROPA SPORTS PRODUCTS INC
13675 Darice Pkwy (44149-3823)
PHONE....................................440 846-9571
Fax: 440 846-9584
Craig Harts, *Branch Mgr*
EMP: 15
SALES (corp-wide): 296.1MM **Privately Held**
SIC: 3949 Sporting & athletic goods
PA: Europa Sports Products, Inc.
11401 Granite St Ste H
Charlotte NC 28273
704 405-2022

(G-17920)
FOUNDATION SOFTWARE INC
17999 Foltz Pkwy (44149-5565)
PHONE....................................330 220-8383
Fax: 330 220-1443
Fred Ode, *CEO*
Michael J Basil, *VP Opers*
Stacey Kazarovich, *Project Mgr*
Lori Adamczyk, *QA Dir*
Denise East, *QA Dir*
EMP: 92
SQ FT: 16,000
SALES (est): 14.3MM **Privately Held**
SIC: 7372 7371 Prepackaged software; software programming applications; custom computer programming services

(G-17921)
FRANJINHAS INC
17656 Fairfax Ln (44136-7206)
PHONE....................................440 463-1523
Clara Lipszyc-Arroyo, *President*
Steven Aurroyo, *Treasurer*
EMP: 6 EST: 1997
SALES (est): 590K **Privately Held**
SIC: 2211 Flannels, cotton

(G-17922)
GARETH STEVENS PUBLISHING LP
23221 Morgan Ct (44149-5100)
PHONE....................................800 542-2595
Roger Rosen, *Partner*
Gary Spears, *Partner*
Jodi Yuhas, *General Mgr*
Jennifer Jenson, *Manager*
Ken Katula, *Manager*
EMP: 150
SALES (est): 5.8MM **Privately Held**
SIC: 2731 Book publishing

(G-17923)
GUARANTEE SPECIALTIES INC
Also Called: Garvin Industries Div
21693 Drake Rd (44149-6614)
P.O. Box 360247 (44136-0005)
PHONE....................................216 451-9744
Fax: 216 451-3332
Armando E Pages, *President*
Ed Hada, *General Mgr*
Carol Braunschweig, *Principal*
▲ EMP: 57
SQ FT: 75,000

SALES (est): 7.2MM **Privately Held**
WEB: www.gsi-garvin.com
SIC: 3463 3469 3465 Plumbing fixture forgings, nonferrous; stamping metal for the trade; automotive stampings

(G-17924)
HDI LANDING GEAR USA INC
Also Called: Heroux Devtek Landing Gear Div
15900 Foltz Pkwy (44149-5531)
PHONE....................................440 783-5255
Tara Kumhall, *General Mgr*
Don Benincasa, *Manager*
EMP: 50
SQ FT: 115,000
SALES (corp-wide): 246.3MM **Privately Held**
SIC: 3728 Alighting (landing gear) assemblies, aircraft
HQ: Hdi Landing Gear Usa, Inc.
663 Montgomery Ave
Springfield OH 45506

(G-17925)
HINCHCLIFF LUMBER COMPANY
Also Called: Hinchcliff Products Co
13550 Falling Water Rd # 105 (44136-4360)
PHONE....................................440 238-5200
Fax: 440 238-5202
Donald Phillips, *Vice Pres*
Jay Philips, *Manager*
John J Whitney, *Admin Sec*
EMP: 5
SALES (corp-wide): 8.8MM **Privately Held**
WEB: www.hinchcliffproducts.com
SIC: 2426 2448 Dimension, hardwood; wood pallets & skids
PA: Hinchcliff Lumber Company
Rr 72
Hendricks WV 26271
304 478-2500

(G-17926)
HMI INDUSTRIES INC (PA)
Also Called: Health Mor At Home Cbp
13325 Darice Pkwy Unit A (44149-3819)
PHONE....................................440 846-7800
Fax: 216 986-8118
Kirk Foley, *CEO*
John Pryor, *President*
Robert Kinney, *Senior VP*
Daniel J Duggan, *Vice Pres*
Julie A Merkle, *Vice Pres*
◆ EMP: 50 EST: 1928
SQ FT: 73,000
SALES (est): 25.2MM **Privately Held**
WEB: www.filterqueen.com
SIC: 3634 Air purifiers, portable

(G-17927)
HOUSE SILVA-STRONGSVILLE INC
Al156 Southpark Mall Al (44136)
Rural Route 4050 Burba, Wooster (44691)
PHONE....................................330 464-6419
Kelly Silva, *President*
EMP: 3
SQ FT: 1,368
SALES (est): 215.9K **Privately Held**
SIC: 3559 Jewelers' machines

(G-17928)
HUGHES CORPORATION (PA)
Also Called: Weschler Instruments
16900 Foltz Pkwy (44149-5520)
PHONE....................................440 238-2550
Fax: 440 238-0660
David E Hughes, *President*
Esther Carpenter, *Principal*
Michael F Dorman, *Exec VP*
Douglas Hughes, *Vice Pres*
Marcia Welcome, *Purch Mgr*
EMP: 30
SQ FT: 11,500
SALES (est): 32MM **Privately Held**
WEB: www.weschler.com
SIC: 5063 3825 Electrical apparatus & equipment; instruments to measure electricity

(G-17929)
IMPERIAL DIE & MFG CO
22930 Royalton Rd (44149-3842)
PHONE....................................440 268-9080
Fax: 440 267-4648
Ronald Lapossy, *President*
Kenneth Lapossy, *Treasurer*
EMP: 13 EST: 1959
SQ FT: 20,000
SALES (est): 2.7MM **Privately Held**
SIC: 3469 3544 Metal stampings; special dies & tools

(G-17930)
INFINIUM WALL SYSTEMS INC
22555 Ascoa Ct (44149-4700)
PHONE....................................440 572-5000
Shawn Gaffney, *President*
Jason Zamecnik, *Project Mgr*
Kenny Goodwin, *Controller*
Mark Fenwick, *Marketing Staff*
Jordan Bates, *Comp Tech*
▼ EMP: 30
SQ FT: 30,000
SALES: 15MM **Privately Held**
WEB: www.infiniumwalls.com
SIC: 2522 Office furniture, except wood

(G-17931)
INSTRUMENTORS INC
22077 Drake Rd (44149-6606)
PHONE....................................440 238-3430
Fax: 440 238-4746
Robert A Heinrich, *President*
Elvera Heinrich, *Corp Secy*
James R Heinrich, *Vice Pres*
David Wolfs, *Engineer*
Michelle Soltis, *Office Mgr*
EMP: 6 EST: 1973
SQ FT: 10,000
SALES (est): 1MM **Privately Held**
WEB: www.instrumentorsinc.com
SIC: 3829 7699 5084 Measuring & controlling devices; scientific equipment repair service; instruments & control equipment

(G-17932)
J & J BECHKE INC (PA)
Also Called: Copy Quick Instant Printing
12931 Pearl Rd (44136-3425)
PHONE....................................440 238-1441
Fax: 440 238-8979
John Bechke, *President*
Joy Bechke, *Vice Pres*
EMP: 7 EST: 1978
SQ FT: 2,200
SALES (est): 1.3MM **Privately Held**
SIC: 2752 Commercial printing, offset

(G-17933)
JATDCO LLC
19963 Progress Dr (44149-3211)
PHONE....................................440 238-6570
Louis James,
Michael Mehwald,
EMP: 4
SALES (est): 322.7K **Privately Held**
SIC: 3465 7692 4213 Automotive stampings; automotive welding; automobiles, transport & delivery

(G-17934)
K & M TOOL & MACHINE CO INC
17383 Foltz Pkwy (44149-5527)
PHONE....................................440 572-5130
Fax: 440 572-5133
Pete Stojsavljevic, *President*
Cynthia Bowen, *Accounts Mgr*
Klara Stojsavljevic, *Admin Sec*
EMP: 3
SQ FT: 8,800
SALES: 500K **Privately Held**
SIC: 3599 7692 Machine shop, jobbing & repair; welding repair

(G-17935)
KALINICH FENCE COMPANY INC
12223 Prospect Rd (44149-2994)
PHONE....................................440 238-6127
Fax: 440 238-2178
Mike Kalinich Sr, *President*
Erma Kalinich, *Corp Secy*
Mike Kalinich Jr, *Vice Pres*
EMP: 18 EST: 1918

SQ FT: 33,000
SALES (est): 3.3MM **Privately Held**
WEB: www.kalinichfenceco.com
SIC: 2499 Fencing, wood; snow fence, wood

(G-17936)
KID CONCOCTIONS COMPANY
18511 Whitemarsh Ln (44149-6863)
PHONE....................................440 572-1800
Danita Thomas, *President*
John Thomas, *Vice Pres*
Edward Johnson, *Manager*
Sandy Shaff, *Manager*
EMP: 4
SALES: 2.1MM **Privately Held**
WEB: www.kidconcoctions.com
SIC: 2731 Books: publishing & printing

(G-17937)
LAKE ERIE RUBBER RECYCLING LLC
19940 Echo Dr (44149-6010)
PHONE....................................440 570-6027
Katherine E Miller, *Admin Asst*
EMP: 4
SALES (est): 441.9K **Privately Held**
SIC: 3069 Reclaimed rubber (reworked by manufacturing processes)

(G-17938)
LEES GRINDING INC
15620 Foltz Pkwy (44149-4741)
P.O. Box 360169 (44136-0003)
PHONE....................................440 572-4610
Fax: 440 572-2411
Nick D Papanikolaou, *President*
Tom Rechin, *Project Mgr*
James Goldman, *Accountant*
Jim Spencer, *Sales Staff*
Karen Allman, *Office Mgr*
EMP: 30 EST: 1961
SQ FT: 20,000
SALES (est): 5.1MM **Privately Held**
WEB: www.leesgrinding.com
SIC: 3599 Machine shop, jobbing & repair

(G-17939)
LUMITEX INC (PA)
8443 Dow Cir (44136-1796)
PHONE....................................440 243-8401
Fax: 440 243-8402
Peter W Broer, *President*
Scott Bogard, *General Mgr*
Tim Corbett, *Mfg Dir*
Jan Ohern, *Production*
Elizabeth Zak, *QC Mgr*
▲ EMP: 90
SQ FT: 19,000
SALES (est): 25.1MM **Privately Held**
WEB: www.lumitex.com
SIC: 3646 3641 3648 3845 Commercial indusl & institutional electric lighting fixtures; electric lamps; lighting equipment; electromedical equipment

(G-17940)
LUMITEX INC
Poly Optical Pdts & Lumitex
8443 Dow Cir (44136-1796)
PHONE....................................949 250-8557
Scott Diestel, *Manager*
EMP: 5
SALES (corp-wide): 25.1MM **Privately Held**
WEB: www.lumitex.com
SIC: 3641 Electric lamps
PA: Lumitex, Inc.
8443 Dow Cir
Strongsville OH 44136
440 243-8401

(G-17941)
MOMENTIVE PRFMCE MTLS QRTZ INC
22557 Lunn Rd (44149-4871)
PHONE....................................440 878-5700
Joseph P Reyes, *President*
Donald Allen, *Maint Spvr*
R S Verboom, *Corp Comm Staff*
Bob Koch, *Marketing Staff*
Bedri Erdem, *Manager*
◆ EMP: 200

SALES (est): 78.7MM
SALES (corp-wide): 2.2B **Publicly Held**
SIC: 2869 3479 3446 3297 Silicones;
   coating of metals with silicon; architectural metalwork; nonclay refractories
HQ: Momentive Performance Materials Inc.
   260 Hudson River Rd
   Waterford NY 12188
   518 237-3330

(G-17942)
MONARCH ENGRAVING INC
8293 Dow Cir (44136-1761)
PHONE.............................440 638-1500
Fax: 440 638-1501
William Pfeil Jr, *President*
David Pfeil, *Corp Secy*
Brian Pfeil, *Vice Pres*
EMP: 23 **EST:** 1953
SQ FT: 20,000
SALES (est): 3.5MM **Privately Held**
SIC: 3083 2899 Laminated plastics plate
   & sheet; chemical preparations

(G-17943)
MTS MEDICATION TECH INC
21550 Drake Rd (44149-6617)
PHONE.............................440 238-0840
Gail Baksi, *Branch Mgr*
EMP: 3
SALES (corp-wide): 692.6MM **Publicly
Held**
WEB: www.mtsp.com
SIC: 3089 3565 Blister or bubble formed
   packaging, plastic; packaging machinery
HQ: Mts Medication Technologies, Inc.
   2003 Gandy Blvd N Ste 800
   Saint Petersburg FL 33702
   727 576-6311

(G-17944)
MUELLER ART COVER & BINDING CO
12005 Alameda Dr (44149-3016)
P.O. Box 360829 (44136-0014)
PHONE.............................440 238-3303
Toll Free:.............................888   -
Fax: 440 238-5574
Edmond Mueller, *President*
Bob Mueller, *COO*
Daniel Mack, *Vice Pres*
Jack Kelly, *Purchasing*
EMP: 45
SQ FT: 38,000
SALES (est): 5.7MM **Privately Held**
WEB: www.muellerartcover.com
SIC: 2782 7336 Looseleaf binders & de-
   vices; graphic arts & related design; silk
   screen design

(G-17945)
NEWBERRY WOOD ENTERPRISES INC (PA)
12223 Prospect Rd (44149-2939)
PHONE.............................440 238-6127
Mike Kalinich, *President*
Michael Kalinich Sr, *President*
Erma Kalinich, *Treasurer*
EMP: 14
SQ FT: 25,000
SALES (est): 1.8MM **Privately Held**
SIC: 2421 Custom sawmill; snow fence
   lath

(G-17946)
NORTH COAST PATTERN INC
10587 Scottsdale Dr (44136-8801)
PHONE.............................440 322-5064
Fax: 440 322-7154
Al Ledyard, *President*
EMP: 4
SQ FT: 4,628
SALES (est): 270K **Privately Held**
SIC: 3543 Foundry patternmaking

(G-17947)
NUTRO INC
11515 Alameda Dr (44149-3006)
PHONE.............................440 572-3800
Walter Klevay, *President*
Christian Nuesser, *Vice Pres*
EMP: 31

SALES (est): 6.4MM
SALES (corp-wide): 42.3MM **Privately
Held**
SIC: 3559 3251 Paint making machinery;
   ceramic glazed brick, clay
PA: Venjakob Maschinenbau Gmbh & Co.
   Kg
   Augsburger Str. 2-6
   Rheda-Wiedenbruck 33378
   524 296-030

(G-17948)
OAK PRINTING COMPANY
19540 Progress Dr (44149-3284)
PHONE.............................440 238-3316
Fax: 440 238-9339
James M Helms, *President*
Alysia Groscost, *General Mgr*
Bobbi Thorsell, *Office Mgr*
Ken Helms, *Technology*
▲ **EMP:** 40 **EST:** 1922
SQ FT: 54,000
SALES (est): 8.3MM **Privately Held**
WEB: www.oakprintingco.com
SIC: 2752 Commercial printing, offset

(G-17949)
OUTOTEC OYJ
Also Called: Outotec North America
11288 Alameda Dr (44149-3001)
PHONE.............................440 783-3336
Tim Robinson, *Branch Mgr*
EMP: 20
SALES (corp-wide): 1.1B **Privately Held**
SIC: 3441 Fabricated structural metal
PA: Outotec Oyj
   Rauhalanpuisto 9
   Espoo 02230
   205 292-11

(G-17950)
PA MA INC
Also Called: Pama Tool & Die
11288 Alameda Dr (44149-3001)
P.O. Box 361459 (44136-0025)
PHONE.............................440 846-3799
Fax: 440 846-3844
Ron Pansil, *President*
Donna Pansil, *Vice Pres*
Danuta Pansil, *Treasurer*
EMP: 7
SQ FT: 8,000
SALES (est): 580K **Privately Held**
SIC: 3544 Special dies & tools

(G-17951)
PPG INDUSTRIES INC
Also Called: Powder Coatings
19699 Progress Dr (44149-3298)
PHONE.............................440 572-2800
Fax: 440 572-0848
Heather Stephan, *Product Mgr*
William Shaw, *Branch Mgr*
Steve Alessandro, *Manager*
Gary Gorrow, *Manager*
Richard Tansey, *Manager*
EMP: 100
SALES (corp-wide): 14.7B **Publicly Held**
SIC: 2851 Paints & allied products
PA: Ppg Industries, Inc.
   1 Ppg Pl
   Pittsburgh PA 15272
   412 434-3131

(G-17952)
PRECISION PRODUCTION INC
8250 Dow Cir (44136-1762)
PHONE.............................216 252-0372
Craig Cook, *President*
John Kocinski, *Plant Mgr*
Mathew A Carson, *Treasurer*
Chris Heath, *Comms Mgr*
▲ **EMP:** 40
SQ FT: 38,000
SALES (est): 8.8MM **Privately Held**
WEB: www.precisionproduction.com
SIC: 3599 Machine shop, jobbing & repair

(G-17953)
PRINT SQUAD LLC
16972 Stag Thicket Ln (44136-6274)
PHONE.............................440 315-5652
Richard Shuba, *Principal*
EMP: 4 **EST:** 2011

SALES (est): 333.1K **Privately Held**
SIC: 2752 Commercial printing, lithographic

(G-17954)
PROFESSIONAL PACKAGING COMPANY (PA)
22360 Royalton Rd (44149-3826)
PHONE.............................440 238-8850
Scott Gilbert, *President*
Sharon Gilbert, *Corp Secy*
Phil Basak, *Controller*
▲ **EMP:** 21
SQ FT: 115,000
SALES (est): 26.8MM **Privately Held**
WEB: www.a-roo.com
SIC: 3081 Packing materials, plastic sheet

(G-17955)
R M TOOL & DIE INC
19768 Progress Dr (44149-3208)
PHONE.............................440 238-6459
Fax: 440 238-6509
Mike Regian, *President*
Steven Regian, *General Mgr*
EMP: 12
SQ FT: 25,000
SALES (est): 3.5MM **Privately Held**
SIC: 3544 Special dies & tools

(G-17956)
RAFTER EQUIPMENT CORPORATION
12430 Alameda Dr (44149-3025)
PHONE.............................440 572-3700
Fax: 440 572-3703
Walter Krenz, *President*
John Hostettler, *Vice Pres*
Paul Rohde, *Vice Pres*
Tyler Sweet, *Safety Dir*
Paul Herman, *Opers Staff*
EMP: 30 **EST:** 1917
SQ FT: 22,500
SALES (est): 6.4MM **Privately Held**
WEB: www.rafterequipment.com
SIC: 3542 3549 3547 3541 Machine
   tools, metal forming type; metalworking
   machinery; rolling mill machinery; ma-
   chine tools, metal cutting type; fabricated
   pipe & fittings

(G-17957)
REPUBLIC RINGS INC
17295 Foltz Pkwy Ste A (44149-5568)
PHONE.............................440 238-2622
Judy Ungerer, *CEO*
EMP: 4
SQ FT: 3,000
SALES (est): 600K **Privately Held**
SIC: 3089 Blister or bubble formed pack-
   aging, plastic

(G-17958)
RITTAL CORP
19541 Winding Trl (44149-8721)
PHONE.............................440 572-4999
Dwight Patterson, *Branch Mgr*
EMP: 170
SALES (corp-wide): 2.2B **Privately Held**
SIC: 3469 Electronic enclosures, stamped
   or pressed metal
HQ: Rittal Corp.
   425 N Martingale Rd # 400
   Schaumburg IL 60173
   847 240-4600

(G-17959)
ROBERT E MCGRATH INC
Also Called: Olympia Candies
11606 Pearl Rd (44136-3320)
PHONE.............................440 572-7747
Fax: 440 572-1819
Robert McGrath, *President*
Celia McGrath, *Vice Pres*
EMP: 25
SQ FT: 15,000
SALES: 750K **Privately Held**
WEB: www.olympiacandy.com
SIC: 5145 5441 2096 2066 Candy;
   candy; potato chips & similar snacks;
   chocolate & cocoa products; ice cream &
   frozen desserts

(G-17960)
SAFETY SIGN COMPANY
19511 Progress Dr Ste 4 (44136-3262)
P.O. Box 360500 (44136-0009)
PHONE.............................440 238-7722
Fax: 440 238-7732
James J Merriman, *President*
Joel G Casas, *Senior VP*
Joe Mackey, *Purchasing*
Cindy O'Connell, *Finance Mgr*
Paul Green, *Sales Staff*
EMP: 50 **EST:** 1952
SQ FT: 42,000
SALES (est): 6.2MM **Privately Held**
WEB: www.safetysignco.com
SIC: 3993 Signs, not made in custom sign
   painting shops

(G-17961)
SCHWEBEL BAKING COMPANY
22626 Royalton Rd (44149-3838)
PHONE.............................440 846-1921
Fax: 440 846-3865
Tom Siegel, *Sales Executive*
Steve Leach, *Manager*
EMP: 154
SALES (corp-wide): 170MM **Privately
Held**
SIC: 2051 Bread, cake & related products
PA: Schwebel Baking Company
   965 E Midlothian Blvd
   Youngstown OH 44502
   330 783-2860

(G-17962)
SEVILLE SAND & GRAVEL INC
12663 Bristol Ln (44149-9240)
P.O. Box 360, Lodi (44254-0360)
PHONE.............................330 948-0168
Fax: 330 948-4186
George D Cross, *President*
Louis Radice, *Corp Secy*
EMP: 22 **EST:** 1958
SQ FT: 600
SALES: 2MM **Privately Held**
WEB: www.sevsg.com
SIC: 1442 Construction sand mining;
   gravel mining

(G-17963)
SGL TECHNIC INC
21945 Drake Rd (44149-6608)
PHONE.............................440 572-3600
Libby Knowles, *President*
John Dickhaut, *Controller*
Alex Olszewski, *Manager*
Roz Bremser, *Info Tech Dir*
▲ **EMP:** 30
SQ FT: 52,000
SALES (est): 4.6MM
SALES (corp-wide): 814MM **Privately
Held**
WEB: www.sglacotec.com
SIC: 3443 Heat exchangers: coolers (after,
   inter), condensers, etc.
HQ: Sgl Carbon, Llc
   10130 Perimeter Pkwy # 500
   Charlotte NC 28116
   704 593-5100

(G-17964)
SHEIBAN JEWELRY INC
16938 Pearl Rd (44136-6053)
PHONE.............................440 238-0616
Fax: 440 878-9066
Tony Sheiban, *President*
Jason Sheiban, *VP Mktg*
EMP: 10
SQ FT: 3,300
SALES (est): 2.6MM **Privately Held**
SIC: 5094 5944 7631 3911 Jewelry; pre-
   cious stones (gems); precious metals;
   jewelry, precious stones & precious met-
   als; watch, clock & jewelry repair; jewelry,
   precious metal

(G-17965)
SHERWIN-WILLIAMS COMPANY
11410 Alameda Dr (44149-3005)
PHONE.............................440 846-4328
Fax: 440 846-4349
Blair Lacour, *President*
Bruce Snyder, *Vice Pres*
Bob Johnston, *Finance*
Chuck Hedberg, *VP Human Res*
Rene Garcia, *Manager*

EMP: 25
SQ FT: 24,150
SALES (corp-wide): 11.8B **Publicly Held**
WEB: www.sherwin.com
SIC: 5231 2851 Paint & painting supplies; wallcoverings; paints & allied products; varnishes; lacquer: bases, dopes, thinner
PA: The Sherwin-Williams Company
101 W Prospect Ave # 1020
Cleveland OH 44115
216 566-2000

(G-17966)
SKINNER SALES GROUP INC
Also Called: Skinner Metal Products
19706 Progress Dr (44149-3208)
P.O. Box 115, Medina (44258-0115)
PHONE..................................440 572-8455
Terry Skinner, *President*
Doug Skinner, *Vice Pres*
EMP: 20
SQ FT: 24,000
SALES: 1.2MM **Privately Held**
SIC: 3441 3443 3449 Fabricated structural metal; fabricated plate work (boiler shop); miscellaneous metalwork

(G-17967)
SLY INC (PA)
8300 Dow Cir Ste 600 (44136-6607)
PHONE..................................440 891-3200
E D Davis, *Principal*
W C Bruce, *Principal*
W C Sly, *Principal*
W W Sly, *Principal*
Sidney C Vessy, *Principal*
EMP: 12 EST: 1874
SQ FT: 36,000
SALES (est): 4.5MM **Privately Held**
WEB: www.slyinc.com
SIC: 3564 Dust or fume collecting equipment, industrial; purification & dust collection equipment

(G-17968)
SMOOTHIE CREATIONS INC
17137 Misty Lake Dr (44136-7361)
PHONE..................................817 313-8212
Samuel Powell II, *Principal*
EMP: 3
SALES (est): 192.8K **Privately Held**
SIC: 2037 Frozen fruits & vegetables

(G-17969)
SPARTON MEDICAL SYSTEMS INC
22740 Lunn Rd (44149-4899)
PHONE..................................440 878-4630
Duane Stierhoff, *Principal*
Michael Kalamasz, *Opers Staff*
Thomas Cowling, *QC Mgr*
Dave Lapeus, *Research*
Tom Hublick, *Controller*
EMP: 94
SALES (est): 21.4MM
SALES (corp-wide): 419.3MM **Publicly Held**
WEB: www.sparton.com
SIC: 3841 Surgical & medical instruments
PA: Sparton Corporation
425 N Martingale Rd
Schaumburg IL 60173
847 762-5800

(G-17970)
SPIEGELBERG MANUFACTURING INC (PA)
Also Called: Stud Welding Associates
12200 Alameda Dr (44149-3021)
PHONE..................................440 324-3042
William Houston, *General Mgr*
Jean L Anderson, *Principal*
Terry S Shilling, *Principal*
Scott Schraff, *Electrical Engi*
Brian Kushinski, *Controller*
EMP: 32
SALES (est): 18.7MM **Privately Held**
SIC: 3548 Welding apparatus

(G-17971)
SROKA INC
21265 Westwood Dr (44149-2905)
PHONE..................................440 572-2811
John Sroka, *President*
▲ EMP: 35

SALES (est): 8.3MM **Privately Held**
SIC: 3537 Industrial trucks & tractors

(G-17972)
SROKA INDUSTRIES INC
21265 Westwood Dr (44149-2905)
P.O. Box 360047 (44136-0001)
PHONE..................................440 572-2811
Fax: 440 572-1137
John Sroka, *President*
Wieslawa Sroka, *Vice Pres*
Adam Sroka, *Info Tech Mgr*
▲ EMP: 30
SQ FT: 60,000
SALES: 2MM **Privately Held**
SIC: 3599 3544 3498 Machine shop, jobbing & repair; special dies & tools; fabricated pipe & fittings

(G-17973)
STEFRA INC
Also Called: E & E Parts Machining
18021 Cliffside Dr (44136-4256)
PHONE..................................440 846-8240
Fax: 216 671-3330
Colleen Ungerer, *CEO*
Frank Ungerer, *President*
Steve Pucha, *Vice Pres*
EMP: 7
SQ FT: 2,900
SALES: 300K **Privately Held**
SIC: 3599 Machine shop, jobbing & repair

(G-17974)
STELFAST INC (PA)
22979 Stelfast Pkwy (44149-5561)
PHONE..................................440 879-0077
Surinder Sakhuja, *CEO*
Simmi Sakhuja, *President*
Todd McRoberts, *Vice Pres*
Dana McLaughlin, *Project Mgr*
Eduardo Garcia, *Warehouse Mgr*
▲ EMP: 32
SQ FT: 85,000
SALES (est): 22.1MM **Privately Held**
WEB: www.stelfast.com
SIC: 3452 Bolts, metal; nuts, metal

(G-17975)
SWAGELOK HY-LEVEL COMPANY (PA)
15400 Foltz Pkwy (44149-4737)
PHONE..................................440 238-1260
Fax: 440 572-1470
Donald M Rebar, *Ch of Bd*
Peter D Rebar, *President*
Arthur J Fabry, *Principal*
Gerald F Franklin, *Principal*
Carl C Heintel, *Principal*
EMP: 200 EST: 1942
SQ FT: 145,000
SALES (est): 32.8MM **Privately Held**
WEB: www.hy-level.com
SIC: 3451 3541 Screw machine products; machine tools, metal cutting type

(G-17976)
TADD SPRING CO INC
15060 Foltz Pkwy (44149-4729)
PHONE..................................440 572-1313
Fax: 440 572-0496
Mark Anguilano, *President*
Leslie Naso, *Purch Agent*
James Hinde, *Engineer*
EMP: 20 EST: 1962
SQ FT: 5,000
SALES (est): 3.2MM **Privately Held**
WEB: www.taddspring.com
SIC: 3495 3493 Precision springs; steel springs, except wire

(G-17977)
TAKEDA PHARMACEUTICALS USA INC
19495 Trotwood Park (44149-4996)
PHONE..................................440 238-0872
Steve Mott, *Principal*
EMP: 3
SALES (corp-wide): 15.4B **Publicly Held**
SIC: 2834 Pharmaceutical preparations
HQ: Takeda Pharmaceuticals U.S.A., Inc.
1 Takeda Pkwy
Deerfield IL 60015
224 554-6500

(G-17978)
TRANSCENDIA INC
22889 Lunn Rd (44149-4800)
P.O. Box 368003, Cleveland (44136-9703)
PHONE..................................440 638-2000
Fax: 440 638-2010
James Carlin, *Branch Mgr*
Scott Keener, *Supervisor*
EMP: 80
SQ FT: 25,000
SALES (corp-wide): 421.8MM **Privately Held**
WEB: www.transilwrap.com
SIC: 3081 Unsupported plastics film & sheet
PA: Transcendia, Inc.
9201 Belmont Ave
Franklin Park IL 60131
847 678-1800

(G-17979)
TSW INDUSTRIES INC
14960 Foltz Pkwy (44149-4727)
PHONE..................................440 572-7200
Fax: 440 572-7506
Tich Wan, *President*
Lee Wan, *Vice Pres*
▲ EMP: 30
SQ FT: 41,000
SALES: 2.3MM **Privately Held**
SIC: 3599 Machine shop, jobbing & repair

(G-17980)
VITAMIN SHOPPE INC
17893 Southpark Ctr (44136-9332)
PHONE..................................440 238-5987
EMP: 26
SALES (corp-wide): 1.2B **Publicly Held**
SIC: 6324 5122 2834 Hospital & medical service plans; vitamins & minerals; vitamin preparations
PA: Vitamin Shoppe, Inc.
300 Harmon Meadow Blvd # 2
Secaucus NJ 07094
201 868-5959

(G-17981)
WALLOVER ENTERPRISES INC (DH)
21845 Drake Rd (44149-6610)
PHONE..................................440 238-9250
George M Marquis, *President*
William C Cutri, *Vice Pres*
Debbie Depompei, *Admin Asst*
EMP: 30
SQ FT: 28,000
SALES (est): 28MM **Privately Held**
SIC: 2992 8734 Oils & greases, blending & compounding; re-refining lubricating oils & greases; product testing laboratories
HQ: Houghton International Inc.
945 Madison Ave
Norristown PA 19403
610 666-4000

(G-17982)
WALLOVER OIL COMPANY INC (DH)
Also Called: Woco
21845 Drake Rd (44149-6610)
PHONE..................................440 238-9250
James I Wallover, *Ch of Bd*
George Marquis, *President*
Maxine Watters, *General Mgr*
William C Cutri, *Vice Pres*
▼ EMP: 33
SQ FT: 28,000
SALES (est): 11.2MM **Privately Held**
SIC: 2992 2841 Oils & greases, blending & compounding; re-refining lubricating oils & greases; soap & other detergents
HQ: Wallover Enterprises Inc.
21845 Drake Rd
Strongsville OH 44149
440 238-9250

(G-17983)
WESTERN RESERVE SLEEVE INC
22360 Royalton Rd (44149-3826)
P.O. Box 361310, Cleveland (44136-0022)
PHONE..................................440 238-8850
Scott Gilbert, *President*
Sharon Gilbert, *Corp Secy*
Phil Basek, *Controller*

EMP: 35
SALES (est): 5.3MM **Privately Held**
SIC: 3081 Packing materials, plastic sheet

(G-17984)
WILLOW TOOL & MACHINING LTD
15110 Foltz Pkwy Ste 1 (44149-4765)
PHONE..................................440 572-2288
Fax: 440 572-0460
Samuel Thomas, *Managing Prtnr*
Teresa Thomas, *Partner*
William A Thomas, *Partner*
EMP: 12 EST: 1972
SQ FT: 7,350
SALES (est): 1.8MM **Privately Held**
WEB: www.willowtool.com
SIC: 3541 3599 Machine tools, metal cutting type; machine shop, jobbing & repair

(G-17985)
WOODPECKERS INC
13700 Prospect Rd (44149-3862)
PHONE..................................440 238-1824
Rich Hummel, *Principal*
EMP: 26
SALES (est): 5.7MM **Privately Held**
SIC: 2499 1751 Decorative wood & woodwork; carpentry work

(G-17986)
YOUR CABINETRY
16488 Pearl Rd (44136-6042)
PHONE..................................440 638-4925
Matt Howells, *Owner*
EMP: 4
SALES (est): 186.9K **Privately Held**
SIC: 2434 Wood kitchen cabinets

(G-17987)
ZORBX INC
17647 Foltz Pkwy (44149-5535)
PHONE..................................440 238-1847
Debbie Mabrouk, *CEO*
Issa Mabrouk, *President*
Joseph Sultan, *Business Dir*
▲ EMP: 25
SQ FT: 30,000
SALES (est): 869.2K **Privately Held**
WEB: www.zorbx.com
SIC: 2841 Detergents, synthetic organic or inorganic alkaline

---

Struthers
Mahoning County

(G-17988)
ADD-A-TRAP LLC
488 Como St (44471-1237)
PHONE..................................330 750-0417
Robert N Davenport, *CEO*
Ray Hassay, *President*
Allan Stratron, *COO*
EMP: 6
SALES: 100K **Privately Held**
SIC: 3088 Plastics plumbing fixtures

(G-17989)
ASTRO SHAPES LLC (PA)
65 Main St (44471-1942)
PHONE..................................330 755-1414
Paul Cene, *President*
Leo Flecton, *General Mgr*
James Dibacco, *Exec VP*
Robert Cene Jr, *Vice Pres*
Rick Pursifull, *Controller*
EMP: 121
SQ FT: 300,000
SALES (est): 99.6MM **Privately Held**
WEB: www.astroshapes.com
SIC: 3354 3086 Aluminum extruded products; insulation or cushioning material, foamed plastic

(G-17990)
ASTRO-COATINGS INC
65 Main St (44471-1942)
P.O. Box 208 (44471-0208)
PHONE..................................330 755-1414
Paul Cene, *President*
Jim Di Bacco, *Exec VP*
Robert Cene Jr, *Vice Pres*
Richard Purcisull, *Finance*

GEOGRAPHIC

EMP: 50
SQ FT: 25,000
SALES: 10MM **Privately Held**
SIC: 3479 Painting of metal products

(G-17991)
GIANNIOS CANDY CO INC (PA)
430 Youngstown Poland Rd (44471-1058)
PHONE.........................330 755-7000
Fax: 330 755-7766
John G Giannios, *President*
EMP: 45
SQ FT: 28,000
SALES (est): 8.5MM **Privately Held**
WEB: www.giannios.com
SIC: 2066 2064 Chocolate candy, solid;
candy & other confectionery products

(G-17992)
JFM INDUSTRIES
111 Elm St (44471-1910)
P.O. Box 5534, Poland (44514-0534)
PHONE.........................330 550-6009
Jason Miller, *Owner*
EMP: 4
SALES (est): 241.1K **Privately Held**
SIC: 3993 Signs & advertising specialties

(G-17993)
KURTZ TOOL & DIE CO INC
164 State St (44471-1956)
P.O. Box 116 (44471-0116)
PHONE.........................330 755-7723
Fax: 330 755-4854
Evelyn Kurtz, *Vice Pres*
Robert Kurtz Sr, *Shareholder*
EMP: 6
SALES (est): 510K **Privately Held**
SIC: 3544 Die sets for metal stamping
(presses)

(G-17994)
L B INDUSTRIES INC
Also Called: Lally Pipe & Tube
534 Lowellville Rd (44471-2077)
P.O. Box 69 (44471-0069)
PHONE.........................330 750-1002
Fax: 330 750-1535
Josh Ball, *Asst Controller*
Jamie Disibio, *Sales Associate*
James Mocker, *Branch Mgr*
Debbie Donattlei, *Manager*
EMP: 36
SALES (corp-wide): 110MM **Privately
Held**
WEB: www.lallypipe.com
SIC: 5051 7692 Pipe & tubing, steel; steel;
welding repair
PA: L B Industries, Inc.
8770 Railroad Dr
Taylor Mill KY 41015
859 431-8300

(G-17995)
MUNROE INCORPORATED
Also Called: Youngstown Plant
25 Union St (44471-1964)
PHONE.........................330 755-7216
Fax: 330 755-0106
Arnie Traud, *Manager*
EMP: 5
SALES (corp-wide): 83.4MM **Privately
Held**
SIC: 3325 3443 3317 Steel foundries;
fabricated plate work (boiler shop); steel
pipe & tubes
HQ: Munroe, Incorporated
1820 N Franklin St
Pittsburgh PA 15233
412 231-0600

(G-17996)
QUALITY BAR INC
17 Union St Ste 7 (44471-1964)
PHONE.........................330 755-0000
Fax: 330 755-0100
Donald A Casey, *Ch of Bd*
Carrie Casey, *President*
Jim Ambrose, *Opers Mgr*
Jim Rugh, *Opers Mgr*
Bob Moy, *Finance Mgr*
EMP: 17
SALES (est): 4.3MM
SALES (corp-wide): 9MM **Privately Held**
WEB: www.qualitybar.com
SIC: 3312 Blast furnaces & steel mills

PA: Casey Equipment Corporation
275 Kappa Dr
Pittsburgh PA 15238
412 963-1111

(G-17997)
R W SIDLEY INCORPORATED
395 Lowellville Rd (44471-2012)
P.O. Box 165 (44471-0165)
PHONE.........................330 750-1661
EMP: 3
SALES (corp-wide): 148.6MM **Privately
Held**
SIC: 3295 Mfg Minerals-Ground/Treated
PA: R. W. Sidley Incorporated
436 Casement Ave
Painesville OH 44077
440 352-9343

(G-17998)
SELAH PAPERIE
130 S Bridge St (44471-1945)
PHONE.........................330 755-2759
Fax: 330 755-2759
Brian Palumbo, *Owner*
EMP: 4
SALES (est): 200K **Privately Held**
WEB: www.selahrestaurant.com
SIC: 2621 Stationery, envelope & tablet pa-
pers

(G-17999)
STEEL VALLEY SIGN
616 Youngstown Poland Rd (44471-1106)
PHONE.........................330 755-7446
EMP: 3
SALES (est): 190.3K **Privately Held**
SIC: 3993 Mfg Signs/Advertising Special-
ties

(G-18000)
**YOUNGSTOWN DIE
DEVELOPMENT**
137 Walton Ave (44471-1054)
P.O. Box 237 (44471-0237)
PHONE.........................330 755-0722
Fax: 330 755-0749
Bob Corll, *President*
Lois Mc Cabe, *President*
Patricia Hynes, *Treasurer*
Robert Corll, *Sales Staff*
EMP: 4 EST: 1959
SQ FT: 13,000
SALES (est): 559.1K **Privately Held**
SIC: 3544 Special dies, tools, jigs & fix-
tures

Stryker
Williams County

(G-18001)
DALTON CORPORATION
310 Ellis St (43557-9329)
P.O. Box 2600 (43557-2600)
PHONE.........................419 682-6328
Jackie Helberg, *Human Res Dir*
Alan Sheets, *Manager*
Jay Sweatland, *Manager*
EMP: 80
SALES (corp-wide): 104.4MM **Privately
Held**
SIC: 3625 Industrial controls: push button,
selector switches, pilot
HQ: The Dalton Corporation
1900 E Jefferson St
Warsaw IN 46580
574 267-8111

(G-18002)
**DALTON STRYKER MCHINING
FCILTY**
310 Ellis St (43557-9329)
PHONE.........................419 682-6328
Joe Derita, *President*
Ron Schmucker, *VP Finance*
EMP: 80
SALES (est): 10.4MM
SALES (corp-wide): 418.5MM **Publicly
Held**
WEB: www.nfco.com
SIC: 3599 Machine & other job shop work

HQ: Neenah Foundry Company
2121 Brooks Ave
Neenah WI 54956
920 725-7000

(G-18003)
FRANKS SAWMILL INC
Rr 195 (43557)
P.O. Box 4600 (43557-4600)
PHONE.........................419 682-3831
Dave Frank, *President*
Mike Meyer, *Corp Secy*
EMP: 10 EST: 1958
SQ FT: 8,000
SALES (est): 1.3MM **Privately Held**
SIC: 2448 Pallets, wood

(G-18004)
JAGGER CONE COMPANY INC
304 Ellis St (43557-9329)
P.O. Box 136 (43557-0136)
PHONE.........................419 682-1816
Jeff Jagger, *President*
Joe Jagger, *Vice Pres*
Carol Jagger, *Treasurer*
Sherry L Jagger, *Admin Sec*
EMP: 4
SALES (est): 200K **Privately Held**
SIC: 2052 Cones, ice cream

(G-18005)
OHIO TIMBERLAND PRODUCTS
102 Railroad Ave (43557-9533)
P.O. Box 330 (43557-0330)
PHONE.........................419 682-6322
Mike Burkholder, *President*
Donna Burkholder, *Corp Secy*
Harley Burkholder, *Vice Pres*
EMP: 10
SQ FT: 15,000
SALES (est): 2.1MM **Privately Held**
SIC: 2411 Poles, posts & pilings: untreated
wood

(G-18006)
**QUADCO REHABILITATION
CENTER (PA)**
Also Called: NORTHWEST PRODUCTS
427 N Defiance St (43557-9472)
PHONE.........................419 682-1011
Fax: 419 682-6097
Chuck Merriman, *Purch Mgr*
Terry Fruth, *CFO*
Jackie Porter, *Finance Asst*
Peggy Keith, *Manager*
Bruce Abell, *Exec Dir*
EMP: 287
SQ FT: 24,000
SALES: 445.7K **Privately Held**
SIC: 8331 2448 2441 Vocational rehabili-
tation agency; wood pallets & skids;
nailed wood boxes & shook

(G-18007)
SAUDER MANUFACTURING CO
Also Called: Stryker Plant
201 Horton St (43557-9310)
PHONE.........................419 682-3061
Fax: 419 446-4051
Luther Gautsche, *Vice Pres*
Marc Fruth, *Vice Pres*
Dan Fleming, *Maintence Staff*
EMP: 125
SQ FT: 46,000
SALES (corp-wide): 550MM **Privately
Held**
WEB: www.saudermfg.com
SIC: 2531 2521 Chairs, portable folding;
wood office furniture
HQ: Sauder Manufacturing Co.
930 W Barre Rd
Archbold OH 43502
419 445-7670

(G-18008)
STRYKER STEEL TUBE LLC
100 Railroad Ave (43557-9533)
P.O. Box 506 (43557-0506)
PHONE.........................419 682-4527
Fax: 419 682-4529
Steve Dominique,
Chris Peterson,
EMP: 10
SALES: 1.2MM **Privately Held**
SIC: 3317 Steel pipe & tubes

(G-18009)
STRYKER WELDING
104 W Mulberry St (43557-7757)
P.O. Box 70 (43557-0070)
PHONE.........................419 682-2301
Fax: 419 682-2301
Jason Baltosser, *Owner*
EMP: 4
SQ FT: 10,000
SALES (est): 500K **Privately Held**
SIC: 7692 Welding repair

(G-18010)
WILLIAMS PORK CO OP
18487 County Road F (43557-9306)
PHONE.........................419 682-9022
Fax: 419 682-1017
Paul Kalmbach, *President*
Ben Cientek, *Manager*
EMP: 9
SALES (est): 458K **Privately Held**
SIC: 2013 Pork, cured: from purchased
meat

Sugar Grove
Fairfield County

(G-18011)
**COMMERCIAL MUSIC SERVICE
CO**
Also Called: Chime Master Systems
6312 Goss Rd (43155-9610)
PHONE.........................740 746-8500
Fax: 740 746-9566
Jeffrey A Crook, *President*
Cyndi McGee, *General Mgr*
▼ EMP: 8
SALES (est): 1.2MM **Privately Held**
WEB: www.chimemaster.com
SIC: 3931 Bells (musical instruments);
chimes & parts (musical instruments)

(G-18012)
JAKES SPORTSWEAR LTD
112 Elm St (43155)
P.O. Box 340 (43155-0340)
PHONE.........................740 746-8356
Jacob Geiger, *Owner*
EMP: 4
SQ FT: 1,680
SALES: 150K **Privately Held**
WEB: www.jakessportswear.com
SIC: 2396 5611 5999 Screen printing on
fabric articles; clothing, sportswear, men's
& boys'; trophies & plaques

(G-18013)
WARTHMAN DRILLING INC
7525 Lancaster Logan Rd (43155)
P.O. Box 360 (43155-0360)
PHONE.........................740 746-9950
Fax: 740 746-9940
Steven Warthman, *President*
EMP: 6
SALES (est): 640K **Privately Held**
SIC: 1781 1381 Water well drilling; drilling
oil & gas wells

Sugarcreek
Tuscarawas County

(G-18014)
A & J WOODWORKING
4012 Winklepleck Rd Nw (44681-7660)
PHONE.........................888 572-9561
Joseph Miller, *Principal*
EMP: 4
SALES (est): 324.4K **Privately Held**
SIC: 2431 Millwork

(G-18015)
**ARCHER-DANIELS-MIDLAND
COMPANY**
Also Called: ADM Animal Nutrition
554 Pleasant Valley Rd Nw (44681-7800)
P.O. Box 486 (44681-0486)
PHONE.........................330 852-3025
Fax: 330 852-3483
Jim Sours, *Marketing Staff*
Doug Miller, *Branch Mgr*

▲ = Import ▼=Export
◆ =Import/Export

EMP: 7
SQ FT: 12,000
SALES (corp-wide): 62.3B Publicly Held
WEB: www.admalliancenutrition.com
SIC: 2048 Prepared feeds
PA: Archer-Daniels-Midland Company
   77 W Wacker Dr Ste 4600
   Chicago IL 60601
   312 634-8100

(G-18016)
BELDEN BRICK COMPANY
Also Called: Tubar Eureka Industrial Group
750 Edelweiss Dr Ne (44681-9501)
P.O. Box 705 (44681-0705)
PHONE..............................330 852-2411
Fax: 330 852-2415
Kenneth L Cook, *Ch of Bd*
Mike Sigman, *General Mgr*
Hemmy Acharya, *Vice Pres*
Rob Snyder, *Sales Executive*
Joyce Nedrow, *Office Admin*
EMP: 46 EST: 1952
SQ FT: 82,000
SALES (est): 11.9MM Privately Held
WEB: www.uhrden.com
SIC: 3535 3561 3537 3536 Conveyors &
  conveying equipment; pumps & pumping
  equipment; industrial trucks & tractors;
  hoists, cranes & monorails; mining ma-
  chinery; construction machinery

(G-18017)
BELDEN BRICK COMPANY LLC
Also Called: Plant 8
700 Edelweiss Dr Ne (44681-9501)
P.O. Box 430 (44681-0430)
PHONE..............................330 456-0031
Doug Mutchelknaus, *Principal*
EMP: 115
**SALES (corp-wide): 6.6MM Privately
Held**
WEB: www.beldenbrick.com
SIC: 3251 3271 Structural brick & blocks;
  brick, concrete
HQ: The Belden Brick Company Llc
  700 Tuscarawas St W Up
  Canton OH 44702
  330 456-0031

(G-18018)
CABIN CREEK GOLF
1361 County Road 108 (44681-9631)
PHONE..............................330 852-4879
Lewis Svchlabch, *Owner*
EMP: 4
SALES (est): 291.6K Privately Held
SIC: 3949 Driving ranges, golf, electronic

(G-18019)
CARLISLE OAK
3872 Township Road 162 (44681-9621)
PHONE..............................330 852-8734
David Miller, *Owner*
EMP: 7
SALES (est): 477.7K Privately Held
SIC: 2511 Wood household furniture

(G-18020)
**CARLISLE PRTG WALNUT
CREEK LTD**
2673 Township Road 421 (44681-9486)
PHONE..............................330 852-9922
Fax: 330 852-3285
Marcus Wengerd, *President*
Dustin Yoder, *Manager*
Heidi Weaver, *Admin Sec*
EMP: 35
SALES (est): 6.6MM Privately Held
SIC: 2621 2791 Catalog, magazine &
  newsprint papers; typesetting

(G-18021)
CREATIVE WOODWORKS
5209 Evans Creek Rd Sw (44681-8034)
PHONE..............................330 897-1432
David Yoder, *Principal*
EMP: 4 EST: 2011
SALES (est): 344.8K Privately Held
SIC: 2431 Millwork

(G-18022)
**DUTCH VALLEY
WOODWORKING INC**
Hc 39 (44681)
P.O. Box 416 (44681-0416)
PHONE..............................330 852-4319
Dale P Mullet, *President*
Ruth Mullet, *Corp Secy*
EMP: 14
SQ FT: 3,200
SALES (est): 1.8MM Privately Held
SIC: 2434 Wood kitchen cabinets

(G-18023)
**EAGLE MACHINERY & SUPPLY
INC**
422 Dutch Valley Dr Ne (44681-7517)
PHONE..............................330 852-1300
Kirk Spillman, *President*
Lori Spillman, *Corp Secy*
Ray Miller, *Plant Mgr*
Timmer Andrew, *Project Mgr*
Dennis McCartney, *Engineer*
▲ EMP: 21
SQ FT: 20,000
SALES (est): 5MM Privately Held
SIC: 3541 Machine tool replacement & re-
  pair parts, metal cutting types

(G-18024)
J & F FURNITURE SHOP
Also Called: Juvenile Furniture Specialties
3521 Township Road 166 (44681-9606)
PHONE..............................330 852-2478
James Miller, *Partner*
Freida Miller, *Partner*
EMP: 4
SALES (est): 534.5K Privately Held
SIC: 5021 2511 Furniture; unfinished furni-
  ture; wood household furniture

(G-18025)
L & M MINERAL CO
2010 County Road 144 (44681-9439)
PHONE..............................330 852-3696
John E Ling Jr, *President*
Merle Mullet, *Treasurer*
EMP: 8
SALES (est): 510K Privately Held
SIC: 1459 1221 Clays (common) quarry-
  ing; shale (common) quarrying; bitumi-
  nous coal & lignite-surface mining

(G-18026)
MIDDAUGH ENTERPRISES INC
Also Called: Idea Works
211 Yoder Ave Nw (44681-9388)
P.O. Box 400 (44681-0400)
PHONE..............................330 852-2471
Steven Middaugh, *President*
Jeri Middaugh, *Corp Secy*
L Wade Middaugh, *Vice Pres*
EMP: 15 EST: 1956
SQ FT: 8,500
SALES (est): 1.9MM Privately Held
WEB: www.middaughprinters.com
SIC: 2752 2759 Commercial printing, off-
  set; imprinting

(G-18027)
**MILLER ENTERPRISES OHIO
LLC**
1360 County Road 108 (44681-9631)
PHONE..............................330 852-4009
Wayne Miller,
Robert Schlabach,
EMP: 5
SQ FT: 5,000
SALES (est): 229.7K Privately Held
SIC: 3061 Automotive rubber goods (me-
  chanical)

(G-18028)
MILLER MANUFACTURING INC
Also Called: Miller Wood Design
2705 Shetler Rd Nw (44681-7604)
P.O. Box 425 (44681-0425)
PHONE..............................330 852-0689
Fax: 330 852-0688
Raymond Miller, *President*
Mellissa Troie, *Accountant*
Mary Miller, *Manager*
▼ EMP: 35

SALES (est): 4.6MM Privately Held
SIC: 2493 2499 2435 2431 Particleboard, plastic laminated; decorative wood
  & woodwork; hardwood veneer & plywood; millwork

(G-18029)
**MULLET ENTERPRISES INC
(PA)**
Also Called: Tmk Farm Service
138 2nd St Nw (44681-7824)
P.O. Box 278 (44681-0278)
PHONE..............................330 852-4681
Fax: 330 852-4683
Larry Tietje, *President*
Raymond Mullet, *Vice Pres*
▼ EMP: 8
SQ FT: 34,000
SALES (est): 8.9MM Privately Held
WEB: www.tmkvalley.com
SIC: 5153 2041 Grain elevators; flour &
  other grain mill products

(G-18030)
PALLET DISTRIBUTORS INC
Also Called: Scenic Wood Products
10343 Copperhead Rd Nw (44681)
PHONE..............................330 852-3531
Martin Troyer, *General Mgr*
EMP: 55
**SALES (corp-wide): 46.7MM Privately
Held**
SIC: 2448 Wood pallets & skids
PA: Pallet Distributors, Inc.
  14701 Detroit Ave Ste 610
  Lakewood OH 44107
  888 805-9670

(G-18031)
PINE ACRES WOODCRAFT
123 Pleasant Valley Rd Nw (44681-8048)
PHONE..............................330 852-0190
Dean Troyer, *Owner*
EMP: 3
SALES (est): 330K Privately Held
SIC: 2514 Metal household furniture

(G-18032)
**PLEASANT VALLEY READY MIX
INC**
559 Pleasant Valley Rd Nw (44681-7800)
P.O. Box 436 (44681-0436)
PHONE..............................330 852-2613
Fax: 330 852-4865
Daniel O Miller, *President*
EMP: 10
SQ FT: 3,000
SALES: 2.2MM Privately Held
SIC: 3273 Ready-mixed concrete;
  masonry materials & supplies

(G-18033)
**PLEASANT VLY TARDROP
TRLRS LLC**
754 Edelweiss Dr Ne (44681-9501)
P.O. Box 395 (44681-0395)
PHONE..............................330 752-4425
Joseph Mullet, *Mng Member*
EMP: 40
SQ FT: 10,000
SALES (est): 7MM Privately Held
SIC: 3715 Trailer bodies

(G-18034)
PROVIA DOOR INC (PA)
Also Called: PROVIA - HERITAGE STONE
2150 State Route 39 (44681-9201)
PHONE..............................330 852-4711
Brian Miller, *President*
Willis Schlabach, *President*
Jeff Yoder, *General Mgr*
Bill Mullet, *Principal*
Freddie Miller, *Vice Pres*
EMP: 180
SQ FT: 280,000
SALES: 140.5MM Privately Held
WEB: www.precisionentry.com
SIC: 3442 5031 Metal doors; door frames,
  all materials

(G-18035)
PROVIA STONE LLC
Also Called: Heritage Stone
1550 County Road 140 (44681-9204)
PHONE..............................740 450-4236

Fax: 740 450-4370
Brian Miller, *President*
Larry Troyer, *CFO*
Lori B Barnes, *Accountant*
Brenda Chism, *Cust Mgr*
William Mullet, *Mng Member*
▼ EMP: 48
SQ FT: 10,000
SALES (est): 6.2MM
**SALES (corp-wide): 140.5MM Privately
Held**
SIC: 3272 Building stone, artificial: con-
  crete
PA: Provia Door, Inc.
  2150 State Route 39
  Sugarcreek OH 44681
  330 852-4711

(G-18036)
RAINBOW BEDDING
3421 Township Road 166 (44681-9605)
PHONE..............................330 852-3127
Paul Miller,
Edna Miller,
▲ EMP: 4
SALES: 600K Privately Held
SIC: 2394 Air cushions & mattresses, can-
  vas

(G-18037)
RNR ENTERPRISES LLC
1361 County Road 108 (44681-9631)
PHONE..............................330 852-3022
Fax: 330 852-9402
Regan R Schlabach,
Lois Schlabach, *Admin Sec*
Robert Schlabach,
EMP: 10
SALES (est): 840K Privately Held
SIC: 2511 Wood household furniture

(G-18038)
SCHLABACH PRINTING LTD
Also Called: Schlabach Printers
798 State Route 93 Nw (44681-7726)
PHONE..............................330 852-4687
Fax: 330 852-2689
Dan Miller, *Partner*
Roman Troyer, *Prdtn Mgr*
EMP: 20
SQ FT: 3,500
SALES (est): 1.6MM Privately Held
WEB: www.schlabachprinters.com
SIC: 2759 2752 Commercial printing;
  commercial printing, lithographic

(G-18039)
SKYLINE CORPORATION
580 Mill St Nw (44681-9561)
PHONE..............................330 852-2483
Fax: 330 852-2748
Bruce Monteith, *Manager*
EMP: 136
SQ FT: 100,000
**SALES (corp-wide): 211.7MM Publicly
Held**
WEB: www.skylinecorp.com
SIC: 2451 3448 2452 Mobile homes; pre-
  fabricated metal buildings; prefabricated
  wood buildings
PA: Skyline Corporation
  2520 Bypass Rd
  Elkhart IN 46514
  574 294-6521

(G-18040)
STONY POINT HARDWOODS
Also Called: Pro Hardware 13074
7842 Stony Point Rd Nw (44681-7642)
PHONE..............................330 852-4512
Fax: 330 852-3445
Mark Shrock, *Owner*
EMP: 16
SALES: 1.8MM Privately Held
SIC: 2448 2435 2431 2426 Pallets,
  wood; hardwood veneer & plywood; mill-
  work; hardwood dimension & flooring
  mills; sawmills & planing mills, general

(G-18041)
STONY POINT METALS LLC
7820 Stony Point Rd Nw (44681-7642)
PHONE..............................330 852-7100
Wes Shrock, *Mng Member*
Mark Shrock,
EMP: 4 EST: 2009

GEOGRAPHIC

SALES (est): 415.7K **Privately Held**
SIC: **3531** 5033 5211 Roofing equipment;
siding, except wood; roofing material

(G-18042)
SUGARCREEK BUDGET
PUBLISHERS
Also Called: Budget Newspaper, The
134 Factory St Ne (44681)
PHONE..................................330 852-4634
Fax: 330 852-4421
Keith Rathbun, *President*
Albert Spector, *Principal*
Beverly Keller, *Editor*
David Spector, *Vice Pres*
Milo Miller, *Accounts Exec*
EMP: 16
SQ FT: 4,800
SALES (est): 952.5K **Privately Held**
WEB: www.thebudgetnewspaper.com
SIC: **2711** Newspapers: publishing only,
not printed on site

(G-18043)
SUGARCREEK PALLETT
681 Belden Pkwy Ne (44681-7699)
PHONE..................................330 852-9812
Jonas Borntrager, *Principal*
EMP: 4
SALES (est): 330.9K **Privately Held**
SIC: **2448** Wood pallets & skids

(G-18044)
SUGARCREEK SHAVINGS LLC
3121 Winklepleck Rd Nw (44681-7656)
PHONE..................................330 763-4239
Ruth Troyer, *Principal*
EMP: 9
SALES (est): 351.5K **Privately Held**
SIC: **2421** Sawdust & shavings

(G-18045)
SUPERB INDUSTRIES INC
330 3rd St Nw (44681-9310)
P.O. Box 708 (44681-0708)
PHONE..................................330 852-0500
Fax: 330 852-9908
John Miller, *President*
Susan Miller, *Treasurer*
Matt Coblentz, *Accountant*
Kevin Bond, *Manager*
Ben Kohler, *Executive*
▲ EMP: 75
SQ FT: 50,000
SALES (est): 17.6MM **Privately Held**
WEB: www.superbdesign.com
SIC: **3678** 3544 Electronic connectors; die
sets for metal stamping (presses)

(G-18046)
TRUPOINT PRODUCTS
Uknown (44681)
P.O. Box 72, Walnut Creek (44687-0072)
PHONE..................................330 204-3302
Myron Miller, *Owner*
EMP: 10
SALES (est): 681.2K **Privately Held**
SIC: **3312** 3495 Wire products, steel or
iron; wire springs

(G-18047)
TUSCO HARDWOODS LLC
Also Called: M & M Hardwoods
10887 Gerber Valley Rd Nw (44681-7932)
PHONE..................................330 852-4281
James Miller, *Manager*
Levi P Miller,
EMP: 14
SQ FT: 10,000
SALES (est): 2.5MM **Privately Held**
SIC: **2448** 2421 Wood pallets & skids;
sawmills & planing mills, general

(G-18048)
VALLEY VIEW WOODCRAFT
Also Called: Valley View Woodcraft & Finshg
1190 Shutt Valley Rd Nw (44681-7743)
PHONE..................................330 852-3000
Bobby Troyer, *Owner*
EMP: 4
SALES: 90K **Privately Held**
SIC: **2519** Lawn & garden furniture, except
wood & metal

(G-18049)
WALNUT CREEK WOOD DESIGN
1689 State Route 39 (44681-9666)
PHONE..................................330 852-9663
Scott Troyer, *Owner*
EMP: 3
SALES (est): 211.6K **Privately Held**
SIC: **2499** Decorative wood & woodwork

(G-18050)
WEAVER BARNS LTD
1696 State Route 39 (44681-9666)
PHONE..................................330 852-2103
Mike Weaver, *General Mgr*
Dustin Miller, *Prdtn Mgr*
Jonathon Beachy, *Controller*
Jonathan Deachy, *Controller*
Mose Miller, *Sales Staff*
EMP: 10
SALES (est): 3.4MM **Privately Held**
WEB: www.weaverbarns.com
SIC: **2452** Prefabricated wood buildings

(G-18051)
WEAVERS FURNITURE LTD
Also Called: Weaver Craft of Sugarcreek
7011 Old Route 39 Nw (44681-7968)
PHONE..................................330 852-2701
Wayne Weaver, *Owner*
Roy R Weaver, *General Mgr*
Kevin Yoder, *Controller*
Martha Weaver,
▲ EMP: 16
SQ FT: 42,000
SALES (est): 2.2MM **Privately Held**
WEB: www.weaverfurniture.com
SIC: **2512** 5023 Upholstered household
furniture; home furnishings

(G-18052)
YODER LUMBER CO INC
3799 County Road 70 (44681-9400)
PHONE..................................330 893-3131
Fax: 330 893-3032
Trent Yoder, *Opers Mgr*
Paul Dow, *Branch Mgr*
EMP: 55
SALES (corp-wide): 30.3MM **Privately
Held**
WEB: www.yoderlumber.com
SIC: **5211** 2435 2426 2421 Planing mill
products & lumber; hardwood veneer &
plywood; hardwood dimension & flooring
mills; sawmills & planing mills, general
PA: Yoder Lumber Co., Inc.
  4515 Township Road 367
  Millersburg OH 44654
  330 893-3121

Sullivan
Ashland County

(G-18053)
BRIARWOOD VALLEY FARMS
502 Us Highway 224 (44880-9771)
P.O. Box 93 (44880-0093)
PHONE..................................419 736-2298
Ladonna Hensen, *Owner*
EMP: 3
SALES (est): 151.4K **Privately Held**
SIC: **2015** Rabbit slaughtering & process-
ing

(G-18054)
EDJEAN TECHNICAL SERVICES
INC
Also Called: Edjetech Services
246 Us Highway 224 Ste A (44880-9765)
PHONE..................................440 647-3300
Fax: 440 647-2400
Douglas Heidenreich, *President*
Joseph Insana, *Vice Pres*
EMP: 4
SALES (est): 610K **Privately Held**
WEB: www.edjetech.com
SIC: **3569** 5084 Filters, general line: in-
dustrial; industrial machinery & equipment

(G-18055)
US SCREEN CO
462 County Road 40 (44880-9727)
P.O. Box 27, Wellington (44090-0027)
PHONE..................................419 736-2400

Mike Dickason, *CEO*
Joanne Dickason, *President*
Matt Dickason, *CFO*
Doug Dickason, *Sales Mgr*
Bob Stevenson, *Sales Staff*
▲ EMP: 4
SQ FT: 8,000
SALES (est): 240K **Privately Held**
SIC: **3496** Screening, woven wire: made
from purchased wire

Sunbury
Delaware County

(G-18056)
BRY-AIR INC
10793 E State Route 37 (43074-9311)
PHONE..................................740 965-2974
Mel Meyers, *President*
Doug Howery, *Exec VP*
Sonali Dutta, *Vice Pres*
Debbie Kemmer, *Purchasing*
Tammy Corrado, *Controller*
▲ EMP: 43 EST: 1964
SQ FT: 40,000
SALES (est): 15.3MM **Privately Held**
WEB: www.bryair.com
SIC: **3585** 3826 3535 3823 Dehumidi-
fiers electric, except portable; environ-
mental testing equipment; conveyors &
conveying equipment; industrial instrmnts
msrmnt display/control process variable;
auto controls regulating residntl & coml
environmt & applncs; blowers & fans

(G-18057)
BUNDY BAKING SOLUTIONS
Also Called: American Pan Company
601 W Cherry St (43074-9803)
PHONE..................................740 965-3008
Brad Moore, *Manager*
Deb Daniels, *Manager*
EMP: 14
SALES (corp-wide): 64MM **Privately
Held**
SIC: **3479** Painting, coating & hot dipping
PA: Russell T. Bundy Associates, Inc.
  417 E Water St Ste 1
  Urbana OH 43078
  937 652-2151

(G-18058)
COUNTER METHOD INC
13767 E State Route 37 (43074-9773)
PHONE..................................614 206-3192
EMP: 3
SALES (est): 165.8K **Privately Held**
SIC: **3131** Counters

(G-18059)
DUFFEE FINISHING INC
4860 N County Line Rd (43074-8305)
PHONE..................................740 965-4848
Fax: 740 965-4603
Robert L Duffee, *President*
Nancy Duffee, *Vice Pres*
EMP: 8
SQ FT: 20,000
SALES (est): 797.8K **Privately Held**
WEB: www.duffeefinishing.com
SIC: **3479** 3399 Painting of metal prod-
ucts; powder; metal

(G-18060)
GERLING AND ASSOCIATES
INC
138 Stelzer Ct (43074-8528)
PHONE..................................740 965-6200
Fax: 740 965-2898
Fred Gerling, *President*
Shannon McElroy, *General Mgr*
Crystal Tieche, *Vice Pres*
Manuel Lopez, *Project Mgr*
Zach Myers, *Opers Mgr*
◆ EMP: 80
SQ FT: 20,000
SALES (est): 29MM **Privately Held**
WEB: www.gerlinggroup.com
SIC: **3711** Mobile lounges (motor vehicle),
assembly of

(G-18061)
GREAT MIDWEST YACHT CO
140 E Granville St (43074)
P.O. Box 364 (43074-0364)
PHONE..................................740 965-4511
Fax: 740 965-3724
Douglas Laber, *President*
EMP: 3
SQ FT: 8,400
SALES: 225K **Privately Held**
SIC: **3732** 3429 5551 Sailboats, building
& repairing; marine hardware; marine
supplies

(G-18062)
HEARTLAND HOME CABINETRY
LTD
35 S Galena Rd Unit C (43074-9010)
PHONE..................................740 936-5100
Terry King, *Principal*
Rod Arthur, *Sales Executive*
EMP: 4 EST: 2009
SALES (est): 526.9K **Privately Held**
SIC: **2434** Wood kitchen cabinets

(G-18063)
ICC SYSTEMS INC
5665 Blue Church Rd # 202 (43074-9695)
PHONE..................................614 524-0299
Fax: 740 524-0263
Harold Arnette, *President*
EMP: 6
SALES (est): 483.1K **Privately Held**
SIC: **7372** Prepackaged software

(G-18064)
INDIAN RIVER INDUSTRIES
Also Called: Village Square Antique Mall
31 E Granville St (43074-9130)
PHONE..................................740 965-4377
Jane Weidner, *Owner*
EMP: 4
SQ FT: 5,184
SALES (est): 31.3K **Privately Held**
SIC: **2541** 2732 5099 5932 Showcases,
except refrigerated: wood; book music:
printing only, not published on site; pam-
phlets: printing only, not published on site;
antiques; antiques

(G-18065)
KI INTEL LLC
11720 Kilbourne Rd (43074-9420)
PHONE..................................740 200-9000
Alex Chang, *Administration*
EMP: 3 EST: 2014
SALES (est): 155.7K **Privately Held**
SIC: **3674** Microprocessors

(G-18066)
LIFES PRODUCTS INC
3319 N State Route 61 (43074-9639)
PHONE..................................740 965-9711
Brenda Ambrose, *CEO*
Tobin Ambrose, *CFO*
EMP: 5
SALES (est): 231.1K **Privately Held**
SIC: **3842** 3841 Trusses, orthopedic &
surgical; medical instruments & equip-
ment, blood & bone work

(G-18067)
MINE EQUIPMENT SERVICES
LLC (PA)
Also Called: Mes
3958 State Route 3 (43074-9660)
P.O. Box 48, Marengo (43334-0048)
PHONE..................................740 936-5427
Christopher Wagner,
Tony Schiavi,
EMP: 22 EST: 2012
SQ FT: 10,000
SALES: 3.4MM **Privately Held**
SIC: **5084** 3535 7699 Industrial machin-
ery & equipment; belt conveyor systems,
general industrial use; construction equip-
ment repair; pumps & pumping equipment
repair; industrial equipment services; in-
dustrial machinery & equipment repair

(G-18068)
NELSON TOOL CORPORATION
388 N County Line Rd (43074-9004)
PHONE..................................740 965-1894
Fax: 740 965-5081

▲ = Import ▼=Export
◆ =Import/Export

Michael Nelson, *President*
Peggy Christ, *CFO*
EMP: 14
SQ FT: 18,200
SALES (est): 1.1MM **Privately Held**
SIC: 3544 Special dies, tools, jigs & fixtures

(G-18069)
OBERFIELDS LLC
471 Kintner Pkwy (43074-8978)
P.O. Box 362, Delaware (43015-0362)
PHONE.................................740 369-7644
Fax: 740 965-2454
Bruce Loris, *President*
Robert Fulton, *Vice Pres*
Earl Freeman, *Facilities Mgr*
EMP: 20
SQ FT: 833
SALES (corp-wide): 17MM **Privately Held**
SIC: 3272 Concrete products, precast
PA: Oberfield's, Llc
528 London Rd
Delaware OH 43015
740 369-7644

(G-18070)
OHASHI TECHNICA USA INC (HQ)
111 Burrer Dr (43074-9323)
PHONE.................................740 965-5115
Hikaru Tateiwa, *President*
Mamoru Shibasaki, *Principal*
Trish Burnside, *Treasurer*
Kazuhiro Maeda, *Accountant*
Cole Croft, *Manager*
▲ **EMP:** 50
SQ FT: 110,000
SALES: 90MM
SALES (corp-wide): 341.6MM **Privately Held**
SIC: 5013 5072 3452 Automotive supplies & parts; automotive supplies; hardware; bolts, nuts, rivets & washers
PA: Ohashi Technica Inc.
4-3-13, Toranomon
Minato-Ku TKY 105-0
354 044-411

(G-18071)
OHASHI TECHNICA USA MFG INC
99 Burrer Dr (43074-9319)
PHONE.................................740 965-9002
Fax: 740 965-9104
Hikaru Tateiwa, *President*
Nobuya Moritani, *Corp Secy*
Eiji Hozumi, *Plant Mgr*
Cole Croft, *Manager*
Yoshi Doyama, *Manager*
EMP: 20
SQ FT: 60,000
SALES (est): 2.8MM
SALES (corp-wide): 341.6MM **Privately Held**
SIC: 3965 Fasteners
HQ: Ohashi Technica U.S.A. Inc.
111 Burrer Dr
Sunbury OH 43074
740 965-5115

(G-18072)
OMEGA ENGINEERING INC
Also Called: Omegadyne
149 Stelzer Ct (43074-8528)
PHONE.................................740 965-9340
Fax: 740 965-9438
Michael Roth, *Editor*
Bruce Lott, *QC Mgr*
Mike Rohde, *Engineer*
Dennis Guy, *Branch Mgr*
Larry Myers, *Manager*
EMP: 50
SALES (corp-wide): 1.6B **Privately Held**
SIC: 3829 3679 3825 Pressure transducers; loads, electronic; instruments to measure electricity
HQ: Omega Engineering, Inc.
800 Connecticut Ave 5n01
Norwalk CT 06854
203 359-1660

(G-18073)
PARROT UNIVERSITY LLC
9000 Cheshire Rd (43074-9382)
PHONE.................................740 965-1965
Stephen Hartman,
EMP: 2
SALES (est): 1MM **Privately Held**
WEB: www.hartmanaviary.com
SIC: 3999 7389 Pet supplies;

(G-18074)
PRECISION FABRICATIONS INC
272 High St (43074-9457)
PHONE.................................937 297-8606
Fax: 614 297-8608
David Steinberger, *President*
EMP: 4
SQ FT: 3,700
SALES: 300K **Privately Held**
SIC: 3082 Rods, unsupported plastic

(G-18075)
PRODUCT TOOLING INC
4290 N 3 Bs And K Rd (43074-9580)
PHONE.................................740 524-2061
Fax: 740 524-2061
Rodney Harp, *President*
Elizabeth Harp, *Corp Secy*
EMP: 7
SQ FT: 3,600
SALES: 500K **Privately Held**
SIC: 3599 7692 3544 Machine shop, jobbing & repair; welding repair; special dies, tools, jigs & fixtures

(G-18076)
RICHARD PAULEY
Also Called: Pauley's Machine Shop
3308 N State Route 61 (43074-9404)
P.O. Box 893 (43074-0893)
PHONE.................................740 965-6897
Richard L Pauley, *Owner*
EMP: 3
SQ FT: 1,250
SALES (est): 224.8K **Privately Held**
SIC: 3599 Machine shop, jobbing & repair

(G-18077)
UNIVERSAL COMPOSITE LLC
Also Called: Uc Trailer Co.
200 Kintner Pkwy (43074-9320)
PHONE.................................614 507-1646
Jennifer Myers,
Steven E Hillman,
Kelly Kelley,
EMP: 25
SALES (est): 4.1MM **Privately Held**
SIC: 3711 Automobile assembly, including specialty automobiles

(G-18078)
WHITS FROZEN CUSTARD
101 W Cherry St Unit A (43074-8029)
PHONE.................................740 965-1427
Rick J Dague, *Principal*
EMP: 3 EST: 2010
SALES (est): 170.2K **Privately Held**
SIC: 2024 Ice cream, bulk

Swanton
Fulton County

(G-18079)
AMBROSIA INC (PA)
395 W Airport Hwy (43558-1445)
P.O. Box 299 (43558-0299)
PHONE.................................419 825-1151
Fax: 419 825-3895
Ann M Albright, *President*
William R Albright, *Corp Secy*
EMP: 5
SQ FT: 31,000
SALES (est): 4.1MM **Privately Held**
SIC: 3999 Candles

(G-18080)
AQUABLOK LTD
230 W Airport Hwy (43558-1471)
PHONE.................................419 402-4170
John Collins, *COO*
EMP: 15

SALES (corp-wide): 2.1MM **Privately Held**
SIC: 3299 Non-metallic mineral statuary & other decorative products
PA: Aquablok, Ltd.
175 Woodland Ave
Swanton OH 43558
419 825-1325

(G-18081)
BROKEN SPINNING WHEEL
14230 Monclova Rd (43558-8711)
PHONE.................................419 825-1609
EMP: 3
SALES (est): 219.5K **Privately Held**
SIC: 2252 Socks

(G-18082)
BYRD PRCUREMENT SPECIALIST INC
12150 Monclova Rd (43558-8706)
PHONE.................................419 936-0019
Jason Byrd, *CEO*
EMP: 4
SALES (est): 248.2K **Privately Held**
SIC: 4813 1522 1389 1521 Telephone communication, except radio; residential construction; construction, repair & dismantling services; patio & deck construction & repair; new construction, single-family houses

(G-18083)
COUNTER CREATION PLUS L L C
106 Church St (43558-1014)
PHONE.................................419 826-7449
Jason J Miller, *Principal*
EMP: 3
SALES (est): 252.5K **Privately Held**
SIC: 3131 Counters

(G-18084)
GRAND AIRE INC (PA)
11777 W Airport Svc Rd (43558-9387)
PHONE.................................419 861-6700
Fax: 419 865-2965
Zachary Cheema, *CEO*
Mike Converse, *Vice Pres*
Mohammad Tariq, *Maintenance Dir*
Art Athar, *Personnel Exec*
Amy Colyer, *Accounts Mgr*
EMP: 21 EST: 1998
SQ FT: 57,000
SALES (est): 10MM **Privately Held**
WEB: www.grandaire.com
SIC: 4522 5172 4512 4581 Air cargo carriers, nonscheduled; petroleum products; air transportation, scheduled; airports, flying fields & services; trucks: freight, baggage, etc.: industrial, except mining; courier services, except by air

(G-18085)
KELLY MACHINE LTD
7245 County Road 1 3 (43558-9532)
PHONE.................................419 825-2006
Francis Gelske, *President*
EMP: 5
SALES: 500K **Privately Held**
SIC: 3599 Machine shop, jobbing & repair

(G-18086)
M L B MOLDED URETHANE PDTS LLC
1680 Us Highway 20a (43558-8663)
P.O. Box 464, Perrysburg (43552-0464)
PHONE.................................419 825-9140
Donald Bates,
Valdemar Lopez,
James Muir,
EMP: 9
SQ FT: 15,000
SALES (est): 1.6MM **Privately Held**
WEB: www.mlbproducts.net
SIC: 3086 Plastics foam products

(G-18087)
PJS CORRUGATED INC
2330 Us Highway 20 (43558-8649)
PHONE.................................419 644-3383
Fax: 419 644-3385
Michael Iozzo, *President*
Priscilla Iozzo, *Corp Secy*
Joseph Iozzo, *Vice Pres*

Toni Bennett, *Bookkeeper*
EMP: 10
SQ FT: 10,000
SALES (est): 2.6MM **Privately Held**
SIC: 2653 Boxes, corrugated: made from purchased materials

(G-18088)
PREFORM TECHNOLOGIES LLC
11362 S Airfield Rd (43558-7900)
P.O. Box 964, Holland (43528-0964)
PHONE.................................419 720-0355
David F Waterman, *Principal*
Jim Sheely, *Officer*
Elizabeth Brady,
Jon Harding, *Maintence Staff*
L Robert Dearduff,
EMP: 4
SQ FT: 7,500
SALES (est): 987.2K **Privately Held**
SIC: 3089 Injection molding of plastics

(G-18089)
SCOTTDEL CUSHION LLC
400 Church St (43558-1199)
PHONE.................................419 825-0432
Fax: 419 825-1523
Kevin Thornton, *CEO*
Todd Bctz, *Vice Pres*
Jamie Quaintance, *Vice Pres*
Jason Lee, *Safety Mgr*
Steve Kerr, *Purch Mgr*
▲ **EMP:** 45 EST: 1943
SQ FT: 185,000
SALES (est): 15.6MM **Privately Held**
WEB: www.scottdel.com
SIC: 3086 Carpet & rug cushions, foamed plastic; insulation or cushioning material, foamed plastic

(G-18090)
SHERIDAN MFG OF OHIO LLC
401 Broadway Ave Rear (43558-1341)
PHONE.................................419 825-2950
Renee McMahon, *Principal*
EMP: 5
SALES (est): 242.4K **Privately Held**
SIC: 3999 Manufacturing industries

(G-18091)
SWANTON WLDG MACHINING CO INC (PA)
407 Broadway Ave (43558-1341)
PHONE.................................419 826-4816
Fax: 419 826-0489
Norm D Zeiter, *CEO*
Chuck Morgan, *President*
Bill Zeiter, *General Mgr*
Jeff Gyurasics, *COO*
Kessler Kody, *Plant Mgr*
EMP: 80
SQ FT: 314,000
SALES (est): 23.3MM **Privately Held**
WEB: www.swantonweld.com
SIC: 3446 3444 3443 3599 Architectural metalwork; sheet metalwork; fabricated plate work (boiler shop); machine & other job shop work

(G-18092)
TOLEDO JET CENTER LLC (PA)
Also Called: Toledo Express
11591 W Airport Svc Rd (43558-9618)
PHONE.................................419 866-9050
Mindy Leppala, *General Mgr*
Bill Pribe, *General Mgr*
William Pribe, *General Mgr*
Mike Romanczuk, *Maint Spvr*
Jack Bohland, *Parts Mgr*
EMP: 11
SALES (est): 950K **Privately Held**
SIC: 3721 4581 Aircraft; aircraft maintenance & repair services

(G-18093)
TRI-COUNTY BLOCK AND BRICK INC
1628 Us 20 Alternate (43558)
PHONE.................................419 826-7060
Fax: 419 825-5405
Roger L Cooley, *President*
Roberta E Cooley, *Corp Secy*
Karen Cooley, *Vice Pres*
Carl Kuhlman, *Vice Pres*
Jennifer Kurt, *Controller*
EMP: 35

GEOGRAPHIC

SQ FT: 4,160
SALES (est): 11.6MM **Privately Held**
WEB: www.tricountyblock.com
SIC: 5211 3271 Lumber & other building
materials; blocks, concrete or cinder:
standard

(G-18094)
VAN ORDERS PALLET
COMPANY INC
2452 County Road 2 (43558-8894)
PHONE..............................419 875-6932
Fax: 419 875-6932
James Van Order, *Ch of Bd*
Casey Van Order, *President*
Patricia Van Order, *Corp Secy*
EMP: 16
SQ FT: 11,000
SALES (est): 898.1K **Privately Held**
SIC: 2448 2441 Pallets, wood; nailed
wood boxes & shook

(G-18095)
WILLYS INC
Also Called: Willy's Fresh Salsa
11305 W Airport Svc Rd (43558-9390)
PHONE..............................419 823-3200
Dennis Dickey, *President*
EMP: 16
SQ FT: 6,000
SALES: 400K **Privately Held**
SIC: 2099 Sauces: gravy, dressing & dip
mixes

Sycamore
Wyandot County

(G-18096)
CREATIVE PLASTIC CONCEPTS
LLC (PA)
206 S Griffith St (44882-9694)
PHONE..............................419 927-9588
Ed Human, *President*
Peg Detray, *Controller*
Regina Orpurt, *Marketing Staff*
EMP: 2
SALES (est): 3.6MM **Privately Held**
SIC: 5085 2499 Bins & containers, stor-
age; clothes dryers (clothes horses),
wood; clothespins, wood

Sylvania
Lucas County

(G-18097)
ADVANCE PRODUCTS
6041 Angleview Dr (43560-1209)
PHONE..............................419 882-8117
Fax: 419 885-3210
David Frantz, *Owner*
James Frantz, *Owner*
EMP: 10
SALES: 1.5MM **Privately Held**
SIC: 3571 3999 Computers, digital, analog
or hybrid; models, except toy

(G-18098)
AFFINITY INFORMATION
MANAGEMET
3359 Silica Rd (43560-9890)
PHONE..............................419 517-2055
EMP: 4
SALES (est): 292.2K **Privately Held**
SIC: 3559 Tire shredding machinery

(G-18099)
AIR CONVERSION
TECHNOLOGY INC
3485 Silica Rd Unit A (43560-8995)
PHONE..............................419 841-1720
Fax: 419 841-1720
Mark E Charpie, *President*
Debra Charpie, *General Mgr*
Scott E Charpie, *Manager*
EMP: 3
SQ FT: 300
SALES: 250K **Privately Held**
SIC: 3592 Pistons & piston rings

(G-18100)
BLUFFTON MOTOR WORKS LLC
Also Called: Toledo Grmtor Blffton Mtr Wrks
5439 Roan Rd (43560-2304)
PHONE..............................419 885-3769
Fax: 419 885-3799
John Toth, *President*
Chad Knight, *Purch Agent*
EMP: 21 EST: 1948
SQ FT: 35,000
SALES (est): 4.8MM **Privately Held**
WEB: www.toledogear.com
SIC: 3566 Reduction gears & gear units for
turbines, except automotive

(G-18101)
BOBBART INDUSTRIES INC
Also Called: American Custom Industries
5035 Alexis Rd Ste 1 (43560-1637)
PHONE..............................419 350-5477
Fax: 419 885-5161
Bart Lea, *President*
Laura Lea, *Corp Secy*
EMP: 25
SQ FT: 45,000
SALES: 1.7MM **Privately Held**
WEB: www.acivette.com
SIC: 3711 3082 7532 3714 Motor vehi-
cles & car bodies; unsupported plastics
profile shapes; top & body repair & paint
shops; motor vehicle parts & accessories;
plastics plumbing fixtures

(G-18102)
CSW OF NY INC
3545 Silica Rd Unit E (43560-9889)
PHONE..............................413 589-1311
Jeffrey Francis, *Principal*
Kevin Abair, *Marketing Staff*
EMP: 15
SALES (corp-wide): 16MM **Privately**
Held
SIC: 2796 3544 Platemaking services;
dies, steel rule
PA: Csw, Inc.
45 Tyburski Rd
Ludlow MA 01056
413 589-1311

(G-18103)
DON-ELL CORPORATION (PA)
Also Called: X M C Division
8450 Central Ave (43560-9747)
P.O. Box 351480, Toledo (43635-1480)
PHONE..............................419 841-7114
Fax: 419 841-1799
Donald R Sell, *Ch of Bd*
Robert N Sell, *President*
Robert Leverton, *Purch Mgr*
EMP: 25 EST: 1956
SQ FT: 12,000
SALES (est): 3.6MM **Privately Held**
SIC: 3679 3089 Electronic switches; mold-
ing primary plastic

(G-18104)
DON-ELL CORPORATION
Also Called: X M C
8456 Central Ave (43560-9747)
PHONE..............................419 841-7114
Fax: 419 841-7202
Jim Krumm, *Manager*
EMP: 8
SALES (corp-wide): 3.1MM **Privately**
Held
SIC: 3089 Injection molding of plastics
PA: Don-Ell Corporation
8450 Central Ave
Sylvania OH 43560
419 841-7114

(G-18105)
DRESCH TOLSON DENTAL
LABS
8730 Resource Park Dr (43560-8939)
PHONE..............................419 842-6730
Fax: 419 842-6731
Joseph Gerace, *Owner*
EMP: 90
SALES (est): 3.1MM **Privately Held**
SIC: 8072 3843 Dental laboratories; den-
tal equipment & supplies

(G-18106)
DURA MAGNETICS INC
5500 Schultz Dr (43560-2384)
PHONE..............................419 882-0591
Fax: 419 882-4052
Donald C Kuchers, *CEO*
Robert M Csortos, *President*
Catherine A Kuchers, *Corp Secy*
Gloria Ferguson, *Purch Agent*
Jim Auld, *Sales Staff*
▲ EMP: 17 EST: 1961
SQ FT: 15,000
SALES (est): 7.2MM **Privately Held**
WEB: www.duramag.com
SIC: 5084 3499 Industrial machinery &
equipment; magnets, permanent: metallic

(G-18107)
GALAXY PRODUCTS INC
3403 Silica Rd (43560-9539)
PHONE..............................419 843-7337
Colleen Sanders, *President*
Richard Sanders, *General Mgr*
Mark Neeley, *Principal*
Roxanne Ott, *Manager*
EMP: 5
SALES (est): 808.9K **Privately Held**
WEB: www.galaxyproducts.com
SIC: 3544 3546 3545 Special dies, tools,
jigs & fixtures; power-driven handtools;
machine tool accessories

(G-18108)
HANSON AGGREGATES LLC
4100 Centennial Rd (43560-9414)
PHONE..............................419 841-3413
Dean Harshman, *Safety Mgr*
Michael Ryan, *Sales Mgr*
Tom Kusmer, *Marketing Staff*
William Kurtz,
EMP: 20
SALES (corp-wide): 16B **Privately Held**
SIC: 1422 Crushed & broken limestone
HQ: Hanson Aggregates Llc
8505 Freport Pkwy Ste 500
Irving TX 75063
469 417-1200

(G-18109)
HANSON AGGREGATES
MIDWEST LLC
8130 Brint Rd (43560-9719)
PHONE..............................419 882-0123
Dean Harshman, *Safety Mgr*
William Kurtz, *Facilities Mgr*
Tom Kusmer, *Engineer*
Ron Tipton, *Branch Mgr*
Lorrie William, *Manager*
EMP: 10
SALES (corp-wide): 16B **Privately Held**
SIC: 1422 Crushed & broken limestone
HQ: Hanson Aggregates Midwest Llc
207 Old Harrods Creek Rd
Louisville KY 40223
502 244-7550

(G-18110)
ICE INDUSTRIES INC (PA)
3810 Herr Rd (43560-8925)
PHONE..............................419 842-3612
Fax: 419 842-1058
Gene Swick, *General Mgr*
Howard Ice, *Principal*
Paul Bishop, *COO*
Jeff Boger, *Exec VP*
Andy Gladwell, *Purch Dir*
▲ EMP: 26
SQ FT: 10,000
SALES: 100MM **Privately Held**
SIC: 3469 Metal stampings

(G-18111)
ICE INDUSTRIES COLUMBUS
INC
3810 Herr Rd (43560-8925)
PHONE..............................419 842-3600
EMP: 8
SALES (est): 821.7K
SALES (corp-wide): 237.2MM **Privately**
Held
SIC: 3469 Mfg Metal Stampings
PA: Ice Industries, Inc.
3810 Herr Rd
Sylvania OH 43560
419 842-3612

(G-18112)
INNOVATIVE HDLG & METALFAB
LLC
7755 Sylvania Ave (43560-9518)
PHONE..............................419 882-7480
Fax: 419 885-1624
Shari Wiseman, *Purchasing*
Ken Fashbaugh, *Accounts Mgr*
Trent Orzechowski, *Accounts Mgr*
Nate Sherman, *Accounts Mgr*
Nick Orzechowski, *Sales Executive*
EMP: 20
SQ FT: 30,000
SALES: 3MM **Privately Held**
WEB: www.innovativehandling.com
SIC: 3535 5084 Conveyors & conveying
equipment; materials handling machinery

(G-18113)
JASON STULLER PRO SHOP
LLC (PA)
5201 Corey Rd (43560-2202)
PHONE..............................419 882-3197
Jason Stuller, *Principal*
EMP: 4
SALES (est): 7.5MM **Privately Held**
SIC: 3949 Golf equipment

(G-18114)
JC AND ASSOCIATES SYLVANIA
LLC
5129 Main St (43560-2125)
PHONE..............................419 824-0011
Jerry Cortese, *Manager*
EMP: 3
SALES (est): 377.7K **Privately Held**
SIC: 3639 Household appliances

(G-18115)
KEVIN K TIDD
Also Called: Arrow Print & Copy
5505 Roan Rd (43560-2306)
PHONE..............................419 885-5603
Fax: 419 885-7783
Kevin K Tidd, *Owner*
EMP: 6
SQ FT: 3,500
SALES (est): 490K **Privately Held**
WEB: www.arrowprint.com
SIC: 2752 2791 2789 Commercial print-
ing, offset; typesetting; bookbinding & re-
lated work

(G-18116)
LUMA ELECTRIC COMPANY
3419 Silica Rd (43560-9539)
PHONE..............................419 843-7842
Fax: 419 843-7984
Daniel Hinds, *President*
Lauren Hinds, *Vice Pres*
EMP: 5
SQ FT: 7,500
SALES (est): 450K **Privately Held**
SIC: 3423 Soldering tools

(G-18117)
MAUMEE BAY KITCHEN & BATH
CENT
Also Called: Maumee Bay Kitchen & Bath Ctr
5758 Main St Ste 1 (43560-1933)
PHONE..............................419 882-4390
Matt Wingate, *Mng Member*
Dori Wingate,
EMP: 3
SALES (est): 314.7K **Privately Held**
SIC: 2499 Kitchen, bathroom & household
ware: wood

(G-18118)
MOLD SHOP INC
8520 Central Ave (43560-9748)
PHONE..............................419 829-2041
Fax: 419 829-2042
Lan Wagner, *President*
Donna Wagner, *Vice Pres*
Blaine Wagner, *Manager*
EMP: 10 EST: 1965
SQ FT: 12,000
SALES (est): 1.2MM **Privately Held**
SIC: 3544 Special dies & tools; forms
(molds), for foundry & plastics working
machinery

(G-18119)
MOORE CHROME PRODUCTS CO
Also Called: Moore Metal Finishing
3525 Silica Rd (43560-9814)
PHONE...................................419 843-3510
Fax: 419 843-3710
Scott Backus, *President*
Larry Huth, *Vice Pres*
Mary Huth, *Vice Pres*
Becky Keifer, *Office Mgr*
Bonnie Armistead, *Manager*
EMP: 25 EST: 1930
SQ FT: 24,000
SALES (est): 3.8MM **Privately Held**
WEB: www.mooremetalfinishing.com
SIC: 3471 Plating of metals or formed products

(G-18120)
MUIR GRAPHICS INC
5454 Alger Dr Ste A (43560-2348)
PHONE...................................309 673-7034
Fax: 419 885-7613
Linda Rider, *President*
Richard Drees, *Vice Pres*
Karen Garner, *Vice Pres*
Suzanne Emerine, *Office Mgr*
EMP: 13
SQ FT: 10,000
SALES (est): 2.2MM **Privately Held**
WEB: www.muir-graphics.com
SIC: 2752 Commercial printing, offset

(G-18121)
NIGHT LIGHTSCAPES
3303 Herr Rd (43560-9780)
PHONE...................................419 304-2486
Tom Walter, *Principal*
EMP: 3
SALES (est): 225.1K **Privately Held**
SIC: 3645 Garden, patio, walkway & yard lighting fixtures: electric

(G-18122)
NORTHERN CONCRETE PIPE INC
3756 Centennial Rd (43560-9734)
PHONE...................................419 841-3361
Jeff Levon, *Principal*
EMP: 10
SALES (corp-wide): 21.3MM **Privately Held**
SIC: 3272 Pipe, concrete or lined with concrete
PA: Northern Concrete Pipe, Inc.
401 Kelton St
Bay City MI 48706
989 892-3545

(G-18123)
POWER SOURCE FUEL LLC
3738 Fairwood Dr (43560-3910)
PHONE...................................419 690-6495
Michael Garza, *Principal*
EMP: 4
SALES (est): 316K **Privately Held**
SIC: 2869 Fuels

(G-18124)
SHARONCO INC
Also Called: Sylvan Studio
5651 Main St (43560-1929)
PHONE...................................419 882-3443
Scott Stampflmeier, *President*
EMP: 8
SALES: 500K **Privately Held**
SIC: 3499 5094 Novelties & giftware, including trophies; trophies

(G-18125)
SILICA PRESS INC
3545 Silica Rd Unit A2 (43560-9889)
PHONE...................................419 843-8500
Fax: 419 843-8501
Joe Ray, *President*
Rudy Severhof, *Accounts Exec*
EMP: 3
SALES (est): 384.6K **Privately Held**
WEB: www.silicapress.com
SIC: 2759 Commercial printing

(G-18126)
STANSLEY MINERAL RESOURCES INC (PA)
3793 Silica Rd B (43560-9814)
PHONE...................................419 843-2813
Rick Stansley, *CEO*
Richard Stansley Jr, *Corp Secy*
Jeff Stansley, *COO*
Mandy Billau, *Manager*
EMP: 35
SQ FT: 10,000
SALES (est): 12.4MM **Privately Held**
SIC: 1442 Gravel mining

(G-18127)
SYLVAN STUDIO INC
5651 Main St (43560-1929)
P.O. Box 59 (43560-0059)
PHONE...................................419 882-3423
Fax: 419 882-8182
Terry E Crandell, *Owner*
Scott Stampflmeier, *COO*
EMP: 7
SQ FT: 5,000
SALES (est): 400K **Privately Held**
WEB: www.sylvanstudio.com
SIC: 2396 7336 Ribbons & bows, cut & sewed; commercial art & graphic design

(G-18128)
V COLLECTION
5630 Main St (43560-1928)
PHONE...................................419 517-0508
Kevin Andrew, *Owner*
EMP: 3
SALES (est): 113.3K **Privately Held**
SIC: 2389 Apparel & accessories

(G-18129)
VAN DELEIGH INDUSTRIES LLC
5611 Bent Oak Rd (43560-1104)
PHONE...................................419 467-2244
Rodney S Brant,
EMP: 4
SALES (est): 542.9K **Privately Held**
SIC: 2679 Paper products, converted

(G-18130)
WORLD PREP INC
8432 Central Ave Ste 10 (43560-9700)
PHONE...................................419 843-3869
Fax: 419 517-6363
David T Krueger, *President*
Sandy Lonchyna, *Sales Staff*
Chip Parsons, *Sales Staff*
Kate Barribalo, *Assistant*
▲ EMP: 4
SQ FT: 2,500
SALES (est): 50K **Privately Held**
WEB: www.worldprep.com
SIC: 3842 First aid, snake bite & burn kits

Tallmadge
Summit County

(G-18131)
A-A1 MACHINE AND SUPPLY CO
Also Called: AA1 Tool and Tech Supply
3130 Klages Blvd (44278-3323)
PHONE...................................440 346-0698
Russ Busse, *President*
EMP: 5
SQ FT: 19,000
SALES: 1MM **Privately Held**
SIC: 3599 Machine shop, jobbing & repair

(G-18132)
AKRON GASKET & PACKG ENTPS INC
445 Northeast Ave (44278-1444)
PHONE...................................330 633-3742
Carter Ray, *CEO*
Craig Ray, *President*
Matthew Ray, *Vice Pres*
John Dodd, *Sales Mgr*
Ralph Wahl, *Accounts Mgr*
▲ EMP: 19
SQ FT: 40,000
SALES: 4MM **Privately Held**
WEB: www.akrongasket.com
SIC: 3053 Gaskets, all materials; packing: steam engines, pipe joints, air compressors, etc.

(G-18133)
ALL-TRA RUBBER PROCESSING
154 Potomac Ave Ste B (44278-2715)
PHONE...................................330 630-1945
Kendell Ashby, *Owner*
Craig Smalley, *Vice Pres*
Micheal Crawford, *Sales Staff*
EMP: 4
SALES (est): 342.8K **Privately Held**
SIC: 2822 Synthetic rubber

(G-18134)
AVTEK INTERNATIONAL INC
382 Commerce St (44278-2135)
PHONE...................................330 633-7500
Fax: 330 634-9947
Thomas Milan, *President*
Venus Earley, *Manager*
▲ EMP: 6
SQ FT: 6,000
SALES (est): 1MM **Privately Held**
SIC: 3651 Household audio equipment

(G-18135)
BASIC PACKAGING LTD
65 Carmen Rd (44278-2125)
P.O. Box 56, Mogadore (44260-0056)
PHONE...................................330 634-9665
Fax: 330 676-0833
Hal Johnson, *President*
Charleigh Gaug, *Office Mgr*
Bob Moodie, *Shareholder*
EMP: 10
SQ FT: 30,000
SALES: 650K **Privately Held**
WEB: www.basicpackaging.com
SIC: 2653 Corrugated & solid fiber boxes

(G-18136)
C L S FINISHING INC
409 Munroe Falls Rd (44278-3339)
P.O. Box 239 (44278-0239)
PHONE...................................330 784-4134
Fax: 330 784-5488
Steven Kenneth Geer, *President*
Vicky Geer, *Manager*
EMP: 10
SALES (est): 900K **Privately Held**
SIC: 3479 Painting of metal products; coating of metals with plastic or resins

(G-18137)
CHEMIONICS CORPORATION
390 Munroe Falls Rd (44278-3399)
PHONE...................................330 733-8834
John Blackfan, *President*
Jim Ferguson, *VP Opers*
Jeff Radler, *Treasurer*
Mike Schmidt, *Finance Dir*
Chris Blackman, *Manager*
▲ EMP: 32 EST: 1978
SQ FT: 80,000
SALES (est): 11.6MM **Privately Held**
WEB: www.chemionics.com
SIC: 2869 3069 3087 2821 Plasticizers, organic: cyclic & acyclic; reclaimed rubber & specialty rubber compounds; custom compound purchased resins; plastics materials & resins

(G-18138)
CIRCLE MOLD INCORPORATED
Also Called: Circle Mold & Machine Co
85 S Thomas Rd (44278-2107)
P.O. Box 513 (44278-0513)
PHONE...................................330 633-7017
Fax: 330 633-7025
Edward A Siciliano, *CEO*
Edward T Siciliano, *President*
Carol Kilway, *Office Mgr*
Agnes Siciliano, *Admin Sec*
EMP: 30
SQ FT: 12,000
SALES (est): 5.3MM **Privately Held**
WEB: www.circlemold.com
SIC: 3544 Forms (molds), for foundry & plastics working machinery

(G-18139)
COMMAND PLASTIC CORPORATION
124 West Ave (44278-2206)
PHONE...................................800 321-8001
Fax: 330 434-8361
Richard S Ames, *President*
Ron Brengartner, *President*
Graham Klintworth, *Vice Pres*
Rob Accord, *Purch Mgr*
Robert Acord, *Human Resources*
▲ EMP: 19
SQ FT: 65,000
SALES: 2MM **Privately Held**
WEB: www.commandplastic.com
SIC: 2671 3081 2673 Plastic film, coated or laminated for packaging; unsupported plastics film & sheet; bags: plastic, laminated & coated

(G-18140)
DES MACHINE SERVICES INC
351 Tacoma Ave (44278-2716)
PHONE...................................330 633-6897
William M Smith, *President*
Debora Smith, *Vice Pres*
EMP: 9
SQ FT: 5,000
SALES (est): 1MM **Privately Held**
SIC: 3599 Machine shop, jobbing & repair

(G-18141)
DIAMOND MOLD & DIE CO
109 E Garwood Dr (44278-1402)
PHONE...................................330 633-5682
Fax: 330 633-7069
Joseph Speer, *President*
Silvia Schaefer, *Vice Pres*
Helene Speer, *Treasurer*
Corinna Phillips, *Admin Sec*
EMP: 14
SQ FT: 5,000
SALES (est): 1MM **Privately Held**
SIC: 3544 Forms (molds), for foundry & plastics working machinery

(G-18142)
DIVERSIFIED READY MIX LTD
1680 Southeast Ave (44278-3466)
PHONE...................................330 628-3355
Todd Steinel, *Principal*
EMP: 3
SALES (est): 269.5K **Privately Held**
SIC: 3273 Ready-mixed concrete

(G-18143)
DOVE CDS INC
290 West Ave Ste J (44278-2143)
PHONE...................................330 928-3430
Fax: 330 928-9644
Larry Adams, *President*
Lisa Ann Adams, *Vice Pres*
Kari Donell, *Graphic Designe*
EMP: 8
SQ FT: 4,800
SALES (est): 1.3MM **Privately Held**
WEB: www.dovetapes.com
SIC: 5961 2791 Record &/or tape (music or video) club, mail order; typesetting

(G-18144)
DROWNED LURE
3295 Klages Blvd (44278-3367)
PHONE...................................330 548-5873
David Mitchell, *Principal*
EMP: 3
SALES (est): 277.5K **Privately Held**
SIC: 3949 Lures, fishing: artificial

(G-18145)
HERMAN MACHINE INC
252 Northeast Ave (44278-1494)
PHONE...................................330 633-3261
Fax: 330 633-9236
Suzanne E Rickards, *President*
Liegh Uhlenhake, *Manager*
EMP: 10
SQ FT: 15,000
SALES (est): 1.6MM **Privately Held**
SIC: 3599 7389 3429 Machine shop, jobbing & repair; grinding, precision: commercial or industrial; clamps, metal

G
E
O
G
R
A

(G-18146)
HORNING STEEL CO
167 Southwest Ave (44278-2293)
PHONE...................................330 633-0028
Fax: 330 475-0297
Jean Horning, *Owner*
EMP: 5
SQ FT: 7,000
SALES (est): 506.1K **Privately Held**
SIC: 3441 Fabricated structural metal

(G-18147)
I R B F COMPANY
195 Potomac Ave Ste A (44278-2714)
P.O. Box 29 (44278-0029)
PHONE...................................330 633-5100
Jennifer A Eldridge, *President*
Linda Kerns, *Office Mgr*
Tom Mountain, *Admin Sec*
EMP: 7
SQ FT: 5,000
SALES (est): 825K **Privately Held**
WEB: www.irbf.com
SIC: 3354 3599 Shapes, extruded alu-
minum; machine shop, jobbing & repair

(G-18148)
**INDUSTRIAL CTRL DSIGN MINT
INC**
Also Called: Industrial Ctrl Design & Maint
311 Geneva Ave (44278-2702)
PHONE...................................330 785-9840
David M Brown Jr, *President*
Jon Coles, *Vice Pres*
Kevin Mitchell, *Director*
EMP: 10
SQ FT: 14,000
SALES (est): 2MM **Privately Held**
WEB: www.icdminc.com
SIC: 3613 7699 5063 Control panels,
electric; engine repair & replacement,
non-automotive; switchboards

(G-18149)
KARG CORPORATION
241 Southwest Ave (44278-2239)
P.O. Box 197 (44278-0197)
PHONE...................................330 633-4916
Fax: 330 633-0235
Michael Karg, *President*
EMP: 15 EST: 1947
SQ FT: 40,000
SALES (est): 4.4MM **Privately Held**
WEB: www.kargcorp.com
SIC: 3552 Braiding machines, textile

(G-18150)
LINEAR ASICS INC
14 Tallmadge Cir (44278-2305)
PHONE...................................330 474-3920
Mike Ward, *CEO*
EMP: 8
SQ FT: 2,000
SALES (est): 330.6K **Privately Held**
SIC: 3674 Semiconductors & related de-
vices

(G-18151)
MANUFACTURING CONCEPTS
409 Munroe Falls Rd (44278-3339)
P.O. Box 493 (44278-0493)
PHONE...................................330 784-9054
Nancy Minne, *Partner*
Sue Brown, *CFO*
Mike Cast, *Manager*
EMP: 12
SQ FT: 14,500
SALES (est): 947.9K **Privately Held**
WEB: www.manufacturingconcepts.com
SIC: 7692 Welding repair

(G-18152)
MARIK SPRING INC
121 Northeast Ave (44278-1947)
PHONE...................................330 564-0617
Fax: 330 633-5528
Greg A Bedrick, *President*
EMP: 19 EST: 1954
SQ FT: 35,000
SALES (est): 4.4MM **Privately Held**
WEB: www.marikspring.com
SIC: 3493 3496 Flat springs, sheet or strip
stock; miscellaneous fabricated wire prod-
ucts

(G-18153)
MARTIN WHEEL CO INC
342 West Ave (44278-2192)
P.O. Box 157 (44278-0157)
PHONE...................................330 633-3278
Fax: 330 633-3303
Jimmy Yang, *CEO*
Thomas J Hartmann, *President*
David Nowlin, *Purch Mgr*
Dolly Yang, *Treasurer*
Darell Ruthruff, *Mktg Dir*
▲ EMP: 100 EST: 1946
SQ FT: 125,000
SALES (est): 23.8MM **Privately Held**
SIC: 3714 3011 Motor vehicle wheels &
parts; pneumatic tires, all types
PA: Americana Development, Inc.
7095 Americana Pkwy
Reynoldsburg OH 43068

(G-18154)
MICROSOL INC
390 Munroe Falls Rd (44278-3338)
PHONE...................................330 733-0086
John Blackfan, *Principal*
EMP: 3
SALES (est): 198.3K **Privately Held**
SIC: 3083 Plastic finished products, lami-
nated

(G-18155)
MIDWEST FABRICATIONS INC
516 Commerce St (44278-2132)
P.O. Box 399 (44278-0399)
PHONE...................................330 633-0191
Fax: 330 633-6302
Robert E Parsons, *President*
Barbara Parsons, *Corp Secy*
Timothy Parsons, *Vice Pres*
William Brown, *Executive*
EMP: 38
SQ FT: 9,000
SALES (est): 4.5MM **Privately Held**
SIC: 3444 Sheet metal specialties, not
stamped

(G-18156)
**MODERN AMERICAN DESIGN
INC**
491 Tacoma Ave (44278-2718)
P.O. Box 419 (44278-0419)
PHONE...................................330 633-0227
Fax: 330 633-9779
Stuart Simcox, *President*
EMP: 5
SQ FT: 7,600
SALES (est): 366.1K **Privately Held**
SIC: 2511 Bookcases, household: wood

(G-18157)
MYERS MOTORS LLC
180 South Ave (44278-2813)
PHONE...................................330 630-7000
Fax: 330 630-3758
Dana S Myers, *President*
Rob Dobson, *Technician*
▲ EMP: 5
SALES (est): 717.7K **Privately Held**
SIC: 3711 Cars, electric, assembly of

(G-18158)
NAP ASSET HOLDINGS LTD
North Amer Products
411 Geneva Ave (44278-2704)
PHONE...................................330 633-0599
Fax: 330 633-0791
Karl Wagner, *Sales Mgr*
Glen McLean, *Branch Mgr*
EMP: 15
SALES (corp-wide): 46.4MM **Privately
Held**
WEB: www.naptools.com
SIC: 2819 7699 Carbides; knife, saw &
tool sharpening & repair
PA: Nap Asset Holdings Ltd.
1180 Wernsing Rd
Jasper IN 47546
812 482-2000

(G-18159)
NORTHEAST COATINGS INC
415 Munroe Falls Rd (44278-3339)
PHONE...................................330 784-7773
Fax: 330 784-8919
Rod Fisher, *President*
Chad Fisher, *Managing Prtnr*

Ruell Fisher, *Vice Pres*
Todd Fisher, *Vice Pres*
EMP: 15
SQ FT: 12,000
SALES: 800K **Privately Held**
SIC: 3471 Finishing, metals or formed
products

(G-18160)
NORTHEAST LASER INC
461 Commerce St (44278-2134)
P.O. Box 295 (44278-0295)
PHONE...................................330 633-2897
Fax: 330 630-0016
Andy Weinsheimer, *President*
EMP: 3
SALES (est): 573K **Privately Held**
SIC: 3699 Laser systems & equipment

(G-18161)
**NORTHESTRN OH FOOT & ANKL
ASOC**
116 East Ave Ste 4 (44278-2300)
PHONE...................................330 633-3445
Theodore Buccilli, *Owner*
Theodore A Buccilli DPM, *Principal*
EMP: 3
SALES (est): 299.8K **Privately Held**
SIC: 3842 Foot appliances, orthopedic

(G-18162)
OWENS CORNING SALES LLC
170 South Ave (44278-2813)
PHONE...................................330 634-0460
Joe Brackman, *Vice Pres*
Richard W Hooper, *Plant Mgr*
Harold Coss, *Purchasing*
Lynn Dewitt, *QC Dir*
Pat Rynd, *Research*
EMP: 140
SALES (corp-wide): 5.6B **Publicly Held**
WEB: www.owenscorning.com
SIC: 3275 3086 Gypsum products; plas-
tics foam products
HQ: Owens Corning Sales, Llc
1 Owens Corning Pkwy
Toledo OH 43659
419 248-8000

(G-18163)
OWENS CORNING SALES LLC
275 Southwest Ave (44278-2232)
PHONE...................................330 633-6735
Fax: 330 633-4939
Patrick Rynd, *Vice Pres*
Joe Brackman, *Branch Mgr*
Chase Boudreaux, *Manager*
EMP: 10
SQ FT: 300
SALES (corp-wide): 5.6B **Publicly Held**
WEB: www.owenscorning.com
SIC: 8711 8731 2821 Engineering serv-
ices; commercial physical research; plas-
tics materials & resins
HQ: Owens Corning Sales, Llc
1 Owens Corning Pkwy
Toledo OH 43659
419 248-8000

(G-18164)
P & P MOLD & DIE INC
1034 S Munroe Rd (44278-3336)
PHONE...................................330 784-8333
Fax: 330 784-8113
Mary Jean Putra, *President*
William Putra, *Treasurer*
Emil Putra, *Admin Sec*
EMP: 17
SQ FT: 6,000
SALES (est): 2.7MM **Privately Held**
SIC: 3599 Machine shop, jobbing & repair

(G-18165)
PROMOLD INC
Also Called: Promold Gauer
487 Commerce St (44278-2134)
PHONE...................................330 633-3532
Stefan K Schler, *President*
Mary Ann Schler, *Vice Pres*
Vickie Miller, *Manager*
EMP: 10
SQ FT: 9,000
SALES (est): 1.6MM **Privately Held**
WEB: www.promoldinc.com
SIC: 3544 Forms (molds), for foundry &
plastics working machinery

(G-18166)
**PYRAMID REBUILD AND MCH
LLC**
123 S Thomas Rd (44278-2101)
PHONE...................................330 633-4452
Jim Leigh,
Jeff Edds,
EMP: 10
SQ FT: 5,000
SALES (est): 1.7MM **Privately Held**
WEB: www.pyramidrebuilders.com
SIC: 3542 Rebuilt machine tools, metal
forming types

(G-18167)
RETCO MOLD & MACHINE
41 Industry St (44278-2127)
PHONE...................................330 633-5725
Marshall Terry, *CEO*
Randy Terry, *Executive*
EMP: 11
SALES (est): 1.3MM **Privately Held**
WEB: www.retcomoldandmachine.com
SIC: 3544 Industrial molds

(G-18168)
SATCO INC
59 Industry St (44278-2127)
PHONE...................................330 630-8866
Fax: 330 630-3377
Waffim Farrah, *President*
▲ EMP: 4
SQ FT: 50,000
SALES (est): 370K **Privately Held**
SIC: 3714 7389 5013 3694 Motor vehicle
engines & parts; motor vehicle transmissions, drive assemblies & parts; transmissions, motor vehicle; packaging & labeling
services; automotive supplies & parts; engine electrical equipment; relays & industrial controls; speed changers, drives &
gears

(G-18169)
SPEELMAN ELECTRIC INC
358 Commerce St (44278-2139)
PHONE...................................330 633-1410
Fax: 330 633-4244
Richard Speelman, *President*
Christeen Parsons, *CFO*
EMP: 80
SQ FT: 7,000
SALES (est): 43.5MM **Privately Held**
WEB: www.speelmanelectric.com
SIC: 3825 1731 Test equipment for elec-
tronic & electric measurement; general
electrical contractor

(G-18170)
STORETEK ENGINEERING INC
399 Commerce St (44278-2134)
PHONE...................................330 294-0678
Jim Crews, *President*
Keith Krebs, *Project Engr*
John Laguardia, *Project Engr*
Bruce Sandacz, *Controller*
EMP: 22
SALES (est): 4.9MM **Privately Held**
SIC: 8711 3559 Engineering services;
electronic component making machinery

(G-18171)
SUNSET GOLF LLC
71 West Ave Ste 6 (44278-2236)
PHONE...................................419 994-5563
Bill Whipple,
Dan Dieghan,
▲ EMP: 37
SQ FT: 40,000
SALES (est): 3.6MM **Privately Held**
WEB: www.sunsetgolfballs.com
SIC: 3949 5941 Golf equipment; sporting
goods & bicycle shops

(G-18172)
TAMARKIN COMPANY
Also Called: Giant Eagle
205 West Ave (44278-2138)
PHONE...................................330 634-0688
Fax: 330 634-0691
EMP: 3
SALES (corp-wide): 8B **Privately Held**
SIC: 2836 Vaccines & other immunizing
products

HQ: The Tamarkin Company
101 Kappa Dr
Pittsburgh PA

(G-18173)
TRANS FOAM INC
281 Southwest Ave (44278-2232)
PHONE..................................330 630-9444
Todd Jordan, *President*
EMP: 9
SALES (est): 1.2MM **Privately Held**
SIC: 3086 Plastics foam products

(G-18174)
VERSATILE MACHINE
402 Commerce St (44278-2135)
PHONE..................................330 618-9895
Darren George, *Owner*
EMP: 8
SALES (est): 335.4K **Privately Held**
SIC: 3599 Machine shop, jobbing & repair

(G-18175)
WALTCO LIFT CORP (DH)
285 Northeast Ave (44278-1431)
P.O. Box 354 (44278-0354)
PHONE..................................330 633-9191
Fax: 330 633-1418
Robert Begg, *QC Mgr*
Chris Adkins, *Design Engr*
Harry Klug, *CFO*
Laura Geyer, *Human Res Dir*
Jody Woods, *Natl Sales Mgr*
▲ EMP: 120
SQ FT: 70,000
SALES (est): 43.2MM
SALES (corp-wide): 4B **Privately Held**
SIC: 3537 3593 Industrial trucks & tractors; fluid power cylinders, hydraulic or pneumatic
HQ: Cargotec Holding, Inc.
415 E Dundee St
Ottawa KS 66067
785 242-2200

(G-18176)
WEB3BOX SOFTWARE LLC
34 Merz Blvd Ste D (44278)
PHONE..................................330 794-7397
EMP: 5
SALES (est): 370K **Privately Held**
SIC: 7372 Prepackaged Software Services

(G-18177)
WHOLE SHOP INC
181 S Thomas Rd (44278-2752)
PHONE..................................330 630-5305
Fax: 330 630-5317
Jerry McClain, *President*
Nancie Scott, *Principal*
◆ EMP: 19
SQ FT: 27,000
SALES (est): 2.4MM **Privately Held**
WEB: www.wholeshopinc.com
SIC: 3441 Fabricated structural metal

(G-18178)
WOODCRAFT PATTERN WORKS INC
210 Southwest Ave (44278-2233)
PHONE..................................330 630-2158
Fax: 330 630-9269
Don A Kessler, *President*
Brian Kessler, *Vice Pres*
EMP: 4
SQ FT: 5,000
SALES (est): 230K **Privately Held**
SIC: 2499 Decorative wood & woodwork

Terrace Park
Hamilton County

(G-18179)
CC PALLETS LLC
212 Cambridge Ave (45174-1138)
PHONE..................................513 442-8766
Tamara Fine, *Principal*
EMP: 3
SALES (est): 119.9K **Privately Held**
SIC: 2448 Pallets, wood & wood with metal

(G-18180)
LAWPAK INC
128 Wrenwood Ln (45174-1045)
PHONE..................................513 831-3900
Theodore Swartz, *President*
EMP: 5
SQ FT: 3,500
SALES: 400K **Privately Held**
WEB: www.elawpak.com
SIC: 2731 5112 Books; publishing & printing; stationery & office supplies

(G-18181)
M D COMPLETE PROF SKINCARE
614 Wooster Pike (45174-1010)
PHONE..................................513 965-3760
EMP: 5
SALES (est): 138.3K **Privately Held**
SIC: 8011 2844 Dermatologist; face creams or lotions

(G-18182)
QUANTUM ATHLETICS LLC
724 Stanton Ave (45174-1250)
PHONE..................................513 248-2966
John Christopher, *Principal*
EMP: 3
SALES (est): 121.3K **Privately Held**
SIC: 3572 Computer storage devices

The Plains
Athens County

(G-18183)
BIMBO BAKERIES USA INC
33 N Plains Rd (45780-1013)
PHONE..................................740 797-4449
Dave Heiners, *Branch Mgr*
EMP: 24
SALES (corp-wide): 11B **Privately Held**
SIC: 2051 Bakery: wholesale or wholesale/retail combined
HQ: Bimbo Bakeries Usa, Inc
255 Business Center Dr # 200
Horsham PA 19044
215 347-5500

(G-18184)
BIMBO BAKERIES USA INC
33 Plains Rd (45780)
PHONE..................................740 797-4449
EMP: 24
SALES (corp-wide): 13.1B **Privately Held**
SIC: 2051 Mfg Bread/Related Products
HQ: Bimbo Bakeries Usa, Inc
255 Business Center Dr
Horsham PA 19044
215 347-5500

(G-18185)
DON GAMERTSFELDER
10416 State Route 682 (45780-1319)
PHONE..................................740 797-4495
Don Gamertsfelder, *Principal*
EMP: 3
SALES (est): 147.4K **Privately Held**
SIC: 1241 Coal mining services

(G-18186)
ELECTRIC MOTOR SVC OF ATHENS
6 E 4th St (45780-1305)
PHONE..................................740 592-1682
Albert W Matters III, *President*
Diane Matters, *Treasurer*
EMP: 10
SALES: 1.4MM **Privately Held**
SIC: 7694 Armature rewinding shops

(G-18187)
TYJEN INC
Also Called: Slater Builders Supply
8 Slater Dr (45780-1321)
PHONE..................................740 797-4064
Fax: 740 797-2922
Mark Vaughn, *President*
EMP: 9
SALES (corp-wide): 2.8MM **Privately Held**
SIC: 3271 Blocks, concrete or cinder: standard

PA: Tyjen Inc
35255 Hocking Dr
Logan OH 43138
740 380-3215

Thompson
Geauga County

(G-18188)
EDMONDS ELEVATOR COMPANY
6777 Sidley Rd (44086-9715)
PHONE..................................216 781-9135
Tina Schaeffer, *President*
Michael Schaeffer, *Vice Pres*
EMP: 19
SQ FT: 5,000
SALES (est): 3.5MM **Privately Held**
SIC: 1796 3534 7699 Installing building equipment; elevators & moving stairways; professional instrument repair services

(G-18189)
PAINE FALLS CENTERPIN LLC
6342 Ledge Rd (44086-9732)
PHONE..................................440 298-3202
Adam N Demarco, *Principal*
EMP: 8
SALES (est): 707.4K **Privately Held**
SIC: 3452 Pins

(G-18190)
QUARTER MILE FABRICATION LLC
7289 Leroy Thompson Rd (44086-9523)
PHONE..................................440 298-1272
Lawrence Gidley, *Principal*
EMP: 3 EST: 2010
SALES (est): 201.3K **Privately Held**
SIC: 3131 Quarters

Thornville
Perry County

(G-18191)
AMERICAN DREAMS INC
1 Shoreline Dr (43076-8957)
PHONE..................................740 385-4444
David Swain, *President*
EMP: 5 EST: 1996
SALES (est): 360K **Privately Held**
WEB: www.coastalhighway.com
SIC: 7372 6531 Prepackaged software; real estate agents & managers

(G-18192)
BUCKEYE LAKE SHOPPER REPORTER
14886 State Route 13 (43076-8954)
PHONE..................................740 246-4741
Sandy Peters, *Principal*
Twila Rodgers, *Manager*
EMP: 4
SALES (est): 205.3K **Privately Held**
SIC: 2711 Newspapers, publishing & printing

(G-18193)
BUCKEYE LAKE WINERY
13750 Rosewood Dr Ne (43076-8117)
PHONE..................................740 246-9890
Tracy Higginbotham, *Principal*
EMP: 7 EST: 2013
SALES (est): 753.8K **Privately Held**
SIC: 2084 Wines, brandy & brandy spirits

(G-18194)
RE CONNORS CONSTRUCTION LTD
13352 Forrest Rd Ne (43076-9164)
PHONE..................................740 644-0261
Thomas Connors, *Owner*
EMP: 9 EST: 2014
SALES (est): 523.9K **Privately Held**
SIC: 1521 1771 1761 3271 Single-family housing construction; general remodeling, single-family houses; concrete work; roofing, siding & sheet metal work; concrete block & brick;

(G-18195)
ROCKS GENERAL MAINTENANCE LLC
10019 Jacksontown Rd (43076-8802)
PHONE..................................740 323-4711
Twila J Stonerock, *Manager*
Michael Stonerock,
Twila Stonerock,
EMP: 7
SALES (est): 1.1MM **Privately Held**
SIC: 3498 Piping systems for pulp paper & chemical industries

(G-18196)
SHELLY COMPANY
80 Park Dr (43076-9397)
PHONE..................................740 246-6315
Dave Bathieck, *Manager*
EMP: 7
SALES (corp-wide): 28.6B **Privately Held**
SIC: 3273 2951 1442 Ready-mixed concrete; asphalt paving mixtures & blocks; construction sand & gravel
HQ: Shelly Company
80 Park Dr
Thornville OH 43076
740 246-6315

(G-18197)
SHELLY MATERIALS INC
8775 Blackbird Ln (43076-9515)
PHONE..................................740 246-5009
Larry Shively, *Vice Pres*
EMP: 25
SALES (corp-wide): 28.6B **Privately Held**
SIC: 2951 Asphalt paving mixtures & blocks
HQ: Shelly Materials, Inc.
80 Park Dr
Thornville OH 43076
740 246-6315

(G-18198)
SHELLY MATERIALS INC (DH)
Also Called: Shelly Company, The
80 Park Dr (43076-9397)
P.O. Box 266 (43076-0266)
PHONE..................................740 246-6315
John Power, *President*
Ted Lemon, *Vice Pres*
Doug Radabaugh, *Treasurer*
John Mahon, *Controller*
Charlie West, *Manager*
EMP: 100 EST: 1938
SALES (est): 552.9MM
SALES (corp-wide): 28.6B **Privately Held**
SIC: 1422 1442 2951 4492 Crushed & broken limestone; construction sand & gravel; concrete, asphaltic (not from refineries); tugboat service
HQ: Shelly Company
80 Park Dr
Thornville OH 43076
740 246-6315

(G-18199)
SILK SCREEN SPECIAL TS INC
9075 Boundaries Rd (43076-9400)
P.O. Box 218 (43076-0218)
PHONE..................................740 246-4843
Fax: 740 246-4850
Steven R Dornon, *President*
EMP: 5
SQ FT: 8,500
SALES (est): 600K **Privately Held**
WEB: www.lakesend.com
SIC: 2759 5199 5947 5699 Screen printing; advertising specialties; novelties; sports apparel; T-shirts, custom printed; novelty merchandise, mail order; clothing, mail order (except women's)

Thurman
Gallia County

(G-18200)
S & J LUMBER CO
3667 Garners Ford Rd (45685-9301)
PHONE..................................740 245-5804
Fax: 740 245-5889
John Smith, *Owner*
Dan Miller, *Manager*
EMP: 30

SQ FT: 3,000
SALES (est): 3.8MM Privately Held
SIC: 2421 Building & structural materials, wood

Tiffin
Seneca County

(G-18201)
A & M PRODUCTS
3060 S County Road 591 (44883-9749)
PHONE..................................419 595-2092
Fax: 419 595-2161
Marion A Lucius, *Owner*
EMP: 3
SQ FT: 4,800
SALES (est): 130K Privately Held
SIC: 2992 2891 Lubricating oils & greases; sealants

(G-18202)
AMERICAN FINE SINTER CO LTD
957 N County Road 11 (44883-9415)
PHONE..................................419 443-8880
Toshihiro Nakashima, *President*
Jeremy A Gibson, *Principal*
Joe Binau, *Controller*
Daren Smith, *Human Res Mgr*
▲ EMP: 125
SQ FT: 80,000
SALES (est): 22.8MM
SALES (corp-wide): 328.5MM Privately Held
SIC: 3519 Parts & accessories, internal combustion engines
PA: Fine Sinter Co., Ltd.
    1189-11, Nishinohora, Akechicho
    Kasugai AIC 480-0
    568 884-355

(G-18203)
AMERICAN SWEET BEAN CO LLC
8133 N Township Road 72a (44883-9335)
PHONE..................................888 995-0007
Charles Fry,
EMP: 5
SALES: 950K Privately Held
SIC: 2099 Food preparations

(G-18204)
APEX TARGET SYSTEMS LLC ◆
37 Heilman St (44883-1802)
PHONE..................................877 224-6692
Jamie Chester, *Mng Member*
EMP: 5 EST: 2016
SALES (est): 159.9K Privately Held
SIC: 3949 Target shooting equipment

(G-18205)
ARNOLD MACHINE INC
19 Heritage Dr (44883-9503)
PHONE..................................419 443-1818
Fax: 419 443-1823
Zachary W Arnold, *President*
EMP: 13
SQ FT: 22,000
SALES (est): 4MM Privately Held
SIC: 3599 Machine shop, jobbing & repair

(G-18206)
ATLAS INDUSTRIES INC
401 Wall St (44883-1369)
PHONE..................................419 447-4730
Fax: 419 447-8456
Jim Clark, *Vice Pres*
David Noble, *Manager*
EMP: 96
SALES (corp-wide): 165.3MM Privately Held
WEB: www.atlasindustries.com
SIC: 3599 3714 Crankshafts & camshafts, machining; manifolds, motor vehicle
PA: Atlas Industries, Inc.
    1750 E State St
    Fremont OH 43420
    419 355-1000

(G-18207)
ATLAS INDUSTRIES INC
401 Wall St (44883-1369)
PHONE..................................419 637-2117

Fax: 419 637-7751
Ted Beavers, *Plant Mgr*
Donald Rickard, *Manager*
Dave Hanthorn, *Manager*
Layne Leemaster, *Maintence Staff*
EMP: 302
SALES (corp-wide): 165.3MM Privately Held
WEB: www.atlasindustries.com
SIC: 3599 5013 3714 Crankshafts & camshafts, machining; automotive supplies & parts; motor vehicle parts & accessories
PA: Atlas Industries, Inc.
    1750 E State St
    Fremont OH 43420
    419 355-1000

(G-18208)
B J PALLETT
525 Wall St (44883-1370)
PHONE..................................419 447-9665
Fax: 419 447-6215
Bernard Breidenbach Jr, *Owner*
EMP: 9
SQ FT: 27,500
SALES (est): 550K Privately Held
SIC: 2448 Wood pallets & skids

(G-18209)
BALLREICH BROS INC
Also Called: Ballreichs Potato Chips Snacks
186 Ohio Ave (44883-1746)
PHONE..................................419 447-1814
Fax: 419 447-5635
Brian Reis, *President*
Joe Biden, *Vice Pres*
Steve Hoover, *Vice Pres*
Ann Dean, *Production*
Joseph Weininger, *Controller*
EMP: 44
SQ FT: 48,000
SALES (est): 10.5MM Privately Held
WEB: www.ballreich.com
SIC: 2096 2099 Potato chips & other potato-based snacks; food preparations

(G-18210)
BOOKMYER LLP
144 S Washington St (44883-2840)
PHONE..................................419 447-3883
Fax: 419 447-6944
Mike Bonham, *Partner*
Mary Hoyda, *Partner*
Barb Patterson, *Partner*
EMP: 5
SALES (est): 431.1K Privately Held
SIC: 2759 Visiting cards (including business): printing

(G-18211)
BRADLEYS BEACONS LTD
Also Called: Whitehouse
296 Hedges St (44883-3120)
PHONE..................................419 447-7560
Donna Bradley, *Mng Member*
David Greene,
Heather Greene,
EMP: 3
SALES (est): 129.6K Privately Held
SIC: 2759 Promotional printing

(G-18212)
BUTT HUT OF AMERICA INC
1972 W Market St (44883-2556)
PHONE..................................419 443-1997
Fax: 419 443-1987
Wendy Waltermyer, *Manager*
Amy Bridinger, *Manager*
Hal Simon, *Director*
EMP: 4
SALES (est): 386K Privately Held
SIC: 2111 5194 Cigarettes; tobacco & tobacco products

(G-18213)
C S BELL CO
170 W Davis St (44883-1337)
P.O. Box 291 (44883-0291)
PHONE..................................419 448-0791
Fax: 419 448-0791
Daniel White, *President*
Mary White, *Vice Pres*
Joan Gongas, *Adv Mgr*
Pat Kesler, *Manager*
EMP: 10

SQ FT: 10,000
SALES (est): 1.1MM Privately Held
WEB: www.csbellco.com
SIC: 3535 3541 Conveyors & conveying equipment; grinding machines, metal-working

(G-18214)
CARMEUSE LIME INC
1967 W County Rd 42 (44883)
PHONE..................................419 986-2000
Amy Kuhn, *Branch Mgr*
EMP: 3 Privately Held
SIC: 1422 Agricultural limestone, ground
HQ: Carmeuse Lime, Inc.
    11 Stanwix St Fl 21
    Pittsburgh PA 15222
    412 995-5500

(G-18215)
CHEMTRANS LOGISTICS INC
281 Hancock St (44883-3115)
PHONE..................................419 447-8041
Kenneth O Stahl, *President*
EMP: 4
SALES (est): 430K Privately Held
SIC: 3537 Trucks: freight, baggage, etc.: industrial, except mining

(G-18216)
CONTINENTAL COML PDTS LLC
1780 S County Road 1 (44883-8800)
PHONE..................................419 447-5000
Curtis Cidler, *Branch Mgr*
EMP: 68
SALES (corp-wide): 113.9MM Publicly Held
SIC: 3089 Injection molded finished plastic products
HQ: Continental Commercial Products, Llc
    11840 Westline Industrial
    Saint Louis MO 63146
    314 656-4301

(G-18217)
CUSTOM MACHINE INC
3315 W Township Road 158 (44883-9453)
PHONE..................................419 986-5122
Fax: 419 986-5204
David Hammer, *President*
Jeffery Hammer, *Vice Pres*
Phyllis Hammer, *Treasurer*
EMP: 30
SQ FT: 19,200
SALES: 3MM Privately Held
WEB: www.custom-machine-inc.com
SIC: 3544 3599 7692 Special dies & tools; machine shop, jobbing & repair; welding repair

(G-18218)
DOREL HOME FURNISHINGS INC
458 2nd Ave (44883-9358)
PHONE..................................419 447-7448
Fax: 419 447-8738
Rick Jackson, *President*
Ron Brown, *Info Tech Mgr*
EMP: 250
SALES (corp-wide): 2.6B Privately Held
WEB: www.dorel.com
SIC: 2511 Console tables: wood; coffee tables: wood; tea wagons: wood
HQ: Dorel Home Furnishings, Inc.
    410 E 1st St S
    Wright City MO 63390
    636 745-3351

(G-18219)
E SYSTEMS DESIGN & AUTOMTN INC
226 Heritage Dr (44883-9504)
P.O. Box 158 (44883-0158)
PHONE..................................419 443-0220
Fax: 419 443-9030
Don Bagent, *President*
Brenda Bagent, *Treasurer*
EMP: 8
SQ FT: 9,000
SALES (est): 1.5MM Privately Held
SIC: 3542 Machine tools, metal forming type

(G-18220)
FIRE TETRAHEDRON JOURNAL
3110 E County Road 50 C (44883-8448)
PHONE..................................567 220-6477
Jennifer Dempsey, *Principal*
EMP: 3
SALES (est): 83.8K Privately Held
SIC: 2711 Newspapers

(G-18221)
FRY FOODS INC
99 Maule Rd (44883-9400)
P.O. Box 837 (44883-0837)
PHONE..................................419 448-0831
Fax: 419 448-8363
Norman Fry, *President*
Beverly Fry, *Vice Pres*
David Fry, *Vice Pres*
Philip Fry, *Vice Pres*
Jerry Kaufman, *Vice Pres*
▼ EMP: 50
SQ FT: 40,000
SALES (est): 21.7MM Privately Held
WEB: www.fryfoods.com
SIC: 2038 2033 Snacks, including onion rings, cheese sticks, etc.; canned fruits & specialties

(G-18222)
HEMPY WATER CONDITIONING INC
Also Called: Hempy Water of Tiffin
227 S Washington St (44883-3085)
PHONE..................................419 448-8885
Justin Wagner, *Office Mgr*
EMP: 4
SALES (corp-wide): 2.3MM Privately Held
SIC: 3589 Water treatment equipment, industrial
PA: Hempy Water Conditioning Inc
    505 Smith St
    Forest OH 45843
    419 273-2531

(G-18223)
J H PLASTICS
4720 W Us Highway 224 (44883-8887)
PHONE..................................419 937-2035
John Defibaugh, *Principal*
EMP: 4
SALES (est): 235.8K Privately Held
SIC: 3089 Plastics products

(G-18224)
JACOBSON MFG - TIFFIN LLC
1988 S County Road 593 (44883-9275)
PHONE..................................419 447-2221
Chris Smith, *Credit Mgr*
Bob Lucius, *Marketing Mgr*
Robert S Kaminski,
EMP: 54
SALES (est): 22.8MM Privately Held
SIC: 3452 Bolts, nuts, rivets & washers
HQ: Continental/Midland, Llc
    24000 S Western Ave
    Park Forest IL 60466
    708 747-1200

(G-18225)
JOHNS WELDING & TOWING INC
850 N County Road 11 (44883-9415)
PHONE..................................419 447-8937
Fax: 419 447-1013
Joseph Keller, *President*
James Keller, *Vice Pres*
EMP: 14
SQ FT: 20,000
SALES (est): 1.8MM Privately Held
SIC: 7549 7692 Towing services; welding repair

(G-18226)
LAMINATE TECHNOLOGIES INC (PA)
Also Called: Lam Tech
161 Maule Rd (44883-9400)
PHONE..................................419 448-0812
Fax: 419 448-0811
Frederick E Zoeller, *President*
Randy Wiser, *General Mgr*
A Louise Zoeller, *Vice Pres*
Greg Storey, *Plant Mgr*
Allan Funkhouser, *CFO*
▲ EMP: 55

SQ FT: 80,000
SALES (est): 28.9MM **Privately Held**
WEB: www.lamtech.net
SIC: 2439 2891 2672 Structural wood members; adhesives & sealants; coated & laminated paper

(G-18227)
LIFETIME IRONWORKS LLC
244 Coe St (44883-3158)
PHONE..................................419 443-0567
David Miller, *Mng Member*
EMP: 3
SALES (est): 235K **Privately Held**
SIC: 3446 Architectural metalwork

(G-18228)
M & B ASPHALT COMPANY INC
Also Called: Maple Grove Materials
2100 W Senc County Rd 42 (44883)
P.O. Box 240, Old Fort (44861-0240)
PHONE..................................419 992-4235
R Chesebro, *Corp Secy*
Farley Wood, *Vice Pres*
Chris Harrison, *Manager*
EMP: 5
SALES (corp-wide): 77.2MM **Privately Held**
SIC: 2951 Asphalt paving mixtures & blocks
PA: M & B Asphalt Company, Inc.
1525 W Seneca Cnty Rd 42
Tiffin OH 44883
419 992-4235

(G-18229)
M G Q INC
Also Called: Maple Grove Companies
1525 W County Road 42 (44883-8457)
P.O. Box 130, Old Fort (44861-0130)
PHONE..................................419 992-4236
Lynn Radabaugh, *President*
Tim Bell, *President*
Bruce Chubb, *Principal*
Nicole Davis, *Principal*
Jeff Murphy, *Principal*
EMP: 45
SALES (est): 3.2MM **Privately Held**
WEB: www.mgq.com
SIC: 4214 1481 Local trucking with storage; mine & quarry services, nonmetallic minerals

(G-18230)
M L ADVERTISING & DESIGN LLC
Also Called: Mlad Graphic Design Services
185 Jefferson St (44883-2865)
PHONE..................................419 447-6523
Fax: 419 447-6550
Mark A Levans, *Mng Member*
EMP: 6
SQ FT: 3,000
SALES: 1MM **Privately Held**
WEB: www.mlad.com
SIC: 7336 2759 Graphic arts & related design; commercial printing

(G-18231)
MAPLE GROVE MATERIALS INC
1525 W City Rd Ste 42 (44883)
PHONE..................................419 992-4235
Tim Bell, *President*
Lynn O Radabaugh, *Vice Pres*
Robert Chesebro, *Treasurer*
EMP: 9
SQ FT: 2,000
SALES (est): 958.9K
SALES (corp-wide): 77.2MM **Privately Held**
SIC: 3281 Limestone, cut & shaped
PA: M & B Asphalt Company, Inc.
1525 W Seneca Cnty Rd 42
Tiffin OH 44883
419 992-4235

(G-18232)
NATIONAL MACHINERY LLC (HQ)
161 Greenfield St (44883-2471)
P.O. Box 747 (44883-0747)
PHONE..................................419 447-5211
Fax: 419 447-5299
John Bolte, *COO*
Christopher Knable, *Engineer*
Terry Zimmerman, *Manager*

Andrew Kalnow,
◆ EMP: 310
SQ FT: 650,000
SALES (est): 98MM
SALES (corp-wide): 120.8MM **Privately Held**
SIC: 3542 Headers; high energy rate metal forming machines; mechanical (pneumatic or hydraulic) metal forming machines
PA: Nm Group Global, Llc
161 Greenfield St
Tiffin OH 44883
419 447-5211

(G-18233)
NM GROUP GLOBAL LLC (PA)
161 Greenfield St (44883-2499)
PHONE..................................419 447-5211
Andrew Kalnow,
EMP: 5
SALES (est): 120.8MM **Privately Held**
SIC: 3542 3599 6799 Forging machinery & hammers; custom machinery; investors

(G-18234)
NMGG CTG LLC (PA)
Also Called: Cleaning Technologies Grp
161 Greenfield St (44883-2499)
PHONE..................................419 447-5211
Andrew H Kalnow, *CEO*
Robert J Foster, *CFO*
EMP: 5
SALES (est): 24.9MM **Privately Held**
SIC: 3569 3541 Blast cleaning equipment, dustless; ultrasonic metal cutting machine tools

(G-18235)
OCECO INC
Also Called: Oceco Co
1616 S County Road 1 (44883-9746)
P.O. Box 159 (44883-0159)
PHONE..................................419 447-0916
Fax: 419 447-5514
Richard Borer, *President*
Julie Morris, *Controller*
Rebecca Mason, *Sales Executive*
EMP: 15
SQ FT: 38,000
SALES (est): 2.7MM **Privately Held**
SIC: 3494 3589 3599 7692 Valves & pipe fittings; sewage treatment equipment; machine shop, jobbing & repair; welding repair; machine tools, metal cutting type

(G-18236)
OGDEN NEWSPAPERS OF OHIO INC
Also Called: Advertising Tribune
320 Nelson St (44883-8956)
P.O. Box 778 (44883-0778)
PHONE..................................419 448-3200
Fax: 419 447-3274
EMP: 85
SALES (est): 6.4MM
SALES (corp-wide): 683.9MM **Privately Held**
SIC: 2711 Newspapers-Publishing/Printing
PA: The Ogden Newspapers Inc
1500 Main St
Wheeling WV 26003
304 233-0100

(G-18237)
PALMER BROS TRANSIT MIX CON
1900 S County Road 1 (44883-8826)
PHONE..................................419 447-2018
Rick Corbeck, *Manager*
Rick Rohrbacher, *Manager*
Tom Weiker, *Manager*
EMP: 8
SALES (corp-wide): 7MM **Privately Held**
SIC: 3273 Ready-mixed concrete
PA: Palmer Bros Transit Mix Concrete Inc
12205 E Gypsy Lane Rd
Bowling Green OH 43402
419 352-4681

(G-18238)
QUICK TAB II INC (PA)
241 Heritage Dr (44883-9504)
P.O. Box 723 (44883-0723)
PHONE..................................419 448-6622
Fax: 419 448-6627

Chuck Daughenbaugh, *CEO*
Mike Daughenbaugh, *Vice Pres*
Jim Hayes, *Opers Mgr*
Marty Ward, *Traffic Mgr*
Brad Distel, *Design Engr*
▼ EMP: 64
SQ FT: 30,000
SALES (est): 12.1MM **Privately Held**
WEB: www.qt2.com
SIC: 2752 5112 2791 2789 Business forms, lithographed; stationery & office supplies; typesetting; bookbinding & related work

(G-18239)
RIVERSIDE ENGINES INC
7381 S State Route 231 (44883-8503)
PHONE..................................419 927-6838
Fax: 419 447-2872
Jan Riedel, *President*
Larry Sarka, *Corp Secy*
EMP: 4
SQ FT: 6,500
SALES: 700K **Privately Held**
SIC: 3714 Motor vehicle parts & accessories

(G-18240)
ROBERT NICKEL
125 Minerva St (44883-1559)
PHONE..................................419 448-8256
Robert Nickel, *Principal*
EMP: 3 EST: 2010
SALES (est): 186.7K **Privately Held**
SIC: 3356 Nickel

(G-18241)
RUSH GRAPHIX LTD
30 Riverside Dr (44883-2332)
P.O. Box 866 (44883-0866)
PHONE..................................419 448-7874
Fax: 419 443-9685
Bill Franklin, *Principal*
EMP: 3
SALES (est): 255.4K **Privately Held**
SIC: 2759 Screen printing

(G-18242)
SARKA SHTMTL & FABRICATION INC
Also Called: Sarka Conveyor
70 Clinton Ave (44883-1620)
PHONE..................................419 447-4377
Fax: 419 447-7263
Kendall T Parker, *President*
Zack Allen, *Sales Staff*
Larry D Sarka, *Shareholder*
EMP: 22
SQ FT: 11,000
SALES (est): 7.8MM **Privately Held**
SIC: 3449 Bars, concrete reinforcing: fabricated steel

(G-18243)
SEISLOVE VAULT & SEPTIC TANKS
Also Called: Seislove Brial Vlts Sptic Tnks
2168 S State Route 100 (44883-3699)
PHONE..................................419 447-5473
Fax: 419 447-5473
EMP: 7 EST: 1946
SQ FT: 13,000
SALES (est): 390K **Privately Held**
SIC: 3272 Burial vaults, concrete or precast terrazzo; septic tanks, concrete

(G-18244)
SENECA SHEET METAL COMPANY
277 Water St (44883-1698)
PHONE..................................419 447-8434
Fax: 419 447-8774
Robert J Fulton, *President*
George H Wells, *Vice Pres*
Dave Bauer, *Purchasing*
Beverly Shaffer, *Manager*
John W Hilbert II, *Incorporator*
EMP: 10
SQ FT: 55,000
SALES: 1MM **Privately Held**
SIC: 3444 1761 Sheet metalwork; sheet metalwork

(G-18245)
SONOCO PRODUCTS COMPANY
60 Heritage Dr (44883-9503)
PHONE..................................419 448-4428
Fax: 419 448-1515
Terry Barfield, *Manager*
EMP: 45
SALES (corp-wide): 4.7B **Publicly Held**
WEB: www.sonoco.com
SIC: 2655 2671 Fiber cans, drums & similar products; packaging paper & plastics film, coated & laminated
PA: Sonoco Products Company
1 N 2nd St
Hartsville SC 29550
843 383-7000

(G-18246)
TAIHO CORPORATION OF AMERICA
194 Heritage Dr (44883-9503)
PHONE..................................419 443-1645
Shigeki Awazu, *President*
Karl Kortlandt, *Vice Pres*
Mike Shannaberger, *Vice Pres*
Mark Gibson, *Prdtn Mgr*
Doug Bouillon, *Maint Spvr*
◆ EMP: 120
SQ FT: 140
SALES (est): 26.4MM
SALES (corp-wide): 916.8MM **Privately Held**
SIC: 3714 3585 3568 Air conditioner parts, motor vehicle; motor vehicle transmissions, drive assemblies & parts; refrigeration & heating equipment; power transmission equipment
PA: Taiho Kogyo Co., Ltd.
3-65, Midorigaoka
Toyota AIC 471-0
565 282-493

(G-18247)
TIFFIN FOUNDRY & MACHINE INC
423 W Adams St (44883-9284)
P.O. Box 37 (44883-0037)
PHONE..................................419 447-3991
Fax: 419 447-7969
Melvin A Jones, *Ch of Bd*
Steven Sobol, *President*
Jack Bour, *Plant Mgr*
Beverly Jones, *Office Mgr*
EMP: 35 EST: 2004
SQ FT: 45,000
SALES (est): 4.3MM **Privately Held**
SIC: 3592 3599 3322 3325 Carburetors, pistons, rings, valves; machine shop, jobbing & repair; malleable iron foundries; steel foundries; gray & ductile iron foundries

(G-18248)
TIFFIN METAL PRODUCTS CO (PA)
450 Wall St (44883-1366)
PHONE..................................419 447-8414
Fax: 419 447-8512
Will Heddles, *President*
Matt Dysard, *General Mgr*
Michael R Reser, *Exec VP*
Ron Myers, *Vice Pres*
Richard M Wyka, *VP Mfg*
▼ EMP: 80 EST: 1903
SQ FT: 120,000
SALES (est): 16MM **Privately Held**
WEB: www.tiffinmetal.com
SIC: 2599 2542 2531 2522 Boards: planning, display, notice; factory furniture & fixtures; lockers (not refrigerated): except wood; public building & related furniture; office furniture, except wood; wood office furniture; wood kitchen cabinets

(G-18249)
TIFFIN SCENIC STUDIOS INC (PA)
Also Called: Atlantic and Prfmce Rigging
146 Riverside Dr (44883-1644)
P.O. Box 39 (44883-0039)
PHONE..................................800 445-1546
Fax: 419 447-5969
Brad Hossler, *President*
Steve Maiberger, *Treasurer*
Mike Griffin, *Accounts Mgr*

Steve Everhart, *Admin Sec*
EMP: 33 **EST:** 1901
SQ FT: 24,000
SALES: 5.5MM **Privately Held**
WEB: www.tiffinscenic.com
SIC: 2391 3999 Draperies, plastic & textile: from purchased materials; stage hardware & equipment, except lighting

(G-18250)
TOLEDO MOLDING & DIE INC
1441 Maule Rd (44883-9130)
PHONE................419 443-9031
Fax: 419 443-9032
Ryan Eley, *Facilities Mgr*
Luke Biller, *Engineer*
Carl Pastorella, *Human Res Mgr*
Ann Wank, *Human Resources*
Dave Spott, *Manager*
EMP: 310
SALES (corp-wide): 426.5MM **Privately Held**
WEB: www.tmdinc.com
SIC: 3089 Automotive parts, plastic
PA: Toledo Molding & Die, Inc.
1429 Coining Dr
Toledo OH 43612
419 470-3950

(G-18251)
VANDILEY INDUSTRIES LTD
3384 N State Route 53 (44883-9391)
P.O. Box 971 (44883-0971)
PHONE................419 618-1970
Matthew S Glick, *Principal*
EMP: 3
SALES (est): 154.1K **Privately Held**
SIC: 3999 Manufacturing industries

(G-18252)
VIEWPOINT GRAPHIC DESIGN
132 S Washington St (44883-2840)
PHONE................419 447-6073
Fax: 419 447-6073
Pete Krupp, *Owner*
Annette Krupp, *Bookkeeper*
Kathleen Ring, *Sales Staff*
EMP: 6
SQ FT: 5,000
SALES (est): 440.5K **Privately Held**
SIC: 2759 Screen printing

(G-18253)
WEBSTER INDUSTRIES INC (PA)
Also Called: Webster Manufacturing Company
325 Hall St (44883-1419)
PHONE................419 447-8232
Fax: 419 448-1618
Andrew J Felter, *President*
Fredric C Spurck, *Chairman*
Dean Bogner, *Vice Pres*
Nicholas D Spurck, *Vice Pres*
Stephen Nedolast, *Opers Mgr*
◆ **EMP:** 295 **EST:** 1876
SQ FT: 250,000
SALES: 55MM **Privately Held**
WEB: www.websterchain.com
SIC: 3535 Bulk handling conveyor systems

Tiltonsville
Jefferson County

(G-18254)
CROFT & SON MFG INC
509 Highland Ave (43963-1110)
P.O. Box 66 (43963-0066)
PHONE................740 859-2200
Fax: 740 859-2700
Samuel E Croft, *President*
Kathy Lester, *Admin Sec*
Shirley Pielech, *Admin Sec*
EMP: 6 **EST:** 1977
SQ FT: 3,600
SALES (est): 779.8K **Privately Held**
SIC: 3599 Machine shop, jobbing & repair

(G-18255)
WALDEN INDUSTRIES INC
Also Called: Belot Concrete Block
101 Walden Ave (43963-1130)
P.O. Box 68 (43963-0068)
PHONE................740 633-5971
John Belot, *President*
Carol Hindman, *Principal*
Barbara Brown, *Manager*
Quinn Ford, *Manager*
Bob Meeker, *Supervisor*
EMP: 35
SALES (est): 3.9MM **Privately Held**
SIC: 1521 3272 3271 Single-family housing construction; concrete products, precast; concrete block & brick

Tipp City
Miami County

(G-18256)
A & B INTERIORS SHINE A BLIND (PA)
Also Called: A&B Interiors
4407 Rudy Rd (45371-9454)
PHONE................937 371-4731
Brenda Perry, *President*
Summer Bishop, *General Mgr*
David Perry, *Vice Pres*
EMP: 7
SALES: 500K **Privately Held**
SIC: 2391 Draperies, plastic & textile: from purchased materials

(G-18257)
ACCU TOOL INC
9765 Julie Ct (45371-9000)
PHONE................937 667-5878
Fax: 937 667-7356
Dale Howard, *President*
Greg Stone, *General Mgr*
Patricia Howard, *Vice Pres*
EMP: 8
SQ FT: 7,500
SALES (est): 790K **Privately Held**
WEB: www.accu-tool.com
SIC: 3544 3599 Special dies & tools; machine shop, jobbing & repair

(G-18258)
ACON INC
11408 Dogleg Rd (45371-9516)
PHONE................513 276-2111
Fax: 937 276-2114
Thomas Mescher, *President*
Susan Hoberty, *Vice Pres*
EMP: 7
SQ FT: 12,000
SALES (est): 1MM **Privately Held**
WEB: www.aconinc.net
SIC: 3625 Noise control equipment

(G-18259)
ACTION BLACKTOP SEALCOATING &
340 E Shoop Rd Bldg B (45371-2497)
PHONE................937 667-4769
John McGee, *Partner*
EMP: 3
SALES: 300K **Privately Held**
SIC: 1771 1799 2951 1611 Driveway contractor; parking lot maintenance; asphalt paving mixtures & blocks; surfacing & paving

(G-18260)
ADAPT-A-PAK INC
9215 State Route 201 (45371-9768)
PHONE................937 845-0386
Russ Miller, *Branch Mgr*
EMP: 22
SALES (corp-wide): 4.7MM **Privately Held**
SIC: 2653 5113 Boxes, corrugated: made from purchased materials; shipping supplies
PA: Adapt-A-Pak, Inc.
1701 Dalton Dr
New Carlisle OH 45344
937 845-0386

(G-18261)
ADCO PRODUCTS INC
65 W Kssler Cwlesville Rd (45371-9333)
PHONE................937 339-6267
Fax: 937 339-1037
George Adkins, *President*
Gary Collins, *COO*
Randy Adkins, *Vice Pres*
Tom Fay, *Opers Mgr*
Tim Defibaugh, *Production*
EMP: 60
SQ FT: 12,500
SALES (est): 10.8MM **Privately Held**
SIC: 3679 2499 Electronic circuits; harness assemblies for electronic use: wire or cable; surveyors' stakes, wood

(G-18262)
AFS TECHNOLOGY LLC
4060 Gibson Dr (45371-9411)
PHONE................937 669-3548
John Tiernan, *President*
Donnie Clarke, *Manager*
Stacy Rueckhaus, *Executive*
EMP: 13
SALES (est): 3.8MM **Privately Held**
SIC: 3523 Elevators, farm

(G-18263)
ALPINE GAGE INC
4325 Lisa Dr (45371-9463)
PHONE................937 669-8665
Dennis Tresslar, *President*
Gene Begley, *Manager*
EMP: 6
SQ FT: 4,400
SALES (est): 901.1K **Privately Held**
SIC: 3825 Instruments for measuring electrical quantities

(G-18264)
B S F INC
320b S 5th St (45371-1625)
PHONE................937 890-6121
Tim Boocher, *Manager*
EMP: 10
SALES (corp-wide): 1.7MM **Privately Held**
SIC: 3498 3568 3599 Couplings, pipe: fabricated from purchased pipe; couplings, shaft: rigid, flexible, universal joint, etc.; machine shop, jobbing & repair
PA: B S F, Inc.
8895 N Dixie Dr
Dayton OH 45414
937 667-4618

(G-18265)
BOOCHERS INC
320 S 5th St (45371-1625)
P.O. Box 25 (45371-0025)
PHONE................937 667-3414
Fax: 937 667-6984
Albert S Boocher, *President*
Tim Boocher, *Vice Pres*
Mary E Boocher, *Admin Sec*
EMP: 4
SQ FT: 4,000
SALES: 600K **Privately Held**
SIC: 3443 Fabricated plate work (boiler shop)

(G-18266)
BR MULCH INC
620 Ginghamsburg Rd (45371-9119)
PHONE................937 667-8288
B G Replogle, *President*
Bartholomew G Replogle, *President*
EMP: 4
SALES (est): 504.5K **Privately Held**
SIC: 2499 Mulch or sawdust products, wood

(G-18267)
BUCKEYE DISTILLERY
130 W Plum St (45371-1843)
PHONE................937 877-1901
Aaron A Lee, *Principal*
EMP: 3
SALES (est): 169.7K **Privately Held**
SIC: 2085 Distillers' dried grains & solubles & alcohol

(G-18268)
C IMPERIAL INC
Also Called: Imperial Castings
1322 Commerce Park Dr (45371-3323)
PHONE................937 669-5620
Larry Haney, *President*
EMP: 6
SQ FT: 9,000
SALES (est): 628.2K **Privately Held**
SIC: 3443 Fabricated plate work (boiler shop)

(G-18269)
CANINE CREATIONS
120b W Broadway St A (45371-1638)
PHONE................937 667-8576
Robert Reidel, *Owner*
Robin Riedel, *Principal*
EMP: 7
SALES (est): 182.4K **Privately Held**
SIC: 0752 3999 Grooming services, pet & animal specialties; pet supplies

(G-18270)
CAPTOR CORPORATION
5040 S County Road 25a (45371-2899)
PHONE................937 667-8484
Fax: 937 667-5133
Donald Cooper, *Ch of Bd*
D Scott Timms, *President*
Ryan Sollmann, *Design Engr*
Carolyn Kiser, *Treasurer*
Mindy Anderson, *Manager*
EMP: 85
SQ FT: 35,000
SALES: 10.7MM **Privately Held**
WEB: www.captorcorp.com
SIC: 3677 Filtration devices, electronic

(G-18271)
CASE CRAFTERS INC
211 S 1st St (45371-1705)
PHONE................937 667-9473
Dan Paugh, *President*
Steven Paugh, *Vice Pres*
EMP: 8
SQ FT: 9,200
SALES: 650K **Privately Held**
WEB: www.casecrafters.com
SIC: 2541 1751 Wood partitions & fixtures; cabinet & finish carpentry

(G-18272)
CHART TECH TOOL INC
4060 Lisa Dr (45371-9499)
P.O. Box 477 (45371-0477)
PHONE................937 667-3543
Fax: 937 667-3613
Eugene Crompton, *President*
Terry Suitts, *Business Mgr*
Lee Scheidweiler, *Vice Pres*
Jeff Crompton, *Mfg Staff*
Mary Ann Crompton, *Controller*
EMP: 20 **EST:** 1965
SQ FT: 30,000
SALES (est): 4.1MM **Privately Held**
WEB: www.ctti-inc.com
SIC: 3541 3545 3544 Machine tools, metal cutting type; gauges (machine tool accessories); special dies, tools, jigs & fixtures

(G-18273)
CONCRETE SEALANTS INC
Also Called: Conseal
9325 State Route 201 (45371-8524)
P.O. Box 176, New Carlisle (45344-0176)
PHONE................937 845-8776
Fax: 937 845-3587
Howard E Wingert, *President*
Gary Biggs, *Plant Mgr*
Cynthia Wingert, *Treasurer*
James E Kear, *Controller*
◆ **EMP:** 50
SQ FT: 100,000
SALES (est): 21.6MM **Privately Held**
WEB: www.conseal.com
SIC: 3053 2891 2821 2822 Gaskets, packing & sealing devices; sealants; plastics materials & resins; synthetic rubber

(G-18274)
DAP PRODUCTS INC
Also Called: Darusta Woodlife Division
875 N 3rd St (45371-3053)
PHONE................937 667-4461

Fax: 937 667-6542
Dave Fuller, *Vice Pres*
Betsy Frappier, *Human Res Mgr*
Gary Williams, *Branch Mgr*
Daniel Witwer, *Manager*
EMP: 110
SALES (corp-wide): 4.8B **Publicly Held**
WEB: www.rpm.net
SIC: 2891 2851 Caulking compounds;
   paints & paint additives
HQ: Dap Products Inc.
   2400 Boston St Ste 200
   Baltimore MD 21224

(G-18275)
DAYTON UNITED METAL SPINNERS
933 York Meadows Dr (45371-2461)
PHONE....................937 222-6732
Fax: 937 275-2818
Doris Dodd, *President*
Jimmie Cochian, *General Mgr*
Pamela Wilks, *Vice Pres*
Tyler Cochran, *Sales Dir*
Vickie Dolbey, *Administration*
EMP: 12
SQ FT: 13,000
SALES (est): 1.8MM **Privately Held**
WEB: www.spinmetal.com
SIC: 3469 7692 3471 Spinning metal for
   the trade; welding repair; polishing, met-
   als or formed products

(G-18276)
DUNCAN TOOL INC
9790 Julie Ct (45371-9000)
PHONE....................937 667-9364
Fax: 937 667-8472
Sandra L Duncan, *President*
Dave Duncan, *Vice Pres*
▲ **EMP:** 10
SQ FT: 5,500
SALES (est): 1.4MM **Privately Held**
WEB: www.duncantool.com
SIC: 3544 3599 Special dies & tools; ma-
   chine shop, jobbing & repair

(G-18277)
FIELD STONE INC
2750 Us Route 40 (45371-9230)
PHONE....................937 898-3236
Paul Carmack, *President*
Shelly Burdge, *Purchasing*
▲ **EMP:** 100 **EST:** 1973
SQ FT: 18,000
SALES (est): 17.4MM **Privately Held**
WEB: www.catlow.com
SIC: 3586 3432 Gasoline pumps, measur-
   ing or dispensing; plumbing fixture fittings
   & trim

(G-18278)
G & M PRECISION MACHINING INC
9785 Wildcat Rd (45371-9421)
PHONE....................937 667-1443
Fax: 937 667-7988
Lori Galovics, *President*
Joe Galovics, *President*
EMP: 6
SQ FT: 10,000
SALES (est): 861K **Privately Held**
SIC: 3599 Machine shop, jobbing & repair

(G-18279)
GILBARCO CATLOW LLC
2750 Us Route 40 (45371-9230)
PHONE....................937 898-3236
Fax: 937 898-0385
Mark Maybee, *President*
Cameron Carmack, *President*
Brian Dodson, *Finance Mgr*
Curtis Hayes, *Manager*
John Spears, *Manager*
EMP: 5
SALES (est): 55.9K **Privately Held**
SIC: 3823 3824 Industrial instrmnts
   msrmnt display/control process variable;
   gas meters, domestic & large capacity: in-
   dustrial; mechanical measuring meters

(G-18280)
GRANT SOLUTIONS
7745 Winding Way N (45371-9254)
PHONE....................937 344-5558
Kevin McDonald, *Owner*

EMP: 5
SALES: 1.5K **Privately Held**
SIC: 3999 Manufacturing industries

(G-18281)
HIGH-TEC INDUSTRIAL SERVICES
15 Industry Park Ct (45371-3060)
P.O. Box 533 (45371-0533)
PHONE....................937 667-1772
Brent Black, *President*
William E Oldham, *President*
Christopher Taylor, *Vice Pres*
Paul Leverette, *Opers Mgr*
EMP: 139
SQ FT: 18,000
SALES (est): 25.3MM **Privately Held**
WEB: www.hightecindustrial.com
SIC: 3589 7349 Commercial cooking &
   foodwarming equipment; building & office
   cleaning services

(G-18282)
INDEPENDENT TRAILER SERVICES
Also Called: Its
4465 Lisa Dr (45371-8341)
PHONE....................937 667-8900
Fax: 937 667-5532
Robert Cyphers, *President*
Todd Cyphers, *Vice Pres*
EMP: 8
SALES: 1MM **Privately Held**
SIC: 3799 Trailers & trailer equipment

(G-18283)
INDIAN CREEK FABRICATORS INC
1350 Commerce Park Dr (45371-3323)
PHONE....................937 667-7214
Fax: 937 667-4093
Andrea Dakin, *President*
Chris Dakin, *General Mgr*
Michael Dakin, *Vice Pres*
Glenn Bielefeld, *Purch Mgr*
Linda Chaney, *Manager*
EMP: 50
SQ FT: 65,000
SALES (est): 11.9MM **Privately Held**
WEB: www.indiancreekfab.com
SIC: 3446 3444 3443 3441 Architectural
   metalwork; sheet metalwork; fabricated
   plate work (boiler shop); fabricated struc-
   tural metal

(G-18284)
IZIT CAIN SHEET METAL CORP
20 N 2nd St (45371-1906)
PHONE....................937 667-6521
Fax: 937 667-1790
Clarence Paul Dehus, *President*
Jeanette Dehus, *Corp Secy*
EMP: 5
SQ FT: 4,000
SALES (est): 775.6K **Privately Held**
SIC: 3444 3699 3599 Sheet metalwork;
   electrical welding equipment; machine &
   other job shop work

(G-18285)
J & B ROGERS INC
Also Called: Airplane Plastics
9785 Julie Ct (45371-9000)
PHONE....................937 669-2677
Fax: 937 669-2777
Jeffrey Rogers, *President*
Rebecca Rogers, *Vice Pres*
EMP: 5
SQ FT: 5,000
SALES: 600K **Privately Held**
WEB: www.airplaneplastics.com
SIC: 3089 Windshields, plastic

(G-18286)
J & L WOOD PRODUCTS INC (PA)
910 Ginghamsburg Rd (45371-9202)
P.O. Box 69 (45371-0069)
PHONE....................937 667-4064
Fax: 937 667-6143
Jeffrey Herzog, *President*
Kevin McClurg, *Vice Pres*
Julie Flannagan, *Manager*
▲ **EMP:** 32
SQ FT: 30,000

SALES (est): 4.4MM **Privately Held**
WEB: www.palletsnskids.com
SIC: 2448 2441 2449 Pallets, wood;
   skids, wood; nailed wood boxes & shook;
   rectangular boxes & crates, wood

(G-18287)
LEVECK LIGHTING PRODUCTS INC (PA)
8415 S State Route 202 (45371-9074)
P.O. Box 24063, Dayton (45424-0063)
PHONE....................937 667-4421
Fax: 937 667-8634
Mary Leveck, *Owner*
Brian Cardinal, *Exec VP*
Robert Leveck Jr, *CFO*
EMP: 25
SQ FT: 6,500
SALES (est): 4.3MM **Privately Held**
SIC: 3229 Bulbs for electric lights

(G-18288)
MADERITE LLC
6915 Roberta Dr (45371-2349)
P.O. Box 351 (45371-0351)
PHONE....................937 570-1042
Kevin R Mader,
EMP: 2
SQ FT: 20,000
SALES: 1MM **Privately Held**
SIC: 2679 Labels, paper: made from pur-
   chased material

(G-18289)
MORE MANUFACTURING LLC
4025 Lisa Dr Ste A (45371-9462)
PHONE....................937 233-3898
Matt Lovelace, *Mng Member*
EMP: 12 **EST:** 2007
SQ FT: 6,000
SALES (est): 2MM **Privately Held**
SIC: 3541 Machine tool replacement & re-
   pair parts, metal cutting types

(G-18290)
MUTUAL TOOL LLC
1350 Commerce Park Dr (45371-3323)
PHONE....................937 667-5818
Bill Baity,
Dean Cooley,
EMP: 80
SQ FT: 31,200
SALES (est): 9.4MM **Privately Held**
WEB: www.mutualtool.com
SIC: 3599 3544 Machine & other job shop
   work; special dies, tools, jigs & fixtures

(G-18291)
ODAWARA AUTOMATION INC
4805 S County Road 25a (45371-2900)
PHONE....................937 667-8433
Fax: 937 667-8435
Takayuki Tsugawa, *CEO*
Christopher Spejna, *President*
David Clark, *Engineer*
Michael Gottfried, *Design Engr*
James Moore, *Controller*
▲ **EMP:** 37
SQ FT: 51,000
SALES: 7.6MM
SALES (corp-wide): 98.4MM **Privately Held**
WEB: www.odawara.com
SIC: 3599 Custom machinery
PA: Odawara Engineering Co., Ltd.
   1577, Matsudasoryo, Matsuda-Machi
   Ashigara Kami-Gun KNG 258-0
   465 831-122

(G-18292)
PECO HOLDINGS CORP (PA)
6555 S State Route 202 (45371-9094)
PHONE....................937 667-4451
Michael Van Haaren, *President*
James Zahora, *Vice Pres*
William Rosenberg, *CFO*
EMP: 11
SALES (est): 20.8MM **Privately Held**
SIC: 3599 3548 3549 Machine shop, job-
   bing & repair; welding apparatus; assem-
   bly machines, including robotic

(G-18293)
PRECISION STRIP INC
315 Park Ave (45371-1887)
PHONE....................937 667-6255

Jerry Huber, *Manager*
EMP: 52
SQ FT: 3,080
SALES (corp-wide): 8.6B **Publicly Held**
WEB: www.precision-strip.com
SIC: 7389 3312 Metal cutting services;
   blast furnaces & steel mills
HQ: Precision Strip Inc.
   86 S Ohio St
   Minster OH 45865
   419 628-2343

(G-18294)
PROCESS EQUIPMENT CO TIPP CITY (HQ)
Also Called: Process Equipment Company
4754 Us Route 40 (45371-9481)
PHONE....................937 667-7105
Fax: 937 667-4798
Michael V Haaren, *President*
James Fisher, *Minister*
James Zahora, *Vice Pres*
William Rosenberg, *CFO*
Krystal Hollenbeck, *Manager*
▲ **EMP:** 74 **EST:** 1945
SQ FT: 360,000
SALES (est): 20.8MM **Privately Held**
WEB: www.processeq.com
SIC: 3599 3548 3549 Machine shop, job-
   bing & repair; welding apparatus; assem-
   bly machines, including robotic
PA: Peco Holdings Corp.
   6555 S State Route 202
   Tipp City OH 45371
   937 667-4451

(G-18295)
PROTO PLASTICS INC
316 Park Ave (45371-1894)
PHONE....................937 667-8416
Fax: 937 667-2536
Thomas Gagnon, *President*
Thomas A Gagnon, *Owner*
Sue Gagnon, *Vice Pres*
▲ **EMP:** 42
SQ FT: 62,000
SALES (est): 10MM **Privately Held**
WEB: www.protoplastics.com
SIC: 3089 3544 Injection molding of plas-
   tics; special dies, tools, jigs & fixtures;
   special dies & tools; jigs: inspection,
   gauging & checking

(G-18296)
REGAL BELOIT AMERICA INC
531 N 4th St (45371-1857)
PHONE....................937 667-2431
Michele Blake, *Division Mgr*
Erik Nordquist, *General Mgr*
Rick Zajchowski, *Vice Pres*
Edward Drye, *Engineer*
Jay Galli, *Engineer*
EMP: 231
SALES (corp-wide): 3.2B **Publicly Held**
SIC: 3621 Motors & generators
HQ: Regal Beloit America, Inc.
   200 State St
   Beloit WI 53511
   608 364-8800

(G-18297)
RPG INDUSTRIES INC
3571 Ginghmsbg Frdrck Rd (45371)
P.O. Box 233, West Milton (45383-0233)
PHONE....................937 698-9801
Robert Ginsburg, *President*
Ernie Booher, *Engineer*
EMP: 6
SQ FT: 3,600
SALES: 500K **Privately Held**
WEB: www.rpgindustries.com
SIC: 3599 Machine & other job shop work

(G-18298)
S-K MOLD & TOOL COMPANY (PA)
955 N 3rd St (45371-3055)
PHONE....................937 339-0299
Fax: 937 667-8240
Samuel K Kingrey, *President*
Chris Byrer, *Business Mgr*
Keith Kingrey, *Vice Pres*
Reed Sevitts, *Vice Pres*
Joy Colby, *Human Res Mgr*
EMP: 45
SQ FT: 76,500

SALES (est): 15.9MM **Privately Held**
WEB: www.skmold.com
SIC: 3544 3599 Special dies & tools; industrial molds; jigs & fixtures; machine
shop, jobbing & repair

(G-18299)
SINBON USA LLC ✪
4265 Gibson Dr (45371-9452)
PHONE.................................937 667-8999
Winnie Chen, *Principal*
Michelle L Cahoon, *Vice Pres*
EMP: 4 EST: 2016
SALES (est): 119.8K **Privately Held**
SIC: 3679 Antennas, receiving

(G-18300)
SOURCEPOINT LOGISTICS LLC
5575 Ross Rd (45371-9710)
PHONE.................................937 604-8209
Fax: 937 506-2257
Jason Wilson, *Mng Member*
Mark Nelson,
EMP: 27
SALES: 1.5MM **Privately Held**
SIC: 3663 7389 3229 Radio & TV com-
munications equipment; ; fiber optics
strands

(G-18301)
SP3 CUTTING TOOLS INC (PA)
835 N Hyatt St (45371-1558)
PHONE.................................937 667-4476
Eric Koik, *President*
Dennis Maude, *CFO*
EMP: 2
SALES (est): 6.7MM **Privately Held**
WEB: www.sp3.com
SIC: 6719 3545 Investment holding com-
panies, except banks; diamond cutting
tools for turning, boring, burnishing, etc.

(G-18302)
T & W TOOL & MACHINE INC
467 N 5th St (45371-1872)
PHONE.................................937 667-2039
Fax: 937 667-1763
Tim Owen, *President*
EMP: 4
SQ FT: 11,000
SALES (est): 300K **Privately Held**
SIC: 3544 3599 Special dies & tools; ma-
chine shop, jobbing & repair

(G-18303)
TEAM AMITY MOLDS & PLASTIC
1435 Commerce Park Dr (45371-2846)
P.O. Box 309 (45371-0309)
PHONE.................................937 667-7856
Leonard L Dickess, *President*
Leonord Dickess, *Owner*
EMP: 80
SALES: 4.3MM **Privately Held**
WEB: www.amitymold.com
SIC: 3089 Molding primary plastic

(G-18304)
TECH MOLD & TOOL CO INC
4333 Lisa Dr (45371-9463)
PHONE.................................937 667-8851
Fax: 937 667-2045
Edward J Weber, *President*
Dan Isenbarger, *Vice Pres*
Arlene Isenbarger, *Admin Sec*
EMP: 7
SQ FT: 5,100
SALES: 800K **Privately Held**
SIC: 3544 Industrial molds

(G-18305)
TIP TOP CANNING CO (PA)
505 S 2nd St (45371-1753)
P.O. Box 126 (45371-0126)
PHONE.................................937 667-3713
Fax: 937 667-3802
George C Timmer, *President*
Scott A Timmer, *Vice Pres*
Matt Timmer, *Prdtn Mgr*
Vicki Davis, *Accounts Exec*
Kristy Boldwin, *Manager*
EMP: 20 EST: 1924
SQ FT: 140,000
SALES (est): 21.9MM **Privately Held**
SIC: 2033 Tomato products: packaged in
cans, jars, etc.

(G-18306)
TROPHY NUT CO (PA)
320 N 2nd St (45371-1960)
P.O. Box 199 (45371-0199)
PHONE.................................937 667-8478
Fax: 937 667-4656
Gerald J Allen, *CEO*
Robert J Bollinger, *President*
Robert N Wilke, *Vice Pres*
Robert Loy, *Facilities Mgr*
David Henning, *Treasurer*
◆ EMP: 49
SQ FT: 85,000
SALES (est): 28.8MM **Privately Held**
WEB: www.trophynut.com
SIC: 2068 5441 Nuts: dried, dehydrated,
salted or roasted; nuts; candy

(G-18307)
TROPHY NUT CO
1567 Harmony Dr (45371-3319)
P.O. Box 199 (45371-0199)
PHONE.................................937 669-5513
Fax: 937 669-5613
Bob Loy, *Manager*
EMP: 6
SALES (corp-wide): 28.8MM **Privately
Held**
WEB: www.trophynut.com
SIC: 2068 Nuts: dried, dehydrated, salted
or roasted
PA: Trophy Nut Co.
320 N 2nd St
Tipp City OH 45371
937 667-8478

(G-18308)
UDECX LLC
320 N 4th St (45371-1803)
PHONE.................................937 830-0374
Tony Desjardins, *CEO*
EMP: 6
SQ FT: 2,200
SALES: 5MM **Privately Held**
SIC: 3089 Floor coverings, plastic

(G-18309)
VISION PROJECTS INC
1350 Commerce Park Dr (45371-3323)
PHONE.................................937 667-8648
George J Minarcek, *CEO*
Chris Dakin, *Treasurer*
EMP: 6
SQ FT: 20,000
SALES (est): 379.1K **Privately Held**
SIC: 3599 Machine shop, jobbing & repair

(G-18310)
**VITAL CONNECTIONS
INCORPORATED**
955 N 3rd St (45371-3055)
PHONE.................................937 667-3880
Fax: 937 667-3935
Samuel Kingrey, *President*
Edward F Hoar, *Vice Pres*
Mark Meister, *Vice Pres*
EMP: 20
SQ FT: 10,000
SALES (est): 3.5MM **Privately Held**
WEB: www.vitalconnections.com
SIC: 3643 Current-carrying wiring devices

(G-18311)
**WENRICK MACHINE AND TOOL
CORP**
4685 Us Route 40 (45371-8339)
PHONE.................................937 667-7307
Fax: 937 667-6796
Tom Wenrick, *President*
Betty Wenrick, *Corp Secy*
EMP: 10
SQ FT: 8,000
SALES: 425K **Privately Held**
SIC: 3599 7692 Machine shop, jobbing &
repair; welding repair

(G-18312)
WRENA LLC
265 Lightner Rd (45371-9228)
PHONE.................................937 667-4403
Fax: 937 667-6949
George J Derr, *Ch of Bd*
Michael R Tanner, *President*
Tom Derr, *Vice Pres*
David Whitehead, *Vice Pres*

Andrew Anderson, *QC Mgr*
EMP: 50
SQ FT: 123,000
SALES (est): 16.9MM **Privately Held**
WEB: www.wrenind.com
SIC: 3465 3544 Automotive stampings;
special dies & tools; jigs & fixtures
HQ: Angstrom Usa Llc
26980 Trolley Indus Dr
Taylor MI 48180
313 295-0100

Tippecanoe
Harrison County

(G-18313)
GARDNER LUMBER CO INC
5805 Laurel Creek Rd Se (44699-9661)
PHONE.................................740 254-4664
Fax: 740 254-4181
Richard Gardner, *President*
Harvey Gardner, *Vice Pres*
EMP: 10 EST: 1938
SALES (est): 1.5MM **Privately Held**
SIC: 2421 2448 5154 Sawmills & planing
mills, general; pallets, wood; cattle

(G-18314)
GRAY-EERING LTD
3158 Sandy Ridge Rd Se (44699-9657)
PHONE.................................740 498-8816
Fax: 740 498-6238
Glenn Gray, *Partner*
Jay Gray, *Partner*
Lainard Gray, *Partner*
Sue Gray, *Partner*
Lisa Gray, *Admin Sec*
EMP: 9
SALES: 600K **Privately Held**
SIC: 3535 3536 3534 Conveyors & con-
veying equipment; mine hoists; elevators
& equipment

Toledo
Lucas County

(G-18315)
1 DAY SIGN
4236 Secor Rd (43623-4238)
PHONE.................................419 475-6060
Fax: 419 475-3278
Thomas E Keller, *Owner*
EMP: 3
SQ FT: 2,400
SALES (est): 220K **Privately Held**
SIC: 3993 Signs & advertising specialties

(G-18316)
A & B TOOL & MANUFACTURING
2921 South Ave (43609-1327)
PHONE.................................419 382-0215
Fax: 419 382-0215
Timothy J Adams, *President*
EMP: 7 EST: 1966
SQ FT: 8,000
SALES (est): 780.1K **Privately Held**
SIC: 3544 Special dies, tools, jigs & fix-
tures

(G-18317)
A & M CHEESE CO
253 Waggoner Blvd (43612-1952)
PHONE.................................419 476-8369
Fax: 419 476-3133
Antonio Sofo, *CEO*
Michael J Sofo, *President*
Joseph J Sofo Jr, *Vice Pres*
Cos Figliomeni, *Controller*
Jim Bradhurst, *Executive*
EMP: 53
SQ FT: 190,000
SALES (est): 8.6MM **Privately Held**
WEB: www.amcheese.com
SIC: 2022 Processed cheese

(G-18318)
ABBOTT TOOL INC
Also Called: ATI
405 Dura Ave (43612-2619)
PHONE.................................419 476-6742
Fax: 419 476-4411

Arthur V Stange, *President*
Kevin Webb, *General Mgr*
Leonard Livecchi, *Vice Pres*
Steve Rogers, *Accountant*
Carl Stange, *Manager*
EMP: 27
SQ FT: 12,000
SALES (est): 5.4MM **Privately Held**
SIC: 3469 7692 Machine parts, stamped
or pressed metal; welding repair

(G-18319)
ACCUSHRED LLC
1114 W Central Ave (43610-1061)
PHONE.................................419 244-7473
Fax: 419 243-4913
Nate Segall, *President*
Barry Gudelman, *Vice Pres*
EMP: 11
SALES (est): 1.1MM **Privately Held**
SIC: 3589 Shredders, industrial & commer-
cial

(G-18320)
**ACE PRODUCTS CO OF
TOLEDO INC**
4902 Douglas Rd (43613-3246)
PHONE.................................419 472-1247
Fax: 419 475-1339
Susan Kennedy, *Ch of Bd*
David W Post, *President*
Duane P Post, *Vice Pres*
Robert C Post, *Treasurer*
Lawrence Runyan, *Manager*
EMP: 4 EST: 1935
SQ FT: 6,800
SALES: 300K **Privately Held**
SIC: 3728 Aircraft parts & equipment

(G-18321)
**ADAMS STREET PUBLISHING
CO**
Also Called: Toledo City Paper
1120 Adams St (43604-5509)
PHONE.................................419 244-9859
Fax: 419 244-9871
Marck Jacobs, *CEO*
Collette Jacobs, *President*
Robin Armstrong, *Accounting Mgr*
Sharon Kornowa, *Accounts Exec*
Sam Rotroff, *Accounts Exec*
EMP: 22
SQ FT: 4,268
SALES (est): 2.6MM **Privately Held**
WEB: www.adamsstreetpublishing.com
SIC: 2721 Magazines: publishing only, not
printed on site

(G-18322)
ADVANTAGE MOLD INC
525 N Wheeling St (43605-1337)
PHONE.................................419 691-5676
Fax: 419 691-5763
Larry J Bolander, *President*
Betsi Frick, *Office Mgr*
Tony Martina, *Manager*
EMP: 8 EST: 1999
SQ FT: 13,000
SALES: 850K **Privately Held**
WEB: www.advantage-mold.com
SIC: 3089 Injection molding of plastics

(G-18323)
**AFFORDABLE STUMP REMOVAL
LLC**
2624 Heysler Rd (43617-1512)
PHONE.................................419 841-8331
Lisa Klebold, *Manager*
Bill Klebold,
EMP: 5
SALES: 230K **Privately Held**
SIC: 2411 0783 Stumps, wood; removal
services, bush & tree

(G-18324)
AIMCO MFG INC
Also Called: Lockrey Manafacturing
203 Matzinger Rd (43612-2624)
PHONE.................................419 476-6572
Mark Makulinski, *President*
Bill Nordolt, *Vice Pres*
John Longfield, *CFO*
James Webb, *Regl Sales Mgr*
Andrew Mathias, *Manager*
EMP: 3

SQ FT: 1,000
SALES (est): 522.3K **Privately Held**
SIC: 3534 Elevators & equipment

(G-18325)
AIRGAS USA LLC
526 Dura Ave (43612-2622)
PHONE....................419 726-2719
Chuck Rainey, *Branch Mgr*
EMP: 3
SALES (corp-wide): 163.9MM **Privately Held**
SIC: 5169 5084 5085 2813 Industrial gases; gases, compressed & liquefied; carbon dioxide; dry ice; welding machinery & equipment; safety equipment; welding supplies; industrial gases; carbon dioxide; nitrous oxide; dry ice, carbon dioxide (solid); industrial inorganic chemicals; calcium carbide
HQ: Airgas Usa, Llc
259 N Radnor Chester Rd # 100
Radnor PA 19087
610 687-5253

(G-18326)
AIRTECH MECHANICAL INC
4444 Monroe St (43613-4732)
PHONE....................419 292-0074
EMP: 12
SALES (est): 2MM **Privately Held**
SIC: 3433 3443 Heating equipment, except electric; cooling towers, metal plate

(G-18327)
ALL AMERICAN SCREEN PRINTING
2607 W Central Ave (43606-3548)
PHONE....................419 475-0696
Jim Schnoering, *Principal*
EMP: 4
SALES (est): 330.6K **Privately Held**
SIC: 2752 Commercial printing, lithographic

(G-18328)
ALLEN ZAHRADNIK INC (PA)
Also Called: Edgewater Canvas Co
5902 Edgewater Dr (43611)
PHONE....................419 729-1201
Fax: 419 729-1713
Allen Zahradnik, *President*
EMP: 5 **EST:** 1952
SQ FT: 5,000
SALES (est): 456.5K **Privately Held**
SIC: 2394 Convertible tops, canvas or boat: from purchased materials

(G-18329)
ALLIED MASK AND TOOLING INC
6051 Telegraph Rd Ste 6 (43612-4573)
PHONE....................419 470-2555
Fax: 419 470-1554
Mike Murray, *President*
EMP: 9
SQ FT: 3,600
SALES (est): 1.4MM **Privately Held**
SIC: 3599 3356 3444 3542 Machine shop, jobbing & repair; nickel; sheet metalwork; forming machine work, sheet metal; electroforming machines

(G-18330)
ALLIED PLASTIC CO INC
3203 South Ave (43609-1103)
PHONE....................419 389-1688
Fax: 419 389-1776
Jeff W Hood, *President*
Leonard K Pudlicki, *Vice Pres*
EMP: 5
SQ FT: 5,000
SALES: 700K **Privately Held**
SIC: 3089 2541 2511 Plastic processing; store fixtures, wood; office fixtures, wood; wood household furniture

(G-18331)
ALRO STEEL CORPORATION
3003 Airport Hwy (43609-1405)
P.O. Box 964 (43697-0964)
PHONE....................419 720-5300
Fax: 419 720-5301
Adam Cristek, *Manager*
Donald Schlatter, *Manager*
EMP: 40

SALES (corp-wide): 1.6B **Privately Held**
WEB: www.alro.com
SIC: 5051 5085 5162 3444 Steel; aluminum bars, rods, ingots, sheets, pipes, plates, etc.; nonferrous metal sheets, bars, rods, etc.; industrial supplies; plastics materials; sheet metalwork
PA: Alro Steel Corporation
3100 E High St
Jackson MI 49203
517 787-5500

(G-18332)
ALS POLISHING SHOP INC
Also Called: Al's Polsg Pltg Powdr Coating
1615 W Laskey Rd (43612-2915)
PHONE....................419 476-8857
Fax: 419 476-0857
Albert R Szymanowski, *CEO*
Richard Szymanowski, *President*
Jamie Szymanowski, *Vice Pres*
Sally Pollock, *Admin Sec*
EMP: 8 **EST:** 1946
SQ FT: 4,800
SALES (est): 964.4K **Privately Held**
SIC: 3471 Polishing, metals or formed products; buffing for the trade; plating of metals or formed products

(G-18333)
ALT CONTROL PRINT
6906 Milrose Ln (43617-1291)
PHONE....................419 841-2467
Hugh Callahan, *Principal*
EMP: 4
SALES (est): 337.5K **Privately Held**
SIC: 2752 Commercial printing, lithographic

(G-18334)
ALT FUEL LLC
1100 King Rd (43617-2002)
P.O. Box 351330 (43635-1330)
PHONE....................419 865-4196
Robert C Barry,
EMP: 3
SALES (est): 206.6K **Privately Held**
SIC: 3999 Manufacturing industries

(G-18335)
AMCRAFT INC
Also Called: Amcraft Manufacturing
5144 Enterprise Blvd (43612-3807)
PHONE....................419 729-7900
Fax: 419 726-3524
David R Frank, *President*
▼ **EMP:** 8
SQ FT: 6,000
SALES (est): 1MM **Privately Held**
WEB: www.amcraftinc.com
SIC: 3423 3544 3469 Hand & edge tools; special dies & tools; metal stampings

(G-18336)
AMERICAN BOTTLING COMPANY
7 Up Bottling Co of Toledo
224 N Byrne Rd (43607-2605)
PHONE....................419 535-0777
Jeff Lark, *Manager*
EMP: 75
SALES (corp-wide): 6.4B **Publicly Held**
WEB: www.cs-americas.com
SIC: 2086 Bottled & canned soft drinks
HQ: The American Bottling Company
5301 Legacy Dr
Plano TX 75024

(G-18337)
AMERICAN CANVAS PRODUCTS INC
2925 South Ave (43609-1327)
PHONE....................419 382-8450
Fax: 419 382-8452
Richard W Jockett, *President*
Andrew Jockett, *Vice Pres*
Jean Cappelletty, *Manager*
Andy Jockett, *Manager*
EMP: 17
SQ FT: 6,000
SALES (est): 1.4MM **Privately Held**
WEB: www.americancanvasproductsinc.com
SIC: 2394 Convertible tops, canvas or boat: from purchased materials

(G-18338)
AMERICAN INTERIORS INC (PA)
302 S Byrne Rd Bldg 100 (43615-6208)
PHONE....................419 324-0365
Fax: 419 535-1899
Steve Essig, *President*
Rick Essig, *Principal*
Doug Montgomery, *Business Mgr*
Lisa Shumway, *Vice Pres*
Scott Elston, *Project Mgr*
◆ **EMP:** 50
SQ FT: 140,000
SALES (est): 22.1MM **Privately Held**
SIC: 2522 Office furniture, except wood

(G-18339)
AMERICAN LASER AND MACHINE LLC
501 Weston St (43609-1128)
PHONE....................419 214-0880
Rusty Obermyer,
Pat Copeland,
EMP: 3
SALES: 15K **Privately Held**
SIC: 3542 Machine tools, metal forming type

(G-18340)
AMERICAN MANUFACTURING INC (PA)
2375 Dorr St Ste F (43607-3407)
PHONE....................419 531-9471
Charles P Gotberg, *President*
Danielle Letellier, *Manager*
▲ **EMP:** 10
SALES (est): 27.6MM **Privately Held**
SIC: 3315 Welded steel wire fabric

(G-18341)
AMERICAN METAL CLEANING INC
2512 Albion St (43610-1215)
PHONE....................419 255-1828
Fax: 419 255-2154
Laura Tobias, *President*
Greg Tobias, *Vice Pres*
EMP: 4
SQ FT: 15,000
SALES (est): 340K **Privately Held**
WEB: www.americanmetalcleaninginc.com
SIC: 3471 5169 Cleaning & descaling metal products; chemicals & allied products

(G-18342)
AMERICAN MNFCTURING OPERATIONS
1931 E Manhattan Blvd (43608-1534)
PHONE....................419 269-1560
Jonathan R Saul, *President*
Kelly Toom, *Office Mgr*
EMP: 8
SALES (est): 900K **Privately Held**
SIC: 3715 Truck trailers

(G-18343)
AMERICAN PAPER CONVERTING LLC
6142 American Rd (43612-3902)
PHONE....................419 729-4782
EMP: 10
SALES (est): 31.8K **Privately Held**
SIC: 2679 Paper Mill

(G-18344)
AMERICAN POSTS LLC
810 Chicago St (43611-3609)
PHONE....................419 720-0652
Jim Rosino, *CFO*
David Feniger, *Mng Member*
EMP: 30
SALES (est): 7.8MM **Privately Held**
WEB: www.americanposts.com
SIC: 3312 5051 Rods, iron & steel: made in steel mills; steel

(G-18345)
AMERICAN STEEL ASSOD PDTS INC
2375 Dorr St Ste F (43607-3407)
PHONE....................419 531-9471
Fax: 419 531-9475
Charles P Gotberg, *President*
Danielle Letellier, *Manager*

EMP: 90
SALES (est): 27.6MM **Privately Held**
SIC: 3441 Fabricated structural metal
PA: American Manufacturing, Inc.
2375 Dorr St Ste F
Toledo OH 43607
419 531-9471

(G-18346)
AMERICAN TOOL AND DIE INC
2024 Champlain St (43611-3700)
PHONE....................419 726-5394
Fax: 419 726-1376
Richard J Russell Jr, *President*
Mike Welsh, *General Mgr*
Paul Philabaum, *Vice Pres*
Gerald Russell, *Vice Pres*
Diana West, *Office Mgr*
EMP: 15 **EST:** 1963
SQ FT: 20,000
SALES (est): 2.7MM **Privately Held**
SIC: 3469 3544 Stamping metal for the trade; special dies, tools, jigs & fixtures

(G-18347)
AMES DEVELOPMENT GROUP LTD
Also Called: Ceen
2339 Drummond Rd (43606-3126)
PHONE....................419 704-7812
Ethan Ames, *Principal*
EMP: 3 **EST:** 2015
SALES (est): 86K **Privately Held**
SIC: 7372 Application computer software

(G-18348)
AMES LOCK SPECIALTIES INC
Also Called: Ames Locksmith
2121 W Sylvania Ave (43613-4436)
PHONE....................419 474-2995
Fax: 419 475-1324
Van Baker, *Principal*
EMP: 5
SALES (est): 338.1K **Privately Held**
SIC: 7699 3089 Locksmith shop; plastic hardware & building products

(G-18349)
ANDERSONS INC
801 S Reynolds Rd (43615-6309)
PHONE....................419 536-0460
Fax: 419 531-1475
Bill Kale, *Manager*
EMP: 7
SALES (corp-wide): 3.9B **Publicly Held**
SIC: 5153 0723 5191 2874 Grain & field beans; grains; grain elevators; crop preparation services for market; cash grain crops market preparation services; farm supplies; fertilizers & agricultural chemicals; seeds & bulbs; phosphatic fertilizers; plant foods, mixed: from plants making phosphatic fertilizer; railroad car repair; rental of railroad cars
PA: The Andersons Inc
1947 Briarfield Blvd
Maumee OH 43537
419 893-5050

(G-18350)
ANDREW & SONS INC
2401 Consaul St (43605-1367)
PHONE....................419 693-0292
Fax: 419 693-0292
Andrew Danisouszky, *President*
Mary Danisouszky, *Corp Secy*
Louis Torda, *Vice Pres*
EMP: 4
SQ FT: 4,800
SALES (est): 378.5K **Privately Held**
SIC: 3599 Machine shop, jobbing & repair

(G-18351)
APEX BOLT & MACHINE COMPANY
Also Called: Apex Metal Fabricating & Mch
5324 Enterprise Blvd (43612-3870)
PHONE....................419 729-3741
Fax: 419 729-2616
William G Foradas, *Ch of Bd*
Michael S Petree, *President*
Luanna M Foradas, *Corp Secy*
Shannon O Connor, *Manager*
Shannyn O'Connell, *Administration*
EMP: 39
SQ FT: 51,000

SALES (est): 8.5MM **Privately Held**
SIC: 3599 Machine & other job shop work

(G-18352)
APEX SOLUTIONS INC
2620 Centennial Rd Ste P (43617-1849)
P.O. Box 8801 (43623-0801)
PHONE.....................................419 843-3434
Fax: 419 843-3436
Bruce Turnbull, *President*
Donald Turnbull, *Vice Pres*
EMP: 5
SALES (est): 1MM **Privately Held**
WEB: www.apexpos.com
SIC: 7372 Prepackaged software

(G-18353)
ARCHER-DANIELS-MIDLAND COMPANY
Also Called: ADM Grain Company
1308 Miami St (43605-3354)
PHONE.....................................419 705-3292
Dan Hines, *Principal*
EMP: 9
SALES (corp-wide): 62.3B **Publicly Held**
SIC: 5153 2048 Grains; prepared feeds
PA: Archer-Daniels-Midland Company
77 W Wacker Dr Ste 4600
Chicago IL 60601
312 634-8100

(G-18354)
ARCLIN USA LLC
6175 American Rd (43612-3901)
PHONE.....................................419 726-5013
Warren Shunk, *Plant Mgr*
David Staley, *Plant Engr*
Rick McCormick, *Manager*
Jeff Elliott, *Data Proc Dir*
Jeff Stone, *Data Proc Dir*
EMP: 25
SALES (corp-wide): 148MM **Privately Held**
SIC: 2891 2821 Adhesives & sealants; plastics materials & resins
HQ: Arclin Usa Llc
1000 Holcomb Woods Pkwy
Roswell GA 30076
678 999-2100

(G-18355)
ARLINGTON RACK & PACKAGING CO
6120 N Detroit Ave (43612-4810)
PHONE.....................................419 476-7700
Fax: 419 470-6290
Michael A Flaum, *President*
Harley Kripke, *Chairman*
Mark Hahm, *Vice Pres*
Robert Kripke, *Vice Pres*
EMP: 8
SQ FT: 110,000
SALES (est): 1.4MM **Privately Held**
SIC: 3714 3086 Motor vehicle parts & accessories; packaging & shipping materials, foamed plastic

(G-18356)
ART & SIGN CORPORATION
5458 Angola Rd (43615-6326)
PHONE.....................................419 865-3336
Michael P Dean, *President*
EMP: 6
SQ FT: 6,400
SALES (est): 520K **Privately Held**
SIC: 7336 7389 3993 Silk screen design; sign painting & lettering shop; displays & cutouts, window & lobby

(G-18357)
ASHCO MANUFACTURING INC
5234 Tulane Ave (43611-1573)
PHONE.....................................419 838-7157
Don Grenier, *President*
EMP: 6
SALES (est): 1MM **Privately Held**
SIC: 3423 3441 Cutting dies, except metal cutting; fabricated structural metal

(G-18358)
AUNT MINNIES FOOD SERVICES INC
702 Searles Rd (43607-2847)
PHONE.....................................419 872-4396
Claudia Brown, *President*

Minnie Sebree, *President*
EMP: 12
SQ FT: 6,000
SALES (est): 1.2MM **Privately Held**
WEB: www.auntminniesfood.com
SIC: 2038 Breakfasts, frozen & packaged

(G-18359)
AUTOMATED MACHINERY SOLUTIONS
6010 N Summit St (43611-1252)
PHONE.....................................419 727-1772
Frank Smith, *Owner*
EMP: 15
SALES (est): 1.8MM **Privately Held**
SIC: 3549 Assembly machines, including robotic

(G-18360)
AUTOTEC ENGINEERING COMPANY
6155 Brent Dr (43611-1083)
PHONE.....................................419 885-2529
Thomas P Ballay, *President*
James Proffitt, *President*
Paul Sieben, *President*
Jim Proffitt, *Vice Pres*
David Puterbaugh, *Project Engr*
EMP: 20
SQ FT: 23,000
SALES (est): 7MM **Privately Held**
WEB: www.autotecinc.com
SIC: 3544 3599 8711 Special dies, tools, jigs & fixtures; custom machinery; designing: ship, boat, machine & product; mechanical engineering

(G-18361)
AXALTA COATING SYSTEMS LLC
1930 Tremainsville Rd (43613-4026)
PHONE.....................................419 478-1211
Fax: 419 470-1716
Scott Landis, *Plant Mgr*
Steve Black, *Manager*
EMP: 35
SALES (corp-wide): 4.1B **Publicly Held**
WEB: www.dupont.com
SIC: 2851 2821 Paints: oil or alkyd vehicle or water thinned; plastics materials & resins
HQ: Axalta Coating Systems, Llc
2001 Market St Fl 36a
Philadelphia PA 19103
215 255-7932

(G-18362)
B & R CUSTOM CHROME
469 Dearborn Ave (43605-1709)
PHONE.....................................419 536-7215
Ary Smith, *Principal*
EMP: 3
SALES (est): 146.8K **Privately Held**
SIC: 3471 Chromium plating of metals or formed products

(G-18363)
BANNER MATTRESS CO INC (PA)
Also Called: Banner Mattress & Furniture Co
2544 N Reynolds Rd (43615-2820)
PHONE.....................................419 324-7181
Fax: 419 324-7115
Matthew Karp, *President*
George Evanoff, *General Mgr*
Barbara Karp, *Corp Secy*
Debbie Brentlinger, *Controller*
Jeff Eldrich, *Manager*
▲ EMP: 5 EST: 1961
SQ FT: 25,000
SALES (est): 15.1MM **Privately Held**
WEB: www.bannermattress.com
SIC: 5712 2515 Furniture stores; mattresses; mattresses & bedsprings

(G-18364)
BASILIUS INC
4338 South Ave (43615-6236)
PHONE.....................................419 536-5810
Fax: 419 536-0391
Scott Basilius, *President*
Dave Keiser, *Vice Pres*
Stephanie Fraser, *Manager*
▲ EMP: 33
SQ FT: 52,000

SALES (est): 6.6MM **Privately Held**
WEB: www.basilius.com
SIC: 3544 Forms (molds), for foundry & plastics working machinery

(G-18365)
BELL BINDERS LLC
320 21st St (43604-5037)
P.O. Box 313 (43697-0313)
PHONE.....................................419 242-3201
Fax: 419 242-3202
Paul Jagielski,
EMP: 15 EST: 1954
SALES (est): 2MM **Privately Held**
SIC: 2782 3089 Looseleaf binders & devices; laminating of plastic

(G-18366)
BETCO CORPORATION LTD
1001 Brown Ave (43607-3942)
PHONE.....................................419 241-2156
John Bird, *Branch Mgr*
EMP: 30
SALES (corp-wide): 138.2MM **Privately Held**
WEB: www.betco.com
SIC: 2841 2842 Detergents, synthetic organic or inorganic alkaline; floor waxes
HQ: Betco Corporation, Ltd.
400 Van Camp Rd
Bowling Green OH 43402
419 241-2156

(G-18367)
BIMBO BAKERIES USA INC
5915 Jason St (43611-1088)
PHONE.....................................419 726-6183
EMP: 3
SALES (corp-wide): 11B **Privately Held**
SIC: 2051 Bread, cake & related products
HQ: Bimbo Bakeries Usa, Inc
255 Business Center Dr # 200
Horsham PA 19044
215 347-5500

(G-18368)
BIONIX DEVELOPMENT CORPORATION (PA)
Also Called: Bionix Radiation Therapy
5154 Enterprise Blvd (43612-3807)
P.O. Box 935 (43697-0935)
PHONE.....................................419 727-8421
Fax: 419 727-8426
Andrew J Milligan, *President*
James J Huttner, *Vice Pres*
Drew Milligan, *Personnel Exec*
Sarah Herzit, *Cust Mgr*
Josh Noble, *Manager*
▲ EMP: 35
SQ FT: 14,000
SALES (est): 9.3MM **Privately Held**
WEB: www.bionix.com
SIC: 3841 3829 Surgical & medical instruments; measuring & controlling devices

(G-18369)
BISON LEATHER CO
7409 W Central Ave (43617-1122)
PHONE.....................................419 517-1737
Barry Cody, *CEO*
EMP: 6
SALES (est): 536.7K **Privately Held**
SIC: 3172 Personal leather goods

(G-18370)
BITUMINOUS PRODUCTS COMPANY
352 George Hardy Dr (43605-1063)
PHONE.....................................419 693-3933
John Krups, *Principal*
EMP: 3 EST: 2010
SALES (est): 290K **Privately Held**
SIC: 2911 Asphalt or asphaltic materials, made in refineries

(G-18371)
BLACK CLOISTER BREWING CO LLC
619 Monroe St (43604-1015)
PHONE.....................................419 481-3891
Kate Matz, *CFO*
Mike Kennedy, *VP Sales*
Thomas Schaeffer,
MO Cherry, *Assistant*
EMP: 4

SALES (est): 361.9K **Privately Held**
SIC: 2082 Beer (alcoholic beverage)

(G-18372)
BLOCK COMMUNICATIONS INC (PA)
Also Called: BCI
405 Madison Ave Ste 2100 (43604-1224)
PHONE.....................................419 724-6212
Allan J Block, *Ch of Bd*
John R Block, *Vice Ch Bd*
Walter H Carstensen, *President*
T P Brown, *Principal*
J K Hamilton, *Principal*
EMP: 14 EST: 1965
SQ FT: 64,100
SALES (est): 626.6MM **Privately Held**
WEB: www.blockcommunications.com
SIC: 4841 4833 2711 Cable television services; television broadcasting stations; newspapers, publishing & printing

(G-18373)
BLUE WATER SATELLITE INC
1510 N Westwood Ave (43606-8202)
PHONE.....................................419 372-0160
Milt Baker, *President*
Jim Harpen, *General Mgr*
Gail Nader, *Business Mgr*
EMP: 8
SALES (est): 862.7K **Privately Held**
SIC: 3826 Environmental testing equipment

(G-18374)
BOBCO ENTERPRISES INC
Also Called: Taylor Mtl Hdlg & Conveyor
2910 Glanzman Rd (43614-3955)
P.O. Box 39, Sylvania (43560-0039)
PHONE.....................................419 867-3560
Toll Free:.....................................888 -
Robert Cordrey, *President*
Pauline Walker, *Accounts Mgr*
EMP: 12
SQ FT: 40,000
SALES (est): 5.8MM **Privately Held**
SIC: 5084 3536 3535 Materials handling machinery; hoists, cranes & monorails; conveyors & conveying equipment

(G-18375)
BOBS CUSTOM STR INTERIORS LLC
5333 Secor Rd Ste 19 (43623-2420)
PHONE.....................................567 316-7490
Robert L Neuenschwander Jr,
EMP: 3
SALES (est): 191.9K **Privately Held**
SIC: 1751 2542 5046 5712 Cabinet & finish carpentry; fixtures, store: except wood; store fixtures; cabinet work, custom

(G-18376)
BOLLIN & SONS INC
Also Called: Bollin Label Systems
6001 Brent Dr (43611-1090)
PHONE.....................................419 693-6573
Fax: 419 697-1682
Mark D Bollin, *President*
Chris Younkman, *Vice Pres*
EMP: 40
SQ FT: 21,000
SALES (est): 15.1MM **Privately Held**
WEB: www.bollin.com
SIC: 2672 5084 7389 2851 Coated & laminated paper; packaging machinery & equipment; design services; paints & allied products; commercial printing; packaging paper & plastics film, coated & laminated

(G-18377)
BOSTON SCNTFIC NRMDLATION CORP
3130 Executive Pkwy (43606-5529)
PHONE.....................................419 720-9510
EMP: 3
SALES (corp-wide): 8.3B **Publicly Held**
SIC: 3841 Surgical & medical instruments
HQ: Boston Scientific Neuromodulation Corporation
25155 Rye Canyon Loop
Valencia CA 91355
661 949-4310

▲ = Import ▼=Export ◆ =Import/Export

(G-18378)
BP PRODUCTS NORTH AMERICA INC
B P Exploration
2450 Hill Ave (43607-3609)
P.O. Box 932 (43697-0932)
PHONE................................419 537-9540
Jim Brahier, *Branch Mgr*
EMP: 16
SQ FT: 11,485
SALES (corp-wide): 183B **Privately Held**
WEB: www.bpproductsnorthamerica.com
SIC: 2911 Petroleum refining
HQ: Bp Products North America Inc.
501 Westlake Park Blvd
Houston TX 77079
281 366-2000

(G-18379)
BPREX PLASTIC PACKAGING INC (DH)
Also Called: Oi Plastic Products Fts Inc
1 Seagate Ste 10 (43604-1563)
PHONE................................419 247-5000
Joseph Lemieux, *CEO*
Kenneth Hicks, *Principal*
Lisa Hysko, *Principal*
EMP: 10
SALES (est): 77.2MM
SALES (corp-wide): 6.4B **Publicly Held**
SIC: 3221 3089 Glass containers; food containers, glass; bottles for packing, bottling & canning; glass; medicine bottles, glass; plastic containers, except foam; cases, plastic; jars, plastic; closures, plastic
HQ: Berry Plastics Corporation
101 Oakley St
Evansville IN 47710
812 424-2904

(G-18380)
BRAD SNODERLY
Also Called: ABC Countertops
444 W Laskey Rd Ste K (43612-3467)
PHONE................................419 476-0184
Fax: 419 476-1330
Brad Snoderly, *Owner*
Anita Snoderly, *Manager*
EMP: 15
SQ FT: 4,400
SALES (est): 1MM **Privately Held**
SIC: 2541 1799 Counter & sink tops; counter top installation

(G-18381)
BRAIN CHILD PRODUCTS LLC
146 Main St (43605-2067)
PHONE................................419 698-4020
Robert Croak,
Emily Marchand, *Assistant*
EMP: 15
SALES (est): 1.3MM **Privately Held**
WEB: www.brainchildproducts.com
SIC: 2822 Silicone rubbers

(G-18382)
BROOKS MANUFACTURING
1102 N Summit St (43604-1816)
PHONE................................419 244-1777
Michael Brooks, *Owner*
EMP: 9
SQ FT: 5,000
SALES (est): 310K **Privately Held**
SIC: 3931 3592 3824 Brass instruments & parts; valves; water meters

(G-18383)
BTW LLC
2226 Greenlawn Dr (43614-5120)
PHONE................................419 382-4443
Paul Long, *President*
EMP: 8
SALES (est): 788.1K **Privately Held**
WEB: www.btw.com
SIC: 2679 5012 Wrappers, paper (unprinted): made from purchased material; automobiles & other motor vehicles

(G-18384)
BUCK EYE PRESSURE WASH
5242 Angola Rd Ste 130 (43615-6334)
P.O. Box 351574 (43635-1574)
PHONE................................419 385-9274
Robert Moeller, *Owner*

EMP: 7 EST: 2001
SALES (est): 745.2K **Privately Held**
SIC: 3452 Washers

(G-18385)
BUILDER TECH WHOLESALE LLC
Also Called: Builder Tech Windows
2931 South Ave (43609-1327)
PHONE................................419 535-7606
Brad Montague,
Lynn Burns,
EMP: 8
SQ FT: 6,000
SALES (est): 290K **Privately Held**
SIC: 3089 Windows, plastic

(G-18386)
C M SLICECHIEF CO
3333 Maple St (43608-1147)
P.O. Box 80206 (43608-0206)
PHONE................................419 241-7647
Fax: 419 241-3513
Susan L Brown, *President*
Barbara Cairl, *Corp Secy*
EMP: 9 EST: 1946
SQ FT: 18,000
SALES (est): 1.2MM **Privately Held**
WEB: www.slicechief.com
SIC: 3556 Slicers, commercial, food

(G-18387)
CAKE ARTS SUPPLIES
Also Called: Cake Arts Supplies & Bakery
2858 W Sylvania Ave (43613-4225)
PHONE................................419 472-4959
Fax: 419 472-9754
Dorothy Bryan, *Owner*
EMP: 5
SALES: 360K **Privately Held**
WEB: www.cakeartssupply.com
SIC: 5999 2051 Cake decorating supplies; cakes, bakery: except frozen

(G-18388)
CANBERRA CORPORATION
3610 N Hlland Sylvania Rd (43615)
PHONE................................419 724-4300
Fax: 419 841-7597
R Bruce Yacko, *President*
James C Lower, *Chairman*
Eddie Morabito, *Business Mgr*
William Schneck, *Corp Secy*
Martin Sikula, *Maintenance Dir*
◆ EMP: 205
SQ FT: 220,000
SALES (est): 83.4MM **Privately Held**
WEB: www.canberracorp.com
SIC: 2842 Specialty cleaning, polishes & sanitation goods; specialty cleaning preparations

(G-18389)
CARLISLE FLUID TECH INC
Also Called: Finishing Brands
320 Phillips Ave (43612-1467)
PHONE................................419 470-2000
Dan Hasselschwert, *General Mgr*
Barry Holt, *Branch Mgr*
Joe Koren, *Info Tech Mgr*
EMP: 190
SALES (corp-wide): 3.6B **Publicly Held**
SIC: 3563 Spraying outfits: metals, paints & chemicals (compressor)
HQ: Carlisle Fluid Technologies, Inc.
11605 N Community Hse
Charlotte NC 28277
704 501-1100

(G-18390)
CAUFFIEL CORPORATION (PA)
3171 N Repub Blvd Ste 102 (43615)
PHONE................................419 843-7262
EMP: 5 EST: 2012
SALES (est): 6.7MM **Privately Held**
SIC: 3549 Mfg Metalworking Machinery

(G-18391)
CELEBRATIONS
Also Called: JM Gourmet Popcorn
2910 Glanzman Rd Unit 1 (43614-3955)
PHONE................................419 381-8088
Fax: 419 381-0042
David Poulos, *Owner*
Cathy Poulos, *Co-Owner*
EMP: 5

SQ FT: 8,000
SALES: 350K **Privately Held**
WEB: www.celebrationsfundraising.com
SIC: 2064 Candy & other confectionery products

(G-18392)
CENTAUR INC (PA)
Also Called: Heidtman Steel Products
2401 Front St (43605-1145)
PHONE................................419 469-8000
Mark Ridenour, *CEO*
John C Bates, *Ch of Bd*
Rita Czerniakowski, *Controller*
▲ EMP: 5
SQ FT: 100,000
SALES (est): 273MM **Privately Held**
SIC: 3312 3316 3999 Sheet or strip, steel, hot-rolled; strip steel, cold-rolled: from purchased hot-rolled; atomizers, toiletry

(G-18393)
CHANTILLY DEVELOPMENT CORP
Acme Specialty Mfg Co
3101 Monroe St (43606-4605)
PHONE................................419 243-8109
Fax: 419 243-9093
Deanna Sifuentes, *General Mgr*
Robert T Skilliter Jr, *Principal*
Thomas Messina, *Plant Mgr*
Bob Sands, *Controller*
Bruce Smith, *Maintence Staff*
EMP: 19
SQ FT: 70,000
SALES (corp-wide): 2MM **Privately Held**
WEB: www.acmespecialty.com
SIC: 3231 3714 3429 3221 Mirrored glass; mirrors, truck & automobile: made from purchased glass; frames, motor vehicle; windshield frames, motor vehicle; manufactured hardware (general); glass containers
PA: Chantilly Development Corp
Wollaston Rd
Unionville PA
419 243-8109

(G-18394)
CHEM-SALES INC
Also Called: C S I
3860 Dorr St (43607-1003)
P.O. Box 351684 (43635-1684)
PHONE................................419 531-4292
Amos Clay Sr, *CEO*
Amos Clay Jr, *President*
Shirley J Clay, *Corp Secy*
EMP: 12
SQ FT: 1,200
SALES (est): 1.3MM **Privately Held**
WEB: www.chemsalesinc.com
SIC: 2869 5087 5169 Industrial organic chemicals; janitors' supplies; chemicals & allied products

(G-18395)
CHEMPACE CORPORATION
339 Arco Dr (43607-2908)
PHONE................................419 535-0101
Fax: 419 535-0531
Richard Shall, *President*
Terry W O'Neill, *Vice Pres*
Sue Klotz, *Controller*
Vicki Horvath, *Accounts Mgr*
Jeff Anderson, *Manager*
▲ EMP: 18 EST: 1968
SQ FT: 12,500
SALES (est): 5.7MM **Privately Held**
WEB: www.chempace.com
SIC: 2842 Cleaning or polishing preparations; degreasing solvent

(G-18396)
CHINA ENTERPRISES INC
Also Called: Chang Audio
5151 Monroe St (43623-3462)
PHONE................................419 885-1485
Fax: 419 885-7148
Stella Lee, *President*
Michael Chang, *Exec VP*
EMP: 7
SALES (est): 827.1K **Privately Held**
WEB: www.changlightspeed.com
SIC: 3651 Household audio equipment

(G-18397)
CHRISTIES CANDIES & MINTS (PA)
2002 Glendale Ave (43614-2801)
PHONE................................419 382-7313
Fax: 419 382-7366
Robert T Christie, *Partner*
Cathy Christie, *Partner*
EMP: 5
SQ FT: 1,900
SALES (est): 742.6K **Privately Held**
SIC: 2064 Candy & other confectionery products

(G-18398)
CLAMPS INC
5960 American Rd E (43612-3966)
PHONE................................419 729-2141
Fax: 419 729-5776
J D Riker, *CEO*
Anthony Carollo, *President*
Tom Shackelford, *Vice Pres*
Glen Jackson, *Treasurer*
Jeanne E Graham, *Admin Sec*
EMP: 25 EST: 1957
SQ FT: 67,000
SALES (est): 5.4MM **Privately Held**
WEB: www.clampsinc.com
SIC: 3496 Miscellaneous fabricated wire products

(G-18399)
CLAYCOR INC
Also Called: Denbro Plastics Company
5924 American Rd E (43612-3950)
PHONE................................419 318-7290
Fax: 419 729-9653
Jack McKisson, *President*
EMP: 10
SQ FT: 10,000
SALES (est): 890K **Privately Held**
SIC: 3089 Molding primary plastic

(G-18400)
CLEAR IMAGES LLC
121 11th St (43604-5829)
PHONE................................419 241-9347
Fax: 419 241-9348
Frank Ozanski, *Mng Member*
Marie Micel,
EMP: 13
SALES (est): 1.5MM **Privately Held**
SIC: 2759 Promotional printing

(G-18401)
CLINTON FOUNDRY LTD
1202 W Bancroft St (43606-4631)
PHONE................................419 243-6885
James D Heninger, *Principal*
Timothy Heninger,
Ronnie L Holbrook,
EMP: 10
SQ FT: 4,500
SALES: 250K **Privately Held**
SIC: 3364 Nonferrous die-castings except aluminum

(G-18402)
CLINTON PATTERN WORKS INC
1215 W Bancroft St. (43606-4632)
PHONE................................419 243-0855
Fax: 419 243-5732
James D Heninger, *President*
Timothy Heninger, *Vice Pres*
David Golaszewski, *Sales Staff*
EMP: 11
SQ FT: 25,000
SALES (est): 1.8MM **Privately Held**
SIC: 3543 Industrial patterns

(G-18403)
COACH INC
5001 Monroe St Ste 1743 (43623-3620)
PHONE................................419 471-9033
Stephanie Rieck, *Branch Mgr*
EMP: 15
SALES (corp-wide): 4.4B **Publicly Held**
WEB: www.coach.com
SIC: 3171 Handbags, women's
PA: Coach, Inc.
10 Hudson Yards
New York NY 10001
212 594-1850

(G-18404)
COCA-COLA REFRESHMENTS USA INC
3970 Catawba St (43612-1404)
PHONE..........................419 476-6622
Paul Kenny, *Manager*
EMP: 110
SALES (corp-wide): 41.8B **Publicly Held**
WEB: www.colasic.net
SIC: 2086 2087 5149 Carbonated beverages, nonalcoholic: bottled & canned; soft drinks: packaged in cans, bottles, etc.; fruit drinks (less than 100% juice): packaged in cans, etc.; syrups, drink; concentrates, drink; groceries & related products
HQ: Coca-Cola Refreshments Usa, Inc.
2500 Windy Ridge Pkwy Se
Atlanta GA 30339
770 989-3000

(G-18405)
COLE ORTHOTICS PROSTHETIC CTR
723 Phillips Ave Bldg F (43612-1351)
PHONE..........................419 476-4248
Fax: 419 476-6655
Daniel P Cole, *Owner*
Cheryl L Coe, *Treasurer*
George Cole, *Director*
EMP: 6
SQ FT: 8,000
SALES (est): 900K **Privately Held**
WEB: www.coleopc.com
SIC: 3842 Braces, orthopedic; limbs, artificial

(G-18406)
COLONIAL FIREWORKS COMPANY
5225 Telegraph Rd (43612-3570)
PHONE..........................419 478-4945
Greg Tremonti, *President*
Ron Greco, *Vice Pres*
Frank Loffredo, *Vice Pres*
Robert Smith, *Vice Pres*
EMP: 10
SALES (est): 1MM **Privately Held**
SIC: 2899 Fireworks

(G-18407)
COMFORT LINE LTD
5500 Enterprise Blvd (43612-3815)
PHONE..........................419 729-8520
Fax: 419 729-8526
Daniel J La Valley, *President*
Richard G La Valley, *President*
Richard Valley, *Plant Mgr*
Victor Wawrzyniak, *Production*
Julianne Stewart, *Purch Agent*
◆ EMP: 100 EST: 1959
SQ FT: 200,000
SALES (est): 23.4MM **Privately Held**
WEB: www.comfortlineinc.com
SIC: 3089 Windows, plastic; doors, folding: plastic or plastic coated fabric

(G-18408)
COMMERCIAL BINDERY INC
2738 Shetland Rd (43617-1518)
PHONE..........................419 517-9914
Jeff Rosenbloom, *President*
Linda Rosenbloom, *Vice Pres*
EMP: 5
SQ FT: 8,000
SALES (est): 450K **Privately Held**
SIC: 2789 Bookbinding & related work

(G-18409)
CONFORMING MATRIX CORPORATION
6255 Suder Ave (43611-1022)
PHONE..........................419 729-3777
Fax: 419 729-3779
Albert J Spelker, *President*
Ella Mae Macarthur, *Principal*
H E Macarthur, *Principal*
Ron Riehle, *Purchasing*
Bob Cheesman, *Engineer*
EMP: 40
SQ FT: 38,000
SALES (est): 12.9MM **Privately Held**
WEB: www.conformingmatrix.com
SIC: 3559 3544 Metal finishing equipment for plating, etc.; plastics working machinery; special dies, tools, jigs & fixtures

(G-18410)
CONNECTRONICS CORP (DH)
2745 Avondale Ave (43607-3232)
P.O. Box 3355 (43607-0355)
PHONE..........................419 537-0020
Fax: 419 537-0007
Thomas Ricketts, *CEO*
Thomas L Ricketts, *CEO*
Lex Potter, *President*
Steven Robinson, *General Mgr*
Al Mocek, *Vice Pres*
EMP: 65
SQ FT: 25,000
SALES (est): 12.4MM
SALES (corp-wide): 1.3B **Publicly Held**
WEB: www.connectronicscorp.com
SIC: 3678 3643 Electronic connectors; connectors & terminals for electrical devices
HQ: Heico Electronic Technologies Corp
3000 Taft St
Hollywood FL 33021
987-6101

(G-18411)
CONSUMER GUILD FOODS INC
5035 Enterprise Blvd (43612-3839)
PHONE..........................419 726-3406
Fax: 419 726-8771
Wilbur R Ascham, *President*
Ann Ascham, *Vice Pres*
Robert J Petrick, *Vice Pres*
EMP: 20 EST: 1966
SQ FT: 14,500
SALES (est): 3.4MM **Privately Held**
SIC: 2035 Dressings, salad: raw & cooked (except dry mixes)

(G-18412)
CONTRERAS PALLETS
1734 Balkan Pl (43613-4606)
PHONE..........................567 277-2447
Fabiola Contreras, *Principal*
EMP: 3
SALES (est): 200.3K **Privately Held**
SIC: 2448 Pallets, wood & wood with metal

(G-18413)
CORILLIAN PAYMENT SOLUTIONS
1946 N 13th St Ste 392 (43604-7265)
PHONE..........................419 244-8048
Mitzi Nowakowski, *Branch Mgr*
EMP: 19
SALES (corp-wide): 5.5B **Publicly Held**
WEB: www.advpres.com
SIC: 7372 Prepackaged software
HQ: Corillian Payment Solutions, Inc
11600 Sunrise Valley Dr # 460
Reston VA

(G-18414)
COTTON FABRICS COMPANY INC
3647 Marine Rd (43609-1019)
P.O. Box 141018 (43614-9011)
PHONE..........................419 389-9904
Fax: 419 389-6500
Michael P Bocian, *President*
Sharyn M Bocian, *Treasurer*
Matt Schober, *Sales Staff*
EMP: 6
SQ FT: 10,000
SALES (est): 490K **Privately Held**
SIC: 2392 5087 5085 Polishing cloths, plain; janitors' supplies; industrial supplies

(G-18415)
CRABAR/GBF INC
Also Called: Printxcel
4444 N Detroit Ave (43612-1978)
P.O. Box 6986 (43612-0986)
PHONE..........................419 269-1720
Tom Fiddle, *General Mgr*
Dan Frederick, *Production*
Janice West, *Sales Staff*
EMP: 22
SQ FT: 52,223
SALES (corp-wide): 568.9MM **Publicly Held**
WEB: www.mail-well.com
SIC: 2752 2761 Commercial printing, lithographic; continuous forms, office & business

HQ: Crabar/Gbf, Inc.
68 Vine St
Leipsic OH 45856
419 943-2141

(G-18416)
CROWN CORK & SEAL USA INC
5201 Enterprise Blvd (43612-3808)
PHONE..........................419 727-8201
Mark Mihal, *Purchasing*
Janelle Stevens, *Purchasing*
Glen Smillie, *Engineer*
John Kupa, *Controller*
Dan Letson, *Sales Staff*
EMP: 40
SALES (corp-wide): 8.2B **Publicly Held**
WEB: www.crowncork.com
SIC: 3411 Metal cans
HQ: Crown Cork & Seal Usa, Inc.
1 Crown Way
Philadelphia PA 19154
215 698-5100

(G-18417)
CULAINE INC
Also Called: Cpg Printing & Graphics
1036 W Laskey Rd (43612-3030)
PHONE..........................419 345-4984
Mike Cutcher, *President*
Elaine R Cutcher, *Vice Pres*
EMP: 6
SQ FT: 4,000
SALES (est): 500K **Privately Held**
SIC: 2759 2752 Commercial printing; commercial printing, lithographic

(G-18418)
CUSTOM DECO SOUTH INC
1343 Miami St (43605-3338)
PHONE..........................419 698-2900
Fax: 419 698-9928
Dean E Stroh, *President*
Hal Mann, *CFO*
Mary Brown, *Manager*
Janet Goerke, *Manager*
F Warden, *Manager*
▲ EMP: 25
SQ FT: 18,000
SALES (est): 2.5MM **Privately Held**
SIC: 2759 3229 Screen printing; tableware, glass or glass ceramic

(G-18419)
CUSTOMERS CAR CARE CENTER
Also Called: Suzuki of Toleda
5299 Monroe St (43623-3139)
PHONE..........................419 841-6646
Robert Fleicher, *Owner*
EMP: 6 EST: 2001
SALES (est): 507K **Privately Held**
SIC: 3559 Automotive related machinery

(G-18420)
CUTTING EDGE CNVERTED PDTS INC
Also Called: Cutting Edge Packaging Pdts
330 Ryder Rd (43607-3104)
PHONE..........................888 720-3343
Hal Fetterman, *CEO*
Eric Thomas, *President*
Garrett Dammin, *Purchasing*
▲ EMP: 20
SQ FT: 60,000
SALES (est): 6.1MM **Privately Held**
WEB: www.usconverting.com
SIC: 2675 Die-cut paper & board

(G-18421)
CWM SMOOTHIE LLC
2859 N Hlland Sylvania Rd (43615)
PHONE..........................419 283-6387
Chris Markho, *Principal*
EMP: 3
SALES (est): 154.2K **Privately Held**
SIC: 2037 Frozen fruits & vegetables

(G-18422)
D & D NEXT DAY SIGNS INC
2112 N Reynolds Rd (43615-3514)
PHONE..........................419 537-9595
Dan Mosher, *President*
EMP: 5
SALES (est): 391.1K **Privately Held**
SIC: 3993 Signs & advertising specialties

(G-18423)
D A L E S CORPORATION
1402 Jackson St (43604-5212)
PHONE..........................419 255-5335
Dale Frantz, *President*
Buzz Kutz, *Vice Pres*
Lisa Frantz, *Admin Sec*
EMP: 12
SQ FT: 10,000
SALES: 2.9MM **Privately Held**
WEB: www.dalescorp.com
SIC: 3991 Paint & varnish brushes

(G-18424)
D L SALKIL LLC
Also Called: Toledo Screw Products
8261 W Bancroft St (43617-1804)
PHONE..........................419 841-3341
EMP: 6
SALES: 500K **Privately Held**
SIC: 3451 Mfg Screw Machine Products

(G-18425)
DAKKOTA INTEGRATED SYSTEMS LLC
315 Matzinger Rd Unit G (43612-2626)
PHONE..........................517 694-6500
James Horwath, *Controller*
EMP: 50
SQ FT: 65,000
SALES (corp-wide): 273.1MM **Privately Held**
SIC: 3711 Motor vehicles & car bodies
PA: Dakkota Integrated Systems, Llc
1875 Holloway Dr
Holt MI 48842
517 694-6500

(G-18426)
DANA CORPORATION
4500 Dorr St (43615-4040)
P.O. Box 1000 (43697-1000)
PHONE..........................419 887-3000
Fax: 419 535-4516
Jeffrey Bowen, *Principal*
Dave Rosquin, *Vice Pres*
Scott Mikesell, *Engineer*
Rodney Filcek, *VP Finance*
Joe Losek, *Sales Staff*
EMP: 29
SALES (est): 4.1MM **Privately Held**
SIC: 3714 Motor vehicle parts & accessories

(G-18427)
DANA LIGHT AXLE MFG LLC
Also Called: Toledo Driveline
3044 Jeep Parkway (43657-0001)
PHONE..........................419 887-3000
EMP: 300
SQ FT: 100,000
SALES (corp-wide): 5.8B **Publicly Held**
SIC: 3714 Motor vehicle parts & accessories
HQ: Dana Light Axle Manufacturing, Llc
3939 Technology Dr
Maumee OH 43537
419 887-3000

(G-18428)
DAVE FOREIGN CARS
6151 American Rd (43612-3901)
PHONE..........................419 727-0685
David Leiber, *Owner*
Jason Leiber, *Vice Pres*
EMP: 4
SALES: 2MM **Privately Held**
SIC: 3711 Automobile bodies, passenger car, not including engine, etc.

(G-18429)
DAY PRE-CAST PRODUCTS CO
801 N Westwood Ave (43607-3561)
PHONE..........................419 536-2909
Fax: 419 536-3412
Michele Filipovich, *Owner*
Richard Day, *Co-Owner*
▲ EMP: 3
SQ FT: 4,800
SALES (est): 320.5K **Privately Held**
SIC: 3272 Chimney caps, concrete; steps, prefabricated concrete; furniture, garden: concrete

(G-18430)
DECO TOOLS INC
1541 Coining Dr (43612-2978)
PHONE.....................419 476-9321
Fax: 419 476-6669
Mike Bollenbacher, *President*
John Schwab, *Project Engr*
Michael Rowley, *Technical Staff*
EMP: 25
SQ FT: 30,000
SALES (est): 6MM Privately Held
WEB: www.decotools.com
SIC: 3563 3991 3842 2672 Spraying outfits: metals, paints & chemicals (compressor); brooms & brushes; surgical appliances & supplies; coated & laminated paper

(G-18431)
DECOMA SYSTEMS INTEGRATION GRO
Also Called: Team Systems
1800 Nathan Dr (43611-1091)
PHONE.....................419 324-3387
Belinda Stronach, *CEO*
Kevin Wickenheiser, *General Mgr*
Nadine Stricker, *Controller*
Ian McColl, *Sales Mgr*
Liz Sechkar, *Manager*
EMP: 100
SALES (est): 22.9MM
SALES (corp-wide): 36.4B Privately Held
WEB: www.decoma.com
SIC: 3465 Body parts, automobile: stamped metal
PA: Magna International Inc
337 Magna Dr
Aurora ON L4G 7
905 726-2462

(G-18432)
DECOR ARCHITECTURAL PRODUCTS
2375 Dorr St Ste E (43607-3400)
PHONE.....................419 537-9493
Fax: 419 537-9493
Terry Creech, *President*
Julie Creech, *Corp Secy*
Jim Tropf, *Manager*
EMP: 5
SQ FT: 5,000
SALES: 350K Privately Held
WEB: www.decorarchitecturalproducts.com
SIC: 3444 3446 Sheet metalwork; architectural metalwork

(G-18433)
DECORATIVE PANELS INTL INC (DH)
Also Called: D P I
2900 Hill Ave (43607-2929)
PHONE.....................419 535-5921
Tim Clark, *President*
Mike Kilbane, *Plant Mgr*
Mike Norman, *Opers Mgr*
Barb Cercone, *Production*
Allen Steiber, *Controller*
▼ EMP: 75
SQ FT: 225,000
SALES (est): 86.8MM
SALES (corp-wide): 16.1B Privately Held
WEB:
www.decorativepanelsinternational.com
SIC: 2435 Hardwood plywood, prefinished; panels, hardwood plywood
HQ: As America, Inc.
1 Centennial Ave Ste 101
Piscataway NJ 08854
732 980-3000

(G-18434)
DEEP SPRINGS TECHNOLOGY LLC
4750 W Bancroft St Ste 1 (43615-3864)
PHONE.....................419 536-5741
Carol Ann Wedding, *President*
Vicky Kurtz, *Managing Prtnr*
Jeff Guy, *Chief Engr*
▲ EMP: 4
SQ FT: 11,000
SALES (est): 762.5K
SALES (corp-wide): 4.8MM Privately Held
WEB: www.teamist.com
SIC: 3532 Mining machinery

PA: Imaging Systems Technology Inc.
4750 W Bancroft St
Toledo OH 43615
419 536-5741

(G-18435)
DETROIT TECHNOLOGIES INC
2959 Nebraska Ave (43607-3124)
PHONE.....................248 647-0400
Steve Phillips, *President*
Mark Oconnor, *General Mgr*
Garry Stanis, *CFO*
Earle Higgins, *Shareholder*
John Mastin, *Admin Sec*
EMP: 5
SQ FT: 4,200
SALES: 800K Privately Held
SIC: 3089 Automotive parts, plastic

(G-18436)
DETROIT TOLEDO FIBER LLC
1245 E Manhattan Blvd (43608-1549)
PHONE.....................248 647-0400
Steven Philips, *President*
Gary Stanis, *CFO*
EMP: 10
SALES (est): 1.3MM Privately Held
SIC: 3714 Motor vehicle engines & parts
PA: Detroit Technologies, Inc.
32500 Telg Rd Ste 207
Bingham Farms MI 48025

(G-18437)
DEVILBISS RANSBURG
320 Phillips Ave (43612-1493)
PHONE.....................419 470-2000
Fax: 419 470-2112
Rolan D Kjosen, *Principal*
Gene Altenburger, *Engineer*
EMP: 19
SALES (est): 4.7MM Privately Held
SIC: 3559 Special industry machinery

(G-18438)
DIGIMATICS INC
Also Called: Architectural Arts
4011 Vermaas Ave (43612-1879)
PHONE.....................419 478-0804
Fax: 419 476-6612
Helen M Bordner, *President*
John Bordner, *Shareholder*
EMP: 8
SQ FT: 10,000
SALES (est): 450K Privately Held
WEB: www.digimaticsinc.com
SIC: 3993 7389 Signs & advertising specialties; electric signs; sign painting & lettering shop

(G-18439)
DISMAT CORPORATION
Also Called: Mc Kay's Food Seasoning
336 N Westwood Ave (43607-3343)
PHONE.....................419 531-8963
Fax: 419 531-8965
John A Donofrio, *President*
Joanne Vick, *Vice Pres*
EMP: 6 EST: 1945
SQ FT: 12,000
SALES (est): 843.7K Privately Held
SIC: 2099 2034 Seasonings: dry mixes; dehydrated fruits, vegetables, soups

(G-18440)
DIVERSIFIED WELDING SERVICES
3541 Marine Rd (43609-1017)
PHONE.....................419 382-1433
Chris Waite, *Owner*
EMP: 3
SALES (est): 213.5K Privately Held
SIC: 7692 Welding repair

(G-18441)
DIVINE PRTG T-SHIRTS & MORE
3433 Monroe St (43606-4140)
PHONE.....................419 241-8208
Karen Hoskins, *Principal*
EMP: 3 EST: 2008
SALES (est): 264.6K Privately Held
SIC: 2759 Commercial printing

(G-18442)
DOLLMAN TECHNICAL SERVICES
2910 Glanzman Rd (43614-3955)
PHONE.....................419 877-9404
Fax: 419 389-4387
James M Dollman, *President*
EMP: 5
SQ FT: 27,084 Privately Held
SIC: 3599 Custom machinery
PA: Dollman Technical Services Inc
5702 Eber Rd
Whitehouse OH 43571

(G-18443)
DOWNTOWN PRINT SHOP
500 Madison Ave Fl 1 (43604-1230)
PHONE.....................419 242-9164
Fax: 419 242-9164
Philip G Cummings, *Partner*
Sharon Cummings, *Partner*
EMP: 3
SQ FT: 2,500
SALES (est): 220K Privately Held
WEB: www.downtownprintshop.com
SIC: 2752 Commercial printing, offset

(G-18444)
DRDC REALTY INC (PA)
4401 Jackman Rd (43612-1529)
PHONE.....................419 478-7091
Marvin K Himmelein, *President*
Gary L Ames, *Vice Pres*
EMP: 3
SQ FT: 12,000
SALES: 491.5K Privately Held
SIC: 3613 6512 7359 Control panels, electric; commercial & industrial building operation; equipment rental & leasing

(G-18445)
DS TECHNOLOGIES GROUP LTD
2537 Wimbledon Park Blvd (43617-2242)
PHONE.....................419 841-5388
Daniel J Kane, *Principal*
▲ EMP: 5
SQ FT: 14,000
SALES: 5MM Privately Held
WEB: www.kanecogroup.com
SIC: 3069 5013 Rubber automotive products; automotive engines & engine parts

(G-18446)
DYNAMICS RESEARCH & DEV
Also Called: Dynamics Manufacturing
4401 Jackman Rd (43612-1529)
PHONE.....................419 478-7091
Marvin K Himmelein, *President*
Gary L Ames, *Vice Pres*
Kathy Hickman, *Manager*
EMP: 3
SQ FT: 6,000
SALES: 192.5K
SALES (corp-wide): 491.5K Privately Held
WEB: www.dynamicsresearch.net
SIC: 3613 5084 Control panels, electric; industrial machinery & equipment
PA: D.R.D.C. Realty Inc
4401 Jackman Rd
Toledo OH 43612
419 478-7091

(G-18447)
DYNETECH LLC
916 N Summit St (43604-1812)
PHONE.....................419 690-4281
Robert Redmond,
EMP: 20 EST: 2005
SALES (est): 2.1MM Privately Held
SIC: 3823 Industrial process control instruments

(G-18448)
E W PERRY SERVICE CO INC
Also Called: Perry Service Co.
4216 W Alexis Rd (43623-1244)
PHONE.....................419 473-1231
Fax: 419 473-3756
Christopher W Perry, *President*
EMP: 4
SQ FT: 3,300

SALES (est): 709.4K Privately Held
SIC: 5023 2391 1799 2591 Window covering parts & accessories; draperies, plastic & textile: from purchased materials; drapery track installation; window blinds

(G-18449)
ECOLOGIC FDSRVICE SLUTIONS LLC
3901 Hill Ave (43607-2636)
PHONE.....................419 467-8758
Lawrence Ohlman,
▲ EMP: 3
SALES (est): 269.3K Privately Held
SIC: 2656 Sanitary food containers

(G-18450)
EDCO INC
Also Called: Edco Tool & Die
5244 Enterprise Blvd # 5 (43612-3871)
PHONE.....................419 726-1595
Fax: 419 726-5904
Jai Singh, *President*
Elie Ghanime, *General Mgr*
Jim Morawski, *Purch Mgr*
Jeff Wheeler, *Engineer*
Hope Schmeling, *Controller*
◆ EMP: 46 EST: 1955
SQ FT: 50,000
SALES (est): 11.1MM
SALES (corp-wide): 379.5MM Privately Held
WEB: www.edcodie.com
SIC: 3544 Special dies, tools, jigs & fixtures
PA: Exco Technologies Limited
130 Spy Crt
Markham ON L3R 5
905 477-3065

(G-18451)
ELAIRE CORPORATION
7944 W Central Ave Ste 10 (43617-1550)
PHONE.....................419 843-2192
Mark Neeley, *President*
EMP: 8
SALES (est): 893.8K Privately Held
SIC: 3999 Manufacturing industries

(G-18452)
ELDEN DRAPERIES OF TOLEDO INC
1845 N Reynolds Rd (43615-3531)
PHONE.....................419 535-1909
Fax: 419 535-8974
Betsy Grubb, *President*
Gary Grubb, *Vice Pres*
EMP: 10
SQ FT: 6,000
SALES: 900K Privately Held
SIC: 2391 5714 Draperies, plastic & textile: from purchased materials; draperies

(G-18453)
ELECTRO PRIME GROUP LLC (PA)
4510 Lint Ave Ste B (43612-2658)
PHONE.....................419 476-0100
Fax: 419 476-9161
Jim Vellequette, *Plant Mgr*
Paul Kamenca, *Production*
Chad Reinbolt, *CFO*
John L Lauffer, *Mng Member*
Brett Grachek, *Info Tech Mgr*
▲ EMP: 70
SQ FT: 20,100
SALES: 20MM Privately Held
WEB: www.electroprime.com
SIC: 3471 5169 Plating & polishing; anti-corrosion products

(G-18454)
ELEMENT MACHINERY LLC
4801 Bennett Rd (43612-2531)
PHONE.....................855 447-7648
Benjamin McGilvery, *CEO*
Samuel McGilvery 40, *President*
Joseph Box, *Vice Pres*
EMP: 6
SQ FT: 20,000
SALES (est): 473.5K Privately Held
SIC: 3547 Rolling mill machinery

GEOGRAPH

(G-18455)
ELEVATOR CNCEPTS BY WURTEC LLC
6200 Brent Dr (43611-1081)
PHONE....................................734 246-4700
Douglas Scott, *President*
Leigh Gaither, *Treasurer*
Kathy Krase, *Manager*
Michael Margin, *Manager*
▲ EMP: 10
SQ FT: 10,000
SALES (est): 1.6MM
SALES (corp-wide): 31.8MM **Privately Held**
WEB: www.elevatorconcepts.com
SIC: 3534 Elevators & equipment
PA: Wurtec, Incorporated
6200 Brent Dr
Toledo OH 43611
419 726-1066

(G-18456)
ERD SPECIALTY GRAPHICS INC
3250 Monroe St (43606-4550)
PHONE....................................419 242-9545
Fax: 419 242-2148
Steve Crouse, *President*
Debbie Crouse, *Admin Sec*
EMP: 12 EST: 1934
SQ FT: 19,500
SALES (est): 2.2MM **Privately Held**
WEB: www.erdgraphics.com
SIC: 2759 7389 Screen printing; emboss-
ing on paper; printers' services: folding,
collating

(G-18457)
ERIE LASER INK LLC
911 Jefferson Ave (43604-5921)
PHONE....................................419 346-0600
Mike Henry, *Mng Member*
EMP: 3
SALES (est): 264.5K **Privately Held**
SIC: 7389 2893 Printers' services: folding,
collating; printing ink

(G-18458)
ERIE STEEL LTD
5540 Jackman Rd (43613-2330)
PHONE....................................419 478-3743
Pat Flynn, *President*
EMP: 50
SALES: 10MM **Privately Held**
SIC: 3398 Metal heat treating

(G-18459)
EXOTHERMICS INC
5040 Enterprise Blvd (43612-3880)
PHONE....................................419 729-9726
Fax: 419 729-9705
Lach Perks, *President*
Rich Lattanzi, *Principal*
Kelly Gonzales, *Corp Secy*
Tina Shultz, *Buyer*
Barb Etling, *Administration*
EMP: 25 EST: 1976
SQ FT: 38,000
SALES (est): 6MM
SALES (corp-wide): 39.3B **Publicly Held**
WEB: www.exothermics.com
SIC: 3443 Heat exchangers, condensers &
components
HQ: Eclipse, Inc.
1665 Elmwood Rd
Rockford IL 61103
815 877-3031

(G-18460)
EXP FUELS INC
3070 Airport Hwy (43609-1406)
PHONE....................................419 382-7713
Victor Safadi, *Principal*
EMP: 4
SALES (est): 345.9K **Privately Held**
SIC: 2869 Fuels

(G-18461)
FAURECIA AUTOMOTIVE HOLDINGS
543 Matzinger Rd (43612-2638)
PHONE....................................419 727-5000
Patrick Szaroletta, *Interim Pres*
Kimberly Jones, *Financial Analy*
Thierry Cappe, *Director*
▲ EMP: 1000

SALES (est): 80.5MM
SALES (corp-wide): 271.8MM **Privately Held**
SIC: 3714 Mufflers (exhaust), motor vehi-
cle
HQ: Faurecia Usa Holdings, Inc.
2800 High Meadow Cir
Auburn Hills MI 48326
248 724-5100

(G-18462)
FAURECIA EXHAUST SYSTEMS INC
5225 Telegraph Rd (43612-3570)
PHONE....................................419 727-5000
Michael Dewitt, *Manager*
EMP: 50
SALES (corp-wide): 271.8MM **Privately Held**
WEB: www.franklin.faurecia.com
SIC: 3714 Motor vehicle parts & acces-
sories
HQ: Faurecia Exhaust Systems, Llc
543 Matzinger Rd
Toledo OH 43612
419 727-5000

(G-18463)
FAURECIA EXHAUST SYSTEMS LLC (DH)
Also Called: Faurecia Exhaust Systems, Inc.
543 Matzinger Rd (43612-2638)
P.O. Box 64010 (43612-0010)
PHONE....................................419 727-5000
Fax: 419 727-5025
Mark Stidham, *President*
Andrew Pontius, *President*
Robert Parmann, *Vice Pres*
Scott McFadden, *Facilities Mgr*
Doug Lapchynski, *Maint Spvr*
▲ EMP: 130
SQ FT: 40,000
SALES (est): 2.2B
SALES (corp-wide): 271.8MM **Privately Held**
WEB: www.franklin.faurecia.com
SIC: 3714 5013 Mufflers (exhaust), motor
vehicle; motor vehicle supplies & new
parts
HQ: Faurecia Usa Holdings, Inc.
2800 High Meadow Cir
Auburn Hills MI 48326
248 724-5100

(G-18464)
FAURECIA USA HOLDINGS INC
543 Matzinger Rd (43612-2638)
PHONE....................................419 727-5000
Jacques Mauge, *Exec VP*
Christophe Schmitt, *Exec VP*
Alex Acket, *Vice Pres*
Anthony Stainer, *Vice Pres*
Nina Valion, *Vice Pres*
EMP: 8
SALES (corp-wide): 271.8MM **Privately Held**
SIC: 3714 Mufflers (exhaust), motor vehi-
cle
HQ: Faurecia Usa Holdings, Inc.
2800 High Meadow Cir
Auburn Hills MI 48326
248 724-5100

(G-18465)
FEDEX OFFICE & PRINT SVCS INC
7007 W Central Ave Unit C (43617-2102)
PHONE....................................419 841-2756
Fax: 419 841-2780
Justin Dotson, *Human Resources*
EMP: 4
SALES (corp-wide): 50.3B **Publicly Held**
SIC: 2752 Commercial printing, litho-
graphic
HQ: Fedex Office And Print Services, Inc.
7900 Legacy Dr
Plano TX 75024
214 550-7000

(G-18466)
FEDEX OFFICE & PRINT SVCS INC
2306 S Reynolds Rd (43614-1417)
PHONE....................................419 866-5464
Dave Prala, *Manager*

EMP: 20
SALES (corp-wide): 50.3B **Publicly Held**
WEB: www.kinkos.com
SIC: 7334 2789 5943 2791 Photocopying
& duplicating services; binding only:
books, pamphlets, magazines, etc.; stationery stores; typesetting; commercial
printing, lithographic
HQ: Fedex Office And Print Services, Inc.
7900 Legacy Dr
Plano TX 75024
214 550-7000

(G-18467)
FENNER DUNLOP (TOLEDO) LLC
146 S Westwood Ave (43607-2948)
P.O. Box 441 (43697-0441)
PHONE....................................419 531-5300
David Hurd, *President*
Cassandra Pan, *President*
Ben Ficklen, *Corp Secy*
Bill Mooney, *CFO*
Bob Greenway, *Controller*
EMP: 50
SQ FT: 100,000
SALES (est): 11.4MM
SALES (corp-wide): 743.7MM **Privately Held**
SIC: 3052 Rubber belting
HQ: Fenner Dunlop Americas, Llc
1000 Omega Dr Ste 1400
Pittsburgh PA 15205

(G-18468)
FENWICK GALLERY OF FINE ARTS (PA)
Also Called: Fenwick Frame Shppe Art Gllery
3433 W Alexis Rd Frnt (43623-1400)
PHONE....................................419 475-1651
Fax: 419 475-9365
Beverly A Freshour, *President*
EMP: 6
SQ FT: 3,000
SALES (est): 634.5K **Privately Held**
SIC: 5999 2499 Art dealers; picture & mir-
ror frames, wood

(G-18469)
FERGUSONS FINISHING INC
Also Called: Universal Bindery
126 N Ontario St (43604-5938)
PHONE....................................419 241-9123
Fax: 419 242-4449
Richard Ferguson, *President*
Janet Ferguson, *Treasurer*
EMP: 20
SQ FT: 15,000
SALES (est): 725K **Privately Held**
WEB: www.universalbindery.com
SIC: 2789 Pamphlets, binding; trade bind-
ing services

(G-18470)
FIBREBOARD CORPORATION (DH)
1 Owens Corning Pkwy (43659-1000)
PHONE....................................419 248-8000
David T Brown, *President*
Roy Dean, *Vice Pres*
Joseph J Mikelonis, *Vice Pres*
Michael Thaman, *CFO*
Ralph A Than, *Treasurer*
▲ EMP: 200 EST: 1917
SALES (est): 24.3MM
SALES (corp-wide): 5.6B **Publicly Held**
SIC: 3089 3272 3296 Siding, plastic; cast
stone, concrete; mineral wool insulation
products
HQ: Owens Corning Sales, Llc
1 Owens Corning Pkwy
Toledo OH 43659
419 248-8000

(G-18471)
FISKE BROTHERS REFINING CO
1500 Oakdale Ave (43605-3843)
P.O. Box 8038 (43605-0038)
PHONE....................................419 691-2491
Fax: 419 693-3806
Tim Everheart, *Plant Mgr*
William Kuhlman, *Manager*
Chris Drain, *MIS Dir*
William Kersey, *Systems Staff*
EMP: 60
SQ FT: 30,000

SALES (corp-wide): 42.1MM **Privately Held**
SIC: 2992 2077 Re-refining lubricating oils
& greases; animal & marine fats & oils
PA: Fiske Brothers Refining Co Inc
129 Lockwood St
Newark NJ 07105
973 589-9150

(G-18472)
FLYNN INC
5540 Jackman Rd (43613-2330)
PHONE....................................419 478-3743
Fax: 419 478-0109
Patrick Flynn, *President*
Michael Mouilleseaux, *General Mgr*
Mary Schira, *Corp Secy*
Doug Kennedy, *Executive*
EMP: 350 EST: 1961
SALES (est): 53.8MM **Privately Held**
WEB: www.erie.com
SIC: 3398 Metal heat treating

(G-18473)
FRIGID UNITS INC
5072 Lewis Ave (43612-3257)
PHONE....................................419 478-4000
Fax: 419 478-4019
Dawn M Heilman, *President*
Mark S Heilman, *Vice Pres*
EMP: 3
SQ FT: 4,000
SALES: 680K **Privately Held**
WEB: www.frigidunits.com
SIC: 3231 Aquariums & reflectors, glass

(G-18474)
FRITZIE FREEZE INC
5137 N Summit St Unit 1 (43611-2754)
PHONE....................................419 727-0818
Chris Schwind, *Principal*
EMP: 3
SALES (est): 201.5K **Privately Held**
SIC: 2024 Ice cream, bulk

(G-18475)
FULTON EQUIPMENT CO (PA)
823 Hamilton St (43607-4477)
PHONE....................................419 290-5393
Fax: 419 255-2950
Richard G Paul Jr, *President*
Anna Okun, *Treasurer*
EMP: 9
SQ FT: 8,000
SALES: 3MM **Privately Held**
SIC: 3441 3444 3443 Fabricated struc-
tural metal; sheet metalwork; fabricated
plate work (boiler shop)

(G-18476)
G H CUTTER SERVICES INC
6203 N Detroit Ave (43612-4818)
PHONE....................................419 476-0476
Fax: 419 476-0778
Gene Hodapp, *President*
Mary Hodapp, *Admin Sec*
EMP: 9
SALES: 750K **Privately Held**
WEB: www.ghcutters.com
SIC: 3599 7389 Machine shop, jobbing &
repair; grinding, precision: commercial or
industrial

(G-18477)
GARDNER SIGNS INC (PA)
3800 Airport Hwy (43615-7106)
PHONE....................................419 385-6669
Fax: 419 385-7046
Weston L Gardner Jr, *CEO*
Scott Gardner, *President*
Jeff Prymas, *General Mgr*
EMP: 17 EST: 1945
SQ FT: 13,000
SALES (est): 3MM **Privately Held**
WEB: www.gardnersigns.com
SIC: 3993 Electric signs; neon signs;
signs, not made in custom sign painting
shops

(G-18478)
GDY INSTALLATIONS INC
302 Arco Dr (43607-2907)
PHONE....................................419 467-0036
Gary Young, *President*
Jeff Young, *Manager*
EMP: 30

SQ FT: 8,430
SALES (est): 3.3MM **Privately Held**
WEB: www.gdyinstallations.com
SIC: 3272 Furniture, church: concrete

(G-18479)
GENERAL MILLS INC
1250 W Laskey Rd (43612-2935)
PHONE..................................419 269-3100
Fax: 419 476-5123
Jennifer Hatcher, *Human Res Dir*
Ann Bombrys, *Branch Mgr*
EMP: 10
SALES (corp-wide): 16.5B **Publicly Held**
WEB: www.generalmills.com
SIC: 2043 Wheat flakes: prepared as cereal breakfast food; oats, rolled: prepared as cereal breakfast food; corn flakes: prepared as cereal breakfast food; rice: prepared as cereal breakfast food
PA: General Mills, Inc.
1 General Mills Blvd
Minneapolis MN 55426
763 764-7600

(G-18480)
GIANT INDUSTRIES INC
900 N Westwood Ave (43607-3261)
PHONE..................................419 531-4600
Fax: 419 531-6836
Raymond Simon, *CEO*
Edward Simon, *President*
Debbie Harrison, *Controller*
Daniel Pietrowski, *Manager*
Wolfgang Drescher, *Admin Sec*
▲ **EMP:** 40
SQ FT: 83,000
SALES (est): 9.5MM **Privately Held**
WEB: www.giantpumps.com
SIC: 3581 3589 5084 3594 Automatic vending machines; car washing machinery; pumps & pumping equipment; fluid power pumps & motors; pumps & pumping equipment; sanitary paper products

(G-18481)
GLOBAL CHEMICAL INC
1925 Nebraska Ave (43607-3830)
PHONE..................................419 242-1004
Tom Oppold, *President*
Barb Ryan, *Administration*
EMP: 4
SALES (est): 360K **Privately Held**
SIC: 2899 Chemical supplies for foundries

(G-18482)
GNRL CHEMICAL L
1661 Campbell St (43607-4322)
PHONE..................................419 255-0193
J Poure, *Principal*
Rick Ryan, *Manager*
EMP: 6
SQ FT: 20,000
SALES (est): 932.3K **Privately Held**
SIC: 2819 Industrial inorganic chemicals

(G-18483)
GOODWILL INDS NW OHIO INC
525 Cherry St (43604-1703)
PHONE..................................419 255-0070
Bob Huber, *Branch Mgr*
EMP: 23
SALES (corp-wide): 19.1MM **Privately Held**
SIC: 3999 Barber & beauty shop equipment
PA: Goodwill Industries Of Northwest Ohio, Inc.
626 N Huron St
Toledo OH 43604
419 255-0070

(G-18484)
GOTTFRIED MEDICAL INC
2920 Centennial Rd (43617-1833)
P.O. Box 8966 (43623-0966)
PHONE..................................419 474-2973
Fax: 419 517-7091
Brent Gottfried, *President*
Pauline Gottfried, *Vice Pres*
Lisa King, *Treasurer*
Brian Genide, *Info Tech Mgr*
EMP: 23
SALES (est): 3.3MM **Privately Held**
WEB: www.gottfriedmedical.com
SIC: 3842 Surgical appliances & supplies

(G-18485)
GRAHAM PACKG PLASTIC PDTS INC (DH)
1 Seagate Ste 10 (43604-1563)
PHONE..................................717 849-8500
Joseph H Lemieux, *Ch of Bd*
Chris Mayrhofer, *Controller*
EMP: 25
SALES (est): 244.9MM
SALES (corp-wide): 9B **Publicly Held**
SIC: 3089 Plastic containers, except foam
HQ: Rexam Limited
Rexam, Rexam Limited
Luton BEDS LU1 3
207 227-4100

(G-18486)
GREAT AMERICAN COOKIE COMPANY
5001 Monroe St Ste Fc13 (43623-7017)
PHONE..................................419 474-9417
Jack Scott, *Owner*
EMP: 12
SQ FT: 400
SALES (est): 244.3K **Privately Held**
SIC: 5461 2052 Cookies; cookies

(G-18487)
GREENWOOD PRINTING & GRAPHICS
3615 Stickney Ave (43608-1307)
PHONE..................................419 727-3275
Fax: 419 727-3515
David Stickley, *Owner*
EMP: 12
SQ FT: 5,700
SALES (est): 800K **Privately Held**
SIC: 2752 Commercial printing, offset

(G-18488)
GREGGS SPECIALTY SERVICES
Also Called: Ch Enterprises
306 Dura Ave (43612-2618)
PHONE..................................419 478-0803
Matthew Haocomb, *President*
EMP: 10
SQ FT: 20,000
SALES (est): 860K **Privately Held**
SIC: 7692 7539 7629 Welding repair; trailer repair; electrical repair shops

(G-18489)
GT TECHNOLOGIES INC
Toledo Stamping
99 N Fearing Blvd (43607-3602)
P.O. Box 596 (43697-0596)
PHONE..................................419 324-7300
Fax: 419 382-8823
Mark Muller, *Branch Mgr*
EMP: 100
SALES (corp-wide): 218.6MM **Privately Held**
SIC: 3714 3469 3465 Motor vehicle engines & parts; metal stampings; automotive stampings
HQ: Gt Technologies, Inc.
5859 E Executive Dr
Westland MI 48185
734 467-8371

(G-18490)
H P STREICHER INC (PA)
2955 Gradwohl Rd (43617-1507)
PHONE..................................419 841-4715
Kurt Smith, *President*
John L Streicher, *Shareholder*
EMP: 2 **EST:** 1860
SQ FT: 3,500
SALES: 5MM **Privately Held**
WEB: www.atlaspaving.com
SIC: 1771 2951 Blacktop (asphalt) work; concrete, asphaltic (not from refineries)

(G-18491)
H&M MACHINE & TOOL LLC
3823 Seiss Ave (43612-1316)
PHONE..................................419 776-9220
Mike Whatley, *Vice Pres*
John Miller, *Mng Member*
Dan Harvey,
EMP: 22
SALES (est): 3.5MM **Privately Held**
SIC: 3544 3543 Industrial molds; industrial patterns

(G-18492)
HA-INTERNATIONAL LLC
4243 South Ave (43615-6233)
PHONE..................................419 537-0096
Michael Hohol, *Branch Mgr*
John Pauley, *Maintence Staff*
EMP: 30
SQ FT: 62,680 **Privately Held**
SIC: 2869 3582 2992 Industrial organic chemicals; commercial laundry equipment; lubricating oils & greases
HQ: Ha-International, Llc
630 Oakmont Ln
Westmont IL 60559
630 575-5700

(G-18493)
HAFNER HARDWOOD CONNECTION LLC
Also Called: Hardwood Connection, The
2845 111th St (43611-2826)
PHONE..................................419 726-4828
Fax: 419 729-0136
Michelle White, *Business Mgr*
Todd Hafner, *Mng Member*
EMP: 6
SQ FT: 5,600
SALES: 300K **Privately Held**
WEB: www.woodworkingtools.com
SIC: 3999 7389 Plaques, picture, laminated; engraving service

(G-18494)
HALE PERFORMANCE COATINGS INC
2282 Albion St (43606-4523)
PHONE..................................419 244-6451
Fax: 419 244-7801
Frederick M Deye, *President*
R A Jefferies Jr, *Principal*
G C Scharfy, *Principal*
J C Straub, *Principal*
Carol Lambrecht, *Treasurer*
EMP: 42 **EST:** 1966
SQ FT: 14,700
SALES: 7MM **Privately Held**
WEB: www.halechrome.com
SIC: 3471 3544 Chromium plating of metals or formed products; special dies, tools, jigs & fixtures

(G-18495)
HANGER PRSTHETCS & ORTHO INC
3435 N Hlland Sylvania Rd (43615)
PHONE..................................419 841-9852
Thomas Sandy, *Manager*
Tom Sandy, *Manager*
EMP: 13
SALES (corp-wide): 460MM **Publicly Held**
SIC: 3842 5999 Prosthetic appliances; orthopedic & prosthesis applications
HQ: Hanger Prosthetics & Orthotics, Inc.
10910 Domain Dr Ste 300
Austin TX 78758
512 777-3800

(G-18496)
HANSEN-MUELLER CO
1800 N Water St (43611)
P.O. Box 50497 (43605-0497)
PHONE..................................419 729-5535
Fax: 419 729-5510
Mike Burget, *Manager*
EMP: 26
SALES (corp-wide): 81.6MM **Privately Held**
WEB: www.hmgrain.com
SIC: 5153 2041 Grains; flour & other grain mill products
PA: Hansen-Mueller Co.
12231 Emmet St Ste 1
Omaha NE 68164
402 491-3385

(G-18497)
HARDWARE UNLIMITED LLC
226 S Reynolds Rd Ste A (43615-5971)
PHONE..................................419 472-8745
Harry Roby,
EMP: 4
SALES (est): 429.2K **Privately Held**
WEB: www.hardwareunlimited.com
SIC: 3429 Cabinet hardware

(G-18498)
HAYES BROS ORNAMENTAL IR WORKS
1830 N Reynolds Rd (43615-3530)
PHONE..................................419 531-1491
Fax: 419 531-1492
Gary M Hayes, *President*
Patrick Hayes, *Vice Pres*
Douglas C Hayes, *Treasurer*
Gregory M Hayes, *Admin Sec*
EMP: 10 **EST:** 1946
SQ FT: 10,000
SALES (est): 1.4MM **Privately Held**
WEB: www.hayesiron.com
SIC: 3446 Railings, prefabricated metal; guards, made from pipe; gates, ornamental metal

(G-18499)
HEARN PLATING CO LTD
3184 Bellevue Rd (43606-1801)
PHONE..................................419 473-9773
Fax: 419 473-0919
Wallace Friedel, *Manager*
John D Drumheller,
Marcia M Drumheller, *Admin Sec*
EMP: 14 **EST:** 1902
SQ FT: 6,400
SALES (est): 2MM **Privately Held**
WEB: www.hearnplating.com
SIC: 3471 Plating of metals or formed products

(G-18500)
HEARTHSIDE FOOD SOLUTIONS LLC
Also Called: Summit Packaging Center
3444 N Summit St (43611-3242)
PHONE..................................419 727-1298
Fax: 419 727-1518
John Weisenberger, *Manager*
EMP: 20
SQ FT: 95,228
SALES (corp-wide): 2.3B **Privately Held**
SIC: 2052 Cookies; crackers, dry
PA: Hearthside Food Solutions, Llc
3250 Lacey Rd Ste 200
Downers Grove IL 60515
630 967-3600

(G-18501)
HEATHERDOWNS LICENSE BUREAU
4460 Heatherdowns Blvd (43614-3113)
PHONE..................................419 381-1109
Fax: 419 381-0250
Pamela Rupp, *Principal*
EMP: 5
SALES (est): 383.7K **Privately Held**
SIC: 3469 Automobile license tags, stamped metal

(G-18502)
HECKS DIRECT MAIL & PRTG SVC (PA)
417 Main St (43605-2057)
PHONE..................................419 697-3505
Fax: 419 691-0752
Edward Heck, *CEO*
EMP: 38 **EST:** 1943
SQ FT: 30,000
SALES (est): 4.2MM **Privately Held**
WEB: www.heckersprinting.com
SIC: 7331 2752 2791 2789 Addressing service; commercial printing, offset; typesetting; bookbinding & related work; commercial printing

(G-18503)
HECKS DIRECT MAIL & PRTG SVC
Also Called: Heck's Diamond Printing
202 W Florence Ave (43605-3304)
P.O. Box 8266 (43605-0266)
PHONE..................................419 661-6028
Fax: 419 661-6036
Cosino Trina, *Vice Pres*
EMP: 25
SALES (corp-wide): 4.2MM **Privately Held**
WEB: www.heckersprinting.com
SIC: 2752 7331 5192 Offset & photolithographic printing; direct mail advertising services; books, periodicals & newspapers

PA: Heck's Direct Mail & Printing Service
　Inc
　417 Main St
　Toledo OH 43605
　419 697-3505

(G-18504)
HEDGES SELECTIVE TOOL & PROD
Also Called: Select Tool & Production
702 W Laskey Rd (43612-3209)
PHONE..............................419 478-8670
Fax: 419 478-8671
Jeff Lachatelle, *President*
Kathryn Lachapelle, *Vice Pres*
Kathy Lachatelle, *Vice Pres*
EMP: 12
SQ FT: 15,048
SALES (est): 1MM **Privately Held**
SIC: 3544 Special dies, tools, jigs & fix-
tures

(G-18505)
HEIDTMAN STEEL PRODUCTS INC (HQ)
2401 Front St (43605-1199)
PHONE..............................419 691-4646
Fax: 419 698-1150
John C Bates, *CEO*
Tim Berra, *President*
F Wm Heidtman, *Principal*
Margery Heidtman, *Principal*
Mark Ridenour, *CFO*
▲ **EMP:** 45 **EST:** 1962
SQ FT: 15,000
SALES (est): 264.3MM
SALES (corp-wide): 273MM **Privately
Held**
WEB: www.heidtman.com
SIC: 3316 3312 Strip steel, cold-rolled:
from purchased hot-rolled; sheet or strip,
steel, hot-rolled
PA: Centaur, Inc.
　2401 Front St
　Toledo OH 43605
　419 469-8000

(G-18506)
HEIDTMAN STEEL PRODUCTS INC
Also Called: Heidtman Toledo Blank
135 N Flearing Blvd (43609)
PHONE..............................419 385-0636
John C Bates, *CEO*
EMP: 87
SALES (corp-wide): 249MM **Privately
Held**
SIC: 3312 Sheet or strip, steel, hot-rolled
HQ: Heidtman Steel Products, Inc.
　2401 Front St
　Toledo OH 43605
　419 691-4646

(G-18507)
HENLY CORPORATION
520 W Laskey Rd (43612-3207)
PHONE..............................419 476-0851
Fax: 419 476-0852
Steven Henly, *President*
Audrey Henly, *Vice Pres*
Mark Henly, *Admin Sec*
EMP: 3 **EST:** 1921
SQ FT: 6,500
SALES: 150K **Privately Held**
SIC: 2499 Woodenware, kitchen & house-
hold

(G-18508)
HILL JOHN
Also Called: R J Displays
3019 E Manhattan Blvd (43611-1714)
PHONE..............................419 727-8666
Fax: 419 727-8677
John R Hill, *Owner*
Shannon Hill, *Bookkeeper*
EMP: 15
SQ FT: 15,000
SALES: 1.1MM **Privately Held**
WEB: www.rjdisplays.com
SIC: 3993 Displays & cutouts, window &
lobby

(G-18509)
HOLLAND ENGRAVING COMPANY
Also Called: Holland Engineering Co
7340 Dorr St (43615-4112)
PHONE..............................419 865-2765
Fax: 419 867-1151
Martin Hartkopf, *President*
Martin Hartkof, *Personnel Exec*
EMP: 12
SQ FT: 15,600
SALES (est): 1.7MM **Privately Held**
WEB: www.holland-eng.com
SIC: 3544 Special dies, tools, jigs & fix-
tures

(G-18510)
HOMEWOOD PRESS INC
400 E State Line Rd (43612-4779)
PHONE..............................419 478-0695
Fax: 419 478-3427
Scott Dubuc, *President*
Mark Dubuc, *Vice Pres*
Dan Curson, *Marketing Staff*
Kyrsten Dubuc, *Marketing Staff*
Linda Rava, *Marketing Staff*
EMP: 30 **EST:** 1922
SQ FT: 11,000
SALES (est): 7.3MM **Privately Held**
WEB: www.homewoodpress.com
SIC: 2752 2791 2789 2759 Commercial
printing, offset; typesetting; bookbinding &
related work; commercial printing

(G-18511)
HOOVER & WELLS INC
Also Called: Rez Stone
2011 Seaman St (43605-1908)
PHONE..............................419 691-9220
Fax: 419 691-8318
Margaret Hoover, *Ch of Bd*
James M Collu, *President*
Barbara Corsini, *President*
John Corsini, *Vice Pres*
James Mc Collum, *Vice Pres*
EMP: 120
SQ FT: 23,448
SALES: 26.9MM **Privately Held**
WEB: www.hooverwells.com
SIC: 1752 2891 2851 Floor laying & floor
work; adhesives & sealants; paints & al-
lied products

(G-18512)
HORWITZ & PINTIS CO
1604 Tracy St (43605-3426)
P.O. Box 60257, Rossford (43460-0257)
PHONE..............................419 666-2220
Fax: 419 666-5760
Steve Horwitz, *President*
Phyllis Horwitz, *Corp Secy*
EMP: 15
SQ FT: 20,000
SALES (est): 4.1MM **Privately Held**
SIC: 5085 3412 2655 Drums, new or re-
conditioned; metal barrels, drums & pails;
fiber cans, drums & similar products

(G-18513)
HOT MAMA FOODS INC
5839 Secor Rd (43623-1421)
PHONE..............................419 474-3402
Fax: 419 474-3403
Mike Barone, *President*
◆ **EMP:** 15
SQ FT: 5,118
SALES (est): 2.1MM **Privately Held**
SIC: 2051 Bread, cake & related products

(G-18514)
I P S TREATMENTS INC
3254 Hill Ave (43607-2911)
PHONE..............................419 241-5955
Fax: 419 241-5040
Fred Pinto, *President*
Manit Vichitchot, *Vice Pres*
EMP: 9
SQ FT: 16,000
SALES (est): 750K **Privately Held**
WEB: www.ipstreatment.com
SIC: 3471 Cleaning, polishing & finishing

(G-18515)
I T W AUTOMOTIVE FINISHING
320 Phillips Ave (43612-1467)
PHONE..............................419 470-2000

Tom Murray, *General Mgr*
Roger Cedoz, *Principal*
John Bland, *Project Mgr*
Marty Selmek, *Engineer*
EMP: 4
SALES (est): 310K **Privately Held**
SIC: 3559 Automotive maintenance equip-
ment

(G-18516)
IGNIO SYSTEMS LLC
444 W Laskey Rd Ste V (43612-3460)
PHONE..............................419 708-0503
Jon Snyder,
Jim Demarest,
EMP: 14
SALES (est): 2.6MM **Privately Held**
SIC: 3821 3625 3822 5063 Ovens, labo-
ratory; motor controls, electric; tempera-
ture controls, automatic; gas burner,
automatic controls; boxes & fittings, elec-
trical

(G-18517)
IMPAC HI-PERFORMANCE MACHINING
5515 Enterprise Blvd (43612-3814)
PHONE..............................419 726-7100
Fax: 419 726-7121
Gerald R Nastachowski, *Owner*
Chris Nastachowski, *Manager*
EMP: 6
SQ FT: 6,000
SALES (est): 300K **Privately Held**
SIC: 3599 Machine shop, jobbing & repair

(G-18518)
IMPACT PRODUCTS LLC (DH)
2840 Centennial Rd (43617-1898)
PHONE..............................419 841-2891
Fax: 800 333-1531
Terry Neal, *CEO*
John Irwin, *President*
John Peggs, *Business Mgr*
John Bandi, *Warehouse Mgr*
Carolyn Helminiak, *Purch Agent*
▲ **EMP:** 140 **EST:** 2001
SQ FT: 155,000
SALES: 120MM
SALES (corp-wide): 15.3B **Publicly Held**
WEB: www.impact-products.com
SIC: 5084 5087 2392 3089 Safety equip-
ment; janitors' supplies; mops, floor &
dust; buckets, plastic; tissue dispensers,
plastic
HQ: S. P. Richards Company
　6300 Highlands Pkwy Se
　Smyrna GA 30082
　770 434-4571

(G-18519)
INCEPTOR INC
1301 Progress Ave (43612-3835)
PHONE..............................419 726-8804
Fax: 419 726-8762
Edward F Pavuk, *President*
EMP: 5
SQ FT: 20,000
SALES (est): 750K **Privately Held**
WEB: www.inceptor.net
SIC: 2842 5169 2865 Cleaning or polish-
ing preparations; sanitation preparations,
disinfectants & deodorants; chemicals &
allied products; dyes, synthetic organic

(G-18520)
INDEPENDENT POWER CONSULTANTS
6051 Telegraph Rd Ste 19 (43612-4560)
PHONE..............................419 476-8383
Fax: 419 476-0416
David Denner, *President*
Patricia M Denner, *Corp Secy*
Michael W Denner, *Vice Pres*
EMP: 7
SALES: 950K **Privately Held**
SIC: 3469 Machine parts, stamped or
pressed metal

(G-18521)
INDICATOR ADVISORY CORPORATION
3061 Shoreland Ave (43611-1251)
PHONE..............................419 726-9000
Robert Kneisley, *President*

EMP: 3
SALES (est): 261.3K **Privately Held**
WEB: www.indicatoradvisory.com
SIC: 2721 2731 Periodicals: publishing
only; books: publishing only

(G-18522)
INDUSTRIAL SCREEN PROCESS (PA)
Also Called: Isps
17 17th St (43604-6708)
P.O. Box 593 (43697-0593)
PHONE..............................419 255-4900
Fax: 419 255-4908
Thomas V Cutcher Sr, *President*
Sharon Cutcher, *Corp Secy*
Thomas V Cutcher II, *Vice Pres*
Teresa House, *Prgrmr*
EMP: 15
SQ FT: 53,000
SALES (est): 2.2MM **Privately Held**
WEB: www.ispsinc.com
SIC: 2759 7373 Screen printing; com-
puter-aided design (CAD) systems serv-
ice

(G-18523)
INITIAL DESIGNS INC
Also Called: Seaway Enterprises
2453 Tremainsville Rd # 2 (43613-3438)
PHONE..............................419 475-3900
Robert W Stauffer, *President*
Carole S Stauffer, *Admin Sec*
EMP: 6
SQ FT: 13,000
SALES: 206.7K **Privately Held**
WEB: www.seawayenterprises.com
SIC: 2395 Embroidery & art needlework

(G-18524)
INNOVATIVE CONTROLS CORP
1354 E Broadway St (43605-3667)
PHONE..............................419 691-6684
Fax: 419 691-0170
Louis M Soltis, *President*
Anson F Schultz, *Vice Pres*
Ken Metzger, *Mfg Staff*
Mark Benton, *Engineer*
John Pavlica, *Engineer*
EMP: 63
SQ FT: 20,000
SALES (est): 14.1MM **Privately Held**
WEB: www.innovativecontrolscorp.com
SIC: 3613 3535 8711 3823 Control pan-
els, electric; conveyors & conveying
equipment; engineering services; indus-
trial instrmnts msrmnt display/control
process variable; relays & industrial con-
trols; food products machinery

(G-18525)
INSTA PLAK INC (PA)
Also Called: Insta-Plak
5025 Dorr St (43615-3855)
PHONE..............................419 537-1555
Fax: 419 537-1511
Rexford E Hardin DDS, *CEO*
Stephen R Hardin, *President*
James Byrd, *Vice Pres*
Betty Hardin, *Admin Sec*
EMP: 12
SQ FT: 7,800
SALES (est): 1.4MM **Privately Held**
SIC: 2499 3993 Decorative wood & wood-
work; signs, not made in custom sign
painting shops

(G-18526)
INTERNATIONAL FUEL SYSTEMS INC
2101 W Sylvania Ave (43613-4436)
PHONE..............................419 475-5276
Fax: 419 475-5277
Chet Craft, *Manager*
Christopher Smith, *Manager*
EMP: 5
SALES (est): 517.2K **Privately Held**
SIC: 2869 Fuels

(G-18527)
INTERTEC CORPORATION
3400 Executive Pkwy (43606-1396)
P.O. Box 2927 (43606-0927)
PHONE..............................419 537-9711
George B Seifried, *President*
Scott A Slater, *Vice Pres*

Darrel G Howard, *Admin Sec*
◆ **EMP:** 300 **EST:** 1978
SQ FT: 1,000
SALES (est): 642.6K **Privately Held**
WEB: www.mspro.com
SIC: 3559 1796 3523 Glass making machinery: blowing, molding, forming, etc.; machinery installation; farm machinery & equipment

(G-18528)
IRONHEAD FABG & CONTG INC
2245 Front St (43605-1231)
PHONE....................................419 690-0000
Anthony Lamantia, *President*
Kathy Lamantia, *CFO*
Nancy Coci, *Manager*
Kelly McCary, *Manager*
Mike Brown, *Executive*
EMP: 65
SQ FT: 33,500
SALES: 10MM **Privately Held**
SIC: 3441 Fabricated structural metal

(G-18529)
IRONHEAD MARINE INC
2245 Front St (43605-1231)
PHONE....................................419 690-0001
Kathy Lamantia, *CFO*
EMP: 20
SALES (est): 3.3MM **Privately Held**
SIC: 3731 Shipbuilding & repairing

(G-18530)
ISHOS BROS FUEL VENTURES INC
2446 W Alexis Rd (43613-2139)
PHONE....................................419 913-5718
Mahir Isho, *Principal*
EMP: 6
SALES (est): 726.5K **Privately Held**
SIC: 2869 Fuels

(G-18531)
J & S INDUSTRIAL MCH PDTS INC
123 Oakdale Ave (43605-3322)
PHONE....................................419 691-1380
Fax: 419 691-0339
Nancy Colyer, *Principal*
Elton E Bowland, *Principal*
George Bowland, *Principal*
John Sehr, *Principal*
Donald R Colyer, *Vice Pres*
EMP: 70 **EST:** 1946
SQ FT: 32,000
SALES (est): 10.3MM **Privately Held**
WEB: www.jsindustrialmachine.com
SIC: 3559 7692 Glass making machinery: blowing, molding, forming, etc.; welding repair

(G-18532)
J M SMUCKER COMPANY
1250 W Laskey Rd (43612-2909)
P.O. Box 357 (43697-0357)
PHONE....................................419 470-7914
Joe Beer, *Plant Mgr*
Ed Labo, *Facilities Mgr*
Stephen Masternak, *Production*
Wayne Clive, *Branch Mgr*
Jill Hojnacki, *MIS Dir*
EMP: 50
SALES (corp-wide): 7.8B **Publicly Held**
WEB: www.smuckers.com
SIC: 2045 2099 Prepared flour mixes & doughs; food preparations
PA: The J M Smucker Company
1 Strawberry Ln
Orrville OH 44667
330 682-3000

(G-18533)
JENSAR MANUFACTURING LLC
1230 S Expressway Dr (43608-1516)
PHONE....................................419 727-8320
Christopher Jakab, *VP Mfg*
Luis Villaflor,
Tom Villaflor,
EMP: 4
SQ FT: 1,200
SALES (est): 659.2K **Privately Held**
SIC: 3089 Injection molding of plastics

(G-18534)
JENSEN & SONS INC
4481 Monroe St (43613-4708)
PHONE....................................419 471-1000
Fax: 419 471-9001
David W Jensen, *President*
James Jensen, *Vice Pres*
EMP: 11 **EST:** 1953
SALES: 1.6MM **Privately Held**
SIC: 3911 Jewelry, precious metal

(G-18535)
JOBSKIN DIV OF TORBOT GROUP
5030 Advantage Dr Ste 101 (43612-3861)
PHONE....................................419 724-1475
Fax: 419 724-1476
Angie Zablocki, *Manager*
EMP: 25
SALES (est): 2.1MM **Privately Held**
SIC: 3842 Bandages & dressings; gauze, surgical

(G-18536)
K-JS MECHANICAL SERVICE
606 New York Ave (43611-3329)
PHONE....................................419 729-1103
Kenneth Lohmeyer, *Owner*
EMP: 11
SQ FT: 4,368
SALES (est): 566.2K **Privately Held**
SIC: 1711 3061 Mechanical contractor; mechanical rubber goods

(G-18537)
KAHUNA BAY SPRAY TAN LLC
Also Called: Artesian Tan
757 Warehouse Rd Ste E-F (43615-6467)
PHONE....................................419 386-2387
A J Licata-Bernath, *Mng Member*
Christopher Bernast,
Andrea J Licata-Bernath,
EMP: 5
SALES (est): 900.9K **Privately Held**
WEB: www.artesiantan.com
SIC: 2844 7299 Face creams or lotions; tanning salon

(G-18538)
KAMALA K TAMIRISA MD
2940 N Mccord Rd (43615-1753)
PHONE....................................419 842-3000
Kamala Tamirisa, *Principal*
EMP: 4 **EST:** 2013
SALES (est): 275K **Privately Held**
SIC: 3845 Electrocardiographs

(G-18539)
KAPIOS LLC
Also Called: Kapios Health
2865 N Reynolds Rd 220d (43615-2068)
PHONE....................................567 661-0772
Justin Hammerling, *CEO*
EMP: 6
SALES (est): 135.3K **Privately Held**
SIC: 7372 8099 Business oriented computer software; health & allied services

(G-18540)
KASPER ENTERPRISES INC
Also Called: Harmon Sign Company
7844 W Central Ave (43617-1530)
PHONE....................................419 829-2121
Fax: 419 841-7160
Daniel C Kasper, *Ch of Bd*
Jeff Kasper, *President*
John E Wagoner, *Principal*
Judith Kasper, *Admin Sec*
EMP: 7
SQ FT: 55,430
SALES (est): 1.8MM **Privately Held**
WEB: www.planetharmon.com
SIC: 3993 Electric signs; neon signs; signs, not made in custom sign painting shops

(G-18541)
KAY TOLEDO TAG INC
6050 Benore Rd (43612-3906)
P.O. Box 5038 (43611-0038)
PHONE....................................419 729-5479
Fax: 419 729-0315
Dan Kay, *President*
EMP: 96 **EST:** 1973
SQ FT: 87,000

SALES (est): 8.7MM
SALES (corp-wide): 568.9MM **Publicly Held**
WEB: www.kaytag.com
SIC: 2752 2679 2759 2671 Commercial printing, offset; tags & labels, paper; commercial printing; packaging paper & plastics film, coated & laminated
PA: Ennis, Inc.
2441 Presidential Pkwy
Midlothian TX 76065
972 775-9801

(G-18542)
KENCRAFT CO INC
821 N Westwood Ave (43607-3561)
PHONE....................................419 536-0333
Fax: 419 536-0944
Ken Spitulski, *President*
Virginia Spitulski, *Corp Secy*
Ginny Spitulski, *Admin Sec*
EMP: 4
SQ FT: 8,000
SALES (est): 575.1K **Privately Held**
WEB: www.kencraftcompany.com
SIC: 5961 5211 2511 Mail order house; millwork & lumber; wood household furniture

(G-18543)
KERN MACHINE TOOL INC
367 E State Line Rd (43612-4709)
P.O. Box 5815 (43613-0815)
PHONE....................................419 470-1206
Frank Kern, *President*
EMP: 4
SQ FT: 10,000
SALES (est): 363K **Privately Held**
WEB: www.kernmachine.com
SIC: 3599 Machine shop, jobbing & repair

(G-18544)
KEYSTONE PRESS INC
1801 Broadway St (43609-3290)
P.O. Box 9183 (43697-9183)
PHONE....................................419 243-7326
Fax: 419 243-1126
Paul A Schultz, *CEO*
David P Schultz, *President*
Andrew C Schultz, *Vice Pres*
Elizabeth Schultz, *Treasurer*
EMP: 8 **EST:** 1921
SQ FT: 9,000
SALES (est): 670K **Privately Held**
SIC: 2752 2759 2796 2791 Commercial printing, lithographic; commercial printing, offset; letterpress printing; platemaking services; typesetting; bookbinding & related work

(G-18545)
KITCHEN DESIGNS PLUS INC
2725 N Reynolds Rd (43615-2031)
PHONE....................................419 536-6605
Fax: 419 531-9652
Pat McKimmy, *President*
EMP: 20
SQ FT: 6,000
SALES (est): 6.4MM **Privately Held**
SIC: 5031 2434 Kitchen cabinets; wood kitchen cabinets

(G-18546)
KLOSTERMAN
660 Sterling St (43609-2351)
PHONE....................................419 242-3400
Mark Haskell, *Owner*
EMP: 4 **EST:** 2010
SALES (est): 366.4K **Privately Held**
SIC: 2051 Bakery: wholesale or wholesale/retail combined

(G-18547)
KNIGHT INDUSTRIES CORP
5949 Telegraph Rd (43612-4548)
PHONE....................................419 478-8550
Fax: 419 478-2311
Carrie Ebeid, *Corp Secy*
Kevin Ebeid, *Vice Pres*
Sandy Carr, *Human Res Dir*
EMP: 38
SQ FT: 104,000
SALES (est): 4.1MM **Privately Held**
WEB: www.knightindcorp.com
SIC: 3211 Picture glass; window glass, clear & colored

(G-18548)
KUHLMAN CORPORATION
444 Kuhlman Dr (43609-2629)
PHONE....................................419 321-1670
Fax: 419 321-1666
Pat Ferry, *Opers Staff*
Dwayne Palmer, *Branch Mgr*
EMP: 50
SALES (corp-wide): 55.6MM **Privately Held**
WEB: www.kuhlman-corp.com
SIC: 3273 Ready-mixed concrete
PA: Kuhlman Corporation
1845 Indian Wood Cir
Maumee OH 43537
419 897-6000

(G-18549)
KUHLMAN ENGINEERING CO
840 Champlain St (43604-3643)
PHONE....................................419 243-2196
Fax: 419 243-8930
Phil Kolling, *President*
Norman Kuhlman, *Vice Pres*
EMP: 10 **EST:** 1916
SQ FT: 7,500
SALES (est): 810K **Privately Held**
WEB: www.kuhlmanengineering.net
SIC: 3444 Sheet metalwork

(G-18550)
KUKA TOLEDO PRODUCTION
3770 Stickney Ave (43608-1310)
PHONE....................................419 727-5500
Lawrence A Drake, *CEO*
Nicole Jackson, *Buyer*
Evan Jenkins, *QC Mgr*
Paul Ambros, *CFO*
Brian Bezrutch, *Controller*
EMP: 247
SALES (est): 32.1MM **Privately Held**
WEB: www.kukausa.com
SIC: 3713 Truck & bus bodies
HQ: Kuka Systems Gmbh
Blucherstr. 144
Augsburg 86165
821 797-0

(G-18551)
KYLE PUBLICATIONS INC
2611 Montebello Rd (43607-1366)
P.O. Box 6469 (43612-0469)
PHONE....................................419 754-4234
Erik R Kyle, *President*
EMP: 5 **EST:** 2001
SALES (est): 446.5K **Privately Held**
SIC: 2721 Magazines: publishing only, not printed on site

(G-18552)
LA PERLA INC (PA)
Also Called: Tortilla Factory
2742 Hill Ave (43607-2926)
PHONE....................................419 534-2074
Fax: 419 534-3230
Santiago Martinez, *President*
EMP: 10
SQ FT: 8,000
SALES: 991K **Privately Held**
WEB: www.laperla.com
SIC: 2099 5141 Tortillas, fresh or refrigerated; groceries, general line

(G-18553)
LAFARGE NORTH AMERICA INC
840 Water St (43604-1832)
PHONE....................................419 241-5256
Fax: 419 241-7915
Chris Peatty, *Manager*
Chris Peatee, *Manager*
EMP: 3
SQ FT: 13,560
SALES (corp-wide): 26.6B **Privately Held**
WEB: www.lafargenorthamerica.com
SIC: 3241 Cement, hydraulic
HQ: Lafarge North America Inc.
8700 W Bryn Mawr Ave Ll
Chicago IL 60631
703 480-3600

(G-18554)
LAPRENSA PUBLICATIONS INC
Also Called: Aztlan Communications
616 Adams St (43604-1420)
PHONE....................................419 242-7744
Fax: 419 255-7700

Becky Mc Queen, *Principal*
Richard Neller, *Principal*
EMP: 6
SALES (est): 471.2K **Privately Held**
SIC: 2711 Newspapers: publishing only, not printed on site

(G-18555)
LEE WILLIAMS MEATS INC (PA)
3002 131st St (43611-2329)
PHONE..................419 729-3893
Fax: 419 729-2058
Barry L Williams, *President*
Richard W Boldt, *Vice Pres*
Mary Jo Cramer, *Treasurer*
Margaret Williams, *Admin Sec*
EMP: 25 EST: 1955
SQ FT: 3,096
SALES (est): 3.7MM **Privately Held**
WEB: www.houseofmeats.com
SIC: 5421 2013 Meat markets, including freezer provisioners; sausages & other prepared meats

(G-18556)
LEEPER PRINTING CO INC
710 S Saint Clair St (43609-2432)
P.O. Box 526 (43697-0526)
PHONE..................419 243-2604
Fax: 419 243-7487
Susan Brooman, *Vice Pres*
Jeffrey Cunningham, *Admin Sec*
EMP: 3
SQ FT: 3,200
SALES (est): 300K **Privately Held**
SIC: 2759 Commercial printing

(G-18557)
LEMSCO INC
Also Called: Lemsco-Girkins
2056 Canton Ave (43620-1945)
PHONE..................419 242-4005
Richard J Baldwin, *President*
Richard Baldwin, *President*
Barbara Baldwin, *Corp Secy*
EMP: 8
SQ FT: 11,000
SALES (est): 1.4MM **Privately Held**
SIC: 7694 5999 Electric motor repair; motors, electric

(G-18558)
LIBBEY GLASS INC (HQ)
300 Madison Ave Fl 4 (43604-2634)
P.O. Box 10060 (43699-0060)
PHONE..................419 325-2100
Fax: 419 325-2585
Richard Reynolds, *Exec VP*
L Frederick Ashton, *Vice Pres*
Daniel P Ibele, *Vice Pres*
Susan A Kovach, *Vice Pres*
Timothy T Paige, *Vice Pres*
◆ **EMP:** 200
SALES (est): 576.1MM
SALES (corp-wide): 796.2MM **Publicly Held**
WEB: www.libbeyglass.com
SIC: 3229 3231 Tableware, glass or glass ceramic; products of purchased glass
PA: Libbey Inc.
300 Madison Ave
Toledo OH 43604
419 325-2100

(G-18559)
LIBBEY GLASS INC
940 Ash St (43611-3846)
PHONE..................419 729-7272
Fax: 419 727-2251
Roberto Rubio, *Vice Pres*
Steve Felix, *Plant Mgr*
Joe Stump, *QC Dir*
Ryan Bockbrader, *Engineer*
Don Gerwin, *Engineer*
EMP: 1200
SALES (corp-wide): 796.2MM **Publicly Held**
WEB: www.libbeyglass.com
SIC: 3229 3421 3262 Tableware, glass or glass ceramic; cutlery; vitreous china table & kitchenware
HQ: Libbey Glass Inc.
300 Madison Ave Fl 4
Toledo OH 43604
419 325-2100

(G-18560)
LIBBEY INC
Also Called: Libbey Glass Factory Outlet
205 S Erie St (43604-8607)
PHONE..................419 244-5697
Fax: 419 254-5012
Kenneth Boerger, *Vice Pres*
Tom Lower, *Manager*
Sarah Verlinde, *Manager*
EMP: 14
SALES (corp-wide): 796.2MM **Publicly Held**
WEB: www.libby.com
SIC: 3851 Eyeglasses, lenses & frames
PA: Libbey Inc.
300 Madison Ave
Toledo OH 43604
419 325-2100

(G-18561)
LIBBEY INC (PA)
300 Madison Ave (43604-1561)
P.O. Box 10060 (43699-0060)
PHONE..................419 325-2100
Fax: 419 727-2473
William A Foley, *Ch of Bd*
Brenda Bennett, *Vice Pres*
Antoine Jordans, *Vice Pres*
Jeff Joyce, *Vice Pres*
Susan A Kovach, *Vice Pres*
▼ **EMP:** 200
SALES: 796.2MM **Publicly Held**
WEB: www.libby.com
SIC: 3229 3262 Glass furnishings & accessories; tableware, glass or glass ceramic; bowls, glass; ashtrays, glass; tableware, vitreous china

(G-18562)
LITHIUM INNOVATIONS CO LLC
3171 N Repub Blvd Ste 101 (43615)
PHONE..................419 725-3525
Ford B Cauffiel, *Principal*
◆ **EMP:** 6
SALES (est): 852.9K **Privately Held**
SIC: 2819 Lithium compounds, inorganic

(G-18563)
LOUISE SWEET LLC
3827 Beechway Blvd (43614-4407)
PHONE..................419 460-5505
Randa Shallal,
EMP: 3
SALES (est): 220.1K **Privately Held**
SIC: 2099 Sauces: gravy, dressing & dip mixes

(G-18564)
LUCAS COUNTY ASPHALT INC
Also Called: Buckeye Asphalt Paving Co
7540 Hollow Creek Dr (43617-1652)
P.O. Box 353094 (43635-3094)
PHONE..................419 476-0705
Fax: 419 476-0700
Stephen A Dolgin, *President*
EMP: 25
SQ FT: 4,800
SALES (est): 1.8MM **Privately Held**
WEB: www.buckeyepaving.com
SIC: 1771 2951 Blacktop (asphalt) work; asphalt & asphaltic paving mixtures (not from refineries)

(G-18565)
M & B MACHINE INC
4801 Bennett Rd (43612-2531)
PHONE..................419 476-8836
Patrick Copeland, *President*
EMP: 12
SQ FT: 5,000
SALES (est): 1.5MM **Privately Held**
SIC: 3599 Machine shop, jobbing & repair

(G-18566)
M & D BRINK INC
Also Called: Printing Press
2128 Eastedge Dr (43614-2059)
PHONE..................419 531-6699
Fax: 419 531-5518
Dolores T Brink, *Principal*
EMP: 5 EST: 2013
SALES (est): 299.1K **Privately Held**
SIC: 2711 Commercial printing & newspaper publishing combined

(G-18567)
M RUSSELL & ASSOCIATES INC
3250 Monroe St (43606-4550)
PHONE..................419 478-8795
Melvyn R Russell, *President*
Kim Sherburne, *Treasurer*
Ann M Russell, *Admin Sec*
EMP: 5
SQ FT: 7,000
SALES (est): 574.8K **Privately Held**
SIC: 2796 Plates & cylinders for rotogravure printing

(G-18568)
M&L PLATING WORKS LLC (PA)
425 Jefferson Ave Ste 520 (43604-1073)
PHONE..................419 255-7701
Glen Matts, *Partner*
Sam Leeviroj, *Partner*
David York, *Plant Mgr*
EMP: 3
SALES (est): 570.3K **Privately Held**
SIC: 3471 Plating of metals or formed products

(G-18569)
MAGIC WOK INC (PA)
Also Called: Magic Wok Enterprises
3352 W Laskey Rd (43623-4030)
PHONE..................419 531-1818
Sutas Pipatjarasgit, *President*
Michele Thrasher, *Accountant*
Deborah Mahlman, *Office Mgr*
Nucharee Pipatjarasgit, *Admin Sec*
EMP: 7
SQ FT: 580
SALES (est): 803K **Privately Held**
WEB: www.magicwok.com
SIC: 5812 2032 Chinese restaurant; ethnic foods: canned, jarred, etc.

(G-18570)
MAGNA MODULAR SYSTEMS INC (DH)
Also Called: Magna Team Systems
1800 Nathan Dr (43611-1091)
PHONE..................419 324-3387
Grahhame Burrow, *CEO*
Keith McMahon, *General Mgr*
Joshua Conley, *Production*
Nadine Stricker, *Manager*
▲ **EMP:** 70
SQ FT: 140,000
SALES (est): 182.2MM
SALES (corp-wide): 36.4B **Privately Held**
SIC: 3714 Motor vehicle body components & frame
HQ: Magna Exteriors Of America, Inc.
750 Tower Dr
Troy MI 48098
248 631-1100

(G-18571)
MAGNETNOTES LTD
946 Kane St Ste A (43612-1372)
PHONE..................419 593-0060
Randall A Boudouris, *CEO*
Tom Stiers, *President*
Lisa Voylis, *Manager*
Joshua Waterfield, *Manager*
EMP: 5
SALES (est): 732.5K **Privately Held**
SIC: 3695 Magnetic tape

(G-18572)
MALLORY PATTERN WORKS INC
5340 Enterprise Blvd (43612-3811)
PHONE..................419 726-8001
Fax: 419 726-7902
Al Antoine, *President*
Janice Mallory, *Treasurer*
Shirley Peschel, *Admin Sec*
EMP: 6 EST: 1960
SQ FT: 6,000
SALES (est): 937.9K **Privately Held**
SIC: 3544 3469 Industrial molds; patterns on metal

(G-18573)
MARKEYS AUDIO/VISUAL INC
24 S Saint Clair St (43604-8736)
PHONE..................419 244-8844
Fax: 419 244-8644
Jason Walton, *Manager*
EMP: 4
SALES (corp-wide): 30.7MM **Privately Held**
WEB: www.markeys.com
SIC: 3651 7819 7622 Household audio & video equipment; video tape or disk reproduction; home entertainment repair services
PA: Markey's Audio/Visual, Inc.
2365 Enterprise Park Pl
Indianapolis IN 46218
317 783-1155

(G-18574)
MARRIK DISH COMPANY LLC
Also Called: Suite Solutions Technologies
4102 Monroe St (43606-2060)
P.O. Box 2891 (43606-0891)
PHONE..................419 475-6538
Fax: 419 475-2672
Steve Ransom, *Manager*
Mark Ralston,
EMP: 25
SALES (est): 4.1MM **Privately Held**
SIC: 3663 Satellites, communications

(G-18575)
MARTINEZ FOOD PRODUCTS LLC
1220 Belmont Ave (43607-4105)
PHONE..................419 720-6973
Mark Catko,
Lillian Catko,
Richard Iott,
Ron Teague,
EMP: 6
SALES (est): 485.2K **Privately Held**
SIC: 2035 Pickles, sauces & salad dressings

(G-18576)
MATURE LIVING NEWS MAGAZINE
3601 W Alexis Rd Ste 112 (43623-1347)
P.O. Box 212, Lambertville MI (48144-0212)
PHONE..................419 241-8880
Diana Calmes, *President*
Lisa Jordan, *Treasurer*
Veronica Smalley, *Admin Sec*
EMP: 4
SALES (est): 190K **Privately Held**
SIC: 2711 Newspapers

(G-18577)
MAUMEE BAY BREWING COMPANY
27 Broadway St Ste A (43604-8701)
PHONE..................419 243-1253
Patricia Appold, *President*
Jen Volpi, *Manager*
EMP: 50
SQ FT: 5,000
SALES (est): 2MM **Privately Held**
SIC: 5812 2082 Chicken restaurant; beer (alcoholic beverage); malt liquors; near beer

(G-18578)
MAUMEE MACHINE & TOOL CORP
2960 South Ave (43609-1328)
PHONE..................419 385-2501
Fax: 419 385-8817
Bruce M Denman, *President*
John S Buescher, *Vice Pres*
Patrick T Denman, *Vice Pres*
EMP: 25 EST: 1966
SALES (est): 3MM **Privately Held**
SIC: 3451 Screw machine products

(G-18579)
MAUMEE PATTERN COMPANY INC
1019 Hazelwood St (43605-3248)
PHONE..................419 693-4968
H Jeffrey Neuman, *President*
Alice Neuman, *Corp Secy*
David Neuman, *Vice Pres*
Mark Neuman, *Vice Pres*
EMP: 30
SQ FT: 13,000
SALES: 3.8MM **Privately Held**
WEB: www.maumeepattern.com
SIC: 3543 3544 Industrial patterns; industrial molds

(G-18580)
MAUMEE VALLEY FABRICATORS INC
Also Called: Escher Division
4801 Bennett Rd (43612-2531)
PHONE......................................419 476-1411
Fax: 419 476-8837
Patrick Copeland, *President*
Karen Coolidge, *General Mgr*
Robert Palmer, *Vice Pres*
Robert N Schuler, *Engineer*
Sue Loucks, *Controller*
EMP: 25 EST: 1978
SQ FT: 54,000
SALES (est): 7.1MM **Privately Held**
WEB: www.maumeevalleyfab.com
SIC: 3443 Heat exchangers, condensers & components

(G-18581)
MECCA REBUILDING & WELDING CO
Also Called: G & J
615 Phillips Ave (43612-1330)
PHONE......................................419 476-8133
George Cole, *President*
Robert Vierling, *Manager*
EMP: 5
SQ FT: 3,536
SALES (est): 300K **Privately Held**
SIC: 7692 Welding repair

(G-18582)
MEL STEVENS U-CART CONCRETE
Also Called: Stevens, Mel U-Cart & Rental
6151 Telegraph Rd (43612-4576)
PHONE......................................419 478-2600
Fax: 419 478-8204
Mel Stevens, *CEO*
Melvin Stevens, *Ch of Bd*
Timothy Stevens, *President*
David Stevens, *Treasurer*
EMP: 4
SQ FT: 4,000
SALES (est): 607K **Privately Held**
SIC: 3273 7353 5261 Ready-mixed concrete; heavy construction equipment rental; nurseries & garden centers; top soil

(G-18583)
MELDRUM MECHANICAL SERVICES
4455 South Ave (43615-6416)
PHONE......................................419 535-3500
Fax: 419 535-3220
Brent R Meldrum Jr, *President*
Martin Donbrosky, *General Mgr*
Jack Drummond, *Mfg Staff*
Debi Meldrum, *Info Tech Mgr*
EMP: 10
SALES (est): 2MM **Privately Held**
SIC: 3599 Machine shop, jobbing & repair

(G-18584)
METZGERS
150 Arco Dr (43607-2903)
PHONE......................................419 861-8611
Tom Metzger, *CEO*
Joe Metzger, *Founder*
John Luscombe, *Vice Pres*
Aaron Miller, *Project Mgr*
Glenn Whaley, *Prdtn Mgr*
EMP: 19
SALES (est): 2.6MM **Privately Held**
SIC: 2752 Commercial printing, offset

(G-18585)
MIDTOWN PALLET & RECYCLING
1987 Hawthorne St (43606)
P.O. Box 397, Stony Ridge (43463-0397)
PHONE......................................419 241-1311
Fax: 419 241-5888
Rita Stang, *President*
EMP: 25
SQ FT: 10,000
SALES (est): 3.6MM **Privately Held**
WEB: www.midtownpallet.com
SIC: 2448 Wood pallets & skids

(G-18586)
MIDWESTERN BAG CO INC
3230 Monroe St (43606-4519)
PHONE......................................419 241-3112
Toney Oneal, *President*
Paulette Lalor, *Vice Pres*
Brian Hoch, *Admin Sec*
EMP: 23
SQ FT: 43,000
SALES: 2.5MM **Privately Held**
SIC: 5199 3069 Bags, baskets & cases; bags, rubber or rubberized fabric

(G-18587)
MISSION CONTROL SYSTEMS INC
3900 Sunforest Ct Ste 119 (43623-4440)
PHONE......................................419 472-3791
Fax: 419 531-0083
Jason Kalb, *President*
EMP: 6
SQ FT: 1,900
SALES (est): 500K **Privately Held**
SIC: 3625 Relays & industrial controls

(G-18588)
MMP TOLEDO
5847 Secor Rd (43623-1421)
PHONE......................................419 472-0505
Fax: 419 472-0505
Steven Heaney, *President*
Teresa Heaney, *Principal*
EMP: 15
SQ FT: 1,500
SALES (est): 2.3MM **Privately Held**
WEB: www.mmptoledo.com
SIC: 2752 Commercial printing, offset

(G-18589)
MOBIS NORTH AMERICA LLC
Also Called: Ommc
3900 Stickney Ave (43608-1314)
PHONE......................................419 729-6700
Adam Hanson, *Production*
Summer Grindle, *Engineer*
Pamela Law, *Engineer*
Phillip Wingate, *Engineer*
KS Noh, *Senior Engr*
EMP: 45
SALES (corp-wide): 17.2B **Privately Held**
SIC: 3711 Chassis, motor vehicle
HQ: Mobis North America, Llc
46501 Commerce Dr
Plymouth MI 48170
248 426-5577

(G-18590)
MON-SAY CORP
Also Called: Ergocan
2735 Dorr St (43607-3240)
P.O. Box 8487 (43623-0487)
PHONE......................................419 720-0163
Terry Netterfield, *President*
EMP: 7
SQ FT: 22,000
SALES (est): 1MM **Privately Held**
SIC: 3089 Bowl covers, plastic

(G-18591)
MONDELEZ GLOBAL LLC
Also Called: Kraft Foods
2221 Front St (43605-1231)
P.O. Box 2208 (43603-2208)
PHONE......................................419 691-5200
Marty Golden, *Engineer*
Diane Gannon, *Design Engr*
Lee Wallace, *Controller*
William Epperson, *Branch Mgr*
Odette Moncayo, *Manager*
EMP: 100 **Publicly Held**
SIC: 2041 Flour & other grain mill products
HQ: Mondelez Global Llc
3 Parkway N Ste 300
Deerfield IL 60015
847 943-4000

(G-18592)
MOSSING MACHINE AND TOOL
5225 Telegraph Rd (43612-3570)
PHONE......................................419 476-5657
Fax: 419 476-3482
Dave S Mossing, *President*
Nancy Mossing, *Vice Pres*
Mark Kohler, *Manager*
EMP: 8
SQ FT: 8,000

SALES (est): 1MM **Privately Held**
SIC: 3599 Machine & other job shop work

(G-18593)
MR&E LTD
3146 W Lincolnshire Blvd (43606-1219)
PHONE......................................419 872-8180
Deane Horne,
▲ EMP: 3
SALES: 950K **Privately Held**
SIC: 3823 Thermocouples, industrial process type

(G-18594)
MV GROUP INC
303 Morris St (43604-8874)
PHONE......................................419 776-1133
Hernan Vasquez, *President*
EMP: 4
SALES: 1MM **Privately Held**
SIC: 3585 Refrigeration & heating equipment

(G-18595)
MY MAJOR FAMILY LLP ✪
5001 Monroe St Ste 1505 (43623-7005)
PHONE......................................567 218-1206
Amati Simmons, *Principal*
Yvette Major, *Principal*
EMP: 4 EST: 2016
SQ FT: 805
SALES (est): 172.4K **Privately Held**
SIC: 3999 Hair & hair-based products

(G-18596)
MY WAY HOME FINDER MAGAZINE
5215 Monroe St Ste 14 (43623-3190)
PHONE......................................419 841-6201
Fax: 419 841-1106
James Moody, *Partner*
EMP: 6
SQ FT: 2,000
SALES: 500K **Privately Held**
WEB: www.iselltoledohomes.com
SIC: 2711 Newspapers

(G-18597)
N-VIRO INTERNATIONAL CORP
2254 Centennial Rd (43617-1870)
P.O. Box 8770 (43623-0770)
PHONE......................................419 535-6374
Timothy R Kasmoch, *Ch of Bd*
Robert W Bohmer, *Exec VP*
James K McHugh, *CFO*
Terri Linnon, *Corp Comm Staff*
EMP: 10
SALES: 1.1MM **Privately Held**
SIC: 3589 4959 Water treatment equipment, industrial; sanitary services

(G-18598)
NATIONAL SAFETY TECH LLC (HQ)
Also Called: Nst
5154 Enterprise Blvd (43612-3807)
PHONE......................................419 727-0552
Andrew Milligan, *President*
John J Skreenock, *General Mgr*
Dr James Huttner, *Vice Pres*
James Vehslage, *Controller*
Paul Czerniakowski, *Sales Mgr*
EMP: 41
SALES (est): 2.8MM
SALES (corp-wide): 9.3MM **Privately Held**
WEB: www.nst-usa.com
SIC: 3825 3826 5084 3829 Test equipment for electronic & electric measurement; analytical instruments; gas testing apparatus; industrial machinery & equipment; measuring & controlling devices
PA: Bionix Development Corporation
5154 Enterprise Blvd
Toledo OH 43612
419 727-8421

(G-18599)
NEMIRE LURES LLC
2144 Ottawa River Rd (43611-1890)
PHONE......................................419 729-1280
John Nemire,
EMP: 5
SALES (est): 315.7K **Privately Held**
WEB: www.nemirelures.com
SIC: 3949 Lures, fishing: artificial

(G-18600)
NETWORK SAVVY LTD
5217 Monroe St Ste A1 (43623-4604)
PHONE......................................419 843-1122
Fax: 419 843-4110
Donald Finnegan Jr, *Owner*
Thom Boyne, *Vice Pres*
Darren Schaible, *Manager*
EMP: 4
SALES (est): 238.2K **Privately Held**
SIC: 7372 Prepackaged software

(G-18601)
NEW DIE INC
2828 E Manhattan Blvd (43611-1710)
PHONE......................................419 726-7581
Richard A Pack, *President*
Ken Coss, *Vice Pres*
Donald R Cousino, *Vice Pres*
Terry Cousino, *Vice Pres*
James David, *Vice Pres*
EMP: 22
SQ FT: 7,500
SALES (est): 3.3MM **Privately Held**
SIC: 3544 Special dies, tools, jigs & fixtures

(G-18602)
NEW HORIZON BAKING COMPANY
1015 New York Ave (43611-3347)
PHONE......................................567 315-8703
EMP: 4
SALES (est): 195.3K **Privately Held**
SIC: 2051 Bread, cake & related products

(G-18603)
NEWFAX CORPORATION (PA)
333 W Woodruff Ave (43604-5025)
P.O. Box 656 (43697-0656)
PHONE......................................419 241-5157
Fax: 419 241-2018
Albert J Gossman Jr, *President*
Greg Scheuerman, *Vice Pres*
Gregory Scheuerman, *Vice Pres*
Darold Forbes, *Manager*
William Scheuerman, *Shareholder*
EMP: 17
SQ FT: 15,000
SALES (est): 1.5MM **Privately Held**
WEB: www.newfaxcorp.com
SIC: 2752 5084 2791 2789 Photo-offset printing; printing trades machinery, equipment & supplies; typesetting; bookbinding & related work

(G-18604)
NEWFAX CORPORATION
Also Called: Mc Graphix Div of Th Newfax
3333 W Wooddrift (43604)
P.O. Box 656 (43697-0656)
PHONE......................................419 893-4557
EMP: 16
SALES (corp-wide): 1.5MM **Privately Held**
SIC: 5084 2752 Wholesales Photoprinting Equipment & Supplies & Reproduction Services
PA: Newfax Corporation
333 W Woodruff Ave
Toledo OH 43604
419 241-5157

(G-18605)
NEXT DAY SIGN
2112 N Reynolds Rd (43615-3514)
PHONE......................................419 537-9595
Fax: 419 537-1881
Dan Mosher, *President*
EMP: 5
SALES: 200K **Privately Held**
SIC: 3993 Signs & advertising specialties

(G-18606)
NEXT SPECIALTY RESINS INC (PA)
8201 W Central Ave (43617-1844)
P.O. Box 365, Addison MI (49220-0365)
PHONE......................................517 547-4600
Rajiv H Naik, *President*
Abhay Prasad, *Principal*
Saurabh H Naik, *Vice Pres*
Jim Harpen, *Sales Mgr*
Angela Matthews, *Manager*
EMP: 30

SQ FT: 250,000
SALES (est): 4.8MM **Privately Held**
SIC: 2821 Melamine resins, melamine-formaldehyde

(G-18607)
NO BURN NORTH AMERICA INC
2930 Centennial Rd (43617-1833)
PHONE.............................419 841-6055
William Kish, *CEO*
Kenneth Rusk, *CFO*
EMP: 15
SQ FT: 9,000
SALES (est): 1.4MM **Privately Held**
WEB: www.noburnna.com
SIC: 2899 Fire retardant chemicals

(G-18608)
NORTH SAILS TOLEDO LLC
5556 Edgewater Dr (43611-2457)
PHONE.............................419 726-2933
Bill Wiggins, *Sales Mgr*
Skip Dieball, *Mng Member*
EMP: 10
SQ FT: 4,800
SALES: 650K **Privately Held**
SIC: 2394 3069 7699 Sails: made from purchased materials; balloons, advertising & toy: rubber; nautical repair services

(G-18609)
NORTH TOLEDO GRAPHICS LLC
Also Called: Nt
5225 Telegraph Rd (43612-3570)
PHONE.............................419 476-8808
Greg Tremonti, *General Mgr*
Dan Priest, *Plant Mgr*
Tom Harris, *Prdtn Mgr*
Shirleen Kistner, *Human Res Mgr*
Jim Jackson, *Manager*
EMP: 95
SQ FT: 210,000
SALES (est): 22.2MM **Privately Held**
WEB: www.northtoledographics.com
SIC: 2752 Commercial printing, lithographic

(G-18610)
NSS ENTERPRISES INC (PA)
Also Called: National Super Service Co
3115 Frenchmens Rd (43607-2918)
PHONE.............................419 531-2121
Fax: 419 531-3761
Mark J Bevington, *President*
Anthony J Colburn, *Principal*
Gary Kreiling, *Regional Mgr*
Phil Meeker, *Vice Pres*
Jim Connell, *Controller*
◆ **EMP:** 150 **EST:** 1911
SQ FT: 160,000
SALES (est): 24.9MM **Privately Held**
WEB: www.nss.com
SIC: 3589 Floor washing & polishing machines, commercial; vacuum cleaners & sweepers, electric: industrial

(G-18611)
NTA GRAPHICS INC
5225 Telegraph Rd (43612-3547)
PHONE.............................419 476-8808
Fax: 419 476-0929
Gregory Tremonti, *President*
Gail Shaffer, *Principal*
David Tremonti, *Vice Pres*
Tom Harris, *Prdtn Mgr*
EMP: 142
SQ FT: 163,000
SALES (est): 16.7MM **Privately Held**
SIC: 2752 Commercial printing, offset

(G-18612)
OASIS MEDITERRANEAN CUISINE
1520 W Laskey Rd (43612-2914)
P.O. Box 8881 (43623-0881)
PHONE.............................419 269-1516
Francois Hashem, *Owner*
Michael Francis, *Manager*
Debbie Losh, *Admin Sec*
◆ **EMP:** 47
SQ FT: 30,000

SALES (est): 5.1MM **Privately Held**
SIC: 2099 2032 Dips, except cheese & sour cream based; dressings, salad: dry mixes; salads, fresh or refrigerated; canned specialties

(G-18613)
OBARS MACHINE AND TOOL COMPANY (PA)
Also Called: Obars Welding & Fabg Div
115 N Westwood Ave 125 (43607-3341)
PHONE.............................419 535-6307
Fax: 419 535-1435
Alvin R Obarski, *Ch of Bd*
Greg Obarski, *President*
Steve Obarski, *General Mgr*
Jeffrey R Obarski, *Exec VP*
Michael Webber, *VP Opers*
EMP: 45 **EST:** 1946
SQ FT: 30,000
SALES (est): 4.2MM **Privately Held**
WEB: www.obarsmachine.com
SIC: 3451 3541 3545 Screw machine products; machine tools, metal cutting type; machine tool accessories

(G-18614)
OFF CONTACT INC
Also Called: Off Contact Productions
4756 W Bancroft St (43615-3902)
PHONE.............................419 255-5546
Allen Schall, *President*
Seth Grossi, *Area Mgr*
Eddie Rusch, *Vice Pres*
Jim Schall, *Marketing Staff*
John Brewer, *Manager*
▲ **EMP:** 15
SQ FT: 9,600
SALES: 900K **Privately Held**
WEB: www.offcontact.com
SIC: 2759 5084 Screen printing; industrial machinery & equipment

(G-18615)
OHIO BLENDERS INC (PA)
Also Called: Alfagreen Supreme
2404 N Summit St (43611-3599)
PHONE.............................419 726-2655
Fax: 419 726-6629
Ken Vaupel, *CEO*
Donald Verhoff, *President*
Becky Lumbrezer-Box, *Corp Secy*
Ronald Yarnell, *Vice Pres*
Devin Conklin, *Controller*
EMP: 11
SQ FT: 6,000
SALES (est): 2.4MM **Privately Held**
SIC: 2048 2047 Prepared feeds; dog & cat food

(G-18616)
OHIO PICKLING & PROCESSING LLC
Also Called: Opp
1149 Campbell St (43607-4467)
PHONE.............................419 241-9601
Fax: 419 241-9635
Thomas Klein, *President*
Mike Balk, *Vice Pres*
Beth Taylor, *Human Res Mgr*
Mike Spencer, *Sales Mgr*
Jeff Philak, *Manager*
▲ **EMP:** 70
SALES (est): 13.5MM
SALES (corp-wide): 203MM **Privately Held**
WEB: www.mnp.com
SIC: 3312 Blast furnaces & steel mills
PA: Mnp Corporation
　　44225 Utica Rd
　　Utica MI 48317
　　586 254-1320

(G-18617)
OHIO SPECIALTY MFG CO
2008 N Hlland Sylvania Rd (43615)
PHONE.............................419 531-5402
Fax: 419 531-6599
Richard Uhl, *President*
Karen S Taylor, *Admin Sec*
▲ **EMP:** 3
SALES: 510K **Privately Held**
SIC: 5085 2448 Boxes, crates, etc., other than paper; cargo containers, wood & wood with metal

(G-18618)
OHIO TRANSITIONAL MACHINE & TL
3940 Castener St (43612-1402)
PHONE.............................419 476-0820
Fax: 419 476-1621
Marten Whalen, *President*
Michelle Hall, *Office Mgr*
EMP: 7
SQ FT: 5,000
SALES: 700K **Privately Held**
SIC: 3599 Machine shop, jobbing & repair

(G-18619)
ONLINE MEGA SELLERS CORP (PA)
Also Called: Distinct Advantage Cabinetry
4236 W Alexis Rd (43623-1255)
PHONE.............................888 384-6468
Timothy Baker, *President*
Craig Poupard, *Vice Pres*
EMP: 8
SQ FT: 250,000
SALES (est): 7.2MM **Privately Held**
SIC: 2434 7371 7373 Wood kitchen cabinets; computer software systems analysis & design, custom; computer software development; systems software development services

(G-18620)
OPC INC
419 N Reynolds Rd (43615-5221)
PHONE.............................419 531-2222
Anne M Cole, *Principal*
EMP: 3
SALES (est): 302.3K **Privately Held**
SIC: 3842 Orthopedic appliances

(G-18621)
ORTHOTIC PROSTHETIC CENTER
Also Called: OPC Inc
419 N Reynolds Rd (43615-5221)
PHONE.............................419 531-2222
Ann Cole, *President*
Jan Posadny, *Office Mgr*
EMP: 5
SALES (est): 460K **Privately Held**
SIC: 3842 Prosthetic appliances; limbs, artificial; orthopedic appliances; braces, orthopedic

(G-18622)
OSTEONOVUS INC
1510 N Westwood Ave (43606-8202)
PHONE.............................617 717-8867
Steven Nemes, *Finance*
Sarit Bhaduri, *Admin Sec*
EMP: 4
SALES (est): 476.5K **Privately Held**
SIC: 3842 Grafts, artificial: for surgery

(G-18623)
OTIS ELEVATOR COMPANY
Also Called: United Technologies
5960 Angola Rd Ste 1 (43615-6381)
PHONE.............................419 867-7758
Tim Collins, *General Mgr*
EMP: 15
SALES (corp-wide): 57.2B **Publicly Held**
WEB: www.otis.com
SIC: 3534 Elevators & equipment
HQ: Otis Elevator Company
　　1 Carrier Pl
　　Farmington CT 06032
　　860 674-3000

(G-18624)
OVERHEAD INC
Also Called: Overhead Door Company
1621 W Alexis Rd (43612-4048)
PHONE.............................419 476-0300
Fax: 419 476-0307
Sandy Wagenfeald, *Site Mgr*
Michael Huss, *Manager*
EMP: 7
SQ FT: 11,470
SALES (corp-wide): 12.4MM **Privately Held**
WEB: www.overheadinc.com
SIC: 3442 5719 5211 Metal doors, sash & trim; fireplace equipment & accessories; garage doors, sale & installation

PA: Overhead Inc.
　　340 New Towne Square Dr
　　Toledo OH 43612
　　419 476-7811

(G-18625)
OWENS CORNING (PA)
1 Owens Corning Pkwy (43659-0001)
PHONE.............................419 248-8000
Fax: 419 248-5337
Michael H Thaman, *Ch of Bd*
Brian D Chambers, *President*
Julian Francis, *President*
Arnaud Genis, *President*
Ava Harter, *Senior VP*
◆ **EMP:** 1000
SQ FT: 400,000
SALES: 5.6B **Publicly Held**
SIC: 3296 2952 3229 3089 Fiberglass insulation; insulation: rock wool, slag & silica minerals; acoustical board & tile, mineral wool; roofing mats, mineral wool; asphalt felts & coatings; glass fibers, textile; yarn, fiberglass; windows, plastic

(G-18626)
OWENS CORNING SALES LLC (HQ)
1 Owens Corning Pkwy (43659-0001)
PHONE.............................419 248-8000
Michael H Thaman, *Ch of Bd*
Rhonda L Brooks, *President*
Carl B Hedlund, *President*
George E Kiemle, *President*
William E Lebaron, *President*
◆ **EMP:** 1000 **EST:** 2006
SQ FT: 400,000
SALES (est): 3.1B
SALES (corp-wide): 5.6B **Publicly Held**
WEB: www.owenscorning.com
SIC: 3296 2952 3229 3089 Fiberglass insulation; insulation: rock wool, slag & silica minerals; acoustical board & tile, mineral wool; roofing mats, mineral wool; asphalt felts & coatings; glass fibers, textile; yarn, fiberglass; windows, plastic; roofing, siding & sheet metal work
PA: Owens Corning
　　1 Owens Corning Pkwy
　　Toledo OH 43659
　　419 248-8000

(G-18627)
OWENS-CORNING CAPITAL LLC
1 Owens Corning Pkwy (43659-0001)
PHONE.............................419 248-8000
EMP: 9
SALES (est): 587.6K
SALES (corp-wide): 5.6B **Publicly Held**
SIC: 3296 Fiberglass insulation
HQ: Owens Corning Sales, Llc
　　1 Owens Corning Pkwy
　　Toledo OH 43659
　　419 248-8000

(G-18628)
OWENS-ILLINOIS DE PUERTO RICO (PA)
Also Called: O-I
1 Seagate (43604-1558)
PHONE.............................419 874-9708
Steve McCracken, *CEO*
Joseph Lemieux, *President*
Michael Paparone, *General Mgr*
Sara Theis, *General Mgr*
Randy Galbraith, *Chairman*
▲ **EMP:** 95
SALES (est): 65.9MM **Privately Held**
SIC: 3221 Glass containers

(G-18629)
P & J INDUSTRIES INC (PA)
4934 Lewis Ave (43612-2825)
P.O. Box 6918 (43612-0918)
PHONE.............................419 726-2675
Fax: 419 726-7509
James E Powers Jr, *President*
James E Powers Sr, *Corp Secy*
Marguerite M Powers, *Vice Pres*
Frank Flanina, *Purchasing*
Sam Amrou, *Manager*
▼ **EMP:** 120

SALES (est): 12.1MM **Privately Held**
SIC: **3471** Plating & polishing; chromium plating of metals or formed products; gold plating; electroplating of metals or formed products

(G-18630)
P & J MANUFACTURING INC
1644 Campbell St (43607-4381)
PHONE................................419 241-7369
Fax: 419 241-3866
Peter James Harvey, *President*
Elizabeth Harvey, *Corp Secy*
William Harvey, *Vice Pres*
EMP: 10
SQ FT: 14,000
SALES: 700K **Privately Held**
WEB: www.pandjmfginc.com
SIC: **7389 3471** Grinding, precision: commercial or industrial; finishing, metals or formed products

(G-18631)
P B FABRICATION MECH CONTR
750 W Laskey Rd (43612-3209)
PHONE................................419 478-4869
Fax: 419 478-4148
Charles W Bailey, *President*
Hubert Backes, *Vice Pres*
EMP: 12
SQ FT: 6,000
SALES (est): 2.9MM **Privately Held**
SIC: **3535 3444 3443 3441** Conveyors & conveying equipment; sheet metalwork; fabricated plate work (boiler shop); fabricated structural metal; aluminum sheet, plate & foil; plumbing, heating, air-conditioning contractors

(G-18632)
P R RACING ENGINES
1951 W Sylvania Ave (43613-4522)
PHONE................................419 472-2277
Fax: 419 472-0932
Jeffery Snyder, *Owner*
EMP: 5
SQ FT: 2,000
SALES (est): 290K **Privately Held**
SIC: **3541** Machine tools, metal cutting type

(G-18633)
PAGE SLOTTING SAW CO INC
3820 Lagrange St (43612-1425)
PHONE................................419 476-7475
Fax: 419 476-9261
James Bouldin, *President*
EMP: 11 EST: 1960
SQ FT: 3,500
SALES (est): 980K **Privately Held**
SIC: **3541** Machine tools, metal cutting type

(G-18634)
PALLET & CONT CORP OF AMER
901 Buckingham St (43607-4410)
PHONE................................419 255-1256
Fax: 419 241-2833
Michael J Burtscher, *President*
Marie J Burtscher, *Vice Pres*
EMP: 8
SQ FT: 39,500
SALES (est): 670K **Privately Held**
SIC: **2448 2653 2449** Pallets, wood; boxes, corrugated: made from purchased materials; containers, plywood & veneer wood

(G-18635)
PATJIM HOLDINGS COMPANY
3444 N Summit St (43611-3242)
PHONE................................419 727-1298
John Weisenberger, *Principal*
EMP: 10
SALES (est): 760.4K **Privately Held**
SIC: **2052** Cookies & crackers

(G-18636)
PEAK ELECTRIC INC
320 N Byrne Rd (43607-2607)
PHONE................................419 726-4848
Milton McIntyre, *President*
Rhys Petee, *Principal*
Lenora McIntyre, *Vice Pres*
Mark Weisenburger, *Sales Staff*

Joyce McIntyre, *Manager*
EMP: 6
SALES (est): 2.4MM **Privately Held**
SIC: **3229** Bulbs for electric lights

(G-18637)
PEDESTRIAN PRESS
2233 Robinwood Ave (43620-1020)
PHONE................................419 244-6488
Jeffrey Kent Nelson, *Principal*
EMP: 4
SALES (est): 276.4K **Privately Held**
SIC: **2741** Miscellaneous publishing

(G-18638)
PEPSI-COLA METRO BTLG CO INC
Also Called: Pepsico
3245 Hill Ave (43607-2936)
PHONE................................419 534-2186
Charlie Powers, *Plant Mgr*
Terry Sandman, *Treasurer*
Terry Sandlin, *Financial Exec*
Bernie Kuminkoski, *Chief Mktg Ofcr*
Michael Hill, *Branch Mgr*
EMP: 30
SALES (corp-wide): 62.8B **Publicly Held**
WEB: www.whitmancorp.com
SIC: **2086** Carbonated soft drinks, bottled & canned
HQ: Pepsi-Cola Metropolitan Bottling Company, Inc.
1111 Westchester Ave
White Plains NY 10604
914 767-6000

(G-18639)
PERFECT MEASURING TAPE COMPANY
1116 N Summit St (43604-1870)
PHONE................................419 243-6811
Fax: 419 243-6811
Andrew C Bohnengel, *President*
Lynn Bohnengel, *General Mgr*
Barrett Bohnengel, *Vice Pres*
Claire Bohnengel, *Vice Pres*
▲ EMP: 8 EST: 1912
SQ FT: 5,000
SALES: 1MM **Privately Held**
WEB: www.cintametrica.com
SIC: **3829 5046** Measuring & controlling devices; scales, except laboratory

(G-18640)
PERFORMANCE SERVICES
828 Warehouse Rd Ste 8 (43615-6480)
PHONE................................419 385-1236
Kirk Moellenberg, *Owner*
EMP: 3
SALES (est): 325.5K **Privately Held**
SIC: **3599** Machine & other job shop work

(G-18641)
PERSTORP POLYOLS INC
600 Matzinger Rd (43612-2695)
PHONE................................419 729-5448
Fax: 419 729-3291
David Wolf, *President*
Chris Yingling, *Plant Mgr*
Laura Inderbitzin, *Purch Mgr*
Larry Fioritto, *Admin Director*
◆ EMP: 109
SQ FT: 3,000
SALES (est): 50.9MM
SALES (corp-wide): 121.8MM **Privately Held**
WEB: www.perstorp.net
SIC: **2819 2851 2821** Elements; paints & allied products; plastics materials & resins
HQ: Perstorp Ab
Perstorp Industripark
Perstorp 284 8
435 380-00

(G-18642)
PEXCO PACKAGING CORP
795 Berdan Ave (43610-1069)
P.O. Box 6540 (43612-0540)
PHONE................................419 470-5935
Fax: 419 470-5940
Bill Buri, *President*
Thomas Jesionowski, *Vice Pres*
Dennis Taylor, *VP Mfg*
Debbie Thomas, *Accountant*
Donna Knaggs, *Clerk*
EMP: 35

SQ FT: 64,000
SALES (est): 9.2MM **Privately Held**
WEB: www.pexcopkg.com
SIC: **2673 3082 3081 2759** Plastic bags: made from purchased materials; unsupported plastics profile shapes; unsupported plastics film & sheet; commercial printing

(G-18643)
PILKINGTON HOLDINGS INC (DH)
Also Called: P H I
811 Madison Ave Fl 1 (43604-5688)
P.O. Box 799 (43697-0799)
PHONE................................419 247-3731
Fax: 419 247-4594
Warren D Knowlton, *CEO*
A R Graham, *President*
Rick Frampton, *Vice Pres*
G M Gray, *Vice Pres*
S P Harris, *Vice Pres*
◆ EMP: 300
SQ FT: 217,000
SALES (est): 622.6MM
SALES (corp-wide): 5.3B **Privately Held**
SIC: **3211** Flat glass
HQ: Pilkington Group Limited
Pilkington Technology Centre Hall Lane
Ormskirk LANCS
169 550-000

(G-18644)
PILKINGTON NORTH AMERICA INC (DH)
811 Madison Ave Fl 1 (43604-5688)
P.O. Box 799 (43697-0799)
PHONE................................419 247-4955
Richard Altman, *President*
Kevin Malpass, *General Mgr*
Gordon Labrech, *Plant Mgr*
Robert Bobel, *Project Mgr*
Demi Salazar, *Facilities Mgr*
◆ EMP: 277
SALES: 20MM
SALES (corp-wide): 5.3B **Privately Held**
WEB: www.low-eglass.com
SIC: **3211** Flat glass; construction glass
HQ: Pilkington Holdings Inc.
811 Madison Ave Fl 1
Toledo OH 43604
419 247-3731

(G-18645)
PISTON AUTOMOTIVE LLC
Also Called: Piston Group
1212 E Alexis Rd (43612-3974)
PHONE................................419 464-0250
Vincent Johnson, *Branch Mgr*
EMP: 75
SALES (corp-wide): 249.9MM **Privately Held**
SIC: **3714** Motor vehicle parts & accessories
PA: Piston Automotive Llc
12723 Telegraph Rd Ste 1
Redford MI 48239
313 541-8674

(G-18646)
PLABELL RUBBER PRODUCTS CORP (PA)
300 S Saint Clair St # 324 (43604)
PHONE................................419 691-5878
John Jaksetic, *President*
Jim Farkas, *Vice Pres*
Randy Reif, *Admin Sec*
EMP: 14
SQ FT: 40,000
SALES (est): 2.7MM **Privately Held**
SIC: **3069 3061** Molded rubber products; mechanical rubber goods

(G-18647)
PLASTEX INDUSTRIES INC
4050 South Ave (43615-6230)
PHONE................................419 531-0189
Susan Smotherman, *President*
Mitch Niemiec, *Plant Mgr*
▲ EMP: 30
SQ FT: 12,000
SALES (est): 5.3MM **Privately Held**
WEB: www.plastex-industries.com
SIC: **3089** Injection molding of plastics

(G-18648)
POLHE TOOL INC
312 W Laskey Rd (43612-3433)
PHONE................................419 476-2433
Fax: 419 476-9168
Jozsef Polhe, *President*
Marianne Polhe, *Treasurer*
Katherina A Arble, *Admin Sec*
EMP: 5
SQ FT: 5,000
SALES (est): 646.2K **Privately Held**
WEB: www.polhetoolinc.com
SIC: **3545** Tools & accessories for machine tools

(G-18649)
POOLES PRINTING & OFFICE SVCS
4036 Monroe St (43606-2144)
PHONE................................419 475-9000
Fax: 419 475-8511
William J Poole Jr, *President*
Scott Poole, *Manager*
EMP: 5 EST: 1965
SQ FT: 5,000
SALES: 500K **Privately Held**
SIC: **2752 2791 2789** Commercial printing, lithographic; typesetting; bookbinding & related work

(G-18650)
POWERBUFF INC
1001 Brown Ave (43607-3942)
PHONE................................419 241-2156
Walter C Anderson, *President*
EMP: 18
SQ FT: 50,000
SALES (est): 2.4MM **Privately Held**
SIC: **3589** Floor washing & polishing machines, commercial

(G-18651)
PRAXAIR INC
6055 Brent Dr (43611-1084)
PHONE................................419 729-7732
EMP: 4
SALES (corp-wide): 10.5B **Publicly Held**
SIC: **2813** Industrial gases
PA: Praxair, Inc.
10 Riverview Dr
Danbury CT 06810
203 837-2000

(G-18652)
PRAXAIR DISTRIBUTION INC
5254 Jackman Rd Ste A (43613-2978)
PHONE................................419 476-0738
Adam Wygast, *Branch Mgr*
EMP: 42
SALES (corp-wide): 10.5B **Publicly Held**
SIC: **2813** Industrial gases
HQ: Praxair Distribution, Inc.
10 Riverview Dr
Danbury CT 06810
203 837-2000

(G-18653)
PRECISION GRAPHIC SERVICES
436 Wade St (43604-3856)
PHONE................................419 241-5189
Fax: 419 241-5414
Kenneth P Breier, *President*
EMP: 15
SQ FT: 10,000
SALES (est): 1.8MM **Privately Held**
WEB: www.pgstoledo.com
SIC: **2759 2789** Embossing on paper; binding only: books, pamphlets, magazines, etc.

(G-18654)
PRECISION STEEL SERVICES INC (PA)
31 E Sylvania Ave (43612-1474)
PHONE................................419 476-5702
Fax: 419 476-4981
David L Kelley, *President*
Greg Forrester, *Vice Pres*
Ramin Kalaty, *Vice Pres*
Jordan Demchyna, *Opers Mgr*
Helen Racckowski, *Purch Mgr*
EMP: 60 EST: 1975
SQ FT: 35,000

SALES (est): 62.4MM **Privately Held**
WEB: www.precision-steel.com
SIC: 5051 3441 3444 Steel; fabricated structural metal; sheet metalwork

(G-18655)
PRESTIGE STORE INTERIORS INC
4500 N Detroit Ave (43612-2644)
PHONE....................................419 476-2106
Fax: 419 476-1682
Jeffrey Simenski, *President*
Blain Stobinski, *Vice Pres*
Brian Falk, *Sales Mgr*
Mike Bastian, *Manager*
Mark Weirich, *Manager*
EMP: 60
SQ FT: 50,000
SALES (est): 10.5MM **Privately Held**
WEB: www.prestigestoreinteriors.com
SIC: 2541 Store fixtures, wood

(G-18656)
PREUSS MOLD & DIE
1010 Matzinger Rd (43612-3823)
PHONE....................................419 729-9100
Fax: 419 729-9120
Jeff Preuss, *Owner*
EMP: 4
SQ FT: 3,700
SALES (est): 300K **Privately Held**
SIC: 3544 Forms (molds), for foundry & plastics working machinery; dies, plastics forming

(G-18657)
PRIDE GAGE ASSOCIATES LLC
7862 W Central Ave Ste D (43617-1549)
PHONE....................................419 318-3793
Chris Grieser, *General Mgr*
William Gstalder,
Christopher Grieser,
Janice Gstalder,
EMP: 2
SALES: 1.3MM **Privately Held**
SIC: 3823 Draft gauges, industrial process type

(G-18658)
PRINT ALL INC
Also Called: A I M Specialists
2375 Dorr St Ste 2 (43607-3407)
PHONE....................................419 534-2880
Fax: 419 536-3294
Ann M Fago, *President*
Irene Fago, *Vice Pres*
EMP: 6
SQ FT: 7,500
SALES (est): 866.4K **Privately Held**
WEB: www.aimspecialists.com
SIC: 2752 7331 Commercial printing, offset; mailing service

(G-18659)
PROJECTS DESIGNED & BUILT
Also Called: PD&b
5949 American Rd E (43612-3950)
PHONE....................................419 726-7400
Fax: 419 726-9884
Ken Martin, *President*
Rita Martin, *Administration*
▼ **EMP:** 21
SQ FT: 16,000
SALES: 6MM **Privately Held**
WEB: www.pdbinc.com
SIC: 3599 Machine shop, jobbing & repair

(G-18660)
PROPERTY ASSIST INC
Also Called: Floorcraft Designs
1755 W Sylvania Ave (43613-4635)
PHONE....................................419 480-1700
James Mann, *President*
Michael Mann, *Vice Pres*
Sunday Sue Mann, *Admin Sec*
EMP: 3
SALES (est): 280K **Privately Held**
SIC: 2426 Flooring, hardwood

(G-18661)
PROTEL SYSTEMS AND SVCS LLC (PA)
3453 Chapel Dr (43615-1640)
PHONE....................................419 913-0825
Denny McBroom,
EMP: 3

SALES (est): 556.8K **Privately Held**
SIC: 7372 Prepackaged software

(G-18662)
Q C PRINTING
Also Called: Qc Prntng By Quality Craft
3650 Upton Ave (43613-5037)
PHONE....................................419 475-4266
Fax: 419 475-1412
Gene Grzymkowski, *Owner*
EMP: 5
SQ FT: 1,200
SALES (est): 300K **Privately Held**
SIC: 2752 Commercial printing, offset

(G-18663)
QUALITY TOOL COMPANY
Also Called: Quality Stamping
577 Mel Simon Dr (43612-4729)
PHONE....................................419 476-8228
Fax: 419 476-5636
James G Pasch, *President*
Michael Pasch, *Vice Pres*
Mike Pasch, *Production*
Mark Schumacher, *QC Mgr*
EMP: 20
SQ FT: 48,000
SALES: 3.2MM **Privately Held**
SIC: 3469 3312 Metal stampings; tool & die steel

(G-18664)
QUIKRETE COMPANIES INC
Also Called: THE QUIKRETE COMPANIES INC
873 Western Ave (43609-2774)
PHONE....................................419 241-1148
Becky Garner, *Manager*
EMP: 25
SQ FT: 10,700 **Privately Held**
WEB: www.quikrete.com
SIC: 3272 3241 Dry mixture concrete; cement, hydraulic
HQ: The Quikrete Companies Llc
3490 Piedmont Rd Ne # 1300
Atlanta GA 30305
404 634-9100

(G-18665)
QUMONT CHEMICAL CO
359 Hamilton St Ste 3 (43604-8548)
PHONE....................................419 241-1057
Donald A Quertinmont, *Owner*
EMP: 3
SALES (est): 299.2K **Privately Held**
SIC: 2899 5169 5113 Water treating compounds; chemicals & allied products; bags, paper & disposable plastic

(G-18666)
R & D CUSTOM MACHINE & TOOL
5961 American Rd E (43612-3950)
PHONE....................................419 727-1700
Fax: 419 727-1704
David Skomer, *President*
Don Loucks, *Senior VP*
Mary Beth Ross, *Manager*
Robert Zink, *Supervisor*
EMP: 25 **EST:** 1982
SQ FT: 16,800
SALES: 4MM **Privately Held**
SIC: 3599 Machine shop, jobbing & repair

(G-18667)
R J ENGINEERING COMPANY INC
2860 Heysler Rd (43617-1536)
PHONE....................................419 843-8651
Julius A Toth, *President*
Kurt Toth, *Vice Pres*
Rhoda J Toth, *Vice Pres*
EMP: 3 **EST:** 1962
SALES: 40K **Privately Held**
SIC: 3829 3524 Measuring & controlling devices; snowblowers & throwers, residential

(G-18668)
RADCO FIRE PROTECTION INC
444 W Laskey Rd Ste S (43612-3460)
PHONE....................................419 476-0102
Douglas W Ward, *President*
EMP: 7
SQ FT: 1,800

SALES (est): 1MM **Privately Held**
SIC: 3569 Sprinkler systems, fire: automatic

(G-18669)
RADCO INDUSTRIES INC
3226 Frenchmens Rd (43607-2996)
PHONE....................................419 531-4731
Fax: 419 531-2134
Richard Anderson, *President*
Mary Anderson, *Vice Pres*
Doug Michael, *Manager*
John Michael, *Manager*
▲ **EMP:** 11 **EST:** 1962
SQ FT: 28,000
SALES (est): 1MM **Privately Held**
WEB: www.radcoindustries.com
SIC: 3599 Custom machinery

(G-18670)
RAGMAN INC
1201 N Summit St (43604-1817)
PHONE....................................419 255-8068
Fax: 419 241-2430
Donald F Billings, *President*
Debbie Billings, *Corp Secy*
EMP: 4
SQ FT: 3,000
SALES: 500K **Privately Held**
SIC: 2394 Sails: made from purchased materials; convertible tops, canvas or boat: from purchased materials; tarpaulins, fabric: made from purchased materials

(G-18671)
RAKA CORPORATION
Also Called: Lockrey Manufacturing
203 Matzinger Rd (43612-2624)
PHONE....................................419 476-6572
Fax: 419 476-1324
Don Vollmar, *CEO*
Mark A Makulinski, *Ch of Bd*
Ron Eaton, *Manager*
Rich Hanus, *Manager*
EMP: 78 **EST:** 1953
SQ FT: 75,000
SALES (est): 19.4MM **Privately Held**
WEB: www.lockreymanufacturing.com
SIC: 3451 3541 3444 Screw machine products; machine tools, metal cutting type; sheet metalwork

(G-18672)
REA POLISHING INC
1606 W Laskey Rd (43612-2916)
PHONE....................................419 470-0216
Fax: 419 476-0064
Jay REA Sr, *President*
Jay REA Jr, *Treasurer*
Tracy REA, *Office Mgr*
EMP: 61
SQ FT: 19,600
SALES: 3MM **Privately Held**
SIC: 3471 Finishing, metals or formed products

(G-18673)
RED WING SHOE COMPANY INC
2122 N Reynolds Rd (43615-3514)
PHONE....................................419 531-1948
Mike Seeger, *Branch Mgr*
EMP: 4
SALES (corp-wide): 599.7MM **Privately Held**
SIC: 3143 Men's footwear, except athletic
PA: Red Wing Shoe Company, Inc.
314 Main St
Red Wing MN 55066
651 388-8211

(G-18674)
REGAL CABINET INC
315 N Holland Sylvania Rd (43615-4907)
PHONE....................................419 865-3932
Jon Kevin Irwin, *President*
Sonja Irwin, *Corp Secy*
William Irwin, *Vice Pres*
EMP: 3 **EST:** 1955
SQ FT: 4,000
SALES (est): 125K **Privately Held**
SIC: 2434 2511 5211 Wood kitchen cabinets; wood household furniture; lumber products; cabinets, kitchen

(G-18675)
RESONANCE GROUP LTD
2300 Chriswood Rd (43617-1258)
PHONE....................................419 509-2245
Tony Chang, *CEO*
Jeffrey Mock,
EMP: 6
SALES (est): 521.9K **Privately Held**
SIC: 3699 Electrical equipment & supplies

(G-18676)
RIKER PRODUCTS INC
4901 Stickney Ave (43612-3716)
P.O. Box 6976 (43612-0976)
PHONE....................................419 729-1626
Gary Frye, *President*
James McDonagh, *Vice Pres*
Brett Leveck, *Opers Staff*
Alan Drake, *Purch Agent*
Jason Dirkman, *Purchasing*
▼ **EMP:** 175
SQ FT: 250,000
SALES (est): 36.7MM **Privately Held**
WEB: www.rikerprod.com
SIC: 3714 3498 Mufflers (exhaust), motor vehicle; exhaust systems & parts, motor vehicle; fabricated pipe & fittings

(G-18677)
RIVER EAST CUSTOM CABINETS
221 S Saint Clair St (43604-8739)
PHONE....................................419 244-3226
Fax: 419 244-3234
Joe Weiser, *President*
John Weiser, *Vice Pres*
Tony Krebs, *Systems Mgr*
EMP: 20
SQ FT: 15,000
SALES: 2.5MM **Privately Held**
WEB: www.rivereastcab.com
SIC: 5712 2434 Cabinet work, custom; wood kitchen cabinets

(G-18678)
ROBERT BECKER IMPRESSIONS INC
4646 Angola Rd (43615-6407)
PHONE....................................419 385-5303
Fax: 419 385-0529
Robert O Becker, *President*
Jennie Becker, *Vice Pres*
EMP: 12 **EST:** 1976
SQ FT: 9,000
SALES (est): 1.2MM **Privately Held**
WEB: www.beckerimpressions.com
SIC: 7334 2752 5044 Blueprinting service; commercial printing, offset; blueprinting equipment

(G-18679)
ROGAR INTERNATIONAL INC
Also Called: N M Hansen Machine and Tool
4015 Dewey St (43612-1415)
P.O. Box 6938 (43612-0938)
PHONE....................................419 476-5500
Fax: 419 476-8169
Ronnie W Clark, *CEO*
Roger Burditt, *Vice Pres*
R Ken Clark, *Treasurer*
James V Schindler, *Admin Sec*
EMP: 15 **EST:** 1909
SQ FT: 30,000
SALES (est): 2.5MM **Privately Held**
SIC: 3599 Machine shop, jobbing & repair

(G-18680)
RONFELDT ASSOCIATES INC
2345 S Byrne Rd (43614-5107)
PHONE....................................419 382-5641
Fax: 419 382-7577
Theodore A Markwood, *President*
Theodore Ronfeldt, *Principal*
Howard Ronfeldt, *Principal*
Zachary Dominique, *Sales Staff*
Robert Wisler, *Director*
EMP: 96
SQ FT: 57,000
SALES (est): 12.5MM
SALES (corp-wide): 100MM **Privately Held**
WEB: www.ronfeldt.com
SIC: 3469 3544 Stamping metal for the trade; special dies, tools, jigs & fixtures

▲ = Import ▼=Export
◆ =Import/Export

PA: Ice Industries, Inc.
3810 Herr Rd
Sylvania OH 43560
419 842-3612

(G-18681)
RONFELDT MANUFACTURING LLC (HQ)
Also Called: Ice Industries Ronfeldt
2345 S Byrne Rd (43614-5107)
PHONE................419 382-5641
Fax: 419 380-9987
Paul Bishop, *President*
Travis Hearn, *General Mgr*
Jeff Morrow, *Prdtn Mgr*
Bill Rawlins, *Purchasing*
Robert Wisler, *Bus Dvlpt Dir*
EMP: 26
SALES (est): 9.2MM
SALES (corp-wide): 100MM **Privately Held**
WEB: www.iceindustries.com
SIC: 3469 Metal stampings
PA: Ice Industries, Inc.
3810 Herr Rd
Sylvania OH 43560
419 842-3612

(G-18682)
ROULET COMPANY
4221 Lewis Ave (43612-1841)
PHONE................419 241-2988
Gary Wahl, *CEO*
Mark Lofgren, *President*
Roger L Bovee, *Vice Pres*
EMP: 5
SQ FT: 7,500
SALES (est): 663.4K **Privately Held**
WEB: www.rouletcompany.com
SIC: 3911 5944 7631 Jewelry, precious metal; jewelry, precious stones & precious metals; jewelry repair services

(G-18683)
SABCO INDUSTRIES INC
4511 South Ave (43615-6418)
PHONE................419 531-5347
Robert Sulier, *President*
John Pershing, *Vice Pres*
CB M Ash, *Treasurer*
▲ EMP: 28 EST: 1961
SQ FT: 35,000
SALES (est): 3.2MM **Privately Held**
WEB: www.kegs.com
SIC: 7699 5085 3993 3412 Tank repair & cleaning services; barrels, new or reconditioned; signs & advertising specialties; metal barrels, drums & pails

(G-18684)
SAN MARCO SUPER MARKETO
Also Called: San Marco Indiana
235 Broadway St (43604-8801)
PHONE................419 469-8963
Oscar Ponce, *President*
EMP: 4
SALES (est): 341.4K **Privately Held**
SIC: 2032 Mexican foods: packaged in cans, jars, etc.

(G-18685)
SAXON PRODUCTS INC
2283 Fulton St (43620-1272)
PHONE................419 241-6771
Edward L Poling, *President*
Tony Berezowski, *Vice Pres*
Mary Mazziotti, *Treasurer*
▲ EMP: 9 EST: 1961
SQ FT: 20,000
SALES (est): 375K **Privately Held**
WEB: www.inpaksystems.com
SIC: 3496 Miscellaneous fabricated wire products

(G-18686)
SCALE TECH LTD
5601 Enterprise Blvd (43612-3816)
PHONE................419 729-5240
Fax: 419 729-0462
Don Wilson, *Principal*
EMP: 5
SALES (est): 125K **Privately Held**
SIC: 3596 Industrial scales

(G-18687)
SCHUSTER MANUFACTURING INC
1508 W Laskey Rd Ste 2 (43612-2936)
PHONE................419 476-5800
Richard J Schuster, *President*
EMP: 3 EST: 1975
SQ FT: 2,600
SALES (est): 371.5K **Privately Held**
SIC: 3544 3599 Jigs & fixtures; machine shop, jobbing & repair

(G-18688)
SEAPORT MOLD & CASTING COMPANY
1215 W Bancroft St (43606-4632)
PHONE................419 243-1422
Fax: 419 243-4445
Michael A Kumor, *President*
Fred Kumor, *Vice Pres*
Chad Martin, *Project Mgr*
EMP: 14
SQ FT: 15,000
SALES (est): 1MM **Privately Held**
SIC: 3369 3543 Nonferrous foundries; industrial patterns

(G-18689)
SEAWAY PATTERN MFG INC
5749 Angola Rd (43615-6319)
PHONE................419 865-5724
Fax: 419 865-1170
Richard Johnston, *President*
EMP: 26 EST: 1962
SQ FT: 30,000
SALES (est): 3.5MM **Privately Held**
WEB: www.seawaypatterninc.com
SIC: 3543 3544 Industrial patterns; industrial molds

(G-18690)
SELECT MATTRESS CO INC
1216 W Bancroft St (43606-4631)
PHONE................419 244-3645
Fax: 419 244-7030
Ruben Gonzalez, *President*
Jose Gonzalez, *Vice Pres*
Arthur Rios, *Treasurer*
Jorge Gonalez, *Admin Sec*
EMP: 13
SQ FT: 41,000
SALES (est): 1.4MM **Privately Held**
SIC: 2515 Mattresses & foundations

(G-18691)
SEM-COM COMPANY INC (PA)
1040 N Westwood Ave (43607-3263)
P.O. Box 8428 (43623-0428)
PHONE................419 537-8813
Fax: 419 537-7054
Michael V Pfaender, *President*
Lawrence V Pfaender, *Chairman*
William Garrett, *Vice Pres*
James Pfaender, *Vice Pres*
Paul Train, *Sales Mgr*
EMP: 18
SQ FT: 22,500
SALES (est): 2.5MM **Privately Held**
WEB: www.sem-com.com
SIC: 3229 3231 2891 Pressed & blown glass; fiber optics strands; products of purchased glass; adhesives & sealants

(G-18692)
SENECA PETROLEUM CO INC
1441 Woodville Rd (43605-3233)
PHONE................419 691-3581
Fax: 419 691-2953
William Matz, *Vice Pres*
Hugh Chapman, *Sales Staff*
Larry Palmer, *Sales Staff*
Dean Friend, *Manager*
EMP: 12
SALES (corp-wide): 22.1MM **Privately Held**
SIC: 2951 2911 Asphalt & asphaltic paving mixtures (not from refineries); petroleum refining
PA: Seneca Petroleum Co., Inc.
13301 Cicero Ave
Crestwood IL 60445
708 396-1100

(G-18693)
SFC GRAPHICS CLEVELAND LTD
Also Called: Sfc Graphic Arts Div
110 E Woodruff Ave (43604-5226)
P.O. Box 877 (43697-0877)
PHONE................419 255-1283
Tom Clark, *CEO*
Paul Clark, *President*
Deb Truscinski, *Human Res Mgr*
EMP: 40
SQ FT: 15,000
SALES (est): 5.2MM **Privately Held**
WEB: www.sfcgraphics.com
SIC: 2752 Commercial printing, lithographic

(G-18694)
SHEAR TECH STEEL LLC
5610 Enterprise Blvd (43612)
PHONE................419 726-6174
Fax: 419 726-4626
Amanda Schaunter, *Manager*
Lisa Jones,
EMP: 6
SQ FT: 70,000
SALES (est): 999.5K **Privately Held**
SIC: 3312 Blast furnaces & steel mills

(G-18695)
SHELLY MATERIALS INC
Also Called: Shelly Liquid Division
352 George Hardy Dr (43605-1063)
PHONE................740 246-6315
John Power, *President*
EMP: 4
SALES (corp-wide): 28.6B **Privately Held**
SIC: 1422 Crushed & broken limestone
HQ: Shelly Materials, Inc.
80 Park Dr
Thornville OH 43076
740 246-6315

(G-18696)
SIGN LADY INC
5981 Telegraph Rd (43612-4548)
PHONE................419 476-9191
Fax: 419 476-9141
Lynn M Ulrich, *President*
Larry Lemerand, *Vice Pres*
EMP: 5
SALES (est): 671.2K **Privately Held**
SIC: 2759 5099 7532 Screen printing; signs, except electric; truck painting & lettering

(G-18697)
SILICONE SOLUTIONS INC
3441 South Ave (43609-1148)
PHONE................419 720-8709
Eric Tudor, *President*
EMP: 3
SALES (est): 943.4K **Privately Held**
SIC: 5169 2869 Adhesives & sealants; silicones

(G-18698)
SLAP N TICKLE LLC
Also Called: Randys
5645 Angola Rd Ste A (43615-6384)
PHONE................419 349-3226
Brian Nutt, *Mng Member*
▲ EMP: 5
SALES (est): 469.7K **Privately Held**
SIC: 3669 Smoke detectors

(G-18699)
SMP MANUFACTURING LLC
Also Called: Select Mattress
1216 W Bancroft St (43606-4631)
PHONE................419 244-3645
Monica Gonzalez, *Principal*
EMP: 3
SALES (est): 320K **Privately Held**
SIC: 2515 Mattresses & foundations

(G-18700)
SOJOURNERS TRUTH
1811 Adams St (43604-5427)
PHONE................419 243-0007
Fletcher Word, *President*
Kevin McQueen, *Vice Pres*
Annette Wright, *Accountant*
EMP: 10

SALES (est): 486.9K **Privately Held**
SIC: 2711 Newspapers

(G-18701)
SONUS-USA INC
3829 Woodley Rd Bldg B (43606-1171)
PHONE................419 474-9324
Dr Vijay Adappa, *Ch of Bd*
William Willis, *Med Doctor*
EMP: 20
SALES (corp-wide): 2.1MM **Privately Held**
WEB: www.sonus.com
SIC: 3842 Hearing aids
HQ: Sonus-Usa, Inc.
5000 Cheshire Pkwy N # 1
Plymouth MN 55446

(G-18702)
SPRINGTIME MANUFACTURING
1121 Hazelwood St (43605-3211)
PHONE................419 697-3720
Fax: 419 697-3891
George Hazel, *Owner*
EMP: 8
SALES (est): 855.9K **Privately Held**
SIC: 3495 5051 Wire springs; metals service centers & offices

(G-18703)
STEPPING STONE ENTERPRISES INC
Also Called: Minuteman Press
5847 Secor Rd (43623-1421)
PHONE................419 472-0505
Fax: 419 472-0554
Steven Heaney, *President*
Vicki Kimler, *Corp Secy*
Ronald R Kimler, *Vice Pres*
Dawn Simmons, *Manager*
Jason Pickens, *Graphic Designe*
EMP: 13
SQ FT: 3,000
SALES (est): 1.7MM **Privately Held**
SIC: 2752 Commercial printing, lithographic

(G-18704)
STERLING PIPE & TUBE INC (PA)
5335 Enterprise Blvd (43612-3810)
PHONE................419 729-9756
Fax: 419 729-2757
Fred Shelar, *President*
Dennis Krout, *Vice Pres*
Jim Swartz, *Opers Mgr*
Bennie Gardner, *CFO*
Christopher Rowe, *Controller*
▲ EMP: 140
SQ FT: 70,000
SALES (est): 27.1MM **Privately Held**
WEB: www.sterlingpipeandtube.com
SIC: 3317 Steel pipe & tubes

(G-18705)
STONECO INC
352 George Hardy Dr (43605-1063)
PHONE................419 693-3933
William Hodges, *Manager*
EMP: 9
SALES (corp-wide): 28.6B **Privately Held**
SIC: 2951 Paving mixtures
HQ: Stoneco, Inc.
1700 Fostoria Ave Ste 200
Findlay OH 45840
419 422-8854

(G-18706)
SUNBEAM PRODUCTS CO LLC
623 Main St (43605-1745)
P.O. Box 8097 (43605-0097)
PHONE................419 691-1551
Todd Lincoln, *Managing Prtnr*
Janice Stoycheff, *Office Mgr*
George Stoycheff,
EMP: 3 EST: 1935
SALES: 370K **Privately Held**
SIC: 2841 7699 Detergents, synthetic organic or inorganic alkaline; industrial equipment services

GEOGRAPHI

(G-18707)
SUNFOREST VISION CENTER INC
3915 Sunforest Ct Ste A (43623-4453)
PHONE..........................419 475-4646
Fax: 419 475-1407
Abraham Sim, *President*
EMP: 3
SALES (est): 326.7K **Privately Held**
SIC: 3851 Eyes, glass & plastic

(G-18708)
SUNSHINE PRODUCTS
760 Warehouse Rd Ste O (43615-6455)
P.O. Box 350786 (43635-0786)
PHONE..........................303 478-4913
Fax: 419 382-7885
Del Short, *Principal*
EMP: 3
SALES (est): 366.3K **Privately Held**
SIC: 3915 Jewelers' materials & lapidary work

(G-18709)
SUPERIOR IMPRESSIONS INC
327 12th St (43604-7531)
PHONE..........................419 244-8676
Douglas A Shelton, *President*
Jeanne Hautaniemi, *Vice Pres*
Dawn Freeman, *Director*
EMP: 8
SQ FT: 6,000
SALES (est): 730K **Privately Held**
SIC: 2752 Commercial printing, offset

(G-18710)
SUPERIOR PACKAGING
2930 Airport Hwy (43609-1404)
PHONE..........................419 380-3335
Steve Davis, *Owner*
Jack Palmer, *Manager*
EMP: 10
SALES (est): 1.6MM **Privately Held**
SIC: 3629 Electronic generation equipment

(G-18711)
SURFACE ENTERPRISES INC
1465 W Alexis Rd (43612-4044)
PHONE..........................419 476-5670
Fax: 419 476-4456
Susan Kroma, *President*
Bill Kroma, *Vice Pres*
Donna Kroma, *Administration*
EMP: 25
SQ FT: 9,000
SALES: 2.4MM **Privately Held**
WEB: www.surfaceenterprises.com
SIC: 2434 Wood kitchen cabinets

(G-18712)
SYRACUSE CHINA COMPANY (DH)
300 Madison Ave (43604-1561)
P.O. Box 10060 (43699-0060)
PHONE..........................419 727-2100
John F Meier, *Ch of Bd*
Richard Reynolds, *Vice Pres*
Willie Purvis, *Plant Mgr*
▲ EMP: 225
SQ FT: 50,000
SALES (est): 16.8MM
SALES (corp-wide): 796.2MM **Publicly Held**
SIC: 3262 Dishes, commercial or household; vitreous china
HQ: Libbey Glass Inc.
　　300 Madison Ave Fl 4
　　Toledo OH 43604
　　419 325-2100

(G-18713)
SYSTEMS SPECIALTY CTRL CO INC
1550 Coining Dr (43612-2905)
PHONE..........................419 478-4156
Fax: 419 478-9642
Edbert A Karcher, *Principal*
Ken Karcher, *Vice Pres*
Tim Stroshine, *Vice Pres*
EMP: 20
SQ FT: 14,000
SALES (est): 5MM **Privately Held**
SIC: 3613 Control panels, electric

(G-18714)
T E HUBLER INC
Also Called: R & T Microcenters of Ohio
236 New Towne Square Dr 1b (43612-4625)
PHONE..........................419 476-2552
Fax: 419 476-8009
Rosalina Hubler, *President*
Carrie Lily, *Info Tech Mgr*
EMP: 3
SQ FT: 2,400
SALES (est): 384.6K **Privately Held**
WEB: www.rtmicrocenters.com
SIC: 5734 7378 3577 5045 Computer & software stores; computer maintenance & repair; computer peripheral equipment; computer software

(G-18715)
TAFT TOOL & PRODUCTION CO
756 S Byrne Rd Ste 1 (43609-1088)
PHONE..........................419 385-2576
Fax: 419 385-7987
Varkes Tavtigian, *President*
Paul Sneider, *General Mgr*
Rose Tavtigian, *Vice Pres*
EMP: 10 EST: 1948
SQ FT: 13,000
SALES (est): 1.1MM **Privately Held**
SIC: 3544 3545 7699 Special dies & tools; gauges (machine tool accessories); industrial machinery & equipment repair

(G-18716)
TECHNOLOGY RESOURCES INC
916 N Summit St (43604-1812)
PHONE..........................419 241-9248
Fax: 419 242-2010
Robert C Redmond, *President*
Dyne Hoenie, *Vice Pres*
Abdul Hashi, *Engineer*
John Meyer, *Engineer*
EMP: 5
SQ FT: 6,000
SALES (est): 951K **Privately Held**
WEB: www.ohiotechresources.com
SIC: 3823 7371 Computer interface equipment for industrial process control; computer software systems analysis & design, custom

(G-18717)
TELEDYNE TECHNOLOGIES INC
1330 W Laskey Rd (43612-2911)
PHONE..........................419 470-3000
Fax: 419 470-3052
Jennifer O'Dell, *General Mgr*
Harley Greenburg, *Vice Pres*
David Plumeau, *Production*
Tony Sticca, *Purch Mgr*
Steve Ryne, *Senior Buyer*
EMP: 100
SALES (corp-wide): 2.1B **Publicly Held**
WEB: www.teledyne.com
SIC: 3511 Gas turbines, mechanical drive
PA: Teledyne Technologies Inc
　　1049 Camino Dos Rios
　　Thousand Oaks CA 91360
　　805 373-4545

(G-18718)
TELEX COMMUNICATIONS INC
Also Called: Toledo Business Journals
5660 Southwyck Blvd # 105 (43614-1597)
PHONE..........................419 865-0972
Fax: 419 244-5773
Sanford Lubin, *President*
Adam Hintz, *Editor*
Wade Kapszukiewicz, *Treasurer*
Jackie Bruecken, *Director*
Michael Carroll, *Director*
EMP: 14
SALES (est): 966.1K **Privately Held**
SIC: 8748 8742 2721 Business consulting; communications consulting; industry specialist consultants; periodicals

(G-18719)
TEMBEC BTLSR INC
2112 Sylvan Ave (43606-4767)
P.O. Box 2570 (43606-0570)
PHONE..........................419 244-5856
Fax: 419 244-9206
James M Lopez, *President*
Lawrence Rowley, *General Mgr*
Dan Wozniak, *Admin Sec*
▲ EMP: 32
SQ FT: 84,000
SALES (est): 9.2MM
SALES (corp-wide): 1.1B **Privately Held**
WEB: www.btlresins.com
SIC: 2821 5169 Plastics materials & resins; industrial chemicals
PA: Tembec Inc
　　4 Place Ville-Marie Bureau 100
　　Montreal QC H3B 2
　　514 871-0137

(G-18720)
TEX-TYLER CORPORATION
Also Called: Viking Paper
5148 Stickney Ave (43612-3721)
PHONE..........................419 729-4951
J Anthony Mooter, *President*
Robert L Walker, *Vice Pres*
Kathleen Malosh, *Office Mgr*
Wendy Logan Rogers, *Manager*
EMP: 29
SQ FT: 60,000
SALES (est): 2.5MM **Privately Held**
SIC: 3444 Sheet metalwork

(G-18721)
TEXTILEATHER CORPORATION (HQ)
3729 Twining St (43608-1315)
PHONE..........................419 729-3731
Fax: 419 729-7556
Robert Cristinzio, *President*
Stephan Walko, *Division Mgr*
Rich Loth, *Purchasing*
David Evans, *Engineer*
Tom Beaschler, *Controller*
▲ EMP: 385
SQ FT: 470,000
SALES (est): 24.6MM
SALES (corp-wide): 143.7MM **Privately Held**
SIC: 3069 Rubber coated fabrics & clothing
PA: Canadian General-Tower Limited
　　52 Middleton St
　　Cambridge ON N1R 5
　　519 623-1630

(G-18722)
THE RUBBER STAMP SHOP
4418 Lewis Ave (43612-1846)
PHONE..........................419 478-4444
Fax: 419 478-8623
Arthur Winzenried, *Owner*
EMP: 3
SQ FT: 7,000
SALES (est): 406.7K **Privately Held**
WEB: www.jillianvillafane.com
SIC: 5112 5999 5943 2672 Marking devices; rubber stamps; stationery stores; coated & laminated paper

(G-18723)
THUNDAWEAR LLC
Also Called: Thundawear Skull Caps
1709 Spielbusch Ave # 100 (43604-5470)
PHONE..........................419 787-2675
Ronald Roberts, *Mng Member*
Gwen Roberts, *Director*
EMP: 4
SALES (est): 215.8K **Privately Held**
SIC: 2353 Hats, caps & millinery

(G-18724)
TIMMYS SANDWICH SHOP
5426 Cresthaven Ln (43614-1218)
PHONE..........................419 350-8267
Timothy Foster, *Owner*
EMP: 6 EST: 2014
SALES (est): 160K **Privately Held**
SIC: 2099 7389 Ready-to-eat meals, salads & sandwiches;

(G-18725)
TIMON J REINHART
Also Called: Timon Tool & Die
1560 W Laskey Rd Ste B (43612-2937)
PHONE..........................419 476-1990
Fax: 419 476-0991
Timon J Reinhart, *Owner*
Tim Reinhart, *Owner*
EMP: 4
SQ FT: 3,800
SALES: 225K **Privately Held**
SIC: 3599 Machine shop, jobbing & repair

(G-18726)
TJ METZGERS INC
207 Arco Dr (43607-2906)
PHONE..........................419 861-8611
Thomas H Metzger, *CEO*
Joseph J Metzger, *President*
Todd Beringer, *Accounts Mgr*
John Luscombe, *Accounts Mgr*
Mary Schuck, *Accounts Mgr*
EMP: 100
SQ FT: 63,146
SALES (est): 20MM **Privately Held**
WEB: www.metzgers.com
SIC: 2752 2759 2789 2791 Commercial printing, lithographic; commercial printing; bookbinding & related work; photocomposition, for the printing trade; color separation, photographic & movie film

(G-18727)
TM MACHINE & TOOL INC
521 Mel Simon Dr (43612-4726)
PHONE..........................419 478-0310
Fax: 419 478-9174
Karyn Weeks, *President*
EMP: 8
SQ FT: 20,000
SALES (est): 770K **Privately Held**
SIC: 3544 3599 Special dies, tools, jigs & fixtures; machine shop, jobbing & repair

(G-18728)
TOLCO CORPORATION
1920 Linwood Ave (43604-5293)
PHONE..........................419 241-1113
Fax: 419 241-3035
George L Notarianni, *President*
Al Carver, *Division Mgr*
James Reising, *Regional Mgr*
Ted Denker, *Purchasing*
Tricia Thomas, *Design Engr*
▲ EMP: 75
SQ FT: 30,000
SALES (est): 32.6MM **Privately Held**
WEB: www.tolco.com
SIC: 5085 3563 3586 3561 Bottler supplies; spraying outfits: metals, paints & chemicals (compressor); vacuum pumps, except laboratory; measuring & dispensing pumps; pumps & pumping equipment; specialty cleaning, polishes & sanitation goods

(G-18729)
TOLEDO AUTOMATIC SCREW CO
2114 Champlain St (43611-3703)
PHONE..........................419 726-3441
Fax: 419 726-0422
James R Park, *President*
Steve Sorge, *Corp Secy*
EMP: 5 EST: 1946
SQ FT: 3,000
SALES: 400K **Privately Held**
SIC: 3451 Screw machine products

(G-18730)
TOLEDO BLADE COMPANY
541 N Superior St (43660-0002)
P.O. Box 921 (43697-0921)
PHONE..........................419 724-6000
Fax: 419 245-6439
Joseph H Zerbey IV, *President*
Jeff Arnett, *Editor*
Mac Arnold, *Editor*
T Barger, *Editor*
Tommy Gallagher, *Editor*
EMP: 423
SALES (est): 28.9MM
SALES (corp-wide): 626.6MM **Privately Held**
SIC: 2711 Newspapers, publishing & printing
PA: Block Communications, Inc.
　　405 Madison Ave Ste 2100
　　Toledo OH 43604
　　419 724-6212

(G-18731)
TOLEDO ENGINEERING CO INC (PA)
Also Called: Teco
3400 Executive Pkwy Ste 4 (43606-1364)
P.O. Box 2927 (43606-0927)
PHONE..........................419 537-9711

George B Seifried, *Ch of Bd*
Todd Seifried, *President*
Geoff Turton, *President*
Eric Kan, *Managing Dir*
Scott A Slater, *Chairman*
▲ EMP: 75
SQ FT: 50,000
SALES (est): 34.8MM **Privately Held**
WEB: www.o2furnace.com
SIC: 3559 Glass making machinery: blowing, molding, forming, etc.

(G-18732)
TOLEDO JOURNAL
3021 Douglas Rd (43606-3504)
P.O. Box 12559 (43606-0159)
PHONE..................................419 472-4521
Fax: 419 472-1604
Myron A Stewart, *Partner*
Sandra Stewart, *Publisher*
EMP: 8
SQ FT: 2,800
SALES (est): 380K **Privately Held**
SIC: 2711 Newspapers: publishing only, not printed on site

(G-18733)
**TOLEDO METAL SPINNING
COMPANY**
1819 Clinton St (43607-1600)
PHONE..................................419 535-5931
Fax: 419 535-0565
Kenneth F Fankhauser, *President*
Craig B Fankhauser, *Vice Pres*
Eric Sankhauser, *Vice Pres*
Dave Johnson, *Safety Mgr*
Eric S Fankhauser, *Treasurer*
▼ EMP: 35 EST: 1929
SQ FT: 100,000
SALES (est): 9.5MM **Privately Held**
WEB: www.toledometalspinning.com
SIC: 3469 3443 Spinning metal for the trade; stamping metal for the trade; cylinders, pressure: metal plate

(G-18734)
**TOLEDO MOBILE MEDIA LLC
(PA)**
757 Warehouse Rd Ste D (43615-6478)
PHONE..................................419 389-0687
John S Demitry, *Mng Member*
EMP: 4
SALES (est): 470.4K **Privately Held**
SIC: 3993 3999 Signs & advertising specialties; advertising display products

(G-18735)
TOLEDO MOLDING & DIE INC
300 Phillips Ave Ste 2002 (43612-1494)
PHONE..................................419 720-3500
Eric Stockard, *Vice Pres*
Pat Sall, *Branch Mgr*
EMP: 100
SALES (corp-wide): 426.5MM **Privately
Held**
WEB: www.tmdinc.com
SIC: 3711 Automobile assembly, including specialty automobiles
PA: Toledo Molding & Die, Inc.
1429 Coining Dr
Toledo OH 43612
419 470-3950

(G-18736)
**TOLEDO MOLDING & DIE INC
(PA)**
Also Called: T M D
1429 Coining Dr (43612-2932)
PHONE..................................419 470-3950
Fax: 419 470-3977
Stephen Ciucci, *President*
Wilda Coyle, *Business Mgr*
David Spotts, *COO*
Joni Schmidt, *Vice Pres*
Brent Mattas, *Plant Mgr*
◆ EMP: 60
SQ FT: 35,000
SALES (est): 426.5MM **Privately Held**
WEB: www.tmdinc.com
SIC: 3089 3544 Injection molded finished plastic products; special dies, tools, jigs & fixtures

(G-18737)
TOLEDO MOLDING & DIE INC
4 E Laskey Rd (43612-3517)
PHONE..................................419 476-0581
Fax: 419 476-1944
Scott Ruskinoff, *Facilities Mgr*
Jeffery Coppler, *Buyer*
Susan Stang, *Buyer*
Rob Olsen, *Engineer*
Joe Pirrone, *Manager*
EMP: 120
SALES (corp-wide): 426.5MM **Privately
Held**
WEB: www.tmdinc.com
SIC: 3089 3544 Injection molded finished plastic products; special dies, tools, jigs & fixtures
PA: Toledo Molding & Die, Inc.
1429 Coining Dr
Toledo OH 43612
419 470-3950

(G-18738)
**TOLEDO OPTICAL
LABORATORY INC**
1201 Jefferson Ave (43604-5852)
P.O. Box 2028 (43603-2028)
PHONE..................................419 248-3384
Fax: 419 321-6361
Irland Tashima, *President*
Robert Lommerse, *General Mgr*
Jeffrey Seymenski, *Vice Pres*
Mary Johnson, *Opers Mgr*
Paula Jahns, *Personnel Exec*
EMP: 52
SQ FT: 10,000
SALES (est): 8.1MM **Privately Held**
SIC: 3851 5048 Eyeglasses, lenses & frames; lenses, ophthalmic; frames, ophthalmic

(G-18739)
TOLEDO PAINT & CHEMICAL CO
33 Blucher St (43607-4403)
P.O. Box 324 (43697-0324)
PHONE..................................419 244-3726
Fax: 419 244-4561
David C Peters, *President*
Frank D Jacobs, *Admin Sec*
EMP: 6
SQ FT: 20,400
SALES (est): 1MM **Privately Held**
SIC: 2851 Paints & paint additives

(G-18740)
TOLEDO PRO FIBERGLASS INC
210 Wade St (43604-8852)
PHONE..................................419 241-9390
Fax: 419 241-9392
Don Jardine, *Vice Pres*
Linda Walters, *Office Mgr*
EMP: 8
SQ FT: 24,000
SALES (est): 500K **Privately Held**
WEB: www.toledopro.com
SIC: 5999 3714 3711 3089 Fiberglass materials, except insulation; motor vehicle parts & accessories; motor vehicles & car bodies; fiberglass doors

(G-18741)
**TOLEDO SCREW PRODUCTS
INC**
8261 W Bancroft St (43617-1804)
PHONE..................................419 841-3341
Fax: 419 841-3341
J Warren Ide, *President*
EMP: 7 EST: 1948
SQ FT: 12,500
SALES (est): 510K **Privately Held**
SIC: 3451 Screw machine products

(G-18742)
TOLEDO SIGNS & DESIGNS LTD
6636 W Bancroft St Ste 2 (43615-3188)
PHONE..................................419 843-1073
Fax: 419 843-3577
Karrie Lyczkowski, *Branch Mgr*
EMP: 3
SALES (corp-wide): 741.2K **Privately
Held**
SIC: 2759 5099 Screen printing; signs, except electric

PA: Toledo Signs & Designs Ltd
1100 N Mccord Rd Ste 1a
Toledo OH 43615
419 843-1073

(G-18743)
TOLEDO STREETS NEWSPAPER
316 N Michigan St Ste 330 (43604-5627)
PHONE..................................419 214-3460
Josh Schuyler, *Principal*
Ken Leslie, *Principal*
EMP: 3
SALES (est): 69.2K **Privately Held**
SIC: 2711 Newspapers

(G-18744)
TOLEDO SWORD NEWSPAPER
3332 Stanhope Dr (43606-1249)
PHONE..................................419 932-0767
Toledo Sword Newspaper, *Principal*
EMP: 4
SALES (est): 185.5K **Privately Held**
SIC: 2711 Newspapers

(G-18745)
**TOLEDO TAPE AND LABEL
COMPANY**
4731 South Ave Ste 3 (43615-6479)
PHONE..................................419 536-8316
Norman L Fisher, *Owner*
Harold Browwing, *Manager*
Harold Browning, *Manager*
EMP: 5
SALES (est): 250K **Privately Held**
SIC: 2754 Rotary photogravure printing

(G-18746)
TOLEDO TICKET COMPANY
3963 Catawba St (43612-1492)
P.O. Box 6876 (43612-0876)
PHONE..................................419 476-5424
Roy L Carter, *Ch of Bd*
Robin G Carter, *Treasurer*
Tom Carter, *Sales Mgr*
Vince Sedlacek, *Manager*
EMP: 50
SQ FT: 50,000
SALES (est): 12.2MM **Privately Held**
WEB: www.toledoticket.com
SIC: 2752 2759 Tickets, lithographed; commercial printing

(G-18747)
TOLEDO TOOL AND DIE CO INC
105 W Alexis Rd (43612-3603)
PHONE..................................419 476-4422
Fax: 419 476-9944
John Vanbelle, *Accounts Mgr*
Francis J Palmer, *Incorporator*
T Kenneth Mattimoe, *Incorporator*
Teresa R Zsigray, *Incorporator*
▲ EMP: 50 EST: 1941
SQ FT: 60,000
SALES (est): 21.2MM **Privately Held**
WEB: www.toledotool.com
SIC: 3469 3544 Metal stampings; special dies, tools, jigs & fixtures

(G-18748)
**TOLEDO WINDOW & AWNING
INC**
3035 W Sylvania Ave (43613-4135)
PHONE..................................419 474-3396
Fax: 419 292-2914
Dennis Whitaker, *President*
Dawn Whitaker, *Vice Pres*
Kevin McFarland, *Sales Staff*
EMP: 7
SQ FT: 2,600
SALES (est): 1.1MM **Privately Held**
WEB: www.toledowindow.com
SIC: 3444 5031 5211 Awnings, sheet metal; doors & windows; doors, storm: wood or metal; windows, storm: wood or metal

(G-18749)
**TOLEDOS RUNWAY RIVALRY
BROUGH**
541 N Superior St (43604-1778)
PHONE..................................419 724-6307
Clarence Espen, *Principal*
Bill Piotrowski, *Editor*
Rona Proudfoot, *Editor*

John Fedderke, *Adv Dir*
EMP: 4
SALES (est): 165.2K **Privately Held**
SIC: 2711 Newspapers

(G-18750)
**TOOLING & COMPONENTS
CORP**
Also Called: Toolcomp
5261 Tractor Rd (43612-3439)
PHONE..................................419 478-9122
Fax: 419 478-1845
David Gonzalez, *President*
Ezekiel Gonzalez, *Vice Pres*
EMP: 12
SQ FT: 5,900
SALES (est): 750K **Privately Held**
WEB: www.toolcomp.com
SIC: 3599 3544 Machine shop, jobbing & repair; special dies, tools, jigs & fixtures

(G-18751)
TORBOT GROUP INC
Also Called: Jobskin Division
5030 Advantage Dr Ste 101 (43612-3861)
PHONE..................................419 724-1475
Greg Johnson, *Branch Mgr*
EMP: 28
SALES (corp-wide): 8.5MM **Privately
Held**
WEB: www.torbot.com
SIC: 3841 Surgical & medical instruments
PA: Torbot Group, Inc.
1367 Elmwood Ave
Cranston RI 02910
401 780-8737

(G-18752)
TOTH INDUSTRIES INC
5102 Enterprise Blvd (43612-3897)
PHONE..................................419 729-4669
Fax: 419 729-3760
Richard Toth, *President*
Thomas Toth, *Vice Pres*
Robert McCullough, *Purchasing*
Ron Gillen, *Engineer*
Chester Skrupa, *Director*
EMP: 70 EST: 1955
SQ FT: 40,000
SALES (est): 16.9MM **Privately Held**
WEB: www.tothindustries.com
SIC: 3599 3594 Machine shop, jobbing & repair; fluid power pumps & motors

(G-18753)
TOUCH OF GLASS
908 Jean Rd (43615-4415)
PHONE..................................419 861-2888
Steven Moder, *Owner*
Jean Moder, *Principal*
EMP: 3 EST: 1991
SALES (est): 144.7K **Privately Held**
SIC: 3229 Pressed & blown glass

(G-18754)
TPR PLASMA CENTER
625 Dorr St (43604-8023)
PHONE..................................419 244-3910
EMP: 3 EST: 2007
SALES (est): 190K **Privately Held**
SIC: 2836 Plasmas

(G-18755)
TRADITIONS SAUCES LLC
606 Durango Dr (43609-1706)
PHONE..................................419 704-4506
Donald Hill, *CEO*
EMP: 5
SALES (est): 60K **Privately Held**
SIC: 2033 Chili sauce, tomato: packaged in cans, jars, etc.

(G-18756)
**TRANSCO RAILWAY PRODUCTS
INC**
4800 Schwartz Rd (43611-1726)
P.O. Box 5009 (43611-0009)
PHONE..................................419 726-3383
Fax: 419 726-3562
Antwan Smith, *Branch Mgr*
EMP: 30
SALES (corp-wide): 104.3MM **Privately
Held**
SIC: 3537 7699 Industrial trucks & tractors; railroad car customizing

HQ: Transco Railway Products Inc.
200 N La Salle St # 1550
Chicago IL 60601
312 427-2818

(G-18757)
TRU-FORM STEEL & WIRE INC
5509 Telegraph Rd (43612-2662)
PHONE......................................765 348-5001
Jeffrey Tuttle, *Branch Mgr*
EMP: 50
SALES (corp-wide): 17.1MM **Privately Held**
SIC: **3315** 3441 Steel wire & related products; fabricated structural metal
PA: Tru-Form Steel & Wire, Inc.
1204 Gilkey Ave
Hartford City IN 47348
765 348-5001

(G-18758)
TRW AUTOMOTIVE US LLC
5915 Jason St (43611-1088)
PHONE......................................419 726-5599
Fax: 419 726-5799
Dennis Burke, *Branch Mgr*
EMP: 55 **Privately Held**
WEB: www.trw.mediaroom.com
SIC: **3469** Metal stampings
HQ: Trw Automotive U.S. Llc
12001 Tech Center Dr
Livonia MI 48150
734 855-2600

(G-18759)
UNITY CABLE TECHNOLOGIES INC
Also Called: Unity Defense Systems, Inc.
1811 Adams St (43604-5427)
PHONE......................................419 322-4118
Annette M Wright, *President*
EMP: 5
SQ FT: 1,500
SALES: 2MM **Privately Held**
SIC: **5063** 3612 3299 3694 Insulators, electrical; wire & cable; current limiting reactors, electrical; tubing for electrical purposes, quartz; engine electrical equipment; combat vehicles

(G-18760)
UNIVERSAL URETHANE PDTS INC
410 1st St (43605-2002)
P.O. Box 50617 (43605-0617)
PHONE......................................419 693-7400
Fax: 419 693-2363
Harry G Conrad, *CEO*
Jeffrey A Conrad, *President*
Scott Conrad, *Vice Pres*
Frank Wilton, *Safety Dir*
Monty Coffman, *Purch Agent*
EMP: 55
SQ FT: 32,000
SALES (est): 10.3MM **Privately Held**
WEB: www.universalurethane.com
SIC: **3069** 3312 3061 2851 Hard rubber & molded rubber products; blast furnaces & steel mills; mechanical rubber goods; paints & allied products; synthetic rubber; platemaking services

(G-18761)
UNLIMITED MACHINE AND TOOL LLC
5139 Tractor Rd Ste C (43612-3432)
PHONE......................................419 269-1730
Tom McCloskey,
Richard Bell,
EMP: 11
SQ FT: 6,000
SALES (est): 852.5K **Privately Held**
WEB: www.unlimmachtool.com
SIC: **3544** 3312 Special dies & tools; tool & die steel & alloys

(G-18762)
UPPER PAW
5746 Staghorn Dr (43614-4561)
PHONE......................................419 277-9000
Jason Bolinger, *Principal*
EMP: 2
SALES (est): 214.7K **Privately Held**
SIC: **3131** Uppers

(G-18763)
V M SYSTEMS INC
3125 Hill Ave (43607-2987)
PHONE......................................419 535-1044
Fax: 419 535-8644
Craig Gabel, *President*
Ronald H Gabel, *President*
Trent Bloomfield, *Vice Pres*
Raymond Klepacz, *Foreman/Supr*
Nicole Snyder, *Manager*
EMP: 100
SQ FT: 24,000
SALES (est): 26MM **Privately Held**
WEB: www.vmsystemsinc.com
SIC: **1711** 3444 Warm air heating & air conditioning contractor; ventilation & duct work contractor; sheet metalwork

(G-18764)
VALLEY PLASTICS CO INC
399 Phillips Ave (43612-1349)
PHONE......................................419 666-2349
David G Thompson, *President*
Ron Tillman, *Business Mgr*
Diane Wade, *Manager*
EMP: 40
SALES (est): 7.8MM **Privately Held**
WEB: www.valleyplasticsinc.com
SIC: **3089** 2542 Plastic processing; partitions & fixtures, except wood

(G-18765)
VANS INC
5001 Monroe St Ste 1560 (43623-7003)
PHONE......................................419 471-1541
Fax: 419 471-1752
Tom Ulrich, *Manager*
EMP: 10
SALES (corp-wide): 12B **Publicly Held**
SIC: **3021** Canvas shoes, rubber soled
HQ: Vans, Inc.
6550 Katella Ave
Cypress CA 90630
714 889-6100

(G-18766)
VENTUREMEDGROUP LTD
2865 N Reynolds Rd 220a (43615-2068)
PHONE......................................567 661-0768
Gary Smith, *CEO*
EMP: 6
SALES: 175K **Privately Held**
SIC: **3841** Surgical & medical instruments

(G-18767)
VERGELINE LLC
1301 N Summit St (43604-1819)
P.O. Box 850, Sylvania (43560-0850)
PHONE......................................419 730-0300
Kristin A Delverne, *Principal*
EMP: 3
SALES (est): 140K **Privately Held**
SIC: **3483** Ammunition, except for small arms

(G-18768)
VIKING PAPER COMPANY (PA)
5148 Stickney Ave (43612-3721)
PHONE......................................419 729-4951
Fax: 419 729-3445
J Anthony Mooter, *President*
Robert Walker, *Vice Pres*
Len Wenderski, *Sales Mgr*
Wendy Loga-Rogers, *Manager*
Bob Schuelke, *Manager*
EMP: 46 EST: 1986
SQ FT: 60,000
SALES (est): 19.9MM **Privately Held**
SIC: **2653** Sheets, corrugated: made from purchased materials

(G-18769)
VILLAGE VOICE PUBLISHING LTD
Also Called: Village Voice of Ottawa Hills
4041 W Central Ave Ste 6 (43606-2213)
PHONE......................................419 537-0286
Yaroslav Kuk, *Managing Prtnr*
Yar0slav Kuk, *Managing Prtnr*
Anthony Bassett, *Partner*
Winifred Kuk, *Partner*
Tony Basset, *Editor*
EMP: 3
SQ FT: 275
SALES (est): 214.5K **Privately Held**
SIC: **2711** Newspapers

(G-18770)
VINTAGE ELECTRIC LTD INC
Also Called: Vintage Heating and Air
3335 Mcgregor Ln (43623-1917)
PHONE......................................419 472-9349
Fax: 419 472-9335
Jacquelyn Crozier, *President*
John Crozier, *Vice Pres*
Lee Sears, *Sales Staff*
EMP: 10
SQ FT: 4,000
SALES: 700K **Privately Held**
SIC: **1711** 7539 5013 5531 Plumbing, heating, air-conditioning contractors; electrical services; automotive supplies & parts; automotive & home supply stores; engine electrical equipment; relays & industrial controls

(G-18771)
WAYNE FRAME PRODUCTS INC
5832 Lakeside Ave (43611-2466)
PHONE......................................419 726-7715
Jack L Bernard, *President*
Margaret Thurber, *Corp Secy*
Gerri Bernard, *Vice Pres*
EMP: 3
SALES (est): 351.6K **Privately Held**
SIC: **3089** Injection molded finished plastic products

(G-18772)
WEST EQUIPMENT COMPANY INC (PA)
1545 E Broadway St (43605-3852)
PHONE......................................419 698-1601
Fax: 419 698-2540
Bernard Erdmann, *CEO*
Paul Erdmann, *President*
Kristi Erdmann, *Principal*
Chad Erdmann, *Vice Pres*
Steve Michaelis, *Marketing Staff*
EMP: 18 EST: 1952
SQ FT: 7,200
SALES (est): 5.8MM **Privately Held**
SIC: **5082** 7699 7359 3496 Construction & mining machinery; construction equipment repair; equipment rental & leasing; slings, lifting: made from purchased wire; wire chain

(G-18773)
WESTROCK COMMERCIAL LLC
1635 Coining Dr (43612-2906)
PHONE......................................419 476-9101
Steve Voorhees, *CEO*
EMP: 8
SALES (corp-wide): 3.9MM **Privately Held**
SIC: **2752** 5112 Commercial printing, lithographic; stationery & office supplies
PA: Westrock Commercial, Llc
501 S 5th St
Richmond VA 23219
770 448-2193

(G-18774)
WHITEFORD INDUSTRIES INC
Also Called: Rehn Co
3323 South Ave (43609-1105)
PHONE......................................419 381-1155
Fax: 419 381-1159
Andy Klumb, *President*
EMP: 13
SQ FT: 9,000
SALES (est): 1.8MM **Privately Held**
WEB: www.rehncompany.com
SIC: **3842** 3451 Atomizers, medical; screw machine products

(G-18775)
WIFIFACE LLC
5424 Westcastle Dr Apt D (43615-2048)
PHONE......................................419 754-4816
Matthew Howenstein, *CEO*
Hassen Alhandy, *Vice Pres*
Marilyn Howenstein, *Manager*
EMP: 3
SALES (est): 101.8K **Privately Held**
SIC: **7372** Prepackaged software

(G-18776)
WIREMAX LTD
705 Wamba Ave (43607-3252)
P.O. Box 3336 (43607-0336)
PHONE......................................419 531-9500

Al Mocek, *President*
Mark Robinson, *Manager*
EMP: 6
SQ FT: 8,000
SALES (est): 1MM **Privately Held**
WEB: www.wiremax.com
SIC: **3643** Current-carrying wiring devices

(G-18777)
WURTEC MANUFACTURING SERVICE
6200 Brent Dr (43611-1081)
PHONE......................................419 726-1066
Steven P Wurth, *President*
Jane A Wurth, *Corp Secy*
▲ EMP: 20
SQ FT: 26,000
SALES (est): 3.7MM **Privately Held**
SIC: **3544** 3993 Special dies, tools, jigs & fixtures; signs, not made in custom sign painting shops

(G-18778)
YARDER MANUFACTURING COMPANY (PA)
722 Phillips Ave (43612-1333)
P.O. Box 6886 (43612-0886)
PHONE......................................419 476-3933
Fax: 419 478-6886
Richard W Yarder, *President*
Jeff Conlan, *General Mgr*
Matt Yarder, *Vice Pres*
Jake Ibarra, *Engineer*
Amy Conlan, *CFO*
EMP: 53
SQ FT: 55,000
SALES (est): 8.5MM **Privately Held**
WEB: www.yardermfg.com
SIC: **3499** Boxes for packing & shipping, metal

(G-18779)
YARDER MANUFACTURING COMPANY
730 Phillips Ave (43612-1333)
PHONE......................................419 269-3474
EMP: 4
SALES (corp-wide): 8.5MM **Privately Held**
SIC: **3499** Boxes for packing & shipping, metal
PA: The Yarder Manufacturing Company
722 Phillips Ave
Toledo OH 43612
419 476-3933

(G-18780)
ZIE BART RHINO LININGS TOLEDO
Also Called: Zie Bart Rhino Linings Toledo
3343 N Hlland Sylvania Rd (43615)
PHONE......................................419 841-2886
Keith Tucker, *Owner*
EMP: 6
SALES: 400K **Privately Held**
SIC: **3713** Truck beds

Toronto
Jefferson County

(G-18781)
EXPRESS ENERGY SVCS OPER LP
1515 Franklin St (43964-1029)
PHONE......................................740 337-4530
EMP: 42
SALES (corp-wide): 986.1MM **Privately Held**
SIC: **1389** Pipe testing, oil field service
PA: Express Energy Services Operating, Lp
9800 Richmond Ave Ste 500
Houston TX 77042
713 625-7400

(G-18782)
F & M COAL COMPANY
3925 County Road 56 (43964-7927)
PHONE......................................740 544-5203
Edward L Fiala, *Partner*
EMP: 3
SALES (est): 260K **Privately Held**
SIC: **1221** Strip mining, bituminous

(G-18783)
K B ELECTRIC MOTOR SERVICE
Also Called: K B Electric Service
915 Banfield Ave (43964-1103)
PHONE.....................................740 537-1346
Sharon Obertance, *President*
Bill Prolago, *Principal*
J B Ash, *Manager*
EMP: 5 **EST:** 1946
SQ FT: 2,000
SALES (est): 75K **Privately Held**
SIC: 7694 Electric motor repair

(G-18784)
RIDGE MACHINE & WELDING CO
1015 Railroad St (43964-1115)
P.O. Box 190 (43964-0190)
PHONE.....................................740 537-2821
Fax: 740 537-5240
David Artman, *President*
Debbie Artman, *Corp Secy*
J Curtis Artman, *Vice Pres*
James R Holland Jr, *Engineer*
EMP: 6 **EST:** 1950
SQ FT: 27,600
SALES: 500K **Privately Held**
SIC: 3599 7692 3398 Machine shop, jobbing & repair; welding repair; metal heat treating

(G-18785)
TITANIUM METALS CORPORATION
Also Called: Timet Toronto
100 Titanium Way (43964-1990)
P.O. Box 309 (43964-0309)
PHONE.....................................740 537-1571
Fax: 740 537-2634
Steve Guzy, *Plant Mgr*
James Pieron, *Plant Mgr*
Duane Faith, *Project Mgr*
Gregg Heil, *Materials Mgr*
Christian Leonhard, *Opers Staff*
EMP: 527
SALES (corp-wide): 223.6B **Publicly Held**
WEB: www.timet.com
SIC: 3566 3356 Speed changers, drives & gears; nonferrous rolling & drawing
HQ: Titanium Metals Corporation
224 Valley Creek Blvd # 200
Exton PA 19341
610 968-1300

(G-18786)
U S ARMY CORPS OF ENGINEERS
Also Called: New Cumberland Lock & Dam
29501 State Rte 7 (43964)
PHONE.....................................740 537-2571
Matt Dillon, *Manager*
David Ciciora, *Network Enginr*
George Schweickert, *Network Enginr*
Brandon Neubig, *Sr Ntwrk Engine*
EMP: 16 **Publicly Held**
WEB: www.sac.usace.army.mil
SIC: 3812 8711 Navigational systems & instruments; engineering services; building construction consultant
HQ: U S Army Corps Of Engineers
441 G Street Nw
Washington DC 20314
804 435-9362

(G-18787)
VALLEY CONVERTING CO INC (PA)
405 Daniels St (43964-1343)
P.O. Box 279 (43964-0279)
PHONE.....................................740 537-2152
Gino Biasi, *Ch of Bd*
Michael D Biasi, *President*
Richard Brandt, *Purch Mgr*
David Pratley, *Controller*
EMP: 50
SQ FT: 107,500
SALES: 11MM **Privately Held**
SIC: 2631 Cardboard

(G-18788)
VALLEY CONVERTING CO INC
310 Loretta Ave (43964-1354)
P.O. Box 279 (43964-0279)
PHONE.....................................740 537-2152

Fax: 740 537-2977
Mike Biasi, *Principal*
EMP: 45
SALES (corp-wide): 11MM **Privately Held**
SIC: 2631 Paperboard mills
PA: Valley Converting Co., Inc.
405 Daniels St
Toronto OH 43964
740 537-2152

Tremont City
Clark County

(G-18789)
MIKE LOPPE
Also Called: Kutrite Manufacturing
2 W Main St (45372)
P.O. Box 186 (45372-0186)
PHONE.....................................937 969-8102
Fax: 937 969-8749
Mike Loppe, *Owner*
Rose Haggey, *Co-Owner*
EMP: 10
SQ FT: 5,500
SALES (est): 640K **Privately Held**
SIC: 3599 7692 3444 Machine shop, jobbing & repair; welding repair; sheet metalwork

Trenton
Butler County

(G-18790)
ELITE MILL SERVICE & CNSTR
5757 Cottonrun Rd (45067-9724)
PHONE.....................................513 422-4234
John A Edester, *President*
EMP: 5
SQ FT: 3,600
SALES (est): 495.2K **Privately Held**
SIC: 3554 1521 Paper industries machinery; single-family housing construction

(G-18791)
EVERSHARPE DEBURRING TOOL CO
10 Baltimore Ave (45067-1513)
PHONE.....................................513 988-6240
Fax: 513 988-6187
David Huff, *President*
Bernice Huff, *Corp Secy*
Roger Sprinkle, *Vice Pres*
EMP: 8 **EST:** 1961
SQ FT: 2,400
SALES: 600K **Privately Held**
WEB: www.eversharpe.com
SIC: 7699 3545 Knife, saw & tool sharpening & repair; machine tool accessories

(G-18792)
GADD LOGGING
823 E Jameson Ct (45067-8621)
PHONE.....................................513 312-3941
Earl Gadd, *Principal*
EMP: 3
SALES (est): 189K **Privately Held**
SIC: 2411 Logging

(G-18793)
GREYFIELD INDUSTRIES INC
3104 Wayne Madison Rd (45067-9746)
PHONE.....................................513 860-1785
George Estes, *President*
Bob Leslie, *Vice Pres*
EMP: 15
SQ FT: 3,500
SALES (est): 4.5MM **Privately Held**
WEB: www.greyfieldindustries.com
SIC: 3661 3429 3663 3651 Telephone & telegraph apparatus; locks or lock sets; radio & TV communications equipment; household audio & video equipment

(G-18794)
JUNEBUGS WASH N DRY
6435 E State St (45067)
PHONE.....................................513 988-5863
Mike Wilson, *Owner*
EMP: 4

SALES (est): 178.5K **Privately Held**
SIC: 3633 Laundry dryers, household or coin-operated

(G-18795)
MAGNODE CORPORATION (PA)
400 E State St (45067-1549)
PHONE.....................................513 988-6351
Fax: 513 988-6357
Arthur W Bidwell, *CEO*
Martin J Bidwell, *President*
Johnie Adams, *Vice Pres*
Ann F Bidwell, *Vice Pres*
Joseph Bidwell, *Vice Pres*
EMP: 125
SQ FT: 100,000
SALES (est): 34MM **Privately Held**
WEB: www.magnode.com
SIC: 3354 Aluminum extruded products

(G-18796)
MILLERCOORS LLC
2525 Wayne Madison Rd (45067-9768)
P.O. Box 168 (45067-0168)
PHONE.....................................513 896-9200
Steve Sharpe, *Purchasing*
Sandra Lewis, *Pub Rel Dir*
Dennis Puffer, *Branch Mgr*
Michael Manning, *Manager*
Kenneth Yangula, *Technician*
EMP: 60
SALES (corp-wide): 4.8B **Publicly Held**
SIC: 2082 Malt beverages
HQ: Millercoors Llc
250 S Wacker Dr Ste 800
Chicago IL 60606
312 496-2700

Trotwood
Montgomery County

(G-18797)
J W DEVERS & SON INC
5 N Broadway St (45426-3555)
P.O. Box 26460 (45426-0460)
PHONE.....................................937 854-3040
Fax: 937 854-3017
Jerry Haupt, *President*
David Henderson, *Corp Secy*
Joseph Wolf, *Vice Pres*
Steve Wolf, *Vice Pres*
Elaine Jones, *Manager*
EMP: 13
SALES: 3MM **Privately Held**
WEB: www.deverstruck.com
SIC: 5012 3715 Truck bodies; trailer bodies

(G-18798)
KASEL ENGINEERING LLC
5911 Wolf Creek Pike (45426-2439)
PHONE.....................................937 854-8875
Donald Kasel,
EMP: 8
SQ FT: 8,000
SALES (est): 1MM **Privately Held**
WEB: www.kaselengineering.com
SIC: 3556 Slicers, commercial, food

(G-18799)
STRYVER MFG INC
15 N Broadway St (45426-3555)
PHONE.....................................937 854-3048
Bruce J Flora, *President*
Lucille Flora, *Corp Secy*
Thomas E Flora, *Vice Pres*
Vinnie Ambos, *QC Mgr*
EMP: 30
SQ FT: 30,000
SALES (est): 6.8MM **Privately Held**
SIC: 3599 3548 Machine shop, jobbing & repair; welding apparatus

(G-18800)
TROTWOOD CORPORATION
11 N Broadway St (45426-3594)
PHONE.....................................937 854-3047
Fax: 937 854-3049
Bruce J Flora, *President*
Lucille Flora, *Corp Secy*
Thomas E Flora, *Vice Pres*
Ron Karka, *Project Mgr*
Dainese Flora, *Financial Exec*
EMP: 40 **EST:** 1932

SQ FT: 30,000
SALES (est): 5MM **Privately Held**
WEB: www.stryver.com
SIC: 3599 Machine shop, jobbing & repair

Troy
Miami County

(G-18801)
3 SIGMA CORPORATION
1985 W Stanfield Rd (45373-2330)
P.O. Box 42627, Middletown (45042-0627)
PHONE.....................................937 440-3400
Tony Rowley, *President*
Brad Beck, *Senior VP*
Terry Cudney, *Vice Pres*
Rick Leonard, *Vice Pres*
Mike Sotzing, *Vice Pres*
▲ **EMP:** 78
SQ FT: 80,000
SALES: 30MM **Privately Held**
WEB: www.3sigma.cc
SIC: 2672 Coated & laminated paper

(G-18802)
AMERICAN ADVNCED ASSMBLIES LLC
37 Harolds Way (45373-4098)
PHONE.....................................937 339-6267
Thomas B Fay, *President*
EMP: 28 **EST:** 2011
SALES: 5.5MM **Privately Held**
SIC: 3679 Harness assemblies for electronic use: wire or cable

(G-18803)
AMERICAN HONDA MOTOR CO INC
101 S Stanfield Rd (45373-2333)
P.O. Box 1010 (45373-8010)
PHONE.....................................937 332-6100
Fax: 937 332-6189
Michael Nitz, *Assistant VP*
Bruce Smith, *Opers Staff*
Denise Clark, *Purch Mgr*
Emily Jordan, *Purch Agent*
Charlotte Davis, *Project Engr*
EMP: 145
SQ FT: 131,000
SALES (corp-wide): 124.7B **Privately Held**
SIC: 5511 3711 Automobiles, new & used; motor vehicles & car bodies
HQ: American Honda Motor Co., Inc.
1919 Torrance Blvd
Torrance CA 90501
310 783-2000

(G-18804)
AMETEK INC
Also Called: Ametek Presto Light Power
66 Industry Ct Ste F (45373-2560)
PHONE.....................................937 440-0800
Patrick Williams, *Principal*
Tom Bolka, *Engineer*
Jeff Harrison, *Regl Sales Mgr*
Matt Bridge, *Software Engr*
EMP: 10
SALES (corp-wide): 3.8B **Publicly Held**
SIC: 5063 3699 Batteries; electrical equipment & supplies
PA: Ametek, Inc.
1100 Cassatt Rd
Berwyn PA 19312
610 647-2121

(G-18805)
ARC ABRASIVES INC
Also Called: A R C
2131 Corporate Dr (45373-1067)
P.O. Box 10 (45373-0010)
PHONE.....................................800 888-4885
Fax: 937 339-4969
Anthony H Stayman, *CEO*
Anthony Stayman, *President*
Erin Marquis, *Purch Agent*
Carlin Temper, *Human Res Mgr*
▲ **EMP:** 76 **EST:** 1960
SALES (est): 71.6MM **Privately Held**
WEB: www.arcabrasives.com
SIC: 5085 3291 2296 Abrasives; abrasive products; tire cord & fabrics

(G-18806)
ATI IRRIGATION LLC
4746 W State Route 55 (45373-7538)
PHONE..................................937 750-2976
Matt Goodin, *President*
EMP: 3 EST: 2008
SALES: 250K **Privately Held**
SIC: 4971 3648 Irrigation systems; outdoor lighting equipment

(G-18807)
BAKEHOUSE BREAD CO INC
Also Called: Bakehouse Bread and Cookie Co
317 Public Sq (45373-3261)
PHONE..................................937 339-8100
Fax: 937 339-8880
Margaret Begg, *CEO*
Steve McLain, *President*
EMP: 20
SQ FT: 4,854
SALES: 480K **Privately Held**
WEB: www.bakehousebread.com
SIC: 2051 Cakes, bakery: except frozen

(G-18808)
CHARACTERS INC
190 Peters Ave Ste A (45373-3995)
PHONE..................................937 335-1976
Fax: 937 339-1773
Esther Marko, *President*
Jason Marko, *Vice Pres*
EMP: 9 EST: 1961
SQ FT: 8,000
SALES (est): 700K **Privately Held**
SIC: 2752 Commercial printing, lithographic

(G-18809)
CITY OF TROY
Also Called: Troy Water Treatment Plant
300 E Staunton Rd (45373-2105)
PHONE..................................937 339-4826
Fax: 937 339-0838
Tim Ray, *Superintendent*
EMP: 10 **Privately Held**
WEB: www.troyohio.gov
SIC: 3589 4941 Sewage & water treatment equipment; water supply
PA: City Of Troy
100 S Market St Ste 1
Troy OH 45373
937 335-2224

(G-18810)
CLOPAY BUILDING PDTS CO INC
1400 W Market St (45373-3889)
PHONE..................................937 440-6403
Tim McNally, *Safety Mgr*
Dusty Brewer, *Engineer*
Mike Kerkman, *Manager*
Brandon Bass, *Manager*
Bonnie Luthman, *Manager*
EMP: 3
SALES (corp-wide): 2B **Publicly Held**
SIC: 2431 3442 2436 Garage doors, overhead: wood; garage doors, overhead: metal; plywood, softwood
HQ: Clopay Building Products Company, Inc.
8585 Duke Blvd
Mason OH 45040
513 770-4800

(G-18811)
CONAGRA BRANDS INC
801 Dye Mill Rd (45373-4223)
PHONE..................................937 440-2800
Dean Hollis, *Human Res Dir*
Scott Adkins, *Branch Mgr*
EMP: 673
SALES (corp-wide): 11.6B **Publicly Held**
SIC: 2099 Food preparations
PA: Conagra Brands, Inc.
222 Merchandise Mart Plz
Chicago IL 60654
312 549-5000

(G-18812)
CONCRETE FEALANTS INC
Also Called: Ohio Precast Concrete Assoc
515 W Water St (45373-2938)
PHONE..................................937 339-0549
Howard W Wingert, *President*
EMP: 53

SALES (est): 4.8MM **Privately Held**
SIC: 3272 Precast terrazo or concrete products

(G-18813)
CROWE MANUFACTURING SERVICES
Also Called: King of The Road
2731 Walnut Ridge Dr (45373-4562)
PHONE..................................800 831-1893
Jamie King, *CEO*
Rob Haviland, *President*
Robert King, *Corp Secy*
Carl Dean, *VP Opers*
Gorden Jones, *QC Dir*
EMP: 60
SQ FT: 140,000
SALES: 10MM **Privately Held**
WEB: www.crowemanufacturing.com
SIC: 3599 3544 Machine & other job shop work; special dies, tools, jigs & fixtures

(G-18814)
DARE ELECTRONICS INC
3245 S County Road 25a (45373-9384)
P.O. Box 419 (45373-0419)
PHONE..................................937 335-0031
Karen Beagle, *President*
Mark Osman, *Mfg Mgr*
Darlene Collopy, *Director*
EMP: 50
SQ FT: 28,750
SALES (est): 9MM **Privately Held**
WEB: www.dareelectronics.com
SIC: 3679 3651 Power supplies, all types: static; amplifiers: radio, public address or musical instrument

(G-18815)
DAYTON SUPERIOR PDTS CO INC
1370 Lytle Rd (45373-9401)
PHONE..................................937 332-1930
Fax: 937 332-1929
Frank Gleason Jr, *Ch of Bd*
Daniel P Gleason, *President*
Lori Enos, *Manager*
EMP: 8
SQ FT: 15,000
SALES: 1.5MM **Privately Held**
SIC: 3714 Motor vehicle transmissions, drive assemblies & parts; clutches, motor vehicle

(G-18816)
DEBRA HARBOUR
Also Called: August Nine Enterprises
251 S Mulberry St # 220 (45373-3585)
P.O. Box 599 (45373-0599)
PHONE..................................937 440-9618
Fax: 937 440-9618
Debra Harbour, *Owner*
Melvin Harbour, *Mfg Staff*
EMP: 8
SQ FT: 1,800
SALES (est): 602.1K **Privately Held**
SIC: 3672 3699 Printed circuit boards; electrical equipment & supplies

(G-18817)
DELTECH POLYMERS CORPORATION
1250 S Union St (45373-4118)
PHONE..................................937 339-3150
Fax: 937 339-7694
Robert Elefante, *Ch of Bd*
Tricia Bonner, *Office Admin*
Rick Jordan, *Supervisor*
EMP: 8
SQ FT: 435,600
SALES (est): 2.8MM **Privately Held**
SIC: 3087 2821 Custom compound purchased resins; polystyrene resins

(G-18818)
DESIGN TECHNOLOGIES & MFG CO
Also Called: Des Tech
2000 Corporate Dr (45373-1069)
PHONE..................................937 335-0757
Fax: 937 339-2961
D Jeffrey Meredith, *President*
Marilyn J Freeman, *Principal*
John E Fulker, *Principal*
Debbie Meredith, *Corp Secy*

William Leffel, *Vice Pres*
EMP: 18
SQ FT: 32,000
SALES (est): 4.3MM **Privately Held**
SIC: 3549 Assembly machines, including robotic

(G-18819)
DESIGNER AWARDS INC
Also Called: Award One
101 S Market St (45373-3324)
PHONE..................................937 339-4444
Fax: 937 335-1750
Scott Breisch, *Shareholder*
EMP: 3
SQ FT: 6,000
SALES (est): 299.6K **Privately Held**
SIC: 5999 2261 7389 Trophies & plaques; screen printing of cotton broadwoven fabrics; engraving service

(G-18820)
DETRICK DESIGN FABRICATION LLC
425 Wisteria Dr (45373-8850)
PHONE..................................937 620-6736
Eugene Detrick,
EMP: 3 EST: 2014
SALES (est): 104K **Privately Held**
SIC: 3499 Novelties & giftware, including trophies; barricades, metal

(G-18821)
ECOTEC LTD LLC
150 Marybill Dr S (45373-1053)
PHONE..................................937 606-2793
Torbjorn Lindgren, *President*
James Keyser, *Vice Pres*
Tom Tag, *Sales Mgr*
▲ EMP: 5 EST: 2012
SQ FT: 2,000
SALES: 2MM **Privately Held**
SIC: 3629 Battery chargers, rectifying or nonrotating

(G-18822)
ERNST ENTERPRISES INC
Troy Ready Mix
805 S Union St (45373-4109)
PHONE..................................937 339-6249
Dwayne Littlejohn, *Manager*
EMP: 22
SQ FT: 7,446
SALES (corp-wide): 191MM **Privately Held**
WEB: www.ernstconcrete.com
SIC: 3273 Ready-mixed concrete
PA: Ernst Enterprises, Inc.
3361 Successful Way
Dayton OH 45414
937 233-5555

(G-18823)
EVENFLO COMPANY INC
1801 W Main St (45373-2303)
PHONE..................................937 773-3971
Fax: 937 778-5429
Nick Baird, *Maint Spvr*
Terressa Knoch, *Purch Agent*
Jeremy Belzyt, *Research*
Kent Newbright, *Engineer*
Alan Wagner, *Plant Engr*
EMP: 100
SALES (corp-wide): 896.7MM **Privately Held**
WEB: www.evenflo.com
SIC: 3944 2519 Games, toys & children's vehicles; child restraint seats, automotive; fiberglass & plastic furniture
HQ: Evenflo Company, Inc.
225 Byers Rd
Miamisburg OH 45342
937 415-3300

(G-18824)
F & B ENGRAVING TLS & SUP LLC
701 W Water St A (45373-2973)
PHONE..................................937 332-7994
Terrance D Blosser, *Owner*
EMP: 3
SQ FT: 1,200
SALES: 148K **Privately Held**
SIC: 3423 5085 Engravers' tools, hand; tools

(G-18825)
F&P AMERICA MFG INC (HQ)
2101 Corporate Dr (45373-1076)
PHONE..................................937 339-0212
Fax: 937 339-0065
Akihide Fukuda, *Ch of Bd*
Masafumi Yamano, *President*
Robert Estep, *Engineer*
Dwane Sloan, *Manager*
Hirp Enomoto, *Admin Sec*
▲ EMP: 244
SQ FT: 400,000
SALES (est): 169.3MM
SALES (corp-wide): 1.6B **Privately Held**
SIC: 3714 Motor vehicle parts & accessories; motor vehicle steering systems & parts; motor vehicle brake systems & parts; motor vehicle body components & frame
PA: F-Tech Inc.
19, Showanuma, Shobucho
Kuki STM 346-0
480 855-211

(G-18826)
FAURECIA EXHAUST SYSTEMS INC
1255 Archer Dr (45373-3841)
PHONE..................................937 339-0551
Clement Quiot, *Managing Dir*
Dirk Stoll, *Managing Dir*
Didier Feral, *Business Mgr*
Joe Galemmo, *Plant Mgr*
Elliton Bulla, *Opers Mgr*
EMP: 300
SALES (corp-wide): 271.8MM **Privately Held**
WEB: www.franklin.faurecia.com
SIC: 3714 Exhaust systems & parts, motor vehicle; manifolds, motor vehicle
HQ: Faurecia Exhaust Systems, Llc
543 Matzinger Rd
Toledo OH 43612
419 727-5000

(G-18827)
FEDEX OFFICE & PRINT SVCS INC
1886 W Main St (45373-2304)
PHONE..................................937 335-3816
Fax: 937 335-1987
Eric Logel, *Manager*
Charles James, *Manager*
EMP: 11
SALES (corp-wide): 50.3B **Publicly Held**
SIC: 7389 7334 5099 2759 Packaging & labeling services; blueprinting service; firearms & ammunition, except sporting; financial note & certificate printing & engraving
HQ: Fedex Office And Print Services, Inc.
7900 Legacy Dr
Plano TX 75024
214 550-7000

(G-18828)
FREUDENBERG-NOK GENERAL PARTNR
Also Called: Verco Seal
1275 Archer Dr (45373-3841)
P.O. Box 844, Spencer IA (51301-0844)
PHONE..................................937 335-3306
Larry Heimilghton, *Manager*
EMP: 30
SALES (corp-wide): 6.9B **Privately Held**
WEB: www.freudenberg-nok.com
SIC: 3053 Gaskets, packing & sealing devices
HQ: Freudenberg-Nok General Partnership
47690 E Anchor Ct
Plymouth MI 48170
734 451-0020

(G-18829)
FTECH R&D NORTH AMERICA INC (HQ)
1191 Horizon West Ct (45373-7560)
PHONE..................................937 339-2777
Sooyoung Ji, *General Mgr*
Bing Liu, *COO*
Donald Bauer, *Administration*
EMP: 56
SQ FT: 50,000

SALES (est): 6.9MM
SALES (corp-wide): 1.6B **Privately Held**
SIC: 8731 3714 Commercial physical research; motor vehicle parts & accessories
PA: F-Tech Inc.
   19, Showanuma, Shobucho
   Kuki STM 346-0
   480 855-211

(G-18830)
GARY COMPTON
Also Called: Tools Plus
3245 Piqua Troy Rd (45373-7794)
PHONE.................................937 339-6829
Fax: 937 335-7289
Gary Compton, *Owner*
EMP: 4
SQ FT: 3,000
SALES: 1.5MM **Privately Held**
WEB: www.toolsplus1.com
SIC: 5251 3559 Tools; automotive related machinery

(G-18831)
GENESIS GRAPHICS
14 N Walnut St Ste 2 (45373-3472)
PHONE.................................937 335-5332
Fax: 937 335-5335
Sam Weiss, *Owner*
EMP: 4
SALES (est): 200K **Privately Held**
SIC: 2759 Commercial printing

(G-18832)
GOKOH CORPORATION (HQ)
1280 Archer Dr (45373-3842)
PHONE.................................937 339-4977
Fax: 937 339-5146
Shuji Hioki, *President*
Steve Kershner, *Managing Dir*
Heiju Hashimoto, *Principal*
Parker Bailey, *Vice Pres*
Inge Voisard, *Accountant*
▲ **EMP:** 15
SQ FT: 16,000
SALES (est): 6.4MM
SALES (corp-wide): 67.7MM **Privately Held**
WEB: www.tellthat.com
SIC: 5085 5084 3544 3559 Industrial supplies; industrial machinery & equipment; machine tools & metalworking machinery; special dies & tools; jigs & fixtures; foundry machinery & equipment; fabricated structural metal
PA: Goko Sangyo Co.,Ltd.
   1-2-2, Higashiryoke
   Kawaguchi STM 332-0
   482 231-493

(G-18833)
GOODRICH CORPORATION
Also Called: UTC Aerospace Systems
101 Waco St (45373-3872)
P.O. Box 340 (45373-0340)
PHONE.................................937 339-3811
Fax: 937 440-3286
Ernie D'Amico, *Vice Pres*
Cynthia Egnotovich, *Vice Pres*
Brian S Gora, *Vice Pres*
Thad Smith, *Facilities Mgr*
Meleah Zarate, *Purch Mgr*
EMP: 750
SALES (corp-wide): 57.2B **Publicly Held**
WEB: www.bfgoodrich.com
SIC: 3728 3714 3721 Aircraft parts & equipment; wheels, motor vehicle; motor vehicle brake systems & parts; aircraft
HQ: Goodrich Corporation
   2730 W Tyvola Rd
   Charlotte NC 28217
   704 423-7000

(G-18834)
HINES BUILDERS INC
1587 Lytle Rd (45373-9488)
PHONE.................................937 335-4586
Fax: 937 339-1694
Harold A Hines, *President*
Michelle Simister, *Bookkeeper*
Scherre Mumpower, *Admin Sec*
EMP: 18
SQ FT: 25,000

SALES (est): 2.1MM **Privately Held**
SIC: 2448 1541 2441 Wood pallets & skids; cargo containers, wood & wood with metal; industrial buildings, new construction; nailed wood boxes & shook

(G-18835)
HOBART BROS STICK ELECTRODE
101 Trade Sq E (45373-2476)
PHONE.................................937 332-5375
Steve Knostman, *Owner*
EMP: 109
SALES (est): 3.2MM **Privately Held**
SIC: 7692 Welding repair

(G-18836)
HOBART BROTHERS COMPANY (HQ)
Also Called: ITW Hobart Brothers
101 Trade Sq E (45373-2488)
PHONE.................................937 332-5439
Fax: 937 332-5224
David Vinson, *President*
Dan Jackson, *General Mgr*
Mark Thibeault, *General Mgr*
W H Hobart Et Al, *Principal*
S E Hobart, *Principal*
◆ **EMP:** 600 EST: 1917
SQ FT: 1,000,000
SALES (est): 365.1MM
SALES (corp-wide): 13.6B **Publicly Held**
SIC: 3548 3537 Welding apparatus; industrial trucks & tractors
PA: Illinois Tool Works Inc.
   155 Harlem Ave
   Glenview IL 60025
   847 724-7500

(G-18837)
HOBART BROTHERS COMPANY
400 Trade Sq E (45373-2463)
PHONE.................................937 332-5338
Stan Wen, *General Mgr*
EMP: 6
SALES (corp-wide): 13.6B **Publicly Held**
SIC: 3548 Welding apparatus
HQ: Hobart Brothers Company
   101 Trade Sq E
   Troy OH 45373
   937 332-5439

(G-18838)
HOBART BROTHERS COMPANY
1260 Bruckner Dr (45373-4354)
PHONE.................................937 332-5023
EMP: 7
SALES (corp-wide): 13.6B **Publicly Held**
SIC: 3548 Welding apparatus
HQ: Hobart Brothers Company
   101 Trade Sq E
   Troy OH 45373
   937 332-5439

(G-18839)
HOBART CABINET COMPANY
301 E Water St (45373-3440)
PHONE.................................937 335-4666
Fax: 937 335-4669
Martin E Hobart, *President*
Helen Sharpe, *Accounts Mgr*
EMP: 9 EST: 1907
SQ FT: 50,000
SALES: 1.1MM **Privately Held**
WEB: www.hobartcabinet.com
SIC: 2522 Office bookcases, wallcases & partitions, except wood; office cabinets & filing drawers: except wood

(G-18840)
HOBART CORPORATION
Also Called: Engineering Dept
401 S Market St (45373)
PHONE.................................937 332-3000
Praveen Reedy, *Vice Pres*
Nigel Mills, *Engineer*
Allison Bruns, *Sales Staff*
Gary Banks, *Manager*
Kevin Rettig, *Manager*
EMP: 50

SALES (corp-wide): 13.6B **Publicly Held**
WEB: www.hobartcorp.com
SIC: 3589 3556 3596 3585 Dishwashing machines, commercial; cooking equipment, commercial; commercial cooking & foodwarming equipment; food products machinery; weighing machines & apparatus; refrigeration equipment, complete; gray & ductile iron foundries
HQ: Hobart Corporation
   701 S Ridge Ave
   Troy OH 45374
   937 332-3000

(G-18841)
HOBART CORPORATION
Also Called: Itwfeg
701 S Ridge Ave (45374-0005)
PHONE.................................937 335-7171
Elaine Everman, *Branch Mgr*
EMP: 50
SALES (corp-wide): 13.6B **Publicly Held**
SIC: 3589 Dishwashing machines, commercial

(G-18842)
HOBART INTERNATIONAL HOLDINGS (HQ)
701 S Ridge Ave (45373-3000)
PHONE.................................937 332-3000
Richard Gleitsmann, *President*
Thomas H Rodgers, *Vice Pres*
Kathy Agenbroad, *Purchasing*
Nigel Mills, *Engineer*
Jeff Davis, *Technology*
EMP: 2
SQ FT: 500,000
SALES (est): 48.1MM
SALES (corp-wide): 13.6B **Publicly Held**
SIC: 3556 Food products machinery
PA: Illinois Tool Works Inc.
   155 Harlem Ave
   Glenview IL 60025
   847 724-7500

(G-18843)
ILLINOIS TOOL WORKS INC
750 Lincoln Ave (45373-3137)
PHONE.................................937 332-2839
Valerie Sweigart, *Principal*
EMP: 92
SALES (corp-wide): 13.6B **Publicly Held**
SIC: 3089 Injection molded finished plastic products
PA: Illinois Tool Works Inc.
   155 Harlem Ave
   Glenview IL 60025
   847 724-7500

(G-18844)
ILLINOIS TOOL WORKS INC
Vulcan Food Equipment Group
401 W Market St (45373-3927)
PHONE.................................519 376-8886
Richard Kice, *Engineer*
Jeff Johnson, *Accounting Mgr*
Holly Roush, *Human Resources*
Cathy Long, *Branch Mgr*
EMP: 92
SALES (corp-wide): 13.6B **Publicly Held**
SIC: 3089 Injection molded finished plastic products; closures, plastic; synthetic resin finished products
PA: Illinois Tool Works Inc.
   155 Harlem Ave
   Glenview IL 60025
   847 724-7500

(G-18845)
INDEPENDENT MACHINE & WLDG INC
35 Marybill Dr S (45373-1033)
PHONE.................................937 339-7330
Glenn Reed, *President*
Dale F Deaton, *Vice Pres*
Carol Owens, *Treasurer*
EMP: 6 EST: 2000
SQ FT: 10,000
SALES: 300K **Privately Held**
SIC: 3599 7692 Machine shop, jobbing & repair; welding repair

(G-18846)
ISHMAEL PRECISION TOOL CORP
Also Called: Iptc
55 Industry Ct (45373-2368)
PHONE.................................937 335-8070
Fax: 937 339-8978
Larry R Ishmael, *President*
Larry Ishmael, *President*
Jackie Mathes, *Principal*
Isaiah Wilmoth, *Principal*
Robert Ishmael, *Vice Pres*
▲ **EMP:** 20 EST: 1978
SQ FT: 32,000
SALES (est): 4.2MM **Privately Held**
SIC: 3544 Special dies & tools

(G-18847)
ITW FOOD EQUIPMENT GROUP LLC
Also Called: Ibex Rapid Cooks
401 W Market St (45373-3927)
PHONE.................................937 332-3000
Gary Simpson, *Exec VP*
EMP: 6
SALES (corp-wide): 13.6B **Publicly Held**
SIC: 3556 Food products machinery
HQ: Itw Food Equipment Group Llc
   701 S Ridge Ave
   Troy OH 45374
   937 332-2396

(G-18848)
ITW FOOD EQUIPMENT GROUP LLC (HQ)
Also Called: Hobart
701 S Ridge Ave (45374-0001)
PHONE.................................937 332-2396
Fax: 937 332-2582
Tom Szafranski, *President*
Chris O Herlihy, *Exec VP*
Gary Duench, *Plant Mgr*
Steve Peditte, *Purchasing*
Ron Grise, *Engineer*
◆ **EMP:** 1100
SALES (est): 452.3MM
SALES (corp-wide): 13.6B **Publicly Held**
SIC: 5046 3556 Restaurant equipment & supplies; food products machinery
PA: Illinois Tool Works Inc.
   155 Harlem Ave
   Glenview IL 60025
   847 724-7500

(G-18849)
JAYNA INC (PA)
15 Marybill Dr S (45373-1033)
PHONE.................................937 335-8922
Fax: 937 339-7581
Damaroo Shah, *President*
Paras Shah, *General Mgr*
Mayank Shah, *Chairman*
Soha Shah, *VP Opers*
Kalyan Chennareddy, *Project Engr*
EMP: 48 EST: 1988
SQ FT: 40,000
SALES (est): 10.7MM **Privately Held**
WEB: www.jayna.com
SIC: 3599 Machine shop, jobbing & repair

(G-18850)
K C CREATIONS
218 Riverside Dr (45373-1412)
PHONE.................................937 748-8181
Ken Cleveland, *President*
Sandra Love, *Vice Pres*
EMP: 3
SQ FT: 10,000
SALES (est): 200K **Privately Held**
WEB: www.cultureworks.org
SIC: 7389 3499 Design, commercial & industrial; novelties & giftware, including trophies

(G-18851)
KENNEDY REPAIR SERVICES
221 S Plum St (45373-3340)
P.O. Box 223 (45373-0223)
PHONE.................................937 332-9118
Dale Kennedy, *President*
EMP: 4
SQ FT: 9,600
SALES: 300K **Privately Held**
SIC: 3599 Machine shop, jobbing & repair

(G-18852)
KERBER SHEETMETAL WORKS INC
Also Called: Ksm Metal Fabrications
104 Foss Way (45373-1430)
PHONE.....................................937 339-6366
Fax: 937 339-6265
Kathleen Kerber, *President*
Daniel J Kerber, *Vice Pres*
Isaac Buehler, *Engineer*
Jim Wilmath, *Sales Mgr*
EMP: 18
SQ FT: 27,000
SALES (est): 3.5MM **Privately Held**
WEB: www.kerbersheetmetal.com
SIC: 3444 Sheet metalwork

(G-18853)
KISER INDUSTRIES LLC
507 Michigan Ave (45373-2142)
PHONE.....................................937 332-6723
EMP: 5 EST: 2012
SALES (est): 280K **Privately Held**
SIC: 3999 Manufacturing Industries, Nec, Nsk

(G-18854)
LUKENS INC
1040 S Dorset Rd (45373-4708)
PHONE.....................................937 440-2500
Fax: 937 440-2551
Michael Van Haaren, *President*
Bill Diederich, *Principal*
Wanda Lukens, *Vice Pres*
EMP: 90
SQ FT: 70,000
SALES (est): 15.1MM **Privately Held**
SIC: 3544 Special dies & tools

(G-18855)
MADER AUTOMOTIVE CENTER INC (PA)
Also Called: Bushong Auto Service
225 S Walnut St (45373-3532)
PHONE.....................................937 339-2681
Fax: 937 339-3544
Dan Mader, *President*
Cristy Mader, *Treasurer*
EMP: 15
SQ FT: 18,000
SALES (est): 2.6MM **Privately Held**
SIC: 5013 5531 3599 Automotive supplies & parts; automotive parts; machine shop, jobbing & repair

(G-18856)
MARIETTA MARTIN MATERIALS INC
Also Called: Troy Sand and Gravel
250 Dye Mill Rd (45373-4280)
PHONE.....................................937 335-8313
Darrell Sparks, *Manager*
Bernard McGuire, *Manager*
EMP: 7
SALES (corp-wide): 3.8B **Publicly Held**
WEB: www.martinmarietta.com
SIC: 1442 Sand mining; gravel mining
PA: Martin Marietta Materials Inc
2710 Wycliff Rd
Raleigh NC 27607
919 781-4550

(G-18857)
MEDWAY TOOL CORP
2100 Corporate Dr (45373-1085)
PHONE.....................................937 335-7717
Fax: 937 335-8393
Tom Drake, *President*
EMP: 23 EST: 1974
SQ FT: 15,000
SALES (est): 3MM **Privately Held**
SIC: 3599 3545 3544 3444 Machine shop, jobbing & repair; machine tool accessories; special dies, tools, jigs & fixtures; sheet metalwork

(G-18858)
NOVACEL INC
421 S Union St (45373-4151)
PHONE.....................................937 335-5611
Andrew Hill, *Managing Dir*
Michael Nuxoll, *Business Mgr*
Tim Shank, *Branch Mgr*
Ron Stoll, *Maintence Staff*
EMP: 160

SALES (corp-wide): 1.9MM **Privately Held**
WEB: www.novacelonline.com
SIC: 2671 Packaging paper & plastics film, coated & laminated
HQ: Novacel, Inc.
21 3rd St
Palmer MA 01069
413 283-3468

(G-18859)
NOVACEL INC
421 Union St (45373-4151)
PHONE.....................................413 283-3468
David Neely, *Manager*
EMP: 45
SALES (corp-wide): 1.9MM **Privately Held**
WEB: www.novacelonline.com
SIC: 2671 Packaging paper & plastics film, coated & laminated
HQ: Novacel, Inc.
21 3rd St
Palmer MA 01069
413 283-3468

(G-18860)
OUTBACK TREE WORKS
808 N Market St (45373-1424)
PHONE.....................................937 332-7300
Eric M Anderson, *Principal*
EMP: 3
SALES (est): 277.6K **Privately Held**
SIC: 3524 Lawn & garden equipment

(G-18861)
PAINTED HILL INV GROUP INC
Also Called: Western Ohio Graphics
402 E Main St (45373-3413)
PHONE.....................................937 339-1756
Anthony W Cockerham, *President*
EMP: 10
SQ FT: 13,000
SALES (est): 800K **Privately Held**
SIC: 2752 2396 3993 2759 Commercial printing, offset; screen printing on fabric articles; signs & advertising specialties; screen printing; graphic arts & related design

(G-18862)
PEAK FOODS LLC
1903 W Main St Ste B (45373-1153)
PHONE.....................................937 440-0707
Fax: 937 440-0706
Steve Vogel, *VP Opers*
Brian Adkins, *Opers Mgr*
Debbie Friend, *Prdtn Mgr*
Chris Whipple, *Materials Mgr*
Patty Krieg, *Purchasing*
EMP: 65
SQ FT: 5,500
SALES (est): 19.4MM **Privately Held**
WEB: www.peakfoods.com
SIC: 2026 Whipped topping, except frozen or dry mix

(G-18863)
POLYMERS BY DESIGN LLC
2150 Monroe Concord Rd (45373-8208)
P.O. Box 303 (45373-0303)
PHONE.....................................937 361-7398
Janet Zelnick, *CEO*
Mark Zelnick, *General Mgr*
EMP: 4
SALES (est): 689.8K **Privately Held**
SIC: 3087 Custom compound purchased resins

(G-18864)
PREMIER TOOL INC
1333 E Main St (45373-3452)
PHONE.....................................937 332-0996
Brady Wilson, *President*
EMP: 5 EST: 2000
SALES: 200K **Privately Held**
SIC: 3599 Machine shop, jobbing & repair

(G-18865)
R T INDUSTRIES INC (PA)
Also Called: CHAMPION INDUSTRIES DIV
110 Foss Way (45373-1430)
PHONE.....................................937 335-5784
Fax: 937 339-6978
Ann Hinkle, *Superintendent*
Karen Mayer, *Superintendent*

Blair Brubaker, *CIO*
Ald Pease, *CTO*
Alan Lange, *Pharmacy Dir*
EMP: 6
SQ FT: 18,000
SALES: 2.3MM **Privately Held**
SIC: 3579 8331 7349 2789 Paper cutters, trimmers & punches; sheltered workshop; janitorial service, contract basis; bookbinding & related work; home for the mentally handicapped

(G-18866)
R&D MACHINE INC
1204 S Crawford St (45373-4134)
PHONE.....................................937 339-2545
Fax: 937 335-2295
Daniel Daffner, *President*
Pam Daffner, *Owner*
EMP: 15
SALES (est): 3.1MM **Privately Held**
SIC: 3312 Tool & die steel

(G-18867)
RAYMATH COMPANY
2323 W State Route 55 (45373-9234)
PHONE.....................................937 335-1860
Fax: 937 335-2500
James M Ruef, *President*
Ray Mathieu, *President*
William Moore, *Chairman*
Rob Smith, *Mfg Mgr*
Tracy Caudill, *Purch Mgr*
▲ EMP: 109
SQ FT: 50,000
SALES: 9.2MM **Privately Held**
WEB: www.raymath.com
SIC: 3541 3544 Machine tools, metal cutting type; special dies & tools

(G-18868)
ROCONEX CORPORATION
20 Marybill Dr S (45373-1034)
PHONE.....................................937 339-2616
Fax: 937 339-1470
Ty Spear, *President*
June Ackerman, *Controller*
June Baker, *Personnel*
Laura Rudy, *Administration*
EMP: 19
SQ FT: 31,000
SALES (est): 3MM **Privately Held**
WEB: www.roconex.com
SIC: 3555 3444 Printing trades machinery; sheet metalwork

(G-18869)
ROSS SPECIAL PRODUCTS INC
2500 W State Route 55 (45373-9511)
PHONE.....................................937 335-8406
Fax: 937 332-9305
Dave Pollard, *President*
Steve Furlong, *General Mgr*
EMP: 17
SQ FT: 13,000
SALES: 900K **Privately Held**
SIC: 3089 3544 Injection molding of plastics; forms (molds), for foundry & plastics working machinery

(G-18870)
S-K MOLD & TOOL COMPANY
2120 Corporate Dr (45373-1085)
P.O. Box 495 (45373-0495)
PHONE.....................................937 339-0299
Vince Hinde, *Branch Mgr*
EMP: 20
SALES (corp-wide): 15.9MM **Privately Held**
WEB: www.skmold.com
SIC: 3544 3599 Special dies & tools; machine shop, jobbing & repair
PA: S-K Mold & Tool Company
955 N 3rd St
Tipp City OH 45371
937 339-0299

(G-18871)
SAN PALLET LLC
1860 State Route 718 (45373-8725)
PHONE.....................................937 271-5308
Richard Sofia, *Mng Member*
EMP: 3

SALES (est): 477.2K **Privately Held**
SIC: 2822 2448 7389 Ethylene-propylene rubbers, EPDM polymers; wood pallets & skids;

(G-18872)
SCHIFFER GROUP INC
Also Called: Minuteman Press
1602 Marby Dr (45373-9264)
PHONE.....................................937 694-8185
Daniel L Schiffer, *President*
EMP: 3
SQ FT: 2,000
SALES: 120K **Privately Held**
SIC: 2752 7336 7319 Commercial printing, lithographic; graphic arts & related design; display advertising service

(G-18873)
SCHWANS HOME SERVICE INC
2991 S County Road 25a (45373-9381)
P.O. Box 148, Tipp City (45371-0148)
PHONE.....................................937 335-4111
Cal Brink, *Branch Mgr*
Larry Oberkfell, *Manager*
EMP: 26
SQ FT: 5,760
SALES (corp-wide): 4.8B **Privately Held**
SIC: 2038 2024 Pizza, frozen; ethnic foods, frozen; ice cream, packaged: molded, on sticks, etc.; ice milk, packaged: molded, on sticks, etc.
HQ: Schwan's Home Service, Inc.
115 W College Dr
Marshall MN 56258
507 532-3274

(G-18874)
SEGNA INC
1316 Barnhart Rd (45373-9510)
PHONE.....................................937 335-6700
Junichi Yakahi, *President*
Jeff Robinson, *Admin Mgr*
◆ EMP: 15 EST: 2001
SQ FT: 2,100
SALES: 3MM **Privately Held**
SIC: 3559 Automotive maintenance equipment

(G-18875)
SEW-EURODRIVE INC
2001 W Main St (45373-1018)
PHONE.....................................937 335-0036
Fax: 937 222-4104
Bruce King, *Vice Pres*
Mayme Larson, *Safety Mgr*
Pete Johnson, *Engineer*
Gene Hart, *Enginr/R&D Mgr*
Jim Allen, *Cust Mgr*
EMP: 100
SQ FT: 32,400
SALES (corp-wide): 2.7B **Privately Held**
WEB: www.seweurodrive.com
SIC: 3566 3714 3699 Speed changers, drives & gears; motor vehicle parts & accessories; electrical equipment & supplies
HQ: Sew-Eurodrive, Inc.
1295 Old Spartanburg Hwy
Lyman SC 29365
864 439-7537

(G-18876)
SLIMLINE SURGICAL DEVICES LLC
Also Called: Canyon Run Engineering
1102 S Market St (45373-4051)
PHONE.....................................937 335-0496
Gary Ward, *President*
Amy Ward, *Principal*
Carly Witmer, *Principal*
EMP: 7
SALES (est): 284.4K **Privately Held**
SIC: 3599 Machine & other job shop work

(G-18877)
SOLOMON INDUSTRIES LLC
3365 Peebles Rd (45373-8437)
PHONE.....................................937 558-5334
Jason David Solomon, *Principal*
EMP: 7
SALES (est): 636.9K **Privately Held**
SIC: 3999 Manufacturing industries

(G-18878)
SPINNAKER COATING LLC
518 E Water St (45373-3400)
PHONE................937 332-6300
Sharon Malone, *Manager*
James Severs, *Manager*
Lou Guzzetti, *CTO*
EMP: 120
SALES (corp-wide): 72.3MM **Privately Held**
SIC: 2672 2891 Labels (unprinted), gummed; made from purchased materials; adhesives & sealants
PA: Spinnaker Coating, Llc
518 E Water St
Troy OH 45373
937 332-6500

(G-18879)
SPINNAKER COATING LLC (PA)
518 E Water St (45373-3400)
PHONE................937 332-6500
Fax: 937 332-6518
Louis A Guzzetti Jr, *CEO*
George E Fuehrer, *Exec VP*
George Fuehrer, *Exec VP*
Stuart A Postle, *Senior VP*
Perry J Schiller, *Senior VP*
▲ EMP: 100
SQ FT: 298,000
SALES (est): 72.3MM **Privately Held**
SIC: 2672 Labels (unprinted), gummed: made from purchased materials

(G-18880)
TROY DAILY NEWS INC (DH)
224 S Market St (45373-3300)
PHONE................937 339-2729
Fax: 937 339-8413
Roy Brown, *President*
Kim Kiehl, *Business Mgr*
Chuck Lobaugh, *Purchasing*
Christopher Dillon, *Info Tech Mgr*
EMP: 35 EST: 1909
SQ FT: 22,000
SALES (est): 30.8MM
SALES (corp-wide): 1.4B **Privately Held**
SIC: 2711 Commercial printing & newspaper publishing combined
HQ: Ocm, Llc
4500 Lyons Rd
Miamisburg OH 45342
937 247-2700

(G-18881)
TROY LAMINATING & COATING INC
421 Union St (45373-4151)
PHONE................937 335-5611
Fax: 937 440-8051
David Bullard, *President*
Mike Desjardins, *Opers Mgr*
Karen Uldrich, *Purch Mgr*
Jeffery Creager, *QC Mgr*
Mike Story, *Controller*
◆ EMP: 100
SALES (est): 47.8MM
SALES (corp-wide): 1.9MM **Privately Held**
WEB: www.troylaminatingandcoating.com
SIC: 2672 Coated paper, except photographic, carbon or abrasive
HQ: Novacel
27 Rue Du Docteur Emile Bataille
Deville Les Rouen 76250
232 827-222

(G-18882)
TROY WEST LLC
Also Called: West Troy
650 Olympic Dr (45373-2306)
PHONE................937 339-2192
Fax: 937 339-7693
Warren Davidson, *CEO*
Diana Griffith, *Manager*
◆ EMP: 3
SQ FT: 45,000
SALES (est): 9.1MM
SALES (corp-wide): 13.5MM **Privately Held**
WEB: www.westtroy.com
SIC: 5051 3544 Stampings, metal; iron & steel (ferrous) products; special dies, tools, jigs & fixtures

PA: Yasotay, Inc.
2678 Arthur Dr
Troy OH

(G-18883)
TUCKERS MOLD POLISHING
3225 E Peterson Rd (45373-7781)
P.O. Box 922 (45373-0922)
PHONE................937 339-3063
John Tucker, *Owner*
EMP: 5
SALES (est): 319.9K **Privately Held**
SIC: 3471 Polishing, metals or formed products

(G-18884)
VALLEY ASPHALT CORPORATION
250 Dye Mill Rd (45373-4280)
PHONE................937 335-3664
James P Jurgensen, *President*
EMP: 3
SALES (corp-wide): 109.5MM **Privately Held**
SIC: 2951 Asphalt paving mixtures & blocks
PA: Valley Asphalt Corporation
11641 Mosteller Rd
Cincinnati OH 45241
513 771-0820

(G-18885)
WESTERN OHIO GRAPHICS
Also Called: Quality Quick Print
402 E Main St (45373-3413)
PHONE................937 335-8769
Bob Hephner, *Owner*
Jeff Marr, *Sales Mgr*
EMP: 11
SQ FT: 13,000
SALES (est): 1MM **Privately Held**
SIC: 2759 2752 Commercial printing; commercial printing, offset

---

Tuppers Plains
Meigs County

(G-18886)
REMRAM RECOVERY LLC
49705 E Park Dr (45783)
P.O. Box 189 (45783-0189)
PHONE................740 667-0092
Ray Maxson, *Mng Member*
EMP: 12
SQ FT: 36,000
SALES: 1MM **Privately Held**
SIC: 3089 Panels, building: plastic

(G-18887)
WECAN FABRICATORS LLC
49425 E Park Dr (45783-9000)
P.O. Box 159 (45783-0159)
PHONE................740 667-0731
Jeffrey Cox, *Mng Member*
Diana Westfall, *Manager*
Stephanie Cox,
EMP: 8
SQ FT: 4,000
SALES (est): 1.5MM **Privately Held**
SIC: 3441 Fabricated structural metal

Twinsburg
Summit County

(G-18888)
A E WILSON HOLDINGS INC
Also Called: Quest Service Labs
2307 E Aurora Rd (44087-1958)
PHONE................330 405-0316
Al Wilson, *President*
Tom Fennell, *General Mgr*
EMP: 8
SALES (est): 709.2K **Privately Held**
WEB: www.questservicelabs.com
SIC: 2759 Commercial printing

(G-18889)
A SIGN ABOVE INC
8982 Dutton Dr (44087-1929)
PHONE................330 723-3650

Fax: 330 963-4519
William A Geschke, *President*
Jack Slegus, *Sales Staff*
EMP: 12
SQ FT: 12,000
SALES: 300K **Privately Held**
SIC: 3993 7319 Signs & advertising specialties; display advertising service

(G-18890)
ACE AMERICAN WIRE DIE CO
9041 Dutton Dr (44087-1930)
PHONE................330 425-7269
Linda Hohl, *President*
EMP: 10
SQ FT: 10,000
SALES (est): 700K **Privately Held**
WEB: www.aawiredie.com
SIC: 3544 Special dies, tools, jigs & fixtures

(G-18891)
ACENSE LLC
8941 Dutton Dr (44087-1939)
PHONE................330 242-0046
John Harley, *CEO*
Glenn Mitchell, *President*
EMP: 4
SALES (est): 179K **Privately Held**
SIC: 3826 Analytical instruments; liquid testing apparatus; gas testing apparatus; gas analyzing equipment

(G-18892)
ACHILLES AEROSPACE PDTS INC
2100 Enterprise Pkwy (44087-2212)
PHONE................330 425-8444
Fax: 330 425-8446
David L Hoyack, *President*
Pam Olah, *Purchasing*
Michael Corfias, *Finance Mgr*
James T Hurt, *Sales Mgr*
J Michael Corfias, *Admin Sec*
EMP: 22
SQ FT: 20,000
SALES (est): 4.8MM **Privately Held**
WEB: www.achillesaerospace.com
SIC: 3728 Aircraft body & wing assemblies & parts

(G-18893)
ACTION PRINTING INC
2307 E Aurora Rd Ste 8 (44087-1952)
PHONE................330 963-7772
Fax: 330 963-7774
John Dodgson, *President*
EMP: 4
SQ FT: 4,500
SALES (est): 616.5K **Privately Held**
SIC: 2752 Commercial printing, lithographic

(G-18894)
ADAPTALL AMERICA INC
9047 Dutton Dr (44087-1930)
PHONE................330 425-4114
Fax: 330 425-7099
C Lane Wood, *President*
Frank Ortis, *Opers Staff*
John Archbold, *Sales Mgr*
Mike Rennie, *Mktg Dir*
Kevin Moore, *Manager*
EMP: 16
SALES (est): 2.4MM **Privately Held**
WEB: www.adaptall.com
SIC: 3494 Pipe fittings

(G-18895)
AJD HOLDING CO (PA)
2181 Enterprise Pkwy (44087-2211)
PHONE................330 405-4477
Fax: 330 425-0092
Frank Defino, *President*
Leonard Defino, *Vice Pres*
Lisa Kowall, *Human Resources*
EMP: 60
SQ FT: 55,000
SALES (est): 72.6MM **Privately Held**
SIC: 3469 3544 3315 3537 Metal stampings; special dies, tools, jigs & fixtures; wire & fabricated wire products; tractors, used in plants, docks, terminals, etc.: industrial

(G-18896)
ALADDINSLIGHTS INC
2201a Pinnacle Pkwy (44087-2367)
PHONE................330 963-6997
Fax: 330 963-6701
Bruce Jenkins, *President*
Jeff Heindel, *VP Admin*
Becky Nedelka, *Manager*
EMP: 9
SQ FT: 20,000
SALES (est): 1.5MM **Privately Held**
WEB: www.plantlighting.com
SIC: 3645 Residential lighting fixtures

(G-18897)
ALBEMARLE CORPORATION
Also Called: Albemarle Sorbent Technologies
1664 Highland Rd (44087-2293)
PHONE................330 425-2354
Richard J Oehlberg, *Exec VP*
Ronald R Landreth, *Vice Pres*
Karen Taylor, *Controller*
Sid Nelson, *Chief Mktg Ofcr*
John White, *Branch Mgr*
EMP: 7
SALES (corp-wide): 2.6B **Publicly Held**
SIC: 3624 8711 8731 Carbon & graphite products; energy conservation engineering; commercial physical research
PA: Albemarle Corporation
4350 Congress St Ste 700
Charlotte NC 28209
980 299-5700

(G-18898)
ALLIED CORPORATION INC (DH)
8920 Canyon Falls Blvd # 120 (44087-1990)
PHONE................330 425-7861
Dan Mongomery, *President*
Jim Williams, *Controller*
Mike Horvath, *Manager*
EMP: 2 EST: 1948
SQ FT: 500
SALES (est): 1.5MM
SALES (corp-wide): 28.6B **Privately Held**
WEB: www.alliedcorporation.com
SIC: 2951 5032 Asphalt paving mixtures & blocks; sand, construction; gravel
HQ: Shelly Company
80 Park Dr
Thornville OH 43076
740 246-6315

(G-18899)
ANGSTROM CORP
9221 Ravenna Rd Ste 1 (44087-2454)
PHONE................330 405-0524
Steven Rasmussen, *President*
EMP: 3
SALES: 500K **Privately Held**
WEB: www.angstromcorp.com
SIC: 3545 Gauges (machine tool accessories)

(G-18900)
ANYTHING PERSONALIZED
9261 Ravenna Rd Ste 10 (44087-2449)
PHONE................330 655-0723
Jennie Duecker, *Principal*
EMP: 3
SALES (est): 167.6K **Privately Held**
SIC: 2395 Art goods for embroidering, stamped: purchased materials

(G-18901)
ARGO TOOL CORPORATION
1962 Case Pkwy (44087-4327)
PHONE................330 425-2407
Fax: 330 487-1546
Laszlo Repay, *President*
Linda Repay, *Vice Pres*
EMP: 12
SQ FT: 6,723
SALES (est): 1.3MM **Privately Held**
SIC: 3544 Special dies & tools

(G-18902)
AUBURN METAL PROCESSING LLC (PA)
1831 Highland Rd (44087-2222)
PHONE................315 253-2565
Linda Krutczek, *Controller*
Steve C Joseph,

▼ **EMP:** 22
SALES (est): 6.4MM **Privately Held**
SIC: 3444 Forming machine work, sheet
metal

(G-18903)
BAUTEC N TECHNOFORM AMER INC
1755 Entp Pkwy Ste 300 (44087)
PHONE..................................330 487-6600
Fax: 216 514-6030
Albert Stankus, *General Mgr*
Linette Flauhaus, *Controller*
Shari Vago, *Office Mgr*
▲ **EMP:** 30
SALES (est): 9.8MM **Privately Held**
SIC: 2431 Windows & window parts & trim,
wood

(G-18904)
BAWLS ACQUISITION LLC
8840 Commons Blvd Ste 101
(44087-4100)
PHONE..................................888 731-9708
John Staudt,
Lisa Karell,
EMP: 3
SQ FT: 2,187
SALES (est): 210K **Privately Held**
SIC: 2086 Carbonated beverages, nonal-
coholic: bottled & canned

(G-18905)
BIRD CONTROL INTERNATIONAL
1393 Highland Rd (44087-2213)
PHONE..................................330 425-2377
Stanley Baker, *President*
Benjamin Baker, *Vice Pres*
Jack Polnick, *Director*
EMP: 25
SALES (est): 1.6MM **Privately Held**
SIC: 2879 2899 Pesticides, agricultural or
household; chemical preparations

(G-18906)
C P ELECTRIC MOTOR REPAIR INC
2212 E Aurora Rd (44087-1926)
PHONE..................................330 425-9593
Fax: 330 425-3105
Michael Chalmers, *President*
Charlotte Papp, *Manager*
EMP: 5
SQ FT: 6,000
SALES (est): 242K **Privately Held**
SIC: 7694 5063 5065 Electric motor re-
pair; motors, electric; electronic parts

(G-18907)
CANADUS POWER SYSTEMS LLC
9347 Ravenna Rd Ste A (44087-2463)
PHONE..................................216 831-6600
Fax: 216 831-6618
Lisa Eston, *Office Mgr*
Jack Scott,
Nelson Mossholder,
EMP: 10
SQ FT: 1,000
SALES (est): 1.6MM **Privately Held**
SIC: 3678 Electronic connectors

(G-18908)
CASE INDUSTRIES INC
9043 Dutton Dr (44087-1930)
P.O. Box 748 (44087-0748)
PHONE..................................330 963-7717
Gunther Meyer, *President*
Susie Meyer, *Treasurer*
Tom Kelly, *Manager*
Douglas Conway, *Shareholder*
Norma Meyer, *Administration*
▲ **EMP:** 5
SQ FT: 5,500
SALES (est): 560K **Privately Held**
SIC: 3089 5065 3469 5063 Injection
molding of plastics; electronic parts; ca-
pacitors, electronic; connectors, elec-
tronic; resistors, electronic; metal
stampings; electrical apparatus & equip-
ment

(G-18909)
CEIA USA LTD
9155 Dutton Dr (44087-1956)
PHONE..................................330 405-3190
Fax: 330 405-3196
Mario Michard, *Regional Mgr*
Doyle Smith, *Warehouse Mgr*
John Zlocki, *Purch Mgr*
James Wardle, *Technical Mgr*
Bruno Carano, *Finance Dir*
▲ **EMP:** 43
SQ FT: 42,316
SALES: 33.9MM **Privately Held**
WEB: www.ceia-usa.com
SIC: 3669 3812 3829 Metal detectors;
magnetic field detection apparatus; mag-
netometers

(G-18910)
CERTECH INC
2181 Pinnacle Pkwy (44087-2365)
PHONE..................................330 405-1033
John Stang, *Branch Mgr*
EMP: 4
SALES (corp-wide): 1.4B **Privately Held**
SIC: 3364 3724 Nonferrous die-castings
except aluminum; airfoils, aircraft engine
HQ: Certech Inc
1 Park Pl W
Wood Ridge NJ 07075
201 842-6800

(G-18911)
CHICOPEE ENGINEERING ASSOC INC
2300 E Enterprise Pkwy (44087-2349)
PHONE..................................413 592-2273
David Pieciak, *President*
Roger Fontaine, *Vice Pres*
EMP: 23 **EST:** 1942
SQ FT: 20,000
SALES (est): 4.4MM **Privately Held**
WEB: www.chiceng.com
SIC: 3677 Filtration devices, electronic

(G-18912)
CHROMASCAPE INC (PA)
Also Called: Amerimulch
2055 Enterprise Pkwy (44087-2209)
PHONE..................................330 998-7574
Fax: 330 425-4240
George Chase, *Ch of Bd*
Joseph Majewski, *President*
Michael Chase, *Counsel*
Tim Carmichael, *Plant Mgr*
Steve Grudzinski, *CFO*
◆ **EMP:** 33
SQ FT: 48,000
SALES (est): 39.7MM **Privately Held**
WEB: www.amerimulch.com
SIC: 2499 Mulch or sawdust products,
wood

(G-18913)
CHURCHILL STEEL PLATE LTD
7851 Bavaria Rd (44087-2263)
PHONE..................................330 425-9000
Jim Stevenson, *President*
Jim Fleming, *Treasurer*
Kirk Mooney, *VP Sales*
Steve Fleming, *Administration*
EMP: 20
SQ FT: 120,000
SALES (est): 5.7MM **Privately Held**
SIC: 3312 Plate, steel

(G-18914)
CLEAN HARBORS ENVMTL SVCS INC
1672 Highland Rd (44087-2219)
PHONE..................................330 425-3825
Dennis Getz, *General Mgr*
Dan Halling, *Manager*
David Wolfe, *Manager*
EMP: 12
SQ FT: 29,322
SALES (corp-wide): 2.7B **Publicly Held**
SIC: 4953 8734 3341 Hazardous waste
collection & disposal; hazardous waste
testing; secondary nonferrous metals
HQ: Clean Harbors Environmental Serv-
ices, Inc.
42 Longwater Dr
Norwell MA 02061
781 792-5000

(G-18915)
CLEVELAND ELECTRIC LABS CO (PA)
1776 Enterprise Pkwy (44087-2246)
PHONE..................................800 447-2207
Fax: 330 425-7209
Jack Allan Lieske, *President*
C M Lemmon, *Principal*
Val Jean Lieske, *Vice Pres*
Don Lieske, *Production*
Travis Smith, *Production*
EMP: 50
SQ FT: 30,000
SALES (est): 10.1MM **Privately Held**
WEB: www.clevelandelectriclabs.com
SIC: 3823 7699 Thermocouples, industrial
process type; industrial machinery &
equipment repair

(G-18916)
CLEVELAND SYRUP CORP (PA)
2200 Highland Rd (44087-2231)
PHONE..................................330 963-1900
Virginia Chaney, *President*
James Chaney, *Vice Pres*
EMP: 4
SQ FT: 50,000
SALES (est): 1.1MM **Privately Held**
SIC: 2087 5149 Syrups, flavoring (except
drink); flour

(G-18917)
COCA-COLA REFRESHMENTS USA INC
1882 Highland Rd (44087-2223)
PHONE..................................330 425-4401
Fax: 330 963-8400
Dan Hanson, *Plant Mgr*
Rick Bodzenski, *Manager*
Timothy Johnson, *Manager*
Tom Hawk, *Maintence Staff*
EMP: 73
SALES (corp-wide): 41.8B **Publicly Held**
WEB: www.cokecce.com
SIC: 2086 Bottled & canned soft drinks
HQ: Coca-Cola Refreshments Usa, Inc.
2500 Windy Ridge Pkwy Se
Atlanta GA 30339
770 989-3000

(G-18918)
COMTEC INCORPORATED
1800 Enterprise Pkwy (44087-2269)
PHONE..................................330 425-8102
Fax: 330 425-9235
Kenneth Drummond, *President*
Fred Rose, *General Mgr*
Nancy Burns, *Purch Agent*
EMP: 12
SQ FT: 10,200
SALES: 1.8MM **Privately Held**
WEB: www.comtecinc.com
SIC: 3823 3625 8711 Computer interface
equipment for industrial process control;
relays & industrial controls; engineering
services

(G-18919)
CONTRACTORS STEEL COMPANY
8383 Boyle Pkwy (44087-2236)
PHONE..................................330 425-3050
Fax: 330 425-8580
Donna Krin, *Sales Staff*
Amy Taylor, *Sales Staff*
Mitch Kubasek, *Manager*
EMP: 49
SQ FT: 58,000
SALES (corp-wide): 101.2MM **Privately
Held**
WEB: www.contractorssteel.com
SIC: 5051 3498 3312 Steel; plates, metal;
sheets, metal; strip, metal; fabricated pipe
& fittings; blast furnaces & steel mills
PA: Contractors Steel Company
36555 Amrhein Rd
Livonia MI 48150
734 464-4000

(G-18920)
CUSTOM SCREEN PRINTING (PA)
Also Called: T Shirts & Soccer Wearhouse
1869 E Aurora Rd Ste 100 (44087-1972)
PHONE..................................330 963-3131
Fax: 330 963-7221
David Tschantz, *Owner*
Mark A Tschantz, *Vice Pres*
EMP: 3
SALES (est): 1.1MM **Privately Held**
SIC: 2759 Screen printing

(G-18921)
DARKO INC
2026 Summit Commerce Park
(44087-2374)
PHONE..................................330 425-9805
Dean Rinicella, *President*
Dan Rinicella Jr, *Vice Pres*
Derek Rinicella, *Vice Pres*
Dominic Dumas, *Project Mgr*
Brenda Smith, *Project Mgr*
▲ **EMP:** 50
SQ FT: 72,000
SALES (est): 19.8MM **Privately Held**
WEB: www.darkoinc.com
SIC: 2541 2542 Shelving, office & store,
wood; office & store showcases & display
fixtures

(G-18922)
DAY-GLO COLOR CORP
1570 Highland Rd (44087-2217)
PHONE..................................216 391-7070
Fax: 330 425-1543
Joe Shaw, *Manager*
EMP: 19
SQ FT: 33,500
SALES (corp-wide): 4.8B **Publicly Held**
WEB: www.dayglo.com
SIC: 2816 Inorganic pigments
HQ: Day-Glo Color Corp.
4515 Saint Clair Ave
Cleveland OH 44103
216 391-7070

(G-18923)
DESCO EQUIPMENT CORP
1903 Case Pkwy (44087-2343)
PHONE..................................330 405-1581
Fax: 330 405-1584
Leo E Henry, *President*
Gene A Gilbert, *Corp Secy*
Dennis Sweeney, *Purch Mgr*
Richard Fleming, *Engineer*
George Hutchins, *Sales Executive*
▲ **EMP:** 26
SQ FT: 50,000
SALES (est): 6.1MM
SALES (corp-wide): 22.7MM **Privately
Held**
WEB: www.descoequipment.com
SIC: 3555 Printing presses
PA: Apex Machine Company
3000 Ne 12th Ter
Oakland Park FL 33334
954 563-0209

(G-18924)
DESIGN AVENUE INC
Also Called: Graphics By Design Avenue
1710 Enterprise Pkwy (44087-2204)
PHONE..................................330 487-5280
Fax: 330 487-5288
Wanda Saltsman, *Admin Sec*
EMP: 6
SQ FT: 5,800
SALES (est): 825.7K **Privately Held**
SIC: 2731 7336 Pamphlets: publishing &
printing; graphic arts & related design

(G-18925)
DIRECT DIGITAL GRAPHICS INC
1716 Enterprise Pkwy (44087-2204)
PHONE..................................330 405-3770
Fax: 330 405-3775
Mike Boswell, *President*
Kimberly Boswell, *Office Mgr*
EMP: 8
SQ FT: 14,000
SALES: 1.1MM **Privately Held**
SIC: 2759 Commercial printing

(G-18926)
DIXON VALVE & COUPLING CO INC
1900 Enterprise Pkwy (44087-2296)
PHONE..................................330 425-3000
Fax: 330 425-1527
Louis Young, *Manager*
EMP: 15

SALES (corp-wide): 270.1MM **Privately Held**
SIC: 3492 5085 Fluid power valves & hose fittings; hose, belting & packing
HQ: Dixon Valve & Coupling Company
800 High St
Chestertown MD 21620

(G-18927)
E S SIGN & DESIGN LLC
Also Called: Es Sign and Design
9478 Ravenna Rd (44087-2104)
PHONE..............................330 405-4799
Fax: 330 405-4798
Mary Ann Serafino, *Area Mgr*
Ben Deak, *Store Mgr*
Chris Serafino,
EMP: 5
SQ FT: 1,384
SALES (est): 474.8K **Privately Held**
SIC: 3993 Signs & advertising specialties

(G-18928)
EASY CARE PRODUCTS INC
8870 Darrow Rd Ste F106 (44087-2178)
PHONE..............................330 405-1380
Mike Crombie, *President*
▲ EMP: 3
SALES (est): 240K **Privately Held**
SIC: 2842 Metal polish

(G-18929)
EPI OF CLEVELAND INC
Also Called: Engineered Products
2224 E Enterprise Pkwy (44087-2393)
PHONE..............................330 468-2872
Fax: 330 650-9805
Robert Knazek, *Vice Pres*
Larry Verbic, *Prdtn Mgr*
EMP: 8
SALES (corp-wide): 14.9MM **Privately Held**
WEB: www.engineeredproducts.com
SIC: 3441 5051 Fabricated structural metal; metals service centers & offices
HQ: E.P.I. Of Cleveland, Inc.
1844 Ardmore Blvd
Pittsburgh PA 15221
330 468-2872

(G-18930)
ERIE CHINESE JOURNAL
9810 Ravenna Rd Ste 1 (44087-1761)
PHONE..............................216 324-2959
Ying Tu, *Owner*
EMP: 4
SALES (est): 273.4K **Privately Held**
SIC: 2711 Newspapers, publishing & printing

(G-18931)
ESSILOR LABORATORIES AMER INC
Also Called: Bell Optical
9221 Ravenna Rd # 3 (44087-2472)
P.O. Box 620 (44087-0620)
PHONE..............................330 425-3003
Ron Sheperd, *Manager*
EMP: 8
SALES (corp-wide): 938.9MM **Privately Held**
WEB: www.crizal.com
SIC: 3851 Eyeglasses, lenses & frames
HQ: Essilor Laboratories Of America, Inc.
13515 N Stemmons Fwy
Dallas TX 75234
972 241-4141

(G-18932)
EXTREME MARINE
2057 E Aurora Rd Ste Lm (44087-1938)
PHONE..............................330 963-7800
Ellaine Penn, *President*
Lawrence Penn, *Vice Pres*
EMP: 5
SALES (est): 360K **Privately Held**
SIC: 3499 Novelties & specialties, metal

(G-18933)
FABRICATING SOLUTIONS INC
7920 Bavaria Rd (44087-2252)
PHONE..............................330 486-0998
Dewey Lockwood, *Principal*
EMP: 13

SALES (est): 2.1MM **Privately Held**
SIC: 3499 3444 Fire- or burglary-resistive products; sheet metalwork

(G-18934)
FACIL NORTH AMERICA INC (DH)
Also Called: Streetsboro Operations
2242 Pinnacle Pkwy # 100 (44087-5301)
PHONE..............................330 487-2500
Fax: 330 626-8155
Rene Achten, *CEO*
Michael REA, *Purch Mgr*
Daniel Michiels, *CFO*
Ray Ardente, *Finance Dir*
◆ EMP: 210
SQ FT: 150,000
SALES (est): 171.9MM
SALES (corp-wide): 5.4K **Privately Held**
WEB: www.flexalloy.com
SIC: 5072 3452 5085 Nuts (hardware); bolts; screws; nuts, metal; fasteners, industrial: nuts, bolts, screws, etc.
HQ: Facil Europe Bvba
Geleenlaan 20
Genk 3600
894 104-50

(G-18935)
FERRUM INDUSTRIES INC (HQ)
1831 Highland Rd (44087-2222)
P.O. Box 360230, Strongsville (44136-0004)
PHONE..............................440 519-1768
Steve Joseph, *President*
Don Moreno, *Vice Pres*
▲ EMP: 5
SALES (est): 493.8K
SALES (corp-wide): 6.4MM **Privately Held**
SIC: 2899 Metal treating compounds
PA: Auburn Metal Processing, Llc
1831 Highland Rd
Twinsburg OH 44087
315 253-2565

(G-18936)
FFR-DSI COMPANY
8181 Darrow Rd (44087-2303)
PHONE..............................330 998-7800
Steve Brenneman, *CFO*
Michelle Owens, *Credit Mgr*
Kim Worron, *Admin Asst*
EMP: 27
SALES (corp-wide): 5.3B **Privately Held**
SIC: 5046 3993 Store fixtures & display equipment; signs & advertising specialties
HQ: Ffr-Dsi Company
1100 Burlington Pike # 2
Florence KY 41042
859 781-7711

(G-18937)
FREEDOM USA INC
Also Called: Avadirect.com
1750 Highland Rd Ste 4 (44087-2244)
PHONE..............................216 503-6374
Fax: 216 503-6355
Alex Sonis, *President*
Gary Muravin, *Vice Pres*
Misha Troshin, *Marketing Staff*
EMP: 10
SQ FT: 8,000
SALES (est): 3.7MM **Privately Held**
WEB: www.avadirect.com
SIC: 3571 7378 Electronic computers; mainframe computers; minicomputers; computer maintenance & repair

(G-18938)
FUCHS LUBRICANTS CO
Also Called: Fuchs Franklin Div
8036 Bavaria Rd (44087-2262)
PHONE..............................330 963-0400
Fax: 330 963-2995
Kipp Kofsky, *Branch Mgr*
Hendrik Noth, *Manager*
Eve Haupt, *Programmer Anys*
EMP: 25
SALES (corp-wide): 2.4B **Privately Held**
WEB: www.fuchs.com
SIC: 4225 2992 2899 2851 General warehousing & storage; lubricating oils & greases; chemical preparations; paints & allied products; specialty cleaning, polishes & sanitation goods

HQ: Fuchs Lubricants Co.
17050 Lathrop Ave
Harvey IL 60426
708 333-8901

(G-18939)
GANZCORP INVESTMENTS INC
Also Called: Mustang Dynamometer
2300 Pinnacle Pkwy (44087-2368)
PHONE..............................330 963-5400
Dean Ganzhorn, *Owner*
Dean K Ganzhorn, *Owner*
Donald W Ganzhorn Jr, *Exec VP*
Paul Bukowski, *Engineer*
Michael Caldwell, *Sales Engr*
◆ EMP: 60
SQ FT: 82,000
SALES (est): 24.6MM **Privately Held**
WEB: www.mustangdyne.com
SIC: 3559 Automotive related machinery

(G-18940)
GARMENT SPECIALTIES INC
1885 E Aurora Rd (44087-1917)
PHONE..............................330 425-2928
Fax: 330 425-3938
Lee Pilous, *President*
EMP: 3
SQ FT: 5,000
SALES: 350K **Privately Held**
WEB: www.garmentspecialties.com
SIC: 2395 Embroidery & art needlework

(G-18941)
GED HOLDINGS INC
9280 Dutton Dr (44087-1967)
PHONE..............................330 963-5401
William Weaver, *President*
Steve Lang, *CFO*
EMP: 141 EST: 2000
SALES (est): 18.3MM **Privately Held**
SIC: 3559 3549 5084 Glass making machinery: blowing, molding, forming, etc.; cutting & slitting machinery; industrial machinery & equipment

(G-18942)
GENERAL DIE CASTERS INC (PA)
2150 Highland Rd (44087-2229)
PHONE..............................330 678-2528
James M Mathias, *CEO*
Thomas J Lennon, *President*
Theresa A Bordelon, *Admin Sec*
▲ EMP: 40
SQ FT: 31,000
SALES (est): 32.6MM **Privately Held**
WEB: www.generaldie.com
SIC: 3364 3363 3544 3369 Zinc & zinc-base alloy die-castings; aluminum die-castings; special dies, tools, jigs & fixtures; nonferrous foundries; aluminum foundries

(G-18943)
GENERAL ELECTRIC COMPANY
8499 Darrow Rd (44087-2309)
PHONE..............................330 425-3755
J E Breen, *Principal*
Tim Kniss, *Draft/Design*
Andrew Shalhoub, *Draft/Design*
Eric Battiest, *Engineer*
Ken Lambach, *Engineer*
EMP: 13
SALES (corp-wide): 123.6B **Publicly Held**
SIC: 1311 Crude petroleum & natural gas
PA: General Electric Company
41 Farnsworth St
Boston MA 02210
617 443-3000

(G-18944)
GENERAL ELECTRIC INTL INC
8941 Dutton Dr (44087-1939)
PHONE..............................330 963-2066
Fax: 330 425-0900
Jeffrey Pack, *Manager*
EMP: 30
SALES (corp-wide): 123.6B **Publicly Held**
SIC: 5084 3561 Compressors, except air conditioning; pumps, oil well & field

HQ: General Electric International, Inc.
191 Rosa Parks St
Cincinnati OH 45202
513 813-9133

(G-18945)
GEORGES DONUTS INC
7995 Darrow Rd (44087-2385)
PHONE..............................330 963-9902
George D Vadaj, *President*
George F Vadaj, *Vice Pres*
EMP: 5
SALES (est): 180K **Privately Held**
SIC: 5461 2051 Doughnuts; doughnuts, except frozen

(G-18946)
GIESECKE & DEVRIENT AMER INC
1960 Enterprise Pkwy (44087-2208)
PHONE..............................330 405-8442
Jim Dooley, *Manager*
EMP: 13 EST: 2013
SALES (est): 2.7MM **Privately Held**
SIC: 2672 Coated & laminated paper

(G-18947)
GIESECKE & DEVRIENT AMER INC
Also Called: G & D Twinsburg
2020 Enterprise Pkwy (44087-2210)
PHONE..............................330 425-1515
Flamarion Pirtouscheg, *Managing Dir*
Tina Atwell, *VP Admin*
Randy Gurganus, *Vice Pres*
Ralf Wintergerst, *Vice Pres*
Dale Ridel, *Plant Mgr*
EMP: 120
SALES (corp-wide): 308.9K **Privately Held**
SIC: 2672 5044 Coated & laminated paper; office equipment
HQ: Giesecke & Devrient America, Inc.
45925 Horseshoe Dr # 100
Dulles VA 20166
703 480-2000

(G-18948)
GIESECKE & DEVRIENT CAN
2020 Enterprise Pkwy (44087-2210)
PHONE..............................330 425-1515
Fax: 330 425-9105
EMP: 9
SALES (est): 1.1MM **Privately Held**
SIC: 3089 Mfg Plastic Products

(G-18949)
GO2 PARTNERS INC
Also Called: Cable Quest
2265 E Entp Pkwy A (44087)
PHONE..............................330 650-5300
Fax: 330 650-6416
Gregg Dipaolo, *Senior VP*
Rebecca Shaffer, *Accounts Mgr*
Peter Rubin, *Branch Mgr*
Brando Melgaard, *Manager*
Nathan Reid, *Software Dev*
EMP: 50
SALES (corp-wide): 38.5MM **Privately Held**
WEB: www.ourpartners.com
SIC: 2752 Business forms, lithographed
PA: Print Management Partners, Inc.
701 Lee St Ste 1050
Des Plaines IL 60016
847 699-2999

(G-18950)
GOLF MARKETING GROUP INC
Also Called: Shot Selector
9221 Ravenna Rd Ste 7 (44087-2454)
PHONE..............................330 963-5155
Fax: 330 963-5137
Dave Zabell, *President*
Marc Mascarillo, *Vice Pres*
Tom Goellner, *Administration*
▲ EMP: 8
SQ FT: 2,000
SALES (est): 1.3MM **Privately Held**
WEB: www.shotselector.com
SIC: 2752 2732 3993 Cards, lithographed; book printing; signs & advertising specialties

GEOGRAPHIC

(G-18951)
GVI MEDICAL DEVICES CORP
Also Called: Gvimd
1470 Enterprise Pkwy (44087-2242)
PHONE..............................330 963-4083
Geoffrey Cochrane, *Engineer*
Traci Pack, *Controller*
Randy Sommerdyke, *Mktg Dir*
Gary Bryant, *Manager*
EMP: 10
SQ FT: 10,000
SALES (est): 928.5K **Privately Held**
SIC: 3845 Magnetic resonance imaging
device, nuclear

(G-18952)
GVI NEURO INC
Also Called: Bio Lum
1470 Enterprise Pkwy (44087-2242)
PHONE..............................330 963-4083
Geoff Cochrane, *CEO*
Michael Tartamella, *Vice Pres*
Traci Pack, *Controller*
EMP: 5
SQ FT: 2,000
SALES (est): 285.3K **Privately Held**
SIC: 3845 Electromedical equipment

(G-18953)
HAHS FACTORY OUTLET
1993 Case Pkwy (44087-4328)
PHONE..............................330 405-4227
Gerry Haas, *Owner*
EMP: 50
SALES (est): 3.5MM **Privately Held**
SIC: 1081 Test boring, metal mining

(G-18954)
HANA MICRODISPLAY TECH INC
2061 Case Pkwy S (44087-2361)
PHONE..............................330 405-4600
Fax: 330 405-4623
John Erdmann, *President*
Paul R Brown Jr, *Vice Pres*
Edward M Stiles III, *Vice Pres*
D Scott Worthington, *Vice Pres*
William Eckert, *Engineer*
▲ EMP: 60
SQ FT: 24,000
SALES (est): 14.2MM **Privately Held**
WEB: www.hanaoh.com
SIC: 3825 Instruments to measure electric-
ity

(G-18955)
HORIZON COMMUNICATIONS INC
Also Called: Dealer Communications
8870 Darrow Rd Ste F106 (44087-2178)
PHONE..............................330 968-6959
Michael Roscoe, *President*
Melissa Green, *Publisher*
Sean Davis, *Marketing Staff*
EMP: 7
SALES (est): 766.2K **Privately Held**
WEB: www.horizoncommunications.net
SIC: 2721 Magazines: publishing & printing

(G-18956)
HYDROMOTIVE ENGINEERING CO
9261 Ravenna Rd Bldg B1b2
(44087-2470)
PHONE..............................330 425-4266
Fax: 330 425-4394
Tom Bucknell, *Owner*
Gary Gruehl, *Enginr/R&D Mgr*
EMP: 6
SQ FT: 8,000
SALES (est): 450K **Privately Held**
SIC: 3429 5088 5551 Marine hardware;
marine supplies; marine supplies & equip-
ment

(G-18957)
IBYCORP
Also Called: Ibycorp Tool & Die
8968 Dutton Dr (44087-1929)
PHONE..............................330 425-8226
Fax: 330 425-8226
Steven Hamori, *President*
Violet Hamori, *Corp Secy*
EMP: 6 EST: 1975
SQ FT: 10,000

SALES: 423.9K **Privately Held**
SIC: 3544 Special dies & tools

(G-18958)
ID CARD SYSTEMS INC
2248 E Enterprise Pkwy (44087-2328)
PHONE..............................330 963-7446
Fax: 330 963-7447
Kenneth Quinn, *President*
Loretta Quinn, *Principal*
Matthew Quinn, *Principal*
Debbie Furillo, *Office Mgr*
EMP: 5
SALES (est): 540K **Privately Held**
WEB: www.idcardsystem.com
SIC: 3999 5043 Identification badges & in-
signia; photographic equipment & sup-
plies

(G-18959)
INDUSTRIAL MOLD INC
Also Called: Industrial Prfctn Mold & Mch
2057 E Aurora Rd (44087-1938)
PHONE..............................330 425-7374
Fax: 330 425-9433
David Kuhary, *President*
Bob Zimmerman, *Vice Pres*
John Ferkul, *Plant Mgr*
Wendy Wloszek, *Engineer*
Emily McElfresh, *Human Res Mgr*
EMP: 24
SQ FT: 8,600
SALES (est): 4.7MM **Privately Held**
WEB: www.industrialmold.com
SIC: 3544 5085 3354 Forms (molds), for
foundry & plastics working machinery; in-
dustrial supplies; aluminum extruded
products

(G-18960)
J T EATON & CO INC
1393 Highland Rd (44087-2213)
PHONE..............................330 425-7801
Fax: 330 425-8353
Stanley Baker, *Chairman*
Bart Baker, *Exec VP*
Benjamin Baker, *Exec VP*
Jack A Polenick, *CFO*
Paul Millet, *Admin Sec*
◆ EMP: 30 EST: 1932
SQ FT: 45,000
SALES (est): 9.5MM **Privately Held**
WEB: www.jteaton.com
SIC: 2879 Exterminating products, for
household or industrial use

(G-18961)
JH INDUSTRIES INC
Also Called: Copperloy
1981 E Aurora Rd (44087-1919)
PHONE..............................330 963-4105
Fax: 330 963-4111
John J Hallack, *President*
Dale Doherty, *Vice Pres*
Jacqueline Hallack, *Vice Pres*
EMP: 30 EST: 1952
SQ FT: 70,000
SALES: 7MM **Privately Held**
WEB: www.copperloy.com
SIC: 3599 3448 3537 3444 Machine
shop, jobbing & repair; ramps: prefabri-
cated metal; docks: prefabricated metal;
industrial trucks & tractors; sheet metal-
work; fabricated plate work (boiler shop);
fabricated structural metal

(G-18962)
KELTEC INC
Also Called: Keltec-Technolab
2300 E Enterprise Pkwy (44087-2349)
PHONE..............................330 425-3100
Fax: 330 425-3550
Edward Kaiser, *President*
Ed Kaiser Sr, *Principal*
Dolores Kaiser, *Vice Pres*
Steve Dixon, *Purch Mgr*
Bill Castrovinci, *Controller*
◆ EMP: 75
SQ FT: 100,000
SALES (est): 23.3MM **Privately Held**
WEB: www.keltecinc.com
SIC: 3569 Separators for steam, gas,
vapor or air (machinery); gas separators
(machinery)

(G-18963)
KES INDUSTRIES LLC (PA)
Also Called: Preform Sealants
8040 Bavaria Rd (44087-2262)
PHONE..............................330 405-2813
Chris Kruty, *General Mgr*
Dan Miller, *QC Mgr*
Guy Swank,
EMP: 5
SQ FT: 18,000
SALES (est): 919.8K **Privately Held**
SIC: 3053 Gaskets, packing & sealing de-
vices

(G-18964)
KING FORGE AND MACHINE COMPANY
Also Called: King Force & Machine
8250 Boyle Pkwy (44087-2234)
PHONE..............................330 963-0600
Fax: 330 425-8106
Raymond W King Jr, *President*
EMP: 10
SQ FT: 10,000
SALES (est): 678K **Privately Held**
SIC: 3462 Flange, valve & pipe fitting forg-
ings, ferrous

(G-18965)
KING-INDIANA FORGE INC
8250 Boyle Pkwy (44087-2234)
PHONE..............................330 425-4250
Raymond W King Jr, *President*
Paula Shirdi, *Controller*
Bonnie Jordan, *Manager*
EMP: 17
SQ FT: 250,000
SALES (est): 1.8MM
SALES (corp-wide): 25.6MM **Privately
Held**
WEB: www.kingforge.com
SIC: 3462 Iron & steel forgings
PA: Ssp Fittings Corp.
8250 Boyle Pkwy
Twinsburg OH 44087
330 425-4250

(G-18966)
KIWI PROMOTIONAL AP & PRTG CO
Also Called: Inc., K.I.W.I.
2170 E Aurora Rd (44087-1924)
PHONE..............................330 487-5115
Fax: 330 487-5440
Mark Candle, *President*
Paul Steels, *Principal*
EMP: 37
SQ FT: 28,000
SALES (est): 4.2MM **Privately Held**
SIC: 2396 2395 Screen printing on fabric
articles; embroidery products, except
schiffli machine

(G-18967)
KRE INC
Also Called: Champion Rivet Company
2181 Enterprise Pkwy (44087-2211)
PHONE..............................216 883-1600
Fax: 216 641-7983
Richard Hendershot, *President*
EMP: 16 EST: 1895
SQ FT: 175,000
SALES (est): 2.2MM **Privately Held**
SIC: 3452 Rivets, metal

(G-18968)
KRISS KREATIONS
Also Called: Edible Arrangement
9224 Darrow Rd (44087-1897)
PHONE..............................330 405-6102
Kristine Brownfield, *Owner*
James Brownfield, *Co-Owner*
EMP: 6
SALES (est): 905.2K **Privately Held**
SIC: 3523 5999 Shakers, tree: nuts, fruits,
etc.; alarm & safety equipment stores

(G-18969)
L J STAR INCORPORATED
2396 Edison Blvd (44087-2376)
P.O. Box 1116 (44087-9116)
PHONE..............................330 405-3040
David Star, *President*
Leonard J Star, *Chairman*
Andrew Oberganec, *COO*

Matthew Hildner, *Research*
Christopher Schrantz, *Controller*
▲ EMP: 20
SQ FT: 10,000
SALES (est): 5.4MM **Privately Held**
WEB: www.ljstar.com
SIC: 3823 Flow instruments, industrial
process type

(G-18970)
LASTING IMPRESSIONS PRINTING
Also Called: Farrell Services
10390 Hanford Ln (44087-1471)
PHONE..............................216 382-8436
Suzy Ebert, *President*
EMP: 3
SALES: 500K **Privately Held**
SIC: 2752 Commercial printing, litho-
graphic

(G-18971)
LEGACY SUPPLIES INC
8252 Darrow Rd Ste E (44087-2392)
P.O. Box 1173 (44087-9173)
PHONE..............................330 405-4565
Fax: 330 405-4566
Mike Corcelli, *President*
Frank Corcelli, *Vice Pres*
EMP: 10 EST: 1998
SALES (est): 1.3MM **Privately Held**
SIC: 3694 5013 Distributors, motor vehicle
engine; motor vehicle supplies & new
parts

(G-18972)
LEIDEN CABINET COMPANY LLC (PA)
2385 Edison Blvd (44087-2376)
PHONE..............................330 425-8555
Fax: 330 425-8557
Thomas Leiden, *CEO*
Chris Rhoa, *COO*
Melissa Hale, *Vice Pres*
Michael Hopp, *Vice Pres*
Stewart Devlin, *Project Mgr*
EMP: 110 EST: 1940
SQ FT: 210,000
SALES (est): 23.7MM **Privately Held**
SIC: 2541 Store fixtures, wood; cabinets,
except refrigerated: show, display, etc.:
wood

(G-18973)
LEXINGTON RUBBER GROUP INC (DH)
Also Called: Qsr
1700 Highland Rd (44087-2221)
P.O. Box 1030 (44087-9030)
PHONE..............................330 425-8472
Fax: 330 305-1045
Randy Ross, *CEO*
Mike Berry, *Plant Mgr*
Roger Schulte, *QC Mgr*
Dennis Welhouse, *CFO*
Robert Martin, *Controller*
▲ EMP: 29
SQ FT: 110,000
SALES: 91.5MM
SALES (corp-wide): 1.2B **Privately Held**
SIC: 3069 Hard rubber & molded rubber
products
HQ: Q Holding Company
1700 Highland Rd
Twinsburg OH 44087
330 425-8472

(G-18974)
LINDE GAS NORTH AMERICA LLC
2045 E Aurora Rd (44087-2280)
PHONE..............................330 425-3989
Brian Coudriet, *Branch Mgr*
EMP: 19
SALES (corp-wide): 17.9B **Privately Held**
SIC: 2813 Oxygen, compressed or lique-
fied
HQ: Linde Gas North America Llc
200 Somerset Corp Blvd # 7000
Bridgewater NJ 08807
908 464-8100

(G-18975)
LTS METROLOGY LLC
Also Called: LTS Scale Company
1500 Enterprise Pkwy (44087-2240)
PHONE..........................330 425-3092
Fax: 330 425-8905
John Mueller,
▲ EMP: 22
SQ FT: 10,000
SALES (est): 4MM **Privately Held**
SIC: 3596 Truck (motor vehicle) scales

(G-18976)
MACTEK CORPORATION
2112 Case Pkwy Ste 1 (44087-2378)
PHONE..........................330 487-5477
Fax: 330 487-0777
Thomas Holmes, *President*
EMP: 12
SQ FT: 1,200
SALES (est): 1.1MM **Privately Held**
SIC: 3559 Electronic component making
machinery

(G-18977)
MAINSTREAM SOFTWARE INC
8848 Commons Blvd Ste 103
(44087-6808)
PHONE..........................330 963-0103
Fax: 330 963-0288
Peter Wallace, *President*
Philip Weiss, *Vice Pres*
Cynthia Trotta, *Project Mgr*
Michelle Brenner, *Accounts Mgr*
Stacey Griffin, *Marketing Mgr*
EMP: 13
SALES (est): 1.3MM **Privately Held**
WEB: www.mainstreams.com
SIC: 7371 7372 Custom computer pro-
gramming services; application computer
software

(G-18978)
MARSAM METALFAB INC
1870 Enterprise Pkwy (44087-2206)
PHONE..........................330 405-1520
Fax: 330 405-1532
Mark Brownfield, *President*
George Dufour, *Marketing Staff*
EMP: 25
SQ FT: 30,000
SALES (est): 3.9MM **Privately Held**
SIC: 1799 3441 7692 3444 Welding on
site; fabricated structural metal; welding
repair; sheet metalwork

(G-18979)
MATHESON TRI-GAS INC
Also Called: Matheson Gas Products
1650 Enterprise Pkwy (44087-2202)
PHONE..........................330 425-4407
Fax: 330 425-1791
Les Gibson, *Opers-Prdtn-Mfg*
EMP: 18
SQ FT: 7,226
SALES (corp-wide): 5.4B **Privately Held**
WEB: www.matheson-trigas.com
SIC: 2813 5084 Industrial gases; welding
machinery & equipment
HQ: Matheson Tri-Gas, Inc.
150 Allen Rd Ste 302
Basking Ridge NJ 07920
908 991-9200

(G-18980)
MATHESON TRI-GAS INC
1650 Enterprise Pkwy (44087-2202)
PHONE..........................440 365-1741
Fax: 440 365-5885
Regis Holland, *Branch Mgr*
EMP: 20
SALES (corp-wide): 5.4B **Privately Held**
WEB: www.vngas.com
SIC: 5169 5085 5099 5172 Industrial
gases; welding supplies; safety equip-
ment & supplies; gases, liquefied petro-
leum (propane); welding repair
HQ: Matheson Tri-Gas, Inc.
150 Allen Rd Ste 302
Basking Ridge NJ 07920
908 991-9200

(G-18981)
MAVAL INDUSTRIES LLC
Also Called: Maval Manufacturing
1555 Enterprise Pkwy (44087-2239)
PHONE..........................330 405-1600
Fax: 330 425-4854
John Dougherty, *President*
Dale Lumby, *Vice Pres*
Dan Denavich, *Engineer*
Meri Vaughn, *Finance*
John C Dougherty, *Manager*
▲ EMP: 203
SQ FT: 88,000
SALES: 30MM
SALES (corp-wide): 9B **Publicly Held**
WEB: www.mavalgear.com
SIC: 3714 8711 Power steering equip-
ment, motor vehicle; consulting engineer
HQ: Borgwarner Pds (Indiana) Inc.
600 Corporation Dr
Pendleton IN 46064
800 372-3555

(G-18982)
MCFLUSION INC
2112 Case Pkwy Ste 8 (44087-2378)
PHONE..........................800 341-8616
Ole Madsen, *President*
Torben Andersen, *Exec VP*
Liza Scurr, *Director*
▲ EMP: 8
SALES (est): 1.5MM **Privately Held**
SIC: 3559 Pharmaceutical machinery

(G-18983)
MEDICAL ELASTOMER DEV INC
Also Called: Qure Medical
1700 Highland Rd (44087-2221)
P.O. Box 1030 (44087-9030)
PHONE..........................330 425-8352
Fax: 330 425-8369
Randy Ross, *CEO*
Christine Delmore, *COO*
Kray David Alan, *Engineer*
Jennifer Petro, *Accounts Mgr*
Adam Shaal, *Sales Associate*
▲ EMP: 30
SQ FT: 20,000
SALES (est): 8.7MM
SALES (corp-wide): 1.2B **Privately Held**
WEB: www.medeladev.com
SIC: 2822 Silicone rubbers
HQ: Q Holding Company
1700 Highland Rd
Twinsburg OH 44087
330 425-8472

(G-18984)
MEDINA SUPPLY COMPANY
1516 Highland Rd (44087-2217)
PHONE..........................330 425-0752
Fax: 330 425-9062
Lowell Perry, *Manager*
EMP: 30
SQ FT: 18,612
SALES (corp-wide): 28.6B **Privately Held**
SIC: 3273 Ready-mixed concrete
HQ: Medina Supply Company
230 E Smith Rd
Medina OH 44256
330 723-3681

(G-18985)
**METAL IMPROVEMENT
COMPANY LLC**
1652 Highland Rd (44087-2219)
PHONE..........................330 425-1490
Fax: 330 425-1494
John O'Brien, *Div Sub Head*
John Obrien, *Div Sub Head*
Kirk Gray, *Manager*
EMP: 28
SALES (corp-wide): 2.1B **Publicly Held**
WEB: www.mic-houston.com
SIC: 3471 3398 Finishing, metals or
formed products; metal heat treating
HQ: Metal Improvement Company, Llc
80 E State Rt 4 Ste 310
Paramus NJ 07652
201 843-7800

(G-18986)
**METALDYNE PWRTRAIN
CMPNNTS INC**
Also Called: Metaldyne Twinsburg
8001 Bavaria Rd (44087-2261)
PHONE..........................330 486-3200
Fax: 440 519-7102
Steve Mitchell, *Plant Mgr*
Derek Funderburk, *Opers Mgr*
Leslie Knapp, *Purch Agent*
Mike Palsha, *Design Engr*
Dave Fallert, *Financial Exec*
EMP: 130
SALES (corp-wide): 3.9B **Publicly Held**
WEB: www.metaldyne.com
SIC: 3312 3519 Tool & die steel; parts &
accessories, internal combustion engines
HQ: Metaldyne Powertrain Components,
Inc.
917 Anderson Rd
Litchfield MI 49252
517 542-5555

(G-18987)
METALLIC RESOURCES INC
2368 E Enterprise Pkwy (44087-2349)
P.O. Box 368 (44087-0368)
PHONE..........................330 425-3155
Fax: 330 425-2180
Stan Rothschild, *President*
Julia Harber, *General Mgr*
William Griffith, *Vice Pres*
John Sprowl, *Vice Pres*
James Boles, *Production*
▲ EMP: 32
SQ FT: 26,000
SALES (est): 10.4MM **Privately Held**
WEB: www.metallicresources.com
SIC: 3356 3339 Solder: wire, bar, acid
core, & rosin core; precious metals
PA: Metallic Solders De Mexico, S. De R.L.
De C.V.
Norte 7 No. 35 A
H. Matamoros TAMPS.
868 811-4301

(G-18988)
**MILES RUBBER & PACKING
COMPANY (PA)**
9020 Dutton Dr (44087-1994)
PHONE..........................330 425-3888
Fax: 330 425-3073
James M Smith, *President*
K J Ertle, *President*
Larry Lempke, *President*
Janet Schickler, *President*
Dennis Baca, *Human Res Mgr*
EMP: 25
SQ FT: 27,800
SALES (est): 3.8MM **Privately Held**
WEB: www.milesrubber-ohio.com
SIC: 3053 3069 Gaskets, packing & seal-
ing devices; sponge rubber & sponge rub-
ber products

(G-18989)
ND INDUSTRIES INC
9051 Dutton Dr (44087-1943)
PHONE..........................330 425-3167
Fax: 330 425-3065
Tom Pennington, *General Mgr*
Mary Croff, *Prdtn Mgr*
George Williamson, *VP Sls/Mktg*
Michael Tohlman, *Sales/Mktg Mgr*
Mike Lynch, *Manager*
EMP: 12
SALES (corp-wide): 90.9MM **Privately
Held**
WEB: www.ndindustries.com
SIC: 2899 Metal treating compounds
PA: Nd Industries, Inc.
1000 N Crooks Rd
Clawson MI 48017
248 288-0000

(G-18990)
**OLIVER PRINTING & PACKG CO
LLC**
1760 Enterprise Pkwy (44087-2291)
PHONE..........................330 425-7890
Fax: 330 425-8138
George Oliver, *President*
Don Karcher, *Sales Staff*
Mike Forst, *Info Tech Dir*
W George Oliver, *Shareholder*

EMP: 62 EST: 1952
SQ FT: 21,000
SALES (est): 19.3MM **Privately Held**
SIC: 2752 Commercial printing, offset

(G-18991)
OMA USA INC
9329 Ravenna Rd Ste A (44087-2457)
PHONE..........................330 487-0602
Mauro Nava, *President*
Antonio Villa, *General Mgr*
Maria Pia Nava, *Vice Pres*
Clara Maria Nava, *Treasurer*
Cristina Monterisi, *Manager*
▲ EMP: 6
SQ FT: 2,860
SALES (est): 570K **Privately Held**
WEB: www.omabraid.com
SIC: 3549 3552 Wiredrawing & fabricating
machinery & equipment, ex. die; braiding
machines, textile

(G-18992)
OMNITHRUSTER INC
2201 Pinnacle Pkwy Ste A (44087-2367)
PHONE..........................330 963-6310
John B De Nault, *Ch of Bd*
Kurt Widmer, *President*
Byron Foreman, *Agent*
EMP: 12
SQ FT: 15,000
SALES: 1.8MM **Privately Held**
WEB: www.omnithruster.com
SIC: 3643 Rail bonds, electric: for propul-
sion & signal circuits

(G-18993)
OMSI TRANSMISSIONS INC
9319 Ravenna Rd Ste A (44087-2462)
PHONE..........................330 405-7350
Renato Soncina, *President*
John Manes, *Admin Sec*
▲ EMP: 3
SALES (est): 479.9K **Privately Held**
WEB: www.omsitrasmissioni.com
SIC: 3714 5088 Axle housings & shafts,
motor vehicle; transportation equipment &
supplies

(G-18994)
P-AMERICAS LLC
2351 Edison Blvd Ste 2 (44087-2384)
PHONE..........................330 963-0090
Fax: 330 963-5537
William Evans, *Manager*
EMP: 22
SALES (corp-wide): 62.8B **Publicly Held**
SIC: 2086 Carbonated soft drinks, bottled
& canned
HQ: P-Americas Llc
1 Pepsi Way
Somers NY

(G-18995)
PARO SERVICES CO (PA)
1755 Entp Pkwy Ste 100 (44087)
PHONE..........................330 467-1300
Daniel N Zelman, *President*
Brian McCue, *COO*
David Debord, *Vice Pres*
Edward J Kubek Jr, *Vice Pres*
Nick La Magna, *Vice Pres*
EMP: 10
SQ FT: 60,000
SALES (est): 85.3MM **Privately Held**
SIC: 7349 2842 Cleaning service, indus-
trial or commercial; cleaning or polishing
preparations

(G-18996)
PENN MACHINE COMPANY
2182 E Aurora Rd (44087-1924)
PHONE..........................814 288-1547
Craig J Opacic, *Sales Mgr*
EMP: 25
SQ FT: 27,000
SALES (corp-wide): 223.6B **Publicly
Held**
WEB: www.pmcgearbox.com
SIC: 3568 3532 3462 Power transmission
equipment; mining machinery; iron & steel
forgings
HQ: Penn Machine Company
106 Station St
Johnstown PA 15905

GEOGRAPHIC

(G-18997)
PEPPERL + FUCHS INC (HQ)
1600 Enterprise Pkwy (44087-2245)
PHONE..................................330 425-3555
Fax: 330 425-4607
Wolfgang Mueller, *President*
Kishore K Kumble, *General Mgr*
Hermann Best, *Managing Dir*
Michael Fuchs, *Managing Dir*
Seitz Juergen, *Managing Dir*
▲ EMP: 130
SQ FT: 55,050
SALES (est): 95MM
SALES (corp-wide): 579.1MM **Privately Held**
WEB: www.pepperlfuchs.com
SIC: 5065 3625 3822 3674 Electronic parts & equipment; relays & industrial controls; auto controls regulating residntl & coml environmt & applncs; semiconductors & related devices
PA: Pepperl + Fuchs Gmbh
Lilienthalstr. 200
Mannheim 68307
621 776-0

(G-18998)
PEPSI-COLA METRO BTLG CO INC
1999 Enterprise Pkwy (44087-2253)
PHONE..................................330 963-0426
Fax: 330 425-4715
Robert Oswald, *Opers Mgr*
Richard Gajewski, *Plant Engr*
Charlie Powers, *Manager*
Frank O'Neill, *Manager*
Chad Damron, *Supervisor*
EMP: 500
SALES (corp-wide): 62.8B **Publicly Held**
WEB: www.joy-of-cola.com
SIC: 2086 5149 Bottled & canned soft drinks; groceries & related products
HQ: Pepsi-Cola Metropolitan Bottling Company, Inc.
1111 Westchester Ave
White Plains NY 10604
914 767-6000

(G-18999)
PEPSI-COLA METRO BTLG CO INC
Also Called: Pepsico
1999 Enterprise Pkwy (44087-2253)
PHONE..................................330 963-5300
Fax: 330 963-5302
Amy Rogers, *CPA*
Charlie Powers, *Branch Mgr*
EMP: 30
SALES (corp-wide): 62.8B **Publicly Held**
WEB: www.whitmancorp.com
SIC: 2086 Carbonated soft drinks, bottled & canned
HQ: Pepsi-Cola Metropolitan Bottling Company, Inc.
1111 Westchester Ave
White Plains NY 10604
914 767-6000

(G-19000)
PERFECTION MOLD & MACHINE CO
2057 E Aurora Rd Ste Hi (44087-1938)
PHONE..................................330 784-5435
Jack Bailey, *President*
Robert Deken, *Finance*
Jenny Schlafer, *Manager*
EMP: 12
SQ FT: 11,000
SALES: 933.7K **Privately Held**
WEB: www.perfectionmold.com
SIC: 3544 Industrial molds

(G-19001)
PERRY WELDING SERVICE INC
2075 Case Pkwy S (44087-2361)
PHONE..................................330 425-2211
Fax: 330 425-2268
Jerry Perry, *President*
Jason Perry, *Foreman/Supr*
Margo Perry, *Treasurer*
EMP: 14 EST: 1974
SQ FT: 12,000

SALES (est): 2.1MM **Privately Held**
SIC: 3599 3469 7692 3544 Custom machinery; machine parts, stamped or pressed metal; welding repair; special dies, tools, jigs & fixtures; fabricated structural metal

(G-19002)
PLATING PERCEPTIONS INC
8815 Herrick Rd (44087-2417)
P.O. Box 81 (44087-0081)
PHONE..................................330 425-4180
Fax: 330 425-1449
Randall Bauer, *President*
James Konicek, *Vice Pres*
Tim Burkhart, *QC Dir*
EMP: 9
SQ FT: 8,000
SALES (est): 1.1MM **Privately Held**
SIC: 3471 Plating of metals or formed products

(G-19003)
POLY-CARB INC
8440 Tower Dr (44087-2000)
P.O. Box 39278, Solon (44139-0278)
PHONE..................................440 248-1223
Fax: 440 248-1513
Puneet Singh, *President*
Ratanjit Sondhe, *Personnel Exec*
Vinod Podar, *Payroll Mgr*
▲ EMP: 40
SQ FT: 55,000
SALES (est): 6.8MM
SALES (corp-wide): 48.1B **Publicly Held**
WEB: www.poly-carb.com
SIC: 2821 Plastics materials & resins; silicone resins
PA: The Dow Chemical Company
2030 Dow Ctr
Midland MI 48674
989 636-1000

(G-19004)
POLYSTAR INC
2030 Midway Dr (44087-1934)
PHONE..................................330 963-5100
Fax: 330 405-6186
David Huston, *CEO*
Mark Pethtel, *Prdtn Mgr*
Robert Hoge, *Manager*
Robert Nightwine, *Director*
EMP: 14
SQ FT: 1,785
SALES (est): 4MM **Privately Held**
SIC: 2655 Containers, laminated phenolic & vulcanized fiber

(G-19005)
PREMIER SHOT COMPANY INC
1666 Enterprise Pkwy (44087-2202)
PHONE..................................330 405-0583
Bob Gillespie, *President*
Bob Armstrong, *Controller*
Tim Carcione, *Manager*
Amelia Wurv, *Administration*
▲ EMP: 6
SQ FT: 10,000
SALES (est): 710K **Privately Held**
WEB: www.premiershot.com
SIC: 3482 Shot, steel (ammunition)

(G-19006)
Q HOLDING COMPANY (HQ)
Also Called: Quality Synthetic Rubber
1700 Highland Rd (44087-2221)
PHONE..................................330 425-8472
Randall Ross, *CEO*
Jason Pettyjohn, *Opers Staff*
Dennis J Welhouse, *CFO*
Kimberly Putnam, *Accounting Mgr*
Richard Jones, *Accountant*
▲ EMP: 385
SQ FT: 41,000
SALES (est): 248.7MM
SALES (corp-wide): 1.2B **Privately Held**
WEB: www.lexingtonprecision.com
SIC: 3061 Mechanical rubber goods
PA: 3i Group Plc
16 Palace Street
London SW1E
207 975-3131

(G-19007)
R A HAMED INTERNATIONAL INC
Also Called: Scott Thomas Furniture
8400 Darrow Rd (44087-2375)
PHONE..................................330 247-0190
Rosemary Hamed, *President*
Scott Hamed, *Vice Pres*
EMP: 12
SQ FT: 19,000
SALES (est): 1.2MM **Privately Held**
WEB: www.scottthomasfurniture.com
SIC: 2511 Wood household furniture

(G-19008)
REUTER-STOKES INC
Also Called: GE Energy Oilfield Technology
8499 Darrow Rd Ste 1 (44087-2398)
PHONE..................................330 425-3755
Fax: 330 425-4045
Leo Zanderschur, *President*
Greg Mellow, *Design Engr*
Damaris Martina, *Manager*
◆ EMP: 260 EST: 1956
SQ FT: 110,000
SALES (est): 58.5MM
SALES (corp-wide): 123.6B **Publicly Held**
SIC: 3829 3826 3823 3812 Nuclear radiation & testing apparatus; environmental testing equipment; industrial instrmnts msrmnt display/control process variable; search & navigation equipment
PA: General Electric Company
41 Farnsworth St
Boston MA 02210
617 443-3000

(G-19009)
RO-MAI INDUSTRIES INC
1605 Enterprise Pkwy (44087-2201)
PHONE..................................330 425-9090
Fax: 330 425-7899
Robert Maier, *President*
▲ EMP: 30
SQ FT: 26,000
SALES (est): 4.7MM **Privately Held**
SIC: 3089 Injection molding of plastics

(G-19010)
ROBERT JAMES SALES INC
1532 Enterprise Pkwy (44087-2240)
P.O. Box 590 (44087-0590)
PHONE..................................330 425-9116
Fax: 330 425-9395
Michael P Luich, *Manager*
EMP: 15
SQ FT: 5,100
SALES (corp-wide): 66.2MM **Privately Held**
SIC: 3312 Stainless steel
PA: Robert James Sales, Inc.
2585 Walden Ave
Cheektowaga NY 14225
716 651-6000

(G-19011)
ROCKWELL AUTOMATION INC
8440 Darrow Rd (44087-2310)
P.O. Box 2167, Milwaukee WI (53201-2167)
PHONE..................................330 425-3211
Fax: 216 487-6117
Michael Sparger, *Principal*
Gina Ward, *Opers Mgr*
Mary Satterlee, *Prdtn Mgr*
Kevin Elkins, *Facilities Mgr*
Noreen Thomas, *Buyer*
EMP: 400 **Publicly Held**
SIC: 3625 Relays & industrial controls
PA: Rockwell Automation, Inc.
1201 S 2nd St
Milwaukee WI 53204

(G-19012)
ROONEY OPTICAL INC (PA)
9221 Ravenna Rd Ste 3 (44087-2454)
PHONE..................................216 267-5600
Fax: 216 267-5580
Gerald J Dougher, *Ch of Bd*
Kevin Dougher, *President*
Dan Trielett, *Info Tech Mgr*
EMP: 50
SQ FT: 20,000

SALES (est): 3.8MM **Privately Held**
WEB: www.rooneyoptical.com
SIC: 3851 Eyeglasses, lenses & frames

(G-19013)
ROYAL CHEMICAL COMPANY LTD
1755 Entp Pkwy Ste 100 (44087)
PHONE..................................330 467-1300
Warren Goldenberg, *Branch Mgr*
EMP: 15
SALES (corp-wide): 8.1MM **Privately Held**
SIC: 2841 Soap: granulated, liquid, cake, flaked or chip; detergents, synthetic organic or inorganic alkaline; scouring compounds
HQ: Royal Chemical Company, Ltd.
8679 Freeway Dr
Macedonia OH 44056
330 467-1300

(G-19014)
RTD ELECTRONICS INC
1632 Entp Pkwy Ste D (44087)
PHONE..................................330 487-0716
Terry L Kellhofer, *President*
EMP: 12
SQ FT: 4,000
SALES (est): 159.5K **Privately Held**
SIC: 3679 Harness assemblies for electronic use: wire or cable

(G-19015)
S & B METAL PRODUCTS INC (PA)
2060 Case Pkwy (44087-2344)
PHONE..................................330 487-5790
Fax: 330 487-5591
Stephen Campbell, *CEO*
Brent Cessna, *General Mgr*
Paul Balliette, *Chairman*
Cindy Balliette, *Corp Secy*
Marianne King, *Controller*
▼ EMP: 50 EST: 1974
SQ FT: 25,000
SALES (est): 6.9MM **Privately Held**
WEB: www.sbmetal.com
SIC: 3444 Sheet metalwork

(G-19016)
SAMUEL STEEL PICKLING COMPANY (PA)
1400 Enterprise Pkwy (44087-2242)
PHONE..................................330 963-3777
Fax: 330 963-0770
Rick Morris, *General Mgr*
Rick Snyder, *Principal*
Michael Evelyn, *Vice Pres*
William Vason, *Opers Mgr*
Ann Huston, *Controller*
EMP: 45
SQ FT: 115,000
SALES: 15MM **Privately Held**
SIC: 7389 5051 3471 3398 Metal slitting & shearing; metals service centers & offices; plating & polishing; metal heat treating; blast furnaces & steel mills

(G-19017)
SCHAFFER GRINDING CO INC
8470 Chamberlin Rd (44087-2085)
PHONE..................................323 724-4476
Fax: 330 425-8082
Chet Schaffer, *General Mgr*
Eric Koleszar, *Plant Mgr*
EMP: 15
SQ FT: 10,000
SALES (corp-wide): 5.1MM **Privately Held**
SIC: 3599 Machine shop, jobbing & repair
PA: Schaffer Grinding Co., Inc.
848 S Maple Ave
Montebello CA
323 724-4476

(G-19018)
SEMATIC USA INC
Also Called: Tyler Elevator Products
7852 Bavaria Rd (44087-2260)
PHONE..................................330 405-3004
Fax: 216 524-9710
Roberto Zappa, *President*
Steve Brunton, *Managing Dir*
Stefano Girardi, *COO*

Bill Novak, *Accounts Mgr*
Bill Kurtz, *Manager*
▲ **EMP:** 35 **EST:** 1959
SQ FT: 35,000
SALES (est): 10.6MM
SALES (corp-wide): 185.8K **Privately Held**
WEB: www.sematic.com
SIC: 3534 Elevators & equipment
HQ: Sematic Spa
  Via Commendatore Francesco Zappa 5
  Osio Sotto BG 24046
  035 481-5100

(G-19019)
SEMTORQ INC
Also Called: Nucam
1953 Case Pkwy S (44087-2359)
P.O. Box 895 (44087-0895)
PHONE.................................330 487-0600
Fax: 330 995-7670
Joseph Seme Jr, *President*
Greg Lanham, *Prdtn Mgr*
Lori Fowers, *Accountant*
Christina Seme, *Admin Sec*
▲ **EMP:** 12
SQ FT: 40,000
SALES (est): 3.5MM **Privately Held**
WEB: www.semtorq.com
SIC: 3549 7692 3594 3548 Assembly machines, including robotic; welding repair; fluid power pumps & motors; welding apparatus; machine tools, metal forming type; screw machine products

(G-19020)
SHELLY MATERIALS INC
8920 Canyon Falls Blvd # 120 (44087-1990)
PHONE.................................330 823-4646
Matt Moten, *Branch Mgr*
EMP: 4
SALES (corp-wide): 28.6B **Privately Held**
SIC: 1422 Crushed & broken limestone
HQ: Shelly Materials, Inc.
  80 Park Dr
  Thornville OH 43076
  740 246-6315

(G-19021)
SPEARFYSH INC
8987 Darrow Rd (44087-1963)
PHONE.................................330 487-0300
Marc Miller, *CEO*
Kim Lewis, *COO*
Rand Lennox, *Chief Engr*
EMP: 11
SQ FT: 1,900
SALES (est): 856.4K **Privately Held**
SIC: 7372 Business oriented computer software

(G-19022)
SSP FITTINGS CORP (PA)
8250 Boyle Pkwy (44087-2200)
PHONE.................................330 425-4250
Jeffrey E King, *CEO*
F B Douglas, *Principal*
O F Douglas, *Principal*
H M Hunter, *Principal*
Betsy S King, *Corp Secy*
▲ **EMP:** 100 **EST:** 1926
SQ FT: 165,000
SALES (est): 25.6MM **Privately Held**
WEB: www.sspfittings.com
SIC: 3494 5085 3498 3492 Pipe fittings; industrial supplies; fabricated pipe & fittings; fluid power valves & hose fittings

(G-19023)
STANLEY PROCTOR & COMPANY INC
2016 Midway Dr (44087-1960)
P.O. Box 446 (44087-0446)
PHONE.................................330 425-7814
Fax: 330 425-3222
John Proctor, *President*
EMP: 18
SALES (est): 2.9MM
SALES (corp-wide): 7.7MM **Privately Held**
WEB: www.stanleyproctor.com
SIC: 3594 Motors: hydraulic, fluid power or air

PA: The Stanley M Proctor Company
  2016 Midway Dr
  Twinsburg OH 44087
  330 425-7814

(G-19024)
STEWART ACQUISITION LLC (PA)
Also Called: Cima Plastics Group
2146 Enterprise Pkwy (44087-2272)
PHONE.................................330 963-0322
Timothy O'Keefe, *Opers Mgr*
J Berkenstock, *Mfg Staff*
James M Stewart,
▲ **EMP:** 45
SQ FT: 44,000
SALES (est): 11.7MM **Privately Held**
WEB: www.cimaplastics.com
SIC: 3089 Injection molding of plastics

(G-19025)
SUMMIT AVIONICS INC
2225 E Entp Pkwy 1a 1 A (44087)
PHONE.................................330 425-1440
Fax: 330 425-8516
Michael Tartamella, *President*
Michael Woods, *CFO*
EMP: 18
SQ FT: 14,000
SALES (est): 1.7MM **Privately Held**
WEB: www.summitavionics.com
SIC: 3728 Aircraft parts & equipment

(G-19026)
SUMMIT PETROLEUM INC
8815 Herrick Rd (44087-2417)
PHONE.................................330 487-5494
William G Kinney, *President*
Sarina Kinney, *Vice Pres*
EMP: 4
SQ FT: 1,500
SALES (est): 868.6K **Privately Held**
SIC: 1311 Crude petroleum production; natural gas production

(G-19027)
TECHNOFORM GL INSUL N AMER INC
1755 Entp Pkwy Ste 300 (44087)
PHONE.................................330 487-6600
Albert Stankus, *General Mgr*
Shari Vago, *Office Mgr*
Dheeraj Corepall, *Manager*
Neil Ji, *Manager*
Steven LI, *Manager*
▲ **EMP:** 25
SQ FT: 50,000
SALES (est): 5.9MM
SALES (corp-wide): 282.3MM **Privately Held**
WEB: www.technoform.us
SIC: 3429 Manufactured hardware (general)
HQ: Technoform Bautec Holding Gmbh
  Friedrichsplatz 8
  Kassel 34117
  561 958-3331

(G-19028)
TOWER TOOL & MANUFACTURING CO
2057 E Aurora Rd Ste No (44087-1938)
PHONE.................................330 425-1623
Fax: 330 425-4757
Lenard Lapchynski, *President*
Kathleen Lapchynski, *Vice Pres*
EMP: 12
SQ FT: 30,000
SALES (est): 1.3MM **Privately Held**
SIC: 3599 3544 3444 Custom machinery; special dies, tools, jigs & fixtures; sheet metalwork

(G-19029)
TRI COUNTY CONCRETE INC (PA)
9423 Darrow Rd (44087-1415)
P.O. Box 665 (44087-0665)
PHONE.................................330 425-4464
Fax: 330 405-3122
Tony Farenacci, *President*
Fred Farenacci, *Vice Pres*
Tony Farecci, *Manager*
Joyce Negrette, *Manager*
EMP: 30

SQ FT: 62,000
SALES (est): 4.4MM **Privately Held**
SIC: 3273 3272 1442 Ready-mixed concrete; concrete products; construction sand & gravel

(G-19030)
TRIONIX RESEARCH LABORATORY
8037 Bavaria Rd (44087-2261)
PHONE.................................330 425-9055
Fax: 330 425-9063
Dr Chun Bin Lim, *President*
Sandy Lim, *Accounts Mgr*
EMP: 6
SQ FT: 150,000
SALES (est): 1.2MM **Privately Held**
SIC: 3844 Nuclear irradiation equipment

(G-19031)
TWIN VENTURES INC
2457 Edison Blvd (44087-2340)
PHONE.................................330 405-3838
Dave Potts, *President*
EMP: 15
SALES (est): 1.5MM **Privately Held**
WEB: www.twinsrealm.com
SIC: 3452 5072 Bolts, nuts, rivets & washers; hardware

(G-19032)
UNIVERSAL ELECTRONICS INC
1864 Entp Pkwy Ste B (44087)
PHONE.................................330 487-1110
Fax: 330 963-7881
Michael Reilly, *Vice Pres*
Jason Etter, *Engineer*
Fred Johnson, *Finance Mgr*
Brian Dean, *Manager*
Anne M Frank, *Manager*
EMP: 80
SALES (corp-wide): 651.3MM **Publicly Held**
WEB: www.ezremote.com
SIC: 3651 Video triggers (remote control TV devices)
PA: Universal Electronics Inc.
  201 Sandpointe Ave Fl 8
  Santa Ana CA 92707
  714 918-9500

(G-19033)
UNIVERSAL RACK & EQUIPMENT CO
Also Called: Universal Coatings Division
8511 Tower Dr (44087-2088)
PHONE.................................330 963-6776
Fax: 330 963-6743
Ken Palik, *President*
John Palik, *Vice Pres*
EMP: 20 **EST:** 1961
SQ FT: 40,000
SALES (est): 1.6MM **Privately Held**
SIC: 3479 3559 3443 Coating of metals with plastic or resins; electroplating machinery & equipment; fabricated plate work (boiler shop)

(G-19034)
US FITTINGS INC
2182 E Aurora Rd (44087-1924)
P.O. Box 746 (44087-0746)
PHONE.................................234 212-9420
Richard K Raymond, *President*
Melanie Schwanek, *Manager*
EMP: 15
SQ FT: 1,500
SALES (est): 2.5MM **Privately Held**
SIC: 3494 Pipe fittings

(G-19035)
VENTURE LIGHTING INTL INC (DH)
2451 E Enterprise Pkwy (44087-2351)
PHONE.................................800 451-2606
Fax: 800 451-2605
Wayne Vespoli, *President*
Sabu Krishnan, *Co-President*
Amy Patrick, *Vice Pres*
Jeff Johanning, *Engineer*
Steve Potts, *CFO*
◆ **EMP:** 68
SQ FT: 330,000

SALES (est): 35.5MM
SALES (corp-wide): 209.5MM **Privately Held**
SIC: 3641 Electric lamps

(G-19036)
VENTURE LIGHTING INTL INC
2451 E Enterprise Pkwy (44087-2351)
PHONE.................................440 248-3510
Don Morrison, *COO*
Matthew Mazzola, *Sales Mgr*
Robin Bienfait, *CIO*
Brian Bidulka, *Officer*
EMP: 15
SALES (corp-wide): 209.5MM **Privately Held**
SIC: 3641 Electric lamps
HQ: Venture Lighting International, Inc.
  2451 E Enterprise Pkwy
  Twinsburg OH 44087
  800 451-2606

(G-19037)
VISIMAX TECHNOLOGIES INC
9177 Dutton Dr (44087-1981)
PHONE.................................330 405-8330
Dane Clark, *President*
Melanie Clark, *Vice Pres*
Lisa Reinhold, *Opers Mgr*
Steve Hales, *Prdtn Mgr*
Paul Van Wagenen, *Sales Associate*
EMP: 12
SALES (est): 1.1MM **Privately Held**
WEB: www.visimaxtechnologies.com
SIC: 3479 Coating electrodes

(G-19038)
WEDGE PRODUCTS INC
2181 Enterprise Pkwy (44087-2211)
PHONE.................................330 405-4477
Fax: 330 425-0091
Anthony J Defino, *President*
Joe Depiero, *Managing Dir*
Frank Defino, *Vice Pres*
Leonard Defino, *Vice Pres*
Donald Ujczo, *Controller*
▲ **EMP:** 300 **EST:** 1925
SQ FT: 55,000
SALES (est): 55.3MM **Privately Held**
WEB: www.wedgeproducts.com
SIC: 3469 3643 Metal stampings; current-carrying wiring devices
PA: A.J.D. Holding Co.
  2181 Enterprise Pkwy
  Twinsburg OH 44087

(G-19039)
WELDON PLASTICS CORPORATION
1962 Case Pkwy (44087-4327)
PHONE.................................330 425-9660
Linda Repay, *President*
Laszlo Repay, *Vice Pres*
EMP: 3
SALES (est): 320K **Privately Held**
SIC: 3089 Plastic processing; molding primary plastic

(G-19040)
WORLDCLASS PROCESSING CORP
1400 Enterprise Pkwy (44087-2242)
PHONE.................................724 251-9000
Daniel Magee, *President*
EMP: 39
SQ FT: 250,000
SALES (est): 5MM
SALES (corp-wide): 1.9B **Privately Held**
WEB: www.wcpcoils.com
SIC: 3479 Etching & engraving
PA: Samuel, Son & Co., Limited
  2360 Dixie Rd
  Mississauga ON L4Y 1
  905 279-5460

(G-19041)
WRWP LLC
Also Called: Western Reserve Wire Products
1920 Case Pkwy S (44087-2358)
PHONE.................................330 425-3421
Fax: 330 425-2400
Cassie Storm, *Buyer*
EMP: 15 **EST:** 2014
SALES (est): 2.9MM **Privately Held**
SIC: 3496 Miscellaneous fabricated wire products

(G-19042)
ZERUST CONSUMER PRODUCTS LLC
9345 Ravenna Rd Unit E (44087-2452)
PHONE..................................330 405-1965
Elliot Dworkin, *Mng Member*
▲ EMP: 3
SALES: 1.5MM **Privately Held**
SIC: 2899 Rust resisting compounds

(G-19043)
ZINKAN ENTERPRISES INC (PA)
1919 Case Pkwy (44087-2343)
PHONE..................................330 487-1500
Thomas W McCrystal, *Principal*
Mr Lou Koenig, *Principal*
◆ EMP: 10
SQ FT: 15,000
SALES (est): 16.1MM **Privately Held**
WEB: www.zinkan.com
SIC: 2899 Chemical preparations

Uhrichsville
Tuscarawas County

(G-19044)
ALERIS ROLLED PRODUCTS INC
7319 Newport Rd Se (44683-6368)
PHONE..................................740 922-2540
Sean M Stack, *CEO*
Daryl Miles, *Opers Mgr*
Donna Svatak, *Purch Agent*
EMP: 4 **Privately Held**
SIC: 3341 3353 Secondary nonferrous metals; aluminum sheet, plate & foil
HQ: Aleris Rolled Products, Inc.
25825 Science Park Dr # 400
Beachwood OH 44122
216 910-3400

(G-19045)
ARMSTRONG CUSTOM MOULDING INC
6408 State Route 800 Se (44683-6302)
PHONE..................................740 922-5931
Fax: 740 922-5900
Todd Armstrong, *President*
James B Armstrong Sr, *Admin Sec*
EMP: 6
SALES (est): 567.1K **Privately Held**
SIC: 2431 2426 Moldings & baseboards, ornamental & trim; hardwood dimension & flooring mills

(G-19046)
CAROLINA STAIR SUPPLY INC (PA)
316 Herrick St (44683-2123)
PHONE..................................740 922-3333
Fax: 740 922-9446
Clair Edwards, *President*
Lynda Hildebrande, *Accounts Mgr*
Linda Hildebrand, *Manager*
▲ EMP: 20
SQ FT: 2,000
SALES (est): 5.7MM **Privately Held**
SIC: 2431 Staircases, stairs & railings

(G-19047)
D & A CUSTOM TRAILER INC
6700 Moores Ridge Rd Se (44683-6573)
PHONE..................................740 922-2205
Dwight Johns, *President*
Anjanette Johns, *Corp Secy*
EMP: 3
SALES (est): 194.5K **Privately Held**
SIC: 3799 Trailers & trailer equipment

(G-19048)
D & B MACHINE WELDING INC
1128 N Main St (44683-1224)
PHONE..................................740 922-4930
Fax: 740 922-9133
Bill Brehm, *President*
Linda Brehm, *Treasurer*
EMP: 4
SQ FT: 4,200
SALES (est): 270K **Privately Held**
SIC: 3599 Machine shop, jobbing & repair

(G-19049)
DJ S WELD
424 N Main St (44683-1837)
PHONE..................................330 432-2206
Dwight Jones, *Owner*
EMP: 4
SALES (est): 407.8K **Privately Held**
SIC: 3443 Weldments

(G-19050)
FABOHIO INC
521 E 7th St (44683-1613)
P.O. Box 434 (44683-0434)
PHONE..................................740 922-4233
Fax: 740 922-4785
Kurt Shelley, *CEO*
Dennis Sautters, *Director*
EMP: 20 EST: 1963
SQ FT: 22,500
SALES: 1.7MM
SALES (corp-wide): 36.8MM **Privately Held**
WEB: www.fabohio.com
SIC: 3089 Plastic containers, except foam
PA: Bowerston Shale Company (Inc)
515 Main St
Bowerston OH 44695
740 269-2921

(G-19051)
HALL SAFETY APPAREL INC
1020 W 1st St (44683-2210)
P.O. Box 392 (44683-0392)
PHONE..................................740 922-3671
Fax: 740 922-4880
Gregory L Schneider, *President*
Delores Schneider, *Vice Pres*
Phillip Schneider, *Admin Sec*
EMP: 14 EST: 1937
SQ FT: 18,000
SALES: 610K **Privately Held**
SIC: 2326 2381 3842 Work apparel, except uniforms; gloves, work: woven or knit, made from purchased materials; radiation shielding aprons, gloves, sheeting, etc.

(G-19052)
IMCO RECYCLING OF OHIO LLC
7335 Newport Rd Se (44683-6368)
PHONE..................................740 922-2373
Fax: 740 922-2377
Sean M Stack, *CEO*
Robert R Holian, *Vice Pres*
Mark Mantooth, *Manager*
▲ EMP: 164
SALES (est): 22.5MM **Privately Held**
WEB: www.imcorecycling.com
SIC: 3341 4953 Aluminum smelting & refining (secondary); recycling, waste materials
HQ: Aleris Rolled Products, Inc.
25825 Science Park Dr # 400
Beachwood OH 44122
216 910-3400

(G-19053)
JOHNSON PRINTING
216 E 5th St (44683-1698)
PHONE..................................740 922-4821
Kevin J Johnson, *Owner*
EMP: 4
SQ FT: 3,000
SALES (est): 245K **Privately Held**
SIC: 2759 2752 Letterpress printing; commercial printing, offset

(G-19054)
K-HILL SIGNAL CO INC
326 W 3rd St (44683-2036)
P.O. Box 432 (44683-0432)
PHONE..................................740 922-0421
Fax: 740 922-0421
William J Hall, *President*
Sally Hall, *Vice Pres*
Kelly Ernandison, *Manager*
Kathy Grandison, *Admin Sec*
EMP: 3 EST: 1935
SQ FT: 4,500
SALES (est): 75K **Privately Held**
WEB: www.khilltrafficcounters.com
SIC: 3669 3824 Traffic signals, electric; fluid meters & counting devices

(G-19055)
NORTH STAR METALS MFG CO
6850 Edwards Ridge Rd Se (44683-5602)
P.O. Box 309, Gnadenhutten (44629-0309)
PHONE..................................740 254-4567
Fax: 740 254-4282
Darren Galbraith, *President*
Ron Fenton, *Vice Pres*
Stephen Weltmer, *Opers Mgr*
Lisa Messner, *Admin Sec*
EMP: 32
SQ FT: 40,000
SALES (est): 7.1MM **Privately Held**
WEB: www.northstarmetals.com
SIC: 3444 Siding, sheet metal

(G-19056)
REAL ALLOY RECYCLING INC
7319 Newport Rd Se (44683-6368)
PHONE..................................740 922-8301
Cynthia Jackson, *CEO*
Mike Wade, *Purch Agent*
Robert Shingle, *Engineer*
EMP: 9
SALES (corp-wide): 1.1B **Publicly Held**
SIC: 3355 Bars, rolled, aluminum
HQ: Real Alloy Recycling, Inc.
3700 Park East Dr Ste 300
Beachwood OH 44122
216 755-8900

(G-19057)
ROSEBUD MINING COMPANY
5600 Pleasant Vly Rd Se (44683-9502)
PHONE..................................740 922-9122
Greg Blainer, *Branch Mgr*
EMP: 33
SALES (corp-wide): 672.6MM **Privately Held**
WEB: www.rosebudmining.com
SIC: 1222 1221 Bituminous coal-underground mining; strip mining, bituminous
PA: Rosebud Mining Company
301 Market St
Kittanning PA 16201
724 545-6222

(G-19058)
SEALCO INC
6566 Superior Rd Se (44683-7487)
P.O. Box 307 (44683-0307)
PHONE..................................740 922-4122
Elmer McClave, *President*
Todd McClave, *Vice Pres*
▲ EMP: 6
SALES (est): 504.6K **Privately Held**
SIC: 2499 2448 Plugs, wood; pallets, wood

(G-19059)
SEYEKCUB INC
615 W 4th St (44683-2007)
PHONE..................................330 324-1394
Robert L Drummond Jr, *President*
EMP: 8
SQ FT: 10,000
SALES (est): 1.3MM **Privately Held**
SIC: 3363 Aluminum die-castings

(G-19060)
STEBBINS ENGINEERING & MFG CO
Also Called: Semco Ceramics
4778 Belden Dr Se (44683-1078)
P.O. Box 90 (44683-0090)
PHONE..................................740 922-3012
Fax: 740 922-6666
Cliff McPherson, *General Mgr*
Mary Wasilewski, *Engineer*
Douglas Miller, *Asst Controller*
William Heimiller, *Human Res Mgr*
Margrate Lavancha, *Executive*
EMP: 26
SALES (corp-wide): 208.4MM **Privately Held**
WEB: www.stebbinseng.com
SIC: 3253 3255 3251 Ceramic wall & floor tile; clay refractories; brick & structural clay tile
PA: The Stebbins Engineering And Manufacturing Company
363 Eastern Blvd
Watertown NY 13601
315 782-3000

(G-19061)
SUPERIOR CLAY CORP
6566 Superior Rd Se (44683-7487)
P.O. Box 352 (44683-0352)
PHONE..................................740 922-4122
Fax: 740 922-6626
Elmer W McClave III, *President*
Joe Berni, *Corp Secy*
Todd M Clave, *Vice Pres*
Tyler McClave, *Vice Pres*
William Johnson, *Purchasing*
◆ EMP: 75 EST: 1936
SQ FT: 190,000
SALES (est): 9.9MM **Privately Held**
WEB: www.superiorclay.com
SIC: 3259 8611 Sewer pipe or fittings, clay; flue lining, clay; wall coping, clay; stove lining, clay; business associations

(G-19062)
TOLLOTI PLASTIC PIPE INC
1830 Barbour Dr Se (44683-1084)
P.O. Box 508 (44683-0508)
PHONE..................................740 922-6911
Jack Homman, *Branch Mgr*
EMP: 5
SALES (corp-wide): 3.8MM **Privately Held**
SIC: 3084 Plastics pipe
PA: Tolloti Plastic Pipe Inc.
102 Barnhill Rd Se
New Philadelphia OH 44663
330 364-6627

(G-19063)
TRADING POST
202 N Water St (44683-1845)
PHONE..................................740 922-1199
Richard Sommers, *Owner*
EMP: 4 EST: 2010
SALES (est): 181.4K **Privately Held**
SIC: 2711 Newspapers, publishing & printing

(G-19064)
UHRICHSVILLE CARBIDE INC
410 N Water St (44683-1849)
PHONE..................................740 922-9197
Fax: 740 922-9524
Bob Septer, *President*
Karen Septer, *Corp Secy*
Eric Septer, *Engineer*
Rhea Septer, *Clerk*
EMP: 17
SALES (est): 1.6MM **Privately Held**
WEB: www.uhrichsvillecarbide.com
SIC: 3545 5072 7699 3546 Cutting tools for machine tools; saw blades; knife, saw & tool sharpening & repair; power-driven handtools; machine tools, metal forming type; saw blades & handsaws

---

Union
Montgomery County

(G-19065)
CONTINENTAL TESTING INC
104 S Main St (45322-3358)
PHONE..................................937 832-3322
Michael Thee, *President*
EMP: 11
SQ FT: 800
SALES: 600K **Privately Held**
WEB: www.continentaltesting.com
SIC: 3829 8734 Measuring & controlling devices; calibration & certification

(G-19066)
FETTERS RACING ENGINE INC
7245 S Rangeline Rd (45322-9600)
PHONE..................................937 698-6411
Fax: 937 698-3951
Larry Fetters, *Owner*
Doug Fetters, *Supervisor*
EMP: 3
SQ FT: 3,500
SALES (est): 443.9K **Privately Held**
SIC: 3714 Motor vehicle engines & parts

(G-19067)
PROCTER & GAMBLE DISTRG LLC
Also Called: Dayton Mixing Center
1800 Union Park Blvd (45377)
P.O. Box 2628, Burlington NC (27216-2628)
PHONE..............................937 387-5189
Robert Fix, *General Mgr*
EMP: 178
SALES (corp-wide): 65.3B **Publicly Held**
SIC: 3999 Advertising display products
HQ: Procter & Gamble Distributing Llc
1 Procter And Gamble Plz
Cincinnati OH 45202
513 983-1100

(G-19068)
TE-CO MANUFACTURING LLC
109 Quinter Farm Rd (45322-9796)
PHONE..............................937 836-0961
Richard Porter, *Mng Member*
▲ EMP: 76 EST: 1926
SQ FT: 40,000
SALES (est): 14.8MM **Privately Held**
WEB: www.te-co.com
SIC: 3545 3829 3544 3429 Machine tool attachments & accessories; vises, machine (machine tool accessories); measuring & controlling devices; special dies, tools, jigs & fixtures; manufactured hardware (general); machine shop, jobbing & repair

Union City
Darke County

(G-19069)
CAL-MAINE FOODS INC
1039 Zumbrum Rd (45390-8646)
PHONE..............................937 968-4874
Fax: 937 968-6586
Chuck Jenkins, *Branch Mgr*
EMP: 35
SALES (corp-wide): 1.5B **Publicly Held**
WEB: www.calmainefoods.com
SIC: 0252 2015 Chicken eggs; eggs, processed: frozen
PA: Cal-Maine Foods, Inc.
3320 W Woodrow Wilson Ave
Jackson MS 39209
601 948-6813

(G-19070)
CHARLES DANIEL YOUNG
Also Called: Fresh Aire Farms
1324 Wasson Rd (45390-9040)
PHONE..............................937 968-3423
Charles Daniel Young, *Owner*
Michelle Young, *Co-Owner*
EMP: 3
SALES: 147K **Privately Held**
SIC: 2875 Compost

(G-19071)
HA-STE MANUFACTURING CO INC
Also Called: Kangaroo Brand Mops
119 E Elm St (45390-1711)
P.O. Box 168 IN (47390-0168)
PHONE..............................937 968-4858
Robin Stewart, *President*
John W Stewart, *Chairman*
Teresa Lehey, *Controller*
Dale Stewart, *Marketing Mgr*
EMP: 25 EST: 1959
SQ FT: 5,500
SALES: 16MM **Privately Held**
WEB: www.hastemops.com
SIC: 2392 Mops, floor & dust

(G-19072)
MBM LUMBER
1588 Cox Rd (45390-9036)
PHONE..............................937 459-7448
Fax: 937 968-6646
Craig Mendenhall, *Partner*
Greg Mendenhall, *Partner*
EMP: 5
SALES: 3.2MM **Privately Held**
SIC: 2421 Sawmills & planing mills, general

(G-19073)
WOODBURY WELDING INC
10393 Oh In State Line Rd (45390-9050)
PHONE..............................937 968-3573
Gary Woodbury, *President*
Jodi Davidson, *Bookkeeper*
EMP: 3
SALES (est): 358.1K **Privately Held**
SIC: 3441 3523 0191 Fabricated structural metal; farm machinery & equipment; general farms, primarily crop

Uniontown
Stark County

(G-19074)
ADVANTAGE TOOL SUPPLY INC
3666 Avanti Ln (44685-8852)
PHONE..............................330 896-8869
Michael Prexta, *President*
Laura Prexta, *Treasurer*
EMP: 3
SALES: 700K **Privately Held**
SIC: 3545 Cutting tools for machine tools

(G-19075)
AMERITECH PUBLISHING INC
Also Called: SBC
1530 Corp Woods Pkwy # 100 (44685-6707)
PHONE..............................330 896-6037
Kim Gergel, *Manager*
Steve Hewitt, *Manager*
EMP: 50
SALES (corp-wide): 163.7B **Publicly Held**
SIC: 2741 Miscellaneous publishing
HQ: Ameritech Publishing, Inc.
23500 Northwestern Hwy
Southfield MI 48075
800 996-4609

(G-19076)
ARATINABOX COMPANIES INC
12910 Cleveland Ave Nw (44685-7207)
PHONE..............................330 699-3421
Chris Magoulick, *President*
Tara Magoulick, *Vice Pres*
EMP: 6
SQ FT: 1,200
SALES: 500K **Privately Held**
SIC: 2329 Athletic (warmup, sweat & jogging) suits: men's & boys'

(G-19077)
BOBIT BUSINESS MEDIA INC
Also Called: Modern Time Dealer
3515 Massillon Rd Ste 350 (44685-6217)
PHONE..............................330 899-2200
Fax: 330 899-2209
Greg Smith, *Branch Mgr*
EMP: 9
SALES (corp-wide): 29.7MM **Privately Held**
WEB: www.bobit.com
SIC: 2721 Magazines: publishing only, not printed on site
PA: Bobit Business Media Inc.
3520 Challenger St
Torrance CA 90503
310 533-2400

(G-19078)
BOMBA S CUSTOM WOODWORKING
3748 Dogwood St Nw (44685-8667)
PHONE..............................330 699-9075
Thomas Bomba, *Principal*
EMP: 4 EST: 2008
SALES (est): 461.1K **Privately Held**
SIC: 2431 Millwork

(G-19079)
CHEMSPEC LTD
Also Called: Chemspec Polymer Additives
1559 Corporate Woods Pkwy (44685-7872)
PHONE..............................330 896-0355
David Moreland, *President*
Chad Smith, *Opers Mgr*
Richard Dee, *CFO*
Richard A Dee, *Manager*
Kevin Coles, *Executive Asst*
◆ EMP: 15
SQ FT: 1,500
SALES (est): 4.6MM
SALES (corp-wide): 109.8K **Privately Held**
WEB: www.chemspecltd.com
SIC: 2891 2952 3011 Adhesives & sealants; mastic roofing composition; automobile tires, pneumatic
HQ: Safic Alcan
3 Rue Bellini
Puteaux 92800
146 926-464

(G-19080)
CHEVRON AE RESOURCES LLC
3500 Massillon Rd Ste 100 (44685-9575)
PHONE..............................330 896-8510
EMP: 24
SALES (corp-wide): 129.9B **Publicly Held**
SIC: 1311 Petroleum/Natural Gas Production
HQ: Chevron Ae Resources Llc
1000 Commerce Dr Fl 4
Pittsburgh PA 15275
800 251-0171

(G-19081)
CRABWARE LTD
3842 Park Ridge Dr (44685-9010)
PHONE..............................330 699-2305
Anna Gambol, *Mng Member*
Charles Gambol,
Rebecca Habel,
Richard Habel,
EMP: 4
SALES (est): 231.6K **Privately Held**
SIC: 7372 Application computer software

(G-19082)
DIEBOLD INCORPORATED
Also Called: North Amer Sls & Svc Ret Div
3800 Tabs Dr (44685-9564)
PHONE..............................330 899-0097
Fax: 330 896-4903
Donn Bohn, *Engineer*
James Lanza, *Human Res Dir*
John Tyler, *Branch Mgr*
Randy Gidcumb, *Program Mgr*
Joseph Altier, *Manager*
EMP: 59
SALES (corp-wide): 3.3B **Publicly Held**
WEB: www.diebold.com
SIC: 3578 Automatic teller machines (ATM)
PA: Diebold Nixdorf, Incorporated
5995 Mayfair Rd
North Canton OH 44720
330 490-4000

(G-19083)
ENVIRONMENT CHEMICAL CORP
2167 Crestwick Dr (44685)
PHONE..............................330 453-5200
Fax: 330 453-9646
Richard Morena, *President*
Dennis Morena, *Vice Pres*
EMP: 4 EST: 2014
SALES (est): 210.9K **Privately Held**
SIC: 2899 Chemical preparations

(G-19084)
FOOT LOGIC INC
2824 Sweitzer Rd (44685-8310)
PHONE..............................330 699-0123
Fax: 330 699-0158
Kathleen Kinsey, *President*
Larry Kinsey, *Vice Pres*
Jennifer Stanton, *Office Mgr*
EMP: 6
SALES: 400K **Privately Held**
WEB: www.footlogic-inc.com
SIC: 3069 3842 Orthopedic sundries, molded rubber; surgical appliances & supplies

(G-19085)
GAYDASH ENTERPRISES INC
Also Called: Gaydash Industries
3640 Tabs Dr (44685-9560)
PHONE..............................330 896-4811
Fax: 330 896-0338
Gerald Gaydash, *President*
Joan Gaydash, *Corp Secy*
Joel Gaydash, *Vice Pres*
EMP: 16
SQ FT: 15,000
SALES (est): 1.8MM **Privately Held**
SIC: 3599 Machine shop, jobbing & repair

(G-19086)
GOODRICH CORPORATION
BF Goodrich Aerospace
1555 Corporate Woods Pkwy (44685-7820)
PHONE..............................330 374-2882
Fax: 330 374-2290
Brian Bowser, *General Mgr*
Jerry Witowski, *Exec VP*
Andrew Chrostowski, *Vice Pres*
Tim Dumbauld, *Vice Pres*
Len Beard, *Engineer*
EMP: 85
SALES (corp-wide): 57.2B **Publicly Held**
WEB: www.bfgoodrich.com
SIC: 3812 Search & navigation equipment
HQ: Goodrich Corporation
2730 W Tyvola Rd
Charlotte NC 28217
704 423-7000

(G-19087)
HIGH TECH MOLD & MACHINE CO
3771 Tabs Dr (44685-9563)
PHONE..............................330 896-4466
Fax: 330 896-4645
Anthony Klisan Jr, *President*
Connie Klisan, *President*
Stephanie Klisan, *President*
Ben Klisan, *Opers Mgr*
EMP: 15
SQ FT: 15,000
SALES (est): 3.1MM **Privately Held**
WEB: www.hightechmold.com
SIC: 3544 3599 Industrial molds; machine shop, jobbing & repair

(G-19088)
KENDEE CANDLES LLC
4761 Buhl Blvd (44685-9617)
PHONE..............................330 899-9898
Kenneth Belile, *Principal*
EMP: 3
SALES (est): 211.1K **Privately Held**
SIC: 3999 Candles

(G-19089)
KOVATCH CASTINGS INC
3743 Tabs Dr (44685-9563)
PHONE..............................330 896-9944
Fax: 330 896-3444
Douglas Kovatch, *President*
Frank E Lysiak, *Vice Pres*
Laura McGee, *Engineer*
Frank Lysik, *CFO*
Bobbi Canterbury, *Sales Staff*
◆ EMP: 195
SQ FT: 65,000
SALES (est): 46.3MM **Privately Held**
WEB: www.kovatchcastings.com
SIC: 3324 3369 3366 3365 Commercial investment castings, ferrous; aerospace investment castings, ferrous; nonferrous foundries; copper foundries; aluminum foundries; steel foundries

(G-19090)
LINDE LLC
4179 Meadow Wood Ln (44685-7716)
PHONE..............................330 608-3008
Karl Kerstetter, *Manager*
EMP: 23
SALES (corp-wide): 17.9B **Privately Held**
SIC: 2813 Industrial gases
HQ: Linde Llc
200 Somerset Corporate Bl
Bridgewater NJ 08807
908 464-8100

(G-19091)
LOUIS ARTHUR STEEL COMPANY
3700 Massillon Rd Ste 360 (44685-9558)
PHONE..............................440 997-5545
Paul Miller, *Project Engr*
EMP: 3

GEOGRAPHIC

SALES (corp-wide): 11.2MM **Privately Held**
SIC: 3441 5051 3444 3443 Fabricated structural metal; steel; sheet metalwork; fabricated plate work (boiler shop)
PA: The Louis Arthur Steel Company
185 Water St
Geneva OH 44041
440 997-5545

(G-19092)
MCAFEE TOOL & DIE INC
1717 Boettler Rd (44685-9588)
PHONE..................................330 896-9555
Fax: 330 896-9549
Gary Mc Afee, *President*
Michael J Francek Jr, *Vice Pres*
Martin Labbe, *Engineer*
Ron Feldner, *Sales Associate*
Peggy Loudon, *Manager*
EMP: 35 **EST:** 1977
SQ FT: 40,000
SALES (est): 6.7MM **Privately Held**
WEB: www.mcafeetool.com
SIC: 3544 3469 Die sets for metal stamping (presses); metal stampings

(G-19093)
PLASTIC CARD INC (PA)
Also Called: Rainbow Printing
3711 Boettler Oaks Dr (44685-7733)
PHONE..................................330 896-5555
Fax: 330 896-5556
Kenneth Thompson, *President*
Rich Krauth, *Vice Pres*
Thomas Thompson, *Vice Pres*
Natasha Millard, *Design Engr*
Rose Dunn, *Human Res Mgr*
▼ **EMP:** 60
SQ FT: 24,000
SALES (est): 7.2MM **Privately Held**
WEB: www.plasticcardfactory.com
SIC: 2396 Printing & embossing on plastics fabric articles

(G-19094)
PLASTICARDS INC (PA)
Also Called: Rainbow Printing
3711 Boettler Oaks Dr (44685-7733)
PHONE..................................330 896-5555
Kenneth Thompson, *President*
Rich Crowft, *Vice Pres*
Thomas Thompson, *Vice Pres*
Patty Lou Thompson, *Admin Sec*
EMP: 46
SQ FT: 20,000
SALES (est): 3.6MM **Privately Held**
WEB: www.magnetguys.com
SIC: 3089 Identification cards, plastic

(G-19095)
PLX INDUSTRIES INC
1505 Corporate Woods Pkwy # 500
(44685-7899)
PHONE..................................330 896-7373
EMP: 4 **EST:** 2013
SALES (est): 92.8K **Privately Held**
SIC: 3999 Manufacturing industries

(G-19096)
RESOURCE AMERICA INC
3500 Massillon Rd Ste 100 (44685-9575)
PHONE..................................330 896-8510
Nancy McGurk, *Manager*
EMP: 30
SALES (corp-wide): 207.5MM **Privately Held**
SIC: 1382 1311 Oil & gas exploration services; crude petroleum & natural gas
HQ: Resource America, Inc.
1 Crescent Dr Ste 203
Philadelphia PA 19112
215 546-5005

(G-19097)
RESOURCE ENERGY INC
3500 Massillon Rd Ste 100 (44685-9575)
PHONE..................................330 896-8510
Michael L Staines, *President*
Jeffrey C Simons, *Exec VP*
Nancy J McGurk, *Treasurer*
EMP: 70

SALES (est): 5.9MM
SALES (corp-wide): 207.5MM **Privately Held**
WEB: www.resourceamerica.com
SIC: 1382 1311 Oil & gas exploration services; crude petroleum production; natural gas production
HQ: Resource America, Inc.
1 Crescent Dr Ste 203
Philadelphia PA 19112
215 546-5005

(G-19098)
SMITH INTERNATIONAL INC
2616 Country Squire St Nw (44685-9471)
PHONE..................................330 497-2999
Tom Colston, *Branch Mgr*
EMP: 5 **Privately Held**
WEB: www.smith-intl.com
SIC: 3533 Oil & gas field machinery
HQ: Smith International, Inc.
1310 Rankin Rd
Houston TX 77073
281 443-3370

(G-19099)
SMITH-FEEMAN INC
2034 Carlile Dr (44685-8856)
PHONE..................................330 434-8882
Fax: 330 434-8788
Vernon Smith, *President*
Joyce Smith, *Vice Pres*
EMP: 15
SALES (est): 1.2MM **Privately Held**
SIC: 2752 Offset & photolithographic printing

(G-19100)
STEERAMERICA INC
Also Called: Steer America
1525 Corporate Woods Pkwy
(44685-7883)
PHONE..................................330 563-4407
Satish Padmanabhan, *CEO*
R Padmanabhan, *Chairman*
Mike Millsaps, *COO*
Sue Arthur, *CFO*
Robert Roden, *Info Tech Mgr*
EMP: 13
SQ FT: 10,000
SALES: 6MM
SALES (corp-wide): 19.6MM **Privately Held**
SIC: 3452 Bolts, nuts, rivets & washers
PA: Steer Engineering Private Limited
No.290, 4th Main, 4th Phase,
Bengaluru KAR
802 372-3309

(G-19101)
SYNTHETIC RUBBER TECHNOLOGY
11021 Wright Rd Nw (44685-9476)
P.O. Box 639 (44685-0639)
PHONE..................................330 494-2221
Rodney A Rose, *President*
EMP: 5
SQ FT: 1,000
SALES (est): 580K **Privately Held**
SIC: 3087 Custom compound purchased resins

(G-19102)
TARGET THOMPSON TECHNOLOGY
3651 Apache St Nw (44685-9114)
PHONE..................................330 699-8000
Rick Thompson, *Owner*
Jesse Thompson, *VP Sales*
EMP: 7
SALES: 450K **Privately Held**
WEB: www.thompsontarget.com
SIC: 3949 Target shooting equipment

(G-19103)
TIN INDIAN PERFORMANCE
2656 Watervale Dr (44685-8354)
PHONE..................................216 214-5485
Kevin Swaney, *Principal*
EMP: 5
SALES (est): 505.3K **Privately Held**
SIC: 3356 Tin

(G-19104)
UNIONTOWN SEPTIC TANKS INC
2781 Raber Rd (44685-8125)
PHONE..................................330 699-3386
James N Kungle, *President*
Jeff Kungle, *Vice Pres*
EMP: 10 **EST:** 1965
SALES: 750K **Privately Held**
SIC: 3272 Septic tanks, concrete

Unionville Center
Union County

(G-19105)
UNIONVILLE CENTER SIGN CO
Also Called: U C Signs
110 W Main St (43077-8000)
P.O. Box 95 (43077-0095)
PHONE..................................614 873-5834
Drew Youngberg, *Owner*
EMP: 4
SALES: 200K **Privately Held**
WEB: www.ucsigns.com
SIC: 3993 Signs & advertising specialties

Uniopolis
Auglaize County

(G-19106)
EAGLE MANUFACTURING INC
88 High St (45888)
P.O. Box 215 (45888-0215)
PHONE..................................419 738-3491
Jay Sargeant, *President*
Elaine Sargeant, *Admin Sec*
EMP: 4
SQ FT: 10,000
SALES (est): 75K **Privately Held**
SIC: 3599 Machine shop, jobbing & repair

University Heights
Cuyahoga County

(G-19107)
CARBOLINE COMPANY
2379 Miramar Blvd (44118-3818)
PHONE..................................800 848-4645
EMP: 4
SALES (corp-wide): 4.8B **Publicly Held**
SIC: 3471 Cleaning, polishing & finishing
HQ: Carboline Company
2150 Schuetz Rd
Saint Louis MO 63146
314 644-1000

(G-19108)
DOAN MACHINERY & EQP CO INC
2636 S Belvoir Blvd (44118-4661)
PHONE..................................216 932-6243
Marguerite Levenson, *President*
EMP: 6 **EST:** 1976
SALES (est): 757.3K **Privately Held**
SIC: 3429 3469 Fireplace equipment, hardware: andirons, grates, screens; bottle openers, stamped metal

(G-19109)
GREAT LAKES DEFENSE SVCS LLC
2319 Miramar Blvd (44118-3818)
PHONE..................................216 272-3450
Alicia Cooney, *President*
Erika Rotko, *Vice Pres*
Christopher Cooney, *Officer*
Jonathan Rotko, *Officer*
EMP: 4
SALES (est): 159.8K **Privately Held**
SIC: 3451 Screw machine products

Upper Arlington
Franklin County

(G-19110)
AUTO DES SYS INC
3518 Riverside Dr (43221-1735)
PHONE..................................614 488-7984
Fax: 614 488-0848
Chris Yessios, *President*
David Kropp, *Vice Pres*
Mathew Holwiski, *Engineer*
Alexandra Yessios, *VP Sales*
Harold Gebel, *Sales Mgr*
EMP: 30
SQ FT: 2,000
SALES (est): 3.4MM **Privately Held**
WEB: www.autodessys.com
SIC: 7371 7372 Computer software development & applications; prepackaged software

(G-19111)
CARDINAL ENERGY GROUP INC (PA)
2665 Fairfax Dr (43220-4518)
PHONE..................................325 762-2112
Timothy W Crawford, *President*
John Jordan, *CFO*
John C May, *Admin Sec*
EMP: 5
SALES: 918.5K **Publicly Held**
SIC: 1382 Oil & gas exploration services

(G-19112)
DAILY GROWLER INC
2812 Fishinger Rd (43221-1129)
P.O. Box 218455 (43221-8455)
PHONE..................................614 656-2337
EMP: 6
SALES (est): 256.9K **Privately Held**
SIC: 2711 Newspapers, publishing & printing

(G-19113)
RANCHO ALEGRE UPPER ARLIN
3140 Kingsdale Ctr (43221-2000)
PHONE..................................614 273-1305
Linda Nunuez, *Branch Mgr*
EMP: 3 **EST:** 2013
SALES (est): 373.3K **Privately Held**
SIC: 3131 Uppers

Upper Sandusky
Wyandot County

(G-19114)
BRIDGESTONE APM COMPANY
235 Commerce Way (43351-9079)
P.O. Box 450 (43351-0450)
PHONE..................................419 294-6989
David Ackman, *Engineer*
Ben Bechstein, *Engineer*
Brent A Blair, *Engineer*
Masanori Okumura, *Engineer*
Cody Grieshop, *Electrical Engi*
EMP: 100
SALES (corp-wide): 30.1B **Privately Held**
SIC: 3061 Automotive rubber goods (mechanical)
HQ: Bridgestone Apm Company
2030 Production Dr
Findlay OH 45840
419 423-9552

(G-19115)
BRIDGESTONE APM COMPANY
Also Called: Seat Division Bridgestone
245 Commerce Way (43351-9079)
PHONE..................................419 294-6304
Fax: 419 294-6308
Fred Rechtenbach, *Principal*
Jim Lafleur, *Engineer*
EMP: 100
SALES (corp-wide): 30.1B **Privately Held**
SIC: 3061 Automotive rubber goods (mechanical)
HQ: Bridgestone Apm Company
2030 Production Dr
Findlay OH 45840
419 423-9552

▲ = Import ▼=Export
◆ =Import/Export

(G-19116)
BUCKEYE READY-MIX
6326 County Highway 61 (43351-9749)
PHONE....................................419 294-2389
Fax: 419 294-6311
Chris Mc Carthy, *Principal*
EMP: 3
SALES (est): 315.3K **Privately Held**
SIC: 3273 Ready-mixed concrete

(G-19117)
CUSTOM GLASS SOLUTIONS UPR SND
12688 State Highway 67 (43351-9411)
PHONE....................................419 294-4921
EMP: 500
SALES (est): 62.5MM
SALES (corp-wide): 27.3B **Privately Held**
SIC: 3231 Laminated glass: made from
   purchased glass; safety glass: made from
   purchased glass
HQ: Custom Glass Solutions Corp.
   2300 Harmon Rd
   Auburn Hills MI 48326
   248 340-1800

(G-19118)
DAILY CHIEF UNION
111 W Wyandot Ave (43351-1367)
P.O. Box 180 (43351-0180)
PHONE....................................419 294-2331
Fax: 419 294-5608
Jack L Barnes, *President*
Tom Martin, *Manager*
Charles G Barnes, *Admin Sec*
EMP: 15
SQ FT: 3,000
SALES (est): 779.2K
SALES (corp-wide): 8MM **Privately Held**
SIC: 2711 Newspapers, publishing & printing
HQ: Hardin County Publishing Co Inc
   201 E Columbus St
   Kenton OH 43326
   419 674-4066

(G-19119)
DESIGN & FABRICATION INC
400 Malabar Dr (43351-9747)
P.O. Box 218 (43351-0218)
PHONE....................................419 294-2414
Mike Reamer, *President*
Cathy Reamer, *Admin Sec*
EMP: 7
SQ FT: 7,200
SALES: 400K **Privately Held**
SIC: 3599 Machine shop, jobbing & repair

(G-19120)
DIAMOND ROLL-UP DOOR INC
295 Commerce Way (43351-9079)
P.O. Box 420 (43351-0420)
PHONE....................................419 294-3373
Fax: 419 294-3329
Ray Van Gunten, *President*
Matthew Baxter, *Corp Secy*
Stephani Kettels, *CFO*
Paul Sleeman, *Director*
▲EMP: 60
SQ FT: 37,500
SALES (est): 14.4MM **Privately Held**
WEB: www.diamondrollupdoor.com
SIC: 3442 Metal doors

(G-19121)
ENGINEERED WIRE PRODUCTS INC (DH)
1200 N Warpole St (43351-9093)
P.O. Box 313 (43351-0313)
PHONE....................................419 294-3817
Fax: 419 294-1019
Bradley W Evers, *Principal*
Jack Helmer, *Vice Pres*
Grafton Redfren, *VP Sales*
Pam Dyer, *Manager*
Kyle Urban, *Maintence Staff*
▲EMP: 101
SALES (est): 23.9MM
SALES (corp-wide): 1.8B **Publicly Held**
WEB: www.keystonesteel.com
SIC: 3496 3315 Miscellaneous fabricated
   wire products; steel wire & related products

HQ: Keystone Consolidated Industries, Inc.
   5430 Lyndon B Johnson Fwy # 1740
   Dallas TX 75240
   800 441-0308

(G-19122)
FARMERS COMMISSION COMPANY (HQ)
520 W Wyandot Ave (43351-1335)
P.O. Box 59 (43351-0059)
PHONE....................................419 294-2371
Fax: 419 294-6348
Eric Parthemore, *President*
Lyle Gottfried, *Treasurer*
Dan Grain, *Manager*
EMP: 22
SALES (est): 17.9MM
SALES (corp-wide): 555.7MM **Privately Held**
WEB: www.farmerscommission.com
SIC: 5191 5999 2041 Fertilizer & fertilizer
   materials; feed & farm supply; flour &
   other grain mill products
PA: Heritage Cooperative, Inc.
   11177 Township Road 133
   West Mansfield OH 43358
   419 294-2371

(G-19123)
FOUNTAIN PK INN UPPER SANDUSKY
101 Westbrook Blvd (43351-9537)
PHONE....................................419 209-1100
Sheila L Sabo, *Principal*
EMP: 3 EST: 2009
SALES (est): 188.7K **Privately Held**
SIC: 3131 Uppers

(G-19124)
HANDY TWINE KNIFE CO
5676 County Highway 330 (43351-9772)
P.O. Box 146 (43351-0146)
PHONE....................................419 294-3130
Fax: 419 294-3130
Lynn L Getz, *President*
John Tschantz, *Vice Pres*
Brian Caldwell, *Treasurer*
Nancy Caldwell, *Manager*
EMP: 9
SQ FT: 1,000
SALES: 875K **Privately Held**
WEB: www.handytwineknife.com
SIC: 3423 5719 Knives, agricultural or industrial; cutlery

(G-19125)
HOT SHOT MOTOR WORKS M LLC
555 S Warpole St Rear (43351-1549)
P.O. Box 297 (43351-0297)
PHONE....................................419 294-1997
Fax: 419 294-6997
Daniel Thompson, *Mng Member*
EMP: 3
SQ FT: 2,600
SALES (est): 220K **Privately Held**
WEB: www.hotshotmotorworks.com
SIC: 3714 5571 Motor vehicle parts & accessories; motorcycle dealers

(G-19126)
ITHACA GUN COMPANY
420 N Warpole St (43351-9301)
PHONE....................................419 294-4113
Dave Dlubak, *President*
Thomas P Killam, *Principal*
Craig Marshall, *Vice Pres*
Bryan Stoops, *Foreman/Supr*
Kevin Gottfried, *Engineer*
▼EMP: 30
SQ FT: 30,000
SALES (est): 5.4MM **Privately Held**
SIC: 3483 Ammunition, except for small arms

(G-19127)
KALMBACH FEEDS INC (PA)
7148 State Highway 199 (43351-9359)
PHONE....................................419 294-3838
Fax: 419 294-4350
Paul M Kalmbach, *President*
Dick Regnier, *CFO*
Deb Christy, *Human Res Mgr*
Sherie McClain, *Human Res Mgr*
Jason Heeter, *Admin Asst*

▲EMP: 110
SALES (est): 28.6MM **Privately Held**
SIC: 2048 Livestock feeds; poultry feeds

(G-19128)
KIRBY AND SONS INC
Also Called: Kirby Sand & Gravel
4876 County Highway 43 (43351-9155)
PHONE....................................419 927-2260
Fax: 419 927-2341
Gene Kirby, *President*
Judi Kirby, *Corp Secy*
Franklin Kirby, *Vice Pres*
Minor Kirby, *Webmaster*
EMP: 12
SALES (est): 2.5MM **Privately Held**
SIC: 1442 4212 Common sand mining;
   gravel mining; dump truck haulage

(G-19129)
LIQUI-BOX CORPORATION
519 Raybestos Dr (43351-9666)
PHONE....................................419 209-9085
Fax: 419 294-1899
EMP: 120
SQ FT: 42,000
SALES (corp-wide): 429MM **Privately Held**
SIC: 3089 3544 Mfg Plastic Molded Parts
PA: Liqui-Box Corporation
   901 E Byrd St Ste 1105
   Richmond VA 43229
   804 325-1400

(G-19130)
M-TEK INC
1111 N Warpole St (43351-9094)
PHONE....................................419 209-0399
Fax: 419 209-0599
Sam Kennedy, *Vice Pres*
Raymond England, *Production*
Rose Myers, *Buyer*
Tracy Wentling, *Buyer*
Bob Graham, *Engineer*
EMP: 600
SALES (corp-wide): 2B **Privately Held**
WEB: www.m-tek.com
SIC: 3465 3714 Moldings or trim, automobile: stamped metal; motor vehicle parts & accessories
HQ: Kasai North America, Inc.
   1020 Volunteer Pkwy
   Manchester TN 37355
   931 728-4122

(G-19131)
MAR-METAL MFG INC
Also Called: Fanci Forms
420 N Warpole St (43351-9301)
PHONE....................................419 447-1102
Floyd Marshall, *President*
Craig Marshall, *Vice Pres*
Kevin Gottfried, *Engineer*
Mark Sendelbach, *Engineer*
Emareeta Grinwold, *Manager*
EMP: 27
SQ FT: 28,000
SALES (est): 5.5MM **Privately Held**
SIC: 3544 Special dies, tools, jigs & fixtures

(G-19132)
MIDWEST OHIO TOOL CO
215 Tarhe Trl (43351-8700)
P.O. Box 269 (43351-0269)
PHONE....................................419 294-1987
Fax: 419 294-5433
Stephanie Kettels, *Principal*
Mike Ruhlen, *Vice Pres*
Mark Lewis, *Sales Staff*
Dan Wessler, *Sales Staff*
EMP: 9
SALES (est): 1.5MM **Privately Held**
SIC: 3545 Precision tools, machinists'

(G-19133)
MIDWEST SPRAY DRYING COMPANY
Also Called: Pro-Soy
422 W Guthrie Dr (43351-1154)
PHONE....................................419 294-4221
Ronald Miller, *President*
Linda Miller, *Corp Secy*
EMP: 5
SQ FT: 44,000

SALES (est): 445K **Privately Held**
SIC: 2099 Seasonings & spices

(G-19134)
NATIONAL LIME AND STONE CO
14407 Township Rd 124 (43351)
PHONE....................................419 294-3049
Fax: 419 294-9460
Michael Keckler, *Manager*
EMP: 4
SALES (corp-wide): 4B **Privately Held**
WEB: www.natlime.com
SIC: 5211 1423 Sand & gravel; crushed & broken granite
PA: The National Lime And Stone Company
   551 Lake Cascade Pkwy
   Findlay OH 45840
   419 422-4341

(G-19135)
NEUMEISTERS CANDY SHOPPE LLC
139 N Sandusky Ave (43351-1253)
PHONE....................................419 294-3647
Fax: 419 294-5702
Diana Hoover, *Manager*
EMP: 3
SALES (est): 273.5K **Privately Held**
WEB: www.neumeisterscandyshoppe.com
SIC: 5441 2064 2066 Candy; candy &
   other confectionery products; chocolate &
   cocoa products

(G-19136)
NEW EEZY-GRO INC
Also Called: Golden Eagle
9841 County Highway 49 (43351-9662)
PHONE....................................419 927-6110
Fax: 419 927-6113
Jerry Taylor, *President*
Joseph Fox, *Branch Mgr*
EMP: 17
SALES (corp-wide): 3.9B **Publicly Held**
WEB: www.eezygro.com
SIC: 2819 5261 Calcium compounds &
   salts, inorganic; fertilizer
HQ: New Eezy-Gro Inc.
   218 Toledo St
   Carey OH
   419 396-3586

(G-19137)
OLEN CORPORATION
6326 County Highway 61 (43351-9749)
PHONE....................................419 294-2611
John Miller, *Branch Mgr*
EMP: 10
SALES (corp-wide): 289.1MM **Privately Held**
SIC: 3273 5032 Ready-mixed concrete;
   stone, crushed or broken
PA: The Olen Corporation
   4755 S High St
   Columbus OH 43207
   614 491-1515

(G-19138)
OVERHEAD DOOR CORPORATION
Also Called: Todco
781 Rt 30w (43351)
PHONE....................................419 294-3874
Fax: 419 294-3017
Mike Traxler, *Manager*
EMP: 10
SALES (corp-wide): 3.1B **Privately Held**
WEB: www.overheaddoor.com
SIC: 3442 3448 2431 Garage doors,
   overhead: metal; ramps: prefabricated
   metal; doors, wood
HQ: Overhead Door Corporation
   2501 S State Hwy 121 Ste
   Lewisville TX 75067
   469 549-7100

(G-19139)
SCHMIDT MACHINE COMPANY
Also Called: S M C
7013 State Highway 199 (43351-9347)
PHONE....................................419 294-3814
Fax: 419 294-2607
Bill, *President*
Randy F Schmidt, *President*
Dorothy M Schmidt, *Principal*
Kevin Schmidt, *Vice Pres*
Darlene Mooney, *Treasurer*

GEOGRAPHIC

EMP: 50 EST: 1935
SQ FT: 2,500
SALES: 19.4MM **Privately Held**
WEB: www.schmidtmachine.com
SIC: 5083 3599 7692 Farm & garden machinery; farm equipment parts & supplies; machine shop, jobbing & repair; welding repair

(G-19140)
SHOOT A WAY INC
3305 Township Highway 47 (43351-9786)
PHONE....................................419 294-4654
John Joseph, *President*
EMP: 10
SALES (est): 1MM **Privately Held**
WEB: www.shootaway.net
SIC: 5699 3949 7389 Sports apparel; team sports equipment; advertising, promotional & trade show services

(G-19141)
SHOOT-A-WAY INC
8706 State Highway 67 (43351-9150)
PHONE....................................419 294-4654
Fax: 419 294-4029
John Joseph, *President*
Shane Adams, *Sales Staff*
Troy G Geiser, *Manager*
EMP: 14
SALES (est): 1.4MM **Privately Held**
WEB: www.shoot-a-way.com
SIC: 3949 Basketball equipment & supplies, general

(G-19142)
SUPERIOR AG-PATOKA VLLY FEED
7148 State Highway 199 (43351-9346)
PHONE....................................419 294-3838
EMP: 17
SALES: 13MM **Privately Held**
SIC: 2048 Prepared Feeds, Nec, Nsk

(G-19143)
UPPER MONUMENT
436 N Sandusky Ave (43351-1072)
PHONE....................................419 310-2387
EMP: 3
SALES (est): 165.6K **Privately Held**
SIC: 3131 Uppers

(G-19144)
UPPER SANDUSKY SENIOR HOUSING
102 Westbrook Blvd (43351-8948)
PHONE....................................419 731-4104
EMP: 3
SALES (est): 235.4K **Privately Held**
SIC: 3131 Uppers

(G-19145)
WANNEMACHER ENTERPRISES INC
Also Called: Wannemacher Packaging
422 W Guthrie Dr (43351-1154)
PHONE....................................419 771-1101
Jerry Jackson, *Director*
Sally Buchholz, *Director*
EMP: 10 EST: 2012
SALES (est): 311.7K **Privately Held**
SIC: 2099 Food preparations

Urbana
Champaign County

(G-19146)
AMERICAN PAN COMPANY (PA)
Also Called: Durashield
417 E Water St Ste 2 (43078-2178)
P.O. Box 628 (43078-0628)
PHONE....................................937 652-3232
Fax: 937 652-1384
Gilbert Bundy, *President*
Michael Cornelis, *Vice Pres*
Curt Marino, *Vice Pres*
Jason Tingley, *Vice Pres*
Jerry Rapp, *Safety Dir*
◆ EMP: 120
SQ FT: 55,800
SALES (est): 31.5MM **Privately Held**
SIC: 3469 Kitchen fixtures & equipment: metal, except cast aluminum

(G-19147)
BISSON CUSTOM PLASTIC
238 Logan St (43078-1234)
PHONE....................................937 653-4966
Delin Bolin, *President*
William Adams, *Principal*
Cindy Bolin, *Manager*
EMP: 3
SALES (est): 370.5K **Privately Held**
SIC: 3089 Plastics products

(G-19148)
BOLDMAN PRINTING LLC
1333 N Main St (43078-1027)
P.O. Box 7 (43078-0007)
PHONE....................................937 653-3431
Fax: 937 653-3314
Wanda Jones, *Owner*
EMP: 4
SQ FT: 3,100
SALES (est): 534.2K **Privately Held**
SIC: 2752 2759 2791 2789 Commercial printing, offset; letterpress printing; typesetting; bookbinding & related work

(G-19149)
BUCK CREEK PALLET
713 Muzzy Rd (43078-9685)
PHONE....................................937 653-3098
Steven Grim, *Principal*
EMP: 3
SALES (est): 288.2K **Privately Held**
SIC: 2448 Wood pallets & skids

(G-19150)
CHRIS HAUGHEY
Also Called: Cupboard Distributing
1463 S Us Highway 68 (43078-8405)
PHONE....................................937 652-3338
Fax: 937 652-3898
Chris Haughey, *Owner*
Lindsey Applegate, *Manager*
EMP: 9
SALES (est): 440K **Privately Held**
WEB: www.cdwood.com
SIC: 2511 Unassembled or unfinished furniture, household: wood

(G-19151)
CMT MACHINING & FABG LLC
1411 Knnard Kingscreek Rd (43078-9505)
P.O. Box 28 (43078-0028)
PHONE....................................937 652-3740
Ted Wallen,
EMP: 14
SQ FT: 22,000
SALES (est): 650K **Privately Held**
WEB: www.cmt-usa.com
SIC: 1761 7692 3599 3544 Sheet metalwork; welding repair; machine shop, jobbing & repair; jigs & fixtures; industrial supplies; rubber & plastics hose & beltings

(G-19152)
COLE PAK INC
1138 Phoenix Dr (43078-8203)
P.O. Box 650 (43078-0650)
PHONE....................................937 652-3910
Fax: 937 652-3602
Deborah Cole, *President*
Shannon Hackathorn, *Principal*
Patrick Maurice, *Principal*
Jason Cole, *Vice Pres*
Rick Cole, *Vice Pres*
EMP: 58
SQ FT: 113,000
SALES (est): 14.6MM **Privately Held**
WEB: www.colepak.com
SIC: 2653 2671 Partitions, solid fiber: made from purchased materials; pads, solid fiber: made from purchased materials; packaging paper & plastics film, coated & laminated

(G-19153)
COLLIERS CSTMIZING FABRICATION
1675 W County Line Rd (43078-9107)
PHONE....................................937 523-0420
Dennie Collier Sr, *Branch Mgr*
EMP: 10
SALES (corp-wide): 3.6MM **Privately Held**
SIC: 3399 Metal powders, pastes & flakes

PA: Collier's Customizing And Fabrication
1675 W County Line Rd
Urbana OH 43078
937 450-6480

(G-19154)
CONTAINER KING INC
955 Lippincott Rd (43078-8305)
PHONE....................................937 652-3087
Nolan W King, *President*
Beth Riblet, *Administration*
EMP: 4
SALES (est): 354.4K **Privately Held**
SIC: 2653 Corrugated & solid fiber boxes

(G-19155)
DANA SIGNS LLC
1052 S Main St Frnt Frnt (43078-2584)
PHONE....................................937 653-3917
James W Dees,
EMP: 3
SALES (est): 389.4K **Privately Held**
SIC: 3993 Signs & advertising specialties

(G-19156)
DAVID BRANDEBERRY
Also Called: U S Graphics
703 Miami St (43078-1909)
P.O. Box 838 (43078-0838)
PHONE....................................937 653-4680
Fax: 937 652-1079
David Brandeberry, *Owner*
EMP: 3
SQ FT: 2,300
SALES (est): 193.4K **Privately Held**
SIC: 2396 2395 Screen printing on fabric articles; pleating & stitching

(G-19157)
DESMOND-STEPHAN MFGCOMPANY
121 W Water St (43078-2048)
P.O. Box 30 (43078-0030)
PHONE....................................937 653-7181
Fax: 937 653-5511
Robert B McConnell, *President*
EMP: 24
SQ FT: 30,000
SALES (est): 5MM **Privately Held**
WEB: www.swirloff.com
SIC: 3423 Hand & edge tools

(G-19158)
GRIMES AEROSPACE COMPANY
Also Called: Honeywell
550 State Route 55 (43078-9482)
PHONE....................................937 484-2001
Rusty Chamberlain, *Materials Mgr*
Bruce Blagg, *Branch Mgr*
Linda Reese, *Executive Asst*
EMP: 300
SALES (corp-wide): 39.3B **Publicly Held**
SIC: 5088 7699 3812 3769 Aircraft & parts; aircraft & heavy equipment repair services; search & navigation equipment; guided missile & space vehicle parts & auxiliary equipment; vehicular lighting equipment
HQ: Grimes Aerospace Company
550 State Route 55
Urbana OH 43078
937 484-2000

(G-19159)
GRIMES AEROSPACE COMPANY
Also Called: Honeywell Lightning & Elec
515 N Russell St (43078-1330)
P.O. Box 247 (43078-0247)
PHONE....................................937 484-2000
Fax: 937 652-3199
Ron King, *Manager*
EMP: 150
SALES (corp-wide): 39.3B **Publicly Held**
SIC: 3728 Aircraft parts & equipment
HQ: Grimes Aerospace Company
550 State Route 55
Urbana OH 43078
937 484-2000

(G-19160)
HALL COMPANY
420 E Water St (43078-2163)
PHONE....................................937 652-1376
Fax: 937 653-7447
James A Hall, *Ch of Bd*
Kyle J Hall, *President*

Rick Hunt, *Vice Pres*
Richard J Walser, *Vice Pres*
Chris Nigh, *Purch Mgr*
EMP: 47 EST: 1954
SQ FT: 38,500
SALES (est): 9.7MM **Privately Held**
WEB: www.hallco.com
SIC: 3679 3993 3471 3444 Electronic switches; signs & advertising specialties; plating & polishing; sheet metalwork; coated & laminated paper; automotive & apparel trimmings

(G-19161)
HEIMANN MANUFACTURING CO
1140 N Main St (43078-1024)
PHONE....................................937 652-1865
Fax: 937 652-1219
Jerrel W Dunham, *President*
Jennifer Young, *Purchasing*
EMP: 5 EST: 1938
SQ FT: 5,000
SALES (est): 629.3K **Privately Held**
SIC: 3544 3542 Special dies, tools, jigs & fixtures; gear rolling machines

(G-19162)
HONEYWELL INTERNATIONAL INC
550 State Route 55 (43078-9482)
P.O. Box 247 (43078-0247)
PHONE....................................937 484-2000
Fax: 937 484-2101
Randy Marker, *Manager*
EMP: 800
SALES (corp-wide): 39.3B **Publicly Held**
WEB: www.honeywell.com
SIC: 3823 3812 3669 3491 Industrial instrmnts msrmnt display/control process variable; temperature instruments: industrial process type; controllers for process variables, all types; programmers, process type; aircraft control systems, electronic; aircraft/aerospace flight instruments & guidance systems; space vehicle guidance systems & equipment; fire alarm apparatus, electric; gas valves & parts, industrial; security control equipment & systems; auto controls regulating residntl & coml environmt & applncs; energy cutoff controls, residential or commercial types; thermostats, except built-in; humidistats: wall, duct & skeleton
PA: Honeywell International Inc.
115 Tabor Rd
Morris Plains NJ 07950
973 455-2000

(G-19163)
HUGHEY & PHILLIPS LLC
240 W Twain Ave (43078-1059)
PHONE....................................937 652-3500
Kay Nance, *General Mgr*
Amy Wolf, *Business Mgr*
Richard Finkbine, *Exec VP*
Jeff Jacobs, *Vice Pres*
Nancy Carter, *Buyer*
EMP: 50
SALES (est): 10MM **Privately Held**
SIC: 3648 Lighting equipment

(G-19164)
JACK WALTERS & SONS CORP
Also Called: Walters Buildings
5045 N Us Highway 68 (43078-9315)
PHONE....................................937 653-8986
Jerry Kauffman, *Manager*
John Martin, *Data Proc Dir*
EMP: 15
SALES (corp-wide): 28MM **Privately Held**
WEB: www.waltersbuildings.com
SIC: 3448 Prefabricated metal buildings
PA: Jack Walters & Sons, Corp.
6600 Midland Ct
Allenton WI 53002
262 629-5521

(G-19165)
JOE REES WELDING
326 W Twain Ave (43078-1061)
PHONE....................................937 652-4067
Joe Rees, *Principal*
EMP: 6
SALES: 440.9K **Privately Held**
SIC: 3441 Fabricated structural metal

(G-19166)
JOHNSON WELDED PRODUCTS INC
Also Called: J W P
625 S Edgewood Ave (43078-8600)
PHONE..........................937 652-1242
Fax: 937 653-4168
Lilli A Johnson, *President*
Clayton W Rose Jr, *Principal*
Burt Bowen, *Safety Mgr*
Steven Brandeberry, *Engineer*
Melody Lucas, *Director*
▼ EMP: 210
SQ FT: 133,000
SALES (est): 57.7MM **Privately Held**
WEB: www.jwp-inc.com
SIC: 3714 Air brakes, motor vehicle

(G-19167)
KOENIG EQUIPMENT INC
Also Called: John Deere Authorized Dealer
3130 E Us Highway 36 (43078-9736)
PHONE..........................937 653-5281
Fax: 937 653-6049
Dale Griest, *Manager*
Gregory Koenig, *Director*
EMP: 15
SALES (corp-wide): 200MM **Privately Held**
WEB: www.koenigequipment.com
SIC: 3524 5082 Lawn & garden equipment; construction & mining machinery
PA: Koenig Equipment, Inc.
15213 State Route 274
Botkins OH 45306
937 693-5000

(G-19168)
LAWNVIEW INDUSTRIES INC
1250 E Us Highway 36 (43078-8002)
P.O. Box 38147 (43078-8147)
PHONE..........................937 653-5217
Fax: 937 653-7516
Micheal Misler, *Director*
EMP: 175
SQ FT: 6,000
SALES: 48K **Privately Held**
SIC: 3999 3914 2392 2499 Plaques, picture, laminated; trophies; towels, fabric & nonwoven: made from purchased materials; surveyors' stakes, wood; packaging & labeling services; carwashes

(G-19169)
MARSHALL PLASTICS INC
590 S Edgewood Ave (43078-2603)
P.O. Box 38126 (43078-8126)
PHONE..........................937 653-4740
Henry Taylor, *President*
Richard T Ricketts, *Principal*
EMP: 9
SALES (est): 620K **Privately Held**
SIC: 3089 Blow molded finished plastic products

(G-19170)
MUMFORDS POTATO CHIPS & DELI
325 N Main St (43078-1605)
PHONE..........................937 653-3491
Fax: 937 652-0490
Randy Leopard, *Partner*
Marilyn Leopard, *Partner*
EMP: 9
SQ FT: 12,000
SALES (est): 742.5K **Privately Held**
SIC: 2096 5411 Potato chips & other potato-based snacks; delicatessens

(G-19171)
ORBIS CORPORATION
200 Elm St (43078-1975)
PHONE..........................937 652-1361
Robert G Neff, *Site Mgr*
Ted Smith, *Purch Mgr*
Tony Bowles, *Engineer*
Jill Thomas, *Director*
EMP: 280
SALES (corp-wide): 1.8B **Privately Held**
WEB: www.orbiscorporation.com
SIC: 3089 Injection molding of plastics
HQ: Orbis Corporation
1055 Corporate Center Dr
Oconomowoc WI 53066
262 560-5000

(G-19172)
PARKER TRUTEC INCORPORATED
Also Called: Nihon Company
4795 Upper Valley Pike (43078-9295)
PHONE..........................937 653-8500
Fax: 937 652-3647
Michael Kleiber, *General Mgr*
Mike REA, *Sales Staff*
Jennifer Baldwin, *Director*
EMP: 90
SALES (corp-wide): 932MM **Privately Held**
SIC: 3479 3471 2899 2851 Painting of metal products; plating & polishing; chemical preparations; paints & allied products
HQ: Parker Trutec Incorporated
4700 Gateway Blvd
Springfield OH 45502
937 323-8833

(G-19173)
PHILLIPS PACKAGING INC
1050 Phoenix Dr Unit B (43078-9547)
PHONE..........................937 484-4702
Fax: 937 484-4449
EMP: 3 **Privately Held**
SIC: 2653 Manufactures Corrugated Products
PA: Phillips Packaging, Inc
120 Fairway Dr
Wilmington OH

(G-19174)
QUEST TOOL & MACHINE LTD
1675 W County Line Rd (43078-9107)
PHONE..........................937 969-8782
Fax: 937 969-8783
Debra Young, *CEO*
Charles Young, *President*
EMP: 20
SQ FT: 22,000
SALES: 1.5MM **Privately Held**
WEB: www.questtool.com
SIC: 3544 Special dies, tools, jigs & fixtures

(G-19175)
RIBLET PACKAGING CO
955 Lippincott Rd (43078-8305)
PHONE..........................937 652-3087
Fax: 937 652-3077
Nolan King, *President*
Jared Riblet, *Treasurer*
Ben Riblet, *Manager*
EMP: 12
SQ FT: 20,000
SALES (est): 1.2MM **Privately Held**
SIC: 2653 Boxes, corrugated: made from purchased materials

(G-19176)
RITTAL CORP
1 Rittal Pl (43078-5003)
PHONE..........................937 399-0500
George Correira, *Business Mgr*
Bethany Brown, *COO*
Jeff Leake, *Vice Pres*
Jim Weist, *Vice Pres*
Lisa Myers, *Transptn Dir*
EMP: 209
SALES (corp-wide): 2.2B **Privately Held**
SIC: 3469 Metal stampings
HQ: Rittal Corp.
425 N Martingale Rd # 400
Schaumburg IL 60173
847 240-4600

(G-19177)
ROBERT ROTHSCHILD FARM LLC
Also Called: Robert Rothschild Market Cafe
3143 E Us Highway 36 (43078-9735)
PHONE..........................937 653-7397
Fax: 937 552-1044
Andy Beister, *President*
Heather Mader, *Human Res Mgr*
Mike Salyer, *IT Specialist*
Robin Louden, *Administration*
Chuck Dyment, *Representative*
▲ EMP: 45
SQ FT: 45,000

SALES (est): 16.5MM **Privately Held**
SIC: 0171 2035 2033 2032 Raspberry farm; pickles, sauces & salad dressings; canned fruits & specialties; canned specialties

(G-19178)
RUTH LEINASARS
Also Called: Urbana Machine & Tool Company
460 E Dallas Rd (43078-8430)
P.O. Box 252 (43078-0252)
PHONE..........................937 484-8542
Fax: 937 864-5145
Lottie Leinasars, *Co-Owner*
Ruth Leinasars, *Co-Owner*
EMP: 5
SQ FT: 2,400
SALES: 600K **Privately Held**
SIC: 3599 Machine shop, jobbing & repair

(G-19179)
SARICA MANUFACTURING COMPANY
240 W Twain Ave (43078-1059)
PHONE..........................937 484-4030
Tod Miller, *Engineer*
Vicki House, *Finance*
Glen Herchik, *VP Sales*
Steven M Schneider, *Mng Member*
Lin Giampetro, *Manager*
EMP: 40
SQ FT: 30,000
SALES (est): 10.8MM **Privately Held**
WEB: www.saricamfg.com
SIC: 3629 Electronic generation equipment

(G-19180)
SHAFFER MANUFACTURING CORP
Also Called: Shaffer Mixers & Proc Eqp
720 S Edgewood Ave (43078-9603)
P.O. Box 64 (43078-0064)
PHONE..........................937 652-2151
Mark Geise, *President*
Kirk Lang, *Vice Pres*
Shane Hayslett, *Project Engr*
Terry Bartsch, *VP Sales*
Marc Ferree, *Sales Engr*
▼ EMP: 50
SQ FT: 60,000
SALES (est): 18.1MM
SALES (corp-wide): 31.5MM **Privately Held**
SIC: 3556 3531 Bakery machinery; construction machinery
PA: American Pan Company
417 E Water St Ste 2
Urbana OH 43078
937 652-3232

(G-19181)
SOLVAIRA SPECIALTIES INC
Also Called: Fiber Sales & Development
1228 Muzzy Rd (43078-9685)
PHONE..........................937 652-2101
Fax: 937 652-2396
Donn Hobson, *Plant Mgr*
Dave McGill, *Branch Mgr*
EMP: 76
SALES (corp-wide): 130.8MM **Privately Held**
WEB: www.ifcfiber.com
SIC: 2823 2834 Cellulosic manmade fibers; pharmaceutical preparations
PA: Solvaira Specialties Inc.
50 Bridge St
North Tonawanda NY 14120
716 693-4040

(G-19182)
SPEEDWAY LLC
Also Called: Speedway Superamerica
725 N Main St (43078-1101)
PHONE..........................937 653-6840
Fax: 937 653-4345
Debra Johnson, *Principal*
Christina Haney, *Manager*
EMP: 3 **Publicly Held**
WEB: www.speedwaynet.com
SIC: 1311 Crude petroleum production
HQ: Speedway Llc
500 Speedway Dr
Enon OH 45323
937 864-3000

(G-19183)
TECH II INC
1765 W County Line Rd (43078)
PHONE..........................937 969-7000
Fax: 937 969-8352
Holly McCutcheon, *CFO*
Tim Peters, *VP Finance*
EMP: 270
SQ FT: 240,500
SALES (corp-wide): 28.2MM **Privately Held**
SIC: 3089 Injection molding of plastics
PA: Tech Ii, Inc.
3100 Upper Valley Pike
Springfield OH 45504
937 969-7300

(G-19184)
TECHNOLOGY PRODUCTS INC
2423 Barger Rd (43078-9129)
PHONE..........................937 653-3412
Fax: 937 653-8716
Sherry Jurgensen, *Principal*
EMP: 4
SALES: 285K **Privately Held**
SIC: 3699 3625 3613 Flight simulators (training aids), electronic; relays & industrial controls; switchgear & switchboard apparatus

(G-19185)
TRIAGE ORTHO GROUP
Also Called: Imperial Orthodontics
132 Lafayette Ave (43078-1420)
P.O. Box 549 (43078-0549)
PHONE..........................937 653-6431
Fax: 937 653-5534
Vincent Gonzalez, *Owner*
Sandra Gonzalez, *Manager*
EMP: 7
SQ FT: 8,900
SALES (est): 490K **Privately Held**
SIC: 5047 2396 Dentists' professional supplies; screen printing on fabric articles

(G-19186)
ULTRA-MET COMPANY
720 N Main St (43078-1102)
PHONE..........................937 653-7133
Brent Sheerer, *President*
Jeff Hartshorn, *President*
Jeff Fox, *Principal*
John Potuzko, *VP Mfg*
Ward Wildman, *Plant Mgr*
◆ EMP: 95 EST: 1964
SQ FT: 50,000
SALES (est): 43MM **Privately Held**
WEB: www.ultra-met.com
SIC: 3545 Cutting tools for machine tools

(G-19187)
WEIDMANN ELECTRICAL TECH INC
700 W Court St (43078-1902)
PHONE..........................937 652-1220
Laura Carneiro, *Principal*
EMP: 60
SALES (corp-wide): 376MM **Privately Held**
SIC: 3644 Insulators & insulation materials, electrical
HQ: Weidmann Electrical Technology Inc.
1 Gordon Mills Way
Saint Johnsbury VT 05819
802 748-8106

(G-19188)
WRIGHT JOHN
Also Called: W Productions
935 N Main St (43078-1005)
PHONE..........................937 653-4570
Fax: 937 653-5543
John Wright, *Owner*
EMP: 4
SALES (est): 294.3K **Privately Held**
SIC: 3993 Signs & advertising specialties

Urbancrest
Franklin County

(G-19189)
HAYDEN VALLEY FOODS INC
3150 Urbancrest Indus (43123-1767)
PHONE..........................614 539-7233
EMP: 22
SALES (corp-wide): 32MM **Privately Held**
SIC: 2032 Canned specialties
PA: Hayden Valley Foods, Inc.
3150 Urbancrest Indus Dr
Urbancrest OH 43123
614 539-7233

(G-19190)
PILKINGTON NORTH AMERICA INC
3440 Centerpoint Dr Ste C (43123-1794)
PHONE..........................419 247-3731
Richard Frampton, *Branch Mgr*
EMP: 223
SALES (corp-wide): 5.3B **Privately Held**
SIC: 3211 Flat glass; construction glass
HQ: Pilkington North America, Inc.
811 Madison Ave Fl 1
Toledo OH 43604
419 247-4955

Utica
Licking County

(G-19191)
A P PRODUCTION & SERVICE
12546 Pleasant Valley Rd (43080-9714)
PHONE..........................740 745-5317
Karen Ashcraft, *President*
EMP: 3
SALES (est): 416.5K **Privately Held**
SIC: 1311 Crude petroleum production

(G-19192)
CARDINAL CT COMPANY
140 Carey St (43080-9004)
PHONE..........................740 892-2324
EMP: 4
SALES (corp-wide): 1B **Privately Held**
SIC: 3231 Products of purchased glass
HQ: Cardinal Ct Company
775 Pririe Ctr Dr Ste 200
Eden Prairie MN 55344

(G-19193)
CATALINA TEMPERING - OHIO INC
140 Carey St (43080-9004)
PHONE..........................740 892-2324
Randy Steinberg, *President*
Michael Torres, *CFO*
Bill Ryan, *Manager*
EMP: 10
SALES: 6MM
SALES (corp-wide): 12.1MM **Privately Held**
SIC: 3231 3211 Products of purchased glass; flat glass
PA: Catalina Tempering, Inc.
1125 E Lanzit Ave
Los Angeles CA 90059
323 789-7800

(G-19194)
J & G SALES
10682 Camp Ohio Rd (43080-9717)
PHONE..........................740 745-5321
John Stemple, *Owner*
EMP: 6
SQ FT: 2,000
SALES (est): 310K **Privately Held**
SIC: 2899 Pyrotechnic ammunition: flares, signals, rockets, etc.

(G-19195)
OILER PROCESSING
Also Called: Oiler's Meat Processing
53 S Central Ave (43080-7708)
P.O. Box 501 (43080-0501)
PHONE..........................740 892-2640
Fax: 740 892-4080

Carmel L Oiler, *Partner*
Linda L Oiler, *Partner*
EMP: 4
SQ FT: 3,000
SALES (est): 368.2K **Privately Held**
SIC: 2011 4222 Meat packing plants; storage, frozen or refrigerated goods

(G-19196)
PERMANENT IMPRESSIONS
12182 Bruce Rd (43080-9484)
PHONE..........................740 892-3045
Cathy Grandstaff, *Owner*
EMP: 3
SALES: 500K **Privately Held**
WEB: www.windyhillkennel.com
SIC: 2395 Embroidery & art needlework

(G-19197)
UTICA HERALD
Also Called: Heartland Communications
60 N Main St (43080-7704)
P.O. Box 515 (43080-0515)
PHONE..........................740 892-2771
Fax: 740 892-2771
Randy Almendinger, *Owner*
James Quinif, *Consultant*
EMP: 3 **EST:** 1878
SQ FT: 3,200
SALES (est): 170K **Privately Held**
SIC: 2711 Job printing & newspaper publishing combined

(G-19198)
VALLEY PETROLEUM INC
25010 Divan Rd (43080-9634)
PHONE..........................740 668-4901
Dennis Dugan, *President*
EMP: 5
SALES (est): 340K **Privately Held**
SIC: 1311 Crude petroleum & natural gas

Valley City
Medina County

(G-19199)
AUTOMATION TOOL & DIE INC
5576 Innovation Dr (44280-9368)
PHONE..........................330 225-8336
Fax: 330 225-6015
William E Bennett, *President*
James R Bennett, *Vice Pres*
Randy Bennett, *Vice Pres*
Michelle Wedlake, *Admin Asst*
EMP: 70
SQ FT: 32,000
SALES (est): 19.2MM **Privately Held**
WEB: www.automationtd.com
SIC: 3544 Special dies & tools

(G-19200)
BOEHM PRESSED STEEL COMPANY
5440 Wegman Dr (44280-9707)
PHONE..........................330 220-8000
Fax: 330 273-9097
Robert J Boehm, *President*
William Reis, *Exec VP*
Judy Kruger, *Accountant*
Wayne Norton, *Accounts Mgr*
Diane Shepherd, *Accounts Mgr*
EMP: 50
SQ FT: 41,000
SALES (est): 14MM **Privately Held**
WEB: www.boehmstampings.com
SIC: 3469 Stamping metal for the trade

(G-19201)
CON-BELT INC
5656 Innovation Dr (44280-9370)
PHONE..........................330 273-2003
Marc Zeitler, *President*
Joe Takacs, *General Mgr*
Darlene Stone, *Controller*
Joe Takis, *Sales Mgr*
Ronald Hannis, *Manager*
EMP: 13
SALES (est): 3.2MM **Privately Held**
WEB: www.conbelt.com
SIC: 3496 Conveyor belts

(G-19202)
CUSTOM SURROUNDINGS INC
6450 Grafton Rd (44280-9762)
P.O. Box 461 (44280-0461)
PHONE..........................330 483-9020
Fax: 330 483-0017
EMP: 14
SQ FT: 25,000
SALES: 2.5MM **Privately Held**
SIC: 2541 2599 Mfg Wood Partitions/Fixtures Mfg Furniture/Fixtures

(G-19203)
EMH INC (PA)
Also Called: Engineered Material Handling
550 Crane Dr (44280-9361)
PHONE..........................330 220-8600
Fax: 330 220-0204
Edis Hazne, *President*
Dave Comiono, *Vice Pres*
Jeff Larouche, *Opers Mgr*
Greg Meyer, *Purch Mgr*
Chris Denison, *Accounts Mgr*
◆ **EMP:** 40
SQ FT: 65,000
SALES (est): 8.9MM **Privately Held**
WEB: www.emh-inc.com
SIC: 3536 8711 3441 Cranes & monorail systems; hoists; engineering services; fabricated structural metal

(G-19204)
FUSERASHI INTL TECH INC
Also Called: F I T
5401 Innovation Dr (44280-9353)
PHONE..........................330 273-0140
Fax: 330 273-0718
Mamoru Shimada, *Principal*
Hal Wagoner, *Plant Mgr*
Frank Oliver, *QC Mgr*
Jeff Wiseman, *QC Mgr*
Kazuyoshi Fujiiu, *Engineer*
▲ **EMP:** 22 **EST:** 1996
SQ FT: 200,000
SALES (est): 9.4MM
SALES (corp-wide): 268.8MM **Privately Held**
WEB: www.fitinc.net
SIC: 3465 Automotive stampings; body parts, automobile: stamped metal
PA: Fuserashi Co., Ltd.
11-74, Takaida
Higashi-Osaka OSK 577-0
667 897-121

(G-19205)
GOOSEFOOT ACRES INC (PA)
Also Called: Goosefoot Acres Cntr For
5879 Center Rd (44280-9315)
P.O. Box 446 (44280-0446)
PHONE..........................330 225-7184
Peter Gail, *President*
Karin Reale, *Corp Secy*
Dominick Reale, *COO*
Wilma Gail, *Vice Pres*
▲ **EMP:** 4
SALES: 2MM **Privately Held**
WEB: www.dandyblend.com
SIC: 2833 5122 Caffeine & derivatives; medicinals & botanicals

(G-19206)
HY-PRODUCTION INC
6000 Grafton Rd (44280-9330)
PHONE..........................330 273-2400
Fax: 330 273-6602
William Kneebusch, *Ch of Bd*
Mathew Roach, *President*
Keith Koprowski, *Vice Pres*
Jim Dorrance, *Purch Agent*
Eugene Waller, *QA Dir*
▲ **EMP:** 124
SQ FT: 60,000
SALES (est): 31.2MM **Privately Held**
WEB: www.hy-production.com
SIC: 3519 3492 3451 3594 Engines, diesel & semi-diesel or dual-fuel; control valves, fluid power: hydraulic & pneumatic; screw machine products; fluid power pumps & motors; machine shop, jobbing & repair

(G-19207)
INDEPENDENT STEEL COMPANY LLC
615 Liverpool Dr (44280-9717)
P.O. Box 472 (44280-0472)
PHONE..........................330 225-7741
Fax: 330 273-6265
Mark Schwertner, *President*
Mark A Schwertner, *Vice Pres*
Esther Stacey, *Controller*
John F Krupinski, *Mng Member*
Kirsten Alonso, *Manager*
▲ **EMP:** 50 **EST:** 1957
SQ FT: 110,000
SALES (est): 26.1MM **Privately Held**
WEB: www.independentsteel.com
SIC: 5051 7389 3316 Steel; metal cutting services; cold finishing of steel shapes
PA: Esmark Steel Group, Llc
2500 Euclid Ave
Chicago Heights IL 60411

(G-19208)
JOSEPH ADAMS CORP
5740 Grafton Rd (44280-9327)
P.O. Box 583 (44280-0583)
PHONE..........................330 225-9125
Fax: 330 225-9105
Patrick Adams, *President*
▲ **EMP:** 10
SQ FT: 100,000
SALES (est): 1.2MM **Privately Held**
SIC: 2087 2833 Flavoring extracts & syrups; botanical products, medicinal: ground, graded or milled

(G-19209)
KRISDALE INDUSTRIES INC
649 Marks Rd (44280-9774)
PHONE..........................330 225-2392
Fax: 330 273-2326
Glenn D Phelan, *President*
EMP: 6
SALES (est): 758.1K **Privately Held**
WEB: www.krisdale.com
SIC: 3544 Jigs & fixtures; special dies & tools

(G-19210)
LIVERPOOL COIL PROCESSING INC
Also Called: Liverpool-Coil-Processing
880 Steel Dr (44280-9310)
PHONE..........................330 558-2600
Fax: 330 558-2666
Theodore Zampetis, *President*
James Fanello, *Vice Pres*
Robert Grissinger, *Treasurer*
David J Hessler, *Admin Sec*
EMP: 101
SQ FT: 223,000
SALES (est): 17.1MM
SALES (corp-wide): 1B **Publicly Held**
WEB: www.shiloh.com
SIC: 3312 Blast furnaces & steel mills
PA: Shiloh Industries, Inc.
880 Steel Dr
Valley City OH 44280
330 558-2600

(G-19211)
LIVERPOOL TOWNSHIP
6700 Center Rd (44280-9435)
P.O. Box 381 (44280-0381)
PHONE..........................330 483-4747
Cathy Keller, *Vice Chairman*
Dale Vasel, *Branch Mgr*
EMP: 7 **Privately Held**
SIC: 3531 9111 Road construction & maintenance machinery; mayors' offices
PA: Liverpool Township
6801 School St
Valley City OH 44280
330 483-3102

(G-19212)
MACK CONCRETE INDUSTRIES INC (HQ)
201 Columbia Rd (44280-9706)
P.O. Box 335 (44280-0335)
PHONE..........................330 483-3111
Richard W Mack, *President*
Betsy Mack, *President*
Barbara Mack, *Corp Secy*
Jim Thompson, *Vice Pres*

Dave Arnold, *Purchasing*
EMP: 12
SQ FT: 20,000
SALES (est): 4.9MM
SALES (corp-wide): 160.1MM **Privately Held**
SIC: 3273 Ready-mixed concrete
PA: Mack Industries, Inc.
 1321 Industrial Pkwy N # 500
 Brunswick OH 44212
 330 460-7005

(G-19213)
MACK INDUSTRIES PA INC (HQ)
201 Columbia Rd (44280-9706)
P.O. Box 335 (44280-0335)
PHONE..................................330 483-3111
Betsy Mack, *President*
Barbara Mack, *Treasurer*
EMP: 100 **EST:** 1952
SQ FT: 7,000
SALES (est): 28.8MM
SALES (corp-wide): 160.1MM **Privately Held**
SIC: 3272 Concrete products, precast
PA: Mack Industries, Inc.
 1321 Industrial Pkwy N # 500
 Brunswick OH 44212
 330 460-7005

(G-19214)
MACK READY MIX CONCRETE INC
201 Columbia Rd (44280-9706)
P.O. Box 335 (44280-0335)
PHONE..................................330 483-3111
Betsy Nesteca, *President*
Richard W Mack, *President*
Barbara Mack, *Corp Secy*
EMP: 5
SQ FT: 40,000
SALES (est): 428.9K
SALES (corp-wide): 160.1MM **Privately Held**
SIC: 3272 1623 Concrete products used to facilitate drainage; sewer line construction
PA: Mack Industries, Inc.
 1321 Industrial Pkwy N # 500
 Brunswick OH 44212
 330 460-7005

(G-19215)
MARTANS FOODS
6460 Grafton Rd (44280-9762)
PHONE..................................330 483-9009
Stephan Kormoczy, *Principal*
EMP: 4
SALES (est): 138.3K **Privately Held**
SIC: 2051 Bread, cake & related products

(G-19216)
MATTHEW KOSTER
Also Called: Servepro of Parma
720 Marks Rd Ste C (44280-9797)
P.O. Box 30008, Parma (44130-0008)
PHONE..................................440 887-9000
Matthew Koster, *Owner*
EMP: 6 **EST:** 2011
SALES (est): 260K **Privately Held**
SIC: 2759 Commercial printing

(G-19217)
MEDINA BLANKING INC (DH)
5580 Wegman Dr (44280-9321)
PHONE..................................330 558-2300
Fax: 330 558-2347
Ted Zampetis, *President*
Ray Love, *Director*
David J Hessler, *Admin Sec*
EMP: 150
SQ FT: 200,000
SALES (est): 16.7MM
SALES (corp-wide): 1B **Publicly Held**
SIC: 3325 3545 3469 Steel foundries; machine tool accessories; metal stampings
HQ: Shiloh Corporation
 880 Steel Dr
 Valley City OH 44280
 330 558-2600

(G-19218)
MIXED LOGIC LLC
5907 E Law Rd (44280-9770)
PHONE..................................440 826-1676

Kevin Borrowman, *Mng Member*
EMP: 7
SALES (est): 584.5K **Privately Held**
WEB: www.mixedlogic.com
SIC: 3699 5999 Electric sound equipment; electronic parts & equipment

(G-19219)
MTD CONSUMER GROUP INC (DH)
5965 Grafton Rd (44280-9329)
PHONE..................................330 225-2600
Steven E Pryatel, *Principal*
▼ **EMP:** 11
SALES (est): 188.3MM
SALES (corp-wide): 2.8B **Privately Held**
SIC: 3524 Lawn & garden tractors & equipment
HQ: Mtd Products Inc
 5965 Grafton Rd
 Valley City OH 44280
 330 225-2600

(G-19220)
MTD HOLDINGS INC (PA)
5965 Grafton Rd (44280-9329)
P.O. Box 368022, Cleveland (44136-9722)
PHONE..................................330 225-2600
Curtis E Moll, *Ch of Bd*
Jason Belsito, *Opers Mgr*
Jeff Deuch, *Treasurer*
Connie Buzek, *Administration*
◆ **EMP:** 500
SALES (est): 2.8B **Privately Held**
SIC: 3524 3544 3469 6141 Lawn & garden equipment; lawnmowers, residential: hand or power; special dies & tools; metal stampings; financing: automobiles, furniture, etc., not a deposit bank

(G-19221)
MTD LLC
5903 Grafton Rd (44280-9329)
P.O. Box 368022, Strongsville (44136-9722)
PHONE..................................800 269-6215
Micah Wolf, *Electrical Engi*
Mark Krecicki, *VP Sales*
Joanne Beganyi, *Sales Mgr*
Jeff Salamon, *Mktg Dir*
Ralph Heysek, *Manager*
EMP: 3
SALES (est): 66K **Privately Held**
SIC: 3524 Lawn & garden equipment

(G-19222)
MTD PRODUCTS INC (HQ)
5965 Grafton Rd (44280-9329)
P.O. Box 368022, Cleveland (44136-9722)
PHONE..................................330 225-2600
Fax: 330 273-7190
Robert T Moll, *CEO*
Jean Hlay, *President*
Blair Cook, *General Mgr*
Gary Siefring, *General Mgr*
Ian Rogers, *Regional Mgr*
◆ **EMP:** 500 **EST:** 1932
SQ FT: 180,000
SALES (est): 2.8B
SALES (corp-wide): 2.8B **Privately Held**
WEB: www.mtdproducts.com
SIC: 3524 Lawn & garden equipment; lawnmowers, residential: hand or power
PA: Mtd Holdings Inc
 5965 Grafton Rd
 Valley City OH 44280
 330 225-2600

(G-19223)
MTD PRODUCTS INC
Industrial Plastics Co Div
680 Liverpool Dr (44280-9717)
P.O. Box 360585, Cleveland (44136-0045)
PHONE..................................330 225-9127
Fax: 330 225-9332
Mark Tyson, *Principal*
Rita Bodey, *Purch Mgr*
Joseph Schilens, *Mktg Dir*
James Leary, *Manager*
EMP: 320
SQ FT: 90,000
SALES (corp-wide): 2.8B **Privately Held**
WEB: www.mtdproducts.com
SIC: 3524 Lawnmowers, residential: hand or power

HQ: Mtd Products Inc
 5965 Grafton Rd
 Valley City OH 44280
 330 225-2600

(G-19224)
MTD PRODUCTS INC
Also Called: Mtd Consumer Products Supply
5903 Grafton Rd (44280-9329)
P.O. Box 368022, Cleveland (44136-9722)
PHONE..................................330 225-1940
Mike Flatt, *Division Mgr*
Ja Rainone, *Principal*
Mickey Leech, *Vice Pres*
Bruce Steenberg, *Draft/Design*
Steven Weiler, *Draft/Design*
EMP: 402
SALES (corp-wide): 2.8B **Privately Held**
WEB: www.mtdproducts.com
SIC: 3524 Lawn & garden equipment
HQ: Mtd Products Inc
 5965 Grafton Rd
 Valley City OH 44280
 330 225-2600

(G-19225)
NORTHLAKE STEEL CORPORATION
5455 Wegman Dr (44280-9707)
PHONE..................................330 220-7717
Fax: 330 220-7718
William K Bissett, *CEO*
Craig O Curie, *President*
Bill Bissett, *Plant Mgr*
Brad Mackenzie, *Prdtn Mgr*
Luke Heinz, *Controller*
▲ **EMP:** 80
SQ FT: 82,000
SALES (est): 24.8MM **Privately Held**
WEB: www.northlakesteelcorp.com
SIC: 3398 3312 Annealing of metal; bar, rod & wire products; bars & bar shapes, steel, cold-finished: own hot-rolled; rods, iron & steel: made in steel mills

(G-19226)
OLIVER SIGNS & GRAPHICS
5880 Myrtle Hill Rd (44280-9724)
P.O. Box 1186, Brunswick (44212-8686)
PHONE..................................330 460-2996
John Oliver, *President*
EMP: 5
SALES (est): 388.2K **Privately Held**
WEB: www.oliversigns.com
SIC: 3993 Signs & advertising specialties

(G-19227)
RAF ACQUISITION CO
Also Called: Republic Anode Fabricators
5478 Grafton Rd (44280-9719)
PHONE..................................440 572-5999
Mike Horonzy, *President*
Michael H Horonzy, *COO*
Jamie O'Conner, *Assistant*
EMP: 15
SQ FT: 20,000
SALES (est): 2.1MM **Privately Held**
WEB: www.repanode.com
SIC: 3471 3479 Chromium plating of metals or formed products; coating of metals & formed products

(G-19228)
S K M L INC
Also Called: Stretcher Pad Company, The
580 Liverpool Dr (44280-9335)
PHONE..................................330 220-7565
Susie Lindenmuth, *President*
David Lindenmuth, *Vice Pres*
Mark Lindenmuth, *Vice Pres*
EMP: 6 **EST:** 1928
SQ FT: 6,000
SALES (est): 1MM **Privately Held**
WEB: www.stretcherpads.com
SIC: 3842 Stretchers

(G-19229)
SCHAEFFLER GROUP USA INC
5370 Wegman Dr (44280-9700)
PHONE..................................330 273-4383
Bruce G Warmbold, *President*
Lisa Aycock, *Warehouse Mgr*
Gabe Vajda, *Engineer*
Rouven Daniel, *Mktg Dir*
Cem Ersahin, *Manager*
EMP: 342

HQ: Mtd Products Inc
 5965 Grafton Rd
 Valley City OH 44280
 330 225-2600

SALES (corp-wide): 56.1B **Privately Held**
WEB: www.ina.com
SIC: 3562 Roller bearings & parts
HQ: Schaeffler Group Usa Inc.
 308 Springhill Farm Rd
 Fort Mill SC 29715
 803 548-8500

(G-19230)
SHILOH AUTOMOTIVE INC
Also Called: Liverpool Manufacturing
880 Steel Dr (44280-9736)
PHONE..................................330 558-2600
Theodore K Zapetis, *President*
Theodore K Zampetis, *President*
Robert J King, *Director*
EMP: 32
SALES (est): 4.8MM
SALES (corp-wide): 1B **Publicly Held**
SIC: 3469 3544 Metal stampings; special dies, tools, jigs & fixtures
PA: Shiloh Industries, Inc.
 880 Steel Dr
 Valley City OH 44280
 330 558-2600

(G-19231)
SHILOH CORPORATION (HQ)
Also Called: Mansfield Blanking Div
880 Steel Dr (44280-9736)
PHONE..................................330 558-2600
Fax: 419 522-2275
Robert Grissinger, *President*
G Loesch, *Exec VP*
Rick Perfetta, *Manager*
David J Hessler, *Admin Sec*
EMP: 335 **EST:** 1950
SQ FT: 275,000
SALES (est): 107.2MM
SALES (corp-wide): 1B **Publicly Held**
SIC: 3469 3544 Metal stampings; special dies & tools
PA: Shiloh Industries, Inc.
 880 Steel Dr
 Valley City OH 44280
 330 558-2600

(G-19232)
SHILOH INDUSTRIES INC
5580 Wegman Dr (44280-9321)
PHONE..................................330 558-2300
Jeff Malik, *Manager*
EMP: 50
SALES (corp-wide): 1B **Publicly Held**
SIC: 3465 Automotive stampings
PA: Shiloh Industries, Inc.
 880 Steel Dr
 Valley City OH 44280
 330 558-2600

(G-19233)
SHILOH INDUSTRIES INC
Ohio Welded Blank
5569 Innovation Dr (44280-9369)
PHONE..................................330 558-2000
Fax: 330 558-2071
Jeff Greene, *Vice Pres*
Daniel Brown, *Manager*
EMP: 600
SALES (corp-wide): 1B **Publicly Held**
WEB: www.shiloh.com
SIC: 3465 Automotive stampings
PA: Shiloh Industries, Inc.
 880 Steel Dr
 Valley City OH 44280
 330 558-2600

(G-19234)
SHILOH INDUSTRIES INC (PA)
880 Steel Dr (44280-9736)
PHONE..................................330 558-2600
Ramzi Y Hermiz, *President*
Kenton Bednarz, *President*
Rich Green, *General Mgr*
Gary Dethomas, *Vice Pres*
Marek Szkiladz, *Engineer*
◆ **EMP:** 4
SALES: 1B **Publicly Held**
WEB: www.shiloh.com
SIC: 3465 3469 3544 Automotive stampings; metal stampings; special dies & tools

---

(G-19235)
SHILOH INDUSTRIES INC
880 Steel Dr (44280-9736)
PHONE...................................330 558-2600
Fax: 216 265-4244
Shyam Rajagopal, *General Mgr*
John R Walker, *Vice Pres*
Stephen J Tomasko, *Human Resources*
Richard Greene, *Manager*
EMP: 799
SALES (corp-wide): 1B **Publicly Held**
WEB: www.shiloh.com
SIC: 3465 3469 3544 Automotive stamp-
ings; metal stampings; special dies &
tools
PA: Shiloh Industries, Inc.
880 Steel Dr
Valley City OH 44280
330 558-2600

(G-19236)
**SUBURBAN ELECTRONICS
ASSEMBLY**
7877 Grafton Rd (44280-9559)
PHONE...................................330 483-4077
EMP: 3 EST: 2004
SQ FT: 2,327
SALES: 400K **Privately Held**
SIC: 3679 Mfg Electronic Components

(G-19237)
WEBB-STILES COMPANY (PA)
Also Called: WEBB-STILES OF ALABAMA
675 Liverpool Dr (44280-9717)
P.O. Box 464 (44280-0464)
PHONE...................................330 225-7761
Fax: 330 225-5532
Donald G Stiles Jr, *President*
Sandra Matthews, *Corp Secy*
Larry Birchler, *Vice Pres*
Michael Davis, *Vice Pres*
Matt Weismann, *Vice Pres*
▲ EMP: 90
SQ FT: 140,000
SALES: 30.6MM **Privately Held**
WEB: www.webb-stiles.com
SIC: 3535 3536 3568 3537 Conveyors &
conveying equipment; monorail systems;
power transmission equipment; industrial
trucks & tractors

(G-19238)
ZION INDUSTRIES INC (PA)
6229 Grafton Rd (44280-9312)
PHONE...................................330 225-3246
Fax: 330 483-3942
Bob Puls, *President*
Dorothy Puls, *Corp Secy*
Micheal Laheta, *Vice Pres*
Randy Lane, *Vice Pres*
Nino Mascioli, *Controller*
EMP: 90 EST: 1977
SQ FT: 16,600
SALES: 11MM **Privately Held**
SIC: 3398 Metal heat treating; brazing
(hardening) of metal

Van Buren
Hancock County

(G-19239)
BENA INC
1390 Township Road 229 (45889-9603)
P.O. Box 77 (45889-0077)
PHONE...................................419 299-3313
Fax: 419 299-3313
Gary Benjamin, *Principal*
Barbara Benjamin, *Corp Secy*
Keith Benjamin, *Vice Pres*
EMP: 9
SQ FT: 5,000
SALES: 1MM **Privately Held**
WEB: www.benainc.com
SIC: 3089 Plastic processing

(G-19240)
**NOSTER RUBBER COMPANY
INC**
1481 Township Road 229 (45889-9603)
P.O. Box 227 (45889-0227)
PHONE...................................419 299-3387
Fax: 419 299-3865
Jeff Wills, *President*

EMP: 12
SQ FT: 20,000
SALES: 2MM **Privately Held**
SIC: 3069 Molded rubber products

Van Wert
Van Wert County

(G-19241)
**ADVANCED BIOLOGICAL MKTG
INC**
375 Bonnewitz Ave (45891-1101)
P.O. Box 222 (45891-0222)
PHONE...................................419 232-2461
Fax: 419 232-4664
Dan Custis, *President*
Leon Bird, *Vice Pres*
Curtis Gordon, *Vice Pres*
Terry Roush, *Vice Pres*
Nicole Gordon, *CFO*
EMP: 14 EST: 2000
SQ FT: 3,500
SALES (est): 3.8MM **Privately Held**
WEB: www.abm1st.com
SIC: 2879 0116 Insecticides & pesticides;
soybeans

(G-19242)
AEROQUIP CORP
1225 W Main St (45891-9362)
PHONE...................................419 238-1190
Fax: 419 238-6833
Don Waggener, *Principal*
EMP: 8
SALES (est): 834.4K **Privately Held**
SIC: 3052 Rubber & plastics hose & belt-
ings

(G-19243)
ALLIANCE AUTOMATION LLC
560 Bonnewitz Ave (45891-1188)
PHONE...................................419 238-2520
Michael Fiedler, *Mng Member*
Tara Reed, *Manager*
Chet Wenninger, *Manager*
Kathleen Fiedler,
Doug Wenninger,
EMP: 13
SALES (est): 4.4MM **Privately Held**
WEB: www.fiedlerelectrical.com
SIC: 3599 Custom machinery

(G-19244)
B M DS FISH N MORE LLC
Also Called: Main Street Ice Cream Parlor
121 South Ave (45891-2350)
PHONE...................................419 238-2722
Marvin Vetter, *Principal*
EMP: 12
SALES (est): 1MM **Privately Held**
SIC: 2024 Ice cream & frozen desserts

(G-19245)
BLUE BELL BIO-MEDICAL INC
1260 Industrial Dr (45891-2433)
PHONE...................................419 238-4442
Fax: 419 238-0226
David R Thompson, *President*
Brandon Miller, *Marketing Staff*
Susan Saam, *Manager*
Suzanne McClure, *Technology*
EMP: 3
SQ FT: 670,000
SALES: 2MM **Privately Held**
WEB: www.bluebellcarts.com
SIC: 3841 Surgical & medical instruments

(G-19246)
BRAUN INDUSTRIES INC
1170 Production Dr (45891-9391)
PHONE...................................419 232-7020
Fax: 419 232-7020
Phillip C Braun, *Ch of Bd*
Kim Elick, *President*
Kimberly Elick, *General Mgr*
Scott Braun, *Senior VP*
Gary Kohls, *Vice Pres*
EMP: 250 EST: 1959
SQ FT: 160,000
SALES (est): 66.1MM **Privately Held**
WEB: www.braunambulances.com
SIC: 3711 Ambulances (motor vehicles),
assembly of

(G-19247)
BUDD CO PLASTICS DIV
1276 Industrial Dr (45891-2466)
PHONE...................................419 238-4332
Fax: 419 238-5734
Frank Macher, *Principal*
EMP: 3
SALES (est): 310.3K **Privately Held**
SIC: 3089 Plastics products

(G-19248)
CONTINENTAL STRL PLAS INC
Also Called: CSP Van Wert
1276 Industrial Dr (45891-2433)
PHONE...................................419 238-4628
Cindy Schlatter, *Opers Mgr*
Nick Greenland, *Engineer*
Gerry Williams, *Engineer*
Tom Harth, *Branch Mgr*
Michael Stump, *Manager*
EMP: 285
SALES (corp-wide): 6.7B **Privately Held**
WEB: www.cs-plastics.com
SIC: 3089 3714 Plastic processing; motor
vehicle parts & accessories
HQ: Continental Structural Plastics, Inc.
255 Rex Blvd
Auburn Hills MI 48326
248 237-7800

(G-19249)
COOL MACHINES INC
740 Fox Rd (45891-2441)
PHONE...................................419 232-4871
David Krendl, *President*
Carlos Usuda, *Treasurer*
Rebecca Schulte, *Human Res Dir*
Ellen Ditto, *Office Mgr*
Andrew Schulte, *Admin Sec*
EMP: 14
SQ FT: 40,000
SALES: 3MM **Privately Held**
WEB: www.coolmachines.com
SIC: 3532 Mining machinery

(G-19250)
COOPER FOODS
Also Called: Cooper Farms Cooked Meat
6893 Us Route 127 (45891)
PHONE...................................419 232-2440
Fax: 419 238-1587
Debra Bashore, *Superintendent*
Paula Fleming, *Principal*
Greg Cooper, *Plant Mgr*
Matthew Barricklow, *Safety Mgr*
Duaine Hampton, *QC Mgr*
EMP: 34 EST: 2009
SALES (est): 6.6MM **Privately Held**
SIC: 2015 Poultry slaughtering & process-
ing

(G-19251)
COOPER HATCHERY INC
Also Called: Cooper Farms Cooked Meats
6793 Us Route 127 (45891-9601)
PHONE...................................419 238-4869
Henry Dues, *Facilities Mgr*
Mike Parker, *Mfg Spvr*
Greg Miller, *Marketing Staff*
Eric Ludwig, *Branch Mgr*
Krista Schroeder, *Manager*
EMP: 130
SALES (corp-wide): 316.9MM **Privately
Held**
WEB: www.cooperfarm.com
SIC: 2015 Poultry slaughtering & process-
ing; poultry slaughtering & processing;
turkey processing & slaughtering
PA: Cooper Hatchery, Inc.
22348 Road 140
Oakwood OH 45873
419 594-3325

(G-19252)
CQT KENNEDY LLC
Also Called: CORNWELL QUALITY TOOLS
1260 Industrial Dr (45891-2433)
PHONE...................................419 238-2442
Raymond Moeller, *President*
George Garifalis, *General Mgr*
Kenneth Wise, *Vice Pres*
Dana Sealscott, *Plant Mgr*
Toni Rose, *Senior Buyer*
EMP: 95
SQ FT: 190,000

SALES: 2.8MM
SALES (corp-wide): 151.2MM **Privately
Held**
SIC: 3469 3841 Boxes: tool, lunch, mail,
etc.: stamped metal; surgical & medical
instruments
PA: The Cornwell Quality Tools Company
667 Seville Rd
Wadsworth OH 44281
330 336-3506

(G-19253)
EATON CORPORATION
Also Called: Mobile Operations
1225 W Main St (45891-9362)
PHONE...................................419 238-1190
Sharon McGuire, *General Mgr*
Dave Abel, *Vice Pres*
Laura Almazan, *Plant Mgr*
Greg Stansake, *Facilities Mgr*
Dave Warnecke, *Purch Mgr*
EMP: 900 **Privately Held**
WEB: www.eaton.com
SIC: 3052 3429 Rubber hose; clamps &
couplings, hose
HQ: Eaton Corporation
1000 Eaton Blvd
Cleveland OH 44122
216 523-5000

(G-19254)
EATON HYDRAULICS LLC
1225 W Main St (45891-9362)
PHONE...................................419 232-7777
Jeffrey Card, *Branch Mgr*
EMP: 21 **Privately Held**
WEB: www.aeroquip-vickers.com
SIC: 3542 3594 3052 3492 Crimping ma-
chinery, metal; fluid power pumps; rubber
hose; hose & tube fittings & assemblies,
hydraulic/pneumatic; power transmission
equipment; aircraft parts & equipment
HQ: Eaton Hydraulics Llc
14615 Lone Oak Rd
Eden Prairie MN 55344
952 937-9800

(G-19255)
EATON-AEROQUIP LLC
Also Called: Eaton Global Hose
1225 W Main St (45891-9362)
PHONE...................................419 238-1190
Steve Brown, *Engineer*
Carey Welker, *Branch Mgr*
Ken Stocklin, *Prgrmr*
EMP: 100 **Privately Held**
SIC: 3052 3492 3429 Rubber hose; plas-
tic hose; hose & tube fittings & assem-
blies, hydraulic/pneumatic; clamps &
couplings, hose; clamps, metal
HQ: Eaton-Aeroquip Llc.
1000 Eaton Blvd
Cleveland OH 44122
216 523-5000

(G-19256)
**EISENHAUER MANUFACTURING
CO**
409 Center St (45891-1135)
P.O. Box 390 (45891-0390)
PHONE...................................419 238-0081
Fax: 419 238-3294
Leigh Eisenhauer Jr, *General Ptnr*
Jim Russell, *General Ptnr*
Cindy Ramsey, *Manager*
EMP: 23 EST: 1944
SQ FT: 50,000
SALES: 4MM **Privately Held**
SIC: 3469 Stamping metal for the trade

(G-19257)
**FEDERAL-MOGUL
CORPORATION**
150 Fisher Ave (45891-1409)
PHONE...................................419 238-1053
Fax: 419 238-5065
Nancy Dohoney, *Purchasing*
Tom Wettig, *QC Dir*
Sean Ford, *Engineer*
Bruce Linn, *Engineer*
Mike Ellerbrock, *Finance Dir*
EMP: 730
SALES (corp-wide): 16.3B **Publicly Held**
SIC: 3053 Oil seals, rubber

▲ = Import　▼=Export
◆ =Import/Export

HQ: Federal-Mogul Corporation
27300 W 11 Mile Rd
Southfield MI 48034
248 354-7700

(G-19258)
GLOBAL PRECISION PARTS INC
7600 Us Route 127 (45891-9363)
PHONE..........................260 563-9030
James A Butz, *Principal*
EMP: 6
SALES (est): 1.1MM **Privately Held**
SIC: 3451 Screw machine products

(G-19259)
GREIF INC
975 Glenn St (45891-2331)
PHONE..........................419 238-0565
Rick Ray, *Plant Mgr*
Greg Wagner, *Human Res Dir*
Daniel Hynes, *Train & Dev Mgr*
Bill Wolverton, *Train & Dev Mgr*
Doug Benner, *Manager*
EMP: 48
SALES (corp-wide): 3.3B **Publicly Held**
WEB: www.greif.com
SIC: 2655 Drums, fiber: made from pur-
chased material
PA: Greif, Inc.
425 Winter Rd
Delaware OH 43015
740 549-6000

(G-19260)
INK AGAIN
115 N Washington St (45891-1705)
PHONE..........................419 232-4465
Dennis Cummings, *Owner*
EMP: 4 **EST:** 2008
SALES (est): 406.6K **Privately Held**
SIC: 3861 Printing equipment, photo-
graphic

(G-19261)
KAM MANUFACTURING INC
1197 Grill Rd (45891-9387)
PHONE..........................419 238-6037
Fax: 419 238-3489
Kim Adams, *Owner*
Stacey Crowle, *Manager*
EMP: 150
SQ FT: 5,500
SALES (est): 9.6MM **Privately Held**
WEB: www.kammfg.com
SIC: 2331 2329 3161 Women's & misses'
blouses & shirts; men's & boys' sports-
wear & athletic clothing; luggage

(G-19262)
KEDAR D ARMY
Also Called: Briarwood Manufacturing
11373 Van Wert Decatur Rd (45891-8401)
PHONE..........................419 238-6929
Fax: 419 238-9916
Kedar D Army, *Owner*
EMP: 4
SALES (est): 323.8K **Privately Held**
SIC: 6512 6515 3799 7692 Nonresiden-
tial building operators; mobile home site
operators; recreational vehicles; welding
repair; fabricated structural metal

(G-19263)
**LEESBURG LOOMS
INCORPORATED**
Also Called: Leesburg Loom & Supply
201 N Cherry St (45891-1210)
PHONE..........................419 238-2738
Fax: 419 238-2963
Jim Myers, *President*
EMP: 7
SQ FT: 90,000
SALES (est): 600K **Privately Held**
SIC: 3552 Fabric forming machinery &
equipment; looms, textile machinery

(G-19264)
LEY EQUIPMENT CO
121 S Walnut St (45891-1720)
P.O. Box 191 (45891-0191)
PHONE..........................419 238-6742
Fax: 419 238-4438
Watson N Ley, *President*
EMP: 5
SQ FT: 32,000

SALES (est): 737.3K
SALES (corp-wide): 754K **Privately Held**
SIC: 3523 Farm machinery & equipment
PA: Ley Industries Inc
121 S Walnut St
Van Wert OH 45891
419 238-6742

(G-19265)
LEY INDUSTRIES INC (PA)
121 S Walnut St (45891-1720)
P.O. Box 191 (45891-0191)
PHONE..........................419 238-6742
Watson N Ley, *President*
Esther Ley, *Vice Pres*
EMP: 6
SQ FT: 32,000
SALES (est): 754K **Privately Held**
SIC: 3523 Farm machinery & equipment

(G-19266)
LIFE STAR RESCUE INC
1171 Production Dr (45891-9390)
P.O. Box 852, Huntington IN (46750-0852)
PHONE..........................419 238-2507
Fax: 419 238-1479
Jim Dondlinger, *President*
Tim Lankenau, *General Mgr*
Dond Linger, *Principal*
Jim Snyder, *Principal*
Lyle Halstead, *Vice Pres*
EMP: 25
SQ FT: 50,000
SALES (est): 9.7MM
SALES (corp-wide): 1.6B **Privately Held**
WEB: www.holmanenterprises.com
SIC: 5521 5012 3713 Pickups & vans,
used; ambulances; ambulance bodies
PA: Holman Enterprises Inc.
244 E Kings Hwy
Maple Shade NJ 08052
856 662-1042

(G-19267)
**MORRIS MAICO HEARING AID
SVC**
117 N Washington St (45891-1705)
PHONE..........................419 232-6200
Rick Morris, *President*
EMP: 6
SALES (est): 259.5K **Privately Held**
SIC: 5999 3842 Hearing aids; hearing aids

(G-19268)
NATIONAL DOOR AND TRIM INC
1189 Grill Rd (45891-9386)
PHONE..........................419 238-9345
Fax: 419 238-2974
E Turnwald, *President*
Thomas Turnwald, *President*
T Turnwald, *Principal*
V Turnwald, *Principal*
Gene Turnwald, *Vice Pres*
▲ **EMP:** 48
SQ FT: 50,000
SALES (est): 8.5MM **Privately Held**
WEB: www.national-door.com
SIC: 2431 Doors & door parts & trim, wood

(G-19269)
**RIDGE TOWNSHIP STONE
QUARRY**
16905 Middle Point Rd (45891-9771)
PHONE..........................419 968-2222
Roger Davis, *President*
EMP: 7
SALES (est): 1.2MM **Privately Held**
SIC: 1422 5032 Crushed & broken lime-
stone; stone, crushed or broken

(G-19270)
**SHUMAKER RACING
COMPONENTS**
11037 Van Wert Decatur Rd (45891-9211)
PHONE..........................419 238-0801
Fax: 419 238-5915
John W Shumaker, *Owner*
EMP: 3 **EST:** 1974
SQ FT: 4,800
SALES (est): 258.6K **Privately Held**
SIC: 3751 3541 Motorcycles & related
parts; machine tools, metal cutting type

(G-19271)
**TECUMSEH PACKG SOLUTIONS
INC**
Also Called: Van Wert Division
1275 Industrial Dr (45891-2432)
PHONE..........................419 238-1122
James Robideau, *Branch Mgr*
EMP: 48
SALES (corp-wide): 8.8MM **Privately
Held**
SIC: 2653 Boxes, corrugated: made from
purchased materials
PA: Tecumseh Packaging Solutions, Inc.
707 S Evans St
Tecumseh MI 49286
517 423-2126

(G-19272)
TIMES BULLETIN MEDIA
700 Fox Rd (45891-2485)
P.O. Box 271 (45891-0271)
PHONE..........................419 238-2285
Fax: 419 238-0447
Ed Gebert, *Editor*
Mike Marchek, *Manager*
Kevin Wannemacher, *Manager*
Tina Byrd, *Director*
EMP: 15 **EST:** 2012
SALES (est): 630.3K **Privately Held**
SIC: 2711 Newspapers

(G-19273)
TOOLCO INC
16913 Wren Landeck Rd (45891-8822)
PHONE..........................419 667-3462
Fax: 419 667-2767
Kenneth D Linton, *President*
Matt Linton, *Vice Pres*
EMP: 4
SQ FT: 5,280
SALES: 100K **Privately Held**
WEB: www.toolcoonline.com
SIC: 3599 3523 Machine shop, jobbing &
repair; harrows: disc, spring, tine, etc.

(G-19274)
UNIVERSAL LETTERING INC
1197 Grill Rd B (45891-9387)
PHONE..........................419 238-9320
Fax: 419 238-1786
Mark Hoops, *President*
Scott Geier, *Controller*
Kendra Roxo, *Manager*
▲ **EMP:** 30
SQ FT: 15,000
SALES (est): 2.8MM **Privately Held**
WEB: www.showjacket.com
SIC: 2339 2329 Women's & misses' jack-
ets & coats, except sportswear; men's &
boys' leather, wool & down-filled outer-
wear

(G-19275)
VAN WERT PALLETS LLC
9042 John Brown Rd (45891-8420)
PHONE..........................419 203-1823
Spencer Wise, *Principal*
EMP: 8 **EST:** 2010
SALES (est): 550K **Privately Held**
SIC: 2448 Pallets, wood & wood with metal

(G-19276)
WILKINSON PRINTING CO
710 W Ervin Rd (45891-1733)
PHONE..........................419 238-3615
Fax: 419 238-3615
Darrell Brant, *Partner*
Dan Brant, *Partner*
EMP: 5 **EST:** 1887
SQ FT: 4,000
SALES (est): 585.4K **Privately Held**
SIC: 2752 2759 Commercial printing, off-
set; letterpress printing

Vandalia
Montgomery County

(G-19277)
ADAIRS PAVERS
50 Lakin Ct (45377-9400)
PHONE..........................937 454-9302
Lonzo Adair, *Principal*
EMP: 4

SALES (est): 8.4K **Privately Held**
SIC: 3531 Pavers

(G-19278)
**ADARE PHARMACEUTICALS
INC (HQ)**
845 Center Dr (45377-3129)
PHONE..........................937 898-9669
Fax: 937 898-9529
John Fraher, *CEO*
David Schloss, *Vice Pres*
Kyle George, *Production*
Muye Akinkuotu, *Engineer*
Jacopo Licciardi, *Human Res Mgr*
▲ **EMP:** 167
SQ FT: 870,000
SALES (est): 72.8MM **Privately Held**
WEB: www.aptalispharma.com
SIC: 2834 Medicines, capsuled or ampuled

(G-19279)
**ALL SRVICE PLASTIC MOLDING
INC**
900 Falls Creek Dr (45377-9685)
PHONE..........................937 890-0322
Joe Minneman, *Branch Mgr*
EMP: 5
SALES (corp-wide): 47.7MM **Privately
Held**
SIC: 3089 Injection molding of plastics
PA: All Service Plastic Molding, Inc.
900 Fall Creek Dr
Vandalia OH 45377
937 890-0322

(G-19280)
**ALL SRVICE PLASTIC MOLDING
INC (PA)**
900 Fall Creek Dr (45377)
P.O. Box 13545, Dayton (45413-0545)
PHONE..........................937 890-0322
Fax: 937 890-1513
Joseph Minneman, *CEO*
Frank Maus, *Principal*
Joe Kavalauskas, *Vice Pres*
Joseph Kavalauskas, *Vice Pres*
Stephanie J Brannon, *Human Res Mgr*
▲ **EMP:** 80
SQ FT: 35,500
SALES (est): 47.7MM **Privately Held**
SIC: 3089 Injection molding of plastics

(G-19281)
**AMERICAN QULTY
FABRICATION INC**
849 Scholz Dr (45377-3121)
PHONE..........................937 667-2861
Fax: 937 667-0761
Joe Beidelschies, *President*
Kevin Nidzorski, *Vice Pres*
Jake Metz, *Sales Executive*
EMP: 5
SQ FT: 14,000
SALES (est): 1.3MM **Privately Held**
SIC: 3441 Building components, structural
steel

(G-19282)
BALANCING COMPANY INC (PA)
898 Center Dr (45377-3130)
PHONE..........................937 898-9111
Fax: 937 898-6145
Donald K Belcher, *President*
Michael W Belcher, *President*
Jack Boeke, *Vice Pres*
Jack Broadwater, *Supervisor*
Don Short, *Director*
EMP: 28 **EST:** 1967
SQ FT: 53,000
SALES (est): 4.5MM **Privately Held**
WEB: www.balco.com
SIC: 3599 8734 3544 Machine & other
job shop work; testing laboratories; spe-
cial dies, tools, jigs & fixtures

(G-19283)
BILL J JERNIGAN INC
Also Called: Microfinish
865 Scholz Dr (45377-3121)
PHONE..........................937 264-1598
Bill J Jernigan, *President*
Gary Warren, *General Mgr*
EMP: 60
SQ FT: 8,000

SALES (est): 5.1MM **Privately Held**
SIC: 3471 Finishing, metals or formed products

(G-19284)
BOSTON STOKER INC (PA)
10855 Engle Rd (45377-9439)
P.O. Box 548 (45377-0548)
PHONE.............................937 890-6401
Fax: 937 890-6403
Donald M Dean, *President*
Sally Dean, *Corp Secy*
Fritz Huber, *Human Res Mgr*
Mindy Friday, *Manager*
EMP: 7
SALES (est): 8.8MM **Privately Held**
WEB: www.bostonstoker.com
SIC: 2095 5499 5993 Coffee roasting (except by wholesale grocers); coffee; tea; gourmet food stores; tobacco stores & stands

(G-19285)
CHALLENGER AVIATION PRODUCTS
4433 Old Springfield Rd (45377-9739)
P.O. Box 577 (45377-0577)
PHONE.............................937 387-6500
Heather Geissler, *CEO*
Linda Rocco, *President*
Susan Rocco, *CFO*
EMP: 5
SQ FT: 5,000
SALES (est): 150K **Privately Held**
SIC: 3724 Aircraft engines & engine parts

(G-19286)
CREATIVE EXTRUDED PRODUCTS INC
3510 Lightner Rd (45377-9735)
PHONE.............................937 667-1618
Don Charles, *General Mgr*
EMP: 57
SALES (corp-wide): 20.3MM **Privately Held**
SIC: 3089 Extruded finished plastic products
PA: Creative Extruded Products, Inc.
1414 Commerce Park Dr
Tipp City OH 45371
937 667-4485

(G-19287)
CROSS COMMUNICATIONS INC
Also Called: Christian Citizen USA
250 N Cassel Rd (45377-9451)
P.O. Box 49365, Dayton (45449-0365)
PHONE.............................937 304-0010
Pendra Snyder, *President*
Rick W Snyder, *Vice Pres*
EMP: 4
SALES (est): 247.1K **Privately Held**
WEB: www.christiancitizen.com
SIC: 2711 Newspapers, publishing & printing

(G-19288)
CROWN EQUIPMENT CORPORATION
Also Called: Crown Lift Trucks
750 Center Dr (45377-3128)
P.O. Box 400 (45377-0400)
PHONE.............................937 454-7545
Fax: 937 898-9452
Jim Schloemer, *Project Mgr*
Ernie Schweitzer, *Draft/Design*
Russ Haley, *Service Mgr*
Lauren Robins, *Branch Mgr*
Barry Dempsey, *Branch Mgr*
EMP: 58
SALES (corp-wide): 5.5B **Privately Held**
SIC: 3537 Lift trucks, industrial: fork, platform, straddle, etc.
PA: Crown Equipment Corporation
44 S Washington St
New Bremen OH 45869
419 629-2311

(G-19289)
DATWYLER SLING SLTIONS USA INC
Also Called: Columbia
875 Center Dr (45377-3129)
PHONE.............................937 387-2800
Mark Bueltel, *Accountant*

Denise Bagaieh, *Human Res Mgr*
Brian Bueltel, *Sales Staff*
◆ EMP: 67
SQ FT: 100,000
SALES (est): 24.2MM
SALES (corp-wide): 1.2B **Privately Held**
WEB: www.columbiaerd.com
SIC: 5085 3069 3061 Seals, industrial; gaskets; molded rubber products; mechanical rubber goods
HQ: Keystone Holdings, Inc.
875 Center Dr
Vandalia OH 45377

(G-19290)
DOOR FABRICATION SERVICES INC
3250 Old Springfield Rd # 1 (45377-9599)
PHONE.............................937 454-9207
Fax: 937 454-9310
Brian Hakers, *Manager*
▲ EMP: 45
SALES (est): 8.7MM
SALES (corp-wide): 1.9B **Publicly Held**
WEB: www.masonite.com
SIC: 5046 2431 Partitions; millwork
PA: Masonite International Corporation
201 N Franklin St
Tampa FL 33602
813 877-2726

(G-19291)
ENCON INC
3435 Stop Eight Rd 8rd (45377)
PHONE.............................937 890-6239
Karin Gaiser, *Branch Mgr*
EMP: 4
SALES (corp-wide): 58.8MM **Privately Held**
SIC: 3089 Molding primary plastic
HQ: Encon, Inc.
6161 Ventnor Ave
Dayton OH 45414
937 898-2603

(G-19292)
GE AVIATION SYSTEMS LLC
740 E National Rd (45377-3062)
PHONE.............................937 898-5881
Elizabeth Jacquemin, *General Mgr*
Kurt Hetico, *VP Opers*
Jennifer Brichacek, *Purch Dir*
Slobodan Gataric, *Engineer*
Joe Jensvold, *Engineer*
EMP: 300
SALES (corp-wide): 123.6B **Publicly Held**
SIC: 3643 Current-carrying wiring devices
HQ: Ge Aviation Systems Llc
1 Neumann Way
Cincinnati OH 45215
513 243-2000

(G-19293)
GE AVIATION SYSTEMS LLC
740 E National Rd (45377-3062)
PHONE.............................937 898-5881
Victor Bonneau, *Branch Mgr*
John Macneil, *Manager*
Gerald Fahringer, *Director*
EMP: 300
SALES (corp-wide): 123.6B **Publicly Held**
SIC: 8711 3643 3625 3624 Aviation &/or aeronautical engineering; current-carrying wiring devices; relays & industrial controls; carbon & graphite products; motors & generators
HQ: Ge Aviation Systems Llc
1 Neumann Way
Cincinnati OH 45215
513 243-2000

(G-19294)
HEPT MACHINE INC
19 E Alkaline Springs Rd (45377-2631)
P.O. Box 486 (45377-0486)
PHONE.............................937 890-5633
Fax: 937 890-9575
Edward W Hept, *President*
Deborah Hept, *Vice Pres*
EMP: 4
SQ FT: 6,000
SALES: 380K **Privately Held**
SIC: 3451 3812 Screw machine products; search & navigation equipment

(G-19295)
HERAEUS PRECIOUS METALS NORTH
970 Industrial Park Dr (45377-3116)
PHONE.............................937 264-1000
Jrgen Heraeus, *Chairman*
Don Peterson, *Facilities Mgr*
Paul Ripplinger, *Controller*
Kayleigh Hahan, *Office Mgr*
Tom Banks, *Manager*
▲ EMP: 31
SQ FT: 28,000
SALES (est): 9.3MM **Privately Held**
SIC: 2869 2819 8731 Industrial organic chemicals; chemicals, high purity: refined from technical grade; chemical laboratory, except testing
HQ: Heraeus Incorporated, Hic
770 Township Line Rd
Yardley PA 19067
212 752-2180

(G-19296)
HIGH TECH ELASTOMERS INC (PA)
885 Scholz Dr (45377-3121)
PHONE.............................937 236-6575
James W Back, *President*
Vicki Back, *Vice Pres*
Russ Thrawford, *Engineer*
▲ EMP: 25
SQ FT: 5,000
SALES (est): 3.3MM **Privately Held**
WEB: www.htei.com
SIC: 3479 2822 Bonderizing of metal or metal products; synthetic rubber

(G-19297)
INTEVA PRODUCTS LLC
Also Called: Inteva - Vandalia Engrg Ctr
707 Crossroads Ct (45377-9675)
PHONE.............................937 280-8500
Fax: 937 356-2000
Mike Stout, *Mfg Staff*
Jerry Webb, *Buyer*
Bill Cook, *Engineer*
Matthew Homan, *Engineer*
Thoai Nguyen, *Engineer*
EMP: 13
SALES (corp-wide): 4.3B **Privately Held**
SIC: 3714 Motor vehicle parts & accessories
HQ: Inteva Products, Llc
1401 Crooks Rd
Troy MI 48084
248 655-8886

(G-19298)
JIMS DONUT SHOP
122 E National Rd (45377-2102)
PHONE.............................937 898-4222
Jim Ashburn, *Owner*
EMP: 3
SALES (est): 129.9K **Privately Held**
SIC: 5461 2051 Bakeries; doughnuts, except frozen

(G-19299)
JPMORGAN CHASE BANK NAT ASSN
806 W National Rd (45377-1016)
PHONE.............................937 443-6260
Debbie Pusey, *Branch Mgr*
EMP: 6
SALES (corp-wide): 105.4B **Publicly Held**
SIC: 3578 Automatic teller machines (ATM)
HQ: Jpmorgan Chase Bank, National Association
1111 Polaris Pkwy
Columbus OH 43240
614 436-3055

(G-19300)
LESLEYS PATTERNS LTD
405 Halifax Dr (45377-2913)
PHONE.............................937 554-4674
Christopher Madden, *Principal*
EMP: 4
SALES (est): 231.8K **Privately Held**
SIC: 3543 Industrial patterns

(G-19301)
MAHLE BEHR DAYTON LLC
250 Northwoods Blvd # 47 (45377-9694)
PHONE.............................937 356-2001
Clayton Brown, *Manager*
EMP: 300 **Privately Held**
SIC: 3714 Motor vehicle parts & accessories
HQ: Mahle Behr Dayton L.L.C.
1600 Webster St
Dayton OH 45404
937 369-2900

(G-19302)
MAHLE BEHR USA INC
Also Called: Delphi
250 Northwoods Blvd # 47 (45377-9694)
PHONE.............................937 356-2001
Fax: 937 356-2008
Clayton Brown, *Branch Mgr*
EMP: 200 **Privately Held**
SIC: 3465 Body parts, automobile: stamped metal
HQ: Mahle Behr Usa Inc.
2700 Daley Dr
Troy MI 48083
248 743-3700

(G-19303)
MASONITE CORPORATION
3250 Old Springfield Rd # 1 (45377-9599)
PHONE.............................937 454-9207
EMP: 96
SALES (corp-wide): 1.9B **Publicly Held**
SIC: 2431 Doors, wood
HQ: Masonite Corporation
1 Tampa City Center 20
Tampa FL 33602
813 877-2726

(G-19304)
MASONITE INTERNATIONAL CORP
875 Center Dr (45377-3129)
PHONE.............................937 454-9308
Geroge Henderson, *President*
EMP: 3
SALES (corp-wide): 1.9B **Publicly Held**
WEB: www.masoniteinternational.com
SIC: 3441 3442 Fabricated structural metal; metal doors, sash & trim
PA: Masonite International Corporation
201 N Franklin St
Tampa FL 33602
813 877-2726

(G-19305)
MISATO COMPUTER PRODUCTS INC
Also Called: Megaform Computer Products
850 Industrial Park Dr (45377-3152)
P.O. Box 667 (45377-0667)
PHONE.............................937 890-8410
Fax: 937 454-1861
James R Browning, *President*
Jenny Browning-Schidecker, *Corp Secy*
▲ EMP: 5
SQ FT: 10,000
SALES (est): 770.6K **Privately Held**
SIC: 2761 Manifold business forms

(G-19306)
MURPHY TRACTOR & EQP CO INC
Also Called: John Deere Authorized Dealer
1015 Industrial Park Dr (45377-3117)
PHONE.............................937 898-4198
Chris Cron, *Manager*
EMP: 8
SALES (corp-wide): 176.9MM **Privately Held**
SIC: 3531 5082 Construction machinery; construction & mining machinery
HQ: Murphy Tractor & Equipment Co., Inc.
5375 N Deere Rd
Park City KS 67219
855 246-9124

(G-19307)
NATIONAL STEEL RULE DIE LLC
3580 Lightner Rd (45377-9735)
P.O. Box 74 (45377-0074)
PHONE.............................937 667-0967
Pete Zelnick, *Managing Prtnr*
David Zelnick, *Partner*

Mark Zelnick, *Partner*
Paul Mason, *Manager*
Sue Waldren, *Info Tech Mgr*
EMP: 6
SQ FT: 5,000
SALES (est): 803K **Privately Held**
WEB: www.nationalsteelruledie.com
SIC: 3423 Cutting dies, except metal cutting

(G-19308)
PHILLIPS COMPANIES
555 Old Springfield Rd (45377-9359)
PHONE..................937 431-7987
EMP: 23
SALES (corp-wide): 13.3MM **Privately Held**
SIC: 1442 Sand mining
PA: Phillips Companies
620 Phillips Dr
Beavercreek Township OH 45434
937 426-5461

(G-19309)
PIQUA CONCRETE CORP
555 Old Springfield Rd (45377-9359)
PHONE..................937 698-7229
Fax: 937 698-7229
Scott Besecker, *Manager*
EMP: 18
SALES (corp-wide): 10.8MM **Privately Held**
WEB: www.piquaconcrete.com
SIC: 3273 Ready-mixed concrete
PA: Piqua Concrete Corp
8395 Piqua Lockington Rd
Piqua OH 45356
937 773-0841

(G-19310)
SAIA-BURGESS LCC
Also Called: Ledex & Dormeyer Products
801 Scholz Dr (45377-3121)
PHONE..................937 898-3621
Fax: 937 898-3624
Christopher Hasson, *President*
Rich Graff, *General Mgr*
Gavin Fielden, *Vice Pres*
Richard Graff, *Plant Mgr*
Chris Stark, *Research*
▲ EMP: 100
SQ FT: 105,000
SALES (est): 30.4MM **Privately Held**
WEB: www.saia-burgessusa.com
SIC: 3714 3643 Motor vehicle parts & accessories; electric switches
HQ: Johnson Electric North America, Inc.
47660 Halyard Dr
Plymouth MI 48170
734 392-5300

(G-19311)
SUBURBAN NEWPAPERS OF DAYTON
Also Called: Vandalia Drummer, The
694 W National Rd (45377-1032)
PHONE..................937 294-7000
Daryl Bigony, *Sales Staff*
Kathleen Belcher, *Executive*
EMP: 3
SALES (corp-wide): 45.6MM **Privately Held**
WEB: www.tcnewsnet.com
SIC: 2711 Commercial printing & newspaper publishing combined
HQ: Suburban Newpapers Of Dayton Inc
3085 Woodman Dr Ste 170
Dayton OH
937 294-7000

(G-19312)
TROY ENGINEERED COMPONENTS AND
Also Called: Teca
800 Scholz Dr (45377-3122)
PHONE..................937 335-8070
Marvin Sauner, *President*
Jack Spencer, *Vice Pres*
Tony Vukufich, *Vice Pres*
Barbara Herbst, *Office Mgr*
Larry Ishmael, *Admin Sec*
EMP: 8
SALES (est): 1MM **Privately Held**
WEB: www.ishmael-precision.com
SIC: 3011 Tire & inner tube materials & related products

(G-19313)
UNIBILT INDUSTRIES INC
8005 Johnson Station Rd (45377)
P.O. Box 373 (45377-0373)
PHONE..................937 890-7570
Fax: 937 890-8303
Douglas Scholz, *President*
Sharon Scholz, *Corp Secy*
Phil Hickman, *Vice Pres*
Jeff Snyder, *Plant Mgr*
Jeff Wintrow, *Purch Dir*
EMP: 50
SQ FT: 80,000
SALES (est): 9.8MM **Privately Held**
WEB: www.unibilt.com
SIC: 2452 Modular homes, prefabricated, wood

(G-19314)
VANDALIA MACHINING INC
884 Center Dr (45377-3130)
PHONE..................937 264-9155
Joe Belcher, *President*
EMP: 4
SQ FT: 6,000
SALES (est): 491K **Privately Held**
WEB: www.vandaliamachining.com
SIC: 3599 Machine & other job shop work

(G-19315)
VANDALIA MASSAGE THERAPY
147 W National Rd (45377-1934)
PHONE..................937 890-8660
Rick Phillips, *Partner*
EMP: 7
SALES (est): 561.1K **Privately Held**
WEB: www.vandaliamassage.com
SIC: 5087 3999 Service establishment equipment; massage machines, electric; barber & beauty shops

(G-19316)
VEOLIA WATER TECHNOLOGIES INC
945 S Brown School Rd (45377-9632)
PHONE..................937 890-4075
Jean De Vauxclairs, *CEO*
George Bellizia, *Opers Spvr*
Gary McFadden, *Purchasing*
Alfonso Salinas, *Technical Mgr*
Paul Houser, *Controller*
EMP: 62 EST: 2004
SALES (est): 16.5MM
SALES (corp-wide): 452.1MM **Privately Held**
SIC: 3589 Water treatment equipment, industrial
PA: Veolia Environnement
21 Rue La Boetie
Paris
185 577-753

(G-19317)
WENTWORTH MOLD INC ELECTRA
Also Called: Electraform Industries Div
852 Scholz Dr (45377-3122)
PHONE..................937 898-8460
Fax: 937 898-1992
Walter T Kuskowski, *CEO*
Tim Bright, *President*
Rick Babington, *Exec VP*
Jeffrey D Barclay, *Vice Pres*
Brian Karns, *Vice Pres*
▲ EMP: 60
SQ FT: 65,000
SALES (est): 14.5MM
SALES (corp-wide): 547.2K **Privately Held**
WEB: www.electraform.com
SIC: 3544 3559 Forms (molds), for foundry & plastics working machinery; plastics working machinery
PA: Wentworth Technologies Company Limited
566 Arvin Ave Suite 3
Stoney Creek ON L8E 5
905 643-9044

(G-19318)
ZED INDUSTRIES INC
3580 Lightner Rd (45377-9735)
P.O. Box 458 (45377-0458)
PHONE..................937 667-8407
Fax: 937 667-3340

Peter Zelnick, *CEO*
Dave Zelnick, *Chairman*
Ken Johnson, *COO*
Mark Zelnick, *Vice Pres*
David Petersime, *Engineer*
EMP: 70 EST: 1969
SQ FT: 30,000
SALES (est): 16.4MM **Privately Held**
WEB: www.zedindustries.com
SIC: 3559 Plastics working machinery

Vanlue
Hancock County

(G-19319)
D & H MEATS INC
400 S Blanchard (45890)
P.O. Box 213 (45890-0213)
PHONE..................419 387-7767
Jared Fry, *President*
EMP: 7
SALES (est): 540K **Privately Held**
SIC: 2011 5421 Meat packing plants; meat & fish markets

(G-19320)
SUNNY SIDE MEATS
505 S Buffalo St (45890)
P.O. Box 101 (45890-0101)
PHONE..................419 387-7812
Patrick Kinley, *Owner*
EMP: 7
SALES (est): 437.8K **Privately Held**
WEB: www.sunnysidemeats.com
SIC: 2011 Meat packing plants

Venedocia
Van Wert County

(G-19321)
KRENDL RACK CO INC
18413 Haver Rd (45894-9420)
PHONE..................419 667-4800
Fax: 419 667-4100
Tony Laman, *President*
Chris Koverman, *Vice Pres*
Jeff Koverman, *Treasurer*
Robin Laman, *Admin Sec*
EMP: 8
SQ FT: 12,000
SALES: 800K **Privately Held**
SIC: 3471 Electroplating & plating

(G-19322)
OHIO ELECTRO-POLISHING CO INC
15085 Main St (45894-9645)
PHONE..................419 667-2281
Marty Koenig, *President*
Randall Koenig, *Vice Pres*
Randy Koenig, *Manager*
James Koenig, *Admin Sec*
EMP: 6 EST: 1963
SQ FT: 15,000
SALES (est): 645.8K **Privately Held**
SIC: 3471 Electroplating of metals or formed products

Vermilion
Erie County

(G-19323)
ARCHITECTURAL AND INDUSTRIAL
Also Called: A & I Metal Finishing
1091 Sunnyside Rd (44089-2759)
PHONE..................440 963-0410
Elizabeth Elden, *Vice Pres*
Christopher W Morris,
EMP: 15
SALES (est): 2.2MM **Privately Held**
WEB: www.aimetalfinishing.com
SIC: 3479 Coating of metals & formed products

(G-19324)
COLEYS INC
1775 Liberty Ave (44089-2510)
P.O. Box 830 (44089-0830)
PHONE..................440 967-5630
Kenneth L Mc Daniel, *President*
Maynard Coleman, *Principal*
Robert J Fetterman, *Principal*
Geraldine Mc Daniel, *Corp Secy*
EMP: 33
SQ FT: 25,000
SALES (est): 7MM **Privately Held**
SIC: 3599 Machine shop, jobbing & repair

(G-19325)
COLEYS INC
1775 Liberty Ave (44089-2510)
PHONE..................440 967-5630
Fax: 440 967-3240
Martha Coleman, *Principal*
EMP: 10
SALES (est): 940K **Privately Held**
SIC: 3545 Machine tool accessories

(G-19326)
FILTER FACTORY-TTN INC
3409 Liberty Ave Ste 100 (44089-2400)
PHONE..................440 963-2034
Dave Skodny, *Principal*
EMP: 6
SALES (est): 752.2K **Privately Held**
SIC: 3569 Filters

(G-19327)
GREAT LAKES DIESEL
5148 Concord Dr (44089-1502)
PHONE..................419 433-9898
Jim Zima, *Owner*
EMP: 3
SALES: 175K **Privately Held**
SIC: 3519 Diesel, semi-diesel or duel-fuel engines, including marine

(G-19328)
HULL BUILDERS SUPPLY INC
685 Main St (44089-1311)
P.O. Box 432 (44089-0432)
PHONE..................440 967-3159
Fax: 440 967-8823
Steve Holovacs, *President*
Ernie Johnson, *Manager*
EMP: 28
SALES: 1,000K **Privately Held**
SIC: 5032 3273 5211 Limestone; ready-mixed concrete; lumber & other building materials

(G-19329)
IRG OPERATING LLC
Also Called: Cleveland Quarries
850 W River Rd (44089-1530)
PHONE..................440 963-4008
Fax: 440 963-4011
Laureen Ramsire, *Office Mgr*
Zach Carpenter, *Mng Member*
EMP: 36
SALES: 3.6MM **Privately Held**
SIC: 1411 Sandstone, dimension-quarrying

(G-19330)
KENDRA SCREEN PRINT
3817 Liberty Ave (44089-2335)
PHONE..................440 967-8820
Ken Roghig, *Owner*
EMP: 3
SALES (est): 154.4K **Privately Held**
SIC: 2759 Screen printing

(G-19331)
KING VINEYARDS
5903 Coen Rd (44089-9524)
PHONE..................440 967-4191
Joseph King, *Owner*
Joan King, *Co-Owner*
EMP: 3
SALES (est): 125.7K **Privately Held**
SIC: 0172 2084 0191 0175 Grapes; wines; general farms, primarily crop; deciduous tree fruits

(G-19332)
LORAIN ARMATURE & MTR REPR INC
960 Sunnyside Rd (44089-2758)
PHONE..................440 967-2620

John W Small, *President*
Roy McGlugritch, *Vice Pres*
EMP: 6
SQ FT: 1,200
SALES (est): 967.6K **Privately Held**
SIC: 7694 Electric motor repair

(G-19333)
MCDANIEL PRODUCTS INC (PA)
Also Called: Automatic Parts
1775 Liberty Ave (44089-2510)
PHONE..............................440 967-5630
Kevin L McDaniel, *President*
Ken McDaniel, *Vice Pres*
EMP: 10
SALES (est): 4MM **Privately Held**
SIC: 3451 Screw machine products

(G-19334)
MCQUEEN ADVERTISING INC
Also Called: McQueen Sign Co
2010 Vermilion Rd (44089-2056)
PHONE..............................440 967-1137
Fax: 440 967-3534
Richard McQueen, *President*
Derrick McQueen, *Vice Pres*
EMP: 4
SALES (est): 402.9K **Privately Held**
SIC: 3993 7311 Signs & advertising specialties; advertising agencies

(G-19335)
PAPER MOON WINERY
2008 State Rd (44089-9602)
PHONE..............................440 967-2500
Sheryl Cawrse, *President*
EMP: 5
SALES (est): 468.9K **Privately Held**
SIC: 2084 Wines, brandy & brandy spirits

(G-19336)
PROMAC INTERNATIONAL INC
1121 Sunnyside Rd (44089-2761)
PHONE..............................440 967-2040
Roger Lewan, *President*
Frank Bobel, *Vice Pres*
▲ **EMP:** 5
SALES (est): 785.5K **Privately Held**
SIC: 3441 Joists, open web steel: long-span series

(G-19337)
VERMILION DOCK MASTERS
858 Vermilion Rd (44089-1834)
PHONE..............................440 244-5370
Thomas Maccarthy, *Owner*
EMP: 4
SALES (est): 140K **Privately Held**
SIC: 3999 Manufacturing industries

Verona
Preble County

(G-19338)
HARVEST LAND CO-OP INC
Also Called: Verona Agriculture Center
141 S Commerce St (45378-5014)
P.O. Box 682 (45378-0682)
PHONE..............................937 884-5526
Fax: 937 884-8904
Mark Gebhardt, *Manager*
EMP: 8
SALES (corp-wide): 321.6MM **Privately Held**
WEB: www.harvestland.com
SIC: 5191 2873 2879 5261 Farm supplies; chemicals, agricultural; herbicides; pesticides; nitrogenous fertilizers; nitrogen solutions (fertilizer); urea; agricultural chemicals; fungicides, herbicides, pesticides, agricultural or household; insecticides, agricultural or household; fertilizer; grain elevators
PA: Harvest Land Co-Op, Inc.
1435 Nw 5th St
Richmond IN 47374
765 962-1527

Versailles
Darke County

(G-19339)
ASPEN MACHINE AND PLASTICS
257 Baker Rd (45380-9317)
PHONE..............................937 526-4644
John Moran, *President*
Mary Moran, *Corp Secy*
EMP: 7
SALES: 1MM **Privately Held**
WEB: www.mtiplasticmfg.com
SIC: 3089 Plastic containers, except foam

(G-19340)
BELSHE INDUSTRIES INC
Also Called: Frenchtown Trailers SL & Sups
11465 Mangen Rd (45380-8419)
P.O. Box 312 (45380-0312)
PHONE..............................937 526-4460
Fax: 937 526-9120
Frank Fullencamp, *Branch Mgr*
EMP: 12
SALES (corp-wide): 6.2MM **Privately Held**
SIC: 3799 Trailers & trailer equipment
PA: Belshe Industries, Inc.
40852 Bob Crouch Rd
Tecumseh OK 74873
405 273-1690

(G-19341)
BEST BITE GRILL LLC
22 N Center St (45380-1201)
PHONE..............................419 344-7462
EMP: 8
SALES (est): 266.9K **Privately Held**
SIC: 5812 2099 Eating places; noodles, fried (Chinese)

(G-19342)
BUCKEYE FEED & GRAIN
895 E Main St (45380-1533)
P.O. Box 19 (45380-0019)
PHONE..............................937 526-3914
Fax: 937 526-3968
Timothy John Weaver, *Partner*
John D Weaver, *Partner*
Charles Krueger, *Manager*
Fred Wells, *Admin Sec*
EMP: 6
SALES (est): 970K **Privately Held**
SIC: 2048 Chicken feeds, prepared

(G-19343)
CANDLE COTTAGE
732 E Main St (45380-1530)
PHONE..............................937 526-4041
Gary Middendorf, *Owner*
Robin Middendorf, *Co-Owner*
EMP: 3
SALES (est): 239.1K **Privately Held**
SIC: 3499 3999 5947 5999 Novelties & giftware, including trophies; candles; gift, novelty & souvenir shop; candle shops

(G-19344)
COTA INTERNATIONAL INC
67 Industrial Pkwy (45380-9759)
PHONE..............................937 526-5520
Fax: 937 526-5505
Linda Cota, *President*
Sandra Cota, *Vice Pres*
Craig Cota, *Treasurer*
Phillip Cota, *Admin Sec*
▲ **EMP:** 12
SQ FT: 5,000
SALES (est): 1.5MM **Privately Held**
WEB: www.cotainternational.com
SIC: 3713 5065 Truck bodies & parts; communication equipment

(G-19345)
DIRECT WIRE SERVICE LLP
100 Subler Dr (45380-9788)
PHONE..............................937 526-4447
Fax: 937 526-9426
Eric Barloge, *Managing Prtnr*
Dave Berger, *Managing Prtnr*
EMP: 8
SQ FT: 6,000

SALES (est): 630K **Privately Held**
WEB: www.directtoolingconcepts.com
SIC: 3599 Machine shop, jobbing & repair

(G-19346)
ERNST SPORTING GDS MINSTER LLC
32 E Main St (45380-1516)
PHONE..............................937 526-9822
Mike Ernst, *Manager*
EMP: 4
SALES (corp-wide): 777.9K **Privately Held**
SIC: 5941 2395 Sporting goods & bicycle shops; embroidery products, except schiffli machine
PA: Ernst Sporting Goods Of Minster, Llc
334 N Main St
Minster OH 45865
419 628-2602

(G-19347)
EXPERT REGRIND SERVICE INC
20 S Pearl St (45380-1221)
PHONE..............................937 526-5662
Fax: 937 526-5662
Micheal Poling, *President*
Bruce Feltz, *Vice Pres*
Pat Gigandet, *Admin Sec*
EMP: 3
SALES: 350K **Privately Held**
SIC: 3545 3544 Cutting tools for machine tools; special dies, tools, jigs & fixtures

(G-19348)
G & C RAW LLC
Also Called: G & C Raw Dog Food
225 N West St (45380-1359)
PHONE..............................937 827-0010
Cathy Manning, *Mng Member*
Gary Manning,
EMP: 9
SQ FT: 1,800
SALES: 315K **Privately Held**
SIC: 2047 Dog food

(G-19349)
J & K PALLET INC
30 Subler Dr (45380-9782)
PHONE..............................937 526-5117
John Shardo, *President*
Jerry Shardo, *Vice Pres*
EMP: 6 **EST:** 1989
SQ FT: 24,000
SALES (est): 898.6K **Privately Held**
SIC: 2448 Pallets, wood & wood with metal

(G-19350)
KINGS COMMAND FOODS LLC
770 N Center St (45380-9610)
PHONE..............................937 526-3553
Pat Solon, *Plant Mgr*
Mack Middendorf, *Branch Mgr*
EMP: 100
SALES (corp-wide): 3.8B **Privately Held**
SIC: 2015 2013 Poultry slaughtering & processing; sausages & other prepared meats
HQ: King's Command Foods, Llc
7622 S 188th St
Kent WA 98032
425 251-6788

(G-19351)
L-K INDUSTRY INC
176 N West St (45380-1210)
PHONE..............................937 526-3000
Karen Stollings, *President*
EMP: 20
SQ FT: 30,000
SALES (est): 2MM **Privately Held**
SIC: 2821 3312 Molding compounds, plastics; tool & die steel & alloys

(G-19352)
MIDMARK CORPORATION (PA)
60 Vista Dr (45380-9310)
PHONE..............................937 526-3662
Fax: 937 526-5206
Anne E D, *President*
Joe Rothstein, *General Mgr*
Greg Blackmore, *COO*
Anne Eiting Klamar, *Vice Pres*
Dick Moorman, *Vice Pres*
◆ **EMP:** 600 **EST:** 1915
SQ FT: 400,000

SALES (est): 390MM **Privately Held**
WEB: www.midmark.com
SIC: 3648 3842 3843 2542 Lighting equipment; stretchers; dental equipment & supplies; partitions & fixtures, except wood; operating tables

(G-19353)
MIDMARK CORPORATION
160 Industrial Pkwy (45380-9757)
PHONE..............................937 526-8387
Anne Eiting Klamar, *Principal*
Jeff Ronek, *Sales Staff*
EMP: 623
SALES (corp-wide): 390MM **Privately Held**
SIC: 3648 Lighting equipment
PA: Midmark Corporation
60 Vista Dr
Versailles OH 45380
937 526-3662

(G-19354)
MORAN TOOL INC
261 Baker Rd (45380-9317)
PHONE..............................937 526-5210
Fax: 937 526-5256
John Moran, *President*
Mary Moran, *Corp Secy*
EMP: 4
SQ FT: 12,000
SALES (est): 582.4K **Privately Held**
SIC: 3544 Special dies & tools

(G-19355)
PALLETS-FM-N-PLC-PACKAGING INC
Also Called: Kamps
10709 Reed Rd (45380-9701)
P.O. Box 37 (45380-0037)
PHONE..............................937 526-9333
Fax: 937 526-5812
Richard A Ware, *President*
Laura Cress, *Clerk*
EMP: 50
SQ FT: 30,000
SALES (est): 7.5MM **Privately Held**
SIC: 2448 Pallets, wood

(G-19356)
PRECISION FAB PRODUCTS INC
10061 Old State Route 121 (45380-9586)
P.O. Box 256 (45380-0256)
PHONE..............................937 526-5681
Eric D Miller, *CEO*
Cindy Miller, *President*
Mary McKinney, *Purchasing*
David Miller, *Treasurer*
EMP: 6
SQ FT: 40,000
SALES (est): 1MM **Privately Held**
SIC: 3069 5712 Foam rubber; furniture stores

(G-19357)
SMITH PALLETS
9855 State Route 121 (45380-9512)
PHONE..............................937 564-6492
Joan M Smith, *Principal*
EMP: 4 **EST:** 2009
SALES (est): 298.4K **Privately Held**
SIC: 2448 Pallets, wood & wood with metal

(G-19358)
VERSAILLES BUILDING SUPPLY
741 N Center St (45380-1512)
P.O. Box 236 (45380-0236)
PHONE..............................937 526-3238
Fax: 937 526-3238
Richard P Huelsman, *President*
EMP: 7
SQ FT: 14,000
SALES: 1.5MM **Privately Held**
SIC: 2431 Millwork; doors, wood; door frames, wood; moldings, wood: unfinished & prefinished

(G-19359)
VPP INDUSTRIES INC
960 E Main St (45380-1555)
PHONE..............................937 526-3775
Vernon Monnin, *President*
Jane Monnin, *Vice Pres*
EMP: 10 **EST:** 1925
SQ FT: 9,600

▲ = Import ▼=Export
◆ =Import/Export

SALES (est): 670K **Privately Held**
WEB: www.vppind.com
SIC: **2711** Commercial printing & newspaper publishing combined

(G-19360)
WEAVER BROS INC (PA)
Also Called: Tri County Eggs
895 E Main St (45380-1533)
P.O. Box 333 (45380-0333)
PHONE................................937 526-3907
Fax: 937 526-4824
Timothy John Weaver, *President*
Audrey Weaver, *Principal*
Geo L Weaver, *Principal*
John D Weaver, *Principal*
Kreg Kohli, *Vice Pres*
▲ EMP: 60 EST: 1931
SQ FT: 20,000
SALES (est): 67.9MM **Privately Held**
SIC: **0252 5143 2015** Chicken eggs; dairy products, except dried or canned; cheese; butter; poultry slaughtering & processing

---

Vickery
Sandusky County

(G-19361)
BSE WELDING & FABRICATING LLC
1787 N State Route 510 (43464-9645)
PHONE................................419 547-1043
Chris Daniel, *Owner*
EMP: 12
SALES (est): 1.4MM **Privately Held**
SIC: **7692** Welding repair

Vienna
Trumbull County

(G-19362)
ADVANCED MICROBEAM INC
4217 King Graves Rd Ste C (44473-9787)
P.O. Box 610 (44473-0610)
PHONE................................330 394-1255
Donald Lesher, *President*
Pamela Lesher, *Vice Pres*
EMP: 4
SQ FT: 6,300
SALES (est): 566K **Privately Held**
WEB: www.advancedmicrobeam.com
SIC: **3577 8731** Computer peripheral equipment; electronic research

(G-19363)
BRAUN MACHINE TECHNOLOGIES LLC
4175 Warren Sharon Rd (44473-9524)
PHONE................................330 777-5433
Ke Sundvall, *Manager*
EMP: 10
SQ FT: 75,000
SALES: 15MM **Privately Held**
SIC: **3291** Abrasive products; abrasive metal & steel products

(G-19364)
DELPHI AUTOMOTIVE SYSTEMS LLC
Also Called: Delphia Pckrd Eea-Wrrn Plnt 47
3400 Aero Park Dr (44473-8704)
P.O. Box 431, Warren (44486-0001)
PHONE................................330 367-6000
Ken Ellsworth, *Branch Mgr*
Frank Lazorishak, *Med Doctor*
David Swipas, *Med Doctor*
Frank Scattino, *Manager*
Jay Shonk, *Manager*
EMP: 120 **Privately Held**
SIC: **3714** Motor vehicle parts & accessories
HQ: Delphi Automotive Systems, Llc
5725 Delphi Dr
Troy MI 48098
248 813-2000

(G-19365)
DIAMOND OILFIELD TECH LLC
4494 Warren Sharon Rd (44473-9642)
P.O. Box 91 (44473-0091)
PHONE................................234 806-4185
Matthew Kleese, *Mng Member*
Peter Karousis, *Mng Member*
EMP: 15
SALES: 2MM **Privately Held**
SIC: **1389** Oil consultants

(G-19366)
LATROBE SPCIALTY MTLS DIST INC (HQ)
1551 Vienna Pkwy (44473-8703)
PHONE................................330 609-5137
Gregory A Pratt, *Ch of Bd*
Timothy R Armstrong, *Vice Pres*
Thomas F Cramsey, *Vice Pres*
James D Dee, *Vice Pres*
Matthew S Enoch, *Vice Pres*
◆ EMP: 80
SQ FT: 189,000
SALES (est): 85.5MM
SALES (corp-wide): 1.8B **Publicly Held**
SIC: **5051 3312** Steel; stainless steel
PA: Carpenter Technology Corporation
2 Meridian Blvd
Wyomissing PA 19610
610 208-2000

(G-19367)
LIDECO LLC
972 Yngtn Kngs Rd Se (44473-8618)
P.O. Box 596 (44473-0596)
PHONE................................330 539-9333
Philip Saloom, *Principal*
EMP: 5
SQ FT: 15,000
SALES (est): 198.4K **Privately Held**
SIC: **3544 3441** Dies & die holders for metal cutting, forming, die casting; fabricated structural metal

(G-19368)
LITCO INTERNATIONAL INC (PA)
1 Litco Dr (44473-9600)
P.O. Box 150 (44473-0150)
PHONE................................330 539-5433
Fax: 330 539-5388
Lionel F Trebilcock, *CEO*
Gary L Trebilcock, *President*
Sharyn McCurdy, *General Mgr*
Bill Smith, *General Mgr*
Gary Sharon, *Vice Pres*
◆ EMP: 30
SQ FT: 13,000
SALES (est): 4.7MM **Privately Held**
WEB: www.litco.com
SIC: **2448 5031** Wood pallets & skids; particleboard

(G-19369)
MACK INDUSTRIES PA INC
2207 Slem Hutchings Rd Ne (44473)
PHONE................................330 638-7680
Fax: 330 638-1277
David Arnold, *Purchasing*
Ron Hoover, *Manager*
EMP: 19
SALES (corp-wide): 160.1MM **Privately Held**
SIC: **3589 3272** Sewage treatment equipment; concrete products
HQ: Mack Industries Of Pennsylvania, Inc.
201 Columbia Rd
Valley City OH 44280
330 483-3111

(G-19370)
MILLWOOD INC (PA)
3708 International Blvd (44473-9796)
PHONE................................330 393-4400
Steven J Miller, *President*
Lionel W Trebilcock, *President*
Kirk Ambrose, *General Mgr*
Gene Gearlds, *Pastor*
Ronald C Ringness, *Exec VP*
◆ EMP: 30
SQ FT: 20,000
SALES (est): 389.8MM **Privately Held**
WEB: www.millwoodinc.com
SIC: **3565 4731** Packaging machinery; freight transportation arrangement

(G-19371)
MILLWOOD NATURAL LLC
3708 International Blvd (44473-9796)
PHONE................................330 393-4400
Lionel Trebilcock, *Partner*
EMP: 95
SALES (est): 12.4MM **Privately Held**
SIC: **3565 4731** Packaging machinery; freight transportation arrangement
PA: Millwood, Inc.
3708 International Blvd
Vienna OH 44473

(G-19372)
NRG SMOOTHIES LLC
1887 Youngstown (44473)
PHONE................................972 800-1002
EMP: 3
SALES (est): 149.4K **Privately Held**
SIC: **2037** Frozen fruits & vegetables

(G-19373)
PROCESS INNOVATIONS INC
4219 King Graves Rd (44473-9708)
P.O. Box 25, Fowler (44418-0025)
PHONE................................330 856-5192
Fax: 330 856-5956
Robert S Crow, *President*
Shane Mealy, *Opers Mgr*
James Clark, *Mfg Staff*
Becky McCauley, *Office Mgr*
EMP: 6
SQ FT: 6,000
SALES: 790K **Privately Held**
WEB: www.processinnovations.com
SIC: **3569 8711** Robots, assembly line: industrial & commercial; engineering services

(G-19374)
RAMON ROBINSON
Also Called: Robinson Wood Products
475 Niles Vienna Rd (44473-9500)
PHONE................................330 883-3244
Ramon Robinson, *Owner*
EMP: 3
SALES (est): 76K **Privately Held**
WEB: www.robinsonswoods.com
SIC: **3944 5092 3952 2851** Craft & hobby kits & sets; arts & crafts equipment & supplies; lead pencils & art goods; paints & allied products

(G-19375)
RIVERSIDE STEEL INC
3102 Warren Sharon Rd (44473-9521)
PHONE................................330 856-5299
Fax: 330 856-7237
John Radu Jr, *President*
John Radu Sr, *Chairman*
Catherine Radu, *Corp Secy*
▼ EMP: 11
SQ FT: 38,000
SALES (est): 2.3MM **Privately Held**
WEB: www.riverside-steel.com
SIC: **3499** Machine bases, metal

(G-19376)
STARR FABRICATING INC
4175 Warren Sharon Rd (44473-9524)
PHONE................................330 394-9891
Fax: 330 394-9890
Thomas B Smith, *President*
EMP: 77 EST: 1965
SALES (est): 13MM **Privately Held**
WEB: www.starrfabricating.com
SIC: **3441 3564 3496 3444** Fabricated structural metal; blowers & fans; miscellaneous fabricated wire products; sheet metalwork; office furniture, except wood

(G-19377)
WATER DROP MEDIA INC
289 Youngstown Kingsvl Se (44473-9601)
PHONE................................234 600-5817
Dustin Ghizzoni, *Principal*
EMP: 7
SALES (est): 494.8K **Privately Held**
SIC: **4899 5999 5099 2759** Data communication services; banners, flags, decals & posters; signs, except electric; screen printing

---

Vincent
Washington County

(G-19378)
BLANEY HARDWOODS OHIO INC (PA)
425 Timberline Dr (45784-5615)
PHONE................................740 678-8288
Fax: 740 678-8163
Randal Blaney, *President*
James Blaney, *Vice Pres*
EMP: 50
SQ FT: 3,000
SALES (est): 5.3MM **Privately Held**
WEB: www.blaneyhardwoods.com
SIC: **2421** Sawmills & planing mills, general; kiln drying of lumber

(G-19379)
DECKER DRILLING INC
11565 State Route 676 (45784-5636)
PHONE................................740 749-3939
Dean Decker, *President*
Pat Decker, *Vice Pres*
Loretta Decker, *Administration*
EMP: 42
SALES (est): 6.6MM **Privately Held**
WEB: www.deandecker.com
SIC: **1381** Redrilling oil & gas wells

(G-19380)
MICRO MACHINE WORKS INC
10499 State Route 339 (45784-5429)
P.O. Box 70, Barlow (45712-0070)
PHONE................................740 678-8471
Fax: 740 678-8119
Linn Yost, *President*
Dan Anstatt, *Sales/Mktg Mgr*
David Yost, *Manager*
EMP: 10
SQ FT: 6,592
SALES: 2MM **Privately Held**
WEB: www.e-mmwi.com
SIC: **3599** Machine shop, jobbing & repair

(G-19381)
U HAUL NEIGHBORHOOD DEALER
6900 State Route 339 (45784-5634)
PHONE................................740 445-4125
Kenneth Meek, *Owner*
EMP: 3
SALES (est): 140K **Privately Held**
SIC: **3585 7539** Air conditioning, motor vehicle; wheel alignment, automotive

---

Vinton
Gallia County

(G-19382)
IVI MINING GROUP LTD
72116 Grey Rd (45686-8410)
P.O. Box 1101, Jackson (45640-7101)
PHONE................................740 418-7745
Jesse Sizemore, *Ch of Bd*
EMP: 7
SQ FT: 5,000
SALES (est): 205.6K **Privately Held**
SIC: **1041 1221 1222** Placer gold mining; bituminous coal surface mining; bituminous coal-underground mining

(G-19383)
STEELIAL WLDG MET FBRCTION INC
Also Called: Steelial Cnstr Met Fabrication
70764 State Route 124 (45686-8545)
PHONE................................740 669-5300
Fax: 740 669-4205
Larry Allen Hedrick Jr, *President*
Deb Karns, *Bookkeeper*
Krista Hedrick, *Manager*
Krista Lynnete Hedrick, *Admin Sec*
EMP: 32 EST: 1998
SQ FT: 40,000
SALES (est): 11MM **Privately Held**
WEB: www.steelial.com
SIC: **1623 3441 3444** Pipe laying construction; fabricated structural metal; sheet metalwork

GEOGRAPHIC

Wadsworth
Medina County

(G-19384)
762MM FIREARMS LLC
Also Called: Elite Tactical Supply
224 High St (44281-1861)
PHONE..440 655-8572
Christian J Thomas,
EMP: 5
SQ FT: 500
SALES: 480K Privately Held
SIC: 3484 5941 Guns (firearms) or gun
parts, 30 mm. & below; firearms

(G-19385)
A & B WOOD DESIGN ASSOC INC
3193 Greenwich Rd (44281-9518)
P.O. Box 88, Oberlin (44074-0088)
PHONE..330 721-2789
Brett Arrowood, President
EMP: 4
SQ FT: 3,000
SALES (est): 282.9K Privately Held
SIC: 7389 2431 5031 5211 Design serv-
ices; moldings & baseboards, ornamental
& trim; molding, all materials; lumber
products

(G-19386)
A T TUBE COMPANY INC
188 S Lyman St (44281-1743)
P.O. Box 123 (44282-0123)
PHONE..330 336-8706
EMP: 3
SQ FT: 4,000
SALES: 500K Privately Held
SIC: 2655 Mfg Fiber Cans/Drums

(G-19387)
ACCEL GROUP INC (PA)
325 Quadral Dr (44281-9571)
PHONE..330 336-0317
Fax: 330 336-1224
Robert Mangus, Vice Pres
Erika Buchholz, Project Mgr
Gwen Vojtush, Project Mgr
Keith Kepes, Purchasing
Todd Rentsch, Purchasing
▲ EMP: 85
SQ FT: 191,000
SALES: 14.3MM Privately Held
WEB: www.accelgrp.com
SIC: 2541 Display fixtures, wood

(G-19388)
ADMIRAL FOUNDRY INC
931 Seville Rd (44281-8316)
PHONE..330 336-7651
William Jackson, President
EMP: 26
SQ FT: 40,000
SALES (est): 2.6MM Privately Held
SIC: 3365 Aluminum foundries

(G-19389)
ADVANCED ELASTOMER SYSTEMS LP
Also Called: Exxon
1000 Seville Rd (44281-8317)
PHONE..330 336-7641
Fax: 330 335-6565
Ronald Campagna, Purchasing
Debra Musch, QC Dir
Robert Latham, Branch Mgr
EMP: 71
SALES (corp-wide): 226B Publicly Held
SIC: 2821 3083 2822 Elastomers, nonvul-
canizable (plastics); laminated plastics
plate & sheet; synthetic rubber
HQ: Advanced Elastomer Systems Lp
388 S Main St Ste 600
Akron OH 44311

(G-19390)
ADVANCED PLASTICS INC
307 Water St (44281-1708)
P.O. Box 720 (44282-0720)
PHONE..330 336-6681

Fax: 330 336-5210
Phil Nye, President
John Davis, Vice Pres
EMP: 11 EST: 1999
SQ FT: 12,000
SALES (est): 1.8MM Privately Held
WEB: www.advancedplastics.net
SIC: 3089 Injection molded finished plastic
products

(G-19391)
AKRON PRODUCTS COMPANY
6600 Ridge Rd (44281-9743)
PHONE..330 576-1750
Chester Marshall Jr, CEO
Francine Kusnir, Accounts Mgr
Joyce Staunton, Manager
EMP: 10
SQ FT: 45,000
SALES: 1MM Privately Held
WEB: www.akronproducts.com
SIC: 3446 Fences or posts, ornamental
iron or steel

(G-19392)
AL FE HEAT TREATING-OHIO INC
979 Seville Rd (44281-8316)
PHONE..330 336-0211
Steve Turner, Manager
EMP: 20 Privately Held
SIC: 3398 Metal heat treating
PA: Al Fe Heat Treating-Ohio, Inc
6920 Pointe Inverness Way # 140
Fort Wayne IN 46804

(G-19393)
ALTERNATIVE FLASH INC
1734 Wall Rd Ste B (44281-8354)
PHONE..330 334-6111
Fax: 330 335-8200
Daniel Broadbent, President
Angelo Savakis, Admin Sec
EMP: 20
SQ FT: 20,000
SALES (est): 2.4MM Privately Held
WEB: www.alternativeflash.com
SIC: 3061 3544 3398 Mechanical rubber
goods; special dies, tools, jigs & fixtures;
metal heat treating

(G-19394)
AMERICAN PRO-MOLD INC
350 State St 7 (44281-1093)
P.O. Box 325 (44282-0325)
PHONE..330 336-4111
Fax: 330 334-2568
Edward F Steinkerchner, President
Roberta Steinkerchner, Corp Secy
Mark E Steinkerchner, Vice Pres
Joan Moore, Purchasing
Nancy Roberts, General Counsel
EMP: 25
SQ FT: 10,000
SALES (est): 3.4MM Privately Held
SIC: 3069 3061 Molded rubber products;
mechanical rubber goods

(G-19395)
APPLIED MATERIALS FINISHING
901 Seville Rd (44281-8316)
PHONE..330 336-5645
Faith Ortiz, Principal
EMP: 25 EST: 2012
SALES (est): 5.1MM Privately Held
SIC: 3341 Secondary nonferrous metals

(G-19396)
BUSSON DIGITAL PRINTING INC
1061 Eastern Rd (44281-9019)
PHONE..330 753-8373
Dennis Busson, President
EMP: 20
SQ FT: 18,000
SALES (est): 3.2MM Privately Held
WEB: www.bussonportraitdirectories.com
SIC: 2752 Commercial printing, litho-
graphic

(G-19397)
CABINET SOURCE
8100 Wadsworth Rd (44281-9527)
PHONE..330 336-5600
Paul Ott, Owner
Pat Ott, Owner
EMP: 4

SALES (est): 177.6K Privately Held
SIC: 2434 Wood kitchen cabinets

(G-19398)
CLAMPCO PRODUCTS INC (PA)
1743 Wall Rd (44281-9558)
PHONE..330 336-8857
Fax: 330 336-4281
James R Venner, President
Jerry Biagini, General Mgr
Linda Venner, Vice Pres
Rich Bobey, Plant Mgr
Joel Kraemer, Opers Staff
◆ EMP: 90
SQ FT: 54,000
SALES (est): 18.2MM Privately Held
WEB: www.clampco.com
SIC: 3429 Clamps, metal; clamps & cou-
plings, hose

(G-19399)
CUSTOM CHEMICAL PACKAGING LLC
303 Water St (44281-1708)
PHONE..330 331-7416
Joanne Blandino, Manager
Scott Sandusky,
EMP: 21
SALES (est): 3MM Privately Held
SIC: 2842 Automobile polish

(G-19400)
CUSTOM SPORTSWEAR IMPRINTS LLC
238 High St (44281-1861)
PHONE..330 335-8326
Dan Gibbs,
EMP: 9
SQ FT: 3,000
SALES (est): 670K Privately Held
SIC: 5199 2759 7389 Advertising special-
ties; screen printing; embroidering of ad-
vertising on shirts, etc.

(G-19401)
D & J ELECTRIC MOTOR REPAIR CO
Also Called: Ohio Belt Control Supply Co
1734 Wall Rd Unit Office (44281-8356)
PHONE..330 336-4343
Fax: 330 335-0075
David Zuchniak, President
John Zuchniak, Vice Pres
EMP: 10
SQ FT: 20,000
SALES (est): 3.2MM Privately Held
SIC: 5013 7694 7629 1731 Automotive
servicing equipment; electric motor repair;
electrical equipment repair services; gen-
eral electrical contractor

(G-19402)
DESHEA PRINTING COMPANY
Also Called: Aldridge Folders
924 Seville Rd (44281-8316)
PHONE..330 336-7601
Sherri Gasser, President
EMP: 6
SALES (est): 406.1K Privately Held
SIC: 2752 Photo-offset printing

(G-19403)
DUNHAMS SPORTS
180 Great Oaks Trl (44281-9465)
PHONE..330 334-3257
EMP: 15
SALES (est): 827.7K Privately Held
SIC: 2329 Men's & boys' sportswear & ath-
letic clothing

(G-19404)
EBNER FURNACES INC
Also Called: Ebnerfab
224 Quadral Dr (44281-8327)
PHONE..330 335-2311
Fax: 330 335-1605
Robert Ebner, President
Ralph Myers, Corp Secy
Kim Swisher, Project Mgr
Mark Weigand, Purch Mgr
Mitch Carver, Purchasing
▲ EMP: 80
SQ FT: 150,000

SALES (est): 49.5MM
SALES (corp-wide): 163.8MM Privately
Held
WEB: www.ebnerfurnaces.com
SIC: 3567 3444 3433 3441 Industrial fur-
naces & ovens; sheet metalwork; heating
equipment, except electric; fabricated
structural metal; fabricated plate work
(boiler shop); fabricated pipe & fittings
HQ: Ebner Verwaltung Gmbh
Ebner-Platz 1
Leonding 4060
732 686-80

(G-19405)
EVANKO WM/BARRINGER RICHD DDS
Also Called: William Evanko Dgs
185 Wadsworth Rd Ste K (44281-9585)
PHONE..330 336-6693
William A Evanko, Manager
William A Evnko, Manager
EMP: 5
SALES (corp-wide): 555.3K Privately
Held
SIC: 3842 Grafts, artificial: for surgery
PA: Evanko, William A & Benninger,
Richard M Dds Inc
6101 34th St W Apt 26e
Bradenton FL 34210
330 721-5009

(G-19406)
FIN TUBE PRODUCTS INC
188 S Lyman St Ste 100 (44281-1743)
PHONE..330 334-3736
Fax: 330 334-3848
Michael Bandrowsky, President
Clare Fahrer, Principal
Paul Ankrim, Vice Pres
William Collins, Admin Sec
EMP: 10
SQ FT: 50,000
SALES (est): 990K Privately Held
WEB: www.fintube.com
SIC: 3443 Finned tubes, for heat transfer

(G-19407)
FLOW LINE OPTIONS CORP
471 E Bergey St (44281-2079)
PHONE..330 331-7331
Fax: 330 331-7172
David Grumney, President
Kathleen Grumney, Vice Pres
EMP: 5
SQ FT: 7,500
SALES (est): 460K Privately Held
WEB: www.flo-corp.com
SIC: 3824 5084 Fluid meters & counting
devices; meters, consumption registering

(G-19408)
GOLDSMITH & EGGLETON LLC
300 1st St (44281-2084)
PHONE..203 855-6000
Robert Eggleton, Vice Pres
Terry Burnell, Controller
Dorianne Smith, Accounting Mgr
Brian Hill, Marketing Staff
David Derhagopian, Mng Member
▲ EMP: 18
SALES (est): 622.4K Privately Held
SIC: 2821 3069 5169 Plastics materials &
resins; reclaimed rubber (reworked by
manufacturing processes); synthetic rub-
ber
HQ: Ravago Holdings America, Inc.
1900 Summit Tower Blvd
Orlando FL 32810
407 875-9595

(G-19409)
H & S TOOL INC
715 Weber Dr (44281-9550)
P.O. Box 393 (44282-0393)
PHONE..330 335-1536
Fax: 330 336-9159
Mark W Hillestad, President
Randy Hall, Prdtn Mgr
Cindy Wasley, Bookkeeper
Diana Dillon, Manager
EMP: 19
SQ FT: 12,500

▲ = Import ▼=Export
◆ =Import/Export

SALES (est): 4.5MM **Privately Held**
WEB: www.handstool.net
SIC: 3545 Tools & accessories for machine tools

(G-19410)
HUBBELL INCORPORATED
8711 Wadsworth Rd (44281-8438)
PHONE...............................330 335-2361
David Terisigni, *Plant Mgr*
Jim Hanreck, *Engineer*
P F King, *Controller*
Harold Brewer, *Product Mgr*
Karl Grabenstetter, *Product Mgr*
EMP: 29
SALES (corp-wide): 3.5B **Publicly Held**
WEB: www.kerite.com
SIC: 3643 Current-carrying wiring devices
PA: Hubbell Incorporated
40 Waterview Dr
Shelton CT 06484
475 882-4000

(G-19411)
HUTNIK COMPANY
Also Called: Ohio Engineering and Mfg Co
350 State St Ste 5 (44281-2417)
PHONE...............................330 336-9700
Victor Hutnik, *President*
Debra Hutnik, *Vice Pres*
EMP: 6
SQ FT: 5,000
SALES: 500K **Privately Held**
SIC: 3599 3443 7389 Machine shop, jobbing & repair; cylinders, pressure; metal plate; design, commercial & industrial

(G-19412)
KEELER ENTERPRISES INC
Also Called: Aldridge Folders
924 Seville Rd (44281-8316)
P.O. Box 269 (44282-0269)
PHONE...............................330 336-7601
Fax: 330 334-1221
Fred Keeler, *President*
Daniel Mills, *Vice Pres*
Sheri Gasser, *Treasurer*
EMP: 8
SQ FT: 10,000
SALES (est): 1.1MM **Privately Held**
WEB: www.aldridgefolders.com
SIC: 2675 2678 Folders, filing, die-cut: made from purchased materials; stationery products

(G-19413)
KEN VENEY INDUSTRIES LLC
690 Weber Dr (44281-9551)
PHONE...............................330 336-5825
Ken Veney,
EMP: 4
SQ FT: 3,800
SALES (est): 503.2K **Privately Held**
SIC: 5531 3089 Automotive parts; automotive parts, plastic

(G-19414)
KLAWHORN INDUSTRIES INC
456 South Blvd (44281-2032)
PHONE...............................330 335-8191
Frank Malec, *President*
Chris Jurey, *Corp Secy*
Fred Hayduk, *Vice Pres*
EMP: 3
SALES (est): 382.3K **Privately Held**
WEB: www.klawhorn.com
SIC: 3423 3524 3634 3541 Hand & edge tools; lawn & garden equipment; housewares, excluding cooking appliances & utensils; machine tools, metal cutting type

(G-19415)
KLEEN POLYMERS INC
145 Rainbow St (44281-1478)
PHONE...............................330 336-4212
Fax: 330 336-4405
John Marefka, *President*
Rick Marefka, *Vice Pres*
Niki Sundling, *Office Mgr*
John Cochran, *Manager*
EMP: 15
SQ FT: 8,000
SALES (est): 3MM **Privately Held**
WEB: www.kleenpolymers.com
SIC: 3061 Mechanical rubber goods

(G-19416)
KRAMER & KIEFER INC
Also Called: Medina Tool & Die
2662 Valley Side Ave (44281-9233)
PHONE...............................330 336-8742
Fax: 330 722-4684
Clayton Kramer, *President*
Robert Kiefer, *Vice Pres*
EMP: 6
SQ FT: 6,500
SALES: 800K **Privately Held**
SIC: 3544 Special dies, tools, jigs & fixtures

(G-19417)
LABELTEK INC
985 Seville Rd (44281-8316)
PHONE...............................330 335-3110
Fax: 330 335-3210
Ronald D Nagy, *President*
Robert Gill, *Vice Pres*
Bryan Conrad, *Sales Executive*
Scott Solomon, *Marketing Staff*
EMP: 58
SQ FT: 35,000
SALES (est): 6.1MM **Privately Held**
WEB: www.labeltek.com
SIC: 2759 Commercial printing

(G-19418)
LUKE ENGINEERING & MFG CORP (PA)
456 South Blvd (44281-2032)
P.O. Box 478 (44282-0478)
PHONE...............................330 335-1501
Fax: 330 336-6738
Fred P Hayduk, *President*
Chris Jurey, *Vice Pres*
◆ EMP: 40 EST: 1946
SQ FT: 37,000
SALES (est): 7.1MM **Privately Held**
SIC: 3471 3559 Anodizing (plating) of metals or formed products; metal finishing equipment for plating, etc.

(G-19419)
MICHAEL DAY ENTERPRISES LLC
9774 Trease Rd (44281-9557)
P.O. Box 151 (44282-0151)
PHONE...............................330 335-5100
Michael F Day, *President*
Kathy Ballash, *Purchasing*
Jana Day, *Manager*
EMP: 5
SALES (est): 1.1MM **Privately Held**
SIC: 2821 Plastics materials & resins; molding compounds, plastics

(G-19420)
MYERS INDUSTRIES INC
Akro-Mils
250 Seville Rd (44281-1020)
P.O. Box 989, Akron (44309-0989)
PHONE...............................330 336-6621
Fax: 330 334-7100
Gary Taylor, *Manager*
Chris Meister, *Maintence Staff*
EMP: 120
SQ FT: 10,000
SALES (corp-wide): 558MM **Publicly Held**
WEB: www.myersind.com
SIC: 3052 3069 3443 2542 Automobile hose, rubber; rubber automotive products; fabricated plate work (boiler shop); partitions & fixtures, except wood
PA: Myers Industries, Inc.
1293 S Main St
Akron OH 44301
330 253-5592

(G-19421)
NO BURN INC
1392 High St Ste 211 (44281-8262)
PHONE...............................330 336-1500
William Kish, *President*
Lindsay Kish, *Marketing Mgr*
Dean Troyer, *Marketing Staff*
EMP: 8
SQ FT: 4,000
SALES (est): 1.4MM **Privately Held**
SIC: 2899 Fire retardant chemicals

(G-19422)
NOVEX INC
258 Main St (44281-1446)
PHONE...............................330 335-2371
Fax: 330 336-8934
Charles Lynn, *President*
Linda Goin, *Purch Mgr*
Paula Lynn, *Admin Sec*
EMP: 14
SQ FT: 15,000
SALES (est): 3.5MM **Privately Held**
WEB: www.novitane.com
SIC: 3052 3069 Rubber belting; sheets, hard rubber; castings, rubber

(G-19423)
P C M CO (PA)
291 W Bergey St (44281-1334)
PHONE...............................330 336-8040
Fax: 330 334-1766
Duane Coffman, *President*
Paul Bebout, *Vice Pres*
Seng Sisouphanah, *Vice Pres*
Roger Beckler, *Engineer*
Brannon Kerr, *Treasurer*
EMP: 37 EST: 1965
SALES (est): 5.8MM **Privately Held**
WEB: www.pcm-lw.com
SIC: 3365 Aluminum & aluminum-based alloy castings

(G-19424)
P-AMERICAS LLC
Also Called: Pepsico
904 Seville Rd (44281-8316)
PHONE...............................330 336-3553
Barbara Headley, *Branch Mgr*
EMP: 123
SQ FT: 50,200
SALES (corp-wide): 62.8B **Publicly Held**
SIC: 2086 Carbonated soft drinks, bottled & canned
HQ: P-Americas Llc
1 Pepsi Way
Somers NY

(G-19425)
PARKER-HANNIFIN CORPORATION
Pneumatic North America
135 Quadral Dr (44281-8326)
PHONE...............................330 336-3511
Fax: 216 334-3335
Ron Hart, *Purchasing*
Dean Sullivan, *Purchasing*
Deborah Kusmier, *HR Admin*
Bill Service, *Marketing Mgr*
Greg Haitz, *Marketing Staff*
EMP: 130
SALES (corp-wide): 11.3B **Publicly Held**
WEB: www.parker.com
SIC: 3621 3643 3593 Electric motor & generator parts; current-carrying wiring devices; fluid power cylinders & actuators
PA: Parker-Hannifin Corporation
6035 Parkland Blvd
Cleveland OH 44124
216 896-3000

(G-19426)
PARKER-HANNIFIN CORPORATION
Also Called: Ips
135 Quadral Dr (44281-8326)
PHONE...............................330 335-6740
Barbara McCall, *Branch Mgr*
EMP: 26
SALES (corp-wide): 11.3B **Publicly Held**
SIC: 3569 Lubricating systems, centralized
PA: Parker-Hannifin Corporation
6035 Parkland Blvd
Cleveland OH 44124
216 896-3000

(G-19427)
PARKER-HANNIFIN CORPORATION
Also Called: Electromechanical North Amer
135 Quadral Dr (44281-8326)
PHONE...............................330 336-3511
Kenneth Sweet, *Branch Mgr*
EMP: 15

SALES (corp-wide): 11.3B **Publicly Held**
WEB: www.parker.com
SIC: 3599 3535 3496 3469 Machine shop, jobbing & repair; conveyors & conveying equipment; miscellaneous fabricated wire products; metal stampings; sheet metalwork; fabricated plate work (boiler shop)
PA: Parker-Hannifin Corporation
6035 Parkland Blvd
Cleveland OH 44124
216 896-3000

(G-19428)
PIN POINT MARKETING LLC
302 Eric Ln (44281-9209)
PHONE...............................330 336-5863
Timothy Davis, *Principal*
EMP: 3
SALES (est): 34.7K **Privately Held**
SIC: 3452 Pins

(G-19429)
PRECISION ALUMINUM INC
733 Weber Dr (44281-9550)
PHONE...............................330 335-2351
Fax: 330 336-4692
Thomas Powell, *President*
Elaine Sheep, *Manager*
EMP: 29
SQ FT: 17,500
SALES (est): 5.7MM **Privately Held**
SIC: 3365 Masts, cast aluminum

(G-19430)
PRECISION ENGINEERED TECH LLC (PA)
1785 Wall Rd (44281-9558)
PHONE...............................330 335-3300
Brian K Murray, *President*
Jerry Mullin, *Vice Pres*
EMP: 6
SALES (est): 4.3MM **Privately Held**
SIC: 3531 Construction machinery

(G-19431)
PROFILE RUBBER CORPORATION
6784 Ridge Rd (44281-9743)
P.O. Box 299, Sharon Center (44274-0299)
PHONE...............................330 239-1703
Fax: 330 239-1196
Lewis Winland, *CEO*
John Winland, *President*
Jeff Winland, *Vice Pres*
EMP: 17 EST: 1961
SQ FT: 12,000
SALES (est): 1.4MM **Privately Held**
WEB: www.profilerubber.com
SIC: 3069 Molded rubber products

(G-19432)
QUALIFORM INC
689 Weber Dr (44281-9550)
PHONE...............................330 336-6777
Andy Antonino, *President*
EMP: 40 EST: 1976
SQ FT: 17,000
SALES (est): 5.7MM **Privately Held**
WEB: www.qualforminc.com
SIC: 3069 3544 3061 Molded rubber products; special dies, tools, jigs & fixtures; mechanical rubber goods

(G-19433)
QUALITY REPRODUCTIONS INC
Also Called: Fine Lines
127 Hartman Rd (44281-9402)
PHONE...............................330 335-5000
Bob Grosser, *President*
Josh Stamper, *Marketing Staff*
EMP: 9
SQ FT: 7,000
SALES (est): 1.5MM **Privately Held**
SIC: 3714 Motor vehicle parts & accessories

(G-19434)
RADICI PLASTICS USA INC
960 Seville Rd (44281-8316)
PHONE...............................330 336-7611
Michael Cain, *CEO*
Danilo Micheletti, *COO*
Mattia Imberti, *CFO*
Shelly A Ray, *Human Res Mgr*
▲ EMP: 95

SQ FT: 235,000
SALES (est): 54.6MM **Privately Held**
WEB: www.radicispandex.com
SIC: 3087 3089 Custom compound purchased resins; plastic processing
HQ: Radici Novacips Spa
　　Via Bedeschi 20
　　Chignolo D'isola BG 24040
　　035 499-7690

(G-19435)
RAYDAR INC OF OHIO
1734 Wall Rd Ste B (44281-8354)
PHONE.................................330 334-6111
Fax: 330 334-7232
Angelo Savakis, *Corp Secy*
Daniel Broadbent, *Vice Pres*
Lisa Matty, *Manager*
Tracy Rowe, *Manager*
Jim Wheeland, *Manager*
EMP: 21
SALES (est): 3.3MM **Privately Held**
WEB: www.raydarrubber.com
SIC: 3069 Molded rubber products

(G-19436)
RBA INC
487 College St (44281-1105)
PHONE.................................330 336-6700
Fax: 330 334-2507
Robert Bault, *President*
Jane Haugh, *Corp Secy*
EMP: 8
SQ FT: 7,000
SALES: 800K **Privately Held**
SIC: 2752 7336 Commercial printing, offset; graphic arts & related design

(G-19437)
REMINGTON PRODUCTS CO
961 Seville Rd (44281-8316)
P.O. Box 506 (44282-0506)
PHONE.................................330 335-1571
Fax: 216 336-9462
Rhonda Newman, *CEO*
Jeff Wert, *Vice Pres*
Ned Goodman, *VP Opers*
Gerry Gross, *Research*
C Kevin McComas, *CFO*
▲ EMP: 110
SQ FT: 102,000
SALES (est): 31.7MM **Privately Held**
WEB: www.remprod.com
SIC: 3069 3131 Boot or shoe products, rubber; orthopedic sundries, molded rubber; footwear cut stock

(G-19438)
ROHRER CORPORATION (PA)
Also Called: Gateway Printing
717 Seville Rd (44281-1091)
P.O. Box 1009 (44282-1009)
PHONE.................................330 335-1541
Fax: 330 336-5147
Scot D Adkins, *President*
Troy Eckstine, *General Mgr*
Carmine Lombardi, *General Mgr*
Scott Nagel, *General Mgr*
David Sander, *General Mgr*
▲ EMP: 170 EST: 1953
SQ FT: 169,000
SALES (est): 130.6MM **Privately Held**
WEB: www.rohrer.com
SIC: 3089 2675 Blister or bubble formed packaging, plastic; die-cut paper & board

(G-19439)
SATTLER COMPANIES INC
1455 Wolf Creek Trl (44281-9742)
P.O. Box 306, Sharon Center (44274-0306)
PHONE.................................330 239-2552
Fax: 330 239-2553
David Sattler, *President*
David F Raynor, *Principal*
Linda Banic, *Vice Pres*
Terry Ake, *Opers Mgr*
Janet Sattler, *Admin Asst*
▲ EMP: 20
SQ FT: 22,600
SALES (est): 3.9MM **Privately Held**
WEB: www.sattlercompanies.com
SIC: 3599 Machine shop, jobbing & repair

(G-19440)
SHELLS INC (PA)
350 State St Ste 8b (44281-2404)
PHONE.................................330 808-5558
Fax: 330 335-1566
Henry C Bray Jr, *President*
Henry Bray Jr, *President*
John Edminister, *Vice Pres*
Jama Neher, *Human Res Mgr*
Keith Johnson, *Accounts Mgr*
EMP: 3 EST: 1972
SQ FT: 85,000
SALES (est): 21MM **Privately Held**
WEB: www.shells.com
SIC: 5051 3543 Foundry products; industrial patterns

(G-19441)
SOPREMA USA INC
310 Quadral Dr (44281-9571)
PHONE.................................330 334-0066
Pierre Bindschedler, *President*
J Bret Treier, *Principal*
Steven P Goetz, *Corp Secy*
Gilbert Lorenzo, *Vice Pres*
Barry Lee, *Research*
EMP: 30
SALES (est): 11MM
SALES (corp-wide): 11.4MM **Privately Held**
WEB: www.soprema.us
SIC: 3069 Roofing, membrane rubber
PA: Holding Soprema
　　14 Rue De Saint Nazaire
　　Strasbourg 67100
　　388 798-400

(G-19442)
SROUFE HEALTHCARE PRODUCTS LLC
961 Seville Rd (44281-8316)
PHONE.................................260 894-4171
Homie Faulkner, *General Mgr*
Remmington Prada, *Controller*
Bob Baugher, *Manager*
Desiree King, *Manager*
Jeff Scott, *CTO*
▲ EMP: 25
SQ FT: 76,800
SALES (est): 4.6MM **Privately Held**
WEB: www.sroufe.com
SIC: 3842 2396 Surgical appliances & supplies; screen printing on fabric articles

(G-19443)
WARNER FABRICATING INC
7812 Hartman Rd (44281-8744)
PHONE.................................330 848-3191
James Warner, *CEO*
Mark Warner, *President*
Karen Perebzak, *Controller*
EMP: 10 EST: 1977
SQ FT: 12,000
SALES: 722.5K **Privately Held**
WEB: www.warnersummit.com
SIC: 3444 Sheet metalwork

(G-19444)
WESTERN ROTO ENGRAVERS INC
Also Called: Wre Color Tech
668 Seville Rd (44281-1080)
PHONE.................................330 336-7636
Fax: 330 336-9172
Dean Ellebruch, *Manager*
EMP: 30
SQ FT: 11,000
SALES (corp-wide): 15.4MM **Privately Held**
WEB: www.wrecolor.com
SIC: 2754 2791 2759 Rotogravure printing; typesetting; commercial printing
PA: Western Roto Engravers, Incorporated
　　533 Banner Ave
　　Greensboro NC 27401
　　336 275-9821

(G-19445)
WIL-MARK FROYO LLC
1090 Williams Reserve Blv (44281-9344)
PHONE.................................330 421-6043
Mark Hotes, *Principal*
EMP: 4
SALES (est): 176.6K **Privately Held**
SIC: 2024 Yogurt desserts, frozen

Wakeman
Huron County

(G-19446)
CONCAST BIRMINGHAM INC
Also Called: Concast Metal Products
14315 State Route 113 (44889-8320)
PHONE.................................440 965-4455
Fax: 440 965-4225
Alfred D Barbour, *President*
John Dorsey, *COO*
Martin Little, *Exec VP*
Dean Mora, *Vice Pres*
Thomas Zadan, *CFO*
▲ EMP: 80
SALES (est): 16.1MM
SALES (corp-wide): 41.1MM **Privately Held**
SIC: 3449 Miscellaneous metalwork
PA: A Cubed Corporation
　　131 Myoma Rd
　　Mars PA 16046
　　724 538-4000

(G-19447)
CUSTOM CHASSIS INC
52826 State Route 303 (44889-9537)
PHONE.................................440 839-5574
Matthew Tipple, *President*
Michael Huhn, *Vice Pres*
Jennifer Tipple, *Office Mgr*
Jack Schartman, *Admin Sec*
▲ EMP: 9
SQ FT: 13,000
SALES (est): 1.2MM **Privately Held**
WEB: www.customchassisinc.com
SIC: 3711 Chassis, motor vehicle

(G-19448)
DURAFLOW INDUSTRIES INC
15706 Garfield Rd (44889-8439)
P.O. Box 574 (44889-0574)
PHONE.................................440 965-5047
Mark Sliman, *Principal*
Anne Sliman, *CFO*
EMP: 8
SALES (est): 938.1K **Privately Held**
SIC: 3999 Barber & beauty shop equipment

(G-19449)
KRAUSHER MACHINING INC
4267 Butler Rd (44889-8212)
PHONE.................................440 839-2828
Dale K Krausher, *President*
Jeffrey Krausher, *Prdtn Mgr*
Barbara Krausher, *CFO*
EMP: 8
SQ FT: 10,000
SALES (est): 1.1MM **Privately Held**
WEB: www.krausher.com
SIC: 3451 Screw machine products

(G-19450)
LAKEWOOD STEEL INC
13616 State Route 113 (44889-9660)
P.O. Box 190, Birmingham (44816-0190)
PHONE.................................440 965-4226
Fax: 440 965-5385
CAM Drennen, *President*
Lori Drennen, *Admin Sec*
EMP: 10
SQ FT: 12,000
SALES (est): 3.8MM **Privately Held**
SIC: 5051 3498 Steel; fabricated pipe & fittings

(G-19451)
M A HARRISON MFG CO INC
14307 State Route 113 (44889-8320)
PHONE.................................440 965-4306
Fax: 440 965-5134
Chad A Harrison, *President*
James Harrison, *Chairman*
Keith Harris, *VP Mfg*
Chad Harrison, *Plant Mgr*
Dave Knowles, *Senior Engr*
EMP: 45
SQ FT: 1,544

SALES (est): 9.5MM **Privately Held**
WEB: www.maharrisonmfg.com
SIC: 3545 3366 Precision tools, machinists'; castings (except die): copper & copper-base alloy; brass foundry

(G-19452)
PAKK SYSTEMS LLC
39 W Main St (44889-9701)
P.O. Box 22 (44889-0022)
PHONE.................................440 839-9999
Adam Frey,
EMP: 6
SQ FT: 4,000
SALES (est): 550K **Privately Held**
SIC: 3545 1799 Machine tool accessories; hydraulic equipment, installation & service

(G-19453)
SUNRISE COOPERATIVE INC
1981 Fitchville River Rd (44889-9326)
PHONE.................................419 929-1568
Fax: 419 929-1960
Jeff Puder, *Branch Mgr*
Pat Fannin, *Manager*
EMP: 12
SALES (corp-wide): 46.5MM **Privately Held**
SIC: 2041 5999 Grain mills (except rice); feed & farm supply
PA: Sunrise Cooperative, Inc.
　　2025 W State St Ste A
　　Fremont OH 43420
　　419 332-6468

(G-19454)
WAKEMAN AUTO AND TRACTOR PARTS
Also Called: Wakeman Power
31 W Main St (44889-9701)
P.O. Box 272 (44889-0272)
PHONE.................................440 839-2835
Fax: 440 839-2500
Chuck Jackson, *President*
EMP: 7 EST: 1969
SQ FT: 5,000
SALES (est): 1MM **Privately Held**
SIC: 3599 5531 Machine shop, jobbing & repair; automotive parts

(G-19455)
WOODWORKS FOR YOU
465 W River Rd (44889)
PHONE.................................440 277-8147
Bruce Bales, *Owner*
EMP: 3
SALES: 500K **Privately Held**
SIC: 2541 Cabinets, except refrigerated: show, display, etc.: wood

---

Walbridge
Wood County

(G-19456)
AK TUBE LLC (DH)
30400 E Broadway St (43465-9568)
PHONE.................................419 661-4150
Erik Anderson, *Vice Pres*
Tom Greco, *Mfg Mgr*
Cheryl Borro, *Purch Mgr*
Stacy Clark, *Purch Agent*
Aaron Klar, *Draft/Design*
▼ EMP: 238 EST: 2001
SQ FT: 330,000
SALES (est): 44.8MM
SALES (corp-wide): 5.8B **Publicly Held**
WEB: www.aktube.com
SIC: 3317 Steel pipe & tubes
HQ: Ak Steel Corporation
　　9227 Centre Pointe Dr
　　West Chester OH 45069
　　513 425-4200

(G-19457)
FISHER METAL FABRICATING
27953 E Broadway St (43465-9408)
PHONE.................................419 838-7200
Pam Manuel, *Principal*
EMP: 14
SALES (est): 2.4MM **Privately Held**
SIC: 3499 Fabricated metal products

(G-19458)
GREAT LAKES WINDOW INC
30499 Tracy Rd (43465-9794)
P.O. Box 1896, Toledo (43603-1896)
PHONE...............................419 666-5555
Fax: 419 666-3618
Lynn Morstadt, *President*
Hans Vetter, *VP Sls/Mktg*
Timothy Albertson, *Finance*
EMP: 600
SQ FT: 170,000
SALES (est): 92.8MM
SALES (corp-wide): 1.9B **Publicly Held**
WEB: www.greatlakeswindow.com
SIC: 3089 5211 Windows, plastic; doors,
folding; plastic or plastic coated fabric;
lumber & other building materials
HQ: Ply Gem Industries, Inc.
5020 Weston Pkwy Ste 400
Cary NC 27513
919 677-3900

(G-19459)
JET TOOL AND PROTOTYPE CO
230 W Perry St (43465-1028)
PHONE...............................419 666-1199
Julius Toth, *President*
David Toth, *Vice Pres*
EMP: 4
SQ FT: 4,400
SALES (est): 260K **Privately Held**
SIC: 3544 Special dies, tools, jigs & fix-
tures

(G-19460)
JONES-HAMILTON CO (PA)
30354 Tracy Rd (43465-9792)
PHONE...............................419 666-9838
Fax: 419 666-1817
J Kern Hamilton, *Ch of Bd*
Robert L James, *President*
Ken Jones, *Division Mgr*
Robert Taylor, *Business Mgr*
Charles Wheeler, *Business Mgr*
◆ EMP: 90
SALES (est): 70.4MM **Privately Held**
WEB: www.jones-hamilton.com
SIC: 2819 Hydrochloric acid; sodium sul-
fate, glauber's salt, salt cake; sulfuric
acid, oleum

(G-19461)
MSC WALBRIDGE COATINGS INC
Also Called: Walbridge Coatings
30610 E Broadway St (43465-9791)
PHONE...............................419 666-6130
Patrick Murley, *CEO*
Jeff Ramsey, *Opers Mgr*
Vasko Rocko, *Engineer*
Jessica Antkowiak, *Credit Mgr*
Dan Hughes, *Sales Mgr*
EMP: 120
SQ FT: 400,000
SALES (est): 38.6MM
SALES (corp-wide): 110.1MM **Privately Held**
WEB: www.mscwalbridgecoatings.com
SIC: 3316 3479 Cold finishing of steel
shapes; galvanizing of iron, steel or end-
formed products
PA: Material Sciences Corporation
6855 Commerce Blvd
Canton MI 48187
734 207-4444

(G-19462)
RESOURCE MECHANICAL INSUL LLC
6842 Commodore Dr (43465-9765)
PHONE...............................248 577-0200
Hussien Shousher, *Mng Member*
EMP: 45 EST: 2008
SALES: 6MM
SALES (corp-wide): 425.3MM **Privately Held**
WEB: www.gemindustrial.com
SIC: 3644 Insulators & insulation materials,
electrical
HQ: Gem Industrial Inc.
6842 Commodore Dr
Walbridge OH 43465
419 467-3287

(G-19463)
RIVERSIDE MCH & AUTOMTN INC
Also Called: Assembly Division
28701 E Broadway St (43465-9625)
PHONE...............................419 855-8308
Denny Meyer, *Manager*
Lisa Spaulding, *Manager*
Amy Millner, *Admin Asst*
EMP: 7
SALES (corp-wide): 9.7MM **Privately Held**
SIC: 3549 Assembly machines, including
robotic
PA: Riverside Machine & Automation, Inc.
1240 N Genoa Clay Ctr Rd
Genoa OH 43430
419 855-8308

(G-19464)
WESTERN STATES ENVELOPE CO
Also Called: Western States Envelope Label
6859 Commodore Dr (43465-9765)
PHONE...............................419 666-7480
Fax: 419 666-8402
Shelly Hinkle, *Manager*
Jim Johnson, *Manager*
EMP: 70
SALES (corp-wide): 209.5MM **Privately Held**
WEB: www.westernstateenvelope.com
SIC: 5112 2677 Envelopes; envelopes
PA: Western States Envelope Company
4480 N 132nd St
Butler WI 53007
262 781-5540

Waldo
Marion County

(G-19465)
CUSTOM CRETE
6928 Gillette Rd (43356-9117)
PHONE...............................740 726-2433
Terry Lowe, *Owner*
EMP: 5
SALES (est): 280K **Privately Held**
SIC: 3444 Sheet metalwork

(G-19466)
NWP MANUFACTURING INC
Also Called: N W P Manufacturing
2862 County Road 146 (43356-9122)
PHONE...............................419 894-6871
John E Werner III, *President*
John Werner, *President*
Jerry Keiesel, *Vice Pres*
EMP: 10
SQ FT: 36,000
SALES (est): 1.1MM **Privately Held**
SIC: 2842 2448 Sweeping compounds, oil
or water absorbent, clay or sawdust; pal-
lets, wood

(G-19467)
OHIGRO INC (PA)
6720 Gillette Rd (43356-9105)
P.O. Box 196 (43356-0196)
PHONE...............................740 726-2429
Fax: 740 726-2574
Jerry Ward, *President*
Jerry A Ward, *President*
James H Ward, *Vice Pres*
David Fierbaugh, *Plant Mgr*
Chris Roe, *Plant Mgr*
EMP: 20
SQ FT: 9,600
SALES (est): 16.9MM **Privately Held**
WEB: www.ohigro.com
SIC: 5191 5261 2875 0723 Fertilizer &
fertilizer materials; fertilizer; fertilizers,
mixing only; crop preparation services for
market

Walhonding
Coshocton County

(G-19468)
DUGAN DRILLING INCORPORATED
27238 New Guilford Rd (43843-9612)
P.O. Box 91, Bladensburg (43005-0091)
PHONE...............................740 668-3811
Guy E Dugan, *President*
Linda Dugan, *Admin Sec*
EMP: 9
SALES: 400K **Privately Held**
SIC: 1381 Drilling oil & gas wells

(G-19469)
ELSAAN ENERGY LLC
26100 Township Road 52 (43843-9768)
PHONE...............................740 294-9399
M Dean Ringwalt, *Principal*
EMP: 7
SALES (est): 426.9K **Privately Held**
SIC: 1389 Oil & gas wells: building, repair-
ing & dismantling

Walnut Creek
Holmes County

(G-19470)
MAST FARM SERVICE LTD
3585 State Rte 39 (44687)
P.O. Box 142 (44687-0142)
PHONE...............................330 893-2972
Eli Mast Jr, *Owner*
EMP: 35
SALES (est): 3.4MM **Privately Held**
SIC: 3499 Fire- or burglary-resistive prod-
ucts

(G-19471)
WALNUT CREEK CHOCOLATE COMPANY
Also Called: Coblentz Chocolate Co
4917 State Rte 515 (44687)
P.O. Box 86 (44687-0086)
PHONE...............................330 893-2995
Fax: 330 893-3913
Jason Coblentz, *President*
Orpha Miller, *Store Mgr*
Amy Yoder, *Mktg Dir*
EMP: 25
SQ FT: 2,000
SALES (est): 4.2MM **Privately Held**
SIC: 2064 2066 5149 5441 Chocolate
covered dates; fruit, chocolate covered
(except dates); chocolate candy, solid;
chocolate; candy

Walton Hills
Cuyahoga County

(G-19472)
CONTROLLIX CORPORATION
Also Called: Walton Hills
21415 Alexander Rd (44146-5512)
PHONE...............................440 232-8757
Fax: 440 232-1893
John Kelly, *CEO*
Cynthia Burry, *Controller*
EMP: 15
SQ FT: 18,000
SALES (est): 4.9MM **Privately Held**
WEB: www.controllix.com
SIC: 3625 5063 Industrial electrical relays
& switches; switches, electric power; elec-
tric controls & control accessories, indus-
trial; electrical apparatus & equipment

(G-19473)
DUNHAM PRODUCTS INC
7400 Northfield Rd (44146-6108)
PHONE...............................440 232-0885
Fax: 440 232-1011
Joseph F Klukan, *CEO*
Rosemary Klukan, *Corp Secy*
Joanna Mann, *Human Res Mgr*
Sarah Johnson, *Manager*

Jay Maslanka, *Manager*
EMP: 15 EST: 1946
SQ FT: 7,700
SALES (est): 3.6MM **Privately Held**
WEB: www.dunhamproducts.com
SIC: 3451 Screw machine products

(G-19474)
MASON STRUCTURAL STEEL INC
Also Called: Mason Steel
7500 Northfield Rd (44146-6187)
PHONE...............................440 439-1040
Fax: 440 439-1077
Leonard N Polster, *CEO*
Keith Polster, *President*
J Moldaver, *Principal*
Joseph Patchan, *Principal*
Sol W Wyman, *Principal*
EMP: 100 EST: 1958
SQ FT: 75,000
SALES (est): 30.1MM **Privately Held**
WEB: www.masonsteel.com
SIC: 3441 5031 5074 Fabricated struc-
tural metal; doors & windows; window
frames, all materials; fireplaces, prefabri-
cated

(G-19475)
POLYMER ADDITIVES INC
7050 Krick Rd (44146-4416)
PHONE...............................216 262-7016
EMP: 3
SALES (corp-wide): 210MM **Privately Held**
SIC: 5169 2899 Chemicals & allied prod-
ucts; chemical preparations; fire retardant
chemicals
HQ: Polymer Additives, Inc.
7500 E Pleasant Valley Rd
Independence OH 44131
216 875-7200

Wapakoneta
Auglaize County

(G-19476)
AMERICAN TRIM LLC
217 Krein Ave (45895)
PHONE...............................419 739-4349
Aaron Art, *Plant Engr*
Randy Fosnaugh, *Branch Mgr*
Kevin Riley, *Graphic Designe*
EMP: 100
SALES (corp-wide): 460MM **Privately Held**
SIC: 3469 Metal stampings; porcelain
enameled products & utensils; ornamen-
tal metal stampings
HQ: American Trim, L.L.C.
1005 W Grand Ave
Lima OH 45801

(G-19477)
AMERICAN TRIM LLC
713 Maple St (45895-2323)
PHONE...............................419 738-9664
Mike Staddon, *Branch Mgr*
Dave Stewart, *Supervisor*
Paul Pellegrini, *Info Tech Mgr*
EMP: 100
SALES (corp-wide): 460MM **Privately Held**
SIC: 3469 Metal stampings; porcelain
enameled products & utensils; ornamen-
tal metal stampings
HQ: American Trim, L.L.C.
1005 W Grand Ave
Lima OH 45801

(G-19478)
AMETEK WESTCHESTER PLASTICS
Also Called: Cpd Chemical Products Division
14101 Cemetery Rd (45895)
PHONE...............................419 739-3200
Ron Gasior, *Manager*
EMP: 110 EST: 1962
SALES (est): 13.9MM **Privately Held**
SIC: 2821 Plastics materials & resins

(G-19479)
ARMIN R JEWETT
607 N Water St (45895-9379)
PHONE.....................................419 647-6644
EMP: 3
SALES: 50K **Privately Held**
SIC: 2499 Mfg Wood Products

(G-19480)
AUGLAIZE WELDING COMPANY INC
106 N Water St (45895-1696)
PHONE.....................................419 738-4422
Fax: 419 738-4422
D A Rummel, *President*
Marjorie Rummel, *Corp Secy*
EMP: 3
SQ FT: 2,500
SALES: 120K **Privately Held**
SIC: 7692 Welding repair

(G-19481)
BECKERMILLS INC
15286 State Route 67 (45895-9121)
PHONE.....................................419 738-3450
Jim L Becker, *Principal*
EMP: 4
SALES (est): 445.5K **Privately Held**
SIC: 3565 Aerating machines, for beverages

(G-19482)
BORNHORST PRINTING COMPANY INC
10139 County Road 25a (45895-8360)
PHONE.....................................419 738-5901
Fax: 419 738-5902
Glenn Bornhorst, *President*
Terri Bornhorst, *Corp Secy*
EMP: 7
SQ FT: 5,200
SALES: 500K **Privately Held**
WEB: www.bornhorstprinting.com
SIC: 2759 Commercial printing

(G-19483)
CBR INDUSTRIAL LLC
20086 Wapakoneta Cridersv (45895-7641)
PHONE.....................................419 645-6447
Rickie Lotz,
EMP: 4
SALES (est): 43.1K **Privately Held**
SIC: 7349 3443 3444 7389 Building & office cleaning services; office cleaning or charring; chutes & troughs; sheet metalwork;

(G-19484)
CREATIVE CURBING AMERICA LLC
1634 Springfield Ave (45895-9483)
PHONE.....................................419 738-7668
Robin William Rosser, *Administration*
EMP: 3
SALES (est): 179K **Privately Held**
SIC: 3272 Well curbing, concrete

(G-19485)
G A WINTZER AND SON COMPANY
12279 S Dixey Hwy (45895)
P.O. Box 406 (45895-0406)
PHONE.....................................419 739-4913
Fax: 419 738-1649
Jim Keack, *General Mgr*
Kirk Azbell, *Sales Staff*
EMP: 70
SALES (corp-wide): 15.7MM **Privately Held**
WEB: www.gawintzer.com
SIC: 2048 Feeds from meat & from meat & vegetable meals
PA: G. A. Wintzer And Son Company
204 W Auglaize St
Wapakoneta OH 45895
419 739-4900

(G-19486)
GATEWAY PACKAGING COMPANY
253 Industrial Dr (45895-9234)
PHONE.....................................419 738-5126
EMP: 4

SALES (est): 88.6K **Privately Held**
SIC: 2759 Flexographic printing

(G-19487)
GENERAL ALUMINUM MFG COMPANY
Also Called: Wapakoneta Plant
13663 Short Rd (45895-8362)
PHONE.....................................419 739-9300
Gary Applegate, *Safety Mgr*
Tina Burd, *Purchasing*
Mike Balazs, *QC Dir*
Glen Meyer, *Engineer*
Lenora Randolph, *Human Res Dir*
EMP: 170
SALES (corp-wide): 1.2B **Publicly Held**
WEB: www.generalaluminum.com
SIC: 3363 3494 3322 3321 Aluminum die-castings; valves & pipe fittings; plumbing & heating valves; malleable iron foundries; cast iron pipe & fittings; motor vehicle parts & accessories; wheels; motor vehicle; motor vehicle brake systems & parts; motor vehicle body components & frame; aerospace investment castings, ferrous
HQ: General Aluminum Mfg. Company
6065 Parkland Blvd
Cleveland OH 44124
440 947-2000

(G-19488)
HOMESTRETCH INC
203 E Auglaize St (45895)
PHONE.....................................419 738-6604
Fax: 419 738-6304
Donna Pest, *President*
EMP: 4 EST: 1992
SALES (est): 251.8K **Privately Held**
SIC: 2759 Commercial printing

(G-19489)
HORIZON OHIO PUBLICATIONS INC
Also Called: Shelby County Review
520 Industrial Dr (45895-9200)
P.O. Box 389 (45895-0389)
PHONE.....................................419 738-2128
Fax: 419 738-5352
Nina Laney, *Sales Staff*
Gayle Masonbrink, *Adv Dir*
Karen Brown, *Advt Staff*
Deb Wez, *Branch Mgr*
Melissa Bartlett, *Manager*
EMP: 32
SALES (corp-wide): 71.4MM **Privately Held**
SIC: 2711 2759 2752 Newspapers, publishing & printing; commercial printing; commercial printing, lithographic
HQ: Horizon Ohio Publications Inc
102 E Spring St
Saint Marys OH 45885
419 394-7414

(G-19490)
HORIZON PUBLICATIONS INC
Also Called: Wapakoneta Daily News
520 Industrial Dr (45895-9200)
PHONE.....................................419 738-2128
Deb Zwez, *Branch Mgr*
EMP: 46
SALES (corp-wide): 71.4MM **Privately Held**
WEB: www.malvern-online.com
SIC: 2711 Newspapers, publishing & printing
PA: Horizon Publications, Inc.
1120 N Carbon St Ste 100
Marion IL 62959
618 993-1711

(G-19491)
INGREDIA INC
Also Called: I D I
625 Commerce Rd (45895-8265)
PHONE.....................................419 738-4060
Gilles Desgrousilliers, *CEO*
Matthieu Arguillere, *President*
Benot Leclercq, *General Mgr*
Kevin Rutter, *Vice Pres*
Leclercq Benoit, *VP Sls/Mktg*
◆ EMP: 23
SQ FT: 39,000

SALES (est): 9MM
SALES (corp-wide): 152.9MM **Privately Held**
WEB: www.ingredia.com
SIC: 2023 Dry, condensed, evaporated dairy products
HQ: Ingredia
51 Avenue Fernand Lobbedez
Arras 62000
321 238-000

(G-19492)
JEWETT SUPPLY
Also Called: Barlamy Supply
607 N Water St (45895-9379)
PHONE.....................................419 738-9882
Rife Jewett, *Partner*
Lisa Hardeman, *Partner*
Amy Jewett, *Partner*
Lori Jewett, *Partner*
Lynn Jewett, *Partner*
EMP: 12
SQ FT: 768
SALES: 90K **Privately Held**
SIC: 2499 Handles, poles, dowels & stakes: wood

(G-19493)
JUDY DUBOIS
Also Called: Auglaize Embroidery Co
4 N Wood St (45895-1660)
PHONE.....................................419 738-6979
Judy Dubois, *Owner*
EMP: 3
SALES (est): 184.2K **Privately Held**
SIC: 2395 Embroidery products, except schiffli machine

(G-19494)
KN RUBBER LLC (HQ)
Also Called: Koneta Rubber
1400 Lunar Dr (45895-9796)
P.O. Box 150 (45895-0150)
PHONE.....................................419 739-4200
Carl Fly, *Facilities Mgr*
Rex Mouland, *Controller*
Eugene Border, *VP Human Res*
John B Kepler,
◆ EMP: 155
SQ FT: 165,000
SALES: 76.2MM
SALES (corp-wide): 193.2MM **Privately Held**
WEB: www.koneta.com
SIC: 3069 Rubber automotive products
PA: Kinderhook Industries, Llc
521 5th Ave Fl 34
New York NY 10175
212 201-6780

(G-19495)
KONETA INC
1400 Lunar Dr (45895-9796)
P.O. Box 150 (45895-0150)
PHONE.....................................419 739-4200
Christopher Keogh, *CEO*
Corwynne Carruthers, *Vice Pres*
Dave Landers, *Vice Pres*
Thomas Tuttle, *Vice Pres*
Denise Neeley, *Purchasing*
▼ EMP: 90
SALES: 23MM **Privately Held**
SIC: 3061 Automotive rubber goods (mechanical)

(G-19496)
M B INDUSTRIES INC (PA)
11158 Infirmary Rd (45895-9413)
PHONE.....................................419 738-4769
Fax: 419 738-5316
Michael Borges, *President*
EMP: 4
SALES (est): 677.1K **Privately Held**
WEB: www.mbind.com
SIC: 3548 2992 Welding & cutting apparatus & accessories; cutting oils, blending: made from purchased materials

(G-19497)
MIDWEST COMPOSITES LLC
302 Krein Ave (45895-2375)
PHONE.....................................419 738-2431
Vern Peak,
EMP: 20

SALES (est): 2.1MM **Privately Held**
SIC: 3229 2231 Glass fiber products; upholstery fabrics, wool

(G-19498)
MIDWEST ELASTOMERS INC
Also Called: MEI
700 Industrial Dr (45895-9200)
P.O. Box 412 (45895-0412)
PHONE.....................................419 738-8844
Fax: 419 738-4411
George Wight, *President*
Ron Clark, *President*
Bill Jacobs, *Principal*
Karen Jacobs, *Principal*
Evan Piland, *Principal*
▲ EMP: 65 EST: 1986
SQ FT: 56,000
SALES: 17.8MM **Privately Held**
WEB: www.midwestelastomers.com
SIC: 2822 3069 Synthetic rubber; reclaimed rubber (reworked by manufacturing processes)

(G-19499)
MIDWEST METAL FABRICATORS
712 Maple St (45895-2324)
PHONE.....................................419 739-7077
Verne E Peake, *Partner*
Jason Neumann, *Partner*
John Neumann, *Partner*
EMP: 10 EST: 2001
SQ FT: 15,500
SALES (est): 1.4MM **Privately Held**
WEB: www.mw-metal.com
SIC: 3444 Sheet metalwork

(G-19500)
MIDWEST METAL FABRICATORS
712 Maple St (45895-2324)
PHONE.....................................419 739-7077
Berne Peake,
EMP: 11
SALES (est): 760K **Privately Held**
SIC: 3444 Sheet metalwork

(G-19501)
MIDWEST SPECIALTIES INC
Also Called: Flexarm
851 Industrial Dr (45895-9243)
PHONE.....................................419 738-8147
Richard D Kennedy, *President*
Brian Hastings, *Plant Mgr*
Jeff Johnson, *Controller*
Penny Kentosh, *Admin Sec*
EMP: 13
SQ FT: 46,000
SALES: 3.5MM **Privately Held**
WEB: www.flexarminc.com
SIC: 3541 3599 3271 Tapping machines; machine shop, jobbing & repair; concrete block & brick

(G-19502)
NATIONAL LIME AND STONE CO
18430 Main Street Rd (45895-9400)
PHONE.....................................419 657-6745
Fax: 419 657-2190
Shaun Place, *Manager*
EMP: 9
SALES (corp-wide): 4B **Privately Held**
WEB: www.natlime.com
SIC: 1422 3281 Crushed & broken limestone; limestone, cut & shaped
PA: The National Lime And Stone Company
551 Lake Cascade Pkwy
Findlay OH 45840
419 422-4341

(G-19503)
OEN CUSTOM CABINETS INC
Also Called: Oen Kitchen & Bath Showroom
8 Willipie St (45895-1969)
PHONE.....................................419 738-8115
Fax: 419 738-8116
Ralph J Oen, *President*
Danielle M Oen, *Vice Pres*
EMP: 3
SALES (est): 398.9K **Privately Held**
SIC: 2434 Wood kitchen cabinets

(G-19504)
ROY HOLTZAPPLE JOHN JOHNS
18526 Williams Rd (45895-7825)
PHONE.....................................419 657-2460
Roy Holtzapple, *Partner*

EMP: 4
SALES (est): 260K **Privately Held**
SIC: 2431 Millwork

(G-19505)
SA-MOR SIGNS
185 Kindle St (45895-8633)
PHONE................................937 441-4950
Don Sleven, *Owner*
EMP: 3
SALES (est): 271.9K **Privately Held**
SIC: 3993 Signs & advertising specialties

(G-19506)
SAFE-GRAIN INC
Also Called: Safe Grain Max Tronix
902 N Dixie Hwy (45895-7738)
PHONE................................513 398-2500
Fax: 419 468-4373
Greg Stevens, *Director*
EMP: 8
SQ FT: 5,000
SALES (corp-wide): 3.4MM **Privately Held**
SIC: 3523 Farm machinery & equipment
PA: Safe-Grain, Inc.
417 Wards Corner Rd Ste B
Loveland OH 45140
513 398-2500

(G-19507)
SIMPLY ELEGANT FORMALS INC
708 N Dixie Hwy (45895-7750)
P.O. Box 127 (45895-0127)
PHONE................................419 738-7722
Brenda Johns, *Principal*
EMP: 3 EST: 2008
SALES (est): 335.3K **Privately Held**
SIC: 2311 Tuxedos: made from purchased materials

(G-19508)
STEVE HENDERSON
1311 Lincoln Hwy (45895-9346)
PHONE................................419 738-6999
EMP: 3
SALES (est): 160K **Privately Held**
SIC: 2411 Logging

(G-19509)
T & S MACHINE INC
712 Maple St (45895-2324)
P.O. Box 579, Ottoville (45876-0579)
PHONE................................419 453-2101
David Kriegel, *President*
William G Petty, *President*
Todd Kriegel, *Vice Pres*
EMP: 18
SQ FT: 2,129
SALES (est): 2.3MM **Privately Held**
WEB: www.tsmachine.com
SIC: 3599 Machine shop, jobbing & repair

(G-19510)
UNITED BUFF & SUPPLY CO INC
2 E Harrison St (45895-1551)
P.O. Box 373 (45895-0373)
PHONE................................419 738-2417
Fax: 419 738-2286
Cora F Slife, *President*
EMP: 8 EST: 1958
SQ FT: 17,000
SALES (est): 710.1K **Privately Held**
SIC: 3291 Buffing or polishing wheels, abrasive or nonabrasive

(G-19511)
VMAXX INC
323 Commerce Rd (45895-8373)
P.O. Box 36, Dover (44622-0036)
PHONE................................419 738-4044
Fax: 419 738-4049
Darren Meyer, *President*
Mark Meyer, *Vice Pres*
Scott Stiles, *Treasurer*
EMP: 10
SQ FT: 20,000
SALES (est): 1.2MM **Privately Held**
WEB: www.vmaxx.biz
SIC: 3542 Extruding machines (machine tools), metal

(G-19512)
WAPAK TOOL & DIE INC
732 Keller Dr (45895-9341)
PHONE................................419 738-6215
Robert H Kantner, *President*
Donald G Kantner, *Corp Secy*
EMP: 4 EST: 1964
SALES: 300K **Privately Held**
SIC: 3544 Special dies, tools, jigs & fixtures

(G-19513)
WHITE FEATHER FOODS INC
Also Called: Whitefeather Foods
13845 Cemetery Rd (45895-8479)
PHONE................................419 738-8975
Fax: 419 738-1952
Stephen L Hengstler, *President*
Dave Jeanneret, *Controller*
EMP: 14
SQ FT: 5,000
SALES: 1MM **Privately Held**
WEB: www.whitefeatherfoods.com
SIC: 2096 2099 Pork rinds; food preparations

(G-19514)
ZIEGLER BROS TOOL & MCH INC
Also Called: Ziegler Brothers Tool & Mch
13790 Infirmary Rd (45895-9358)
PHONE................................419 738-6048
Fax: 419 738-6048
Aretha Ziegler, *President*
Teresa Koon, *Bookkeeper*
EMP: 7
SQ FT: 5,000
SALES (est): 200K **Privately Held**
SIC: 3599 Machine shop, jobbing & repair

Warren
Trumbull County

(G-19515)
ADS MACHINERY CORP
1201 Vine Ave Ne Ste 1 (44483-3834)
P.O. Box 1027 (44482-1027)
PHONE................................330 399-3601
Fax: 330 399-1190
Dale Minton, *President*
K Ramalingham, *Vice Pres*
John Schofer, *Purch Dir*
Patricia S Beil, *CFO*
K Ramalinga, *Sales Executive*
EMP: 75 EST: 1956
SQ FT: 57,000
SALES (est): 16.3MM **Privately Held**
WEB: www.adsmachinery.com
SIC: 3549 3547 Metalworking machinery; rolling mill machinery

(G-19516)
ADVANCED CUSTOM SOUND
1894 Elm Rd Ne (44483-4030)
PHONE................................330 372-9900
Daniel Mezbethh, *Owner*
EMP: 8
SALES (est): 1.1MM **Privately Held**
SIC: 3651 Audio electronic systems

(G-19517)
AJAX TOCCO MAGNETHERMIC CORP (HQ)
1745 Overland Ave Ne (44483-2860)
PHONE................................330 372-8511
Fax: 330 372-8644
Thomas Illencik, *President*
Keith Anderson, *General Mgr*
Gary Andrews, *General Mgr*
John Caruso, *General Mgr*
Chun Lee, *General Mgr*
◆ EMP: 200 EST: 2002
SQ FT: 200,000
SALES (est): 18.6MM
SALES (corp-wide): 1.2B **Publicly Held**
WEB: www.ajaxtocco.com
SIC: 3567 7699 3612 Metal melting furnaces, industrial: electric; industrial machinery & equipment repair; electric furnace transformers

PA: Park-Ohio Holdings Corp.
6065 Parkland Blvd Ste 1
Cleveland OH 44124
440 947-2000

(G-19518)
ALAN BJ COMPANY
3566 Larchmont Ave Ne (44483-2400)
PHONE................................330 372-1201
▲ EMP: 4
SALES (est): 590.2K **Privately Held**
SIC: 2899 Fireworks

(G-19519)
ALPHABET INC (HQ)
8640 E Market St (44484-2346)
PHONE................................330 856-3366
Fax: 330 856-6011
Mark Tervalon, *President*
Cloyd Abruzzo, *Vice Pres*
Michael Jocola, *Vice Pres*
John Norris, *Facilities Mgr*
Susie Martinez, *Accounting Mgr*
EMP: 100 EST: 1977
SALES (est): 64.7MM
SALES (corp-wide): 695.9MM **Publicly Held**
WEB: www.alphabet.com
SIC: 3679 Harness assemblies for electronic use: wire or cable
PA: Stoneridge, Inc.
39675 Mackenzie Dr # 400
Novi MI 48377
248 489-9300

(G-19520)
AM WARREN LLC
Also Called: Arcelormittal Warren
2234 Main Ave Sw (44481)
PHONE................................330 841-2800
Lou Schorsch, *CEO*
Jeff Foster, *Manager*
EMP: 3
SALES (est): 104.8K **Privately Held**
SIC: 3441 Fabricated structural metal

(G-19521)
AMERICAN STEEL & ALLOYS LLC
4000 Mahoning Ave Nw (44483-1924)
PHONE................................330 847-0487
Mordechai Korf, *Principal*
EMP: 40
SALES (est): 5.7MM **Privately Held**
SIC: 3312 Tool & die steel & alloys

(G-19522)
AMERICAN WAY MANUFACTURING INC
1871 Henn Pkwy Sw (44481-8659)
P.O. Box 189, North Jackson (44451-0189)
PHONE................................330 824-2353
Robert E Platt, *President*
Joe Montgomerry, *Controller*
William Ezbeth, *Sales Mgr*
Cindy Fryer, *Manager*
John Resey, *Manager*
EMP: 27
SALES (est): 6.3MM **Privately Held**
WEB: www.americanwaymfg.com
SIC: 3089 Fences, gates & accessories: plastic

(G-19523)
AML INDUSTRIES INC
520 Pine Ave Se Ste 1 (44483-5763)
P.O. Box 4110 (44482-4110)
PHONE................................330 399-5000
Fax: 330 399-5005
Terry L Kartzer, *President*
Robert Hartsough, *Vice Pres*
Elizabeth Cione, *Finance Mgr*
Stacy Jerina, *Financial Analy*
Marie Vickers, *Manager*
▲ EMP: 26
SQ FT: 30,000
SALES: 6.7MM **Privately Held**
WEB: www.amlube.com
SIC: 2992 Lubricating oils

(G-19524)
ANN PRINTING & PROMOTIONS
269 E Market St (44481-1205)
PHONE................................330 399-6564
Tom Opalka, *Owner*
EMP: 3

SALES (est): 281.9K **Privately Held**
SIC: 2752 Commercial printing, offset

(G-19525)
ASTRO TECHNICAL SERVICES INC
2401 Parkman Rd Nw (44485-1758)
PHONE................................330 394-7350
Fax: 330 394-4643
Myron Watts, *Ch of Bd*
Michael Watts, *President*
Paul Ryan, *General Mgr*
Martin Watts, *Vice Pres*
F Adams, *Project Engr*
EMP: 23
SALES (est): 3.6MM
SALES (corp-wide): 65.5MM **Privately Held**
WEB: www.astrotec.com
SIC: 3599 Custom machinery
PA: Astro Manufacturing & Design, Inc.
34459 Curtis Blvd
Eastlake OH 44095
888 215-1746

(G-19526)
BASELINE PRINTING INC
1262 Youngstown Rd Se (44484-4242)
PHONE................................330 369-3204
Rey Collazo, *President*
Carolyn Collazo, *Treasurer*
EMP: 3 EST: 1970
SQ FT: 3,000
SALES: 320K **Privately Held**
SIC: 2752 Commercial printing, offset

(G-19527)
BEE JAX INC
156 Vermont Ave Sw (44485-2657)
PHONE................................330 373-0500
Bill T Jackson Jr, *President*
Bill Jackson, *President*
EMP: 3 EST: 1997
SALES (est): 823.5K **Privately Held**
SIC: 3545 Vises, machine (machine tool accessories)

(G-19528)
BEHLKE DALENE
Also Called: Ram Racewares
958 Tod Ave Nw (44485-2826)
PHONE................................330 399-6780
Dalene Behlke, *Owner*
EMP: 3
SALES (est): 171.8K **Privately Held**
SIC: 3751 5013 Motorcycles, bicycles & parts; motorcycle parts

(G-19529)
BLOOM INDUSTRIES INC
Also Called: Incredible Plastics
1052 Mahoney Ave Nw (44483)
PHONE................................330 898-3878
Fax: 330 898-3874
Ted E Bloom, *President*
Paul Fridley, *Controller*
EMP: 60
SQ FT: 95,000
SALES (est): 9.9MM **Privately Held**
SIC: 3089 3544 Injection molding of plastics; special dies, tools, jigs & fixtures

(G-19530)
BOSTON SCNTFIC NRMDLATION CORP
2174 Sarkies Dr Ne (44483-4262)
PHONE................................330 372-2652
P A Martof, *Principal*
EMP: 154
SALES (corp-wide): 8.3B **Publicly Held**
SIC: 3842 Hearing aids
HQ: Boston Scientific Neuromodulation Corporation
25155 Rye Canyon Loop
Valencia CA 91355
661 949-4310

(G-19531)
BUCKEYE MEDICAL TECH LLC
405 Niles Cortland Rd Se # 202 (44484-2460)
PHONE................................330 719-9868
Terry B Philibin,
EMP: 7 EST: 2009
SALES (est): 262.6K **Privately Held**
SIC: 3841 Surgical & medical instruments

(G-19532)
BUDDY BACKYARD INC
140 Dana St Ne (44483-3845)
PHONE..............................330 393-9353
Jan Kiftler, *President*
Pam Chrisopouios, *Manager*
▲ EMP: 25
SALES (est): 4.9MM **Privately Held**
SIC: 3559 Automotive related machinery

(G-19533)
C & P METALS INC
2880 Sferra Ave Nw (44483-2272)
PHONE..............................724 510-4293
EMP: 5
SALES (est): 218.2K **Privately Held**
SIC: 3399 Metal fasteners

(G-19534)
CHARLES MFG CO
3021 Sferra Ave Nw (44483-2268)
PHONE..............................330 395-3490
Fax: 330 395-3034
David Frazier, *President*
Christine M Frazier, *Corp Secy*
Mark Frazier, *Sales Mgr*
EMP: 13
SQ FT: 10,000
SALES (est): 2.4MM **Privately Held**
WEB: www.charlesmfg.com
SIC: 3441 5039 Fabricated structural
metal; architectural metalwork

(G-19535)
**CLARKWESTERN DIETRICH
BUILDING**
Also Called: Clark Dietrich Building
1985 N River Rd Ne (44483-2527)
PHONE..............................330 372-5564
EMP: 7
SALES (corp-wide): 8.1B **Privately Held**
SIC: 3444 8711 3081 Studs & joists,
sheet metal; engineering services; vinyl
film & sheet
HQ: Clarkwestern Dietrich Building Sys-
tems Llc
9100 Centre Pointe Dr # 210
West Chester OH 45069

(G-19536)
COLOR 3 EMBROIDERY INC
387 Chestnut Ave Ne (44483-5856)
P.O. Box 870 (44482-0870)
PHONE..............................330 652-9495
Fax: 330 652-9487
Traci Miller, *President*
Don Wiley, *Vice Pres*
EMP: 8
SQ FT: 3,600
SALES (est): 375K **Privately Held**
WEB: www.color3.com
SIC: 2395 Embroidery & art needlework

(G-19537)
CONDO INCORPORATED
3869 Niles Rd Se (44484-3548)
PHONE..............................330 609-6021
John Condoleon, *CEO*
Janice Schneider, *Accounts Mgr*
EMP: 55
SQ FT: 40,000
SALES: 4MM **Privately Held**
WEB: www.warrenscrewmachine.com
SIC: 3451 Screw machine products

(G-19538)
CSC LTD
4000 Mahoning Ave Nw (44483-1924)
PHONE..............................330 841-6011
Fax: 330 841-7108
Butch John, *Manager*
EMP: 4
SALES (est): 546.3K **Privately Held**
SIC: 3312 Blast furnaces & steel mills

(G-19539)
CURRENT INC
455 N River Rd Nw (44483-2250)
PHONE..............................330 392-5151
Todd Buratti, *CEO*
EMP: 8
SALES (corp-wide): 11.5MM **Privately
Held**
WEB: www.currentcomposites.com
SIC: 2821 Thermosetting materials

PA: Current, Inc.
30 Tyler Street Ext
East Haven CT 06512
203 469-1337

(G-19540)
D M V SUPPLY CORPORATION
Also Called: United Safety Authority
3047 Anderson Anthony (44481-9450)
PHONE..............................330 847-0450
Virginia Chicoine, *President*
David Chicoine, *Vice Pres*
Michael Chicoine, *Vice Pres*
EMP: 3
SQ FT: 2,200
SALES: 800K **Privately Held**
WEB: www.unitedsafetyauthority.com
SIC: 2672 5084 Tape, pressure sensitive:
made from purchased materials; safety
equipment

(G-19541)
**DELPHI AUTOMOTIVE SYSTEMS
LLC**
Warren Plant 11
1265 N River Rd Ne Plant11 (44483-2352)
P.O. Box 431 (44486-0001)
PHONE..............................248 813-2000
Donald R Dedow, *Opers-Prdtn-Mfg*
Jon Anderson, *Purchasing*
James Spencer, *Branch Mgr*
EMP: 300 **Privately Held**
SIC: 3357 Automotive wire & cable, except
ignition sets: nonferrous
HQ: Delphi Automotive Systems, Llc
5725 Delphi Dr
Troy MI 48098
248 813-2000

(G-19542)
**DELPHI AUTOMOTIVE SYSTEMS
LLC**
4551 Research Prwy (44483)
PHONE..............................330 306-1000
Robert Verhotz, *Engineer*
Bob Verhotz, *Manager*
Robert Seidler, *Director*
EMP: 400 **Privately Held**
WEB: www.delphiauto.com
SIC: 3714 Air conditioner parts, motor vehi-
cle
HQ: Delphi Automotive Systems, Llc
5725 Delphi Dr
Troy MI 48098
248 813-2000

(G-19543)
DIETRICH INDUSTRIES INC
Also Called: Dietrich Metal Framing
1300 Phoenix Rd Ne (44483-2851)
PHONE..............................330 372-4014
Fax: 330 372-4859
Greg Samsa, *Branch Mgr*
Theresa Naylor, *Manager*
Carrie Probst, *Personnel Assit*
EMP: 200
SALES (corp-wide): 2.8B **Publicly Held**
WEB: www.dietrichmetalframing.com
SIC: 3441 Building components, structural
steel
HQ: Dietrich Industries, Inc.
200 W Old Wilson Brdge Rd
Worthington OH 43085
800 873-2604

(G-19544)
DIETRICH INDUSTRIES INC
1985 N River Rd Ne (44483-2527)
PHONE..............................330 372-2868
Fax: 330 372-4055
Bill Tomlinson, *Purch Agent*
Joe Labus, *Manager*
EMP: 180
SALES (corp-wide): 2.8B **Publicly Held**
WEB: www.dietrichmetalframing.com
SIC: 3312 Primary finished or semifinished
shapes
HQ: Dietrich Industries, Inc.
200 W Old Wilson Brdge Rd
Worthington OH 43085
800 873-2604

(G-19545)
**DRAKE MANUFACTURING SVCS
CO**
4371 N Leavitt Rd Nw (44485-1199)
PHONE..............................330 847-7291
Fax: 330 847-6323
James Vosmik, *President*
Don Lacertosa, *Vice Pres*
Gary Cantelmi, *Engineer*
Casey Downs, *Engineer*
Stig Mowatt, *Treasurer*
▲ EMP: 90 EST: 1972
SQ FT: 47,000
SALES (est): 27.6MM **Privately Held**
WEB: www.drakemfg.com
SIC: 3541 Machine tool replacement & re-
pair parts, metal cutting types; drilling &
boring machines; grinding machines, met-
alworking

(G-19546)
DROP ZONE LTD
3680 N River Rd Ne (44484-1031)
PHONE..............................234 806-4604
EMP: 4
SALES (est): 272.2K **Privately Held**
SIC: 3949 Shooting equipment & supplies,
general

(G-19547)
EMT INC
1201 Vine Ave Ne Ste 2 (44483-3834)
PHONE..............................330 399-6939
Fax: 330 393-6940
David F Gerback, *President*
Wanda S Gerback, *Vice Pres*
Merinda Stephenson, *Office Mgr*
EMP: 4
SQ FT: 7,000
SALES: 250K **Privately Held**
WEB: www.emtinc.biz
SIC: 3613 Control panels, electric

(G-19548)
EVERETT INDUSTRIES INC
3601 Larchmont Ave Ne (44483-2447)
P.O. Box 2068 (44484-0068)
PHONE..............................330 372-3700
Fax: 330 372-3118
William Everett, *President*
Roy Williams, *Vice Pres*
Carol Gintert, *Office Mgr*
Estate of Charles T Everett, *Shareholder*
EMP: 24 **EST: 1962**
SQ FT: 25,000
SALES (est): 3.9MM **Privately Held**
WEB: www.everett-ind.com
SIC: 3291 Abrasive wheels & grindstones,
not artificial

(G-19549)
**FAURECIA EXHAUST SYSTEMS
LLC**
1849 Ellsworth Bailey Rd (44481-9234)
PHONE..............................330 824-2807
Fax: 330 824-0089
Dana Bower, *Branch Mgr*
Robert Guertin, *Supervisor*
EMP: 182
SALES (corp-wide): 271.8MM **Privately
Held**
WEB: www.franklin.faurecia.com
SIC: 3714 Mufflers (exhaust), motor vehi-
cle
HQ: Faurecia Exhaust Systems, Llc
543 Matzinger Rd
Toledo OH 43612
419 727-5000

(G-19550)
FINE LINE TOOL AND DIE INC
Also Called: Fabco Tool and Machine
1804 Roberts Ln Ne (44483-3665)
PHONE..............................330 782-8139
Tom Huskin, *President*
EMP: 14
SQ FT: 7,000
SALES: 1.5MM **Privately Held**
SIC: 3544 Extrusion dies

(G-19551)
FLEX-STRUT INC
2900 Commonwealth Ave Ne (44483-2831)
PHONE..............................330 372-9999
Fax: 330 372-3666

Dale H Gebhardt, *President*
Larry Mears, *Vice Pres*
Jerry Selina, *Controller*
Mark Mirini, *Admin Sec*
EMP: 75
SQ FT: 52,000
SALES (est): 29.1MM **Privately Held**
WEB: www.flexstrut.com
SIC: 3441 3429 Fabricated structural
metal; manufactured hardware (general)

(G-19552)
GARBER MACHINE CO
1788 Drexel Ave Nw (44485-2120)
PHONE..............................330 399-4181
Roger L Garber, *Owner*
EMP: 3
SALES (est): 189.7K **Privately Held**
SIC: 3599 Machine shop, jobbing & repair

(G-19553)
GENERAL MOTORS LLC
2300 Hallock Young Rd Sw (44481-9238)
PHONE..............................330 824-5000
Fax: 330 824-7477
Daniel Wood, *Superintendent*
Jim Hiller, *Engineer*
Thomas E Will, *Engineer*
Jerry Butler, *Human Res Dir*
Jennifer Tremayne, *Human Resources*
EMP: 1053
SALES (corp-wide): 166.3MM **Publicly
Held**
SIC: 3711 Automobile assembly, including
specialty automobiles
HQ: General Motors Llc
300 Renaissance Ctr L1
Detroit MI 48243

(G-19554)
GENERAL MOTORS LLC
2369 Ellsworth Bailey Rd (44481-9235)
PHONE..............................330 824-5840
John Berestecki, *Plant Mgr*
Bruce Pierson, *Plant Mgr*
Thomas Will, *Engrg Dir*
Richard Whittington, *Engineer*
Richard Beany, *Finance*
EMP: 277
SALES (corp-wide): 166.3MM **Publicly
Held**
SIC: 3465 3714 Automotive stampings;
motor vehicle parts & accessories
HQ: General Motors Llc
300 Renaissance Ctr L1
Detroit MI 48243

(G-19555)
GLUNT INDUSTRIES INC
319 N River Rd Nw (44483-2248)
PHONE..............................330 399-7585
Fax: 330 399-0387
Dennis Glunt, *President*
Mary Ann Patrick, *Principal*
Gary Shells, *Principal*
Harold Glunt, *Vice Pres*
Stuart Gladstone, *CFO*
▲ EMP: 125
SQ FT: 150,000
SALES (est): 28.3MM **Privately Held**
SIC: 3599 3549 3444 Machine shop, job-
bing & repair; custom machinery; metal-
working machinery; sheet metalwork

(G-19556)
**HANGER PRSTHETCS & ORTHO
INC**
8029 E Market St (44484-2229)
PHONE..............................330 856-6990
Joseph Whiteside, *Branch Mgr*
EMP: 7
SALES (corp-wide): 460MM **Publicly
Held**
SIC: 3842 Limbs, artificial
HQ: Hanger Prosthetics & Orthotics, Inc.
10910 Domain Dr Ste 300
Austin TX 78758
512 777-3800

(G-19557)
HARSCO CORPORATION
Harsco Minerals International
101 Tidewater St Ne (44483-2434)
PHONE..............................330 372-1781
Brian Conlon, *Branch Mgr*
EMP: 75

SALES (corp-wide): 1.4B **Publicly Held**
SIC: 2816 2899 Metallic & mineral pigments; chemical preparations
PA: Harsco Corporation
350 Poplar Church Rd
Camp Hill PA 17011
717 763-7064

(G-19558)
HARVEST SAND AND GRAVEL INC
522 Perkins Dr Nw (44483-4616)
PHONE..............................330 372-4408
Herbert Cottrell, *President*
Dick Gurley, *Vice Pres*
EMP: 4
SALES: 304.7K **Privately Held**
SIC: 1442 Construction sand & gravel

(G-19559)
INCREDIBLE SOLUTIONS INC
1052 Mahoning Ave Nw (44483-4622)
PHONE..............................330 898-3878
Ted Bloom, *CEO*
Paul Fridley, *CFO*
▲ **EMP:** 16
SALES: 5.9MM **Privately Held**
WEB: www.bloomindustries.com
SIC: 2821 Molding compounds, plastics

(G-19560)
INTERNATIONAL STEEL GROUP
2234 Main Street Ext Sw (44481-9602)
PHONE..............................330 841-2800
Rodney Mott, *President*
Jeff Foster, *General Mgr*
EMP: 135
SALES (est): 17.6MM **Privately Held**
WEB: www.internationalsteelgroup.com
SIC: 3312 1011 Blast furnaces & steel mills; iron ores
HQ: Arcelormittal Usa Llc
1 S Dearborn St Ste 1800
Chicago IL 60603
312 346-0300

(G-19561)
J & L WELDING FABRICATING INC
140 Dana St Ne (44483-3845)
PHONE..............................330 393-9353
Fax: 330 392-9311
Larry Grossa, *CEO*
Janet Kistler, *President*
EMP: 17
SALES (est): 3.3MM **Privately Held**
SIC: 3449 7692 3444 3441 Bars, concrete reinforcing: fabricated steel; welding repair; sheet metalwork; fabricated structural metal

(G-19562)
J W GOSS CO INC (PA)
Also Called: Reds Auto Glass Shop
410 South St Sw (44483-5737)
P.O. Box 1066 (44482-1066)
PHONE..............................330 395-0739
Fax: 330 395-0739
EMP: 14
SQ FT: 20,000
SALES (est): 1.6MM **Privately Held**
SIC: 7536 3429 Auto Glass Replacement Mfg Hardware

(G-19563)
JB INDUSTRIES LTD (PA)
160 Clifton Dr Ne Ste 4 (44484-1820)
PHONE..............................330 856-4587
Fax: 330 856-4587
Bruce O Bancroft, *VP Mfg*
Mary Martin, *Draft/Design*
John E Bancroft,
EMP: 14
SQ FT: 1,800
SALES (est): 2.5MM **Privately Held**
WEB: www.jb-industries.com
SIC: 8711 3599 Industrial engineers; machine shop, jobbing & repair; custom machinery

(G-19564)
JUST QUILT IT INC
2298 High St Nw (44483-1292)
PHONE..............................330 469-6956
Dorothy Bettiker, *Owner*
EMP: 4 EST: 2010

SALES (est): 366.8K **Privately Held**
SIC: 2395 Quilting & quilting supplies

(G-19565)
KELLOGG COMPANY
655 N River Rd Nw (44483-2254)
PHONE..............................330 306-1500
EMP: 385
SALES (corp-wide): 13B **Publicly Held**
SIC: 2043 Cereal breakfast foods
PA: Kellogg Company
1 Kellogg Sq
Battle Creek MI 49017
269 961-2000

(G-19566)
KLEESE DEVELOPMENT ASSOCIATES
103 W Market St Ste 300 (44481-1017)
PHONE..............................330 392-7899
Fax: 330 392-9022
Mary Ann Kleese, *CEO*
Nick S Perod, *Principal*
Edward A Kleese, *Vice Pres*
EMP: 4
SALES (est): 2.7MM **Privately Held**
WEB: www.kleesedevelop.com
SIC: 1381 Drilling oil & gas wells

(G-19567)
LAIRD CONTROLS HOLDINGS INC (HQ)
655 N River Rd Nw Ste A (44483-2254)
PHONE..............................234 806-0018
Rick Morse, *President*
Lori Grace, *Corp Secy*
Thomas McFall, *Vice Pres*
Kathy Vincent, *Executive Asst*
EMP: 24
SALES (est): 20MM
SALES (corp-wide): 950.5MM **Privately Held**
WEB: www.cattron.com
SIC: 3625 7622 5065 5063 Relays & industrial controls; communication equipment repair; communication equipment; closed circuit television; electric alarms & signaling equipment; equipment rental & leasing; hoists, cranes & monorails
PA: Laird Plc
100 Pall Mall
London SW1Y
207 468-4040

(G-19568)
LAIRD CONTROLS NORTH AMER INC (DH)
Also Called: Remtron
655 N River Rd Nw Ste A (44483-2254)
PHONE..............................234 806-0018
Rick Morse, *General Mgr*
Wendy Reed, *Opers Mgr*
Lori Grace, *Finance Dir*
Deborah Montgomery, *Administration*
◆ **EMP:** 19
SQ FT: 25,000
SALES (est): 17.9MM
SALES (corp-wide): 950.5MM **Privately Held**
WEB: www.cattron-theimeg.com
SIC: 3625 Relays & industrial controls
HQ: Laird Controls Holdings Inc
655 N River Rd Nw Ste A
Warren OH 44483
234 806-0018

(G-19569)
LAIRD TECHNOLOGIES INC
655 N River Rd Nw (44483-2254)
PHONE..............................234 806-0105
EMP: 8
SALES (corp-wide): 950.5MM **Privately Held**
SIC: 3443 Nuclear shielding, metal plate
HQ: Laird Technologies, Inc.
3481 Rider Trl S
Earth City MO 63045
636 898-6000

(G-19570)
LIBERTY STEEL INDUSTRIES INC (PA)
2207 Larchmont Ave Ne (44483-2834)
P.O. Box 70 (44482-0070)
PHONE..............................330 372-6363

James T Weller, *President*
Joe Dubaj, *General Mgr*
Phil Latmardo, *CFO*
EMP: 55 EST: 2015
SALES (est): 24MM **Privately Held**
SIC: 3469 Metal stampings

(G-19571)
LIBERTY STEEL INDUSTRIES INC
900 Dietz Rd Ne (44483-2755)
PHONE..............................330 372-6363
James T Weller, *President*
EMP: 49
SALES (corp-wide): 24MM **Privately Held**
SIC: 3469 Metal stampings
PA: Liberty Steel Industries, Inc.
2207 Larchmont Ave Ne
Warren OH 44483
330 372-6363

(G-19572)
LINDE LLC
2000 Pine Ave Se (44483-6550)
PHONE..............................330 394-4541
Rick Julius, *Manager*
EMP: 6
SALES (corp-wide): 17.9B **Privately Held**
SIC: 2813 Industrial gases
HQ: Linde Llc
200 Somerset Corporate Bl
Bridgewater NJ 08807
908 464-8100

(G-19573)
LITCO MANUFACTURING LLC
1512 Phoenix Rd Ne (44483-2855)
P.O. Box 150, Vienna (44473-0150)
PHONE..............................330 539-5433
Lionel F Trebilcock, *CEO*
Raymond W Snider, *Principal*
Gary Tredilcock, *COO*
Gwen Matricardi, *Accountant*
▲ **EMP:** 17
SALES: 1.2MM
SALES (corp-wide): 4.7MM **Privately Held**
SIC: 2448 Wood pallets & skids
PA: Litco International, Inc.
1 Litco Dr
Vienna OH 44473
330 539-5433

(G-19574)
LRB TOOL & DIE LTD
3303 Parkman Rd Nw (44481-9142)
PHONE..............................330 898-5783
Lee Ann Westenselder, *Corp Secy*
Leeann Westenfelder, *Treasurer*
George Pearce, *Mng Member*
EMP: 10
SALES: 750K **Privately Held**
SIC: 3544 Special dies, tools, jigs & fixtures

(G-19575)
MACKLAND CO INC
Also Called: Hal Mar Printing
155 North St Nw (44483-3715)
P.O. Box 84 (44482-0084)
PHONE..............................330 399-5034
Fax: 330 399-8070
Doreen Romack, *President*
Victor A Romack, *Vice Pres*
EMP: 4 EST: 1972
SQ FT: 9,000
SALES: 200K **Privately Held**
SIC: 2752 Commercial printing, offset

(G-19576)
MAGNA SEATING AMERICA INC
Also Called: Intier Sting Systems-Lordstown
1702 Henn Pkwy Sw (44481-8656)
PHONE..............................330 824-3101
Sean Ewing, *Branch Mgr*
Gary Lawson, *Info Tech Mgr*
EMP: 250
SALES (corp-wide): 36.4B **Privately Held**
SIC: 3714 2531 Motor vehicle parts & accessories; seats, automobile
HQ: Magna Seating Of America, Inc.
39600 Lewis Dr Ste 216
Novi MI 48377
248 553-8094

(G-19577)
MAGNEFORCE INC
155 Shaffer Dr Ne (44484-1842)
P.O. Box 8508 (44484-0508)
PHONE..............................330 856-9300
Fax: 330 856-9301
Richard Miller, *President*
David Miller, *Vice Pres*
Linda Stango, *Admin Sec*
EMP: 10
SQ FT: 5,900
SALES (est): 1.7MM **Privately Held**
WEB: www.magneforce.com
SIC: 3567 Induction heating equipment

(G-19578)
MATALCO (US) INC
5120 Tod Ave Sw (44481-9748)
PHONE..............................234 806-0600
Armand Sanguigni, *President*
EMP: 4 **Privately Held**
SIC: 3363 Aluminum die-castings

(G-19579)
MSSL WIRING SYSTEM INC (HQ)
8640 E Market St (44484-2346)
PHONE..............................330 856-3344
Jitender Mahajan, *President*
Duncan Reid, *COO*
EMP: 99
SQ FT: 24,570
SALES (est): 36.8MM
SALES (corp-wide): 781.8MM **Privately Held**
SIC: 3679 Harness assemblies for electronic use: wire or cable
PA: Motherson Sumi Systems Limited
11th Floor, Plot No.1, Sector-127,
Noida UP 20130
120 667-9270

(G-19580)
NOVELIS CORPORATION
390 Griswold St Ne (44483-2738)
P.O. Box 1151 (44482-1151)
PHONE..............................330 841-3456
Patricia Peterson, *Purchasing*
R J Kovach, *Finance Other*
Mervyn W Bell, *Branch Mgr*
Ronald Borkes, *Manager*
EMP: 93
SALES (corp-wide): 5B **Privately Held**
SIC: 3355 3353 Aluminum rolling & drawing; aluminum sheet, plate & foil
HQ: Novelis Corporation
3560 Lenox Rd Ne Ste 2000
Atlanta GA 30326
404 760-4000

(G-19581)
OAKES FOUNDRY INC
700 Bronze Rd Ne (44483-2720)
PHONE..............................330 372-4010
Fax: 330 372-2842
Grant Oakes, *President*
Chas Antinone, *General Mgr*
Roger Johnson, *Prdtn Mgr*
EMP: 21 EST: 1929
SQ FT: 2,000
SALES (est): 5MM **Privately Held**
WEB: www.oakesfoundry.com
SIC: 3366 Castings (except die): bronze; castings (except die): copper & copper-base alloy

(G-19582)
OGDEN NEWSPAPERS INC
Also Called: Tribune Chronicle
240 Franklin St Se (44483-5711)
PHONE..............................330 841-1600
Fax: 330 841-1721
Doug Chapin, *Editor*
Bob Coupland, *Editor*
Joseph Landsberger, *Editor*
Brenda Linert, *Editor*
Theresa Munnell, *Editor*
EMP: 210
SALES (corp-wide): 617.1MM **Privately Held**
SIC: 2711 2752 Newspapers: publishing only, not printed on site; commercial printing, lithographic
PA: The Ogden Newspapers Inc
1500 Main St
Wheeling WV 26003
304 233-0100

GEOGRAPHIC

(G-19583)
OHIO STAR FORGE CO
4000 Mahoning Ave Nw (44482-1924)
P.O. Box 430 (44482-0430)
PHONE..............................330 847-6360
Fax: 330 847-6368
William J Orbach, *CEO*
William Orbach, *Plant Mgr*
David James, *Maint Spvr*
Mark Presley, *Maint Spvr*
Dorothy Daley, *Opers Staff*
▲ EMP: 84
SQ FT: 150,000
SALES (est): 18.7MM
SALES (corp-wide): 3.9B **Privately Held**
WEB: www.ohiostar.com
SIC: 3463 Automotive forgings, nonferrous
PA: Daido Steel Co., Ltd.
    1-1-10, Higashisakura, Higashi-Ku
    Nagoya AIC 461-0
    529 637-501

(G-19584)
OHIO TRAILER INC
1899 Tod Ave Sw (44485-4221)
P.O. Box 3010 (44485-0010)
PHONE..............................330 392-4444
John Miller, *President*
Chuck Everman, *Systems Staff*
EMP: 18
SQ FT: 20,000
SALES (est): 1.6MM **Privately Held**
SIC: 5231 7692 7538 3444 Paint, glass
& wallpaper; welding repair; general auto-
motive repair shops; sheet metalwork

(G-19585)
**ORTHOTICS & PROSTHETICS
REHAB**
Also Called: Billock, John N Cpo
700 Howland Wilson Rd Se (44484-2512)
PHONE..............................330 856-2553
Fax: 330 856-4619
John N Billock, *Director*
Kathleen A Fike, *Admin Dir*
EMP: 11
SQ FT: 9,000
SALES (est): 1.5MM **Privately Held**
WEB: www.oandpcenter.com
SIC: 3842 8011 Braces, orthopedic; limbs,
artificial; offices & clinics of medical doc-
tors

(G-19586)
PHOENIX TOOL CO INC
1351 Phoenix Rd Ne (44483-2899)
PHONE..............................330 372-4627
Fax: 330 372-5158
Eric Fredenburg, *President*
Jeff Copeland, *Vice Pres*
Betty L Fredenburg, *Treasurer*
Joel Fredenburg, *Treasurer*
Harlan R Fredenburg, *Shareholder*
EMP: 8 EST: 1949
SQ FT: 5,000
SALES (est): 800K **Privately Held**
WEB: www.phoenixtoolco.com
SIC: 3599 Machine shop, jobbing & repair

(G-19587)
PORTAGE RESOURCES INC
8650 Kimblewick Ln Ne (44484-2068)
PHONE..............................330 872-3827
William R Templeton, *President*
Norman Darl Templeton, *Vice Pres*
Robert P Templeton, *Treasurer*
Eric A Templeton, *Admin Sec*
EMP: 4
SQ FT: 800
SALES (est): 330K **Privately Held**
SIC: 1381 Drilling oil & gas wells

(G-19588)
PPG INDUSTRIES INC
2823 Ellsworth Bailey Rd (44481-9201)
PHONE..............................330 824-2537
Fax: 330 824-3661
Charles Bunch, *Branch Mgr*
EMP: 24
SALES (corp-wide): 14.7B **Publicly Held**
WEB: www.ppg.com
SIC: 2851 Paints & allied products
PA: Ppg Industries, Inc.
    1 Ppg Pl
    Pittsburgh PA 15272
    412 434-3131

(G-19589)
PREMIUM MEATS INC
241 Logan Ave Ne (44483-5841)
PHONE..............................330 394-8651
Michael Kassos, *President*
Matthew Kassos, *Vice Pres*
Harriet Kassos, *Manager*
Parisa Tos, *Manager*
EMP: 15
SQ FT: 27,000
SALES (est): 3.2MM **Privately Held**
WEB: www.premiummeats.com
SIC: 2011 Meat packing plants

(G-19590)
PRODUCTION PACKAGING INC
5232 Tod Ave Sw Ste 12 (44481-9729)
PHONE..............................330 392-4155
Brad Yergan, *President*
Deborah Hasley, *Manager*
EMP: 12
SQ FT: 108,000
SALES (est): 1MM **Privately Held**
SIC: 2631 Container, packaging &
boxboard

(G-19591)
RAPTIS COFFEE INC
341 Main Ave Sw (44481-1044)
PHONE..............................330 399-7011
Ilias Raptis, *President*
Marianne Raptis, *Corp Secy*
George Raptis, *Vice Pres*
EMP: 3
SQ FT: 8,000
SALES: 200K **Privately Held**
WEB: www.raptiscoffee.com
SIC: 2095 Roasted coffee; coffee roasting
(except by wholesale grocers)

(G-19592)
RED HOT STUDIOS
728 Shadowood Ln Se (44484-2441)
PHONE..............................330 609-7446
Fax: 330 609-7446
William L Snyder, *Owner*
EMP: 4
SQ FT: 3,000
SALES: 350K **Privately Held**
WEB: www.redhotstudios.com
SIC: 3993 Signs & advertising specialties;
displays & cutouts, window & lobby

(G-19593)
**REINFORCEMENT SYSTEMS
OHIO LLC**
Also Called: Merksteijn
3121 W Market St (44485-3070)
PHONE..............................330 469-6958
Mark Cornman, *CFO*
John Banko, *Manager*
Peter Van Merksteijn,
William Gallenz,
Mark Marvin,
▲ EMP: 8
SALES (est): 990K **Privately Held**
SIC: 3315 Wire & fabricated wire products

(G-19594)
RESCO PRODUCTS INC
1929 Larchmont Ave Ne (44483-3507)
PHONE..............................330 372-3716
Ryan Marshall, *Buyer*
EMP: 30
SALES (corp-wide): 192.1MM **Privately
Held**
SIC: 3255 3272 Clay refractories; con-
crete products, precast
PA: Resco Products, Inc.
    1 Robinson Plz Ste 300
    Pittsburgh PA 15205
    412 494-4491

(G-19595)
**RICHMOND CONCRETE
PRODUCTS**
Also Called: Portage Septic Tank
3640 Kibler Toot Rd Sw (44481-9159)
PHONE..............................330 673-7892
Wayne Richmond, *President*
Lou Richmond, *Corp Secy*
Nicole Richmond, *Treasurer*
EMP: 5
SALES (est): 598.4K **Privately Held**
SIC: 3272 Septic tanks, concrete

(G-19596)
**RINALDI AND PACKARD
INDUSTRIES**
Also Called: Northeastern Machinery
775 And A Half Nles Rd Se (44483)
PHONE..............................330 395-4942
Fax: 330 395-4942
Kevin Rinaldi, *President*
Barb Rinaldi, *Corp Secy*
EMP: 3
SQ FT: 1,250
SALES (est): 230K **Privately Held**
SIC: 3599 Machine shop, jobbing & repair

(G-19597)
SANESE SERVICES INC
Also Called: Sanese Vending Company
2590 Elm Rd Ne (44483-2904)
PHONE..............................330 494-5900
Fax: 330 494-8059
Kris Holzopsel, *Manager*
Kris Holzopfel, *Executive*
EMP: 50
SALES (corp-wide): 117.4MM **Privately
Held**
WEB: www.sanese.com
SIC: 5962 2099 Sandwich & hot food
vending machines; food preparations
PA: Sanese Services, Inc.
    2590 Elm Rd Ne
    Warren OH 44483
    614 436-1234

(G-19598)
SCHAEFER EQUIPMENT INC
1590 Phoenix Rd Ne (44483-2896)
PHONE..............................330 372-4006
Fax: 330 372-4089
Rich Barnhart, *CEO*
Barry Anderson, *Vice Pres*
David Cline, *Research*
▲ EMP: 80
SQ FT: 101,000
SALES (est): 23.2MM
SALES (corp-wide): 2.9B **Publicly Held**
WEB: www.schaeferequipment.net
SIC: 3462 Iron & steel forgings; railroad
wheels, axles, frogs or other equipment:
forged
HQ: Wabtec Corporation
    1001 Airbrake Ave
    Wilmerding PA 15148

(G-19599)
SCOTT EMERSON
Also Called: Master Street Engineering
2541 Larchmont Ave Ne (44483-2840)
PHONE..............................330 372-1040
Scott Emerson, *Owner*
EMP: 8
SQ FT: 2,400
SALES (est): 117K **Privately Held**
SIC: 3714 Frames, motor vehicle

(G-19600)
SHALELOGIX LLC
1800 N River Rd Ne (44483-2442)
PHONE..............................234 600-5839
Jason Nicholas,
EMP: 7
SALES (est): 739.2K **Privately Held**
SIC: 1389 Impounding & storing salt water,
oil & gas field

(G-19601)
**SPECIALTIES MDS INDUCTION
LTD**
762 E Market St (44481-1214)
PHONE..............................330 394-3338
Fax: 330 394-3486
David G Moyer, *President*
John Bevlin, *Partner*
Ron Snyder, *Partner*
EMP: 4
SQ FT: 16,000
SALES (est): 638.6K **Privately Held**
SIC: 3567 Induction heating equipment

(G-19602)
SUMMIT STREET NEWS INC
645 Summit St Nw (44485-2811)
P.O. Box 1270 (44482-1270)
PHONE..............................330 609-5600
Kenneth Heyman, *Principal*
EMP: 5
SALES (est): 242.8K **Privately Held**
SIC: 2711 Newspapers, publishing & print-
ing

(G-19603)
SUPERIOR CUP INC
448 E Market St (44481-1208)
PHONE..............................330 393-6187
Fax: 330 393-6199
Steve Papadimas, *President*
EMP: 27
SQ FT: 24,000
SALES (est): 8MM **Privately Held**
SIC: 2656 Sanitary food containers; cups,
paper: made from purchased material

(G-19604)
TECNOCAP LLC
Also Called: Warren Metal Lithography
2100 Griswold St Ne (44483-2750)
PHONE..............................330 392-7222
Brian Bates, *Plant Mgr*
Patti Davis, *Controller*
Bob Macosko, *Sales Dir*
Ric Smith, *Manager*
EMP: 52
SALES (corp-wide): 54.4MM **Privately
Held**
SIC: 3354 2752 Aluminum extruded prod-
ucts; lithographing on metal
HQ: Tecnocap Llc
    1701 Wheeling Ave
    Glen Dale WV 26038
    304 845-3402

(G-19605)
THERM-O-LINK INC
Also Called: Vulkor
621 Dana St Ne Ste 5 (44483-3977)
PHONE..............................330 393-7600
Emil Foriska, *Mfg Staff*
John Mullen, *Manager*
Bryan Crouch, *Supervisor*
EMP: 7
SQ FT: 18,000
SALES (corp-wide): 41.2MM **Privately
Held**
WEB: www.tolwire.com
SIC: 3357 Nonferrous wiredrawing & insu-
lating
PA: Therm-O-Link, Inc.
    10513 Freedom St
    Garrettsville OH 44231
    330 527-2124

(G-19606)
THERM-O-LINK OF TEXAS INC
621 Dana St Ne Ste V (44483-3977)
PHONE..............................330 393-4300
Ronald M Krisher, *President*
EMP: 4 EST: 2015
SALES (est): 206.2K **Privately Held**
SIC: 3357 Nonferrous wiredrawing & insu-
lating

(G-19607)
THOMAS ENTERPRISES
263 Lowell Ave Ne (44483-5843)
PHONE..............................330 394-4483
Fax: 330 394-4483
Tim C Thomas, *Partner*
Zach Economos, *Partner*
EMP: 6
SALES: 100K **Privately Held**
SIC: 3672 3822 Printed circuit boards;
auto controls regulating residntl & coml
environmt & applncs

(G-19608)
**THOMAS STEEL STRIP
CORPORATION**
Also Called: Tata Steel Plating
2518 W Market St (44485)
PHONE..............................330 841-6429
Fax: 330 841-6187
William Boyd, *President*
Jonathan M Jarvis, *Vice Pres*
Kim Grey, *Safety Mgr*
John McHale, *Manager*
Malcom Loucks, *Info Tech Dir*
▲ EMP: 300
SALES (est): 82.1MM
SALES (corp-wide): 5.5B **Privately Held**
WEB: www.corusgroup.com
SIC: 3316 Cold finishing of steel shapes

▲ = Import ▼=Export
◆ =Import/Export

HQ: Tata Steel Europe Limited
30 Millbank
London SW1P
207 717-4444

(G-19609)
TMS INTERNATIONAL LLC
4000 Mahoning Ave Nw (44483-1924)
P.O. Box 1819 (44482-1819)
PHONE................................330 847-0844
EMP: 28 Privately Held
SIC: 3295 Minerals, Ground Or Treated,
Nsk

(G-19610)
TRI COUNTY VKING WARRIORS
Also Called: Tri County Viking Warriors
1745 Ogden Ave Nw (44483-3029)
PHONE................................330 646-4632
James Toney, *CEO*
Ashley Toney, *President*
EMP: 45
SALES (est): 1.4MM **Privately Held**
SIC: 3949 7389 Guards: football, basket-
ball, soccer, lacrosse, etc.; masks:
hockey, baseball, football, etc.;

(G-19611)
**TRUMBULL CEMENT
PRODUCTS CO**
2185 Larchmont Ave Ne (44483-2894)
PHONE................................330 372-4342
Fax: 330 372-4165
Jeffrey Carbone, *President*
Julie Carbone, *Treasurer*
Darla Carbone, *Admin Sec*
EMP: 6
SQ FT: 5,000
SALES: 1MM **Privately Held**
SIC: 3271 5211 5032 Blocks, concrete or
cinder: standard; lumber & other building
materials; brick, stone & related material

(G-19612)
**TRUMBULL COUNTY LEGAL
NEWS**
108 Main Ave Sw Ste 700 (44481-1010)
P.O. Box 707 (44482-0707)
PHONE................................330 392-7112
Cheryl Biviano, *President*
EMP: 3
SALES (est): 180K **Privately Held**
SIC: 7313 2711 Newspaper advertising
representative; newspapers

(G-19613)
**TRUMBULL ENGRG ASSEMBLY
& MCH**
Also Called: Team
172 Forest St Nw (44483-3704)
P.O. Box 1877 (44482-1877)
PHONE................................330 394-6628
Fax: 330 394-8881
Shelby J Green, *President*
EMP: 4
SALES (est): 485.6K **Privately Held**
SIC: 3599 Machine shop, jobbing & repair

(G-19614)
**TRUMBULL MANUFACTURING
INC**
400 Dietz Rd Ne (44483-2749)
P.O. Box 30 (44482-0030)
PHONE................................330 393-6624
Murray Miller, *President*
Dennis Parks, *General Mgr*
Julian Lehman, *Treasurer*
Dennis Sabol, *VP Human Res*
Chick Haering, *VP Sales*
▲ **EMP:** 89
SQ FT: 16,000
SALES (est): 14MM **Privately Held**
SIC: 3432 3433 5074 Plumbing fixture fit-
tings & trim; heating equipment, except
electric; plumbing & hydronic heating sup-
plies

(G-19615)
TRUMBULL MOBILE MEALS INC
323 E Market St (44481-1207)
PHONE................................330 394-2538
Fax: 330 394-6058
Lynn Carine, *Manager*
Sandra Mathews, *Exec Dir*
EMP: 10

SQ FT: 3,567
SALES: 339.9K **Privately Held**
SIC: 8322 2051 Individual & family serv-
ices; bakery, for home service delivery

(G-19616)
ULTIMATE PRINTING CO INC
6090 Mahoning Ave Nw C (44481-9495)
PHONE................................330 847-2941
Fax: 330 847-2942
Richard Wilms, *President*
William Pugh, *Vice Pres*
Linda Overmier, *Office Mgr*
EMP: 6
SQ FT: 3,000
SALES (est): 430K **Privately Held**
SIC: 2752 Commercial printing, litho-
graphic

(G-19617)
VANGUARD DIE & MACHINE INC
2070 Mcmyler St Nw (44485-2615)
PHONE................................330 394-4170
Fax: 330 395-3505
EMP: 20
SQ FT: 6,000
SALES: 1.5MM **Privately Held**
SIC: 3599 Machine Shop

(G-19618)
**VINDICATOR PRINTING
COMPANY**
Also Called: News Office, Beauro
135 Pine Ave Se Ste 208 (44481-1249)
PHONE................................330 392-0176
Fax: 330 392-5202
Tom Wills, *Branch Mgr*
EMP: 4
SALES (corp-wide): 51.8MM **Privately
Held**
WEB: www.vindy.com
SIC: 2711 Newspapers
PA: The Vindicator Printing Company
107 Vindicator Sq
Youngstown OH 44503
330 747-1471

(G-19619)
VULKOR INCORPORATED (PA)
621 Dana St Ne Ste V (44483-3977)
PHONE................................330 393-7600
Fax: 330 393-7909
David J Campbell, *President*
Deborah Steen, *Controller*
Ronald M Krisher, *Shareholder*
Richard Thompson, *Shareholder*
EMP: 24
SQ FT: 780
SALES (est): 6MM **Privately Held**
SIC: 3357 Nonferrous wiredrawing & insu-
lating

(G-19620)
**WARREN CONCRETE AND
SUPPLY CO**
1113 Parkman Rd Nw (44485-2497)
P.O. Box 1408 (44482-1408)
PHONE................................330 393-1581
Harry N Hamilton, *President*
David H Hamilton, *President*
James Hamilton, *Vice Pres*
Richard Hamilton, *Vice Pres*
EMP: 18
SQ FT: 2,000
SALES (est): 2.6MM **Privately Held**
SIC: 3273 5211 5032 Ready-mixed con-
crete; lumber & other building materials;
brick, stone & related material

(G-19621)
**WARREN FABRICATING
CORPORATION (PA)**
3240 Mahoning Ave Nw (44483-2054)
P.O. Box 1032 (44482-1032)
PHONE................................330 847-0596
Fax: 330 847-8114
John C Rebhan, *President*
Eric Rebhan, *President*
William E Marsteller, *Principal*
Robert M Platt Sr, *Principal*
David Della Donna, *Vice Pres*
◆ **EMP:** 90 EST: 1966
SQ FT: 380,000

SALES: 84.7MM **Privately Held**
WEB: www.warfab.com
SIC: 3441 3599 3547 3532 Fabricated
structural metal; machine shop, jobbing &
repair; rolling mill machinery; mining machinery; sheet metalwork; fabricated plate
work (boiler shop)

(G-19622)
**WARREN FIRE EQUIPMENT INC
(PA)**
6880 Tod Ave Sw (44481-8628)
PHONE................................330 824-3523
Fax: 330 824-8303
Robert R Malone, *President*
Lynda L Malone, *COO*
Richard D Garrity, *Vice Pres*
Gayle Paulus, *Accountant*
Mickey Dewitt, *Sales Staff*
EMP: 21 EST: 1920
SQ FT: 8,400
SALES (est): 4MM **Privately Held**
WEB: www.warrenfireequip.com
SIC: 5999 2899 Fire extinguishers; fire ex-
tinguisher charges

(G-19623)
WARREN SCREW MACHINE INC
3869 Niles Rd Se (44484-3548)
PHONE................................330 609-6020
John Condoleon, *President*
Janice Schneider, *Manager*
EMP: 26
SALES (est): 5.7MM **Privately Held**
SIC: 3451 Screw machine products

(G-19624)
**WARREN STEEL SPECIALTIES
CORP**
1309 Niles Rd Se (44484-5106)
P.O. Box 1391 (44482-1391)
PHONE................................330 399-8360
Fax: 330 399-8371
Christopher Shape, *President*
Frederick Shape, *Vice Pres*
Vicki McClain, *Manager*
Barbara Shape, *Admin Sec*
EMP: 15 EST: 1931
SQ FT: 21,000
SALES (est): 1.1MM **Privately Held**
WEB: www.warrensteel.com
SIC: 2542 3499 Stands, merchandise dis-
play: except wood; strapping, metal

(G-19625)
WATERPRO
2926 Commonwealth Ave Ne (44483-2831)
PHONE................................330 372-3565
Vern Parker, *Owner*
Kirk Parker, *Vice Pres*
EMP: 13
SALES (est): 1.2MM **Privately Held**
SIC: 3561 Pumps & pumping equipment

(G-19626)
WELD-ACTION COMPANY INC
2100 N River Rd Ne (44483-2598)
PHONE................................330 372-1063
Fax: 330 372-5858
Todd Huna, *President*
EMP: 6 EST: 1960
SQ FT: 7,158
SALES: 1.5MM **Privately Held**
WEB: www.weldaction.com
SIC: 5084 3548 Welding machinery &
equipment; welding & cutting apparatus &
accessories

(G-19627)
XPRESSIONS LLC
707 Meadowbrook Ave Se (44484-4555)
PHONE................................330 898-8591
Anthony L Jones,
EMP: 3
SALES (est): 257.9K **Privately Held**
SIC: 3552 Textile machinery

(G-19628)
ZEKELMAN INDUSTRIES INC
Also Called: Wheatland Tube Company
901 Dietz Rd Ne (44483-2748)
PHONE................................330 373-4410
Jim Cunningham, *Engng Exec*
Teri Aljoe, *Branch Mgr*
EMP: 153

SALES (corp-wide): 637.5MM **Privately
Held**
SIC: 3312 3317 Blast furnaces & steel
mills; steel pipe & tubes
HQ: Wheatland Tube, Llc
227 W Monroe St Ste 2600
Chicago IL 60606
312 275-1600

Warrensville Heights
Cuyahoga County

(G-19629)
B & F MANUFACTURING CO
19050 Cranwood Pkwy (44128-4047)
PHONE................................216 518-0333
Fax: 216 518-0376
Marsha Kutsikovich, *President*
EMP: 10
SQ FT: 10,000
SALES (est): 1.6MM **Privately Held**
SIC: 3599 Machine shop, jobbing & repair

(G-19630)
**CHARLES HUFFMAN &
ASSOCIATES**
19214 Gladstone Rd (44122-6626)
PHONE................................216 295-0850
Charles Huffman, *Manager*
EMP: 6
SALES (corp-wide): 300K **Privately Held**
SIC: 2759 Commercial printing
PA: Charles Huffman & Associates
17325 Euclid Ave Ste 4002
Cleveland OH 44112
216 295-0850

(G-19631)
CHEM 1 INC
19220 Miles Rd (44128-4106)
PHONE................................216 475-7443
Sam Zemaitis, *President*
▲ **EMP:** 5
SQ FT: 42,000
SALES (est): 2.8MM **Privately Held**
SIC: 2842 Cleaning or polishing prepara-
tions

(G-19632)
EMBEDDED PLANET INC
4760 Richmond Rd Ste 400 (44128-5979)
PHONE................................216 245-4180
Fax: 216 461-4329
Mark Lowdermilk, *CEO*
Timothy J Callahan, *Ch of Bd*
Scott Szewcyk, *Opers Mgr*
Steve Cloud, *Sales Staff*
Nancy Beatty, *Info Tech Mgr*
EMP: 15
SQ FT: 8,000
SALES (est): 3.1MM **Privately Held**
WEB: www.embeddedplanet.com
SIC: 7371 3577 Custom computer pro-
gramming services; computer peripheral
equipment

(G-19633)
**GE MEDICAL SYSTEMS
INFORMATION**
18683 S Miles Rd (44128-4239)
PHONE................................216 663-2110
Ken Koons, *Electrical Engi*
Jason Hisrich, *Branch Mgr*
Kathleen Bradley, *Master*
EMP: 3
SALES (corp-wide): 123.6B **Publicly
Held**
SIC: 3845 Patient monitoring apparatus;
electrocardiographs; defibrillator; respira-
tory analysis equipment, electromedical
HQ: Ge Medical Systems Information Tech-
nologies, Inc.
9900 W Innovation Dr
Wauwatosa WI 53226

(G-19634)
POLIMEROS USA LLC
26210 Emery Rd Ste 202 (44128-5770)
PHONE................................216 591-0162
Jose Antonio Chacon,
EMP: 15
SALES (est): 2.5MM **Privately Held**
SIC: 3089 Air mattresses, plastic

(G-19635)
**SPECIAL METALS
CORPORATION (DH)**
4832 Richmond Rd Ste 100 (44128-5993)
PHONE..............................216 755-3030
Ken Buck, *President*
Joseph Snowden, *President*
Gregory De Vito, *Sr Corp Ofcr*
James M Hensler, *Vice Pres*
Stanton D Kirk, *Vice Pres*
▲ **EMP:** 461
SQ FT: 14,000
SALES (est): 654.9MM
SALES (corp-wide): 223.6B **Publicly
Held**
SIC: 3356 Nickel & nickel alloy: rolling,
drawing or extruding
HQ: Precision Castparts Corp.
4650 Sw Mcdam Ave Ste 300
Portland OR 97239
503 946-4800

(G-19636)
VORTEX METALS LTD
19200 Cranwood Pkwy (44128-4043)
P.O. Box 1303, Bath (44210-1303)
PHONE..............................216 365-2300
Eric J Henkel, *President*
Denise Henkel, *Vice Pres*
Lorna Melby, *Office Mgr*
▲ **EMP:** 8
SALES (est): 1.2MM **Privately Held**
SIC: 3444 Sheet metalwork

(G-19637)
WHITMORE PRODUCTIONS INC
Also Called: Whitmore's Bbq
20209 Harvard Ave (44122-6808)
PHONE..............................216 752-3960
Virgil Whitmore, *President*
Vance Whitmore, *Vice Pres*
Esther Whitmore, *Treasurer*
Kim Whitmore, *Admin Sec*
EMP: 11
SQ FT: 1,500
SALES (est): 1.2MM **Privately Held**
WEB: www.whitmoreproductions.com
SIC: 2099 Sauces: dry mixes

Washington Court Hou
Fayette County

(G-19638)
**COURTHOUSE
MANUFACTURING LLC**
Also Called: Chappell Door Company
1730 Wash Ave Solar Ln (43160)
PHONE..............................740 335-2727
Fax: 740 335-8049
James Traynor, *Controller*
Wayne Gooley, *Mng Member*
EMP: 38 **EST:** 1955
SQ FT: 84,000
SALES (est): 6.7MM **Privately Held**
WEB: www.chappelldoor.net
SIC: 2431 Doors, wood; window frames,
wood

(G-19639)
HEARTLAND STEEL INC
1629 S Fayette St (43160)
PHONE..............................740 333-5401
Terry L Lee, *President*
Randy Frevert, *Principal*
Thomas Miller, *Principal*
EMP: 12
SALES (est): 1.9MM **Privately Held**
SIC: 3312 Structural shapes & pilings,
steel

(G-19640)
STARK TRUSS COMPANY INC
2000 Landmark Blvd (43160)
P.O. Box 8, Wshngtn CT Hs (43160-0008)
PHONE..............................740 335-4156
Fax: 740 335-6144
Javan Yoder, *Vice Pres*
Jeff Coulter, *Branch Mgr*
EMP: 50
SQ FT: 12,000

SALES (corp-wide): 230.5MM **Privately
Held**
WEB: www.starktruss.com
SIC: 2439 Trusses, wooden roof
PA: Stark Truss Company, Inc.
109 Miles Ave Sw
Canton OH 44710
330 478-2100

(G-19641)
YUSA CORPORATION
151 Jamison Rd Sw (43160)
PHONE..............................740 335-0335
Fax: 740 335-0330
Takeyoshi Usui, *President*
Roger Williams, *Engineer*
Greg Niehaus, *CFO*
Yoshiji Iwamoto, *Treasurer*
Andy Brown, *Accounting Mgr*
▲ **EMP:** 1046
SQ FT: 250,000
SALES (est): 228.8MM
SALES (corp-wide): 173.1MM **Privately
Held**
SIC: 3069 Rubber covered motor mounting
rings (rubber bonded); bushings, rubber;
tubing, rubber
PA: Yamashita Rubber Co.,Ltd.
1239, Kamekubo
Fujimino STM 356-0
492 622-121

Washingtonville
Columbiana County

(G-19642)
KEEN MANUFACTURING INC
240 High St (44490)
PHONE..............................330 427-0045
Fax: 330 427-0800
Terry Turvey, *President*
Tressa Turvey, *Corp Secy*
Mike Prychodczenko, *Office Mgr*
EMP: 5
SQ FT: 7,000
SALES: 350K **Privately Held**
WEB: www.keenmanufacturing.com
SIC: 3491 Industrial valves

(G-19643)
TURVEY ENGINEERING
Also Called: TS Engineering
240 High St (44490)
P.O. Box 334 (44490-0334)
PHONE..............................330 427-0125
Terry Turvey, *President*
EMP: 5
SALES (est): 543K **Privately Held**
WEB: www.tsengineering.com
SIC: 3625 Industrial controls: push button,
selector switches, pilot

(G-19644)
W M INC
275 High St (44490)
PHONE..............................330 427-6115
Fax: 330 427-6784
Richard Owsley, *President*
EMP: 31 **EST:** 1952
SQ FT: 30,000
SALES (est): 3.9MM **Privately Held**
SIC: 3469 Metal stampings

Waterford
Washington County

(G-19645)
**AIR HEATER SEAL COMPANY
INC**
15710 Waterford Rd (45786-5001)
P.O. Box 8 (45786-0008)
PHONE..............................740 984-2146
Fax: 740 984-4275
Randy Townsend, *Owner*
Mable Townsend, *Corp Secy*
Kevin Stewart, *Purch Dir*
Edward Hensler, *Engineer*
Janet Farley, *Manager*
EMP: 23
SQ FT: 4,500

SALES (est): 4.9MM **Privately Held**
WEB: www.airheaterseal.com
SIC: 3053 3441 Gaskets, packing & seal-
ing devices; fabricated structural metal

(G-19646)
E Z GROUT CORPORATION
Also Called: Ezg Manufacturing
405 Watertown Rd (45786-5248)
PHONE..............................740 749-3512
Damian Lang, *President*
Daniel Kern, *Plant Mgr*
Robert Myers, *Plant Engr*
Douglas Taylor, *CFO*
Dan McCutcheun, *Sales Executive*
▲ **EMP:** 25
SALES: 9.7MM **Privately Held**
WEB: www.ezgrout.com
SIC: 3423 Masons' hand tools

(G-19647)
**GLOBE METALLURGICAL INC
(DH)**
Also Called: Globe Specialty Metals
County Road 32 (45786)
P.O. Box 157, Beverly (45715-0157)
PHONE..............................740 984-2361
Fax: 740 984-8536
Jeff Bradley, *President*
Eli David, *General Mgr*
Alan Kestenbaum, *Chairman*
Marlin Perkins, *Vice Pres*
Jeff Watson, *Vice Pres*
◆ **EMP:** 141
SALES (est): 177.1MM
SALES (corp-wide): 2.3MM **Privately
Held**
WEB: www.globemetallurgical.com
SIC: 3339 3313 2819 Silicon refining (pri-
mary, over 99% pure); silicon; silicon, epitaxial
(silicon alloy); ferrosilicon, not made in
blast furnaces; industrial inorganic chemi-
cals
HQ: Globe Specialty Metals, Inc.
600 Brickell Ave Ste 3100
Miami FL 33131
786 509-6900

(G-19648)
GYM PRO LLC
50 Washington St (45786-5337)
P.O. Box 50 (45786-0050)
PHONE..............................740 984-4143
Fax: 740 984-2017
Daryl J Van Dyne, *General Mgr*
Karen S Vandyne, *Mng Member*
EMP: 3
SALES: 250K **Privately Held**
SIC: 3949 5999 2759 Sporting & athletic
goods; trophies & plaques; screen print-
ing

(G-19649)
LAMINATE SHOP
1145 Klinger Rd (45786-5347)
P.O. Box 1218, Marietta (45750-6218)
PHONE..............................740 749-3536
Tim Strahler, *President*
EMP: 10
SQ FT: 25,000
SALES (est): 870K **Privately Held**
SIC: 3083 5211 1799 Laminated plastics
plate & sheet; cabinets, kitchen; counter
top installation

(G-19650)
LWR ENTERPRISES INC
4310 Sparling Rd (45786-5170)
P.O. Box 245 (45786-0245)
PHONE..............................740 984-0036
Jay A Porter, *President*
EMP: 5
SALES (est): 674.2K **Privately Held**
SIC: 3449 Miscellaneous metalwork

Waterville
Lucas County

(G-19651)
ALLSTATES REFR CONTRS LLC
218 Mechanic St B (43566-1438)
P.O. Box 256 (43566-0256)
PHONE..............................419 878-4691

Fax: 419 878-8054
David T Boothe, *Mng Member*
EMP: 15
SQ FT: 1,000
SALES: 1MM **Privately Held**
SIC: 3567 Industrial furnaces & ovens

(G-19652)
AQUILA PHARMATECH LLC
8225 Farnsworth Rd Ste A7 (43566-9781)
PHONE..............................419 386-2527
Han Chen, *Mng Member*
EMP: 3
SALES (est): 229.5K **Privately Held**
WEB: www.aquilapharmatech.com
SIC: 3559 Chemical machinery & equip-
ment

(G-19653)
CARRUTH STUDIO INC (PA)
1178 Farnsworth Rd (43566-1074)
PHONE..............................419 878-3060
Fax: 419 878-3261
George Carruth, *President*
Debbie Carruth, *Corp Secy*
Jan Ford, *Human Resources*
Ruth Ott, *Manager*
EMP: 13
SQ FT: 13,600
SALES (est): 2.8MM **Privately Held**
WEB: www.carruthstudio.com
SIC: 3269 3272 Art & ornamental ware,
pottery; concrete products

(G-19654)
CRUM MANUFACTURING INC
1265 Wtrville Monclova Rd (43566-1067)
PHONE..............................419 878-9779
Ernest Crum Jr, *President*
Douglas Waldie, *Vice Pres*
Hank Briggs, *Opers Mgr*
Chad Graham, *Opers Mgr*
Jonathan Rodebaugh, *QC Mgr*
EMP: 25
SQ FT: 23,000
SALES (est): 5.7MM **Privately Held**
WEB: www.crummfg.com
SIC: 3544 3599 3462 Special dies, tools,
jigs & fixtures; machine & other job shop
work; automotive forgings, ferrous: crank-
shaft, engine, axle, etc.

(G-19655)
DATA MOLD AND TOOL INC
160 Concord St (43566-1417)
PHONE..............................419 878-9861
Jeff Suess, *President*
Doris Suess, *Treasurer*
EMP: 7
SQ FT: 7,500
SALES: 580K **Privately Held**
SIC: 3544 Forms (molds), for foundry &
plastics working machinery

(G-19656)
DUVALL WOODWORKING INC
Also Called: American Products
7551 Dutch Rd (43566-9732)
PHONE..............................419 878-9581
Fax: 419 878-9580
Thomas Duvall, *President*
Karen Zielinski, *Admin Asst*
EMP: 14
SQ FT: 12,000
SALES (est): 1.3MM **Privately Held**
SIC: 2499 Kitchen, bathroom & household
ware: wood

(G-19657)
FRANKLIN
Also Called: Rrysburg Sunoco
747 Michigan Ave (43566-1052)
PHONE..............................419 699-5757
EMP: 3
SALES (est): 254.5K **Privately Held**
SIC: 2869 Fuels

(G-19658)
FURNACE TECHNOLOGIES INC
Also Called: Furn Tech
1070 Disher Dr (43566-1079)
PHONE..............................419 878-2100
Fax: 419 878-4455
Tim Fisher, *President*
Julie Harry, *Admin Asst*
EMP: 63

SALES (est): 12.5MM **Privately Held**
WEB: www.thermeq.com
SIC: 3567 Industrial furnaces & ovens

(G-19659)
HANSON AGGREGATES MIDWEST LLC
600 S River Rd (43566-9754)
P.O. Box 49 (43566-0049)
PHONE....................419 878-2006
Paul Carbaugh, *Branch Mgr*
EMP: 9
SALES (corp-wide): 16B **Privately Held**
SIC: 2951 Asphalt paving mixtures & blocks
HQ: Hanson Aggregates Midwest Llc
207 Old Harrods Creek Rd
Louisville KY 40223
502 244-7550

(G-19660)
JOHNS MANVILLE CORPORATION
7500 Dutch Rd (43566-9731)
PHONE....................419 878-8111
Rhonda Francis, *Principal*
Brent Harrill, *Accounts Mgr*
Tiffany Hausauer, *Program Mgr*
Song-Ping Dai, *Manager*
Ben Guess, *Supervisor*
EMP: 400
SALES (corp-wide): 223.6B **Publicly Held**
WEB: www.jm.com
SIC: 3296 3297 3229 2273 Mineral wool; nonclay refractories; pressed & blown glass; carpets & rugs
HQ: Johns Manville Corporation
717 17th St Ste 800
Denver CO 80202
303 978-2000

(G-19661)
KAUFMAN ENGINEERED SYSTEMS INC
1260 Wtrville Monclova Rd (43566-1066)
PHONE....................419 878-9727
Fax: 419 878-9726
Andrew J Quinn, *President*
Charles R Kaufman, *President*
Robert J Kaufman, *Vice Pres*
Connie Kosbab, *Accounting Mgr*
Mary Jo Burkert, *Manager*
EMP: 72 **EST:** 1957
SQ FT: 66,250
SALES (est): 25MM **Privately Held**
WEB: www.kaufmanengsys.com
SIC: 3567 3565 Industrial furnaces & ovens; packaging machinery

(G-19662)
LABCRAFT INC
1070 Disher Dr (43566-1079)
PHONE....................419 878-4400
Timothy J Fisher, *President*
EMP: 11
SALES (est): 710.2K **Privately Held**
WEB: www.labcraft.com
SIC: 3499 Machine bases, metal

(G-19663)
MAUMEE VALLEY MEMORIALS INC (DH)
Also Called: Americraft Bronze Co
111 Anthony Wayne Trl (43566-1373)
PHONE....................419 878-9030
Fax: 419 878-3906
Richard Kimball, *President*
Mike Faehnle, *General Mgr*
Pat Braun, *Bookkeeper*
Kathleen Noaker, *Sales Staff*
EMP: 12
SQ FT: 2,500
SALES (est): 9.3MM
SALES (corp-wide): 9MM **Privately Held**
SIC: 5999 3281 Monuments & tombstones; cut stone & stone products
HQ: Swenson Granite Company Llc
369 N State St
Concord NH 03301
603 225-4322

(G-19664)
PAHL READY MIX CONCRETE INC
600 S River Rd (43566-9754)
P.O. Box 49 (43566-0049)
PHONE....................419 636-4238
Thomas Weber, *Owner*
Brock Mealer, *Manager*
EMP: 13
SALES (corp-wide): 4.9MM **Privately Held**
SIC: 3273 Ready-mixed concrete
PA: Pahl Ready Mix Concrete, Inc.
14586 Us Highway 127 Ew
Bryan OH 43506
419 636-4238

(G-19665)
REEBAR DIE CASTING INC
1177 Farnsworth Rd (43566-1036)
PHONE....................419 878-7591
Fax: 419 878-8289
Byron G Reed, *President*
Joyce Reed, *Corp Secy*
Byron David Reed, *Vice Pres*
EMP: 15
SQ FT: 22,000
SALES (est): 2.5MM **Privately Held**
SIC: 3364 3089 Zinc & zinc-base alloy die-castings; injection molded finished plastic products

(G-19666)
RIMER ENTERPRISES INC
Also Called: Kelic
916 Rimer Dr (43566-1019)
P.O. Box 27 (43566-0027)
PHONE....................419 878-8156
Fax: 419 878-6218
Chuck Meyers, *Owner*
Kathy Smith, *Business Mgr*
Eric Nathe, *Corp Secy*
EMP: 30
SQ FT: 25,000
SALES (est): 6.9MM **Privately Held**
SIC: 3324 Commercial investment castings, ferrous

(G-19667)
SEAGATE PLASTICS COMPANY (PA)
1110 Disher Dr (43566-1256)
PHONE....................419 878-5010
Fax: 419 878-9512
Kevin Fink, *President*
▲ **EMP:** 39
SQ FT: 50,000
SALES (est): 11.9MM **Privately Held**
WEB: www.seagateplastics.com
SIC: 3089 Extruded finished plastic products

(G-19668)
T J F INC
Also Called: Thermeq Co
1070 Disher Dr (43566-1079)
PHONE....................419 878-4400
Timothy Fisher, *President*
Ernest Seeman, *Director*
Elizabeth Kramp, *Admin Sec*
EMP: 16
SALES (est): 4.4MM **Privately Held**
SIC: 3585 3433 Refrigeration & heating equipment; heating equipment, except electric

(G-19669)
TECH SYSTEMS INC
1070 Disher Dr (43566-1079)
PHONE....................419 878-2100
Tim Fisher, *President*
EMP: 25
SALES (est): 2.3MM **Privately Held**
SIC: 3441 Fabricated structural metal

(G-19670)
WATERVILLE SHEET METAL COMPANY
1210 Wtrville Monclova Rd (43566-1000)
PHONE....................419 878-5050
Fax: 419 878-7829
Ron Kelso, *President*
Rita Hitchner, *Business Mgr*
EMP: 6
SQ FT: 12,000

SALES (est): 3.7MM **Privately Held**
SIC: 3444 Sheet metalwork

Wauseon
Fulton County

(G-19671)
AMERICAN POWER PULL CORP
115 E Linfoot St (43567-1005)
P.O. Box 109 (43567-0109)
PHONE....................419 335-7050
Edward S Kraemer, *President*
Gabriella Stover, *Engineer*
▲ **EMP:** 8 **EST:** 1919
SQ FT: 36,600
SALES (est): 1.7MM **Privately Held**
WEB: www.americanpowerpull.com
SIC: 3423 3531 3536 Jacks: lifting, screw or ratchet (hand tools); winches; hoists, cranes & monorails

(G-19672)
BILLS SPORTS CENTER
1495 N Shoop Ave (43567-1824)
PHONE....................419 335-2405
Bill Drummer, *Principal*
EMP: 4
SALES (est): 504K **Privately Held**
SIC: 3842 Hearing aids

(G-19673)
BUSSE KNIFE CO
Also Called: Busse Combat Knives
11651 County Road 12 (43567-9622)
PHONE....................419 923-6471
Jerry Busse, *President*
Kendra Spiess, *Manager*
EMP: 30
SQ FT: 37,000
SALES (est): 3.1MM **Privately Held**
WEB: www.swampratknives.com
SIC: 3421 Cutlery

(G-19674)
CONCEPT PRINTING OF WAUSEON
775 N Shoop Ave (43567-1839)
P.O. Box 503 (43567-0503)
PHONE....................419 335-6627
Fax: 419 335-0490
Kim M Clark, *President*
Kristene Clark, *Corp Secy*
EMP: 5
SALES: 300K **Privately Held**
SIC: 2752 Commercial printing, lithographic

(G-19675)
E & J DEMARK INC (PA)
1115 N Ottokee St (43567-1911)
P.O. Box 416 (43567-0416)
PHONE....................419 337-5866
Fax: 419 337-5089
J Edwin Hecock, *President*
Boonie L Hecock, *Vice Pres*
EMP: 16
SQ FT: 29,000
SALES (est): 5MM **Privately Held**
WEB: www.demrk.com
SIC: 3545 3599 Machine tool accessories; machine shop, jobbing & repair

(G-19676)
E & J DEMARK INC
1115 N Ottokee St (43567-1911)
PHONE....................419 337-5866
Bonnie Hecock, *Principal*
EMP: 6
SALES (corp-wide): 5MM **Privately Held**
WEB: www.demrk.com
SIC: 3545 Machine tool accessories
PA: E & J Demark, Inc.
1115 N Ottokee St
Wauseon OH 43567
419 337-5866

(G-19677)
FINE LINES LASER ENGRAVING
12825 County Road 14 (43567-9660)
PHONE....................419 337-6313
James Ballmer, *Principal*
EMP: 3 **EST:** 2012

SALES (est): 227.5K **Privately Held**
SIC: 2796 Platemaking services

(G-19678)
FULTON INDUSTRIES INC (PA)
135 E Linfoot St (43567-1000)
P.O. Box 377 (43567-0377)
PHONE....................419 335-3015
Fax: 419 335-3215
John Razzano, *President*
Glenn Badenhop, *President*
Kim Griggs, *Exec VP*
Ned Griggs, *Exec VP*
Robert E Swanson, *Treasurer*
EMP: 70
SQ FT: 170,000
SALES (est): 15.1MM **Privately Held**
WEB: www.fultonindoh.com
SIC: 3469 3648 Metal stampings; flashlights

(G-19679)
GAZETTE PUBLISHING COMPANY
Also Called: Fulton County Expositor
1270 N Shoop Ave Ste A (43567-2211)
PHONE....................419 335-2010
Jason A Manner, *Editor*
Janice May, *Manager*
EMP: 15
SALES (corp-wide): 8.2MM **Privately Held**
WEB: www.theoberlinnews.com
SIC: 7313 2711 Newspaper advertising representative; newsstand; newspapers
PA: The Gazette Publishing Company
42 S Main St
Oberlin OH 44074
419 483-4190

(G-19680)
GUARDIAN ENGINEERING & MFG CO
965 Fairway Ln (43567-9234)
PHONE....................419 335-1784
Michael Christman, *President*
EMP: 2
SALES: 1.2MM **Privately Held**
SIC: 8711 3469 3599 Machine tool design; metal stampings; custom machinery

(G-19681)
HAAS DOOR COMPANY
320 Sycamore St (43567-1100)
PHONE....................419 337-9900
Edward Nofziger, *President*
Carol Nofziger, *Corp Secy*
Tom Moyer, *Plant Mgr*
EMP: 200
SQ FT: 150,000
SALES (est): 24.3MM **Privately Held**
SIC: 3442 Garage doors, overhead: metal

(G-19682)
HILL MANUFACTURING INC
318 W Chestnut St (43567-1369)
P.O. Box 241 (43567-0241)
PHONE....................419 335-5006
Fax: 419 335-7953
Marion Hill, *President*
Carl T Hill, *Vice Pres*
Kevin Levitas, *Vice Pres*
George Chmura, *Sales Mgr*
▲ **EMP:** 50 **EST:** 1948
SQ FT: 55,000
SALES (est): 10.8MM **Privately Held**
WEB: www.hillmfginc.com
SIC: 3469 Stamping metal for the trade

(G-19683)
INTERACTIVE FINCL SOLUTIONS
Also Called: Mrdd Solutions
122 S Fulton St (43567-1350)
PHONE....................419 335-1280
Lynn Miller, *President*
Jeff Rutledge, *Vice Pres*
EMP: 15 **EST:** 1997
SALES: 1.2MM **Privately Held**
WEB: www.mrddsolutions.com
SIC: 7372 Prepackaged software

(G-19684)
INTERNATIONAL AUTOMOTIVE
555 W Linfoot St (43567-9558)
PHONE..............................419 335-1000
Robert S Miller, *President*
Scott Weed, *Manager*
EMP: 600 Privately Held
WEB: www.iaaawards.com
SIC: 3714 Motor vehicle parts & accessories
HQ: International Automotive Components
Group North America, Inc.
28333 Telegraph Rd
Southfield MI 48034
248 455-7000

(G-19685)
J & B FEED CO INC
140 S Brunell St (43567-1387)
PHONE..............................419 335-5821
Fax: 419 335-0271
Kerry Ackerman, *President*
EMP: 4
SQ FT: 1,200
SALES (est): 370K Privately Held
SIC: 5999 2048 5191 Feed & farm supply; prepared feeds; animal feeds

(G-19686)
L GARBERS SONS SAWMILLING LLC
6444 County Road 12 (43567-9641)
PHONE..............................419 335-6362
David Garber,
Kathryn Garber,
Martin Garber,
EMP: 5 EST: 1999
SALES (est): 707.2K Privately Held
SIC: 2421 Sawmills & planing mills, general

(G-19687)
LATROBE SPECIALTY MTLS CO LLC
14614 County Road H (43567-9796)
PHONE..............................419 335-8010
Fax: 419 330-2508
Gary Joslyn, *Engineer*
Robert J Smith, *Sales/Mktg Mgr*
Jowania Wilson, *Human Res Dir*
Cheryl Bookheimer, *Branch Mgr*
Bob Smith, *Manager*
EMP: 76
SALES (corp-wide): 1.8B Publicly Held
SIC: 3312 Tool & die steel
HQ: Latrobe Specialty Metals Company, Llc
2626 Ligonier St
Latrobe PA 15650
724 537-7711

(G-19688)
LEAR CORPORATION
Also Called: Sheridan Mfg
447 E Walnut St (43567-1278)
PHONE..............................419 335-6010
Fax: 419 337-9527
Norman Wachtman, *Purchasing*
Dianne Blosser, *Human Res Mgr*
Gerry Lauber, *Sales Mgr*
Cary Wood, *Branch Mgr*
EMP: 200
SQ FT: 80,000
SALES (corp-wide): 18.5B Publicly Held
SIC: 2531 Seats, automobile
PA: Lear Corporation
21557 Telegraph Rd
Southfield MI 48033
248 447-1500

(G-19689)
MASTER VAC INCORPORATED
741 Parkview St (43567-1241)
PHONE..............................419 335-7796
D Ross Strayer, *President*
Virgie Strayer, *Vice Pres*
EMP: 3
SALES (est): 184.6K Privately Held
SIC: 3479 Coating of metals with plastic or resins

(G-19690)
MULTI CAST LLC
225 E Linfoot St (43567-1007)
PHONE..............................419 335-0010
Fax: 419 337-4263

Edward Metzger, *Vice Pres*
Mike Schnipke, *Mng Member*
Robin Mininger, *Manager*
Ted Metzger, *Advisor*
EMP: 37 EST: 1930
SQ FT: 42,500
SALES: 5MM Privately Held
WEB: www.multi-cast.com
SIC: 3365 Aluminum foundries

(G-19691)
NEBRASKA INDUSTRIES CORP
447 E Walnut St (43567-1278)
PHONE..............................419 335-6010
Michael Hemphill, *President*
Dave Verbey, *Vice Pres*
Norman Wachtman, *Purchasing*
Ray Cox, *CFO*
Dianne Blosser, *Manager*
EMP: 38
SQ FT: 95,000
SALES (est): 5.9MM Privately Held
WEB: www.nebraskaindustries.com
SIC: 3469 3089 3714 3465 Metal stampings; injection molding of plastics; motor vehicle parts & accessories; automotive stampings

(G-19692)
NOFZIGER DOOR SALES INC (PA)
Also Called: Haas Doors
320 Sycamore St (43567-1100)
PHONE..............................419 337-9900
Fax: 419 337-5973
Edward L Nofziger, *President*
Carol Nofziger, *Corp Secy*
Dawn Haas, *Vice Pres*
Marty Haas, *Sales Executive*
Jan Trask, *Director*
EMP: 173
SQ FT: 200,000
SALES (est): 31.9MM Privately Held
WEB: www.haasdoor.com
SIC: 3442 Metal doors; garage doors, overhead: metal; garage door, installation or erection; doors, wood or metal, except storm

(G-19693)
PERFECTION FINISHERS INC
1151 N Ottokee St (43567-1911)
PHONE..............................419 337-8015
Fax: 419 335-2943
Gerald Haack, *CEO*
Kelly Flanigan, *Manager*
Susan Krueger, *Manager*
EMP: 25
SQ FT: 80,000
SALES (est): 3.1MM Privately Held
WEB: www.perfectionfinishers.com
SIC: 3479 Coating of metals with plastic or resins

(G-19694)
SILVER CREEK LOG HOMES
5350 County Road 16 (43567-8708)
PHONE..............................419 335-3220
Fax: 419 335-2832
Andrew Davis, *Owner*
Bonnie Davis, *Co-Owner*
EMP: 3
SALES (est): 315.3K Privately Held
WEB: www.silvercreekloghomes.com
SIC: 2452 1521 Log cabins, prefabricated, wood; single-family housing construction

(G-19695)
TC BROS CHOPPERS LLC
12052 Us Highway 20a (43567-9638)
PHONE..............................419 265-9399
Tyler R Cobb,
Tim E Cobb,
▲ EMP: 6 EST: 2008
SQ FT: 6,425
SALES: 1.2MM Privately Held
SIC: 3751 Motorcycles & related parts

(G-19696)
TOMAHAWK PRINTING (PA)
Also Called: Mustang Multi Graphics
229 N Fulton St (43567-1171)
PHONE..............................419 335-3161
Richard L Elrod, *President*
Carol Elrod, *Admin Sec*
EMP: 10

SQ FT: 32,000
SALES (est): 1.1MM Privately Held
WEB: www.mustangink.com
SIC: 2752 Commercial printing, offset

(G-19697)
TOMAHAWK PRINTING INC
229 N Fulton St (43567-1171)
P.O. Box 413 (43567-0413)
PHONE..............................419 335-3161
Fax: 419 335-0239
Jerry Dehnbostel, *President*
Shawn Ferguson, *Opers Mgr*
Lolita Dehnbostel, *Treasurer*
Amy Gifford, *Manager*
EMP: 12 EST: 1938
SQ FT: 3,000
SALES (est): 1.1MM Privately Held
WEB: www.tomahawkprinting.com
SIC: 2752 2789 Commercial printing, offset; binding only: books, pamphlets, magazines, etc.

(G-19698)
TURKEYFOOT CREEK CREAMERY
11313 County Road D (43567-9574)
PHONE..............................419 335-0224
Del Burkholder, *Principal*
EMP: 3
SALES (est): 144.5K Privately Held
SIC: 2021 Creamery butter

(G-19699)
UNLIMTED RCOVERY SOLUTIONS LLC
2701 S Eberd Rd Ste B (43567)
PHONE..............................419 868-4888
Brandon Johnson,
EMP: 45
SALES (est): 2.5MM Privately Held
SIC: 3713 Dump truck bodies

(G-19700)
WAUSEON MACHINE & MFG INC (PA)
995 Enterprise Ave (43567-9333)
PHONE..............................419 337-0940
Fax: 419 335-1640
Russell P Dominique, *CEO*
Eric Patty, *President*
Andrew Rausch, *General Mgr*
Douglas A Weddelman, *Principal*
Cindy Baker, *Purch Agent*
▲ EMP: 75 EST: 1985
SQ FT: 24,000
SALES (est): 18.4MM Privately Held
WEB: www.wauseonmachine.com
SIC: 3599 3441 3559 7629 Machine shop, jobbing & repair; fabricated structural metal; automotive related machinery; electrical repair shops; rolling mill machinery; special dies, tools, jigs & fixtures

(G-19701)
WAUSEON SILO & COAL COMPANY
Also Called: Wauseon Precast
535 Wood St (43567-1248)
PHONE..............................419 335-6041
Fax: 419 335-1538
Barton L Frazier, *President*
Scott Frazier, *Manager*
EMP: 10
SQ FT: 41,000
SALES: 739.9K Privately Held
SIC: 3272 5251 Covers, catch basin: concrete; septic tanks, concrete; steps, prefabricated concrete; builders' hardware

(G-19702)
WYSE INDUSTRIAL CARTS INC
10510 County Road 12 (43567-9237)
PHONE..............................419 923-7353
Fax: 419 923-7354
Gene Wyse, *President*
Randy Wyse, *Vice Pres*
Steve Lauber, *Webmaster*
EMP: 12
SQ FT: 20,000
SALES (est): 2.2MM Privately Held
WEB: www.wyseindustrialcarts.com
SIC: 3448 Ramps: prefabricated metal

(G-19703)
ZIMMERMAN SHTMTL STL & WLDG
1179 N Ottokee St (43567-1911)
PHONE..............................419 335-3806
Dennis M Zimmerman, *Owner*
EMP: 3
SQ FT: 2,100
SALES (est): 160K Privately Held
SIC: 3441 Fabricated structural metal

Waverly
Pike County

(G-19704)
C & C MOBILE HOMES LLC
Also Called: Colburn Dairy
1580 Valley Rd (45690-9532)
PHONE..............................740 663-5535
Murrell Colburn, *Mng Member*
Imogene Colburn, *Mng Member*
EMP: 4
SALES: 100K Privately Held
SIC: 2451 Mobile homes

(G-19705)
CLEARFIELD OHIO HOLDINGS INC
300 E 2nd St (45690-1323)
PHONE..............................740 947-5121
Brian Jonard, *Branch Mgr*
EMP: 67
SALES (corp-wide): 11.4MM Privately Held
SIC: 1389 Gas field services
PA: Clearfield Ohio Holdings Inc
Radnor Corp Ctr Bdg5 40
Radnor PA 19087
610 293-0410

(G-19706)
CST ZERO DISCHARGED CAR WASH S
223 Virginia Ln (45690-9639)
PHONE..............................740 947-5480
EMP: 3 EST: 1995
SALES (est): 130K Privately Held
SIC: 3589 3826 Water And Enviromental Saving

(G-19707)
D & M WELDING & RADIATOR
9093 State Route 220 (45690-9734)
PHONE..............................740 947-9032
Hank Dyke, *Partner*
Chuck Myers, *Partner*
EMP: 4
SQ FT: 2,400
SALES (est): 278.5K Privately Held
SIC: 7692 7539 1799 Welding repair; radiator repair shop, automotive; welding on site

(G-19708)
ECHO ENVIRONMENTAL WAVERLY LLC
479 Indl Pk Dr (45690)
PHONE..............................740 286-2810
Alan Stockmeister, *CEO*
EMP: 12
SALES (est): 2.1MM Privately Held
SIC: 3341 Copper smelting & refining (secondary)

(G-19709)
GEO-TECH POLYMERS LLC
423 Hopewell Rd (45690-9700)
PHONE..............................614 797-2300
Fax: 614 797-2301
Doug Collins, *President*
Aimee McDonald, *Director*
▼ EMP: 17
SALES (est): 5.2MM
SALES (corp-wide): 105MM Privately Held
SIC: 2821 Plastics materials & resins
PA: Wastren Advantage, Inc.
1571 Shyville Rd
Piketon OH 45661
970 254-1277

▲ = Import ▼ =Export
◆ =Import/Export

(G-19710)
HADSELL CHEMICAL PROC LLC
9329 State Route 220 (45690-9012)
PHONE................................740 941-1792
Bob Walton Jr, *President*
G Todd Schulte, *Exec VP*
Jenny Chamberlin, *Vice Pres*
Jonathan Eaton, *Vice Pres*
EMP: 39
SALES (est): 8.9MM **Privately Held**
SIC: 2821 3565 1541 Molding compounds, plastics; packaging machinery; industrial buildings & warehouses

(G-19711)
HOT SPOT
Also Called: Bronze and Beautiful
800 W 2nd St (45690-9701)
PHONE................................740 947-8888
Jeff Straughtenburger, *Owner*
EMP: 3
SALES (est): 193.2K **Privately Held**
SIC: 3648 Sun tanning equipment, incl. tanning beds

(G-19712)
J&R PALLET LTD
1100 Travis Rd (45690-9086)
PHONE................................740 226-1112
Ramona Southworth, *Principal*
EMP: 4
SALES (est): 225K **Privately Held**
SIC: 2448 Pallets, wood & wood with metal

(G-19713)
NEWS WATCHMAN & PAPER
Also Called: Acm Ohio
860 W Emmitt Ave Ste 5 (45690-1080)
P.O. Box 151 (45690-0151)
PHONE................................740 947-2149
Fax: 740 947-1344
Norman Guilliland, *Principal*
Carrie Humble, *Principal*
EMP: 10
SALES (est): 461.2K **Privately Held**
WEB: www.newswatchman.com
SIC: 2711 7313 Newspapers, publishing & printing; newspaper advertising representative

(G-19714)
OAK CHIPS INC
306 W North St (45690-1032)
PHONE................................740 947-4159
EMP: 7 EST: 2014
SALES (est): 694.9K **Privately Held**
SIC: 2448 Wood pallets & skids

(G-19715)
OHIO CANDLE CO INC
7040 Us Rte 23 (45690)
P.O. Box 103, Piketon (45661-0103)
PHONE................................740 289-8000
William Purpeco, *President*
Ed Purpeco, *Vice Pres*
Melinda Purpeco, *Treasurer*
Rebecca Purpeco, *Admin Sec*
EMP: 3
SALES: 350K **Privately Held**
SIC: 3999 Candles

(G-19716)
PERFORMANX SPECIALTY CHEM LLC
423 Hopewell Rd (45690-9700)
PHONE................................614 300-7001
Kim Pellock, *Branch Mgr*
EMP: 6
SALES (corp-wide): 943.5K **Privately Held**
SIC: 2834 Pharmaceutical preparations
PA: Performanx Specialty Chemicals, Llc
300 Westdale Ave
Westerville OH 43082
614 300-7001

(G-19717)
PIKE COUNTY PAPER INC
14572 Us Highway 23 Ste C (45690-9448)
PHONE................................740 947-5522
Fax: 740 947-3515
David Ringer, *Treasurer*
Carrie Lawson, *Manager*
EMP: 14
SQ FT: 800

SALES (est): 670K **Privately Held**
WEB: www.news-watch.com
SIC: 2741 Newsletter publishing

(G-19718)
PIKE TOOL & MANUFACTURING CO
754 W 2nd St (45690-9701)
PHONE................................740 947-7462
Fax: 740 947-8287
James E Hambrick, *President*
Dal Hambrick, *Admin Sec*
EMP: 3
SQ FT: 4,800
SALES (est): 75K **Privately Held**
SIC: 3545 Machine tool accessories

(G-19719)
PRINTEX INCORPORATED
Also Called: Fomerly Daniels Printing Den
101 Victory Dr (45690-1062)
PHONE................................740 947-8800
Todd Schobelock, *Manager*
EMP: 3
SALES (corp-wide): 1.6MM **Privately Held**
SIC: 2752 Commercial printing, lithographic
PA: Printex, Incorporated
185 E Main St
Chillicothe OH 45601
740 773-0088

(G-19720)
VR WAVERLY INC (DH)
Also Called: Van Rob Waverly
611 W 2nd St (45690-9701)
PHONE................................740 947-7763
Dennis Berry, *CEO*
Edward Konyen, *General Mgr*
Randy Myers, *General Mgr*
David Albert, *CFO*
Chris Dawson, *Controller*
▲ EMP: 81
SALES (est): 42.9MM
SALES (corp-wide): 1.4B **Privately Held**
SIC: 3465 Automotive stampings
HQ: Kirchhoff Automotive Gmbh
Stefanstr. 2
Iserlohn 58638
237 121-10

Wayne
Wood County

(G-19721)
BRADNER OIL COMPANY INC
Wayne Rd (43466)
PHONE................................419 288-2945
Robert Harstter, *President*
Carla Harstter, *Vice Pres*
EMP: 3
SALES: 500K **Privately Held**
SIC: 1389 5172 Oil & gas field services; petroleum products

Waynesburg
Stark County

(G-19722)
ACE ASSEMBLY PACKAGING INC
133 N Mill St (44688-9124)
P.O. Box 55 (44688-0055)
PHONE................................330 866-9117
Fax: 330 866-9118
Dency S Cilona, *President*
EMP: 30
SALES (est): 2.3MM **Privately Held**
SIC: 7389 3999 Packaging & labeling services; manufacturing industries

(G-19723)
BAUGHMANS MACHINE & WELD SHOP
6498 June Rd Nw (44688-9433)
PHONE................................330 866-9243
Paul Baughman, *President*
John Baughaman, *Vice Pres*
Kathy Miller, *Treasurer*

EMP: 8
SQ FT: 960
SALES (est): 632.4K **Privately Held**
SIC: 7692 Welding repair

(G-19724)
E & M LIBERTY WELDING INC
141 James St (44688)
PHONE................................330 866-2338
Mark Crowe, *Partner*
Earl Ecenbarger, *Partner*
Kim Crowe, *Office Mgr*
EMP: 8
SALES: 50K **Privately Held**
SIC: 7692 1711 Welding repair; boiler & furnace contractors

(G-19725)
GRODHAUS & YOUNG INC
144 Niles Ave (44688)
P.O. Box 565 (44688-0565)
PHONE................................330 866-3321
Fax: 330 866-2910
Barry Grodhaus, *President*
Barry Gradhaus, *Treasurer*
▲ EMP: 16 EST: 1953
SQ FT: 25,000
SALES (est): 1MM **Privately Held**
SIC: 7692 7699 Welding repair; industrial machinery & equipment repair

(G-19726)
OS POWER TONG INC
7330 Minerva Rd Se (44688-9340)
P.O. Box 694 (44688-0694)
PHONE................................330 866-3815
Thomas R Orlando, *President*
Steven Nicholson, *Vice Pres*
EMP: 4
SALES (est): 410K **Privately Held**
SIC: 1389 Gas field services

(G-19727)
PETROS CONCRETE INC (PA)
7105 Lardon Rd Nw (44688-9604)
PHONE................................330 868-6130
John Petros, *President*
EMP: 6
SALES (est): 626.5K **Privately Held**
SIC: 3273 Ready-mixed concrete

(G-19728)
TERRA STAR INC
111 N Main St (44688-9437)
P.O. Box 42223, Oklahoma City OK (73123-3223)
PHONE................................405 200-1336
Bradley Wittrock, *CEO*
Justin Keiser, *Foreman/Supr*
Tommy Peck, *Foreman/Supr*
Rindi Cochran, *Accounting Mgr*
EMP: 13
SALES (corp-wide): 12.6MM **Privately Held**
SIC: 1389 Cementing oil & gas well casings
PA: Terra Star Inc
6106 Nw 63rd St
Warr Acres OK 73132
405 200-1336

(G-19729)
WMRE OF OHIO-AMERICAN LLC
7916 Chapel St Se (44688-9754)
PHONE................................713 328-7345
Ginger Kaladas,
EMP: 3
SALES (est): 270K **Privately Held**
SIC: 2836 5122 Biological products, except diagnostic; biologicals & allied products

---
Waynesville
Warren County

(G-19730)
INDICATOR SHOP
8875 Bellbrook Rd (45068-9741)
PHONE................................513 897-0055
Mary Conley, *Owner*
EMP: 3

SALES: 140K **Privately Held**
SIC: 3829 Measuring & controlling devices

(G-19731)
JOHN PURDUM
Also Called: Brass Lantern Antiques
100 S Main St (45068-8954)
P.O. Box 597 (45068-0597)
PHONE................................513 897-9686
Fax: 513 897-7901
John Purdum, *Owner*
EMP: 6
SQ FT: 3,720
SALES (est): 315.3K **Privately Held**
WEB: www.purdumantiques.com
SIC: 5932 5399 2519 7011 Antiques; country general stores; household furniture, except wood or metal: upholstered; hotels & motels; eating places

(G-19732)
OUTHOUSE PAPER ETC INC
319 Collett Rd (45068-9306)
P.O. Box 101, Cuba (45177-0101)
PHONE................................937 382-2800
Shelley Taylor, *President*
EMP: 6
SQ FT: 3,250
SALES (est): 453K **Privately Held**
SIC: 2679 Paperboard products, converted

(G-19733)
PATRICK M DAVIDSON
Also Called: Davidson Meat Processing Plant
6490 Corwin Ave (45068-9722)
PHONE................................513 897-2971
Patrick M Davidson, *Owner*
EMP: 6
SQ FT: 3,000
SALES: 80K **Privately Held**
SIC: 0751 2013 2011 Slaughtering: custom livestock services; sausages & other prepared meats; meat packing plants

(G-19734)
R & M IMPORTS
3313 Harlan Carroll Rd (45068-9414)
P.O. Box 60, Harveysburg (45032-0060)
PHONE................................513 897-5015
Fax: 513 897-7278
Randall Thatcher, *Owner*
Edward Thatcher, *Principal*
▲ EMP: 5
SQ FT: 2,520
SALES (est): 380K **Privately Held**
WEB: www.randmimports.com
SIC: 3873 Watches, clocks, watchcases & parts

(G-19735)
ROSE OF SHARON ENTERPRISES
9243 Old Stage Rd (45068-8831)
P.O. Box 984 (45068-0984)
PHONE................................937 862-4543
Sharon Willard, *Owner*
James Willard, *Co-Owner*
EMP: 3
SALES: 250K **Privately Held**
SIC: 3999 Potpourri

(G-19736)
TROPICAL OHIO SMOOTHIE INC
2019 E State Route 73 (45068-8716)
PHONE................................937 673-6218
Chet Hakanson, *Principal*
EMP: 4
SALES (est): 233.4K **Privately Held**
SIC: 2037 Frozen fruits & vegetables

Wellington
Lorain County

(G-19737)
ARC ELEC
18637 State Route 511 (44090-9700)
PHONE................................440 774-2800
EMP: 10 **Privately Held**
SIC: 9111 3699 1731 Executive offices; electrical equipment & supplies; electrical work

GEOGRAPHIC

(G-19738)
BOOS MAKE & TAKE
676 N Main St (44090-1040)
PHONE..............................440 647-0000
Terry Jenkins, *Manager*
EMP: 4
SALES (est): 378.5K Privately Held
SIC: 3911 Cigar & cigarette accessories

(G-19739)
CLEVELAND CITY FORGE INC
46950 State Route 18 (44090-9791)
PHONE..............................440 647-5400
Fax: 440 647-4185
Richard Kovach, *President*
Jim Evans, *Purch Mgr*
Ken Wrona, *CFO*
Kenneth Kovach, *Treasurer*
Drew Maddock, *Admin Sec*
EMP: 40
SQ FT: 200,000
SALES (est): 10.2MM Privately Held
WEB: www.clevelandcityforge.com
SIC: 3441 Fabricated structural metal

(G-19740)
E D M STAR-ONE INC
745 Shiloh Ave (44090-1190)
PHONE..............................440 647-0600
Fax: 440 647-0600
Howard White, *President*
Samuel White, *Vice Pres*
Michael White, *Treasurer*
Mayetta Haynes, *Manager*
Timothy White, *Admin Sec*
EMP: 10
SQ FT: 6,500
SALES (est): 800K Privately Held
WEB: www.star-one-edm.com
SIC: 3312 Blast furnaces & steel mills

(G-19741)
ECO MECHANICAL LLC
47559 Hughes Rd (44090-9717)
PHONE..............................440 610-9253
James McKnight, *President*
EMP: 3
SQ FT: 1,000
SALES: 414.8K Privately Held
SIC: 3569 Testing chambers for altitude,
temperature, ordnance, power

(G-19742)
EDWARD W DANIEL LLC
46950 State Route 18 S (44090-9791)
PHONE..............................440 647-1960
Fax: 216 295-9744
Ken Wrona, *CFO*
Robert Oriti,
Stuart W Cordell,
EMP: 36 EST: 1922
SQ FT: 75,000
SALES (est): 5.8MM Privately Held
WEB: www.ewdaniel.com
SIC: 3429 5085 3494 3463 Manufac-
tured hardware (general); industrial sup-
plies; valves & pipe fittings; nonferrous
forgings; iron & steel forgings; bolts, nuts,
rivets & washers

(G-19743)
**FOREST CITY TECHNOLOGIES
INC (PA)**
299 Clay St (44090-1128)
P.O. Box 86 (44090-0086)
PHONE..............................440 647-2115
Fax: 440 647-2644
John D Cloud Sr, *President*
Jeffrey R Petras, *COO*
Charles Schillig, *Vice Pres*
David Snowball, *Vice Pres*
R Gary Thomas, *Vice Pres*
▲ EMP: 430 EST: 1955
SQ FT: 50,000
SALES (est): 305.9MM Privately Held
SIC: 3053 Gaskets & sealing devices; gas-
kets, all materials

(G-19744)
**FOREST CITY TECHNOLOGIES
INC**
232 Maple St (44090-1164)
P.O. Box 86 (44090-0086)
PHONE..............................440 647-2115
Chuck Shilleg, *Manager*

Larry Buehler, *Maintence Staff*
EMP: 500
SALES (corp-wide): 305.9MM Privately
Held
SIC: 3053 Gaskets & sealing devices; gas-
kets, all materials
PA: Forest City Technologies, Inc.
299 Clay St
Wellington OH 44090
440 647-2115

(G-19745)
**FOREST CITY TECHNOLOGIES
INC**
Also Called: Forest City Tech Plant 4
401 Magyar St (44090-1278)
P.O. Box 86 (44090-0086)
PHONE..............................440 647-2115
Bob Nelson, *General Mgr*
Jeni Dubena, *Admin Asst*
EMP: 150
SALES (corp-wide): 305.9MM Privately
Held
SIC: 3053 Gasket materials
PA: Forest City Technologies, Inc.
299 Clay St
Wellington OH 44090
440 647-2115

(G-19746)
**FOREST CITY TECHNOLOGIES
INC**
Also Called: Adelphia
299 Clay St (44090-1128)
P.O. Box 86 (44090-0086)
PHONE..............................440 647-2115
Buzz Bernning, *Manager*
EMP: 120
SALES (corp-wide): 305.9MM Privately
Held
SIC: 3053 Gasket materials
PA: Forest City Technologies, Inc.
299 Clay St
Wellington OH 44090
440 647-2115

(G-19747)
**FOREST CITY TECHNOLOGIES
INC**
Also Called: Technofab
234 Maple St (44090-1164)
P.O. Box 86 (44090-0086)
PHONE..............................440 647-2115
EMP: 4
SALES (corp-wide): 305.9MM Privately
Held
SIC: 3053 Gaskets, packing & sealing de-
vices
PA: Forest City Technologies, Inc.
299 Clay St
Wellington OH 44090
440 647-2115

(G-19748)
**HUNTINGTON HARDWOOD LBR
CO INC**
28211 Baker Rd (44090-9349)
P.O. Box 5, Spencer (44275-0005)
PHONE..............................440 647-2283
Dennis Emary, *President*
EMP: 7
SALES (est): 625.4K Privately Held
SIC: 2411 2431 Logging; millwork

(G-19749)
L & L FABRICATING LLC
46419 Whitney Rd (44090-9846)
PHONE..............................440 647-6649
Larry Gilles, *Owner*
Linda Gilles, *Owner*
EMP: 4
SALES: 350K Privately Held
WEB: www.llfab.com
SIC: 3999 Education aids, devices & sup-
plies

(G-19750)
MD TOOL & DIE INC
755 Industrial Ave (44090-1193)
P.O. Box 298 (44090-0298)
PHONE..............................440 647-6456
Fax: 440 647-1007
Michael Donovan, *President*
Linda Donovan, *Admin Sec*
EMP: 4

SQ FT: 2,400
SALES (est): 478.4K Privately Held
SIC: 3544 Special dies, tools, jigs & fix-
tures

(G-19751)
NN INC
125 Bennett St (44090-1202)
PHONE..............................440 647-4711
EMP: 4
SALES (corp-wide): 833.4MM Publicly
Held
SIC: 3562 Ball bearings & parts
PA: Nn, Inc.
207 Mockingbird Ln Ste 10
Johnson City TN 37604
423 743-9151

(G-19752)
PRECISION FITTINGS LLC
709 N Main St (44090-1089)
PHONE..............................440 647-4143
Fax: 440 647-5030
Christopher H Lake, *President*
Dan Puskas, *Safety Mgr*
Larry Szabo, *Purch Mgr*
Dick Ross, *QC Mgr*
Bill Thorn, *Draft/Design*
▲ EMP: 49 EST: 1947
SQ FT: 65,000
SALES (est): 10.9MM Privately Held
WEB: www.precisionfittings.com
SIC: 3452 3451 3498 3494 Bolts, nuts,
rivets & washers; screw machine prod-
ucts; fabricated pipe & fittings; valves &
pipe fittings

(G-19753)
**ROCHESTER MANUFACTURING
INC**
Also Called: ELECTROBURR
24765 Quarry Rd (44090-9293)
PHONE..............................440 647-2463
David Younglas, *CEO*
Scott Frombaugh, *President*
Rose Alferio, *Manager*
EMP: 16
SQ FT: 14,000
SALES: 1.2MM Privately Held
WEB: www.rochestermfg.com
SIC: 3599 Machine shop, jobbing & repair

(G-19754)
SECTIONAL STAMPING INC
Also Called: Wellington Stamping
350 Maple St (44090-1171)
PHONE..............................440 647-2100
Fax: 440 647-5350
Jack Falcon, *President*
James Fanello, *Vice Pres*
Louis Jones, *Production*
Keith Brenning, *QC Dir*
Beth Moore, *Human Res Mgr*
EMP: 280
SQ FT: 200,000
SALES (est): 62.2MM
SALES (corp-wide): 1B Publicly Held
SIC: 3469 Metal stampings
HQ: Shiloh Corporation
880 Steel Dr
Valley City OH 44280
330 558-2600

(G-19755)
SHILOH INDUSTRIES INC
350 Maple St (44090-1171)
PHONE..............................440 647-2100
SRI Perumal, *Plant Mgr*
Kevin Cleary, *Manager*
Butch Thompson, *Manager*
Tom Strick, *Director*
Ray Weaver, *Executive*
EMP: 799
SALES (corp-wide): 1B Publicly Held
SIC: 3465 Automotive stampings
PA: Shiloh Industries, Inc.
880 Steel Dr
Valley City OH 44280
330 558-2600

(G-19756)
TITE SEAL CASE COMPANY INC
Also Called: Forest City Tech
299 Clay St (44090-1128)
P.O. Box 86 (44090-0086)
PHONE..............................440 647-2371

Fax: 440 647-5207
John Cloud, *President*
Dave Snowball, *Vice Pres*
Sharon Regal, *Cust Mgr*
Kevin Gallatin, *CTO*
EMP: 4 EST: 1948
SQ FT: 1,000
SALES (est): 80K Privately Held
WEB: www.forestcitytech.com
SIC: 3317 Steel pipe & tubes

(G-19757)
WELLINGTON MANUFACTURING
200 Erie St (44090-1268)
PHONE..............................440 647-1162
Fax: 440 647-0254
Gary Petshe, *Principal*
EMP: 3
SALES (est): 241.7K Privately Held
SIC: 3999 Manufacturing industries

(G-19758)
**WHIRLAWAY CORPORATION
(HQ)**
720 Shiloh Ave (44090-1190)
PHONE..............................440 647-4711
Roderick R Baty, *CEO*
James R Widders, *Vice Pres*
Jeff Haag, *Engineer*
Mike Hluszti, *Engineer*
Tony Jones, *Controller*
▲ EMP: 175 EST: 1973
SALES (est): 66.9MM
SALES (corp-wide): 833.4MM Publicly
Held
WEB: www.whirlawaycorporation.com
SIC: 3714 3451 3469 Motor vehicle brake
systems & parts; screw machine prod-
ucts; appliance parts, porcelain enameled
PA: Nn, Inc.
207 Mockingbird Ln Ste 10
Johnson City TN 37604
423 743-9151

(G-19759)
WHIRLAWAY CORPORATION
125 Bennett St (44090-1202)
PHONE..............................440 647-4711
Fax: 440 647-9384
Thomas G Zupan, *Principal*
Tony Jones, *Controller*
EMP: 150
SALES (corp-wide): 833.4MM Publicly
Held
WEB: www.whirlawaycorporation.com
SIC: 3714 3451 Motor vehicle parts & ac-
cessories; screw machine products
HQ: Whirlaway Corporation
720 Shiloh Ave
Wellington OH 44090
440 647-4711

(G-19760)
WHIRLAWAY CORPORATION
Whirlaway Cincinatti, A Div Nn
720 Shiloh Ave (44090-1190)
PHONE..............................440 647-4711
Richard Eichmann, *Branch Mgr*
EMP: 20
SALES (corp-wide): 833.4MM Publicly
Held
WEB: www.whirlawaycorporation.com
SIC: 3714 3451 Motor vehicle parts & ac-
cessories; screw machine products
HQ: Whirlaway Corporation
720 Shiloh Ave
Wellington OH 44090
440 647-4711

Wellston
Jackson County

(G-19761)
**BROWN-FORMAN
CORPORATION**
Also Called: Blue Grass Cooperage - Jackson
468 Salem Church Rd (45692)
P.O. Box 528, Jackson (45640-0528)
PHONE..............................740 384-3027
James Gulley, *Branch Mgr*
Jo E Boggs, *Admin Asst*
EMP: 27

SALES (corp-wide): 4B Publicly Held
WEB: www.brown-forman.com
SIC: 2429 2449 Cooperage stock products: staves, headings, hoops, etc.; wood containers
PA: Brown-Forman Corporation
850 Dixie Hwy
Louisville KY 40210
502 585-1100

(G-19762)
DAVIS CAULKING & SEALANT LLC
199 Garfield Rd (45692-9746)
PHONE..................................740 286-3825
Arnold Davis, *Principal*
EMP: 4 EST: 2008
SALES (est): 431.3K Privately Held
SIC: 2891 Sealants

(G-19763)
GEM BEVERAGES INC
106 E 11th St (45692-1713)
PHONE..................................740 384-2411
Fax: 740 384-2411
Rex Holzapfel, *President*
EMP: 12 EST: 1995
SALES (est): 1.7MM Privately Held
SIC: 2086 Soft drinks: packaged in cans, bottles, etc.

(G-19764)
J-FAB
21 N Wisconsin Ave (45692-1149)
P.O. Box 622 (45692-0622)
PHONE..................................740 384-2649
Nick Rypert Sr, *Partner*
Bryan Rypert, *Partner*
EMP: 5 EST: 1999
SALES (est): 298.3K Privately Held
SIC: 3999 Manufacturing industries

(G-19765)
J-VAC INDUSTRIES INC
202 S Pennsylvania Ave (45692-1797)
PHONE..................................740 384-2155
Frank Declemente, *President*
Richard Moore, *Director*
Ann Ogletree, *Director*
EMP: 74
SQ FT: 8,300
SALES: 19.7K Privately Held
SIC: 8331 3269 Sheltered workshop; art & ornamental ware, pottery

(G-19766)
JACK HUFFMAN
1210 Hiram West Rd (45692-9536)
PHONE..................................740 384-5178
ADM Jack Huffman, *Owner*
Jack Huffman, *Owner*
EMP: 3
SALES (est): 115.5K Privately Held
SIC: 3281 Cut stone & stone products

(G-19767)
PILLSBURY COMPANY LLC
2403 S Pennsylvania Ave (45692-9503)
P.O. Box 151 (45692-0151)
PHONE..................................740 286-2170
Fax: 740 384-6986
Michael Davis, *Vice Pres*
Peter Erickson, *Vice Pres*
Daniel Malina, *Vice Pres*
Kristen Wenker, *Vice Pres*
John Komor, *Plant Mgr*
EMP: 15
SALES (corp-wide): 16.5B Publicly Held
WEB: www.pillsbury.com
SIC: 2041 2033 Flour & other grain mill products; canned fruits & specialties
HQ: The Pillsbury Company Llc
1 General Mills Blvd
Minneapolis MN 55426

(G-19768)
SEYMOURS LOGGING
1085 Loop Rd (45692-9768)
PHONE..................................740 288-1825
Ralph Seymour, *Partner*
EMP: 12
SALES (est): 1MM Privately Held
SIC: 2411 Wood chips, produced in the field; pole cutting contractors

(G-19769)
SOUTHERN OHIO WOOD
1085 Loop Rd (45692-9768)
P.O. Box 452, Hamden (45634-0452)
PHONE..................................740 288-1825
Ralph Seymour, *Owner*
EMP: 7
SALES (est): 354.4K Privately Held
SIC: 2421 Sawmills & planing mills, general

(G-19770)
SUPERIOR HARDWOODS OHIO INC (PA)
134 Wellston Indus Pk Rd (45692)
P.O. Box 606 (45692-0606)
PHONE..................................740 384-5677
Fax: 740 384-2985
Emmett Conway Jr, *President*
EMP: 60
SALES (est): 9.3MM Privately Held
SIC: 2421 2426 Sawmills & planing mills, general; hardwood dimension & flooring mills

(G-19771)
T&R LOGGING LLC
1085 Loop Rd (45692-9768)
P.O. Box 452, Hamden (45634-0452)
PHONE..................................740 288-1825
Ralph Seymour, *Principal*
EMP: 3
SALES (est): 182.6K Privately Held
SIC: 2411 Logging camps & contractors

(G-19772)
WELLSTON AEROSOL MFG CO INC
105 W A St (45692-1113)
P.O. Box 326 (45692-0326)
PHONE..................................740 384-2320
Fax: 740 384-2320
Norma Lockard, *President*
Dan Lockard Jr, *Vice Pres*
EMP: 25 EST: 1957
SALES (est): 4.9MM Privately Held
SIC: 2813 Aerosols

(G-19773)
WILKETT ENTERPRISES LLC
Also Called: Dirt Works Excavating
109 Mitchell Dr 4 (45692-9204)
PHONE..................................740 384-2890
Gregory Wilkett, *Principal*
EMP: 6
SALES: 350K Privately Held
SIC: 3531 Construction machinery

Wellsville
Columbiana County

(G-19774)
CIMBAR PERFORMANCE MNRL WV LLC
2400 Clark Ave (43968-1070)
PHONE..................................330 532-2034
John H Waters, *President*
Roger Smith, *Manager*
EMP: 24
SALES (est): 3.9MM
SALES (corp-wide): 26.2MM Privately Held
WEB: www.cimbar.com
SIC: 3295 Minerals, ground or otherwise treated
PA: United Minerals And Properties, Inc.
49 Jackson Lake Rd Ste O
Chatsworth GA 30705
770 387-0319

(G-19775)
STEVENSON MFG CO
Also Called: Stevco
1 1st St (43968)
PHONE..................................330 532-1581
Fax: 330 532-1120
Timothy Lynch, *President*
Todd Lynch, *Vice Pres*
Lisa De Ardo, *Controller*
EMP: 8 EST: 1800
SQ FT: 115,000

SALES (est): 1.2MM Privately Held
WEB: www.stevensonmfg.com
SIC: 3541 3599 Grinding machines, metalworking; machine shop, jobbing & repair

(G-19776)
WELLSVILLE FOUNDRY INC
18150 Fife Coal Rd (43968-9760)
P.O. Box 424 (43968-0424)
PHONE..................................330 532-2995
Fax: 330 532-3424
Chuck H Gilmore, *President*
Patsy Frontone, *Principal*
Gerald M Kelly, *Principal*
James K Kelly, *Principal*
Jodi Griffith, *Manager*
EMP: 30
SQ FT: 17,000
SALES (est): 8MM Privately Held
WEB: www.wellsvillefoundry.com
SIC: 3321 Gray & ductile iron foundries

(G-19777)
YELLOW CREEK CASTING COMPANY
18141 Fife Coal Rd (43968-9760)
PHONE..................................330 532-4608
Fax: 330 532-9635
Ron Kelly, *President*
Erin Kelly, *Prdtn Mgr*
Jeanne Kelly, *Treasurer*
Lois Kelly, *Treasurer*
Gerald Kelly, *Sales Staff*
EMP: 20
SQ FT: 4,500
SALES (est): 3.2MM Privately Held
WEB: www.yellowcreekcasting.com
SIC: 3321 3322 Gray iron castings; malleable iron foundries

West Alexandria
Preble County

(G-19778)
AMS GLOBAL LTD
119 E Dayton St (45381-1209)
PHONE..................................937 620-1036
Terrence Brennan, *Partner*
Anna Matthews, *Partner*
EMP: 14
SQ FT: 10,000
SALES: 700K Privately Held
SIC: 3089 Plastic processing

(G-19779)
DOW CHEMICAL COMPANY
10 Electric St (45381-1212)
PHONE..................................937 839-4612
David Kistner, *Director*
EMP: 76
SALES (corp-wide): 48.1B Publicly Held
SIC: 2821 Thermoplastic materials
PA: The Dow Chemical Company
2030 Dow Ctr
Midland MI 48674
989 636-1000

(G-19780)
JOHN M HAND
Also Called: Treasured Times Enterprises
6417 Enterprise Rd (45381-9500)
PHONE..................................937 902-1327
John M Hand, *Principal*
EMP: 4
SALES (est): 263K Privately Held
SIC: 2431 Millwork

(G-19781)
REXARC INTERNATIONAL INC
35 E 3rd St (45381-1231)
P.O. Box 7 (45381-0007)
PHONE..................................937 839-4604
Fax: 937 839-5897
Robert Moyer, *CEO*
James P Bowman, *President*
Ann C Smith, *Principal*
Joseph R Smith, *Chairman*
Galen Woodhouse, *CFO*
▼ EMP: 25
SQ FT: 96,000

SALES (est): 6.6MM Privately Held
SIC: 3498 3548 3569 Manifolds, pipe: fabricated from purchased pipe; gas welding equipment; gas generators

(G-19782)
ROGUE MANUFACTURING INC
304 Stotler Rd (45381-1261)
PHONE..................................937 839-4026
Paul Kasperski, *President*
EMP: 5
SALES (est): 442.1K Privately Held
SIC: 3531 Construction machinery

(G-19783)
ROHM AND HAAS COMPANY
10 Electric St (45381-1299)
PHONE..................................937 839-4612
Kathy Schultz, *Plant Mgr*
Cristan Popio, *Engineer*
Carlos Quinones, *Branch Mgr*
Clayton Woodgeard, *Maintence Staff*
EMP: 110
SALES (corp-wide): 48.1B Publicly Held
WEB: www.rohmhaas.com
SIC: 2821 Plastics materials & resins
HQ: Rohm And Haas Company
100 N Independence Mall W
Philadelphia PA 19106
215 592-3000

(G-19784)
TWIN VALLEY METALCRAFT ASM LLC
4739 Enterprise Rd (45381-9518)
PHONE..................................937 787-4634
Fax: 937 787-4862
Debra L Purdy,
David R Purdy,
EMP: 6
SQ FT: 7,000
SALES: 340K Privately Held
SIC: 3451 3429 3599 Screw machine products; aircraft hardware; machine shop, jobbing & repair

(G-19785)
VILLAGE OF WEST ALEXANDRIA (PA)
16 N Main St Unit 2 (45381-1191)
P.O. Box 265 (45381-0265)
PHONE..................................937 839-4168
Fax: 937 839-4209
Carol Lunssord, *Mayor*
Mitchell Suggs, *Mayor*
EMP: 4 EST: 1985
SALES (est): 1.7MM Privately Held
WEB: www.walexpreb.org
SIC: 3589 Sewage & water treatment equipment

(G-19786)
WEBERS BODY & FRAME
2017 State Route 503 N (45381-9701)
PHONE..................................937 839-5946
David P Weber, *President*
EMP: 9
SALES (est): 875.3K Privately Held
SIC: 7532 7536 7692 Body shop, automotive; automotive glass replacement shops; welding repair

(G-19787)
WYSONG GRAVEL CO INC (PA)
Also Called: Camden Ready Mix
2332 State Route 503 N (45381)
PHONE..................................937 456-4539
John D Wysong, *President*
Carroll Wysong, *Vice Pres*
EMP: 10
SQ FT: 1,500
SALES (est): 3.1MM Privately Held
SIC: 1442 Gravel mining

(G-19788)
WYSONG GRAVEL CO INC
2032 State Route 503 N (45381-9701)
PHONE..................................937 839-5497
Carroll Wysong, *Vice Pres*
EMP: 9
SALES (corp-wide): 3.1MM Privately Held
SIC: 1442 Gravel mining

GEOGRAPHIC

PA: Wysong Gravel Co Inc
2332 State Route 503 N
West Alexandria OH 45381
937 456-4539

West Carrollton
Montgomery County

(G-19789)
AERO JET WASH LLC
440 Fame Rd (45449-2315)
PHONE..866 381-7955
Shawn Tadayon, *Mng Member*
Mike Vahedy, *Mng Member*
EMP: 10
SQ FT: 4,400
SALES (est): 1.3MM **Privately Held**
WEB: www.aerojetwash.com
SIC: 3724 4581 Aircraft engines & engine
parts; aircraft cleaning & janitorial service

(G-19790)
APPVION INC
1030 W Alex Bell Rd (45449-1923)
PHONE..937 859-8261
Fax: 937 847-7153
Roxanne Webb, *Safety Mgr*
J Pequignot, *Purchasing*
Doniece Gatliff, *Human Res Dir*
Mark Ferguson, *Manager*
Tod Downy, *Manager*
EMP: 400
SALES (corp-wide): 690.3MM **Privately
Held**
WEB: www.appletonpapers.com
SIC: 2672 2621 Coated paper, except
photographic, carbon or abrasive; paper
mills
HQ: Appvion, Inc.
825 E Wisconsin Ave
Appleton WI 54911
920 734-9841

(G-19791)
BARTLEY LAWN SERVICE LLC
Also Called: Bartleys Lawn Services
69 W Alex Bell Rd (45449-1912)
PHONE..937 435-8884
Todd Bartley, *Mng Member*
EMP: 4
SALES (est): 30K **Privately Held**
SIC: 0782 0783 3711 Lawn services; or-
namental shrub & tree services; motor ve-
hicles & car bodies

(G-19792)
**FOURTEEN VENTURES GROUP
LLC**
3131 W Alex Bell Rd (45449-2832)
PHONE..937 866-2341
Richard Dobson, *Mng Member*
EMP: 8 EST: 2014
SALES (est): 776.5K **Privately Held**
SIC: 3993 Signs & advertising specialties

(G-19793)
GITI TECH GROUP LTD
440 Fame Rd (45449-2315)
PHONE..866 381-7955
Shahin Tadayon, *Managing Dir*
Maggie Tadayon, *Administration*
EMP: 5 EST: 2011
SALES: 500K **Privately Held**
SIC: 3563 Air & gas compressors

(G-19794)
**WEST CARROLLTON
PARCHMENT**
400 E Dixie Dr (45449-1827)
PHONE..513 594-3341
Cameron Lonergan, *President*
Jeff Whitt, *Maint Spvr*
Scott Sheridan, *VP Sales*
EMP: 25
SALES (est): 6.5MM **Privately Held**
SIC: 2759 Flexographic printing

West Chester
Butler County

(G-19795)
ABB INC
7759 Lakota Springs Dr (45069-1455)
PHONE..513 874-4730
Fax: 513 874-4736
Pat Mueller, *Branch Mgr*
EMP: 76
SALES (corp-wide): 33.8B **Privately Held**
WEB: www.elsterelectricity.com
SIC: 3612 Transformers, except electric
HQ: Abb Inc.
12040 Regency Pkwy # 200
Cary NC 27518
919 856-2360

(G-19796)
ACCUFAB INC
9059 Sutton Pl (45011-9316)
P.O. Box 62433, Cincinnati (45262-0433)
PHONE..513 942-1929
Fax: 513 942-1931
Geneva Morgan, *President*
James Morgan, *Vice Pres*
Kerry Ward, *CFO*
Greg Davis, *Manager*
EMP: 7
SQ FT: 6,500
SALES (est): 1.2MM **Privately Held**
WEB: www.cincy-accufab.com
SIC: 3444 Sheet metalwork

(G-19797)
ACTIVE ROADS LLC
7641 Kirkwood Dr (45069-4702)
PHONE..937 242-6555
Randy Hinders,
Joshua Deaton,
Michael Kirshteyn,
EMP: 3 EST: 2014
SALES (est): 170.1K **Privately Held**
SIC: 3599 Custom machinery

(G-19798)
**ADDIS GLASS FABRICATING
INC**
9418 Sutton Pl (45011-9698)
PHONE..513 860-3340
Fax: 513 860-3444
Kevin Addis, *President*
Kevin J Addis, *Principal*
Penni Addis, *Corp Secy*
Mark Kile, *Vice Pres*
▲ **EMP:** 19
SQ FT: 39,000
SALES (est): 1.6MM **Privately Held**
SIC: 3211 3231 Flat glass; products of
purchased glass

(G-19799)
**AEG PHOTOCONDUCTOR
CORPORATION**
6929 Tylersville Rd # 18 (45069-1590)
PHONE..513 874-4939
Manfred Wagner, *President*
Kevin Gilmore, *Vice Pres*
Wolfgang Tietze, *Vice Pres*
Thomas Schank, *QC Dir*
Heribert Weber, *Treasurer*
▲ **EMP:** 60
SQ FT: 32,000
SALES (est): 4.2MM
SALES (corp-wide): 8.7MM **Privately
Held**
SIC: 3861 3699 3674 Photographic
equipment & supplies; electrical equip-
ment & supplies; semiconductors & re-
lated devices
PA: Hologic Hitec-Imaging Gmbh
Max-Planck-Str. 7
Warstein 59581
290 286-10

(G-19800)
**AGENT TECHNOLOGIES INC
(PA)**
8216 Princeton Glendale (45069-1675)
PHONE..513 942-9444
Ben Moore, *President*
Benjamin E Moore, *President*
EMP: 4

SALES (est): 546.5K **Privately Held**
WEB: www.agenttech.com
SIC: 7371 3613 Computer software development & applications; control panels,
electric

(G-19801)
AK STEEL CORPORATION
Also Called: AK Steel Corp Copy Center
9227 Centre Pointe Dr (45069-4822)
P.O. Box 8702 (45071-8702)
PHONE..513 425-5000
J L Wainscott, *President*
EMP: 82
SALES (corp-wide): 5.8B **Publicly Held**
SIC: 3312 Blast furnaces & steel mills
HQ: Ak Steel Corporation
9227 Centre Pointe Dr
West Chester OH 45069
513 425-4200

(G-19802)
AK STEEL CORPORATION (HQ)
9227 Centre Pointe Dr (45069-4822)
PHONE..513 425-4200
James Wainscott, *President*
Bill Cro, *General Mgr*
Roger K Newport, *COO*
Kirk W Reich, *Exec VP*
Keith J Howell, *Senior VP*
◆ **EMP:** 303
SQ FT: 136,000
SALES (est): 2.8B
SALES (corp-wide): 5.8B **Publicly Held**
WEB: www.ketnar.org
SIC: 3312 Blast furnaces & steel mills;
sheet or strip, steel, hot-rolled; coated or
plated products; sheet or strip, steel, cold-
rolled: own hot-rolled
PA: Ak Steel Holding Corporation
9227 Centre Pointe Dr
West Chester OH 45069
513 425-5000

(G-19803)
**AK STEEL HOLDING
CORPORATION (PA)**
9227 Centre Pointe Dr (45069-4822)
PHONE..513 425-5000
Roger K Newport, *CEO*
Kirk W Reich, *President*
Darren Callihan, *General Mgr*
Greg Cappiello, *General Mgr*
Tom Thompson, *General Mgr*
◆ **EMP:** 300
SALES: 5.8B **Publicly Held**
WEB: www.aksteel.com
SIC: 3312 Blast furnaces & steel mills;
sheet or strip, steel, hot-rolled; coated or
plated products; sheet or strip, steel, cold-
rolled: own hot-rolled

(G-19804)
**ALMO PROCESS TECHNOLOGY
INC**
8849 Brookside Ave # 101 (45069-7114)
PHONE..513 402-2566
Tom Schroeder, *President*
Dixon F Miller, *Principal*
Brian Smith, *Sales Staff*
▲ **EMP:** 6
SALES: 5MM **Privately Held**
SIC: 3443 3535 Separators, industrial
process: metal plate; belt conveyor sys-
tems, general industrial use

(G-19805)
ANOTEX INDUSTRIES INC
4914 Rialto Rd (45069-2927)
PHONE..513 860-1165
Fax: 513 860-4795
Diem Pham, *President*
Vinh Pham, *Vice Pres*
Dominic Pham, *Admin Mgr*
Thao Pham, *Shareholder*
EMP: 7
SQ FT: 6,000
SALES: 1MM **Privately Held**
SIC: 3479 Coating, rust preventive

(G-19806)
APEX CIRCUITS INC
Also Called: Apex Crcits Elctrnic Dsign Man
5100 Excello Ct (45069-3090)
P.O. Box 1190 (45071-1190)
PHONE..513 942-4400

Fax: 513 881-7177
Ken Rensing, *President*
Rob Troescher, *Corp Secy*
JC Privett, *Sales Staff*
EMP: 5
SQ FT: 10,900
SALES (est): 3MM **Privately Held**
WEB: www.apexcircuits.com
SIC: 3613 3625 Control panels, electric;
industrial controls: push button, selector
switches, pilot

(G-19807)
**AQUA TECHNOLOGY GROUP
LLC**
8104 Beckett Center Dr (45069-5015)
PHONE..513 298-1183
Chris Davis, *Info Tech Mgr*
Greg Davis,
Joe Davis,
EMP: 8
SQ FT: 15,428
SALES: 250K **Privately Held**
SIC: 7363 5085 3823 3824 Industrial
help service; industrial supplies; industrial
process control instruments; fluid meters
& counting devices; indicating instru-
ments, electric

(G-19808)
AQUAPRO SYSTEMS LLC
4438 Muhlhauser Rd # 500 (45011-9775)
PHONE..877 278-2797
EMP: 15 EST: 2004
SALES: 2MM **Privately Held**
SIC: 7389 3585 ; heating & air condition-
ing combination units

(G-19809)
ARRAY TELEPRESENCE INC
9480 Meridian Way (45069-6527)
PHONE..800 779-7480
Harold Williams, *CEO*
Steve Lambert, *Director*
EMP: 5
SALES: 2MM **Privately Held**
SIC: 3651 Video camera-audio recorders,
household use

(G-19810)
ASHLAND LLC
Also Called: Valvoline
9451 Meridian Way (45069-6525)
PHONE..513 682-2405
EMP: 4
SALES (corp-wide): 4.9B **Publicly Held**
SIC: 2899 Chemical preparations
HQ: Ashland Llc
50 E Rivercenter Blvd # 1600
Covington KY 41011
859 815-3333

(G-19811)
ASLAN WORLDWIDE
8583 Rupp Farm Dr (45069-4526)
PHONE..513 671-0671
Josh Stebbins, *Principal*
EMP: 10
SALES (est): 1MM **Privately Held**
SIC: 2441 Boxes, wood

(G-19812)
B L ANDERSON CO INC
8887 Eagle Ridge Ct (45069-4544)
PHONE..765 463-1518
Cindy Sell, *Business Mgr*
Matt Boone, *Sales Staff*
Nick Dornbusch, *Sales Staff*
EMP: 4
SALES (corp-wide): 8.6MM **Privately
Held**
SIC: 3589 Sewage & water treatment
equipment
PA: B L Anderson Co Inc
4801 Tazer Dr
Lafayette IN 47905
765 463-1518

(G-19813)
BAG-PACK INC
Also Called: Bagpack
9486 Sutton Pl (45011-9698)
PHONE..513 346-3900
Fax: 513 346-3903
Steven Dreyer, *President*
David Hezlep, *Business Mgr*

Ronald C Dreyer, *Vice Pres*
Nancy Kennedy, *Admin Asst*
Pat Weiland, *Admin Asst*
EMP: 30
SQ FT: 40,000
SALES (est): 7.3MM **Privately Held**
WEB: www.bag-pack.com
SIC: 2673 Plastic bags: made from pur-
chased materials

(G-19814)
BARNES GROUP INC
9826 Crescent Park Dr (45069-3800)
PHONE........................513 759-3528
Rick Dehner, *Branch Mgr*
EMP: 1388
SALES (corp-wide): 1.2B **Publicly Held**
SIC: 3724 Aircraft engines & engine parts
PA: Barnes Group Inc.
123 Main St
Bristol CT 06010
860 583-7070

(G-19815)
BARNES GROUP INC
Also Called: Windsor Airmotive
9826 Crescent Park Dr (45069-3800)
PHONE........................513 779-6888
Jerry Bach, *Branch Mgr*
EMP: 1434
SALES (corp-wide): 1.2B **Publicly Held**
WEB: www.barnesgroupinc.com
SIC: 3724 Aircraft engines & engine parts
PA: Barnes Group Inc.
123 Main St
Bristol CT 06010
860 583-7070

(G-19816)
**BELLWYCK PACKG SOLUTIONS
INC**
Also Called: Bellwyck Clinical Services
8946 Global Way (45069-7071)
PHONE........................513 874-1200
Bruce Wells, *CFO*
Dawn Pohl, *Manager*
EMP: 4
SALES (est): 575.7K **Privately Held**
SIC: 2834 Pharmaceutical preparations

(G-19817)
BESI MANUFACTURING INC (PA)
9087 Sutton Pl (45011-9316)
PHONE........................513 874-0232
Fax: 513 874-0579
William Moore, *President*
Sue Weaver, *Vice Pres*
Tom Moore, *Traffic Mgr*
Dave Moore, *Production*
Brittany Weaver, *Sales Staff*
▲ **EMP:** 24
SQ FT: 17,500
SALES (est): 11.4MM **Privately Held**
WEB: www.besi-inc.com
SIC: 2399 Seat covers, automobile; seat
belts, automobile & aircraft

(G-19818)
BISON USA CORP
5225 Muhlhauser Rd (45011-9327)
PHONE........................513 713-0513
EMP: 5
SALES (est): 73.6K
SALES (corp-wide): 12.1MM **Privately
Held**
SIC: 8711 3999 3549 Engineering serv-
ices; atomizers, toiletry; metalworking ma-
chinery
PA: Bison Chucks S A
Ul. Mysliwska 13
Bialystok 15-56
507 181-243

(G-19819)
BMA METALS GROUP INC
7770 W Chester Rd Ste 120 (45069-4157)
PHONE........................513 874-5152
Jeanne Beebe, *President*
EMP: 3
SALES: 950K **Privately Held**
SIC: 3449 Miscellaneous metalwork

(G-19820)
BORKE MOLD SPECIALIST INC
9541 Glades Dr (45011-9410)
PHONE........................513 870-8000

Fax: 513 870-8008
Fritz Borke, *President*
Patty Borke, *Admin Sec*
EMP: 18
SQ FT: 14,000
SALES (est): 3.5MM **Privately Held**
WEB: www.borkemold.com
SIC: 3544 Industrial molds

(G-19821)
**BRAININ-ADVANCE INDUSTRIES
LLC**
Also Called: Pep Brainin Fairfield Division
4348 Le Saint Ct (45014-5486)
PHONE........................513 874-9760
Fax: 513 874-9764
Barry Eyre, *Plant Mgr*
William Willings, *Mfg Staff*
Carl Dearman, *Manager*
EMP: 25
SALES (corp-wide): 833.4MM **Publicly
Held**
WEB: www.brainin.com
SIC: 3469 3544 Stamping metal for the
trade; special dies & tools
HQ: Brainin-Advance Industries Llc
48 Frank Mossberg Dr
Attleboro MA 02703
508 226-1200

(G-19822)
C-TECH INDUSTRIES LLC
8950 Global Way (45069-7071)
P.O. Box 1157 (45071-1157)
PHONE........................877 755-7311
Fax: 513 867-9310
Levi Harper, *Opers Mgr*
Donna Heitfeld, *Production*
Chris Lantow, *Marketing Staff*
Patt Glynm, *Manager*
Donna Heifeld, *Manager*
▲ **EMP:** 18
SALES (est): 3.7MM **Privately Held**
SIC: 3625 Mfg Relays/Industrial Controls

(G-19823)
CARDINAL HEALTH 414 LLC
9866 Windisch Rd Bldg 3 (45069-3806)
PHONE........................513 759-1900
Tommy Ward, *Branch Mgr*
EMP: 9
SALES (corp-wide): 121.5B **Publicly
Held**
SIC: 2834 2835 Pharmaceutical prepara-
tions; radioactive diagnostic substances
HQ: Cardinal Health 414, Llc
7000 Cardinal Pl
Dublin OH 43017
614 757-5000

(G-19824)
**CEDAR ELEC HOLDINGS CORP
(PA)**
5440 W Chester Rd (45069-2950)
PHONE........................513 870-8500
David Thornhill, *CEO*
Sally Washlow, *President*
Jonathan La, *Controller*
EMP: 2
SALES (est): 139.8MM **Privately Held**
SIC: 3812 5088 Navigational systems &
instruments; navigation equipment & sup-
plies

(G-19825)
CFM INTERNATIONAL INC (PA)
6440 Aviation Way (45069-4546)
P.O. Box 15514, Cincinnati (45215-0514)
PHONE........................513 552-2787
Fax: 513 243-2994
Gael Meheust, *President*
Cedric Goubet, *Exec VP*
Allen Paxson, *Exec VP*
Pierre Bry, *Vice Pres*
Maria Deacon, *Vice Pres*
EMP: 28
SALES (est): 14MM **Privately Held**
WEB: www.cfm56.com
SIC: 3724 Aircraft engines & engine parts

(G-19826)
CHASING FIREFLIES LLC
5568 W Chester Rd (45069-2914)
PHONE........................206 574-4500
Gregory Henchel, *Manager*
EMP: 6

SALES (corp-wide): 3.5B **Publicly Held**
SIC: 2741 Catalogs: publishing & printing
HQ: Chasing Fireflies, Llc
835 S Fidalgo St
Seattle WA 98108
206 574-4500

(G-19827)
CHEMINSTRUMENTS INC (PA)
510 Commercial Dr (45014-7593)
PHONE........................513 860-1598
Fax: 513 860-1597
Richard Muny, *President*
Keith Muny, *Vice Pres*
Pat Santurri, *Vice Pres*
Matt Johnson, *Prdtn Mgr*
Judith Muny, *Treasurer*
▲ **EMP:** 8
SQ FT: 15,000
SALES (est): 1.7MM **Privately Held**
WEB: www.cheminstruments.com
SIC: 3821 Laboratory apparatus & furniture

(G-19828)
CHEMINSTRUMENTS INC
Also Called: Chemical Instruments
510 Commercial Dr (45014-7593)
PHONE........................513 860-1598
Keith Muny, *Manager*
EMP: 7
SALES (corp-wide): 1.7MM **Privately
Held**
WEB: www.cheminstruments.com
SIC: 3821 Chemical laboratory apparatus
PA: Cheminstruments, Inc
510 Commercial Dr
West Chester OH 45014
513 860-1598

(G-19829)
**CHEMSULTANTS
INTERNATIONAL INC**
Also Called: Chem Instruments
510 Commercial Dr (45014-7593)
PHONE........................513 860-1598
Brian Bresser, *Sales Mgr*
Keith Muny, *Manager*
EMP: 7
SALES (corp-wide): 4.2MM **Privately
Held**
SIC: 3821 Laboratory apparatus & furniture
PA: Chemsultants International, Inc.
9079 Tyler Blvd
Mentor OH 44060
440 974-3080

(G-19830)
CINCINNATI COLD DRAWN INC
9108 Sutton Pl (45011-9317)
PHONE........................513 874-3296
Fax: 513 874-1525
William H Ward, *President*
Terry Bien, *Exec VP*
Pam Fitzpatrick, *Opers-Prdtn-Mfg*
Pam Stephenson, *Finance*
EMP: 4
SQ FT: 30,000
SALES (est): 1.3MM
SALES (corp-wide): 51.7MM **Privately
Held**
WEB: www.cincinnaticolddrawn.com
SIC: 3316 Cold finishing of steel shapes
PA: Ashley F. Ward, Inc.
7490 Easy St
Mason OH 45040
513 398-1414

(G-19831)
**CINCINNATI GUTTER SUPPLY
INC**
9345 Prnceton Glendale Rd (45011-9707)
PHONE........................513 825-0500
Clarence Mollett, *Principal*
Radford Mollett, *Manager*
EMP: 5
SQ FT: 12,000
SALES (est): 458.9K **Privately Held**
SIC: 1761 3444 5082 Roofing, siding &
sheet metal work; metal roofing & roof
drainage equipment; contractors' materi-
als

(G-19832)
CINCINNATI PRINTERS CO INC
9053 Le Saint Dr (45014-2242)
PHONE........................513 860-9053

A James Yockey, *President*
Lynett Bourgeous, *Manager*
Peggy Cahill, *Manager*
Rebecca Dressman, *Manager*
EMP: 13
SQ FT: 25,000
SALES (est): 2MM **Privately Held**
WEB: www.cintiprinters.com
SIC: 2752 Commercial printing, offset

(G-19833)
CIP INTERNATIONAL INC
Also Called: Commercial Interior Products
9575 Le Saint Dr (45014-5447)
PHONE........................513 874-9925
Fax: 513 874-6246
Thomas Huff, *Ch of Bd*
Kathleen Huff, *President*
Mark Elmlinger, *Vice Pres*
Philip Huff, *Vice Pres*
Brian Hubbard, *Project Dir*
◆ **EMP:** 83 **EST:** 1975
SQ FT: 140,000
SALES: 33MM **Privately Held**
WEB: www.cipinternational.net
SIC: 7389 2541 Interior designer; lettering
& sign painting services; store fixtures,
wood; cabinets, except refrigerated:
show, display, etc.: wood

(G-19834)
**CLARKDIETRICH BLDG
SYSTEMS LLC**
9100 Centre Pointe Dr # 210 (45069-4846)
PHONE........................513 870-1100
Chris Ernst, *Manager*
Ruth Castle, *Info Tech Dir*
EMP: 125
SALES (corp-wide): 8.1B **Privately Held**
WEB: www.clarksteel.com
SIC: 3444 Studs & joists, sheet metal
HQ: Clarkwestern Dietrich Building Sys-
tems Llc
9100 Centre Pointe Dr # 210
West Chester OH 45069

(G-19835)
**CLARKWESTERN DIETRICH
BUILDING (DH)**
9100 Centre Pointe Dr # 210 (45069-4846)
PHONE........................513 870-1100
Fax: 513 870-1300
Bill Courtney, *CEO*
Chris Fiste, *Project Mgr*
James Graham, *Engineer*
Erica Thompson, *Project Engr*
Paul Gaitan, *VP Finance*
▼ **EMP:** 8
SQ FT: 80,000
SALES (est): 193MM
SALES (corp-wide): 8.1B **Privately Held**
SIC: 3444 8711 3081 Studs & joists,
sheet metal; engineering services; vinyl
film & sheet
HQ: Marubeni-Itochu Steel America Inc.
150 E 42nd St Fl 7
New York NY 10017
212 660-6000

(G-19836)
CLEAR PACKAGING FILMS INC
9053 Le Saint Dr (45014-2242)
PHONE........................513 860-9053
James Yockey, *President*
Becky Spahni, *Accountant*
EMP: 4
SQ FT: 25,000
SALES: 3.5MM **Privately Held**
SIC: 3081 Plastic film & sheet

(G-19837)
CONE OF WEST CHESTER
6855 Tylersville Rd (45069-1415)
PHONE........................513 779-7040
Fax: 513 779-8100
Keith Wren, *President*
EMP: 20
SALES (est): 1.2MM **Privately Held**
WEB: www.thecone.com
SIC: 2024 Ice cream & frozen desserts

(G-19838)
CONTECH BRIDGE SOLUTIONS LLC (DH)
Also Called: Bridgetek
9025 Cntrpinte Dr Ste 400 (45069)
PHONE..................513 645-7000
Fax: 513 763-8213
Michael M Rafi, *Principal*
Bill McAdory, *Vice Pres*
Joe Wojciechowski, *Controller*
Dave Kunkel, *VP Finance*
Marie Bikers, *Accountant*
EMP: 15
SQ FT: 1,440
SALES (est): 15.4MM **Privately Held**
SIC: 3272 Concrete products, precast
HQ: Contech Engineered Solutions Llc
9025 Ctr Pinte Dr Ste 400
West Chester OH 45069
513 645-7000

(G-19839)
CONTECH CNSTR PDTS HLDINGS INC
9025 Centre Pointe Dr # 400 (45069-9700)
PHONE..................513 645-7000
Joseph Salerno, *General Mgr*
Ronald Keating, *Principal*
Scott Becher, *COO*
Godfrey Little, *COO*
Phil Perry, *COO*
EMP: 1 EST: 2012
SALES (est): 8.9MM
SALES (corp-wide): 200.8MM **Privately Held**
SIC: 3443 Fabricated plate work (boiler shop)
HQ: Apax Partners, L.P.
601 Lexington Ave Fl 53
New York NY 10022
212 753-6300

(G-19840)
CONTECH ENGNERED SOLUTIONS INC
9025 Centre Pointe Dr # 400 (45069-9700)
PHONE..................513 645-7000
Michael Rafi, *President*
Dan Priest, *General Mgr*
J Paul Allen, *Vice Pres*
Michael Carfagno, *Vice Pres*
Ken Dombroski, *Project Mgr*
EMP: 1300
SALES (est): 175.6MM **Privately Held**
SIC: 3444 3084 3317 3441 Sheet metalwork; culverts, sheet metal; plastics pipe; steel pipe & tubes; fabricated structural metal; fabricated plate work (boiler shop)

(G-19841)
CONTECH ENGNERED SOLUTIONS LLC (HQ)
9025 Ctr Pinte Ste 400 (45069)
PHONE..................513 645-7000
Mike Rafi, *President*
Vernon B Cameron, *President*
MO Heshmati, *President*
Thomas P Slabe, *President*
Steve R Spanagel, *President*
◆ EMP: 150
SQ FT: 75,000
SALES (est): 563.1MM **Privately Held**
WEB: www.conteches.com
SIC: 3444 3084 3317 3441 Sheet metalwork; culverts, sheet metal; plastics pipe; steel pipe & tubes; fabricated structural metal; fabricated plate work (boiler shop)

(G-19842)
CONTECH STRMWTER SOLUTIONS LLC
9025 Centre Pointe Dr # 400 (45069-9700)
PHONE..................513 645-7000
Rick Stepien, *President*
Jeffrey S Lee, *Senior VP*
Kim Stiver, *QC Dir*
Doug Witten, *Sales Mgr*
Frank Birney, *Regl Sales Mgr*
EMP: 8
SALES (est): 1.4MM **Privately Held**
SIC: 3677 Filtration devices, electronic
HQ: Contech Engineered Solutions Llc
9025 Ctr Pinte Dr Ste 400
West Chester OH 45069
513 645-7000

(G-19843)
CONTROL INTERFACE INC
517 Commercial Dr (45014-7594)
PHONE..................513 874-2062
Fax: 513 874-2099
Tom Osborn, *President*
Ryan Osborn, *Project Mgr*
Chris Ingram, *Engineer*
▲ EMP: 8
SQ FT: 5,000
SALES (est): 1.6MM **Privately Held**
WEB: www.controlinterface.com
SIC: 3613 Control panels, electric

(G-19844)
CORNERSTONE BRANDS INC
Also Called: Grandinroad Catalog
5568 W Chester Rd (45069-2914)
PHONE..................866 668-5962
David Cleavinger, *Branch Mgr*
EMP: 7
SALES (corp-wide): 3.5B **Publicly Held**
SIC: 3199 Dog furnishings: collars, leashes, muzzles, etc.: leather
HQ: Cornerstone Brands, Inc.
5568 W Chester Rd
West Chester OH 45069
513 603-1000

(G-19845)
CORNERSTONE INDUSTRIES LCC
Also Called: Adam Printing
10132 Mosteller Ln (45069-3872)
PHONE..................513 871-4546
Fax: 513 871-4635
Andy Werth,
Amy Werth,
EMP: 3 EST: 1963
SQ FT: 4,200
SALES (est): 455.5K **Privately Held**
WEB: www.adamprinting.com
SIC: 2752 2791 2759 Commercial printing, offset; typesetting; letterpress printing

(G-19846)
CR BRANDS INC (DH)
8790 Beckett Rd (45069-2904)
PHONE..................513 860-5039
Richard Owen, *CEO*
Mark Winterholder, *Vice Pres*
Vickie Bridges, *Senior Buyer*
John Samoya, *CFO*
Patrick Couch, *Accountant*
EMP: 82
SQ FT: 5,000
SALES (est): 29.9MM
SALES (corp-wide): 1B **Publicly Held**
WEB: www.redoxbrands.com
SIC: 2841 5169 3999 Soap & other detergents; detergents & soaps, except specialty cleaning; atomizers, toiletry
HQ: Cr Holding, Inc.
9100 Centre Pointe Dr
West Chester OH 45069
513 860-5039

(G-19847)
CR HOLDING INC (HQ)
9100 Centre Pointe Dr (45069-4846)
PHONE..................513 860-5039
Richard Owen, *CEO*
John Samoya, *VP Finance*
EMP: 8
SQ FT: 5,000
SALES (est): 29.9MM
SALES (corp-wide): 1B **Publicly Held**
SIC: 2841 Soap: granulated, liquid, cake, flaked or chip; detergents, synthetic organic or inorganic alkaline
PA: Ares Capital Corporation
245 Park Ave Fl 44
New York NY 10167
212 750-7300

(G-19848)
CRANE TRAINING USA INC
7908 Cincinnati Dayton Rd H (45069-6629)
PHONE..................513 755-2177
Alan Stein, *President*
Sandy Stein, *Vice Pres*
Melissa Saylor, *Sales Mgr*
EMP: 6
SALES (est): 520K **Privately Held**
WEB: www.cranetraining.com
SIC: 3536 Hoists, cranes & monorails

(G-19849)
CRYOVAC INC
7410 Union Centre Blvd (45014-2286)
PHONE..................513 771-7770
Sharon Drysdale, *Opers-Prdtn-Mfg*
Meredith Werdon, *Marketing Staff*
EMP: 10
SALES (corp-wide): 6.7B **Publicly Held**
WEB: www.cryovac.com
SIC: 3086 Packaging & shipping materials, foamed plastic
HQ: Cryovac, Inc.
2415 Cascade Pointe Blvd
Charlotte NC 28208
980 430-7000

(G-19850)
CUMMINS BRIDGEWAY LLC
5400 Rialto Rd (45069-3092)
PHONE..................513 563-6670
Ron Brunot, *Business Mgr*
Peter Zelinskas, *Marketing Staff*
Robert Fontilla, *Branch Mgr*
EMP: 40
SALES (corp-wide): 17.5B **Publicly Held**
WEB: www.cummins.com
SIC: 3519 Internal combustion engines
HQ: Cummins Bridgeway, Llc
21810 Clessie Ct
New Hudson MI 48165
248 573-1600

(G-19851)
CUSTOM MILLCRAFT CORP
9092 Le Saint Dr (45014-2241)
PHONE..................513 874-7080
Jody Corbett, *Owner*
Fernando Cruz, *Project Mgr*
Tony Diamond, *Project Mgr*
Dave Donnelly, *Project Mgr*
Tyler Kasse, *Project Mgr*
EMP: 25
SQ FT: 56,000
SALES (est): 5.3MM **Privately Held**
WEB: www.custommillcraft.com
SIC: 2521 2522 2542 Cabinets, office: wood; office furniture, except wood; partitions & fixtures, except wood

(G-19852)
DEE SIGN CO (PA)
Also Called: Diversified Sign
6163 Allen Rd (45069-3855)
PHONE..................513 779-3333
Fax: 513 779-3344
Braden R Huenefeld, *Ch of Bd*
Mike Farrell, *General Mgr*
Craig Dixon, *Vice Pres*
Joe Kolks, *CFO*
Roger Kistner, *Accounts Mgr*
▼ EMP: 40
SQ FT: 125,000
SALES (est): 16MM **Privately Held**
WEB: www.dee-sign.com
SIC: 3993 Signs & advertising specialties

(G-19853)
DEE SIGN USA LLC
6163 Allen Rd (45069-3855)
PHONE..................513 779-3333
Joe Kolks, *CFO*
Braden R Huenefeld, *Mng Member*
EMP: 7
SALES (est): 753.9K **Privately Held**
SIC: 3993 Signs & advertising specialties

(G-19854)
DWLLR INC
Also Called: Dwllr Labs
6556 Lakeside Dr (45069-7677)
PHONE..................513 400-5544
Khisaun Ferguson, *Principal*
EMP: 6 EST: 2013
SALES (est): 246.4K **Privately Held**
SIC: 7371 7372 7389 Computer software writing services; computer software development; business oriented computer software;

(G-19855)
ELSEVIER INC
8080 Beckett Center Dr # 225 (45069-1968)
PHONE..................513 942-5070
Marsha Campbell, *Principal*
Curt Kohler, *Technology*
EMP: 3
SALES (corp-wide): 8.4B **Privately Held**
WEB: www.elsevierfoundation.org
SIC: 2741 Technical manual & paper publishing
HQ: Elsevier Inc.
230 Park Ave Fl 8
New York NY 10169
212 633-3773

(G-19856)
EMERSON ELECTRIC CO
4400 Muhlhauser Rd (45011-9708)
PHONE..................513 942-1118
Joel Duvall, *Regional Mgr*
Mike Uhl, *Branch Mgr*
EMP: 8
SALES (corp-wide): 14.5B **Publicly Held**
SIC: 3823 Industrial instrmnts msrmnt display/control process variable
PA: Emerson Electric Co.
8000 West Florissant Ave
Saint Louis MO 63136
314 553-2000

(G-19857)
EMS/HOOPTECH (PA)
9185 Le Saint Dr (45014-5467)
PHONE..................513 829-7768
Fax: 513 829-7769
Mark Mason, *Owner*
EMP: 3
SALES (est): 530.2K **Privately Held**
WEB: www.hooptechproducts.com
SIC: 2395 Embroidery products, except schiffli machine

(G-19858)
ENERSYS
9436 Meridian Way (45069-6527)
PHONE..................513 737-2268
Fax: 513 737-7942
Karyl McKnight, *Manager*
EMP: 92
SALES (corp-wide): 2.3B **Publicly Held**
SIC: 3691 Lead acid batteries (storage batteries)
PA: Enersys
2366 Bernville Rd
Reading PA 19605
610 208-1991

(G-19859)
ESCORT INC (HQ)
5440 W Chester Rd (45069-9004)
PHONE..................513 870-8500
Fax: 513 870-8509
Mark Carrm, *President*
John A Malone, *Senior VP*
Tim Coomer, *Vice Pres*
David Workman, *CFO*
Victoria Woofter, *Officer*
▲ EMP: 90 EST: 1997
SQ FT: 32,000
SALES (est): 39.8MM
SALES (corp-wide): 139.8MM **Privately Held**
WEB: www.escortradar.com
SIC: 3812 Radar systems & equipment
PA: Cedar Electronics Holdings Corp.
5440 W Chester Rd
West Chester OH 45069
513 870-8500

(G-19860)
ESTECH INC
6217 Centre Park Dr (45069-3866)
PHONE..................805 895-1263
Tamer Ibrahim, *Principal*
EMP: 4
SALES (est): 390K **Privately Held**
SIC: 3841 Surgical & medical instruments

(G-19861)
F A TECH CORP
9065 Sutton Pl (45011-9316)
PHONE..................513 942-1920
Fax: 513 942-3282
Michael Michimi, *President*
Jay Smith, *Prdtn Mgr*
Deron Beebe, *Senior Engr*
Kiyotaka Kondo, *Design Engr*
EMP: 35
SALES (est): 4.6MM **Privately Held**
WEB: www.brazer.com
SIC: 3599 Machine & other job shop work

(G-19862)
FEDEX OFFICE & PRINT SVCS INC
7785 Cox Ln (45069-6549)
PHONE.................................513 777-1079
Fax: 513 777-1386
Joshua Miller, *Branch Mgr*
EMP: 4
SALES (corp-wide): 50.3B **Publicly Held**
SIC: 2752 Commercial printing, litho-graphic
HQ: Fedex Office And Print Services, Inc.
7900 Legacy Dr
Plano TX 75024
214 550-7000

(G-19863)
FEINBLANKING LIMITED INC
9461 Le Saint Dr (45014-5447)
PHONE.................................513 860-2100
EMP: 8
SQ FT: 25,000
SALES (est): 860K **Privately Held**
SIC: 3469 Mfg Metal Stampings

(G-19864)
FISHER CONTROLS INTL LLC
5453 W Chester Rd (45069-2963)
PHONE.................................513 285-6000
EMP: 3
SALES (corp-wide): 14.5B **Publicly Held**
SIC: 3491 Automatic regulating & control valves
HQ: Fisher Controls International Llc
205 S Center St
Marshalltown IA 50158
641 754-3011

(G-19865)
FLOTURN INC (PA)
4236 Thunderbird Ln (45014-5482)
PHONE.................................513 860-8040
Fax: 513 860-8044
R V Glutting, *President*
John Deatley, *Engineer*
Don Spillane, *CFO*
Denise Fornshell, *Controller*
Sonya Finley, *HR Admin*
◆ EMP: 184 EST: 1962
SQ FT: 75,000
SALES (est): 83.7MM **Privately Held**
WEB: www.floturn.com
SIC: 3599 Machine shop, jobbing & repair

(G-19866)
FOAM CONCEPTS & DESIGN INC
4602 Muhlhauser Rd (45011-9708)
PHONE.................................513 860-5589
Jeff Labermeier, *President*
Al Peck, *General Mgr*
Jim Knabb, *Sales Mgr*
Amy Hesselbrock, *Manager*
EMP: 19
SQ FT: 40,500
SALES (est): 2.4MM **Privately Held**
SIC: 3086 Packaging & shipping materials, foamed plastic

(G-19867)
FRECON ENGINEERING
Also Called: Frecon Technologies
9319 Prnceton Glendale Rd (45011-9707)
PHONE.................................513 874-8981
Fax: 513 682-4732
Fred J Pfirrmann, *Owner*
Edwin A Pfirrmann, *Co-Owner*
EMP: 5 EST: 1963
SQ FT: 500
SALES: 400K **Privately Held**
WEB: www.frecontechnologies.com
SIC: 3545 Machine tool attachments & accessories

(G-19868)
FRECON TECHNOLOGIES INC
9319 Prnceton Glendale Rd (45011-9707)
PHONE.................................513 874-8981
Fax: 513 874-8982
Fred J Pfirrmann, *President*
▲ EMP: 15
SQ FT: 6,000

SALES: 1.2MM **Privately Held**
SIC: 5084 3544 7539 Machine tools & accessories; special dies, tools, jigs & fixtures; machine shop, automotive

(G-19869)
FRITO-LAY NORTH AMERICA INC
7781 Service Center Dr (45069-2440)
PHONE.................................513 759-1000
Fax: 513 759-1050
Dan Carley, *Manager*
Bryan Barnes, *Manager*
EMP: 200
SALES (corp-wide): 62.8B **Publicly Held**
WEB: www.fritolay.com
SIC: 2096 Potato chips & similar snacks; potato chips & other potato-based snacks; tortilla chips; corn chips & other corn-based snacks
HQ: Frito-Lay North America, Inc.
7701 Legacy Dr
Plano TX 75024

(G-19870)
FURNACE CONTROL CORP
8904 Beckett Rd (45069-7054)
PHONE.................................513 772-1000
Eric Boltz, *President*
Patrick Torok, *Vice Pres*
Yvonne Spooner, *VP Sls/Mktg*
EMP: 22
SQ FT: 2,000
SALES: 2MM **Privately Held**
WEB: www.furnacecontrol.com
SIC: 3829 3822 Gas detectors; electric heat proportioning controls, modulating controls

(G-19871)
G F FRANK AND SONS INC
9075 Le Saint Dr (45014-2242)
PHONE.................................513 870-9075
Fax: 513 870-0579
George P Frank, *President*
John Frank, *Vice Pres*
Mark Frank, *Vice Pres*
Donna Chitwood, *Manager*
EMP: 15
SQ FT: 40,000
SALES (est): 3.6MM **Privately Held**
SIC: 3556 3599 Food products machinery; machine shop, jobbing & repair

(G-19872)
GE AVIATION SYSTEMS LLC
Also Called: Rapid Quality Manufacturing
5223 Muhlhauser Rd (45011-9327)
PHONE.................................513 889-5150
James C Taylor, *Branch Mgr*
EMP: 15
SALES (corp-wide): 123.6B **Publicly Held**
SIC: 3313 Alloys, additive, except copper: not made in blast furnaces
HQ: Ge Aviation Systems Llc
1 Neumann Way
Cincinnati OH 45215
513 243-2000

(G-19873)
GE HONDA AERO ENGINES LLC
9050 Centre Pointe Dr (45069-4874)
PHONE.................................513 552-4322
Bill Dwyer, *CEO*
Steven J Shaknaitis, *President*
Bill Myers, *Principal*
Jun Yanada, *Vice Pres*
Satoshi Kawarada, *Engineer*
EMP: 11
SALES (est): 1.6MM **Privately Held**
SIC: 3519 Internal combustion engines; parts & accessories, internal combustion engines; jet propulsion engines

(G-19874)
GENERAL ELECTRIC COMPANY
9050 Centre Pointe Dr (45069-4874)
PHONE.................................513 243-9317
CHI Tang, *Branch Mgr*
EMP: 13
SALES (corp-wide): 123.6B **Publicly Held**
SIC: 3511 Turbines & turbine generator sets

PA: General Electric Company
41 Farnsworth St
Boston MA 02210
617 443-3000

(G-19875)
GENERAL ELECTRIC COMPANY
9100 Centre Pointe Dr # 4 (45069-4846)
PHONE.................................513 552-5364
Paul Kemme, *Senior Engr*
Tod Steen, *Treasurer*
Dave Hartshorne, *Manager*
EMP: 3
SALES (est): 94.6K **Privately Held**
SIC: 3724 Aircraft engines & engine parts

(G-19876)
GLOBAL HEALTH SERVICES INC
8087 Cincinnati Dayton Rd B (45069-2003)
PHONE.................................513 777-8111
Fax: 513 777-0741
Beth Townsend, *CEO*
Dave Townsend, *Vice Pres*
Cammie Mitrione, *Consultant*
Vivian Brown,
EMP: 4
SALES (est): 529.2K **Privately Held**
WEB: www.ghs-inc.com
SIC: 2836 Vaccines

(G-19877)
GLOBAL PACKAGING & EXPORTS INC (PA)
9166 Sutton Pl (45011-9317)
P.O. Box 62687, Cincinnati (45262-0687)
PHONE.................................513 454-2020
Lori Jordan, *President*
Shawn McClinton, *Manager*
EMP: 6
SQ FT: 19,000
SALES (est): 1.8MM **Privately Held**
WEB: www.globalpkg.com
SIC: 2448 2441 4783 Skids, wood; cases, wood; packing goods for shipping; crating goods for shipping

(G-19878)
GLOBAL PARTNERS USA CO INC
7544 Bermuda Trce (45069-6324)
PHONE.................................513 276-4981
Rudy Shephard, *Principal*
EMP: 3
SALES (est): 186K **Privately Held**
SIC: 3953 Stationery embossers, personal

(G-19879)
GRAPHEL CORPORATION
Also Called: Carbon Products
6115 Centre Park Dr (45069-3869)
P.O. Box 369 (45071-0369)
PHONE.................................513 779-6166
Fax: 513 777-8959
Cliff Kersker, *President*
Jaime Portillo, *President*
Mark Grammer, *CFO*
David Miller, *Finance Other*
Melody West, *Sales Staff*
EMP: 140 EST: 1965
SQ FT: 35,000
SALES (est): 64.2MM **Privately Held**
WEB: www.graphel.com
SIC: 5052 3599 3624 Coal & other minerals & ores; machine shop, jobbing & repair; electrodes, thermal & electrolytic uses: carbon, graphite
PA: Graphite Metallizing Corp
1050 Nepperhan Ave
Yonkers NY 10703
914 968-8400

(G-19880)
HATFIELD INDUSTRIES LLC
9717 Flagstone Way (45069-7042)
PHONE.................................513 225-0456
Raymond Carl Hatfield, *Principal*
EMP: 3
SALES (est): 273.7K **Privately Held**
SIC: 3585 Heating equipment, complete

(G-19881)
HERITAGE BAG COMPANY
4255 Thunderbird Ln (45014-5483)
PHONE.................................513 874-3311
Fax: 513 874-3543
Craig Quinn, *Prdtn Mgr*

Gary Munsch, *Manager*
Jim Kelley, *Manager*
Ted Tucker, *Director*
Margo Coley, *Executive*
EMP: 100
SALES (est): 2.2B **Publicly Held**
WEB: www.heritage-bag.com
SIC: 2673 Trash bags (plastic film): made from purchased materials
HQ: Heritage Bag Company
501 Gateway Pkwy
Roanoke TX 76262
972 241-5525

(G-19882)
HI TECH AERO SPARES
9436 Meridian Way (45069-6527)
PHONE.................................513 942-4150
Fax: 513 942-4305
Tom Wahl, *Principal*
EMP: 3
SALES (est): 248.2K **Privately Held**
SIC: 3812 Aircraft/aerospace flight instruments & guidance systems

(G-19883)
INTERMEC INC
9290 Le Saint Dr (45014-5454)
PHONE.................................513 874-5882
Juri Lazdrins, *Vice Pres*
Robert Young, *Manager*
Dave Flaherty, *Info Tech Mgr*
EMP: 10
SALES (corp-wide): 39.3B **Publicly Held**
WEB: www.unova.com
SIC: 3577 Computer peripheral equipment
HQ: Intermec, Inc.
16201 25th Ave W
Lynnwood WA 98087
425 348-2600

(G-19884)
INTERMEC TECHNOLOGIES CORP
9290 Le Saint Dr (45014-5454)
PHONE.................................513 874-5882
Gerald Witte, *Branch Mgr*
Jerry Witt, *MIS Dir*
EMP: 13
SALES (corp-wide): 39.3B **Publicly Held**
WEB: www.intermec.net
SIC: 3577 2759 7372 Computer peripheral equipment; commercial printing; prepackaged software
HQ: Intermec Technologies Corporation
16201 25th Ave W
Lynnwood WA 98087
425 348-2600

(G-19885)
INTERMEC ULTRA PRINT INC
Also Called: Intermec Media Products
9290 Le Saint Dr (45014-5454)
PHONE.................................513 874-5882
Fax: 513 874-8487
Darell Thomas, *Prdtn Mgr*
Dave Cashman, *Sales/Mktg Mgr*
Tim Breidenbaugh, *Controller*
Robert Young, *Finance*
Jerry Vianello, *Human Res Dir*
EMP: 250 EST: 1973
SQ FT: 65,000
SALES (est): 29.7MM
SALES (corp-wide): 39.3B **Publicly Held**
WEB: www.intermec.net
SIC: 2759 Flexographic printing
HQ: Intermec Technologies Corporation
16201 25th Ave W
Lynnwood WA 98087
425 348-2600

(G-19886)
IT XCEL CONSULTING LLC
Also Called: Xgs.it
7112 Office Park Dr (45069-2261)
PHONE.................................513 847-8261
Fax: 513 942-1457
Dennis Hollstegge, *Mng Member*
Mark Hollstegge,
EMP: 15
SQ FT: 1,880
SALES (est): 5.2MM **Privately Held**
WEB: www.xgsit.com
SIC: 2752 7379 Commercial printing, lithographic; computer related consulting services

(G-19887)
KC ROBOTICS INC
9000 Le Saint Dr (45014-2241)
PHONE.....................................513 860-4442
Kenneth P Carrier Jr, *President*
Jack Justice, *General Mgr*
Crystal Vezey, *Business Mgr*
Constance M Carrier, *Corp Secy*
Paul Carrier, *Opers Mgr*
◆ EMP: 21
SQ FT: 18,000
SALES: 4.1MM Privately Held
WEB: www.kcrobotics.com
SIC: 5084 7699 7373 3569 Robots, in-
   dustrial; industrial equipment services;
   systems integration services; assembly
   machines, non-metalworking

(G-19888)
KIMBERLY-CLARK
CORPORATION
9277 Centre Pointe Dr # 200 (45069-4963)
PHONE.....................................513 794-1005
Woody Bowling, *Manager*
EMP: 209
SALES (corp-wide): 18.2B Publicly Held
WEB: www.kimberly-clark.com
SIC: 2676 Sanitary paper products
PA: Kimberly-Clark Corporation
   351 Phelps Dr
   Irving TX 75038
   972 281-1200

(G-19889)
KZ SOLUTIONS INC
9440 Sutton Pl (45011-9698)
PHONE.....................................513 942-9378
Mike Lichon, *President*
Randy Johnson, *General Mgr*
Ed Zenni, *Treasurer*
EMP: 6
SALES: 2.5MM Privately Held
SIC: 3625 Actuators, industrial

(G-19890)
LAKOTA PRINTING INC
7967 Cincinnati Dayton Rd J (45069-3578)
P.O. Box 876 (45071-0876)
PHONE.....................................513 755-3666
Fax: 513 755-3667
EMP: 3
SQ FT: 10,000
SALES (est): 230K Privately Held
SIC: 7334 2752 Photocopying & Offset
   Printing

(G-19891)
LAURA DAWSON
7827 Plantation Dr (45069-2266)
PHONE.....................................513 777-2513
Laura Dawson, *Owner*
EMP: 5
SQ FT: 1,000
SALES (est): 180K Privately Held
SIC: 2342 7389 Foundation garments,
   women's; design services

(G-19892)
LEM PRODUCTS HOLDING LLC
Also Called: L.E.M. Products
4440 Muhlhauser Rd # 300 (45011-9767)
PHONE.....................................513 202-1188
Hill Kohnen, *CEO*
Michael Hess, *COO*
Timothy O'Connor, *Vice Pres*
Carol Pucci, *Purchasing*
Chris Whitaker, *Manager*
▲ EMP: 20
SALES (est): 7.9MM Privately Held
WEB: www.lemproducts.com
SIC: 3556 3949 Cutting, chopping, grind-
   ing, mixing & similar machinery; hunting
   equipment

(G-19893)
LIBERTY SPORTSWEAR LLC
6929 Tylersville Rd Ste 9 (45069-1591)
PHONE.....................................513 755-8740
Fax: 513 755-0031
Mark Scott, *Owner*
EMP: 6
SQ FT: 1,800
SALES (est): 529K Privately Held
WEB: www.libertysportswear.com
SIC: 2759 Commercial printing

(G-19894)
LIGHTING CONCEPTS &
CONTROLS
9753 Crescent Park Dr (45069-3893)
PHONE.....................................513 761-6360
Dave Robinson, *President*
May Robinson, *CFO*
Ron Browning, *Sales Staff*
EMP: 6
SALES (est): 550K Privately Held
WEB: www.lightingconcepts.net
SIC: 3645 Residential lighting fixtures

(G-19895)
LONG-STANTON MFG COMPANY
9388 Sutton Pl (45011-9702)
PHONE.....................................513 874-8020
Fax: 513 874-4242
Daniel B Cunningham, *President*
Marvin Cunningham, *General Mgr*
Richard Hassinger, *General Mgr*
Tom Kachovec, *COO*
Steve Scales, *Opers Staff*
▲ EMP: 50
SQ FT: 66,000
SALES (est): 11.7MM Privately Held
WEB: www.longstanton.com
SIC: 3444 7692 3469 3544 Sheet metal-
   work; welding repair; metal stampings;
   special dies, tools, jigs & fixtures; fabri-
   cated plate work (boiler shop)

(G-19896)
LOST TECHNOLOGY LLP
9501 Woodland Hills Dr (45011-9300)
P.O. Box 8257 (45069-8257)
PHONE.....................................513 685-0054
Larry Hansonsmith, *Partner*
EMP: 7
SALES: 500K Privately Held
WEB: www.losttech.com
SIC: 7372 Educational computer software

(G-19897)
MARTIN MARIETTA MATERIALS
INC
Also Called: Martin Marietta Aggregate
9277 Centre Pointe Dr # 250 (45069-4844)
P.O. Box 30013, Raleigh NC (27622-0013)
PHONE.....................................513 701-1140
Harry Charles, *Manager*
EMP: 40
SALES (corp-wide): 3.8B Publicly Held
WEB: www.martinmarietta.com
SIC: 1423 1422 3295 3297 Crushed &
   broken granite; crushed & broken lime-
   stone; magnesite, crude: ground, calcined
   or dead-burned; nonclay refractories; con-
   struction sand & gravel
PA: Martin Marietta Materials Inc
   2710 Wycliff Rd
   Raleigh NC 27607
   919 781-4550

(G-19898)
MARTIN-BROWER COMPANY
LLC
Also Called: Distribution Center
4260 Port Union Rd (45011-9768)
PHONE.....................................513 773-2301
Ryan Rozen, *General Mgr*
EMP: 275 Privately Held
SIC: 2013 2015 5087 Frozen meats from
   purchased meat; poultry, processed:
   frozen; restaurant supplies
HQ: The Martin-Brower Company L L C
   6250 N River Rd Ste 9000
   Rosemont IL 60018
   847 227-6500

(G-19899)
MECC-USA LLC (PA)
Also Called: Umecc
9468 Meridian Way (45069-6527)
PHONE.....................................513 891-0301
George He, *President*
Bernhard Schiefer, *Treasurer*
▲ EMP: 7
SALES (est): 1MM Privately Held
WEB: www.mecc-usa.com
SIC: 3429 Manufactured hardware (gen-
   eral)

(G-19900)
MERCHANTS METALS LLC
Also Called: Meadow Burke Products
8760 Global Way Bldg 1 (45069-7066)
PHONE.....................................513 942-0268
Debbie Humbert, *General Mgr*
EMP: 15
SALES (corp-wide): 1.8B Privately Held
SIC: 3315 Wire & fabricated wire products
HQ: Merchants Metals Llc
   211 Perimeter Center Pkwy
   Atlanta GA 30346
   770 741-0300

(G-19901)
MILLWOOD INC
4438 Muhlhauser Rd # 100 (45011-9776)
PHONE.....................................513 860-4567
Antonio Delgado, *Branch Mgr*
Frank Hyatt, *Executive*
EMP: 17 Privately Held
SIC: 3565 5084 Packaging machinery;
   packaging machinery & equipment
PA: Millwood, Inc.
   3708 International Blvd
   Vienna OH 44473

(G-19902)
MITEL (DELAWARE) INC
Also Called: Inter Tel
9100 W Chester Towne Ctr (45069-3106)
PHONE.....................................513 733-8000
John J Catalano, *Vice Pres*
Dan Ziezerink, *Branch Mgr*
EMP: 25
SALES (corp-wide): 1.1B Privately Held
WEB: www.inter-tel.com
SIC: 3661 5045 4813 5065 Telephone &
   telegraph apparatus; computer software;
   long distance telephone communications;
   telephone equipment; telephone & tele-
   phone equipment installation; equipment
   rental & leasing
HQ: Mitel (Delaware). Inc.
   1146 N Alma School Rd
   Mesa AZ 85201
   480 449-8900

(G-19903)
MODEL GRAPHICS & MEDIA INC
2614 Crescentville Rd (45069-3819)
PHONE.....................................513 541-2355
Steve Fleissner, *President*
Barb Fleissner, *Vice Pres*
Ed Kruse, *Controller*
EMP: 48
SQ FT: 38,000
SALES (est): 13.8MM Privately Held
WEB: www.modelgraphicsinc.com
SIC: 2679 Labels, paper: made from pur-
   chased material

(G-19904)
NEASE CO LLC (DH)
Also Called: Nease Performance Chemicals
9774 Windisch Rd (45069-3808)
PHONE.....................................513 587-2800
Fax: 513 587-2828
Steve Preda, *Plant Mgr*
Terry Herdemann, *Maint Spvr*
Frank Canepa, *Opers Staff*
Ed Hamilton, *Production*
Ryan Vikan, *Research*
▲ EMP: 10
SALES (est): 19.1MM Privately Held
SIC: 2819 Catalysts, chemical
HQ: Wp Mannheim Gmbh
   Sandhofer Str. 96
   Mannheim 68305
   621 765-40

(G-19905)
NEPTUNE CHEMICAL PUMP
COMPANY
9393 Princetone Glendale (45011-9707)
PHONE.....................................513 870-3239
Michael Dowse, *CEO*
EMP: 3
SALES (corp-wide): 6.7B Publicly Held
SIC: 3586 3561 Measuring & dispensing
   pumps; pumps & pumping equipment
HQ: Neptune Chemical Pump Company
   295 Dekalb Pike
   North Wales PA 19454
   215 699-8700

(G-19906)
NORCAL SIGNS INC
6163 Allen Rd (45069-3855)
PHONE.....................................513 779-6982
Braden R Huenefeld, *Principal*
EMP: 3
SALES (est): 171.9K Privately Held
SIC: 3993 Signs & advertising specialties

(G-19907)
OGARA HESS EISENHARDT
9113 Le Saint Dr (45014-5453)
PHONE.....................................513 346-1300
Fax: 513 874-2558
N Carpinello, *Principal*
Nazzareno E Paciotti, *CFO*
Marc Wolfrum, *Data Proc Staff*
▲ EMP: 7
SALES (est): 1.4MM Privately Held
SIC: 3711 Motor vehicles & car bodies

(G-19908)
OHIO ALUMINUM CHEMICALS
LLC
4544 Muhlhauser Rd (45011-9708)
PHONE.....................................513 860-3842
Richard Rosen,
EMP: 6
SALES (est): 430K Privately Held
SIC: 2899 Chemical preparations

(G-19909)
OMER J SMITH INC
Also Called: Paper Products Company
9112 Le Saint Dr (45014-5452)
PHONE.....................................513 921-4717
Fax: 513 251-5553
Dennis J Smith II, *President*
Denny J Smith II, *Vice Pres*
Mary Smith, *Vice Pres*
Mary C Smith, *Admin Sec*
▲ EMP: 30
SQ FT: 80,000
SALES (est): 7.3MM Privately Held
WEB: www.paperproductscompany.com
SIC: 2653 Boxes, corrugated: made from
   purchased materials

(G-19910)
OPW INC
Also Called: Opw Engineering Systems
9393 Prnceton Glendale Rd (45011-9707)
PHONE.....................................800 422-2525
David Crouse, *President*
Richard Jones, *Vice Pres*
James Walton, *Vice Pres*
Fred Wilking, *Vice Pres*
Ronald Shryock, *Info Tech Mgr*
▲ EMP: 559
SQ FT: 250,000
SALES (est): 55.2K
SALES (corp-wide): 6.7B Publicly Held
SIC: 3594 Fluid power pumps
PA: Dover Corporation
   3005 Highland Pkwy # 200
   Downers Grove IL 60515
   630 541-1540

(G-19911)
OPW FUELING COMPONENTS
INC (HQ)
Also Called: Opw Engineered Systems
9393 Prnceton Glendale Rd (45011-9707)
PHONE.....................................800 422-2525
Fax: 800 421-3297
David Crouse, *President*
Greg Kennedy, *Opers Staff*
Martha Owens, *Credit Mgr*
◆ EMP: 32
SALES (est): 70.4MM
SALES (corp-wide): 6.7B Publicly Held
WEB: www.dovercorporation.com
SIC: 2899 Fuel treating compounds
PA: Dover Corporation
   3005 Highland Pkwy # 200
   Downers Grove IL 60515
   630 541-1540

(G-19912)
PARKER-HANNIFIN
CORPORATION
9050 Centre Pointe Dr # 310 (45069-4874)
PHONE.....................................513 847-1758
Rick Stumpf, *Branch Mgr*
EMP: 123

SALES (corp-wide): 11.3B **Publicly Held**
SIC: 3594 Fluid power pumps & motors
PA: Parker-Hannifin Corporation
6035 Parkland Blvd
Cleveland OH 44124
216 896-3000

(G-19913)
PFIZER INC
9878 Windisch Rd (45069-3806)
PHONE..................................513 342-9056
EMP: 3
SALES (corp-wide): 52.8B **Publicly Held**
SIC: 2834 Pharmaceutical preparations
PA: Pfizer Inc.
235 E 42nd St
New York NY 10017
212 733-2323

(G-19914)
PHASE ARRAY COMPANY LLC
9365 Allen Rd (45069-3846)
PHONE..................................513 785-0801
Dominique Braconnier,
◆ **EMP:** 7
SQ FT: 3,000
SALES (est): 168.3K **Privately Held**
SIC: 3599 Custom machinery

(G-19915)
PIPE PRODUCTS INC (DH)
5122 Rialto Rd (45069-2923)
PHONE..................................513 587-7532
Fax: 513 881-7784
Stephen Tino, President
Thomas L Cuni, Principal
Steven Kushner, Vice Pres
Danny Sweeney, Vice Pres
Joe Dugan, Project Mgr
▲ **EMP:** 63
SQ FT: 65,000
SALES (est): 53.5MM
SALES (corp-wide): 20.8B **Privately Held**
WEB: www.ferguson.com
SIC: 5051 3498 5085 Pipe & tubing,
steel; pipe fittings, fabricated from pur-
chased pipe; pipe sections fabricated
from purchased pipe; valves & fittings
HQ: Ferguson Enterprises, Inc.
12500 Jefferson Ave
Newport News VA 23602
757 874-7795

(G-19916)
PMCO LLC
Also Called: PM Company
9220 Glades Dr (45011-8821)
PHONE..................................513 825-7626
Mike Webster, President
Stuart Blair, CFO
Jeff Neale, Human Res Mgr
▲ **EMP:** 140 **EST:** 1905
SQ FT: 85,000
SALES (est): 96.1MM **Privately Held**
WEB: www.pmcompany.com
SIC: 2679 Paper products, converted

(G-19917)
POLE/ZERO ACQUISITION INC
5558 Union Centre Dr (45069-4821)
PHONE..................................513 870-9060
Fax: 513 870-9064
Larry Ochs, Vice Pres
Dave Daniels, Prdtn Mgr
Joe Cormican, Engineer
John Creatura, Engineer
Art Zekis, Sales Engr
EMP: 180
SQ FT: 50,000
SALES (est): 61.3MM
SALES (corp-wide): 6.7B **Publicly Held**
WEB: www.emxo.com
SIC: 3663 Radio & television switching
equipment
PA: Dover Corporation
3005 Highland Pkwy # 200
Downers Grove IL 60515
630 541-1540

(G-19918)
PRECISION DIE & STAMPING INC
9800 Harwood Ct (45014-7589)
PHONE..................................513 942-8220
Greg Johnson, President
Mike Stephens, Principal

Trina Johnson, Office Mgr
EMP: 8
SQ FT: 6,500
SALES (est): 1.3MM **Privately Held**
WEB: www.precisiondie.com
SIC: 3312 Tool & die steel

(G-19919)
PRECISION ENVIRONMENTS INC (PA)
Also Called: Precison Clean Rooms
9830 Windisch Rd (45069-3806)
PHONE..................................513 847-1510
Douglas J Cooper, President
Michael Hall, Corp Secy
EMP: 23 **EST:** 2009
SQ FT: 8,000
SALES (est): 16MM **Privately Held**
SIC: 3829 5085 Measuring & controlling
devices; clean room supplies

(G-19920)
PREMIER COATINGS LTD
9390 Le Saint Dr (45014-5446)
PHONE..................................513 942-1070
Brandon Stock, General Mgr
Josh Walters, Manager
EMP: 14 **EST:** 1999
SQ FT: 20,000
SALES (est): 775.6K **Privately Held**
WEB: www.premiercoatings.com
SIC: 3291 1721 Coated abrasive prod-
ucts; painting & paper hanging

(G-19921)
PROCTER & GAMBLE COMPANY
8868 Beckett Rd (45069-2902)
PHONE..................................513 672-4044
Carlos Lange, Opers Mgr
Garrett Cain, Manager
Valsa Vettikkal, Technology
EMP: 417
SALES (corp-wide): 65.3B **Publicly Held**
SIC: 2844 Toilet preparations
PA: The Procter & Gamble Company
1 Procter And Gamble Plz
Cincinnati OH 45202
513 983-1100

(G-19922)
PROCTER & GAMBLE COMPANY
8256 Union Centre Blvd (45069-7056)
PHONE..................................513 634-9600
Troy Embree, Engineer
Nathan Gill, Engineer
David Howell, Engineer
Pam Dunnon, Branch Mgr
Mark Morrow, Manager
EMP: 205
SALES (corp-wide): 65.3B **Publicly Held**
WEB: www.pg.com
SIC: 2841 Soap & other detergents
PA: The Procter & Gamble Company
1 Procter And Gamble Plz
Cincinnati OH 45202
513 983-1100

(G-19923)
PROCTER & GAMBLE COMPANY
8611 Beckett Rd (45069-4868)
PHONE..................................513 634-9110
Dimitris Collias, Research
Leroy Kocher, Research
Steve Bush, Engineer
Jon Calderas, Engineer
Nancy Jackson, Engineer
EMP: 205
SALES (corp-wide): 65.3B **Publicly Held**
WEB: www.pg.com
SIC: 2841 2676 2844 2079 Soap: granulated, liquid, cake, flaked or chip; detergents, synthetic organic or inorganic
alkaline; towels, napkins & tissue paper
products; diapers, paper (disposable):
made from purchased paper; deodorants,
personal; hair preparations, including
shampoos; cosmetic preparations; oral
preparations; shortening & other solid edible fats; margarine & margarine oils;
pharmaceutical preparations; cough medicines; cold remedies
PA: The Procter & Gamble Company
1 Procter And Gamble Plz
Cincinnati OH 45202
513 983-1100

(G-19924)
QPI CINCINNATI LLC
6455 Gano Rd (45069-4830)
PHONE..................................513 755-2670
Eduardo Rosado, Owner
EMP: 3
SQ FT: 50,000
SALES (est): 28.7MM **Privately Held**
SIC: 2676 Infant & baby paper products

(G-19925)
QUALITURN INC
9081 Le Saint Dr (45014-2242)
PHONE..................................513 868-3333
Fax: 513 868-0333
Mike Barber, President
EMP: 24
SQ FT: 1,500
SALES (est): 5.1MM **Privately Held**
SIC: 3599 Machine shop, jobbing & repair

(G-19926)
QUANTUM COMMERCE LLC
6748 Dimmick Rd (45069-3931)
P.O. Box 1640 (45071-1640)
PHONE..................................513 777-0737
Gregory Workman II, Principal
EMP: 4
SALES (est): 273.9K **Privately Held**
SIC: 3572 Computer storage devices

(G-19927)
QUASONIX INC (PA)
6025 Schumacher Park Dr (45069-4812)
PHONE..................................513 942-1287
Terrance Hill, President
Tim O'Connell, Engineer
Sean Wilson, Engineer
Pamela S Hill, Treasurer
Pamela Salyers, Accountant
EMP: 26
SQ FT: 15,000
SALES: 15MM **Privately Held**
WEB: www.quasonix.com
SIC: 5065 3663 3812 3669 Communica-
tion equipment; airborne radio communi-
cations equipment; antennas, radar or
communications; intercommunication sys-
tems, electric

(G-19928)
QUEEN CITY POLYMERS INC (PA)
6101 Schumacher Park Dr (45069-3818)
PHONE..................................513 779-0990
Fax: 513 779-0993
James M Powers, President
James L Powers, Principal
Kelli Alder, Controller
Greg Hendren, Director
EMP: 40
SQ FT: 33,000
SALES (est): 6.5MM **Privately Held**
WEB: www.qcpinc.net
SIC: 3089 5162 Plastic processing; plas-
tics products

(G-19929)
R L INDUSTRIES INC
9355 Le Saint Dr (45014-5458)
PHONE..................................513 874-2800
John R Gierl, Principal
Joe Lassandro, Sls & Mktg Exec
EMP: 75 **EST:** 1962
SALES (est): 7.5MM
SALES (corp-wide): 17.2MM **Privately Held**
SIC: 3089 Plastic & fiberglass tanks
PA: R L Holdings, Inc.
9355 Le Saint Dr
West Chester OH 45014
513 874-2800

(G-19930)
REPUBLIC WIRE INC
5525 Union Centre Dr (45069-4820)
PHONE..................................513 860-1800
Fax: 513 860-8818
Ron Rosenbeck, Principal
Steve Hart, Engineer
Mark Huelsebusch, CFO
Lisa Shepherd, Accountant
Doug Chandler, Regl Sales Mgr
▲ **EMP:** 75
SQ FT: 175,000

SALES (est): 53.2MM **Privately Held**
WEB: www.republicwire.com
SIC: 3351 3315 Wire, copper & copper
alloy; steel wire & related products

(G-19931)
RETTERBUSH GRAPHIC AND PACKG
6187 Schumacher Park Dr (45069-3818)
PHONE..................................513 779-4466
Fax: 513 779-3993
Joseph Retterbush, President
Denny Meador, Vice Pres
EMP: 20
SQ FT: 5,000
SALES (est): 4.5MM **Privately Held**
SIC: 2671 2754 Paper coated or lami-
nated for packaging; labels: gravure print-
ing

(G-19932)
REV38 LLC
8888 Beckett Rd (45069)
PHONE..................................937 572-4000
Erick Carlson, Branch Mgr
EMP: 6
SALES (corp-wide): 680.6K **Privately Held**
SIC: 3663 Radio & TV communications
equipment
PA: Rev38 Llc
650 N Alex Rd
West Carrollton OH 45449
937 269-9641

(G-19933)
RIOTECH INTERNATIONAL LTD (PA)
Also Called: Queen City Polymers
6101 Schumacher Park Dr (45069-3818)
PHONE..................................513 779-0990
James M Powers, Partner
Jerry Pavone, COO
Kelli Alder, Controller
EMP: 2
SQ FT: 40,000
SALES (est): 9.1MM **Privately Held**
SIC: 3089 Plastic kitchenware, tableware &
houseware

(G-19934)
RIVERCITY WOODWORKING INC
9837 Harwood Ct (45014-7588)
PHONE..................................513 860-1900
Fax: 513 870-5943
Richard Neubauer Jr, President
EMP: 6
SQ FT: 10,000
SALES (est): 1.1MM **Privately Held**
SIC: 2541 Store fixtures, wood

(G-19935)
ROBOWORLD MOLDED PRODUCTS LLC ✪
Also Called: Pendant Armor
8216 Princeton Glendale (45069-1675)
PHONE..................................513 720-6900
Christian Tur, President
EMP: 4 **EST:** 2016
SALES (est): 247.5K **Privately Held**
SIC: 3061 7389 Mechanical rubber goods;

(G-19936)
ROCKWELL AUTOMATION INC
9355 Allen Rd (45069-3846)
PHONE..................................513 942-9828
Fax: 513 942-9085
Jim Sell, District Mgr
Christopher Gist, Research
Heidi Latsko, Sales Staff
Michael Schutte, Sales Staff
Mike Kmetz, Manager
EMP: 80
SQ FT: 16,000 **Publicly Held**
SIC: 3625 Relays & industrial controls
PA: Rockwell Automation, Inc.
1201 S 2nd St
Milwaukee WI 53204

(G-19937)
RPS AMERICA INC (PA)
8808 Beckett Center Dr (45069)
PHONE..................................937 231-9339
Roberto Facci, President
Edward Kwiatkowski, Vice Pres

EMP: 2
SQ FT: 18,800
SALES: 5MM Privately Held
SIC: 3699 Electrical equipment & supplies

(G-19938)
RR DONNELLEY & SONS COMPANY
8740 Global Way (45069-7066)
PHONE..................................513 870-4040
EMP: 7
SALES (corp-wide): 6.9B Publicly Held
SIC: 2657 Folding paperboard boxes
PA: R. R. Donnelley & Sons Company
   35 W Wacker Dr Ste 3650
   Chicago IL 60601
   312 326-8000

(G-19939)
RR DONNELLEY & SONS COMPANY
Also Called: RR Donnelley
8720 Global Way (45069-7066)
PHONE..................................513 552-1512
Brad Hull, Manager
EMP: 7
SALES (corp-wide): 6.9B Publicly Held
WEB: www.rrdonnelley.com
SIC: 2759 Promotional printing
PA: R. R. Donnelley & Sons Company
   35 W Wacker Dr Ste 3650
   Chicago IL 60601
   312 326-8000

(G-19940)
RSA CONTROLS INC
6422 Fountains Blvd (45069-2101)
PHONE..................................513 476-6277
Ruth McWilliams, Principal
EMP: 4
SALES (est): 356.8K Privately Held
SIC: 3823 Thermal conductivity instruments, industrial process type

(G-19941)
SAFEWAY SAFETY STEP LLC
Also Called: Cleancut
5242 Rialto Rd (45069-2921)
PHONE..................................513 942-7837
Chris Stafford, President
Randy Slattery, VP Opers
EMP: 10 EST: 2000
SALES (est): 1.1MM Privately Held
SIC: 3088 Tubs (bath, shower & laundry), plastic

(G-19942)
SCHNEIDER ELECTRIC USA INC
Also Called: Square D Field Services
9870 Crescent Park Dr (45069-3800)
PHONE..................................513 755-4231
Angela Fay, Purch Agent
Brian Cassell, Financial Exec
Tim Miracle, Mktg Dir
Jean-Pascal Tricoire, Branch Mgr
EMP: 152
SALES (corp-wide): 241K Privately Held
SIC: 3613 3643 3612 3823 Switchgear & switchboard apparatus; power circuit breakers; switches, electric power except snap, push button, etc.; switchboards & parts, power; bus bars (electrical conductors); connectors & terminals for electrical devices; power transformers, electric; controllers for process variables, all types; relays & industrial controls; motor controls, electric; relays, electric power; switches, electronic applications; electrical apparatus & equipment
HQ: Schneider Electric Usa, Inc.
   800 Federal St
   Andover MA 01810
   978 975-9600

(G-19943)
SCHNEIDER ELECTRIC USA INC
9870 Crescent Park Dr (45069-3800)
PHONE..................................513 755-5000
John Blaylock, General Mgr
Jerry Earl, Plant Mgr
Angela Fay, Purch Mgr
Ryan Back, Senior Buyer
Daniel Lee, Finance
EMP: 75

SALES (corp-wide): 241K Privately Held
WEB: www.squared.com
SIC: 3613 3643 3612 3823 Switchgear & switchboard apparatus; bus bars (electrical conductors); power transformers, electric; controllers for process variables, all types; relays & industrial controls; electrical apparatus & equipment
HQ: Schneider Electric Usa, Inc.
   800 Federal St
   Andover MA 01810
   978 975-9600

(G-19944)
SENTRILOCK LLC
7701 Service Center Dr (45069-2440)
PHONE..................................513 618-5800
Scott R Fisher, President
Scott Richardson, General Mgr
Scott Farmer, Vice Pres
John G Wenker, Vice Pres
John Gill, Opers Staff
EMP: 83
SQ FT: 7,000
SALES: 16.5MM Privately Held
WEB: www.sentrilock.com
SIC: 2542 Mail racks & lock boxes, postal service: except wood

(G-19945)
SHAW INDUSTRIES INC
4436 Muhlhauser Rd # 100 (45011-9774)
PHONE..................................513 942-3692
Fax: 513 942-6276
Jim Brown, Branch Mgr
EMP: 6
SALES (corp-wide): 223.6B Publicly Held
WEB: www.shawinc.com
SIC: 3999 Barber & beauty shop equipment
HQ: Shaw Industries, Inc.
   616 E Walnut Ave
   Dalton GA 30721
   706 278-3812

(G-19946)
SINE WALL LLC
7162 Liberty Ste 105 (45069)
PHONE..................................919 453-2011
Heather Hardwick, Credit Mgr
Timothy Brereton, Mng Member
EMP: 5 EST: 2009
SALES (est): 38.2K Privately Held
SIC: 3446 Architectural metalwork

(G-19947)
SPICY OLIVE LLC (PA)
7671 Cox Ln (45069-6546)
PHONE..................................513 847-4397
Theresa A Banks, Principal
EMP: 12
SALES (est): 22.4MM Privately Held
SIC: 2079 Olive oil

(G-19948)
STABLE STEP LLC
8930 Global Way (45069-7071)
PHONE..................................513 825-1888
Rhonda Newman, CEO
EMP: 23
SALES (est): 755.3K Privately Held
SIC: 3842 Foot appliances, orthopedic

(G-19949)
STERLING COATING
9048 Port Union Rialto Rd (45069-2937)
PHONE..................................513 942-4900
Fax: 513 942-4901
Craig Lowe, General Mgr
EMP: 4
SALES (est): 356.9K Privately Held
SIC: 3479 Etching & engraving

(G-19950)
SUGAR CREEK PACKING CO
4235 Thunderbird Ln (45014-5483)
PHONE..................................513 874-4422
Jeff Shutte, Branch Mgr
EMP: 140
SALES (corp-wide): 739.8MM Privately Held
SIC: 2013 2011 Bacon, side & sliced: from purchased meat; meat packing plants

PA: Sugar Creek Packing Co.
   2101 Kenskill Ave
   Wshngtn Ct Hs OH 43160
   740 335-7440

(G-19951)
SUGAR CREEK PACKING CO
4585 Muhlhauser Rd (45011-9788)
PHONE..................................513 874-4422
Fax: 513 551-5252
John Richardson, Ch of Bd
EMP: 5
SALES (corp-wide): 739.8MM Privately Held
SIC: 2013 2011 Sausages & other prepared meats; meat packing plants
PA: Sugar Creek Packing Co.
   2101 Kenskill Ave
   Wshngtn Ct Hs OH 43160
   740 335-7440

(G-19952)
SYNDICATE PRINTERS INC
7291 Saint Ives Pl (45069-4647)
PHONE..................................513 779-3625
Ambrish K Bansal, Principal
EMP: 3
SALES (est): 23.3K Privately Held
SIC: 2752 Commercial printing, lithographic

(G-19953)
SYSTECON INC
6121 Schumacher Park Dr (45069-3818)
PHONE..................................513 777-7722
Fax: 513 777-0259
Terrence Moses, CEO
Martin P Tierney, President
Bill Bell, Engineer
Jim Schlachter, Engineer
Linda Morckel, Human Resources
EMP: 70
SQ FT: 60,000
SALES: 29MM Privately Held
WEB: www.systecon.com
SIC: 3561 Pumps & pumping equipment

(G-19954)
TEMPAC LLC
7370 Avenel Ct (45069-4649)
PHONE..................................513 505-9700
Heidi Temming, Psychologist
Dave R Temming,
EMP: 2
SQ FT: 1,500
SALES (est): 3MM Privately Held
SIC: 2011 5131 Meat packing plants; labels

(G-19955)
TENACITY MANUFACTURING COMPANY
4455 Muhlhauser Rd (45011-9788)
PHONE..................................513 821-0201
Fax: 513 821-7511
Layne Meader, President
Jerry Crowder, Vice Pres
Jim Fox, Prdtn Mgr
Tim Baumgardner, Treasurer
EMP: 28 EST: 1905
SQ FT: 36,500
SALES (est): 3.2MM
SALES (corp-wide): 17.3MM Privately Held
SIC: 3469 2782 Machine parts, stamped or pressed metal; looseleaf binders & devices
PA: Enduro Binders, Inc.
   6480 Enduro Dr
   Washington MO 63090
   636 239-0140

(G-19956)
THOMPSON CULVERT COMPANY LLC (DH)
9025 Centre Pointe Dr # 400 (45069-4984)
PHONE..................................513 645-7000
William S Thompson, President
Warren J Randle, Vice Pres
Chris Hill, Executive
EMP: 10
SQ FT: 21,400
SALES (est): 2.4MM Privately Held
WEB: www.thompsonculvert.com
SIC: 3444 3564 3498 Pipe, sheet metal; blowers & fans; fabricated pipe & fittings

HQ: Contech Engineered Solutions Llc
   9025 Ctr Pinte Dr Ste 400
   West Chester OH 45069
   513 645-7000

(G-19957)
THREE BOND INTERNATIONAL INC (DH)
6184 Schumacher Park Dr (45069-4802)
PHONE..................................513 779-7300
Fax: 513 779-7375
Kazunori Shibayama, President
Dave Barkley, Plant Mgr
Sergio Balcarcel, Prdtn Mgr
Jeff Speed, Engineer
Masato Suzuki, CFO
▲ EMP: 60
SALES: 39.5MM Privately Held
SIC: 2891 Adhesives & sealants
HQ: Threebond Co., Ltd.
   4-3-3, Minamiosawa
   Hachioji TKY 192-0
   426 705-333

(G-19958)
THYSSENKRUPP BILSTEIN AMER INC
4440 Muhlhauser Rd (45011-9767)
PHONE..................................513 881-7600
Jimmy Brentle, Manager
EMP: 25
SALES (corp-wide): 44.2B Privately Held
SIC: 5013 3714 Motor vehicle supplies & new parts; motor vehicle parts & accessories
HQ: Thyssenkrupp Bilstein Of America, Inc.
   8685 Bilstein Blvd
   Hamilton OH 45015
   513 881-7600

(G-19959)
TOKIN AMERICA CORPORATION
9844 Windisch Rd (45069-3806)
PHONE..................................513 644-9743
Motoaki Suzuki, President
Cherie McKenney, Manager
EMP: 3
SQ FT: 8,500
SALES: 130K
SALES (corp-wide): 19.2MM Privately Held
SIC: 3548 Welding apparatus
PA: Tokin Corporation
   1509, Okubocho, Nishi-Ku
   Hamamatsu SZO 432-8
   534 855-555

(G-19960)
TREY CORRUGATED INC
9048 Port Union Rialto Rd (45069-2937)
PHONE..................................513 942-4800
Fax: 513 942-4801
Tim Cossey, President
Mark Gibson, Controller
Jeff Altom, Manager
EMP: 98
SALES: 48MM
SALES (corp-wide): 27.3B Privately Held
SIC: 2653 Sheets, corrugated: made from purchased materials
HQ: Georgia-Pacific Corrugated Iii Llc
   5645 W 82nd St
   Indianapolis IN 46278

(G-19961)
TRIANGLE LABEL INC
6392 Gano Rd (45069-4809)
PHONE..................................513 242-2822
Scott Kenner, President
EMP: 9
SQ FT: 5,000
SALES (est): 117.3K Privately Held
SIC: 2759 Labels & seals: printing; tags: printing

(G-19962)
TSS TECHNOLOGIES INC (PA)
Also Called: TSS Medical
8800 Global Way (45069-7070)
PHONE..................................513 772-7000
Brent Nichols, President
Kriss Cloninger, Managing Dir
Leila B Nichols, Principal
Charles P Taft, Principal
Ruth Zimmerman, Principal
▲ EMP: 105

▲ = Import ▼=Export
◆ =Import/Export

SQ FT: 75,000
SALES (est): 129.5MM **Privately Held**
WEB: www.tss.com
SIC: 3599 8711 Machine shop, jobbing & repair; mechanical engineering

(G-19963)
TSS TECHNOLOGIES INC
8800 Global Way (45069-7070)
PHONE..............................513 772-7000
Brent Nichols, *Manager*
EMP: 7
SALES (corp-wide): 129.5MM **Privately Held**
SIC: 3599 Machine shop, jobbing & repair
PA: Tss Technologies, Inc.
8800 Global Way
West Chester OH 45069
513 772-7000

(G-19964)
TSS TECHNOLOGIES INC
8800 Global Way (45069-7070)
PHONE..............................513 772-7000
Phil Jones,
EMP: 45
SALES (corp-wide): 129.5MM **Privately Held**
SIC: 3699 Electrical equipment & supplies
PA: Tss Technologies, Inc.
8800 Global Way
West Chester OH 45069
513 772-7000

(G-19965)
TVH PARTS CO
8950 Global Way (45069-7071)
PHONE..............................877 755-7311
EMP: 18
SALES (corp-wide): 189.7MM **Privately Held**
SIC: 3625 Relays & industrial controls
PA: Tvh Parts Co.
16355 S Lone Elm Rd
Olathe KS 66062
913 829-1000

(G-19966)
U S THERMAL INC
9846 Crescent Park Dr (45069-3800)
PHONE..............................513 777-7763
Fax: 513 777-7761
Dan Reagan, *President*
Walter Stevenson, *General Mgr*
EMP: 5
SQ FT: 4,000
SALES (est): 696.4K **Privately Held**
SIC: 3639 Hot water heaters, household

(G-19967)
UNITED PROCESS CONTROLS INC (DH)
8904 Beckett Rd (45069-7054)
PHONE..............................414 462-8200
Patrick Torok, *Vice Pres*
Jennifer Beach, *Controller*
▼ **EMP:** 40 **EST:** 2007
SALES (est): 5.9MM
SALES (corp-wide): 85.7K **Privately Held**
SIC: 3824 Fluid meters & counting devices
HQ: Nitrex Metal Inc
3474 Boul Poirier
Saint-Laurent QC H4R 2
514 335-7191

(G-19968)
UNIVERSAL MACHINE PRODUCTS
9060 Goldpark Dr (45011-9764)
PHONE..............................513 860-4530
Fax: 513 860-3653
Brian Bogan, *President*
EMP: 4
SQ FT: 6,400
SALES (est): 400K **Privately Held**
SIC: 3599 Machine & other job shop work

(G-19969)
UPA TECHNOLOGY INC
8963 Cncnnati Columbus Rd (45069-3513)
P.O. Box 8172 (45069-8172)
PHONE..............................513 755-1380
Michael Justice, *President*
Susan Justice, *Vice Pres*
◆ **EMP:** 11
SQ FT: 4,500

SALES (est): 2MM **Privately Held**
WEB: www.upa.com
SIC: 3829 7699 Measuring & controlling devices; professional instrument repair services

(G-19970)
VIP-SUPPLY CHAIN SOLUTIONS LLC (PA)
Also Called: VIP-Scs
9166 Sutton Pl (45011-9317)
PHONE..............................513 454-2020
Lori Jordan,
Mike Francis,
EMP: 4 **EST:** 2012
SQ FT: 30,000
SALES (est): 1.8MM **Privately Held**
SIC: 7389 5085 4731 2449 Packaging & labeling services; inventory computing service; boxes, crates, etc., other than paper; freight transportation arrangement; rectangular boxes & crates, wood

(G-19971)
WEST CHESTER LOCK CO LLC
6847 Lakota Plaza Dr (45069-6006)
P.O. Box 8052 (45069-8052)
PHONE..............................513 777-6486
Rod Herdman,
EMP: 8
SQ FT: 2,000
SALES (est): 562.4K **Privately Held**
SIC: 3429 Door locks, bolts & checks

(G-19972)
WESTROCK COMPANY
Also Called: Rocktenn Merchandising Display
9245 Meridian Way (45069-6523)
PHONE..............................513 860-5546
Bob Akers, *Ltd Ptnr*
EMP: 35
SALES (corp-wide): 14.1B **Publicly Held**
WEB: www.rocktenn.com
SIC: 2653 Hampers, solid fiber: made from purchased materials
HQ: Westrock Rkt Company
504 Thrasher St
Norcross GA 30071
770 448-2193

(G-19973)
WESTROCK CONVERTING COMPANY
9266 Meridian Way (45069-6521)
PHONE..............................513 860-0225
EMP: 117
SALES (corp-wide): 14.1B **Publicly Held**
SIC: 2631 Container board
HQ: Westrock Converting Company
504 Thrasher St
Norcross GA 30071
770 246-9982

(G-19974)
WRR CREATIVE CONCEPTS LLC
Also Called: Walton, Rego and Roy
6082 Ash Hill Ct (45069-6663)
PHONE..............................513 659-2284
Randall James Walton,
EMP: 4
SALES (est): 1,000K **Privately Held**
SIC: 3089 Plastics products

(G-19975)
YOCKEY GROUP INC
9053 Le Saint Dr (45014-2242)
PHONE..............................513 860-9053
A James Yockey, *President*
Becky Spahni, *Accountant*
EMP: 30 **EST:** 1998
SALES (est): 1.5MM **Privately Held**
SIC: 2759 Commercial printing

West Chester
Hamilton County

(G-19976)
ACE MANUFACTURING COMPANY
Also Called: Ace Sanitary
5452 Spellmire Dr (45246-4842)
PHONE..............................513 541-2490
Fax: 513 541-2492

Charles H Tobias Jr, *Principal*
M R Fredwest, *Principal*
Donald A Schenck, *Principal*
Sherry Miller, *Controller*
Greg Evans, *Regl Sales Mgr*
▲ **EMP:** 32
SQ FT: 27,500
SALES (est): 6MM **Privately Held**
WEB: www.acemanco.com
SIC: 3599 3492 Hose, flexible metallic; hose & tube fittings & assemblies, hydraulic/pneumatic

(G-19977)
ADVANCEPIERRE FOODS INC
9990 Prnceton Glendale Rd (45246-1116)
PHONE..............................513 874-8741
Eileen Ordway, *Manager*
EMP: 4 **Publicly Held**
SIC: 2013 Sausages & other prepared meats
HQ: Advancepierre Foods, Inc.
9987 Carver Rd Ste 500
Blue Ash OH 45242
513 874-8741

(G-19978)
AGEAN MARBLE MANUFACTURING
9756 Prnceton Glendale Rd (45246-1015)
PHONE..............................513 874-1475
Fax: 513 874-3352
Gary Bolte, *Chairman*
Lois Bolte, *Corp Secy*
Chris Bolte, *Vice Pres*
EMP: 15
SQ FT: 26,000
SALES (est): 2MM **Privately Held**
SIC: 3272 5211 5091 3431 Art marble, concrete; bathroom fixtures, equipment & supplies; spa equipment & supplies; hot tubs; metal sanitary ware; cut stone & stone products; wood kitchen cabinets

(G-19979)
AJJ ENTERPRISES LLC
4636 Interstate Dr (45246-1110)
PHONE..............................513 755-9562
Jason Wahl, *Webmaster*
Adam Brinkman,
Jonathan Back,
▲ **EMP:** 10
SQ FT: 10,000
SALES (est): 1.2MM **Privately Held**
SIC: 3944 Games, toys & children's vehicles

(G-19980)
AN ENVIRONMENTAL INKS
5150 Duff Dr (45246-1311)
PHONE..............................513 870-0288
Fax: 513 870-0290
Jeff Tyree, *Manager*
EMP: 22
SALES (corp-wide): 940.5K **Privately Held**
SIC: 2893 Printing ink
HQ: Environmental Inks And Coatings Canada Ltd.
1 Quality Products Rd
Morganton NC 28655
828 433-1922

(G-19981)
APACHE HOSE & BELTING CO INC
9965 Farr Ct (45246-1119)
PHONE..............................513 587-8313
Mark Benedetti, *Administration*
EMP: 66
SALES (corp-wide): 94.7MM **Privately Held**
SIC: 3496 Conveyor belts
PA: Apache Hose & Belting Company, Inc.
4805 Bowling St Sw
Cedar Rapids IA 52404
319 365-0471

(G-19982)
ATLAS MACHINE AND SUPPLY INC
4985 Provident Dr (45246-1020)
PHONE..............................502 584-7262
Fax: 513 874-4263
Kurt Colwell, *Div Sub Head*

Sonny Welker, *Manager*
EMP: 32
SALES (corp-wide): 50.1MM **Privately Held**
WEB: www.atlasmachine.com
SIC: 5084 3599 Industrial machinery & equipment; machine shop, jobbing & repair
PA: Atlas Machine And Supply, Inc.
7000 Global Dr
Louisville KY 40258
502 584-7262

(G-19983)
AUTOMATIC EQUIPMENT CORP
Also Called: AEC Magnetics
4699 Interstate Dr (45246-1109)
PHONE..............................513 771-3833
Fax: 513 326-3614
William R Klaus, *President*
Pat Klaus, *Vice Pres*
H Hamilton, *Mfg Staff*
▲ **EMP:** 11 **EST:** 1960
SQ FT: 12,000
SALES (est): 1.6MM **Privately Held**
WEB: www.aecmagnetics.com
SIC: 3499 Magnets, permanent: metallic

(G-19984)
BEIERSDORF INC
5232 E Provident Dr (45246-1040)
PHONE..............................513 682-7300
Fax: 513 682-5351
Gayle Gao, *President*
Dan Heil, *Opers Mgr*
John Parrish, *Maint Spvr*
Melanie Peck, *Human Res Mgr*
Catherine Greaves, *Human Resources*
EMP: 168
SALES (corp-wide): 10.7B **Privately Held**
WEB: www.bdfusa.com
SIC: 2844 5122 3842 2841 Face creams or lotions; antiseptics; bandages & dressings; stockinette, surgical; soap: granulated, liquid, cake, flaked or chip; tape, pressure sensitive: made from purchased materials
HQ: Beiersdorf, Inc.
45 Danbury Rd
Wilton CT 06897
203 563-5800

(G-19985)
BUILDING CTRL INTEGRATORS LLC
10174 International Blvd (45246-4846)
PHONE..............................513 860-9600
David Milar, *General Mgr*
EMP: 7
SALES (corp-wide): 14.1MM **Privately Held**
SIC: 3822 Temperature controls, automatic
PA: Building Control Integrators, Llc
383 N Liberty St
Powell OH 43065
614 334-3300

(G-19986)
CAE RANSOHOFF INC
4933 Provident Dr (45246-1020)
PHONE..............................513 870-0100
EMP: 7
SALES (est): 470K **Privately Held**
SIC: 3569 General Industrial Machinery, Nec, Nsk

(G-19987)
CECO ENVIRONMENTAL CORP
Effox-Flextor
9759 Inter Ocean Dr (45246-1027)
PHONE..............................513 874-8915
Mark Lefke, *COO*
Patrick Mayer, *Vice Pres*
David Meinking, *Vice Pres*
Bill Holthaus, *Plant Mgr*
Dave Fritsch, *Project Mgr*
EMP: 27
SALES (corp-wide): 417MM **Publicly Held**
SIC: 3443 3441 Fabricated plate work (boiler shop); fabricated structural metal
PA: Ceco Environmental Corp.
4625 Red Bank Rd Ste 200
Cincinnati OH 45227
513 458-2600

(G-19988)
CHASE INDUSTRIES INC (PA)
Also Called: Chase Doors
10021 Commerce Park Dr (45246-1333)
PHONE...................................513 860-5565
Fax: 513 860-0933
Jeffrey Stark, *CEO*
Tony Bartelson, *General Mgr*
Mike Hegner, *General Mgr*
Alan D Baker, *Corp Secy*
Todd Ray, *Exec VP*
▲ EMP: 80
SQ FT: 280,000
SALES (est): 194.4MM **Privately Held**
WEB: www.restaurantdoors.com
SIC: 3442 Metal doors, sash & trim

(G-19989)
CLARKE FIRE PRTECTION PDTS INC
133 Circle Freeway Dr (45246-1203)
PHONE...................................513 771-2200
EMP: 4
SALES (corp-wide): 277.1MM **Privately Held**
SIC: 3519 Diesel, semi-diesel or duel-fuel engines, including marine
HQ: Clarke Fire Protection Products, Inc.
3133 E Kemper Rd
Cincinnati OH 45241
513 771-2200

(G-19990)
CLEANING TECH GROUP LLC (HQ)
4933 Provident Dr (45246-1020)
PHONE...................................513 870-0100
Bernard A Bosse, *President*
Pam Kamp, *General Mgr*
Randi Rabe, *Production*
Tammy George, *Purch Mgr*
Carl Stroh, *Engineer*
▲ EMP: 127
SQ FT: 32,780
SALES (est): 24.9MM **Privately Held**
SIC: 3699 Cleaning equipment, ultrasonic, except medical & dental
PA: Nmgg Ctg Llc
161 Greenfield St
Tiffin OH 44883
419 447-5211

(G-19991)
CLEANING TECH GROUP LLC
Ransohoff Division
4933 Provident Dr (45246-1020)
PHONE...................................513 870-0100
Fax: 513 870-0105
James T McEachen, *President*
Chuck Meutsch, *VP Admin*
Jeff Mills, *Vice Pres*
Mark Huffman, *Mfg Dir*
Dan Bingle, *Opers Mgr*
EMP: 50
SALES (corp-wide): 24.9MM **Privately Held**
SIC: 3569 3599 Blast cleaning equipment; dustless; custom machinery
HQ: Cleaning Technologies Group, Llc
4933 Provident Dr
West Chester OH 45246
513 870-0100

(G-19992)
CMA SUPPLY COMPANY INC
Also Called: C M A Supply Company
9984 Commerce Park Dr (45246-1332)
PHONE...................................513 942-6663
Fax: 513 942-7546
Ken Townsley, *Opers Mgr*
Carrie Shafer, *Purchasing*
Alan Monnin, *Branch Mgr*
Dave McKinney, *Manager*
Rich Emery,
EMP: 12
SALES (corp-wide): 11.8MM **Privately Held**
SIC: 5032 3444 Concrete building products; concrete forms, sheet metal
PA: C.M.A. Supply Company, Inc.
3201 Roosevelt Ave
Indianapolis IN 46218
317 545-4446

(G-19993)
CONTRACT PCKG DIST SPECIALISTS
Also Called: C P D S
236 Circle Freeway Dr (45246-1206)
PHONE...................................513 942-0300
Martha Cahall, *CEO*
M Todd Hampton, *Vice Pres*
Carolyn Stephens, *Controller*
James Cahall,
Kyle Cahall,
EMP: 15
SQ FT: 160,000
SALES (est): 1.7MM **Privately Held**
SIC: 4226 2653 4783 3086 Special warehousing & storage; corrugated & solid fiber boxes; packing goods for shipping; plastics foam products

(G-19994)
CTL-AEROSPACE INC (PA)
Also Called: OEM
5616 Spellmire Dr (45246-4898)
PHONE...................................513 874-1118
Fax: 513 874-2499
James T Irwin, *President*
Lynne Malyn, *General Mgr*
Robert W Buechner, *Principal*
Vicki Osborne, *Principal*
John Irwin, *Vice Pres*
EMP: 205 EST: 1946
SQ FT: 100,000
SALES (est): 42.3MM **Privately Held**
WEB: www.ctlaerospace.com
SIC: 3728 Aircraft parts & equipment; aircraft body & wing assemblies & parts; airframe assemblies, except for guided missiles; aircraft propellers & associated equipment

(G-19995)
CTL-AEROSPACE INC
9970 International Blvd (45246-4852)
PHONE...................................513 874-7900
JC Owen, *President*
Ed Shaffer, *Manager*
EMP: 60
SALES (corp-wide): 42.3MM **Privately Held**
WEB: www.ctlaerospace.com
SIC: 3728 Aircraft parts & equipment
PA: Ctl-Aerospace, Inc.
5616 Spellmire Dr
West Chester OH 45246
513 874-1118

(G-19996)
CUSTOM CARBIDE CUTTER INC
133 Circle Freeway Dr (45246-1203)
PHONE...................................513 851-6363
Fax: 513 851-6379
Steven Long, *President*
Nancy Long, *Admin Sec*
EMP: 15
SQ FT: 5,000
SALES (est): 2.8MM **Privately Held**
WEB: www.customcarbidecutter.com
SIC: 3545 Drill bits, metalworking

(G-19997)
DC CONTROLS LLC
Also Called: Coffey and Associates
4836 Duff Dr Ste E (45246-1194)
PHONE...................................513 225-0813
David Coffey, *Mng Member*
EMP: 7
SALES (est): 1MM **Privately Held**
SIC: 3315 Wire & fabricated wire products

(G-19998)
E2 MERCHANDISING INC
9706 Inter Ocean Dr (45246-1028)
PHONE...................................513 860-5444
Chris Kin, *President*
Henry Kin, *Managing Prtnr*
Gary Nagel, *Vice Pres*
Michelle Heywood, *Manager*
▼ EMP: 20
SALES (est): 2.8MM **Privately Held**
SIC: 2542 Racks, merchandise display or storage: except wood

(G-19999)
ECKEL INDUSTRIES INC
Rubbair Door
10021 Commerce Park Dr (45246-1333)
PHONE...................................978 772-0480
Scott Salem, *Sales Staff*
Alex Eckel, *Branch Mgr*
EMP: 30
SALES (corp-wide): 9.7MM **Privately Held**
WEB: www.eckelacoustic.com
SIC: 3089 3069 Doors, folding: plastic or plastic coated fabric; hard rubber & molded rubber products
PA: Eckel Industries, Inc.
155 Fawcett St Ste 1
Cambridge MA 02138
617 491-3221

(G-20000)
EMPIRE PACKING COMPANY LP
Also Called: Cincinnatti Processing
113 Circle Freeway Dr (45246-1203)
PHONE...................................513 942-5400
Fax: 513 870-6068
Dennis Hioghmas, *General Mgr*
Dennis Hilgeman, *Plant Mgr*
EMP: 60
SALES (corp-wide): 110.7MM **Privately Held**
WEB: www.ledbetterfoods.com
SIC: 5147 2013 2011 Meats, fresh; sausages & other prepared meats; meat packing plants
PA: Empire Packing Company, L.P.
1837 Harbor Ave
Memphis TN 38113
901 948-4788

(G-20001)
FIRE-END & CROKER CORP
4690 Interstate Dr Ste P (45246-1142)
PHONE...................................513 870-0517
Bob Orth, *General Mgr*
EMP: 4
SALES (corp-wide): 12.7MM **Privately Held**
SIC: 3699 Fire control or bombing equipment, electronic
PA: Fire-End & Croker Corp.
7 Westchester Plz Ste 267
Elmsford NY 10523
914 592-3640

(G-20002)
FLAVOR SYSTEMS INTERNATIONAL
9930 Commerce Park Dr (45246-1332)
PHONE...................................513 870-0420
Thomas L Cuni, *Principal*
EMP: 5
SALES (est): 530K **Privately Held**
SIC: 2087 Extracts, flavoring

(G-20003)
FLAVOR SYSTEMS INTL INC (HQ)
5404 Duff Dr (45246-1323)
PHONE...................................513 870-4900
Fax: 513 870-4909
William W Wasz, *President*
William Baker, *Vice Pres*
John Disebastian, *Vice Pres*
Tim Fahey, *CFO*
Linda Gwozdz, *Regl Sales Mgr*
▲ EMP: 40
SQ FT: 50,000
SALES (est): 7.9MM
SALES (corp-wide): 865.3MM **Privately Held**
WEB: www.flavorsystems.com
SIC: 2087 Flavoring extracts & syrups
PA: Frutarom Industries Ltd
25/27 Hashaish
Haifa 26291
996 038-00

(G-20004)
FRUTAROM USA HOLDING INC (DH)
5404 Duff Dr (45246-1323)
PHONE...................................201 861-9500
Ori Yehudai, *CEO*
ARI Rosenthal, *General Mgr*
Amos Anatot, *Exec VP*

Alon Granot, *CFO*
EMP: 5
SALES (est): 2.6MM
SALES (corp-wide): 865.3MM **Privately Held**
SIC: 2869 Flavors or flavoring materials, synthetic
HQ: Frutarom Usa Inc.
5404 Duff Dr
West Chester OH 45246
513 870-4900

(G-20005)
FRUTAROM USA INC (HQ)
5404 Duff Dr (45246-1323)
PHONE...................................513 870-4900
Ori Yehudai, *President*
Alon Granot, *Senior VP*
Luis Gayo, *Vice Pres*
Arial Salmanovici, *CFO*
Michael J Gill, *Treasurer*
◆ EMP: 120
SQ FT: 360,000
SALES (est): 45MM
SALES (corp-wide): 865.3MM **Privately Held**
WEB: www.frutarommeer.com
SIC: 2099 2833 2087 Spices, including grinding; botanical products, medicinal: ground, graded or milled; extracts, flavoring
PA: Frutarom Industries Ltd
25/27 Hashaish
Haifa 26291
996 038-00

(G-20006)
FRUTAROM USA INC
9950 Commerce Park Dr (45246-1332)
PHONE...................................513 870-4900
Reed Lynn, *General Mgr*
Sheryl Protheroe, *QC Mgr*
Kelvin Gray, *Manager*
Anton Horstmann, *Administration*
EMP: 12
SALES (corp-wide): 865.3MM **Privately Held**
SIC: 2099 Spices, including grinding
HQ: Frutarom Usa Inc.
5404 Duff Dr
West Chester OH 45246
513 870-4900

(G-20007)
FRUTAROM USA INC
9930 Commerce Park Dr (45246-1332)
PHONE...................................513 870-4900
EMP: 4
SALES (corp-wide): 865.3MM **Privately Held**
SIC: 2099 Spices, including grinding
HQ: Frutarom Usa Inc.
5404 Duff Dr
West Chester OH 45246
513 870-4900

(G-20008)
FRUTAROM USA INC
10139 Commerce Park Dr (45246-1335)
PHONE...................................513 870-4900
Ori Yehudai, *CEO*
EMP: 5
SALES (corp-wide): 865.3MM **Privately Held**
SIC: 2833 Medicinals & botanicals
HQ: Frutarom Usa Inc.
5404 Duff Dr
West Chester OH 45246
513 870-4900

(G-20009)
GARVEY PRODUCTS INC (HQ)
5428 Duff Dr (45246-1323)
PHONE...................................513 771-8710
Jeff Griffin, *President*
Bill Fischer, *Regl Sales Mgr*
Brian Bellman, *Manager*
Terrie Yearion, *Executive*
▲ EMP: 27
SALES (est): 2.2MM
SALES (corp-wide): 4.6B **Privately Held**
SIC: 3953 Marking devices
PA: Taylor Corporation
1725 Roe Crest Dr
North Mankato MN 56003
507 625-2828

(G-20010)
GOYAL ENTERPRISES INC
Also Called: Bharat Trading
4836 Business Center Way (45246-1318)
P.O. Box 1728 (45071-1728)
PHONE..................................513 874-9303
Fax: 513 777-3911
Kavita Goyal, *President*
Arun Goyal, *General Mgr*
EMP: 10
SQ FT: 4,500
SALES (est): 1.2MM **Privately Held**
WEB: www.gemini-jewelers.com
SIC: 5094 5944 3911 Jewelry & precious
stones; jewelry, precious stones & pre-
cious metals; bracelets, precious metal

(G-20011)
GRAHAM PACKAGING
COMPANY LP
290 Circle Freeway Dr (45246-1206)
PHONE..................................513 874-1770
Fax: 513 860-8439
Kevin George, *Manager*
Russ Stegman, *Administration*
EMP: 43 **Privately Held**
WEB: www.grahampackaging.com
SIC: 3089 3085 Plastic containers, except
foam; plastics bottles
HQ: Graham Packaging Company, L.P.
700 Indian Springs Dr # 100
Lancaster PA 17601
717 849-8500

(G-20012)
HANSEN SCAFFOLDING LLC
(PA)
193 Circle Freeway Dr (45246-1203)
PHONE..................................513 574-9000
Fax: 513 574-5322
Aaron Hansen, *President*
Jennifer McDonald, *Principal*
EMP: 15
SQ FT: 22,000
SALES (est): 3.1MM **Privately Held**
WEB: www.hiloclimbers.com
SIC: 7359 3446 Equipment rental & leas-
ing; scaffolds, mobile or stationary: metal

(G-20013)
HARGIS INDUSTRIES LP
Also Called: Sealtite Building Fasteners
9950 Prnceton Glendale Rd (45246-1116)
PHONE..................................513 874-5905
Fax: 513 874-5903
David Quel, *Manager*
EMP: 40
SALES (corp-wide): 48.4MM **Privately**
Held
WEB: www.sealtite.com
SIC: 5085 3452 Fasteners, industrial:
nuts, bolts, screws, etc.; bolts, nuts, rivets
& washers
PA: Hargis Industries, Lp
6357 Reynolds Rd
Tyler TX 75708
903 592-2826

(G-20014)
HORNER INDUSTRIAL
SERVICES INC
4721 Interstate Dr (45246-1111)
PHONE..................................513 874-8722
Mark Wolma, *Vice Pres*
Scott Hartley, *Manager*
EMP: 15
SALES (corp-wide): 47.3MM **Privately**
Held
SIC: 7694 Armature rewinding shops
PA: Horner Industrial Services, Inc.
1521 E Washington St
Indianapolis IN 46201
317 639-4261

(G-20015)
ICEE USA
44 Carnegie Way (45246-1224)
PHONE..................................513 771-0630
Fax: 513 771-3826
Bob Keegan, *Principal*
Robert Keegan, *Director*
EMP: 4
SALES (est): 261.5K **Privately Held**
SIC: 2024 Ice cream & frozen desserts

(G-20016)
INTELLIGRATED INC
10045 International Blvd (45246-4845)
PHONE..................................513 874-0788
Fax: 513 881-5251
Lee Yarberry, *VP Mfg*
Jon Tutuncu, *Opers Staff*
James Ketcham, *Engineer*
Steve Luebbe, *Accountant*
Cindi Andres, *Comptroller*
EMP: 20
SALES (corp-wide): 39.3B **Publicly Held**
SIC: 3535 5084 7371 Conveyors & con-
veying equipment; industrial machinery &
equipment; custom computer program-
ming services
HQ: Intelligrated, Inc.
7901 Innovation Way
Mason OH 45040
866 936-7300

(G-20017)
J & K CABINETRY
INCORPORATED
9920 Prnceton Glendale Rd (45246-1116)
PHONE..................................513 860-3461
Zhi WEI Huang, *Administration*
EMP: 4 EST: 2014
SALES (est): 486.2K **Privately Held**
SIC: 2434 Wood kitchen cabinets

(G-20018)
J BEISCHEL ELECTRIC
10175 International Blvd (45246-4840)
PHONE..................................513 860-3290
Thomas Popp, *Principal*
EMP: 7
SALES (est): 1MM **Privately Held**
SIC: 3699 Electrical equipment & supplies

(G-20019)
JOHNNY CHIN INSURANCE
AGENCY
Also Called: State Farm Insurance
9676 Cncnnati Columbus Rd (45241-1071)
PHONE..................................513 777-8695
Fax: 513 755-5722
Johnny Chin, *President*
Angela Chin, *Office Mgr*
EMP: 3
SALES: 3MM **Privately Held**
SIC: 6411 2741 Insurance agents & bro-
kers; miscellaneous publishing

(G-20020)
LASTING FIRST IMPRESSIONS
INC
Also Called: Heartland Thermography
36 Carnegie Way (45246-1224)
PHONE..................................513 870-6900
Fax: 513 870-6920
Douglas Rodenfels, *President*
Laurie Rodenfels, *Admin Sec*
EMP: 19
SQ FT: 10,000
SALES (est): 2.3MM **Privately Held**
SIC: 2752 Commercial printing, offset

(G-20021)
LOUIS TRAUTH DAIRY LLC (HQ)
9991 Commerce Park Dr (45246-1331)
P.O. Box 721770, Newport KY (41072-
1770)
PHONE..................................859 431-7553
Greg Engles, *CEO*
Rachael A Gonzalez, *Principal*
Steven J Kemps, *Principal*
Gary Sparks, *Senior VP*
Dan Smith, *Vice Pres*
EMP: 260 EST: 1920
SQ FT: 160,000
SALES (est): 50.4MM **Publicly Held**
WEB: www.trauthdairy.com
SIC: 5143 5149 2033 2026 Dairy prod-
ucts, except dried or canned; milk &
cream, fluid; ice cream & ices; butter;
beverages, except coffee & tea; mineral
or spring water bottling; tea; canned fruits
& specialties; fluid milk; ice cream &
frozen desserts

(G-20022)
MAGNUM PIERING INC
156 Circle Freeway Dr (45246-1204)
PHONE..................................513 759-3348

Brian Dwyer, *President*
Bill Bonekemper, *Vice Pres*
Randy Bonhaus, *Controller*
Michael Dwyer, *Sales Staff*
Sharon Appelman, *Admin Sec*
EMP: 30
SALES (est): 9MM
SALES (corp-wide): 19.4MM **Privately**
Held
WEB: www.magnumpiering.com
SIC: 3441 3561 Fabricated structural
metal; pumps & pumping equipment
PA: Dwyer Companies, Inc.
6083 Schumacher Park Dr
West Chester OH 45069
513 777-0998

(G-20023)
MAI MEDIA GROUP LLC
Also Called: Eye3data
9624 Cincinnati Columbus (45241-4123)
PHONE..................................513 779-0604
Erum Ansari,
EMP: 5
SALES (est): 892.2K
SALES (corp-wide): 2.2B **Privately Held**
SIC: 3699 5065 Security control equip-
ment & systems; security control equip-
ment & systems
HQ: Point Blank Enterprises, Inc.
2102 Sw 2nd St
Pompano Beach FL 33069
954 630-0900

(G-20024)
MANUFACTURERS
REPRESENTATIVES
Also Called: Mri
7432 Heathcock Ct (45241-3641)
PHONE..................................513 467-6669
Ron Creamer, *CEO*
Henry J Carota, *President*
Pete Schneider, *Vice Pres*
Glenda Carota, *Treasurer*
EMP: 3
SALES (est): 285.4K **Privately Held**
SIC: 3069 Water bottles, rubber

(G-20025)
MCCC SPORTSWEAR INC
9944 Prnceton Glendale Rd (45246-1116)
PHONE..................................513 583-9210
Fax: 513 583-0874
Marta Callahan, *President*
Sue Kollstedt, *Vice Pres*
Jennifer Snyder, *Marketing Staff*
Max Cole, *Manager*
Robert Seyfried, *Manager*
▲ EMP: 30
SQ FT: 45,000
SALES: 8MM **Privately Held**
WEB: www.mccc-sportswear.com
SIC: 5137 2395 5136 Women's & chil-
dren's clothing; embroidery & art needle-
work; men's & boys' clothing

(G-20026)
MED CENTER SYSTEMS LLC
10179 Commerce Park Dr (45246-1335)
PHONE..................................513 942-6066
Paul Brelo, *General Mgr*
Tina Powell, *Accounting Mgr*
David Griffiths, *Accountant*
David Cooper,
Martin Cooper,
EMP: 3
SALES: 750K **Privately Held**
SIC: 3089 Plastic containers, except foam

(G-20027)
MEKA SIGNS ENTERPRISES INC
Also Called: Signs By Tomorrow
10126 Prncton Glendale Rd (45246-1200)
PHONE..................................513 942-5494
Fax: 513 942-5495
Kevin Moe, *President*
EMP: 3
SALES: 150K **Privately Held**
SIC: 3993 Signs & advertising specialties

(G-20028)
MH LOGISTICS CORP
Also Called: Mh Equipment
106 Circle Freeway Dr (45246-1204)
PHONE..................................513 681-2200
Robert Sattler, *Vice Pres*

Angie Hickman, *Project Mgr*
Brad Barrow, *Controller*
Matt Guye, *Accounts Mgr*
Carl Traub, *Sales Staff*
EMP: 55
SALES (corp-wide): 238.6MM **Privately**
Held
WEB: www.mhlogistics.com
SIC: 3537 Industrial trucks & tractors
PA: M.H. Logistics Corp.
2001 Hartman
Chillicothe IL 61523
309 579-8030

(G-20029)
MICROTEK FINISHING LLC
5579 Spellmire Dr (45246-4841)
PHONE..................................513 766-5600
Tim Bell, *Vice Pres*
Tim Dell, *Director*
▲ EMP: 22
SQ FT: 5,000
SALES (est): 3.1MM **Privately Held**
WEB: www.MicroTekFinishing.com
SIC: 3471 Polishing, metals or formed
products

(G-20030)
MIDWEST FILTRATION LLC
9775 International Blvd (45246-4855)
PHONE..................................513 874-6510
Steven Vollmer, *CEO*
Frank Strittmatter, *President*
Chris Noe, *Business Mgr*
Russ Halstad, *Vice Pres*
James Valentine, *Plant Mgr*
▲ EMP: 50
SQ FT: 110,000
SALES (est): 24.6MM **Privately Held**
WEB: www.midwestfiltration.com
SIC: 3569 2653 Filters, general line: in-
dustrial; corrugated & solid fiber boxes

(G-20031)
MILSO MIDWEST
4739 Interstate Dr (45246-1111)
PHONE..................................513 745-0760
Fax: 513 745-0790
Steve Duffy, *Principal*
EMP: 3
SALES (est): 120K **Privately Held**
SIC: 3995 Burial caskets

(G-20032)
NORTHROP GRUMMAN
SYSTEMS CORP
460 W Crescentville Rd (45246-1221)
PHONE..................................513 881-3296
William Thompson, *General Mgr*
Brian Harrigan, *Opers Mgr*
Michael Chapman, *Facilities Mgr*
Jason Brach, *Engineer*
Thurman Brown, *Engineer*
EMP: 270 **Publicly Held**
WEB: www.sperry.ngc.com
SIC: 3663 Radio & TV communications
equipment
HQ: Northrop Grumman Systems Corpora-
tion
2980 Fairview Park Dr
Falls Church VA 22042
703 280-2900

(G-20033)
OCTAL EXTRUSION CORP
5399 E Provident Dr (45246-1044)
PHONE..................................513 881-6100
Joe Barenberg, *CEO*
Eric O'Bryant, *Human Resources*
John Dennis, *Manager*
EMP: 50
SQ FT: 130,000
SALES: 18MM **Privately Held**
SIC: 2631 Container, packaging &
boxboard
PA: Octal Holding Saoc
Alawak Building Next To Nissan Show-
room
Muscat
220 307-00

(G-20034)
PACKAGE DESIGN & MFG INC
Also Called: PDM
4740 Interstate Dr Ste K (45246-1146)
PHONE..................................513 874-7364

Fax: 513 874-7017
Patrick Kallmyer, *General Mgr*
Jane Jahn, *Manager*
EMP: 11
SALES (corp-wide): 10.7MM **Privately Held**
WEB: www.packdm.com
SIC: 2621 Paper mills
PA: Package Design & Manufacturing, Inc.
12424 Emerson Dr
Brighton MI 48116
248 486-4390

(G-20035)
PERFECTION BAKERIES INC
374 Circle Freeway Dr C (45246-1260)
PHONE.................................513 942-1442
Jeri Meinking, *Principal*
EMP: 37
SALES (corp-wide): 567MM **Privately Held**
SIC: 2051 Bread, all types (white, wheat, rye, etc): fresh or frozen
PA: Perfection Bakeries, Inc.
350 Pearl St
Fort Wayne IN 46802
260 424-8245

(G-20036)
PF MANAGEMENT INC
Also Called: Pfmi
9990 Prnceton Glendale Rd (45246-1116)
PHONE.................................513 874-8741
Norbert E Woodhams, *President*
EMP: 7
SQ FT: 220,000
SALES (est): 470.7K
SALES (corp-wide): 951.3MM **Privately Held**
SIC: 8741 2015 2051 Management services; chicken slaughtering & processing; bread, cake & related products
HQ: Pierre Holding Corp
9990 Prnceton Glendale Rd
West Chester OH 45246
513 874-8741

(G-20037)
PIERRE HOLDING CORP (HQ)
9990 Prnceton Glendale Rd (45246-1116)
PHONE.................................513 874-8741
Fax: 513 874-7180
Norbert E Wooadhams, *President*
Robert C Naylor, *Senior VP*
Joseph W Meyers, *CFO*
EMP: 7
SQ FT: 220,000
SALES (est): 224.5MM
SALES (corp-wide): 951.3MM **Privately Held**
SIC: 2013 2015 2051 Prepared beef products from purchased beef; prepared pork products from purchased pork; chicken slaughtering & processing; bread, cake & related products
PA: Madison Dearborn Partners Iv Lp
70 W Madison St Ste 3800
Chicago IL 60602
312 895-1000

(G-20038)
POLYMET CORPORATION
10073 Commerce Park Dr (45246-1333)
PHONE.................................513 874-3586
Fax: 513 874-2880
Bill Mosier, *President*
Thomas J Dagenback, *Vice Pres*
Keith Brody, *Purch Mgr*
Chris Phillips, *Purchasing*
Todd Centers, *Plant Engr Mgr*
▲ **EMP:** 45
SQ FT: 47,000
SALES (est): 11MM **Privately Held**
WEB: www.polymetcorp.com
SIC: 3496 3548 3341 3315 Miscellaneous fabricated wire products; welding apparatus; secondary nonferrous metals; steel wire & related products

(G-20039)
PPG INDUSTRIES INC
Also Called: PPG 4341
9304 Cincinnati Columbus (45241-6101)
PHONE.................................513 779-2727
EMP: 24

SALES (corp-wide): 14.7B **Publicly Held**
WEB: www.ppg.com
SIC: 2851 Paints & allied products
PA: Ppg Industries, Inc.
1 Ppg Pl
Pittsburgh PA 15272
412 434-3131

(G-20040)
PRINT ZONE
9588 Cncnnati Columbus Rd (45241-1112)
PHONE.................................513 733-0067
B Ariapad, *Principal*
EMP: 4
SALES (est): 425.2K **Privately Held**
SIC: 2752 Commercial printing, lithographic

(G-20041)
PROFESSIONAL CASE INC
Also Called: PCI
9790 Inter Ocean Dr (45246-1028)
PHONE.................................513 682-2520
Fax: 513 682-2525
Thomas Brown, *President*
Erin Biel, *Vice Pres*
Paul Biel, *Vice Pres*
EMP: 10 **EST:** 1978
SQ FT: 7,000
SALES (est): 1.5MM **Privately Held**
WEB: www.professionalcase.com
SIC: 3161 Cases, carrying

(G-20042)
PURE LIGHT TECHNOLOGY LLC
9624 Cincinnati Columbus (45241-4123)
PHONE.................................513 779-7474
Scot Heck, *CEO*
Pat Heck, *Principal*
Adam Combs, *COO*
EMP: 4
SQ FT: 1,000
SALES (est): 207.2K **Privately Held**
SIC: 5047 3641 8742 5063 Instruments, surgical & medical; health lamps, infrared or ultraviolet; sales (including sales management) consultant; hanging & fastening devices, electrical; sterilizers, hospital & surgical

(G-20043)
QUALITY ENVELOPE INC
9792 Inter Ocean Dr (45246-1028)
PHONE.................................513 942-7578
Robert Lester, *President*
Rick Doxtator, *Vice Pres*
Jeffery Leatherwood Sr, *Vice Pres*
EMP: 6
SALES (est): 1.2MM **Privately Held**
WEB: www.qenvelopes.com
SIC: 2677 Envelopes

(G-20044)
QUEEN CITY TECHNOLOGIES
34 W Crescentville Rd (45246)
P.O. Box 157026, Cincinnati (45215-7026)
PHONE.................................513 253-1312
Aaron Hoffman, *Principal*
EMP: 10
SALES (est): 521.3K **Privately Held**
SIC: 7371 7372 Computer software development; business oriented computer software

(G-20045)
READING ROCK INC (PA)
4600 Devitt Dr (45246-1104)
P.O. Box 46387, Cincinnati (45246-0387)
PHONE.................................513 874-2345
Fax: 513 874-2520
Gordon Rich, *President*
Kevin Forrest, *General Mgr*
Steve Hanrahan, *Assistant VP*
Dallas Moore, *Assistant VP*
Mark Swortwood, *Vice Pres*
▲ **EMP:** 150
SQ FT: 64,000
SALES (est): 32.2MM **Privately Held**
WEB: www.readingrock.com
SIC: 3271 2951 Blocks, concrete or cinder: standard; paving blocks, concrete; asphalt paving mixtures & blocks

(G-20046)
SAF-HOLLAND INC
246 Circle Freeway Dr (45246-1206)
PHONE.................................513 874-7888
EMP: 3 **Privately Held**
SIC: 3714 3715 3568 3537 Motor vehicle parts & accessories; trailer hitches; motor vehicle; truck trailers; power transmission equipment; industrial trucks & tractors; bolts, nuts, rivets & washers
HQ: Saf-Holland, Inc.
1950 Industrial Blvd
Muskegon MI 49442
231 773-3271

(G-20047)
SCHINDLER ELEVATOR CORPORATION
5426 Duff Dr (45246-1323)
PHONE.................................513 341-2600
Catherine Morgan, *Manager*
Sean Cain, *Network Mgr*
EMP: 40
SALES (corp-wide): 9.5B **Privately Held**
WEB: www.us.schindler.com
SIC: 3534 Elevators & equipment
HQ: Schindler Elevator Corporation
20 Whippany Rd
Morristown NJ 07960
973 397-6500

(G-20048)
SEI INC
10004 International Blvd (45246-4839)
PHONE.................................513 942-6170
EMP: 11 **Privately Held**
SIC: 2741 Miscellaneous publishing
PA: Sei, Inc.
3854 Broadmoor Ave Se # 101
Grand Rapids MI 49512

(G-20049)
SEXTON INDUSTRIAL INC
366 Circle Freeway Dr (45246-1208)
PHONE.................................513 530-5555
Abbe Sexton, *President*
Dan Towne, *Corp Secy*
Ron Sexton, *Vice Pres*
Vikie Masnith, *Office Mgr*
EMP: 150
SQ FT: 85,000
SALES (est): 43.5MM **Privately Held**
WEB: www.artisanmechanical.com
SIC: 1711 3443 Mechanical contractor; industrial vessels, tanks & containers

(G-20050)
SLUSH PUPPIE
44 Carnegie Way (45246-1224)
PHONE.................................513 771-0940
Will Radcliff, *Ch of Bd*
Dan Keating, *President*
Dennis Harney, *Vice Pres*
Mike Kornbluth, *Sales Mgr*
Diane Menzer, *Marketing Staff*
EMP: 90
SQ FT: 40,000
SALES (est): 7.6MM **Privately Held**
WEB: www.slushpuppie.net
SIC: 2087 5078 Syrups, drink; cocktail mixes, nonalcoholic; soda fountain equipment, refrigerated

(G-20051)
SOLEXY USA LLC
10168 International Blvd (45246-4846)
PHONE.................................513 860-5465
Fax: 513 860-5464
Vince Rohrig, *VP Sales*
Mark Peters,
Steve Wells,
▲ **EMP:** 8
SQ FT: 8,000
SALES (est): 1.8MM
SALES (corp-wide): 249.3K **Privately Held**
SIC: 3357 Communication wire
HQ: Solexy Srl
Via Enrico Fermi 2
Desenzano Del Garda BS
030 787-0787

(G-20052)
SONOCO PRODUCTS COMPANY
Sonoco Consumer Products
4633 Dues Dr (45246-1008)
PHONE.................................513 870-3985
Fax: 513 870-3989
Mark Boston, *Plant Mgr*
Sachin Patel, *Engineer*
Lowern Laster, *Manager*
EMP: 45
SALES (corp-wide): 4.7B **Publicly Held**
WEB: www.sonoco.com
SIC: 2655 2656 Cans, composite: foil-fiber & other: from purchased fiber; sanitary food containers
PA: Sonoco Products Company
1 N 2nd St
Hartsville SC 29550
843 383-7000

(G-20053)
SPLICENET INC
9624 Cincinnati Columbus (45241-4100)
PHONE.................................513 563-3533
James B Lisk, *CEO*
James Gast, *President*
EMP: 4
SALES (est): 583.6K **Privately Held**
WEB: www.splice.net
SIC: 7372 7373 Prepackaged software; systems integration services

(G-20054)
SSI MANUFACTURING INC
9615 Inter Ocean Dr (45246-1029)
PHONE.................................513 761-7757
Fax: 513 761-2677
John R Monday, *President*
Carl Thiem, *Vice Pres*
EMP: 15
SQ FT: 13,500
SALES: 1MM **Privately Held**
WEB: www.ssimfg.com
SIC: 1751 2522 Cabinet building & installation; filing boxes, cabinets & cases: except wood

(G-20055)
STOLLE MILK BIOLOGICS INC
4735 Devitt Dr (45246-1105)
PHONE.................................513 489-7997
Fax: 513 489-7267
Con F Sterling Jr, *CEO*
Daniel Gingerich, *Vice Pres*
Dr Robert Stohrer, *Vice Pres*
Chris McPhillips, *Manager*
Young Lee, *Director*
▲ **EMP:** 176
SQ FT: 1,000
SALES (est): 7.8MM **Privately Held**
WEB: www.smbimilk.com
SIC: 2023 Powdered milk

(G-20056)
STOROPACK INC (DH)
Also Called: Foam Pac Materials Company
4758 Devitt Dr (45246-1106)
PHONE.................................513 874-0314
Fax: 513 874-2955
Hans Reichenecker, *Ch of Bd*
Daniel Wachter, *President*
Thomas G Eckel, *Vice Pres*
Joe Lagrasta, *Vice Pres*
Lester Whisnant, *Vice Pres*
▲ **EMP:** 50
SQ FT: 35,000
SALES: 110MM
SALES (corp-wide): 447.2MM **Privately Held**
WEB: www.storopack.com
SIC: 5199 3086 2671 Packaging materials; packaging & shipping materials, foamed plastic; packaging paper & plastics film, coated & laminated
HQ: Storopack Deutschland Gmbh + Co. Kg
Untere Rietstr. 30
Metzingen 72555
712 316-40

(G-20057)
SWISHER HYGIENE INC
5579 Spellmire Dr (45246-4841)
PHONE.................................513 870-4830
EMP: 3 **Privately Held**
SIC: 3582 Commercial laundry equipment

PA: Swisher Hygiene Inc.
350 E Las Olas Blvd
Fort Lauderdale FL 33301

(G-20058)
TEKTRONIX INC
9639 Inter Ocean Dr Dr2 (45246-1029)
PHONE.................................513 870-4729
EMP: 23
SALES (corp-wide): 6.2B Publicly Held
SIC: 3825 Instruments to measure electricity
HQ: Tektronix, Inc.
14150 Sw Karl Braun Dr
Beaverton OR 97005
800 833-9200

(G-20059)
TOTES ISOTONER CORPORATION (PA)
9655 International Blvd (45246-4861)
PHONE.................................513 682-8200
Fax: 513 682-2602
Doug Gernert, President
Liza Rockhill, Business Mgr
John Cardito, Vice Pres
Jason Herr, Vice Pres
James Pierce, Vice Pres
▲ EMP: 18 EST: 1924
SQ FT: 450,000
SALES (est): 8.4MM Privately Held
WEB: www.isotoner.com
SIC: 2381 3151 2211 3021 Gloves, woven or knit: made from purchased materials; leather gloves & mittens; umbrella cloth, cotton; rubber & plastics footwear; umbrellas; stockings: men's, women's & children's; raincoats; leather garments; men's & boys' clothing

(G-20060)
TOTES ISOTONER HOLDINGS CORP (PA)
9655 International Blvd (45246-4861)
PHONE.................................513 682-8200
Daniel S Rajczak, CEO
Doug Baker, Principal
Joshua Beckenstein, Vice Pres
Donna Deye, CFO
Preston Cruser, Info Tech Dir
▲ EMP: 200 EST: 1994
SALES (est): 116MM Privately Held
SIC: 2381 3151 2211 3021 Gloves, woven or knit: made from purchased materials; leather gloves & mittens; umbrella cloth, cotton; rubber & plastics footwear; umbrellas; stockings: men's, women's & children's; raincoats; leather garments

(G-20061)
TRICO BELTING & SUPPLY COMPANY (HQ)
9965 Farr Ct (45246-1119)
P.O. Box 62385, Cincinnati (45262-0385)
PHONE.................................513 860-8400
Fax: 513 860-5505
John Schafer, President
John Shafer, President
Mark Benedetti, Vice Pres
Michael Lader, Vice Pres
Brian Grady, Purch Mgr
▲ EMP: 40
SQ FT: 65,000
SALES (est): 13.8MM
SALES (corp-wide): 94.7MM Privately Held
WEB: www.tricobelt.com
SIC: 5084 3535 Conveyor systems; conveyors & conveying equipment
PA: Apache Hose & Belting Company, Inc.
4805 Bowling St Sw
Cedar Rapids IA 52404
319 365-0471

(G-20062)
TSK AMERICA CO LTD
9668 Inter Ocean Dr (45246-1030)
PHONE.................................513 942-4002
Fax: 513 942-4003
Takeshi Takeuchi, President
▲ EMP: 10

SALES: 3MM Privately Held
SIC: 3562 3568 5051 Ball & roller bearings; ball bearings & parts; roller bearings & parts; bearings, bushings & blocks; joints & couplings; metals service centers & offices; iron & steel (ferrous) products

(G-20063)
UNITED GROUP SERVICES INC (PA)
9740 Near Dr (45246-1013)
PHONE.................................800 633-9690
Daniel Freese, President
Kevin Sell, Vice Pres
Bob Erhart, Purchasing
Brian Harvey, CFO
Mary E Strunk, Human Res Mgr
EMP: 200
SQ FT: 45,500
SALES: 50.4MM Privately Held
WEB: www.united-gs.com
SIC: 3498 1711 Fabricated pipe & fittings; process piping contractor; mechanical contractor

(G-20064)
UNIVAR USA INC
4600 Dues Dr (45246-1009)
PHONE.................................513 714-5264
Vicki Turner, Personnel Exec
Gary Southern, Branch Mgr
Rob Couch, Manager
EMP: 150
SQ FT: 129,100
SALES (corp-wide): 8B Publicly Held
SIC: 5169 2819 2869 2899 Industrial chemicals; industrial inorganic chemicals; industrial organic chemicals; chemical preparations; specialty cleaning, polishes & sanitation goods
HQ: Univar Usa Inc.
17411 Ne Union Hill Rd
Redmond WA 98052
331 777-6000

(G-20065)
UPSIDE INNOVATIONS LLC
5470 Spellmire Dr (45246-4842)
PHONE.................................513 889-2492
Kevin Sharp, President
Sean Faller, Design Engr
Amy Langford, Accounting Mgr
Rick Hofer, Accounts Mgr
Bill Carroll, Sales Staff
EMP: 5
SALES (est): 702.9K Privately Held
SIC: 3448 3444 3446 Ramps: prefabricated metal; canopies, sheet metal; stairs, staircases, stair treads: prefabricated metal

(G-20066)
V I P PRINTING & DESIGN
4836 Duff Dr Ste A (45246-1194)
PHONE.................................513 777-7468
Douglas Rinnert, Owner
EMP: 4
SQ FT: 3,000
SALES (est): 354.5K Privately Held
SIC: 2752 Commercial printing, offset

(G-20067)
VALCO CINCINNATI INC (PA)
Also Called: Valco Melton
497 Circle Freeway Dr # 490 (45246-1257)
P.O. Box 465619, Cincinnati (45246-5619)
PHONE.................................513 874-6550
Richard Santefort, President
Sergio Contreras, Project Mgr
William Schlensker, Buyer
Mark Lickert, Purchasing
Scott Chalk, Engineer
▲ EMP: 180
SQ FT: 43,000
SALES (est): 45.7MM Privately Held
WEB: www.valco-cp.com
SIC: 3586 3561 Measuring & dispensing pumps; industrial pumps & parts

(G-20068)
VALCO CINCINNATI INC
411 Circle Freeway Dr (45246-1284)
PHONE.................................513 874-6550
EMP: 3

SALES (corp-wide): 45.7MM Privately Held
SIC: 3586 Measuring & dispensing pumps
PA: Valco Cincinnati, Inc.
497 Circle Freeway Dr # 490
West Chester OH 45246
513 874-6550

(G-20069)
VALCO MELTON INC
411 Circle Freeway Dr (45246-1213)
PHONE.................................513 874-6550
Austin Koehler, Principal
▲ EMP: 34
SALES (est): 8MM Privately Held
SIC: 3663 Radio & TV communications equipment

(G-20070)
XEROX CORPORATION
4622 Interstate Dr (45246-1110)
PHONE.................................513 860-8600
Chad Ward, Manager
EMP: 12
SALES (corp-wide): 10.7B Publicly Held
WEB: www.xerox.com
SIC: 3861 Photocopy machines
PA: Xerox Corporation
201 Merritt 7
Norwalk CT 06851
203 968-3000

(G-20071)
YKK AP AMERICA INC
Also Called: YKK USA
5406 Spellmire Dr (45246-4842)
PHONE.................................513 942-7200
Fax: 513 682-2123
Phil Blizzard, Manager
EMP: 13
SALES (corp-wide): 750.5MM Privately Held
WEB: www.ykkap.com
SIC: 3442 3449 Sash, door or window: metal; metal doors; curtain wall, metal
HQ: Ykk Ap America Inc.
270 Riverside Pkwy Sw A
Austell GA 30168
678 838-6000

(G-20072)
ZARTIC LLC (DH)
9990 Prnceton Glendale Rd (45246-1116)
PHONE.................................513 874-8741
Norbert E Woodhams,
Joseph W Meyers,
Robert C Naylor,
EMP: 65 EST: 1956
SQ FT: 29,159
SALES (est): 58.5MM Publicly Held
SIC: 2013 2015 Frozen meats from purchased meat; poultry, processed: frozen
HQ: Advancepierre Foods, Inc.
9987 Carver Rd Ste 500
Blue Ash OH 45242
513 874-8741

West Farmington
Trumbull County

(G-20073)
ACRYLIC ARTS
3698 G P Easterly Rd (44491-8700)
PHONE.................................440 537-0300
Justine Conklin, Owner
Shannon Conklin, Owner
EMP: 4
SALES (est): 307K Privately Held
SIC: 3089 Aquarium accessories, plastic

(G-20074)
ALPHA MACHINING LLC
394 E Main St (44491-8726)
P.O. Box 195 (44491-0195)
PHONE.................................330 889-2207
Fax: 330 889-2375
Connie Blair, CFO
Gary Blair, Manager
EMP: 3
SALES: 200K Privately Held
SIC: 3599 Amusement park equipment

(G-20075)
REYNOLDS INDUSTRIES INC
380 W Main St (44491-9712)
P.O. Box 6 (44491-0006)
PHONE.................................330 889-9466
Fax: 330 889-9466
Gregory A Reynolds, President
EMP: 25
SQ FT: 3,500
SALES (est): 2.9MM Privately Held
SIC: 3069 4783 Rubber hardware; packing goods for shipping

West Jefferson
Madison County

(G-20076)
BUCKEYE READY-MIX LLC
6600 State Route 29 (43162-9746)
PHONE.................................614 879-6316
Fax: 614 879-6393
Don Harsh, Branch Mgr
EMP: 7
SALES (corp-wide): 42.4MM Privately Held
SIC: 3273 Ready-mixed concrete
PA: Buckeye Ready-Mix, Llc
7657 Taylor Rd Sw
Reynoldsburg OH 43068
614 575-2132

(G-20077)
CONDUIT PIPE PRODUCTS COMPANY
1501 W Main St (43162-9627)
PHONE.................................614 879-9114
John Rodgers, President
Tim McGhee, Principal
Brenda Somar, Accountant
Robert Harran, Human Res Dir
Ellen Robb, Sales Staff
EMP: 60
SALES (est): 15.7MM
SALES (corp-wide): 163.7MM Privately Held
WEB: www.conduitpipe.com
SIC: 3317 Steel pipe & tubes
PA: The Phoenix Forge Group Llc
1020 Macarthur Rd
Reading PA 19605
800 234-8665

(G-20078)
FISHER CAST STEEL PRODUCTS INC (PA)
6 W Town St (43162-1293)
P.O. Box 1368, Delaware (43015-8368)
PHONE.................................614 879-8325
Fax: 614 879-7965
John Harmeyer, President
Richard Metcalf, Principal
Max Robbins, Principal
Ryan Onley, VP Opers
Michelle Hansberry, Prdtn Mgr
▲ EMP: 42
SQ FT: 800
SALES (est): 10.9MM Privately Held
WEB: www.fishercaststeel.com
SIC: 3325 Alloy steel castings, except investment

(G-20079)
JEFFERSON INDUSTRIES CORP (PA)
Also Called: J I C
6670 State Route 29 (43162-9677)
PHONE.................................614 879-5300
Fax: 614 879-5605
Shiro Shimokagi, President
Curtis A Loveland, Principal
Kazuhiko Hara, Vice Pres
Hassan Saadat, Vice Pres
Bob Allen, Accounting Mgr
▲ EMP: 152
SQ FT: 370,000
SALES: 320MM Privately Held
WEB: www.jic-ohio.com
SIC: 3711 Chassis, motor vehicle

(G-20080)
KELLOGG COMPANY
125 Enterprise Pkwy (43162-9414)
PHONE.................................614 879-9659

Richard Emerson, *Principal*
Alan Tinker, *Manager*
EMP: 385
SALES (corp-wide): 13B **Publicly Held**
SIC: 2043 Cereal breakfast foods
PA: Kellogg Company
　1 Kellogg Sq
　Battle Creek MI 49017
　269 961-2000

(G-20081)
M H EBY INC
　4435 State Route 29 (43162-9544)
　P.O. Box 137 (43162-0137)
　PHONE..............................614 879-6901
　Fax: 614 879-6904
　EMP: 50 **Privately Held**
　SIC: 5012 3444 Whol Autos/Motor Vehicles Mfg Sheet Metalwork

(G-20082)
PHOENIX FORGE GROUP LLC
Capitol Manufacturing Division
　1501 W Main St (43162-9627)
　PHONE..............................800 848-6125
　Fax: 614 879-7785
Mark McIntosh, *VP Sales*
Anita Woods, *Sales Associate*
David R Halman, *Branch Mgr*
EMP: 220
SALES (corp-wide): 163.7MM **Privately Held**
　SIC: 3498 Pipe fittings, fabricated from purchased pipe
PA: The Phoenix Forge Group Llc
　1020 Macarthur Rd
　Reading PA 19605
　800 234-8665

(G-20083)
R L PARSONS & SON EQUIPMENT CO
Also Called: Micro Mower
　7155 State Route 142 Se (43162-9591)
　P.O. Box 28 (43162-0028)
　PHONE..............................614 879-7601
　Fax: 614 879-7605
Ralph L Parsons Jr, *President*
Mary Parsons, *Corp Secy*
Ralph L Parsons III, *Vice Pres*
Julie Walker, *Vice Pres*
▲ **EMP:** 4
SQ FT: 11,000
SALES (est): 610K **Privately Held**
WEB: www.bomfordcenter.com
SIC: 5083 3523 Farm implements; grounds mowing equipment

(G-20084)
TOAGOSEI AMERICA INC
Also Called: Krazy Glue
　1450 W Main St (43162-9747)
　PHONE..............................614 718-3855
　Fax: 614 879-6959
Tonio Kambayashi, *President*
Kenichi Ohashi, *Plant Mgr*
Terry Cheatam, *Prdtn Mgr*
Shawn Bennett, *Purchasing*
Pam Ray, *Purchasing*
▲ **EMP:** 100
SQ FT: 64,000
SALES (est): 22.7MM
SALES (corp-wide): 1.1B **Privately Held**
WEB: www.toagosei.net
SIC: 2891 Adhesives
PA: Toagosei Co., Ltd.
　1-14-1, Nishishimbashi
　Minato-Ku TKY 105-0
　335 977-215

West Lafayette
Coshocton County

(G-20085)
CABOT LUMBER INC
　304 E Union Ave (43845-1250)
　P.O. Box 101 (43845-0101)
　PHONE..............................740 545-7109
　Fax: 740 545-6438
Donald Cabot, *President*
Dennis E Cabot, *Treasurer*
Kenneth Cabot, *Admin Sec*
EMP: 9

SQ FT: 14,000
SALES (est): 1.3MM **Privately Held**
SIC: 5031 2448 Lumber: rough, dressed & finished; pallets, wood

(G-20086)
GLENN RAVENS WINERY
　56183 County Road 143 (43845)
　PHONE..............................740 545-1000
Bob Guilliams, *Principal*
EMP: 25
SALES (est): 2.9MM **Privately Held**
WEB: www.ravensglenn.com
SIC: 2084 Wines

(G-20087)
JONES METAL PRODUCTS COMPANY (PA)
Also Called: JONES ZYLON COMPANY
　200 N Center St (43845-1270)
　P.O. Box 179 (43845-0179)
　PHONE..............................740 545-6381
　Fax: 740 545-9690
Marion M Sutton, *Ch of Bd*
Daniel P Erb III, *President*
Harold R Howell, *Vice Pres*
Carole M Loos, *Vice Pres*
Fred Williams, *Vice Pres*
EMP: 90 **EST:** 1923
SQ FT: 140,000
SALES (est): 9.5MM **Privately Held**
WEB: www.joneszylon.com
SIC: 3842 3444 3469 Surgical appliances & supplies; forming machine work, sheet metal; metal stampings

(G-20088)
JONES METAL PRODUCTS COMPANY
Jones-Zylon Company
　305 N Center St (43845-1001)
　PHONE..............................740 545-6341
Todd Kohl, *Manager*
EMP: 40
SALES (corp-wide): 9.5MM **Privately Held**
WEB: www.joneszylon.com
SIC: 5047 3842 Hospital equipment & supplies; surgical appliances & supplies
PA: Jones Metal Products Company
　200 N Center St
　West Lafayette OH 43845
　740 545-6381

(G-20089)
JONESZYLON COMPANY LLC
　300 N Center St (43845-1002)
　P.O. Box 149 (43845-0149)
　PHONE..............................740 545-6341
　Fax: 740 545-6671
Robert Zachrich, *President*
Tracey Zachrich, *Principal*
Julie Smith, *Sales Staff*
EMP: 9
SQ FT: 20,000
SALES (est): 1.2MM **Privately Held**
SIC: 3089 5046 Plastic kitchenware, tableware & houseware; food warming equipment

(G-20090)
YANKEE WIRE CLOTH PRODUCTS INC
　221 W Main St (43845-1103)
　P.O. Box 58 (43845-0058)
　PHONE..............................740 545-9129
　Fax: 740 545-6323
William D Timmons, *President*
Mary Timmons, *Exec VP*
EMP: 45 **EST:** 1963
SQ FT: 35,000
SALES (est): 8.7MM **Privately Held**
WEB: www.yankeewire.com
SIC: 3496 Screening, woven wire: made from purchased wire

West Liberty
Logan County

(G-20091)
BAC TECHNOLOGIES LTD
Also Called: Burkett Advnced Composite Tech
　8115 Calland Rd (43357-9604)
　PHONE..............................937 465-2228
Jerald S Burkett,
EMP: 5
SALES (est): 830.3K **Privately Held**
WEB: www.bactechnologies.com
SIC: 5031 3542 Composite board products, woodboard; spinning, spline rolling & winding machines

(G-20092)
HOLDREN BROTHERS INC
　301 Runkle St (43357-9476)
　P.O. Box 459 (43357-0459)
　PHONE..............................937 465-7050
　Fax: 937 465-0525
Shirley Holdren, *President*
Dennis Watkins, *Plant Mgr*
Ronda Deleon, *Admin Mgr*
EMP: 10
SQ FT: 4,800
SALES: 1.3MM **Privately Held**
WEB: www.holdrenbrothers.com
SIC: 3599 3589 7692 3549 Machine & other job shop work; commercial cleaning equipment; welding repair; metalworking machinery

(G-20093)
LOGAN ENTERPRISES INC
　8844 Us Highway 68 N (43357)
　P.O. Box 819 (43357-0819)
　PHONE..............................937 465-8170
　Fax: 937 465-9140
Laurel M McCombs, *President*
EMP: 3
SQ FT: 4,700
SALES (est): 494.8K **Privately Held**
WEB: www.loganent.com
SIC: 3823 Temperature instruments: industrial process type

(G-20094)
MARRIE S CANDIES LLC
Also Called: Marie's Candies
　311 Zanesfield Rd (43357-9563)
　P.O. Box 766 (43357-0766)
　PHONE..............................937 465-3061
　Fax: 937 465-3336
Rebecca Craig, *Owner*
Kathy King, *Office Mgr*
EMP: 30
SQ FT: 4,100
SALES (est): 3.3MM **Privately Held**
WEB: www.mariescandies.com
SIC: 2064 5441 Candy bars, including chocolate covered bars; candy

(G-20095)
WILGUSS AUTOMOTIVE MACHINE
　216 Runkle St (43357-9442)
　PHONE..............................937 465-0043
John R Wilgus, *Owner*
EMP: 4
SQ FT: 2,600
SALES: 81K **Privately Held**
SIC: 7699 3599 7538 Lawn mower repair shop; machine shop, jobbing & repair; general automotive repair shops

West Manchester
Preble County

(G-20096)
BEEVINWOOD INC
　5748 Clark Rd (45382-9608)
　PHONE..............................937 678-9910
Contance Pitts, *President*
EMP: 3
SALES (est): 213.9K **Privately Held**
SIC: 2731 Book publishing

(G-20097)
DARI FREEZE
　414 N Main St (45382-9700)
　PHONE..............................937 678-6171
Mary James, *Owner*
Michael James, *Co-Owner*
EMP: 4
SALES: 75K **Privately Held**
SIC: 5812 2024 Ice cream, soft drink & soda fountain stands; ice cream & frozen desserts

(G-20098)
ROWE PREMIX INC
　10107 Us Rr 127 Box N (45382)
　P.O. Box 205 (45382-0205)
　PHONE..............................937 678-9015
Gene Rowe, *President*
Sharon Rowe, *Vice Pres*
Kathy Hoover, *Office Mgr*
EMP: 12
SQ FT: 5,000
SALES: 1.7MM **Privately Held**
SIC: 2048 Feed premixes; feed supplements

West Mansfield
Logan County

(G-20099)
INDUSTRIAL PULLEY & MACHINE CO
　E Center St (43358)
　P.O. Box 35 (43358-0035)
　PHONE..............................937 355-4910
　Fax: 937 355-2001
Raleigh Oliver, *CEO*
Steve Oliver, *President*
Cindy Bettinger, *Corp Secy*
Tim Oliver, *Vice Pres*
EMP: 8
SQ FT: 12,000
SALES: 850K **Privately Held**
SIC: 3429 Pulleys metal

(G-20100)
M & M CONCEPTS INC
Also Called: Cmg Company Plant 2
　2633 State Route 292 (43358-9523)
　PHONE..............................937 355-1115
　Fax: 937 355-1117
Thomas P McGrady, *President*
Mark Guthrie, *Vice Pres*
Larry Vermillion, *Vice Pres*
Kris Carpenter, *Treasurer*
Alexa McGrady, *Admin Sec*
EMP: 8
SQ FT: 14,000
SALES (est): 1.2MM **Privately Held**
SIC: 7692 Welding repair

(G-20101)
M J S OIL INC
Also Called: Smith Marathon Distributing
　23296 Treaty Line Rd (43358-9624)
　PHONE..............................937 982-3519
Mark Smith, *President*
Julia Smith, *Admin Sec*
EMP: 3
SALES (est): 459.2K **Privately Held**
SIC: 2869 Fuels

(G-20102)
NATURE PURE LLC
　26560 Storms Rd (43358-9662)
　P.O. Box 127, Raymond (43067-0127)
　PHONE..............................937 358-2364
Kurt Lausecker, *CEO*
Sandra Lausecker, *CEO*
EMP: 15
SALES (corp-wide): 3.5MM **Privately Held**
SIC: 0252 2015 Chicken eggs; egg processing
PA: Nature Pure Llc
　26586 State Route 739
　Raymond OH 43067
　937 358-2364

(G-20103)
ROCKHOLD STONE QUARRY INC
20620 Spangler Rd (43358-9653)
PHONE..................937 358-2224
Fax: 937 358-2561
Benjie Evans, *Superintendent*
EMP: 7
SALES (est): 361.8K **Privately Held**
SIC: 1429 Crushed & broken stone

West Millgrove
Wood County

(G-20104)
MAC RITCHIE MATERIALS INC
6126 S Main St (43467)
PHONE..................419 288-2790
Fax: 419 288-3313
Donald B Mac Ritchie, *President*
Ronald Mac Ritchie, *Vice Pres*
EMP: 12 **EST:** 1911
SQ FT: 4,000
SALES (est): 973.8K **Privately Held**
SIC: 1422 Crushed & broken limestone

West Milton
Miami County

(G-20105)
BOYDS MACHINE AND MET FINSHG
7650 S Kssler Frderick Rd (45383-8790)
PHONE..................937 698-5623
Fax: 937 698-4674
Larry E Boyd, *President*
Stephen Boyd, *Vice Pres*
Tina Lakin, *Manager*
EMP: 17
SQ FT: 1,800
SALES (est): 900K **Privately Held**
SIC: 3599 Machine & other job shop work

(G-20106)
COATE CONCRETE PRODUCTS INC (PA)
7330 W State Route 571 (45383-9741)
P.O. Box 159 (45383-0159)
PHONE..................937 698-4181
Fax: 937 698-6618
Craig Coate, *President*
Paul Harris, *Sales Staff*
Cindy Coate, *Office Mgr*
Travis Coate, *Office Mgr*
EMP: 5 **EST:** 1925
SQ FT: 22,500
SALES (est): 3.1MM **Privately Held**
SIC: 3272 Burial vaults, concrete or precast terrazzo; septic tanks, concrete

(G-20107)
MIAMI CONTROL SYSTEMS INC
955 S Main St (45383-1364)
P.O. Box 96 (45383-0096)
PHONE..................937 698-5725
Andy Minniear, *President*
Will Dewey, *Vice Pres*
Aaron Levy, *Design Engr*
Lois Meek, *Manager*
EMP: 9
SQ FT: 7,500
SALES (est): 2MM **Privately Held**
WEB: www.miamicontrol.com
SIC: 3625 Relays & industrial controls

(G-20108)
MIAMI GRAPHICS SERVICES INC
225 N Jay St (45383-1706)
P.O. Box 194 (45383-0194)
PHONE..................937 698-4013
Fax: 937 698-3811
Norma Parmenter, *President*
Charles Parmenter, *Vice Pres*
EMP: 10
SQ FT: 8,500
SALES (est): 576.5K **Privately Held**
SIC: 2759 Commercial printing

(G-20109)
OLD MASON WINERY INC
4199 S Iddings Rd (45383-8741)
PHONE..................937 698-1122
Jeff Clark, *President*
Donna Clarke, *Vice Pres*
EMP: 9
SALES (est): 751K **Privately Held**
SIC: 2084 Wines

(G-20110)
ROBERTSON CABINETS INC
1090 S Main St (45383-1365)
PHONE..................937 698-3755
Fax: 937 698-3894
William Robertson Sr, *Ch of Bd*
Jeff Yantis, *President*
Judith Robertson, *Vice Pres*
Brian Smith, *Draft/Design*
EMP: 20
SQ FT: 22,000
SALES: 1.9MM **Privately Held**
WEB: www.about-rci.com
SIC: 2541 2431 Cabinets, except refrigerated: show, display, etc.: wood; bar fixtures, wood; millwork

West Salem
Wayne County

(G-20111)
CENSTAR COATINGS INC
11829 Jeffrey Rd (44287-9219)
PHONE..................330 723-8000
Jim Feterle, *President*
EMP: 6
SQ FT: 6,000
SALES (est): 682.5K **Privately Held**
SIC: 3069 Sheeting, rubber or rubberized fabric

(G-20112)
COMMODITY BLENDERS INC
Also Called: CBI
10510 Myers Rd (44287-9043)
PHONE..................419 846-3155
Bruce Keener, *President*
Deanna Keener, *Vice Pres*
EMP: 9
SQ FT: 14,000
SALES (est): 1.3MM **Privately Held**
SIC: 2048 Livestock feeds

(G-20113)
HAYNN CONSTRUCTION CO INC
14866 N Elyria Rd (44287-8958)
P.O. Box 346 (44287-0346)
PHONE..................419 853-4747
Tony Brown, *President*
Laura Fryman, *Corp Secy*
Jerry Fryman, *Vice Pres*
EMP: 6
SALES (est): 1MM **Privately Held**
WEB: www.haynncorp.com
SIC: 3567 Industrial furnaces & ovens

(G-20114)
JOHNSON BROS RUBBER CO INC (PA)
42 W Buckeye St (44287-9747)
P.O. Box 812 (44287-0812)
PHONE..................419 853-4122
Fax: 419 853-4062
Lawrence G Cooke, *President*
Joyce Porter, *COO*
Eric Vail, *Vice Pres*
Jeff Garrigues, *Purchasing*
Larry Adkins, *Engineer*
▲ **EMP:** 100 **EST:** 1947
SQ FT: 70,000
SALES (est): 54.4MM **Privately Held**
SIC: 5199 3061 Foams & rubber; mechanical rubber goods

(G-20115)
LATTASBURG LUMBERWORKS CO LLC
9399 Lattasburg Rd (44287-9725)
PHONE..................330 202-7671
Pascal King-Smith, *Principal*
EMP: 6
SQ FT: 1,500

SALES (est): 1.1MM **Privately Held**
WEB: www.lattasburglumberworks.com
SIC: 2435 Hardwood veneer & plywood

(G-20116)
PAROBEK TRUCKING CO
192 State Route 42 (44287-9130)
PHONE..................419 869-7500
Keigm Parobek, *Owner*
EMP: 6
SALES (est): 480.1K **Privately Held**
SIC: 3537 4213 4212 Industrial trucks & tractors; trucking, except local; local trucking, without storage

(G-20117)
SUNNY SIDE FEEDS LLC
6371 W Pleasant Home Rd (44287-9573)
PHONE..................330 635-1455
Wade Mahoney, *Principal*
Randy Tegtmeier, *Principal*
EMP: 5 **EST:** 2013
SQ FT: 12,000
SALES: 500K **Privately Held**
SIC: 2048 Bird food, prepared

West Union
Adams County

(G-20118)
BROWN PUBLISHING CO
Also Called: People's Defender
229 N Cross St (45693-1266)
P.O. Box 308 (45693-0308)
PHONE..................937 544-2391
Fax: 937 544-2298
Roy Brown, *CEO*
Terry Rigdon, *Accounts Exec*
EMP: 12
SQ FT: 5,000
SALES (est): 500K **Privately Held**
SIC: 2711 Newspapers, publishing & printing

(G-20119)
COLUMBUS INDUSTRIES INC
11545 State Route 41 (45693-9434)
PHONE..................937 544-6896
Fax: 937 544-6239
Eric Pontious, *VP Sls/Mktg*
Harold Pontius, *Branch Mgr*
EMP: 11
SALES (corp-wide): 186.9MM **Privately Held**
SIC: 3999 Barber & beauty shop equipment
PA: Columbus Industries, Inc.
2938 State Route 752
Ashville OH 43103
740 983-2552

(G-20120)
DINSMORE INC
Also Called: Purvis Milling Co
11780 State Route 41 (45693-8025)
P.O. Box 32 (45693-0032)
PHONE..................937 544-3332
Ron Dinsmore, *President*
Diane Dinsmore, *Corp Secy*
EMP: 8
SQ FT: 12,000
SALES (est): 1MM **Privately Held**
SIC: 3524 5999 Lawn & garden equipment; feed & farm supply

(G-20121)
J MCCOY LUMBER CO LTD
733 Vaughn Ridge Rd (45693-9620)
P.O. Box 306, Peebles (45660-0306)
PHONE..................937 544-2968
Fax: 937 544-2021
Jack McCoy, *Owner*
EMP: 3
SALES (corp-wide): 7.7MM **Privately Held**
SIC: 5031 2426 2431 Lumber, plywood & millwork; dimension, hardwood; moldings, wood: unfinished & prefinished
PA: J. Mccoy Lumber Co. Ltd
6 N Main St
Peebles OH 45660
937 587-3423

(G-20122)
JERRY TADLOCK
Also Called: Tadlock Trailer Sales
5645 State Route 125 (45693-9332)
PHONE..................937 544-2851
Jerry Tadlock, *Owner*
EMP: 5
SALES: 400K **Privately Held**
WEB: www.tadlocktrailersales.com
SIC: 5599 5531 3715 Utility trailers; truck equipment & parts; truck trailers

(G-20123)
KENNETH SCHROCK
Also Called: Ridgeway Lumber
3735 Wheat Ridge Rd (45693-9428)
PHONE..................937 544-7566
Kenneth Schrock, *Owner*
Carol Schrock, *Owner*
EMP: 5
SALES: 280K **Privately Held**
SIC: 7389 2448 Log & lumber broker; pallets, wood

(G-20124)
MILLERS MINI BARNS
1587 Wheat Ridge Rd (45693-9735)
PHONE..................937 544-6317
Gerald Miller, *Owner*
EMP: 6
SALES (est): 493.9K **Privately Held**
SIC: 2452 Prefabricated wood buildings

(G-20125)
SCHROCK JOHN
Also Called: Wheat Ridge Pallet & Lumber
61 Poole Rd (45693-9736)
PHONE..................937 544-8457
John Schrock, *Owner*
Melissa Black, *Accountant*
EMP: 9
SALES (est): 1MM **Privately Held**
SIC: 2448 Pallets, wood

West Unity
Williams County

(G-20126)
AGB LLC
15188 Us Highway 127 (43570-9502)
PHONE..................419 924-5216
Andrew Brehm,
EMP: 5
SALES (est): 914.5K **Privately Held**
SIC: 3469 Metal stampings

(G-20127)
CONVERSION TECH INTL INC
700 Oak St (43570-9457)
P.O. Box 707 (43570-0707)
PHONE..................419 924-5566
Chester Cromwell, *President*
Jason Cromwell, *Principal*
Celeste Engel, *CFO*
Linda Johnston, *Manager*
▲ **EMP:** 33
SQ FT: 130,000
SALES (est): 8.6MM **Privately Held**
WEB: www.conversiontechnologies.com
SIC: 2891 7389 Adhesives; laminating service

(G-20128)
H K K MACHINING CO
1201 Oak St (43570-9435)
PHONE..................419 924-5116
Fax: 419 924-5387
Duane E King, *President*
Sharon King, *Vice Pres*
Tyson King, *VP Prdtn*
Sheila Bowers, *Office Mgr*
EMP: 20
SQ FT: 23,500
SALES (est): 3.7MM **Privately Held**
WEB: www.hkkmach.com
SIC: 3599 Machine shop, jobbing & repair

(G-20129)
HARDLINE INTERNATIONAL INC
Also Called: Rimm Kleen Systems
1107 Oak St (43570-9429)
PHONE..................419 924-9556
Robert Warmingham, *President*

EMP: 10
SQ FT: 12,000
SALES (est): 1.6MM **Privately Held**
WEB: www.rimmkleensystems.com
SIC: 3479 Aluminum coating of metal products

(G-20130)
JACOBY PACKING CO
Also Called: Jacoby Old Smokehouse
505 S Main St (43570-9734)
P.O. Box 466 (43570-0466)
PHONE................................419 924-2684
Fax: 419 924-2684
James Kieffer, *Owner*
Jim Keifer, *Partner*
EMP: 8
SALES: 750K **Privately Held**
SIC: 2011 Meat packing plants

(G-20131)
KAMCO INDUSTRIES
1000 Oak St (43570-9432)
PHONE................................419 551-9211
Brian Myers, *Manager*
EMP: 3 EST: 2014
SALES (est): 268.8K **Privately Held**
SIC: 3089 Injection molded finished plastic products; thermoformed finished plastic products

(G-20132)
KAMCO INDUSTRIES INC (HQ)
1001 E Jackson St (43570-9414)
PHONE................................419 924-5511
Fax: 419 924-2610
Bryan Barshel, *Assistant VP*
Joe Tubbs, *Vice Pres*
Allan Benien, *VP Opers*
Dave Rothenberger, *Manager*
Kenny Walz, *Manager*
◆ EMP: 370
SQ FT: 160,000
SALES (est): 82.1MM
SALES (corp-wide): 120.6MM **Privately Held**
WEB: www.kamcoind.com
SIC: 3089 Injection molded finished plastic products; thermoformed finished plastic products
PA: Kumi Kasei Co., Ltd.
47-1, Kandahigashimatsushitacho
Chiyoda-Ku TKY
352 981-511

(G-20133)
MIDWEST PRODUCTION MACHINING
Also Called: Midwest Machine
10484 State Route 191 (43570-9506)
P.O. Box 464 (43570-0464)
PHONE................................419 924-5616
Fax: 419 924-5610
Chad Oxender, *President*
Julie Oxender, *Vice Pres*
EMP: 3
SQ FT: 6,000
SALES (est): 500K **Privately Held**
SIC: 3599 Machine shop, jobbing & repair

(G-20134)
RAVAGO AMERICAS LLC
Trinity Specialty Compounding
600 Oak St (43570-9545)
PHONE................................419 924-9090
Fax: 419 924-9191
Timothy L Walkowski, *General Mgr*
Ken Ziegenbusch, *Plant Mgr*
EMP: 19 **Privately Held**
SIC: 3089 Plastic processing
HQ: Ravago Americas Llc
1900 Summit Tower Blvd
Orlando FL 32810
407 875-9595

(G-20135)
RUPCOL INC
509 Parkway St (43570-9575)
PHONE................................419 924-5215
Fax: 419 924-5378
Burdel Colon, *President*
David Colon, *Vice Pres*
EMP: 4
SQ FT: 24,000

SALES: 750K **Privately Held**
SIC: 3448 1541 Prefabricated metal buildings; prefabricated building erection, industrial

(G-20136)
VISION COLOR LLC
214 S Defiance St (43570-9620)
P.O. Box 264 (43570-0264)
PHONE................................419 924-9450
Richard Bacon, *President*
Vicki Davis, *Office Mgr*
Adam Bacon, *Comp Lab Dir*
EMP: 8
SALES (est): 1.5MM **Privately Held**
WEB: www.visioncolorllc.com
SIC: 3089 Injection molding of plastics

Westerville
Delaware County

(G-20137)
AMERICAN CERAMIC SOCIETY (PA)
Also Called: Pottery Making Illustrate
600 N Cleveland Ave # 210 (43082-6921)
PHONE................................614 890-4700
Fax: 614 899-6109
Marcus Bailey, *Publisher*
Pat Janeway, *Editor*
Bill Jones, *Editor*
Paul Holbrook, *COO*
Lora Saiber, *Treasurer*
EMP: 35
SQ FT: 10,126
SALES: 7.3MM **Privately Held**
WEB: www.ceramics.org
SIC: 8621 2721 Professional membership organizations; engineering association; scientific membership association; periodicals: publishing & printing

(G-20138)
ANRO LOGISTICS INC
7473 Bentley Pl (43082-8662)
PHONE................................614 428-7490
William Anderson, *Principal*
EMP: 4
SALES (est): 250.3K **Privately Held**
SIC: 4789 3444 Transportation services; sheet metalwork

(G-20139)
BAKERWELL INC
6295 Maxtown Rd Ste 300 (43082-8885)
P.O. Box 1678 (43086-1678)
PHONE................................614 898-7590
Fax: 614 898-0053
Rex Baker, *President*
Jeff Baker, *Corp Secy*
EMP: 51 EST: 1981
SALES (est): 2.9MM **Privately Held**
WEB: www.bakerwell.com
SIC: 1382 Oil & gas exploration services

(G-20140)
BRIGHTSTAR PROPANE & FUELS
Also Called: Guttman Oil
6190 Frost Rd (43082-9027)
PHONE................................614 891-8395
Fax: 614 890-6221
Richard Guttman, *President*
EMP: 4
SALES (est): 215.1K **Privately Held**
SIC: 5984 1389 2869 Propane gas, bottled; construction, repair & dismantling services; fuels

(G-20141)
BUCKEYE BUSINESS FORMS INC
Also Called: Proforma Buckeye
7307 Red Bank Rd (43082-8241)
PHONE................................614 882-1890
Fax: 614 895-6407
Ann Kaylor Patton, *President*
Ken Short, *Controller*
James Patton, *Admin Sec*
EMP: 6
SQ FT: 13,500

SALES (est): 1.4MM **Privately Held**
WEB: www.bbf.cc
SIC: 7311 2752 7331 Advertising agencies; commercial printing, offset; mailing service

(G-20142)
CENTURY GRAPHICS INC
9101 Hawthorne Pt (43082-9231)
PHONE................................614 895-7698
Fax: 614 431-1063
Richard Bonham, *President*
EMP: 40
SQ FT: 26,000
SALES (est): 4.8MM **Privately Held**
WEB: www.centurygr.com
SIC: 2752 2796 2789 2759 Commercial printing, lithographic; commercial printing, offset; platemaking services; bookbinding & related work; commercial printing

(G-20143)
CHARISMA PRODUCTS INC
6342 Worthington Rd (43082-9446)
PHONE................................614 846-8888
Gary L Chiero, *President*
Kathleen A Chiero, *Treasurer*
EMP: 3 EST: 1977
SQ FT: 3,400
SALES (est): 276.6K **Privately Held**
SIC: 2396 Screen printing on fabric articles; apparel & other linings, except millinery; millinery materials & supplies

(G-20144)
CHERYL & CO (HQ)
646 Mccorkle Blvd (43082-8778)
PHONE................................614 776-1500
Fax: 614 891-8599
Cheryl L Krueger, *President*
Bob Happle, *General Mgr*
Charles Fraas, *Vice Pres*
Lisa Henry, *Vice Pres*
James W Krueger, *Vice Pres*
▲ EMP: 225 EST: 1981
SALES (est): 86MM
SALES (corp-wide): 1.1B **Publicly Held**
WEB: www.cherylandco.com
SIC: 2052 Cookies
PA: 1-800-Flowers.Com, Inc.
1 Old Country Rd Ste 500
Carle Place NY 11514
516 237-6000

(G-20145)
DERN TROPHIES CORP
Also Called: Dern Trophy Mfg
6225 Frost Rd (43082-9027)
PHONE................................614 895-3260
Ronald M Spohn, *President*
B Thomas Dern, *Vice Pres*
Thomas Dern, *Vice Pres*
▲ EMP: 12
SQ FT: 20,000
SALES (est): 1.6MM **Privately Held**
WEB: www.dern-trophy.com
SIC: 3499 5094 3993 Trophies, metal, except silver; trophies; signs & advertising specialties

(G-20146)
E - I CORP
214 Hoff Rd Unit M (43082-7157)
PHONE................................614 899-2282
Fax: 614 899-0304
Glenn Meek, *Principal*
Lisa Tiburzio, *Purchasing*
▲ EMP: 12
SALES (est): 2.4MM **Privately Held**
SIC: 3589 Sewage treatment equipment

(G-20147)
E STAR AEROSPACE CORPORATION
470 Olde Worthington Rd # 200 (43082-8985)
PHONE................................614 396-6868
Ely Bachir, *CEO*
EMP: 3
SALES: 500K **Privately Held**
SIC: 3721 Research & development on aircraft by the manufacturer

(G-20148)
EDWARD ORTON JR CRMIC FNDATION
6991 S Old 3c Hwy (43082-9026)
P.O. Box 2760 (43086-2760)
PHONE................................614 895-2663
Edward Orton, *Principal*
Jim Litzinger, *Manager*
Joseph Homeny, *Director*
EMP: 30
SQ FT: 42,000
SALES (est): 808.3K **Privately Held**
SIC: 3269 Cones, pyrometric: earthenware

(G-20149)
EMC CORPORATION
Also Called: Emc2
9200 Worthington Rd # 200 (43082-7801)
PHONE................................614 865-4200
Kelly Hampton, *Sales Mgr*
Jake Cleveland, *Manager*
Tony Leonard, *Director*
EMP: 89
SALES (corp-wide): 67.1B **Publicly Held**
WEB: www.emc.com
SIC: 3572 Computer storage devices
HQ: Emc Corporation
176 South St
Hopkinton MA 01748
508 435-1000

(G-20150)
EMERSON NETWORK POWER SYSTEM
610 Executive Campus Dr (43082-8870)
PHONE................................614 841-6309
Frank Bibens, *President*
Ramon Torres, *Business Mgr*
Mike Endsley, *Vice Pres*
Greg Fromknecht, *Vice Pres*
Lauri Turevon, *Sls & Mktg Exec*
EMP: 8
SQ FT: 1,000
SALES (est): 2.7MM
SALES (corp-wide): 14.5B **Publicly Held**
WEB: www.gotoemerson.com
SIC: 3823 3491 Industrial instrmnts msrmnt display/control process variable; industrial valves
PA: Emerson Electric Co.
8000 West Florissant Ave
Saint Louis MO 63136
314 553-2000

(G-20151)
ERIC NICKEL
5563 Covington Meadows Ct (43082-8371)
PHONE................................614 818-2488
Eric Nickel, *Principal*
EMP: 3
SALES (est): 183.7K **Privately Held**
SIC: 3356 Nickel

(G-20152)
EXELON ENERGY COMPANY
470 Olde Worthington Rd # 375 (43082-7907)
PHONE................................614 797-4377
Sheree Petrone, *Principal*
EMP: 14
SALES (corp-wide): 31.3B **Publicly Held**
SIC: 1389 Gas field services
HQ: Exelon Energy Company
300 Exelon Way
Kennett Square PA 19348
312 394-7158

(G-20153)
GAIN LLC
8475 Fallgold Ln (43082-9745)
PHONE................................440 396-6613
Greg Miller, *Co-Owner*
Nugeen Aftab, *Co-Owner*
Alex Chudik, *Co-Owner*
EMP: 4
SALES (est): 154.7K **Privately Held**
SIC: 7372 Application computer software

(G-20154)
GANGER ENTERPRISES INC
Also Called: Northwest Printing
214 Hoff Rd Unit D (43082-7156)
PHONE................................614 776-3985
William E Ganger Jr, *President*
EMP: 3

SQ FT: 3,000
SALES (est): 260K **Privately Held**
WEB: www.geography.uwo.ca
SIC: 2752 2789 Commercial printing, offset; bookbinding & related work

(G-20155)
GLASS MEDIC INC
Also Called: Glass Medic America
6996 Four Seasons Dr (43082-8533)
PHONE...................800 356-4009
Fax: 614 891-9227
John Robinson, *President*
Paul Syfko, *Officer*
▲ **EMP:** 3
SQ FT: 2,200
SALES: 1MM
SALES (corp-wide): 2.9B **Privately Held**
WEB: www.glassmedic.com
SIC: 3423 Cutters, glass
PA: D'ieteren Sa
Rue Du Mail 50
Bruxelles 1050
322 536-5111

(G-20156)
GUITAMMER COMPANY
Also Called: Buttkicker
6117 Maxtown Rd (43082-9051)
P.O. Box 82 (43086-0082)
PHONE...................614 898-9370
Mark A Luden, *Ch of Bd*
Lawrence L Lemoine, *COO*
Marvin Clamme, *VP Engrg*
▲ **EMP:** 7
SQ FT: 15,000
SALES: 1.5MM **Privately Held**
WEB: www.thebuttkicker.com
SIC: 3679 Transducers, electrical

(G-20157)
HARRIS MACKESSY & BRENNAN
Also Called: Hmb Information Sys Developers
570 Polaris Pkwy Ste 125 (43082-7924)
PHONE...................614 221-6831
Fax: 614 221-6856
Thomas Harris, *President*
Tom Harris, *President*
Patrick Brennan, *Vice Pres*
Mark Buchy, *Vice Pres*
Owen Myers, *Project Mgr*
EMP: 150
SQ FT: 9,000
SALES (est): 36.4MM **Privately Held**
WEB: www.hmbnet.com
SIC: 8742 3577 Management consulting services; decoders, computer peripheral equipment

(G-20158)
IMAGE PRINT INC
214 Hoff Rd Unit D (43082-7156)
PHONE...................614 776-3985
Alan Lang, *General Mgr*
EMP: 6 EST: 2009
SALES (est): 803.4K **Privately Held**
SIC: 2759 Commercial printing

(G-20159)
IMT DEFENSE CORP
5386 Club Dr (43082-8312)
PHONE...................614 891-8812
James Hacking, *Ch of Bd*
Remo Assini, *President*
Randall Sweeney, *Office Mgr*
EMP: 7
SALES (est): 590K **Privately Held**
SIC: 3812 Defense systems & equipment

(G-20160)
INTEK INC
751 Intek Way (43082-9057)
PHONE...................614 895-0301
Fax: 614 895-0319
Joseph W Harpster, *President*
Phil Snyder, *COO*
Marilyn Y C Harpster, *Exec VP*
Thomas Krallman, *Engineer*
Eugeniu Morari, *Engineer*
▼ **EMP:** 22
SQ FT: 12,800

SALES: 2.7MM **Privately Held**
WEB: www.intekflow.com
SIC: 3823 8732 Industrial flow & liquid measuring instruments; commercial non-physical research

(G-20161)
IQ SOLUTIONS GROUP LLC
570 Polaris Pkwy Ste 110 (43082-7902)
PHONE...................855 367-4774
Tom Richardson,
EMP: 12
SALES (est): 3.6MM **Privately Held**
SIC: 7372 4822 Business oriented computer software; telegraph & other communications

(G-20162)
JBW SYSTEMS INC
5840 Chandler Ct (43082-9049)
P.O. Box 1530 (43086-1530)
PHONE...................614 882-5008
James Watkins, *President*
Billie L Watkins, *Vice Pres*
EMP: 10
SQ FT: 5,000
SALES (est): 1.2MM **Privately Held**
WEB: www.jbwsystems.com
SIC: 3559 3531 Chemical machinery & equipment; construction machinery

(G-20163)
JOHNSTONS BANKS INC
6927 Sherbrook Dr (43082-8568)
PHONE...................614 499-4374
Mary J Johnston, *Principal*
EMP: 5
SALES (est): 567.6K **Privately Held**
SIC: 3961 Costume jewelry

(G-20164)
JST LLC
Also Called: Lifecubby
6240 Frost Rd Ste C (43082-6928)
PHONE...................614 423-7815
Susan Testaguzza, *CEO*
James Testaguzza, *Vice Pres*
EMP: 7
SALES (est): 184.8K **Privately Held**
SIC: 7372 Educational computer software

(G-20165)
LAKE SHORE CRYOTRONICS INC (PA)
575 Mccorkle Blvd (43082-8888)
PHONE...................614 891-2243
Fax: 614 818-1600
Michael S Swartz, *President*
John M Swartz, *Chairman*
Karen Lint, *COO*
Brad Dodrill, *Vice Pres*
Ed Maloof, *Vice Pres*
EMP: 110
SQ FT: 60,000
SALES (est): 20.1MM **Privately Held**
WEB: www.lakeshore.com
SIC: 3812 3825 3679 3823 Search & navigation equipment; measuring instruments & meters, electric; cryogenic cooling devices for infrared detectors, masers; industrial instrmnts msrmnt display/control process variable; temperature sensors, except industrial process & aircraft; tachometer, centrifugal

(G-20166)
LANCASTER COLONY CORPORATION (PA)
380 Polaris Pkwy Ste 400 (43082-8069)
PHONE...................614 224-7141
Fax: 614 469-8219
John B Gerlach Jr, *Ch of Bd*
David A Ciesinski, *President*
Douglas A Fell, *CFO*
Christine Wallen, *Accountant*
Vandy Cameron, *Accounts Exec*
◆ **EMP:** 25 EST: 1961
SALES: 1.1B **Publicly Held**
WEB: www.lancastercolony.com
SIC: 2035 2038 Dressings, salad: raw & cooked (except dry mixes); seasonings & sauces, except tomato & dry; frozen specialties

(G-20167)
LANCASTER COLONY CORPORATION
Also Called: Lancaster Colony Design Group
380 Polaris Pkwy Ste 400 (43082-8069)
PHONE...................614 792-9774
Fax: 614 792-9778
Doug Covell, *Manager*
EMP: 13
SALES (corp-wide): 1.1B **Publicly Held**
WEB: www.lancastercolony.com
SIC: 2035 Dressings, salad: raw & cooked (except dry mixes)
PA: Lancaster Colony Corporation
380 Polaris Pkwy Ste 400
Westerville OH 43082
614 224-7141

(G-20168)
LANCASTER COLONY CORPORATION
380 Polaris Pkwy Ste 400 (43082-8069)
PHONE...................614 224-7141
EMP: 55
SALES (corp-wide): 1.1B **Publicly Held**
SIC: 2035 Dressings, salad: raw & cooked (except dry mixes)
PA: Lancaster Colony Corporation
380 Polaris Pkwy Ste 400
Westerville OH 43082
614 224-7141

(G-20169)
M&M GREAT ADVENTURES LLC
586 Deer Trl (43082-6410)
PHONE...................937 344-1415
Michael Pennington, *Mng Member*
Mary Ellen Pennington, *Mng Member*
▼ **EMP:** 3 EST: 2009
SALES (est): 233.1K **Privately Held**
SIC: 3949 5199 7389 Camping equipment & supplies; general merchandise, non-durable;

(G-20170)
MARK RASCHE
Also Called: Rasche Cabinetmakers
6962 Harlem Rd (43082-9247)
PHONE...................614 882-1810
Fax: 614 882-1810
EMP: 3
SQ FT: 6,000
SALES: 100K **Privately Held**
SIC: 2511 7641 2522 2521 Mfg Wood Household Furn Reupholstery/Furn Repair Mfg Nonwood Office Furn Mfg Wood Office Furn

(G-20171)
MCNISH CORPORATION
Also Called: E & I
214 Hoff Rd Unit M (43082-7157)
PHONE...................614 899-2282
Roger Randolph, *Purchasing*
Nicole Favorite, *Marketing Staff*
Glenn E Meek, *Branch Mgr*
EMP: 7
SALES (corp-wide): 33.2MM **Privately Held**
WEB: www.walker-process.com
SIC: 3589 Sewage treatment equipment
PA: Mcnish Corporation
840 N Russell Ave
Aurora IL 60506
630 892-7921

(G-20172)
NEW YORK FROZEN FOODS
380 Polaris Pkwy Ste 400 (43082-8069)
P.O. Box 297737, Columbus (43229-7737)
PHONE...................614 846-2232
Thomas E Moloney, *Principal*
Tim Tate, *Sales Staff*
EMP: 11
SALES (est): 2.7MM **Privately Held**
SIC: 3421 Table & food cutlery, including butchers'

(G-20173)
NOLAN MANUFACTURING LLC
Also Called: Nolan Mfg Co - Electronics Div
493 Blue Heron Ct (43082-7448)
PHONE...................614 859-2302
Andrew Nolan, *President*
EMP: 3

SALES (est): 158.2K **Privately Held**
SIC: 3613 Power connectors, electric

(G-20174)
ONEVISION CORPORATION (PA)
5805 Chandler Ct Ste A (43082-9076)
PHONE...................614 794-1144
Neil E Morris, *President*
Steve Bettencourt, *Engineer*
EMP: 4
SQ FT: 3,200
SALES: 1MM **Privately Held**
WEB: www.onevisioncorp.com
SIC: 3823 Industrial instrmnts msrmnt display/control process variable

(G-20175)
ORANGE LEAF
750 N State St (43082-9066)
PHONE...................614 898-5323
Don Stanley, *Principal*
EMP: 3
SALES (est): 194.8K **Privately Held**
SIC: 2024 Ice cream, bulk

(G-20176)
ORTON EDWARD JR CRMIC FNDATION
6991 S Old 3c Hwy (43082-9026)
P.O. Box 2760 (43086-2760)
PHONE...................614 895-2663
Jonathan Hinton, *Ch of Bd*
J Gary Childress, *General Mgr*
Dr Stephen Freiman, *Trustee*
Dr John Morral, *Trustee*
Dr James Williams, *Trustee*
▼ **EMP:** 31
SQ FT: 34,260
SALES: 5MM **Privately Held**
WEB: www.ortonceramic.com
SIC: 3269 3826 3825 8748 Cones, pyrometric: earthenware; analytical instruments; instruments to measure electricity; testing services

(G-20177)
OSTEO SOLUTION
117 Commerce Park Dr (43082-6063)
PHONE...................614 485-9790
Tom Meyer, *Principal*
EMP: 4
SALES (est): 506.3K **Privately Held**
SIC: 3842 Orthopedic appliances

(G-20178)
PARADISE LEMONADE
Also Called: Giant Lemonade Cup
12897 Hatch Rd (43082-9512)
PHONE...................740 816-0771
Theresa Dronsfield, *Owner*
Morgan Dronsfield, *Principal*
Todd Dronsfield, *Principal*
EMP: 10
SALES (est): 375.1K **Privately Held**
SIC: 2086 7389 Lemonade: packaged in cans, bottles, etc.;

(G-20179)
PERFORMANX SPECIALTY CHEM LLC (PA)
300 Westdale Ave (43082-8962)
PHONE...................614 300-7001
Michael Suver, *President*
Kim Pellock, *Controller*
EMP: 5 EST: 2014
SQ FT: 2,500
SALES (est): 943.5K **Privately Held**
SIC: 2834 Emulsions, pharmaceutical

(G-20180)
QUADRIGA AMERICAS LLC (DH)
480 Olde Worthington Rd # 350 (43082-7067)
PHONE...................614 890-6090
Roger Taylor, *CEO*
Candice Deluca, *Vice Pres*
Scott Scriba, *Vice Pres*
Scott Lai, *Controller*
Howard Watts, *Technology*
EMP: 3
SQ FT: 5,000
SALES (est): 2.1MM **Privately Held**
SIC: 2741

HQ: Quadriga Worldwide Limited
　　Forum 1
　　Reading BERKS RG7 4
　　118 930-6030

(G-20181)
QUALITY BAKERY COMPANY INC (DH)
380 Polaris Pkwy Ste 400　(43082-8069)
PHONE..................................614 846-2232
Bruce Rosa, *President*
EMP: 5
SALES (est): 9MM
SALES (corp-wide): 1.1B **Publicly Held**
WEB: www.marzetti.com
SIC: 2051　Bread, cake & related products
HQ: T.Marzetti Company
　　380 Polaris Pkwy Ste 400
　　Westerville OH 43082
　　614 846-2232

(G-20182)
REVOLUTION GROUP INC
600 N Cleveland Ave # 110　(43082-6921)
PHONE..................................614 212-1111
Richard Snide, *President*
Polly Clavijo, *Vice Pres*
Greg Huddleston, *Vice Pres*
Firas Alnemer, *Engineer*
Carlos Clavijo, *CFO*
EMP: 80
SALES (est): 6.9MM **Privately Held**
SIC: 7379　7372　4813　8741　Computer related consulting services; prepackaged software; ; ; management services

(G-20183)
RKE TRUCKING CO
6305 Frost Rd　(43082-9027)
PHONE..................................614 891-1786
Fax: 614 891-1767
Ed Deim, *President*
Michael Hrabcak, *President*
Valerie Clark, *Accountant*
EMP: 15
SALES (est): 3.5MM **Privately Held**
SIC: 3713　Automobile wrecker truck bodies

(G-20184)
ROCKWELL AUTOMATION INC
350 Worthington Rd Ste A　(43082-8327)
PHONE..................................614 776-3021
Fax: 614 898-9401
John Fossen, *Manager*
Robert Billy, *Manager*
Paul Burgan, *Technology*
EMP: 80 **Publicly Held**
SIC: 3625　Relays & industrial controls
PA: Rockwell Automation, Inc.
　　1201 S 2nd St
　　Milwaukee WI 53204

(G-20185)
SKLADANY ENTERPRISES INC
Also Called: SKLADANY PRINTING CENTER
695 Mccorkle Blvd　(43082-8790)
PHONE..................................614 823-6883
Fax: 614 823-6890
Thomas Skladany, *President*
Debbie Skladany, *Vice Pres*
Dave Packard, *Foreman/Supr*
Lisa Esty, *Personnel Exec*
Michael Niezgoda, *VP Sales*
EMP: 8
SALES: 1MM **Privately Held**
WEB: www.skladany.com
SIC: 2752　Commercial printing, offset

(G-20186)
SMARTV COMPANY LLC
480 Olde Worthington Rd　(43082-8954)
PHONE..................................614 890-6090
Michael Infante, *CEO*
Kyle Virgin, *President*
Seale Moorer, *Chairman*
Casey Flynn, *Vice Pres*
Shane Pierce, *Vice Pres*
EMP: 22
SALES (est): 1.5MM **Privately Held**
SIC: 7929　5199　3429　Entertainment service; advertising specialties; animal traps, iron or steel

(G-20187)
STANLEY INDUSTRIAL & AUTO LLC
Mac Tools
505 N Cleveland Ave # 200　(43082-7130)
PHONE..................................614 755-7089
Chuck Turner, *Controller*
Laurita Adams, *Administration*
EMP: 150
SALES (corp-wide): 11.4B **Publicly Held**
WEB: www.stanleyworks.com
SIC: 3469　3423　5251　2542　Boxes: tool, lunch, mail, etc.: stamped metal; hand & edge tools; tools; partitions & fixtures, except wood
HQ: Stanley Industrial & Automotive, Llc
　　505 N Cleveland Ave
　　Westerville OH 43082
　　614 755-7000

(G-20188)
STANLEY INDUSTRIAL & AUTO LLC (HQ)
505 N Cleveland Ave　(43082-7130)
PHONE..................................614 755-7000
Joanna Sohovich, *President*
Larry Harper, *President*
Joe McCormack, *President*
James Ray, *President*
Brett Shaw, *President*
▲ EMP: 72
SALES (est): 283.6MM
SALES (corp-wide): 11.4B **Publicly Held**
SIC: 3429　3546　3423　3452　Builders' hardware; power-driven handtools; hand & edge tools; bolts, nuts, rivets & washers
PA: Stanley Black & Decker, Inc.
　　1000 Stanley Dr
　　New Britain CT 06053
　　860 225-5111

(G-20189)
STEELES DISPLAY CASES
5665 State Route 605 S　(43082-9647)
PHONE..................................740 965-6426
Mike Steele, *Owner*
Sherrie Steele, *Co-Owner*
EMP: 4
SALES (est): 200K **Privately Held**
SIC: 2541　Store & office display cases & fixtures

(G-20190)
SUPERMEDIA LLC
470 Olde Worthington Rd　(43082-8985)
PHONE..................................614 216-6566
Adrienne Wilson, *Principal*
EMP: 4 EST: 2011
SALES (est): 209K **Privately Held**
SIC: 2741　Directories, telephone: publishing only, not printed on site

(G-20191)
TG CAN TECHNOLOGY USA INC
470 Olde Worthington Rd　(43082-8985)
PHONE..................................614 410-6672
Ian Williams, *President*
Carl Horning, *Manager*
▲ EMP: 3
SALES (est): 174.6K **Privately Held**
SIC: 3411　Metal cans; beverage cans, metal: except beer

(G-20192)
TMARZETTI COMPANY
380 Polaris Pkwy Ste 400　(43082-8069)
PHONE..................................614 268-3722
Fax: 614 261-3248
Doug Fell, *Vice Pres*
Cara Stamm, *VP Opers*
William M Mogollon, *Prdtn Mgr*
Doug Taylor, *Safety Mgr*
David Lawson, *Opers Staff*
EMP: 180
SALES (corp-wide): 1.1B **Publicly Held**
SIC: 2035　Dressings, salad: raw & cooked (except dry mixes)
HQ: T.Marzetti Company
　　380 Polaris Pkwy Ste 400
　　Westerville OH 43082
　　614 846-2232

(G-20193)
TMARZETTI COMPANY (HQ)
Also Called: Inn Maid Products
380 Polaris Pkwy Ste 400　(43082-8069)
PHONE..................................614 846-2232
Fax: 614 848-8330
David Ciesinski, *President*
Doug Fell, *Vice Pres*
Ernie Grindstaff, *Vice Pres*
Jeff Harris, *Vice Pres*
Bob Holtcamp, *Vice Pres*
◆ EMP: 147 EST: 1927
SQ FT: 28,000
SALES (est): 492.5MM
SALES (corp-wide): 1.1B **Publicly Held**
SIC: 2035　2098　Dressings, salad: raw & cooked (except dry mixes); noodles (e.g. egg, plain & water), dry
PA: Lancaster Colony Corporation
　　380 Polaris Pkwy Ste 400
　　Westerville OH 43082
　　614 224-7141

(G-20194)
WESTERVILLE ENDOSCOPY CTR LLC
300 Polaris Pkwy Ste 1500　(43082-7990)
PHONE..................................614 568-1666
Tammy Blankenship, *Principal*
EMP: 12
SALES (est): 1.8MM **Privately Held**
SIC: 3845　8011　Gastroscopes, electromedical; internal medicine, physician/surgeon

(G-20195)
WESTERVILLE LAWN & GARDEN
5064 S Old 3c Hwy　(43082-9249)
PHONE..................................740 936-8452
Eugene Green, *Owner*
EMP: 5
SQ FT: 1,668
SALES: 500K **Privately Held**
SIC: 3524　Lawn & garden equipment

(G-20196)
WORTHINGTON CYLINDER CORP
333 Maxtown Rd　(43082-8757)
PHONE..................................614 840-3800
Fax: 614 840-3850
Craig Breedlove, *Vice Pres*
Mary Luers, *Vice Pres*
Bob Katarba, *Plant Mgr*
Lou Saggio, *Opers Staff*
Carl McLaughlin, *Engineer*
EMP: 200
SQ FT: 12,880
SALES (corp-wide): 2.8B **Publicly Held**
SIC: 3443　Cylinders, pressure: metal plate
HQ: Worthington Cylinder Corporation
　　200 W Wlson Bridge Rd
　　Worthington OH 43085
　　614 840-3210

┌─────────────────────┐
│ **Westerville** │
│ *Franklin County* │
└─────────────────────┘

(G-20197)
ALCATEL CO
4571 Cautela Dr　(43081-9657)
PHONE..................................818 878-4485
Frank Myers, *Property Mgr*
EMP: 3 EST: 2015
SALES (est): 195K **Privately Held**
SIC: 3661　Telephone & telegraph apparatus

(G-20198)
ALLEN PRESS
6132 Batavia Rd　(43081-3515)
PHONE..................................614 891-4413
James Tiedt, *President*
EMP: 3
SQ FT: 6,000
SALES: 130K **Privately Held**
SIC: 2752　Commercial printing, offset

(G-20199)
ANDERSON PRINTING & SUPPLY LLC
237 E Broadway Ave　(43081-1646)
P.O. Box 2125　(43086-2125)
PHONE..................................614 891-1100
Nicole Lynn Anderson, *Mng Member*
Dawn Sims, *Manager*
EMP: 5
SALES (est): 370K **Privately Held**
SIC: 2752　Commercial printing, lithographic

(G-20200)
AVCOM SMT INC
213 E Broadway Ave　(43081-1656)
P.O. Box 1516　(43086-1516)
PHONE..................................614 882-8176
Paul Wiese, *President*
Barbara Wiese, *Vice Pres*
Scott Wiese, *Marketing Staff*
EMP: 12
SQ FT: 10,000
SALES (est): 2.5MM **Privately Held**
WEB: www.avcomsmt.com
SIC: 3672　Printed circuit boards

(G-20201)
B L F ENTERPRISES INC
Also Called: Great Harvest Bread
445 S State St　(43081-2956)
PHONE..................................937 642-6425
Bruce Fowler, *President*
Linda Fowler, *Corp Secy*
EMP: 10
SQ FT: 2,000
SALES (est): 490.1K **Privately Held**
SIC: 5461　2052　2051　Bread; cookies & crackers; bread, cake & related products

(G-20202)
BLIND OUTLET (PA)
574 W Schrock Rd　(43081-8996)
PHONE..................................614 895-2002
Fax: 614 895-2003
David Bornhorst, *President*
Diane Bornhorst, *Vice Pres*
Stephanie Bornhorst, *Vice Pres*
Roger Bornhorst, *Treasurer*
EMP: 9
SQ FT: 2,400
SALES: 1.5MM **Privately Held**
SIC: 2591　5719　5023　Blinds vertical; vertical blinds; vertical blinds

(G-20203)
BLUELOGOS INC
Also Called: Sullivan Company, The
130 Graphic Way　(43081-2360)
PHONE..................................614 898-9971
Fax: 614 898-0882
David Duhl, *CEO*
Susan Eckles, *Opers Staff*
EMP: 17
SQ FT: 5,760
SALES (est): 1.6MM **Privately Held**
WEB: www.wearbarndmatters.com
SIC: 2759　Screen printing

(G-20204)
COLUMBUS PRESCR REHABILITATION
Also Called: The Mobility Store
975 Eastwind Dr Ste 155　(43081-3344)
PHONE..................................614 294-1600
Fax: 614 429-2201
Mark A Witchey, *President*
Brad Hannan, *Sales Mgr*
Peggy Rankan, *Manager*
Jack A Witchey, *Admin Sec*
EMP: 6
SQ FT: 50,000
SALES: 1.7MM **Privately Held**
WEB: www.themobilitystore.com
SIC: 3842　7352　Wheelchairs; medical equipment rental

(G-20205)
CREATIVE PRINT SOLUTIONS LLC
71 Granby Pl W　(43081-1205)
PHONE..................................614 989-1747
Jay Broyles,
EMP: 3

SALES: 252K **Privately Held**
SIC: 2759 Commercial printing

(G-20206)
CRUISE QUARTERS AND TOURS
730 Mohican Way (43081-3048)
PHONE..............................614 891-6089
EMP: 3
SALES (est): 153K **Privately Held**
SIC: 3131 Quarters

(G-20207)
CURV IMAGING LLC
841 Green Crest Dr (43081-2838)
P.O. Box 360641, Columbus (43236-0641)
PHONE..............................614 890-2878
Bernie Sigal, *President*
Reta Sigal, *Vice Pres*
Carrie Cartwright, *Art Dir*
EMP: 6
SALES: 1MM **Privately Held**
SIC: 2752 Commercial printing, lithographic

(G-20208)
DARIFILL INC
750 Green Crest Dr (43081-2837)
PHONE..............................614 890-3274
Fax: 614 890-4230
Steve Aspery, *President*
Eric Rousculp, *Vice Pres*
Jack Spencer, *Vice Pres*
▲ EMP: 18
SALES (est): 6.2MM **Privately Held**
WEB: www.darifill.com
SIC: 3565 Packaging machinery

(G-20209)
DEVRIES & ASSOCIATES INC
Also Called: Fastsigns
654 Brooksedge Blvd Ste A (43081-2962)
PHONE..............................614 890-3821
Mary Devries, *President*
Scott Oliphant, *Accounts Exec*
EMP: 14
SALES (est): 1.2MM **Privately Held**
SIC: 3993 Signs & advertising specialties

(G-20210)
DEVRIES & ASSOCIATES INC (PA)
Also Called: Fastsigns
5117 E Main St (43081)
PHONE..............................614 860-0103
Fax: 614 860-0159
Thomas R De Vries, *President*
Mary L De Vries, *CFO*
EMP: 7
SALES (est): 1MM **Privately Held**
SIC: 3993 Signs & advertising specialties

(G-20211)
DSC SUPPLY COMPANY LLC
237 E Broadway Ave Ste A (43081-1646)
P.O. Box 2125 (43086-2125)
PHONE..............................614 891-1100
Nikki Anderson, *President*
EMP: 7
SALES (est): 817K **Privately Held**
SIC: 2759 Commercial printing

(G-20212)
ELAN DESIGNS INC
10 E Schrock Rd 110 (43081-2915)
PHONE..............................614 985-5600
Nelia Anderson, *President*
Neilia Anderson, *President*
EMP: 6
SALES (est): 581.2K **Privately Held**
WEB: www.elandesigns.com
SIC: 3524 Lawn & garden equipment

(G-20213)
EN-HANCED PRODUCTS INC
229 E Broadway Ave (43081-1656)
PHONE..............................614 882-7400
James M Hance, *President*
EMP: 7
SALES (est): 1.2MM **Privately Held**
SIC: 3443 Fabricated plate work (boiler shop)

(G-20214)
FEDEX OFFICE & PRINT SVCS INC
604 W Schrock Rd (43081-8996)
PHONE..............................614 898-0000
Rob Heinz, *Manager*
Eric Baker, *Manager*
EMP: 40
SALES (corp-wide): 50.3B **Publicly Held**
WEB: www.kinkos.com
SIC: 7334 2759 2396 Photocopying & duplicating services; commercial printing; automotive & apparel trimmings
HQ: Fedex Office And Print Services, Inc.
7900 Legacy Dr
Plano TX 75024
214 550-7000

(G-20215)
GENERAL PARTS INC
Also Called: Carquest Auto Parts
24 E Schrock Rd (43081-2915)
PHONE..............................614 891-6014
Fax: 614 891-0856
Sherrie Rowlison, *Branch Mgr*
EMP: 4
SALES (corp-wide): 9.5B **Publicly Held**
WEB: www.carquest.com
SIC: 5013 5531 3599 Automotive supplies & parts; automotive parts; machine shop, jobbing & repair
HQ: General Parts, Inc.
2635 E Millbrook Rd Ste C
Raleigh NC 27604
919 573-3000

(G-20216)
H G SCHNEIDER COMPANY
291 Broad St (43081-1603)
PHONE..............................614 882-6944
Fax: 614 523-1662
Constance Schneider, *President*
Harold Schneider, *Vice Pres*
EMP: 6
SALES: 200K **Privately Held**
WEB: www.unikix.net
SIC: 3452 Spring pins, metal

(G-20217)
HALF PRICE BKS REC MGZINES INC
561 S State St (43081-2923)
PHONE..............................614 776-5551
Doug Gruney, *Manager*
EMP: 17
SALES (corp-wide): 250.9MM **Privately Held**
SIC: 2721 Magazines: publishing & printing
PA: Half Price Books, Records, Magazines, Incorporated
5803 E Northwest Hwy
Dallas TX 75231
214 379-8000

(G-20218)
INDUSTRIAL FABRICATORS INC
265 E Broadway Ave (43081-1646)
PHONE..............................614 882-7423
Fax: 614 882-3162
Frederick R Landig Jr, *President*
Frederick Landig Sr, *President*
Tom Persinger, *Human Res Mgr*
EMP: 38 EST: 1964
SQ FT: 98,000
SALES (est): 8.3MM **Privately Held**
WEB: www.ifab.com
SIC: 3499 Boxes for packing & shipping, metal

(G-20219)
JEFFREY REEDY
Also Called: Computer Forms Printing
237 E Broadway Ave Ste D (43081-1646)
PHONE..............................614 794-9292
Fax: 614 794-9387
Jeffrey Reedy, *Owner*
EMP: 3
SQ FT: 2,500
SALES (est): 170K **Privately Held**
SIC: 2759 2752 Commercial printing; commercial printing, lithographic

(G-20220)
KOKOSING MATERIALS INC
6189 Westerville Rd (43081-4057)
P.O. Box 334, Fredericktown (43019-0334)
PHONE..............................614 891-5090
Fax: 614 891-4434
Jason Schopp, *Manager*
Donald Cobb, *Manager*
EMP: 7
SALES (corp-wide): 18.1MM **Privately Held**
WEB: www.kokosingmaterials.biz
SIC: 2951 Asphalt & asphaltic paving mixtures (not from refineries)
PA: Kokosing Materials, Inc.
17531 Waterford Rd
Fredericktown OH 43019
740 694-9585

(G-20221)
KUFBAG INC
1333 Cobblestone Ave (43081-4581)
PHONE..............................614 589-8687
Glenda L Hill-Foster, *CEO*
John Foster, *CFO*
EMP: 4
SQ FT: 2,400
SALES (est): 317.4K **Privately Held**
WEB: www.kufbag.com
SIC: 3842 Surgical appliances & supplies

(G-20222)
LABELDATA
275 Old County Line Rd I (43081-1081)
PHONE..............................614 891-5858
Scott Bendger, *Owner*
EMP: 3 EST: 2007
SALES: 600K **Privately Held**
SIC: 3565 Packing & wrapping machinery

(G-20223)
MC VAY VENTURES INC
Also Called: Wm Caxton Printing
40 W College Ave (43081-2104)
PHONE..............................614 890-1516
Larry Mc Vay, *President*
Pat Krause, *Bookkeeper*
EMP: 4
SQ FT: 1,200
SALES (est): 597.6K **Privately Held**
WEB: www.caxtonprinting.com
SIC: 2752 Commercial printing, offset

(G-20224)
MICRO INDUSTRIES CORPORATION (PA)
8399 Green Meadows Dr N (43081)
PHONE..............................740 548-7878
Fax: 614 882-6357
John Curran, *CEO*
Michael Curran, *President*
Amanda Curran, *Vice Pres*
William Jackson, *Vice Pres*
Jeffrey Price, *Mfg Staff*
EMP: 67
SQ FT: 52,000
SALES (est): 17.1MM **Privately Held**
WEB: www.microindustries.com
SIC: 8711 3674 Engineering services; semiconductor circuit networks; microcircuits, integrated (semiconductor)

(G-20225)
NAIL ART
Also Called: Nail Artist
5470 Westerville Rd (43081-9361)
PHONE..............................614 899-7155
H Meadows, *Owner*
EMP: 3
SALES (est): 130K **Privately Held**
SIC: 3999 7231 Fingernails, artificial; manicurist, pedicurist

(G-20226)
NANAK BAKERY
895 S State St (43081-3345)
PHONE..............................614 882-0882
EMP: 8
SALES (est): 280K **Privately Held**
SIC: 2051 Mfg Bread/Related Products

(G-20227)
OHIO SHELTERALL INC
Also Called: Moore Outdoor Sign Craftsman
6060 Westerville Rd (43081-4048)
PHONE..............................614 882-1110
Fax: 614 882-5686
Steve P Moore, *President*
Tom Moore, *Vice Pres*
Ellen Moore, *Treasurer*
Dave Moore, *Admin Sec*
EMP: 10
SALES (est): 880K **Privately Held**
WEB: www.ohioagriculture.gov
SIC: 7312 7389 7338 3993 Outdoor advertising services; sign painting & lettering shop; secretarial & typing service; signs & advertising specialties

(G-20228)
OPTIMUM SYSTEM PRODUCTS INC (PA)
Also Called: Optimum Graphics
921 Eastwind Dr Ste 133 (43081-3363)
PHONE..............................614 885-4464
Fax: 614 885-4454
John Martin, *CEO*
Dorothy Martin, *President*
Anthony Danna, *Senior Buyer*
Phil Osborn, *Marketing Staff*
Anita Pasco, *Marketing Staff*
EMP: 40
SQ FT: 75,000
SALES (est): 11.7MM **Privately Held**
WEB: www.optimumsystem.com
SIC: 2752 5112 Business form & card printing, lithographic; business forms

(G-20229)
PRECISION Q SYSTEMS LLC
285 Old County Line Rd B (43081-1886)
PHONE..............................614 286-5142
J R Gaines, *Director*
EMP: 3
SALES (est): 182.7K **Privately Held**
WEB: www.low-nox.com
SIC: 3491 Valves, automatic control

(G-20230)
PRESS RESOURCE LLC
237 E Broadway Ave (43081-1646)
PHONE..............................614 794-9000
Joseph Fullen, *Principal*
Jerry Holcolmb,
EMP: 3
SALES (est): 334.6K **Privately Held**
SIC: 2741 Miscellaneous publishing

(G-20231)
PRINT SOLUTIONS TODAY LLC
100 Dorchester Sq N # 101 (43081-7304)
PHONE..............................614 848-4500
David D Dinning, *Mng Member*
EMP: 4
SQ FT: 1,200
SALES: 4MM **Privately Held**
SIC: 2752 Commercial printing, lithographic

(G-20232)
RISING MOON CUSTOM APPAREL
19 E College Ave (43081-2101)
PHONE..............................614 882-1336
Fax: 614 846-0255
Sue M Swihart, *Owner*
Robert Swihart, *Co-Owner*
EMP: 4
SALES: 400K **Privately Held**
SIC: 2759 Screen printing

(G-20233)
ROBIN ENTERPRISES COMPANY
111 N Otterbein Ave (43081-5703)
P.O. Box 6180 (43086-6180)
PHONE..............................614 891-0250
Fax: 614 891-4398
Brad Hance, *President*
Julie Stewart, *General Mgr*
John Kaufman, *Mfg Staff*
Bill Rippel, *Engineer*
Shane Gruber, *Accounting Dir*
EMP: 120
SQ FT: 90,000

SALES: 22MM **Privately Held**
WEB: www.robinent.com
SIC: **2752** 2789 2791 Commercial printing, offset; bookbinding & related work;
typesetting

(G-20234)
SOURCEPAC INC
275 Old County Line Rd L (43081-1082)
PHONE................................614 899-0744
Lawrence Savage, *President*
EMP: 4
SALES (est): 735.5K **Privately Held**
WEB: www.simplysourcepac.com
SIC: **2671** Packaging paper & plastics film,
coated & laminated

(G-20235)
TAHOE INTERACTIVE SYSTEMS
INC
60 Nadine Pl N (43081-2518)
P.O. Box 820 (43086-0820)
PHONE................................614 891-2323
Fax: 614 882-5805
Paul Coleman, *President*
EMP: 18
SQ FT: 12,000
SALES: 1MM **Privately Held**
SIC: **7372** 7375 7371 Prepackaged soft-
ware; information retrieval services; cus-
tom computer programming services

(G-20236)
TECHNOPRINT INC
Also Called: Inkwell, The
515 S State St (43081-2921)
PHONE................................614 899-1403
Fax: 614 899-1139
Pat Patel, *President*
David Umbreit, *Supervisor*
Diane L Burchetp-Patel, *Admin Sec*
EMP: 10
SQ FT: 1,800
SALES: 620K **Privately Held**
SIC: **2752** 7334 Commercial printing, litho-
graphic; photocopying & duplicating serv-
ices

(G-20237)
THOMAS TOOL & MOLD
COMPANY
271 Broad St (43081-1603)
PHONE................................614 890-4978
Fax: 614 890-1314
James W Thomas, *President*
James P Thomas, *Vice Pres*
EMP: 11
SQ FT: 7,500
SALES: 1.3MM **Privately Held**
WEB: www.ttmco.com
SIC: **3544** Forms (molds), for foundry &
plastics working machinery

(G-20238)
TOP HAT DESIGNS
776 Autumn Branch Rd (43081-3104)
PHONE................................614 898-1962
Mary Jo Lee, *Owner*
EMP: 5
SALES (est): 180K **Privately Held**
SIC: **2389** Theatrical costumes

(G-20239)
TRACEWELL POWER INC
567 Enterprise Dr (43081-8883)
PHONE................................614 846-6175
Larry Tracewell, *President*
Larry Martin, *CFO*
EMP: 25
SQ FT: 100,000
SALES (est): 3.9MM
SALES (corp-wide): 29.3MM **Privately**
Held
SIC: **3679** Power supplies, all types: static
PA: Tracewell Systems, Inc.
567 Enterprise Dr
Lewis Center OH 43035
614 846-6175

(G-20240)
WES-GARDE COMPONENTS
GROUP INC
300 Enterprise Dr (43081-8840)
PHONE................................614 885-0319
Joe Jeenan, *General Mgr*

EMP: 6
SALES (corp-wide): 61.4MM **Privately**
Held
SIC: **5065** 3625 5063 Electronic parts &
equipment; switches, electric power;
switches, except electronic
PA: Wes-Garde Components Group, Inc.
2820 Drane Field Rd
Lakeland FL 33811
863 644-7564

(G-20241)
WEST-CAMP PRESS INC
39 Collegeview Rd (43081-1463)
PHONE................................614 818-6279
Fax: 614 882-7380
Ed Evina, *Principal*
Dave Mars, *Principal*
Dave Holscher, *COO*
Tamara Dolder, *Vice Pres*
Dave Marsh, *Plant Mgr*
▲ EMP: 75 EST: 1961
SQ FT: 55,000
SALES (est): 21.4MM **Privately Held**
WEB: www.westcamp.com
SIC: **2752** 2796 2791 2789 Commercial
printing, lithographic; platemaking serv-
ices; typesetting; bookbinding & related
work; commercial printing

(G-20242)
WORLD DEVELOPMENT &
CONSLT LLC
Also Called: Vicrobiz
855 S Sunbury Rd (43081-9553)
PHONE................................614 805-4450
Ron Paul, *President*
▼ EMP: 3
SALES (est): 180K **Privately Held**
SIC: **1442** Construction sand & gravel

Westfield Center
Medina County

(G-20243)
ALL SPORT PRINTWEAR INC
8606 N Leroy Rd (44251-9745)
P.O. Box 5001 (44251-5001)
PHONE................................330 887-6505
Tom Pickering, *President*
R Cary Blair, *Principal*
Steve Elder, *Vice Pres*
Andy Schiesswohl, *VP Sales*
Westfield Wares, *Manager*
EMP: 10
SQ FT: 2,800
SALES: 1.5MM
SALES (corp-wide): 1.7B **Privately Held**
SIC: **2395** 5699 Embroidery & art needle-
work; sports apparel
HQ: Westfield Insurance Company
1 Park Cir
Westfield Center OH 44251
800 243-0210

(G-20244)
J WILLIAMS & ASSOCIATES INC
8761 Virginia Dr (44251-9755)
P.O. Box 727 (44251-0727)
PHONE................................330 887-1392
Jeffery Williams, *President*
Lori Williams, *Sales Staff*
Michael Williams, *Sales Staff*
EMP: 4
SALES (est): 504.7K **Privately Held**
SIC: **3469** Metal stampings

Westlake
Cuyahoga County

(G-20245)
ADVANCED ARM DYNAMICS
Also Called: Great Lakes Center Excellence
30701 Clemens Rd Ste C (44145-1074)
PHONE................................440 617-6601
Brian Waryck, *Manager*
EMP: 3
SALES (corp-wide): 11.1MM **Privately**
Held
SIC: **3842** Prosthetic appliances

PA: Advanced Arm Dynamics
123 W Torrance Blvd # 203
Redondo Beach CA 90277
310 372-3050

(G-20246)
ADVANCED
TRANSLATION/CNSLTNG
Also Called: Spanish Portugese Translation
3751 Willow Run (44145-5720)
PHONE................................440 716-0820
Hugo R Urizar, *Owner*
EMP: 30
SALES (est): 1.4MM **Privately Held**
SIC: **7389** 2791 Translation services; type-
setting

(G-20247)
AEROCASE INCORPORATED
Also Called: Odell Electronic Cleaning Stns
1061 Bradley Rd (44145-1044)
PHONE................................440 617-9294
Fax: 440 779-0730
John Koniarczyk, *President*
Deborah Koniarczyk, *Vice Pres*
Aaron Nix, *Director*
EMP: 10
SALES (est): 1.8MM **Privately Held**
WEB: www.aerocaseinc.com
SIC: **3089** 2441 Cases, plastic; cases,
wood

(G-20248)
ALLEGRA PRINTING & IMAGING
LLC
Also Called: Allegra Print & Imaging
1486 Barclay Blvd (44145-6822)
PHONE................................440 449-6989
Bruce Wilson,
EMP: 7
SALES (est): 628.5K **Privately Held**
SIC: **2752** Commercial printing, offset

(G-20249)
ALUMINUM LINE PRODUCTS
COMPANY (PA)
Also Called: Alpco
24460 Sperry Cir (44145-1591)
PHONE................................440 835-8880
Fax: 440 835-8879
Edward Murray, *Principal*
Chris Harrington, *Vice Pres*
Guy Martin, *Vice Pres*
Vicki Black, *Purchasing*
Pat Wessel, *Purchasing*
◆ EMP: 100 EST: 1960
SQ FT: 100,000
SALES: 100MM **Privately Held**
WEB: www.aluminumline.com
SIC: **5051** 3365 3999 Metals service cen-
ters & offices; aluminum foundries; barber
& beauty shop equipment

(G-20250)
AMERICAN LAWYERS CO INC
(PA)
Also Called: American Lawyers Quarterly
853 Westpoint Pkwy # 710 (44145-1546)
PHONE................................440 333-5190
Edward D Familo, *President*
Thomas W Hamilton, *Exec VP*
Nancy Hamilton, *Bookkeeper*
Jeremy Brown, *Manager*
Judy Taylor, *Manager*
EMP: 11
SQ FT: 4,000 **Privately Held**
WEB: www.alqlist.com
SIC: **2721** Periodicals: publishing only

(G-20251)
AMERICAN MERCHANT SERVIC
3076 Waterfall Way (44145-6811)
PHONE................................216 598-3100
Ramzy Assad, *Owner*
Mike Assad, *Office Mgr*
EMP: 4 EST: 2010
SALES: 400K **Privately Held**
SIC: **3578** 7699 Automatic teller machines
(ATM); automated teller machine (ATM)
repair

(G-20252)
AMERICAN OFFICE SERVICES
INC
30257 Clemens Rd Unit C (44145-1082)
PHONE................................440 899-6888
Fax: 440 961-8035
Scott C Ashbrook, *President*
Margo L Ashbrook, *Vice Pres*
Kristen M Ashbrook, *Treasurer*
EMP: 6
SQ FT: 8,000
SALES: 1.7MM **Privately Held**
SIC: **7641** 2531 Office furniture repair &
maintenance; stadium seating

(G-20253)
AMERICAN TCHNICAL
COATINGS INC
Also Called: A T C
28045 Ranney Pkwy Ste H (44145-1144)
PHONE................................440 401-2270
Charles Inglefield, *President*
Mark Hawthorne, *Engineer*
Brian Barry, *Info Tech Mgr*
EMP: 6
SALES (est): 867.3K **Privately Held**
SIC: **3479** Coating of metals & formed
products

(G-20254)
ANCHOR CHEMICAL CO INC
(PA)
777 Canterbury Rd (44145-1499)
PHONE................................440 871-1660
Diana Firth, *Ch of Bd*
Mark Atzel, *Vice Pres*
▼ EMP: 3
SQ FT: 6,000
SALES (est): 456.3K **Privately Held**
WEB: www.anchorlube.com
SIC: **2992** Lubricating oils & greases; cut-
ting oils, blending: made from purchased
materials

(G-20255)
APPLIED MARKETING
SERVICES
Also Called: Ibeda Inc Sprflash Gas Equip
28825 Ranney Pkwy (44145-1173)
PHONE................................440 716-9962
David J Marquard, *President*
C V Guggenviller, *CFO*
Jane Binzer, *Sales Staff*
Laura Frederick, *Manager*
▲ EMP: 28
SQ FT: 20,000
SALES (est): 9.6MM **Privately Held**
WEB: www.applied-inc.com
SIC: **3569** 8742 Gas producers, genera-
tors & other gas related equipment; mar-
keting consulting services; new products
& services consultants

(G-20256)
ASSOC TALENTS INC
3700 Greenbriar Cir (44145-5436)
PHONE................................440 716-1265
Carol Gantz, *President*
EMP: 3
SALES (est): 150K **Privately Held**
SIC: **2395** 5099 Embroidery & art needle-
work; durable goods

(G-20257)
BONNE BELL LLC (PA)
1006 Crocker Rd (44145-1094)
PHONE................................440 835-2440
Fax: 440 835-3404
Tony Giovanini, *Vice Pres*
Renee Nowak, *Finance Dir*
Lisa Henry, *Accounts Mgr*
Jess A Bell Jr, *Mng Member*
Henry Reitinger, *Info Tech Dir*
▲ EMP: 8 EST: 1927
SQ FT: 40,000
SALES (est): 36MM **Privately Held**
SIC: **2844** Cosmetic preparations; toilet
preparations; colognes; face creams or
lotions

(G-20258)
BORCHERS AMERICAS INC (HQ)
Also Called: Om Group
811 Sharon Dr (44145-1522)
PHONE..............................440 899-2950
Fax: 440 808-7117
Joseph Scaminace, *CEO*
William Reidy, *Managing Prtnr*
Susan Vicha, *Research*
James Shakour, *Engineer*
Shannon Craig, *Human Res Mgr*
◆ EMP: 60
SQ FT: 30,000
SALES (est): 40.8MM
SALES (corp-wide): 461.6MM **Privately Held**
SIC: 8731 2819 2899 2992 Commercial physical research; industrial inorganic chemicals; chemical preparations; lubricating oils & greases; industrial organic chemicals
PA: The Jordan Company L P
399 Park Ave Fl 30
New York NY 10022
212 572-0800

(G-20259)
BRAZING SERVICE INC
24480 Sperry Cir (44145-1593)
PHONE..............................440 871-1120
Fax: 440 871-1121
Robert Deucher, *President*
Robert Doucher, *President*
EMP: 5
SQ FT: 4,000
SALES (est): 390K **Privately Held**
SIC: 3398 Brazing (hardening) of metal

(G-20260)
CLEAR IMAGE TECHNOLOGY LLC
26202 Detroit Rd Ste 340 (44145-2480)
PHONE..............................440 366-4330
Subba Shankar,
▲ EMP: 5
SALES (est): 538.3K **Privately Held**
WEB: www.clearimg.com
SIC: 3845 Endoscopic equipment, electromedical

(G-20261)
CLOROX SALES COMPANY
24500 Center Ridge Rd # 240 (44145-5601)
PHONE..............................440 892-1700
EMP: 25
SALES (corp-wide): 5.5B **Publicly Held**
SIC: 2812 Mfg Alkalies/Chlorine
HQ: The Clorox Sales Company
1221 Broadway Ste 13
Oakland CA 94612
510 271-7000

(G-20262)
COACH INC
183 Main St (44145-6980)
PHONE..............................440 871-0103
Alicia Wood, *Manager*
EMP: 15
SALES (corp-wide): 4.4B **Publicly Held**
WEB: www.coach.com
SIC: 3171 Handbags, women's
PA: Coach, Inc.
10 Hudson Yards
New York NY 10001
212 594-1850

(G-20263)
DIAMOND RESERVE INC
Also Called: National Diamond Tl & Coating
801 Sharon Dr (44145-1522)
PHONE..............................440 892-7877
Fax: 440 892-4590
William Pastis, *CEO*
Tom Abersold, *President*
Diana Smith, *Manager*
EMP: 10
SQ FT: 2,000
SALES (est): 1.6MM **Privately Held**
WEB: www.diamondreserve.com
SIC: 3545 Diamond cutting tools for turning, boring, burnishing, etc.

(G-20264)
DOME DRILLING CO (PA)
Also Called: Dome Resources
2001 Crocker Rd Ste 420 (44145-6967)
PHONE..............................440 892-9434
Jon O Newton, *President*
James E Gessel, *Vice Pres*
Noreen C Mc Kinney, *Vice Pres*
James A Carney, *Treasurer*
John James Carney, *Admin Sec*
EMP: 6 EST: 1981
SQ FT: 1,200
SALES (est): 1.5MM **Privately Held**
SIC: 1311 1382 Crude petroleum production; natural gas production; oil & gas exploration services

(G-20265)
DOME ENERGICORP
2001 Crocker Rd Ste 420 (44145-6967)
PHONE..............................440 892-4900
John J Carney, *Ch of Bd*
Jon O Newton, *President*
James A Carney, *Admin Sec*
EMP: 4
SQ FT: 1,500
SALES (est): 224.3K **Privately Held**
SIC: 1382 8741 Oil & gas exploration services; financial management for business

(G-20266)
EDGEWELL PER CARE BRANDS LLC
25225 Detroit Rd (44145-2536)
P.O. Box 450777 (44145-0616)
PHONE..............................440 835-7500
Fax: 440 835-7837
Claire Marie Langkau, *Principal*
Dennis Crawford, *Engineer*
EMP: 98
SALES (corp-wide): 2.3B **Publicly Held**
WEB: www.eveready.com
SIC: 3421 Razor blades & razors
HQ: Edgewell Personal Care Brands, Llc
6 Research Dr
Shelton CT 06484
203 944-5500

(G-20267)
ENERGIZER MANUFACTURING INC
25225 Detroit Rd (44145-2536)
PHONE..............................440 835-7866
◆ EMP: 67
SALES (corp-wide): 1.6B **Publicly Held**
WEB: www.eveready.com
SIC: 3691 Storage batteries; alkaline cell storage batteries; batteries, rechargeable; lead acid batteries (storage batteries)
HQ: Energizer Manufacturing, Inc.
533 Maryville Univ Dr
Saint Louis MO 63141
314 985-2000

(G-20268)
FRANKIES GRAPHICS INC
3770 Windsong Ct (44145-5483)
PHONE..............................440 979-0824
Frank Fusco, *President*
EMP: 3
SALES (est): 100K **Privately Held**
SIC: 2752 Commercial printing, lithographic

(G-20269)
FUEL G USA LLC
1457 Mendelssohn Dr (44145-2346)
PHONE..............................440 617-0950
Azdiher Abuhamdeh, *Principal*
EMP: 3 EST: 2011
SALES (est): 174.6K **Privately Held**
SIC: 2869 Fuels

(G-20270)
G I PLASTEK INC
24700 Center Ridge Rd # 8 (44145-5636)
PHONE..............................440 230-1942
Charles Lagasse Jr, *CEO*
Susan Winger, *General Mgr*
Graham Gund, *Principal*
James Lyman, *Principal*
Shelly Trochemenko, *Treasurer*
EMP: 7
SQ FT: 3,000

SALES (est): 854.4K **Privately Held**
SIC: 3089 Plastic processing

(G-20271)
GENERAL BAR INC
25000 Center Ridge Rd # 3 (44145-4108)
PHONE..............................440 835-2000
Fax: 440 835-3636
Charles Sonnhalter, *President*
Robert Sonnhalter, *Publisher*
Michael Sonnhalter, *Vice Pres*
EMP: 18
SQ FT: 1,500
SALES (est): 1.4MM **Privately Held**
WEB: www.generalbar.com
SIC: 2741 8111 Directories: publishing only, not printed on site; legal services

(G-20272)
GIBRALTAR INDUSTRIES INC
26314 Center Ridge Rd (44145-4028)
PHONE..............................440 617-9230
Alan W Douglas, *Principal*
EMP: 3
SALES (corp-wide): 1B **Publicly Held**
SIC: 3999 Barber & beauty shop equipment
PA: Gibraltar Industries, Inc.
3556 Lake Shore Rd # 100
Buffalo NY 14219
716 826-6500

(G-20273)
GRIFFIN CIDER WORKS LLC
2165 Elmwood Dr (44145-3128)
PHONE..............................440 785-7418
EMP: 7
SALES (est): 510.4K **Privately Held**
SIC: 2037 Fruit juices

(G-20274)
HANGER PRSTHETCS & ORTHO INC
29101 Health Campus Dr # 104 (44145-5270)
PHONE..............................440 892-6665
Joe Garcia, *Branch Mgr*
Frank Zingales, *Exec Dir*
EMP: 6
SALES (corp-wide): 460MM **Publicly Held**
SIC: 3824 Speedometers
HQ: Hanger Prosthetics & Orthotics, Inc.
10910 Domain Dr Ste 300
Austin TX 78758
512 777-3800

(G-20275)
HENKEL CORPORATION
Also Called: Loctite
26235 1st St (44145-1439)
PHONE..............................440 250-7700
Beth Schlenger, *Business Anlyst*
James Heginbotham, *Branch Mgr*
Jennifer Gaba, *Manager*
Chris Igielinski, *Manager*
Anna Mulgrew, *Manager*
EMP: 202
SALES (corp-wide): 19.7B **Privately Held**
SIC: 2843 Surface active agents
HQ: Henkel Corporation
1 Henkel Way
Rocky Hill CT 06067
860 571-5100

(G-20276)
HIGH PERFORMANCE SERVO LLC
1477 E Crossings Pl (44145-6247)
PHONE..............................440 541-3529
Peter Ganczarski, *President*
EMP: 5 EST: 2012
SALES (est): 330K **Privately Held**
SIC: 3621 Coils, for electric motors or generators

(G-20277)
HMS INDUSTRIES LLC
27995 Ranney Pkwy (44145-1178)
PHONE..............................440 899-0001
Rick Kucinski, *Engineer*
Neal Saluja, *Sales Staff*
Biri Saluja, *Mng Member*
Catherine Saluga, *Manager*
Joanne Sibert, *Manager*
▲ EMP: 8

SQ FT: 10,000
SALES (est): 1.7MM **Privately Held**
WEB: www.wanxiang.com
SIC: 3562 5085 Roller bearings & parts; industrial supplies

(G-20278)
HYLAND SOFTWARE INC (HQ)
28500 Clemens Rd (44145-1145)
PHONE..............................440 788-5000
Fax: 440 788-5100
Bill Priemer, *CEO*
Christopher J Hyland, *Ch of Bd*
Miguel A Zubizarreta, *Exec VP*
Noreen Kilbane, *Senior VP*
Brenda Kirk, *Senior VP*
EMP: 1800
SQ FT: 150,000
SALES (est): 616.2MM **Privately Held**
WEB: www.onbase.com
SIC: 7372 Application computer software
PA: Thoma Cressey Bravo, Inc.
300 N La Salle Dr # 4350
Chicago IL 60654
312 254-3300

(G-20279)
JTEKT NORTH AMERICA CORP (HQ)
Also Called: Koyo Bearings
29570 Clemens Rd (44145-1007)
P.O. Box 45028 (44145-0028)
PHONE..............................440 835-1000
Fax: 440 835-9347
Hirouki Kaijima, *CEO*
Mike Davidson, *COO*
Ken Hopkins, *COO*
Gary Bourque, *Senior VP*
James Gregory, *Senior VP*
▲ EMP: 195
SQ FT: 70,000
SALES (est): 780.1MM
SALES (corp-wide): 11.9B **Privately Held**
WEB: www.koyousa.com
SIC: 5085 3562 Industrial supplies; ball & roller bearings
PA: Jtekt Corporation
3-5-8, Minamisemba, Chuo-Ku
Osaka OSK 542-0
662 718-451

(G-20280)
KAEDEN CORPORATION
Also Called: Kaeden Books
806 Sharon Dr Ste F (44145-7701)
P.O. Box 16190, Rocky River (44116-0190)
PHONE..............................440 617-1400
Fax: 440 617-1403
Craig Urmston, *President*
Kathlene Urmston, *Vice Pres*
Lisa Stenger, *Accounts Exec*
Anthony Vaoenveno, *Manager*
Grant Urmston, *Director*
▲ EMP: 6
SQ FT: 5,000
SALES (est): 1.1MM **Privately Held**
WEB: www.kaeden.com
SIC: 2731 Book publishing

(G-20281)
LAMOR CORPORATION
841 Hamlet Ln Apt A2 (44145-1673)
PHONE..............................440 871-8000
Thomas Mackey, *CEO*
James Mackey, *President*
Jamie Roehm, *CFO*
▲ EMP: 15
SQ FT: 3,600
SALES (est): 2MM **Privately Held**
WEB: www.lamor.com
SIC: 2899 Oil absorption equipment

(G-20282)
LS STARRETT COMPANY
Webber Gage Div
24500 Detroit Rd (44145-2580)
PHONE..............................440 835-0005
Fax: 440 892-9555
David D Friedel, *Plant Mgr*
D Wickes, *Research*
Carl Stearns, *Engineer*
Brian Morris, *Project Engr*
Roger U Wellington Jr, *CFO*
EMP: 80
SQ FT: 35,000

G E O G R A P H I C

SALES (corp-wide): 209.6MM **Publicly Held**
WEB: www.starrett.com
SIC: 3545 3829 3823 Gauge blocks; measuring tools & machines, machinists' metalworking type; measuring & controlling devices; industrial instrmnts msrmnt display/control process variable
PA: The L S Starrett Company
121 Crescent St
Athol MA 01331
978 249-3551

(G-20283)
MMI TEXTILES INC
Also Called: Ndw Textiles
29260 Clemens Rd Bldg Ii (44145-1020)
PHONE....................................440 899-8050
Amy Hammond, *President*
Joseph Hammond, *Vice Pres*
Nickolas Rivera, *Production*
Molly Feiklowicz, *Human Resources*
▲ EMP: 10
SQ FT: 3,300
SALES (est): 4.9MM **Privately Held**
WEB: www.mmitextiles.com
SIC: 2211 2221 2262 5131 Duck, cotton; manmade & synthetic broadwoven fabrics; chemical coating or treating: manmade broadwoven fabrics; broadwoven fabrics

(G-20284)
MPC INC
835 Canterbury Rd (44145-1420)
PHONE....................................440 835-1405
Peter S Bodonyi, *President*
Joyce Bodonyi, *Corp Secy*
Christopher M Holick, *Vice Pres*
EMP: 15
SQ FT: 14,000
SALES (est): 1.8MM **Privately Held**
WEB: www.mpcsilentwall.com
SIC: 3296 5044 2493 Acoustical board & tile, mineral wool; office equipment; bulletin boards, cork; bulletin boards, wood

(G-20285)
NORDSON CORPORATION (PA)
28601 Clemens Rd (44145-1119)
PHONE....................................440 892-1580
Fax: 440 892-9507
Joseph P Keithley, *Ch of Bd*
Michael F Hilton, *President*
Suprotik Das, *Managing Dir*
J Leaheey, *Counsel*
Robert A Dunn, *Senior VP*
◆ EMP: 58 EST: 1935
SQ FT: 28,000
SALES: 1.8B **Publicly Held**
WEB: www.nordson.com
SIC: 3563 Spraying outfits: metals, paints & chemicals (compressor); robots for industrial spraying, painting, etc.

(G-20286)
NOVO FOAM PRODUCTS LLC
1991 Crocker Rd Ste 600 (44145-6976)
PHONE....................................440 892-3325
EMP: 4
SALES (est): 310K **Privately Held**
SIC: 2821 Mfg Plastic Materials/Resins

(G-20287)
OAKMOOR PALLET
795 Sharon Dr Ste 210 (44145-1542)
PHONE....................................216 926-1858
Michael Keating, *Owner*
EMP: 3 EST: 2011
SALES (est): 318.1K **Privately Held**
SIC: 2448 Pallets, wood & wood with metal

(G-20288)
OAKMOOR PALLET
795 Sharon Dr (44145-1542)
PHONE....................................440 385-7340
EMP: 4
SALES (est): 335K **Privately Held**
SIC: 2448 Pallets, wood & wood with metal

(G-20289)
OMAR MCDOWELL CO
25109 Detroit Rd Ste 320 (44145-2544)
PHONE....................................440 808-2280
Fax: 440 808-2266
O'Mar McDowell, *Principal*

Erin McDowell, *Treasurer*
EMP: 4
SALES (est): 580.5K **Privately Held**
SIC: 3559 Sewing machines & attachments, industrial

(G-20290)
OPEN SIDED MRI CLEVELAND LLC
30400 Detroit Rd Ste 30 (44145-1872)
PHONE....................................804 217-7114
Fax: 440 808-0289
Sharon Keeling, *Principal*
EMP: 3 EST: 2000
SALES (est): 330K **Privately Held**
SIC: 3845 Ultrasonic scanning devices, medical

(G-20291)
PARTY ANIMAL INC
909 Crocker Rd (44145-1030)
PHONE....................................440 471-1030
Jim Cantrall, *President*
Phyllis Cantrall, *Vice Pres*
Jeff Kuzmanoff, *Traffic Mgr*
Danielle Stark, *Opers Staff*
Julie Koenig, *VP Sales*
▲ EMP: 7
SQ FT: 3,800
SALES (est): 1.1MM **Privately Held**
WEB: www.metronet.net
SIC: 2399 Banners, made from fabric

(G-20292)
PENGUIN ENTERPRISES INC
Also Called: PS Copy
869 Canterbury Rd Ste 2 (44145-1492)
PHONE....................................440 899-5110
Fax: 440 899-5113
Phil Seman, *President*
Jim Seman, *Sales Mgr*
EMP: 35
SALES (est): 4.4MM **Privately Held**
WEB: www.ncsports.com
SIC: 2752 2796 2791 2789 Commercial printing, lithographic; commercial printing, offset; platemaking services; typesetting; bookbinding & related work; commercial printing

(G-20293)
PINES MANUFACTURING INC (PA)
Also Called: Pines Technology
29100 Lakeland Blvd (44145)
PHONE....................................440 835-5553
Fax: 440 835-5556
Donald Rebar, *Ch of Bd*
Ian Williamson, *President*
Mickey McNamara, *Plant Mgr*
Dan Wilczynski, *Plant Mgr*
Darlene Wenzler, *Purchasing*
▲ EMP: 43
SQ FT: 48,000
SALES (est): 13.6MM **Privately Held**
WEB: www.pines-mfg.com
SIC: 5084 3542 3549 3547 Industrial machinery & equipment; bending machines; metalworking machinery; rolling mill machinery

(G-20294)
PINES MANUFACTURING INC
Also Called: H & H Tooling
30505 Clemens Rd (44145-1011)
PHONE....................................440 835-5553
John Aragon, *Foreman/Supr*
Lynn Bohn, *Purchasing*
Janet Brosius, *Human Res Dir*
Lonnie Smiley, *Branch Mgr*
Shirley Willits, *Administration*
EMP: 45 **Privately Held**
WEB: www.pines-mfg.com
SIC: 3544 8661 3547 3498 Special dies, tools, jigs & fixtures; religious organizations; rolling mill machinery; fabricated pipe & fittings
PA: Pines Manufacturing, Inc.
29100 Lakeland Blvd
Westlake OH 44145

(G-20295)
PINNACLE SALES INC
159 Crocker Park Blvd # 400 (44145-8131)
P.O. Box 45376 (44145-0376)
PHONE....................................440 777-2544

James G Loparich, *President*
EMP: 3
SALES (est): 319.4K **Privately Held**
SIC: 5044 5085 3999 Office equipment; industrial supplies; barber & beauty shop equipment

(G-20296)
PIPE LINE DEVELOPMENT COMPANY
Also Called: Plidco Ppline Repr Ppline Mint
870 Canterbury Rd (44145-1490)
PHONE....................................440 871-5700
Fax: 440 871-9577
Kimberly Smith, *President*
Julie Tcel, *Purchasing*
Julie Teel, *Purchasing*
Mary Smith, *QC Mgr*
Reinhard Bauer, *Engineer*
▲ EMP: 90 EST: 1949
SQ FT: 70,000
SALES (est): 26.7MM **Privately Held**
WEB: www.plidco.com
SIC: 3498 Pipe fittings, fabricated from purchased pipe

(G-20297)
PREMAR MANUFACTURING LTD
803 Sharon Dr (44145-1522)
PHONE....................................440 250-0373
Jonathan Krapf, *Partner*
Janet Krapf, *Partner*
EMP: 3
SALES (est): 468.6K **Privately Held**
WEB: www.premar.com
SIC: 3399 Flakes, metal

(G-20298)
Q-LAB CORPORATION (PA)
800 Canterbury Rd (44145-1419)
PHONE....................................440 835-8700
Fax: 440 835-8738
Douglas M Grossman, *President*
Brad Reis, *Vice Pres*
Ron Roberts, *Vice Pres*
Gary Simecek, *Vice Pres*
Kirk Wilhelm, *CFO*
▲ EMP: 53 EST: 1956
SQ FT: 40,000
SALES (est): 18.8MM **Privately Held**
WEB: www.q-lab.com
SIC: 3823 3829 3826 Industrial instrmnts msrmnt display/control process variable; measuring & controlling devices; analytical instruments

(G-20299)
R AND J CORPORATION
Also Called: Haynes Manufacturing Company
24142 Detroit Rd (44145-1515)
PHONE....................................440 871-6009
Fax: 440 871-0855
Beth Kloos, *President*
Timothy Kloos, *Vice Pres*
Sheri Bohning, *Purchasing*
Ric Thornton, *Project Engr*
Joanne Randolph, *Sales Staff*
EMP: 42 EST: 1902
SQ FT: 23,000
SALES (est): 17.1MM **Privately Held**
WEB: www.haynesmfg.com
SIC: 3556 5084 7389 3053 Food products machinery; food industry machinery; design, commercial & industrial; gaskets, packing & sealing devices; lubricating oils & greases

(G-20300)
RAM SENSORS INC
875 Canterbury Rd Ste 875 (44145-1488)
PHONE....................................440 835-3540
Connie Field, *Manager*
EMP: 8
SALES (corp-wide): 3.1MM **Privately Held**
WEB: www.ramsensors.com
SIC: 3315 Wire, steel: insulated or armored
PA: Ram Sensors Inc
875 Canterbury Rd
Cleveland OH 44145
440 835-3540

(G-20301)
RECTOR INC
Also Called: Profiles In Diversity Journal
1991 Crocker Rd Ste 320 (44145-6971)
P.O. Box 45605, Cleveland (44145-0605)
PHONE....................................440 892-0444
Jim Rector, *President*
John Murphey, *Editor*
Damian Johnson, *Mktg Dir*
James Gorman, *Info Tech Dir*
EMP: 7
SQ FT: 1,000
SALES (est): 680K **Privately Held**
WEB: www.diversityjournal.com
SIC: 2721 Magazines: publishing only, not printed on site

(G-20302)
RESOURCE DEVELOPMENT CO LLC
30205 Clemens Rd Ste B (44145-1055)
PHONE....................................440 617-9087
P Connaughton, *Branch Mgr*
EMP: 4
SALES (corp-wide): 27.3MM **Privately Held**
SIC: 2741 Technical manuals: publishing only, not printed on site
HQ: Resource Development Company, Llc
2930 S Yale Ave
Tulsa OK 74114
248 646-2300

(G-20303)
ROBERT A REICH COMPANY
24930 Detroit Rd D (44145-2528)
P.O. Box 45490 (44145-0490)
PHONE....................................440 808-0033
Fax: 440 808-0055
Robert A Reich III, *President*
Page Reich, *Corp Secy*
Adam J Reich, *Vice Pres*
EMP: 4
SQ FT: 6,000
SALES (est): 310K **Privately Held**
SIC: 3399 Metal fasteners

(G-20304)
ROMARK INDUSTRIES INC
24500 Center Ridge Rd # 250 (44145-5602)
PHONE....................................440 333-5480
Sheryl P Greenleaf, *President*
Alan R Greenleaf, *Vice Pres*
▲ EMP: 5
SQ FT: 1,200
SALES: 2MM **Privately Held**
SIC: 3462 Railroad, construction & mining forgings

(G-20305)
S J T ENTERPRISES INC
28045 Ranney Pkwy Ste B (44145-1144)
PHONE....................................440 617-1100
Timothy J Smith, *President*
Tami Haggerty, *Graphic Designe*
▲ EMP: 22
SQ FT: 17,000
SALES (est): 2.2MM **Privately Held**
WEB: www.sjtent.com
SIC: 2741 Miscellaneous publishing

(G-20306)
SCOTT FETZER COMPANY (DH)
28800 Clemens Rd (44145-1197)
PHONE....................................440 892-3000
Robert McBride, *CEO*
William Stephans, *Treasurer*
John Gretta, *Asst Treas*
Trish Scanlon, *Admin Sec*
EMP: 13
SQ FT: 2,000
SALES: 2.8MM
SALES (corp-wide): 223.6B **Publicly Held**
SIC: 2731 2741 5961 Textbooks: publishing only, not printed on site; atlases: publishing only, not printed on site; books, mail order (except book clubs)
HQ: Bhsf Inc.
1440 Kiewit Plz
Omaha NE 68131
402 346-1400

(G-20307)
SEST INC
24509 Annie Ln (44145-4144)
PHONE..................................440 777-9777
Ashwin Shah, *President*
EMP: 10 EST: 1997
SQ FT: 1,000
SALES (est): 986.1K **Privately Held**
WEB: www.sest.com
SIC: 8711 7373 7372 7371 Engineering services; computer-aided engineering (CAE) systems service; application computer software; computer software development & applications; computer software development

(G-20308)
SHAMROCK COMPANIES INC (PA)
24090 Detroit Rd (44145-1513)
P.O. Box 450980 (44145-0623)
PHONE..................................440 899-9510
Fax: 440 899-3288
Tim Connor, *CEO*
Robert E Troop, *Ch of Bd*
Tom Backus, *Business Mgr*
Dave Fechter, *COO*
Matthew Balmer, *Plant Mgr*
▲ EMP: 65
SQ FT: 42,500
SALES (est): 100.1MM **Privately Held**
WEB: www.shamrockcompanies.net
SIC: 5112 5199 7336 7389 Business forms; advertising specialties; art design services; brokers' services; commercial printing, gravure; pleating & stitching

(G-20309)
SPECTRE SENSORS INC (PA)
2392 Georgia Dr (44145-5806)
PHONE..................................440 250-0372
Glen Keller, *Ch of Bd*
John Keller, *President*
EMP: 4
SALES: 4MM **Privately Held**
WEB: www.spectresensors.com
SIC: 3612 Electronic meter transformers

(G-20310)
SPECTRE SENSORS INC
2392 Georgia Dr (44145-5806)
PHONE..................................440 250-0616
EMP: 5
SALES (corp-wide): 4MM **Privately Held**
SIC: 3612 Electronic meter transformers
PA: Spectre Sensors, Inc.
2392 Georgia Dr
Westlake OH 44145
440 250-0372

(G-20311)
STAR METAL PRODUCTS CO INC (PA)
30405 Clemens Rd (44145-1018)
PHONE..................................440 899-7000
Fax: 440 899-7171
John C Murray, *CEO*
Rita A Dunham, *Principal*
Mary C Reidy, *Principal*
Arthur Stenzel, *Principal*
Eleanor V Murray, *Treasurer*
EMP: 60 EST: 1958
SQ FT: 24,000
SALES (est): 12MM **Privately Held**
WEB: www.starmetal.com
SIC: 3545 Machine tool attachments & accessories

(G-20312)
STARBRINGER MEDIA GROUP LTD
871 Canterbury Rd Ste B (44145-1482)
PHONE..................................440 871-5448
Sharon Klingler, *President*
EMP: 4
SALES (est): 335.1K **Privately Held**
WEB: www.starbringermedia.com
SIC: 2741 Miscellaneous publishing

(G-20313)
STRUERS INC (HQ)
24766 Detroit Rd (44145-2525)
PHONE..................................440 871-0071
Fax: 440 871-8188
Bente Freiberg, *President*

Christopher Sopko, *President*
Bill Thompson, *General Mgr*
Roland Zale, *Opers Mgr*
Steen Jensen, *Treasurer*
◆ EMP: 58 EST: 1875
SALES (est): 13.2MM
SALES (corp-wide): 111.8MM **Privately Held**
WEB: www.logitech-us.com
SIC: 3829 Measuring & controlling devices
PA: Struers Aps
Pederstrupvej 84
Ballerup 2750
446 008-00

(G-20314)
SWORD FURS
25112 Center Ridge Rd (44145-4115)
PHONE..................................440 249-5001
Jim Sword, *Owner*
EMP: 3
SALES (est): 120K **Privately Held**
SIC: 3999 Furs

(G-20315)
THE SHELBY CO
865 Canterbury Rd (44145-1420)
PHONE..................................440 871-9901
Fax: 440 871-0326
Richard J Rapacz, *President*
Sue Hintze, *Exec VP*
Wayne McGan, *Controller*
EMP: 33 EST: 1923
SQ FT: 50,000
SALES (est): 8.8MM **Privately Held**
WEB: www.shelbycompany.com
SIC: 2657 2653 Folding paperboard boxes; display items, corrugated: made from purchased materials

(G-20316)
TIMCAL AMERICA INC
29299 Clemens Rd Ste 1l (44145-1051)
PHONE..................................440 871-7504
Fax: 440 871-6026
Davide Cattaneo, *General Mgr*
Axel Wappler, *Principal*
Fabrizio Corti, *Senior VP*
Ivan M Ini, *Senior VP*
Fabio Rota, *Senior VP*
▲ EMP: 7
SALES (est): 1.1MM
SALES (corp-wide): 1.2MM **Privately Held**
SIC: 3624 Carbon & graphite products
HQ: Imerys Graphite & Carbon Switzerland Sa
Strada Industriale 12
Bodio TI
918 732-010

(G-20317)
VISIBLE SOLUTIONS INC (PA)
1991 Crocker Rd Ste 222 (44145-6971)
PHONE..................................440 925-2810
Sandra L Haftl, *President*
Lyle Storey, *Vice Pres*
Debby Kitchell, *Office Mgr*
EMP: 4
SQ FT: 850 **Privately Held**
WEB: www.visi-sol.com
SIC: 2899 3714 Deicing or defrosting fluid; windshield wiper systems, motor vehicle

(G-20318)
VISION GRAPHIX INC
Also Called: AlphaGraphics Westlake
29260 Clemens Rd Ste A (44145-1076)
PHONE..................................440 835-6540
Jeff Brant Jr, *President*
Eleanor Brant, *Treasurer*
EMP: 4
SQ FT: 4,000
SALES (est): 600K **Privately Held**
WEB: www.visiongraphixinc.com
SIC: 2752 Commercial printing, lithographic

(G-20319)
WESTERN/SCOTT FETZER COMPANY
Also Called: Western Enterprises
875 Bassett Rd (44145-1142)
PHONE..................................440 871-2160
John McCluskey, *Plant Mgr*
Dan Hrdlicka, *Purch Agent*

Gary Heeman, *Branch Mgr*
Byron Crampton, *Manager*
Allan Pratt, *Manager*
EMP: 250
SALES (corp-wide): 223.6B **Publicly Held**
SIC: 3635 Household vacuum cleaners
HQ: Western/Scott Fetzer Company
28800 Clemens Rd
Westlake OH 44145

(G-20320)
WESTERN/SCOTT FETZER COMPANY (DH)
28800 Clemens Rd (44145-1134)
PHONE..................................440 892-3000
Robert D McBride, *CEO*
Kenneth Semelsberger, *Ch of Bd*
John Gretta, *Treasurer*
◆ EMP: 45
SALES (est): 43.2MM
SALES (corp-wide): 223.6B **Publicly Held**
SIC: 3635 Household vacuum cleaners
HQ: The Scott Fetzer Company
28800 Clemens Rd
Westlake OH 44145
440 892-3000

(G-20321)
WIDE AREA MEDIA LLC
24500 Center Ridge Rd # 205 (44145-5602)
P.O. Box 45285 (44145-0285)
PHONE..................................440 356-3133
Roger Vichill, *Vice Pres*
Nicholas Praenkner, *Officer*
Brian Clancy,
EMP: 3
SALES (est): 421K **Privately Held**
WEB: www.wideareamedia.com
SIC: 8742 3993 Management consulting services; electric signs; scoreboards, electric

(G-20322)
WOODBURY VINEYARDS INC (PA)
2001 Crocker Rd Ste 440 (44145-6968)
PHONE..................................440 835-2828
Joseph D Carney, *CEO*
Gary F Woodbury, *COO*
EMP: 2
SALES (est): 1.5MM **Privately Held**
WEB: www.woodburyvineyards.com
SIC: 2084 Wines

(G-20323)
XIM PRODUCTS INC
1169 Bassett Rd (44145-1112)
P.O. Box 45516 (44145-0516)
PHONE..................................440 871-4737
Fax: 440 871-3027
Richard Hardy, *President*
Gary Hannah, *Vice Pres*
Joseph Wolf, *Vice Pres*
Stephen Sabanos, *Accounts Mgr*
▲ EMP: 21 EST: 1935
SQ FT: 30,000
SALES (est): 4.1MM **Privately Held**
WEB: www.ximbonder.com
SIC: 2851 Paints & allied products

Weston
Wood County

(G-20324)
CRESSET CHEMICAL CO INC (PA)
13255 Main St (43569-9544)
P.O. Box 367 (43569-0367)
PHONE..................................419 669-2041
Fax: 419 669-2200
George F Baty, *Ch of Bd*
Mike Baty, *President*
Robert Criner, *Purchasing*
Jim Renda, *VP Sales*
Michael Baez, *Sales Mgr*
▼ EMP: 10 EST: 1946
SQ FT: 2,000

SALES (est): 1.9MM **Privately Held**
WEB: www.cresset.com
SIC: 2899 2841 Chemical preparations; soap & other detergents

(G-20325)
CRESSET CHEMICAL CO INC
13490 Silver St (43569-9522)
PHONE..................................419 669-2041
George Baty, *Manager*
EMP: 10
SALES (corp-wide): 1.9MM **Privately Held**
WEB: www.cresset.com
SIC: 2841 Soap & other detergents
PA: Cresset Chemical Co Inc
13255 Main St
Weston OH 43569
419 669-2041

(G-20326)
MCM PRECISION CASTINGS INC
13133 Beech St (43569-9516)
PHONE..................................419 669-3226
Fax: 419 669-3227
Donald Marion, *President*
Roger Davis, *Financial Exec*
Abbey Strayer, *Manager*
EMP: 20
SQ FT: 7,896
SALES: 1.2MM **Privately Held**
SIC: 3369 Castings, except die-castings, precision

(G-20327)
VITAKRAFT SUN SEED INC
20584 Long Judson Rd (43569-9639)
P.O. Box 33, Bowling Green (43402-0033)
PHONE..................................419 832-1641
Brent Weinmann, *President*
Jim Roe, *Purch Mgr*
Sue Stokes, *Bookkeeper*
Debbie Thomas, *Sales Staff*
Ron Reid, *Manager*
▲ EMP: 60
SQ FT: 50,000
SALES (est): 13MM **Privately Held**
WEB: www.sunseed.com
SIC: 2048 2047 Bird food, prepared; feeds, specialty: mice, guinea pig, etc.; dog & cat food

---

Wharton
Wyandot County

(G-20328)
COUPLED PRODUCTS LLC
200 E Wyandotte St (43359)
PHONE..................................419 294-3827
Joe Kochan, *Manager*
EMP: 200
SQ FT: 3,000
SALES (corp-wide): 120.3MM **Privately Held**
SIC: 3714 Motor vehicle parts & accessories
PA: Coupled Products Llc
2651 S 600 E
Columbia City IN 46725
260 248-3200

Wheelersburg
Scioto County

(G-20329)
CONNIES CANDLES
9103 Ohio River Rd (45694-1927)
P.O. Box 97 (45694-0097)
PHONE..................................740 574-1224
Connie Potters, *Owner*
William Potters, *Co-Owner*
EMP: 6 EST: 1997
SALES: 300K **Privately Held**
WEB: www.conniescandles.com
SIC: 3999 Candles

(PA)=Parent Co (HQ)=Headquarters (DH)=Div Headquarters
✪ = New Business established in last 2 years

GEOGRAPHIC

(G-20330)
FORREST RAWLINS
Also Called: Rawlins Pallet & Lumber
902 Great Meadow Rd (45694-8465)
PHONE...................................740 778-3366
Forrest Rawlins, *Owner*
Debra Rawlins, *Co-Owner*
EMP: 4
SQ FT: 5,000
SALES: 150K **Privately Held**
SIC: 2448 Wood pallets & skids

(G-20331)
FUHRMANN ORCHARDS LLC
510 Hansgen Morgan Rd (45694-8839)
PHONE...................................740 776-6406
Fax: 740 766-7557
Paul William Fuhrmann, *Partner*
Susan Fuhrmann, *Partner*
EMP: 5
SALES (est): 355.2K **Privately Held**
SIC: 0175 0161 2099 0181 Peach or-
chard; apple orchard; nectarine orchard;
cantaloupe farm; pepper farm, sweet &
hot (vegetables); cider, nonalcoholic; bed-
ding plants, growing of

(G-20332)
GREG BLUME
Also Called: Copyrite Printing
7459 Ohio River Rd (45694)
P.O. Box 388 (45694-0388)
PHONE...................................740 574-2308
Fax: 740 574-5713
Greg Blume, *Owner*
EMP: 6
SALES: 330K **Privately Held**
SIC: 2752 5999 2791 2789 Commercial
printing, lithographic; commercial printing,
offset; trophies & plaques; typesetting;
bookbinding & related work

(G-20333)
**PATRIOT HOLDINGS UNLIMITED
LLC**
Also Called: Patriot Building Solutions
956 Patriot Ridge Dr (45694-7822)
P.O. Box 58 (45694-0058)
PHONE...................................740 574-2112
Michael Russell, *Mng Member*
Kimberly Russell,
EMP: 4
SQ FT: 4,400
SALES: 50K **Privately Held**
SIC: 6553 3272 Real property subdividers
& developers, cemetery lots only; building
materials, except block or brick: concrete

(G-20334)
SHIRT STOP LLC
11769 Gallia Pike Rd (45694-8438)
PHONE...................................740 574-4774
Peggy Ruggles, *Partner*
Terri Laxton, *Partner*
EMP: 4
SALES (est): 466.5K **Privately Held**
SIC: 2261 Screen printing of cotton broad-
woven fabrics

(G-20335)
**TRI-AMERICA CONTRACTORS
INC (PA)**
1664 State Route 522 (45694-7828)
PHONE...................................740 574-0148
Teresa Smith, *CEO*
Scott Taylor, *President*
John Mauk, *General Mgr*
Gregory Stanley, *General Mgr*
Paul Montgomery, *Superintendent*
EMP: 37
SQ FT: 34,000
SALES: 12MM **Privately Held**
WEB: www.triaminc.com
SIC: 3498 3441 1629 Fabricated pipe &
fittings; fabricated structural metal; indus-
trial plant construction

(G-20336)
**TRI-AMERICA CONTRACTORS
INC**
1664 State Route 522 (45694-7828)
PHONE...................................740 574-0148
Fax: 740 574-1440
Teresa Smith, *Branch Mgr*
EMP: 22

SALES (corp-wide): 12MM **Privately
Held**
SIC: 3498 Fabricated pipe & fittings
PA: Tri-America Contractors, Inc.
1664 State Route 522
Wheelersburg OH 45694
740 574-0148

Whitehouse
Lucas County

(G-20337)
BASF CORPORATION
Coatings & Colorants Division
6125 Industrial Pkwy (43571-9595)
P.O. Box 2757 (43571-0757)
PHONE...................................419 877-0876
Fax: 419 877-0798
Kenneth Terry, *Engrg Dir*
Karl A Schnapp, *Administration*
EMP: 136
SQ FT: 20,000
SALES (corp-wide): 60.8B **Privately Held**
WEB: www.basf.com
SIC: 2869 Industrial organic chemicals
HQ: Basf Corporation
100 Park Ave
Florham Park NJ 07932
973 245-6000

(G-20338)
BITTERSWEET INC (PA)
Also Called: Bittersweet Farms
12660 Archbold Whthuse Rd (43571-9566)
PHONE...................................419 875-6986
Fax: 419 875-5593
Julie Horns, *General Mgr*
Connie Olinger, *Vice Pres*
Valerie French, *Manager*
Vicki Obee-Hilty, *Exec Dir*
Charles Flowers, *Exec Dir*
EMP: 49
SQ FT: 20,000
SALES: 6.8MM **Privately Held**
WEB: www.bittersweetfarms.org
SIC: 8361 2032 8052 Home for the men-
tally handicapped; canned specialties; in-
termediate care facilities

(G-20339)
G L HELLER CO INC
6246 Industrial Pkwy (43571-9594)
PHONE...................................419 877-5122
Fax: 419 877-9267
Gary Lee Heller, *President*
M Jean Heller, *Corp Secy*
Todd Heller, *Manager*
EMP: 14
SQ FT: 17,000
SALES (est): 2.1MM **Privately Held**
SIC: 3599 Machine & other job shop work

(G-20340)
GENERAL INTL PWR PDTS LLC
6243 Industrial Pkwy (43571-9594)
PHONE...................................419 877-5234
Craig Valentine, *President*
EMP: 6
SALES (est): 961.6K
SALES (corp-wide): 9.1MM **Privately
Held**
SIC: 3553 Woodworking machinery
PA: Dmt Holdings, Inc.
33400 9th Ave S Ste 104
Federal Way WA 98003
253 545-0015

(G-20341)
KENNAMETAL INC
6325 Industrial Pkwy (43571-9792)
PHONE...................................419 877-5358
Jerry Natter, *Engineer*
Fred Morgan, *Manager*
Dennis Wittenmeyer, *Manager*
Lloyd Stamper, *Software Dev*
Richard Canada, *Administration*
EMP: 118
SALES (corp-wide): 2.1B **Publicly Held**
SIC: 3545 Cutting tools for machine tools
PA: Kennametal Inc.
600 Grant St Ste 5100
Pittsburgh PA 15219
412 248-8200

(G-20342)
NOVA INDUSTRIAL MACHINE CO
10843 Little Creek Dr (43571-9516)
PHONE...................................419 535-0800
Fax: 419 535-0670
Larry J Barney, *President*
Scott Horen, *Project Mgr*
EMP: 12
SQ FT: 12,000
SALES (est): 1.7MM **Privately Held**
SIC: 3549 Coiling machinery

(G-20343)
PROHOS INC
10755 Logan St (43571-9698)
PHONE...................................419 877-0153
Fax: 419 877-0920
William A Green, *President*
Joan Green, *Corp Secy*
Kevin Green, *Vice Pres*
EMP: 9
SQ FT: 18,000
SALES (est): 920K **Privately Held**
WEB: www.prohos-inc.com
SIC: 3599 Machine shop, jobbing & repair

(G-20344)
**PROHOS MANUFACTURING CO
INC**
10755 Logan St (43571-9698)
PHONE...................................419 877-0153
William Green, *President*
Joan Green, *Corp Secy*
Kevin Green, *Vice Pres*
EMP: 8
SQ FT: 18,000
SALES: 600K **Privately Held**
SIC: 3599 Machine shop, jobbing & repair;
machine & other job shop work

(G-20345)
**REXAM BEVERAGE CAN
COMPANY**
10444 Waterville St (43571-9175)
PHONE...................................419 877-0401
David Lewis, *Branch Mgr*
EMP: 120
SQ FT: 220,000
SALES (corp-wide): 9B **Publicly Held**
SIC: 3411 3354 Metal cans; aluminum ex-
truded products
HQ: Rexam Beverage Can Company
8770 W Bryn Mawr Ave Fl 8
Chicago IL 60631
773 399-3000

Wickliffe
Lake County

(G-20346)
ABB AUTOMATION INC
29801 Euclid Ave (44092-1898)
PHONE...................................440 347-9668
Mark Taft, *Manager*
EMP: 425
SALES (est): 75.4MM **Privately Held**
SIC: 3822 Hydronic controls

(G-20347)
ABB INC
Also Called: ABB Electric Systems
29801 Euclid Ave (44092-1898)
PHONE...................................440 585-8500
Fax: 440 585-8172
Al Yedid, *Branch Mgr*
Rick Hamblen, *Manager*
Prentice Trickette, *Manager*
Patrick Farmer, *IT/INT Sup*
Anders Sjoelin, *Admin Sec*
EMP: 75
SALES (corp-wide): 33.8B **Privately Held**
WEB: www.elsterelectricity.com
SIC: 3612 Transformers, except electric;
power & distribution transformers; distri-
bution transformers, electric; electronic
meter transformers
HQ: Abb Inc.
12040 Regency Pkwy # 200
Cary NC 27518
919 856-2360

(G-20348)
ABB INC
Also Called: Bailey Controls
1400 Worden Rd (44092)
PHONE...................................440 585-8500
Fax: 440 585-5101
William Sulivan, *Branch Mgr*
EMP: 250
SALES (corp-wide): 33.8B **Privately Held**
WEB: www.elsterelectricity.com
SIC: 3823 5084 Industrial instrmnts
msrmnt display/control process variable;
controllers for process variables, all types;
instruments & control equipment; control-
ling instruments & accessories; indicating
instruments & accessories
HQ: Abb Inc.
12040 Regency Pkwy # 200
Cary NC 27518
919 856-2360

(G-20349)
ABB INC
29801 Euclid Ave (44092-1898)
PHONE...................................440 585-8500
Steve Hawkins, *Principal*
EMP: 5
SALES (corp-wide): 33.8B **Privately Held**
WEB: www.elsterelectricity.com
SIC: 3823 Industrial instrmnts msrmnt dis-
play/control process variable
HQ: Abb Inc.
12040 Regency Pkwy # 200
Cary NC 27518
919 856-2360

(G-20350)
**ACCURATE PLASMA CUTTING
INC**
1271 E 289th St (44092-2358)
P.O. Box 310 (44092-0310)
PHONE...................................440 943-1655
Fax: 440 943-2550
Gary Smith, *President*
EMP: 12
SALES (est): 2MM **Privately Held**
SIC: 3541 Plasma process metal cutting
machines

(G-20351)
**AJAX MANUFACTURING
COMPANY**
Also Called: Ajax - Ceco Manufacturing Co
29100 Lakeland Blvd (44092-2323)
PHONE...................................440 295-0244
Fax: 440 295-0245
Charlie Crout, *President*
Edward Lyons, *Business Mgr*
Barry Yost, *Purch Mgr*
Jack Specker, *Purchasing*
Johanna Markko, *Sales Staff*
▲ EMP: 21
SALES (est): 4.6MM
SALES (corp-wide): 1.2B **Publicly Held**
WEB: www.ajax-ceco.com
SIC: 3542 Forging machinery & hammers
HQ: Park-Ohio Industries, Inc.
6065 Parkland Blvd Ste 1
Cleveland OH 44124
440 947-2000

(G-20352)
**AJAX TOCCO MAGNETHERMIC
CORP**
Also Called: Pines Engineering
29100 Lakeland Blvd (44092-2323)
PHONE...................................440 278-7200
Thomas Illencik, *President*
Kile F Snyder, *General Mgr*
James Focareto, *Vice Pres*
Dianne Schwab, *Associate*
EMP: 193
SALES (corp-wide): 1.2B **Publicly Held**
SIC: 3542 Machine tools, metal forming
type; brakes, metal forming
HQ: Ajax Tocco Magnethermic Corporation
1745 Overland Ave Ne
Warren OH 44483
330 372-8511

(G-20353)
AMERICAN CONTROLS INC
1340 Lloyd Rd (44092-2381)
PHONE...................................440 944-9735
Fax: 440 944-3076

▲ = Import ▼=Export
◆ =Import/Export

Donald G Nettis, *President*
Don Nettis Sr, *Vice Pres*
Nancy Mann, *Accounts Mgr*
▲ **EMP:** 20
SQ FT: 25,000
SALES (est): 4.4MM **Privately Held**
SIC: 3613 8711 Control panels, electric;
electrical or electronic engineering

(G-20354)
ANDY RUSSO JR INC
Also Called: A R J
29200 Anderson Rd (44092-2312)
PHONE..............................440 585-1456
Andy Russo Jr, *President*
Richard J Silvestro, *Principal*
EMP: 15
SQ FT: 30,000
SALES (est): 2.2MM **Privately Held**
WEB: www.arjinc.net
SIC: 1761 3444 Ceilings, metal: erection &
repair; sheet metalwork

(G-20355)
BACO MANUFACTURING CORP
29175 Anderson Rd (44092-2357)
P.O. Box 329 (44092-0329)
PHONE..............................440 585-5858
Fax: 440 585-5397
John Garron, *President*
Marion Gulic, *President*
Robert A Gulic, *President*
EMP: 4
SQ FT: 4,000
SALES: 600K **Privately Held**
SIC: 3599 Machine shop, jobbing & repair

(G-20356)
BAR TECH SERVICE INC
30012 Lakeland Blvd (44092-1745)
PHONE..............................440 943-5286
Fax: 440 943-5296
Randy Demell, *President*
EMP: 5
SALES (est): 591.3K **Privately Held**
WEB: www.bartechdesign.com
SIC: 3541 Machine tool replacement & re-
pair parts, metal cutting types

(G-20357)
BERTIN STEEL PROCESSING INC
1271 E 289th St Ste 1 (44092-2358)
PHONE..............................440 943-0094
Fax: 440 585-1532
Bernard D'Ambrosi, *President*
Denny Perrino, *Vice Pres*
Fritz Michalk, *Plant Mgr*
Jim Connelley, *QC Mgr*
Tina Kaplan, *Controller*
▲ **EMP:** 47
SQ FT: 300,000
SALES (est): 7.8MM **Privately Held**
WEB: www.bertinsteel.com
SIC: 3312 Blast Furnace-Steel Works

(G-20358)
BEST PLATING RACK CORP
1321 E 289th St (44092-2350)
PHONE..............................440 944-3270
Robert Evatz, *Owner*
Barbara Evatz, *Co-Owner*
William Evatz, *Co-Owner*
EMP: 12
SALES (est): 1.4MM **Privately Held**
SIC: 3471 Plating of metals or formed
products

(G-20359)
BICKFORD LABORATORIES INC
Also Called: Bickford Flavors
1197 E 305th St (44092-1520)
PHONE..............................440 354-7747
Fax: 216 531-2006
Barbara Sofer, *President*
EMP: 5
SQ FT: 2,000
SALES: 100K **Privately Held**
WEB: www.bickfordflavors.com
SIC: 2087 Flavoring extracts & syrups

(G-20360)
BISON WLDG & FABRICATION INC
29301 Clayton Ave (44092-1907)
PHONE..............................440 944-4770

Fax: 440 944-7028
Theresa Bice, *President*
Lloyd Bice, *Vice Pres*
EMP: 5
SQ FT: 15,000
SALES: 675.1K **Privately Held**
SIC: 3441 Fabricated structural metal

(G-20361)
BREWER COMPANY
30060 Lakeland Blvd (44092-1745)
PHONE..............................440 944-3800
Fax: 440 944-1492
S Choromanski, *General Mgr*
Stephen Root, *Div Sub Head*
EMP: 25
SQ FT: 73,188
SALES (corp-wide): 50MM **Privately
Held**
WEB: www.thebrewerco.com
SIC: 2952 Coating compounds, tar
PA: The Brewer Company
1354 Us Route 50
Milford OH 45150
800 394-0017

(G-20362)
CLEVELAND SPECIAL TOOL INC
1351 E 286th St (44092-2505)
PHONE..............................440 944-1600
Fax: 440 944-1900
Jim Treblas, *President*
EMP: 13 **EST:** 1966
SQ FT: 6,000
SALES (est): 2.3MM **Privately Held**
SIC: 3599 Machine shop, jobbing & repair

(G-20363)
CP CHEMICALS GROUP LP
Also Called: CP Trading Group
28960 Lakeland Blvd (44092-2321)
PHONE..............................440 833-3000
Joseph Patrick III, *President*
Joe Patrick, *Purchasing*
Vince Cardella, *Manager*
EMP: 54
SALES (est): 10MM **Privately Held**
SIC: 2899 Chemical preparations

(G-20364)
DSM INDUSTRIES INC
1340 E 289th St (44092-2304)
PHONE..............................440 585-1100
Scott Soble, *President*
David Soble, *Controller*
John Dempsey, *Manager*
Chris Fisher, *MIS Dir*
▲ **EMP:** 16
SQ FT: 106,000
SALES (est): 3.7MM **Privately Held**
WEB: www.diamondshine.com
SIC: 2841 Soap: granulated, liquid, cake,
flaked or chip; detergents, synthetic or-
ganic or inorganic alkaline

(G-20365)
EUCLID SPRING CO
30006 Lakeland Blvd (44092-1745)
PHONE..............................440 943-3213
Fax: 440 943-4668
James L Marsey, *President*
Donald Seaburn, *Principal*
William J Marsey, *Vice Pres*
EMP: 22 **EST:** 1950
SQ FT: 7,000
SALES (est): 4MM **Privately Held**
WEB: www.euclidspring.com
SIC: 3493 Coiled flat springs

(G-20366)
GREAT LAKES CRUSHING LTD
30831 Euclid Ave (44092-1042)
PHONE..............................440 944-5500
Fax: 440 953-8461
Mark M Belich, *General Ptnr*
Maxine Belich, *Manager*
EMP: 47 **EST:** 1996
SQ FT: 10,000
SALES (est): 23.9MM **Privately Held**
SIC: 1429 7359 1623 1629 Igneous rock,
crushed & broken-quarrying; equipment
rental & leasing; office machine rental, ex-
cept computers; underground utilities con-
tractor; land clearing contractor; grading

(G-20367)
HAWTHORNE TOOL LLC
1340 Lloyd Rd Ste C (44092-2381)
PHONE..............................440 516-1891
Dominic Rega, *President*
Don G Nettis,
EMP: 10
SALES (est): 860K **Privately Held**
SIC: 3544 Dies & die holders for metal cut-
ting, forming, die casting; die springs

(G-20368)
HI TECMETAL GROUP INC
Also Called: Brite Brazing
28910 Lakeland Blvd (44092-2321)
PHONE..............................440 373-5101
Fax: 440 426-6837
Scott Featherston, *Engineer*
Duane Heinrich, *Manager*
EMP: 40
SALES (corp-wide): 22.9MM **Privately
Held**
SIC: 3398 7692 Metal heat treating; weld-
ing repair
PA: Hi Tecmetal Group Inc
1101 E 55th St
Cleveland OH 44103
216 881-8100

(G-20369)
KINETIC TECHNOLOGIES INC
1350 Rockefeller Rd (44092-1930)
PHONE..............................440 943-4111
Larry Tyler, *President*
John Neumann, *Vice Pres*
Amy Blueter, *VP Opers*
Irene Vail, *Manager*
EMP: 17
SQ FT: 1,000
SALES (est): 5.3MM **Privately Held**
WEB: www.ktecinc.com
SIC: 3537 Industrial trucks & tractors

(G-20370)
LUBRIZOL CORPORATION (HQ)
Also Called: Lubricant Additives
29400 Lakeland Blvd (44092-2298)
PHONE..............................440 943-4200
Fax: 440 347-2616
James L Hambrick, *President*
Rick Deel, *Fire Chief*
Tom Weyenberg, *Business Mgr*
Stephen F Kirk, *COO*
Donald W Bogus, *Vice Pres*
◆ **EMP:** 1300
SALES (est): 5.9B
SALES (corp-wide): 223.6B **Publicly
Held**
WEB: www.lubrizol.com
SIC: 2899 2869 Oil treating compounds;
industrial organic chemicals
PA: Berkshire Hathaway Inc.
3555 Farnam St Ste 1440
Omaha NE 68131
402 346-1400

(G-20371)
MASTER GRINDING COMPANY INC
28917 Anderson Rd (44092-2307)
PHONE..............................440 944-3680
Fax: 440 944-3681
Brad Brown, *President*
Joy Brown, *Vice Pres*
Rich Fairbanks, *Manager*
EMP: 3
SQ FT: 3,000
SALES: 300K **Privately Held**
SIC: 3541 Grinding machines, metalwork-
ing

(G-20372)
MATTEO ALUMINUM INC
1261 E 289th St (44092-2367)
PHONE..............................440 585-5213
Fax: 440 558-5214
Steve Matteo, *President*
EMP: 20
SQ FT: 25,444
SALES: 13MM **Privately Held**
SIC: 3444 3449 Gutters, sheet metal; mis-
cellaneous metalwork

(G-20373)
MULTI LAPPING SERVICE INC
30032 Lakeland Bvld (44092)
PHONE..............................440 944-7592
Fax: 440 943-9875
Donna Wohr, *President*
Enos Adkins III, *Vice Pres*
Michael Adkins, *Vice Pres*
EMP: 12
SQ FT: 72,000
SALES: 1.2MM **Privately Held**
SIC: 3829 Whole body counters, nuclear

(G-20374)
NOVEON FCC INC
29400 Lakeland Blvd (44092-2201)
PHONE..............................440 943-4200
Charles P Cooley III, *Senior VP*
▼ **EMP:** 5
SALES (est): 986.1K
SALES (corp-wide): 223.6B **Publicly
Held**
SIC: 2869 2899 Industrial organic chemi-
cals; chemical preparations
HQ: The Lubrizol Corporation
29400 Lakeland Blvd
Wickliffe OH 44092
440 943-4200

(G-20375)
OMCO HOLDINGS INC (PA)
30396 Lakeland Blvd (44092-1748)
PHONE..............................440 944-2100
Ben Yorks, *Ch of Bd*
Gary Schuster, *President*
Edward F Gleason, *Exec VP*
Robert Stephenson, *Vice Pres*
Clark Lichtinger, *Purch Agent*
EMP: 33
SALES (est): 60.9MM **Privately Held**
SIC: 3449 Miscellaneous metalwork

(G-20376)
P O MCINTIRE COMPANY (PA)
29191 Anderson Rd (44092-2357)
PHONE..............................440 269-1848
Fax: 440 269-1446
James Goglin, *President*
Scott Goglin, *Vice Pres*
Mitchell Pete, *Manager*
EMP: 27 **EST:** 1938
SQ FT: 12,000
SALES: 1.8MM **Privately Held**
WEB: www.pomcintire.com
SIC: 3545 3544 Cutting tools for machine
tools; reamers, machine tool; jigs & fix-
tures

(G-20377)
P R W TOOL INC
30036 Lakeland Blvd (44092-1745)
PHONE..............................440 585-3373
Fax: 440 585-3373
Bill Satyshur, *President*
David Satyshur, *Vice Pres*
EMP: 3
SQ FT: 3,000
SALES: 60K **Privately Held**
SIC: 3599 Machine shop, jobbing & repair

(G-20378)
PANELTECH LLC
1430 Lloyd Rd (44092-2320)
PHONE..............................440 516-1300
Andrea Christensen, *Principal*
EMP: 11
SALES (est): 2.2MM **Privately Held**
SIC: 3825 Test equipment for electronic &
electric measurement

(G-20379)
PARKER-HANNIFIN CORPORATION
Hose Products Div
30240 Lakeland Blvd (44092-1797)
PHONE..............................440 943-5700
Fax: 440 585-2028
James Blaha, *Principal*
Robert Kennedy, *Project Engr*
Laura McLean, *Credit Staff*
Paul Sirko, *Human Res Mgr*
Tom Zimmerman, *Marketing Staff*
EMP: 271
SQ FT: 145,000

SALES (corp-wide): 11.3B **Publicly Held**
WEB: www.parker.com
SIC: 3714 3492 Motor vehicle parts & accessories; fluid power valves & hose fittings
PA: Parker-Hannifin Corporation
6035 Parkland Blvd
Cleveland OH 44124
216 896-3000

(G-20380)
PARKER-HANNIFIN CORPORATION
Hose Products
30240 Lakeland Blvd (44092-1797)
PHONE................................218 534-3148
Fax: 218 534-3050
Greg Barber, *Engineer*
Lonnie Gallup, *Branch Mgr*
EMP: 60
SALES (corp-wide): 11.3B **Publicly Held**
WEB: www.parker.com
SIC: 3451 3492 Screw machine products; fluid power valves & hose fittings
PA: Parker-Hannifin Corporation
6035 Parkland Blvd
Cleveland OH 44124
216 896-3000

(G-20381)
PARKER-HANNIFIN CORPORATION
Also Called: Industrial Hose Product Div
30242 Lakeland Blvd (44092-1747)
PHONE................................440 943-5700
Fax: 440 943-3129
Shelby Scanlon, *General Mgr*
Dan Barrett, *Branch Mgr*
Robert Griffin, *IT/INT Sup*
EMP: 36
SALES (corp-wide): 11.3B **Publicly Held**
WEB: www.parker.com
SIC: 3492 Hose & tube fittings & assemblies, hydraulic/pneumatic; hose & tube couplings, hydraulic/pneumatic
PA: Parker-Hannifin Corporation
6035 Parkland Blvd
Cleveland OH 44124
216 896-3000

(G-20382)
PCC CERAMIC GROUP 1
1470 E 289th St (44092-2306)
PHONE................................440 516-3672
Daren Kennedy, *Vice Pres*
EMP: 9
SALES (est): 450K **Privately Held**
SIC: 3253 Floor tile, ceramic

(G-20383)
PMC INDUSTRIES CORP
Also Called: A Park Ohio Company
29100 Lakeland Blvd (44092-2323)
PHONE................................440 943-3300
Fax: 440 944-1974
Jim Guthrie, *Area Mgr*
Edward K Novak, *Vice Pres*
Stan Arko, *Plant Mgr*
Steve Grasser, *Opers Mgr*
Mark Widemire, *Mfg Staff*
▲ **EMP:** 85 **EST:** 1912
SQ FT: 125,000
SALES (est): 18.9MM
SALES (corp-wide): 1.2B **Publicly Held**
WEB: www.pmcindustries.com
SIC: 3317 Steel pipe & tubes
HQ: Park-Ohio Industries, Inc.
6065 Parkland Blvd Ste 1
Cleveland OH 44124
440 947-2000

(G-20384)
PRECIOUS METAL PLATING CO
30335 Palisades Pkwy (44092-1598)
PHONE................................440 585-7117
Fax: 440 585-0479
Thomas Talty Jr, *President*
EMP: 22
SQ FT: 14,000
SALES (est): 2.5MM **Privately Held**
WEB: www.preciousmetalplating.com
SIC: 3471 Electroplating of metals or formed products; gold plating

(G-20385)
REGAL DIAMOND PRODUCTS CORP
1405 E 286th St (44092-2506)
P.O. Box 198 (44092-0198)
PHONE................................440 944-7700
Fax: 440 944-7722
Steve Brewer, *President*
Bob Gray, *Sales Mgr*
Robert Gray, *Sales Mgr*
Michele Brewer, *Manager*
▼ **EMP:** 22 **EST:** 1958
SQ FT: 16,500
SALES (est): 3.1MM **Privately Held**
SIC: 3291 3545 3425 Abrasive wheels & grindstones, not artificial; cutting tools for machine tools; saw blades & handsaws

(G-20386)
RESEARCH ABRASIVE PRODUCTS INC
1400 E 286th St (44092-2507)
PHONE................................440 944-3200
Fax: 440 944-0317
Ken Dixon Jr, *President*
Margaret Tripp, *Corp Secy*
Kathy Matt, *Vice Pres*
William Dixon, *Warehouse Mgr*
EMP: 40
SQ FT: 32,000
SALES (est): 5.3MM **Privately Held**
WEB: www.researchabrasive.com
SIC: 3291 Wheels, abrasive

(G-20387)
SPEEDWAY LLC
Also Called: Speedway Superamerica 3027
29201 Euclid Ave (44092-2359)
PHONE................................440 943-0044
EMP: 10
SALES (corp-wide): 82.4B **Publicly Held**
SIC: 1311 Crude Petroleum & Natural Gas
HQ: Speedway Llc
500 Speedway Dr
Enon OH 45323
937 864-3000

(G-20388)
THERMAL TREATMENT CENTER INC
Nettleton Steel Treating Div
28910 Lakeland Blvd (44092-2321)
PHONE................................440 943-4555
Fax: 440 943-4730
Rodney Holstein, *Manager*
EMP: 47
SQ FT: 13,000
SALES (corp-wide): 21MM **Privately Held**
WEB: www.htg.cc
SIC: 3398 Metal heat treating; brazing (hardening) of metal
HQ: Thermal Treatment Center Inc
1101 E 55th St
Cleveland OH 44103
216 881-8100

(G-20389)
UMICORE SPCLTY MTLS RECYCL LLC
28960 Lakeland Blvd (44092-2321)
PHONE................................440 833-3000
Steffan Jannis, *CEO*
Ravila Gupta, *President*
Karen Micharg, *Treasurer*
EMP: 40
SALES (est): 10.9MM
SALES (corp-wide): 3B **Privately Held**
SIC: 3341 Recovery & refining of nonferrous metals
HQ: Umicore Usa Inc.
3600 Glenwood Ave Ste 250
Raleigh NC 27612

(G-20390)
UNITED HYDRAULICS
29627 Lakeland Blvd (44092-2203)
PHONE................................440 585-0906
John Birkic, *President*
EMP: 15
SALES (est): 1.3MM **Privately Held**
WEB: www.unitedhydraulics.com
SIC: 3593 5084 Fluid power cylinders, hydraulic or pneumatic; industrial machinery & equipment

(G-20391)
UNIVERSAL METAL PRODUCTS INC (PA)
Also Called: Hercules
29980 Lakeland Blvd (44092-1744)
P.O. Box 130 (44092-0130)
PHONE................................440 943-3040
Fax: 440 585-4032
Hugh S Seaholm, *CEO*
Cesar Pina, *General Mgr*
Norman Allison, *VP Admin*
Ken Bateman, *Vice Pres*
Eric Bowser, *Vice Pres*
▲ **EMP:** 190
SQ FT: 15,000
SALES: 60MM **Privately Held**
WEB: www.ump-inc.com
SIC: 3469 Metal stampings

Wilberforce
Greene County

(G-20392)
SPEEDWAY LLC
Also Called: Speedway Superamerica 5839
1455 Brush Row Rd (45384-1300)
PHONE................................937 372-7129
EMP: 10 **Publicly Held**
WEB: www.speedwaynet.com
SIC: 1311 Crude petroleum production
HQ: Speedway Llc
500 Speedway Dr
Enon OH 45323
937 864-3000

Willard
Huron County

(G-20393)
CAROLS ULTRA STITCH & VARIETY
122 S Myrtle Ave (44890-1425)
PHONE................................419 935-8991
Carol Barnett, *Owner*
EMP: 8
SQ FT: 4,000
SALES (est): 547.7K **Privately Held**
SIC: 5699 2395 Customized clothing & apparel; T-shirts, custom printed; embroidery products, except schiffli machine

(G-20394)
DONALD SCHLOEMER
Also Called: Schloemer, Don Masonry
2441 Niver Rd (44890-9669)
PHONE................................419 933-2002
Donald Schloemer, *Owner*
EMP: 4
SALES: 350K **Privately Held**
SIC: 1741 3272 Chimney construction & maintenance; concrete products, precast

(G-20395)
GUARDIAN MANUFACTURING CO LLC
Also Called: Guardian Gloves
302 S Conwell Ave (44890-9525)
PHONE................................419 933-2711
Gene Lamoreaux, *President*
Ron Vanderpool, *Treasurer*
▲ **EMP:** 25
SQ FT: 100,000
SALES (est): 5.8MM **Privately Held**
WEB: www.guardian-mfg.com
SIC: 3069 3842 Medical & laboratory rubber sundries & related products; surgical appliances & supplies

(G-20396)
LSC COMMUNICATIONS US LLC
Also Called: Building Maintenance Dept
1145 S Conwell Ave (44890-9392)
PHONE................................419 935-0111
Glenn Baker, *Branch Mgr*
EMP: 109

SALES (corp-wide): 12.4B **Publicly Held**
WEB: www.rrdonnelley.com
SIC: 2754 2759 2752 2732 Commercial printing, gravure; catalogs: gravure printing, not published on site; magazines: gravure printing, not published on site; directories: gravure printing, not published on site; letterpress printing; commercial printing, offset; books: printing & binding; direct mail advertising services; graphic arts & related design
HQ: Lsc Communications Us, Llc
191 N Wacker Dr Ste 1400
Chicago IL 60606
844 572-5720

(G-20397)
MTD PRODUCTS INC
Midwest Industries
979 S Conwell Ave (44890-9301)
PHONE................................419 935-6611
Fax: 419 935-6611
Rob Fox, *General Mgr*
Jeff Diamond, *Safety Mgr*
Jeff Dymond, *Safety Mgr*
Roy King, *QC Dir*
Steve Wilson, *Engineer*
EMP: 800
SQ FT: 480,000
SALES (corp-wide): 2.8B **Privately Held**
WEB: www.mtdproducts.com
SIC: 3524 Lawn & garden equipment
HQ: Mtd Products Inc
5965 Grafton Rd
Valley City OH 44280
330 225-2600

(G-20398)
NUTRIFRESH EGGS
342 Plymouth East Rd (44890-9579)
PHONE................................567 224-7676
Dean Steiner, *Managing Prtnr*
EMP: 5
SALES: 500K **Privately Held**
SIC: 2015 Chicken, processed: fresh

(G-20399)
PEPPERIDGE FARM INCORPORATED
3320 State Route 103 E (44890-9777)
PHONE................................419 933-2611
Fax: 419 933-3804
Elaine Danhoff, *Safety Mgr*
Thomas Gremmer, *Purchasing*
William Kaltenbach, *Human Res Dir*
George Litvak, *Branch Mgr*
Donald Tomasvewski, *Manager*
EMP: 9
SALES (corp-wide): 7.9B **Publicly Held**
WEB: www.pepperidgefarm.com
SIC: 5461 2052 Bakeries; cookies & crackers
HQ: Pepperidge Farm, Incorporated
595 Westport Ave
Norwalk CT 06851
203 846-7000

(G-20400)
RR DONNELLEY & SONS COMPANY
Willard Mfg Div
1145 S Conwell Ave (44890-9392)
PHONE................................419 935-0111
Fax: 419 933-5480
Casey Cuzmicki, *Div Sub Head*
Robert Jones, *Plant Mgr*
Robert Gospodarek, *Opers-Prdtn-Mfg*
Brad Lee, *Purchasing*
Jerry Grundish, *Research*
EMP: 980
SALES (corp-wide): 6.9B **Publicly Held**
WEB: www.rrdonnelley.com
SIC: 2741 2732 2759 2752 Directories: publishing & printing; books: printing only; commercial printing; commercial printing, lithographic
PA: R. R. Donnelley & Sons Company
35 W Wacker Dr Ste 3650
Chicago IL 60601
312 326-8000

(G-20401)
SNEAKY PETE BAND
4418 N Greenfield Rd (44890-9527)
PHONE................................419 933-6251
EMP: 3

SALES (est): 140K **Privately Held**
SIC: 2836 Mfg Biological Products

(G-20402)
TIN SHED LLC
6 S Myrtle Ave (44890-1423)
PHONE..........................330 636-2524
EMP: 4
SALES (est): 370.9K **Privately Held**
SIC: 3356 Tin

(G-20403)
V & R MOLDED PRODUCTS INC
181 Us Highway 224 W (44890-9788)
PHONE..........................419 752-4171
EMP: 10
SQ FT: 23,000
SALES (est): 82.3K **Privately Held**
SIC: 3089 Mfg Plastic Products

(G-20404)
WEAVER BOOS CONSULTANTS INC
1145 S Conwell Ave (44890-9392)
PHONE..........................419 933-5216
Dirk Hiler, *Manager*
EMP: 14
SALES (corp-wide): 37MM **Privately Held**
SIC: 2731 Book publishing
PA: Weaver Boos Consultants, Inc.
35 E Wacker Dr Ste 1250
Chicago IL 60601
312 922-1030

(G-20405)
WILLARD TIMES JUNCTION
211 S Myrtle Ave (44890-1407)
P.O. Box 368 (44890-0368)
PHONE..........................419 935-0184
Fax: 419 933-2031
Scott Gove, *Owner*
EMP: 13
SALES (est): 414.4K **Privately Held**
SIC: 2711 Newspapers

Williamsburg
Clermont County

(G-20406)
AEC BREWS LLC DBA OLD FRHUSE B
Also Called: Old Firehouse Brewery
237 W Main St (45176-1342)
PHONE..........................513 536-9071
Adam Cowan,
Lori Ward,
EMP: 6
SALES: 750K **Privately Held**
SIC: 2082 Malt liquors

(G-20407)
FTK MANUFACTURING LLC
1514 Lost Lake Ct (45176-9640)
PHONE..........................513 218-7237
Christopher L Loes,
EMP: 3
SALES (est): 423.7K **Privately Held**
SIC: 3575 Computer terminals, monitors & components

(G-20408)
G & L MACHINING INC
299 N 3rd St (45176-8101)
PHONE..........................513 724-2600
Fax: 513 724-2602
Gary Abrams, *President*
Leslie Abrams, *President*
EMP: 8
SQ FT: 4,000
SALES (est): 1MM **Privately Held**
SIC: 3599 Machine shop, jobbing & repair

(G-20409)
IV M TOOL & DIE
3227 Us Highway 50 (45176-6202)
PHONE..........................513 625-6464
Fax: 513 625-3929
Patti Mallaley, *Owner*
EMP: 4
SQ FT: 15,000

SALES (est): 411.7K **Privately Held**
SIC: 3599 3544 Machine shop, jobbing & repair; special dies, tools, jigs & fixtures

(G-20410)
PATCHES LLC
1696 Pin Oak Ln (45176-9106)
PHONE..........................513 304-4882
Jeff Clock, *Principal*
EMP: 3
SALES (est): 240K **Privately Held**
SIC: 2298 Cargo nets

(G-20411)
R & L WOOD PRODUCTS
16137 Eastwood Rd (45176-9338)
PHONE..........................937 444-2496
Robert L Lodwick, *Owner*
Pam Loudwick, *Vice Pres*
EMP: 7
SALES (est): 370K **Privately Held**
SIC: 2421 Lumber: rough, sawed or planed; kiln drying of lumber

(G-20412)
STEPHEN J PAGE
143 Winding Trails Dr (45176-1475)
PHONE..........................865 951-3316
Stephen Page, *Owner*
EMP: 3
SALES (est): 102.6K **Privately Held**
SIC: 2511 2521 2541 7389 Wood household furniture; wood office furniture; store & office display cases & fixtures;

(G-20413)
W&W ROCK SAND AND GRAVEL
1451 Maple Grove Rd (45176-9636)
P.O. Box 640 (45176-0640)
PHONE..........................513 266-3708
Rick A Wuebold, *Principal*
EMP: 6
SALES (est): 250K **Privately Held**
SIC: 1442 Construction sand & gravel

(G-20414)
WOLFE OIL COMPANY LLC
2944 Quitter Rd (45176-8211)
PHONE..........................513 732-6220
Lance Wolfe, *Principal*
EMP: 3
SALES (est): 230K **Privately Held**
SIC: 3559 Petroleum refinery equipment

(G-20415)
ZIPPER MANUFACTURING LLC
16698 Edgington Rd (45176-6531)
PHONE..........................937 444-0904
William A Dunn, *Principal*
EMP: 6 EST: 2008
SALES (est): 517.4K **Privately Held**
SIC: 3965 Zipper

Williamsfield
Ashtabula County

(G-20416)
PREMIER STAMPING AND ASSEMBLY
Also Called: Premiere Stamping
7924 Mill St (44093-9757)
PHONE..........................440 293-8961
Fax: 440 293-8096
Christopher Mott, *President*
Nikki Mott, *Corp Secy*
EMP: 3
SQ FT: 9,000
SALES (est): 200K **Privately Held**
SIC: 3469 3444 Metal stampings; sheet metalwork

(G-20417)
VALLEY VENEER & LUMBER CO
4261 Us Route 322 (44093-9717)
PHONE..........................440 293-6025
Fax: 440 293-5161
Lynn Tabor, *President*
Jackie Tabor, *Treasurer*
Betty Ann Green, *Admin Sec*
EMP: 13
SQ FT: 6,000

SALES (est): 820K **Privately Held**
SIC: 2421 2435 2426 2411 Sawmills & planing mills, general; hardwood veneer & plywood; hardwood dimension & flooring mills; logging

Williamsport
Pickaway County

(G-20418)
R GORDON JONES INC
Also Called: Jet Electric
20849 Five Points Pike (43164-9708)
PHONE..........................740 986-8381
Fax: 740 986-6481
R Gordon Jones, *President*
Marcia Eyre, *Manager*
EMP: 5
SQ FT: 5,000
SALES (est): 1MM **Privately Held**
WEB: www.jetelectric.com
SIC: 3621 Motors & generators

(G-20419)
ROOF TO ROAD LLC
27910 Chillicothe Pike (43164-9654)
PHONE..........................740 986-6923
Stephen Johnson, *Mng Member*
Slyvia Johnson, *Agent*
Alfred Johnson,
EMP: 7
SALES (est): 1.4MM **Privately Held**
SIC: 2951 Road materials, bituminous (not from refineries)

Williston
Ottawa County

(G-20420)
DURIVAGE PATTERN & MFG CO
20522 State Route 579 W (43468)
P.O. Box 337 (43468-0337)
PHONE..........................419 836-8655
Fax: 419 836-7100
Gary Durivage, *President*
Gretchen Durivage, *Corp Secy*
Larry Durivage, *Vice Pres*
Ron Miller, *Vice Pres*
EMP: 30
SQ FT: 24,000
SALES (est): 4.9MM **Privately Held**
WEB: www.durivagepattern.com
SIC: 3469 3544 3369 3365 Patterns on metal; industrial molds; nonferrous foundries; aluminum foundries; steel foundries; laminated plastics plate & sheet

Willoughby
Lake County

(G-20421)
A & D PRINTING CO
Also Called: Sterling Media
38287 Airport Pkwy Ste A (44094-8066)
PHONE..........................440 975-8001
Fax: 440 975-8002
Dean Sterling, *President*
Terri Richter, *Manager*
EMP: 5
SQ FT: 2,000
SALES: 400K **Privately Held**
SIC: 2752 Commercial printing, offset

(G-20422)
A M D
4580 Beidler Rd (44094-4602)
PHONE..........................440 918-8930
Mike Bollas, *Manager*
EMP: 3
SALES (est): 387.7K **Privately Held**
SIC: 3674 Integrated circuits, semiconductor networks, etc.

(G-20423)
A&S MACHINE
38363 Western Pkwy Unit 1 (44094-8843)
PHONE..........................440 946-3976

Allan Bockhoff, *Owner*
EMP: 4
SALES (est): 412.8K **Privately Held**
SIC: 3599 Machine shop, jobbing & repair

(G-20424)
ACE GRINDING CO
37518 N Industrial Pkwy (44094-6279)
PHONE..........................440 951-6760
Fax: 440 951-3882
Brian Danolfo, *President*
Jackie King, *Administration*
EMP: 6
SQ FT: 12,000
SALES (est): 657.7K **Privately Held**
SIC: 3999 Custom pulverizing & grinding of plastic materials; education aids, devices & supplies

(G-20425)
ADVANCED RV LLC
4590 Hamann Pkwy (44094-5630)
PHONE..........................440 283-0405
Mike Neundorfer, *President*
EMP: 4 EST: 2012
SALES (est): 554.8K **Privately Held**
SIC: 3716 7519 7532 Motor homes; motor home rental; mobile home & trailer repair

(G-20426)
AIRCRAFT WELDING INC
38335 Apollo Pkwy Unit 1 (44094-7795)
PHONE..........................440 951-3863
Fax: 440 510-4501
Michael Horvath, *President*
David Horvath, *Vice Pres*
Stephen Gron, *Plant Mgr*
Patricia Horvath, *Admin Sec*
EMP: 8 EST: 1990
SQ FT: 6,500
SALES: 1MM **Privately Held**
WEB: www.aircraftweldinginc.com
SIC: 7692 Welding repair

(G-20427)
ALD GROUP LLC
34201 Melinz Pkwy Unit A (44095-4018)
P.O. Box 435, Cleveland (44107-0435)
PHONE..........................440 942-9800
Fax: 440 942-2987
Don Defonzo, *General Mgr*
Don Difonzo, *Mng Member*
EMP: 6
SQ FT: 10,000
SALES (est): 818.7K **Privately Held**
WEB: www.aldgroup.net
SIC: 3541 Machine tool replacement & repair parts, metal cutting types

(G-20428)
ALL-CRAFT WELLMAN PRODUCTS
4839 E 345th St (44094-4671)
PHONE..........................440 946-9646
Fax: 440 946-9648
Gil Wellman, *President*
Ed Nagy, *Sales Staff*
Charlene Thomas, *Office Mgr*
EMP: 15
SQ FT: 8,000
SALES: 500K **Privately Held**
SIC: 3953 3451 3499 Letters (marking devices), metal; screw machine products; tablets, bronze or other metal

(G-20429)
AMD FABRICATORS INC
4580 Beidler Rd (44094-4602)
PHONE..........................440 946-8855
Fax: 440 269-6986
Michael Watts, *President*
Randy Hampton, *Vice Pres*
Gus Deangelo, *CFO*
Donna Nowak, *Sales Executive*
Jeff Lehr, *Info Tech Mgr*
EMP: 20
SQ FT: 50,000
SALES (est): 3.3MM **Privately Held**
SIC: 3444 Sheet metalwork

(G-20430)
AMETCO MANUFACTURING CORP
4326 Hamann Pkwy (44094-5626)
P.O. Box 1210 (44096-1210)
PHONE..................440 951-4300
Fax: 440 951-2542
Steve G Mitrovich, *President*
Greg Mitrovich, *Vice Pres*
Rona Mitrovich, *Vice Pres*
Ludwig Weber, *Inv Control Mgr*
Dean Maurer, *Sales Staff*
▲ EMP: 38 EST: 1966
SQ FT: 85,000
SALES (est): 11.9MM **Privately Held**
WEB: www.ametco.com
SIC: 3315 Steel wire & related products

(G-20431)
AMFM INC
Also Called: Omega One
38373 Pelton Rd (44094-7719)
PHONE..................440 953-4545
Fax: 440 953-3774
Morgun McIntosh, *President*
John Drcar, *Opers Mgr*
Jaune Meadows, *Manager*
▲ EMP: 37
SALES (est): 6MM **Privately Held**
SIC: 2241 Braids, textile

(G-20432)
ANDERSON BROTHERS ENTPS INC
38180 Airport Pkwy (44094-8021)
PHONE..................440 269-3920
Fax: 440 269-3929
H W Domeck, *President*
Tenneth Anderson, *President*
Donald Anderson, *Vice Pres*
Theresa Inman, *Controller*
EMP: 20 EST: 1945
SQ FT: 52,000
SALES (est): 5.2MM
SALES (corp-wide): 42.6MM **Privately Held**
SIC: 2033 Vegetables: packaged in cans, jars, etc.
PA: The Fremont Company
802 N Front St
Fremont OH 43420
419 334-8995

(G-20433)
API PATTERN WORKS INC
4456 Hamann Pkwy (44094-5628)
PHONE..................440 269-1766
Jesse Baden, *President*
Michael Scanlon, *Corp Secy*
Ryan Yeager, *Manager*
EMP: 45
SQ FT: 20,000
SALES: 3MM **Privately Held**
SIC: 3543 Industrial patterns

(G-20434)
APOLLO PRODUCTS INC
4456 Hamann Pkwy (44094-5628)
PHONE..................440 269-8551
Fax: 440 269-1768
Jess Baden, *President*
Michael Scanlon, *Corp Secy*
Katy Baden, *Manager*
EMP: 15
SQ FT: 5,000
SALES (est): 2.5MM **Privately Held**
SIC: 3544 3545 Special dies, tools, jigs & fixtures; machine tool accessories

(G-20435)
APOLLO WELDING & FABG INC (PA)
35600 Curtis Blvd (44095-4109)
PHONE..................440 942-0227
John Turkalj, *President*
Mary Turkalj, *Corp Secy*
Doug Barth, *Vice Pres*
EMP: 20
SQ FT: 25,000
SALES (est): 3.5MM **Privately Held**
SIC: 3599 Machine shop, jobbing & repair

(G-20436)
APPLIED CONCEPTS INC
Also Called: Applied Bingo Mate
36445 Biltmore Pl Ste E (44094-8228)
PHONE..................440 229-5033
John Adams, *President*
Bryan Massie, *General Mgr*
John Q Adams, *Corp Secy*
Tom Marzella, *Vice Pres*
Valeria Stachowicz, *Manager*
EMP: 11
SQ FT: 3,000
SALES (est): 1.5MM **Privately Held**
SIC: 3944 Electronic game machines, except coin-operated

(G-20437)
APR TOOL INC
4712 Beidler Rd Ste A (44094-4604)
PHONE..................440 946-0393
Fax: 440 975-0711
Robert Zietz, *President*
Joe Zeitz, *Vice Pres*
John Zeitz, *Vice Pres*
EMP: 9 EST: 1974
SQ FT: 3,200
SALES (est): 907.5K **Privately Held**
SIC: 3599 3544 Machine shop, jobbing & repair; dies & die holders for metal cutting, forming, die casting

(G-20438)
AQUA LILY PRODUCTS LLC
4485 Glenbrook Rd (44094-8219)
PHONE..................480 588-6731
Craig Cushman, *Branch Mgr*
EMP: 28
SALES (corp-wide): 3.3MM **Privately Held**
SIC: 3086 Plastics foam products
PA: Aqua Lily Products, Llc
4485 Glenbrook Rd
Willoughby OH 44094
951 246-9610

(G-20439)
AQUA LILY PRODUCTS LLC (PA)
4485 Glenbrook Rd (44094-8219)
PHONE..................951 246-9610
Craig Cushman, *Principal*
Brian Cannon,
Donna Cannon,
EMP: 13
SALES: 3.3MM **Privately Held**
SIC: 3086 7389 Padding, foamed plastic;

(G-20440)
ARTISTIC FINISHES INC
38357 Apollo Pkwy (44094-7723)
PHONE..................440 951-7850
Fax: 440 951-0783
Michael Credico, *President*
Bonnie Credico, *Corp Secy*
Robert Fine, *Vice Pres*
Jim Fiorello, *Purchasing*
EMP: 18
SALES (est): 1.7MM **Privately Held**
WEB: www.artisticfinishes.net
SIC: 2541 2511 Store fixtures, wood; wood household furniture

(G-20441)
ASCENDTECH INC
4772 E 355th St (44094-4632)
PHONE..................216 458-1101
Igor Lapinskiy, *President*
Gary Lapinskiy, *General Mgr*
Jerry Latin, *Office Mgr*
Roman Aronovich, *Supervisor*
EMP: 35
SALES (est): 8.1MM **Privately Held**
SIC: 5045 7379 3571 7378 Computers, peripherals & software; computer related maintenance services; electronic computers; computer peripheral equipment repair & maintenance; electrical repair shops; scrap & waste materials

(G-20442)
B V GRINDING MACHINING INC
1438 E 363rd St (44095-4136)
PHONE..................440 918-1884
Fax: 440 918-1877
Ivica Begovic, *President*
Mary Begovic, *Office Mgr*

EMP: 8
SALES (est): 1.2MM **Privately Held**
WEB: www.bvgrinding.com
SIC: 3541 Grinding machines, metalworking

(G-20443)
BENDER CYCLE & MACHINE CORP
1476 E 359th St (44095-4123)
PHONE..................440 946-0681
Fax: 440 946-5248
Ronald Bender, *President*
EMP: 5
SQ FT: 3,500
SALES (est): 430K **Privately Held**
SIC: 3599 Machine shop, jobbing & repair

(G-20444)
BESCAST INC
4600 E 355th St (44094-4699)
PHONE..................440 946-5300
Fax: 440 946-8437
David M Brown, *Principal*
John W Gallagher, *Principal*
Mike McCraith, *Area Mgr*
Russ Gallagher, *Vice Pres*
George M Brown Jr, *Vice Pres*
▲ EMP: 170 EST: 1945
SQ FT: 85,000
SALES (est): 40.9MM **Privately Held**
WEB: www.bescast.com
SIC: 3324 Aerospace investment castings, ferrous

(G-20445)
BRANDTS CANDIES
1238 Lost Nation Rd (44094-7325)
PHONE..................440 942-1016
Fax: 440 942-7330
Theodore Prindle, *President*
Barbara Tabernick, *Manager*
EMP: 7 EST: 1948
SQ FT: 3,000
SALES: 700K **Privately Held**
WEB: www.brandts-candies.com
SIC: 5441 2066 Candy, nut & confectionery stores; chocolate & cocoa products

(G-20446)
BRONCO MACHINE INC
38411 Apollo Pkwy (44094-7725)
PHONE..................440 951-5015
Fax: 440 951-7939
Michael Bronaka, *President*
Ann Turpin, *Vice Pres*
Diana Bronaka, *Treasurer*
EMP: 10 EST: 1962
SQ FT: 6,000
SALES (est): 1.6MM **Privately Held**
WEB: www.broncomachine.com
SIC: 3451 Screw machine products

(G-20447)
BUD INDUSTRIES INC (PA)
4605 E 355th St (44094-4600)
PHONE..................440 946-3200
Blair K Haas, *President*
Stephen H Haas, *President*
Duane Berhent, *General Mgr*
Greg A Haas, *Vice Pres*
Dan Lucas, *Mfg Staff*
▲ EMP: 4 EST: 1928
SQ FT: 170,000
SALES (est): 17.4MM **Privately Held**
WEB: www.budind.com
SIC: 3469 3672 3644 3643 Electronic enclosures, stamped or pressed metal; printed circuit boards; noncurrent-carrying wiring services; current-carrying wiring devices; switchgear & switchboard apparatus; partitions & fixtures, except wood

(G-20448)
BUDZAR INDUSTRIES INC
38241 Willoughby Pkwy (44094-7582)
PHONE..................440 530-1000
Fax: 440 918-0606
Edward S Young, *Ch of Bd*
David F Young, *President*
Andrea Gallion, *Purch Agent*
Wayne Schaeffer, *Engineer*
Zach Weber, *Design Engr*
▲ EMP: 63
SQ FT: 50,000

SALES (est): 26.5MM
SALES (corp-wide): 86MM **Privately Held**
WEB: www.budzar.com
SIC: 3585 3822 3823 3634 Refrigeration & heating equipment; auto controls regulating residntl & coml environmt & applncs; temperature instruments: industrial process type; electric housewares & fans
PA: Shelburne Corp
20001 Shelburne Rd
Shaker Heights OH 44118
216 321-9177

(G-20449)
BULLSEYE DART SHOPPE INC
950c Erie Rd (44095-1811)
PHONE..................440 951-9277
Fax: 440 951-4290
Thomas Nazarak, *President*
Steve Nazark, *QC Mgr*
Bob Farley, *Manager*
▲ EMP: 8
SQ FT: 14,000
SALES (est): 679.5K **Privately Held**
WEB: www.bullseyetcnaz.com
SIC: 3949 Billiard & pool equipment & supplies, general

(G-20450)
C G MANUFACTURING COMPANY INC
36490 Reading Ave (44094-8207)
PHONE..................440 951-8555
Fax: 440 951-8083
John Corrigan, *President*
Andrea Zacher, *Office Mgr*
EMP: 25
SQ FT: 22,000
SALES: 3.6MM **Privately Held**
SIC: 3599 Machine shop, jobbing & repair

(G-20451)
C L M ASSOCIATES
4312 Parklawn Dr (44094-7955)
PHONE..................440 942-8861
Fax: 440 942-8861
Craig L Mackey, *President*
Todd M Mackey, *Corp Secy*
David B Mackey, *Vice Pres*
Carol L Mackey, *Manager*
EMP: 5
SALES: 100K **Privately Held**
SIC: 2711 Newspapers: publishing only, not printed on site

(G-20452)
CARBIDE SPECIALIST INC
36430 Reading Ave Ste 10 (44094-8220)
PHONE..................440 951-4027
Fax: 440 954-9094
Ray Northern, *President*
Naomi Northern, *Corp Secy*
EMP: 12
SALES: 200K **Privately Held**
SIC: 3544 Wire drawing & straightening dies

(G-20453)
CASTMOR PRODUCTS INC
4708 Beidler Rd (44094-4604)
P.O. Box 70 (44096-0070)
PHONE..................440 953-1103
Fax: 440 953-1243
Edward A Marvin, *President*
Craig Marvin, *Vice Pres*
EMP: 4
SQ FT: 4,800
SALES: 1MM **Privately Held**
SIC: 3369 Zinc & zinc-base alloy castings, except die-castings

(G-20454)
CENTER LINE DRILLING INC
33000 Lakeland Blvd (44095-5203)
PHONE..................440 951-5920
Mike Burgess, *President*
David Rockefeller, *Vice Pres*
EMP: 3
SALES: 370K **Privately Held**
WEB: www.centerlinedrilling.com
SIC: 3599 Machine shop, jobbing & repair

(G-20455)
CHAGRIN VLY STL ERECTORS INC
Also Called: Ruple Trucking
4500 Hamann Pkwy (44094-5630)
PHONE................................440 975-1556
Victoria Ruple, *President*
John Ruple, *President*
Nancy Janke, *Manager*
EMP: 13
SQ FT: 10,040
SALES: 4MM **Privately Held**
SIC: 3441 1791 4213 1796 Fabricated structural metal; structural steel erection; trucking, except local; machine moving & rigging

(G-20456)
CHIPS MANUFACTURING INC
35720 Lakeland Blvd (44095-5307)
PHONE................................440 946-3666
Frank Cipriano, *President*
EMP: 8
SQ FT: 7,200
SALES (est): 1.2MM **Privately Held**
SIC: 3599 Machine shop, jobbing & repair

(G-20457)
COCA-COLA COMPANY
4800 E 355th St (44094-4634)
PHONE................................440 269-1433
Valerie Nobacco, *Manager*
EMP: 60
SALES (corp-wide): 41.8B **Publicly Held**
WEB: www.colasic.net
SIC: 2086 Bottled & canned soft drinks
PA: The Coca-Cola Company
1 Coca Cola Plz Nw
Atlanta GA 30313
404 676-2121

(G-20458)
COIT TOOL COMPANY INC
38134 Western Pkwy Unit 3 (44094-7588)
PHONE................................440 946-3377
Fax: 440 946-3324
Russell P Bliss, *President*
Judy Arnold, *Office Mgr*
EMP: 10
SQ FT: 6,400
SALES (est): 1.8MM **Privately Held**
SIC: 3599 Machine shop, jobbing & repair

(G-20459)
COLLATED PRODUCTS CORP
35595 Curtis Blvd Unit D (44095-4100)
PHONE................................440 946-1950
Jeff Wright, *President*
EMP: 10
SQ FT: 8,000
SALES (est): 1.3MM **Privately Held**
SIC: 3579 Binding machines, plastic & adhesive

(G-20460)
COMMERCIAL ANODIZING CO
38387 Apollo Pkwy (44094-7791)
PHONE................................440 942-8384
Fax: 440 942-3229
Mark S Swetel, *President*
Shirley Swetel, *Corp Secy*
Sherry Blake, *Director*
EMP: 20
SQ FT: 20,000
SALES (est): 2.3MM **Privately Held**
SIC: 3471 Anodizing (plating) of metals or formed products; coloring & finishing of aluminum or formed products

(G-20461)
CONCORDE CASTINGS INC
34000 Lakeland Blvd (44095-5213)
PHONE................................440 953-0053
Fax: 440 953-1675
Joe Weber, *President*
EMP: 4 **EST:** 2015
SALES (est): 325K **Privately Held**
SIC: 3369 Nonferrous foundries

(G-20462)
CONN-SELMER INC
Also Called: Eastlake Mfg Facility
34199 Curtis Blvd (44095-4008)
PHONE................................440 946-6100
Richard Vacha, *Prdtn Mgr*

David Jackson, *Purch Mgr*
Robert Stone, *Manager*
Derek Bowen, *Manager*
Shelly Matthys, *Manager*
EMP: 300
SQ FT: 140,000
SALES (corp-wide): 189.9MM **Privately Held**
WEB: www.conn-selmer.com
SIC: 3931 Musical instruments
HQ: Conn-Selmer, Inc.
600 Industrial Pkwy
Elkhart IN 46516
574 522-1675

(G-20463)
CORTEST INC
38322 Apollo Pkwy (44094-7724)
PHONE................................440 942-1235
Fax: 440 942-0327
Allen F Denzine, *President*
Stephen Kubiak, *Project Engr*
Wendy Peren, *Office Mgr*
Gary Mazurk, *Manager*
Marsha Denzine, *Admin Sec*
EMP: 14
SQ FT: 10,000
SALES (est): 2.9MM **Privately Held**
SIC: 3821 5084 Laboratory apparatus & furniture; industrial machinery & equipment

(G-20464)
COUNTY OF LAKE
Also Called: Lake Cnty Deptmntl Retrdtn/Dvl
2100 Joseph Lloyd Pkwy (44094-8032)
PHONE................................440 269-2193
Fax: 440 269-2191
Wiegand Ken, *Plant Mgr*
Carol Krider, *Production*
Marcie Barbic, *Sls & Mktg Exec*
Michael Betz, *Sales Executive*
Gary Metelko, *Director*
EMP: 72 **Privately Held**
WEB: www.lakecountyohio.gov
SIC: 8322 8331 3441 Individual & family services; job training & vocational rehabilitation services; fabricated structural metal
PA: County Of Lake
8 N State St Ste 215
Painesville OH 44077
440 350-2500

(G-20465)
CREST AWNING & HOME IMPRV CO
1571 E 361st St Bldg 1 (44095-5328)
PHONE................................440 942-3092
EMP: 3
SALES: 300K **Privately Held**
SIC: 3444 Mfg Alluminum Awnings

(G-20466)
D & D QUALITY MACHINING CO INC
36495 Reading Ave (44094-8208)
PHONE................................440 942-2772
Zarko Duvnjak, *President*
Steve Drazetic, *Manager*
EMP: 15
SALES (est): 2.1MM **Privately Held**
SIC: 3599 Machine shop, jobbing & repair

(G-20467)
D S H MACHINE CO
36255 Reading Ave Ste A (44094-8236)
PHONE................................440 946-4311
Fax: 440 946-4311
Kenneth Lekes, *President*
Diane P Sustar, *Corp Secy*
EMP: 4
SQ FT: 6,000
SALES (est): 422K **Privately Held**
SIC: 3599 Machine shop, jobbing & repair

(G-20468)
DAI CERAMICS INC
38240 Airport Pkwy (44094-8023)
PHONE................................440 946-6964
Fax: 440 951-2106
Richard Ruggerio, *President*
Carole Coughlin, *Purch Mgr*
EMP: 65
SQ FT: 40,000

SALES (est): 10.3MM **Privately Held**
WEB: www.daiceramics.com
SIC: 3253 Ceramic wall & floor tile

(G-20469)
DAN NOVAK
Also Called: Nova Metal Products
1455 E 328th St (44095-3457)
PHONE................................440 269-1741
Dan Novak, *Owner*
Nick Novak, *Engineer*
EMP: 5
SALES: 400K **Privately Held**
SIC: 3449 Miscellaneous metalwork

(G-20470)
DANIELS BROTHERS FUEL CO
38700 Pelton Rd (44094-7745)
PHONE................................440 942-1800
Fax: 440 942-1577
Daniel Mitchell, *President*
EMP: 3 **EST:** 2012
SALES (est): 226.4K **Privately Held**
SIC: 2869 Fuels

(G-20471)
DE MILTA SAND AND GRAVEL
921 Erie Rd (44095-1812)
PHONE................................440 942-2015
Fax: 440 918-1300
Nick De Milta, *President*
Joseph De, *Vice Pres*
Joe De Milta, *Vice Pres*
EMP: 15
SQ FT: 1,800
SALES (est): 1.9MM **Privately Held**
SIC: 1442 Common sand mining; gravel mining

(G-20472)
DE-KO INC
38334 Willoughby Pkwy (44094-7584)
PHONE................................440 951-2585
Dennis Kog, *President*
Roberta Ernst, *Manager*
EMP: 5
SQ FT: 10,400
SALES (est): 1.6MM **Privately Held**
SIC: 5084 1796 3441 Cranes, industrial; machinery installation; fabricated structural metal

(G-20473)
DESIGNER CNTEMPORARY LAMINATES
37105 Code Ave (44094-6337)
PHONE................................440 946-8207
Fax: 440 946-9652
Robert Krauss, *President*
EMP: 8
SQ FT: 5,600
SALES (est): 480K **Privately Held**
WEB: www.dclweb.net
SIC: 3083 2541 Plastic finished products, laminated; cabinets, except refrigerated: show, display, etc.: wood

(G-20474)
DOCMANN PRINTING & ASSOC INC
4889 E 345th St (44094-4606)
PHONE................................440 975-1775
Fax: 440 975-4975
Todd Brichmann, *President*
James E Docherty, *Vice Pres*
Lauren Gizzo, *Graphic Designe*
EMP: 7
SQ FT: 14,000
SALES (est): 1.3MM **Privately Held**
WEB: www.docmann.com
SIC: 2752 Commercial printing, lithographic

(G-20475)
DUKE GRAPHICS INC
Also Called: Duke Printing
33212 Lakeland Blvd (44095-5205)
PHONE................................440 946-0606
Fax: 440 946-1627
Blake A Leduc, *President*
Thomas Chubb, *Vice Pres*
David Firestone, *Purch Mgr*
Karin Lucas, *Purch Mgr*
Ron Jewett, *Accounts Exec*
EMP: 33
SQ FT: 24,000

SALES (est): 8.1MM **Privately Held**
WEB: www.dukeprint.com
SIC: 2752 Commercial printing, offset

(G-20476)
DUKE MANUFACTURING INC
38205 Western Pkwy (44094-7591)
PHONE................................440 951-1879
Jeff Newmark, *President*
Robert Zaucha, *Vice Pres*
Timo Henk, *Engineer*
▲ **EMP:** 30
SQ FT: 18,000
SALES (est): 4.9MM **Privately Held**
WEB: www.dmcmachining.com
SIC: 3599 Machine shop, jobbing & repair

(G-20477)
DURA BILT DRAPERY & UPHOLSTERY
4041 Erie St (44094-7871)
PHONE................................440 269-8438
Helen T Luskin, *President*
James F Luskin, *Treasurer*
Gerard M Luskin, *Admin Sec*
EMP: 12
SQ FT: 4,000
SALES (est): 1MM **Privately Held**
SIC: 2512 7641 Upholstered household furniture; furniture refinishing; reupholstery

(G-20478)
EAGLE WLDG & FABRICATION INC
1766 Joseph Lloyd Pkwy (44094-8028)
PHONE................................440 946-0692
Fax: 440 942-5584
Mareo Paulic, *President*
Nick Paulic, *Vice Pres*
Milan Paulic, *Treasurer*
Amy Murphy, *Office Mgr*
William Schwenner, *Admin Sec*
EMP: 20
SQ FT: 15,500
SALES (est): 4.4MM **Privately Held**
WEB: www.eagle-welding.com
SIC: 3443 3699 7692 3444 Fabricated plate work (boiler shop); laser systems & equipment; welding repair; sheet metalwork

(G-20479)
EASTLAKE MACHINE PRODUCTS INC
1956 Joseph Lloyd Pkwy (44094-8030)
PHONE................................440 953-1014
Fax: 440 953-1086
Ivan Saric, *President*
Richard Moroscak, *Principal*
Sandra Saric, *Manager*
EMP: 43
SQ FT: 14,000
SALES (est): 5.1MM **Privately Held**
SIC: 3599 3451 Machine shop, jobbing & repair; screw machine products

(G-20480)
ERICSON MANUFACTURING CO
4323 Hamann Pkwy (44094-5625)
PHONE................................440 951-8000
Fax: 440 951-1867
John Ericson III, *President*
Diane Contreraz, *General Mgr*
Chris Ericson, *Vice Pres*
William Murphy, *Foreman/Supr*
Mike Higgins, *Maint Spvr*
◆ **EMP:** 80
SQ FT: 25,000
SALES (est): 27.1MM **Privately Held**
WEB: www.ericson.com
SIC: 3643 3648 Electric connectors; plugs, electric; connectors, electric cord; lighting equipment

(G-20481)
EUCLID DESIGN & MANUFACTURING
38333 Willoughby Pkwy (44094-7585)
PHONE................................440 942-0066
Fax: 440 942-0059
Don Nemeth, *President*
Sue Nemeth, *Vice Pres*
EMP: 10 **EST:** 1972
SQ FT: 8,000

SALES (est): 800K **Privately Held**
SIC: **3544** Special dies, tools, jigs & fixtures

(G-20482)
EUCLID PRODUCTS CO INC
Also Called: Main Fare Box Division
3625 Lost Nation Rd (44094-7790)
PHONE..............................440 942-7310
Fax: 440 942-4184
Bruce T Finke, *President*
EMP: 9
SQ FT: 24,000
SALES: 1MM **Privately Held**
WEB: www.epco-mfb.com
SIC: **3567 3829 3565 3365** Heating units & devices, industrial: electric; fare registers for street cars, buses, etc.; packaging machinery; aluminum foundries; packaging paper & plastics film, coated & laminated

(G-20483)
F & J GRINDING INC
36495 Reading Ave (44094-8208)
PHONE..............................440 942-4430
Fax: 440 942-1185
Joe Faraguna, *President*
EMP: 4
SQ FT: 3,600
SALES (est): 525.8K **Privately Held**
SIC: **3599** Grinding castings for the trade

(G-20484)
FABTECH OHIO
38311 Apollo Pkwy Ste 3 (44094-7760)
PHONE..............................440 942-0811
Ron Beech, *President*
EMP: 3
SQ FT: 5,000
SALES (est): 260K **Privately Held**
SIC: **3444** Sheet metalwork

(G-20485)
FAITH TOOL & MANUFACTURING
36575 Reading Ave (44094-8210)
PHONE..............................440 951-5934
Fax: 440 951-4956
Robert Levak, *Principal*
Donna Levak, *Vice Pres*
EMP: 8
SALES: 910K **Privately Held**
SIC: **3544** Industrial molds

(G-20486)
FEEDALL INC
38379 Pelton Rd (44094-7719)
PHONE..............................440 942-8100
Fax: 440 942-5710
Roger W Winslow Jr, *President*
Steve Steinor, *Design Engr*
Randy Sparks, *Sales Mgr*
Jackie Nagle, *Manager*
Michael J O'Brien, *Admin Sec*
EMP: 12
SQ FT: 15,300
SALES: 3.7MM **Privately Held**
WEB: www.feedall.com
SIC: **3535 3545** Conveyors & conveying equipment; hopper feed devices

(G-20487)
FIONAS FINERIES
Also Called: Fellow's
9077 Billings Rd (44094-9573)
PHONE..............................440 796-7426
Christine Fellows, *Owner*
Thomas Overhausen, *Owner*
EMP: 3
SALES: 950K **Privately Held**
SIC: **2386** Garments, leather

(G-20488)
FIRENZA STONE INC
36420 Biltmore Pl Ste 4 (44094-8232)
PHONE..............................440 953-8883
Fax: 440 953-8266
Anthony Fimiani, *Principal*
Jon Fimiani, *Principal*
Michael Fimiani, *Principal*
▲ EMP: 8
SALES (est): 1.6MM **Privately Held**
WEB: www.firenzastone.com
SIC: **3423** Stonecutters' hand tools

(G-20489)
FIRST MACHINE & TOOL CORP
38181 Airport Pkwy (44094-8038)
PHONE..............................440 269-8644
Fax: 440 269-8645
Mladen Laush, *President*
Herman Lackner, *Vice Pres*
EMP: 12
SQ FT: 5,600
SALES (est): 1.4MM **Privately Held**
WEB: www.firstmachinegages.com
SIC: **3544** Jigs: inspection, gauging & checking

(G-20490)
FLORLINE DISPLAY PRODUCTS CORP
38160 Western Pkwy (44094-7588)
PHONE..............................440 975-9449
Patricia Primozic, *President*
Randy Primozic, *Corp Secy*
James Primozic, *Vice Pres*
EMP: 3
SQ FT: 60,000
SALES (est): 341.5K **Privately Held**
WEB: www.floralinedisplay.com
SIC: **3585** Counters & counter display cases, refrigerated

(G-20491)
FLUID LINE PRODUCTS INC
38273 Western Pkwy (44094-7591)
P.O. Box 1000 (44096-1000)
PHONE..............................440 946-9470
Fax: 440 946-9472
John Skalicki, *Ch of Bd*
John J Hetzer, *President*
Stella Ann Hetzer, *Corp Secy*
Zelko Skalicki, *Vice Pres*
Robert Skalicki, *Admin Asst*
EMP: 128
SQ FT: 62,000
SALES (est): 23.5MM **Privately Held**
WEB: www.fluidline.com
SIC: **3492** Fluid power valves & hose fittings

(G-20492)
FOCUS MANUFACTURING INC
Also Called: Libra Industries
38127 Willoughby Pkwy (44094-7581)
PHONE..............................440 946-8766
Fax: 440 946-8022
Ronald K Brehm, *President*
Jeff Waterman, *Vice Pres*
Peter Snitzer, *Engineer*
Richard Scebbi, *Treasurer*
Bruce Vanek, *Admin Sec*
EMP: 16
SQ FT: 6,000
SALES: 1.3MM **Privately Held**
SIC: **3599** Machine shop, jobbing & repair

(G-20493)
FUSION AUTOMATION INC (HQ)
4658 E 355th St (44094-4630)
PHONE..............................440 602-5595
Kent Williams, *President*
Ann Moore, *Vice Pres*
Bruce Williams, *Vice Pres*
Roger Barker, *Technical Mgr*
Jim Meschewski, *CFO*
EMP: 2
SALES: 10MM
SALES (corp-wide): 20.1MM **Privately Held**
SIC: **3548 3356 3423 3398** Soldering equipment, except hand soldering irons; solder: wire, bar, acid core, & rosin core; hand & edge tools; metal heat treating; secondary nonferrous metals; chemical preparations
PA: Fusion Incorporated
    4658 E 355th St
    Willoughby OH 44094
    440 946-3300

(G-20494)
FUSION INCORPORATED
4658 E 355th St (44094-4630)
PHONE..............................440 946-3300
Christopher T Turner, *President*
Deke Morrow, *Vice Pres*
Tina Ashlock, *Admin Asst*
Jamie Broveak, *Administration*
▲ EMP: 44

SALES (est): 9.6MM **Privately Held**
SIC: **3511** Hydraulic turbines

(G-20495)
FUSION INCORPORATED
4711 Topps Indus Pkwy (44094-4635)
PHONE..............................440 946-3300
Kent Williams, *President*
Roger Barker, *Research*
Roger Lohrey, *Engineer*
Tony Straniero, *VP Mktg*
Dick Lamb, *CTO*
EMP: 30
SALES (corp-wide): 20.1MM **Privately Held**
WEB: www.fai-uk.com
SIC: **3356 3548** Nonferrous rolling & drawing; welding apparatus
PA: Fusion Incorporated
    4658 E 355th St
    Willoughby OH 44094
    440 946-3300

(G-20496)
G-M-I INC
4822 E 355th St (44094-4634)
PHONE..............................440 953-8811
Fax: 440 953-9631
Donald J Restly, *President*
Carol L Restly, *Corp Secy*
G Pacanosky, *Opers Mgr*
EMP: 9
SQ FT: 9,200
SALES (est): 1.3MM **Privately Held**
WEB: www.gmiincusa.com
SIC: **3053** Gaskets, packing & sealing devices

(G-20497)
GEARTEC INC
4245 Hamann Pkwy (44094-5623)
PHONE..............................440 953-3900
Fax: 440 953-3906
Elizabeth Masitto, *Principal*
Mike Wendolowski, *Engineer*
Betty Masitto, *Controller*
Dan Smyntek, *Sales Staff*
Bill Stohr, *Manager*
▲ EMP: 8
SALES (est): 1.8MM **Privately Held**
SIC: **3714** Gears, motor vehicle

(G-20498)
GENERAL PRECISION CORPORATION
4553 Beidler Rd (44094-4646)
PHONE..............................440 951-9380
Fax: 440 921-3200
Allen Ernst, *President*
Jerome Walker, *Vice Pres*
EMP: 7
SALES: 600K **Privately Held**
WEB: www.generalprecisioncorp.com
SIC: **8711 3365** Engineering services; machinery castings, aluminum

(G-20499)
GLENRIDGE MACHINE CO
4610 Beidler Rd (44094-4603)
PHONE..............................440 975-1055
Fax: 440 975-3490
Mark Negrelli Jr, *Ch of Bd*
Jerry Negrelli, *President*
Mark Negrelli III, *Vice Pres*
Michael Genzen, *Engineer*
Gary Mann, *CFO*
▲ EMP: 33
SQ FT: 66,000
SALES (est): 7.8MM **Privately Held**
WEB: www.glenridgemachine.com
SIC: **3599 7692** Machine shop, jobbing & repair; welding repair

(G-20500)
GOOD FORTUNES INC
1486 E 361st St (44095-3174)
P.O. Box 43419, Cleveland (44143-0419)
PHONE..............................440 942-2888
Gene Yee, *President*
Yuet Yee, *Principal*
EMP: 12
SQ FT: 5,000
SALES (est): 1.4MM **Privately Held**
WEB: www.goodfortunecookies.com
SIC: **2052** Bakery products, dry; cookies

(G-20501)
GRADEWORKS
10655 Hickory Hill Ct (44094-9418)
PHONE..............................440 487-4201
Matthew Clem, *Principal*
EMP: 6
SALES (est): 599.1K **Privately Held**
SIC: **3531** Road construction & maintenance machinery

(G-20502)
H & R METAL FINISHING INC
1650 E 361st St Unit L (44095-5334)
PHONE..............................440 942-6656
Fax: 440 942-6635
Rosemarie Cruz, *President*
Hermes C Cruz, *Managing Dir*
Rose Espendez, *Corp Secy*
Rose M Cruz, *Manager*
EMP: 6
SQ FT: 3,600
SALES (est): 731.2K **Privately Held**
WEB: www.hrmetal.com
SIC: **3471** Finishing, metals or formed products

(G-20503)
HEISLER TOOL COMPANY
38228 Western Pkwy (44094-7590)
PHONE..............................440 951-2424
Fax: 440 951-3299
Timothy M McCord, *President*
Susan McCord, *Vice Pres*
EMP: 15
SQ FT: 22,000
SALES (est): 2.1MM **Privately Held**
WEB: www.heislertool.com
SIC: **3599 3549** Custom machinery; metalworking machinery

(G-20504)
HI TECMETAL GROUP INC
HI Tech Aero
34800 Lakeland Blvd (44095-5224)
PHONE..............................440 946-2280
Fax: 440 946-2283
Scott St Claire, *Branch Mgr*
Scott Stclair, *Manager*
EMP: 27
SQ FT: 17,433
SALES (corp-wide): 22.9MM **Privately Held**
SIC: **3398 7692** Metal heat treating; brazing (hardening) of metal; welding repair
PA: Hi Tecmetal Group Inc
    1101 E 55th St
    Cleveland OH 44103
    216 881-8100

(G-20505)
HUDCO MANUFACTURING INC
38250 Western Pkwy (44094-7590)
PHONE..............................440 951-4040
Fax: 440 951-1870
Donald M Hudak, *President*
Joan L Hudak, *Corp Secy*
◆ EMP: 8
SQ FT: 6,000
SALES (est): 1.3MM **Privately Held**
WEB: www.hudcomfg.com
SIC: **3531** Construction machinery; rock crushing machinery, portable; concrete grouting equipment

(G-20506)
HYDRAULIC PRODUCTS INC
4540 Beidler Rd (44094-4602)
PHONE..............................440 946-4575
Joseph Focareto, *President*
Mary Arhar, *Controller*
▲ EMP: 8
SALES (est): 992.8K **Privately Held**
SIC: **3593 7699 3594** Fluid power cylinders, hydraulic or pneumatic; hydraulic equipment repair; fluid power pumps & motors

(G-20507)
HYLUN MACHINE CO INC
9220 Woods Way Dr (44094-9370)
PHONE..............................440 256-8755
Kim Hyder, *President*
Bonnie Hyder, *Corp Secy*
EMP: 4 EST: 1974
SQ FT: 5,000

▲ = Import ▼=Export
◆ =Import/Export

SALES (est): 362.5K **Privately Held**
SIC: 3599 Machine shop, jobbing & repair

(G-20508)
IDA CONTROLS
38593 Bell Rd (44094-7519)
PHONE..........................440 785-8457
Vince Difranco, *Owner*
EMP: 8
SALES (est): 1.2MM **Privately Held**
SIC: 3613 Switchgear & switchboard apparatus

(G-20509)
IMAGING SCIENCES LLC
38174 Willoughby Pkwy (44094-7580)
PHONE..........................440 975-9640
Geoffrey R Brown, *President*
Geoffrey Brown, *President*
Simon Rogers, *Marketing Staff*
Brenda Brown,
Charles Vendeville,
EMP: 9
SQ FT: 18,000
SALES (est): 1.7MM **Privately Held**
WEB: www.imaging-sciences.com
SIC: 3211 Construction glass

(G-20510)
INTEGRA ENCLOSURES INC (PA)
7750 Pyler Blvd (44094)
P.O. Box 1870, Mentor (44061-1870)
PHONE..........................440 269-4966
Fax: 440 269-4977
Jim McWilliams, *President*
Deb Tasel, *Manager*
EMP: 6
SQ FT: 30,000
SALES: 3.4MM **Privately Held**
WEB: www.integraenclosures.com
SIC: 3089 Injection molding of plastics; thermoformed finished plastic products

(G-20511)
INTELITOOL MANUFACTURING SVCS
36335 Reading Ave Ste 4 (44094-8200)
PHONE..........................440 953-1071
Gary Struna, *President*
William Tulloch, *Senior VP*
Scott Webb, *Manager*
Collen Mocz, *Admin Sec*
EMP: 6
SQ FT: 10,500
SALES (est): 885.6K **Privately Held**
WEB: www.intelitoolinc.com
SIC: 2542 Fixtures, office: except wood

(G-20512)
INTERLAKE INDUSTRIES INC (PA)
4732 E 355th St (44094-4632)
PHONE..........................440 942-0800
Lisa M Habe, *Ch of Bd*
Mark Groenstein, *General Mgr*
Norm Valentino Sr, *Senior VP*
Dan Valentino, *Vice Pres*
John Ellis, *Controller*
EMP: 3
SQ FT: 3,000
SALES (est): 25.6MM **Privately Held**
WEB: www.interlakestamping.com
SIC: 3469 Stamping metal for the trade

(G-20513)
INTERLAKE STAMPING OHIO INC
4732 E 355th St (44094-4632)
PHONE..........................440 942-0800
Fax: 440 942-0212
Lisa M Habe, *President*
Mark Groenstein, *General Mgr*
Dan Valentino, *Vice Pres*
John Ellis, *Comptroller*
Liz Tolbert, *Director*
EMP: 40 EST: 1957
SQ FT: 36,000
SALES: 10.9MM
SALES (corp-wide): 25.6MM **Privately Held**
WEB: www.interlakestamping.com
SIC: 3469 Metal stampings

PA: Interlake Industries, Inc.
4732 E 355th St
Willoughby OH 44094
440 942-0800

(G-20514)
J E M INDUSTRIES INC
950 Erie Rd (44095-1811)
PHONE..........................440 951-4884
Fax: 440 951-2191
James Morgan, *President*
Elizabeth Morgan, *Admin Sec*
EMP: 12
SQ FT: 10,000
SALES (est): 1.9MM **Privately Held**
SIC: 3585 Parts for heating, cooling & refrigerating equipment

(G-20515)
JAMES L WEREB
Also Called: Wereb Metal Fabricating
38005 Apollo Pkwy Ste 2 (44094-7759)
PHONE..........................440 942-2405
James L Wereb, *Owner*
EMP: 3 EST: 1990
SQ FT: 2,400
SALES (est): 323K **Privately Held**
SIC: 3446 3599 Railings, bannisters, guards, etc.: made from metal pipe; stairs, staircases, stair treads: prefabricated metal; machine shop, jobbing & repair

(G-20516)
JOHN WOLF & CO INC
36420 Biltmore Pl Ste 1 (44094-8232)
PHONE..........................440 942-0083
John R Wolf, *President*
EMP: 3
SQ FT: 1,600
SALES (est): 280.7K **Privately Held**
SIC: 3812 Airspeed instrumentation (aeronautical instruments)

(G-20517)
JOURNAL REGISTER COMPANY
Journal, The
7085 Mentor Ave (44094-7948)
PHONE..........................440 951-0000
Fax: 440 975-2293
Stephen Roszczyk, *Principal*
Dave Wilson, *Systems Mgr*
Douglas Fuller, *Director*
EMP: 225
SALES (corp-wide): 745.5MM **Privately Held**
WEB: www.journalregister.com
SIC: 2711 Newspapers
PA: Journal Register Company
5 Hanover Sq Fl 25
New York NY 10004
212 257-7212

(G-20518)
KALCOR COATINGS COMPANY
37721 Stevens Blvd (44094-6231)
PHONE..........................440 946-4700
Cori Zucker, *President*
Don Mihalik, *Vice Pres*
Carol McGee, *Traffic Mgr*
Roger Lafrance, *Research*
Sheryl Herwood, *Controller*
▲ EMP: 25 EST: 1961
SQ FT: 55,000
SALES (est): 7MM **Privately Held**
SIC: 2851 Paints & paint additives; lacquers, varnishes, enamels & other coatings

(G-20519)
KEB INDUSTRIES INC
2166 Joseph Lloyd Pkwy (44094-8032)
PHONE..........................440 953-4623
Fax: 440 953-9209
Brad Butler, *President*
EMP: 8
SQ FT: 6,500
SALES (est): 820K **Privately Held**
WEB: www.kebkollets.com
SIC: 3545 Precision tools, machinists'

(G-20520)
KENNEDY GROUP INCORPORATED (PA)
38601 Kennedy Pkwy (44094-7395)
PHONE..........................440 951-7660

Bertram Kennedy, *CEO*
Michael R Kennedy, *President*
Marybeth Whelan, *Regional Mgr*
Todd Kennedy, *COO*
Mary Lou Kennedy, *Vice Pres*
▲ EMP: 83
SQ FT: 80,000
SALES (est): 36.4MM **Privately Held**
WEB: www.kennedygrp.com
SIC: 2679 2673 3089 3565 Tags & labels, paper; bags: plastic, laminated & coated; garment bags (plastic film): made from purchased materials; plastic containers, except foam; boxes, plastic; cases, plastic; packaging machinery; nailed wood boxes & shook

(G-20521)
KJ MACHINING SYSTEMS INC
38254 Airport Pkwy Unit C (44094-8023)
PHONE..........................440 975-8624
Jonathan Deblasi, *President*
EMP: 5
SQ FT: 2,500
SALES (est): 220K **Privately Held**
WEB: www.kjmsinc.com
SIC: 3599 Machine shop, jobbing & repair

(G-20522)
KOPACHKO MACHINING INC
38341 Western Pkwy (44094-7528)
PHONE..........................440 953-3988
Robert Kopachko, *President*
Lois Kopachko, *Vice Pres*
EMP: 5
SQ FT: 4,800
SALES: 300K **Privately Held**
SIC: 3599 Machine shop, jobbing & repair

(G-20523)
KOTTLER METAL PRODUCTS CO INC
1595 Lost Nation Rd (44094-7329)
PHONE..........................440 946-7473
Barry Feldman, *President*
Harold Feldman, *Vice Pres*
Mike Mangan, *Mfg Staff*
Ron McCloud, *Mfg Staff*
Pat Garrett, *Sales Mgr*
▲ EMP: 25 EST: 1914
SALES: 7.4MM **Privately Held**
WEB: www.kottlermetal.com
SIC: 3498 3441 7692 3547 Pipe sections fabricated from purchased pipe; tube fabricating (contract bending & shaping); fabricated structural metal; welding repair; rolling mill machinery

(G-20524)
LAKE COMMUNITY NEWS
Also Called: Painesville Pride
36081 Lake Shore Blvd # 5 (44095-1578)
P.O. Box 814, Mantua (44255-0814)
PHONE..........................440 946-2577
Fax: 440 946-0527
Deanne Nelisse, *President*
Gordon Moser, *Finance*
EMP: 7
SALES: 300K **Privately Held**
SIC: 2711 Newspapers: publishing only, not printed on site

(G-20525)
LANDERWOOD INDUSTRIES INC
4245 Hamann Pkwy (44094-5623)
PHONE..........................440 233-4234
James H Weaver III, *President*
Betty Horowitz, *Controller*
EMP: 30
SQ FT: 30,000
SALES (est): 2.9MM **Privately Held**
WEB: www.geartecinc.com
SIC: 3462 Gears, forged steel

(G-20526)
LANGA TOOL & MACHINE INC
36430 Reading Ave Ste 1 (44094-8220)
PHONE..........................440 953-1138
Fax: 440 953-1399
William Langa, *President*
Winzy Langa, *Manager*
EMP: 20
SQ FT: 7,000
SALES (est): 2.7MM **Privately Held**
SIC: 3599 Machine shop, jobbing & repair

(G-20527)
LAPA LOWE ENTERPRISES LLC
Also Called: Gas & Grills
5900 Som Center Rd Ste 16 (44094-3044)
PHONE..........................440 944-9410
Fax: 440 944-9412
Lacy Lowe, *Mng Member*
EMP: 3
SALES: 260K **Privately Held**
SIC: 3631 Barbecues, grills & braziers (outdoor cooking)

(G-20528)
LOKRING TECHNOLOGY LLC
38376 Apollo Pkwy (44094-7724)
PHONE..........................440 942-0880
Bill Lennon, *President*
Vijay Raghu, *Materials Mgr*
Zsolt Harsanyi, *Purchasing*
Cody Durio, *Sales Associate*
Chuck Leaberry, *Manager*
▲ EMP: 54
SALES (est): 28.8MM **Privately Held**
SIC: 3312 Pipes & tubes

(G-20529)
LOST NATION FUEL
3525 Lost Nation Rd (44094-7753)
PHONE..........................440 951-9088
Dan Triplett, *Principal*
EMP: 4
SALES (est): 432.6K **Privately Held**
SIC: 2869 Fuels

(G-20530)
LURE INC
38040 3rd St (44094-6139)
PHONE..........................440 951-8862
Giovana Kustella, *President*
Nick Kustella, *Vice Pres*
EMP: 20 EST: 2001
SALES (est): 1.3MM **Privately Held**
WEB: www.baitdriver.com
SIC: 3949 Lures, fishing: artificial

(G-20531)
M L GRINDING CO
34620 Lakeland Blvd (44095-5222)
PHONE..........................440 975-9111
Fax: 440 975-9311
Fred Lazar, *Owner*
EMP: 3 EST: 1975
SQ FT: 4,000
SALES (est): 140K **Privately Held**
SIC: 3599 Grinding castings for the trade

(G-20532)
MAGNETIC RESONANCE TECH
4261 Hamann Pkwy (44094-5623)
PHONE..........................440 942-2922
Michael Profeta, *President*
Kathleen Profeta, *Vice Pres*
Claudia Toth, *Manager*
EMP: 5
SQ FT: 20,000
SALES: 1.5MM **Privately Held**
WEB: www.mritechnologies.com
SIC: 3845 Magnetic resonance imaging device, nuclear

(G-20533)
MAGNUS ENGINEERED EQP LLC
4500 Beidler Rd (44094-4602)
PHONE..........................440 942-8488
William Martin, *President*
Bill Martin, *COO*
Jeffrey Mendrala, *CFO*
Daniel Ackroyd, *Sales Staff*
Chelsea Mendrala, *Mktg Dir*
EMP: 26
SQ FT: 38,000
SALES: 4MM **Privately Held**
SIC: 3699 Cleaning equipment, ultrasonic, except medical & dental

(G-20534)
MANICO INC
37105 Code Ave (44094-6337)
P.O. Box 509 (44096-0509)
PHONE..........................440 946-5333
Fax: 440 946-7756
Nicholas Manta, *President*
EMP: 6
SQ FT: 12,000

SALES: 500K **Privately Held**
WEB: www.manico.com
SIC: 3491 3823 Pressure valves & regulators, industrial; regulators (steam fittings); water works valves; flow instruments, industrial process type

(G-20535)
MAR-BAL PULTRUSION INC
38310 Apollo Pkwy (44094-7724)
PHONE...............................440 953-0456
Fax: 440 953-1831
Allen J Goryance, *President*
James Gortance, *Vice Pres*
EMP: 10
SQ FT: 10,000
SALES: 1MM **Privately Held**
SIC: 2519 Furniture, household: glass, fiberglass & plastic

(G-20536)
MARC INDUSTRIES INC
Also Called: Best Snow Plow
35140 Lakeland Blvd (44095-5228)
PHONE...............................440 944-9305
Fax: 440 946-8507
Howard Hren, *President*
Salvatore Lazzano, *Vice Pres*
Dan Chase, *Info Tech Dir*
EMP: 8
SQ FT: 8,000
SALES (est): 630K **Privately Held**
WEB: www.bestsnowplow.com
SIC: 3441 3711 Fabricated structural metal; snow plows (motor vehicles), assembly of

(G-20537)
MARK-N-MEND INC
38151 Airport Pkwy Ste 54 (44094-8050)
PHONE...............................440 951-2003
Fax: 440 951-2140
Melvin L March, *General Mgr*
Carol Burry, *Office Mgr*
Todd March, *Admin Sec*
EMP: 3
SQ FT: 5,000
SALES: 200K **Privately Held**
WEB: www.marknmend.com
SIC: 2752 Transfers, decalcomania or dry: lithographed

(G-20538)
MARKETING COMM RESOURCE INC
4800 E 345th St (44094-4607)
PHONE...............................440 484-3010
Dominic Tiunno, *CEO*
Frank Tiunno, *Exec VP*
EMP: 57
SALES (est): 6.9MM **Privately Held**
SIC: 4961 2759 Air conditioning supply services; laser printing

(G-20539)
MARTIN MACHINE CO INC
37151 Ben Hur Ave Ste D (44094-6349)
P.O. Box 136 (44096-0136)
PHONE...............................440 946-5174
Fax: 440 946-9366
James Martin, *President*
EMP: 5
SQ FT: 3,000
SALES: 600K **Privately Held**
SIC: 3599 Machine shop, jobbing & repair

(G-20540)
MAY THREAD GRINDING CO
38401 Apollo Pkwy Ste F (44094-7757)
PHONE...............................440 953-0678
Fax: 440 953-1484
Richard May, *President*
Shelby May, *President*
EMP: 4
SQ FT: 1,200
SALES: 500K **Privately Held**
SIC: 3599 Machine shop, jobbing & repair

(G-20541)
MCATTACK MACHINE LLC
38338 Apollo Pkwy Bldg 2 (44094-7796)
PHONE...............................440 946-3855
Sharon McIntire,
EMP: 3
SALES (est): 489.1K **Privately Held**
SIC: 3599 Industrial machinery

(G-20542)
MCTT MACHINE TOOL INC
Also Called: T T Machine Tool
38131 Arprt Pkwy Unit 207 (44094)
PHONE...............................440 946-9559
Tadija Erceg, *President*
Tom Erceg, *Vice Pres*
Milka Erceg, *Treasurer*
EMP: 3
SQ FT: 1,700
SALES (est): 412K **Privately Held**
SIC: 3599 Machine shop, jobbing & repair

(G-20543)
MEIBUHR CO INC
38301 Apollo Pkwy Ste 1 (44094-7758)
P.O. Box 317 (44096-0317)
PHONE...............................440 942-9375
Fax: 440 942-9375
A Scott Lining, *Vice Pres*
Jeannie Lining, *Vice Pres*
Kurt Lining, *Vice Pres*
Jason Salaty, *Vice Pres*
Timothy Lining, *VP Mfg*
EMP: 4
SALES: 200K **Privately Held**
WEB: www.meibuhr.com
SIC: 3449 Miscellaneous metalwork

(G-20544)
MEISTER MEDIA WORLDWIDE INC (PA)
37733 Euclid Ave (44094-5992)
PHONE...............................440 942-2000
Fax: 440 942-0662
Gary T Fitzgerald, *Ch of Bd*
Eric Davis, *Publisher*
Homero Ontiveros, *Publisher*
Rick Welder, *Publisher*
Laura Drotleff, *Editor*
EMP: 100 **EST:** 1932
SQ FT: 29,000
SALES (est): 19.5MM **Privately Held**
WEB: www.meistermedia.com
SIC: 2721 Magazines: publishing only, not printed on site

(G-20545)
MELINZ INDUSTRIES INC (PA)
Also Called: Riverview Raquetball Club
34099 Melinz Pkwy Unit D (44095-4001)
PHONE...............................440 946-3512
Adolph Melinz, *President*
Jeff Sloat, *Treasurer*
Nancy Sloat, *Admin Sec*
EMP: 10
SQ FT: 11,000
SALES (est): 1.2MM **Privately Held**
SIC: 7999 3599 Racquetball club, non-membership; machine & other job shop work

(G-20546)
MENTOR TOOL INC
990 Erie Rd Unit D (44095-1813)
PHONE...............................440 942-5273
Fax: 440 942-5934
John Elersich, *President*
Skip Schwab, *Corp Secy*
John Elerisch, *Personnel Exec*
EMP: 4
SQ FT: 2,000
SALES: 250K **Privately Held**
SIC: 3599 Machine shop, jobbing & repair

(G-20547)
METAL QUALITY PRODUCTS CO INC
34640 Lakeland Blvd (44095-5222)
PHONE...............................440 942-0787
Fax: 440 942-0980
Eugene Horvat, *President*
Luba Horvat, *Vice Pres*
Vince Borovic, *Purchasing*
Eva Miller, *Enginr/R&D Mgr*
Vlado Dujmovic, *Sales Staff*
EMP: 6
SQ FT: 10,000
SALES (est): 758.4K **Privately Held**
WEB: www.metalqualityproducts.com
SIC: 3599 Machine shop, jobbing & repair

(G-20548)
MICONVI PROPERTIES INC
Also Called: Bevcorp Properties
4711 E 355th St (44094-4631)
PHONE...............................440 954-3500
Michael Connelly, *President*
Vicki Connelly, *Corp Secy*
Timothy Frantz, *Senior VP*
John Adamczak, *Draft/Design*
Kevin Sweeney, *Engineer*
◆ **EMP:** 40
SQ FT: 25,000
SALES (est): 8.2MM **Privately Held**
SIC: 3565 Bottling machinery: filling, capping, labeling

(G-20549)
MIKA METAL FABRICATING CO
4530 Hamann Pkwy (44094-5630)
PHONE...............................440 951-5500
Fax: 440 951-0754
Fred J G Mika, *President*
Jack W Grootegoed, *General Mgr*
Fred G Mika, *Vice Pres*
Scott M Mika, *Vice Pres*
Jim Gunvalsen, *Sales Mgr*
EMP: 45
SQ FT: 78,000
SALES (est): 14.3MM **Privately Held**
SIC: 3444 Sheet metalwork

(G-20550)
MILLENNIUM MCH TECHLONLOGY LLC
38323 Apollo Pkwy Ste 7 (44094-7761)
PHONE...............................440 269-8080
Jeffrey J Downs, *Mng Member*
EMP: 11
SALES (est): 1.7MM **Privately Held**
SIC: 3599 Machine shop, jobbing & repair

(G-20551)
MIRMAT CNC MACHINING INC
4550 Hamann Pkwy (44094-5630)
PHONE...............................440 951-2410
Miroslav Vujovic, *President*
EMP: 5
SALES (est): 617.8K **Privately Held**
SIC: 3599 Machine & other job shop work

(G-20552)
NATIONAL ROLLER DIE INC
4750 Beidler Rd Unit 4 (44094-4663)
PHONE...............................440 951-3850
Kelly Johnson, *CEO*
Will Corral, *President*
Jeff Watt, *Superintendent*
EMP: 10
SALES (est): 1.1MM **Privately Held**
WEB: www.nrdi.net
SIC: 3544 Special dies & tools

(G-20553)
NEUNDORFER INC
Also Called: Neundorfer Engineering Service
4590 Hamann Pkwy (44094-5691)
PHONE...............................440 942-8990
Fax: 440 942-6824
Michael Neundorfer, *CEO*
Jean Ockuly, *Vice Pres*
Conne Tuttle, *Vice Pres*
Steve Ostanek, *Human Res Mgr*
Maggie Zeller, *Manager*
EMP: 42
SQ FT: 38,000
SALES (est): 7.6MM **Privately Held**
WEB: www.neundorfer.com
SIC: 8711 3564 Pollution control engineering; precipitators, electrostatic

(G-20554)
NEWAY STAMPING & MFG INC
4820 E 345th St (44094-4607)
P.O. Box 1023 (44096-1023)
PHONE...............................440 951-8500
Fax: 440 951-1108
Adam Bowden, *President*
Jason H Bowden, *Vice Pres*
Matthew J Bowden, *Vice Pres*
Lois Wimberly, *Purchasing*
Ray Pribula, *Engineer*
EMP: 85
SQ FT: 15,000
SALES (est): 22.8MM **Privately Held**
WEB: www.newaystamping.com
SIC: 3469 3544 Stamping metal for the trade; special dies, tools, jigs & fixtures

(G-20555)
NORBAR TORQUE TOOLS INC
36400 Biltmore Pl (44094-8221)
PHONE...............................440 953-1175
Keith Daiber, *President*
Bernice Daiber, *Corp Secy*
Terry Daiber, *Vice Pres*
Sam Ortolani, *Natl Sales Mgr*
Laura Russ, *Sales Staff*
▲ **EMP:** 12
SQ FT: 5,000
SALES (est): 3.8MM **Privately Held**
WEB: www.norbar.com
SIC: 5072 3423 Hand tools; wrenches, hand tools

(G-20556)
NORTHEAST BROACH & TOOL
990 Erie Rd Unit H (44095-1813)
PHONE...............................440 918-0048
Herb Eierman, *President*
Hannah Norder, *Corp Secy*
Tom Norder, *Exec VP*
EMP: 3
SALES: 200K **Privately Held**
SIC: 3545 Broaches (machine tool accessories)

(G-20557)
NORTHEASTERN RFRGN CORP
38274 Western Pkwy (44094-7590)
PHONE...............................440 942-7676
Fax: 440 942-0129
Carol A Primozic, *President*
James A Primozic, *Vice Pres*
Fern Peters, *Info Tech Mgr*
EMP: 20
SQ FT: 11,000
SALES (est): 5MM **Privately Held**
WEB: www.nrcinc.net
SIC: 3585 1711 7623 Refrigeration equipment, complete; heating & air conditioning contractors; refrigeration repair service

(G-20558)
NRC INC
Also Called: Northeastern Process Cooling
38160 Western Pkwy (44094-7588)
PHONE...............................440 975-9449
Fax: 440 918-9043
Randolph J Primozic, *President*
Patricia A Primozic, *Corp Secy*
Dave Dragolich, *Project Mgr*
Thomas Galon, *Project Mgr*
EMP: 30
SALES (est): 5.4MM **Privately Held**
SIC: 3585 Refrigeration equipment, complete

(G-20559)
NUPRO COMPANY
4800 E 345th St (44094-4607)
PHONE...............................440 951-9729
Fax: 216 951-4872
F J Callahan Jr, *Ch of Bd*
William Cosgrove, *President*
Ivan Begovic, *Plant Mgr*
Amy D Frank, *Project Mgr*
William C Gurley, *Project Mgr*
EMP: 250
SQ FT: 60,000
SALES (est): 18.5MM
SALES (corp-wide): 1.1B **Privately Held**
WEB: www.swagelok.com
SIC: 3494 3569 3564 3491 Valves & pipe fittings; filters, general line: industrial; blowers & fans; industrial valves
PA: Swagelok Company
    29500 Solon Rd
    Solon OH 44139
    440 248-4600

(G-20560)
OHIO BROACH & MACHINE COMPANY
35264 Topps Indus Pkwy (44094-4684)
PHONE...............................440 946-1040
Fax: 440 946-6475
Charles P Van De Motter, *CEO*
Christopher C Van De Motter, *President*
Louis B Komaromy, *Principal*

Walter Kuskin, *Principal*
Neil Van De Motter, *Vice Pres*
▼ EMP: 34 EST: 1956
SQ FT: 52,000
SALES (est): 6.7MM **Privately Held**
WEB: www.ohiobroach.com
SIC: 3541 7699 3545 3599 Broaching machines; knife, saw & tool sharpening & repair; machine tool accessories; machine shop, jobbing & repair

(G-20561)
OHIO CARBON BLANK INC (PA)
38403 Pelton Rd (44094-7721)
PHONE....................................440 953-9302
Fax: 440 953-5829
Scott Boncha, *President*
Dale McCartney, *President*
Lonnie Kirby, *Prdtn Mgr*
Susan Furman, *Mfg Staff*
EMP: 5
SQ FT: 2,000
SALES (est): 2.4MM **Privately Held**
WEB: www.ohiocarbonblank.com
SIC: 3624 Carbon & graphite products

(G-20562)
ORANGE BLOSSOM PRESS INC
38005 Brown Ave (44094-5836)
P.O. Box 93417, Cleveland (44101-5417)
PHONE....................................216 781-8655
Fax: 216 781-6336
Greg Patt, *President*
Donna Lirrivee-Cohen, *Corp Secy*
John O'Hara, *Vice Pres*
EMP: 8 EST: 1976
SQ FT: 6,000
SALES: 776K **Privately Held**
WEB: www.orangeblossompress.com
SIC: 2752 2791 2789 Commercial printing, offset; typesetting; bookbinding & related work

(G-20563)
P M MACHINE INC
38205 Western Pkwy (44094-7591)
PHONE....................................440 942-6537
Tom Decumbe, *President*
Jack Hostutler, *Prdtn Mgr*
EMP: 15
SQ FT: 10,000
SALES (est): 1.2MM **Privately Held**
SIC: 3089 Injection molding of plastics

(G-20564)
PACE CONSOLIDATED INC (PA)
Also Called: Pace Engineering
4800 Beidler Rd (44094-4605)
PHONE....................................440 942-1234
Fax: 440 942-5725
Craig Wallace, *CEO*
Randy Murphy, *Vice Pres*
Stephen Sherbondy, *Vice Pres*
Michelle Schroeder, *Human Res Mgr*
John Casalina, *Manager*
◆ EMP: 95
SQ FT: 120,000
SALES (est): 27.5MM **Privately Held**
SIC: 3531 Construction machinery

(G-20565)
PACE ENGINEERING INC
4800 Beidler Rd (44094-4605)
PHONE....................................440 942-1234
Craig R Wallace, *CEO*
John Casalina, *Manager*
EMP: 105 EST: 1963
SQ FT: 120,000
SALES (est): 7.7MM
SALES (corp-wide): 27.5MM **Privately Held**
WEB: www.paceparts.net
SIC: 3531 Construction machinery
PA: Pace Consolidated, Inc.
4800 Beidler Rd
Willoughby OH 44094
440 942-1234

(G-20566)
PALESH & ASSOCIATES INC
3659 Lost Nation Rd (44094-7756)
PHONE....................................440 942-9168
Fax: 440 953-4529
Frank G Palesh III, *CEO*
Michelle Mahoney, *Personnel Exec*
Lynn Elliott, *Manager*

EMP: 5
SQ FT: 12,000
SALES (est): 460K **Privately Held**
WEB: www.palesh.com
SIC: 7629 3621 5063 7699 Electrical equipment repair services; motors, electric; motors, electric; industrial machinery & equipment repair

(G-20567)
PAULO PRODUCTS COMPANY
Also Called: American Brzing Div Paulo Pdts
4428 Hamann Pkwy (44094-5628)
PHONE....................................440 942-0153
Fax: 440 946-3091
Andrew Muto, *Area Mgr*
Bob Muto, *Branch Mgr*
Jim Loveland, *Manager*
EMP: 38
SALES (corp-wide): 95.3MM **Privately Held**
WEB: www.paulo.com
SIC: 7692 1799 Brazing; coating of concrete structures with plastic
PA: Paulo Products Company
5711 W Park Ave
Saint Louis MO 63110
314 647-7500

(G-20568)
PHIL MATIC SCREW PRODUCTS INC
1457 E 357th St (44095-4127)
P.O. Box 1178 (44096-1178)
PHONE....................................440 942-7290
Fax: 440 942-1007
Larry E Phillis, *President*
Richard Phillis, *Vice Pres*
Fraser Young, *Vice Pres*
Cindy Young, *Office Mgr*
EMP: 14
SQ FT: 11,300
SALES (est): 2.2MM **Privately Held**
WEB: www.philmatic.com
SIC: 3599 Machine shop, jobbing & repair

(G-20569)
PIP PRINTING
35401 Euclid Ave Ste 109 (44094-4561)
PHONE....................................440 951-2606
Fax: 440 951-2607
Tom Jones, *Owner*
EMP: 3
SALES (est): 199.7K **Privately Held**
SIC: 2752 Commercial printing, offset

(G-20570)
PLASTIC FABRICATION SVCS INC
Also Called: Pierce Ohio
38167 Airport Pkwy Unit 1 (44094-8020)
P.O. Box 242, Grand River (44045-0242)
PHONE....................................440 953-9990
Richard Pierce, *President*
EMP: 3
SALES (est): 469.5K **Privately Held**
WEB: www.plastictanks.com
SIC: 3086 Plastics foam products

(G-20571)
PM COAL COMPANY LLC
9717 Chillicothe Rd (44094-9200)
PHONE....................................440 256-7624
Scott Brown, *President*
Jack M Grinwis, *Partner*
EMP: 5
SALES (est): 256.7K **Privately Held**
SIC: 1221 Bituminous coal surface mining

(G-20572)
PMC GAGE INC (PA)
Also Called: PMC Lonestar
38383 Willoughby Pkwy (44094-7585)
PHONE....................................440 953-1672
Fax: 440 953-3301
Nicholas Bosworth, *CEO*
Ann Gross, *General Mgr*
Teri Feldmann, *QC Mgr*
Randi Peterson, *Accountant*
Danija Jones, *Sales Staff*
EMP: 50

SALES (est): 10.7MM **Privately Held**
WEB: www.pmclonestar.com
SIC: 3545 3826 3829 Measuring tools & machines, machinists' metalworking type; analytical instruments; measuring & controlling devices

(G-20573)
PMC MERCURY (PA)
38383 Willoughby Pkwy (44094-7585)
PHONE....................................440 953-3300
Nick Boxworth, *President*
John Selesky, *Sales Associate*
EMP: 7
SQ FT: 38,000
SALES (est): 2.1MM **Privately Held**
WEB: www.mercurygage.com
SIC: 3545 Gauges (machine tool accessories)

(G-20574)
POLYFLEX LLC
4803 E 345th St (44094-4606)
PHONE....................................440 946-0758
Timothy Reed,
Scott Janda,
EMP: 10
SALES (est): 1.6MM **Privately Held**
SIC: 2297 Nonwoven fabrics

(G-20575)
POSITIVE SAFETY MFR CO
34099 Melinz Pkwy Unit A (44095-4001)
PHONE....................................440 951-2130
Jeff Sloat, *President*
Nancy Sloat, *Vice Pres*
Fred Tomazic, *Vice Pres*
Dale Snyder, *Office Mgr*
EMP: 15
SQ FT: 11,000
SALES (est): 1.3MM **Privately Held**
SIC: 3625 Control equipment, electric

(G-20576)
POWER-PACK CONVEYOR COMPANY
38363 Airport Pkwy (44094-7562)
PHONE....................................440 975-9955
Fax: 440 975-0505
Kevin Ensinger, *President*
James L Ensinger, *President*
Donnell Ensinger, *Exec VP*
Harry Cook, *VP Mfg*
Eric Ensinger, *CFO*
EMP: 25 EST: 1929
SQ FT: 48,000
SALES: 5.6MM **Privately Held**
WEB: www.power-packconveyor.com
SIC: 3535 5084 3531 Conveyors & conveying equipment; unit handling conveying systems; belt conveyor systems, general industrial use; bucket type conveyor systems; industrial machinery & equipment; road construction & maintenance machinery

(G-20577)
PRECISE TOOL & DIE COMPANY
38128 Willoughby Pkwy (44094-7580)
P.O. Box 1055 (44096-1055)
PHONE....................................440 951-9173
Fax: 440 951-7524
Steve Hunyadi, *CEO*
Eva Pinkerton, *President*
Rodger Ashburn, *Purch Mgr*
Elizabeth Hunyadi, *Treasurer*
Frank Corrao, *Sales Executive*
▲ EMP: 35
SQ FT: 22,000
SALES (est): 9.9MM **Privately Held**
WEB: www.precisetoolanddie.com
SIC: 3599 Machine shop, jobbing & repair

(G-20578)
PRECISION HONING INC
33000 Lakeland Blvd (44095-5203)
PHONE....................................440 942-7339
Fax: 440 942-4554
Don Bard, *President*
EMP: 4
SQ FT: 10,000
SALES (est): 488.4K **Privately Held**
SIC: 3541 Honing & lapping machines

(G-20579)
PRIME TIME MACHINE INC
38302 Arprt Pkwy Unit 10 (44094)
PHONE....................................440 942-7410
James R Vaughn, *President*
EMP: 3
SQ FT: 5,000
SALES (est): 260K **Privately Held**
SIC: 3544 Special dies & tools; jigs & fixtures

(G-20580)
PROGRESSIVE LABELS LLC
38601 Kennedy Pkwy (44094-7395)
PHONE....................................570 688-9636
Albert C Walck III,
EMP: 12
SQ FT: 10,000
SALES (est): 1.8MM **Privately Held**
WEB: www.progressivelabels.com
SIC: 2672 Tape, pressure sensitive: made from purchased materials

(G-20581)
QUALITY CNC MACHINING INC
38195 Airport Pkwy (44094-8038)
PHONE....................................440 942-0542
Fax: 440 953-8069
Joseph Katic, *President*
Sandro Marusic, *General Mgr*
EMP: 12
SQ FT: 8,000
SALES (est): 2.2MM **Privately Held**
SIC: 3599 Machine shop, jobbing & repair

(G-20582)
QUALITY FRP FABRICATIONS
1450 E 363rd St (44095-4136)
PHONE....................................440 942-9067
Fax: 440 946-5374
Robert Archbold, *Owner*
EMP: 7
SQ FT: 3,000
SALES (est): 675.2K **Privately Held**
SIC: 3089 Pallets, plastic

(G-20583)
QUALITY SCREW PRODUCTS INC
38302 Arprt Pkwy Unit 15 (44094)
PHONE....................................440 975-1828
Fax: 440 975-1824
Frank Fiorta, *President*
Michele Fiorta, *Vice Pres*
Edward Krukowski, *Treasurer*
EMP: 3
SQ FT: 3,100
SALES: 300K **Privately Held**
SIC: 3599 Machine shop, jobbing & repair

(G-20584)
QUALITY SPECIALISTS INC
Also Called: Www.slidepartsexpress.com
1428 E 363rd St (44095-4136)
PHONE....................................440 946-9129
Fax: 440 946-9711
Kenneth Bateman, *President*
Rosemary Bateman, *Vice Pres*
EMP: 8
SQ FT: 6,000
SALES (est): 991.2K **Privately Held**
WEB: www.qualityspecialists.com
SIC: 3544 3599 Special dies & tools; custom machinery

(G-20585)
QUALTECH TECHNOLOGIES INC
1685b Joseph Lloyd Pkwy (44094-8044)
PHONE....................................440 946-8081
Dave Vance, *President*
Brian McCoy, *Opers Mgr*
Joel Wolnik, *Prdtn Mgr*
Mike Trebuchon, *Purch Mgr*
Rick Cardinale, *QC Mgr*
▲ EMP: 50 EST: 2002
SQ FT: 18,000
SALES (est): 15.7MM **Privately Held**
WEB: www.qualtechinc.com
SIC: 3699 3672 Electrical equipment & supplies; printed circuit boards

(G-20586)
RACEDIRECTOR LLC
38613 Andrews Ridge Way (44094-7830)
PHONE....................................440 940-6675
Craig Rowe, *Manager*
EMP: 3
SALES (est): 71.1K **Privately Held**
SIC: 7372 Application computer software

(G-20587)
**REID ASSET MANAGEMENT
COMPANY**
Also Called: Magnus Equipment
4500 Beidler Rd (44094-4602)
PHONE....................................440 942-8488
Scott Miller, *Branch Mgr*
EMP: 30
SALES (corp-wide): 9.9MM **Privately
Held**
WEB: www.magnusequipment.com
SIC: 2842 Specialty cleaning, polishes &
sanitation goods
PA: Reid Asset Management Company
9555 Rockside Rd Ste 350
Cleveland OH 44125
216 642-3223

(G-20588)
RIMECO PRODUCTS INC
38198 Willoughby Pkwy (44094-7580)
PHONE....................................440 918-1220
Fax: 440 918-1224
Valentine Ribic, *President*
John Ribic, *Vice Pres*
Rok Ribic, *Prdtn Mgr*
Mateja Ackworth, *Purch Mgr*
Albin Lampic, *Financial Exec*
EMP: 7
SQ FT: 12,000
SALES (est): 1.2MM **Privately Held**
WEB: www.rimecoproducts.com
SIC: 3599 Machine shop, jobbing & repair

(G-20589)
**RINOS WOODWORKING SHOP
INC**
36475 Biltmore Pl (44094-8222)
PHONE....................................440 946-1718
Fax: 440 946-5665
Rino Ritosa, *President*
Alto Ritosa, *Vice Pres*
Dan Ritosa, *Vice Pres*
▲ EMP: 19 EST: 1982
SQ FT: 15,000
SALES (est): 1.6MM **Privately Held**
WEB: www.rinoswoodworking.com
SIC: 2541 2431 Cabinets, except refriger-
ated: show, display, etc.: wood; millwork

(G-20590)
RONSON MANUFACTURING INC
9933 Chillicothe Rd (44094-9733)
PHONE....................................440 256-1463
Fax: 440 256-1465
Ronald J Ducca, *President*
Bonnie Webb, *Vice Pres*
EMP: 5
SQ FT: 10,000
SALES (est): 743.2K **Privately Held**
SIC: 3452 Bolts, metal; nuts, metal;
screws, metal

(G-20591)
**SAWYER TECHNICAL
MATERIALS LLC (HQ)**
Also Called: Sawyer Crystal Systems
35400 Lakeland Blvd (44095-5304)
PHONE....................................440 951-8770
Cynthia Clement, *Controller*
Kelly Scott, *Mng Member*
Fred Taylor, *Mng Member*
▲ EMP: 35
SQ FT: 100,000
SALES (est): 8MM **Privately Held**
WEB: www.sawyerresearch.com
SIC: 3679 3471 Quartz crystals, for elec-
tronic application; plating & polishing
PA: Foreasia International Inc.
7f, 6, Hsiang Yang Rd.,
Taipei City TAP
223 817-122

(G-20592)
**SCHUPP ADVANCED
MATERIALS LLC**
10770 Chillicothe Rd (44094-5102)
PHONE....................................440 488-6416
John Schupp,
EMP: 3
SALES (est): 169.1K **Privately Held**
SIC: 3679 Quartz crystals, for electronic
application

(G-20593)
SERVICE STAMPINGS INC
4700 Hamann Pkwy (44094-5616)
PHONE....................................440 946-2330
Fax: 440 946-6486
Thurston Reid, *Ch of Bd*
Christopher T Reid, *President*
Robert A Stohlman, *Vice Pres*
Donald Bowen, *VP Mfg*
Jefferey J Campbell, *Treasurer*
EMP: 31 EST: 1956
SQ FT: 28,000
SALES: 4MM **Privately Held**
WEB: www.servicestampings.com
SIC: 3469 Stamping metal for the trade

(G-20594)
SERVICE STORAGE INTL INC
Also Called: Ssi
38316 Airport Pkwy (44094-7579)
PHONE....................................440 951-7579
Craig Budreo, *President*
Donna Budreo, *Vice Pres*
EMP: 7
SQ FT: 1,000
SALES (est): 1.4MM **Privately Held**
WEB: www.servicestorage.com
SIC: 3572 Computer auxiliary storage units

(G-20595)
SHAFTS MFG
1585 E 361st St Unit G1 (44095-5329)
PHONE....................................440 942-6012
Berndy Heckelmann, *Principal*
EMP: 8
SALES (est): 573.4K **Privately Held**
SIC: 3999 Manufacturing industries

(G-20596)
SHERBROOKE METALS
36490 Reading Ave (44094-8207)
P.O. Box 689 (44096-0689)
PHONE....................................440 942-3520
Randy Spoth, *President*
Nancy Spoth, *Treasurer*
Laura Krus, *Admin Sec*
EMP: 22
SQ FT: 9,000
SALES (est): 8MM **Privately Held**
WEB: www.sherbrookemetals.com
SIC: 3624 3823 3548 Electrodes, thermal
& electrolytic uses: carbon, graphite; in-
dustrial instrmnts msrmnt display/control
process variable; welding apparatus

(G-20597)
SIGNS PDQ INC
35160 Topps Industrial Pk (44094-4675)
PHONE....................................440 951-6651
Fax: 440 943-2472
Brenda O'Toole, *President*
Don O'Toole, *Vice Pres*
Marge Mackey, *CFO*
Bronson Reed, *Controller*
Frank Smith, *Sales Staff*
EMP: 4
SALES (est): 506.8K **Privately Held**
WEB: www.signspdq.com
SIC: 3993 Signs & advertising specialties

(G-20598)
SKRL DIE CASTING INC
34580 Lakeland Blvd (44095-5221)
PHONE....................................440 946-7200
Fax: 440 946-2929
Sandra Szuch, *President*
EMP: 75 EST: 1967
SQ FT: 30,000
SALES (est): 14.1MM **Privately Held**
SIC: 3544 Special dies, tools, jigs & fix-
tures

(G-20599)
**SLABE MACHINE PRODUCTS
CO**
4659 Hamann Pkwy (44094-5631)
PHONE....................................440 946-6555
Fax: 440 946-7657
Edward Slabe Jr, *President*
Tracy Cermak, *General Mgr*
Brendan Slabe, *Vice Pres*
Nadin Sakalic, *Opers Mgr*
Dale Thompson, *Engineer*
▲ EMP: 100
SQ FT: 58,000
SALES (est): 26MM **Privately Held**
WEB: www.slabemachine.com
SIC: 3451 Screw machine products

(G-20600)
SLOAT INC
34099 Melinz Pkwy Unit A (44095-4001)
PHONE....................................440 951-9554
Jeff Sloat, *President*
EMP: 6
SALES (est): 750K **Privately Held**
SIC: 2892 Primary explosives, fuses & det-
onators

(G-20601)
SMOLIC MACHINE CO
37127 Ben Hur Ave (44094-6333)
PHONE....................................440 946-1747
Fax: 440 946-9139
Joseph Smolic Sr, *President*
Emil Smolic, *General Mgr*
EMP: 4
SQ FT: 10,500
SALES: 1.5MM **Privately Held**
SIC: 3599 Machine shop, jobbing & repair

(G-20602)
SONOMA GRINDING
37195 Ben Hur Ave Ste E (44094-6348)
PHONE....................................440 918-7990
Joe Filipovic, *Owner*
Sabina Filipovic, *Office Mgr*
EMP: 6
SALES (est): 379.8K **Privately Held**
SIC: 3599 Machine shop, jobbing & repair

(G-20603)
SPENCE TECHNOLOGIES INC
Also Called: R.W.
4752 Topps Indus Pkwy (44094-4636)
PHONE....................................440 946-3035
William Spence, *President*
Gail Spence, *Treasurer*
EMP: 18
SQ FT: 10,320
SALES (est): 3.1MM **Privately Held**
SIC: 3599 Machine shop, jobbing & repair

(G-20604)
**SPINKS MACHINE PRODUCTS
CO**
37939 Stevens Blvd (44094-6235)
PHONE....................................440 951-5814
Fax: 440 951-3775
Donald R Spinks, *Owner*
Donald Spinks, *Owner*
Gregory Spinks, *Vice Pres*
John Holliday, *Branch Mgr*
EMP: 3
SQ FT: 6,400
SALES (est): 170K **Privately Held**
SIC: 3599 Machine shop, jobbing & repair

(G-20605)
STEEL TECHNOLOGIES LLC
Steel Technologies Ohio
220 Joseph Lloyd Pkwy (44094)
PHONE....................................440 946-8666
Rick Furber, *Vice Pres*
Marina Monteiro, *Human Res Mgr*
Pam Patterson, *Manager*
EMP: 70 **Privately Held**
WEB: www.steeltechnologies.com
SIC: 3316 Cold finishing of steel shapes
HQ: Steel Technologies Llc
700 N Hurstbourne Pkwy
Louisville KY 40222
502 245-2110

(G-20606)
STICKER CORPORATION (PA)
Also Called: Reighart Steel Products
37877 Elm St (44094-6243)
PHONE....................................440 946-2100
Douglas Reighart, *President*
Laura Schwarz, *Bookkeeper*
Michael Devirro, *Manager*
EMP: 18 EST: 1947
SQ FT: 18,000
SALES (est): 3.8MM **Privately Held**
WEB: www.stickercorp.com
SIC: 3585 3549 3547 3443 Heating
equipment, complete; metalworking ma-
chinery; rolling mill machinery; fabricated
plate work (boiler shop); heating equip-
ment, except electric

(G-20607)
T & S DISCOUNT TIRES INC
Also Called: Gear Products Co
36525 Reading Ave (44094-8210)
PHONE....................................440 951-9084
David Takacs, *President*
EMP: 4 EST: 1971
SQ FT: 14,000
SALES (est): 574K **Privately Held**
SIC: 3462 Gears, forged steel

(G-20608)
TABLOX INC
4821 E 345th St (44094-4606)
PHONE....................................440 953-1951
Fax: 440 953-0506
Dana Talcott, *President*
Pam Cleverly, *Vice Pres*
Aaron Talcott, *QC Mgr*
EMP: 9
SQ FT: 16,000
SALES (est): 955K **Privately Held**
WEB: www.tablox.com
SIC: 3471 Finishing, metals or formed
products

(G-20609)
TC SERVICE CO
Also Called: Top Cat Air Tools
38285 Pelton Rd (44094-7740)
PHONE....................................440 954-7500
Fax: 440 954-7118
Edgar G Henry, *President*
Gerald J Henry, *Principal*
Valeria S Henry, *Principal*
Andy Henry, *Engrg Mgr*
M Anne Henry, *Admin Sec*
EMP: 40
SQ FT: 60,000
SALES (est): 7.6MM **Privately Held**
WEB: www.tcservice.com
SIC: 3546 Power-driven handtools

(G-20610)
TDC SYSTEMS INC
38296 Western Pkwy (44094-7590)
PHONE....................................440 953-5918
Fax: 440 953-5955
Tony Kalar, *President*
Diana Kalar, *Vice Pres*
EMP: 5
SQ FT: 2,500
SALES: 700K **Privately Held**
SIC: 3721 Research & development on air-
craft by the manufacturer

(G-20611)
**TECHNICAL TRANSLATION
SERVICES (PA)**
37841 Euclid Ave Ste 7 (44094-5981)
PHONE....................................440 942-3130
J M Crouvisier, *President*
Nikki Bell, *Mktg Dir*
EMP: 1
SQ FT: 10,000
SALES (est): 1.3MM **Privately Held**
WEB: www.onelap.com
SIC: 7389 7819 7812 2791 Translation
services; film processing, editing & titling:
motion picture; audio-visual program pro-
duction; typesetting

(G-20612)
TELLING INDUSTRIES LLC (PA)
4420 Sherwin Rd (44094-7994)
PHONE....................................440 974-3370
Harbour Garrett, *Accounting Mgr*
Art Vaccariello, *Sales Mgr*

Edward Slish, *Mng Member*
Troy Frank,
Tom Gallagher,
◆ **EMP:** 10
SQ FT: 400,000
SALES (est): 31.8MM **Privately Held**
WEB: www.tellingindustries.com
SIC: 3316 Bars, steel, cold finished, from purchased hot-rolled

(G-20613)
TELLING INDUSTRIES LLC
4420 Sherwin Rd Ste 3 (44094-7995)
PHONE..............................928 681-2010
EMP: 10
SALES (corp-wide): 31.5MM **Privately Held**
SIC: 3316 Mfg Cold-Rolled Steel Sheet
PA: Telling Industries, Llc
4420 Sherwin Rd
Willoughby OH 44094
440 974-3370

(G-20614)
TETRAD ELECTRONICS INC (PA)
2048 Joseph Lloyd Pkwy (44094-8032)
PHONE..............................440 946-6443
Fax: 440 946-6062
Ronald K Brehm, *President*
Jeffrey Waterman, *Vice Pres*
Richard Scebbi, *Treasurer*
Paul Carani, *Director*
Bruce Vanek, *Admin Sec*
EMP: 61
SQ FT: 14,000
SALES (est): 9.7MM **Privately Held**
WEB: www.tetradelec.com
SIC: 3672 Printed circuit boards

(G-20615)
TIMAR ENTERPRISES INC
Also Called: Timco Machine Co
35665 Curtis Blvd Unit 5 (44095-4111)
PHONE..............................440 942-4001
Fax: 440 951-0092
Timothy R Sarver Sr, *President*
Mary E Sarver, *Treasurer*
EMP: 3
SQ FT: 4,800
SALES (est): 450K **Privately Held**
SIC: 3599 Machine shop, jobbing & repair

(G-20616)
TITAN MANUFACTURING LLC
4730 Beidler Rd (44094-4604)
PHONE..............................440 942-2258
Marcel Uhrich, *Principal*
EMP: 4
SQ FT: 1,680
SALES (est): 380K **Privately Held**
WEB: www.titansoap.com
SIC: 3599 Machine shop, jobbing & repair

(G-20617)
TKR METAL FABRICATING LLC
Also Called: T-Fab
37552 N Industrial Pkwy (44094-6214)
PHONE..............................440 221-2770
Kevin Humphreys, *Vice Pres*
Timothy Herbert, *Vice Pres*
EMP: 5 **EST:** 2010
SQ FT: 7,000
SALES (est): 214.9K **Privately Held**
SIC: 3444 Machine guards, sheet metal

(G-20618)
TOKU AMERICA INC
Also Called: Striker Hydraulic Breakers
3900 Ben Hur Ave Ste 3 (44094-6398)
PHONE..............................440 954-9923
David Nakamura, *President*
Chris Baruffa, *Controller*
Jan Gomez, *Manager*
Akinori Kihara, *Admin Sec*
▲ **EMP:** 13
SQ FT: 15,000
SALES (est): 3.7MM
SALES (corp-wide): 73.4MM **Privately Held**
SIC: 3531 Crushers, portable
PA: Toku Pneumatic Co.,Ltd.
4-3-4, Katakasu, Hakata-Ku
Fukuoka FUK 812-0
924 720-275

(G-20619)
TOM THUMB CLIP CO INC
36300 Lkeland Blvd Unit 2 (44095)
P.O. Box 709 (44096-0709)
PHONE..............................440 953-9606
Fax: 440 951-7175
Jennifer Baxter, *President*
June Baxter, *Vice Pres*
EMP: 10 **EST:** 1947
SALES (est): 650K **Privately Held**
WEB: www.tomthumbclip.com
SIC: 3496 Clips & fasteners, made from purchased wire

(G-20620)
TRU-FAB TECHNOLOGY INC
34820 Lakeland Blvd (44095-5224)
PHONE..............................440 954-9760
Fax: 440 954-9761
John J Stegh, *President*
Connie Stegh, *Treasurer*
Andrea Kornodich, *Data Proc Dir*
EMP: 10
SQ FT: 15,000
SALES (est): 1.8MM **Privately Held**
SIC: 3599 7692 Custom machinery; welding repair

(G-20621)
TRUCAST INC
4382 Hamann Pkwy (44094-5683)
PHONE..............................440 942-4923
Jesse Baden, *President*
Brad Nicholson, *General Mgr*
Ray Newcomb, *Financial Exec*
Dave Longstreth, *Sales Executive*
Carl McCollister, *Manager*
EMP: 60
SQ FT: 20,000
SALES (est): 2.5MM **Privately Held**
SIC: 3599 Machine & other job shop work

(G-20622)
TRV INCORPORATED
4860 E 345th St (44094-4607)
PHONE..............................440 951-7722
Fax: 440 951-3629
Peter Kolaric, *President*
Rudy Kolaric, *General Mgr*
Tom Kolaric, *Vice Pres*
Victoria Kolaric, *Treasurer*
EMP: 30
SALES (est): 6.4MM **Privately Held**
SIC: 3599 Machine shop, jobbing & repair

(G-20623)
TWO M PRECISION CO INC
Also Called: United Hydraulics
1747 Joseph Lloyd Pkwy # 3 (44094-8067)
PHONE..............................440 946-2120
Fax: 440 946-2120
Mate Brkic, *President*
Nate Brkic, *Vice Pres*
Frank Bortnick, *Purchasing*
Doris Brkic, *Treasurer*
EMP: 45
SQ FT: 35,000
SALES (est): 7.2MM **Privately Held**
WEB: www.twomprecision.com
SIC: 3599 3569 7692 Machine shop, jobbing & repair; grinding castings for the trade; filter elements, fluid, hydraulic line; welding repair

(G-20624)
UNIVERSAL J&Z MACHINE LLC
4781 E 355th St (44094-4631)
PHONE..............................216 486-2220
Marina Grman, *President*
Joseph Grman, *Vice Pres*
Jose Padilla, *Prdtn Mgr*
EMP: 24
SQ FT: 5,000
SALES (est): 450K **Privately Held**
SIC: 3599 Machine shop, jobbing & repair

(G-20625)
US MOLDING MACHINERY CO INC
38294 Pelton Rd (44094-7765)
PHONE..............................440 918-1701
Fax: 440 918-1720
Zac Cohen, *President*
Jerry Harper, *Vice Pres*
Robert Luck, *Vice Pres*
Bill Sprowls, *Vice Pres*

Roger Anderson, *Plant Engr*
EMP: 28
SQ FT: 12,500
SALES (est): 4.9MM **Privately Held**
WEB: www.usmolding.com
SIC: 3089 7699 Injection molding of plastics; industrial equipment services

(G-20626)
USA FOILS INC
Also Called: US Foils
38264 Willoughby Pkwy (44094-7583)
PHONE..............................440 975-1145
Michael Jach, *President*
Michael P McNamara, *Principal*
▲ **EMP:** 7
SALES (est): 2MM **Privately Held**
WEB: www.usfoils.com
SIC: 3497 Metal foil & leaf

(G-20627)
USM ACQUISITION CORPORATION (PA)
Also Called: Universal Machine
2002 Joseph Lloyd Pkwy (44094-8032)
PHONE..............................440 975-8600
Lisa Netiss, *President*
Jay Rust, *General Mgr*
EMP: 12
SALES (est): 17.7MM **Privately Held**
WEB: www.usmonline.com
SIC: 3599 3541 Machine shop, jobbing & repair; machine tools, metal cutting type

(G-20628)
USM PRECISION PRODUCTS INC
Also Called: U S M
2002 Joseph Lloyd Pkwy (44094-8032)
PHONE..............................440 975-8600
Donald R Nettis, *President*
Ken Marvar, *Vice Pres*
Laurie Olver, *Controller*
Derek West, *VP Sales*
Katherine Culmer, *Admin Asst*
EMP: 100
SQ FT: 55,000
SALES (est): 17.7MM **Privately Held**
WEB: www.usmonline.com
SIC: 3599 Machine shop, jobbing & repair
PA: Usm Acquisition Corporation
2002 Joseph Lloyd Pkwy
Willoughby OH 44094
440 975-8600

(G-20629)
WEISS NORTH AMERICA INC
3860 Ben Hur Ave Unit 2 (44094-6377)
PHONE..............................440 269-8031
Bill Eppich, *Vice Pres*
Brian Romanini, *Opers Staff*
Carl Borgione Jr, *Accounts Mgr*
Jason Berry, *Regl Sales Mgr*
Don Geisler, *Regl Sales Mgr*
▲ **EMP:** 17
SALES: 14MM
SALES (corp-wide): 174.5K **Privately Held**
SIC: 3569 Liquid automation machinery & equipment
HQ: Weiss Gmbh
Siemensstr. 17
Buchen (Odenwald) 74722
628 152-080

(G-20630)
WILLOUGHBY BREWING COMPANY
4057 Erie St (44094-7804)
PHONE..............................440 975-0202
Fax: 440 975-1080
Jeremy Vanhorn, *Managing Prtnr*
Steve McAdams, *General Mgr*
Lisa Fallon, *Manager*
Jason Sims, *Manager*
Rick Seibt, *Director*
EMP: 80
SQ FT: 1,200
SALES (est): 9.9MM **Privately Held**
WEB: www.willoughbybrewing.com
SIC: 2082 5812 Malt beverages; eating places

(G-20631)
WILLOW HILL INDUSTRIES LLC
37611 Euclid Ave (44094-5923)
PHONE..............................440 942-3003
Fax: 440 942-1617
Dave Lozano, *Project Engr*
Ronald A Bone,
EMP: 80
SALES (est): 8.1MM **Privately Held**
WEB: www.whindustries.com
SIC: 3469 Metal stampings

(G-20632)
WIRED INC
38849 Courtland Dr (44094-7509)
PHONE..............................440 567-8379
David Allen, *Principal*
EMP: 5
SALES (est): 481.7K **Privately Held**
SIC: 3629 Electrical industrial apparatus

(G-20633)
X PRESS PRINTING SERVICES INC
4405 Glenbrook Rd (44094-8219)
PHONE..............................440 951-8848
Fax: 440 951-8842
John Platko, *President*
Don Advey, *Manager*
Kerri Kautzman, *Graphic Designe*
EMP: 11
SALES (est): 820K **Privately Held**
SIC: 2759 Commercial printing

(G-20634)
Z & Z MANUFACTURING INC
4765 E 355th St (44094-4631)
PHONE..............................440 953-2800
Tom Zovko, *President*
Jure Zovko, *General Mgr*
Mary Yanick, *Manager*
EMP: 18
SQ FT: 20,000
SALES (est): 2.5MM **Privately Held**
WEB: www.z-zmfg.com
SIC: 3599 Machine shop, jobbing & repair

(G-20635)
ZITNIK ENTERPRISES INC
Also Called: D M Z Machine Co
35530 Lakeland Blvd (44095-5305)
PHONE..............................440 951-0089
Dusan Mark Zitnik, *Owner*
Bill Hufgard, *Controller*
EMP: 4
SQ FT: 5,000
SALES (est): 433.4K **Privately Held**
SIC: 3599 Machine shop, jobbing & repair

(G-20636)
ZUKOWSKI RACK CO
1647 E 361st St (44095-5331)
PHONE..............................440 942-5889
Dan Zukowski, *President*
Francis Zukowski, *President*
EMP: 5
SQ FT: 6,000
SALES: 250K **Privately Held**
SIC: 2542 Racks, merchandise display or storage: except wood

Willoughby Hills
Lake County

(G-20637)
ATLANTIC CO
26651 Curtiss Wright Pkwy (44092-2832)
PHONE..............................440 944-8988
Fax: 440 944-1294
F Joseph Callahan, *Ch of Bd*
William Cosgrove, *President*
Thomas Janock, *Treasurer*
EMP: 50 **EST:** 1959
SQ FT: 30,000
SALES (est): 5.1MM
SALES (corp-wide): 1.1B **Privately Held**
WEB: www.swagelok.com
SIC: 3432 Plumbing fixture fittings & trim
PA: Swagelok Company
29500 Solon Rd
Solon OH 44139
440 248-4600

(G-20638)
BUTERA MANUFACTURING INC
2935 Lynn Dr (44092-1419)
P.O. Box 349, Wickliffe (44092-0349)
PHONE....................................440 516-3698
Fax: 440 953-8583
Richard E Butera, *CEO*
Brian Butera, *President*
Kim Butera, *Corp Secy*
EMP: 18
SQ FT: 50,000
SALES (est): 1.8MM **Privately Held**
SIC: 3429 5941 Animal traps, iron or steel;
hunting equipment

(G-20639)
IDCOMM LLC
32315 White Rd (44092-1339)
PHONE....................................661 250-4081
Gary Marsh, *Principal*
Karen Marsh, *Principal*
EMP: 5
SALES (est): 423.5K **Privately Held**
SIC: 3679 Microwave components

(G-20640)
**KIRTLAND CPITL PARTNERS III
LP (PA)**
2550 Som Center Rd # 105 (44094-9655)
PHONE....................................440 585-9010
Fax: 440 585-9699
John F Turben, *Partner*
Corrine Menary, *Partner*
Jack Withrow, *CFO*
◆ **EMP:** 1
SALES (est): 41.2MM **Privately Held**
WEB: www.kirtlandcapital.com
SIC: 3085 2821 Plastics bottles; polyvinyl
chloride resins (PVC)

(G-20641)
MICRO PRODUCTS CO INC
26653 Curtiss Wright Pkwy (44092-2832)
PHONE....................................440 943-0258
Fax: 440 943-1599
Arthur Anton, *President*
Reese Armstrong, *Safety Mgr*
Scott Tracy, *Engineer*
Frank Roddy, *CFO*
Debbie Rubble, *Accountant*
EMP: 70 **EST:** 1981
SQ FT: 10,000
SALES (est): 4.1MM
SALES (corp-wide): 1.1B **Privately Held**
WEB: www.swagelok.com
SIC: 3471 7389 Plating & polishing; grind-
ing, precision: commercial or industrial
PA: Swagelok Company
29500 Solon Rd
Solon OH 44139
440 248-4600

(G-20642)
NEUROS MEDICAL INC
35010 Chardon Rd Ste 210 (44094-9011)
PHONE....................................440 951-2565
Jon J Snyder, *President*
Joe Schwoebel, *Vice Pres*
Mark Teague, *CFO*
Zi-Ping Fang, *CTO*
EMP: 8
SQ FT: 4,275
SALES (est): 700K **Privately Held**
SIC: 3845 Electromedical equipment

(G-20643)
NIKLEE CO
2959 Canterbury Ct (44092-1467)
PHONE....................................440 944-0082
Linda Motuza, *President*
Rick Motuza, *Vice Pres*
EMP: 5
SALES (est): 380K **Privately Held**
WEB: www.niklee.com
SIC: 2759 Screen printing

(G-20644)
SWAGELOK COMPANY
26653 Curtiss Wright Pkwy (44092-2832)
P.O. Box 31300, Independence (44131-
0300)
PHONE....................................440 248-4600
EMP: 66

SALES (corp-wide): 1.1B **Privately Held**
SIC: 3491 3599 Pressure valves & regulators, industrial; machine shop, jobbing &
repair
PA: Swagelok Company
29500 Solon Rd
Solon OH 44139
440 248-4600

(G-20645)
SWAGELOK COMPANY
Also Called: Swagelok Biopharm Services Co
26651 Curtiss Wright Pkwy (44092-2832)
PHONE....................................440 944-8988
Pierre Fischer, *Regional Mgr*
Chuck Pereksta, *Manager*
Brian Muckenthaler, *Manager*
EMP: 20
SALES (corp-wide): 1.1B **Privately Held**
WEB: www.swagelok.com
SIC: 3494 Valves & pipe fittings
PA: Swagelok Company
29500 Solon Rd
Solon OH 44139
440 248-4600

Willowick
Lake County

(G-20646)
ALLEN MOLD & DIE INC
850 Charles St (44095-4302)
PHONE....................................440 944-1819
Bernard Deak, *President*
Roger Eastabrooks, *Vice Pres*
EMP: 4
SQ FT: 3,300
SALES (est): 381.9K **Privately Held**
SIC: 3544 Forms (molds), for foundry &
plastics working machinery

(G-20647)
E E CONTROLS INC
30301 Fairway Blvd (44095-4647)
P.O. Box 5098, Willoughby (44095-0098)
PHONE....................................440 585-5554
Fax: 440 942-2330
Rollin Randolph, *President*
Wanda Randolph, *Accounting Dir*
EMP: 3
SQ FT: 3,500
SALES (est): 263.4K **Privately Held**
SIC: 7699 3823 Industrial equipment serv-
ices; industrial process control instru-
ments

(G-20648)
JHS TOYZ LLC
Also Called: Wireless Toyz of Eastlake
35125 Vine St (44095-5147)
PHONE....................................440 946-6600
Michael Corrado,
EMP: 10
SALES (est): 1.6MM
SALES (corp-wide): 8.1MM **Privately
Held**
SIC: 3669 Communications equipment
PA: Wireless Toyz, Inc.
7499 Middlebelt Rd
West Bloomfield MI 48322
248 426-8200

(G-20649)
PEER PANTRY LLC
30901 Lake Shore Blvd (44095-3609)
PHONE....................................216 236-4087
Marcus Allen Coleman,
EMP: 5
SALES (est): 139.9K **Privately Held**
SIC: 2099 Food preparations

(G-20650)
**PUBLIC SAFETY OHIO
DEPARTMENT**
Also Called: Ross County License Bureau
31517 Vine St (44095-3561)
PHONE....................................440 943-5545
Fax: 440 943-4180
Cynthia Marfisi, *General Mgr*
EMP: 6 **Privately Held**
SIC: 3469 9221 Automobile license tags,
stamped metal; police protection;

HQ: Ohio Department Of Public Safety
1970 W Broad St Fl 5
Columbus OH 43223
614 466-3383

Willshire
Van Wert County

(G-20651)
PHOTO STAR
307 State St (45898)
PHONE....................................419 495-2696
Fax: 419 495-2143
Judith E Bunner, *Owner*
EMP: 3 **EST:** 1895
SQ FT: 1,500
SALES (est): 203.4K **Privately Held**
SIC: 2711 Newspapers, publishing & print-
ing

Wilmington
Clinton County

(G-20652)
ABBOT IMAGE SOLUTIONS LLC
185 Park Dr (45177-2040)
PHONE....................................937 382-6677
Greg Abbott, *Owner*
Jamie Warren, *Director*
EMP: 3 **EST:** 2012
SALES: 9MM **Privately Held**
SIC: 3993 Signs & advertising specialties

(G-20653)
**AHRESTY WILMINGTON
CORPORATION**
2627 S South St (45177-2926)
PHONE....................................937 382-6112
Fax: 937 382-5871
Kenichi Nonaka, *President*
Justin Rummer, *Vice Pres*
Darrell Wyatt, *Opers Staff*
Zachary Cox, *Engineer*
Cheryl Goodman, *Controller*
▲ **EMP:** 378
SQ FT: 334,000
SALES: 29MM
SALES (corp-wide): 1.2B **Privately Held**
WEB: www.ahresty.com
SIC: 3363 Aluminum die-castings
PA: Ahresty Corporation
1-2, Nakahara, Mitsuyacho
Toyohashi AIC 441-3
532 652-170

(G-20654)
ALKERMES INC
265 Olinger Cir (45177-2484)
PHONE....................................937 382-5642
Fax: 937 382-5949
Mark Stejbach, *Senior VP*
Carl Oberweiser, *Mfg Mgr*
Greg Anderson, *Facilities Mgr*
Brandon Baird, *Mfg Spvr*
Nathan Hardyman, *Mfg Spvr*
EMP: 40
SQ FT: 12,000 **Privately Held**
WEB: www.alkermes.com
SIC: 2834 Pharmaceutical preparations
HQ: Alkermes, Inc.
852 Winter St
Waltham MA 02451
781 609-6000

(G-20655)
**ATEC DIVERSFD WLDG
FABRICATION**
Also Called: A T E C Diversified
466 Dehan Rd (45177-9771)
PHONE....................................937 546-4399
David Sanford, *Owner*
EMP: 5 **EST:** 2001
SALES (est): 304.7K **Privately Held**
WEB: www.atecdiversified.com
SIC: 1389 Oil field services

(G-20656)
BARBARA A LIEURANCE
180 E Sugartree St (45177-2333)
PHONE....................................937 382-2864

Barbara Lieurance, *Principal*
EMP: 6 **Privately Held**
SIC: 9621 3469 Licensing agencies; auto-
mobile license tags, stamped metal

(G-20657)
**BUSH SPECIALTY VEHICLES
INC**
80 Park Dr (45177-2038)
PHONE....................................937 382-5502
Larry Vanover, *Vice Pres*
EMP: 15 **EST:** 2001
SALES (est): 3.3MM
SALES (corp-wide): 569.9MM **Privately
Held**
WEB: www.bushinteriors.com
SIC: 3713 Specialty motor vehicle bodies
HQ: Element Fleet Management (Us) Corp.
655 Business Center Dr
Horsham PA 19044
267 960-4000

(G-20658)
CHAMPION BRIDGE COMPANY
261 E Sugartree St (45177-2316)
PHONE....................................937 382-2521
Fax: 937 382-1477
Randy Dell, *President*
Gale Gerard, *Vice Pres*
Kathrine Morgans, *Office Mgr*
Debbie Laufer, *Manager*
Christopher Stevens, *Manager*
EMP: 20 **EST:** 1934
SQ FT: 30,000
SALES (est): 5.7MM **Privately Held**
SIC: 3441 Fabricated structural metal

(G-20659)
CLIFFCO STANDS INC
Also Called: Wilmington Precision Machining
397 Starbuck Rd (45177-8875)
PHONE....................................937 382-3700
Fax: 937 382-4993
Steve Garrison, *Principal*
David D Clay, *Principal*
Clifton Hamilton, *Principal*
Dan Reeves, *Engineer*
Cynthia E Garrison, *Office Mgr*
EMP: 24 **EST:** 1996
SQ FT: 9,000
SALES (est): 5.7MM **Privately Held**
SIC: 3544 Special dies & tools

(G-20660)
**COMPTON METAL PRODUCTS
INC**
416 Steele Rd (45177-9332)
PHONE....................................937 382-2403
Fax: 937 382-2403
James Compton, *President*
Kandi Compton, *Admin Sec*
EMP: 82 **EST:** 1929
SQ FT: 2,000
SALES (est): 2.4MM **Privately Held**
SIC: 7699 3599 7692 Engine repair & re-
placement, non-automotive; machine
shop, jobbing & repair; welding repair

(G-20661)
COX PRINTING CO
Also Called: Cox Painting
1087 Wayne Rd (45177-2024)
PHONE....................................937 382-2312
Fax: 937 382-0362
Pamela Olds, *President*
Ramona Cox, *President*
Frank A Cox, *Consultant*
EMP: 7
SQ FT: 2,600
SALES (est): 470K **Privately Held**
SIC: 2752 2759 2789 Commercial print-
ing, offset; letterpress printing; bookbind-
ing & related work

(G-20662)
**CUSTOM MOLDED PRODUCTS
LLC**
92 Grant St (45177-2362)
PHONE....................................937 382-1070
Fax: 937 382-6995
Rick Carver, *Plant Mgr*
Kevin Hamilton, *Purch Mgr*
Marsha Leigh, *Manager*
Norman Allen Jr,
▲ **EMP:** 84

SQ FT: 11,000
SALES (est): 17.1MM **Privately Held**
WEB: www.custommolded.com
SIC: 3089 Injection molding of plastics

(G-20663)
DESIGNER SET
529 S Walnut St (45177-2718)
P.O. Box 150 (45177-0150)
PHONE..............................937 382-8000
Fax: 937 382-0768
Annette Bickel, *Owner*
EMP: 3
SQ FT: 4,000
SALES (est): 234.3K **Privately Held**
WEB: www.designerset.com
SIC: 2759 Commercial printing

(G-20664)
EDWARD KEITER & SONS
1235 Stone Rd (45177-9680)
PHONE..............................937 382-3249
Edward Keiter, *Owner*
Steve Keiter, *Co-Owner*
EMP: 4
SALES (est): 310K **Privately Held**
SIC: 2048 Livestock feeds

(G-20665)
GRANDPAS POTTERY
3558 W State Route 73 (45177-9292)
PHONE..............................937 382-6442
Fax: 937 382-7975
Ray Storer, *Owner*
Betty Storer, *Co-Owner*
EMP: 4
SALES: 50K **Privately Held**
SIC: 3269 Pottery cooking & kitchen articles

(G-20666)
GRAPHICS TO GO LLC
761 S Nelson Ave (45177-2517)
PHONE..............................937 382-4100
Tracy L Addison, *Mng Member*
EMP: 5
SALES (est): 442.5K **Privately Held**
SIC: 2759 Commercial printing; screen printing

(G-20667)
HALE MANUFACTURING LLC
1065 Wayne Rd (45177-2024)
PHONE..............................937 382-2127
David Hale, *President*
EMP: 10 EST: 1947
SQ FT: 10,000
SALES (est): 1.4MM **Privately Held**
SIC: 3599 Machine shop, jobbing & repair

(G-20668)
HANSON AGGREGATES EAST LLC
1481 S Us Highway 68 (45177-8929)
PHONE..............................937 382-2557
Gerald Mercer, *Manager*
EMP: 15
SALES (corp-wide): 16B **Privately Held**
SIC: 3272 3273 3251 Precast terrazo or concrete products; ready-mixed concrete; concrete block & brick; brick & structural clay tile
HQ: Hanson Aggregates East Llc
3131 Rdu Center Dr
Morrisville NC 27560
919 380-2500

(G-20669)
HOOD PACKAGING CORPORATION
Also Called: Southern Bag
1961 Rombach Ave (45177-1997)
P.O. Box 745 (45177-0745)
PHONE..............................937 382-6681
Zachary Williams, *Controller*
Jerry Cowin, *Sales Staff*
Bill Terrill, *Branch Mgr*
EMP: 200
SQ FT: 150,000
SALES (corp-wide): 857.2MM **Privately Held**
WEB: www.hoodpkg.com
SIC: 2674 2673 Shipping bags or sacks, including multiwall & heavy duty; bags: plastic, laminated & coated

HQ: Hood Packaging Corporation
25 Woodgreen Pl
Madison MS 39110
601 853-7260

(G-20670)
MELVIN GRAIN CO
413 Melvin Rd (45177-9675)
PHONE..............................937 382-1249
Mike Keither, *Owner*
Ed Keither, *Partner*
Jim Keither, *Partner*
Steve Keither, *Partner*
EMP: 4 EST: 1944
SALES: 30K **Privately Held**
SIC: 3999 Custom pulverizing & grinding of plastic materials

(G-20671)
MONEY JEWELRY VAULTS
236 E Sugartree St (45177-2317)
PHONE..............................937 366-6391
EMP: 3
SALES (est): 140K **Privately Held**
SIC: 3272 Mfg Concrete Products

(G-20672)
ORANGE FRAZER PRESS INC
37 1/2 W Main St (45177-2236)
P.O. Box 214 (45177-0214)
PHONE..............................937 382-3196
Marcy Hawley, *President*
John Baskin, *Vice Pres*
Sarah Hawley, *Marketing Staff*
Kelsey Swindler, *Marketing Staff*
Alyson Rua, *Graphic Designe*
EMP: 7
SQ FT: 2,000
SALES (est): 1MM **Privately Held**
WEB: www.orangefrazer.com
SIC: 2731 Books: publishing only

(G-20673)
POLARIS INDUSTRIES INC
3435 Airborne Rd Ste A (45177-8951)
PHONE..............................937 283-1200
Scott W Wine, *Branch Mgr*
EMP: 40
SALES (corp-wide): 4.5B **Publicly Held**
SIC: 3799 All terrain vehicles (ATV)
PA: Polaris Industries Inc.
2100 Highway 55
Medina MN 55340
763 542-0500

(G-20674)
PRAXAIR DISTRIBUTION INC
105 Praxair Way (45177-7189)
PHONE..............................937 283-3400
Chris Lawson, *Branch Mgr*
EMP: 6
SALES (corp-wide): 10.5B **Publicly Held**
SIC: 2813 5084 Industrial gases; carbon dioxide; dry ice, carbon dioxide (solid); oxygen, compressed or liquefied; welding machinery & equipment
HQ: Praxair Distribution, Inc.
10 Riverview Dr
Danbury CT 06810
203 837-2000

(G-20675)
QUALI-TEE DESIGN SPORTS
Also Called: Quali-Tee Design Sportswear
59 W Sugartree St (45177-2225)
PHONE..............................937 382-7997
Fax: 937 382-7997
James Evans, *President*
Todd Evans, *Vice Pres*
Scott Faughn, *Sales Staff*
Terri Gehlbach, *Manager*
EMP: 18
SALES (est): 1.1MM **Privately Held**
SIC: 7336 2395 5699 5999 Silk screen design; swiss loom embroideries; sports apparel; trophies & plaques; screen printing

(G-20676)
R & B MACHINING INC (PA)
2695 Progress Way (45177-7702)
PHONE..............................937 698-3528
Fax: 937 382-6727
Randy Workman, *President*
Betty Workman, *President*
Melissa Pinkerton, *Purch Mgr*

Ethan Long, *Sales Staff*
EMP: 4
SQ FT: 4,000
SALES (est): 7.8MM **Privately Held**
WEB: www.rbmachining.com
SIC: 3599 Machine shop, jobbing & repair

(G-20677)
R & B MACHINING INC
2695 Progress Way (45177-7702)
PHONE..............................937 382-6710
Joe Eramo, *CEO*
Mike Burnett, *Engineer*
Kevin Camp, *Engineer*
John Wiget, *Manager*
EMP: 35
SALES (corp-wide): 7.8MM **Privately Held**
SIC: 3599 3542 Machine shop, jobbing & repair; bending machines
PA: R & B Machining, Inc.
2695 Progress Way
Wilmington OH 45177

(G-20678)
RTPROCESS LLC
311 Davids Dr (45177-2431)
PHONE..............................937 366-6215
Ali Kerr, *General Mgr*
EMP: 4
SQ FT: 8,000
SALES (est): 410K **Privately Held**
SIC: 2819 Industrial inorganic chemicals

(G-20679)
TIMBERTECH LIMITED (DH)
894 Prairie Rd (45177-8847)
PHONE..............................937 655-8766
Fax: 937 655-8827
Tom Gramlich, *President*
Kevin Brennan, *Senior VP*
Paul Bizzarri, *Vice Pres*
Steve Thomas, *Vice Pres*
Ralph Baker, *Plant Mgr*
◆ EMP: 221
SALES (est): 82.5MM
SALES (corp-wide): 1.2B **Publicly Held**
WEB: www.timbertech.com
SIC: 3089 Plastic hardware & building products
HQ: C.P.G. International, Inc.
888 N Keyser Ave
Scranton PA 18504
570 558-8000

(G-20680)
TRI STATE MEDIA LLC
325 Davids Dr (45177-2431)
PHONE..............................513 933-0101
John Clary, *President*
Colleen Abney, *Office Mgr*
EMP: 15 EST: 2001
SQ FT: 10,500
SALES: 5MM **Privately Held**
SIC: 2679 Labels, paper: made from purchased material

(G-20681)
W L AREHART COMPUTING SYSTEMS
555 Fife Rd (45177-8901)
PHONE..............................937 383-4710
Fax: 937 383-4511
William Arehart Jr, *Owner*
Anita Hobart, *Director*
EMP: 5
SALES (est): 200K **Privately Held**
SIC: 7379 7372 Data processing consultant; prepackaged software

(G-20682)
WILMINGTON FOREST PRODUCTS
5562 S Us Highway 68 (45177-7112)
PHONE..............................937 382-5013
Fax: 937 382-7813
Thomas D Driscoll, *President*
Mary B Driscoll, *Vice Pres*
EMP: 6
SQ FT: 7,500
SALES (est): 739.8K **Privately Held**
SIC: 2421 Sawmills & planing mills, general

Wilmot
Stark County

(G-20683)
AMISH DOOR INC (PA)
Also Called: Amish Door Restaurant
1210 Winesburg Rd (44689)
P.O. Box 215 (44689-0215)
PHONE..............................330 359-5464
Fax: 330 359-7159
Milo Miller, *President*
Eric Gerber, *Vice Pres*
Yvonne Torrence, *Treasurer*
Katherine Miller, *Shareholder*
EMP: 155
SQ FT: 7,500
SALES (est): 22.4MM **Privately Held**
WEB: www.amishdoor.com
SIC: 5947 5812 7011 2051 Gift shop; restaurant, family: independent; hotels & motels; bread, cake & related products

(G-20684)
COSMO CORPORATION
Also Called: Cosmo Plastics Co
211 N Winesburg Rd (44689)
PHONE..............................330 359-5429
Fax: 330 359-1013
Vicky Wartcentruber, *Manager*
Dennis Snyder, *Executive*
EMP: 100
SQ FT: 12,000
SALES (corp-wide): 39.1K **Privately Held**
SIC: 3089 Injection molding of plastics
HQ: Cosmo Corporation
30201 Aurora Rd
Cleveland OH 44139
440 498-7500

(G-20685)
DAVID E EASTERDAY AND CO INC
Also Called: Easterday & Co
1225c Us Route 62 (44689-9601)
PHONE..............................330 359-0700
David E Easterday, *President*
Valeria Easterday, *Corp Secy*
Terri Siders, *Office Mgr*
EMP: 12
SQ FT: 40,000
SALES (est): 3.3MM **Privately Held**
SIC: 2851 Varnishes

(G-20686)
HARDWOOD SOLUTIONS
112 E Main St (44689)
PHONE..............................330 359-5755
Brian Kyle, *Principal*
EMP: 6
SALES (est): 787K **Privately Held**
SIC: 2499 Decorative wood & woodwork

(G-20687)
WEAVER LUMBER CO
1925 Us Route 62 (44689-9604)
PHONE..............................330 359-5091
Robert Weaver, *Owner*
EMP: 6
SALES (est): 522.7K **Privately Held**
SIC: 2421 Custom sawmill

(G-20688)
WENGERD WOOD INC
2000 Us Route 62 (44689-9606)
PHONE..............................330 359-4300
Fax: 330 359-4301
Weyne Wengerd, *President*
Dean Wengerd, *Corp Secy*
EMP: 9
SALES: 1.2MM **Privately Held**
SIC: 2499 Decorative wood & woodwork

Winchester
Adams County

(G-20689)
ACELA BIOMEDICAL
3455 Cross Rd (45697-9477)
PHONE..............................937 544-8618
Andrew Culbertson, *CEO*

EMP: 15
SALES (est): 823.5K **Privately Held**
SIC: 3841 3842 3845 5047 Inhalators, surgical & medical; atomizers, medical; electromedical equipment; electro-medical equipment; laboratory equipment, except medical or dental

(G-20690)
BETTER BUILT BARNS (PA)
10628 Russellville Winchs (45697-9636)
PHONE..............................606 348-6146
Lyndon Yoder, *Owner*
EMP: 4
SQ FT: 4,000
SALES (est): 886.5K **Privately Held**
SIC: 3448 Prefabricated metal buildings

(G-20691)
CANTRELL RFINERY SLS TRNSP INC
18856 State Route 136 (45697-9793)
P.O. Box 175 (45697-0175)
PHONE..............................937 695-0318
Robert Cantrell, *President*
Kathy Jodrey, *Vice Pres*
EMP: 15 EST: 2008
SALES (est): 1.9MM **Privately Held**
SIC: 3559 Petroleum refinery equipment

(G-20692)
EZ WALL LLC ✪
3455 Cross Rd (45697-9477)
PHONE..............................800 424-8251
Andrew R Culbertson, *Principal*
EMP: 3 EST: 2016
SALES (est): 161.9K **Privately Held**
SIC: 3589 Commercial cleaning equipment

(G-20693)
FOX HOLLOW PALLET
3519 Graces Run Rd (45697-9763)
PHONE..............................937 386-2872
Freeman Yutzy, *Owner*
EMP: 3
SALES (est): 80K **Privately Held**
SIC: 2448 Pallets, wood

(G-20694)
LEROY YUTZY
Also Called: Fox Hollow Pallet
191 Russellville Rd (45697-9635)
PHONE..............................937 386-2872
EMP: 4
SALES (est): 170K **Privately Held**
SIC: 2448 Mfg Wood Pallets/Skids

(G-20695)
MACA PLASTICS INC
3455 Cross Rd (45697-9477)
PHONE..............................937 544-8618
Andrew R Culbertson, *CEO*
Brion Howelett, *Business Mgr*
Donna Smith, *Human Resources*
EMP: 14 EST: 1995
SQ FT: 25,000
SALES: 1.8MM **Privately Held**
WEB: www.macaplastics.com
SIC: 3714 3089 Motor vehicle parts & accessories; injection molding of plastics

(G-20696)
N & W MACHINING & FABRICATING
8 Mathias Rd (45697-9727)
PHONE..............................937 695-5582
Fax: 937 695-5584
Junior Nesbitt, *President*
Julene Nesbitt, *Corp Secy*
EMP: 9 EST: 1996
SQ FT: 10,000
SALES (est): 1.1MM **Privately Held**
SIC: 3599 Machine shop, jobbing & repair

Windham
Portage County

(G-20697)
HARBISONWALKER INTL INC
9686 E Center St (44288-1050)
P.O. Box 490 (44288-0490)
PHONE..............................330 326-2010
Fax: 330 326-2169

John Stock, *Branch Mgr*
EMP: 22
SQ FT: 300,000
SALES (corp-wide): 923MM **Privately Held**
WEB: www.hwr.com
SIC: 3255 Clay refractories
HQ: Harbisonwalker International, Inc.
1305 Cherrington Pkwy # 100
Moon Township PA 15108
412 375-6600

(G-20698)
KNUKONCEPTZCOM LTD
7227 Anderson Rd (44288-9702)
PHONE..............................216 310-6555
William Greenberg, *Mng Member*
▲ **EMP:** 5
SQ FT: 5,000
SALES (est): 848K **Privately Held**
SIC: 3651 Household audio & video equipment

Windsor
Ashtabula County

(G-20699)
HERSHBERGER MANUFACTURING
Also Called: Eagle Hardwoods
7584 Rockwood Rd (44099-9741)
P.O. Box 336 (44099-0336)
PHONE..............................440 272-5555
Fax: 440 272-5564
John Hershberger, *Owner*
EMP: 20
SQ FT: 6,500
SALES: 4.1MM **Privately Held**
SIC: 2448 4212 Pallets, wood; local trucking, without storage

(G-20700)
HILLSIDE PALLET
8552 Cox Rd (44099-9729)
PHONE..............................440 272-5425
Norman Byler, *Partner*
Timothy Miller, *Partner*
EMP: 7
SALES (est): 450K **Privately Held**
SIC: 2448 Pallets, wood & wood with metal

Winesburg
Holmes County

(G-20701)
9444 OHIO HOLDING CO
1658 Us Route 62 E (44690)
P.O. Box 181 (44690-0181)
PHONE..............................330 359-6291
Fax: 330 359-0035
Robert Ramseyer, *President*
Brian Bailey, *General Mgr*
EMP: 45
SQ FT: 5,500
SALES (est): 19.9MM **Privately Held**
WEB: www.alpinelace.com
SIC: 2022 Cheese, natural & processed

(G-20702)
CASE FARMS OF OHIO INC (HQ)
Also Called: Case Farms Chicken
1818 County Rd 160 (44690)
P.O. Box 185 (44690-0185)
PHONE..............................330 359-7141
Fax: 330 359-6482
Thomas Shelton, *President*
James Witt, *Safety Mgr*
Mike Popowycz, *CFO*
EMP: 200 EST: 1947
SQ FT: 8,000
SALES (est): 37.8MM
SALES (corp-wide): 413.7MM **Privately Held**
WEB: www.casefarms.com
SIC: 2015 2011 Poultry slaughtering & processing; meat packing plants
PA: Case Foods, Inc.
385 Pilch Rd
Troutman NC 28166
704 528-4501

(G-20703)
FROSTY TWINS
2236 Main St (44690)
P.O. Box 183 (44690-0183)
PHONE..............................330 359-0708
Frosty Twins, *Principal*
EMP: 5 EST: 2014
SALES (est): 307.8K **Privately Held**
SIC: 2024 Ice cream & frozen desserts

(G-20704)
H & S OPERATING COMPANY INC
2581 County Rd 160 (44690)
P.O. Box 82 (44690-0082)
PHONE..............................330 830-8178
Eric Smith, *President*
Ervin Hostetler, *Corp Secy*
EMP: 3
SALES (est): 291.8K **Privately Held**
SIC: 1321 Natural gas liquids

(G-20705)
MARIC DRILLING COMPANY INC
2581 County Rd 160 (44690)
P.O. Box 82 (44690-0082)
PHONE..............................330 830-8178
Eric Smith, *President*
Martha Smith, *Corp Secy*
EMP: 12
SALES (est): 955.1K **Privately Held**
SIC: 1381 Drilling oil & gas wells

(G-20706)
MERIDIAN INDUSTRIES INC
Also Called: Kent Elastomer Products
7369 Peabody Kent Rd (44690)
P.O. Box 186 (44690-0186)
PHONE..............................330 359-5447
Keith Wengerd, *QC Dir*
Robert Oborn, *Branch Mgr*
EMP: 75
SALES (corp-wide): 374.1MM **Privately Held**
WEB: www.meridiancompanies.com
SIC: 3069 3949 Tubing, rubber; sporting & athletic goods
PA: Meridian Industries, Inc.
735 N Water St Ste 630
Milwaukee WI 53202
414 224-0610

(G-20707)
ROBIN INDUSTRIES INC
Also Called: Holmco Division
7227 State Route 515 (44690)
P.O. Box 188 (44690-0188)
PHONE..............................330 359-5418
Paul Rogers, *Principal*
Patty Frazier, *Production*
Rahul Patil, *Manager*
Steve Case, *Lab Dir*
EMP: 120
SALES (corp-wide): 73.3MM **Privately Held**
WEB: www.robin-industries.com
SIC: 3069 3061 Molded rubber products; mechanical rubber goods
PA: Robin Industries, Inc.
6500 Rockside Rd Ste 230
Independence OH 44131
216 631-7000

(G-20708)
WINESBURG MEATS INC
2181 Us Rte 62 (44690)
P.O. Box 202 (44690-0202)
PHONE..............................330 359-5092
Marion Pacula, *President*
EMP: 8
SQ FT: 5,500
SALES: 750K **Privately Held**
SIC: 2011 5421 Meat packing plants; meat markets, including freezer provisioners

Wingett Run
Washington County

(G-20709)
JAMES L WILLIAMS
Also Called: Gas Enterprise Company
52 Tr 12 (45789)
PHONE..............................740 865-3382

James L Williams, *Owner*
EMP: 4
SALES: 234.8K **Privately Held**
SIC: 1389 Gas field services

Wintersville
Jefferson County

(G-20710)
ANTHONY MINING CO INC
72 Airport Rd (43953-9204)
PHONE..............................740 266-8100
Fax: 740 266-8200
Mike Carapellotti, *President*
Albert Carapellotti, *Administration*
EMP: 6
SALES (est): 425.7K **Privately Held**
SIC: 1241 Coal mining services

(G-20711)
JOHNDAVID D JONES
Also Called: Ssk Industries
590 Woodvue Ln (43953-9029)
PHONE..............................740 264-0176
Johndavid D Jones, *Owner*
EMP: 4
SALES: 400K **Privately Held**
SIC: 3482 5941 Pellets & BB's, pistol & air rifle ammunition; sporting goods & bicycle shops

(G-20712)
P-AMERICAS LLC
450 Luray Dr (43953-3971)
PHONE..............................740 266-6121
Mark Heil, *Manager*
EMP: 24
SQ FT: 8,000
SALES (corp-wide): 62.8B **Publicly Held**
SIC: 2086 Carbonated soft drinks, bottled & canned
HQ: P-Americas Llc
1 Pepsi Way
Somers NY

(G-20713)
ROBS CREATIVE SCREEN PRINTING (PA)
Also Called: Rob's Specialties
350 Cadiz Rd (43953-3926)
PHONE..............................740 264-6383
Fax: 740 264-6378
Kathy Jo Barker, *President*
Kathy Barker, *President*
Robert Barker, *Vice Pres*
EMP: 3
SALES: 400K **Privately Held**
WEB: www.robsts.com
SIC: 2741 5699 5661 2791 Miscellaneous publishing; T-shirts, custom printed; bathing suits; women's shoes; typesetting; commercial printing, lithographic; pleating & stitching

(G-20714)
STEUBEN COAL-ANTHONY MIN LTD
72 Airport Rd (43953-9204)
PHONE..............................740 266-8100
Michael B Carapellotti,
EMP: 5
SALES (est): 398.2K **Privately Held**
SIC: 1241 Coal mining services

Woodsfield
Monroe County

(G-20715)
CHRISTMAN SUPPLY CO INC
239 Oaklawn Ave (43793-9066)
PHONE..............................740 472-0046
Fax: 740 472-0106
Charles Christman, *President*
Mark Christman, *Corp Secy*
Paul Christman, *Vice Pres*
EMP: 4 EST: 1932
SQ FT: 2,700

▲ = Import ▼=Export
◆ =Import/Export

SALES (est): 812.6K **Privately Held**
WEB: www.chrismansearch.com
SIC: 5031 3273 Building materials, exterior; building materials, interior; ready-mixed concrete

(G-20716)
COUNTRY CLIPPINS
237 S Main St (43793-1024)
PHONE...................................740 472-5228
Leslie Cisler, *Principal*
EMP: 3
SALES (est): 140K **Privately Held**
SIC: 3999 Barber & beauty shop equipment

(G-20717)
D&D LOGGING
52759 State Route 379 (43793-9222)
PHONE...................................740 679-2573
Bruce Stephen, *Owner*
EMP: 3
SALES (est): 138.9K **Privately Held**
SIC: 2411 Logging camps & contractors

(G-20718)
J C L S ENTERPRISES LLC
Also Called: Sew It Seams
742 Lewisville Rd (43793-9061)
P.O. Box 150 (43793-0150)
PHONE...................................740 472-0314
Christina Seawash,
EMP: 7
SALES (est): 100K **Privately Held**
SIC: 2331 2321 Blouses, women's & juniors': made from purchased material; sport shirts, men's & boys': from purchased materials

(G-20719)
MEDI HOME HEALTH AGENCY INC
117 S Main St (43793-1022)
PHONE...................................740 472-3220
Kim Warner, *Branch Mgr*
EMP: 3
SALES (corp-wide): 197.9MM **Privately Held**
SIC: 2086 Bottled & canned soft drinks
HQ: Medi Home Health Agency Inc
105 Main St
Steubenville OH 43953
740 266-3977

(G-20720)
MONROE COUNTY BEACON INC
103 E Court St (43793-1110)
P.O. Box 70 (43793-0070)
PHONE...................................740 472-0734
Fax: 740 472-0735
Murray Cohen, *President*
EMP: 13
SQ FT: 3,500
SALES: 577.9K
SALES (corp-wide): 1.1MM **Privately Held**
WEB: www.delphosherald.com
SIC: 2711 Newspapers
PA: Herald Delphos Inc
405 N Main St
Delphos OH 45833
419 695-0015

(G-20721)
MONROE DRILLING OPERATIONS
46886 Moore Ridge Rd (43793-9483)
PHONE...................................740 472-0866
Kerry Brown, *Owner*
EMP: 8
SALES (est): 1.4MM **Privately Held**
SIC: 3533 Oil & gas drilling rigs & equipment

(G-20722)
WARD MOLD & MACHINE
317 Fairground Rd (43793-9308)
PHONE...................................740 472-5303
Gary Ward, *Owner*
EMP: 4
SALES (est): 220K **Privately Held**
SIC: 3544 Forms (molds), for foundry & plastics working machinery

(G-20723)
WOODSFELD TRUE VLUE HM CTR INC
218 State Rte 78 (43793)
P.O. Box 30 (43793-0030)
PHONE...................................740 472-1651
Fax: 740 472-0730
Walter L Kemp, *President*
Charles Orum, *Corp Secy*
Sally Kemp, *Vice Pres*
Troy Kemp, *Manager*
EMP: 15
SQ FT: 12,000
SALES (est): 4MM **Privately Held**
SIC: 5251 2421 Hardware; lumber: rough, sawed or planed

Woodville
Sandusky County

(G-20724)
CHIPPEWA TOOL & MFG CO
1101 Oak St (43469-9792)
P.O. Box 158 (43469-0158)
PHONE...................................419 849-2790
Fax: 419 849-2894
Jim Kusian, *President*
Dave Perry, *Manager*
EMP: 10 EST: 1965
SQ FT: 8,600
SALES (est): 990K **Privately Held**
SIC: 3545 3544 Precision tools, machinists'; special dies & tools

(G-20725)
CONCRETE MATERIAL SUPPLY LLC
875 E Main St (43469-9814)
PHONE...................................419 261-6404
Tom Bischoff Jr, *Principal*
EMP: 3
SALES (est): 240K **Privately Held**
SIC: 1771 3272 Concrete work; concrete products

(G-20726)
MODERN TRADE COMMUNICATIONS
109 Portage St (43469-1236)
PHONE...................................419 849-3109
Fax: 419 849-3367
Ron Rado, *Vice Pres*
John Thomas, *Sales Mgr*
Cassidy Thomas, *Mktg Coord*
John Morris, *Manager*
EMP: 7
SALES (corp-wide): 1.5MM **Privately Held**
WEB: www.metalarchitecture.com
SIC: 2721 Trade journals: publishing only, not printed on site
PA: Modern Trade Communications Inc
8833 Gross Point Rd # 308
Skokie IL 60077
847 674-2200

(G-20727)
TRUMBULL INC
Also Called: True Value
850 1/2 Water St (43469-9740)
PHONE...................................419 849-3561
Phil Trumbull, *President*
Joyce Trumbull, *Corp Secy*
EMP: 4 EST: 1850
SALES (est): 415.5K **Privately Held**
SIC: 3999 Painting instrument dials

Wooster
Wayne County

(G-20728)
201 E LIBERTY ST
201 E Liberty St (44691-4325)
PHONE...................................234 249-0145
Pranav Arora, *CEO*
EMP: 7
SQ FT: 200
SALES (est): 341.1K **Privately Held**
SIC: 3229 Glassware, industrial

(G-20729)
7&7 WOODWORKING
11080 Ashland Rd (44691-9339)
PHONE...................................330 347-6574
Jake S Cassady, *Principal*
EMP: 4
SALES (est): 260K **Privately Held**
SIC: 2431 Millwork

(G-20730)
ABS MATERIALS INC
Also Called: AMC
1909 Old Mansfield Rd (44691-9359)
PHONE...................................330 234-7999
J Gary McDaniel, *CEO*
Stephen Spoonamore, *President*
Glenn Johnso, *COO*
Steve Jolly, *Vice Pres*
Jane Leisure, *Engineer*
EMP: 69
SALES (est): 650.3K **Privately Held**
SIC: 2869 Industrial organic chemicals

(G-20731)
ADVANCED DRAINAGE SYSTEMS INC
3113 W Old Lincoln Way (44691-3262)
PHONE...................................330 264-4949
Fax: 330 262-4211
Barry Girvin, *Manager*
EMP: 52
SALES (corp-wide): 1.2B **Publicly Held**
WEB: www.ads-pipe.com
SIC: 3084 3083 Plastics pipe; laminated plastics plate & sheet
PA: Advanced Drainage Systems, Inc.
4640 Trueman Blvd
Hilliard OH 43026
614 658-0050

(G-20732)
AIRGAS
115 N Smyser Rd (44691-3230)
PHONE...................................330 345-1257
Ryan Joyce, *Manager*
EMP: 4
SALES (est): 318.9K **Privately Held**
SIC: 3548 5084 Welding & cutting apparatus & accessories; instruments & control equipment

(G-20733)
AKRON BRASS COMPANY
343 Venture Blvd (44691-7564)
PHONE...................................309 444-4440
Dan Peters, *President*
Thomas H Hudak, *President*
Dan Reese, *Opers Mgr*
Michael Peck, *Director*
Joseph R Daprile, *Admin Sec*
EMP: 25
SALES (est): 5MM **Privately Held**
WEB: www.akronbrass.com
SIC: 3364 3569 Brass & bronze die-castings; firefighting apparatus & related equipment; firefighting apparatus

(G-20734)
AKRON BRASS COMPANY
1615 Old Mansfield Rd (44691-7211)
PHONE...................................330 264-5678
Dan Peters, *Superintendent*
Richard Wuescher, *Vice Pres*
Lonnie Lashbrook, *Prdtn Mgr*
Jason Farley, *Opers Staff*
Karla Berger, *Purchasing*
EMP: 300
SALES (corp-wide): 2.1B **Publicly Held**
WEB: www.v-mux.com
SIC: 3647 3569 Vehicular lighting equipment; firefighting apparatus & related equipment
HQ: Akron Brass Company
343 Venture Blvd
Wooster OH 44691

(G-20735)
AKRON BRASS COMPANY (DH)
343 Venture Blvd (44691-7564)
P.O. Box 86 (44691-0086)
PHONE...................................330 264-5678
Fax: 330 264-2944
Sean Tillinghast, *President*
Will Leach, *District Mgr*
Steve Lynn, *District Mgr*
Kurt Mohn, *District Mgr*

Joseph R Daprile, *Vice Pres*
▲ EMP: 325
SQ FT: 20,000
SALES: 115.1MM
SALES (corp-wide): 2.1B **Publicly Held**
WEB: www.v-mux.com
SIC: 3647 3699 Vehicular lighting equipment; electrical equipment & supplies
HQ: Akron Brass Holding Corp.
343 Venture Blvd
Wooster OH 44691
330 264-5678

(G-20736)
AKRON BRASS HOLDING CORP (HQ)
343 Venture Blvd (44691-7564)
PHONE...................................330 264-5678
Sean Tillinghast, *President*
EMP: 2
SALES (est): 115.1MM
SALES (corp-wide): 2.1B **Publicly Held**
SIC: 3647 3699 6719 Vehicular lighting equipment; electrical equipment & supplies; investment holding companies, except banks
PA: Idex Corporation
1925 W Field Ct Ste 200
Lake Forest IL 60045
847 498-7070

(G-20737)
ALAN MANUFACTURING INC
3927 E Lincoln Way (44691-8997)
P.O. Box 24875, Cleveland (44124-0875)
PHONE...................................330 262-1555
Richard Bluestone, *President*
▲ EMP: 36 EST: 1993
SQ FT: 110,000
SALES (est): 3.6MM **Privately Held**
SIC: 3444 3822 1711 1761 Sheet metalwork; auto controls regulating residntl & coml environmt & applncs; plumbing, heating, air-conditioning contractors; roofing, siding & sheet metal work

(G-20738)
ALBRIGHT RADIATOR INC
331 N Hillcrest Dr (44691-3722)
P.O. Box 214 (44691-0214)
PHONE...................................330 264-8886
Fax: 330 264-8878
Dave Albright, *President*
Scott Albright, *Corp Secy*
EMP: 6 EST: 1928
SQ FT: 4,000
SALES (est): 876.4K **Privately Held**
SIC: 7539 7692 3714 Radiator repair shop, automotive; welding repair; radiators & radiator shells & cores, motor vehicle

(G-20739)
APPALACHIAN EQUIPMENT CO LLC
2054 Great Trails Dr (44691-3740)
PHONE...................................330 345-2251
John Collier, *Mng Member*
Joshua Collier, *Mng Member*
EMP: 3
SALES (est): 380K **Privately Held**
SIC: 3533 Oil & gas field machinery

(G-20740)
ARTFINDERS
Also Called: Artfind Tile
143 S Market St (44691-4838)
PHONE...................................330 264-7706
Fax: 330 264-7709
Brigid O'Connor, *President*
EMP: 3
SQ FT: 10,000
SALES (est): 125K **Privately Held**
SIC: 3253 5032 5211 Ceramic wall & floor tile; ceramic wall & floor tile; tile, ceramic

(G-20741)
ARTIFLEX MANUFACTURING LLC (HQ)
Also Called: Gerstco Division
1425 E Bowman St (44691-3185)
P.O. Box 6011 (44691-6011)
PHONE...................................330 262-2015
Fax: 330 262-3001
Erin Hoffmann, *President*

Randy Zeigler, *President*
Steve Delmoro, *Mfg Dir*
Vince Cover, *Plant Mgr*
Bruce Bunce, *Production*
▲ **EMP:** 428 **EST:** 1860
SQ FT: 1,200,000
SALES (est): 173.9MM
SALES (corp-wide): 2.8B **Publicly Held**
WEB: www.artiflexmfg.com
SIC: 3465 3469 Body parts, automobile:
stamped metal; metal stampings
PA: Worthington Industries, Inc.
200 W Old Wlson Bridge Rd
Worthington OH 43085
614 438-3210

(G-20742)
AT PALLET
4224 E Messner Rd (44691-9406)
PHONE..........................330 264-3903
Armando Pacheco, *Principal*
EMP: 3 **EST:** 2008
SALES (est): 173.5K **Privately Held**
SIC: 2448 Pallets, wood & wood with metal

(G-20743)
ATKINSON PRINTING INC
2876 N Applecreek Rd (44691-7942)
PHONE..........................330 669-3515
Fax: 330 669-3013
James Atkinson, *President*
James D Atkinson Jr, *Corp Secy*
EMP: 5 **EST:** 1970
SQ FT: 5,200
SALES (est): 655.3K **Privately Held**
SIC: 2752 Commercial printing, offset

(G-20744)
**AUTOMATION WELDING
SYSTEM**
3132 E Lincoln Way (44691-3757)
P.O. Box 35 (44691-0035)
PHONE..........................330 263-1176
Jim Horst, *Partner*
EMP: 3
SALES (est): 221.2K **Privately Held**
SIC: 7692 Welding repair

(G-20745)
BAARON ABRASIVES INC
Also Called: Easton-Mccarthy Division
2015 Great Trails Dr (44691-3741)
P.O. Box 194 (44691-0194)
PHONE..........................330 263-7737
Fax: 330 263-4440
Terry Perrine, *President*
Treva Wickwire, *Purch Agent*
Daryl Perrine, *Treasurer*
EMP: 4 **EST:** 1972
SQ FT: 10,000
SALES (est): 400K **Privately Held**
WEB: www.baaronabrasives.com
SIC: 3291 5085 Abrasive products; indus-
trial supplies

(G-20746)
BAUER CORPORATION (PA)
Also Called: Bauer Ladder
2540 Progress Dr (44691-7970)
P.O. Box 165 (44691-0165)
PHONE..........................800 321-4760
Fax: 330 264-4888
Mark McConnell, *President*
Ward McConnel, *Chairman*
John Vasichko, *Vice Pres*
John D Vasichko, *Engineer*
Beth Raff, *Accountant*
EMP: 30
SQ FT: 71,500
SALES (est): 16.9MM **Privately Held**
WEB: www.bauerladder.com
SIC: 5082 3499 3446 3441 Ladders;
metal ladders; architectural metalwork;
fabricated structural metal

(G-20747)
**BC INVESTMENT
CORPORATION (PA)**
1505 E Bowman St (44691-3128)
P.O. Box 165 (44691-0165)
PHONE..........................330 262-3070
Norman L Miller Jr, *President*
EMP: 6
SQ FT: 72,500

SALES (est): 8.4MM **Privately Held**
SIC: 2499 3499 4213 3089 Ladders &
stepladders, wood; ladders, wood; metal
ladders; trucking, except local; plastic processing

(G-20748)
BISHOP WELL SERVICE CORP
416 N Bauer Rd (44691-8626)
P.O. Box 511 (44691-0511)
PHONE..........................330 264-2023
David Bishop, *President*
Tom Patton, *Principal*
EMP: 9
SQ FT: 6,000
SALES (est): 814.2K **Privately Held**
SIC: 1389 Oil field services

(G-20749)
BLAZE OIL & GAS INC
1699 Nupp Dr (44691-1113)
P.O. Box 1407 (44691-7087)
PHONE..........................330 345-6700
EMP: 3 **EST:** 1967
SALES (est): 84K **Privately Held**
SIC: 1311 Crude Petroleum/Natural Gas
Production

(G-20750)
BOREMAN HARDWOODS INC
4470 W Old Lincoln Way (44691-3236)
PHONE..........................330 262-0403
Fax: 330 264-0452
Russell Boreman, *President*
Maralee Boreman, *Admin Sec*
EMP: 5
SQ FT: 1,620
SALES (est): 440K **Privately Held**
WEB: www.boremanhardwoods.com
SIC: 2411 Timber, cut at logging camp

(G-20751)
**BOSCH REXROTH
CORPORATION**
Mannesmann Rexroth
1683 Enterprise Pkwy (44691-7967)
PHONE..........................330 263-3300
Fax: 330 263-3330
Bob Warren, *Facilities Mgr*
Dan Brownson, *Design Engr*
Mike Bickel, *Branch Mgr*
Charles Back, *Manager*
Veronica Reiwald, *Manager*
EMP: 500
SQ FT: 225,000
SALES (corp-wide): 236.4MM **Privately
Held**
WEB: www.us.rexroth.com
SIC: 3594 3494 3491 Pumps, hydraulic
power transfer; expansion joints pipe; in-
dustrial valves
HQ: Bosch Rexroth Corporation
14001 S Lakes Dr
Charlotte NC 28273
847 645-3600

(G-20752)
BOXES & SUCH
1118 Mindy Ln (44691-5427)
PHONE..........................440 237-7122
Ed Allen, *President*
Roberta Allen, *CFO*
EMP: 3
SALES (est): 282.8K **Privately Held**
SIC: 2441 Boxes, wood

(G-20753)
BUCKEYE CORRUGATED INC
Also Called: Buckeye Container Division
3350 Long Rd (44691-7953)
PHONE..........................330 264-6336
Fax: 330 264-0127
Bill Randquist, *General Mgr*
Jeff Stansberry, *Plant Mgr*
Jon McGurk, *Sales Mgr*
Bob Peters, *Cust Mgr*
Jack Nebesky, *Manager*
EMP: 100
SALES (corp-wide): 196.7MM **Privately
Held**
WEB: www.buckeyecorrugated.com
SIC: 2653 Corrugated & solid fiber boxes
PA: Buckeye Corrugated, Inc
822 Kumho Dr Ste 400
Fairlawn OH 44333
330 576-0590

(G-20754)
BUCKEYE OIL PRODUCING CO
544 E Liberty St (44691-3602)
P.O. Box 129 (44691-0129)
PHONE..........................330 264-8847
Fax: 330 264-4222
Mark Lytle, *President*
Steve Sigler, *Vice Pres*
Cheryl Becker, *Manager*
EMP: 15
SQ FT: 10,000
SALES (est): 2.5MM **Privately Held**
WEB: www.buckeyeoilinc.com
SIC: 1311 1381 Crude petroleum & natu-
ral gas production; natural gas produc-
tion; drilling oil & gas wells

(G-20755)
BUCKEYE VEAL SERVICES
1046 N Applecreek Rd (44691-9528)
PHONE..........................740 489-5145
Fax: 330 262-8870
Steve Bond, *Branch Mgr*
▲ **EMP:** 9
SALES (est): 1.4MM **Privately Held**
SIC: 2011 Veal from meat slaughtered on
site

(G-20756)
BUILT-RITE BOX & CRATE INC
608 Freedlander Rd (44691-4704)
P.O. Box 1051 (44691-7051)
PHONE..........................330 263-0936
Fax: 330 262-4252
John C Meenan, *President*
Jodie L Meenan, *Corp Secy*
Dave Schaeufele, *Vice Pres*
EMP: 20
SQ FT: 10,000
SALES (est): 3.5MM **Privately Held**
WEB: www.builtritebox.com
SIC: 2441 2448 Boxes, wood; cases,
wood; skids, wood

(G-20757)
**CLARK-FOWLER ENTERPRISES
INC**
Also Called: Clark-Fowler Elc Mtr & Sups
510 W Henry St (44691-4773)
P.O. Box 310, Westerville (43086-0310)
PHONE..........................330 262-0906
Fax: 330 262-9126
Don Clark, *President*
Douglas Fowler, *Vice Pres*
Jeff Gentry, *Sales Staff*
Doug Fowler, *Sales Executive*
Nason Clark, *Manager*
EMP: 24 **EST:** 1995
SQ FT: 5,000
SALES (est): 5.8MM **Privately Held**
SIC: 7694 5063 Electric motor repair;
rewinding stators; motors, electric; power
transmission equipment, electric

(G-20758)
CLEARWATER SYSTEMS INC
1799 Akron Rd (44691-2513)
PHONE..........................330 262-5515
Fax: 330 263-1967
Ellery E Horn, *Branch Mgr*
EMP: 14
SALES (corp-wide): 31MM **Privately
Held**
SIC: 3589 Water treatment equipment, in-
dustrial
PA: Clearwater Systems, Inc.
1411 Vernon Odom Blvd
Akron OH 44320
330 821-2382

(G-20759)
COIL TECHNOLOGY INC
Also Called: Coil Tek
2109 Great Trails Dr (44691-3738)
P.O. Box 540 (44691-0540)
PHONE..........................330 601-1350
Andrew Cary, *President*
Annette Cary, *CFO*
▼ **EMP:** 3
SQ FT: 1,500
SALES: 600K **Privately Held**
WEB: www.coiltek.com
SIC: 3541 Machine tools, metal cutting
type

(G-20760)
**COLLIER WELL EQP & SUP INC
(PA)**
3310 Columbus Rd (44691-9134)
PHONE..........................330 345-3968
Fax: 330 345-7191
Doug Drughal, *President*
Bill Stanton, *Shareholder*
EMP: 16
SQ FT: 14,000
SALES (est): 5.8MM **Privately Held**
SIC: 1389 3444 4212 Construction, repair
& dismantling services; sheet metalwork;
local trucking, without storage

(G-20761)
CRYOPLUS INC
2429 N Millborne Rd (44691-9539)
PHONE..........................330 683-3375
Kathi Bond, *President*
Hobart Bond, *Vice Pres*
Ross Miller, *Treasurer*
EMP: 4
SALES: 72.1K **Privately Held**
WEB: www.cryoplus.com
SIC: 3399 Cryogenic treatment of metal

(G-20762)
DAISY BRAND LLC
3600 N Geyers Chapel Rd (44691-9641)
PHONE..........................330 202-4376
David M Sokolsky, *Mng Member*
EMP: 18
SALES (corp-wide): 197.7MM **Privately
Held**
SIC: 2026 Milk processing (pasteurizing,
homogenizing, bottling)
PA: Daisy Brand, Llc
12750 Merit Dr Ste 600
Dallas TX 75251
972 726-0800

(G-20763)
DANROC CORP
326 N Hillcrest Dr (44691-3745)
PHONE..........................330 262-0712
Christopher Jeffers, *Principal*
EMP: 4
SALES (est): 454K **Privately Held**
SIC: 2759 Screen printing

(G-20764)
**DAVID A WALDRON &
ASSOCIATES (PA)**
2285 Eagle Pass A (44691-5322)
P.O. Box 766 (44691-0766)
PHONE..........................330 264-7275
David A Waldron, *President*
EMP: 6
SQ FT: 2,000
SALES (est): 1.4MM **Privately Held**
SIC: 1311 8999 6512 Crude petroleum &
natural gas; geological consultant; com-
mercial & industrial building operation

(G-20765)
DINOS DRIVE THRU LLC
1541 Jones Ave (44691-4523)
PHONE..........................330 263-1111
EMP: 4
SALES (est): 261.2K **Privately Held**
SIC: 2082 Beer (alcoholic beverage)

(G-20766)
DOME DRILLING CO
4489 E Lincoln Way (44691-8602)
PHONE..........................330 262-5113
James Gessel, *Branch Mgr*
EMP: 3
SALES (corp-wide): 1.5MM **Privately
Held**
SIC: 1311 1382 Crude petroleum produc-
tion; oil & gas exploration services
PA: Dome Drilling Co
2001 Crocker Rd Ste 420
Westlake OH 44145
440 892-9434

(G-20767)
DRAGON PRODUCTS LTD
3310 Columbus Rd (44691-9134)
PHONE..........................330 345-3968
EMP: 4

SALES (corp-wide): 350.1MM **Privately Held**
SIC: **3443** Fuel tanks (oil, gas, etc.): metal plate
HQ: Dragon Products, Ltd.
1655 Louisiana St
Beaumont TX 77701
409 833-2665

(G-20768)
E S H INC
Also Called: Mc Products
390 W South St (44691-4762)
P.O. Box 1524 (44691-7089)
PHONE..................................330 345-1010
Bill Barnes, *President*
EMP: 4
SALES (est): 338.9K **Privately Held**
SIC: **3569** Firefighting apparatus & related equipment

(G-20769)
E-PAK MANUFACTURING LLC
1109 Pittsburg Ave (44691-3805)
P.O. Box 269 (44691-0269)
PHONE..................................800 235-1632
Fax: 330 264-2664
Aden Yoder, *General Mgr*
Kyle Schlabach, *Sales Mgr*
Bryan Mullet, *Mng Member*
▼ EMP: 75
SQ FT: 12,000
SALES (est): 19.1MM **Privately Held**
SIC: **3443** 3441 Dumpsters, garbage; fabricated structural metal

(G-20770)
EXPERT TS
Also Called: Expertise
221 Beall Ave (44691-3674)
PHONE..................................330 263-4588
Anna Gerig, *President*
EMP: 5
SALES (est): 200K **Privately Held**
SIC: **2759** 2395 Screen printing; embroidery & art needlework

(G-20771)
F J DESIGNS INC
Also Called: Cat's Meow Village, The
2163 Great Trails Dr (44691-3738)
PHONE..................................330 264-1377
Fax: 330 263-0219
Faline Jones, *CEO*
Chris Ciha, *Vice Pres*
Brent Rice, *Vice Pres*
George Pethtel, *Facilities Mgr*
EMP: 20
SQ FT: 7,000
SALES (est): 5.2MM **Privately Held**
WEB: www.fjdesign.com
SIC: **2499** 2759 3993 Novelties, wood fiber; commercial printing; signs & advertising specialties

(G-20772)
FEW ATMTIVE GL APPLCATIONS INC
1660 Enterprise Pkwy (44691-7968)
PHONE..................................234 249-1880
Andre Jenrich, *President*
▲ EMP: 3
SQ FT: 12,000
SALES (est): 350K **Privately Held**
SIC: **3089** Windshields, plastic

(G-20773)
FRANKLIN GAS & OIL COMPANY LLC
1615 W Old Lincoln Way (44691-3329)
P.O. Box 1005 (44691-7005)
PHONE..................................330 264-8739
Fax: 330 264-0796
James C Morgan, *Mng Member*
James Morgan III,
John J Morgan,
EMP: 7
SQ FT: 4,000
SALES (est): 920.2K **Privately Held**
SIC: **1311** Crude petroleum & natural gas production

(G-20774)
FRITO-LAY NORTH AMERICA INC
1626 Old Mansfield Rd (44691-9056)
PHONE..................................972 334-7000
Fax: 330 262-0105
Jim Barnard, *Plant Mgr*
Bill Luther, *Purchasing*
Tim Tayerle, *Controller*
Mark Vantrease, *Manager*
Larry Neidig, *Manager*
EMP: 234
SALES (corp-wide): 62.8B **Publicly Held**
WEB: www.fritolay.com
SIC: **2099** 2096 Food preparations; potato chips & similar snacks
HQ: Frito-Lay North America, Inc.
7701 Legacy Dr
Plano TX 75024

(G-20775)
GDC INC
1700 Old Mansfield Rd (44691-7212)
PHONE..................................574 533-3128
Lonnie Abney, *COO*
EMP: 10
SALES (corp-wide): 41.6MM **Privately Held**
SIC: **2822** 2869 2891 3069 Synthetic rubber; perfumes, flavorings & food additives; adhesives & sealants; medical & laboratory rubber sundries & related products; plastics foam products
PA: Gdc, Inc.
815 Logan St
Goshen IN 46528
574 533-3128

(G-20776)
GLASS SENSORS LLC
770 Spruce St (44691-4605)
PHONE..................................330 234-7999
Kevin Spence, *Principal*
EMP: 4
SALES (est): 280K **Privately Held**
SIC: **3829** Measuring & controlling devices

(G-20777)
GLOBAL BODY & EQUIPMENT CO
Also Called: C & C Metal Products
2061 Sylvan Rd (44691-3849)
P.O. Box 857 (44691-0857)
PHONE..................................330 264-6640
Fax: 330 264-3585
Robert Lapsley, *President*
Bob Lapsley, *President*
Bryan Deeken, *Manager*
EMP: 100
SALES: 17MM **Privately Held**
WEB: www.cncmetalproducts.com
SIC: **3599** Machine & other job shop work

(G-20778)
GLORIAS
2023 Portage Rd (44691-1909)
PHONE..................................330 264-8963
Gloria Cantleberry, *Owner*
EMP: 6
SALES (est): 200K **Privately Held**
SIC: **2395** Emblems, embroidered

(G-20779)
GREEN ENERGY INC
4489 E Lincoln Way (44691-8602)
PHONE..................................330 262-5112
Stephen R Gessel, *President*
Debra J Falde, *Corp Secy*
James E Gessel, *Vice Pres*
Carl Robert Gessel, *Treasurer*
EMP: 7
SQ FT: 3,700
SALES: 900K **Privately Held**
SIC: **1311** Crude petroleum & natural gas

(G-20780)
GRT UTILICORP INC
9268 Ashland Rd (44691-9235)
PHONE..................................330 264-8444
Fax: 330 264-2252
Rod Zimmermen, *President*
Rod Zimmerman, *President*
Thomas Funk, *Vice Pres*
Rick Fliger, *Foreman/Supr*
Lisa Scott, *Controller*

◆ EMP: 20
SQ FT: 7,840
SALES (est): 4.7MM **Privately Held**
WEB: www.grtutilicorp.com
SIC: **3541** 5084 Drilling & boring machines; industrial machine parts

(G-20781)
H & H EQUIPMENT INC
Also Called: Snyder Hot Shot
6247 Ashland Rd (44691-9233)
PHONE..................................330 264-5400
Fax: 330 264-0327
Gerald Snyder, *President*
EMP: 6
SQ FT: 8,400
SALES (est): 610K **Privately Held**
SIC: **3715** Truck trailers

(G-20782)
HACKWORTH ELECTRIC MOTORS INC
4952 Cleveland Rd (44691-1195)
PHONE..................................330 345-6049
Fax: 330 345-1937
Jeffery K Hackworth, *President*
Brenda K Hackworth, *Vice Pres*
Sharon Sayre, *Office Mgr*
EMP: 7
SQ FT: 5,000
SALES (est): 1.1MM **Privately Held**
SIC: **7694** 5063 7692 Electric motor repair; motors, electric; welding repair

(G-20783)
HACKWORTH OIL FIELD ELECTRIC
Also Called: Hackworth Electrical Contrs In
4931 Cleveland Rd (44691-1161)
PHONE..................................330 345-6504
Fax: 330 345-1344
Jerry Hackworth, *President*
Brenda S Hackworth, *Corp Secy*
EMP: 4
SQ FT: 40,000
SALES (est): 541.7K **Privately Held**
SIC: **1389** Servicing oil & gas wells

(G-20784)
HORIZONTAL EQP MANUFACTORING
3310 Columbus Rd (44691-9134)
P.O. Box 145, Southern Pines NC (28388-0145)
PHONE..................................330 264-2229
Leo Barbera, *President*
EMP: 4
SQ FT: 40,000
SALES (est): 439.8K **Privately Held**
SIC: **3532** Auger mining equipment

(G-20785)
ILLUSIONS SCREENPRINTING
334 E South St Ste 3 (44691-4318)
PHONE..................................330 263-7770
Charles Steinman, *Owner*
EMP: 4
SQ FT: 4,500
SALES (est): 190K **Privately Held**
SIC: **2759** Screen printing

(G-20786)
INGREDIENT INNOVATIONS INTL CO
146 S Bever St (44691-4326)
PHONE..................................330 262-4440
Charles Brain, *President*
Michael Schwing, *Business Mgr*
Brett Wright, *QC Mgr*
Mindy Brain, *Marketing Staff*
Scott Peters, *Director*
EMP: 7
SQ FT: 12,000
SALES: 9MM **Privately Held**
SIC: **2099** Food preparations

(G-20787)
INKTASTIC INC
5214 Cleveland Rd (44691-1156)
PHONE..................................330 345-0911
Fax: 330 345-3053
Alan Dail, *President*
Angela Smith - Dail, *President*
Joyce Dial, *Treasurer*
Amber Marshall, *Creative Dir*

EMP: 18
SALES (est): 2MM **Privately Held**
SIC: **2759** Commercial printing

(G-20788)
INTERNATIONAL PAPER COMPANY
689 Palmer St (44691-3197)
P.O. Box 1047 (44691-7045)
PHONE..................................330 264-1322
Fax: 330 262-4037
Jim Gracey, *General Mgr*
Carol Collins, *Plant Mgr*
Mike Filyaw, *Human Res Dir*
Allan Szirony, *Sales Mgr*
Rick Oberg, *Marketing Mgr*
EMP: 109
SALES (corp-wide): 21B **Publicly Held**
WEB: www.internationalpaper.com
SIC: **2653** Boxes, corrugated: made from purchased materials
PA: International Paper Company
6400 Poplar Ave
Memphis TN 38197
901 419-9000

(G-20789)
JAMES R BERNHARDT PRODUCING
6717 Cleveland Rd (44691-9619)
P.O. Box 638 (44691-0638)
PHONE..................................330 345-5306
John Bernhardt, *Owner*
EMP: 3
SALES (est): 225.6K **Privately Held**
SIC: **1311** Crude petroleum & natural gas

(G-20790)
JAMES R SMAIL INC
2285 Eagle Pass Ste B (44691-5322)
P.O. Box 1157 (44691-7082)
PHONE..................................330 264-7500
James R Smail, *President*
Mark A Sparr, *Vice Pres*
EMP: 7
SALES (est): 780K **Privately Held**
SIC: **1381** Drilling oil & gas wells

(G-20791)
JNP GROUP LLC
449 Freedlander Rd (44691-4734)
P.O. Box 1022 (44691-7022)
PHONE..................................800 735-9645
James Pooler,
EMP: 6 EST: 2011
SALES (est): 705.8K **Privately Held**
SIC: **3585** 7389 Refrigeration & heating equipment

(G-20792)
JPMORGAN CHASE BANK NAT ASSN
141 N Walnut St (44691-4807)
PHONE..................................330 287-5102
Chris Foy, *Branch Mgr*
EMP: 6
SALES (corp-wide): 105.4B **Publicly Held**
SIC: **3578** Automatic teller machines (ATM)
HQ: Jpmorgan Chase Bank, National Association
1111 Polaris Pkwy
Columbus OH 43240
614 436-3055

(G-20793)
JUST BASIC SPORTS INC
Also Called: Pizzazz
1615 N Geyers Chapel Rd (44691-9563)
PHONE..................................330 264-7771
Bill Older, *President*
Freddick Older, *Vice Pres*
EMP: 3 EST: 1999
SQ FT: 4,500
SALES: 518.4K
SALES (corp-wide): 50.4K **Privately Held**
SIC: **5091** 3949 Sporting & recreation goods; sporting & athletic goods
PA: Older Bros, Inc
408 N Bever St
Wooster OH 44691
330 262-1065

(G-20794)
KENOIL INC
1537 Blachleyville Rd (44691-9752)
P.O. Box 1085 (44691-7081)
PHONE..............................330 262-1144
Steve Fleisher, *Vice Pres*
Martha Morris, *Office Mgr*
EMP: 50 EST: 1982
SALES (est): 2.7MM **Privately Held**
SIC: 1311 Crude petroleum & natural gas
production

(G-20795)
KETMAN CORPORATION
Also Called: Wooster Book Company, The
205 W Liberty St (44691-4831)
PHONE..............................330 262-1688
David Wiesenberg, *President*
Carol A Rueger, *Corp Secy*
EMP: 8
SQ FT: 7,500
SALES: 750K **Privately Held**
WEB: www.woosterbook.com
SIC: 5942 2731 8742 Book stores; books:
publishing only; industry specialist con-
sultants

(G-20796)
KILLBUCK CREEK OIL CO
2538 Columbus Rd (44691-4466)
PHONE..............................330 601-0921
Jim Shoots, *Owner*
EMP: 4
SALES (est): 284.9K **Privately Held**
SIC: 1311 Crude petroleum & natural gas

(G-20797)
KORDA MANUFACTURING INC
3927 E Lincoln Way (44691-8997)
PHONE..............................330 262-1555
Fax: 330 262-1556
Dan Korda, *President*
EMP: 61
SALES (est): 8.8MM **Privately Held**
SIC: 3444 Sheet metalwork

(G-20798)
LUK CLUTCH SYSTEMS LLC (DH)
3401 Old Airport Rd (44691-9544)
PHONE..............................330 264-4383
David Marlar, *Vice Pres*
Ann Pierson, *Purchasing*
Nigel Gurney, *Engineer*
Darlene John, *Controller*
Darlene Johns, *Controller*
▲ EMP: 50
SQ FT: 400,000
SALES (est): 117MM
SALES (corp-wide): 56.1B **Privately Held**
WEB: www.luk-us.com
SIC: 3714 3568 3566 Motor vehicle parts
& accessories; clutches, motor vehicle;
power transmission equipment; speed
changers, drives & gears
HQ: Luk Usa Llc
3401 Old Airport Rd
Wooster OH 44691
330 264-4383

(G-20799)
LUK TRANSMISSION SYSTEMS LLC
3401 Old Airport Rd (44691-9544)
PHONE..............................330 264-4383
Darlene Johns, *Controller*
Marc McGrath,
◆ EMP: 640
SALES (est): 228.8MM
SALES (corp-wide): 56.1B **Privately Held**
SIC: 3714 3566 Motor vehicle parts & ac-
cessories; speed changers, drives &
gears
HQ: Luk Usa Llc
3401 Old Airport Rd
Wooster OH 44691
330 264-4383

(G-20800)
LUK USA LLC (DH)
3401 Old Airport Rd (44691-9544)
PHONE..............................330 264-4383
Fax: 330 202-6288
Klaus Rosenfeld, *CEO*
Marc McGrath, *President*

Rob Chapman, *COO*
Marc McCgrath, *Vice Pres*
Ashi Uppal, *Vice Pres*
▲ EMP: 257
SALES (est): 345.8MM
SALES (corp-wide): 56.1B **Privately Held**
SIC: 3714 Motor vehicle parts & acces-
sories
HQ: Schaeffler Group Usa Inc.
308 Springhill Farm Rd
Fort Mill SC 29715
803 548-8500

(G-20801)
MAINTENANCE + INC
1051 W Liberty St (44691-3307)
P.O. Box 408 (44691-0408)
PHONE..............................330 264-6262
Fax: 330 264-2578
William Neckermann, *President*
Robert Huebner, *Opers Staff*
◆ EMP: 12
SQ FT: 10,000
SALES (est): 4MM **Privately Held**
SIC: 2992 Lubricating oils & greases

(G-20802)
MARCUM DEVELOPMENT LLC
2245 Flickinger Hill Rd (44691-9064)
PHONE..............................330 466-8231
Howard Marcum Jr, *Mng Member*
Sonny Marcum, *Manager*
EMP: 5
SALES: 250K **Privately Held**
SIC: 3089 Pallets, plastic

(G-20803)
MCCANN TOOL & DIE INC
Also Called: J R Tool & Die
3230 Columbus Rd (44691-8430)
PHONE..............................330 264-8820
Fax: 330 264-8248
Jess R McCann Sr, *President*
Nellie McCann, *Corp Secy*
J R McCann Jr, *Vice Pres*
EMP: 11 EST: 1982
SQ FT: 6,500
SALES: 500K **Privately Held**
SIC: 3599 3089 Machine shop, jobbing &
repair; injection molding of plastics

(G-20804)
MCELROY CONTRACT PACKAGING
249 S Bauer Rd (44691-3803)
P.O. Box 597 (44691-0597)
PHONE..............................330 262-0855
Fax: 330 264-9784
Larry McElroy, *President*
Steve McElroy, *Vice Pres*
Lorrie Mendenhall, *Manager*
Judie McElroy, *Admin Sec*
EMP: 15 EST: 1978
SQ FT: 14,500
SALES (est): 3.6MM **Privately Held**
WEB: www.mcelroypackaging.com
SIC: 4783 2675 2653 Packing goods for
shipping; crating goods for shipping; die-
cut paper & board; pads, corrugated:
made from purchased materials

(G-20805)
METAL DYNAMICS CO
4047 Unit A Lincoln Way (44691)
P.O. Box 1348 (44691-7086)
PHONE..............................330 601-0748
Wendy K Bowman, *Principal*
EMP: 4
SALES (est): 460K **Privately Held**
SIC: 3441 Fabricated structural metal

(G-20806)
METALS USA CRBN FLAT RLLED INC (DH)
1070 W Liberty St (44691-3308)
P.O. Box 999 (44691-0999)
PHONE..............................330 264-8416
Don Gingery, *President*
Tom Pacek, *Purch Mgr*
Jeffrey Aultz, *Sls & Mktg Exec*
James Zimmermann, *CFO*
Brian Schmidt, *Treasurer*
▲ EMP: 102
SQ FT: 140,000

SALES (est): 70.3MM
SALES (corp-wide): 8.6B **Publicly Held**
SIC: 3312 5051 Blast furnaces & steel
mills; steel
HQ: Metals Usa, Inc.
2400 E Coml Blvd Ste 905
Fort Lauderdale FL 33308
954 202-4000

(G-20807)
METROMEDIA TECHNOLOGIES INC
1061 Venture Blvd (44691-9358)
PHONE..............................330 264-2501
Fax: 330 262-9147
Richard Beaudoin, *Foreman/Supr*
Carl Udell, *Purchasing*
D Parsons, *Engineer*
Ralph Degliotta, *Manager*
Trent Mullet, *Director*
EMP: 80
SALES (corp-wide): 52.7MM **Privately Held**
WEB: www.mmt.com
SIC: 3993 Signs & advertising specialties
PA: Metromedia Technologies, Inc.
810 7th Ave Fl 29
New York NY 10019
212 273-2100

(G-20808)
MIDWAY SWISS TURN INC
2160 Great Trails Dr (44691-3711)
PHONE..............................330 264-4300
Jim Rahz, *President*
Jaymie Rahz, *Admin Sec*
EMP: 5
SALES (est): 558.6K **Privately Held**
SIC: 3599 Machine shop, jobbing & repair

(G-20809)
MILITARY RESOURCES LLC
1036 Burbank Rd (44691)
PHONE..............................330 263-1040
EMP: 50
SALES (corp-wide): 3MM **Privately Held**
SIC: 3559 7389 Mfg Misc Industry Ma-
chinery Business Services
PA: Military Resources, Llc
1834 Cleveland Rd Ste 301
Wooster OH 44691
330 309-9970

(G-20810)
MILITARY RESOURCES LLC (PA)
1834 Cleveland Rd Ste 301 (44691-2206)
PHONE..............................330 309-9970
William D Johnson, *CEO*
Arthur Summerville,
Roger Williams,
EMP: 9
SQ FT: 3,000
SALES: 3MM **Privately Held**
WEB: www.militaryresources.com
SIC: 7389 3559 Design, commercial & in-
dustrial; ammunition & explosives, loading
machinery

(G-20811)
MORRISON CUSTOM WELDING INC
1435 S Honeytown Rd (44691-8914)
PHONE..............................330 264-0626
Fax: 330 264-0628
Mark Morrison, *President*
Dave Samerdak, *Project Mgr*
EMP: 12
SALES (est): 2.1MM **Privately Held**
WEB: www.morrisonwelding.com
SIC: 3441 Fabricated structural metal for
bridges

(G-20812)
MORTON BUILDINGS INC
1055 Columbus Avenue Ext (44691-9701)
PHONE..............................330 345-6188
Fax: 330 345-5790
Gary Schodorf, *Manager*
EMP: 14
SALES (corp-wide): 499.4MM **Privately Held**
WEB: www.mortonbuildings.com
SIC: 3448 5039 Prefabricated metal build-
ings; prefabricated structures

PA: Morton Buildings, Inc.
252 W Adams St
Morton IL 61550
800 447-7436

(G-20813)
MURR CORPORATION
Also Called: Murr Printing and Graphics
201 N Buckeye St (44691-3501)
PHONE..............................330 264-2223
Fax: 330 262-1628
Joseph F Murr, *President*
Earl Martin, *District Mgr*
Jodi Robison, *Graphic Designe*
EMP: 14 EST: 1980
SQ FT: 5,800
SALES (est): 2.2MM **Privately Held**
WEB: www.murrprinting.com
SIC: 2752 5943 Commercial printing, off-
set; office forms & supplies

(G-20814)
NATIONAL LIME AND STONE CO
Also Called: National Lime Stone
1455 Timken Rd (44691-8346)
P.O. Box 1154 (44691-7082)
PHONE..............................330 262-1317
Dave Webber, *Manager*
EMP: 3
SALES (corp-wide): 4B **Privately Held**
WEB: www.natlime.com
SIC: 1422 Limestones, ground
PA: The National Lime And Stone Company
551 Lake Cascade Pkwy
Findlay OH 45840
419 422-4341

(G-20815)
NEON NIGHTS
2239 W Smithvl Wstrn Rd (44691-8501)
PHONE..............................330 345-9907
Bill Brown, *CEO*
EMP: 14
SALES (est): 1MM **Privately Held**
SIC: 3993 Neon signs

(G-20816)
NORTH CENTRAL CONCRETE DESIGN
Also Called: Nccd
3331 E Lincoln Way (44691-3762)
PHONE..............................419 606-1908
Daniel Zawacki, *President*
Mike Wiseman, *Vice Pres*
Lori Crum, *Treasurer*
EMP: 13
SALES: 2.5MM **Privately Held**
SIC: 3271 1741 Blocks, concrete: insulat-
ing; concrete block masonry laying

(G-20817)
NORTH EAST FUEL INC
3927 Cleveland Rd (44691-1223)
PHONE..............................330 264-4454
Timothy E Miller, *Principal*
EMP: 3
SALES (est): 233.3K **Privately Held**
SIC: 2869 Fuels

(G-20818)
NORTHEAST TUBULAR SERVICE INC
Also Called: Northeast Piping Supply
6740 E Lincoln Way (44691-8643)
PHONE..............................330 262-1881
Rick Casper, *President*
William Meismer, *Vice Pres*
EMP: 3
SALES (est): 310K **Privately Held**
SIC: 3312 5541 Primary finished or semi-
finished shapes; gasoline service stations

(G-20819)
OLEN CORPORATION
3001 Prairie Ln (44691-9441)
PHONE..............................330 262-6821
EMP: 5
SALES (corp-wide): 289.1MM **Privately Held**
SIC: 1442 Construction sand & gravel
PA: The Olen Corporation
4755 S High St
Columbus OH 43207
614 491-1515

(G-20820)
PETRO EVALUATION SERVICES INC
3927 Cleveland Rd (44691-1223)
PHONE.............................330 264-4454
Fax: 330 345-6617
Jay G Henthorne Jr, *President*
Kelly Smith, *Office Mgr*
EMP: 4
SQ FT: 3,000
SALES (est): 719.6K **Privately Held**
SIC: 1311 8748 Crude petroleum & natural gas; business consulting

(G-20821)
PONDEROSA CONSULTING SERVICES (PA)
4060 Millbrook Rd (44691-8400)
P.O. Box 357 (44691-0357)
PHONE.............................330 264-2298
Robert Breneman, *President*
EMP: 4
SALES (est): 860K **Privately Held**
SIC: 1381 8748 Drilling oil & gas wells; business consulting

(G-20822)
PPG INDUSTRIES INC
Also Called: PPG 5414
239 W Liberty St (44691-4831)
PHONE.............................330 262-9741
Tim Miles, *Manager*
EMP: 24
SALES (corp-wide): 14.7B **Publicly Held**
WEB: www.ppg.com
SIC: 2851 Paints & allied products
PA: Ppg Industries, Inc.
1 Ppg Pl
Pittsburgh PA 15272
412 434-3131

(G-20823)
PRAIRIE LANE CORPORATION
Also Called: Prairie Lane Gravel Co
4489 Prairie Ln (44691-9442)
P.O. Box 233 (44691-0233)
PHONE.............................330 262-3322
Fax: 330 264-5469
Ralph Miller, *President*
Chris McCarthy, *Sales Staff*
James Lanham, *Admin Sec*
EMP: 7 EST: 1954
SQ FT: 2,400
SALES (est): 1.2MM **Privately Held**
SIC: 1442 7032 6519 Construction sand & gravel; sporting & recreational camps; farm land leasing

(G-20824)
PRAXAIR INC
4265 E Lincoln Way Unit A (44691-8666)
PHONE.............................330 264-6633
Fax: 330 264-6948
Larry Sauriol, *Business Mgr*
Randy Mick, *Project Mgr*
Gerry Parker, *Manager*
EMP: 19
SALES (corp-wide): 10.5B **Publicly Held**
SIC: 2813 Industrial gases
PA: Praxair, Inc.
10 Riverview Dr
Danbury CT 06810
203 837-2000

(G-20825)
PRENTKE ROMICH COMPANY (PA)
1022 Heyl Rd (44691-9744)
P.O. Box 76079, Cleveland (44101-4203)
PHONE.............................330 202-5800
Fax: 330 263-4829
Barry Romich, *Ch of Bd*
Dave Moffat, *President*
Katie Phillips, *Managing Dir*
Edwin M Prentke, *Principal*
Herman Taber, *Principal*
EMP: 118
SQ FT: 8,000

SALES (est): 24.8MM **Privately Held**
WEB: www.prentrom.com
SIC: 3822 3663 3577 3841 Auto controls regulating residntl & coml environmt & applncs; radio & TV communications equipment; computer peripheral equipment; surgical & medical instruments; measuring & controlling devices; telephone & telegraph apparatus

(G-20826)
R & M WELDING CO
5663 Shreve Rd (44691-9122)
PHONE.............................330 264-4788
Mark Mellor, *Owner*
EMP: 3
SALES: 100K **Privately Held**
SIC: 7692 Welding repair

(G-20827)
RBB SYSTEMS INC (PA)
4265 E Lincoln Way Unit C (44691-8666)
PHONE.............................330 263-4502
Fax: 330 567-3925
Bruce Hendrick, *President*
Richard L Beery, *Principal*
Michele Hendrick, *Treasurer*
Micky Henrick, *Accountant*
Ruth Ferrell, *Sales Staff*
EMP: 65
SQ FT: 20,000
SALES: 7.9MM **Privately Held**
WEB: www.rbbsystems.com
SIC: 3625 Relays & industrial controls

(G-20828)
RBB SYSTEMS INC
4265 E Lincoln Way Unit C (44691-8666)
PHONE.............................330 263-4502
Chris Blum, *Managing Dir*
Ross Lilley, *Managing Dir*
Carl Sheler, *Controller*
Ruth Ferrell, *Sales Dir*
Bruce Hendrick, *Branch Mgr*
EMP: 70
SALES (corp-wide): 7.9MM **Privately Held**
WEB: www.rbbsystems.com
SIC: 3625 Relays & industrial controls
PA: Rbb Systems, Inc.
4265 E Lincoln Way Unit C
Wooster OH 44691
330 263-4502

(G-20829)
RICELAND CABINET INC
326 N Hillcrest Dr Ste A (44691-3745)
PHONE.............................330 601-1071
Leroy Miller, *President*
David A Miller, *Principal*
Paul A Miller, *Principal*
Wanda Mullet, *Principal*
Myron Miller, *Corp Secy*
EMP: 92 EST: 1979
SQ FT: 24,220
SALES (est): 14.5MM **Privately Held**
WEB: www.ricelandcabinet.com
SIC: 2434 3281 2541 Wood kitchen cabinets; cut stone & stone products; wood partitions & fixtures

(G-20830)
RIVERVIEW INDUS WD PDTS INC
646 Industrial Blvd (44691-8926)
P.O. Box 408, Smithville (44677-0408)
PHONE.............................330 669-8509
Fax: 330 264-4417
Michael Meenan, *President*
Edward Nettleton, *General Mgr*
Cherly Coblentz, *Controller*
EMP: 60
SQ FT: 17,000
SALES (est): 8.9MM **Privately Held**
WEB: www.riverviewpallet.com
SIC: 2448 Cargo containers, wood; pallets, wood; skids, wood

(G-20831)
SANTMYER OIL CO OF ASHLAND (HQ)
1055 W Old Lincoln Way (44691-3398)
PHONE.............................330 262-6501
Terry Santmyer, *President*
Joe Miller, *Vice Pres*
Randy Ruggles, *Vice Pres*

Dave First, *Treasurer*
EMP: 1
SQ FT: 1,000
SALES: 1.4MM
SALES (corp-wide): 104.2MM **Privately Held**
SIC: 5172 5983 1382 Fuel oil; fuel oil dealers; oil & gas exploration services
PA: Santmyer Oil Co., Inc.
3000 Old Airport Rd
Wooster OH 44691
330 262-6501

(G-20832)
SCOT INDUSTRIES INC
6578 Ashland Rd (44691-9233)
P.O. Box 1106 (44691-7081)
PHONE.............................330 262-7585
Fax: 330 263-4702
David Speigle, *Vice Pres*
Mike Bannert, *Plant Mgr*
Cody Wesson, *Prdtn Mgr*
Bob Gralinski, *Facilities Mgr*
Tammy Myers, *Human Resources*
EMP: 40
SQ FT: 2,018
SALES (corp-wide): 190.2MM **Privately Held**
WEB: www.scotindustries.com
SIC: 5051 7389 3498 3471 Steel; pipe & tubing, steel; metal cutting services; fabricated pipe & fittings; plating & polishing
PA: Scot Industries, Inc.
3756 Fm 250 N
Lone Star TX 75668
903 639-2551

(G-20833)
SEAMAN CORPORATION (PA)
1000 Venture Blvd (44691-9358)
PHONE.............................330 262-1111
Fax: 330 263-6950
Richard N Seaman, *President*
James E Dye, *COO*
Scott Gipson, *Vice Pres*
Carol Momchilou, *Vice Pres*
Raj Venkataraman, *Vice Pres*
◆ EMP: 130
SQ FT: 90,000
SALES (est): 124.9MM **Privately Held**
WEB: www.seamancorp.com
SIC: 2221 Nylon broadwoven fabrics; polyester broadwoven fabrics

(G-20834)
SHEARER FARM INC (PA)
Also Called: John Deere Authorized Dealer
7762 Cleveland Rd (44691-7700)
PHONE.............................330 345-9023
Fax: 330 345-9348
Brian Giauque, *President*
Gerald Shearer, *Principal*
EMP: 45 EST: 1937
SQ FT: 9,400
SALES (est): 59.5MM **Privately Held**
WEB: www.shearerequipment.com
SIC: 3523 5082 Fertilizing machinery, farm; construction & mining machinery

(G-20835)
SIGN DESIGN WOOSTER INC
1537 W Old Lincoln Way (44691-3327)
PHONE.............................330 262-8838
Ken Stiffler, *President*
Stephanie Stiffler, *Corp Secy*
EMP: 8
SQ FT: 2,000
SALES (est): 674.3K **Privately Held**
WEB: www.signdesignwooster.com
SIC: 3993 Signs & advertising specialties

(G-20836)
SMITHVILLE MANUFACTURING CO
6563 Cleveland Rd (44691-9690)
PHONE.............................330 345-5818
Fax: 330 345-5855
Allen Nayman, *President*
John Neubert, *Purchasing*
Corrie Eash, *Finance*
EMP: 30
SQ FT: 624
SALES (est): 3.9MM **Privately Held**
SIC: 3469 3544 Metal stampings; special dies & tools

(G-20837)
SOL-FLY TECHNOLOGIES LLC
3098 Tamarack Ln (44691-9023)
PHONE.............................330 465-8883
Austin Doerr, *Owner*
EMP: 8
SALES (est): 625K **Privately Held**
SIC: 3679 Electronic components

(G-20838)
SPEED NORTH AMERICA INC
1700a Old Mansfield Rd (44691)
P.O. Box 79r
PHONE.............................330 202-7775
Fax: 330 202-7779
Emmanuel Legrand, *President*
Bryan Franczek, *General Mgr*
Arnold Legrand, *Director*
◆ EMP: 38
SALES (est): 10MM
SALES (corp-wide): 36.5K **Privately Held**
SIC: 3524 Hedge trimmers, electric
HQ: Tecomec Srl
Strada Della Mirandola 11
Reggio Emilia RE 42124
052 295-9001

(G-20839)
STAHL/SCOTT FETZER COMPANY (DH)
Also Called: Arbortech
3201 W Old Lincoln Way (44691-3298)
PHONE.............................800 277-8245
Fax: 330 264-3319
Craig Aszkler, *President*
Rick Horn, *General Mgr*
Bob Businger, *Vice Pres*
Thomas J Boyer, *Design Engr*
W W T Stephens, *Treasurer*
EMP: 115
SQ FT: 70,000
SALES (est): 23.5MM
SALES (corp-wide): 223.6B **Publicly Held**
SIC: 3715 Trailer bodies
HQ: The Scott Fetzer Company
28800 Clemens Rd
Westlake OH 44145
440 892-3000

(G-20840)
TEKFOR INC
Also Called: Tekfor USA
3690 Long Rd (44691-7962)
PHONE.............................330 202-7420
Kevin Weldi, *President*
Antonio Clausi, *Project Mgr*
Steve Weatherwax, *Purch Agent*
Robin Martin, *QC Mgr*
Duke Brinkman, *Engineer*
▲ EMP: 265
SQ FT: 100,000
SALES (est): 77.3MM
SALES (corp-wide): 453.1K **Privately Held**
WEB: www.tekfor.com
SIC: 3462 Automotive forgings, ferrous: crankshaft, engine, axle, etc.
HQ: Neumayer Tekfor Holding Gmbh
Hauptstr. 115
Offenburg 77652

(G-20841)
TRICOR INDUSTRIAL INC (PA)
3225 W Old Lincoln Way (44691-3258)
P.O. Box 752 (44691-0752)
PHONE.............................330 264-3299
Fax: 330 262-7311
Nancy A Stitzlein, *CEO*
Michael D Stitzlein, *President*
▲ EMP: 77
SQ FT: 140,000
SALES: 50MM **Privately Held**
WEB: www.tricormetals.com
SIC: 5085 5051 5169 3444 Industrial supplies; fasteners, industrial: nuts, bolts, screws, etc.; metals service centers & offices; chemicals & allied products; sheet metalwork

(G-20842)
UNITED TITANIUM INC (PA)
3450 Old Airport Rd (44691-9581)
PHONE.............................330 264-2111
Fax: 330 263-1336
C Michael Reardon, *President*

Charlie Gray, *Vice Pres*
Bill Hileman, *Plant Mgr*
Rebecca Chewning, *Purch Mgr*
Shanon Jones, *Purch Mgr*
▲ **EMP:** 117
SQ FT: 150,000
SALES (est): 17.3MM **Privately Held**
WEB: www.unitedtitanium.com
SIC: 3452 Bolts, nuts, rivets & washers

(G-20843)
VERTICAL RUNNER
207 S Market St (44691-4723)
PHONE....................330 262-3000
Adam Johnson, *Principal*
EMP: 4
SALES (est): 412.8K **Privately Held**
SIC: 2591 Blinds vertical

(G-20844)
WASTE WATER POLLUTION CONTROL
Also Called: Wooster
1123 Columbus Rd (44691-4617)
PHONE....................330 263-5290
Fax: 330 263-5291
Jim Borton, *Managing Prtnr*
Michael Hunter, *Manager*
Curt Denning, *Manager*
Damien Johnson, *Officer*
Brian Perry, *Officer*
EMP: 12
SALES (est): 1.5MM **Privately Held**
SIC: 3589 4953 Water treatment equipment, industrial; refuse systems

(G-20845)
WAYNE COUNTY RUBBER INC
1205 E Bowman St (44691-3182)
PHONE....................330 264-5553
Fax: 330 262-7274
Laurie Schang, *President*
Arnie Berkowitz, *General Mgr*
Gary Oaklief, *Plant Mgr*
Bob Lowe, *CFO*
Jamie Pampa, *Manager*
EMP: 30
SQ FT: 170,000
SALES (est): 10.2MM **Privately Held**
SIC: 2822 3069 Synthetic rubber; custom compounding of rubber materials

(G-20846)
WESTERMAN INC
Also Called: Wooster Tool and Supply Co
899 Venture Blvd (44691-7521)
P.O. Box 915 (44691-0915)
PHONE....................330 262-6946
Brian Householder, *Branch Mgr*
EMP: 65
SALES (corp-wide): 2.8B **Publicly Held**
WEB: www.westermancompanies.com
SIC: 3566 3443 3533 3823 Reduction gears & gear units for turbines, except automotive; industrial vessels, tanks & containers; gas field machinery & equipment; oil field machinery & equipment; flow instruments, industrial process type; boat lifts; pumps, oil well & field
HQ: Westerman, Inc.
245 N Broad St
Bremen OH 43107
740 569-4143

(G-20847)
WESTERMAN ACQUISITION CO LLC
Also Called: Woosco
776 Kemrow Ave (44691-4857)
P.O. Box 915 (44691-0915)
PHONE....................330 264-2447
Fax: 330 262-1760
Terry McGhee, *President*
Scott Carpenter, *Exec VP*
Judith Van Buren, *Admin Sec*
EMP: 23 **EST:** 1924
SQ FT: 31,000
SALES (est): 3.2MM
SALES (corp-wide): 2.8B **Publicly Held**
WEB: www.westermancompanies.com
SIC: 3599 7692 Machine & other job shop work; welding repair
HQ: Westerman, Inc.
245 N Broad St
Bremen OH 43107
740 569-4143

(G-20848)
WHITE JEWELERS
211 E Liberty St (44691-4347)
PHONE....................330 264-3324
Fax: 330 264-6220
Heather Maxwell, *Owner*
EMP: 6 **EST:** 1928
SQ FT: 500
SALES (est): 547.1K **Privately Held**
SIC: 5944 7631 3911 Jewelry, precious stones & precious metals; watch repair; jewelry repair services; jewelry, precious metal

(G-20849)
WOOSTER DAILY RECORD INC (HQ)
Also Called: Farmer Hub
212 E Liberty St (44691-4348)
PHONE....................330 264-1125
Fax: 330 264-3756
Charles Dix, *President*
Stephanie Kandel, *Editor*
Katherine Ryder, *Editor*
David E Dix, *Vice Pres*
Robert C Dix Jr, *Vice Pres*
EMP: 120
SQ FT: 25,000
SALES (est): 60.8MM
SALES (corp-wide): 567.1MM **Privately Held**
SIC: 2711 Newspapers, publishing & printing
PA: Wooster Republican Printing Co
212 E Liberty St
Wooster OH
330 264-3511

(G-20850)
WOOSTER PRODUCTS INC (PA)
1000 Spruce St (44691-4682)
P.O. Box 6005 (44691-6005)
PHONE....................330 264-2844
Fax: 216 262-4151
G K Arora, *President*
Poonam A Harvey, *COO*
Dr Urmil Arora, *Vice Pres*
Wayne Kasserman, *Prdtn Mgr*
Rashmi Jeirath, *VP Finance*
▼ **EMP:** 70
SQ FT: 100,000
SALES (est): 13.1MM **Privately Held**
WEB: www.wooster-products.com
SIC: 3446 2851 Stairs, staircases, stair treads: prefabricated metal; paints & allied products; lacquers, varnishes, enamels & other coatings

(G-20851)
WOOSTER PRODUCTS INC
Also Called: Plant 2
1000 Spruce St (44691-4682)
P.O. Box 6005 (44691-6005)
PHONE....................330 264-2854
Adrienne Rodgers, *Branch Mgr*
EMP: 20
SALES (corp-wide): 13.1MM **Privately Held**
WEB: www.wooster-products.com
SIC: 3446 Stairs, staircases, stair treads: prefabricated metal
PA: Wooster Products Inc
1000 Spruce St
Wooster OH 44691
330 264-2844

(G-20852)
WORTHINGTON CYLINDER CORP
899 Venture Blvd (44691-7521)
PHONE....................330 262-1762
Zach Lenhart, *Manager*
EMP: 191
SALES (corp-wide): 2.8B **Publicly Held**
SIC: 3443 Cylinders, pressure: metal plate
HQ: Worthington Cylinder Corporation
200 W Old Wlson Bridge Rd
Worthington OH 43085
614 840-3210

Worthington
Franklin County

(G-20853)
AERO TUBE & CONNECTOR COMPANY
7100 N High St (43085-2316)
PHONE....................614 885-2514
Richard O Chakroff, *President*
Barbara M Chakroff, *Corp Secy*
Christopher Norman, *Vice Pres*
EMP: 7 **EST:** 1954
SQ FT: 4,000
SALES (est): 664.9K **Privately Held**
SIC: 3728 Aircraft parts & equipment

(G-20854)
ALASKAN FALLS BOTTLING COMPANY
6950 Wrthington Galena Rd (43085-2309)
PHONE....................614 888-9280
Fax: 614 888-0383
C William McBee, *President*
EMP: 7
SALES (est): 460.7K
SALES (corp-wide): 497.5MM **Privately Held**
WEB: www.liquibox.com
SIC: 2086 Bottled & canned soft drinks
PA: Liqui-Box Corporation
480 Schrock Rd Ste G
Columbus OH 43229
614 888-9280

(G-20855)
ALBRIGHT ALBRIGHT & SCHN
89 E Wilson Bridge Rd D (43085-2379)
PHONE....................614 825-4829
EMP: 5
SALES (est): 398.4K **Privately Held**
SIC: 3851 Contact lenses

(G-20856)
ALVITO CUSTOM IMPRINTS
7469 Wrthington Galena Rd (43085-6713)
PHONE....................614 846-8986
Dominique Romanilli, *Owner*
EMP: 4
SALES (est): 308.7K **Privately Held**
SIC: 2752 Commercial printing, lithographic

(G-20857)
AMETEK INC
530 Lakeview Plaza Blvd C (43085-4710)
PHONE....................302 636-5401
EMP: 9 **EST:** 1986
SALES (est): 1MM **Privately Held**
SIC: 3621 Motors & generators

(G-20858)
BESTTRANSPORTCOM INC
400 W Wilson Bridge Rd (43085-2259)
PHONE....................614 888-2378
Fax: 614 433-9748
Michael Dolan, *President*
Scott Cummans, *Vice Pres*
Alain Gauthier, *Vice Pres*
Pete Scolieri, *Sales Dir*
Patrick Ryan, *Sales Executive*
EMP: 30
SQ FT: 11,000
SALES (est): 5.7MM **Privately Held**
WEB: www.besttransport.com
SIC: 7372 Prepackaged software

(G-20859)
CGAS EXPLORATION INC (HQ)
110 E Wilson Bridge Rd # 250 (43085-2317)
PHONE....................614 436-4631
Kenneth Kirk, *President*
William Grubaugh, *Exec VP*
Marilyn Ennis, *Vice Pres*
John Erwin, *CFO*
EMP: 7
SQ FT: 27,500

SALES: 20MM
SALES (corp-wide): 21.7MM **Privately Held**
WEB: www.cgasinc.com
SIC: 1311 1382 Crude petroleum production; natural gas production; oil & gas exploration services
PA: Cgas Inc
110 E Wilson Bridge Rd # 250
Worthington OH 43085
614 975-4697

(G-20860)
CGAS INC (PA)
110 E Wilson Bridge Rd # 250 (43085-2317)
PHONE....................614 975-4697
Kenneth Kirk, *President*
William Grubaugh, *Exec VP*
Kurt Pritz, *Vice Pres*
John O Erwin, *CFO*
Steve Schultheis, *Controller*
EMP: 5
SQ FT: 36,000
SALES (est): 21.7MM **Privately Held**
SIC: 1311 Crude petroleum production; natural gas production

(G-20861)
COLUMBUS MOBILITY SPECIALIST
6330 Proprietors Rd Ste F (43085-3296)
PHONE....................614 825-8996
Fax: 614 431-9690
Brian Marcun, *President*
Scott Grassette, *Vice Pres*
EMP: 3
SQ FT: 5,000
SALES (est): 452.3K **Privately Held**
SIC: 3713 Specialty motor vehicle bodies

(G-20862)
CUSTOM GLASS SOLUTIONS CORP
600 Lkview Plz Blvd Ste A (43085)
PHONE....................614 987-1390
Neale Yeomanf, *CEO*
EMP: 100
SALES (est): 4.6MM
SALES (corp-wide): 27.3B **Privately Held**
SIC: 3229 Pressed & blown glass
HQ: Guardian Industries Corp.
2300 Harmon Rd
Auburn Hills MI 48326
248 340-1800

(G-20863)
DIETRICH INDUSTRIES INC
200 W Old Wlson Bridge Rd (43085-2247)
PHONE....................614 438-3210
Richard Berdik, *President*
Dave Cunkelman, *Purchasing*
John Meyers, *Sales Staff*
Lisa Churma, *Executive Asst*
Debra Merritt, *Admin Asst*
EMP: 19
SALES (corp-wide): 2.8B **Publicly Held**
WEB: www.dietrichmetalframing.com
SIC: 3441 Building components, structural steel
HQ: Dietrich Industries, Inc.
200 W Old Wilson Brdge Rd
Worthington OH 43085
800 873-2604

(G-20864)
DIETRICH INDUSTRIES INC
200 W Old Wlson Bridge Rd (43085-2247)
PHONE....................614 438-3210
Kevin Parker, *Mktg Dir*
Bill Wick, *Manager*
William Dietrich, *Manager*
EMP: 30
SQ FT: 66,613
SALES (corp-wide): 2.8B **Publicly Held**
WEB: www.dietrichmetalframing.com
SIC: 3316 3441 Cold finishing of steel shapes; building components, structural steel
HQ: Dietrich Industries, Inc.
200 W Old Wilson Brdge Rd
Worthington OH 43085
800 873-2604

(G-20865)
DYNAMIC SENSOR SYSTEMS LLC
510 E Wilson Bridge Rd (43085-2373)
PHONE......................................614 430-2888
Paul Swetnam, *Owner*
David Swetnam,
EMP: 2
SALES: 1.1MM **Privately Held**
SIC: 3812 Radar systems & equipment

(G-20866)
GEOPETRO LLC
7100 N High St Ste 303 (43085-2316)
PHONE......................................614 885-9350
Ron Ullman, *Opers Staff*
Paul L Archer, *Mng Member*
Paul Archer,
EMP: 2
SQ FT: 1,000
SALES (est): 1MM **Privately Held**
SIC: 1311 Crude petroleum production;
natural gas production

(G-20867)
GEORGE R SILCOTT RAILWAY EQUIP
564 E Dublin Granville Rd (43085-3166)
PHONE......................................614 885-7224
Fax: 614 885-6521
George R Silcot, *Principal*
EMP: 4
SALES (est): 244.3K **Privately Held**
SIC: 3743 Railroad equipment

(G-20868)
GUARDIAN INDUSTRIES CORP
600 Lkview Plz Blvd Ste A (43085)
PHONE......................................614 431-6309
Paul Janisse, *Branch Mgr*
EMP: 40
SALES (corp-wide): 27.3B **Privately Held**
SIC: 3211 Flat glass
HQ: Guardian Industries Corp.
2300 Harmon Rd
Auburn Hills MI 48326
248 340-1800

(G-20869)
HAMAN ENTERPRISES INC
Also Called: Haman Midwest
7525 Pingue Dr (43085-1715)
PHONE......................................614 888-7574
Fax: 614 846-2257
Tod Haman, *Owner*
Paul Baronda, *Production*
John Donnelly, *Manager*
Steve Mitchell, *Manager*
▲ EMP: 19
SQ FT: 24,000
SALES (est): 4.2MM **Privately Held**
WEB: www.southprint.net
SIC: 2752 2759 Commercial printing, litho-
graphic; calendars: printing

(G-20870)
HANNIBAL CO INC
Also Called: Heartland Bread & Roll
6536 Proprietors Rd (43085-3233)
PHONE......................................614 846-5060
Rebecca Henderson, *President*
EMP: 10
SALES (est): 888.3K **Privately Held**
SIC: 2051 Breads, rolls & buns

(G-20871)
IGLOO PRESS LLC
39 W New England Ave (43085-3535)
PHONE......................................614 787-5528
Ian Brown, *Principal*
EMP: 3
SALES (est): 255.9K **Privately Held**
SIC: 2741 Miscellaneous publishing

(G-20872)
INPACO CORPORATION
6950 Wrthington Galena Rd (43085-2309)
PHONE......................................614 888-9288
Ken J Swanson, *CEO*
◆ EMP: 14
SALES: 32.6MM
SALES (corp-wide): 497.5MM **Privately Held**
SIC: 2673 Plastic bags: made from pur-
chased materials

PA: Liqui-Box Corporation
480 Schrock Rd Ste G
Columbus OH 43229
614 888-9280

(G-20873)
INSLEY PRINTING INC
666 High St Ste 400 (43085-4135)
P.O. Box 387 (43085-0387)
PHONE......................................614 885-5973
Fax: 614 885-5141
Paul Insley, *President*
EMP: 5
SQ FT: 2,500
SALES (est): 629.5K **Privately Held**
SIC: 2752 Commercial printing, offset

(G-20874)
JUAL CORPORATION
Also Called: Tecsis Corp Delta Metrics
771 Dearborn Park Ln F (43085-5720)
PHONE......................................614 430-0683
Alex Khrakovsky, *President*
Erin Baby, *Admin Asst*
EMP: 30
SALES (est): 3.9MM
SALES (corp-wide): 402.9MM **Privately Held**
WEB: www.deltametrics.com
SIC: 3823 Industrial instrmnts msrmnt dis-
play/control process variable
HQ: Wika Holding, L P
1000 Wiegand Blvd
Lawrenceville GA 30043
770 513-8200

(G-20875)
KNAPE INDUSTRIES INC
6592 Proprietors Rd (43085-3233)
PHONE......................................614 885-3016
John Knape, *President*
Joyce Knape, *Vice Pres*
EMP: 22 EST: 1970
SQ FT: 14,000
SALES (est): 4.1MM **Privately Held**
WEB: www.knapeindustries.com
SIC: 3599 Machine shop, jobbing & repair

(G-20876)
L S MANUFACTURING INC
480 E Wilson Bridge Rd C (43085-2372)
PHONE......................................614 885-7988
Fax: 614 885-7985
Glenn Liebert, *President*
Joyce Rhea, *Office Mgr*
Mary P Liebert, *Admin Sec*
EMP: 3
SALES: 100K **Privately Held**
SIC: 2499 5999 Trophy bases, wood; tro-
phies & plaques

(G-20877)
M S ABBOTT JEWELERS
Also Called: Worthington Jewelers
692 High St (43085-4106)
PHONE......................................614 430-8800
Fax: 614 433-9988
Joe Davis, *Partner*
Mark Abbott, *Partner*
Bob Capace, *Partner*
Pajet Davis, *Principal*
EMP: 9
SALES (est): 1.4MM **Privately Held**
SIC: 3911 Jewelry, precious metal

(G-20878)
METTLER-TOLEDO LLC
Also Called: Toledo Scales & Systems
720 Dearborn Park Ln (43085-5703)
PHONE......................................614 438-4511
Fax: 614 438-4770
Todd Manifold, *Opers Mgr*
Russ Vires, *Engineer*
John Hoggatt, *Project Engr*
Doug Woeste, *Train & Dev Mgr*
Gary Wilkins, *Manager*
EMP: 81
SALES (corp-wide): 2.5B **Publicly Held**
WEB: www.mtnw.com
SIC: 3596 Industrial scales
HQ: Mettler-Toledo, Llc
1900 Polaris Pkwy Fl 6
Columbus OH 43240
614 438-4511

(G-20879)
METTLER-TOLEDO LLC
Toledo Scales & Systems
1150 Dearborn Dr (43085-4766)
PHONE......................................614 438-4390
Fax: 614 438-4459
Todd Manifold, *General Mgr*
William Miller, *Engineer*
James Million, *Engineer*
Bud Wagstaff, *Engineer*
Thomas Reuter, *Controller*
EMP: 200
SALES (corp-wide): 2.5B **Publicly Held**
WEB: www.mtnw.com
SIC: 3596 Industrial scales
HQ: Mettler-Toledo, Llc
1900 Polaris Pkwy Fl 6
Columbus OH 43240
614 438-4511

(G-20880)
MICROWELD ENGINEERING INC
7451 Oakmeadows Dr (43085-1713)
PHONE......................................614 847-9410
Fax: 614 885-5670
Robert Lloyd, *President*
Daniel Mitchell, *Vice Pres*
EMP: 11
SALES (est): 1.5MM **Privately Held**
WEB: www.microweldengineering.com
SIC: 3369 8731 7692 3728 Aerospace
castings, nonferrous: except aluminum;
commercial physical research; welding re-
pair; aircraft parts & equipment

(G-20881)
MORK PROCESS INC
400 W Wilson Bridge Rd # 130
(43085-2259)
PHONE......................................330 928-3700
Fax: 330 928-3746
Christopher Yessayan, *CEO*
Lennart Samuelson, *Sr Corp Ofcr*
Ole Madsen, *Vice Pres*
Michael Port, *Vice Pres*
▲ EMP: 20
SALES (est): 2.9MM **Privately Held**
WEB: www.morkusa.com
SIC: 3589 High pressure cleaning equip-
ment

(G-20882)
PENGUIN SERV ICE
530 Lakeview Plaza Blvd (43085-4710)
PHONE......................................614 848-6511
Pete Bahill, *Principal*
EMP: 3
SALES (est): 193.6K **Privately Held**
SIC: 2097 Manufactured ice

(G-20883)
PRECISION SPECIALTY METALS INC
Also Called: Worthington Steel
200 W Old Wlson Bridge Rd (43085-2247)
PHONE......................................323 475-3200
Mark A Russell, *President*
Ronald Archibetue, *General Mgr*
Pat Clark, *Principal*
Perry Madison, *Principal*
Tony Gallegos, *Vice Pres*
▲ EMP: 65
SQ FT: 369,750
SALES: 60MM
SALES (corp-wide): 2.8B **Publicly Held**
WEB: www.psm-inc.com
SIC: 3312 Blast furnaces & steel mills;
sheet or strip, steel, cold-rolled: own hot-
rolled; stainless steel
HQ: The Worthington Steel Company
200 W Old Wlson Bridge Rd
Worthington OH 43085
614 438-3210

(G-20884)
RECYCLED SYSTEMS FURNITURE INC
Also Called: Rsfi Office Furniture
401 E Wilson Bridge Rd (43085-2320)
PHONE......................................614 880-9110
Fax: 614 880-9112
Ron Morris, *President*
Jim Ellison, *Vice Pres*
Joanne Simmons, *Office Admin*
EMP: 25

SQ FT: 100,000
SALES (est): 4.4MM **Privately Held**
WEB: www.rsfi.com
SIC: 7641 5712 2522 Office furniture re-
pair & maintenance; office furniture; office
furniture, except wood

(G-20885)
ROBERT MIDKIFF
Also Called: American Imprssions Sportswear
6969 Wrthington Galena Rd (43085-2322)
PHONE......................................614 848-6677
Robert Midkiff, *President*
Marianne Collins, *Vice Pres*
Amy Haines, *Vice Pres*
Jason Jamison, *Prdtn Mgr*
EMP: 9
SALES (est): 1MM **Privately Held**
SIC: 2396 Screen printing on fabric articles

(G-20886)
S O S GRAPHICS & PRINTING INC
445 E Wilson Bridge Rd (43085-2320)
PHONE......................................614 846-8229
Fax: 614 846-7335
Maryann Ondecko, *President*
EMP: 4
SQ FT: 3,400
SALES (est): 390K **Privately Held**
SIC: 2752 2791 5112 Commercial print-
ing, offset; typesetting; albums, scrap-
books & binders; office supplies

(G-20887)
SEVEN-OGUN INTERNATIONAL LLC
670 Lkview Plz Blvd Ste K (43085)
PHONE......................................614 888-8939
Fernanda Aler, *Mng Member*
Antonio Machado,
EMP: 5
SQ FT: 1,700
SALES (est): 500K **Privately Held**
SIC: 3496 3411 Conveyor belts; food &
beverage containers

(G-20888)
SIEMENS INDUSTRY INC
530 Lkview Plz Blvd Ste D (43085)
PHONE......................................614 846-9540
Fax: 614 430-2980
Joe Kaiser, *CEO*
Brad Kreuzer, *Sales Mgr*
David Makarius, *Sales Engr*
Angela Meek, *Social Dir*
Jennifer Taylor, *Admin Asst*
EMP: 80
SALES (est): 10.2MM **Privately Held**
SIC: 3822 Building services monitoring
controls, automatic

(G-20889)
SPIRAX SARCO INC
500 W Wilson Bridge Rd # 145
(43085-2238)
PHONE......................................803 714-2023
EMP: 4
SALES (corp-wide): 932.4MM **Privately Held**
WEB: www.spiraxsarco.com
SIC: 3494 Steam fittings & specialties
HQ: Spirax Sarco, Inc.
1150 Northpoint Blvd
Blythewood SC 29016
803 714-2000

(G-20890)
TATUM PETROLEUM CORPORATION
667 Lkview Plz Blvd Ste E (43085)
P.O. Box 2607, Zanesville (43702-2607)
PHONE......................................740 819-6810
Fax: 614 888-3621
Zachary Thomas Tatum, *President*
EMP: 6
SQ FT: 2,400
SALES (est): 890.1K **Privately Held**
SIC: 1311 Crude petroleum production

(G-20891)
TECSIS LP
771 Dearborn Park Ln F (43085-5720)
PHONE......................................614 430-0683
Fax: 614 431-6957

Bruce Yohr, *President*
Rob Turner, *Sales Mgr*
Brent Hart, *Marketing Mgr*
Bill Schwartz, *Manager*
Vera Dubrovsky, *Info Tech Mgr*
EMP: 50
SALES (est): 11.5MM
SALES (corp-wide): 48.3MM **Privately Held**
SIC: 3823 Industrial instrmnts msrmnt display/control process variable
PA: Tecsis Gmbh
     Carl-Legien-Str. 40-44
     Offenbach Am Main 63073
     695 806-0

(G-20892)
UNITED STATE PLTG BUMPER SVC
1937 W Dblin Granville Rd (43085-3346)
PHONE................................614 403-4666
EMP: 3
SALES (est): 128.1K **Privately Held**
SIC: 3471 Plating of metals or formed products

(G-20893)
WHEMPYS CORP
6969 Worth Galena Rd P (43085-2322)
PHONE................................614 888-6670
Fax: 614 888-6650
David Reed, *President*
Kathy Reed, *Corp Secy*
Eugene Reed, *Manager*
EMP: 9
SQ FT: 2,000
SALES: 500K **Privately Held**
WEB: www.whempys.com
SIC: 5719 1711 7349 1741 Fireplace equipment & accessories; heating systems repair & maintenance; chimney cleaning; chimney construction & maintenance; chimney caps, concrete

(G-20894)
WHITNEY HOUSE
666 High St Ste 102 (43085-4135)
PHONE................................614 396-7846
EMP: 3
SALES (est): 162.3K **Privately Held**
SIC: 2711 Newspapers

(G-20895)
WORTHINGTON CYLINDER CORP (HQ)
200 W Old Wlson Bridge Rd (43085-2247)
PHONE................................614 840-3210
Fax: 614 438-3083
Carol L Barnum, *Principal*
Theodore Armbruster, *Vice Pres*
Jim Knox, *Vice Pres*
Bob Kotarba, *Plant Mgr*
Sheryl Sorrell, *QC Mgr*
◆ **EMP:** 185
SQ FT: 125,000
SALES (est): 531.3MM
SALES (corp-wide): 2.8B **Publicly Held**
SIC: 3443 Cylinders, pressure: metal plate
PA: Worthington Industries, Inc.
     200 W Old Wlson Bridge Rd
     Worthington OH 43085
     614 438-3210

(G-20896)
WORTHINGTON INDUSTRIES INC (PA)
200 W Old Wlson Bridge Rd (43085-2247)
PHONE................................614 438-3210
John P McConnell, *Ch of Bd*
Geoffrey G Gilmore, *President*
John G Lamprinakos, *President*
Mark A Russell, *President*
John Messmer, *Area Mgr*
EMP: 250
SQ FT: 117,700
SALES: 2.8B **Publicly Held**
WEB: www.worthingtonindustries.com
SIC: 3316 3449 3443 3325 Strip steel, cold-rolled: from purchased hot-rolled; fabricated bar joists & concrete reinforcing bars; cylinders, pressure: metal plate; alloy steel castings, except investment

(G-20897)
WORTHINGTON INDUSTRIES INC (HQ)
200 W Old Wlson Bridge Rd (43085-2247)
PHONE................................614 438-3077
Fax: 614 438-3171
John P McConnell, *CEO*
John H McConnell, *Ch of Bd*
Jeffrey Bell, *Regional Mgr*
Virgil Winland, *Senior VP*
Edward A Ferkany, *Vice Pres*
EMP: 2400
SALES (est): 228.8MM
SALES (corp-wide): 2.8B **Publicly Held**
WEB: www.worthingtonindustries.com
SIC: 3316 Cold finishing of steel shapes; cold-rolled strip or wire
PA: Worthington Industries, Inc.
     200 W Old Wlson Bridge Rd
     Worthington OH 43085
     614 438-3210

(G-20898)
WORTHINGTON INDUSTRIES LSG LLC
200 W Old Wlson Bridge Rd (43085-2247)
PHONE................................614 438-3210
EMP: 4
SALES (est): 311.9K **Privately Held**
SIC: 3316 Cold finishing of steel shapes

(G-20899)
WORTHINGTON PALLET
160 Tucker Dr (43085-3064)
PHONE................................614 888-1573
Lynn Lazorik-Tucker, *Owner*
EMP: 3
SALES (est): 179.3K **Privately Held**
SIC: 2448 Pallets, wood & wood with metal

(G-20900)
WORTHINGTON STEEL COMPANY (HQ)
200 W Old Wlson Bridge Rd (43085-2247)
PHONE................................614 438-3210
Fax: 614 840-4681
John H Mc Connell, *Ch of Bd*
Donal H Malenick, *President*
Mark A Russell, *President*
John Graf, *General Mgr*
Brad Kern, *Opers Mgr*
EMP: 249
SALES (est): 90.5MM
SALES (corp-wide): 2.8B **Publicly Held**
SIC: 3316 3471 3312 Cold-rolled strip or wire; plating & polishing; blast furnaces & steel mills
PA: Worthington Industries, Inc.
     200 W Old Wlson Bridge Rd
     Worthington OH 43085
     614 438-3210

(G-20901)
WORTHNGTON STL CMPNY-BALTIMORE (HQ)
200 W Old Wlson Bridge Rd (43085-2247)
PHONE................................410 574-5835
Don Pulver, *Vice Pres*
Chris Sekella, *Vice Pres*
Bruce Miller, *Plant Mgr*
Jerry Connolly, *Purch Agent*
Tim Lewis, *Controller*
EMP: 21 EST: 1937
SQ FT: 168,000
SALES (est): 9.2MM
SALES (corp-wide): 2.8B **Publicly Held**
SIC: 3316 5051 3471 3312 Sheet, steel, cold-rolled: from purchased hot-rolled; metals service centers & offices; plating & polishing; blast furnaces & steel mills
PA: Worthington Industries, Inc.
     200 W Old Wlson Bridge Rd
     Worthington OH 43085
     614 438-3210

Wshngtn CT Hs
Fayette County

(G-20902)
BONHAM ENTERPRSISES
Also Called: Bonham Doors & Openers
2555 Us Highway 62 Ne (43160-9073)
PHONE................................740 333-0501
Barry Bonham, *Owner*
EMP: 3
SALES: 200K **Privately Held**
SIC: 5211 3699 Garage doors, sale & installation; door opening & closing devices, electrical

(G-20903)
BWD WOODWORK LLC
4271 Bush Rd Nw (43160-9552)
PHONE................................740 335-9766
Fax: 740 335-5923
William F Seyfang,
Derek Seyfang,
EMP: 4 EST: 1980
SQ FT: 10,000
SALES: 500K **Privately Held**
SIC: 5031 5713 3442 2431 Millwork; floor covering stores; metal doors, sash & trim; millwork; hardwood dimension & flooring mills

(G-20904)
C H WASHINGTON WATER PLAN
220 Park Ave (43160-1181)
PHONE................................740 636-2382
Joe Burbage, *Director*
EMP: 4
SALES (est): 421.2K **Privately Held**
SIC: 3823 Water quality monitoring & control systems

(G-20905)
CRESTAR CRUSTS INC
Also Called: Crestar Foods
1104 Clinton Ave (43160-1215)
PHONE................................740 335-4813
Fax: 740 335-3908
Richard Hayward, *President*
Mike Lauren, *CFO*
Dan Walsh, *Controller*
EMP: 400 EST: 1998
SQ FT: 120,000
SALES (est): 37MM
SALES (corp-wide): 224.5MM **Privately Held**
WEB: www.richelieufoods.com
SIC: 2041 Pizza dough, prepared
PA: Richelieu Foods, Inc.
     222 Forbes Rd Ste 401
     Braintree MA 02184
     781 786-6800

(G-20906)
DOMTAR PAPER COMPANY LLC
1803 Lowes Blvd (43160-8611)
PHONE................................740 333-0003
Sue Wiggins, *Branch Mgr*
Jim Fink, *Manager*
EMP: 85
SALES (corp-wide): 5.6B **Privately Held**
SIC: 2679 Paper products, converted
HQ: Domtar Paper Company, Llc
     100 Kingsley Park Dr
     Fort Mill SC 29715
     803 802-7500

(G-20907)
DOUG MARINE MOTORS INC
1120 Clinton Ave (43160-1215)
PHONE................................740 335-3700
Fax: 740 333-3966
Doug Marine, *President*
Bill D Marine, *Admin Sec*
EMP: 31
SQ FT: 8,000
SALES (est): 9.8MM **Privately Held**
WEB: www.dougmarinemotors.com
SIC: 5511 7538 5531 5012 Automobiles, new & used; general automotive repair shops; automotive & home supply stores; automobiles & other motor vehicles; motor vehicle parts & accessories

(G-20908)
FEATHERWEIGHT TURF INC
2250 Kenskill Ave (43160-9142)
PHONE................................920 452-4861
Emil Stauber, *President*
Virginia Stauber, *Vice Pres*
EMP: 9 EST: 1931
SQ FT: 5,000
SALES: 600K **Privately Held**
SIC: 3199 Equestrian related leather articles

(G-20909)
FIBER TECH INDUSTRIES INC
2000 Kenskill Ave (43160-9311)
PHONE................................740 636-3232
Harris Armstrong, *CEO*
Wayne Durnin, *Vice Pres*
Mike Caskey, *Plant Mgr*
Terry Kegan, *Mfg Staff*
Jerry Kroll, *CFO*
EMP: 75
SQ FT: 180,000
SALES (est): 16MM
SALES (corp-wide): 26.5MM **Privately Held**
WEB: www.fiber-tech.net
SIC: 3083 Laminated plastics plate & sheet
PA: Celstar Group Inc
     40 N Main St Ste 1730
     Dayton OH 45423
     937 224-1730

(G-20910)
HALLIDAY HOLDINGS INC
1544 Old Us 35 Se (43160-8624)
P.O. Box 700 (43160-0700)
PHONE................................740 335-1430
Fax: 740 335-6502
John Halliday, *President*
William Halliday II, *Vice Pres*
Melanie Vince, *Manager*
EMP: 40
SQ FT: 50,000
SALES (est): 6.8MM **Privately Held**
WEB: www.hallidaylumber.com
SIC: 2448 2426 Pallets, wood; dimension, hardwood

(G-20911)
IHEARTCOMMUNICATIONS INC
Also Called: Wcho AM
1535 N North St (43160-1111)
P.O. Box 94, Chillicothe (45601-0094)
PHONE................................740 335-0941
Dan Latham, *Manager*
EMP: 14
SALES (corp-wide): 6.2B **Publicly Held**
SIC: 4832 2711 Radio broadcasting stations; newspapers
HQ: Iheartcommunications, Inc.
     200 E Basse Rd
     San Antonio TX 78209
     210 822-2828

(G-20912)
J K PRECAST LLC
1001 Armbrust Ave (43160-2457)
PHONE................................740 335-2188
James E Kimmey, *Owner*
EMP: 8 EST: 2000
SQ FT: 20,500
SALES: 900K **Privately Held**
SIC: 3272 3089 Septic tanks, concrete; septic tanks, plastic

(G-20913)
JAMES KIMMEY
Also Called: J K Precast
1000 Armbrust Ave (43160-1392)
PHONE................................740 335-5746
Fax: 740 335-1957
James Kimmey, *Owner*
EMP: 13
SALES (est): 75.3K **Privately Held**
SIC: 3272 Septic tanks, concrete

(G-20914)
JIM DAVIS
Also Called: Print Shop, The
1020 Leesburg Ave (43160-1272)
PHONE................................740 335-8030
James Davis, *Owner*
EMP: 6
SQ FT: 6,500

▲ = Import ▼=Export
◆ =Import/Export

SALES (est): 584.1K Privately Held
SIC: 2752 2791 2759 2396 Commercial printing, offset; typesetting; commercial printing; automotive & apparel trimmings

(G-20915)
KROGER CO
548 Clinton Ave (43160-1299)
PHONE....................................740 335-4030
Fax: 740 333-3827
William Drum, *Manager*
EMP: 110
SALES (corp-wide): 115.3B Publicly Held
WEB: www.kroger.com
SIC: 5411 5122 2051 Supermarkets, chain; drugs, proprietaries & sundries; bread, cake & related products
PA: The Kroger Co
1014 Vine St Ste 1000
Cincinnati OH 45202
513 762-4000

(G-20916)
MELVIN STONE COMPANY LLC
3333 Plano Rd (43160-9105)
PHONE....................................740 998-5016
Fax: 740 773-7820
Randy Grooms, *Principal*
EMP: 4
SALES (corp-wide): 109.5MM Privately Held
SIC: 5211 1422 Masonry materials & supplies; crushed & broken limestone
HQ: The Melvin Stone Company Llc
228 Melvin Rd
Wilmington OH
937 584-2486

(G-20917)
MILLWORK DESIGNS INC
230 Topaz Ln (43160-1745)
PHONE....................................740 335-5203
Stephen Willis, *President*
Marsha Willis, *Vice Pres*
EMP: 3
SALES: 120K Privately Held
SIC: 2431 2499 Millwork; decorative wood & woodwork

(G-20918)
NORWESCO INC
2424 Kenskill Ave (43160-9309)
PHONE....................................740 335-6236
Jeff Pauley, *Principal*
EMP: 17
SQ FT: 14,000
SALES (corp-wide): 49MM Privately Held
WEB: www.ncmmolding.com
SIC: 3089 Plastic & fiberglass tanks
PA: Norwesco, Inc.
4365 Steiner St
Saint Bonifacius MN 55375
952 446-1945

(G-20919)
PHILIP ARMBRUST
Also Called: Armbrust Concrete
4939 Branen Dr (43160-9716)
PHONE....................................740 335-7285
Philip Armbrust, *Owner*
EMP: 4
SQ FT: 6,000
SALES (est): 280K Privately Held
SIC: 3273 Ready-mixed concrete

(G-20920)
PRINT SHOP
1020 Leesburg Ave (43160-1272)
PHONE....................................740 335-8030
James Davis, *Owner*
EMP: 7
SQ FT: 3,000
SALES (est): 400.3K Privately Held
SIC: 2711 2752 Newspapers; commercial printing, offset

(G-20921)
PROEPO SOFTWARE LTD
609 E Paint St (43160-1509)
PHONE....................................937 243-3825
EMP: 3
SALES (est): 112.2K Privately Held
SIC: 7372 Prepackaged software

(G-20922)
QUALITEE DESIGN SPORTSWEAR CO (PA)
1270 Us Highway 22 Nw # 9 (43160-9187)
PHONE....................................740 333-8337
Jim Evans, *CEO*
Todd Evans, *President*
Shelli Cartwright, *Manager*
EMP: 10
SQ FT: 6,500
SALES (est): 1.9MM Privately Held
SIC: 7336 2395 5999 2759 Silk screen design; embroidery & art needlework; trophies & plaques; screen printing

(G-20923)
RAM MACHINING INC
806 Delaware St (43160-1552)
PHONE....................................740 333-5522
Fax: 740 333-5522
Rick Miller, *President*
Barb Massie, *Admin Sec*
EMP: 6
SALES: 100K Privately Held
WEB: www.rammachining.com
SIC: 3599 Machine shop, jobbing & repair

(G-20924)
RICHELIEU FOODS INC
1104 Clinton Ave (43160-1278)
PHONE....................................740 335-4813
Richard Hayward, *Principal*
Jason Yoakum, *Plant Mgr*
Dan Walsh, *Controller*
Dave Meltzer, *Sales Dir*
EMP: 11
SALES (est): 1.4MM Privately Held
SIC: 2038 Breakfasts, frozen & packaged

(G-20925)
RITEN INDUSTRIES INCORPORATED
1100 Lakeview Ave (43160-1037)
P.O. Box 340 (43160-0340)
PHONE....................................740 335-5353
Fax: 740 355-4622
Andrew Lachelt, *President*
Mitchell Kirby, *VP Mfg*
Scott Robinson, *Purch Agent*
Mark Underwood, *Engineer*
Tricia Simon, *Controller*
EMP: 40
SQ FT: 28,500
SALES (est): 11.8MM Privately Held
WEB: www.riten.com
SIC: 3545 Machine tool attachments & accessories

(G-20926)
ROSS CO REDI MIX CO INC
1865 Old Us 35 Se (43160-8687)
PHONE....................................740 333-6833
Mark Crabtree, *Principal*
EMP: 3
SALES (est): 205.5K Privately Held
SIC: 3273 Ready-mixed concrete

(G-20927)
SUGAR CREEK PACKING CO (PA)
2101 Kenskill Ave (43160-9404)
PHONE....................................740 335-7440
Fax: 740 333-3962
John Richardson, *CEO*
Michael Richardson, *COO*
Rob Howe, *Vice Pres*
Darren Kleinsorge, *Plant Mgr*
Jeff Litteral, *Plant Mgr*
◆ EMP: 400 EST: 1966
SQ FT: 80,000
SALES (est): 739.8MM Privately Held
WEB: www.sugarcreek.com
SIC: 2013 2011 Bacon, side & sliced; from purchased meat; meat packing plants

(G-20928)
WCH MOLDING LLC
1850 Lowes Blvd (43160-8611)
PHONE....................................740 335-6320
Gene J Kuzma, *President*
Jeff Kuzma, *Treasurer*
EMP: 20

SALES (est): 3.4MM
SALES (corp-wide): 26.1MM Privately Held
WEB: www.gkpackaging.com
SIC: 3089 Molding primary plastic
PA: Gk Packaging, Inc.
7680 Commerce Pl
Plain City OH 43064
614 873-3900

(G-20929)
WCR INCORPORATED
809 Delaware St (43160-1551)
PHONE....................................740 333-3448
EMP: 21
SALES (corp-wide): 39.9MM Privately Held
SIC: 3443 Heat exchangers, plate type
PA: Wcr Inc
2377 Commerce Center Blvd B
Fairborn OH 45324
937 223-0703

(G-20930)
WESTROCK CP LLC
1010 Mead St (43160-9310)
PHONE....................................770 448-2193
Larry Markham, *QC Dir*
Mark Badgley, *Branch Mgr*
EMP: 93
SALES (corp-wide): 14.1B Publicly Held
WEB: www.smurfit-stone.com
SIC: 2653 5113 3412 Boxes, corrugated: made from purchased materials; corrugated & solid fiber boxes; metal barrels, drums & pails
HQ: Westrock Cp, Llc
504 Thrasher St
Norcross GA 30071

(G-20931)
WEYERHAEUSER COMPANY
Also Called: Washington Crt Hse Converting
1803 Lowes Blvd (43160-8611)
PHONE....................................740 335-4480
Fax: 740 335-6190
Jim Fink, *Manager*
EMP: 61
SALES (corp-wide): 6.3B Publicly Held
SIC: 2653 Corrugated boxes, partitions, display items, sheets & pad
PA: Weyerhaeuser Company
220 Occidental Ave S
Seattle WA 98104
206 539-3000

Wyoming
Hamilton County

(G-20932)
JOHN MCHAEL PRIESTER ASSOC INC
Also Called: Power Engineering Technology
266 Elm Ave (45215-4328)
PHONE....................................513 761-8605
John E Priester, *President*
Jayne Priester, *Corp Secy*
EMP: 3
SQ FT: 2,800
SALES (est): 367.7K
SALES (corp-wide): 207.1MM Privately Held
SIC: 1796 3823 Power generating equipment installation; industrial process control instruments
PA: Gai Consultants, Inc.
385 E Waterfront Dr Fl 1
Homestead PA 15120
412 476-2000

Xenia
Greene County

(G-20933)
ACTION AIR & HYDRAULICS INC
1087 Bellbrook Ave (45385-4011)
P.O. Box 655 (45385-0655)
PHONE....................................937 372-8614
Peter J Pacier, *CEO*
Pat Minnela, *Corp Secy*
EMP: 6

SQ FT: 2,500
SALES (est): 769.6K Privately Held
SIC: 3822 Auto controls regulating residntl & coml environmt & applncs; energy cut-off controls, residential or commercial types

(G-20934)
ADELPHI ENTERPRISES
1340 Gultice Rd (45385-9628)
PHONE....................................937 372-3791
Barbara Klawonn, *Owner*
EMP: 3
SALES (est): 78.7K Privately Held
SIC: 2741 Miscellaneous publishing

(G-20935)
ALPHABET EMBROIDERY STUDIOS
Also Called: Americas Best Cstm Digitizing
1291 Bellbrook Ave (45385-4015)
PHONE....................................937 372-6557
Fax: 937 372-9990
Dee Thompson, *President*
Mark Thompson, *Vice Pres*
EMP: 17
SQ FT: 10,000
SALES: 530K Privately Held
WEB: www.alphabetembroidery.com
SIC: 2395 Embroidery products, except schiffli machine

(G-20936)
AMERICAN METAL TECH LLC
Also Called: Destin Die Casting, LLC
851 Bellbrook Ave (45385-4057)
PHONE....................................937 347-1111
Bob Trieber, *Branch Mgr*
EMP: 60
SALES (corp-wide): 64.9MM Privately Held
SIC: 3542 Die casting & extruding machines
PA: American Metal Technologies Llc
8213 Durand Ave
Sturtevant WI 53177
262 633-1756

(G-20937)
B5 SYSTEMS INC
1463 Bellbrook Ave (45385-4019)
PHONE....................................937 372-4768
Philip Burke, *President*
Judd Burke, *Vice Pres*
Mark Keller, *Vice Pres*
Mike Martin, *Prdtn Mgr*
Greg Ridge, *Info Tech Mgr*
EMP: 8
SALES (est): 2MM Privately Held
SIC: 3679 Electronic circuits

(G-20938)
BEAUTIFUL BITES
609 S Columbus St (45385-5665)
PHONE....................................937 397-4225
Monica Leslie, *Owner*
EMP: 5
SALES (est): 141.1K Privately Held
SIC: 2053 Cakes, bakery: frozen

(G-20939)
BOB EVANS FARMS INC
640 Birch Rd (45385-7600)
P.O. Box 44 (45385-0044)
PHONE....................................937 372-4493
Fax: 937 372-4176
Henry King, *Safety Mgr*
Debra Arnold, *Human Res Mgr*
Tom Sefton, *Manager*
George Furman, *Manager*
EMP: 85
SQ FT: 3,000
SALES (corp-wide): 1.3B Publicly Held
SIC: 2011 Sausages from meat slaughtered on site
PA: Bob Evans Farms, Inc.
8111 Smiths Mill Rd
New Albany OH 43054
614 491-2225

(G-20940)
BURKE PRODUCTS INC
1355 Enterprise Ln (45385-6504)
PHONE....................................937 372-3516
Fax: 937 372-8540
Shiv Bakhshi, *President*

GEOGRAPHIC

Katie Scott, *General Mgr*
Aaron Bakshi, *Vice Pres*
Angela Copsey, *Purch Mgr*
Greg Ridge, *Engineer*
▲ **EMP:** 20 **EST:** 1966
SQ FT: 10,000
SALES (est): 4.5MM **Privately Held**
WEB: www.burkeproducts.com
SIC: 3674 3599 Solid state electronic de-
vices; machine shop, jobbing & repair

(G-20941)
CEMEX CNSTR MTLS ATL LLC
Also Called: Cem - Fairborn Plant
3250 Linebaugh Rd (45385-8567)
PHONE...................................937 878-8651
John Cass, *Manager*
EMP: 78
SALES (corp-wide): 12B **Privately Held**
SIC: 3241 Masonry cement
HQ: Cemex Construction Materials Atlantic,
   Llc
   1501 Belvedere Rd
   West Palm Beach FL 33406
   561 833-5555

(G-20942)
**CIL ISOTOPE SEPARATIONS
LLC**
1689 Burnett Dr (45385-5691)
PHONE...................................937 376-5413
Fax: 937 376-5499
Joel Bradley, *CEO*
Peter Dodwell, *President*
Maureen Duffy, *Vice Pres*
Steve Igo, *Vice Pres*
Bill Roos, *Manager*
▲ **EMP:** 10
SQ FT: 8,000
SALES (est): 2.9MM
SALES (corp-wide): 11.7B **Privately Held**
WEB: www.isotope.com
SIC: 2819 Industrial inorganic chemicals
HQ: Cambridge Isotope Laboratories, Inc.
   3 Highwood Dr
   Tewksbury MA 01876
   978 749-8000

(G-20943)
CITY OF XENIA
Also Called: Xenia City Water Treatment Div
1831 Us Route 68 N (45385-9547)
PHONE...................................937 376-7269
Roger Beehler, *Branch Mgr*
EMP: 26 **Privately Held**
SIC: 3589 Water treatment equipment, in-
dustrial
PA: City Of Xenia
   101 N Detroit St
   Xenia OH 45385
   937 376-7231

(G-20944)
**CLARKSVILLE STAVE &
LUMBER CO**
2808 Jasper Rd (45385-9425)
PHONE...................................937 376-4618
Fax: 937 376-1413
Martha Valentine, *President*
Charles Valentine, *Vice Pres*
Chuck Valentine, *Vice Pres*
EMP: 9
SQ FT: 10,800
SALES (est): 900K **Privately Held**
SIC: 2421 5031 5211 Sawmills & planing
mills, general; lumber: rough, dressed &
finished; lumber products

(G-20945)
DAILY GAZETTE
1836 W Park Sq (45385-2668)
PHONE...................................937 372-4444
Fred Gibson, *Publisher*
EMP: 36
SALES (est): 1.2MM
SALES (corp-wide): 1.4B **Privately Held**
WEB: www.brownpublishing.com
SIC: 2711 2791 2752 Newspapers, pub-
lishing & printing; typesetting; commercial
printing, lithographic
HQ: Ocm, Llc
   4500 Lyons Rd
   Miamisburg OH 45342
   937 247-2700

(G-20946)
DAYTON TRACTOR & CRANE
1861 Us Route 42 S (45385-7350)
PHONE...................................937 317-5014
Dave Younkin, *Principal*
EMP: 3
SALES (est): 654.4K **Privately Held**
SIC: 5082 3469 Construction & mining
machinery; metal stampings

(G-20947)
DESTIN DIE CASTING LLC
851 Bellbrook Ave (45385-4057)
PHONE...................................937 347-1111
San Santharam,
EMP: 45
SALES (est): 6.1MM
SALES (corp-wide): 64.9MM **Privately
Held**
SIC: 3363 Aluminum die-castings
PA: American Metal Technologies Llc
   8213 Durand Ave
   Sturtevant WI 53177
   262 633-1756

(G-20948)
DODDS MONUMENT INC (PA)
123 W Main St (45385-2914)
PHONE...................................937 372-2736
Fax: 937 374-4342
Eric Fogarty, *President*
Rebecca Fogarty, *Corp Secy*
Neil Fogarty, *Exec VP*
Larry Morrison, *Vice Pres*
Courtney Parks, *Manager*
▲ **EMP:** 3
SQ FT: 7,500
SALES (est): 3MM **Privately Held**
WEB: www.doddsmonuments.com
SIC: 5999 3281 Monuments, finished to
custom order; gravestones, finished;
monuments, cut stone (not finishing or let-
tering only); tombstones, cut stone (not
finishing or lettering only)

(G-20949)
**ESTERLINE GEORGIA US LLC
(HQ)**
600 Bellbrook Ave (45385-4053)
PHONE...................................937 372-7579
Mark Saturno, *Vice Pres*
EMP: 45 **EST:** 2014
SQ FT: 200,000
SALES: 30MM
SALES (corp-wide): 175.8MM **Privately
Held**
SIC: 3577 Computer peripheral equipment
PA: Esterline Belgium Bvba
   President Kennedypark 35a
   Kortrijk 8500
   562 031-14

(G-20950)
**FAIRBORN CEMENT COMPANY
LLC**
3250 Linebaugh Rd (45385-8567)
PHONE...................................937 879-8393
Gerald Essl, *President*
Ray Meier, *Vice Pres*
EMP: 110
SALES (est): 3MM
SALES (corp-wide): 1.1B **Publicly Held**
SIC: 3241 Natural cement
PA: Eagle Materials Inc.
   3811 Turtle Creek Blvd # 1100
   Dallas TX 75219
   214 432-2000

(G-20951)
**FILE SHARPENING COMPANY
INC**
Also Called: Save Edge USA
360 W Church St (45385-2900)
PHONE...................................937 376-8268
Fax: 937 376-8052
George Whyde, *President*
Randy Stout, *Manager*
▲ **EMP:** 25
SALES (est): 7.8MM **Privately Held**
SIC: 5085 7699 3423 3315 Industrial
tools; knife, saw & tool sharpening & re-
pair; hand & edge tools; steel wire & re-
lated products

(G-20952)
FIVEPOINT LLC
825 Bellbrook Ave Unit B (45385-4076)
PHONE...................................937 374-3193
John Caldwell,
Edward Crowley,
Gregory Robinson,
EMP: 12
SQ FT: 70,000
SALES (est): 1.7MM **Privately Held**
WEB: www.5point.com
SIC: 3575 Computer terminals

(G-20953)
G2 DIGITAL SOLUTIONS
1841 Trebein Rd (45385-9558)
PHONE...................................937 241-6003
Vincent W Cowie, *Owner*
EMP: 10
SQ FT: 1,200
SALES: 1.7MM **Privately Held**
SIC: 3663 Radio & TV communications
equipment

(G-20954)
H & K PALLET SERVICES
1039 Jasper Ave (45385-3303)
PHONE...................................937 608-1140
Jonathon Holley, *Administration*
EMP: 4
SALES (est): 190.3K **Privately Held**
SIC: 2448 Pallets, wood & wood with metal

(G-20955)
HERSHEY CREAMERY CO
1065 S Columbus St (45385-9641)
PHONE...................................937 374-0688
Fax: 937 374-0692
John Derocher, *Manager*
EMP: 9
SALES (est): 698K **Privately Held**
SIC: 2066 5143 Chocolate; dairy products,
except dried or canned

(G-20956)
IDIALOGS LLC
121 Pawleys Plantation Ct (45385-9120)
PHONE...................................937 372-2890
Ira Goldstein,
EMP: 8 **EST:** 2012
SALES (est): 531.7K **Privately Held**
SIC: 7372 Application computer software

(G-20957)
JADE TOOL CO INC
1280 Burnett Dr (45385-5687)
PHONE...................................937 376-4740
Fax: 937 376-4603
Jeff Sakalaskas, *President*
Dan Baker, *Corp Secy*
EMP: 9
SQ FT: 3,600
SALES: 490K **Privately Held**
SIC: 3599 Machine shop, jobbing & repair

(G-20958)
JCL EQUIPMENT CO INC
915 Trumbull St (45385-3644)
P.O. Box 396 (45385-0396)
PHONE...................................937 374-1010
Fax: 937 374-0666
Jim Lunay, *President*
Allan Liming, *Manager*
EMP: 9
SQ FT: 23,000
SALES (est): 1.9MM **Privately Held**
WEB: www.jclequipment.com
SIC: 3531 5084 Road construction &
maintenance machinery; industrial ma-
chinery & equipment

(G-20959)
KEY MOBILITY SERVICES LTD
1944 Us Route 68 N (45385-9552)
PHONE...................................937 374-3226
Fax: 937 374-4460
Angela Adams, *General Mgr*
Cecil Tubey, *General Mgr*
Terrence R Tubey,
EMP: 4
SALES (est): 260K **Privately Held**
WEB: www.keymobility.com
SIC: 5999 7532 5047 3999 Hospital
equipment & supplies; van conversion;
hospital equipment & furniture; wheelchair
lifts

(G-20960)
LAKOTA INDUSTRIES INC
Also Called: Lakota Archery
1463 Bellbrook Ave (45385-4019)
PHONE...................................937 532-6394
Richard Williamson, *CEO*
Daniel Obrovac, *CFO*
EMP: 3
SQ FT: 5,000
SALES (est): 225.8K **Privately Held**
WEB: www.lakota-industries.com
SIC: 3949 Bows, archery

(G-20961)
LIMING PRINTING INC
Also Called: Screenplay Printing
1450 S Patton St (45385-7406)
PHONE...................................937 374-2646
Fax: 937 374-0111
Brian Liming, *President*
Alan Liming, *Treasurer*
EMP: 10
SQ FT: 6,700
SALES (est): 850K **Privately Held**
WEB: www.screenplayprinting.com
SIC: 2752 2759 7336 2791 Commercial
printing, offset; commercial printing; silk
screen design; typesetting

(G-20962)
**MAHLE BEHR SERVICE
AMERICA LLC**
1003 Bellbrook Ave (45385-4011)
PHONE...................................937 369-2610
Ricardo Studebaker, *Manager*
EMP: 3 **Privately Held**
SIC: 3714 Radiators & radiator shells &
cores, motor vehicle
HQ: Mahle Behr Service America L.L.C.
   5020 Augusta Dr
   Fort Worth TX 76106
   817 740-3791

(G-20963)
MARMAC CO
1231 Bellbrook Ave (45385-4015)
P.O. Box 157 (45385-0157)
PHONE...................................937 372-8093
Fax: 937 372-7101
Gary Walthall, *President*
Sharon L Walthall, *Exec VP*
EMP: 6 **EST:** 1954
SQ FT: 17,060
SALES (est): 2.9MM **Privately Held**
WEB: www.marmacco.com
SIC: 3569 Jacks, hydraulic

(G-20964)
**NATIONAL CARTON & COATING
CO**
1439 Lavelle Dr (45385-5679)
PHONE...................................937 347-1042
Fax: 937 372-9809
James Yost, *President*
Charles S Goodwin, *Principal*
Jim Bailey, *Facilities Mgr*
Greg Swartz, *Sales Executive*
Frances Hames, *Manager*
EMP: 80
SALES (est): 20.3MM **Privately Held**
WEB: www.nationalcarton.com
SIC: 2631 Packaging board

(G-20965)
OHIO MODEL PLANES
Also Called: Ohio Model Products
199 Stratford Ln (45385-8959)
PHONE...................................937 372-0603
John Drake, *Owner*
▲ **EMP:** 5
SALES (est): 352.6K **Privately Held**
SIC: 3999 Airplane models, except toy

(G-20966)
OHTA PRESS US INC
1125 S Patton St (45385-5671)
PHONE...................................937 374-3382
Fax: 937 374-3387
Shigeki Ikuta, *President*
▲ **EMP:** 15
SQ FT: 12,000
SALES (est): 2.6MM **Privately Held**
SIC: 3714 Motor vehicle parts & acces-
sories

▲ = Import ▼=Export
◆ =Import/Export

(G-20967)
PRINTING CENTER OF XENIA
402 W Church St (45385-2908)
PHONE...................................937 372-1687
Sandra Smittkamp, *Owner*
EMP: 4
SALES (est): 389.8K **Privately Held**
SIC: 2752 Commercial printing, lithographic

(G-20968)
PROIMAGE PRINTING & DESIGN LLC
1803 Roxbury Dr (45385-4932)
PHONE...................................937 312-9544
Carol A Hurt, *Principal*
EMP: 9
SALES (est): 1MM **Privately Held**
SIC: 2752 Commercial printing, lithographic

(G-20969)
R AND D INDUSTRIES UNLIMITED
1030 Mcpherson Rd (45385-7327)
PHONE...................................937 502-1374
Douglas Lapchynski, *Principal*
EMP: 3
SALES (est): 203.4K **Privately Held**
SIC: 3999 Manufacturing industries

(G-20970)
RBS TECHNOLOGIES LLC
1488 Champions Way (45385-7086)
PHONE...................................937 320-8189
Raymond Siferd, *President*
Raymond E Siferd,
EMP: 5
SALES (est): 334.6K **Privately Held**
SIC: 3674 Semiconductors & related devices

(G-20971)
SANDY SMITTCAMP
Also Called: Printing Center, The
402 W Church St (45385-2908)
PHONE...................................937 372-1687
Fax: 937 372-1746
Sandy Smittcamp, *Owner*
EMP: 3
SQ FT: 3,200
SALES (est): 270K **Privately Held**
SIC: 2752 2791 2789 2759 Business form & card printing, lithographic; typesetting; bookbinding & related work; commercial printing

(G-20972)
SAS AUTOMATION LLC
1200 S Patton St (45385-5672)
PHONE...................................937 372-5255
Fax: 937 372-5555
Trent P Fisher, *President*
CAM Coalson, *Draft/Design*
Eric Roetter, *Accounts Mgr*
Tom Lakes, *Sales Executive*
Robert Lord, *Marketing Staff*
EMP: 18
SQ FT: 16,000
SALES (est): 5.3MM **Privately Held**
WEB: www.sas-automation.com
SIC: 3569 Robots, assembly line: industrial & commercial

(G-20973)
SPI INC
Also Called: S P I
1170 S Patton St (45385-5670)
PHONE...................................937 374-2700
William J Shannon Jr, *President*
Donna L Shannon, *Corp Secy*
Thomas R Heffernan, *Vice Pres*
Cindy Elliot, *Accountant*
Michael Rosenberger, *Manager*
▲ **EMP:** 9
SQ FT: 28,000
SALES (est): 3.5MM **Privately Held**
WEB: www.spi-connects.com
SIC: 5065 5063 3678 3679 Connectors, electronic; electrical apparatus & equipment; electronic connectors; harness assemblies for electronic use: wire or cable

(G-20974)
SPINTECH LLC
Also Called: Smart Tooling
1150 S Patton St (45385-5670)
PHONE...................................937 912-3250
Charley Hilton, *Business Mgr*
Jayme Everhart, *Accounting Mgr*
Patrick J Hood, *Mng Member*
Ernie Havens, *CTO*
Crystal Phillips, *Admin Asst*
EMP: 13
SALES (est): 2.7MM **Privately Held**
SIC: 3544 Special dies, tools, jigs & fixtures

(G-20975)
STEINBARGER PRECISION CNC INC
634 Cincinnati Ave (45385-5013)
PHONE...................................937 376-0322
Steve Steinbarger, *President*
EMP: 6
SQ FT: 1,000
SALES (est): 500K **Privately Held**
SIC: 3549 Drawing machinery

(G-20976)
SUBURBAN NEWPAPERS OF DAYTON
Also Called: Fairborn Herald
1836 W Park Sq (45385-2668)
PHONE...................................937 878-3993
Fax: 937 272-3385
Fred Gibson, *Manager*
EMP: 37
SALES (corp-wide): 45.6MM **Privately Held**
WEB: www.tcnewsnet.com
SIC: 2711 Newspapers: publishing only, not printed on site
HQ: Suburban Newpapers Of Dayton Inc
3085 Woodman Dr Ste 170
Dayton OH
937 294-7000

(G-20977)
SUPERION INC
1285 S Patton St (45385-5673)
PHONE...................................937 374-0033
Fax: 937 374-0032
Alton Choiniere, *President*
Kelly Huffman, *Purchasing*
Masaru Yokokawa, *Treasurer*
John McGlone, *Manager*
Carolyn Evans, *Data Proc Staff*
▲ **EMP:** 40
SQ FT: 12,000
SALES (est): 5.7MM
SALES (corp-wide): 18.2MM **Privately Held**
WEB: www.superioninc.com
SIC: 3423 3541 3545 3425 Knives, agricultural or industrial; machine tools, metal cutting type; machine tool accessories; saw blades & handsaws
PA: Sanyo Tool Mfg,Co, Ltd.
3-6-21, Osaki
Shinagawa-Ku TKY 141-0
334 906-821

(G-20978)
TDL TOOL INC
1296 S Patton St (45385-5672)
PHONE...................................937 374-0055
Fax: 937 374-0057
Steve Mangan, *President*
Dan Mangan, *Vice Pres*
Dave Galpin, *Manager*
EMP: 21
SQ FT: 16,000
SALES (est): 3.6MM **Privately Held**
WEB: www.tdltool.com
SIC: 3599 Machine & other job shop work

(G-20979)
THE WOOD SHED
Also Called: Cdracks
2665 Trebein Rd (45385-9563)
PHONE...................................937 429-3355
Fax: 937 429-4745
James Rusch, *Owner*
EMP: 4
SALES (est): 404.8K **Privately Held**
WEB: www.cdracks.com
SIC: 2599 Cabinets, factory

(G-20980)
TIMAC MANUFACTURING COMPANY
825 Bellbrook Ave (45385-4075)
P.O. Box 329 (45385-0329)
PHONE...................................937 372-3305
Fax: 937 372-3710
Tim McIntire, *President*
EMP: 12
SQ FT: 5,000
SALES (est): 2MM **Privately Held**
WEB: www.timacspring.com
SIC: 3493 Coiled flat springs

(G-20981)
TJAR INNOVATIONS LLC
1004 Cincinnati Ave (45385-9353)
P.O. Box 357 (45385-0357)
PHONE...................................937 347-1999
Tony Arsenault, *Vice Pres*
Anthony Arsenault,
EMP: 12
SALES (est): 2.4MM **Privately Held**
WEB: www.tjarinnovations.com
SIC: 3089 Injection molding of plastics

(G-20982)
TREMAC CORPORATION
550 Bellbrook Ave (45385-4051)
P.O. Box 34 (45385-0034)
PHONE...................................937 372-8662
Fax: 937 372-7275
Scott McIntire, *President*
Scott Mc Intire, *President*
Brad Johnson, *Prdtn Mgr*
Brenda Day, *Admin Sec*
EMP: 28 **EST:** 1960
SQ FT: 37,000
SALES (est): 5.2MM **Privately Held**
SIC: 3493 Steel springs, except wire

(G-20983)
TRIAD GOVERNMENTAL SYSTEMS
358 N Monroe St (45385-3442)
PHONE...................................937 376-5446
Tod A Rapp, *President*
EMP: 27
SALES (est): 2.6MM **Privately Held**
WEB: www.triadgsi.com
SIC: 7371 7372 Computer software development; prepackaged software

(G-20984)
VALLEY ASPHALT CORPORATION
782 N Valley Rd (45385)
PHONE...................................937 426-7682
Jim Jurgenson, *Manager*
James P Jurgensen II, *Manager*
EMP: 3
SALES (corp-wide): 109.5MM **Privately Held**
SIC: 2951 Asphalt & asphaltic paving mixtures (not from refineries)
PA: Valley Asphalt Corporation
11641 Mosteller Rd
Cincinnati OH 45241
513 771-0820

(G-20985)
VISUAL INFORMATION INSTITUTE
Also Called: V I I Craft
1065 Lower Bellbrook Rd (45385-7308)
PHONE...................................937 376-4361
Fax: 937 376-2802
John H Harshbarger Jr, *Principal*
Rebecca J Shaw, *Business Mgr*
June S Harshbarger, *Vice Pres*
Karen S Pellerin, *Vice Pres*
Rita Bohon, *Purch Agent*
EMP: 18 **EST:** 1964
SQ FT: 18,000
SALES (est): 1.1MM **Privately Held**
WEB: www.videoinstruments.com
SIC: 3444 3672 2759 3825 Sheet metalwork; printed circuit boards; commercial printing; instruments to measure electricity

(G-20986)
W H K COMPANY
1720 State Route 380 (45385-8788)
PHONE...................................937 372-3368

William H Kingsolver, *Owner*
EMP: 3
SALES (est): 116.6K **Privately Held**
SIC: 2499 Decorative wood & woodwork

(G-20987)
WA HAMMOND DRIERITE CO LTD
138 Dayton Ave (45385-2830)
P.O. Box 460 (45385-0460)
PHONE...................................937 376-2927
Fax: 937 376-1977
Joan L Hammond, *Partner*
James F Hammond, *Partner*
Sandy Corbean, *Office Mgr*
EMP: 21 **EST:** 1932
SQ FT: 80,000
SALES: 5.9MM **Privately Held**
WEB: www.drierite.com
SIC: 2879 Defoliants

(G-20988)
WADES WOODWORKING INC
1427 Bellbrook Ave (45385-4064)
PHONE...................................937 374-6470
Fax: 937 374-6472
Wade A Smith, *President*
Sandy Smith, *Admin Sec*
EMP: 10
SQ FT: 13,000
SALES: 1MM **Privately Held**
WEB: www.wadeswoodworking.com
SIC: 1751 2599 Cabinet & finish carpentry; cabinets, factory

(G-20989)
WOODSON DISTRIBUTION LLC
1470 Deer Creek Dr Ste 7 (45385-8038)
PHONE...................................937 864-9013
Desmond Woodson, *General Mgr*
Kino Henderson, *Office Mgr*
EMP: 3
SALES (est): 147.9K **Privately Held**
SIC: 3999 Manufacturing industries

Yellow Springs
Greene County

(G-20990)
BUSHWORKS INCORPORATED
144 Cliff St Ste A (45387-2099)
PHONE...................................937 767-1713
Fax: 937 767-1722
John Bush, *President*
EMP: 8
SQ FT: 8,000
SALES (est): 520K **Privately Held**
SIC: 2499 Woodenware, kitchen & household

(G-20991)
GRAPHICOM PRESS INC
302 Orton Rd (45387-1321)
PHONE...................................937 767-1916
Phyllis D Schmidt, *President*
Eric K Schmidt, *Corp Secy*
Ronald G Schmidt, *Vice Pres*
EMP: 5
SALES (est): 470K **Privately Held**
SIC: 2721 Periodicals

(G-20992)
HAMILTON ARTS INC
750 Union St (45387-1740)
P.O. Box 293 (45387-0293)
PHONE...................................937 767-1834
Arnold Adoff, *President*
Virginia Hamilton, *Webmaster*
EMP: 3
SALES: 250K **Privately Held**
WEB: www.virginiahamilton.com
SIC: 2731 Books: publishing & printing

(G-20993)
HUNTINGTON INSTRUMENTS INC
303 N Walnut St (45387-2041)
P.O. Box 718 (45387-0718)
PHONE...................................937 767-7001
Fax: 937 767-7699
Jeffrey Huntington, *President*
Lee C Huntington, *Treasurer*
EMP: 4

SALES (est): 320K **Privately Held**
WEB: www.huntingtoninstruments.com
SIC: 3823 Industrial instrmnts msrmnt display/control process variable

(G-20994)
KENWAY CORP
Also Called: Oak Heritage
504 Xenia Ave (45387-1838)
PHONE...................................937 767-1660
Linda Greenway, *President*
Keeth Kinney, *Vice Pres*
EMP: 3
SALES (est): 180K **Privately Held**
SIC: 2511 Wood household furniture

(G-20995)
MIAMI VALLEY EDUCTL CMPT ASSN
Also Called: Mveca
330 E Enon Rd (45387-1415)
PHONE...................................937 767-1468
Fax: 937 767-1793
Joan Corbitt, *Treasurer*
Brian Hoehner, *Info Tech Dir*
Kelly Kilbarger, *Comp Spec*
Norma Stewart, *Director*
Gary Bosserman, *Director*
EMP: 13
SQ FT: 2,900
SALES (est): 2MM **Privately Held**
WEB: www.mveca.com
SIC: 7372 7374 Prepackaged software; computer time-sharing

(G-20996)
MORRIS BEAN & COMPANY
777 E Hyde Rd (45387-9726)
PHONE...................................937 767-7301
Fax: 937 767-7301
Edward Myers, *President*
Debbie Whitt, *Opers Mgr*
Dennis Cloyd, *Engineer*
Beth Umina, *Engineer*
William Magro, *CFO*
EMP: 175 EST: 1932
SQ FT: 185,000
SALES (est): 35.8MM **Privately Held**
WEB: www.morrisbean.com
SIC: 3365 3769 3369 Aluminum & aluminum-based alloy castings; guided missile & space vehicle parts & auxiliary equipment; nonferrous foundries

(G-20997)
OHIO SILVER CO
245 Xenia Ave (45387-1832)
PHONE...................................937 767-8261
Marcia Wallgren, *Owner*
EMP: 4 EST: 1971
SQ FT: 1,500
SALES (est): 230K **Privately Held**
SIC: 5944 3911 5094 Jewelry stores; jewelry, precious metal; jewelry

(G-20998)
RITA CAZ JWLY STUDIO & GALLERY
220 Xenia Ave Ste 2 (45387-1865)
P.O. Box 487 (45387-0487)
PHONE...................................937 767-7713
Fax: 937 767-2766
Mark Crockett, *President*
EMP: 5
SALES (est): 471.9K **Privately Held**
SIC: 3911 5944 Jewelry, precious metal; jewelry stores

(G-20999)
SILVER MAPLE PUBLICATIONS
1308 Corry St (45387-1312)
P.O. Box 846 (45387-0846)
PHONE...................................937 767-1259
Barbara Fleming, *President*
EMP: 3
SALES (est): 118.6K **Privately Held**
WEB: www.silvermaplepublications.com
SIC: 2731 Book publishing

(G-21000)
VERNAY MANUFACTURING INC (HQ)
120 E South College St (45387-1623)
PHONE...................................937 767-7261
Thomas Allen, *President*

Andy Woodward, *Vice Pres*
Robin Thompson, *Human Resources*
Mahmoud Kardan, *Manager*
Hugh Barnett, *Admin Sec*
▲ EMP: 22
SQ FT: 40,000
SALES (est): 22.2MM
SALES (corp-wide): 196.6MM **Privately Held**
SIC: 3069 Molded rubber products
PA: Vernay Laboratories, Inc.
2077 Cnvntion Ctr Cncurse
Atlanta GA 30337
404 994-2000

(G-21001)
YELLOW SPRINGS NEWS INC
253 And A Half Xenia Ave (45387)
PHONE...................................937 767-7373
Fax: 937 767-2254
Robert Hasek, *Adv Mgr*
Diane Chiddister, *Office Mgr*
Mike Ruddell, *Director*
EMP: 11 EST: 1880
SQ FT: 4,000
SALES (est): 817.2K **Privately Held**
WEB: www.ysnews.com
SIC: 2711 Job printing & newspaper publishing combined

(G-21002)
YELLOW SPRINGS POTTERY
222 Xenia Ave Ste 1 (45387-1866)
PHONE...................................937 767-1666
Janet Murie, *Principal*
Eliza Bush, *Principal*
Marcia Cochran, *Principal*
Jerry Davis, *Principal*
Kim Kramer, *Principal*
EMP: 10
SALES (est): 633.2K **Privately Held**
SIC: 5023 3269 Pottery; pottery products

(G-21003)
YOUNGS JERSEY DAIRY INC
Also Called: Golden Jersey Inn
6880 Springfield Xenia Rd (45387-9610)
PHONE...................................937 325-0629
Fax: 937 325-3226
C Daniel Young, *President*
C Robert Young, *President*
Brian Patterson, *General Mgr*
William H Young, *Vice Pres*
Debra Whittaker, *Treasurer*
EMP: 300 EST: 1964
SQ FT: 35,000
SALES (est): 12.1MM **Privately Held**
SIC: 5812 5451 5947 7999 Ice cream stands or dairy bars; family restaurants; dairy products stores; gift shop; golf driving range; miniature golf course operation; dairy farms; ice cream & frozen desserts

(G-21004)
YSI ENVIRONMENTAL INC
Also Called: Ysie
1725 Brannum Ln (45387-1107)
PHONE...................................937 767-7241
Richard Omlor, *President*
EMP: 200
SALES (est): 58K **Privately Held**
SIC: 3823 Water quality monitoring & control systems

(G-21005)
YSI INCORPORATED (DH)
Also Called: Yellow Springs International
1700 Brannum Ln 1725 (45387-1106)
PHONE...................................937 767-7241
Fax: 937 767-2045
Richard J Omlor, *President*
Ron Geis, *General Mgr*
Darrin Honious, *General Mgr*
Sham Chaudhari, *Regional Mgr*
David Lee, *Regional Mgr*
◆ EMP: 100
SQ FT: 120,000
SALES (est): 35.2MM **Publicly Held**
SIC: 3826 3823 3841 Water testing apparatus; industrial instrmnts msrmnt display/control process variable; temperature measurement instruments, industrial; diagnostic apparatus, medical

HQ: O.I. Corporation
151 Graham Rd
College Station TX 77845
979 690-1711

Yorkshire
Darke County

(G-21006)
ROBERT WINNER SONS INC (PA)
Also Called: Winner's Meat Service
8544 State Route 705 (45388-9784)
P.O. Box 39, Osgood (45351-0039)
PHONE...................................419 582-4321
Fax: 419 582-2123
Brian K Winner, *President*
Alan Winner, *Senior VP*
Ted Winner, *Vice Pres*
Terrance Winner, *Vice Pres*
Steven Winner, *Treasurer*
EMP: 40 EST: 1928
SQ FT: 6,500
SALES: 33.9MM **Privately Held**
SIC: 0213 0751 5154 5147 Hog feedlot; slaughtering: custom livestock services; hogs; meats & meat products; sausages & other prepared meats; meat packing plants

---
Yorkville
Jefferson County

(G-21007)
OHIO COATINGS COMPANY
2100 Tin Plate Pl (43971-1053)
PHONE...................................740 859-5500
James Tennant, *President*
Yong Sig Bin, *Exec VP*
Phillip E Withum, *Vice Pres*
Emerson McKimmie, *Manager*
Ken Kinyo, *Supervisor*
EMP: 73
SQ FT: 134,000
SALES (est): 13.9MM **Privately Held**
WEB: www.ohiocoatingscompany.com
SIC: 3479 2819 3312 3398 Painting, coating & hot dipping; tin (stannic/stannous) compounds or salts, inorganic; coated or plated products; annealing of metal; surface burner controls, temperature

---
Youngstown
Mahoning County

(G-21008)
1ST CHOICE WEB SOLUTION INC
3000 Belmont Ave (44505-1846)
PHONE...................................330 503-1591
Bill Arfaras, *CEO*
EMP: 3 EST: 2013
SALES (est): 201.1K **Privately Held**
SIC: 3555 Printing presses

(G-21009)
4S COMPANY
3730 Mahoning Ave (44515-3020)
PHONE...................................330 792-5518
Debra Woodford, *President*
EMP: 10
SALES: 350K **Privately Held**
SIC: 3999 Manufacturing industries

(G-21010)
A A S AMELS SHEET META L INC
222 Steel St (44509-2547)
P.O. Box 2407 (44509-0407)
PHONE...................................330 793-9326
Fax: 330 793-0072
Andrew A Samuels Jr, *President*
George Timar, *Admin Sec*
EMP: 40
SQ FT: 12,000

SALES (est): 6.7MM **Privately Held**
SIC: 1711 3585 3564 3444 Ventilation & duct work contractor; warm air heating & air conditioning contractor; refrigeration & heating equipment; blowers & fans; sheet metalwork; fabricated plate work (boiler shop)

(G-21011)
A UNITED
Also Called: AM & PM United
5234 Southern Blvd Ste D (44512-2245)
PHONE...................................330 782-6005
Tony Mark, *Owner*
EMP: 4 EST: 1997
SALES (est): 387.5K **Privately Held**
SIC: 2951 Asphalt paving mixtures & blocks

(G-21012)
AARDVARK SPORTSWEAR INC
5329 Mahoning Ave (44515-2417)
PHONE...................................330 793-9428
Fax: 330 793-7963
Linda Davies, *President*
EMP: 5 EST: 1982
SALES (est): 303.8K **Privately Held**
SIC: 2759 2395 5699 Screen printing; embroidery products, except schiffli machine; sports apparel

(G-21013)
ABI ORTHTC/PROSTHETIC LABS LTD (HQ)
930 Trailwood Dr (44512-5007)
PHONE...................................330 758-1143
Fax: 330 758-2361
William W De Toro,
Arthur W Guilford,
Kevin Hawkins,
Richard A Riffle,
Joseph W Whiteside,
EMP: 20 EST: 1978
SALES (est): 1.4MM
SALES (corp-wide): 460MM **Publicly Held**
SIC: 3842 Braces, orthopedic; prosthetic appliances
PA: Hanger, Inc.
10910 Domain Dr Ste 300
Austin TX 78758
512 777-3800

(G-21014)
ACCUFORM MANUFACTURING INC
2750 Intertech Dr (44509-4023)
PHONE...................................330 797-9291
Fax: 330 797-9255
Bob Hockenberry, *President*
Joe Hensley, *QC Mgr*
Thomas Manos, *Treasurer*
EMP: 32
SQ FT: 1,056
SALES (est): 5.3MM **Privately Held**
WEB: www.accuformmfg.com
SIC: 3599 3543 3544 Machine shop, jobbing & repair; foundry patternmaking; special dies, tools, jigs & fixtures

(G-21015)
ACE LUMBER COMPANY
1039 Poland Ave (44502-2138)
P.O. Box 508 (44501-0508)
PHONE...................................330 744-3167
Fax: 330 744-1226
Herbert Soss, *President*
Steve Hill, *Opers Staff*
Steven Hill, *Purchasing*
Julie Soss, *Shareholder*
Susan Soss, *Shareholder*
EMP: 13
SQ FT: 300,000
SALES (est): 2.1MM **Privately Held**
WEB: www.acelumberco.com
SIC: 2431 5211 Millwork; lumber products

(G-21016)
ACME STEAK & SEAFOOD INC
31 Bissell Ave (44505-2707)
P.O. Box 688 (44501-0688)
PHONE...................................330 270-8000
Fax: 330 270-8006
Michael A Mike II, *President*
EMP: 10

SALES (est): 7.5MM **Privately Held**
WEB: www.acmesteak.com
SIC: **5146** 5113 5149 5147 Seafoods; disposable plates, cups, napkins & eating utensils; canned goods: fruit, vegetables, seafood, meats, etc.; meats, fresh; dairy products, except dried or canned; meat packing plants

(G-21017)
ADVANCED MARKING SYSTEMS INC (PA)
Also Called: Advanced Printing
6000 Mahoning Ave Ste 50 (44515-2248)
PHONE..................................330 792-8239
Fax: 330 792-1738
Fred Fye, *Ch of Bd*
Carol L Fye, *President*
Rita Baun, *Office Mgr*
EMP: 5
SQ FT: 3,000
SALES (est): 401.6K **Privately Held**
WEB: www.advancedmarkingsystems.com
SIC: **2752** 5112 Commercial printing, offset; marking devices

(G-21018)
AEROLITE EXTRUSION COMPANY
4605 Lake Park Rd (44512-1891)
PHONE..................................330 782-1127
Fax: 330 782-3061
Thomas E Hutch Jr, *President*
John D Hutch, *Principal*
Paul J Hutch, *Principal*
Thomas E Hutch, *Principal*
David Camacci, *CFO*
EMP: 90
SQ FT: 200,000
SALES (est): 22.9MM **Privately Held**
WEB: www.aeroext.com
SIC: **3354** 3444 Shapes, extruded aluminum; sheet metalwork

(G-21019)
AIRMACHINESCOM INC
4705 Belmont Ave (44505-1013)
PHONE..................................330 759-1620
Donald R Taylor, *President*
William A Taylor, *Vice Pres*
EMP: 5
SQ FT: 5,000
SALES: 500K **Privately Held**
SIC: **3546** Drills, portable, except rock: electric or pneumatic

(G-21020)
ALLIED CONSOLIDATED INDUSTRIES (PA)
2100 Poland Ave (44502-2751)
PHONE..................................330 744-0808
John Ramun, *President*
Louise Ramun, *Admin Sec*
EMP: 104
SQ FT: 24,000
SALES (est): 34.1MM **Privately Held**
SIC: **3535** 3531 Conveyors & conveying equipment; construction machinery

(G-21021)
ALUMO EXTRUSIONS & MFR COMPANY
3749 Mahoning Ave Ste 2 (44515-3052)
PHONE..................................330 779-3333
Fax: 330 799-7264
Frank Moulin, *President*
John Moulin, *Vice Pres*
Rose Palermo, *Admin Sec*
EMP: 20 EST: 1975
SQ FT: 66,000
SALES (est): 5.8MM **Privately Held**
SIC: **5039** 5031 3089 Doors, sliding; doors, garage; doors, folding: plastic or plastic coated fabric

(G-21022)
AM GRAPHICS
20 S Maryland Ave (44509-2807)
PHONE..................................330 799-7319
Alfred Eusanio, *Owner*
EMP: 3
SQ FT: 3,500

SALES (est): 200K **Privately Held**
SIC: **2759** 7336 3993 2396 Screen printing; commercial art & graphic design; signs & advertising specialties; automotive & apparel trimmings

(G-21023)
AMERICAN FUTURE SYSTEMS INC
970 Windham Ct Ste 1b (44512-5082)
PHONE..................................330 758-0277
Fax: 330 758-0771
Michael Boziar, *Branch Mgr*
EMP: 12
SALES (corp-wide): 140.8MM **Privately Held**
SIC: **2759** Publication printing
PA: American Future Systems, Inc.
370 Technology Dr
Malvern PA 19355
610 695-8600

(G-21024)
AMTECH TOOL AND MACHINE INC
100 Mcclurg Rd (44512-6738)
PHONE..................................330 758-8215
Fax: 330 758-3325
Fred Coss, *President*
Melinda Coss, *Treasurer*
EMP: 13
SQ FT: 6,200
SALES (est): 2.1MM **Privately Held**
SIC: **3544** 3599 3441 Special dies, tools, jigs & fixtures; machine shop, jobbing & repair; fabricated structural metal

(G-21025)
AMTHOR STEEL INC
5019 Belmont Ave (44505-1019)
PHONE..................................330 759-0200
Fax: 330 759-8755
Raymond G Makara, *Project Engr*
George Ohlin, *Manager*
EMP: 7
SALES (corp-wide): 900MM **Privately Held**
SIC: **3312** Blast furnaces & steel mills
PA: Amthor Steel, Inc.
1717 Gaskell Ave
Erie PA 16503
814 452-4700

(G-21026)
ANATOMICAL CONCEPTS INC
1399 E Western Reserve Rd (44514-5224)
PHONE..................................330 757-3569
Fax: 330 757-3634
William W De Toro, *President*
William W Detoro, *President*
Richard Siegel, *General Mgr*
Richard A Riffle, *Vice Pres*
Joe Finocchi, *Financial Exec*
EMP: 15
SQ FT: 1,600
SALES (est): 1.2MM **Privately Held**
WEB: www.prafo.com
SIC: **3842** Braces, orthopedic

(G-21027)
ARMADA FORTRESS LLC
Also Called: Pennsylvania Hill
6971 Southern Blvd Ste B (44512-4652)
PHONE..................................330 953-2185
Danny Chew, *President*
EMP: 6
SALES (est): 679.1K
SALES (corp-wide): 3.8MM **Privately Held**
SIC: **2511** Wood household furniture
PA: Amish Furniture Mart, Inc.
401 E County Road 200n
Arcola IL 61910
217 268-4504

(G-21028)
AUSTINTOWN METAL WORKS INC
45 Victoria Rd (44515-2023)
PHONE..................................330 259-4673
Fax: 330 259-4675
Jim Myers, *President*
EMP: 19

SALES (est): 3MM **Privately Held**
SIC: **3444** 3449 Sheet metalwork; bars, concrete reinforcing: fabricated steel

(G-21029)
AUSTINTOWN PRINTING INC
Also Called: Kwik Kopy Printing
5015 Mahoning Ave Ste 3 (44515-1701)
P.O. Box 312, North Lima (44452-0312)
PHONE..................................330 797-0099
Fax: 330 797-0097
Sue Roberts, *President*
Timothy Clymer, *Manager*
EMP: 5
SQ FT: 1,620
SALES (est): 692.1K **Privately Held**
WEB: www.austintownprinting.com
SIC: **2759** Thermography

(G-21030)
AZTEC MANUFACTURING INC
4325 Simon Rd (44512-1327)
PHONE..................................330 783-9747
Fax: 330 783-0092
Jim Rutana, *Owner*
EMP: 20
SQ FT: 6,000
SALES (est): 2.4MM **Privately Held**
WEB: www.aztecmetalfab.com
SIC: **3365** 3444 Aluminum foundries; sheet metalwork

(G-21031)
BAKER PLASTICS INC
900 Mahoning Ave (44502-1488)
PHONE..................................330 743-3142
Fax: 330 743-3143
Bonnie Baker, *President*
Robert E Baker, *Chairman*
Ruth Luarde, *Admin Sec*
EMP: 7 EST: 1946
SQ FT: 15,000
SALES (est): 1.3MM **Privately Held**
WEB: www.bakerplastics.com
SIC: **3089** 3993 5099 5046 Novelties, plastic; signs & advertising specialties; displays & cutouts, window & lobby; signs, not made in custom sign painting shops; advertising novelties; novelties, durable; store fixtures & display equipment; advertising specialties

(G-21032)
BOARDMAN MOLDED PRODUCTS INC
1110 Thalia Ave (44512-1825)
P.O. Box 1858 (44501-1858)
PHONE..................................330 788-2401
Fax: 330 788-9665
Ronald N Kessler, *President*
Milton Kessler, *Principal*
George Lolakis, *Plant Mgr*
Katheline Ayles, *Manager*
▲ EMP: 80 EST: 1976
SQ FT: 85,000
SALES (est): 22.8MM **Privately Held**
SIC: **3089** 3466 3429 2273 Injection molding of plastics; crowns & closures; manufactured hardware (general); carpets & rugs

(G-21033)
BOLTECH INCORPORATED
1201 Crescent St (44502-1303)
P.O. Box 749 (44501-0749)
PHONE..................................330 746-6881
Alex Benyo, *President*
C R Pallante, *Principal*
Brian Benyo, *Vice Pres*
Lucas Bacon, *Webmaster*
EMP: 9 EST: 1998
SQ FT: 6,500
SALES (est): 1.5MM **Privately Held**
WEB: www.boltechinc.com
SIC: **3537** Trucks, tractors, loaders, carriers & similar equipment

(G-21034)
BRENTWOOD ORIGINALS INC
1309 N Meridian Rd (44509-1099)
PHONE..................................330 793-2255
Fax: 330 793-1434
Beth Foley, *Safety Dir*
Debbie Martin, *Warehouse Mgr*
Natasha Richardson, *Design Engr*
Monica Wills, *Design Engr*

Candace Crum, *Personnel*
EMP: 330
SQ FT: 130,000
SALES (corp-wide): 196.3MM **Privately Held**
WEB: www.brentwoodoriginals.com
SIC: **2392** Pillows, bed: made from purchased materials
PA: Brentwood Originals, Inc.
20639 S Fordyce Ave
Carson CA 90810
310 637-6804

(G-21035)
BRIER HILL SLAG COMPANY (PA)
18 Hogue St (44502-1425)
PHONE..................................330 743-8170
Scott Marucci, *President*
William Gaffney, *Corp Secy*
Nicki Williams, *Admin Sec*
EMP: 10
SQ FT: 700
SALES (est): 659.4K **Privately Held**
SIC: **3295** Slag, crushed or ground

(G-21036)
BRILEX INDUSTRIES INC
101 Andrews Ave (44503-1607)
PHONE..................................330 744-1114
Jessica Llyod, *Branch Mgr*
EMP: 100 **Privately Held**
SIC: **3542** 3549 3441 Machine tools, metal forming type; metalworking machinery; fabricated structural metal
PA: Brilex Industries, Inc.
1201 Crescent St
Youngstown OH 44502

(G-21037)
BRILEX INDUSTRIES INC (PA)
1201 Crescent St (44502-1303)
P.O. Box 749 (44501-0749)
PHONE..................................330 744-1114
Fax: 330 744-1125
Brian Benyo, *President*
Alex M Benyo, *Vice Pres*
Steve Davinsizer, *Vice Pres*
Robert Fent, *Project Mgr*
Bud Geddis, *Mfg Mgr*
▲ EMP: 160
SQ FT: 54,000
SALES (est): 44.4MM **Privately Held**
WEB: www.brilex.com
SIC: **3441** 3542 3549 Fabricated structural metal; machine tools, metal forming type; metalworking machinery

(G-21038)
BROCKER MACHINE INC
1530 Poland Ave (44502-2188)
PHONE..................................330 744-5858
Fax: 330 744-0377
Brad Brocker, *President*
EMP: 11
SQ FT: 10,000
SALES: 1.4MM **Privately Held**
SIC: **3599** Machine shop, jobbing & repair

(G-21039)
BUDS SIGN SHOP INC
892 Mahoning Ave (44502-1414)
PHONE..................................330 744-5555
Fax: 330 744-3927
Robert Perkins, *President*
Barbara Perkins, *Vice Pres*
EMP: 10
SQ FT: 10,000
SALES (est): 1.1MM **Privately Held**
WEB: www.budsignshop.com
SIC: **3993** Signs & advertising specialties

(G-21040)
BUSINESS JOURNAL
Also Called: Business Journal, The
25 E Boardman St Ste 306 (44503-1803)
P.O. Box 714 (44501-0714)
PHONE..................................330 744-5023
Fax: 330 744-5838
Andrea Wood, *President*
EMP: 15
SQ FT: 2,700
SALES (est): 1.4MM **Privately Held**
WEB: www.business-journal.com
SIC: **2721** Trade journals: publishing & printing

(G-21041)
**C M L CONCRETE
CONSTRUCTION**
482 Garden Valley Ct (44512-6503)
PHONE................................330 758-8314
Carman Lofaro, *President*
EMP: 4
SALES (est): 566.3K **Privately Held**
SIC: 3444 Concrete forms, sheet metal

(G-21042)
**CANFIELD INDUSTRIES INC
(PA)**
8510 Foxwood Ct (44514-4301)
PHONE................................800 554-5071
Fax: 330 758-8912
John R Rasmussen, *President*
John Simon, *President*
Charles P Henderson, *Principal*
Ruth Smedley, *Principal*
Nancy M Williard, *Principal*
EMP: 2
SQ FT: 35,000
SALES (est): 27.5MM **Privately Held**
WEB: www.canfieldconnector.com
SIC: 7389 3491 3678 3677 Purchasing
service; industrial valves; electronic con-
nectors; electronic coils, transformers &
other inductors; fluid power valves & hose
fittings

(G-21043)
**CARDIAC ARRHYTHMIA
ASSOCIATES**
3622 Belmont Ave Ste 1112 (44505-1450)
PHONE................................330 759-8169
Mita Raheja, *Owner*
EMP: 3
SALES (est): 343.7K **Privately Held**
SIC: 8011 3845 Cardiologist & cardio-vas-
cular specialist; pacemaker, cardiac

(G-21044)
CARNEY PLASTICS INC
1010 W Rayen Ave (44502-1317)
PHONE................................330 746-8273
Fax: 330 746-8276
Sean Carney, *President*
EMP: 9
SALES (est): 1.4MM **Privately Held**
WEB: www.carneyplastics.com
SIC: 3089 5162 Plastic processing; plas-
tics products

(G-21045)
**CENTRAL HEATING & COOLING
INC**
5626 South Ave Ste 1 (44512-2461)
PHONE................................330 782-7100
Fax: 330 782-2222
Joseph Del Fraino, *President*
EMP: 5
SALES (est): 891.1K **Privately Held**
SIC: 3585 1711 Refrigeration & heating
equipment; plumbing, heating, air-condi-
tioning contractors

(G-21046)
CENTRAL OPTICAL INC
6981 Southern Blvd Ste B (44512-4657)
PHONE................................330 783-9660
Fax: 330 783-9721
Lloyd Yazbek, *President*
Richard J Thomas, *Co-President*
Pamela A Thomas, *Treasurer*
Linda Yasbeck, *Accounting Dir*
Sue Cadman, *Accountant*
▲ EMP: 28
SQ FT: 10,000
SALES (est): 4.9MM **Privately Held**
WEB: www.centraloptical.com
SIC: 3851 5995 Eyeglasses, lenses &
frames; optical goods stores

(G-21047)
**CITY MACHINE TECHNOLOGIES
INC (PA)**
773 W Rayen Ave (44502-1112)
P.O. Box 1466 (44501-1466)
PHONE................................330 747-2639
Fax: 330 747-3205
Michael J Kovach, *President*
Sam Frasco, *Controller*
Doug Meek, *Finance Mgr*

Paul Goske, *VP Mktg*
Sam Farsco, *Officer*
EMP: 18 EST: 1986
SQ FT: 17,000
SALES (est): 13.7MM **Privately Held**
WEB: www.cmtcompanies.com
SIC: 3621 7694 3599 7692 Motors &
generators; armature rewinding shops;
machine shop, jobbing & repair; welding
repair; industrial trucks & tractors

(G-21048)
**CITY MACHINE TECHNOLOGIES
INC**
Electric Machinery Division
825 Martin Luther King Jr (44502-1105)
P.O. Box 1466 (44501-1466)
PHONE................................330 740-8186
Michael J Kovach, *President*
Mike Perello, *QC Mgr*
Robert Puharich, *Supervisor*
EMP: 40
SALES (corp-wide): 13.7MM **Privately
Held**
WEB: www.cmtcompanies.com
SIC: 3599 7694 3621 3568 Machine
shop, jobbing & repair; armature rewind-
ing shops; motors & generators; power
transmission equipment
PA: City Machine Technologies, Inc.
773 W Rayen Ave
Youngstown OH 44502
330 747-2639

(G-21049)
**CITY MACHINE TECHNOLOGIES
INC**
Electric Machinery Division
773 W Rayen Ave (44502-1112)
P.O. Box 1466 (44501-1466)
PHONE................................330 747-2639
Michael Kovach, *Manager*
EMP: 50
SALES (corp-wide): 13.7MM **Privately
Held**
WEB: www.cmtcompanies.com
SIC: 3599 3613 Machine shop, jobbing &
repair; control panels, electric
PA: City Machine Technologies, Inc.
773 W Rayen Ave
Youngstown OH 44502
330 747-2639

(G-21050)
**CITY MACHINE TECHNOLOGIES
INC**
Lifting Magnet Division
448 Andrews Ave (44505-3063)
P.O. Box 1466 (44501-1466)
PHONE................................330 747-2639
Doug Meek, *Manager*
EMP: 7
SALES (corp-wide): 13.7MM **Privately
Held**
WEB: www.cmtcompanies.com
SIC: 3599 3613 Machine shop, jobbing &
repair; control panels, electric
PA: City Machine Technologies, Inc.
773 W Rayen Ave
Youngstown OH 44502
330 747-2639

(G-21051)
CITY PRINTING CO INC
122 Oak Hill Ave (44502-1428)
PHONE................................330 747-5691
Fax: 330 747-6907
Joseph A Valentini, *President*
Irene Valentini, *Controller*
Tony Valentini, *Director*
Jean Kochera, *Admin Sec*
EMP: 20 EST: 1920
SQ FT: 11,000
SALES: 92.7K **Privately Held**
WEB: www.cityprinting.com
SIC: 2752 Commercial printing, litho-
graphic

(G-21052)
CLASSIC OPTICAL LABS INC
3710 Belmont Ave (44505-1406)
P.O. Box 1341 (44501-1341)
PHONE................................330 759-8245
Fax: 330 759-8300
Dawn Friedkin, *President*
Bob Sherman, *Purch Agent*

Martin Willingale, *CFO*
Amy Needles, *VP Human Res*
Amy Barnes, *Human Resources*
▲ EMP: 195
SQ FT: 30,000
SALES (est): 13.2MM **Privately Held**
WEB: www.classicoptical.com
SIC: 3851 Ophthalmic goods

(G-21053)
COCA-COLA COMPANY
531 E Indianola Ave (44502-2395)
PHONE................................330 783-1982
Fax: 330 788-2056
David Gray, *Opers Mgr*
John Flynt, *Branch Mgr*
EMP: 60
SALES (corp-wide): 41.8B **Publicly Held**
WEB: www.colasic.net
SIC: 2086 Bottled & canned soft drinks
PA: The Coca-Cola Company
1 Coca Cola Plz Nw
Atlanta GA 30313
404 676-2121

(G-21054)
**COMMERCIAL BAR &
CABINETRY**
Also Called: Commercial Cabinets
12 S Worthington St (44502-1336)
PHONE................................330 743-1420
Fax: 330 743-1420
James Pupino, *Owner*
EMP: 6
SQ FT: 5,000
SALES: 450K **Privately Held**
SIC: 2434 Wood kitchen cabinets

(G-21055)
**COMPREHENSIVE LOGISTICS
CO INC**
365 Victoria Rd (44515-2027)
PHONE................................330 793-0504
Tom Welsh, *Sales Executive*
Doug Caswell, *Branch Mgr*
Edward H Jones, *Manager*
Trey Lyda, *Director*
EMP: 50 **Privately Held**
SIC: 8742 4226 3714 3711 Management
consulting services; special warehousing
& storage; motor vehicle parts & acces-
sories; motor vehicles & car bodies
PA: Comprehensive Logistics Co., Inc.
4944 Belmont Ave Ste 202
Youngstown OH 44505

(G-21056)
CONISON TOOL AND DIE INC
8100 Southern Blvd (44512-6307)
PHONE................................330 758-1574
Fax: 330 758-5633
Edward Straub, *President*
Michelle Straub, *President*
EMP: 9
SQ FT: 3,500
SALES: 890K **Privately Held**
SIC: 3599 Machine & other job shop work

(G-21057)
CONSTRUCTION BULLETIN INC
4178 Market St Lowr (44512-1116)
PHONE................................330 782-3733
Fax: 330 782-8110
EMP: 6
SQ FT: 2,000
SALES (est): 280K **Privately Held**
SIC: 2711 Newspapers-Publishing/Printing

(G-21058)
**CROWN ELEC SVCS &
AUTOMTN INC**
102 Javit Ct (44515-2409)
PHONE................................330 270-9890
Fax: 330 270-9895
Bob Messerly, *Branch Mgr*
EMP: 6
SALES (corp-wide): 35.3MM **Privately
Held**
SIC: 8711 3823 3594 Electrical or elec-
tronic engineering; industrial instrmnts
msrmnt display/control process variable;
fluid power pumps & motors

HQ: Crown Electrical Services & Automation Inc.
5960 Southport Rd
Portage IN 46368
972 929-4700

(G-21059)
CUBBISON COMPANY (PA)
380 Victoria Rd (44515-2054)
PHONE................................330 793-2481
Fax: 330 793-8471
Timothy Merrifield, *President*
Ken Baytosh, *Purchasing*
Sheila Scheel, *Financial Exec*
Kathy Sipe, *Marketing Mgr*
Judy Cornelius, *Manager*
EMP: 67
SQ FT: 27,000
SALES: 7.6MM **Privately Held**
WEB: www.cubbison.com
SIC: 3469 3993 3479 Metal stampings;
name plates: except engraved, etched,
etc.: metal; etching & engraving

(G-21060)
**CUSTOM TARPAULIN
PRODUCTS INC**
8095 Southern Blvd (44512-6336)
PHONE................................330 758-1801
Fax: 330 758-9872
Beth Robinson, *Corp Secy*
Brian Robinson, *Vice Pres*
Sharon Morocco, *Manager*
EMP: 19
SALES (est): 2.2MM **Privately Held**
WEB: www.customtarpaulin.com
SIC: 2394 Tarpaulins, fabric: made from
purchased materials

(G-21061)
CUSTOMER PRINTING INC
Also Called: Pegasus Printing Group
592 Industrial Rd (44509-2917)
PHONE................................330 629-8676
EMP: 15
SALES (est): 2.9MM **Privately Held**
SIC: 2752 Commercial Printing, Litho-
graphic

(G-21062)
D & L GAS ENERGY LTD
2761 Salt Springs Rd (44509-1035)
PHONE................................330 792-9524
Ben W Lupo, *President*
Susan Faith, *Controller*
EMP: 125
SALES (est): 10.3MM **Privately Held**
SIC: 3533 8742 Oil & gas drilling rigs &
equipment; management consulting serv-
ices

(G-21063)
DAILY LEGAL NEWS INC
100 E Federal St Ste 126 (44503-1834)
PHONE................................330 747-7777
Fax: 330 747-3977
John Burleson, *President*
Leann Bryce, *Manager*
Kim Pearson, *Manager*
EMP: 5
SALES (est): 270.4K **Privately Held**
WEB: www.dlnnews.com
SIC: 2711 Newspapers

(G-21064)
DATCO MFG COMPANY INC
4605 Lake Park Rd (44512-1814)
PHONE................................330 787-1127
John Kerns, *Principal*
EMP: 45
SALES (corp-wide): 8MM **Privately Held**
SIC: 3999 Atomizers, toiletry
PA: Datco Mfg. Company, Inc.
4605 Lake Park Rd
Youngstown OH 44512
330 781-6100

(G-21065)
DATCO MFG COMPANY INC (PA)
4605 Lake Park Rd (44512-1814)
PHONE................................330 781-6100
Thomas E Hutch Jr, *President*
EMP: 45
SQ FT: 32,000

SALES (est): 8MM **Privately Held**
SIC: **3354** 3444 Aluminum extruded products; sheet metalwork

(G-21066)
DEKAY FABRICATORS INC
295 S Meridian Rd (44509-2924)
PHONE......................................330 793-0826
Fax: 330 797-5433
Bryan Kennedy, *President*
EMP: 8
SQ FT: 10,000
SALES: 100K **Privately Held**
SIC: **3498** Tube fabricating (contract bending & shaping)

(G-21067)
DESIGN TRAC INC
4136 Logan Way (44505-5703)
PHONE......................................330 759-3131
Gary Gasser, *CEO*
Mark Gasser, *President*
Cindy Gasser, *Treasurer*
Cathy Gasser, *Admin Sec*
EMP: 5
SQ FT: 3,000
SALES (est): 390K **Privately Held**
SIC: **2522** Office furniture, except wood

(G-21068)
**DIAMOND SPARKLER MFG CO
(PA)**
555 Martin Luther King Jr (44502-1102)
PHONE......................................330 746-1064
Fax: 330 746-0070
Bruce J Zoldan, *President*
John Reiss, *Plant Mgr*
EMP: 1
SQ FT: 30,000
SALES: 8.1MM **Privately Held**
SIC: **2899** Fireworks

(G-21069)
DIGITAL GRAPHICS
4589 Dobbins Rd (44514-2398)
PHONE......................................330 707-1720
Tom Donegan, *Owner*
EMP: 4
SALES (est): 248.3K **Privately Held**
SIC: **2759** Commercial printing

(G-21070)
DIRUSSOS SAUSAGE INC
1035 W Rayen Ave (44502-1316)
PHONE......................................330 744-1208
Fax: 330 744-4523
Robert Dirusso, *President*
Michael Testa, *Prdtn Mgr*
Brenda Gioppo, *Manager*
EMP: 30
SQ FT: 8,000
SALES (est): 4.9MM **Privately Held**
SIC: **2013** Sausages & other prepared meats

(G-21071)
**DON WALTER KITCHEN DISTRS
INC**
260 Victoria Rd (44515-2024)
PHONE......................................330 793-9338
Betty Kern, *Manager*
EMP: 5
SALES (corp-wide): 17.8MM **Privately Held**
SIC: **2599** 5211 Cabinets, factory; cabinets, kitchen
PA: Don Walter Kitchen Distributors, Inc.
260 Victoria Rd
Youngstown OH 44515
330 793-9338

(G-21072)
**DR PEPPER BOTTLERS
ASSOCIATES**
500 Pepsi Pl (44502-1432)
PHONE......................................330 746-7651
Fax: 330 746-0557
Danny Rittenberry, *Principal*
EMP: 3
SALES (est): 128.7K **Privately Held**
SIC: **2086** Soft drinks: packaged in cans, bottles, etc.

(G-21073)
**EASTERDAYS PRINTING
CENTER**
86 Boardman Poland Rd (44512-4602)
PHONE......................................330 726-1182
John Easterday, *President*
Sharlene Easterday, *Treasurer*
EMP: 4
SALES (est): 500K **Privately Held**
SIC: **5112** 2752 2791 2789 Stationery & office supplies; commercial printing, offset; typesetting; bookbinding & related work

(G-21074)
EINSTRUCTION CORP
255 W Federal St (44503-1207)
PHONE......................................940 565-0004
EMP: 6
SALES (est): 308.6K
SALES (corp-wide): 180.1MM **Privately Held**
SIC: **7372** Prepackaged software
PA: Turning Technologies, Llc
255 W Federal St
Youngstown OH 44503
330 746-3015

(G-21075)
**EINSTRUCTION CORPORATION
(HQ)**
255 W Federal St (44503-1207)
PHONE......................................330 746-3015
Rich Fennessy, *CEO*
Mike Logan, *Regional Mgr*
Michael Ottiano, *Engineer*
Tim Torno, *CFO*
Mike Torrenti, *Sales Dir*
▲ EMP: 100
SQ FT: 8,000
SALES (est): 49.1MM
SALES (corp-wide): 180.1MM **Privately Held**
WEB: www.einstruction.com
SIC: **7371** 7379 5045 7372 Computer software development; computer related consulting services; computers, peripherals & software; prepackaged software
PA: Turning Technologies, Llc
255 W Federal St
Youngstown OH 44503
330 746-3015

(G-21076)
EJ USA INC
4150 Simon Rd (44512-1322)
PHONE......................................330 782-3900
Fax: 330 781-1044
Bill Denidovich, *Manager*
EMP: 16 **Privately Held**
WEB: www.ejiw.com
SIC: **3449** 3321 Custom roll formed products; manhole covers, metal
HQ: Ej Usa, Inc.
301 Spring St
East Jordan MI 49727
800 874-4100

(G-21077)
**ENERGY RESOURCES OF
AMERICA IN**
6075 Silica Rd Ste B (44515-1081)
PHONE......................................330 953-1813
Fax: 330 533-8474
Joseph Glista, *President*
EMP: 3
SALES (est): 442.5K **Privately Held**
WEB: www.energyresourcesofamerica.com
SIC: **1381** Drilling oil & gas wells

(G-21078)
EPCO EXTRUSION PAINTING CO
4605 Lake Park Rd (44512-1814)
PHONE......................................330 781-6100
Fax: 330 781-6115
Thomas E Hutch Jr, *President*
EMP: 45
SALES (est): 7.3MM **Privately Held**
SIC: **3479** Aluminum coating of metal products

(G-21079)
**ESSENTIAL PATHWAYS OHIO
LLC**
726 E Boston Ave (44502-2420)
PHONE......................................330 518-3091
Andrea Dawson,
EMP: 3
SALES (est): 108K **Privately Held**
SIC: **5699** 5661 7389 5044 Sports apparel; customized clothing & apparel; men's shoes; women's shoes; ; typewriters; radio & TV communications equipment

(G-21080)
EXAL CORPORATION (PA)
1 Performance Pl (44502-2099)
PHONE......................................330 744-9505
Fax: 330 744-1124
Michael Mapes, *CEO*
Delfin Gibert, *President*
Keith Clark, *Vice Pres*
Brenda Oman, *Vice Pres*
Keith Mitchell, *Project Mgr*
◆ EMP: 35
SQ FT: 476,000
SALES (est): 113.9MM **Privately Held**
WEB: www.exal.com
SIC: **3411** 3354 Aluminum cans; aluminum extruded products

(G-21081)
EXTENDIT COMPANY
601 Jones St (44502-2161)
PHONE......................................330 743-4343
Fax: 330 743-4397
Henry M Garlick, *President*
Mike Schlueter, *Office Mgr*
EMP: 6
SQ FT: 50,000
SALES (est): 1MM **Privately Held**
WEB: www.extenditco.com
SIC: **2891** Sealants

(G-21082)
**FALMER SCREW PDTS & MFG
INC**
690 Mcclurg Rd (44512-6407)
PHONE......................................330 758-0593
Rick Dravecky, *President*
George Dravecky, *Corp Secy*
Joseph Dravecky, *Vice Pres*
EMP: 15
SQ FT: 30,000
SALES (est): 2.9MM **Privately Held**
WEB: www.falmerinc.com
SIC: **3599** 3451 Machine & other job shop work; screw machine products

(G-21083)
**FARMERS NATIONAL BANC
CORP**
102 W Western Reserve Rd (44514-3522)
PHONE......................................330 726-8896
Fax: 330 726-0506
Rochelle Baer, *Site Mgr*
Lynn Kaschak, *Branch Mgr*
EMP: 12
SALES (corp-wide): 95.7MM **Publicly Held**
SIC: **2782** Bank checkbooks & passbooks
PA: Farmers National Banc Corp.
20 S Broad St
Canfield OH 44406
330 533-3341

(G-21084)
**FINE LINE EMBROIDERY
COMPANY**
4660 Lake Park Rd (44512-1813)
PHONE......................................330 788-9070
Michael David, *Owner*
EMP: 5 **Privately Held**
WEB: www.fineline-emb.com
SIC: **2395** Pleating & stitching
PA: Fine Line Embroidery Company, Inc
20525 Detroit Rd Ste 9
Rocky River OH 44116

(G-21085)
FIRELINE INC
8560 Foxwood Ct (44514-4301)
PHONE......................................330 259-0647
Barbara Burley, *Branch Mgr*
EMP: 20

SALES (corp-wide): 17MM **Privately Held**
SIC: **3299** Non-metallic mineral statuary & other decorative products; ceramic fiber
PA: Fireline, Inc.
300 Andrews Ave
Youngstown OH 44505
330 743-1164

(G-21086)
FIRELINE INC (PA)
Also Called: Fireline Tcon
300 Andrews Ave (44505-3061)
PHONE......................................330 743-1164
Fax: 330 743-3117
Barbara Burley, *President*
Robert A Wimer, *President*
Klaus-Markus Peters, *General Mgr*
Ed Ress, *Exec VP*
Dave Riggs, *Vice Pres*
▼ EMP: 78
SQ FT: 85,000
SALES (est): 18.7MM **Privately Held**
SIC: **3299** Non-metallic mineral statuary & other decorative products; insulsleeves (foundry materials); ceramic fiber

(G-21087)
**FITHIAN-WILBERT BURIAL VLT
CO**
6234 Market St (44512-3329)
PHONE......................................330 758-2327
Fax: 330 758-1815
Heather Davis, *President*
EMP: 14 **EST:** 1924
SALES (est): 1.3MM **Privately Held**
SIC: **3272** Burial vaults, concrete or precast terrazzo

(G-21088)
FOOD 4 YOUR SOUL
3957 S Schenley Ave (44511-3428)
PHONE......................................330 402-4073
Michelle White, *Owner*
EMP: 10
SALES (est): 330.7K **Privately Held**
SIC: **2099** Food preparations

(G-21089)
FORGE INDUSTRIES INC (PA)
4450 Market St (44512-1512)
PHONE......................................330 782-8301
Fax: 330 782-4064
William T James II, *Ch of Bd*
Carl G James, *President*
W Thomas James III, *Vice Pres*
Dan Maisonville, *CFO*
Robert Ruester, *Controller*
▲ EMP: 1250 **EST:** 1900
SQ FT: 1,500
SALES (est): 588.6MM **Privately Held**
WEB: www.forgeindustries.com
SIC: **5085** 3566 3599 3531 Bearings; power transmission equipment & apparatus; gears, power transmission, except automotive; machine shop, jobbing & repair; road construction & maintenance machinery; insurance brokers; industrial equipment services

(G-21090)
GARVEY CORPORATION
Also Called: M7 Technologies
1019 Ohio Works Dr (44510-1078)
PHONE......................................330 779-0700
Fax: 330 797-0471
Michael S Garvey, *President*
Jeanette Garvey, *Treasurer*
EMP: 25
SQ FT: 20,000
SALES (est): 6MM **Privately Held**
SIC: **3599** Machine shop, jobbing & repair

(G-21091)
GASSER CHAIR CO INC (PA)
4136 Logan Way (44505-1797)
PHONE......................................330 534-2234
Fax: 330 759-2227
Gary L Gasser, *CEO*
Mark E Gasser, *President*
Cindy Gasser, *Vice Pres*
Jimmy Elenz, *Project Mgr*
Rick Williams, *Opers Mgr*
◆ EMP: 25
SQ FT: 22,000

SALES (est): 24.7MM **Privately Held**
WEB: www.gasserchair.com
SIC: **2531** 2521 Chairs, table & arm; chairs, office: padded, upholstered or plain: wood

(G-21092)
GASSER CHAIR CO INC
4136 Logan Way (44505-1797)
PHONE.....................330 534-2234
Fax: 330 534-9844
Scott Gasser, *Manager*
EMP: 15
SQ FT: 8,900
SALES (corp-wide): 24.7MM **Privately Held**
WEB: www.gasserchair.com
SIC: **5021** 2522 2512 2531 Chairs; chairs, office: padded or plain, except wood; chairs: upholstered on wood frames; chairs, portable folding; chairs, table & arm
PA: Gasser Chair Co., Inc.
　　4136 Logan Way
　　Youngstown OH 44505
　　330 534-2234

(G-21093)
GASSER CHAIR CO INC
Also Called: Production Div
2457 Logan Ave (44505)
PHONE.....................330 759-2234
Frank Joy, *Vice Pres*
Evelyn McCabe, *Controller*
EMP: 100
SALES (corp-wide): 24.7MM **Privately Held**
WEB: www.gasserchair.com
SIC: **2531** 2522 2521 2511 Chairs, table & arm; office furniture, except wood; wood office furniture; wood household furniture
PA: Gasser Chair Co., Inc.
　　4136 Logan Way
　　Youngstown OH 44505
　　330 534-2234

(G-21094)
GEI OF COLUMBIANA INC
4040 Lake Park Rd (44512-1801)
PHONE.....................330 783-0270
Michael C Schuler, *President*
Larry Fiedler, *Traffic Mgr*
Patricia McMahon, *Purchasing*
Rosemary Athey, *Controller*
Terry M Maloney, *Human Res Mgr*
EMP: 62
SALES (est): 7.2MM **Privately Held**
SIC: **3354** 3471 Shapes, extruded aluminum; polishing, metals or formed products; finishing, metals or formed products; anodizing (plating) of metals or formed products

(G-21095)
GENERAL ELECTRIC COMPANY
280 N Meridian Rd (44509-1858)
PHONE.....................330 793-3911
Fax: 330 270-5230
Art Holmes, *Opers Mgr*
George Lopuchovsky, *Opers Mgr*
George Lupuzhovky, *Branch Mgr*
E Malloy, *Manager*
David Chapman, *Systems Mgr*
EMP: 230
SALES (corp-wide): 123.6B **Publicly Held**
SIC: **3641** 3356 Filaments, for electric lamps; nonferrous rolling & drawing
PA: General Electric Company
　　41 Farnsworth St
　　Boston MA 02210
　　617 443-3000

(G-21096)
GENERAL EXTRUSIONS INC
Also Called: Gei
4040 Lake Park Rd (44512-1801)
P.O. Box 3488 (44513-3488)
PHONE.....................330 783-0270
Fax: 330 788-1250
Herbert F Schuler, *President*
Rosemary Athey, *General Mgr*
Ted Allen, *Plant Mgr*
Jason Andre, *Opers Staff*
Patricia McMahon, *Purchasing*

EMP: 58
SQ FT: 220,000
SALES (est): 21.1MM **Privately Held**
WEB: www.genext.com
SIC: **3354** 3471 Shapes, extruded aluminum; polishing, metals or formed products

(G-21097)
GENEVA LIBERTY STEEL LTD (PA)
Also Called: Genmak Geneva Liberty
947 Martin Luther King Jr (44502-1106)
P.O. Box 6124 (44501-6124)
PHONE.....................330 740-0103
Fax: 330 740-0113
David T McLeroy, *Partner*
Joe Ruess, *General Mgr*
Enzo Dechellis, *CFO*
Barb McLeroy, *Human Res Mgr*
Dave Bauschard, *Regl Sales Mgr*
EMP: 55
SQ FT: 85,000
SALES (est): 44.1MM **Privately Held**
SIC: **3316** 7389 Strip steel, flat bright, cold-rolled: purchased hot-rolled; scrap steel cutting

(G-21098)
GENEX TOOL & DIE INC
4000 Lake Park Rd (44512)
PHONE.....................330 788-2466
Fax: 330 782-6170
Herbert F Schuler, *President*
Patricia McMahon, *Purch Agent*
Rosemary Athey, *Finance Mgr*
Rob Schwartz, *VP Sales*
Michael Schuler, *Admin Sec*
EMP: 11
SQ FT: 23,000
SALES (est): 1MM **Privately Held**
WEB: www.genext.com
SIC: **3541** Machine tools, metal cutting type

(G-21099)
GEORGE A MITCHELL COMPANY
557 Mcclurg Rd (44512-6443)
P.O. Box 3727 (44513-3727)
PHONE.....................330 758-5777
Fax: 330 758-7263
George A Mitchell, *President*
Patricia Jasinski, *Corp Secy*
Mark A Mitchell, *Vice Pres*
Paul F Russo, *Vice Pres*
Gary Sansenbaugher, *Engineer*
▼ EMP: 20
SQ FT: 22,000
SALES (est): 4.7MM **Privately Held**
WEB: www.mitchellmachinery.com
SIC: **3542** 3541 3594 3547 Extruding machines (machine tools), metal; machine tools, metal cutting type; rolling mill machinery

(G-21100)
GIA RUSSA (PA)
Also Called: John Zidian Company
574 Mcclurg Rd (44512-6405)
PHONE.....................330 743-6050
Loren Grossman, *Warehouse Mgr*
Anita Galo, *Credit Mgr*
Doug Koller, *Regl Sales Mgr*
John Grossman, *Director*
EMP: 17 EST: 2011
SALES (est): 2.5MM **Privately Held**
SIC: **2032** Italian foods: packaged in cans, jars, etc.

(G-21101)
GL INTERNATIONAL LLC
Also Called: Gli Pool Products
215 Sinter Ct (44510-1076)
PHONE.....................330 744-8812
Fax: 330 744-4653
Mike Loccisano, *VP Opers*
Scott Grdina, *Opers Mgr*
John Bushling, *Opers Staff*
Glen Hensley, *Opers Staff*
Linda Burgett, *Purchasing*
▲ EMP: 130
SALES (est): 19.8MM **Privately Held**
SIC: **3949** Swimming pools, plastic

(G-21102)
GRALE TECHNOLOGIES INC
1019 Ohio Works Dr (44510-1078)
P.O. Box 1001, Aliquippa PA (15001-0801)
PHONE.....................724 683-8141
Fred Persi, *Partner*
Michael Garvey, *Partner*
James Osterloh, *Partner*
EMP: 3
SALES (est): 128K **Privately Held**
SIC: **3829** Measuring & controlling devices

(G-21103)
GREAT LAKES TELCOM LTD
Also Called: Broadband Hospitality
590 E Western Reserve Rd (44514-3354)
PHONE.....................330 629-8848
Vincent Lucci Jr, *Partner*
Jeanne Mafodda, *Vice Pres*
Jeanne Dunn, *VP Opers*
Ed Santor, *VP Sales*
Larry Borders, *Manager*
EMP: 30
SQ FT: 9,200
SALES (est): 8.7MM **Privately Held**
WEB: www.broadbandhospitality.com
SIC: **4813** 3663 ; satellites, communications

(G-21104)
GRENGA MACHINE & WELDING
56 Wayne Ave (44502-1938)
PHONE.....................330 743-1113
Fax: 330 743-1114
Joe Grenga, *Owner*
Todd Grenga, *Sales Staff*
Glen Graham, *Director*
EMP: 10
SQ FT: 30,000
SALES (est): 2.1MM **Privately Held**
SIC: **5051** 5084 3599 3443 Steel; industrial machinery & equipment; machine shop, jobbing & repair; fabricated plate work (boiler shop); fabricated structural metal; blast furnaces & steel mills

(G-21105)
GRINDING EQUIPMENT & MCHY LLC
15 S Worthington St (44502-1335)
PHONE.....................330 747-2313
Fax: 330 747-4211
James Johnson, *President*
Tracy Gross, *Office Mgr*
Fredrick Houston, *Mng Member*
EMP: 13
SQ FT: 10,000
SALES: 1.5MM **Privately Held**
WEB: www.gem-usa.com
SIC: **3547** Grinding equipment, rolling mill

(G-21106)
GUNDERSON RAIL SERVICES LLC
Also Called: Greenbrier Rail Services
3710 Hendricks Rd Bldg 2a (44515-1537)
PHONE.....................330 792-6521
Adam Strysseler, *Manager*
EMP: 20
SALES (corp-wide): 2.6B **Publicly Held**
SIC: **3743** 3444 3441 Railroad equipment; sheet metalwork; fabricated structural metal
HQ: Gunderson Rail Services Llc
　　1 Centerpointe Dr Ste 200
　　Lake Oswego OR 97035
　　503 684-7000

(G-21107)
HATTENBACH COMPANY
52 E Myrtle Ave (44507-1268)
PHONE.....................330 744-2732
Fax: 330 744-3890
Roy Guerrieri, *Branch Mgr*
EMP: 20
SALES (corp-wide): 15MM **Privately Held**
WEB: www.hattenbach.com
SIC: **5078** 1711 2434 2541 Commercial refrigeration equipment; refrigeration contractor; wood kitchen cabinets; cabinets, except refrigerated: show, display, etc.: wood

PA: The Hattenbach Company
　　5309 Hamilton Ave
　　Cleveland OH 44114
　　216 881-5200

(G-21108)
HOMER G WALLER JR
Also Called: Yse
3142 Southern Blvd (44507-1836)
PHONE.....................330 788-4023
Fax: 330 788-4593
Homer G Waller Jr, *Owner*
Allen Waller, *Admin Sec*
EMP: 4
SQ FT: 3,800
SALES: 350K **Privately Held**
SIC: **3589** High pressure cleaning equipment

(G-21109)
HOWARD GRANT CORPORATION
Also Called: Vector Laboratories
316 Alexander St (44502-2117)
P.O. Box 47, Lowellville (44436-0047)
PHONE.....................330 743-3151
Fax: 330 743-3155
Morgan Geddes, *President*
Claudia Hirschochs, *Vice Pres*
Patty Meehan, *Sales Mgr*
Loree Forman, *Shareholder*
Charles Kortan, *Shareholder*
EMP: 6
SQ FT: 8,000
SALES: 507.4K **Privately Held**
WEB: www.vectorchemicals.com
SIC: **2841** Detergents, synthetic organic or inorganic alkaline

(G-21110)
HUDSON FASTENERS INC
241 W Federal St 512 (44503-1207)
PHONE.....................330 270-9500
Lisa Kleinhandler, *President*
Cris Young, *Exec VP*
EMP: 4
SQ FT: 3,000
SALES (est): 590K **Privately Held**
WEB: www.hudsonfasteners.com
SIC: **5072** 3452 3429 Bolts; nuts (hardware); screws; washers (hardware); wood screws; metal fasteners

(G-21111)
HYNES INDUSTRIES INC (PA)
Also Called: Roll Formed Products Co Div
3805 Hericks Rd (44515)
P.O. Box 2459 (44509-0459)
PHONE.....................330 799-3221
Fax: 330 799-9098
William W Bresnahan, *Ch of Bd*
William J Bresnahan, *President*
D R Golding, *President*
C A Covington Jr, *Principal*
Joseph S Donchess, *Principal*
▲ EMP: 106
SQ FT: 154,000
SALES (est): 62.6MM **Privately Held**
WEB: www.hynesind.com
SIC: **5051** 3449 3316 3441 Metals service centers & offices; strip, metal; custom roll formed products; wire, flat, cold-rolled strip: not made in hot-rolled mills; fabricated structural metal

(G-21112)
I-DEE-X INC
Also Called: Idx Supply Division
4302 Lake Park Rd (44512-1830)
PHONE.....................330 788-2186
Fax: 330 788-4320
Martin Mayer Jr, *President*
EMP: 4
SQ FT: 5,400
SALES: 388.6K **Privately Held**
SIC: **5085** 3544 Industrial supplies; special dies & tools

(G-21113)
IMDS CORPORATION
Also Called: Imds Defense Systems
840 Mcclurg Rd (44512-6411)
PHONE.....................330 747-4637
Robert A Hill Jr, *President*
Robert Holecko, *Purchasing*
Linda Spencer, *Sales Staff*

▲ = Import ▼=Export
◆ =Import/Export

Joseph Pivovar, *Manager*
Larry D Sztary, *Manager*
EMP: 10
SQ FT: 18,600
SALES (est): 1.2MM **Privately Held**
WEB: www.imds-ohio.com
SIC: 3599 8711 Machine shop, jobbing & repair; industrial engineers

(G-21114)
INDUCTION IRON INCORPORATED
3710 Hendricks Rd Bldg 1 (44515-1537)
PHONE.....................330 501-8852
Robert Macklin, *Manager*
EMP: 5
SALES (corp-wide): 4.5MM **Privately Held**
SIC: 5093 3444 Ferrous metal scrap & waste; sheet metalwork
PA: Induction Iron Incorporated
13909 N Dale Mabry Hwy # 203
Tampa FL 33618
813 969-3300

(G-21115)
INDUSTRIAL MILL MAINTENANCE
1609 Wilson Ave Ste 2 (44506-1838)
P.O. Box 1465 (44501-1465)
PHONE.....................330 746-1155
Fax: 330 747-7017
Michael McCarthy Sr, *President*
Kathy McCarthy, *Vice Pres*
EMP: 50
SQ FT: 5,600
SALES: 4MM **Privately Held**
SIC: 3471 1721 3444 3441 Sand blasting of metal parts; industrial painting; sheet metalwork; fabricated structural metal

(G-21116)
INK FACTORY INC
2750 Salt Springs Rd (44509-1034)
PHONE.....................330 799-0888
Charles Nannicola, *President*
Kevin McHenry, *Vice Pres*
Jeff Joseph, *Manager*
EMP: 4
SQ FT: 12,000
SALES (est): 438K **Privately Held**
WEB: www.nannicola.com
SIC: 2893 3944 2899 Printing ink; games, toys & children's vehicles; chemical preparations

(G-21117)
INNERSOURCE INC
755 Wick Ave (44505-2826)
PHONE.....................330 799-7619
Fax: 330 799-5222
Gloria B Byce, *President*
Terri Gallagher, *Corp Secy*
Margaret Byce, *Vice Pres*
EMP: 11
SALES (est): 1.1MM **Privately Held**
WEB: www.innersource.com
SIC: 3993 Signs & advertising specialties

(G-21118)
INNOVATION EXHIBITS INC
85 Karago Ave Ste 1&2 (44512-5969)
P.O. Box 3198 (44513-3198)
PHONE.....................330 726-1324
Monica Gable, *President*
EMP: 5
SALES (corp-wide): 1.2MM **Privately Held**
WEB: www.innovationexhibits.com
SIC: 3993 Signs & advertising specialties
PA: Innovation Exhibits, Inc.
850 Mcclurg Rd
Youngstown OH 44512
330 726-1324

(G-21119)
INTERNATIONAL DIES CO INC
117 S Blaine Ave (44506-1800)
PHONE.....................330 744-7951
Fax: 330 744-7958
Ted Lyda, *President*
EMP: 6
SQ FT: 13,400
SALES (est): 410K **Privately Held**
SIC: 3544 Extrusion dies

(G-21120)
INTIGRAL INC
45 Karago Ave (44512-5950)
PHONE.....................440 439-0980
Michael McHugh, *Manager*
EMP: 27
SALES (corp-wide): 50.1MM **Privately Held**
WEB: www.edgeseal.com
SIC: 3231 Insulating glass: made from purchased glass
PA: Intigral, Inc.
7850 Northfield Rd
Bedford OH 44146
440 439-0980

(G-21121)
IRON CITY WOOD PRODUCTS INC
900 Albert St (44505-2968)
PHONE.....................330 755-2772
Fax: 330 755-2709
David S Muslovski, *President*
Denise Muslovski, *Vice Pres*
Christina Yanssens, *Vice Pres*
Tina Yanssens, *Asst Mgr*
EMP: 48
SQ FT: 2,560
SALES (est): 8.5MM **Privately Held**
WEB: www.ironcitywoodproducts.com
SIC: 2448 Pallets, wood

(G-21122)
J TREHARN CO INC
1024 Mahoning Ave Ste 5 (44502-1452)
PHONE.....................330 743-8215
Sherry Treharn, *President*
EMP: 18
SQ FT: 20,000
SALES: 2.5MM **Privately Held**
WEB: www.jltreharn.com
SIC: 2511 Wood household furniture

(G-21123)
JAMEN TOOL & DIE CO (PA)
Also Called: Truex Tool & Die Div
4450 Lake Park Rd (44512-1809)
PHONE.....................330 788-6521
Fax: 330 788-5735
Antonette Chicone, *Vice Pres*
Carmen Chicone Jr, *Shareholder*
Paul Chicone, *Shareholder*
EMP: 19 EST: 1965
SQ FT: 5,000
SALES (est): 8.6MM **Privately Held**
SIC: 3544 Extrusion dies

(G-21124)
JAMEN TOOL & DIE CO
Also Called: Mor-X Plastics
914 E Indianola Ave (44502-2674)
PHONE.....................330 782-6731
Fax: 330 782-0868
Bob Marcum, *Manager*
EMP: 22
SALES (corp-wide): 8.6MM **Privately Held**
SIC: 3544 Special dies, tools, jigs & fixtures
PA: Jamen Tool & Die Co.
4450 Lake Park Rd
Youngstown OH 44512
330 788-6521

(G-21125)
JAMESTOWN INDUSTRIES INC
650 N Meridian Rd Ste 3 (44509-1233)
PHONE.....................330 779-0670
Fax: 330 779-0671
Clark Babb, *Manager*
EMP: 60
SQ FT: 32,000
SALES (corp-wide): 11MM **Privately Held**
SIC: 3493 Steel springs, except wire
PA: Jamestown Industries, Inc.
2210 Arbor Blvd Ste 99
Moraine OH 45439
937 643-5354

(G-21126)
JEWISH JOURNAL MONTHLY MAG
505 Gypsy Ln (44504-1314)
PHONE.....................330 746-3251
Sherry Weinblatt, *Principal*

Alla Verkhlin, *Office Admin*
Sam Cooperman, *Exec Dir*
Cristal Vincent, *Asst Admin*
Debbie Kascak, *Social Worker*
EMP: 4
SALES: 150K **Privately Held**
WEB: www.jewishyoungstown.org
SIC: 2711 Newspapers, publishing & printing

(G-21127)
JONES & ASSOC ADVG & DESIGN
5015 Mahoning Ave Ste 1 (44515-1701)
PHONE.....................330 799-6876
Diane Jones, *Owner*
EMP: 3 EST: 2009
SALES: 100K **Privately Held**
SIC: 5949 5099 3993 2759 Sewing, needlework & piece goods; signs, except electric; signs & advertising specialties; screen printing; T-shirts, custom printed

(G-21128)
KIND SPECIAL ALLOYS US LLC
1221 Velma Ct (44512-1829)
PHONE.....................330 788-2437
Lora Hull, *Office Mgr*
Susanne Wildner,
EMP: 4
SALES (est): 177.3K **Privately Held**
SIC: 3312 Tool & die steel & alloys

(G-21129)
KIRALY TOOL AND DIE INC
1250 Crescent St (44502-1303)
PHONE.....................330 744-5773
Fax: 330 744-5753
Steve Kiraly, *President*
Shari Kiraly, *Vice Pres*
Kyle Kiraly, *Controller*
Larry Diedrick, *Supervisor*
EMP: 10
SQ FT: 9,500
SALES: 750K **Privately Held**
WEB: www.kiralytool.com
SIC: 3542 3544 Machine tools, metal forming type; special dies, tools, jigs & fixtures

(G-21130)
L M ENGINEERING INC
2720 Intertech Dr (44509-4023)
PHONE.....................330 270-2400
Fax: 330 270-2424
Joann Laguardia, *President*
William Laguardia, *Corp Secy*
Dave Young, *Plant Mgr*
David Hendrick, *Engineer*
Samuel Bowser, *Design Engr*
EMP: 25
SQ FT: 40,000
SALES (est): 5.4MM **Privately Held**
SIC: 3161 Musical instrument cases; cases, carrying

(G-21131)
LAKE PARK TOOL & MACHINE LLC
1221 Velma Ct (44512-1829)
PHONE.....................330 788-2437
Fax: 330 788-4946
Oscar Lund, *President*
Dave Cornelius, *Principal*
Susanne Wildner, *Principal*
EMP: 13
SALES (est): 572.6K **Privately Held**
SIC: 3429 Manufactured hardware (general)

(G-21132)
LARICCIAS ITALIAN FOODS
7438 Southern Blvd (44512-5629)
PHONE.....................330 729-0222
Fax: 330 726-9729
Tessa Lariccia, *President*
Michael Allegretto, *Vice Pres*
Michael Allegritto, *Vice Pres*
EMP: 10 EST: 1910
SQ FT: 4,000
SALES (est): 1.2MM **Privately Held**
SIC: 5411 2098 2035 Grocery stores, independent; macaroni & spaghetti; pickles, sauces & salad dressings

(G-21133)
LARRYS DRIVE THRU & MINI MART
3305 Center Rd (44514-2204)
PHONE.....................330 953-0512
Diana M Ornelas, *Principal*
EMP: 3 EST: 2011
SALES (est): 204.9K **Privately Held**
SIC: 5411 2082 2084 Convenience stores; beer (alcoholic beverage); wines

(G-21134)
LIBERTY PATTERN AND MOLD INC
1131 Meadowbrook Ave (44512-1822)
PHONE.....................330 788-9463
John Plaskett, *President*
EMP: 7
SQ FT: 4,800
SALES: 400K **Privately Held**
WEB: www.libpattern.com
SIC: 3543 Industrial patterns

(G-21135)
LUBE DEPOT
6122 Market St (44512-3326)
PHONE.....................330 758-0570
Rex McMasters, *General Mgr*
EMP: 5
SALES (est): 312.8K **Privately Held**
SIC: 3559 Automotive maintenance equipment

(G-21136)
M A K FABRICATING INC
1609 Wilson Ave (44506-1838)
P.O. Box 212 (44501-0212)
PHONE.....................330 747-0040
Dan Maccarthy, *President*
EMP: 10
SQ FT: 54,000
SALES (est): 1.4MM **Privately Held**
SIC: 3499 Fire- or burglary-resistive products

(G-21137)
M F Y INC
Also Called: Youngstown Metal Fabricating
1640 Wilson Ave (44506-1839)
PHONE.....................330 747-1334
Fax: 330 747-3511
Andrew Weaver Jr, *President*
Bob Straley, *Administration*
EMP: 15
SQ FT: 35,000
SALES (est): 1.5MM **Privately Held**
SIC: 3446 Architectural metalwork; stairs, staircases, stair treads: prefabricated metal

(G-21138)
M I P INC
701 Jones St (44502-2160)
PHONE.....................330 744-0215
Fax: 330 744-3544
Richard B Weaver Jr, *President*
Leigh Marsden, *President*
Melvin Weaver Jr, *President*
Russel W Brown, *Vice Pres*
Judy W Milton, *Vice Pres*
EMP: 19
SQ FT: 50,000
SALES: 2.1MM **Privately Held**
SIC: 3471 Finishing, metals or formed products; electroplating of metals or formed products

(G-21139)
M MANUFACTURING INC
75 S Turner Rd (44515-4319)
P.O. Box 4052, Austintown (44515-0052)
PHONE.....................330 793-6806
Fax: 330 793-3366
James Molnar, *President*
Charlene Delbone, *Admin Sec*
EMP: 3
SALES: 300K **Privately Held**
WEB: www.mmanufacturing.com
SIC: 3799 Trailers & trailer equipment

(G-21140)
MAGNETIC ANALYSIS CORPORATION
675 Mcclurg Rd (44512-6408)
PHONE.....................330 758-1367

Fax: 330 758-5393
Joseph Baldauff, *Regional Mgr*
Joseph V Vitulli, *Vice Pres*
Manuel Morales, *Manager*
Clifford Guarino, *Info Tech Mgr*
EMP: 15
SQ FT: 19,000
SALES (corp-wide): 34.9MM **Privately Held**
WEB: www.mac-ndt.com
SIC: 3829 Testing equipment: abrasion, shearing strength, etc.
PA: Magnetic Analysis Corporation
　103 Fairview Pk Dr Ste 2
　Elmsford NY 10523
　914 530-2000

(G-21141)
MARK RITE CO
206 Evergreen Dr (44514-3706)
PHONE................................330 757-7229
Margaret Broadwater, *Principal*
EMP: 4
SALES (est): 169.9K **Privately Held**
SIC: 3953 Marking devices; textile marking stamps, hand: rubber or metal

(G-21142)
MCHENRY INDUSTRIES INC
85 Victoria Rd (44515-2023)
PHONE................................330 799-8930
Fax: 330 799-5051
Robert P Willison, *President*
Ron Musilli Sr, *President*
Ronald Musilli, *Vice Pres*
Ronald Kovach, *Human Res Dir*
EMP: 24 **EST:** 1964
SQ FT: 20,000
SALES (est): 6.1MM **Privately Held**
WEB: www.mchenryindustries.com
SIC: 3083 3315 Thermoplastic laminates: rods, tubes, plates & sheet; steel wire & related products

(G-21143)
MERIDIAN ARTS AND GRAPHICS
16 Belgrade St (44505-1818)
PHONE................................330 759-9099
Fax: 330 759-5113
Ted Webb, *President*
Robert Millham, *Vice Pres*
Cheryl Millham, *Admin Sec*
EMP: 11
SQ FT: 10,000
SALES (est): 1.1MM **Privately Held**
WEB: www.meridianarts.com
SIC: 7336 2752 Art design services; lithographing on metal

(G-21144)
MERIDIAN MANUFACTURING COMPANY
1191 N Meridian Rd (44509-1018)
PHONE................................330 793-9632
James Povhe, *President*
EMP: 3
SQ FT: 687
SALES (est): 220K **Privately Held**
SIC: 3599 Machine & other job shop work

(G-21145)
MID-STATE SALES INC
Also Called: Youngstown Rubber Products
854 Mahoning Ave (44502-1408)
PHONE................................330 744-2158
James B Tomaino, *Manager*
EMP: 8
SALES (corp-wide): 26.5MM **Privately Held**
WEB: www.midstate-sales.com
SIC: 5085 3492 Rubber goods, mechanical; hose & tube fittings & assemblies, hydraulic/pneumatic
PA: Mid-State Sales, Inc.
　1101 Gahanna Pkwy
　Columbus OH 43230
　614 864-1811

(G-21146)
MILLER CURBER COMPANY LLC
4020 Simon Rd (44512-1320)
PHONE................................330 782-8081
Fax: 330 782-1047

James B Rochette, *President*
Jim Rochette, *General Mgr*
Randall Best, *Vice Pres*
E Russell, *Manager*
Hank Rochette,
▲ **EMP:** 10
SQ FT: 20,000
SALES (est): 2.2MM **Privately Held**
WEB: www.millerspreader.com
SIC: 3531 Road construction & maintenance machinery

(G-21147)
MODERN BUILDERS SUPPLY INC (PA)
Also Called: Polaris Technologies
302 Mcclurg Rd (44512-6401)
P.O. Box 9393 (44513-0393)
PHONE................................330 729-2690
Fax: 330 729-2696
Kevin Leggett, *CEO*
Larry Leggett, *Ch of Bd*
Kevin Buchholtz, *General Mgr*
Eric Leggett, *Vice Pres*
Jack Marstellar, *Vice Pres*
EMP: 200
SQ FT: 40,000
SALES (est): 437.3MM **Privately Held**
WEB: www.polaristechnologies.com
SIC: 5032 3089 3446 3442 Brick, stone & related material; windows, plastic; doors, folding: plastic or plastic coated fabric; architectural metalwork; metal doors, sash & trim

(G-21148)
NATIONAL TOOL & EQUIPMENT INC
60 Karago Ave (44512-5949)
PHONE................................330 629-8665
Fax: 330 629-8750
James Simon Jr, *CEO*
Anthony Vross, *President*
Alex Simon, *Admin Sec*
EMP: 10
SQ FT: 8,000
SALES (est): 747.6K **Privately Held**
SIC: 7699 5084 5072 5251 Engine repair & replacement, non-automotive; tool repair services; fans, industrial; hand tools; power tools & accessories; tools; asphalt felts & coatings

(G-21149)
NELIS PRINTING CO
5146 Sterling Ave (44515-3952)
PHONE................................330 757-4114
Fax: 330 755-2974
David Nelis, *Owner*
EMP: 3 **EST:** 1953
SALES (est): 227.2K **Privately Held**
SIC: 2752 2759 Commercial printing, offset; letterpress printing

(G-21150)
NOMIS PUBLICATIONS INC
Also Called: Boardman Printing
8570 Foxwood Ct (44514-4301)
P.O. Box 5159 (44514-0159)
PHONE................................330 965-2380
Fax: 330 965-2381
Lucille Mc Guire, *President*
Margaret Rouzzo, *Corp Secy*
Kim Graham, *Vice Pres*
Dana Depillo, *Marketing Staff*
Peggy Rouzzo, *Executive*
EMP: 15
SQ FT: 7,000
SALES (est): 1.6MM **Privately Held**
WEB: www.yelobk.com
SIC: 2741 2711 2752 2759 Directories: publishing only, not printed on site; newspapers: publishing only, not printed on site; commercial printing, offset; commercial printing

(G-21151)
NORTHERN STATES METALS COMPANY
3207 Innovation Pl (44509-4025)
PHONE................................860 521-6001
Robert Voytilla, *Branch Mgr*
EMP: 60
SQ FT: 4,000

SALES (corp-wide): 21.6MM **Privately Held**
WEB: www.extrusions.com
SIC: 3354 Aluminum extruded products
PA: Northern States Metals Company
　3207 Innovation Pl
　Youngstown OH 44509
　330 799-1855

(G-21152)
ODYSSEY CELLARS INC
4033 Hopkins Rd (44511-3442)
PHONE................................330 782-0177
Ed Goist, *President*
EMP: 3
SALES (est): 169.4K **Privately Held**
SIC: 2084 Wines

(G-21153)
OGR PUBLISHING INC
Also Called: O Gauge Railroading
33 Sheridan Rd Ste 1 (44514-1680)
PHONE................................330 757-3020
Fax: 330 757-3771
Richard P Melvin, *President*
Linda Melvin, *Accounting Mgr*
EMP: 7
SQ FT: 4,000
SALES (est): 545.3K **Privately Held**
WEB: www.webhostsvc.com
SIC: 2741 Miscellaneous publishing

(G-21154)
OHIO FLAME
7655 Spring Park Dr (44512-5328)
P.O. Box 3368 (44513-3368)
PHONE................................330 953-0863
EMP: 3 **EST:** 2011
SALES (est): 181.6K **Privately Held**
SIC: 3272 Fireplace & chimney material: concrete

(G-21155)
OHIO FOAM CORPORATION
1201 Ameritech Blvd (44509-4022)
PHONE................................330 799-4553
Fax: 330 799-4565
Jerry Necastro, *Vice Pres*
Terri Lady, *Human Res Mgr*
Pete Kesler, *Sales Mgr*
Jerry Mouser, *Branch Mgr*
EMP: 25
SALES (corp-wide): 13MM **Privately Held**
WEB: www.ohiofoam.com
SIC: 3069 Medical & laboratory rubber sundries & related products
PA: Ohio Foam Corporation
　820 Plymouth St
　Bucyrus OH 44820
　419 563-0399

(G-21156)
OHIO VALLEY ENERGY SYSTEMS
200 Victoria Rd Bldg 4 (44515-2093)
PHONE................................330 799-2268
Charles W Masters, *President*
John Moore, *Director*
Daniel Notar, *Planning*
EMP: 2
SQ FT: 9,000
SALES (est): 2MM **Privately Held**
SIC: 1381 1382 Drilling oil & gas wells; oil & gas exploration services

(G-21157)
ONEALS TARPAULIN & AWNING CO
Also Called: Air Locke Dock Seal Division
549 W Indianola Ave (44511-2460)
PHONE................................330 788-6504
Fax: 330 788-6705
Greg O'Neal, *President*
Dan O'Neal, *Vice Pres*
Larry O'Neal, *Admin Sec*
EMP: 17 **EST:** 1935
SQ FT: 32,000
SALES: 800K **Privately Held**
WEB: www.onealawnings.com
SIC: 2394 3448 Canvas & related products; awnings, fabric: made from purchased materials; tarpaulins, fabric: made from purchased materials; prefabricated metal buildings

(G-21158)
P & L HEAT TREATING & GRINDING
948 Poland Ave (44502-2137)
PHONE................................330 746-8081
David Maxwell Sr, *Principal*
EMP: 8
SALES (est): 643.9K **Privately Held**
SIC: 7699 7389 3398 Knife, saw & tool sharpening & repair; grinding, precision: commercial or industrial; metal heat treating

(G-21159)
P & L HEAT TRTING GRINDING INC
313 E Wood St (44503-1691)
PHONE................................330 746-1339
Fax: 330 746-7029
William H Pociask, *President*
Ken Malysa, *QC Mgr*
Larion Senderov, *Supervisor*
Helen Premec, *Admin Sec*
EMP: 28
SQ FT: 16,000
SALES (est): 5.9MM **Privately Held**
WEB: www.plheattreatinggrinding.com
SIC: 3398 3599 3471 Metal heat treating; grinding castings for the trade; plating & polishing

(G-21160)
P & L METALCRAFTS LLC
1050 Ohio Works Dr (44510-1077)
PHONE................................330 793-2178
Fax: 330 793-2182
Mary Ann Troy, *Office Mgr*
John Lyras, *Mng Member*
EMP: 12 **EST:** 1959
SALES (est): 3.2MM
SALES (corp-wide): 20.5MM **Privately Held**
WEB: www.metalcrafts.com
SIC: 3446 3444 3441 Ornamental metalwork; sheet metalwork; fabricated structural metal
PA: Jolley Industrial Supply Co., Inc.
　105 Agate Way 109
　Sharon PA 16146
　724 981-5400

(G-21161)
P-AMERICAS LLC
Also Called: Pepsico
500 Pepsi Pl (44502-1432)
PHONE................................330 746-7652
Richard Plant, *Manager*
Ransom Lane, *Manager*
EMP: 105
SALES (corp-wide): 62.8B **Publicly Held**
SIC: 2086 5149 4225 Bottled & canned soft drinks; groceries & related products; general warehousing & storage
HQ: P-Americas Llc
　1 Pepsi Way
　Somers NY

(G-21162)
PANELMATIC INC
Also Called: Panelmatic Youngstown
1125 Meadowbrook Ave (44512-1884)
PHONE................................330 782-8007
Fax: 330 782-0047
Gary M Urso, *Branch Mgr*
EMP: 29
SALES (corp-wide): 32MM **Privately Held**
WEB: www.panelmatic.com
SIC: 3613 8711 Control panels, electric; cubicles (electric switchboard equipment); designing: ship, boat, machine & product
PA: Panelmatic, Inc.
　258 Donald Dr
　Fairfield OH 45014
　513 829-3666

(G-21163)
PANELMATIC YOUNGSTOWN INC
1125 Meadowbrook Ave (44512-1884)
PHONE................................330 782-8007
Richard Leach, *President*
Cory Jones, *General Mgr*
David D Adamson, *CFO*
▼ **EMP:** 40

▲ = Import ▼ =Export
◆ =Import/Export

SQ FT: 44,000
SALES (est): 7.7MM
SALES (corp-wide): 32MM **Privately
Held**
WEB: www.panelmatic.com
SIC: 3613 Control panels, electric; cubicles
(electric switchboard equipment)
PA: Panelmatic, Inc.
258 Donald Dr
Fairfield OH 45014
513 829-3666

(G-21164)
**PARK PLC PRNTG CPYG &
DGTL IMG**
3410 Canfield Rd Ste B (44511-2713)
PHONE..................................330 799-1739
Kay F Probst, *President*
EMP: 6
SALES (est): 434.6K **Privately Held**
SIC: 2759 Commercial printing

(G-21165)
**PARKER-HANNIFIN
CORPORATION**
1911 Logan Ave (44505-2673)
PHONE..................................330 740-8366
Michael Wood, *Principal*
EMP: 126
SALES (corp-wide): 11.3B **Publicly Held**
SIC: 3594 Fluid power pumps
PA: Parker-Hannifin Corporation
6035 Parkland Blvd
Cleveland OH 44124
216 896-3000

(G-21166)
**PARKER-HANNIFIN
CORPORATION**
Mobile Cylinder Division
58 Hubbard Rd (44505-3117)
PHONE..................................330 743-6893
Fax: 330 740-8636
Dave Olson, *General Mgr*
Bob Smith, *Engineer*
Stanley Hetrick, *IT/INT Sup*
Beth Mistovich, *Admin Asst*
EMP: 11
SALES (corp-wide): 11.3B **Publicly Held**
WEB: www.parker.com
SIC: 3593 Fluid power cylinders, hydraulic
or pneumatic
PA: Parker-Hannifin Corporation
6035 Parkland Blvd
Cleveland OH 44124
216 896-3000

(G-21167)
**PATRICIAN FURNITURE
BUILDERS**
1097 Wick Ave (44505-2860)
PHONE..................................330 746-6354
Kenneth Mason, *President*
Louis Loverde, *Admin Sec*
EMP: 4
SQ FT: 15,000
SALES: 400K **Privately Held**
SIC: 2511 Wood household furniture

(G-21168)
PATRIOT SEATING INC
1584 Tamarisk Trl (44514-3632)
PHONE..................................330 779-0768
Fax: 330 779-0261
Kenneth Altiero, *President*
Sam Marocco, *Vice Pres*
EMP: 13
SALES (est): 1.2MM **Privately Held**
SIC: 2522 Office furniture, except wood

(G-21169)
PERFETTES SAUSAGE LLC
1264 S Schenley Ave (44511-1255)
PHONE..................................330 792-0775
Chris Burton,
Joe Perfette,
EMP: 3
SALES (est): 155.7K **Privately Held**
SIC: 2013 5812 Sausages & other pre-
pared meats; sandwiches & submarines
shop

(G-21170)
PESCE BAKING COMPANY LTD
45 N Hine St (44506-1203)
PHONE..................................330 746-6537
Fax: 330 746-6672
Gary Cellone, *Partner*
Dean Cellone,
EMP: 25
SALES (est): 2.4MM **Privately Held**
SIC: 2051 Bread, cake & related products

(G-21171)
**PLASTIC PRODUCTS AND
SUPPLY**
1305 Lilac St (44502-1309)
PHONE..................................330 744-5076
Fax: 330 744-5957
Craig Wylie, *President*
Sidney Wiley, *Corp Secy*
EMP: 3 EST: 1945
SQ FT: 9,000
SALES: 286K **Privately Held**
SIC: 7389 3089 Engraving service; plastic
processing

(G-21172)
POLY TEC EAST INC
550 N Meridian Rd (44509-1226)
PHONE..................................330 799-7876
Tracey A Hoffman, *President*
Kelly A Kempf, *Corp Secy*
Kerry L Thomas, *Vice Pres*
Cheryl Dunn, *Asst Treas*
Jennifer Skowron, *Administration*
▲ EMP: 8
SALES (est): 590K **Privately Held**
SIC: 3083 Laminated plastic sheets

(G-21173)
POLYTECH COMPONENT CORP
8469 Southern Blvd (44512-6709)
PHONE..................................330 726-3235
Fax: 330 726-2202
Paul Colby, *President*
Robert Barber, *Vice Pres*
Michael Durina, *Vice Pres*
William White, *Treasurer*
Illene Colby, *Admin Sec*
EMP: 25
SQ FT: 6,000
SALES: 2.5MM **Privately Held**
SIC: 3599 Machine shop, jobbing & repair

(G-21174)
**PPG ARCHITECTURAL FINISHES
INC**
Also Called: Glidden Professional Paint Ctr
4440 Market St Unit 127 (44512-1512)
PHONE..................................330 788-2421
Fax: 330 788-2303
Selina Bell, *Sales/Mktg Mgr*
EMP: 5
SALES (corp-wide): 14.7B **Publicly Held**
WEB: www.gliddenpaint.com
SIC: 2891 Adhesives
HQ: Ppg Architectural Finishes, Inc.
1 Ppg Pl
Pittsburgh PA 15272
412 434-3131

(G-21175)
**PRECISION FOAM FABRICATION
INC**
2716 Intertech Dr (44509-4023)
PHONE..................................330 270-2440
Fax: 330 370-2424
Joann Laguargia, *President*
Brendan McCloud, *General Mgr*
Bill Laguardia Jr, *Treasurer*
Paula Rich, *Manager*
EMP: 15
SALES (est): 2.8MM **Privately Held**
WEB: www.precisionfoam.com
SIC: 3086 Plastics foam products

(G-21176)
PRECISION OF OHIO INC
3850 Hendricks Rd (44515-1528)
PHONE..................................330 793-0900
Fax: 330 793-9098
Mike Pallotta, *Manager*
▲ EMP: 18
SALES (est): 3.9MM **Privately Held**
SIC: 3354 Aluminum extruded products

(G-21177)
**PRESSED COFFEE BAR &
EATERY**
215 Lincoln Ave (44503-1013)
PHONE..................................330 746-8030
EMP: 4
SALES (est): 163.8K **Privately Held**
SIC: 2741 Miscellaneous publishing

(G-21178)
PRINTING 3D PARTS INC
16 Belgrade St (44505-1818)
PHONE..................................330 759-9099
Theodore Webb, *President*
Paul Palovich, *Vice Pres*
EMP: 4
SALES (est): 192.5K **Privately Held**
SIC: 3089 Synthetic resin finished products

(G-21179)
PRINTING DEPOT INC
3828 Southern Blvd (44507-2078)
PHONE..................................330 783-5341
Fax: 330 783-9508
Sandy Parker, *President*
Kevin Farr, *Vice Pres*
EMP: 3
SALES: 150K **Privately Held**
SIC: 2759 Commercial printing

(G-21180)
**PROUT BOILER HTG & WLDG
INC**
3124 Temple St (44510-1048)
PHONE..................................330 744-0293
Fax: 330 744-0717
Wes Prout, *President*
Richard Dalleske, *Vice Pres*
Wesley Prou, *Info Tech Dir*
Linda Prout, *Shareholder*
Donald Raybuck, *Admin Sec*
EMP: 50 EST: 1945
SQ FT: 3,000
SALES (est): 10.1MM **Privately Held**
WEB: www.proutboiler.com
SIC: 1711 7692 3443 Boiler maintenance
contractor; heating & air conditioning con-
tractors; plumbing contractors; mechani-
cal contractor; welding repair; fabricated
plate work (boiler shop)

(G-21181)
**QUALITY SEATING COMPANY
INC**
4136 Logan Way (44505-5703)
PHONE..................................330 747-0181
Frank J Joy, *President*
Roger E Gasser, *Vice Pres*
Evelyn Mihin, *CFO*
EMP: 35 EST: 1978
SQ FT: 45,000
SALES (est): 3MM **Privately Held**
SIC: 2599 2531 Restaurant furniture,
wood or metal; public building & related
furniture

(G-21182)
R & M FLUID POWER INC
7953 Southern Blvd (44512-6091)
PHONE..................................330 758-2766
Fax: 330 758-2095
Robert Gustafson Sr, *Ch of Bd*
Robert Gustafson II, *Vice Pres*
Jennifer Kenetz, *Treasurer*
Melissa Ricciardi, *Admin Sec*
EMP: 25
SQ FT: 40,000
SALES (est): 5.5MM **Privately Held**
WEB: www.rmfluidpower.com
SIC: 3593 5084 Fluid power cylinders &
actuators; hydraulic systems equipment &
supplies

(G-21183)
R T COMMUNICATIONS INC
Also Called: Sprint Signs & Graphics
6031 Applecrest Dr (44512-3143)
PHONE..................................330 726-7892
Fax: 330 726-4443
David Touvelle, *President*
Rick Rush, *Corp Secy*
EMP: 4
SALES: 125K **Privately Held**
SIC: 2499 7374 Signboards, wood; com-
puter graphics service

(G-21184)
R W SIDLEY INCORPORATED
3424 Oregon Ave (44509-1075)
PHONE..................................330 793-7374
Fax: 330 793-5761
Dave Moore, *Managing Dir*
Gary Hawkins, *Manager*
Jeff Hochendoner, *Manager*
Janey Mental, *Manager*
EMP: 25
SALES (corp-wide): 143.8MM **Privately
Held**
WEB: www.rwsidleyinc.com
SIC: 5032 3273 Brick, stone & related ma-
terial; ready-mixed concrete
PA: R. W. Sidley Incorporated
436 Casement Ave
Painesville OH 44077
440 352-9343

(G-21185)
RAM Z NEON
1227 E Indianola Ave (44502-2645)
PHONE..................................330 788-5121
Greg Ramsey, *Partner*
Jeff Ramsey, *Partner*
Walt Woznak, *Partner*
EMP: 4
SALES: 180K **Privately Held**
SIC: 3993 Signs & advertising specialties

(G-21186)
RB FABRICATORS INC
4021 Mahoning Ave (44515-2904)
PHONE..................................330 779-0263
Fax: 330 779-0045
James E Sullivan, *President*
EMP: 15
SQ FT: 72,000
SALES: 1.5MM **Privately Held**
WEB: www.rbfabricators.com
SIC: 3441 Fabricated structural metal

(G-21187)
REGAL TOOL & DIE INC
712 Andrews Ave (44505-2942)
PHONE..................................330 746-6644
Fax: 330 746-7208
Gary S Kiraly, *President*
EMP: 8
SQ FT: 7,400
SALES: 1MM **Privately Held**
WEB: www.regaltooldie.com
SIC: 3544 Special dies & tools

(G-21188)
RICCI ANTHONY
Also Called: Rich Print
755 Boardman Canfield Rd (44512-4300)
PHONE..................................330 758-5761
Anthony Ricci, *President*
EMP: 4
SALES (est): 280K **Privately Held**
SIC: 2752 7334 2791 2789 Commercial
printing, lithographic; photocopying & du-
plicating services; typesetting; bookbind-
ing & related work

(G-21189)
RL SMITH PRINTING CO
4030 Simon Rd (44512-1320)
PHONE..................................330 747-9590
Ronald Smith, *Principal*
Tim Ruffo, *Marketing Staff*
EMP: 10
SALES (est): 1.2MM **Privately Held**
SIC: 2759 Commercial printing

(G-21190)
RNW HOLDINGS INC
200 Division Street Ext (44510-1000)
P.O. Box 478 (44501-0478)
PHONE..................................330 792-0600
Fax: 330 792-1459
Major Hammond, *Branch Mgr*
Thomas Norris, *Director*
EMP: 40
SALES (corp-wide): 52.8MM **Privately
Held**
SIC: 5093 1795 3341 Scrap & waste ma-
terials; wrecking & demolition work; sec-
ondary nonferrous metals
HQ: Rnw Holdings, Inc.
26949 Chagrin Blvd # 305
Cleveland OH 44122
216 831-0510

(G-21191)
ROBERTS GRAPHIC CENTER
5375 Market St (44512-2252)
PHONE...........................330 788-4642
Fax: 330 788-5600
Robert Patrick, *Owner*
EMP: 5
SQ FT: 1,500
SALES (est): 504K **Privately Held**
SIC: 2752 7336 Commercial printing, off-set; graphic arts & related design

(G-21192)
ROCKYS GYM
1285 Boardman Canfield Rd (44512-4058)
PHONE...........................330 965-0464
Robert Nemcik, *Owner*
EMP: 3
SALES (est): 201.6K **Privately Held**
SIC: 3949 Gymnasium equipment

(G-21193)
ROMAN CTHLIC DOCESE YOUNGSTOWN
Also Called: Catholic Exponent
144 W Wood St Fl 1 (44503-1030)
P.O. Box 6787 (44501-6787)
PHONE...........................330 744-8451
Fax: 330 744-2848
Lou Jacquet, *Manager*
EMP: 8
SALES (corp-wide): 23.6MM **Privately Held**
WEB: www.stjosephmantua.com
SIC: 2711 Newspapers, publishing & printing
PA: Roman Catholic Diocese Of Youngstown
144 W Wood St
Youngstown OH 44503
330 744-8451

(G-21194)
RUST BELT BREWING LLC
1744 Overlook Ave (44509-2101)
PHONE...........................330 423-3818
Kenneth Blair, *Principal*
EMP: 5
SALES (est): 316.1K **Privately Held**
SIC: 2082 Malt beverages

(G-21195)
S & W CUSTOM TOPS INC
4300 Simon Rd (44512-1326)
PHONE...........................330 788-2525
Fax: 330 788-1863
Edward Sullivan, *President*
Phyllis Sullivan, *Vice Pres*
EMP: 6
SQ FT: 3,500
SALES: 550K **Privately Held**
SIC: 2434 1751 Wood kitchen cabinets; cabinet building & installation

(G-21196)
SAMMARTINO WELDING & AUTO SLS
155 W Indianola Ave (44507-1460)
PHONE...........................330 782-6086
Fax: 330 782-5727
Dayne C Sammartino, *Owner*
Dayne Sammartino, *Owner*
EMP: 4
SQ FT: 3,200
SALES (est): 244.7K **Privately Held**
SIC: 7538 7692 5521 General automotive repair shops; automotive welding; automobiles, used cars only

(G-21197)
SCHWEBEL BAKING COMPANY (PA)
965 E Midlothian Blvd (44502-2869)
P.O. Box 6018 (44501-6018)
PHONE...........................330 783-2860
Fax: 330 782-1774
Paul Schwebel, *President*
Zach Gross, *Division Mgr*
George Lockyer, *Division Mgr*
Bruce Raber, *District Mgr*
Alyson Winick, *Vice Pres*
EMP: 450 EST: 1906
SQ FT: 125,000

SALES: 170MM **Privately Held**
WEB: www.schwebels.com
SIC: 2051 Bread, cake & related products

(G-21198)
SDS NATIONAL LLC
Also Called: SDS Logistics Services
19 Colonial Dr Ste 27 (44505-2162)
PHONE...........................330 759-8066
Fax: 330 288-0265
Andrew Weiss, *CEO*
Tom Shapiro, *COO*
Annette Kelly, *Traffic Dir*
Samuel Shapiro,
Frank Venzdio,
EMP: 6
SALES (est): 1.8MM **Privately Held**
WEB: www.sdslogistics.com
SIC: 3559 4731 Recycling machinery; freight transportation arrangement

(G-21199)
SEIFERT PRINTING COMPANY
Also Called: Minuteman Press
3200 Belmont Ave Ste 11 (44505-1862)
PHONE...........................330 759-7414
Fax: 330 759-1783
Dean W Seifert Sr, *President*
Dawn Seifert, *Manager*
EMP: 4
SQ FT: 2,000
SALES (est): 400K **Privately Held**
SIC: 2752 Commercial printing, lithographic

(G-21200)
SHADE YOUNGSTOWN & ALUMINUM CO
Also Called: Richards Intrors Bldg Cmpnents
3335 South Ave (44502-2407)
P.O. Box 8627, Warren (44484-0627)
PHONE...........................330 782-2373
Fax: 330 788-1526
Richard Gula, *Owner*
EMP: 8
SQ FT: 15,000
SALES: 1.6MM **Privately Held**
SIC: 1542 2591 3444 3442 Commercial & office buildings, renovation & repair; venetian blinds; awnings, sheet metal; metal doors, sash & trim; millwork; canvas & related products

(G-21201)
SHELLY AND SANDS INC
Also Called: Mar Zane
2800 Center Rd (44514)
PHONE...........................330 743-8850
Bill Castle, *Manager*
EMP: 3
SALES (corp-wide): 301.4MM **Privately Held**
WEB: www.shellyandsands.com
SIC: 2951 Asphalt paving mixtures & blocks
PA: Shelly And Sands, Inc.
3570 S River Rd
Zanesville OH 43701
740 453-0721

(G-21202)
SHENANGO VALLEY SAND AND GRAV (PA)
7240 Glenwood Ave (44512-4800)
PHONE...........................330 758-9100
John Cernica, *President*
EMP: 4
SQ FT: 900
SALES (est): 955.9K **Privately Held**
WEB: www.pymatuning.com
SIC: 1442 Common sand mining; gravel mining

(G-21203)
SIFTED SWEET SHOP LLC
4496 Mahoning Ave Ste 905 (44515-1601)
PHONE...........................216 901-7100
Nichelle Hall, *Principal*
EMP: 4
SALES (est): 149.8K **Privately Held**
SIC: 2051 Cakes, bakery: except frozen

(G-21204)
SIMON ROOFING AND SHTMTL CORP (PA)
70 Karago Ave (44512-5949)
PHONE...........................330 629-7392
Fax: 330 629-7399
James Simon Jr, *President*
Rich Serignese, *General Mgr*
Gene Washington, *Managing Dir*
Rocco Augustine, *Vice Pres*
Rick Cook, *Vice Pres*
EMP: 105
SQ FT: 30,000
SALES: 77.7MM **Privately Held**
WEB: www.simonroofing.com
SIC: 1761 2952 Roofing contractor; asphalt felts & coatings

(G-21205)
SOLAR ARTS GRAPHIC DESIGNS
824 Tod Ave (44502-1326)
PHONE...........................330 744-0535
Fax: 330 744-0776
Daniel Klingensmith, *President*
Catherine Klingensmith, *Vice Pres*
EMP: 6
SALES (est): 250K **Privately Held**
WEB: www.solar-arts.com
SIC: 2396 5199 Printing & embossing on plastics fabric articles; advertising specialties

(G-21206)
SPACE-LINKS INC
1110 Thalia Ave (44512-1825)
PHONE...........................330 788-2401
Ronald N Kessler, *President*
Jennifer Morris, *Office Mgr*
Katheline Allz, *Manager*
EMP: 20
SQ FT: 15,000
SALES (est): 2.8MM **Privately Held**
WEB: www.spacelinks1.com
SIC: 3069 Mats or matting, rubber

(G-21207)
SPACELINKS ENTERPRISES INC
1110 Thalia Ave (44512-1825)
PHONE...........................330 788-2401
Daniel Kessler, *President*
EMP: 60
SQ FT: 90,000
SALES: 7MM **Privately Held**
SIC: 2273 Mats & matting

(G-21208)
SPARTAN FABRICATION
230 Mcclurg Rd (44512-6740)
PHONE...........................330 758-3512
Fax: 330 758-3969
Joe Steppo, *Owner*
EMP: 4
SALES (est): 449.2K **Privately Held**
SIC: 3599 Machine & other job shop work

(G-21209)
SPECIAL T FOODS LLC
6834 Pinebrook Ct (44515-5588)
P.O. Box 4992, Austintown (44515-0992)
PHONE...........................330 793-8697
Joseph A Potkonicky Jr, *Principal*
EMP: 3
SALES (est): 155.3K **Privately Held**
SIC: 2099 Food preparations

(G-21210)
SPECIALTY SWITCH CO
525 Mcclurg Rd (44512-6406)
PHONE...........................330 427-3000
Terry Turvey, *President*
Piotr Blaszczyk, *General Mgr*
Gary Skinner, *Purch Agent*
Marjorie Turvey, *Treasurer*
EMP: 15
SQ FT: 7,000
SALES: 700K **Privately Held**
WEB: www.specialtyswitch.com
SIC: 3679 5063 Electronic switches; electrical apparatus & equipment

(G-21211)
SPECTRUM METAL FINISHING INC
535 Bev Rd (44512-6490)
PHONE...........................330 758-8358
Neil Chrisman, *President*
Janet Toth, *Controller*
Shane Percival, *Manager*
Greg Sheets, *Manager*
Thomas Hutch, *Admin Sec*
▼ EMP: 57
SQ FT: 60,000
SALES (est): 14.1MM **Privately Held**
WEB: www.spectrummetal.com
SIC: 3479 Painting of metal products

(G-21212)
STEEL FORMING INC (DH)
Also Called: Commercial Metal Forming
1775 Logan Ave (44505-2622)
P.O. Box 599 (44501-0599)
PHONE...........................714 532-6321
Fax: 330 740-8599
Bob Messaros, *President*
John Fischer, *Vice Pres*
Michael Conglose, *Opers Staff*
Marie Votino, *Buyer*
Zach Divencenzo, *Engineer*
▲ EMP: 203 EST: 2001
SQ FT: 150,000
SALES (est): 59.1MM
SALES (corp-wide): 349.7MM **Privately Held**
WEB: www.cmforming.com
SIC: 3469 Metal stampings

(G-21213)
SUGAR SHOWCASE
1725 S Raccoon Rd (44515-4588)
PHONE...........................330 792-9154
Cheryl Bair, *Principal*
EMP: 4 EST: 1965
SQ FT: 2,000
SALES (est): 130K **Privately Held**
SIC: 5461 3089 7999 Cakes; molding primary plastic; cake or pastry decorating instruction

(G-21214)
SULMONA ENEGRY LLC
46 N Phelps St (44503-1130)
PHONE...........................234 736-3749
Jamie Garayua,
EMP: 4 EST: 2011
SALES (est): 100K **Privately Held**
SIC: 1389 Gas field services

(G-21215)
SUMMCO INC
Also Called: Fastsigns
6981 Southern Blvd Ste D (44512-4657)
PHONE...........................330 965-7446
Fax: 330 965-0973
Jay Summer, *President*
EMP: 7
SALES (est): 550K **Privately Held**
SIC: 3993 Signs & advertising specialties

(G-21216)
T & W STAMPING INC
207 N Four Mile Run Rd (44515-3008)
PHONE...........................330 270-0891
Christopher D Smith, *Principal*
EMP: 5
SALES (est): 601.4K **Privately Held**
SIC: 3469 Metal stampings

(G-21217)
T C REDI MIX YOUNGSTOWN INC (PA)
2400 Poland Ave (44502-2782)
PHONE...........................330 755-2143
Fax: 330 755-2281
Sherry Andrews, *President*
Susan Kirkwood, *Corp Secy*
Sandra Raider, *Vice Pres*
EMP: 20
SQ FT: 3,000
SALES (est): 4.1MM **Privately Held**
SIC: 3273 5211 Ready-mixed concrete; lumber & other building materials

(G-21218)
TAYLOR-WINFIELD TECH INC (HQ)
Also Called: Taylor Winfield Indus Wldg Eqp
3200 Innovation Pl (44509-4025)
P.O. Box 779 (44501-0779)
PHONE................................330 259-8500
Alex Benyo, *President*
Brian Benyo, *Vice Pres*
Frank Deley, *Vice Pres*
Blake Rhein, *Vice Pres*
Todd Zamski, *CFO*
EMP: 50
SQ FT: 25,000
SALES (est): 14MM **Privately Held**
SIC: 3548 Welding apparatus

(G-21219)
THE FLORAND COMPANY
1776 Cherry St Ste A (44506-1859)
PHONE................................330 747-8986
Fax: 330 743-8245
Andrew Hirt, *President*
Kevin Carney, *Vice Pres*
Florence Hirt, *Treasurer*
EMP: 20
SALES (est): 4.1MM **Privately Held**
WEB: www.florand.com
SIC: 3312 Plate, sheet & strip, except coated products

(G-21220)
THOMAS MFG
696 Mcclurg Rd Ste 8 (44512-6432)
PHONE................................330 758-2384
Andrew Martin, *Principal*
EMP: 3
SALES (est): 243.8K **Privately Held**
SIC: 3999 Manufacturing industries

(G-21221)
THOMAS PANELS INC
696 Mcclurg Rd (44512-6432)
PHONE................................330 758-2384
Andrew J Martin II, *Principal*
EMP: 15
SALES: 3MM **Privately Held**
SIC: 2452 Panels & sections, prefabricated, wood

(G-21222)
TIMEKAP INC
Also Called: Timekap Indus Sls Svc & Mch
2315 Belmont Ave (44505-2404)
PHONE................................330 747-2122
Fax: 330 747-2210
Patrick Chrystal, *President*
Scott Lawrence, *Vice Pres*
Nicole Overly, *Manager*
EMP: 6
SQ FT: 15,000
SALES (est): 876.8K **Privately Held**
SIC: 3599 Machine shop, jobbing & repair

(G-21223)
TMI INC
6475 Victoria East Rd (44515-2051)
P.O. Box 4596 (44515-0596)
PHONE................................330 270-9780
Fax: 330 270-9845
Michael J Myhal Jr, *President*
Bob Hurst, *Project Mgr*
Rebecca Myhal, *Admin Sec*
▼ EMP: 28
SQ FT: 30,000
SALES (est): 5.8MM **Privately Held**
SIC: 3069 Molded rubber products

(G-21224)
TOROK SUPPLY COMPANY
52 S Meridian Rd (44509-2638)
PHONE................................330 799-6677
Victor Torok Jr, *President*
Jean Torok, *Vice Pres*
EMP: 3
SQ FT: 12,000
SALES: 450K **Privately Held**
SIC: 5075 3444 Warm air heating & air conditioning; electrical heating equipment; air conditioning equipment, except room units; sheet metalwork; elbows, for air ducts, stovepipes, etc.: sheet metal

(G-21225)
TOWING ELECTRICAL SYSTEMS
150 Victoria Rd (44515-2037)
PHONE................................330 793-3887
Donald Thomas, *President*
Frank Cassese, *Business Mgr*
Henry Limoge, *Vice Pres*
Adam Dizelbess, *Opers Mgr*
Chris Barcey, *Project Engr*
▲ EMP: 5
SQ FT: 10,000
SALES (est): 1.2MM **Privately Held**
SIC: 3694 Engine electrical equipment; electrical apparatus & equipment

(G-21226)
TRAFFIC DETECTORS & SIGNS INC
7521 Forest Hill Ave (44514-2635)
PHONE................................330 707-9060
Leila M Meris, *Principal*
EMP: 6
SALES (est): 618.9K **Privately Held**
SIC: 1611 3993 Highway signs & guardrails; signs & advertising specialties

(G-21227)
TRANSIT SITTINGS OF NA
295 S Meridian Rd (44509-2924)
PHONE................................330 797-2516
Wayne Donitzen, *Office Mgr*
EMP: 6
SALES (est): 350K **Privately Held**
SIC: 3498 Fabricated pipe & fittings

(G-21228)
TRESCO INTERNATIONAL LTD CO
1637 Bluebell Trl (44514-5215)
PHONE................................330 757-8131
▲ EMP: 5
SQ FT: 5,400
SALES (est): 390K **Privately Held**
SIC: 3645 Mfg Residential Lighting Fixtures

(G-21229)
TRI COUNTY ASPHALT MATERIALS
405 Andrews Ave (44505-3062)
P.O. Box 338, North Lima (44452-0338)
PHONE................................330 549-2852
Jo Anne Vernal, *President*
Richard Vernal, *Treasurer*
EMP: 2
SALES: 2.7MM
SALES (corp-wide): 10.9MM **Privately Held**
SIC: 3531 Asphalt plant, including gravel-mix type
PA: R T Vernal Paving Inc
11299 South Ave
North Lima OH 44452
330 549-2852

(G-21230)
TRI-R DIES INC
556 Bev Rd (44512-6420)
PHONE................................330 758-8050
Fax: 330 758-7419
Benjamin Morucci, *President*
David Ciolli, *Info Tech Mgr*
Mary Morucci, *Admin Sec*
EMP: 30 EST: 1978
SQ FT: 6,000
SALES (est): 4.5MM **Privately Held**
WEB: www.trirdies.com
SIC: 3544 Extrusion dies; special dies & tools

(G-21231)
TURNING TECHNOLOGIES LLC (PA)
255 W Federal St (44503-1207)
PHONE................................330 259-7516
Fax: 330 259-7615
Mike Broderick, *CEO*
Dave Kauer, *President*
Ethan Cohen, *COO*
Sheila Hura, *Vice Pres*
Kevin Owens, *Vice Pres*
EMP: 145
SQ FT: 26,200

SALES (est): 180.1MM **Privately Held**
WEB: www.turningtechnologies.com
SIC: 7372 Business oriented computer software; educational computer software

(G-21232)
TURNING TECHNOLOGIES LLC
265 W Federal St (44503-1207)
PHONE................................330 746-3015
EMP: 9
SALES (corp-wide): 180.1MM **Privately Held**
SIC: 7372 Business oriented computer software
PA: Turning Technologies, Llc
255 W Federal St
Youngstown OH 44503
330 746-3015

(G-21233)
U S WEATHERFORD L P
1100 Performance Pl (44502-4001)
PHONE................................330 746-2502
Terry Storvoll, *Manager*
EMP: 250 **Privately Held**
SIC: 3498 Fabricated pipe & fittings
HQ: U S Weatherford L P
2000 Saint James Pl
Houston TX 77056
713 836-4000

(G-21234)
V & M STAR LP
2669 Mrtn Luthr Kg Jr Bld (44510)
PHONE................................330 742-6300
Brian R Colquhoun, *Principal*
Garrett Francis, *Manager*
▲ EMP: 41 EST: 2012
SALES (est): 9.6MM **Privately Held**
SIC: 3061 Oil & gas field machinery rubber goods (mechanical)

(G-21235)
VALLOUREC STAR LP (HQ)
2669 M L K J Blvd (44510)
PHONE................................330 742-6300
Judson Wallace, *President*
Diana Franco, *Project Mgr*
Bill Ferguson, *Buyer*
Jason Lehman, *Buyer*
Danielle Williamson, *Buyer*
▲ EMP: 203
SALES (est): 185.6MM
SALES (corp-wide): 6MM **Privately Held**
SIC: 3317 Pipes, seamless steel
PA: Vallourec
27 Avenue Du General Leclerc
Boulogne Billancourt 92100
149 093-500

(G-21236)
VEIN CENTER AND MEDSPA
Also Called: Vein Center, The
965 Windham Ct Ste 2 (44512-5088)
PHONE................................330 629-9400
Fax: 330 629-9441
Richard A Michaels MD, *Owner*
Ellaine Kosa, *Receptionist*
EMP: 4
SALES (est): 520.7K **Privately Held**
WEB: www.the-vein-center.com
SIC: 8011 2844 Offices & clinics of medical doctors; cosmetic preparations

(G-21237)
VETERANS REPRESENTATIVE CO LLC
1584 Tamarisk Trl (44514-3632)
PHONE................................330 779-0768
James Altiero Jr,
Shirley Bennett, *Administration*
Kenneth Altiero,
Gerald Ragozine,
EMP: 10
SQ FT: 800
SALES: 500K **Privately Held**
SIC: 2522 Chairs, office: padded or plain, except wood

(G-21238)
VICTOR ORGAN COMPANY
5340 Mahoning Ave (44515-2415)
PHONE................................330 792-1321
Victor Marsilo, *Owner*
EMP: 8
SQ FT: 6,500

SALES (est): 330K **Privately Held**
SIC: 3931 7699 Organs, all types: pipe, reed, hand, electronic, etc.; organ tuning & repair

(G-21239)
VICTORIA VENTURES INC (PA)
425 Victoria Rd Ste 427 (44515-2029)
PHONE................................330 793-9321
John M Antonucci, *President*
Eileen Rinehart, *Principal*
EMP: 2
SALES (est): 2.7MM **Privately Held**
SIC: 6799 5182 5181 2082 Venture capital companies; wine & distilled beverages; beer & ale; malt beverages

(G-21240)
VINDICATOR BOARDMAN OFFICE
8075 Southern Blvd (44512-6306)
PHONE................................330 259-1732
EMP: 3
SALES (est): 128.3K **Privately Held**
SIC: 2711 Newspapers

(G-21241)
VINYL TOOL & DIE COMPANY INC
1144 Meadowbrook Ave (44512-1821)
PHONE................................330 782-0254
Fax: 330 782-0466
Paul Chicone, *President*
Carmen Chicone Jr, *Corp Secy*
Carmen Chicone Sr, *Vice Pres*
EMP: 12
SALES (est): 1.2MM **Privately Held**
SIC: 3544 Extrusion dies

(G-21242)
VINYLUME PRODUCTS INC
3745 Hendricks Rd (44515-1506)
PHONE................................330 799-2000
Fax: 330 799-2119
Jack M White, *CEO*
Orlando White, *President*
Jack Cappabianca, *Purch Mgr*
Kathy Simpson, *Data Proc Staff*
Helen White, *Admin Sec*
EMP: 70
SQ FT: 200,000
SALES (est): 14.9MM **Privately Held**
WEB: www.vinylume.com
SIC: 3089 3442 3211 Window frames & sash, plastic; metal doors, sash & trim; flat glass

(G-21243)
WARRIOR IMPORTS INC
Also Called: Hardcore Offroad Tires
112 S Meridian Rd (44509-2640)
PHONE................................954 935-5536
Ray Starr, *President*
Corey Burt, *Principal*
▲ EMP: 20
SQ FT: 100,000
SALES (est): 20MM **Privately Held**
SIC: 3262 Vitreous china table & kitchenware

(G-21244)
YELLOW TANG INTERIORS LLC
1255 Barbie Dr (44512-3702)
PHONE................................330 629-9279
John R Boris Jr,
EMP: 8
SALES (est): 861.3K **Privately Held**
SIC: 2521 Wood office furniture

(G-21245)
YOUNGSTOWN ARC ENGRAVING CO
Also Called: Youngstown Lithographing Co
380 Victoria Rd (44515-2026)
PHONE................................330 793-2471
E Craig Olsen, *President*
Tim Merrifield, *Exec VP*
George B Snyder, *Vice Pres*
Ken Baytosh, *Purchasing*
Terry Dunn, *Marketing Staff*
EMP: 26 EST: 1900
SQ FT: 30,000

SALES (est): 2.9MM **Privately Held**
WEB: www.youngstownwholesale.com
SIC: 2752 2796 7335 2791 Commercial printing, lithographic; commercial printing, offset; photoengraving plates, linecuts or halftones; commercial photography; typesetting; bookbinding & related work; commercial printing

(G-21246)
YOUNGSTOWN BENDING ROLLING
3710 Hendricks Rd Bldg 2b (44515-1537)
PHONE.................................330 799-2227
Daniel Kish, *Principal*
EMP: 16
SALES (est): 3.2MM **Privately Held**
SIC: 3531 Railroad related equipment

(G-21247)
YOUNGSTOWN BOLT & SUPPLY CO
340 N Meridian Rd (44509-1246)
PHONE.................................330 799-3201
Fax: 330 799-3591
Al Fedorisin, *President*
Lorraine Fedorisin, *Vice Pres*
EMP: 6
SQ FT: 20,000
SALES (est): 700K **Privately Held**
SIC: 5085 3965 Fasteners, industrial; nuts, bolts, screws, etc.; fasteners

(G-21248)
YOUNGSTOWN BURIAL VAULT CO
546 E Indianola Ave (44502-2320)
PHONE.................................330 782-0015
Fax: 330 782-0012
Charles Phillips, *President*
EMP: 9 EST: 1945
SQ FT: 4,000
SALES (est): 1.2MM **Privately Held**
SIC: 3272 Burial vaults, concrete or precast terrazzo

(G-21249)
YOUNGSTOWN CASKET CO INC
450 Melbourne Ave (44512-4410)
PHONE.................................330 758-2008
John R Kiefer, *President*
Robert Kiefer, *Corp Secy*
EMP: 6
SQ FT: 7,500
SALES (est): 530K **Privately Held**
SIC: 3995 Burial caskets

(G-21250)
YOUNGSTOWN CURVE FORM INC
1102 Rigby St (44506-1500)
PHONE.................................330 744-3028
Fax: 330 744-4405
Frank Laskay, *President*
EMP: 10 EST: 1964
SQ FT: 7,800
SALES (est): 1.5MM **Privately Held**
SIC: 5031 2541 Building materials, interior; table or counter tops, plastic laminated

(G-21251)
YOUNGSTOWN FENCE INC
235 E Indianola Ave (44507-1546)
PHONE.................................330 788-8110
Fax: 330 788-8112
Frank J Mikitaw, *President*
Suzanne Mikitaw, *Vice Pres*
EMP: 6
SQ FT: 34,000
SALES (est): 800K **Privately Held**
SIC: 1799 5211 2499 Fence construction; fencing; fencing, wood

(G-21252)
YOUNGSTOWN HARD CHROME PLATING
8451 Southern Blvd (44512-6709)
P.O. Box 3508 (44513-3508)
PHONE.................................330 758-9721
Fax: 330 758-3954
Richard S McCarthy, *President*
Daniel J McCarthy, *Vice Pres*
Butch Ritter, *Office Mgr*
EMP: 28 EST: 1962

SQ FT: 35,000
SALES (est): 3.3MM **Privately Held**
WEB: www.youngstownhardchrome.com
SIC: 3471 3599 Chromium plating of metals or formed products; grinding castings for the trade

(G-21253)
YOUNGSTOWN LETTER SHOP INC
615 N Meridian Rd (44509-1229)
PHONE.................................330 793-4935
Fax: 330 793-4927
Jean Tuscano, *President*
Scott Turke, *Vice Pres*
Kathy Cressman, *Manager*
EMP: 9
SQ FT: 5,000
SALES: 1.7MM **Privately Held**
SIC: 7331 2752 7521 Direct mail advertising services; commercial printing, offset; parking garage

(G-21254)
YOUNGSTOWN PLASTIC TOOLING (PA)
1209 Velma Ct (44512-1829)
PHONE.................................330 782-7222
Fax: 330 782-1854
Donald J Liga, *President*
Janet Liga, *Admin Sec*
EMP: 26
SQ FT: 20,000
SALES (est): 3.3MM **Privately Held**
WEB: www.yptm.com
SIC: 3559 8711 Plastics working machinery; machine tool design; mechanical engineering

(G-21255)
YOUNGSTOWN PRE-PRESS INC
3691 Leharps Dr (44515-1437)
P.O. Box 2375 (44509-0375)
PHONE.................................330 793-3690
Fax: 330 793-8155
Kenneth Slater, *President*
Gary P Dobrindt, *Vice Pres*
Brian Dickens, *Admin Sec*
EMP: 14
SQ FT: 4,000
SALES (est): 1.5MM **Privately Held**
SIC: 7336 2752 Art design services; lithographing on metal

(G-21256)
YOUNGSTOWN SPECIALTY MTLS INC
571 Andrews Ave (44505-3064)
PHONE.................................330 259-1110
Frank Wadlinger, *CEO*
Michael Miklus, *Vice Pres*
Richard Wadlinger, *CFO*
EMP: 8
SQ FT: 20,000
SALES (est): 1.8MM **Privately Held**
WEB: www.yngspecmetals.com
SIC: 3499 3053 Strapping, metal; gaskets; packing & sealing devices

(G-21257)
YOUNGSTOWN TOOL & DIE COMPANY
1261 Poland Ave (44502-2192)
PHONE.................................330 747-4464
Fax: 330 747-5623
Lawrence Stanislav, *President*
William Yurchyk, *Controller*
Allison Martinco, *Office Mgr*
Eric Houck, *Data Proc Staff*
EMP: 62 EST: 1961
SQ FT: 12,800
SALES (est): 10MM **Privately Held**
WEB: www.youngstowntool.com
SIC: 3544 3354 Special dies & tools; extrusion dies; aluminum extruded products

(G-21258)
YOUNGSTOWN TUBE CO
401 Andrews Ave (44505-3062)
PHONE.................................330 743-7414
Fax: 330 743-3185
William Veri, *President*
Kimberly Hahn, *Manager*
EMP: 30
SQ FT: 93,000

SALES (est): 6.9MM **Privately Held**
WEB: www.youngstowntube.com
SIC: 3312 Pipes, iron & steel; tubes, steel & iron

(G-21259)
YRP INDUSTRIES INC
854 Mahoning Ave (44502-1408)
P.O. Box 444 (44501-0444)
PHONE.................................330 533-2524
James Tomaino, *CEO*
EMP: 4
SALES (est): 284.2K **Privately Held**
SIC: 3011 Tire & inner tube materials & related products

(G-21260)
YSD INDUSTRIES INC
3710 Henricks Rd (44515)
P.O. Box 346, Berwick PA (18603-0346)
PHONE.................................330 792-6521
Fax: 330 792-2422
Jerome D Hines, *President*
Bruce Wylie, *Vice Pres*
Michael Feschak, *CFO*
Karen Flavell, *Human Resources*
Ralph Boland, *Director*
▲ EMP: 100
SQ FT: 30,000
SALES (est): 23.4MM **Privately Held**
SIC: 5088 3444 3441 Railroad equipment & supplies; sheet metalwork; fabricated structural metal

---

Zaleski
Vinton County

(G-21261)
LMP MACHINE LLC
115 E Chestnut St (45698)
P.O. Box 255 (45698-0255)
PHONE.................................740 596-4559
Fax: 740 596-4979
Mark Peters,
Lawrence M Peters,
EMP: 9
SQ FT: 4,800
SALES (est): 760K **Privately Held**
SIC: 3599 Machine shop, jobbing & repair

Zanesfield
Logan County

(G-21262)
QUANTUM WORLD TECHNOLOGIES
6973 Township Road 177 (43360-9717)
PHONE.................................937 747-3018
Hollis L Smith, *Principal*
EMP: 3
SALES (est): 178.5K **Privately Held**
SIC: 3572 Computer storage devices

Zanesville
Muskingum County

(G-21263)
5 BS INC (PA)
Also Called: B-Wear Sportswear
1000 5 Bs Dr (43701-7630)
P.O. Box 520 (43702-0520)
PHONE.................................740 454-8453
Fax: 740 455-6794
Todd Biles, *President*
Steven R Baldwin, *Principal*
Leland Biles, *Principal*
Larry R King, *Principal*
John Klies, *Vice Pres*
▲ EMP: 250
SQ FT: 170,000
SALES (est): 54.1MM **Privately Held**
WEB: www.5bs.com
SIC: 2339 2395 Athletic clothing: women's, misses' & juniors'; embroidery products, except schiffli machine

(G-21264)
ACE TRUCK EQUIPMENT CO
1130 Newark Rd (43701-2619)
P.O. Box 2605 (43702-2605)
PHONE.................................740 453-0551
Fax: 740 453-7023
Robert D Beitzel, *CEO*
David Beitzel, *President*
Shawn Hampp, *Sales Staff*
Dora Beitzel, *Admin Sec*
EMP: 21
SQ FT: 30,500
SALES (est): 4MM **Privately Held**
WEB: www.acetruck.net
SIC: 5531 5012 3713 Truck equipment & parts; truck bodies; trucks, commercial; truck tractors; trailers for trucks, new & used; truck & bus bodies

(G-21265)
ADAMS BROTHERS INC
1501 Woodlawn Ave (43701-5955)
P.O. Box 27 (43702-0027)
PHONE.................................740 819-0323
Fax: 740 452-7567
William Adams IV, *President*
William H Adams III, *President*
Nancy Adams, *Vice Pres*
Williams H Adams IV, *Vice Pres*
Katie Brown, *Treasurer*
EMP: 12 EST: 1908
SALES (est): 1.4MM **Privately Held**
SIC: 3273 5211 Ready-mixed concrete; lumber & other building materials

(G-21266)
ADKEL CORP (PA)
Also Called: Custom Bobbin Winding
2920 Newark Rd (43701-7759)
P.O. Box 2369 (43702-2369)
PHONE.................................740 452-6973
Fax: 740 452-4156
Doral S Mills Jr, *President*
Dale Young, *General Mgr*
EMP: 6
SQ FT: 15,000
SALES (est): 587.7K **Privately Held**
SIC: 3677 Coil windings, electronic; electronic transformers

(G-21267)
AK STEEL CORPORATION
1724 Linden Ave (43701-2307)
P.O. Box 1520 (43702-1520)
PHONE.................................740 450-5600
Douglas C Garvin, *General Mgr*
Bill Adams, *Safety Mgr*
L Davis, *Purchasing*
Edward S Siedlak, *Senior Engr*
Ted E Hill, *Enginr/R&D Mgr*
EMP: 315
SALES (corp-wide): 5.8B **Publicly Held**
WEB: www.ketnar.org
SIC: 3312 3316 Blast furnaces & steel mills; cold finishing of steel shapes
HQ: Ak Steel Corporation
9227 Centre Pointe Dr
West Chester OH 45069
513 425-4200

(G-21268)
ALC HOLDINGS INC
4005 All American Way (43701-7251)
PHONE.................................740 452-2500
Perry Jacobson, *Ch of Bd*
Steven Silverman, *Vice Ch Bd*
Claude Brown Jr, *President*
Trevor Greening, *General Mgr*
Dave Crane, *Exec VP*
EMP: 120 EST: 2007
SALES: 14.3MM **Privately Held**
SIC: 3089 Prefabricated plastic buildings

(G-21269)
ALFRED NICKLES BAKERY INC
Also Called: Nickles Bakery 45
1147 Newark Rd (43701-2618)
PHONE.................................740 453-6522
Fax: 740 453-7311
Les Bell, *General Mgr*
Brian Rexroad, *Manager*
EMP: 30

SALES (corp-wide): 205MM **Privately Held**
WEB: www.nicklesbakery.com
SIC: 2051 5461 Bread, cake & related products; bakeries
PA: Alfred Nickles Bakery, Inc.
26 Main St N
Navarre OH 44662
330 879-5635

(G-21270)
ALLIED MACHINE WORKS INC
120 Graham St (43701-3100)
P.O. Box 2743 (43702-2743)
PHONE.................................740 454-2534
Fax: 740 454-2544
Richard J Straker, *President*
Patricia Folden, *Principal*
Richard Goldsmith, *Sales Staff*
EMP: 8
SQ FT: 56,058
SALES: 750K **Privately Held**
WEB: www.allliedmachineworks.com
SIC: 3599 7629 3533 Machine shop, jobbing & repair; machine & other job shop work; electrical repair shops; oil & gas field machinery

(G-21271)
AMERICAN BAND SAW CO
4049 Newark Rd (43701-8727)
PHONE.................................740 452-8168
Fax: 740 454-8524
Bob Holbein, *Owner*
EMP: 5
SALES: 300K **Privately Held**
WEB:
www.americanbandsawcompany.com
SIC: 2221 Textile mills, broadwoven: silk & manmade, also glass

(G-21272)
ANCHOR GLASS CONTAINER CORP
Zanesville Mould Division
1555 Fairview Rd (43701-8889)
P.O. Box 2340 (43702-2340)
PHONE.................................740 452-2743
Fax: 740 452-7730
Steve Brock, *Superintendent*
Shane McLoughlin, *Opers Mgr*
Mark Perrine, *Purchasing*
Cheryl Carothers, *HR Admin*
Jim Walters, *CIO*
EMP: 202
SALES (corp-wide): 2.3B **Privately Held**
WEB: www.anchorglass.com
SIC: 3321 3221 3544 Gray iron ingot molds, cast; glass containers; special dies, tools, jigs & fixtures
HQ: Anchor Glass Container Corporation
401 E Jackson St Ste 1100
Tampa FL 33602

(G-21273)
AXION STRL INNOVATIONS LLC (PA) ✪
1100 Brandywine Blvd H (43701-7303)
P.O. Box 3708 (43702)
PHONE.................................740 452-2500
Claude Brown, *President*
Dave Crane, *Exec VP*
Matt Elli, *Exec VP*
Donald Fallon, *CFO*
Allen Kronstadt,
EMP: 17 EST: 2016
SALES (est): 12.2MM **Privately Held**
SIC: 3089 Extruded finished plastic products

(G-21274)
BALLAS EGG PRODUCTS CORP
40 N 2nd St (43701-3402)
P.O. Box 2217 (43702-2217)
PHONE.................................614 453-0386
Fax: 740 453-0491
Leonard Ballas, *President*
Joseph G Saliba, *Vice Pres*
Craig Ballas, *Admin Sec*
▼ EMP: 100 EST: 1961
SQ FT: 200,000
SALES (est): 16.1MM **Privately Held**
SIC: 2015 5144 Egg processing; eggs, processed: desiccated (dried); eggs, processed: frozen; eggs

(G-21275)
BARNES ADVERTISING CORP
1580 Fairview Rd (43701-0934)
P.O. Box 277 (43702-0277)
PHONE.................................740 453-6836
Fax: 740 453-3780
Maryjane Shackelford, *President*
Roderick W Barnes, *President*
John Barnes, *Vice Pres*
Joe Panzica, *Sales Mgr*
Chad Demattei, *Accounts Exec*
EMP: 13
SALES (est): 1.5MM **Privately Held**
SIC: 7312 3993 Outdoor advertising services; signs & advertising specialties

(G-21276)
BATTERY UNLIMITED
2350 Adamsville Rd (43701-6949)
PHONE.................................740 452-5030
Fax: 740 453-5027
Kent Curry, *Owner*
EMP: 6
SQ FT: 2,500
SALES: 900K **Privately Held**
WEB: www.batteryunlimited.com
SIC: 5063 5531 5999 7699 Batteries; batteries, dry cell; batteries, automotive & truck; batteries, non-automotive; battery service & repair; battery testers, electrical

(G-21277)
BE PRODUCTS INC
Also Called: Ballas Egg Products
40 N 2nd St (43701-3402)
P.O. Box 2217 (43702-2217)
PHONE.................................740 453-0386
Criag Ballas, *President*
Craig Ballas, *President*
Leonard Ballas, *Vice Pres*
EMP: 100
SQ FT: 125,000
SALES (est): 15.1MM **Privately Held**
SIC: 2015 Egg processing

(G-21278)
BIGGYS AUTO BUFFET
806 W Main St (43701-3142)
PHONE.................................740 455-4663
Zack Wagner, *Principal*
EMP: 7
SALES (est): 350K **Privately Held**
SIC: 3711 Automobile bodies, passenger car, not including engine, etc.

(G-21279)
BILCO COMPANY
3400 Jim Granger Dr (43701-7231)
PHONE.................................740 455-9020
EMP: 50
SALES (corp-wide): 532.9MM **Privately Held**
WEB: www.bilco.com
SIC: 3442 3272 Metal doors; areaways, basement window: concrete
HQ: The Bilco Company
37 Water St
West Haven CT 06516
203 934-6363

(G-21280)
BISHOP MACHINE TOOL & DIE
Also Called: Bishop Machine Shop
2304 Hoge Ave (43701-2166)
PHONE.................................740 453-8818
Fax: 740 453-6750
Robert L Bishop, *Partner*
John R Bishop, *Partner*
Alva Bishop Jr, *Manager*
EMP: 10 EST: 1964
SQ FT: 2,000
SALES (est): 1.2MM **Privately Held**
SIC: 3599 3953 Machine shop, jobbing & repair; marking devices

(G-21281)
BROCKS WELDING & REPAIR SVC
3985 East Pike (43701-8008)
PHONE.................................740 453-3943
Charles Brock, *President*
Myrtle Ann Brock, *Corp Secy*
Marsha Brock, *Vice Pres*
EMP: 4

SALES (est): 501.3K **Privately Held**
SIC: 7692 7629 Welding repair; electrical repair shops

(G-21282)
BUCKEYE COMPANIES (PA)
999 Zane St (43701-3863)
P.O. Box 1480 (43702-1480)
PHONE.................................740 452-3641
C E Straker, *President*
Stephen R Straker, *President*
M Dean Cole, *Corp Secy*
EMP: 31
SALES (est): 18.4MM **Privately Held**
SIC: 3533 5083 Drill rigs; agricultural machinery & equipment

(G-21283)
BUCKEYE ENERGY RESOURCES INC
Also Called: Seth Enterprises
999 Zane St (43701-3863)
PHONE.................................740 452-9506
Charles E Straker, *CEO*
Stephen Straker, *President*
C E Staker, *Chairman*
M Dean Cole, *Corp Secy*
Larry S Messner, *Treasurer*
EMP: 6
SALES (est): 967.6K
SALES (corp-wide): 16.6MM **Privately Held**
WEB: www.buckeyedrill.com
SIC: 4213 1311 Trucking, except local; crude petroleum & natural gas
PA: Buckeye Companies
999 Zane St
Zanesville OH 43701
740 452-3641

(G-21284)
BUCKINGHAM COAL COMPANY LLC
11 N 4th St (43701-3409)
P.O. Box 340 (43702-0340)
PHONE.................................740 767-2907
Fax: 740 347-4003
Clay Graham, *CEO*
EMP: 80 EST: 1994
SALES (est): 18.7MM
SALES (corp-wide): 1.4B **Publicly Held**
SIC: 1241 Coal mining services
PA: Westmoreland Coal Company
9540 Maroon Cir Unit 200
Englewood CO 80112
855 922-6463

(G-21285)
CAMERON DRILLING CO INC
3636 Adamsville Rd (43701-6954)
PHONE.................................740 453-3300
Fax: 740 453-6299
James H Cameron, *President*
Richard M Cameron, *Vice Pres*
EMP: 12 EST: 1966
SQ FT: 3,000
SALES (est): 150K **Privately Held**
SIC: 1311 Crude petroleum production; natural gas production

(G-21286)
CAPITAL PROSTHETIC &
4035 Northpointe Dr A (43701-7647)
PHONE.................................740 453-9545
Fax: 740 453-1799
Lisa Crawford, *Branch Mgr*
EMP: 3
SALES (corp-wide): 2.9MM **Privately Held**
SIC: 3842 Limbs, artificial; braces, orthopedic
PA: Capital Prosthetic And Orthotic Center, Inc.
4678 Larwell Dr
Columbus OH 43220
614 451-0446

(G-21287)
CARL RITTBERGER SR INC
1900 Lutz Ln (43701-9260)
PHONE.................................740 452-2767
Fax: 740 452-6001
Andrew Rittberger, *President*
Pauline Butler, *Corp Secy*
EMP: 32
SQ FT: 100,000

SALES (est): 4.4MM **Privately Held**
SIC: 2011 2013 Beef products from beef slaughtered on site; pork products from pork slaughtered on site; sausages & other prepared meats

(G-21288)
CASTING SOLUTIONS LLC
2345 Licking Rd (43701-2728)
P.O. Box 3148 (43702-3148)
PHONE.................................740 452-9371
Fax: 740 452-9371
Jeremiah Clegg, *President*
Adam Kolbe, *Maint Spvr*
Susan Stotts, *Purch Mgr*
Dan Cooper, *Engineer*
Deb Rollman, *Credit Mgr*
EMP: 106
SALES (est): 23MM
SALES (corp-wide): 172.4MM **Publicly Held**
WEB: www.burnhamfoundry.com
SIC: 3321 Gray iron castings
PA: Burnham Holdings, Inc.
1241 Harrisburg Ave
Lancaster PA 17603
717 390-7800

(G-21289)
CLEARPATH UTLITY SOLUTIONS LLC
8155 Ridge Rd (43701-8283)
PHONE.................................740 661-4240
Maureen E Riley, *Principal*
Rodney Riley, *Principal*
Maureen Riley, *Manager*
EMP: 10
SALES (est): 2.9MM **Privately Held**
SIC: 1381 Directional drilling oil & gas wells

(G-21290)
CLOSETS BY MIKE
517 Winton Ave (43701-1918)
PHONE.................................740 607-2212
Michael Lmills, *Principal*
EMP: 3
SALES (est): 175.8K **Privately Held**
SIC: 3088 Shower stalls, fiberglass & plastic

(G-21291)
COCA-COLA COMPANY
154 S 7th St (43701-4332)
PHONE.................................740 452-3608
Fax: 740 452-7003
Linda Kuhn, *Vice Pres*
Dave Llewellen, *Manager*
EMP: 30
SALES (corp-wide): 41.8B **Publicly Held**
WEB: www.colasic.net
SIC: 2086 Bottled & canned soft drinks
PA: The Coca-Cola Company
1 Coca Cola Plz Nw
Atlanta GA 30313
404 676-2121

(G-21292)
COLUMBIA MACHINE COMPANY
961 Hughes St (43701-4388)
PHONE.................................740 452-1736
John Mc Cutcheon, *President*
EMP: 4
SQ FT: 5,500
SALES: 250K **Privately Held**
SIC: 3599 Machine shop, jobbing & repair

(G-21293)
COLUMBUS EQUIPMENT COMPANY
818 Lee St (43701-3375)
PHONE.................................740 455-4036
Dan Minnis, *Branch Mgr*
EMP: 3
SALES (corp-wide): 93.6MM **Privately Held**
SIC: 1442 Construction sand mining
PA: The Columbus Equipment Company
2323 Performance Way
Columbus OH 43207
614 437-0352

(PA)=Parent Co (HQ)=Headquarters (DH)=Div Headquarters
✪ = New Business established in last 2 years

2017 Harris Ohio
Industrial Directory

861

GEOGRAPHIC

(G-21294)
CONNS POTATO CHIP CO INC (PA)
1805 Kemper Ct (43701-4634)
PHONE..................................740 452-4615
Fax: 740 452-9272
Monte Hunter, *President*
Thomas George Sr, *Vice Pres*
John George, *Plant Mgr*
EMP: 30 EST: 1952
SQ FT: 100,000
SALES (est): 8.1MM Privately Held
SIC: 2096 5963 Potato chips & other po-
tato-based snacks; snacks, direct sales

(G-21295)
CREATIVE PACKAGING LLC
1781 Kemper Ct (43701-4606)
P.O. Box 305 (43702-0305)
PHONE..................................740 452-8497
Fax: 740 452-2437
Tim Deerman, *Controller*
Jim Theisen, *Sales Mgr*
Keith Imhoff, *Mng Member*
Ed Sims, *Manager*
Caitlin Grimm, *Admin Sec*
EMP: 48
SQ FT: 125,000
SALES (est): 19.9MM Privately Held
WEB: www.creativepkg.net
SIC: 2653 2671 Corrugated & solid fiber
boxes; packaging paper & plastics film,
coated & laminated

(G-21296)
CRUDE OIL COMPANY
1819 Newark Rd (43701-2631)
PHONE..................................740 452-3335
Sharp Ellen P, *Owner*
EMP: 3 EST: 1943
SALES (est): 230.8K Privately Held
SIC: 1311 Crude petroleum production

(G-21297)
CUSTOM COIL & TRANSFORMER CO
2900 Newark Rd (43701-7759)
P.O. Box 8063 (43702-8063)
PHONE..................................740 452-5211
Marty Lucas, *President*
Martin C Lucas, *President*
Pam Lucas, *Admin Sec*
EMP: 50
SQ FT: 9,000
SALES: 1MM Privately Held
SIC: 3621 3677 3612 Coils, for electric
motors or generators; electronic coils,
transformers & other inductors; transform-
ers, except electric

(G-21298)
DEBOLT MACHINE INC
4208 West Pike (43701-8289)
PHONE..................................740 454-8082
Paul W Debolt, *President*
EMP: 5
SQ FT: 3,600
SALES: 250K Privately Held
SIC: 3999 7539 3519 Models, general,
except toy; machine shop, automotive; in-
ternal combustion engines

(G-21299)
DMV CORPORATION
1024 Military Rd (43701-1343)
P.O. Box 878 (43702-0878)
PHONE..................................740 452-4787
Fax: 740 452-4501
Allan Patterson, *President*
Pat Burkhart, *Director*
EMP: 9
SQ FT: 1,500
SALES: 1MM Privately Held
WEB: www.dmvcorp.com
SIC: 3851 Ophthalmic goods

(G-21300)
DOW CAMERON OIL & GAS LLC
5555 Eden Park Dr (43701-7052)
PHONE..................................740 452-1568
Kathy S Shatto, *Manager*
Dow Cameron,
EMP: 8

SALES (est): 1.3MM Privately Held
SIC: 1389 Oil & gas wells: building, repairing & dismantling

(G-21301)
DR PEPPER BOTTLING COMPANY
335 N 6th St (43701-3636)
PHONE..................................740 452-2721
Rick Stone, *Principal*
EMP: 3
SALES (est): 182.4K Privately Held
SIC: 2086 Soft drinks: packaged in cans,
bottles, etc.

(G-21302)
DRESDEN SPECIALTIES INC
Also Called: Tom's Print Shop
710 Main St (43701-3732)
P.O. Box 146 (43702-0146)
PHONE..................................740 452-7100
Dean Cole, *Manager*
EMP: 5
SALES (corp-wide): 558.2K Privately
Held
WEB: www.socialsupper.com
SIC: 2752 2759 Commercial printing, off-
set; letterpress printing
PA: Dresden Specialties Inc
    305 Main St
    Dresden OH 43821
    740 754-2451

(G-21303)
EAST BALT OHIO LLC (DH)
3005 E Pointe Dr (43701-7263)
P.O. Box 256, Dublin (43017-0256)
PHONE..................................740 454-6876
Fax: 740 454-3131
Mark Bendix, *CEO*
David Dvorak, *Exec VP*
Shelly Holden, *Exec VP*
David Watkins, *Exec VP*
Daniel Harrison, *Vice Pres*
EMP: 10 EST: 1975
SQ FT: 200,000
SALES (est): 63.9MM
SALES (corp-wide): 1.4B Privately Held
SIC: 2051 Buns, bread type: fresh or
frozen

(G-21304)
EAST BALT OHIO LLC
3005 E Pointe Dr (43701-7263)
PHONE..................................740 454-6876
Dan Augburgur, *General Mgr*
EMP: 5
SALES (corp-wide): 1.4B Privately Held
SIC: 2051 Buns, bread type: fresh or
frozen
HQ: East Balt Ohio, Llc
    3005 E Pointe Dr
    Zanesville OH 43701
    740 454-6876

(G-21305)
EAST BALT US LLC
750 Airport Rd (43701-9694)
P.O. Box 256, Dublin (43017-0256)
PHONE..................................740 454-6876
Fax: 740 588-5860
David Marion, *Manager*
EMP: 8
SALES (corp-wide): 1.4B Privately Held
SIC: 2051 Buns, bread type: fresh or
frozen
HQ: East Balt Us, Llc
    1801 W 31st Pl
    Chicago IL 60608

(G-21306)
ECLIPSE RESOURCES - OHIO LLC
4900 Boggs Rd (43701-9491)
P.O. Box 910 (43702-0910)
PHONE..................................740 452-4503
Benjamin W Hulburt, *Mng Member*
Bruce Carpenter, *Manager*
Drew Gray, *Manager*
Christopher K Hulburt,
Thomas S Liberatore,
EMP: 42
SALES (est): 11MM
SALES (corp-wide): 235MM Publicly
Held
SIC: 1381 Drilling oil & gas wells

HQ: Eclipse Resources I, Lp
    2121 Old Gteburg Rd Ste 1
    State College PA 16803
    814 308-9754

(G-21307)
EMEGA TECHNOLOGIES LLC
205 N 5th St (43701-3507)
PHONE..................................740 407-3712
Donald E Duffy, *CEO*
EMP: 4
SQ FT: 1,000
SALES: 1MM Privately Held
SIC: 3699 Electrical equipment & supplies

(G-21308)
FINELINE IMPRINTS INC
516 State St (43701-3237)
P.O. Box 2688 (43702-2688)
PHONE..................................740 453-1083
Fax: 740 452-3550
Robert Kessler, *President*
Tom Baughman, *Prdtn Mgr*
EMP: 20
SQ FT: 12,000
SALES (est): 1.9MM Privately Held
WEB: www.finelineimprints.com
SIC: 5999 2396 3993 2395 Trophies &
plaques; screen printing on fabric articles;
signs & advertising specialties; pleating &
stitching

(G-21309)
FLOW-LINER SYSTEMS LTD
4830 Northpointe Dr (43701-7273)
PHONE..................................800 348-0020
Jeff Tanner, *CEO*
Hartman Ralph, *Personnel Exec*
Pamela Davis, *Marketing Staff*
Brent Musselman, *Manager*
EMP: 28 EST: 2000
SQ FT: 30,000
SALES (est): 6MM Privately Held
WEB: www.flow-liner.com
SIC: 3589 1799 Sewage & water treat-
ment equipment; epoxy application

(G-21310)
FORMATION CEMENTING INC
1800 Timber Port Dr (43701)
P.O. Box 2667 (43702-2667)
PHONE..................................740 453-6926
Brian G Jasper, *President*
Rae Anne Jasper, *Admin Sec*
EMP: 7
SQ FT: 500
SALES: 2MM Privately Held
SIC: 1389 Oil & gas wells: building, repair-
ing & dismantling; servicing oil & gas
wells

(G-21311)
FRANKLINS PRINTING COMPANY
984 Beverly Ave (43701-1413)
PHONE..................................740 452-6375
Fax: 740 455-6229
Everett Jackson Jr, *President*
Alice Lucille Jackson, *Corp Secy*
EMP: 10
SQ FT: 7,000
SALES (est): 900K Privately Held
SIC: 2752 7331 2791 2789 Commercial
printing, lithographic; addressing service;
mailing service; typesetting; bookbinding
& related work

(G-21312)
FRIESINGERS INC
120 Graham St (43701-4393)
PHONE..................................740 452-9480
Fax: 740 452-2705
Michael F La Plante, *President*
EMP: 3
SQ FT: 18,000
SALES (est): 330K Privately Held
SIC: 3449 Miscellaneous metalwork

(G-21313)
G & J PEPSI-COLA BOTTLERS INC
Also Called: Pepsico
335 N 6th St (43701-3636)
PHONE..................................740 452-2721
Rick Stone, *Branch Mgr*
EMP: 85

SALES (corp-wide): 490.5MM Privately
Held
WEB: www.gjpepsi.com
SIC: 2086 5149 Carbonated soft drinks,
bottled & canned; groceries & related
products
PA: G & J Pepsi-Cola Bottlers Inc
    9435 Waterstone Blvd # 390
    Cincinnati OH 45249
    513 785-6060

(G-21314)
GANNETT CO INC
Also Called: Times Recorder, The
3871 Gorsky Dr (43701-6429)
PHONE..................................740 452-4561
Fax: 740 453-9417
Chuck Martin, *Loan Officer*
Rhonda McGee, *Personnel*
Tom Russo, *Sales Staff*
Karie Sargent, *Sales Staff*
Greg Baumer, *Advt Staff*
EMP: 60
SALES (corp-wide): 3B Publicly Held
WEB: www.gannett.com
SIC: 2711 Newspapers
PA: Gannett Co., Inc.
    7950 Jones Branch Dr
    Mc Lean VA 22102
    703 854-6000

(G-21315)
GENERAL MACHINE & SUPPLY CO
Also Called: GM Management
3135 Lookout Dr (43701-1690)
PHONE..................................740 453-4804
Lynne A Sprague, *President*
Robert T Sprague, *Vice Pres*
EMP: 5
SALES: 150K Privately Held
SIC: 3599 5085 Machine shop, jobbing &
repair; industrial supplies

(G-21316)
H & R TOOL & MACHINE CO INC
Also Called: Zanesville Bearing Div
18 Jefferson St (43701-4904)
P.O. Box 1444 (43702-1444)
PHONE..................................740 452-0784
Fax: 740 452-4529
William Hill, *President*
Charlene Hill, *Corp Secy*
EMP: 8
SALES (est): 660K Privately Held
SIC: 3599 5013 7538 3544 Machine
shop, jobbing & repair; automotive sup-
plies & parts; engine rebuilding: automo-
tive; special dies, tools, jigs & fixtures

(G-21317)
HANGER PRSTHETCS & ORTHO INC
930 Orchard Hill Rd (43701-7311)
PHONE..................................740 454-6215
Vern Hostetler, *Manager*
EMP: 5
SALES (corp-wide): 460MM Publicly
Held
SIC: 8071 5999 3842 Medical laborato-
ries; artificial limbs; limbs, artificial
HQ: Hanger Prosthetics & Orthotics, Inc.
    10910 Domain Dr Ste 300
    Austin TX 78758
    512 777-3800

(G-21318)
HANNON COMPANY
Electric Motor & Service Co
218 Adams St (43701-4902)
P.O. Box 667 (43702-0667)
PHONE..................................740 453-0527
Fax: 740 453-5087
John Haswell, *Manager*
EMP: 24
SALES (corp-wide): 27.2MM Privately
Held
WEB: www.hanco.com
SIC: 7694 7699 5063 Electric motor re-
pair; welding equipment repair; motors,
electric
PA: The Hannon Company
    1605 Waynesburg Dr Se
    Canton OH 44707
    330 456-4728

(G-21319)
HOPEWELL OIL & GAS DEV CO
1615 W Main St (43701-3157)
P.O. Box 2776 (43702-2776)
PHONE.................................740 452-9326
Jerry S Henderson, President
EMP: 6
SALES (est): 1.1MM Privately Held
SIC: 1311 1381 Crude petroleum production; natural gas production; drilling oil & gas wells

(G-21320)
HYDRO SUPPLY CO
3112 East Pike (43701-8975)
PHONE.................................740 454-3842
Fax: 740 454-7953
Charles William Kimble, President
Judy K Kimble, Corp Secy
Bill Kimble, Purchasing
Tim Hampp, Sales Staff
EMP: 12
SQ FT: 6,500
SALES (est): 3.4MM Privately Held
WEB: www.hydrosupply.com
SIC: 5084 7699 3599 Hydraulic systems equipment & supplies; industrial machinery & equipment repair; machine shop, jobbing & repair

(G-21321)
IG WATTEEUW USA LLC
1000 Linden Ave (43701-3098)
PHONE.................................740 588-1722
Dan Bucur, CEO
EMP: 11
SQ FT: 51,946
SALES: 5MM
SALES (corp-wide): 29.6MM Privately Held
SIC: 3714 5085 Gears, motor vehicle; gears
HQ: Ig Watteeuw International Nv
Kampveldstraat 51
Oostkamp 8020
508 269-07

(G-21322)
J A B WELDING SERVICE INC
Also Called: Bakers Welding
2820 S River Rd (43701-7184)
PHONE.................................740 453-5868
Fax: 740 453-7765
Jeffrey A Baker, President
Cyndy Baker, Vice Pres
EMP: 12
SQ FT: 20,000
SALES (est): 2MM Privately Held
SIC: 7692 Welding repair

(G-21323)
JILLIANS LTD
3935 Northpointe Dr (43701-7361)
PHONE.................................740 450-7766
Gail Garland,
Jill Jones,
EMP: 3
SQ FT: 1,200
SALES (est): 378.5K Privately Held
SIC: 2335 Bridal & formal gowns

(G-21324)
JOE MCCLELLAND INC (PA)
Also Called: O K Coal & Concrete
98 E La Salle St (43701-6281)
P.O. Box 1815 (43702-1815)
PHONE.................................740 452-3036
Fax: 740 455-8781
Joe Mc Clelland, President
Jack Mc Clelland, Vice Pres
Michael McClelland, Vice Pres
Richard Mc Clelland, Treasurer
Joe Nesselroad, Manager
EMP: 25 EST: 1934
SQ FT: 1,500
SALES (est): 6.1MM Privately Held
WEB: www.okcoalandconcrete.com
SIC: 3273 7992 1442 Ready-mixed concrete; public golf courses; construction sand & gravel

(G-21325)
KELLOGG COMPANY
1675 Fairview Rd (43701-8890)
PHONE.................................740 453-5501
Fax: 740 430-2105

Gary Pilnick, Owner
Debra Kurtz, Vice Pres
EMP: 125
SALES (corp-wide): 13B Publicly Held
WEB: www.kelloggs.com
SIC: 2043 Cereal breakfast foods
PA: Kellogg Company
1 Kellogg Sq
Battle Creek MI 49017
269 961-2000

(G-21326)
KESSLER SIGN COMPANY (PA)
Also Called: Kessler Outdoor Advertising
2669 National Rd (43701-8257)
P.O. Box 785 (43702-0785)
PHONE.................................740 453-0668
Fax: 740 453-5301
Robert Kessler, President
Rodger Kessler, Vice Pres
Elaine Kessler-Kuntz, Treasurer
Mark Cox, Accounts Exec
Natalie Kessler, Accounts Exec
EMP: 50
SQ FT: 25,000
SALES (est): 7.4MM Privately Held
WEB: www.kesslersignco.com
SIC: 3993 7312 Signs, not made in custom sign painting shops; outdoor advertising services

(G-21327)
MANSFIELD ASPHALT PAVING INC
Also Called: Shelly and Shells
3570 S River Rd (43701-7731)
P.O. Box 1585 (43702-1585)
PHONE.................................740 453-0721
Richard Mc Clelland, President
EMP: 12
SALES (est): 834.6K
SALES (corp-wide): 301.4MM Privately Held
WEB: www.shellyandsands.com
SIC: 2951 Asphalt paving mixtures & blocks
PA: Shelly And Sands, Inc.
3570 S River Rd
Zanesville OH 43701
740 453-0721

(G-21328)
MAR-ZANE INC (HQ)
Also Called: Mar-Zane Materials
3570 S River Rd (43701-7731)
P.O. Box 1585 (43702-1585)
PHONE.................................740 453-0721
Fax: 740 454-3144
Gerald N Little, President
Wade Hamm, Vice Pres
Mike Cline, Controller
EMP: 12
SQ FT: 5,000
SALES (est): 9.3MM
SALES (corp-wide): 301.4MM Privately Held
SIC: 2951 Asphalt paving mixtures & blocks
PA: Shelly And Sands, Inc.
3570 S River Rd
Zanesville OH 43701
740 453-0721

(G-21329)
MOCK WOODWORKING COMPANY LLC
4400 West Pike (43701-9208)
PHONE.................................740 452-2701
Fax: 740 452-9304
Wilbur Mock, Vice Pres
Tim Gifford, Project Mgr
Pracilla Rhoads, Accounts Mgr
Douglas F Mock, Mng Member
EMP: 44
SQ FT: 46,000
SALES (est): 7.3MM Privately Held
WEB: www.mockwoodworking.com
SIC: 2434 2541 2531 Wood kitchen cabinets; office fixtures, wood; store fixtures, wood; public building & related furniture

(G-21330)
MOMENTIVE SPECIALTY CHEM INC
Borden
2055 Grief Rd (43701-2759)
PHONE.................................740 452-5451
Fax: 740 452-4706
EMP: 12
SALES (corp-wide): 2.6B Privately Held
SIC: 2869 Mfg Industrial Organic Chemicals
HQ: Momentive Specialty Chemicals Inc.
180 E Broad St Fl 26
Columbus OH 43215
614 225-4000

(G-21331)
NEFF MACHINERY AND SUPPLIES
Also Called: Neff Parts
112 S Shawnee Ave (43701-6221)
P.O. Box 1822 (43702-1822)
PHONE.................................740 454-0128
Fax: 740 454-8433
Robert Neff, President
EMP: 30
SQ FT: 20,000
SALES (est): 3.6MM Privately Held
SIC: 3599 5084 5013 Machine & other job shop work; machine tools & accessories; motor vehicle supplies & new parts

(G-21332)
NESTLE PURINA PETCARE COMPANY
5 N 2nd St (43701-3402)
P.O. Box 38 (43702-0038)
PHONE.................................740 454-8575
Carol Kagenski, Human Res Mgr
Dante Benincasa, Manager
EMP: 100
SALES (corp-wide): 88.4B Privately Held
WEB: www.purina.com
SIC: 2047 Dog & cat food
HQ: Nestle Purina Petcare Company
901 Chouteau Ave
Saint Louis MO 63102
314 982-1000

(G-21333)
NEW WAYNE INC
Also Called: Wayne Manufacturing
1555 Ritchey Pkwy (43701-7050)
PHONE.................................740 453-3454
Fax: 740 674-7006
Michael Higgins, President
Kurt Paul, Vice Pres
Mike Paul, CFO
Jennifer James, Admin Sec
EMP: 8 EST: 1953
SQ FT: 40,000
SALES: 1.8MM Privately Held
SIC: 3441 3443 Fabricated structural metal; fabricated plate work (boiler shop)

(G-21334)
NORTHPOINTE CABINETRY LLC
4800 Frazeysburg Rd (43701-8928)
PHONE.................................740 455-4045
Robert Corbett, Mng Member
Nancy Corbett, Manager
EMP: 5 EST: 2011
SALES (est): 712K Privately Held
SIC: 2434 1522 Wood kitchen cabinets; hotel/motel & multi-family home renovation & remodeling

(G-21335)
O E M HYDRAULICS INC
1150 Newark Rd (43701-2619)
P.O. Box 2969 (43702-2969)
PHONE.................................740 454-1201
Fax: 740 454-4809
Daniel Perone, President
EMP: 3
SQ FT: 10,000
SALES (est): 432.1K Privately Held
SIC: 3494 Valves & pipe fittings

(G-21336)
OHIO NATURAL GAS SERVICES INC
5600 East Pike (43701-8013)
PHONE.................................740 796-3305

Fax: 740 844-0450
John Busch, President
EMP: 4
SALES: 200K Privately Held
SIC: 1389 Oil field services

(G-21337)
OHIO STONEWARE LLC
34 N 3rd St (43701-3404)
PHONE.................................740 450-4415
Fax: 740 450-4430
Ross Pattison, Owner
Milman Linn, General Mgr
Tiffany Pattison,
EMP: 12 EST: 2005
SALES (est): 1.6MM Privately Held
WEB: www.ohiostoneware.com
SIC: 3269 Stoneware pottery products

(G-21338)
OWENS-BROCKWAY GLASS CONT INC
1700 State St (43701-3116)
PHONE.................................740 455-4500
Fax: 740 455-4514
Tom Latier, QC Dir
John Elliot, Branch Mgr
Peggy Guy, Director
Alaine Sherman, Director
Mike Spinks, Maintence Staff
EMP: 100
SALES (corp-wide): 6.7B Publicly Held
SIC: 3221 Glass containers
HQ: Owens-Brockway Glass Container Inc.
1 Michael Owens Way
Perrysburg OH 43551
567 336-8449

(G-21339)
OXFORD MINING COMPANY INC
1855 Kemper Ct (43701-4634)
PHONE.................................740 588-0190
Joe Douglas, Branch Mgr
EMP: 11
SALES (corp-wide): 1.4B Publicly Held
SIC: 1221 Bituminous coal & lignite-surface mining
HQ: Oxford Mining Company, Inc.
544 Chestnut St
Coshocton OH 43812
740 622-6302

(G-21340)
PEABODY COAL COMPANY
2810 East Pike Apt 3 (43701-9197)
PHONE.................................740 450-2420
J T Kneen, Principal
EMP: 312
SALES (corp-wide): 4.7B Publicly Held
SIC: 1241 Coal mining services
HQ: Peabody Coal Company
701 Market St
Saint Louis MO 63101
314 342-3400

(G-21341)
PLASKOLITE INC
1175 5 Bs Dr (43701-7376)
PHONE.................................740 450-1109
Fax: 740 450-1128
Mark Gringley, Branch Mgr
EMP: 100
SALES (corp-wide): 166.8MM Privately Held
WEB: www.plaskolite.com
SIC: 2821 3083 Acrylic resins; laminated plastic sheets
PA: Plaskolite Llc
1770 Joyce Ave
Columbus OH 43219
614 294-3281

(G-21342)
PORTERS WELDING INC (PA)
601 Linden Ave (43701-3397)
PHONE.................................740 452-4181
Fax: 740 452-3823
Virginia Porter, President
Daryl Porter, Vice Pres
Kimberly Browning, Admin Sec
EMP: 10
SQ FT: 70,000
SALES (est): 1.6MM Privately Held
SIC: 3441 Fabricated structural metal

(G-21343)
PORTO PUMP INC
Also Called: Zanesville Terminal Warehouse
8th And South St (43702)
P.O. Box 1003 (43702-1003)
PHONE...........................740 454-2576
Clarence Goss, *President*
Dorothy Goss, *Corp Secy*
David Goss, *Vice Pres*
Terry Goss, *Vice Pres*
EMP: 4
SALES (est): 533.7K **Privately Held**
SIC: 3586 Measuring & dispensing pumps

(G-21344)
PRAXAIR INC
130 N 3rd St (43701-3406)
PHONE...........................740 453-0346
Scott Sills, *Manager*
EMP: 3
SALES (corp-wide): 10.5B **Publicly Held**
SIC: 2813 Industrial gases
PA: Praxair, Inc.
10 Riverview Dr
Danbury CT 06810
203 837-2000

(G-21345)
PRECISION FABG & STAMPING
1755 Kemper Ct (43701-4606)
P.O. Box 2065 (43702-2065)
PHONE...........................740 453-7310
Fax: 740 453-3533
Charlie Sode, *President*
Christine Sode, *Corp Secy*
EMP: 9
SQ FT: 10,000
SALES (est): 1.4MM **Privately Held**
WEB: www.precisionfabricating.com
SIC: 3469 Metal stampings

(G-21346)
PRINT MASTERS LTD
941 W Main St (43701-3143)
PHONE...........................740 450-2885
Tom Bughman, *President*
Monica Bughman, *Partner*
EMP: 5
SALES: 300K **Privately Held**
SIC: 2752 Commercial printing, litho-
graphic

(G-21347)
PSC HOLDINGS INC (PA)
109 Graham St (43701-3103)
P.O. Box 2277 (43702-2277)
PHONE...........................740 454-6253
Dan Pottmeyer, *Principal*
Kelly Hartman, *Principal*
Jim Rose, *Principal*
Cathy Brown, *Accounting Mgr*
Chris Berns, *Sales Mgr*
EMP: 6
SALES: 83.5MM **Privately Held**
SIC: 1389 Hydraulic fracturing wells

(G-21348)
RANDY R WILSON
5100 Manchester Dr (43701-9090)
PHONE...........................740 454-4440
Randy R Wilson, *Principal*
EMP: 3
SALES (est): 190.3K **Privately Held**
SIC: 3131 Quarters

(G-21349)
S & S AGGREGATES INC (HQ)
3570 S River Rd (43701-7731)
P.O. Box 1585 (43702-1585)
PHONE...........................740 453-0721
Gerald Little, *President*
Wade Hamm, *Exec VP*
Brian Heller, *Manager*
EMP: 2 EST: 1923
SQ FT: 15,000
SALES: 50MM
SALES (corp-wide): 301.4MM **Privately
Held**
SIC: 1442 3272 3271 Sand mining; gravel
mining; concrete products; concrete block
& brick
PA: Shelly And Sands, Inc.
3570 S River Rd
Zanesville OH 43701
740 453-0721

(G-21350)
SHELLY AND SANDS INC (PA)
3570 S River Rd (43701-9052)
P.O. Box 1585 (43702-1585)
PHONE...........................740 453-0721
Fax: 740 455-3144
Richard H McClelland, *President*
Gerald N Little, *President*
Larry E Young, *Vice Pres*
Mike Cline, *Controller*
EMP: 12 EST: 1942
SQ FT: 5,000
SALES (est): 301.4MM **Privately Held**
WEB: www.shellyandsands.com
SIC: 1611 1442 2951 Highway & street
paving contractor; construction sand min-
ing; gravel mining; asphalt & asphaltic
paving mixtures (not from refineries)

(G-21351)
SHELLY AND SANDS INC
3570 S River Rd (43701-9052)
PHONE...........................740 453-0721
Matt Kelley, *Vice Pres*
EMP: 35
SALES (corp-wide): 301.4MM **Privately
Held**
WEB: www.shellyandsands.com
SIC: 1611 2951 1442 1771 Highway &
street paving contractor; asphalt & as-
phaltic paving mixtures (not from refiner-
ies); construction sand & gravel; concrete
work
PA: Shelly And Sands, Inc.
3570 S River Rd
Zanesville OH 43701
740 453-0721

(G-21352)
**SHIRLEY KS STORAGE TRAYS
LLC**
1150 Newark Rd (43701-2619)
P.O. Box 2519 (43702-2519)
PHONE...........................740 868-8140
Carrie Matheney, *President*
Dick Watts, *Plant Mgr*
Devin Hall, *Mktg Coord*
Amanda Huber, *Office Mgr*
EMP: 8
SALES (est): 1.8MM **Privately Held**
SIC: 3089 Plastic containers, except foam

(G-21353)
SIDNEY STIERS
Also Called: Stiers Countertop Sales
620 Moxahala Ave (43701-5528)
PHONE...........................740 454-7368
Fax: 740 454-7368
Sidney Stiers, *Owner*
EMP: 4
SQ FT: 4,200
SALES (est): 350.8K **Privately Held**
SIC: 2541 2434 Counter & sink tops;
wood kitchen cabinets

(G-21354)
SIDWELL MATERIALS INC
4200 Maysville Pike (43701-9372)
P.O. Box 192, White Cottage (43791-0192)
PHONE...........................740 849-2394
Jeffrey R Sidwell, *President*
Stan Archer, *General Mgr*
Jackie Harlow, *Manager*
EMP: 130
SALES (est): 21.3MM **Privately Held**
SIC: 1795 4953 2951 1422 Demolition,
buildings & other structures; rubbish col-
lection & disposal; asphalt paving mix-
tures & blocks; crushed & broken
limestone; brick, stone & related material

(G-21355)
**SOUTHEAST OHIO TIMBER
PDTS CO**
Also Called: Industrial Crate & Lumber Div
67 Beech Rock Dr (43701-6348)
PHONE...........................740 344-2570
Fax: 740 453-6764
Thomas H York, *President*
George Fouch, *Vice Pres*
EMP: 8
SQ FT: 15,000
SALES (est): 870K **Privately Held**
SIC: 2435 2448 Veneer stock, hardwood;
pallets, wood

(G-21356)
SPRINTER MARKING INC
1805 Chandlersville Rd (43701-4644)
PHONE...........................740 453-1000
Bob Bishop, *President*
John Bishop, *Treasurer*
Al Bishop, *Admin Sec*
EMP: 15
SQ FT: 6,000
SALES (est): 1.4MM **Privately Held**
WEB: www.sprintermarking.com
SIC: 3953 Marking devices; date stamps,
hand: rubber or metal

(G-21357)
STEVEN L LONES
3275 Carnation Rd (43701-9815)
PHONE...........................740 452-8851
Steven L Lones, *Owner*
EMP: 4
SALES (est): 243.4K **Privately Held**
SIC: 3494 7389 Pipe fittings;

(G-21358)
T & K HEINS CORPORATION
Also Called: American Speedy Printing
1326 Brandywine Blvd (43701-1089)
PHONE...........................740 452-6006
Fax: 740 452-5116
Thomas Heins, *President*
Katherin Heins, *President*
Alex Abernethy, *Consultant*
James Heins, *Representative*
EMP: 5
SQ FT: 1,250
SALES (est): 743.3K **Privately Held**
SIC: 2752 Commercial printing, offset

(G-21359)
**UNIQUE STRAIGHT LINE &
SFETY S**
2776 Coopermill Rd (43701-7041)
PHONE...........................740 452-2724
Lori Wickham, *Principal*
EMP: 3
SALES (est): 260.5K **Privately Held**
SIC: 3993 Signs & advertising specialties

(G-21360)
US WATER COMPANY LLC
Also Called: Culligan
1115 Newark Rd (43701-2618)
PHONE...........................740 453-0604
Richard Dovenbarger, *Manager*
EMP: 9
SALES (corp-wide): 8MM **Privately Held**
WEB: www.culliganmiami.com
SIC: 5999 7389 2899 5074 Water purifi-
cation equipment; water softener service;
water treating compounds; plumbing &
hydronic heating supplies
PA: U.S. Water Company, Llc
270 W Palatine Rd
Wheeling IL 60090
815 526-3375

(G-21361)
**VICTOR MCKENZIE DRILLING
CO**
3596 Maple Ave Ste A (43701-1686)
P.O. Box 3323 (43702-3323)
PHONE...........................740 453-0834
Victor McKenzie, *President*
Sandy McKenzie, *Corp Secy*
EMP: 27
SALES (est): 1.5MM **Privately Held**
SIC: 1381 Drilling oil & gas wells

(G-21362)
WHITE MACHINE & MFG CO (PA)
120 Graham St (43701-3100)
PHONE...........................740 453-3444
Fax: 740 453-5861
Kenneth F Vlah, *President*
EMP: 18 EST: 1955
SQ FT: 20,000
SALES (est): 2.1MM **Privately Held**
SIC: 3599 3441 Machine & other job shop
work; fabricated structural metal

(G-21363)
WORTHINGTON FOODS INC
1675 Fairview Rd (43701-8890)
PHONE...........................740 453-5501
Fax: 740 453-7789
Jackie Minarik, *Principal*
Ronald McDermott, *Vice Pres*
Tim Simon, *Safety Mgr*
Jay Brewer, *Engineer*
Stacy Huelsman, *Engineer*
▲ EMP: 87
SALES (est): 7.9MM **Privately Held**
SIC: 2038 Frozen specialties

(G-21364)
Y CITY RECYCLING LLC
4005 All American Way (43701-7251)
PHONE...........................740 452-2500
Brian Coll, *CEO*
Matt Elli, *Vice Pres*
EMP: 70
SALES (est): 7.6MM **Privately Held**
SIC: 3089 Plastic processing

(G-21365)
ZANE CASKET COMPANY INC
1201 Hall Ave (43701-3859)
P.O. Box 2113 (43702-2113)
PHONE...........................740 452-4680
Fax: 740 452-8993
Robert C Dougherty, *President*
William L Dougherty, *Vice Pres*
EMP: 20
SALES (est): 1.4MM **Privately Held**
SIC: 3995 Burial caskets

(G-21366)
ZANE PETROLEUM INC
Also Called: Hopewell Oil and Gas
1615 W Main St (43701-3157)
P.O. Box 2776 (43702-2776)
PHONE...........................740 454-8779
Fax: 740 452-6760
Jerry S Henderson, *President*
EMP: 10
SQ FT: 4,000
SALES (est): 1.3MM **Privately Held**
SIC: 1382 Oil & gas exploration services

(G-21367)
ZANESVILLE NEWSPAPER
34 S 4th St (43701-3417)
PHONE...........................740 452-4561
Dan Shaw, *Principal*
EMP: 3
SALES (est): 118.3K **Privately Held**
SIC: 2711 Newspapers

(G-21368)
ZANESVILLE TOOL GRINDING
624 Main St (43701-3625)
PHONE...........................740 453-9356
Fax: 740 453-9356
Jerry Richardson, *Owner*
EMP: 3 EST: 1971
SALES (est): 150.3K **Privately Held**
SIC: 7699 3599 Knife, saw & tool sharp-
ening & repair; machine shop, jobbing &
repair

(G-21369)
**ZANESVLLE CNFECTIONARY
HSE LLC**
2200 Linden Ave (43701)
PHONE...........................740 452-7501
Michael Ryan, *President*
EMP: 25 EST: 2013
SALES (est): 2.1MM **Privately Held**
SIC: 2064 Chocolate candy, except solid
chocolate

Zoarville
Tuscarawas County

(G-21370)
BUCKEYE FRANKLIN CO
3471 New Zoarville Rd Ne (44656-9707)
P.O. Box 117 (44656-0117)
PHONE...........................330 859-2465
Fax: 330 859-2466
R Dean Smith, *President*
Hazel Yockey, *Asst Sec*
EMP: 12
SQ FT: 15,000
SALES (est): 732.8K **Privately Held**
SIC: 1311 Natural gas production

(G-21371)
LEGACY OAK AND
HARDWOODS LLC
7138 Mount Pleasant Rd Ne (44656-8992)
PHONE.................................330 859-2656
Renee Kirtley,
EMP: 12
SALES: 800K **Privately Held**
SIC: 2511 Wood household furniture

GEOGRAPHIC

SIC INDEX

Standard Industrial Classification Alphabetical Index

SIC NO	PRODUCT

A

3291 Abrasive Prdts
2891 Adhesives & Sealants
3563 Air & Gas Compressors
3585 Air Conditioning & Heating Eqpt
3721 Aircraft
3724 Aircraft Engines & Engine Parts
3728 Aircraft Parts & Eqpt, NEC
2812 Alkalies & Chlorine
3363 Aluminum Die Castings
3354 Aluminum Extruded Prdts
3365 Aluminum Foundries
3355 Aluminum Rolling & Drawing, NEC
3353 Aluminum Sheet, Plate & Foil
3483 Ammunition, Large
3826 Analytical Instruments
2077 Animal, Marine Fats & Oils
1231 Anthracite Mining
2389 Apparel & Accessories, NEC
3446 Architectural & Ornamental Metal Work
7694 Armature Rewinding Shops
3292 Asbestos products
2952 Asphalt Felts & Coatings
3822 Automatic Temperature Controls
3581 Automatic Vending Machines
3465 Automotive Stampings
2396 Automotive Trimmings, Apparel Findings, Related Prdts

B

2673 Bags: Plastics, Laminated & Coated
2674 Bags: Uncoated Paper & Multiwall
3562 Ball & Roller Bearings
2836 Biological Prdts, Exc Diagnostic Substances
1221 Bituminous Coal & Lignite: Surface Mining
1222 Bituminous Coal: Underground Mining
2782 Blankbooks & Looseleaf Binders
3312 Blast Furnaces, Coke Ovens, Steel & Rolling Mills
3564 Blowers & Fans
3732 Boat Building & Repairing
3452 Bolts, Nuts, Screws, Rivets & Washers
2732 Book Printing, Not Publishing
2789 Bookbinding
2731 Books: Publishing & Printing
3131 Boot & Shoe Cut Stock & Findings
2342 Brassieres, Girdles & Garments
2051 Bread, Bakery Prdts Exc Cookies & Crackers
3251 Brick & Structural Clay Tile
3991 Brooms & Brushes
3995 Burial Caskets
2021 Butter

C

3578 Calculating & Accounting Eqpt
2064 Candy & Confectionery Prdts
2033 Canned Fruits, Vegetables & Preserves
2032 Canned Specialties
2394 Canvas Prdts
3624 Carbon & Graphite Prdts
2895 Carbon Black
3955 Carbon Paper & Inked Ribbons
3592 Carburetors, Pistons, Rings & Valves
2273 Carpets & Rugs
2823 Cellulosic Man-Made Fibers
3241 Cement, Hydraulic
3253 Ceramic Tile
2043 Cereal Breakfast Foods
2022 Cheese
1479 Chemical & Fertilizer Mining
2899 Chemical Preparations, NEC
2361 Children's & Infants' Dresses & Blouses
3261 China Plumbing Fixtures & Fittings
3262 China, Table & Kitchen Articles
2066 Chocolate & Cocoa Prdts
2111 Cigarettes
2121 Cigars
3255 Clay Refractories
1459 Clay, Ceramic & Refractory Minerals, NEC
1241 Coal Mining Svcs
3479 Coating & Engraving, NEC
2095 Coffee
3316 Cold Rolled Steel Sheet, Strip & Bars
3582 Commercial Laundry, Dry Clean & Pressing Mchs
2759 Commercial Printing

2754 Commercial Printing: Gravure
2752 Commercial Printing: Lithographic
3646 Commercial, Indl & Institutional Lighting Fixtures
3669 Communications Eqpt, NEC
3577 Computer Peripheral Eqpt, NEC
3572 Computer Storage Devices
3575 Computer Terminals
3271 Concrete Block & Brick
3272 Concrete Prdts
3531 Construction Machinery & Eqpt
1442 Construction Sand & Gravel
2679 Converted Paper Prdts, NEC
3535 Conveyors & Eqpt
2052 Cookies & Crackers
3366 Copper Foundries
1021 Copper Ores
2298 Cordage & Twine
2653 Corrugated & Solid Fiber Boxes
3961 Costume Jewelry & Novelties
2261 Cotton Fabric Finishers
2211 Cotton, Woven Fabric
3466 Crowns & Closures
1311 Crude Petroleum & Natural Gas
1423 Crushed & Broken Granite
1422 Crushed & Broken Limestone
1429 Crushed & Broken Stone, NEC
3643 Current-Carrying Wiring Devices
2391 Curtains & Draperies
3087 Custom Compounding Of Purchased Plastic Resins
3281 Cut Stone Prdts
3421 Cutlery
2865 Cyclic-Crudes, Intermediates, Dyes & Org Pigments

D

3843 Dental Eqpt & Splys
2835 Diagnostic Substances
2675 Die-Cut Paper & Board
3544 Dies, Tools, Jigs, Fixtures & Indl Molds
1411 Dimension Stone
2047 Dog & Cat Food
3942 Dolls & Stuffed Toys
2591 Drapery Hardware, Window Blinds & Shades
2381 Dress & Work Gloves
2034 Dried Fruits, Vegetables & Soup
1381 Drilling Oil & Gas Wells

E

3263 Earthenware, Whiteware, Table & Kitchen Articles
3634 Electric Household Appliances
3641 Electric Lamps
3694 Electrical Eqpt For Internal Combustion Engines
3629 Electrical Indl Apparatus, NEC
3699 Electrical Machinery, Eqpt & Splys, NEC
3845 Electromedical & Electrotherapeutic Apparatus
3313 Electrometallurgical Prdts
3675 Electronic Capacitors
3677 Electronic Coils & Transformers
3679 Electronic Components, NEC
3571 Electronic Computers
3678 Electronic Connectors
3676 Electronic Resistors
3471 Electroplating, Plating, Polishing, Anodizing & Coloring
3534 Elevators & Moving Stairways
3431 Enameled Iron & Metal Sanitary Ware
2677 Envelopes
2892 Explosives

F

2241 Fabric Mills, Cotton, Wool, Silk & Man-Made
3499 Fabricated Metal Prdts, NEC
3498 Fabricated Pipe & Pipe Fittings
3443 Fabricated Plate Work
3069 Fabricated Rubber Prdts, NEC
3441 Fabricated Structural Steel
2399 Fabricated Textile Prdts, NEC
2295 Fabrics Coated Not Rubberized
2297 Fabrics, Nonwoven
3523 Farm Machinery & Eqpt
3965 Fasteners, Buttons, Needles & Pins
1061 Ferroalloy Ores, Except Vanadium
2875 Fertilizers, Mixing Only
2655 Fiber Cans, Tubes & Drums
2091 Fish & Seafoods, Canned & Cured
3211 Flat Glass

2087 Flavoring Extracts & Syrups
2045 Flour, Blended & Prepared
2041 Flour, Grain Milling
3824 Fluid Meters & Counters
3593 Fluid Power Cylinders & Actuators
3594 Fluid Power Pumps & Motors
3492 Fluid Power Valves & Hose Fittings
2657 Folding Paperboard Boxes
3556 Food Prdts Machinery
2099 Food Preparations, NEC
3149 Footwear, NEC
2053 Frozen Bakery Prdts
2037 Frozen Fruits, Juices & Vegetables
2038 Frozen Specialties
2371 Fur Goods
2599 Furniture & Fixtures, NEC

G

3944 Games, Toys & Children's Vehicles
3524 Garden, Lawn Tractors & Eqpt
3053 Gaskets, Packing & Sealing Devices
2369 Girls' & Infants' Outerwear, NEC
3221 Glass Containers
3231 Glass Prdts Made Of Purchased Glass
1041 Gold Ores
3321 Gray Iron Foundries
2771 Greeting Card Publishing
3769 Guided Missile/Space Vehicle Parts & Eqpt, NEC
3764 Guided Missile/Space Vehicle Propulsion Units & parts
3761 Guided Missiles & Space Vehicles
2861 Gum & Wood Chemicals
3275 Gypsum Prdts

H

3423 Hand & Edge Tools
3425 Hand Saws & Saw Blades
3171 Handbags & Purses
3429 Hardware, NEC
2426 Hardwood Dimension & Flooring Mills
2435 Hardwood Veneer & Plywood
2353 Hats, Caps & Millinery
3433 Heating Eqpt
3536 Hoists, Cranes & Monorails
2252 Hosiery, Except Women's
2392 House furnishings: Textile
3142 House Slippers
3639 Household Appliances, NEC
3651 Household Audio & Video Eqpt
3631 Household Cooking Eqpt
2519 Household Furniture, NEC
3633 Household Laundry Eqpt
3632 Household Refrigerators & Freezers
3635 Household Vacuum Cleaners

I

2097 Ice
2024 Ice Cream
2819 Indl Inorganic Chemicals, NEC
3823 Indl Instruments For Meas, Display & Control
3569 Indl Machinery & Eqpt, NEC
3567 Indl Process Furnaces & Ovens
3537 Indl Trucks, Tractors, Trailers & Stackers
2813 Industrial Gases
2869 Industrial Organic Chemicals, NEC
3543 Industrial Patterns
1446 Industrial Sand
3491 Industrial Valves
2816 Inorganic Pigments
3825 Instrs For Measuring & Testing Electricity
3519 Internal Combustion Engines, NEC
3462 Iron & Steel Forgings
1011 Iron Ores

J

3915 Jewelers Findings & Lapidary Work
3911 Jewelry: Precious Metal

K

1455 Kaolin & Ball Clay
2253 Knit Outerwear Mills

L

3821 Laboratory Apparatus & Furniture
2258 Lace & Warp Knit Fabric Mills
3952 Lead Pencils, Crayons & Artist's Mtrls

SIC NO	PRODUCT

2386 Leather & Sheep Lined Clothing
3151 Leather Gloves & Mittens
3199 Leather Goods, NEC
3111 Leather Tanning & Finishing
3648 Lighting Eqpt, NEC
3274 Lime
3996 Linoleum & Hard Surface Floor Coverings, NEC
2085 Liquors, Distilled, Rectified & Blended
2411 Logging
2992 Lubricating Oils & Greases
3161 Luggage

M

2098 Macaroni, Spaghetti & Noodles
3545 Machine Tool Access
3541 Machine Tools: Cutting
3542 Machine Tools: Forming
3599 Machinery & Eqpt, Indl & Commercial, NEC
3322 Malleable Iron Foundries
2082 Malt Beverages
2761 Manifold Business Forms
3999 Manufacturing Industries, NEC
3953 Marking Devices
2515 Mattresses & Bedsprings
3829 Measuring & Controlling Devices, NEC
3586 Measuring & Dispensing Pumps
2011 Meat Packing Plants
3568 Mechanical Power Transmission Eqpt, NEC
2833 Medicinal Chemicals & Botanical Prdts
2329 Men's & Boys' Clothing, NEC
2325 Men's & Boys' Separate Trousers & Casual Slacks
2321 Men's & Boys' Shirts
2311 Men's & Boys' Suits, Coats & Overcoats
2322 Men's & Boys' Underwear & Nightwear
2326 Men's & Boys' Work Clothing
3143 Men's Footwear, Exc Athletic
3412 Metal Barrels, Drums, Kegs & Pails
3411 Metal Cans
3442 Metal Doors, Sash, Frames, Molding & Trim
3497 Metal Foil & Leaf
3398 Metal Heat Treating
2514 Metal Household Furniture
1081 Metal Mining Svcs
1099 Metal Ores, NEC
3469 Metal Stampings, NEC
3549 Metalworking Machinery, NEC
2026 Milk
2023 Milk, Condensed & Evaporated
2431 Millwork
3296 Mineral Wool
3295 Minerals & Earths: Ground Or Treated
3532 Mining Machinery & Eqpt
3496 Misc Fabricated Wire Prdts
2741 Misc Publishing
3449 Misc Structural Metal Work
1499 Miscellaneous Nonmetallic Mining
2451 Mobile Homes
3061 Molded, Extruded & Lathe-Cut Rubber Mechanical Goods
3716 Motor Homes
3714 Motor Vehicle Parts & Access
3711 Motor Vehicles & Car Bodies
3751 Motorcycles, Bicycles & Parts
3621 Motors & Generators
3931 Musical Instruments

N

1321 Natural Gas Liquids
2711 Newspapers: Publishing & Printing
2873 Nitrogenous Fertilizers
3297 Nonclay Refractories
3644 Noncurrent-Carrying Wiring Devices
3364 Nonferrous Die Castings, Exc Aluminum
3463 Nonferrous Forgings
3369 Nonferrous Foundries: Castings, NEC
3357 Nonferrous Wire Drawing
3299 Nonmetallic Mineral Prdts, NEC
1481 Nonmetallic Minerals Svcs, Except Fuels

O

2522 Office Furniture, Except Wood
3579 Office Machines, NEC
1382 Oil & Gas Field Exploration Svcs
1389 Oil & Gas Field Svcs, NEC
3533 Oil Field Machinery & Eqpt
3851 Ophthalmic Goods
3827 Optical Instruments
3489 Ordnance & Access, NEC
3842 Orthopedic, Prosthetic & Surgical Appliances/Splys

SIC NO	PRODUCT

P

3565 Packaging Machinery
2851 Paints, Varnishes, Lacquers, Enamels
2671 Paper Coating & Laminating for Packaging
2672 Paper Coating & Laminating, Exc for Packaging
3554 Paper Inds Machinery
2621 Paper Mills
2631 Paperboard Mills
2542 Partitions & Fixtures, Except Wood
2951 Paving Mixtures & Blocks
3951 Pens & Mechanical Pencils
2844 Perfumes, Cosmetics & Toilet Preparations
2721 Periodicals: Publishing & Printing
3172 Personal Leather Goods
2879 Pesticides & Agricultural Chemicals, NEC
2911 Petroleum Refining
2834 Pharmaceuticals
3652 Phonograph Records & Magnetic Tape
2874 Phosphatic Fertilizers
3861 Photographic Eqpt & Splys
2035 Pickled Fruits, Vegetables, Sauces & Dressings
3085 Plastic Bottles
3086 Plastic Foam Prdts
3083 Plastic Laminated Plate & Sheet
3084 Plastic Pipe
3088 Plastic Plumbing Fixtures
3089 Plastic Prdts
3082 Plastic Unsupported Profile Shapes
3081 Plastic Unsupported Sheet & Film
2821 Plastics, Mtrls & Nonvulcanizable Elastomers
2796 Platemaking & Related Svcs
2395 Pleating & Stitching For The Trade
3432 Plumbing Fixture Fittings & Trim, Brass
3264 Porcelain Electrical Splys
2096 Potato Chips & Similar Prdts
3269 Pottery Prdts, NEC
2015 Poultry Slaughtering, Dressing & Processing
3546 Power Hand Tools
3612 Power, Distribution & Specialty Transformers
3448 Prefabricated Metal Buildings & Cmpnts
2452 Prefabricated Wood Buildings & Cmpnts
7372 Prepackaged Software
2048 Prepared Feeds For Animals & Fowls
3229 Pressed & Blown Glassware, NEC
3692 Primary Batteries: Dry & Wet
3399 Primary Metal Prdts, NEC
3339 Primary Nonferrous Metals, NEC
3334 Primary Production Of Aluminum
3331 Primary Smelting & Refining Of Copper
3672 Printed Circuit Boards
2893 Printing Ink
3555 Printing Trades Machinery & Eqpt
2999 Products Of Petroleum & Coal, NEC
2531 Public Building & Related Furniture
2611 Pulp Mills
3561 Pumps & Pumping Eqpt

R

3663 Radio & T V Communications, Systs & Eqpt, Broadcast/Studio
3671 Radio & T V Receiving Electron Tubes
3743 Railroad Eqpt
3273 Ready-Mixed Concrete
2493 Reconstituted Wood Prdts
3695 Recording Media
3625 Relays & Indl Controls
3645 Residential Lighting Fixtures
2044 Rice Milling
2384 Robes & Dressing Gowns
3547 Rolling Mill Machinery & Eqpt
3351 Rolling, Drawing & Extruding Of Copper
3356 Rolling, Drawing-Extruding Of Nonferrous Metals
3021 Rubber & Plastic Footwear
3052 Rubber & Plastic Hose & Belting

S

2068 Salted & Roasted Nuts & Seeds
2656 Sanitary Food Containers
2676 Sanitary Paper Prdts
2013 Sausages & Meat Prdts
2421 Saw & Planing Mills
3596 Scales & Balances, Exc Laboratory
3451 Screw Machine Prdts
3812 Search, Detection, Navigation & Guidance Systs & Instrs
3341 Secondary Smelting & Refining Of Nonferrous Metals
3674 Semiconductors
3589 Service Ind Machines, NEC
2652 Set-Up Paperboard Boxes
3444 Sheet Metal Work
3731 Shipbuilding & Repairing

SIC NO	PRODUCT

2079 Shortening, Oils & Margarine
3993 Signs & Advertising Displays
2262 Silk & Man-Made Fabric Finishers
2221 Silk & Man-Made Fiber
3914 Silverware, Plated & Stainless Steel Ware
3484 Small Arms
3482 Small Arms Ammunition
2841 Soap & Detergents
2086 Soft Drinks
2436 Softwood Veneer & Plywood
2075 Soybean Oil Mills
2842 Spec Cleaning, Polishing & Sanitation Preparations
3559 Special Ind Machinery, NEC
2429 Special Prdt Sawmills, NEC
3566 Speed Changers, Drives & Gears
3949 Sporting & Athletic Goods, NEC
2678 Stationery Prdts
3511 Steam, Gas & Hydraulic Turbines & Engines
3325 Steel Foundries, NEC
3324 Steel Investment Foundries
3317 Steel Pipe & Tubes
3493 Steel Springs, Except Wire
3315 Steel Wire Drawing & Nails & Spikes
3691 Storage Batteries
3259 Structural Clay Prdts, NEC
2439 Structural Wood Members, NEC
2063 Sugar, Beet
2843 Surface Active & Finishing Agents, Sulfonated Oils
3841 Surgical & Medical Instrs & Apparatus
3613 Switchgear & Switchboard Apparatus
2824 Synthetic Organic Fibers, Exc Cellulosic
2822 Synthetic Rubber (Vulcanizable Elastomers)

T

3795 Tanks & Tank Components
3661 Telephone & Telegraph Apparatus
2393 Textile Bags
2269 Textile Finishers, NEC
2299 Textile Goods, NEC
3552 Textile Machinery
2284 Thread Mills
2296 Tire Cord & Fabric
3011 Tires & Inner Tubes
2131 Tobacco, Chewing & Snuff
3799 Transportation Eqpt, NEC
3792 Travel Trailers & Campers
3713 Truck & Bus Bodies
3715 Truck Trailers
2791 Typesetting

U

1094 Uranium, Radium & Vanadium Ores

V

3494 Valves & Pipe Fittings, NEC
3647 Vehicular Lighting Eqpt

W

3873 Watch & Clock Devices & Parts
2385 Waterproof Outerwear
3548 Welding Apparatus
7692 Welding Repair
2046 Wet Corn Milling
2084 Wine & Brandy
3495 Wire Springs
2331 Women's & Misses' Blouses
2335 Women's & Misses' Dresses
2339 Women's & Misses' Outerwear, NEC
2337 Women's & Misses' Suits, Coats & Skirts
3144 Women's Footwear, Exc Athletic
2341 Women's, Misses' & Children's Underwear & Nightwear
2441 Wood Boxes
2449 Wood Containers, NEC
2511 Wood Household Furniture
2512 Wood Household Furniture, Upholstered
2434 Wood Kitchen Cabinets
2521 Wood Office Furniture
2448 Wood Pallets & Skids
2499 Wood Prdts, NEC
2491 Wood Preserving
2517 Wood T V, Radio, Phono & Sewing Cabinets
2541 Wood, Office & Store Fixtures
3553 Woodworking Machinery
2231 Wool, Woven Fabric

X

3844 X-ray Apparatus & Tubes

Y

2281 Yarn Spinning Mills
2282 Yarn Texturizing, Throwing, Twisting & Winding Mills

SIC INDEX

Standard Industrial Classification Numerical Index

SIC NO	PRODUCT

10 METAL MINING
1011 Iron Ores
1021 Copper Ores
1041 Gold Ores
1061 Ferroalloy Ores, Except Vanadium
1081 Metal Mining Svcs
1094 Uranium, Radium & Vanadium Ores
1099 Metal Ores, NEC

12 COAL MINING
1221 Bituminous Coal & Lignite: Surface Mining
1222 Bituminous Coal: Underground Mining
1231 Anthracite Mining
1241 Coal Mining Svcs

13 OIL AND GAS EXTRACTION
1311 Crude Petroleum & Natural Gas
1321 Natural Gas Liquids
1381 Drilling Oil & Gas Wells
1382 Oil & Gas Field Exploration Svcs
1389 Oil & Gas Field Svcs, NEC

14 MINING AND QUARRYING OF NONMETALLIC MINERALS, EXCEPT FUELS
1411 Dimension Stone
1422 Crushed & Broken Limestone
1423 Crushed & Broken Granite
1429 Crushed & Broken Stone, NEC
1442 Construction Sand & Gravel
1446 Industrial Sand
1455 Kaolin & Ball Clay
1459 Clay, Ceramic & Refractory Minerals, NEC
1479 Chemical & Fertilizer Mining
1481 Nonmetallic Minerals Svcs, Except Fuels
1499 Miscellaneous Nonmetallic Mining

20 FOOD AND KINDRED PRODUCTS
2011 Meat Packing Plants
2013 Sausages & Meat Prdts
2015 Poultry Slaughtering, Dressing & Processing
2021 Butter
2022 Cheese
2023 Milk, Condensed & Evaporated
2024 Ice Cream
2026 Milk
2032 Canned Specialties
2033 Canned Fruits, Vegetables & Preserves
2034 Dried Fruits, Vegetables & Soup
2035 Pickled Fruits, Vegetables, Sauces & Dressings
2037 Frozen Fruits, Juices & Vegetables
2038 Frozen Specialties
2041 Flour, Grain Milling
2043 Cereal Breakfast Foods
2044 Rice Milling
2045 Flour, Blended & Prepared
2046 Wet Corn Milling
2047 Dog & Cat Food
2048 Prepared Feeds For Animals & Fowls
2051 Bread, Bakery Prdts Exc Cookies & Crackers
2052 Cookies & Crackers
2053 Frozen Bakery Prdts
2063 Sugar, Beet
2064 Candy & Confectionery Prdts
2066 Chocolate & Cocoa Prdts
2068 Salted & Roasted Nuts & Seeds
2075 Soybean Oil Mills
2077 Animal, Marine Fats & Oils
2079 Shortening, Oils & Margarine
2082 Malt Beverages
2084 Wine & Brandy
2085 Liquors, Distilled, Rectified & Blended
2086 Soft Drinks
2087 Flavoring Extracts & Syrups
2091 Fish & Seafoods, Canned & Cured
2095 Coffee
2096 Potato Chips & Similar Prdts
2097 Ice
2098 Macaroni, Spaghetti & Noodles
2099 Food Preparations, NEC

21 TOBACCO PRODUCTS
2111 Cigarettes
2121 Cigars
2131 Tobacco, Chewing & Snuff

22 TEXTILE MILL PRODUCTS
2211 Cotton, Woven Fabric

2221 Silk & Man-Made Fiber
2231 Wool, Woven Fabric
2241 Fabric Mills, Cotton, Wool, Silk & Man-Made
2252 Hosiery, Except Women's
2253 Knit Outerwear Mills
2258 Lace & Warp Knit Fabric Mills
2261 Cotton Fabric Finishers
2262 Silk & Man-Made Fabric Finishers
2269 Textile Finishers, NEC
2273 Carpets & Rugs
2281 Yarn Spinning Mills
2282 Yarn Texturizing, Throwing, Twisting & Winding Mills
2284 Thread Mills
2295 Fabrics Coated Not Rubberized
2296 Tire Cord & Fabric
2297 Fabrics, Nonwoven
2298 Cordage & Twine
2299 Textile Goods, NEC

23 APPAREL AND OTHER FINISHED PRODUCTS MADE FROM FABRICS AND SIMILAR MATERIAL
2311 Men's & Boys' Suits, Coats & Overcoats
2321 Men's & Boys' Shirts
2322 Men's & Boys' Underwear & Nightwear
2325 Men's & Boys' Separate Trousers & Casual Slacks
2326 Men's & Boys' Work Clothing
2329 Men's & Boys' Clothing, NEC
2331 Women's & Misses' Blouses
2335 Women's & Misses' Dresses
2337 Women's & Misses' Suits, Coats & Skirts
2339 Women's & Misses' Outerwear, NEC
2341 Women's, Misses' & Children's Underwear & Nightwear
2342 Brassieres, Girdles & Garments
2353 Hats, Caps & Millinery
2361 Children's & Infants' Dresses & Blouses
2369 Girls' & Infants' Outerwear, NEC
2371 Fur Goods
2381 Dress & Work Gloves
2384 Robes & Dressing Gowns
2385 Waterproof Outerwear
2386 Leather & Sheep Lined Clothing
2389 Apparel & Accessories, NEC
2391 Curtains & Draperies
2392 House furnishings: Textile
2393 Textile Bags
2394 Canvas Prdts
2395 Pleating & Stitching For The Trade
2396 Automotive Trimmings, Apparel Findings, Related Prdts
2399 Fabricated Textile Prdts, NEC

24 LUMBER AND WOOD PRODUCTS, EXCEPT FURNITURE
2411 Logging
2421 Saw & Planing Mills
2426 Hardwood Dimension & Flooring Mills
2429 Special Prdt Sawmills, NEC
2431 Millwork
2434 Wood Kitchen Cabinets
2435 Hardwood Veneer & Plywood
2436 Softwood Veneer & Plywood
2439 Structural Wood Members, NEC
2441 Wood Boxes
2448 Wood Pallets & Skids
2449 Wood Containers, NEC
2451 Mobile Homes
2452 Prefabricated Wood Buildings & Cmpnts
2491 Wood Preserving
2493 Reconstituted Wood Prdts
2499 Wood Prdts, NEC

25 FURNITURE AND FIXTURES
2511 Wood Household Furniture
2512 Wood Household Furniture, Upholstered
2514 Metal Household Furniture
2515 Mattresses & Bedsprings
2517 Wood T V, Radio, Phono & Sewing Cabinets
2519 Household Furniture, NEC
2521 Wood Office Furniture
2522 Office Furniture, Except Wood
2531 Public Building & Related Furniture
2541 Wood, Office & Store Fixtures
2542 Partitions & Fixtures, Except Wood
2591 Drapery Hardware, Window Blinds & Shades
2599 Furniture & Fixtures, NEC

26 PAPER AND ALLIED PRODUCTS
2611 Pulp Mills
2621 Paper Mills
2631 Paperboard Mills
2652 Set-Up Paperboard Boxes
2653 Corrugated & Solid Fiber Boxes
2655 Fiber Cans, Tubes & Drums
2656 Sanitary Food Containers
2657 Folding Paperboard Boxes
2671 Paper Coating & Laminating for Packaging
2672 Paper Coating & Laminating, Exc for Packaging
2673 Bags: Plastics, Laminated & Coated
2674 Bags: Uncoated Paper & Multiwall
2675 Die-Cut Paper & Board
2676 Sanitary Paper Prdts
2677 Envelopes
2678 Stationery Prdts
2679 Converted Paper Prdts, NEC

27 PRINTING, PUBLISHING, AND ALLIED INDUSTRIES
2711 Newspapers: Publishing & Printing
2721 Periodicals: Publishing & Printing
2731 Books: Publishing & Printing
2732 Book Printing, Not Publishing
2741 Misc Publishing
2752 Commercial Printing: Lithographic
2754 Commercial Printing: Gravure
2759 Commercial Printing
2761 Manifold Business Forms
2771 Greeting Card Publishing
2782 Blankbooks & Looseleaf Binders
2789 Bookbinding
2791 Typesetting
2796 Platemaking & Related Svcs

28 CHEMICALS AND ALLIED PRODUCTS
2812 Alkalies & Chlorine
2813 Industrial Gases
2816 Inorganic Pigments
2819 Indl Inorganic Chemicals, NEC
2821 Plastics, Mtrls & Nonvulcanizable Elastomers
2822 Synthetic Rubber (Vulcanizable Elastomers)
2823 Cellulosic Man-Made Fibers
2824 Synthetic Organic Fibers, Exc Cellulosic
2833 Medicinal Chemicals & Botanical Prdts
2834 Pharmaceuticals
2835 Diagnostic Substances
2836 Biological Prdts, Exc Diagnostic Substances
2841 Soap & Detergents
2842 Spec Cleaning, Polishing & Sanitation Preparations
2843 Surface Active & Finishing Agents, Sulfonated Oils
2844 Perfumes, Cosmetics & Toilet Preparations
2851 Paints, Varnishes, Lacquers, Enamels
2861 Gum & Wood Chemicals
2865 Cyclic-Crudes, Intermediates, Dyes & Org Pigments
2869 Industrial Organic Chemicals, NEC
2873 Nitrogenous Fertilizers
2874 Phosphatic Fertilizers
2875 Fertilizers, Mixing Only
2879 Pesticides & Agricultural Chemicals, NEC
2891 Adhesives & Sealants
2892 Explosives
2893 Printing Ink
2895 Carbon Black
2899 Chemical Preparations, NEC

29 PETROLEUM REFINING AND RELATED INDUSTRIES
2911 Petroleum Refining
2951 Paving Mixtures & Blocks
2952 Asphalt Felts & Coatings
2992 Lubricating Oils & Greases
2999 Products Of Petroleum & Coal, NEC

30 RUBBER AND MISCELLANEOUS PLASTICS PRODUCTS
3011 Tires & Inner Tubes
3021 Rubber & Plastic Footwear
3052 Rubber & Plastic Hose & Belting
3053 Gaskets, Packing & Sealing Devices
3061 Molded, Extruded & Lathe-Cut Rubber Mechanical Goods
3069 Fabricated Rubber Prdts, NEC
3081 Plastic Unsupported Sheet & Film
3082 Plastic Unsupported Profile Shapes
3083 Plastic Laminated Plate & Sheet
3084 Plastic Pipe

SIC

SIC NO	PRODUCT

3085 Plastic Bottles
3086 Plastic Foam Prdts
3087 Custom Compounding Of Purchased Plastic Resins
3088 Plastic Plumbing Fixtures
3089 Plastic Prdts

31 LEATHER AND LEATHER PRODUCTS

3111 Leather Tanning & Finishing
3131 Boot & Shoe Cut Stock & Findings
3142 House Slippers
3143 Men's Footwear, Exc Athletic
3144 Women's Footwear, Exc Athletic
3149 Footwear, NEC
3151 Leather Gloves & Mittens
3161 Luggage
3171 Handbags & Purses
3172 Personal Leather Goods
3199 Leather Goods, NEC

32 STONE, CLAY, GLASS, AND CONCRETE PRODUCTS

3211 Flat Glass
3221 Glass Containers
3229 Pressed & Blown Glassware, NEC
3231 Glass Prdts Made Of Purchased Glass
3241 Cement, Hydraulic
3251 Brick & Structural Clay Tile
3253 Ceramic Tile
3255 Clay Refractories
3259 Structural Clay Prdts, NEC
3261 China Plumbing Fixtures & Fittings
3262 China, Table & Kitchen Articles
3263 Earthenware, Whiteware, Table & Kitchen Articles
3264 Porcelain Electrical Splys
3269 Pottery Prdts, NEC
3271 Concrete Block & Brick
3272 Concrete Prdts
3273 Ready-Mixed Concrete
3274 Lime
3275 Gypsum Prdts
3281 Cut Stone Prdts
3291 Abrasive Prdts
3292 Asbestos products
3295 Minerals & Earths: Ground Or Treated
3296 Mineral Wool
3297 Nonclay Refractories
3299 Nonmetallic Mineral Prdts, NEC

33 PRIMARY METAL INDUSTRIES

3312 Blast Furnaces, Coke Ovens, Steel & Rolling Mills
3313 Electrometallurgical Prdts
3315 Steel Wire Drawing & Nails & Spikes
3316 Cold Rolled Steel Sheet, Strip & Bars
3317 Steel Pipe & Tubes
3321 Gray Iron Foundries
3322 Malleable Iron Foundries
3324 Steel Investment Foundries
3325 Steel Foundries, NEC
3331 Primary Smelting & Refining Of Copper
3334 Primary Production Of Aluminum
3339 Primary Nonferrous Metals, NEC
3341 Secondary Smelting & Refining Of Nonferrous Metals
3351 Rolling, Drawing & Extruding Of Copper
3353 Aluminum Sheet, Plate & Foil
3354 Aluminum Extruded Prdts
3355 Aluminum Rolling & Drawing, NEC
3356 Rolling, Drawing-Extruding Of Nonferrous Metals
3357 Nonferrous Wire Drawing
3363 Aluminum Die Castings
3364 Nonferrous Die Castings, Exc Aluminum
3365 Aluminum Foundries
3366 Copper Foundries
3369 Nonferrous Foundries: Castings, NEC
3398 Metal Heat Treating
3399 Primary Metal Prdts, NEC

34 FABRICATED METAL PRODUCTS, EXCEPT MACHINERY AND TRANSPORTATION EQUIPMENT

3411 Metal Cans
3412 Metal Barrels, Drums, Kegs & Pails
3421 Cutlery
3423 Hand & Edge Tools
3425 Hand Saws & Saw Blades
3429 Hardware, NEC
3431 Enameled Iron & Metal Sanitary Ware
3432 Plumbing Fixture Fittings & Trim, Brass
3433 Heating Eqpt
3441 Fabricated Structural Steel
3442 Metal Doors, Sash, Frames, Molding & Trim
3443 Fabricated Plate Work
3444 Sheet Metal Work
3446 Architectural & Ornamental Metal Work
3448 Prefabricated Metal Buildings & Cmpnts
3449 Misc Structural Metal Work

3451 Screw Machine Prdts
3452 Bolts, Nuts, Screws, Rivets & Washers
3462 Iron & Steel Forgings
3463 Nonferrous Forgings
3465 Automotive Stampings
3466 Crowns & Closures
3469 Metal Stampings, NEC
3471 Electroplating, Plating, Polishing, Anodizing & Coloring
3479 Coating & Engraving, NEC
3482 Small Arms Ammunition
3483 Ammunition, Large
3484 Small Arms
3489 Ordnance & Access, NEC
3491 Industrial Valves
3492 Fluid Power Valves & Hose Fittings
3493 Steel Springs, Except Wire
3494 Valves & Pipe Fittings, NEC
3495 Wire Springs
3496 Misc Fabricated Wire Prdts
3497 Metal Foil & Leaf
3498 Fabricated Pipe & Pipe Fittings
3499 Fabricated Metal Prdts, NEC

35 INDUSTRIAL AND COMMERCIAL MACHINERY AND COMPUTER EQUIPMENT

3511 Steam, Gas & Hydraulic Turbines & Engines
3519 Internal Combustion Engines, NEC
3523 Farm Machinery & Eqpt
3524 Garden, Lawn Tractors & Eqpt
3531 Construction Machinery & Eqpt
3532 Mining Machinery & Eqpt
3533 Oil Field Machinery & Eqpt
3534 Elevators & Moving Stairways
3535 Conveyors & Eqpt
3536 Hoists, Cranes & Monorails
3537 Indl Trucks, Tractors, Trailers & Stackers
3541 Machine Tools: Cutting
3542 Machine Tools: Forming
3543 Industrial Patterns
3544 Dies, Tools, Jigs, Fixtures & Indl Molds
3545 Machine Tool Access
3546 Power Hand Tools
3547 Rolling Mill Machinery & Eqpt
3548 Welding Apparatus
3549 Metalworking Machinery, NEC
3552 Textile Machinery
3553 Woodworking Machinery
3554 Paper Inds Machinery
3555 Printing Trades Machinery & Eqpt
3556 Food Prdts Machinery
3559 Special Ind Machinery, NEC
3561 Pumps & Pumping Eqpt
3562 Ball & Roller Bearings
3563 Air & Gas Compressors
3564 Blowers & Fans
3565 Packaging Machinery
3566 Speed Changers, Drives & Gears
3567 Indl Process Furnaces & Ovens
3568 Mechanical Power Transmission Eqpt, NEC
3569 Indl Machinery & Eqpt, NEC
3571 Electronic Computers
3572 Computer Storage Devices
3575 Computer Terminals
3577 Computer Peripheral Eqpt, NEC
3578 Calculating & Accounting Eqpt
3579 Office Machines, NEC
3581 Automatic Vending Machines
3582 Commercial Laundry, Dry Clean & Pressing Mchs
3585 Air Conditioning & Heating Eqpt
3586 Measuring & Dispensing Pumps
3589 Service Ind Machines, NEC
3592 Carburetors, Pistons, Rings & Valves
3593 Fluid Power Cylinders & Actuators
3594 Fluid Power Pumps & Motors
3596 Scales & Balances, Exc Laboratory
3599 Machinery & Eqpt, Indl & Commercial, NEC

36 ELECTRONIC AND OTHER ELECTRICAL EQUIPMENT AND COMPONENTS, EXCEPT COMPUTER

3612 Power, Distribution & Specialty Transformers
3613 Switchgear & Switchboard Apparatus
3621 Motors & Generators
3624 Carbon & Graphite Prdts
3625 Relays & Indl Controls
3629 Electrical Indl Apparatus, NEC
3631 Household Cooking Eqpt
3632 Household Refrigerators & Freezers
3633 Household Laundry Eqpt
3634 Electric Household Appliances
3635 Household Vacuum Cleaners
3639 Household Appliances, NEC
3641 Electric Lamps
3643 Current-Carrying Wiring Devices

3644 Noncurrent-Carrying Wiring Devices
3645 Residential Lighting Fixtures
3646 Commercial, Indl & Institutional Lighting Fixtures
3647 Vehicular Lighting Eqpt
3648 Lighting Eqpt, NEC
3651 Household Audio & Video Eqpt
3652 Phonograph Records & Magnetic Tape
3661 Telephone & Telegraph Apparatus
3663 Radio & T V Communications, Systs & Eqpt, Broadcast/Studio
3669 Communications Eqpt, NEC
3671 Radio & T V Receiving Electron Tubes
3672 Printed Circuit Boards
3674 Semiconductors
3675 Electronic Capacitors
3676 Electronic Resistors
3677 Electronic Coils & Transformers
3678 Electronic Connectors
3679 Electronic Components, NEC
3691 Storage Batteries
3692 Primary Batteries: Dry & Wet
3694 Electrical Eqpt For Internal Combustion Engines
3695 Recording Media
3699 Electrical Machinery, Eqpt & Splys, NEC

37 TRANSPORTATION EQUIPMENT

3711 Motor Vehicles & Car Bodies
3713 Truck & Bus Bodies
3714 Motor Vehicle Parts & Access
3715 Truck Trailers
3716 Motor Homes
3721 Aircraft
3724 Aircraft Engines & Engine Parts
3728 Aircraft Parts & Eqpt, NEC
3731 Shipbuilding & Repairing
3732 Boat Building & Repairing
3743 Railroad Eqpt
3751 Motorcycles, Bicycles & Parts
3761 Guided Missiles & Space Vehicles
3764 Guided Missile/Space Vehicle Propulsion Units & parts
3769 Guided Missile/Space Vehicle Parts & Eqpt, NEC
3792 Travel Trailers & Campers
3795 Tanks & Tank Components
3799 Transportation Eqpt, NEC

38 MEASURING, ANALYZING AND CONTROLLING INSTRUMENTS; PHOTOGRAPHIC, MEDICAL AN

3812 Search, Detection, Navigation & Guidance Systs & Instrs
3821 Laboratory Apparatus & Furniture
3822 Automatic Temperature Controls
3823 Indl Instruments For Meas, Display & Control
3824 Fluid Meters & Counters
3825 Instrs For Measuring & Testing Electricity
3826 Analytical Instruments
3827 Optical Instruments
3829 Measuring & Controlling Devices, NEC
3841 Surgical & Medical Instrs & Apparatus
3842 Orthopedic, Prosthetic & Surgical Appliances/Splys
3843 Dental Eqpt & Splys
3844 X-ray Apparatus & Tubes
3845 Electromedical & Electrotherapeutic Apparatus
3851 Ophthalmic Goods
3861 Photographic Eqpt & Splys
3873 Watch & Clock Devices & Parts

39 MISCELLANEOUS MANUFACTURING INDUSTRIES

3911 Jewelry: Precious Metal
3914 Silverware, Plated & Stainless Steel Ware
3915 Jewelers Findings & Lapidary Work
3931 Musical Instruments
3942 Dolls & Stuffed Toys
3944 Games, Toys & Children's Vehicles
3949 Sporting & Athletic Goods, NEC
3951 Pens & Mechanical Pencils
3952 Lead Pencils, Crayons & Artist's Mtrls
3953 Marking Devices
3955 Carbon Paper & Inked Ribbons
3961 Costume Jewelry & Novelties
3965 Fasteners, Buttons, Needles & Pins
3991 Brooms & Brushes
3993 Signs & Advertising Displays
3995 Burial Caskets
3996 Linoleum & Hard Surface Floor Coverings, NEC
3999 Manufacturing Industries, NEC

73 BUSINESS SERVICES

7372 Prepackaged Software

76 MISCELLANEOUS REPAIR SERVICES

7692 Welding Repair
7694 Armature Rewinding Shops

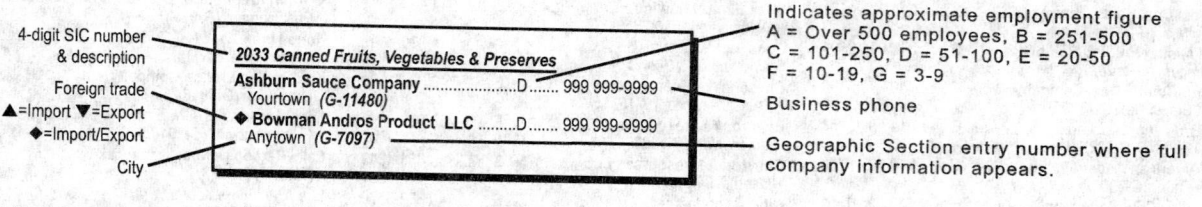

4-digit SIC number & description

Foreign trade
▲=Import ▼=Export
◆=Import/Export

City

2033 Canned Fruits, Vegetables & Preserves
Ashburn Sauce Company ....D..... 999 999-9999
Yourtown *(G-11480)*
◆ Bowman Andros Product LLC ....D...... 999 999-9999
Anytown *(G-7097)*

Indicates approximate employment figure
A = Over 500 employees, B = 251-500
C = 101-250, D = 51-100, E = 20-50
F = 10-19, G = 3-9

Business phone

Geographic Section entry number where full company information appears.

See footnotes for symbols and codes identification.

- The SIC codes in this section are from the latest Standard Industrial Classification manual published by the U.S. Government's Office of Management and Budget. For more information regarding SICs, see the Explanatory Notes.
- Companies may be listed under multiple classifications.

10 METAL MINING

1011 Iron Ores

Bloom Lake Iron Ore Mine Ltd..............A..... 216 694-5700
Cleveland *(G-4918)*
Cliffs & Associates Ltd ....G...... 216 694-5700
Cleveland *(G-5088)*
Cliffs Michigan Operation ....E...... 216 694-5303
Cleveland *(G-5090)*
Cliffs Mining Company ....F...... 216 694-5700
Cleveland *(G-5091)*
Cliffs Minnesota Minerals Co ....A..... 216 694-5700
Cleveland *(G-5092)*
Cliffs Natural Resources Inc ....D...... 216 694-5700
Cleveland *(G-5093)*
Empire Iron Mining Partnership ....G...... 216 694-5700
Cleveland *(G-5277)*
▲ Hibbing Taconite A Joint Ventr ....G...... 216 694-5700
Cleveland *(G-5512)*
International Steel Group ....C...... 330 841-2800
Warren *(G-19560)*
◆ Northshore Mining Company ....G...... 216 694-5700
Cleveland *(G-5914)*
The Cleveland-Cliffs Iron Co ....C...... 216 694-5700
Cleveland *(G-6308)*
Tilden Mining Company LC ....A..... 216 694-5278
Cleveland *(G-6325)*
▼ United Taconite LLC ....G...... 218 744-7800
Cleveland *(G-6388)*
Wabush Mines Cliffs Mining Co ....A..... 216 694-5700
Cleveland *(G-6438)*

1021 Copper Ores

◆ Warrenton Copper LLC ....E...... 636 456-3488
Cleveland *(G-6447)*

1041 Gold Ores

Ivi Mining Group Ltd ....G...... 740 418-7745
Vinton *(G-19382)*

1061 Ferroalloy Ores, Except Vanadium

General Electric Company ....D...... 330 343-8841
Dover *(G-8987)*
▲ Rhenium Alloys Inc ....D...... 440 365-7388
North Ridgeville *(G-15401)*

1081 Metal Mining Svcs

Alloy Metal Exchange LLC ....E...... 216 478-0200
Bedford Heights *(G-1477)*
Hahs Factory Outlet..............................E...... 330 405-4227
Twinsburg *(G-18953)*
Hopedale Mining LLC ....E...... 740 937-2225
Hopedale *(G-11118)*
Metokote Corporation............................G...... 419 996-7800
Lima *(G-12058)*
Mining Reclamation Inc ....F...... 740 327-5555
Dresden *(G-9033)*
Omega Cementing Co ....G...... 330 695-7147
Apple Creek *(G-646)*

1094 Uranium, Radium & Vanadium Ores

◆ AMG Vanadium LLC ....G...... 740 435-4600
Cambridge *(G-2444)*
Centrus Energy Corp.............................C...... 740 897-2457
Piketon *(G-16217)*

1099 Metal Ores, NEC

Al Chem Specialties LLC.......................G...... 440 255-2826
Mentor *(G-13515)*
Alcoa Inc ....F...... 216 391-3885
Cleveland *(G-4743)*
Alcoa Inc ....E...... 608 363-5214
Newburgh Heights *(G-15068)*

12 COAL MINING

1221 Bituminous Coal & Lignite: Surface Mining

American Coal Co ....G...... 740 926-1372
Alledonia *(G-484)*
B&N Coal Inc ....D...... 740 783-3575
Dexter City *(G-8954)*
Bramhi Inc ....G...... 740 367-0467
Bidwell *(G-1674)*
CAM Co Inc ....G...... 740 922-4533
Dennison *(G-8943)*
Cliffs Logan County Coal LLC ....G...... 216 694-5700
Cleveland *(G-5089)*
Coal Services Inc ....D...... 740 795-5220
Powhatan Point *(G-16488)*
Commercial Minerals Inc ....G...... 330 549-2165
North Lima *(G-15313)*
D & D Mining Co Inc ....F...... 330 549-3127
New Springfield *(G-14950)*
Daron Coal Company LLC ....C...... 614 643-0337
Cadiz *(G-2417)*
East Fairfield Coal Co ....E...... 330 542-1010
Petersburg *(G-16177)*
Edwards Auger Mining Inc ....G...... 330 339-7318
New Philadelphia *(G-14896)*
F & M Coal Company ....G...... 740 544-5203
Toronto *(G-18782)*
Holmes Limestone Co ....G...... 330 893-2721
Berlin *(G-1649)*
Ivi Mining Group Ltd ....G...... 740 418-7745
Vinton *(G-19382)*
J & D Mining Inc ....E...... 330 339-4935
New Philadelphia *(G-14904)*
Kenneth Mc Beth ....G...... 740 922-9494
Dennison *(G-8945)*
King Quarries Inc ....G...... 740 732-2923
Caldwell *(G-2429)*
L & M Mineral Co ....G...... 330 852-3696
Sugarcreek *(G-18025)*
Marietta Coal Co ....F...... 740 695-2197
Saint Clairsville *(G-16795)*
Morning Sun Technologies Inc..............G...... 513 461-1417
Oxford *(G-15841)*
Murray American Energy Inc ....A..... 740 338-3100
Saint Clairsville *(G-16796)*
Nacco Industries Inc ....E...... 440 229-5151
Cleveland *(G-5848)*
Oxford Min Cmpany-Kentucky LLC ......C...... 740 622-6302
Coshocton *(G-7905)*
Oxford Mining Company Inc ....D...... 740 342-7666
New Lexington *(G-14850)*
Oxford Mining Company Inc ....G...... 740 622-6302
Coshocton *(G-7906)*
Oxford Mining Company Inc ....F...... 740 588-0190
Zanesville *(G-21339)*
PM Coal Company LLC ....G...... 440 256-7624
Willoughby *(G-20571)*
Rayle Coal Co ....G...... 740 695-2197
Saint Clairsville *(G-16805)*

Rosebud Mining Company.....................E 740 768-2097
Bergholz *(G-1642)*
Rosebud Mining Company.....................E 740 922-9122
Uhrichsville *(G-19057)*
Sands Hill Coal Hauling Co Inc.............E 740 384-4211
Hamden *(G-10657)*
Straight Creek Bushman LLC................G 513 732-1698
Batavia *(G-1226)*
Ted Tipple ....G 740 432-3263
Cambridge *(G-2479)*
Thompson Brothers Mining Co ....F 330 549-3979
New Springfield *(G-14952)*
W B Coal Company Inc...........................F 614 221-0101
Columbus *(G-7745)*
Westmoreland Resources Gp LLC.......F 740 622-6302
Coshocton *(G-7914)*

1222 Bituminous Coal: Underground Mining

▲ American Energy Corporation ....B 740 926-2430
Beallsville *(G-1307)*
Coal Services Inc ....D 740 795-5220
Powhatan Point *(G-16488)*
Ivi Mining Group Ltd ....G 740 418-7745
Vinton *(G-19382)*
Kenamerican Resources Inc..................G 740 338-3100
Saint Clairsville *(G-16793)*
Maple Creek Mining Inc ....G 740 926-9205
Alledonia *(G-485)*
Murray Energy Corporation ....G 740 338-3100
Saint Clairsville *(G-16797)*
Rosebud Mining Company.....................E 740 658-4217
Freeport *(G-10119)*
Rosebud Mining Company.....................E 740 768-2097
Bergholz *(G-1642)*
Rosebud Mining Company.....................E 740 922-9122
Uhrichsville *(G-19057)*
Rosebud Mining Company.....................E 330 222-2334
Carrollton *(G-2964)*
Sterling Mining Corporation ....F 330 549-2165
North Lima *(G-15323)*
West Ridge Resources Inc.....................G 740 338-3100
Saint Clairsville *(G-16813)*

1231 Anthracite Mining

Coal Services Inc ....D 740 795-5220
Powhatan Point *(G-16488)*

1241 Coal Mining Svcs

▲ American Energy Corporation ....B 740 926-2430
Beallsville *(G-1307)*
Anthony Mining Co Inc...........................G 740 266-8100
Wintersville *(G-20710)*
Appalachian Fuels LLC ....G 606 928-0460
Dublin *(G-9045)*
Boich Companies LLC............................G 614 221-0101
Columbus *(G-6845)*
Buckingham Coal Company LLC ....D 740 767-2907
Zanesville *(G-21284)*
Coal Resources Inc...............................F 740 338-3100
Saint Clairsville *(G-16786)*
Coal Services Inc ....D 740 795-5220
Powhatan Point *(G-16488)*
Consol Coal Company ....D 740 942-4353
Cadiz *(G-2415)*
Don Gamertsfelder.................................G 740 797-4495
The Plains *(G-18185)*
Duncan Brothers Drilling Inc.................F 330 426-9507
East Palestine *(G-9234)*

SIC

Duncan Brothers Drilling Inc ....F 330 426-9507
East Palestine *(G-9235)*
▼ Global Coal Sales Group LLC ....G 614 221-0101
Columbus *(G-7119)*
Global Mining Holding Co LLC ....G 614 221-0101
Columbus *(G-7120)*
Harrison County Coal Company ....E 740 338-3100
Saint Clairsville *(G-16791)*
Kurtz Bros Inc ....E 614 491-0868
Groveport *(G-10632)*
North American Auger Mining ....G 740 622-8782
Coshocton *(G-7902)*
Ohio Valley Coal Company ....B 740 926-1351
Saint Clairsville *(G-16801)*
Ohio Valley Resources Inc ....E 740 795-5220
Saint Clairsville *(G-16802)*
Ohio Valley Transloading Co ....A 740 795-4967
Saint Clairsville *(G-16803)*
Oxford Mining Company Inc ....G 330 878-5120
Strasburg *(G-17827)*
Oxford Mining Company LLC ....G 740 622-6302
Coshocton *(G-7907)*
Oxford Mining Inc ....G 330 339-4546
Stone Creek *(G-17725)*
Peabody Coal Company ....B 740 450-2420
Zanesville *(G-21340)*
Resource Fuels LLC ....G 614 221-0101
Columbus *(G-7558)*
Rosebud Mining Company ....E 330 222-2334
Carrollton *(G-2964)*
Sandusky Dock Corporation ....F 419 626-1214
Sandusky *(G-17000)*
State Line Resources Inc ....G 330 426-9611
Negley *(G-14732)*
Steuben Coal-Anthony Min Ltd ....G 740 266-8100
Wintersville *(G-20714)*
Strata Mine Services Inc ....G 740 695-6880
Saint Clairsville *(G-16810)*
Strata Mine Services LLC ....F 740 695-0488
Saint Clairsville *(G-16811)*
Suncoke Energy Nc ....E 513 727-5571
Middletown *(G-14086)*

13 OIL AND GAS EXTRACTION

1311 Crude Petroleum & Natural Gas

A P Production & Service ....G 740 745-5317
Utica *(G-19191)*
A S Nf Producing Inc ....G 330 933-0622
Hartville *(G-10815)*
AB Resources LLC ....E 440 922-1098
Brecksville *(G-2031)*
Alliance Petroleum Corporation ....E 330 493-0440
Canton *(G-2599)*
American Rodpump Ltd ....G 440 987-9457
Dublin *(G-9044)*
B & J Drilling Company Inc ....G 740 599-6700
Danville *(G-8083)*
Bakerwell Inc ....E 330 276-2161
Killbuck *(G-11592)*
Barclay Petroleum Inc ....G 740 569-4327
Bremen *(G-2079)*
Belden & Blake Corporation ....E 330 602-5551
Dover *(G-8968)*
Beucler Brothers Inc ....G 330 735-2267
Dellroy *(G-8897)*
Blaze Oil & Gas Inc ....G 330 345-6700
Wooster *(G-20749)*
Bpi Energy Holdings Inc ....G 281 556-6200
Solon *(G-17272)*
Brendel Producing Company ....G 330 854-4151
Canton *(G-2628)*
Broad Street Energy Company ....G 614 228-0326
Columbus *(G-6865)*
Broad Street Financial Company ....G 614 228-0326
Columbus *(G-6866)*
BT Energy Corporation ....G 740 373-6134
Fleming *(G-9911)*
Buckeye Energy Resources Inc ....G 740 452-9506
Zanesville *(G-21283)*
Buckeye Franklin Co ....F 330 859-2465
Zoarville *(G-21370)*
Buckeye Oil Producing Co ....F 330 264-8847
Wooster *(G-20754)*
Cac Energy Ltd ....G 937 867-5593
Dayton *(G-8206)*
Cameron Drilling Co Inc ....F 740 453-3300
Zanesville *(G-21285)*
Carlton Oil Corp ....G 740 473-2629
Newport *(G-15126)*
▲ Carol Mickley ....G 740 599-7870
Danville *(G-8086)*
Cgas Exploration Inc ....G 614 436-4631
Worthington *(G-20859)*
Cgas Inc ....G 614 975-4697
Worthington *(G-20860)*
Chesapeake Energy Corporation ....E 740 695-1623
Saint Clairsville *(G-16785)*
Chevron Ae Resources LLC ....E 330 896-8510
Uniontown *(G-19080)*
Chevron Ae Resources LLC ....E 330 654-4343
Deerfield *(G-8771)*
City of Lancaster ....E 740 687-6670
Lancaster *(G-11697)*
Columbia Energy Group ....G 614 460-4683
Columbus *(G-6945)*
Columbia Gas Meter Shop ....F 614 460-5519
Columbus *(G-6946)*
Columbia Midstream Group LLC ....F 330 542-1095
New Middletown *(G-14875)*
Crude Oil Company ....G 740 452-3335
Zanesville *(G-21296)*
D & L Energy Inc ....E 330 270-1201
Canton *(G-2675)*
David A Waldron & Associates ....G 330 264-7275
Wooster *(G-20764)*
Derrick Petroleum Inc ....G 740 668-5711
Bladensburg *(G-1707)*
Dome Drilling Co ....G 440 892-9434
Westlake *(G-20264)*
Dome Drilling Co ....G 330 262-5113
Wooster *(G-20766)*
Drillex Inc ....G 440 255-7500
Mentor *(G-13564)*
East Ohio Gas Company ....G 740 439-2721
Byesville *(G-2400)*
Edco Producing ....G 419 947-2515
Mount Gilead *(G-14558)*
Elkhead Gas & Oil Co ....G 740 763-3966
Newark *(G-15002)*
Enrevo Pyro LLC ....G 203 517-5002
Brookfield *(G-2124)*
Equity Oil & Gas Funds Inc ....G 234 231-1004
Stow *(G-17747)*
Everflow Eastern Partners LP ....E 330 533-2692
Canfield *(G-2555)*
Excalibur Exploration Inc ....G 330 966-7003
Greentown *(G-10486)*
Foltz & Foltz Ltd Partnership ....G 330 488-1898
East Canton *(G-9192)*
Franklin Gas & Oil Company LLC ....G 330 264-8739
Wooster *(G-20773)*
General Electric Company ....F 330 425-3755
Twinsburg *(G-18943)*
Geopetro LLC ....G 614 885-9350
Worthington *(G-20866)*
Green Energy Inc ....G 330 262-5112
Wooster *(G-20779)*
Gulfport Energy Corporation ....E 740 251-0407
Saint Clairsville *(G-16790)*
H & S Drilling Co Inc ....G 740 828-2411
Frazeysburg *(G-10074)*
H I Smith Oil & Gas Inc ....G 330 279-2361
Holmesville *(G-11101)*
Hanini Seven Oil ....G 216 857-0172
Cleveland *(G-5478)*
Hess Corporation ....G 740 346-0581
Steubenville *(G-17698)*
Hopco Resources Inc ....G 614 882-8533
Columbus *(G-7167)*
Hopewell Oil & Gas Dev Co ....G 740 452-9326
Zanesville *(G-21319)*
Hunter Eureka Pipeline LLC ....F 740 374-2940
Marietta *(G-12791)*
Icon Energy Systems Inc ....G 937 423-4786
Greenville *(G-10505)*
Interstate Gas Supply Inc ....D 614 659-5000
Dublin *(G-9090)*
James R Bernhardt Producing ....G 330 345-5306
Wooster *(G-20789)*
Jerry Moore Inc ....G 330 877-1155
Hartville *(G-10825)*
John D Oil and Gas Company ....G 440 255-6325
Mentor *(G-13620)*
Kenoil Inc ....E 330 262-1144
Wooster *(G-20794)*
Kilbarger Investments Inc ....G 740 385-6019
Logan *(G-12183)*
Killbuck Creek Oil Co ....G 330 601-0921
Wooster *(G-20796)*
King Drilling Co ....G 330 769-3434
Seville *(G-17077)*
◆ Koch Knight LLC ....D 330 488-1651
East Canton *(G-9194)*
Konoil Inc ....G 330 499-9811
Canton *(G-2757)*
Kramer Exploration Company ....G 740 362-1805
Delaware *(G-8866)*
Lagc Ltd ....G 419 886-2141
Fredericktown *(G-10105)*
Lake Region Oil Inc ....F 330 837-4767
Dalton *(G-8073)*
Lee A Williams Jr ....G 419 225-6751
Lima *(G-12038)*
Marietta Resources Corporation ....F 740 373-6305
Marietta *(G-12803)*
Mason Producing Inc ....G 740 913-0686
Galena *(G-10247)*
MFC Drilling Inc ....F 740 622-5600
Coshocton *(G-7898)*
Midland Oil Co ....G 740 787-2557
Brownsville *(G-2199)*
MRC Global (us) Inc ....F 614 475-4033
Gahanna *(G-10221)*
MRC Global (us) Inc ....E 330 686-4988
Stow *(G-17777)*
National Gas & Oil Company ....G 740 344-2102
Newark *(G-15036)*
Northwood Energy Corporation ....E 614 457-1024
Columbus *(G-7403)*
Orion Petro Corporation ....G 330 364-8155
Atwater *(G-901)*
P & S Energy Inc ....G 330 652-2525
Mineral Ridge *(G-14309)*
Penick Gas & Oil ....G 740 323-3040
Newark *(G-15045)*
Petro Evaluation Services Inc ....G 330 264-4454
Wooster *(G-20820)*
Profit Energy Company Inc ....G 740 472-1018
Jerusalem *(G-11385)*
Purvi Oil Inc ....G 419 207-8234
Ashland *(G-769)*
R C Poling Company Inc ....G 740 939-0023
Junction City *(G-11411)*
R D Holder Oil Co Inc ....G 740 522-3136
Heath *(G-10852)*
RCM Engineering Company ....G 330 666-0575
Akron *(G-368)*
Resource America Inc ....E 330 896-8510
Uniontown *(G-19096)*
Resource Energy Inc ....D 330 896-8510
Uniontown *(G-19097)*
Robert Barr ....F 740 826-7325
New Concord *(G-14821)*
Rodco Petroleum Inc ....G 330 477-9823
Canton *(G-2842)*
Saint Croix Ltd ....G 330 666-1544
Akron *(G-395)*
Sheridan One Stop Carryout ....G 740 687-1300
Lancaster *(G-11751)*
Southeastern Natural Gas Co ....G 740 385-8583
Logan *(G-12195)*
Speedway LLC ....F 330 874-4616
Bolivar *(G-1946)*
Speedway LLC ....F 440 943-0044
Wickliffe *(G-20387)*
Speedway LLC ....G 330 644-2730
New Franklin *(G-14832)*
Speedway LLC ....G 937 653-6840
Urbana *(G-19182)*
Speedway LLC ....F 614 418-9325
Columbus *(G-7643)*
Speedway LLC ....F 513 829-3223
Fairfield *(G-9722)*
Speedway LLC ....F 937 390-6651
Springfield *(G-17649)*
Speedway LLC ....F 614 861-6397
Reynoldsburg *(G-16607)*
Speedway LLC ....G 330 339-7770
New Philadelphia *(G-14928)*
Speedway LLC ....F 937 372-7129
Wilberforce *(G-20392)*
Speedway LLC ....F 513 683-2034
Cincinnati *(G-4441)*
Speedway LLC ....F 330 468-3320
Macedonia *(G-12485)*
Speedway LLC ....F 330 343-9469
Dover *(G-9018)*
Speedway LLC ....F 419 468-9773
Galion *(G-10288)*

Speedway LLC ....F....... 440 988-8014
Amherst *(G-608)*

Standard Energy Company ....G....... 614 885-1901
Columbus *(G-7650)*

Stocker & Sitler Inc ....G....... 614 888-9588
Columbus *(G-7657)*

Stocker & Sitler Oil Company ....G....... 614 888-9588
Columbus *(G-7658)*

Stonebridge Operating Co LLC ....G....... 740 373-6134
Fleming *(G-9914)*

Summit Petroleum Inc ....G....... 330 487-5494
Twinsburg *(G-19026)*

T JS Oil & Gas Inc ....G....... 740 623-0192
Coshocton *(G-7912)*

Tatum Petroleum Corporation ....G....... 740 819-6810
Worthington *(G-20890)*

Temple Oil & Gas Company ....G....... 740 452-7878
Crooksville *(G-7954)*

Triad Hunter LLC ....F....... 740 374-2940
Marietta *(G-12845)*

Triad Hunter LLC ....G....... 740 374-2940
Marietta *(G-12846)*

U S Fuel Development Co ....G....... 614 486-0614
Columbus *(G-7716)*

Valley Petroleum Inc ....G....... 740 668-4901
Utica *(G-19198)*

Viking Intl Resources Co Inc ....G....... 304 628-3878
Marietta *(G-12849)*

W H Patten Drilling Co Inc ....G....... 330 674-3046
Millersburg *(G-14279)*

W P Brown Enterprises Inc ....G....... 740 685-2594
Byesville *(G-2413)*

William S Miller Inc ....G....... 330 223-1794
Kensington *(G-11421)*

Williams Partners LP ....C....... 330 966-3674
North Canton *(G-15284)*

Xto Energy Inc ....D....... 740 671-9901
Bellaire *(G-1502)*

1321 Natural Gas Liquids

A Plus Propane LLC ....G....... 419 399-4445
Paulding *(G-15998)*

Consolidated Gas Coop Inc ....G....... 419 946-6600
Mount Gilead *(G-14557)*

H & S Operating Company Inc ....G....... 330 830-8178
Winesburg *(G-20704)*

Husky Marketing and Supply Co ....E....... 614 210-2300
Dublin *(G-9087)*

Markwest Energy Partners LP ....G....... 740 942-0463
Cadiz *(G-2419)*

Markwest Utica Emg LLC ....G....... 740 942-4810
Jewett *(G-11386)*

Nimco Inc ....G....... 740 596-4477
Mc Arthur *(G-13332)*

RCM Engineering Company ....G....... 330 666-0575
Akron *(G-368)*

United Landmark Llc ....G....... 740 852-2062
London *(G-12222)*

1381 Drilling Oil & Gas Wells

Advent Drilling Inc ....E....... 330 497-2533
Canton *(G-2589)*

Anderson Energy Inc ....G....... 740 678-8608
Fleming *(G-9909)*

Artex Oil Company ....E....... 740 373-3313
Marietta *(G-12763)*

Bakerwell Service Rigs Inc ....F....... 330 276-2161
Killbuck *(G-11593)*

Bancequity Petroleum Corp ....G....... 330 468-5935
Macedonia *(G-12436)*

Brendel Producing Company ....G....... 330 854-4151
Canton *(G-2628)*

Buckeye Oil Producing Co ....F....... 330 264-8847
Wooster *(G-20754)*

Camphire Drilling Inc ....G....... 740 599-6928
Danville *(G-8085)*

Clarence Tussel Jr ....G....... 440 576-3415
Jefferson *(G-11360)*

Clearpath Utlity Solutions LLC ....F....... 740 661-4240
Zanesville *(G-21289)*

Columbus Oilfield Exploration ....G....... 614 895-9520
Powell *(G-16468)*

D Anderson Corp ....G....... 330 433-0606
Canton *(G-2676)*

Decker Drilling Inc ....E....... 740 749-3939
Vincent *(G-19379)*

Directional One Svcs Inc USA ....G....... 740 371-5031
Marietta *(G-12779)*

Dnl Oil Corp ....G....... 740 342-4970
New Lexington *(G-14847)*

Domestic Oil & Gas Co Inc ....G....... 440 232-3150
Cleveland *(G-5203)*

Doris Kimble ....E....... 330 343-1226
Dover *(G-8977)*

Drillex Inc ....G....... 440 255-7500
Mentor *(G-13564)*

Dugan Drilling Incorporated ....G....... 740 668-3811
Walhonding *(G-19468)*

Echo Drilling Inc ....G....... 740 254-4127
Gnadenhutten *(G-10406)*

Eclipse Resources - Ohio LLC ....E....... 740 452-4503
Zanesville *(G-21306)*

Energy Resources of America In ....G....... 330 953-1813
Youngstown *(G-21077)*

Frank Csapo ....G....... 330 435-4458
Creston *(G-7939)*

Fredebaugh Well Drilling Co ....F....... 440 357-6924
Grand River *(G-10448)*

Future Productions Inc ....G....... 330 478-0477
Canton *(G-2709)*

G & H Drilling Inc ....E....... 330 674-4868
Millersburg *(G-14216)*

Geocore Drilling Inc ....G....... 419 864-4011
Cardington *(G-2910)*

Groundhogs 2000 LLC ....G....... 440 653-1647
Oakwood Village *(G-15625)*

H & A Drilling ....G....... 740 763-2575
Newark *(G-15016)*

H & D Drilling Co Inc ....G....... 740 745-2236
Frazeysburg *(G-10073)*

Hocking Hills Energy & Well SE ....G....... 740 385-6690
Logan *(G-12176)*

Hopewell Oil & Gas Dev Co ....G....... 740 452-9326
Zanesville *(G-21319)*

Interden Industries Inc ....G....... 419 368-9011
Lakeville *(G-11651)*

J D Drilling Co ....E....... 740 949-2512
Racine *(G-16504)*

J Valtier Gas and Oil Co Inc ....G....... 740 342-2839
Malta *(G-12537)*

JAC Construction Ohio Llc ....G....... 440 564-5005
Newbury *(G-15097)*

Jackson Wells Services ....G....... 419 886-2017
Bellville *(G-1571)*

James R Smail Inc ....G....... 330 264-7500
Wooster *(G-20790)*

Jersey West Drilling Inc ....G....... 513 398-0774
Mason *(G-13049)*

Keito Gas Inc ....G....... 740 374-5463
Marietta *(G-12796)*

Kilbarger Construction Inc ....C....... 740 385-5531
Logan *(G-12182)*

King Energy Inc ....G....... 330 297-5508
Ravenna *(G-16536)*

Kirk Excavating & Construction ....E....... 614 444-4008
Columbus *(G-7262)*

Kleese Development Associates ....G....... 330 392-7899
Warren *(G-19566)*

Lee Oil & Gas Inc ....G....... 937 223-8891
Oakwood *(G-15608)*

Maric Drilling Company Inc ....F....... 330 830-8178
Winesburg *(G-20705)*

Moore Well Services Inc ....E....... 330 650-4443
Mogadore *(G-14381)*

▲ Ngo Development Corporation ....F....... 740 344-3790
Newark *(G-15039)*

Nomac Drilling LLC ....G....... 330 476-7040
Carrollton *(G-2962)*

Nomac Drilling LLC ....F....... 724 324-2205
Saint Clairsville *(G-16798)*

Oak Dale Drilling Inc ....G....... 740 385-5888
Logan *(G-12187)*

Ohio L & M Company Inc ....G....... 330 493-0440
Canton *(G-2800)*

Ohio Valley Energy Systems ....G....... 330 799-2268
Youngstown *(G-21156)*

Oogeep ....G....... 740 587-0410
Granville *(G-10463)*

Osair Inc ....G....... 440 974-6500
Mentor *(G-13675)*

P & S Energy Inc ....G....... 330 652-2525
Mineral Ridge *(G-14309)*

PAC Drilling O & G LLC ....G....... 330 874-3781
Bolivar *(G-1941)*

Palmer Properties LLC ....G....... 419 938-3114
Perrysville *(G-16174)*

Parrot Energy Company ....G....... 330 637-0151
Cortland *(G-7873)*

Paul A Grim Inc ....G....... 740 385-9637
Logan *(G-12190)*

Petro Quest Inc ....G....... 740 593-3800
Athens *(G-881)*

Pine Top Inc ....G....... 330 929-2492
Akron *(G-340)*

Pinnacle Drilling LLC ....F....... 330 276-1096
Killbuck *(G-11597)*

Ponderosa Consulting Services ....G....... 330 264-2298
Wooster *(G-20821)*

Portage Resources Inc ....G....... 330 872-3827
Warren *(G-19587)*

Professional Oilfield Services ....G....... 740 685-5168
Byesville *(G-2409)*

Quality Oil & Gas Corp ....G....... 330 821-6375
Alliance *(G-534)*

R & J Drilling Company Inc ....G....... 740 763-3991
Frazeysburg *(G-10076)*

Rj Drilling Company Inc ....G....... 740 763-3991
Nashport *(G-14707)*

Rockbottom Oil & Gas ....G....... 740 374-2478
Marietta *(G-12825)*

Sabre Energy Corporation ....G....... 740 685-8266
Lore City *(G-12294)*

Smith Smith & Deyarman ....G....... 330 866-5521
Magnolia *(G-12519)*

Stratagraph Ne Inc ....E....... 740 373-3091
Marietta *(G-12838)*

Summit Drilling Company Inc ....F....... 800 775-5537
Akron *(G-419)*

Temple Oil & Gas Company ....G....... 740 452-7878
Crooksville *(G-7954)*

Tiger Oil Inc ....G....... 614 837-5552
Canal Winchester *(G-2538)*

Timco Inc ....F....... 740 685-2594
Byesville *(G-2410)*

Top Drilling Corporation ....F....... 304 477-3333
Marietta *(G-12842)*

Transcontinental Oil & Gas ....G....... 330 995-0777
Aurora *(G-950)*

U S Fuel Development Co ....G....... 614 486-0614
Columbus *(G-7716)*

Victor McKenzie Drilling Co ....E....... 740 453-0834
Zanesville *(G-21361)*

Warren Drilling Co Inc ....G....... 740 783-2775
Dexter City *(G-8958)*

Warthman Drilling Inc ....G....... 740 746-9950
Sugar Grove *(G-18013)*

Well Service Group Inc ....F....... 330 308-0880
New Philadelphia *(G-14939)*

1382 Oil & Gas Field Exploration Svcs

Alliance Petroleum Corporation ....E....... 330 493-0440
Canton *(G-2599)*

Alteirs Oil Inc ....G....... 740 347-4335
Corning *(G-7858)*

▲ American Envmtl Group Ltd ....B....... 330 659-5930
Richfield *(G-16613)*

Antero Resources Corporation ....C....... 303 357-7310
Caldwell *(G-2423)*

Atlas America Inc ....E....... 330 339-3155
New Philadelphia *(G-14885)*

Bakerwell Inc ....D....... 614 898-7590
Westerville *(G-20139)*

Bands Company Inc ....G....... 330 674-0446
Millersburg *(G-14196)*

Barclay Petroleum Inc ....G....... 740 569-4327
Bremen *(G-2079)*

Beck Energy Corp ....F....... 330 297-6891
Ravenna *(G-16517)*

Belden & Blake Corporation ....E....... 330 602-5551
Dover *(G-8968)*

Bergstein Oil & Gas Partnr ....G....... 513 771-6220
Cincinnati *(G-3446)*

Bocor Holdings LLC ....G....... 330 494-1221
Canton *(G-2624)*

C & A Land and Energy LLC ....G....... 606 434-1420
New Philadelphia *(G-14888)*

Capital City Energy Group Inc ....G....... 614 485-3110
Columbus *(G-6898)*

Capital Oil & Gas Inc ....G....... 330 533-1828
Austintown *(G-971)*

Cardinal Energy Group Inc ....G....... 325 762-2112
Upper Arlington *(G-19111)*

Carrizo Oil & Gas Inc ....G....... 740 432-5463
Cambridge *(G-2450)*

Cgas Exploration Inc ....G....... 614 436-4631
Worthington *(G-20859)*

Chevron Ae Resources LLC ....E....... 330 654-4343
Deerfield *(G-8771)*

Clarence Tussel Jr ....G....... 440 576-3415
Jefferson *(G-11360)*

Columbus Oilfield Exploration ....G...... 614 895-9520
Powell **(G-16468)**

David R Hill Inc ....G...... 740 685-5168
Byesville **(G-2397)**

Deep Resources LLC ....F...... 419 869-7441
Polk **(G-16388)**

Delmar E Hicks ....G...... 740 354-4333
Portsmouth **(G-16434)**

Dlz Ohio Inc ....C...... 614 888-0040
Columbus **(G-7033)**

Dome Drilling Co ....G...... 440 892-9434
Westlake **(G-20264)**

Dome Drilling Co ....G...... 330 262-5113
Wooster **(G-20766)**

Dome Energicorp ....G...... 440 892-4900
Westlake **(G-20265)**

Dunn S Tank Service Inc ....G...... 330 863-2200
Malvern **(G-12542)**

Eastern Reserve Development ....G...... 614 319-3179
Columbus **(G-7045)**

Elkhead Gas & Oil Co ....G...... 740 763-3966
Newark **(G-15002)**

Everflow Eastern Partners LP ....E...... 330 533-2692
Canfield **(G-2555)**

Flint Ridge Energy ....G...... 740 344-1351
Newark **(G-15007)**

H & S Drilling Co Inc ....G...... 740 828-2411
Frazeysburg **(G-10074)**

Hocking Hills Energy & Well SE ....G...... 740 385-6690
Logan **(G-12176)**

Husky Marketing and Supply Co ....E...... 614 210-2300
Dublin **(G-9087)**

John D Oil and Gas Company ....G...... 440 255-6325
Mentor **(G-13620)**

K Petroleum Inc ....F...... 614 532-5420
Gahanna **(G-10214)**

Mori Shuji ....G...... 614 459-1296
Columbus **(G-7369)**

New World Energy Resources ....F...... 740 344-4087
Newark **(G-15038)**

Ngo Development Corporation ....F...... 740 622-9560
Coshocton **(G-7901)**

Ohio Valley Energy Systems ....G...... 330 799-2268
Youngstown **(G-21156)**

Pine Top Inc ....G...... 330 929-2492
Akron **(G-340)**

Precision Geophysical Inc ....E...... 330 674-2198
Millersburg **(G-14256)**

Precision Geophysical Inc ....F...... 740 849-3044
Mount Perry **(G-14593)**

Quantum Energy LLC ....F...... 440 285-7381
Chardon **(G-3175)**

Range Rsurces - Appalachia LLC ....E...... 330 866-3301
Dover **(G-9009)**

Reserve Energy Exploration Co ....G...... 440 543-0770
Chagrin Falls **(G-3117)**

Resource America Inc ....E...... 330 896-8510
Uniontown **(G-19096)**

Resource Energy Inc ....D...... 330 896-8510
Uniontown **(G-19097)**

Santmyer Oil Co of Ashland ....G...... 330 262-6501
Wooster **(G-20831)**

Standard Energy Company ....G...... 614 885-1901
Columbus **(G-7650)**

Standard Oil Company ....G...... 419 691-2460
Oregon **(G-15718)**

Stryker Energy LLC ....G...... 440 446-9214
Cleveland **(G-6257)**

Summit Well Services Inc ....G...... 330 223-1074
East Rochester **(G-9251)**

Triad Energy Corporation ....E...... 740 374-2940
Marietta **(G-12844)**

True North Energy LLC ....E...... 440 442-0060
Mayfield Heights **(G-13323)**

Whitacre Enterprises Inc ....F...... 740 934-2331
Graysville **(G-10470)**

Wilkes Energy Inc ....G...... 330 252-4560
Akron **(G-472)**

Wrp Energy Inc ....G...... 330 533-1921
Canfield **(G-2582)**

Zane Petroleum Inc ....F...... 740 454-8779
Zanesville **(G-21366)**

1389 Oil & Gas Field Svcs, NEC

A W Tipka Oil & Gas Inc ....G...... 330 364-4333
Dover **(G-8962)**

Acer Contracting LLC ....G...... 702 236-5917
Columbus **(G-6688)**

Acuren Inspection Inc ....D...... 937 228-9729
Dayton **(G-8135)**

Acuren Inspection Inc ....E...... 330 733-8160
Akron **(G-30)**

Acuren Inspection Inc ....E...... 513 671-7073
Cincinnati **(G-3353)**

Ajami Holdings Group LLC ....G...... 216 396-6089
Richmond Heights **(G-16651)**

Altheirs Oil Inc ....G...... 740 347-4335
Corning **(G-7859)**

Altier Brothers Inc ....F...... 740 347-4329
Corning **(G-7860)**

Appalachian Oilfield Svcs LLC ....G...... 337 216-0066
Sardis **(G-17035)**

Appalachian Well Surveys Inc ....G...... 740 255-7652
Cambridge **(G-2446)**

Atec Diversfd Wldg Fabrication ....G...... 937 546-4399
Wilmington **(G-20655)**

Bakerwell Inc ....E...... 330 276-2161
Killbuck **(G-11592)**

Barnes Services LLC ....G...... 440 319-2088
Maple Heights **(G-12727)**

▲ Bdi Inc ....C...... 216 642-9100
Cleveland **(G-4898)**

Bearcat Construction Inc ....G...... 513 314-0867
Mason **(G-12987)**

Belden & Blake Corporation ....E...... 330 602-5551
Dover **(G-8968)**

Bill Hall Well Service ....G...... 330 695-4671
Fredericksburg **(G-10078)**

Binder Oil Field Construction ....G...... 330 484-3680
Magnolia **(G-12515)**

Bishop Well Service Corp ....G...... 330 264-2023
Wooster **(G-20748)**

BJ Oilfield Services Ltd ....G...... 419 768-2408
Cardington **(G-2908)**

Boyce Ltd ....G...... 614 236-8901
Columbus **(G-6851)**

Bradner Oil Company Inc ....G...... 419 288-2945
Wayne **(G-19721)**

Brightstar Propane & Fuels ....G...... 614 891-8395
Westerville **(G-20140)**

Byrd Prcurement Specialist Inc ....G...... 419 936-0019
Swanton **(G-18082)**

Canton Oil Well Service Inc ....F...... 330 494-1221
Canton **(G-2643)**

Carper Well Service Inc ....F...... 740 374-2567
Marietta **(G-12771)**

Catress LLC ....G...... 740 695-0918
Saint Clairsville **(G-16784)**

Circleville Oil Co ....G...... 740 477-3341
Circleville **(G-4625)**

Clearfield Ohio Holdings Inc ....D...... 740 947-5121
Waverly **(G-19705)**

Collier Well Eqp & Sup Inc ....G...... 330 345-3968
Wooster **(G-20760)**

Complete Energy Services Inc ....F...... 440 577-1070
Pierpont **(G-16211)**

Countryside Pumping Inc ....G...... 330 628-0058
Mogadore **(G-14371)**

Crescent Services LLC ....G...... 405 603-1200
Cambridge **(G-2453)**

D & D Energy Co ....F...... 330 495-1631
Canton **(G-2674)**

Dansco Mfg & Pmpg Unit Svc LP ....G...... 330 452-3677
Canton **(G-2678)**

Decker Well Service LLC ....G...... 740 678-2970
Fleming **(G-9912)**

Diamond Oilfield Tech LLC ....F...... 234 806-4185
Vienna **(G-19365)**

Diesel Fltrtion Spcialists LLC ....G...... 740 698-0255
New Marshfield **(G-14871)**

Dover Atwood Corp ....G...... 330 809-0630
Massillon **(G-13125)**

Dow Cameron Oil & Gas LLC ....G...... 740 452-1568
Zanesville **(G-21300)**

Dp Operating Company Inc ....G...... 330 938-2172
Beloit **(G-1582)**

Dp2 Energy LLC ....G...... 330 376-5068
Akron **(G-156)**

Echo Drilling Inc ....G...... 740 498-8560
Newcomerstown **(G-15112)**

Elite Property Group LLC ....F...... 216 316-8222
Cleveland **(G-5272)**

Elsaan Energy LLC ....G...... 740 294-9399
Walhonding **(G-19469)**

EP Ferris & Associates Inc ....G...... 614 299-2999
Columbus **(G-7063)**

Erodetech Inc ....G...... 330 725-9181
Medina **(G-13407)**

Everflow Eastern Partners LP ....G...... 330 537-3863
Salem **(G-16889)**

Exelon Energy Company ....F...... 614 797-4377
Westerville **(G-20152)**

Express Energy Svcs Oper LP ....E...... 740 337-4530
Toronto **(G-18781)**

Fishburn Tank Truck Service ....D...... 419 253-6031
Marengo **(G-12750)**

Formation Cementing Inc ....G...... 740 453-6926
Zanesville **(G-21310)**

Franks Casing ....G...... 330 236-4264
Massillon **(G-13133)**

Fts International Inc ....B...... 330 754-2375
East Canton **(G-9193)**

Gas Analytical Services Inc ....G...... 330 539-4267
Girard **(G-10389)**

Global Oilfield Services LLC ....G...... 419 756-8027
Mansfield **(G-12613)**

Granger Pipeline Corporation ....G...... 330 454-8095
Canton **(G-2718)**

Greer & Whitehead Cnstr Inc ....E...... 513 202-1757
Harrison **(G-10781)**

Hackworth Oil Field Electric ....G...... 330 345-6504
Wooster **(G-20783)**

Harmon John ....G...... 740 934-2032
Graysville **(G-10469)**

Hill & Associates Inc ....G...... 740 685-5168
Byesville **(G-2403)**

HI Oilfield Services LLC ....G...... 740 783-1156
Caldwell **(G-2427)**

Infinity Oilfield Services LLC ....G...... 570 567-7027
Newcomerstown **(G-15116)**

Interden Industries Inc ....G...... 419 368-9011
Lakeville **(G-11651)**

J Valtier Gas and Oil Co Inc ....G...... 740 342-2839
Malta **(G-12537)**

James Engineering Inc ....G...... 740 373-9521
Marietta **(G-12794)**

James L Williams ....G...... 740 865-3382
Wingett Run **(G-20709)**

Karlco Oilfield Services Inc ....F...... 440 576-3415
Jefferson **(G-11363)**

Kbc Services ....F...... 513 693-3743
Loveland **(G-12365)**

Kelchner Inc ....C...... 937 704-9890
Springboro **(G-17486)**

Killbuck Oilfield Services ....G...... 330 276-6706
Killbuck **(G-11596)**

Ksn Clearing LLC ....F...... 304 269-3306
Gallipolis **(G-10303)**

Lakeside Sport Shop Inc ....G...... 330 637-2862
Cortland **(G-7870)**

Loken Oil Field Services LLC ....G...... 740 749-3495
Marietta **(G-12799)**

Maan Power Services LLC ....E...... 740 609-3020
Bridgeport **(G-2091)**

Mac Oil Field Service Inc ....F...... 330 674-7371
Millersburg **(G-14244)**

Martz Well Service ....G...... 330 323-7417
Canton **(G-2770)**

MGM Construction Inc ....F...... 440 234-7660
Berea **(G-1627)**

Natural Gas Construction Inc ....G...... 330 364-9240
Dover **(G-9005)**

Naw Petroleum Service ....G...... 740 464-7988
Chillicothe **(G-3253)**

Northeastern Oilfield Svcs LLC ....G...... 330 581-3304
Canton **(G-2794)**

Oaktree Wireline LLC ....G...... 330 352-7250
New Philadelphia **(G-14919)**

Ohio L & M Company Inc ....E...... 330 493-0440
Canton **(G-2800)**

Ohio Natural Gas Services Inc ....G...... 740 796-3305
Zanesville **(G-21336)**

Omega Cementing Co ....G...... 330 695-7147
Apple Creek **(G-646)**

OS Power Tong Inc ....G...... 330 866-3815
Waynesburg **(G-19726)**

Ottawa Oil Co Inc ....F...... 419 425-3301
Findlay **(G-9874)**

Performance Technologies LLC ....G...... 330 875-1216
Louisville **(G-12324)**

Personnel Selection Services ....F...... 440 835-3255
Cleveland **(G-5994)**

Petrox Inc ....F...... 330 653-5526
Streetsboro **(G-17867)**

Pettigrew Pumping Inc ....G...... 330 297-7900
Ravenna **(G-16550)**

Pluggers Inc ....G...... 330 383-7692
Niles **(G-15175)**

Predict Inc ....F...... 216 642-3223
Cleveland **(G-6039)**

PSC Holdings Inc .... G 740 454-6253
  Zanesville *(G-21347)*

Pyramid Treating Inc .... G 330 325-2811
  Atwater *(G-902)*

R & B Enterprises USA Inc .... G 330 674-2227
  Millersburg *(G-14257)*

R & J Drilling Company Inc .... G 740 763-3991
  Frazeysburg *(G-10076)*

R Anthony Enterprises LLC .... F 419 341-0961
  Marion *(G-12894)*

Ralph Robinson Inc .... G 740 385-2747
  Logan *(G-12192)*

Ream and Haager Laboratory .... F 330 343-3711
  Dover *(G-9010)*

Renegade Well Services LLC .... G 330 488-6055
  Canton *(G-2836)*

Ruscilli Real Estate Services .... F 614 923-6400
  Dublin *(G-9135)*

Sanders Fredrick Excvtg Co Inc .... G 330 297-7980
  Ravenna *(G-16555)*

Scassa Asphalt Inc .... F 330 830-2039
  Massillon *(G-13200)*

Schlumberger Limited .... G 330 878-0794
  Strasburg *(G-17828)*

Shalelogix LLC .... G 234 600-5839
  Warren *(G-19600)*

Standard Oil Company .... G 419 691-2460
  Oregon *(G-15718)*

Stevens Oil & Gas LLC .... G 740 374-4542
  Marietta *(G-12835)*

▲ Stingray Energy Services .... E 405 648-4177
  Belmont *(G-1580)*

Stocker & Sitler Oil Company .... G 614 888-9588
  Columbus *(G-7658)*

Stonebridge Oilfield Svcs LLC .... D 740 373-6134
  Marietta *(G-12837)*

Stratagraph Ne Inc .... E 740 373-3091
  Marietta *(G-12838)*

Sulmona Enegry LLC .... G 234 736-3749
  Youngstown *(G-21214)*

Surveying Cannon Land .... G 740 342-2835
  New Lexington *(G-14856)*

Terra Star Inc .... F 405 200-1336
  Waynesburg *(G-19728)*

Timothy Sinfield .... E 740 685-3684
  Pleasant City *(G-16368)*

Tk Gas Services Inc .... E 740 826-0303
  New Concord *(G-14822)*

Trico Corporation .... C 216 642-3223
  Cleveland *(G-6364)*

Triple J Oilfield Services LLC .... G 740 483-9030
  Hannibal *(G-10764)*

United Chart Processors Inc .... G 740 373-5801
  Marietta *(G-12847)*

Universal Well Services Inc .... E 330 264-1109
  Millersburg *(G-14275)*

Vanguard Oil & Gas .... G 330 223-1074
  East Rochester *(G-9252)*

Varco LP .... E 440 277-8696
  Lorain *(G-12289)*

W Pole Contracting Inc .... F 330 325-7177
  Ravenna *(G-16570)*

Washita Valley Enterprises Inc .... E 330 510-1568
  Louisville *(G-12334)*

Wenger Pipeline Construction .... E 330 828-8803
  Dalton *(G-8080)*

Williams John F Oil Field Svcs .... G 740 622-7692
  Jackson *(G-11333)*

Wolfe Creek Farms .... G 740 962-4563
  Malta *(G-12538)*

Wrights Well Service .... G 740 380-9602
  Logan *(G-12197)*

Wyoming Casing Service Inc .... E 330 479-8785
  Canton *(G-2904)*

14 MINING AND QUARRYING OF NONMETALLIC MINERALS, EXCEPT FUELS

1411 Dimension Stone

C & C Marble & Granite LLC .... F 614 873-1919
  Hilliard *(G-10937)*

C F Poeppelman Inc .... E 937 448-2191
  Bradford *(G-2025)*

Connolly Construction Co Inc .... G 937 644-8831
  Marysville *(G-12936)*

▲ Designer Stone Co .... G 740 492-1300
  Port Washington *(G-16423)*

Family Memorials .... G 330 477-4900
  Canton *(G-2700)*

Gerald Christman .... G 740 838-2475
  Lewisville *(G-11948)*

Gregory Stone Co Inc .... G 937 275-7455
  Dayton *(G-8380)*

Helmart Company Inc .... G 513 941-3095
  Cincinnati *(G-3876)*

Heritage Marble of Ohio Inc .... E 614 436-1464
  Columbus *(G-7151)*

Irg Operating LLC .... E 440 963-4008
  Vermilion *(G-19329)*

Jim Nier Construction Inc .... F 740 289-2629
  Piketon *(G-16221)*

Marble Cliff Limestone Inc .... G 614 488-3030
  Hilliard *(G-10959)*

National Lime and Stone Co .... D 419 562-0771
  Bucyrus *(G-2354)*

North Hill Marble & Granite Co .... F 330 253-2179
  Akron *(G-318)*

North Shore Stone Inc .... E 614 870-7531
  Columbus *(G-7401)*

Ohio Beauty Inc .... G 330 644-2241
  Akron *(G-322)*

S E Johnson Companies Inc .... F 419 893-8731
  Maumee *(G-13290)*

▲ Stone Statements Incorporated .... E 513 489-7866
  Cincinnati *(G-4470)*

Stoneco Inc .... C 419 422-8854
  Findlay *(G-9895)*

1422 Crushed & Broken Limestone

Acme Company .... D 330 758-2313
  Poland *(G-16381)*

Allgeier & Son Inc .... F 513 574-3735
  Cincinnati *(G-3378)*

Bluffton Stone Co .... E 419 358-6941
  Bluffton *(G-1909)*

Carmeuse Lime Inc .... G 419 986-2000
  Tiffin *(G-18214)*

Chalk Outline Pictures .... G 216 291-3944
  Cleveland *(G-5013)*

Chesterhill Stone Co .... E 740 849-2338
  East Fultonham *(G-9198)*

Conag Inc .... E 419 394-8870
  Saint Marys *(G-16837)*

Drummond Dolomite Inc .... F 440 942-7000
  Mentor *(G-13565)*

Duff Quarry Inc .... F 937 686-2811
  Huntsville *(G-11212)*

Duff Quarry Inc .... F 419 273-2518
  Forest *(G-9920)*

Erie Sand & Gravel Co Inc .... G 216 961-1010
  Cleveland *(G-5296)*

Feikert Sand & Gravel Co Inc .... E 330 674-0038
  Millersburg *(G-14215)*

Gerald Christman .... G 740 838-2475
  Lewisville *(G-11948)*

Hanson Aggregates East LLC .... E 937 587-2671
  Peebles *(G-16021)*

Hanson Aggregates East LLC .... D 419 483-4390
  Castalia *(G-2976)*

Hanson Aggregates East LLC .... E 937 364-2311
  Hillsboro *(G-10999)*

Hanson Aggregates LLC .... E 419 841-3413
  Sylvania *(G-18108)*

Hanson Aggregates Midwest Inc .... E 419 399-4846
  Paulding *(G-16004)*

Hanson Aggregates Midwest LLC .... F 419 882-0123
  Sylvania *(G-18109)*

Hanson Aggregates Midwest LLC .... G 419 983-2211
  Bloomville *(G-1728)*

King Limestone Inc .... F 740 638-3942
  Cumberland *(G-7956)*

▲ Lang Stone Company Inc .... D 614 235-4099
  Columbus *(G-7284)*

Latham Limestone LLC .... G 740 493-2677
  Latham *(G-11765)*

Mac Ritchie Materials Inc .... F 419 288-2790
  West Millgrove *(G-20104)*

Marietta Martin Materials Inc .... F 937 884-5814
  Brookville *(G-2190)*

Martin Marietta Materials Inc .... D 513 353-1400
  North Bend *(G-15206)*

Martin Marietta Materials Inc .... E 513 701-1140
  West Chester *(G-19897)*

Melvin Stone Company LLC .... G 740 998-5016
  Wshngtn CT Hs *(G-20916)*

Miami River Stone Co .... F 937 492-5412
  Sidney *(G-17202)*

Millersville Lime Inc 3 .... D 419 986-2019
  Bettsville *(G-1669)*

National Lime and Stone Co .... C 419 396-7671
  Carey *(G-2921)*

National Lime and Stone Co .... G 419 657-6745
  Wapakoneta *(G-19502)*

National Lime and Stone Co .... G 330 262-1317
  Wooster *(G-20814)*

National Lime and Stone Co .... E 740 548-4206
  Delaware *(G-8872)*

National Lime and Stone Co .... E 419 228-3434
  Lima *(G-12062)*

National Lime and Stone Co .... E 740 387-3485
  Marion *(G-12889)*

National Lime and Stone Co .... E 419 642-6690
  Columbus Grove *(G-7796)*

National Lime and Stone Co .... G 216 883-9840
  Cleveland *(G-5857)*

National Lime and Stone Co .... E 419 423-3400
  Findlay *(G-9866)*

National Lime and Stone Co .... D 419 562-0771
  Bucyrus *(G-2354)*

Ohio Asphaltic Limestone Corp .... F 937 364-2191
  Hillsboro *(G-11009)*

◆ Omya Industries Inc .... D 513 387-4600
  Blue Ash *(G-1847)*

Oster Sand and Gravel Inc .... G 330 833-2649
  Massillon *(G-13190)*

Piqua Materials Inc .... E 937 773-4824
  Piqua *(G-16305)*

Piqua Materials Inc .... E 513 771-0820
  Cincinnati *(G-4240)*

R W Sidley Incorporated .... F 440 352-9343
  Painesville *(G-15914)*

Ridge Township Stone Quarry .... G 419 968-2222
  Van Wert *(G-19269)*

Sharon Stone Inc .... G 740 732-7100
  Caldwell *(G-2432)*

Shelly Materials Inc .... G 740 246-6315
  Toledo *(G-18695)*

Shelly Materials Inc .... G 330 274-0802
  Mantua *(G-12721)*

Shelly Materials Inc .... G 330 722-2190
  Medina *(G-13480)*

Shelly Materials Inc .... G 330 364-4411
  Dover *(G-9014)*

Shelly Materials Inc .... G 330 823-4646
  Twinsburg *(G-19020)*

Shelly Materials Inc .... G 330 673-3646
  Kent *(G-11527)*

Shelly Materials Inc .... E 740 666-5841
  Ostrander *(G-15789)*

Shelly Materials Inc .... D 740 246-6315
  Thornville *(G-18198)*

Sidwell Materials Inc .... C 740 849-2394
  Zanesville *(G-21354)*

Stoneco Inc .... E 419 393-2555
  Oakwood *(G-15619)*

Stoneco Inc .... E 419 893-7645
  Maumee *(G-13298)*

Suever Stone Company .... F 419 331-1945
  Lima *(G-12097)*

The National Lime and Stone Co .... G 330 455-5722
  North Canton *(G-15271)*

Wagner Quarries Company .... E 419 625-8141
  Sandusky *(G-17021)*

White Rock Quarry L P .... A 419 855-8388
  Clay Center *(G-4655)*

Wysong Stone Co .... F 937 962-2559
  Lewisburg *(G-11942)*

1423 Crushed & Broken Granite

Bradley Stone Industries LLC .... F 440 519-3277
  Solon *(G-17273)*

Martin Marietta Materials Inc .... F 513 701-1120
  Mason *(G-13060)*

Martin Marietta Materials Inc .... E 513 701-1140
  West Chester *(G-19897)*

Martin Marietta Materials Inc .... E 937 766-2351
  Cedarville *(G-2982)*

Martin Marietta Materials Inc .... E 513 871-7152
  Cincinnati *(G-4063)*

National Lime and Stone Co .... G 419 294-3049
  Upper Sandusky *(G-19134)*

National Lime and Stone Co .... G 330 339-2144
  New Philadelphia *(G-14918)*

National Lime and Stone Co .... G 216 883-9840
  Cleveland *(G-5857)*

1429 Crushed & Broken Stone, NEC

Great Lakes Crushing Ltd ....E 440 944-5500
  Wickliffe *(G-20366)*
Melvin Stone Company LLC ....G 937 453-2032
  Sabina *(G-16773)*
Riverrock Recycl Crushing LLC ......G 937 325-2052
  Springfield *(G-17640)*
Rockhold Stone Quarry Inc ....G 937 358-2224
  West Mansfield *(G-20103)*
Sands Hill Mining LLC ....F 740 384-4211
  Hamden *(G-10658)*
Southern Ohio Materials ....G 937 386-3200
  Seaman *(G-17043)*
Stoneco Inc. ....G 419 686-3311
  Portage *(G-16428)*

1442 Construction Sand & Gravel

Alden Sand & Gravel Co Inc ....F 330 928-3249
  Cuyahoga Falls *(G-7963)*
Allen Harper. ....G 740 543-3919
  Amsterdam *(G-609)*
Arden J Neer Sr ....F 937 585-6733
  Bellefontaine *(G-1519)*
Barrett Paving Materials Inc ....C 513 271-6200
  Middletown *(G-14101)*
Beck Sand & Gravel Inc ....G 330 626-3863
  Ravenna *(G-16518)*
Beldex Land Company LLC ....G 740 783-3575
  Dexter City *(G-8955)*
Big Bills Trucking LLC ....G 614 850-0626
  Hilliard *(G-10934)*
Bonsal American Inc ....E 513 398-7300
  Cincinnati *(G-3460)*
C F Poeppelman Inc. ....E 937 448-2191
  Bradford *(G-2025)*
Carl E Oeder Sons Sand & Grav ......F 513 494-1555
  Lebanon *(G-11787)*
Central Allied Enterprises Inc ....G 330 879-2132
  Navarre *(G-14711)*
Central Ready Mix LLC ....E 513 402-5001
  Cincinnati *(G-3515)*
Clay LBC Co ....G 740 492-5055
  Newcomerstown *(G-15111)*
Columbus Equipment Company ....G 740 455-4036
  Zanesville *(G-21293)*
De Milta Sand and Gravel ....F 440 942-2015
  Willoughby *(G-20471)*
Demmy Sand and Gravel LLC ....E 937 325-8840
  Springfield *(G-17543)*
Feikert Sand & Gravel Co Inc ....E 330 674-0038
  Millersburg *(G-14215)*
Fenner Enterprises Inc ....G 937 698-7048
  Ludlow Falls *(G-12426)*
Fisher Sand & Gravel Inc ....G 330 745-9239
  Norton *(G-15512)*
Fleming Construction Co ....E 740 494-2177
  Prospect *(G-16496)*
FML Resin LLC ....E 440 214-3200
  Chesterland *(G-3207)*
FML Sand LLC ....G 440 214-3200
  Chesterland *(G-3208)*
FML Terminal Logistics LLC ....D 440 214-3200
  Chesterland *(G-3209)*
Foundry Sand Service LLC ....G 330 823-6152
  Sebring *(G-17045)*
Fouremans Sand & Gravel Inc ....G 937 547-1005
  Greenville *(G-10498)*
Gravel Doctor of Ohio LLC ....G 844 472-8353
  Millersport *(G-14293)*
Gravel-Tech ....G 513 703-3672
  Morrow *(G-14546)*
Hanson Aggregates East ....G 513 353-1100
  Cleves *(G-6515)*
Hanson Aggregates East LLC ....E 740 773-2172
  Chillicothe *(G-3242)*
Harvest Sand and Gravel Inc ....G 330 372-4408
  Warren *(G-19558)*
Haueter Construction Co ....G 440 834-8220
  Newbury *(G-15094)*
Hilltop Basic Resources Inc ....E 513 651-5000
  Cincinnati *(G-3884)*
Hilltop Basic Resources Inc ....G 937 878-8631
  Fairborn *(G-9624)*
Hilltop Basic Resources Inc ....F 937 882-6357
  Springfield *(G-17573)*
Hilltop Basic Resources Inc ....F 937 859-3616
  Miamisburg *(G-13817)*
Hilltop Basic Resources Inc ....E 513 621-1500
  Cincinnati *(G-3885)*

Hocking Valley Concrete Inc ....F 740 385-2165
  Logan *(G-12177)*
Holmes Supply Corp. ....G 330 279-2634
  Holmesville *(G-11105)*
Hugo Sand Company ....G 216 570-1212
  Kent *(G-11471)*
J P Sand & Gravel Company ....E 614 497-0083
  Lockbourne *(G-12147)*
James Bunnell Inc ....F 513 353-1100
  Cleves *(G-6516)*
James Ryan Soloman ....F 740 659-2304
  Glenford *(G-10398)*
Joe McClelland Inc ....E 740 452-3036
  Zanesville *(G-21324)*
John L Garber Materials Corp ....F 419 884-1567
  Mansfield *(G-12628)*
Keeney Sand & Stone Inc ....G 440 254-4582
  Painesville *(G-15894)*
Ken Heuser & Gary Gravel ....G 513 752-4159
  Cincinnati *(G-3981)*
Kenmore Construction Co Inc ....E 330 832-8888
  Massillon *(G-13162)*
Kipps Gravel Company Inc ....F 513 732-1024
  Batavia *(G-1199)*
Kirby and Sons Inc ....F 419 927-2260
  Upper Sandusky *(G-19128)*
L & I Natural Resources Inc ....G 513 683-2045
  Loveland *(G-12369)*
Lakeside Sand & Gravel Inc ....E 330 274-2569
  Mantua *(G-12714)*
M J Coates Construction Co ....G 937 886-9546
  Dayton *(G-8462)*
M J Coates Construction Co ....G 937 886-9546
  Dayton *(G-8463)*
Marietta Martin Materials Inc ....E 937 335-8313
  Troy *(G-18856)*
Marietta Martin Materials Inc ....F 919 781-4550
  Brookville *(G-2189)*
Marietta Martin Materials Inc ....E 937 766-2351
  Cedarville *(G-2981)*
Martin Marietta Materials Inc ....E 513 200-2303
  Harrison *(G-10789)*
Martin Marietta Materials Inc ....E 513 701-1140
  West Chester *(G-19897)*
Masons Sand and Gravel Co ....G 614 491-3611
  Obetz *(G-15655)*
Massillon Materials Inc ....E 330 837-4767
  Dalton *(G-8074)*
Mecco Inc. ....E 513 422-3651
  Middletown *(G-14061)*
Mechanicsburg Sand & Gravel ....F 937 834-2606
  Mechanicsburg *(G-13358)*
Medina Supply Company ....G 330 723-3681
  Medina *(G-13445)*
Morrow Gravel Company Inc ....E 513 771-0820
  Cincinnati *(G-4124)*
Morrow Gravel Company Inc ....F 513 899-2000
  Morrow *(G-14549)*
National Lime and Stone Co ....G 330 339-2144
  New Philadelphia *(G-14918)*
National Lime and Stone Co ....E 614 497-0083
  Lockbourne *(G-12150)*
National Lime and Stone Co ....G 216 883-9840
  Cleveland *(G-5857)*
National Lime and Stone Co ....C 419 396-7671
  Carey *(G-2921)*
Nelson Sand & Gravel Inc ....F 440 224-0198
  Kingsville *(G-11606)*
Oeder Carl E Sons Sand & Grav ......E 513 494-1238
  Lebanon *(G-11820)*
Ohio Valley Sand LLC ....G 740 661-4240
  New Philadelphia *(G-14920)*
Olen Corporation ....G 330 262-6821
  Wooster *(G-20819)*
Olen Corporation ....G 740 745-5865
  Saint Louisville *(G-16829)*
▼ Osborne Materials Company ....G 440 357-7026
  Grand River *(G-10452)*
Oscar Brugmann Sand & Gravel ....F 330 274-8224
  Mantua *(G-12719)*
Oster Sand and Gravel Inc ....G 330 494-5472
  Canton *(G-2805)*
Oster Sand and Gravel Inc ....G 330 874-3322
  Bolivar *(G-1940)*
Oster Sand and Gravel Inc ....G 330 833-2649
  Massillon *(G-13190)*
Phillips Companies ....G 937 426-5461
  Beavercreek Township *(G-1386)*
Phillips Companies ....E 937 431-7987
  Vandalia *(G-19308)*

Phillips Ready Mix Co. ....D 937 426-5151
  Beavercreek Township *(G-1388)*
Phoenix Asphalt Company Inc ....G 330 339-4935
  Magnolia *(G-12518)*
Piketon Sand & Gravel ....G 740 289-2316
  Piketon *(G-16227)*
Prairie Lane Corporation ....G 330 262-3322
  Wooster *(G-20823)*
Premier Silica LLC ....E 740 599-7773
  Howard *(G-11124)*
R W Sidley Incorporated ....E 440 564-2221
  Newbury *(G-15102)*
Riverside Sand & Gravel Co ....G 330 673-2021
  Kent *(G-11517)*
Rjw Trucking Company Ltd ....E 740 363-5343
  Delaware *(G-8883)*
Robert Perez Carpentry ....G 330 497-0043
  Canton *(G-2840)*
Roger Hall ....G 740 778-2861
  South Webster *(G-17451)*
Rolo Sand & Gravel ....G 740 886-7407
  Proctorville *(G-16491)*
Rupp Construction Inc ....F 330 855-2781
  Marshallville *(G-12920)*
S & S Aggregates Inc ....G 740 453-0721
  Zanesville *(G-21349)*
S & S Aggregates Inc ....F 419 938-5604
  Perrysville *(G-16175)*
Sant Sand & Gravel Co ....G 740 397-0000
  Mount Vernon *(G-14644)*
Seville Sand & Gravel Inc ....E 330 948-0168
  Strongsville *(G-17962)*
Shamrock Materials Inc. ....F 513 988-0647
  Cincinnati *(G-4411)*
Shelly and Sands Inc ....E 740 453-0721
  Zanesville *(G-21350)*
Shelly and Sands Inc ....E 740 453-0721
  Zanesville *(G-21351)*
Shelly Company ....F 740 687-4420
  Lancaster *(G-11750)*
Shelly Company ....G 740 246-6315
  Thornville *(G-18196)*
Shelly Materials Inc. ....E 740 775-4567
  Chillicothe *(G-3275)*
Shelly Materials Inc. ....G 330 673-3646
  Kent *(G-11527)*
Shelly Materials Inc. ....G 740 745-5965
  Newark *(G-15053)*
Shelly Materials Inc. ....D 740 246-6315
  Thornville *(G-18198)*
Shenango Valley Sand and Grav ....G 330 758-9100
  Youngstown *(G-21202)*
Small Sand & Gravel Inc ....E 740 427-3130
  Gambier *(G-10317)*
Smith Concrete Co. ....E 740 373-7441
  Dover *(G-9015)*
Sober Sand & Gravel Co ....G 330 325-7088
  Ravenna *(G-16557)*
Solomons Mines Inc ....G 330 337-0123
  Salem *(G-16928)*
Stafford Gravel Inc. ....G 419 298-2440
  Edgerton *(G-9336)*
Stansley Mineral Resources Inc ....E 419 843-2813
  Sylvania *(G-18126)*
Stocker Concrete Company ....F 740 254-4626
  Gnadenhutten *(G-10411)*
Stocker Sand & Gravel Co ....F 740 254-4635
  Gnadenhutten *(G-10412)*
Streamside Materials Llc ....G 419 423-1290
  Findlay *(G-9896)*
▲ Technisand Inc ....G 440 285-3132
  Chardon *(G-3181)*
Tiger Sand & Gravel LLC ....F 330 833-6325
  Massillon *(G-13205)*
Tipp Stone Inc ....G 937 890-4051
  Dayton *(G-8717)*
Tri County Concrete Inc ....E 330 425-4464
  Twinsburg *(G-19029)*
Turkeyfoot Hill Sand & Gravel ....G 330 899-1997
  Akron *(G-449)*
Twinsburg Development Corp ....G 440 357-5562
  Grand River *(G-10454)*
W&W Rock Sand and Gravel ....G 513 266-3708
  Williamsburg *(G-20413)*
Ward Construction Co ....F 419 943-2450
  Leipsic *(G-11879)*
Watson Gravel Inc. ....E 513 422-3781
  Middletown *(G-14095)*
Watson Gravel Inc. ....E 513 863-0070
  Hamilton *(G-10757)*

Wayne Concrete Company ....F 937 545-9919
Medway *(G-13502)*

Weber Sand & Gravel Inc ....F 419 298-2388
Edgerton *(G-9338)*

Weber Sand & Gravel Inc ....G 419 636-7920
Bryan *(G-2326)*

Welch Holdings Inc ....E 513 353-3220
Cincinnati *(G-4584)*

▼ World Development & Conslt LLC ....G 614 805-4450
Westerville *(G-20242)*

Wysong Gravel Co Inc ....F 937 456-4539
West Alexandria *(G-19787)*

Wysong Gravel Co Inc ....G 937 452-1523
Camden *(G-2489)*

Wysong Gravel Co Inc ....G 937 839-5497
West Alexandria *(G-19788)*

X L Sand and Gravel Co Inc ....F 330 426-9876
Negley *(G-14733)*

Young Sand & Gravel Co Inc ....F 419 994-3040
Loudonville *(G-12307)*

1446 Industrial Sand

▼ C E D Process Minerals Inc ....F 330 666-5500
Akron *(G-106)*

Fairmount Minerals LLC ....A 269 926-9450
Chesterland *(G-3204)*

◆ Fairmount Santrol Holdings Inc ....G 800 255-7263
Chesterland *(G-3205)*

Fairmount Water Solutions LLC ....G 440 285-3132
Newbury *(G-15090)*

I P Contractors LLC ....G 330 452-1643
Canton *(G-2735)*

Jim Nier Construction Inc ....F 740 289-2629
Piketon *(G-16221)*

Kistler Instrument Corp ....G 937 268-5920
Dayton *(G-8442)*

Parry Co ....G 740 884-4893
Chillicothe *(G-3258)*

Premier Silica LLC ....E 740 659-2241
Glenford *(G-10400)*

Premier Silica LLC ....E 740 599-7773
Howard *(G-11124)*

Standex International Corp ....E 513 871-3777
Cincinnati *(G-4457)*

1455 Kaolin & Ball Clay

State Line Resources Inc ....G 330 426-9611
Negley *(G-14732)*

1459 Clay, Ceramic & Refractory Minerals, NEC

American Colloid Company ....G 419 445-9085
Archbold *(G-662)*

Blue Jay Entps of Tscrwas Cnty ....G 330 874-2048
Bolivar *(G-1928)*

E J Bognar Inc ....F 330 426-9292
East Palestine *(G-9236)*

L & M Mineral Co ....G 330 852-3696
Sugarcreek *(G-18025)*

▲ Valley Clay Mining Co ....F 740 697-0620
Roseville *(G-16734)*

1479 Chemical & Fertilizer Mining

Cargill Incorporated ....C 216 651-7200
Cleveland *(G-4977)*

◆ Everris NA Inc ....E 614 726-7100
Dublin *(G-9074)*

Morton International LLC ....G 513 941-1578
Cincinnati *(G-4125)*

1481 Nonmetallic Minerals Svcs, Except Fuels

Aluchem of Jackson Inc ....E 740 286-2455
Jackson *(G-11309)*

Barr Engineering Incorporated ....F 614 892-0162
Columbus *(G-6807)*

Barr Engineering Incorporated ....E 614 714-0299
Columbus *(G-6808)*

Fgb International LLC ....G 440 359-0000
Cleveland *(G-5341)*

Longyear Company ....E 740 373-2190
Marietta *(G-12800)*

M G Q Inc ....E 419 992-4236
Tiffin *(G-18229)*

Masters Group Inc ....G 440 893-1900
Chagrin Falls *(G-3103)*

Robin Industries Inc ....E 330 893-3501
Berlin *(G-1652)*

▲ Sandy Creek Mining Co Inc ....G 419 435-5891
Fostoria *(G-9993)*

Stoepfel Drilling Co ....G 419 532-3307
Ottawa *(G-15811)*

Tom Hudson ....G 937 393-1285
Hillsboro *(G-11016)*

Tresslers Plumbing LLC ....G 419 784-2142
Defiance *(G-8812)*

1499 Miscellaneous Nonmetallic Mining

Asphalt Materials Inc ....F 419 693-0626
Oregon *(G-15702)*

Graftech Holdings Inc ....A 216 676-2000
Independence *(G-11256)*

Kellstone ....G 419 621-8140
Sandusky *(G-16976)*

Mar-Zane Inc ....G 419 529-2086
Ontario *(G-15689)*

Massillon Metaphysics ....G 330 837-1653
Massillon *(G-13174)*

National Lime and Stone Co ....G 330 339-2144
New Philadelphia *(G-14918)*

National Lime and Stone Co ....G 216 883-9840
Cleveland *(G-5857)*

Shelly Liquid Division ....G 216 781-9264
Cleveland *(G-6187)*

20 FOOD AND KINDRED PRODUCTS

2011 Meat Packing Plants

Acme Steak & Seafood Inc ....F 330 270-8000
Youngstown *(G-21016)*

American Foods Group LLC ....E 513 733-8898
Cincinnati *(G-3388)*

Baltic Country Meats ....G 330 897-7025
Baltic *(G-1065)*

Bob Evans Farms Inc ....D 937 372-4493
Xenia *(G-20939)*

Bob Evans Farms Inc ....F 740 245-5305
Bidwell *(G-1673)*

Bob Evans Farms Inc ....B 614 491-2225
New Albany *(G-14750)*

▲ Buckeye Veal Services ....G 740 489-5145
Wooster *(G-20755)*

C J Kraft Enterprises Inc ....E 740 653-9606
Lancaster *(G-11694)*

Canaan Country Meats ....G 330 435-4778
Creston *(G-7938)*

Carl Rittberger Sr Inc ....E 740 452-2767
Zanesville *(G-21287)*

Case Farms of Ohio Inc ....C 330 359-7141
Winesburg *(G-20702)*

Caven and Sons Meat Packing Co ......F 937 368-3841
Conover *(G-7822)*

D & H Meats Inc ....G 419 387-7767
Vanlue *(G-19319)*

Dalton Veal ....G 330 828-8337
Dalton *(G-8066)*

Dee-Jays Cstm Butchering Proc ....G 740 694-7492
Fredericktown *(G-10099)*

Empire Packing Company LP ....D 513 942-5400
West Chester *(G-20000)*

Fresh Mark Inc ....A 330 332-8508
Salem *(G-16893)*

◆ Fresh Mark Inc ....B 330 834-3669
Massillon *(G-13135)*

Gortons Inc ....E 216 362-1050
Cleveland *(G-5439)*

Hartville Locker Service Inc ....G 330 877-9547
Hartville *(G-10823)*

Heffelfingers Meats Inc ....E 419 368-7131
Jeromesville *(G-11384)*

Honey Baked Ham Company LLC ....G 513 474-0022
Cincinnati *(G-3894)*

Horst Packing Inc ....G 330 482-2997
Columbiana *(G-6620)*

Industrial Packaging Products ....G 440 734-2663
Cleveland *(G-5567)*

J M Meat Processing ....G 740 259-3030
Mc Dermott *(G-13342)*

Jacoby Packing Co ....G 419 924-2684
West Unity *(G-20130)*

◆ John Morrell & Co ....C 513 782-3800
Cincinnati *(G-3953)*

John Stehlin & Sons Co Inc ....F 513 385-6164
Cincinnati *(G-3955)*

Jones Processing ....G 330 772-2193
Hartford *(G-10814)*

Karn Meats Inc ....E 614 252-3712
Columbus *(G-7251)*

King Kold Inc ....E 937 836-2731
Englewood *(G-9529)*

Links Country Meats ....G 419 683-2195
Crestline *(G-7931)*

Mahan Packing Co Inc ....G 330 889-2454
Bristolville *(G-2099)*

Mannings Packing Co ....G 937 446-3263
Sardinia *(G-17030)*

Marshallville Packing Co Inc ....E 330 855-2871
Marshallville *(G-12918)*

Mc Connells Market ....G 740 765-4300
Richmond *(G-16647)*

New Riegel Cafe Inc ....E 419 595-2255
New Riegel *(G-14947)*

Northside Meat Co Inc ....G 513 681-4111
Cincinnati *(G-4163)*

Ohio Farms Packing Co Ltd ....G 330 435-6400
Creston *(G-7942)*

Ohio Packing Company ....D 614 445-0627
Columbus *(G-7426)*

Ohio Packing Company ....D 614 445-0627
Columbus *(G-7427)*

Oiler Processing ....G 740 892-2640
Utica *(G-19195)*

Patrick M Davidson ....G 513 897-2971
Waynesville *(G-19733)*

Pine Ridge Processing ....G 740 749-3166
Fleming *(G-9913)*

Premium Meats Inc ....F 330 394-8651
Warren *(G-19589)*

Presslers Meats Inc ....F 330 644-5636
Akron *(G-350)*

Reuss Meats Inc ....F 513 874-3200
Fairfield *(G-9710)*

Robert Winner Sons Inc ....G 937 548-7513
Greenville *(G-10520)*

Robert Winner Sons Inc ....E 419 582-4321
Yorkshire *(G-21006)*

Rxpert Consultants LLC ....G 614 579-9384
Columbus *(G-7580)*

Shaker Valley Foods Inc ....E 216 961-8600
Cleveland *(G-6182)*

Shirer Brothers Meats ....G 740 796-3214
Adamsville *(G-9)*

Signature Beef LLC ....G 740 468-3579
Pleasantville *(G-16375)*

Smokin TS Smokehouse ....G 440 577-1117
Jefferson *(G-11371)*

Strasburg Provision Inc ....E 330 878-1059
Strasburg *(G-17830)*

◆ Sugar Creek Packing Co ....B 740 335-7440
Wshngtn CT Hs *(G-20927)*

Sugar Creek Packing Co ....B 937 268-6601
Dayton *(G-8687)*

Sugar Creek Packing Co ....C 513 874-4422
West Chester *(G-19950)*

Sugar Creek Packing Co ....G 513 874-4422
West Chester *(G-19951)*

Sunny Side Meats ....G 419 387-7812
Vanlue *(G-19320)*

Tempac LLC ....E 513 505-9700
West Chester *(G-19954)*

Tri-State Beef Co Inc ....E 513 579-1722
Cincinnati *(G-4521)*

Troyers Trail Bologna Inc ....G 330 893-2414
Dundee *(G-9183)*

Trumbull Locker Plant Inc ....G 440 474-4631
Rock Creek *(G-16686)*

V H Cooper & Co Inc ....E 419 678-4853
Saint Henry *(G-16824)*

V H Cooper & Co Inc ....B 419 678-4853
Saint Henry *(G-16823)*

V H Cooper & Co Inc ....C 419 375-4116
Fort Recovery *(G-9961)*

Werling and Sons Inc ....F 937 338-3281
Burkettsville *(G-2370)*

Whitefeather Meats LLC ....G 330 435-6300
Creston *(G-7944)*

Winesburg Meats Inc ....G 330 359-5092
Winesburg *(G-20708)*

Youngs Locker Service Inc ....F 740 599-6833
Danville *(G-8093)*

2013 Sausages & Meat Prdts

A To Z Portion Ctrl Meats Inc ....E 419 358-2926
Bluffton *(G-1906)*

▲ Advancepierre Foods Inc ....B 513 874-8741
Blue Ash *(G-1734)*

Advancepierre Foods Inc ....G 513 874-8741
West Chester *(G-19977)*

Advancperre Foods Holdings Inc .... G 800 969-2747
 Blue Ash *(G-1735)*
American Foods Group LLC .... E 513 733-8898
 Cincinnati *(G-3388)*
Amish Wedding Foods Inc .... E 330 674-9199
 Millersburg *(G-14193)*
Brentmoor Hams LLC .... G 513 677-0813
 Loveland *(G-12344)*
Brinkman Turkey Farms Inc .... F 419 365-5127
 Findlay *(G-9802)*
Carl Rittberger Sr Inc .... E 740 452-2767
 Zanesville *(G-21287)*
Caven and Sons Meat Packing Co .... F 937 368-3841
 Conover *(G-7822)*
◆ Cincinnati Meat Processing Inc .... D 513 682-6000
 Cincinnati *(G-3559)*
D D D Hams Inc .... G 440 487-9572
 Solon *(G-17281)*
Dirussos Sausage Inc .... E 330 744-1208
 Youngstown *(G-21070)*
Dumas Meats Inc .... G 330 628-3438
 Mogadore *(G-14373)*
Edelmann Provision Company .... D 513 881-5800
 Harrison *(G-10776)*
Empire Packing Company LP .... D 513 942-5400
 West Chester *(G-20000)*
Fink Meat Company Inc .... G 937 390-2750
 Springfield *(G-17558)*
Frank Brunckhorst Company LLC .... G 614 662-5300
 Groveport *(G-10622)*
◆ Fresh Mark Inc .... B 330 834-3669
 Massillon *(G-13135)*
Fresh Mark Inc .... B 330 832-7491
 Massillon *(G-13136)*
Fresh Mark Inc .... A 330 332-8508
 Salem *(G-16893)*
Hoffman Meat Processing .... G 419 864-3994
 Cardington *(G-2911)*
Honeybaked Ham Company .... E 513 583-9700
 Cincinnati *(G-3895)*
Hormel Foods Corp Svcs LLC .... E 513 563-0211
 Cincinnati *(G-3898)*
John Krusinski .... F 216 441-0100
 Cleveland *(G-5619)*
John Stehlin & Sons Co Inc .... F 513 385-6164
 Cincinnati *(G-3955)*
Johns Jerky & Snack Meats LLC .... G 937 207-7008
 South Charleston *(G-17426)*
Jtm Provisions Company Inc .... B 513 367-4900
 Harrison *(G-10787)*
Karn Meats Inc .... E 614 252-3712
 Columbus *(G-7251)*
Keith Grimm .... G 419 899-2725
 Sherwood *(G-17146)*
Kenosha Beef International Ltd .... C 614 771-1330
 Columbus *(G-7256)*
Keystone Foods LLC .... E 419 257-2341
 North Baltimore *(G-15193)*
King Kold Inc .... E 937 836-2731
 Englewood *(G-9529)*
Kings Command Foods LLC .... D 937 526-3553
 Versailles *(G-19350)*
Kraft Heinz Foods Company .... B 740 622-0523
 Coshocton *(G-7896)*
Lee Williams Meats Inc .... E 419 729-3893
 Toledo *(G-18555)*
Lous Sausage Ltd .... F 216 752-5060
 Cleveland *(G-5710)*
Mama Mias Foods Inc .... G 216 281-2188
 Cleveland *(G-5737)*
Marshallville Packing Co Inc .... E 330 855-2871
 Marshallville *(G-12918)*
Martin-Brower Company LLC .... B 513 773-2301
 West Chester *(G-19898)*
Ohio Packing Company .... D 614 445-0627
 Columbus *(G-7427)*
Old Country Sausage Kitchen .... G 216 662-5988
 Cleveland *(G-5936)*
Patrick M Davidson .... G 513 897-2971
 Waynesville *(G-19733)*
Peggys Pride .... G 614 464-2511
 Columbus *(G-7475)*
Perfettes Sausage LLC .... G 330 792-0775
 Youngstown *(G-21169)*
Pettisville Meats Inc .... F 419 445-0921
 Pettisville *(G-16183)*
Pierre Holding Corp .... G 513 874-8741
 West Chester *(G-20037)*
Queen City Sausage & Provision .... E 513 541-5581
 Cincinnati *(G-4320)*

Raddells Sausage .... G 216 486-1944
 Cleveland *(G-6085)*
Rays Sausage Inc .... G 216 921-8782
 Cleveland *(G-6092)*
Robert Winner Sons Inc .... E 419 582-4321
 Yorkshire *(G-21006)*
Sausage Shoppe .... G 216 351-5213
 Cleveland *(G-6163)*
Schad Meats Inc .... G 513 520-4888
 Cincinnati *(G-4385)*
Simply Unique Snacks LLC .... G 513 223-7736
 Cincinnati *(G-4422)*
Steven Yant .... G 937 596-0497
 Jackson Center *(G-11348)*
Strasburg Provision Inc .... G 330 878-1059
 Strasburg *(G-17830)*
◆ Sugar Creek Packing Co .... B 740 335-7440
 Wshngtn CT Hs *(G-20927)*
Sugar Creek Packing Co .... G 937 268-6601
 Dayton *(G-8687)*
Sugar Creek Packing Co .... C 513 874-4422
 West Chester *(G-19950)*
Sugar Creek Packing Co .... G 513 874-4422
 West Chester *(G-19951)*
Sunrise Foods Inc .... E 614 276-2880
 Columbus *(G-7667)*
Tea Hills Gourmet Chicken Pdts .... G 419 685-1689
 Loudonville *(G-12305)*
Tri-State Beef Co Inc .... G 513 579-1722
 Cincinnati *(G-4521)*
Weaver Meats Inc .... F 440 639-1954
 Painesville *(G-15938)*
▲ White Castle System Inc .... B 614 228-5781
 Columbus *(G-7761)*
▲ Wild Joes Inc .... G 513 681-9200
 Cincinnati *(G-4594)*
Williams Pork Co Op .... G 419 682-9022
 Stryker *(G-18010)*
Youngs Locker Service Inc .... F 740 599-6833
 Danville *(G-8093)*
Zartic LLC .... D 513 874-8741
 West Chester *(G-20072)*

2015 Poultry Slaughtering, Dressing & Processing

▲ Advancepierre Foods Inc .... B 513 874-8741
 Blue Ash *(G-1734)*
▼ Ballas Egg Products Corp .... D 614 453-0386
 Zanesville *(G-21274)*
BE Products Inc .... D 740 453-0386
 Zanesville *(G-21277)*
Briarwood Valley Farms .... G 419 736-2298
 Sullivan *(G-18053)*
Brinkman Turkey Farms Inc .... F 419 365-5127
 Findlay *(G-9802)*
Cal-Maine Foods Inc .... E 937 337-9576
 Rossburg *(G-16735)*
Cal-Maine Foods Inc .... E 937 968-4874
 Union City *(G-19069)*
Case Farms of Ohio Inc .... C 330 359-7141
 Winesburg *(G-20702)*
Case Farms of Ohio Inc .... F 330 878-7118
 Strasburg *(G-17822)*
Cooper Foods .... E 419 232-2440
 Van Wert *(G-19250)*
Cooper Hatchery Inc .... E 419 238-4869
 Van Wert *(G-19251)*
Cooper Hatchery Inc .... C 419 594-3325
 Oakwood *(G-15615)*
Fort Recovery Equity Inc .... E 419 375-4119
 Fort Recovery *(G-9950)*
Fort Recovery Equity Exchange .... E 937 338-8901
 Rossburg *(G-16736)*
Freak-N-Fries Inc .... G 440 453-1877
 Lagrange *(G-11625)*
Gerber Farm Division Inc .... G 800 362-7381
 Kidron *(G-11590)*
Hemmelgarn & Sons Inc .... D 419 678-2351
 Coldwater *(G-6563)*
Just Natural Provision Company .... E 216 431-7922
 Cleveland *(G-5626)*
Kings Command Foods LLC .... D 937 526-3553
 Versailles *(G-19350)*
Koch Meat Co Inc .... B 513 874-3500
 Fairfield *(G-9674)*
Martin-Brower Company LLC .... B 513 773-2301
 West Chester *(G-19898)*
Medina Foods Inc .... E 330 725-1390
 Litchfield *(G-12138)*

Nature Pure LLC .... F 937 358-2364
 West Mansfield *(G-20102)*
Nutrifresh Eggs .... G 567 224-7676
 Willard *(G-20398)*
▲ Ohio Fresh Eggs LLC .... G 740 893-7200
 Croton *(G-7955)*
Ohio Fresh Eggs LLC .... E 937 354-2233
 Mount Victory *(G-14657)*
Pf Management Inc .... G 513 874-8741
 West Chester *(G-20036)*
Pierre Holding Corp .... G 513 874-8741
 West Chester *(G-20037)*
Roots Poultry Inc .... F 419 332-0041
 Fremont *(G-10180)*
V H Cooper & Co Inc .... B 419 678-4853
 Saint Henry *(G-16823)*
V H Cooper & Co Inc .... C 419 375-4116
 Fort Recovery *(G-9961)*
▲ Weaver Bros Inc .... D 937 526-3907
 Versailles *(G-19360)*
Whitewater Processing Co .... D 513 367-4133
 Harrison *(G-10812)*
Zartic LLC .... D 513 874-8741
 West Chester *(G-20072)*

2021 Butter

Black Radish Creamery Ltd .... G 614 323-6016
 New Albany *(G-14749)*
Butt Kickn Creamery Inc .... G 419 482-6610
 Perrysburg *(G-16072)*
Dairy Farmers America Inc .... E 330 670-7800
 Medina *(G-13400)*
Fairmont Creamery LLC .... G 216 357-2560
 Cleveland *(G-5320)*
Land OLakes Inc .... C 330 678-1578
 Kent *(G-11485)*
Minerva Dairy Inc .... D 330 868-4196
 Minerva *(G-14334)*
Turkeyfoot Creek Creamery .... G 419 335-0224
 Wauseon *(G-19698)*

2022 Cheese

9444 Ohio Holding Co .... E 330 359-6291
 Winesburg *(G-20701)*
A & M Cheese Co .... D 419 476-8369
 Toledo *(G-18317)*
Amish Wedding Foods Inc .... E 330 674-9199
 Millersburg *(G-14193)*
▲ Biery Cheese Co .... C 330 875-3381
 Louisville *(G-12310)*
Brewster Cheese Company .... C 330 767-3492
 Brewster *(G-2083)*
Bunker Hill Cheese Co Inc .... D 330 893-2131
 Millersburg *(G-14207)*
Dairy Farmers America Inc .... E 330 670-7800
 Medina *(G-13400)*
Es Steiner Dairy LLC .... F 330 897-5555
 Baltic *(G-1069)*
◆ Great Lakes Cheese Co Inc .... B 440 834-2500
 Hiram *(G-11036)*
Guggisberg Cheese Inc .... E 330 893-2550
 Millersburg *(G-14219)*
Hans Rothenbuhler & Son Inc .... E 440 632-6000
 Middlefield *(G-13939)*
▲ Holmes Cheese Co .... D 330 674-6451
 Millersburg *(G-14229)*
Inter American Products Inc .... E 800 645-2233
 Cincinnati *(G-3927)*
Kathys Krafts and Kollectibles .... G 423 787-3709
 Medina *(G-13431)*
Kraft House No 5 .... G 614 396-9091
 Powell *(G-16475)*
Kraft of Writing .... G 614 620-2476
 Columbus *(G-7266)*
▲ Lake Erie Frozen Foods Mfg Co ...... E 419 289-9204
 Ashland *(G-749)*
Lakeview Farms LLC .... G 419 695-9925
 Delphos *(G-8912)*
Lakeview Farms LLC .... C 419 695-9925
 Delphos *(G-8913)*
▲ Miceli Dairy Products Co .... D 216 791-6222
 Cleveland *(G-5797)*
Middlefield Mix Inc .... F 440 632-0157
 Middlefield *(G-13960)*
Middlfeld Original Cheese Coop .... E 440 632-5567
 Middlefield *(G-13964)*
Minerva Dairy Inc .... D 330 868-4196
 Minerva *(G-14334)*
Oakvale Farm Cheese Inc .... G 740 857-1230
 London *(G-12217)*

Pearl Valley Cheese Inc ....E 740 545-6002
  Fresno (G-10197)
Schindlers Broad Run Chese Hse ....F 330 343-4108
  Dover (G-9011)
Tri State Dairy ....G 419 542-8788
  Hicksville (G-10908)
Tri State Dairy LLC ....F 330 897-5555
  Baltic (G-1078)
Wood Kraft ....G 440 487-4634
  Garrettsville (G-10336)

2023 Milk, Condensed & Evaporated

Aggregate Tersornance LLC ....G 330 418-4751
  Canton (G-2590)
Alifet USA Inc ....G 513 793-8033
  Blue Ash (G-1740)
Eagle Family Foods Group LLC ....E 330 382-3725
  Richfield (G-16621)
▲ Freedom Health LLC ....E 330 562-0888
  Aurora (G-920)
Hans Rothenbuhler & Son Inc ....E 440 632-6000
  Middlefield (G-13939)
Healthy Living ....G 937 962-4705
  Lewisburg (G-11934)
▲ Infinit Nutrition LLC ....F 513 791-3500
  Blue Ash (G-1815)
◆ Ingredia Inc ....G 419 738-4060
  Wapakoneta (G-19491)
Innovated Health LLC ....G 330 858-0651
  Cuyahoga Falls (G-8010)
Instantwhip-Columbus Inc ....E 614 871-9447
  Grove City (G-10564)
▲ Instantwhip-Dayton Inc ....F 937 235-5930
  Dayton (G-8410)
Instantwhip-Dayton Inc ....G 937 435-4371
  Dayton (G-8411)
◆ J M Smucker Company ....A 330 682-3000
  Orrville (G-15742)
Kerry Flavor Systems Us LLC ....D 513 771-4682
  Cincinnati (G-3985)
L & F Lauch LLC ....G 513 732-5805
  Batavia (G-1200)
Lifestyle Nutraceuticals Ltd ....F 513 376-7218
  Cincinnati (G-4022)
▼ Milnot Company ....G 888 656-3245
  Gahanna (G-10220)
Minerva Dairy Inc ....D 330 868-4196
  Minerva (G-14334)
Moo Technologies Inc ....G 513 732-5805
  Batavia (G-1209)
Muscle Feast LLC ....G 888 734-3634
  Hebron (G-10877)
Muscle Feast LLC ....F 740 877-8808
  Hebron (G-10878)
Nestle Usa Inc ....C 216 524-7738
  Cleveland (G-5872)
Nestle Usa Inc ....C 216 524-3397
  Cleveland (G-5873)
Nestle Usa Inc ....C 440 349-5757
  Solon (G-17347)
Nestle Usa Inc ....D 216 861-8350
  Cleveland (G-5874)
Rich Products Corporation ....C 614 771-1117
  Hilliard (G-10976)
Smithfoods Orrville Inc ....C 330 684-6502
  Orrville (G-15765)
▲ Stolle Milk Biologics Inc ....C 513 489-7997
  West Chester (G-20055)
Tmarzetti Company ....C 614 279-8673
  Columbus (G-7697)
Toomey Inc ....C 513 831-4771
  Milford (G-14178)
Wileys Finest LLC ....G 740 622-1072
  Coshocton (G-7916)
▲ Yoders Cider Barn ....F 740 668-4961
  Gambier (G-10319)

2024 Ice Cream

3 Dips ....G 937 247-5914
  Miamisburg (G-13777)
ABC Refreshments LLC ....F 866 382-5575
  Euclid (G-9563)
Archies Too ....D 419 427-2663
  Findlay (G-9790)
Awesome Yogurt LLC ....G 937 643-0879
  Dayton (G-8176)
B M DS Fish N More LLC ....F 419 238-2722
  Van Wert (G-19244)
Bacconis Lickety Split ....G 330 924-0418
  Cortland (G-7861)

Better Than Sex Ice Cream LLC ....G 614 444-5505
  Columbus (G-6823)
Bojos Cream ....G 330 270-3332
  Austintown (G-970)
Broughton Foods Company ....C 740 373-4121
  Marietta (G-12768)
Cone of West Chester ....E 513 779-7040
  West Chester (G-19837)
Country Caterers Inc ....G 740 389-1013
  Marion (G-12863)
Country Maid Ice Cream Inc ....G 330 659-6830
  Richfield (G-16619)
Country Parlour Ice Cream Co ....F 440 237-4040
  Cleveland (G-5134)
CTB Consulting LLC ....F 216 712-7764
  Rocky River (G-16697)
Dairy Shed ....G 937 848-3504
  Bellbrook (G-1506)
Dari Freeze ....G 937 678-6171
  West Manchester (G-20097)
Dietsch Brothers Incorporated ....E 419 422-4474
  Findlay (G-9816)
Double Dippin Inc ....G 937 847-2572
  Miamisburg (G-13802)
Fritzie Freeze Inc ....F 419 727-0818
  Toledo (G-18474)
Frosty Twins ....G 330 359-0708
  Winesburg (G-20703)
Froyo Twist ....G 440 974-1001
  Mentor (G-13586)
Gibson Bros Inc ....E 440 774-2401
  Oberlin (G-15641)
Graeters Manufacturing Co ....D 513 721-3323
  Cincinnati (G-3843)
Home City Ice ....G 859 441-1700
  Aberdeen (G-1)
Home City Ice Company ....F 419 562-4953
  Delaware (G-8860)
Honeybaked Ham Company ....E 513 583-9700
  Cincinnati (G-3895)
ICEE USA ....G 513 771-0630
  West Chester (G-20015)
International Brand Services ....F 513 376-8209
  Cincinnati (G-3930)
Jim H Niemeyer ....F 419 422-2465
  Findlay (G-9845)
Johnsons Real Ice Cream Co ....E 614 231-0014
  Columbus (G-7241)
Joshua Leigh Enterprises Inc ....G 330 244-9200
  Canton (G-2749)
Louis Trauth Dairy LLC ....B 859 431-7553
  West Chester (G-20021)
▲ Malleys Candies ....D 216 362-8700
  Lakewood (G-11674)
Mitchell Bros Ice Cream Inc ....F 216 861-2799
  Cleveland (G-5824)
Orange Leaf ....G 614 898-5323
  Westerville (G-20175)
▲ Pierres French Ice Cream Inc ....E 216 431-2555
  Cleveland (G-6006)
Reiter Dairy of Akron Inc ....E 419 424-5060
  Findlay (G-9882)
Robert E McGrath Inc ....E 440 572-7747
  Strongsville (G-17959)
◆ Royal Ice Cream Co ....D 216 432-1144
  Cleveland (G-6139)
Schwans Home Service Inc ....E 419 222-9977
  Lima (G-12088)
Schwans Home Service Inc ....E 937 335-4111
  Troy (G-18873)
Smithfoods Inc ....G 330 683-8710
  Orrville (G-15764)
Springdale Ice Cream Beverage ....E 513 699-4984
  Cincinnati (G-4447)
St Clairsville Dairy Queen ....G 740 635-1800
  Saint Clairsville (G-16808)
Stella Lou LLC ....F 937 935-9536
  Powell (G-16483)
Superior Tasting Products Inc ....E 614 442-0622
  Columbus (G-7668)
The Dannon Company Inc ....E 513 229-0092
  Mason (G-13098)
The Dannon Company Inc ....B 419 628-3861
  Minster (G-14363)
Tmarzetti Company ....C 614 279-8673
  Columbus (G-7697)
Toft Dairy Inc ....E 419 625-4376
  Sandusky (G-17016)
United Dairy Inc ....G 740 633-1451
  Martins Ferry (G-12927)

United Dairy Farmers Inc ....C 513 396-8700
  Cincinnati (G-4538)
Weldon Ice Cream Company ....G 740 467-2400
  Millersport (G-14299)
Welsh Farms LLC ....G 513 723-4487
  Cincinnati (G-4585)
Whit S Frozen Custard ....G 740 927-0025
  Pataskala (G-15990)
Whits Frozen Custard ....G 740 965-1427
  Sunbury (G-18078)
Wil-Mark Froyo LLC ....G 330 421-6043
  Wadsworth (G-19445)
Wild Penguin Llc ....G 513 533-4356
  Cincinnati (G-4595)
Yagoot ....G 513 791-6600
  Cincinnati (G-4617)
Youngs Jersey Dairy Inc ....B 937 325-0629
  Yellow Springs (G-21003)
ZS Cream & Bean ....G 440 652-6369
  Hinckley (G-11032)

2026 Milk

American Confections Co LLC ....G 614 888-8838
  Columbus (G-6734)
Arps Dairy Inc ....F 419 782-9116
  Defiance (G-8779)
Auburn Dairy Products Inc ....G 614 488-2536
  Columbus (G-6785)
Borden Dairy Co Cincinnati LLC ....G 513 948-8811
  Cincinnati (G-3461)
Borden Dairy Company Ohio LLC ....C 216 671-2300
  Cleveland (G-4925)
Broughton Foods Company ....G 740 373-4121
  Marietta (G-12768)
Broughton Foods Company ....F 800 598-7545
  South Point (G-17434)
Consun Food Industries Inc ....D 440 322-6301
  Elyria (G-9397)
Dairy Farmers America Inc ....G 330 670-7800
  Medina (G-13400)
Daisy Brand LLC ....F 330 202-4376
  Wooster (G-20762)
Dallas Instantwhip Inc ....G 614 488-2536
  Columbus (G-7009)
Dip It Good Foods Inc ....G 330 219-3137
  Newton Falls (G-15132)
Instantwhip Connecticut Inc ....F 614 488-2536
  Columbus (G-7192)
Instantwhip Detroit Inc ....G 614 488-2536
  Columbus (G-7193)
Instantwhip Detroit Inc ....F 800 544-9447
  Columbus (G-7194)
Instantwhip Foods Inc ....G 614 488-2536
  Columbus (G-7195)
Instantwhip of Buffalo Inc ....G 614 488-2536
  Columbus (G-7196)
Instantwhip Products Co PA ....F 614 488-2536
  Columbus (G-7197)
Instantwhip-Chicago Inc ....G 614 488-2536
  Columbus (G-7198)
Instantwhip-Columbus Inc ....E 614 871-9447
  Grove City (G-10564)
▲ Instantwhip-Dayton Inc ....F 937 235-5930
  Dayton (G-8410)
Instantwhip-Dayton Inc ....G 937 435-4371
  Dayton (G-8411)
Instantwhip-Syracuse Inc ....F 614 488-2536
  Columbus (G-7199)
Lakeview Farms Inc ....D 419 695-9925
  Delphos (G-8911)
Lakeview Farms LLC ....E 419 695-9925
  Delphos (G-8912)
Lakeview Farms LLC ....C 419 695-9925
  Delphos (G-8913)
Louis Instantwhip-St Inc ....F 614 488-2536
  Columbus (G-7305)
Louis Trauth Dairy LLC ....B 859 431-7553
  West Chester (G-20021)
Ohio Processors Inc ....G 740 852-9243
  Columbus (G-7428)
Peak Foods Llc ....D 937 440-0707
  Troy (G-18862)
Philadelphia Instantwhip Inc ....G 614 488-2536
  Columbus (G-7482)
Reiter Dairy of Akron Inc ....E 937 323-5777
  Springfield (G-17637)
Reiter Dairy of Akron Inc ....E 419 424-5060
  Findlay (G-9882)
Smith Dairy Products Company ....E 740 927-2688
  Reynoldsburg (G-16605)

S I C

Smithfoods Inc ....G 330 683-8710
Orrville (G-15764)
Snowville Creamery LLC ....E 740 698-2301
Pomeroy (G-16391)
Toft Dairy Inc ....D 419 625-4376
Sandusky (G-17016)
United Dairy Inc ....C 740 633-1451
Martins Ferry (G-12927)
United Dairy Farmers Inc ....C 513 396-8700
Cincinnati (G-4538)

2032 Canned Specialties

Abbott Laboratories ....A 614 624-3191
Columbus (G-6671)
Beckman & Gast Company ....F 419 678-4195
Saint Henry (G-16815)
Bittersweet Inc ....E 419 875-6986
Whitehouse (G-20338)
Clovervale Farms Inc ....D 440 960-0146
Amherst (G-595)
Conagra Brands Inc ....B 419 445-8015
Archbold (G-669)
D & A Rofael Enterprises Inc ....G 513 751-4929
Cincinnati (G-3628)
Disalvos Deli & Italian Store ....G 937 298-5053
Dayton (G-8306)
Elizabeths Closet ....G 513 646-5025
Maineville (G-12522)
Food Designs Inc ....F 216 651-9221
Cleveland (G-5366)
Gia Russa ....F 330 743-6050
Youngstown (G-21100)
Hayden Valley Foods Inc ....E 614 539-7233
Urbancrest (G-19189)
JES Foods/Celina Inc ....E 419 586-4192
Celina (G-3004)
Lifo Enterprises Inc ....G 513 225-8801
Loveland (G-12371)
Magic Wok Inc ....G 419 531-1818
Toledo (G-18569)
▼ Milnot Company ....G 888 656-3245
Gahanna (G-10220)
▲ More Than Gourmet Inc ....E 330 762-6652
Akron (G-302)
◆ Oasis Mediterranean Cuisine ....E 419 269-1516
Toledo (G-18612)
P3 Secure LLC ....E 937 610-5500
Dayton (G-8559)
Randall Foods Inc ....G 513 793-6525
Cincinnati (G-4329)
▲ Robert Rothschild Farm LLC ....E 937 653-7397
Urbana (G-19177)
San Marco Super Marketo ....G 419 469-8963
Toledo (G-18684)
Silgan Can Company ....F 419 592-1010
Napoleon (G-14699)
Skyline Chili Inc ....C 513 874-1188
Fairfield (G-9719)
Troyer Cheese Inc ....E 330 893-2479
Millersburg (G-14274)
Werling Meats Inc ....G 419 375-0037
Burkettsville (G-2371)
Whiteys Food Systems Inc ....G 330 659-4070
Richfield (G-16646)
Wornick Company ....B 800 860-4555
Blue Ash (G-1899)
Wornick Company ....A 513 552-7463
Blue Ash (G-1900)
Wornick Holding Company Inc ....A 513 794-9800
Blue Ash (G-1901)
Worthmore Food Products Co ....F 513 559-1473
Cincinnati (G-4605)

2033 Canned Fruits, Vegetables & Preserves

Anderson Brothers Entps Inc ....E 440 269-3920
Willoughby (G-20432)
Beckman & Gast Co Inc ....D 419 678-4195
Saint Henry (G-16814)
Beckman & Gast Company ....F 419 678-4195
Saint Henry (G-16815)
Bellisio Foods Inc ....A 740 286-5505
Jackson (G-11311)
▲ Bossa Nova Beverage Group Inc ...F 513 483-3300
Blue Ash (G-1753)
Buckeye Sauce Corporation ....F 216 751-0440
Cleveland (G-4944)
Campbell Soup Company ....D 419 592-1010
Napoleon (G-14674)
▲ Cincinnati Preserving Company .....F 513 771-2000
Cincinnati (G-3563)

Clovervale Farms Inc ....D 440 960-0146
Amherst (G-595)
Coopers Mill ....F 419 562-4215
Bucyrus (G-2336)
◆ Country Pure Foods Inc ....C 330 848-6875
Akron (G-131)
Dominion Liquid Tech LLC ....E 513 272-2824
Cincinnati (G-3663)
▼ Fremont Company ....D 419 334-8995
Fremont (G-10146)
Fremont Company ....D 419 334-8995
Fremont (G-10147)
Fremont Company ....E 419 363-2924
Rockford (G-16691)
▼ Fry Foods Inc ....D 419 448-0831
Tiffin (G-18221)
Garden of Flavor LLC ....G 216 702-7991
Cleveland (G-5396)
Gofast LLC ....G 419 562-8027
Bucyrus (G-2346)
Great Western Juice Company ....F 216 475-5770
Cleveland (G-5457)
Guys Barbeque Inc ....G 330 872-7256
Newton Falls (G-15133)
Hermann Pickle Company ....E 330 527-2696
Garrettsville (G-10324)
Hirzel Canning Company ....E 419 287-3288
Pemberville (G-16028)
▲ Hirzel Canning Company ....E 419 693-0531
Northwood (G-15482)
Hirzel Canning Company ....F 419 523-3225
Ottawa (G-15796)
Inter American Products Inc ....E 800 645-2233
Cincinnati (G-3927)
J M Smucker Company ....G 330 497-0073
Canton (G-2743)
◆ J M Smucker Company ....A 330 682-3000
Orrville (G-15742)
JES Foods Inc ....E 216 883-8987
Cleveland (G-5612)
JES Foods/Celina Inc ....E 419 586-7446
Celina (G-3004)
Kraft Heinz Company ....A 330 837-8331
Massillon (G-13165)
Landec Corporation ....D 419 931-1095
Bowling Green (G-1995)
Louis Trauth Dairy LLC ....B 859 431-7553
West Chester (G-20021)
▲ Meiers Wine Cellars Inc ....E 513 891-2900
Cincinnati (G-4082)
Milos Whole World Gourmet LLC ......D 740 589-6456
Athens (G-877)
▲ Natural Country Farms Inc ....G 330 753-2293
Akron (G-311)
▲ Ohio Pure Foods Inc ....D 330 753-2293
Akron (G-326)
Pillsbury Company LLC ....F 740 286-2170
Wellston (G-19767)
Pillsbury Company LLC ....D 419 845-3751
Caledonia (G-2441)
▼ Portion Pac Inc ....B 513 398-0400
Mason (G-13074)
RC Industries Inc ....E 330 879-5486
Navarre (G-14726)
▲ Robert Rothschild Farm LLC ....E 937 653-7397
Urbana (G-19177)
▼ Smucker International Inc ....G 330 682-3000
Orrville (G-15766)
The Fremont Kraut Company ....D 419 332-6481
Fremont (G-10187)
Tip Top Canning Co ....E 937 667-3713
Tipp City (G-18305)
Traditions Sauces LLC ....G 419 704-4506
Toledo (G-18755)
Two Grandmothers Gourmet Kit ....G 614 746-0888
Reynoldsburg (G-16611)
Uncle Jesters Fine Foods LLC ....G 937 550-1025
Miamisburg (G-13873)
▲ Yoders Cider Barn ....F 740 668-4961
Gambier (G-10319)

2034 Dried Fruits, Vegetables & Soup

Dismat Corporation ....G 419 531-8963
Toledo (G-18439)
Green Gourmet Foods LLC ....E 740 400-4212
Baltimore (G-1082)
▲ Hirzel Canning Company ....E 419 693-0531
Northwood (G-15482)
◆ Kanan Enterprises Inc ....C 440 248-8484
Solon (G-17325)

Kanan Enterprises Inc ....F 440 349-0719
Solon (G-17326)
Raw Real and Wonderful LLC ....F 614 529-8606
Hilliard (G-10975)

2035 Pickled Fruits, Vegetables, Sauces & Dressings

Belton Foods ....E 937 890-7768
Dayton (G-8184)
Bob Evans Farms Inc ....B 614 491-2225
New Albany (G-14750)
Consumer Guild Foods Inc ....E 419 726-3406
Toledo (G-18411)
Food Specialties Co ....G 513 761-1242
Cincinnati (G-3766)
Fremont Company ....E 419 363-2924
Rockford (G-16691)
Hinkle Fine Foods Inc ....G 937 836-3665
Englewood (G-9523)
◆ J M Smucker Company ....A 330 682-3000
Orrville (G-15742)
JES Foods/Celina Inc ....E 419 586-7446
Celina (G-3004)
▲ Kaiser Foods Inc ....E 513 621-2053
Cincinnati (G-3969)
Kaiser Foods Inc ....F 513 241-6833
Cincinnati (G-3970)
◆ Lancaster Colony Corporation ....E 614 224-7141
Westerville (G-20166)
Lancaster Colony Corporation ....G 614 792-9774
Westerville (G-20167)
Lancaster Colony Corporation ....D 614 224-7141
Westerville (G-20168)
Lariccias Italian Foods ....F 330 729-0222
Youngstown (G-21132)
Martinez Food Products LLC ....G 419 720-6973
Toledo (G-18575)
▲ Niidex Enterprise LLC ....G 614 653-8526
Columbus (G-7393)
▼ Portion Pac Inc ....B 513 398-0400
Mason (G-13074)
Randys Pickles LLC ....G 440 864-6611
Cleveland (G-6090)
RC Industries Inc ....E 330 879-5486
Navarre (G-14726)
Ribs King Inc ....G 513 791-1942
Cincinnati (G-4341)
▲ Robert Rothschild Farm LLC ....E 937 653-7397
Urbana (G-19177)
SOO Nyeo Won Inc ....G 562 569-8390
Lorain (G-12279)
Sunrise Foods Inc ....E 614 276-2880
Columbus (G-7667)
Tmarzetti Company ....C 614 268-3722
Westerville (G-20192)
◆ Tmarzetti Company ....C 614 846-2232
Westerville (G-20193)
Tmarzetti Company ....G 216 292-5655
Bedford (G-1467)
Tmarzetti Company ....C 614 277-3577
Grove City (G-10602)
Uncle Jesters Fine Foods LLC ....G 937 550-1025
Miamisburg (G-13873)
Waymakers Inc ....G 330 352-1096
Akron (G-469)
Wellys Horseradish ....G 419 334-3134
Fremont (G-10194)
◆ Woeber Mustard Mfg Co ....C 937 323-6281
Springfield (G-17680)

2037 Frozen Fruits, Juices & Vegetables

Beverages Holdings LLC ....E 513 483-3300
Blue Ash (G-1750)
Big Gus Onion Rings Inc ....E 216 883-9045
Cleveland (G-4912)
◆ Country Pure Foods Inc ....C 330 848-6875
Akron (G-131)
Creek Smoothies LLC ....G 937 429-1519
Beavercreek (G-1328)
Cwm Smoothie LLC ....G 419 283-6387
Toledo (G-18421)
Elations Company ....F 513 483-3300
Blue Ash (G-1782)
Griffin Cider Works LLC ....G 440 785-7418
Westlake (G-20273)
Heinz Foreign Investment Co ....G 330 837-8331
Massillon (G-13146)
▲ HJ Heinz Company LP ....A 330 837-8331
Massillon (G-13150)

▲ Lake Erie Frozen Foods Mfg Co ....E 419 289-9204
  Ashland *(G-749)*

National Fruit Vegetable Tech ....E 740 400-4055
  Columbus *(G-7383)*

▲ Natural Country Farms Inc ....G 330 753-2293
  Akron *(G-311)*

▲ Nestle Prepared Foods Company ....A 440 248-3600
  Solon *(G-17344)*

Nestle Prepared Foods Company ....D 440 349-5757
  Solon *(G-17345)*

NRG Smoothies LLC ....G 972 800-1002
  Vienna *(G-19372)*

Old World Foods Inc ....G 216 341-5665
  Cleveland *(G-5937)*

Schwans Home Service Inc ....E 419 222-9977
  Lima *(G-12088)*

Simply Unique Snacks LLC ....G 513 223-7736
  Cincinnati *(G-4422)*

Smoothie Creations Inc ....G 817 313-8212
  Strongsville *(G-17968)*

Smoothie-Licious ....G 513 742-2260
  Batavia *(G-1223)*

Tri-State Special Events Inc ....G 513 221-2962
  Cincinnati *(G-4523)*

Tropical Ohio Smoothie Inc ....G 937 673-6218
  Waynesville *(G-19736)*

2038 Frozen Specialties

Ascot Valley Foods LLC ....G 330 376-9411
  Cuyahoga Falls *(G-7970)*

Athens Foods Inc ....C 216 676-8500
  Cleveland *(G-4853)*

Aunt Minnies Food Services Inc ....F 419 872-4396
  Toledo *(G-18358)*

Bellisio Foods Inc ....A 740 286-5505
  Jackson *(G-11311)*

Brilista Foods Company Inc ....G 614 299-4132
  Columbus *(G-6861)*

Chef 2 Chef Foods ....G 216 696-0080
  Cleveland *(G-5024)*

Classic Recipe Chili Inc ....G 513 771-1441
  Cincinnati *(G-3584)*

Clovervale Farms Inc ....D 440 960-0146
  Amherst *(G-595)*

Empress Chili ....E 513 312-9589
  Blue Ash *(G-1785)*

Frozen Specialties Inc ....C 419 445-9015
  Archbold *(G-674)*

▼ Frozen Specialties Inc ....E 419 445-9015
  Perrysburg *(G-16100)*

▼ Fry Foods Inc ....E 419 448-0831
  Tiffin *(G-18221)*

FSI/Mfp Inc ....G 419 445-9015
  Archbold *(G-675)*

Hudson Village Pizza Inc ....G 330 968-4563
  Stow *(G-17763)*

▲ Kahiki Foods Inc ....C 614 322-3180
  Gahanna *(G-10215)*

King Kold Inc ....G 937 836-2731
  Englewood *(G-9529)*

▲ Lake Erie Frozen Foods Mfg Co .....E 419 289-9204
  Ashland *(G-749)*

◆ Lancaster Colony Corporation ....E 614 224-7141
  Westerville *(G-20166)*

▲ Nestle Prepared Foods Company ...A 440 248-3600
  Solon *(G-17344)*

Nestle Prepared Foods Company ....D 440 349-5757
  Solon *(G-17345)*

Paleomd LLC ....G 248 854-0031
  Bedford *(G-1452)*

Richelieu Foods Inc ....F 740 335-4813
  Wshngtn CT Hs *(G-20924)*

Rsw Distributors LLC ....D 502 587-8877
  Blue Ash *(G-1863)*

Schwans Home Service Inc ....E 937 335-4111
  Troy *(G-18873)*

Skyline Chili Inc ....C 513 874-1188
  Fairfield *(G-9719)*

▲ Stouffer Corporation ....G 440 349-5757
  Solon *(G-17387)*

Sunrise Foods Inc ....E 614 276-2880
  Columbus *(G-7667)*

▲ Worthington Foods Inc ....D 740 453-5501
  Zanesville *(G-21363)*

2041 Flour, Grain Milling

1-2-3 Gluten Free Inc ....G 216 378-9233
  Chagrin Falls *(G-3046)*

Ardent Mills LLC ....F 419 994-4181
  Loudonville *(G-12296)*

Ardent Mills LLC ....E 614 274-2545
  Columbus *(G-6770)*

Bunge North America Foundation ....G 419 483-5340
  Bellevue *(G-1547)*

Cargill Incorporated ....E 937 236-1971
  Dayton *(G-8210)*

Countyline Co-Op Inc ....F 419 287-3241
  Pemberville *(G-16026)*

Crestar Crusts Inc ....B 740 335-4813
  Wshngtn CT Hs *(G-20905)*

Farmers Commission Company ....E 419 294-2371
  Upper Sandusky *(G-19122)*

Fowlers Milling Co Inc ....G 440 286-2024
  Chardon *(G-3154)*

Friends of Bears Mill Inc ....G 937 548-5112
  Greenville *(G-10500)*

General Mills Inc ....D 513 770-0558
  Mason *(G-13026)*

General Mills Inc ....E 513 563-8866
  Cincinnati *(G-3818)*

Grain Craft Inc ....E 216 621-3206
  Cleveland *(G-5444)*

H Nagel & Son Co ....F 513 665-4550
  Cincinnati *(G-3859)*

H Nagel & Son Co ....G 513 665-4550
  Cincinnati *(G-3860)*

Hansen-Mueller Co ....E 419 729-5535
  Toledo *(G-18496)*

I Dream of Cakes ....G 937 533-6024
  Eaton *(G-9310)*

Indie-Peasant Enterprises ....G 740 590-8240
  Athens *(G-872)*

◆ International Multifoods Corp ....G 330 682-3000
  Orrville *(G-15741)*

Jaz Foods Inc ....G 800 456-7115
  Canton *(G-2746)*

Keynes Bros Inc ....E 740 385-6824
  Logan *(G-12181)*

Legacy Farmers Cooperative ....F 419 423-2611
  Findlay *(G-9851)*

Mennel Milling Company ....G 419 436-5130
  Fostoria *(G-9985)*

Mondelez Global LLC ....D 419 691-5200
  Toledo *(G-18591)*

▼ Mullet Enterprises Inc ....G 330 852-4681
  Sugarcreek *(G-18029)*

Mullet Enterprises Inc ....G 330 897-3911
  Bakersville *(G-1063)*

Pettisville Grain Co ....E 419 446-2547
  Pettisville *(G-16182)*

Pillsbury Company LLC ....F 740 286-2170
  Wellston *(G-19767)*

Pillsbury Company LLC ....D 419 845-3751
  Caledonia *(G-2441)*

Pioneer Hi-Bred Intl Inc ....E 419 748-8051
  Grand Rapids *(G-10443)*

Premier Feeds LLC ....G 937 584-2411
  Sabina *(G-16776)*

Star of West Milling Company ....E 330 673-2941
  Kent *(G-11532)*

Sunrise Cooperative Inc ....G 419 929-1568
  Wakeman *(G-19453)*

Sunrise Cooperative Inc ....F 419 628-4705
  Minster *(G-14362)*

2043 Cereal Breakfast Foods

General Mills Inc ....D 513 771-8200
  Cincinnati *(G-3817)*

General Mills Inc ....F 419 269-3100
  Toledo *(G-18479)*

General Mills Inc ....E 513 563-8866
  Cincinnati *(G-3818)*

Kellogg Company ....E 513 772-8980
  Cincinnati *(G-3979)*

Kellogg Company ....B 614 879-9659
  West Jefferson *(G-20080)*

Kellogg Company ....B 330 306-1500
  Warren *(G-19565)*

Kellogg Company ....B 513 792-2700
  Cincinnati *(G-3980)*

Kellogg Company ....A 614 855-3437
  Delaware *(G-8864)*

Kellogg Company ....C 740 453-5501
  Zanesville *(G-21325)*

Niese Farms ....G 419 347-1204
  Crestline *(G-7932)*

Olde Man Granola LLC ....F 419 819-9576
  Findlay *(G-9872)*

▼ Seven Hills Foods Ltd ....G 513 518-3704
  Cincinnati *(G-4410)*

Treehouse Private Brands Inc ....B 740 654-8880
  Lancaster *(G-11758)*

Treehouse Private Brands Inc ....G 740 654-8880
  Lancaster *(G-11759)*

2044 Rice Milling

Cargill Incorporated ....G 513 625-2863
  Goshen *(G-10413)*

2045 Flour, Blended & Prepared

▼ Abitec Corporation ....E 614 429-6464
  Columbus *(G-6678)*

Alamarra Inc ....G 800 336-3007
  Mentor *(G-13516)*

Aspen Mulling Company ....G 970 925-5027
  Bedford *(G-1400)*

Athens Foods Inc ....C 216 676-8500
  Cleveland *(G-4853)*

B & D Commissary LLC ....E 740 743-3890
  Mount Perry *(G-14590)*

B O K Inc ....C 937 322-9588
  Springfield *(G-17520)*

Fleetchem ....F 513 539-1111
  Monroe *(G-14401)*

J M Smucker Company ....E 419 470-7914
  Toledo *(G-18532)*

J M Smucker Company ....E 440 323-5100
  Elyria *(G-9442)*

Mid American Ventures Inc ....F 216 524-0974
  Cleveland *(G-5804)*

▼ Procter & Gamble Mfg Co ....F 513 983-1100
  Cincinnati *(G-4290)*

Rich Products Corporation ....C 614 771-1117
  Hilliard *(G-10976)*

2046 Wet Corn Milling

Cargill Incorporated ....E 937 236-1971
  Dayton *(G-8210)*

Tate Lyle Ingrdnts Amricas LLC ....D 937 235-4074
  Dayton *(G-8704)*

2047 Dog & Cat Food

About and Dogs LLC ....G 440 263-8989
  Hudson *(G-11153)*

Big Heart Pet Brands ....C 412 222-2200
  Orrville *(G-15731)*

Bil-Jac Foods Inc ....E 330 722-7888
  Medina *(G-13377)*

G & C Raw LLC ....G 937 827-0010
  Versailles *(G-19348)*

Hartz Mountain Corporation ....D 513 877-2131
  Pleasant Plain *(G-16372)*

▲ IAMS Company ....B 800 675-3849
  Mason *(G-13038)*

IAMS Company ....C 419 943-4267
  Leipsic *(G-11870)*

IAMS Company ....D 937 962-2624
  Lewisburg *(G-11935)*

In Good Hlth & Animal Wellness ....G 330 908-1234
  Northfield *(G-15467)*

▼ Kelly Foods Corporation ....E 330 722-8855
  Medina *(G-13433)*

Lakeshore Feed & Seed Inc ....G 216 961-5729
  Cleveland *(G-5677)*

Land OLakes Inc ....E 330 879-2158
  Massillon *(G-13166)*

Lucky Paws LLC ....G 859 620-2525
  Cincinnati *(G-4037)*

Mars Petcare Us Inc ....E 614 878-7242
  Columbus *(G-7319)*

Nestle Purina Petcare Company ....D 740 454-8575
  Zanesville *(G-21332)*

Nom Nom Nom ....G 614 302-4815
  Columbus *(G-7396)*

Ohio Blenders Inc ....F 419 726-2655
  Toledo *(G-18615)*

◆ Ohio Pet Foods Inc ....E 330 424-1431
  Lisbon *(G-12130)*

Pro-Pet LLC ....E 419 394-3374
  Saint Marys *(G-16849)*

◆ Pro-Pet LLC ....G 419 394-3374
  Saint Marys *(G-16850)*

Rex M & Kim P Bellville ....F 937 256-2526
  Dayton *(G-8628)*

Royal Canin USA Inc ....G 937 962-7352
  Lewisburg *(G-11941)*

▲ Vitakraft Sun Seed Inc ....D 419 832-1641
  Weston *(G-20327)*

SIC

2048 Prepared Feeds For Animals & Fowls

2nd Roe LLC ....G...... 419 499-3031
Monroeville *(G-14423)*

Agri-Products Inc ....G...... 216 831-5890
Cleveland *(G-4732)*

Archer-Daniels-Midland Company ......E...... 419 435-6633
Fostoria *(G-9966)*

Archer-Daniels-Midland Company ......G...... 330 852-3025
Sugarcreek *(G-18015)*

Archer-Daniels-Midland Company ......G...... 419 705-3292
Toledo *(G-18353)*

Buckeye Feed & Grain.........................G...... 937 526-3914
Versailles *(G-19342)*

Centerra Co-Op ....E...... 330 769-3469
Seville *(G-17072)*

Centerra Co-Op ....E...... 800 362-9598
Jefferson *(G-11358)*

Centerra Co-Op ....E...... 419 281-2153
Ashland *(G-717)*

Commodity Blenders Inc ....E...... 419 846-3155
West Salem *(G-20112)*

Cooper Farms Inc ....D...... 419 375-4116
Fort Recovery *(G-9946)*

Cooper Farms Inc ....E...... 419 375-4119
Fort Recovery *(G-9947)*

Cooper Farms Inc ....F...... 419 375-4619
Fort Recovery *(G-9948)*

Cooper Hatchery Inc ....C...... 419 594-3325
Oakwood *(G-15615)*

Direct Action Co Inc ....F...... 330 364-3219
Dover *(G-8976)*

Edward Keiter & Sons ....G...... 937 382-3249
Wilmington *(G-20664)*

Four Natures Keepers Inc ....F...... 740 363-8007
Delaware *(G-8845)*

G A Wintzer and Son Company ....D...... 419 739-4913
Wapakoneta *(G-19485)*

Geauga Feed and Grain Supply.........G...... 440 564-5000
Newbury *(G-15092)*

Gerber & Sons Inc ....G...... 330 897-6201
Baltic *(G-1072)*

Granville Milling Co ....G...... 740 345-1305
Newark *(G-15015)*

▲ Hamlet Protein Inc ....E...... 567 525-5627
Findlay *(G-9835)*

Hanby Farms Inc ....E...... 740 763-3554
Nashport *(G-14705)*

Hartz Mountain Corporation ....D...... 513 877-2131
Pleasant Plain *(G-16372)*

▲ Holmes By Products Co ....E...... 330 893-2322
Millersburg *(G-14228)*

▲ IAMS Company................................B...... 800 675-3849
Mason *(G-13038)*

◆ International Multifoods Corp ....G...... 330 682-3000
Orrville *(G-15741)*

J & B Feed Co Inc ....G...... 419 335-5821
Wauseon *(G-19685)*

Jroll LLC ....F...... 330 661-0600
Medina *(G-13430)*

Juana Williams ....G...... 614 351-9844
Columbus *(G-7247)*

▲ Kalmbach Feeds Inc ....C...... 419 294-3838
Upper Sandusky *(G-19127)*

▼ Kelly Foods Corporation ....E...... 330 722-8855
Medina *(G-13433)*

Lakeshore Feed & Seed Inc ....G...... 216 961-5729
Cleveland *(G-5677)*

Land OLakes Inc ....E...... 330 879-2158
Massillon *(G-13166)*

Le Summer Kidron Inc ....E...... 330 857-2031
Apple Creek *(G-642)*

Legacy Farmers Cooperative............F...... 419 423-2611
Findlay *(G-9851)*

Lizzie Maes Birdseed & Dg Co...........G...... 330 927-1795
Rittman *(G-16678)*

▲ Magnus International Group Inc ....G...... 216 592-8355
Chagrin Falls *(G-3100)*

Manco Inc ....G...... 937 962-2661
Lewisburg *(G-11937)*

Mid-Wood Inc ....F...... 419 257-3331
North Baltimore *(G-15195)*

Nature Pure LLC.................................E...... 937 358-2364
Raymond *(G-16576)*

Occidental Chemical Corp ....E...... 513 242-2900
Cincinnati *(G-4172)*

Ocean Providence Columbus LLC.....G...... 614 272-5973
Columbus *(G-7411)*

Ohio Blenders Inc ....F...... 419 726-2655
Toledo *(G-18615)*

◆ Ohio Pet Foods Inc ....E...... 330 424-1431
Lisbon *(G-12130)*

Pettisville Grain Co ....E...... 419 446-2547
Pettisville *(G-16182)*

Premier Feeds LLC ....G...... 937 584-2411
Sabina *(G-16776)*

Pro-Pet LLC ....E...... 419 394-3374
Saint Marys *(G-16849)*

◆ Pro-Pet LLC ....G...... 419 394-3374
Saint Marys *(G-16850)*

Provimi North America Inc ....D...... 937 770-2400
Lewisburg *(G-11940)*

◆ Provimi North America Inc ....B...... 937 770-2400
Brookville *(G-2197)*

Psd Partners LLC ....F...... 419 294-3838
Carey *(G-2925)*

Purina Mills LLC ....G...... 330 682-1951
Orrville *(G-15755)*

▼ Republic Mills Inc ....F...... 419 758-3511
Okolona *(G-15669)*

Ridley USA Inc ....F...... 800 837-8222
Botkins *(G-1953)*

Ridley USA Inc ....F...... 937 693-6393
Botkins *(G-1954)*

Rogers Mill Inc ....G...... 330 227-3214
Rogers *(G-16715)*

Rowe Premix Inc ....F...... 937 678-9015
West Manchester *(G-20098)*

Stahl Farm Market ....F...... 330 325-0640
Ravenna *(G-16562)*

Sunny Side Feeds LLC ....G...... 330 635-1455
West Salem *(G-20117)*

Sunrise Cooperative Inc ....G...... 419 629-2338
New Bremen *(G-14794)*

Superior Ag-Patoka Vlly Feed ....F...... 419 294-3838
Upper Sandusky *(G-19142)*

Tenda Horse Products LLC ....G...... 740 694-8836
Fredericktown *(G-10111)*

Terry A Johnson ....G...... 614 561-0706
Etna *(G-9552)*

Toledo Alfalfa Mills Inc ....G...... 419 836-3705
Oregon *(G-15720)*

Verhoff Alfalfa Mills Inc ....G...... 419 653-4161
New Bavaria *(G-14776)*

▼ Verhoff Alfalfa Mills Inc ....G...... 419 523-4767
Ottawa *(G-15813)*

▲ Vitakraft Sun Seed Inc ....D...... 419 832-1641
Weston *(G-20327)*

Woodstock Products Inc ....G...... 216 641-3811
Cleveland *(G-6477)*

Yarnell Bros Inc ....G...... 419 278-2831
Deshler *(G-8952)*

2051 Bread, Bakery Prdts Exc Cookies & Crackers

614 Cupcakes LLC ....G...... 614 245-8800
New Albany *(G-14744)*

7 Little Cupcakes ....G...... 419 252-0858
Perrysburg *(G-16060)*

A Bun In Oven ....G...... 419 559-3056
Fremont *(G-10121)*

A Cupcake A Day LLC........................G...... 330 389-1247
Stow *(G-17727)*

A Pop of Elegance LLC ....G...... 330 225-4724
Brunswick *(G-2201)*

A Spoon Fulla Sugar LLC...................F...... 513 683-0444
Cincinnati *(G-3336)*

Abby Girl Sweets Cupcakery ....G...... 513 335-0898
Cincinnati *(G-3343)*

▲ Alfred Nickles Bakery Inc ....B...... 330 879-5635
Navarre *(G-14708)*

Alfred Nickles Bakery Inc ....E...... 740 453-6522
Zanesville *(G-21269)*

Alfred Nickles Bakery Inc ....F...... 937 256-3762
Dayton *(G-8143)*

Amish Door Inc ....C...... 330 359-5464
Wilmot *(G-20683)*

An Baiceir Bakery ....G...... 740 739-0501
Etna *(G-9554)*

Angry Cupcakes Productions LLC......G...... 216 229-2394
Cleveland *(G-4813)*

Atlas Produce LLC ....G...... 937 223-1446
Dayton *(G-8168)*

Auntie Annes ....G...... 330 652-1939
Niles *(G-15144)*

B & J Baking Company Inc ....F...... 513 541-2386
Cincinnati *(G-3432)*

B L F Enterprises Inc ....F...... 937 642-6425
Westerville *(G-20201)*

Bake ME Happy LLC ....G...... 614 477-3642
Columbus *(G-6802)*

Baked & More LLC ....G...... 330 324-4981
Louisville *(G-12309)*

Bakehouse Bread Co Inc ....E...... 937 339-8100
Troy *(G-18807)*

Bakers Choice Distributing ....G...... 330 273-5745
Brunswick *(G-2210)*

Beckers Bakeshop Inc ....F...... 216 752-4161
Cleveland *(G-4901)*

◆ Berlin Natural Bakery Inc ....E...... 330 893-2734
Berlin *(G-1645)*

Bimbo Bakeries Usa Inc ....G...... 419 726-6183
Toledo *(G-18367)*

Bimbo Bakeries Usa Inc ....E...... 740 797-4449
The Plains *(G-18183)*

Bimbo Bakeries Usa Inc ....E...... 740 797-4449
The Plains *(G-18184)*

Bites Baking Company LLC ....G...... 614 457-6092
Dublin *(G-9055)*

Blue Cottage Bakery LLC ....G...... 216 221-9733
Lakewood *(G-11658)*

Bonbonneri Inc ....F...... 513 321-3399
Cincinnati *(G-3458)*

Borden Bakers Inc ....G...... 614 457-9800
Columbus *(G-6847)*

Bread Kneads Inc ....G...... 419 422-3863
Findlay *(G-9801)*

Breaking Bread Pizza Company ....E...... 614 754-4777
Lewis Center *(G-11891)*

Buns of Delaware Inc ....E...... 740 363-2867
Delaware *(G-8826)*

Busken Bakery Inc ....G...... 513 671-8454
Cincinnati *(G-3488)*

Busken Bakery Inc ....G...... 513 791-6736
Cincinnati *(G-3489)*

Cake Arts Supplies ....G...... 419 472-4959
Toledo *(G-18387)*

Calvary Christian Ch of Ohio ....E...... 740 828-9000
Frazeysburg *(G-10071)*

Carlas Cake Pops Cnfctions LLC ......G...... 614 321-9280
Columbus *(G-6909)*

Caryns Cuisine ....G...... 614 237-4143
Columbus *(G-6915)*

Champa Ventures LLC ....G...... 614 726-1801
Dublin *(G-9062)*

Cincy Cupcakes LLC ....G...... 513 985-4440
Cincinnati *(G-3572)*

Colossal Cupcakes ....G...... 216 322-7656
Lakewood *(G-11660)*

Cora Cupcakes ....G...... 440 227-7145
Painesville *(G-15870)*

Country Crust Bakery ....G...... 888 860-2940
Bainbridge *(G-1057)*

Crispie Creme of Chillicothe ....E...... 740 774-3770
Chillicothe *(G-3235)*

Crumbs Inc ....F...... 740 592-3803
Athens *(G-859)*

Cupcake Divaz ....G...... 216 509-3850
North Ridgeville *(G-15365)*

Cupcake Wishes ....G...... 440 315-3856
North Ridgeville *(G-15366)*

Cupcake Wishes Ltd ....G...... 440 934-5550
Avon *(G-992)*

Cupcakes For A Cure..........................G...... 419 764-1719
Perrysburg *(G-16080)*

Dandi Enterprises Inc ....F...... 419 516-9070
Solon *(G-17282)*

Danis Sweet Cupcakes ....G...... 614 581-8978
Centerburg *(G-3030)*

Desserts By Sandy LLC ....G...... 513 385-8755
Cincinnati *(G-3650)*

Destination Donuts LLC ....G...... 614 370-0754
Columbus *(G-7022)*

Dulcelicious Cupcakes and More ....G...... 440 385-7706
Cleveland *(G-5221)*

DUrso Bakery Inc ....F...... 330 652-4741
Niles *(G-15150)*

Dutch Cntry Apple Dmplings Inc........D...... 330 683-0646
Orrville *(G-15735)*

East Balt Ohio LLC ....G...... 740 454-6876
Zanesville *(G-21303)*

East Balt Ohio LLC ....G...... 740 454-6876
Zanesville *(G-21304)*

East Balt Us LLC ....G...... 740 454-6876
Zanesville *(G-21305)*

Eat Moore Cupcakes...........................G...... 513 713-8139
Batavia *(G-1178)*

Empire Bakery Commissary LLC ....C...... 513 793-6241
Blue Ash *(G-1784)*

Evans Bakery Inc G 937 228-4151
Dayton *(G-8334)*
Fields Associates Inc G 513 426-8652
Cincinnati *(G-3755)*
Flowers Bakeries LLC E 330 724-1604
Akron *(G-191)*
Fragapane Bakeries Inc G 440 779-6050
North Olmsted *(G-15335)*
Garys Chesecakes Fine Desserts G 513 574-1700
Cincinnati *(G-3800)*
George Weston Co G 614 868-7565
Columbus *(G-7110)*
Georges Donuts Inc G 330 963-9902
Twinsburg *(G-18945)*
Geyers Markets Inc D 419 468-9477
Galion *(G-10271)*
Gibson Bros Inc E 440 774-2401
Oberlin *(G-15641)*
Gigis Cupcakes of Kenwood G 513 985-4440
Cincinnati *(G-3823)*
Giminetti Baking Company E 513 751-7655
Cincinnati *(G-3826)*
Glorious Cupcakes G 216 544-2325
Medina *(G-13418)*
Gluten-Free Expressions G 740 928-0338
Hebron *(G-10868)*
Go Cupcake G 937 299-4985
Dayton *(G-8374)*
Graeters Manufacturing Co D 513 721-3323
Cincinnati *(G-3843)*
▼ **Grandmas Fruit Cakes** G 614 761-1118
Dublin *(G-9080)*
Hannibal Co Inc F 614 846-5060
Worthington *(G-20870)*
Heinens Inc D 330 562-5297
Aurora *(G-924)*
Hoffmans Country Market G 740 216-0115
Logan *(G-12179)*
Home Bakery F 419 678-3018
Coldwater *(G-6564)*
◆ **Hot Mama Foods Inc** F 419 474-3402
Toledo *(G-18513)*
I Heart Cupcakes G 614 787-3896
Columbus *(G-7179)*
International Multifoods Corp G 440 323-5100
Elyria *(G-9432)*
J M Smucker Company E 440 323-5100
Elyria *(G-9442)*
▲ **Jasmine Distributing Ltd** E 216 251-9420
Cleveland *(G-5608)*
Jeffs Bakery G 937 890-9703
Dayton *(G-8427)*
Jims Donut Shop G 937 898-4222
Vandalia *(G-19298)*
Jtm Provisions Company Inc B 513 367-4900
Harrison *(G-10787)*
K & B Acquisitions Inc F 937 253-1163
Dayton *(G-8432)*
K Cupcakes G 440 576-3464
Jefferson *(G-11362)*
Kellogg Company B 513 271-3500
Cincinnati *(G-3978)*
Kennedys Bakery Inc E 740 432-2301
Cambridge *(G-2461)*
Klosterman G 419 242-3400
Toledo *(G-18546)*
Klosterman Baking Co E 513 242-5667
Cincinnati *(G-3995)*
Klosterman Baking Co F 513 398-2707
Mason *(G-13053)*
Klosterman Baking Co G 614 338-8111
Columbus *(G-7264)*
Klosterman Baking Co D 513 242-1004
Cincinnati *(G-3996)*
Klosterman Baking Co Inc E 937 322-9588
Springfield *(G-17587)*
Klosterman Baking Co Inc G 937 743-9021
Springboro *(G-17487)*
Kmart Supercenter G 440 974-7300
Cleveland *(G-5660)*
Krispy Kreme Doughnut Corp F 614 798-0812
Columbus *(G-7268)*
Kroger Co C 513 742-9500
Cincinnati *(G-4004)*
Kroger Co C 937 743-5900
Springboro *(G-17488)*
Kroger Co C 740 335-4030
Wshngtn CT Hs *(G-20915)*
Kroger Co C 740 264-5057
Steubenville *(G-17702)*
Kroger Co D 419 423-2065
Findlay *(G-9848)*
Kroger Co C 614 263-1766
Columbus *(G-7271)*
Kroger Co C 614 575-3742
Columbus *(G-7272)*
Kroger Co C 740 671-5164
Bellaire *(G-1499)*
Kroger Co D 513 683-4001
Maineville *(G-12526)*
Kroger Co C 937 277-0950
Dayton *(G-8447)*
Kroger Co D 740 374-2523
Marietta *(G-12798)*
Kustom Cases LLC G 240 380-6275
Dayton *(G-8448)*
M Mazzone & Sons Bakery Inc G 216 631-6511
Cleveland *(G-5718)*
Main Street Gourmet LLC C 330 929-0000
Cuyahoga Falls *(G-8022)*
Martans Foods G 330 483-9009
Valley City *(G-19215)*
McHappys Donuts of Parkersburg G 740 593-8744
Athens *(G-875)*
McL Inc D 614 861-6259
Columbus *(G-7336)*
Meeks Pastry Shop G 419 782-4871
Defiance *(G-8803)*
Morselicious Cupcakes G 216 408-7508
Brookpark *(G-2167)*
Mustard Seed Health Fd Mkt Inc E 440 519-3663
Solon *(G-17342)*
My Lady Muffins LLC G 937 854-5317
Dayton *(G-8516)*
Nanak Bakery G 614 882-0882
Westerville *(G-20226)*
Nanbrands LLC G 513 313-9581
Cincinnati *(G-4136)*
New Bakery of Zanesville LLC B 614 764-3100
Dublin *(G-9112)*
New Horizon Baking Company G 567 315-8703
Toledo *(G-18602)*
New Horizons Baking Company C 419 668-8226
Norwalk *(G-15553)*
New York Frozen Foods Inc B 216 292-5655
Bedford *(G-1447)*
Nikkicakes G 330 606-5745
Cuyahoga Falls *(G-8029)*
Norcia Bakery E 330 454-1077
Canton *(G-2790)*
Olde Home Market LLC G 614 738-3975
Grove City *(G-10580)*
▲ **Orlando Baking Company** C 216 361-1872
Cleveland *(G-5948)*
Osmans Pies Inc E 330 607-9083
Stow *(G-17786)*
Perfection Bakeries Inc D 614 866-8171
Blacklick *(G-1703)*
Perfection Bakeries Inc D 419 221-2359
Lima *(G-12068)*
Perfection Bakeries Inc E 513 942-1442
West Chester *(G-20035)*
Perfection Bakeries Inc D 937 492-2220
Sidney *(G-17208)*
Perkins & Marie Callenders LLC C 513 881-7900
Fairfield *(G-9702)*
Pesce Baking Company Ltd E 330 746-6537
Youngstown *(G-21170)*
Pf Management Inc G 513 874-8741
West Chester *(G-20036)*
Pierre Holding Corp G 513 874-8741
West Chester *(G-20037)*
Polkadot Cupcakery Limited G 614 304-1368
Columbus *(G-7502)*
Quality Bakery Company Inc G 614 846-2232
Westerville *(G-20181)*
Quality Bakery Company Inc E 614 224-1424
Columbus *(G-7534)*
Reineckers Bakery Ltd G 330 467-2221
Macedonia *(G-12480)*
Rich Products Corporation C 614 771-1117
Hilliard *(G-10976)*
Riesbeck Food Markets Inc C 740 695-3401
Saint Clairsville *(G-16806)*
Royal Gateau G 216 351-3553
Cleveland *(G-6138)*
Rudys Strudel Shop G 440 886-4430
Cleveland *(G-6143)*
Saras Little Cupcakes G 419 305-7914
Saint Marys *(G-16854)*
Schulers Bakery Inc E 937 323-4154
Springfield *(G-17647)*
Schwebel Baking Company B 330 783-2860
Youngstown *(G-21197)*
Schwebel Baking Company C 440 846-1921
Strongsville *(G-17961)*
Schwebel Baking Company G 740 435-9857
Cambridge *(G-2475)*
Schwebel Baking Company D 330 783-2860
Hebron *(G-10884)*
Schwebel Baking Company C 440 248-1500
Solon *(G-17376)*
Servatii Inc F 513 231-4455
Cincinnati *(G-4406)*
Servatii Inc F 513 271-5040
Cincinnati *(G-4407)*
Sifted Sweet Shop LLC G 216 901-7100
Youngstown *(G-21203)*
Sinful Sweets LLC G 330 721-0916
Medina *(G-13481)*
Slice of Heaven Bakery G 419 656-6606
Clyde *(G-6547)*
Smashing Events and Baking G 513 415-9693
Cincinnati *(G-3318)*
Squire Shoppe Bakery G 440 964-3303
Ashtabula *(G-839)*
Steubenville Bakery G 740 282-6851
Steubenville *(G-17714)*
Sugar Shack G 419 961-4016
Mansfield *(G-12686)*
Sweet GS Cupcakery Ltd G 419 610-8507
Columbus *(G-7671)*
Sweet Mobile Cupcakery G 440 465-7333
Bay Village *(G-1246)*
Sweet Persuasions LLC G 614 216-9052
Pickerington *(G-16206)*
Ta Die For Gourmet Cupcakes G 740 751-4586
Marion *(G-12905)*
▲ **Taste of Belgium LLC** G 513 381-3280
Cincinnati *(G-4494)*
Thurns Bakery & Deli E 614 221-9246
Columbus *(G-7693)*
Trumbull Mobile Meals Inc F 330 394-2538
Warren *(G-19615)*
Unger Kosher Bakery Inc E 216 321-7176
Cleveland Heights *(G-6502)*
Wal-Bon of Ohio Inc F 740 423-6351
Belpre *(G-1595)*
Wal-Bon of Ohio Inc D 740 423-8178
Belpre *(G-1596)*
Were Rolling Pretzle Company G 419 784-0762
Defiance *(G-8813)*
▲ **White Castle System Inc** B 614 228-5781
Columbus *(G-7761)*
You Dough Girl LLC G 330 207-5031
Salem *(G-16937)*

2052 Cookies & Crackers

Adrians Place G 513 651-2154
Cincinnati *(G-3357)*
Annes Auntie Pretzels E 614 418-7021
Columbus *(G-6758)*
B L F Enterprises Inc F 937 642-6425
Westerville *(G-20201)*
Basic Grain Products Inc D 419 678-2304
Coldwater *(G-6553)*
Beckers Bakeshop Inc F 216 752-4161
Cleveland *(G-4901)*
▲ **Cheryl & Co** C 614 776-1500
Westerville *(G-20144)*
Cheryl & Co D 614 776-1500
Obetz *(G-15653)*
Cleveland Bean Sprout Inc F 216 881-2112
Cleveland *(G-5049)*
Consolidated Biscuit Company F 419 293-2911
Mc Comb *(G-13336)*
Cookie Bouquets Inc G 614 888-2171
Columbus *(G-6980)*
CTB Consulting LLC F 216 712-7764
Rocky River *(G-16697)*
Four Generations Inc G 330 784-2243
Lakemore *(G-11644)*
Frischco Inc G 740 363-7537
Delaware *(G-8846)*
Good Fortunes Inc F 440 942-2888
Willoughby *(G-20500)*
Great American Cookie Company F 419 474-9417
Toledo *(G-18486)*
Hearthside Food Solutions LLC E 419 727-1298
Toledo *(G-18500)*

Hearthside Food Solutions LLC ....A 419 293-2911
Mc Comb (G-13338)
Hen of Woods LLC ....G 513 833-7357
Cincinnati (G-3877)
J & J Snack Foods Corp ....G 440 248-2084
Solon (G-17319)
Jagger Cone Company Inc ....G 419 682-1816
Stryker (G-18004)
K & R Pretzel Co ....G 937 299-2231
Dayton (G-8433)
Keebler Company ....E 513 271-3500
Cincinnati (G-3976)
Keebler Company ....E 614 836-3094
Columbus (G-7253)
Keebler Company ....E 513 671-0880
Cincinnati (G-3977)
Kellogg Company ....B 513 271-3500
Cincinnati (G-3978)
Kennedys Bakery Inc ....E 740 432-2301
Cambridge (G-2461)
Kroger Co ....C 740 671-5164
Bellaire (G-1499)
Kroger Co ....D 614 462-2000
Columbus (G-7270)
Kroger Co ....D 513 683-4001
Maineville (G-12526)
Kroger Co ....C 937 277-0950
Dayton (G-8447)
Kroger Co ....D 740 374-2523
Marietta (G-12798)
Lenas Amish Granola ....G 330 600-1599
Shreve (G-17160)
◆ LLC Brand Castle ....F 216 292-7700
Bedford Heights (G-1487)
Main Street Gourmet LLC ....C 330 929-0000
Cuyahoga Falls (G-8022)
Mar Chele Inc ....G 937 833-3400
Brookville (G-2188)
Nonnies Goodies LLC ....G 419 435-4685
Fostoria (G-9989)
Norcia Bakery ....E 330 454-1077
Canton (G-2790)
▼ Norse Dairy Systems LP ....B 614 421-5297
Columbus (G-7398)
Osmans Pies Inc ....G 330 607-9083
Stow (G-17786)
Patjim Holdings Company ....F 419 727-1298
Toledo (G-18635)
Pepperidge Farm Incorporated ....G 419 933-2611
Willard (G-20399)
Rudys Strudel Shop ....G 440 886-4430
Cleveland (G-6143)
Rykrisp Llc ....G 843 338-0750
Cincinnati (G-4371)
S-L Distribution Company Inc ....G 440 786-9990
Bedford (G-1458)
S-L Snacks Real Estate Inc ....B 440 786-9990
Bedford (G-1459)
Schulers Bakery Inc ....E 937 323-4154
Springfield (G-17647)
Shades of Sugar Ltd ....G 614 776-5998
Galena (G-10249)
Snyders-Lance Inc ....G 614 856-4616
Grove City (G-10596)
Snyders-Lance Inc ....C 419 289-0787
Ashland (G-778)
Y Z Enterprises Inc ....E 419 893-8777
Maumee (G-13310)

2053 Frozen Bakery Prdts

Atk2 Inc ....G 513 661-5869
Cincinnati (G-3424)
Bartells Cupcakery ....G 330 957-1793
Austintown (G-969)
Beautiful Bites ....G 937 397-4225
Xenia (G-20938)
Chefs Pantry Inc ....G 440 288-0146
Amherst (G-594)
Cleveland Bagel Company LLC ....G 216 385-7723
Cleveland (G-5048)
Junebugs Cupcaked ....G 937 723-9040
Dayton (G-8430)
Kissicakes - N-Sweets LLC ....G 614 940-2779
Columbus (G-7263)
Main Street Gourmet LLC ....C 330 929-0000
Cuyahoga Falls (G-8022)
Mammas Mandel ....G 513 827-2457
Mason (G-13059)

2063 Sugar, Beet

Michigan Sugar Company ....F 419 332-9931
Fremont (G-10170)
Michigan Sugar Company ....G 419 423-1666
Findlay (G-9860)

2064 Candy & Confectionery Prdts

69 Taps ....G 330 253-4554
Akron (G-14)
Al Meda Chocolates Inc ....G 419 446-2676
Archbold (G-661)
American Health Packaging ....D 614 492-8177
Columbus (G-6738)
▲ Anthony-Thomas Candy Company ..C .. 614 274-8405
Columbus (G-6759)
Anthony-Thomas Candy Company ....G 614 870-8899
Columbus (G-6760)
Arnolds Candies Inc ....G 330 733-4022
Akron (G-73)
Becky Knapp ....G 330 854-4400
Canal Fulton (G-2498)
Buckeye Chocolate Co ....F 440 564-8086
Middlefield (G-13919)
Celebrations ....G 419 381-8088
Toledo (G-18391)
Chocolate Pig Inc ....G 440 461-4511
Cleveland (G-5029)
Christies Candies & Mints ....G 419 382-7313
Toledo (G-18397)
Cincinnatti Premier Candy LLC ....E 513 253-0079
Cincinnati (G-3571)
Coffelt Candy Inc ....G 937 399-8772
Springfield (G-17533)
Coons Homemade Candies ....G 740 496-4141
Harpster (G-10765)
Crawford Acquisition Corp ....F 216 486-0702
Cleveland (G-5141)
Daffins Candies ....G 330 545-0325
Girard (G-10385)
◆ Decko Products Inc ....D 419 626-5757
Sandusky (G-16957)
Doschers Candies Inc ....F 513 381-8656
Cincinnati (G-3666)
E R B Enterprises Inc ....G 740 948-9174
Jeffersonville (G-11379)
Ervan Guttman Co ....G 513 791-0767
Cincinnati (G-3718)
Fawn Confectionery ....F 513 574-9612
Cincinnati (G-3742)
Giannios Candy Co Inc ....E 330 755-7000
Struthers (G-17991)
Gibson Bros Inc ....E 440 774-2401
Oberlin (G-15641)
Gift Cove Inc ....G 419 285-2920
Put In Bay (G-16498)
Good Nutrition LLC ....F 216 534-6617
Oakwood Village (G-15624)
Graeters Manufacturing Co ....D 513 721-3323
Cincinnati (G-3843)
Great Lakes Popcorn Company ....G 419 732-3080
Port Clinton (G-16401)
Gwen Rosenberg Enterprises LLC ....G 330 678-1893
Kent (G-11465)
▲ Hake Head LLC ....E 614 291-2244
Columbus (G-7138)
Humphrey Company ....F 216 662-6629
Cleveland (G-5537)
Kevin G Ryba Inc ....G 419 627-2010
Huron (G-11230)
Light Vision ....E 513 351-9444
Cincinnati (G-4023)
▲ Malleys Candies ....D 216 362-8700
Lakewood (G-11674)
Malleys Candies Inc ....G 216 529-6262
Cleveland (G-5736)
Marrie S Candies LLC ....E 937 465-3061
West Liberty (G-20094)
Marshas Buckeyes LLC ....G 419 872-7666
Perrysburg (G-16120)
▲ McJak Candy Company LLC ....E 330 722-3531
Medina (G-13441)
Milk & Honey ....F 330 492-5884
Canton (G-2782)
Nestle R&D Center Inc ....F 440 349-5757
Solon (G-17346)
Neumeisters Candy Shoppe LLC ......G 419 294-3647
Upper Sandusky (G-19135)
Normant Candy Co ....F 419 886-4214
Mansfield (G-12659)

PA & Jjs Fruity Smiles Inc ....G 937 449-0999
Dayton (G-8560)
Piqua Chocolate Company Inc ....G 937 773-1981
Piqua (G-16301)
Popped ....F 330 678-1893
Kent (G-11504)
Rcs Brewhouse ....G 440 984-3103
Amherst (G-607)
Richards Maple Products Inc ....G 440 286-4160
Chardon (G-3176)
Snyders-Lance Inc ....G 614 856-4616
Grove City (G-10596)
Suzin L Chocolatiers ....F 440 323-3372
Elyria (G-9496)
Sweet Melissas ....G 440 333-6357
Rocky River (G-16712)
Temos Inc ....B 330 376-7229
Akron (G-432)
Walnut Creek Chocolate Company ....E 330 893-2995
Walnut Creek (G-19471)
White House Chocolate ....G 440 834-3133
Middlefield (G-14005)
Wittichs Candies Inc ....G 740 474-3313
Circleville (G-4649)
Yost Candy Co ....E 330 828-2777
Dalton (G-8081)
Zanesville Cnfectionary Hse LLC ......E 740 452-7501
Zanesville (G-21369)

2066 Chocolate & Cocoa Prdts

American Confections Co LLC ....G 614 888-8838
Columbus (G-6734)
▲ Anthony-Thomas Candy Company ..C .. 614 274-8405
Columbus (G-6759)
Becky Knapp ....G 330 854-4400
Canal Fulton (G-2498)
▲ Benjamin P Forbes Company ....F 440 838-4400
Broadview Heights (G-2104)
Brandts Candies ....G 440 942-1016
Willoughby (G-20445)
Brownie Points Inc ....G 614 860-8470
Columbus (G-6868)
Campbells Candies ....G 330 493-1805
Canton (G-2635)
Cheryl & Co ....D 614 776-1500
Obetz (G-15653)
Chocolate Pig Inc ....G 440 461-4511
Cleveland (G-5029)
Dietsch Brothers Incorporated ....E 419 422-4474
Findlay (G-9816)
E R B Enterprises Inc ....G 740 948-9174
Jeffersonville (G-11379)
Fannie May Cnfctons Brands Inc ......A 330 494-0833
North Canton (G-15230)
Fawn Confectionery ....F 513 574-9612
Cincinnati (G-3742)
Giannios Candy Co Inc ....E 330 755-7000
Struthers (G-17991)
Godiva Chocolatier Inc ....E 216 831-9414
Beachwood (G-1273)
Golden Turtle Chocolate Fctry ....G 513 932-1990
Lebanon (G-11805)
Gorant Chocolatier LLC ....C 330 726-8821
Boardman (G-1921)
Graeters Manufacturing Co ....D 513 721-3323
Cincinnati (G-3843)
▲ Harry London Candies Inc ....C 330 494-0833
North Canton (G-15239)
Hartville Chocolates Inc ....F 330 877-1999
Hartville (G-10822)
Haute Chocolate Inc ....E 513 793-9999
Montgomery (G-14432)
Hershey Creamery Co ....G 937 374-0688
Xenia (G-20955)
▼ L C F Inc ....E 330 877-3322
Hartville (G-10828)
Mageros Candies ....G 330 534-1146
Hubbard (G-11134)
▲ Malleys Candies ....D 216 362-8700
Lakewood (G-11674)
Malleys Candies Inc ....G 216 529-6262
Cleveland (G-5736)
Maverick Chocolate Company ....G 513 381-0561
Cincinnati (G-4068)
Milk & Honey ....G 330 492-5884
Canton (G-2782)
Neumeisters Candy Shoppe LLC ......G 419 294-3647
Upper Sandusky (G-19135)
Robert E McGrath Inc ....E 440 572-7747
Strongsville (G-17959)

Sugars Sweets Ltd ....G 513 936-0104
Cincinnati *(G-4474)*

Walnut Creek Chocolate Company ....E 330 893-2995
Walnut Creek *(G-19471)*

2068 Salted & Roasted Nuts & Seeds

▲ Anthony-Thomas Candy Company ..C 614 274-8405
Columbus *(G-6759)*

Back Development LLC ....G 937 671-7896
Cleveland *(G-4887)*

◆ Kanan Enterprises Inc ....C 440 248-8484
Solon *(G-17325)*

Kanan Enterprises Inc ....F 440 349-0719
Solon *(G-17326)*

▲ Malleys Candies ....D 216 362-8700
Lakewood *(G-11674)*

Nuts Are Good Inc ....F 586 619-2400
Columbus *(G-7406)*

Simply Unique Snacks LLC ....G 513 223-7736
Cincinnati *(G-4422)*

Southside Wolfies ....G 419 422-5450
Findlay *(G-9893)*

Thorfood LLC ....E 419 626-4375
Sandusky *(G-17014)*

◆ Trophy Nut Co ....E 937 667-8478
Tipp City *(G-18306)*

Trophy Nut Co ....G 937 669-5513
Tipp City *(G-18307)*

2075 Soybean Oil Mills

Archer-Daniels-Midland Company ....E 419 435-6633
Fostoria *(G-9966)*

Bunge North America Foundation ....D 740 383-1181
Marion *(G-12859)*

Bunge North America Foundation ....D 419 692-6010
Delphos *(G-8903)*

Bunge North America Foundation ....G 419 483-5340
Bellevue *(G-1547)*

Bunge North America Foundation ....G 740 426-6332
Jeffersonville *(G-11378)*

Cargill Incorporated ....D 937 498-4555
Sidney *(G-17170)*

Pioneer Hi-Bred Intl Inc ....E 419 748-8051
Grand Rapids *(G-10443)*

Schlessman Seed Co ....E 419 499-2572
Milan *(G-14116)*

Solae LLC ....C 419 483-0400
Bellevue *(G-1560)*

Solae LLC ....G 419 483-5340
Bellevue *(G-1561)*

2077 Animal, Marine Fats & Oils

Archer-Daniels-Midland Company ....E 419 435-6633
Fostoria *(G-9966)*

Cargill Incorporated ....D 937 498-4555
Sidney *(G-17170)*

Darling International Inc ....F 216 651-9300
Cleveland *(G-5167)*

Fiske Brothers Refining Co ....D 419 691-2491
Toledo *(G-18471)*

Griffin Industries LLC ....G 216 696-2588
Cleveland *(G-5459)*

Inland Products Inc ....E 614 443-3425
Columbus *(G-7188)*

Wileys Finest LLC ....G 740 622-1072
Coshocton *(G-7916)*

2079 Shortening, Oils & Margarine

Cincinnati Biorefining Corp ....G 513 482-8800
Cincinnati *(G-3543)*

◆ Cincinnati Renewable Fuels LLC .....D 513 482-8800
Cincinnati *(G-3565)*

Garden of Delight LLC ....G 513 300-7205
Cincinnati *(G-3797)*

Inter American Products Inc ....E 800 645-2233
Cincinnati *(G-3927)*

Kerry Flavor Systems Us LLC ....D 513 771-4682
Cincinnati *(G-3985)*

▲ Lms LLC ....G 513 981-1412
Cincinnati *(G-4031)*

◆ Olivamed Corporation ....G 937 401-0821
Franklin *(G-10042)*

Olive Serafino Oils Balsamics ....G 440 773-0200
Cleveland *(G-5939)*

Olive Smuckers Oil ....G 513 646-7103
Cincinnati *(G-4184)*

Olive Tap ....G 330 721-6500
Medina *(G-13453)*

Procter & Gamble Company ....C 513 634-9110
West Chester *(G-19923)*

Procter & Gamble Company ....C 410 527-5735
Grove City *(G-10586)*

Procter & Gamble Company ....B 513 983-1100
Cincinnati *(G-4286)*

▼ Procter & Gamble Mfg Co ....F 513 983-1100
Cincinnati *(G-4290)*

Spicy Olive LLC ....F 513 847-4397
West Chester *(G-19947)*

Spicy Olive LLC ....G 513 376-9061
Cincinnati *(G-4442)*

Wileys Finest LLC ....G 740 622-1072
Coshocton *(G-7916)*

2082 Malt Beverages

Actual Brewing ....F 614 636-3825
Columbus *(G-6692)*

AEC Brews LLC DBA Old Frhuse B .....G 513 536-9071
Williamsburg *(G-20406)*

American Craft Brewery LLC ....C 513 412-3200
Cincinnati *(G-3387)*

Anheuser-Busch LLC ....B 614 847-6213
Columbus *(G-6757)*

Barbeque Integrated Inc ....D 614 430-0572
Columbus *(G-6640)*

Barnstorm Brewing Company LLC ......G 419 852-9366
Coldwater *(G-6551)*

Birdfish Brewing Company LLC ....G 330 397-4010
Columbiana *(G-6606)*

Black Cloister Brewing Co LLC ....G 419 481-3891
Toledo *(G-18371)*

Brew Kettle Inc ....F 440 234-8788
Strongsville *(G-17898)*

Brewery Real Estate Partnr ....G 614 224-9023
Columbus *(G-6856)*

Brewery X LLC ....G 513 240-3600
Cincinnati *(G-3471)*

Brewpub Restaurant Corp ....D 614 228-2537
Columbus *(G-6857)*

Brufist LLC ....G 330 221-4472
Bowling Green *(G-1974)*

Burgie Brauerei Inc ....G 740 344-1620
Newark *(G-14990)*

Carry Grandview Out ....G 614 487-0305
Columbus *(G-6913)*

Choice Brands ....G 740 598-4121
Mingo Junction *(G-14347)*

Cineen Inc ....G 440 236-3658
Columbia Station *(G-6583)*

Columbus Kombucha Company LLC ..G 614 262-0000
Columbus *(G-6959)*

Commissary Brewing ....G 614 636-3164
Columbus *(G-6972)*

Dayton Heidelberg Distrg Co ....C 440 989-1027
Lorain *(G-12243)*

Dinos Drive Thru LLC ....F 330 263-1111
Wooster *(G-20765)*

District Brewing Co Inc ....G 614 224-3626
Columbus *(G-7032)*

Eagles Club ....G 740 962-6490
McConnelsville *(G-13349)*

Elevator Brewing Company LLC ....G 614 679-2337
Columbus *(G-7052)*

Euclid Brewing Company LLC ....G 216 289-5100
Euclid *(G-9578)*

Green Room Brewing LLC ....G 614 596-3655
Columbus *(G-7131)*

Guys Brewing Gear ....G 330 554-9362
Kent *(G-11464)*

Hill James R & Hill Earley W ....G 740 591-4203
Albany *(G-480)*

Jackie Os Pub Brewery LLC ....D 740 274-0777
Athens *(G-873)*

Larrys Drive Thru & Mini Mart ....G 330 953-0512
Youngstown *(G-21133)*

Marios Drive Thru ....G 330 452-8793
Canton *(G-2769)*

Marks Brew Thru ....G 330 699-1755
Akron *(G-287)*

Maumee Bay Brewing Company ....E 419 243-1253
Toledo *(G-18577)*

McKinleys Meadery LLC ....G 740 928-0229
Hebron *(G-10873)*

Millercoors LLC ....D 513 896-9200
Trenton *(G-18796)*

Minnicks Drive-Thru ....G 513 868-6126
Hamilton *(G-10725)*

Nine Giant Brewing LLC ....G 510 220-5104
Cincinnati *(G-4157)*

North High Brewing LLC ....F 614 407-5278
Columbus *(G-7400)*

Platform Beers LLC ....F 440 539-3245
Cleveland *(G-6016)*

Pop A Top Cruise Thru ....G 419 947-5855
Mount Gilead *(G-14565)*

▲ Rivertown Brewing Company LLC ....E 513 827-9280
Cincinnati *(G-4350)*

Rocky River Brewing Co ....E 440 895-2739
Rocky River *(G-16708)*

Rust Belt Brewing LLC ....G 330 423-3818
Youngstown *(G-21194)*

Schuster Beverage Marketing ....G 614 764-1420
Dublin *(G-9140)*

Seventh Son Brewing Co ....E 614 783-4217
Columbus *(G-7612)*

Sgt S Drive Thru ....G 937 378-3813
Georgetown *(G-10365)*

Snyder Intl Brewing Group LLC ....G 216 619-7424
Cleveland *(G-6215)*

South Side Drive Thru ....G 937 295-2927
Fort Loramie *(G-9940)*

Southern Glazers Wine & Sprt ....D 513 755-7082
Fairfield *(G-9721)*

▲ The Great Lakes Brewing Co ....D 216 771-4404
Cleveland *(G-6313)*

Thirsty Dog Brewing Co ....G 330 252-8740
Akron *(G-440)*

Tom Bad Brewing LLC ....G 513 871-4677
Cincinnati *(G-4512)*

Two Bandits Brewing Co LLC ....G 419 636-4045
Bryan *(G-2324)*

Unbridled Brewing Company LLC ....F 937 361-2573
Middletown *(G-14091)*

Victoria Ventures Inc ....G 330 793-9321
Youngstown *(G-21239)*

Wedco LLC ....G 513 309-0781
Mount Orab *(G-14587)*

Westend Brewing LLC ....G 513 922-0289
Cincinnati *(G-4587)*

Willoughby Brewing Company ....D 440 975-0202
Willoughby *(G-20630)*

Wright Designs Inc ....G 216 524-6662
Cleveland *(G-6484)*

2084 Wine & Brandy

Breitenbach Wine Cellar Inc ....G 330 343-3603
Dover *(G-8970)*

Buckeye Lake Winery ....G 740 246-9890
Thornville *(G-18193)*

Camelot Cellars Winery ....G 614 441-8860
Columbus *(G-6891)*

Chalet Debonne Vineyards Inc ....F 440 466-3485
Madison *(G-12499)*

CWC Partners LLC ....G 567 208-1573
Findlay *(G-9815)*

Deluca Vineyards ....G 440 685-4242
North Bloomfield *(G-15216)*

Drake Brothers Ltd ....G 415 819-4941
Columbus *(G-7039)*

Europia Gourmet Foods LLC ....G 614 460-3000
Columbus *(G-7068)*

Ferrante Wine Farm Inc ....E 440 466-8466
Geneva *(G-10347)*

Firelands Winery ....E 419 625-5474
Sandusky *(G-16965)*

Gar-Nays Winery ....G 419 668-6802
Collins *(G-6575)*

Georgetown Vineyards LLC ....F 740 435-3222
Cambridge *(G-2458)*

Gillig Custom Winery Inc ....G 419 202-6057
Findlay *(G-9831)*

Glenn Ravens Winery ....E 740 545-1000
West Lafayette *(G-20086)*

Hillside Winery ....G 419 456-3108
Gilboa *(G-10379)*

Hundley Cellars LLC ....G 843 368-5016
Geneva *(G-10351)*

John Christ Winery Inc ....G 440 933-9672
Avon Lake *(G-1035)*

Kelleys Island Wine Co ....G 419 746-2678
Kelleys Island *(G-11419)*

King Vineyards ....G 440 967-4191
Vermilion *(G-19331)*

Klingshirn Winery Inc ....G 440 933-6666
Avon Lake *(G-1036)*

Lamont Enterprises Inc ....G 330 677-4400
Kent *(G-11484)*

Larrys Drive Thru & Mini Mart ....G 330 953-0512
Youngstown *(G-21133)*

S I C

Markko Vineyard ....G...... 440 593-3197
Conneaut (G-7815)
Mastropietro Winery Inc ....G...... 330 547-2151
Berlin Center (G-1656)
▲ Meiers Wine Cellars Inc ....E...... 513 891-2900
Cincinnati (G-4082)
Moyer Vineyards Inc ....E...... 937 549-2957
Manchester (G-12550)
Mt Carmel Brewing Company ....G...... 513 519-7161
Cincinnati (G-4129)
Muirfield Wine Company LLC ....G...... 614 799-9222
Dublin (G-9107)
Odyssey Cellars Inc ....G...... 330 782-0177
Youngstown (G-21152)
Old Mason Winery Inc ....G...... 937 698-1122
West Milton (G-20109)
Old Mill Winery Inc ....F...... 440 466-5560
Geneva (G-10354)
Olde Schlhuse Vnyrd Winery LLC ....G...... 937 273-6023
Eldorado (G-9347)
Paper Moon Winery ....G...... 440 967-2500
Vermilion (G-19335)
Rainbow Hills Vineyards Inc ....G...... 740 545-9305
Newcomerstown (G-15122)
Renee Barrett Winery ....G...... 513 471-1340
Cincinnati (G-4336)
Rockside Winery & Vineyards LL ....G...... 740 687-4414
Lancaster (G-11749)
Sand Hollow Winery ....G...... 740 323-3959
Heath (G-10856)
Sandra Weddington ....G...... 740 417-4286
Delaware (G-8885)
School House Winery LLC ....G...... 330 602-9463
Dover (G-9012)
Shade Text Book Service Inc ....G...... 740 696-1323
Shade (G-17079)
Shawne Springs Winery ....G...... 740 623-0744
Coshocton (G-7909)
Stoney Ridge Winery Ltd ....G...... 419 636-3500
Bryan (G-2321)
Thorncreek Winery & Garden ....G...... 330 562-9245
Aurora (G-949)
Via Vecchia Winery ....G...... 614 469-4940
Columbus (G-7739)
Virant Family Winery Inc ....G...... 440 466-6279
Geneva (G-10358)
Winery At Spring Hill Inc ....G...... 440 466-0626
Geneva (G-10359)
Wines For You ....G...... 440 946-1420
Mentor (G-13770)
Woodbury Vineyards Inc ....G...... 440 835-2828
Westlake (G-20322)

2085 Liquors, Distilled, Rectified & Blended

Buckeye Distillery ....G...... 937 877-1901
Tipp City (G-18267)
Catawba Island Brewing Co ....G...... 419 960-7764
Port Clinton (G-16396)
Cleveland Whiskey LLC ....G...... 216 881-8481
Cleveland (G-5086)
Crooked Handle Brewing Co LLC ....G...... 937 241-5965
Springboro (G-17477)
Crystal Spirits LLC ....G...... 937 228-0201
Dayton (G-8253)
Five Points Distillery LLC ....G...... 937 776-4634
Dayton (G-8344)
Indian Creek Distillery ....G...... 937 846-1443
New Carlisle (G-14803)
Luxco Inc ....E...... 216 671-6300
Cleveland (G-5713)
Smedleys Bar and Grill ....G...... 216 941-0124
Cleveland (G-6212)
Western Reserve Distillers LLC ....G...... 330 671-0347
Hudson (G-11208)

2086 Soft Drinks

7 Up of Marietta Inc ....E...... 740 423-9230
Little Hocking (G-12141)
Abbott Laboratories ....A...... 614 624-3191
Columbus (G-6671)
Alaskan Falls Bottling Company ....G...... 614 888-9280
Worthington (G-20854)
American Bottling Company ....D...... 614 237-4201
Columbus (G-6730)
American Bottling Company ....D...... 937 236-0333
Dayton (G-8151)
American Bottling Company ....E...... 740 922-5253
Midvale (G-14104)
American Bottling Company ....E...... 740 377-4371
South Point (G-17432)

American Bottling Company ....D...... 740 423-9230
Little Hocking (G-12142)
American Bottling Company ....D...... 614 237-4201
Columbus (G-6731)
American Bottling Company ....E...... 419 229-7777
Lima (G-11988)
American Bottling Company ....D...... 419 535-0777
Toledo (G-18336)
American Bottling Company ....D...... 513 381-4891
Cincinnati (G-3384)
American Bottling Company ....E...... 419 529-6773
Mansfield (G-12560)
American Bottling Company ....C...... 513 242-5151
Cincinnati (G-3385)
Arizona Beverage Company LLC ....D...... 516 837-1999
Cincinnati (G-3413)
Bawls Acquisition LLC ....C...... 888 731-9708
Twinsburg (G-18904)
Belton Foods ....E...... 937 890-7768
Dayton (G-8184)
Beverages Holdings LLC ....E...... 513 483-3300
Blue Ash (G-1750)
Borden Dairy Co Cincinnati LLC ....C...... 513 948-8811
Cincinnati (G-3461)
Burton Bottling Company Inc ....E...... 216 681-0025
Cleveland (G-4950)
Cadbury Schweppes Bottling ....G...... 614 238-0469
Columbus (G-6887)
Cincinnati Marlins Inc ....C...... 513 761-3320
Cincinnati (G-3558)
Cleveland Coca-Cola Btlg Inc ....C...... 216 690-2653
Bedford Heights (G-1480)
Coca-Cola ....G...... 937 446-4644
Sardinia (G-17027)
Coca-Cola Bottling Co Cnsld ....G...... 419 422-3743
Lima (G-12000)
Coca-Cola Bottling Co Cnsld ....E...... 740 353-3133
Portsmouth (G-16433)
Coca-Cola Bottling Co Cnsld ....E...... 419 229-2000
Lima (G-12001)
Coca-Cola Bottling Co Cnsld ....B...... 513 527-6600
Cincinnati (G-3595)
Coca-Cola Bottling Co Cnsld ....D...... 937 878-5000
Dayton (G-8235)
Coca-Cola Company ....C...... 614 491-6305
Columbus (G-6942)
Coca-Cola Company ....D...... 614 863-7200
Columbus (G-6943)
Coca-Cola Company ....D...... 330 783-1982
Youngstown (G-21053)
Coca-Cola Company ....E...... 419 522-2653
Mansfield (G-12582)
Coca-Cola Company ....F...... 937 446-4644
Sardinia (G-17028)
Coca-Cola Company ....D...... 440 324-3335
Elyria (G-9396)
Coca-Cola Company ....E...... 740 452-3608
Zanesville (G-21291)
Coca-Cola Company ....C...... 513 898-7800
Blue Ash (G-1767)
Coca-Cola Company ....D...... 440 269-1433
Willoughby (G-20457)
Coca-Cola Refreshments USA Inc ....C...... 419 476-6622
Toledo (G-18404)
Coca-Cola Refreshments USA Inc ....D...... 330 425-4401
Twinsburg (G-18917)
Copper Mountain Beverages LLC ....G...... 513 484-9550
Cincinnati (G-3610)
◆ Country Pure Foods Inc ....C...... 330 848-6875
Akron (G-131)
Creekside Springs LLC ....E...... 330 679-1010
Salineville (G-16941)
Csv Inc ....F...... 937 438-1142
Dayton (G-8254)
Currier Richard & James ....G...... 440 988-4132
Amherst (G-596)
Delite Fruit Juices ....G...... 614 470-4333
Columbus (G-7019)
Diverse Acquisitions Group LLC ....F...... 888 232-1546
Centerville (G-3040)
Dominion Liquid Tech LLC ....E...... 513 272-2824
Cincinnati (G-3663)
Dr Pepper Bottlers Associates ....G...... 330 746-7651
Youngstown (G-21072)
Dr Pepper Bottling Company ....G...... 740 452-2721
Zanesville (G-21301)
Dr Pepper Snapple Group ....G...... 419 529-6773
Mansfield (G-12596)
Dr Pepper Snapple Group Inc ....D...... 614 237-4201
Columbus (G-7036)

Dr Pepper Snapple Group Inc ....D...... 614 237-4201
Columbus (G-7037)
Dr Pepper/Seven Up Inc ....D...... 419 229-7777
Lima (G-12005)
Dragon Beverage Inc ....G...... 614 506-5592
Columbus (G-7038)
Fbg Bottling Group LLC ....F...... 614 554-4646
Columbus (G-7077)
G & J Pepsi-Cola Bottlers Inc ....B...... 740 354-9191
Franklin Furnace (G-10069)
G & J Pepsi-Cola Bottlers Inc ....F...... 513 785-6060
Cincinnati (G-3789)
G & J Pepsi-Cola Bottlers Inc ....D...... 937 392-4937
Ripley (G-16666)
G & J Pepsi-Cola Bottlers Inc ....C...... 513 896-3700
Hamilton (G-10694)
G & J Pepsi-Cola Bottlers Inc ....A...... 614 253-8771
Columbus (G-7104)
G & J Pepsi-Cola Bottlers Inc ....D...... 740 452-2721
Zanesville (G-21313)
G & J Pepsi-Cola Bottlers Inc ....E...... 740 774-2148
Chillicothe (G-3239)
G & J Pepsi-Cola Bottlers Inc ....D...... 740 593-3366
Athens (G-867)
Gehm & Sons Limited ....G...... 330 724-8423
Akron (G-202)
Gem Beverages Inc ....F...... 740 384-2411
Wellston (G-19763)
Gordon Brothers Btlg Group Inc ....G...... 330 337-8754
Salem (G-16894)
Haus Mathias ....G...... 330 533-5305
Canfield (G-2557)
Hornell Brewing Co Inc ....G...... 516 812-0384
Cincinnati (G-3899)
Jmike LLC ....G...... 740 525-1734
Marietta (G-12795)
Kroger Co ....C...... 513 671-2790
Cincinnati (G-4003)
L & F Lauch LLC ....G...... 513 732-5805
Batavia (G-1200)
L & J Drive Thru ....G...... 330 767-2185
Brewster (G-2085)
Life Support Development Ltd ....G...... 614 221-1765
Columbus (G-7294)
Lynn Lyons ....G...... 740 599-7811
Danville (G-8089)
Medi Home Health Agency Inc ....G...... 740 472-3220
Woodsfield (G-20719)
▲ Meiers Wine Cellars Inc ....E...... 513 891-2900
Cincinnati (G-4082)
National Beverage Corp ....E...... 614 491-5415
Obetz (G-15657)
▲ Natural Country Farms Inc ....G...... 330 753-2293
Akron (G-311)
▲ Niagara Bottling LLC ....F...... 614 751-7420
Gahanna (G-10224)
Nurture Brands LLC ....C...... 513 307-2338
Cincinnati (G-4168)
Ohio Beverage Systems Inc ....F...... 216 475-3900
Cleveland (G-5929)
▲ Ohio Pure Foods Inc ....D...... 330 753-2293
Akron (G-326)
Our Heart Health Care Svcs LLC ....G...... 614 943-5216
Columbus (G-7448)
P-Americas LLC ....E...... 740 266-6121
Wintersville (G-20712)
P-Americas LLC ....B...... 513 948-5100
Cincinnati (G-4207)
P-Americas LLC ....C...... 614 253-8771
Columbus (G-7452)
P-Americas LLC ....C...... 440 323-5524
Elyria (G-9474)
P-Americas LLC ....C...... 330 336-3553
Wadsworth (G-19424)
P-Americas LLC ....C...... 330 837-4224
Massillon (G-13191)
P-Americas LLC ....C...... 937 328-6750
Springfield (G-17621)
P-Americas LLC ....E...... 330 963-0090
Twinsburg (G-18994)
P-Americas LLC ....C...... 330 746-7652
Youngstown (G-21161)
P-Americas LLC ....E...... 419 227-3541
Lima (G-12065)
Paradise Lemonade ....F...... 740 816-0771
Westerville (G-20178)
Pepsi-Cola Metro Btlg Co Inc ....B...... 937 461-4664
Dayton (G-8570)
Pepsi-Cola Metro Btlg Co Inc ....C...... 614 261-8193
Columbus (G-7477)

Pepsi-Cola Metro Btlg Co Inc...............B.......330 963-0426
  Twinsburg (G-18998)

Pepsi-Cola Metro Btlg Co Inc...............E.......330 963-5300
  Twinsburg (G-18999)

Pepsi-Cola Metro Btlg Co Inc...............E.......419 534-2186
  Toledo (G-18638)

Scioto Coca Cola...............................G.......740 474-2180
  Circleville (G-4641)

SD Ip Holdings Company.....................G.......513 483-3300
  Blue Ash (G-1866)

Shasta Beverages Inc..........................E.......614 491-5415
  Obetz (G-15659)

Skinny Piggy Kombucha LLC..................G.......513 646-5753
  Cincinnati (G-4425)

▼ Smucker International Inc..................G.......330 682-3000
  Orrville (G-15766)

Smucker Natural Foods Inc...................E.......330 682-3000
  Orrville (G-15767)

▼ Sunny Delight Beverage Co................D.......513 483-3300
  Blue Ash (G-1876)

Vinnies Drive Thru..............................G.......419 225-5272
  Lima (G-12109)

Your Bottled Water LLC.......................G.......740 443-6079
  Piketon (G-16230)

Youthtopia LLC..................................G.......740 525-1734
  Marietta (G-12851)

2087 Flavoring Extracts & Syrups

Abbott Laboratories............................A.......614 624-3191
  Columbus (G-6671)

Agrana Fruit Us Inc.............................C.......937 693-3821
  Anna (G-620)

▲ Bayswater Beverages LLC.................312 224-8012
  Cincinnati (G-3441)

Beck Flavors Inc................................G.......513 889-1268
  Loveland (G-12342)

Belton Foods....................................E.......937 890-7768
  Dayton (G-8184)

▲ Berghausen Corporation..................E.......513 541-5631
  Cincinnati (G-3445)

Bickford Laboratories Inc....................G.......440 354-7747
  Wickliffe (G-20359)

Cargill Incorporated...........................G.......937 236-1971
  Dayton (G-8210)

Cleveland Syrup Corp.........................G.......330 963-1900
  Twinsburg (G-18916)

Coca-Cola Refreshments USA Inc..........C.......419 476-6622
  Toledo (G-18404)

Dominion Liquid Tech LLC....................E.......513 272-2824
  Cincinnati (G-3663)

Flavor Systems International.................513 870-0420
  West Chester (G-20002)

▲ Flavor Systems Intl Inc....................E.......513 870-4900
  West Chester (G-20003)

◆ Frutarom USA Inc...........................C.......513 870-4900
  West Chester (G-20005)

Givaudan Flavors Corporation...............F.......513 948-8000
  Cincinnati (G-3829)

Givaudan Flavors Corporation...............B.......513 948-8000
  Cincinnati (G-3828)

Givaudan Flvors Fragrances Inc.............513 948-8000
  Cincinnati (G-3830)

Givaudan Fragrances Corp....................B.......513 948-3428
  Cincinnati (G-3832)

◆ Givaudan Roure US Inc....................G.......513 948-8000
  Cincinnati (G-3833)

Great Western Juice Company..............F.......216 475-5770
  Cleveland (G-5457)

Inter American Products Inc..................E.......800 645-2233
  Cincinnati (G-3927)

◆ J M Smucker Company.....................A.......330 682-3000
  Orrville (G-15742)

▲ Joseph Adams Corp........................F.......330 225-9125
  Valley City (G-19208)

◆ Mane Inc......................................D.......513 248-9876
  Lebanon (G-11815)

Mane Inc...D.......513 248-9876
  Lebanon (G-11816)

Mapledale Farm Inc...........................F.......440 286-3389
  Chardon (G-3166)

Roare-Q LLC.....................................G.......419 801-4040
  Bowling Green (G-2014)

Sensoryeffects Flavor Company............E.......419 782-5010
  Defiance (G-8809)

▲ Sensus LLC....................................F.......513 892-7100
  Hamilton (G-10737)

Slush Puppie....................................D.......513 771-0940
  West Chester (G-20050)

Synergy Flavors (oh) LLC....................G.......513 892-7100
  Hamilton (G-10743)

Tate Lyle Ingrdnts Amricas LLC............D.......937 236-5906
  Dayton (G-8703)

2091 Fish & Seafoods, Canned & Cured

Strasburg Provision Inc.......................E.......330 878-1059
  Strasburg (G-17830)

2095 Coffee

Altraserv LLC...................................G.......614 889-2500
  Dublin (G-9041)

Boston Stoker Inc..............................G.......937 890-6401
  Vandalia (G-19284)

Crooked River Coffee Co......................G.......440 442-8330
  Cleveland (G-5142)

Essential Wonders Inc.........................G.......888 525-5282
  Cuyahoga Falls (G-7992)

Euclid Coffee Co Inc...........................G.......216 481-3330
  Cleveland (G-5299)

▲ Folger Coffee Company....................F.......800 937-9745
  Orrville (G-15737)

Generations Coffee Company LLC...........E.......440 546-0901
  Brecksville (G-2051)

Good Beans Coffee Roasters LLC...........G.......513 310-9516
  Milford (G-14145)

Harbor Perk LLC................................G.......440 964-9277
  Ashtabula (G-812)

Inter American Products Inc..................E.......800 645-2233
  Cincinnati (G-3927)

Little Ghost Roasters..........................G.......614 325-2065
  Columbus (G-7301)

Mc Concepts Llc................................G.......330 933-6402
  Canton (G-2774)

▲ Millstone Coffee Inc.......................D.......513 983-1100
  Cincinnati (G-4108)

▲ Pmd Enterprises Inc.......................F.......440 546-0901
  Brecksville (G-2070)

Raptis Coffee Inc...............................G.......330 399-7011
  Warren (G-19591)

Stonefruit Coffee Co...........................G.......330 509-2787
  Canfield (G-2577)

▼ Wallingford Coffee Mills Inc..............D.......513 771-3131
  Cincinnati (G-4578)

2096 Potato Chips & Similar Prdts

ABC Refreshments LLC.......................F.......866 382-5575
  Euclid (G-9563)

Ballreich Bros Inc..............................E.......419 447-1814
  Tiffin (G-18209)

Basic Grain Products Inc......................614 408-3091
  Coldwater (G-6552)

Basic Grain Products Inc......................D.......419 678-2304
  Coldwater (G-6553)

Birds Eye Foods Inc............................E.......330 854-0818
  Canal Fulton (G-2499)

Conns Potato Chip Co Inc.....................G.......740 452-4615
  Zanesville (G-21294)

Daniel Meenan.................................G.......330 756-2818
  Beach City (G-1247)

Dure Foods Us LLC.............................F.......614 409-9030
  Columbus (G-7040)

Frito-Lay North America Inc..................C.......513 759-1000
  West Chester (G-19869)

Frito-Lay North America Inc..................D.......330 477-7009
  Canton (G-2708)

Frito-Lay North America Inc..................E.......419 595-2338
  New Riegel (G-14946)

Frito-Lay North America Inc..................C.......513 229-3000
  Mason (G-13023)

Frito-Lay North America Inc..................C.......972 334-7000
  Wooster (G-20774)

Gold N Krisp Chips & Pretzels...............G.......330 832-8395
  Massillon (G-13140)

Grippo Potato Chip Co Inc....................D.......513 923-1900
  Cincinnati (G-3854)

Herr Foods Incorporated......................E.......740 773-8282
  Chillicothe (G-3243)

Jones Potato Chip Co..........................F.......419 529-9424
  Mansfield (G-12629)

Kroger Co..D.......614 462-2000
  Columbus (G-7270)

Mike-Sells Potato Chip Co....................E.......937 228-9400
  Dayton (G-8499)

Mumfords Potato Chips & Deli...............G.......937 653-3491
  Urbana (G-19170)

Pats Delicious LLC.............................G.......614 441-7047
  Columbus (G-7466)

Robert E McGrath Inc.........................F.......440 572-7747
  Strongsville (G-17959)

◆ Rudolph Foods Company Inc.............C.......909 383-7463
  Lima (G-12087)

Savory Foods Inc...............................D.......740 354-6655
  Portsmouth (G-16451)

◆ Shearers Foods LLC........................A.......330 834-4030
  Massillon (G-13201)

◆ Snack Alliance Inc..........................E.......330 767-3426
  Massillon (G-13202)

Waffle House Inc...............................E.......937 746-6830
  Franklin (G-10062)

Waffle House Inc...............................F.......513 539-8372
  Monroe (G-14419)

White Feather Foods Inc......................F.......419 738-8975
  Wapakoneta (G-19513)

▲ Wyandot Inc..................................B.......740 383-4031
  Marion (G-12916)

2097 Ice

Donahues Hilltop Ice Company..............F.......740 432-3348
  Cambridge (G-2455)

Haller Enterprises Inc.........................F.......330 733-9693
  Akron (G-211)

Home City Ice Company.......................513 574-1800
  Cincinnati (G-3892)

Home City Ice Company.......................E.......513 851-4040
  Cincinnati (G-3893)

Home City Ice Company.......................937 461-6028
  Dayton (G-8392)

Home City Ice Company.......................216 429-0535
  Cleveland (G-5519)

Home City Ice Company.......................F.......419 562-4953
  Delaware (G-8860)

Home City Ice Company.......................440 439-5001
  Bedford (G-1429)

Home City Ice Company.......................614 836-2877
  Groveport (G-10625)

J Davis Sales and Assoc LLC................G.......330 947-2038
  Atwater (G-899)

Lori Holding Co.................................740 342-3230
  New Lexington (G-14848)

Luc Ice Inc.......................................G.......419 734-2201
  Port Clinton (G-16404)

Millersburg Ice Co.............................330 674-3016
  Millersburg (G-14249)

Olmsted Ice Inc.................................E.......440 235-8411
  Olmsted Twp (G-15682)

Penguin Serv Ice...............................G.......614 848-6511
  Worthington (G-20882)

Velvet Ice Cream Company...................F.......419 562-2009
  Bucyrus (G-2363)

Wings Way Drive Thru Inc....................G.......330 533-2788
  Salem (G-16935)

Zygo Inc..G.......513 281-0888
  Cincinnati (G-4621)

2098 Macaroni, Spaghetti & Noodles

Big Noodle LLC..................................G.......614 558-7170
  Columbus (G-6828)

Chieffos Frozen Foods Inc....................G.......330 652-1222
  Niles (G-15146)

Fusion Noodle Co..............................G.......740 589-5511
  Athens (G-866)

▲ International Noodle Company.............F.......614 888-0665
  Lewis Center (G-11902)

Lariccias Italian Foods........................F.......330 729-0222
  Youngstown (G-21132)

▲ Mrs Mllers Hmmade Noodles Ltd........F.......330 694-5814
  Fredericksburg (G-10089)

Sommers Co.....................................G.......888 906-7452
  Holmesville (G-11112)

T & R Noodles LLC.............................G.......614 537-4710
  New Lexington (G-14857)

Tmarzetti Company............................F.......330 674-2993
  Millersburg (G-14270)

◆ Tmarzetti Company.........................C.......614 846-2232
  Westerville (G-20193)

YAR Corporation................................G.......330 652-1222
  Niles (G-15190)

2099 Food Preparations, NEC

Advancperre Foods Holdings Inc............G.......800 969-2747
  Blue Ash (G-1735)

Agrana Fruit Us Inc.............................C.......937 693-3821
  Anna (G-620)

Alacwin Nutrition Corporation...............G.......614 961-6479
  Columbus (G-6713)

Allenbaugh Foods LLC.........................G.......216 952-3984
  Lakewood (G-11655)

American Foods Dist Co LLC.................G.......614 218-4049
  Blacklick (G-1687)

American Sweet Bean Co LLC................G.......888 995-0007
  Tiffin (G-18203)

S
I
C

Amir International Foods Inc ....G...... 614 332-1742
Grove City (G-10543)

Amish Wedding Foods Inc ....E...... 330 674-9199
Millersburg (G-14193)

▲ Andys Mdterranean Fd Pdts LLC ....G...... 513 281-9791
Cincinnati (G-3404)

Artic Diamond ....G...... 513 742-4921
Cincinnati (G-3416)

Artistic Foods Incorporated ....G...... 330 401-1313
Lodi (G-12157)

Aspen Mulling Company ....G...... 970 925-5027
Bedford (G-1400)

Atlantic Investment ....G...... 440 567-5054
Lorain (G-12233)

Ballreich Bros Inc ....E...... 419 447-1814
Tiffin (G-18209)

Barkett Fruit Co Inc ....E...... 330 364-6645
Dover (G-8967)

Basic Grain Products Inc ....D...... 419 678-2304
Coldwater (G-6553)

Beatty Foods LLC ....G...... 330 327-2442
Canton (G-2619)

Beckwith Orchards Inc ....F...... 330 673-6433
Kent (G-11433)

Best Bite Grill LLC ....E...... 419 344-7462
Versailles (G-19341)

Big Gus Onion Rings Inc ....E...... 216 883-9045
Cleveland (G-4912)

Bob Evans Farms Inc ....B...... 614 491-2225
New Albany (G-14750)

Bread Kneads Inc ....G...... 419 422-3863
Findlay (G-9801)

Chemtura Corporation ....E...... 440 324-6060
Elyria (G-9393)

Chez Rama Restaurant ....G...... 614 237-9315
Columbus (G-6926)

Cincinnatti Premier Candy LLC ....E...... 513 253-0079
Cincinnati (G-3571)

Clovervale Farms Inc ....D...... 440 960-0146
Amherst (G-595)

▲ Coalescence LLC ....E...... 614 861-3639
Columbus (G-6941)

Conagra Brands Inc ....C...... 513 229-0305
Mason (G-13006)

Conagra Brands Inc ....F...... 740 465-3912
Morral (G-14539)

Conagra Brands Inc ....A...... 937 440-2800
Troy (G-18811)

Conagra Brands Inc ....B...... 419 445-8015
Archbold (G-669)

Country Parlour Ice Cream Co ....F...... 440 237-4040
Cleveland (G-5134)

Cuyahoga Vending Co Inc ....E...... 440 353-9595
North Ridgeville (G-15368)

Daniel Meenan ....G...... 330 756-2818
Beach City (G-1247)

Deer Creek Honey Farms Ltd ....G...... 740 852-0899
London (G-12208)

Dik Jaxon Products Co ....G...... 937 890-7350
Dayton (G-8305)

Dismat Corporation ....E...... 419 531-8963
Toledo (G-18439)

Dno Inc ....D...... 614 231-3601
Columbus (G-7034)

Dole Fresh Vegetables Inc ....C...... 937 525-4300
Springfield (G-17546)

Domino Foods Inc ....D...... 216 432-3222
Cleveland (G-5205)

Feinkost Ingredient Co U S A ....G...... 330 948-3006
Lodi (G-12161)

Firehouse Foods ....G...... 614 592-8115
Columbus (G-7088)

Food 4 Your Soul ....F...... 330 402-4073
Youngstown (G-21088)

Food Designs Inc ....F...... 216 651-9221
Cleveland (G-5366)

Frank L Harter & Son Inc ....G...... 513 574-1330
Cincinnati (G-3778)

Fremont Company ....E...... 419 363-2924
Rockford (G-16691)

Fresh Table LLC ....G...... 513 381-3774
Cincinnati (G-3783)

Freshway Foods Inc ....C...... 937 498-4664
Sidney (G-17190)

Frito-Lay North America Inc ....C...... 972 334-7000
Wooster (G-20774)

Frito-Lay North America Inc ....D...... 330 477-7009
Canton (G-2708)

Frog Ranch Foods Ltd ....F...... 740 767-3705
Glouster (G-10404)

◆ Frutarom USA Inc ....C...... 513 870-4900
West Chester (G-20005)

Frutarom USA Inc ....F...... 513 870-4900
West Chester (G-20006)

Frutarom USA Inc ....E...... 513 870-4900
West Chester (G-20007)

Fuhrmann Orchards LLC ....G...... 740 776-6406
Wheelersburg (G-20331)

Ganeden Biotech Inc ....E...... 440 229-5200
Mayfield Heights (G-13315)

General Mills Inc ....D...... 513 771-8200
Cincinnati (G-3817)

Gold Star Chili Inc ....E...... 513 631-1990
Cincinnati (G-3839)

Goodell Farms ....G...... 330 274-2161
Mantua (G-12711)

Graffiti Foods Limited ....F...... 614 759-1921
Columbus (G-7126)

Great Lakes Popcorn Company ....E...... 419 732-3080
Port Clinton (G-16401)

▲ Greencore USA Inc ....D...... 513 645-1985
Cincinnati (G-3850)

Grippo Potato Chip Co Inc ....D...... 513 923-1900
Cincinnati (G-3854)

▲ Gsi of Ohio LLC ....D...... 216 431-3344
Cleveland (G-5462)

H & K Products Inc ....G...... 419 659-5110
Columbus Grove (G-7795)

Haus Mathias ....G...... 330 533-5305
Canfield (G-2557)

Hays Orchard & Cider Mill LLC ....F...... 330 482-2924
Columbiana (G-6619)

Heather Creek Foods LLC ....E...... 330 792-8654
North Jackson (G-15291)

Herold Salads Inc ....E...... 216 991-7500
Cleveland (G-5505)

Hiland Group Incorporated ....D...... 330 499-8404
Canton (G-2728)

Homestat Farm Ltd ....G...... 614 718-3060
Dublin (G-9085)

Honeybaked Ham Company ....E...... 513 583-9700
Cincinnati (G-3895)

Indie-Peasant Enterprises ....G...... 740 590-8240
Athens (G-872)

Infant Food Project Inc ....E...... 614 239-5763
Columbus (G-7186)

Ingredient Innovations Intl Co ....G...... 330 262-4440
Wooster (G-20786)

Injoy Foods LLC ....G...... 614 798-2033
Dublin (G-9089)

Inter American Products Inc ....E...... 800 645-2233
Cincinnati (G-3927)

◆ J M Smucker Company ....A...... 330 682-3000
Orrville (G-15742)

J M Smucker Company ....D...... 513 482-8000
Cincinnati (G-3936)

J M Smucker Company ....E...... 419 470-7914
Toledo (G-18532)

J M Smucker Company ....E...... 440 323-5100
Elyria (G-9442)

John Krusinski ....F...... 216 441-0100
Cleveland (G-5619)

Kerry Flavor Systems Us LLC ....D...... 513 771-4682
Cincinnati (G-3985)

Koch Foods of Cincinnati LLC ....G...... 513 874-3500
Fairfield (G-9673)

Kraft Heinz Company ....A...... 330 837-8331
Massillon (G-13165)

Krema Products Inc ....G...... 614 889-4824
Dublin (G-9097)

Kroger Co ....D...... 614 462-2000
Columbus (G-7270)

La Perla Inc ....F...... 419 534-2074
Toledo (G-18552)

Lakeview Farms LLC ....E...... 419 695-9925
Delphos (G-8913)

Louise Sweet LLC ....G...... 419 460-5505
Toledo (G-18563)

Main Street Gourmet LLC ....C...... 330 929-0000
Cuyahoga Falls (G-8022)

◆ Mane Inc ....D...... 513 248-9876
Lebanon (G-11815)

Miami Valley Pizza Hut Inc ....E...... 419 586-5900
Celina (G-3009)

Mid American Ventures Inc ....F...... 216 524-0974
Cleveland (G-5804)

Midwest Spray Drying Company ....G...... 419 294-4221
Upper Sandusky (G-19133)

▲ National Foods Packaging Inc ....F...... 216 415-7102
Cleveland (G-5856)

Nestle Brands Company ....F...... 440 264-6600
Solon (G-17343)

◆ Oasis Mediterranean Cuisine ....E...... 419 269-1516
Toledo (G-18612)

Oceanside Foods ....G...... 440 554-7810
Avon Lake (G-1042)

Ohio Hickory Harvest Brand Pro ....E...... 330 644-6266
Akron (G-324)

Ohio Processors Inc ....E...... 740 852-9243
London (G-12218)

Peer Pantry LLC ....G...... 216 236-4087
Willowick (G-20649)

Perez Foods LLC ....C...... 419 264-0303
Holgate (G-11039)

Pfizer Inc ....F...... 937 746-3603
Franklin (G-10044)

Pita Wrap LLC ....G...... 330 886-8091
Boardman (G-1922)

▼ Procter & Gamble Mfg Co ....F...... 513 983-1100
Cincinnati (G-4290)

Purushealth LLC ....F...... 800 601-0580
Shaker Heights (G-17093)

Rich Products Corporation ....C...... 614 771-1117
Hilliard (G-10976)

Ritchie Foods LLC ....G...... 440 354-7474
Fairport Harbor (G-9772)

Roare-Q LLC ....G...... 419 801-4040
Bowling Green (G-2014)

Rossi Pasta Factory Inc ....F...... 740 376-2065
Marietta (G-12826)

◆ Rudolph Foods Company Inc ....C...... 909 383-7463
Lima (G-11687)

▲ Sandridge Food Corporation ....G...... 330 725-2348
Medina (G-13474)

Sandridge Food Corporation ....C...... 330 725-8883
Medina (G-13475)

Sanese Services Inc ....E...... 330 494-5900
Warren (G-19597)

Savor Seasonings LLC ....G...... 513 732-2333
Batavia (G-1222)

◆ Sensoryffcts Powdr Systems Inc ....D...... 419 783-5518
Defiance (G-8810)

Sharpys Food Systems LLC ....G...... 440 232-9601
Oakwood Village (G-15627)

Simple Products LLC ....G...... 330 674-2448
Millersburg (G-14263)

▼ Smucker International Inc ....G...... 330 682-3000
Orrville (G-15766)

Special t Foods LLC ....G...... 330 793-8697
Youngstown (G-21209)

Special t Foods LLC ....G...... 330 533-9493
Canfield (G-2574)

Staceys Kitchen Limited ....G...... 614 921-1290
Hilliard (G-10980)

Sticky Petes Maple Syrup ....G...... 740 662-2726
Athens (G-886)

Sugarbush Creek Farm ....G...... 440 636-5371
Middlefield (G-13994)

Sunrise Foods Inc ....E...... 614 276-2880
Columbus (G-7667)

Tarrier Foods Corp ....E...... 614 876-8594
Columbus (G-7678)

Timmys Sandwich Shop ....G...... 419 350-8267
Toledo (G-18724)

Tom Pallas Industries Inc ....G...... 216 622-0230
Cleveland (G-6331)

Toms Country Place Inc ....E...... 440 934-4553
Avon (G-1016)

Tortilla ....G...... 614 557-3367
Reynoldsburg (G-16609)

Tortilleria El Maizal LLP ....G...... 330 209-9344
Massillon (G-13206)

Tortilleria La Bamba ....G...... 216 515-1600
Cleveland (G-6340)

▼ Tortilleria La Bamba LLC ....G...... 216 469-0410
Cleveland (G-6341)

Twenty Second Cntury Foods LLC ....G...... 419 866-6343
Maumee (G-13305)

Unger Kosher Bakery Inc ....E...... 216 321-7176
Cleveland Heights (G-6502)

Veggie Valley Farm LLC ....G...... 330 866-2712
Sandyville (G-17023)

Wake Robin Fermented Foods LLC ....G...... 216 961-9944
Cleveland (G-6442)

Wal-Bon of Ohio Inc ....D...... 740 423-8178
Belpre (G-1596)

▼ Wallingford Coffee Mills Inc ....D...... 513 771-3131
Cincinnati (G-4578)

Wannemacher Enterprises Inc ....F...... 419 771-1101
Upper Sandusky (G-19145)

Western Reserve Foods LLC ....G....... 330 770-0885
Chagrin Falls (G-3073)

White Castle System Inc ....E....... 513 563-2290
Cincinnati (G-4591)

White Feather Foods Inc ....F....... 419 738-8975
Wapakoneta (G-19513)

Whitmore Productions Inc ....F....... 216 752-3960
Warrensville Heights (G-19637)

Wildcat Creek Farms Inc ....F....... 419 263-2549
Payne (G-16019)

Willys Inc ....F....... 419 823-3200
Swanton (G-18095)

◆ Woeber Mustard Mfg Co ....C....... 937 323-6281
Springfield (G-17680)

▲ Zidian Manufacturing Inc ....G....... 330 965-8455
Boardman (G-1926)

21 TOBACCO PRODUCTS

2111 Cigarettes

Avail Vapor LLC ....G....... 440 716-6027
North Olmsted (G-15327)

Avail Vapor LLC ....G....... 440 365-5440
Elyria (G-9377)

Butt Hut of America Inc ....G....... 419 443-1997
Tiffin (G-18212)

Itg Brands LLC ....G....... 614 431-0044
Columbus (G-7215)

Low Bobs Discount Tobacco ....G....... 513 727-1430
Middletown (G-14055)

Memphis Smokehouse Inc ....G....... 216 351-5321
Cleveland (G-5782)

2121 Cigars

American Western Inc ....E....... 513 662-8802
Cincinnati (G-3394)

Cigars of Cincy ....G....... 513 931-5926
Cincinnati (G-3533)

Guari Inc ....G....... 330 733-4005
Akron (G-208)

2131 Tobacco, Chewing & Snuff

Ev Liquids LLC ....G....... 614 622-9617
Columbus (G-7069)

Great Midwest Tobacco Inc ....G....... 513 745-0450
Cincinnati (G-3846)

Hookah Rush ....G....... 614 267-6463
Columbus (G-7166)

Smoke Rings Inc ....G....... 419 420-9966
Findlay (G-9890)

22 TEXTILE MILL PRODUCTS

2211 Cotton, Woven Fabric

Akron Cotton Products Inc ....G....... 330 434-7171
Akron (G-38)

▲ Anita Plastics Inc ....G....... 216 831-5773
Solon (G-17260)

Associated Hygienic Pdts LLC ....B....... 770 497-9800
Delaware (G-8822)

Canton Sterilized Wiping Cloth ....G....... 330 455-5179
Canton (G-2648)

Canvas Salon and Skin Bar ....G....... 614 336-3942
Powell (G-16465)

Carmens Installation Co ....F....... 216 371-5633
Cleveland (G-4979)

Cleveland Drapery Stitch Inc ....F....... 216 252-3857
Cleveland (G-5060)

Compass Energy LLC ....D....... 866 665-2225
Cleveland (G-5110)

Custom Craft Drap Inc ....G....... 330 929-5728
Cuyahoga Falls (G-7984)

Custom Marine Canvas Training ....G....... 419 732-8362
Port Clinton (G-16397)

▲ F H Bonn Co Inc ....D....... 937 323-7024
Springfield (G-17556)

Fabric Square Shop ....G....... 330 752-3044
Stow (G-17751)

Franjinhas Inc ....G....... 440 463-1523
Strongsville (G-17921)

Grow With Me- Creations ....G....... 800 850-1889
Hartville (G-10821)

Keepsakes Etc ....G....... 330 559-6716
Canfield (G-2560)

Linsalata Capital Partners Fun ....G....... 440 684-1400
Cleveland (G-5703)

Lumenomics Inc ....E....... 614 798-3500
Lewis Center (G-11906)

Mary James Inc ....E....... 419 599-2941
Napoleon (G-14689)

▲ Mmi Textiles Inc ....F....... 440 899-8050
Westlake (G-20283)

Moleman ....G....... 513 662-3017
Cincinnati (G-4118)

Nancys Draperies ....F....... 330 855-7751
Marshallville (G-12919)

Noble Denim Workshop ....G....... 513 560-5640
Cincinnati (G-4161)

◆ Omnova Solutions Inc ....C....... 216 682-7000
Beachwood (G-1287)

Osnaburg Quilt Fibr Art Guild ....G....... 330 488-2591
East Canton (G-9195)

Silver Threads Inc ....E....... 614 733-0099
Plain City (G-16359)

▲ Sk Textile Inc ....C....... 323 581-8986
Cincinnati (G-4424)

◆ Standard Textile Co Inc ....B....... 513 761-9255
Cincinnati (G-4455)

The Max ....G....... 440 357-0036
Painesville (G-15929)

▲ Totes Isotoner Corporation ....F....... 513 682-8200
West Chester (G-20059)

▲ Totes Isotoner Holdings Corp ....C....... 513 682-8200
West Chester (G-20060)

◆ Tranzonic Companies ....C....... 216 535-4300
Richmond Heights (G-16656)

Tranzonic Companies ....C....... 440 446-0643
Cleveland (G-6350)

Twin Design AP Promotions Ltd ....G....... 937 732-6798
Dayton (G-8734)

◆ Tz Acquisition Corp ....A....... 216 535-4300
Richmond Heights (G-16658)

Weiskopf Industries Corp ....E....... 440 442-4400
Cleveland (G-6454)

Winspec Inc ....G....... 440 834-9068
Middlefield (G-14006)

2221 Silk & Man-Made Fiber

American Band Saw Co ....G....... 740 452-8168
Zanesville (G-21271)

▲ Anita Plastics Inc ....G....... 216 831-5773
Solon (G-17260)

▲ Architectural Fiberglass Inc ....E....... 216 641-8300
Cleveland (G-4825)

C S A Enterprises ....G....... 740 342-9367
New Lexington (G-14845)

Chautauqua Fiberglass & Plasti ....G....... 513 423-8840
Middletown (G-14028)

Cleveland Drapery Stitch Inc ....F....... 216 252-3857
Cleveland (G-5060)

Detroit Technologies Inc ....E....... 937 492-2708
Sidney (G-17179)

Ets Schaefer LLC ....E....... 330 468-6600
Macedonia (G-12448)

◆ King Bag and Manufacturing Co ....G....... 513 541-5440
Cincinnati (G-3990)

Lumenomics Inc ....E....... 614 798-3500
Lewis Center (G-11906)

M C L Window Coverings Inc ....G....... 513 868-6000
Hamilton (G-10719)

▲ Mmi Textiles Inc ....F....... 440 899-8050
Westlake (G-20283)

Owens Corning Sales LLC ....B....... 740 587-3562
Granville (G-10464)

P C R Restorations Inc ....F....... 419 747-7957
Mansfield (G-12666)

Schmelzer Industries Inc ....E....... 740 743-2866
Somerset (G-17419)

◆ Seaman Corporation ....C....... 330 262-1111
Wooster (G-20833)

Snyder Manufacturing Co Ltd ....G....... 330 343-4456
Dover (G-9017)

Sunshine Performance Glass Inc ....G....... 330 562-8600
Aurora (G-948)

Yoders Nylon Halter Shop ....G....... 330 893-3479
Millersburg (G-14290)

2231 Wool, Woven Fabric

Midwest Composites LLC ....E....... 419 738-2431
Wapakoneta (G-19497)

▲ Orr Felt Company ....D....... 937 773-0551
Piqua (G-16296)

Resistflame Acquisition Corp ....G....... 513 561-5223
Cincinnati (G-4337)

2241 Fabric Mills, Cotton, Wool, Silk & Man-Made

A & P Technology Inc ....E....... 513 688-3200
Cincinnati (G-3287)

A & P Technology Inc ....D....... 513 688-3200
Cincinnati (G-3288)

A & P Technology Inc ....E....... 513 688-3200
Cincinnati (G-3289)

A & P Technology Inc ....E....... 513 688-3200
Cincinnati (G-3290)

▲ A & P Technology Inc ....E....... 513 688-3200
Cincinnati (G-3291)

▲ Amfm Inc ....E....... 440 953-4545
Willoughby (G-20431)

Armotec Materials Corporation ....G....... 216 476-2766
Cleveland (G-4832)

Champion Webbing Company Inc ....G....... 330 920-1007
Cuyahoga Falls (G-7978)

Community Action Program Corp ....F....... 740 374-8501
Marietta (G-12776)

Crane Consumables LLC ....G....... 513 539-9980
Middletown (G-14034)

◆ Db Rediheat Inc ....E....... 216 361-0530
Cleveland (G-5175)

▲ Denizen Inc ....F....... 937 615-9561
Piqua (G-16261)

▲ Grove Engineered Products Inc ....G....... 419 659-5939
Columbus Grove (G-7794)

Joe Busby ....G....... 513 821-1716
Cincinnati (G-3949)

◆ Keuchel & Associates Inc ....E....... 330 945-9455
Cuyahoga Falls (G-8017)

▲ Mitchellace Inc ....E....... 740 354-2813
Portsmouth (G-16444)

Paxar Corporation ....G....... 937 681-4541
Dayton (G-8567)

Piland Parts ....G....... 330 686-3083
Stow (G-17787)

▲ Samsel Rope & Marine Supply Co .....E....... 216 241-0333
Cleveland (G-6156)

▲ Shore To Shore Inc ....D....... 937 866-1908
Dayton (G-8656)

Shurtape Technologies LLC ....B....... 440 937-7000
Avon (G-1011)

▲ Sole Choice Inc ....E....... 740 354-2813
Portsmouth (G-16456)

◆ Spunfab Ltd ....G....... 330 945-9455
Cuyahoga Falls (G-8049)

US Cotton LLC ....B....... 216 676-6400
Cleveland (G-6399)

Vacuflo Factory ....G....... 330 875-2450
Louisville (G-12333)

2252 Hosiery, Except Women's

Broken Spinning Wheel ....G....... 419 825-1609
Swanton (G-18081)

Disante Socks ....G....... 614 481-3243
Columbus (G-7028)

Forepleasure ....G....... 330 821-1293
Alliance (G-509)

Hype Socks ....G....... 614 506-5248
Columbus (G-7172)

2253 Knit Outerwear Mills

Digitek Corp ....F....... 513 794-3190
Blue Ash (G-1775)

E Retailing Associates LLC ....D....... 614 300-5785
Columbus (G-7043)

Embroidme ....G....... 330 484-8484
Canton (G-2697)

◆ Factory Direct International ....E....... 419 425-9636
Findlay (G-9821)

Fine Points Inc ....F....... 216 229-6644
Cleveland (G-5346)

Gibbs E & Associates LLC ....G....... 614 939-1672
New Albany (G-14760)

Heritage Inc ....G....... 614 860-1185
Reynoldsburg (G-16594)

Okm LLC ....G....... 216 272-6375
Cleveland (G-5935)

▲ Pjs Wholesale Inc ....G....... 614 402-9363
Columbus (G-7487)

TIS Incorporated ....G....... 614 291-3950
Columbus (G-7695)

Wonder-Shirts Inc ....G....... 917 679-2336
Dublin (G-9166)

S
I
C

2258 Lace & Warp Knit Fabric Mills

Murray Fabrics Inc ....F 216 881-4041
Cleveland *(G-5840)*

2261 Cotton Fabric Finishers

◆ Air Waves Inc ....C 740 548-1200
Lewis Center *(G-11883)*

Apparel Screen Printing Inc ....G 513 733-9495
Cincinnati *(G-3408)*

▲ Ares Sportswear Ltd ....D 614 767-1950
Hilliard *(G-10926)*

▲ Atlantis Sportswear Inc ....E 937 773-0680
Piqua *(G-16250)*

CSP Graphics Inc ....F 216 426-2660
Cleveland *(G-5144)*

Designer Awards Inc ....G 937 339-4444
Troy *(G-18819)*

▼ Duracote Corporation ....E 330 296-9600
Ravenna *(G-16526)*

Fryes Soccer Shoppe ....G 937 832-2230
Englewood *(G-9520)*

Graphic Plus ....G 740 701-1860
Chillicothe *(G-3241)*

Image Group Inc ....G 419 866-3300
Holland *(G-11065)*

◆ Image Group of Toledo Inc ....E 419 866-3300
Holland *(G-11066)*

Phantasm Designs ....G 419 538-6737
Ottawa *(G-15804)*

Precision Imprint ....G 740 592-5916
Athens *(G-882)*

Prism Prints Inc ....G 614 294-4981
Columbus *(G-7520)*

◆ Professional Image Inc ....F 513 984-1111
Cincinnati *(G-4296)*

Rapid Signs & More Inc ....G 513 553-4040
New Richmond *(G-14944)*

Resistflame Acquisition Corp ....G 513 561-5223
Cincinnati *(G-4337)*

Screen Printing Show House ....G 614 252-2202
Columbus *(G-7603)*

Shirt Stop LLC ....G 740 574-4774
Wheelersburg *(G-20334)*

Three Cord LLC ....G 419 445-2673
Archbold *(G-698)*

Uptown Dog The Inc ....G 740 592-4600
Athens *(G-889)*

Zenos Activewear Inc ....G 614 443-0070
Columbus *(G-7787)*

2262 Silk & Man-Made Fabric Finishers

717 Inc ....G 440 925-0402
Lakewood *(G-11652)*

B Richardson Inc ....F 330 724-2122
Akron *(G-80)*

Cincinnati Advg Pdts LLC ....E 513 346-7310
Cincinnati *(G-3537)*

Creatia Inc ....G 937 368-3100
Fletcher *(G-9915)*

E & E Screen Prtg & Cstm EMB ....G 614 235-2177
Columbus *(G-7042)*

Evolution Crtive Solutions LLC ....E 513 681-4450
Cincinnati *(G-3725)*

Fcs Graphics Inc ....G 216 771-5177
Cleveland *(G-5330)*

Flashions Sportswear Ltd ....G 937 323-5885
Springfield *(G-17560)*

Great Oppurtunities Inc ....G 614 868-1899
Columbus *(G-7130)*

▲ Mmi Textiles Inc ....F 440 899-8050
Westlake *(G-20283)*

Ohio Flock-Cote Company Inc ....G 440 498-3877
Solon *(G-17354)*

Phantasm Designs ....G 419 538-6737
Ottawa *(G-15804)*

Resistflame Acquisition Corp ....G 513 561-5223
Cincinnati *(G-4337)*

Scenic Screen ....G 419 468-3110
Galion *(G-10285)*

Sportsco Imprinting ....G 513 641-5111
Cincinnati *(G-4443)*

◆ Tranzonic Companies ....C 216 535-4300
Richmond Heights *(G-16656)*

Tranzonic Companies ....C 440 446-0643
Cleveland *(G-6350)*

◆ Tz Acquisition Corp ....A 216 535-4300
Richmond Heights *(G-16658)*

Wayne Sporting Goods ....G 937 236-6665
Dayton *(G-8748)*

Wizard Graphics Inc ....G 419 354-3098
Bowling Green *(G-2021)*

2269 Textile Finishers, NEC

Creative Commercial Finishing ....G 513 722-9393
Loveland *(G-12347)*

Grace Imaging LLC ....G 419 874-2127
Perrysburg *(G-16104)*

Nettting Technologies LLC ....G 330 298-0022
Ravenna *(G-16543)*

Pelz Lettering Inc ....G 419 625-3567
Sandusky *(G-16996)*

◆ Trebnick Systems Inc ....E 937 743-1550
Springboro *(G-17512)*

2273 Carpets & Rugs

Absorbcore LLC ....G 440 614-0457
North Olmsted *(G-15324)*

Alliance Carpet Cushion Co ....D 740 966-5001
Johnstown *(G-11388)*

B and L Sales Inc ....G 330 279-2007
Millersburg *(G-14195)*

▲ Boardman Molded Products Inc ......D 330 788-2401
Youngstown *(G-21032)*

Buckeye Volleyball Center LLC ....G 614 764-1075
Powell *(G-16463)*

Crown Dielectric Inds Inc ....C 614 224-5161
Columbus *(G-7001)*

Davies Since 1900 ....G 419 756-4212
Mansfield *(G-12593)*

◆ Durable Corporation ....D 419 668-8138
Norwalk *(G-15535)*

International Automotive ....B 937 492-1225
Sidney *(G-17195)*

Johns Manville Corporation ....B 419 878-8111
Waterville *(G-19660)*

Kadee Industries Newco Inc ....F 440 439-8650
Bedford *(G-1435)*

Mohawk Industries Inc ....C 800 837-3812
Grove City *(G-10574)*

Remnant Room ....G 937 938-7350
Dayton *(G-8624)*

Spacelinks Enterprises Inc ....D 330 788-2401
Youngstown *(G-21207)*

◆ Tranzonic Companies ....C 216 535-4300
Richmond Heights *(G-16656)*

Tranzonic Companies ....C 440 446-0643
Cleveland *(G-6350)*

Wholesale Carpet Outlet Inc ....G 937 447-4265
Gettysburg *(G-10376)*

Xt Innovations Ltd ....G 419 562-1989
Bucyrus *(G-2366)*

Zahler Enterprises LLC ....G 614 870-7872
Columbus *(G-7785)*

2281 Yarn Spinning Mills

▲ Specilty Fbrics Converting Inc ....E 706 637-3000
Fairlawn *(G-9760)*

Yarn Shop Inc ....G 614 457-7836
Columbus *(G-7782)*

2282 Yarn Texturizing, Throwing, Twisting & Winding Mills

Alliance Carpet Cushion Co ....D 740 966-5001
Johnstown *(G-11388)*

US Greentech ....G 513 371-5520
Cincinnati *(G-4546)*

2284 Thread Mills

Alvin L Roepke ....F 419 862-3891
Elmore *(G-9360)*

2295 Fabrics Coated Not Rubberized

Alron ....G 330 477-3405
Strasburg *(G-17819)*

Automated Packaging Systems ....G 330 342-0205
Streetsboro *(G-17841)*

Bexley Fabrics Inc ....G 614 231-7272
Columbus *(G-6825)*

▲ Biothane Coated Webbing Corp ......E 440 327-0485
North Ridgeville *(G-15361)*

▲ Buschman Corporation ....F 216 431-6633
Cleveland *(G-4951)*

▼ Duracote Corporation ....E 330 296-9600
Ravenna *(G-16526)*

Durez Corporation ....C 567 295-6400
Kenton *(G-11546)*

Excello Fabric Finishers Inc ....F 740 622-7444
Coshocton *(G-7889)*

Gvc Plastics & Metals LLC ....G 440 232-9360
Bedford *(G-1427)*

Laserflex Corporation ....D 614 850-9600
Hilliard *(G-10958)*

Ohio Metalizing LLC ....G 330 830-1092
Massillon *(G-13185)*

Omnova Overseas Inc ....C 330 869-4200
Fairlawn *(G-9757)*

Prints & Paints Flr Cvg Co Inc ....E 419 462-5663
Galion *(G-10283)*

◆ Schneller LLC ....C 330 676-7183
Kent *(G-11522)*

Shaheen Oriental Rug Co Inc ....F 330 493-9000
Canton *(G-2846)*

Spectroglass Corp ....G 614 297-0412
Columbus *(G-7640)*

Trim Systems Operating Corp ....C 614 289-5360
New Albany *(G-14774)*

2296 Tire Cord & Fabric

▲ Akro Polychem Inc ....G 330 864-0360
Fairlawn *(G-9737)*

▲ ARC Abrasives Inc ....D 800 888-4885
Troy *(G-18805)*

Cleveland Canvas Goods Mfg Co ....E 216 361-4567
Cleveland *(G-5050)*

Mfh Partners Inc ....F 440 461-4100
Cleveland *(G-5795)*

Midwest Precision Products ....F 440 237-9500
Cleveland *(G-5811)*

2297 Fabrics, Nonwoven

Autoneum North America Inc ....B 419 693-0511
Oregon *(G-15703)*

Polyflex LLC ....F 440 946-0758
Willoughby *(G-20574)*

▲ Toyobo Kureha America Co Ltd ......E 513 771-6788
Cincinnati *(G-4515)*

2298 Cordage & Twine

Capital Connection Cabling ....G 330 620-6311
Akron *(G-109)*

Connect Television ....G 614 876-4402
Hilliard *(G-10943)*

Patches LLC ....G 513 304-4882
Williamsburg *(G-20410)*

Phoenix/Electrotek LLC ....E 740 681-1412
Lancaster *(G-11739)*

▲ R C Packaging Systems ....F 248 684-6363
Mentor *(G-13711)*

Wire Holdings LLC ....G 216 731-9191
Cleveland *(G-6467)*

2299 Textile Goods, NEC

Big Productions Inc ....G 440 775-0015
Oberlin *(G-15635)*

Construction Techniques Inc ....F 216 267-7310
Cleveland *(G-5121)*

▲ Cusc International Ltd ....G 513 881-2000
Hamilton *(G-10682)*

Dayton Bag & Burlap Co ....F 937 253-1722
Dayton *(G-8268)*

Johnston-Morehouse-Dickey Co ....G 614 866-0452
Columbus *(G-7242)*

Johnston-Morehouse-Dickey Co ....G 330 405-6050
Macedonia *(G-12464)*

Meridian Industries Inc ....E 330 359-5809
Beach City *(G-1248)*

Nanomeld LLC ....G 740 477-5900
Circleville *(G-4634)*

▲ NC Works Inc ....E 937 514-7781
Franklin *(G-10039)*

▲ Ohio Table Pad Company ....F 419 872-6400
Perrysburg *(G-16130)*

▲ Ohio Table Pad of Indiana ....F 419 872-6400
Perrysburg *(G-16132)*

▼ Ribbon Technology Corporation ....F 614 864-5444
Gahanna *(G-10229)*

Tops Inc ....G 440 954-9451
Mentor *(G-13749)*

23 APPAREL AND OTHER FINISHED PRODUCTS MADE FROM FABRICS AND SIMILAR MATERIAL

2311 Men's & Boys' Suits, Coats & Overcoats

American Commodore Tuxedos...........G....... 440 324-2889
  Elyria (G-9370)
Bea-Ecc Apparels Inc ....G....... 216 650-6336
  Cleveland (G-4899)
Cinderella..G....... 937 312-9969
  Dayton (G-8229)
Contingncy Prcrments Group LLC.......G....... 513 204-9590
  Maineville (G-12521)
▲ Fechheimer Brothers Company ....C....... 513 793-7819
  Blue Ash (G-1792)
Global Gear LLC ....G....... 941 830-0531
  Chagrin Falls (G-3088)
Government Specialty Pdts LLC ....G....... 937 672-9473
  Dayton (G-8375)
Hugo Boss Usa Inc ....B....... 216 671-8100
  Cleveland (G-5536)
◆ Lion Apparel Inc ....C....... 937 898-1949
  Dayton (G-8458)
Simply Elegant Formals Inc ....G....... 419 738-7722
  Wapakoneta (G-19507)
Tom James Company ....F....... 614 488-8400
  Columbus (G-7698)
Vgs Inc ....C....... 216 431-7800
  Cleveland (G-6413)
Wahconah Group Inc ....F....... 216 923-0570
  Cleveland (G-6441)

2321 Men's & Boys' Shirts

J C L S Enterprises LLC ....G....... 740 472-0314
  Woodsfield (G-20718)
One Universal Brands LLC ....G....... 513 362-4326
  Cincinnati (G-4188)
Professional Image Apparel Inc ....F....... 513 984-1111
  Cincinnati (G-4295)
Pvh Corp ....G....... 330 562-4440
  Aurora (G-941)

2322 Men's & Boys' Underwear & Nightwear

Tranzonic Companies............................B....... 216 535-4300
  Richmond Heights (G-16657)

2325 Men's & Boys' Separate Trousers & Casual Slacks

Levi Strauss & Co ....F....... 513 539-7822
  Monroe (G-14410)

2326 Men's & Boys' Work Clothing

3n1 Mens Fashion.................................G....... 513 851-3610
  Cincinnati (G-3325)
▲ Affordable Med Scrubs LLC ....E....... 419 222-1088
  Lima (G-11982)
All-Bilt Uniform Corp ....E....... 513 793-5400
  Blue Ash (G-1742)
Ansell Healthcare Products LLC ....C....... 740 295-5414
  Coshocton (G-7880)
Aresgear...G....... 518 966-2737
  Columbus (G-6771)
Barton-Carey Medical Products ....E....... 419 887-1285
  Maumee (G-13230)
Carhartt Inc ....G....... 513 657-7130
  Cincinnati (G-3501)
Cintas Corporation ....F....... 513 336-6300
  Mason (G-12997)
Cintas Corporation ....D....... 513 631-5750
  Cincinnati (G-3578)
◆ Cintas Corporation ....A....... 513 459-1200
  Cincinnati (G-3577)
Cintas Corporation No 2 ....D....... 330 966-7800
  Canton (G-2655)
Cintas Sales Corporation ....B....... 513 459-1200
  Cincinnati (G-3579)
Cleveland Canvas Goods Mfg Co........D....... 216 361-4567
  Cleveland (G-5050)
DCW Acquisition Inc ....F....... 216 451-0666
  Cleveland (G-5179)
Eagle Rock Brand Cons LLC ....G....... 614 403-4802
  Plain City (G-16338)
▲ Euclid Vidaro Manufacturing Co.......D....... 330 673-7413
  Kent (G-11457)
Hall Safety Apparel Inc ....F....... 740 922-3671
  Uhrichsville (G-19051)

▲ Hands On International LLC ....G....... 513 502-9000
  Mason (G-13034)
High Lvel Fshion Athletes Foot ....G....... 614 577-8800
  Columbus (G-7155)
Kip-Craft Incorporated ....D....... 216 898-5500
  Cleveland (G-5656)
Lawft..G....... 419 422-5293
  Findlay (G-9850)
Linsalata Capital Partners Fun ....G....... 440 684-1400
  Cleveland (G-5703)
▲ Morning Pride Mfg LLC ....A....... 937 264-2662
  Dayton (G-8508)
Mypro Apparel LLC ....G....... 419 462-9464
  Ontario (G-15690)
Postal Uniform Xpress ....D....... 513 621-4787
  Cincinnati (G-4253)
Professional Image Apparel Inc ....F....... 513 984-1111
  Cincinnati (G-4295)
▲ RG Barry Corporation ....C....... 614 864-6400
  Pickerington (G-16203)
▲ Rich Industries Inc ....E....... 330 339-4113
  New Philadelphia (G-14924)
Rons Texstyles LLC ....G....... 513 936-9975
  Columbus (G-7571)
Seven Mile Creek Corporation ....F....... 937 456-3320
  Eaton (G-9322)
◆ Standard Textile Co Inc ....B....... 513 761-9255
  Cincinnati (G-4455)
◆ Tranzonic Companies ....C....... 216 535-4300
  Richmond Heights (G-16656)
Tranzonic Companies............................C....... 440 446-0643
  Cleveland (G-6350)
◆ Tz Acquisition Corp ....A....... 216 535-4300
  Richmond Heights (G-16658)
Unifirst Corporation ....D....... 216 658-6900
  Independence (G-11279)
Vgs Inc ....C....... 216 431-7800
  Cleveland (G-6413)
▲ Wagoner Stores Inc ....G....... 937 836-3636
  Englewood (G-9544)

2329 Men's & Boys' Clothing, NEC

Adidas North America Inc ....G....... 513 360-2979
  Monroe (G-14389)
Afi Brands LLC......................................G....... 614 999-6426
  Dublin (G-9038)
Aratinabox Companies Inc ....G....... 330 699-3421
  Uniontown (G-19076)
Carrera Holdings Inc ....G....... 216 687-1311
  Cleveland (G-4984)
Dunhams Sports ....F....... 330 334-3257
  Wadsworth (G-19403)
Fanz Stop ....G....... 937 310-1436
  Bellbrook (G-1508)
Hilliard Cat Shack LLC ....G....... 614 527-9711
  Hilliard (G-10952)
Inner Fire Sports LLC ....G....... 719 244-6622
  Cincinnati (G-3922)
J America LLC ....G....... 614 914-2091
  Columbus (G-7216)
Kam Manufacturing Inc ....C....... 419 238-6037
  Van Wert (G-19261)
Noxgear LLC..G....... 937 248-1860
  Columbus (G-7404)
Outdoor Army Store of Ashtabula..........F....... 440 992-8791
  Ashtabula (G-828)
Promotions Plus Inc ....G....... 440 582-2855
  Broadview Heights (G-2116)
Quality Sewing Inc ....G....... 216 475-0411
  Cleveland (G-6074)
Riegle Colors ....G....... 937 548-8444
  Greenville (G-10519)
▲ Rocky Brands Inc ....B....... 740 753-1951
  Nelsonville (G-14736)
Sacks Bruce & Associates ....G....... 419 537-0623
  Ottawa Hills (G-15819)
Torso...G....... 614 421-7663
  Columbus (G-7700)
Under Armour Inc ....G....... 330 995-9557
  Aurora (G-953)
▲ Universal Lettering Inc ....E....... 419 238-9320
  Van Wert (G-19274)
▲ Vesi Incorporated ....E....... 513 563-6002
  Cincinnati (G-4567)

2331 Women's & Misses' Blouses

Afi Brands LLC......................................G....... 614 999-6426
  Dublin (G-9038)
J C L S Enterprises LLC ....G....... 740 472-0314
  Woodsfield (G-20718)

Kam Manufacturing Inc ....C....... 419 238-6037
  Van Wert (G-19261)
Quality Sewing Inc ....G....... 216 475-0411
  Cleveland (G-6074)
▲ Rocky Brands Inc ....B....... 740 753-1951
  Nelsonville (G-14736)

2335 Women's & Misses' Dresses

Finishing Touch ....F....... 440 263-9264
  Cleveland (G-5348)
Jillians Ltd ....G....... 740 450-7766
  Zanesville (G-21323)
Lavander Bridal Salon ....F....... 330 602-0333
  Dover (G-8997)
Quality Sewing Inc ....G....... 216 475-0411
  Cleveland (G-6074)
S & C Newman Enterprises Inc............G....... 740 772-7433
  Chillicothe (G-3274)

2337 Women's & Misses' Suits, Coats & Skirts

◆ Cintas Corporation ....A....... 513 459-1200
  Cincinnati (G-3577)
Cintas Corporation ....D....... 513 631-5750
  Cincinnati (G-3578)
Cintas Corporation No 2 ....D....... 330 966-7800
  Canton (G-2655)
▲ Fechheimer Brothers Company ....C....... 513 793-7819
  Blue Ash (G-1792)
Lucio Vanni LLC ....G....... 440 823-6103
  Rocky River (G-16701)
◆ Standard Textile Co Inc ....B....... 513 761-9255
  Cincinnati (G-4455)

2339 Women's & Misses' Outerwear, NEC

▲ 5 BS Inc ....C....... 740 454-8453
  Zanesville (G-21263)
Barton-Carey Medical Products ....E....... 419 887-1285
  Maumee (G-13230)
Carrera Holdings Inc ....G....... 216 687-1311
  Cleveland (G-4984)
Fanz Stop ....G....... 937 310-1436
  Bellbrook (G-1508)
▲ Fechheimer Brothers Company ....C....... 513 793-7819
  Blue Ash (G-1792)
Hipsy LLC ....G....... 513 403-5333
  Fairfield (G-9665)
Inner Fire Sports LLC ....G....... 719 244-6622
  Cincinnati (G-3922)
Kip-Craft Incorporated ....D....... 216 898-5500
  Cleveland (G-5656)
Lena Fiore Inc.......................................F....... 330 468-3226
  Akron (G-270)
Majestic Sportswear Company.............G....... 937 773-1144
  Piqua (G-16290)
Owl Be Sweatin ....G....... 513 260-2026
  Cincinnati (G-4205)
Rita Fishel Inc.......................................E....... 740 775-1957
  Chillicothe (G-3272)
▲ Rocky Brands Inc ....B....... 740 753-1951
  Nelsonville (G-14736)
▲ Universal Lettering Inc ....E....... 419 238-9320
  Van Wert (G-19274)
▲ Vesi Incorporated ....E....... 513 563-6002
  Cincinnati (G-4567)

2341 Women's, Misses' & Children's Underwear & Nightwear

Skinnywear LLC ....G....... 216 310-5599
  Cleveland (G-6208)
Tranzonic Companies............................B....... 216 535-4300
  Richmond Heights (G-16657)

2342 Brassieres, Girdles & Garments

▲ Kern Manufacturing Inc ....G....... 216 464-5490
  Cleveland (G-5650)
Laura Dawson ....G....... 513 777-2513
  West Chester (G-19891)

2353 Hats, Caps & Millinery

▲ Barbs Graffiti Inc ....E....... 216 881-5550
  Cleveland (G-4889)
Bows Barrettes & Baubles ....F....... 440 247-2697
  Moreland Hills (G-14537)
◆ Factory Direct International.................E....... 419 425-9636
  Findlay (G-9821)
Genesco Inc..G....... 330 633-8179
  Akron (G-204)

S I C

Genesco Inc ....G...... 513 947-1200
Cincinnati *(G-3307)*

Lids Corporation ....F...... 419 621-8742
Sandusky *(G-16980)*

Lids Corporation ....G...... 440 974-9127
Mentor *(G-13633)*

Lids Corporation ....F...... 440 779-4998
North Olmsted *(G-15341)*

▲ Pukka Inc ....E...... 419 429-7808
Findlay *(G-9881)*

Thomas Creative Apparel Inc ....E...... 419 929-1506
New London *(G-14867)*

Thundawear LLC ....G...... 419 787-2675
Toledo *(G-18723)*

▲ Wagoner Stores Inc ....G...... 937 836-3636
Englewood *(G-9544)*

2361 Children's & Infants' Dresses & Blouses

▲ RG Barry Corporation ....RG..... 614 864-6400
Pickerington *(G-16203)*

Tween Brands Inc ....F...... 937 435-6928
Dayton *(G-8733)*

2369 Girls' & Infants' Outerwear, NEC

Rita Fishel Inc ....E...... 740 775-1957
Chillicothe *(G-3272)*

2371 Fur Goods

Reliable Fur Co ....G...... 513 288-5093
New Richmond *(G-14945)*

2381 Dress & Work Gloves

C & G Associates Inc ....G...... 419 756-6583
Mansfield *(G-12573)*

▲ Chester West Holdings Inc ....C...... 800 647-1900
Sharonville *(G-17113)*

Hall Safety Apparel Inc ....F...... 740 922-3671
Uhrichsville *(G-19051)*

Independent Protection Systems ....G...... 330 832-7992
Massillon *(G-13156)*

Pristine Exteriors ....G...... 330 957-5664
New Franklin *(G-14830)*

▲ Totes Isotoner Corporation ....F...... 513 682-8200
West Chester *(G-20059)*

▲ Totes Isotoner Holdings Corp ....C...... 513 682-8200
West Chester *(G-20060)*

▲ Wcm Holdings Inc ....G...... 513 705-2100
Cincinnati *(G-4581)*

2384 Robes & Dressing Gowns

Thomas Creative Apparel Inc ....E...... 419 929-1506
New London *(G-14867)*

2385 Waterproof Outerwear

Grow With Me- Creations ....G...... 800 850-1889
Hartville *(G-10821)*

2386 Leather & Sheep Lined Clothing

Fionas Fineries ....F...... 440 796-7426
Willoughby *(G-20487)*

2389 Apparel & Accessories, NEC

Akron Design & Costume Co ....G...... 330 644-4849
Akron *(G-40)*

Costume Specialists Inc ....E...... 614 464-2115
Columbus *(G-6987)*

Costume Specialists Inc ....E...... 614 464-2115
Columbus *(G-6988)*

Direct Disposables LLC ....G...... 440 717-3335
Brecksville *(G-2043)*

▲ Donegal Bay Ltd ....F...... 216 360-9966
Cleveland *(G-5207)*

▲ Fire-Dex LLC ....D...... 330 723-0000
Medina *(G-13410)*

Inner Fire Sports LLC ....G...... 719 244-6622
Cincinnati *(G-3922)*

Jki Sales ....G...... 614 581-5498
Columbus *(G-7233)*

▲ Kern Manufacturing Inc ....G...... 216 464-5490
Cleveland *(G-5650)*

L Brands Inc ....C...... 614 479-2000
Columbus *(G-7275)*

M M A Authentics LLC ....G...... 614 274-1141
Columbus *(G-7309)*

Novak Supply LLC ....G...... 216 741-5112
Cleveland *(G-5919)*

Promo Costumes Inc ....F...... 740 383-5176
Marion *(G-12893)*

Rageon Inc ....E...... 617 633-0544
Cleveland *(G-6088)*

▲ Rich Industries Inc ....E...... 330 339-4113
New Philadelphia *(G-14924)*

▲ Rocky Brands Inc ....B...... 740 753-1951
Nelsonville *(G-14736)*

Salindia LLC ....G...... 614 501-4799
Columbus *(G-7587)*

Schenz Theatrical Supply Inc ....F...... 513 542-6100
Cincinnati *(G-4387)*

Snaps Inc ....G...... 419 477-5100
Mount Cory *(G-14554)*

Stagecraft Costuming Inc ....F...... 513 541-7150
Cincinnati *(G-4451)*

◆ Standard Textile Co Inc ....B...... 513 761-9255
Cincinnati *(G-4455)*

▲ Status Mens Accessories ....G...... 440 232-6700
Cleveland *(G-6242)*

Tactical Revolution LLC ....G...... 419 348-9526
Ottawa *(G-15812)*

Thomas Creative Apparel Inc ....E...... 419 929-1506
New London *(G-14867)*

Top Hat Designs ....G...... 614 898-1962
Westerville *(G-20238)*

V Collection ....G...... 419 517-0508
Sylvania *(G-18128)*

Walter F Stephens Jr Inc ....E...... 937 746-0521
Franklin *(G-10063)*

2391 Curtains & Draperies

A & B Interiors Shine A Blind ....G...... 937 371-4731
Tipp City *(G-18256)*

A Designers Workroom ....G...... 513 251-7396
Cincinnati *(G-3334)*

Accent Drapery Co Inc ....E...... 614 488-0741
Columbus *(G-6683)*

Anthony Decorative Fabrics and ....G...... 937 299-4637
Moraine *(G-14466)*

Biaginis Draperies ....G...... 614 876-1706
Hilliard *(G-10933)*

Carter Drapery Service Inc ....G...... 419 289-2530
Ashland *(G-716)*

Drapery Stitch of Delphos ....G...... 419 692-3921
Delphos *(G-8906)*

E W Perry Service Co Inc ....G...... 419 473-1231
Toledo *(G-18448)*

Elden Draperies of Toledo Inc ....F...... 419 535-1909
Toledo *(G-18452)*

Janson Industries ....D...... 330 455-7029
Canton *(G-2745)*

Silver Threads Inc ....E...... 614 733-0099
Plain City *(G-16359)*

▲ Sk Textile Inc ....E...... 323 581-8986
Cincinnati *(G-4424)*

Specialty Drapery Workroom ....G...... 330 864-4190
Akron *(G-410)*

Stan Rileys Custom Draperies ....G...... 513 821-3732
Cincinnati *(G-4452)*

◆ Standard Textile Co Inc ....B...... 513 761-9255
Cincinnati *(G-4455)*

Style-Line Incorporated ....E...... 614 291-0600
Columbus *(G-7664)*

Tiffin Scenic Studios Inc ....E...... 800 445-1546
Tiffin *(G-18249)*

Vocational Services Inc ....C...... 216 431-8085
Cleveland *(G-6424)*

Wahlies Cstm Cft Drapery Uphl ....G...... 419 229-1731
Lima *(G-12111)*

Willet Enterprises ....G...... 937 298-8622
Dayton *(G-8758)*

Wise Window Treatment Inc ....F...... 216 676-4080
Cleveland *(G-6470)*

2392 House furnishings: Textile

A & W Table Pad Co ....F...... 800 541-0271
Cleveland *(G-4667)*

Ace-Tex Enterprises Inc ....F...... 513 829-8899
Hamilton *(G-10661)*

Aunties Attic ....E...... 740 548-5059
Lewis Center *(G-11886)*

Brentwood Originals Inc ....B...... 330 793-2255
Youngstown *(G-21034)*

▲ Casco Mfg Solutions Inc ....D...... 513 681-0003
Cincinnati *(G-3504)*

Cotton Fabrics Company Inc ....G...... 419 389-9904
Toledo *(G-18414)*

◆ Db Rediheat Inc ....E...... 216 361-0530
Cleveland *(G-5175)*

DCW Acquisition Inc ....F...... 216 451-0666
Cleveland *(G-5179)*

◆ Down-Lite International Inc ....C...... 513 229-3696
Mason *(G-13011)*

▲ Downhome Inc ....E...... 513 921-3373
Cincinnati *(G-3670)*

Eastern Slipcover Company Inc ....G...... 440 951-2310
Mentor *(G-13569)*

▼ Easy Way Leisure Corporation ....C...... 513 731-5640
Cincinnati *(G-3687)*

F K Holding Inc ....F...... 513 641-1400
Cincinnati *(G-3735)*

Guardian Co Inc ....G...... 216 721-2262
Cleveland *(G-5464)*

Ha-Ste Manufacturing Co Inc ....E...... 937 968-4858
Union City *(G-19071)*

Henty USA ....F...... 513 984-5590
Cincinnati *(G-3879)*

▲ Impact Products LLC ....C...... 419 841-2891
Toledo *(G-18518)*

Innocor Foam Tech - Acp Inc ....G...... 419 647-4172
Spencerville *(G-17460)*

Lawnview Industries Inc ....C...... 937 653-5217
Urbana *(G-19168)*

▲ Master Mfg Co Inc ....E...... 216 641-0500
Cleveland *(G-5758)*

Nanofilm Ltd ....G...... 216 674-1430
Cleveland *(G-5851)*

▲ National Seating Company ....D...... 219 872-7295
New Albany *(G-14766)*

Ohio Table Pad Company ....F...... 419 872-6400
Perrysburg *(G-16131)*

▲ Ohio Table Pad Company ....F...... 419 872-6400
Perrysburg *(G-16130)*

◆ Saturday Knight Ltd ....D...... 513 641-1400
Cincinnati *(G-4379)*

Seven Mile Creek Corporation ....F...... 937 456-3320
Eaton *(G-9322)*

Sewline Products Inc ....F...... 419 929-1114
New London *(G-14866)*

Silver Threads Inc ....E...... 614 733-0099
Plain City *(G-16359)*

Stan Rileys Custom Draperies ....G...... 513 821-3732
Cincinnati *(G-4452)*

Wise Window Treatment Inc ....F...... 216 676-4080
Cleveland *(G-6470)*

2393 Textile Bags

Capital City Awning Company ....E...... 614 221-5404
Columbus *(G-6897)*

Cleveland Canvas Goods Mfg Co ....D...... 216 361-4567
Cleveland *(G-5050)*

DCW Acquisition Inc ....F...... 216 451-0666
Cleveland *(G-5179)*

▲ Hdt Expeditionary Systems Inc ....C...... 216 438-6111
Solon *(G-17309)*

Jordan E Armour ....E...... 330 252-0290
Akron *(G-242)*

◆ King Bag and Manufacturing Co ....E...... 513 541-5440
Cincinnati *(G-3990)*

Lamports Filter Media Inc ....F...... 216 881-2050
Cleveland *(G-5679)*

Loctote LLC ....G...... 614 407-0882
Blacklick *(G-1700)*

Luxaire Cushion Co ....F...... 330 872-0995
Newton Falls *(G-15135)*

Polka DOT Pin Cushion Inc ....G...... 330 659-0233
Richfield *(G-16632)*

Queen City Carpets LLC ....F...... 513 823-8238
Cincinnati *(G-4314)*

▲ Rich Industries Inc ....E...... 330 339-4113
New Philadelphia *(G-14924)*

Sailors Tailor Inc ....G...... 937 862-7781
Spring Valley *(G-17469)*

Seven Mile Creek Corporation ....F...... 937 456-3320
Eaton *(G-9322)*

2394 Canvas Prdts

A B C Sign Inc ....F...... 513 241-8884
Cincinnati *(G-3332)*

▼ Advantage Tent Fittings Inc ....F...... 740 773-3015
Chillicothe *(G-3226)*

Allen Zahradnik Inc ....G...... 419 729-1201
Toledo *(G-18328)*

American Canvas Products Inc ....F...... 419 382-8450
Toledo *(G-18337)*

Awning Fabri Caters Inc ....G...... 216 476-4888
Cleveland *(G-4878)*

Berlin Boat Covers ....G...... 330 547-7600
Berlin Center *(G-1654)*

Canvas Exchange Inc ....G...... 216 749-2233
Cleveland *(G-4967)*

Canvas Products Co .... F 440 232-8716
Bedford *(G-1411)*

Canvas Specialty Mfg Co .... G 216 881-0647
Cleveland *(G-4968)*

Capital City Awning Company .... E 614 221-5404
Columbus *(G-6897)*

Catawba Canvas Company LLC .... G 419 797-2050
Port Clinton *(G-16395)*

▼ Celina Tent Inc .... E 419 586-3610
Celina *(G-2990)*

▼ Chalfant Sew Fabricators Inc .... E 216 521-7922
Cleveland *(G-5012)*

Cleveland Canvas Goods Mfg Co .... D 216 361-4567
Cleveland *(G-5050)*

Crown Dielectric Inds Inc .... C 614 224-5161
Columbus *(G-7001)*

Custom Canvas & Boat Repair .... F 419 732-3314
Lakeside *(G-11646)*

Custom Tarpaulin Products Inc .... F 330 758-1801
Youngstown *(G-21060)*

DCW Acquisition Inc .... F 216 451-0666
Cleveland *(G-5179)*

Electra Tarp Inc .... F 330 477-7168
Canton *(G-2696)*

Embedee LLC .... G 419 678-7007
Coldwater *(G-6558)*

Forest City Companies Inc .... E 216 586-5279
Cleveland *(G-5369)*

Galion Canvas Products Co .... G 419 468-5333
Galion *(G-10269)*

Glawe Manufacturing Co Inc .... E 937 754-0064
Fairborn *(G-9623)*

Griffin Fisher Co Inc .... G 513 961-2110
Cincinnati *(G-3853)*

▲ Hdt Expeditionary Systems Inc .... C 216 438-6111
Solon *(G-17309)*

Hogan Awning Inc .... G 440 352-4033
Grand River *(G-10450)*

Independent Awning & Canvas Co .... G 937 223-9661
Dayton *(G-8401)*

J & W Canvas Company .... G 330 652-7678
Mineral Ridge *(G-14306)*

Lesch Boat Cover Canvas Co LLC .... G 419 668-6374
Norwalk *(G-15550)*

Lumenomics Inc .... E 614 798-3500
Lewis Center *(G-11906)*

◆ Main Awning & Tent Inc .... G 513 621-6947
Cincinnati *(G-4054)*

National Bias Fabric Co .... E 216 361-0530
Cleveland *(G-5853)*

North Sails Toledo LLC .... F 419 726-2933
Toledo *(G-18608)*

Odyssey Canvas Works Inc .... G 937 392-4422
Ripley *(G-16668)*

▲ Ohio Awning & Manufacturing Co .... E 216 861-2400
Cleveland *(G-5928)*

ONeals Tarpaulin & Awning Co .... F 330 788-6504
Youngstown *(G-21157)*

P C R Restorations Inc .... F 419 747-7957
Mansfield *(G-12666)*

Phillips Awning Co .... G 740 653-2433
Lancaster *(G-11738)*

Queen City Awning & Tent Co .... E 513 530-9660
Cincinnati *(G-4313)*

R F W Holdings Inc .... G 440 331-8300
Cleveland *(G-6082)*

Ragman Inc .... G 419 255-8068
Toledo *(G-18670)*

▲ Rainbow Bedding .... G 330 852-3127
Sugarcreek *(G-18036)*

▲ Rainbow Industries Inc .... G 937 323-6493
Springfield *(G-17633)*

Raven Industries Inc .... G 937 323-4625
Springfield *(G-17634)*

Rex Manufacturing Co .... G 419 224-5751
Lima *(G-12083)*

Sailors Tailor Inc .... G 937 862-7781
Spring Valley *(G-17469)*

▲ Samsel Rope & Marine Supply Co .... E 216 241-0333
Cleveland *(G-6156)*

Schaaf Co Inc .... G 513 241-7044
Cincinnati *(G-4384)*

▲ Scherba Industries Inc .... D 330 273-3200
Brunswick *(G-2256)*

Shade Youngstown & Aluminum Co .... G 330 782-2373
Youngstown *(G-21200)*

Shur-Co LLC .... G 330 297-0888
Ravenna *(G-16556)*

South Akron Awning Co .... F 330 848-7611
Akron *(G-409)*

Stan Rileys Custom Draperies .... G 513 821-3732
Cincinnati *(G-4452)*

Tarpco Inc .... F 330 677-8277
Kent *(G-11535)*

Tarped Out Inc .... F 330 325-7722
Ravenna *(G-16565)*

Tri County Tarp Inc .... E 419 288-3350
Bradner *(G-2030)*

William Thompson .... G 440 232-4363
Aurora *(G-956)*

Wolf G T Awning & Tent Co .... F 937 548-4161
Greenville *(G-10529)*

2395 Pleating & Stitching For The Trade

▲ 5 BS Inc .... C 740 454-8453
Zanesville *(G-21263)*

A Graphic Solution .... F 216 228-7223
Cleveland *(G-4672)*

A To Z Wear Ltd .... G 513 923-4662
Cincinnati *(G-3337)*

Aardvark Sportswear Inc .... G 330 793-9428
Youngstown *(G-21012)*

Absolute Impressions Inc .... G 614 840-0599
Lewis Center *(G-11882)*

Action Sports Apparel Inc .... G 330 848-9300
Norton *(G-15503)*

Aida Embroidery & Printing .... G 440 498-8981
Solon *(G-17250)*

All For Show Inc .... G 440 729-7186
Chesterland *(G-3197)*

All Sport Printwear Inc .... F 330 887-6505
Westfield Center *(G-20243)*

Alley Cat Designs Inc .... G 937 885-7950
Dayton *(G-8145)*

Alphabet Embroidery Studios .... F 937 372-6557
Xenia *(G-20935)*

Alphabet Soup Inc .... G 330 467-4418
Macedonia *(G-12434)*

Anything Personalized .... G 330 655-0723
Twinsburg *(G-18900)*

Apparel Impressions Inc .... G 513 247-0555
Cincinnati *(G-3407)*

Appleheart .... G 937 384-0430
Miamisburg *(G-13784)*

Assoc Talents Inc .... G 440 716-1265
Westlake *(G-20256)*

▲ Atlantis Sportswear Inc .... E 937 773-0680
Piqua *(G-16250)*

Aubrey Rose Apparel LLC .... G 513 728-2681
Cincinnati *(G-3428)*

Avina Specialties Inc .... G 419 592-5646
Napoleon *(G-14672)*

B D P Services Inc .... D 740 828-9685
Nashport *(G-14703)*

Barbs Custom Embroidery .... G 419 393-2226
Defiance *(G-8781)*

Barbs Embroidery .... G 614 875-9933
Grove City *(G-10545)*

▲ Barbs Graffiti Inc .... E 216 881-5550
Cleveland *(G-4889)*

Big Kahuna Graphics Inc .... G 330 455-2625
Canton *(G-2622)*

Cal Sales Embroidery .... G 440 236-3820
Columbia Station *(G-6582)*

Campbell Signs & Apparel LLC .... F 330 386-4768
East Liverpool *(G-9205)*

Carols Ultra Stitch & Variety .... G 419 935-8991
Willard *(G-20393)*

Carter Evans Enterprises Inc .... G 614 920-2276
Granville *(G-10455)*

▲ Catania Medallic Specialty .... E 440 933-9595
Avon Lake *(G-1026)*

Charles Wisvari .... F 740 671-9960
Bellaire *(G-1497)*

Cheryl A Lucas .... G 614 755-2100
Columbus *(G-6925)*

CNG Business Group .... G 614 771-0877
Hilliard *(G-10941)*

Collegiate Connection .... G 419 352-8333
Bowling Green *(G-1982)*

Color 3 Embroidery Inc .... G 330 652-9495
Warren *(G-19536)*

Craco Embroidery Inc .... G 513 563-6999
Cincinnati *(G-3617)*

David Brandeberry .... G 937 653-4680
Urbana *(G-19156)*

Design Original Inc .... F 937 596-5121
Jackson Center *(G-11339)*

Dimensions Three Inc .... G 614 539-5180
Grove City *(G-10554)*

Eastgate Custom Graphics Ltd .... G 513 528-7922
Cincinnati *(G-3686)*

Elegant Embroidery Llc .... G 440 878-0904
Strongsville *(G-17916)*

Embroid ME .... G 216 459-9250
Cleveland *(G-5275)*

Embroidered ID Inc .... G 440 974-8113
Mentor *(G-13572)*

Embroidery Design Group LLC .... F 614 798-8152
Columbus *(G-7055)*

Ems/Hooptech .... G 513 829-7768
West Chester *(G-19857)*

Ernst Sporting Gds Minster LLC .... G 937 526-9822
Versailles *(G-19346)*

Expert TS .... G 330 263-4588
Wooster *(G-20770)*

Fastpatch Ltd .... F 513 367-1838
Harrison *(G-10777)*

Fcs Graphics Inc .... G 216 771-5177
Cleveland *(G-5330)*

Fine Line Embroidery Company .... G 330 788-9070
Youngstown *(G-21084)*

Fine Line Embroidery Company .... G 440 331-7030
Rocky River *(G-16699)*

Fineline Imprints Inc .... E 740 453-1083
Zanesville *(G-21308)*

Finn Graphics Inc .... E 513 941-6161
Cincinnati *(G-3756)*

Gail Berner .... G 937 322-0314
Springfield *(G-17563)*

Garment Specialties Inc .... G 330 425-2928
Twinsburg *(G-18940)*

Glorias .... G 330 264-8963
Wooster *(G-20778)*

Good JP .... G 419 207-8484
Ashland *(G-735)*

Graphic Stitch Inc .... G 937 642-6707
Marysville *(G-12945)*

Graphix Junction .... G 234 284-8392
Hudson *(G-11176)*

Great Oppurtunities Inc .... G 614 868-1899
Columbus *(G-7130)*

H & H Screen Process Inc .... G 937 253-7520
Dayton *(G-8381)*

Hang Time Group Inc .... G 216 771-5885
Cleveland *(G-5476)*

Heller Acquisitions Inc .... G 937 833-2676
Brookville *(G-2186)*

Ideal Drapery Company Inc .... F 330 745-9873
Barberton *(G-1121)*

Initial Designs Inc .... G 419 475-3900
Toledo *(G-18523)*

Initially Yours .... G 216 228-4478
Lakewood *(G-11669)*

J America LLC .... G 614 914-2091
Columbus *(G-7216)*

Jane Valentine .... G 330 452-3154
North Canton *(G-15244)*

Jaquas Monogramming & Design .... G 419 422-2244
Findlay *(G-9844)*

Jetts Embroideries .... G 937 981-3716
Greenfield *(G-10481)*

Joan B Mailloux .... G 361 992-5311
Mansfield *(G-12627)*

Judy Dubois .... G 419 738-6979
Wapakoneta *(G-19493)*

Just Quilt It Inc .... G 330 469-6956
Warren *(G-19564)*

K Ventures Inc .... F 419 678-2308
Coldwater *(G-6566)*

Kathy Simecek .... G 440 886-2468
Cleveland *(G-5635)*

Kens His & Hers Shop Inc .... G 330 872-3190
Newton Falls *(G-15134)*

Kiwi Promotional AP & Prtg Co .... E 330 487-5115
Twinsburg *(G-18966)*

Kts Cstm Lgs/Xclsvely You Inc .... G 440 285-9803
Chardon *(G-3161)*

Kts Custom Logos .... G 440 285-9803
Chardon *(G-3162)*

Kuhls Hot Sportspot .... F 513 474-2282
Cincinnati *(G-4006)*

Lion Clothing Inc .... G 419 692-9981
Delphos *(G-8914)*

Locker Room Lettering Ltd .... G 419 359-1761
Castalia *(G-2977)*

Logan Screen Printing .... G 740 385-3303
Logan *(G-12185)*

Logo This .... G 419 445-1355
Archbold *(G-685)*

SIC

Lynns Logos Inc .... G 440 786-1156
Cleveland (G-5714)

M & Y Marketing .... G 937 322-3423
Springfield (G-17595)

▲ McCc Sportswear Inc .... E 513 583-9210
West Chester (G-20025)

Mr Emblem Inc .... G 419 697-1888
Oregon (G-15710)

National Ntwrk EMB Prfssionals .... G 502 212-7500
Stow (G-17782)

Novak J F Manufacturing Co LLC .... G 216 741-5112
Cleveland (G-5918)

Oasis Embroidery .... G 614 785-7266
Columbus (G-7408)

Pelz Lettering Inc .... G 419 625-3567
Sandusky (G-16996)

Permanent Impressions .... G 740 892-3045
Utica (G-19196)

Personal Stitch Monogramming .... G 440 282-7707
Amherst (G-605)

Phantasm Designs .... G 419 538-6737
Ottawa (G-15804)

Precision Imprint .... G 740 592-5916
Athens (G-882)

Quali-Tee Design Sports .... F 937 382-7997
Wilmington (G-20675)

Qualitee Design Sportswear Co .... F 740 333-8337
Wshngtn CT Hs (G-20922)

Quality Image Embroidery & AP .... G 440 230-1109
Broadview Heights (G-2117)

Quality Rubber Stamp Inc .... G 614 235-2700
Columbus (G-7536)

Quality Stitch Embroidery Inc .... G 614 237-0480
Columbus (G-7537)

Quickstitch Plus LLC .... G 614 476-3186
Columbus (G-7539)

R Sportswear LLC .... G 937 748-3507
Springboro (G-17504)

Randy Gray .... G 513 533-3200
Cincinnati (G-4330)

Red Barn Screen Printing & EMB ...... F 740 474-6657
Circleville (G-4640)

Robs Creative Screen Printing .... G 740 264-6383
Wintersville (G-20713)

Route 14 Storage Inc .... G 330 296-0084
Ravenna (G-16553)

▲ Shamrock Companies Inc .... D 440 899-9510
Westlake (G-20308)

Sovereign Stitch .... G 440 829-0678
Avon Lake (G-1052)

Spectrum Embroidery Inc .... G 937 847-9905
Dayton (G-8669)

Sportsco Imprinting .... G 513 641-5111
Cincinnati (G-4443)

Stepp Sewing Service .... G 513 248-0822
Milford (G-14175)

Sun Shine Awards .... F 740 425-2504
Barnesville (G-1161)

Superior Image Llc .... F 513 771-4565
Cincinnati (G-4484)

T & L Custom Screening Inc .... G 937 237-3121
Dayton (G-8695)

Tag Sportswear LLC .... G 330 456-8867
Canton (G-2866)

Tech Wear Embroidery Company .... G 740 344-1276
Newark (G-15062)

Thompson Assoc Hudson Ohio .... G 330 655-2142
Hudson (G-11204)

Threaded Image .... G 513 683-9069
Loveland (G-12394)

Trademark Solutions .... G 740 374-9779
Marietta (G-12843)

Truck Stop Embroidery .... G 419 257-2860
North Baltimore (G-15200)

Twin Design AP Promotions Ltd .... G 937 732-6798
Dayton (G-8734)

Unisport Inc .... F 419 529-4727
Ontario (G-15696)

United Sport Apparel .... F 330 722-0818
Medina (G-13493)

Vasil Co Inc .... G 419 562-2901
Bucyrus (G-2362)

Vector International Corp .... G 440 942-2002
Mentor (G-13766)

Walnut Hill Shop .... G 740 828-3346
Frazeysburg (G-10077)

Wizard Graphics Inc .... G 419 354-3098
Bowling Green (G-2021)

Writely Sew LLC .... G 513 728-2682
Cincinnati (G-4609)

▲ Zimmer Enterprises Inc .... E 937 428-1057
Dayton (G-8768)

2396 Automotive Trimmings, Apparel Findings, Related Prdts

A C Hadley - Printing Inc .... G 937 426-0952
Beavercreek (G-1314)

Aardvark Graphic Enterprises L .... F 419 352-3197
Bowling Green (G-1963)

ABC Lettering & Embroidery .... G 216 321-8338
Lakewood (G-11653)

Action Sports Apparel Inc .... G 330 848-9300
Norton (G-15503)

Activewares .... G 419 994-5932
Loudonville (G-12295)

Adcraft Decals Inc .... E 216 524-2934
Cleveland (G-4702)

◆ Air Waves Inc .... C 740 548-1200
Lewis Center (G-11883)

Akron Felt & Chenille Mfg Co .... F 330 733-7778
Akron (G-43)

Am Graphics .... G 330 799-7319
Youngstown (G-21022)

▲ Angell-Demmel North Amer Corp ...D 937 461-5800
Dayton (G-8158)

◆ Anomatic Corporation .... B 740 522-2203
New Albany (G-14745)

Art Tees Inc .... G 614 338-8337
Columbus (G-6774)

Art Works .... G 740 425-5765
Barnesville (G-1158)

▲ Atlantis Sportswear Inc .... E 937 773-0680
Piqua (G-16250)

B D P Services Inc .... D 740 828-9685
Nashport (G-14703)

Bates Metal Products Inc .... D 740 498-8371
Port Washington (G-16422)

Big Kahuna Graphics Inc .... G 330 455-2625
Canton (G-2622)

Brandon Screen Printing .... F 419 229-9837
Lima (G-11996)

Brown Cnty Bd Mntal Rtardation .... E 937 378-4891
Georgetown (G-10364)

Cal Sales Embroidery .... G 440 236-3820
Columbia Station (G-6582)

Camela Nitschke Ribbonry .... G 419 872-0073
Perrysburg (G-16073)

Charisma Products Inc .... G 614 846-8888
Westerville (G-20143)

Charizma Corp .... G 216 621-2220
Cleveland (G-5014)

Charles Wisvari .... F 740 671-9960
Bellaire (G-1497)

Crabar/Gbf Inc .... G 419 943-2141
Leipsic (G-11868)

David Brandeberry .... G 937 653-4680
Urbana (G-19156)

Design Original Inc .... F 937 596-5121
Jackson Center (G-11339)

Detailed Athletic Wear Co Inc .... G 513 541-0884
Cincinnati (G-3651)

Detroit Technologies Inc .... E 937 492-2708
Sidney (G-17179)

Dresden Specialties Inc .... G 740 754-2451
Dresden (G-9032)

Dupli-Systems Inc .... C 440 234-9415
Strongsville (G-17913)

E L Frueh Inc .... F 419 222-9741
Lima (G-12007)

Eastgate Custom Graphics Ltd .... G 513 528-7922
Cincinnati (G-3686)

Ed Thomas .... G 937 325-4300
Springfield (G-17551)

Elken Co .... G 513 459-7207
Maineville (G-12523)

Fair Publishing House Inc .... E 419 668-3746
Norwalk (G-15540)

Fedex Office & Print Svcs Inc .... E 614 898-0000
Westerville (G-20214)

Fineline Imprints Inc .... E 740 453-1083
Zanesville (G-21308)

Fried Daddy .... G 937 854-4542
Dayton (G-8351)

Gail Berner .... G 937 322-0314
Springfield (G-17563)

Gail Zeilmann .... G 440 888-4858
Cleveland (G-5391)

General Theming Contrs LLC .... C 614 252-6342
Columbus (G-7108)

Gotcha Covered .... G 513 829-7555
Fairfield (G-9661)

▼ Greenfield Research Inc .... C 937 981-7763
Greenfield (G-10478)

Greenfield Research Inc .... G 937 876-9224
Greenfield (G-10479)

Griffin Fisher Co Inc .... G 513 961-2110
Cincinnati (G-3853)

H & H Screen Process Inc .... G 937 253-7520
Dayton (G-8381)

Hall Company .... E 937 652-1376
Urbana (G-19160)

Hayes Reconditioning Group .... G 937 299-8013
Dayton (G-8387)

▲ Hfi LLC .... B 614 491-0700
Canal Winchester (G-2525)

Hfi LLC .... C 614 491-0700
Canal Winchester (G-2526)

Hollywood Imprints LLC .... F 614 501-6040
Gahanna (G-10211)

Hunt Products Inc .... E 440 667-2457
Newburgh Heights (G-15075)

J America LLC .... G 614 914-2091
Columbus (G-7216)

J&D Beck Co Inc .... G 419 224-0027
Lima (G-12033)

Jakes Sportswear Ltd .... G 740 746-8356
Sugar Grove (G-18012)

Jerry Pulfer .... G 937 778-1861
Piqua (G-16283)

Jetts Embroideries .... G 937 981-3716
Greenfield (G-10481)

Jim Davis .... G 740 335-8030
Wshngtn CT Hs (G-20914)

Jls Funeral Home .... F 614 625-1220
Columbus (G-7234)

Johnson Brothers Holdings LLC .... G 614 868-5273
Columbus (G-7240)

Kam-Awards Inc .... G 513 631-5553
Cincinnati (G-3971)

Kemper Automotive .... G 800 783-8004
Franklin (G-10030)

Kent Stow Screen Printing Inc .... F 330 923-5118
Akron (G-255)

Kiwi Promotional AP & Prtg Co .... E 330 487-5115
Twinsburg (G-18966)

Lesch Boat Cover Canvas Co LLC ...... G 419 668-6374
Norwalk (G-15550)

Logan Screen Printing .... G 740 385-3303
Logan (G-12185)

Lund Printing Co .... G 330 628-4047
Akron (G-277)

M & H Screen Printing .... G 740 522-1957
Newark (G-15031)

Madison Group Inc .... G 216 362-9000
Cleveland (G-5727)

Mr Emblem Inc .... G 419 697-1888
Oregon (G-15710)

National Bias Fabric Co .... E 216 361-0530
Cleveland (G-5853)

Nicholas Ray Enterprises LLC .... G 330 454-4811
Canton (G-2788)

Northeastern Plastics Inc .... G 330 453-5925
Canton (G-2795)

Ohio State Institute of Fin .... G 614 861-8811
Reynoldsburg (G-16596)

Outsourcing Services Inc .... F 330 963-2710
Solon (G-17357)

Painted Hill Inv Group Inc .... F 937 339-1756
Troy (G-18861)

Peska Inc .... F 440 998-4664
Ashtabula (G-831)

Pieco Inc .... E 419 422-5335
Findlay (G-9878)

Pieco Inc .... D 937 399-5100
Springfield (G-17628)

Pinky & Thumb LLC .... G 614 939-5216
New Albany (G-14769)

▼ Plastic Card Inc .... D 330 896-5555
Uniontown (G-19093)

▲ Plus Mark LLC .... E 216 252-6770
Cleveland (G-6018)

Pro Companies Inc .... G 614 738-1222
Pickerington (G-16201)

Puttco Inc .... G 937 299-1527
Dayton (G-8604)

Quality Rubber Stamp Inc .... G 614 235-2700
Columbus (G-7536)

Quality Spt & Silk Screen Sp .... G 513 769-8300
Cincinnati (G-4309)

R & A Sports Inc ....E 216 289-2254
  Euclid *(G-9603)*

Randy Gray ....G 513 533-3200
  Cincinnati *(G-4330)*

Robert Midkiff ....G 614 848-6677
  Worthington *(G-20885)*

▲ S S T Enterprises Inc ....D 330 343-2656
  New Philadelphia *(G-14927)*

Schilling Graphics Inc ....E 419 468-1037
  Galion *(G-10286)*

Screen Works Inc ....E 937 264-9111
  Dayton *(G-8650)*

Simply Canvas Inc ....E 330 436-6500
  Akron *(G-402)*

Solar Arts Graphic Designs ....G 330 744-0535
  Youngstown *(G-21205)*

Spirit Avionics Ltd ....F 614 358-0333
  Columbus *(G-7645)*

▲ Sroufe Healthcare Products LLC .....E 260 894-4171
  Wadsworth *(G-19442)*

Standard Prototyping Ideals ....G 614 837-9180
  Pickerington *(G-16205)*

Sweaty Bands LLC ....E 513 871-1222
  Cincinnati *(G-4489)*

Swocat Design Inc ....G 440 282-4700
  Lorain *(G-12284)*

Sylvan Studio Inc ....G 419 882-3423
  Sylvania *(G-18127)*

T & L Custom Screening Inc ....G 937 237-3121
  Dayton *(G-8695)*

Tee Creations ....G 937 878-2822
  Fairborn *(G-9632)*

Telempu N Hayashi Amer Corp ....G 513 932-9319
  Lebanon *(G-11843)*

Tendon Manufacturing Inc ....E 216 663-3200
  Cleveland *(G-6305)*

Tim L Humbert ....F 330 497-4944
  Canton *(G-2870)*

Triage Ortho Group ....G 937 653-6431
  Urbana *(G-19185)*

Trim Systems Operating Corp ....C 740 772-5998
  Chillicothe *(G-3281)*

▲ Universal Drect Flfllment Corp .....C 330 650-5000
  Hudson *(G-11206)*

Vasil Co Inc ....G 419 562-2901
  Bucyrus *(G-2362)*

Vector International Corp ....G 440 942-2002
  Mentor *(G-13766)*

▲ Vgu Industries Inc ....E 216 676-9093
  Cleveland *(G-6414)*

▼ W J Egli Company Inc ....F 330 823-3666
  Alliance *(G-551)*

West & Barker Inc ....E 330 652-9923
  Niles *(G-15189)*

Wizard Graphics Inc ....G 419 354-3098
  Bowling Green *(G-2021)*

Woodrow Manufacturing Co ....E 937 399-9333
  Springfield *(G-17682)*

Yi Xing Inc ....G 614 785-9631
  Columbus *(G-7784)*

Zenos Activewear Inc ....G 614 443-0070
  Columbus *(G-7787)*

Zide Sport Shop of Ohio Inc ....F 740 373-8199
  Marietta *(G-12852)*

2399 Fabricated Textile Prdts, NEC

Akron Felt & Chenille Mfg Co ....F 330 733-7778
  Akron *(G-43)*

Annin & Co ....D 740 622-4447
  Coshocton *(G-7878)*

▲ Besi Manufacturing Inc ....E 513 874-0232
  West Chester *(G-19817)*

Buckeye Seating LLC ....G 330 473-2379
  Millersburg *(G-14205)*

Crown Dielectric Inds Inc ....C 614 224-5161
  Columbus *(G-7001)*

Exochem Corporation ....F 330 426-9898
  East Palestine *(G-9239)*

Flag Lady Inc ....G 614 263-1776
  Columbus *(G-7090)*

Griffin Fisher Co Inc ....G 513 961-2110
  Cincinnati *(G-3853)*

Kanel Brothers Supply ....G 330 499-4802
  Canton *(G-2750)*

Kolhfab Cstm Plstic Fbrication ....G 937 237-2098
  Dayton *(G-8444)*

Markers Inc ....G 440 933-5927
  Avon Lake *(G-1039)*

▲ Party Animal Inc ....G 440 471-1030
  Westlake *(G-20291)*

Perimeter Technologies Inc ....F 513 322-5453
  Cincinnati *(G-4229)*

Rex Manufacturing Co ....G 419 224-5751
  Lima *(G-12083)*

School Maintenance Supply Inc ......G 513 376-8670
  Blue Ash *(G-1865)*

School Pride Limited ....E 614 568-0697
  Columbus *(G-7598)*

Seven Mile Creek Corporation ....F 937 456-3320
  Eaton *(G-9322)*

Sewline Products Inc ....F 419 929-1114
  New London *(G-14866)*

▲ Specity Fbrics Converting Inc ......E 706 637-3000
  Fairlawn *(G-9760)*

Tk Holdings Inc ....E 937 778-9713
  Piqua *(G-16315)*

TS Trim Industries Inc ....B 740 593-5958
  Athens *(G-888)*

Ver Mich Ltd ....G 330 493-7330
  Canton *(G-2896)*

Vitamin Lac ....F 440 548-5294
  Middlefield *(G-14003)*

24 LUMBER AND WOOD PRODUCTS, EXCEPT FURNITURE

2411 Logging

A & M Logging ....G 740 543-3171
  Salineville *(G-16939)*

A & P Wood Products Inc ....G 419 673-1196
  Kenton *(G-11543)*

Affordable Stump Removal LLC ....G 419 841-8331
  Toledo *(G-18323)*

Alfman Logging LLC ....G 740 982-6227
  Crooksville *(G-7948)*

Appalachia Wood Inc ....F 740 596-2551
  Mc Arthur *(G-13328)*

Art Saylor Logging ....F 740 682-6188
  Oak Hill *(G-15594)*

B Hogenkamp & R Harlamert ....G 419 925-0526
  Celina *(G-2986)*

Baker Logging ....G 740 686-2817
  Belmont *(G-1578)*

Beachs Trees Selective Harvest ......F 513 289-5976
  Cincinnati *(G-3294)*

Beekman Logging ....G 740 493-2763
  Piketon *(G-16216)*

Biedenbach Logging ....G 740 732-6477
  Sarahsville *(G-17024)*

Blair Logging ....G 740 934-2730
  Lower Salem *(G-12415)*

Blankenship Logging LLC ....G 740 372-3833
  Otway *(G-15826)*

Bolon Timber LLC ....G 740 567-4102
  Lewisville *(G-11947)*

Boreman Hardwoods Inc ....G 330 262-0403
  Wooster *(G-20750)*

Brett Purdum ....G 740 626-2890
  South Salem *(G-17449)*

Broty Enterprises Inc ....G 330 674-6900
  Millersburg *(G-14203)*

Brown Forest Products ....G 937 544-1515
  Otway *(G-15828)*

Busy Bee Lumber ....G 330 674-1305
  Millersburg *(G-14209)*

C & B Logging Inc ....G 740 347-4844
  Glouster *(G-10403)*

C & L Erectors & Riggers Inc ....E 740 332-7185
  Laurelville *(G-11769)*

Chester F Hale ....G 740 379-2437
  Patriot *(G-15993)*

Chili Logging Ltd ....G 740 545-9502
  Fresno *(G-10196)*

Chipmunk Logging & Lumber LLC .....G 440 834-4660
  Middlefield *(G-13923)*

Chub Gibsons Logging ....G 740 884-4079
  Chillicothe *(G-3233)*

Coldwell Family Tree Farm ....G 330 506-9012
  Salineville *(G-16940)*

Crisenbery Logging LLC ....G 740 256-1439
  Patriot *(G-15994)*

Custom Material Hdlg Eqp LLC ....G 513 235-5336
  Cincinnati *(G-3626)*

D&D Logging ....G 740 679-2573
  Woodsfield *(G-20717)*

D&M Fencing LLC ....G 419 604-0698
  Spencerville *(G-17459)*

David Adkins Logging ....G 740 533-0297
  Kitts Hill *(G-11620)*

Denver Adkins ....F 740 682-3123
  Oak Hill *(G-15595)*

Dunagan Logging ....G 740 599-9368
  Danville *(G-8087)*

Erichar Inc ....G 216 402-2628
  Cleveland *(G-5293)*

Ervin Lee Logging ....G 330 771-0039
  Minerva *(G-14321)*

▼ Facemyer Lumber Co Inc ....G 740 992-5965
  Pomeroy *(G-16389)*

For Every Home ....G 740 710-1253
  Jackson *(G-11314)*

Gadd Logging ....G 513 312-3941
  Trenton *(G-18792)*

Gerald D Damron ....G 740 894-3680
  Chesapeake *(G-3188)*

GM Logging ....G 740 501-0819
  Johnstown *(G-11399)*

H & H Tree Service LLC ....G 440 632-0551
  Middlefield *(G-13938)*

Haessly Lumber Sales Co ....D 740 373-6681
  Marietta *(G-12788)*

Huntington Hardwood Lbr Co Inc ......G 440 647-2283
  Wellington *(G-19748)*

Ingles Logging ....G 740 379-2909
  Patriot *(G-15995)*

Ingles Logging ....G 740 379-2760
  Patriot *(G-15996)*

▼ Itl California LLC ....F 216 831-4734
  Cleveland *(G-5590)*

J & J Logging ....G 740 896-2827
  Lowell *(G-12402)*

J D Knisley Logging ....G 740 634-3207
  Bainbridge *(G-1058)*

J K Logging & Chipwood Company .....G 330 738-3571
  Salineville *(G-16942)*

Jacobs & Sons Logging LLC ....G 419 678-3802
  Saint Henry *(G-16820)*

Jason C Gibson ....F 740 663-4520
  Chillicothe *(G-3246)*

Jeffrey Adams Logging Inc ....G 740 634-2286
  Bainbridge *(G-1059)*

Jim Logging LLC ....G 330 340-4863
  Millersburg *(G-14235)*

JM Logging Inc ....G 740 441-0941
  Gallipolis *(G-10301)*

John Byler ....G 330 627-7635
  Carrollton *(G-2957)*

John J Yoder Logging ....G 330 749-6324
  Apple Creek *(G-641)*

Knauff Bros Logging & Lumber ....F 740 634-2432
  Bainbridge *(G-1060)*

◆ Krajewski Corp ....C 740 522-1147
  Newark *(G-15028)*

L&L Excavating & Land Clearing ....G 740 682-7823
  Oak Hill *(G-15600)*

Litzinger Logging ....G 740 743-2245
  Somerset *(G-17416)*

M H Logging & Lumber ....G 740 694-1988
  Fredericktown *(G-10106)*

McFadden Logging ....G 740 599-6902
  Danville *(G-8090)*

Michael D Strickland ....G 740 682-6902
  Oak Hill *(G-15601)*

Milestone Ventures LLC ....G 317 908-2093
  Granville *(G-10462)*

Miller & Son Logging ....G 330 738-2031
  Mechanicstown *(G-13360)*

Miller Logging ....G 440 693-4001
  Middlefield *(G-13965)*

Miller Logging Inc ....G 330 279-4721
  Holmesville *(G-11109)*

Millwood Lumber Inc ....E 740 254-4681
  Gnadenhutten *(G-10408)*

Ned A Shreve ....G 740 732-6465
  Sarahsville *(G-17025)*

NY Logging & Lumber ....G 740 679-2085
  Quaker City *(G-16500)*

Oakbridge Timber Framing ....G 419 994-1052
  Loudonville *(G-12301)*

Ohio Timberland Products ....F 419 682-6322
  Stryker *(G-18005)*

Omega Logging Inc ....G 330 534-0378
  Hubbard *(G-11137)*

Perkins Logging LLC ....G 740 288-7311
  Chillicothe *(G-3261)*

Perkins Wood Products ....G 740 884-4046
  Chillicothe *(G-3262)*

Powell Logging ....G 740 372-6131
  Otway *(G-15831)*

SIC

Randy Carter Logging Inc....G....740 634-2604
Bainbridge (G-1062)
Ray H Miller Trucking and Log....G....330 378-2131
Big Prairie (G-1684)
Ray L Lute LL....G....740 372-7703
Lucasville (G-12424)
Robby Yoder....G....740 679-2776
Quaker City (G-16501)
Robert Ashcraft....G....740 667-3690
Guysville (G-10654)
Roger L Best....G....740 590-9133
Stockport (G-17723)
Ross Tmber Harvstg For MGT Inc....G....513 383-6933
Batavia (G-1220)
Select Logging....G....419 564-0361
Marengo (G-12754)
Seymours Logging....F....740 288-1825
Wellston (G-19768)
Shellenbarger Excavating & Log....G....740 397-9949
Mount Vernon (G-14647)
Sissel Logging LLC....G....740 858-4613
Portsmouth (G-16454)
Stark Truss Company Inc....D....419 298-3777
Edgerton (G-9337)
Steve Henderson....G....419 738-6999
Wapakoneta (G-19508)
Superior Hardwoods of Ohio....D....740 384-6862
Jackson (G-11327)
T J Ellis Enterprises Inc....G....419 224-1969
Lima (G-12100)
T&R Logging LLC....G....740 288-1825
Wellston (G-19771)
Terry G Sickles....G....740 286-8880
Ray (G-16574)
Top Notch Logging....G....330 466-1780
Apple Creek (G-650)
Valley Veneer & Lumber Co....F....440 293-6025
Williamsfield (G-20417)
Vorhees Logging LLC....G....740 385-0216
Rockbridge (G-16690)
Warner Hildebrant....G....740 286-1903
South Webster (G-17452)
Watson Logging....G....740 985-4465
Pomeroy (G-16392)
Y&B Logging....G....440 437-1053
Orwell (G-15784)
Yoder Logging....G....740 679-2635
Quaker City (G-16502)

2421 Saw & Planing Mills

Andy A Raber....G....330 893-0400
Millersburg (G-14194)
Appalachia Wood Inc....F....740 596-2551
Mc Arthur (G-13328)
Automated Bldg Components Inc....E....419 257-2152
North Baltimore (G-15191)
Baillie Lumber Co LP....E....419 462-2000
Galion (G-10254)
Barker Lumber....G....740 289-2424
Piketon (G-16215)
Beach City Lumber LLC....G....330 878-4097
Strasburg (G-17821)
Beaver Wood Products....E....740 226-6211
Beaver (G-1310)
Beiting Farms....G....740 384-5127
Jackson (G-11310)
Blaney Hardwoods Ohio Inc....E....740 678-8288
Vincent (G-19378)
Blankenship Lumber Inc....G....740 372-0191
Otway (G-15827)
Bruewer Woodwork Mfg Co....D....513 353-3505
Cleves (G-6507)
Cherokee Hardwoods Inc....F....440 632-0322
Middlefield (G-13922)
Clarksville Stave & Lumber Co....G....937 376-4618
Xenia (G-20944)
Clear Run Lumber Co....G....740 747-2665
Marengo (G-12748)
Clyde Ferenbaugh....G....740 397-0287
Mount Vernon (G-14617)
Coblentz Brothers Inc....E....330 857-7211
Apple Creek (G-634)
Conover Lumber Company Inc....F....937 368-3010
Conover (G-7823)
Crownover Lumber Co Inc....D....740 596-5229
Mc Arthur (G-13330)
D&M Fencing LLC....G....419 604-0698
Spencerville (G-17459)
Del Holdash....G....440 427-0611
North Olmsted (G-15329)
Denoon Lumber Company LLC....D....740 768-2220
Bergholz (G-1641)
Dexter Hardwoods Inc....G....740 783-4141
Dexter City (G-8956)
DIA Enterprises Inc....G....740 802-7075
New Bloomington (G-14777)
Don Puckett Lumber Inc....F....740 887-4191
Londonderry (G-12227)
Dues Jersey Farm....G....419 678-2102
Coldwater (G-6557)
Facemyer Forest Products Inc....F....740 992-7425
Middleport (G-14010)
▼ Facemyer Lumber Co Inc....F....740 992-5965
Pomeroy (G-16389)
Fivecoat Lumber Inc....F....740 254-4681
Gnadenhutten (G-10407)
Frickco Inc....G....740 887-2017
South Bloomingville (G-17422)
Gardner Lumber Co Inc....F....740 254-4664
Tippecanoe (G-18313)
Gary Brown Farm & Sawmill....G....740 372-5022
Otway (G-15830)
Green Brothers Enterprises....G....937 444-3323
Sardinia (G-17029)
Gross Lumber Inc....E....330 683-2055
Apple Creek (G-638)
Haessly Lumber Sales Co....D....740 373-6681
Marietta (G-12788)
▼ Hartzell Hardwoods Inc....D....937 773-7054
Piqua (G-16272)
▲ Hess & Gault Lumber Co....G....419 281-3105
Ashland (G-739)
Hillcrest Lumber Ltd....G....330 359-5721
Apple Creek (G-639)
▼ Itl Corp....E....216 831-3140
Cleveland (G-5591)
Kaufman Mulch Inc....G....330 893-3676
Millersburg (G-14236)
Knisley Lumber....F....740 634-2935
Bainbridge (G-1061)
Koppers Ind Inc....G....740 776-2149
Portsmouth (G-16440)
Koppers Industries Inc....E....740 776-3238
Portsmouth (G-16441)
Kreis Sawmill....G....937 537-1248
Marysville (G-12955)
L Garbers Sons Sawmilling LLC....G....419 335-6362
Wauseon (G-19686)
Lansing Bros Sawmill....G....937 588-4291
Piketon (G-16223)
Lantz Lumber & Saw Shop....G....740 286-5658
Jackson (G-11318)
Leppert Companies Inc....G....614 889-2818
Dublin (G-9099)
Marathon At Sawmill....F....614 734-0836
Columbus (G-7317)
MB Manufacturing Corp....G....513 682-1461
Fairfield (G-9682)
Mbm Lumber....G....937 459-7448
Union City (G-19072)
McMillion Lock & Key....G....937 473-5342
Covington (G-7926)
Miller Logging Inc....E....330 279-4721
Holmesville (G-11109)
Miller Lumber Co Inc....E....330 674-0273
Millersburg (G-14247)
Mohler Lumber Company....E....330 499-5461
North Canton (G-15250)
Newberry Wood Enterprises Inc....F....440 238-6127
Strongsville (G-17945)
▼ Ohio Valley Veneer Inc....E....740 493-2901
Piketon (G-16225)
Omega Logging Inc....G....330 534-0378
Hubbard (G-11137)
P & R Hardwoods....G....937 452-3753
Camden (G-2487)
Piada Sawmill LLC....G....614 389-2069
Dublin (G-9125)
Plaza At Sawmill Pl....G....614 889-6121
Columbus (G-7497)
R & D Hilltop Lumber Inc....E....740 342-3051
New Lexington (G-14852)
R & L Wood Products....G....937 444-2496
Williamsburg (G-20411)
R J Dobay Enterprises Inc....G....440 834-4580
Burton (G-2382)
R M Wood Co....G....419 845-2661
Mount Gilead (G-14566)
Raber Lumber Co....G....330 893-2797
Charm (G-3184)
Ramona Southworth....G....740 226-8202
Beaver (G-1311)
Residents of Sawmill Park....G....614 659-6678
Dublin (G-9131)
Roseville Hardwood....G....740 221-8712
Roseville (G-16732)
Runkles Sawmill LLC....G....937 663-0115
Saint Paris (G-16864)
S & J Lumber Co....E....740 245-5804
Thurman (G-18200)
Salt Creek Lumber Company Inc....G....330 695-3500
Fredericksburg (G-10093)
Saw Siefker Mill....G....419 339-1956
Delphos (G-8917)
Sawmill Crossing....G....614 766-1685
Columbus (G-7592)
Sawmill Eye Associates Inc....G....440 724-0396
Broadview Heights (G-2118)
Sawmill Eye Associates Inc....G....614 734-2685
Columbus (G-7593)
Sawmill Road Management Co LLC....E....937 342-9071
Springfield (G-17646)
Sawmill Station....G....614 434-6147
Dublin (G-9139)
▼ Select Enterprises Inc....F....724 588-4141
Kinsman (G-11611)
Siefker Sawmill....G....419 339-1956
Elida (G-9358)
Southern Ohio Wood....G....740 288-1825
Wellston (G-19769)
Sphon Associates Inc....G....614 741-4002
Gahanna (G-10236)
Stark Truss Company Inc....E....330 756-3050
Beach City (G-1251)
▲ Stephen M Trudick....E....440 834-1891
Burton (G-2385)
Stony Point Hardwoods....F....330 852-4512
Sugarcreek (G-18040)
Stutzman Brothers Sawmill....G....440 272-5179
Middlefield (G-13992)
Sugarcreek Shavings LLC....G....330 763-4239
Sugarcreek (G-18044)
Superior Hardwoods of Ohio....E....740 596-2561
Mc Arthur (G-13333)
Superior Hardwoods of Ohio....D....740 384-6862
Jackson (G-11327)
Superior Hardwoods Ohio Inc....D....740 384-5677
Wellston (G-19770)
Superior Hardwoods Ohio Inc....E....740 439-2727
Cambridge (G-2477)
Supply Dynamics LLC....F....513 965-2000
Loveland (G-12392)
T & D Thompson Inc....E....740 332-8515
Laurelville (G-11772)
◆ Taylor Lumber Worldwide Inc....C....740 259-6222
Mc Dermott (G-13344)
Three H Lumber....G....740 473-2515
Newport (G-15127)
Timbermill Ltd....G....740 862-3426
Baltimore (G-1089)
Trumbull County Dry Kilns Inc....F....330 562-3367
Aurora (G-952)
Trumbull County Hardwoods....E....440 632-0555
Middlefield (G-13998)
Tusco Hardwoods LLC....F....330 852-4281
Sugarcreek (G-18047)
United Hardwoods Ltd....G....330 878-9510
Strasburg (G-17832)
Valley Veneer & Lumber Co....F....440 293-6025
Williamsfield (G-20417)
W O Hardwoods Inc....G....740 425-1588
Barnesville (G-1162)
Wagner Farms & Sawmill LLC....F....419 653-4126
Leipsic (G-11878)
Walnut Creek Lumber Co Ltd....E....330 852-4559
Dundee (G-9185)
▲ Walnut Creek Planing Ltd....D....330 893-3244
Millersburg (G-14281)
Wappoo Wood Products Inc....E....937 492-1166
Sidney (G-17233)
Weaver Lumber Co....G....330 359-5091
Wilmot (G-20687)
Wilmington Forest Products....G....937 382-5013
Wilmington (G-20682)
Woodsfeld True Vlue HM Ctr Inc....F....740 472-1651
Woodsfield (G-20723)
Wooldridge Lumber Co....D....740 289-4912
Piketon (G-16229)
Wrights Saw Mill....G....937 773-2546
Piqua (G-16316)

▼ Yoder Lumber Co Inc ....D 330 893-3121
Millersburg (G-14288)

Yoder Lumber Co Inc ....E 330 674-1435
Millersburg (G-14289)

Yoder Lumber Co Inc ....D 330 893-3131
Sugarcreek (G-18052)

2426 Hardwood Dimension & Flooring Mills

Armstrong Custom Moulding Inc ....G 740 922-5931
Uhrichsville (G-19045)

Baillie Lumber Co LP ....E 419 462-2000
Galion (G-10254)

Beaver Wood Products ....E 740 226-6211
Beaver (G-1310)

Bwd Woodwork LLC ....G 740 335-9766
Wshngtn CT Hs (G-20903)

Canfield Manufacturing Co Inc ....G 330 533-3333
North Jackson (G-15289)

Carter-Jones Lumber Company ....C 330 674-9060
Millersburg (G-14211)

Cherokee Hardwoods Inc ....F 440 632-0322
Middlefield (G-13922)

Creative Concepts ....G 216 513-6463
Medina (G-13398)

Crownover Lumber Co Inc ....D 740 596-5229
Mc Arthur (G-13330)

Denoon Lumber Company LLC ......D 740 768-2220
Bergholz (G-1641)

Dutch Heritage Woodcraft ....E 330 893-2211
Berlin (G-1648)

Gross Lumber Inc ....E 330 683-2055
Apple Creek (G-638)

Haessly Lumber Sales Co ....D 740 373-6681
Marietta (G-12788)

Halliday Holdings Inc ....E 740 335-1430
Wshngtn CT Hs (G-20910)

▼ Hardwood Flrg & Paneling Inc .....D 440 834-1710
Middlefield (G-13940)

▼ Hartzell Hardwoods Inc ....D 937 773-7054
Piqua (G-16272)

Hillcrest ....G 740 824-4849
Brinkhaven (G-2097)

Hillside Wood Ltd ....E 330 359-5991
Millersburg (G-14225)

Hinchcliff Lumber Company ....G 440 238-5200
Strongsville (G-17925)

Hochstetler Wood ....F 330 893-2384
Millersburg (G-14226)

Holmes Lumber & Bldg Ctr Inc ....C 330 674-9060
Millersburg (G-14231)

Itl LLC ....B 216 831-3140
Beachwood (G-1274)

▼ Itl Corp ....E 216 831-3140
Cleveland (G-5591)

J McCoy Lumber Co Ltd ....F 937 587-3423
Peebles (G-16022)

J McCoy Lumber Co Ltd ....G 937 544-2968
West Union (G-20121)

Kelco Hardwood Floors Inc ....G 440 354-0974
Painesville (G-15895)

Knisley Lumber ....F 740 634-2935
Bainbridge (G-1061)

Little Cottage Company ....G 330 893-4212
Millersburg (G-14241)

Marsh Valley Forest Pdts Ltd ....G 440 632-1889
Middlefield (G-13953)

Mid Ohio Wood Products Inc ....E 740 323-0427
Newark (G-15033)

Mohler Lumber Company ....E 330 499-5461
North Canton (G-15250)

▼ Ohio Valley Veneer Inc ....E 740 493-2901
Piketon (G-16225)

Plank and Hide Co ....F 513 378-3194
Cincinnati (G-4242)

◆ Prestige Enterprise Intl Inc ....D 513 469-6044
Blue Ash (G-1855)

Property Assist Inc ....G 419 480-1700
Toledo (G-18660)

◆ Robbins Inc ....E 513 871-8988
Cincinnati (G-4352)

Siefker Sawmill ....G 419 339-1956
Elida (G-9358)

▲ Stephen M Trudick ....E 440 834-1891
Burton (G-2385)

Stony Point Hardwoods ....F 330 852-4512
Sugarcreek (G-18040)

Superior Hardwoods of Ohio ....E 740 596-2561
Mc Arthur (G-13333)

Superior Hardwoods Ohio Inc ....D 740 384-5677
Wellston (G-19770)

Superior Hardwoods Ohio Inc ....E 740 439-2727
Cambridge (G-2477)

T & D Thompson Inc ....E 740 332-8515
Laurelville (G-11772)

Trumbull County Dry Kilns Inc ......F 330 562-3367
Aurora (G-952)

Trumbull County Hardwoods ....F 440 632-0555
Middlefield (G-13998)

Valley Veneer & Lumber Co ....F 440 293-6025
Williamsfield (G-20417)

Valleyview Wood Turning Co ....D 330 763-0407
Millersburg (G-14277)

Wagner Farms & Sawmill LLC ....F 419 653-4126
Leipsic (G-11878)

▲ Walnut Creek Planing Ltd ....D 330 893-3244
Millersburg (G-14281)

Wappoo Wood Products Inc ....E 937 492-1166
Sidney (G-17233)

Woodcraft Industries Inc ....D 440 437-7811
Orwell (G-15783)

Woodcraft Industries Inc ....C 440 632-9655
Middlefield (G-14007)

Woodcraft Manufacturing Co ....E 740 927-6609
Pataskala (G-15992)

Wooden Horse ....G 740 503-5243
Baltimore (G-1091)

Yoder Lumber Co Inc ....D 330 893-3131
Sugarcreek (G-18052)

▼ Yoder Lumber Co Inc ....D 330 893-3121
Millersburg (G-14288)

2429 Special Prdt Sawmills, NEC

Brown-Forman Corporation ....E 740 384-3027
Wellston (G-19761)

2431 Millwork

7&7 Woodworking ....G 330 347-6574
Wooster (G-20729)

7d Marketing Inc ....F 330 721-8822
Medina (G-13362)

A & B Wood Design Assoc Inc ....G 330 721-2789
Wadsworth (G-19385)

A & J Woodworking ....G 888 572-9561
Sugarcreek (G-18014)

A & J Woodworking Inc ....G 419 695-5655
Delphos (G-8898)

A & M Woodworking ....G 330 893-1331
Millersburg (G-14189)

A C Shutters Inc ....G 216 429-2424
Cleveland (G-4669)

A W S Incorporated ....G 419 352-5397
Bowling Green (G-1962)

Ace Lumber Company ....F 330 744-3167
Youngstown (G-21015)

▲ Action Industries Ltd ....E 216 252-7800
Cleveland (G-4698)

Adams Custom Woodworking ....F 513 761-1395
Cincinnati (G-3355)

▼ Advantage Tent Fittings Inc ......F 740 773-3015
Chillicothe (G-3226)

Ailes Millwork Inc ....F 330 678-4300
Kent (G-11424)

Aj Stineburg Wdwkg Studio LLC .....G 614 526-9480
Columbus (G-6706)

All Around Garage Door Inc ....G 440 759-5079
North Ridgeville (G-15357)

All Pro Ovrhd Door Systems LLC .....G 614 444-3667
Columbus (G-6721)

Amarr Company ....G 216 573-7100
Independence (G-11248)

Amcan Stair & Rail LLC ....F 937 781-3084
Springfield (G-17516)

American Home Products LLC ....G 800 684-3434
(G-4784)

American Woodwork Specialty Co .....E 937 263-1053
Dayton (G-8156)

Anderson Door Co ....E 216 475-5700
Cleveland (G-4809)

Architectural Door Systems LLC .....G 513 808-9900
Lebanon (G-11780)

Armstrong Custom Moulding Inc .....G 740 922-5931
Uhrichsville (G-19045)

◆ Arrow Tru-Line Inc ....E 419 446-2785
Archbold (G-666)

Art Woodworking & Mfg Co ....G 513 681-2986
Cincinnati (G-3415)

Automated Bldg Components Inc .....E 419 257-2152
North Baltimore (G-15191)

Baird Brothers Sawmill Inc ....C 330 533-3122
Canfield (G-2549)

▲ Bautec N Technoform Amer Inc .....E 330 487-6600
Twinsburg (G-18903)

Bay World International Inc ....E 419 525-2222
Mansfield (G-12565)

Beechvale Laminating ....F 330 674-2804
Millersburg (G-14198)

Berlin Woodworking ....G 330 893-3234
Millersburg (G-14202)

Berry Woodworking ....F 513 734-6133
Amelia (G-569)

Bomba S Custom Woodworking ....G 330 699-9075
Uniontown (G-19078)

Brogan Machine Shop ....G 513 683-9054
Loveland (G-12345)

Bruewer Woodwork Mfg Co ....D 513 353-3505
Cleves (G-6507)

Buckeye Products ....G 740 969-4718
Amanda (G-560)

Bwd Woodwork LLC ....G 740 335-9766
Wshngtn CT Hs (G-20903)

C & W Custom Wdwkg Co Inc ....E 513 891-6340
Blue Ash (G-1757)

C Square Lumber Products ....F 740 557-3129
Stockport (G-17722)

Carden Door Company LLC ....G 513 459-2233
Mason (G-12990)

▲ Carolina Stair Supply Inc ....G 740 922-3333
Uhrichsville (G-19046)

Carter-Jones Lumber Company ......C 330 674-9060
Millersburg (G-14211)

▲ Cascade Ohio Inc ....B 440 593-5800
Conneaut (G-7801)

Cassady Woodworks Inc ....E 937 256-7948
Dayton (G-8099)

Cincinnati Wood Products Co ....G 513 542-0569
Cincinnati (G-3569)

Cincinnati Woodworks Inc ....G 513 241-6412
Cincinnati (G-3570)

Cindoco Wood Products Co ....G 937 444-2504
Mount Orab (G-14577)

Clark Township Garage ....G 330 897-4844
Baltic (G-1066)

Clark Wood Specialties Inc ....G 330 499-8711
Clinton (G-6534)

◆ Clopay Building Pdts Co Inc ....E 513 770-4800
Mason (G-12998)

Clopay Building Pdts Co Inc ....E 937 526-4301
Russia (G-16762)

Clopay Building Pdts Co Inc ....E 937 440-6403
Troy (G-18810)

▲ Clopay Corporation ....C 800 282-2260
Mason (G-12999)

Corns Quality Woodworking LLC .....E 419 589-4899
Mansfield (G-12585)

Cortland Hardwood Products LLC .....E 330 638-3232
Cortland (G-7865)

Country Comfort Woodworking ....G 330 695-4408
Fredericksburg (G-10081)

Courthouse Manufacturing LLC ......E 740 335-2727
Washington Court Hou (G-19638)

Cox Interior Inc ....G 614 473-9169
Columbus (G-6993)

Creative Millwork Ohio Inc ....G 440 992-3566
Ashtabula (G-799)

Creative Woodworks ....G 330 897-1432
Sugarcreek (G-18021)

Crowes Cabinets Inc ....G 330 536-2545
Lowellville (G-12406)

Curves and More Woodworking ....G 614 239-7837
Columbus (G-7003)

D & L Overhead Door Co Ltd ....G 440 255-9720
Mentor (G-13557)

Darby Creek Millwork Co ....G 614 873-3267
Plain City (G-16331)

Dendratec Ltd ....G 330 473-4878
Dalton (G-8067)

Denoon Lumber Company LLC ......D 740 768-2220
Bergholz (G-1641)

Design-N-Wood LLC ....G 937 419-0479
Sidney (G-17177)

Display Dynamics Inc ....F 937 832-2830
Englewood (G-9516)

Division Overhead Door Inc ....E 513 872-0888
Cincinnati (G-3659)

Dlwoodworking ....G 740 927-2693
Pataskala (G-15969)

▲ Door Fabrication Services Inc ......G 937 454-9207
Vandalia (G-19290)

Door Guys Inc ....F 419 562-3376
Bucyrus (G-2339)

Dublin Millwork Co Inc ....E 614 889-7776
Dublin (G-9069)

Dutch Heritage Woodcraft ....E 330 893-2211
Berlin (G-1648)

Ernest Warther and Sons Inc ....F 330 343-7513
Dover (G-8984)

Evil Corporation Corporation ....G 937 902-5921
Dayton (G-8335)

Fairfield Woodworks Ltd ....G 740 689-1953
Lancaster (G-11715)

Farmstead Acres Woodworking ....G 330 695-6492
Fredericksburg (G-10086)

Fdi Cabinetry LLC ....G 513 353-4500
Cleves (G-6514)

Fifth Avenue Lumber Co ....D 614 833-6655
Canal Winchester (G-2524)

▼ Fixture Dimensions Inc ....E 513 360-7512
Middletown (G-14041)

Flottemesch Anthony & Son ....F 513 561-1212
Cincinnati (G-3762)

Forum III Inc ....F 513 961-5123
Cincinnati (G-3773)

▼ Gateway Industrial Pdts Inc ....F 440 324-4112
Elyria (G-9425)

Gdw Woodworking LLC ....G 513 494-3041
South Lebanon (G-17429)

Gerstenslager Construction ....G 330 832-3604
Massillon (G-13139)

Great Lakes Stair & Mllwk Co ....G 330 225-2005
Hinckley (G-11024)

Gross & Sons Custom Millwork ....G 419 227-0214
Lima (G-12020)

Hawk Engine & Machine ....G 440 582-0900
North Royalton (G-15424)

Heartland Stairway Ltd ....G 330 279-2554
Millersburg (G-14220)

Hinckley Wood Products ....G 330 220-9999
Hinckley (G-11025)

Hj Systems Inc ....F 614 351-9777
Columbus (G-7161)

Hoehnes Custom Woodworking ....G 937 693-8008
Anna (G-623)

Holes Custom Woodworking ....G 419 586-8171
Celina (G-3002)

Holmes Lumber & Bldg Ctr Inc ....C 330 674-9060
Millersburg (G-14231)

Hoover Group ....G 419 525-3159
Shiloh (G-17149)

Hrh Door Corp ....D 440 593-5226
Conneaut (G-7809)

◆ Hrh Door Corp ....A 850 208-3400
Mount Hope (G-14572)

Hrh Door Corp ....E 513 674-9300
Cincinnati (G-3900)

Huntington Hardwood Lbr Co Inc ....G 440 647-2283
Wellington (G-19748)

Hyde Park Lumber Company ....E 513 271-1500
Cincinnati (G-3903)

Idx Corporation ....C 937 401-3225
Dayton (G-8400)

Inter Cab Corporation ....G 216 351-0770
Cleveland (G-5576)

J A H Woodworking LLC ....G 740 266-6949
Bloomingdale (G-1723)

J McCoy Lumber Co Ltd ....F 937 587-3423
Peebles (G-16022)

J McCoy Lumber Co Ltd ....G 937 544-2968
West Union (G-20121)

Jaco Inc ....G 513 722-3947
Loveland (G-12364)

Jeld-Wen Inc ....B 740 397-1144
Mount Vernon (G-14625)

Jeld-Wen Inc ....C 740 964-1431
Etna (G-9557)

Jeld-Wen Inc ....E 740 397-3403
Mount Vernon (G-14626)

Jh Woodworking LLC ....G 330 276-7600
Killbuck (G-11595)

Joe P Fischer Woodcraft ....G 513 530-9600
Blue Ash (G-1819)

John M Hand ....G 937 902-1327
West Alexandria (G-19780)

Judy Mills Company Inc ....E 513 271-4241
Cincinnati (G-3962)

K D Hardwoods Inc ....G 440 834-1772
Burton (G-2379)

Kacy Stairs ....F 740 599-5201
Howard (G-11123)

Khempco Bldg Sup Co Ltd Partnr ....D 740 549-0465
Delaware (G-8865)

L & L Ornamental Iron Co ....F 513 353-1930
Cleves (G-6520)

▲ L J Smith Inc ....C 740 269-2221
Bowerston (G-1958)

Laborie Enterprises LLC ....G 419 686-6245
Portage (G-16425)

LAtelier Custom Woodworking ....G 234 759-3359
North Lima (G-15320)

▲ LE Smith Company ....D 419 636-4555
Bryan (G-2310)

Lehman & Sons ....G 330 857-7404
Orrville (G-15745)

Liechty Specialties Inc ....G 419 445-6696
Archbold (G-683)

Lima Millwork Inc ....E 419 331-3303
Elida (G-9351)

Lj Woodworking ....G 330 359-3216
Dundee (G-9175)

Longs Custom Doors ....G 419 339-2331
Lima (G-12049)

M H Woodworking LLC ....G 330 893-3929
Millersburg (G-14243)

M21 Industries LLC ....D 937 781-1377
Dayton (G-8465)

Mandi A Tripp ....G 740 380-1216
Rockbridge (G-16689)

Maple Hill Woodworking ....G 330 674-2500
Millersburg (G-14245)

Marsh Industries Inc ....E 330 308-8667
New Philadelphia (G-14912)

Martin Bauder Woodworking LLC ....G 513 735-0659
Milford (G-14160)

Masco Cbinetry Middlefield LLC ....B 440 437-8537
Orwell (G-15778)

Masonite Corporation ....D 937 454-9207
Vandalia (G-19303)

Menard Inc ....E 513 250-4566
Cincinnati (G-4084)

Menard Inc ....E 419 998-4348
Lima (G-12053)

Midwest Woodworking Co Inc ....G 513 631-6684
Cincinnati (G-4106)

Miller and Slay Wdwkg LLC ....G 513 265-3816
Mason (G-13063)

▼ Miller Manufacturing Inc ....E 330 852-0689
Sugarcreek (G-18028)

Mills Customs Woodworks ....G 216 407-3600
Cleveland (G-5818)

Millwood Wholesale Inc ....F 330 359-6109
Dundee (G-9177)

Millwork Designs Inc ....G 740 335-5203
Wshngtn CT Hs (G-20917)

Millwork Fabricators Inc ....G 937 299-5452
Moraine (G-14508)

Mohican Wood Products ....G 740 599-5655
Butler (G-2393)

Morey Woodworking LLC ....G 937 623-5280
Piqua (G-16293)

Mount Hope Planing ....F 330 359-0538
Millersburg (G-14250)

Nagele Manufacturing Co Inc ....G 216 433-1100
Cleveland (G-5849)

National Access Design LLC ....F 513 351-3400
Cincinnati (G-4137)

▲ National Door and Trim Inc ....E 419 238-9345
Van Wert (G-19268)

Nauvoo Custom Woodworking ....G 440 632-9502
Middlefield (G-13974)

North View Woodworking ....G 330 359-6286
Dundee (G-9174)

Noteworthy Woodworking ....G 330 297-0509
Ravenna (G-16545)

Oak Front Inc ....G 330 948-4500
Lodi (G-12167)

Oak Pointe Stair Systems Inc ....E 740 498-9820
Newcomerstown (G-15120)

Ohio Woodworking Co Inc ....G 513 631-0870
Cincinnati (G-4181)

Overhead Door Corporation ....D 740 383-6376
Marion (G-12892)

Overhead Door Corporation ....F 419 294-3874
Upper Sandusky (G-19138)

P & T Millwork Inc ....E 440 543-2151
Chagrin Falls (G-3109)

Paragon Woodworking LLC ....G 614 402-1459
Columbus (G-7461)

Pease Industies Inc ....B 513 870-3600
Fairfield (G-9700)

Peninsula Hardwoods Inc ....G 330 657-2701
Peninsula (G-16039)

Pete Emmert Co ....G 740 455-3924
Nashport (G-14706)

Pickens Window Service Inc ....F 513 931-4432
Cincinnati (G-4235)

Pj Woodwork LLC ....G 419 886-0008
Bellville (G-1574)

Pleasant Valley Wdwkg LLC ....G 440 636-5860
Middlefield (G-13983)

Ply Gem Industries Inc ....C 937 492-1111
Sidney (G-17210)

Precision Wood Products Inc ....E 937 787-3523
Camden (G-2488)

Premium Panel & Tread ....G 330 695-9979
Fredericksburg (G-10090)

R C Moore Lumber Co ....F 740 732-4950
Caldwell (G-2431)

R Carney Thomas ....G 740 342-3388
New Lexington (G-14853)

Rebsco Inc ....F 937 548-2246
Greenville (G-10517)

Renewal By Andersen LLC ....G 614 781-9600
Columbus (G-6658)

Reserve Millwork Inc ....E 216 531-6982
Bedford (G-1457)

Richardson Woodworking ....G 614 893-8850
Blacklick (G-1705)

▲ Rinos Woodworking Shop Inc ....F 440 946-1718
Willoughby (G-20589)

Riverside Cnstr Svcs Inc ....E 513 723-0900
Cincinnati (G-4349)

Robertson Cabinets Inc ....G 937 698-3755
West Milton (G-20110)

Roettger Hardwood Inc ....F 937 693-6811
Kettlersville (G-11589)

Roy Holtzapple John Johns ....E 419 657-2460
Wapakoneta (G-19504)

S & S Panel ....G 330 412-6735
Orrville (G-15761)

S R Door Inc ....D 740 927-3558
Hebron (G-10883)

Sauder Wdwkg Co Welfare Tr ....G 419 446-2711
Archbold (G-693)

Sawdust ....G 740 862-0612
Baltimore (G-1088)

Scarred Hands Wood Creations ....G 740 975-2835
Etna (G-9562)

Schreiner Cstm Stairs & Mllwk ....F 419 435-8935
Fostoria (G-9994)

Screenmobile Inc ....G 614 868-8663
Radnor (G-16507)

Select Woodworking Inc ....F 513 948-9901
Cincinnati (G-4402)

Seneca Millwork Inc ....E 419 435-6671
Fostoria (G-9995)

Shade Youngstown & Aluminum Co ....G 330 782-2373
Youngstown (G-21200)

Shawnee Wood Products Inc ....G 440 632-1771
Middlefield (G-13989)

Sheridan Woodworks Inc ....F 216 663-9333
Cleveland (G-6188)

Sommers Wood N Door Company ....G 614 873-3506
Plain City (G-16361)

Stainwood Products ....F 440 244-1352
Lorain (G-12280)

Star Door & Sash Co Inc ....F 419 841-3396
Berkey (G-1643)

Stein Inc ....F 419 747-2611
Mansfield (G-12683)

▲ Stephen M Trudick ....E 440 834-1891
Burton (G-2385)

Stoney Acres Woodworking Llc ....G 440 834-0717
Burton (G-2386)

Stony Point Hardwoods ....F 330 852-4512
Sugarcreek (G-18040)

Stratton Creek Wood Works LLC ....F 330 876-0005
Kinsman (G-11612)

Stull Woodworks ....G 937 698-8181
Ludlow Falls (G-12428)

Summit Millwork LLC ....G 330 920-4000
Cuyahoga Falls (G-8051)

Swartz Woodworking ....G 330 359-6359
Millersburg (G-14266)

Swiss Woodcraft Inc ....G 330 925-1807
Rittman (G-16683)

Sylvan Forge Inc ....G 440 237-3626
North Royalton (G-15453)

T & D Thompson Inc ....E 740 332-8515
Laurelville (G-11772)

Thermolock Mfg LLC ....E 513 771-6555
Hamilton (G-10745)

Timberlane Woodworking ....G...... 419 895-9945
  Greenwich *(G-10537)*

Touchstone Woodworks ....G...... 330 297-1313
  Ravenna *(G-16566)*

Trimtec Systems Ltd ....F...... 614 820-0340
  Grove City *(G-10607)*

Turnwood Industries Inc ....E...... 330 278-2421
  Hinckley *(G-11031)*

▼ Universal Production Corp ....C...... 740 522-1147
  Newark *(G-15065)*

V & W Woodcraft ....G...... 330 674-0073
  Millersburg *(G-14276)*

Versailles Building Supply ....G...... 937 526-3238
  Versailles *(G-19358)*

Village Woodworking ....G...... 740 326-4461
  Fredericktown *(G-10115)*

Vinylmax Corporation ....D...... 800 847-3736
  Hamilton *(G-10754)*

Volpe Millwork ....G...... 216 581-0200
  Cleveland *(G-6427)*

Walnut Creek Woodworking LLC ....G...... 513 504-3520
  Bethel *(G-1665)*

Wedge Hardwood Products ....G...... 330 525-7775
  Alliance *(G-552)*

▲ Wittrock Wdwkg & Mfg Co Inc ....D...... 513 891-5800
  Blue Ash *(G-1896)*

Woodcraft Industries Inc ....C...... 440 632-9655
  Middlefield *(G-14007)*

Woodcraft Industries Inc ....D...... 440 437-7811
  Orwell *(G-15783)*

Woodcraft Manufacturing Co ....E...... 740 927-6609
  Pataskala *(G-15992)*

Woodland Woodworking ....G...... 330 897-7282
  Baltic *(G-1079)*

Woodworks Unlimited ....G...... 740 574-4523
  Franklin Furnace *(G-10070)*

Wyman Woodworking ....G...... 614 338-0615
  Columbus *(G-7779)*

▼ Yoder Lumber Co Inc ....D...... 330 893-3121
  Millersburg *(G-14288)*

Yoder Window & Siding Ltd ....F...... 330 695-6960
  Fredericksburg *(G-10095)*

Yoder Woodworking ....G...... 740 399-9400
  Butler *(G-2394)*

▲ Yutzy Woodworking Ltd ....C...... 330 359-6166
  Millersburg *(G-14292)*

2434 Wood Kitchen Cabinets

4-B Wood Specialties Inc ....F...... 330 769-2188
  Seville *(G-17067)*

A & J Woodworking Inc ....G...... 419 695-5655
  Delphos *(G-8898)*

Affordable Cabinet Doors ....G...... 513 734-9663
  Bethel *(G-1664)*

Agean Marble Manufacturing ....F...... 513 874-1475
  West Chester *(G-19978)*

Ailes Millwork Inc ....F...... 330 678-4300
  Kent *(G-11424)*

Al-Co Products Inc ....F...... 419 399-3867
  Latty *(G-11767)*

Alpine Cabinets Inc ....G...... 330 273-2131
  Hinckley *(G-11021)*

Approved Plumbing Co ....F...... 216 663-5063
  Cleveland *(G-4820)*

Baird Cabinet Shop Inc ....G...... 330 837-9075
  Massillon *(G-13113)*

Benchmark Cabinets ....E...... 740 397-4615
  Mount Vernon *(G-14609)*

Benchmark Cabinets ....E...... 740 694-1144
  Fredericktown *(G-10096)*

Bestway Cabinets LLC ....G...... 614 306-3518
  Hilliard *(G-10932)*

Bison Builders LLC ....F...... 614 636-0365
  Columbus *(G-6832)*

Bowes Mill and Cabinet LLC ....G...... 440 236-3255
  Columbia Station *(G-6581)*

Bricolage Inc ....G...... 614 853-6789
  Grove City *(G-10547)*

Brower Products Inc ....D...... 937 563-1111
  Cincinnati *(G-3482)*

Bruewer Woodwork Mfg Co ....D...... 513 353-3505
  Cleves *(G-6507)*

Cabinet Concepts Inc ....G...... 440 232-4644
  Cleveland *(G-4960)*

Cabinet Source ....G...... 330 336-5600
  Wadsworth *(G-19397)*

Cabinet Specialties Inc ....E...... 330 695-3463
  Fredericksburg *(G-10079)*

Cabinet Systems Inc ....G...... 440 237-1924
  Cleveland *(G-4961)*

Cabinetry By Ebbing ....G...... 419 678-2191
  Celina *(G-2988)*

Cabinets Inc ....G...... 740 377-4629
  South Point *(G-17435)*

Canton Cabinet Co ....G...... 330 455-2585
  Canton *(G-2637)*

Cardinal Custom Cabinets Ltd ....G...... 216 281-1570
  Cleveland *(G-4975)*

Care Cabinetry Inc ....G...... 216 481-7445
  Euclid *(G-9570)*

Carnegie Plas Cabinetry Inc ....G...... 216 451-3300
  Cleveland *(G-4981)*

Carter-Jones Lumber Company ....C...... 330 674-9060
  Millersburg *(G-14211)*

Cedee Cedar Inc ....F...... 740 363-3148
  Delaware *(G-8831)*

Chesterland Cabinet Company ....G...... 440 564-1157
  Newbury *(G-15083)*

Cirjak Furniture and Design ....G...... 330 296-8035
  Ravenna *(G-16521)*

Clancys Cabinet Shop ....E...... 419 445-4455
  Archbold *(G-668)*

▼ Clark Son Actn Liquidation Inc ....G...... 330 866-9330
  East Sparta *(G-9254)*

Cleveland Custom Cabinets LLC ....G...... 213 663-0606
  Cleveland *(G-5056)*

Colonial Cabinets Inc ....F...... 440 355-9663
  Lagrange *(G-11624)*

Commercial Bar & Cabinetry ....G...... 330 743-1420
  Youngstown *(G-21054)*

Contemporary Cabinets Inc ....G...... 937 833-1135
  Brookville *(G-2178)*

Crane Plumbing LLC ....E...... 419 522-4211
  Mansfield *(G-12587)*

Custom Woodworking Inc ....G...... 419 456-3330
  Ottawa *(G-15791)*

D Lewis Inc ....G...... 740 695-2615
  Saint Clairsville *(G-16788)*

Dgl Woodworking Inc ....F...... 937 837-7091
  Dayton *(G-8302)*

Distinctive Surfaces LLC ....F...... 614 431-0898
  Columbus *(G-7031)*

Dover Cabinet Inc ....F...... 330 343-9074
  Dover *(G-8978)*

Dutch Valley Woodworking Inc ....F...... 330 852-4319
  Sugarcreek *(G-18022)*

E J Skok Industries ....G...... 216 292-7533
  Bedford *(G-1422)*

East Oberlin Cabinets ....G...... 440 775-1166
  Oberlin *(G-15637)*

Ernst Custom Cabinets LLC ....G...... 513 376-9554
  Cincinnati *(G-3717)*

Fairfield Woodworks Ltd ....G...... 740 689-1953
  Lancaster *(G-11715)*

Fdi Cabinetry LLC ....G...... 513 353-4500
  Cleves *(G-6514)*

Fine Wood Design Inc ....G...... 440 327-0751
  North Ridgeville *(G-15374)*

Fleetwood Custom Countertops ....F...... 740 965-9833
  Johnstown *(G-11398)*

Flottemesch Anthony & Son ....F...... 513 561-1212
  Cincinnati *(G-3762)*

Formware Inc ....G...... 614 231-9387
  Columbus *(G-7093)*

Forum III Inc ....F...... 513 961-5123
  Cincinnati *(G-3773)*

Franklin Cabinet Company Inc ....F...... 937 743-9606
  Franklin *(G-10023)*

Gillard Construction Inc ....F...... 740 376-9744
  Marietta *(G-12786)*

Hampshire Co ....E...... 937 773-3493
  Piqua *(G-16268)*

Harold Flory ....G...... 937 473-3030
  Covington *(G-7924)*

Hattenbach Company ....G...... 330 744-2732
  Youngstown *(G-21107)*

Hattenbach Company ....D...... 216 881-5200
  Cleveland *(G-5485)*

Heartland Home Cabinetry Ltd ....G...... 740 936-5100
  Sunbury *(G-18062)*

Holmes Lumber & Bldg Ctr Inc ....C...... 330 674-9060
  Millersburg *(G-14231)*

Idx Corporation ....C...... 937 401-3225
  Dayton *(G-8400)*

Inter Cab Corporation ....G...... 216 351-0770
  Cleveland *(G-5576)*

J & K Cabinetry Incorporated ....G...... 513 860-3461
  West Chester *(G-20017)*

J & L Door ....G...... 330 684-1496
  Dalton *(G-8071)*

James F Seme ....G...... 440 759-6455
  Berea *(G-1623)*

◆ Kellogg Cabinets Inc ....E...... 614 833-9596
  Canal Winchester *(G-2529)*

Kelly Cabinet Company LLC ....G...... 614 563-2971
  Powell *(G-16474)*

Kinnemyers Cornerstone Cab Inc ....G...... 513 353-3030
  Cleves *(G-6518)*

Kinsella Manufacturing Co Inc ....F...... 513 561-5285
  Cincinnati *(G-3991)*

Kitchen Designs Plus Inc ....E...... 419 536-6605
  Toledo *(G-18545)*

Kitchen Works Inc ....G...... 440 353-0939
  North Ridgeville *(G-15385)*

▲ Kitchens By Rutenschroer Inc ....F...... 513 251-8333
  Cincinnati *(G-3994)*

Lima Millwork Inc ....E...... 419 331-3303
  Elida *(G-9351)*

M A Miller ....G...... 440 636-5697
  Middlefield *(G-13951)*

Malco Laminated Inc ....G...... 513 541-8300
  Cincinnati *(G-4055)*

Marsh Industries Inc ....E...... 330 308-8667
  New Philadelphia *(G-14912)*

Masco Cabinetry LLC ....B...... 740 286-5033
  Jackson *(G-11320)*

◆ Masco Cbinetry Middlefield LLC ....A...... 440 632-5333
  Middlefield *(G-13955)*

Masco Cbinetry Middlefield LLC ....D...... 440 632-5058
  Middlefield *(G-13956)*

Masco Cbinetry Middlefield LLC ....B...... 440 437-8537
  Orwell *(G-15778)*

Midwest Woodworking Co Inc ....E...... 513 631-6684
  Cincinnati *(G-4106)*

Miller Cabinet Company LLC ....E...... 614 873-4221
  Plain City *(G-16351)*

Mock Woodworking Company LLC ....E...... 740 452-2701
  Zanesville *(G-21329)*

Mro Built Inc ....D...... 330 526-0555
  North Canton *(G-15252)*

Nagele Manufacturing Co Inc ....E...... 216 433-1100
  Cleveland *(G-5849)*

Navigator Construction LLC ....G...... 330 244-0221
  North Canton *(G-15254)*

Northeast Cabinet Co LLC ....E...... 614 759-0800
  Columbus *(G-7402)*

Northpointe Cabinetry LLC ....G...... 740 455-4045
  Zanesville *(G-21334)*

Oakwood Furniture Inc ....G...... 740 896-3162
  Lowell *(G-12403)*

Oen Custom Cabinets Inc ....G...... 419 738-8115
  Wapakoneta *(G-19503)*

Ohio River Valley Cabinet ....G...... 740 975-8846
  Newark *(G-15042)*

Old Mill Custom Cabinetry Co ....G...... 419 423-8897
  Findlay *(G-9871)*

Online Mega Sellers Corp ....G...... 888 384-6468
  Toledo *(G-18619)*

Peters Cabinetry ....G...... 937 884-7514
  Brookville *(G-2196)*

Phil D De Mint ....G...... 740 474-7777
  Circleville *(G-4636)*

Pleasant Valley Wdwkg LLC ....G...... 440 636-5860
  Middlefield *(G-13983)*

Precision Woodwork Ltd ....G...... 440 257-3002
  Mentor *(G-13696)*

Profiles In Design Inc ....F...... 513 751-2212
  Cincinnati *(G-4297)*

R Carney Thomas ....G...... 740 342-3388
  New Lexington *(G-14853)*

Red Barn Cabinet Co ....G...... 937 884-9800
  Arcanum *(G-659)*

Regal Cabinet Inc ....G...... 419 865-3932
  Toledo *(G-18674)*

Reserve Millwork Inc ....E...... 216 531-6982
  Bedford *(G-1457)*

Riceland Cabinet Inc ....D...... 330 601-1071
  Wooster *(G-20829)*

Richard Benhase & Associates ....F...... 513 772-1896
  Cincinnati *(G-4343)*

Riggenbach Kitchens ....G...... 330 669-2113
  Smithville *(G-17242)*

River East Custom Cabinets ....E...... 419 244-3226
  Toledo *(G-18677)*

Riverside Cnstr Svcs Inc ....E...... 513 723-0900
  Cincinnati *(G-4349)*

Roberts Cabinetry LLC ....G...... 330 421-4374
  Medina *(G-13469)*

Roettger Hardwood Inc ....F...... 937 693-6811
  Kettlersville *(G-11589)*

Royal Cabinet Design Co Inc ....F 216 267-5330
Cleveland **(G-6137)**
Ruede Cabinet Company ....G..... 614 875-8717
Lockbourne **(G-12151)**
S & G Manufacturing Group LLC ....C 614 529-0100
Hilliard **(G-10977)**
S & W Custom Tops Inc ....G...... 330 788-2525
Youngstown **(G-21195)**
Schrock Woodworking ....G 740 489-5229
Freeport **(G-10120)**
Shawnee Wood Products Inc ....G...... 440 632-1771
Middlefield **(G-13989)**
Showcase Cab Mar Rstoration LL ....G...... 419 626-6715
Sandusky **(G-17008)**
Sidney Stiers ....G...... 740 454-7368
Zanesville **(G-21353)**
Snows Wood Shop Inc ....E 419 836-3805
Oregon **(G-15716)**
Specified Structures Inc ....G...... 330 753-0693
Barberton **(G-1149)**
Summit Custom Cabinets ....G...... 740 345-1734
Newark **(G-15061)**
Surface Enterprises Inc ....E 419 476-5670
Toledo **(G-18711)**
TDS Custom Cabinets LLC ....G...... 614 517-2220
Columbus **(G-7680)**
Tenkotte Tops Inc ....G...... 513 738-7300
Harrison **(G-10810)**
Thomas Cabinet Shop Inc ....F 937 847-8239
Dayton **(G-8711)**
▼ Tiffin Metal Products Co ....D 419 447-8414
Tiffin **(G-18248)**
Trail Cabinet ....G...... 330 893-3791
Dundee **(G-9181)**
Trutech Cabinetry ....G...... 614 338-0680
Columbus **(G-7713)**
Turnwood Industries Inc ....E 330 278-2421
Hinckley **(G-11031)**
Unique Woodmasters LLC ....G...... 419 268-9663
Celina **(G-3025)**
Virgils Kitchens Inc ....G...... 440 355-5058
Lagrange **(G-11641)**
Wengerd Cabinets ....G...... 330 231-0879
Millersburg **(G-14285)**
Westgerdes Cabinets ....G...... 419 375-2113
Fort Recovery **(G-9963)**
Wilson Cabinet Co ....G...... 330 276-8711
Killbuck **(G-11601)**
Woodcraft Industries Inc ....D 440 437-7811
Orwell **(G-15783)**
Woodcraft Industries Inc ....C 440 632-9655
Middlefield **(G-14007)**
Wurms Woodworking Company ....E 419 492-2184
New Washington **(G-14966)**
Xxx Intrntional Amusements Inc ....E 216 671-6900
Cleveland **(G-6487)**
Yoder Cabinets Ltd ....G...... 614 873-5186
Plain City **(G-16366)**
Your Cabinetry ....G...... 440 638-4925
Strongsville **(G-17986)**

2435 Hardwood Veneer & Plywood

A & M Kiln Dry Ltd ....F 330 852-0505
Dundee **(G-9170)**
▲ American Veneer Edgebanding ....G...... 740 928-0266
Newark **(G-14981)**
▲ Arkansas Face Veneer Co Inc ....E 937 773-6295
Piqua **(G-16249)**
Automated Bldg Components Inc ....E 419 257-2152
North Baltimore **(G-15191)**
Beaver Wood Products ....E 740 226-6211
Beaver **(G-1310)**
Bruewer Woodwork Mfg Co ....D 513 353-3505
Cleves **(G-6507)**
Carl C Andre Inc ....G...... 614 864-0123
Brice **(G-2087)**
Carter Woodcraft Center ....G...... 330 872-6474
Newton Falls **(G-15130)**
▼ Decorative Panels Intl Inc ....D 419 535-5921
Toledo **(G-18433)**
▲ Dimension Hardwood Veneers Inc ......E 419 272-2245
Edon **(G-9340)**
◆ Erath Veneer Corp Virginia ....F 540 483-5223
Granville **(G-10458)**
Fifth Avenue Lumber Co ....G...... 614 833-6655
Canal Winchester **(G-2524)**
Haessly Lumber Sales Co ....D 740 373-6681
Marietta **(G-12788)**
Hartzell Industries Inc ....F 937 773-6295
Piqua **(G-16273)**

Knisley Lumber ....F 740 634-2935
Bainbridge **(G-1061)**
Lattasburg Lumberworks Co LLC ....G...... 330 202-7671
West Salem **(G-20115)**
Miller Crist ....F 330 359-7877
Fredericksburg **(G-10088)**
▼ Miller Manufacturing Inc ....E 330 852-0689
Sugarcreek **(G-18028)**
Mohler Lumber Company ....G...... 330 499-5461
North Canton **(G-15250)**
▼ Ohio Valley Veneer Inc ....F 740 493-2901
Piketon **(G-16225)**
S & G Manufacturing Group LLC ....C 614 529-0100
Hilliard **(G-10977)**
▲ Sims-Lohman Inc ....E 513 651-3510
Cincinnati **(G-4423)**
Southeast Ohio Timber Pdts Co ....G...... 740 344-2570
Zanesville **(G-21355)**
Starecasing Systems Inc ....G...... 312 203-5632
Columbus **(G-7654)**
Stony Point Hardwoods ....F 330 852-4512
Sugarcreek **(G-18040)**
Valley Veneer & Lumber Co ....F 440 293-6025
Williamsfield **(G-20417)**
Wappoo Wood Products Inc ....F 937 492-1166
Sidney **(G-17233)**
Yoder Lumber Co Inc ....D 330 893-3131
Sugarcreek **(G-18052)**

2436 Softwood Veneer & Plywood

▲ American Veneer Edgebanding ....G...... 740 928-0266
Newark **(G-14981)**
Beaver Wood Products ....E 740 226-6211
Beaver **(G-1310)**
◆ Clopay Building Pdts Co Inc ....E 513 770-4800
Mason **(G-12998)**
Clopay Building Pdts Co Inc ....G...... 937 526-4301
Russia **(G-16762)**
Clopay Building Pdts Co Inc ....G...... 937 440-6403
Troy **(G-18810)**
S & G Manufacturing Group LLC ....C 614 529-0100
Hilliard **(G-10977)**
Wappoo Wood Products Inc ....E 937 492-1166
Sidney **(G-17233)**

2439 Structural Wood Members, NEC

Amish Timber Framers ....F 330 658-5699
Doylestown **(G-9026)**
Automated Bldg Components Inc ....E 419 257-2152
North Baltimore **(G-15191)**
Baker McMillen Co ....E 330 923-3303
Stow **(G-17734)**
Buckeye Components LLC ....E 330 482-5163
Columbiana **(G-6608)**
Building Concepts Inc ....F 419 298-2371
Edgerton **(G-9326)**
Byler Truss ....G...... 330 465-5412
Ashland **(G-715)**
C & M Truss LLC ....F 937 446-3400
Sardinia **(G-17026)**
Carter-Jones Lumber Company ....C 330 674-9060
Millersburg **(G-14211)**
Columbus Roof Trusses Inc ....E 614 272-6464
Columbus **(G-6964)**
Columbus Roof Trusses Inc ....F 740 763-3000
Newark **(G-14994)**
Contract Building Components ....E 937 644-0739
Marysville **(G-12938)**
Dutchcraft Truss Component Inc ....F 330 862-2220
Minerva **(G-14320)**
Fifth Avenue Lumber Co ....D 614 833-6655
Canal Winchester **(G-2524)**
Four Js Bldg Components LLC ....F 740 886-6112
Scottown **(G-17039)**
Holmes Lumber & Bldg Ctr Inc ....C 330 674-9060
Millersburg **(G-14231)**
Khempco Bldg Sup Co Ltd Partnr ....D 740 549-0465
Delaware **(G-8865)**
▲ Laminate Technologies Inc ....D 419 448-0812
Tiffin **(G-18226)**
M & G Truss Rafters ....G...... 740 667-3166
Coolville **(G-7834)**
Ohio Valley Truss Co ....E 937 393-3995
Hillsboro **(G-11010)**
Ohio Valley Truss Co ....G...... 937 393-3995
Hillsboro **(G-11011)**
Orica Ground Support Inc ....D 740 377-9146
South Point **(G-17443)**
Pioneer Homes Inc ....G...... 419 737-2371
Pioneer **(G-16238)**

Proline Truss ....F 419 895-9980
Shiloh **(G-17154)**
R & L Truss Inc ....F 419 587-3440
Grover Hill **(G-10653)**
Redbuilt LLC ....E 740 363-0870
Delaware **(G-8882)**
Richland Laminated Columns LLC ....F 419 895-0036
Greenwich **(G-10535)**
Schilling Truss Inc ....F 740 984-2396
Beverly **(G-1671)**
Socar of Ohio Inc ....D 419 596-3100
Continental **(G-7828)**
Stark Truss Company Inc ....D 330 478-2100
Canton **(G-2859)**
Stark Truss Company Inc ....E 740 335-4156
Washington Court Hou **(G-19640)**
Stark Truss Company Inc ....D 419 298-3777
Edgerton **(G-9337)**
Stark Truss Company Inc ....E 330 756-3050
Beach City **(G-1251)**
Stark Truss Company Inc ....F 330 478-2100
Canton **(G-2858)**
Strait & Lamp Lumber Co Inc ....E 614 833-6655
Canal Winchester **(G-2537)**
▲ Thomas Do-It Center Inc ....E 740 446-2002
Gallipolis **(G-10310)**
Truss Worx LLC ....G...... 419 363-2100
Rockford **(G-16693)**
Waynedale Truss & Panel Co ....G...... 330 683-4471
Dalton **(G-8079)**
Waynedale Truss and Panel Co ....E 330 698-7373
Apple Creek **(G-651)**
Woodcraft Floor & Roof Trusses ....G...... 740 927-9015
Pataskala **(G-15991)**
Woodcraft Manufacturing Co ....E 740 927-6609
Pataskala **(G-15992)**

2441 Wood Boxes

Aerocase Incorporated ....F 440 617-9294
Westlake **(G-20247)**
Aslan Worldwide ....F 513 671-0671
West Chester **(G-19811)**
Boxes & Such ....G...... 440 237-7122
Wooster **(G-20752)**
Buckeye Diamond Logistics Inc ....C 937 462-8361
South Charleston **(G-17424)**
Built-Rite Box & Crate Inc ....E 330 263-0936
Wooster **(G-20756)**
Caravan Packaging Inc ....F 440 243-4100
Cleveland **(G-4974)**
Cassady Woodworks Inc ....E 937 256-7948
Dayton **(G-8099)**
Cedar Craft Products Inc ....E 614 759-1600
Blacklick **(G-1692)**
Clark Rm Inc ....E 419 425-9889
Findlay **(G-9808)**
Custom Displays LLC ....G...... 330 454-8850
Bolivar **(G-1931)**
Damar Products Inc ....G...... 937 492-9023
Sidney **(G-17174)**
Damar Products Inc ....F 937 492-9023
Sidney **(G-17175)**
Dp Products LLC ....E 440 834-9663
Burton **(G-2373)**
Fca LLC ....F 309 644-2424
Clayton **(G-4658)**
Forest City Companies Inc............E 216 586-5279
Cleveland **(G-5369)**
Global Packaging & Exports Inc ....G...... 513 454-2020
West Chester **(G-19877)**
H Gerstner & Sons Inc ....F 937 228-1662
Dayton **(G-8382)**
Hann Manufacturing Inc ....F 740 962-3752
McConnelsville **(G-13352)**
Hawthorne Caravan & Assoc LLC ......F 440 366-9065
Elyria **(G-9428)**
Hines Builders Inc ....F 937 335-4586
Troy **(G-18834)**
▲ J & L Wood Products Inc ....E 937 667-4064
Tipp City **(G-18286)**
▲ Kennedy Group Incorporated ....D 440 951-7660
Willoughby **(G-20520)**
Lima Pallet Company Inc ....E 419 229-5736
Lima **(G-12041)**
Ohio Box & Crate Inc ....F 440 526-3133
Burton **(G-2381)**
Packaging Materials Svcs LLC ....F 330 745-9722
Norton **(G-15520)**
Packaging Plus Inc ....G...... 304 429-5900
Dayton **(G-8562)**

Quadco Rehabilitation Center ....B 419 682-1011
  Stryker (G-18006)
Schaefer Box & Pallet Co ....E 513 738-2500
  Hamilton (G-10736)
Scorpion Case Mfg LLC ....F 614 274-7246
  Dublin (G-9141)
Sterling Industries Inc ....F 419 523-3788
  Ottawa (G-15810)
Thomas J Weaver Inc ....F 740 622-2040
  Coshocton (G-7913)
Traveling & Recycle Wood Pdts ....F 419 968-2649
  Middle Point (G-13899)
Van Orders Pallet Company Inc ....F 419 875-6932
  Swanton (G-18094)
World Express Packaging Corp ....G 216 634-9000
  Cleveland (G-6479)
Zak Box Co Inc ....G 216 961-5636
  Cleveland (G-6491)

2448 Wood Pallets & Skids

A & D Wood Products Inc ....G 419 331-8859
  Elida (G-9349)
A & M Pallet ....F 937 295-3093
  Russia (G-16760)
A & M Pallet Shop Inc ....F 440 632-1941
  Middlefield (G-13911)
A W Taylor Lumber Incorporated ....F 440 577-1889
  Pierpont (G-16210)
A-Z Packaging Company ....F 614 444-8441
  Columbus (G-6670)
A2z Pallets LLC ....G 513 652-9026
  Cincinnati (G-3340)
AAA Plastics and Pallets Ltd ....G 330 844-2556
  North Lawrence (G-15305)
Able Pallet Mfg & Repr ....F 614 444-2115
  Columbus (G-6681)
Akron Crate and Pallet LLC ....G 330 524-8955
  Kent (G-11425)
American Built Custom Pallets ....G 330 532-4780
  Lisbon (G-12116)
Anderson Pallet & Packg Inc ....E 937 962-2614
  Lewisburg (G-11931)
Arrowhead Pallets LLC ....F 440 693-4241
  Middlefield (G-13915)
At Pallet ....G 330 264-3903
  Wooster (G-20742)
B & B Pallet Co ....G 419 435-4530
  Fostoria (G-9967)
B J Pallett ....G 419 447-9665
  Tiffin (G-18208)
B M Pallets ....G 740 634-2659
  Hillsboro (G-10996)
Belco Works Inc ....B 740 695-0500
  Saint Clairsville (G-16782)
Bonded Pallets ....G 513 541-1855
  Cincinnati (G-3459)
Brookhill Center Industries ....C 419 876-3932
  Ottawa (G-15790)
Buck Creek Pallet ....G 937 653-3098
  Urbana (G-19149)
Buckeye Diamond Logistics Inc ....C 937 462-8361
  South Charleston (G-17424)
Buckeye Pallett ....G 330 359-5919
  Millersburg (G-14204)
Built-Rite Box & Crate Inc ....E 330 263-0936
  Wooster (G-20756)
Buy The Pallet LLC ....G 440 521-0073
  Broadview Heights (G-2107)
Cabot Lumber Inc ....G 740 545-7109
  West Lafayette (G-20085)
Caesarcreek Pallets Ltd ....F 937 416-4447
  Jamestown (G-11351)
Carrillo Pallets LLC ....G 513 942-2210
  Cincinnati (G-3503)
CC Pallets LLC ....G 513 442-8766
  Terrace Park (G-18179)
Chep (usa) Inc ....E 614 497-9448
  Columbus (G-6924)
Cimino Box Inc ....G 216 961-7377
  Cleveland (G-5033)
Clark Rm Inc ....E 419 425-9889
  Findlay (G-9808)
Cleveland Cstm Pllet Crate Inc ....E 216 881-1414
  Cleveland (G-5055)
Clover Pallet LLC ....G 330 454-5592
  Canton (G-2660)
Coblentz Brothers Inc ....G 330 857-7211
  Apple Creek (G-634)
Contreras Pallets ....G 567 277-2447
  Toledo (G-18412)

Cottonwood Pallet Inc ....G 419 468-9703
  Galion (G-10260)
Cox Wood Product Inc ....F 740 372-4735
  Otway (G-15829)
Crosscreek Pallet Co ....G 440 632-1940
  Middlefield (G-13926)
Cs Products ....G 330 452-8566
  Canton (G-2672)
Custom Palet Manufacturing ....G 440 693-4603
  Middlefield (G-13927)
D M Pallet Service Inc ....F 614 491-0881
  Columbus (G-7006)
D P Products Inc ....G 440 834-9663
  Middlefield (G-13929)
Damar Products Inc ....G 937 492-9023
  Sidney (G-17174)
Damar Products Inc ....F 937 492-9023
  Sidney (G-17175)
Dan S Miller & David S Miller ....G 937 464-9061
  Belle Center (G-1512)
Daves Pallets ....G 740 525-4938
  Belpre (G-1585)
Dj Pallets ....G 216 701-9183
  Columbia Station (G-6588)
▲ Emergency Products & RES Inc ....G 330 673-5003
  Kent (G-11455)
Findlay Pallet Inc ....G 419 423-0511
  Findlay (G-9824)
Fisher Pallet ....G 440 632-0863
  Middlefield (G-13934)
Forrest Rawlins ....G 740 778-3366
  Wheelersburg (G-20330)
Fox Hollow Pallet ....G 937 386-2872
  Winchester (G-20693)
Frankes Wood Products LLC ....E 937 642-0706
  Marysville (G-12944)
Franks Sawmill Inc ....F 419 682-3831
  Stryker (G-18003)
Gallagher Lumber Co ....G 330 274-2333
  Mantua (G-12710)
Gardner Lumber Co Inc ....F 740 254-4664
  Tippecanoe (G-18313)
Garys Pallet Sales ....G 330 569-7676
  Hiram (G-11035)
George Biniker Wooden Pallets ....F 419 666-3185
  Perrysburg (G-16101)
Global Packaging & Exports Inc........G 513 454-2020
  West Chester (G-19877)
Grant Street Pallet Inc ....G 330 424-0355
  Lisbon (G-12120)
Gross Lumber Inc ....E 330 683-2055
  Apple Creek (G-638)
H & K Pallet Services ....G 937 608-1140
  Xenia (G-20954)
Hacker Wood Products Inc ....G 513 737-4462
  Hamilton (G-10700)
Haessly Lumber Sales Co ....D 740 373-6681
  Marietta (G-12788)
Halliday Holdings Inc ....E 740 335-1430
  Wshngtn CT Hs (G-20910)
Hann Box Works ....E 740 962-3752
  McConnelsville (G-13351)
Hann Manufacturing Inc ....E 740 962-3752
  McConnelsville (G-13352)
Hershberger Manufacturing ....E 440 272-5555
  Windsor (G-20699)
Hillside Pallet ....E 440 272-5425
  Windsor (G-20700)
Hinchcliff Lumber Company ....E 440 238-5200
  Strongsville (G-17925)
Hines Builders Inc ....F 937 335-4586
  Troy (G-18834)
Hope Timber & Marketing Group ....F 740 344-1788
  Newark (G-15019)
Hope Timber Pallet Recycl Inc ....E 740 344-1788
  Newark (G-15021)
Ifco Systems North America Inc ....D 330 669-2726
  Smithville (G-17240)
Ifco Systems Us LLC ....G 513 769-0377
  Cincinnati (G-3910)
▲ Inca Presswood-Pallets Ltd ....E 330 343-3361
  Dover (G-8992)
Industrial Hardwood Inc ....G 419 666-2503
  Perrysburg (G-16111)
Inland Hardwood Corporation ....D 740 373-7187
  Marietta (G-12793)
Iron City Wood Products Inc ....G 330 755-2772
  Youngstown (G-21121)
J & K Pallet Inc ....G 937 526-5117
  Versailles (G-19349)

▲ J & L Wood Products Inc ....E 937 667-4064
  Tipp City (G-18286)
J D L Hardwoods ....G 440 272-5630
  Middlefield (G-13943)
J E Johnson Pallett Inc ....G 614 424-9663
  Columbus (G-7217)
J I T Pallets Inc ....G 330 424-0355
  Lisbon (G-12124)
J Smokin ....G 330 466-7087
  Rittman (G-16677)
J&R Pallet Ltd ....G 740 226-1112
  Waverly (G-19712)
JIT Packaging Inc ....E 330 562-8080
  Aurora (G-927)
Joe Barrett ....G 216 385-2384
  East Liverpool (G-9220)
Joe Gonda Company Inc ....F 440 458-6000
  Elyria (G-9443)
Ken Harper ....C 740 439-4452
  Byesville (G-2406)
Kenneth Schrock ....G 937 544-7566
  West Union (G-20123)
Kmak Group LLC ....F 937 308-1023
  London (G-12214)
Kountry Pride Enterprises ....G 330 868-3345
  Minerva (G-14330)
L N S Pallets ....G 330 936-7507
  Navarre (G-14718)
Lake Wood Product Inc ....G 419 832-0150
  Grand Rapids (G-10441)
Langston Pallets ....G 937 492-8769
  Sidney (G-17198)
Lawrence Pallets & Solutions ....G 740 259-4283
  Lucasville (G-12421)
Leroy Yutzy ....G 937 386-2872
  Winchester (G-20694)
Lima Pallet Company Inc ....E 419 229-5736
  Lima (G-12041)
◆ Litco International Inc ....E 330 539-5433
  Vienna (G-19368)
▲ Litco Manufacturing LLC ....F 330 539-5433
  Warren (G-19573)
Lumberjack Pallet Recycl LLC ....G 513 821-7543
  Cincinnati (G-4039)
Martin Pallet Inc ....E 330 832-5309
  Massillon (G-13172)
Melt Inc ....G 330 426-3545
  Negley (G-14731)
Mid Ohio Wood Products Inc ....E 740 323-0427
  Newark (G-15033)
Mid Ohio Wood Recycling Inc ....G 419 673-8470
  Kenton (G-11558)
Middlefield Pallet Inc ....E 440 632-0553
  Middlefield (G-13961)
Midtown Pallet & Recycling ....E 419 241-1311
  Toledo (G-18585)
Miller Pallet Company ....G 937 464-4483
  Belle Center (G-1514)
Millwood Inc ....D 330 857-3075
  Apple Creek (G-645)
Millwood Inc ....E 614 409-9680
  Columbus (G-7355)
Millwood Inc ....E 330 359-5220
  Dundee (G-9176)
Mjc Enterprises Inc ....G 330 669-3744
  Sterling (G-17684)
Montgomerys Pallet Service ....G 330 297-6677
  Ravenna (G-16542)
◆ Morgan Wood Products Inc ....F 614 336-4000
  Powell (G-16480)
Mt Eaton Pallet Ltd ....E 330 893-2986
  Millersburg (G-14251)
Mulch World ....G 419 873-6852
  Perrysburg (G-16123)
Nwp Manufacturing Inc ....F 419 894-6871
  Waldo (G-19466)
Oak Chips Inc ....G 740 947-4159
  Waverly (G-19714)
Oakmoor Pallet ....G 216 926-1858
  Westlake (G-20287)
Oakmoor Pallet ....G 440 385-7340
  Westlake (G-20288)
Ohio Box & Crate Inc ....F 440 526-3133
  Burton (G-2381)
▲ Ohio Specialty Mfg Co ....G 419 531-5402
  Toledo (G-18617)
Ohio State Pallet Corp ....G 614 332-3961
  Homer (G-11113)
Ohio Wood Recycling Inc ....E 614 491-0881
  Columbus (G-7437)

Employee Codes: A=Over 500 employees, B=251-500
C=101-250, D=51-100, E=20-50, F=10-19, G=3-9

2017 Harris Ohio
Industrial Directory

901

SIC

Olympic Forest Products Co ....F 216 421-2775
Cleveland *(G-5940)*

P R U Industries Inc ....F 937 746-8702
Franklin *(G-10043)*

Packaging Plus Inc ....G 304 429-5900
Dayton *(G-8562)*

Pallet & Cont Corp of Amer ....G 419 255-1256
Toledo *(G-18634)*

Pallet Distributors Inc ....D 330 852-3531
Sugarcreek *(G-18030)*

Pallet Guys ....G 440 897-3001
North Royalton *(G-15441)*

Pallet Pros ....G 440 537-9087
Grafton *(G-10434)*

Pallet Specs Plus LLC ....F 513 351-3200
Norwood *(G-15573)*

Pallet World Inc ....E 419 874-9333
Perrysburg *(G-16144)*

Pallets-Fm-N-plc-packaging Inc ....E 937 526-9333
Versailles *(G-19355)*

Parks West Pallet Llc ....G 440 693-4651
Middlefield *(G-13979)*

Paul E Cekovich ....G 330 424-3213
Lisbon *(G-12132)*

Pettits Pallets Inc ....G 614 351-4920
Derby *(G-8947)*

Plains Precut Ltd ....G 330 893-3300
Millersburg *(G-14255)*

Precise Pallets LLC ....G 513 560-8236
Batavia *(G-1217)*

Precision Pallet Inc ....G 419 381-8191
Ottawa Hills *(G-15818)*

Premier Pallet & Recycling ....F 330 767-2221
Navarre *(G-14724)*

▲ Prime Wood Craft Inc ....F 216 738-2222
Brunswick *(G-2248)*

Quadco Rehabilitation Center ....B 419 682-1011
Stryker *(G-18006)*

Quadco Rehabilitation Center ....D 419 445-1950
Archbold *(G-691)*

Quality Pllets Recyclables LLC ....G 419 396-3244
Carey *(G-2926)*

Queen City Pallets ....F 513 200-6426
Cincinnati *(G-4318)*

R C Family Wood Products ....G 937 295-2393
Fort Loramie *(G-9935)*

Raber Lumber Co ....G 330 893-2797
Charm *(G-3184)*

Rettig Family Pallets Inc ....F 419 264-1540
Holgate *(G-11040)*

Richland Newhope Industries ....C 419 774-4400
Mansfield *(G-12671)*

Riverview Indus WD Pdts Inc ....D 330 669-8509
Wooster *(G-20830)*

Riverview Indus WD Pdts Inc ....F 330 669-8509
Smithville *(G-17243)*

Russell L Garber ....G 937 548-6224
Greenville *(G-10521)*

S & M Products ....G 419 272-2054
Blakeslee *(G-1708)*

S & S Pallets ....G 513 967-7432
Milford *(G-14171)*

S & S Pallett ....G 740 372-0238
Mc Dermott *(G-13343)*

San Pallet LLC ....G 937 271-5308
Troy *(G-18871)*

Schaefer Box & Pallet Co ....E 513 738-2500
Hamilton *(G-10736)*

Schnider Pallet LLC ....G 440 632-5346
Middlefield *(G-13987)*

Schrock John ....G 937 544-8457
West Union *(G-20125)*

▲ Schuetz Container ....E 419 872-2295
Perrysburg *(G-16148)*

▲ Sealco Inc ....G 740 922-4122
Uhrichsville *(G-19058)*

Shaw Pallets & Specialties ....G 740 498-7892
Newcomerstown *(G-15123)*

Silvesco Inc ....F 740 373-6661
Marietta *(G-12830)*

Slats and Nails Inc ....G 330 866-1008
East Sparta *(G-9255)*

Smith Pallets ....G 937 564-6492
Versailles *(G-19357)*

Southeast Ohio Timber Pdts Co ....G 740 344-2570
Zanesville *(G-21355)*

Southern Ohio Lumber LLC ....E 614 436-4472
Peebles *(G-16025)*

Specialty Pallet & Design Ltd ....E 330 857-0257
Orrville *(G-15768)*

Specialty Pallet Entps LLC ....G 419 673-0247
Kenton *(G-11569)*

Sterling Industries Inc ....F 419 523-3788
Ottawa *(G-15810)*

Stony Point Hardwoods ....F 330 852-4512
Sugarcreek *(G-18040)*

Stumptown Lbr Pallet Mills Ltd ....F 740 757-2275
Somerton *(G-17421)*

Sugarcreek Pallett ....G 330 852-9812
Sugarcreek *(G-18043)*

T & D Thompson Inc ....E 740 332-8515
Laurelville *(G-11772)*

T&A Pallets Inc ....G 330 968-4743
Ravenna *(G-16564)*

Terry Lumber and Supply Co ....F 330 659-6800
Peninsula *(G-16043)*

Thomas J Weaver Inc ....F 740 622-2040
Coshocton *(G-7913)*

Timber Products Inc ....G 440 693-4098
Middlefield *(G-13995)*

Tolson Pallet Mfg Inc ....F 937 787-3511
Gratis *(G-10468)*

Traveling & Recycle Wood Pdts ....F 419 968-2649
Middle Point *(G-13899)*

Tri State Pallet Inc ....G 937 323-5210
Springfield *(G-17667)*

Tri State Pallet Inc ....F 937 746-8702
Franklin *(G-10060)*

Troyers Pallet Shop ....G 330 897-1038
Fresno *(G-10201)*

Troymill Manufacturing Inc ....F 440 632-5580
Middlefield *(G-13997)*

Tusco Hardwoods LLC ....F 330 852-4281
Sugarcreek *(G-18047)*

Ultimate Pallet & Trucking LLC ....G 440 693-4090
Middlefield *(G-13999)*

Universal Pallets Inc ....G 614 444-1095
Columbus *(G-7724)*

Universal Pallets Inc ....E 614 444-1095
Columbus *(G-7725)*

Valley View Pallets Partners ....G 740 393-9282
Danville *(G-8092)*

Van Orders Pallet Company Inc ....F 419 875-6932
Swanton *(G-18094)*

Van Wert Pallets LLC ....G 419 203-1823
Van Wert *(G-19275)*

Weaver Pallet Ltd ....G 330 682-4022
Apple Creek *(G-652)*

Winesburg Hardwood Lumber Co ....E 330 893-2705
Dundee *(G-9186)*

Wjf Enterprises LLC ....F 513 871-7320
Cincinnati *(G-4601)*

Woodford Logistics ....D 513 417-8453
South Charleston *(G-17427)*

Worthington Pallet ....G 614 888-1573
Worthington *(G-20899)*

▼ Yoder Lumber Co Inc ....D 330 893-3121
Millersburg *(G-14288)*

Yoder Lumber Co Inc ....E 330 674-1435
Millersburg *(G-14289)*

Zak Box Co Inc ....G 216 961-5636
Cleveland *(G-6491)*

2449 Wood Containers, NEC

A-Z Packaging Company ....F 614 444-8441
Columbus *(G-6670)*

Brown-Forman Corporation ....E 740 384-3027
Wellston *(G-19761)*

Cassis Packaging Co ....F 937 223-8563
Dayton *(G-8214)*

Clark Rm Inc ....E 419 425-9889
Findlay *(G-9808)*

Custom Built Crates Inc ....E 513 248-4422
Milford *(G-14135)*

Denoon Lumber Company LLC ....D 740 768-2220
Bergholz *(G-1641)*

Dp Products LLC ....G 440 834-9663
Burton *(G-2373)*

Frankes Wood Products LLC ....E 937 642-0706
Marysville *(G-12944)*

Greif Inc ....E 740 657-6500
Delaware *(G-8848)*

Greif Inc ....F 740 549-6000
Delaware *(G-8850)*

Greif Inc ....E 740 549-6000
Delaware *(G-8847)*

Haessly Lumber Sales Co ....D 740 373-6681
Marietta *(G-12788)*

Hann Box Works ....E 740 962-3752
McConnelsville *(G-13351)*

▲ J & L Wood Products Inc ....E 937 667-4064
Tipp City *(G-18286)*

Joe Gonda Company Inc ....F 440 458-6000
Elyria *(G-9443)*

Lefco Worthington LLC ....E 216 432-4422
Cleveland *(G-5691)*

Longaberger Company ....A 740 828-4000
Frazeysburg *(G-10075)*

Overseas Packing LLC ....F 440 232-2917
Bedford *(G-1451)*

Pallet & Cont Corp of Amer ....G 419 255-1256
Toledo *(G-18634)*

Patriotic Buildings LLC ....G 740 853-3970
Patriot *(G-15997)*

Schaefer Box & Pallet Co ....E 513 738-2500
Hamilton *(G-10736)*

Silvesco Inc ....F 740 373-6661
Marietta *(G-12830)*

T & D Thompson Inc ....E 740 332-8515
Laurelville *(G-11772)*

Terry Lumber and Supply Co ....F 330 659-6800
Peninsula *(G-16043)*

Traveling & Recycle Wood Pdts ....F 419 968-2649
Middle Point *(G-13899)*

VIP-Supply Chain Solutions LLC ....G 513 454-2020
West Chester *(G-19970)*

2451 Mobile Homes

C & C Mobile Homes LLC ....G 740 663-5535
Waverly *(G-19704)*

▲ Ellis & Watts Intl LLC ....G 513 752-9000
Batavia *(G-1183)*

Holiday Homes Inc ....F 513 353-9777
Harrison *(G-10782)*

Manufactured Housing Entps Inc ....C 419 636-4511
Bryan *(G-2313)*

Mobile Conversions Inc ....F 513 797-1991
Amelia *(G-580)*

Skyline Corporation ....C 330 852-2483
Sugarcreek *(G-18039)*

Sun Communities Inc ....G 740 548-1942
Lewis Center *(G-11922)*

2452 Prefabricated Wood Buildings & Cmpnts

Al Yoder Construction Company ....G 330 359-5726
Millersburg *(G-14191)*

Americraft Stor Buildings Ltd ....G 330 877-6900
Hartville *(G-10816)*

Carter-Jones Lumber Company ....F 440 834-8164
Middlefield *(G-13920)*

▲ Cconly Inc ....F 614 607-2288
Delaware *(G-8830)*

Consolidatd Analytical Sys Inc ....F 513 542-1200
Cleves *(G-6511)*

Ecoponics Group LLC ....G 330 819-1233
Kent *(G-11453)*

Everything In America ....G 347 871-6872
Cleveland *(G-5310)*

Fifth Avenue Lumber Co ....D 614 833-6655
Canal Winchester *(G-2524)*

Gillard Construction Inc ....F 740 376-9744
Marietta *(G-12786)*

Hershbergers Dutch Market LLP ....E 740 489-5322
Old Washington *(G-15671)*

Hochstetler Milling LLC ....E 419 368-0004
Loudonville *(G-12298)*

J L Wannemacher Sales & Svc ....F 419 453-3445
Ottoville *(G-15823)*

Millers Mini Barns ....G 937 544-6317
West Union *(G-20124)*

Millers Storage Barns LLC ....E 330 893-3293
Millersburg *(G-14248)*

Mohican Log Homes Inc ....G 419 994-4088
Loudonville *(G-12299)*

Morton Buildings Inc ....D 419 675-2311
Kenton *(G-11561)*

Patio Enclosures ....F 513 733-4646
Cincinnati *(G-4213)*

Premier Construction Company ....E 513 874-2611
Fairfield *(G-9704)*

Rona Enterprises Inc ....G 740 927-9971
Pataskala *(G-15981)*

Silver Creek Log Homes ....G 419 335-3220
Wauseon *(G-19694)*

Skyline Corporation ....C 330 852-2483
Sugarcreek *(G-18039)*

Smiths Sawdust Studio ....G 740 484-4656
Bethesda *(G-1667)*

Thomas Panels Inc ....F 330 758-2384
Youngstown (G-21221)

Twin Oaks Barn ....F 330 893-3126
Dundee (G-9184)

Unibilt Industries Inc ....E 937 890-7570
Vandalia (G-19313)

Vinyl Design Corporation ....E 419 283-4009
Holland (G-11095)

Weaver Barns Ltd ....F 330 852-2103
Sugarcreek (G-18050)

2491 Wood Preserving

Appalachia Wood Inc ....F 740 596-2551
Mc Arthur (G-13328)

Appalachian Wood Floors Inc ....D 740 354-4572
Portsmouth (G-16430)

Clark Rm Inc ....E 419 425-9889
Findlay (G-9808)

Couch Business Development Inc ....F 937 253-1099
Dayton (G-8244)

ISK Americas Incorporated ....E 440 357-4600
Painesville (G-15892)

Joseph Sabatino ....G 330 332-5879
Salem (G-16904)

Luxus Products LLC ....G 937 444-6500
Mount Orab (G-14582)

Preserving Your Memories ....G 614 861-4283
Reynoldsburg (G-16600)

Ufp Blanchester LLC ....E 937 783-2443
Blanchester (G-1717)

Ufp Hamilton LLC ....F 513 285-7190
Hamilton (G-10752)

US Pro Painters ....G 937 298-2142
Springfield (G-17671)

Wood Duck Enterprises Ltd ....G 937 426-0506
Beavercreek (G-1366)

2493 Reconstituted Wood Prdts

Amerilam Laminating ....G 440 235-4687
Cleveland (G-4797)

Aristocrat Industries Inc ....F 740 694-2752
Mount Vernon (G-14608)

Celcore Inc ....F 440 234-7888
Cleveland (G-5001)

Decker Custom Wood Llc ....G 419 332-3464
Fremont (G-10141)

Frankes Wood Products LLC ....E 937 642-0706
Marysville (G-12944)

▲ GMI Companies Inc ....C 513 932-3445
Lebanon (G-11804)

GMI Companies Inc ....G 937 981-0244
Greenfield (G-10476)

◆ Michael Kaufman Companies Inc ...F 330 673-4881
Kent (G-11490)

Michael Kaufman Companies Inc ....F 330 673-4881
Kent (G-11491)

▼ Miller Manufacturing Inc ....E 330 852-0689
Sugarcreek (G-18028)

Mpc Inc ....F 440 835-1405
Westlake (G-20284)

Ohio Plywood Box ....G 513 242-9125
Cincinnati (G-4179)

Profile Products LLC ....F 330 452-2630
Canton (G-2828)

▼ Tectum Inc ....C 740 345-9691
Newark (G-15063)

Tri-State Supply Co Inc ....F 614 272-6767
Columbus (G-7709)

US Greenfiber LLC ....F 419 692-7015
Delphos (G-8924)

Wico Products Inc ....G 937 783-0000
Blanchester (G-1718)

2499 Wood Prdts, NEC

77 Coach Supply Ltd ....E 330 674-1454
Millersburg (G-14187)

Adco Products Inc ....D 937 339-6267
Tipp City (G-18261)

Adroit Thinking Inc ....F 419 542-9363
Hicksville (G-10898)

American Wood Fibers Inc ....E 740 420-3233
Circleville (G-4623)

Anderson Co ....G 419 396-7056
Carey (G-2914)

▼ AP Tech Group Inc ....F 513 761-8111
Blue Ash (G-1743)

Armin R Jewett ....G 419 647-6644
Wapakoneta (G-19479)

Attractive Kitchens & Flrg LLC ....G 440 406-9299
Elyria (G-9376)

▲ Baker McMillen Co ....D 330 923-8300
Stow (G-17733)

Baker McMillen Co ....E 330 923-3303
Stow (G-17734)

Barkman Products LLC ....G 330 893-2520
Millersburg (G-14197)

Bc Investment Corporation ....G 330 262-3070
Wooster (G-20747)

Berlin Wood Products Inc ....E 330 893-3281
Berlin (G-1646)

Blang Acquisition LLC ....F 937 223-2155
Dayton (G-8190)

Bonfoey Co ....F 216 621-0178
Cleveland (G-4924)

BR Mulch Inc ....G 937 667-8288
Tipp City (G-18266)

Brown Wood Products Company ....G 330 339-8000
New Philadelphia (G-14886)

▲ Buhi Imports ....G 440 224-0013
North Kingsville (G-15303)

Bushworks Incorporated ....G 937 767-1713
Yellow Springs (G-20990)

Cado Door & Design Inc ....G 330 343-4288
New Philadelphia (G-14889)

Canfield Manufacturing Co Inc ....G 330 533-3333
North Jackson (G-15289)

Cass Frames Inc ....G 419 468-2863
Galion (G-10257)

Cedar Chest ....G 937 878-9097
Fairborn (G-9616)

◆ Chromascape Inc ....E 330 998-7574
Twinsburg (G-18912)

◆ Cincinnati Dowel & WD Pdts Co ....E 937 444-2502
Mount Orab (G-14576)

◆ CM Paula Company ....E 513 759-7473
Mason (G-13002)

Colby Woodworking Inc ....G 937 224-7676
Dayton (G-8236)

▲ Columbus Washboard Company Ltd ....F
740 380-3828
Logan (G-12173)

Company Front Awards ....G 440 636-5493
Middlefield (G-13924)

Cornerstone Spclty WD Pdts LLC ....D 513 772-5560
Cincinnati (G-3611)

Creative Plastic Concepts LLC ....G 419 927-9588
Sycamore (G-18096)

Crosco Wood Products ....G 330 857-0228
Dalton (G-8065)

Dalton Wood Products Inc ....G 330 682-0727
Orrville (G-15734)

Decorative Veneer Inc ....G 216 741-5511
Cleveland (G-5180)

Duvall Woodworking Inc ....F 419 878-9581
Waterville (G-19656)

Ely Road Reel Company Ltd ....E 330 683-1818
Apple Creek (G-637)

F J Designs Inc ....E 330 264-1377
Wooster (G-20771)

Family Woodworks LLC ....G 740 289-4071
Piketon (G-16220)

Fenwick Gallery of Fine Arts ....G 419 475-1651
Toledo (G-18468)

Frame Depot Inc ....G 330 652-7865
Niles (G-15153)

Frame Shoppe ....G 513 232-3970
Cincinnati (G-3775)

◆ Frame USA ....E 513 577-7107
Cincinnati (G-3776)

Frame Warehouse ....G 614 861-4582
Reynoldsburg (G-16591)

▲ G R K Manufacturing Co Inc ....E 513 863-3131
Hamilton (G-10697)

Garick LLC ....E 216 581-0100
Cleveland (G-5398)

Ginnys Custom Framing Gallery ....G 419 468-7240
Galion (G-10272)

Global Wood Products LLC ....G 440 442-5859
Highland Heights (G-10913)

▲ Good Wood Inc ....G 740 484-1500
Belmont (G-1579)

▲ Greenes Fence Co Inc ....G 216 464-3160
Solon (G-17305)

Gregoire Moulin ....G 614 861-4582
Reynoldsburg (G-16593)

Growers Choice Ltd ....G 330 262-8754
Shreve (G-17156)

Hackman Frames LLC ....F 614 841-0007
Columbus (G-7137)

▼ Handicraft LLC ....G 216 295-1950
Cleveland (G-5475)

Hardwood Solutions ....G 330 359-5755
Wilmot (G-20686)

Hardwood Store Inc ....G 937 864-2899
Enon (G-9547)

Hauser Services Llc ....E 440 632-5126
Middlefield (G-13941)

Henly Corporation ....G 419 476-0851
Toledo (G-18507)

Herbert Wood Products Inc ....G 440 834-1410
Middlefield (G-13942)

Hit Trophy Inc ....G 419 445-5356
Archbold (G-681)

▲ Holmes Wheel Shop Inc ....E 330 279-2891
Holmesville (G-11106)

Homestead Collections ....G 419 422-8286
Findlay (G-9841)

Hope Timber & Marketing Group ....F 740 344-1788
Newark (G-15019)

Hope Timber Mulch Inc ....G 740 344-1788
Newark (G-15020)

House of 10000 Picture Frames ....G 937 254-5541
Dayton (G-8393)

Insta Plak Inc ....E 419 537-1555
Toledo (G-18525)

Irvine Wood Recovery Inc ....E 513 831-0060
Miamiville (G-13894)

J & R Woodworking ....G 330 893-0713
Millersburg (G-14234)

J R Custom Unlimited ....E 513 894-9800
Hamilton (G-10710)

Jewett Supply ....F 419 738-9882
Wapakoneta (G-19492)

Judith C Zell ....G 740 385-0386
Logan (G-12180)

Kalinich Fence Company Inc ....F 440 238-6127
Strongsville (G-17935)

Kaufman Mulch Inc ....G 330 893-3676
Millersburg (G-14236)

Kennewegs Wood Products ....G 330 832-1540
Massillon (G-13163)

L S Manufacturing Inc ....G 614 885-7988
Worthington (G-20876)

Latham Lumber & Pallet Co Inc ....F 740 493-2707
Latham (G-11766)

Lawnview Industries Inc ....C 937 653-5217
Urbana (G-19168)

Lazars Art Gllery Crtive Frmng ....G 330 477-8351
Canton (G-2759)

Mad River Topsoil Inc ....G 937 882-6115
Springfield (G-17598)

Marcum Crew Cut Inc ....G 740 862-3400
Baltimore (G-1084)

Mark Nelson ....F 740 282-5334
Steubenville (G-17704)

Maumee Bay Kitchen & Bath Cent ....G 419 882-4390
Sylvania (G-18117)

▲ Mi-Lar Fence Co Inc ....G 216 464-3160
Solon (G-17337)

Mikes Mill Shop Inc ....G 419 538-6091
Ottawa (G-15801)

▼ Miller Manufacturing Inc ....E 330 852-0689
Sugarcreek (G-18028)

Millwork Designs Inc ....G 740 335-5203
Wshngtn CT Hs (G-20917)

Minotas Trophies & Awards ....G 440 720-1288
Cleveland (G-5823)

Mollard Conducting Batons Inc ....F 330 659-7081
Bath (G-1239)

Mt Perry Foods Inc ....D 740 743-3890
Mount Perry (G-14592)

Mulch Madness LLC ....F 330 920-9900
Aurora (G-935)

Mulch Makers of Ohio Inc ....G 330 753-3090
Norton (G-15518)

Mulch Man ....E 937 866-5370
Dayton (G-8114)

National Pallet & Mulch LLC ....F 937 237-1643
Dayton (G-8521)

Newbury Woodworks ....G 440 564-5273
Newbury (G-15100)

▲ P & R Specialty Inc ....E 937 773-0263
Piqua (G-16297)

P & T Millwork Inc ....E 440 543-2151
Chagrin Falls (G-3109)

Peters Family Enterprises Inc ....G 419 339-0555
Elida (G-9355)

▲ Puttmann Industries Inc ....F 513 202-9444
Harrison (G-10797)

R M Wood Co ....G 419 845-2661
Mount Gilead (G-14566)

R T Communications Inc..................G....... 330 726-7892
  Youngstown *(G-21183)*

Randy Lewis Inc................................F....... 330 784-0456
  Akron *(G-365)*

Red Lion Nursery Inc........................G....... 937 704-9840
  Lebanon *(G-11832)*

Revonoc Inc.....................................G....... 440 548-3491
  Parkman *(G-15953)*

Rightway Food Service......................G....... 419 223-4075
  Lima *(G-12084)*

Roe Transportation Entps Inc...........G....... 937 497-7161
  Sidney *(G-17217)*

Ryanworks Inc..................................G....... 937 438-1282
  Dayton *(G-8641)*

◆ Scotts Company LLC....................A....... 937 644-3729
  Marysville *(G-12967)*

▲ Sealco Inc....................................G....... 740 922-4122
  Uhrichsville *(G-19058)*

Sign Technologies LLC.....................G....... 937 439-3970
  Dayton *(G-8658)*

Signature Sign Co Inc.......................F....... 216 426-1234
  Cleveland *(G-6204)*

Singleton Reels Inc...........................E....... 330 274-2961
  Mantua *(G-12722)*

Smith P K Woodcarving LLC..............G....... 513 271-7077
  Louisville *(G-12329)*

▲ Solid Dimensions Inc...................G....... 419 663-1134
  Norwalk *(G-15564)*

Sonoco Products Company................E....... 614 759-8470
  Columbus *(G-7631)*

Steeles 5 Acre Mill Inc.....................F....... 419 542-9363
  Hicksville *(G-10906)*

Tayjus Personalized Woodworks.........G....... 440 427-9145
  Olmsted Falls *(G-15676)*

Todd W Goings..................................G....... 740 389-5842
  Marion *(G-12907)*

W H K Company.................................G....... 937 372-3368
  Xenia *(G-20986)*

▲ Walnut Creek Planing Ltd.............D....... 330 893-3244
  Millersburg *(G-14281)*

Walnut Creek Wood Design................G....... 330 852-9663
  Sugarcreek *(G-18049)*

Warthers Music Box Bells..................G....... 330 343-4706
  Dover *(G-9024)*

Wengerd Wood Inc.............................G....... 330 359-4300
  Wilmot *(G-20688)*

Wood Trader Inc.................................G....... 216 397-7671
  Cleveland Heights *(G-6503)*

▲ Woodcor America Inc....................G....... 614 277-2930
  Grove City *(G-10610)*

Woodcraft Pattern Works Inc..............G....... 330 630-2158
  Tallmadge *(G-18178)*

Wooden Creations..............................G....... 419 874-6367
  Perrysburg *(G-16171)*

Woodpeckers Inc...............................E....... 440 238-1824
  Strongsville *(G-17985)*

Woodworks Design.............................G....... 440 693-4414
  Middlefield *(G-14008)*

Wurms Woodworking Company...........E....... 419 492-2184
  New Washington *(G-14966)*

▼ Yoder Lumber Co Inc....................D....... 330 893-3121
  Millersburg *(G-14288)*

Youngstown Fence Inc.......................G....... 330 788-8110
  Youngstown *(G-21251)*

Zaenkert Surveying Essentials...........G....... 513 738-2917
  Okeana *(G-15668)*

25 FURNITURE AND FIXTURES

2511 Wood Household Furniture

Allied Plastic Co Inc..........................G....... 419 389-1688
  Toledo *(G-18330)*

Andal Woodworking............................F....... 330 897-8059
  Baltic *(G-1064)*

◆ Archbold Furniture Co...................E....... 567 444-4666
  Archbold *(G-665)*

Ariels Oak Inc....................................E....... 330 343-7453
  Sherrodsville *(G-17145)*

Armada Fortress LLC.........................G....... 330 953-2185
  Youngstown *(G-21027)*

Artistic Finishes Inc..........................F....... 440 951-7850
  Willoughby *(G-20440)*

Basic Cases Inc.................................G....... 216 662-3900
  Cleveland *(G-4896)*

Battershell Cabinets...........................G....... 419 542-6448
  Hicksville *(G-10901)*

Benners Custom Woodworking............G....... 513 932-9159
  Lebanon *(G-11783)*

Berlin Gardens Gazebos Ltd...............E....... 330 893-3411
  Berlin *(G-1644)*

Briar Hill Furniture............................G....... 330 223-2109
  Kensington *(G-11420)*

Cabinet Systems Inc..........................G....... 440 237-1924
  Cleveland *(G-4961)*

▼ Canal Dover Furniture LLC...........D....... 330 359-5375
  Millersburg *(G-14210)*

Carlisle Oak.......................................G....... 330 852-8734
  Sugarcreek *(G-18019)*

Cedar Outdoor Furniture Inc..............G....... 330 863-2580
  Malvern *(G-12540)*

Chris Haughey...................................G....... 937 652-3338
  Urbana *(G-19150)*

Cirjak Furniture and Design...............G....... 330 296-8035
  Ravenna *(G-16521)*

▲ Clearwater Wood Group LLC........G....... 567 644-9951
  Hebron *(G-10862)*

Colonial Woodcraft Inc.......................F....... 513 779-8088
  Lebanon *(G-11789)*

Criswell Furniture..............................G....... 330 695-2082
  Fredericksburg *(G-10082)*

Diversified Products & Svcs..............C....... 740 393-6202
  Mount Vernon *(G-14619)*

Dorel Home Furnishings Inc............C....... 419 447-7448
  Tiffin *(G-18218)*

Dutch Heritage Woodcraft..................E....... 330 893-2211
  Berlin *(G-1648)*

Dutch Legacy LLC..............................G....... 330 359-0270
  Dundee *(G-1645)*

Dutch Valley Woodcraft Ltd...............G....... 330 695-2364
  Fredericksburg *(G-10084)*

East Oberlin Cabinets........................G....... 440 775-1166
  Oberlin *(G-15637)*

Feslers Refinishing............................G....... 740 622-4849
  Coshocton *(G-7890)*

Fleetwood Custom Countertops...........F....... 740 965-9833
  Johnstown *(G-11398)*

Flottemesch Anthony & Son................F....... 513 561-1212
  Cincinnati *(G-3762)*

◆ Foundations Worldwide Inc............E....... 330 722-5033
  Medina *(G-13412)*

Furniture By Otmar Inc.....................F....... 937 435-2039
  Dayton *(G-8355)*

Furniture By Otmar Inc.....................G....... 513 891-5141
  Cincinnati *(G-3787)*

▲ G R K Manufacturing Co Inc.........E....... 513 863-3131
  Hamilton *(G-10697)*

Gasser Chair Co Inc.........................D....... 330 759-2234
  Youngstown *(G-21093)*

Grabo Interiors Inc.............................G....... 216 391-6677
  Cleveland *(G-5442)*

Green Acres Furniture Ltd..................F....... 330 359-6251
  Navarre *(G-14713)*

◆ Greenway Home Products Inc.........F....... 419 874-6770
  Perrysburg *(G-16105)*

▲ Hen House Inc..............................G....... 419 663-3377
  Norwalk *(G-15544)*

Hidden View Woodworking...................G....... 330 674-5196
  Millersburg *(G-14224)*

Hochstetler Wood...............................F....... 330 893-2384
  Millersburg *(G-14226)*

Hochstetler Wood Ltd..........................F....... 330 893-1601
  Millersburg *(G-14227)*

Holmes Panel.....................................G....... 330 897-5040
  Baltic *(G-1074)*

Hopewood Inc.....................................G....... 330 359-5656
  Millersburg *(G-14232)*

Idx Corporation..................................C....... 937 401-3225
  Dayton *(G-8400)*

Installed Building Pdts LLC................E....... 614 308-9900
  Columbus *(G-7190)*

Integral Design Inc.............................F....... 216 524-0555
  Cleveland *(G-5574)*

J & F Furniture Shop.........................G....... 330 852-2478
  Sugarcreek *(G-18024)*

J Treharn Co Inc................................F....... 330 743-8215
  Youngstown *(G-21122)*

J-J Berlin Woodcraft Inc.....................G....... 330 893-9171
  Berlin *(G-1650)*

Jeffco Sheltered Workshop.................E....... 740 264-4608
  Steubenville *(G-17701)*

Joe P Fischer Woodcraft.....................G....... 513 474-4316
  Cincinnati *(G-3950)*

Ken Harper..C....... 740 439-4452
  Byesville *(G-2406)*

Kencraft Co Inc..................................G....... 419 536-0333
  Toledo *(G-18542)*

Kenway Corp......................................G....... 937 767-1660
  Yellow Springs *(G-20994)*

▲ Kitchens By Rutenschroer Inc......F....... 513 251-8333
  Cincinnati *(G-3994)*

Lauber Manufacturing Co ....G....... 419 446-2450
  Archbold *(G-682)*

Legacy Oak and Hardwoods LLC.........F....... 330 859-2656
  Zoarville *(G-21371)*

Lima Millwork Inc..............................E....... 419 331-3303
  Elida *(G-9351)*

Mark Rasche......................................G....... 614 882-1810
  Westerville *(G-20170)*

Masco Cbinetry Middlefield LLC..........D....... 440 632-5058
  Middlefield *(G-13956)*

Michaels Pre-Cast Con Pdts...............F....... 513 683-1292
  Loveland *(G-12374)*

Mielke Furniture Repair Inc................G....... 419 625-4572
  Sandusky *(G-16989)*

Miller Cabinet LLC............................G....... 614 873-4221
  Plain City *(G-16351)*

Millwood Wholesale Inc.....................F....... 330 359-6109
  Dundee *(G-9177)*

Modern American Design Inc..............G....... 330 633-0227
  Tallmadge *(G-18156)*

N Wasserstrom & Sons Inc...............D....... 614 737-5410
  Columbus *(G-7378)*

Nagele Manufacturing Co Inc.............E....... 216 433-1100
  Cleveland *(G-5849)*

▲ P Graham Dunn Inc.....................D....... 330 828-2105
  Dalton *(G-8076)*

Paradise Inc......................................G....... 330 928-3789
  Cuyahoga Falls *(G-8031)*

Patrician Furniture Builders................G....... 330 746-6354
  Youngstown *(G-21167)*

▲ Progressive Furniture Inc.............E....... 419 446-4500
  Archbold *(G-690)*

R A Hamed International Inc................F....... 330 247-0190
  Twinsburg *(G-19007)*

▲ R D Cook Company LLC.................G....... 614 262-0550
  Columbus *(G-7543)*

Regal Cabinet Inc..............................G....... 419 865-3932
  Toledo *(G-18674)*

Richard Benhase & Associates...........F....... 513 772-1896
  Cincinnati *(G-4343)*

Richmonds Woodworks Inc..................F....... 330 343-8184
  New Philadelphia *(G-14925)*

Rnr Enterprises LLC..........................F....... 330 852-3022
  Sugarcreek *(G-18037)*

▲ Senator International Inc...............E....... 419 887-5806
  Maumee *(G-13291)*

Simmons Company.............................G....... 614 871-8088
  Grove City *(G-10595)*

Specialty Services Inc........................G....... 614 421-1599
  Columbus *(G-7638)*

Stark Truss Company Inc..................D....... 330 478-2100
  Canton *(G-2859)*

Stark Truss Company Inc..................D....... 419 298-3777
  Edgerton *(G-9337)*

Stephen J Page...................................G....... 865 951-3316
  Williamsburg *(G-20412)*

Swigart Refinishing Company.............G....... 937 254-1141
  Dayton *(G-8692)*

▲ Textiles Inc....................................G....... 740 852-0782
  London *(G-12220)*

Textiles Inc.......................................G....... 614 529-8642
  Hilliard *(G-10986)*

Thomas Hora......................................G....... 740 622-1386
  Fresno *(G-10200)*

Touchpint Cmplete Slutions LLC.........G....... 419 919-3222
  Celina *(G-3024)*

Trailway Wood....................................F....... 330 893-9966
  Dundee *(G-9182)*

Tri State Countertop Service...............G....... 740 354-3663
  Portsmouth *(G-16458)*

Vocational Services Inc.....................C....... 216 431-8085
  Cleveland *(G-6424)*

Waller Brothers Stone Company..........E....... 740 858-1948
  Mc Dermott *(G-13345)*

Weaver Woodcraft L L C.....................G....... 330 695-2150
  Apple Creek *(G-653)*

Western & Southern Lf Insur Co.........A....... 513 629-1800
  Cincinnati *(G-4588)*

Western Reserve Furniture Co............G....... 440 235-6216
  North Olmsted *(G-15351)*

▼ Wine Cellar Innovations LLC.........C....... 513 321-3733
  Cincinnati *(G-4599)*

Yoders Woodworking...........................G....... 888 818-0568
  Millersburg *(G-14291)*

2512 Wood Household Furniture, Upholstered

Central Design Services.......................G....... 513 829-7027
  Fairfield *(G-9652)*

Decor At 124 ....G 260 319-4213
  Convoy (G-7831)
Dura Bilt Drapery & Upholstery ....F 440 269-8438
  Willoughby (G-20477)
Fortner Upholstering Inc ....F 614 475-8282
  Columbus (G-7095)
Franklin Cabinet Company Inc ....E 937 743-9606
  Franklin (G-10023)
▲ G R K Manufacturing Co Inc ....C 513 863-3131
  Hamilton (G-10697)
Gasser Chair Co Inc ....F 330 534-2234
  Youngstown (G-21092)
▲ H Goodman Inc ....D 216 341-0200
  Newburgh Heights (G-15070)
Hallmark Industries Inc ....E 937 864-7378
  Enon (G-9545)
Hallmark Industries Inc ....E 937 864-7378
  Enon (G-9546)
Hopewood Inc ....G 330 359-5656
  Millersburg (G-14232)
Joseph G Betz & Sons ....G 513 481-0322
  Cincinnati (G-3958)
Kenneth Shannon ....G 513 777-8888
  Liberty Twp (G-11975)
▲ Kroehler Furniture Mfg Co Inc ....B 828 459-9865
  Columbus (G-7269)
LAtelier Custom Woodworking ....G 234 759-3359
  North Lima (G-15320)
Mastercraft Mfg Inc ....G 330 893-3366
  Berlin (G-1651)
Njm Furniture Outlet Inc ....F 330 893-3514
  Millersburg (G-14254)
Quality Fabrications LLC ....G 330 695-2478
  Fredericksburg (G-10091)
Robert Mayo Industries ....G 330 426-2587
  East Palestine (G-9244)
Stiglers Woodworks ....G 513 733-3009
  Cincinnati (G-4468)
▲ Weavers Furniture Ltd ....F 330 852-2701
  Sugarcreek (G-18051)

2514 Metal Household Furniture

◆ Albion Industries Inc ....E 440 238-1955
  Strongsville (G-17885)
▲ Angels Landing Inc ....G 513 687-3681
  Moraine (G-14465)
Bailey & Jensen Inc ....F 937 272-1784
  Centerville (G-3036)
C-Link Enterprises LLC ....F 937 222-2829
  Dayton (G-8205)
Cabintpak Kitchens of Columbus ....G 614 294-4646
  Columbus (G-6886)
Installed Building Pdts LLC ....E 614 308-9900
  Columbus (G-7190)
◆ Invacare Corporation ....A 440 329-6000
  Elyria (G-9435)
Invacare Corporation ....D 800 333-6900
  Elyria (G-9436)
▲ Invacare Holdings Corporation ....G 440 329-6000
  Elyria (G-9438)
Invacare International Corp ....G 440 329-6000
  Elyria (G-9439)
▲ Mantua Manufacturing Co ....D 800 333-8333
  Bedford (G-1440)
◆ Medallion Lighting Corporation ....E 440 255-8383
  Mentor (G-13650)
Metal Fabricating Corporation ....D 216 631-8121
  Cleveland (G-5787)
Pine Acres Woodcraft ....G 330 852-0190
  Sugarcreek (G-18031)
▲ Sunnest Service LLC ....E 740 283-2815
  Steubenville (G-17717)

2515 Mattresses & Bedsprings

Ahmf Inc ....E 614 921-1223
  Columbus (G-6704)
▲ Banner Mattress Co Inc ....G 419 324-7181
  Toledo (G-18363)
▲ Casco Mfg Solutions Inc ....D 513 681-0003
  Cincinnati (G-3504)
Central Ohio Mat Company ....G 740 627-7261
  Mount Vernon (G-14614)
▲ H Goodman Inc ....D 216 341-0200
  Newburgh Heights (G-15070)
Heritage Sleep Products LLC ....E 440 437-4425
  Orwell (G-15776)
Homecare Mattress Inc ....F 937 746-2556
  Franklin (G-10027)
Innocor Foam Tech - Acp Inc ....F 419 647-4172
  Spencerville (G-17460)

Lcmf Inc ....E 513 860-9988
  Fairfield (G-9677)
Leggett & Platt Incorporated ....E 440 322-4865
  Elyria (G-9452)
Midwest Quality Bedding Inc ....G 614 504-5971
  Columbus (G-7352)
Midwest Quality Bedding Inc ....F 614 504-5971
  Plain City (G-16350)
National Bedding Company LLC ....C 513 421-4094
  Cincinnati (G-4139)
Ohio Mattress ....G 740 739-8219
  Lancaster (G-11736)
Original Mattress Factory Inc ....G 614 291-8085
  Columbus (G-7446)
Original Mattress Factory Inc ....G 216 661-8388
  Cleveland (G-5947)
Original Mattress Factory Inc ....G 513 752-6600
  Cincinnati (G-3313)
Protective Industrial Polymers ....F 440 327-0015
  North Ridgeville (G-15396)
▲ Quilting Inc ....D 614 504-5971
  Plain City (G-16356)
Sealy Mattress Company ....C 330 725-4146
  Medina (G-13477)
Sealy Mattress Mfg Co Inc ....D 800 697-3259
  Medina (G-13478)
Select Mattress Co Inc ....F 419 244-3645
  Toledo (G-18690)
Smp Manufacturing LLC ....G 419 244-3645
  Toledo (G-18699)
SSP Tennessee LLC ....G 614 279-8850
  Columbus (G-7649)
Tep Bedding Grp Inc ....E 440 437-7700
  Orwell (G-15779)
Timken Foundation ....G 330 452-1144
  Canton (G-2875)
Tru Comfort Mattress ....G 614 595-8600
  Dublin (G-9156)
Walter F Stephens Jr Inc ....E 937 746-0521
  Franklin (G-10063)
▲ White Dove Mattress Ltd ....E 216 341-0200
  Newburgh Heights (G-15081)

2517 Wood T V, Radio, Phono & Sewing Cabinets

Innerwood & Company ....F 513 677-2229
  Loveland (G-12360)
Kraftmaid Trucking Inc ....D 440 632-2531
  Middlefield (G-13449)
Masco Cabinetry LLC ....A 440 632-2547
  Middlefield (G-13954)
▲ Progressive Furniture Inc ....E 419 446-4500
  Archbold (G-690)
Xxx Intrntional Amusements Inc ....E 216 671-6900
  Cleveland (G-6487)

2519 Household Furniture, NEC

Bulk Carrier Trnsp Eqp Co ....E 330 339-3333
  New Philadelphia (G-14887)
Daniels Amish Collection LLC ....C 330 276-0110
  Killbuck (G-11594)
Daniels Amish Collection LLC ....G 330 359-0400
  Dundee (G-9171)
Entertainment Junction ....D 513 326-1100
  Cincinnati (G-3710)
Evenflo Company Inc ....D 937 773-3971
  Troy (G-18823)
◆ Evenflo Company Inc ....C 937 415-3300
  Miamisburg (G-13806)
G Keener & Co ....G 937 846-1210
  New Carlisle (G-14801)
Hershy Way Ltd ....G 330 893-2809
  Millersburg (G-14223)
John Purdum ....G 513 897-9686
  Waynesville (G-19731)
Kenwood Pool Distributors Inc ....G 513 793-7080
  Cincinnati (G-3984)
▲ Kitchens By Rutenschroer Inc ....F 513 251-8333
  Cincinnati (G-3994)
Mar-Bal Pultrusion Inc ....G 440 953-0456
  Willoughby (G-20535)
Norwalk Custom Order Furn LLC ....C 419 744-3200
  Norwalk (G-15556)
Office Magic Inc ....F 510 782-6100
  Medina (G-13452)
Poly Concepts LLC ....G 419 678-3300
  Saint Henry (G-16821)
Sailors Tailor Inc ....G 937 862-7781
  Spring Valley (G-17469)

◆ Sauder Woodworking Co ....A 419 446-3828
  Archbold (G-694)
Sauder Woodworking Co ....G 419 446-2711
  Archbold (G-695)
Valley View Woodcraft ....G 330 852-3000
  Sugarcreek (G-18048)

2521 Wood Office Furniture

August Incorporated ....E 937 434-2520
  Dayton (G-8171)
Basic Cases Inc ....G 216 662-3900
  Cleveland (G-4896)
▲ Buzz Seating Inc ....F 877 263-5737
  Cincinnati (G-3490)
Cabinet Systems Inc ....G 440 237-1924
  Cleveland (G-4961)
Creative Woodworks ....G 440 355-8155
  Grafton (G-10422)
Custom Millcraft Corp ....E 513 874-7080
  West Chester (G-19851)
DIng Products ....G 440 442-7777
  Cleveland (G-5195)
Dutch Design Products LLC ....E 330 674-1167
  Fredericksburg (G-10083)
▼ Dvuv LLC ....G 216 741-5511
  Cleveland (G-5226)
East Woodworking Company ....G 216 791-5950
  Cleveland (G-5240)
Frontier Signs & Displays Inc ....G 513 367-0813
  Harrison (G-10779)
◆ Gasser Chair Co Inc ....E 330 534-2234
  Youngstown (G-21091)
Gasser Chair Co Inc ....D 330 759-2234
  Youngstown (G-21093)
Geograph Industries Inc ....E 513 202-9200
  Harrison (G-10780)
Global Design Factory LLC ....G 330 322-8775
  Hudson (G-11174)
▲ GMI Companies Inc ....C 513 932-3445
  Lebanon (G-11804)
GMI Companies Inc ....G 937 981-0244
  Greenfield (G-10476)
H S Morgan Limited Partnership ....G 513 870-4400
  Fairfield (G-9663)
▲ Hoge Lumber Company ....E 419 753-2263
  New Knoxville (G-14836)
Idx Corporation ....C 937 401-3225
  Dayton (G-8400)
Innerwood & Company ....F 513 677-2229
  Loveland (G-12360)
Innovative Woodworking Inc ....G 513 531-1940
  Cincinnati (G-3923)
Interior Products Co Inc ....F 216 641-1919
  Cleveland (G-5578)
LAtelier Custom Woodworking ....G 234 759-3359
  North Lima (G-15320)
Lima Millwork Inc ....G 419 331-3303
  Elida (G-9351)
Macwood Inc ....G 614 279-7676
  Columbus (G-7312)
Mark Rasche ....G 614 882-1810
  Westerville (G-20170)
Miller Cabinet Company LLC ....E 614 873-4221
  Plain City (G-16351)
▲ National Electro-Coatings Inc ....D 216 898-0080
  Cleveland (G-5855)
R Carney Thomas ....G 740 342-3388
  New Lexington (G-14853)
Richard Benhase & Associates ....F 513 772-1896
  Cincinnati (G-4343)
Sauder Manufacturing Co ....C 419 682-3061
  Stryker (G-18007)
Specialty Services Inc ....G 614 421-1599
  Columbus (G-7638)
Stephen J Page ....G 865 951-3316
  Williamsburg (G-20412)
Symatic Inc ....E 330 225-1510
  Brunswick (G-2260)
▼ Tiffin Metal Products Co ....D 419 447-8414
  Tiffin (G-18248)
▼ Workstream Inc ....D 513 870-4400
  Fairfield (G-9733)
Yellow Tang Interiors LLC ....G 330 629-9279
  Youngstown (G-21244)

2522 Office Furniture, Except Wood

◆ American Interiors Inc ....E 419 324-0365
  Toledo (G-18338)
Axess International LLC ....G 330 460-4840
  Brunswick (G-2208)

S I C

▲ Casco Mfg Solutions Inc ....D 513 681-0003
  Cincinnati *(G-3504)*
Custom Millcraft Corp ....E 513 874-7080
  West Chester *(G-19851)*
Design Trac Inc ....G 330 759-3131
  Youngstown *(G-21067)*
Dgl Woodworking Inc ....F 937 837-7091
  Dayton *(G-8302)*
East Woodworking Company ....E 216 791-5950
  Cleveland *(G-5240)*
Edsal Sandusky Corporation ....C 419 626-5465
  Sandusky *(G-16960)*
Ergo Desktop LLC ....E 567 890-3746
  Celina *(G-2995)*
Frontier Signs & Displays Inc ....G 513 367-0813
  Harrison *(G-10779)*
Furniture Concepts Inc ....F 216 292-9100
  Cleveland *(G-5385)*
Gasser Chair Co Inc ....F 330 534-2234
  Youngstown *(G-21092)*
Gasser Chair Co Inc ....D 330 759-2234
  Youngstown *(G-21093)*
Geograph Industries Inc ....E 513 202-9200
  Harrison *(G-10780)*
▲ GMI Companies Inc ....C 513 932-3445
  Lebanon *(G-11804)*
GMI Companies Inc ....G 937 981-0244
  Greenfield *(G-10476)*
H S Morgan Limited Partnership ....G 513 870-4400
  Fairfield *(G-9663)*
Hobart Cabinet Company ....E 937 335-4666
  Troy *(G-18839)*
▼ Infinium Wall Systems Inc ....E 440 572-5000
  Strongsville *(G-17930)*
Innovative Woodworking Inc ....E 513 531-1940
  Cincinnati *(G-3923)*
Jsc Employee Leasing Corp ....F 330 773-8971
  Akron *(G-245)*
◆ Kellogg Cabinets Inc ....E 614 833-9596
  Canal Winchester *(G-2529)*
Lakeside Cabins Ltd ....G 419 896-2299
  Shiloh *(G-17150)*
▲ M/W International Inc ....F 440 526-6900
  Brecksville *(G-2063)*
Mark Rasche ....E 614 882-1810
  Westerville *(G-20170)*
Marsh Industries Inc ....D 330 308-8667
  New Philadelphia *(G-14912)*
Metal Fabricating Corporation ....D 216 631-8121
  Cleveland *(G-5787)*
▲ National Electro-Coatings Inc ....D 216 898-0080
  Cleveland *(G-5855)*
Office Magic Inc ....E 510 782-6100
  Medina *(G-13452)*
Patriot Seating Inc ....F 330 779-0768
  Youngstown *(G-21168)*
Pucel Enterprises Inc ....D 216 881-4604
  Cleveland *(G-6061)*
▲ R B Mfg Co ....F 419 626-9464
  Sandusky *(G-16999)*
Recycled Systems Furniture Inc ....E 614 880-9110
  Worthington *(G-20884)*
Right Fit Ergonomics LLC ....G 330 674-0977
  Millersburg *(G-14260)*
Service Pdts Group of Bucyrus ....G 419 562-4456
  Bucyrus *(G-2359)*
Ssi Manufacturing Inc ....F 513 761-7757
  West Chester *(G-20054)*
Starr Fabricating Inc ....D 330 394-9891
  Vienna *(G-19376)*
▼ Tiffin Metal Products Co ....D 419 447-8414
  Tiffin *(G-18248)*
Veterans Representative Co LLC ....F 330 779-0768
  Youngstown *(G-21237)*
▼ Workstream Inc ....D 513 870-4400
  Fairfield *(G-9733)*

2531 Public Building & Related Furniture

Absolutely Paper Established ....G 216 932-4822
  Cleveland *(G-4688)*
Adient US LLC ....C 937 383-5200
  Greenfield *(G-10472)*
American Office Services Inc ....G 440 899-6888
  Westlake *(G-20252)*
Ap-Alternatives LLC ....F 419 267-5280
  Ridgeville Corners *(G-16663)*
Bell Vault & Monument Works ....E 937 866-2444
  Miamisburg *(G-13785)*
Brocar Products Inc ....E 513 922-2888
  Cincinnati *(G-3477)*

▲ C E White Co ....D 419 492-2157
  New Washington *(G-14958)*
City of Conneaut ....G 440 599-7071
  Conneaut *(G-7802)*
City of Kent ....F 330 673-8897
  Kent *(G-11438)*
Columbiana Metro Hsing Auth ....E 330 385-6662
  East Liverpool *(G-9207)*
County of Summit ....G 330 865-8065
  Akron *(G-132)*
Franklin Cabinet Company Inc ....G 937 743-9606
  Franklin *(G-10023)*
◆ Gasser Chair Co Inc ....E 330 534-2234
  Youngstown *(G-21091)*
Gasser Chair Co Inc ....D 330 759-2234
  Youngstown *(G-21093)*
Gasser Chair Co Inc ....F 330 534-2234
  Youngstown *(G-21092)*
General Motors LLC ....A 216 265-5000
  Cleveland *(G-5419)*
Global Furnishings Inc ....G 216 595-0901
  Beachwood *(G-1272)*
▲ GMI Companies Inc ....C 513 932-3445
  Lebanon *(G-11804)*
GMI Companies Inc ....G 937 981-0244
  Greenfield *(G-10476)*
▲ Gra-Mag Truck Intr Systems LLC ....E 740 490-1000
  London *(G-12211)*
Gramag LLC ....E 614 875-8435
  Grove City *(G-10559)*
▲ Grand-Rock Company Inc ....E 440 639-2000
  Painesville *(G-15884)*
◆ Granite Industries Inc ....D 419 445-4733
  Archbold *(G-679)*
Hann Manufacturing Inc ....E 740 962-3752
  McConnelsville *(G-13352)*
International Automotive ....B 937 492-1225
  Sidney *(G-17195)*
Johnson Controls Inc ....D 419 636-4211
  Bryan *(G-2307)*
Johnson Controls Inc ....D 216 587-0100
  Cleveland *(G-5621)*
Johnson Controls Inc ....D 513 671-6338
  Cincinnati *(G-3956)*
Lear Corporation ....C 419 335-6010
  Wauseon *(G-19688)*
Lear Corporation ....F 614 850-8630
  Columbus *(G-7289)*
Lorain County Metro Pk Dst ....G 440 327-3626
  North Ridgeville *(G-15388)*
Magna International Amer Inc ....E 905 853-3604
  Ridgeville Corners *(G-16665)*
Magna Seating America Inc ....D 440 846-5680
  Sheffield Village *(G-17126)*
Magna Seating America Inc ....C 330 824-3101
  Warren *(G-19576)*
McGill Septic Tank Co ....E 330 876-2171
  Kinsman *(G-11610)*
Michaels Pre-Cast Con Pdts ....F 513 683-1292
  Loveland *(G-12374)*
Mock Woodworking Company LLC ....E 740 452-2701
  Zanesville *(G-21329)*
Modern Manufacturing Inc ....F 513 251-3600
  Cincinnati *(G-4116)*
N Wasserstrom & Sons Inc ....D 614 737-5410
  Columbus *(G-7378)*
Oberfields LLC ....E 614 252-0955
  Columbus *(G-7410)*
Quality Seating Company Inc ....E 330 747-0181
  Youngstown *(G-21181)*
▲ Sauder Manufacturing Co ....C 419 445-7670
  Archbold *(G-692)*
Sauder Manufacturing Co ....C 419 682-3061
  Stryker *(G-18007)*
▲ Setex Inc ....B 419 394-7800
  Saint Marys *(G-16855)*
▲ Shiffler Equipment Sales Inc ....E 440 285-9175
  Chardon *(G-3179)*
Soft Touch Wood LLC ....E 330 545-4204
  Girard *(G-10395)*
▲ Systems Jay LLC Nanogate ....C 419 524-3778
  Mansfield *(G-12688)*
▼ Tiffin Metal Products Co ....D 419 447-8414
  Tiffin *(G-18248)*
Tri-State Supply Co Inc ....F 614 272-6767
  Columbus *(G-7709)*
Trim Systems Operating Corp ....C 614 289-5360
  New Albany *(G-14774)*
W C Heller & Co Inc ....F 419 485-3176
  Montpelier *(G-14457)*

Wurms Woodworking Company ....E 419 492-2184
  New Washington *(G-14966)*
Yanfeng US Automotive ....D 419 662-4905
  Northwood *(G-15499)*

2541 Wood, Office & Store Fixtures

119c Landis Display Co ....G 937 307-9499
  Franklin *(G-10003)*
3jd Inc ....F 513 324-9655
  Moraine *(G-14462)*
7d Marketing Inc ....F 330 721-8822
  Medina *(G-13362)*
A & J Woodworking Inc ....G 419 695-5655
  Delphos *(G-8898)*
A J Construction Co ....G 330 539-9544
  Girard *(G-10380)*
A-Display Service Corp ....F 614 469-1230
  Columbus *(G-6669)*
▲ Accel Group Inc ....D 330 336-0317
  Wadsworth *(G-19387)*
Accent Manufacturing Inc ....F 330 724-7704
  Norton *(G-15500)*
Action Group Inc ....D 614 868-8868
  Blacklick *(G-1686)*
AG Industries Inc ....E 216 252-7300
  Cleveland *(G-4730)*
Allied Plastic Co Inc ....G 419 389-1688
  Toledo *(G-18330)*
American Interior Design Inc ....F 216 663-0606
  Cleveland *(G-4785)*
Amtekco Industries Inc ....G 614 228-6525
  Columbus *(G-6750)*
Amtekco Industries Inc ....D 614 228-6590
  Columbus *(G-6749)*
▲ Archer Counter Design Inc ....G 513 396-7526
  Cincinnati *(G-3410)*
Artistic Finishes Inc ....F 440 951-7850
  Willoughby *(G-20440)*
Automated Bldg Components Inc ....E 419 257-2152
  North Baltimore *(G-15191)*
Baker Store Equipment Company ....F 216 475-5900
  Shaker Heights *(G-17084)*
Bauman Custom Woodworking LLC ....G 330 482-4330
  Salem *(G-16875)*
Benchmark Cabinets ....E 740 694-1144
  Fredericktown *(G-10096)*
Brad Snoderly ....F 419 476-0184
  Toledo *(G-18380)*
Brower Products Inc ....D 937 563-1111
  Cincinnati *(G-3482)*
Bruewer Woodwork Mfg Co ....D 513 353-3505
  Cleves *(G-6507)*
C & D Counters ....G 740 259-5529
  Lucasville *(G-12417)*
Cameo Countertops Inc ....G 419 865-6371
  Holland *(G-11048)*
◆ Cap & Associates Incorporated ....C 614 863-3363
  Columbus *(G-6893)*
Case Crafters Inc ....G 937 667-9473
  Tipp City *(G-18271)*
Cassady Woodworks Inc ....G 937 256-7948
  Dayton *(G-8099)*
◆ CIP International Inc ....D 513 874-9925
  West Chester *(G-19833)*
Couch Business Development Inc ....F 937 253-1099
  Dayton *(G-8244)*
Counter Concepts Inc ....G 330 848-4848
  Doylestown *(G-9028)*
Counter- Advice Inc ....F 937 291-1600
  Franklin *(G-10014)*
Countertop Sales ....F 614 626-4476
  Columbus *(G-6991)*
Countertop Xpress ....G 440 358-0500
  Painesville *(G-15871)*
Crane Plumbing LLC ....E 419 522-4211
  Mansfield *(G-12587)*
Creative Products Inc ....E 419 866-5501
  Holland *(G-11049)*
Custom Counter Tops & Spc Co ....G 330 637-4856
  Cortland *(G-7867)*
Custom Design Cabinets & Tops ....G 440 639-9900
  Painesville *(G-15872)*
Custom Surroundings Inc ....F 330 483-9020
  Valley City *(G-19202)*
D Lewis Inc ....G 740 695-2615
  Saint Clairsville *(G-16788)*
▲ Darko Inc ....E 330 425-9805
  Twinsburg *(G-18921)*
▲ Dell Fixtures Inc ....E 614 449-1750
  Columbus *(G-7020)*

Designer Cntemporary Laminates ....G...... 440 946-8207
Willoughby (G-20473)

Display Dynamics Inc ....F...... 937 832-2830
Englewood (G-9516)

Diversified Products & Svcs ....C...... 740 393-6202
Mount Vernon (G-14619)

Dovetail Dimensions ....G...... 330 674-9533
Millersburg (G-14212)

E J Skok Industries ....E...... 216 292-7533
Bedford (G-1422)

▼ Fixture Dimensions Inc ....E...... 513 360-7512
Middletown (G-14041)

Fleetwood Custom Countertops ....F...... 740 965-9833
Johnstown (G-11398)

Form-A-Top Products Inc ....G...... 440 779-9452
North Olmsted (G-15334)

▲ Formatech Inc ....E...... 330 273-2800
Brunswick (G-2225)

▲ Formica Corporation ....E...... 513 786-3400
Cincinnati (G-3772)

Formware Inc ....G...... 614 231-9387
Columbus (G-7093)

Forum III Inc ....F...... 513 961-5123
Cincinnati (G-3773)

Franklin Cabinet Company Inc ....E...... 937 743-9606
Franklin (G-10023)

▲ G & W Products LLC ....C...... 513 860-4050
Fairfield (G-9660)

▲ Gabriel Logan LLC ....D...... 740 380-6809
Logan (G-12174)

Gary L Gast ....G...... 419 626-5915
Sandusky (G-16968)

Geograph Industries Inc ....E...... 513 202-9200
Harrison (G-10780)

GMI Companies Inc ....E...... 937 981-7724
Greenfield (G-10477)

▲ GMI Companies Inc ....C...... 513 932-3445
Lebanon (G-11804)

GMI Companies Inc ....G...... 937 981-0244
Greenfield (G-10476)

Hattenbach Company ....D...... 216 881-5200
Cleveland (G-5485)

Hattenbach Company ....E...... 330 744-2732
Youngstown (G-21107)

Hawthorne Caravan & Assoc LLC ......F...... 440 366-9065
Elyria (G-9428)

Helmart Company Inc ....G...... 513 941-3095
Cincinnati (G-3876)

Home Stor & Off Solutions Inc ....F...... 216 362-4660
Cleveland (G-5521)

Imperial Countertops ....F...... 216 851-0888
Cleveland (G-5555)

Indian River Industries ....G...... 740 965-4377
Sunbury (G-18064)

▲ Innovative Retail Displays Inc ....F...... 937 237-7708
Dayton (G-8406)

Kbi Group Inc ....G...... 614 873-5825
Plain City (G-16346)

Kdm Signs Inc ....E...... 513 769-3900
Cincinnati (G-3974)

◆ Kellogg Cabinets Inc ....E...... 614 833-9596
Canal Winchester (G-2529)

Kinsella Manufacturing Co Inc ....F...... 513 561-5285
Cincinnati (G-3991)

Kitchen & Bath Factory Inc ....G...... 440 510-8111
Mentor (G-13623)

▲ Kitchens By Rutenschroer Inc ....F...... 513 251-8333
Cincinnati (G-3994)

▲ LE Smith Company ....D...... 419 636-4555
Bryan (G-2310)

Leiden Cabinet Company LLC ....C...... 330 425-8555
Twinsburg (G-18972)

Leiden Cabinet Company LLC ....E...... 330 878-7790
Strasburg (G-17825)

Lima Millwork Inc ....E...... 419 331-3303
Elida (G-9351)

M21 Industries LLC ....D...... 937 781-1377
Dayton (G-8465)

Macwood Inc ....G...... 614 279-7676
Columbus (G-7312)

Malco Laminated Inc ....G...... 513 541-8300
Cincinnati (G-4055)

Mespo Woodworking ....G...... 440 693-4041
Middlefield (G-13958)

Miami Valley Counters & Spc ....G...... 937 865-0562
Miamisburg (G-13831)

◆ Michael Kaufman Companies Inc ....F...... 330 673-4881
Kent (G-11490)

Michael Kaufman Companies Inc ....F...... 330 673-4881
Kent (G-11491)

Midwest Woodworking Co Inc ....E...... 513 631-6684
Cincinnati (G-4106)

Miller Cabinet Company LLC ....E...... 614 873-4221
Plain City (G-16351)

Mock Woodworking Company LLC .....E...... 740 452-2701
Zanesville (G-21329)

Modern Designs Inc ....G...... 330 644-1771
Akron (G-299)

Murray Display Fixtures Ltd ....G...... 614 554-9461
Grove City (G-10575)

Nagele Manufacturing Co Inc ....E...... 216 433-1100
Cleveland (G-5849)

Norton Industries Inc ....F...... 888 357-2345
Lakewood (G-11676)

Ohio Woodworking Co Inc ....E...... 513 631-0870
Cincinnati (G-4181)

Partitions Plus LLC ....F...... 419 422-2600
Findlay (G-9877)

Pfi Displays Inc ....E...... 330 925-9015
Rittman (G-16681)

Prestige Store Interiors Inc ....D...... 419 476-2106
Toledo (G-18655)

▲ Profac Inc ....C...... 440 942-0205
Mentor (G-13698)

◆ Ptmj Enterprises ....F...... 440 543-8000
Solon (G-17365)

▲ R D Cook Company LLC ....G...... 614 262-0550
Columbus (G-7543)

Randys Countertops Inc ....F...... 740 881-5831
Powell (G-16482)

Reserve Millwork Inc ....E...... 216 531-6982
Bedford (G-1457)

Riceland Cabinet Inc ....D...... 330 601-1071
Wooster (G-20829)

Richard B Linneman ....E...... 513 922-5537
Cincinnati (G-4342)

▲ Rinos Woodworking Shop Inc ....F...... 440 946-1718
Willoughby (G-20589)

Rivercity Woodworking Inc ....G...... 513 860-1900
West Chester (G-19934)

Robertson Cabinets Inc ....E...... 937 698-3755
West Milton (G-20110)

Roy L Bayes ....G...... 614 274-6729
Columbus (G-7575)

Scio Laminated Products Inc ....E...... 740 945-1321
Scio (G-17038)

Shur Fit Distributors Inc ....E...... 937 746-0567
Franklin (G-10053)

Sidney Stiers ....G...... 740 454-7368
Zanesville (G-21353)

Skeeles Manufacturing Corp ....F...... 614 274-4700
Columbus (G-7626)

Steeles Display Cases ....G...... 740 965-6426
Westerville (G-20189)

Stephen J Page ....G...... 865 951-3316
Williamsburg (G-20412)

Stephen R Lilley ....G...... 513 899-4400
Morrow (G-14551)

Stoller Custom Cabinetry ....G...... 330 939-6555
Sterling (G-17685)

Summit Custom Cabinets ....G...... 740 345-1734
Newark (G-15061)

Symatic Inc ....E...... 330 225-1510
Brunswick (G-2260)

Tenkotte Tops Inc ....G...... 513 738-7300
Harrison (G-10810)

Thiels Replacement Systems Inc ....D...... 419 289-6139
Ashland (G-781)

Thomas Cabinet Shop Inc ....F...... 937 847-8239
Dayton (G-8711)

Thomas Hora ....D...... 740 622-1386
Fresno (G-10200)

Tim Crabtree ....G...... 740 286-4535
Jackson (G-11329)

Tri-Co Industries ....G...... 740 927-1928
Pataskala (G-15988)

Trumbull Industries Inc ....E...... 330 434-6174
Akron (G-448)

Ultrabuilt Play Systems Inc ....F...... 419 652-2294
Nova (G-15580)

Vances Department Store ....F...... 937 549-2188
Manchester (G-12552)

Vances Department Store ....F...... 937 549-3033
Manchester (G-12553)

▼ W J Egli Company Inc ....F...... 330 823-3666
Alliance (G-551)

Wilsonart LLC ....E...... 614 876-1515
Columbus (G-7765)

▼ Wine Cellar Innovations LLC ....F...... 513 321-3733
Cincinnati (G-4599)

Witt-Gor Inc ....G...... 419 659-2151
Columbus Grove (G-7798)

Wood Specialists ....G...... 440 639-9797
Mentor (G-13772)

Woodworks For You ....G...... 440 277-8147
Wakeman (G-19455)

Xxx Intrntional Amusements Inc ....E...... 216 671-6900
Cleveland (G-6487)

Youngstown Curve Form Inc ....F...... 330 744-3028
Youngstown (G-21250)

2542 Partitions & Fixtures, Except Wood

3-D Technical Services Inc ....E...... 937 746-2901
Franklin (G-10004)

Acrylicon Inc ....G...... 614 263-2086
Columbus (G-6691)

B-R-O-T Incorporated ....E...... 216 267-5335
Cleveland (G-4886)

Bates Metal Products Inc ....D...... 740 498-8371
Port Washington (G-16422)

Bedford Cabinet Inc ....G...... 440 439-4830
Cleveland (G-4903)

▼ Benko Products Inc ....F...... 440 934-2180
Sheffield Village (G-17121)

Bobs Custom Str Interiors LLC ....G...... 567 316-7490
Toledo (G-18375)

▲ Bud Industries Inc ....G...... 440 946-3200
Willoughby (G-20447)

Busch & Thiem Inc ....E...... 419 625-7515
Sandusky (G-16952)

◆ Cap & Associates Incorporated ......C...... 614 863-3363
Columbus (G-6893)

Ceemco Incorporated ....D...... 513 563-8822
Cincinnati (G-3511)

Component Systems Inc ....E...... 216 252-9292
Cleveland (G-5113)

Control Electric Co ....E...... 216 671-8010
Columbia Station (G-6586)

▲ Crescent Metal Products Inc.........C...... 440 350-1100
Mentor (G-13555)

Custom Millcraft Corp ....E...... 513 874-7080
West Chester (G-19851)

D Lewis Inc ....G...... 740 695-2615
Saint Clairsville (G-16788)

▲ Darko Inc ....G...... 330 425-9805
Twinsburg (G-18921)

▲ Dell Fixtures Inc ....E...... 614 449-1750
Columbus (G-7020)

Display Dynamics Inc ....F...... 937 832-2830
Englewood (G-9516)

Dwayne Bennett Industries ....G...... 440 466-5724
Geneva (G-10345)

▼ E2 Merchandising Inc ....E...... 513 860-5444
West Chester (G-19998)

Easy Board Inc ....G...... 440 205-8836
Mentor (G-13570)

Environmental Wall Systems ....G...... 440 542-6600
Hudson (G-11170)

▲ Formatech Inc ....E...... 330 273-2800
Brunswick (G-2225)

◆ Gallo Displays Inc ....E...... 216 431-9500
Cleveland (G-5393)

GMR Furniture Services Ltd ....F...... 216 244-5072
Parma (G-15959)

▲ Gwp Holdings Inc ....D...... 513 860-4050
Fairfield (G-9662)

Heat Seal LLC ....C...... 216 341-2022
Cleveland (G-5491)

HP Manufacturing Company Inc........D...... 216 361-6500
Cleveland (G-5530)

◆ Industrial Mfg Co LLC ....F...... 440 838-4700
Brecksville (G-2055)

Integral Design Inc ....F...... 216 524-0555
Cleveland (G-5574)

Intelitool Manufacturing Svcs ....G...... 440 953-1071
Willoughby (G-20511)

Jhg Retail Services LLC ....F...... 216 447-0831
Cincinnati (G-3945)

◆ Kellogg Cabinets Inc ....E...... 614 833-9596
Canal Winchester (G-2529)

▲ M/W International Inc ....F...... 440 526-6900
Brecksville (G-2063)

Marlite Inc ....C...... 330 343-6621
Dover (G-8998)

◆ Marlite Inc ....C...... 330 343-6621
Dover (G-8999)

Metal Fabricating Corporation ....D...... 216 631-8121
Cleveland (G-5787)

Metrodeck Inc ....F...... 513 541-4370
Cincinnati (G-4095)

▲ Mfs Supply LLC ....F 440 248-5300
  Solon *(G-17336)*
◆ Midmark Corporation ....A 937 526-3662
  Versailles *(G-19352)*
▲ Mills Company ....E 740 375-0770
  Marion *(G-12885)*
▲ Modern Store Fixtures Inc ....F 330 427-6906
  Garrettsville *(G-10331)*
Mro Built Inc ....D 330 526-0555
  North Canton *(G-15252)*
Myers Industries Inc ....C 330 336-6621
  Wadsworth *(G-19420)*
Ohio Displays Inc ....F 216 961-5600
  Elyria *(G-9470)*
▲ Organized Living Inc ....E 513 489-9300
  Cincinnati *(G-4194)*
◆ Panacea Products Corporation .....E 614 850-7000
  Columbus *(G-7456)*
Panacea Products Corporation ....D 614 429-6320
  Columbus *(G-7457)*
Paul Yoder ....G 740 439-5811
  Senecaville *(G-17059)*
▲ Pete Gaietto & Associates Inc .....D 513 771-0903
  Cincinnati *(G-4230)*
Pfi Displays Inc ....G 330 925-9015
  Rittman *(G-16681)*
Pucel Enterprises Inc ....D 216 881-4604
  Cleveland *(G-6061)*
Qualco LLC ....G 614 257-7408
  Columbus *(G-7533)*
Rack Processing Company Inc ....E 937 294-1911
  Moraine *(G-14521)*
Rack Processing Company Inc ....G 937 294-1911
  Moraine *(G-14522)*
Ray Communications Inc ....G 330 686-0226
  Stow *(G-17795)*
Republic Storage Systems LLC ......C 330 438-5800
  Canton *(G-2839)*
Richard B Linneman ....G 513 922-5537
  Cincinnati *(G-4342)*
Sentrilock LLC ....D 513 618-5800
  West Chester *(G-19944)*
Stanley Industrial & Auto LLC ....C 614 755-7089
  Westerville *(G-20187)*
◆ Summa Holdings Inc ....G 440 838-4700
  Cleveland *(G-6261)*
Sunrise Cooperative Inc ....E 419 683-4600
  Crestline *(G-7936)*
◆ Ternion Inc ....E 216 642-6180
  Cleveland *(G-6307)*
▼ Tiffin Metal Products Co ....D 419 447-8414
  Tiffin *(G-18248)*
Tri County Tarp Inc ....F 419 288-3350
  Bradner *(G-2030)*
Unarco Material Handling Inc ....G 419 384-3211
  Pandora *(G-15948)*
Valley Plastics Co Inc ....E 419 666-2349
  Toledo *(G-18764)*
▼ W J Egli Company Inc ....F 330 823-3666
  Alliance *(G-551)*
Warren Steel Specialties Corp ....F 330 399-8360
  Warren *(G-19624)*
Witt-Gor Inc ....G 419 659-2151
  Columbus Grove *(G-7798)*
Zak Box Co Inc ....G 216 961-5636
  Cleveland *(G-6491)*
Zukowski Rack Co ....G 440 942-5889
  Willoughby *(G-20636)*

2591 Drapery Hardware, Window Blinds & Shades

11 92 Holdings LLC ....E 216 920-7790
  Chagrin Falls *(G-3047)*
ARC Blinds Inc ....G 513 889-4864
  Liberty Twp *(G-11971)*
Blind Factory Showroom ....E 614 771-6549
  Hilliard *(G-10935)*
Blind Outlet ....G 614 895-2002
  Westerville *(G-20202)*
Cincinnati Window Shade Inc ....G 513 398-8510
  Mason *(G-12995)*
Cincinnati Window Shade Inc ....F 513 631-7200
  Cincinnati *(G-3568)*
Custom Blind Corporation ....F 937 643-2907
  Dayton *(G-8257)*
E W Perry Service Co Inc ....G 419 473-1231
  Toledo *(G-18448)*
Gannons Discount Blinds ....G 216 398-2761
  Cleveland *(G-5394)*

Hang-UPS Instllation Group Inc ....G 614 239-7004
  Columbus *(G-7141)*
Hob Enterprises LLC ....G 440 290-8861
  Mentor *(G-13603)*
Lumenomics Inc ....G 614 798-3500
  Lewis Center *(G-11906)*
M C L Window Coverings Inc ....G 513 868-6000
  Hamilton *(G-10719)*
▲ Mag Resources LLC ....G 330 294-0494
  Barberton *(G-1126)*
Miles Pk Vntian Blind Shds Mfg ....G 216 239-0850
  Beachwood *(G-1279)*
Optimun Blinds Inc ....G 740 598-5808
  Brilliant *(G-2094)*
Shade Youngstown & Aluminum Co ..G 330 782-2373
  Youngstown *(G-21200)*
Simex Inc ....G 304 665-1104
  Columbus *(G-7622)*
Vertical Runner ....G 330 262-3000
  Wooster *(G-20843)*

2599 Furniture & Fixtures, NEC

Adkins Marlena ....G 216 704-2751
  Cleveland *(G-4704)*
After Werk ....G 513 661-9375
  Cincinnati *(G-3365)*
Aster Industries Inc ....F 330 762-7965
  Akron *(G-75)*
Belmont Community Hospital ....B 740 671-1216
  Bellaire *(G-1496)*
Bio Fit Engineered Prqcucts ....D 419 823-1089
  Bowling Green *(G-1973)*
Bolons Custom Kitchens Inc ....F 330 499-0092
  Canton *(G-2625)*
Brodwill LLC ....G 513 258-2716
  Cincinnati *(G-3479)*
Cateringstone ....G 513 410-1064
  Cincinnati *(G-3506)*
CC & Sj of Ohio Inc ....G 614 878-7291
  Columbus *(G-6917)*
Columbia Cabinets Inc ....G 440 748-1010
  Columbia Station *(G-6584)*
Custom Sink Top Mfg ....F 440 245-6220
  Lorain *(G-12242)*
Custom Surroundings Inc ....F 330 483-9020
  Valley City *(G-19202)*
Don Walter Kitchen Distrs Inc ....G 330 793-9338
  Youngstown *(G-21071)*
Donkey Coffee & Espresso ....E 740 594-7353
  Athens *(G-862)*
Epix Tube Co Inc ....D 937 529-4858
  Dayton *(G-8328)*
Flipside Inc ....G 440 600-7274
  Chagrin Falls *(G-3059)*
Franklin Cabinet Company Inc ....E 937 743-9606
  Franklin *(G-10023)*
▲ GMI Companies Inc ....C 513 932-3445
  Lebanon *(G-11804)*
GMI Companies Inc ....G 937 981-0244
  Greenfield *(G-10476)*
Home Idea Center Inc ....F 419 375-4951
  Fort Recovery *(G-9954)*
Howard B Claflin Co ....G 330 928-1704
  Cuyahoga Falls *(G-8009)*
Joseph Knapp ....F 330 832-3515
  Massillon *(G-13160)*
Kinnemyers Cornerstone Cab Inc ....G 513 353-3030
  Cleves *(G-6518)*
Lasting Impression Llc ....G 614 806-1186
  Columbus *(G-7287)*
▲ Master Mfg Co Inc ....E 216 641-0500
  Cleveland *(G-5758)*
McLeod Bar Group LLC ....F 614 299-2099
  Columbus *(G-7337)*
◆ Michael Kaufman Companies Inc ..F 330 673-4881
  Kent *(G-11490)*
Michael Kaufman Companies Inc .....F 330 673-4881
  Kent *(G-11491)*
Modroto ....G 800 772-7659
  Ashtabula *(G-821)*
Mro Built Inc ....D 330 526-0555
  North Canton *(G-15252)*
Pegasus Products Company Inc ....G 330 677-1123
  Kent *(G-11500)*
Quadra - Tech Inc ....D 614 445-0690
  Columbus *(G-7532)*
Quality Seating Company Inc ....E 330 747-0181
  Youngstown *(G-21181)*
Rightway Food Service ....G 419 223-4075
  Lima *(G-12084)*

Success Technologies Inc ....G 614 761-0008
  Powell *(G-16484)*
Suds ....G 937 273-6007
  Eldorado *(G-9348)*
Textiles Inc ....G 614 529-8642
  Hilliard *(G-10986)*
The Wood Shed ....G 937 429-3355
  Xenia *(G-20979)*
▼ Tiffin Metal Products Co ....D 419 447-8414
  Tiffin *(G-18248)*
Touchpint Cmplete Slutions LLC .....G 419 919-3222
  Celina *(G-3024)*
Tri-Co Industries ....G 740 927-1928
  Pataskala *(G-15988)*
Vivo Brothers LLC ....F 330 629-8686
  Poland *(G-16387)*
Wades Woodworking Inc ....F 937 374-6470
  Xenia *(G-20988)*
Wood Works ....G 330 674-0333
  Millersburg *(G-14287)*

26 PAPER AND ALLIED PRODUCTS

2611 Pulp Mills

Caraustar Industries Inc ....F 216 961-5060
  Cleveland *(G-4973)*
Caraustar Industries Inc ....D 740 862-4167
  Baltimore *(G-1081)*
▲ Cheney Pulp and Paper Company ..E 937 746-9991
  Franklin *(G-10012)*
Flegal Brothers Inc ....F 419 298-3539
  Edgerton *(G-9331)*
Green Recycling Works LLC ....G 513 278-7111
  Cincinnati *(G-3849)*
Greif Packaging LLC ....C 330 879-2101
  Massillon *(G-13144)*
Itran Electronics Recycling ....G 330 659-0801
  Richfield *(G-16628)*
▼ Newpage Energy Services LLC ......A 877 855-7243
  Miamisburg *(G-13840)*
Newpage Holding Corporation ....A 877 855-7243
  Miamisburg *(G-13842)*
Polymer Tech & Svcs Inc ....E 740 929-5500
  Heath *(G-10851)*
Riverview Productions Inc ....G 740 441-1150
  Gallipolis *(G-10308)*
Rumpke Transportation Co LLC ....C 513 242-4600
  Cincinnati *(G-4367)*
SMA Plastics LLC ....G 330 627-1377
  Carrollton *(G-2966)*
Verso Corporation ....G 901 369-4105
  Miamisburg *(G-13875)*
◆ Verso Paper Holding LLC ....B 877 855-7243
  Miamisburg *(G-13876)*
Waste Parchment Inc ....E 330 674-6868
  Millersburg *(G-14282)*
World Wide Recyclers Inc ....F 614 554-3296
  Columbus *(G-7774)*

2621 Paper Mills

▲ Ahlstrom West Carrollton LLC ....C 937 859-3621
  Dayton *(G-8140)*
▲ Ampac Plastics LLC ....B 513 671-1777
  Cincinnati *(G-3399)*
Appvion Inc ....B 937 859-8261
  West Carrollton *(G-19790)*
B & B Paper Converters Inc ....F 216 941-8100
  Cleveland *(G-4880)*
BASF Corporation ....E 216 867-1040
  Independence *(G-11251)*
Blue Ridge Paper Products Inc ....C 440 235-7200
  Olmsted Falls *(G-15674)*
Carlisle Prtg Walnut Creek Ltd ....E 330 852-9922
  Sugarcreek *(G-18020)*
Crown Envelope LLC ....C 513 771-5070
  Cincinnati *(G-3621)*
D C S Specialty Packaging Inc ....F 937 615-0100
  Piqua *(G-16258)*
Duracorp LLC ....E 740 549-3336
  Lewis Center *(G-11896)*
Eagle Wright Innovations Inc ....G 937 640-8093
  Moraine *(G-14482)*
Evergreen Packaging Inc ....G 440 235-7200
  Olmsted Falls *(G-15675)*
Georgia-Pacific ....C 330 794-4444
  Mogadore *(G-14376)*
Graphic Paper Products Corp ....D 937 325-5503
  Springfield *(G-17564)*
Greif Inc ....C 330 879-2936
  Massillon *(G-13143)*

Gvs Industries Inc......G....... 513 887-8660
Hamilton *(G-10699)*
Hanchett Paper Company......E....... 513 782-4440
Cincinnati *(G-3865)*
Honey Cell Inc Mid West......E....... 513 360-0280
Monroe *(G-14405)*
International Paper Company......C....... 800 473-0830
Middletown *(G-14049)*
International Paper Company......B....... 877 447-2737
Milford *(G-14153)*
International Paper Company......G....... 440 428-5116
Madison *(G-12507)*
International Paper Company......G....... 513 248-6365
Loveland *(G-12362)*
International Paper Company......F....... 740 439-3527
Byesville *(G-2404)*
International Paper Company......G....... 419 675-2534
Kenton *(G-11551)*
International Paper Company......G....... 513 248-6000
Loveland *(G-12363)*
International Paper Company......B....... 419 673-0711
Kenton *(G-11553)*
JMJ Paper Inc......F....... 216 941-8100
Avon Lake *(G-1034)*
▲ Ken AG Inc......E....... 419 281-1204
Ashland *(G-747)*
Kimberly-Clark Corporation......C....... 513 864-3780
Cincinnati *(G-3989)*
Kn8designs LLC......G....... 859 380-5926
Cincinnati *(G-3997)*
Metro Recycling Company......G....... 513 251-1800
Cincinnati *(G-4094)*
Mohawk Fine Papers Inc......E....... 440 969-2000
Ashtabula *(G-822)*
▼ Newpage Energy Services LLC......A....... 877 855-7243
Miamisburg *(G-13840)*
Newpage Holding Corporation......A....... 877 855-7243
Miamisburg *(G-13842)*
Novolex Holdings Inc......D....... 740 397-2555
Mount Vernon *(G-14634)*
Novolex Holdings Inc......B....... 937 746-1933
Franklin *(G-10041)*
▲ Novolyte Technologies Inc......E....... 216 867-1040
Cleveland *(G-5920)*
Owens Corning Sales LLC......D....... 614 399-3915
Mount Vernon *(G-14635)*
P H Glatfelter Company......D....... 740 772-3111
Chillicothe *(G-3256)*
Package Design & Mfg Inc......F....... 513 874-7364
West Chester *(G-20034)*
▲ Plus Mark LLC......E....... 216 252-6770
Cleveland *(G-6018)*
▲ Polymer Packaging Inc......D....... 330 832-2000
Massillon *(G-13195)*
◆ Ranpak Corp......C....... 440 354-4445
Concord Township *(G-7799)*
Resolute FP US Inc......B....... 216 961-3900
Cleveland *(G-6107)*
Resolute FP US Inc......B....... 614 443-6300
Columbus *(G-7557)*
Resolute FP US Inc......B....... 513 242-3671
Cincinnati *(G-4338)*
Selah Paperie......G....... 330 755-2759
Struthers *(G-17998)*
T J Target......G....... 330 658-3057
Doylestown *(G-9031)*
Thedkahn LLC......G....... 239 961-8757
Amelia *(G-586)*
Transmit Identity LLC......G....... 330 576-4732
Stow *(G-17810)*
Veritiv Operating Company......C....... 513 242-0800
Fairfield *(G-9728)*
Verso Corporation......D....... 901 369-4105
Miamisburg *(G-13875)*
◆ Verso Paper Holding LLC......B....... 877 855-7243
Miamisburg *(G-13876)*
Wausau Paper Corp......C....... 513 217-3623
Middletown *(G-14096)*
Wausau Ppr Towel & Tissue LLC......C....... 513 424-2999
Middletown *(G-14097)*
Welch Packaging Group Inc......E....... 614 870-2000
Columbus *(G-7755)*
◆ West Carrollton Converting Inc......D....... 937 859-3621
Dayton *(G-8753)*
Westrock Cp LLC......B....... 513 745-2586
Cincinnati *(G-4589)*
Westrock Cp LLC......B....... 740 622-0581
Coshocton *(G-7915)*
Westrock CP LLC......C....... 937 898-2115
Dayton *(G-8754)*

2631 Paperboard Mills

Ball Corporation......D....... 330 244-2800
Canton *(G-2615)*
▲ Buckeye Boxes Inc......D....... 614 274-8484
Columbus *(G-6870)*
Caraustar Industries Inc......E....... 513 871-7112
Cincinnati *(G-3497)*
Caraustar Industries Inc......E....... 330 665-7700
Copley *(G-7841)*
Caraustar Industries Inc......D....... 740 862-4167
Baltimore *(G-1081)*
Centor Inc......F....... 800 321-3391
Perrysburg *(G-16076)*
Centor Inc......C....... 800 321-3391
Berlin *(G-1647)*
Churmac Industries Inc......E....... 740 773-5800
Chillicothe *(G-3234)*
Cincinnati Bindery & Packg Inc......G....... 859 816-0282
Cincinnati *(G-3542)*
Coburn Inc......D....... 419 368-4051
Hayesville *(G-10843)*
Corpad Company Inc......D....... 419 522-7818
Mansfield *(G-12586)*
Custom Aluminum Boxes......G....... 440 864-2664
Elyria *(G-9400)*
Derby Fabg Solutions LLC......E....... 937 498-4054
Sidney *(G-17176)*
Diversipak Inc......G....... 513 321-7884
Cincinnati *(G-3658)*
Elite Ship Packaging System......G....... 216 502-6798
Cleveland *(G-5273)*
▲ Fibercorr Mills LLC......D....... 330 837-5151
Massillon *(G-13131)*
Folding Carton Service Inc......F....... 419 281-4099
Ashland *(G-734)*
G S K Inc......G....... 937 547-1611
Greenville *(G-10501)*
Galion Packaging Co Inc......G....... 419 468-2548
Galion *(G-10270)*
Georgia-Pacific LLC......C....... 740 477-3347
Circleville *(G-4631)*
Graphic Packaging Intl Inc......C....... 513 424-4200
Middletown *(G-14044)*
Graphic Packaging Intl Inc......C....... 440 248-4370
Solon *(G-17301)*
Greif Paper Packg & Svcs LLC......D....... 740 549-6000
Delaware *(G-8855)*
International Cont Systems LLC......F....... 216 481-8219
Cleveland *(G-5580)*
International Paper Company......C....... 740 383-4061
Marion *(G-12877)*
International Paper Company......C....... 740 363-9882
Delaware *(G-8862)*
Jlt Packaging Cincinnati Inc......E....... 513 933-0250
Lebanon *(G-11810)*
◆ Loroco Industries Inc......E....... 513 891-9544
Blue Ash *(G-1828)*
Martin Paper Products Inc......E....... 740 756-9271
Carroll *(G-2944)*
Miami Valley Paper LLC......F....... 937 746-6451
Franklin *(G-10036)*
Multi-Color Corporation......C....... 513 396-5600
Cincinnati *(G-4131)*
National Bias Fabric Co......E....... 216 361-0530
Cleveland *(G-5853)*
National Carton & Coating Co......D....... 937 347-1042
Xenia *(G-20964)*
Octal Extrusion Corp......E....... 513 881-6100
West Chester *(G-20033)*
▲ P & R Specialty Inc......E....... 937 773-0263
Piqua *(G-16297)*
Pactiv LLC......C....... 614 771-5400
Columbus *(G-7454)*
Production Packaging Inc......F....... 330 392-4155
Warren *(G-19590)*
Quilting Creations Intl......E....... 330 874-4741
Bolivar *(G-1945)*
Safeway Packaging Inc......D....... 419 629-3200
New Bremen *(G-14793)*
▲ Smith-Lustig Paper Box Mfg Co......E....... 216 621-0453
Bedford *(G-1462)*
Sonoco Products Company......C....... 330 688-8247
Munroe Falls *(G-14665)*
Sonoco Products Company......D....... 740 927-2525
Johnstown *(G-11404)*
Sonoco Products Company......E....... 614 759-8470
Columbus *(G-7631)*
Sonoco Products Company......D....... 513 455-6003
Blue Ash *(G-1870)*
Third Party Service Ltd......F....... 419 872-2312
Perrysburg *(G-16158)*
Valley Converting Co Inc......E....... 740 537-2152
Toronto *(G-18787)*
Valley Converting Co Inc......E....... 740 537-2152
Toronto *(G-18788)*
Verso Corporation......D....... 901 369-4105
Miamisburg *(G-13875)*
Wayne Signer Enterprises Inc......E....... 513 841-1351
Cincinnati *(G-4580)*
Westrock Converting Company......C....... 513 860-0225
West Chester *(G-19973)*
Westrock Cp LLC......B....... 740 622-0581
Coshocton *(G-7915)*
Westrock Cp LLC......E....... 614 445-6850
Columbus *(G-7759)*
Westrock Mwv LLC......C....... 937 495-6323
Kettering *(G-11588)*

2652 Set-Up Paperboard Boxes

A To Z Paper Box Co......G....... 330 325-8722
Rootstown *(G-16718)*
Boxit Corporation......D....... 216 631-6900
Cleveland *(G-4927)*
Boxit Corporation......G....... 216 416-9475
Cleveland *(G-4928)*
Graphic Paper Products Corp......D....... 937 325-5503
Springfield *(G-17564)*
▲ Piqua Paper Box Company......E....... 937 773-0313
Piqua *(G-16306)*
R and D Incorporated......E....... 216 581-6328
Maple Heights *(G-12738)*
Sandusky Packaging Corporation......E....... 419 626-8520
Sandusky *(G-17005)*

2653 Corrugated & Solid Fiber Boxes

1923 W 25th St Inc......G....... 216 696-7529
Cleveland *(G-4664)*
A-Kobak Container Company......F....... 330 225-7791
Hinckley *(G-11020)*
Acrylicon Inc......G....... 614 263-2086
Columbus *(G-6691)*
Adapt-A-Pak Inc......E....... 937 845-0386
Tipp City *(G-18260)*
▲ Akers Packaging Service Inc......C....... 513 422-6312
Middletown *(G-14016)*
Akers Packaging Solutions Inc......E....... 513 422-6312
Middletown *(G-14017)*
▲ Alpha Container Co Inc......F....... 937 644-5511
Marysville *(G-12931)*
American Corrugated Pdts Inc......C....... 614 870-2000
Columbus *(G-6735)*
American Made Corrugated Packg......F....... 937 981-2111
Greenfield *(G-10473)*
Archbold Container Corp......C....... 800 446-2520
Archbold *(G-664)*
Argrov Box Co......F....... 937 898-1700
Dayton *(G-8163)*
B & B Box Company Inc......F....... 419 872-5600
Perrysburg *(G-16067)*
Basic Packaging Ltd......F....... 330 634-9665
Tallmadge *(G-18135)*
BDS Packaging Inc......D....... 937 643-0530
Moraine *(G-14468)*
Bruce Box Co Inc......G....... 740 533-0670
Franklin Furnace *(G-10066)*
Bryan Packaging Inc......F....... 419 636-2600
Bryan *(G-2287)*
Buckeye Boxes Inc......G....... 937 599-2551
Bellefontaine *(G-1523)*
▲ Buckeye Boxes Inc......D....... 614 274-8484
Columbus *(G-6870)*
Buckeye Boxes Inc......E....... 614 274-8484
Columbus *(G-6871)*
Buckeye Corrugated Inc......G....... 330 576-0590
Fairlawn *(G-9744)*
Buckeye Corrugated Inc......D....... 330 264-6336
Wooster *(G-20753)*
Cambridge Packaging Inc......E....... 740 432-3351
Cambridge *(G-2449)*
▲ Cameron Packaging Inc......G....... 419 222-9404
Lima *(G-11999)*
Charles Messina......D....... 216 663-3344
Cleveland *(G-5016)*
Chillicothe Packaging Corp......E....... 740 773-5800
Chillicothe *(G-3232)*
Clecorr Inc......E....... 216 961-5500
Cleveland *(G-5047)*
Cole Pak Inc......D....... 937 652-3910
Urbana *(G-19152)*

S I C

Combined Container Board ....D 513 530-5700
Cincinnati *(G-3598)*

Container King Inc ....G 937 652-3087
Urbana *(G-19154)*

Containercraft Inc ....F 419 884-2414
Mansfield *(G-12584)*

Contract Pckg Dist Specialists ....F 513 942-0300
West Chester *(G-19993)*

Creative Packaging LLC ....E 740 452-8497
Zanesville *(G-21295)*

Digital Color Intl LLC ....E 330 762-6959
Akron *(G-152)*

Family Packaging Inc ....G 937 325-4106
Springfield *(G-17557)*

General Packaging Products ....E 330 725-7731
Medina *(G-13416)*

Georgia-Pacific LLC ....C 740 477-3347
Circleville *(G-4631)*

Graphic Paper Products Corp ....G 937 325-5503
Springfield *(G-17564)*

Green Bay Packaging Inc ....C 419 332-5593
Fremont *(G-10157)*

Green Bay Packaging Inc ....D 513 228-5560
Lebanon *(G-11806)*

Greif Inc ....E 740 549-6000
Delaware *(G-8847)*

Greif Inc ....E 740 657-6500
Delaware *(G-8849)*

Greif Inc ....G 740 549-6000
Delaware *(G-8851)*

Greif Inc ....E 740 657-6500
Delaware *(G-8848)*

Greif U S Holdings Inc ....G 740 549-6000
Delaware *(G-8856)*

Hinkle Manufacturing Inc ....D 419 666-5550
Perrysburg *(G-16107)*

Honeymoon Paper Products Inc ....D 513 755-7200
Fairfield *(G-9666)*

▲ Innomark Perm Disply Grp LLC ......F 513 285-1040
Fairfield *(G-9668)*

Innovative Packaging LLC ....F 419 222-6071
Lima *(G-12030)*

International Paper Company ....C 330 264-1322
Wooster *(G-20788)*

International Paper Company ....C 937 456-4131
Eaton *(G-9311)*

International Paper Company ....C 740 397-5215
Mount Vernon *(G-14623)*

International Paper Company ....C 740 363-9882
Delaware *(G-8862)*

International Paper Company ....C 740 369-7691
Delaware *(G-8863)*

International Paper Company ....D 740 522-3123
Newark *(G-15023)*

International Paper Company ....C 330 626-7300
Streetsboro *(G-17858)*

Jamestown Cont Cleveland Inc ....B 216 831-3700
Cleveland *(G-5606)*

Jet Container Company ....G 614 444-2133
Columbus *(G-7230)*

JIT Packaging Inc ....E 330 562-8080
Aurora *(G-927)*

Jordon Auto Service & Tire Inc ....G 216 214-6528
Cleveland *(G-5622)*

Joseph T Snyder Industries ....G 216 883-6900
Cleveland *(G-5623)*

Kennedy Mint Inc ....D 440 572-3222
Cleveland *(G-5645)*

▲ Lewisburg Container Company ....C 937 962-2681
Lewisburg *(G-11936)*

▲ Marshalltown Packaging Inc ....G 641 753-5272
Columbus *(G-7320)*

Martin Paper Products Inc ....E 740 756-9271
Carroll *(G-2944)*

McElroy Contract Packaging ....F 330 262-0855
Wooster *(G-20804)*

Menasha Packaging Company LLC ......F 740 773-8204
Chillicothe *(G-3251)*

Miami Vly Packg Solutions Inc ....F 937 224-1800
Dayton *(G-8492)*

Mid Ohio Packaging LLC ....G 740 383-9200
Marion *(G-12884)*

Midwest Box Company ....E 216 281-9021
Cleveland *(G-5807)*

Midwest Container Corporation ....E 513 870-3000
Fairfield *(G-9684)*

▲ Midwest Filtration LLC ....E 513 874-6510
West Chester *(G-20030)*

Mount Vernon Packaging Inc ....F 740 397-3221
Mount Vernon *(G-14632)*

N-Stock Box Inc ....E 513 423-0319
Middletown *(G-14067)*

Nicofibers Inc ....G 740 394-2491
Shawnee *(G-17116)*

Northeast Box Company ....D 440 992-5500
Ashtabula *(G-827)*

Novolex Holdings Inc ....B 937 746-1933
Franklin *(G-10041)*

▲ Omer J Smith Inc ....E 513 921-4717
West Chester *(G-19909)*

Orora North America ....G 513 539-8274
Monroe *(G-14411)*

Packaging Corporation America ....D 513 424-3542
Middletown *(G-14073)*

Packaging Corporation America ....G 419 282-5809
Ashland *(G-762)*

Packaging Corporation America ....G 513 860-1145
Fairfield *(G-9697)*

Packaging Corporation America ....G 513 582-0690
Cincinnati *(G-4208)*

Packaging Corporation America ....D 740 344-1126
Newark *(G-15044)*

Packaging Corporation America ....G 330 644-9542
Akron *(G-330)*

Pactiv LLC ....G 330 644-9542
Akron *(G-331)*

Pallet & Cont Corp of Amer ....G 419 255-1256
Toledo *(G-18634)*

Pax Corrugated Products Inc ....D 513 932-9855
Lebanon *(G-11826)*

Phillips Packaging Inc ....G 937 484-4702
Urbana *(G-19173)*

Pjs Corrugated Inc ....F 419 644-3383
Swanton *(G-18087)*

Pratt (jet Corr) Inc ....E 937 390-7100
Springfield *(G-17629)*

Pratt Industries USA Inc ....D 513 770-0851
Mason *(G-13075)*

▲ Prestige Display and Packg LLC ......E 513 285-1040
Fairfield *(G-9705)*

Pro-Pak Industries Inc ....G 419 729-0751
Maumee *(G-13288)*

R and D Incorporated ....E 216 581-6328
Maple Heights *(G-12738)*

Riblet Packaging Co ....F 937 652-3087
Urbana *(G-19175)*

Riverview Packaging Inc ....E 937 743-9530
Franklin *(G-10049)*

Safeway Packaging Inc ....D 419 629-3200
New Bremen *(G-14793)*

Schwarz Partners Packaging LLC ....F 317 290-1140
Sidney *(G-17222)*

Skybox Investments Inc ....E 419 525-6013
Mansfield *(G-12679)*

▲ Smith-Lustig Paper Box Mfg Co ....E 216 621-0453
Bedford *(G-1462)*

Sobel Corrugated Cntrs Inc ....C 216 475-2100
Cleveland *(G-6216)*

Sonoco Products Company ....E 614 759-8470
Columbus *(G-7631)*

Square One Solutions LLC ....F 419 425-5445
Findlay *(G-9894)*

Systems Pack Inc ....E 330 467-5729
Macedonia *(G-12493)*

Tavens Container Inc ....D 216 883-3333
Bedford *(G-1464)*

Tecumseh Packg Solutions Inc ....E 419 238-1122
Van Wert *(G-19271)*

Temple Inland ....G 513 425-0830
Middletown *(G-14087)*

The Shelby Co ....E 440 871-9901
Westlake *(G-20315)*

Trey Corrugated Inc ....D 513 942-4800
West Chester *(G-19960)*

Unipac Inc ....E 740 929-2000
Hebron *(G-10893)*

US Corrugated Inc ....C 740 681-1600
Lancaster *(G-11760)*

US Corrugated of Massillon ....F 216 663-3344
Maple Heights *(G-12743)*

Valley Containers Inc ....F 330 544-2244
Mineral Ridge *(G-14314)*

Value Added Packaging Inc ....F 937 832-9595
Englewood *(G-9542)*

Verso Corporation ....G 901 369-4105
Miamisburg *(G-13875)*

Viking Paper Company ....E 419 729-4951
Toledo *(G-18768)*

▼ Warwick Products Company ....E 216 334-1200
Cleveland *(G-6448)*

Westrock Company ....E 513 860-5546
West Chester *(G-19972)*

Westrock Cp LLC ....B 513 745-2400
Blue Ash *(G-1893)*

Westrock Cp LLC ....C 330 297-0841
Ravenna *(G-16571)*

Westrock CP LLC ....D 770 448-2193
Wshngtn CT Hs *(G-20930)*

Westrock Rkt Company ....G 330 296-5155
Ravenna *(G-16572)*

Weyerhaeuser Co Containeerboar ....F 740 397-5215
Mount Vernon *(G-14655)*

Weyerhaeuser Company ....D 740 335-4480
Wshngtn CT Hs *(G-20931)*

Wood Specialists ....G 440 639-9797
Mentor *(G-13772)*

2655 Fiber Cans, Tubes & Drums

A T Tube Company Inc ....G 330 336-8706
Wadsworth *(G-19386)*

Acme Spirally Wound Paper Pdts ....F 216 267-2950
Cleveland *(G-4694)*

Advanced Paper Tube Inc ....F 216 281-5691
Cleveland *(G-4717)*

Artistic Composite & Mold Co ....G 330 352-6632
Litchfield *(G-12137)*

Astro Qcb Inc ....B 513 921-8811
Cincinnati *(G-3422)*

Burch Plastics Corp ....G 440 835-2059
Cleveland *(G-4948)*

Caraustar Industrial and Con ....E 330 868-4111
Minerva *(G-14318)*

Caraustar Industries Inc ....G 330 665-7700
Copley *(G-7841)*

Companies of North Coast LLC ....G 216 398-8550
Cleveland *(G-5109)*

Dayton Industrial Drum Inc ....E 937 253-8933
Dayton *(G-8103)*

Erdie Industries Inc ....E 440 288-0166
Lorain *(G-12245)*

Erie Container Corporation ....G 216 631-1650
Cleveland *(G-5294)*

Greif Inc ....E 419 238-0565
Van Wert *(G-19259)*

Greif Inc ....D 937 548-4111
Delaware *(G-8852)*

Greif Inc ....E 740 657-6500
Delaware *(G-8848)*

Greif Inc ....E 740 549-6000
Delaware *(G-8847)*

Greif Bros Corp Ohio Inc ....E 740 549-6000
Delaware *(G-8853)*

Haul-Away Containers Inc ....G 440 546-1879
Richfield *(G-16626)*

Horwitz & Pintis Co ....F 419 666-2220
Toledo *(G-18512)*

Howard B Claflin Co ....G 330 928-1704
Cuyahoga Falls *(G-8009)*

Hpc Holdings LLC ....F 330 666-3751
Fairlawn *(G-9753)*

▲ Midwest Specialty Pdts Co Inc ....F 513 874-7070
Fairfield *(G-9685)*

Modroto ....G 800 772-7659
Ashtabula *(G-821)*

Newkor Inc ....E 216 631-7800
Cleveland *(G-5880)*

Nicofibers Inc ....G 740 394-2491
Shawnee *(G-17116)*

▲ North Coast Composites Inc ....E 216 398-8550
Cleveland *(G-5893)*

Ohio Paper Tube Co ....G 330 478-5171
Canton *(G-2802)*

Operational Support Svcs LLC ....F 419 425-0889
Findlay *(G-9873)*

Polystar Inc ....F 330 963-5100
Twinsburg *(G-19004)*

Shockakhan Express LLC ....G 614 432-3133
Groveport *(G-10644)*

Sonoco Products Company ....D 937 429-0040
Beavercreek Township *(G-1390)*

Sonoco Products Company ....E 513 870-3985
West Chester *(G-20052)*

Sonoco Products Company ....E 419 448-4428
Tiffin *(G-18245)*

Sonoco Products Company ....C 330 688-8247
Munroe Falls *(G-14665)*

Sonoco Products Company ....E 614 759-8470
Columbus *(G-7631)*

Transport Container Corp ....G 614 459-8140
Columbus *(G-7707)*

2656 Sanitary Food Containers

◆ **American Greetings Corporation** ......A 216 252-7300
Cleveland (G-4782)

Century Intermediate Holdg Co ....F 216 252-7300
Cleveland (G-5006)

Clovernook Center For The Bli ....C 513 522-3860
Cincinnati (G-3590)

▲ **Ecologic Fdsrvice Slutions LLC** ....G 419 467-8758
Toledo (G-18449)

Gibson Greetings Inc ....G 216 252-7300
Cleveland (G-5428)

Huhtamaki Inc ....B 513 201-1525
Batavia (G-1192)

Huhtamaki Inc ....B 937 746-9700
Franklin (G-10028)

International Paper Company ....C 800 422-4657
Kenton (G-11552)

International Paper Company ....B 419 673-0711
Kenton (G-11553)

▲ **Island Aseptics LLC** ....C 740 685-2548
Byesville (G-2405)

▼ **Norse Dairy Systems LP** ....B 614 421-5297
Columbus (G-7398)

Novolex Holdings Inc ....B 937 746-1933
Franklin (G-10041)

Ohio State Plastics ....F 614 299-5618
Columbus (G-7430)

Pactiv LLC ....D 815 547-1200
Columbus (G-7453)

Premier Industries Inc ....E 513 271-2550
Cincinnati (G-4266)

Ricking Paper and Specialty Co ....G 513 825-3551
Cincinnati (G-4345)

Sonoco Products Company ....E 513 870-3985
West Chester (G-20052)

▲ **Sunamericaconverting LLC** ....D 330 821-6300
Alliance (G-542)

Superior Cup Inc ....E 330 393-6187
Warren (G-19603)

Taylor Company ....G 513 271-2550
Cincinnati (G-4496)

Verso Corporation ....D 901 369-4105
Miamisburg (G-13875)

Washington Products Inc ....F 330 837-5101
Massillon (G-13211)

2657 Folding Paperboard Boxes

American Corrugated Pdts Inc ....C 614 870-2000
Columbus (G-6735)

Americraft Carton Inc ....E 419 668-1006
Norwalk (G-15525)

Ample Industries Inc ....C 937 746-9700
Franklin (G-10007)

B & L Labels and Packg Co Inc ....G 937 773-9080
Piqua (G-16252)

Bell Ohio Inc ....F 605 332-6721
Groveport (G-10616)

Boxit Corporation ....G 216 416-9475
Cleveland (G-4928)

Boxit Corporation ....D 216 631-6900
Cleveland (G-4927)

▲ **Carton Service Incorporated** ....C 419 342-5010
Shelby (G-17134)

▲ **Chilcote Company** ....C 216 781-6000
Cleveland (G-5028)

Graphic Packaging Intl Inc ....C 740 387-6543
Marion (G-12869)

Graphic Packaging Intl Inc ....C 513 424-4200
Middletown (G-14044)

Graphic Packaging Intl Inc ....C 440 248-4370
Solon (G-17301)

Jefferson Smurfit Corporation ....F 440 248-4370
Solon (G-17321)

Oak Hills Carton Co ....E 513 948-4200
Cincinnati (G-4171)

Rohrer Corporation ....C 440 542-3100
Solon (G-17371)

RR Donnelley & Sons Company ....G 513 870-4040
West Chester (G-19938)

Sandusky Packaging Corporation ....E 419 626-8520
Sandusky (G-17005)

Star Pizza Box ....E 740 967-1105
Johnstown (G-11405)

The Shelby Co ....E 440 871-9901
Westlake (G-20315)

Therm-O-Packaging Suppliers ....F 440 543-5188
Chagrin Falls (G-3126)

Unipac Inc ....E 740 929-2000
Hebron (G-10893)

Yuckon International Corp ....G 216 361-2103
Cleveland (G-6488)

2671 Paper Coating & Laminating for Packaging

▲ **ABC Packaging Direct LLC** ....G 440 934-1477
Avon (G-979)

Adaptive Data Inc ....F 937 436-2343
Centerville (G-3032)

Amatech Inc ....E 614 252-2506
Columbus (G-6729)

American Corrugated Pdts Inc ....C 614 870-2000
Columbus (G-6735)

American Corrugated Pdts Inc ....E 800 248-6840
Columbus (G-6736)

▲ **Angell-Demmel North Amer Corp** ....D 937 461-5800
Dayton (G-8158)

Austin Tape and Label Inc ....D 330 928-7999
Stow (G-17731)

Bemis Company Inc ....E 419 334-9465
Fremont (G-10128)

Bollin & Sons Inc ....E 419 693-6573
Toledo (G-18376)

▲ **Central Coated Products Inc** ....D 330 821-9830
Alliance (G-503)

Central Ohio Paper & Packg Inc ....G 614 492-8956
Groveport (G-10618)

Central Ohio Paper & Packg Inc ....F 419 621-9239
Huron (G-11219)

Cole Pak Inc ....D 937 652-3910
Urbana (G-19152)

▲ **Command Plastic Corporation** ....F 800 321-8001
Tallmadge (G-18139)

Cpg - Ohio LLC ....D 513 825-4800
Cincinnati (G-3616)

Crabar/Gbf Inc ....G 419 943-2141
Leipsic (G-11868)

Creative Packaging LLC ....E 740 452-8497
Zanesville (G-21295)

▲ **Custom Products Corporation** ....D 440 528-7100
Solon (G-17280)

▲ **Dayton Fruit Tree Label Co** ....G 937 223-4650
Dayton (G-8274)

Douglas Michalske ....G 216 631-0567
Cleveland (G-5210)

E-Z Stop Service Center ....D 330 448-2236
Brookfield (G-2123)

Engineered Films Division ....F 419 884-8150
Mansfield (G-12601)

▲ **Engineered Films Division** ....G 419 884-8150
Lexington (G-11950)

Esperia Holdings LLC ....G 714 249-7888
Oak Harbor (G-15589)

Euclid Products Co Inc ....G 440 942-7310
Willoughby (G-20482)

Future Polytech Inc ....E 419 763-1352
Saint Henry (G-16816)

Gauntlet Awards & Engraving ....G 937 890-5811
Dayton (G-8357)

Georgia-Pacific LLC ....C 740 477-3347
Circleville (G-4631)

Gt Industrial Supply Inc ....G 513 771-7000
Cincinnati (G-3856)

Harris & Company Inc ....F 330 332-4127
Salem (G-16899)

Hooven - Dayton Corp ....D 937 233-4473
Miamisburg (G-13818)

Hunt Products Inc ....E 440 667-2457
Newburgh Heights (G-15075)

▲ **Inno-Pak Holding Inc** ....G 740 363-0090
Delaware (G-8861)

International Paper Company ....C 740 363-9882
Delaware (G-8862)

Jerry Pulfer ....G 937 778-1861
Piqua (G-16283)

Johnson Energy Company ....G 937 435-5401
Miamisburg (G-13822)

Joseph T Snyder Industries ....G 216 883-6900
Cleveland (G-5623)

Kapstone Container Corporation ....C 330 562-6111
Aurora (G-928)

Kay Toledo Tag Inc ....D 419 729-5479
Toledo (G-18541)

▲ **Kroy LLC** ....C 216 426-5600
Cleveland (G-5666)

Liqui-Box Corporation ....C 419 289-9696
Ashland (G-750)

◆ **Loroco Industries Inc** ....E 513 891-9544
Blue Ash (G-1828)

Marlen Manufacturing & Dev Co ....E 216 292-7546
Bedford (G-1442)

Multi-Color Corporation ....D 513 943-0080
Batavia (G-1212)

National Glass Service Group ....F 614 652-3699
Dublin (G-9109)

Newpage Group Inc ....E 937 242-9500
Miamisburg (G-13841)

Next Design & Build LLC ....G 330 907-3042
Akron (G-314)

▲ **Next Generation Films Inc** ....C 419 884-8150
Lexington (G-11951)

◆ **Nilpeter Usa Inc** ....C 513 489-4400
Cincinnati (G-4156)

North American Plas Chem Inc ....E 216 531-3400
Euclid (G-9595)

Novacel Inc ....C 937 335-5611
Troy (G-18858)

Novacel Inc ....E 413 283-3468
Troy (G-18859)

Novolex Holdings Inc ....D 740 397-2555
Mount Vernon (G-14634)

Packaging Material Direct Inc ....G 989 482-8400
Solon (G-17358)

Paxar Corporation ....G 937 681-4541
Dayton (G-8567)

Perfect Packaging ....G 419 662-1700
Northwood (G-15487)

Perfection Packaging Inc ....G 614 866-8558
Gahanna (G-10226)

Plastic Works Inc ....F 440 331-5575
Cleveland (G-6014)

Plastipak Packaging Inc ....B 937 596-6142
Jackson Center (G-11344)

▲ **Polychem Corporation** ....E 440 357-1500
Mentor (G-13691)

Polychem Corporation ....E 440 357-1500
Mentor (G-13692)

Prime Industries Inc ....E 440 288-3626
Lorain (G-12268)

Proampac LLC ....E 513 671-1777
Cincinnati (G-4275)

Raven Industries Inc ....E 937 323-4625
Springfield (G-17634)

Retterbush Graphic and Packg ....E 513 779-4466
West Chester (G-19931)

Richards and Simmons Inc ....G 614 268-3909
Columbus (G-7561)

Safeway Packaging Inc ....D 419 629-3200
New Bremen (G-14793)

Schilling Graphics Inc ....E 419 468-1037
Galion (G-10286)

Schwarz Partners Packaging LLC ....F 317 290-1140
Sidney (G-17222)

Shurtape Technologies LLC ....B 440 937-7000
Avon (G-1011)

◆ **Shurtech Brands LLC** ....C 440 937-7000
Avon (G-1012)

Signode Industrial Group LLC ....E 513 248-2990
Loveland (G-12387)

Sonoco Products Company ....E 419 448-4428
Tiffin (G-18245)

Sonoco Products Company ....E 614 759-8470
Columbus (G-7631)

Sonoco Prtective Solutions Inc ....G 419 420-0029
Findlay (G-9891)

Sourcepac Inc ....G 614 899-0744
Westerville (G-20234)

Springdot Inc ....D 513 542-4000
Cincinnati (G-4448)

Sterling Paper Company Inc ....F 513 242-3678
Monroe (G-14414)

▲ **Storopack Inc** ....E 513 874-0314
West Chester (G-20056)

▲ **Stretchtape Inc** ....E 216 486-9400
Cleveland (G-6251)

Superior Label Systems Inc ....B 513 336-0825
Mason (G-13092)

▼ **Tce International Ltd** ....F 800 962-2376
Perry (G-16059)

Tcp Inc ....G 330 836-4239
Fairlawn (G-9764)

Tech/III Inc ....E 513 482-7500
Cincinnati (G-4497)

Therm-O-Packaging Suppliers ....F 440 543-5188
Chagrin Falls (G-3126)

Thomas Products Co Inc ....E 513 756-9009
Cincinnati (G-4507)

Universal Packg Systems Inc ....B 513 674-9400
Cincinnati (G-4542)

SIC

Universal Packg Systems Inc ....B 513 732-2000
Batavia *(G-1231)*

Universal Packg Systems Inc ....E 513 735-4777
Batavia *(G-1232)*

▲ Virgail Industries Inc ....G 740 928-6001
Hebron *(G-10894)*

Westrock Cp LLC ....B 513 745-2400
Blue Ash *(G-1893)*

Zebco Industries Inc ....F 740 654-4510
Lancaster *(G-11763)*

Zech Printing Industries Inc ....E 937 748-2776
Cincinnati *(G-4618)*

2672 Paper Coating & Laminating, Exc for Packaging

21st Century Printers Inc ....G 513 771-4150
Cincinnati *(G-3322)*

▲ 3 Sigma Corporation ....D 937 440-3400
Troy *(G-18801)*

3M Company ....D 330 725-1444
Medina *(G-13361)*

A-1 Printing Inc ....F 419 562-3111
Bucyrus *(G-2330)*

Adcraft Decals Inc ....E 216 524-2934
Cleveland *(G-4702)*

Admiral Products Company Inc ....E 216 671-0600
Cleveland *(G-4706)*

▲ Ahlstrom West Carrollton LLC ......C 937 859-3621
Dayton *(G-8140)*

All-Seasons Paper Company ....E 440 826-1700
Cleveland *(G-4760)*

▲ Ameri-Cal Corporation ....F 330 725-7735
Medina *(G-13368)*

Appvion Inc ....B 937 859-8261
West Carrollton *(G-19790)*

Austin Tape and Label Inc ....D 330 928-7999
Stow *(G-17731)*

Avery Dennison Corporation ....C 440 358-4691
Painesville *(G-15856)*

Avery Dennison Corporation ....B 440 358-3700
Painesville *(G-15857)*

Avery Dennison Corporation ....G 216 267-8700
Cleveland *(G-4871)*

Avery Dennison Corporation ....G 800 282-8379
Painesville *(G-15858)*

Avery Dennison Corporation ....D 440 358-3408
Painesville *(G-15859)*

Avery Dennison Corporation ....C 614 418-7740
New Albany *(G-14748)*

Avery Dennison Corporation ....D 440 358-2828
Mentor *(G-13530)*

Avery Dennison Corporation ....C 440 266-2500
Mentor *(G-13531)*

Avery Dennison Corporation ....C 440 358-2930
Mentor *(G-13532)*

Avery Dennison Corporation ....F 513 682-7500
Cincinnati *(G-3430)*

B & L Labels and Packg Co Inc ......G 937 773-9080
Piqua *(G-16252)*

Beiersdorf Inc ....C 513 682-7300
West Chester *(G-19984)*

Bemis Company Inc ....E 419 334-9465
Fremont *(G-10128)*

Bemis Company Inc ....E 330 923-5281
Akron *(G-87)*

Boehm Inc ....E 614 875-9010
Grove City *(G-10546)*

Bollin & Sons Inc ....E 419 693-6573
Toledo *(G-18376)*

CCL Label Inc ....C 216 676-2703
Cleveland *(G-4998)*

CCL Label Inc ....E 440 878-7000
Brunswick *(G-2215)*

CCL Label Inc ....B 440 878-7277
Strongsville *(G-17900)*

▲ Central Coated Products Inc ....D 330 821-9830
Alliance *(G-503)*

Coating Applications Intl LLC ....G 513 956-5222
Cincinnati *(G-3594)*

◆ Cortape Inc ....F 330 929-6700
Cuyahoga Falls *(G-7982)*

D M V Supply Corporation ....G 330 847-0450
Warren *(G-19540)*

Deco Tools Inc ....E 419 476-9321
Toledo *(G-18430)*

Gary I Teach Jr ....G 614 582-7483
London *(G-12210)*

GBS Corp ....E 330 929-8050
Stow *(G-17758)*

GBS Corp ....C 330 863-1828
Malvern *(G-12545)*

▲ GBS Corp ....C 330 494-5330
North Canton *(G-15233)*

Giesecke & Devrient Amer Inc ....F 330 405-8442
Twinsburg *(G-18946)*

Giesecke & Devrient Amer Inc ....G 330 425-1515
Twinsburg *(G-18947)*

Hall Company ....E 937 652-1376
Urbana *(G-19160)*

Harris & Company Inc ....F 330 332-4127
Salem *(G-16899)*

Hooven - Dayton Corp ....D 937 233-4473
Miamisburg *(G-13818)*

▲ ID Images LLC ....D 330 220-7300
Brunswick *(G-2234)*

Illinois Tool Works Inc ....G 937 393-4271
Hillsboro *(G-11004)*

Imerys Usa Inc ....F 920 687-0872
Blue Ash *(G-1813)*

Jamac Inc ....F 419 625-9790
Sandusky *(G-16974)*

▼ Kardol Quality Products LLC ....E 513 933-8206
Blue Ash *(G-1822)*

▼ Kent Adhesive Products Co ....D 330 678-1626
Kent *(G-11475)*

Lam Pro Inc ....F 216 426-0661
Cleveland *(G-5678)*

▲ Laminate Technologies Inc ....D 419 448-0812
Tiffin *(G-18226)*

◆ Loroco Industries Inc ....E 513 891-9544
Blue Ash *(G-1828)*

Marlen Manufacturing & Dev Co ......E 216 292-7546
Bedford *(G-1442)*

Master Label Company Inc ....G 419 625-8095
Sandusky *(G-16986)*

Miami Valley Paper LLC ....F 937 746-6451
Franklin *(G-10036)*

▲ Miller Studio Inc ....D 330 339-1100
New Philadelphia *(G-14916)*

◆ Morgan Adhesives Company LLC ...B 330 688-1111
Stow *(G-17775)*

Mr Label Inc ....E 513 681-2088
Cincinnati *(G-4128)*

▲ Multi-Color Corporation ....F 513 381-1480
Batavia *(G-1211)*

▼ Newpage Energy Services LLC ....A 877 855-7243
Miamisburg *(G-13840)*

Newpage Holding Corporation ....A 877 855-7243
Miamisburg *(G-13842)*

◆ Nilpeter Usa Inc ....C 513 489-4400
Cincinnati *(G-4156)*

▲ Northcoast Tape & Label Inc ....G 440 439-3200
Cleveland *(G-5902)*

Novolex Holdings Inc ....D 740 397-2555
Mount Vernon *(G-14634)*

Ohio Laminating & Binding Inc ....E 614 771-4868
Hilliard *(G-10966)*

Oliver Products Company ....F 513 860-6880
Hamilton *(G-10729)*

Paxar Corporation ....G 937 681-4541
Dayton *(G-8567)*

Pilot Production Solutions LLC ....E 513 602-1467
Mason *(G-13073)*

Progressive Labels LLC ....F 570 688-9636
Willoughby *(G-20580)*

Roemer Industries Inc ....D 330 448-2000
Masury *(G-13216)*

RR Donnelley & Sons Company ....E 440 774-2101
Oberlin *(G-15647)*

▲ Sensical Inc ....D 216 641-1141
Solon *(G-17378)*

Shurtape Technologies LLC ....B 440 937-7000
Avon *(G-1011)*

Specialty Adhesive Film Co ....G 513 353-1885
Cleves *(G-6526)*

Spinnaker Coating LLC ....C 937 332-6300
Troy *(G-18878)*

▲ Spinnaker Coating LLC ....D 937 332-6500
Troy *(G-18879)*

◆ SRC Liquidation LLC ....A 937 221-1000
Dayton *(G-8672)*

Storad Label Co ....F 740 382-6440
Marion *(G-12904)*

▲ Stretchtape Inc ....E 216 486-9400
Cleveland *(G-6251)*

Superior Label Systems Inc ....B 513 336-0825
Mason *(G-13092)*

◆ Technicote Inc ....E 800 358-4448
Miamisburg *(G-13868)*

Technicote Westfield Inc ....D 937 859-4448
Miamisburg *(G-13869)*

Tekni-Plex Inc ....E 419 491-2407
Holland *(G-11088)*

The Rubber Stamp Shop ....G 419 478-4444
Toledo *(G-18722)*

Thomas Products Co Inc ....E 513 756-9009
Cincinnati *(G-4507)*

Thomas Tape and Supply Company ...F 937 325-6414
Springfield *(G-17663)*

◆ Troy Laminating & Coating Inc ......D 937 335-5611
Troy *(G-18881)*

Unitherm Inc ....G 937 278-1900
Dayton *(G-8738)*

USA Label Express Inc ....E 330 874-1001
Bolivar *(G-2948)*

▲ Waytek Corporation ....E 937 743-6142
Franklin *(G-10065)*

2673 Bags: Plastics, Laminated & Coated

Accutech Films Inc ....F 419 678-8700
Coldwater *(G-6549)*

Advanced Poly-Packaging Inc ....E 330 785-4000
Akron *(G-33)*

◆ Ampac Holdings LLC ....A 513 671-1777
Cincinnati *(G-3397)*

Ampac Packaging LLC ....D 513 671-1777
Cincinnati *(G-3398)*

▲ Atlapac Corp ....B 614 252-2121
Columbus *(G-6782)*

Automated Packg Systems Inc ....D 330 342-2000
Bedford *(G-1401)*

Automated Packg Systems Inc ....C 330 663-2000
Cleveland *(G-4866)*

B K Plastics Inc ....G 937 473-2087
Covington *(G-7920)*

Bag-Pack Inc ....E 513 346-3900
West Chester *(G-19813)*

▲ Buckeye Boxes Inc ....B 614 274-8484
Columbus *(G-6870)*

Charter Nex Films - Delaware ....E 740 369-2770
Delaware *(G-8832)*

Charter Nex Holding Company ....E 740 369-2770
Delaware *(G-8833)*

▲ Command Plastic Corporation ......F 800 321-8001
Tallmadge *(G-18139)*

Cpg - Ohio LLC ....D 513 825-4800
Cincinnati *(G-3616)*

Dayton Industrial Drum Inc ....E 937 253-8933
Dayton *(G-8103)*

▲ Engineered Films Division ....G 419 884-8150
Lexington *(G-11950)*

◆ Factory Direct International ....E 419 425-9636
Findlay *(G-9821)*

◆ Flavorseal LLC ....D 440 937-3900
Avon *(G-995)*

General Films Inc ....D 888 436-3456
Covington *(G-7923)*

Hcf of Bowling Green Inc ....G 419 999-2010
Lima *(G-12022)*

Heritage Bag Company ....D 513 874-3311
West Chester *(G-19881)*

Hood Packaging Corporation ....G 937 382-6681
Wilmington *(G-20669)*

◆ Inpaco Corporation ....F 614 888-9288
Worthington *(G-20872)*

▲ Kennedy Group Incorporated ....D 440 951-7660
Willoughby *(G-20520)*

L & C Plastic Bags Inc ....G 937 473-2968
Covington *(G-7925)*

◆ Liqui-Box Corporation ....D 614 888-9280
Columbus *(G-7300)*

Liqui-Box Corporation ....C 419 289-9696
Ashland *(G-750)*

Mid-West Poly Pak Inc ....E 330 658-2921
Doylestown *(G-9029)*

Multiplast Systems Inc ....F 440 349-0800
Solon *(G-17341)*

Next Generation Bag Inc ....B 419 884-1327
Mansfield *(G-12658)*

▲ Next Generation Films Inc ....C 419 884-8150
Lexington *(G-11951)*

North American Plas Chem Inc ....E 216 531-3400
Euclid *(G-9595)*

▼ Packaging Materials Inc ....E 740 432-6337
Cambridge *(G-2471)*

Pexco Packaging Corp ....E 419 470-5935
Toledo *(G-18642)*

Pitt Plastics Inc ....D 614 868-8660
Columbus *(G-7486)*

▲ Poly Works ....G....... 419 678-3758
   Coldwater (G-6569)

Primary Packaging Incorporated.........D....... 330 874-3131
   Bolivar (G-1943)

Safeway Packaging Inc ....D....... 419 629-3200
   New Bremen (G-14793)

Vee Gee Enterprise Corporation.........G....... 330 493-9780
   Canton (G-2895)

2674 Bags: Uncoated Paper & Multiwall

◆ Ampac Holdings LLC ....A....... 513 671-1777
   Cincinnati (G-3397)

Cleveland Canvas Goods Mfg Co.........D....... 216 361-4567
   Cleveland (G-5050)

Gibson Greetings Inc ....G....... 216 252-7300
   Cleveland (G-5428)

Greif Inc ....E....... 740 657-6500
   Delaware (G-8848)

Greif Inc ....E....... 740 549-6000
   Delaware (G-8847)

Home Care Products LLC ....G....... 919 693-1002
   Chagrin Falls (G-3092)

Hood Packaging Corporation ....C....... 937 382-6681
   Wilmington (G-20669)

▲ Mid-America Packaging LLC ....G....... 330 963-4199
   New Philadelphia (G-14914)

2675 Die-Cut Paper & Board

A G Ruff Paper Specialties Co ....G....... 513 891-7990
   Blue Ash (G-1731)

A H Pelz Co ....G....... 216 861-1882
   Cleveland (G-4674)

Alliance Indus Masking Inc ....G....... 937 681-5569
   Dayton (G-8146)

Art Guild Binders Inc ....E....... 513 242-3000
   Cincinnati (G-3414)

▲ Buckeye Boxes Inc ....D....... 614 274-8484
   Columbus (G-6870)

Ccw Group Pacesetter Inc ....C....... 740 474-0122
   Circleville (G-4624)

Commercial Cutng Graphics LLC ....D....... 419 526-4800
   Mansfield (G-12583)

Consuetudo Abscisum Inc ....G....... 419 281-8002
   Ashland (G-725)

Cornerstone Indus Holdings ....G....... 440 893-9144
   Chagrin Falls (G-3054)

▲ Cutting Edge Cnverted Pdts Inc ....E....... 888 720-3343
   Toledo (G-18420)

D A Stirling Inc ....G....... 330 923-3195
   Cuyahoga Falls (G-7985)

Forest Converting Company Inc ....G....... 513 631-4190
   Cincinnati (G-3769)

GBS Corp ....C....... 330 863-1828
   Malvern (G-12545)

▲ GBS Corp ....C....... 330 494-5330
   North Canton (G-15233)

Georgia-Pacific LLC ....C....... 740 477-3347
   Circleville (G-4631)

Harris & Company Inc ....F....... 330 332-4127
   Salem (G-16899)

Harris Paper Crafts Inc ....F....... 614 299-2141
   Columbus (G-7145)

Honeymoon Paper Products Inc ....D....... 513 755-7200
   Fairfield (G-9666)

Hunt Products Inc ....E....... 440 667-2457
   Newburgh Heights (G-15075)

Keeler Enterprises Inc ....G....... 330 336-7601
   Wadsworth (G-19412)

▼ Kent Adhesive Products Co ....D....... 330 678-1626
   Kent (G-11475)

▲ Keyah International Trdg LLC ....E....... 937 399-3140
   Springfield (G-17586)

Lam Pro Inc ....F....... 216 426-0661
   Cleveland (G-5678)

◆ Loroco Industries Inc ....E....... 513 891-9544
   Blue Ash (G-1828)

McElroy Contract Packaging ....F....... 330 262-0855
   Wooster (G-20804)

Nordec Inc ....D....... 330 940-3700
   Stow (G-17784)

▲ P & R Specialty Inc ....E....... 937 773-0263
   Piqua (G-16297)

Paxar Corporation.........................G....... 937 681-4541
   Dayton (G-8567)

Paycard USA Inc ....F....... 702 216-6801
   Dublin (G-9118)

▲ Printers Bindery Services Inc ....D....... 513 821-8039
   Cincinnati (G-4271)

R D Thompson Paper Pdts Co Inc ......E....... 419 994-3614
   Loudonville (G-12303)

R W Michael Printing Co ....G....... 330 923-9277
   Akron (G-363)

▲ Rohrer Corporation.....................C....... 330 335-1541
   Wadsworth (G-19438)

Smead Manufacturing Company ....C....... 740 385-5601
   Logan (G-12194)

Spencer-Walker Press Inc ....F....... 740 344-6110
   Newark (G-15055)

Springdot Inc ....D....... 513 542-4000
   Cincinnati (G-4448)

Stat Industries Inc ....G....... 513 860-4482
   Hamilton (G-10741)

Stat Industries Inc ....G....... 740 779-6561
   Chillicothe (G-3277)

Stat Industries Inc ....G....... 740 779-6561
   Chillicothe (G-3278)

Stuart Company ....F....... 513 621-9462
   Cincinnati (G-4471)

Vya Inc ....E....... 513 772-5400
   Cincinnati (G-4573)

Williams Steel Rule Die Co................F....... 216 431-3232
   Cleveland (G-6464)

2676 Sanitary Paper Prdts

◆ Absorbent Products Company Inc ....E....... 419 352-5353
   Bowling Green (G-1965)

◆ Aci Industries Converting Ltd ....E....... 740 368-4160
   Delaware (G-8816)

B & B Necessities ....G....... 330 995-0489
   Aurora (G-909)

Cbl Products ....G....... 216 321-2599
   Cleveland (G-4997)

Georgia-Pacific LLC ....F....... 513 336-4200
   Mason (G-13027)

▲ Giant Industries Inc ....E....... 419 531-4600
   Toledo (G-18480)

Gibson Greetings Inc ....G....... 216 252-7300
   Cleveland (G-5428)

▲ Health Care Products Inc ....E....... 419 678-9620
   Coldwater (G-6562)

Kimberly-Clark Corporation ....C....... 513 794-1005
   West Chester (G-19888)

Linsalata Capital Partners Fun ....G....... 440 684-1400
   Cleveland (G-5703)

▲ Little Busy Bodies LLC ....E....... 513 351-5700
   Cincinnati (G-4029)

▲ Novex Products Incorporated.........C....... 440 244-3330
   Lorain (G-12264)

PGT Healthcare LLP ....G....... 513 983-1100
   Cincinnati (G-4234)

Playtex Manufacturing Inc ....D....... 937 498-4710
   Sidney (G-17209)

▲ Principle Business Entps Inc ....C....... 419 352-1551
   Bowling Green (G-2009)

Procter & Gamble Company ....C....... 513 983-1100
   Cincinnati (G-4278)

Procter & Gamble Company ....C....... 513 934-3406
   Oregonia (G-15722)

Procter & Gamble Company ....C....... 513 626-2500
   Blue Ash (G-1857)

◆ Procter & Gamble Company ....B....... 513 983-1100
   Cincinnati (G-4277)

Procter & Gamble Company ....C....... 513 634-9110
   West Chester (G-19923)

Procter & Gamble Company ....B....... 513 983-1100
   Cincinnati (G-4286)

Procter & Gamble Company ....C....... 410 527-5735
   Grove City (G-10586)

Procter & Gamble Far East Inc ....C....... 513 983-1100
   Cincinnati (G-4289)

▼ Procter & Gamble Paper Pdts Co .....F....... 513 983-1100
   Cincinnati (G-4291)

Procter & Gamble Paper Pdts Co ....E....... 513 983-2222
   Cincinnati (G-4292)

Qpi Cincinnati LLC........................C....... 513 755-2670
   West Chester (G-19924)

▲ Tambrands Sales Corp ....C....... 513 983-1100
   Cincinnati (G-4492)

◆ Tranzonic Companies ....C....... 216 535-4300
   Richmond Heights (G-16656)

Tranzonic Companies ....B....... 216 535-4300
   Richmond Heights (G-16657)

Tranzonic Companies ....C....... 440 446-0643
   Cleveland (G-6350)

Tri Con Distribution LLC ....G....... 937 399-3312
   Springfield (G-17666)

◆ Tz Acquisition Corp.....................A....... 216 535-4300
   Richmond Heights (G-16658)

Wausau Ppr Towel & Tissue LLC ....C....... 513 424-2999
   Middletown (G-14097)

2677 Envelopes

◆ Ampac Holdings LLC ....A....... 513 671-1777
   Cincinnati (G-3397)

Bayley Envelope Inc ....G....... 330 821-2150
   Alliance (G-498)

Church Budget Monthly Inc ....D....... 330 337-1122
   Salem (G-16881)

Church-Budget Envelope Company ....E....... 800 446-9780
   Salem (G-16882)

▲ Envelope 1 Inc ....D....... 330 482-3900
   Columbiana (G-6615)

Envelope Mart of Ohio Inc ....E....... 440 365-8177
   Elyria (G-9421)

Ohio Envelope Manufacturing Co ....E....... 216 267-2920
   Cleveland (G-5933)

Pac Worldwide Corporation ....E....... 513 217-3200
   Middletown (G-14071)

Pac Worldwide Corporation ....D....... 800 610-9367
   Middletown (G-14072)

Quality Envelope Inc ....G....... 513 942-7578
   West Chester (G-20043)

◆ SRC Liquidation LLC ....A....... 937 221-1000
   Dayton (G-8672)

Tcp Inc......................................G....... 330 836-4239
   Fairlawn (G-9764)

United Envelope LLC ....D....... 513 542-4700
   Cincinnati (G-4539)

Western States Envelope Co ....D....... 419 666-7480
   Walbridge (G-19464)

2678 Stationery Prdts

◆ American Greetings Corporation.......A....... 216 252-7300
   Cleveland (G-4782)

▼ Bookfactory LLC ....E....... 937 226-7100
   Dayton (G-8191)

CCL Label Inc ....C....... 216 676-2703
   Cleveland (G-4998)

CCL Label Inc ....E....... 440 878-7000
   Brunswick (G-2215)

Century Intermediate Holdg Co ....C....... 216 252-7300
   Cleveland (G-5006)

◆ CM Paula Company ....E....... 513 759-7473
   Mason (G-13002)

Keeler Enterprises Inc ....G....... 330 336-7601
   Wadsworth (G-19412)

▲ Nature Friendly Products LLC ....C....... 216 464-5490
   Cleveland (G-5861)

▲ Primary Colors Design Corp ....G....... 419 903-0403
   Ashland (G-768)

Selco Industries Inc ....C....... 419 861-0336
   Holland (G-11085)

▲ Steel City Corporation ....E....... 330 792-7663
   Ashland (G-779)

Westrock Mwv LLC ....A....... 937 495-6323
   Dayton (G-8755)

2679 Converted Paper Prdts, NEC

4 Walls Com LLC..........................F....... 216 432-1400
   Cleveland (G-4666)

Acme Label & Tag Inc ....G....... 440 729-1040
   Chesterland (G-3194)

Adaptive Data Inc.........................F....... 937 436-2343
   Centerville (G-3032)

◆ American Greetings Corporation.......A....... 216 252-7300
   Cleveland (G-4782)

American Paper Converting LLC.........F....... 419 729-4782
   Toledo (G-18343)

Avery Dennison Corporation ....C....... 440 358-4691
   Painesville (G-15856)

Btw LLC ....G....... 419 382-4443
   Toledo (G-18383)

▼ Buckeye Paper Co Inc ....E....... 330 477-5925
   Canton (G-2630)

▲ Buschman Corporation ....F....... 216 431-6633
   Cleveland (G-4951)

Caraustar Industries Inc ....F....... 216 961-5060
   Cleveland (G-4973)

Caraustar Industries Inc ....E....... 330 665-7700
   Copley (G-7841)

CCL Label Inc ....C....... 216 676-2703
   Cleveland (G-4998)

Century Intermediate Holdg Co ....F....... 216 252-7300
   Cleveland (G-5006)

▼ Century Marketing Corporation.........C....... 419 354-2591
   Bowling Green (G-1978)

▲ CMC Daymark Corporation ....C....... 419 354-2591
   Bowling Green (G-1980)

▲ Corrchoice Inc ....D....... 330 833-5705
   Massillon (G-13122)

Davidson Converting Inc ....G...... 330 626-2118
Streetsboro *(G-17848)*

Domtar Paper Company LLC ....D...... 740 333-0003
Wshngtn CT Hs *(G-20906)*

E-Z Grader Company ....G...... 440 247-7511
Chagrin Falls *(G-3057)*

Federal Barcode Label Systems.......G...... 440 748-8060
North Ridgeville *(G-15373)*

▲ Fibercorr Mills LLC ....D...... 330 837-5151
Massillon *(G-13131)*

▲ Formica Corporation ....E...... 513 786-3400
Cincinnati *(G-3772)*

Gatton Packaging Inc ....G...... 419 886-2577
Bellville *(G-1569)*

GBS Corp ....E...... 330 929-8050
Stow *(G-17758)*

Gemini Fiber Corporation ....F...... 330 874-4131
Bolivar *(G-1935)*

▲ General Data Company Inc ....C...... 513 752-7978
Cincinnati *(G-3304)*

General Data Company Inc ....E...... 513 752-7978
Cincinnati *(G-3305)*

Gibson Greetings Inc ....G...... 216 252-7300
Cleveland *(G-5428)*

Graphic Paper ....F...... 419 526-4123
Mansfield *(G-12619)*

Greif Inc ....D...... 330 879-2101
Navarre *(G-14714)*

Harris Paper Crafts Inc ....F...... 614 299-2141
Columbus *(G-7145)*

Hooven - Dayton Corp ....D...... 937 233-4473
Miamisburg *(G-13818)*

Inline Label Company ....F...... 513 217-5662
Middletown *(G-14048)*

Joshua Enterprises Inc ....G...... 419 872-9699
Perrysburg *(G-16115)*

Jr Kennel Mfg ....G...... 937 780-6104
Leesburg *(G-11853)*

Kay Toledo Tag Inc ....D...... 419 729-5479
Toledo *(G-18541)*

Keithley Enterprises Inc ....G...... 937 890-1878
Dayton *(G-8434)*

▲ Kennedy Group Incorporated ....D...... 440 951-7660
Willoughby *(G-20520)*

▼ Kent Adhesive Products Co ....D...... 330 678-1626
Kent *(G-11475)*

▲ Label Aid Inc ....F...... 419 433-2888
Huron *(G-11231)*

Maderite LLC ....G...... 937 570-1042
Tipp City *(G-18288)*

Media Procurement Services Inc.....G...... 513 977-3000
Cincinnati *(G-4077)*

Mid-States Packaging Inc ....E...... 937 843-3243
Lewistown *(G-11946)*

Millcraft Group LLC ....D...... 216 441-5500
Cleveland *(G-5817)*

Model Graphics & Media Inc ....E...... 513 541-2355
West Chester *(G-19903)*

Mondi Akrosil LLC ....C...... 740 653-4102
Lancaster *(G-11731)*

▲ Multi-Color Corporation ....F...... 513 381-1480
Batavia *(G-1211)*

Oak Hills Carton Co ....E...... 513 948-4200
Cincinnati *(G-4171)*

▲ Ohio Packaging ....E...... 330 833-2884
Massillon *(G-13186)*

Orbytel Print and Packg Inc ....G...... 216 267-8734
Cleveland *(G-5946)*

Outhouse Paper Etc Inc ....G...... 937 382-2800
Waynesville *(G-19732)*

Paper Service Inc ....F...... 330 227-3546
Lisbon *(G-12131)*

◆ Paper Systems Incorporated ....C...... 937 746-6841
Springboro *(G-17494)*

Paxar Corporation ....G...... 937 681-4541
Dayton *(G-8567)*

▲ Pmco LLC ....E...... 513 825-7626
West Chester *(G-19916)*

Rivercor LLC ....E...... 330 784-1113
Akron *(G-375)*

Roberds Converting Co Inc ....E...... 513 683-6667
Loveland *(G-12381)*

▼ Scratch-Off Systems Inc ....E...... 216 649-7800
Brecksville *(G-2071)*

▲ Shore To Shore Inc ....D...... 937 866-1908
Dayton *(G-8656)*

Signode Industrial Group LLC ....E...... 513 248-2990
Loveland *(G-12387)*

Stumps Converting Inc ....F...... 419 492-2542
New Washington *(G-14965)*

Tekni-Plex Inc ....E...... 419 491-2407
Holland *(G-11088)*

▼ The Magic Seal Paper Pdts Co .....F...... 614 299-1185
Columbus *(G-7691)*

Tri State Media LLC ....F...... 513 933-0101
Wilmington *(G-20680)*

Unique Covers ....G...... 419 925-9600
Maria Stein *(G-12761)*

Van Deleigh Industries LLC ....G...... 419 467-2244
Sylvania *(G-18129)*

◆ Vemuri International LLC ....G...... 513 483-6300
Vandalia *(G-4559)*

Vista Industrial Packaging LLC ....D...... 800 454-6117
Columbus *(G-7743)*

W/S Packaging Group Inc ....E...... 513 459-2400
Mason *(G-13102)*

Warren Printing & Off Pdts Inc ....F...... 419 523-3635
Ottawa *(G-15814)*

Wolff House Art Papers Inc ....G...... 740 501-3766
Mount Vernon *(G-14656)*

27 PRINTING, PUBLISHING, AND ALLIED INDUSTRIES

2711 Newspapers: Publishing & Printing

Aak Kings Mills LLC ....G...... 513 598-4460
Mason *(G-12978)*

Acm Ohio LLC ....G...... 740 286-2187
Jackson *(G-11308)*

Active Daily Living LLC ....G...... 513 607-6769
Cincinnati *(G-3352)*

Adams Publishing Group LLC ....G...... 740 592-6612
Athens *(G-854)*

Adult Daily Living LLC ....G...... 330 612-7941
Barberton *(G-1093)*

Advance Reporter ....G...... 419 485-4851
Montpelier *(G-14438)*

Akron Legal News Inc ....F...... 330 296-7578
Akron *(G-46)*

Alliance Publishing Co Inc ....C...... 330 453-1304
Alliance *(G-495)*

Alliance Publishing Co Inc ....F...... 330 868-5222
Minerva *(G-14316)*

American City Bus Journals Inc.......E...... 513 337-9450
Cincinnati *(G-3386)*

American City Bus Journals Inc.......G...... 937 528-4400
Dayton *(G-8152)*

American Community Newspapers......G...... 614 888-4567
Columbus *(G-6733)*

American Israelite Co ....G...... 513 621-3145
Cincinnati *(G-3390)*

American Jrnl of Drmtpathology ....G...... 440 542-0041
Solon *(G-17257)*

American Lithuanian Press ....G...... 216 531-8150
Cleveland *(G-4787)*

▲ Amos Press Inc ....C...... 937 498-2111
Sidney *(G-17168)*

Antwerp Bee-Argus ....G...... 419 258-8161
Antwerp *(G-627)*

Applelane Press LLC ....G...... 440 543-6747
Chagrin Falls *(G-3048)*

Archbold Buckeye Inc ....F...... 419 445-4466
Archbold *(G-663)*

Arens Corporation ....F...... 937 473-2028
Covington *(G-7918)*

Arens Corporation ....G...... 937 473-2028
Covington *(G-7919)*

Ashland Publishing Co ....A...... 419 281-0581
Ashland *(G-708)*

B G News ....E...... 419 372-2601
Bowling Green *(G-1969)*

Bakers Print Shop ....G...... 740 423-1717
Little Hocking *(G-12143)*

Barbara A Eisenhardt ....G...... 614 436-9690
Columbus *(G-6806)*

Bellefontaine Examiner ....G...... 937 592-3060
Bellefontaine *(G-1522)*

Block Communications Inc ....F...... 419 724-6212
Toledo *(G-18372)*

Bloomville Gazette Inc ....G...... 419 426-3491
Attica *(G-892)*

Bluffton News Pubg & Prtg Co ....F...... 419 358-8010
Bluffton *(G-1907)*

Boardman News ....G...... 330 758-6397
Boardman *(G-1920)*

Brecksville Broadview Gazette.........E...... 440 526-7977
Brecksville *(G-2038)*

Brookville Star ....G...... 937 833-2545
Brookville *(G-2177)*

Brothers Publishing Co LLC ....E...... 937 548-3330
Greenville *(G-10490)*

Brown Publishing Co ....F...... 937 544-2391
West Union *(G-20118)*

Brown Publishing Co Inc ....G...... 740 286-2187
Jackson *(G-11313)*

Brown Publishing Inc LLC ....G...... 513 794-5040
Blue Ash *(G-1756)*

Brv Inc ....F...... 513 977-3000
Cincinnati *(G-3483)*

Bryan Publishing Company ....D...... 419 636-1111
Bryan *(G-2288)*

Buchtelite ....E...... 330 972-6184
Akron *(G-101)*

Buckeye Lake Shopper Reporter ......G...... 740 246-4741
Thornville *(G-18192)*

Buckeye Post ....G...... 330 724-2800
Akron *(G-102)*

Business First Columbus Inc ....E...... 614 461-4040
Columbus *(G-6878)*

C L M Associates ....G...... 440 942-8861
Willoughby *(G-20451)*

Cameco Communications ....G...... 937 840-9490
Hillsboro *(G-10997)*

Carrollton Publishing Company ....F...... 330 627-5591
Carrollton *(G-2954)*

Cathie D Hubbard ....E...... 937 593-0316
Bellefontaine *(G-1524)*

Catholic Diocese of Columbus ....G...... 614 224-5195
Columbus *(G-6916)*

Caxton New Stand ....G...... 216 861-1600
Cleveland *(G-4996)*

Central Ohio Printing Corp ....D...... 740 852-1616
London *(G-12203)*

Chagrin Valley Publishing Co ....C...... 440 247-5335
Chagrin Falls *(G-3051)*

Chesterland News Inc ....F...... 440 729-7667
Chesterland *(G-3200)*

Chronicle Telegram ....D...... 330 725-4166
Medina *(G-13387)*

Chronicle Your Life Story ....G...... 614 456-7576
Columbus *(G-6928)*

Cincinnati Crt Index Press Inc ....F...... 513 241-1450
Cincinnati *(G-3546)*

Citizens USA ....G...... 937 280-2001
Dayton *(G-8232)*

Clermont Sun Publishing Co ....G...... 937 444-3441
Mount Orab *(G-14578)*

Cleveland Citizen Pubg Co ....G...... 216 861-4283
Cleveland *(G-5052)*

Cleveland Jewish Publ Co ....G...... 216 454-8300
Cleveland *(G-5067)*

Cleveland Jewish Publ Co Fdn ....G...... 216 454-8300
Beachwood *(G-1261)*

Coffee News ....G...... 330 688-0952
Stow *(G-17741)*

Columbus Alive Inc ....F...... 614 221-2449
Columbus *(G-6947)*

Columbus Messenger Company ......E...... 614 272-5422
Columbus *(G-6961)*

Columbus Messenger Company ......G...... 740 852-0809
London *(G-12205)*

Columbus-Sports Publications ....F...... 614 486-2202
Columbus *(G-6969)*

Comcorp Inc ....B...... 718 981-1234
Cleveland *(G-5102)*

Construction Bulletin Inc ....G...... 330 782-3733
Youngstown *(G-21057)*

Consumers News Services Inc ....C...... 740 888-6000
Lewis Center *(G-11893)*

Copley Ohio Newspapers Inc ....D...... 585 598-0030
Canton *(G-2668)*

Copley Ohio Newspapers Inc ....C...... 330 364-5577
New Philadelphia *(G-14892)*

Copley Ohio Newspapers Inc ....D...... 330 833-2631
Massillon *(G-13121)*

Coshocton County Advertiser ....G...... 740 295-3435
Coshocton *(G-7884)*

County Classifieds ....G...... 937 592-8847
Bellefontaine *(G-1525)*

Cox Media Group Ohio Inc ....A...... 937 225-2000
Dayton *(G-8245)*

Cox Media Group Ohio Inc ....G...... 937 743-6700
Franklin *(G-10016)*

Cox Newspapers LLC ....E...... 513 696-4500
Liberty Township *(G-11959)*

Cox Newspapers LLC ....F...... 937 866-3331
Miamisburg *(G-13794)*

Cox Newspapers LLC ....D...... 937 225-2000
Dayton *(G-8246)*

Cox Newspapers LLC ....D 513 863-8200
Liberty Township (G-11960)

Cox Newspapers LLC ....G 513 523-4139
Oxford (G-15835)

Crain Communications Inc ....D 330 836-9180
Akron (G-133)

Crain Communications Inc ....E 216 522-1383
Cleveland (G-5140)

Cross Communications Inc ....G 937 304-0010
Vandalia (G-19287)

Cuyahoga Co Med Examiner S Off ....G 216 721-5610
Cleveland (G-5156)

Daily Agency Inc ....F 937 456-9808
Eaton (G-9304)

Daily Chief Union ....F 419 294-2331
Upper Sandusky (G-19118)

Daily Dog ....G 419 708-4923
Holland (G-11053)

Daily Fostoria Review Co ....C 419 435-6641
Fostoria (G-9969)

Daily Gazette ....E 937 372-4444
Xenia (G-20945)

Daily Growler Inc ....G 614 656-2337
Upper Arlington (G-19112)

Daily Legal News Inc ....G 330 747-7777
Youngstown (G-21063)

Daily Needs Assistance ....F 614 824-8340
Plain City (G-16330)

Daily Needs Personal Care LLC ....G 614 598-8383
Ashville (G-850)

Daily Reporter ....E 614 224-4835
Columbus (G-7008)

Daily Squawk LLC ....G 937 426-6247
Dayton (G-8101)

Dayton City Paper New LLC ....F 937 222-8855
Dayton (G-8270)

Dayton Dailey News ....F 937 743-2387
Franklin (G-10017)

Dayton Weekly News ....G 937 223-8060
Dayton (G-8289)

Defiance Publishing Co ....A 419 784-5441
Defiance (G-8788)

Delaware Gazette Company ....D 740 363-1161
Delaware (G-8836)

Delphos Herald Inc ....D 419 695-0015
Delphos (G-8904)

Delphos Herald Inc ....G 419 399-4015
Paulding (G-16003)

Delphos Herald Inc ....D 419 695-0015
Delphos (G-8905)

Digicom Inc ....G 216 642-3838
Independence (G-11252)

Dispatch Printing Company ....C 740 548-5331
Lewis Center (G-11895)

Dispatch Printing Company ....E 614 885-6020
Columbus (G-7030)

Dog Daily ....G 216 624-0735
Cleveland (G-5202)

Douthit Communications Inc ....D 419 625-5825
Sandusky (G-16958)

Dow Jones & Company Inc ....E 419 352-4696
Bowling Green (G-1987)

Eastern Ohio Newspapers Inc ....G 740 633-1131
Martins Ferry (G-12924)

Easy Side Publishing Co Inc ....G 216 721-1674
Cleveland (G-5242)

Erie Chinese Journal ....G 216 324-2959
Twinsburg (G-18930)

Euclid Media Group LLC ....E 216 241-7550
Cleveland (G-5301)

EW Scripps Company ....E 513 977-3000
Cincinnati (G-3728)

Farmland News LLC ....F 419 445-9456
Archbold (G-672)

Fire Tetrahedron Journal ....G 567 220-6477
Tiffin (G-18220)

First Catholc Slovak Union U S ....F 216 642-9406
Cleveland (G-5349)

Fostoria Focus Inc ....F 419 435-6397
Fostoria (G-9976)

Franklin Communications Inc ....D 614 459-9769
Columbus (G-7097)

Full Gospel Baptist Times ....G 614 279-3307
Columbus (G-7102)

Funny Times Inc ....G 216 371-8600
Cleveland (G-5383)

Gannett Co Inc ....C 740 345-4053
Newark (G-15009)

Gannett Co Inc ....D 513 721-2700
Cincinnati (G-3795)

Gannett Co Inc ....E 740 654-1321
Lancaster (G-11718)

Gannett Co Inc ....C 740 773-2111
Chillicothe (G-3240)

Gannett Co Inc ....E 419 521-7341
Marion (G-12866)

Gannett Co Inc ....E 740 295-3435
Coshocton (G-7892)

Gannett Co Inc ....D 740 452-4561
Zanesville (G-21314)

Gannett Co Inc ....F 419 332-5511
Fremont (G-10151)

Gannett Co Inc ....C 419 522-3311
Mansfield (G-12609)

Gannett Co Inc ....F 740 349-1100
Newark (G-15010)

Gannett Co Inc ....G 419 562-3333
Mansfield (G-12610)

Gannett Publishing Svcs LLC ....D 419 522-3311
Mansfield (G-12611)

Gannett Stllite Info Ntwrk Inc ....D 513 721-2700
Cincinnati (G-3796)

Gannett Stllite Info Ntwrk Inc ....G 513 576-1800
Milford (G-14143)

Gannett Stllite Info Ntwrk LLC ....D 419 334-1012
Fremont (G-10152)

Gate West Coast Ventures LLC ....F 513 891-1000
Blue Ash (G-1802)

Gazette Editorial Department ....G 330 725-6220
Medina (G-13415)

Gazette Publishing Company ....E 419 483-4190
Oberlin (G-15640)

Gazette Publishing Company ....F 419 335-2010
Wauseon (G-19679)

Graphic Publications Inc ....D 330 343-4377
Dover (G-8988)

Greenhills Journal ....F 513 825-2525
Cincinnati (G-3851)

Hamilton Journal News Inc ....D 513 863-8200
Liberty Township (G-11963)

Hardin County Publishing Co ....E 419 674-4066
Kenton (G-11549)

Harrison News Herald Inc ....F 740 942-2118
Cadiz (G-2418)

Heartland Education Community ....F 330 684-3034
Orrville (G-15739)

Heartland Publications LLC ....F 740 446-2342
Gallipolis (G-10300)

Herald House ....G 740 967-8044
Johnstown (G-11401)

Herald Looms ....G 330 948-1080
Lodi (G-12162)

Herald Reflector Inc ....E 419 668-3771
Norwalk (G-15545)

Highschoolball Inc ....G 844 472-2551
North Royalton (G-15425)

Hirt Publishing Co Inc ....E 419 946-3010
Mount Gilead (G-14562)

Hirt Publishing Co Inc ....G 419 523-5709
Ottawa (G-15794)

Hirt Publishing Co Inc ....F 419 523-5709
Ottawa (G-15795)

Holland Springfield Journal ....G 419 874-2528
Perrysburg (G-16108)

Holmes County Hub Inc ....G 330 674-1811
Millersburg (G-14230)

Horizon Ohio Publications Inc ....F 419 394-7414
Saint Marys (G-16840)

Horizon Ohio Publications Inc ....E 419 738-2128
Wapakoneta (G-19489)

Horizon Publications Inc ....G 419 628-2369
Minster (G-14355)

Horizon Publications Inc ....E 419 738-2128
Wapakoneta (G-19490)

Hubbard Publishing Co ....E 937 592-3060
Bellefontaine (G-1533)

Huron Hometown News ....G 419 433-1401
Huron (G-11225)

Iheartcommunications Inc ....F 740 335-0941
Wshngtn CT Hs (G-20911)

Iheartcommunications Inc ....D 419 223-2060
Lima (G-12026)

Impact Publications ....G 740 928-5541
Buckeye Lake (G-2329)

Indian Lake Shoppers Edge ....G 937 843-6600
Russells Point (G-16756)

Ironton Publications Inc ....A 740 532-1441
Ironton (G-11294)

James Oshea ....G 614 262-3188
Columbus (G-7226)

Jewish Journal Monthly Mag ....G 330 746-3251
Youngstown (G-21126)

Job News ....G 513 984-5724
Blue Ash (G-1818)

Job News USA ....F 614 310-1700
Columbus (G-7236)

Journal Bkr ....G 440 245-6901
Lorain (G-12250)

Journal Register Company ....C 440 951-0000
Willoughby (G-20517)

Journal Register Company ....C 440 245-6901
Lorain (G-12251)

Kent State University ....G 330 672-2586
Kent (G-11482)

King Media Enterprises Inc ....G 216 588-6700
Cleveland (G-5554)

Knowles Press Inc ....G 330 877-9345
Hartville (G-10827)

Knox County Printing Co ....G 740 848-4032
Galion (G-10278)

Kroner Publications Inc ....G 330 544-5500
Niles (G-15167)

La Voz Hispania Newspaper ....G 614 274-5505
Columbus (G-7279)

Lake Community News ....G 440 946-2577
Willoughby (G-20524)

Lakewood Observer Inc ....G 216 712-7070
Lakewood (G-11672)

Laprensa Publications Inc ....G 419 242-7744
Toledo (G-18554)

Leader Publications Inc ....E 330 665-9595
Fairlawn (G-9756)

Leaf & Thorn Press ....G 614 396-6055
Columbus (G-6651)

Legal News Publishing Co ....E 216 696-3322
Cleveland (G-5692)

Lets Golf Daily Inc ....G 330 966-3373
North Canton (G-15246)

Lisa Arters ....G 330 435-1804
Creston (G-7940)

Lorain Journal ....G 440 245-6900
Lorain (G-12257)

Lore Inc ....G 513 969-8481
Milford (G-14159)

Louisville Herald Inc ....G 330 875-5610
Louisville (G-12318)

M & D Brink Inc ....G 419 531-6699
Toledo (G-18566)

Mansfield Journal Co ....G 330 364-8641
New Philadelphia (G-14910)

Mark Daily ....G 937 369-5358
Eaton (G-9318)

Marketing Essentials LLC ....F 419 629-0080
New Bremen (G-14789)

Marrow County Sentinel ....G 419 946-3010
Mount Gilead (G-14564)

Marysville Newspaper Inc ....G 740 943-2214
Richwood (G-16660)

Marysville Newspaper Inc ....E 937 644-9111
Marysville (G-12957)

Mature Living News Magazine ....G 419 241-8880
Toledo (G-18576)

Merrill Corporation ....C 614 801-4700
Grove City (G-10571)

Messenger Publishing Company ....C 740 592-6612
Athens (G-876)

Mickens Inc ....G 419 533-2401
Liberty Center (G-11955)

Mickens Inc ....G 419 943-2590
Leipsic (G-11872)

Mirror ....E 419 893-8135
Maumee (G-13284)

Mirror Publishing Co Inc ....E 419 893-8135
Maumee (G-13285)

Monroe County Beacon Inc ....F 740 472-0734
Woodsfield (G-20720)

Morgan County Publishing Co ....G 740 962-3377
McConnelsville (G-13356)

My Way Home Finder Magazine ....G 419 841-6201
Toledo (G-18596)

Napoleon Inc ....E 419 592-5055
Napoleon (G-14691)

Neighborhood News Pubg Co ....G 216 441-2141
Cleveland (G-5867)

New Urban Distributors LLC ....G 216 373-2349
Cleveland (G-5879)

News Democrat ....G 937 378-6161
Miamisburg (G-13843)

News Watchman & Paper ....F 740 947-2149
Waverly (G-19713)

Newspaper Holding Inc ....D...... 440 998-2323
Ashtabula (G-826)
Newspaper Network Central OH ....G...... 419 524-3545
Mansfield (G-12657)
Newspaper Solutions LLC ....G...... 937 694-9370
Englewood (G-9535)
Nomis Publications Inc ....F...... 330 965-2380
Youngstown (G-21150)
North Coast Voice Mag ....G...... 440 415-0999
Geneva (G-10353)
Northeast Scene Inc ....E...... 216 241-7550
Cleveland (G-5907)
Ocm LLC ....E...... 937 247-2700
Miamisburg (G-13844)
Ogden Newspapers Inc ....E...... 330 332-4601
Salem (G-16917)
Ogden Newspapers Inc ....D...... 740 283-4711
Steubenville (G-17708)
Ogden Newspapers Inc ....C...... 330 841-1600
Warren (G-19582)
Ogden Newspapers of Ohio Inc ....D...... 419 448-3200
Tiffin (G-18236)
Ogden Newspapers Ohio Inc ....E...... 330 424-9541
Lisbon (G-12129)
Ohio Community Media ....G...... 740 848-4064
Fredericktown (G-10107)
Ohio News Network ....D...... 614 460-3700
Columbus (G-7423)
Ohio Newspaper Services Inc ....F...... 614 486-6677
Columbus (G-7424)
Ohio Newspapers Foundation ....G...... 614 486-6677
Columbus (G-7425)
Ohio University ....C...... 740 593-4010
Athens (G-880)
Our Daily Bread ....G...... 513 621-6364
Cincinnati (G-4201)
Outdoor News Service ....G...... 419 734-5172
Port Clinton (G-16408)
▲ Outlook Publishing Inc ....F...... 614 268-8525
Columbus (G-7450)
Pataskala Post ....F...... 740 964-6226
Pataskala (G-15977)
Patriot ....G...... 419 864-8411
Cardington (G-2913)
Peebles Messenger Newspaper ....G...... 937 587-1451
Peebles (G-16023)
Perry County Tribune ....F...... 740 342-4121
New Lexington (G-14851)
Photo Star ....G...... 419 495-2696
Willshire (G-20651)
Plain Dealer Publishing Co ....F...... 216 999-5000
Cleveland (G-6010)
Plain Dealer Publishing Co ....G...... 614 228-8200
Columbus (G-7488)
Plain Dealer Publishing Co ....A...... 216 999-5000
Cleveland (G-6011)
Pride of Geneva ....G...... 440 466-5695
Geneva (G-10356)
Print Shop ....G...... 740 335-8030
Wshngtn CT Hs (G-20920)
Progressive Communications ....D...... 740 397-5333
Mount Vernon (G-14640)
Progressor Times ....G...... 419 396-7567
Carey (G-2924)
Ptr Daily LLC ....G...... 330 673-1990
Stow (G-17793)
Pulse Journal ....E...... 513 829-7900
Liberty Township (G-11965)
R & C Lortcher LLC ....G...... 419 663-1531
Norwalk (G-15560)
Ray Barnes Newspaper Inc ....G...... 419 674-4066
Kenton (G-11566)
Record Publishing Co ....D...... 330 541-9400
Kent (G-11513)
Register Herald Office ....F...... 937 456-5553
Eaton (G-9321)
Reporter Newspaper Inc ....F...... 330 535-7061
Akron (G-371)
Richardson Publishing Company ....F...... 330 753-1068
Barberton (G-1146)
Ripley Bee ....G...... 937 392-4321
Ripley (G-16669)
Robert Tuneberg ....G...... 440 899-9277
Bay Village (G-1244)
Roman Cthlic Docese Youngstown ....G...... 330 744-8451
Youngstown (G-21193)
Royalton Recorder ....G...... 440 237-2235
North Royalton (G-15450)
Rural Urban Record Inc ....G...... 440 236-8982
Columbia Station (G-6598)

Sandusky Newspapers Inc ....C...... 419 625-5500
Sandusky (G-17004)
Scripps Media Inc ....D...... 513 977-3000
Cincinnati (G-4392)
Sdg News Group Inc ....F...... 419 929-3411
New London (G-14865)
Sentinel Daily ....G...... 740 992-2155
Pomeroy (G-16390)
Sesh Communications ....F...... 513 851-1693
Cincinnati (G-4408)
Seven Hills Reporter ....G...... 216 524-9515
Seven Hills (G-17064)
Shelby Daily Globe Inc ....E...... 419 342-4276
Shelby (G-17142)
Shree Krupa Inc ....G...... 216 781-6054
Cleveland (G-6197)
Smart Business Network Inc ....E...... 440 250-7000
Cleveland (G-6210)
Sojourners Truth ....F...... 419 243-0007
Toledo (G-18700)
Sound Publishing Holding Inc ....G...... 330 996-3000
Akron (G-408)
Southeast Publications Inc ....F...... 740 732-2341
Caldwell (G-2433)
Springfield Newspapers Inc ....E...... 937 323-5533
Springfield (G-17653)
Standard Printing Co Inc ....E...... 419 586-2371
Celina (G-3019)
Star Newspaper ....G...... 614 622-5930
Columbus (G-7652)
Stumbo Publishing Co ....G...... 419 529-2847
Ontario (G-15695)
Suburban Newpapers of Dayton ....G...... 937 236-4990
Dayton (G-8686)
Suburban Newpapers of Dayton ....E...... 937 878-3993
Xenia (G-20976)
Suburban Newpapers of Dayton ....G...... 937 294-7000
Vandalia (G-19311)
Sugarcreek Budget Publishers ....F...... 330 852-4634
Sugarcreek (G-18042)
Summit Street News Inc ....G...... 330 609-5600
Warren (G-19602)
Telegram ....F...... 740 286-3604
Jackson (G-11328)
The Beacon Journal Pubg Co ....B...... 330 996-3140
Akron (G-435)
The Cleveland Jewish Publ Co ....G...... 216 454-8300
Beachwood (G-1300)
The Gazette Printing Co Inc ....G...... 440 593-6030
Conneaut (G-7820)
The Jeffersonian ....G...... 740 498-7117
Newcomerstown (G-15125)
Times Bulletin Media ....F...... 419 238-2285
Van Wert (G-19272)
Times Journal ....F...... 740 286-2187
Jackson (G-11330)
Toledo Blade Company ....B...... 419 724-6000
Toledo (G-18730)
Toledo Journal ....G...... 419 472-4521
Toledo (G-18732)
Toledo Streets Newspaper ....G...... 419 214-3460
Toledo (G-18743)
Toledo Sword Newspaper ....G...... 419 932-0767
Toledo (G-18744)
Toledos Runway Rivalry Brough ....G...... 419 724-6307
Toledo (G-18749)
Trading Post ....G...... 740 922-1199
Uhrichsville (G-19063)
Travelers Vacation Guide ....G...... 440 582-4949
North Royalton (G-15456)
Tribune Printing Inc ....G...... 419 542-7764
Hicksville (G-10909)
Trogdon Publishing Inc ....E...... 330 721-7678
Medina (G-13491)
Troy Daily News Inc ....E...... 937 339-2729
Troy (G-18880)
Truax Printing Inc ....E...... 419 994-4166
Loudonville (G-12306)
Trumbull County Legal News ....G...... 330 392-7112
Warren (G-19612)
University Sports Publications ....E...... 614 291-6416
Columbus (G-7726)
Utica Herald ....G...... 740 892-2771
Utica (G-19197)
Venice Cornerstone Newspaper ....G...... 513 738-7151
Hamilton (G-10753)
Village Reporter ....G...... 419 485-4851
Montpelier (G-14456)
Village Voice Publishing Ltd ....G...... 419 537-0286
Toledo (G-18769)

Villager Publishing Co Inc ....G...... 330 527-5761
Garrettsville (G-10335)
Vindicator ....G...... 330 755-0135
Campbell (G-2493)
Vindicator Boardman Office ....G...... 330 259-1732
Youngstown (G-21240)
Vindicator Printing Company ....G...... 330 392-0176
Warren (G-19618)
Voice Media Group Inc ....D...... 216 241-7550
Cleveland (G-6425)
Vpp Industries Inc ....F...... 937 526-3775
Versailles (G-19359)
Weekly Brothers Cnty Line Far ....G...... 330 674-4195
Millersburg (G-14284)
Weekly Chatter ....G...... 740 336-4704
Belpre (G-1597)
Weekly Juicery ....G...... 513 321-0680
Cincinnati (G-4582)
Weirton Daily Times ....F...... 740 283-4711
Steubenville (G-17720)
Welch Publishing Co ....E...... 419 874-2528
Perrysburg (G-16168)
Welch Publishing Co ....G...... 419 666-5344
Rossford (G-16750)
Whitney House ....G...... 614 396-7846
Worthington (G-20894)
Willard Times Junction ....F...... 419 935-0184
Willard (G-20405)
Winkler Co Inc ....G...... 937 294-2662
Dayton (G-8761)
Wooster Daily Record Inc ....C...... 330 264-1125
Wooster (G-20849)
World Journal ....G...... 216 458-0988
Cleveland (G-6480)
Yellow Springs News Inc ....F...... 937 767-7373
Yellow Springs (G-21001)
Your Daily Bargains ....G...... 330 715-8324
Stow (G-17818)
Your Daily Motivation Ydm Fitn ....G...... 440 954-1038
Painesville (G-15946)
Zanesville Newspaper ....G...... 740 452-4561
Zanesville (G-21367)

2721 Periodicals: Publishing & Printing

614 Media Group LLC ....D...... 614 488-4400
Columbus (G-6665)
A R Harding Publishing Company ....F...... 614 231-5735
Columbus (G-6668)
Acoustical Publications Inc ....G...... 440 835-0101
Bay Village (G-1241)
Adams Street Publishing Co ....E...... 419 244-9859
Toledo (G-18321)
Advanced Mdia Publications Inc ....F...... 440 260-9910
Cleveland (G-4716)
Advanstar Communications Inc ....F...... 440 243-8100
North Olmsted (G-15325)
Agri Communicators Inc ....E...... 614 273-0465
Columbus (G-6702)
AGS Custom Graphics Inc ....D...... 330 963-7770
Macedonia (G-12433)
Alcohol & Drug Addiction Svcs ....E...... 216 348-4830
Cleveland (G-4744)
Alternative Press Magazine Inc ....E...... 216 631-1510
Cleveland (G-4771)
American Ceramic Society ....E...... 614 890-4700
Westerville (G-20137)
American Heart Association Inc ....F...... 419 740-6180
Maumee (G-13223)
American Lawyers Co Inc ....F...... 440 333-5190
Westlake (G-20250)
▲ Amos Press Inc ....C...... 937 498-2111
Sidney (G-17168)
◆ Angstrom Graphics Inc ....C...... 216 271-5300
Cleveland (G-4814)
Arens Corporation ....F...... 937 473-2028
Covington (G-7918)
Arens Corporation ....G...... 937 473-2028
Covington (G-7919)
▲ Asm International ....D...... 440 338-5151
Novelty (G-15582)
Babcox Media Inc ....D...... 330 670-1234
Akron (G-82)
Baker Media Group LLC ....F...... 330 253-0056
Akron (G-83)
▲ Benjamin Media Inc ....E...... 330 467-7588
Brecksville (G-2036)
Bluffton News Pubg & Prtg Co ....F...... 419 358-8010
Bluffton (G-1907)
Bobit Business Media Inc ....G...... 330 899-2200
Uniontown (G-19077)

Buckeye Prep Report Magazine ....G.... 614 855-6977
New Albany *(G-14752)*
Business Journal ....F.... 330 744-5023
Youngstown *(G-21040)*
C & S Associates Inc ....E.... 440 461-9661
Highland Heights *(G-10910)*
Camargo Publications Inc ....G.... 513 779-7177
Cincinnati *(G-3495)*
Carmel Trader Publishing Inc ....E.... 330 478-9200
Canton *(G-2650)*
Cars and Parts Magazine ....C.... 937 498-0803
Sidney *(G-17171)*
Center For Inquiry Inc ....G.... 330 671-7192
Peninsula *(G-16035)*
CFM Religion Pubg Group LLC ....E.... 513 931-4050
Cincinnati *(G-3520)*
Charlotte M Peters ....G.... 216 798-8997
Cleveland *(G-5017)*
Cincinnati Magazine ....G.... 513 421-4300
Cincinnati *(G-3557)*
City Girl Magazine LLC ....G.... 216 481-4110
Cleveland *(G-5034)*
City of Parma ....G.... 440 885-8816
Cleveland *(G-5037)*
City Visitor Inc ....G.... 216 661-6666
Cleveland *(G-5039)*
Clipper Magazine LLC ....G.... 937 534-0470
Moraine *(G-14472)*
Columbus Bride ....D.... 614 888-4567
Columbus *(G-6948)*
Communication Resources Inc ....E.... 800 992-2144
Canton *(G-2665)*
Construction Journal Ltd ....F.... 440 826-4700
Cleveland *(G-5120)*
Crain Communications Inc ....E.... 216 522-1383
Cleveland *(G-5140)*
Crain Communications Inc ....D.... 330 836-9180
Akron *(G-133)*
Cruisin Times Magazine ....G.... 440 331-4615
Rocky River *(G-16696)*
Curt Harler Inc ....G.... 440 238-4556
Cleveland *(G-5147)*
Dispatch Printing Company ....E.... 614 885-6020
Columbus *(G-7030)*
Dominion Enterprises ....E.... 216 472-1870
Cleveland *(G-5204)*
Downey Enterprises Inc ....G.... 740 587-4258
Granville *(G-10457)*
▲ F+w Media Inc ....B.... 513 531-2690
Blue Ash *(G-1791)*
Family Motor Coach Assn Inc ....E.... 513 474-3622
Cincinnati *(G-3738)*
Family Motor Coaching Inc ....D.... 513 474-3622
Cincinnati *(G-3739)*
Family Values Magazine ....G.... 419 566-1102
Mansfield *(G-12602)*
Fontanelle Group Inc ....G.... 440 834-8900
Burton *(G-2375)*
Gardner Business Media Inc ....E.... 513 527-8800
Cincinnati *(G-3799)*
Generals Books ....G.... 614 870-1861
Columbus *(G-7109)*
Gie Media Inc ....E.... 800 456-0707
Cleveland *(G-5430)*
Gongwer News Service Inc ....F.... 614 221-1992
Columbus *(G-7123)*
Gongwer News Service Inc ....G.... 614 221-1992
Columbus *(G-7124)*
Graphic Publications Inc ....E.... 330 674-2300
Millersburg *(G-14218)*
Graphicom Press Inc ....G.... 937 767-1916
Yellow Springs *(G-20991)*
Great Lakes Publishing Company ....D.... 216 771-2833
Cleveland *(G-5455)*
Greater Cincinnati Bowl Assn ....E.... 513 761-7387
Cincinnati *(G-3847)*
Guitar Digest Inc ....F.... 740 592-4614
Athens *(G-870)*
Hacienda Publications LLC ....G.... 216 202-5440
Euclid *(G-9585)*
Half Price Bks Rec Mgzines Inc ....F.... 614 776-5551
Westerville *(G-20217)*
Half Price Bks Rec Mgzines Inc ....F.... 440 255-2581
Mentor *(G-13599)*
Harvey Whitney Books Company ....F.... 513 793-3555
Cincinnati *(G-3869)*
Highlights For Children Inc ....C.... 614 486-0631
Hilliard *(G-10951)*
Horizon Communications Inc ....G.... 330 968-6959
Twinsburg *(G-18955)*
Housetrends ....G.... 513 794-4103
Blue Ash *(G-1809)*
In Box Publications LLC ....G.... 330 592-4288
Akron *(G-231)*
Incorporated Trst Gspl Wk Scty ....D.... 216 749-2100
Cleveland *(G-5560)*
Indicator Advisory Corporation ....G.... 419 726-9000
Toledo *(G-18521)*
Institute Mthmtical Statistics ....G.... 216 295-2340
Shaker Heights *(G-17090)*
Jadlyn Inc ....G.... 330 670-9545
Akron *(G-238)*
Kaleidoscope Magazine LLC ....E.... 216 566-5500
Cleveland *(G-5631)*
Kent Information Services Inc ....G.... 330 672-2110
Kent *(G-11479)*
Kenyon Review ....G.... 740 427-5208
Gambier *(G-10316)*
Kyle Publications Inc ....G.... 419 754-4234
Toledo *(G-18551)*
Larry C White ....G.... 330 386-3228
East Liverpool *(G-9224)*
Lavish Lyfe Magazine ....G.... 937 938-5816
Dayton *(G-8453)*
Legal News Publishing Co ....E.... 216 696-3322
Cleveland *(G-5692)*
Lippincott & Peto Inc ....F.... 330 864-2122
Akron *(G-271)*
▲ Lorenz Corporation ....D.... 937 228-6118
Dayton *(G-8460)*
Lyle Printing & Publishing Co ....E.... 330 337-3419
Salem *(G-16909)*
Lyle Printing & Publishing Co ....F.... 330 337-7172
Salem *(G-16910)*
Marketing Directions Inc ....G.... 440 835-5550
Cleveland *(G-5747)*
Marketing Essentials LLC ....F.... 419 629-0080
New Bremen *(G-14789)*
Marula Publishing LLC ....G.... 513 549-5218
Cincinnati *(G-4064)*
Matthew Bender & Company Inc ....C.... 518 487-3000
Miamisburg *(G-13827)*
Medquest Communications Inc ....E.... 216 391-9100
Cleveland *(G-5776)*
Meister Media Worldwide Inc ....D.... 440 942-2000
Willoughby *(G-20544)*
◆ Midwest Exposure Magazine ....G.... 937 626-6738
Dayton *(G-8495)*
Miller Publishing Company ....G.... 937 866-3331
Miamisburg *(G-13837)*
Modern Trade Communications ....G.... 419 849-3109
Woodville *(G-20726)*
Morrison Media Group-Cmj LLP ....G.... 216 973-4005
Cleveland *(G-5834)*
National Mortgage Weekley ....G.... 330 674-2887
Millersburg *(G-14253)*
▲ New Track Media LLC ....F.... 513 421-6500
Blue Ash *(G-1844)*
North Coast Business Journal ....G.... 419 734-4838
Port Clinton *(G-16407)*
North Coast Minority Media LLC ....E.... 216 407-4327
Cleveland *(G-5899)*
Northeast Scene Inc ....E.... 216 241-7550
Cleveland *(G-5907)*
Ohio Association Realtors Inc ....E.... 614 228-6675
Columbus *(G-7415)*
Ohio Designer Craftsmen Entps ....F.... 614 486-7119
Columbus *(G-7419)*
Ohio State University ....F.... 614 292-6930
Columbus *(G-7434)*
Open House Magazine Inc ....G.... 614 523-7775
Columbus *(G-7443)*
Organic Spa Magazine Ltd ....G.... 440 331-5750
Rocky River *(G-16704)*
Pardson Inc ....F.... 740 373-5285
Marietta *(G-12813)*
Pearson Education Inc ....F.... 614 876-0371
Columbus *(G-7471)*
Pearson Education Inc ....F.... 614 841-3700
Columbus *(G-7472)*
Peninsula Publishing LLC ....G.... 330 524-3359
Peninsula *(G-16040)*
Pink Corner Office Inc ....G.... 614 547-9350
Lewis Center *(G-11910)*
Pjl Enterprise Inc ....D.... 937 293-1415
Moraine *(G-14513)*
Pjl Enterprise Inc ....E.... 937 293-1415
Moraine *(G-14514)*
Plus Publications Inc ....G.... 740 345-5542
Newark *(G-15046)*
Prehistoric Antiquities ....G.... 937 747-2225
North Lewisburg *(G-15308)*
Professional Reports Corp ....G.... 330 492-6063
Canton *(G-2826)*
Province of St John The Baptis ....D.... 513 241-5615
Cincinnati *(G-4301)*
Publishing Group Ltd ....F.... 614 572-1240
Columbus *(G-7526)*
Quad/Graphics Inc ....A.... 513 932-1064
Lebanon *(G-11830)*
Rector Inc ....G.... 440 892-0444
Westlake *(G-20301)*
Reel Image ....G.... 937 296-9036
Dayton *(G-8621)*
Relx Inc ....E.... 937 865-6800
Miamisburg *(G-13851)*
Relx Inc ....F.... 937 865-6800
Miamisburg *(G-13852)*
Rubber World Magazine Inc ....F.... 330 864-2122
Akron *(G-381)*
Sabre Publishing ....G.... 440 243-4300
Berea *(G-1634)*
SC Solutions Inc ....G.... 614 317-7119
Grove City *(G-10592)*
Schuster Beverage Marketing ....G.... 614 764-1420
Dublin *(G-9140)*
Sesh Communications ....F.... 513 851-1693
Cincinnati *(G-4408)*
Sheep & Farm Life Inc ....G.... 419 492-2364
New Washington *(G-14964)*
▲ St Media Group Intl Inc ....D.... 513 421-2050
Blue Ash *(G-1873)*
▲ Standard Publishing LLC ....C.... 513 931-4050
Cincinnati *(G-4453)*
Sterling Associates Inc ....G.... 330 630-3500
Akron *(G-418)*
Suburban Communications Inc ....E.... 440 632-0130
Middlefield *(G-13993)*
Target Printing & Graphics ....G.... 937 228-0170
Dayton *(G-8700)*
Telex Communications Inc ....F.... 419 865-0972
Toledo *(G-18718)*
Toastmasters International ....F.... 937 429-2680
Dayton *(G-8118)*
United Advg Publications Inc ....G.... 513 469-8818
Cincinnati *(G-4537)*
University Sports Publications ....E.... 614 291-6416
Columbus *(G-7726)*
US Brands Inc ....G.... 216 595-9700
Cleveland *(G-6398)*
Vela ....G.... 614 500-0150
Salesville *(G-16938)*
Venue Lifestyle & Event Guide ....F.... 513 405-6822
Cincinnati *(G-4563)*
Virtus Stunts LLC ....G.... 440 543-0472
Chagrin Falls *(G-3132)*
Welch Publishing Co ....E.... 419 874-2528
Perrysburg *(G-16168)*
Wordcross Enterprises Inc ....F.... 614 410-4140
Columbus *(G-7773)*
Xray Media Ltd ....G.... 513 751-9641
Cincinnati *(G-4615)*
Youngs Publishing Inc ....F.... 937 259-6575
Beavercreek *(G-1367)*
Z Track Magazine ....G.... 614 764-1703
Dublin *(G-9167)*

2731 Books: Publishing & Printing

American Academic Press ....G.... 216 906-2518
Bedford *(G-1396)*
American Legal Publishing Corp ....E.... 513 421-4248
Cincinnati *(G-3391)*
Anderson Publishing Co ....D.... 513 474-9305
Miamisburg *(G-13783)*
▲ Asm International ....D.... 440 338-5151
Novelty *(G-15582)*
B & S Transport Inc ....G.... 330 767-4319
Navarre *(G-14709)*
B&D Productions Inc ....F.... 216 961-0310
Cleveland *(G-4885)*
▼ Bearing Precious Seed ....G.... 513 575-1706
Milford *(G-14124)*
Beevinwood Inc ....G.... 937 678-9910
West Manchester *(G-20096)*
▲ Bendon Inc ....D.... 419 207-3600
Ashland *(G-712)*
▼ Bookfactory LLC ....E.... 937 226-7100
Dayton *(G-8191)*
Bookmasters Inc ....C.... 419 281-1802
Ashland *(G-713)*

SIC

Carmel Trader Publishing Inc E 330 478-9200
Canton (G-2650)
Cengage Learning Inc C 513 234-5967
Mason (G-12993)
Communication Resources Inc E 800 992-2144
Canton (G-2665)
Conway Greene Co Inc G 216 619-8091
Cleveland (G-5128)
CSS Publishing Co Inc E 419 227-1818
Lima (G-12002)
▲ Dalmatian Press LLC E 419 207-3600
Ashland (G-728)
Decent Hill Publishers LLC G 216 548-1255
Hilliard (G-10948)
Design Avenue Inc G 330 487-5280
Twinsburg (G-18924)
Dialogue House Associates Inc G 216 342-5170
Beachwood (G-1266)
Dreamscape Media LLC G 877 983-7326
Holland (G-11056)
Eastword Publications Dev G 216 781-9594
Cleveland (G-5241)
Elloras Cave Publishing Inc E 330 253-3521
Akron (G-163)
▲ F+w Media Inc B 513 531-2690
Blue Ash (G-1791)
Frasernet Inc G 216 691-6686
Cleveland (G-5379)
Gardner Business Media Inc E 513 527-8800
Cincinnati (G-3799)
Gareth Stevens Publishing LP C 800 542-2595
Strongsville (G-17922)
Gie Media Inc E 800 456-0707
Cleveland (G-5430)
▲ Golf Galaxy Golfworks Inc C 740 328-4193
Newark (G-15014)
Grand Unification Press Inc G 330 683-1187
Orrville (G-15738)
Gray & Company Publishers G 216 431-2665
Cleveland (G-5448)
Hamilton Arts Inc G 937 767-1834
Yellow Springs (G-20992)
Harvey Whitney Books Company F 513 793-3555
Cincinnati (G-3869)
Highlights Press Inc G 614 487-2767
Columbus (G-7156)
Hubbard Company E 419 784-4455
Defiance (G-8794)
Indicator Advisory Corporation G 419 726-9000
Toledo (G-18521)
Instruction & Design Concepts G 937 439-2698
Dayton (G-8412)
J S C Publishing G 614 424-6911
Columbus (G-7219)
Jack C Keir Inc F 513 422-4860
Middletown (G-14051)
Just Business Inc F 866 577-3303
Dayton (G-8431)
▲ Kaeden Corporation G 440 617-1400
Westlake (G-20280)
Katherine A Stull Inc G 440 349-3977
Solon (G-17327)
Kelley Communication Dev G 937 298-6132
Dayton (G-8435)
Kendall/Hunt Publishing Co D 877 275-4725
Cincinnati (G-3982)
Kent State University F 330 672-7913
Kent (G-11481)
Ketman Corporation G 330 262-1688
Wooster (G-20795)
Kid Concoctions Company G 440 572-1800
Strongsville (G-17936)
Kovels Antiques Inc F 216 752-2252
Cleveland (G-5664)
Lachina Publishing Svcs Inc E 216 292-7959
Cleveland (G-5674)
Lawpak Inc G 513 831-3900
Terrace Park (G-18180)
Leap Publishing Services Inc F 234 738-0082
Stow (G-17768)
Lloyd Library & Museum G 513 721-3707
Cincinnati (G-4030)
Marysville Newspaper Inc E 937 644-9111
Marysville (G-12957)
▲ Master Communications Inc G 208 821-3473
Blue Ash (G-1833)
Matthew Bender & Company Inc C 518 487-3000
Miamisburg (G-13827)
McDonald & Woodward Pubg Co G 740 321-1140
Granville (G-10460)
McGraw-Hill Global Educatn LLC B 614 755-4151
Blacklick (G-1702)
McGraw-Hill School Education H B 419 207-7400
Ashland (G-753)
McGraw-Hill School Education H B 614 430-4000
Columbus (G-6652)
McNamaras Pub Inc G 216 671-8820
Cleveland (G-5772)
Micropress America LLC G 513 746-0689
Cincinnati (G-4102)
National Directory Morticians G 440 247-3561
Chagrin Falls (G-3065)
Neal Publications Inc G 419 874-4787
Perrysburg (G-16125)
Neola Inc G 330 926-0514
Stow (G-17783)
Neola Inc F 740 622-5341
Coshocton (G-7900)
North Coast Media LLC E 216 706-3700
Cleveland (G-5898)
Northstar Publishing G 330 721-9126
Medina (G-13450)
Nurdcon LLC G 614 208-5898
Canal Winchester (G-2534)
OFA Services Inc F 614 884-1203
Columbus (G-7413)
Ohio Psychlogy Pblications Inc G 614 861-1999
Columbus (G-7429)
One Liberty Street G 419 352-6298
Bowling Green (G-2004)
Orange Frazer Press Inc G 937 382-3196
Wilmington (G-20672)
Pardson Inc F 740 373-5285
Marietta (G-12813)
▲ Precision Metalforming Assn E 216 241-1482
Independence (G-11271)
Province of St John The Baptis D 513 241-5615
Cincinnati (G-4301)
Relx Inc C 937 865-6800
Miamisburg (G-13853)
Relx Inc E 937 865-6800
Miamisburg (G-13851)
Reynolds Industries Group LLC E 614 864-6199
Blacklick (G-1704)
River Corp G 513 641-3355
Cincinnati (G-4348)
SC Solutions Inc G 614 317-7119
Grove City (G-10592)
Scott Fetzer Company F 440 892-3000
Westlake (G-20306)
Silver Maple Publications G 937 767-1259
Yellow Springs (G-20999)
Simon & Schuster Inc C 614 876-0371
Columbus (G-7623)
Spanish Lngage Productions Inc G 614 737-3424
Alexandria (G-481)
Sparkpeople Inc E 513 651-2062
Cincinnati (G-4439)
▲ St Media Group Intl Inc D 513 421-2050
Blue Ash (G-1873)
Swagg Productions2015llc F 614 815-1173
Reynoldsburg (G-16608)
Talbot Drake Incorporated G 216 441-5600
Cleveland (G-6293)
Teachers Publishing Group F 614 486-0631
Hilliard (G-10985)
Tgs International Inc E 330 893-2428
Millersburg (G-14268)
Vista Research Group LLC G 419 281-3927
Ashland (G-784)
Weaver Boos Consultants Inc F 419 933-5216
Willard (G-20404)
Wolters Kluwer Clinical Drug D 330 650-6506
Hudson (G-11210)
Woodburn Press LLC G 937 293-9245
Dayton (G-8764)
World Harvest Church Inc C 614 837-1990
Canal Winchester (G-2542)
▲ Zaner-Bloser Inc D 614 486-0221
Columbus (G-7786)

2732 Book Printing, Not Publishing

▼ 48 Hr Books Inc E 330 374-6917
Akron (G-13)
All Systems Colour Inc G 937 859-9701
Dayton (G-8144)
Amerilam Laminating G 440 235-4687
Cleveland (G-4797)
Bip Printing Solutions LLC F 216 832-5673
Beachwood (G-1259)
▼ C J Krehbiel Company C 513 271-6035
Cincinnati (G-3493)
D B Hess Company G 330 676-2006
Kent (G-11445)
Digicom Inc G 216 642-3838
Independence (G-11252)
▲ Golf Marketing Group Inc G 330 963-5155
Twinsburg (G-18950)
Hf Group LLC F 440 729-2445
Chesterland (G-3210)
Hf Group LLC A 440 729-9411
Chesterland (G-3211)
Hf Group LLC D 440 729-9411
Chesterland (G-3212)
Hubbard Company E 419 784-4455
Defiance (G-8794)
Indian River Industries G 740 965-4377
Sunbury (G-18064)
J & L Management Corporation G 440 205-1199
Mentor (G-13614)
Lsc Communications Us LLC C 419 935-0111
Willard (G-20396)
Morse Enterprises Inc G 513 229-3600
Mason (G-13066)
Naomi Kight G 937 278-0040
Dayton (G-8517)
Printex Incorporated F 740 773-0088
Chillicothe (G-3268)
Quebecor World Johnson Hardin A 614 326-0299
Cincinnati (G-4312)
RR Donnelley & Sons Company A 419 935-0111
Willard (G-20400)
Society of The Precious Blood E 419 925-4516
Celina (G-3018)

2741 Misc Publishing

360 Communications LLC G 330 329-2013
Akron (G-12)
Aaronyx Publishing G 419 747-2400
Mansfield (G-12555)
Adelphi Enterprises G 937 372-3791
Xenia (G-20934)
Albert Bickel G 513 530-5700
Cincinnati (G-3375)
Align Assess Achieve LLC G 614 505-6820
Columbus (G-6716)
All County Phone Directories G 419 865-2464
Holland (G-11044)
American City Bus Journals Inc E 513 337-9450
Cincinnati (G-3386)
American Guild of English Hand G 937 438-0085
Cincinnati (G-3389)
American Legal Publishing Corp E 513 421-4248
Cincinnati (G-3391)
Ameritech Publishing Inc D 614 895-6123
Columbus (G-6744)
Ameritech Publishing Inc E 330 896-6037
Uniontown (G-19075)
▲ Amos Press Inc C 937 498-2111
Sidney (G-17168)
Anadem Inc G 614 262-2539
Columbus (G-6751)
Anderson Publishing Co D 513 474-9305
Miamisburg (G-13783)
AT&T Corp A 614 223-8236
Columbus (G-6780)
B G News E 419 372-2601
Bowling Green (G-1969)
Bcmr Publications LLC G 740 441-7778
Gallipolis (G-10291)
Beaver Productions G 330 352-4603
Akron (G-86)
Beckenhorst Press Inc G 614 451-6461
Columbus (G-6817)
Becker Gallagher Legal Pubg F 513 677-5044
Cincinnati (G-3442)
Begashaw & Associates G 614 329-1630
Columbus (G-6820)
Berry Co F 877 742-3779
Hudson (G-11161)
Berry Company G 513 768-7800
Cincinnati (G-3448)
Blue Line Painting LLC G 440 951-2583
Cleveland (G-4919)
▲ Cartoon Books Inc G 614 224-4487
Columbus (G-6914)
Cbd Media Holdings LLC G 513 217-9483
Cincinnati (G-3507)
Ceja Publishing G 216 319-0268
Cleveland (G-5000)

Champion Directories Inc .... F 419 668-1280
Norwalk (G-15530)

Chasing Fireflies LLC .... G 206 574-4500
West Chester (G-19826)

Checkered Express Inc .... F 330 530-8169
Girard (G-10384)

Christian Blue Pages .... F 937 847-2583
Miamisburg (G-13792)

Cincinnati Bell Inc .... F 513 565-2210
Cincinnati (G-3541)

Clark Optimization LLC .... E 330 417-2164
Canton (G-2658)

Collegiate Directories Inc .... G 440 835-1172
Cleveland (G-5098)

▲ Competitive Press Inc .... G 330 289-1968
Copley (G-7842)

Computer Workshop Inc .... E 614 798-9505
Dublin (G-9065)

Computer Workshop Inc .... G 216 901-0106
Cleveland (G-5114)

Computercrafts .... G 614 231-7559
Columbus (G-6974)

Consumer Source Inc .... G 513 621-7300
Cincinnati (G-3605)

Copy Source Inc .... G 937 642-7140
Marysville (G-12939)

County Classifieds .... G 937 592-8847
Bellefontaine (G-1525)

Cox Publishing Hq .... G 937 225-2000
Dayton (G-8247)

D B Hess Company .... G 330 676-2006
Kent (G-11445)

▲ Darby Creek Publishing .... F 614 873-7958
Plain City (G-16332)

Deemsys Inc .... D 614 322-9928
Gahanna (G-10206)

Deward Publishing Co Ltd .... G 800 300-9778
Chillicothe (G-3236)

Dickman Directories Inc .... G 740 548-6130
Lewis Center (G-11894)

Diocesan Publications Inc Ohio .... E 614 718-9500
Dublin (G-9068)

Discover Publications .... G 614 785-1111
Columbus (G-7029)

Dodge Data & Analytics LLC .... G 513 345-8200
Cincinnati (G-3660)

Douthit Communications Inc .... E 419 621-2142
Sandusky (G-16959)

Douthit Communications Inc .... D 419 625-5825
Sandusky (G-16958)

Educational Publisher Inc .... G 614 485-0721
Columbus (G-7046)

Elbern Publications .... G 614 235-2643
Columbus (G-7051)

Elloras Cave Publishing Inc .... E 330 253-3521
Akron (G-163)

Elsevier Inc .... G 513 942-5070
West Chester (G-19855)

Evans Creative Group LLC .... G 614 657-9439
Columbus (G-7072)

Express Care .... F 740 266-2501
Steubenville (G-17694)

F and W Publications Inc .... G 513 531-2690
Cincinnati (G-3734)

Fax Medley Group Inc .... G 513 272-1932
Cincinnati (G-3743)

Fgm Media Inc .... G 440 376-0487
North Royalton (G-15419)

Fire Ball Press .... G 614 280-0100
Columbus (G-7087)

Fish Express .... G 513 661-3000
Cincinnati (G-3758)

Fleetmaster Express Inc .... C 419 425-0666
Findlay (G-9826)

Franklin Covey Co .... G 513 792-0099
Cincinnati (G-3779)

Free Bird Publications Ltd .... G 216 673-0229
Brunswick (G-2226)

General Bar Inc .... F 440 835-2000
Westlake (G-20271)

Gordon Bernard Co Inc .... E 513 248-7600
Milford (G-14146)

Gordon Bernard Company LLC .... E 513 248-7600
Milford (G-14147)

Gospel Trumpet Publishing .... G 937 548-9876
Greenville (G-10503)

Graphic Paper Products Corp .... D 937 325-5503
Springfield (G-17564)

Great Works Publishing Inc .... F 440 926-1100
Grafton (G-10428)

Guadalupe Publishing Inc .... G 614 450-2474
Etna (G-9556)

▲ Haines & Company Inc .... C 330 494-9111
North Canton (G-15237)

Haines Criss Cross .... G 330 494-9111
North Canton (G-15238)

Haines Publishing Inc .... D 330 494-9111
Canton (G-2722)

Hampton Publishing Company .... G 513 777-9543
Liberty Township (G-11964)

Hanover Publishing Co .... G 440 838-0911
Brecksville (G-2054)

Herff Jones LLC .... E 330 678-8138
Stow (G-17762)

Hibu Inc .... E 614 468-7900
Columbus (G-6650)

Igloo Press LLC .... G 614 787-5528
Worthington (G-20871)

Immigration Law Systems Inc .... G 614 252-3078
Columbus (G-7184)

Incorporated Trustees Gospel W ...... D 216 749-1428
Cleveland (G-5561)

Interweave Press LLC .... G 513 531-2690
Blue Ash (G-1817)

IPA Ltd .... F 614 523-3974
Columbus (G-7210)

Johnny Chin Insurance Agency .... G 513 777-8695
West Chester (G-20019)

Kaylee Ryan Publishing LLC .... G 937 446-3926
Lake Waynoka (G-11643)

Kennedy Catalogs LLC .... G 513 753-1518
Batavia (G-1196)

L & S Liette Express .... G 419 394-7077
Saint Marys (G-16842)

L M Berry and Company .... A 937 296-2121
Moraine (G-14500)

Lake Publishing Inc .... G 440 299-8500
Mentor (G-13628)

Lanier & Associates Inc .... G 216 391-7735
Cleveland (G-5681)

Latte Living .... G 440 364-2201
Cleveland (G-5685)

Lexisnexis Group .... C 937 865-6800
Miamisburg (G-13825)

Lily Tiger Press .... E 513 591-0817
Cincinnati (G-4025)

Local Insight Yellow Pages Inc .... C 330 650-7100
Hudson (G-11188)

▲ Lorenz Corporation .... D 937 228-6118
Dayton (G-8460)

LPC Publishing Co .... G 216 721-1800
Cleveland (G-5711)

Ludwig Music Publishing Co .... F 440 926-1100
Grafton (G-10433)

M Grafix LLC .... F 419 528-8665
Mansfield (G-12638)

M R I Education Foundation .... C 513 281-3400
Cincinnati (G-4043)

Marketing Essentials LLC .... F 419 629-0080
New Bremen (G-14789)

Massie Publishing LLC .... G 740 446-4543
Gallipolis (G-10305)

Masterpiece Publisher L P .... G 513 948-1000
Cincinnati (G-4065)

Matly Digital Solutions LLC .... G 513 860-3435
Fairfield (G-9681)

Matthew R Copp .... G 614 276-8959
Columbus (G-7325)

Mia Express Inc .... G 330 896-8180
Akron (G-297)

Mp Printing & Design Inc .... G 740 456-2045
Portsmouth (G-16445)

Network Communications Inc .... G 614 934-1919
Gahanna (G-10223)

New Century Sales LLC .... G 513 422-3631
Middletown (G-14070)

Nomis Publications Inc .... F 330 965-2380
Youngstown (G-21150)

North Bend Express .... G 513 481-4623
Cincinnati (G-4162)

Ogr Publishing Inc .... G 330 757-3020
Youngstown (G-21153)

Ohio Printed Products Inc .... G 330 659-0909
Richfield (G-16630)

Ohlinger Publishing Svcs Inc .... F 614 261-5360
Columbus (G-7438)

ONeil & Associates Inc .... C 937 865-0800
Miamisburg (G-13847)

Organized Lightning LLC .... G 407 965-2730
Blue Ash (G-1850)

P&M Publishing .... G 740 353-3300
Portsmouth (G-16447)

Paula and Julies Cookbooks LLC ...... G 614 863-1193
Columbus (G-7469)

Pauler Communications Inc .... G 440 243-1229
Richfield (G-16631)

Pedestrian Press .... G 419 244-6488
Toledo (G-18637)

Peebles Creative Group Inc .... G 614 487-2011
Dublin (G-9120)

Penton Business Media Inc .... A 216 696-7000
Cleveland (G-5990)

Permaguide .... E 330 456-8519
Canton (G-2811)

Phoenix Graphix Pubg Svcs LLC ...... G 740 587-3659
Granville (G-10465)

Pike County Paper Inc .... F 740 947-5522
Waverly (G-19717)

Pixslap Inc .... G 937 559-2671
Middletown (G-14076)

▲ Posterservice Incorporated .... G 513 577-7100
Cincinnati (G-4254)

Powerhouse Factories Inc .... F 513 719-6417
Cincinnati (G-4256)

Press Resource LLC .... G 614 794-9000
Westerville (G-20230)

Pressed Coffee Bar & Eatery .... G 330 746-8030
Youngstown (G-21177)

Promatch Solutions LLC .... G 937 299-0185
Springboro (G-17500)

Propress Inc .... F 216 631-8200
Cleveland (G-6056)

Province of St John The Baptis .... D 513 241-5615
Cincinnati (G-4301)

Prowrite Inc .... G 614 864-2004
Reynoldsburg (G-16601)

Psa Consulting Inc .... C 513 382-4315
Cincinnati (G-4302)

Publishing Group Ltd .... F 614 572-1240
Columbus (G-7526)

Puhd .... G 216 244-3336
Bedford (G-1455)

Purebred Publishing Inc .... G 614 339-5393
Columbus (G-7527)

Quadriga Americas LLC .... G 614 890-6090
Westerville (G-20180)

Quaker Express Stamping Inc .... F 330 332-9266
Salem (G-16921)

Questline Inc .... E 614 255-3166
Dublin (G-9129)

Rawhide Software Inc .... G 419 878-0857
Bowling Green (G-2010)

▼ Rcl Publishing Group LLC .... G 972 390-6400
Cincinnati (G-4333)

Recob Great Lakes Express Inc .... G 216 265-7940
Cleveland (G-6093)

Research and Development Group ..... G 614 261-0454
Columbus (G-7556)

Resource Development Co LLC .... G 440 617-9087
Westlake (G-20302)

Robs Creative Screen Printing .... G 740 264-6383
Wintersville (G-20713)

RR Donnelley & Sons Company .... A 419 935-0111
Willard (G-20400)

▲ S J T Enterprises Inc .... E 440 617-1100
Westlake (G-20305)

S&P Global Inc .... E 216 749-9779
Cleveland (G-6152)

Samhain Publishing Ltd (llc) .... G 513 453-4688
Cincinnati (G-4378)

SC Solutions Inc .... G 614 317-7119
Grove City (G-10592)

Scott Fetzer Company .... F 440 892-3000
Westlake (G-20306)

Scrambl-Gram Inc .... F 419 635-2321
Port Clinton (G-16414)

Sea Bird Publications Inc .... G 513 869-2200
Fairfield (G-9715)

See Ya There Inc .... G 614 856-9037
Millersport (G-14298)

Sei Inc .... F 513 942-6170
West Chester (G-20048)

Senior Impact Publication .... F 513 791-8800
Cincinnati (G-4404)

Sentinel USA Inc .... F 740 345-6412
Newark (G-15052)

Sevell + Sevell Inc .... G 614 341-9700
Columbus (G-7611)

Shoppers Compass .... G 419 947-9234
Mount Gilead (G-14567)

Simon & Schuster Inc ... C ... 614 876-0371
Columbus *(G-7623)*
Singer Press ... G ... 216 595-9400
Beachwood *(G-1299)*
Snap-On Business Solutions ... B ... 330 659-1600
Richfield *(G-16639)*
Snook Advertising Al Publisher ... F ... 614 866-3333
Reynoldsburg *(G-16606)*
Specialty Gas Publishing Inc ... G ... 216 226-3796
Cleveland *(G-6224)*
Star Brite Express Car WA ... G ... 330 674-0062
Millersburg *(G-14264)*
Starbringer Media Group Ltd ... G ... 440 871-5448
Westlake *(G-20312)*
Suburban Communications Inc ... E ... 440 632-0130
Middlefield *(G-13993)*
Success Pro Publications ... G ... 614 497-5674
Columbus *(G-7666)*
Supermedia LLC ... G ... 614 216-6566
Westerville *(G-20190)*
Terewell Inc ... G ... 216 334-6897
Cleveland *(G-6306)*
Thickemz Entertainment LLC ... G ... 404 399-4255
Cuyahoga Falls *(G-8056)*
Thunder Dreamer Publishing ... G ... 419 424-2004
Findlay *(G-9903)*
Tiny Lion Music Groups ... G ... 419 874-7353
Perrysburg *(G-16160)*
Trogdon Publishing Inc ... E ... 330 721-7678
Medina *(G-13491)*
Trogdon Publishing Inc ... G ... 330 620-2407
Powell *(G-16486)*
▲ **Universal Drect Flfllment Corp** ... C ... 330 650-5000
Hudson *(G-11206)*
User Friendly Phone Book LLC ... E ... 216 674-6500
Independence *(G-11281)*
Van-Griner LLC ... G ... 419 733-7951
Cincinnati *(G-4555)*
Visual Education Association ... G ... 937 325-5503
Springfield *(G-17673)*
Walter H Drane Co Inc ... G ... 216 514-1022
Beachwood *(G-1305)*
Willis Music Company ... F ... 513 671-3288
Cincinnati *(G-4597)*
Wizard Publications Inc ... F ... 808 821-1214
Lancaster *(G-11762)*
Woodburn Press LLC ... G ... 937 293-9245
Dayton *(G-8764)*
▲ **Zoo Publishing Inc** ... E ... 513 824-8297
Blue Ash *(G-1905)*

2752 Commercial Printing: Lithographic

1455 Group LLC ... G ... 330 494-9074
Canton *(G-2583)*
21st Century Printers Inc ... G ... 513 771-4150
Cincinnati *(G-3322)*
4 Over LLC ... F ... 937 610-0629
Dayton *(G-8123)*
A & D Printing Co ... G ... 440 975-8001
Willoughby *(G-20421)*
A F Krainz Co ... G ... 216 431-4341
Cleveland *(G-4671)*
A Grade Notes Inc ... G ... 614 766-9999
Dublin *(G-9034)*
A-1 Printing Inc ... F ... 419 562-3111
Bucyrus *(G-2330)*
A-A Blueprint Co Inc ... E ... 330 794-8803
Akron *(G-22)*
Academy Graphic Comm Inc ... E ... 216 661-2550
Cleveland *(G-4689)*
Acme Duplicating Co ... G ... 216 241-1241
Cleveland *(G-4692)*
Acme Printing Co Inc ... G ... 419 626-4426
Sandusky *(G-16944)*
Action Printing & Photography ... G ... 419 332-9615
Fremont *(G-10123)*
Action Printing Inc ... G ... 330 963-7772
Twinsburg *(G-18893)*
▲ **Activities Press Inc** ... E ... 440 953-1200
Mentor *(G-13509)*
Adcraft Decals Inc ... E ... 216 524-2934
Cleveland *(G-4702)*
Adkins & Co Inc ... G ... 216 521-6323
Cleveland *(G-4705)*
Admark Printing Inc ... G ... 937 833-5111
Brookville *(G-2173)*
Admiral Products Company Inc ... E ... 216 671-0600
Cleveland *(G-4706)*
Advanatage Print Solut ... G ... 614 519-2392
Columbus *(G-6695)*
Advanced Graphics of Dayton ... G ... 937 228-2221
Dayton *(G-8138)*
Advanced Marking Systems Inc ... G ... 330 792-8239
Youngstown *(G-21017)*
Advantage Printing Inc ... G ... 614 272-8259
Columbus *(G-6698)*
Aero Printing Inc ... G ... 419 695-2931
Delphos *(G-8899)*
AGS Custom Graphics Inc ... D ... 330 963-7770
Macedonia *(G-12433)*
◆ **Air Waves Inc** ... C ... 740 548-1200
Lewis Center *(G-11883)*
Akron Litho-Print Company Inc ... F ... 330 434-3145
Akron *(G-47)*
Akron Thermography Inc ... E ... 330 896-9712
Akron *(G-59)*
▲ **Alberts Screen Print Inc** ... C ... 330 753-7559
Norton *(G-15505)*
All American Screen Printing ... G ... 419 475-0696
Toledo *(G-18327)*
All Print Ltd ... F ... 440 349-6868
Solon *(G-17252)*
All Systems Colour Inc ... G ... 937 859-9701
Dayton *(G-8144)*
Allegra Print & Imaging ... F ... 419 427-8095
Findlay *(G-9789)*
Allegra Printing & Imaging LLC ... G ... 440 449-6989
Westlake *(G-20248)*
Allen Graphics Inc ... G ... 440 349-4100
Solon *(G-17253)*
Allen Kenard Printing Inc ... F ... 440 323-7405
Elyria *(G-9369)*
Allen Press ... G ... 614 891-4413
Westerville *(G-20198)*
Alliance Printing & Publishing ... F ... 513 422-7611
Middletown *(G-14019)*
Alliance Publishing Co Inc ... C ... 330 453-1304
Alliance *(G-495)*
Alpha Print Specialties ... G ... 440 282-1150
Lorain *(G-12231)*
AlphaGraphics 507 Inc ... G ... 440 878-9700
Strongsville *(G-17886)*
Alt Control Print ... G ... 419 841-2467
Toledo *(G-18333)*
Alvito Custom Imprints ... G ... 614 846-8986
Worthington *(G-20856)*
American Colorscans Inc ... E ... 614 895-0233
Columbus *(G-6732)*
American Inks and Coatings Co ... F ... 513 552-7200
Fairfield *(G-9641)*
American Printing Inc ... F ... 330 630-1121
Akron *(G-68)*
Anderson Graphics Inc ... E ... 330 745-2165
Barberton *(G-1098)*
Anderson Printing & Supply LLC ... G ... 614 891-1100
Westerville *(G-20199)*
Angel Prtg & Reproduction Co ... F ... 216 631-5225
Cleveland *(G-4812)*
▲ **Angell-Demmel North Amer Corp** ... D ... 937 461-5800
Dayton *(G-8158)*
◆ **Angstrom Graphics Inc** ... C ... 216 271-5300
Cleveland *(G-4814)*
Angstrom Graphics Inc Midwest ... B ... 216 271-5300
Cleveland *(G-4815)*
◆ **Angstrom Graphics Southeast** ... G ... 216 271-5300
Cleveland *(G-4816)*
Ann Printing & Promotions ... G ... 330 399-6564
Warren *(G-19524)*
Anthony Business Forms Inc ... F ... 937 253-0072
Dayton *(G-8096)*
Aran Inc ... G ... 216 464-1508
Cleveland *(G-4821)*
Arens Corporation ... F ... 937 473-2028
Covington *(G-7918)*
Arens Corporation ... G ... 937 473-2028
Covington *(G-7919)*
Armstrong S Printing Ex LLC ... G ... 937 276-7794
Dayton *(G-8164)*
Arnold Printing Inc ... G ... 330 494-1191
Canton *(G-2606)*
Art Printing Co Inc ... G ... 419 281-4371
Ashland *(G-705)*
Art Pro Graphics ... G ... 216 236-6465
Seven Hills *(G-17060)*
Ashland Inc Valvoline Instant ... G ... 330 653-3926
Hudson *(G-11159)*
Atkinson Printing Inc ... G ... 330 669-3515
Wooster *(G-20743)*
Avon Lake Printing ... G ... 440 933-2078
Avon Lake *(G-1024)*
Avondale Printing Inc ... G ... 330 477-1180
Canton *(G-2610)*
B & B Printing Graphics Inc ... F ... 419 893-7068
Maumee *(G-13228)*
B2 Incorporated ... G ... 330 244-9510
North Canton *(G-15221)*
Baise Enterprises Inc ... G ... 614 444-3171
Columbus *(G-6801)*
Bang Printing of Ohio Inc ... F ... 800 678-1222
Kent *(G-11432)*
Bansal Enterprises Inc ... F ... 330 633-9355
Akron *(G-84)*
Barberton Magic Press Printing ... G ... 330 753-9578
Barberton *(G-1107)*
Barberton Printcraft ... G ... 330 848-3000
Barberton *(G-1109)*
Barnhart Printing Corp ... F ... 330 456-2279
Canton *(G-2616)*
Baseline Printing Inc ... G ... 330 369-3204
Warren *(G-19526)*
Bates Printing Inc ... F ... 330 833-5830
Massillon *(G-13114)*
Bay Business Forms Inc ... F ... 937 322-3000
Springfield *(G-17521)*
Bay Village Printing Inc ... G ... 440 892-2005
Cleveland *(G-4897)*
BCT Alarm Services Inc ... G ... 440 669-8153
Amherst *(G-591)*
Beach Company ... F ... 740 622-0905
Coshocton *(G-7882)*
Beckman Xmo ... F ... 614 864-3305
Columbus *(G-6818)*
Belle Printing ... G ... 937 592-5161
Bellefontaine *(G-1521)*
Bemis Company Inc ... E ... 330 923-5281
Akron *(G-87)*
Berea Printing Company ... G ... 440 243-1080
Berea *(G-1605)*
Bethart Enterprises Inc ... F ... 513 863-6161
Hamilton *(G-10675)*
Betley Printing Co ... G ... 216 206-5600
Cleveland *(G-4910)*
Bill Wyatt Inc ... G ... 330 535-1113
Mentor *(G-13535)*
Bindery & Spc Pressworks Inc ... D ... 614 873-4623
Plain City *(G-16326)*
Bloch Printing Company ... G ... 330 576-6760
Copley *(G-7840)*
Blt Inc ... F ... 513 631-5050
Norwood *(G-15571)*
Blue Crescent Enterprises Inc ... G ... 440 878-9700
Strongsville *(G-17897)*
Blueserv Reprograhics LLC ... G ... 937 426-6410
Beavercreek *(G-1370)*
Bock & Pierce Enterprises ... G ... 513 474-9500
Cincinnati *(G-3455)*
Bodnar Printing Co Inc ... F ... 440 277-8295
Lorain *(G-12234)*
Boehm Inc ... E ... 614 875-9010
Grove City *(G-10546)*
Boehr Print ... G ... 419 358-1350
Findlay *(G-9799)*
Bogart Imprinting ... G ... 419 659-2840
Columbus Grove *(G-7790)*
Bohlender Engraving Company ... F ... 513 621-4095
Cincinnati *(G-3457)*
Boldman Printing LLC ... G ... 937 653-3431
Urbana *(G-19148)*
Bookmasters Inc ... C ... 419 281-1802
Ashland *(G-713)*
▲ **Bottomline Ink Corporation** ... E ... 419 897-8000
Perrysburg *(G-16068)*
Box King LLC ... G ... 937 322-8117
Springfield *(G-17524)*
Bpm Realty Inc ... E ... 614 221-6811
Columbus *(G-6852)*
Bramkamp Printing Company Inc ... E ... 513 241-1865
Blue Ash *(G-1754)*
Brandon Screen Printing ... F ... 419 229-9837
Lima *(G-11996)*
Brent Carter Enterprises Inc ... G ... 513 731-1440
Cincinnati *(G-3468)*
Brentwood Printing & Sty ... G ... 513 522-2679
Cincinnati *(G-3469)*
Bricolage Inc ... G ... 614 853-6789
Grove City *(G-10547)*
Broadway Offset Printing Co ... F ... 216 391-3800
Cleveland *(G-4932)*
Brooke Printers Inc ... G ... 614 235-6800
Lancaster *(G-11692)*

Brookville Star.....G..... 937 833-2545
Brookville *(G-2177)*
Brothers Printing Co Inc.....F..... 216 621-6050
Cleveland *(G-4938)*
Buckeye Business Forms Inc.....G..... 614 882-1890
Westerville *(G-20141)*
Buckeye Cstm Screen Print EMB.....F..... 614 237-0196
Columbus *(G-6872)*
Bucyrus Graphics Inc.....F..... 419 562-2906
Bucyrus *(G-2333)*
Busson Digital Printing Inc.....E..... 330 753-8373
Wadsworth *(G-19396)*
C Massouh Printing Co Inc.....F..... 330 408-7330
Canal Fulton *(G-2500)*
C Massouh Printing Co Inc.....G..... 330 832-6334
Massillon *(G-13116)*
Canton Graphic Arts Service.....G..... 330 456-9868
Canton *(G-2641)*
Capehart Enterprises LLC.....F..... 614 769-7746
Columbus *(G-6895)*
Capozzolo Printers Inc.....G..... 513 542-7874
Cincinnati *(G-3496)*
Carbonless On Demandcom.....F..... 330 837-8611
Massillon *(G-13119)*
Cardinal Printing Inc.....G..... 330 773-7300
Akron *(G-111)*
Carl Graphics Company.....G..... 740 382-6583
Marion *(G-12861)*
Cats Printing Inc.....G..... 216 381-8181
Cleveland *(G-4995)*
Central Ohio Printing Corp.....D..... 740 852-1616
London *(G-12203)*
Century Graphics Inc.....E..... 614 895-7698
Westerville *(G-20142)*
▼ **Century Marketing Corporation**.....C..... 419 354-2591
Bowling Green *(G-1978)*
Characters Inc.....G..... 937 335-1976
Troy *(G-18808)*
Charger Press Inc.....F..... 513 542-3113
Miamitown *(G-13886)*
Child Evngelism Fellowship Inc.....E..... 440 218-4982
Cuyahoga Falls *(G-7979)*
Child Evngelism Fellowship Inc.....E..... 419 756-7799
Mansfield *(G-12579)*
Cincinnati Print Solutions LLC.....G..... 513 943-9500
Amelia *(G-570)*
Cincinnati Printers Co Inc.....F..... 513 860-9053
West Chester *(G-19832)*
City of Cleveland.....F..... 216 664-3013
Cleveland *(G-5035)*
City Printing Co Inc.....E..... 330 747-5691
Youngstown *(G-21051)*
Clark Associates Inc.....G..... 419 334-3838
Fremont *(G-10138)*
Cleveland Letter Service Inc.....E..... 216 781-8300
Chagrin Falls *(G-3052)*
Cleveland Offset Press Co Inc.....G..... 440 845-9137
Cleveland *(G-5071)*
Clints Printing Inc.....G..... 937 426-2771
Beavercreek *(G-1373)*
Cnb LLC.....G..... 419 528-3109
Ontario *(G-15685)*
Cns Inc.....G..... 513 631-7073
Cincinnati *(G-3593)*
Cold Duck Screen Prtg & EMB Co.....G..... 330 426-1900
East Palestine *(G-9231)*
Color Bar Printing Centers Inc.....E..... 216 595-3939
Cleveland *(G-5099)*
Coloramic Process Inc.....F..... 440 275-1199
Austinburg *(G-959)*
Commercial Prtg of Greenvill.....G..... 937 548-3835
Greenville *(G-10494)*
Concept Printing of Wauseon.....G..... 419 335-6627
Wauseon *(G-19674)*
▲ **Consoldated Graphics Group Inc**.....C..... 216 881-9191
Cleveland *(G-5116)*
Copley Ohio Newspapers Inc.....C..... 330 364-5577
New Philadelphia *(G-14892)*
Copley Ohio Newspapers Inc.....D..... 330 833-2631
Massillon *(G-13121)*
Copy Right of Ohio LLC.....G..... 614 431-1303
Plain City *(G-16328)*
Cornerstone Industries Lcc.....G..... 513 871-4546
West Chester *(G-19845)*
Cornerstone Printing Inc.....G..... 614 861-2138
Reynoldsburg *(G-16585)*
Corporate Dcment Solutions Inc.....F..... 513 595-8200
Cincinnati *(G-3613)*
COS Blueprint Inc.....F..... 330 376-0022
Akron *(G-130)*
County Classifieds.....G..... 937 592-8847
Bellefontaine *(G-1525)*
Covap Inc.....F..... 513 793-1855
Blue Ash *(G-1769)*
Cowgill Printing Co.....G..... 216 741-2076
Parma *(G-15955)*
Cox Printing Co.....G..... 937 382-2312
Wilmington *(G-20661)*
Cpmm Services Group Inc.....F..... 614 447-0165
Columbus *(G-6996)*
Crabar/Gbf Inc.....E..... 419 269-1720
Toledo *(G-18415)*
Crabar/Gbf Inc.....D..... 419 943-2141
Leipsic *(G-11867)*
Crabar/Gbf Inc.....E..... 740 622-0222
Coshocton *(G-7887)*
Crabar/Gbf Inc.....G..... 419 943-2141
Leipsic *(G-11868)*
Crain-Tharp Printing Inc.....G..... 740 345-9823
Newark *(G-14998)*
Creative Impressions Inc.....F..... 937 435-5296
Dayton *(G-8250)*
Crest Craft Company.....F..... 513 271-4858
Blue Ash *(G-1770)*
Crown Printing Inc.....G..... 740 477-2511
Circleville *(G-4626)*
Culaine Inc.....G..... 419 345-4984
Toledo *(G-18417)*
Curless Printing Company.....E..... 937 783-2403
Blanchester *(G-1712)*
Curry Copy Center of Lakewood.....G..... 216 521-5775
Lakewood *(G-11661)*
Curv Imaging LLC.....G..... 614 890-2878
Westerville *(G-20207)*
Customer Printing Inc.....F..... 330 629-8676
Youngstown *(G-21061)*
Customer Service Systems Inc.....G..... 330 677-2877
Kent *(G-11442)*
Cwh Graphics LLC.....G..... 866 241-8515
Bedford Heights *(G-1482)*
D & J Printing Inc.....D..... 330 678-5868
Kent *(G-11443)*
D & S Crtive Cmmunications Inc.....D..... 419 524-6699
Mansfield *(G-12591)*
D M J F Inc.....G..... 440 845-1155
Cleveland *(G-5162)*
Daily Gazette.....E..... 937 372-4444
Xenia *(G-20945)*
▲ **Dana Graphics Inc**.....G..... 513 351-4400
Cincinnati *(G-3638)*
Danner Press Corp.....G..... 330 454-5692
Canton *(G-2677)*
Dansizen Printing Co Inc.....G..... 330 966-4962
North Canton *(G-15226)*
Daubenmires Printing.....G..... 513 425-7223
Middletown *(G-14036)*
Daves Printing.....G..... 513 221-0182
Cincinnati *(G-3641)*
David A and Mary A Mathis.....G..... 330 837-8611
Massillon *(G-13124)*
David Butler Tax Service.....G..... 419 626-8086
Sandusky *(G-16956)*
Debandale Printing Inc.....G..... 330 725-5122
Medina *(G-13401)*
Deerfield Ventures Inc.....G..... 614 875-0688
Grove City *(G-10553)*
Delores E OBeirn.....G..... 440 582-3610
Cleveland *(G-5182)*
Delphos Herald Inc.....D..... 419 695-0015
Delphos *(G-8904)*
Delphos Herald Inc.....D..... 419 695-0015
Delphos *(G-8905)*
Deshea Printing Company.....G..... 330 336-7601
Wadsworth *(G-19402)*
Dewitt Group Inc.....F..... 614 847-5919
Columbus *(G-7024)*
Digital Color Intl LLC.....E..... 330 762-6959
Akron *(G-152)*
Directconnectgroup Ltd.....A..... 216 281-2866
Cleveland *(G-5196)*
Dispatch Printing Company.....E..... 614 885-6020
Columbus *(G-7030)*
Distributor Graphics Inc.....G..... 440 260-0024
Cleveland *(G-5198)*
Dixie Flyer & Printing Co.....G..... 937 687-0088
New Lebanon *(G-14841)*
Dla Document Services.....G..... 216 522-3535
Cleveland *(G-5201)*
Dla Document Services.....E..... 937 257-6014
Dayton *(G-8104)*
Docmann Printing & Assoc Inc.....G..... 440 975-1775
Willoughby *(G-20474)*
Doll Inc.....G..... 419 586-7880
Celina *(G-2992)*
Domicone Printing Inc.....G..... 937 878-3080
Fairborn *(G-9619)*
Donnelley Financial LLC.....F..... 216 621-8384
Cleveland *(G-5208)*
Dorothy Crooker.....G..... 513 385-0888
Cincinnati *(G-3665)*
Double b Printing LLC.....G..... 740 593-7393
Athens *(G-863)*
Doug Smith.....G..... 740 345-1398
Newark *(G-15000)*
Douglas Michalske.....G..... 216 631-0567
Cleveland *(G-5210)*
DOV Graphics Inc.....E..... 513 241-5150
Cincinnati *(G-3668)*
Dove Graphics Inc.....G..... 440 238-1800
Cleveland *(G-5212)*
Downtown Print Shop.....G..... 419 242-9164
Toledo *(G-18443)*
Dresden Specialties Inc.....G..... 740 452-7100
Zanesville *(G-21302)*
Dresden Specialties Inc.....G..... 740 754-2451
Dresden *(G-9032)*
Dsk Imaging LLC.....F..... 513 554-1797
Blue Ash *(G-1777)*
Duke Graphics Inc.....E..... 440 946-0606
Willoughby *(G-20475)*
Duncan Press Corporation.....E..... 330 477-4529
Canton *(G-2694)*
Dupli-Systems Inc.....C..... 440 234-9415
Strongsville *(G-17913)*
Durbin Minuteman Press.....G..... 513 791-9171
Blue Ash *(G-1778)*
◆ **Dynamic Design & Systems Inc**.....G..... 440 708-1010
Chagrin Falls *(G-3085)*
E L Frueh Inc.....F..... 419 222-9741
Lima *(G-12007)*
E T & K Inc.....G..... 440 777-7375
North Olmsted *(G-15331)*
E T & K Inc.....G..... 440 888-4780
Cleveland *(G-5234)*
Eagle Advertising.....G..... 216 881-0800
Cleveland *(G-5236)*
Eagle Printing & Graphics LLC.....G..... 937 773-7900
Piqua *(G-16263)*
Earl D Arnold Printing Company.....E..... 513 533-6900
Cincinnati *(G-3685)*
Easterdays Printing Center.....G..... 330 726-1182
Youngstown *(G-21073)*
▲ **Echographics Inc**.....G..... 440 846-2330
North Ridgeville *(G-15371)*
Edwards Electrical & Mech.....E..... 614 485-2003
Columbus *(G-7047)*
Eg Enterprise Services Inc.....F..... 216 431-3300
Cleveland *(G-5260)*
Elyria Copy Center Inc.....G..... 440 323-4145
Elyria *(G-9412)*
Empire Printing Inc.....G..... 513 242-3900
Cincinnati *(G-3700)*
Emta Inc.....G..... 440 734-6464
North Olmsted *(G-15332)*
Engler Printing Co.....G..... 419 332-2181
Fremont *(G-10144)*
Enlarging Arts Inc.....G..... 330 434-3433
Akron *(G-168)*
Enquirer Printing Co Inc.....F..... 513 241-1956
Cincinnati *(G-3707)*
Enquirer Printing Company.....G..... 513 241-1956
Cincinnati *(G-3708)*
Envoi Design Inc.....G..... 513 651-4229
Cincinnati *(G-3711)*
▲ **Etched Metal Company**.....E..... 440 248-0240
Solon *(G-17290)*
Eugene Stewart.....G..... 937 898-1117
Dayton *(G-8333)*
▲ **Eurostampa North America Inc**.....D..... 513 821-2275
Cincinnati *(G-3721)*
Eveready Printing Inc.....E..... 216 587-2389
Cleveland *(G-5307)*
Evolution Crtive Solutions Inc.....E..... 513 681-4450
Cincinnati *(G-3724)*
Excelsior Printing Co.....G..... 740 927-2934
Pataskala *(G-15970)*
Exchange Printing Company.....G..... 330 773-7842
Akron *(G-173)*
Exec-U-Print Inc.....G..... 440 333-6484
Rocky River *(G-16698)*

F P C Printing Inc G 937 743-8136
Franklin *(G-10020)*
Fair Publishing House Inc E 419 668-3746
Norwalk *(G-15540)*
Fairchild Printing Co G 216 641-4192
Cleveland *(G-5319)*
Far Corner G 330 767-3734
Navarre *(G-14712)*
Fedex Corporation G 740 687-0334
Lancaster *(G-11716)*
Fedex Office & Print Svcs Inc G 513 777-1079
West Chester *(G-19862)*
Fedex Office & Print Svcs Inc G 614 356-1639
Dublin *(G-9076)*
Fedex Office & Print Svcs Inc G 419 841-2756
Toledo *(G-18465)*
Fedex Office & Print Svcs Inc G 614 478-1180
Columbus *(G-7079)*
Fedex Office & Print Svcs Inc G 513 754-1482
Mason *(G-13021)*
Fedex Office & Print Svcs Inc G 440 605-0191
Richmond Heights *(G-16653)*
Fedex Office & Print Svcs Inc F 330 376-6002
Akron *(G-183)*
Fedex Office & Print Svcs Inc E 419 866-5464
Toledo *(G-18466)*
▲ **Fine Line Graphics Corp** C 614 486-0276
Columbus *(G-7085)*
Fine Print LLC G 419 702-7087
Lakeside Marblehead *(G-11648)*
Finn Graphics Inc E 513 941-6161
Cincinnati *(G-3756)*
Fleet Graphics Inc G 937 252-2552
Dayton *(G-8345)*
Flemish Investments Inc G 419 625-4073
Sandusky *(G-16967)*
Flowers Print Inc G 937 429-3823
Beavercreek *(G-1338)*
Folks Creative Printers Inc E 740 383-6326
Marion *(G-12865)*
Follow Print Club On Facebook G 216 707-2579
Cleveland *(G-5365)*
Foote Printing Company F 216 431-1757
Cleveland *(G-5367)*
Fortec Litho Central LLC G 330 463-1265
Streetsboro *(G-17853)*
Fourjays Inc G 216 741-8258
Parma *(G-15958)*
Frame Warehouse G 614 861-4582
Reynoldsburg *(G-16591)*
Franchise Services Inc G 513 731-1440
Cincinnati *(G-3777)*
Frank J Prucha & Associates G 216 642-3838
Cleveland *(G-5378)*
Frankies Graphics Inc G 440 979-0824
Westlake *(G-20268)*
Franklins Printing Company F 740 452-6375
Zanesville *(G-21311)*
Fremont Quick Print G 419 334-8808
Helena *(G-10895)*
Friends Service Co Inc F 800 427-1704
Dayton *(G-8352)*
Friends Service Co Inc G 800 427-1704
Kent *(G-11459)*
Friends Service Co Inc D 419 427-1704
Findlay *(G-9828)*
Frisby Printing Company G 330 665-4565
Fairlawn *(G-9750)*
Fx Digital Media Inc E 216 241-4040
Cleveland *(G-5387)*
G A Spring Advertising G 330 343-9030
Dover *(G-8986)*
G S Link & Associates G 513 722-2457
Goshen *(G-10415)*
▲ **Galaxy Balloons Incorporated** C 216 476-3360
Cleveland *(G-5392)*
Galley Printing Inc E 330 220-5577
Brunswick *(G-2228)*
Ganger Enterprises Inc G 614 776-3985
Westerville *(G-20154)*
Gannett Co Inc C 740 773-2111
Chillicothe *(G-3240)*
Gannett Co Inc E 740 295-3435
Coshocton *(G-7892)*
Gannett Stllite Info Ntwrk LLC D 419 334-1012
Fremont *(G-10152)*
Gaspar Services LLC G 330 467-8292
Macedonia *(G-12455)*
Gazette Publishing Company E 419 483-4190
Oberlin *(G-15640)*
GBS Corp C 330 863-1828
Malvern *(G-12545)*
Genesis Quality Printing Inc G 440 975-5700
Mentor *(G-13592)*
Genie Repros Inc E 216 965-0213
Cleveland *(G-5422)*
George D Kanaan & Associates G 440 243-6410
Berea *(G-1617)*
Gerald L Hermann Co Inc F 513 661-1818
Cincinnati *(G-3822)*
Gergel-Kellem Company Inc D 216 398-2000
Cleveland *(G-5425)*
Geygan Enterprises Inc F 513 932-4222
Lebanon *(G-11803)*
Globus Printing & Packg Co Inc D 419 628-2381
Minster *(G-14354)*
Go Calendars G 513 755-1555
Liberty Township *(G-11962)*
Go2 Partners Inc E 330 650-5300
Twinsburg *(G-18949)*
Golden Graphics Ltd F 419 673-6260
Kenton *(G-11548)*
▲ **Golf Marketing Group Inc** G 330 963-5155
Twinsburg *(G-18950)*
Gordon Bernard Co Inc E 513 248-7600
Milford *(G-14146)*
Gordon Bernard Company LLC E 513 248-7600
Milford *(G-14147)*
Gordons Graphics Inc G 330 863-2322
Malvern *(G-12546)*
Grant John G 937 298-0633
Dayton *(G-8376)*
Graphic Expressions Signs G 330 422-7446
Streetsboro *(G-17856)*
Graphic Paper Products Corp D 937 325-5503
Springfield *(G-17564)*
Graphic Paper Products Corp G 937 322-7711
Springfield *(G-17565)*
Graphic Solutions Company F 513 484-3067
Cincinnati *(G-3845)*
Graphic Touch Inc G 330 337-3341
Salem *(G-16896)*
Graphic TS G 614 836-2613
Groveport *(G-10624)*
Graphicsource Inc G 440 248-9200
Solon *(G-17302)*
Graphtech Communications Inc F 216 676-1020
Cleveland *(G-5447)*
Grayson Graphics Inc G 740 927-7080
Pataskala *(G-15971)*
Great Lakes Engraving Corp G 419 867-1607
Maumee *(G-13262)*
▲ **Great Lakes Integrated Inc** D 216 651-1500
Cleveland *(G-5452)*
Great Lakes Integrated Inc E 440 892-7760
Avon Lake *(G-1030)*
Great Lakes Lithograph F 216 651-1500
Cleveland *(G-5453)*
Great Lakes Printing Inc D 440 993-8781
Ashtabula *(G-810)*
Green Leaf Printing and Design G 937 222-3634
Dayton *(G-8378)*
Greenwood Printing & Graphics F 419 727-3275
Toledo *(G-18487)*
Greg Blume G 740 574-2308
Wheelersburg *(G-20332)*
Gregg Macmillan G 513 248-2121
Milford *(G-14148)*
Gtlp Holdings LLC E 513 489-6700
Cincinnati *(G-3857)*
H&An LLC G 740 435-0200
Cambridge *(G-2460)*
▲ **Haines & Company Inc** C 330 494-9111
North Canton *(G-15237)*
▲ **Haman Enterprises Inc** F 614 888-7574
Worthington *(G-20869)*
Harbro LLC G 810 229-4755
Lakewood *(G-11666)*
Harper Engraving & Printing Co D 614 276-0700
Columbus *(G-7144)*
Harris & Company Inc F 330 332-4127
Salem *(G-16899)*
Harris Hawk G 800 459-4295
Mason *(G-13036)*
Hartco Printing Company G 614 761-1292
Dublin *(G-9083)*
Hartman Printing Co G 419 946-2854
Mount Gilead *(G-14561)*
Hartmann Incorporated F 513 276-7318
Blue Ash *(G-1805)*
Hawks & Associates Inc E 513 752-4311
Cincinnati *(G-3308)*
Headlee Enterprises Ltd G 614 785-0011
Columbus *(G-6649)*
Hecks Direct Mail & Prtg Svc E 419 661-6028
Toledo *(G-18503)*
Hecks Direct Mail & Prtg Svc E 419 697-3505
Toledo *(G-18502)*
Heitkamp & Kremer Printing G 419 925-4121
Celina *(G-3001)*
Henry Bussman G 614 224-0417
Columbus *(G-7150)*
Herald Inc E 419 492-2133
New Washington *(G-14960)*
Herff Jones Inc G 740 821-3109
Portsmouth *(G-16438)*
Heritage Press Inc E 419 289-9209
Ashland *(G-738)*
Heskamp Printing Co Inc G 513 871-6770
Cincinnati *(G-3881)*
Hilleary-Whitaker Inc G 614 766-4694
Columbus *(G-7157)*
Hkm Drect Mkt Cmmnications Inc C 216 651-9500
Cleveland *(G-5516)*
Hollys Custom Print Inc E 740 928-2697
Hebron *(G-10871)*
Holmes Printing Solutions LLC G 330 234-9699
Fredericksburg *(G-10087)*
Holmes W & Sons Printing F 937 325-1509
Springfield *(G-17574)*
Homewood Press Inc E 419 478-0695
Toledo *(G-18510)*
Horizon Ohio Publications Inc E 419 738-2128
Wapakoneta *(G-19489)*
Hoster Graphics Company Inc F 614 299-9770
Columbus *(G-7168)*
HOT Graphic Services Inc E 419 242-7000
Northwood *(G-15483)*
Howland Printing Inc G 330 637-8255
Cortland *(G-7869)*
Hubbard Company E 419 784-4455
Defiance *(G-8794)*
Hubbard Publishing Co E 937 592-3060
Bellefontaine *(G-1533)*
Hudson Printing of Medina LLC G 330 591-4800
Medina *(G-13424)*
Icandi Graphics LLC G 330 723-8337
Medina *(G-13425)*
Ideas & Ad Ventures Inc G 513 542-7154
Cincinnati *(G-3909)*
Image Concepts Inc F 216 524-9000
Cleveland *(G-5550)*
Image Print Inc G 614 430-8470
Columbus *(G-7182)*
◆ **In-Touch Corp** G 440 268-0881
Cleveland *(G-5559)*
Info-Graphics Inc G 440 498-1640
Solon *(G-17315)*
Ink Inc G 330 875-4789
Louisville *(G-12316)*
Ink Well G 614 861-7113
Gahanna *(G-10212)*
Innomark Communications LLC E 937 454-5555
Dayton *(G-8404)*
Insley Printing Inc G 614 885-5973
Worthington *(G-20873)*
Insta-Print Inc G 216 741-6500
Cleveland *(G-5573)*
Instant Replay G 937 592-0534
Bellefontaine *(G-1534)*
Integrity Print Solutions Inc G 330 818-0161
Akron *(G-233)*
International Cntr Artfcial or G 440 358-1102
Painesville *(G-15891)*
Irwin Engraving & Printing Co G 216 391-7300
Cleveland *(G-5589)*
It XCEL Consulting LLC F 513 847-8261
West Chester *(G-19886)*
J & J Bechke Inc G 440 238-1441
Strongsville *(G-17932)*
J & K Printing G 330 456-5306
Canton *(G-2742)*
J & L Management Corporation G 440 205-1199
Mentor *(G-13614)*
J & P Investments Inc F 513 821-2299
Cincinnati *(G-3933)*
J P Quality Printing Inc G 216 791-6303
Cleveland *(G-5598)*
▲ **Jack G Walker** F 440 352-4222
Mentor *(G-13617)*

Jakprints Inc ....C 877 246-3132
Cleveland *(G-5605)*
Jarman Printing Company LLC ....G 330 823-8585
Alliance *(G-519)*
Jaymac Systems Inc ....G 440 498-0810
Solon *(G-17320)*
Jeffrey Reedy ....G 614 794-9292
Westerville *(G-20219)*
Jim Davis ....G 740 335-8030
Wshngtn CT Hs *(G-20914)*
Jk Digital Publishing LLC ....E 937 299-0185
Springboro *(G-17484)*
JM Printing ....G 740 412-8666
Circleville *(G-4632)*
Joe The Printer Guy LLC ....G 216 651-3880
Lakewood *(G-11670)*
John Kolesar and Sons Inc ....G 216 221-7117
Cleveland *(G-5618)*
John S Swift Company Inc ....F 513 721-4147
Cincinnati *(G-3954)*
Johnson Printing ....G 740 922-4821
Uhrichsville *(G-19053)*
Jones Printing Services Inc ....G 440 946-7300
Eastlake *(G-9277)*
Joseph Berning Printing Co ....F 513 721-0781
Cincinnati *(G-3957)*
Joseph Scarberry ....G 740 522-1551
Newark *(G-15025)*
K B Printing ....G 614 771-1222
Columbus *(G-7249)*
Kad Holdings Inc ....G 614 792-3399
Dublin *(G-9093)*
Kader Printing LLC ....G 440 668-1579
North Royalton *(G-15429)*
Kahny Printing Inc ....E 513 251-2911
Cincinnati *(G-3968)*
Kay Toledo Tag Inc ....D 419 729-5479
Toledo *(G-18541)*
Kee Printing Inc ....G 937 456-6851
Eaton *(G-9312)*
Keener Printing Inc ....F 216 531-7595
Cleveland *(G-5640)*
Kehl-Kolor Inc ....E 419 281-3107
Ashland *(G-746)*
Kehoe Brothers Printing Inc ....G 216 351-4100
Cleveland *(G-5641)*
Keithley Enterprises Inc ....G 937 890-1878
Dayton *(G-8434)*
Kelly Prints LLC ....G 440 356-6361
North Olmsted *(G-15340)*
Kendall & Sons Company ....G 937 222-6996
Dayton *(G-8436)*
Kennedy Graphics Inc ....G 419 223-9825
Lima *(G-12035)*
Kennedy Mint Inc ....D 440 572-3222
Cleveland *(G-5645)*
Kennedy Printing Co ....F 419 422-1802
Findlay *(G-9847)*
Kenwel Printers Inc ....E 614 261-1011
Columbus *(G-7257)*
Kever Incorporated ....G 614 552-9000
Columbus *(G-7258)*
Kevin K Tidd ....G 419 885-5603
Sylvania *(G-18115)*
Key Maneuvers Inc ....G 440 285-0774
Chardon *(G-3159)*
Key Press Inc ....G 513 721-1203
Cincinnati *(G-3987)*
Keystone Press Inc ....G 419 243-7326
Toledo *(G-18544)*
Keystone Printing & Copy Cat ....G 740 354-6542
Portsmouth *(G-16439)*
Keystone Printing Co ....G 330 385-9519
East Liverpool *(G-9223)*
Kimpton Printing & Spc Co ....F 330 467-1640
Macedonia *(G-12466)*
Klingstedt Brothers Company ....F 330 456-8319
Canton *(G-2755)*
KMS 2000 Inc ....F 330 454-9444
Canton *(G-2756)*
Knowles Press Inc ....G 330 877-9345
Hartville *(G-10827)*
Knox County Printing Co ....G 740 848-4032
Galion *(G-10278)*
Kovacevic Printing Inc ....G 440 887-1000
Cleveland *(G-5663)*
Krok Printing Inc ....G 330 652-8198
Niles *(G-15166)*
Kuwatch Printing LLC ....G 513 759-5850
Liberty Twp *(G-11976)*

L & H Printing ....G 937 855-4512
Germantown *(G-10370)*
L & T Collins Inc ....G 740 345-4494
Newark *(G-15029)*
L B L Lithographers Inc ....G 440 350-0106
Painesville *(G-15896)*
Lake Erie Graphics Inc ....E 216 575-1333
Brookpark *(G-2166)*
Lakota Printing Inc ....G 513 755-3666
West Chester *(G-19890)*
Landen Desktop Pubg Ctr Inc ....G 513 683-5181
Loveland *(G-12370)*
Lanz Printing Co Inc ....G 614 221-1724
Columbus *(G-7285)*
Larry C White ....G 330 386-3228
East Liverpool *(G-9224)*
Laser Images Inc ....G 419 668-8348
Norwalk *(G-15549)*
Lasting First Impressions Inc ....F 513 870-6900
West Chester *(G-20020)*
Lasting Impressions Printing ....G 216 382-8436
Twinsburg *(G-18970)*
Laurenee Ltd LLC ....G 513 662-2225
Cincinnati *(G-4015)*
Lee Corporation ....F 513 771-3602
Cincinnati *(G-4019)*
Legal News Publishing Co ....E 216 696-3322
Cleveland *(G-5692)*
Letter Shop ....G 937 981-3117
Greenfield *(G-10482)*
Letterman Printing Inc ....G 513 523-1111
Oxford *(G-15839)*
Lilienthal Southeastern Inc ....F 740 439-1640
Cambridge *(G-2464)*
Liming Printing Inc ....F 937 374-2646
Xenia *(G-20961)*
Lindsey Graphics Inc ....G 330 995-9241
Aurora *(G-933)*
Lobo Awrds Screen Prtg Graphix ....G 740 972-9087
Marion *(G-12880)*
Lorain Printing Company ....E 440 288-6000
Lorain *(G-12258)*
Loris Printing Inc ....G 419 626-6648
Sandusky *(G-16981)*
Lsc Communications Us LLC ....C 419 935-0111
Willard *(G-20396)*
Lund Printing Co ....G 330 628-4047
Akron *(G-277)*
Lyle Printing & Publishing Co ....E 330 337-3419
Salem *(G-16909)*
Mabar Printing Service ....G 419 257-3659
North Baltimore *(G-15194)*
Mac Printing Company ....G 937 393-1101
Hillsboro *(G-11007)*
Mackland Co Inc ....G 330 399-5034
Warren *(G-19575)*
Mansfield Journal Co ....G 330 364-8641
New Philadelphia *(G-14910)*
Marbee Inc ....G 419 422-9441
Findlay *(G-9858)*
Marco Printed Products Co ....E 937 433-7030
Dayton *(G-8477)*
Marco Printed Products Co Inc ....G 937 433-5680
Dayton *(G-8478)*
Margaret Trentman ....G 513 948-1700
Cincinnati *(G-4059)*
Mariotti Printing Co LLC ....G 440 245-4120
Lorain *(G-12259)*
Mark Advertising Agency Inc ....F 419 626-9000
Sandusky *(G-16985)*
Mark-N-Mend Inc ....G 440 951-2003
Willoughby *(G-20537)*
Marles Business Systems Inc ....G 440 268-8380
Brooklyn Heights *(G-2142)*
Marshalls Thrifty Print Inc ....G 513 984-5513
Cincinnati *(G-4062)*
Martin Printing Co ....G 419 224-9176
Lima *(G-12051)*
Martys Print Shop ....G 740 373-3454
Marietta *(G-12804)*
Marysville Printing Company ....G 937 644-4959
Marysville *(G-12958)*
◆ Mass-Marketing Inc ....C 513 860-6200
Fairfield *(G-9679)*
Master Printing Company ....E 216 351-2246
Cleveland *(G-5759)*
Mathews Printing Company ....F 614 444-1010
Columbus *(G-7324)*
Maumee Quick Print Inc ....G 419 893-4321
Maumee *(G-13280)*

Maximum Graphix Inc ....G 440 353-3301
North Ridgeville *(G-15390)*
Mc Sign Company ....C 440 209-6200
Mentor *(G-13649)*
Mc Vay Ventures Inc ....G 614 890-1516
Westerville *(G-20223)*
McKinnon Printing Inc ....F 330 929-5769
Cuyahoga Falls *(G-8025)*
McMath & Sheets Unlimited Inc ....G 216 381-0010
Cleveland *(G-5771)*
◆ McNerney & Associates LLC ....E 513 241-9951
Cincinnati *(G-4070)*
Mercer Color Corporation ....G 419 678-8273
Coldwater *(G-6568)*
Meridian Arts and Graphics ....F 330 759-9099
Youngstown *(G-21143)*
Messenger Publishing Company ....C 740 592-6612
Athens *(G-876)*
Metzgers ....F 419 861-8611
Toledo *(G-18584)*
Miami Valley Press Inc ....G 937 547-0771
Greenville *(G-10511)*
Michael R Kelly ....G 614 491-1745
Obetz *(G-15656)*
Middaugh Enterprises Inc ....F 330 852-2471
Sugarcreek *(G-18026)*
Middleton Printing Co Inc ....G 614 294-7277
Gahanna *(G-10219)*
Mike B Crawford ....G 330 673-7944
Kent *(G-11492)*
Milford Printers ....E 513 831-6630
Milford *(G-14162)*
Milford Printers ....G 513 831-6630
Milford *(G-14163)*
Millstream Press Inc ....F 419 422-9745
Findlay *(G-9863)*
Milo Bennett Corp ....G 419 874-1492
Perrysburg *(G-16122)*
Minuteman Press ....G 440 946-3311
Mentor *(G-13658)*
Minuteman Press ....G 419 782-8002
Defiance *(G-8805)*
Minuteman Press ....G 513 772-0500
Cincinnati *(G-4109)*
Minuteman Press ....G 614 337-2334
Columbus *(G-7357)*
Minuteman Press ....G 937 429-8610
Beavercreek *(G-1352)*
Minuteman Press Inc ....G 513 741-9056
Cincinnati *(G-4110)*
Minuteman Press of Athens LLC ....G 740 593-7393
Athens *(G-878)*
Minuteman Press of Elyria ....G 440 365-9377
Elyria *(G-9463)*
Minutman Press Frfeld Cnty LLC ....G 740 689-1992
Lancaster *(G-11730)*
Mizer Printing & Graphics ....G 740 942-3343
Cadiz *(G-2421)*
Mmp Printing Inc ....E 513 381-0990
Cincinnati *(G-4112)*
Mmp Toledo ....F 419 472-0505
Toledo *(G-18588)*
Monks Copy Shop Inc ....G 614 885-7228
Columbus *(G-7367)*
Montview Corporation ....G 330 723-3409
Medina *(G-13449)*
Morse Enterprises Inc ....G 513 229-3600
Mason *(G-13066)*
Muir Graphics Inc ....F 309 673-7034
Sylvania *(G-18120)*
Mullin Print Solutions ....G 216 383-2901
Euclid *(G-9594)*
Multi-Color Australia LLC ....B 513 381-1480
Batavia *(G-1210)*
Murr Corporation ....F 330 264-2223
Wooster *(G-20813)*
Mustang Printing ....F 419 592-2746
Napoleon *(G-14690)*
Nari Inc ....G 440 960-2280
Monroeville *(G-14427)*
National Bank Note Company ....G 216 281-7792
Cleveland *(G-5852)*
Nelis Printing Co ....G 330 757-4114
Youngstown *(G-21149)*
Network Printing & Graphics ....F 614 230-2084
Columbus *(G-7387)*
Newfax Corporation ....F 419 241-5157
Toledo *(G-18603)*
Newfax Corporation ....F 419 893-4557
Toledo *(G-18604)*

SIC

Employee Codes: A=Over 500 employees, B=251-500
C=101-250, D=51-100, E=20-50, F=10-19, G=3-9
2017 Harris Ohio
Industrial Directory
923

Newhouse & Faulkner Inc ....G....513 721-1660
Cincinnati *(G-4150)*
Newmast Mktg & Communications ....E....614 837-1200
Columbus *(G-7389)*
Newspaper Holding Inc ....D....440 998-2323
Ashtabula *(G-826)*
Newton Falls Printing ....G....330 872-3532
Newton Falls *(G-15137)*
Nickum Enterprises Inc ....G....513 561-2292
Cincinnati *(G-4154)*
Nomis Publications Inc ....F....330 965-2380
Youngstown *(G-21150)*
North Coast Litho Inc ....E....216 881-1952
Cleveland *(G-5897)*
North Toledo Graphics LLC ....D....419 476-8808
Toledo *(G-18609)*
Northeast Blueprint & Sup Co ....G....216 261-7500
Cleveland *(G-5903)*
Northwest Print Inc ....G....419 385-3375
Perrysburg *(G-16127)*
Nova Creative Group Inc ....F....937 291-8653
Dayton *(G-8533)*
◆ **Novelty Advertising Co Inc** ....E....740 622-3113
Coshocton *(G-7903)*
Nta Graphics Inc ....C....419 476-8808
Toledo *(G-18611)*
O Connor Office Pdts & Prtg ....G....740 852-2209
London *(G-12216)*
O T Packaging ....G....330 482-2224
Columbiana *(G-6626)*
▲ **Oak Printing Company** ....E....440 238-3316
Strongsville *(G-17948)*
Odyssey Press Inc ....F....614 410-0356
Huron *(G-11236)*
Office Print N Copy ....G....740 695-3616
Saint Clairsville *(G-16799)*
Ogden Newspapers Inc ....C....330 841-1600
Warren *(G-19582)*
▲ **Ohio Art Company** ....D....419 636-3141
Bryan *(G-2315)*
Old Trail Printing Company ....C....614 443-4852
Columbus *(G-7440)*
Oliver Printing & Packg Co LLC ....D....330 425-7890
Twinsburg *(G-18990)*
Olmsted Printing Inc ....G....440 234-2600
Berea *(G-1631)*
▼ **One-Write Company** ....E....740 654-2128
Lancaster *(G-11737)*
Onetouchpoint East Corp ....D....513 421-1600
Cincinnati *(G-4189)*
Optimum System Products Inc ....E....614 885-4464
Westerville *(G-20228)*
Orange Blossom Press Inc ....G....216 781-8655
Willoughby *(G-20562)*
Oregon Village Print Shoppe ....F....937 222-9418
Dayton *(G-8552)*
Orrville Printing Co Inc ....G....330 682-5066
Orrville *(G-15752)*
Orwell Printing ....G....440 285-2233
Chardon *(G-3171)*
Oscar Hicks ....G....937 435-4350
Dayton *(G-8553)*
Our Nine LLC ....G....614 844-6655
Columbus *(G-7449)*
Page One Group ....G....740 397-4240
Mount Vernon *(G-14636)*
Painesville Publishing Co ....G....440 354-4142
Austinburg *(G-964)*
Painted Hill Inv Group Inc ....F....937 339-1756
Troy *(G-18861)*
Papworth Prints ....G....614 428-6137
Columbus *(G-7460)*
Paragon Press ....G....513 281-9911
Cincinnati *(G-4211)*
▲ **Paragraphics Inc** ....E....330 493-1074
Canton *(G-2806)*
Patio Printing Inc ....G....614 785-9553
Columbus *(G-7463)*
Patterson-Britton Printing ....G....216 781-7997
Cleveland *(G-5981)*
Paul Stipkovich ....G....330 499-7391
North Canton *(G-15258)*
Paul/Jay Associates ....G....740 676-8776
Bellaire *(G-1500)*
Paxar Corporation ....G....937 681-4541
Dayton *(G-8567)*
PDQ Printing Service ....F....216 241-5443
Cleveland *(G-5985)*
Peck Engraving Co ....E....216 221-1556
Cleveland *(G-5987)*
Peerless Printing Company ....F....513 721-4657
Cincinnati *(G-4221)*
Pen-Ann Corporation ....G....740 373-2054
Marietta *(G-12815)*
Penguin Enterprises Inc ....E....440 899-5110
Westlake *(G-20292)*
Penny Printing Inc ....G....330 645-2955
Akron *(G-334)*
Performa La Mar Printing Inc ....G....440 632-9800
Middlefield *(G-13981)*
Perrons Printing Company ....E....440 236-8870
Columbia Station *(G-6593)*
Phil Vedda & Sons Inc ....G....216 671-2222
Cleveland *(G-6000)*
Pinnacle Press Inc ....F....330 453-7060
Canton *(G-2813)*
PIP and Huds LLC ....G....740 208-5519
Gallipolis *(G-10307)*
PIP Printing ....G....440 951-2606
Willoughby *(G-20569)*
Plain Dealer Publishing Co ....A....216 999-5000
Cleveland *(G-6011)*
PM Graphics Inc ....E....330 650-0861
Streetsboro *(G-17868)*
Pooles Printing & Office Svcs ....G....419 475-9000
Toledo *(G-18649)*
Porath Business Services Inc ....F....216 626-0060
Cleveland *(G-6021)*
Post Printing Co ....D....859 254-7714
Minster *(G-14359)*
Power Management Inc ....E....937 222-2909
Dayton *(G-8580)*
Preferred Printing ....G....937 492-6961
Sidney *(G-17212)*
Preisser Inc ....E....614 345-0199
Columbus *(G-7514)*
Premier Printing and Packg Inc ....G....937 436-5290
Dayton *(G-8589)*
Premier Printing Corporation ....F....216 478-9720
Cleveland *(G-6042)*
Premier Printing Solutions ....G....740 374-2836
Marietta *(G-12819)*
Press For Less Printing Firm I ....G....931 912-4606
Lebanon *(G-11829)*
Pressmark Inc ....G....740 373-6005
Marietta *(G-12820)*
Prestige Printing ....G....937 236-8468
Dayton *(G-8590)*
Priesman Printery ....G....419 898-2526
Oak Harbor *(G-15593)*
Prime Printing Inc ....E....937 438-3707
Dayton *(G-8594)*
Print A Copy ....G....440 845-9039
Cleveland *(G-6049)*
Print All Inc ....G....419 534-2880
Toledo *(G-18658)*
Print Craft Inc ....G....513 931-6828
Cincinnati *(G-4270)*
▼ **Print Direct For Less 2 Inc** ....E....440 236-8870
Columbia Station *(G-6595)*
Print Factory Pll ....G....330 549-9640
North Lima *(G-15321)*
▲ **Print Marketing Inc** ....E....330 625-1500
Homerville *(G-11114)*
Print Masters Ltd ....G....740 450-2885
Zanesville *(G-21346)*
Print Shop ....G....740 335-8030
Wshngtn CT Hs *(G-20920)*
Print Shop Design and Print ....G....440 232-2391
Bedford *(G-1454)*
Print Shop of Canton Inc ....G....330 497-3212
Canton *(G-2822)*
Print Solutions Today LLC ....G....614 848-4500
Westerville *(G-20231)*
Print Squad LLC ....G....440 315-5652
Strongsville *(G-17953)*
Print Syndicate LLC ....F....614 519-0341
Columbus *(G-7518)*
Print Zone ....G....513 733-0067
West Chester *(G-20040)*
Print-Digital Incorporated ....G....330 686-5945
Stow *(G-17792)*
Printcraft Inc ....G....440 599-8903
Conneaut *(G-7817)*
Printed Image ....F....614 221-1412
Columbus *(G-7519)*
Printers Devil Inc ....F....330 650-1218
Hudson *(G-11194)*
Printers Emergency Service LLC ....G....513 421-7799
Cincinnati *(G-4272)*
Printex Incorporated ....F....740 773-0088
Chillicothe *(G-3268)*
Printex Incorporated ....G....740 947-8800
Waverly *(G-19719)*
Printing Arts Press ....F....740 397-6106
Mount Vernon *(G-14639)*
Printing Center of Xenia ....G....937 372-1687
Xenia *(G-20967)*
Printing Connection Inc ....G....216 898-4878
Brookpark *(G-2168)*
Printing Express ....G....937 276-7794
Moraine *(G-14517)*
Printing Express Inc ....G....740 532-7003
Ironton *(G-11299)*
Printing For Less ....G....937 743-8268
Springboro *(G-17499)*
Printing Service Company ....D....937 425-6100
Miamisburg *(G-13848)*
Printing Services ....E....440 708-1999
Chagrin Falls *(G-3114)*
Printing System Inc ....F....330 375-9128
Akron *(G-351)*
Printmanagement Llc ....E....513 272-7000
Cincinnati *(G-4273)*
Printpoint Printing Inc ....G....937 223-9041
Dayton *(G-8595)*
Printprod Inc ....F....937 228-2181
Dayton *(G-8596)*
Printzone ....G....513 733-0067
Cincinnati *(G-4274)*
Pro Companies Inc ....G....614 738-1222
Pickerington *(G-16201)*
Pro Printing Inc ....G....614 276-8366
Columbus *(G-7521)*
Pro-Decal Inc ....G....330 484-0089
Canton *(G-2825)*
Professional Screen Printing ....G....740 687-0760
Lancaster *(G-11742)*
Profile Digital Printing LLC ....E....937 866-4241
Dayton *(G-8599)*
Proforma Print & Imaging ....G....216 520-8400
Dublin *(G-9128)*
Progressive Communications ....D....740 397-5333
Mount Vernon *(G-14640)*
Progressive Printers Inc ....D....937 222-1267
Dayton *(G-8601)*
Progressive Printing Services ....G....330 534-8501
Hubbard *(G-11138)*
Proimage Printing & Design LLC ....G....937 312-9544
Xenia *(G-20968)*
Promatch Solutions LLC ....F....937 299-0185
Springboro *(G-17500)*
Province of St John The Baptis ....D....513 241-5615
Cincinnati *(G-4301)*
Q C Printing ....G....419 475-4266
Toledo *(G-18662)*
Quad/Graphics Inc ....A....513 932-1064
Lebanon *(G-11830)*
Quad/Graphics Inc ....C....614 276-4800
Columbus *(G-7531)*
Quality Publishing Co ....F....513 863-8210
Hamilton *(G-10733)*
Quebecor World Johnson Hardin ....A....614 326-0299
Cincinnati *(G-4312)*
Queen City Reprographics ....C....513 326-2300
Cincinnati *(G-4319)*
Quez Media Marketing Inc ....F....216 910-0202
Cleveland *(G-6077)*
Quick As A Wink Printing Co ....F....419 224-9786
Lima *(G-12079)*
▼ **Quick Tab II Inc** ....D....419 448-6622
Tiffin *(G-18238)*
Quick Tech Graphics Inc ....E....937 743-5952
Springboro *(G-17502)*
R & J Bardon Inc ....G....614 457-5500
Columbus *(G-7541)*
R & J Printing Enterprises Inc ....F....330 343-1242
Dover *(G-9008)*
R & W Printing Company ....G....513 575-0131
Loveland *(G-12379)*
R B Robinson Inc ....G....440 543-5547
Chagrin Falls *(G-3116)*
R Design & Printing Co ....G....614 299-1420
Columbus *(G-7544)*
▲ **R S C Sales Company** ....E....423 581-4916
Dayton *(G-8612)*
R W Michael Printing Co ....G....330 923-9277
Akron *(G-363)*
R&D Marketing Group Inc ....G....216 398-9100
Brooklyn Heights *(G-2145)*

Randd Assoc Prtg & Promotions ....G 937 294-1874
Dayton (G-8617)

Rba Inc ....G 330 336-6700
Wadsworth (G-19436)

Red Vette Printing Company ....G 740 364-1766
Granville (G-10466)

Renco Printing Inc ....G 216 267-5585
Cleveland (G-6100)

▲ Repro Acquisition Company LLC ......E 216 738-3800
Cleveland (G-6104)

Reynolds and Reynolds Company ....F 419 584-7000
Celina (G-3017)

Rhoads Printing Center Inc ....G 330 678-2042
Kent (G-11516)

Ricci Anthony ....G 330 758-5761
Youngstown (G-21188)

▲ Richardson Printing Corp ....D 740 373-5362
Marietta (G-12824)

Robert Becker Impressions Inc ....F 419 385-5303
Toledo (G-18678)

Robert H Shackelford ....G 330 364-2221
New Philadelphia (G-14926)

Roberts Graphic Center ....G 330 788-4642
Youngstown (G-21191)

Robin Enterprises Company ....C 614 891-0250
Westerville (G-20233)

Robs Creative Screen Printing ....G 740 264-6383
Wintersville (G-20713)

Rohrer Corporation ....C 440 542-3100
Solon (G-17371)

Rotary Forms Press Inc ....E 937 393-3426
Hillsboro (G-11013)

RPI Color Service Inc ....D 513 471-4040
Cincinnati (G-4363)

RR Donnelley & Sons Company ....E 440 774-2101
Oberlin (G-15647)

RR Donnelley & Sons Company ....A 419 935-0111
Willard (G-20400)

Ruda Print & Graphics ....G 419 331-7832
Lima (G-12086)

Rutobo Inc ....G 614 236-2948
Columbus (G-7579)

Ryans Newark Leader Ex Prtg ....F 740 522-2149
Newark (G-15051)

S & S Printing Service Inc ....G 937 228-9411
Dayton (G-8643)

S and K Painting ....G 330 505-1910
Niles (G-15184)

S Beckman Print & G ....E 614 864-2232
Columbus (G-7581)

S O S Graphics & Printing Inc ....G 614 846-8229
Worthington (G-20886)

Sandusky Newspapers Inc ....C 419 625-5500
Sandusky (G-17004)

Sandy Smittcamp ....G 937 372-1687
Xenia (G-20971)

Sanscan Inc ....G 330 332-9365
Salem (G-16926)

Schaffner Publication Inc ....E 419 732-2154
Port Clinton (G-16413)

Schiffer Group Inc ....G 937 694-8185
Troy (G-18872)

Schilling Graphics Inc ....E 419 468-1037
Galion (G-10286)

Schlabach Printing Ltd ....E 330 852-4687
Sugarcreek (G-18038)

Schuerholz Printing Inc ....G 937 294-5218
Dayton (G-8647)

Scorecards Unlimited LLC ....G 614 885-0796
Columbus (G-7602)

Scratch Off Works ....G 440 333-4302
Rocky River (G-16709)

Screen Printing Unlimited ....G 419 621-2335
Sandusky (G-17007)

▼ Scrip-Safe Security Products ....E 513 697-7789
Loveland (G-12384)

Sdg News Group Inc ....F 419 929-3411
New London (G-14865)

Seemless Design & Printing LLC ....G 513 871-2366
Cincinnati (G-4397)

Seifert Printing Company ....G 330 759-7414
Youngstown (G-21199)

Selby Service/Roxy Press Inc ....G 513 241-3445
Cincinnati (G-4400)

▲ Sensical Inc ....D 216 641-1141
Solon (G-17378)

Sentry Graphics Inc ....G 440 735-0850
Northfield (G-15471)

Sfc Graphics Cleveland Ltd ....E 419 255-1283
Toledo (G-18693)

Shallow Lake Corp ....G 614 883-6350
Lewis Center (G-11917)

Sharon Printing Co Inc ....G 330 239-1684
Sharon Center (G-17110)

Sharp Enterprises Inc ....F 937 295-2965
Fort Loramie (G-9939)

▲ Shawnee Systems Inc ....D 513 561-9932
Cincinnati (G-4414)

Shelby Printing Inc ....E 419 342-3171
Shelby (G-17143)

Ship Print E Sell ....G 614 459-1205
Columbus (G-7616)

Shreve Printing LLC ....F 330 567-2341
Shreve (G-17163)

Sidney Printing Works Inc ....E 513 542-4000
Cincinnati (G-4416)

Sitler Printer Inc ....G 330 482-4463
Columbiana (G-6632)

Sjpm Inc ....G 614 475-4571
Gahanna (G-10233)

Skladany Enterprises Inc ....G 614 823-6883
Westerville (G-20185)

Slimans Printery Inc ....F 330 454-9141
Canton (G-2851)

Slutzkers Quickprint Center ....G 440 244-0330
Lorain (G-12278)

SMI Holdings Inc ....F 740 927-3464
Pataskala (G-15986)

Smith-Feeman Inc ....F 330 434-8882
Uniontown (G-19099)

Snow Printing Co Inc ....F 419 229-7669
Lima (G-12093)

◆ Source3media Inc ....E 330 467-9003
Macedonia (G-12483)

Sourcelink Ohio LLC ....C 937 885-8000
Miamisburg (G-13862)

South End Printing Co ....G 216 341-0669
Cleveland (G-6222)

Southeast Publications Inc ....F 740 732-2341
Caldwell (G-2433)

SP Mount Printing Company ....E 216 881-3316
Cleveland (G-6223)

SPAOS Inc ....G 937 890-0783
Dayton (G-8666)

Specialty Lithographing Co ....G 513 621-0222
Cincinnati (G-4440)

Spencer-Walker Press Inc ....F 740 344-6110
Newark (G-15055)

Sportsartcom ....G 330 903-0895
Copley (G-7856)

Springdot Inc ....D 513 542-4000
Cincinnati (G-4448)

Springfield Engraving Company ....G 937 390-0011
Springfield (G-17651)

Sprint Print Inc ....G 740 622-4429
Coshocton (G-7910)

Standard Register Inc ....E 860 870-2063
Dayton (G-8676)

Standard Register Inc ....G 937 228-5800
Dayton (G-8679)

Stapins Qick Cpy/Print Ctr LLC ....G 330 296-0123
Ravenna (G-16563)

Star Calendar & Printing Co ....G 216 741-3223
Cleveland (G-6237)

Star Printing Company Inc ....G 330 376-0514
Akron (G-415)

Starr Printing Services Inc ....G 513 241-7708
Cincinnati (G-4460)

Start Printing ....G 513 424-2121
Middletown (G-14085)

State-Mate Company ....G 740 392-9487
Mount Vernon (G-14652)

Stationery Shop Inc ....G 330 376-2033
Akron (G-416)

Stein-Palmer Printing Co ....G 740 633-3894
Saint Clairsville (G-16809)

Stephen Andrews Inc ....G 330 725-2672
Lodi (G-12170)

Stepping Stone Enterprises Inc ....F 419 472-0505
Toledo (G-18703)

Stevenson Color Inc ....C 513 321-7500
Cincinnati (G-4466)

Stick-It Graphics LLC ....G 330 407-0142
New Philadelphia (G-14930)

Streamline Printing ....G 740 549-0330
Lewis Center (G-11921)

Streichers Enterprises Inc ....G 419 423-8606
Findlay (G-9897)

Suburban Press Inc ....E 216 961-0766
Cleveland (G-6260)

Summit Printing & Graphics ....G 330 645-7644
Akron (G-421)

Sun Art Decals Inc ....G 440 234-9045
Berea (G-1636)

Superior Impressions Inc ....G 419 244-8676
Toledo (G-18709)

Superprinter Inc ....G 440 277-0787
Lorain (G-12282)

Superprinter Ltd ....G 440 277-0787
Lorain (G-12283)

Swimmer Printing Inc ....G 216 623-1005
Cleveland (G-6281)

Syndicate Printers Inc ....G 513 779-3625
West Chester (G-19952)

T & K Heins Corporation ....G 740 452-6006
Zanesville (G-21358)

T D Dynamics Inc ....F 216 881-0800
Cleveland (G-6288)

T H E B Inc ....G 216 391-4800
Cleveland (G-6290)

Target Printing & Graphics ....G 937 228-0170
Dayton (G-8700)

Taylor Quick Print ....G 740 439-2208
Cambridge (G-2478)

▼ Tce International Ltd ....F 800 962-2376
Perry (G-16059)

Tcp Inc ....G 330 836-4239
Fairlawn (G-9764)

Technoprint Inc ....F 614 899-1403
Westerville (G-20236)

Tecnocap LLC ....D 330 392-7222
Warren (G-19604)

The Gazette Printing Co Inc ....D 440 576-9125
Jefferson (G-11373)

The Gazette Printing Co Inc ....G 440 593-6030
Conneaut (G-7820)

Thrifty Print ....G 440 360-7826
North Olmsted (G-15349)

Timely Tours Inc ....G 419 734-3751
Port Clinton (G-16418)

Tiny Printing Co ....G 614 920-0800
Pickerington (G-16208)

Tj Metzgers Inc ....D 419 861-8611
Toledo (G-18726)

TL Krieg Offset Inc ....E 513 542-1522
Cincinnati (G-4511)

Toledo Ticket Company ....E 419 476-5424
Toledo (G-18746)

Tomahawk Printing ....F 419 335-3161
Wauseon (G-19696)

Tomahawk Printing Inc ....F 419 335-3161
Wauseon (G-19697)

Tope Printing Inc ....G 330 674-4993
Millersburg (G-14271)

Tradewinds Prin Twear ....G 740 214-5005
Roseville (G-16733)

◆ Transfer Express Inc ....D 440 918-1900
Mentor (G-13755)

Traxium LLC ....E 330 572-8200
Stow (G-17811)

◆ Trebnick Systems Inc ....E 937 743-1550
Springboro (G-17512)

Tri-State Publishing Company ....E 740 283-3686
Steubenville (G-17719)

Tribune Printing Inc ....G 419 542-7764
Hicksville (G-10909)

Ultimate Printing Co Inc ....G 330 847-2941
Warren (G-19616)

Ultra Impressions Inc ....G 440 951-4777
Mentor (G-13758)

Ultra Printing & Design Inc ....G 440 887-0393
Cleveland (G-6380)

United Prtrs & Lithographers ....G 216 771-2759
Cleveland (G-6386)

▼ United Trade Printers LLC ....E 614 326-4829
Dublin (G-9158)

University of Cincinnati ....F 513 556-5042
Cincinnati (G-4543)

USA Quickprint Inc ....F 330 455-5119
Canton (G-2892)

V & C Enterprises Co ....G 614 221-1412
Columbus (G-7729)

V I P Printing & Design ....G 513 777-7468
West Chester (G-20066)

Valley Graphics ....G 330 652-0484
Niles (G-15187)

Valley Printing & Graphics ....G 330 364-5010
Dover (G-9023)

Variety Printing ....G 216 676-9815
Brookpark (G-2171)

◆ Vectra Inc .... F 614 351-6868
  Columbus (G-7733)

Victory Direct LLC .... G 614 626-0000
  Gahanna (G-10240)

Villager Publishing Co Inc .... G 330 527-5761
  Garrettsville (G-10335)

Vision Graphics .... G 330 665-4451
  Copley (G-7857)

Vision Graphix Inc .... G 440 835-6540
  Westlake (G-20318)

Visual Art Graphic Services .... E 330 274-2775
  Mantua (G-12725)

Vya Inc .... E 513 772-5400
  Cincinnati (G-4573)

W C Sims Co Inc .... G 937 325-7035
  Springfield (G-17674)

Walter Graphics Inc .... G 419 522-5261
  Mansfield (G-12702)

Warren Printing & Off Pdts Inc .... F 419 523-3635
  Ottawa (G-15814)

Wasserstrom Company .... F 614 228-2233
  Columbus (G-7751)

Watkins Printing Company .... E 614 297-8270
  Columbus (G-7752)

Welch Publishing Co .... E 419 874-2528
  Perrysburg (G-16168)

West Bend Printing & Pubg Inc .... G 419 258-2000
  Antwerp (G-632)

▲ West-Camp Press Inc .... D 614 818-6279
  Westerville (G-20241)

Western Ohio Graphics .... G 937 335-8769
  Troy (G-18885)

Western Reserve Graphics .... G 440 729-9527
  Chesterland (G-3223)

Westrock Commercial LLC .... G 419 476-9101
  Toledo (G-18773)

▲ Wfsr Holdings LLC .... A 877 735-4966
  Dayton (G-8757)

Whiskey Fox Corporation .... F 440 779-6767
  North Olmsted (G-15352)

White Tiger Inc .... F 740 852-4873
  London (G-12223)

Wholesale Printers Ltd .... G 440 354-5788
  Painesville (G-15940)

Wilkinson Printing Co .... G 419 238-3615
  Van Wert (G-19276)

William J Bergen & Co .... G 440 248-6132
  Solon (G-17414)

William J Dupps .... G 419 734-2126
  Port Clinton (G-16419)

Williams Design & Printing Ser .... G 937 320-9449
  Beavercreek (G-1365)

Williams Executive Entps Inc .... G 440 887-1000
  Middleburg Heights (G-13910)

Wilson Prtg Graphics of London .... G 740 852-5934
  London (G-12224)

Wirick Press Inc .... G 330 273-3488
  Brunswick (G-2269)

Woodrow Manufacturing Co .... E 937 399-9333
  Springfield (G-17682)

Xpress Print Inc .... F 330 494-7246
  Louisville (G-12335)

Yes Press Printing Co .... G 330 535-8398
  Akron (G-477)

Youngs Screenprinting & Embro .... G 330 922-5777
  Cuyahoga Falls (G-8063)

Youngstown ARC Engraving Co .... E 330 793-2471
  Youngstown (G-21245)

Youngstown Letter Shop Inc .... G 330 793-4935
  Youngstown (G-21253)

Youngstown Pre-Press Inc .... F 330 793-3690
  Youngstown (G-21255)

Yuckon International Corp .... G 216 361-2103
  Cleveland (G-6488)

Z P Enterprises Inc .... G 513 863-3393
  Hamilton (G-10758)

Zip Laser Systems Inc .... G 740 286-6613
  Jackson (G-11335)

2754 Commercial Printing: Gravure

Admiral Products Company Inc .... E 216 671-0600
  Cleveland (G-4706)

◆ Angstrom Graphics Inc .... C 216 271-5300
  Cleveland (G-4814)

Anthony Business Forms Inc .... F 937 253-0072
  Dayton (G-8096)

Barberton Magic Press Printing .... G 330 753-9578
  Barberton (G-1107)

Business Fnctnality Forms Svcs .... G 614 557-9420
  Gahanna (G-10205)

Cham Cor Industries Inc .... G 740 967-9015
  Johnstown (G-11395)

Clipper Magazine LLC .... G 937 534-0470
  Moraine (G-14472)

Dulle Associates .... G 513 723-9600
  Cincinnati (G-3674)

Dupli-Systems Inc .... C 440 234-9415
  Strongsville (G-17913)

E-Z Stop Service Center .... D 330 448-2236
  Brookfield (G-2123)

Graphic Paper Products Corp .... D 937 325-5503
  Springfield (G-17564)

Graphic Paper Products Corp .... G 937 322-7711
  Springfield (G-17565)

Hotcardscom Inc .... E 216 241-4040
  Cleveland (G-5528)

Klingstedt Brothers Company .... F 330 456-8319
  Canton (G-2755)

▲ Label Print Technologies LLC .... G 800 475-4030
  Mogadore (G-14380)

Lloyd F Helber .... E 740 756-9607
  Carroll (G-2943)

Lsc Communications Us LLC .... C 419 935-0111
  Willard (G-20396)

M PI Label Systems .... G 330 938-2134
  Sebring (G-17047)

Miami Valley Press Inc .... G 937 547-0771
  Greenville (G-10511)

Mpi Labels of Baltimore Inc .... F 330 938-2134
  Sebring (G-17049)

Multi-Color Australia LLC .... B 513 381-1480
  Batavia (G-1210)

Multi-Color Corporation .... D 513 943-0080
  Batavia (G-1212)

Ohio Envelope Manufacturing Co .... E 216 267-2920
  Cleveland (G-5933)

▲ Ohio Gravure Technologies Inc .... E 937 439-1582
  Miamisburg (G-13846)

Quad/Graphics Inc .... A 513 932-1064
  Lebanon (G-11830)

Retterbush Graphic and Packg .... E 513 779-4466
  West Chester (G-19931)

Revenue Management Group LLC .... G 419 993-2200
  Lima (G-12082)

▼ Scratch-Off Systems Inc .... E 216 649-7800
  Brecksville (G-2071)

▲ Shamrock Companies Inc .... G 440 899-9510
  Westlake (G-20308)

Standard Register Inc .... G 866 541-0937
  Dayton (G-8680)

Standard Register Inc .... G 937 228-5800
  Dayton (G-8679)

Toledo Tape and Label Company .... G 419 536-8316
  Toledo (G-18745)

◆ Trebnick Systems Inc .... E 937 743-1550
  Springboro (G-17512)

W L Beck Printing & Design .... G 330 762-3020
  Akron (G-467)

Western Roto Engravers Inc .... E 330 336-7636
  Wadsworth (G-19444)

▲ Wfsr Holdings LLC .... A 877 735-4966
  Dayton (G-8757)

Wilmer .... G 419 678-6000
  Coldwater (G-6574)

World Color (usa) Corp .... G 847 230-1547
  Oberlin (G-15649)

2759 Commercial Printing

3dlt LLC .... F 513 452-3358
  Cincinnati (G-3324)

4d Screenprinting Ltd .... G 513 353-1070
  Cleves (G-6504)

A C Hadley - Printing Inc .... G 937 426-0952
  Beavercreek (G-1314)

A E Wilson Holdings Inc .... G 330 405-0316
  Twinsburg (G-18888)

A Screen Printed Products .... G 419 352-1535
  Bowling Green (G-1961)

A Sign For The Times Inc .... G 216 297-2977
  Cleveland (G-4678)

A Special Touch Embroidery LLC .... G 740 858-2241
  Portsmouth (G-16429)

A To Z Paper Box Co .... G 330 325-8722
  Rootstown (G-16718)

A Z Printing Inc .... G 513 733-3900
  Cincinnati (G-3338)

A Z Printing Inc .... G 513 745-0700
  Cincinnati (G-3339)

A-A Blueprint Co Inc .... E 330 794-8803
  Akron (G-22)

Aardvark Screen Prtg & EMB LLC .... F 419 354-6686
  Bowling Green (G-1964)

Aardvark Sportswear Inc .... G 330 793-9428
  Youngstown (G-21012)

Abl Screen Printing .... G 440 914-0093
  Solon (G-17247)

Able Printing Company .... G 614 294-4547
  Columbus (G-6682)

Ace Transfer Company .... G 937 398-1103
  Springfield (G-17514)

Acme Printing Co Inc .... G 419 626-4426
  Sandusky (G-16944)

Ad Source Inc .... G 330 468-2934
  Peninsula (G-16033)

Adcraft Decals Inc .... E 216 524-2934
  Cleveland (G-4702)

Admiral Products Company Inc .... E 216 671-0600
  Cleveland (G-4706)

▼ Advanced Specialty Products .... D 419 882-6528
  Bowling Green (G-1966)

Adyl Inc .... G 330 797-8700
  Austintown (G-968)

Aero Fulfillment Services Corp .... D 800 225-7145
  Mason (G-12979)

Agnone-Kelly Enterprises Inc .... G 800 634-6503
  Cincinnati (G-3367)

AGS Custom Graphics Inc .... D 330 963-7770
  Macedonia (G-12433)

Akos Promotions Inc .... G 513 398-6324
  Mason (G-12980)

Akron Litho-Print Company Inc .... F 330 434-3145
  Akron (G-47)

Albert Bramkamp Printing Co .... G 513 641-1069
  Cincinnati (G-3376)

▲ Alberts Screen Print Inc .... C 330 753-7559
  Norton (G-15505)

Alfacomp Inc .... G 216 459-1790
  Cleveland (G-4751)

Allied Silk Screen Inc .... G 937 223-4921
  Dayton (G-8148)

Alpha Bus Forms & Prtg LLC .... G 419 999-5138
  Lima (G-11987)

Alvin L Roepke .... F 419 862-3891
  Elmore (G-9360)

Am Graphics .... G 330 799-7319
  Youngstown (G-21022)

American Future Systems Inc .... G 330 758-0277
  Youngstown (G-21023)

Amerigraph Llc .... G 614 278-8000
  Columbus (G-6743)

Ameriprint .... G 440 235-6094
  Olmsted Falls (G-15673)

Amtech Inc .... G 440 238-2141
  Strongsville (G-17888)

Anderson Graphics Inc .... E 330 745-2165
  Barberton (G-1098)

Anthony Business Forms Inc .... F 937 253-0072
  Dayton (G-8096)

Anthony-Lee Screen Prtg Inc .... F 419 683-1861
  Crestline (G-7928)

Appleheart .... G 937 384-0430
  Miamisburg (G-13784)

Art Brands LLC .... E 614 755-4278
  Blacklick (G-1688)

Art Printing Co Inc .... G 419 281-4371
  Ashland (G-705)

Art Tees Inc .... G 614 338-8337
  Columbus (G-6774)

Ashton LLC .... G 614 833-4165
  Pickerington (G-16186)

Associated Graphics Inc .... F 614 873-1273
  Plain City (G-16321)

Assocted Vsual Cmmncations Inc .... E 330 452-4449
  Canton (G-2608)

Atlas Printing and Embroidery .... G 440 882-3537
  Cleveland (G-4856)

Atrium Corp .... G 740 966-8200
  Johnstown (G-11390)

August Graphics Inc .... G 216 381-5503
  Cleveland (G-4858)

Austin Tape and Label Inc .... D 330 928-7999
  Stow (G-17731)

Austintown Printing Inc .... G 330 797-0099
  Youngstown (G-21029)

Axent Graphics LLC .... G 216 362-7560
  Brookpark (G-2152)

B & D Graphics Inc .... G 513 641-0855
  Cincinnati (G-3431)

Baise Enterprises Inc .... G 614 444-3171
  Columbus (G-6801)

Bar Codes Unlimited Inc ....G...... 937 434-2633
Dayton (G-8181)

Barnhart Printing Corp ....F...... 330 456-2279
Canton (G-2616)

Basinger Inc ....G...... 614 771-8300
Columbus (G-6813)

Bates Printing Inc ....F...... 330 833-5830
Massillon (G-13114)

Bayard Inc ....G...... 937 293-1415
Moraine (G-14467)

Bemis Company Inc ....E...... 330 923-5281
Akron (G-87)

Benchmark Prints ....F...... 419 332-7640
Fremont (G-10129)

Berea Printing Company ....G...... 440 243-1080
Berea (G-1605)

Betley Printing Co ....G...... 216 206-5600
Cleveland (G-4910)

Better Living Concepts Inc ....F...... 330 494-2213
Canton (G-2621)

Bindery & Spc Pressworks Inc ....D...... 614 873-4623
Plain City (G-16326)

Bizzy Bee Printing Inc ....G...... 614 771-1222
Columbus (G-6833)

Blue Ribbon Screen Graphics ....G...... 216 226-6200
Avon (G-986)

Bluelogos Inc ....F...... 614 898-9971
Westerville (G-20203)

Bob King Sign Company Inc ....G...... 330 753-2679
Akron (G-94)

Bock & Pierce Enterprises ....G...... 513 474-9500
Cincinnati (G-3455)

Boehm Inc ....E...... 614 875-9010
Grove City (G-10546)

Bohlender Engraving Company ....F...... 513 621-4095
Cincinnati (G-3457)

Boldman Printing LLC ....G...... 937 653-3431
Urbana (G-19148)

Bollin & Sons Inc ....E...... 419 693-6573
Toledo (G-18376)

Bookmyer LLP ....G...... 419 447-3883
Tiffin (G-18210)

Bornhorst Printing Company Inc .....G...... 419 738-5901
Wapakoneta (G-19482)

Bradleys Beacons Ltd ....G...... 419 447-7560
Tiffin (G-18211)

Brahler Inc ....G...... 330 966-7730
Canton (G-2627)

Brakers Publishing & Prtg Svc ....G...... 440 576-0136
Jefferson (G-11357)

Bramkamp Printing Company Inc ....E...... 513 241-1865
Blue Ash (G-1754)

Broadway Printing LLC ....G...... 513 621-3429
Cincinnati (G-3475)

Brothers Printing Co Inc ....F...... 216 621-6050
Cleveland (G-4938)

Brune Printing Co ....G...... 419 399-2756
Paulding (G-16002)

Buckeye Cstm Screen Print EMB ....F...... 614 237-0196
Columbus (G-6872)

Bullseye Activewear Inc ....G...... 330 220-1720
Brunswick (G-2214)

Burns & Rink Enterprises LLC ....G...... 513 421-7799
Cincinnati (G-3487)

Bush Inc ....E...... 216 362-6700
Cleveland (G-4952)

C A I R Ohio ....G...... 513 281-8200
Blue Ash (G-1758)

C P S Enterprises Inc ....F...... 216 441-7969
Cleveland (G-4957)

Campbell Signs & Apparel LLC ....F...... 330 386-4768
East Liverpool (G-9205)

Candy Print Shop ....G...... 937 390-6458
Springfield (G-17526)

Canvas 123 Inc ....G...... 312 805-0563
Akron (G-108)

Cap City Direct LLC ....F...... 614 252-6245
Columbus (G-6894)

Carbonless & Cut Sheet Forms ....F...... 740 826-1700
New Concord (G-14817)

Carey Color Llc/Cincinnati ....F...... 513 241-5210
Cincinnati (G-3499)

Carnegie Promotions Inc ....G...... 440 442-2099
Cleveland (G-4982)

Carroll Exhibit and Print Svcs ....G...... 216 361-2325
Cleveland (G-4985)

▲ Casad Company Inc ....F...... 419 586-9457
Coldwater (G-6555)

Cds Signs ....G...... 513 563-7446
Cincinnati (G-3508)

Centennial Screen Printing ....G...... 419 422-5548
Findlay (G-9805)

Century Graphics Inc ....E...... 614 895-7698
Westerville (G-20142)

Century Marketing Corporation ....G...... 419 354-2591
Bowling Green (G-1977)

▼ Century Marketing Corporation ...C...... 419 354-2591
Bowling Green (G-1978)

Charles Huffman & Associates ....G...... 216 295-0850
Warrensville Heights (G-19630)

Cincinnati Convertors Inc ....F...... 513 731-6600
Cincinnati (G-3545)

Cincinnati Enquirer ....E...... 513 721-2700
Cincinnati (G-3549)

Cincinnati Print Solutions LLC ....G...... 513 943-9500
Amelia (G-570)

Ckm Ventures LLC ....G...... 216 623-0370
Cleveland (G-5040)

Clear Images LLC ....F...... 419 241-9347
Toledo (G-18400)

Cleveland Copy & Prtg Svc LLC ......G...... 216 861-0324
Cleveland (G-5054)

▼ Cleveland Menu Printing Inc ....E...... 216 241-5256
Cleveland (G-5069)

Cleveland Printwear Inc ....G...... 216 521-5500
Cleveland (G-5073)

Cloverleaf Office Slutions LLC ....G...... 614 219-9050
Hilliard (G-10939)

Club 513 LLC ....G...... 800 530-2574
Cincinnati (G-3591)

▲ CMC Group Inc ....D...... 419 352-9567
Bowling Green (G-1981)

Cnr Marketing Ltd ....G...... 937 293-1030
Dayton (G-8233)

Cns Inc ....G...... 513 631-7073
Cincinnati (G-3593)

Cold Duck Screen Prtg & EMB Co ...G...... 330 426-1900
East Palestine (G-9231)

Collegiate Connection ....G...... 419 352-8333
Bowling Green (G-1982)

Color Process Inc ....E...... 440 268-7100
Strongsville (G-17905)

Coloring Book Solutions LLC ....F...... 419 281-9641
Ashland (G-723)

Columbus Humungous Apparel LLC ....G...... 614 824-2657
Columbus (G-6955)

Comdoc Inc ....G...... 330 899-8000
Columbus (G-6970)

Commercial Decal of Ohio Inc ....E...... 330 385-7178
East Liverpool (G-9208)

Concept 9 Inc ....G...... 614 294-3743
Columbus (G-6976)

▲ Consolidated Graphics Group Inc ....C...... 216 881-9191
Cleveland (G-5116)

Consolidated Graphics Inc ....C...... 740 654-2112
Lancaster (G-11699)

Consolidated Web ....G...... 216 881-7816
Cleveland (G-5119)

Contemprary Image Labeling Inc ......G...... 513 583-5699
Lebanon (G-11791)

Copy Cats Printing LLC ....G...... 440 345-5966
Cleveland (G-5132)

Copy Source Inc ....G...... 937 642-7140
Marysville (G-12939)

Cornerstone Industries Lcc ....G...... 513 871-4546
West Chester (G-19845)

Corporate Dcment Solutions Inc ......F...... 513 595-8200
Cincinnati (G-3613)

Corporate Supply LLC ....G...... 614 876-8400
Columbus (G-6986)

Coso Media LLC ....G...... 330 904-5889
Hudson (G-11166)

Cotton Pickin Tees & Caps ....G...... 419 636-3595
Bryan (G-2291)

Cox Printing Co ....G...... 937 382-2312
Wilmington (G-20661)

Crabar/Gbf Inc ....G...... 419 943-2141
Leipsic (G-11868)

Crabro Printing Inc ....G...... 740 533-3404
Ironton (G-11291)

Creative Documents Solutions ....G...... 740 389-4252
Marion (G-12864)

Creative Print Solutions LLC ....G...... 614 989-1747
Westerville (G-20205)

Crest Graphics Inc ....F...... 513 271-2200
Cincinnati (G-3619)

Culaine Inc ....G...... 419 345-4984
Toledo (G-18417)

▲ Custom Deco South Inc ....E...... 419 698-2900
Toledo (G-18418)

▲ Custom Products Corporation ......D...... 440 528-7100
Solon (G-17280)

Custom Screen Printing ....G...... 330 963-3131
Twinsburg (G-18920)

Custom Sportswear Imprints LLC .....G...... 330 335-8326
Wadsworth (G-19400)

Customer Service Systems Inc ....G...... 330 677-2877
Kent (G-11442)

▲ D B Hess Company ....E...... 330 678-5868
Kent (G-11444)

D B Hess Company ....G...... 330 676-2006
Kent (G-11445)

D&D Design Concepts Inc ....F...... 513 752-2191
Batavia (G-1176)

▲ Dana Graphics Inc ....G...... 513 351-4400
Cincinnati (G-3638)

Danner Press Corp ....G...... 330 454-5692
Canton (G-2677)

Danroc Corp ....G...... 330 262-0712
Wooster (G-20763)

Data Image ....E...... 740 763-7017
Heath (G-10846)

Dayton Mailing Services Inc ....G...... 937 222-5056
Dayton (G-8279)

DCS Technologies Corporation ....E...... 937 743-4060
Franklin (G-10018)

Debandale Printing Inc ....G...... 330 725-5122
Medina (G-13401)

Dee Printing Inc ....F...... 614 777-8700
Columbus (G-7017)

Design Graphics Group Inc ....E...... 419 354-8717
Bowling Green (G-1984)

Designer Set ....G...... 937 382-8000
Wilmington (G-20663)

Dietrich Von Hildebrand Legacy ....G...... 703 496-7821
Steubenville (G-17691)

Digital Graphics ....G...... 330 707-1720
Youngstown (G-21069)

Digital Shorts Inc ....G...... 937 228-1700
Dayton (G-8304)

Digital Visuals Inc ....G...... 513 420-9466
Middletown (G-14037)

Diocesan Publications Inc Ohio ....E...... 614 718-9500
Dublin (G-9068)

Direct Digital Graphics Inc ....G...... 330 405-3770
Twinsburg (G-18925)

Divine Prtg T-Shirts & More ....G...... 419 241-8208
Toledo (G-18441)

DK & J Inc ....G...... 216 357-3090
Cleveland (G-5200)

Docupros Inc ....G...... 513 242-7700
Blue Ash (G-1776)

Domicone Printing Inc ....G...... 937 878-3080
Fairborn (G-9619)

Dominion Labels & Forms ....G...... 419 784-1041
Defiance (G-8789)

▲ Donprint Inc ....E...... 847 573-7777
Strongsville (G-17911)

Doug Smith ....G...... 740 345-1398
Newark (G-15000)

Douglas Michalske ....G...... 216 631-0567
Cleveland (G-5210)

DOV Graphics Inc ....E...... 513 241-5150
Cincinnati (G-3668)

Dresden Specialties Inc ....G...... 740 452-7100
Zanesville (G-21302)

Dresden Specialties Inc ....G...... 740 754-2451
Dresden (G-9032)

Drycal Inc ....G...... 440 974-1999
Mentor (G-13566)

DSC Supply Company LLC ....G...... 614 891-1100
Westerville (G-20211)

Dupli-Systems Inc ....C...... 440 234-9415
Strongsville (G-17913)

Durbin Minuteman Press ....G...... 513 791-9171
Blue Ash (G-1778)

Dyenamo Distributing ....F...... 419 462-9474
Galion (G-10264)

◆ Dynamic Design & Systems Inc ....G...... 440 708-1010
Chagrin Falls (G-3085)

E & E Nameplates Inc ....F...... 419 468-3617
Galion (G-10265)

E L Frueh Inc ....F...... 419 222-9741
Lima (G-12007)

Eagle Image Inc ....F...... 513 662-3000
Cincinnati (G-3683)

Earl D Arnold Printing Company ....E...... 513 533-6900
Cincinnati (G-3685)

Eastern Graphic Arts ....G...... 419 994-5815
Loudonville (G-12297)

S I C

Ebel-Binder Printing Co .... G 513 471-1067
Cincinnati (G-3688)

▲ Echographics Inc .... G 440 846-2330
North Ridgeville (G-15371)

Embroidme Co .... G 614 933-9194
Columbus (G-7056)

Empire Printing Inc .... G 513 242-3900
Cincinnati (G-3700)

Emta Inc .... G 440 734-6464
North Olmsted (G-15332)

Erd Specialty Graphics Inc .... F 419 242-9545
Toledo (G-18456)

Everythings Image Inc .... F 513 469-6727
Blue Ash (G-1789)

Evolution Crtive Solutions LLC .... E 513 681-4450
Cincinnati (G-3725)

Exact Software North Amer LLC .... C 978 539-6186
Dublin (G-9075)

Exchange Printing Company .... G 330 773-7842
Akron (G-173)

Expert TS .... G 330 263-4588
Wooster (G-20770)

Express Graphic Prtg & Design .... G 513 728-3344
Cincinnati (G-3731)

Exxcite Marketing Inc .... G 513 271-4550
Cincinnati (G-3733)

F J Designs Inc .... E 330 264-1377
Wooster (G-20771)

Fair Publishing House Inc .... E 419 668-3746
Norwalk (G-15540)

Federal Barcode Label Systems .... G 440 748-8060
North Ridgeville (G-15373)

Fedex Office & Print Svcs Inc .... E 614 898-0000
Westerville (G-20214)

Fedex Office & Print Svcs Inc .... F 937 335-3816
Troy (G-18827)

Fine Line Embroidery Company .... G 440 331-7030
Rocky River (G-16699)

Firelands Fas-Print LLC .... G 419 668-3045
Norwalk (G-15541)

First Impression Wear .... G 937 456-3900
Eaton (G-9306)

First Stop Signs and Decals .... G 330 343-1859
New Philadelphia (G-14899)

Five Star Graphics Inc .... G 330 545-5077
Girard (G-10388)

Flex Pro Label Inc .... G 513 489-4417
Blue Ash (G-1795)

Folks Creative Printers Inc .... E 740 383-6326
Marion (G-12865)

Foote Printing Company .... F 216 431-1757
Cleveland (G-5367)

▲ Forward Movement Publications .... F 513 721-6659
Cincinnati (G-3774)

Freeport Press Inc .... C 740 658-3315
Freeport (G-10118)

Fulton Sign & Decal Inc .... G 440 951-1515
Mentor (G-13587)

Functional Imaging Ltd .... G 740 689-2466
Lancaster (G-11717)

Future Screen Inc .... G 440 838-5055
Cleveland (G-5386)

G Q Business Products .... G 513 792-4750
Blue Ash (G-1801)

G2 Print Plus .... F 614 276-0500
Columbus (G-7105)

Gail Berner .... G 937 322-0314
Springfield (G-17563)

Gail Zeilmann .... G 440 888-4858
Cleveland (G-5391)

Gateway Packaging Company .... G 419 738-5126
Wapakoneta (G-19486)

GBS Corp .... E 330 929-8050
Stow (G-17758)

▲ GBS Corp .... C 330 494-5330
North Canton (G-15233)

GCI Digital Imaging Inc .... F 513 521-7446
Cincinnati (G-3802)

▲ General Data Company Inc .... C 513 752-7978
Cincinnati (G-3304)

General Theming Contrs LLC .... G 614 252-6342
Columbus (G-7108)

Genesis Graphics .... G 937 335-5332
Troy (G-18831)

Genesis Quality Printing Inc .... G 440 975-5700
Mentor (G-13592)

Geygan Enterprises Inc .... F 513 932-4222
Lebanon (G-11803)

Glauners Wholesale Inc .... G 216 398-7088
Cleveland (G-5432)

Glavin Industries Inc .... E 440 349-0049
Solon (G-17297)

Glen D Lala .... G 937 274-7770
Dayton (G-8366)

Golden Graphics Ltd .... F 419 673-6260
Kenton (G-11548)

Good JP .... G 419 207-8484
Ashland (G-735)

Gordon Bernard Company LLC .... E 513 248-7600
Milford (G-14147)

Gordons Graphics Inc .... G 330 863-2322
Malvern (G-12546)

Grady McCauley Incorporated .... D 330 494-9444
North Canton (G-15236)

Grant John .... G 937 298-0633
Dayton (G-8376)

Graphic Paper Products Corp .... G 937 325-3912
Springfield (G-17566)

Graphic Stitch Inc .... G 937 642-6707
Marysville (G-12945)

Graphic Touch Inc .... G 330 337-3341
Salem (G-16896)

Graphics To Go LLC .... G 937 382-4100
Wilmington (G-20666)

Graphix Junction .... G 234 284-8392
Hudson (G-11176)

Great Lakes Printing Inc .... D 440 993-8781
Ashtabula (G-810)

Gym Pro LLC .... G 740 984-4143
Waterford (G-19648)

H & H Screen Process Inc .... G 937 253-7520
Dayton (G-8381)

▲ Haines & Company Inc .... C 330 494-9111
North Canton (G-15237)

▲ Haman Enterprises Inc .... F 614 888-7574
Worthington (G-20869)

Handcrafted Jewelry Inc .... G 330 650-9011
Hudson (G-11178)

Harper Engraving & Printing Co .... D 614 276-0700
Columbus (G-7144)

Harris & Company Inc .... G 330 332-4127
Salem (G-16899)

Hartman Distributing LLC .... D 740 616-7764
Heath (G-10847)

Hawks & Associates Inc .... E 513 752-4311
Cincinnati (G-3308)

Heartland Publications LLC .... F 860 664-1075
Miamisburg (G-13816)

Heartland Publications LLC .... F 740 446-2342
Gallipolis (G-10300)

Hecks Direct Mail & Prtg Svc .... E 419 697-3505
Toledo (G-18502)

Heskamp Printing Co Inc .... G 513 871-6770
Cincinnati (G-3881)

Hilltop Printing .... G 419 782-9898
Defiance (G-8793)

Hkm Drect Mkt Cmmnications Inc ..... E 440 934-3060
Sheffield Village (G-17122)

Hkm Drect Mkt Cmmnications Inc ..... E 330 395-9538
Cleveland (G-5517)

Hkm Drect Mkt Cmmnications Inc ..... C 216 651-9500
Cleveland (G-5516)

Hoffee John .... G 330 868-3553
Minerva (G-14325)

Hollys Custom Print Inc .... E 740 928-2697
Hebron (G-10871)

Holmes Prcut/Troyer Imprinting .... G 330 359-0000
Dundee (G-9173)

Homeguard Products Inc .... G 616 846-0804
Baltimore (G-1083)

Homestretch Inc .... G 419 738-6604
Wapakoneta (G-19488)

Homestretch Sportswear Inc .... F 419 678-4282
Saint Henry (G-16818)

Homewood Press Inc .... E 419 478-0695
Toledo (G-18510)

Hooven - Dayton Corp .... G 937 233-4473
Miamisburg (G-13818)

Horizon Ohio Publications Inc .... E 419 738-2128
Wapakoneta (G-19489)

Humtown Pattern Company .... D 330 482-5555
Columbiana (G-6621)

Hyde Brothers Prtg & Mktg LLC .... G 740 373-2054
Marietta (G-12792)

Hypodermic Designs LLC .... G 614 203-4048
Columbus (G-7174)

Illusions Screenprinting .... G 330 263-7770
Wooster (G-20785)

Image Print Inc .... G 614 776-3985
Westerville (G-20158)

Imagemart Inc .... G 216 486-4767
Cleveland (G-5552)

Imagine This Renovations .... G 330 833-6739
Navarre (G-14716)

Impressions - A Print Shop .... G 440 449-6966
Cleveland (G-5558)

Industrial Screen Process .... F 419 255-4900
Toledo (G-18522)

Inktastic Inc .... F 330 345-0911
Wooster (G-20787)

Innomark Communications LLC .... C 513 285-1040
Miamisburg (G-13819)

Innovtive Crtive Solutions LLC .... E 614 491-9638
Groveport (G-10626)

▲ Innovtive Lbling Solutions Inc ...... D 513 860-2457
Hamilton (G-10706)

Inskeep Brothers Inc .... F 614 898-6620
Columbus (G-7189)

Instant Impressions Inc .... G 614 538-9844
Columbus (G-7191)

Integrity Printing .... G 937 331-5390
Dayton (G-8414)

Intermec Technologies Corp .... F 513 874-5882
West Chester (G-19884)

Intermec Ultra Print Inc .... C 513 874-5882
West Chester (G-19885)

International Advg Concepts .... G 440 331-4733
Cleveland (G-5579)

International Business Solutio .... F 937 853-0348
Dayton (G-8415)

Irwin Engraving & Printing Co .... G 216 391-7300
Cleveland (G-5589)

J & K Printing .... G 330 456-5306
Canton (G-2742)

J P Quality Printing Inc .... G 216 791-6303
Cleveland (G-5598)

J-M Designs Inc .... G 419 794-2114
Maumee (G-13269)

▲ Jack G Walker .... F 440 352-4222
Mentor (G-13617)

Jarman Printing Company LLC .... G 330 823-8585
Alliance (G-519)

Jazz Textile Impressions .... G 419 242-5940
Maumee (G-13270)

Jeffrey Reedy .... G 614 794-9292
Westerville (G-20219)

Jim Davis .... G 740 335-8030
Wshngtn CT Hs (G-20914)

Jjkb Enterprises LLC .... G 513 731-4332
Cincinnati (G-3946)

Joe Paxton .... G 614 424-9000
Columbus (G-7237)

Joe Sestito .... G 614 871-7778
Grove City (G-10566)

John C Starr .... G 740 852-5592
London (G-12213)

Johnson Printing .... G 740 922-4821
Uhrichsville (G-19053)

Jones & Assoc Advg & Design .... G 330 799-6876
Youngstown (G-21127)

Jscs Group Inc .... G 513 563-4900
Cincinnati (G-3961)

▲ Kaufman Container Company .... C 216 898-2000
Cleveland (G-5636)

Kay Toledo Tag Inc .... D 419 729-5479
Toledo (G-18541)

Kdm Signs Inc .... C 513 769-1932
Cincinnati (G-3975)

Kee Printing Inc .... G 937 456-6851
Eaton (G-9312)

Kehoe Brothers Printing Inc .... G 216 351-4100
Cleveland (G-5641)

Keithley Enterprises Inc .... G 937 890-1878
Dayton (G-8434)

Kendra Screen Print .... G 440 967-8820
Vermilion (G-19330)

Kens His & Hers Shop Inc .... G 330 872-3190
Newton Falls (G-15134)

Kenwel Printers Inc .... E 614 261-1011
Columbus (G-7257)

Keteli Teamwear LLC .... G 740 373-7969
Marietta (G-12797)

Key Marketing Group .... G 440 748-3479
Grafton (G-10432)

Key Press Inc .... G 513 721-1203
Cincinnati (G-3987)

Keystone Press Inc .... G 419 243-7326
Toledo (G-18544)

Keystone Printing & Copy Cat .... G 740 354-6542
Portsmouth (G-16439)

KMS 2000 Inc F 330 454-9444
Canton *(G-2756)*
▲ **Kramer Graphics Inc** E 937 296-9600
Moraine *(G-14499)*
Krok Printing Inc G 330 652-8198
Niles *(G-15166)*
KS Designs Inc G 513 241-5953
Cincinnati *(G-4005)*
Labeltek Inc D 330 335-3110
Wadsworth *(G-19417)*
Lake Screen Printing Inc G 440 244-5707
Lorain *(G-12254)*
Lamar D Steiner G 330 466-1479
Millersburg *(G-14239)*
Lamar Proforma G 440 285-2277
Chardon *(G-3163)*
Landen Desktop Pubg Ctr Inc G 513 683-5181
Loveland *(G-12370)*
Larmax Inc G 513 984-0783
Blue Ash *(G-1825)*
Laser Printing Solutions Inc F 216 351-4444
Cleveland *(G-5684)*
Laughing Star Montessory G 513 683-5682
Maineville *(G-12527)*
Lazer Systems Inc F 513 641-4002
Cincinnati *(G-4016)*
Lee Corporation F 513 771-3602
Cincinnati *(G-4019)*
Leeper Printing Co Inc G 419 243-2604
Toledo *(G-18556)*
Legendary Ink Inc G 614 766-5101
Columbus *(G-7290)*
Lesher Printers Inc E 419 332-8253
Fremont *(G-10163)*
Letterman Printing Inc G 513 523-1111
Oxford *(G-15839)*
Liberty Sportswear LLC G 513 755-8740
West Chester *(G-19893)*
Lilienthal Southeastern Inc F 740 439-1640
Cambridge *(G-2464)*
Lima Sporting Goods Inc E 419 222-1036
Lima *(G-12046)*
Liming Printing Inc F 937 374-2646
Xenia *(G-20961)*
Locker Room Inc G 419 445-9600
Archbold *(G-684)*
Locker Room Lettering Ltd G 419 359-1761
Castalia *(G-2977)*
Logan Screen Printing G 740 385-3303
Logan *(G-12185)*
Logos On Lee G 216 862-5226
Cleveland *(G-5708)*
Loris Printing Inc G 419 626-6648
Sandusky *(G-16981)*
Lsc Communications Us LLC C 419 935-0111
Willard *(G-20396)*
LSI Industries Inc E 513 793-3200
Blue Ash *(G-1829)*
Lund Printing Co G 330 628-4047
Akron *(G-277)*
Lyle Printing & Publishing Co E 330 337-3419
Salem *(G-16909)*
M L Advertising & Design LLC G 419 447-6523
Tiffin *(G-18230)*
M PI Label Systems G 330 938-2134
Sebring *(G-17047)*
Mac Printing Company G 937 393-1101
Hillsboro *(G-11007)*
Madison Graphics G 216 226-5770
Cleveland *(G-5726)*
Madison Press Inc G 216 521-3789
Lakewood *(G-11673)*
Magnetic Mktg Solutions LLC G 513 721-3801
Cincinnati *(G-4053)*
Marazita Graphics Inc G 330 773-6462
Akron *(G-283)*
Marbee Inc G 419 422-9441
Findlay *(G-9858)*
Marcus Uppe Inc D 216 263-4000
Cleveland *(G-5742)*
Margaret Trentman G 513 948-1700
Cincinnati *(G-4059)*
Mariotti Printing Co LLC G 440 245-4120
Lorain *(G-12259)*
Markethatch Co Inc F 330 376-6363
Akron *(G-285)*
Marketing Comm Resource Inc D 440 484-3010
Willoughby *(G-20538)*
Martin Printing Co G 419 224-9176
Lima *(G-12051)*

Marysville Printing Company G 937 644-4959
Marysville *(G-12958)*
Matthew Koster G 440 887-9000
Valley City *(G-19216)*
McDaniel Envelope Co Inc F 330 868-5929
Minerva *(G-14332)*
McPc Imaging and Printing LLC G 419 627-9872
Sandusky *(G-16987)*
Meders Special Tees G 513 921-3800
Cincinnati *(G-4076)*
Metro Flex Inc G 937 299-5360
Moraine *(G-14506)*
Meyers Printing & Design Inc G 937 461-6000
Dayton *(G-8488)*
Miami Graphics Services Inc F 937 698-4013
West Milton *(G-20108)*
Miami Valley Press Inc G 937 547-0771
Greenville *(G-10511)*
▲ **Microplex Printware Corp** F 440 374-2424
Bedford *(G-1443)*
Mid Ohio Screen Print Inc G 614 875-1774
Grove City *(G-10572)*
Mid West Dry Sift G 614 946-3797
Columbus *(G-7348)*
Middaugh Enterprises Inc F 330 852-2471
Sugarcreek *(G-18026)*
Middleton Printing Co Inc G 614 294-7277
Gahanna *(G-10219)*
Mike B Crawford G 330 673-7944
Kent *(G-11492)*
Minuteman Press of Athens LLC G 740 593-7393
Athens *(G-878)*
Miracle Documents G 513 651-2222
Cincinnati *(G-4111)*
ML Erectors LLC G 440 328-3227
Elyria *(G-9464)*
Mmp Printing Inc E 513 381-0990
Cincinnati *(G-4112)*
Modern Displays Inc G 513 471-1639
Cincinnati *(G-4114)*
Mojo Sportsgear G 614 864-6656
Columbus *(G-7362)*
Moonshine Screen Printing Inc F 513 523-7775
Oxford *(G-15840)*
Morrison Sign Company Inc E 614 276-1181
Columbus *(G-7371)*
Morse Enterprises Inc G 513 229-3600
Mason *(G-13066)*
Mound Printing Company Inc E 937 866-2872
Miamisburg *(G-13838)*
Mpi Labels of Baltimore Inc F 330 938-2134
Sebring *(G-17049)*
Mr Label Inc E 513 681-2088
Cincinnati *(G-4128)*
Multi-Color Australia LLC B 513 381-1480
Batavia *(G-1210)*
▲ **Multi-Color Corporation** F 513 381-1480
Batavia *(G-1211)*
Multi-Color Corporation D 513 943-0080
Batavia *(G-1212)*
Nelis Printing Co G 330 757-4114
Youngstown *(G-21149)*
Network Printing & Graphics F 614 230-2084
Columbus *(G-7387)*
News Gazette Printing Company F 419 227-2527
Lima *(G-12063)*
Newton Falls Printing G 330 872-3532
Newton Falls *(G-15137)*
Niklee Co G 440 944-0082
Willoughby Hills *(G-20643)*
◆ **Nilpeter Usa Inc** C 513 489-4400
Cincinnati *(G-4156)*
Nomis Publications Inc F 330 965-2380
Youngstown *(G-21150)*
Nordec Inc D 330 940-3700
Stow *(G-17784)*
Northeastern Plastics Inc G 330 453-5925
Canton *(G-2795)*
▲ **Novavision Inc** D 419 354-1427
Bowling Green *(G-2003)*
Novex Systems LLC E 330 659-3546
Akron *(G-320)*
Odyssey Press Inc F 614 410-0356
Huron *(G-11236)*
Odyssey Spirits Inc F 330 562-1523
Aurora *(G-938)*
▲ **Off Contact Inc** F 419 255-5546
Toledo *(G-18614)*
Ohio Envelope Manufacturing Co E 216 267-2920
Cleveland *(G-5933)*

Ohio Flexible Packaging Co F 513 494-1800
South Lebanon *(G-17430)*
Old Trail Printing Company C 614 443-4852
Columbus *(G-7440)*
Onetouchpoint East Corp D 513 421-1600
Cincinnati *(G-4189)*
▼ **Packaging Materials Inc** E 740 432-6337
Cambridge *(G-2471)*
Painted Hill Inv Group Inc F 937 339-1756
Troy *(G-18861)*
Papel Couture G 614 848-5700
Columbus *(G-7458)*
Paper Occasions G 614 761-8880
Dublin *(G-9116)*
Paragon Press G 513 281-9911
Cincinnati *(G-4211)*
Park PLC Prntg Cpyg & Dgtl IMG G 330 799-1739
Youngstown *(G-21164)*
Park Press Direct G 419 626-4426
Sandusky *(G-16993)*
Peebles Creative Group Inc G 614 487-2011
Dublin *(G-9120)*
Penca Design Group Ltd G 440 210-4422
Painesville *(G-15910)*
Penguin Enterprises Inc E 440 899-5110
Westlake *(G-20292)*
Penton Media Inc A 216 696-7000
Cleveland *(G-5991)*
Pep Pony Express Printing Inc G 513 542-4882
Cincinnati *(G-4222)*
Perfection Printing F 513 874-2173
Fairfield *(G-9701)*
Pexco Packaging Corp E 419 470-5935
Toledo *(G-18642)*
PJ Bush Associates Inc E 216 362-6700
Cleveland *(G-6009)*
Pops Printed Apparel LLC G 614 372-5651
Columbus *(G-7504)*
Post Printing Co D 859 254-7714
Minster *(G-14359)*
Powell Prints LLC G 614 771-4830
Hilliard *(G-10971)*
Precision Graphic Services F 419 241-5189
Toledo *(G-18653)*
Precision Imprint G 740 592-5916
Athens *(G-882)*
▲ **Premier Southern Ticket Co Inc** E 513 489-6700
Cincinnati *(G-4267)*
Premiere Printing & Signs Inc G 330 688-6244
Stow *(G-17791)*
Press of Ohio Inc E 330 678-5868
Kent *(G-11506)*
Primal Screen Inc E 330 677-1766
Kent *(G-11507)*
Printcraft Inc G 440 599-8903
Conneaut *(G-7817)*
Printex Incorporated F 740 773-0088
Chillicothe *(G-3268)*
Printing Depot Inc G 330 783-5341
Youngstown *(G-21179)*
Profile Digital Printing LLC E 937 866-4241
Dayton *(G-8599)*
Proforma Advantage G 440 781-5255
Mayfield Village *(G-13325)*
Proforma Steinbacher & Assoc G 330 241-5370
Medina *(G-13463)*
Proforma Systems Advantage G 419 224-8747
Lima *(G-12076)*
Progressive Printers Inc D 937 222-1267
Dayton *(G-8601)*
Proline Screenwear G 440 205-3700
Mentor *(G-13702)*
PS Graphics Inc G 440 356-9656
Rocky River *(G-16706)*
Quali-Tee Design Sports F 937 382-7997
Wilmington *(G-20675)*
Qualitee Design Sportswear Co F 740 333-8337
Wshngtn CT Hs *(G-20922)*
Quality Print Shop Inc G 740 992-3345
Middleport *(G-14011)*
Quebecor World Johnson Hardin A 614 326-0299
Cincinnati *(G-4312)*
Queen City Office Machine F 513 251-7200
Cincinnati *(G-4317)*
Quick As A Wink Printing Co F 419 224-9786
Lima *(G-12079)*
Quick Tech Business Forms Inc E 937 743-5952
Springboro *(G-17501)*
R C L Enterprises Inc G 972 390-6500
Cincinnati *(G-4323)*

SIC

Employee Codes: A=Over 500 employees, B=251-500
C=101-250, D=51-100, E=20-50, F=10-19, G=3-9

R W Michael Printing Co ....G....... 330 923-9277
   Akron (G-363)

R&D Marketing Group Inc ....G....... 216 398-9100
   Brooklyn Heights (G-2145)

Research and Development Group ....G....... 614 261-0454
   Columbus (G-7556)

Reynolds and Reynolds Company ....G....... 937 485-4771
   Dayton (G-8629)

Reynolds and Reynolds Company ....F....... 419 584-7000
   Celina (G-3017)

Richardson Supply LLC ....G....... 614 539-3033
   Grove City (G-10589)

Rising Moon Custom Apparel ....G....... 614 882-1336
   Westerville (G-20232)

Rl Smith Printing Co ....F....... 330 747-9590
   Youngstown (G-21189)

Robert Esterman ....G....... 513 541-3311
   Cincinnati (G-4353)

Robert H Shackelford ....G....... 330 364-2221
   New Philadelphia (G-14926)

Rotary Printing Company ....G....... 419 668-4821
   Norwalk (G-15563)

RR Donnelley & Sons Company ......G....... 513 552-1512
   West Chester (G-19939)

RR Donnelley & Sons Company ......B....... 740 928-6110
   Hebron (G-10882)

RR Donnelley & Sons Company ......D....... 330 562-5250
   Streetsboro (G-17872)

RR Donnelley & Sons Company ......A....... 419 935-0111
   Willard (G-20400)

RR Donnelley & Sons Company ......E....... 440 774-2101
   Oberlin (G-15647)

Rush Graphix Ltd ....G....... 419 448-7874
   Tiffin (G-18241)

▲ Ruthie Ann Inc ....F....... 800 231-3567
   New Paris (G-14881)

Rutland Plastic Tech Inc ....G....... 614 846-3055
   Columbus (G-7578)

Ryans Newark Leader Ex Prtg ....F....... 740 522-2149
   Newark (G-15051)

S F Mock & Associates LLC ....F....... 937 438-0196
   Dayton (G-8644)

Sams Graphic Industries ....F....... 330 821-4710
   Alliance (G-536)

Samuels Products Inc ....E....... 513 891-4456
   Blue Ash (G-1864)

Sandy Smittcamp ....G....... 937 372-1687
   Xenia (G-20971)

Saturn Press Inc ....G....... 440 232-3344
   Bedford (G-1460)

Schilling Graphics Inc ....E....... 419 468-1037
   Galion (G-10286)

Schlabach Printing Ltd ....E....... 330 852-4687
   Sugarcreek (G-18038)

▼ Scratch-Off Systems Inc ....E....... 216 649-7800
   Brecksville (G-2071)

Screen Craft Plastics ....G....... 440 286-4060
   Chardon (G-3178)

Screen Tech Graphics ....G....... 740 695-7950
   Saint Clairsville (G-16807)

Scriptype Publishing Inc ....E....... 330 659-0303
   Richfield (G-16635)

Selby Service/Roxy Press Inc ....G....... 513 241-3445
   Cincinnati (G-4400)

Seneca Label Inc ....E....... 440 237-1600
   Cleveland (G-6180)

▲ Sensical Inc ....D....... 216 641-1141
   Solon (G-17378)

Sevell + Sevell Inc ....G....... 614 341-9700
   Columbus (G-7611)

Sharon Printing Co Inc ....G....... 330 239-1684
   Sharon Center (G-17110)

Shirtwork ....G....... 937 322-7507
   Springfield (G-17648)

Shops By Todd Inc ....G....... 937 458-3192
   Beavercreek (G-1360)

Shreve Printing LLC ....F....... 330 567-2341
   Shreve (G-17163)

Sign Lady Inc ....G....... 419 476-9191
   Toledo (G-18696)

Signs By George ....G....... 216 394-2095
   Brookfield (G-2126)

Silica Press Inc ....G....... 419 843-8500
   Sylvania (G-18125)

Silk Screen Special TS Inc ....G....... 740 246-4843
   Thornville (G-18199)

Sitler Printer Inc ....G....... 330 482-4463
   Columbiana (G-6632)

Slimans Printery Inc ....F....... 330 454-9141
   Canton (G-2851)

Slutzkers Quickprint Center ....G....... 440 244-0330
   Lorain (G-12278)

Small Dog Printing ....G....... 614 777-7620
   Hilliard (G-10979)

Smartbill Ltd ....F....... 740 928-6909
   Hebron (G-10885)

SMS Communications Inc ....E....... 216 374-6686
   Shaker Heights (G-17095)

Snow Printing Co Inc ....F....... 419 229-7669
   Lima (G-12093)

Snyder Printing LLC ....G....... 740 353-3947
   Portsmouth (G-16455)

Solution Ventures Inc ....G....... 440 242-1658
   Avon Lake (G-1051)

Somerset Commercial Prtg Co ....G....... 740 536-7187
   Rushville (G-16753)

South End Printing Co ....G....... 216 341-0669
   Cleveland (G-6222)

Spear USA Inc ....C....... 513 459-1100
   Mason (G-13088)

Special Touch Midnight Press ....G....... 740 596-5380
   South Bloomingville (G-17423)

Specialtee Sportswear & Design ....G....... 614 877-0976
   Orient (G-15724)

Specialty Printing and Proc ....F....... 614 322-9035
   Columbus (G-7637)

Spectrum Embroidery Inc ....G....... 937 847-9905
   Dayton (G-8669)

Spencer-Walker Press Inc ....G....... 740 345-4494
   Newark (G-15056)

Spencer-Walker Press Inc ....F....... 740 344-6110
   Newark (G-15055)

Sports Express ....G....... 330 297-1112
   Ravenna (G-16559)

Springdot Inc ....D....... 513 542-4000
   Cincinnati (G-4448)

◆ SRC Liquidation LLC ....A....... 937 221-1000
   Dayton (G-8672)

▲ SRI Ohio Inc ....D....... 740 653-5800
   Lancaster (G-11755)

Srm Graphics Inc ....G....... 614 263-4433
   Columbus (G-7648)

Stadvec Inc ....G....... 330 644-7724
   Barberton (G-1150)

Standard Register Inc ....C....... 419 678-6000
   Coldwater (G-6572)

Standard Register Inc ....C....... 614 277-7500
   Grove City (G-10598)

Standard Register Inc ....E....... 860 870-2063
   Dayton (G-8676)

Standout Stickers Inc ....G....... 877 449-7703
   Medina (G-13483)

Star Calendar & Printing Co ....G....... 216 741-3223
   Cleveland (G-6237)

Star Printing Company Inc ....E....... 330 376-0514
   Akron (G-415)

Starr Printing Services Inc ....G....... 513 241-7708
   Cincinnati (G-4460)

State-Mate Company ....G....... 740 392-9487
   Mount Vernon (G-14652)

Stationery Shop Inc ....G....... 330 376-2033
   Akron (G-416)

Stephen Andrews Inc ....G....... 330 725-2672
   Lodi (G-12170)

Stephens Publishing Co Inc ....G....... 419 626-5592
   Sandusky (G-17010)

Steves Sports Inc ....G....... 440 735-0044
   Bedford Heights (G-1494)

Stolle Machinery Company LLC ....C....... 937 497-5400
   Sidney (G-17230)

▲ Studio Eleven Inc ....E....... 937 295-2225
   Fort Loramie (G-9941)

Studs N Hip Hop ....G....... 614 477-0786
   Columbus (G-7663)

Suburban Press Inc ....E....... 216 961-0766
   Cleveland (G-6260)

▲ Suntwist Corp ....E....... 800 935-3534
   Maple Heights (G-12741)

Superior Label Systems Inc ....B....... 513 336-0825
   Mason (G-13092)

T & L Custom Screening Inc ....G....... 937 237-3121
   Dayton (G-8695)

T K L Lettering ....G....... 937 832-2091
   Englewood (G-9540)

Tag ....G....... 614 921-1732
   Columbus (G-7674)

Tech/III Inc ....E....... 513 482-7500
   Cincinnati (G-4497)

Tewell & Associates ....G....... 440 543-5190
   Chagrin Falls (G-3125)

The Label Team Inc ....F....... 330 332-1067
   Salem (G-16929)

Thomas Allen Co ....G....... 330 823-8487
   Alliance (G-544)

Thomas Products Co Inc ....E....... 513 756-9009
   Cincinnati (G-4507)

Tj Metzgers ....D....... 419 861-8611
   Toledo (G-18726)

Toledo Signs & Designs Ltd ....G....... 419 843-1073
   Toledo (G-18742)

Toledo Ticket Company ....E....... 419 476-5424
   Toledo (G-18746)

Tope Printing Inc ....G....... 330 674-4993
   Millersburg (G-14271)

◆ Transfer Express Inc ....D....... 440 918-1900
   Mentor (G-13755)

Traxium LLC ....E....... 330 572-8200
   Stow (G-17811)

◆ Trebnick Systems Inc ....E....... 937 743-1550
   Springboro (G-17512)

Tree Free Resources LLC ....F....... 740 751-4844
   Marion (G-12908)

Triangle Label Inc ....G....... 513 242-2822
   West Chester (G-19961)

Trinity Printing Co ....F....... 513 469-1000
   Cincinnati (G-4526)

▲ Underground Sport Shop Inc ....F....... 513 751-1662
   Cincinnati (G-4535)

Unisport Inc ....F....... 419 529-4727
   Ontario (G-15696)

United Sport Apparel ....F....... 330 722-0818
   Medina (G-13493)

Unlimited Promotions Inc ....G....... 513 844-2211
   Fairfield (G-9727)

Uptown Dog The Inc ....G....... 740 592-4600
   Athens (G-889)

US Government Publishing Off ....G....... 614 469-5657
   Columbus (G-7727)

Vagabond Creations Inc ....G....... 937 298-1124
   Moraine (G-14536)

Value Added Business Svcs Co ....G....... 614 854-9755
   Jackson (G-11332)

▲ Vgu Industries Inc ....E....... 216 676-9093
   Cleveland (G-6414)

Victory Postcards Inc ....G....... 614 764-8975
   Columbus (G-7740)

Viewpoint Graphic Design ....G....... 419 447-6073
   Tiffin (G-18252)

Vision Press Inc ....G....... 440 357-6362
   Painesville (G-15937)

Visual Information Institute ....F....... 937 376-4361
   Xenia (G-20985)

Vya Inc ....E....... 513 772-5400
   Cincinnati (G-4573)

Ward/Kraft Forms of Ohio Inc ....D....... 740 694-0015
   Fredericktown (G-10116)

Warren Printing & Off Pdts Inc ....F....... 419 523-3635
   Ottawa (G-15814)

Water Drop Media Inc ....G....... 234 600-5817
   Vienna (G-19377)

Watson Haran & Company Inc ....G....... 937 436-1414
   Dayton (G-8747)

West Carrollton Parchment ....E....... 513 594-3341
   West Carrollton (G-19794)

▲ West-Camp Press Inc ....D....... 614 818-6279
   Westerville (G-20241)

Western Ohio Graphics ....F....... 937 335-8769
   Troy (G-18885)

Western Reserve Printing ....G....... 330 650-9800
   Hudson (G-11209)

Western Roto Engravers Inc ....E....... 330 336-7636
   Wadsworth (G-19444)

▲ Wfsr Holdings LLC ....A....... 877 735-4966
   Dayton (G-8757)

Wilkinson Printing Co ....G....... 419 238-3615
   Van Wert (G-19276)

William J Bergen & Co ....G....... 440 248-6132
   Solon (G-17414)

William J Dupps ....G....... 419 734-2126
   Port Clinton (G-16419)

Williams Steel Rule Die Co ....F....... 216 431-3232
   Cleveland (G-6464)

Wingate Packaging South ....E....... 513 745-8600
   Blue Ash (G-1895)

Wirick Press Inc ....G....... 330 273-3488
   Brunswick (G-2269)

Wolfe Associates Inc ....G....... 614 461-5000
   Columbus (G-7771)

X Press Printing Services Inc ....F....... 440 951-8848
   Willoughby (G-20633)

Yi Xing Inc....G.... 614 785-9631
Columbus *(G-7784)*
Yockey Group Inc....E.... 513 860-9053
West Chester *(G-19975)*
Youngstown ARC Engraving Co....E.... 330 793-2471
Youngstown *(G-21245)*
Zech Printing Industries Inc....E.... 937 748-2776
Cincinnati *(G-4618)*
Zenos Activewear Inc....G.... 614 443-0070
Columbus *(G-7787)*
Zippity Print....G.... 216 438-0001
Cleveland *(G-6497)*

2761 Manifold Business Forms

Anderson Graphics Inc....E.... 330 745-2165
Barberton *(G-1098)*
Anthony Business Forms Inc....F.... 937 253-0072
Dayton *(G-8096)*
Crabar/Gbf Inc....E.... 419 269-1720
Toledo *(G-18415)*
Crabar/Gbf Inc....G.... 419 943-2141
Leipsic *(G-11868)*
▲ Custom Products Corporation....D.... 440 528-7100
Solon *(G-17280)*
Delores E OBeirn....G.... 440 582-3610
Cleveland *(G-5182)*
Dupli-Systems Inc....C.... 440 234-9415
Strongsville *(G-17913)*
Eleet Cryogenics Inc....E.... 330 874-4009
Bolivar *(G-1933)*
Feld Printing Co....G.... 513 271-6806
Cincinnati *(G-3749)*
GBS Corp....C.... 330 863-1828
Malvern *(G-12545)*
▲ GBS Corp....C.... 330 494-5330
North Canton *(G-15233)*
Geygan Enterprises Inc....F.... 513 932-4222
Lebanon *(G-11803)*
Highland Computer Forms Inc....D.... 937 393-4215
Hillsboro *(G-11001)*
Hubert Enterprises Inc....G.... 513 367-8600
Harrison *(G-10783)*
▲ Kroy LLC....C.... 216 426-5600
Cleveland *(G-5666)*
Lakeshore Graphic Industries....F.... 419 626-8631
Sandusky *(G-16978)*
Little Printing Company....E.... 937 773-4595
Piqua *(G-16286)*
▲ Misato Computer Products Inc....G.... 937 890-8410
Vandalia *(G-19305)*
Print-Digital Incorporated....G.... 330 686-5945
Stow *(G-17792)*
Quick Tech Graphics Inc....E.... 937 743-5952
Springboro *(G-17502)*
Reynolds and Reynolds Company....F.... 419 584-7000
Celina *(G-3017)*
Reynolds and Reynolds Company....E.... 937 449-4039
Dayton *(G-8630)*
Reynolds and Reynolds Company....F.... 937 485-2805
Beavercreek *(G-1379)*
Rotary Forms Press Inc....E.... 937 393-3426
Hillsboro *(G-11013)*
RR Donnelley & Sons Company....E.... 440 774-2101
Oberlin *(G-15647)*
S F Mock & Associates LLC....F.... 937 438-0196
Dayton *(G-8644)*
▲ Shawnee Systems Inc....D.... 513 561-9932
Cincinnati *(G-4414)*
◆ SRC Liquidation LLC....A.... 937 221-1000
Dayton *(G-8672)*
Standard Register Inc....F.... 513 772-8860
Cincinnati *(G-4454)*
Standard Register Inc....F.... 513 563-9700
Blue Ash *(G-1874)*
Standard Register Inc....G.... 440 974-1611
Mentor *(G-13730)*
Standard Register Inc....D.... 216 265-9612
Richfield *(G-16640)*
Standard Register Inc....E.... 860 870-2063
Dayton *(G-8676)*
Standard Register Inc....F.... 732 356-0081
Dayton *(G-8677)*
Standard Register Inc....G.... 480 763-1900
Dayton *(G-8678)*
Standard Register Inc....D.... 937 221-3347
Grove City *(G-10599)*
Standard Register Inc....G.... 937 228-5800
Dayton *(G-8679)*
Tcp Inc....G.... 330 836-4239
Fairlawn *(G-9764)*

Thomas Products Co Inc....E.... 513 756-9009
Cincinnati *(G-4507)*
Unit Sets Inc....E.... 937 840-6123
Hillsboro *(G-11017)*
▲ Wfsr Holdings LLC....A.... 877 735-4966
Dayton *(G-8757)*

2771 Greeting Card Publishing

◆ American Greetings Corporation....A.... 216 252-7300
Cleveland *(G-4782)*
American Greetings Corporation....G.... 216 685-9167
Cleveland *(G-4783)*
Century Intermediate Holdg Co....F.... 216 252-7300
Cleveland *(G-5006)*
Frogs In Bloom....G.... 330 678-9508
Kent *(G-11460)*
Gibson Greetings Inc....G.... 216 252-7300
Cleveland *(G-5428)*
Naptime Productions LLC....F.... 419 662-9521
Rossford *(G-16743)*
▲ Plus Mark LLC....E.... 216 252-6770
Cleveland *(G-6018)*
Those Charc From Cleve Inc....F.... 216 252-7300
Cleveland *(G-6323)*
Vagabond Creations Inc....G.... 937 298-1124
Moraine *(G-14536)*

2782 Blankbooks & Looseleaf Binders

A H Pelz Co....G.... 216 861-1882
Cleveland *(G-4674)*
Acco Brands Corporation....E.... 937 495-5723
Kettering *(G-11572)*
Art Guild Binders Inc....E.... 513 242-3000
Cincinnati *(G-3414)*
Beck & Orr Inc....G.... 614 276-8809
Columbus *(G-6816)*
Bell Binders LLC....F.... 419 242-3201
Toledo *(G-18365)*
▲ Chilcote Company....C.... 216 781-6000
Cleveland *(G-5028)*
Custom Cut UPS Scapbooking....G.... 330 698-5164
Apple Creek *(G-635)*
Cuyahoga Community College....G.... 216 987-4744
Cleveland *(G-5157)*
Deluxe Corporation....C.... 330 342-1500
Hudson *(G-11168)*
Dupli-Systems Inc....C.... 440 234-9415
Strongsville *(G-17913)*
Ed Thomas....G.... 937 325-4300
Springfield *(G-17551)*
Elken Co....G.... 513 459-7207
Maineville *(G-12523)*
Farmers National Banc Corp....F.... 330 726-8896
Youngstown *(G-21083)*
Gotta Groove Records Inc....E.... 216 431-7373
Cleveland *(G-5440)*
Lilienthal Southeastern Inc....F.... 740 439-1640
Cambridge *(G-2464)*
M & R Phillips Enterprises....F.... 740 323-0580
Newark *(G-15032)*
Mueller Art Cover & Binding Co....E.... 440 238-3303
Strongsville *(G-17944)*
My Scrapbook Paradise LLC....G.... 419 584-1393
Celina *(G-3011)*
Quick Tech Graphics Inc....E.... 937 743-5952
Springboro *(G-17502)*
Scrapbook Gallery....G.... 419 523-4419
Ottawa *(G-15807)*
Tenacity Manufacturing Company....E.... 513 821-0201
West Chester *(G-19955)*
W N Albums and Frames Inc....G.... 800 325-5179
Cleveland *(G-6435)*
William Exline Inc....E.... 216 941-0800
Cleveland *(G-6463)*

2789 Bookbinding

21st Century Printers Inc....G.... 513 771-4150
Cincinnati *(G-3322)*
A-1 Printing Inc....F.... 419 562-3111
Bucyrus *(G-2330)*
A-A Blueprint Co Inc....E.... 330 794-8803
Akron *(G-22)*
AAA Laminating & Bindery....G.... 513 860-2680
Fairfield *(G-9637)*
▲ Activities Press Inc....E.... 440 953-1200
Mentor *(G-13509)*
AGS Custom Graphics Inc....D.... 330 963-7770
Macedonia *(G-12433)*
Allen Graphics Inc....G.... 440 349-4100
Solon *(G-17253)*

Anderson Graphics Inc....E.... 330 745-2165
Barberton *(G-1098)*
Aran Inc....G.... 216 464-1508
Cleveland *(G-4821)*
Archival Conservation Center....G.... 513 861-3268
Cincinnati *(G-3412)*
Art Guild Binders Inc....E.... 513 242-3000
Cincinnati *(G-3414)*
B & B Bindery Inc....G.... 330 722-5430
Medina *(G-13375)*
Baise Enterprises Inc....G.... 614 444-3171
Columbus *(G-6801)*
Barnhart Printing Corp....F.... 330 456-2279
Canton *(G-2616)*
Bernard Specialty Co....G.... 216 881-2200
Cleveland *(G-4907)*
Bill Wyatt Inc....G.... 330 535-1113
Mentor *(G-13535)*
Bindery & Spc Pressworks Inc....D.... 614 873-4623
Plain City *(G-16326)*
Bindery Tech Inc....F.... 440 934-3247
Avon *(G-985)*
Bindusa....F.... 513 247-3000
Blue Ash *(G-1751)*
Bip Printing Solutions LLC....F.... 216 832-5673
Beachwood *(G-1259)*
Blains Folding Service Inc....G.... 216 631-4700
Cleveland *(G-4914)*
Bock & Pierce Enterprises....G.... 513 474-9500
Cincinnati *(G-3455)*
Boldman Printing LLC....G.... 937 653-3431
Urbana *(G-19148)*
Bookbinders Incorporated....G.... 330 848-4980
Barberton *(G-1111)*
Bookcolor Bindery Services....E.... 614 252-2941
Columbus *(G-6846)*
▼ Bookfactory LLC....E.... 937 226-7100
Dayton *(G-8191)*
Century Graphics Inc....E.... 614 895-7698
Westerville *(G-20142)*
Cleveland Letter Service Inc....E.... 216 781-8300
Chagrin Falls *(G-3052)*
Clints Printing Inc....G.... 937 426-2771
Beavercreek *(G-1373)*
Commercial Bindery Inc....G.... 419 517-9914
Toledo *(G-18408)*
▲ Consolidated Graphics Group Inc....C.... 216 881-9191
Cleveland *(G-5116)*
Copley Ohio Newspapers Inc....C.... 330 364-5577
New Philadelphia *(G-14892)*
COS Blueprint Inc....F.... 330 376-0022
Akron *(G-130)*
Cott Systems Inc....D.... 614 847-4405
Columbus *(G-6989)*
Cox Printing Co....G.... 937 382-2312
Wilmington *(G-20661)*
Customformed Products Inc....F.... 937 388-0480
Miamisburg *(G-13795)*
D & S Crtive Cmmunications Inc....D.... 419 524-6699
Mansfield *(G-12591)*
▲ D B Hess Company....E.... 330 678-5868
Kent *(G-11444)*
D B Hess Company....G.... 330 676-2006
Kent *(G-11445)*
Dayton Bindery Service Inc....E.... 937 235-3111
Dayton *(G-8269)*
Debandale Printing Inc....G.... 330 725-5122
Medina *(G-13401)*
Delphos Herald Inc....D.... 419 695-0015
Delphos *(G-8905)*
Douglas Michalske....G.... 216 631-0567
Cleveland *(G-5210)*
Durbin Minuteman Press....G.... 513 791-9171
Blue Ash *(G-1778)*
E L Frueh Inc....F.... 419 222-9741
Lima *(G-12007)*
E Z Binderys....G.... 513 733-0005
Cincinnati *(G-3680)*
Earl D Arnold Printing Company....E.... 513 533-6900
Cincinnati *(G-3685)*
Easterdays Printing Center....G.... 330 726-1182
Youngstown *(G-21073)*
Eugene Stewart....G.... 937 898-1117
Dayton *(G-8333)*
Fedex Office & Print Svcs Inc....E.... 419 866-5464
Toledo *(G-18466)*
Fedex Office & Print Svcs Inc....E.... 937 436-0677
Dayton *(G-8339)*
Fedex Office & Print Svcs Inc....F.... 614 575-0800
Reynoldsburg *(G-16590)*

Fedex Office & Print Svcs Inc ....E 216 573-1511
Cleveland *(G-5333)*

Fergusons Finishing Inc ....E 419 241-9123
Toledo *(G-18469)*

Folks Creative Printers Inc ....E 740 383-6326
Marion *(G-12865)*

Frank J Prucha & Associates ....G 216 642-3838
Cleveland *(G-5378)*

Franklins Printing Company ....F 740 452-6375
Zanesville *(G-21311)*

G W Steffen Bookbinders Inc ....E 330 963-0300
Macedonia *(G-12454)*

Ganger Enterprises Inc ....G 614 776-3985
Westerville *(G-20154)*

Golden Graphics Ltd ....F 419 673-6260
Kenton *(G-11548)*

Grant John ....G 937 298-0633
Dayton *(G-8376)*

▲ Great Lakes Integrated Inc ....D 216 651-1500
Cleveland *(G-5452)*

Greg Blume ....G 740 574-2308
Wheelersburg *(G-20332)*

Harris & Company Inc ....F 330 332-4127
Salem *(G-16899)*

Harris Paper Crafts Inc ....F 614 299-2141
Columbus *(G-7145)*

Hecks Direct Mail & Prtg Svc ....E 419 697-3505
Toledo *(G-18502)*

Henry Bussman ....G 614 224-0417
Columbus *(G-7150)*

Homewood Press Inc ....E 419 478-0695
Toledo *(G-18510)*

Hopewell Industries Inc ....D 740 622-3563
Coshocton *(G-7895)*

ICI Binding Corp ....E 440 729-2445
Chesterland *(G-3213)*

Innomark Communications LLC ....E 937 454-5555
Dayton *(G-8404)*

Irvin Oslin Inc ....G 216 361-7555
Cleveland *(G-5588)*

▲ Jack G Walker ....F 440 352-4222
Mentor *(G-13617)*

Kad Holdings Inc ....G 614 792-3399
Dublin *(G-9093)*

Kehl-Kolor Inc ....G 419 281-3107
Ashland *(G-746)*

Kenwel Printers Inc ....E 614 261-1011
Columbus *(G-7257)*

Kevin K Tidd ....G 419 885-5603
Sylvania *(G-18115)*

Keystone Press Inc ....G 419 243-7326
Toledo *(G-18544)*

Keystone Printing & Copy Cat ....G 740 354-6542
Portsmouth *(G-16439)*

L B Folding Co Inc ....G 216 961-0888
Cleveland *(G-5670)*

Laipplys Prtg Mktg Sltions Inc ....G 740 387-9282
Marion *(G-12879)*

Lam Pro Inc ....E 216 426-0661
Cleveland *(G-5678)*

Lee Corporation ....F 513 771-3602
Cincinnati *(G-4019)*

Legal News Publishing Co ....E 216 696-3322
Cleveland *(G-5692)*

Lilienthal Southeastern Inc ....F 740 439-1640
Cambridge *(G-2464)*

Lund Printing Co ....G 330 628-4047
Akron *(G-277)*

Macke Brothers Inc ....D 513 771-7500
Cincinnati *(G-4048)*

Mmp Printing Inc ....E 513 381-0990
Cincinnati *(G-4112)*

Monco Enterprises Inc ....A 937 461-0034
Dayton *(G-8507)*

Montview Corporation ....G 330 723-3409
Medina *(G-13449)*

Nari Inc ....G 440 960-2280
Monroeville *(G-14427)*

Network Printing & Graphics ....F 614 230-2084
Columbus *(G-7387)*

Newfax Corporation ....F 419 241-5157
Toledo *(G-18603)*

North End Press Incorporated ....E 740 653-6514
Lancaster *(G-11734)*

Ohio Laminating & Binding Inc ....E 419 771-4868
Hilliard *(G-10966)*

Old Trail Printing Company ....C 614 443-4852
Columbus *(G-7440)*

Onetouchpoint East Corp ....D 513 421-1600
Cincinnati *(G-4189)*

Orange Blossom Press Inc ....G 216 781-8655
Willoughby *(G-20562)*

Orrville Printing Co Inc ....G 330 682-5066
Orrville *(G-15752)*

Painesville Publishing Co ....G 440 354-4142
Austinburg *(G-964)*

Patricia Lee Burd ....G 513 302-4860
Cincinnati *(G-4214)*

Penguin Enterprises Inc ....E 440 899-5110
Westlake *(G-20292)*

Pooles Printing & Office Svcs ....G 419 475-9000
Toledo *(G-18649)*

Precision Graphic Services ....F 419 241-5189
Toledo *(G-18653)*

Prime Printing Inc ....E 937 438-3707
Dayton *(G-8594)*

Print-Digital Incorporated ....G 330 686-5945
Stow *(G-17792)*

Printed Image ....F 614 221-1412
Columbus *(G-7519)*

▲ Printers Bindery Services Inc ....D 513 821-8039
Cincinnati *(G-4271)*

Progressive Folding Binding Co ....G 216 621-1893
Northfield *(G-15470)*

Promatch Solutions LLC ....F 937 299-0185
Springboro *(G-17500)*

▼ Quick Tab II Inc ....D 419 448-6622
Tiffin *(G-18238)*

R T Industries Inc ....G 937 335-5784
Troy *(G-18865)*

R W Michael Printing Co ....G 330 923-9277
Akron *(G-363)*

▲ Repro Acquisition Company LLC .....E 216 738-3800
Cleveland *(G-6104)*

Ricci Anthony ....G 330 758-5761
Youngstown *(G-21188)*

Rmt Holdings Inc ....F 419 221-1168
Lima *(G-12085)*

Robert Esterman ....G 513 541-3311
Cincinnati *(G-4353)*

Robert H Shackelford ....G 330 364-2221
New Philadelphia *(G-14926)*

Robin Enterprises Company ....C 614 891-0250
Westerville *(G-20233)*

Ryans Newark Leader Ex Prtg ....F 740 522-2149
Newark *(G-15051)*

Sandy Smittcamp ....G 937 372-1687
Xenia *(G-20971)*

Slutzkers Quickprint Center ....G 440 244-0330
Lorain *(G-12278)*

Spencer-Walker Press Inc ....F 740 344-6110
Newark *(G-15055)*

Spring Grove Manufacturing ....F 513 542-6900
Cincinnati *(G-4445)*

Springdale Bindery LLC ....G 513 772-8500
Cincinnati *(G-4446)*

Springfield Engraving Company ....G 937 390-0011
Springfield *(G-17651)*

Standard Register Inc ....G 937 228-5800
Dayton *(G-8679)*

Star Printing Company Inc ....E 330 376-0514
Akron *(G-415)*

Strong Bindery ....G 216 231-0001
Cleveland *(G-6256)*

Suburban Press Inc ....G 216 961-0766
Cleveland *(G-6260)*

Target Printing & Graphics ....G 937 228-0170
Dayton *(G-8700)*

The Bookseller Inc ....G 330 865-5831
Akron *(G-436)*

Tj Metzgers Inc ....D 419 861-8611
Toledo *(G-18726)*

TL Krieg Offset Inc ....E 513 542-1522
Cincinnati *(G-4511)*

Tomahawk Printing Inc ....F 419 335-3161
Wauseon *(G-19697)*

Traxium LLC ....E 330 572-8200
Stow *(G-17811)*

Watkins Printing Company ....G 614 297-8270
Columbus *(G-7752)*

▲ West-Camp Press Inc ....D 614 818-6279
Westerville *(G-20241)*

▲ Wfsr Holdings LLC ....A 877 735-4966
Dayton *(G-8757)*

William J Dupps ....G 419 734-2126
Port Clinton *(G-16419)*

Youngstown ARC Engraving Co ....E 330 793-2471
Youngstown *(G-21245)*

2791 Typesetting

21st Century Printers Inc ....G 513 771-4150
Cincinnati *(G-3322)*

A-1 Printing Inc ....F 419 562-3111
Bucyrus *(G-2330)*

A-A Blueprint Co Inc ....E 330 794-8803
Akron *(G-22)*

▲ Activities Press Inc ....E 440 953-1200
Mentor *(G-13509)*

Advanced Translation/Cnsltng ....E 440 716-0820
Westlake *(G-20246)*

AGS Custom Graphics Inc ....D 330 963-7770
Macedonia *(G-12433)*

Ajeh & Company Unlimited ....G 440 729-2367
Chesterland *(G-3196)*

Alfacomp Inc ....G 216 459-1790
Cleveland *(G-4751)*

Anderson Graphics Inc ....E 330 745-2165
Barberton *(G-1098)*

Anthony Business Forms Inc ....F 937 253-0072
Dayton *(G-8096)*

Art Printing Co Inc ....G 419 281-4371
Ashland *(G-705)*

Art Tees Inc ....G 614 338-8337
Columbus *(G-6774)*

Asist Inc ....F 614 451-6744
Columbus *(G-6777)*

Baise Enterprises Inc ....G 614 444-3171
Columbus *(G-6801)*

Beer Communications Inc ....G 419 756-6882
Mansfield *(G-12566)*

Bill Wyatt Inc ....G 330 535-1113
Mentor *(G-13535)*

Bindery & Spc Pressworks Inc ....D 614 873-4623
Plain City *(G-16326)*

Blt Inc ....F 513 631-5050
Norwood *(G-15571)*

Bock & Pierce Enterprises ....G 513 474-9500
Cincinnati *(G-3455)*

Boldman Printing LLC ....G 937 653-3431
Urbana *(G-19148)*

Bookmasters Inc ....C 419 281-1802
Ashland *(G-713)*

Brothers Publishing Co LLC ....E 937 548-3330
Greenville *(G-10490)*

Camelot Typesetting Company ....G 216 574-8973
Cleveland *(G-4964)*

Canton Graphic Arts Service ....G 330 456-9868
Canton *(G-2641)*

Capozzolo Printers Inc ....G 513 542-7874
Cincinnati *(G-3496)*

Carlisle Prtg Walnut Creek Ltd ....E 330 852-9922
Sugarcreek *(G-18020)*

Clints Printing Inc ....G 937 426-2771
Beavercreek *(G-1373)*

Cold Duck Screen Prtg & EMB Co ....G 330 426-1900
East Palestine *(G-9231)*

Colortech Graphics & Printing ....F 614 766-2400
Columbus *(G-6944)*

▲ Consoldated Graphics Group Inc .....C 216 881-9191
Cleveland *(G-5116)*

Copley Ohio Newspapers Inc ....C 330 364-5577
New Philadelphia *(G-14892)*

Cornerstone Industries Lcc ....G 513 871-4546
West Chester *(G-19845)*

COS Blueprint Inc ....F 330 376-0022
Akron *(G-130)*

Crabar/Gbf Inc ....G 419 943-2141
Leipsic *(G-11868)*

Customer Service Systems Inc ....G 330 677-2877
Kent *(G-11442)*

D & S Crtive Cmmunications Inc ....D 419 524-6699
Mansfield *(G-12591)*

Daily Gazette ....G 937 372-4444
Xenia *(G-20945)*

Daubenmires Printing ....G 513 425-7223
Middletown *(G-14036)*

Debandale Printing Inc ....G 330 725-5122
Medina *(G-13401)*

Dorothy Crooker ....G 513 385-0888
Cincinnati *(G-3665)*

Douglas Michalske ....G 216 631-0567
Cleveland *(G-5210)*

DOV Graphics Inc ....G 513 241-5150
Cincinnati *(G-3668)*

Dove Cds Inc ....G 330 928-3430
Tallmadge *(G-18143)*

E L Frueh Inc ....F 419 222-9741
Lima *(G-12007)*

Earl D Arnold Printing Company ....E 513 533-6900
Cincinnati (G-3685)

Easterdays Printing Center ....G 330 726-1182
Youngstown (G-21073)

Emta Inc ....G 440 734-6464
North Olmsted (G-15332)

Eugene Stewart ....G 937 898-1117
Dayton (G-8333)

Fedex Office & Print Svcs Inc ....E 937 436-0677
Dayton (G-8339)

Fedex Office & Print Svcs Inc ....E 614 621-1100
Columbus (G-7080)

Fedex Office & Print Svcs Inc ....F 614 575-0800
Reynoldsburg (G-16590)

Fedex Office & Print Svcs Inc ....E 216 573-1511
Cleveland (G-5333)

Fedex Office & Print Svcs Inc ....E 419 866-5464
Toledo (G-18466)

Flexoplate Inc ....E 513 489-0433
Blue Ash (G-1796)

Frank J Prucha & Associates ....G 216 642-3838
Cleveland (G-5378)

Franklins Printing Company ....F 740 452-6375
Zanesville (G-21311)

Gazette Publishing Company ....E 419 483-4190
Oberlin (G-15640)

Genesis Quality Printing Inc ....G 440 975-5700
Mentor (G-13592)

George D Kanaan & Associates ....G 440 243-6410
Berea (G-1617)

Geygan Enterprises Inc ....F 513 932-4222
Lebanon (G-11803)

Graphic Image ....G 937 320-0302
Beavercreek (G-1341)

Graphic Touch Inc ....G 330 337-3341
Salem (G-16896)

Greg Blume ....G 740 574-2308
Wheelersburg (G-20332)

Harlan Graphic Arts Svcs Inc ....E 513 251-5700
Cincinnati (G-3866)

Hecks Direct Mail & Prtg Svc ....E 419 697-3505
Toledo (G-18502)

Henderson Builders Inc ....G 419 665-2684
Gibsonburg (G-10377)

Heritage Press Inc ....E 419 289-9209
Ashland (G-738)

Hilleary-Whitaker Inc ....G 614 766-4694
Columbus (G-7157)

Hkm Drect Mkt Cmmnications Inc ....C 216 651-9500
Cleveland (G-5516)

Homewood Press Inc ....E 419 478-0695
Toledo (G-18510)

HOT Graphic Services Inc ....E 419 242-7000
Northwood (G-15483)

Hubbard Publishing Co ....E 937 592-3060
Bellefontaine (G-1533)

Image Industries Inc ....G 937 832-7969
Englewood (G-9524)

Imprints ....G 330 650-0467
Hudson (G-11181)

▲ Jack G Walker ....F 440 352-4222
Mentor (G-13617)

Jim Davis ....G 740 335-8030
Wshngtn CT Hs (G-20914)

Kad Holdings Inc ....G 614 792-3399
Dublin (G-9093)

Keener Printing Inc ....F 216 531-7595
Cleveland (G-5640)

Kehl-Kolor Inc ....E 419 281-3107
Ashland (G-746)

Kevin K Tidd ....G 419 885-5603
Sylvania (G-18115)

Keystone Press Inc ....G 419 243-7326
Toledo (G-18544)

Keystone Printing & Copy Cat ....G 740 354-6542
Portsmouth (G-16439)

La Dua Inc ....G 440 243-9600
Olmsted Twp (G-15679)

Landen Desktop Pubg Ctr Inc ....G 513 683-5181
Loveland (G-12370)

Larry C White ....G 330 386-3228
East Liverpool (G-9224)

Laurenee Ltd LLC ....G 513 662-2225
Cincinnati (G-4015)

Lee Corporation ....F 513 771-3602
Cincinnati (G-4019)

Legal News Publishing Co ....E 216 696-3322
Cleveland (G-5692)

Liming Printing Inc ....F 937 374-2646
Xenia (G-20961)

Lund Printing Co ....G 330 628-4047
Akron (G-277)

M Web Type Inc ....G 614 272-8973
Columbus (G-7310)

Margaret Trentman ....G 513 948-1700
Cincinnati (G-4059)

Middleton Printing Co Inc ....G 614 294-7277
Gahanna (G-10219)

Mmp Printing Inc ....E 513 381-0990
Cincinnati (G-4112)

Montview Corporation ....G 330 723-3409
Medina (G-13449)

Nari Inc ....G 440 960-2280
Monroeville (G-14427)

Network Printing & Graphics ....F 614 230-2084
Columbus (G-7387)

Newfax Corporation ....F 419 241-5157
Toledo (G-18603)

Newspaper Holding Inc ....D 440 998-2323
Ashtabula (G-826)

Old Trail Printing Company ....C 614 443-4852
Columbus (G-7440)

Onetouchpoint East Corp ....D 513 421-1600
Cincinnati (G-4189)

Orange Blossom Press Inc ....G 216 781-8655
Willoughby (G-20562)

Orrville Printing Co Inc ....G 330 682-5066
Orrville (G-15752)

Painesville Publishing Co ....G 440 354-4142
Austinburg (G-964)

Paul/Jay Associates ....G 740 676-8776
Bellaire (G-1500)

Penguin Enterprises Inc ....E 440 899-5110
Westlake (G-20292)

Performa La Mar Printing Inc ....G 440 632-9800
Middlefield (G-13981)

Photo-Type Engraving Company ....F 614 308-1900
Columbus (G-7483)

Photo-Type Engraving Company ....F 614 308-7914
Columbus (G-7484)

Plott Graphic Directions Inc ....G 614 475-0217
Columbus (G-7500)

Pooles Printing & Office Svcs ....G 419 475-9000
Toledo (G-18649)

Preisser Inc ....E 614 345-0199
Columbus (G-7514)

Prime Printing Inc ....E 937 438-3707
Dayton (G-8594)

Printed Image ....F 614 221-1412
Columbus (G-7519)

Printing Arts Press ....F 740 397-6106
Mount Vernon (G-14639)

Progressive Communications ....D 740 397-5333
Mount Vernon (G-14640)

Quad/Graphics Inc ....C 614 276-4800
Columbus (G-7531)

Quick As A Wink Printing Co ....F 419 224-9786
Lima (G-12079)

▼ Quick Tab II Inc ....D 419 448-6622
Tiffin (G-18238)

Quick Tech Graphics Inc ....E 937 743-5952
Springboro (G-17502)

R & W Printing Company ....G 513 575-0131
Loveland (G-12379)

R B Robinson Inc ....G 440 543-5547
Chagrin Falls (G-3116)

R W Michael Printing Co ....G 330 923-9277
Akron (G-363)

Registered Images Inc ....G 859 781-9200
Cincinnati (G-4335)

Ricci Anthony ....G 330 758-5761
Youngstown (G-21188)

River Corp ....G 513 641-3355
Cincinnati (G-4348)

Robert Esterman ....G 513 541-3311
Cincinnati (G-4353)

Robin Enterprises Company ....C 614 891-0250
Westerville (G-20233)

Robs Creative Screen Printing ....G 740 264-6383
Wintersville (G-20713)

▲ Royal Acme Corporation ....E 216 241-1477
Cleveland (G-6136)

RR Donnelley & Sons Company ....G 614 221-8385
Columbus (G-7576)

Ryans Newark Leader Ex Prtg ....F 740 522-2149
Newark (G-15051)

S O S Graphics & Printing Inc ....G 614 846-8229
Worthington (G-20886)

Sandy Smittcamp ....G 937 372-1687
Xenia (G-20971)

Sharon Printing Co Inc ....G 330 239-1684
Sharon Center (G-17110)

Sjpm Inc ....G 614 475-4571
Gahanna (G-10233)

South End Printing Co ....G 216 341-0669
Cleveland (G-6222)

Spencer-Walker Press Inc ....F 740 344-6110
Newark (G-15055)

Springfield Engraving Company ....G 937 390-0011
Springfield (G-17651)

▲ St Media Group Intl Inc ....D 513 421-2050
Blue Ash (G-1873)

Stationery Shop Inc ....G 330 376-2033
Akron (G-416)

Stumbo Publishing Co ....G 419 529-2847
Ontario (G-15695)

Suburban Press Inc ....E 216 961-0766
Cleveland (G-6260)

Target Business Services ....F 614 866-4065
Pickerington (G-16207)

Target Printing & Graphics ....G 937 228-0170
Dayton (G-8700)

Technical Translation Services ....G 440 942-3130
Willoughby (G-20611)

Tim L Humbert ....F 330 497-4944
Canton (G-2870)

Tj Metzgers Inc ....D 419 861-8611
Toledo (G-18726)

Ulrich Rubber Stamp Company ....G 419 339-9939
Elida (G-9359)

W L Beck Printing & Design ....G 330 762-3020
Akron (G-467)

Watkins Printing Company ....E 614 297-8270
Columbus (G-7752)

▲ West-Camp Press Inc ....D 614 818-6279
Westerville (G-20241)

Western Roto Engravers Inc ....E 330 336-7636
Wadsworth (G-19444)

▲ Wfsr Holdings LLC ....A 877 735-4966
Dayton (G-8757)

Winkler Co Inc ....G 937 294-2662
Dayton (G-8761)

Wolters Kluwer Clinical Drug ....D 330 650-6506
Hudson (G-11210)

Youngstown ARC Engraving Co ....E 330 793-2471
Youngstown (G-21245)

2796 Platemaking & Related Svcs

Acme Printing Co Inc ....G 419 626-4426
Sandusky (G-16944)

▲ Amos Press Inc ....C 937 498-2111
Sidney (G-17168)

Anderson & Vreeland Inc ....D 419 636-5002
Bryan (G-2278)

Art-American Printing Plates ....E 216 241-4420
Cleveland (G-4836)

B & B Trophies & Awards ....G 330 225-6193
Brunswick (G-2209)

Bock & Pierce Enterprises ....G 513 474-9500
Cincinnati (G-3455)

Bomen Marking Products Inc ....G 440 582-0053
Cleveland (G-4922)

Capital Engraving Company ....G 440 237-7760
Cleveland (G-4970)

Carey Color Inc ....D 330 239-1835
Sharon Center (G-17103)

Carey Color Inc /cincinnati ....E 513 241-5210
Cincinnati (G-3498)

Centec Cast Metal Products ....G 419 355-1414
Fremont (G-10135)

Century Graphics Inc ....E 614 895-7698
Westerville (G-20142)

Converters/Prepress Inc ....G 937 743-0935
Carlisle (G-2929)

Csw of Ny Inc ....F 413 589-1311
Sylvania (G-18102)

Custom Cntrwght Plate Proc Inc ....G 330 448-2347
Masury (G-13214)

Customer Service Systems Inc ....G 330 677-2877
Kent (G-11442)

Dorothy Crooker ....G 513 385-0888
Cincinnati (G-3665)

E C Shaw Co ....E 513 721-6334
Cincinnati (G-3677)

Earl D Arnold Printing Company ....E 513 533-6900
Cincinnati (G-3685)

Econo Products Inc ....F 330 923-4101
Cuyahoga Falls (G-7989)

Fine Lines Laser Engraving ....G 419 337-6313
Wauseon (G-19677)

Flexoplate Inc ....E 513 489-0433
  Blue Ash *(G-1796)*

FT Group Inc ....E 937 746-6439
  Cincinnati *(G-3786)*

Grant John ....G 937 298-0633
  Dayton *(G-8376)*

▲ Great Lakes Integrated Inc ....D 216 651-1500
  Cleveland *(G-5452)*

Great Lakes Integrated Inc ....E 440 892-7760
  Avon Lake *(G-1030)*

Hadronics Inc ....D 513 321-9350
  Cincinnati *(G-3861)*

Harris Paper Crafts Inc ....F 614 299-2141
  Columbus *(G-7145)*

Jerry Pulfer ....G 937 778-1861
  Piqua *(G-16283)*

Kehl-Kolor Inc ....E 419 281-3107
  Ashland *(G-746)*

Keystone Press Inc ....E 419 243-7326
  Toledo *(G-18544)*

Lazer Systems Inc ....F 513 641-4002
  Cincinnati *(G-4016)*

Linger Photo Engraving Corp ....G 513 579-1380
  Cincinnati *(G-4026)*

Litho-Craft Lithography Inc ....E 513 542-6404
  Cincinnati *(G-4028)*

M Russell & Associates Inc ....G 419 478-8795
  Toledo *(G-18567)*

Mark-All Enterprises LLC ....E 800 433-3615
  Akron *(G-284)*

Massillon Plaque Company ....F 330 494-4199
  Canton *(G-2771)*

Master Marking Company Inc ....E 330 688-6797
  Stow *(G-17772)*

Northmont Sign Co Inc ....G 937 890-0372
  Dayton *(G-8528)*

Peck Engraving Co ....E 216 221-1556
  Cleveland *(G-5987)*

Penguin Enterprises Inc ....E 440 899-5110
  Westlake *(G-20292)*

Pinnacle Graphics & Imaging ....F 216 781-1800
  Cleveland *(G-6008)*

Plate Engraving Corporation ....F 330 239-2155
  Medina *(G-13462)*

Precision Reflex Inc ....F 419 629-2603
  New Bremen *(G-14792)*

Prime Printing Inc ....E 937 438-3707
  Dayton *(G-8594)*

Quality Rubber Stamp Inc ....G 614 235-2700
  Columbus *(G-7536)*

R E May Inc ....F 216 771-6332
  Cleveland *(G-6081)*

R W Michael Printing Co ....G 330 923-9277
  Akron *(G-363)*

Registered Images Inc ....G 859 781-9200
  Cincinnati *(G-4335)*

Roban Inc ....G 330 794-1059
  Lakemore *(G-11645)*

Robert H Shackelford ....G 330 364-2221
  New Philadelphia *(G-14926)*

Sams Graphic Industries ....F 330 821-4710
  Alliance *(G-536)*

Shamrock Plastics Inc ....F 740 392-5555
  Mount Vernon *(G-14646)*

South End Printing Co ....G 216 341-0669
  Cleveland *(G-6222)*

Springfield Engraving Company ....G 937 390-0011
  Springfield *(G-17651)*

Stevenson Color Inc ....C 513 321-7500
  Cincinnati *(G-4466)*

Summit Finishing Technologies ....G 937 424-5512
  Moraine *(G-14533)*

Universal Urethane Pdts Inc ....D 419 693-7400
  Toledo *(G-18760)*

▲ West-Camp Press Inc ....D 614 818-6279
  Westerville *(G-20241)*

Westrock CP LLC ....C 937 898-2115
  Dayton *(G-8754)*

Williams Steel Rule Die Co ....F 216 431-3232
  Cleveland *(G-6464)*

◆ Wood Graphics Inc ....E 513 771-6300
  Cincinnati *(G-4603)*

Youngstown ARC Engraving Co ....E 330 793-2471
  Youngstown *(G-21245)*

28 CHEMICALS AND ALLIED PRODUCTS

2812 Alkalies & Chlorine

▲ Ashta Chemicals Inc ....D 440 997-5221
  Ashtabula *(G-793)*

Church & Dwight Co Inc ....D 740 852-3621
  London *(G-12204)*

Church & Dwight Co Inc ....F 419 992-4244
  Old Fort *(G-15670)*

Clorox Company ....F 513 445-1840
  Mason *(G-13001)*

Clorox Sales Company ....E 440 892-1700
  Westlake *(G-20261)*

Gbc Metals LLC ....G 330 823-1700
  Alliance *(G-510)*

◆ GFS Chemicals Inc ....E 740 881-5501
  Powell *(G-16472)*

Jci Jones Chemicals Inc ....F 330 825-2531
  New Franklin *(G-14826)*

▲ National Colloid Company ....E 740 282-1171
  Steubenville *(G-17706)*

National Lime and Stone Co ....C 419 396-7671
  Carey *(G-2921)*

Occidental Chemical Corp ....E 513 242-2900
  Cincinnati *(G-4172)*

Occidental Chemical Corp ....E 330 764-3441
  Medina *(G-13451)*

PPG Industries Inc ....E 419 683-2400
  Crestline *(G-7935)*

▲ Valvsys LLC ....G 513 539-1234
  Monroe *(G-14417)*

2813 Industrial Gases

Air Products and Chemicals Inc ....D 513 420-3663
  Middletown *(G-14013)*

Air Products and Chemicals Inc ....F 216 781-2801
  Cleveland *(G-4734)*

Air Products and Chemicals Inc ....G 513 242-9215
  Cincinnati *(G-3369)*

Airgas Merchant Gases LLC ....E 330 454-1330
  Canton *(G-2593)*

Airgas Usa LLC ....F 419 228-2828
  Lima *(G-11983)*

Airgas Usa LLC ....G 440 232-6397
  Oakwood Village *(G-15622)*

Airgas USA LLC ....F 513 563-9400
  Cincinnati *(G-3371)*

Airgas USA LLC ....E 937 228-8594
  Dayton *(G-8142)*

Airgas USA LLC ....G 419 726-2719
  Toledo *(G-18325)*

C A P Industries Inc ....F 937 773-1824
  Piqua *(G-16254)*

Continental Carbonic Pdts Inc ....G 614 491-4327
  Obetz *(G-15654)*

Continental Carbonic Pdts Inc ....G 937 316-6160
  Greenville *(G-10495)*

Delille Oxygen Company ....E 614 444-1177
  Columbus *(G-7018)*

Delille Oxygen Company ....G 937 325-9595
  Springfield *(G-17541)*

Endurance Manufacturing Inc ....G 330 628-2600
  Mogadore *(G-14374)*

Eveready Products Corporation ....F 216 661-2755
  Cleveland *(G-5308)*

▲ Gayston Corporation ....C 937 743-6050
  Miamisburg *(G-13812)*

Gsf Energy LLC ....G 513 825-0504
  Cincinnati *(G-3855)*

Hydrogen Energy Systems LLC ....G 330 236-0358
  Akron *(G-227)*

Ihod USA LLC ....G 216 459-7179
  Cleveland *(G-5549)*

Ineos Americas LLC ....B 419 226-1200
  Lima *(G-12028)*

◆ Invacare Corporation ....A 440 329-6000
  Elyria *(G-9435)*

Invacare Corporation ....D 800 333-6900
  Elyria *(G-9436)*

Linde Gas North America LLC ....F 614 846-7048
  Columbus *(G-7297)*

Linde Gas North America LLC ....F 330 425-3989
  Twinsburg *(G-18974)*

Linde LLC ....E 330 608-3008
  Uniontown *(G-19090)*

Linde LLC ....E 419 435-8153
  Fostoria *(G-9982)*

Linde LLC ....E 513 831-4742
  Miamiville *(G-13895)*

Linde LLC ....E 216 533-7256
  Cleveland *(G-5700)*

Linde LLC ....E 419 227-9585
  Lima *(G-12047)*

Linde LLC ....G 330 394-4541
  Warren *(G-19572)*

Linde LLC ....E 419 221-5043
  Lima *(G-12048)*

Linde LLC ....G 419 822-3909
  Delta *(G-8937)*

Matheson Tri-Gas Inc ....E 513 727-9638
  Middletown *(G-14060)*

Matheson Tri-Gas Inc ....F 330 425-4407
  Twinsburg *(G-18979)*

Matheson Tri-Gas Inc ....F 419 865-8881
  Holland *(G-11071)*

National Gas & Oil Corporation ....E 740 344-2102
  Newark *(G-15037)*

Neo Tech ....G 937 845-0999
  New Carlisle *(G-14809)*

Neon ....G 216 761-4782
  Cleveland *(G-5868)*

Neon Health Services Inc ....E 216 231-7700
  Cleveland *(G-5869)*

Neon Hussy LLC ....G 513 374-7644
  Columbus *(G-7386)*

Neon Light Manufacturing Co ....G 216 851-1000
  Cleveland *(G-5870)*

Neon Paintbrush ....G 419 436-1202
  Fostoria *(G-9987)*

Northeast OH Neighborhood Heal ....C 216 231-7700
  Cleveland *(G-5905)*

Nyeco Gas Inc ....G 419 447-2712
  Sandusky *(G-16990)*

Osair Inc ....G 440 974-6500
  Mentor *(G-13675)*

▲ Plasti-Kote Co Inc ....C 330 725-4511
  Medina *(G-13459)*

Praxair Inc ....D 440 994-1000
  Ashtabula *(G-834)*

Praxair Inc ....E 216 778-5555
  Cleveland *(G-6029)*

Praxair Inc ....E 440 237-8690
  Cleveland *(G-6030)*

Praxair Inc ....G 419 698-8005
  Oregon *(G-15713)*

Praxair Inc ....G 740 453-0346
  Zanesville *(G-21344)*

Praxair Inc ....G 419 729-7732
  Toledo *(G-18651)*

Praxair Inc ....G 937 323-6408
  Springfield *(G-17630)*

Praxair Inc ....F 330 264-6633
  Wooster *(G-20824)*

Praxair Inc ....E 419 652-3562
  Cleveland *(G-6031)*

Praxair Inc ....G 419 422-1353
  Lima *(G-12071)*

Praxair Inc ....G 440 944-8844
  Cleveland *(G-6032)*

Praxair Inc ....F 740 374-5525
  Marietta *(G-12818)*

Praxair Inc ....E 330 453-9904
  Canton *(G-2818)*

Praxair Inc ....D 419 666-5206
  Rossford *(G-16746)*

Praxair Inc ....G 330 825-4449
  Barberton *(G-1142)*

Praxair Distribution Inc ....F 614 443-7687
  Columbus *(G-7512)*

Praxair Distribution Inc ....G 419 422-1353
  Lima *(G-12072)*

Praxair Distribution Inc ....G 513 821-2192
  Cincinnati *(G-4263)*

Praxair Distribution Inc ....G 937 283-3400
  Wilmington *(G-20674)*

Praxair Distribution Inc ....G 419 221-0517
  Lima *(G-12073)*

Praxair Distribution Inc ....G 419 476-0738
  Toledo *(G-18652)*

Reliable Mfg Co LLC ....G 740 756-9373
  Carroll *(G-2945)*

Welders Supply Inc ....F 216 241-1696
  Cleveland *(G-6456)*

Wellston Aerosol Mfg Co Inc ....E 740 384-2320
  Wellston *(G-19772)*

Wright Brothers Inc ....F 513 731-2222
  Cincinnati *(G-4606)*

Wright Brothers Global Gas LLC..........G...... 513 731-2222
Cincinnati (G-4607)

▲ Zenex International.............................E...... 440 232-4155
Bedford (G-1475)

2816 Inorganic Pigments

Americhem Inc.......................................E...... 330 926-3185
Cuyahoga Falls (G-7964)

▲ Americhem Inc...................................D...... 330 929-4213
Cuyahoga Falls (G-7965)

Ampacet Corporation...........................C...... 740 929-5521
Newark (G-14982)

▲ Chromaflo Technologies Corp..........C...... 440 997-0081
Ashtabula (G-795)

Chromaflo Technologies Corp.............C...... 513 733-5111
Cincinnati (G-3532)

Chromaflo Technologies Corp.............C...... 440 997-5137
Ashtabula (G-796)

Colormatrix Group Inc..........................G...... 216 622-0100
Berea (G-1608)

Colormatrix Holdings Inc......................G...... 440 930-3162
Berea (G-1609)

Colortrend USA LLC.............................G...... 513 733-5111
Cincinnati (G-3597)

Cristal USA Inc.....................................C...... 440 994-1400
Ashtabula (G-800)

▲ Day-Glo Color Corp............................C...... 216 391-7070
Cleveland (G-5173)

Day-Glo Color Corp...............................C...... 216 391-7070
Cleveland (G-5174)

Day-Glo Color Corp...............................F...... 216 391-7070
Twinsburg (G-18922)

▲ Degussa Incorporated........................G...... 513 733-5111
Cincinnati (G-3646)

◆ Eckart America Corporation..............D...... 440 954-7600
Painesville (G-15876)

◆ Ferro Corporation..............................D...... 216 875-5600
Mayfield Heights (G-13313)

Ferro International Svcs Inc..................G...... 216 875-5600
Mayfield Heights (G-13314)

General Color Investments Inc.............D...... 330 868-4161
Minerva (G-14322)

Harsco Corporation..............................G...... 330 372-1781
Warren (G-19557)

Ironics Inc...G...... 330 652-0583
Niles (G-15162)

ISK Americas Incorporated...................E...... 440 357-4600
Painesville (G-15892)

Leonhardt Plating Company..................E...... 513 242-1410
Cincinnati (G-4020)

Lightstab Ltd Co...................................G...... 216 751-5800
Shaker Heights (G-17091)

Obron Atlantic Corporation..................D...... 440 954-7600
Painesville (G-15905)

◆ PMC Specialties Group Inc................E...... 513 242-3300
Cincinnati (G-4246)

PMC Specialties Group Inc....................G...... 513 242-3300
Cincinnati (G-4247)

Polyone Corporation.............................C...... 419 668-4844
Norwalk (G-15559)

Revlis Corporation...............................E...... 330 535-2108
Barberton (G-1145)

Rti Niles...G...... 330 455-4010
Niles (G-15182)

Spectrum Dispersions Inc.....................F...... 330 296-0600
Ravenna (G-16558)

Sun Chemical Corporation....................C...... 513 681-5950
Cincinnati (G-4477)

Sun Chemical Corporation....................B...... 513 681-5950
Cincinnati (G-4480)

◆ Thorworks Industries Inc...................E...... 419 626-4375
Sandusky (G-17015)

Vwm-Republic Inc................................F...... 216 271-1400
Cleveland (G-6433)

Whiterock Pigments Inc........................G...... 216 391-7765
Cleveland (G-6460)

2819 Indl Inorganic Chemicals, NEC

Adna Inc...G...... 614 397-4974
Dublin (G-9036)

Airgas Usa LLC.....................................G...... 440 232-6397
Oakwood Village (G-15622)

Airgas USA LLC.....................................G...... 419 726-2719
Toledo (G-18325)

▲ Akron Dispersions Inc........................E...... 330 666-0045
Copley (G-7838)

▲ Alchem Corporation............................G...... 330 725-2436
Medina (G-13366)

Aldrich Chemical..................................D...... 937 859-1808
Miamisburg (G-13781)

Allyn Corp..G...... 614 442-3900
Columbus (G-6727)

Alpha Zeta Holdings Inc........................G...... 216 271-1601
Cleveland (G-4770)

▲ Americhem Inc...................................D...... 330 929-4213
Cuyahoga Falls (G-7965)

Amresco LLC...C...... 440 349-2805
Cleveland (G-4798)

Arboris LLC...E...... 740 522-9350
Newark (G-14983)

Arizona Chemical Company LLC............C...... 330 343-7701
Dover (G-8964)

▲ Baerlocher Production Usa LLC..........E...... 513 482-6300
Cincinnati (G-3434)

▲ Baerlocher USA LLC............................F...... 330 364-6000
Dover (G-8965)

BASF Catalysts LLC..............................B...... 440 322-3741
Elyria (G-9379)

BASF Catalysts LLC..............................E...... 216 867-1047
Independence (G-11250)

BASF Catalysts LLC..............................D...... 216 360-5005
Cleveland (G-4894)

BASF Corporation.................................A...... 513 482-3000
Cincinnati (G-3438)

BASF Corporation.................................G...... 614 662-5682
Columbus (G-6812)

BLaster Corporation.............................G...... 216 901-5800
Cleveland (G-4916)

Bleachtech LLC.....................................E...... 216 921-1980
Seville (G-17071)

Bond Chemicals Inc..............................F...... 330 725-5935
Medina (G-13379)

◆ Borchers Americas Inc......................D...... 440 899-2950
Westlake (G-20258)

C Soltesz Co...G...... 614 529-5494
Columbus (G-6885)

C T Chemicals Inc.................................G...... 513 336-6160
Lebanon (G-11785)

Calgon Carbon Corporation..................C...... 614 258-9501
Columbus (G-6888)

▲ Calvary Industries Inc.......................E...... 513 874-1113
Fairfield (G-9649)

▲ Capital Resin Corporation..................D...... 614 445-7177
Columbus (G-6901)

Chem Masters.......................................G...... 440 428-2105
Madison (G-12500)

Chem Technologies Ltd.........................E...... 440 632-9311
Middlefield (G-13921)

Chemours Company Fc LLC....................F...... 513 941-4121
North Bend (G-15203)

Chemtrade Chemicals US LLC...............G...... 513 422-6319
Middletown (G-14029)

◆ Cil Isotope Separations LLC..............F...... 937 376-5413
Xenia (G-20942)

Cincinnati Specialties LLC....................C...... 513 242-3300
Cincinnati (G-3566)

◆ Columbia Chemical Corporation.......E...... 330 225-3200
Brunswick (G-2217)

Compliance Elements LLC.....................G...... 419 217-1793
Bellevue (G-1549)

▲ Coolant Control Inc............................E...... 513 471-8770
Cincinnati (G-3609)

Coulton Chemical.................................G...... 419 698-8181
Oregon (G-15706)

Creative Elements Studio.....................G...... 330 606-2068
Mogadore (G-14372)

Crop Production Services Inc................E...... 513 941-4100
North Bend (G-15204)

Curtis Chemical Inc..............................G...... 330 656-2514
Hudson (G-11167)

Custom Metal Shearing Inc...................F...... 937 233-6950
Dayton (G-8260)

Db Parent Inc..G...... 513 475-3265
Cincinnati (G-3644)

Df Consumer Products...........................F...... 440 239-4795
Berea (G-1611)

Diversified Brands...............................G...... 216 595-8777
Bedford (G-1419)

▲ Dover Chemical Corporation..............C...... 330 343-7711
Dover (G-8979)

Dpa Investments Inc............................F...... 440 992-7039
Ashtabula (G-804)

Drs Industries Inc................................D...... 419 861-0334
Holland (G-11057)

Dubois Chemicals Inc...........................F...... 513 868-9662
Hamilton (G-10684)

E I Du Pont De Nemours & Co................G...... 330 929-2961
Stow (G-17745)

Elco Corporation..................................E...... 440 997-6131
Ashtabula (G-805)

Elf Atochem NA OH...............................G...... 740 363-1351
Delaware (G-8841)

Enerchem Incorporated........................G...... 513 745-0580
Cincinnati (G-3703)

▲ Engelhard Corp..................................G...... 440 322-3741
Elyria (G-9420)

Eomg Harko Holdings LLC.....................G...... 216 781-0083
Cleveland (G-5287)

Extreme Elements................................G...... 330 325-2807
Akron (G-175)

Ferro Corporation................................D...... 216 577-7144
Bedford (G-1423)

▲ Gabriel Performance Pdts LLC...........G...... 440 992-3200
Akron (G-197)

Gabriel Performance Pdts LLC..............G...... 440 992-3200
Ashtabula (G-809)

General Electric Company.....................D...... 216 268-3846
Cleveland (G-5417)

◆ GFS Chemicals Inc.............................E...... 740 881-5501
Powell (G-16472)

GFS Chemicals Inc................................D...... 614 224-5345
Columbus (G-7112)

GFS Chemicals Inc................................G...... 740 881-5501
Columbus (G-7113)

GFS Chemicals Inc................................D...... 614 351-5347
Columbus (G-7114)

◆ Globe Metallurgical Inc.....................G...... 740 984-2361
Waterford (G-19647)

Gnrl Chemical L....................................G...... 419 255-0193
Toledo (G-18482)

Graphite Sales Inc...............................G...... 419 652-3388
Nova (G-15578)

Helena Chemical Company....................G...... 419 596-3806
Continental (G-7826)

Helena Chemical Company....................G...... 614 275-4200
Columbus (G-7148)

▲ Heraeus Precious Metals North.........E...... 937 264-1000
Vandalia (G-19295)

Hilltop Energy Inc................................E...... 330 859-2108
Mineral City (G-14301)

Ineos Americas LLC..............................B...... 419 226-1200
Lima (G-12028)

Johnson Mtthey Prcess Tech Inc..........E...... 330 298-7005
Ravenna (G-16535)

◆ Jones-Hamilton Co............................D...... 419 666-9838
Walbridge (G-19460)

Kerry Flavor Systems Us LLC................E...... 513 539-7373
Monroe (G-14407)

◆ Lithium Innovations Co LLC...............G...... 419 725-3525
Toledo (G-18562)

Littlern Corporation.............................D...... 330 848-8847
Barberton (G-1124)

M & G Polymers Usa LLC......................E...... 330 239-7400
Sharon Center (G-17107)

McGean-Rohco Inc................................D...... 216 441-4900
Newburgh Heights (G-15076)

Metals and Additives Corp Inc.............F...... 740 654-6555
Pleasantville (G-16373)

▲ Molecular Research Center................F...... 513 841-0900
Cincinnati (G-4117)

◆ Nachurs Alpine Solutions Corp..........E...... 740 382-5701
Marion (G-12888)

Nap Asset Holdings Ltd.........................F...... 330 633-0599
Tallmadge (G-18158)

▲ National Colloid Company...................E...... 740 282-1171
Steubenville (G-17706)

▲ Nease Co LLC.....................................F...... 513 587-2800
West Chester (G-19904)

New Eezy-Gro Inc.................................F...... 419 927-6110
Upper Sandusky (G-19136)

Occidental Chemical Corp.....................E...... 513 242-2900
Cincinnati (G-4172)

▲ Occidental Chemical Durez................G...... 419 675-5300
Kenton (G-11563)

Ohio Coatings Company........................D...... 740 859-5500
Yorkville (G-21007)

Ohio Metal Working Products................E...... 330 455-2009
Canton (G-2801)

Ohio Oxide Corporation Del..................F...... 740 654-6555
Pleasantville (G-16374)

Omnova Solutions Inc..........................D...... 330 734-1237
Akron (G-328)

◆ Omnova Solutions Inc........................C...... 216 682-7000
Beachwood (G-1287)

Omnova Wallcovering USA Inc..............G...... 216 682-7000
Beachwood (G-1288)

Omya Distribution LLC..........................G...... 513 387-4600
Blue Ash (G-1846)

Pcs Phosphate Company Inc..................E...... 513 738-1261
Harrison (G-10794)

Pennex Aluminum ....D...... 330 427-6704
Leetonia *(G-11863)*

◆ Perstorp Polyols Inc ....C...... 419 729-5448
Toledo *(G-18641)*

◆ PMC Specialties Group Inc ....E...... 513 242-3300
Cincinnati *(G-4246)*

PMC Specialties Group Inc ....G...... 513 242-3300
Cincinnati *(G-4247)*

▲ Polymerics Inc ....E...... 330 434-6665
Cuyahoga Falls *(G-8034)*

◆ Porocel Industries LLC ....G...... 513 733-8519
Cincinnati *(G-4249)*

PQ Corporation ....G...... 216 341-2578
Newburgh Heights *(G-15078)*

Press Chemical & Phrm Lab ....G...... 614 863-2802
Columbus *(G-7515)*

Process Sltions For Indust Inc .....G...... 330 702-1685
Canfield *(G-2570)*

PVS Chemical Solutions Inc ....F...... 330 666-0888
Copley *(G-7853)*

Rapid Blanket Restorer Corp ....G...... 330 821-6326
Painesville *(G-15916)*

Rtprocess LLC ....G...... 937 366-6215
Wilmington *(G-20678)*

Saint-Gobain Ceramics Plas Inc ...A...... 330 673-5860
Stow *(G-17797)*

Saint-Gobain Ceramics Plas Inc ...C...... 440 834-0061
Hiram *(G-11037)*

Shepherd Chemical Company ....F...... 513 200-6987
Cincinnati *(G-4415)*

Shepherd Chemical Company ....F...... 513 731-1110
Norwood *(G-15574)*

Shepherd Chemical Company ....F...... 513 424-7276
Middletown *(G-14083)*

Solvay USA Inc ....E...... 513 482-5700
Cincinnati *(G-4436)*

Tate Lyle Ingrdnts Amricas LLC .....D...... 937 236-5906
Dayton *(G-8703)*

TEC Line Inc ....G...... 740 881-5948
Lewis Center *(G-11924)*

▲ Three Leaf Inc ....G...... 888 308-1007
Hamilton *(G-10746)*

Total Plastics Inc ....G...... 440 205-9700
Mentor *(G-13751)*

Tru-Chem Company Inc ....F...... 614 888-2436
Columbus *(G-7711)*

▲ Union Camp Corp ....G...... 330 343-7701
Dover *(G-9022)*

◆ United Initiators Inc ....D...... 440 326-2416
Elyria *(G-9505)*

Univar USA Inc ....C...... 513 714-5264
West Chester *(G-20064)*

▲ Zaclon LLC ....E...... 216 271-1601
Cleveland *(G-6489)*

2821 Plastics, Mtrls & Nonvulcanizable Elastomers

1999 Pvc Partner Inc ....G...... 440 930-1000
Avon Lake *(G-1022)*

20/20 Custom Molded Plast ....D...... 419 485-2020
Montpelier *(G-14437)*

A Schulman Inc ....D...... 330 666-3751
Fairlawn *(G-9736)*

A Schulman Inc ....C...... 330 773-2700
Akron *(G-19)*

A Schulman Inc ....F...... 330 630-3315
Akron *(G-20)*

A Schulman Inc ....C...... 330 630-0308
Akron *(G-21)*

Absolute Polymers Inc ....F...... 888 850-0455
Salem *(G-16866)*

Ada Solutions Inc ....E...... 440 576-0423
Jefferson *(G-11355)*

Advanced Elastomer Systems LP ...D...... 330 336-7641
Wadsworth *(G-19389)*

Advanced Fiber Technology Inc 513 860-4446
Bucyrus *(G-2331)*

Al-Co Products Inc ....F...... 419 399-3867
Latty *(G-11767)*

Altera Polymers LLC ....G...... 864 973-7000
Jefferson *(G-11356)*

American Polymer Standards ....G...... 440 255-2211
Mentor *(G-13520)*

Americas Styrenics LLC ....D...... 740 533-4017
Hanging Rock *(G-10761)*

Ametek Westchester Plastics 419 739-3200
Wapakoneta *(G-19478)*

Amros Industries Inc ....E...... 216 433-0010
Cleveland *(G-4799)*

Arclin USA LLC ....E...... 419 726-5013
Toledo *(G-18354)*

Arizona Chemical Company LLC .....C...... 330 343-7701
Dover *(G-8964)*

▼ Armorsource LLC ....E...... 740 928-0070
Hebron *(G-10861)*

Ashland LLC ....E...... 513 557-3100
Cincinnati *(G-3418)*

Asi Investment Holding Co ....D...... 330 666-3751
Fairlawn *(G-9738)*

▲ Aurora Plastics Inc ....D...... 330 422-0700
Streetsboro *(G-17840)*

Aviles Construction Company ....E...... 216 939-1084
Cleveland *(G-4873)*

Axalta Coating Systems LLC ....E...... 419 478-1211
Toledo *(G-18361)*

BCi and V Investments Inc ....D...... 330 538-0660
North Jackson *(G-15287)*

Biobent Holdings LLC ....G...... 513 658-5560
Columbus *(G-6830)*

Biobent Holdings LLC ....G...... 513 658-5560
Columbus *(G-6831)*

▲ Biothane Coated Webbing Corp ...E...... 440 327-0485
North Ridgeville *(G-15361)*

Bricolage Inc ....G...... 614 853-6789
Grove City *(G-10547)*

▲ Buckeye Polymers Inc ....G...... 330 948-3007
Lodi *(G-12158)*

Cameo Countertops Inc ....G...... 419 865-6371
Holland *(G-11048)*

▲ Capital Resin Corporation ....D...... 614 445-7177
Columbus *(G-6901)*

▲ Chemionics Corporation ....E...... 330 733-8834
Tallmadge *(G-18137)*

Clyde Tool & Die Inc ....G...... 419 547-9574
Clyde *(G-6538)*

Composite Technical Svcs LLC .....G...... 937 660-3783
Kettering *(G-11578)*

◆ Concrete Sealants Inc ....E...... 937 845-8776
Tipp City *(G-18273)*

Cornerstone Indus Holdings ....G...... 440 893-9144
Chagrin Falls *(G-3054)*

Covestro LLC ....C...... 740 929-2015
Hebron *(G-10863)*

Crane Blending Center ....E...... 614 542-1199
Columbus *(G-6997)*

Crane Plastics Mfg Ltd ....G...... 614 754-3700
Columbus *(G-6998)*

▲ Crg Plastics Inc ....F...... 937 298-2025
Dayton *(G-8251)*

▲ Crown Plastics Co ....D...... 513 367-0238
Harrison *(G-10775)*

Current Inc ....G...... 330 392-5151
Warren *(G-19539)*

Deltech Polymers Corporation ....G...... 937 339-3150
Troy *(G-18817)*

Denney Plastics Machining LLC .....F...... 330 308-5300
New Philadelphia *(G-14894)*

Dentsply International Inc ....D...... 419 865-9497
Maumee *(G-13256)*

Dlhbowles Inc ....F...... 330 478-2503
Canton *(G-2692)*

Dow Chemical Company ....G...... 937 839-4612
West Alexandria *(G-19779)*

Dow Chemical Company ....F...... 937 254-1550
Dayton *(G-8309)*

Dow Chemical Company ....E...... 740 533-4000
Ironton *(G-11292)*

Durez Corporation ....C...... 567 295-6400
Kenton *(G-11546)*

E C Shaw Co ....E...... 513 721-6334
Cincinnati *(G-3677)*

E I Du Pont De Nemours & Co ....E...... 740 474-0220
Circleville *(G-4627)*

E I Du Pont De Nemours & Co ....E...... 740 474-0635
Circleville *(G-4628)*

E P S Specialists Ltd Inc ....F...... 513 489-3676
Cincinnati *(G-3679)*

Eagle Elastomer Inc ....E...... 330 923-7070
Peninsula *(G-16037)*

Eaton Corporation ....C...... 330 562-9111
Aurora *(G-917)*

◆ Emerald Performance Mtls LLC ...E...... 330 916-6700
Cuyahoga Falls *(G-7990)*

Emerald Performance Mtls LLC .....D...... 330 374-2418
Akron *(G-164)*

Emerald Specialty Polymers LLC ...E...... 330 374-2424
Akron *(G-166)*

Ep Bollinger LLC ....A...... 513 941-1101
Cincinnati *(G-3712)*

Eps Specialties Ltd Inc ....F...... 513 489-3676
Cincinnati *(G-3714)*

◆ Etna Products Incorporated ....E...... 440 543-9845
Chagrin Falls *(G-3087)*

◆ Evans Adhesive Corporation Ltd ...E...... 614 451-2665
Columbus *(G-7070)*

Farmed Materials Inc ....G...... 513 680-4046
Cincinnati *(G-3740)*

◆ Ferro Corporation ....D...... 216 875-5600
Mayfield Heights *(G-13313)*

Flex Technologies Inc ....E...... 330 897-6311
Baltic *(G-1071)*

▼ Flexsys America LP ....D...... 330 666-4111
Akron *(G-190)*

Freeman Manufacturing & Sup Co ...E...... 440 934-1902
Avon *(G-996)*

▼ Geo-Tech Polymers LLC ....F...... 614 797-2300
Waverly *(G-19709)*

Georgia-Pacific LLC ....E...... 614 491-9100
Columbus *(G-7111)*

▲ Global Biochem ....G...... 513 792-2218
Cincinnati *(G-3835)*

▲ Goldsmith & Eggleton LLC ....F...... 203 855-6000
Wadsworth *(G-19408)*

◆ Great Lakes Textiles Inc ....E...... 440 439-1300
Solon *(G-17304)*

Grit Guard Inc ....G...... 937 592-9003
Bellefontaine *(G-1531)*

Hadsell Chemical Proc LLC ....E...... 740 941-1792
Waverly *(G-19710)*

Hancor Inc ....D...... 419 424-8225
Findlay *(G-9837)*

▲ Hexa Americas Inc ....E...... 937 497-7900
Sidney *(G-17192)*

Hexion Inc ....B...... 614 225-4000
Columbus *(G-7152)*

Hexion Inc ....D...... 614 759-6227
Gahanna *(G-10210)*

◆ Hexion LLC ....D...... 614 225-4000
Columbus *(G-7153)*

▲ Hexpol Compounding LLC ....E...... 440 834-4644
Burton *(G-2377)*

▲ Hfi LLC ....B...... 614 491-0700
Canal Winchester *(G-2525)*

Hfi Manufacturing Holdings LLC .....G...... 614 491-0700
Canal Winchester *(G-2528)*

Hggc Citadel Plas Holdings Inc .....G...... 330 666-3751
Fairlawn *(G-9752)*

Hpc Holdings LLC ....F...... 330 666-3751
Fairlawn *(G-9753)*

Ic3d LLC ....G...... 614 260-5631
Columbus *(G-7180)*

ICP Adhesives and Sealants Inc ...G...... 330 753-4585
Norton *(G-15513)*

▲ Ier Fujikura Inc ....C...... 330 425-7121
Macedonia *(G-12458)*

Illinois Tool Works Inc ....C...... 513 489-7600
Blue Ash *(G-1812)*

▲ Incredible Solutions Inc ....F...... 330 898-3878
Warren *(G-19559)*

Ineos LLC ....D...... 419 226-1200
Lima *(G-12027)*

◆ Ineos ABS (usa) LLC ....C...... 513 467-2400
Addyston *(G-10)*

Ineos USA LLC ....D...... 419 226-1200
Lima *(G-12029)*

Integrated Chem Concepts Inc ....E...... 440 838-5666
Brecksville *(G-2056)*

Intergroup International Ltd ....D...... 216 965-0257
Euclid *(G-9586)*

▲ International Technical ....E...... 330 505-1218
Niles *(G-15161)*

Isochem Incorporated ....G...... 614 775-9328
New Albany *(G-14762)*

▲ J P Industrial Products Inc ....G...... 330 424-1110
Lisbon *(G-12125)*

◆ Jain America Foods Inc ....G...... 614 850-9400
Columbus *(G-7222)*

◆ Jain America Holdings Inc ....D...... 614 850-9400
Columbus *(G-7223)*

Jjc Plastics Ltd ....G...... 330 334-3637
Norton *(G-15516)*

▲ JMS Industries Inc ....E...... 937 325-3502
Springfield *(G-17581)*

▼ Kardol Quality Products LLC ....G...... 513 933-8206
Blue Ash *(G-1822)*

Kathom Manufacturing Co Inc ....E...... 513 868-8890
Hamilton *(G-10715)*

Kiley Mold Company LLC ....G...... 513 875-3223
Fayetteville *(G-9784)*

◆ Kirtland Cpitl Partners III LP ....G 440 585-9010
  Willoughby Hills (G-20640)
Kraton Polymers US LLC ....B 740 423-7571
  Belpre (G-1589)
L-K Industry Inc..............................E 937 526-3000
  Versailles (G-19351)
Liberty Plastics LLC ....G 330 627-6677
  Carrollton (G-2960)
Louisville Molded Products ....G 330 877-9740
  Hartville (G-10829)
Ltg Polymers Limited ....G 330 854-5609
  Massillon (G-13168)
Lubrizol Advanced Mtls Inc ....E 440 933-0400
  Avon Lake (G-1037)
▲ Maintenance Repair Supply Inc ......E 740 922-3006
  Midvale (G-14109)
▲ Mar-Bal Inc ....D 440 543-7526
  Chagrin Falls (G-3101)
Mar-Bal Inc ....D 440 543-7526
  Chagrin Falls (G-3102)
Materion Brush Inc ....E 440 960-5660
  Lorain (G-12260)
Meggitt (erlanger) LLC ....D 513 851-5550
  Cincinnati (G-4080)
◆ Mexichem Specialty Resins Inc ....E 440 930-1435
  Avon Lake (G-1040)
Michael Day Enterprises LLC ....G 330 335-5100
  Wadsworth (G-19419)
Mitsubishi Chls Perf Plyrs Inc ....D 419 483-2931
  Bellevue (G-1553)
Modern Plastics Recovery Inc ....F 419 622-4611
  Haviland (G-10842)
Mold Surface Textures ....G 330 678-8590
  Kent (G-11494)
▼ Momentive Performance Mtls Inc ....B 614 986-2495
  Columbus (G-7365)
▲ Multibase Inc ....D 330 666-0505
  Copley (G-7850)
▲ Mum Industries Inc ....E 440 269-4966
  Mentor (G-13663)
Nano Innovations LLC ....G 614 203-5706
  Columbus (G-7379)
▼ Nanosperse LLC ....G 937 296-5030
  Kettering (G-11583)
National Polymer Dev Co Inc ....F 440 708-1245
  Chagrin Falls (G-3105)
Nexeo Solutions LLC ....F 800 531-7106
  Dublin (G-9113)
Next Specialty Resins Inc ....E 517 547-4600
  Toledo (G-18606)
Nona Composites LLC ....G 937 490-4814
  Beavercreek (G-1376)
Nova Chemicals Inc ....D 440 352-3381
  Painesville (G-15904)
Novo Foam Products LLC ....G 440 892-3325
  Westlake (G-20286)
Occidental Chemical Corp ....E 513 242-2900
  Cincinnati (G-4172)
Ohio Foam Corporation....................F 419 492-2151
  New Washington (G-14963)
Orica Ground Support Inc ....D 740 377-9146
  South Point (G-17443)
OSI Global Sourcing LLC ....C 614 471-4800
  Columbus (G-7447)
▲ Ovation Polymer Technology and ....E 330 723-5686
  Medina (G-13455)
Owens Corning Sales LLC ....F 330 633-6735
  Tallmadge (G-18163)
Pace Mold & Machine LLC ....G 330 879-1777
  Massillon (G-13192)
Pahuja Inc ....D 614 864-3989
  Gahanna (G-10225)
Performnce Plymr Solutions Inc ....F 937 298-3713
  Moraine (G-14512)
◆ Perstorp Polyols Inc ....C 419 729-5448
  Toledo (G-18641)
◆ Pet Processors LLc ....D 440 354-4321
  Painesville (G-15911)
Pf Polymers LLC ....E 567 712-7046
  Lima (G-12069)
Pitt Plastics Inc ....E 614 868-8660
  Columbus (G-7486)
Plaskolite Inc ....D 740 450-1109
  Zanesville (G-21341)
▲ Plaskolite LLC ....C 614 294-3281
  Columbus (G-7489)
Plaskolite LLC ....B 614 294-7294
  Columbus (G-7490)
Plasti-Kemm Inc ....G 330 239-1555
  Medina (G-13458)

Plastic Compounders Inc ....E 740 432-7371
  Cambridge (G-2472)
Plastic Regrinders Inc ....G 740 659-2346
  Glenford (G-10399)
▼ Plastic Selection Group Inc ....G 614 464-2008
  Columbus (G-7492)
Poly Green Technologies LLC ....G 419 529-9909
  Ontario (G-15694)
▲ Poly-Carb Inc ....E 440 248-1223
  Twinsburg (G-19003)
▲ Polygroup Inc ....E 877 476-5972
  Maineville (G-12531)
▼ Polymer Concepts Inc ....G 440 953-9605
  Mentor (G-13693)
▲ Polymer Packaging Inc ....D 330 832-2000
  Massillon (G-13195)
Polymerics Inc ....E 330 677-1131
  Kent (G-11503)
▲ Polymerics Inc ....E 330 434-6665
  Cuyahoga Falls (G-8034)
Polynew Inc ....G 330 897-3202
  Baltic (G-1076)
Polynt Composites USA Inc ....E 816 391-6000
  Sandusky (G-16997)
Polyone Corporation ....F 740 423-7571
  Belpre (G-1594)
Polyone Corporation ....D 440 930-1000
  Avon Lake (G-1044)
Polyone Corporation ....D 440 930-3754
  Avon Lake (G-1045)
Polyone Corporation ....D 440 933-2000
  Avon Lake (G-1046)
Polyone Corporation ....D 440 930-1000
  North Baltimore (G-15197)
Polyone Corporation ....D 330 834-3812
  Massillon (G-13196)
◆ Polyone Corporation ....D 440 930-1000
  Avon Lake (G-1047)
PPG Industries Inc ....E 419 683-2400
  Crestline (G-7935)
Ppi Holding Company ....E 216 514-1840
  Cleveland (G-6028)
▼ Premix Inc ....C 440 224-2181
  North Kingsville (G-15304)
▲ Prime Conduit Inc ....F 216 464-3400
  Cleveland (G-6046)
Prime Industries Inc ....E 440 288-3626
  Lorain (G-12268)
Pro Mold Design Inc ....G 440 352-1212
  Mentor (G-13697)
Proficient Plastics Inc ....F 440 205-9700
  Mentor (G-13700)
▲ Progressive Foam Tech Inc ....C 330 756-3200
  Beach City (G-1250)
Queen City Foam Inc ....G 513 741-7722
  Cincinnati (G-4315)
▲ Rauh Polymers Inc ....G 330 376-1120
  Akron (G-367)
Ray Fogg Construction Inc ....F 216 351-7976
  Cleveland (G-6091)
▲ Renegade Materials Corporation......E 508 579-7888
  Miamisburg (G-13854)
▲ Resinoid Engineering Corp ....D 847 673-1050
  Hebron (G-10881)
◆ Rochling Glastic Composites LP ......E 216 486-0100
  Cleveland (G-6125)
Rohm and Haas Company ....C 513 733-2100
  Cincinnati (G-4357)
Rohm and Haas Company ....C 937 839-4612
  West Alexandria (G-19783)
Saco Aei Polymers Inc ....F 330 995-1600
  Aurora (G-947)
▲ Scott Bader Inc ....G 330 920-4410
  Stow (G-17799)
Scott Molders Incorporated ....D 330 673-5777
  Kent (G-11524)
Sherwood Rtm Corp ....G 330 875-7151
  Louisville (G-12328)
Sonoco Prtective Solutions Inc ....D 419 420-0029
  Findlay (G-9892)
Sorbothane Inc ....E 330 678-9444
  Kent (G-11530)
STC International Co Ltd ....G 561 308-6002
  Lebanon (G-11842)
Stopol Equipment Sales LLC ....G 440 499-0030
  Brunswick (G-2258)
Sunprene Company ....D 330 666-3751
  Fairlawn (G-9762)
▲ Tembec Btlsr Inc ....E 419 244-5856
  Toledo (G-18719)

Triple Arrow Industries Inc ....G 614 437-5588
  Marysville (G-12976)
◆ Uniloy Milacron Inc ....D 513 487-5000
  Batavia (G-1230)
Versa-Pak Ltd ....E 419 586-5466
  Celina (G-3026)
Vinyl Profiles Acquisition LLC ....E 330 538-0660
  North Jackson (G-15301)
Wilsonart LLC ....E 614 876-1515
  Columbus (G-7765)
Winsell Incorporated ....G 330 836-7421
  Akron (G-473)

2822 Synthetic Rubber (Vulcanizable Elastomers)

Advanced Elastomer Systems LP ....D 330 336-7641
  Wadsworth (G-19389)
All-Tra Rubber Processing ....G 330 630-1945
  Tallmadge (G-18133)
Brain Child Products LLC ....F 419 698-4020
  Toledo (G-18381)
Bridgestone Procurement Holdin ....A 337 882-1200
  Akron (G-98)
◆ Brp Manufacturing Company ....E 800 858-0482
  Lima (G-11998)
Canton OH Rubber Speclty Prods ......G 330 454-3847
  Canton (G-2642)
▲ Cardinal Rubber Company Inc ....E 330 745-2191
  Barberton (G-1113)
◆ Concrete Sealants Inc ....E 937 845-8776
  Tipp City (G-18273)
Covestro LLC ....E 740 929-2015
  Hebron (G-10863)
Dupont Prfmce Elastomers LLC ....C 330 929-6934
  Stow (G-17744)
Dupont Prfmce Elastomers LLC ....C 330 929-6934
  Akron (G-158)
E I Du Pont De Nemours & Co ....E 330 929-2961
  Stow (G-17745)
Elastostar Rubber Corp ....E 614 841-4400
  Columbus (G-7050)
Eliokem Inc ....E 330 734-1100
  Fairlawn (G-9749)
▼ Flexsys America LP ....D 330 666-4111
  Akron (G-190)
Gdc Inc ....F 574 533-3128
  Wooster (G-20775)
▲ High Tech Elastomers Inc ....E 937 236-6575
  Vandalia (G-19296)
Kraton Emplyees Recreation CLB.......G 740 423-7571
  Belpre (G-1588)
Kraton Polymers US LLC ....B 740 423-7571
  Belpre (G-1589)
Lyondell Chemical Company ....D 513 530-4000
  Cincinnati (G-4042)
Matterworks ....G 740 200-0071
  Heath (G-10850)
▲ Medical Elastomer Dev Inc ....E 330 425-8352
  Twinsburg (G-18983)
Meggitt (erlanger) LLC ....D 513 851-5550
  Cincinnati (G-4080)
◆ Mexichem Specialty Resins Inc ....E 440 930-1435
  Avon Lake (G-1040)
▲ Midwest Elastomers Inc ....D 419 738-8844
  Wapakoneta (G-19498)
Mohican Industries Inc ....F 330 869-0500
  Akron (G-300)
Mondo Polymer Technologies Inc ......E 740 376-9396
  Reno (G-16577)
Polyshield Corporation ....F 614 755-7674
  Pickerington (G-16200)
Protective Industrial Polymers ....F 440 327-0015
  North Ridgeville (G-15396)
San Pallet LLC ....G 937 271-5308
  Troy (G-18871)
▲ Shincor Silicones Inc ....G 330 630-9460
  Akron (G-400)
Toyo Seiki Usa Inc ....G 513 546-9657
  Blue Ash (G-1882)
▲ Tradex International Inc ....D 216 651-4788
  Cleveland (G-6345)
Universal Urethane Pdts Inc ....D 419 693-7400
  Toledo (G-18760)
Vibronic ....F 937 274-1114
  Dayton (G-8742)
Wayne County Rubber Inc ....E 330 264-5553
  Wooster (G-20845)

S I C

2823 Cellulosic Man-Made Fibers

3M Company ....C...... 440 323-6161
Elyria (G-9366)

▼ Flexsys America LP ....D...... 330 666-4111
Akron (G-190)

Laser Horizons ....G...... 330 208-0575
Norton (G-15517)

▼ Mfg Composite Systems Company ..B...... 440 997-5851
Ashtabula (G-820)

◆ Morgan Adhesives Company LLC ..B...... 330 688-1111
Stow (G-17775)

Solvaira Specialties Inc ....D...... 937 652-2101
Urbana (G-19181)

2824 Synthetic Organic Fibers, Exc Cellulosic

Bridge Components Incorporated ....G...... 614 873-0777
Columbus (G-6858)

▲ Buckeye Polymers Inc ....E...... 330 948-3007
Lodi (G-12158)

▲ Dowco LLC ....E...... 330 773-6654
Akron (G-155)

Ecm Biofilms Inc ....G...... 440 350-1400
Painesville (G-15877)

◆ Mytee Products Inc ....F...... 440 591-4301
Aurora (G-936)

Ohio Plastics Belting Co ....G...... 330 882-6764
New Franklin (G-14828)

Omnova Solutions Inc ....C...... 330 628-6550
Mogadore (G-14382)

Organic Roots Horticulture LLC ....G...... 330 620-1108
Ravenna (G-16546)

Success Technologies Inc ....G...... 614 761-0008
Powell (G-16484)

2833 Medicinal Chemicals & Botanical Prdts

Amresco LLC ....D...... 440 349-2805
Solon (G-17259)

Amresco LLC ....C...... 440 349-2805
Cleveland (G-4798)

Avitae USA LLC ....G...... 216 416-3461
Cleveland (G-4874)

B&A Holstic Food and Herbs ....F...... 614 747-2885
Columbus (G-6797)

Badizo LLC ....G...... 844 344-3833
Stow (G-17732)

Biofocus Inc ....G...... 937 890-3068
Dayton (G-8188)

Frutarom USA Inc ....G...... 513 870-4900
West Chester (G-20008)

◆ Frutarom USA Inc ....C...... 513 870-4900
West Chester (G-20005)

▲ Goosefoot Acres Inc ....G...... 330 225-7184
Valley City (G-19205)

Graminex LLC ....F...... 419 278-1023
Deshler (G-8951)

▲ Joseph Adams Corp ....F...... 330 225-9125
Valley City (G-19208)

Odacs Inc ....G...... 513 761-0539
Cincinnati (G-4173)

Ohio Valley Herbal Products ....G...... 330 382-1229
East Liverpool (G-9225)

Patenthealth LLC ....G...... 330 208-1111
North Canton (G-15257)

Pfizer Inc ....C...... 937 746-3603
Franklin (G-10044)

Pharmacia Hepar LLC ....D...... 937 746-3603
Franklin (G-10045)

Plymouth Healthcare Pdts LLC ....F...... 440 542-0762
Solon (G-17362)

▲ Polar Products Inc ....G...... 330 253-9973
Stow (G-17789)

Press Chemical & Phrm Lab ....G...... 614 863-2802
Columbus (G-7515)

Proctoer & Gamble ....G...... 513 983-1100
Blue Ash (G-1859)

Satellite Gear Inc ....F...... 216 514-8668
Cleveland (G-6162)

USB Corporation ....D...... 216 765-5000
Cleveland (G-6401)

Valley Vitamins II Inc ....E...... 330 533-0051
Columbus (G-7731)

Vdm Biochemicals LLC ....G...... 440 786-9400
Bedford (G-1470)

2834 Pharmaceuticals

Abbott Laboratories ....A...... 614 624-7677
Columbus (G-6672)

Abbott Laboratories ....D...... 614 624-6627
Columbus (G-6673)

Abbott Laboratories ....A...... 614 624-3078
Columbus (G-6674)

Abbott Laboratories ....A...... 614 624-6627
Columbus (G-6675)

Abbott Laboratories ....A...... 614 624-6088
Columbus (G-6676)

Abbott Laboratories ....A...... 614 624-3191
Columbus (G-6671)

Abbott Nutrition Mfg Inc ....E...... 614 624-7485
Columbus (G-6677)

▼ Abitec Corporation ....E...... 614 429-6464
Columbus (G-6678)

▲ Adare Pharmaceuticals Inc ....C...... 937 898-9669
Vandalia (G-19278)

Advanced Medical Solutions Inc ....G...... 937 291-0069
Centerville (G-3033)

Aeromics Inc ....G...... 216 772-1004
Cleveland (G-4721)

Affinity Therapeutics LLC ....G...... 216 224-9364
Cleveland (G-4728)

Alkermes Inc ....E...... 937 382-5642
Wilmington (G-20654)

Allergan Inc ....G...... 614 623-8140
Powell (G-16462)

Amerisourcebergen Corporation ......D...... 614 497-3665
Lockbourne (G-12145)

▼ Amish Country Essentials LLC ......G...... 330 674-3088
Millersburg (G-14192)

Analiza Inc ....F...... 216 432-9050
Cleveland (G-4801)

Aprecia Pharmaceuticals Co ....E...... 513 204-1369
Blue Ash (G-1744)

Astellas Pharma Us Inc ....E...... 614 409-2953
Groveport (G-10615)

Athersys Inc ....E...... 216 431-9900
Cleveland (G-4854)

Aultwrks Occupational Medicine ....F...... 330 491-9675
Canton (G-2609)

Barr Laboratories Inc ....B...... 513 731-9900
Cincinnati (G-3437)

BASF Corporation ....G...... 614 662-5682
Columbus (G-6812)

Bellwyck Packg Solutions Inc ....G...... 513 874-1200
West Chester (G-19816)

Berlin Industries Inc ....F...... 330 549-2100
North Lima (G-15310)

Bigmar Inc ....E...... 740 966-5800
Johnstown (G-11391)

Biorx LLC ....C...... 866 442-4679
Cincinnati (G-3450)

Bnoat Oncology ....G...... 330 285-2537
Akron (G-93)

Bristol-Myers Squibb Company ....E...... 800 321-1335
Columbus (G-6642)

Buderer Drug Co ....G...... 419 626-3429
Sandusky (G-16950)

Buderer Drug Company Inc ....F...... 419 627-2800
Sandusky (G-16951)

Buderer Drug Company Inc ....F...... 419 873-2800
Perrysburg (G-16070)

Buderer Drug Company Inc ....G...... 440 934-3100
Avon (G-987)

Bulk Molding Compounds Inc ....D...... 419 874-7941
Perrysburg (G-16071)

Cabell Huntington ....G...... 740 867-2665
Chesapeake (G-3185)

Calcol Inc ....E...... 216 245-6301
Shaker Heights (G-17086)

Camargo Phrm Svcs LLC ....F...... 513 561-3329
Blue Ash (G-1761)

Caps ....G...... 216 524-0418
Cleveland (G-4972)

▲ Cardinal Health 414 LLC ....C...... 614 757-5000
Dublin (G-9058)

Cardinal Health 414 LLC ....G...... 513 759-1900
West Chester (G-19823)

Cardinal Health 414 LLC ....G...... 614 473-0786
Columbus (G-6906)

Casselberry Clinic Inc ....G...... 440 995-0555
Cleveland (G-4990)

CBS Pharmacy ....G...... 740 366-9082
Newark (G-14992)

Chester Labs Inc ....E...... 513 458-3871
Cincinnati (G-3526)

◆ Chester Packaging LLC ....C...... 513 458-3840
Cincinnati (G-3527)

Chewrite Co ....D...... 937 746-5509
Springboro (G-17476)

Clearwater One LLC ....F...... 216 554-4747
Cleveland (G-5046)

Cleobrothers & Company LLC ....F...... 614 985-3639
Columbus (G-6936)

Clinical Specialties Inc ....D...... 888 873-7888
Brecksville (G-2040)

CMC Pharmaceuticals Inc ....G...... 216 600-9430
Cleveland (G-5094)

Dayton Laser & Aesthetic Medic ....G...... 937 208-8282
Dayton (G-8278)

Dow Chemical Company ....F...... 937 254-1550
Dayton (G-8309)

Dr Hess Products LLC ....G...... 800 718-8022
Ashland (G-729)

Essence Maker ....G...... 440 729-3894
Chesterland (G-3203)

Eyescience Labs LLC ....G...... 614 885-7100
Powell (G-16471)

Family Medical Clinic & Laser ....G...... 740 345-2767
Newark (G-15006)

◆ Ferro Corporation ....D...... 216 875-5600
Mayfield Heights (G-13313)

▲ Flow Dry Technology Inc ....C...... 937 833-2161
Brookville (G-2183)

Fluence Therapeutics ....G...... 216 780-5220
Akron (G-192)

Forest Pharmaceuticals Inc ....C...... 513 271-6800
Cincinnati (G-3770)

Forest Pharmaceuticals Inc ....C...... 513 271-6800
Cincinnati (G-3771)

Forrest Pharmaceuticals ....G...... 513 791-1701
Blue Ash (G-1799)

Fred W Albrecht Grocery Co ....C...... 330 922-4057
Stow (G-17757)

Fresenius Usa Inc ....E...... 330 837-2575
Massillon (G-13134)

Fresenius Usa Inc ....E...... 440 734-7474
North Olmsted (G-15336)

Ftd Investments LLC ....C...... 937 833-2161
Brookville (G-2184)

Gateway Biotechnology Inc ....G...... 314 747-7199
Rootstown (G-16722)

▲ Gebauer Company ....E...... 216 581-3030
Cleveland (G-5405)

Glaxosmithkline LLC ....E...... 937 623-2680
Columbus (G-7116)

Glaxosmithkline LLC ....E...... 440 552-2895
North Ridgeville (G-15376)

Glaxosmithkline LLC ....E...... 330 608-2365
Copley (G-7847)

Glaxosmithkline LLC ....E...... 614 570-5970
Columbus (G-7117)

Glaxosmithkline LLC ....E...... 330 241-4447
Medina (G-13417)

Graminex LLC ....F...... 419 278-1023
Deshler (G-8951)

Harry and David LLC ....G...... 740 929-7100
Hebron (G-10869)

Isp Chemicals LLC ....D...... 614 876-3637
Columbus (G-7214)

Libido Edge Labs LLC ....G...... 740 344-1401
Newark (G-15030)

◆ Lubrizol Advanced Mtls Inc ....F...... 216 447-5000
Brecksville (G-2061)

Medpace Holdings Inc ....G...... 513 579-9911
Cincinnati (G-4079)

Mercurio Biotec LLC ....F...... 214 507-8031
Dublin (G-9102)

Meridian Bioscience Inc ....B...... 513 271-3700
Cincinnati (G-4085)

Middletown Pharmacy Inc ....G...... 513 705-6252
Middletown (G-14063)

Millers Liniments LLC ....G...... 440 548-5800
Middlefield (G-13966)

Molorokalin Inc ....F...... 330 629-1332
Canfield (G-2566)

Mp Biomedicals LLC ....C...... 440 337-1200
Solon (G-17340)

Mvp Pharmancy ....G...... 614 449-8000
Columbus (G-7375)

N M R Inc ....G...... 513 530-9075
Cincinnati (G-4135)

N8 Medical Inc ....G...... 614 537-7246
Dublin (G-9108)

Nanofiber Solutions Inc ....G...... 614 559-9065
Columbus (G-7380)

Nigerian Assn Pharmacists & PH ....G...... 513 861-2329
Cincinnati (G-4155)

Nitto Denko Avecia Inc ....F...... 513 679-3000
Cincinnati (G-4158)

Nnodum Pharmaceuticals Corp ... F ... 513 861-2329
Cincinnati *(G-4160)*
▲ **Norwich Overseas Inc** ... F ... 513 983-1100
Mason *(G-13068)*
Nostrum Laboratories Inc ... E ... 419 636-1168
Bryan *(G-2314)*
Novartis Corporation ... D ... 919 577-5000
Cincinnati *(G-4165)*
Nutralab Inc ... G ... 513 561-0471
Cincinnati *(G-4169)*
Nutrimir LLC ... G ... 614 600-2478
Delaware *(G-8875)*
Oak Tree Intl Holdings Inc ... F ... 702 462-7295
Elyria *(G-9469)*
Oakwood Laboratories LLC ... E ... 440 359-0000
Oakwood Village *(G-15626)*
Oakwood Laboratories LLC ... F ... 440 505-2011
Solon *(G-17352)*
Omnicare Phrm of Midwest LLC ... D ... 513 719-2600
Cincinnati *(G-4186)*
Organon Inc ... G ... 440 729-2290
Chesterland *(G-3218)*
Patenthealth LLC ... G ... 330 208-1111
North Canton *(G-15257)*
Patheon Pharmaceuticals Inc ... C ... 513 948-7942
Cincinnati *(G-4212)*
PBM Covington LLC ... F ... 937 473-2050
Covington *(G-7927)*
Performanx Specialty Chem LLC ... G ... 614 300-7001
Westerville *(G-20179)*
Performanx Specialty Chem LLC ... G ... 614 300-7001
Waverly *(G-19716)*
Pfizer Inc ... G ... 513 342-9056
West Chester *(G-19913)*
Pfizer Inc ... C ... 614 496-0990
Dublin *(G-9124)*
Pfizer Inc ... D ... 216 591-0642
Beachwood *(G-1290)*
Pfizer Inc ... C ... 937 746-3603
Franklin *(G-10044)*
Pharmacia Hepar LLC ... D ... 937 746-3603
Franklin *(G-10045)*
Pharmaforce Inc ... E ... 614 436-2222
Columbus *(G-7481)*
Pharmaforce Inc ... F ... 614 436-2222
Hilliard *(G-10969)*
Polgenix Inc ... G ... 440 537-9691
Cleveland *(G-6019)*
Polynt Composites USA Inc ... E ... 816 391-6000
Sandusky *(G-16997)*
Principled Dynamics Inc ... G ... 419 351-6303
Holland *(G-11079)*
Procter & Gamble Company ... C ... 513 983-1100
Cincinnati *(G-4281)*
Procter & Gamble Company ... B ... 513 983-1100
Cincinnati *(G-4286)*
Procter & Gamble Company ... C ... 513 634-9110
West Chester *(G-19923)*
Procter & Gamble Company ... C ... 410 527-5735
Grove City *(G-10586)*
Protein Express Inc ... G ... 513 769-9654
Cincinnati *(G-4300)*
RC Outsourcing LLC ... G ... 330 536-8500
Lowellville *(G-12412)*
Retinagenix LLC ... G ... 440 808-9334
Cleveland *(G-6108)*
River City Pharma ... D ... 513 870-1680
Fairfield *(G-9711)*
Rohm and Haas Chemicals LLC ... G ... 513 733-2100
Cincinnati *(G-4356)*
Roxane Laboratories Inc ... C ... 614 276-4000
Columbus *(G-7574)*
Rx Institutional Services LLC ... G ... 330 505-1979
Mineral Ridge *(G-14310)*
Safe Rx Pharmacies Inc ... G ... 740 377-4162
South Point *(G-17447)*
Safecor Health LLC ... F ... 781 933-8780
Columbus *(G-7583)*
Sara Wood Pharmaceuticals LLC ... G ... 513 833-5502
Mason *(G-13085)*
Scicompro - LLC ... G ... 513 680-8686
Mason *(G-13086)*
Sermonix Pharmaceuticals ... G ... 614 864-4919
Columbus *(G-7609)*
Sironrx Therapeutics Inc ... G ... 216 445-5588
Cleveland *(G-6206)*
Solvaira Specialties Inc ... D ... 937 652-2101
Urbana *(G-19181)*
Specialized Pharmaceuticals ... G ... 330 453-3067
Canton *(G-2853)*
Specialized Pharmaceuticals ... G ... 419 371-2081
Lima *(G-12095)*
Suarez Corporation Industries ... E ... 330 494-4282
Canton *(G-2861)*
Summit Research Group ... G ... 330 689-1778
Stow *(G-17806)*
Takeda Pharmaceuticals USA Inc ... G ... 440 238-0872
Strongsville *(G-17977)*
Tersus Pharmaceuticals ... F ... 440 951-2451
Mentor *(G-13745)*
Teva Womens Health Inc ... C ... 513 731-9900
Cincinnati *(G-4503)*
Tri-Tech Laboratories Inc ... D ... 740 927-2817
Johnstown *(G-11408)*
USB Corporation ... D ... 216 765-5000
Cleveland *(G-6401)*
Venture Therapeutics Inc ... G ... 614 430-3300
New Albany *(G-14775)*
Vitamin Shoppe Inc ... E ... 440 238-5987
Strongsville *(G-17980)*
Warner Chlcott Phrmcticals Inc ... F ... 513 983-1100
Cincinnati *(G-4579)*
West-Ward Pharmaceuticals Corp ... G ... 614 276-4000
Columbus *(G-7758)*
Xellia Pharmaceuticals USA LLC ... E ... 847 986-7984
Bedford *(G-1473)*
Z M O Company Inc ... G ... 614 875-0230
Grove City *(G-10611)*

2835 Diagnostic Substances

Apollo Medical Devices LLC ... G ... 440 935-5027
Cleveland *(G-4819)*
Cardinal Health 414 LLC ... G ... 614 473-0786
Columbus *(G-6906)*
▲ **Cardinal Health 414 LLC** ... C ... 614 757-5000
Dublin *(G-9058)*
Cardinal Health 414 LLC ... G ... 513 759-1900
West Chester *(G-19823)*
Core Quantum Technologies Inc ... G ... 614 214-7210
Columbus *(G-6984)*
Diagnostic Hybrids Inc ... C ... 740 593-1784
Athens *(G-861)*
Diramed LLC ... F ... 614 487-3660
Columbus *(G-7026)*
Enlyton Ltd ... G ... 614 888-9220
Columbus *(G-7059)*
Filament LLC ... G ... 614 732-0754
Columbus *(G-7083)*
GE Health ... F ... 513 241-5955
Cincinnati *(G-3809)*
John P Ellis Clinic Podiatry ... G ... 440 460-0444
Cleveland *(G-5620)*
Meridian Bioscience Inc ... B ... 513 271-3700
Cincinnati *(G-4085)*
Meridian Life Science Inc ... D ... 513 271-3700
Cincinnati *(G-4086)*
Nanofiber Solutions Inc ... G ... 614 559-9065
Columbus *(G-7380)*
Navidea Biopharmaceuticals Inc ... D ... 614 793-7500
Dublin *(G-9110)*
Perkinelmer Hlth Sciences Inc ... E ... 330 825-4525
Akron *(G-336)*
Petnet Solutions Inc ... G ... 865 218-2000
Cincinnati *(G-4232)*
Petnet Solutions Inc ... G ... 865 218-2000
Cleveland *(G-5996)*
Petnet Solutions Cleveland LLC ... G ... 865 218-2000
Cleveland *(G-5997)*
Prostate Theranostics LLC ... G ... 216 595-1968
Beachwood *(G-1291)*
Sarcokinetics LLC ... G ... 414 477-9585
Cleveland *(G-6159)*
Thermo Fisher Scientific Inc ... C ... 800 871-8909
Oakwood Village *(G-15630)*
USB Corporation ... D ... 216 765-5000
Cleveland *(G-6401)*

2836 Biological Prdts, Exc Diagnostic Substances

Automatic Bacterial Injection ... F ... 216 378-1336
Bedford *(G-1402)*
Bio-Blood Components Inc ... E ... 614 294-3183
Columbus *(G-6829)*
Carbogene USA LLC ... G ... 215 378-4306
Columbus *(G-6904)*
Columbus Serum Co ... G ... 614 793-0615
Columbus *(G-6965)*
Copernicus Therapeutics Inc ... F ... 216 707-1776
Cleveland *(G-5131)*
Csl Plasma Inc ... E ... 937 325-4200
Springfield *(G-17537)*
Decaria Brothers Inc ... G ... 330 385-0825
East Liverpool *(G-9212)*
Edzplace ... G ... 216 289-4834
Euclid *(G-9577)*
EMD Millipore Corporation ... C ... 513 631-0445
Norwood *(G-15572)*
Ferro Corporation ... D ... 216 577-7144
Bedford *(G-1423)*
General Envmtl Science Corp ... G ... 216 464-0680
Cleveland *(G-5418)*
Global Health Services Inc ... G ... 513 777-8111
West Chester *(G-19876)*
Microbiological Labs Inc ... G ... 330 626-2264
Streetsboro *(G-17862)*
No Rinse Laboratories LLC ... G ... 937 746-7357
Springboro *(G-17492)*
Octapharma Plasma Inc ... G ... 216 518-0322
Maple Heights *(G-12735)*
Octapharma Plasma Inc ... G ... 216 252-6811
Cleveland *(G-5926)*
Perkinelmer Hlth Sciences Inc ... E ... 330 825-4525
Akron *(G-336)*
Plasmacare Inc ... G ... 614 231-5322
Columbus *(G-7491)*
Protein Express Laboratories ... G ... 513 769-9654
Blue Ash *(G-1860)*
Safewhite Inc ... G ... 614 340-1450
Columbus *(G-7586)*
Sellyourmaccom ... G ... 513 965-1144
Blue Ash *(G-1868)*
Sneaky Pete Band ... G ... 419 933-6251
Willard *(G-20401)*
Star Spangled Spectacular Inc ... G ... 419 879-3502
Lima *(G-12096)*
Supply Dynamics LLC ... F ... 513 965-2000
Loveland *(G-12392)*
Talecris Plasma Resources ... G ... 937 275-5996
Dayton *(G-8698)*
Tamarkin Company ... G ... 330 634-0688
Tallmadge *(G-18172)*
Tamarkin Company ... G ... 614 878-8942
Columbus *(G-7675)*
Tpr Plasma Center ... G ... 419 244-3910
Toledo *(G-18754)*
Venom Exterminating LLC ... G ... 330 637-3366
Cortland *(G-7876)*
Venom Towing LLC ... G ... 937 344-6530
Springboro *(G-17513)*
Wmre of Ohio-American LLC ... G ... 713 328-7345
Waynesburg *(G-19729)*

2841 Soap & Detergents

AIN Industries Inc ... G ... 440 781-0950
Cleveland *(G-4733)*
▼ **Amish Country Essentials LLC** ... G ... 330 674-3088
Millersburg *(G-14192)*
Beiersdorf Inc ... C ... 513 682-7300
West Chester *(G-19984)*
Betco Corporation Ltd ... E ... 419 241-2156
Toledo *(G-18366)*
◆ **Chester Packaging LLC** ... C ... 513 458-3840
Cincinnati *(G-3527)*
Cincinnati - Vulcan Company ... D ... 513 242-5300
Cincinnati *(G-3535)*
Cleaning Lady Inc ... F ... 419 589-5566
Mansfield *(G-12581)*
Colgate-Palmolive Company ... C ... 212 310-2000
Cambridge *(G-2452)*
Cr Brands Inc ... D ... 513 860-5039
West Chester *(G-19846)*
Cr Holding Inc ... G ... 513 860-5039
West Chester *(G-19847)*
Cresset Chemical Co Inc ... F ... 419 669-2041
Weston *(G-20325)*
▼ **Cresset Chemical Co Inc** ... F ... 419 669-2041
Weston *(G-20324)*
▲ **DSM Industries Inc** ... F ... 440 585-1100
Wickliffe *(G-20364)*
Edmar Chemical Company ... G ... 440 247-9560
Chagrin Falls *(G-3058)*
▲ **Emco Electric International** ... G ... 440 878-1199
Strongsville *(G-17917)*
Equipment Spcalists Dayton LLC ... G ... 937 415-2151
Dayton *(G-8330)*
EZ Brite Brands Inc ... F ... 440 871-7817
Cleveland *(G-5316)*
▲ **Fairy Dust Ltd Inc** ... F ... 513 251-0065
Cincinnati *(G-3736)*

S I C

▲ Foam-Tex Solutions Corp ....G....... 216 889-2702
Cleveland *(G-5364)*

Guardian Co Inc ....G....... 216 721-2262
Cleveland *(G-5464)*

Henkel Corporation ....E....... 740 363-1351
Delaware *(G-8859)*

Howard Grant Corporation ....G....... 330 743-3151
Youngstown *(G-21109)*

Jabco & Associates Inc ....G....... 513 752-0600
Amelia *(G-578)*

Jtm Products Inc ....E....... 440 287-2302
Solon *(G-17324)*

◆ KAO USA Inc ....B....... 513 421-1400
Cincinnati *(G-3972)*

▼ Kardol Quality Products LLC ....G....... 513 933-8206
Blue Ash *(G-1822)*

▲ Kutol Products Company Inc ....C....... 513 527-5500
Sharonville *(G-17114)*

Lubrizol Advanced Mtls Inc ....F....... 419 352-5565
Bowling Green *(G-1998)*

Mix-Masters Inc ....F....... 513 228-2800
Lebanon *(G-11817)*

New Vulco Mfg & Sales Co LLC ....D....... 513 242-2672
Cincinnati *(G-4149)*

◆ Noveon Incorporated ....G....... 216 447-5000
Brecksville *(G-2067)*

Oliver Chemical Co Inc ....G....... 513 541-4540
Cincinnati *(G-4185)*

Our Detergent Inc ....G....... 419 589-5571
Mansfield *(G-12665)*

◆ Pilot Chemical Company Ohio ....E....... 513 326-0600
Cincinnati *(G-4236)*

Pilot Chemical Company Ohio ....E....... 513 733-4880
Cincinnati *(G-4237)*

◆ Pilot Chemical Corp ....F....... 513 326-0600
Cincinnati *(G-4238)*

Pilot Chemical Corp ....E....... 513 424-9700
Middletown *(G-14075)*

▼ Polar Inc ....F....... 937 297-0911
Moraine *(G-14516)*

Procter & Gamble Company ....A....... 513 626-2500
Blue Ash *(G-1856)*

Procter & Gamble Company ....C....... 513 634-9600
West Chester *(G-19922)*

Procter & Gamble Company ....C....... 513 634-9110
West Chester *(G-19923)*

Procter & Gamble Company ....G....... 513 627-7779
Cincinnati *(G-4287)*

Procter & Gamble Company ....C....... 410 527-5735
Grove City *(G-10586)*

Procter & Gamble Company ....B....... 513 983-1100
Cincinnati *(G-4286)*

◆ Procter & Gamble Company ....B....... 513 983-1100
Cincinnati *(G-4277)*

▼ Procter & Gamble Mfg Co ....F....... 513 983-1100
Cincinnati *(G-4290)*

Procter & Gamble Mfg Co ....G....... 513 626-6882
Blue Ash *(G-1858)*

Procter & Gamble Mfg Co ....C....... 419 226-5500
Lima *(G-12075)*

Renegade Brands LLC ....G....... 216 342-4347
Cleveland *(G-6101)*

RES Q Cleaning Solutions Inc ....G....... 740 964-9494
Reynoldsburg *(G-16602)*

Royal Chemical Company Ltd ....F....... 330 467-1300
Twinsburg *(G-19013)*

▲ St Bernard Soap Company ....B....... 513 242-2227
Cincinnati *(G-4450)*

◆ State Industrial Products Corp ....B....... 877 747-6986
Cleveland *(G-6239)*

State Industrial Products Corp ....E....... 740 929-5800
Hebron *(G-10886)*

Sunbeam Products Co LLC ....G....... 419 691-1551
Toledo *(G-18706)*

Trillium Health Care Products ....G....... 513 242-2227
Cincinnati *(G-4525)*

US Industrial Lubricants Inc ....F....... 513 541-2225
Cincinnati *(G-4547)*

▼ Wallover Oil Company Inc ....E....... 440 238-9250
Strongsville *(G-17982)*

▼ Washing Systems LLC ....C....... 800 272-1974
Loveland *(G-12399)*

Woodspirits Limited Inc ....G....... 937 663-5025
Saint Paris *(G-16865)*

▲ Zorbx Inc ....E....... 440 238-1847
Strongsville *(G-17987)*

2842 Spec Cleaning, Polishing & Sanitation Preparations

Advanced Cleaning Tech LLC ....G....... 614 504-5433
Plain City *(G-16318)*

▲ Alco-Chem Inc ....E....... 330 253-3535
Akron *(G-61)*

All Prem Cleaners Inc ....G....... 440 349-3649
Solon *(G-17251)*

Allen Drain Service Inc ....G....... 330 253-4206
Kent *(G-11426)*

Alumin Nu Corp ....G....... 216 421-2116
Cleveland *(G-4772)*

Aman & Co Inc ....G....... 330 854-1122
Canal Fulton *(G-2495)*

American Chemical Products ....F....... 216 267-7722
Cleveland *(G-4780)*

Babcock & Wilcox Megtec ....G....... 614 258-9501
Columbus *(G-6799)*

◆ Betco Corporation Ltd ....C....... 419 241-2156
Bowling Green *(G-1972)*

Betco Corporation Ltd ....E....... 419 241-2156
Toledo *(G-18366)*

Bevclean Products Inc ....G....... 937 233-5000
Dayton *(G-8187)*

BLaster Corporation ....G....... 216 901-5800
Cleveland *(G-4916)*

Boyd Sanitation ....G....... 740 697-7940
Roseville *(G-16727)*

◆ Canberra Corporation ....C....... 419 724-4300
Toledo *(G-18388)*

Capital Chemical Co ....E....... 330 494-9535
Canton *(G-2649)*

Carolyn Chemical Company ....G....... 614 252-5000
Columbus *(G-6911)*

Cedar Point Laundry ....G....... 419 627-2274
Sandusky *(G-16953)*

▲ Chem 1 Inc ....G....... 216 475-7443
Warrensville Heights *(G-19631)*

Chemical Methods Inc ....E....... 216 476-8400
Strongsville *(G-17901)*

▲ Chempace Corporation ....F....... 419 535-0101
Toledo *(G-18395)*

◆ Chester Packaging LLC ....C....... 513 458-3840
Cincinnati *(G-3527)*

Cincinnati - Vulcan Company ....D....... 513 242-5300
Cincinnati *(G-3535)*

Clayton Manufacturing Company ....F....... 513 563-1300
Cincinnati *(G-3585)*

Cleaning By Sndra Msters Touch ....F....... 216 524-6827
Seven Hills *(G-17061)*

Clorox Company ....F....... 513 445-1840
Mason *(G-13001)*

Consolidated Coatings Corp ....E....... 216 514-7596
Cleveland *(G-5118)*

Custom Chemical Packaging LLC ....E....... 330 331-7416
Wadsworth *(G-19399)*

▲ D & J Distributing & Mfg ....E....... 419 865-2552
Holland *(G-11052)*

D C Filter & Chemical Inc ....G....... 419 626-3967
Sandusky *(G-16955)*

Diversey Inc ....G....... 513 326-8300
Cincinnati *(G-3657)*

▲ Easy Care Products Inc ....G....... 330 405-1380
Twinsburg *(G-18928)*

Ecolab Inc ....G....... 513 932-0830
Lebanon *(G-11796)*

Edmar Chemical Company ....G....... 440 247-9560
Chagrin Falls *(G-3058)*

EMD Millipore Corporation ....C....... 513 631-0445
Norwood *(G-15572)*

EZ Brite Brands Inc ....F....... 440 871-7817
Cleveland *(G-5316)*

Ferro Corporation ....D....... 216 577-7144
Bedford *(G-1423)*

◆ Fresh Products LLC ....D....... 419 531-9741
Perrysburg *(G-16099)*

Fuchs Lubricants Co ....E....... 330 963-0400
Twinsburg *(G-18938)*

Glister Inc ....G....... 614 252-6400
Columbus *(G-7118)*

◆ Gojo Industries Inc ....C....... 330 255-6000
Akron *(G-206)*

Gojo Industries Inc ....E....... 330 255-6000
Cuyahoga Falls *(G-8004)*

Gojo Industries Inc ....C....... 330 255-6525
Stow *(G-17760)*

Gojo Industries Inc ....C....... 330 922-4522
Cuyahoga Falls *(G-8005)*

Guardian Co Inc ....G....... 216 721-2262
Cleveland *(G-5464)*

Henkel Corporation ....E....... 740 363-1351
Delaware *(G-8859)*

Henkel Corporation ....C....... 216 475-3600
Cleveland *(G-5498)*

Inceptor Inc ....G....... 419 726-8804
Toledo *(G-18519)*

Intercontinental Chemical Corp ....E....... 513 541-7100
Cincinnati *(G-3928)*

Jackson Deluxe Cleaners Ltd ....G....... 419 592-2826
Napoleon *(G-14686)*

James C Robinson ....G....... 513 969-7482
Cincinnati *(G-3941)*

Jason Incorporated ....F....... 513 860-3400
Hamilton *(G-10711)*

Jax Wax Inc ....F....... 614 476-6769
Columbus *(G-7228)*

Jeyes US Holdings Inc ....B....... 614 984-2896
New Albany *(G-14764)*

K-O-K Products Inc ....F....... 740 548-0526
Galena *(G-10245)*

▼ Kardol Quality Products LLC ....G....... 513 933-8206
Blue Ash *(G-1822)*

Kcs Cleaning Service ....F....... 740 418-5479
Oak Hill *(G-15599)*

Kinzua Environmental Inc ....E....... 216 881-4040
Cleveland *(G-5655)*

Kleen Test Products Corp ....F....... 330 878-5586
Strasburg *(G-17824)*

▲ Kona Blackbird Inc ....F....... 440 285-3189
Chardon *(G-3160)*

L-Mor Inc ....F....... 216 541-2224
Cleveland *(G-5672)*

Leesburg Modern Sales Inc ....G....... 937 780-2613
Leesburg *(G-11854)*

Leonhardt Plating Company ....E....... 513 242-1410
Cincinnati *(G-4020)*

Malco Products Inc ....E....... 330 753-0361
Akron *(G-281)*

McGean-Rohco Inc ....D....... 216 441-4900
Newburgh Heights *(G-15076)*

Milsek Furniture Polish Inc ....G....... 330 542-2700
Petersburg *(G-16178)*

Mix-Masters Inc ....F....... 513 228-2800
Lebanon *(G-11817)*

Mold Masters Intl Inc ....C....... 440 953-0220
Mentor *(G-13659)*

Nanofilm Ltd ....E....... 216 674-1430
Cleveland *(G-5851)*

▲ National Colloid Company ....E....... 740 282-1171
Steubenville *(G-17706)*

New Vulco Mfg & Sales Co LLC ....D....... 513 242-2672
Cincinnati *(G-4149)*

New Waste Concepts Inc ....G....... 419 872-2190
Perrysburg *(G-16126)*

◆ Nilodor Inc ....E....... 800 443-4321
Bolivar *(G-1939)*

Nwp Manufacturing Inc ....G....... 419 894-6871
Waldo *(G-19466)*

Ohio Auto Supply Company ....E....... 330 454-5105
Canton *(G-2798)*

Ohio Mills Corporation ....G....... 216 431-3979
Cleveland *(G-5934)*

Oliver Chemical Co Inc ....G....... 513 541-4540
Cincinnati *(G-4185)*

Orchem Corporation ....E....... 513 874-9700
Cincinnati *(G-4193)*

Paro Services Co ....F....... 330 467-1300
Twinsburg *(G-18995)*

Pats Nu-Style Cleaners Inc ....G....... 216 676-4855
Cleveland *(G-5980)*

Pilot Chemical Company Ohio ....E....... 513 733-4880
Cincinnati *(G-4237)*

Pilot Chemical Corp ....E....... 513 424-9700
Middletown *(G-14075)*

Polynt Composites USA Inc ....E....... 816 391-6000
Sandusky *(G-16997)*

◆ Procter & Gamble Company ....B....... 513 983-1100
Cincinnati *(G-4277)*

Procter & Gamble Company ....B....... 513 983-1100
Cincinnati *(G-4286)*

Procter & Gamble Far East Inc ....C....... 513 983-1100
Cincinnati *(G-4289)*

Procter & Gamble Mfg Co ....C....... 419 226-5500
Lima *(G-12075)*

Q2power Technologies Inc ....G....... 740 415-2073
Lancaster *(G-11743)*

Reid Asset Management Company ....E....... 440 942-8488
Willoughby *(G-20587)*

◆ Republic Powdered Metals Inc ....D....... 330 225-3192
Medina *(G-13467)*

Rose Products and Services Inc ....E 614 443-7647
Columbus (G-7573)

◆ RPM International Inc ....D 330 273-5090
Medina (G-13471)

S C Johnson & Son Inc ....E 513 665-3600
Cincinnati (G-4372)

Saint Ctherines Metalworks Inc ....G 216 409-0576
Cleveland (G-6155)

Scottissue LLC ....E 937 293-2139
Moraine (G-14527)

Sevan At-Ndustrial Pnt Abr Ltd ....G 614 258-4747
Columbus (G-7610)

Shur Clean Usa LLC ....E 513 341-5486
Liberty Township (G-11968)

Skybryte Company Inc ....G 216 771-1590
Cleveland (G-6209)

Smart Sonic Corporation ....G 818 610-7900
Cleveland (G-6211)

Solutions Plus Inc ....E 513 943-9600
Amelia (G-583)

◆ Spartan Chemical Company Inc ......E 419 897-5551
Maumee (G-13297)

◆ State Industrial Products Corp..........B 877 747-6986
Cleveland (G-6239)

▼ Strib Industries Inc ....E 216 281-1155
Cleveland (G-6252)

Sun Cleaners & Laundry Inc ....G 740 756-4749
Carroll (G-2948)

▲ Tolco Corporation ....D 419 241-1113
Toledo (G-18728)

◆ Tranzonic Companies ....C 216 535-4300
Richmond Heights (G-16656)

Tranzonic Companies............................C 440 446-0643
Cleveland (G-6350)

◆ Tremco Incorporated ....B 216 292-5000
Beachwood (G-1303)

Trigon Industries Inc.............................G 937 299-1350
Oakwood (G-15612)

▲ Troy Chemical Industries Inc ....F 440 834-4408
Burton (G-2387)

◆ Tz Acquisition Corp...........................A 216 535-4300
Richmond Heights (G-16658)

Univar USA Inc ....G 513 714-5264
West Chester (G-20064)

US Industrial Lubricants Inc ....E 513 541-2225
Cincinnati (G-4547)

Valspar Corporation ....C 330 830-6000
Massillon (G-13209)

▼ Ventco Inc ....F 440 834-8888
Middlefield (G-14001)

Vitex Corporation ....F 216 883-0920
Cleveland (G-6423)

Wilkshire Dry Cleaners LLC ....G 330 674-7696
Millersburg (G-14286)

Wise Consumer Products Company......G 513 484-6530
Montgomery (G-14436)

▲ Woodbine Products Company ....F 330 725-0165
Medina (G-13497)

2843 Surface Active & Finishing Agents, Sulfonated Oils

BASF Corporation...................................G 614 662-5682
Columbus (G-6812)

▲ Berghausen Corporation...................E 513 541-5631
Cincinnati (G-3445)

Henkel Corporation................................C 440 250-7700
Westlake (G-20275)

▲ Peter Cremer North America LP ....D 513 471-7200
Cincinnati (G-4231)

◆ Pilot Chemical Company Ohio ....E 513 326-0600
Cincinnati (G-4236)

Pilot Chemical Company Ohio ....E 513 733-4880
Cincinnati (G-4237)

◆ Pilot Chemical Corp ....F 513 326-0600
Cincinnati (G-4238)

Southern Express Lubes Inc ....F 937 278-5807
Dayton (G-8662)

2844 Perfumes, Cosmetics & Toilet Preparations

Abbott Laboratories................................A 614 624-3078
Columbus (G-6674)

▼ Abitec Corporation............................E 614 429-6464
Columbus (G-6678)

Aeroscena LLC ....F 800 671-1890
Cleveland (G-4723)

▼ Amish Country Essentials LLC..........G 330 674-3088
Millersburg (G-14192)

◆ Art of Beauty Company Inc ....F 216 438-6363
Bedford (G-1399)

Ashland Specialty Ingredients...............D 302 594-5000
Dublin (G-9048)

Ashland Specialty Ingredients...............D 614 529-3311
Columbus (G-6776)

B & P Company Inc ....G 937 298-0265
Dayton (G-8177)

Barbasol LLC...E 419 903-0738
Ashland (G-711)

▲ Bath & Body Works LLC....................B 614 856-6000
Reynoldsburg (G-16582)

Beiersdorf Inc ....C 513 682-7300
West Chester (G-19984)

Bertsherm Products Inc ....G 440 268-8389
Cleveland (G-4908)

Biocurv Medical Instruments ....G 330 451-1628
Canton (G-2623)

Bocchi Laboraties Ohio LLC ....B 661 673-8500
New Albany (G-14751)

▲ Bonne Bell LLC.................................G 440 835-2440
Westlake (G-20257)

▲ Cameo Inc...E 419 661-9611
Perrysburg (G-16074)

Dayton Environmental.............................F 937 478-1536
Dayton (G-8102)

▲ Donegal Bay Ltd................................F 216 360-9966
Cleveland (G-5207)

Dover Wipes Company ....F 513 983-1100
Cincinnati (G-3669)

Edgewell Personal Care LLC..................C 937 492-1057
Sidney (G-17183)

Erik V Lamb ....G 330 962-1540
Copley (G-7846)

Expressive Scents By A ....G 513 254-5399
Cincinnati (G-3732)

Facial Sensation Products ....G 937 293-2280
Oakwood (G-15607)

Fantastic Sams Hair Care Salon............G 740 456-4296
Portsmouth (G-16435)

Galleria Co ....G 513 983-1490
Cincinnati (G-3794)

Garden Art Innovations LLC ....G 330 697-0007
Barberton (G-1116)

◆ Gojo Industries Inc ....C 330 255-6000
Akron (G-206)

Gojo Industries Inc ....C 330 255-6525
Stow (G-17760)

Gojo Industries Inc ....G 330 922-4522
Cuyahoga Falls (G-8005)

Hair & Nail Impressions..........................G 937 399-0221
Springfield (G-17567)

Honey Gold Company ....G 330 688-5502
Kent (G-11470)

House of Delara Fragrances ....G 216 651-5803
Cleveland (G-5529)

Jackson David Do ....F 419 872-3201
Perrysburg (G-16113)

John Frieda Prof Hair Care Inc ....E 800 521-3189
Cincinnati (G-3952)

Kahuna Bay Spray Tan LLC....................G 419 386-2387
Toledo (G-18537)

◆ KAO USA Inc ....B 513 421-1400
Cincinnati (G-3972)

LOreal Usa Inc.......................................A 440 248-3700
Cleveland (G-5709)

LS Bombshelles ....G 513 254-6898
Cincinnati (G-4036)

Luminex Home Decor ....A 513 563-1113
Blue Ash (G-1831)

M D Complete Prof Skincare ....G 513 965-3760
Terrace Park (G-18181)

▲ Madaen Natural Products Inc ....G 800 600-1445
Cuyahoga Falls (G-8021)

Mantra Haircare LLC ....F 440 526-3304
Broadview Heights (G-2113)

Meridian Industries Inc...........................E 330 359-5809
Beach City (G-1248)

Natural Beauty Products Inc...................F 513 420-9400
Middletown (G-14068)

▲ Natural Essentials Inc.......................E 330 562-8022
Aurora (G-937)

Natures Simple Solution Inc ....G 440 567-6913
Cleveland (G-5862)

▲ Nehemiah Manufacturing Co LLC .....E 513 351-5700
Cincinnati (G-4143)

Oasis Consumer Healthcare LLC...........G 216 394-0544
Cleveland (G-5924)

Oil Bar LLC ....F 614 880-3950
Columbus (G-6657)

◆ Oils By Nature Incorporated.............G 330 468-8897
Hudson (G-11190)

▲ OKeeffes Working Hands Creme.......F 800 275-2718
Cincinnati (G-4182)

Olay LLC...G 787 535-2191
Blue Ash (G-1845)

Olfactorium Corp Inc ....G 216 663-8831
Cleveland (G-5938)

Pfizer Inc ....C 937 746-3603
Franklin (G-10044)

◆ Procter & Gamble Company ....B 513 983-1100
Cincinnati (G-4277)

Procter & Gamble Company ....E 513 266-4375
Cincinnati (G-4279)

Procter & Gamble Company ....E 513 871-7557
Cincinnati (G-4280)

Procter & Gamble Company ....F 513 482-6789
Cincinnati (G-4282)

Procter & Gamble Company ....E 513 672-4044
West Chester (G-19921)

Procter & Gamble Company ....E 513 634-5069
Cincinnati (G-4283)

Procter & Gamble Company ....E 513 627-7115
Cincinnati (G-4284)

Procter & Gamble Company ....C 513 948-2462
Cincinnati (G-4285)

Procter & Gamble Company ....B 513 983-1100
Cincinnati (G-4286)

Procter & Gamble Company ....B 513 945-0340
Cincinnati (G-4288)

Procter & Gamble Company ....E 513 622-1000
Mason (G-13078)

Procter & Gamble Company ....C 513 626-2500
Blue Ash (G-1857)

Procter & Gamble Company ....C 513 634-9110
West Chester (G-19923)

Procter & Gamble Company ....C 410 527-5735
Grove City (G-10586)

Procter & Gamble Far East Inc ....C 513 983-1100
Cincinnati (G-4289)

▼ Procter & Gamble Mfg Co ....F 513 983-1100
Cincinnati (G-4290)

▲ Proft & Gamble ....G 513 945-0340
Cincinnati (G-4298)

Redex Industries Inc ....F 330 332-9800
Salem (G-16924)

Sally Beauty Supply LLC ....G 330 823-7476
Alliance (G-535)

Scarlett Kitty LLC ....F 678 438-3796
Dayton (G-8646)

Sentinel Consumer Products Inc ....D 801 825-5671
Mentor (G-13720)

Skin ....G 937 222-0222
Dayton (G-8660)

Sysco Guest Supply LLC ....F 440 960-2515
Lorain (G-12285)

Universal Packg Systems Inc ....B 513 674-9400
Cincinnati (G-4542)

Universal Packg Systems Inc ....B 513 732-2000
Batavia (G-1231)

Universal Packg Systems Inc ....E 513 735-4777
Batavia (G-1232)

US Cotton LLC ....B 216 676-6400
Cleveland (G-6399)

Vein Center and Medspa ....G 330 629-9400
Youngstown (G-21236)

▲ Woodbine Products Company ....F 330 725-0165
Medina (G-13497)

2851 Paints, Varnishes, Lacquers, Enamels

◆ Akron Paint & Varnish Inc ....D 330 773-8911
Akron (G-50)

Akzo Nobel Coatings Inc ....C 614 294-3361
Columbus (G-6709)

Akzo Nobel Coatings Inc ....F 937 322-2671
Springfield (G-17515)

Akzo Nobel Coatings Inc ....C 614 294-3361
Columbus (G-6711)

Akzo Nobel Inc ....C 205 323-5201
Columbus (G-6712)

All Coatings Co Inc ....G 330 821-3806
Alliance (G-489)

Aluminum Coating Manufacturers ....E 216 341-2000
Cleveland (G-4774)

American Paint Recyclers LLC ....G 888 978-6558
Middle Point (G-13897)

▲ Americhem Inc ....D 330 929-4213
Cuyahoga Falls (G-7965)

▲ Aps-Materials Inc ....D 937 278-6547
Dayton (G-8161)

SIC

Avion Manufacturing Company ....G...... 330 220-1989
  Brunswick (G-2207)

Axalt Powde Coati Syste Usa I ....F...... 614 600-4104
  Hilliard (G-10929)

Axalta Coating Systems LLC ....E...... 419 478-1211
  Toledo (G-18361)

Baker Built Products Inc ....G...... 419 965-2646
  Ohio City (G-15660)

◆ BASF Construction Chem LLC ....E...... 216 831-5500
  Cleveland (G-4895)

Basic Coatings LLC ....E...... 419 241-2156
  Bowling Green (G-1971)

Bollin & Sons Inc ....E...... 419 693-6573
  Toledo (G-18376)

Brinkman LLC ....F...... 419 204-5934
  Lima (G-11997)

Cahill Services Inc ....G...... 216 410-5595
  Lakewood (G-11659)

Cansto Coatings Ltd ....F...... 216 231-6115
  Cleveland (G-4965)

Cansto Paint and Varnish Co ....G...... 216 231-6115
  Cleveland (G-4966)

Certon Technologies Inc ....F...... 440 786-7185
  Bedford (G-1414)

Cetek Ltd ....E...... 216 362-3900
  Cleveland (G-5010)

Cleveland Pigment Blending LLC ....G...... 330 794-6960
  Akron (G-126)

◆ Coloramics LLC ....E...... 614 876-1171
  Hilliard (G-10942)

◆ Comex North America Inc ....D...... 303 307-2100
  Cleveland (G-5103)

Consolidated Coatings Corp ....E...... 216 514-7596
  Cleveland (G-5118)

Continental Products Company ....E...... 216 383-3932
  Euclid (G-9573)

Continental Products Company ....E...... 216 531-0710
  Cleveland (G-5126)

CPI Industrial Co ....E...... 614 445-0800
  Columbus (G-6995)

Creative Commercial Finishing ....G...... 513 722-9393
  Loveland (G-12347)

Dap Products Inc ....C...... 937 667-4461
  Tipp City (G-18274)

David E Easterday and Co Inc ....F...... 330 359-0700
  Wilmot (G-20685)

▲ Day-Glo Color Corp ....C...... 216 391-7070
  Cleveland (G-5173)

Day-Glo Color Corp ....C...... 216 391-7070
  Cleveland (G-5174)

Deco Plas Properties LLC ....E...... 419 485-0632
  Montpelier (G-14443)

Dolgencorp LLC ....G...... 740 289-4790
  Piketon (G-16219)

Dudick Inc ....D...... 330 562-1970
  Streetsboro (G-17851)

Dynafloor Systems Inc ....F...... 330 467-6005
  Solon (G-17283)

Envirnmntal Prtctive Ctngs LLC ....G...... 740 363-6180
  Ostrander (G-15786)

Epoxy Systems Blstg Cating Inc ....E...... 513 924-1800
  Cleves (G-6513)

Ferro Corporation ....D...... 216 577-7144
  Bedford (G-1423)

Ferro Corporation ....G...... 216 481-0238
  Cleveland (G-5338)

Ferro Corporation ....C...... 216 875-6178
  Cleveland (G-5337)

◆ Ferro Corporation ....D...... 216 875-5600
  Mayfield Heights (G-13313)

Filament LLC ....G...... 614 732-0754
  Columbus (G-7083)

Fuchs Lubricants Co ....E...... 330 963-0400
  Twinsburg (G-18938)

General Electric Company ....D...... 216 268-3846
  Cleveland (G-5417)

Genvac Aerospace Corp ....F...... 440 646-9986
  Cleveland (G-5424)

Harrison Paint Company ....E...... 330 455-5120
  Canton (G-2724)

Henkel Corporation ....C...... 216 475-3600
  Cleveland (G-5498)

Hess Advanced Technology Inc ....G...... 937 268-4377
  Huber Heights (G-11148)

Hexpol Compounding LLC ....C...... 440 834-4644
  Burton (G-2376)

Hoover & Wells Inc ....C...... 419 691-9220
  Toledo (G-18511)

Hytek Coatings Inc ....G...... 513 424-0131
  Middletown (G-14046)

Janet Sullivan ....G...... 419 658-2333
  Ney (G-15142)

▲ Kalcor Coatings Company ....E...... 440 946-4700
  Willoughby (G-20518)

▼ Kardol Quality Products LLC ....E...... 513 933-8206
  Blue Ash (G-1822)

Kars Ohio LLC ....G...... 614 655-1099
  Pataskala (G-15973)

Karyall-Telday Inc ....E...... 216 281-4063
  Cleveland (G-5633)

Leonhardt Plating Company ....E...... 513 242-1410
  Cincinnati (G-4020)

Mameco International Inc ....F...... 216 752-4400
  Cleveland (G-5738)

Mansfield Paint Co Inc ....F...... 330 725-2436
  Medina (G-13439)

Matrix Sys Auto Finishes LLC ....D...... 248 668-8135
  Massillon (G-13177)

Meggitt (erlanger) LLC ....D...... 513 851-5550
  Cincinnati (G-4080)

Metalcrete Industries Inc ....G...... 440 526-5600
  Cleveland (G-5790)

Mid America Chemical Corp ....G...... 216 749-0100
  Cleveland (G-5803)

Myko Industries ....G...... 216 431-0900
  Cleveland (G-5845)

▼ Nanosperse LLC ....G...... 937 296-5030
  Kettering (G-11583)

▲ North Shore Strapping Inc ....G...... 216 661-5200
  Brooklyn Heights (G-2144)

▲ Npa Coatings Inc ....C...... 216 651-5900
  Cleveland (G-5921)

Parker Trutec Incorporated ....D...... 937 653-8500
  Urbana (G-19172)

Parkins Asphalt Sealing ....G...... 419 422-2399
  Findlay (G-9876)

◆ Perstorp Polyols Inc ....C...... 419 729-5448
  Toledo (G-18641)

Pittsburgh Glass Works LLC ....B...... 419 683-2400
  Crestline (G-7933)

▲ Plasti-Kote Co Inc ....C...... 330 725-4511
  Medina (G-13459)

▲ Polymerics Inc ....E...... 330 434-6665
  Cuyahoga Falls (G-8034)

Polynt Composites USA Inc ....C...... 816 391-6000
  Sandusky (G-16997)

Polyone Corporation ....C...... 419 668-4844
  Norwalk (G-15559)

▲ Postle Industries Inc ....E...... 216 265-9000
  Cleveland (G-6022)

PPG Architectural Finishes Inc ....E...... 216 328-1581
  Cleveland (G-6025)

PPG Architectural Finishes Inc ....G...... 330 477-8165
  Canton (G-2817)

PPG Industries Inc ....G...... 330 825-0831
  Barberton (G-1140)

PPG Industries Inc ....D...... 440 572-2800
  Strongsville (G-17951)

PPG Industries Inc ....G...... 740 774-8734
  Chillicothe (G-3264)

PPG Industries Inc ....E...... 216 671-7793
  Cleveland (G-6026)

PPG Industries Inc ....E...... 513 576-0360
  Milford (G-14167)

PPG Industries Inc ....C...... 740 474-3161
  Circleville (G-4637)

PPG Industries Inc ....E...... 740 774-7600
  Chillicothe (G-3265)

PPG Industries Inc ....F...... 740 774-7600
  Chillicothe (G-3266)

PPG Industries Inc ....E...... 419 683-2400
  Crestline (G-7935)

PPG Industries Inc ....E...... 513 231-3200
  Cincinnati (G-4259)

PPG Industries Inc ....E...... 740 474-3945
  Circleville (G-4638)

PPG Industries Inc ....E...... 513 829-6006
  Fairfield (G-9703)

PPG Industries Inc ....E...... 513 661-5220
  Cincinnati (G-4260)

PPG Industries Inc ....G...... 614 277-0620
  Grove City (G-10584)

PPG Industries Inc ....G...... 614 921-9228
  Hilliard (G-10972)

PPG Industries Inc ....E...... 513 424-1241
  Middletown (G-14077)

PPG Industries Inc ....E...... 513 984-6761
  Cincinnati (G-4261)

PPG Industries Inc ....G...... 614 939-2365
  Columbus (G-7509)

PPG Industries Inc ....E...... 614 268-2609
  Columbus (G-7510)

PPG Industries Inc ....E...... 513 779-2727
  West Chester (G-20039)

PPG Industries Inc ....E...... 513 242-3050
  Cincinnati (G-4262)

PPG Industries Inc ....E...... 614 501-7360
  Reynoldsburg (G-16597)

PPG Industries Inc ....G...... 330 262-9741
  Wooster (G-20822)

PPG Industries Inc ....E...... 513 576-3100
  Milford (G-14168)

PPG Industries Inc ....E...... 330 824-2537
  Warren (G-19588)

PPG Industries Ohio Inc ....G...... 740 363-9610
  Delaware (G-8878)

PPG Industries Ohio Inc ....D...... 216 486-5300
  Euclid (G-9600)

◆ PPG Industries Ohio Inc ....A...... 216 671-0050
  Cleveland (G-6027)

Precisions Paint Systems LLC ....F...... 740 894-6224
  South Point (G-17444)

Premier Ink Systems Inc ....F...... 513 367-4700
  Harrison (G-10796)

Priest Services Inc ....G...... 440 333-1123
  Mayfield Heights (G-13321)

▲ Prism Powder Coatings Ltd ....E...... 330 225-5626
  Brunswick (G-2249)

Ramon Robinson ....G...... 330 883-3244
  Vienna (G-19374)

◆ Republic Powdered Metals Inc ....D...... 330 225-3192
  Medina (G-13467)

Robert Raack ....G...... 216 932-6127
  Cleveland Heights (G-6501)

Roger Hoover ....G...... 330 857-1815
  Orrville (G-15760)

RPM Consumer Holding Company ....G...... 330 273-5090
  Medina (G-13470)

◆ RPM International Inc ....G...... 330 273-5090
  Medina (G-13471)

Ruscoe Company ....G...... 330 253-8148
  Akron (G-383)

Schilling Enamels Company ....G...... 216 252-6242
  Cleveland (G-6164)

Schilling Enterprises Inc ....G...... 216 252-6242
  Cleveland (G-6165)

Sheffield Bronze Paint Corp ....E...... 216 481-8330
  Cleveland (G-6186)

Sherwin-Williams Company ....A...... 216 566-2000
  Cleveland (G-6189)

Sherwin-Williams Company ....G...... 440 282-2310
  Lorain (G-12275)

Sherwin-Williams Company ....G...... 330 253-6625
  North Canton (G-15264)

Sherwin-Williams Company ....E...... 614 539-8456
  Grove City (G-10594)

Sherwin-Williams Company ....E...... 440 846-4328
  Strongsville (G-17965)

Sherwin-Williams Company ....G...... 216 662-3300
  Cleveland (G-6190)

Sherwin-Williams Company ....G...... 330 528-0124
  Hudson (G-11198)

◆ Sherwn-Wllams Auto Fnshes Corp ...C...... 216 332-8330
  Cleveland (G-6191)

Sherwn-Wllams Intl Hldings Inc ....G...... 216 566-2000
  Cleveland (G-6192)

Spectrum Dispersions Inc ....F...... 330 296-0600
  Ravenna (G-16558)

Suncolor Corporation ....G...... 330 499-7010
  North Canton (G-15270)

Superior Printing Ink Co Inc ....G...... 216 328-1720
  Cleveland (G-6268)

▲ Teknol Inc ....D...... 937 264-0190
  Dayton (G-8708)

The Euclid Chemical Company ....D...... 216 531-9222
  Cleveland (G-6310)

◆ Thorworks Industries Inc ....E...... 419 626-4375
  Sandusky (G-17015)

Toledo Paint & Chemical Co ....G...... 419 244-3726
  Toledo (G-18739)

◆ Tremco Incorporated ....B...... 216 292-5000
  Beachwood (G-1303)

Treved Exteriors ....G...... 513 771-3888
  Cincinnati (G-4520)

Trexler Rubber Co Inc ....E...... 330 296-9677
  Ravenna (G-16567)

Universal Urethane Pdts Inc ....D...... 419 693-7400
  Toledo (G-18760)

Valspar Corporation ....C...... 330 830-6000
  Massillon (G-13209)

▼ Waterlox Coatings Corporation ....F 216 641-4877
  Cleveland *(G-6450)*
▼ Wooster Products Inc ....D 330 264-2844
  Wooster *(G-20850)*
X-Treme Finishes Inc ....F 330 474-0614
  Medina *(G-13498)*
▲ Xim Products Inc ....E 440 871-4737
  Westlake *(G-20323)*
▲ Zircoa Inc ....C 440 248-0500
  Cleveland *(G-6498)*

2861 Gum & Wood Chemicals

Arizona Chemical Company LLC ....C 330 343-7701
  Dover *(G-8964)*
Tanning ....G 937 233-4554
  Dayton *(G-8699)*

2865 Cyclic-Crudes, Intermediates, Dyes & Org Pigments

Accel Corporation ....F 440 327-7418
  Avon *(G-980)*
Altivia Petrochemicals LLC ....E 740 532-3420
  Haverhill *(G-10836)*
Americas Styrenics LLC ....D 740 533-4017
  Hanging Rock *(G-10761)*
Americhem Inc ....E 330 926-3185
  Cuyahoga Falls *(G-7964)*
▲ Americhem Inc ....D 330 929-4213
  Cuyahoga Falls *(G-7965)*
▲ Berghausen Corporation ....E 513 541-5631
  Cincinnati *(G-3445)*
Chromaflo Technologies Corp ....C 513 733-5111
  Cincinnati *(G-3532)*
▲ Chromaflo Technologies Corp ....C 440 997-0081
  Ashtabula *(G-795)*
◆ Cleveland FP Inc ....D 216 249-4900
  Cleveland *(G-5061)*
Colormatrix Group Inc ....G 216 622-0100
  Berea *(G-1608)*
Colormatrix Holdings Inc ....C 440 930-3162
  Berea *(G-1609)*
Dorum Color Co Inc ....G 330 773-1900
  Akron *(G-154)*
▲ Emerald Hilton Davis LLC ....D 513 841-0057
  Cincinnati *(G-3694)*
Exciton Inc ....F 937 252-2989
  Dayton *(G-8336)*
Ferro Corporation ....F 330 682-8015
  Orrville *(G-15736)*
Ferro Corporation ....C 216 875-6178
  Cleveland *(G-5337)*
Flint Group US LLC ....D 513 771-1900
  Cincinnati *(G-3761)*
Hexpol Compounding LLC ....C 440 834-4644
  Burton *(G-2376)*
Inceptor Inc ....G 419 726-8804
  Toledo *(G-18519)*
Kingscote Chemicals Inc ....G 937 886-9100
  Miamisburg *(G-13824)*
◆ Marathon Petroleum Company LP ....F 419 422-2121
  Findlay *(G-9855)*
Norlab Inc ....G 440 282-5265
  Lorain *(G-12262)*
Office Link Inc ....G 440 498-1364
  Solon *(G-17353)*
▲ Polymerics Inc ....E 330 434-6665
  Cuyahoga Falls *(G-8034)*
Polyone Corporation ....C 419 668-4844
  Norwalk *(G-15559)*
Polyone Corporation ....G 216 622-0100
  Berea *(G-1632)*
◆ Republic Powdered Metals Inc ....D 330 225-3192
  Medina *(G-13467)*
◆ RPM International Inc ....D 330 273-5090
  Medina *(G-13471)*
Ruscoe Company ....E 330 253-8148
  Akron *(G-384)*
Spectrum Dispersions Inc ....F 330 296-0600
  Ravenna *(G-16558)*
Sun Chemical Corporation ....C 513 681-5950
  Cincinnati *(G-4477)*
Sun Chemical Corporation ....D 513 753-9550
  Amelia *(G-585)*
Sun Chemical Corporation ....E 513 830-8667
  Cincinnati *(G-4481)*
Thermocolor LLC ....E 419 626-5677
  Sandusky *(G-17012)*
Thermocolor LLC ....F 419 626-5677
  Sandusky *(G-17013)*

▲ Tri Chem Inc ....G 330 677-1213
  Kent *(G-11539)*

2869 Industrial Organic Chemicals, NEC

▼ Abitec Corporation ....E 614 429-6464
  Columbus *(G-6678)*
ABS Materials Inc ....D 330 234-7999
  Wooster *(G-20730)*
Adr Fuel Inc ....G 419 872-2178
  Perrysburg *(G-16061)*
Advanced Engine Tech LLC ....G 937 439-0224
  Bellbrook *(G-1503)*
Akzo Nobel Chemicals LLC ....G 419 229-0088
  Lima *(G-11985)*
▲ Alco-Chem Inc ....E 330 253-3535
  Akron *(G-61)*
Aldrich Chemical ....D 937 859-1808
  Miamisburg *(G-13781)*
Alpha Zeta Holdings Inc ....G 216 271-1601
  Cleveland *(G-4770)*
AMA Fuel Services LLC ....G 513 836-3800
  Lebanon *(G-11779)*
Ampacet Corporation ....C 740 929-5521
  Newark *(G-14982)*
Andersons Marathon Ethanol LLC ......G 937 316-3700
  Greenville *(G-10488)*
Ashland Inc ....C 800 283-4823
  Columbus *(G-6775)*
B P Oil Company ....G 513 671-4107
  Cincinnati *(G-3433)*
B-F Processing LLC ....G 614 225-4000
  Columbus *(G-6798)*
Bam Fuel Inc ....G 740 397-6674
  Howard *(G-11122)*
BASF Corporation ....G 937 547-6700
  Greenville *(G-10489)*
BASF Corporation ....C 419 877-0876
  Whitehouse *(G-20337)*
BASF Corporation ....G 614 662-5682
  Columbus *(G-6812)*
BASF Corporation ....G 513 482-3000
  Cincinnati *(G-3439)*
Beloit Fuel LLC ....G 330 584-1915
  North Benton *(G-15212)*
▲ Biowish Technologies Inc ....G 312 572-6700
  Cincinnati *(G-3451)*
Bonded Chemicals Inc ....G 330 723-4570
  Medina *(G-13380)*
◆ Borchers Americas Inc ....D 440 899-2950
  Westlake *(G-20258)*
Borden Chemical Foundry LLC ....E 614 225-4000
  Columbus *(G-6849)*
Brightstar Propane & Fuels ....G 614 891-8395
  Westerville *(G-20140)*
Canton Fuel ....G 330 455-3400
  Canton *(G-2639)*
Canton OH Rubber Speclty Prods ....G 330 454-3847
  Canton *(G-2642)*
Cargill Incorporated ....F 513 941-7400
  Cincinnati *(G-3500)*
▲ Carson-Saeks Inc ....E 937 278-5311
  Dayton *(G-8213)*
Catholic Charity Hispanic Off ....F 216 696-2197
  Cleveland *(G-4994)*
Champion Company ....D 937 324-5681
  Springfield *(G-17531)*
Chem-Sales Inc ....F 419 531-4292
  Toledo *(G-18394)*
Chemcore Inc ....F 937 228-6118
  Dayton *(G-8228)*
▲ Chemionics Corporation ....E 330 733-8834
  Tallmadge *(G-18137)*
◆ Chempak International LLC ....G 440 543-8511
  Chagrin Falls *(G-3079)*
Clariant Corporation ....G 513 791-2964
  Blue Ash *(G-1766)*
Coil Specialty Chemicals LLC ....G 740 236-2407
  Marietta *(G-12775)*
Corrugated Chemicals Inc ....G 513 561-7773
  Cincinnati *(G-3614)*
Coshocton Ethanol LLC ....E 740 623-3046
  Coshocton *(G-7885)*
Creative Fuels LLC ....G 330 923-2222
  Cuyahoga Falls *(G-7983)*
Cwru Irland Cncer Ctr Cellular ....G 216 368-1007
  Cleveland *(G-5160)*
Daniels Brothers Fuel Co ....G 440 942-1800
  Willoughby *(G-20470)*
Detrex Corporation ....E 440 997-6131
  Ashtabula *(G-802)*

Dnd Emulsions Inc ....G 419 525-4988
  Mansfield *(G-12595)*
▲ Dover Chemical Corporation ....C 330 343-7711
  Dover *(G-8979)*
Dow Corning Corporation ....C 330 319-1127
  Copley *(G-7844)*
▼ Dubois Chemicals Inc ....B 513 731-6350
  Cincinnati *(G-3673)*
East Side Fuel Plus Operations ....G 419 563-0777
  Bucyrus *(G-2341)*
Eco Chem Alternative Fuels LLC ....G 614 764-3835
  Dublin *(G-9072)*
Eco Fuel Solution LLC ....G 440 282-8592
  Amherst *(G-598)*
Elco Corporation ....E 440 997-6131
  Ashtabula *(G-805)*
▼ Elco Corporation ....D 800 321-0467
  Cleveland *(G-5262)*
Emerald Polymer Additives LLC ....D 330 374-2424
  Akron *(G-165)*
Enzyme Catalyzed Polymers LLC ....G 330 310-1072
  Akron *(G-170)*
Enzyme Industries of The U S A ....G 740 929-4975
  Newark *(G-15003)*
Eqm Technologies & Energy Inc ....F 513 825-7500
  Cincinnati *(G-3715)*
Equistar Chemicals LP ....E 513 530-4000
  Cincinnati *(G-3716)*
Es Manufacturing Inc ....G 888 331-3443
  Newark *(G-15005)*
Evonik Corporation ....D 513 554-8969
  Cincinnati *(G-3726)*
Exp Fuels Inc ....G 419 382-7713
  Toledo *(G-18460)*
Ferro Corporation ....D 216 577-7144
  Bedford *(G-1423)*
Flow Polymers LLC ....C 216 249-4900
  Cleveland *(G-5360)*
Fly Race Fuels LLC ....G 419 744-9402
  North Fairfield *(G-15285)*
Fostoria Ethanol LLC ....E 419 436-0954
  Fostoria *(G-9975)*
Franklin ....G 419 699-5757
  Waterville *(G-19657)*
Franklin Fueling Systems ....G 513 231-7840
  Cincinnati *(G-3780)*
Frutarom USA Holding Inc ....G 201 861-9500
  West Chester *(G-20004)*
Fuel America ....G 419 586-5609
  Celina *(G-2998)*
Fuel G USA LLC ....G 440 617-0950
  Westlake *(G-20269)*
Gdc Inc ....F 574 533-3128
  Wooster *(G-20775)*
Geo Specialty Chemical ....G 330 650-0237
  Hudson *(G-11172)*
◆ GFS Chemicals Inc ....E 740 881-5501
  Powell *(G-16472)*
GFS Chemicals Inc ....D 614 224-5345
  Columbus *(G-7112)*
Givaudan ....F 513 482-2536
  Cincinnati *(G-3827)*
Givaudan Flavors Corporation ....B 513 948-8000
  Cincinnati *(G-3828)*
Givaudan Flvors Fragrances Inc ....G 513 948-8000
  Cincinnati *(G-3830)*
◆ Givaudan Fragrances Corp ....B 513 948-3428
  Cincinnati *(G-3831)*
Givaudan Fragrances Corp ....B 513 948-3428
  Cincinnati *(G-3832)*
◆ Givaudan Roure US Inc ....G 513 948-8000
  Cincinnati *(G-3833)*
▲ Global Biochem ....G 513 792-2218
  Cincinnati *(G-3835)*
Greater Ohio Ethanol LLC ....G 567 940-9500
  Lima *(G-12019)*
Green Fuel Today ....G 440 925-7820
  Grafton *(G-10429)*
Green Harvest Energy LLC ....F 330 716-3068
  Columbiana *(G-6618)*
Greene Fuel Plaza Inc ....G 937 532-4826
  Kettering *(G-11580)*
Guardian Lima LLC ....E 567 940-9500
  Lima *(G-12021)*
Ha-International LLC ....E 419 537-0096
  Toledo *(G-18492)*
▲ Hardy Industrial Tech LLC ....D 440 350-6300
  Painesville *(G-15887)*
Harrison 20 Mtd Borefinery LLC ....G 740 796-4797
  Adamsville *(G-8)*

S
I
C

▲ Heraeus Precious Metals North........E 937 264-1000
Vandalia (G-19295)
Hill & Griffith Company ....G....... 513 921-1075
Cincinnati (G-3882)
Homeland AG Fuels LLC........................G....... 216 763-1004
Cleveland (G-5522)
▲ Hunt Imaging LLC ....E 440 826-0433
Berea (G-1620)
◆ Image Armor LLC ....G....... 877 673-4377
New Philadelphia (G-14903)
Ineos Americas LLC ....B 419 226-1200
Lima (G-12028)
Insightfuel LLC....................................F 330 998-7380
Macedonia (G-12460)
International Fuel Systems Inc.............G....... 419 475-5276
Toledo (G-18526)
Ishos Bros Fuel Ventures Inc................G....... 586 634-0187
Maumee (G-13268)
Ishos Bros Fuel Ventures Inc................G....... 419 913-5718
Toledo (G-18530)
▲ J R M Chemical Inc ....F 216 475-8488
Cleveland (G-5600)
▼ Jatrodiesel Inc.................................F 937 847-8050
Miamisburg (G-13821)
K & E Chemical Co Inc ....F 216 341-0500
Cleveland (G-5627)
Karl Industries Inc................................G....... 330 562-4100
Aurora (G-929)
Kerry Flavor Systems Us LLC ....E 513 539-7373
Monroe (G-14407)
L and S Express Fuel Center ....G....... 330 549-9566
North Lima (G-15319)
Leaf Lono Earth Alterntv Fuels.............G....... 614 829-7159
Canal Winchester (G-2530)
Littlern Corporation ....G....... 330 848-8847
Barberton (G-1124)
Lost Nation Fuel...................................G....... 440 951-9088
Willoughby (G-20529)
◆ Lubrizol Corporation.........................A 440 943-4200
Wickliffe (G-20370)
Lyondell Chemical Company................E 440 352-9393
Fairport Harbor (G-9767)
Lyondell Chemical Company................D 513 530-4000
Cincinnati (G-4042)
M J S Oil Inc...G....... 937 982-3519
West Mansfield (G-20101)
Marion Ethanol LLC ....E 740 383-4400
Marion (G-12882)
Mart Plus Fuel ....G....... 216 261-0420
Euclid (G-9591)
Martin M Hardin....................................G....... 740 282-1234
Steubenville (G-17705)
Michelman Inc ....E 513 793-7766
Cincinnati (G-4099)
Mid America Chemical Corp ....G....... 216 749-0100
Cleveland (G-5803)
Momentive Performance Mtls Inc..........C 740 928-7010
Hebron (G-10874)
Momentive Performance Mtls Inc..........A 440 878-5705
Richmond Heights (G-16655)
▼ Momentive Performance Mtls Inc.....B 614 986-2495
Columbus (G-7365)
◆ Momentive Prfmce Mtls Qrtz Inc.......C 440 878-5700
Strongsville (G-17941)
Momentive Specialty Chem Inc............F 740 452-5451
Zanesville (G-21330)
Mp Biomedicals LLC............................C 440 337-1200
Solon (G-17340)
◆ Nachurs Alpine Solutions Corp ....E 740 382-5701
Marion (G-12888)
Nanofilm Ltd ....E 216 674-1430
Cleveland (G-5851)
▲ Nanotech West Lab...........................F 614 688-3055
Columbus (G-7381)
▲ National Colloid Company ....E 740 282-1171
Steubenville (G-17706)
Nationwide Chemical Products ....G....... 419 714-7075
Perrysburg (G-16124)
Nease Co LLC......................................D 513 738-1255
Harrison (G-10793)
New Mulch In A Bottle Limited..............G....... 724 290-2341
Marietta (G-12810)
North East Fuel Inc ....G....... 330 264-4454
Wooster (G-20817)
▼ Noveon Fcc Inc ....G....... 440 943-4200
Wickliffe (G-20374)
Occidental Chemical Corp ....E 513 242-2900
Cincinnati (G-4172)
Ohio Biosystems Coop Inc ....G....... 419 980-7663
Loudonville (G-12302)
Ohio Chemical Two...............................G....... 614 482-8073
Columbus (G-7417)
Ohio State University............................E 614 292-7656
Columbus (G-7431)
Orion Engineered Carbons LLC ....D 740 423-9571
Belpre (G-1592)
Oxyrase Inc...F 419 589-8800
Ontario (G-15692)
P S P Inc...E 330 283-5635
Kent (G-11498)
Patriot Energy LLC ....D 330 923-4442
Cuyahoga Falls (G-8032)
▲ Permco Inc...C 330 626-2801
Streetsboro (G-17866)
Polychem Dispersions Inc ....E 800 545-3530
Middlefield (G-13984)
Power Source Fuel LLC.........................G....... 419 690-6495
Sylvania (G-18123)
▲ Reclamation Technologies Inc.........D 419 867-8990
Bowling Green (G-2011)
Reclamation Technologies Inc ....F 419 867-8990
Bowling Green (G-2012)
▲ Research Organics LLC ....D 216 883-8025
Cleveland (G-6105)
Rex American Resources Corp ....C 937 276-3931
Dayton (G-8627)
▲ Rezkem Chemicals LLC ....F 330 653-9104
Hudson (G-11196)
Ronald T Dodge Co...............................F 937 439-4497
Dayton (G-8638)
Shepherd Chemical Company ....F 513 200-6987
Cincinnati (G-4415)
▲ Shincor Silicones Inc........................G....... 330 630-9460
Akron (G-400)
Silicone Solutions Inc............................F 330 920-3125
Cuyahoga Falls (G-8045)
Silicone Solutions Inc............................G....... 419 720-8709
Toledo (G-18697)
Speedway LLC ....A 937 864-3000
Enon (G-9550)
◆ Struktol Company America LLC ......C 330 928-5188
Stow (G-17805)
Summit Ethanol LLC..............................E 419 943-7447
Leipsic (G-11877)
Symrise Inc..C 440 324-6060
Elyria (G-9498)
Syrgis Holdings Inc ....G....... 859 356-8000
Blue Ash (G-1879)
◆ Systech Environmental Corp ....E 800 888-8011
Dayton (G-8693)
◆ Tedia Company Inc...........................D 513 874-5340
Fairfield (G-9723)
Top Fuel Coatings ....G....... 330 758-1166
Poland (G-16385)
Trugreen Cleaners LLC.........................G....... 740 703-1063
Chillicothe (G-3282)
Twin Rvers Tech - Pnsville LLC ....D 440 350-6300
Painesville (G-15935)
Ultimate Chem Solutions Inc ....E 440 998-6751
Ashtabula (G-843)
◆ United Initiators Inc ....D 440 326-2416
Elyria (G-9505)
Univar USA Inc ....C 513 714-5264
West Chester (G-20064)
Vadose Syn Fuels Inc ....G....... 330 564-0545
Munroe Falls (G-14667)
Valero Renewable Fuels Co LLC ....D 740 437-6211
Bloomingburg (G-1721)
▲ Vantage Specialty Ingredients ....E 937 264-1222
Englewood (G-9543)
Vetz USA Inc ....G....... 937 237-8764
Dayton (G-8741)
Wacker Chemical Corporation..............E 330 899-0847
Canton (G-2899)
West Erie Fuel ....G....... 440 282-3493
Lorain (G-12292)
▲ Zaclon LLC ....E 216 271-1601
Cleveland (G-6489)

2873 Nitrogenous Fertilizers

Advancing Eco-Agriculture LLC............G....... 800 495-6603
Middlefield (G-13912)
Agrium Advanced Tech US Inc..............G....... 614 276-5103
Columbus (G-6703)
Agrium US Inc ....D 513 941-4100
North Bend (G-15201)
Airgas Inc...G....... 419 695-7085
Delphos (G-8900)
Alpha Omega Bioremediation LLC........F 614 287-2600
Columbus (G-6728)
Amsoil Inc..G....... 614 274-9851
Columbus (G-6746)
Crop Production Services Inc...............E 513 941-4100
North Bend (G-15204)
Deerfield Farms Service Inc..................D 800 589-8606
Deerfield (G-8772)
Everris NA Inc ....E 800 492-8255
Dublin (G-9073)
Harvest Land Co-Op Inc ....G....... 937 884-5526
Verona (G-19338)
Hyponex Corporation ....D 937 644-0011
Marysville (G-12953)
Hyponex Corporation ....E 330 262-1300
Shreve (G-17157)
Icgc The Andersons Inc ....G....... 419 893-5050
Maumee (G-13267)
Ineos Americas LLC ....B 419 226-1200
Lima (G-12028)
Pcs Nitrogen Inc.....................................B 419 226-1200
Lima (G-12066)
Pcs Nitrogen Ohio LP ....G....... 419 879-8989
Lima (G-12067)
R & J AG Manufacturing Inc ....F 419 962-4707
Ashland (G-770)
Scotts Company LLC..............................E 614 863-3920
Gahanna (G-10231)
Scotts Company LLC..............................F 937 454-2782
Dayton (G-8649)
Scotts Company LLC..............................E 614 733-0462
Plain City (G-16357)
◆ Scotts Company LLC ....A 937 644-3729
Marysville (G-12967)
Scotts Company LLC..............................E 440 899-9339
Bay Village (G-1245)
Scotts Miracle-Gro Company.................D 330 684-0421
Orrville (G-15763)
Scotts Miracle-Gro Company.................E 937 578-5065
Marysville (G-12969)
Scotts Miracle-Gro Products ....E 937 644-0011
Marysville (G-12970)
Summers Organization LLC...................E 740 286-1322
Jackson (G-11326)
Synagro Midwest Inc ....F 937 384-0669
Miamisburg (G-13866)
▼ Turf Care Supply Corp ....B 877 220-1014
Brunswick (G-2264)

2874 Phosphatic Fertilizers

Andersons Inc...C 419 893-5050
Maumee (G-13224)
Andersons Inc...G....... 419 536-0460
Toledo (G-18349)
Auto-Tap Inc ....E 216 671-1043
Cleveland (G-4864)
Occidental Chemical Corp ....E 513 242-2900
Cincinnati (G-4172)
◆ Scotts Company LLC ....A 937 644-3729
Marysville (G-12967)

2875 Fertilizers, Mixing Only

All Ways Green Lawn & Turf LLC ....G....... 937 763-4766
Seaman (G-17040)
Charles Daniel Young ....G....... 937 968-3423
Union City (G-19070)
City of Columbus ....E 614 645-3152
Lockbourne (G-12146)
Compost Cincy..G....... 513 278-8178
Cincinnati (G-3602)
Countyline Co-Op Inc ....F 419 287-3241
Pemberville (G-16026)
Crop Production Services Inc................G....... 419 274-2701
Hamler (G-10759)
Crop Production Services Inc................F 740 869-3369
Mount Sterling (G-14597)
Crop Production Services Inc................E 513 941-4100
North Bend (G-15204)
Crop Production Services Inc................G....... 614 873-4253
Milford Center (G-14181)
Gardenscape ....E 419 445-6561
Archbold (G-676)
Garick LLC..E 216 581-0100
Cleveland (G-5398)
Growmark Fs LLC...................................F 330 386-7626
East Liverpool (G-9216)
Hoopes Fertilizer Works Inc...................G....... 330 894-2121
East Rochester (G-9250)
Hoopes Fertilizer Works Inc...................G....... 330 821-3550
Alliance (G-516)
Hyponex Corporation ....D 937 644-0011
Marysville (G-12953)

Hyponex Corporation ....E 330 262-1300
Shreve (G-17157)

Insta-Gro Manufacturing Inc ....G 419 845-3046
Caledonia (G-2438)

Jefferson Landmark Inc ....F 740 944-1971
Bloomingdale (G-1724)

Kurtz Bros Compost Services ....G 330 864-2621
Akron (G-263)

Legacy Farmers Cooperative ....F 419 423-2611
Findlay (G-9851)

Lesco Inc ....G 740 549-2141
Lewis Center (G-11905)

Lesco Inc ....F 740 633-6366
Martins Ferry (G-12925)

Luckey Farmers Inc ....G 419 287-3275
Bradner (G-2027)

Midwest Compost Inc ....F 419 547-7979
Clyde (G-6542)

◆ Nachurs Alpine Solutions Corp ....E 740 382-5701
Marion (G-12888)

Ohigro Inc ....E 740 726-2429
Waldo (G-19467)

Opal Diamond LLC ....G 330 653-5876
Rocky River (G-16703)

Ottokee Group Inc ....E 419 636-1932
Bryan (G-2316)

Price Farms Organics Ltd ....F 740 369-1000
Delaware (G-8880)

Rod McLellan Company ....E 513 644-0011
Marysville (G-12966)

Roe Transportation Entps Inc ....G 937 497-7161
Sidney (G-17217)

Rural Farm Distributors Co ....G 419 747-6807
Mansfield (G-12673)

Tyler Grain & Fertilizer Co ....F 330 669-2341
Smithville (G-17246)

Werlor Inc ....E 419 784-4285
Defiance (G-8814)

2879 Pesticides & Agricultural Chemicals, NEC

A Best Trmt & Pest Ctrl Sups ....G 330 434-5555
Akron (G-17)

Advanced Biological Mktg Inc ....F 419 232-2461
Van Wert (G-19241)

BASF Corporation ....G 614 662-5682
Columbus (G-6812)

Bird Control International ....E 330 425-2377
Twinsburg (G-18905)

Dow Chemical Company ....F 937 254-1550
Dayton (G-8309)

E I Du Pont De Nemours & Co ....C 330 364-6002
Dover (G-8983)

Harvest Land Co-Op Inc ....G 937 884-5526
Verona (G-19338)

◆ J T Eaton & Co Inc ....E 330 425-7801
Twinsburg (G-18960)

Mercer Landmark Inc ....G 419 363-3391
Rockford (G-16692)

Modern AG Supply Inc ....G 419 753-3484
New Knoxville (G-14838)

Mystic Chemical Products Co ....G 216 251-4416
Cleveland (G-5846)

▲ Quality Borate Co LLC ....F 216 896-1949
Cleveland (G-6069)

◆ Scotts Company LLC ....A 937 644-3729
Marysville (G-12967)

Scotts Miracle-Gro Company ....E 937 578-5065
Marysville (G-12969)

WA Hammond Drierite Co Ltd ....E 937 376-2927
Xenia (G-20987)

2891 Adhesives & Sealants

A & M Products ....G 419 595-2092
Tiffin (G-18201)

Adchem Adhesives Inc ....F 440 526-1976
Cleveland (G-4701)

◆ Akron Paint & Varnish Inc ....D 330 773-8911
Akron (G-50)

Akzo Nobel Paints LLC ....G 513 242-0530
Cincinnati (G-3374)

Alpha Coatings Inc ....C 419 435-5111
Fostoria (G-9964)

Aluminum Coating Manufacturers ...E 216 341-2000
Cleveland (G-4774)

Arclin ....G 877 689-9145
Holland (G-11045)

Arclin USA LLC ....E 419 726-5013
Toledo (G-18354)

Avery Dennison Corporation ....B 440 358-3700
Painesville (G-15857)

Besten Equipment Inc ....E 216 581-1166
Solon (G-17267)

▲ Boltaron Inc ....D 740 498-5900
Newcomerstown (G-15109)

Borden Chemical Inc ....E 614 225-4000
Columbus (G-6848)

Brewer Company ....G 513 576-6300
Cincinnati (G-3470)

Brewer Company ....E 614 279-8688
Columbus (G-6855)

▲ Cardinal Rubber Company Inc ......E 330 745-2191
Barberton (G-1113)

Certon Technologies Inc ....F 440 786-7185
Bedford (G-1414)

▲ Chemmasters Inc ....E 440 428-2105
Madison (G-12501)

◆ Chemspec Ltd ....F 330 896-0355
Uniontown (G-19079)

Choice Brands Adhesives Ltd ....G 513 772-1234
Cincinnati (G-3530)

Cincinnati Assn For The Blind ....C 513 221-8558
Cincinnati (G-3539)

◆ Concrete Sealants Inc ....E 937 845-8776
Tipp City (G-18273)

Consolidated Coatings Corp ....E 216 514-7596
Cleveland (G-5118)

Continental Products Company ....E 216 531-0710
Cleveland (G-5126)

▲ Conversion Tech Intl Inc ....E 419 924-5566
West Unity (G-20127)

Cornerstone Indus Holdings ....G 440 893-9144
Chagrin Falls (G-3054)

▲ CP Industries Inc ....F 740 763-2886
Newark (G-14997)

Dap Products Inc ....C 937 667-4461
Tipp City (G-18274)

Davis Caulking & Sealant LLC ....G 740 286-3825
Wellston (G-19762)

Dental Sealants ....G 440 582-3466
North Royalton (G-15417)

Durez Corporation ....C 567 295-6400
Kenton (G-11546)

Dyna Tech Molding & Beta ....G 330 296-2315
Ravenna (G-16527)

Econo Products Inc ....F 330 923-4101
Cuyahoga Falls (G-7989)

▲ Egc Enterprises Inc ....E 440 285-5835
Chardon (G-3151)

Elaston Company ....E 330 863-2865
Malvern (G-12543)

▲ Engineered Mtls Systems Inc ....E 740 362-4444
Delaware (G-8843)

Entrochem Inc ....F 614 946-7602
Columbus (G-7061)

◆ Evans Adhesive Corporation Ltd ....E 614 451-2665
Columbus (G-7070)

Evans Adhesive Corporation Ltd .....G 614 451-2665
Columbus (G-7071)

Extendit Company ....G 330 743-4343
Youngstown (G-21081)

Fairchild Labs LLC ....E 614 235-7040
Columbus (G-7076)

▼ Fairmount Santrol Inc ....G 440 214-3200
Chesterland (G-3206)

▲ Federal Process Corporation ....E 216 464-6440
Cleveland (G-5332)

Foam Seal Inc ....D 216 881-8111
Cleveland (G-5363)

Freedom Asphalt Sealant & Line .....G 937 416-1053
Miamisburg (G-13811)

Gdc Inc ....F 574 533-3128
Wooster (G-20775)

▲ Gold Key Processing Inc ....C 440 632-0901
Middlefield (G-13937)

Har Equipment Sales Inc ....G 440 786-7189
Bedford (G-1428)

Hartline Products Coinc ....G 216 291-2303
Cleveland (G-5482)

Hartline Products Coinc ....G 216 851-7189
Cleveland (G-5483)

HB Fuller Company ....E 513 719-3600
Blue Ash (G-1806)

HB Fuller Company ....G 513 719-3600
Blue Ash (G-1807)

Henkel Corporation ....C 216 475-3600
Cleveland (G-5498)

Henkel Corporation ....D 513 830-0260
Cincinnati (G-3878)

Hexpol Compounding LLC ....C 440 834-4644
Burton (G-2376)

Hoover & Wells Inc ....C 419 691-9220
Toledo (G-18511)

Hydratech Engineered Pdts LLC .....F 513 827-9169
Cincinnati (G-3904)

ICP Adhesives and Sealants Inc .....G 330 753-4585
Norton (G-15513)

Illinois Tool Works Inc ....C 513 489-7600
Blue Ash (G-1812)

Imperial Adhesives ....E 513 351-1300
Cincinnati (G-3914)

Invisible Repair Products Inc ....G 330 798-0441
Akron (G-236)

Jetcoat LLC ....E 800 394-0047
Columbus (G-7232)

Kcg Inc ....G 614 238-9450
Columbus (G-7252)

▲ Laminate Technologies Inc ....D 419 448-0812
Tiffin (G-18226)

Leesburg Modern Sales Inc ....F 937 780-2613
Leesburg (G-11854)

▲ LMI Custom Mixing LLC ....D 740 435-0444
Cambridge (G-2465)

Lord Corporation ....C 440 992-0193
Ashtabula (G-818)

Lord Corporation ....C 440 333-5750
Rocky River (G-16700)

◆ Lubrizol Advanced Mtls Inc ....E 216 447-5000
Brecksville (G-2061)

Mactac Americas LLC ....G 330 688-1111
Stow (G-17771)

Mameco International Inc ....F 216 752-4400
Cleveland (G-5738)

Marlen Manufacturing & Dev Co .....E 216 292-7546
Bedford (G-1442)

Metalcrete Industries Inc ....G 440 526-5600
Cleveland (G-5790)

Millennium Adhesive Pdts Inc ....F 440 708-1212
Chagrin Falls (G-3064)

Millennium Adhesive Products ....G 440 708-1212
Chagrin Falls (G-3104)

Mitsubishi Chls Perf Plyrs Inc ....D 419 483-2931
Bellevue (G-1553)

◆ Morgan Adhesives Company LLC ...B 330 688-1111
Stow (G-17775)

▼ Nanosperse LLC ....G 937 296-5030
Kettering (G-11583)

National Adhesives Inc ....F 513 683-8650
Cincinnati (G-4138)

National Applied Cnstr Pdts ....G 330 644-3117
Akron (G-310)

National Polymer Inc ....F 440 708-1245
Chagrin Falls (G-3106)

National Starch Chemical ....G 513 830-0260
Cincinnati (G-4141)

▲ Nova Films and Foils Inc ....F 440 201-1300
Bedford (G-1448)

Novagard Solutions Inc ....F 216 881-3890
Cleveland (G-5917)

P & T Products Inc ....E 419 621-1966
Sandusky (G-16992)

▲ Paramelt Argueso Kindt Inc ....G 216 252-4122
Cleveland (G-5963)

▲ Polymerics Inc ....G 330 434-6665
Cuyahoga Falls (G-8034)

PPG Architectural Finishes Inc ....G 330 788-2421
Youngstown (G-21174)

PPG Architectural Finishes Inc ....G 440 942-7708
Mentor (G-13694)

PPG Architectural Finishes Inc ....G 614 846-0097
Columbus (G-7508)

PPG Architectural Finishes Inc ....C 419 433-5664
Huron (G-11238)

PPG Architectural Finishes Inc ....G 513 563-0220
Cincinnati (G-4258)

PRC - Desoto International Inc ....F 800 772-9378
Chillicothe (G-3267)

◆ Premier Building Solutions Inc ....D 330 244-2907
Massillon (G-13197)

Priest Services Inc ....G 440 333-1123
Mayfield Heights (G-13321)

Quest Solutions Group LLC ....G 513 703-4520
Liberty Township (G-11966)

▲ Renegade Materials Corporation ...E 508 579-7888
Miamisburg (G-13854)

◆ Republic Powdered Metals Inc ....D 330 225-3192
Medina (G-13467)

Royal Adhesives & Sealants LLC .....G 440 708-1212
Chagrin Falls (G-3118)

RPM Consumer Holding Company ....G....... 330 273-5090
Medina *(G-13470)*

◆ RPM International Inc ....D....... 330 273-5090
Medina *(G-13471)*

▼ Rubex Inc ....F....... 614 875-6343
Grove City *(G-10590)*

Ruscoe Company ....E....... 330 253-8148
Akron *(G-383)*

Savare Corporation ....G....... 614 255-2878
Columbus *(G-7590)*

◆ Savare Specialty Adhesives LLC ...E....... 614 255-2648
Delaware *(G-8886)*

Sealant Solutions ....G....... 614 599-8000
Columbus *(G-7605)*

Sem-Com Company Inc ....F....... 419 537-8813
Toledo *(G-18691)*

▲ Shincor Silicones Inc ....G....... 330 630-9460
Akron *(G-400)*

Signature Salants Coatings LLC ....G....... 513 922-8723
Cleves *(G-6525)*

Silicone Solutions Inc ....F....... 330 920-3125
Cuyahoga Falls *(G-8045)*

▲ Sirrus Inc ....E....... 513 448-0308
Loveland *(G-12388)*

Sonoco Products Company ....G....... 937 429-0040
Beavercreek Township *(G-1390)*

Southern Adhsives Coatings Inc ...G....... 513 561-8440
Cincinnati *(G-4438)*

Specialty Adhesive Film Co ....G....... 513 353-1885
Cleves *(G-6526)*

Spectrum Adhesives Inc ....F....... 740 763-2886
Newark *(G-15054)*

Spinnaker Coating LLC ....C....... 937 332-6300
Troy *(G-18878)*

Sportsmaster ....F....... 440 257-3900
Mentor *(G-13728)*

Summitville Tiles Inc ....E....... 330 868-6463
Minerva *(G-14344)*

▲ Sunstar Engrg Americas Inc ......G....... 937 746-8575
Springboro *(G-17508)*

Tara Acquisition Group ....F....... 614 754-4777
Lewis Center *(G-11923)*

Tech-Bond Solutions ....G....... 614 327-8884
Carroll *(G-2949)*

◆ Technical Rubber Company Inc ...B....... 740 967-9015
Johnstown *(G-11407)*

Technicote Inc ....E....... 330 928-1476
Cuyahoga Falls *(G-8053)*

▲ Teknol Inc ....D....... 937 264-0190
Dayton *(G-8708)*

The Euclid Chemical Company ......F....... 216 292-5000
Beachwood *(G-1301)*

▲ Thermagon Inc ....D....... 216 939-2300
Cleveland *(G-6315)*

◆ Thorworks Industries Inc ....E....... 419 626-4375
Sandusky *(G-17015)*

Three Bond International Inc ....E....... 937 610-3000
Dayton *(G-8713)*

▲ Three Bond International Inc ......D....... 513 779-7300
West Chester *(G-19957)*

▲ Toagosei America Inc ....G....... 614 718-3855
West Jefferson *(G-20084)*

Tremco Incorporated ....C....... 216 752-4401
Cleveland *(G-6354)*

◆ Tremco Incorporated ....B....... 216 292-5000
Beachwood *(G-1303)*

Tremco Incorporated ....E....... 419 289-2050
Ashland *(G-782)*

◆ Truseal Technologies Inc ....E....... 216 910-1500
Solon *(G-17408)*

◆ United McGill Corporation ....E....... 614 829-1200
Groveport *(G-10648)*

Valspar Corporation ....C....... 330 830-6000
Massillon *(G-13209)*

▲ Waytek Corporation ....E....... 937 743-6142
Franklin *(G-10065)*

2892 Explosives

▲ Additive Technology Inc ....G....... 419 968-2777
Middle Point *(G-13896)*

▲ Austin Powder Company ....D....... 216 464-2400
Cleveland *(G-4860)*

Austin Powder Company ....C....... 740 596-5286
Mc Arthur *(G-13329)*

Austin Powder Company ....E....... 740 968-1555
Saint Clairsville *(G-16780)*

◆ Austin Powder Holdings Company .D....... 216 464-2400
Cleveland *(G-4861)*

Hilltop Energy Inc ....E....... 330 859-2108
Mineral City *(G-14301)*

Regal Technology Corporation ....G....... 614 272-7644
Columbus *(G-7553)*

Sloat Inc ....G....... 440 951-9554
Willoughby *(G-20600)*

Viking Explosives LLC ....E....... 218 263-8845
Cleveland *(G-6419)*

2893 Printing Ink

Actega North America Inc ....G....... 513 489-5691
Blue Ash *(G-1733)*

American Inks and Coatings Co .....F....... 513 552-7200
Fairfield *(G-9641)*

An Environmental Inks ....E....... 513 870-0288
West Chester *(G-19980)*

▲ Braden-Sutphin Ink Company ......C....... 216 271-2300
Cleveland *(G-4929)*

Braden-Sutphin Ink Company ....G....... 614 443-9100
Columbus *(G-6853)*

Braden-Sutphin Ink Company ....E....... 937 704-9047
Carlisle *(G-2928)*

▼ Dischem Inc ....G....... 330 494-5210
Canton *(G-2690)*

▲ DOT-2-Dot Inc ....F....... 440 891-9388
Cleveland *(G-5209)*

◆ Eckart America Corporation ....D....... 440 954-7600
Painesville *(G-15876)*

Erie Laser Ink LLC ....G....... 419 346-0600
Toledo *(G-18457)*

Ferro Corporation ....G....... 216 875-6178
Cleveland *(G-5337)*

Flint Group US LLC ....G....... 513 934-6500
Lebanon *(G-11800)*

Flint Group US LLC ....F....... 216 267-1927
Cleveland *(G-5357)*

Flint Group US LLC ....D....... 513 771-1900
Cincinnati *(G-3761)*

▲ Glass Coatings & Concepts LLC ....E....... 513 539-5300
Monroe *(G-14403)*

Grand Rapids Printing Ink Co ....G....... 859 261-4530
Cincinnati *(G-3844)*

Ink Factory Inc ....G....... 330 799-0888
Youngstown *(G-21116)*

Ink Production Services Inc ....F....... 513 733-9338
Cincinnati *(G-3921)*

◆ Ink Technology Corporation ....E....... 216 486-6720
Cleveland *(G-5569)*

INX International Ink Co ....F....... 513 282-2920
Lebanon *(G-11809)*

INX International Ink Co ....F....... 440 239-1766
Cleveland *(G-5585)*

Kennedy Ink Company Inc ....F....... 513 871-2515
Cincinnati *(G-3983)*

Kennedy Ink Company Inc ....G....... 937 461-5600
Dayton *(G-8437)*

Premier Ink Systems Inc ....F....... 513 367-4700
Harrison *(G-10796)*

Sun Chemical Corporation ....D....... 513 671-0407
Cincinnati *(G-4476)*

Sun Chemical Corporation ....D....... 419 891-3514
Maumee *(G-13299)*

Sun Chemical Corporation ....D....... 513 753-9550
Amelia *(G-585)*

Sun Chemical Corporation ....E....... 513 681-5950
Cincinnati *(G-4478)*

Sun Chemical Corporation ....E....... 937 743-8055
Franklin *(G-10055)*

Sun Chemical Corporation ....E....... 513 771-4030
Cincinnati *(G-4479)*

Sun Chemical Corporation ....E....... 513 830-8667
Cincinnati *(G-4481)*

Superior Printing Ink Co Inc ....G....... 216 328-1720
Cleveland *(G-6268)*

Wikoff Color Corporation ....G....... 513 423-0727
Middletown *(G-14099)*

2895 Carbon Black

▲ Jacobi Carbons Inc ....E....... 215 546-3900
Columbus *(G-7221)*

North Central Processing Inc ....G....... 216 623-1090
Cleveland *(G-5891)*

2899 Chemical Preparations, NEC

Abraxus Salt Inc ....G....... 440 743-7669
Cleveland *(G-4687)*

Ace Gasket Manufacturing Co ......G....... 513 271-6321
Cincinnati *(G-3349)*

Advanced Chem Solutions Inc ......G....... 216 692-3005
Orrville *(G-15728)*

Advanced Chem Solutions Inc ......G....... 330 283-5157
Medina *(G-13363)*

▲ Akron Dispersions Inc ....E....... 330 666-0045
Copley *(G-7838)*

Akzo Nobel Chemicals LLC ....G....... 419 229-0088
Lima *(G-11985)*

Akzo Nobel Coatings Inc ....G....... 614 294-3361
Columbus *(G-6710)*

▲ Alan BJ Company ....G....... 330 372-1201
Warren *(G-19518)*

Aldrich Chemical ....D....... 937 859-1808
Miamisburg *(G-13781)*

Allyn Corp ....G....... 614 442-3900
Columbus *(G-6727)*

▲ American Fireworks Company Inc ..F....... 330 650-1776
Hudson *(G-11156)*

◆ American Metal Chemical Corp .....E....... 330 725-4501
Medina *(G-13369)*

American Metal Chemical Corp ......G....... 440 244-1800
Lorain *(G-12232)*

Amresco LLC ....E....... 440 349-2805
Cleveland *(G-4798)*

Anchor Corporation ....G....... 614 836-9590
Columbus *(G-6753)*

Andersons Lawn Fert Div Inc ....F....... 419 893-5050
Maumee *(G-13226)*

▲ Aps-Materials Inc ....G....... 937 278-6547
Dayton *(G-8161)*

Aqua Science Inc ....E....... 614 252-5000
Columbus *(G-6766)*

Aquablue Inc ....G....... 330 343-0220
New Philadelphia *(G-14884)*

Ashland LLC ....G....... 614 790-3333
Dublin *(G-9047)*

Ashland LLC ....G....... 513 682-2405
West Chester *(G-19810)*

Ashland LLC ....E....... 419 998-8728
Lima *(G-11995)*

◆ Ask Chemicals LP ....C....... 614 763-0384
Dublin *(G-9049)*

Atotech USA Inc ....D....... 216 398-0550
Cleveland *(G-4857)*

Attia Applied Sciences Inc ....F....... 740 369-1891
Delaware *(G-8823)*

Aufbackgroundscreeningcom ....G....... 216 831-4113
Beachwood *(G-1258)*

Babcock & Wilcox Megtec ....C....... 614 258-9501
Columbus *(G-6799)*

◆ BASF Construction Chem LLC ......E....... 216 831-5500
Cleveland *(G-4895)*

BASF Corporation ....G....... 614 662-5682
Columbus *(G-6812)*

Bernard Laboratories Inc ....E....... 513 681-7373
Cincinnati *(G-3447)*

Biofocus Inc ....G....... 937 890-3068
Dayton *(G-8188)*

Bird Control International ....E....... 330 425-2377
Twinsburg *(G-18905)*

Blackthorn LLC ....F....... 937 836-9296
Clayton *(G-4657)*

BLaster Corporation ....E....... 216 901-5800
Cleveland *(G-4916)*

Bluefoot Industrial LLC ....F....... 740 314-5299
Steubenville *(G-17689)*

Bond Chemicals Inc ....F....... 330 725-5935
Medina *(G-13379)*

Bond Distributing LLC ....G....... 440 461-7920
Cleveland *(G-4923)*

◆ Borchers Americas Inc ....D....... 440 899-2950
Westlake *(G-20258)*

▲ Braden-Sutphin Ink Company ......C....... 216 271-2300
Cleveland *(G-4929)*

Brewer Industries LLC ....G....... 216 469-0808
Chagrin Falls *(G-3050)*

Broco Products Inc ....G....... 216 531-0880
Cleveland *(G-4933)*

Bulk Molding Compounds Inc ....D....... 419 874-7941
Perrysburg *(G-16071)*

Capital Chemical Co ....E....... 330 494-9535
Canton *(G-2649)*

Cargill Incorporated ....C....... 330 745-0031
Akron *(G-112)*

Cargill Incorporated ....F....... 513 941-7400
Cincinnati *(G-3500)*

Cargill Incorporated ....C....... 216 651-7200
Cleveland *(G-4977)*

◆ Celsus Laboratories Inc ....E....... 513 772-8130
Cincinnati *(G-3512)*

Chem Technologies Ltd ....E....... 440 632-9311
Middlefield *(G-13921)*

Chemical Methods Inc ....E....... 216 476-8400
Strongsville *(G-17901)*

▲ Chemmasters Inc .... E 440 428-2105
Madison (G-12501)

Chemtech Inc .... F 330 454-2127
Canton (G-2653)

Cinchempro Inc .... C 513 724-6111
Batavia (G-1171)

Cincinnati - Vulcan Company .... D 513 242-5300
Cincinnati (G-3535)

City of Mount Vernon .... G 740 393-9508
Mount Vernon (G-14615)

Colonial Fireworks Company .... F 419 478-4945
Toledo (G-18406)

▲ Coolant Control Inc .... E 513 471-8770
Cincinnati (G-3609)

▲ Coventya Inc .... E 216 351-1500
Brooklyn Heights (G-2136)

CP Chemicals Group LP .... D 440 833-3000
Wickliffe (G-20363)

Creative Commercial Finishing ..... G 513 722-9393
Loveland (G-12347)

▼ Cresset Chemical Co Inc .... F 419 669-2041
Weston (G-20324)

Cytec Industries Inc .... G 740 374-7171
Marietta (G-12777)

▲ Dayton Superior Corporation ..... C 937 866-0711
Miamisburg (G-13798)

Diamond Sparkler Mfg Co .... G 330 746-1064
Youngstown (G-21068)

Distillata Company .... D 216 771-2900
Cleveland (G-5197)

▲ Dover Chemical Corporation ...... C 330 343-7711
Dover (G-8979)

Dpa Investments Inc .... G 440 992-3377
Ashtabula (G-803)

E I Du Pont De Nemours & Co ..... E 330 929-2961
Stow (G-17745)

E3 Materials LLC .... G 330 972-6457
Akron (G-159)

▲ Eagle Fireworks Co. .... G 740 373-3357
Marietta (G-12782)

Eagle Fireworks Co .... G 740 758-5649
Quaker City (G-16499)

Earth Safe Chemical LLC .... G 419 648-7801
Harrod (G-10813)

Elco Corporation .... E 440 997-6131
Ashtabula (G-805)

EMD Millipore Corporation .... C 513 631-0445
Norwood (G-15572)

Emerald Performance Mtls LLC .... D 513 841-4000
Cincinnati (G-3695)

Emerald Performance Mtls LLC .... D 330 374-2418
Akron (G-164)

◆ Emery Oleochemicals LLC .... C 513 762-2500
Cincinnati (G-3699)

Ensign Product Company Inc .... G 216 341-5911
Cleveland (G-5284)

Envirnmntal Prtctive Ctngs LLC .... G 740 363-6180
Ostrander (G-15786)

Enviro Polymers & Chemicals ...... G 937 427-1315
Beavercreek (G-1336)

Environment Chemical Corp .... G 330 453-5200
Uniontown (G-19083)

◆ Etna Products Incorporated .... E 440 543-9845
Chagrin Falls (G-3087)

Ferro Corporation .... D 216 875-5600
Cleveland (G-5336)

Ferro Corporation .... C 216 875-6178
Cleveland (G-5337)

▲ Ferrum Industries Inc .... G 440 519-1768
Twinsburg (G-18935)

Flame Safe of Northern Ohio .... G 419 626-6204
Sandusky (G-16966)

▼ Flexsys America LP .... D 330 666-4111
Akron (G-190)

▲ Fort Amanda Specialties LLC .... D 419 229-0088
Lima (G-12015)

▲ Foseco Inc .... G 440 826-4548
Cleveland (G-5374)

Fuchs Lubricants Co .... E 330 963-0400
Twinsburg (G-18938)

Fusion Automation Inc .... G 440 602-5595
Willoughby (G-20493)

▼ Fusion Ceramics Inc .... E 330 627-5821
Carrollton (G-2956)

◆ Gasflux Company .... G 440 365-1941
Elyria (G-9424)

GE Betz Inc .... E 330 339-2292
New Philadelphia (G-14900)

General Electric Company .... D 216 268-3846
Cleveland (G-5417)

◆ GFS Chemicals Inc .... E 740 881-5501
Powell (G-16472)

GFS Chemicals Inc .... D 614 224-5345
Columbus (G-7112)

Global Chemical Inc .... G 419 242-1004
Toledo (G-18481)

Harsco Corporation .... D 330 372-1781
Warren (G-19557)

◆ Hexion LLC .... D 614 225-4000
Columbus (G-7153)

Hexpol Compounding LLC .... C 440 834-4644
Burton (G-2376)

Hill & Griffith Company .... G 513 921-1075
Cincinnati (G-3882)

▲ Hunt Imaging LLC .... E 440 826-0433
Berea (G-1620)

▲ I P Specrete Inc .... G 216 721-2050
Cleveland (G-5547)

Ink Factory Inc .... G 330 799-0888
Youngstown (G-21116)

Interlube Corporation .... F 513 531-1777
Cincinnati (G-3929)

International Paper Company .... C 740 363-9882
Delaware (G-8862)

J & G Sales .... G 740 745-5321
Utica (G-19194)

▲ James Sorgi .... G 330 653-5180
Hudson (G-11186)

Jay Tackett .... G 740 779-1715
Frankfort (G-9999)

Jeff Pendergrass .... G 513 575-1226
Milford (G-14156)

Joules Angstrom UV Printing .... E 740 964-9113
Etna (G-9558)

K2 Petroleum & Supply LLC .... G 937 503-2614
Cincinnati (G-3966)

▲ Key Resin Company .... F 513 943-4225
Batavia (G-1198)

▲ Kona Blackbird Inc .... F 440 285-3189
Chardon (G-3160)

▲ Lamor Corporation .... F 440 871-8000
Westlake (G-20281)

Leonhardt Plating Company .... E 513 242-1410
Cincinnati (G-4020)

Lfg Specialties LLC .... E 419 424-4999
Findlay (G-9852)

▲ Liquid Development Company ..... G 216 641-9366
Independence (G-11265)

◆ Lubrizol Advanced Mtls Inc .... F 216 447-5000
Brecksville (G-2061)

Lubrizol Advanced Mtls Inc .... E 440 933-0400
Avon Lake (G-1037)

◆ Lubrizol Corporation .... A 440 943-4200
Wickliffe (G-20370)

Lubrizol Corporation .... E 440 357-7064
Painesville (G-15898)

Luxfer Magtech Inc .... E 513 772-3066
Cincinnati (G-4040)

Lynx Chemical .... G 513 856-9161
Franklin (G-10033)

Magnesium Technologies Corp ..... G 330 659-3003
Independence (G-11266)

McGean-Rohco Inc .... D 216 441-4900
Newburgh Heights (G-15076)

Merry X-Ray Chemical Corp .... G 614 219-2011
Hilliard (G-10960)

Midwest Fireworks Mfg Co II .... G 330 584-7000
Deerfield (G-8774)

▼ Midwest Industrial Supply Inc .... D 330 456-3121
Canton (G-2780)

◆ Milacron LLC .... E 513 487-5000
Blue Ash (G-1842)

Momentive Performance 281 325-3536
Columbus (G-7364)

Monarch Engraving Inc .... E 440 638-1500
Strongsville (G-17942)

Morgan Advanced Ceramics Inc ... C 440 232-8604
Bedford (G-1445)

Morton Salt Inc .... F 440 354-9901
Painesville (G-15902)

Morton Salt Inc .... C 330 925-3015
Rittman (G-16680)

▲ National Colloid Company .... G 740 282-1171
Steubenville (G-17706)

▲ Natural Essentials Inc .... E 330 562-8022
Aurora (G-937)

Natures Own Source LLC .... G 440 838-5135
Brecksville (G-2065)

ND Industries Inc .... F 330 425-3167
Twinsburg (G-18989)

Nelson Professional Mktg Inc ...... G 513 482-6150
Cincinnati (G-4144)

New Vulco Mfg & Sales Co LLC ... D 513 242-2672
Cincinnati (G-4149)

No Burn Inc .... G 330 336-1500
Wadsworth (G-19421)

No Burn North America Inc .... F 419 841-6055
Toledo (G-18607)

▲ Noco Company .... B 216 464-8131
Solon (G-17350)

▲ Nof Metal Coatings N Amer Inc ... E 440 285-2231
Chardon (G-3168)

▲ Northern Chem Blnding Corp Inc ... G 216 781-7799
Cleveland (G-5909)

▼ Noveon Fcc Inc .... G 440 943-4200
Wickliffe (G-20374)

Obersons Nurs & Landscapes Inc ... F 513 894-0669
Fairfield (G-9692)

Ohio Aluminum Chemicals LLC .... G 513 860-3842
West Chester (G-19908)

Oil Bar LLC .... G 614 501-9815
Columbus (G-7439)

Oliver Chemical Co Inc .... G 513 541-4540
Cincinnati (G-4185)

◆ Opw Fueling Components Inc ..... E 800 422-2525
West Chester (G-19911)

Parker Trutec Incorporated .... D 937 653-8500
Urbana (G-19172)

Pazco Inc .... E 216 447-9581
Cleveland (G-5982)

Phantom Fireworks .... E 740 927-6943
Millersport (G-14296)

Phantom Fireworks Inc .... E 740 927-6943
Millersport (G-14297)

Phantom Fireworks Inc .... F 419 237-2185
Fayette (G-9777)

▼ Plating Process Systems Inc ...... G 440 951-9667
Mentor (G-13689)

Polymer Additives Inc .... E 216 875-7200
Independence (G-11269)

Polymer Additives Inc .... G 216 262-7016
Walton Hills (G-19475)

Polymer Additives Holdings Inc .... G 216 875-7200
Independence (G-11270)

Polymerics Inc .... E 330 677-1131
Kent (G-11503)

Premier Ink Systems Inc .... F 513 367-4700
Harrison (G-10796)

Prestige Fireworks LLC .... F 513 492-7726
Mason (G-13077)

Pyro-Chem Corporation .... F 740 377-2244
South Point (G-17445)

▲ Pyrotechnics By Presutti Inc ...... F 740 699-1224
Bellaire (G-1501)

▲ Quaker Chemical Corporation .... D 513 422-9600
Middletown (G-14080)

Qualico Inc .... G 216 271-2550
Cleveland (G-6067)

▲ Ques Industries Inc .... F 216 267-8989
Cleveland (G-6076)

Quikrete Companies Inc .... E 614 885-4406
Columbus (G-7540)

Qumont Chemical Co .... G 419 241-1057
Toledo (G-18665)

▲ Railtech Boutet Inc .... D 419 592-5050
Napoleon (G-14695)

Railtech Matweld Inc .... G 419 592-5050
Napoleon (G-14696)

Railtech Matweld Inc .... F 419 591-3770
Napoleon (G-14697)

Rambasek Realty Inc .... F 937 228-1189
Dayton (G-8616)

◆ Republic Powdered Metals Inc .... D 330 225-3192
Medina (G-13467)

▲ Research Organics LLC .... D 216 883-8025
Cleveland (G-6105)

▲ Rhenium Alloys Inc .... D 440 365-7388
North Ridgeville (G-15401)

Rotech Products Incorporated ...... G 216 476-3722
Cleveland (G-6135)

▲ Rozzi Company Inc .... E 513 683-0620
Loveland (G-12382)

◆ RPM International Inc .... D 330 273-5090
Medina (G-13471)

Sam Abdallah .... E 330 532-3900
Hammondsville (G-10760)

▲ SC Fire Protection Ltd .... G 330 468-3300
Macedonia (G-12481)

Sika Corporation .... G 740 375-3020
Marion (G-12900)

Sika Corporation ....D 740 387-9224
  Marion *(G-12901)*

Solvay USA Inc ....E 513 482-5700
  Cincinnati *(G-4436)*

Spectra Group Limited Inc ....G 419 837-9783
  Millbury *(G-14186)*

Sports Care Products Inc ....G 216 663-8110
  Cleveland *(G-6227)*

▲ SRC Worldwide Inc ....F 216 941-6115
  Cleveland *(G-6230)*

St Bernard Insulation LLC ....F 513 266-2158
  Cincinnati *(G-4449)*

◆ State Industrial Products Corp ......B 877 747-6986
  Cleveland *(G-6239)*

Summitville Tiles Inc ....E 330 868-6463
  Minerva *(G-14344)*

Sun & Soil LLC ....G 513 575-5900
  Loveland *(G-12391)*

Sun Chemical Corporation ....D 513 671-0407
  Cincinnati *(G-4476)*

◆ Superior Flux & Mfg Co ....F 440 349-3000
  Cleveland *(G-6264)*

Superior Printing Ink Co Inc ....F 513 221-4707
  Blue Ash *(G-1877)*

▲ Surtec Inc ....G 440 239-9710
  Brunswick *(G-2259)*

Tate Lyle Ingrdnts Amricas LLC ....D 937 236-5906
  Dayton *(G-8703)*

▲ Teknol Inc ....D 937 264-0190
  Dayton *(G-8708)*

◆ The Euclid Chemical Company ......E 800 321-7628
  Cleveland *(G-6309)*

The Euclid Chemical Company ....F 216 531-9222
  Cleveland *(G-6311)*

Tidewater Products Inc ....G 419 873-0223
  Perrysburg *(G-16159)*

Tidewater Products Inc ....G 419 534-9870
  Ottawa Hills *(G-15820)*

Truco Inc ....B 216 631-1000
  Cleveland *(G-6370)*

U S Chemical & Plastics ....G 740 254-4311
  Massillon *(G-13208)*

United Lubricants Corporation ....D 513 422-9600
  Middletown *(G-14092)*

Univar USA Inc ....C 513 714-5264
  West Chester *(G-20064)*

US Water Company LLC ....G 740 453-0604
  Zanesville *(G-21360)*

Vesuvius U S A Corporation ....E 440 593-1800
  Conneaut *(G-7821)*

Vesuvius U S A Corporation ....E 440 816-3051
  Cleveland *(G-6411)*

Viking Group Inc ....G 937 443-0433
  Dayton *(G-8743)*

Visible Solutions Inc ....G 440 925-2810
  Westlake *(G-20317)*

Wagers Inc ....G 513 825-6300
  Okeana *(G-15666)*

Warren Fire Equipment Inc ....E 330 824-3523
  Warren *(G-19622)*

Wicktek Inc ....E 724 329-8310
  Cincinnati *(G-4593)*

▲ Wild Berry Incense Inc ....F 513 523-8583
  Oxford *(G-15846)*

Worthington Industries Inc ....E 937 556-6111
  Mount Orab *(G-14588)*

Wrl of Indiana Inc ....A 419 289-8700
  Ashland *(G-786)*

▲ Zerust Consumer Products LLC ......G 330 405-1965
  Twinsburg *(G-19042)*

◆ Zinkan Enterprises Inc ....G 330 487-1500
  Twinsburg *(G-19043)*

Zircon Industries Inc ....G 216 595-0200
  Cleveland *(G-6499)*

29 PETROLEUM REFINING AND RELATED INDUSTRIES

2911 Petroleum Refining

Aecom Energy & Cnstr Inc ....C 419 698-6277
  Oregon *(G-15701)*

Appal Energy ....G 740 448-4605
  Amesville *(G-589)*

Appalachian Solvents LLC ....G 740 680-3649
  Cambridge *(G-2445)*

Arizona Chemical Company LLC ....C 330 343-7701
  Dover *(G-8964)*

Ashland LLC ....G 513 557-3100
  Cincinnati *(G-3418)*

Babcock & Wilcox Megtec ....G 614 340-4154
  Columbus *(G-6800)*

Bituminous Products Company ....G 419 693-3933
  Toledo *(G-18370)*

Blanchard Pipe Line Co LLC ....G 419 422-2121
  Findlay *(G-9796)*

Blanchard Refining Company LLC ......G 419 422-2121
  Findlay *(G-9797)*

Blanchard Terminal Company LLC .....G 419 422-2121
  Findlay *(G-9798)*

Blaster Chemical Co Inc ....G 216 901-5800
  Cleveland *(G-4915)*

BLaster Corporation ....E 216 901-5800
  Cleveland *(G-4916)*

Bloom Center Biodiesel LLC ....G 937 585-6412
  Lewistown *(G-11943)*

BP Products North America Inc ....G 937 461-3621
  Dayton *(G-8192)*

BP Products North America Inc ....F 419 537-9540
  Toledo *(G-18378)*

BP Products North America Inc ....G 419 636-2249
  Bryan *(G-2284)*

Capital City Oil Inc ....G 740 397-4483
  Mount Vernon *(G-14612)*

Certified Oil Company Inc ....G 614 421-7500
  Columbus *(G-6920)*

Chemours Company Fc LLC ....D 740 989-5202
  Little Hocking *(G-12144)*

Citgo Petroleum Corporation ....G 419 698-8055
  Oregon *(G-15705)*

Cyberutility LLC ....G 216 291-8723
  Cleveland *(G-5161)*

Dark Continent ....G 330 454-7804
  Canton *(G-2679)*

Diesel Recon Service Inc ....G 513 625-1887
  Pleasant Plain *(G-16370)*

Enrevo Pyro LLC ....G 203 517-5002
  Brookfield *(G-2124)*

Foam Seal Inc ....D 216 881-8111
  Cleveland *(G-5363)*

Grace Petroleum Inc ....G 330 484-0709
  Canton *(G-2717)*

Husky Energy ....F 614 766-5633
  Dublin *(G-9086)*

Hydrodec Inc ....F 330 454-8202
  Canton *(G-2733)*

▼ Hydrodec of North America LLC .....E 330 454-8202
  Canton *(G-2734)*

Isp Lima LLC ....E 419 998-8700
  Lima *(G-12031)*

Jet Fuel Tech Inc ....G 614 463-1986
  Columbus *(G-7231)*

K2 Petroleum & Supply LLC ....G 937 503-2614
  Cincinnati *(G-3966)*

Knox Energy Inc ....F 740 927-6731
  Pataskala *(G-15974)*

Knox Energy Inc ....G 740 787-1391
  Mount Perry *(G-14591)*

◆ Koch Knight LLC ....D 330 488-1651
  East Canton *(G-9194)*

Lavy Inc ....G 937 692-8189
  Arcanum *(G-657)*

▲ Lima Refining Company ....B 419 226-2300
  Lima *(G-12042)*

Lima Refining Company ....D 419 226-2300
  Lima *(G-12043)*

Lube Depot ....G 330 854-6345
  Canal Fulton *(G-2506)*

Marathon Oil Company ....E 419 422-2121
  Findlay *(G-9854)*

Marathon Petroleum Corporation ....B 419 422-2121
  Findlay *(G-9856)*

Marathon Petroleum Supply LLC ....A 419 422-2121
  Findlay *(G-9857)*

Mid-Town Petro Acquisition LLC ....G 219 728-5149
  Blue Ash *(G-1840)*

Novagard Solutions Inc ....F 216 881-3890
  Cleveland *(G-5917)*

Ohio Biofuels ....G 614 886-6518
  Cincinnati *(G-4174)*

Residue National LLC ....G 614 309-8963
  Dublin *(G-9132)*

Santmyer Oil Co of Ashland ....G 419 289-8815
  Ashland *(G-775)*

Seneca Petroleum Co Inc ....F 419 691-3581
  Toledo *(G-18692)*

Sherwood Valve LLC ....F 216 264-5023
  Brookfield *(G-6193)*

Sports Care Products Inc ....G 216 663-8110
  Cleveland *(G-6227)*

Standard Oil Company ....E 419 698-6200
  Oregon *(G-15717)*

Stark Materials Inc ....E 330 497-1648
  Canton *(G-2856)*

▲ STP Products Manufacturing Co ......D 440 352-6176
  Painesville *(G-15923)*

Sunoco Inc ....E 216 912-2579
  Akron *(G-423)*

Troy Valley Petroleum ....G 937 604-0012
  Dayton *(G-8730)*

Usalco LLC ....G 440 993-2721
  Ashtabula *(G-844)*

Vertex Refining OH LLC ....E 419 668-8373
  Norwalk *(G-15565)*

2951 Paving Mixtures & Blocks

A United ....G 330 782-6005
  Youngstown *(G-21011)*

Action Blacktop Sealcoating & ....G 937 667-4769
  Tipp City *(G-18259)*

All Coatings Co Inc ....G 330 821-3806
  Alliance *(G-489)*

Allied Corporation Inc ....G 330 425-7861
  Twinsburg *(G-18898)*

Aluminum Coating Manufacturers ....E 216 341-2000
  Cleveland *(G-4774)*

Ashland LLC ....G 513 557-3100
  Cincinnati *(G-3418)*

Asphalt Fabrics & Specialties ....G 440 786-1077
  Solon *(G-17262)*

Asphalt Materials Inc ....G 740 373-3040
  Marietta *(G-12764)*

Asphalt Materials Inc ....F 740 374-5100
  Marietta *(G-12765)*

Asphalt Services & Cnstr ....G 330 995-6044
  Aurora *(G-907)*

Atlas Roofing Corporation ....G 937 746-9941
  Franklin *(G-10008)*

B & S Blacktop Co ....G 513 797-5759
  New Richmond *(G-14940)*

Baileys Asphalt Sealing ....F 740 453-9409
  South Zanesville *(G-17453)*

Barrett Paving Materials Inc ....C 513 271-6200
  Middletown *(G-14101)*

Bluffton Stone Co ....E 419 358-6941
  Bluffton *(G-1909)*

Bowerston Shale Company ....E 740 269-2921
  Bowerston *(G-1957)*

Brewer Company ....G 614 279-8688
  Columbus *(G-6855)*

▲ Brewer Company ....G 800 394-0017
  Milford *(G-14127)*

Brown Construction & Paving ....G 513 494-0095
  Morrow *(G-14544)*

Buckeye Sealcoating ....F 330 658-3377
  Doylestown *(G-9027)*

Canton Asphalt Co ....G 330 499-6888
  Canton *(G-2636)*

Central Ohio Asphalt LLC ....G 419 768-4211
  Chesterville *(G-3224)*

Central Oil Asphalt Corp ....G 614 224-8111
  Columbus *(G-6919)*

Concord Paving Co ....G 440 354-8580
  Painesville *(G-15866)*

D & R Supply Inc ....G 330 855-3781
  Marshallville *(G-12917)*

D and D Asp Sealcoating LLC ....G 614 288-3597
  Pickerington *(G-16189)*

Erie Materials Inc ....G 419 483-4648
  Castalia *(G-2975)*

Full Circle Technologies LLC ....G 216 650-0007
  Pepper Pike *(G-16046)*

Grand River Asphalt ....G 440 352-2254
  Grand River *(G-10449)*

H P Streicher Inc ....G 419 841-4715
  Toledo *(G-18490)*

Hanson Aggregates Midwest LLC ....G 419 983-2211
  Bloomville *(G-1728)*

Hanson Aggregates Midwest LLC ....G 419 878-2006
  Waterville *(G-19659)*

Heritage Group Inc ....G 330 875-5566
  Louisville *(G-12314)*

Holmes Supply Corp ....G 330 279-2634
  Holmesville *(G-11105)*

Husac Paving ....G 513 200-2818
  Harrison *(G-10784)*

Hy-Grade Corporation ....E 216 341-7711
  Cleveland *(G-5541)*

Image Pavement Maintenance ....E 937 833-9200
  Brookville *(G-2187)*

John R Jurgensen Co .... G 937 293-3112
Springfield (G-17582)

Kokosing Materials Inc .... F 419 522-2715
Mansfield (G-12634)

Kokosing Materials Inc .... E 740 745-3341
Saint Louisville (G-16827)

Kokosing Materials Inc .... G 614 891-5090
Westerville (G-20220)

Kokosing Materials Inc .... E 614 491-1199
Columbus (G-7265)

Koksing Material Inc .... G 330 721-2775
Medina (G-13434)

Koski Construction Co .... G 440 997-5337
Ashtabula (G-815)

La Rose Paving Co Inc .... G 440 632-0330
Middlefield (G-13950)

Lake Erie Asphalt Paving Inc .... G 440 526-5191
Brecksville (G-2060)

Lucas County Asphalt Inc .... E 419 476-0705
Toledo (G-18564)

Lynn James Contracting LLC .... G 419 467-4505
Delta (G-8938)

M & B Asphalt Company Inc .... G 419 992-4235
Tiffin (G-18228)

Mansfield Asphalt Paving Inc .... F 740 453-0721
Zanesville (G-21327)

Mar-Zane Inc .... F 740 453-0721
Zanesville (G-21328)

Mar-Zane Inc .... G 740 782-1240
Bethesda (G-1666)

Mar-Zane Inc .... G 740 685-5178
Byesville (G-2407)

Mar-Zane Inc .... G 330 626-2079
Mantua (G-12716)

Marathon Petroleum Company LP .... B 330 478-5000
Canton (G-2767)

◆ Marathon Petroleum Company LP .... F 419 422-2121
Findlay (G-9855)

Massillon Asphalt Co .... G 330 833-6330
Massillon (G-13173)

Miller Bros Paving Inc .... F 419 445-1015
Archbold (G-687)

Morris Paving .... F 740 373-2457
Marietta (G-12809)

Morrow Gravel Company Inc .... E 513 771-0820
Cincinnati (G-4124)

Mt Pleasant Blacktopping Inc .... G 513 874-3777
Fairfield (G-9688)

Newton Asphalt Paving Inc .... F 330 878-5648
Strasburg (G-17826)

▲ Reading Rock Inc .... C 513 874-2345
West Chester (G-20045)

Robert Gorey .... G 330 725-7272
Medina (G-13468)

Roof To Road LLC .... G 740 986-6923
Williamsport (G-20419)

Russell Standard Corporation .... G 330 733-9400
Akron (G-389)

Rutland Township .... G 740 742-2805
Bidwell (G-1678)

S E Johnson Companies Inc .... F 419 893-8731
Maumee (G-13290)

Seal Master Corporation .... E 330 673-8410
Kent (G-11525)

Seneca Petroleum Co Inc .... F 419 691-3581
Toledo (G-18692)

Shalersville Asphalt Co .... E 440 834-4294
Burton (G-2384)

Shelly and Sands Inc .... G 330 743-8850
Youngstown (G-21201)

Shelly and Sands Inc .... F 740 373-6495
Marietta (G-12828)

Shelly and Sands Inc .... D 740 859-2104
Rayland (G-16575)

Shelly and Sands Inc .... E 740 453-0721
Zanesville (G-21351)

Shelly and Sands Inc .... F 740 453-0721
Zanesville (G-21350)

Shelly Company .... G 740 474-6255
Circleville (G-4642)

Shelly Company .... G 740 246-6315
Thornville (G-18196)

Shelly Materials Inc .... G 419 229-2741
Lima (G-12090)

Shelly Materials Inc .... E 740 246-5009
Thornville (G-18197)

Shelly Materials Inc .... G 740 446-7789
Gallipolis (G-10309)

Shelly Materials Inc .... E 740 666-5841
Ostrander (G-15789)

Shelly Materials Inc .... G 330 673-3646
Kent (G-11527)

Shelly Materials Inc .... G 419 273-2510
Forest (G-9922)

Shelly Materials Inc .... D 740 246-6315
Thornville (G-18198)

Sidwell Materials Inc .... C 740 849-2394
Zanesville (G-21354)

Smalls Asphalt Paving Inc .... E 740 427-4096
Gambier (G-10318)

Specialty Technology & Res .... G 614 870-0744
Columbus (G-7639)

Star Seal of Ohio Inc .... G 614 870-1590
Columbus (G-7653)

Stark Materials Inc .... E 330 497-1648
Canton (G-2856)

Stoneco Inc .... C 419 422-8854
Findlay (G-9895)

Stoneco Inc .... G 419 693-3933
Toledo (G-18705)

Stoneco Inc .... E 419 393-2555
Oakwood (G-15619)

◆ Thorworks Industries Inc .... E 419 626-4375
Sandusky (G-17015)

Unique Paving Materials Corp .... E 216 341-7711
Cleveland (G-6383)

Valley Asphalt Corporation .... G 513 381-0652
Morrow (G-14552)

Valley Asphalt Corporation .... G 937 426-7682
Xenia (G-20984)

Valley Asphalt Corporation .... G 937 335-3664
Troy (G-18884)

Valley Asphalt Corporation .... G 513 353-2171
Cleves (G-6531)

Valley Asphalt Corporation .... G 513 784-1476
Cincinnati (G-4552)

Valley Asphalt Corporation .... G 513 561-1551
Cincinnati (G-4551)

Walls Bros Asphalt Co Inc .... G 937 548-7158
Greenville (G-10526)

Wilson Blacktop Corporation .... E 740 635-3566
Martins Ferry (G-12928)

York Paving Co .... F 740 594-3600
Athens (G-891)

2952 Asphalt Felts & Coatings

Aluminum Coating Manufacturers .... E 216 341-2000
Cleveland (G-4774)

American Orginal Bldg Pdts LLC .... F 330 786-3000
Akron (G-67)

Atlas Roofing Corporation .... C 937 746-9941
Franklin (G-10008)

▲ Brewer Company .... G 800 394-0017
Milford (G-14127)

Brewer Company .... E 440 944-3800
Wickliffe (G-20361)

Brewer Company .... E 614 279-8688
Columbus (G-6855)

Brewer Company .... G 513 576-6300
Cincinnati (G-3470)

C Green & Sons Incorporated .... F 740 745-2998
Saint Louisville (G-16826)

Certainteed Corporation .... C 419 499-2581
Milan (G-14110)

◆ Chemspec Ltd .... F 330 896-0355
Uniontown (G-19079)

Classic Metals Ltd .... G 330 763-1162
Holmesville (G-11100)

Consolidated Coatings Corp .... E 216 514-7596
Cleveland (G-5118)

▼ Custom Seal Inc .... E 419 334-1020
Fremont (G-10140)

Dnd Emulsions Inc .... G 419 525-4988
Mansfield (G-12595)

Garland Industries Inc .... G 216 641-7500
Cleveland (G-5399)

Garland/Dbs Inc .... C 216 641-7500
Cleveland (G-5400)

Hy-Grade Corporation .... E 216 341-7711
Cleveland (G-5541)

▼ Hyload Inc .... F 330 336-6604
Seville (G-17075)

Iko Production Inc .... E 937 746-4561
Franklin (G-10029)

▼ Isaiah Industries Inc .... E 937 773-9840
Piqua (G-16280)

Johns Manville Corporation .... D 419 499-1400
Milan (G-14114)

Kettering Roofing & Shtmtl .... F 513 281-6413
Cincinnati (G-3986)

Metal Sales Manufacturing Corp .... E 440 576-9070
Jefferson (G-11367)

Midwest Industrial Products .... G 216 771-8555
Cleveland (G-5810)

▲ Midwest Trmnals Tledo Intl Inc .... G 419 897-6868
Maumee (G-13283)

National Tool & Equipment Inc .... F 330 629-8665
Youngstown (G-21148)

◆ Owens Corning .... A 419 248-8000
Toledo (G-18625)

Owens Corning Sales LLC .... C 330 764-7800
Medina (G-13456)

◆ Owens Corning Sales LLC .... A 419 248-8000
Toledo (G-18626)

P C R Inc .... F 330 945-7721
Akron (G-329)

Qualico Inc .... G 216 271-2550
Cleveland (G-6067)

Riverside Sand & Gravel Co .... G 330 673-2021
Kent (G-11517)

Simon Roofing and Shtmtl Corp .... C 330 629-7392
Youngstown (G-21204)

Sr Products .... G 330 998-6500
Macedonia (G-12486)

◆ State Industrial Products Corp .... B 877 747-6986
Cleveland (G-6239)

Surface-All Inc .... G 440 428-2233
Port Clinton (G-16416)

Terry Asphalt Materials Inc .... E 513 874-6192
Hamilton (G-10744)

◆ Thorworks Industries Inc .... E 419 626-4375
Sandusky (G-17015)

Topps Products Inc .... G 216 271-2550
Cleveland (G-6338)

Transtar Holding Company .... G 800 359-3339
Cleveland (G-6349)

◆ Tremco Incorporated .... B 216 292-5000
Beachwood (G-1303)

Truco Inc .... B 216 631-1000
Cleveland (G-6370)

2992 Lubricating Oils & Greases

A & M Products .... G 419 595-2092
Tiffin (G-18201)

Advanced Engine Tech LLC .... G 937 439-0224
Bellbrook (G-1503)

Advanced Fluids Inc .... G 216 692-3050
Cleveland (G-4713)

Aerospace Lubricants Inc .... F 614 878-3600
Columbus (G-6701)

American Ultra Specialties Inc .... F 330 656-5000
Hudson (G-11157)

▲ Aml Industries Inc .... E 330 399-5000
Warren (G-19523)

Amsoil Inc .... G 614 274-9851
Columbus (G-6746)

▼ Anchor Chemical Co Inc .... G 440 871-1660
Westlake (G-20254)

Apex Advanced Technologies LLC .... G 216 898-1595
Cleveland (G-4818)

▲ Bechem Lubrication Tech LLC .... G 440 543-9845
Chagrin Falls (G-3077)

BLaster Corporation .... E 216 901-5800
Cleveland (G-4916)

Blendzall Inc .... G 740 633-1333
Martins Ferry (G-12922)

◆ Borchers Americas Inc .... D 440 899-2950
Westlake (G-20258)

Cambridge Mill Products Inc .... G 330 863-1121
Malvern (G-12539)

Chemical Methods Inc .... E 216 476-8400
Strongsville (G-17901)

▲ Chemical Solvents Inc .... E 216 741-9310
Cleveland (G-5025)

Cincinnati - Vulcan Company .... D 513 242-5300
Cincinnati (G-3535)

Commercial Lubricants Inc .... G 614 475-5952
Columbus (G-6971)

Digilube Systems Inc .... F 937 748-2209
Springboro (G-17479)

Diversified Technology Inc .... G 330 722-4995
Medina (G-13403)

Dnd Emulsions Inc .... G 419 525-4988
Mansfield (G-12595)

Douglas W & B C Richardson .... G 440 247-5262
Chagrin Falls (G-3055)

Dubro Oil Corporation .... G 216 696-2646
Cleveland (G-5218)

Eni USA R & M Co Inc .... F 330 723-6457
Medina (G-13405)

S I C

Ensign Product Company Inc...............G....... 216 341-5911
Cleveland (G-5284)

◆ Etna Products Incorporated............E....... 440 543-9845
Chagrin Falls (G-3087)

Fiske Brothers Refining Co................D....... 419 691-2491
Toledo (G-18471)

Fuchs Lubricants Co.........................E....... 330 963-0400
Twinsburg (G-18938)

▲ Functional Products Inc..................E....... 330 963-3060
Macedonia (G-12452)

▲ G W Smith and Sons Inc................E....... 937 253-5114
Dayton (G-8105)

Ha-International LLC........................E....... 419 537-0096
Toledo (G-18492)

▼ Into Great Brands Inc....................F....... 888 771-5656
Gahanna (G-10213)

J J Merlin Systems Inc......................G....... 330 666-8609
Copley (G-7848)

Jtm Products Inc.............................E....... 440 287-2302
Solon (G-17324)

Koki Laboratories Inc......................E....... 330 773-7669
Akron (G-262)

Lcp Tech Inc..................................G....... 513 271-1389
Cincinnati (G-4017)

Lubrizol Corporation.......................E....... 440 357-7064
Painesville (G-15898)

M B Industries Inc...........................G....... 419 738-4769
Wapakoneta (G-19496)

▲ Magnus International Group Inc.......G....... 216 592-8355
Chagrin Falls (G-3100)

◆ Maintenance + Inc........................F....... 330 264-6262
Wooster (G-20801)

Mar Mor Inc...................................G....... 216 961-6900
Cleveland (G-5740)

◆ Master Chemical Corporation..........D....... 419 874-7902
Perrysburg (G-16121)

McGlaughln Oil Compny/Fas Lube......E....... 614 231-2518
Columbus (G-7334)

Melanda Inc...................................G....... 330 833-0517
Massillon (G-13179)

Metal Forming Lubricants Inc............G....... 440 458-5730
Elyria (G-9461)

New Vulco Mfg & Sales Co LLC...........D....... 513 242-2672
Cincinnati (G-4149)

▲ North Shore Strapping Inc..............E....... 216 661-5200
Brooklyn Heights (G-2144)

Oil Etc Inc.....................................G....... 513 933-8280
Lebanon (G-11822)

Oliver Chemical Co Inc.....................G....... 513 541-4540
Cincinnati (G-4185)

Paramount Products........................G....... 419 832-0235
Grand Rapids (G-10442)

Perma-Fix of Dayton Inc...................E....... 937 268-6501
Dayton (G-8571)

Petroliance..................................G....... 614 475-5952
Columbus (G-7480)

Petroliance LLC..............................G....... 216 441-7200
Cleveland (G-5999)

Phymet Inc....................................F....... 937 743-8061
Springboro (G-17496)

▲ Plasti-Kote Co Inc........................C....... 330 725-4511
Medina (G-13459)

▲ Quaker Chemical Corporation.........D....... 513 422-9600
Middletown (G-14080)

R and J Corporation.........................E....... 440 871-6009
Westlake (G-20299)

Reladyne Inc..................................E....... 513 489-6000
Blue Ash (G-1862)

Renite Company.............................F....... 614 253-5509
Columbus (G-7554)

Shooters Choice LLC........................G....... 440 834-8888
Middlefield (G-13990)

Spec Mask Ohio LLC.........................G....... 440 522-3055
Kirtland (G-11616)

Specialty Technologies Inc...............G....... 330 638-0744
Cortland (G-7875)

Starchem Inc..................................G....... 513 458-8262
Cincinnati (G-4458)

◆ State Industrial Products Corp.........B....... 877 747-6986
Cleveland (G-6239)

Triad Energy Corporation.................E....... 740 374-2940
Marietta (G-12844)

United Lubricants Corporation...........D....... 513 422-9600
Middletown (G-14092)

Universal Oil Inc.............................E....... 216 771-4300
Cleveland (G-6391)

US Industrial Lubricants Inc..............E....... 513 541-2225
Cincinnati (G-4547)

▼ Ventco Inc...................................F....... 440 834-8888
Middlefield (G-14001)

Wallover Enterprises Inc...................E....... 440 238-9250
Strongsville (G-17981)

Wallover Enterprises Inc...................F....... 440 238-9250
East Liverpool (G-9228)

▼ Wallover Oil Company Inc...............E....... 440 238-9250
Strongsville (G-17982)

Wallover Oil Hamilton Inc.................F....... 513 896-6692
Hamilton (G-10756)

Western Reserve Lubricants..............G....... 440 951-5700
Painesville (G-15939)

2999 Products Of Petroleum & Coal, NEC

Citi 2 Citi Logistics..........................G....... 614 306-4109
Columbus (G-6930)

30 RUBBER AND MISCELLANEOUS PLASTICS PRODUCTS

3011 Tires & Inner Tubes

◆ 31 Inc.......................................D....... 740 498-8324
Newcomerstown (G-15107)

American Airless Inc.........................E....... 614 552-0146
Reynoldsburg (G-16580)

B & S Transport Inc..........................G....... 330 767-4319
Navarre (G-14709)

BF Diversified Svcs...........................G....... 330 869-5203
Akron (G-91)

◆ Bkt USA Inc................................F....... 330 836-1090
Fairlawn (G-9743)

Bridgestone Americas Inc..................E....... 330 379-7000
Akron (G-97)

Bridgestone Firestone.......................E....... 614 523-2259
Columbus (G-6641)

Bridgestone Ret Operations LLC..........F....... 330 379-6220
Akron (G-99)

Buckman Machine Works Inc..............G....... 330 525-7665
Homeworth (G-11115)

C N C Wholesale..............................G....... 330 832-9525
Massillon (G-13117)

◆ Chemspec Ltd.............................F....... 330 896-0355
Uniontown (G-19079)

Continental Tire Americas LLC............E....... 419 633-4221
Bryan (G-2290)

Contitech North America Inc...............E....... 440 225-5363
Akron (G-129)

◆ Cooper Tire & Rubber Company.......A....... 419 423-1321
Findlay (G-9811)

Cooper Tire & Rubber Company..........E....... 419 424-4202
Findlay (G-9812)

Cooper Tire & Rubber Company..........D....... 419 424-4384
Findlay (G-9813)

▲ Cooper Tire Vhcl Test Ctr Inc..........E....... 419 423-1321
Findlay (G-9814)

F M P Enterprises Inc........................G....... 330 920-8059
Cuyahoga Falls (G-7994)

Goodrich Corporation.......................G....... 216 429-4655
Brooklyn Heights (G-2140)

Goodyear Tire & Rubber Company.......A....... 330 796-2121
Akron (G-207)

Goodyear Tire & Rubber Company.......G....... 216 265-1800
Cleveland (G-5438)

Gregs Eagle Tire Co Inc.....................G....... 330 837-1983
Massillon (G-13142)

▲ Grove Engineered Products Inc........G....... 419 659-5939
Columbus Grove (G-7794)

H & H Industries Inc.........................G....... 740 682-7721
Oak Hill (G-15596)

Intertex World Resources Inc.............G....... 770 214-5551
Canton (G-2739)

▲ Martin Wheel Co Inc.....................D....... 330 633-3278
Tallmadge (G-18153)

PPG Industries Inc............................G....... 614 921-9228
Hilliard (G-10972)

Sumitomo Rubber Usa LLC..................E....... 419 347-1067
Shelby (G-17144)

◆ Technical Rubber Company Inc.........B....... 740 967-9015
Johnstown (G-11407)

Titan Tire Corporation......................B....... 419 633-4221
Bryan (G-2323)

▲ Trelleborg Wheel Systems Ameri......E....... 866 633-8473
Akron (G-444)

Troy Engineered Components and.......G....... 937 335-8070
Vandalia (G-19312)

Truflex Rubber Products Co................C....... 740 967-9015
Johnstown (G-11409)

Umd Contractors Inc.........................F....... 740 694-8614
Fredericktown (G-10114)

Yrp Industries Inc............................G....... 330 533-2524
Youngstown (G-21259)

3021 Rubber & Plastic Footwear

Advantage Products Corporation.........F....... 513 489-2283
Blue Ash (G-1736)

American Doll Accessories..................G....... 740 590-8458
Coolville (G-7833)

Cobblers Corner LLC.........................F....... 330 482-4005
Columbiana (G-6610)

Crocs Inc......................................F....... 330 954-1963
Aurora (G-914)

◆ Factory Direct International.............E....... 419 425-9636
Findlay (G-9821)

Georgia Boot LLC.............................D....... 740 753-1951
Nelsonville (G-14734)

Mulhern Belting Inc..........................E....... 201 337-5700
Fairfield (G-9689)

Nwc HUD Corp II..............................G....... 419 228-8400
Lima (G-12064)

▲ Totes Isotoner Corporation.............F....... 513 682-8200
West Chester (G-20059)

▲ Totes Isotoner Holdings Corp..........C....... 513 682-8200
West Chester (G-20060)

Vans Inc..F....... 419 471-1541
Toledo (G-18765)

3052 Rubber & Plastic Hose & Belting

Aeroquip Corp.................................G....... 419 238-1190
Van Wert (G-19242)

Aeroquip-Vickers Inc........................G....... 216 523-5000
Cleveland (G-4722)

Allied Fabricating & Wldg Co..............E....... 614 751-6664
Columbus (G-6725)

Cmt Machining & Fabg LLC.................F....... 937 652-3740
Urbana (G-19151)

Contitech North America Inc...............E....... 440 225-5363
Akron (G-129)

Cooper-Standard Automotive Inc........B....... 419 352-3533
Bowling Green (G-1983)

Eaton Corporation...........................A....... 419 238-1190
Van Wert (G-19253)

Eaton Corporation...........................C....... 330 274-0743
Aurora (G-916)

Eaton Hydraulics LLC........................E....... 419 232-7777
Van Wert (G-19254)

Eaton-Aeroquip Inc..........................D....... 419 891-7775
Maumee (G-13258)

▲ Eaton-Aeroquip Llc.......................C....... 216 523-5000
Cleveland (G-5254)

Eaton-Aeroquip Llc..........................D....... 419 238-1190
Van Wert (G-19255)

▲ Engineered Plastics Corp...............E....... 330 376-7700
Akron (G-167)

Fenner Dunlop (toledo) LLC...............E....... 419 531-5300
Toledo (G-18467)

Goodyear Tire & Rubber Company.......A....... 330 796-2121
Akron (G-207)

▼ Hbd/Thermoid Inc........................C....... 937 593-5010
Bellefontaine (G-1532)

Kent Elastomer Products Inc..............G....... 800 331-4762
Mogadore (G-14379)

▲ Kent Elastomer Products Inc...........C....... 330 673-1011
Kent (G-11478)

Kentak Products Company..................D....... 330 386-3700
East Liverpool (G-9221)

▲ Kentak Products Company...............E....... 330 382-2000
East Liverpool (G-9222)

Kentak Products Company..................G....... 330 532-6211
East Palestine (G-9240)

Mechanical Elastomerics Inc..............G....... 330 863-1014
Malvern (G-12547)

▲ Milligan Workshops Inc..................E....... 419 353-0099
Bowling Green (G-2002)

Myers Industries Inc.........................G....... 330 336-6621
Wadsworth (G-19420)

◆ Myers Industries Inc......................E....... 330 253-5592
Akron (G-309)

Novex Inc......................................F....... 330 335-2371
Wadsworth (G-19422)

Parker-Hannifin Corporation..............G....... 330 296-2871
Ravenna (G-16549)

Polychem Corporation......................G....... 419 547-1400
Clyde (G-6543)

Roller Source Inc.............................F....... 440 748-4033
Columbia Station (G-6596)

▲ Salem-Republic Rubber Company.....E....... 330 938-2016
Sebring (G-17052)

Sperry Rice Manufacturing LLC...........F....... 330 276-2801
Killbuck (G-11600)

◆ Sumiriko Ohio Inc.........................C....... 419 358-2121
Bluffton (G-1916)

Summers Acquisition Corp.................G....... 740 373-0303
Marietta *(G-12839)*

Summers Acquisition Corp.................G....... 419 526-5800
Mansfield *(G-12687)*

Summers Acquisition Corp.................G....... 419 423-5800
Findlay *(G-9898)*

Universal Plastics Inc.........................E....... 440 942-7510
Mentor *(G-13762)*

◆ Watteredge LLC.............................D....... 440 933-6110
Avon Lake *(G-1055)*

3053 Gaskets, Packing & Sealing Devices

◆ Accel Performance Group LLC.........C....... 216 658-6413
Independence *(G-11245)*

Ace Gasket Manufacturing Co.............G....... 513 271-6321
Cincinnati *(G-3349)*

Air Heater Seal Company Inc..............E....... 740 984-2146
Waterford *(G-19645)*

▲ Akron Gasket & Packg Entps Inc.....F....... 330 633-3742
Tallmadge *(G-18132)*

Alternative Surface Grinding................E....... 330 273-3443
Brunswick *(G-2205)*

▲ Ashtabula Rubber Co.......................C....... 440 992-2195
Ashtabula *(G-794)*

Blackthorn LLC...................................F....... 937 836-9296
Clayton *(G-4657)*

▲ Chestnut Holdings Inc......................G....... 330 849-6503
Akron *(G-122)*

▲ Cincinnati Gasket Pkg Mfg Inc.........E....... 513 761-3458
Cincinnati *(G-3550)*

Columbus Gasket and Sup Co LLC......G....... 614 878-6041
Columbus *(G-6952)*

▲ Columbus Gasket Co Inc..................G....... 614 878-6041
Columbus *(G-6953)*

◆ Concrete Sealants Inc......................E....... 937 845-8776
Tipp City *(G-18273)*

Cornerstone Indus Holdings................G....... 440 893-9144
Chagrin Falls *(G-3054)*

Dan-Loc LLC......................................G....... 937 778-0485
Piqua *(G-16259)*

Dana Incorporated..............................B....... 419 887-3000
Maumee *(G-13246)*

▲ Dana Limited...................................B....... 630 697-3783
Maumee *(G-13249)*

Die-Cut Products Co...........................E....... 216 771-6994
Cleveland *(G-5193)*

▲ Durox Company...............................D....... 440 238-5350
Strongsville *(G-17914)*

▲ Egc Enterprises Inc.........................E....... 440 285-5835
Chardon *(G-3151)*

Epg Inc..D....... 330 995-5125
Aurora *(G-919)*

Epg Inc..F....... 330 995-9725
Streetsboro *(G-17852)*

Essential Sealing Products Inc............G....... 440 543-8108
Chagrin Falls *(G-3086)*

Excelsior Solutions.............................G....... 937 848-2569
Spring Valley *(G-17467)*

Faurecia Exhaust Systems Inc............B....... 937 743-0551
Franklin *(G-10021)*

Federal-Mogul Corporation.................C....... 740 432-2393
Cambridge *(G-2457)*

Federal-Mogul Corporation.................A....... 419 238-1053
Van Wert *(G-19257)*

▲ Ferrotherm Corporation....................C....... 216 883-9350
Cleveland *(G-5339)*

▲ Flow Dry Technology Inc..................C....... 937 833-2161
Brookville *(G-2183)*

Foam Seal Inc....................................D....... 216 881-8111
Cleveland *(G-5363)*

▲ Forest City Technologies Inc............B....... 440 647-2115
Wellington *(G-19743)*

Forest City Technologies Inc...............B....... 440 647-2115
Wellington *(G-19744)*

Forest City Technologies Inc...............C....... 440 647-2115
Wellington *(G-19745)*

Forest City Technologies Inc...............C....... 440 647-2115
Wellington *(G-19746)*

Forest City Technologies Inc...............C....... 440 647-2115
Wellington *(G-19747)*

▲ Fouty & Company Inc.......................G....... 419 693-0017
Oregon *(G-15709)*

Freudenberg-Nok General Partnr.........E....... 937 335-3306
Troy *(G-18828)*

Freudenberg-Nok General Partnr.........C....... 419 427-5221
Findlay *(G-9827)*

G-M-I Inc...G....... 440 953-8811
Willoughby *(G-20496)*

Gasko Fabricated Products LLC...........E....... 330 239-1781
Medina *(G-13414)*

High Quality Plastics...........................G....... 419 422-8290
Findlay *(G-9839)*

Hunt Products Inc...............................E....... 440 667-2457
Newburgh Heights *(G-15075)*

▲ Ier Fujikura Inc...............................C....... 330 425-7121
Macedonia *(G-12458)*

Industry Products Co..........................B....... 937 778-0585
Piqua *(G-16279)*

▲ Ishikawa Gasket America Inc...........F....... 419 353-7300
Bowling Green *(G-1990)*

Ishikawa Gasket America Inc..............C....... 419 353-7300
Bowling Green *(G-1991)*

Jbm Technologies Inc.........................E....... 419 368-4362
Hayesville *(G-10844)*

Jet Rubber Company...........................G....... 330 325-1821
Rootstown *(G-16723)*

Johnson Bros Rubber Co Inc...............E....... 419 752-4814
Greenwich *(G-10531)*

Jtm Products Inc................................E....... 440 287-2302
Solon *(G-17324)*

K Wm Beach Mfg Co Inc.....................E....... 937 399-3838
Springfield *(G-17584)*

Kes Industries LLC..............................G....... 330 405-2813
Twinsburg *(G-18963)*

May Lin Silicone Products Inc..............C....... 330 825-9019
Barberton *(G-1129)*

Mechanical Dynamics Analis Ltd..........E....... 440 946-0082
Euclid *(G-9592)*

Miami Valley Gasket Co Inc.................C....... 937 228-0781
Dayton *(G-8490)*

Middlefield Plastics Inc.......................C....... 440 834-4638
Middlefield *(G-13962)*

Midwest Industrial Rubber Inc.............F....... 614 876-3110
Hilliard *(G-10963)*

Miles Rubber & Packing Company........C....... 330 425-3888
Twinsburg *(G-18988)*

Neff-Perkins Company.........................C....... 440 632-1658
Middlefield *(G-13975)*

Netherland Rubber Company................C....... 513 733-0883
Cincinnati *(G-4146)*

Newman Sanitary Gasket Company.......E....... 513 932-7379
Lebanon *(G-11818)*

▲ Nitto Denko Auto Ohio Inc...............C....... 937 773-4820
Piqua *(G-16295)*

Novagard Solutions Inc.......................E....... 216 881-3890
Cleveland *(G-5917)*

▲ Ohio Gasket and Shim Co Inc...........E....... 330 630-0626
Akron *(G-323)*

P & E Sales Ltd..................................G....... 330 829-0100
Alliance *(G-532)*

▲ P & R Specialty Inc.........................F....... 937 773-0263
Piqua *(G-16297)*

Paramont Machine Company LLC..........E....... 330 339-3489
New Philadelphia *(G-14921)*

◆ Parker-Hannifin Corporation.............B....... 216 896-3000
Cleveland *(G-5973)*

Parker-Hannifin Corporation.................F....... 216 896-3000
Cleveland *(G-5976)*

Paul J Tatulinski Ltd...........................B....... 330 584-8251
North Benton *(G-15213)*

Phoenix Associates............................E....... 440 543-9701
Chagrin Falls *(G-3112)*

Produce Packaging Inc........................C....... 216 391-6129
Cleveland *(G-6052)*

Quanex Ig Systems Inc.......................C....... 740 439-2338
Cambridge *(G-2473)*

◆ Quanex Ig Systems Inc....................C....... 216 910-1519
Solon *(G-17366)*

R and J Corporation............................F....... 440 871-6009
Westlake *(G-20299)*

▲ Royal Acme Corporation...................C....... 216 241-1477
Cleveland *(G-6136)*

Rubbertec Industrial Pdts Co...............C....... 740 657-3345
Lewis Center *(G-11916)*

▲ Saint-Gobain Prfmce Plas Corp.........C....... 440 836-6900
Solon *(G-17375)*

▲ SKF Usa Inc....................................F....... 440 720-1500
Highland Heights *(G-10920)*

▲ Soffseal Inc....................................E....... 513 367-0028
Harrison *(G-10804)*

▲ Sur-Seal Corporation........................C....... 513 574-8500
Cincinnati *(G-4485)*

Sur-Seal Corporation..........................C....... 513 574-8500
Harrison *(G-10808)*

Thermodyn Corporation......................C....... 419 874-5100
Perrysburg *(G-16157)*

Treaty City Industries Inc....................F....... 937 548-9000
Greenville *(G-10525)*

Tri-Seal LLC.......................................C....... 330 821-1166
Alliance *(G-549)*

▲ Vertex Inc.......................................E....... 330 628-6230
Mogadore *(G-14387)*

Youngstown Specialty Mtls Inc............G....... 330 259-1110
Youngstown *(G-21256)*

3061 Molded, Extruded & Lathe-Cut Rubber Mechanical Goods

Alloy Extrusion Company....................E....... 330 677-4946
Kent *(G-11427)*

Alternative Flash Inc..........................E....... 330 334-6111
Wadsworth *(G-19393)*

American Pro-Mold Inc........................E....... 330 336-4111
Wadsworth *(G-19394)*

ARC Rubber Inc..................................F....... 440 466-4555
Geneva *(G-10343)*

▲ Ashtabula Rubber Co.......................C....... 440 992-2195
Ashtabula *(G-794)*

Bridgestone APM Company..................D....... 419 294-6989
Upper Sandusky *(G-19114)*

Bridgestone APM Company..................C....... 419 294-6304
Upper Sandusky *(G-19115)*

◆ Brp Manufacturing Company.............E....... 800 858-0482
Lima *(G-11998)*

Canton OH Rubber Speclty Prods.........G....... 330 454-3847
Canton *(G-2642)*

▲ Cardinal Rubber Company Inc...........E....... 330 745-2191
Barberton *(G-1113)*

Chardon Custom Polymers LLC............F....... 440 285-2161
Chardon *(G-3143)*

Clark Rbr Plastic Intl Sls Inc...............C....... 440 953-9514
Mentor *(G-13544)*

Colonial Rubber Company....................E....... 330 296-2831
Ravenna *(G-16523)*

▲ Contitech North America Inc.............F....... 330 664-7180
Fairlawn *(G-9747)*

◆ Datwyler Sling Sltions USA Inc..........D....... 937 387-2800
Vandalia *(G-11999)*

Duramax Global Corp...........................D....... 440 834-5400
Hiram *(G-11033)*

Elbex Corporation...............................E....... 330 673-3233
Kent *(G-11454)*

Epg Inc..D....... 330 995-5125
Aurora *(G-919)*

Epg Inc..F....... 330 995-9725
Streetsboro *(G-17852)*

Extruded Silicon Products Inc..............E....... 330 733-0101
Mogadore *(G-14375)*

Frankes Wood Products LLC.................E....... 937 642-0706
Marysville *(G-12944)*

Harwood Rubber Products Inc..............E....... 330 923-3256
Cuyahoga Falls *(G-8008)*

Hygenic Acquisition Co........................C....... 330 633-8460
Akron *(G-228)*

◆ Hygenic Corporation........................C....... 330 633-8460
Akron *(G-229)*

▲ Ier Fujikura Inc...............................C....... 330 425-7121
Macedonia *(G-12458)*

Jakmar Incorporated...........................F....... 513 631-4303
Cincinnati *(G-3938)*

▲ Johnson Bros Rubber Co Inc............E....... 419 853-4122
West Salem *(G-20114)*

K-Js Mechanical Service......................F....... 419 729-1103
Toledo *(G-18536)*

Karman Rubber Company.....................E....... 330 864-2161
Akron *(G-251)*

Kleen Polymers Inc.............................F....... 330 336-4212
Wadsworth *(G-19415)*

▼ Koneta Inc......................................D....... 419 739-4200
Wapakoneta *(G-19495)*

▲ Lauren Manufacturing LLC...............B....... 330 339-3373
New Philadelphia *(G-14909)*

Macdivitt Rubber Company LLC............E....... 440 259-5937
Perry *(G-16054)*

Mantaline Corporation........................D....... 330 274-2264
Mantua *(G-12715)*

Martin Industries Inc..........................E....... 419 862-2694
Elmore *(G-9364)*

Meridian Industries Inc.......................D....... 330 673-1011
Kent *(G-11488)*

▲ Midlands Millroom Supply Inc...........E....... 330 453-9100
Canton *(G-2779)*

Midwest Industrial Rubber Inc.............F....... 614 876-3110
Hilliard *(G-10963)*

Miller Enterprises Ohio LLC.................G....... 330 852-4009
Sugarcreek *(G-18027)*

▲ Milligan Workshops Inc....................E....... 419 353-0099
Bowling Green *(G-2002)*

Neff-Perkins Company.........................C....... 440 632-1658
Middlefield *(G-13975)*

Ohio Elastomers ....G....... 440 354-9750
Perry (G-16055)

Ottawa Rubber Company ....F....... 419 865-1378
Holland (G-11075)

Plabell Rubber Products Corp ....F....... 419 691-5878
Toledo (G-18646)

Polycraft Products Inc ....G....... 513 353-3334
Cleves (G-6523)

▲ Q Holding Company ....B....... 330 425-8472
Twinsburg (G-19006)

Qualiform Inc ....E....... 330 336-6777
Wadsworth (G-19432)

Quanex Ig Systems Inc ....C....... 740 439-2338
Cambridge (G-2473)

◆ Quanex Ig Systems Inc ....C....... 216 910-1519
Solon (G-17366)

Robin Industries Inc ....E....... 330 893-3501
Berlin (G-1652)

Robin Industries Inc ....C....... 330 359-5418
Winesburg (G-20707)

Robin Industries Inc ....C....... 330 695-9300
Fredericksburg (G-10092)

Robin Industries Inc ....G....... 216 267-3554
Cleveland (G-6124)

Roboworld Molded Products LLC ....G....... 513 720-6900
West Chester (G-19935)

Rubber-Tech Inc ....F....... 937 274-1114
Dayton (G-8640)

Saint-Gobain Prfmce Plas Corp ......C....... 330 798-6981
Akron (G-396)

Saint-Gobain Prfmce Plas Corp ......B....... 614 889-2220
Dublin (G-9137)

▲ Shreiner Sole Co Inc ....F....... 330 276-6135
Killbuck (G-11599)

◆ Soffseal Inc ....E....... 513 367-0028
Harrison (G-10804)

Taradon Rubber Co Inc ....E....... 330 896-3143
Akron (G-428)

▲ Tigerpoly Manufacturing Inc ....B....... 614 871-0045
Grove City (G-10601)

▲ Trelleborg Wheel Systems Ameri ..E....... 866 633-8473
Akron (G-444)

▲ United Feed Screws Ltd ....F....... 330 798-5532
Akron (G-456)

Universal Urethane Pdts Inc ....D....... 419 693-7400
Toledo (G-18760)

▲ V & M Star LP ....E....... 330 742-6300
Youngstown (G-21234)

▲ Vertex Inc ....E....... 330 628-6230
Mogadore (G-14387)

Woodlawn Rubber Co ....F....... 513 489-1718
Blue Ash (G-1898)

Yokohama Tire Corporation ....C....... 440 352-3321
Painesville (G-15945)

3069 Fabricated Rubber Prdts, NEC

Abeon Medical Corporation ....G....... 440 262-6000
Brecksville (G-2032)

Action Rubber Co Inc ....F....... 937 866-5975
Dayton (G-8134)

Aeroquip-Vickers Inc ....G....... 216 523-5000
Cleveland (G-4722)

American Pro-Mold Inc ....E....... 330 336-4111
Wadsworth (G-19394)

American Rubber Products Co ....G....... 440 461-0900
Solon (G-17258)

Ansell Healthcare Products LLC ......D....... 740 622-4311
Coshocton (G-7879)

Ansell Healthcare Products LLC ......G....... 740 295-5414
Coshocton (G-7880)

ARC Rubber Inc ....F....... 440 466-4555
Geneva (G-10343)

▲ Ashtabula Rubber Co ....A....... 440 992-2195
Ashtabula (G-794)

◆ B D G Wrap-Tite Inc ....A....... 440 349-5400
Solon (G-17263)

Bedell-Kraus Flexographic and ....E....... 330 688-4881
Stow (G-17735)

◆ Blair Rubber Company ....D....... 330 769-5583
Seville (G-17070)

Boomerang Rubber Inc ....E....... 937 693-4611
Botkins (G-1950)

◆ Brp Manufacturing Company ....E....... 800 858-0482
Lima (G-11998)

C & M Rubber Co Inc ....F....... 937 299-2782
Dayton (G-8203)

Canton OH Rubber Speclty Prods ....G....... 330 454-3847
Canton (G-2642)

▲ Cardinal Rubber Company Inc .....E....... 330 745-2191
Barberton (G-1113)

Censtar Coatings Inc ....G....... 330 723-8000
West Salem (G-20111)

Cep Holdings LLC ....G....... 330 665-2900
Fairlawn (G-9745)

▼ Chalfant Sew Fabricators Inc ....E....... 216 521-7922
Cleveland (G-5012)

Champion Manufacturing Inc ....G....... 419 253-7930
Marengo (G-12747)

Chardon Custom Polymers LLC ....F....... 440 285-2161
Chardon (G-3143)

▲ Chemionics Corporation ....E....... 330 733-8834
Tallmadge (G-18137)

Clark Rbr Plastic Intl Sls Inc ....D....... 440 953-9514
Mentor (G-13544)

Clearly Visible Mobile Wash ....G....... 440 543-9299
Chagrin Falls (G-3080)

Cleveland Rubber Products LLC ....G....... 440 564-7100
Newbury (G-15084)

Colonial Rubber Company ....G....... 330 296-2831
Ravenna (G-16523)

▲ Columbus Gasket Co Inc ....G....... 614 878-6041
Columbus (G-6953)

◆ Contitech Usa Inc ....F....... 330 664-7000
Fairlawn (G-9748)

Crushproof Tubing Co ....E....... 419 293-2111
Mc Comb (G-13337)

◆ Custom Rubber Corporation ....D....... 216 391-2928
Cleveland (G-5151)

Custom Stamp Makers Inc ....G....... 216 351-1470
Cleveland (G-5152)

Dacon Industries Co ....E....... 330 298-9491
Ravenna (G-16524)

Dandy Products Inc ....E....... 513 625-3000
Goshen (G-10414)

◆ Datwyler Sling Sltions USA Inc ....D....... 937 387-2800
Vandalia (G-19289)

◆ Deruijter Intl USA Inc ....F....... 419 678-3909
Coldwater (G-6556)

Die-Cut Products Co ....E....... 216 771-6994
Cleveland (G-5193)

▲ Ds Technologies Group Ltd ....G....... 419 841-5388
Toledo (G-18445)

▲ DTR Equipment Inc ....F....... 419 692-3000
Delphos (G-8907)

◆ Durable Corporation ....F....... 419 668-8138
Norwalk (G-15535)

Eagle Elastomer Inc ....E....... 330 923-7070
Peninsula (G-16037)

▲ Eaton-Aeroquip Llc ....C....... 216 523-5000
Cleveland (G-5254)

Eckel Industries Inc ....E....... 978 772-0480
West Chester (G-19999)

Econo Products Inc ....F....... 330 923-4101
Cuyahoga Falls (G-7989)

Enduro Rubber Company ....G....... 330 296-9603
Ravenna (G-16529)

▲ Enterprise / Ameriseal Inc ....G....... 937 284-3003
South Charleston (G-17425)

Farmed Materials Inc ....E....... 513 680-4046
Cincinnati (G-3740)

▲ Fenner Dunlop Port Clinton Inc ....C....... 419 635-2191
Port Clinton (G-16399)

◆ Firestone Polymers LLC ....D....... 330 379-7000
Akron (G-187)

▼ Flexsys America LP ....D....... 330 666-4111
Akron (G-190)

Foot Logic Inc ....G....... 330 699-0123
Uniontown (G-19084)

Formco Inc ....G....... 330 966-2111
Canton (G-2706)

Foxtronix Inc ....G....... 937 866-2112
Miamisburg (G-13810)

G Grafton Machine & Rubber ....F....... 330 297-1062
Ravenna (G-16530)

Garro Tread Corporation ....G....... 330 376-3125
Akron (G-198)

Gdc Inc ....F....... 574 533-3128
Wooster (G-20775)

◆ Gold Key Processing Inc ....C....... 440 632-0901
Middlefield (G-13937)

▲ Goldsmith & Eggleton LLC ....F....... 203 855-6000
Wadsworth (G-19408)

◆ Green Tokai Co Ltd ....A....... 937 833-5444
Brookville (G-2185)

▲ Guardian Manufacturing Co LLC ...E....... 419 933-2711
Willard (G-20395)

Hhi Company Inc ....G....... 330 455-3983
Canton (G-2727)

Hygenic Acquisition Co ....G....... 330 633-8460
Akron (G-228)

◆ Hygenic Corporation ....C....... 330 633-8460
Akron (G-229)

▼ Hyload Inc ....F....... 330 336-6604
Seville (G-17075)

Hytech Silicone Products Inc ....G....... 330 297-1888
Ravenna (G-16533)

▲ Ier Fujikura Inc ....C....... 330 425-7121
Macedonia (G-12458)

Innocor Foam Tech - Acp Inc ....F....... 419 647-4172
Spencerville (G-17460)

International Automotive ....F....... 330 279-6557
Holmesville (G-11108)

Jet Rubber Company ....G....... 330 325-1821
Rootstown (G-16723)

K F D Inc ....C....... 330 773-4300
Akron (G-246)

Karman Rubber Company ....E....... 330 864-2161
Akron (G-251)

Keener Rubber Company ....F....... 330 821-1880
Alliance (G-521)

Kent Sporting Goods Co Inc ....E....... 330 674-2233
Millersburg (G-14237)

▲ Killian Latex Inc ....C....... 330 644-6746
Akron (G-256)

Kiltex Corporation ....C....... 330 644-6746
Akron (G-257)

◆ Kn Rubber LLC ....C....... 419 739-4200
Wapakoneta (G-19494)

Koroseal Interior Products LLC ....G....... 330 668-7600
Fairlawn (G-9755)

Lake Erie Rubber Recycling LLC ....G....... 440 570-6027
Strongsville (G-17937)

Lanxess Corporation ....C....... 440 279-2367
Chardon (G-3164)

▲ Lauren International Ltd ....C....... 330 339-3373
New Philadelphia (G-14908)

▲ Lauren Manufacturing LLC ....B....... 330 339-3373
New Philadelphia (G-14909)

▲ Lexington Rubber Group Inc ....C....... 330 425-8472
Twinsburg (G-18973)

◆ Ludlow Composites Corporation ...C....... 419 332-5531
Fremont (G-10168)

Luxx Ultra-Tech Inc ....G....... 330 483-6051
Medina (G-13438)

Macdivitt Rubber Company LLC ....F....... 440 259-5937
Perry (G-16054)

Maine Rubber Preforms LLC ....G....... 216 210-2094
Middlefield (G-13952)

Mameco International Inc ....F....... 216 752-4400
Cleveland (G-5738)

Manufacturers Representatives ....G....... 513 467-6669
West Chester (G-20024)

▲ Maple City Rubber Company ....E....... 419 668-8261
Norwalk (G-15551)

Martin Industries Inc ....E....... 419 862-2694
Elmore (G-9364)

Martin Rubber Company ....F....... 330 336-6604
Seville (G-17078)

▲ Master Mfg Co Inc ....E....... 216 641-0500
Cleveland (G-5758)

May Lin Silicone Products Inc ....G....... 330 825-9019
Barberton (G-1129)

Meridian Industries Inc ....D....... 330 359-5447
Winesburg (G-20706)

Meridian Industries Inc ....G....... 330 673-1011
Kent (G-11488)

Merrico Inc ....G....... 419 525-2711
Mansfield (G-12646)

▲ Meteor Sealing Systems LLC ....C....... 330 343-9595
Dover (G-9001)

▲ Midwest Elastomers Inc ....D....... 419 738-8844
Wapakoneta (G-19498)

Midwestern Bag Co Inc ....E....... 419 241-3112
Toledo (G-18586)

Miles Rubber & Packing Company ....G....... 330 425-3888
Twinsburg (G-18988)

Mitchell Plastics Inc ....G....... 330 825-2461
Barberton (G-1131)

MPS Manufacturing Company LLC ....G....... 330 343-1435
New Philadelphia (G-14917)

Mullins Rubber Products Inc ....D....... 937 233-4211
Dayton (G-8514)

Myers Industries Inc ....C....... 330 336-6621
Wadsworth (G-19420)

◆ Myers Industries Inc ....G....... 330 253-5592
Akron (G-309)

Neff-Perkins Company ....C....... 440 632-1658
Middlefield (G-13975)

Newact Inc ....F....... 513 321-5177
Batavia (G-1213)

Newell Brands Inc ....G 330 733-1184
Kent (G-11496)

Niles Roll Service Inc ....F 330 544-0026
Niles (G-15172)

North Sails Toledo LLC ....F 419 726-2933
Toledo (G-18608)

Noster Rubber Company Inc ....F 419 299-3387
Van Buren (G-19240)

▲ Novatex North America Inc ....D 419 282-4264
Ashland (G-757)

Novex Inc ....G 330 335-2371
Wadsworth (G-19422)

Ohio Foam Corporation ....G 614 252-4877
Columbus (G-7421)

Ohio Foam Corporation ....G 419 563-0399
Bucyrus (G-2355)

Ohio Foam Corporation ....G 330 799-4553
Youngstown (G-21155)

Ohio Foam Corporation ....F 419 492-2151
New Washington (G-14963)

▲ Okamoto Sandusky Mfg LLC ....D 419 626-1633
Sandusky (G-16991)

◆ Omnova Solutions Inc ....C 216 682-7000
Beachwood (G-1287)

◆ Park-Ohio Holdings Corp ....F 440 947-2000
Cleveland (G-5966)

◆ Park-Ohio Industries Inc ....F 440 947-2000
Cleveland (G-5967)

◆ Park-Ohio Products Inc ....C 216 961-7200
Cleveland (G-5969)

Paullin Driveway Sealing ....G 419 289-2228
Ashland (G-763)

Perfect Products Company ....E 330 863-1466
Malvern (G-12548)

◆ Performance Additives ....G 330 365-9256
New Philadelphia (G-14922)

▲ Philpott Rubber LLC ....E 330 225-3344
Brunswick (G-2243)

Pinnacle Roller Co ....F 513 369-4830
Cincinnati (G-4239)

▲ Pioneer National Latex Inc ....D 419 289-3300
Ashland (G-766)

Plabell Rubber Products Corp ....F 419 691-5878
Toledo (G-18646)

Plan B Toys Ltd ....G 614 751-6605
Groveport (G-10642)

▲ Polymerics Inc ....E 330 434-6665
Cuyahoga Falls (G-8034)

Ppafco Inc ....G 614 488-7259
Columbus (G-7507)

Prcc Holdings Inc ....C 330 798-4790
Akron (G-346)

Precision Component & Mch Inc ....E 740 867-6366
Chesapeake (G-3189)

Precision Fab Products Inc ....G 937 526-5681
Versailles (G-19356)

▲ Preferred Compounding Corp ....C 330 798-4790
Copley (G-7852)

Premiere Medical Resources Inc ....E 330 923-5899
Cuyahoga Falls (G-8036)

Pritt Enterprises Inc ....F 330 453-2142
Canton (G-2823)

Profile Rubber Corporation ....F 330 239-1703
Wadsworth (G-19431)

Q Model Inc ....E 330 673-0473
Barberton (G-1144)

Qualiform Inc ....E 330 336-6777
Wadsworth (G-19432)

◆ R C A Rubber Company ....D 330 784-1291
Akron (G-361)

R C Musson Rubber Co ....E 330 773-7651
Akron (G-362)

◆ R T H Processing Inc ....D 419 692-3000
Delphos (G-8916)

Raydar Inc of Ohio ....E 330 334-6111
Wadsworth (G-19435)

▲ Remington Products Co ....C 330 335-1571
Wadsworth (G-19437)

◆ Republic Powdered Metals Inc ....D 330 225-3192
Medina (G-13467)

Reynolds Industries Inc ....E 330 889-9466
West Farmington (G-20075)

Richard L Gibson ....F 937 964-1521
Springfield (G-17638)

Robin Industries Inc ....C 330 359-5418
Winesburg (G-20707)

Robin Industries Inc ....C 330 695-9300
Fredericksburg (G-10092)

Robin Industries Inc ....G 216 267-3554
Cleveland (G-6124)

Robin Industries Inc ....E 330 893-3501
Berlin (G-1652)

◆ Roppe Corporation ....B 419 435-8546
Fostoria (G-9991)

Roppe Holding Company ....G 419 435-6601
Fostoria (G-9992)

▲ RPM International Inc ....D 330 273-5090
Medina (G-13471)

Rub-R-Road Inc ....G 330 678-7050
Kent (G-11521)

▲ Rubber Associates Inc ....G 330 745-2186
New Franklin (G-14831)

Rubber-Tech Inc ....F 937 274-1114
Dayton (G-8640)

▲ Safeguard Technology Inc ....E 330 995-5200
Streetsboro (G-17873)

▲ Salem-Republic Rubber Company ....E 330 938-2016
Sebring (G-17052)

▲ Scherba Industries Inc ....D 330 273-3200
Brunswick (G-2256)

▲ Shreiner Sole Co Inc ....F 330 276-6135
Killbuck (G-11599)

▲ Sml Inc ....G 330 668-6555
Akron (G-406)

▲ Soffseal Inc ....E 513 367-0028
Harrison (G-10804)

Soprema USA Inc ....E 330 334-0066
Wadsworth (G-19441)

Sorbothane Inc ....E 330 678-9444
Kent (G-11530)

Space-Links Inc ....E 330 788-2401
Youngstown (G-21206)

▲ Sparton Enterprises Inc ....E 330 745-6088
Norton (G-15521)

Spiralcool Company ....F 419 483-2510
Bellevue (G-1562)

Starpoint Extrusions LLC ....E 330 825-2373
Norton (G-15522)

◆ Sumiriko Ohio Inc ....C 419 358-2121
Bluffton (G-1916)

▲ Sur-Seal Corporation ....C 513 574-8500
Cincinnati (G-4485)

◆ Survitec Group (usa) Inc ....E 330 239-4331
Sharon Center (G-17111)

Tahoma Enterprises Inc ....D 330 745-9016
Barberton (G-1151)

▼ Tahoma Rubber & Plastics Inc ....G 330 745-9016
Barberton (G-1152)

Tallmadge Finishing Co Inc ....E 330 633-7466
Akron (G-426)

Taradon Rubber Co Inc ....F 330 896-3143
Akron (G-428)

Tarkett Inc ....E 440 708-9366
Chagrin Falls (G-3124)

▲ Tarkett Inc ....D 800 899-8916
Solon (G-17398)

▲ Textileather Corporation ....B 419 729-3731
Toledo (G-18721)

Tmac Machine Inc ....G 330 673-0621
Kent (G-11537)

▼ TMI Inc ....E 330 270-9780
Youngstown (G-21223)

Trexler Rubber Co Inc ....E 330 296-9677
Ravenna (G-16567)

Tristan Rubber Molding Inc ....E 330 499-4055
North Canton (G-15278)

Truflex Rubber Products Co ....C 740 967-9015
Johnstown (G-11409)

Ultimate Rb Inc ....F 419 692-3000
Delphos (G-8922)

▲ Universal Polymer & Rubber Ltd ......C 440 632-1691
Middlefield (G-14000)

Universal Urethane Pdts Inc ....D 419 693-7400
Toledo (G-18760)

University Plastic Surgery ....G 216 778-4450
Cleveland (G-6394)

US 261 Corp ....G 216 531-7143
Cleveland (G-6397)

Usui International Corporation ....E 513 448-0410
Cincinnati (G-4548)

Valley Rubber Mixing Inc ....F 330 434-4442
Akron (G-462)

▲ Vernay Manufacturing Inc ....E 937 767-7261
Yellow Springs (G-21000)

▲ Vertex Inc ....E 330 628-6230
Mogadore (G-14387)

Wayne County Rubber Inc ....E 330 264-5553
Wooster (G-20845)

West & Barker Inc ....E 330 652-9923
Niles (G-15189)

Woodbridge Group ....C 419 334-3666
Fremont (G-10195)

Woodlawn Rubber Co ....F 513 489-1718
Blue Ash (G-1898)

▲ Yokohama Inds Amricas Ohio Inc ....D 440 352-3321
Painesville (G-15944)

▲ Yusa Corporation ....A 740 335-0335
Washington Court Hou (G-19641)

3081 Plastic Unsupported Sheet & Film

▲ Advanced Polymer Coatings Ltd ....E 440 937-6218
Avon (G-982)

American Insulation Tech LLC ....F 513 733-4248
Milford (G-14120)

◆ Ampac Holdings LLC ....A 513 671-1777
Cincinnati (G-3397)

Automated Packg Systems Inc ....C 330 626-2313
Streetsboro (G-17842)

Automated Packg Systems Inc ....C 216 663-2000
Cleveland (G-4866)

Avery Dennison Corporation ....E 440 358-3466
Painesville (G-15855)

Avery Dennison Corporation ....D 440 358-3408
Painesville (G-15859)

▲ Berry Plastics Filmco Inc ....D 330 562-6111
Aurora (G-911)

Blako Industries Inc ....E 419 246-6172
Dunbridge (G-9168)

▲ Boltaron Inc ....D 740 498-5900
Newcomerstown (G-15109)

Buckeye Diamond Logistics Inc ....G 937 644-2194
Marysville (G-12934)

CCL Label Inc ....C 216 676-2703
Cleveland (G-4998)

CCL Label Inc ....E 440 878-7000
Brunswick (G-2215)

◆ Champion Win Co Cleveland LLC ......E 440 899-2562
Macedonia (G-12440)

Charter Nex Films - Delaware ....E 740 369-2770
Delaware (G-8832)

Charter Nex Holding Company ....E 740 369-2770
Delaware (G-8833)

Clarkwestern Dietrich Building ....G 330 372-5564
Warren (G-19535)

▼ Clarkwestern Dietrich Building ....G 513 870-1100
West Chester (G-19835)

Clear Packaging Films Inc ....G 513 860-9053
West Chester (G-19836)

Clondalkin Group ....G 440 324-2222
Elyria (G-9395)

▲ Clopay Corporation ....C 800 282-2260
Mason (G-12999)

Clopay Corporation ....G 440 542-9215
Solon (G-17278)

Clopay Corporation ....G 513 742-1984
Cincinnati (G-3589)

◆ Clopay Plastic Products Co Inc ....D 513 770-4800
Mason (G-13000)

▲ Command Plastic Corporation ....F 800 321-8001
Tallmadge (G-18139)

Cool Seal Usa LLC ....F 419 666-1111
Perrysburg (G-16079)

▲ Crown Plastics Co ....D 513 367-0238
Harrison (G-10775)

Dayton Molded Urethanes LLC ....D 937 279-9987
Dayton (G-8280)

◆ DJM Plastics Ltd ....F 419 424-5250
Findlay (G-9817)

Dow Chemical Company ....C 419 423-6500
Findlay (G-9818)

Dow Chemical Company ....F 937 254-1550
Dayton (G-8309)

E I Du Pont De Nemours & Co ....E 740 474-0220
Circleville (G-4627)

▲ Entrotech Inc ....F 614 946-7602
Columbus (G-7062)

▲ General Data Company Inc ....C 513 752-7978
Cincinnati (G-3304)

General Films Inc ....D 888 436-3456
Covington (G-7923)

▲ Graphic Art Systems Inc ....E 216 581-9050
Cleveland (G-5446)

Industry Products Co ....B 937 778-0585
Piqua (G-16279)

▲ IVEX Protective Packaging Inc ....E 937 498-9298
Sidney (G-17196)

◆ Jain America Foods Inc ....G 614 850-9400
Columbus (G-7222)

◆ Jain America Holdings Inc ....D 614 850-9400
Columbus (G-7223)

James McGuire .... G 614 483-9825
Columbus (G-7225)

Kapstone Container Corporation ...... C 330 562-6111
Aurora (G-928)

Klockner Pentaplast Amer Inc .... D 937 548-7272
Greenville (G-10508)

Koroseal Interior Products LLC .... C 330 668-7600
Fairlawn (G-9755)

Liqui-Box Corporation .... C 419 289-9696
Ashland (G-750)

◆ Liqui-Box Corporation .... D 614 888-9280
Columbus (G-7300)

◆ Ludlow Composites Corporation ..... C 419 332-5531
Fremont (G-10168)

▲ MAI-Weave LLC .... D 937 322-1698
Springfield (G-17600)

▲ Mar-Bal Inc .... D 440 543-7526
Chagrin Falls (G-3101)

Mar-Bal Inc .... D 440 543-7526
Chagrin Falls (G-3102)

▲ North Shore Strapping Inc .... E 216 661-5200
Brooklyn Heights (G-2144)

North Shore Strapping Inc .... D 216 661-5200
Cleveland (G-5900)

◆ Omnova Solutions Inc .... E 216 682-7000
Beachwood (G-1287)

Orbis Rpm LLC .... G 740 772-6355
Chillicothe (G-3255)

Orbis Rpm LLC .... F 419 355-8310
Fremont (G-10173)

▼ Packaging Materials Inc .... E 740 432-6337
Cambridge (G-2471)

Pexco Packaging Corp .... E 419 470-5935
Toledo (G-18642)

◆ Plastic Suppliers Inc .... E 614 471-9100
Columbus (G-7493)

Plastic Suppliers Inc .... D 614 475-8010
Columbus (G-7494)

Plastic Suppliers Inc .... E 614 475-8010
Columbus (G-7495)

Plastic Works Inc .... G 419 433-6576
Huron (G-11237)

PMC Acquisitions Inc .... E 419 429-0042
Findlay (G-9879)

Polyone Corporation .... D 937 548-1395
Greenville (G-10513)

Polyone Corporation .... C 800 727-4338
Greenville (G-10514)

Polyone Corporation .... E 937 548-2133
Greenville (G-10515)

Polyone Corporation .... C 419 399-4050
Paulding (G-16013)

◆ Polyone Corporation .... D 440 930-1000
Avon Lake (G-1047)

Premier Material Concepts LLC .... D 419 429-0042
Findlay (G-9880)

▲ Priority Custom Molding Inc .... F 937 431-8770
Beavercreek Township (G-1389)

▲ Professional Packaging Company .. E 440 238-8850
Strongsville (G-17954)

Profusion Industries LLC .... C 800 938-2858
Fairlawn (G-9758)

Profusion Industries LLC .... D 740 374-6400
Marietta (G-12821)

Putnam Plastics Inc .... G 937 866-6261
Dayton (G-8603)

Quality Poly Corp .... F 330 453-9559
Canton (G-2829)

Raven Industries Inc .... G 937 323-4625
Springfield (G-17634)

▲ Renegade Materials Corporation ... E 508 579-7888
Miamisburg (G-13854)

Ritrama Inc .... E 216 851-7208
Cleveland (G-6116)

Rotary Products Inc .... F 740 747-2623
Ashley (G-790)

Rotary Products Inc .... F 740 747-2623
Ashley (G-791)

▲ Scherba Industries Inc .... D 330 273-3200
Brunswick (G-2256)

Snyder Manufacturing Co Ltd .... G 330 343-4456
Dover (G-9017)

Specialty Films Inc .... E 614 471-9100
Columbus (G-7635)

▲ Summit Plastic Company .... D 330 633-3668
Akron (G-420)

Team Plastics Inc .... F 216 251-8270
Cleveland (G-6296)

▲ Tradex International Inc .... D 216 651-4788
Cleveland (G-6345)

Transcendia Inc .... C 740 929-5100
Hebron (G-10891)

Transcendia Inc .... D 440 638-2000
Strongsville (G-17978)

Tsp Inc .... E 513 732-8900
Batavia (G-1229)

United Converting Inc .... G 614 863-9972
Columbus (G-7719)

Valfilm LLC .... E 419 423-6500
Findlay (G-9904)

Vinyl Building Products LLC .... B 513 539-4444
Monroe (G-14418)

▲ Walton Plastics Inc .... E 440 786-7711
Bedford (G-1472)

Western Reserve Sleeve Inc .... E 440 238-8850
Strongsville (G-17983)

World Connections Corps .... E 419 363-2681
Rockford (G-16694)

3082 Plastic Unsupported Profile Shapes

ABC Inoac Exterior Systems LLC ...... C 419 334-8951
Fremont (G-10122)

▲ Advanced Composites Inc .... C 937 575-9800
Sidney (G-17165)

▲ Akron Polymer Products Inc .... E 330 628-5551
Akron (G-52)

▲ Alkon Corporation .... D 419 355-9111
Fremont (G-10124)

Alkon Corporation .... E 614 799-6650
Dublin (G-9039)

Bobbart Industries Inc .... E 419 350-5477
Sylvania (G-18101)

▲ Deceuninck North America LLC .... B 513 539-5466
Monroe (G-14399)

Dlhbowles Inc .... D 330 488-0716
East Canton (G-9191)

Dlhbowles Inc .... B 330 478-2503
Canton (G-2691)

▼ Duracote Corporation .... E 330 296-9600
Ravenna (G-16526)

Global Manufacturing Solutions .... F 937 236-8315
Dayton (G-8367)

Granger Plastic Company .... E 513 424-1955
Middletown (G-14043)

HP Manufacturing Company Inc .... D 216 361-6500
Cleveland (G-5530)

Inventive Extrusions Corp .... E 330 874-3000
Bolivar (G-1937)

Kentak Products Company .... D 330 386-3700
East Liverpool (G-9221)

▲ Kentak Products Company .... E 330 382-2000
East Liverpool (G-9222)

Kentak Products Company .... G 330 532-6211
East Palestine (G-9240)

▲ Machining Technologies Inc .... E 419 862-3110
Elmore (G-9363)

Meridian Industries Inc .... D 330 673-1011
Kent (G-11488)

New Image Plastics Mfg Co .... G 330 854-3010
Canal Fulton (G-2509)

Normandy Products Company .... D 440 632-5050
Middlefield (G-13976)

Pexco Packaging Corp .... E 419 470-5935
Toledo (G-18642)

Plasto-Tech Corporation .... F 440 323-6300
Elyria (G-9479)

Precision Fabrications Inc .... G 937 297-8606
Sunbury (G-18074)

Quality Poly Corp .... F 330 453-9559
Canton (G-2829)

Roach Wood Products & Plas Inc ..... G 740 532-4855
Ironton (G-11301)

Universal Plastics Inc .... E 440 942-7510
Mentor (G-13762)

Wurms Woodworking Company .... E 419 492-2184
New Washington (G-14966)

3083 Plastic Laminated Plate & Sheet

Advanced Drainage Systems Inc ...... D 330 264-4949
Wooster (G-20731)

Advanced Drainage Systems Inc ...... D 419 599-9565
Napoleon (G-14669)

Advanced Drainage Systems Inc ...... E 419 424-8324
Findlay (G-9788)

Advanced Elastomer Systems LP ...... D 330 336-7641
Wadsworth (G-19389)

Aetna Plastics Corp .... D 330 274-2855
Mantua (G-12706)

Applied Medical Technology Inc .... E 440 717-4000
Brecksville (G-2034)

Arthur Corporation .... D 419 433-7202
Huron (G-11216)

▲ Biothane Coated Webbing Corp .... E 440 327-0485
North Ridgeville (G-15361)

Blt Inc .... F 513 631-5050
Norwood (G-15571)

Bruewer Woodwork Mfg Co .... D 513 353-3505
Cleves (G-6507)

Bulk Molding Compounds Inc .... D 419 874-7941
Perrysburg (G-16071)

Cool Seal Usa LLC .... F 419 666-1111
Perrysburg (G-16079)

Counter Concepts Inc .... F 330 848-4848
Doylestown (G-9028)

Cuda Composites LLC .... G 937 499-0360
Dayton (G-8256)

Designer Cntemporary Laminates ..... G 440 946-8207
Willoughby (G-20473)

▼ Duracote Corporation .... E 330 296-9600
Ravenna (G-16526)

Durivage Pattern & Mfg Co .... E 419 836-8655
Williston (G-20420)

◆ Elster Perfection Corporation .... D 440 428-1171
Geneva (G-10346)

Fdi Cabinetry LLC .... G 513 353-4500
Cleves (G-6514)

Fiber Tech Industries Inc .... D 740 636-3232
Wshngtn CT Hs (G-20909)

▲ Fowler Products Inc .... F 419 683-4057
Crestline (G-7929)

Franklin Cabinet Company Inc .... E 937 743-9606
Franklin (G-10023)

General Electric Company .... D 740 623-5366
Coshocton (G-7893)

Great Lakes Textiles Inc .... E 440 201-1300
Bedford (G-1425)

◆ Hancor Inc .... B 614 658-0050
Hilliard (G-10950)

Hrh Door Corp .... D 440 593-5226
Conneaut (G-7809)

Idx Corporation .... C 937 401-3225
Dayton (G-8400)

Iko Production Inc .... E 937 746-4561
Franklin (G-10029)

Ilpea Industries Inc .... C 330 562-2916
Aurora (G-926)

International Laminating Corp .... E 937 254-8181
Dayton (G-8417)

◆ Interntnal Cnvrter Cldwell Inc .... C 740 732-5665
Caldwell (G-2428)

Laminate Shop .... F 740 749-3536
Waterford (G-19649)

McHenry Industries Inc .... E 330 799-8930
Youngstown (G-21142)

Meridian Industries Inc .... D 330 673-1011
Kent (G-11488)

◆ Meridienne International Inc .... G 330 274-8317
Mantua (G-12717)

Microsol Inc .... G 330 733-0086
Tallmadge (G-18154)

Monarch Engraving Inc .... E 440 638-1500
Strongsville (G-17942)

▲ Organized Living Inc .... E 513 489-9300
Cincinnati (G-4194)

Parker-Hannifin Corporation .... C 330 296-2871
Ravenna (G-16548)

Plaskolite Inc .... D 740 450-1109
Zanesville (G-21341)

Plaskolite LLC .... B 614 294-7294
Columbus (G-7490)

Plextrusions Inc .... G 330 668-2587
North Ridgeville (G-15394)

▲ Poly TEC East Inc .... G 330 799-7876
Youngstown (G-21172)

Polyone Corporation .... C 419 399-4050
Paulding (G-16013)

Quality Rubber Stamp Inc .... G 614 235-2700
Columbus (G-7536)

Raven Industries Inc .... G 937 323-4625
Springfield (G-17634)

Recto Molded Products Inc .... D 513 871-5544
Cincinnati (G-4334)

▲ Resinoid Engineering Corp .... D 847 673-1050
Hebron (G-10881)

◆ Rochling Glastic Composites LP .... C 216 486-0100
Cleveland (G-6125)

◆ Rowmark LLC .... D 419 425-8974
Findlay (G-9884)

Saint-Gobain Prfmce Plas Corp .... C 330 798-6981
Akron (G-396)

Schneller LLC ....D...... 330 673-1299
Kent (G-11523)
Shamrock Plastics Inc ....F...... 740 392-5555
Mount Vernon (G-14646)
Shurtape Technologies LLC ....B...... 440 937-7000
Avon (G-1011)
▲ **Snyder Manufacturing Inc** ....D...... 330 343-4456
Dover (G-9016)
Snyder Manufacturing Co Ltd ....G...... 330 343-4456
Dover (G-9017)
Somerset Galleries Inc ....G...... 614 443-0003
Columbus (G-7630)
Southern Cabinetry Inc ....E...... 740 245-5992
Bidwell (G-1679)
Specialty Adhesive Film Co ....E...... 513 353-1885
Cleves (G-6526)
Spring Grove Manufacturing ....F...... 513 542-0185
Cincinnati (G-4444)
Techniform Industries Inc ....E...... 419 332-8484
Fremont (G-10186)
Trim Systems Operating Corp ....C...... 614 289-5360
New Albany (G-14774)
Ultratech Polymers Inc ....F...... 330 945-9410
Cuyahoga Falls (G-8060)
V & A Process Inc ....F...... 440 288-8137
Lorain (G-12288)
Victory Store Fixtures Inc ....F...... 740 499-3494
La Rue (G-11623)
Wurms Woodworking Company ......E...... 419 492-2184
New Washington (G-14966)

3084 Plastic Pipe

ADS Ventures Inc ....G...... 614 658-0050
Hilliard (G-10922)
Advanced Drainage of Ohio Inc ....D...... 614 658-0050
Hilliard (G-10924)
Advanced Drainage Systems Inc ....E...... 740 852-9554
London (G-12198)
Advanced Drainage Systems Inc ....D...... 513 863-1384
Hamilton (G-10662)
Advanced Drainage Systems Inc ....D...... 330 264-4949
Wooster (G-20731)
▼ **Advanced Drainage Systems Inc** ..D...... 614 658-0050
Hilliard (G-10925)
Advanced Drainage Systems Inc ....E...... 419 599-9565
Napoleon (G-14669)
Advanced Drainage Systems Inc ....D...... 740 852-2980
London (G-12199)
Advanced Drainage Systems Inc ....E...... 419 424-8324
Findlay (G-9788)
Aetna Plastics Corp ....G...... 330 274-2855
Mantua (G-12706)
Baughman Tile Company ....D...... 800 837-3160
Paulding (G-16000)
Cantex Inc ....D...... 330 995-3665
Aurora (G-912)
Contech Engnered Solutions Inc ......A...... 513 645-7000
West Chester (G-19840)
Contech Engnered Solutions LLC ....D...... 513 645-7000
Middletown (G-14032)
◆ **Contech Engnered Solutions LLC** ....C...... 513 645-7000
West Chester (G-19841)
Drain Products LLC ....G...... 419 230-4549
Lakeview (G-11649)
Drainage Products Inc ....E...... 419 622-6951
Haviland (G-10838)
Dura-Line Corporation ....D...... 440 322-1000
Elyria (G-9407)
◆ **Elster Perfection Corporation** ......D...... 440 428-1171
Geneva (G-10346)
▲ **Fowler Products Inc** ....F...... 419 683-4057
Crestline (G-7929)
◆ **Hancor Holding Corporation** ....B...... 419 422-6521
Findlay (G-9836)
◆ **Hancor Inc** ....B...... 614 658-0050
Hilliard (G-10950)
Hancor Inc ....D...... 419 424-8222
Findlay (G-9838)
Hancor Inc ....D...... 419 424-8225
Findlay (G-9837)
Harrison Mch & Plastic Corp ....E...... 330 569-3128
Garrettsville (G-10323)
Nupco Inc ....G...... 419 629-2259
New Bremen (G-14791)
Plas-Tanks Industries Inc ....E...... 513 942-3800
Hamilton (G-10730)
Savko Plastic Pipe & Fittings ....F...... 614 885-8420
Columbus (G-7591)
Tolloti Pipe LLC ....F...... 330 364-6627
New Philadelphia (G-14935)

Tolloti Plastic Pipe Inc ....E...... 330 364-6627
New Philadelphia (G-14936)
Tolloti Plastic Pipe Inc ....G...... 740 922-6911
Uhrichsville (G-19062)
Utility Solutions Inc ....G...... 740 369-4300
Delaware (G-8892)

3085 Plastic Bottles

▲ **Al Root Company** ....C...... 330 723-4359
Medina (G-13364)
Al Root Company ....C...... 330 725-6677
Medina (G-13365)
Alpha Packaging Holdings Inc ....B...... 216 252-5595
Cleveland (G-4768)
▲ **Alpla Inc** ....F...... 419 991-9484
Lima (G-12114)
Amcor Rigid Plastics Usa LLC ....D...... 419 483-4343
Bellevue (G-1541)
Eco-Groupe Inc ....E...... 937 898-2603
Dayton (G-8318)
◆ **Encon Inc** ....C...... 937 898-2603
Dayton (G-8325)
▲ **GK Packaging Inc** ....D...... 614 873-3900
Plain City (G-16342)
Graham Packaging Company LP ....E...... 740 439-4242
Cambridge (G-2459)
Graham Packaging Company LP ....E...... 419 334-4197
Fremont (G-10155)
Graham Packaging Company LP ....E...... 513 874-1770
West Chester (G-20011)
Graham Packaging Pet Tech Inc ....C...... 419 334-4197
Fremont (G-10156)
Graham Packg Plastic Pdts Inc ......C...... 419 421-8037
Findlay (G-9833)
◆ **Kirtland Cpitl Partners III LP** ......G...... 440 585-9010
Willoughby Hills (G-20640)
▲ **Novatex North America Inc** ....D...... 419 282-4264
Ashland (G-757)
▲ **Phoenix Technologies Intl LLC** ....C...... 419 353-7738
Bowling Green (G-2007)
Plastipak Packaging Inc ....C...... 330 725-0205
Medina (G-13461)
Plastipak Packaging Inc ....B...... 937 596-6142
Jackson Center (G-11344)
Plastipak Packaging Inc ....C...... 740 928-4435
Hebron (G-10880)
Pure Water Global Inc ....E...... 419 737-2352
Pioneer (G-16242)
Quality-Service Products Inc ....F...... 614 447-9522
Columbus (G-7538)
Rexam PLC ....F...... 330 893-2451
Millersburg (G-14258)
Ring Container Tech LLC ....E...... 937 492-0961
Sidney (G-17216)
Silgan Plastics LLC ....C...... 419 523-3737
Ottawa (G-15808)
Southeastern Container Inc ....D...... 419 352-6300
Bowling Green (G-2016)

3086 Plastic Foam Prdts

A K Athletic Equipment Inc ....E...... 614 920-3069
Canal Winchester (G-2518)
ADS Ventures Inc ....G...... 614 658-0050
Hilliard (G-10922)
ADS Worldwide Inc ....G...... 614 658-0050
Hilliard (G-10923)
▼ **Advanced Drainage Systems Inc** ..D...... 614 658-0050
Hilliard (G-10925)
Amatech Inc ....E...... 614 252-2506
Columbus (G-6729)
American Corrugated Pdts Inc ....E...... 614 870-2000
Columbus (G-6735)
American Corrugated Pdts Inc ....G...... 800 248-6840
Columbus (G-6736)
American Foam Products Inc ....E...... 440 352-3434
Painesville (G-15850)
Aqua Lily Products LLC ....D...... 480 588-6731
Willoughby (G-20438)
Aqua Lily Products LLC ....F...... 951 246-9610
Willoughby (G-20439)
Archbold Container Corp ....C...... 800 446-2520
Archbold (G-664)
Arkay Industries Inc ....E...... 513 360-0390
Monroe (G-14392)
Arlington Rack & Packaging Co ......G...... 419 476-7700
Toledo (G-18355)
▼ **Armaly LLC** ....E...... 740 852-3621
London (G-12200)
Astro Shapes LLC ....C...... 330 755-1414
Struthers (G-17989)

Atlas Roofing Corporation ....C...... 937 746-9941
Franklin (G-10008)
Austin Foam Plastics Inc ....E...... 614 921-0824
Columbus (G-6789)
B B Bradley Company Inc ....D...... 440 354-2005
Painesville (G-15860)
B B Bradley Company Inc ....C...... 614 777-5600
Columbus (G-6796)
Bentley World-Packaging Ltd ....F...... 440 232-1100
Bedford (G-1407)
Contract Pckg Dist Specialists ....F...... 513 942-0300
West Chester (G-19993)
Cryovac Inc ....E...... 513 771-7770
West Chester (G-19849)
Custom Foam Products Inc ....E...... 937 295-2700
Fort Loramie (G-9928)
Dayton Polymeric Products Inc ......E...... 937 279-9987
Dayton (G-8282)
Dow Chemical Company ....C...... 740 533-4000
Ironton (G-11292)
Dow Chemical Company ....E...... 937 254-1550
Dayton (G-8309)
Energy Storage Technologies ....E...... 937 312-0114
Dayton (G-8326)
Extol of Ohio Inc ....E...... 419 668-2072
Norwalk (G-15538)
Fabricated Packaging Mtls Inc ....E...... 740 681-1750
Lancaster (G-11712)
Fabricated Packaging Mtls Inc ....F...... 740 654-3492
Lancaster (G-11713)
Foam Concepts & Design Inc ....E...... 513 860-5589
West Chester (G-19866)
Gdc Inc ....E...... 574 533-3128
Wooster (G-20775)
▲ **Greif Packaging LLC** ....D...... 740 549-6000
Delaware (G-8854)
▲ **Hfi LLC** ....B...... 614 491-0700
Canal Winchester (G-2525)
Hinkle Manufacturing Inc ....D...... 419 666-5550
Perrysburg (G-16107)
Hitti Enterprises Inc ....F...... 440 243-4100
Cleveland (G-5514)
ICP Adhesives and Sealants Inc ......G...... 330 753-4585
Norton (G-15513)
Interior Dnnage Spcialites Inc ....F...... 614 291-0900
Columbus (G-7203)
J P Industrial Products Inc ....E...... 330 424-3388
Lisbon (G-12126)
◆ **Jain America Foods Inc** ....G...... 614 850-9400
Columbus (G-7222)
◆ **Jain America Holdings Inc** ....D...... 614 850-9400
Columbus (G-7223)
Jason Incorporated ....D...... 419 668-4474
Milan (G-14113)
▲ **Johnsonite Inc** ....B...... 440 632-3441
Middlefield (G-13948)
M L B Molded Urethane Pdts LLC ....G...... 419 825-9140
Swanton (G-18086)
◆ **Myers Industries Inc** ....E...... 330 253-5592
Akron (G-309)
◆ **Ohio Decorative Products LLC** ......C...... 419 647-9033
Spencerville (G-17463)
Ohio Foam Corporation ....E...... 614 252-4877
Columbus (G-7421)
Owens Corning Sales LLC ....C...... 330 634-0460
Tallmadge (G-18162)
Pacemaker Plastic Company Inc ......E...... 740 498-4181
Newcomerstown (G-15121)
Packages Anything Anywhere ....G...... 937 298-1939
Dayton (G-8561)
Palpac Industries Inc ....F...... 419 523-3230
Ottawa (G-15803)
Paragon Custom Plastics Inc ....E...... 419 636-6060
Bryan (G-2318)
Plastic Fabrication Svcs Inc ....G...... 440 953-9990
Willoughby (G-20570)
Plastic Forming Company Inc ....E...... 330 830-5167
Massillon (G-13194)
Plastic Works Inc ....F...... 440 331-5575
Cleveland (G-6014)
Plymouth Foam Incorporated ....E...... 740 254-1188
Gnadenhutten (G-10410)
Polycel Incorporated ....E...... 614 252-2400
Columbus (G-7503)
Precision Foam Fabrication Inc ......F...... 330 270-2440
Youngstown (G-21175)
Prime Industries Inc ....E...... 440 288-3626
Lorain (G-12268)
Protective Packg Solutions LLC ......F...... 513 769-5777
Cincinnati (G-4299)

S
I
C

▲ S & A Industries Corporation ....D 330 733-6040
　Akron (G-390)
Sash Foam Works Inc ....G 419 522-4074
　Mansfield (G-12676)
▲ Scott Port-A-Fold Inc ....E 419 748-8880
　Napoleon (G-14698)
▲ Scottdel Cushion LLC ....E 419 825-0432
　Swanton (G-18089)
Skybox Packaging LLC ....D 419 525-7209
　Mansfield (G-12680)
▼ Smithers-Oasis Company ....F 330 945-5100
　Kent (G-11528)
Smithers-Oasis Company ....F 330 673-5831
　Kent (G-11529)
Solo Products Inc ....F 513 321-7884
　Cincinnati (G-4435)
Sonoco Prtective Solutions Inc ......D 419 420-0029
　Findlay (G-9892)
Special Design Products Inc ......E 614 272-6700
　Columbus (G-7634)
▲ Storopack Inc ....E 513 874-0314
　West Chester (G-20056)
Surface Dynamics Inc ....G 513 772-6635
　Cincinnati (G-4486)
Team Wendy LLC ....D 216 738-2518
　Cleveland (G-6297)
Technifab Inc ....E 440 934-8324
　Avon (G-1013)
Technifab Inc ....D 440 934-8324
　Avon (G-1014)
◆ Technifab Inc ....E 440 934-8324
　Avon (G-1015)
▲ Thermal Visions Inc ....G 740 587-4025
　Granville (G-10467)
Toy & Sport Trends Inc ....E 419 748-8880
　Napoleon (G-14700)
Trans Foam Inc ....G 330 630-9444
　Tallmadge (G-18173)
Truechoicepack Corp ....E 937 630-3832
　Dayton (G-8732)
Unique-Chardan Inc ....E 419 636-6900
　Bryan (G-2325)
US Foam Corporation ....G 513 528-9800
　Cincinnati (G-4545)
Zebco Industries Inc ....F 740 654-4510
　Lancaster (G-11763)
Zing Pac Inc ....G 440 248-7997
　Cleveland (G-6495)

3087 Custom Compounding Of Purchased Plastic Resins

▲ Accel Corporation ....D 440 934-7711
　Avon (G-981)
▲ Advanced Composites Inc ....C 937 575-9800
　Sidney (G-17165)
◆ Aurora Plastics Inc ....D 330 422-0700
　Streetsboro (G-17840)
▲ Chemionics Corporation ....E 330 733-8834
　Tallmadge (G-18137)
▲ Chromaflo Technologies Corp ....C 440 997-0081
　Ashtabula (G-795)
Chromaflo Technologies Corp .....C 513 733-5111
　Cincinnati (G-3532)
Deltech Polymers Corporation .....G 937 339-3150
　Troy (G-18817)
Dyneon LLC ....E 859 334-4500
　Cincinnati (G-3676)
Flex Technologies Inc ....E 330 897-6311
　Baltic (G-1071)
Freeman Manufacturing & Sup Co ...E 440 934-1902
　Avon (G-996)
General Color Investments Inc .....D 330 868-4161
　Minerva (G-14322)
Hexpol Compounding LLC ....C 440 834-4644
　Burton (G-2376)
▲ Hexpol Compounding LLC ....C 440 834-4644
　Burton (G-2377)
▲ Killian Latex Inc ....F 330 644-6746
　Akron (G-256)
McCann Plastics Inc ....D 330 499-1515
　Canton (G-2776)
▼ Nanosperse LLC ....G 937 296-5030
　Kettering (G-11583)
Omnova Solutions Inc ....C 330 628-6550
　Mogadore (G-14382)
Polymers By Design LLC ....G 937 361-7398
　Troy (G-18863)
Polyone Corporation ....F 573 468-6513
　North Baltimore (G-15196)

Polyone Corporation ....C 419 668-4844
　Norwalk (G-15559)
◆ Polyone Corporation ....D 440 930-1000
　Avon Lake (G-1047)
Polyone Corporation ....D 440 930-1000
　North Baltimore (G-15197)
▲ Radici Plastics Usa Inc ....D 330 336-7611
　Wadsworth (G-19434)
Rutland Plastic Tech Inc ....G 614 846-3055
　Columbus (G-7578)
Synthetic Rubber Technology ......G 330 494-2221
　Uniontown (G-19101)
Thermafab Alloy Inc ....E 216 861-0540
　Olmsted Falls (G-15677)
Tymex Plastics Inc ....E 216 429-8950
　Cleveland (G-6378)
Valspar Corporation ....C 330 830-6000
　Massillon (G-13209)

3088 Plastic Plumbing Fixtures

Add-A-Trap LLC ....G 330 750-0417
　Struthers (G-17988)
Bobbart Industries Inc ....E 419 350-5477
　Sylvania (G-18101)
Carolina Color Corporation ....E 740 363-6622
　Delaware (G-8828)
Certified Walk In Tubs ....F 614 436-4848
　Columbus (G-6921)
Cfrc Wtr & Enrgy Solutions Inc ....G 216 479-0290
　Cleveland (G-5011)
▲ Cincinnati Machines Inc ....A 513 536-2432
　Batavia (G-1172)
Closets By Mike ....G 740 607-2212
　Zanesville (G-21290)
◆ Crane Plumbing LLC ....F 419 522-4211
　Mansfield (G-12588)
Cultured Marble Inc ....G 330 549-2282
　North Lima (G-15314)
▲ Dbhl Inc ....F 216 267-7100
　Cleveland (G-5176)
▼ E L Mustee & Sons Inc ....D 216 267-3100
　Brookpark (G-2158)
◆ Hancor Inc ....B 614 658-0050
　Hilliard (G-10950)
◆ Lubrizol Advanced Mtls Inc .....F 216 447-5000
　Brecksville (G-2061)
Mansfield Plumbing Pdts LLC .....E 330 496-2301
　Big Prairie (G-1682)
◆ Mansfield Plumbing Pdts LLC ...A 419 938-5211
　Perrysville (G-16173)
Marble Arch Products Inc ....F 937 746-8388
　Franklin (G-10034)
Meese Inc ....D 440 998-1202
　Ashtabula (G-819)
Nibco Inc ....E 513 228-1426
　Lebanon (G-11819)
Pro-Kleen Industrial Svcs Inc ......E 740 689-1886
　Lancaster (G-11741)
Righter Plumbing ....G 614 604-7197
　Pataskala (G-15980)
Safeway Safety Step Llc ....F 513 942-7837
　West Chester (G-19941)
Tower Industries Ltd ....E 330 837-2216
　Massillon (G-13207)
▼ W T Inc ....F 419 224-6942
　Lima (G-12110)

3089 Plastic Prdts

1 888 U Pitch It ....G 440 796-9028
　Mentor (G-13503)
3M Company ....C 440 323-6161
　Elyria (G-9366)
6s Products LLC ....G 937 394-7440
　Anna (G-619)
A & A Discount Tire ....G 330 863-1936
　Carrollton (G-2950)
A Aabaco Plastics Inc ....F 216 663-9494
　Cleveland (G-4668)
A C Shutters Inc ....G 216 429-2424
　Cleveland (G-4669)
A Schulman Inc ....G 330 498-4840
　North Canton (G-15217)
AB Plastics Inc ....G 513 576-6333
　Milford (G-14119)
ABC Plastics Inc ....E 330 948-3322
　Lodi (G-12154)
Acco Brands USA LLC ....A 937 495-6323
　Kettering (G-11573)
Accurate Plastics LLC ....F 330 346-0048
　Kent (G-11422)

Accutech Plastic Molding Inc ......G 937 233-0017
　Dayton (G-8133)
Achill Island Composites LLC ......G 440 838-1746
　Brecksville (G-2033)
◆ Aco Polymer Products Inc ....E 440 285-7000
　Mentor (G-13508)
Acorn Products Inc ....B 614 222-4400
　Columbus (G-6689)
Acrylic Arts ....G 440 537-0300
　West Farmington (G-20073)
Advanced Drainage Systems Inc ...F 419 384-3140
　Pandora (G-15947)
Advanced Plastic Systems Inc .....E 614 759-6550
　Gahanna (G-10202)
Advanced Plastics Inc ....F 330 336-6681
　Wadsworth (G-19390)
Advantage Mold Inc ....G 419 691-5676
　Toledo (G-18322)
Aerocase Incorporated ....F 440 617-9294
　Westlake (G-20247)
Aetna Plastics Corp ....E 330 274-2855
　Mantua (G-12706)
Air Plastics Inc ....F 513 469-1074
　Blue Ash (G-1737)
▲ Akron Polymer Products Inc .....E 330 628-5551
　Akron (G-52)
▲ Akron Porcelain & Plastics Co ...C 330 745-2159
　Akron (G-53)
ALC Holdings Inc ....C 740 452-2500
　Zanesville (G-21268)
All Around Garage Door Inc ....C 440 759-5079
　North Ridgeville (G-15357)
All Srvice Plastic Molding Inc .....E 937 415-3674
　Fairborn (G-9614)
All Srvice Plastic Molding Inc .....G 937 890-0322
　Vandalia (G-19279)
▲ All Srvice Plastic Molding Inc ...D 937 890-0322
　Vandalia (G-19280)
▲ Alliance Equipment Company Inc ...F 330 821-2291
　Alliance (G-493)
Allied Custom Molded Products ....G 614 291-0629
　Columbus (G-6724)
▲ Allied Moulded Products Inc .....B 419 636-4217
　Bryan (G-2275)
Allied Plastic Co Inc ....G 419 389-1688
　Toledo (G-18330)
Alpha Packaging Holdings Inc .....B 216 252-5595
　Cleveland (G-4768)
◆ Alsco Metals Corporation ....E 740 983-2571
　Dennison (G-8942)
Alumo Extrusions & Mfr Company ...E 330 779-3333
　Youngstown (G-21021)
Amclo Group Inc ....C 216 791-8400
　Cleveland (G-4776)
Amcor Rigid Plastics Usa LLC .....E 419 592-1998
　Napoleon (G-14670)
AMD Plastics LLC ....E 216 289-4862
　Euclid (G-9565)
American Molded Plastics Inc .....F 330 872-3838
　Newton Falls (G-15128)
American Molding Company Inc ....G 330 620-6799
　Barberton (G-1097)
▲ American Plastic Tech Inc ....D 440 632-5203
　Middlefield (G-13914)
American Way Manufacturing Inc ...E 330 824-2353
　Warren (G-19522)
Ames Lock Specialties Inc ....G 419 474-2995
　Toledo (G-18348)
Ampacet Corporation ....E 513 247-5400
　Cincinnati (G-3400)
Amrex Inc ....G 330 678-7050
　Kent (G-11430)
AMS Global Ltd ....F 937 620-1036
　West Alexandria (G-19778)
◆ Anchor Hocking LLC ....A 740 681-6478
　Lancaster (G-11687)
▲ Angell-Demmel North Amer Corp ...D 937 461-5800
　Dayton (G-8158)
Apollo Plastics Inc ....F 440 951-7774
　Mentor (G-13525)
Arkay Industries Inc ....G 513 360-0390
　Monroe (G-14392)
Arkay Plastics Alabama Inc ....G 513 360-0390
　Monroe (G-14393)
▼ Armaly LLC ....E 740 852-3621
　London (G-12200)
Armeton US Co ....G 419 554-1866
　Norwalk (G-15526)
Arthur Corporation ....D 419 433-7202
　Huron (G-11216)

Company	City	Code	Phone
Artisan Mold Co Inc	Grafton (G-10419)	G	440 926-4511
Aspec Inc	Cincinnati (G-3420)	G	513 561-9922
Aspen Machine and Plastics	Versailles (G-19339)	G	937 526-4644
Associated Materials LLC	Cuyahoga Falls (G-7971)	B	330 929-1811
Associated Mtls Holdings LLC	Cuyahoga Falls (G-7972)	A	330 929-1811
▲ Associated Plastics Corp	Ada (G-5)	D	419 634-3910
◆ Astra Products of Ohio Ltd	Ravenna (G-16516)	D	330 296-0112
Astro Qcb Inc	Cincinnati (G-3422)	B	513 921-8811
▲ Atc Group Inc	Andover (G-612)	D	440 293-4064
Atc Nymold Corporation	Andover (G-614)	G	440 293-4064
Atc Nymold Corporation	Andover (G-615)	G	440 293-4064
Auld Company	Columbus (G-6786)	E	614 454-1010
Automation Plastics Corp	Aurora (G-908)	D	330 562-5148
Axion Strl Innovations LLC	Zanesville (G-21273)	F	740 452-2500
▲ B & B Molded Products Inc	Napoleon (G-14673)	E	419 592-8700
Bakelite N Sumitomo Amer Inc	Kenton (G-11545)	G	419 675-1282
Baker Plastics Inc	Youngstown (G-21031)	G	330 743-3142
▲ Baldie Import and Export Corp	Cincinnati (G-3435)	G	513 503-0953
◆ Ball Bounce and Sport Inc	Ashland (G-710)	B	419 289-9310
Bc Investment Corporation	Wooster (G-20747)	G	330 262-3070
Beach Mfg Plastic Molding Div	New Carlisle (G-14797)	D	937 882-6400
Bell Binders LLC	Toledo (G-18365)	F	419 242-3201
Bena Inc	Van Buren (G-19239)	G	419 299-3313
Bennett Plastics Inc	Cambridge (G-2447)	E	740 432-2209
Berlekamp Plastics Inc	Fremont (G-10130)	F	419 334-4481
Berman Industries Inc	Blue Ash (G-1749)	F	513 874-7477
▼ Berry Plas Technical Svcs Inc	Kent (G-11435)	F	330 995-3459
Berry Plastics Corporation	Streetsboro (G-17843)	F	330 896-6700
Bisson Custom Plastic	Urbana (G-19147)	G	937 653-4966
Bkhn Inc	Milford (G-14126)	D	513 831-4402
Black Diamnd Eco Solutions LLC	Eastlake (G-9259)	G	877 892-3370
Blackthorn LLC	Clayton (G-4657)	F	937 836-9296
Bloom Industries Inc	Warren (G-19529)	D	330 898-3878
Bloomdale Plastics Co	Bloomdale (G-1719)	E	419 454-5135
▲ Boardman Molded Products Inc	Youngstown (G-21032)	D	330 788-2401
Bourbon Plastics Inc	Cuyahoga Falls (G-7975)	E	574 342-0893
Bprex Closures LLC	Maumee (G-13232)	D	812 424-2904
▲ Bprex Halthcare Brookville Inc	Perrysburg (G-16069)	C	847 541-9700
Bprex Plastic Packaging Inc	Toledo (G-18379)	F	419 247-5000
Brighteye Innovations LLC	Akron (G-100)	F	800 573-0052
Brown Company of Findlay Ltd	Findlay (G-9803)	E	419 425-3002
Bta Enterprises Inc	Dayton (G-8201)	G	937 277-0881
Bu E Comp Inc	Bloomville (G-1725)	G	419 284-3381
Buckeye Design & Engr Svc LLC	Fort Recovery (G-9945)	G	419 375-4241
Buckeye Stamping Company	Columbus (G-6875)	D	614 445-0059
◆ Buckhorn Inc	Milford (G-14128)	E	513 831-4402
▼ Buckhorn Material Hdlg Group	Milford (G-14129)	D	513 831-4402
Budd Co Plastics Div	Van Wert (G-19247)	G	419 238-4332
Buecomp Inc	Bloomville (G-1726)	E	419 284-3840
Bugh Vinyl Products Inc	Canton (G-2631)	G	330 305-0978
Builder Tech Wholesale LLC	Toledo (G-18385)	G	419 535-7606
▲ C A Joseph Co	East Liverpool (G-9204)	G	330 385-6869
C B & S Spouting Inc	Miamisburg (G-13788)	G	937 866-1600
C-Mold Inc	Greenfield (G-10474)	E	937 981-7797
Cantex Inc	Aurora (G-912)	D	330 995-3665
Caraustar Industries Inc	Copley (G-7841)	E	330 665-7700
Cardinal Products Inc	North Royalton (G-15413)	G	440 237-8280
Carney Plastics Inc	Youngstown (G-21044)	G	330 746-8273
Carolina Color Corp Ohio	Delaware (G-8827)	E	740 363-6622
Carson Industries LLC	Napoleon (G-14675)	G	419 592-2309
▲ Case Industries Inc	Twinsburg (G-18908)	G	330 963-7717
▲ Cell-O-Core Co	Sharon Center (G-17104)	E	330 239-4370
◆ Centrex Plastics LLC	Findlay (G-9806)	C	419 423-1213
Century Container LLC	New Waterford (G-14969)	E	330 457-2367
Century Container LLC	Columbiana (G-6609)	G	330 457-2367
Century Mold Company Inc	Middletown (G-14027)	D	513 539-9283
Cep Holdings LLC	Fairlawn (G-9745)	G	330 665-2900
▲ Champion Opco LLC	Cincinnati (G-3521)	B	513 924-4858
Champion Opco LLC	Maumee (G-13234)	D	419 740-5193
Champion Window Co of Akron	Macedonia (G-12441)	E	330 474-3024
Chatelain Plastics Inc	Findlay (G-9807)	G	419 422-4323
Checkpoint Systems Inc	Canton (G-2652)	C	330 456-7776
Chemigon LLC	Akron (G-121)	G	330 592-1875
Chica Bands LLC	Cincinnati (G-3528)	G	513 871-4300
Chuck Meadors Plastics Co	Jefferson (G-11359)	F	440 813-4466
▲ CK Technologies LLC	Montpelier (G-14441)	C	419 485-1110
Claflin Company Inc	Hudson (G-11163)	G	330 650-0582
Clark Rbr Plastic Intl Sls Inc	Mentor (G-13544)	D	440 953-9514
Classic Laminations Inc	Cleveland (G-5042)	E	440 735-1333
Claycor Inc	Toledo (G-18399)	F	419 318-7290
Clear Fold Door Inc	Cleveland (G-5045)	G	440 735-1351
▲ Clearsonic Manufacturing Inc	Hudson (G-11164)	G	330 650-1420
Cleveland Plastic Fabricat	Euclid (G-9572)	F	216 797-7300
Cleveland Reclaim Inds Inc	Lorain (G-12238)	F	440 282-4917
Cleveland Specialty Pdts Inc	Cleveland (G-5079)	E	216 281-8300
◆ CM Paula Company	Mason (G-13002)	E	513 759-7473
◆ Cobra Plastics Inc	Macedonia (G-12442)	D	330 425-3669
▲ Comdess Company Inc	Seville (G-17073)	F	330 769-2094
◆ Comfort Line Ltd	Toledo (G-18407)	D	419 729-8520
Composite Advantage LLC	Dayton (G-8240)	E	937 723-9031
Composite Technologies Co LLC	Dayton (G-8241)	D	937 228-2880
Continental Coml Pdts LLC	Tiffin (G-18216)	D	419 447-5000
Continental Strl Plas Inc	Conneaut (G-7803)	C	440 945-4800
Continental Strl Plas Inc	Carey (G-2917)	B	419 396-1980
Continental Strl Plas Inc	Van Wert (G-19248)	B	419 238-4628
Continental Strl Plas Inc	North Baltimore (G-15192)	C	419 257-2231
Converge Group Inc	Ashland (G-726)	F	419 281-0000
Core Composites Cincinnati LLC	Batavia (G-1174)	A	513 724-6111
Core Molding Technologies Inc	Columbus (G-6983)	B	614 870-5000
Corvac Composites LLC	Greenfield (G-10475)	G	248 807-0969
Cosmo Corporation	Wilmot (G-20684)	D	330 359-5429
Country Molding	Newbury (G-15085)	G	440 564-5235
▲ CP Technologies Company	Blacklick (G-1693)	E	614 866-9200
Creative Extruded Products Inc	Vandalia (G-19286)	D	937 667-1618
Creative Plastics Intl	Jackson Center (G-11338)	F	937 596-6769
▲ Crg Plastics Inc	Dayton (G-8251)	F	937 298-2025
Crown Cork & Seal Usa Inc	Lancaster (G-11702)	D	740 681-3000
Ctc Plastics	Dayton (G-8255)	B	937 228-9184
Custom Molded Foam Products	Lorain (G-12241)	G	440 288-8951
▲ Custom Molded Products LLC	Wilmington (G-20662)	D	937 382-1070
Custom Pultrusions Inc	Aurora (G-915)	E	330 562-5201
Customized Vinyl Sales	East Palestine (G-9232)	G	330 518-3238
D & D Plastics Inc	Akron (G-139)	F	330 376-0668
D J Metro Mold & Die Inc	North Royalton (G-15416)	G	440 237-1130
D K Manufacturing	Lancaster (G-11704)	D	740 654-5566
D M Tool & Plastics Inc	Brookville (G-2180)	F	937 962-4140
D M Tool & Plastics Inc	Lewisburg (G-11932)	F	937 962-4140
D Martone Industries Inc	Middlefield (G-13928)	E	440 632-5800
Dadco Inc	Cincinnati (G-3636)	F	513 489-2244
Dadco Inc	Cincinnati (G-3635)	G	513 489-2244
Daddy Katz LLC	Moraine (G-14474)	G	937 296-0347
Dak Enterprises Inc	Marysville (G-12941)	F	740 828-3291
David Wolfe Design Inc	Akron (G-142)	F	330 633-6124
▲ Dawn Enterprises Inc	Cleveland (G-5172)	E	216 642-5506
▲ Dayton Superior Corporation	Miamisburg (G-13798)	C	937 866-0711
Deflecto LLC	Dover (G-8975)	E	330 602-0840
▲ Deimling/Jeliho Plastics Inc	Amelia (G-572)	D	513 752-6653
Design Molded Plastics Inc	Macedonia (G-12444)	C	330 963-4400
Detroit Technologies Inc	Toledo (G-18435)	G	248 647-0400
Diamond Plastics Inc	Dunkirk (G-9187)	D	419 759-3838
▲ Dimcogray Corporation	Centerville (G-3039)	D	937 433-7600
◆ Dimex LLC	Marietta (G-12778)	C	740 374-3100
▲ Dinesol Plastics Inc	Niles (G-15149)	C	330 544-7171
◆ DJM Plastics Ltd	Findlay (G-9817)	F	419 424-5250
DK Manfcturing Frazeysburg Inc	Frazeysburg (G-10072)	E	740 828-3291

DK Manufacturing Lancaster Inc..........D 740 654-5566
Lancaster *(G-11710)*

Dlhbowles Inc..........................E 330 479-7595
Canton *(G-2693)*

Dlhbowles Inc..........................D 330 488-0716
East Canton *(G-9191)*

Dlhbowles Inc..........................B 330 478-2503
Canton *(G-2691)*

Doglok Inc...............................G 440 223-1836
Perry *(G-16049)*

▲ Dometic Sanitation Corporation ......D 330 439-5550
Big Prairie *(G-1680)*

Don-Ell Corporation ....G 419 841-7114
Sylvania *(G-18104)*

Don-Ell Corporation ....E 419 841-7114
Sylvania *(G-18103)*

Doyle Manufacturing Inc ....D 419 865-2548
Holland *(G-11055)*

▲ Dreco Inc..............................C 440 327-6021
North Ridgeville *(G-15370)*

Drs Industries Inc......................E 419 861-0334
Holland *(G-11057)*

Drummond Corp ....F 440 834-9660
Middlefield *(G-13931)*

Dublin Plastics Inc ....G 216 641-5904
Cleveland *(G-5217)*

Duo-Corp.................................E 330 549-2149
North Lima *(G-15315)*

Dyna Vac Plastics Inc ....G 937 773-0092
Piqua *(G-16262)*

Dynamic Plastics Inc ....G 937 437-7261
New Paris *(G-14879)*

▲ Dynamic Polymers LLC.................G 614 575-1222
Columbus *(G-7041)*

Eaton Corporation ....C 330 274-0743
Aurora *(G-916)*

Eckel Industries Inc ....E 978 772-0480
West Chester *(G-19999)*

Eclipse Blind Systems Inc ....C 330 296-0112
Ravenna *(G-16528)*

▲ Edge Plastics Inc ....C 419 522-6696
Mansfield *(G-12598)*

Eger Products Inc ....E 513 735-1400
Batavia *(G-1179)*

Electr-Gnral Plas Corp Clumbus ....G 614 871-2915
Grove City *(G-10557)*

Electro-Cap International Inc ....F 937 456-6099
Eaton *(G-9305)*

Elkhart Plastics ....E 419 965-2103
Ohio City *(G-15661)*

Elliott Mfg Co ....F 937 833-4430
Brookville *(G-2182)*

Elra Industries Inc ....G 513 868-6228
Hamilton *(G-10688)*

◆ Elster Perfection Corporation ....D 440 428-1171
Geneva *(G-10346)*

Encon Inc ....G 937 890-6239
Vandalia *(G-19291)*

◆ Encon Inc.............................C 937 898-2603
Dayton *(G-8325)*

▲ Encore Industries Inc ....E 419 626-8000
Sandusky *(G-16961)*

Encore Plastics Corporation ....D 740 432-1652
Cambridge *(G-2456)*

▲ Encore Plastics Corporation ....F 419 626-8000
Sandusky *(G-16962)*

Endura Plastics Inc ....D 440 951-4466
Kirtland *(G-11613)*

Engineered Profiles LLC ....C 614 754-3700
Columbus *(G-7058)*

Enginred Plstic Components Inc ....C 513 228-0298
Lebanon *(G-11797)*

Enkon LLC ....F 937 898-2603
Dayton *(G-8327)*

◆ Enpac LLC.............................E 440 975-0070
Eastlake *(G-9268)*

▼ Enpress LLC...........................E 440 510-0108
Eastlake *(G-9269)*

Erie Lake Plastic Inc ....F 440 333-4880
Cleveland *(G-5295)*

▲ Ernie Green Industries Inc ....G 614 219-1423
Columbus *(G-7064)*

Evans Industries Inc ....F 330 453-1122
Canton *(G-2698)*

Everyware Global Inc ....D 740 687-2500
Lancaster *(G-11711)*

Extreme Custom Spools ....G 330 533-6936
Canfield *(G-2556)*

Extrudex Limited Partnership ....E 440 352-7101
Painesville *(G-15879)*

▲ F K Holding Inc.......................F 513 641-1400
Cincinnati *(G-3735)*

Fabohio Inc ....E 740 922-4233
Uhrichsville *(G-19050)*

Fabri-Form Company ....D 740 826-5000
New Concord *(G-14818)*

Fastformingcom LLC ....F 330 927-3277
Rittman *(G-16674)*

Fci Inc ....D 216 251-5200
Cleveland *(G-5329)*

▲ Ferriot Inc...........................C 330 786-3000
Akron *(G-185)*

▲ Few Atmtive GL Applcations Inc ......G 234 249-1880
Wooster *(G-20772)*

▲ Fibreboard Corporation ....C 419 248-8000
Toledo *(G-18470)*

First Choice Packaging Inc ....C 419 333-4100
Fremont *(G-10145)*

Flambeau Inc ....E 440 632-3752
Middlefield *(G-13935)*

Flambeau Inc ....D 440 632-1631
Middlefield *(G-13936)*

Flambeau Inc ....C 330 239-0202
Sharon Center *(G-17106)*

Flex Technologies Inc ....D 330 359-5415
Mount Eaton *(G-14555)*

Formtech Enterprises Inc ....G 330 688-2171
Stow *(G-17755)*

▼ Foundation Industries Inc ....D 330 564-1250
Akron *(G-193)*

Fountain Specialists Inc ....G 513 831-5717
Milford *(G-14142)*

▲ Fowler Products Inc...................F 419 683-4057
Crestline *(G-7929)*

▼ Fox Lite Inc..........................E 937 864-1966
Fairborn *(G-9622)*

Frantz Medical Development Ltd ....G 212 308-4860
Mentor *(G-13582)*

Fremont Plastic Products Inc ....G 419 332-6407
Fremont *(G-10150)*

▲ Fukuvi Usa Inc........................D 937 236-7288
Dayton *(G-8354)*

▲ Fypon Ltd.............................C 800 446-3040
Maumee *(G-13260)*

G & J Extrusions Inc ....G 330 753-0162
New Franklin *(G-14824)*

G I Plastek Inc ....G 440 230-1942
Westlake *(G-20270)*

▲ G M R Technology Inc ....G 440 992-6003
Ashtabula *(G-808)*

G S K Inc ....G 937 547-1611
Greenville *(G-10501)*

Gadjets Inc ....G 937 274-2111
Dayton *(G-8356)*

▼ Gateway Industrial Pdts Inc ....F 440 324-4112
Elyria *(G-9425)*

Genesis Plastic Tech LLC ....D 440 542-0722
Solon *(G-17296)*

▲ Gentek Building Products Inc ....F 800 548-4542
Cuyahoga Falls *(G-8003)*

▼ Ghp II LLC............................C 740 687-2500
Lancaster *(G-11719)*

Giesecke & Devrient Can ....G 330 425-1515
Twinsburg *(G-18948)*

Gilkey Window Company Inc ....G 513 769-9663
Cincinnati *(G-3824)*

▲ Gilkey Window Company Inc ....D 513 769-4527
Cincinnati *(G-3825)*

Global Plastic Tech Inc ....E 330 963-6830
Brecksville *(G-2053)*

Gorell Enterprises Inc ....B 724 465-1800
Streetsboro *(G-17855)*

Graham Packaging Co Europe LLC ....C 513 398-5000
Mason *(G-13032)*

Graham Packaging Company LP ....E 513 874-1770
West Chester *(G-20011)*

Graham Packaging Company LP ....E 419 334-4197
Fremont *(G-10155)*

Graham Packg Plastic Pdts Inc ....E 717 849-8500
Toledo *(G-18485)*

Great Lakes Window Inc ....A 419 666-5555
Walbridge *(G-19458)*

Greenlight Optics LLC ....E 513 247-9777
Loveland *(G-12354)*

Greenville Technology Inc ....G 937 642-6744
Marysville *(G-12946)*

▲ Greenville Technology Inc ....A 937 548-3217
Greenville *(G-10504)*

Greif Inc ....E 740 549-6000
Delaware *(G-8847)*

Greif Inc ....E 740 657-6500
Delaware *(G-8848)*

H & H Engineered Molded Pdts ....D 440 415-1814
Geneva *(G-10348)*

H P Manufacturing Co ....D 216 361-6500
Cleveland *(G-5469)*

▲ Hadlock Plastics LLC ....C 440 466-4876
Geneva *(G-10349)*

Hamilton Custom Molding Inc ....G 513 844-6643
Hamilton *(G-10702)*

Hancor Inc ....D 419 424-8225
Findlay *(G-9837)*

◆ Hancor Inc............................B 614 658-0050
Hilliard *(G-10950)*

Hang-It-All Curtain System LLC ....G 614 275-0954
Columbus *(G-7140)*

Hanlon Industries Inc ....F 216 261-7056
Cleveland *(G-5479)*

Harbor Industrial Corp ....F 440 599-8366
Conneaut *(G-7807)*

▲ Harmony Systems and Svc Inc ....D 937 778-1082
Piqua *(G-16270)*

Harrison Mch & Plastic Corp ....E 330 569-3128
Garrettsville *(G-10323)*

Hartville Plastics Inc ....D 330 877-9090
Hartville *(G-10824)*

Hathaway Stamp Co ....F 513 621-1052
Cincinnati *(G-3871)*

▼ Haviland Plastic Products Co ....E 419 622-3110
Haviland *(G-10841)*

Hendrickson International Corp ....D 740 929-5600
Hebron *(G-10870)*

Hfi Inc ....G 614 491-0700
Canal Winchester *(G-2527)*

Hl Lite Plastic Products ....G 614 235-9050
Columbus *(G-7154)*

Hl Tek Mold ....E 440 942-4090
Mentor *(G-13601)*

Hi-Tech Extrusions Ltd ....E 440 286-4000
Chardon *(G-3156)*

Holm Industries Inc ....D 330 562-2900
Aurora *(G-925)*

▲ Horsemens Pride Inc ....E 800 232-7950
Streetsboro *(G-17857)*

HP Manufacturing Company Inc ....D 216 361-6500
Cleveland *(G-5530)*

Hrh Door Corp ....D 440 593-5226
Conneaut *(G-7809)*

Hub Plastics Inc ....D 614 861-1791
Blacklick *(G-1698)*

Hudson Extrusions Inc ....G 330 653-6015
Hudson *(G-11180)*

Huhtamaki Inc ....B 937 987-3078
New Vienna *(G-14955)*

Hy-Tech Products ....F 440 537-1257
Elyria *(G-9430)*

Hycomp LLC ....D 440 234-2002
Cleveland *(G-5542)*

Hydrant Hat LLC ....G 440 224-1007
Kingsville *(G-11604)*

IAC Holmesville LLC ....F 330 279-4505
Holmesville *(G-11107)*

IAC Sidney LLC ....G 937 492-1225
Sidney *(G-17194)*

▲ ICO Products LLC ....C 419 867-3900
Holland *(G-11064)*

ICO Technology Inc ....G 330 666-3751
Fairlawn *(G-9754)*

Illinois Tool Works Inc ....G 937 332-2839
Troy *(G-18843)*

Illinois Tool Works Inc ....B 419 636-3161
Bryan *(G-2302)*

Illinois Tool Works Inc ....D 519 376-8886
Troy *(G-18844)*

Ilpea Industries Inc ....C 330 562-2916
Aurora *(G-926)*

▲ Impact Products LLC ....C 419 841-2891
Toledo *(G-18518)*

Imperial Plastics Inc ....D 330 927-5065
Rittman *(G-16675)*

Industrial Container Svcs LLC ....E 513 921-2056
Cincinnati *(G-3916)*

Industrial Farm Tank Inc ....E 937 843-2972
Lewistown *(G-11944)*

Inhance Technologies LLC ....F 614 846-6400
Columbus *(G-7187)*

Injection Molding Specialist ....G 440 639-7896
Painesville *(G-15890)*

Innovation Plastics LLC ....E 513 818-1771
Fostoria *(G-9980)*

Innovations In Plastic Inc..................G...... 216 541-6060
  Cleveland (G-5571)

Integra Enclosures Inc..................G...... 440 269-4966
  Willoughby (G-20510)

Integral Design Inc..................F...... 216 524-0555
  Cleveland (G-5574)

International Automotive..................B...... 419 332-1587
  Fremont (G-10159)

International Automotive..................A...... 419 433-5653
  Huron (G-11228)

International Supply Corp..................G...... 513 793-0393
  Cincinnati (G-3931)

◆ Interntnal Cnvrter Cldwell Inc..........C...... 740 732-5665
  Caldwell (G-2428)

Interntnal Plstic Cmpnents Inc..................F...... 330 744-0625
  Campbell (G-2490)

▼ Interpak Inc..................E...... 440 974-8999
  Mentor (G-13611)

Inventive Extrusions Corp..................E...... 330 874-3000
  Bolivar (G-1937)

▲ Iten Industries Inc..................C...... 440 997-6134
  Ashtabula (G-813)

J & B Rogers Inc..................G...... 937 669-2677
  Tipp City (G-18285)

J & M Construction LLP..................G...... 740 454-8986
  Hopewell (G-11119)

J & O Plastics Inc..................G...... 330 927-3169
  Rittman (G-16676)

J H Plastics..................G...... 419 937-2035
  Tiffin (G-18223)

J K Plastics Co..................G...... 440 632-1482
  Middlefield (G-13944)

J K Precast LLC..................G...... 740 335-2188
  Wshngtn CT Hs (G-20912)

Jack Gruber..................G...... 740 408-2718
  Cardington (G-2912)

Jaco Manufacturing Company..................D...... 440 234-4000
  Berea (G-1621)

Jaco Manufacturing Company..................F...... 440 234-4000
  Berea (G-1622)

▲ Janorport LLC..................E...... 330 564-0232
  Mogadore (G-14378)

Jeffrey Brandewie..................G...... 937 726-7765
  Fort Loramie (G-9933)

Jensar Manufacturing LLC..................G...... 419 727-8320
  Toledo (G-18533)

Jjc Products Inc..................G...... 330 666-4582
  Akron (G-240)

Johnston-Morehouse-Dickey Co..................G...... 614 866-0452
  Columbus (G-7242)

Johnston-Morehouse-Dickey Co..................G...... 330 405-6050
  Macedonia (G-12464)

Joneszylon Company LLC..................G...... 740 545-6341
  West Lafayette (G-20089)

Jos-Tech Inc..................E...... 330 678-3260
  Kent (G-11474)

▲ Joslyn Manufacturing Company..................E...... 330 467-8111
  Macedonia (G-12465)

JPS Technologies Inc..................G...... 513 984-6400
  Blue Ash (G-1820)

JPS Technologies Inc..................F...... 513 984-6400
  Blue Ash (G-1821)

Just Plastics Inc..................E...... 419 468-5506
  Galion (G-10277)

Ka Molded Products..................G...... 419 884-3375
  Mansfield (G-12631)

Kamco Industries..................G...... 419 551-9211
  West Unity (G-20131)

◆ Kamco Industries Inc..................B...... 419 924-5511
  West Unity (G-20132)

Kar-Del Plastics Inc..................G...... 419 289-9739
  Ashland (G-744)

Kasai North America Inc..................F...... 614 356-1494
  Dublin (G-9094)

Kathom Manufacturing Co Inc..................E...... 513 868-8890
  Hamilton (G-10715)

Ken Veney Industries LLC..................G...... 330 336-5825
  Wadsworth (G-19413)

▲ Kennedy Group Incorporated..................D...... 440 951-7660
  Willoughby (G-20520)

Kennick Mold & Die Inc..................G...... 216 631-3535
  Cleveland (G-5646)

Kittyhawk Molding Company Inc..................E...... 937 746-3663
  Carlisle (G-2932)

Klw Plastics Inc..................G...... 678 674-2990
  Monroe (G-14408)

Klw Plastics Inc..................G...... 513 539-2673
  Monroe (G-14409)

Koroseal Interior Products LLC..................C...... 330 668-7600
  Fairlawn (G-9755)

Kurz-Kasch Inc..................C...... 740 498-8343
  Newcomerstown (G-15117)

▲ Kurz-Kasch Inc..................C...... 740 498-8343
  Newcomerstown (G-15118)

▲ Kurzkasch Inc Wilm Div..................F...... 740 498-8345
  Newcomerstown (G-15119)

L C Liming & Sons Inc..................G...... 513 876-2555
  Felicity (G-9786)

Laird Plastics Inc..................F...... 614 272-0777
  Columbus (G-7280)

Lam Pro Inc..................F...... 216 426-0661
  Cleveland (G-5678)

◆ Lancaster Commercial Pdts LLC..................E...... 740 286-5081
  Columbus (G-7282)

◆ Landmark Plastic Corporation..................C...... 330 785-2200
  Akron (G-267)

Larmco Windows Inc..................E...... 216 502-2832
  Cleveland (G-5683)

▲ Laszeray Technology LLC..................D...... 440 582-8430
  North Royalton (G-15243)

Lee Plastic Company LLC..................F...... 937 456-5720
  Eaton (G-9316)

Lenz Inc..................E...... 937 277-9364
  Dayton (G-8456)

Lion Helmet Molding..................G...... 937 297-0760
  Kettering (G-11582)

Lion Mold & Machine Inc..................G...... 330 688-4248
  Stow (G-17770)

Liqui-Box Corporation..................C...... 419 209-9085
  Upper Sandusky (G-19129)

Liqui-Box Corporation..................G...... 419 289-9696
  Ashland (G-750)

◆ Liqui-Box Corporation..................D...... 614 888-9280
  Columbus (G-7300)

Louis G Freeman Co..................G...... 513 263-1720
  Batavia (G-1202)

Lpi Legacy Plastics LLC..................F...... 270 827-1318
  Cincinnati (G-4035)

M L C Technologies Inc..................G...... 513 874-7792
  Hamilton (G-10720)

▼ M T M Molded Products Company..................E...... 937 890-7461
  Dayton (G-8464)

M W Solutions LLC..................F...... 419 782-1611
  Defiance (G-8800)

Maca Plastics Inc..................F...... 937 544-8618
  Winchester (G-20695)

▲ Mag-Nif Inc..................D...... 440 946-4308
  Mentor (G-13643)

Magnum Molding Inc..................G...... 937 368-3040
  Conover (G-7824)

▲ Mahar Spar Industries Inc..................G...... 216 249-7143
  Cleveland (G-5731)

Majestic Plastics Inc..................G...... 937 593-9500
  Bellefontaine (G-1536)

◆ Malish Corporation..................C...... 440 951-5356
  Mentor (G-13644)

▲ Mar-Bal Inc..................D...... 440 543-7526
  Chagrin Falls (G-3101)

Mar-Bal Inc..................D...... 440 543-7526
  Chagrin Falls (G-3102)

Marcum Development LLC..................G...... 330 466-8231
  Wooster (G-20802)

Marshall Plastics Inc..................G...... 937 653-4740
  Urbana (G-19169)

Mastic Home Exteriors Inc..................C...... 937 497-7008
  Sidney (G-17199)

Matrix Cable and Mould..................G...... 513 832-2577
  Cincinnati (G-4067)

Matrix Plastics Co Inc..................G...... 330 666-7730
  Medina (G-13440)

Maverick Corporation..................E...... 513 469-9919
  Blue Ash (G-1835)

McCann Tool & Die Inc..................G...... 330 264-8820
  Wooster (G-20803)

MCS Midwest LLC..................F...... 513 217-0805
  Franklin (G-10035)

Mdi of Ohio Inc..................E...... 937 866-2345
  Miamisburg (G-13829)

Med Center Systems LLC..................G...... 513 942-6066
  West Chester (G-20026)

Meese Inc..................D...... 440 998-1202
  Ashtabula (G-819)

Mega Plastics Co..................G...... 330 527-2211
  Garrettsville (G-10330)

Meggitt (erlanger) LLC..................D...... 513 851-5550
  Cincinnati (G-4080)

▲ Mercury Plastics Inc..................C...... 440 632-5281
  Middlefield (G-13957)

Metro Recycling Company..................G...... 513 251-1800
  Cincinnati (G-4094)

Mexus Holdings Inc..................F...... 937 832-2307
  Englewood (G-9532)

▲ Miami Valley Plastics Inc..................E...... 937 273-3200
  Eldorado (G-9346)

Mibtach Enterprises Inc..................G...... 513 941-0387
  Cincinnati (G-4098)

Middlefield Plastics Inc..................E...... 440 834-4638
  Middlefield (G-13962)

Midwest Molding Inc..................E...... 614 873-1572
  Plain City (G-16349)

Midwest Plastic Systems Inc..................G...... 513 553-4380
  New Richmond (G-14943)

▲ Milacron LLC..................E...... 513 536-2000
  Batavia (G-1206)

Minotas Trophies & Awards..................G...... 440 720-1288
  Cleveland (G-5823)

Modern Builders Supply Inc..................C...... 330 729-2690
  Youngstown (G-21147)

Modern Builders Supply Inc..................F...... 419 526-0002
  Mansfield (G-12651)

▲ Modern Store Fixtures Inc..................F...... 330 427-6906
  Garrettsville (G-10331)

Molded Extruded..................G...... 216 475-5491
  Bedford Heights (G-1490)

▼ Molded Fiber Glass Companies..................A...... 440 997-5851
  Ashtabula (G-823)

Molded Fiber Glass Companies..................B...... 440 997-5851
  Ashtabula (G-824)

Molders World Inc..................F...... 513 469-6653
  Blue Ash (G-1843)

Molding Dynamics Inc..................F...... 440 786-8100
  Bedford (G-1444)

Moldmakers Inc..................F...... 419 673-0902
  Kenton (G-11559)

▲ Molten North America Corp..................C...... 419 425-2700
  Findlay (G-9865)

Mon-Say Corp..................G...... 419 720-0163
  Toledo (G-18590)

Montville Plastics & Rbr LLC..................D...... 440 548-3211
  Parkman (G-15952)

▲ Moore Industries Inc..................D...... 419 485-5572
  Montpelier (G-14449)

Mor-Lite Co Inc..................G...... 513 661-8587
  Cincinnati (G-4122)

Mos International Inc..................F...... 330 329-0905
  Stow (G-17776)

MTI Acquisition LLC..................E...... 740 929-2065
  Hebron (G-10876)

MTS Medication Tech Inc..................G...... 440 238-0840
  Strongsville (G-17943)

Mustang Aerial Services Inc..................G...... 740 373-9262
  Reno (G-16578)

Mvp Plastics Inc..................F...... 330 872-4451
  Middlefield (G-13970)

Mwe of Ohio..................G...... 419 777-7192
  Galion (G-10280)

Mye Automotive Inc..................G...... 330 253-5592
  Akron (G-308)

◆ Myers Industries Inc..................B...... 330 253-5592
  Akron (G-309)

Myers Industries Inc..................E...... 440 632-1006
  Middlefield (G-13971)

National Access Design LLC..................F...... 513 351-3400
  Cincinnati (G-4137)

National Fleet Svcs Ohio LLC..................F...... 440 930-5177
  Avon Lake (G-1041)

National Molded Products Inc..................E...... 440 365-3400
  Elyria (G-9466)

NBC Industries Inc..................F...... 216 651-9800
  Cleveland (G-5863)

Nebraska Industries Corp..................E...... 419 335-6010
  Wauseon (G-19691)

▲ Next Generation Films Inc..................C...... 419 884-8150
  Lexington (G-11951)

▲ Nifco America Corporation..................B...... 614 920-6800
  Canal Winchester (G-2532)

Nifco America Corporation..................G...... 614 836-3808
  Canal Winchester (G-2533)

Nifco America Corporation..................C...... 614 836-8691
  Groveport (G-10637)

▲ Nissen Chemitec America Inc..................C...... 740 852-3200
  London (G-12215)

Nitrojection..................G...... 440 834-8790
  Chesterland (G-3217)

North Canton Plastics Inc..................E...... 330 497-0071
  Canton (G-2792)

North Coast Custom Molding Inc..................F...... 419 905-6447
  Dunkirk (G-9188)

Northshore Mold Inc..................G...... 440 838-8212
  Cleveland (G-5915)

SIC

Northwest Molded Plastics ....G........ 419 459-4414
Edon *(G-9342)*

Norwesco Inc ....F 740 335-6236
Wshngtn CT Hs *(G-20918)*

Norwesco Inc ....E 740 654-6402
Lancaster *(G-11735)*

▲ Novatex North America Inc ....D 419 282-4264
Ashland *(G-757)*

O A R Vinyl Windows & Siding ....G........ 440 636-5573
Middlefield *(G-13978)*

Octsys Security Corp ....G........ 614 470-4510
Columbus *(G-7412)*

Oe Plastics LLC ....G........ 513 847-8101
Liberty Twp *(G-11977)*

Ohio Plastics Company ....G........ 740 828-3291
Newark *(G-15041)*

▲ Ohio Precision Molding Inc ....E 330 745-9393
Barberton *(G-1135)*

Olan Plastics Inc ....E 614 834-6526
Canal Winchester *(G-2535)*

Oldcastle Precast Inc ....E 419 592-2309
Napoleon *(G-14692)*

Omega Polymer Technologies Inc ....G........ 330 562-5201
Aurora *(G-939)*

Omega Pultrusions Incorporated ....C 330 562-5201
Aurora *(G-940)*

Opti Mold Inc ....G........ 440 248-9179
Solon *(G-17356)*

Orbis Corporation ....B 937 652-1361
Urbana *(G-19171)*

Orbis Corporation ....C 440 974-3857
Mentor *(G-13673)*

Orbit Manufacturing Inc ....E 513 732-6097
Batavia *(G-1215)*

Orzen Extruded Polymers ....G........ 330 298-9550
Ravenna *(G-16547)*

▲ Osburn Associates Inc ....F 740 385-5732
Logan *(G-12188)*

◆ Owens Corning ....A 419 248-8000
Toledo *(G-18625)*

◆ Owens Corning Sales LLC ....A 419 248-8000
Toledo *(G-18626)*

P & S Welding Co ....G........ 330 274-2850
Mantua *(G-12720)*

P C R Restorations Inc ....F 419 747-7957
Mansfield *(G-12666)*

P M Machine Inc ....F 440 942-6537
Willoughby *(G-20563)*

▲ P P E Inc ....D 440 322-8577
Elyria *(G-9473)*

P S Plastics Inc ....F 614 262-7070
Columbus *(G-7451)*

▲ Paarlo Plastics Inc ....D 330 494-3798
North Canton *(G-15256)*

Pace Mold & Machine LLC ....G........ 330 879-1777
Massillon *(G-13192)*

Pahuja Inc ....D 614 864-3989
Gahanna *(G-10225)*

Palpac Industries Inc ....F 419 523-3230
Ottawa *(G-15803)*

Paragon Plastics ....G........ 330 542-9825
New Middletown *(G-14878)*

Parker-Hannifin Corporation ....D 330 673-2700
Kent *(G-11499)*

▲ Pave Technology Co ....E 937 890-1592
Dayton *(G-8566)*

Pease Industies Inc ....B 513 870-3600
Fairfield *(G-9700)*

Pendaform Company ....E 740 826-5000
New Concord *(G-14819)*

Pendaform Company ....E 740 826-5000
New Concord *(G-14820)*

Performance Plastics Ltd ....E 513 321-8404
Cincinnati *(G-4227)*

Perimeter Technologies Inc ....F 513 322-5453
Cincinnati *(G-4229)*

Philpott Indus Plas Entps Ltd ....G........ 330 225-3344
Brunswick *(G-2242)*

Pilot Plastics Inc ....G........ 330 920-1718
Peninsula *(G-16041)*

▲ Pinnacle Industrial Entps Inc ......C 419 352-8688
Bowling Green *(G-2008)*

Pioneer Custom Molding Inc ....E 419 737-3252
Pioneer *(G-16237)*

Pioneer Plastics Corporation ....C 330 896-2356
Akron *(G-341)*

Plas-Tanks Industries Inc ....E 513 942-3800
Hamilton *(G-10730)*

Plas-TEC Corp ....D 419 272-2731
Edon *(G-9343)*

▲ Plastex Industries Inc ....E 419 531-0189
Toledo *(G-18647)*

Plastic Enterprises Inc ....E 440 324-3240
Elyria *(G-9478)*

▼ Plastic Extrusion Technologies ......E 440 632-5611
Middlefield *(G-13982)*

Plastic Forming Company Inc ....E 330 830-5167
Massillon *(G-13194)*

Plastic Materials Inc ....E 330 468-5706
Macedonia *(G-12472)*

Plastic Materials Inc ....E 330 468-0184
Macedonia *(G-12473)*

▲ Plastic Moldings Company Llc ....C 513 921-5040
Blue Ash *(G-1851)*

Plastic Products and Supply ....G........ 330 744-5076
Youngstown *(G-21171)*

Plastic Works Inc ....G........ 419 433-6576
Huron *(G-11237)*

Plasticards Inc ....G........ 330 896-5555
Uniontown *(G-19094)*

Plastics Converting Solutions ....G........ 330 722-2537
Medina *(G-13460)*

Plastics Group Inc ....G........ 630 325-1210
Fremont *(G-10175)*

Plastics Mentor LLC ....G........ 440 352-1357
Mentor *(G-13688)*

Plastikos Corporation ....E 513 732-0961
Batavia *(G-1216)*

Plastipak Packaging Inc ....C 740 928-4435
Hebron *(G-10880)*

Plastipak Packaging Inc ....C 937 596-5166
Jackson Center *(G-11345)*

Plate Engraving Corporation ....F 330 239-2155
Medina *(G-13462)*

PMC Smart Solutions LLC ....E 513 921-5040
Blue Ash *(G-1852)*

Podnar Plastics Inc ....E 330 673-2255
Kent *(G-11501)*

Podnar Plastics Inc ....E 330 673-2255
Kent *(G-11502)*

Polimeros Usa LLC ....F 216 591-0162
Warrensville Heights *(G-19634)*

▲ Polyfill LLC ....E 937 493-0041
Sidney *(G-17211)*

▼ Polymer & Steel Tech Inc ....E 440 510-0108
Eastlake *(G-9285)*

Polymer Tech & Svcs Inc ....E-...... 740 929-5500
Heath *(G-10851)*

Polyone Corporation ....D 937 548-1395
Greenville *(G-10513)*

Polyone Corporation ....E 419 399-4050
Paulding *(G-16013)*

Polystar Inc ....E 234 678-9020
Stow *(G-17790)*

Positool Technologies Inc ....G........ 330 220-4002
Brunswick *(G-2245)*

Possible Plastics Inc ....G........ 614 277-2100
Grove City *(G-10583)*

Pouchr LLC ....G........ 216 990-0535
Cleveland *(G-6024)*

Ppafco Inc ....F 614 488-7259
Columbus *(G-7507)*

Precision Custom Products Inc ....E 937 585-4011
De Graff *(G-8769)*

Precision Mfg & Assembly LLC ....D 937 252-3507
Dayton *(G-8586)*

Precision Polymers Inc ....G........ 614 322-9951
Reynoldsburg *(G-16599)*

◆ Precision Thrmplstc Componts ....D 419 227-4500
Lima *(G-12115)*

Preferred Solutions Inc ....F 216 642-1200
Seven Hills *(G-17062)*

Preform Technologies LLC ....G........ 419 720-0355
Swanton *(G-18088)*

▼ Premix Inc ....C 440 224-2181
North Kingsville *(G-15304)*

Pretium Packaging LLC ....C 419 943-3733
Leipsic *(G-11874)*

Priamus System Technology ....G........ 330 273-3393
Brunswick *(G-2247)*

Prime Engineered Plastics Corp ....F 330 452-5110
Canton *(G-2821)*

Printing 3d Parts Inc ....G........ 330 759-9099
Youngstown *(G-21178)*

▲ Priority Custom Molding Inc ....F 937 431-8770
Beavercreek Township *(G-1389)*

Professional Plastics Corp ....G........ 614 336-2498
Dublin *(G-9127)*

Profile Plastics Inc ....E 330 452-7000
Canton *(G-2827)*

Profusion Industries LLC ....G........ 800 938-2858
Fairlawn *(G-9758)*

Progressive Molding Tech ....G........ 330 220-7030
Medina *(G-13464)*

Progrssive Molding Bolivar Inc ....C 330 874-3000
Bolivar *(G-1944)*

Protec Industries Incorporated ....D 440 937-4142
Avon *(G-1004)*

▲ Proto Plastics Inc ....E 937 667-8416
Tipp City *(G-18295)*

Proto-Mold Products Co Inc ....E 937 778-1959
Piqua *(G-16308)*

▲ Ptc Enterprises Inc ....E 419 272-2524
Edon *(G-9344)*

▲ PVS Plastics Technology Corp ....E 937 233-4376
Huber Heights *(G-11151)*

Pyramid Plastics Inc ....E 216 641-5904
Cleveland *(G-6065)*

Quality Blow Molding Inc ....D 440 458-6550
Elyria *(G-9481)*

Quality Frp Fabrications ....G........ 440 942-9067
Willoughby *(G-20582)*

Quality Innovative Pdts LLC ....G........ 330 990-9888
Akron *(G-356)*

Qube Corporation ....F 440 543-2393
Chagrin Falls *(G-3115)*

Queen City Polymers Inc ....E 513 779-0990
West Chester *(G-19928)*

Queen City Polymers Inc ....E 937 236-2710
Dayton *(G-8607)*

R A M Plastics Co Inc ....E 330 549-3107
North Lima *(G-15322)*

R and S Technologies Inc ....F 419 483-3691
Bellevue *(G-1555)*

R Dunn Mold Inc ....E 937 773-3388
Piqua *(G-16309)*

R L Industries Inc ....D 513 874-2800
West Chester *(G-19929)*

▲ Radici Plastics Usa Inc ....D 330 336-7611
Wadsworth *(G-19434)*

▲ Rage Corporation ....G........ 614 771-4771
Hilliard *(G-10974)*

Randy Lewis Inc ....F 330 784-0456
Akron *(G-365)*

Ravago Americas LLC ....F 419 924-9090
West Unity *(G-20134)*

Raven Concealment Systems LLC ....G........ 440 508-9000
North Ridgeville *(G-15399)*

▲ Reactive Resin Products Co ....E 419 666-6119
Perrysburg *(G-16146)*

Recto Molded Products Inc ....C 513 871-5544
Cincinnati *(G-4334)*

Reebar Die Casting Inc ....F 419 878-7591
Waterville *(G-19665)*

Remram Recovery LLC ....F 740 667-0092
Tuppers Plains *(G-18886)*

Replex Mirror Company ....D 740 397-5535
Mount Vernon *(G-14641)*

Republic Rings Inc ....G........ 440 238-2622
Strongsville *(G-17957)*

Reserve Industries Inc ....E 440 871-2796
Bay Village *(G-1243)*

Resinoid Engineering Corp ....E 740 928-2220
Heath *(G-10854)*

▲ Resinoid Engineering Corp ....D 847 673-1050
Hebron *(G-10881)*

▼ Resource Mtl Hdlg & Recycl Inc .....E 440 834-0727
Middlefield *(G-13985)*

Retterbush Fiberglass Corp ....E 937 778-1936
Piqua *(G-16310)*

Revere Plas Systems Group LLC ....B 419 547-6918
Clyde *(G-6544)*

▲ Revere Plastics Systems LLC ....B 419 547-6918
Clyde *(G-6545)*

Rexles Inc ....G........ 419 732-8188
Port Clinton *(G-16411)*

▲ Rez-Tech Corporation ....E 330 673-4009
Kent *(G-11515)*

RG Mold ....G........ 419 868-9390
Holland *(G-11081)*

▲ Rhino Rubber LLC ....F 877 744-6603
North Canton *(G-15262)*

Riotech International Ltd ....G........ 513 779-0990
West Chester *(G-19933)*

Rlr Industries Inc ....G........ 440 951-9501
Mentor *(G-13716)*

▲ Ro-MAI Industries Inc ....E 330 425-9090
Twinsburg *(G-19009)*

◆ Rochling Glastic Composites LP .....C 216 486-0100
Cleveland *(G-6125)*

▲ Rohrer Corporation ... C ... 330 335-1541
Wadsworth (G-19438)

Roppe Holding Company ... G ... 419 435-6601
Fostoria (G-9992)

Ross Special Products Inc ... F ... 937 335-8406
Troy (G-18869)

Roswell Inc ... G ... 419 433-4709
Huron (G-11241)

Roto Solutions Inc ... D ... 330 279-2424
Holmesville (G-11110)

Rotosolutions Inc ... F ... 419 903-0800
Ashland (G-774)

◆ Rowmark LLC ... D ... 419 425-8974
Findlay (G-9884)

Rowmark LLC ... D ... 419 429-0042
Findlay (G-9885)

▲ Royal Plastics Inc ... C ... 440 352-1357
Mentor (G-13717)

RPM Consumer Holding Company ... G ... 330 273-5090
Medina (G-13470)

▲ RTS Companies (us) Inc ... E ... 440 275-3077
Austinburg (G-965)

Rubbermaid Incorporated ... C ... 330 733-7771
Mogadore (G-14383)

Rutland Plastic Tech Inc ... G ... 614 846-3055
Columbus (G-7578)

Ryan Development Corp ... E ... 937 587-2266
Peebles (G-16024)

S&T Automotive America LLC ... G ... 248 649-1020
Grove City (G-10591)

▲ S&V Industries Inc ... G ... 330 666-1986
Medina (G-13472)

Saint-Gobain Prfmce Plas Corp ... C ... 330 296-9948
Ravenna (G-16554)

▲ Saint-Gobain Prfmce Plas Corp ... C ... 440 836-6900
Solon (G-17375)

Sajar Plastics Inc ... D ... 440 632-5203
Middlefield (G-13986)

Samuel Strapping Systems Inc ... D ... 740 522-2500
Heath (G-10855)

Sanborn Plastics Corp ... D ... 440 286-4122
Chardon (G-3177)

Schmidt Progressive LLC ... E ... 513 934-2600
Lebanon (G-11837)

Scott Molders Incorporated ... D ... 330 673-5777
Kent (G-11524)

▲ Seagate Plastics Company ... E ... 419 878-5010
Waterville (G-19667)

▼ Sentry Protection LLC ... G ... 216 228-3200
Lakewood (G-11679)

Shelly Fisher ... D ... 419 522-6696
Mansfield (G-12677)

Shiloh Industries Inc ... F ... 937 236-5100
Dayton (G-8655)

Shirley KS Storage Trays LLC ... G ... 740 868-8140
Zanesville (G-21352)

Skribs Tool and Die Inc ... E ... 440 951-7774
Mentor (G-13724)

Soft-Lite LLC ... C ... 330 528-3400
Streetsboro (G-17876)

Solon ... G ... 440 498-1798
Solon (G-17383)

Solus Indus Innovations LLC ... G ... 440 356-1933
Rocky River (G-16711)

Solvay Spclty Polymers USA LLC ... E ... 740 373-9242
Marietta (G-12833)

Sonoco Products Company ... E ... 614 759-8470
Columbus (G-7631)

Sonoco Prtective Solutions Inc ... D ... 419 420-0029
Findlay (G-9892)

Southeastern Container Inc ... D ... 419 352-6300
Bowling Green (G-2016)

▲ Specialty Plas Fabrications ... G ... 513 856-9475
Hamilton (G-10740)

▲ Spectrum Plastics Corporation ... G ... 330 926-9766
Cuyahoga Falls (G-8048)

▲ Speedline Corporation ... G ... 440 914-1122
Solon (G-17386)

Springfield Plastics Inc ... F ... 937 322-6071
Springfield (G-17654)

Springseal Inc ... F ... 330 626-0673
Ravenna (G-16560)

Stanek E F and Assoc Inc ... C ... 216 341-7700
Macedonia (G-12490)

▲ Stanley Electric US Co Inc ... B ... 740 852-5200
London (G-12219)

Starks Plastics LLC ... G ... 513 541-4591
Cincinnati (G-4459)

State Tool and Die Inc ... G ... 216 267-6030
Cleveland (G-6241)

◆ Step2 Company LLC ... B ... 866 429-5200
Streetsboro (G-17879)

Step2 Company LLC ... B ... 419 938-6343
Perrysville (G-16176)

◆ Step2 Holdings LLC ... A ... 330 656-0440
Streetsboro (G-17880)

Sterilite Corporation ... B ... 330 830-2204
Massillon (G-13204)

Stewart Acquisition LLC ... E ... 800 376-4466
Kirtland (G-11617)

▲ Stewart Acquisition LLC ... E ... 330 963-0322
Twinsburg (G-19024)

Stopol Equipment Sales LLC ... G ... 440 499-0030
Brunswick (G-2258)

Stuchell Products LLC ... E ... 330 821-4299
Alliance (G-541)

◆ Style Crest Inc ... B ... 419 332-7369
Fremont (G-10184)

Style Crest Enterprises Inc ... D ... 419 355-8586
Fremont (G-10185)

Sugar Showcase ... G ... 330 792-9154
Youngstown (G-21213)

Sun State Plastics Inc ... E ... 330 494-5220
Canton (G-2863)

Superior Fibers Inc ... B ... 740 394-2491
Shawnee (G-17117)

▲ Systems Jay LLC Nanogate ... C ... 419 524-3778
Mansfield (G-12688)

T&M Plastics Co Inc ... G ... 216 651-7700
Cleveland (G-6291)

Tahoma Enterprises Inc ... D ... 330 745-9016
Barberton (G-1151)

▼ Tahoma Rubber & Plastics Inc ... D ... 330 745-9016
Barberton (G-1152)

Tapco Holdings Inc ... G ... 800 771-4486
Franklin (G-10057)

Team Amity Molds & Plastic ... D ... 937 667-7856
Tipp City (G-18303)

Tech II Inc ... B ... 937 969-7000
Urbana (G-19183)

Tech-Way Industries Inc ... D ... 937 746-1004
Franklin (G-10058)

Technimold Plus Inc ... G ... 937 492-4077
Port Jefferson (G-16421)

▲ Tema Isenmann Inc ... G ... 859 252-0613
Cincinnati (G-4500)

Tetra Mold & Tool Inc ... E ... 937 845-1651
New Carlisle (G-14814)

Tez Tool & Fabrication Inc ... G ... 440 323-2300
Elyria (G-9500)

Th Plastics Inc ... C ... 419 352-2770
Bowling Green (G-2017)

Th Plastics Inc ... F ... 419 425-5825
Findlay (G-9901)

Th Plastics Inc ... C ... 419 425-5825
Findlay (G-9902)

Thermoform Products LLC ... G ... 330 686-2050
Stow (G-17808)

Thermoplastic Accessories Corp ... E ... 614 771-4777
Hilliard (G-10987)

▲ Thogus Products Company ... D ... 440 933-8850
Avon Lake (G-1053)

▲ Tigerpoly Manufacturing Inc ... B ... 614 871-0045
Grove City (G-10601)

Timbertech Limited ... F ... 614 443-4891
Columbus (G-7694)

◆ Timbertech Limited ... C ... 937 655-8766
Wilmington (G-20679)

Tjar Innovations LLC ... F ... 937 347-1999
Xenia (G-20981)

Tmd Wek North LLC ... C ... 440 576-6940
Jefferson (G-11374)

▲ Todd Smith Products ... G ... 216 529-0525
Lakewood (G-11680)

Toledo Molding & Die Inc ... B ... 419 443-9031
Tiffin (G-18250)

◆ Toledo Molding & Die Inc ... D ... 419 470-3950
Toledo (G-18736)

Toledo Molding & Die Inc ... C ... 419 692-6022
Delphos (G-8919)

Toledo Molding & Die Inc ... C ... 419 476-0581
Toledo (G-18737)

Toledo Pro Fiberglass Inc ... G ... 419 241-9390
Toledo (G-18740)

▲ Tom Smith Industries Inc ... C ... 937 832-1555
Clayton (G-4663)

Tooling Tech Holdings LLC ... G ... 937 295-3672
Fort Loramie (G-9942)

Total Plastics Inc ... G ... 440 891-1140
Cleveland (G-6342)

Toth Mold & Die Inc ... F ... 440 232-8530
Cleveland (G-6343)

▲ Tradex International Inc ... D ... 216 651-4788
Cleveland (G-6345)

Treemen Industries Inc ... E ... 330 965-3777
Boardman (G-1925)

Trellborg Sling Prfiles US Inc ... E ... 330 995-9725
Aurora (G-951)

Tri-Craft Inc ... E ... 440 826-1050
Cleveland (G-6358)

Triaxis Machine & Tool LLC ... G ... 440 230-0303
North Royalton (G-15457)

▲ Trifecta Tool & Engrg LLC ... G ... 937 291-0933
Dayton (G-8724)

Trilogy Plastics Inc ... C ... 330 821-4700
Alliance (G-550)

Trilogy Plastics Inc ... E ... 440 893-5522
Chagrin Falls (G-3129)

▲ Trilogy Plastics Inc ... G ... 330 875-1789
Louisville (G-12331)

Trimold LLC ... B ... 740 474-7591
Circleville (G-4648)

Triple Diamond Plastics LLC ... D ... 419 533-0085
Liberty Center (G-11956)

Truechoicepack Corp ... E ... 937 630-3832
Dayton (G-8732)

Tsp Inc ... E ... 513 732-8900
Batavia (G-1229)

Turbo Machine & Tool Inc ... G ... 216 651-1940
Cleveland (G-6375)

U S Development Corp ... E ... 570 966-5990
Kent (G-11540)

U S Development Corp ... E ... 330 673-6900
Kent (G-11541)

Udecx LLC ... G ... 937 830-0374
Tipp City (G-18308)

Unique Plastics LLC ... G ... 419 352-0066
Bowling Green (G-2018)

Unique-Chardan Inc ... E ... 419 636-6900
Bryan (G-2325)

United Security Seals Inc ... E ... 614 443-7633
Columbus (G-7721)

▲ Universal Polymer & Rubber Ltd ... C ... 440 632-1691
Middlefield (G-14000)

Upl International Inc ... E ... 330 433-2860
North Canton (G-15280)

▲ US Coexcell Inc ... E ... 419 897-9110
Maumee (G-13306)

US Molding Machinery Co Inc ... E ... 440 918-1701
Willoughby (G-20625)

V & R Molded Products Inc ... F ... 419 752-4171
Willard (G-20403)

Valley Plastics Co Inc ... E ... 419 666-2349
Toledo (G-18764)

Vast Mold & Tool Co Inc ... G ... 440 942-7585
Mentor (G-13765)

Venture Packaging Inc ... B ... 419 465-2534
Monroeville (G-14430)

Venture Packaging Midwest Inc ... G ... 419 465-2534
Monroeville (G-14431)

◆ Venture Plas Middlefield LLC ... E ... 440 834-0704
Middlefield (G-14002)

▲ Venture Plastics Inc ... C ... 330 872-5774
Newton Falls (G-15141)

Vicas Manufacturing Co Inc ... E ... 513 791-7741
Cincinnati (G-4568)

Vinyl Design Corporation ... E ... 419 283-4009
Holland (G-11095)

Vinylmax Corporation ... D ... 800 847-3736
Hamilton (G-10754)

Vinylume Products Inc ... D ... 330 799-2000
Youngstown (G-21242)

Vision Color LLC ... G ... 419 924-9450
West Unity (G-20136)

Vlchek Plastics ... G ... 440 632-1631
Middlefield (G-14004)

Vts Co Ltd ... G ... 419 273-4010
Forest (G-9924)

▼ Warwick Products Company ... E ... 216 334-1200
Cleveland (G-6448)

Wayne Frame Products Inc ... G ... 419 726-7715
Toledo (G-18771)

Wayne Pak Ltd ... F ... 440 323-8744
Elyria (G-9509)

Wch Molding LLC ... E ... 740 335-6320
Wshngtn CT Hs (G-20928)

Weldon Plastics Corporation ... G ... 330 425-9660
Twinsburg (G-19039)

West & Barker Inc ... E ... 330 652-9923
Niles (G-15189)

West Extrusion LLC ....G...... 330 744-0625
Campbell (G-2494)
West Pharmaceutical Svcs Inc ....G...... 513 741-3004
Cincinnati (G-4586)
Westar Plastics Llc ....G...... 419 636-1333
Bryan (G-2327)
White Co David ....G...... 440 247-2920
Novelty (G-15584)
Win Cd Inc ....F...... 330 929-1999
Cuyahoga Falls (G-8062)
Windsor Mold Inc ....E...... 419 484-2400
Bellevue (G-1565)
▲ Windsor Mold USA Inc ....E...... 419 483-0653
Bellevue (G-1566)
Wisco Products Incorporated ....E...... 937 228-2101
Dayton (G-8763)
▲ World Class Plastics Inc ....D...... 937 843-3003
Russells Point (G-16759)
▲ World Resource Solutons Corp.......G...... 614 733-3737
Plain City (G-16364)
▲ Worthignton Products Inc ....G...... 330 452-7400
Canton (G-2903)
Wrr Creative Concepts LLC ....G...... 513 659-2284
West Chester (G-19974)
Wyatt Industries LLC ....G...... 330 954-1790
Streetsboro (G-17883)
Y City Recycling LLC ....D...... 740 452-2500
Zanesville (G-21364)
▲ Yachiyo of America Inc ....D...... 614 876-3220
Columbus (G-7781)
Yanfeng US Automotive ....B...... 419 636-4211
Bryan (G-2328)
Yngstn Plastic Fabrication ....G...... 330 743-6404
Petersburg (G-16179)
Ypf Corporation ....G...... 330 743-6404
Petersburg (G-16180)
▲ Zehrco-Giancola Composites Inc....C...... 440 994-6317
Ashtabula (G-847)
Zehrco-Giancola Composites Inc..........G...... 440 576-9941
Jefferson (G-11377)

31 LEATHER AND LEATHER PRODUCTS

3111 Leather Tanning & Finishing

▲ Old West Industries Inc ....G...... 513 889-0500
Hamilton (G-10728)
Premier Tanning & Nutrition ....G...... 419 342-6259
Shelby (G-17141)

3131 Boot & Shoe Cut Stock & Findings

Bean Counter LLC ....G...... 419 636-0705
Bryan (G-2282)
Bond Quarters Horses ....G...... 614 354-4028
Freeport (G-10117)
Buckeye Counters ....G...... 330 682-0902
Orrville (G-15732)
Classic Countertops LLC ....G...... 330 882-4220
Akron (G-125)
Counter Creation Plus L L C ....G...... 419 826-7449
Swanton (G-18083)
Counter Method Inc ....G...... 614 206-3192
Sunbury (G-18058)
Counter Rhythm Group ....G...... 513 379-6587
Cincinnati (G-3615)
Cruise Quarters ....G...... 614 777-6022
Hilliard (G-10944)
Cruise Quarters and Tours ....G...... 614 891-6089
Westerville (G-20206)
Dicks Counter D M ....G...... 440 322-3312
Elyria (G-9404)
Fountain Pk Inn Upper Sandusky.........G...... 419 209-1100
Upper Sandusky (G-19123)
French Quarter LLC ....G...... 614 781-0588
Columbus (G-7101)
Halvey Quarter Horses ....G...... 614 648-0483
Blacklick (G-1697)
Home Quarters North Canto ....G...... 330 806-5336
North Canton (G-15240)
Hudson Leather Ltd ....G...... 419 485-8531
Pioneer (G-16234)
J Liu of Upper Arlington Inc ....G...... 614 313-1268
Columbus (G-7218)
Latin Quarter ....G...... 513 271-5400
Cincinnati (G-4014)
McClellan Rand L ....G...... 614 462-4782
Columbus (G-7329)
Perfume Counter ....G...... 513 885-5989
Cincinnati (G-4228)

Quarter Bistro ....G...... 513 271-5400
Cincinnati (G-4311)
Quarter Mile Fabrication LLC..............G...... 440 298-1272
Thompson (G-18190)
Rancho Alegre Upper Arlin ....G...... 614 273-1305
Upper Arlington (G-19113)
Randy R Wilson ....G...... 740 454-4440
Zanesville (G-21348)
▲ Remington Products Co ....C...... 330 335-1571
Wadsworth (G-19437)
Selbys Upper Deck Company ....G...... 513 451-5981
Cincinnati (G-4401)
Sentinel Consumer Products Inc ....D...... 801 825-5671
Mentor (G-13720)
Upper Cut ....G...... 740 397-0330
Mount Vernon (G-14653)
Upper Echelon Bar LLC ....G...... 513 531-2814
Cincinnati (G-4544)
Upper Monument ....G...... 419 310-2387
Upper Sandusky (G-19143)
Upper Paw ....G...... 419 277-9000
Toledo (G-18762)
Upper Sandusky Senior Housing ....G...... 419 731-4104
Upper Sandusky (G-19144)
Upper Sarahsville LLC ....G...... 740 732-2071
Caldwell (G-2434)
Upperroom Action Ministries ....G...... 330 848-9246
Akron (G-459)
Whits Frozen Custard of Upper ....G...... 614 230-2213
Columbus (G-7762)
Yabos Tacos ....G...... 614 824-2485
Columbus (G-7780)

3142 House Slippers

Gold Toe Moretz Holdings Corp ....G...... 740 948-0004
Jeffersonville (G-11380)
▲ Principle Business Entps Inc ....C...... 419 352-1551
Bowling Green (G-2009)

3143 Men's Footwear, Exc Athletic

▲ Acor Orthopaedic Inc ....D...... 216 662-4500
Cleveland (G-4695)
Georgia Boot LLC ....G...... 740 753-1951
Nelsonville (G-14734)
Red Wing Shoe Company Inc ....G...... 419 531-1948
Toledo (G-18673)
▲ RG Barry Corporation ....G...... 614 864-6400
Pickerington (G-16203)
▲ Rocky Brands Inc ....B...... 740 753-1951
Nelsonville (G-14736)
Rocky Brands Inc ....D...... 740 753-1951
Nelsonville (G-14737)
Rocky Brands Inc ....A...... 740 753-9100
Nelsonville (G-14738)

3144 Women's Footwear, Exc Athletic

▲ Acor Orthopaedic Inc ....D...... 216 662-4500
Cleveland (G-4695)
Georgia Boot LLC ....D...... 740 753-1951
Nelsonville (G-14734)
▲ RG Barry Corporation ....C...... 614 864-6400
Pickerington (G-16203)
▲ Rocky Brands Inc ....B...... 740 753-1951
Nelsonville (G-14736)

3149 Footwear, NEC

NTS Enterprises Ltd ....G...... 513 531-1166
Cincinnati (G-4167)

3151 Leather Gloves & Mittens

▲ Totes Isotoner Corporation ....F...... 513 682-8200
West Chester (G-20059)
▲ Totes Isotoner Holdings Corp..........C...... 513 682-8200
West Chester (G-20060)

3161 Luggage

Buckeye Stamping Company ....D...... 614 445-0059
Columbus (G-6875)
Cleveland Canvas Goods Mfg Co..........D...... 216 361-4567
Cleveland (G-5050)
Clipper Products Inc ....G...... 513 688-7300
Cincinnati (G-3295)
Eagle Creek Inc ....D...... 513 385-4442
Cincinnati (G-3682)
Hawthorne Caravan & Assoc LLC.........F...... 440 366-9065
Elyria (G-9428)
Kam Manufacturing Inc ....C...... 419 238-6037
Van Wert (G-19261)

L M Engineering Inc ....E...... 330 270-2400
Youngstown (G-21130)
Plastic Forming Company Inc ....E...... 330 830-5167
Massillon (G-13194)
Professional Case Inc ....F...... 513 682-2520
West Chester (G-20041)
Professional Image Apparel Inc ....F...... 513 984-1111
Cincinnati (G-4295)
▲ Tia Marie & Company ....G...... 513 521-8694
Cincinnati (G-4509)
Travelers Custom Case Inc ....F...... 216 621-8447
Cleveland (G-6351)
▲ UNI Corp ....E...... 330 489-6500
Canton (G-2883)
Whitman Corporation ....G...... 513 541-3223
Okeana (G-15667)

3171 Handbags & Purses

Coach Inc ....F...... 330 491-8658
Canton (G-2661)
Coach Inc ....F...... 513 539-8087
Monroe (G-14398)
Coach Inc ....F...... 614 885-6184
Columbus (G-6644)
Coach Inc ....G...... 419 471-9033
Toledo (G-18403)
Coach Inc ....F...... 440 871-0103
Westlake (G-20262)
Gro2 Bags & Accessories LLC ....G...... 740 622-0928
Coshocton (G-7894)
▲ Hugo Bosca Company Inc ....G...... 937 323-5523
Springfield (G-17578)
Judith Leiber LLC ....E...... 614 449-4217
Columbus (G-7248)
Ravenworks Deer Skin ....G...... 937 354-5151
Mount Victory (G-14658)

3172 Personal Leather Goods

Bison Leather Co ....G...... 419 517-1737
Toledo (G-18369)
Down Home ....G...... 740 393-1186
Mount Vernon (G-14620)
Ed Thomas ....G...... 937 325-4300
Springfield (G-17551)
Global Payments Inc ....G...... 440 356-0325
Cleveland (G-5433)
Hamilton Manufacturing Corp ....E...... 419 867-4858
Holland (G-11063)
▲ Hugo Bosca Company Inc ....G...... 937 323-5523
Springfield (G-17578)
Ravenworks Deer Skin ....G...... 937 354-5151
Mount Victory (G-14658)
Williams Leather Products Inc ....G...... 740 223-1604
Marion (G-12914)

3199 Leather Goods, NEC

AM Retail Group Inc ....G...... 513 539-7837
Monroe (G-14391)
Berlin Custom Leather Ltd ....G...... 330 674-3768
Millersburg (G-14200)
Brighton Collectibles LLC ....E...... 614 418-7561
Columbus (G-6860)
Charm Harness and Boot Ltd ....F...... 330 893-0402
Charm (G-3183)
Cornerstone Brands Inc ....G...... 866 668-5962
West Chester (G-19844)
Cromwell Aleene ....G...... 937 547-2281
Greenville (G-10496)
Diy Holster LLC ....G...... 419 921-2168
Elyria (G-9405)
Dnd Products Inc ....G...... 440 286-7275
Chardon (G-3150)
Dog Depot ....G...... 513 771-9274
Cincinnati (G-3661)
Dpi Inc ....G...... 419 273-1400
Forest (G-9919)
Dwayne Hall ....G...... 740 685-5270
Senecaville (G-17058)
Ervin Yoder ....G...... 330 359-5862
Mount Hope (G-14570)
Featherweight Turf Inc ....G...... 920 452-4861
Wshngtn CT Hs (G-20908)
▲ Hamilton Animal Products LLC ....E...... 937 293-9994
Moraine (G-14492)
▲ Holmes Wheel Shop Inc ....E...... 330 279-2891
Holmesville (G-11106)
In Good Hlth & Animal Wellness ....G...... 330 908-1234
Northfield (G-15467)
LLC Bowman Leather ....G...... 330 893-1954
Millersburg (G-14242)

Lockbourne AG Center Inc ....G...... 614 491-0635
　Lockbourne (G-12148)
Maysville Harness Shop Ltd ....G...... 330 695-9977
　Apple Creek (G-644)
Rantek Products LLC ....G...... 419 485-2421
　Montpelier (G-14451)
Straight Razor Designes ....G...... 330 598-1414
　Medina (G-13484)
◆ Tarahill Inc ....E...... 706 864-0808
　Columbus (G-7676)
▼ Trd Leathers ....G...... 216 631-6233
　Cleveland (G-6352)
Whitman Corporation ....G...... 513 541-3223
　Okeana (G-15667)
Yoders Harness Shop ....G...... 440 632-1505
　Middlefield (G-14009)

32 STONE, CLAY, GLASS, AND CONCRETE PRODUCTS

3211 Flat Glass

3-G Incorporated ....G...... 513 921-4515
　Cincinnati (G-3323)
▲ Addis Glass Fabricating Inc ....F...... 513 860-3340
　West Chester (G-19798)
AGC Flat Glass North Amer Inc ....G...... 937 292-7784
　Bellefontaine (G-1516)
AGC Flat Glass North Amer Inc ....G...... 937 599-3131
　Bellefontaine (G-1517)
◆ Anchor Hocking Corporation ....D...... 740 681-6461
　Lancaster (G-11689)
Catalina Tempering - Ohio Inc ....F...... 740 892-2324
　Utica (G-19193)
▲ Continental GL Sls & Inv Group .....B...... 614 679-1201
　Powell (G-16469)
Custom GL Sltons Millbury Corp ....C...... 419 855-7706
　Millbury (G-14183)
Dela-Glassware Ltd LLC ....G...... 740 369-6737
　Delaware (G-8835)
Glass Fabricators Inc ....G...... 216 529-1919
　Lakewood (G-11665)
▲ Glasstech Inc ....C...... 419 661-9500
　Perrysburg (G-16103)
Guardian Industries Corp ....E...... 614 431-6309
　Worthington (G-20868)
Imaging Sciences LLC ....G...... 440 975-9640
　Willoughby (G-20509)
Knight Industries Corp ....E...... 419 478-8550
　Toledo (G-18547)
Machined Glass Specialist Inc ....F...... 937 743-6166
　Springboro (G-17489)
Mentor Glass Supplies and Repr .....G...... 440 255-9444
　Mentor (G-13651)
◆ Pilkington Holdings Inc ....B...... 419 247-3731
　Toledo (G-18643)
Pilkington North America Inc ....C...... 800 547-9280
　Northwood (G-15488)
Pilkington North America Inc ....B...... 419 247-3211
　Rossford (G-16745)
Pilkington North America Inc ....C...... 419 247-3731
　Urbancrest (G-19190)
◆ Pilkington North America Inc ....B...... 419 247-4955
　Toledo (G-18644)
Poma GL Specialty Windows Inc ......G...... 330 965-1000
　Boardman (G-1923)
PPG Industries Inc ....E...... 419 683-2400
　Crestline (G-7935)
S R Door Inc ....D...... 740 927-3558
　Hebron (G-10883)
Schodorf Truck Body & Eqp Co ....E...... 614 228-6793
　Columbus (G-7596)
Sonalysts Inc ....E...... 937 429-9711
　Beavercreek (G-1362)
Taylor Products Inc ....E...... 419 263-2313
　Payne (G-16018)
Therm-All Inc ....E...... 440 779-9494
　North Olmsted (G-15348)
Trulite GL Alum Solutions LLC ....D...... 740 929-2443
　Hebron (G-10892)
Vinylume Products Inc ....D...... 330 799-2000
　Youngstown (G-21242)
Wt Acquisition Company Ltd ....E...... 513 577-7980
　Cincinnati (G-4610)
Yoder Window & Siding Ltd ....G...... 330 857-4530
　Fredericksburg (G-10094)

3221 Glass Containers

Anchor Glass Container Corp ....C...... 740 452-2743
　Zanesville (G-21272)

◆ Anchor Hocking LLC ....A...... 740 681-6478
　Lancaster (G-11687)
Bprex Plastic Packaging Inc ....F...... 419 247-5000
　Toledo (G-18379)
Chantilly Development Corp ....F...... 419 243-8109
　Toledo (G-18393)
Dura Temp Corporation ....F...... 419 866-4348
　Holland (G-11058)
▲ G&M Media Packaging Inc ....F...... 419 636-5461
　Bryan (G-2297)
▼ Ghp II LLC ....C...... 740 687-2500
　Lancaster (G-11719)
◆ Owens-Brockway Glass Cont Inc ...C...... 567 336-8449
　Perrysburg (G-16139)
Owens-Brockway Glass Cont Inc .....D...... 740 455-4500
　Zanesville (G-21338)
◆ Owens-Brockway Packaging Inc .....C...... 567 336-5000
　Perrysburg (G-16140)
Owens-Illinois Inc ....B...... 567 336-5000
　Perrysburg (G-16141)
▲ Owens-Illinois De Puerto Rico ....D...... 419 874-9708
　Toledo (G-18628)
▲ Owens-Illinois General Inc ....B...... 567 336-5000
　Perrysburg (G-16142)
◆ Owens-Illinois Group Inc ....A...... 567 336-5000
　Perrysburg (G-16143)
Pyromatics Corp ....F...... 440 352-3500
　Mentor (G-13704)

3229 Pressed & Blown Glassware, NEC

201 E Liberty St ....G...... 234 249-0145
　Wooster (G-20728)
Adria Scientific GL Works Co ....G...... 440 474-6691
　Geneva (G-10339)
All State GL Block Fctry Inc ....G...... 440 205-8410
　Mentor (G-13519)
◆ Anchor Hocking LLC ....A...... 740 681-6478
　Lancaster (G-11687)
Anchor Hocking Consmr GL Corp .....G...... 740 653-2527
　Lancaster (G-11688)
Anderson Glass Co Inc ....E...... 614 476-4877
　Columbus (G-6756)
Angel Glass Lost ....G...... 419 353-2831
　Bowling Green (G-1967)
Axis Led Group LLC ....G...... 614 633-7955
　Dublin (G-9051)
Brubaker Metalcrafts Inc ....G...... 937 456-5834
　Eaton (G-9300)
Celstar Group Inc ....G...... 937 224-1730
　Dayton (G-8218)
▲ Cincinnati Gasket Pkg Mfg Inc ....E...... 513 761-3458
　Cincinnati (G-3550)
▲ Custom Deco South Inc ....G...... 419 698-2900
　Toledo (G-18418)
Custom Glass Solutions Corp ....D...... 614 987-1390
　Worthington (G-20862)
Dal-Little Fabricating Inc ....G...... 216 883-3323
　Cleveland (G-5163)
▲ Echo EMR Inc ....F...... 937 322-4972
　Springfield (G-17550)
▲ Eye Lighting Intl N Amer Inc ....C...... 440 350-7000
　Mentor (G-13576)
General Electric Company ....D...... 740 385-2114
　Logan (G-12175)
General Electric Company ....A...... 330 373-1400
　Niles (G-15155)
▼ Ghp II LLC ....C...... 740 687-2500
　Lancaster (G-11719)
Glass Axis ....G...... 614 291-4250
　Columbus (G-7115)
▲ Glasstech Inc ....C...... 419 661-9500
　Perrysburg (G-16103)
▲ Global Glass Block Inc ....G...... 216 731-2333
　Euclid (G-9581)
Industrial Fiberglass Spc Inc ....E...... 937 222-9000
　Dayton (G-8402)
International Automotive ....A...... 419 433-5653
　Huron (G-11228)
Jack Pine Studio ....G...... 614 291-0699
　Columbus (G-7220)
Jjs3 Foundation ....E...... 513 751-3292
　Cincinnati (G-3947)
▲ John Krizay Inc ....D...... 330 332-5607
　Salem (G-16903)
Johns Manville Corporation ....B...... 419 878-8111
　Waterville (G-19660)
Katies Light House LLC ....E...... 419 645-5451
　Cridersville (G-7946)
Knoble Glass & Metal Inc ....G...... 513 753-1246
　Cincinnati (G-3998)

Leveck Lighting Products Inc ....E...... 937 667-4421
　Tipp City (G-18287)
◆ Libbey Glass Inc ....C...... 419 325-2100
　Toledo (G-18558)
Libbey Glass Inc ....A...... 419 729-7272
　Toledo (G-18559)
▼ Libbey Inc ....C...... 419 325-2100
　Toledo (G-18561)
Matthews Art Glass ....G...... 419 335-2448
　Archbold (G-686)
▼ Mfg Composite Systems Company ..B...... 440 997-5851
　Ashtabula (G-820)
Midwest Composites LLC ....E...... 419 738-2431
　Wapakoneta (G-19497)
Modern China Inc ....E...... 330 938-6104
　Sebring (G-17048)
Molded Fiber Glass Research ....E...... 440 994-5100
　Ashtabula (G-825)
▲ Mosser Glass Incorporated ....E...... 740 439-1827
　Cambridge (G-2468)
Nextgen Fiber Optics LLC ....G...... 513 549-4691
　Cincinnati (G-4152)
◆ Owens Corning ....A...... 419 248-8000
　Toledo (G-18625)
◆ Owens Corning Sales LLC ....A...... 419 248-8000
　Toledo (G-18626)
Peak Electric Inc ....G...... 419 726-4848
　Toledo (G-18636)
Pgw Auto Glass LLC ....E...... 419 993-2421
　Lima (G-12070)
◆ PLC Connections LLC ....F...... 614 279-1796
　Columbus (G-7498)
PPG Industries Inc ....E...... 419 683-2400
　Crestline (G-7935)
R G C Inc ....E...... 513 683-3110
　Loveland (G-12380)
Robert Coleman ....G...... 740 393-4336
　Mount Vernon (G-14642)
Scottrods LLC ....E...... 419 499-2705
　Monroeville (G-14428)
Sem-Com Company Inc ....F...... 419 537-8813
　Toledo (G-18691)
Sourcepoint Logistics LLC ....E...... 937 604-8209
　Tipp City (G-18300)
Srico Inc ....G...... 614 799-0664
　Columbus (G-7647)
Techneglas Inc ....E...... 419 873-2000
　Perrysburg (G-16155)
Technical Glass Products Inc ....G...... 425 396-8420
　Perrysburg (G-16156)
▲ Tencate Advanced Armor USA Inc ..D...... 740 928-0326
　Hebron (G-10888)
Touch of Glass ....E...... 419 861-2888
　Toledo (G-18753)
Variety Glass Inc ....F...... 740 432-3643
　Cambridge (G-2481)
Wilson Optical Laboratory Inc ....E...... 440 357-7000
　Mentor (G-13769)

3231 Glass Prdts Made Of Purchased Glass

A & B Iron & Metal Company ....F...... 937 228-1561
　Dayton (G-8125)
A Service Glass Inc ....F...... 937 426-4920
　Beavercreek (G-1315)
▲ Addis Glass Fabricating Inc ....F...... 513 860-3340
　West Chester (G-19798)
▲ AGC Automotive Americas ....D...... 937 599-3131
　Bellefontaine (G-1515)
AGC Flat Glass North Amer Inc ....G...... 937 599-3131
　Bellefontaine (G-1517)
American Woodwork Specialty Co .....E...... 937 263-1053
　Dayton (G-8156)
◆ Anchi Inc ....A...... 740 653-2527
　Lancaster (G-11686)
Anderson Glass Co Inc ....E...... 614 476-4877
　Columbus (G-6756)
Architectural Art Glass Studio ....G...... 513 731-7336
　Milford (G-14122)
▲ Atc Lighting & Plastics Inc ....G...... 440 466-7670
　Andover (G-613)
◆ Auto Temp Inc ....C...... 513 732-6969
　Batavia (G-1164)
◆ Basco Manufacturing Company ....C...... 513 573-1900
　Mason (G-12986)
Beach Manufacturing Co ....G...... 937 882-6372
　Donnelsville (G-8960)
Bruening Glass Works Inc ....G...... 440 333-4768
　Cleveland (G-4940)
Cadenza Enterprises LLC ....G...... 937 428-6058
　Dayton (G-8207)

SIC

Cardinal CT Company .... G 740 892-2324
Utica (G-19192)

Catalina Tempering - Ohio Inc .... F 740 892-2324
Utica (G-19193)

Champion Window Co of Toledo .... E 419 841-0154
Perrysburg (G-16077)

Chantilly Development Corp .... F 419 243-8109
Toledo (G-18393)

Colleen D Turner .... G 419 886-4810
Bellville (G-1568)

Commercial Vehicle Group Inc .... A 614 289-5360
New Albany (G-14753)

▲ Crystal Art Imports Inc .... F 614 505-6001
Columbus (G-7002)

Custom GL Sltons Millbury Corp .... C 419 855-7706
Millbury (G-14183)

Custom Glass Solutions Upr Snd .... B 419 294-4921
Upper Sandusky (G-19117)

Domair Transmore Inc .... F 513 771-1516
Cincinnati (G-3662)

Dresden Specialties Inc .... G 740 754-2451
Dresden (G-9032)

▲ East Palestine Decorating LLC .... F 330 426-9600
East Palestine (G-9238)

▲ Enclosure Suppliers LLC .... E 513 782-3900
Cincinnati (G-3701)

Etching Concepts .... G 419 691-9086
Rossford (G-16740)

Fergusons Cut Glass Works .... F 419 734-0808
Marblehead (G-12744)

Fire Nation Ltd .... F 419 866-6288
Holland (G-11061)

▲ Franklin Art Glass Studios .... E 614 221-2972
Columbus (G-7096)

Frigid Units Inc .... G 419 478-4000
Toledo (G-18473)

General Electric Company .... D 740 385-2114
Logan (G-12175)

General Glass & Screen Inc .... G 440 350-9033
Mentor (G-13591)

Ghp II LLC .... B 740 681-6825
Lancaster (G-11720)

Glass Seale Ltd .... G 513 733-1464
Cincinnati (G-3834)

Glass Surface Systems Inc .... D 330 745-8500
Barberton (G-1119)

▲ Glasstech Inc .... C 419 661-9500
Perrysburg (G-16103)

Great Day Improvements LLC .... G 330 468-0700
Macedonia (G-12456)

Hall Creations .... G 330 357-2428
Kent (G-11468)

Installed Building Pdts LLC .... E 614 308-9900
Columbus (G-7190)

▲ Intigral Inc .... C 440 439-0980
Bedford (G-1432)

Intigral Inc .... E 440 439-0980
Youngstown (G-21120)

Jafe Decorating Co Inc .... E 937 547-1888
Greenville (G-10506)

Kessler Studios Inc .... G 513 683-7500
Loveland (G-12366)

Kimmatt Corp .... G 937 228-3811
Dayton (G-8441)

◆ Libbey Glass Inc .... C 419 325-2100
Toledo (G-18558)

Macpherson Engineering Inc .... E 440 243-6565
Berea (G-1625)

Marchione Studio Inc .... G 330 454-7408
Canton (G-2768)

Middlefield Glass Incorporated .... E 440 632-5699
Middlefield (G-13959)

Monarch Ig Inc .... F 330 897-2302
Baltic (G-1075)

▲ North Central Insulation Inc .... F 419 886-2030
Bellville (G-1573)

Ohio Mirror Technologies Inc .... F 419 399-5903
Paulding (G-16010)

Ohio Mirror Technologies Inc .... F 419 399-5903
Paulding (G-16011)

Oldcastle Buildingenvelope Inc .... G 419 887-1228
Maumee (G-13287)

Oldcastle Buildingenvelope Inc .... D 419 661-5079
Perrysburg (G-16133)

▲ Pei Liquidation Company .... C 330 467-4267
Macedonia (G-12470)

Perfection Glass .... G 614 920-0652
Pickerington (G-16199)

Pilkington North America Inc .... B 419 247-3211
Rossford (G-16745)

Pittsburgh Glass Works LLC .... D 740 774-7600
Chillicothe (G-3263)

Potters Industries LLC .... E 216 621-0840
Cleveland (G-6023)

PPG Industries Inc .... E 419 683-2400
Crestline (G-7935)

Pyromatics Corp .... G 440 352-3500
Mentor (G-13704)

R G C Inc .... F 513 683-3110
Loveland (G-12380)

R M Yates Co Inc .... G 216 441-0900
Cleveland (G-6084)

Radiant Arts Inc .... G 330 879-0013
Navarre (G-14725)

Rumpke Transportation Co LLC .... C 513 242-4600
Cincinnati (G-4367)

▲ Safelite Glass Corp .... A 614 210-9000
Columbus (G-7584)

▲ Safelite Group Inc .... A 614 210-9000
Columbus (G-7585)

Scs Construction Services Inc .... E 513 929-0260
Cincinnati (G-4393)

Sem-Com Company Inc .... F 419 537-8813
Toledo (G-18691)

Shiloh Hotglass .... G 937 274-7222
Dayton (G-8654)

Solon Glass Center Inc .... F 440 248-5018
Cleveland (G-6218)

Standing Rock Designery .... G 330 650-9089
Hudson (G-11202)

Strategic Materials Inc .... G 740 349-9523
Newark (G-15059)

Studio Arts & Glass Inc .... F 330 494-9779
Canton (G-2860)

Taylor Products Inc .... E 419 263-2313
Payne (G-16017)

Taylor Products Inc .... E 419 263-2313
Payne (G-16018)

Technicolor Usa Inc .... A 614 474-8821
Circleville (G-4646)

Tiger Mirror Corporation .... G 419 855-3146
Clay Center (G-4654)

Trio Insulated Glass Inc .... G 614 276-1647
Columbus (G-7710)

Trulite GL Alum Solutions LLC .... D 740 929-2443
Hebron (G-10892)

Tyseka .... G 419 860-9585
Lima (G-12107)

Vidonish Studios .... G 419 884-1119
Mansfield (G-12701)

Whitney Stained Glass Studio .... G 216 348-1616
Cleveland (G-6461)

3241 Cement, Hydraulic

Appc Plumbing Co .... G 330 722-7754
Medina (G-13372)

Asphalt Services Ohio Inc .... E 614 864-4600
Columbus (G-6778)

Cemex Cnstr Mtls ATL LLC .... D 937 878-8651
Xenia (G-20941)

Cincinnati Blacktop Company .... F 513 681-0952
Cincinnati (G-3544)

Essroc Cement Corp .... F 330 499-9100
Middlebranch (G-13900)

Essroc Cement Corp .... G 614 497-2001
Columbus (G-7067)

Fairborn Cement Company LLC .... C 937 879-8393
Xenia (G-20950)

Hartline Products Coinc .... G 216 851-7189
Cleveland (G-5483)

Hudecek Cement Inc .... G 216 676-0362
Cleveland (G-5534)

Huron Cement Products Company ..... E 419 433-4161
Huron (G-11224)

▲ Kona Blackbird Inc .... F 440 285-3189
Chardon (G-3160)

Lafarge North America Inc .... C 419 399-4861
Paulding (G-16009)

Lafarge North America Inc .... G 216 781-9330
Cleveland (G-5676)

Lafarge North America Inc .... G 419 241-5256
Toledo (G-18553)

Lafarge North America Inc .... F 419 897-7656
Maumee (G-13274)

Lafarge North America Inc .... G 740 423-5900
Belpre (G-1590)

Lozinak & Sons Inc .... G 440 877-1819
North Royalton (G-15433)

Murphy James Construction LLC .... E 740 667-3626
Coolville (G-7836)

Myko Industries .... G 216 431-0900
Cleveland (G-5845)

Quikrete Companies Inc .... E 614 885-4406
Columbus (G-7540)

Quikrete Companies Inc .... E 419 241-1148
Toledo (G-18664)

Quikrete Companies Inc .... E 330 296-6080
Ravenna (G-16551)

Riverside Sand & Gravel Co .... G 330 673-2021
Kent (G-11517)

St Marys Cement Inc (us) .... G 937 642-4573
Marysville (G-12972)

Wallseye Concrete Corp .... F 440 235-1800
Cleveland (G-6444)

Wallseye Concrete Corp .... F 419 483-2738
Castalia (G-2978)

3251 Brick & Structural Clay Tile

Afc Company .... F 330 533-5581
Canfield (G-2545)

Armstrong World Industries Inc .... D 614 771-9307
Hilliard (G-10927)

Belden Brick Company LLC .... C 330 456-0031
Sugarcreek (G-18017)

Boral Bricks Inc .... G 937 294-1548
Franklin (G-10010)

Bowerston Shale Company .... E 740 763-3921
Newark (G-14988)

Bowerston Shale Company .... G 740 269-2921
Bowerston (G-1957)

Glen-Gery Corporation .... D 419 845-3321
Caledonia (G-2437)

Glen-Gery Corporation .... E 419 468-4890
Galion (G-10274)

Glen-Gery Corporation .... E 419 468-5002
Iberia (G-11243)

Hanson Aggregates East LLC .... F 937 382-2557
Wilmington (G-20668)

Kepcor Inc .... E 330 868-6434
Minerva (G-14327)

▲ Kona Blackbird Inc .... F 440 285-3189
Chardon (G-3160)

LBC Clay Co LLC .... G 330 674-0674
Millersburg (G-14240)

Minteq International Inc .... G 330 343-8821
Dover (G-9003)

Morgan Advanced Ceramics Inc .... C 440 232-8604
Bedford (G-1445)

Nutro Inc .... E 440 572-3800
Strongsville (G-17947)

Resco Products Inc .... E 740 682-7794
Oak Hill (G-15605)

Stebbins Engineering & Mfg Co .... E 740 922-3012
Uhrichsville (G-19060)

Whitacre Greer Company .... E 330 823-1610
Alliance (G-553)

Wk Brick Company .... G 614 416-6700
Columbus (G-7767)

3253 Ceramic Tile

Artfinders .... G 330 264-7706
Wooster (G-20740)

Carolex Company Inc .... E 330 386-9529
East Liverpool (G-9206)

Dai Ceramics Inc .... D 440 946-6964
Willoughby (G-20468)

Epro Inc .... E 419 426-5053
Bloomville (G-1727)

Florida Tile Inc .... G 513 891-1122
Blue Ash (G-1797)

Florida Tile Inc .... G 614 436-2511
Columbus (G-7091)

Florida Tile Inc .... G 937 293-5151
Miamisburg (G-13809)

▲ Ironrock Capital Incorporated ...... D 330 484-4887
Canton (G-2741)

Kepcor Inc .... F 330 868-6434
Minerva (G-14327)

Mohawk Industries Inc .... C 800 837-3812
Grove City (G-10574)

▲ Ohio Tile & Marble Co .... E 513 541-4211
Cincinnati (G-4180)

PCC Ceramic Group 1 .... F 440 516-3672
Wickliffe (G-20382)

◆ Seneca Tiles Inc .... D 419 426-3561
Attica (G-895)

Stebbins Engineering & Mfg Co .... E 740 922-3012
Uhrichsville (G-19060)

▲ Studio Vertu Inc .... E 513 241-9038
Cincinnati (G-4472)

Summitville Tiles Inc ....C.... 330 868-6771
Minerva *(G-14343)*
Tarkett USA Inc ....C.... 440 543-8916
Solon *(G-17399)*
Wccv Floor Coverings Inc ....E.... 330 688-0114
Peninsula *(G-16044)*

3255 Clay Refractories

Afc Company ....F.... 330 533-5581
Canfield *(G-2545)*
Bowerston Shale Company ....E.... 740 269-2921
Bowerston *(G-1957)*
Glen-Gery Corporation ....E.... 419 468-5002
Iberia *(G-11243)*
Glen-Gery Corporation ....D.... 419 845-3321
Caledonia *(G-2437)*
Harbisonwalker Intl Inc ....D.... 740 682-7711
Oak Hill *(G-15597)*
Harbisonwalker Intl Inc ....E.... 330 326-2010
Windham *(G-20697)*
Harbisonwalker Intl Inc ....E.... 513 576-6240
Batavia *(G-1191)*
Harbisonwalker Intl Inc ....F.... 330 868-4141
Minerva *(G-14323)*
I Cerco Inc ....D.... 740 982-2050
Crooksville *(G-7950)*
Lakeway Mfg Inc ....E.... 419 433-3030
Huron *(G-11232)*
Magneco/Metrel Inc ....E.... 330 426-9468
Negley *(G-14730)*
Minteq International Inc ....E.... 330 343-8821
Dover *(G-9003)*
▲ **Nock and Son Company** ....G.... 440 871-5525
Cleveland *(G-5885)*
Nock and Son Company ....F.... 740 682-7741
Oak Hill *(G-15602)*
Resco Products Inc ....E.... 330 372-3716
Warren *(G-19594)*
Resco Products Inc ....E.... 740 682-7794
Oak Hill *(G-15605)*
Resco Products Inc ....D.... 330 488-1226
East Canton *(G-9197)*
▲ **Selas Heat Technology Co LLC** ....E.... 800 523-6500
Streetsboro *(G-17875)*
Specialty Ceramics Inc ....D.... 330 482-0800
Columbiana *(G-6633)*
Stebbins Engineering & Mfg Co ....E.... 740 922-3012
Uhrichsville *(G-19060)*
Summitville Tiles Inc ....E.... 330 868-6463
Minerva *(G-14344)*
UNI-Ref United Refractories Co ....E.... 513 563-9955
Cincinnati *(G-4536)*
▲ **Wahl Refractory Solutions LLC** ....D.... 419 334-2658
Fremont *(G-10193)*
Whitacre Greer Company ....E.... 330 823-1610
Alliance *(G-553)*

3259 Structural Clay Prdts, NEC

Baughman Tile Company ....D.... 800 837-3160
Paulding *(G-16000)*
Clay Logan Products Company ....D.... 740 385-2184
Logan *(G-12172)*
Haviland Drainage Products Co ....F.... 419 622-4611
Haviland *(G-10840)*
▲ **Ludowici Roof Tile Inc** ....D.... 740 342-1995
New Lexington *(G-14849)*
Nr Lee Restoration Ltd ....G.... 419 692-2233
Delphos *(G-8915)*
◆ **Superior Clay Corp** ....D.... 740 922-4122
Uhrichsville *(G-19061)*

3261 China Plumbing Fixtures & Fittings

▼ **A C Products Co** ....D.... 330 698-1105
Apple Creek *(G-633)*
Aabel Plumbing Inc ....E.... 937 434-4343
Dayton *(G-8127)*
Accent Manufacturing Inc ....F.... 330 724-7704
Norton *(G-15500)*
As America Inc ....G.... 330 337-2219
Salem *(G-16873)*
As America Inc ....G.... 615 873-2410
Mansfield *(G-12563)*
Bridgits Bath LLC ....G.... 937 259-1960
Dayton *(G-8194)*
Crane Plumbing LLC ....E.... 419 522-4211
Mansfield *(G-12587)*
◆ **Crane Plumbing LLC** ....F.... 419 522-4211
Mansfield *(G-12588)*
Crane Plumbing LLC ....C.... 419 522-0321
Mansfield *(G-12589)*
Dittmar Sales and Service ....G.... 740 653-7933
Lancaster *(G-11709)*
East Woodworking Company ....G.... 216 791-5950
Cleveland *(G-5240)*
▲ **F K Holding Inc** ....F.... 513 641-1400
Cincinnati *(G-3735)*
◆ **Mansfield Plumbing Pdts LLC** ....A.... 419 938-5211
Perrysville *(G-16173)*

3262 China, Table & Kitchen Articles

Libbey Glass Inc ....A.... 419 729-7272
Toledo *(G-18559)*
▼ **Libbey Inc** ....C.... 419 325-2100
Toledo *(G-18561)*
▲ **Syracuse China Company** ....C.... 419 727-2100
Toledo *(G-18712)*
▲ **Warrior Imports Inc** ....E.... 954 935-5536
Youngstown *(G-21243)*

3263 Earthenware, Whiteware, Table & Kitchen Articles

Added Touch Decorating Gallery ....G.... 419 747-3146
Ontario *(G-15684)*
Modern China Inc ....E.... 330 938-6104
Sebring *(G-17048)*
Us Inc ....G.... 513 791-1162
Blue Ash *(G-1887)*
West Ohio Tool & Mfg LLC ....G.... 419 678-4745
Saint Henry *(G-16825)*

3264 Porcelain Electrical Splys

▲ **Akron Porcelain & Plastics Co** ....C.... 330 745-2159
Akron *(G-53)*
CAM-Lem Inc ....G.... 216 391-7750
Cleveland *(G-4963)*
▲ **Channel Products Inc** ....D.... 440 423-0113
Chesterland *(G-3199)*
Crane Plumbing LLC ....C.... 419 522-0321
Mansfield *(G-12589)*
▲ **Electrodyne Company Inc** ....F.... 513 732-2822
Batavia *(G-1180)*
Ferro Corporation ....C.... 216 875-6178
Cleveland *(G-5337)*
Fram Group Operations LLC ....G.... 937 316-3000
Greenville *(G-10499)*
Fram Group Operations LLC ....A.... 419 436-5827
Fostoria *(G-9979)*
▲ **Materion Brush Inc** ....D.... 216 486-4200
Mayfield Heights *(G-13317)*
Petro Ware Inc ....D.... 740 982-1302
Crooksville *(G-7953)*

3269 Pottery Prdts, NEC

All Fired Up Pnt Your Own Pot ....G.... 330 865-5858
Copley *(G-7839)*
Annies Mud Pie Shop LLC ....G.... 513 871-2529
Cincinnati *(G-3405)*
Beaumont Brothers Stoneware ....G.... 740 982-0055
Crooksville *(G-7949)*
Benzle Porcelain Company Inc ....G.... 614 876-2159
Hilliard *(G-10931)*
Bodycote Imt Inc ....E.... 740 852-5000
London *(G-12201)*
Bosco Pup Co LLC ....G.... 614 833-0349
Pickerington *(G-16187)*
Carruth Studio Inc ....F.... 419 878-3060
Waterville *(G-19653)*
▲ **Clay Burley Products Co** ....E.... 740 452-3633
Roseville *(G-16728)*
Clay Burley Products Co ....E.... 740 697-0221
Roseville *(G-16729)*
◆ **E R Advanced Ceramics Inc** ....E.... 330 426-9433
East Palestine *(G-9237)*
Edward Orton Jr Crmic Fndation ....E.... 614 895-2663
Westerville *(G-20148)*
Gosun Inc ....F.... 513 709-2519
Cincinnati *(G-3841)*
Grandpas Pottery ....G.... 937 382-6442
Wilmington *(G-20665)*
J-Vac Industries Inc ....D.... 740 384-2155
Wellston *(G-19765)*
Javanation ....F.... 419 584-1705
Celina *(G-3003)*
Kiln of Hyde Park Inc ....F.... 513 321-3307
Cincinnati *(G-3988)*
Klopfenstein Art Equipment ....G.... 419 884-2900
Mansfield *(G-12633)*
Larose Industries LLC ....E.... 419 237-1600
Fayette *(G-9776)*
Mad Potter LLC ....G.... 513 770-5585
Mason *(G-13057)*
Marchione Studio Inc ....G.... 330 454-7408
Canton *(G-2768)*
Ohio Stoneware LLC ....F.... 740 450-4415
Zanesville *(G-21337)*
▼ **Orton Edward Jr Crmic Fndation** ....E.... 614 895-2663
Westerville *(G-20176)*
Potter House ....G.... 419 584-1705
Celina *(G-3015)*
Spirit of Clay ....G.... 440 684-0001
Cleveland *(G-6226)*
Stoneware Palace Ltd ....G.... 614 529-6974
Columbus *(G-7659)*
Strictly Stitchery Inc ....F.... 440 543-7128
Cleveland *(G-6254)*
Yellow Springs Pottery ....F.... 937 767-1666
Yellow Springs *(G-21002)*

3271 Concrete Block & Brick

All Ohio Ready Mix Concrete ....G.... 419 841-3838
Perrysburg *(G-16062)*
American Concrete Products ....F.... 937 224-1433
Dayton *(G-8153)*
B & S Blacktop Co ....G.... 513 797-5759
New Richmond *(G-14940)*
Belden Brick Company LLC ....C.... 330 456-0031
Sugarcreek *(G-18017)*
Bryce Hill Inc ....E.... 937 663-4152
Saint Paris *(G-16859)*
Bryce Hill Inc ....G.... 937 325-0651
Springfield *(G-17525)*
Cantelli Block and Brick Inc ....E.... 419 433-0102
Huron *(G-11218)*
Cement Products Inc ....E.... 419 524-4342
Mansfield *(G-12578)*
Charles Svec Inc ....E.... 216 662-5200
Maple Heights *(G-12730)*
Dearth Resources Inc ....G.... 937 325-0651
Springfield *(G-17539)*
Dearth Resources Inc ....G.... 937 663-4171
Springfield *(G-17540)*
Frankie Tatum ....G.... 614 216-1556
Gahanna *(G-10207)*
Gennaro Pavers ....G.... 330 536-6825
Lowellville *(G-12409)*
Green Vision Materials Inc ....F.... 440 564-5500
Newbury *(G-15093)*
Hanson Aggregates East LLC ....E.... 740 773-2172
Chillicothe *(G-3242)*
Hanson Aggregates East LLC ....F.... 937 382-2557
Wilmington *(G-20668)*
Hazelbaker Industries Ltd ....E.... 614 276-2631
Columbus *(G-7146)*
ICC Safety Service Inc ....G.... 614 261-4557
Columbus *(G-7181)*
J P Sand & Gravel Company ....E.... 614 497-0083
Lockbourne *(G-12147)*
K & L Ready Mix Inc ....F.... 419 532-3585
Kalida *(G-11413)*
Kathy Edie ....G.... 740 763-4887
Newark *(G-15026)*
Koltcz Concrete Block Co ....E.... 440 232-3630
Bedford *(G-1437)*
Mapes Concrete Construction ....G.... 513 245-2631
Cincinnati *(G-4057)*
Martin Block Company ....G.... 740 286-7507
Jackson *(G-11319)*
Medina Supply Company ....G.... 440 234-1321
Berea *(G-1626)*
Midwest Specialties Inc ....F.... 419 738-8147
Wapakoneta *(G-19501)*
National Lime and Stone Co ....E.... 614 497-0083
Lockbourne *(G-12150)*
North Central Concrete Design ....F.... 419 606-1908
Wooster *(G-20816)*
Oberfields LLC ....E.... 614 491-7643
Columbus *(G-7409)*
Oberfields LLC ....F.... 614 252-0955
Columbus *(G-7410)*
▲ **Osborne Inc** ....E.... 440 942-7000
Mentor *(G-13677)*
Portsmouth Block Inc ....F.... 740 353-4113
Portsmouth *(G-16448)*
Quality Block & Supply Inc ....E.... 330 364-4411
Mount Eaton *(G-14556)*
R W Sidley Incorporated ....E.... 440 564-2221
Newbury *(G-15102)*
RE Connors Construction Ltd ....G.... 740 644-0261
Thornville *(G-18194)*

▲ Reading Rock Inc .... C 513 874-2345
West Chester *(G-20045)*

S & S Aggregates Inc .... G 740 453-0721
Zanesville *(G-21349)*

Simon & Simon Blue Pond Inc ...... G 330 928-2298
Cuyahoga Falls *(G-8046)*

▲ Snyder Concrete Products Inc .... E 937 885-5176
Moraine *(G-14528)*

Snyder Concrete Products Inc ...... G 937 224-1433
Dayton *(G-8661)*

St Henry Tile Co Inc .... E 419 678-4841
Saint Henry *(G-16822)*

St Henry Tile Co Inc .... F 937 548-1101
Greenville *(G-10523)*

Stiger Pre Cast Inc .... G 740 482-2313
Nevada *(G-14743)*

Stocker Concrete Company .... F 740 254-4626
Gnadenhutten *(G-10411)*

Stocker Sand & Gravel Co .... F 740 254-4635
Gnadenhutten *(G-10412)*

Sunny Brook Pressed Con Co .... G 330 673-7667
Kent *(G-11534)*

Tri-County Block and Brick Inc ...... E 419 826-7060
Swanton *(G-18093)*

Trumbull Cement Products Co .... G 330 372-4342
Warren *(G-19611)*

Turner Vault .... G 419 223-6861
Lima *(G-12106)*

Tyjen Inc .... G 740 380-3215
Logan *(G-12196)*

Tyjen Inc .... G 740 797-4064
The Plains *(G-18187)*

Walden Industries Inc .... E 740 633-5971
Tiltonsville *(G-18255)*

William Dauch Concrete Company .... F 419 668-4458
Norwalk *(G-15567)*

3272 Concrete Prdts

A K Ready Mix LLC .... F 740 286-8900
Jackson *(G-11307)*

◆ Aco Polymer Products Inc .... E 440 285-7000
Mentor *(G-13508)*

Adler & Company Inc .... F 513 248-1500
Cincinnati *(G-3356)*

Aetna Plastics Corp .... G 330 274-2855
Mantua *(G-12706)*

Agean Marble Manufacturing .... F 513 874-1475
West Chester *(G-19978)*

Akron Vault Company Inc .... F 330 784-5475
Akron *(G-60)*

Ald Precast Corp .... G 614 449-3366
Columbus *(G-6714)*

Alexander Wilbert Vault Co .... G 419 468-3477
Galion *(G-10252)*

Allen Enterprises Inc .... G 740 532-5913
Ironton *(G-11288)*

▲ American Spring Wire Corp .... C 216 292-4620
Bedford Heights *(G-1478)*

Andras Corp .... G 440 323-2528
Elyria *(G-9373)*

Art Columbus Memorial Inc .... G 614 221-9333
Columbus *(G-6773)*

Ash Sewer & Drain Service .... G 330 376-9714
Akron *(G-74)*

Ashland Monument Company Inc ..... G 419 281-2688
Ashland *(G-706)*

B & B Cast Stone Co Inc .... G 740 697-0008
Roseville *(G-16726)*

Babbert Real Estate Inv Co Ltd ..... D 614 837-8444
Canal Winchester *(G-2519)*

Baird Concrete Products Inc .... F 740 623-8600
Coshocton *(G-7881)*

▲ Baswa Acoustics North Amer LLC .. F ... 216 475-7197
Bedford *(G-1404)*

Baxter Burial Vault Service .... E 513 641-1010
Cincinnati *(G-3440)*

Baxter Holdings Inc .... E 513 860-3593
Hamilton *(G-10673)*

Bell Burial Vault Co .... G 513 896-9044
Hamilton *(G-10674)*

Bell Vault & Monument Works .... E 937 866-2444
Miamisburg *(G-13785)*

Bilco Company .... E 740 455-9020
Zanesville *(G-21279)*

Bluffton Precast Concrete Co .... F 419 358-6946
Bluffton *(G-1908)*

Brock Burial Vault Inc .... G 740 894-5246
South Point *(G-17433)*

Buckeye Vault Service Inc .... G 419 747-1976
Mansfield *(G-12571)*

Carey Precast Concrete Company .... G 419 396-7142
Carey *(G-2915)*

Carruth Studio Inc .... F 419 878-3060
Waterville *(G-19653)*

Cashen Inc .... G 440 428-1148
Madison *(G-12497)*

Cement Products Inc .... E 419 524-4342
Mansfield *(G-12578)*

Cemex Materials LLC .... D 937 268-6706
Dayton *(G-8219)*

Cemex Materials LLC .... E 937 268-6706
Dayton *(G-8220)*

Charles Svec Inc .... E 216 662-5200
Maple Heights *(G-12730)*

Click Burial Vault and Mfg Co .... G 330 343-1143
New Philadelphia *(G-14891)*

Coate Concrete Products Inc .... G 937 698-4181
West Milton *(G-20106)*

Complete Cylinder Service Inc ...... G 513 772-1500
Cincinnati *(G-3600)*

Concrete Fealants Inc .... D 937 339-0549
Troy *(G-18812)*

Concrete Material Supply LLC .... G 419 261-6404
Woodville *(G-20725)*

Contech Bridge Solutions LLC .... F 937 878-2170
Dayton *(G-8243)*

Contech Bridge Solutions LLC .... F 513 645-7000
West Chester *(G-19838)*

Cox Inc .... F 740 858-4400
Lucasville *(G-12418)*

Creative Curbing America LLC .... G 419 738-7668
Wapakoneta *(G-19484)*

Crummitt & Son Vault Corp .... G 304 281-2420
Martins Ferry *(G-12923)*

Dalaco Materials LLC .... F 513 893-5483
Liberty Twp *(G-11974)*

▲ Day Pre-Cast Products Co .... G 419 536-2909
Toledo *(G-18429)*

Dennis Constuction Sanitation ...... G 419 332-8301
Fremont *(G-10142)*

Donald Schloemer .... G 419 933-2002
Willard *(G-20394)*

Douglas Industries LLC .... E 740 775-2400
Chillicothe *(G-3237)*

Douglas S Kutz .... G 440 238-8426
Strongsville *(G-17912)*

E A Cox Inc .... G 740 858-4400
Lucasville *(G-12419)*

E C Babbert Inc .... D 614 837-8444
Canal Winchester *(G-2523)*

E C S Corp .... F 440 323-1707
Elyria *(G-9409)*

E Pompili & Sons Inc .... G 216 581-8080
Cleveland *(G-5233)*

Ellinger Monument Inc .... G 740 385-3687
Rockbridge *(G-16688)*

Encore Precast LLC .... F 513 726-5678
Seven Mile *(G-17065)*

Evan Ragouzis Co .... G 513 242-5900
Hamilton *(G-10689)*

Everly Concrete Products .... G 740 635-1415
Bridgeport *(G-2089)*

Fabcon Companies LLC .... D 614 875-8601
Grove City *(G-10558)*

▲ Fibreboard Corporation .... C 419 248-8000
Toledo *(G-18470)*

▲ Fin Pan Inc .... F 513 870-9200
Hamilton *(G-10692)*

Fithian-Wilbert Burial Vlt Co .... F 330 758-2327
Youngstown *(G-21087)*

Fort Loramie Cast Stone Pdts .... G 937 420-2257
Fort Loramie *(G-9931)*

Fort Stben Burial Estates Assn ...... G 740 266-6101
Steubenville *(G-17695)*

Forterra Pipe & Precast LLC .... G 330 467-7890
Macedonia *(G-12451)*

Forterra Pipe & Precast LLC .... E 937 268-6707
Dayton *(G-8348)*

Forterra Pipe & Precast LLC .... G 937 268-6707
Dayton *(G-8349)*

Fountain Specialists Inc .... G 513 831-5717
Milford *(G-14142)*

Galena Vault Ltd .... G 740 965-2200
Galena *(G-10242)*

Gallipolis Vault Co Inc .... G 740 446-3357
Gallipolis *(G-10297)*

Gdy Installations Inc .... E 419 467-0036
Toledo *(G-18478)*

Green Forward Technologies LLC .... G 513 607-9639
Cincinnati *(G-3848)*

Hanson Aggregates East LLC .... E 330 467-7890
Macedonia *(G-12457)*

Hanson Aggregates East LLC .... F 937 382-2557
Wilmington *(G-20668)*

Hanson Aggregates East LLC .... E 740 773-2172
Chillicothe *(G-3242)*

Hanson Concrete Products Ohio ..... E 614 443-4846
Columbus *(G-7143)*

Harn Vault Service Inc .... F 330 832-1995
Minerva *(G-14324)*

Haviland Culvert Company .... G 419 622-6951
Haviland *(G-10839)*

Hazelbaker Industries Ltd .... E 614 276-2631
Columbus *(G-7146)*

Headwaters Incorporated .... F 989 671-1500
Manchester *(G-12549)*

High Concrete Group LLC .... C 937 748-2412
Springboro *(G-17483)*

Highland Stone .... G 937 364-2311
Hillsboro *(G-11003)*

Hilles Burial Vaults Inc .... G 330 823-2251
Alliance *(G-514)*

Hilltop Basic Resources Inc .... E 513 621-1500
Cincinnati *(G-3885)*

Hilltop Stone Llc .... G 513 651-5000
Cincinnati *(G-3886)*

Huron Cement Products Company .... E 419 433-4161
Huron *(G-11224)*

J K Precast LLC .... G 740 335-2188
Wshngtn CT Hs *(G-20912)*

Jackson Monument Inc .... G 740 286-1590
Jackson *(G-11316)*

James Kimmey .... F 740 335-5746
Wshngtn CT Hs *(G-20913)*

Janell Inc .... G 740 532-9111
Ironton *(G-11295)*

▲ Jet Stream International Inc ...... E 330 505-9988
Niles *(G-15164)*

Jim Bumen Construction Company ... G 740 663-2659
Chillicothe *(G-3247)*

K M B Inc .... G 330 889-3451
Bristolville *(G-2098)*

Kcg Inc .... G 614 238-9450
Columbus *(G-7252)*

Koppers Industries Inc .... E 740 776-3238
Portsmouth *(G-16441)*

KSA Limited Partnership .... E 740 776-3238
Portsmouth *(G-16442)*

L B Weiss Construction Inc .... G 440 205-1774
Mentor *(G-13625)*

Landon Vault Company .... F 614 443-5505
Columbus *(G-7283)*

▲ Lang Stone Company Inc .... D 614 235-4099
Columbus *(G-7284)*

Latorre Concrete Cnstr Inc .... E 614 257-1401
Columbus *(G-7288)*

Lindsay Package Systems Inc .... G 330 854-4511
Canal Fulton *(G-2504)*

▼ Lindsay Precast Inc .... E 330 854-6282
Canal Fulton *(G-2505)*

Mack Industries .... C 419 353-7081
Bowling Green *(G-1999)*

Mack Industries Inc .... G 330 460-7005
Brunswick *(G-2237)*

Mack Industries PA Inc .... D 330 483-3111
Valley City *(G-19213)*

Mack Industries PA Inc .... F 330 638-7680
Vienna *(G-19369)*

Mack Ready Mix Concrete Inc .... G 330 483-3111
Valley City *(G-19214)*

Mansfield Brick & Supply Co .... G 419 526-1191
Mansfield *(G-12641)*

Marblelife of Central Ohio .... G 614 837-6146
Pickerington *(G-16197)*

McGill Septic Tank Co .... E 330 876-2171
Kinsman *(G-11610)*

Metro Mech Inc .... G 216 641-6262
Cleveland *(G-5792)*

Michaels Pre-Cast Con Pdts .... F 513 683-1292
Loveland *(G-12374)*

Millinium 3 Inc .... G 513 770-3122
Mason *(G-13064)*

Money Jewelry Vaults .... G 937 366-6391
Wilmington *(G-20671)*

Motz Mobile Containers Inc .... G 513 772-6689
Cincinnati *(G-4127)*

National Center For Composite ...... E 937 297-9450
Dayton *(G-8518)*

Neher Burial Vault Company .... F 937 399-4494
Springfield *(G-17617)*

Next Dimension Components Inc.........F 440 576-0194
Jefferson *(G-11368)*

North American Cast Stone Inc.........G 440 286-1999
Chardon *(G-3169)*

Northern Concrete Pipe Inc.........F 419 841-3361
Sylvania *(G-18122)*

▲ Norwalk Concrete Inds Inc.........E 419 668-8167
Norwalk *(G-15554)*

Norwalk Concrete Inds Inc.........E 419 668-8167
Norwalk *(G-15555)*

O K Brugmann Jr & Sons Inc.........F 330 274-2106
Mantua *(G-12718)*

Oberfields LLC.........D 740 369-7644
Delaware *(G-8876)*

Oberfields LLC.........E 740 369-7644
Sunbury *(G-18069)*

Oberfields LLC.........F 614 252-0955
Columbus *(G-7410)*

Oberfields LLC.........G 937 885-3711
Dayton *(G-8538)*

Oberfields LLC.........E 614 491-7643
Columbus *(G-7409)*

Ohio Cast Stone Co LLC.........G 614 524-0666
Ashville *(G-852)*

Ohio Cast Stone Co LLC.........G 614 444-2278
Columbus *(G-7416)*

Ohio Flame.........G 330 953-0863
Youngstown *(G-21154)*

Oldcastle Apg Midwest Inc.........D 440 949-1815
Sheffield Village *(G-17128)*

Olde Wood Ltd.........E 330 866-1441
Magnolia *(G-12517)*

One Wish LLC.........F 800 505-6883
Beachwood *(G-1289)*

Orrville Trucking & Grading Co.........E 330 682-4010
Orrville *(G-15753)*

Outdoor Supply.........G 440 256-3338
Kirtland *(G-11615)*

P L M Corporation.........G 216 341-8008
Cleveland *(G-5956)*

Paper Vault.........G 614 859-5538
Columbus *(G-7459)*

Patriot Holdings Unlimited LLC.........G 740 574-2112
Wheelersburg *(G-20333)*

Pavestone LLC.........E 513 474-3783
Cincinnati *(G-4218)*

Pawnee Maintenance Inc.........D 740 373-6861
Marietta *(G-12814)*

Poland Concrete Products Inc.........G 330 757-1241
Poland *(G-16384)*

Precast Services Inc.........G 614 428-4541
Reynoldsburg *(G-16598)*

Premere Precast Products.........F 740 533-3333
Ironton *(G-11298)*

Premiere Con Solutions LLC.........F 419 737-9808
Pioneer *(G-16241)*

Prestress Services Inds LLC.........C 859 299-0461
Columbus *(G-7516)*

Prestress Services Inds LLC.........E 614 871-2900
Grove City *(G-10585)*

▼ Provia Stone LLC.........E 740 450-4236
Sugarcreek *(G-18035)*

Quaker City Septic Tanks LLC.........G 330 427-2239
Leetonia *(G-11864)*

Quikrete Companies Inc.........E 614 885-4406
Columbus *(G-7540)*

Quikrete Companies Inc.........E 513 367-6135
Harrison *(G-10798)*

Quikrete Companies Inc.........E 419 241-1148
Toledo *(G-18664)*

Quikrete Companies Inc.........E 330 296-6080
Ravenna *(G-16551)*

R W Sidley Inc.........F 440 224-2664
Kingsville *(G-11607)*

R W Sidley Incorporated.........E 440 564-2221
Newbury *(G-15102)*

Ramp Creek III Ltd.........G 740 522-0660
Heath *(G-10853)*

Redi Rock Structures Oki LLC.........G 513 965-9221
Milford *(G-14169)*

Reed Elvin Burl II.........G 937 399-3242
Springfield *(G-17636)*

Resco Products Inc.........E 330 372-3716
Warren *(G-19594)*

Richmond Concrete Products.........G 330 673-7892
Warren *(G-19595)*

River Cities Vault Inc.........F 740 237-0010
Ironton *(G-11300)*

Rock Decor Company.........G 330 857-7625
Orrville *(G-15759)*

S & S Aggregates Inc.........G 740 453-0721
Zanesville *(G-21349)*

Seislove Vault & Septic Tanks.........G 419 447-5473
Tiffin *(G-18243)*

Septic Products Inc.........G 419 282-5933
Ashland *(G-777)*

Shaw Wilbert Vaults LLC.........G 740 498-7438
Newcomerstown *(G-15124)*

Shelly Materials Inc.........G 614 801-9105
Grove City *(G-10593)*

Shock Precast.........G 419 426-0535
Attica *(G-896)*

Sickels Septic Tanks Inc.........G 740 593-8302
Athens *(G-884)*

Sky Vault Ltd.........G 740 549-0623
Lewis Center *(G-11919)*

Smith Concrete Co.........E 740 373-7441
Dover *(G-9015)*

▲ Snyder Concrete Products Inc.........E 937 885-5176
Moraine *(G-14528)*

Snyder Concrete Products Inc.........F 513 539-7686
Monroe *(G-14413)*

Spoerr Precast Concrete Inc.........F 419 625-9132
Sandusky *(G-17009)*

St Henry Tile Co Inc.........F 937 548-1101
Greenville *(G-10523)*

Stiger Pre Cast Inc.........G 740 482-2313
Nevada *(G-14743)*

Stuart Burial Vault Company.........F 740 569-4158
Bremen *(G-2080)*

▲ Sunjoy Industries Group Inc.........G 740 283-2815
Steubenville *(G-17716)*

Thomas-Wilbert Vault Co Inc.........G 740 695-5671
Saint Clairsville *(G-16812)*

Tri County Concrete Inc.........E 330 425-4464
Twinsburg *(G-19029)*

Tri-Way Rebar Inc.........G 330 882-8043
Akron *(G-447)*

Turner Vault.........G 419 223-6861
Lima *(G-12106)*

Turner Vault Co.........E 419 537-1133
Northwood *(G-15493)*

Uniontown Septic Tanks Inc.........F 330 699-3386
Uniontown *(G-19104)*

USA Precast Concrete Limited.........G 330 854-9600
Canal Fulton *(G-2516)*

Walden Industries Inc.........E 740 633-5971
Tiltonsville *(G-18255)*

Wauseon Silo & Coal Company.........F 419 335-6041
Wauseon *(G-19701)*

Whempys Corp.........G 614 888-6670
Worthington *(G-20893)*

William Dauch Concrete Company.........F 419 668-4458
Norwalk *(G-15567)*

Wilson Concrete Products Inc.........E 937 885-7965
Dayton *(G-8759)*

Wilsons Country Creations.........F 330 377-4190
Killbuck *(G-11602)*

Wine Vault Enterprises LLC.........G 614 850-0047
Hilliard *(G-10993)*

Wysong Concrete Products LLC.........G 513 874-3109
Fairfield *(G-9734)*

Youngstown Burial Vault Co.........G 330 782-0015
Youngstown *(G-21248)*

3273 Ready-Mixed Concrete

ACE Ready Mix Company Inc.........G 330 745-8125
Norton *(G-15501)*

Ace Ready Mix Concrete Co Inc.........F 330 745-8125
Norton *(G-15502)*

Adams Brothers Inc.........F 740 819-0323
Zanesville *(G-21265)*

Alexis Concrete Enterprise Inc.........F 440 366-0031
Elyria *(G-9368)*

Allega Concrete Corp.........G 216 447-0814
Cleveland *(G-4762)*

Anderson Concrete Corp.........C 614 443-0123
Columbus *(G-6755)*

Arrow Coal Grove Inc.........G 740 532-6143
Ironton *(G-11289)*

ASAP Ready Mix Inc.........G 513 797-1774
Amelia *(G-568)*

Associated Associates Inc.........G 330 626-3300
Mantua *(G-12707)*

Avon Concrete Corporation.........G 440 937-6264
Avon *(G-984)*

Baker-Shindler Contracting Co.........G 419 399-4841
Cecil *(G-2979)*

Baker-Shindler Contracting Co.........E 419 782-5080
Defiance *(G-8780)*

Buckeye Ready-Mix.........G 419 294-2389
Upper Sandusky *(G-19116)*

Buckeye Ready-Mix LLC.........G 740 967-4801
Johnstown *(G-11393)*

Buckeye Ready-Mix LLC.........G 614 879-6316
West Jefferson *(G-20076)*

Buckeye Ready-Mix LLC.........F 740 387-8846
Marion *(G-12858)*

Buckeye Ready-Mix LLC.........E 614 575-2132
Reynoldsburg *(G-16583)*

Buckeye Ready-Mix LLC.........G 937 642-2951
Marysville *(G-12935)*

Buckeye Ready-Mix LLC.........F 740 654-4423
Lancaster *(G-11693)*

C F Poeppelman Inc.........G 937 448-2191
Bradford *(G-2025)*

Caldwell Lumber & Supply Co.........E 740 732-2306
Caldwell *(G-2425)*

Caldwell Redi Mix Company.........G 740 732-2906
Caldwell *(G-2426)*

Caldwell Redi Mix Company.........G 740 685-6554
Byesville *(G-2395)*

Camden Ready Mix Co.........F 937 456-4539
Camden *(G-2484)*

Carbros.........G 330 375-5000
Akron *(G-110)*

Carr Bros Inc.........G 440 232-3700
Bedford *(G-1412)*

Carr Bros Bldrs Sup & Coal Co.........E 440 232-3700
Cleveland *(G-4983)*

Castalia Trenching & Ready Mix.........F 419 684-5502
Castalia *(G-2973)*

Cement Products Inc.........E 419 524-4342
Mansfield *(G-12578)*

Cemex USA Inc.........F 937 879-8350
Fairborn *(G-9617)*

Central Ready Mix LLC.........E 513 402-5001
Cincinnati *(G-3515)*

Central Ready Mix LLC.........G 513 367-1939
Cleves *(G-6508)*

Central Ready-Mix of Ohio LLC.........E 614 252-3452
Cincinnati *(G-3516)*

Central Ready-Mix Ohio LLC.........E 614 252-3452
Cincinnati *(G-3517)*

Chappell-Zimmerman Inc.........E 330 337-8711
Salem *(G-16880)*

Christman Supply Co Inc.........G 740 472-0046
Woodsfield *(G-20715)*

Citywide Materials Inc.........E 513 533-1111
Cincinnati *(G-3581)*

Consumeracq Inc.........F 440 277-9305
Lorain *(G-12239)*

Consumers Builders Supply Co.........E 440 277-9306
Lorain *(G-12240)*

Cremeans Concrete and Sup Co.........G 740 446-1142
Gallipolis *(G-10293)*

D W Dickey and Son Inc.........E 330 424-1441
Lisbon *(G-12119)*

Dan K Williams Inc.........E 419 893-3251
Maumee *(G-13236)*

Dan Shrock Cement.........G 440 548-2498
Parkman *(G-15951)*

Dearth Resources Inc.........G 937 325-0651
Springfield *(G-17539)*

Dearth Resources Inc.........G 937 663-4171
Springfield *(G-17540)*

Diano Construction and Sup Co.........E 330 456-7229
Canton *(G-2687)*

Diversified Ready Mix Ltd.........G 330 628-3355
Tallmadge *(G-18142)*

Eci.........G 419 483-2738
Castalia *(G-2974)*

Ernst Enterprises Inc.........F 937 878-9378
Fairborn *(G-9620)*

Ernst Enterprises Inc.........E 937 233-5555
Dayton *(G-8331)*

Ernst Enterprises Inc.........E 513 874-8300
Lebanon *(G-11798)*

Ernst Enterprises Inc.........E 937 848-6811
Bellbrook *(G-1507)*

Ernst Enterprises Inc.........E 937 866-9441
Carrollton *(G-2955)*

Ernst Enterprises Inc.........E 937 339-6249
Troy *(G-18822)*

Ernst Enterprises Inc.........E 614 443-9456
Columbus *(G-7065)*

Feikert Sand & Gravel Co Inc.........E 330 674-0038
Millersburg *(G-14215)*

G Big Inc.........E 740 867-5758
Chesapeake *(G-3187)*

G Big Inc ... G ... 740 532-9123
Ironton *(G-11293)*

Geauga Concrete Inc ... F ... 440 338-4915
Newbury *(G-15091)*

Grafton Ready Mix Concret Inc ... E ... 440 926-2911
Grafton *(G-10427)*

Hanson Aggregates East LLC ... E ... 740 773-2172
Chillicothe *(G-3242)*

Hanson Aggregates East LLC ... E ... 937 364-2311
Hillsboro *(G-10999)*

Hanson Aggregates East LLC ... F ... 937 382-2557
Wilmington *(G-20668)*

Hanson Aggregates East LLC ... E ... 937 587-2671
Peebles *(G-16021)*

Hensel Ready Mix ... G ... 419 253-9200
Marengo *(G-12751)*

Hensel Ready Mix Inc ... F ... 419 675-1808
Kenton *(G-11550)*

Hilltop Basic Resources Inc ... E ... 937 878-8631
Fairborn *(G-9624)*

Hilltop Basic Resources Inc ... E ... 513 621-1500
Cincinnati *(G-3885)*

Hilltop Basic Resources Inc ... F ... 513 651-5000
Cincinnati *(G-3884)*

Hocking Valley Concrete Inc ... F ... 740 385-2165
Logan *(G-12177)*

Hocking Valley Concrete Inc ... G ... 740 385-2165
Logan *(G-12178)*

Hull Builders Supply Inc ... E ... 440 967-3159
Vermilion *(G-19328)*

Hull Ready Mix Concrete Inc ... F ... 419 625-8070
Sandusky *(G-16972)*

Huron Cement Products Company ... E ... 419 433-4161
Huron *(G-11224)*

Huth Ready Mix & Supply Co ... F ... 330 833-4191
Massillon *(G-13152)*

IMI-Irving Materials Inc ... G ... 513 844-8444
Hamilton *(G-10704)*

In The Mix Dj Service ... G ... 330 704-2833
North Canton *(G-15242)*

Ioppolo Concrete Corporation ... E ... 440 439-6606
Bedford *(G-1433)*

Irving Materials Inc ... F ... 513 844-8444
Hamilton *(G-10708)*

Irving Materials Inc ... F ... 513 523-7127
Oxford *(G-15838)*

Joe McClelland Inc ... E ... 740 452-3036
Zanesville *(G-21324)*

K & L Ready Mix Inc ... F ... 419 523-4376
Ottawa *(G-15798)*

K & L Ready Mix Inc ... F ... 419 532-3585
Kalida *(G-11413)*

K & L Ready Mix Inc ... F ... 419 293-2937
Mc Comb *(G-13339)*

K M B Inc ... E ... 330 889-3451
Bristolville *(G-2098)*

Kuhlman Corporation ... E ... 419 321-1670
Toledo *(G-18548)*

Kuhlman Corporation ... E ... 419 897-6000
Maumee *(G-13273)*

Lancaster West Side Coal Co ... F ... 740 862-4713
Lancaster *(G-11725)*

M & R Redi Mix Inc ... E ... 419 445-7771
Pettisville *(G-16181)*

M & R Redi Mix Inc ... G ... 419 748-8442
Mc Clure *(G-13335)*

Mack Concrete Industries Inc ... F ... 330 483-3111
Valley City *(G-19212)*

Mack Concrete Industries Inc ... G ... 330 784-7008
Akron *(G-279)*

Market Ready ... G ... 513 289-9231
Maineville *(G-12528)*

Marvin Mix ... G ... 614 774-9337
Columbus *(G-7322)*

Maysville Ready Mix Concr ... G ... 937 795-2020
Aberdeen *(G-2)*

McGovney Ready Mix Inc ... E ... 740 353-4111
Portsmouth *(G-16443)*

Mecco Inc ... E ... 513 422-3651
Middletown *(G-14061)*

Medina Supply Company ... E ... 330 425-0752
Twinsburg *(G-18984)*

Medina Supply Company ... E ... 330 723-3681
Medina *(G-13445)*

Mel Stevens U-Cart Concrete ... G ... 419 478-2600
Toledo *(G-18582)*

Miami Valley Ready Mix Inc ... E ... 513 738-2616
Harrison *(G-10791)*

Mini-Mix Inc ... G ... 740 345-3186
Newark *(G-15034)*

Moritz Concrete Inc ... E ... 419 529-3232
Mansfield *(G-12652)*

Moritz Materials Inc ... E ... 419 281-0575
Ashland *(G-755)*

Nalcon Ready Mix Inc ... G ... 419 422-4341
Kenton *(G-11562)*

National Lime and Stone Co ... E ... 419 423-3400
Findlay *(G-9866)*

National Lime and Stone Co ... G ... 330 339-2144
New Philadelphia *(G-14918)*

National Lime and Stone Co ... G ... 216 883-9840
Cleveland *(G-5857)*

Nissen Lumber & Coal Co Inc ... G ... 419 836-8035
Oregon *(G-15711)*

O K Brugmann Jr & Sons Inc ... F ... 330 274-2106
Mantua *(G-12718)*

Olen Corporation ... F ... 419 294-2611
Upper Sandusky *(G-19137)*

Orrville Trucking & Grading Co ... E ... 330 682-4010
Orrville *(G-15753)*

▲ Osborne Inc ... E ... 440 942-7000
Mentor *(G-13677)*

Osborne Inc ... E ... 216 771-0010
Cleveland *(G-5949)*

Pahl Ready Mix Concrete Inc ... F ... 419 636-4238
Bryan *(G-2317)*

Pahl Ready Mix Concrete Inc ... F ... 419 636-4238
Waterville *(G-19664)*

Palmer Bros Transit Mix Con ... F ... 419 332-6363
Fremont *(G-10174)*

Palmer Bros Transit Mix Con ... F ... 419 352-4681
Bowling Green *(G-2006)*

Palmer Bros Transit Mix Con ... G ... 419 447-2018
Tiffin *(G-18237)*

Palmer Bros Transit Mix Con ... F ... 419 686-2366
Portage *(G-16427)*

Paul R Lipp & Son Inc ... F ... 330 227-9614
Rogers *(G-16714)*

Petros Concrete Inc ... G ... 330 868-6130
Waynesburg *(G-19727)*

Philip Armbrust ... G ... 740 335-7285
Wshngtn CT Hs *(G-20919)*

Phillips Companies ... E ... 937 426-5461
Beavercreek Township *(G-1387)*

Phillips Ready Mix Co ... D ... 937 426-5151
Beavercreek Township *(G-1388)*

Piqua Concrete Corp ... E ... 937 773-0841
Piqua *(G-16302)*

Piqua Concrete Corp ... F ... 937 698-7229
Vandalia *(G-19309)*

Piqua Concrete Corp ... G ... 937 855-0410
Germantown *(G-10372)*

Placecrete Inc ... F ... 937 298-2121
Moraine *(G-14515)*

Pleasant Valley Ready Mix Inc ... F ... 330 852-2613
Sugarcreek *(G-18032)*

Quadcast ... G ... 330 854-4511
Canal Fulton *(G-2511)*

Quality Block & Supply Inc ... E ... 330 364-4411
Mount Eaton *(G-14556)*

Quality Ready Mix Inc ... E ... 419 738-2817
Bluffton *(G-1914)*

Quality Ready Mix Inc ... G ... 419 394-9097
Saint Marys *(G-16851)*

Quality Ready Mix Inc ... F ... 419 394-8870
Saint Marys *(G-16852)*

Quikrete Companies Inc ... E ... 513 367-6135
Harrison *(G-10798)*

Quikrete Companies Inc ... E ... 330 296-6080
Ravenna *(G-16551)*

R W Sidley Incorporated ... E ... 440 564-2221
Newbury *(G-15102)*

R W Sidley Incorporated ... F ... 330 499-5616
Canton *(G-2834)*

R W Sidley Incorporated ... E ... 330 793-7374
Youngstown *(G-21184)*

Rinker Materials ... G ... 330 654-2511
Diamond *(G-8959)*

Rockport Cnstr & Mtls Inc ... E ... 216 432-9465
Cleveland *(G-6126)*

Ross Co Redi Mix Co Inc ... G ... 740 333-6833
Wshngtn CT Hs *(G-20926)*

Ross-Co Redi-Mix Co Inc ... F ... 740 775-4466
Chillicothe *(G-3273)*

Rw Sidley Inc ... G ... 330 545-1964
Girard *(G-10394)*

S J Roth Enterprises Inc ... E ... 513 242-8400
Cincinnati *(G-4373)*

Sakrete Inc ... E ... 513 242-3644
Cincinnati *(G-4377)*

Sardinia Concrete Company ... E ... 513 248-0090
Milford *(G-14172)*

Sardinia Concrete Company ... F ... 513 248-0090
Lebanon *(G-11836)*

Sardinia Ready Mix Inc ... G ... 937 446-2523
Sardinia *(G-17031)*

Sardinia Ready Mix Inc ... F ... 937 446-2523
Sardinia *(G-17032)*

Schwab Industries Inc ... F ... 330 364-4411
Dover *(G-9013)*

Scioto Ready Mix LLC ... D ... 740 924-9273
Pataskala *(G-15983)*

Scioto Readymix Co ... G ... 614 491-0773
Columbus *(G-7601)*

Scsrm Concrete Company Ltd ... E ... 937 533-1001
Sidney *(G-17223)*

Shelly Company ... G ... 740 246-6315
Thornville *(G-18196)*

Smith Concrete Co ... E ... 740 373-7441
Dover *(G-9015)*

Spurlino Materials LLC ... E ... 513 705-0111
Middletown *(G-14084)*

Spurlino Materials LLC ... G ... 513 202-1111
Cleves *(G-6527)*

St Henry Tile Co Inc ... E ... 419 678-4841
Saint Henry *(G-16822)*

Stamm Contracting Co Inc ... E ... 330 274-8230
Mantua *(G-12723)*

Stark Ready Mix & Supply Co ... E ... 330 580-4307
Canton *(G-2857)*

Stocker Concrete Company ... F ... 740 254-4626
Gnadenhutten *(G-10411)*

T C Redi Mix Youngstown Inc ... E ... 330 755-2143
Youngstown *(G-21217)*

Tech Ready Mix Inc ... E ... 216 361-5000
Cleveland *(G-6299)*

▲ Terminal Ready-Mix Inc ... E ... 440 288-0181
Lorain *(G-12286)*

Tow Path Ready Mix ... F ... 740 286-2131
Jackson *(G-11331)*

Tow Path Ready Mix ... G ... 740 259-3222
Lucasville *(G-12425)*

Tri County Concrete Inc ... E ... 330 425-4464
Twinsburg *(G-19029)*

Tri County Concrete Inc ... F ... 330 425-4464
Cleveland *(G-6357)*

Twin Cities Concrete Co ... F ... 330 343-4491
Dover *(G-9021)*

Twin Cities Concrete Co ... G ... 330 627-2158
Carrollton *(G-2968)*

United Ready Mix Inc ... E ... 216 696-1600
Cleveland *(G-6387)*

W G Lockhart Construction Co ... D ... 330 745-6520
Akron *(G-466)*

W M Dauch Concrete Inc ... G ... 419 562-6917
Bucyrus *(G-2364)*

Warren Concrete and Supply Co ... F ... 330 393-1581
Warren *(G-19620)*

Wells Group LLC ... F ... 740 532-9240
Ironton *(G-11304)*

Westview Concrete Corp ... E ... 440 458-5800
Elyria *(G-9510)*

William Dauch Concrete Company ... F ... 419 668-4458
Norwalk *(G-15567)*

William Oeder Ready Mix Inc ... E ... 513 899-3901
Martinsville *(G-12930)*

Williams Concrete Inc ... F ... 419 893-3251
Maumee *(G-13309)*

Winters Products Inc ... F ... 740 286-4149
Jackson *(G-11334)*

3274 Lime

Bluffton Stone Co ... E ... 419 358-6941
Bluffton *(G-1909)*

Carmeuse Lime Inc ... E ... 419 986-5200
Bettsville *(G-1668)*

▼ Graymont Dolime (oh) Inc ... D ... 419 855-8682
Genoa *(G-10360)*

Hanson Aggregates East LLC ... E ... 937 587-2671
Peebles *(G-16021)*

Hanson Aggregates East LLC ... D ... 419 483-4390
Castalia *(G-2976)*

Huron Lime Inc ... E ... 419 433-2141
Huron *(G-11226)*

Mineral Processing Company ... G ... 419 396-3501
Carey *(G-2920)*

Naked Lime ... D ... 937 485-1932
Beavercreek *(G-1375)*

National Lime and Stone Co ... C ... 419 396-7671
Carey *(G-2921)*

Piqua Materials Inc ....E 937 773-4824
Piqua *(G-16305)*

Shelly Materials Inc ....E 740 666-5841
Ostrander *(G-15789)*

Sugarcreek Lime Service ....G 330 364-4460
Dover *(G-9019)*

Wollam AG Center Inc ....F 419 596-3896
Continental *(G-7830)*

3275 Gypsum Prdts

California Ceramic Supply Co ....G 216 531-9185
Euclid *(G-9569)*

Caraustar Industries Inc ....E 330 665-7700
Copley *(G-7841)*

Ernst Enterprises Inc ....F 419 222-2015
Lima *(G-12011)*

Mineral Processing Company ....G 419 396-3501
Carey *(G-2920)*

Next Sales LLC ....G 330 704-4126
Dover *(G-9006)*

Owens Corning Sales LLC ....C 330 634-0460
Tallmadge *(G-18162)*

Priest Services Inc ....G 440 333-1123
Mayfield Heights *(G-13321)*

Priest Services Inc ....F 440 333-1123
Rocky River *(G-16705)*

United States Gypsum Company .....B 419 734-3161
Gypsum *(G-10655)*

3281 Cut Stone Prdts

Accent Manufacturing Inc ....F 330 724-7704
Norton *(G-15500)*

Agean Marble Manufacturing ....F 513 874-1475
West Chester *(G-19978)*

Akron Cultured Marble Pdts LLC ....G 330 628-6757
Mogadore *(G-14366)*

Al-Co Products Inc ....F 419 399-3867
Latty *(G-11767)*

Angelina Stone & Marble Ltd ....G 740 633-3360
Bridgeport *(G-2088)*

Artistic Memorials Ltd ....G 419 873-0433
Perrysburg *(G-16066)*

Barta Viorel ....G 440 735-1699
Bedford *(G-1403)*

Bartan Design Inc ....G 216 267-6474
Cleveland *(G-4892)*

Bell Burial Vault Co ....G 513 896-9044
Hamilton *(G-10674)*

Bell Vault & Monument Works ....E 937 866-2444
Miamisburg *(G-13785)*

Briar Hill Stone Company ....E 330 377-5100
Glenmont *(G-10402)*

Brocks Chimney ....G 740 819-2489
Nashport *(G-14704)*

Brower Products Inc ....D 937 563-1111
Cincinnati *(G-3482)*

▲ Canton Cut Stone Co ....G 330 456-8408
North Canton *(G-15223)*

Cardinal Aggregate ....F 419 872-4380
Perrysburg *(G-16075)*

Carmeuse Lime Inc ....E 419 638-2511
Millersville *(G-14300)*

Cascade Cut Stone ....G 419 422-4341
Findlay *(G-9804)*

▲ Castelli Marble Inc ....G 216 361-2410
Cleveland *(G-4993)*

Classic Stone Company Inc ....F 614 833-3946
Columbus *(G-6934)*

▲ Cleveland Granite & Marble LLC ..E 216 291-7637
Cleveland *(G-5063)*

Columbus Marble Products Inc ....F 614 766-2786
Dublin *(G-9063)*

Crane Plumbing LLC ....E 419 522-4211
Mansfield *(G-12587)*

Creative Countertops Ohio LLC ....F 937 540-9450
Englewood *(G-9514)*

Creative Design Marble Inc ....G 937 434-8892
Dayton *(G-8248)*

Custar Stone Co ....F 419 669-4327
Napoleon *(G-14676)*

▲ Custom Cast Marbleworks Inc ......E 513 769-6505
Cincinnati *(G-3625)*

▼ Cutting Edge Countertops Inc ......E 419 873-9500
Perrysburg *(G-16081)*

D J Decorative Stone Inc ....G 937 848-6462
Bellbrook *(G-1505)*

▲ Distinctive Marble & Gran Inc ......F 614 760-0003
Plain City *(G-16335)*

▲ Dodds Monument Inc ....G 937 372-2736
Xenia *(G-20948)*

Drake Monument Company ....G 937 399-7941
Springfield *(G-17547)*

Engineered Marble Inc ....G 614 308-0041
Columbus *(G-7057)*

Fostoria Monument Co ....G 419 435-0373
Fostoria *(G-9978)*

Gallipolis Vault Co Inc ....G 740 446-3357
Gallipolis *(G-10297)*

▲ Granex Industries Inc ....F 440 248-4915
Solon *(G-17300)*

Hanson Aggregates East LLC ....E 937 364-2311
Hillsboro *(G-10999)*

HBK Stoneworks ....G 740 817-2244
Johnstown *(G-11400)*

Heritage Marble of Ohio Inc ....E 614 436-1464
Columbus *(G-7151)*

Jack Huffman ....G 740 384-5178
Wellston *(G-19766)*

Jalco Industries Inc ....F 740 286-3808
Jackson *(G-11317)*

Keystone Granite and Tile Inc ....G 614 541-9749
Columbus *(G-7261)*

Korkan Granite Co Inc ....F 330 677-1883
Kent *(G-11483)*

▲ Lang Stone Company Inc ....D 614 235-4099
Columbus *(G-7284)*

Lima Millwork Inc ....E 419 331-3303
Elida *(G-9351)*

▲ Lind Stoneworks Ltd ....G 614 866-9733
Columbus *(G-7296)*

Linden Monuments ....G 419 468-4130
Galion *(G-10279)*

Maple Grove Materials Inc ....G 419 992-4235
Tiffin *(G-18231)*

Marble Works ....G 216 496-7745
Cleveland *(G-5741)*

Marsh Industries Inc ....E 330 308-8667
New Philadelphia *(G-14912)*

Maumee Valley Memorials Inc ....F 419 878-9030
Waterville *(G-19663)*

Medina Supply Company ....E 330 723-3681
Medina *(G-13445)*

Melvin Stone Co LLC ....G 513 771-0820
Cincinnati *(G-4083)*

◆ Michael Kaufman Companies Inc ..F 330 673-4881
Kent *(G-11490)*

Michael Kaufman Companies Inc .....F 330 673-4881
Kent *(G-11491)*

▲ Milano Monuments LLC ....G 216 362-1199
Cleveland *(G-5814)*

National Lime and Stone Co ....G 419 657-6745
Wapakoneta *(G-19502)*

National Lime and Stone Co ....D 419 562-0771
Bucyrus *(G-2354)*

National Lime and Stone Co ....C 419 396-7671
Carey *(G-2921)*

North Hill Marble & Granite Co ....G 330 253-2179
Akron *(G-318)*

OBrien Cut Stone Company ....E 216 663-7800
Cleveland *(G-5925)*

Ohio Beauty Inc ....G 330 644-2241
Akron *(G-322)*

Ohio Centech ....G 513 477-8779
Cincinnati *(G-4175)*

▲ Ohio Tile & Marble Co ....E 513 541-4211
Cincinnati *(G-4180)*

Pavestone LLC ....D 513 474-3783
Cincinnati *(G-4218)*

Pietra Naturale Inc ....F 937 438-8882
Dayton *(G-8576)*

Piqua Granite & Marble Co Inc ....G 937 773-2000
Piqua *(G-16304)*

▲ Quarrymasters Inc ....G 330 612-0474
Canton *(G-2830)*

Rainbow Cultured Marble ....F 330 225-3400
Brunswick *(G-2251)*

Riceland Cabinet Inc ....D 330 601-1071
Wooster *(G-20829)*

▲ Rome Marble Inc ....G 216 431-0334
Cleveland *(G-6131)*

Schena Company Ltd ....G 419 868-5207
Holland *(G-11083)*

Solon Granite Memorial Works ....G 440 248-6606
Solon *(G-17384)*

▲ Studio Vertu Inc ....E 513 241-9038
Cincinnati *(G-4472)*

Suburban Marble and Granite Co .....G 216 281-5557
Cleveland *(G-6259)*

▲ Take It For Granite LLC ....F 513 735-0555
Cincinnati *(G-3319)*

▲ Traditional Marble & Gran Ltd ......F 419 625-3966
Milan *(G-14117)*

Transtar Holding Company ....G 800 359-3339
Cleveland *(G-6349)*

Trustone Distributors Co ....G 513 469-0335
Cincinnati *(G-4531)*

Waller Brothers Stone Company ....E 740 858-1948
Mc Dermott *(G-13345)*

Western Ohio Cut Stone Ltd ....E 937 492-4722
Sidney *(G-17235)*

3291 Abrasive Prdts

Abrasive Source Inc ....F 937 526-9753
Russia *(G-16761)*

▲ Abrasive Technology Inc ....C 740 548-4100
Lewis Center *(G-11880)*

Action Super Abrasive Pdts Inc ....E 330 673-7333
Kent *(G-11423)*

◆ Ali Industries Inc ....C 937 878-3946
Fairborn *(G-9613)*

▲ Alliance Abrasives LLC ....F 330 823-7957
Alliance *(G-490)*

▲ ARC Abrasives Inc ....D 800 888-4885
Troy *(G-18805)*

B & P Polishing Inc ....F 330 753-4202
Barberton *(G-1102)*

Baaron Abrasives Inc ....G 330 263-7737
Wooster *(G-20745)*

Braun Machine Technologies LLC .....G 330 777-5433
Vienna *(G-19363)*

Buckeye Abrasive Inc ....F 330 753-1041
Barberton *(G-1112)*

▲ Cleveland Granite & Marble LLC ...E 216 291-7637
Cleveland *(G-5063)*

Coastal Diamond Incorporated ....G 440 946-7171
Mentor *(G-13548)*

▲ Diamond Innovations Inc ....B 614 438-2000
Columbus *(G-7025)*

▲ Even-Cut Abrasive Company ....D 216 881-9595
Cleveland *(G-5306)*

Everett Industries Inc ....E 330 372-3700
Warren *(G-19548)*

▲ Golden Dynamic Inc ....G 614 575-1222
Columbus *(G-7122)*

▲ Hec Investments Inc ....C 937 278-9123
Dayton *(G-8388)*

Inner City Abrasives LLC ....E 216 391-4402
Cleveland *(G-5570)*

Innovation Sales LLC ....G 330 239-0400
Medina *(G-13426)*

Jason Incorporated ....F 513 860-3400
Hamilton *(G-10711)*

◆ Lawrence Industries Inc ....E 216 518-7000
Cleveland *(G-5687)*

▲ Lexington Abrasives Inc ....D 330 821-1166
Alliance *(G-522)*

Maxion Wheels Sedalia LLC ....F 330 794-2300
Akron *(G-290)*

▲ Mill-Rose Company ....C 440 255-9171
Mentor *(G-13657)*

Nanolap Technologies LLC ....E 877 658-4949
Englewood *(G-9534)*

National Lime and Stone Co ....C 419 396-7671
Carey *(G-2921)*

Noritake Co Inc ....E 513 234-0770
Mason *(G-13067)*

Ohio Slitting & Storage ....E 937 452-1108
Camden *(G-2486)*

▲ Performance Abrasives Inc ....G 513 733-9283
Cincinnati *(G-4224)*

Performance Superabrasives LLC .....G 440 946-7171
Mentor *(G-13685)*

Premier Coatings Ltd ....F 513 942-1070
West Chester *(G-19920)*

▲ Qibco Buffing Pads Inc ....F 937 743-0805
Carlisle *(G-2935)*

▼ Regal Diamond Products Corp ......E 440 944-7700
Wickliffe *(G-20385)*

Research Abrasive Products Inc ....E 440 944-3200
Wickliffe *(G-20386)*

Schumann Enterprises Inc ....E 216 267-6850
Cleveland *(G-6166)*

Steel Warehouse of Ohio LLC ....D 888 225-3760
Cleveland *(G-6246)*

▲ Sure-Foot Industries Corp ....E 440 234-4446
Cleveland *(G-6275)*

Tomson Steel Company ....E 513 420-8600
Middletown *(G-14089)*

▲ Unisand Incorporated ....E 330 722-0222
Medina *(G-13492)*

S I C

United Buff & Supply Co Inc ....G...... 419 738-2417
Wapakoneta *(G-19510)*
Universal Ground Cullet Inc ....G...... 419 637-2630
Gibsonburg *(G-10378)*
◆ US Technology Corporation ....E...... 330 455-1181
Canton *(G-2891)*
US Technology Media Inc ....F...... 330 874-3094
Bolivar *(G-1947)*
Vibra Finish Co ....E...... 513 870-6300
Fairfield *(G-9729)*
Wright Buffing Wheel Company ....G...... 330 424-7887
Lisbon *(G-12136)*

3292 Asbestos products

Pop/Pos Advantage ....G...... 440 543-9452
Chagrin Falls *(G-3113)*
▲ Texas Tile Manufacturing LLC ....E...... 713 869-5811
Solon *(G-17404)*

3295 Minerals & Earths: Ground Or Treated

6062 Holdings LLC ....G...... 216 359-9005
Beachwood *(G-1252)*
Acme Company ....D...... 330 758-2313
Poland *(G-16381)*
▲ Advanced Quartz Fabrication ....F...... 440 350-4567
Chardon *(G-3138)*
Allega Slag Recovery Inc ....E...... 216 447-0814
Cleveland *(G-4763)*
▲ Aluchem Inc ....E...... 513 733-8519
Cincinnati *(G-3382)*
Brier Hill Slag Company ....F...... 330 743-8170
Youngstown *(G-21035)*
Cimbar Performance Mnrl WV LLC ....E...... 330 532-2034
Wellsville *(G-19774)*
Dubro Oil Corporation ....G...... 216 696-2646
Cleveland *(G-5218)*
Edw C Levy Co ....E...... 330 484-6328
Canton *(G-2695)*
Edw C Levy Co ....E...... 419 822-8286
Delta *(G-8931)*
EMD Millipore Corporation ....C...... 513 631-0445
Norwood *(G-15572)*
GRB Holdings Inc ....D...... 937 236-3250
Dayton *(G-8377)*
Harsco Corporation ....G...... 740 367-7322
Cheshire *(G-3192)*
Industrial Quartz Corp ....E...... 440 942-0909
Mentor *(G-13606)*
Ironics Inc ....G...... 330 652-0583
Niles *(G-15162)*
J R Goslee Co ....F...... 330 723-4904
Medina *(G-13428)*
Martin Marietta Materials Inc ....E...... 513 701-1140
West Chester *(G-19897)*
Mineral Met Inc ....G...... 216 641-3555
Cleveland *(G-5820)*
Premier Silica LLC ....E...... 740 659-2241
Glenford *(G-10400)*
Premier Silica LLC ....E...... 740 599-7773
Howard *(G-11124)*
Pyrotek Incorporated ....C...... 440 349-8800
Aurora *(G-942)*
R W Sidley Incorporated ....E...... 330 750-1661
Struthers *(G-17997)*
▲ Seaforth Mineral & Ore Co Inc ....F...... 216 292-5820
Cleveland *(G-6176)*
Sharon Stone Co ....G...... 740 374-3236
Dexter City *(G-8957)*
Stein Steel Mill Services Inc ....F...... 440 526-9301
Broadview Heights *(G-2120)*
Tms International LLC ....E...... 330 847-0844
Warren *(G-19609)*
Tms International Corporation ....F...... 740 223-0091
Marion *(G-12906)*
Trans Ash Inc ....F...... 859 341-1528
Cincinnati *(G-4518)*

3296 Mineral Wool

American Insulation Tech LLC ....F...... 513 733-4248
Milford *(G-14120)*
Autoneum North America Inc ....B...... 419 693-0511
Oregon *(G-15703)*
Blackthorn LLC ....F...... 937 836-9296
Clayton *(G-4657)*
Brendons Fiber Works ....G...... 614 353-6599
Columbus *(G-6854)*
Corrosion Resistant Technology ....G...... 440 543-1320
Chagrin Falls *(G-3083)*
Cpic Automotive Inc ....G...... 740 587-3262
Granville *(G-10456)*

Derby Fabg Solutions LLC ....E...... 937 498-4054
Sidney *(G-17176)*
▼ Extol of Ohio Inc ....E...... 419 668-2072
Norwalk *(G-15537)*
▲ Fibreboard Corporation ....C...... 419 248-8000
Toledo *(G-18470)*
Johns Manville Corporation ....B...... 419 878-8111
Waterville *(G-19660)*
Johns Manville Corporation ....A...... 419 784-7000
Defiance *(G-8795)*
Johns Manville Corporation ....C...... 419 784-7000
Defiance *(G-8796)*
Johns Manville Corporation ....C...... 419 467-8189
Maumee *(G-13271)*
Johns Manville Corporation ....C...... 419 878-8111
Defiance *(G-8797)*
McGill Airpressure LLC ....G...... 614 882-5455
Columbus *(G-7332)*
Midwest Acoust-A-Fiber Inc ....E...... 740 363-6247
Delaware *(G-8871)*
Mpc Inc ....F...... 440 835-1405
Westlake *(G-20284)*
▲ Nitto Denko Auto Ohio Inc ....C...... 937 773-4820
Piqua *(G-16295)*
Owens Corning ....E...... 419 248-8000
Navarre *(G-14723)*
Owens Corning ....C...... 740 964-1727
Pataskala *(G-15976)*
◆ Owens Corning ....A...... 419 248-8000
Toledo *(G-18625)*
◆ Owens Corning Sales LLC ....A...... 419 248-8000
Toledo *(G-18626)*
Owens Corning Sales LLC ....C...... 740 328-2300
Newark *(G-15043)*
Owens Corning Sales LLC ....E...... 614 539-0830
Grove City *(G-10581)*
Owens Corning Sales LLC ....D...... 614 399-3915
Mount Vernon *(G-14635)*
Owens-Corning Capital LLC ....G...... 419 248-8000
Toledo *(G-18627)*
◆ Premier Manufacturing Corp ....D...... 216 941-9700
Cleveland *(G-6041)*
▲ Refractory Specialties Inc ....E...... 330 938-2101
Sebring *(G-17050)*
Silvercote LLC ....G...... 330 748-8500
Macedonia *(G-12482)*
Sorbothane Inc ....E...... 330 678-9444
Kent *(G-11530)*
▼ Tectum Inc ....C...... 740 345-9691
Newark *(G-15063)*

3297 Nonclay Refractories

A & M Refractories Inc ....E...... 740 456-8020
New Boston *(G-14778)*
◆ Allied Mineral Products Inc ....B...... 614 876-0244
Columbus *(G-6726)*
Castruction Company Inc ....F...... 330 332-9622
Salem *(G-16879)*
▲ E I Ceramics LLC ....D...... 513 772-7001
Cincinnati *(G-3678)*
Ets Schaefer LLC ....E...... 330 468-6600
Macedonia *(G-12448)*
General Electric Company ....G...... 740 928-7010
Hebron *(G-10867)*
Harbisonwalker Intl Inc ....D...... 740 682-7711
Oak Hill *(G-15597)*
I Cerco Inc ....D...... 740 982-2050
Crooksville *(G-7950)*
Impact Armor Technologies LLC ....F...... 216 706-2024
Cleveland *(G-5554)*
Johns Manville Corporation ....B...... 419 878-8111
Waterville *(G-19660)*
Magneco/Metrel Inc ....E...... 330 426-9468
Negley *(G-14730)*
Martin Marietta Materials Inc ....E...... 513 701-1140
West Chester *(G-19897)*
Minteq International Inc ....E...... 330 343-8821
Dover *(G-9003)*
◆ Momentive Prfmce Mtls Qrtz Inc ....C...... 440 878-5700
Strongsville *(G-17941)*
▲ Nock and Son Company ....G...... 440 871-5525
Cleveland *(G-5885)*
Ohio Vly Stmpng-Assemblies Inc ....E...... 419 522-0983
Mansfield *(G-12663)*
Plibrico Company LLC ....E...... 740 682-7755
Oak Hill *(G-15604)*
Pyromatics Corp ....F...... 440 352-3500
Mentor *(G-13704)*
Refractory Coating Tech Inc ....E...... 330 683-2200
Orrville *(G-15757)*

▲ Refractory Specialties Inc ....E...... 330 938-2101
Sebring *(G-17050)*
Resco Products Inc ....E...... 740 682-7794
Oak Hill *(G-15605)*
Ruscoe Company ....E...... 330 253-8148
Akron *(G-383)*
Saint-Gobain Ceramics Plas Inc ....A...... 330 673-5860
Stow *(G-17797)*
UNI-Ref United Refractories Co ....E...... 513 563-9955
Cincinnati *(G-4536)*
▲ US Refractory Products LLC ....E...... 440 386-4580
North Ridgeville *(G-15408)*
▲ Vacuform ....E...... 330 938-9674
Sebring *(G-17057)*
Vesuvius U S A Corporation ....E...... 419 986-5126
Bettsville *(G-1670)*
▲ Wahl Refractory Solutions LLC ....D...... 419 334-2658
Fremont *(G-10193)*
▲ Zircoa Inc ....C...... 440 248-0500
Cleveland *(G-6498)*

3299 Nonmetallic Mineral Prdts, NEC

Aquablok Ltd ....F...... 419 402-4170
Swanton *(G-18080)*
Architectural Products Dev ....G...... 216 631-6260
Cleveland *(G-4826)*
Astro Met Inc ....E...... 513 772-1242
Cincinnati *(G-3421)*
B & B Cast Stone Co Inc ....G...... 740 697-0008
Roseville *(G-16726)*
Brady A Lantz Enterprises Inc ....G...... 513 742-4921
Cincinnati *(G-3466)*
Carmeuse Lime Inc ....G...... 216 961-1010
Cleveland *(G-4980)*
Cultured Marble Inc ....G...... 330 549-2282
North Lima *(G-15314)*
Custom Fountains Inc ....F...... 513 398-1447
Mason *(G-13007)*
Dayton Wright Composite ....G...... 937 469-3962
Dayton *(G-8292)*
▲ Exochem Corporation ....E...... 800 807-7464
Lorain *(G-12247)*
Fillous & Ruppel Inc ....G...... 216 431-0470
Cleveland *(G-5344)*
Fireline Inc ....E...... 330 259-0647
Youngstown *(G-21085)*
▼ Fireline Inc ....D...... 330 743-1164
Youngstown *(G-21086)*
Functional Imaging Ltd ....G...... 740 689-2466
Lancaster *(G-11717)*
▲ Great Lakes Glasswerks Inc ....G...... 440 358-0460
Painesville *(G-15885)*
Holmes Supply Corp ....G...... 330 279-2634
Holmesville *(G-11105)*
Kent Paverbrick LLC ....G...... 330 995-7000
Aurora *(G-930)*
Maverick Corporation ....F...... 513 469-9919
Blue Ash *(G-1835)*
▲ Mazzolini Artcraft Co Inc ....F...... 216 431-7529
Cleveland *(G-5767)*
▲ Miller Studio Inc ....D...... 330 339-1100
New Philadelphia *(G-14916)*
▲ R W Sidley Incorporated ....E...... 440 352-9343
Painesville *(G-15913)*
Richtech Industries Inc ....G...... 440 937-4401
Avon *(G-1009)*
Roberts Group Inc ....G...... 614 486-0497
Columbus *(G-7569)*
Scioto Ceramic Products Inc ....E...... 614 436-0405
Columbus *(G-7600)*
◆ Seves Glass Block Inc ....G...... 440 627-6257
Broadview Heights *(G-2119)*
Southwest Greens Ohio LLC ....F...... 614 389-6042
Columbus *(G-7633)*
Stephen R Lilley ....G...... 513 899-4400
Morrow *(G-14551)*
The Fischer & Jirouch Company ....G...... 216 361-3840
Cleveland *(G-6312)*
Unity Cable Technologies Inc ....G...... 419 322-4118
Toledo *(G-18759)*

33 PRIMARY METAL INDUSTRIES

3312 Blast Furnaces, Coke Ovens, Steel & Rolling Mills

A-1 Welding & Fabricating Inc ....F...... 440 233-8474
Lorain *(G-12230)*
◆ Aco Polymer Products Inc ....E...... 440 285-7000
Mentor *(G-13508)*

Adams Fabricating Inc ....G 330 866-2986
East Sparta (G-9253)

AK Steel Corporation ....B 419 755-3011
Mansfield (G-12557)

AK Steel Corporation ....B 740 450-5600
Zanesville (G-21267)

AK Steel Corporation ....A 740 829-2206
Coshocton (G-7877)

AK Steel Corporation ....B 513 425-3694
Middletown (G-14014)

AK Steel Corporation ....F 513 425-3593
Middletown (G-14015)

AK Steel Corporation ....D 513 425-5000
West Chester (G-19801)

AK Steel Corporation ....G 513 231-2552
Cincinnati (G-3373)

◆ AK Steel Corporation ....B 513 425-4200
West Chester (G-19802)

◆ AK Steel Holding Corporation ....B 513 425-5000
West Chester (G-19803)

◆ Akers America Inc ....G 330 757-4100
Poland (G-16382)

Alba Manufacturing Inc ....D 513 874-0551
Fairfield (G-9640)

▲ All Ohio Threaded Rod Co Inc ....E 216 426-1800
Cleveland (G-4757)

Allegheny Ludlum LLC ....E 330 875-2244
Louisville (G-12308)

Allen Alloys ....G 330 422-1814
Streetsboro (G-17837)

Alro Steel Corporation ....E 937 253-6121
Dayton (G-8149)

American Culvert & Fabg Co ....F 740 432-6334
Cambridge (G-2443)

American Mfg & Engrg Co ....G 440 899-9400
Cleveland (G-4791)

American Posts LLC ....E 419 720-0652
Toledo (G-18344)

American Processing LLC ....G 216 486-4600
Cleveland (G-4793)

American Steel & Alloys LLC ....E 330 847-0487
Warren (G-19521)

Amthor Steel Inc ....G 330 759-0200
Youngstown (G-21025)

Anchor Pattern Company ....G 614 443-2221
Columbus (G-6754)

Applied Innovations ....G 330 837-5694
Massillon (G-13109)

▲ Arcelormittal Cleveland LLC ....C 216 429-6000
Cleveland (G-4823)

Arcelormittal Obetz LLC ....E 614 492-8287
Columbus (G-6769)

Arcelormittal USA LLC ....D 330 659-9100
Richfield (G-16614)

Arrowstrip Inc ....E 740 633-2609
Martins Ferry (G-12921)

B & G Tool Company ....G 614 451-2538
Columbus (G-6795)

B-K Tool & Design Inc ....G 419 532-3890
Kalida (G-11412)

Barberton Steel Industries Inc ....E 330 745-6837
Barberton (G-1110)

▲ Bcast Stainless Products LLC ....F 614 873-3945
Plain City (G-16325)

Benjamin Steel Company Inc ....E 937 233-1212
Springfield (G-17522)

▲ Bertin Steel Processing Inc ....E 440 943-0094
Wickliffe (G-20357)

Brenmar Construction Inc ....D 740 286-2151
Jackson (G-11312)

Bridge Components Inds Inc ....G 614 873-0777
Columbus (G-6859)

▲ Buschman Corporation ....F 216 431-6633
Cleveland (G-4951)

C & R Inc ....E 614 497-1130
Groveport (G-10617)

◆ Canton Drop Forge Inc ....B 330 477-4511
Canton (G-2638)

Carter Scott-Browne ....E 513 398-3970
Mason (G-12992)

▲ Centaur Inc ....G 419 469-8000
Toledo (G-18392)

▲ Challenger Hardware Company ....F 216 591-1141
Brooklyn Heights (G-2134)

Charles C Lewis Company ....F 440 439-3150
Cleveland (G-5015)

Charter Manufacturing Co Inc ....A 216 883-3800
Cleveland (G-5022)

Churchill Steel Plate Ltd ....E 330 425-9000
Twinsburg (G-18913)

▲ Cleveland Track Material Inc ....D 216 641-4000
Cleveland (G-5082)

Cleveland Track Material Inc ....F 216 641-4000
Cleveland (G-5083)

Cohen Brothers Inc ....G 513 422-3696
Middletown (G-14031)

Columbus Processing Co LLC ....G 614 492-8287
Columbus (G-6963)

Community Care On Wheels ....F 330 882-5506
Clinton (G-6535)

Contractors Steel Company ....E 330 425-3050
Twinsburg (G-18919)

Crest Bending Inc ....E 419 492-2108
New Washington (G-14959)

Csc Ltd ....G 330 841-6011
Warren (G-19538)

Custom Blast & Coat Inc ....G 419 225-6024
Lima (G-12003)

D Johnson Services ....G 330 386-4588
East Liverpool (G-9210)

Dan Nemes American Racing ....G 216 749-4203
Brooklyn Heights (G-2137)

Deaks Form Tools Inc ....G 440 286-2353
Chardon (G-3149)

Die Services Ltd ....G 216 883-5800
Cleveland (G-5192)

Dietrich Industries Inc ....C 330 372-2868
Warren (G-19544)

▲ Diversifd OH Vlly Eqpt & Srvcs ....F 740 458-9881
Clarington (G-4651)

DMG Tool & Die LLC ....G 937 407-0810
Bellefontaine (G-1529)

E D M Star-One Inc ....F 440 647-0600
Wellington (G-19740)

Eastern Automated Piping ....G 740 535-8184
Mingo Junction (G-14348)

Egypt Structural Steel Proc ....E 419 628-2375
Minster (G-14352)

◆ Elster Perfection Corporation ....D 440 428-1171
Geneva (G-10346)

▲ Ernst Metal Technologies LLC ....E 937 434-3133
Moraine (G-14485)

Esm Products Inc ....G 937 492-4644
Celina (G-2996)

Falcon Fab and Finishes LLC ....G 740 820-4458
Lucasville (G-12420)

Famous Industries Inc ....C 740 397-8842
Mount Vernon (G-14622)

FBC Chemical Corporation ....F 216 341-2000
Cleveland (G-5328)

Ferguson Fire Fabrication Inc ....F 614 299-2070
Columbus (G-7081)

Forge Products Corporation ....D 216 231-2600
Cleveland (G-5370)

▲ Franklin Iron & Metal Corp ....C 937 253-8184
Dayton (G-8350)

▲ Fulton County Processing Ltd ....D 419 822-9266
Delta (G-8933)

Garden Street Iron & Metal ....E 513 853-3700
Cincinnati (G-3798)

George Manufacturing Inc ....E 513 932-1067
Lebanon (G-11801)

GKN Sinter Metals LLC ....C 740 441-3203
Gallipolis (G-10298)

Grace Metals Ltd ....G 234 380-1433
Hudson (G-11175)

Gregory Roll Form Inc ....D 330 477-4800
Canton (G-2720)

Grenga Machine & Welding ....F 330 743-1113
Youngstown (G-21104)

Hadronics Inc ....D 513 321-9350
Cincinnati (G-3861)

Harvard Coil Processing Inc ....E 216 883-6366
Cleveland (G-5484)

Heartland Steel Inc ....F 740 333-5401
Washington Court Hou (G-19639)

Heidtman Steel Products Inc ....D 419 385-0636
Toledo (G-18506)

▲ Heidtman Steel Products Inc ....E 419 691-4646
Toledo (G-18505)

Hi-Tech Wire Inc ....D 419 678-8376
Saint Henry (G-16817)

Hmt Associates Inc ....E 216 369-0109
Broadview Heights (G-2110)

Holgate Metal Fab Inc ....F 419 599-2000
Napoleon (G-14682)

Humble Construction Co ....E 614 888-8960
Columbus (G-7169)

Ideal Steel Inc ....E 937 525-9161
Springfield (G-17580)

International Steel Group ....C 330 841-2800
Warren (G-19560)

J & L Steel Bar LLC ....G 440 526-0050
Broadview Heights (G-2111)

J&J Precision Fabricators ....F 330 482-4964
Columbiana (G-6623)

Jck Industries ....E 419 433-6277
Huron (G-11229)

John Maneely Company ....E 724 342-6851
Niles (G-15165)

K K Tool Co ....E 937 325-1373
Springfield (G-17583)

Kind Special Alloys Us LLC ....G 330 788-2437
Youngstown (G-21128)

◆ Kirtland Capital Partners LP ....E 216 593-0100
Beachwood (G-1276)

▲ L&H Threaded Rods Corp ....C 937 294-6666
Moraine (G-14501)

L-K Industry Inc ....E 937 526-3000
Versailles (G-19351)

Lapham-Hickey Steel Corp ....E 614 443-4881
Columbus (G-7286)

◆ Latrobe Spcialty Mtls Dist Inc ....D 330 609-5137
Vienna (G-19366)

Latrobe Specialty Mtls Co LLC ....D 419 335-8010
Wauseon (G-19687)

Liverpool Coil Processing Inc ....C 330 558-2600
Valley City (G-19210)

▲ Lokring Technology LLC ....D 440 942-0880
Willoughby (G-20528)

Long View Steel Corp ....F 419 747-1108
Mansfield (G-12637)

Louis G Freeman Co ....E 419 334-9709
Fremont (G-10167)

Lukjan Metal Products Inc ....C 440 599-8127
Conneaut (G-7814)

Majestic Steel Management Co ....E 440 786-2666
Cleveland (G-5732)

Major Metals Company ....E 419 886-4600
Mansfield (G-12639)

Matandy Steel & Metal Pdts LLC ....D 513 844-2277
Hamilton (G-10723)

Maull Tool & Die Supply Llc ....G 513 646-4229
Loveland (G-12373)

Mc Cully Supply & Sales Inc ....G 330 497-2211
Canton (G-2775)

▲ McDonald Steel Corporation ....C 330 530-9118
Mc Donald (G-13347)

McWane Inc ....B 740 622-6651
Coshocton (G-7897)

Metaldyne Pwrtrain Cmpnnts Inc ....C 330 486-3200
Twinsburg (G-18986)

▲ Metals USA Crbn Flat Rlled Inc ....C 330 264-8416
Wooster (G-20806)

Metals USA Crbn Flat Rlled Inc ....D 937 882-6354
Springfield (G-17604)

▲ Miba Sinter USA LLC ....F 740 962-4242
McConnelsville (G-13355)

Mid-America Steel Corp ....E 800 282-3466
Cleveland (G-5805)

Middletown Tube Works Inc ....E 513 727-0080
Middletown (G-14064)

▼ Mtr Martco LLC ....D 513 424-5307
Middletown (G-14065)

New Age Design & Tool Inc ....F 440 355-5400
Lagrange (G-11634)

Nichidai America Corporation ....E 419 423-7511
Findlay (G-9867)

North American Steel Company ....E 216 475-7300
Cleveland (G-5890)

North Jckson Specialty Stl LLC ....E 330 538-9621
North Jackson (G-15295)

▲ North Shore Strapping Inc ....E 216 661-5200
Brooklyn Heights (G-2144)

◆ North Star Bluescope Steel LLC ....B 419 822-2399
Delta (G-8939)

Northeast Tubular Service Inc ....G 330 262-1881
Wooster (G-20818)

▲ Northlake Steel Corporation ....D 330 220-7717
Valley City (G-19225)

Nuflux LLC ....G 330 399-1122
Cortland (G-7872)

Ohio Coatings Company ....D 740 859-5500
Yorkville (G-21007)

▼ Ohio Gratings Inc ....B 330 477-6707
Canton (G-2799)

▲ Ohio Pickling & Processing LLC ....D 419 241-9601
Toledo (G-18616)

Ohio Steel Sheet & Plate Inc ....E 800 827-2401
Hubbard (G-11136)

▲ Ohio Valley Alloy Services Inc ....E 740 373-1900
Marietta *(G-12811)*

OReilly Precision Tool Inc ....E 937 526-4677
Russia *(G-16767)*

Pelletier Brothers Mfg ....F 740 774-4704
Chillicothe *(G-3260)*

Pemjay Inc ....E 740 254-4591
Gnadenhutten *(G-10409)*

Pendleton Mold & Machine LLC ....G 440 998-0041
Ashtabula *(G-830)*

Phillips Mfg and Tower Co ....D 419 347-1720
Shelby *(G-17140)*

▲ Pilgrim-Harp Co ....G 440 249-4185
Avon *(G-1003)*

◆ Pioneer Equipment Company ....F 330 857-6340
Dalton *(G-8078)*

▲ Pioneer Pipe Inc ....B 740 376-2400
Marietta *(G-12816)*

Plymouth Locomotive Svc LLC ....G 419 896-2854
Shiloh *(G-17152)*

Precision Die & Stamping Inc ....G 513 942-8220
West Chester *(G-19918)*

Precision Laser & Forming ....F 419 943-4350
Leipsic *(G-11873)*

▲ Precision Specialty Metals Inc ....D 323 475-3200
Worthington *(G-20883)*

Precision Strip Inc ....D 937 667-6255
Tipp City *(G-18293)*

Precision Wood & Metal Co ....G 419 221-1512
Lima *(G-12074)*

Premier Metal Trading LLC ....G 440 247-9494
Chagrin Falls *(G-3068)*

▲ Prime Conduit Inc ....F 216 464-3400
Cleveland *(G-6046)*

▼ Qual-Fab Inc ....E 440 327-5000
Avon *(G-1005)*

Quality Bar Inc ....F 330 755-0000
Struthers *(G-17996)*

Quality Tool Company ....E 419 476-8228
Toledo *(G-18663)*

R&D Machine Inc ....F 937 339-2545
Troy *(G-18866)*

Racelite South Coast Inc ....F 216 581-4600
Maple Heights *(G-12739)*

Republic Engineered Products ....E 440 277-2000
Lorain *(G-12271)*

Republic Steel Inc ....C 330 438-5533
Canton *(G-2837)*

◆ Republic Steel Inc ....D 330 438-5435
Canton *(G-2838)*

Republic Steel Inc ....E 440 277-2000
Lorain *(G-12272)*

Robert James Sales Inc ....F 330 425-9116
Twinsburg *(G-19010)*

Robs Welding Technologies Ltd ....G 937 890-4963
Dayton *(G-8637)*

Romarc Enterprises Inc ....F 419 287-4837
Pemberville *(G-16030)*

Rti Alloys ....G 330 652-9952
Niles *(G-15177)*

Rti International Metals Inc ....D 330 471-1844
Canton *(G-2845)*

S & J Precision Inc ....G 937 296-0068
Moraine *(G-14524)*

▲ S&V Industries Inc ....G 330 666-1986
Medina *(G-13472)*

Samuel Steel Pickling Company ......E 330 963-3777
Twinsburg *(G-19016)*

Schaefer Group Inc ....G 419 897-2883
Perrysburg *(G-16147)*

Sedlak ....G 330 908-2200
Richfield *(G-16636)*

Seilkop Industries Inc ....E 513 353-3090
Miamitown *(G-13892)*

Seneca Railroad & Mining Co ....F 419 483-7764
Bellevue *(G-1559)*

Sertek LLC ....D 614 504-5828
Dublin *(G-9143)*

Shear Service Inc ....G 216 341-2700
Cleveland *(G-6185)*

Shear Tech Steel LLC ....G 419 726-6174
Toledo *(G-18694)*

Stainless Specialties Inc ....E 440 942-4242
Eastlake *(G-9287)*

Steel Technologies LLC ....E 419 523-5199
Ottawa *(G-15809)*

▲ Stein Inc ....F 440 526-9301
Cleveland *(G-6248)*

Steve Vore Welding and Steel ....F 419 375-4087
Fort Recovery *(G-9959)*

◆ Superior Forge & Steel Corp ....D 419 222-4412
Lima *(G-12098)*

Systems Jay LLC Nanogate ....E 419 747-1096
Mansfield *(G-12689)*

T J Tool Works Inc ....G 440 439-1388
Bedford *(G-1463)*

The Florand Company ....G 330 747-8986
Youngstown *(G-21219)*

Thrift Tool Inc ....G 937 275-3600
Dayton *(G-8714)*

Timken Receivables Corporation ......G 234 262-3000
North Canton *(G-15275)*

Timkensteel Corporation ....B 330 471-7000
Canton *(G-2876)*

Timkensteel Corporation ....G 330 517-7300
Akron *(G-441)*

Timkensteel Corporation ....C 330 438-3000
Canton *(G-2878)*

Timkensteel Corporation ....D 937 456-8002
Eaton *(G-9324)*

Timkensteel Corporation ....C 330 438-3000
Canton *(G-2879)*

Trupoint Products ....F 330 204-3302
Sugarcreek *(G-18046)*

United Security Seals Inc ....E 614 443-7633
Columbus *(G-7721)*

United States Steel Corp ....A 440 240-2500
Lorain *(G-12287)*

Universal Metals Cutting Inc ....G 330 580-5192
Canton *(G-2890)*

Universal Urethane Pdts Inc ....D 419 693-7400
Toledo *(G-18760)*

Unlimited Machine and Tool LLC ......F 419 269-1730
Toledo *(G-18761)*

V & S Schuler Engineering Inc ....D 330 452-5200
Canton *(G-2893)*

West Motorsports Inc ....G 330 350-0375
Akron *(G-470)*

Western Reserve Metals Inc ....E 330 448-4092
Masury *(G-13218)*

WH Fetzer & Sons Mfg Inc ....G 419 687-8237
Plymouth *(G-16380)*

Wire Holdings LLC ....G 216 731-9191
Cleveland *(G-6467)*

▼ Witt Industries Inc ....D 513 871-5700
Mason *(G-13103)*

Wodin Inc ....E 440 439-4222
Cleveland *(G-6474)*

Worthington Industries Inc ....D 419 822-2500
Delta *(G-8941)*

Worthington Industries Inc ....C 513 539-9291
Monroe *(G-14420)*

Worthington Steel Company ....C 614 438-3210
Worthington *(G-20900)*

Worthngton Stl Cmpny-Baltimore ....E 410 574-5835
Worthington *(G-20901)*

◆ Xtek Inc ....B 513 733-7800
Cincinnati *(G-4616)*

Youngstown Tube Co ....E 330 743-7414
Youngstown *(G-21258)*

Zekelman Industries Inc ....C 740 432-2146
Cambridge *(G-2483)*

Zekelman Industries Inc ....C 330 373-4410
Warren *(G-19628)*

3313 Electrometallurgical Prdts

Castlebar Corporation ....C 330 451-6511
Canton *(G-2651)*

▲ Cleveland Tungsten Inc ....G 440 786-0800
Bedford *(G-1415)*

GE Aviation Systems LLC ....F 513 552-5663
Cincinnati *(G-3805)*

GE Aviation Systems LLC ....C 513 733-1611
Cincinnati *(G-3807)*

GE Aviation Systems LLC ....F 513 889-5150
West Chester *(G-19872)*

◆ Globe Metallurgical Inc ....C 740 984-2361
Waterford *(G-19647)*

H C Starck Inc ....B 216 692-3990
Euclid *(G-9584)*

▲ Marietta Eramet Inc ....C 740 374-1000
Marietta *(G-12802)*

Morris Technologies Inc ....C 513 733-1611
Cincinnati *(G-4123)*

◆ Real Alloy Holding Inc ....D 216 755-8800
Beachwood *(G-1292)*

▲ Rhenium Alloys Inc ....D 440 365-7388
North Ridgeville *(G-15401)*

Slice Mfg LLC ....G 330 733-7600
Akron *(G-404)*

Tungsten Sltons Group Intl Inc ....G 440 708-3096
Chagrin Falls *(G-3130)*

3315 Steel Wire Drawing & Nails & Spikes

Advance Industries Group LLC ....E 216 741-1800
Cleveland *(G-4707)*

Advance Wire Forming Inc ....F 216 432-3250
Cleveland *(G-4711)*

AJD Holding Co ....D 330 405-4477
Twinsburg *(G-18895)*

Aluminum Fence & Mfg Co ....G 330 755-3323
Burton *(G-2372)*

▲ American Manufacturing Inc ....F 419 531-9471
Toledo *(G-18340)*

▲ American Spring Wire Corp ....C 216 292-4620
Bedford Heights *(G-1478)*

▲ American Wire & Cable Company ...E 440 235-1140
Olmsted Twp *(G-15678)*

▲ Ametco Manufacturing Corp ....E 440 951-4300
Willoughby *(G-20430)*

◆ Barrette Outdoor Living Inc ....B 440 891-0790
Middleburg Heights *(G-13903)*

Bayloff Stmped Pdts Knsman Inc .....D 330 876-4511
Kinsman *(G-11608)*

Bekaert Corporation ....C 330 683-5060
Orrville *(G-15729)*

Bekaert Corporation ....F 330 683-5060
Orrville *(G-15730)*

Bekaert Corporation ....E 330 835-5124
Fairlawn *(G-9740)*

Bekaert Corporation ....C 330 867-3325
Fairlawn *(G-9741)*

◆ Bekaert North America MGT Corp ...C ... 330 867-3325
Fairlawn *(G-9742)*

▲ Brushes Inc ....E 216 267-8084
Cleveland *(G-4942)*

Butler Processing Inc ....E 513 874-1400
Hamilton *(G-10678)*

Cambridge Cable Service Co ....G 740 685-5775
Byesville *(G-2396)*

Ceco Machine & Tool ....G 937 264-3047
Dayton *(G-8217)*

Contour Forming Inc ....G 740 345-9777
Newark *(G-14996)*

Custom Cltch Jint Hydrlics Inc ....F 216 431-1630
Cleveland *(G-5149)*

D M L Steel Tech ....F 513 737-9911
Liberty Twp *(G-11973)*

D&M Fencing LLC ....G 419 604-0698
Spencerville *(G-17459)*

▲ Dayton Superior Corporation ....C 937 866-0711
Miamisburg *(G-13798)*

DC Controls LLC ....G 513 225-0813
West Chester *(G-19997)*

Electroduct LLC ....E 330 220-9300
Brunswick *(G-2223)*

▲ Engineered Wire Products Inc ....C 419 294-3817
Upper Sandusky *(G-19121)*

Euclid Steel & Wire Inc ....F 216 731-6744
Euclid *(G-9580)*

Falcon Fab and Finishes LLC ....G 740 820-4458
Lucasville *(G-12420)*

▲ Fenix LLC ....F 419 739-3400
Fostoria *(G-9971)*

▲ File Sharpening Company Inc ....E 937 376-8268
Xenia *(G-20951)*

◆ Garda Arch Fab LLC ....G 216 431-6300
Cleveland *(G-5395)*

Genesis Steel Corp ....G 740 282-2300
Steubenville *(G-17696)*

Glebus Alloys LLC ....F 330 867-9999
Stow *(G-17759)*

Hawthorne Wire Ltd ....F 216 712-4747
Lakewood *(G-11667)*

Hawthorne Wire Services Ltd ....G 216 712-4747
Lakewood *(G-11668)*

Hsm Wire International Inc ....G 330 244-8501
North Canton *(G-15241)*

▲ Injection Alloys Incorporated ....F 513 422-8819
Middletown *(G-14047)*

John A & William J Wiechart ....G 419 647-4617
Spencerville *(G-17461)*

▲ JR Manufacturing Inc ....C 419 375-8021
Fort Recovery *(G-9956)*

▲ Madsen Wire Products Inc ....E 937 829-6561
Dayton *(G-8468)*

▲ Marlin Thermocouple Wire Inc ....E 440 835-1950
Cleveland *(G-5750)*

Master-Halco Inc ....E 513 869-7600
Fairfield *(G-9680)*

McHenry Industries Inc ....E 330 799-8930
Youngstown (G-21142)
Merchants Metals LLC ....F 513 942-0268
West Chester (G-19900)
▼ Midwestern Industries Inc ....C 330 837-4203
Massillon (G-13180)
▲ Murphy Industries Inc ....E 740 387-7890
Marion (G-12887)
▲ Noco Company ....B 216 464-8131
Solon (G-17350)
Partners Manufacturing Group ....G 419 468-8516
Galion (G-10281)
▲ Polymet Corporation ....E 513 874-3586
West Chester (G-20038)
Ram Sensors Inc ....G 440 835-3540
Westlake (G-20300)
Ram Sensors Inc ....F 440 835-3540
Cleveland (G-6089)
Randy Lewis Inc ....F 330 784-0456
Akron (G-365)
▲ Reinforcement Systems Ohio LLC ....G 330 469-6958
Warren (G-19593)
▲ Republic Steel Wire Proc LLC ....E 440 996-0740
Solon (G-17368)
▲ Republic Wire Inc ....D 513 860-1800
West Chester (G-19930)
▲ Richards Whl Fence Co Inc ....E 330 773-0423
Akron (G-373)
Robertson Incorporated ....E 937 323-3747
Springfield (G-17644)
S & S Wldg Fabg Machining Inc ....E 330 392-7878
Newton Falls (G-15139)
Seneca Wire Group Inc ....G 419 435-9261
Fostoria (G-9996)
▲ Solon Specialty Wire Co ....E 440 248-7600
Cleveland (G-6219)
Stephens Pipe & Steel LLC ....C 740 869-2257
Mount Sterling (G-14604)
▲ Stop Stick Ltd ....E 513 202-5500
Harrison (G-10806)
Summit Engineered Products ....F 330 854-5388
Canal Fulton (G-2514)
Sunrise Cooperative Inc ....E 419 683-4600
Crestline (G-7936)
Tru-Form Steel & Wire Inc ....E 765 348-5001
Toledo (G-18757)
Wire Holdings LLC ....G 216 731-9191
Cleveland (G-6467)
Wire Products Company Inc ....C 216 267-0777
Cleveland (G-6469)

3316 Cold Rolled Steel Sheet, Strip & Bars

AK Steel Corporation ....B 740 450-5600
Zanesville (G-21267)
AK Steel Corporation ....A 740 829-2206
Coshocton (G-7877)
◆ Akers America Inc ....G 330 757-4100
Poland (G-16382)
Akron Rebar Co ....E 216 433-0000
Cleveland (G-4740)
▲ All Ohio Threaded Rod Co Inc ......E 216 426-1800
Cleveland (G-4757)
Allegheny Ludlum LLC ....E 330 875-2244
Louisville (G-12308)
Alro Steel Corporation ....E 937 253-6121
Dayton (G-8149)
▲ American Spring Wire Corp ....C 216 292-4620
Bedford Heights (G-1478)
Bar Processing Corporation ....D 330 872-0914
Newton Falls (G-15129)
▲ Bcs Metal Prep LLC ....E 440 663-1100
Solon (G-17266)
Bekaert Corporation ....C 330 683-5060
Orrville (G-15729)
Benjamin Steel Company Inc ....E 937 233-1212
Springfield (G-17522)
▲ Centaur Inc ....G 419 469-8000
Toledo (G-18392)
Cincinnati Cold Drawn Inc ....G 513 874-3296
West Chester (G-19830)
Clark Grave Vault Company ....C 614 294-3761
Columbus (G-6933)
Columbia Steel and Wire Inc ....G 330 468-2709
Northfield (G-15463)
Consolidated Metal Pdts Inc ....C 513 251-2624
Cincinnati (G-3604)
Denne Industries Inc ....E 440 365-0600
Elyria (G-9401)
Dietrich Industries Inc ....E 614 438-3210
Worthington (G-20864)

Elgin Fastener Group LLC ....E 216 481-4400
Cleveland (G-5271)
Ferrolux Metals Co Ohio LLC ....G 216 671-6161
Macedonia (G-12449)
Formetal Inc ....F 419 898-2211
Oak Harbor (G-15591)
Geneva Liberty Steel Ltd ....D 330 740-0103
Youngstown (G-21097)
◆ Greer Steel Company ....C 330 343-8811
Dover (G-8989)
H S Processing LP ....E 216 641-6995
Cleveland (G-5470)
▲ Heidtman Steel Products Inc ....E 419 691-4646
Toledo (G-18505)
▲ Hynes Industries Inc ....C 330 799-3221
Youngstown (G-21111)
▲ Independent Steel Company LLC .....E 330 225-7741
Valley City (G-19207)
Lakeway Mfg Inc ....E 419 433-3030
Huron (G-11232)
LLC Ring Masters ....E 330 832-1511
Massillon (G-13167)
Mid-America Steel Corp ....E 800 282-3466
Cleveland (G-5805)
MSC Walbridge Coatings Inc ....C 419 666-6130
Walbridge (G-19461)
▲ New Dimension Metals Corp ....E 937 299-2233
Moraine (G-14510)
Nucor Bright Bar Orville LLC ....F 330 682-5555
Orrville (G-15751)
Pilot-Run Stamping Company ....E 440 255-8821
Mentor (G-13687)
Precision Strip Inc ....E 419 674-4186
Kenton (G-11564)
Raco Cutting Inc ....G 937 293-1228
Moraine (G-14523)
Republic Steel Inc ....F 330 837-7024
Massillon (G-13199)
Steel Technologies LLC ....D 440 946-8666
Willoughby (G-20605)
◆ Superior Forge & Steel Corp ....D 419 222-4412
Lima (G-12098)
Tecumseh Redevelopment Inc ....G 330 659-9100
Richfield (G-16643)
◆ Telling Industries LLC ....F 440 974-3370
Willoughby (G-20612)
Telling Industries LLC ....F 928 681-2010
Willoughby (G-20613)
Telling Industries LLC ....D 740 435-8900
Cambridge (G-2480)
▲ Thomas Steel Strip Corporation ....B 330 841-6429
Warren (G-19608)
Thompson Steel Company Inc ....D 419 399-4803
Paulding (G-16014)
Western Reserve Metals Inc ....E 330 448-4092
Masury (G-13218)
Worthington Industries Inc ....C 614 438-3210
Worthington (G-20896)
Worthington Industries Inc ....F 614 438-3113
Columbus (G-7776)
Worthington Industries Inc ....F 614 438-3190
Columbus (G-7777)
Worthington Industries Inc ....A 614 438-3077
Worthington (G-20897)
Worthington Industries Lsg LLC ......G 614 438-3210
Worthington (G-20898)
Worthington Steel Company ....C 614 438-3210
Worthington (G-20900)
Worthington Steel Company ....C 216 441-8300
Cleveland (G-6483)
Worthington Stl Cmpny-Baltimore .....E 410 574-5835
Worthington (G-20901)

3317 Steel Pipe & Tubes

▼ AK Tube LLC ....C 419 661-4150
Walbridge (G-19456)
All Steel Structures Inc ....G 330 312-3131
Carrollton (G-2951)
Alro Steel Corporation ....E 937 253-6121
Dayton (G-8149)
▲ Arcelormittal Tubular ....D 740 382-3979
Marion (G-12855)
Arcelormittal Tubular ....A 419 347-2424
Shelby (G-17132)
Arcelormittal USA LLC ....D 419 347-2424
Shelby (G-17133)
Benjamin Steel Company Inc ....E 937 233-1212
Springfield (G-17522)
Bull Moose Tube Company ....G 330 448-4878
Masury (G-13213)

Busch & Thiem Inc..................E 419 625-7515
Sandusky (G-16952)
Chart International Inc...............D 440 753-1490
Cleveland (G-5021)
▲ Commercial Honing LLC ....D 330 343-8896
Dover (G-8971)
Conduit Pipe Products Company ......D 614 879-9114
West Jefferson (G-20077)
Contech Engnered Solutions Inc ......A 513 645-7000
West Chester (G-19840)
Contech Engnered Solutions LLC .....D 513 645-7000
Middletown (G-14032)
◆ Contech Engnered Solutions LLC ...C 513 645-7000
West Chester (G-19841)
Crest Bending Inc ....E 419 492-2108
New Washington (G-14959)
General Machine & Saw Company ....E 740 375-5730
Marion (G-12867)
▲ Jackson Tube Service Inc ....C 937 773-8550
Piqua (G-16282)
James O Emert Jr ....G 330 650-6990
Hudson (G-11185)
Jmc Steel Group ....E 216 910-3700
Beachwood (G-1275)
John Maneely Company ....E 724 342-6851
Niles (G-15165)
◆ Kirtland Capital Partners LP ....E 216 593-0100
Beachwood (G-1276)
Major Metals Company ....E 419 886-4600
Mansfield (G-12639)
Mid-Ohio Tubing LLC ....E 419 883-2066
Butler (G-2392)
Mid-Ohio Tubing LLC ....D 419 886-0220
Bellville (G-1572)
Munroe Incorporated ....G 330 755-7216
Struthers (G-17995)
Phillips Mfg and Tower Co ....D 419 347-1720
Shelby (G-17140)
▲ PMC Industries Corp ....D 440 943-3300
Wickliffe (G-20383)
PWS Welding & Mtg ....F 330 385-6922
East Liverpool (G-9226)
▲ Reliacheck Manufacturing Inc ......E 440 933-6162
Avon Lake (G-1048)
Shawcor Inc ....C 513 683-7800
Loveland (G-12386)
◆ Specialty Pipe & Tube Inc ....F 330 505-8262
Mineral Ridge (G-14311)
▲ Sterling Pipe & Tube Inc ....C 419 729-9756
Toledo (G-18704)
Stryker Steel Tube LLC ....E 419 682-4527
Stryker (G-18008)
T & D Fabricating Inc ....E 440 951-5646
Eastlake (G-9292)
TI Group Auto Systems LLC ....C 740 929-2049
Hebron (G-10890)
Timkensteel Corporation ....G 330 471-7000
Canton (G-2877)
Tite Seal Case Company Inc ....G 440 647-2371
Wellington (G-19756)
Tubetech Inc ....E 330 426-9476
East Palestine (G-9247)
Unison Industries LLC ....B 937 426-0621
Dayton (G-8121)
United Tube Corporation ....D 330 725-4196
Medina (G-13494)
▲ Vallourec Star LP ....C 330 742-6300
Youngstown (G-21235)
▲ Welded Tubes Inc ....G 216 378-2092
Orwell (G-15781)
Welded Tubes Inc ....F 440 437-5144
Orwell (G-15782)
Woodsage LLC ....E 419 866-8000
Holland (G-11098)
Zekelman Industries Inc ....C 740 432-2146
Cambridge (G-2483)
Zekelman Industries Inc ....C 330 373-4410
Warren (G-19628)

3321 Gray Iron Foundries

A C Williams Co Inc ....E 330 296-6110
Ravenna (G-16511)
Advanced Metals Group LLC ....C 937 492-4134
Sidney (G-17166)
Akron Gear & Engineering Inc ....E 330 773-6608
Akron (G-45)
Amsted Industries Incorporated ......C 614 836-2323
Groveport (G-10612)
Anchor Glass Container Corp ....C 740 452-2743
Zanesville (G-21272)

Arcelormittal Tubular ....A 419 347-2424
Shelby *(G-17132)*

Arconic Inc ....A 216 641-3600
Newburgh Heights *(G-15069)*

Blanchester Foundry Co Inc ....F 937 783-2091
Blanchester *(G-1711)*

Cast Metals Incorporated ....E 419 278-2010
Deshler *(G-8948)*

Castco Inc ....E 440 365-2333
Elyria *(G-9390)*

Casting Solutions LLC ....C 740 452-9371
Zanesville *(G-21288)*

Castings Usa Inc ....G 330 339-3611
New Philadelphia *(G-14890)*

Chris Erhart Foundry & Mch Co ....E 513 421-6550
Cincinnati *(G-3531)*

Col-Pump Company Inc ....D 330 482-1029
Columbiana *(G-6611)*

D Picking & Co ....G 419 562-5016
Bucyrus *(G-2337)*

▲ Dd Foundry Inc ....C 216 362-4100
Brookpark *(G-2156)*

Domestic Casting Company LLC ....C 717 532-6615
Delaware *(G-8839)*

Ej Usa Inc ....E 216 692-3001
Cleveland *(G-5261)*

Ej Usa Inc ....G 614 871-2436
Grove City *(G-10556)*

Ej Usa Inc ....F 330 782-3900
Youngstown *(G-21076)*

◆ Ellwood Engineered Castings Co ....C 330 568-3000
Hubbard *(G-11130)*

Engines Inc of Ohio ....D 740 377-9874
South Point *(G-17437)*

Foote Foundry LLC ....D 740 694-1595
Fredericktown *(G-10102)*

Ford Motor Company ....A 216 676-3989
Brookpark *(G-2160)*

General Aluminum Mfg Company ....C 419 739-9300
Wapakoneta *(G-19487)*

General Motors LLC ....A 419 782-2244
Defiance *(G-8790)*

Hamilton Brass & Alum Castings ....E 513 867-0400
Hamilton *(G-10701)*

Hobart Corporation ....E 937 332-3000
Troy *(G-18840)*

Hobart Corporation ....C 937 332-2797
Piqua *(G-16277)*

Kenton Iron Products Inc ....E 419 674-4178
Kenton *(G-11554)*

Kenton Iron Products Inc ....E 419 674-4178
Kenton *(G-11555)*

Knapp Foundry Co Inc ....F 330 434-0916
Akron *(G-261)*

Korff Holdings LLC ....C 330 332-1566
Salem *(G-16905)*

Liberty Casting Company LLC ....D 740 363-1941
Delaware *(G-8868)*

McWane Inc ....B 740 622-6651
Coshocton *(G-7897)*

Miami-Cast Inc ....E 937 866-2951
Miamisburg *(G-13833)*

Monroe Water System ....G 740 472-1030
Sardis *(G-17036)*

Oak Hill Foundry & Mch Works ....E 740 682-7746
Oak Hill *(G-15603)*

OS Kelly Corporation ....E 937 322-4921
Springfield *(G-17620)*

▼ Osco Industries Inc ....B 740 354-3183
Portsmouth *(G-16446)*

Osco Industries Inc ....C 740 286-5004
Jackson *(G-11323)*

Pioneer City Casting Company ....E 740 423-7533
Belpre *(G-1593)*

Piqua Champion Foundry Inc ....E 937 773-3375
Piqua *(G-16300)*

Quality Castings Company ....B 330 682-6871
Orrville *(G-15756)*

▲ Rotek Incorporated ....C 330 562-4000
Aurora *(G-945)*

Sancast Inc ....E 740 622-8660
Coshocton *(G-7908)*

St Marys Foundry Inc ....C 419 394-3346
Saint Marys *(G-16856)*

T & B Foundry Company ....D 216 391-4200
Cleveland *(G-6285)*

Tangent Air Inc ....E 740 474-1114
Circleville *(G-4645)*

Tiffin Foundry & Machine Inc ....E 419 447-3991
Tiffin *(G-18247)*

Tri Cast Limited Partnership ....E 330 733-8718
Akron *(G-445)*

Tri-Cast Inc ....E 330 733-8718
Akron *(G-446)*

▲ Wallace Forge Company ....D 330 488-1203
Canton *(G-2900)*

Wellsville Foundry Inc ....E 330 532-2995
Wellsville *(G-19776)*

Whemco-Ohio Foundry Inc ....C 419 222-2111
Lima *(G-12112)*

Yellow Creek Casting Company ....E 330 532-4608
Wellsville *(G-19777)*

3322 Malleable Iron Foundries

Ej Usa Inc ....E 216 692-3001
Cleveland *(G-5261)*

◆ Ellwood Engineered Castings Co ....C 330 568-3000
Hubbard *(G-11130)*

General Aluminum Mfg Company ....C 419 739-9300
Wapakoneta *(G-19487)*

General Motors LLC ....A 419 782-2244
Defiance *(G-8790)*

Kenton Iron Products Inc ....E 419 674-4178
Kenton *(G-11554)*

Osco Industries Inc ....C 740 286-5004
Jackson *(G-11323)*

Pioneer City Casting Company ....E 740 423-7533
Belpre *(G-1593)*

Sancast Inc ....E 740 622-8660
Coshocton *(G-7908)*

St Marys Foundry Inc ....C 419 394-3346
Saint Marys *(G-16856)*

T & B Foundry Company ....D 216 391-4200
Cleveland *(G-6285)*

Tiffin Foundry & Machine Inc ....E 419 447-3991
Tiffin *(G-18247)*

Tooling Technology LLC ....G 937 295-3672
Fort Loramie *(G-9943)*

Whemco-Ohio Foundry Inc ....C 419 222-2111
Lima *(G-12112)*

Yellow Creek Casting Company ....E 330 532-4608
Wellsville *(G-19777)*

3324 Steel Investment Foundries

▲ Alcon Industries Inc ....D 216 961-1100
Cleveland *(G-4745)*

B W Grinding Co ....E 419 923-1376
Lyons *(G-12431)*

▲ Bescast Inc ....C 440 946-5300
Willoughby *(G-20444)*

Brost Foundry Company ....E 216 641-1131
Cleveland *(G-4936)*

Caspa Home Page Inc ....G 216 781-0748
Cleveland *(G-4989)*

▲ Castalloy Inc ....D 216 961-7990
Cleveland *(G-4992)*

▲ Consolдted Precision Pdts Corp ....C 909 595-2252
Cleveland *(G-5117)*

▲ Dd Foundry Inc ....C 216 362-4100
Brookpark *(G-2156)*

General Aluminum Mfg Company ....C 419 739-9300
Wapakoneta *(G-19487)*

Harbor Castings Inc ....E 231 733-1053
Cuyahoga Falls *(G-8006)*

Harbor Castings Inc ....E 330 499-7178
Cuyahoga Falls *(G-8007)*

Howmet Castings & Services Inc ....B 216 641-4400
Newburgh Heights *(G-15073)*

◆ Howmet Corporation ....E 800 242-9898
Newburgh Heights *(G-15074)*

Interntnal Precision Cast Sups ....G 330 342-0407
Hudson *(G-11182)*

Island Castings Inc ....D 231 733-1053
North Canton *(G-15243)*

◆ Kovatch Castings Inc ....C 330 896-9944
Uniontown *(G-19089)*

Mercury Machine Co ....D 440 349-3222
Solon *(G-17335)*

Mold Masters Intl Inc ....C 440 953-0220
Mentor *(G-13659)*

PCC Airfoils LLC ....C 330 868-6441
Minerva *(G-14337)*

PCC Airfoils LLC ....C 440 255-9770
Mentor *(G-13683)*

Rimer Enterprises Inc ....E 419 878-8156
Waterville *(G-19666)*

▲ Steel Ceilings Inc ....E 740 967-1063
Johnstown *(G-11406)*

Summit Resources Group Inc ....G 330 653-3992
Hudson *(G-11203)*

▲ Xapc Co ....D 216 362-4100
Cleveland *(G-6486)*

3325 Steel Foundries, NEC

▲ Alcon Industries Inc ....D 216 961-1100
Cleveland *(G-4745)*

Anointed Design & Technologies ......G 330 826-1493
Massillon *(G-13108)*

Arcelormittal Cleveland LLC ....E 216 429-6000
Cleveland *(G-4824)*

Aza Enterprises LLC ....G 740 678-8482
Fleming *(G-9910)*

◆ B-Tek Scales LLC ....E 330 471-8900
Canton *(G-2613)*

Brost Foundry Company ....E 216 641-1131
Cleveland *(G-4936)*

Castings Usa Inc ....G 330 339-3611
New Philadelphia *(G-14890)*

▲ Columbus Steel Castings Co ....A 614 444-2121
Columbus *(G-6967)*

▲ Dd Foundry Inc ....C 216 362-4100
Brookpark *(G-2156)*

Durivage Pattern & Mfg Co ....E 419 836-8655
Williston *(G-20420)*

Engines Inc of Ohio ....D 740 377-9874
South Point *(G-17437)*

▲ Evertz Technology Service Usa ....E 513 422-8400
Middletown *(G-14040)*

▲ Fisher Cast Steel Products Inc ....E 614 879-8325
West Jefferson *(G-20078)*

Harbor Castings Inc ....E 231 733-1053
Cuyahoga Falls *(G-8006)*

Harbor Castings Inc ....E 330 499-7178
Cuyahoga Falls *(G-8007)*

Island Castings Inc ....D 231 733-1053
North Canton *(G-15243)*

▲ Jmac Inc ....F 614 436-2418
Columbus *(G-7235)*

Korff Holdings LLC ....C 330 332-1566
Salem *(G-16905)*

◆ Kovatch Castings Inc ....C 330 896-9944
Uniontown *(G-19089)*

Lakeway Mfg Inc ....E 419 433-3030
Huron *(G-11232)*

Medina Blanking Inc ....C 330 558-2300
Valley City *(G-19217)*

Munroe Incorporated ....G 330 755-7216
Struthers *(G-17995)*

▲ PC Campana Inc ....E 440 246-6500
Lorain *(G-12266)*

Precision Polymer Casting LLC ....G 440 343-0461
Moreland Hills *(G-14538)*

Rampp Company ....E 740 373-7886
Marietta *(G-12822)*

◆ Sandusky International Inc ....C 419 626-5340
Sandusky *(G-17002)*

Santos Industrial Ltd ....E 937 299-7333
Moraine *(G-14525)*

▲ Sawbrook Steel Castings Co ....D 513 554-1700
Cincinnati *(G-4381)*

Sns Nano Fiber Technology LLC ....G 330 655-0030
Hudson *(G-11200)*

Steel Service Plus Ltd ....F 216 391-9000
Cleveland *(G-6244)*

Tecumseh Redevelopment Inc ....G 330 659-9100
Richfield *(G-16643)*

Tiffin Foundry & Machine Inc ....E 419 447-3991
Tiffin *(G-18247)*

United Engineering & Fndry Co ....F 330 456-2761
Canton *(G-2885)*

Whemco-Ohio Foundry Inc ....C 419 222-2111
Lima *(G-12112)*

Worthington Industries Inc ....C 513 539-9291
Monroe *(G-14420)*

Worthington Industries Inc ....C 614 438-3210
Worthington *(G-20896)*

Worthngton Stelpac Systems LLC ......C 614 438-3205
Columbus *(G-7778)*

3331 Primary Smelting & Refining Of Copper

▲ Bryan Metals LLC ....G 419 636-4571
Bryan *(G-2286)*

Hildreth Mfg LLC ....E 740 375-5832
Marion *(G-12875)*

▲ Sam Dong Ohio Inc ....D 740 363-1985
Delaware *(G-8884)*

3334 Primary Production Of Aluminum

◆ Alcan Primary Products Corp ....A 440 460-3300
Independence *(G-11247)*

Alcoa Inc ....F 216 391-3885
Cleveland (G-4743)

Alcoa Inc ....E 608 363-5214
Newburgh Heights (G-15068)

Benjamin Steel Company Inc ....E 937 233-1212
Springfield (G-17522)

Boggs Recycling Inc ....G 800 837-8101
Newbury (G-15082)

D-Flite Mfg LLC ....G 419 485-3081
Montpelier (G-14442)

Fabrication Group LLC ....E 216 251-1125
Cleveland (G-5318)

Homan Metals LLC ....G 513 721-5010
Cincinnati (G-3891)

Imperial Alum - Minerva LLC ....D 330 868-7765
Minerva (G-14326)

Kaiser Aluminum Fab Pdts LLC .....C 740 522-1151
Heath (G-10848)

▲ Ormet Corporation ....A 740 483-1381
Hannibal (G-10763)

◆ Real Alloy Holding Inc ....D 216 755-8800
Beachwood (G-1292)

▲ Real Alloy Specification Inc ....D 260 563-7461
Beachwood (G-1295)

▼ Specialized Castings Ltd ....F 937 669-5620
Greenville (G-10522)

Wagner Rustproofing Co Inc ....E 216 361-4930
Cleveland (G-6440)

3339 Primary Nonferrous Metals, NEC

◆ Aci Industries Ltd ....E 740 368-4160
Delaware (G-8815)

▲ Advanced Materials Products ....G 330 650-4000
Hudson (G-11154)

▲ American Friction Tech LLC ....D 216 823-0861
Cleveland (G-4781)

▲ American Spring Wire Corp ....C 216 292-4620
Bedford Heights (G-1478)

Bradley Metal Fabrication ....F 216 881-7400
Shaker Heights (G-17085)

Galt Alloys Inc Main Ofc ....G 330 453-4678
Canton (G-2710)

Gdc Industries LLC ....G 937 367-7229
Beavercreek (G-1339)

General Electric Company ....D 330 343-8841
Dover (G-8987)

◆ Globe Metallurgical Inc ....C 740 984-2361
Waterford (G-19647)

H C Starck Inc ....E 216 692-6990
Euclid (G-9583)

H C Starck Inc ....B 216 692-3990
Euclid (G-9584)

Hamilton Rti Inc ....G 330 652-9951
Niles (G-15157)

▲ Magnesium Refining Tech Inc ......E 419 483-9199
Cleveland (G-5729)

Magnesium Refining Tech Inc ....E 419 483-9199
Bellevue (G-1552)

Materion Brush Inc ....A 419 862-2745
Elmore (G-9365)

▲ Materion Brush Inc ....D 216 486-4200
Mayfield Heights (G-13317)

◆ Materion Corporation ....C 216 486-4200
Mayfield Heights (G-13318)

▲ Metallic Resources Inc ....E 330 425-3155
Twinsburg (G-18987)

Ohio Valley Specialty Company ......F 740 373-2276
Marietta (G-12812)

▲ Quality Gold Inc ....B 513 942-7659
Fairfield (G-9706)

▲ Rhenium Alloys Inc ....D 440 365-7388
North Ridgeville (G-15401)

Rml Tool Inc ....G 216 941-1615
Cleveland (G-6120)

Rti Finance Corp ....G 330 652-9952
Niles (G-15178)

Silicon Processors Inc ....G 740 373-2252
Marietta (G-12829)

Swift Manufacturing Co Inc ....G 740 237-4405
Ironton (G-11302)

▲ Zircoa Inc ....G 440 248-0500
Cleveland (G-6498)

3341 Secondary Smelting & Refining Of Nonferrous Metals

A & B Iron & Metal Company ....F 937 228-1561
Dayton (G-8125)

▲ A J Oster Foils LLC ....D 330 823-1700
Alliance (G-486)

Able Alloy Inc ....F 216 251-6110
Cleveland (G-4685)

◆ Aci Industries Ltd ....E 740 368-4160
Delaware (G-8815)

Agmet LLC ....F 216 663-8200
Cleveland (G-4731)

Aleris Rolled Pdts Sls Corp ....G 216 910-3400
Cleveland (G-4748)

Aleris Rolled Products Inc ....G 216 910-3400
Beachwood (G-1256)

Aleris Rolled Products Inc ....D 740 983-2571
Ashville (G-848)

Aleris Rolled Products Inc ....G 740 922-2540
Uhrichsville (G-19044)

Applied Materials Finishing ....E 330 336-5645
Wadsworth (G-19395)

Auris Noble LLC ....D 330 321-6649
Fairlawn (G-9739)

Auris Noble LLC ....E 330 685-3748
Akron (G-77)

Beck Aluminum Alloys Ltd ....D 216 861-4455
Mayfield Heights (G-13311)

City Scrap & Salvage Co ....E 330 753-5051
Akron (G-124)

Clean Harbors Envmtl Svcs Inc ......F 330 425-3825
Twinsburg (G-18914)

Cohen Brothers Inc ....G 513 422-3696
Middletown (G-14031)

Continental Metal Proc Co ....F 216 268-0000
Cleveland (G-5124)

Continental Metal Proc Co ....E 216 268-0000
Cleveland (G-5125)

Echo Environmental Waverly LLC .....F 740 286-2810
Waverly (G-19708)

▲ Fpt Cleveland LLC ....C 216 441-3800
Cleveland (G-5376)

▲ Franklin Iron & Metal Corp ....C 937 253-8184
Dayton (G-8350)

Fusion Automation Inc ....G 440 602-5595
Willoughby (G-20493)

G A Avril Company ....F 513 641-0566
Cincinnati (G-3790)

Garden Street Iron & Metal ....E 513 853-3700
Cincinnati (G-3798)

Gnw Aluminum Inc ....E 330 821-7955
Alliance (G-511)

▲ Grandview Materials Inc ....G 614 488-6998
Lewis Center (G-11899)

HC Starck (ohio) Inc ....B 216 692-3990
Cleveland (G-5487)

I H Schlezinger Inc ....E 614 252-1188
Columbus (G-7178)

◆ I Schumann & Co LLC ....C 440 439-2300
Bedford (G-1430)

▲ Imco Recycling of Ohio LLC ....C 740 922-2373
Uhrichsville (G-19052)

Lake County Auto Recyclers ....G 440 428-2886
Painesville (G-15897)

Lakeside Industrial Pdts Corp ......G 440 366-0052
Elyria (G-9449)

Masters Group Inc ....G 440 893-1900
Chagrin Falls (G-3103)

Materion Brush Inc ....A 419 862-2745
Elmore (G-9365)

▲ Materion Brush Inc ....D 216 486-4200
Mayfield Heights (G-13317)

◆ Materion Corporation ....C 216 486-4200
Mayfield Heights (G-13318)

Metal Improvement Company LLC ......E 513 489-6484
Blue Ash (G-1838)

Metal Shredders Inc ....E 937 866-0777
Miamisburg (G-13830)

Metalico Akron Inc ....E 330 376-1400
Akron (G-295)

Metals Recovery Services LLC ....G 614 870-0364
Columbus (G-7342)

Midwest Iron and Metal Co ....D 937 222-5992
Dayton (G-8496)

Moskowitz Bros Inc ....E 513 242-2100
Cincinnati (G-4126)

▲ National Bronze and Metals ....E 440 277-1226
Lorain (G-12261)

◆ Oakwood Industries Inc ....D 440 232-8700
Bedford (G-1450)

▲ Ohio Valley Alloy Services Inc ...E 740 373-1900
Marietta (G-12811)

Panama Jewelers LLC ....G 440 376-6987
Painesville (G-15909)

▲ Polymet Corporation ....E 513 874-3586
West Chester (G-20038)

Precision Strip Inc ....C 419 674-4186
Kenton (G-11564)

Quality Molded ....C 330 645-6653
Akron (G-358)

R L S Corporation ....E 740 773-1440
Chillicothe (G-3270)

◆ Real Alloy Holding Inc ....D 216 755-8800
Beachwood (G-1292)

Real Alloy Recycling Inc ....E 216 755-8900
Beachwood (G-1293)

Real Alloy Specialty Products ......F 440 563-3487
Rock Creek (G-16685)

Real Alloy Specialty Products ......E 440 322-0072
Elyria (G-9483)

River Smelting & Ref Mfg Co ....E 216 459-2100
Cleveland (G-6117)

Rnw Holdings Inc ....E 330 792-0600
Youngstown (G-21190)

Rti International Metals Inc ....D 330 471-1844
Canton (G-2845)

Rumpke Transportation Co LLC ....C 513 242-4600
Cincinnati (G-4367)

▲ Sawbrook Steel Castings Co ....D 513 554-1700
Cincinnati (G-4381)

Shaneway Inc ....G 330 868-2220
Minerva (G-14342)

Thyssenkrupp Materials NA Inc ......D 216 883-8100
Independence (G-11277)

Umicore Spclty Mtls Recycl LLC .....C 440 833-3000
Wickliffe (G-20389)

Victory White Metal Company ....E 216 271-7200
Cleveland (G-6418)

W R G Inc ....E 216 351-8494
Cleveland (G-6436)

Wall Colmonoy Corporation ....F 937 278-9111
Cincinnati (G-4576)

3351 Rolling, Drawing & Extruding Of Copper

◆ Alcan Corporation ....E 440 460-3307
Cleveland (G-4741)

▲ American Wire & Cable Company ....E 440 235-1140
Olmsted Twp (G-15678)

Arem Co ....F 440 974-6740
Mentor (G-13526)

Avtron Aerospace Inc ....C 216 750-5152
Cleveland (G-4875)

▲ Bryan Metals LLC ....G 419 636-4571
Bryan (G-2286)

◆ Chase Brass and Copper Co LLC ....B 419 485-3193
Montpelier (G-14440)

Commconnect ....G 937 414-0505
Dayton (G-8238)

Federal Metal Company ....D 440 232-8700
Cleveland (G-5331)

Jj Seville LLC ....F 330 769-2071
Seville (G-17076)

▲ Materion Brush Inc ....D 216 486-4200
Mayfield Heights (G-13317)

◆ Materion Corporation ....C 216 486-4200
Mayfield Heights (G-13318)

▲ Republic Wire Inc ....D 513 860-1800
West Chester (G-19930)

Stoutheart Corporation ....G 401 434-7640
Chagrin Falls (G-3123)

T & D Fabricating Inc ....E 440 951-5646
Eastlake (G-9292)

3353 Aluminum Sheet, Plate & Foil

▲ A J Oster Foils LLC ....D 330 823-1700
Alliance (G-486)

Alcoa Inc ....C 330 848-4000
Barberton (G-1096)

Alcoa Inc ....F 216 391-3885
Cleveland (G-4743)

Alcoa Inc ....E 608 363-5214
Newburgh Heights (G-15068)

Aleris Rolled Products Inc ....G 740 922-2540
Uhrichsville (G-19044)

Arconic Inc ....C 330 835-6000
Mogadore (G-14368)

B&B Distributors LLC ....F 440 324-1293
Elyria (G-9378)

◆ Interntnal Cnvrter Cldwell Inc ...C 740 732-5665
Caldwell (G-2428)

▲ Monarch Steel Company Inc ....E 216 587-8000
Cleveland (G-5830)

Nichols Aluminum-Alabama LLC ....C 256 353-1550
Beachwood (G-1284)

Novelis Corporation ....D 330 841-3456
Warren (G-19580)

S
I
C

P B Fabrication Mech Contr ....F 419 478-4869
Toledo *(G-18631)*

Sheffield Metals Cleveland LLC ....F 800 283-5262
Sheffield Village *(G-17130)*

3354 Aluminum Extruded Prdts

Accu-Tek Tool & Die Inc ....G...... 330 726-1946
Salem *(G-16867)*

Aerolite Extrusion Company ....D 330 782-1127
Youngstown *(G-21018)*

◆ Alanod Westlake Metal Ind Inc ....E 440 327-8184
North Ridgeville *(G-15356)*

Aleris Corporation ....G...... 216 910-3400
Cleveland *(G-4746)*

▲ Aleris International Inc ....E 216 910-3400
Beachwood *(G-1253)*

Allen Morgan Trucking & Repair ......G...... 330 336-5192
Norton *(G-15506)*

Aluminum Extruded Shapes Inc ....C 513 563-2205
Cincinnati *(G-3383)*

▲ American Aluminum Extrusions ....C 330 458-0300
Canton *(G-2602)*

Arem Co ....F 440 974-6740
Mentor *(G-13526)*

Astro Shapes LLC ....G...... 330 755-1414
Struthers *(G-17989)*

BRT Extrusions Inc ....C 330 544-0177
Niles *(G-15145)*

Bug-Barrier Screen Corp ....G...... 330 723-2551
Medina *(G-13384)*

Central Aluminum Company LLC ......E 614 491-5700
Obetz *(G-15652)*

Compliant Access Products LLC ....G...... 513 518-4525
Cleves *(G-6510)*

Datco Mfg Company Inc ....E 330 781-6100
Youngstown *(G-21065)*

◆ Exal Corporation ....E 330 744-9505
Youngstown *(G-21080)*

▲ Extrudex Aluminum Inc ....C 330 538-4444
North Jackson *(G-15290)*

Gei of Columbiana Inc ....D 330 783-0270
Youngstown *(G-21094)*

General Extrusions Inc ....D 330 783-0270
Youngstown *(G-21096)*

Hydro Aluminum Fayetteville ....G...... 937 492-9194
Sidney *(G-17193)*

I R B F Company ....G...... 330 633-5100
Tallmadge *(G-18147)*

Industrial Mold Inc ....E 330 425-7374
Twinsburg *(G-18959)*

▼ Isaiah Industries Inc ....E 937 773-9840
Piqua *(G-16280)*

James C Denier Co Inc ....C 513 385-6272
Cincinnati *(G-3939)*

▲ Kit MB Systems Inc ....E 330 945-4500
Akron *(G-260)*

▲ Klb Industries Inc ....E 937 592-9010
Bellefontaine *(G-1535)*

Knoble Glass & Metal Inc ....E 513 753-1246
Cincinnati *(G-3998)*

L & L Ornamental Iron Co ....F 513 353-1930
Cleves *(G-6520)*

Langstons Ultmate Clg Svcs Inc ....F 330 298-9150
Ravenna *(G-16537)*

Loxcreen Company Inc ....E 513 539-2255
Middletown *(G-14056)*

Magnode Corporation ....C 513 988-6351
Trenton *(G-18795)*

▲ National Metal Shapes Inc ....E 740 363-9559
Delaware *(G-8873)*

Navarre Industries Inc ....E 330 767-3003
Navarre *(G-14721)*

Northern States Metals Company ......D 860 521-6001
Youngstown *(G-21151)*

▲ Orrvilon Inc ....C 330 684-9400
Orrville *(G-15754)*

Owens Corning Sales Inc ....G...... 740 983-1300
Ashville *(G-853)*

Patton Aluminum Products Inc ....F 937 845-9404
New Carlisle *(G-14811)*

▲ Precision of Ohio Inc ....F 330 793-0900
Youngstown *(G-21176)*

Rexam Beverage Can Company ....C 419 877-0401
Whitehouse *(G-20345)*

Rexam Beverage Can Company ....E 419 334-4461
Fremont *(G-10178)*

Sheet Angle Bar Met Fbrication ....E 513 829-8600
Fairfield *(G-9716)*

Star Extruded Shapes Inc ....B 330 533-9863
Canfield *(G-2575)*

▲ Star Fab Inc ....C 330 533-9863
Canfield *(G-2576)*

Star Fab Inc ....E 330 482-1601
Columbiana *(G-6634)*

T & D Fabricating Inc ....E 440 951-5646
Eastlake *(G-9292)*

Tecnocap LLC ....G...... 330 392-7222
Warren *(G-19604)*

Tri County Tarp Inc ....E 419 288-3350
Bradner *(G-2030)*

Vari-Wall Tube Specialists Inc ....E 330 482-0000
Columbiana *(G-6637)*

Youngstown Tool & Die Company ......D 330 747-4464
Youngstown *(G-21257)*

Zarbana Alum Extrusions LLC ....E 330 482-5092
Columbiana *(G-6639)*

3355 Aluminum Rolling & Drawing, NEC

◆ Alcan Corporation ....E 440 460-3307
Cleveland *(G-4741)*

Aleris Corporation ....G...... 216 910-3400
Cleveland *(G-4746)*

▲ Aleris International Inc ....E 216 910-3400
Beachwood *(G-1253)*

Aleris Rm Inc ....E 216 910-3400
Beachwood *(G-1255)*

▲ Aleris Rolled Products LLC ....E 216 910-3400
Cleveland *(G-4749)*

Aluminum Extrusion Tech LLC ....G...... 330 533-3994
Canfield *(G-2548)*

Amh Holdings LLC ....A 330 929-1811
Cuyahoga Falls *(G-7966)*

Amh Holdings II Inc ....A 330 929-1811
Cuyahoga Falls *(G-7967)*

Eastman Kodak Company ....E 937 259-3000
Kettering *(G-11579)*

Eastman Kodak Company ....E 937 259-3000
Dayton *(G-8317)*

Homan Metals LLC ....E 513 721-5010
Cincinnati *(G-3891)*

Kaiser Aluminum Fab Pdts LLC ....C 740 522-1151
Heath *(G-10848)*

Max Mighty Inc ....F 937 862-9530
Spring Valley *(G-17468)*

Novelis Corporation ....D 330 841-3456
Warren *(G-19580)*

Nuvox ....G...... 614 232-9115
Columbus *(G-7407)*

Powermount Systems Inc ....E 740 499-4330
La Rue *(G-11622)*

Real Alloy Recycling Inc ....G...... 740 922-8301
Uhrichsville *(G-19056)*

Real Alloy Specialty Products ....C 216 755-8836
Beachwood *(G-1294)*

Waxco International Inc ....F 937 746-4845
Miamisburg *(G-13879)*

3356 Rolling, Drawing-Extruding Of Nonferrous Metals

Air Craft Wheels LLC ....G...... 440 937-7903
Ravenna *(G-16513)*

Allied Mask and Tooling Inc ....G...... 419 470-2555
Toledo *(G-18329)*

API Machining Fabrication Inc ....G...... 740 369-0455
Delaware *(G-8821)*

Artistic Composite & Mold Co ....G...... 330 352-6632
Litchfield *(G-12137)*

BCi and V Investments Inc ....D 330 538-0660
North Jackson *(G-15287)*

Bunting Bearings LLC ....E 419 522-3323
Mansfield *(G-12572)*

◆ Canton Drop Forge Inc ....B 330 477-4511
Canton *(G-2638)*

Castlebar Corporation ....G...... 330 451-6511
Canton *(G-2651)*

Chris Nckel Cstm Ltherwork LLC ....G...... 614 262-2672
Columbus *(G-6927)*

▲ Cleanlife Energy LLC ....F 216 661-7872
Cleveland *(G-5044)*

Consolidated Metal Pdts Inc ....C 513 251-2624
Cincinnati *(G-3604)*

Contour Forming Inc ....E 740 345-9777
Newark *(G-14996)*

Curtiss-Wright Flow Ctrl Corp ....D 216 267-3200
Cleveland *(G-5148)*

Economy Flame Hardening Inc ....G...... 216 431-9333
Cleveland *(G-5255)*

Economy Straightening Service ....G...... 216 432-4410
Cleveland *(G-5256)*

Eric Nickel ....G...... 614 818-2488
Westerville *(G-20151)*

Fusion Automation Inc ....G...... 440 602-5595
Willoughby *(G-20493)*

Fusion Incorporated ....E 440 946-3300
Willoughby *(G-20495)*

G A Avril Company ....F 513 731-5133
Cincinnati *(G-3791)*

G A Avril Company ....F 513 641-0566
Cincinnati *(G-3790)*

Gem City Metal Tech LLC ....G...... 937 252-8998
Dayton *(G-8362)*

General Electric Company ....D 330 343-8841
Dover *(G-8987)*

General Electric Company ....C 330 793-3911
Youngstown *(G-21095)*

H C Starck Inc ....B 216 692-3990
Euclid *(G-9584)*

Kilroy Company ....D 440 951-8700
Eastlake *(G-9278)*

Lite Metals Company ....E 330 296-6110
Ravenna *(G-16539)*

▲ Materion Brush Inc ....D 216 486-4200
Mayfield Heights *(G-13317)*

◆ Materion Corporation ....C 216 486-4200
Mayfield Heights *(G-13318)*

Mestek Inc ....D 419 288-2703
Bradner *(G-2029)*

Metal Merchants Usa Inc ....G...... 330 723-3228
Medina *(G-13447)*

▲ Metallic Resources Inc ....E 330 425-3155
Twinsburg *(G-18987)*

▲ Nova Machine Products Inc ....C 216 267-3200
Middleburg Heights *(G-13907)*

▲ Patriot Special Metals Inc ....G...... 330 538-9621
North Jackson *(G-15296)*

Patriot Special Metals Inc ....D 330 580-9600
Canton *(G-2809)*

▲ Rhenium Alloys Inc ....D 440 365-7388
North Ridgeville *(G-15401)*

▼ Rmi Titanium Company LLC ....G...... 330 652-9952
Niles *(G-15176)*

Robert Nickel ....G...... 419 448-8256
Tiffin *(G-18240)*

Rti International Metals Inc ....E 330 544-7633
Niles *(G-15180)*

Rti International Metals Inc ....G...... 330 652-9955
Niles *(G-15181)*

▲ Special Metals Corporation ....B 216 755-3030
Warrensville Heights *(G-19635)*

Steven Nickel ....G...... 419 732-3377
Port Clinton *(G-16415)*

Tailwind Technologies Inc ....E 937 778-4200
Piqua *(G-16313)*

Th Magnesium Inc ....G...... 513 285-7568
Cincinnati *(G-4504)*

Tin Indian Performance ....G...... 216 214-5485
Uniontown *(G-19103)*

Tin Shed LLC ....G...... 330 636-2524
Willard *(G-20402)*

Tin Wizard Heating and Cooling ....G...... 330 468-7884
Macedonia *(G-12494)*

Tin-Sau LLC ....G...... 419 586-8886
Celina *(G-3023)*

Titanium Contractors Ltd ....G...... 513 256-2152
Cincinnati *(G-4510)*

Titanium Industries Inc ....G...... 216 661-4610
Independence *(G-11278)*

Titanium Lacrosse LLC ....F 614 562-8082
Lewis Center *(G-11926)*

Titanium Metals Corporation ....A 740 537-1571
Toronto *(G-18785)*

Titanium Trout LLC ....G...... 440 543-3187
Chagrin Falls *(G-3127)*

Victory White Metal Company ....F 216 641-2575
Cleveland *(G-6416)*

▲ Victory White Metal Company ....D 216 271-1400
Cleveland *(G-6417)*

▲ Water Star Inc ....G...... 440 564-1001
Newbury *(G-15106)*

3357 Nonferrous Wire Drawing

◆ Alcan Corporation ....E 440 460-3307
Cleveland *(G-4741)*

▲ American Wire & Cable Company ....E 440 235-1140
Olmsted Twp *(G-15678)*

▲ Arnco Corporation ....C 800 847-7661
Elyria *(G-9375)*

Astro Industries Inc ....E 937 429-5900
Beavercreek *(G-1319)*

AT&T Corp ....G 513 792-9300
  Cincinnati (G-3423)
Composite Concepts Inc ....G 440 247-3844
  Mason (G-13005)
▲ Connectors Unlimited Inc ....E 440 357-1161
  Painesville (G-15868)
Delphi Automotive Systems LLC ....B 248 813-2000
  Warren (G-19541)
▲ Electra - Cord Inc ....D 330 832-8124
  Massillon (G-13129)
Electrovations Inc ....E 330 274-3558
  Aurora (G-918)
General Electric Company ....D 330 343-8841
  Dover (G-8987)
HM Wire International Inc ....G 330 244-8501
  Canton (G-2729)
Integrated Systems Professiona ....G 614 875-0104
  Grove City (G-10565)
Legrand North America LLC ....B 937 224-0639
  Moraine (G-14503)
Master Magnetics Inc ....F 740 373-0909
  Marietta (G-12805)
Mueller Electric Company Inc ....E 216 771-5225
  Akron (G-307)
▲ Murphy Industries Inc ....E 740 387-7890
  Marion (G-12887)
Ohio Associated Entps LLC ....E 440 354-3148
  Painesville (G-15908)
Radix Wire Co ....D 216 731-9191
  Cleveland (G-6086)
Radix Wire Co ....D 216 731-9191
  Cleveland (G-6087)
Radix Wire Company ....E 330 995-3677
  Aurora (G-943)
▼ Ribbon Technology Corporation ......F 614 864-5444
  Gahanna (G-10228)
Schneider Electric Usa Inc ....B 513 523-4171
  Oxford (G-15843)
Scott Fetzer Company ....C 216 267-9000
  Cleveland (G-6168)
▲ Solexy Usa LLC ....G 513 860-5465
  West Chester (G-20051)
▲ Therm-O-Link Inc ....D 330 527-2124
  Garrettsville (G-10334)
Therm-O-Link Inc ....G 330 393-7600
  Warren (G-19605)
Therm-O-Link of Texas Inc ....G 330 393-4300
  Warren (G-19606)
Veteran Industries LLC ....G 937 751-2133
  Columbus (G-7737)
Vulkor Incorporated ....E 330 393-7600
  Warren (G-19619)
Xponet Inc ....E 440 354-6617
  Painesville (G-15943)

3363 Aluminum Die Castings

▲ Ahresty Wilmington Corporation ......B 937 382-6112
  Wilmington (G-20653)
Akron Foundry Co ....C 330 745-3101
  Akron (G-44)
Alumacast LLC ....G 419 584-1473
  Celina (G-2985)
▲ American Light Metals LLC ....C 330 467-0750
  Macedonia (G-12435)
Apex Aluminum Die Cast Co Inc ....E 937 773-0432
  Piqua (G-16248)
Buckeye Aluminum Foundry Inc ....G 440 428-7180
  Madison (G-12496)
Cast Specialties Inc ....E 216 292-7393
  Cleveland (G-4991)
CSM Horvath Ledgebrook ....G 419 522-1133
  Mansfield (G-12590)
Custom Industries Inc ....G 216 251-2804
  Cleveland (G-5150)
Destin Die Casting LLC ....E 937 347-1111
  Xenia (G-20947)
Enterprise Machine Inc ....F 513 541-4031
  Cincinnati (G-3709)
◆ Fort Recovery Industries Inc ....C 419 375-4121
  Fort Recovery (G-9951)
General Aluminum Mfg Company ....C 419 739-9300
  Wapakoneta (G-19487)
General Die Casters Inc ....D 330 467-6700
  Northfield (G-15466)
▲ General Die Casters Inc ....E 330 678-2528
  Twinsburg (G-18942)
J & M Precision Die Cast Inc ....F 440 365-7388
  Elyria (G-9441)
Matalco (us) Inc ....G 234 806-0600
  Warren (G-19578)

Matalco (us) Inc ....F 330 452-4760
  Canton (G-2772)
Model Pattern & Foundry Co ....E 513 542-2322
  Cincinnati (G-4113)
◆ Ohio Decorative Products LLC ....C 419 647-9033
  Spencerville (G-17463)
▼ Omni Die Casting Inc ....E 330 830-5500
  Massillon (G-13188)
◆ Park-Ohio Holdings Corp ....F 440 947-2000
  Cleveland (G-5966)
◆ Park-Ohio Industries Inc ....C 440 947-2000
  Cleveland (G-5967)
Plaster Process Castings Co ....E 216 663-1814
  Cleveland (G-6012)
Ramco Electric Motors Inc ....D 937 548-2525
  Greenville (G-10516)
Ravana Industries Inc ....G 330 536-4015
  Lowellville (G-12411)
Reliable Castings Corporation ....D 937 497-5217
  Sidney (G-17215)
▲ Ross Casting & Innovation LLC ....B 937 497-4500
  Sidney (G-17219)
Seilkop Industries Inc ....E 513 761-1035
  Cincinnati (G-4398)
Seilkop Industries Inc ....F 513 679-5680
  Cincinnati (G-4399)
Seyekcub Inc ....G 330 324-1394
  Uhrichsville (G-19059)
SRS Die Casting Holdings LLC ....G 330 467-0750
  Macedonia (G-12487)
SRS Light Metals Inc ....G 330 467-0750
  Macedonia (G-12488)
▲ Thompson Aluminum Casting Co ......D 216 206-2781
  Cleveland (G-6322)
Tooling Technology LLC ....D 937 295-3672
  Fort Loramie (G-9943)
United States Drill Head Co ....E 513 941-0300
  Cincinnati (G-4540)
Yoder Industries Inc ....C 937 278-5769
  Dayton (G-8766)

3364 Nonferrous Die Castings, Exc Aluminum

Akron Brass Company ....E 309 444-4440
  Wooster (G-20733)
American Bronze Corporation ....E 216 341-7800
  Cleveland (G-4779)
▲ American Light Metals LLC ....C 330 467-0750
  Macedonia (G-12435)
Cast Specialties Inc ....E 216 292-7393
  Cleveland (G-4991)
Certech Inc ....G 330 405-1033
  Twinsburg (G-18910)
Clinton Foundry Ltd ....F 419 243-6885
  Toledo (G-18401)
Custom Industries Inc ....G 216 251-2804
  Cleveland (G-5150)
D Picking & Co ....G 419 562-5016
  Bucyrus (G-2337)
▲ Dd Foundry Inc ....C 216 362-4100
  Brookpark (G-2156)
Elektron N Magnesium Amer Inc ....E 419 424-8878
  Findlay (G-9819)
▲ Empire Brass Co ....E 216 431-6565
  Cleveland (G-5276)
Federal Metal Company ....D 440 232-8700
  Cleveland (G-5331)
▲ General Die Casters Inc ....E 330 678-2528
  Twinsburg (G-18942)
General Die Casters Inc ....D 330 467-6700
  Northfield (G-15466)
Hamilton Brass & Alum Castings ....E 513 867-0400
  Hamilton (G-10701)
M & M Dies Inc ....E 216 883-6628
  Cleveland (G-5715)
Martina Metal LLC ....G 614 291-9700
  Columbus (G-7321)
Model Pattern & Foundry Co ....E 513 542-2322
  Cincinnati (G-4113)
◆ Oakwood Industries Inc ....D 440 232-8700
  Bedford (G-1450)
Omni USA Inc ....D 330 830-5500
  Massillon (G-13189)
Plaster Process Castings Co ....E 216 663-1814
  Cleveland (G-6012)
Ray Lewis & Son Incorporated ....E 937 644-4015
  Marysville (G-12965)
Reebar Die Casting Inc ....F 419 878-7591
  Waterville (G-19665)

Ryder-Heil Bronze Inc ....E 419 562-2841
  Bucyrus (G-2358)
SRS Die Casting Holdings LLC ....G 330 467-0750
  Macedonia (G-12487)
SRS Light Metals Inc ....G 330 467-0750
  Macedonia (G-12488)
Support Svc LLC ....G 419 617-0660
  Lexington (G-11954)
Tessec LLC ....E 937 985-3552
  Dayton (G-8709)
▲ Thompson Aluminum Casting Co ......D 216 206-2781
  Cleveland (G-6322)
Yoder Industries Inc ....G 937 890-4322
  Dayton (G-8767)
Yoder Industries Inc ....C 937 278-5769
  Dayton (G-8766)

3365 Aluminum Foundries

Acuity Brands Lighting Inc ....B 740 349-4343
  Newark (G-14979)
Admiral Foundry Inc ....E 330 336-7651
  Wadsworth (G-19388)
Advanced Metals Group LLC ....C 937 492-4134
  Sidney (G-17166)
Air Craft Wheels LLC ....G 440 937-7903
  Ravenna (G-16513)
Akron Foundry Co ....C 330 745-3101
  Akron (G-44)
Akron Foundry Co ....C 330 745-3101
  Barberton (G-1095)
Alumalloy Metalcasting Company ....C 440 930-2222
  Avon Lake (G-1023)
◆ Aluminum Line Products Company ..D 440 835-8880
  Westlake (G-20249)
Anchor Foundry & Machine Inc ....C 330 453-3441
  Canton (G-2603)
Aztec Manufacturing Inc ....C 330 783-9747
  Youngstown (G-21030)
Boscott Metals Inc ....F 937 448-2018
  Bradford (G-2024)
Brost Foundry Company ....E 216 641-1131
  Cleveland (G-4936)
C M M S - Re LLC ....F 513 489-5111
  Blue Ash (G-1760)
Calphalon Corporation ....C 419 666-8700
  Rossford (G-16737)
Cast Metals Technology Inc ....G 740 363-1690
  Delaware (G-8829)
Castek Aluminum Inc ....E 440 365-2333
  Elyria (G-9391)
▲ Clinton Machine Co Inc ....G 330 882-6743
  New Franklin (G-14823)
▲ Consoldted Precision Pdts Corp ......C 909 595-2252
  Cleveland (G-5117)
Cushman Foundry LLC ....E 513 984-5570
  Blue Ash (G-1773)
▲ Dd Foundry Inc ....C 216 362-4100
  Brookpark (G-2156)
Durivage Pattern & Mfg Co ....E 419 836-8655
  Williston (G-20420)
▲ Enprotech Industrial Tech LLC ....C 216 883-3220
  Cleveland (G-5283)
Euclid Products Co Inc ....C 440 942-7310
  Willoughby (G-20482)
Francis Manufacturing Company ....C 937 526-4551
  Russia (G-16763)
▲ General Aluminum Mfg Company .....B 440 947-2000
  Cleveland (G-5410)
General Aluminum Mfg Company ....E 330 297-1020
  Ravenna (G-16531)
General Aluminum Mfg Company ....B 440 593-6225
  Conneaut (G-7805)
▲ General Die Casters Inc ....E 330 678-2528
  Twinsburg (G-18942)
General Motors LLC ....A 419 782-2244
  Defiance (G-8790)
General Precision Corporation ....G 440 951-9380
  Willoughby (G-20498)
Globe Motors Inc ....C 937 228-3171
  Dayton (G-8369)
Howmet Aluminum Casting Inc ....E 216 641-4340
  Newburgh Heights (G-15072)
Htci Co ....F 937 845-1204
  New Carlisle (G-14802)
I A B F Inc ....G 614 279-4498
  Columbus (G-7177)
◆ Kovatch Castings Inc ....C 330 896-9944
  Uniontown (G-19089)
Lite Metals Company ....E 330 296-6110
  Ravenna (G-16539)

Lockheed Martin Investments ....F 937 429-0100
Beavercreek *(G-1349)*

Lodi Foundry Co Inc ....E 330 948-1516
Lodi *(G-12164)*

Mansfield Brass & Alum Corp ....D 419 492-2154
New Washington *(G-14961)*

Merit Foundry Co Inc ....G 216 741-4282
Cleveland *(G-5785)*

Metal-Mation Inc ....F 216 651-1083
Cleveland *(G-5789)*

Miller Casting Inc ....F 330 482-2923
Columbiana *(G-6624)*

Model Pattern & Foundry Co ....E 513 542-2322
Cincinnati *(G-4113)*

Morris Bean & Company ....C 937 767-7301
Yellow Springs *(G-20996)*

Mpe Aeroengines Inc ....G 937 878-3800
Huber Heights *(G-11150)*

Multi Cast LLC ....E 419 335-0010
Wauseon *(G-19690)*

Myron D Budd ....G 330 682-5866
Orrville *(G-15749)*

Nelson Aluminum Foundry Inc ....G 440 543-1941
Chagrin Falls *(G-3107)*

New London Foundry Inc ....F 419 929-2073
New London *(G-14863)*

New Mansfield Brass & Alum Co ....E 419 492-2166
New Washington *(G-14962)*

Non-Ferrous Casting Co ....G 937 228-1162
Dayton *(G-8525)*

▲ Ohio Aluminum Industries Inc ....C 216 641-8865
Cleveland *(G-5927)*

OKeefe Casting Co ....G 440 277-5427
Lorain *(G-12265)*

P C M Co ....G 330 336-8040
Wadsworth *(G-19423)*

▲ Palmer Engineered Products Inc ....G 937 322-1481
Springfield *(G-17622)*

Piqua Emery Cutter & Fndry Co ....D 937 773-4134
Piqua *(G-16303)*

Precision Aluminum Inc ....G 330 335-2351
Wadsworth *(G-19429)*

▲ Pride Cast Metals Inc ....D 513 541-1295
Cincinnati *(G-4268)*

Quality Match Plate Co ....F 330 889-2462
Southington *(G-17454)*

▲ Range Kleen Mfg Inc ....B 419 331-8000
Elida *(G-9356)*

Reliable Castings Corporation ....D 937 497-5217
Sidney *(G-17215)*

Reliable Pattern Works Inc ....G 440 232-8820
Cleveland *(G-6099)*

▲ Ross Aluminum Castings LLC ....C 937 492-4134
Sidney *(G-17218)*

Rotocast Technologies Inc ....E 330 798-9091
Akron *(G-379)*

S M C Aluminum Foundry Inc ....F 419 257-2175
North Baltimore *(G-15198)*

▲ Sawbrook Steel Castings Co ....D 513 554-1700
Cincinnati *(G-4381)*

Seilkop Industries Inc ....E 513 679-5680
Cincinnati *(G-4399)*

▲ Stripmatic Products Inc ....E 216 241-7143
Cleveland *(G-6255)*

▲ Thompson Aluminum Casting Co ....D 216 206-2781
Cleveland *(G-6322)*

Tooling Technology LLC ....D 937 295-3672
Fort Loramie *(G-9943)*

Tri - Flex of Ohio Inc ....F 330 705-7084
North Canton *(G-15277)*

TW Corporation ....E 440 461-3234
Akron *(G-450)*

◆ US Metalcraft Inc ....E 419 692-4962
Delphos *(G-8925)*

Yoder Industries Inc ....F 937 890-4322
Dayton *(G-8767)*

Yoder Industries Inc ....C 937 278-5769
Dayton *(G-8766)*

Zephyr Industries Inc ....G 419 281-4485
Ashland *(G-787)*

3366 Copper Foundries

A & H Automotive Industries ....G 614 235-1759
Columbus *(G-6666)*

Accurate Products Company ....G 740 498-7202
Newcomerstown *(G-15108)*

▲ Advance Bronze Inc ....D 330 948-1231
Lodi *(G-12155)*

Advanced Propeller Systems ....G 937 409-1038
Dayton *(G-8094)*

Anchor Bronze and Metals Inc ....E 440 549-5653
Cleveland *(G-4802)*

Brost Foundry Company ....E 216 641-1131
Cleveland *(G-4936)*

Brost Foundry Company ....F 419 522-1133
Mansfield *(G-12570)*

Bunting Bearings LLC ....E 419 522-3323
Mansfield *(G-12572)*

▲ Bunting Bearings LLC ....D 419 866-7000
Holland *(G-11047)*

Calmego Specialized Pdts LLC ....F 937 669-5620
Greenville *(G-10491)*

▲ Cincinnati Valve Company ....F 513 471-8258
Cincinnati *(G-3567)*

▲ Climax Metal Products Company ....D 440 943-8898
Mentor *(G-13547)*

Connell Limited Partnership ....D 877 534-8986
Northfield *(G-15464)*

D Picking & Co ....E 419 562-5016
Bucyrus *(G-2337)*

▲ Daido Metal Bellefontaine LLC ....C 937 592-5010
Bellefontaine *(G-1526)*

E I Du Pont De Nemours & Co ....C 216 901-3600
Cleveland *(G-5232)*

◆ Falcon Foundry Company ....D 330 536-6221
Lowellville *(G-12407)*

Foundry Artist Inc ....B 216 391-9030
Cleveland *(G-5375)*

Hadronics Inc ....D 513 321-9350
Cincinnati *(G-3861)*

◆ Kovatch Castings Inc ....C 330 896-9944
Uniontown *(G-19089)*

M A Harrison Mfg Co Inc ....E 440 965-4306
Wakeman *(G-19451)*

Maass Midwest Mfg Inc ....G 419 894-6424
Arcadia *(G-654)*

▲ McNeil Industries Inc ....E 440 951-7756
Painesville *(G-15901)*

▲ Meierjohan-Wengler Inc ....F 513 771-6074
Cincinnati *(G-4081)*

Model Pattern & Foundry Co ....E 513 542-2322
Cincinnati *(G-4113)*

National Brass Company Inc ....G 216 651-8530
Cleveland *(G-5854)*

▲ National Bronze and Metals ....E 440 277-1226
Lorain *(G-12261)*

Non-Ferrous Casting Co ....G 937 228-1162
Dayton *(G-8525)*

Oakes Foundry Inc ....E 330 372-4010
Warren *(G-19581)*

OKeefe Casting Co ....G 440 277-5427
Lorain *(G-12265)*

Piqua Emery Cutter & Fndry Co ....D 937 773-4134
Piqua *(G-16303)*

▲ Pride Cast Metals Inc ....D 513 541-1295
Cincinnati *(G-4268)*

R E H Company Inc ....D 513 242-0011
Cincinnati *(G-4324)*

▲ Randall Bearings Inc ....F 419 223-1075
Lima *(G-12080)*

Randall Bearings Inc ....F 419 678-2486
Coldwater *(G-6570)*

▲ S C Industries Inc ....E 216 732-9000
Euclid *(G-9605)*

▲ Semco ....D 800 848-5764
Marion *(G-12899)*

Snair Co ....F 614 873-7020
Plain City *(G-16360)*

▲ Stripmatic Products Inc ....E 216 241-7143
Cleveland *(G-6255)*

Whip Guide Co ....F 440 543-5151
Chagrin Falls *(G-3133)*

3369 Nonferrous Foundries: Castings, NEC

A C Williams Co Inc ....E 330 296-6110
Ravenna *(G-16511)*

Air Craft Wheels LLC ....G 440 937-7903
Ravenna *(G-16513)*

Akron Foundry Co ....C 330 745-3101
Akron *(G-44)*

▲ Alcon Industries Inc ....D 216 961-1100
Cleveland *(G-4745)*

Apex Aluminum Die Cast Co Inc ....E 937 773-0432
Piqua *(G-16248)*

Auld Company ....E 614 454-1010
Columbus *(G-6786)*

Brost Foundry Company ....E 216 641-1131
Cleveland *(G-4936)*

Bunting Bearings LLC ....E 419 522-3323
Mansfield *(G-12572)*

Castmor Products Inc ....G 440 953-1103
Willoughby *(G-20453)*

▲ Catania Medallic Specialty ....E 440 933-9595
Avon Lake *(G-1026)*

Computational Engineering Svcs ....G 513 745-0313
Blue Ash *(G-1768)*

Concorde Castings Inc ....G 440 953-0053
Willoughby *(G-20461)*

Consoldted Precision Pdts Corp ....E 440 953-0053
Eastlake *(G-9263)*

Curtiss-Wright Flow Ctrl Corp ....D 216 267-3200
Cleveland *(G-5148)*

Custom Industries Inc ....G 216 251-2804
Cleveland *(G-5150)*

▲ Dd Foundry Inc ....C 216 362-4100
Brookpark *(G-2156)*

Dmk Industries Inc ....F 513 727-4549
Middletown *(G-14038)*

Durivage Pattern & Mfg Co ....E 419 836-8655
Williston *(G-20420)*

◆ Ellwood Engineered Castings Co ....C 330 568-3000
Hubbard *(G-11130)*

Francis Manufacturing Company ....C 937 526-4551
Russia *(G-16763)*

▼ Garfield Alloys Inc ....F 216 587-4843
Cleveland *(G-5397)*

▲ General Aluminum Mfg Company ....B 440 947-2000
Cleveland *(G-5410)*

General Aluminum Mfg Company ....E 330 297-1020
Ravenna *(G-16531)*

General Aluminum Mfg Company ....E 440 593-6225
Conneaut *(G-7805)*

▲ General Die Casters Inc ....E 330 678-2528
Twinsburg *(G-18942)*

General Motors LLC ....A 419 782-2244
Defiance *(G-8790)*

Globe Motors Inc ....C 937 228-3171
Dayton *(G-8369)*

Harbor Castings Inc ....E 330 499-7178
Cuyahoga Falls *(G-8007)*

I A B F Inc ....G 614 279-4498
Columbus *(G-7177)*

◆ Kovatch Castings Inc ....C 330 896-9944
Uniontown *(G-19089)*

Liberty Die Casting Company ....G 419 636-3971
Bryan *(G-2312)*

Lite Metals Company ....E 330 296-6110
Ravenna *(G-16539)*

Materion Brush Inc ....A 419 862-2745
Elmore *(G-9365)*

McM Precision Castings Inc ....E 419 669-3226
Weston *(G-20326)*

Microweld Engineering Inc ....F 614 847-9410
Worthington *(G-20880)*

Morris Bean & Company ....C 937 767-7301
Yellow Springs *(G-20996)*

Nelson Aluminum Foundry Inc ....G 440 543-1941
Chagrin Falls *(G-3107)*

New London Foundry Inc ....F 419 929-2073
New London *(G-14863)*

▲ Nova Machine Products Inc ....C 216 267-3200
Middleburg Heights *(G-13907)*

◆ Ohio Decorative Products LLC ....E 419 647-9033
Spencerville *(G-17463)*

PCC Airfoils LLC ....C 330 868-6441
Minerva *(G-14337)*

PCC Airfoils LLC ....B 740 982-6025
Crooksville *(G-7952)*

PCC Airfoils LLC ....C 216 692-7900
Cleveland *(G-5983)*

◆ PCC Airfoils LLC ....E 216 831-3590
Cleveland *(G-5984)*

PCC Airfoils LLC ....C 440 255-9770
Mentor *(G-13683)*

Piqua Emery Cutter & Fndry Co ....D 937 773-4134
Piqua *(G-16303)*

Ray Lewis & Son Incorporated ....E 937 644-4015
Marysville *(G-12965)*

Reliable Castings Corporation ....D 937 497-5217
Sidney *(G-17215)*

▲ Ross Aluminum Castings LLC ....C 937 492-4134
Sidney *(G-17218)*

Sam Americas Inc ....H 330 628-1118
Mogadore *(G-14384)*

◆ Sandusky International Inc ....C 419 626-5340
Sandusky *(G-17002)*

▲ Sawbrook Steel Castings Co ....D 513 554-1700
Cincinnati *(G-4381)*

Seaport Mold & Casting Company ....F 419 243-1422
Toledo *(G-18688)*

Seilkop Industries Inc ....F 513 679-5680
Cincinnati *(G-4399)*

St Marys Foundry Inc ....C 419 394-3346
Saint Marys *(G-16856)*

T & B Foundry Company ....D 216 391-4200
Cleveland *(G-6285)*

▲ Technology House The Ltd ....D 440 248-3025
Solon *(G-17400)*

Telcon LLC ....C 330 562-5566
Streetsboro *(G-17881)*

▲ Thompson Aluminum Casting Co ....D 216 206-2781
Cleveland *(G-6322)*

▲ Voss Industries Inc ....C 216 771-0870
Cleveland *(G-6429)*

Warren Castings Inc ....F 216 883-2520
Cleveland *(G-6446)*

Yoder Industries Inc ....C 937 278-5769
Dayton *(G-8766)*

3398 Metal Heat Treating

A M Castle & Co ....D 330 425-7000
Bedford *(G-1394)*

Accuphase Metal Treating LLC ....G 937 610-5934
Moraine *(G-14463)*

Advanced Flame Hardening Inc ....G 216 431-0370
Cleveland *(G-4712)*

Akron Steel Treating Co ....E 330 773-8211
Akron *(G-58)*

Al Fe Heat Treating-Ohio Inc ....E 330 336-0211
Wadsworth *(G-19392)*

Al-Fe Heat Treating Inc ....E 419 782-7200
Defiance *(G-8776)*

Allegheny Ludlum LLC ....E 330 875-2244
Louisville *(G-12308)*

Alternative Flash Inc ....E 330 334-6111
Wadsworth *(G-19393)*

Amac Enterprises Inc ....C 216 362-1880
Parma *(G-15954)*

American Metal Proc Co LLC ....E 216 486-4600
Cleveland *(G-4789)*

▲ American Metal Treating Co ....E 216 431-4492
Cleveland *(G-4790)*

American Quality Stripping ....E 419 625-6288
Sandusky *(G-16946)*

American Steel Treating Inc ....E 419 662-5500
Perrysburg *(G-16063)*

American Steel Treating Inc ....E 419 874-2044
Perrysburg *(G-16064)*

Analytic Stress Relieving Inc ....G 804 271-7198
Northwood *(G-15476)*

▲ Arcelormittal Columbus LLC ....C 614 492-6800
Columbus *(G-6768)*

Atmosphere Annealing LLC ....D 330 478-0314
Kenton *(G-11544)*

B&C Machine Co LLC ....B 330 745-4013
Barberton *(G-1103)*

Bekaert Corporation ....C 330 683-5060
Orrville *(G-15729)*

Bob Lanes Welding Inc ....F 740 373-3567
Marietta *(G-12767)*

Bodycote lmt Inc ....E 740 852-5000
London *(G-12201)*

Bodycote Thermal Proc Inc ....E 614 444-1181
Columbus *(G-6843)*

Bodycote Thermal Proc Inc ....F 440 473-2020
Cleveland *(G-4921)*

Bodycote Thermal Proc Inc ....E 513 921-2300
Cincinnati *(G-3456)*

Bodycote Thermal Proc Inc ....G 740 852-4955
London *(G-12202)*

Bowdil Company ....F 800 356-8663
Canton *(G-2626)*

Brazing Service Inc ....G 440 871-1120
Westlake *(G-20259)*

▲ Byron Products Inc ....D 513 870-9111
Fairfield *(G-9648)*

Certified Heat Treating Inc ....E 937 866-0245
Dayton *(G-8222)*

Cincinnati Gearing Systems Inc ....D 513 527-8600
Cincinnati *(G-3552)*

Cleveland Hollow Boring Inc ....G 216 883-1926
Cleveland *(G-5065)*

▲ Clifton Steel Company ....D 216 662-6111
Maple Heights *(G-12731)*

Colonial Surface Solutions Inc ....E 419 358-0129
Bluffton *(G-1910)*

Colonial Surface Solutions Inc ....D 419 659-5639
Columbus Grove *(G-7793)*

Columbus Coatings Company ....D 614 492-6800
Columbus *(G-6949)*

Commercial Steel Treating Co ....F 216 431-8204
Cleveland *(G-5105)*

Dayton Forging Heat Treating ....D 937 253-4126
Dayton *(G-8273)*

Derrick Company Inc ....E 513 321-8122
Cincinnati *(G-3648)*

Detroit Flame Hardening Co ....E 216 531-4273
Euclid *(G-9574)*

Detroit Flame Hardening Co ....F 513 942-1400
Fairfield *(G-9658)*

Dewitt Inc ....G 216 662-0800
Maple Heights *(G-12732)*

▲ Die Co Inc ....E 440 942-8856
Eastlake *(G-9265)*

▲ Dowa Tht America Inc ....E 419 354-4144
Bowling Green *(G-1988)*

Ellison Srfc Tech - Mexico LLC ....B 513 770-4900
Mason *(G-13014)*

Erie Steel Ltd ....E 419 478-3743
Toledo *(G-18458)*

Euclid Heat Treating Co ....D 216 481-8444
Euclid *(G-9579)*

Fbf Limited ....E 513 541-6300
Cincinnati *(G-3746)*

Flynn Inc ....B 419 478-3743
Toledo *(G-18472)*

Franklin Field Service ....G 614 885-1779
Columbus *(G-7098)*

Fusion Automation Inc ....G 440 602-5595
Willoughby *(G-20493)*

General Steel Corporation ....F 216 883-4200
Cleveland *(G-5421)*

Gerdau Macsteel Atmosphere Ann ....D 330 478-0314
Canton *(G-2713)*

Gt Technologies Inc ....C 419 782-8955
Defiance *(G-8792)*

H & M Metal Processing Co ....E 330 745-3075
Akron *(G-210)*

H & S Steel Treating Inc ....F 330 678-5245
Kent *(G-11466)*

Harvard Metal Treating Inc ....G 216 271-4424
Newburgh Heights *(G-15071)*

Heat Treating Inc ....E 937 325-3121
Springfield *(G-17570)*

Heat Treating Inc ....F 937 325-3121
Springfield *(G-17571)*

Heat Treating Inc ....G 614 759-9963
Gahanna *(G-10209)*

Heat Treating Technologies ....E 419 224-8324
Lima *(G-12023)*

HI Tecmetal Group Inc ....E 216 881-8100
Cleveland *(G-5508)*

HI Tecmetal Group Inc ....E 440 373-5101
Wickliffe *(G-20368)*

HI Tecmetal Group Inc ....E 440 946-2280
Willoughby *(G-20504)*

HI Tecmetal Group Inc ....F 216 941-0440
Cleveland *(G-5509)*

Hmt Inc ....G 440 599-7005
Conneaut *(G-7808)*

Isostatic Pressing Svcs LLC ....G 614 370-2140
Columbus *(G-7213)*

▲ J W Harris Co Inc ....F 216 481-8100
Euclid *(G-9587)*

Kando of Cincinnati Inc ....E 513 459-7782
Lebanon *(G-11811)*

Kowalski Heat Treating Co ....F 216 631-4411
Cleveland *(G-5665)*

Lapham-Hickey Steel Corp ....E 614 443-4881
Columbus *(G-7286)*

Metal Improvement Company LLC ....E 513 489-6484
Blue Ash *(G-1838)*

Metal Improvement Company LLC ....E 330 425-1490
Twinsburg *(G-18985)*

Metallurgical Service Inc ....E 937 294-2681
Moraine *(G-14505)*

Miller Consolidated Industries ....E 937 294-2681
Moraine *(G-14507)*

Moore Mc Millen Holdings ....D 330 745-3075
Cuyahoga Falls *(G-8027)*

National Peening ....G 216 342-9155
Bedford Heights *(G-1491)*

▲ Neturen America Corporation ....F 513 863-1900
Hamilton *(G-10726)*

▲ Northlake Steel Corporation ....D 330 220-7717
Valley City *(G-19225)*

Northwind Industries Inc ....E 216 433-0666
Cleveland *(G-5916)*

Ohio Coatings Company ....D 740 859-5500
Yorkville *(G-21007)*

Ohio Flame Hardening Company ......G 513 336-6160
Lebanon *(G-11821)*

Ohio Flame Hardening Company ......E 513 733-5162
Cincinnati *(G-4177)*

Ohio Metallurgical Service Inc ....D 440 365-4104
Elyria *(G-9471)*

P & L Heat Treating & Grinding ....G 330 746-8081
Youngstown *(G-21158)*

P & L Heat Trting Grinding Inc ....E 330 746-1339
Youngstown *(G-21159)*

▲ Parker Trutec Incorporated ....D 937 323-8833
Springfield *(G-17625)*

Pike Machine Products Co ....E 216 731-1880
Euclid *(G-9597)*

Pressure Technology Ohio Inc ....E 215 628-1975
Painesville *(G-15912)*

Pride Investments LLC ....F 937 461-1121
Dayton *(G-8591)*

Ridge Machine & Welding Co ....G 740 537-2821
Toronto *(G-18784)*

Ropama Inc ....F 440 358-1304
Painesville *(G-15919)*

Samuel Steel Pickling Company ....E 330 963-3777
Twinsburg *(G-19016)*

Surface Enhancement Tech LLC ......F 513 561-1520
Cincinnati *(G-4487)*

Team Inc ....F 614 263-1808
Columbus *(G-7681)*

Team Cooperheat Mqs ....G 614 501-7304
Columbus *(G-7682)*

Techniques Surfaces Usa Inc ....G 937 323-2556
Springfield *(G-17661)*

Thermal Solutions Inc ....G 614 263-1808
Columbus *(G-7692)*

Thermal Treatment Center Inc ....E 216 881-8100
Cleveland *(G-6317)*

Thermal Treatment Center Inc ....E 216 883-4820
Cleveland *(G-6318)*

Thermal Treatment Center Inc ....E 440 943-4555
Wickliffe *(G-20388)*

Thermal Treatment Center Inc ....F 216 941-0440
Cleveland *(G-6319)*

Thompson Steel Company Inc ....D 419 399-4803
Paulding *(G-16014)*

Universal Heat Treating Inc ....E 216 641-2000
Cleveland *(G-6390)*

USA Heat Treating Inc ....E 216 587-4700
Cleveland *(G-6400)*

Vicon Fabricating Company Ltd ....E 440 205-6700
Mentor *(G-13767)*

Wall Colmonoy Corporation ....F 937 278-9111
Cincinnati *(G-4576)*

Weiss Industries Inc ....E 419 526-2480
Mansfield *(G-12704)*

Winston Heat Treating Inc ....E 937 226-0110
Dayton *(G-8762)*

◆ Xtek Inc ....B 513 733-7800
Cincinnati *(G-4616)*

Zion Industries Inc ....D 330 225-3246
Valley City *(G-19238)*

3399 Primary Metal Prdts, NEC

Additive Metal Alloys Ltd ....G 800 687-6110
Holland *(G-11043)*

Aerotech Industries Inc ....G 216 881-6660
Cleveland *(G-4725)*

Altana ....G 440 954-7600
Painesville *(G-15849)*

Bogie Industries Inc Ltd ....E 330 745-3105
Akron *(G-95)*

Bricolage Inc ....G 614 853-6789
Grove City *(G-10547)*

C & P Metals Inc ....G 724 510-4293
Warren *(G-19533)*

Colliers Cstmizing Fabrication ....F 937 523-0420
Urbana *(G-19153)*

Cryoplus Inc ....G 330 683-3375
Wooster *(G-20761)*

▼ Destiny Manufacturing Inc ....E 330 273-9000
Brunswick *(G-2220)*

Diamond Metals Dist Inc ....E 216 898-7900
Cleveland *(G-5189)*

Duffee Finishing Inc ....G 740 965-4848
Sunbury *(G-18059)*

◆ Eckart America Corporation ....D 440 954-7600
Painesville *(G-15876)*

Elgin Fastener Group LLC ....F 812 717-2544
Brecksville *(G-2046)*

◆ Ferro Corporation ....D 216 875-5600
Mayfield Heights *(G-13313)*

Hilti Inc	F	614 258-8384	
Columbus (G-7158)			
J & K Powder Coating	G	330 540-6145	
Mineral Ridge (G-14305)			
▲ Key Finishes LLC	G	614 351-8393	
Columbus (G-7260)			
Key Principal Partners Corp	F	888 539-3322	
Cleveland (G-5651)			
Legacy Finishing Inc	G	937 743-7278	
Franklin (G-10032)			
Liberty Steel Pressed Pdts LLC	G	330 538-2236	
North Jackson (G-15294)			
Masters Group Inc	G	440 893-1900	
Chagrin Falls (G-3103)			
Matandy Steel & Metal Pdts LLC	D	513 844-2277	
Hamilton (G-10723)			
Materion Technical Mtls Inc	D	216 486-4200	
Cleveland (G-5761)			
▲ Midwest Motor Supply Co	C	800 233-1294	
Columbus (G-7351)			
National Fasteners Inc	G	216 771-6473	
Brooklyn Heights (G-2143)			
Nuflux LLC	G	330 399-1122	
Cortland (G-7872)			
Obron Atlantic Corporation	D	440 954-7600	
Painesville (G-15905)			
Ohio Valley Manufacturing Inc	D	419 522-5818	
Mansfield (G-12662)			
▲ Powder Alloy Corporation	E	513 984-4016	
Loveland (G-12378)			
Powdermet Inc	E	216 404-0053	
Euclid (G-9598)			
Premar Manufacturing Ltd	G	440 250-0373	
Westlake (G-20297)			
▼ Rmi Titanium Company LLC	E	330 652-9952	
Niles (G-15176)			
Robert A Reich Company	G	440 808-0033	
Westlake (G-20303)			
Royal Powder Corporation	G	216 898-0074	
Cleveland (G-6140)			
◆ Shinagawa Advanced Materials A	E	330 628-1118	
Mogadore (G-14385)			
Stein Inc	D	440 277-6148	
Lorain (G-12281)			
▲ Stein Inc	F	440 526-9301	
Cleveland (G-6248)			
Stein Inc	B	216 883-7444	
Cleveland (G-6249)			
Stonebrook Machine	G	440 951-5013	
Eastlake (G-9289)			
Topkote Inc	G	440 428-0525	
Madison (G-12512)			
▼ Transmet Corporation	G	614 276-5522	
Columbus (G-7706)			
Tru-Har Products	G	330 338-6826	
Hudson (G-11205)			
◆ Truck Fax Inc	G	216 921-8866	
Cleveland (G-6369)			
▲ Waterford Tank Fabrication Ltd	D	740 984-4100	
Beverly (G-1672)			

34 FABRICATED METAL PRODUCTS, EXCEPT MACHINERY AND TRANSPORTATION EQUIPMENT

3411 Metal Cans

Amcor Rigid Plastics Usa LLC	G	419 483-4343	
Bellevue (G-1542)			
◆ Anchor Hocking LLC	A	740 681-6478	
Lancaster (G-11687)			
Ball Arosol Specialty Cont Inc	C	330 534-9273	
Hubbard (G-11128)			
Ball Corporation	C	419 423-3071	
Findlay (G-9792)			
Ball Corporation	G	330 244-2313	
North Canton (G-15222)			
Ball Corporation	D	614 771-9112	
Columbus (G-6804)			
Ball Corporation	F	330 534-7418	
Hubbard (G-11129)			
Ball Metal Beverage Cont Corp	C	419 423-3071	
Findlay (G-9793)			
Broodle Brands LLC	F	855 276-6353	
Cincinnati (G-3480)			
Buckeye Stamping Company	G	614 445-0059	
Columbus (G-6875)			
Busch Properties Inc	G	614 888-0946	
Columbus (G-6877)			

BWAY Corporation	E	513 388-2200	
Cincinnati (G-3491)			
Cardinal Welding Inc	G	330 426-2404	
East Palestine (G-9229)			
Cleveland Steel Container Corp	E	330 656-5600	
Streetsboro (G-17845)			
Container Manufacturing Ltd	G	937 264-2370	
Dayton (G-8242)			
Crown Cork & Seal Usa Inc	E	419 727-8201	
Toledo (G-18416)			
Crown Cork & Seal Usa Inc	B	330 833-1011	
Massillon (G-13123)			
Crown Cork & Seal Usa Inc	E	740 681-6593	
Lancaster (G-11703)			
Crown Cork & Seal Usa Inc	E	740 681-3000	
Lancaster (G-11702)			
▲ Encore Plastics Corporation	F	419 626-8000	
Sandusky (G-16962)			
◆ Exal Corporation	E	330 744-9505	
Youngstown (G-21080)			
G W Cobb Co	F	216 341-0100	
Cleveland (G-5389)			
▲ G&M Media Packaging Inc	F	419 636-5461	
Bryan (G-2297)			
▼ Ghp II LLC	E	740 687-2500	
Lancaster (G-11719)			
Independent Can Company	E	440 593-5300	
Conneaut (G-7810)			
Industrial Container Svcs LLC	E	513 921-8811	
Cincinnati (G-3917)			
Industrial Container Svcs LLC	D	614 864-1900	
Blacklick (G-1699)			
▲ Organized Living Inc	E	513 489-9300	
Cincinnati (G-4194)			
▲ Packaging Specialties Inc	E	330 723-6000	
Medina (G-13457)			
Rexam Beverage Can Company	E	419 877-0401	
Whitehouse (G-20345)			
Rexam Beverage Can Company	C	419 334-4461	
Fremont (G-10178)			
Reynolds Metals Company LLC	F	614 228-7390	
Columbus (G-7560)			
Seven-Ogun International LLC	G	614 888-8939	
Worthington (G-20887)			
Sidney Can & Tool LLC	G	937 492-0977	
Sidney (G-17226)			
▲ SSP Industrial Group Inc	G	330 665-2900	
Fairlawn (G-9761)			
▲ Tg Can Technology USA Inc	G	614 410-6672	
Westerville (G-20191)			
▼ Witt Industries Inc	D	513 871-5700	
Mason (G-13103)			

3412 Metal Barrels, Drums, Kegs & Pails

Astro Qcb Inc	B	513 921-8811	
Cincinnati (G-3422)			
Bentley World-Packaging Ltd	F	440 232-1100	
Bedford (G-1407)			
Champion Company	D	937 324-5681	
Springfield (G-17532)			
Champion Company	D	937 324-5681	
Springfield (G-17531)			
Cleveland Steel Container Corp	E	330 656-5600	
Streetsboro (G-17845)			
Cleveland Steel Container Corp	E	330 544-2271	
Niles (G-15147)			
Cqcb Inc	B	614 864-1900	
Blacklick (G-1694)			
Fluid-Bag LLC	G	513 310-9550	
Blue Ash (G-1798)			
Georgia-Pacific LLC	C	740 477-3347	
Circleville (G-4631)			
Green Bay Packaging Inc	C	419 332-5593	
Fremont (G-10157)			
Green Bay Packaging Inc	D	513 228-5560	
Lebanon (G-11806)			
Greif Inc	E	740 657-6500	
Delaware (G-8848)			
Greif Inc	E	740 549-6000	
Delaware (G-8847)			
Hawthorne Caravan & Assoc LLC	F	440 366-9065	
Elyria (G-9428)			
Horwitz & Pintis Co	F	419 666-2220	
Toledo (G-18512)			
Industrial Container Svcs LLC	E	513 921-8811	
Cincinnati (G-3917)			
Industrial Container Svcs LLC	D	614 864-1900	
Blacklick (G-1699)			
Mauser Usa LLC	E	614 856-5982	
Gahanna (G-10217)			

Mauser Usa LLC	D	513 398-1300	
Mason (G-13061)			
Mauser USA LLC	E	614 856-5982	
Columbus (G-7328)			
Mobile Mini Inc	F	614 449-8655	
Columbus (G-7360)			
North Coast Container Corp	D	216 441-6214	
Cleveland (G-5894)			
Overseas Packing LLC	F	440 232-2917	
Bedford (G-1451)			
▲ Packaging Specialties Inc	E	330 723-6000	
Medina (G-13457)			
Rexam Beverage Can Company	C	419 334-4461	
Fremont (G-10178)			
▲ Sabco Industries Inc	E	419 531-5347	
Toledo (G-18683)			
Schwarz Partners Packaging LLC	F	317 290-1140	
Sidney (G-17222)			
▲ SSP Industrial Group Inc	G	330 665-2900	
Fairlawn (G-9761)			
Syme Inc	G	330 723-6000	
Medina (G-13486)			
Tavens Container Inc	G	216 883-3333	
Bedford (G-1464)			
▲ Unican Ohio LLC	G	419 636-5461	
Fremont (G-10191)			
▲ Werk-Brau Company	G	419 422-2912	
Findlay (G-9907)			
Westrock Cp LLC	C	330 297-0841	
Ravenna (G-16571)			
Westrock Cp LLC	B	513 745-2400	
Blue Ash (G-1893)			
Westrock CP LLC	D	770 448-2193	
Wshngtn CT Hs (G-20930)			
▼ Witt Industries Inc	D	513 871-5700	
Mason (G-13103)			

3421 Cutlery

A & P Tech Services Inc	G	330 535-1700	
Akron (G-16)			
Acorn Products Inc	B	614 222-4400	
Columbus (G-6689)			
Advetech Inc	E	330 533-2227	
Canfield (G-2543)			
◆ Air Technical Industries Inc	E	440 951-5191	
Mentor (G-13512)			
◆ Alliance Knife Inc	E	513 367-9000	
Harrison (G-10768)			
American Punch Co Inc	E	216 731-4501	
Euclid (G-9566)			
▲ American Quicksilver Co	G	513 871-4517	
Cincinnati (G-3393)			
Badurik Butcher Block	G	330 652-2333	
Mineral Ridge (G-14303)			
Busse Knife Co	E	419 923-6471	
Wauseon (G-19673)			
Chief General Office	G	419 782-0950	
Defiance (G-8784)			
Cut Off Blades Inc	G	440 543-2947	
Chagrin Falls (G-3084)			
Dan Wilzynski	G	800 531-3343	
Columbus (G-7010)			
Edgewell Per Care Brands LLC	D	937 228-0105	
Dayton (G-8319)			
Edgewell Per Care Brands LLC	D	440 835-7500	
Westlake (G-20266)			
Edgewell Per Care Brands LLC	D	330 527-2191	
Garrettsville (G-10320)			
Edgewell Per Care Brands LLC	E	440 572-1336	
Cleveland (G-5259)			
El Nuevo Naranjo	G	614 863-4212	
Galloway (G-10312)			
Ernest Warther and Sons Inc	F	330 343-7513	
Dover (G-8984)			
▲ Evolution Resources LLC	G	937 438-2390	
Centerville (G-3041)			
▲ Fred Marvin and Associates Inc	G	330 784-9211	
Stow (G-17756)			
General Cutlery Inc	F	419 332-2316	
Fremont (G-10154)			
Klenk Industries Inc	D	330 453-7857	
Canton (G-2754)			
Kne LLC	G	859 356-1690	
Fairfield (G-9672)			
Libbey Glass Inc	A	419 729-7272	
Toledo (G-18559)			
Lt Wright Handcrafted Knife Co	F	740 317-1404	
Steubenville (G-17703)			
New York Frozen Foods	F	614 846-2232	
Westerville (G-20172)			

◆ Npk Construction Equipment Inc......D...... 440 232-7900
   Bedford *(G-1449)*

◆ Procter & Gamble Company............B...... 513 983-1100
   Cincinnati *(G-4277)*

Starbucks Corporation.....................G...... 513 754-5700
   Mason *(G-13091)*

Tom Fucito Inc.................................G...... 513 273-2092
   Oxford *(G-15844)*

3423 Hand & Edge Tools

A W C Inc..G...... 216 831-0550
   Cleveland *(G-4679)*

▲ Abhushan LLC..............................G...... 614 789-0632
   Dublin *(G-9035)*

Acme Company.................................D...... 330 758-2313
   Poland *(G-16381)*

Acorn Products Inc..........................B...... 614 222-4400
   Columbus *(G-6689)*

Advetech Inc....................................E...... 330 533-2227
   Canfield *(G-2544)*

Advetech Inc....................................E...... 330 533-2227
   Canfield *(G-2543)*

◆ Alliance Knife Inc..........................E...... 513 367-9000
   Harrison *(G-10768)*

▼ Amcraft Inc...................................G...... 419 729-7900
   Toledo *(G-18335)*

▲ American Power Pull Corp..............G...... 419 335-7050
   Wauseon *(G-19671)*

Ames Companies Inc........................E...... 740 783-2535
   Dexter City *(G-8953)*

ASG...F...... 216 486-6163
   Cleveland *(G-4845)*

Ashco Manufacturing Inc..................G...... 419 838-7157
   Toledo *(G-18357)*

Bartter & Sons................................G...... 419 651-0374
   Jeromesville *(G-11383)*

Bergman Safety Spanner Co Inc.......G...... 419 691-1462
   Northwood *(G-15478)*

Buckeye Gear Co.............................F...... 216 292-7998
   Chagrin Falls *(G-3078)*

C-H Tool & Die.................................G...... 740 397-7214
   Mount Vernon *(G-14610)*

Calvin Lanier...................................E...... 937 952-4221
   Dayton *(G-8208)*

Cannon Salt & Supply Inc.................G...... 440 232-1700
   Bedford *(G-1410)*

CB Manufacturing & Sls Co Inc.........D...... 937 866-5986
   Dayton *(G-8216)*

▲ CB Manufacturing & Sls Co Inc......D...... 937 866-5986
   Miamisburg *(G-13790)*

Chrisnik Inc.....................................G...... 513 738-2920
   Okeana *(G-15663)*

Cleveland Iron Workers Members......G...... 216 687-2290
   Cleveland *(G-5066)*

Cornwell Quality Tools Company.......D...... 330 628-2627
   Mogadore *(G-14370)*

Crystal Carvers Inc.........................G...... 800 365-9782
   Powell *(G-16470)*

D & M Saw & Tool Inc.....................G...... 513 871-5433
   Cincinnati *(G-3630)*

Desmond-Stephan Mfgcompany........E...... 937 653-7181
   Urbana *(G-19157)*

▲ E Z Grout Corporation...................E...... 740 749-3512
   Waterford *(G-19646)*

E Z Rout Inc....................................G...... 330 467-4814
   Northfield *(G-15465)*

Edgerton Forge Inc..........................D...... 419 298-2333
   Edgerton *(G-9327)*

▲ Electric Eel Mfg Co Inc.................G...... 937 323-4644
   Springfield *(G-17552)*

Empire Plow Company Inc.................E...... 216 641-2290
   Cleveland *(G-5278)*

Eric Mondene...................................G...... 740 965-2842
   Galena *(G-10241)*

▲ Everhard Products Inc...................C...... 330 453-7786
   Canton *(G-2699)*

F & B Engraving Tls & Sup LLC........G...... 937 332-7994
   Troy *(G-18824)*

Falcon Industries Inc.......................F...... 330 723-0099
   Medina *(G-13409)*

Fiery Chillcom.................................G...... 800 575-4180
   Akron *(G-186)*

▲ File Sharpening Company Inc.........E...... 937 376-8268
   Xenia *(G-20951)*

▲ Firenza Stone Inc.........................G...... 440 953-8883
   Willoughby *(G-20488)*

▼ Furukawa Rock Drill USA Co Ltd....E...... 330 673-5826
   Kent *(G-11462)*

Fusion Automation Inc.....................G...... 440 602-5595
   Willoughby *(G-20493)*

▲ Glass Medic Inc...........................G...... 800 356-4009
   Westerville *(G-20155)*

Handy Twine Knife Co.....................G...... 419 294-3424
   Upper Sandusky *(G-19124)*

Harbor Freight Tools Usa Inc............E...... 937 415-0770
   Dayton *(G-8385)*

Hutchinson-Stevens Inc...................G...... 216 281-8585
   Cleveland *(G-5540)*

▲ J & H Manufacturing LLC..............F...... 330 482-2636
   Columbiana *(G-6622)*

J and S Tool Incorporated................E...... 216 676-8330
   Cleveland *(G-5595)*

▲ Jbc Technologies Inc....................D...... 440 327-4522
   North Ridgeville *(G-15383)*

Klawhorn Industries Inc...................G...... 330 335-8191
   Wadsworth *(G-19414)*

Knight Ergonomics Inc.....................F...... 440 746-0044
   Brecksville *(G-2059)*

◆ Komar Industries Inc.....................E...... 614 836-2366
   Groveport *(G-10629)*

Luma Electric Company....................G...... 419 843-7842
   Sylvania *(G-18116)*

Martin Sprocket & Gear Inc.............D...... 419 485-5515
   Montpelier *(G-14448)*

▲ Matco Tools Corporation 1.............B...... 330 929-4949
   Stow *(G-17773)*

Midwest Knife Grinding Inc...............G...... 330 854-1030
   Canal Fulton *(G-2508)*

Myers Industries Inc........................E...... 440 632-1006
   Middlefield *(G-13971)*

Myers Industries Inc........................D...... 440 632-0230
   Middlefield *(G-13972)*

National Steel Rule Die LLC.............G...... 937 667-0967
   Vandalia *(G-19307)*

▲ Norbar Torque Tools Inc...............F...... 440 953-1175
   Willoughby *(G-20555)*

North Coast Holdings Inc..................G...... 330 535-7177
   Akron *(G-316)*

North Pk Innovations Group Inc........C...... 440 247-4600
   Solon *(G-17351)*

Oldforge Tools Inc...........................G...... 330 535-7177
   Akron *(G-327)*

Panacea Products Corporation.........D...... 614 429-6320
   Columbus *(G-7457)*

Randolph Tool Company Inc.............F...... 330 877-4923
   Hartville *(G-10832)*

▲ Rex International USA Inc...............E...... 800 321-7950
   Ashtabula *(G-837)*

◆ Ridge Tool Company......................A...... 440 323-5581
   Elyria *(G-9486)*

Ridge Tool Manufacturing Co...........A...... 440 323-5581
   Elyria *(G-9488)*

▲ S & H Industries Inc.....................G...... 216 831-0550
   Cleveland *(G-6145)*

Sewer Rodding Equipment Co...........E...... 419 991-2065
   Lima *(G-12089)*

Silver Expressions...........................G...... 740 687-0144
   Lancaster *(G-11752)*

Simon Ellis Superabrasives..............G...... 937 226-0683
   Dayton *(G-8659)*

Simonds International LLC................E...... 978 424-0100
   Kimbolton *(G-11603)*

Spa Pool Covers Inc........................G...... 440 235-9981
   North Royalton *(G-15452)*

Stanley Access Tech LLC.................G...... 440 461-5500
   Cleveland *(G-6235)*

Stanley Industrial & Auto LLC...........C...... 614 755-7089
   Westerville *(G-20187)*

▲ Stanley Industrial & Auto LLC.......D...... 614 755-7000
   Westerville *(G-20188)*

◆ Step2 Company LLC......................B...... 866 429-5200
   Streetsboro *(G-17879)*

Step2 Company LLC.........................B...... 419 938-6343
   Perrysville *(G-16176)*

Stride Tool LLC...............................C...... 440 247-4600
   Solon *(G-17388)*

Sumitomo Elc Carbide Mfg Inc.........F...... 440 354-0600
   Grand River *(G-10453)*

▲ Summit Tool Company....................D...... 330 535-7177
   Akron *(G-422)*

▲ Superion Inc................................E...... 937 374-0033
   Xenia *(G-20977)*

Toolovation LLC..............................G...... 216 514-3022
   Cleveland *(G-6336)*

▲ Wright Tool Company....................G...... 330 848-0600
   Barberton *(G-1157)*

3425 Hand Saws & Saw Blades

▲ Blade Manufacturing Co Inc...........F...... 614 294-1649
   Columbus *(G-6840)*

Callahan Cutting Tools Inc...............G...... 614 294-1649
   Columbus *(G-6889)*

Cammel Saw Company Inc................F...... 330 477-3764
   Canton *(G-2634)*

Dynatech Systems Inc......................E...... 440 365-1774
   Elyria *(G-9408)*

Form-A-Chip Inc...............................G...... 937 223-4135
   Dayton *(G-8347)*

J and S Tool Incorporated................E...... 216 676-8330
   Cleveland *(G-5595)*

Joes Saw Shop................................G...... 440 834-1196
   Burton *(G-2378)*

◆ M K Morse Company......................B...... 330 453-8187
   Canton *(G-2762)*

Martindale Electric Company............E...... 216 521-8567
   Cleveland *(G-5754)*

▲ Peerless Saw Company..................E...... 614 836-5790
   Groveport *(G-10640)*

▼ Regal Diamond Products Corp........E...... 440 944-7700
   Wickliffe *(G-20385)*

▲ Superion Inc................................E...... 937 374-0033
   Xenia *(G-20977)*

Uhrichsville Carbide Inc...................F...... 740 922-9197
   Uhrichsville *(G-19064)*

Wolff Tool & Manufacturing Co.........F...... 440 933-7797
   Avon Lake *(G-1056)*

3429 Hardware, NEC

AB Bonded Locksmiths Inc...............G...... 513 531-7334
   Cincinnati *(G-3342)*

Acorn Technology Corporation..........E...... 216 663-1244
   Cleveland *(G-4697)*

▲ Action Coupling & Eqp Inc.............D...... 330 279-4242
   Holmesville *(G-11099)*

Aeroquip-Vickers Inc........................G...... 216 523-5000
   Cleveland *(G-4722)*

▲ Allfasteners Usa LLC.....................F...... 440 232-6060
   Medina *(G-13367)*

Aluminum Bearing Co of America.......G...... 216 267-8560
   Cleveland *(G-4773)*

Ampex Metal Products Company........E...... 216 267-9242
   Brookpark *(G-2151)*

Annin & Co.......................................D...... 740 622-4447
   Coshocton *(G-7878)*

Architectural Door Systems LLC........G...... 513 808-9900
   Lebanon *(G-11780)*

▲ Arnco Corporation........................C...... 800 847-7661
   Elyria *(G-9375)*

Arrow Tru-Line Inc...........................D...... 419 636-7013
   Bryan *(G-2279)*

Baker McMillen Co...........................E...... 330 923-3303
   Stow *(G-17734)*

▲ Boardman Molded Products Inc......D...... 330 788-2401
   Youngstown *(G-21032)*

Bowes Manufacturing Inc.................F...... 216 378-2110
   Solon *(G-17271)*

▲ Brass Accents Inc.........................E...... 330 332-9500
   Salem *(G-16876)*

Butera Manufacturing Inc.................F...... 440 516-3698
   Willoughby Hills *(G-20638)*

Butera Manufacturing Inds................G...... 216 761-8800
   Cleveland *(G-4953)*

▲ Case-Maul Clamps Inc...................F...... 419 668-6563
   Norwalk *(G-15529)*

Chantilly Development Corp..............F...... 419 243-8109
   Toledo *(G-18393)*

◆ Clampco Products Inc....................D...... 330 336-8857
   Wadsworth *(G-19398)*

▲ Cleveland Hdwr & Forging Co.........E...... 216 641-5200
   Cleveland *(G-5064)*

Cleveland Steel Specialty Co............E...... 216 464-9400
   Bedford Heights *(G-1481)*

▲ CT Hydraulics Inc.........................F...... 440 437-2101
   Orwell *(G-15774)*

Curtiss-Wright Flow Ctrl Corp..........D...... 216 267-3200
   Cleveland *(G-5148)*

Custom Metal Works Inc..................F...... 419 668-7831
   Norwalk *(G-15531)*

Dayton Metal Products Company.......G...... 937 849-0071
   Cincinnati *(G-3643)*

Dayton Superior Corporation............E...... 937 682-4015
   Rushsylvania *(G-16751)*

Desco Corporation...........................G...... 614 888-8855
   New Albany *(G-14757)*

Design Magnetics Ltd.......................G...... 234 380-5500
   Hudson *(G-11169)*

Detroit Technologies Inc...................E...... 937 492-2708
   Sidney *(G-17179)*

▲ Die Co Inc...................................E...... 440 942-8856
   Eastlake *(G-9265)*

SIC

Doan Machinery & Eqp Co Inc ....G...... 216 932-6243
　University Heights *(G-19108)*

Eaton Corporation ....A...... 419 238-1190
　Van Wert *(G-19253)*

Eaton Corporation ....C...... 330 274-0743
　Aurora *(G-916)*

▲ Eaton-Aeroquip Llc ....C...... 216 523-5000
　Cleveland *(G-5254)*

Eaton-Aeroquip Llc ....D...... 419 238-1190
　Van Wert *(G-19255)*

Edward W Daniel LLC ....E...... 440 647-1960
　Wellington *(G-19742)*

Element14 US Holdings Inc ....G...... 330 523-4280
　Richfield *(G-16622)*

◆ Elster Perfection Corporation ....D...... 440 428-1171
　Geneva *(G-10346)*

Exact Pipe Tools ....G...... 330 922-8150
　Cuyahoga Falls *(G-7993)*

Exline Manufacturing Co Inc ....G...... 937 866-1515
　Miamisburg *(G-13808)*

Fastenal Company ....G...... 419 629-3024
　New Bremen *(G-14787)*

Faull & Son LLC ....F...... 330 652-4341
　Niles *(G-15152)*

▲ Federal Equipment Company ....D...... 513 621-5260
　Cincinnati *(G-3747)*

First Francis Company Inc ....E...... 440 352-8927
　Painesville *(G-15881)*

Flex-Strut Inc ....D...... 330 372-9999
　Warren *(G-19551)*

Florida Production Engrg Inc ....G...... 937 996-4361
　New Madison *(G-14869)*

◆ Fort Recovery Industries Inc ....C...... 419 375-4121
　Fort Recovery *(G-9951)*

Fortner Upholstering Inc ....F...... 614 475-8282
　Columbus *(G-7095)*

Gateway Concrete Forming Svcs ......D...... 513 353-2000
　Miamitown *(G-13887)*

Great Midwest Yacht Co ....G...... 740 965-4511
　Sunbury *(G-18061)*

Greyfield Industries Inc ....F...... 513 860-1785
　Trenton *(G-18793)*

▲ Group Industries Inc ....E...... 216 271-0702
　Cleveland *(G-5461)*

Hardware Unlimited LLC ....G...... 419 472-8745
　Toledo *(G-18447)*

Hawthorne Bolt Works Corp ....G...... 330 723-0555
　Medina *(G-13419)*

▼ Hbd/Thermoid Inc ....G...... 937 593-5010
　Bellefontaine *(G-1532)*

Hearth & Home Technologies LLC ....G...... 513 874-4770
　Cincinnati *(G-3875)*

Hebco Products Inc ....A...... 419 562-7987
　Bucyrus *(G-2347)*

Heller Machine Products Inc ....G...... 216 281-2951
　Cleveland *(G-5496)*

▲ Hercules Industries Inc ....E...... 740 494-2620
　Prospect *(G-16497)*

Herman Machine Inc ....F...... 330 633-3261
　Tallmadge *(G-18145)*

▲ Hfi LLC ....B...... 614 491-0700
　Canal Winchester *(G-2525)*

Hillman Group Inc ....G...... 800 800-4900
　Parma *(G-15962)*

Hudson Fasteners Inc ....G...... 330 270-9500
　Youngstown *(G-21110)*

Hydromotive Engineering Co ....G...... 330 425-4266
　Twinsburg *(G-18956)*

▲ Independence 2 LLC ....F...... 800 414-0545
　Hubbard *(G-11131)*

Industrial Pulley & Machine Co ....G...... 937 355-4910
　West Mansfield *(G-20099)*

International Automotive ....A...... 419 433-5653
　Huron *(G-11228)*

J B Kepple Sheet Metal ....G...... 740 393-2971
　Mount Vernon *(G-14624)*

J L R Products Inc ....F...... 330 832-9557
　Massillon *(G-13158)*

J W Goss Co Inc ....G...... 330 395-0739
　Warren *(G-19562)*

John Stieg & Associates ....G...... 614 889-7954
　Dublin *(G-9092)*

Kasai North America Inc ....F...... 614 356-1494
　Dublin *(G-9094)*

▲ Kirk Key Interlock Company LLC ...E...... 330 833-8223
　North Canton *(G-15245)*

L & W Inc ....D...... 734 397-6300
　Avon *(G-999)*

Lake Park Tool & Machine LLC ....F...... 330 788-2437
　Youngstown *(G-21131)*

Langenau Manufacturing Company .....F...... 216 651-3400
　Cleveland *(G-5680)*

Leetonia Tool Company ....F...... 330 427-6944
　Leetonia *(G-11861)*

▲ Marlboro Manufacturing Inc ....E...... 330 935-2221
　Alliance *(G-526)*

▲ Master Mfg Co Inc ....E...... 216 641-0500
　Cleveland *(G-5758)*

▲ Matdan Corporation ....D...... 513 794-0500
　Blue Ash *(G-1834)*

Maumee Hose & Fitting Inc ....G...... 419 893-7252
　Maumee *(G-13279)*

▲ Mecc-Usa LLC ....G...... 513 891-0301
　West Chester *(G-19899)*

Meese Inc ....D...... 440 998-1202
　Ashtabula *(G-819)*

Midlake Products & Mfg Co ....D...... 330 875-4202
　Louisville *(G-12319)*

▲ Miller Studio Inc ....D...... 330 339-1100
　New Philadelphia *(G-14916)*

Minderman Marine Products Inc ....G...... 419 732-2626
　Port Clinton *(G-16406)*

▲ Morgal Machine Tool Co ....G...... 937 325-5561
　Springfield *(G-17607)*

▼ Napoleon Spring Works Inc ....C...... 419 445-1010
　Archbold *(G-688)*

Netherland Rubber Company ....E...... 513 733-0883
　Cincinnati *(G-4146)*

▲ Nova Machine Products Inc ....C...... 216 267-3200
　Middleburg Heights *(G-13907)*

Ohio Hydraulics Inc ....E...... 513 771-2590
　Cincinnati *(G-4178)*

Ottawa Products Co ....E...... 419 836-5115
　Curtice *(G-7958)*

PA Stratton & Co Inc ....G...... 419 660-9979
　Collins *(G-6576)*

Paddock Corporation ....E...... 440 543-0631
　Chagrin Falls *(G-3110)*

◆ Premier Farnell Holding Inc ....E...... 330 523-4273
　Richfield *(G-16633)*

Progressive Machine Die Inc ....E...... 330 405-6600
　Macedonia *(G-12478)*

▲ R & R Tool Inc ....E...... 937 783-8665
　Blanchester *(G-1715)*

R H Industries Inc ....E...... 216 281-5210
　Cleveland *(G-6083)*

Racelite South Coast Inc ....E...... 216 581-4600
　Maple Heights *(G-12739)*

▲ Samsel Rope & Marine Supply Co ...E...... 216 241-0333
　Cleveland *(G-6156)*

Sensible Products Inc ....G...... 330 659-4212
　Richfield *(G-16637)*

Sheet Metal Products Co Inc ....G...... 440 392-9000
　Mentor *(G-13722)*

Sky Climber Fasteners LLC ....G...... 740 816-9830
　Delaware *(G-8889)*

Smartv Company LLC ....G...... 614 890-6090
　Westerville *(G-20186)*

▲ Stanley Industrial & Auto LLC ....D...... 614 755-7000
　Westerville *(G-20188)*

Strawser Hydrant Maintenance ....G...... 614 875-1514
　Grove City *(G-10600)*

Strutt Products LLC ....G...... 330 889-2727
　Bristolville *(G-2100)*

▲ Summers Acquisition Corp ....E...... 216 941-7700
　Cleveland *(G-6262)*

Summers Acquisition Corp ....G...... 419 526-5800
　Mansfield *(G-12687)*

Summers Acquisition Corp ....G...... 440 946-5611
　Eastlake *(G-9291)*

Summers Acquisition Corp ....G...... 419 423-5800
　Findlay *(G-9898)*

◆ Superior Metal Products Inc ....E...... 419 228-1145
　Lima *(G-12099)*

Supply International Inc ....G...... 740 282-8604
　Steubenville *(G-17718)*

▲ Te-Co Manufacturing LLC ....D...... 937 836-0961
　Union *(G-19068)*

▲ Technoform GL Insul N Amer Inc ...E...... 330 487-6600
　Twinsburg *(G-19027)*

Texmaster Tools Inc ....F...... 740 965-8778
　Fredericktown *(G-10112)*

Thermo-Rite Mfg Company ....G...... 330 633-8680
　Akron *(G-439)*

▲ Top Tier Storage Prodcuts LLC ......G...... 937 242-6133
　Centerville *(G-3045)*

▲ Trim Parts Inc ....E...... 513 934-0815
　Lebanon *(G-11845)*

Trim Systems Operating Corp ....C...... 614 289-5360
　New Albany *(G-14774)*

▲ Triton Products LLC ....F...... 440 248-5480
　Solon *(G-17407)*

Trust Manufacturing LLC ....F...... 216 531-8787
　Euclid *(G-9612)*

Twin Valley Metalcraft Asm LLC ....G...... 937 787-4634
　West Alexandria *(G-19784)*

United Die & Mfg Co ....E...... 330 938-6141
　Sebring *(G-17056)*

Van Lock Co Inc ....F...... 513 561-9692
　Cincinnati *(G-4554)*

Verhoff Machine & Welding Inc ....C...... 419 596-3202
　Continental *(G-7829)*

▲ Voss Industries Inc ....C...... 216 771-0870
　Cleveland *(G-6429)*

Voss Industries Inc ....D...... 216 771-7655
　Cleveland *(G-6430)*

Wallen Commercial Hardware ....G...... 937 426-5711
　Beavercreek Township *(G-1392)*

Washington Products Inc ....F...... 330 837-5101
　Massillon *(G-13211)*

Wecall Inc ....G...... 440 437-8202
　Orwell *(G-15780)*

West Chester Lock Co LLC ....G...... 513 777-6486
　West Chester *(G-19971)*

▲ Whiteside Manufacturing Co ....E...... 740 363-1179
　Delaware *(G-8896)*

Wilson Bohannan Company ....D...... 740 382-3639
　Marion *(G-12915)*

Winzeler Stamping Co ....D...... 419 485-3147
　Montpelier *(G-14458)*

▲ Worthington Products Inc ....D...... 330 452-7400
　Canton *(G-2903)*

3431 Enameled Iron & Metal Sanitary Ware

Accent Manufacturing Inc ....F...... 330 724-7704
　Norton *(G-15500)*

Agean Marble Manufacturing ....E...... 513 874-1475
　West Chester *(G-19978)*

BJ Equipment Ltd ....F...... 614 497-1776
　Columbus *(G-6834)*

Crane Plumbing LLC ....E...... 419 522-4211
　Mansfield *(G-12587)*

◆ Crane Plumbing LLC ....E...... 419 522-4211
　Mansfield *(G-12588)*

Extrudex Limited Partnership ....E...... 440 352-7101
　Painesville *(G-15879)*

◆ Mansfield Plumbing Pdts LLC ....A...... 419 938-5211
　Perrysville *(G-16173)*

Murdock Inc ....F...... 513 471-7700
　Cincinnati *(G-4132)*

Zurn Industries LLC ....F...... 814 455-0921
　Hilliard *(G-10994)*

3432 Plumbing Fixture Fittings & Trim, Brass

▲ American Brass Manufacturing ....E...... 216 431-6565
　Cleveland *(G-4778)*

As America Inc ....C...... 614 497-9384
　Groveport *(G-10614)*

As America Inc ....G...... 330 337-2219
　Salem *(G-16873)*

As America Inc ....G...... 615 873-2410
　Mansfield *(G-12563)*

Atlantic Co ....E...... 440 944-8988
　Willoughby Hills *(G-20637)*

Carr Supply Co ....G...... 937 316-6300
　Greenville *(G-10492)*

Carr Supply Co ....G...... 937 276-2555
　Dayton *(G-8211)*

Cfrc Wtr & Enrgy Solutions Inc ....G...... 216 479-0290
　Cleveland *(G-5011)*

◆ CMI Holding Company Crawford .....D...... 419 468-9122
　Galion *(G-10259)*

Dittmar Sales and Service ....G...... 740 653-7933
　Lancaster *(G-11709)*

▲ Empire Brass Co ....E...... 216 431-6565
　Cleveland *(G-5276)*

▲ Field Stone Inc ....G...... 937 898-3236
　Tipp City *(G-18277)*

◆ Fort Recovery Industries Inc ....E...... 419 375-4121
　Fort Recovery *(G-9951)*

Fort Recovery Industries Inc ....E...... 419 375-3005
　Fort Recovery *(G-9952)*

▼ Krendl Machine Company ....D...... 419 692-3060
　Delphos *(G-8910)*

Langenau Manufacturing Company ....F...... 216 651-3400
　Cleveland *(G-5680)*

Lsq Manufacturing Inc ....G...... 330 725-4905
　Medina *(G-13437)*

Maass Midwest Mfg Inc ....G...... 419 894-6424
　Arcadia *(G-654)*

◆ Mansfield Plumbing Pdts LLC ....A 419 938-5211
Perrysville *(G-16173)*

National Brass Company Inc ....G 216 651-8530
Cleveland *(G-5854)*

Next Gerenation Crimping ....G 440 237-6300
North Royalton *(G-15437)*

Scotts Miracle-Gro Products ....E 937 644-0011
Marysville *(G-12970)*

Toolbold Corporation ....E 440 543-1660
Cleveland *(G-6335)*

▲ Trumbull Manufacturing Inc ....D 330 393-6624
Warren *(G-19614)*

W A S P Inc ....G 740 439-2398
Cambridge *(G-2482)*

▲ Waxman Industries Inc ....C 440 439-1830
Cleveland *(G-6452)*

Winsupply Inc ....F 937 346-0600
Springfield *(G-17679)*

Zekelman Industries Inc ....C 740 432-2146
Cambridge *(G-2483)*

3433 Heating Eqpt

Accent Manufacturing Inc ....F 330 724-7704
Norton *(G-15500)*

Air Enterprises LLC ....E 330 794-9770
Akron *(G-34)*

Air Entrprises Acquisition LLC ....C 330 794-9770
Akron *(G-35)*

Airtech Mechanical Inc ....F 419 292-0074
Toledo *(G-18326)*

Aitken Products Inc ....G 440 466-5711
Geneva *(G-10341)*

▲ Beckett Air Incorporated ....D 440 327-9999
North Ridgeville *(G-15359)*

◆ Beckett Gas Inc ....C 440 327-3141
North Ridgeville *(G-15360)*

BMC Holdings Inc ....G 419 636-1194
Bryan *(G-2283)*

Burner Technology Unlimited ....G 440 232-6181
Cleveland *(G-4949)*

◆ Dcm Manufacturing Inc ....E 216 265-8006
Cleveland *(G-5178)*

▲ Dmi Products Inc ....F 440 975-8645
Mentor *(G-13562)*

▲ Duro Dyne Midwest Corp ....B 513 870-6000
Hamilton *(G-10685)*

▲ Ebner Furnaces Inc ....D 330 335-2311
Wadsworth *(G-19404)*

▲ Enerco Group Inc ....E 216 916-3000
Cleveland *(G-5280)*

Enerco Technical Products Inc ....C 216 916-3000
Cleveland *(G-5281)*

Es Thermal Inc ....E 440 323-3291
Elyria *(G-9422)*

Ets Schaefer LLC ....E 330 468-6600
Macedonia *(G-12448)*

Famous Industries Inc ....D 740 685-2592
Byesville *(G-2401)*

Firestone Sheet Metal Inc ....E 330 337-9551
Salem *(G-16890)*

First Solar Inc ....B 419 661-1478
Perrysburg *(G-16096)*

Glo-Quartz Electric Heater Co ....E 440 255-9701
Mentor *(G-13593)*

Grid Industrial Heating Inc ....G 330 332-9931
Salem *(G-16897)*

◆ Hartzell Fan Inc ....C 937 773-7411
Piqua *(G-16271)*

Hdt Ep Inc ....C 216 438-6111
Solon *(G-17307)*

Hdt Expeditionary Systems Inc ....F 440 466-6640
Geneva *(G-10350)*

▼ Hunter Defense Tech Inc ....E 216 438-6111
Solon *(G-17312)*

Infinity Plus ....G 937 828-1350
Mechanicsburg *(G-13357)*

Iosil Energy Corporation ....F 614 295-8680
Groveport *(G-10627)*

Lakeway Mfg Inc ....E 419 433-3030
Huron *(G-11232)*

▲ Mr Heater Inc ....E 216 916-3000
Cleveland *(G-5838)*

Nbbi ....G 614 888-8320
Columbus *(G-7385)*

North Amrcn Sstnable Enrgy Ltd ....G 440 539-7133
Parma *(G-15963)*

▲ Onix Corporation ....G 800 844-0076
Perrysburg *(G-16135)*

Panelbloc Inc ....G 440 974-8877
Mentor *(G-13679)*

◆ Qual-Fab Inc ....E 440 327-5000
Avon *(G-1005)*

◆ Rbi Solar Inc ....G 513 242-2051
Cincinnati *(G-4332)*

◆ RW Beckett Corporation ....C 440 327-1060
North Ridgeville *(G-15402)*

Selas Heat Technology Co LLC ....G 216 662-8800
Streetsboro *(G-17874)*

▲ Selas Heat Technology Co LLC ....E 800 523-6500
Streetsboro *(G-17875)*

Sgm Co Inc ....E 440 255-1190
Mentor *(G-13721)*

Shark Solar LLC ....G 216 630-7395
Medina *(G-13479)*

Specialty Ceramics Inc ....D 330 482-0800
Columbiana *(G-6633)*

▲ Spectrum Inc ....F 440 951-6061
Brooklyn Heights *(G-2147)*

Stelter and Brinck Inc ....E 513 367-9300
Harrison *(G-10805)*

Sticker Corporation ....F 440 946-2100
Willoughby *(G-20606)*

Suarez Corporation Industries ....F 330 494-5504
Canton *(G-2862)*

Swagelok Company ....C 440 349-5836
Solon *(G-17393)*

T J F Inc ....F 419 878-4400
Waterville *(G-19668)*

Thermo Systems Technology ....E 216 292-8250
Cleveland *(G-6320)*

▲ Trumbull Manufacturing Inc ....D 330 393-6624
Warren *(G-19614)*

Turbonics Inc ....G 216 741-8300
Cleveland *(G-6376)*

UNI-Ref United Refractories Co ....E 513 563-9955
Cincinnati *(G-4536)*

▼ Willard Kelsey Solar Group LLC ....E 419 931-2001
Perrysburg *(G-16170)*

Wood Stove Shed ....G 419 562-1545
Bucyrus *(G-2365)*

Ws Thermal Process Tech Inc ....G 440 385-6829
Lorain *(G-12293)*

3441 Fabricated Structural Steel

A & E Butscha Co ....G 513 761-1919
Cincinnati *(G-3329)*

▲ A & G Manufacturing Co Inc ....E 419 468-7433
Galion *(G-10250)*

A+ Engineering Fabrication Inc ....F 419 832-0748
Grand Rapids *(G-10439)*

A-1 Fabricators Finishers LLC ....D 513 724-0383
Batavia *(G-1163)*

Accu-Tech Manufacturing Co ....F 330 848-8100
Akron *(G-27)*

Accurate Fab LLC ....G 330 562-0566
Streetsboro *(G-17833)*

Ace Boiler & Welding Co Inc ....G 330 745-4443
Barberton *(G-1092)*

Advance Industrial Mfg Inc ....E 614 871-3333
Grove City *(G-10539)*

Advance Industries Group LLC ....E 216 741-1800
Cleveland *(G-4707)*

Advanced Onsight Welding Svcs ....G 513 924-1400
Cincinnati *(G-3359)*

Air Heater Seal Company Inc ....E 740 984-2146
Waterford *(G-19645)*

Akron Rebar Co ....E 330 745-7100
Akron *(G-54)*

Albert Freytag Inc ....E 419 628-2018
Minster *(G-14349)*

▲ Alcon Industries Inc ....D 216 961-1100
Cleveland *(G-4745)*

Allied Fabricating & Wldg Co ....E 614 751-6664
Columbus *(G-6725)*

Alro Steel Corporation ....E 937 253-6121
Dayton *(G-8149)*

Alsteel Fabricators Inc ....G 330 652-4344
Mineral Ridge *(G-14302)*

▲ Alufab Inc ....G 513 528-7281
Cincinnati *(G-3293)*

AM Warren LLC ....G 330 841-2800
Warren *(G-19520)*

Ambassador Steel Corporation ....F 740 382-9969
Marion *(G-12854)*

Ameco USA Metal Fabrication ....G 440 899-9400
Cleveland *(G-4777)*

▼ American Ir Met Cleveland LLC ....E 216 266-0518
Cleveland *(G-4786)*

American Qulty Fabrication Inc ....G 937 667-2861
Vandalia *(G-19281)*

American Steel Assod Pdts Inc ....D 419 531-9471
Toledo *(G-18345)*

Ameridian Specialty Services ....E 513 769-0150
Cincinnati *(G-3396)*

Amrod Bridge & Iron LLC ....E 330 530-8230
Mc Donald *(G-13346)*

Amtank Armor LLC ....G 216 252-1500
Cleveland *(G-4800)*

Amtech Tool and Machine Inc ....G 330 758-8215
Youngstown *(G-21024)*

Amto Acquisition Corp ....F 419 347-1185
Shelby *(G-17131)*

Anstine Machining Corp ....F 330 821-4365
Alliance *(G-496)*

Ap-Alternatives LLC ....F 419 267-5280
Ridgeville Corners *(G-16663)*

▲ Appian Manufacturing Corp ....E 614 445-2230
Columbus *(G-6762)*

Applied Energy Tech Inc ....E 419 537-9052
Maumee *(G-13227)*

Applied Engneered Surfaces Inc ....F 440 366-0440
Elyria *(G-9374)*

Arcalloy Metal Fabrication ....G 800 822-9402
Akron *(G-71)*

Arctech Fabricating Inc ....E 937 525-9353
Springfield *(G-17518)*

▲ Armor Consolidated Inc ....C 513 923-5260
Mason *(G-12982)*

▲ Armor Metal Group Mason Inc ....C 513 769-0700
Mason *(G-12983)*

Arrow Fabricating Co ....E 216 641-0490
Novelty *(G-15581)*

Ashco Manufacturing Inc ....G 419 838-7157
Toledo *(G-18357)*

Aster Elements Inc ....E 440 942-2799
Mentor *(G-13527)*

◆ Astro-TEC Mfg Inc ....E 330 854-2209
Canal Fulton *(G-2497)*

Avenue Fabricating Inc ....E 513 752-1911
Batavia *(G-1165)*

Banks Manufacturing Company ....F 440 458-8661
Grafton *(G-10420)*

Bauer Corporation ....E 800 321-4760
Wooster *(G-20746)*

Bcfab Inc ....E 419 532-2899
Fort Jennings *(G-9925)*

Berran Industrial Group Inc ....E 330 253-5800
Akron *(G-89)*

Best Fab Co ....G 440 328-3254
Elyria *(G-9381)*

Best Process Solutions Inc ....E 330 220-1440
Brunswick *(G-2212)*

Bethel Engineering and Eqp Inc ....E 419 568-1100
New Hampshire *(G-14833)*

Bickers Metal Products Inc ....E 513 353-4000
Miamitown *(G-13884)*

Bird Equipment LLC ....E 330 549-1004
North Lima *(G-15311)*

Bison Wldg & Fabrication Inc ....G 440 944-4770
Wickliffe *(G-20360)*

Blackburns Fabrication Inc ....E 614 875-0784
Columbus *(G-6838)*

Blevins Metal Fabrication Inc ....E 419 522-6082
Mansfield *(G-12567)*

Boardman Steel Inc ....D 330 758-0951
Columbiana *(G-6607)*

Bradley Metal Fabrication Llc ....F 216 881-7400
Cleveland *(G-4930)*

Breitinger Company ....C 419 526-4255
Mansfield *(G-12569)*

▲ Brilex Industries Inc ....C 330 744-1114
Youngstown *(G-21037)*

Brilex Industries Inc ....D 330 744-1114
Youngstown *(G-21036)*

▲ Buck Equipment Inc ....E 614 539-3039
Grove City *(G-10548)*

Buckeye Fbricators of Leetonia ....G 330 427-0330
Leetonia *(G-11858)*

Buckeye Steel Incorporated ....F 740 425-2306
Barnesville *(G-1159)*

Burghardt Manufacturing Inc ....G 330 253-7590
Akron *(G-103)*

Burghardt Metal Fabg Inc ....F 330 794-1830
Akron *(G-104)*

C A Joseph Co ....F 330 532-4646
Irondale *(G-11287)*

C-N-D Industries Inc ....E 330 478-8811
Massillon *(G-13118)*

Camelot Manufacturing Inc ....F 419 678-2603
Coldwater *(G-6554)*

CCM Welding Inc .... G 330 630-2521
Akron *(G-113)*

Ceco Environmental Corp .... E 513 874-8915
West Chester *(G-19987)*

Central Ohio Fabricators LLC .... E 740 393-3892
Mount Vernon *(G-14613)*

Chagrin Vly Stl Erectors Inc .... F 440 975-1556
Willoughby *(G-20455)*

Champion Bridge Company .... E 937 382-2521
Wilmington *(G-20658)*

Charles Mfg Co .... F 330 395-3490
Warren *(G-19534)*

Charles Ray Evans .... F 740 967-3669
Johnstown *(G-11396)*

Chattanooga Laser Cutting LLC .... E 513 779-7200
Cincinnati *(G-3524)*

Chc Manufacturing Inc .... E 513 821-7757
Cincinnati *(G-3525)*

Chc Manufacturing Inc .... G 614 527-1606
Columbus *(G-6923)*

Christman Fabricators Inc .... G 330 477-8077
Canton *(G-2654)*

Cincinnati Industrial McHy Inc .... C 513 923-5600
Mason *(G-12994)*

Cincy Glass Inc .... G 513 241-0455
Cincinnati *(G-3573)*

◆ Clermont Steel Fabricators LLC .... D 513 732-6033
Batavia *(G-1173)*

Cleveland City Forge Inc .... E 440 647-5400
Wellington *(G-19739)*

▲ Clifton Steel Company .... D 216 662-6111
Maple Heights *(G-12731)*

Clipsons Metal Working Inc .... G 513 772-6393
Cincinnati *(G-3588)*

Cohen Brothers Inc .... E 513 422-3696
Middletown *(G-14031)*

Com-Fab Inc .... E 740 857-1107
Plain City *(G-16327)*

Commercial Mtal Fbricators Inc ...... E 937 233-4911
Dayton *(G-8239)*

Concord Fabricators Inc .... E 614 875-2500
Grove City *(G-10550)*

Contech Engnered Solutions Inc ..... A 513 645-7000
West Chester *(G-19840)*

Contech Engnered Solutions LLC ..... D 513 645-7000
Middletown *(G-14032)*

◆ Contech Engnered Solutions LLC ... C 513 645-7000
West Chester *(G-19841)*

▲ Continental GL Sls & Inv Group .... B 614 679-1201
Powell *(G-16469)*

County of Lake .... D 440 269-2193
Willoughby *(G-20464)*

Coventry Steel Services Inc .... F 216 883-4477
Cleveland *(G-5136)*

Cramers Inc .... E 330 477-4571
Canton *(G-2670)*

Creative Fab & Welding LLC .... E 937 780-5000
Leesburg *(G-11851)*

Curtiss-Wright Flow Control .... D 513 528-7900
Cincinnati *(G-3297)*

D T Kothera Inc .... G 440 632-1651
Middlefield *(G-13930)*

Dal-Little Fabricating Inc .... G 216 883-3323
Cleveland *(G-5163)*

Davis Fabricators Inc .... E 419 898-5297
Oak Harbor *(G-15588)*

De-Ko Inc .... E 440 951-2585
Willoughby *(G-20472)*

Debra-Kuempel Inc .... D 513 271-6500
Cincinnati *(G-3645)*

Debs Welding & Fabrication .... G 330 376-2242
Akron *(G-143)*

Defiance Metal Products WI Inc ...... C 920 426-9207
Defiance *(G-8787)*

Diamond Mfg Bluffton Ltd .... D 419 358-0129
Bluffton *(G-1911)*

Diamond Wipes Intl Inc .... D 419 562-3575
Bucyrus *(G-2338)*

Dietrich Industries Inc .... C 330 372-4014
Warren *(G-19543)*

Dietrich Industries Inc .... F 614 438-3210
Worthington *(G-20863)*

Dietrich Industries Inc .... D 216 472-1511
Cleveland *(G-5194)*

Dietrich Industries Inc .... E 614 438-3210
Worthington *(G-20864)*

▲ Diversifd OH Vlly Eqpt & Srvcs .... F 740 458-9881
Clarington *(G-4651)*

DMC Welding Incorporated .... G 330 877-1935
Hartville *(G-10820)*

Dover Conveyor Inc .... E 740 922-9390
Midvale *(G-14106)*

Dover Tank and Plate Company ...... E 330 343-4443
Dover *(G-8982)*

◆ Dracool-Usa Inc .... E 937 743-5899
Carlisle *(G-2930)*

Dwayne Bennett Industries .... E 440 466-5724
Geneva *(G-10345)*

E B P Inc .... E 216 241-2550
Cleveland *(G-5230)*

E W Welding & Fabricating .... G 440 826-9038
Berea *(G-1612)*

▼ E-Pak Manufacturing LLC .... D 800 235-1632
Wooster *(G-20769)*

▲ Ebner Furnaces Inc .... D 330 335-2311
Wadsworth *(G-19404)*

Egypt Structural Steel Proc .... E 419 628-2375
Minster *(G-14352)*

▲ Electromech Technologies LLC ...... B 216 706-2960
Cleveland *(G-5270)*

◆ Emh Inc .... G 330 220-8600
Valley City *(G-19203)*

EPI of Cleveland Inc .... G 330 468-2872
Twinsburg *(G-18929)*

▲ Erico International Corp .... A 440 349-2630
Solon *(G-17288)*

Erico International Corp .... B 440 248-0100
Solon *(G-17289)*

Evers Welding Co Inc .... E 513 385-7352
Cincinnati *(G-3723)*

F M Machine Co .... E 330 773-8237
Akron *(G-177)*

Fab Shop Inc .... E 513 860-1332
Hamilton *(G-10690)*

▲ Fabco Inc .... E 419 421-4740
Findlay *(G-9820)*

▲ Falls Welding & Fabg Inc .... G 330 253-3437
Akron *(G-180)*

Fastfeed Corp .... G 330 948-7333
Lodi *(G-12160)*

Fenix Fabrication Inc .... E 330 745-8731
Akron *(G-184)*

Fiedeldey Stl Fabricators Inc .... E 513 353-3300
Cincinnati *(G-3751)*

Fincom Corporation .... G 330 456-8341
Canton *(G-2703)*

Flex-Strut Inc .... D 330 372-9999
Warren *(G-19551)*

Foster Products Inc .... E 513 735-9770
Batavia *(G-1186)*

Franck and Fric Incorporated ...... D 216 524-4451
Cleveland *(G-5377)*

Frederick Steel Company LLC ...... E 513 821-6400
Cincinnati *(G-3782)*

Fulton Equipment Co .... G 419 290-5393
Toledo *(G-18475)*

Fwt LLC .... G 419 542-1420
Hicksville *(G-10902)*

G & R Welding & Machining .... G 937 323-9353
Springfield *(G-17562)*

▲ G & W Products LLC .... C 513 860-4050
Fairfield *(G-9660)*

Galion-Godwin Truck Bdy Co LLC .... D 330 359-5495
Millersburg *(G-14217)*

Gardner Metal Craft Inc .... G 513 539-4538
Monroe *(G-14402)*

Garland Welding Co Inc .... F 330 536-6506
Lowellville *(G-12408)*

Gb Fabrication Company .... E 419 347-1835
Shelby *(G-17136)*

Gen III .... G 614 737-8744
Columbus *(G-7107)*

General Steel Corporation .... F 216 883-4200
Cleveland *(G-5421)*

George Steel Fabricating Inc ...... E 513 932-2887
Lebanon *(G-11802)*

Gilson Machine & Tool Co Inc .... E 419 592-2911
Napoleon *(G-14678)*

GL Nause Co Inc .... E 513 722-9500
Loveland *(G-12353)*

Glenwood Erectors Inc .... G 330 652-9616
Niles *(G-15156)*

▲ Gokoh Corporation .... F 937 339-4977
Troy *(G-18832)*

Gold Star Met Fabg & Repr Inc ..... F 440 353-3233
North Ridgeville *(G-15377)*

▲ Goyal Industries Inc .... E 419 522-7099
Mansfield *(G-12618)*

Graber Metal Works Inc .... E 440 237-8422
North Royalton *(G-15422)*

Green Point Metals Inc .... E 937 743-4075
Franklin *(G-10025)*

Grenga Machine & Welding .... F 330 743-1113
Youngstown *(G-21104)*

Griffin Industries LLC .... G 216 696-2588
Cleveland *(G-5459)*

Gunderson Rail Services LLC .... E 330 792-6521
Youngstown *(G-21106)*

▲ Gwp Holdings Inc .... D 513 860-4050
Fairfield *(G-9662)*

▲ H B Products Inc .... E 937 492-7031
Sidney *(G-17191)*

Halman Industries .... F 440 992-4239
Ashtabula *(G-811)*

▲ Halvorsen Company .... E 216 341-7500
Cleveland *(G-5473)*

Hanson Concrete Products Ohio ..... E 614 443-4846
Columbus *(G-7143)*

Hays Fabricating & Welding .... E 937 325-0031
Springfield *(G-17568)*

Herman Manufacturing LLC .... F 216 251-6400
Cleveland *(G-5504)*

High Production Technology LLC ..... F 419 591-7000
Napoleon *(G-14680)*

Holgate Metal Fab Inc .... F 419 599-2000
Napoleon *(G-14682)*

▲ Horizon Metals Inc .... E 440 235-3338
Berea *(G-1618)*

Horning Steel Co .... G 330 633-0028
Tallmadge *(G-18146)*

Howden North America Inc .... E 330 721-7374
Medina *(G-13422)*

Hr Machine LLC .... G 937 222-7644
Beavercreek *(G-1345)*

Hunkar Technologies Inc .... C 513 272-1010
Cincinnati *(G-3902)*

▲ Hynes Industries Inc .... C 330 799-3221
Youngstown *(G-21111)*

Hyq Technologies LLC .... G 513 225-6911
Oxford *(G-15837)*

Indian Creek Fabricators Inc ...... E 937 667-7214
Tipp City *(G-18283)*

Industrial Hanger Conveyor Co ...... G 419 332-2661
Fremont *(G-10158)*

Industrial Mill Maintenance .... E 330 746-1155
Youngstown *(G-21115)*

Ironfab LLC .... F 614 443-3900
Columbus *(G-7211)*

Ironhead Fabg & Contg Inc .... D 419 690-0000
Toledo *(G-18528)*

J & L Specialty Steel Inc .... G 330 875-6200
Louisville *(G-12317)*

J & L Welding Fabricating Inc .... F 330 393-9353
Warren *(G-19561)*

J A Donadee Corporation .... E 330 533-3305
Canfield *(G-2559)*

J A McMahon Incorporated .... E 330 652-2588
Niles *(G-15163)*

J Horst Manufacturing Co .... D 330 828-2216
Dalton *(G-8072)*

J P Suggins Mobile Welding .... E 216 566-7131
Cleveland *(G-5599)*

J&J Precision Machine Ltd .... E 330 923-5783
Cuyahoga Falls *(G-8012)*

Jab Sales Inc .... G 440 446-0606
Cleveland *(G-5603)*

James C Denier Co Inc .... G 513 385-6272
Cincinnati *(G-3939)*

Jayron Fabrication LLC .... G 740 335-3184
Leesburg *(G-11852)*

Jh Industries Inc .... E 330 963-4105
Twinsburg *(G-18961)*

Joe Rees Welding .... G 937 652-4067
Urbana *(G-19165)*

Jomac Ltd .... G 330 627-7727
Carrollton *(G-2958)*

▲ JR Manufacturing Inc .... C 419 375-8021
Fort Recovery *(G-9956)*

Js Fabrications Inc .... G 419 333-0323
Fremont *(G-10161)*

K & L Die & Manufacturing .... G 419 895-1301
Greenwich *(G-10532)*

Kecoat LLC .... E 330 527-0215
Garrettsville *(G-10327)*

Kedar D Army .... G 419 238-6929
Van Wert *(G-19262)*

Kellys Welding & Fabricating .... G 440 593-6040
Conneaut *(G-7811)*

Kings Welding and Fabg Inc .... E 330 738-3592
Mechanicstown *(G-13359)*

Kirk Welding & Fabricating ....G.... 216 961-6403
Cleveland *(G-5658)*

Kirwan Industries Inc ....G.... 513 333-0766
Cincinnati *(G-3993)*

▲ **Kottler Metal Products Co Inc** ....E.... 440 946-7473
Willoughby *(G-20523)*

Kramer Power Equipment Co ....F.... 937 456-2232
Eaton *(G-9313)*

L & W Inc ....D.... 734 397-6300
Avon *(G-999)*

Lake Erie Ship Repair ....F.... 440 624-0025
Jefferson *(G-11366)*

▲ **Langdon Inc** ....E.... 513 733-5955
Cincinnati *(G-4011)*

Lapham-Hickey Steel Corp ....E.... 614 443-4881
Columbus *(G-7286)*

Laserflex Corporation ....D.... 614 850-9600
Hilliard *(G-10958)*

Lauren Yoakam ....G.... 440 365-3952
Elyria *(G-9450)*

Lazarus Steel LLC ....G.... 216 391-3245
Cleveland *(G-5689)*

▲ **Lefeld Welding & Stl Sups Inc** ....E.... 419 678-2397
Coldwater *(G-6567)*

Lideco LLC ....G.... 330 539-9333
Vienna *(G-19367)*

Lilly Industries Inc ....E.... 419 946-7908
Mount Gilead *(G-14563)*

Livingston & Company Ltd ....G.... 513 553-6430
New Richmond *(G-14941)*

Louis Arthur Steel Company ....G.... 440 997-5545
Geneva *(G-10352)*

Louis Arthur Steel Company ....G.... 440 997-5545
Uniontown *(G-19091)*

Lyco Corporation ....E.... 330 534-3330
Lowellville *(G-12410)*

M & H Fabricating Co Inc ....F.... 937 325-8708
Springfield *(G-17593)*

M & M Fabrication Inc ....F.... 740 779-3071
Chillicothe *(G-3249)*

M & W Welding Inc ....G.... 614 224-0501
Columbus *(G-7307)*

Machine Tool & Fab Corp ....F.... 419 435-7676
Fostoria *(G-9983)*

Mad River Fabricating Ltd ....G.... 937 322-6521
Springfield *(G-17597)*

Mad River Steel Ltd ....G.... 937 845-4046
New Carlisle *(G-14806)*

Magnesium Products Group Inc ....G.... 310 971-5799
Maumee *(G-13277)*

Magnum Piering Inc ....E.... 513 759-3348
West Chester *(G-20022)*

Mahoning Valley Fabricators ....F.... 330 793-8995
Austintown *(G-975)*

▼ **Manifold & Phalor Inc** ....E.... 614 920-1200
Canal Winchester *(G-2531)*

Manitowoc Company Inc ....G.... 920 746-3332
Cleveland *(G-5739)*

Marc Industries Inc ....G.... 440 944-9305
Willoughby *(G-20536)*

Marsam Metalfab Inc ....E.... 330 405-1520
Twinsburg *(G-18978)*

Martina Metal LLC ....E.... 614 291-9700
Columbus *(G-7321)*

Marysville Steel Inc ....E.... 937 642-5971
Marysville *(G-12959)*

Mason Structural Steel Inc ....D.... 440 439-1040
Walton Hills *(G-19474)*

Masonite International Corp ....G.... 937 454-9308
Vandalia *(G-19304)*

Maverick Innvtive Slutions LLC ....E.... 419 281-7944
Ashland *(G-752)*

Mc Brown Industries Inc ....F.... 419 963-2800
Findlay *(G-9859)*

McNeil Group Inc ....E.... 614 298-0300
Columbus *(G-7338)*

McNeil Holdings LLC ....G.... 614 298-0300
Columbus *(G-7339)*

McNichols Company ....G.... 877 884-4653
Cincinnati *(G-4071)*

McWane Inc ....B.... 740 622-6651
Coshocton *(G-7897)*

Mercury Iron & Steel ....F.... 440 349-1500
Solon *(G-17334)*

Metal Dynamics Co ....G.... 330 601-0748
Wooster *(G-20805)*

Metal Man Inc ....G.... 614 830-0968
Groveport *(G-10636)*

Metal Sales Manufacturing Corp ....E.... 440 576-9070
Jefferson *(G-11367)*

Metlweb ....E.... 513 563-8822
Cincinnati *(G-4093)*

Miami Steel Fabricators Inc ....G.... 937 299-5550
Dayton *(G-8489)*

Mikes Welding ....G.... 937 675-6587
Jamestown *(G-11352)*

Miracle Welding Inc ....G.... 513 746-9977
Franklin *(G-10037)*

Mobile Mini Inc ....F.... 614 449-8655
Columbus *(G-7360)*

Mohican Steel Fabricators Inc ....G.... 419 994-4802
Loudonville *(G-12300)*

Monnig Welding Co ....G.... 513 241-5156
Cincinnati *(G-4119)*

Morrison Custom Welding Inc ....F.... 330 264-0626
Wooster *(G-20811)*

Navpar Inc ....G.... 513 738-2230
Harrison *(G-10792)*

Nct Technologies Group Inc ....E.... 937 882-6800
New Carlisle *(G-14808)*

Neidert Fabricating Inc ....G.... 330 753-3331
Barberton *(G-1133)*

New Wayne Inc ....G.... 740 453-3454
Zanesville *(G-21333)*

Northeast Ohio Contractors LLC ....G.... 216 269-7881
Cleveland *(G-5906)*

Northern Boiler Company ....F.... 216 961-3033
Cleveland *(G-5908)*

▲ **Northern Manufacturing Co Inc** ....C.... 419 898-2821
Oak Harbor *(G-15592)*

Northwest Installations Inc ....E.... 419 423-5738
Findlay *(G-9869)*

Northwind Industries Inc ....E.... 216 433-0666
Cleveland *(G-5916)*

▼ **Ohio Gratings Inc** ....B.... 330 477-6707
Canton *(G-2799)*

Ohio Steel Industries Inc ....E.... 740 927-9500
Pataskala *(G-15975)*

Ohio Structures Inc ....E.... 330 547-7705
Berlin Center *(G-1657)*

Ohio Structures Inc ....E.... 330 533-0084
Canfield *(G-2568)*

Olson Sheet Metal Cnstr Co ....G.... 330 745-8225
Barberton *(G-1136)*

Orica Ground Support Inc ....B.... 740 269-8100
Bowerston *(G-1960)*

Outotec Oyj ....E.... 440 783-3336
Strongsville *(G-17949)*

Overhead Door Corporation ....D.... 740 383-6376
Marion *(G-12892)*

Ozone Systems Svcs Group Inc ....G.... 513 899-4131
Morrow *(G-14550)*

P & L Metalcrafts LLC ....F.... 330 793-2178
Youngstown *(G-21160)*

P B Fabrication Mech Contr ....F.... 419 478-4869
Toledo *(G-18631)*

Pcy Enterprises Inc ....E.... 513 241-5566
Cincinnati *(G-4219)*

Perfections Fabricators Inc ....F.... 440 365-5850
Elyria *(G-9477)*

Perry Welding Service Inc ....F.... 330 425-2211
Twinsburg *(G-19001)*

Phillips & Sons Welding & Fabg ....G.... 440 428-1625
Geneva *(G-10355)*

Phoenix Metal Works Inc ....G.... 937 274-5555
Dayton *(G-8573)*

Pioneer Machine Inc ....G.... 330 948-6500
Lodi *(G-12168)*

▲ **Pioneer Pipe Inc** ....B.... 740 376-2400
Marietta *(G-12816)*

PJs Fabricating Inc ....E.... 330 478-1120
Canton *(G-2814)*

Pjs Towing Inc ....E.... 330 478-1120
Canton *(G-2815)*

Porters Welding Inc ....F.... 740 452-4181
Zanesville *(G-21342)*

Precision International LLC ....E.... 330 793-0900
Akron *(G-348)*

Precision Quincy Shelters Inc ....B.... 888 312-5442
Mason *(G-13076)*

Precision Steel Services Inc ....D.... 419 476-5702
Toledo *(G-18654)*

Precision Tower Products LLC ....G.... 740 362-7876
Delaware *(G-8879)*

Precision Welding & Mfg ....F.... 937 444-6925
Mount Orab *(G-14585)*

Precision Welding Corporation ....E.... 216 524-6110
Cleveland *(G-6037)*

Pro Fab Industries Inc ....G.... 317 297-0461
Dundee *(G-9179)*

Pro-Fab Inc ....E.... 330 644-0044
Akron *(G-352)*

Production Support Inc ....F.... 937 526-3897
Russia *(G-16768)*

Professional Fabricators Inc ....G.... 216 362-1208
Cleveland *(G-6054)*

▲ **Promac International Inc** ....G.... 440 967-2040
Vermilion *(G-19336)*

Pucel Enterprises Inc ....D.... 216 881-4604
Cleveland *(G-6061)*

Q S I Fabrication ....G.... 419 832-1680
Grand Rapids *(G-10444)*

Qc Industrial Inc ....G.... 740 642-5004
Chillicothe *(G-3269)*

Quality Steel Fabrication ....F.... 937 492-9503
Sidney *(G-17213)*

R L Torbeck Industries Inc ....D.... 513 367-0080
Harrison *(G-10800)*

R S V Wldg Fbrcation Machining ....F.... 419 592-0993
Napoleon *(G-14694)*

Rads LLC ....F.... 330 671-0464
Berea *(G-1633)*

Railing Crafters Ltd ....G.... 440 506-9336
Painesville *(G-15915)*

Rance Industries Inc ....F.... 330 482-1745
Columbiana *(G-6629)*

RB Fabricators Inc ....F.... 330 779-0263
Youngstown *(G-21186)*

Rbm Environmental and Cnstr ....E.... 419 693-5840
Oregon *(G-15715)*

Redbuilt LLC ....E.... 740 363-0870
Delaware *(G-8882)*

Republic Storage Systems LLC ....C.... 330 438-5800
Canton *(G-2839)*

Retays Welding Company ....E.... 440 327-4100
North Ridgeville *(G-15400)*

Rezmann Karoly ....G.... 216 441-4357
Cleveland *(G-6110)*

Richard Steel Company Inc ....G.... 216 520-6390
Cleveland *(G-6111)*

Ripley Metalworks Ltd ....E.... 937 392-4992
Ripley *(G-16670)*

Rittman Inc ....D.... 330 927-6855
Rittman *(G-16682)*

Riwco Corp ....F.... 937 322-6521
Springfield *(G-17641)*

Robs Welding Technologies Ltd ....G.... 937 890-4963
Dayton *(G-8637)*

▼ **Rol- Fab Inc** ....E.... 216 662-2500
Cleveland *(G-6130)*

Romar Metal Fabricating Inc ....G.... 740 682-7731
Oak Hill *(G-15606)*

Rose Metal Industries LLC ....F.... 216 881-3355
Cleveland *(G-6132)*

Rose Metal Industries LLC ....E.... 216 426-8615
Cleveland *(G-6133)*

Royal Welding Inc ....G.... 513 829-9353
Fairfield *(G-9713)*

Rti International Metals Inc ....G.... 330 544-9470
Niles *(G-15179)*

S & G Manufacturing Group LLC ....C.... 614 529-0100
Hilliard *(G-10977)*

▲ **Sausser Steel Company Inc** ....F.... 419 422-9632
Findlay *(G-9888)*

Sautter Brothers ....G.... 419 468-7443
Galion *(G-10284)*

Schoonover Industries Inc ....E.... 419 289-8332
Ashland *(G-776)*

Seeburger Greenhouse ....G.... 419 832-1834
Grand Rapids *(G-10446)*

Service Iron & Steel Company ....G.... 330 253-9147
Akron *(G-399)*

Shaffer Metal Fab Inc ....E.... 937 492-1384
Sidney *(G-17225)*

Sharon Manufacturing Inc ....E.... 330 239-1561
Sharon Center *(G-17109)*

Signa Stortech Systems Inc ....E.... 214 357-0411
Canton *(G-2849)*

Sintered Metal Industries Inc ....F.... 330 650-4000
Hudson *(G-11199)*

Skinner Sales Group Inc ....E.... 440 572-8455
Strongsville *(G-17966)*

▲ **Smith Truck Cranes & Eqp Co** ....F.... 330 929-3303
Cuyahoga Falls *(G-8047)*

Snair Co ....F.... 614 873-7020
Plain City *(G-16360)*

Socar of Ohio Inc ....D.... 419 596-3100
Continental *(G-7828)*

Somerville Manufacturing Inc ....E.... 740 336-7847
Marietta *(G-12834)*

Employee Codes: A=Over 500 employees, B=251-500
C=101-250, D=51-100, E=20-50, F=10-19, G=3-9

Specialty Steel Solutions ....G....... 567 674-0011
Kenton (G-11570)

Spradlin Bros Welding Co ....F....... 800 219-2182
Springfield (G-17650)

Ss Metal Fabricators Inc ....G....... 937 226-9957
Dayton (G-8673)

St Lawrence Steel Corporation ....E....... 330 562-9000
Streetsboro (G-17878)

Stainless Specialties Inc ....E....... 440 942-4242
Eastlake (G-9287)

Starr Fabricating Inc ....D....... 330 394-9891
Vienna (G-19376)

▼ Steel & Alloy Utility Pdts Inc ....E....... 330 530-2220
Mc Donald (G-13348)

▲ Steel Eqp Specialists Inc ....D....... 330 823-8260
Alliance (G-540)

Steel Quest Inc ....G....... 513 772-5030
Cincinnati (G-4462)

Steel Services Inc ....G....... 513 353-4173
North Bend (G-15208)

Steelcon LLC ....G....... 330 457-4003
New Waterford (G-14975)

Steelial Wldg Met Fbrction Inc ....E....... 740 669-5300
Vinton (G-19383)

Steeltec Products LLC ....E....... 216 681-1114
Cleveland (G-6247)

Steve Vore Welding and Steel ....F....... 419 375-4087
Fort Recovery (G-9959)

Stock Mfg & Design Co Inc ....D....... 513 353-3600
Cleves (G-6528)

Straightaway Fabrications Ltd ....E....... 419 281-9440
Ashland (G-780)

Suburban Metal Products Inc ....F....... 740 474-4237
Circleville (G-4644)

Suburban Stl Sup Co Ltd Partnr ....G....... 317 783-6555
Columbus (G-7665)

Sulecki Precision Products ....G....... 440 255-5454
Mentor (G-13740)

Summers Acquisition Corp ....G....... 419 423-5800
Findlay (G-9898)

Superior Soda Service LLC ....G....... 937 657-9700
Beavercreek (G-1381)

Superior Welding Co ....F....... 614 252-8539
Columbus (G-7669)

Surface Recovery Tech LLC ....F....... 937 879-5864
Fairborn (G-9631)

T & K Welding Co Inc ....G....... 216 432-0221
Cleveland (G-6287)

Taflan Steel & Welding Inc ....G....... 740 635-0841
Bridgeport (G-2093)

Tarrier Steel Company Inc ....E....... 614 444-4000
Columbus (G-7679)

Tech Dynamics Inc ....F....... 419 666-1666
Perrysburg (G-16153)

Tech Systems Inc ....E....... 419 878-2100
Waterville (G-19669)

The Mansfield Strl & Erct Co ....F....... 419 522-5911
Mansfield (G-12695)

The Mansfield Strl & Erct Co ....F....... 419 747-6571
Mansfield (G-12696)

Thomas Steel Inc ....E....... 419 483-7540
Bellevue (G-1563)

Transco Railway Products Inc ....D....... 330 872-0934
Newton Falls (G-15140)

Tri-America Contractors Inc ....E....... 740 574-0148
Wheelersburg (G-20335)

Tri-Fab Inc ....E....... 330 337-3425
Salem (G-16931)

Tri-State Fabricators Inc ....E....... 513 752-5005
Amelia (G-587)

Triangle Precision Industries ....D....... 937 299-6776
Dayton (G-8723)

Tru-Fab Inc ....F....... 937 435-1733
Dayton (G-8731)

Tru-Form Steel & Wire Inc ....G....... 765 348-5001
Toledo (G-18757)

Turn-Key Industrial Svcs LLC ....D....... 614 274-1128
Columbus (G-7714)

U M D Automated Systems Inc ....D....... 740 694-8614
Fredericktown (G-10113)

Union Fabricating & Machine Co ....G....... 419 626-5963
Sandusky (G-17018)

Unique Fabrications Inc ....F....... 419 355-1700
Fremont (G-10192)

▲ Universal Fabg Cnstr Svcs Inc ....D....... 614 274-1128
Columbus (G-7723)

Updegraff Inc ....G....... 216 621-7600
Cleveland (G-6395)

Upright Steel LLC ....E....... 216 923-0852
Cleveland (G-6396)

V & S Schuler Engineering Inc ....D....... 330 452-5200
Canton (G-2893)

Valco Industries Inc ....E....... 937 399-7400
Springfield (G-17672)

Verhoff Machine & Welding Inc ....C....... 419 596-3202
Continental (G-7829)

Vicon Fabricating Company Ltd ....E....... 440 205-6700
Mentor (G-13767)

Viking Fabricators Inc ....E....... 740 374-5246
Marietta (G-12848)

W & W Custom Fabrication Inc ....G....... 513 353-4617
Cleves (G-6532)

Warmus and Associates Inc ....F....... 330 659-4440
Bath (G-1240)

◆ Warren Fabricating Corporation ....D....... 330 847-0596
Warren (G-19621)

▲ Waterford Tank Fabrication Ltd ....D....... 740 984-4100
Beverly (G-1672)

▲ Wauseon Machine & Mfg Inc ....D....... 419 337-0940
Wauseon (G-19700)

Wecan Fabricators LLC ....E....... 740 667-0731
Tuppers Plains (G-18887)

Welage Corporation ....F....... 513 681-2300
Cincinnati (G-4583)

Weldfab Inc ....G....... 440 563-3310
Rock Creek (G-16687)

Welding Improvement Company ....G....... 330 424-9666
Lisbon (G-12135)

Weldtec Inc ....E....... 419 394-9440
Celina (G-3027)

Weldtec Ltd ....E....... 419 394-9440
Celina (G-3028)

Wernke Wldg & Stl Erection Co ....F....... 513 353-4173
North Bend (G-15210)

Wernli Realty Inc ....D....... 937 258-7878
Beavercreek (G-1384)

Westwood Fbrction Shtmetal Inc ....G....... 937 837-0494
Dayton (G-8756)

White Machine & Mfg Co ....F....... 740 453-3444
Zanesville (G-21362)

◆ Whole Shop Inc ....F....... 330 630-5305
Tallmadge (G-18177)

Winston Campbell LLC ....G....... 614 274-7015
Columbus (G-7766)

Wirenet Inc ....F....... 513 774-7759
Loveland (G-12400)

Wiseman Bros Fabg & Stl Ltd ....F....... 740 988-5121
Beaver (G-1313)

▼ Witt Industries Inc ....D....... 513 871-5700
Mason (G-13103)

Wm Lang & Sons Company ....F....... 513 541-3304
Cincinnati (G-4602)

Woodbury Welding Inc ....G....... 937 968-3573
Union City (G-19073)

Worthington Industries Inc ....C....... 513 539-9291
Monroe (G-14420)

Worthngton Stelpac Systems LLC ....G....... 937 747-2370
North Lewisburg (G-15309)

▲ Ysd Industries Inc ....D....... 330 792-6521
Youngstown (G-21260)

Ziegler Engineering Inc ....E....... 440 582-8515
North Royalton (G-15461)

Zimmerman Shtmtl Stl & Wldg ....G....... 419 335-3806
Wauseon (G-19703)

3442 Metal Doors, Sash, Frames, Molding & Trim

A B Siemer Inc ....B....... 614 888-8855
Columbus (G-6667)

A C Shutters Inc ....G....... 216 429-2424
Cleveland (G-4669)

All Around Garage Door Inc ....G....... 440 759-5079
North Ridgeville (G-15357)

All Pro Ovrhd Door Systems LLC ....G....... 614 444-3667
Columbus (G-6721)

Allied Window Inc ....E....... 513 559-1212
Cincinnati (G-3379)

Aluminum Color Industries Inc ....E....... 330 536-6295
Lowellville (G-12404)

Amarr Company ....G....... 216 573-7100
Independence (G-11248)

American Window Pdts of Ohio ....F....... 330 830-0274
Massillon (G-13107)

American Woodwork Specialty Co ....E....... 937 263-1053
Dayton (G-8156)

Anderson Door Co ....E....... 216 475-5700
Cleveland (G-4809)

Angel Window Mfg Corp ....G....... 440 891-1006
Berea (G-1601)

Arched Casings Inc ....G....... 614 873-1196
Plain City (G-16320)

Associated Materials LLC ....B....... 330 929-1811
Cuyahoga Falls (G-7971)

Associated Mtls Holdings LLC ....A....... 330 929-1811
Cuyahoga Falls (G-7972)

Bilco Company ....E....... 740 455-9020
Zanesville (G-21279)

Brainerd Industries Inc ....E....... 937 228-0488
Miamisburg (G-13786)

Bug-Barrier Screen Corp ....G....... 330 723-2551
Medina (G-13384)

Burt Manufacturing Company Inc ....C....... 330 762-0061
Akron (G-105)

Bwd Woodwork LLC ....G....... 740 335-9766
Wshngtn CT Hs (G-20903)

Capitol Aluminum & Glass Corp ....D....... 800 331-8268
Bellevue (G-1548)

▲ Cascade Ohio Inc ....B....... 440 593-5800
Conneaut (G-7801)

Central Ohio Rtrctable Screens ....G....... 614 868-5080
Radnor (G-16506)

▲ Champion Opco LLC ....E....... 513 924-4858
Cincinnati (G-3521)

◆ Champion Win Co Cleveland LLC ....E....... 440 899-2562
Macedonia (G-12440)

Champion Window Co of Toledo ....F....... 419 841-0154
Perrysburg (G-16077)

▲ Chase Industries Inc ....D....... 513 860-5565
West Chester (G-19988)

◆ Clopay Building Pdts Co Inc ....E....... 513 770-4800
Mason (G-12998)

Clopay Building Pdts Co Inc ....G....... 937 526-4301
Russia (G-16762)

Clopay Building Pdts Co Inc ....G....... 937 440-6403
Troy (G-18810)

▲ Clopay Corporation ....C....... 800 282-2260
Mason (G-12999)

Custom Hitch and Trailer/ Over ....G....... 740 289-3925
Piketon (G-16218)

Dale Kestler ....G....... 513 871-9000
Cincinnati (G-3637)

Desco Corporation ....C....... 614 888-8855
New Albany (G-14757)

▲ Diamond Roll-Up Door Inc ....D....... 419 294-3373
Upper Sandusky (G-19120)

Division Overhead Door Inc ....F....... 513 872-0888
Cincinnati (G-3659)

Dj & Woodies Vinyl Frontier ....G....... 740 623-2818
Coshocton (G-7888)

Duo-Corp ....E....... 330 549-2149
North Lima (G-15315)

Dynaco Usa Inc ....G....... 419 227-3000
Lima (G-12006)

Euclid Jalousies Inc ....E....... 440 953-1112
Cleveland (G-5300)

▲ Fab Tech Inc ....G....... 330 926-9556
Brecksville (G-2049)

Francis-Schulze Co ....E....... 937 295-3941
Russia (G-16764)

Friends Ornamental Iron Co ....G....... 216 431-6710
Cleveland (G-5382)

Haas Door Company ....C....... 419 337-9900
Wauseon (G-19681)

◆ Hrh Door Corp ....A....... 850 208-3400
Mount Hope (G-14572)

Hrh Door Corp ....E....... 513 674-9300
Cincinnati (G-3900)

Hrh Door Corp ....G....... 330 896-2175
Millersburg (G-14233)

Hrh Door Corp ....C....... 330 828-2291
Dalton (G-8070)

Installed Building Pdts LLC ....E....... 614 308-9900
Columbus (G-7190)

Kawneer Company Inc ....F....... 216 252-3203
Cleveland (G-5637)

Larson Manufacturing Co Inc ....F....... 419 435-9400
Fostoria (G-9981)

▲ Lean Factory America LLC ....G....... 513 297-3086
Cincinnati (G-4018)

Loxcreen Company Inc ....F....... 513 539-2255
Middletown (G-14056)

M-D Building Products Inc ....B....... 513 539-2255
Middletown (G-14057)

Machine Tool & Fab Corp ....F....... 419 435-7676
Fostoria (G-9983)

Masonite International Corp ....G....... 937 454-9308
Vandalia (G-19304)

Mestek Inc ....D....... 419 288-2703
Holland (G-11072)

Mestek Inc ....D 419 288-2703
Bradner (G-2029)

Midwest Curtainwalls Inc ....D 216 641-7900
Cleveland (G-5809)

Modern Builders Supply Inc ....C 330 729-2690
Youngstown (G-21147)

National Access Design LLC ....F 513 351-3400
Cincinnati (G-4137)

Nofziger Door Sales Inc ....G 419 337-9900
Wauseon (G-19692)

Nofziger Door Sales Inc ....F 419 445-2961
Archbold (G-689)

▲ Orrvilon Inc ....C 330 684-9400
Orrville (G-15754)

Otter Group LLC ....F 937 315-1199
Dayton (G-8554)

Overhead Door Corporation ....D 740 383-6376
Marion (G-12892)

Overhead Door Corporation ....F 419 294-3874
Upper Sandusky (G-19138)

Overhead Door Corporation ....D 330 674-7015
Mount Hope (G-14573)

Overhead Door Corporation ....D 330 674-7015
Mount Hope (G-14574)

Overhead Inc ....G 419 476-0300
Toledo (G-18624)

Paul Miracle ....G 513 575-3113
Loveland (G-12376)

Pease Industies Inc ....B 513 870-3600
Fairfield (G-9700)

Phillips Manufacturing Co ....D 330 652-4335
Niles (G-15173)

Provia Door Inc ....C 330 852-4711
Sugarcreek (G-18034)

Quality Security Door & Mfg Co .....G 440 246-0770
Lorain (G-12269)

Quanex Screens LLC ....G 419 662-5001
Perrysburg (G-16145)

Renewal By Andersen LLC ....G 614 781-9600
Columbus (G-6658)

S R Door Inc ....D 740 927-3558
Hebron (G-10883)

▲ Select Security Screen Co Ltd ....F 216 362-1850
Cleveland (G-6179)

Shade Youngstown & Aluminum Co ...G 330 782-2373
Youngstown (G-21200)

Shurtape Technologies LLC ....B 440 937-7000
Avon (G-1011)

▲ Stephen M Trudick ....E 440 834-1891
Burton (G-2385)

Stoett Industries Inc ....E 419 542-0247
Hicksville (G-10907)

Superior Weld and Fabg Co Inc ......G 216 249-5122
Cleveland (G-6272)

Tdm LLC ....G 440 969-1442
Ashtabula (G-840)

▲ Therma-Tru Corp ....E 419 891-7400
Maumee (G-13301)

Thermal Industries Inc ....G 216 464-0674
Cleveland (G-6316)

Thomas J Weaver Inc ....F 740 622-2040
Coshocton (G-7913)

Traichal Construction Company ....E 800 255-3667
Niles (G-15186)

Tri County Door Service Inc ....F 216 531-2245
Euclid (G-9611)

Vinylume Products Inc ....D 330 799-2000
Youngstown (G-21242)

Warren Door ....E 330 652-6346
Niles (G-15188)

YKK AP America Inc ....F 513 942-7200
West Chester (G-20071)

3443 Fabricated Plate Work

A A S Amels Sheet Meta L Inc ....E 330 793-9326
Youngstown (G-21010)

A & E Butscha Co ....G 513 761-1919
Cincinnati (G-3329)

▲ A & G Manufacturing Co Inc ....E 419 468-7433
Galion (G-10250)

A C Knox Inc ....G 513 921-5028
Cincinnati (G-3333)

A H Marty Co Ltd ....F 216 641-8950
Cleveland (G-4673)

A M Castle & Co ....D 330 425-7000
Bedford (G-1394)

A Metalcraft Associates Inc ....G 937 693-4008
Botkins (G-1949)

A P O Holdings Inc ....E 330 455-8925
Canton (G-2585)

A-1 Welding & Fabricating Inc ....F 440 233-8474
Lorain (G-12230)

Acme Boiler Co Inc ....G 216 961-2471
Cleveland (G-4691)

Advance Industrial Mfg Inc ....E 614 871-3333
Grove City (G-10539)

Advanced Welding Co ....E 937 746-6800
Franklin (G-10005)

Aetna Plastics Corp ....G 330 274-2855
Mantua (G-12706)

Airtech Mechanical Inc ....F 419 292-0074
Toledo (G-18326)

All American Welding Co ....G 614 224-7752
Columbus (G-6720)

▼ Alloy Engineering Company ....D 440 243-6800
Berea (G-1600)

▲ Allpass Corporation ....F 440 998-6300
Ashtabula (G-792)

▲ Almo Process Technology Inc ....G 513 402-2566
West Chester (G-19804)

Alpha Sintered Metals LLC ....F 330 220-5800
Brunswick (G-2204)

▲ American Tank & Fabricating Co ....D 216 252-1500
Cleveland (G-4796)

AMF Bruns America Lp ....G 877 506-3770
Hudson (G-11158)

▲ Amko Service Company ....E 330 364-8857
Midvale (G-14105)

Apex Welding Incorporated ....F 440 232-6770
Bedford (G-1398)

Ares Inc ....D 419 635-2175
Port Clinton (G-16393)

▲ Armor Consolidated Inc ....C 513 923-5260
Mason (G-12982)

▲ Armor Metal Group Mason Inc ......C 513 769-0700
Mason (G-12983)

▲ AT&f Advanced Metals LLC ....E 330 684-1122
Cleveland (G-4851)

Austin Engineering Inc ....G 330 848-0815
Barberton (G-1100)

Ayling and Reichert Co Consent ......E 419 898-2471
Oak Harbor (G-15586)

◆ Babcock & Wilcox Company ....A 330 753-4511
Barberton (G-1104)

Babcock & Wilcox Nuclr Oprtns ......F 330 860-1010
Barberton (G-1105)

Babcock & Wilcox Powr Generatn ...E 330 753-4511
Barberton (G-1106)

Baxter Holdings Inc ....E 513 860-3593
Hamilton (G-10673)

▲ Bico Akron Inc ....D 330 794-1716
Mogadore (G-14369)

BJ Equipment Ltd ....F 614 497-1776
Columbus (G-6834)

Blackwood Sheet Metal Inc ....G 614 291-3115
Columbus (G-6839)

Blevins Metal Fabrication Inc ....E 419 522-6082
Mansfield (G-12567)

Boochers Inc ....G 937 667-3414
Tipp City (G-18265)

Breitinger Company ....C 419 526-4255
Mansfield (G-12569)

Brighton Truedge ....G 513 771-2300
Cincinnati (G-3474)

Brown-Singer Co ....F 513 422-9619
Middletown (G-14024)

▼ Buckeye Fabricating Co ....E 937 746-9822
Springboro (G-17475)

Buckeye Stamping Company ....D 614 445-0059
Columbus (G-6875)

C & C Fabrication Inc ....G 419 354-3535
Bowling Green (G-1975)

C & R Inc ....G 614 497-1130
Groveport (G-10617)

C A Joseph Co ....F 330 532-4646
Irondale (G-11287)

C Imperial Inc ....G 937 669-5620
Tipp City (G-18268)

▲ CA Litzler Co Inc ....C 216 267-8020
Cleveland (G-4958)

Capital Tool Company ....C 216 661-5750
Cleveland (G-4971)

▲ Cardinal Pumps Exchangers Inc ....F 330 332-8558
Salem (G-16878)

Cbr Industrial Llc ....G 419 645-6447
Wapakoneta (G-19483)

Ceco Environmental Corp ....E 513 874-8915
West Chester (G-19987)

Ceco Group Inc ....E 513 458-2600
Cincinnati (G-3510)

Centerline Machine Inc ....G 937 322-4887
Springfield (G-17529)

Central Fabricators Inc ....E 513 621-1240
Cincinnati (G-3514)

Chart Asia Inc ....C 440 753-1490
Cleveland (G-5018)

Chart Industries Inc ....A 440 753-1490
Cleveland (G-5019)

Chart Industries Inc ....E 440 753-1490
Cleveland (G-5020)

Chart International Inc ....D 440 753-1490
Cleveland (G-5021)

Chempure Products Corporation ......G 330 874-4300
Bolivar (G-1930)

Chute Source LLC ....F 330 475-0377
Akron (G-123)

Cleveland Steel Specialty Co ....E 216 464-9400
Bedford Heights (G-1481)

Cleveland Track Material Inc ....F 216 641-4000
Cleveland (G-5083)

▲ Clifton Steel Company ....D 216 662-6111
Maple Heights (G-12731)

◆ Columbiana Boiler Company LLC ...E 330 482-3373
Columbiana (G-6612)

▲ Columbiana Holding Co Inc ....G 330 482-3373
Columbiana (G-6613)

Commercial Mtal Fbricators Inc ....E 937 233-4911
Dayton (G-8239)

Compco Industries Incorporated ......D 330 482-6488
Columbiana (G-6614)

Containment Solutions Inc ....C 419 874-8765
Perrysburg (G-16078)

Contech Cnstr Pdts Hldings Inc ....G 513 645-7000
West Chester (G-19839)

Contech Engnered Solutions Inc ......A 513 645-7000
West Chester (G-19840)

Contech Engnered Solutions LLC .....F 513 425-5337
Middletown (G-14033)

Contech Engnered Solutions LLC .....D 513 645-7000
Middletown (G-14032)

◆ Contech Engnered Solutions LLC ...C 513 645-7000
West Chester (G-19841)

Convault of Ohio Inc ....G 614 252-8422
Columbus (G-6979)

Cooper-Standard Automotive Inc ......B 740 342-3523
New Lexington (G-14846)

Cramers Inc ....E 330 477-4571
Canton (G-2670)

Curtiss-Wright Flow Control ....D 513 735-2538
Batavia (G-1175)

Curtiss-Wright Flow Control ....D 513 528-7900
Cincinnati (G-3296)

Curtiss-Wright Flow Ctrl Corp ....D 513 528-7900
Cincinnati (G-3298)

Dabar Industries LLC ....F 614 873-3949
Plain City (G-16329)

David S Rodgers ....G 740 490-5843
Plain City (G-16334)

Debra-Kuempel Inc ....D 513 271-6500
Cincinnati (G-3645)

▲ Defiance Metal Products Co ....B 419 784-5332
Defiance (G-8785)

Deibel Manufacturing LLC ....G 330 482-3351
Leetonia (G-11859)

Diller Metals Inc ....G 419 943-3364
Leipsic (G-11869)

Dj S Weld ....G 330 432-2206
Uhrichsville (G-19049)

Dover Tank and Plate Company ....E 330 343-4443
Dover (G-8982)

Dragon Products Ltd ....G 330 345-3968
Wooster (G-20767)

Ds Express Carriers Inc ....G 419 433-6200
Norwalk (G-15534)

▲ Dynamic Control North Amer Inc ....F 513 860-5094
Hamilton (G-10686)

▼ E-Pak Manufacturing LLC ....D 800 235-1632
Wooster (G-20769)

Eagle Wldg & Fabrication Inc ....E 440 946-0692
Willoughby (G-20478)

▲ Eaton Fabricating Company Inc ......E 440 926-3121
Grafton (G-10425)

▲ Ebner Furnaces Inc ....D 330 335-2311
Wadsworth (G-19404)

Efco Corp ....E 614 876-1226
Columbus (G-7048)

Eleet Cryogenics Inc ....E 330 874-4009
Bolivar (G-1933)

Elliott Machine Works Inc ....E 419 468-4709
Galion (G-10267)

▲ Ellis & Watts Intl LLC	G	513 752-9000
Batavia *(G-1183)*		
En-Hanced Products Inc	G	614 882-7400
Westerville *(G-20213)*		
▲ Enerfab Inc	B	513 641-0500
Cincinnati *(G-3704)*		
▲ Enk Tenofour LLC	G	419 661-1465
Northwood *(G-15480)*		
Exothermics Inc	E	419 729-9726
Toledo *(G-18459)*		
▲ Fabco Inc	E	419 421-4740
Findlay *(G-9820)*		
Fabrication Shop Inc	F	419 435-7934
Fostoria *(G-9970)*		
Fabstar Tanks Inc	F	419 587-3639
Grover Hill *(G-10652)*		
▲ Falls Welding & Fabg Inc	G	330 253-3437
Akron *(G-180)*		
Farasey Steel Fabricators Inc	F	216 641-1853
Cleveland *(G-5324)*		
Fiba Technologies Inc	D	330 602-7300
Midvale *(G-14107)*		
Fin Tube Products Inc	F	330 334-3736
Wadsworth *(G-19406)*		
Firstenergy Corp	E	419 321-7114
Oak Harbor *(G-15590)*		
Firstnrgy Nclear Gnration Corp	G	330 761-4370
Akron *(G-189)*		
Fred Winner	G	419 582-2421
New Weston *(G-14977)*		
FSRc Tanks Inc	E	234 221-2015
Bolivar *(G-1934)*		
Fulton Equipment Co	G	419 290-5393
Toledo *(G-18475)*		
Gaspar Inc	D	330 477-2222
Canton *(G-2711)*		
▲ Gayston Corporation	C	937 743-6050
Miamisburg *(G-13812)*		
▲ General Technologies Inc	E	419 747-1800
Mansfield *(G-12612)*		
▲ General Tool Company	C	513 733-5500
Cincinnati *(G-3820)*		
Gerald H Smith	G	740 446-3455
Bidwell *(G-1676)*		
GL Nause Co Inc	E	513 722-9500
Loveland *(G-12353)*		
Graber Metal Works Inc	E	440 237-8422
North Royalton *(G-15422)*		
Grenga Machine & Welding	F	330 743-1113
Youngstown *(G-21104)*		
H P E Inc	F	330 833-3161
Massillon *(G-13145)*		
▲ Halvorsen Company	E	216 341-7500
Cleveland *(G-5473)*		
Hamilton Tanks LLC	F	614 445-8446
Columbus *(G-7139)*		
▲ Hammelmann Corporation	F	937 859-8777
Miamisburg *(G-13814)*		
Hard Chrome Plating Consultant	G	216 631-9090
Cleveland *(G-5480)*		
Harsco Corporation	E	216 961-1570
Cleveland *(G-5481)*		
Hason USA Corp	E	513 248-0287
Milford *(G-14150)*		
Hershey Machine	E	330 674-2718
Millersburg *(G-14222)*		
Hutnik Company	E	330 336-9700
Wadsworth *(G-19411)*		
Hydraulic Specialists Inc	E	740 922-3343
Midvale *(G-14108)*		
▼ Hydro-Thrift Corporation	E	330 837-5141
Massillon *(G-13154)*		
Hyq Technologies LLC	G	513 225-6911
Oxford *(G-15837)*		
I L R Inc	G	216 587-2212
Cleveland *(G-5546)*		
Indian Creek Fabricators Inc	E	937 667-7214
Tipp City *(G-18283)*		
Industrial Container Svcs LLC	E	513 921-2056
Cincinnati *(G-3916)*		
Industrial Container Svcs LLC	E	513 921-8811
Cincinnati *(G-3917)*		
Industrial Container Svcs LLC	D	614 864-1900
Blacklick *(G-1699)*		
Industrial Farm Tank Inc	G	937 843-2972
Lewistown *(G-11944)*		
▲ Industrial Repair & Mfg Inc	E	419 822-4232
Delta *(G-8936)*		
Ironman Metalworks LLC	G	614 907-6629
Groveport *(G-10628)*		

J B Kepple Sheet Metal	G	740 393-2971
Mount Vernon *(G-14624)*		
Jacp Inc	G	513 353-3660
Miamitown *(G-13888)*		
▲ Jergens Inc	C	216 486-5540
Cleveland *(G-5610)*		
Jh Industries Inc	E	330 963-4105
Twinsburg *(G-18961)*		
JMw Welding and Mfg	E	330 484-2428
Canton *(G-2748)*		
Kard Welding Inc	E	419 628-2598
Minster *(G-14356)*		
Kendall Holdings Ltd	E	614 486-4750
Columbus *(G-7255)*		
◆ Kirk & Blum Manufacturing Co	C	513 458-2600
Cincinnati *(G-3992)*		
Kirk & Blum Manufacturing Co	E	419 782-9885
Defiance *(G-8798)*		
Laird Technologies Inc	G	234 806-0105
Warren *(G-19569)*		
▲ Langdon Inc	E	513 733-5955
Cincinnati *(G-4011)*		
Lapham-Hickey Steel Corp	E	614 443-4881
Columbus *(G-7286)*		
Lion Industries LLC	E	740 699-0012
Saint Clairsville *(G-16794)*		
Liquid Luggers LLC	E	330 426-2538
East Palestine *(G-9241)*		
▲ Long-Stanton Mfg Company	E	513 874-8020
West Chester *(G-19895)*		
Louis Arthur Steel Company	G	440 997-5545
Geneva *(G-10352)*		
Louis Arthur Steel Company	G	440 997-5545
Uniontown *(G-19091)*		
▼ Loveman Steel Corporation	D	440 232-6200
Bedford *(G-1439)*		
M & H Fabricating Co Inc	G	937 325-8708
Springfield *(G-17594)*		
M & M Certified Welding Inc	F	330 467-1729
Macedonia *(G-12467)*		
M T Metals LLC	G	330 809-6465
Massillon *(G-13169)*		
Mack Iron Works Company	E	419 626-3712
Sandusky *(G-16984)*		
Macleod Inc	G	513 771-9560
Miamitown *(G-13889)*		
Mahle Behr USA Inc	A	937 369-2000
Dayton *(G-8472)*		
Manco Manufacturing Co	G	419 925-4152
Maria Stein *(G-12759)*		
▼ Marathon Industrial Cntrs Inc	F	440 324-2748
Elyria *(G-9458)*		
Mark One Manufacturing Ltd	E	419 628-4405
Minster *(G-14358)*		
Maumee Valley Fabricators Inc	E	419 476-1411
Toledo *(G-18580)*		
McGill Airpressure LLC	E	614 882-5455
Columbus *(G-7332)*		
Mercury Iron & Steel	F	440 349-1500
Solon *(G-17334)*		
Metal Fabricating Corporation	D	216 631-8121
Cleveland *(G-5787)*		
▼ Midwestern Industries Inc	C	330 837-4203
Massillon *(G-13180)*		
Modern Sheet Metal Works Inc	E	513 353-3666
Miamitown *(G-13890)*		
Modern Welding Co Ohio Inc	E	740 344-9425
Newark *(G-15035)*		
Moore Mr Specialty Company	G	330 332-1229
Salem *(G-16916)*		
◆ Morris Material Handling Inc	G	937 525-5520
Springfield *(G-17608)*		
Munroe Incorporated	G	330 755-7216
Struthers *(G-17995)*		
Myers Industries Inc	C	330 336-6621
Wadsworth *(G-19420)*		
Nbw Inc	E	216 377-1700
Cleveland *(G-5864)*		
▲ Netshape Technologies Mim Inc	F	440 248-5456
Solon *(G-17348)*		
New Wayne Inc	G	740 453-3454
Zanesville *(G-21333)*		
North High Marathon	G	937 444-1894
Mount Orab *(G-14584)*		
Northwest Installations Inc	E	419 423-5738
Findlay *(G-9869)*		
◆ Ohio Heat Transfer Ltd	F	740 695-0635
Saint Clairsville *(G-16800)*		
Oil Skimmers Inc	E	440 237-4600
North Royalton *(G-15440)*		

P B Fabrication Mech Contr	F	419 478-4869
Toledo *(G-18631)*		
◆ Park Corporation	B	216 267-4870
Cleveland *(G-5965)*		
Parker-Hannifin Corporation	F	330 336-3511
Wadsworth *(G-19427)*		
Pcy Enterprises Inc	E	513 241-5566
Cincinnati *(G-4219)*		
▲ Pioneer Pipe Inc	B	740 376-2400
Marietta *(G-12816)*		
Plastran Inc	G	440 237-8404
Cleveland *(G-6015)*		
Polymer Steel Corp	E	330 562-6906
Streetsboro *(G-17869)*		
Prout Boiler Htg & Wldg Inc	E	330 744-0293
Youngstown *(G-21180)*		
Pucel Enterprises Inc	D	216 881-4604
Cleveland *(G-6061)*		
Quintus Technologies LLC	E	614 891-2732
Lewis Center *(G-11912)*		
▲ R B Mfg Co	F	419 626-9464
Sandusky *(G-16999)*		
Rampp Company	E	740 373-7886
Marietta *(G-12822)*		
RCE Heat Exchangers LLC	E	330 627-0300
Carrollton *(G-2963)*		
Rcr Partnership	G	419 340-1202
Genoa *(G-10362)*		
Rebsco Inc	F	937 548-2246
Greenville *(G-10517)*		
Retays Welding Company	E	440 327-4100
North Ridgeville *(G-15400)*		
Rezmann Karoly	G	216 441-4357
Cleveland *(G-6110)*		
Rhodes Manufacturing Co Inc	E	740 743-2614
Somerset *(G-17418)*		
▲ Ridge Corporation	D	614 421-7434
Etna *(G-9561)*		
Rimrock Holdings Corporation	E	614 471-5926
Columbus *(G-7564)*		
Rose Metal Industries LLC	F	216 881-3355
Cleveland *(G-6132)*		
RPI of Indiana Inc	E	330 279-2421
Holmesville *(G-11111)*		
S-P Company Inc	F	330 482-0200
Columbiana *(G-6631)*		
▲ Sausser Steel Company Inc	F	419 422-9632
Findlay *(G-9888)*		
Schweizer Dipple Inc	D	440 786-8090
Cleveland *(G-6167)*		
Sexton Industrial Inc	C	513 530-5555
West Chester *(G-20049)*		
▲ Sgl Technic Inc	E	440 572-3600
Strongsville *(G-17963)*		
Sharon Manufacturing Inc	E	330 239-1561
Sharon Center *(G-17109)*		
Shelburne Corp	G	216 321-9177
Shaker Heights *(G-17094)*		
Skinner Sales Group Inc	E	440 572-8455
Strongsville *(G-17966)*		
Snair Co	F	614 873-7020
Plain City *(G-16360)*		
Space Dynamics Corp	E	513 792-9800
Blue Ash *(G-1871)*		
Spradlin Bros Welding Co	F	800 219-2182
Springfield *(G-17650)*		
St Lawrence Steel Corporation	E	330 562-9000
Streetsboro *(G-17878)*		
Standard Welding & Steel Pdts	F	330 273-2777
Medina *(G-13482)*		
▼ Steel & Alloy Utility Pdts Inc	E	330 530-2220
Mc Donald *(G-13348)*		
Steel Valley Tank & Welding	G	740 598-4994
Brilliant *(G-2095)*		
Steve Vore Welding and Steel	F	419 375-4087
Fort Recovery *(G-9959)*		
Sticker Corporation	F	440 946-2100
Willoughby *(G-20606)*		
▲ Strohecker Incorporated	E	330 426-9496
East Palestine *(G-9245)*		
Swagelok Company	D	440 349-5934
Solon *(G-17392)*		
Swanton Wldg Machining Co Inc	D	419 826-4816
Swanton *(G-18091)*		
Thermogenics Corp	G	513 247-7963
Cincinnati *(G-4505)*		
▼ Toledo Metal Spinning Company	E	419 535-5931
Toledo *(G-18733)*		
Tonns Fabrication	G	614 989-5097
Orient *(G-15725)*		

Triangle Precision Industries..............D...... 937 299-6776
  Dayton *(G-8723)*

Triumph Thermal Systems LLC..........C...... 419 273-2511
  Forest *(G-9923)*

TW Tank LLC...............................G...... 419 334-2664
  Fremont *(G-10189)*

Universal Hydraulik USA Corp...........G...... 419 873-6340
  Perrysburg *(G-16164)*

Universal Rack & Equipment Co........E...... 330 963-6776
  Twinsburg *(G-19033)*

▲ Val-Co Pax Inc.......................D...... 717 354-4586
  Coldwater *(G-6573)*

Varo Energy Services LLC..............G...... 914 437-6906
  Dublin *(G-9161)*

Verhoff Machine & Welding Inc.........C...... 419 596-3202
  Continental *(G-7829)*

Viking Fabricators Inc..................E...... 740 374-5246
  Marietta *(G-12848)*

Vortec Corporation......................E...... 513 686-8210
  Blue Ash *(G-1891)*

◆ Warren Fabricating Corporation.....D...... 330 847-0596
  Warren *(G-19621)*

Washington Products Inc...............F...... 330 837-5101
  Massillon *(G-13211)*

Wastequip Manufacturing Co LLC......E...... 330 674-1119
  Millersburg *(G-14283)*

◆ Wcr Inc..............................E...... 937 223-0703
  Fairborn *(G-9635)*

Wcr Incorporated.......................E...... 740 333-3448
  Wshngtn CT Hs *(G-20929)*

Westerman Inc...........................D...... 330 262-6946
  Wooster *(G-20846)*

Will-Burt Company......................G...... 330 682-7015
  Orrville *(G-15772)*

▲ Will-Burt Company...................B...... 330 682-7015
  Orrville *(G-15770)*

▲ Worthington Products Inc............G...... 330 452-7400
  Canton *(G-2903)*

Worthington Cylinder Corp.............C...... 740 569-4143
  Bremen *(G-2082)*

Worthington Cylinder Corp.............C...... 330 262-1762
  Wooster *(G-20852)*

◆ Worthington Cylinder Corp...........C...... 614 840-3210
  Worthington *(G-20895)*

Worthington Cylinder Corp.............C...... 440 576-5847
  Jefferson *(G-11376)*

Worthington Cylinder Corp.............C...... 614 438-7900
  Columbus *(G-7775)*

Worthington Cylinder Corp.............C...... 614 840-3800
  Westerville *(G-20196)*

Worthington Industries Inc.............C...... 614 438-3210
  Worthington *(G-20896)*

3444 Sheet Metal Work

A A S Amels Sheet Meta L Inc.........E...... 330 793-9326
  Youngstown *(G-21010)*

A & C Welding Inc......................E...... 330 762-4777
  Peninsula *(G-16032)*

A & E Butscha Co........................G...... 513 761-1919
  Cincinnati *(G-3329)*

▲ A & G Manufacturing Co Inc..........E...... 419 468-7433
  Galion *(G-10250)*

A A A Professional Htg & Coolg........G...... 513 933-0564
  Lebanon *(G-11773)*

A C Shutters Inc........................G...... 216 429-2424
  Cleveland *(G-4669)*

A M Castle & Co.........................D...... 330 425-7000
  Bedford *(G-1394)*

Aba Gutters Inc.........................G...... 440 729-2177
  Chesterland *(G-3193)*

Accufab Inc.............................G...... 513 942-1929
  West Chester *(G-19796)*

▲ Acro Tool & Die Company.............D...... 330 773-5173
  Akron *(G-29)*

Adjustable Kicker LLC..................G...... 740 362-9170
  Delaware *(G-8817)*

Advance Metal Products Inc............F...... 216 741-1800
  Cleveland *(G-4709)*

Advanced Welding Co....................E...... 937 746-6800
  Franklin *(G-10005)*

Aerolite Extrusion Company............D...... 330 782-1127
  Youngstown *(G-21018)*

Ahemco LLC.............................F...... 513 385-0555
  Cincinnati *(G-3368)*

Ahner Fabricating & Shtmtl Inc........E...... 419 626-6641
  Sandusky *(G-16945)*

Akron Foundry Co........................E...... 330 745-3101
  Barberton *(G-1095)*

▲ Alan Manufacturing Inc..............E...... 330 262-1555
  Wooster *(G-20737)*

Aleris Rolled Products Inc.............D...... 740 983-2571
  Ashville *(G-848)*

All Metal Fabricators Inc..............F...... 216 267-0033
  Cleveland *(G-4755)*

Allen County Fabrication Inc...........E...... 419 227-7447
  Lima *(G-11986)*

Allfab Inc..............................F...... 614 491-4944
  Columbus *(G-6723)*

Allied Fabricating & Wldg Co..........E...... 614 751-6664
  Columbus *(G-6725)*

Allied Mask and Tooling Inc............G...... 419 470-2555
  Toledo *(G-18329)*

Alloy Fabricators Inc..................E...... 330 948-3535
  Lodi *(G-12156)*

Alro Steel Corporation.................E...... 419 720-5300
  Toledo *(G-18331)*

◆ Alsco Metals Corporation............E...... 740 983-2571
  Dennison *(G-8942)*

Alumetal Manufacturing Company.......E...... 419 268-2311
  Coldwater *(G-6550)*

Aluminum Color Industries Inc.........E...... 330 536-6295
  Lowellville *(G-12404)*

Aluminum Extruded Shapes Inc.........C...... 513 563-2205
  Cincinnati *(G-3383)*

AMD Fabricators Inc....................E...... 440 946-8855
  Willoughby *(G-20429)*

American Culvert & Fabg Co............F...... 740 432-6334
  Cambridge *(G-2443)*

▲ American Frame Corporation..........D...... 419 893-5595
  Maumee *(G-13222)*

Americas Best Siding Co................G...... 419 589-5900
  Mansfield *(G-12562)*

Amh Holdings LLC.......................A...... 330 929-1811
  Cuyahoga Falls *(G-7966)*

▲ Ampp Incorporated...................C...... 419 666-4747
  Perrysburg *(G-16065)*

Anchor Metal Processing Inc...........F...... 216 362-6463
  Cleveland *(G-4804)*

Anchor Metal Processing Inc...........E...... 216 362-1850
  Cleveland *(G-4805)*

Andy Russo Jr Inc......................F...... 440 585-1456
  Wickliffe *(G-20354)*

Anro Logistics Inc.....................G...... 614 428-7490
  Westerville *(G-20138)*

Antique Auto Sheet Metal Inc..........E...... 937 833-4422
  Brookville *(G-2174)*

Apex Welding Incorporated.............F...... 440 232-6770
  Bedford *(G-1398)*

Architectural Daylighting LLC..........G...... 330 460-5000
  Medina *(G-13373)*

Architectural Sheet Metals LLC........G...... 216 361-9952
  Cleveland *(G-4827)*

▲ Armor Consolidated Inc..............C...... 513 923-5260
  Mason *(G-12982)*

▲ Armor Metal Group Mason Inc........C...... 513 769-0700
  Mason *(G-12983)*

Art Fremont Iron Co.....................E...... 419 332-5554
  Fremont *(G-10125)*

Associated Materials LLC..............G...... 937 236-5679
  Dayton *(G-8166)*

▼ Auburn Metal Processing LLC.........E...... 315 253-2565
  Twinsburg *(G-18902)*

Austintown Metal Works Inc............F...... 330 259-4673
  Youngstown *(G-21028)*

Autoneum North America Inc............B...... 419 693-0511
  Oregon *(G-15703)*

Avon Lake Sheet Metal Co..............E...... 440 933-3505
  Avon Lake *(G-1025)*

Aztec Manufacturing Inc...............E...... 330 783-9747
  Youngstown *(G-21030)*

B Y G Industries Inc...................G...... 216 961-5436
  Cleveland *(G-4884)*

B-R-O-T Incorporated...................E...... 216 267-5335
  Cleveland *(G-4886)*

Bainter Machining Company.............G...... 740 653-2422
  Lancaster *(G-11691)*

Baltimore Fabricators Inc..............E...... 740 862-6016
  Baltimore *(G-1080)*

Bayloff Stmped Pdts Knsman Inc........D...... 330 876-4511
  Kinsman *(G-11608)*

Beacon Metal Fabricators Inc..........F...... 216 391-7444
  Cleveland *(G-4900)*

Berran Industrial Group Inc............E...... 330 253-5800
  Akron *(G-89)*

Bickers Metal Products Inc.............E...... 513 353-4000
  Miamitown *(G-13884)*

BJ Equipment Ltd.......................F...... 614 497-1776
  Columbus *(G-6834)*

Blesco Services.........................G...... 614 871-4900
  Mount Sterling *(G-14596)*

Blevins Metal Fabrication Inc..........E...... 419 522-6082
  Mansfield *(G-12567)*

Bob Lanes Welding Inc..................F...... 740 373-3567
  Marietta *(G-12767)*

Bogie Industries Inc Ltd...............E...... 330 745-3105
  Akron *(G-95)*

Breitinger Company......................C...... 419 526-4255
  Mansfield *(G-12569)*

BT Investments II Inc..................G...... 937 434-4321
  Dayton *(G-8200)*

Buckeye Metal Works Inc................F...... 614 239-8000
  Columbus *(G-6873)*

Bud Corp................................G...... 740 967-9992
  Johnstown *(G-11394)*

Budde Sheet Metal Works Inc...........E...... 937 224-0868
  Dayton *(G-8202)*

Burt Manufacturing Company Inc........C...... 330 762-0061
  Akron *(G-105)*

Busch & Thiem Inc......................E...... 419 625-7515
  Sandusky *(G-16952)*

C & R Inc...............................E...... 614 497-1130
  Groveport *(G-10617)*

C A Joseph Co...........................F...... 330 532-4646
  Irondale *(G-11287)*

C G C Systems Inc.......................G...... 330 678-3261
  Kent *(G-11437)*

C L W Inc...............................G...... 740 374-8443
  Marietta *(G-12769)*

C M L Concrete Construction............G...... 330 758-8314
  Youngstown *(G-21041)*

C-N-D Industries Inc...................G...... 330 478-8811
  Massillon *(G-13118)*

Cabletek Wiring Products Inc...........E...... 800 562-9378
  Elyria *(G-9387)*

Carroll Distrg & Cnstr Sup Inc.........E...... 513 422-3327
  Middletown *(G-14026)*

Carroll Distrg & Cnstr Sup Inc.........G...... 614 564-9799
  Columbus *(G-6912)*

Cbr Industrial Llc......................G...... 419 645-6447
  Wapakoneta *(G-19483)*

Ceco Group Inc..........................E...... 513 458-2600
  Cincinnati *(G-3510)*

Centria Inc.............................D...... 740 432-7351
  Cambridge *(G-2451)*

Chagrin Metal Fabricating Inc..........E...... 440 946-6342
  Eastlake *(G-9262)*

Champion Window Co of Toledo..........E...... 419 841-0154
  Perrysburg *(G-16077)*

Chute Source LLC........................F...... 330 475-0377
  Akron *(G-123)*

Cincinnati Gutter Supply Inc...........G...... 513 825-0500
  West Chester *(G-19831)*

Cinfab LLC..............................C...... 513 396-6100
  Cincinnati *(G-3575)*

Clarkdietrich Bldg Systems LLC........C...... 513 870-1100
  West Chester *(G-19834)*

Clarkwestern Dietrich Building.........G...... 330 372-5564
  Warren *(G-19535)*

▼ Clarkwestern Dietrich Building......G...... 513 870-1100
  West Chester *(G-19835)*

Cleveland Steel Specialty Co...........E...... 216 464-9400
  Bedford Heights *(G-1481)*

CMA Supply Company Inc................F...... 513 942-6663
  West Chester *(G-19992)*

Collier Well Eqp & Sup Inc.............F...... 330 345-3968
  Wooster *(G-20760)*

Color Brite Company Inc................G...... 216 441-4117
  Cleveland *(G-5100)*

Columbus Steelmasters Inc.............F...... 614 231-2141
  Columbus *(G-6968)*

Commercial Mtal Fbricators Inc........E...... 937 233-4911
  Dayton *(G-8239)*

Compco Industries Incorporated.......D...... 330 482-6488
  Columbiana *(G-6614)*

Contech Engnered Solutions Inc........A...... 513 645-7000
  West Chester *(G-19840)*

Contech Engnered Solutions LLC........D...... 513 645-7000
  Middletown *(G-14032)*

Contech Engnered Solutions LLC........G...... 614 477-1171
  Columbus *(G-6977)*

◆ Contech Engnered Solutions LLC......C...... 513 645-7000
  West Chester *(G-19841)*

Contour Forming Inc.....................E...... 740 345-9777
  Newark *(G-14996)*

Controls and Sheet Metal Inc..........E...... 513 721-3610
  Cincinnati *(G-3607)*

COW Industries Inc......................E...... 614 443-6537
  Columbus *(G-6992)*

Cramers Inc.............................E...... 330 477-4571
  Canton *(G-2670)*

CRC Metal Products .... G 740 966-0475
Johnstown (G-11397)

Creative Concepts .... G 216 513-6463
Medina (G-13398)

Crest Awning & Home Imprv Co .... G 440 942-3092
Willoughby (G-20465)

Crest Products Inc .... F 440 942-5770
Mentor (G-13556)

▲ Crown Electric Engrg & Mfg LLC ..... E 513 539-7394
Middletown (G-14035)

Custom Crete .... G 740 726-2433
Waldo (G-19465)

Custom Duct & Supply Co Inc .... G 937 228-2058
Dayton (G-8258)

Custom Enclosures Corp .... G 330 786-9000
Akron (G-137)

Custom Metal Products Inc .... F 614 855-2263
New Albany (G-14756)

Custom Metal Shearing Inc .... F 937 233-6950
Dayton (G-8260)

D & D Metal Supply Inc .... F 513 272-1246
Cincinnati (G-3629)

▲ D B S Stinless Stl Fabricators .... G 513 856-9600
Hamilton (G-10683)

Datco Mfg Company Inc .... E 330 781-6100
Youngstown (G-21065)

David Cox .... G 740 254-4858
Gnadenhutten (G-10405)

Decor Architectural Products .... G 419 537-9493
Toledo (G-18432)

Delafoil Pennsylvania Inc .... D 610 327-9565
Perrysburg (G-16083)

Delma Corp .... D 937 253-2142
Dayton (G-8296)

Di Lorio Sheet Metal Inc .... F 216 961-3703
Cleveland (G-5187)

Die-Cut Products Co .... E 216 771-6994
Cleveland (G-5193)

Dimensional Metals Inc .... D 740 927-3633
Reynoldsburg (G-16586)

Dover Tank and Plate Company .... E 330 343-4443
Dover (G-8982)

Duct Fabricators Inc .... G 216 391-2400
Cleveland (G-5219)

Ducts Inc .... G 216 391-2400
Cleveland (G-5220)

▲ Duro Dyne Midwest Corp .... B 513 870-6000
Hamilton (G-10685)

Dynamic Weld Corporation .... E 419 582-2900
Osgood (G-15785)

E & K Products Co Inc .... E 216 631-2510
Cleveland (G-5229)

E B P Inc .... E 216 241-2550
Cleveland (G-5230)

Eagle Wldg & Fabrication Inc .... E 440 946-0692
Willoughby (G-20478)

▲ Eastern Sheet Metal Inc .... D 513 793-3440
Blue Ash (G-1781)

▲ Eaton Fabricating Company Inc .... F 440 926-3121
Grafton (G-10425)

▲ Ebner Furnaces Inc .... D 330 335-2311
Wadsworth (G-19404)

Edwards Sheet Metal Works Inc .... F 740 694-0010
Fredericktown (G-10101)

Efco Corp .... E 614 876-1226
Columbus (G-7048)

Elg Inc .... E 216 518-0476
Maple Heights (G-12734)

Elsass Fabricating Ltd .... G 937 394-7169
Anna (G-622)

Enterprise Welding & Fabg Inc .... C 440 354-4128
Mentor (G-13574)

F M Sheet Metal Fabrication .... G 937 362-4357
Quincy (G-16503)

Fab Steel Co Inc .... F 419 666-5100
Northwood (G-15481)

▲ Fabco Inc .... E 419 421-4740
Findlay (G-9820)

Fabcraft Inc .... G 440 286-6700
Chardon (G-3152)

Fabricating Solutions Inc .... F 330 486-0998
Twinsburg (G-18933)

Fabrication Unlimited LLC .... G 937 492-3166
Sidney (G-17189)

Fabtech Ohio .... G 440 942-0811
Willoughby (G-20484)

Falcon Industries Inc .... G 330 723-0099
Medina (G-13409)

Famous Industries Inc .... C 740 397-8842
Mount Vernon (G-14622)

Famous Industries Inc .... E 330 535-1811
Akron (G-181)

▲ Feather Lite Innovations Inc .... E 937 743-9008
Springboro (G-17480)

Firestone Sheet Metal Inc .... E 330 337-9551
Salem (G-16890)

First Francis Company Inc .... E 440 352-8927
Painesville (G-15881)

Flood Heliarc Inc .... F 614 835-3929
Groveport (G-10621)

Franck and Fric Incorporated .... D 216 524-4451
Cleveland (G-5377)

Franklin Frames and Cycles .... G 740 763-3838
Newark (G-15008)

Fred Winner .... G 419 582-2421
New Weston (G-14977)

Fulton Equipment Co .... E 419 290-5393
Toledo (G-18475)

G & C Drainage Supplies Inc .... G 513 563-8616
Cincinnati (G-3788)

G T Metal Fabricators Inc .... F 440 237-8745
Cleveland (G-5388)

Galion LLC .... C 419 468-5214
Galion (G-10268)

Galion-Godwin Truck Bdy Co LLC .... D 330 359-5495
Millersburg (G-14217)

Gaspar Inc .... D 330 477-2222
Canton (G-2711)

Gdm Mailbox Company LLC .... G 419 433-3022
Huron (G-11221)

Geist Co Inc .... F 216 771-2200
Cleveland (G-5406)

Gem City Metal Tech LLC .... E 937 252-8998
Dayton (G-8362)

General Awning Company Inc .... F 216 749-0110
Cleveland (G-5411)

▲ General Technologies Inc .... E 419 747-1800
Mansfield (G-12612)

▲ General Tool Company .... C 513 733-5500
Cincinnati (G-3820)

▲ Gentek Building Products Inc .... F 800 548-4542
Cuyahoga Falls (G-8003)

George Manufacturing Inc .... E 513 932-1067
Lebanon (G-11801)

Gilson Screen Incorporated .... E 419 256-7711
Malinta (G-12534)

GL Nause Co Inc .... E 513 722-9500
Loveland (G-12353)

▲ Glunt Industries Inc .... C 330 399-7585
Warren (G-19555)

GNI Erectors .... E 614 465-7260
Galloway (G-10314)

Gomech Ltd .... E 419 419-4446
Maumee (G-13261)

Graber Metal Works Inc .... E 440 237-8422
North Royalton (G-15422)

Great Day Improvements LLC .... G 330 468-0700
Macedonia (G-12456)

Gunderson Rail Services LLC .... E 330 792-6521
Youngstown (G-21106)

Gundlach Sheet Metal Works Inc .... E 419 626-4525
Sandusky (G-16971)

Gutter Topper Ltd .... G 513 797-5800
Batavia (G-1189)

▲ Gwp Holdings Inc .... D 513 860-4050
Fairfield (G-9662)

▲ H B Products Inc .... E 937 492-7031
Sidney (G-17191)

Hall Company .... E 937 652-1376
Urbana (G-19160)

Halls Sheet Metal Fabrication .... G 740 965-9264
Galena (G-10243)

▲ Halvorsen Company .... E 216 341-7500
Cleveland (G-5473)

Harray LLC .... G 888 568-8371
Cincinnati (G-3867)

Harrison Mch & Plastic Corp .... E 330 569-3128
Garrettsville (G-10323)

Hartley Machine Inc .... G 330 821-0343
Alliance (G-513)

Hartzell Manufacturing Co Inc .... F 937 859-5955
Miamisburg (G-13815)

HCC Holdings Inc .... G 800 203-1155
Cleveland (G-5488)

Heidtman Steel Products Inc .... D 216 641-6995
Cleveland (G-5494)

Hennig Inc .... G 513 247-0838
Blue Ash (G-1808)

▲ Hidaka Usa Inc .... E 614 889-8611
Dublin (G-9084)

Higgins Building Mtls No 2 LLC .... G 740 395-5410
Jackson (G-11315)

Highway Safety Corp .... F 740 387-6991
Marion (G-12874)

Hoffman Machining & Repair LLC .... G 419 547-9204
Clyde (G-6540)

Holgate Metal Fab Inc .... F 419 599-2000
Napoleon (G-14682)

Home Sheet Metal & Roofing Co .... G 419 562-7806
Bucyrus (G-2348)

Hvac Inc .... F 330 343-5511
Dover (G-8991)

Indian Creek Fabricators Inc .... E 937 667-7214
Tipp City (G-18283)

Induction Iron Incorporated .... G 330 501-8852
Youngstown (G-21114)

Industrial Hanger Conveyor Co .... G 419 332-2661
Fremont (G-10158)

Industrial Mill Maintenance .... E 330 746-1155
Youngstown (G-21115)

Interlock Industries Inc .... E 440 576-9070
Jefferson (G-11361)

Interstate Contractors LLC .... E 513 372-5393
Mason (G-13048)

▼ Isaiah Industries Inc .... E 937 773-9840
Piqua (G-16280)

Izit Cain Sheet Metal Corp .... E 937 667-6521
Tipp City (G-18284)

J & L Welding Fabricating Inc .... F 330 393-9353
Warren (G-19561)

J B Kepple Sheet Metal .... G 740 393-2971
Mount Vernon (G-14624)

J N Linrose Mfg LLC .... E 513 867-5500
Hamilton (G-10709)

J O Y Aluminum Products Inc .... F 513 797-1100
Batavia (G-1193)

Jacobs Mechanical Co .... G 513 681-6800
Cincinnati (G-3937)

Jeffery A Burns .... G 419 845-2129
Caledonia (G-2439)

Jh Industries Inc .... E 330 963-4105
Twinsburg (G-18961)

Jim Nier Construction Inc .... F 740 289-3925
Piketon (G-16222)

John Baird .... G 216 440-3595
Spencer (G-17456)

Johnson-Nash Metal Pdts Inc .... F 513 874-7022
Fairfield (G-9671)

Joining Metals Inc .... F 440 259-1790
Perry (G-16051)

Jones Metal Products Company .... D 740 545-6381
West Lafayette (G-20087)

Joseph T Ryerson & Son Inc .... D 513 542-5800
Columbus (G-7245)

Joyce Manufacturing Co .... D 440 239-9100
Berea (G-1624)

Kerber Sheetmetal Works Inc .... F 937 339-6366
Troy (G-18852)

Kettering Roofing & Shtmtl .... F 513 281-6413
Cincinnati (G-3986)

Kilroy Company .... D 440 951-8700
Eastlake (G-9278)

◆ Kirk & Blum Manufacturing Co .... C 513 458-2600
Cincinnati (G-3992)

Kirk & Blum Manufacturing Co .... E 419 782-9885
Defiance (G-8798)

Kirk Williams Company Inc .... D 614 875-9023
Grove City (G-10568)

Knight Manufacturing Co Inc .... G 740 676-5516
Shadyside (G-17082)

Korda Manufacturing Inc .... D 330 262-1555
Wooster (G-20797)

Kramer Power Equipment Co .... F 937 456-2232
Eaton (G-9313)

Kuhlman Engineering Co .... F 419 243-2196
Toledo (G-18549)

Kuhn Fabricating Inc .... G 440 277-4182
Lorain (G-12253)

L C Systems Inc .... G 614 235-9430
Dublin (G-9098)

L&M Sheet Metal Ltd .... G 513 858-6173
Fairfield (G-9676)

◆ Lake Shore Electric Corp .... E 440 232-0200
Bedford (G-1438)

Lambert Sheet Metal Inc .... F 614 237-0384
Columbus (G-7281)

▲ Langdon Inc .... E 513 733-5955
Cincinnati (G-4011)

Lima Sheet Metal Machine & Mfg .... E 419 229-1161
Lima (G-12045)

Locker Konnection Services LLC.........G....... 419 334-3956
Fremont (G-10166)
▲ Long-Stanton Mfg Company............E....... 513 874-8020
West Chester (G-19895)
Louis Arthur Steel Company.................G....... 440 997-5545
Geneva (G-10352)
Louis Arthur Steel Company.................G....... 440 997-5545
Uniontown (G-19091)
Lowry Furnace Company Inc................G....... 330 745-4822
Akron (G-276)
LSI Industries Inc..................................E....... 513 793-3200
Blue Ash (G-1829)
▲ Lt Enterprises of Ohio LLC..............E....... 330 526-6908
North Canton (G-15247)
Lukjan Metal Products Inc....................C....... 440 599-8127
Conneaut (G-7814)
Lund Equipment Co Inc.........................E....... 330 659-4800
Bath (G-1238)
M H EBY Inc...E....... 614 879-6901
West Jefferson (G-20081)
M3 Technologies Inc...............................F....... 216 898-9936
Cleveland (G-5721)
Mack Iron Works Company....................E....... 419 626-3712
Sandusky (G-16984)
Maines Brothers Tin Shop.....................G....... 937 393-1633
Hillsboro (G-11008)
Mantych Metalworking Inc....................E....... 937 258-1373
Dayton (G-8111)
Marsam Metalfab Inc..............................E....... 330 405-1520
Twinsburg (G-18978)
Martina Metal LLC..................................E....... 614 291-9700
Columbus (G-7321)
Matandy Steel & Metal Pdts LLC..........D....... 513 844-2277
Hamilton (G-10723)
Matteo Aluminum Inc.............................E....... 440 585-5213
Wickliffe (G-20372)
McGill Airflow LLC.................................F....... 614 829-1200
Columbus (G-7331)
◆ McGill Airflow LLC...............................G....... 614 829-1200
Groveport (G-10634)
◆ McGill Corporation..............................F....... 614 829-1200
Groveport (G-10635)
McWane Inc..B....... 740 622-6651
Coshocton (G-7897)
Medway Tool Corp..................................E....... 937 335-7717
Troy (G-18857)
Meese Inc...D....... 440 998-1202
Ashtabula (G-819)
Mestek Inc..D....... 419 288-2703
Holland (G-11072)
Mestek Inc..D....... 419 288-2703
Bradner (G-2029)
Met L Fab Inc...F....... 513 561-4289
Cincinnati (G-4088)
Metal Fabricating Corporation..............D....... 216 631-8121
Cleveland (G-5787)
Metal Sales Manufacturing Corp..........E....... 440 576-9070
Jefferson (G-11367)
Metal Technology Systems Inc.............G....... 513 563-1882
Cincinnati (G-4089)
Metal-Max Inc..G....... 330 673-9926
Kent (G-11489)
▲ Metalworking Group Holdings..........C....... 513 521-4119
Cincinnati (G-4091)
Metlweb...E....... 513 563-8822
Cincinnati (G-4093)
Metrodeck Inc...F....... 513 541-4370
Cincinnati (G-4095)
Michael Fabricating Inc.........................G....... 330 325-8636
Rootstown (G-16724)
Mid-America Gutters Inc.......................G....... 513 671-3505
Cincinnati (G-4105)
▲ Mid-Ohio Products Inc......................D....... 614 771-2795
Hilliard (G-10962)
Midwest Fabrications Inc......................E....... 330 633-0191
Tallmadge (G-18155)
Midwest Metal Fabricators....................F....... 419 739-7077
Wapakoneta (G-19499)
Midwest Metal Fabricators....................F....... 419 739-7077
Wapakoneta (G-19500)
Midwest Metal Products LLC................E....... 614 539-7322
Grove City (G-10573)
Midwest Spray Booths...........................G....... 937 439-6600
Dayton (G-8497)
Mika Metal Fabricating Co.....................E....... 440 951-5500
Willoughby (G-20549)
Mike Loppe...F....... 937 969-8102
Tremont City (G-18789)
Mings Heating & AC...............................G....... 216 721-2007
Cleveland (G-5821)
◆ Modern Ice Equipment & Sup Co......E....... 513 367-2101
Cincinnati (G-4115)
Modern Manufacturing Inc....................F....... 513 251-3600
Cincinnati (G-4116)
Mor-Lite Co Inc......................................G....... 513 661-8587
Cincinnati (G-4122)
▲ MRS Industrial Inc..............................E....... 614 308-1070
Columbus (G-7372)
Muehlenkamp Properties Inc................E....... 513 745-0874
Cincinnati (G-4130)
◆ N Wasserstrom & Sons Inc...............C....... 614 228-5550
Columbus (G-7377)
Neal Miller..G....... 440 296-5322
Pierpont (G-16214)
Nel-Ack Sheet Metal Inc.......................G....... 440 357-7844
Painesville (G-15903)
Niles Manufacturing & Finshg..............C....... 330 544-0402
Niles (G-15171)
▲ Nissin Precision N Amer Inc.............D....... 937 836-1910
Englewood (G-9536)
Norstar Aluminum Molds Inc................D....... 440 632-0853
Middlefield (G-13977)
North Coast Profile Inc.........................G....... 330 823-7777
Alliance (G-531)
North Star Metals Mfg Co......................E....... 740 254-4567
Uhrichsville (G-19055)
Northwest Installations Inc...................E....... 419 423-5738
Findlay (G-9869)
Northwind Industries Inc.......................E....... 216 433-0666
Cleveland (G-5916)
Nufab Sheet Metal..................................G....... 937 235-2030
Dayton (G-8535)
Obr Cooling Towers Inc........................E....... 419 243-3443
Rossford (G-16744)
Ohio Blow Pipe Company......................E....... 216 681-7379
Cleveland (G-5930)
▼ Ohio Gratings Inc................................B....... 330 477-6707
Canton (G-2799)
Ohio Steel Sheet & Plate Inc.................E....... 800 827-2401
Hubbard (G-11136)
Ohio Trailer Inc.......................................F....... 330 392-4444
Warren (G-19584)
▼ Options Plus Incorporated.................F....... 740 694-9811
Fredericktown (G-10108)
Owens Corning Sales Inc......................G....... 740 983-1300
Ashville (G-853)
P & L Metalcrafts LLC............................F....... 330 793-2178
Youngstown (G-21160)
P B Fabrication Mech Contr...................F....... 419 478-4869
Toledo (G-18631)
Parker-Hannifin Corporation.................F....... 330 336-3511
Wadsworth (G-19427)
Patio Room Factory Inc.........................G....... 614 449-7900
Columbus (G-7464)
Patterson & Sons Inc..............................F....... 419 281-0897
Nova (G-15579)
Paul Wilke & Son Inc..............................F....... 513 921-3163
Cincinnati (G-4217)
Pcy Enterprises Inc................................E....... 513 241-5566
Cincinnati (G-4219)
▲ Pei Liquidation Company...................C....... 330 467-4267
Macedonia (G-12470)
Pei Liquidation Company.......................E....... 615 781-5020
Macedonia (G-12471)
Pennant Moldings Inc.............................C....... 937 584-5411
Sabina (G-16775)
Phillips Awning Co.................................G....... 740 653-2433
Lancaster (G-11738)
Phillips Manufacturing Co......................D....... 330 652-4335
Niles (G-15173)
▲ Phillips Shtmtl Fabrications...............G....... 937 223-2722
Dayton (G-8572)
Pioneer Fabrication.................................G....... 419 737-9464
Alvordton (G-558)
Plas-Tanks Industries Inc......................E....... 513 942-3800
Hamilton (G-10730)
Precise Metal Form Inc..........................F....... 419 636-5221
Bryan (G-2319)
Precision Mtal Fabrication Inc...............D....... 937 235-9261
Dayton (G-8587)
Precision Steel Services Inc..................D....... 419 476-5702
Toledo (G-18654)
Precision Welding Corporation..............E....... 216 524-6110
Cleveland (G-6037)
Premier Stamping and Assembly...........G....... 440 293-8961
Williamsfield (G-20416)
Priest Millwright Service.......................G....... 937 780-3405
Leesburg (G-11856)
Production Manufacturing Inc................E....... 513 892-2331
Hamilton (G-10731)
Prototype Fabricators Co.......................G....... 216 252-0080
Cleveland (G-6058)
Providence Group Inc.............................E....... 440 350-4615
Mentor (G-13703)
Quality Craftsman Inc.............................F....... 740 474-9685
Circleville (G-4639)
Quality Steel Fabrication........................F....... 937 492-9503
Sidney (G-17213)
Quass Sheet Metal Inc............................G....... 330 477-4841
Canton (G-2831)
▲ R B Mfg Co...F....... 419 626-9464
Sandusky (G-16999)
R L Torbeck Industries Inc.....................D....... 513 367-0080
Harrison (G-10800)
Raka Corporation....................................D....... 419 476-6572
Toledo (G-18671)
Range One Products & Fabg..................F....... 330 533-1151
Canfield (G-2571)
Rapid Machine Inc..................................F....... 419 737-2377
Pioneer (G-16243)
Related Metals Inc...................................G....... 330 799-4866
Canfield (G-2572)
Rex Burnett..G....... 740 927-4669
Etna (G-9560)
Rexam Beverage Can Company.............C....... 419 334-4461
Fremont (G-10178)
Rezmann Karoly.......................................G....... 216 441-4357
Cleveland (G-6110)
Ridge Enterprises Inc..............................G....... 740 867-3456
Chesapeake (G-3190)
Ridgeview Sheet Metal............................G....... 330 674-3768
Millersburg (G-14259)
▲ Robinson Fin Machines Inc.................E....... 419 674-4152
Kenton (G-11567)
▲ Rockwell Metals Company LLC.........F....... 440 242-2420
Lorain (G-12273)
Roconex Corporation...............................F....... 937 339-2616
Troy (G-18868)
Romar Metal Fabricating Inc...................G....... 740 682-7731
Oak Hill (G-15606)
Royalton Archtctral Fbrication................F....... 440 582-0400
North Royalton (G-15447)
▼ S & B Metal Products Inc.....................E....... 330 487-5790
Twinsburg (G-19015)
S & D Architectural Metals......................G....... 440 582-2560
North Royalton (G-15451)
S & G Manufacturing Group LLC............C....... 614 529-0100
Hilliard (G-10977)
S & R Sheet Metal....................................G....... 937 865-9236
Dayton (G-8642)
S L M Inc...G....... 216 651-0666
Cleveland (G-6150)
Salsbury Industries Inc............................G....... 614 409-1600
Columbus (G-7588)
Samuel Clark...F....... 614 855-2263
New Albany (G-14772)
Saringer Sheet Metal Inc..........................E....... 216 447-9755
Independence (G-11274)
▲ Sausser Steel Company Inc.................F....... 419 422-9632
Findlay (G-9888)
Scharenberg Sheet Metal.........................G....... 740 664-2431
New Marshfield (G-14872)
Schoonover Industries Inc.......................E....... 419 289-8332
Ashland (G-776)
Schweizer Dipple Inc................................D....... 440 786-8090
Cleveland (G-6167)
Scott Fetzer Company..............................C....... 216 267-9000
Cleveland (G-6168)
Selmco Metal Fabricators Inc...................F....... 937 498-1331
Sidney (G-17224)
Seneca Sheet Metal Company..................F....... 419 447-8434
Tiffin (G-18244)
Shade Youngstown & Aluminum Co.........G....... 330 782-2373
Youngstown (G-21200)
◆ Shadetree Systems LLC........................F....... 614 844-5990
Columbus (G-7614)
Shaffer Metal Fab Inc...............................E....... 937 492-1384
Sidney (G-17225)
Shape Supply Inc.......................................G....... 513 863-6695
Hamilton (G-10738)
Sheet Angle Bar Met Fbrication...............G....... 513 829-8600
Fairfield (G-9716)
Sheet Metal Products Co Inc....................E....... 440 392-9000
Mentor (G-13722)
Shriner Sheet Metal Inc............................F....... 330 435-6735
Creston (G-7943)
▲ Siata Ds Inc..G....... 216 503-7200
Beachwood (G-1298)
▼ Sidney Manufacturing Company.........E....... 937 492-4154
Sidney (G-17227)

SIC

Smith Rn Sheet Metal Shop Inc .... E 740 653-5011
Lancaster *(G-11753)*

Snair Co .... F 614 873-7020
Plain City *(G-16360)*

Somerville Manufacturing Inc .... E 740 336-7847
Marietta *(G-12834)*

Spradlin Bros Welding Co .... F 800 219-2182
Springfield *(G-17650)*

▲ Staber Industries Inc .... E 614 836-5995
Groveport *(G-10645)*

Standard Technologies LLC .... D 419 332-6434
Fremont *(G-10183)*

Starr Fabricating Inc .... D 330 394-9891
Vienna *(G-19376)*

▼ Steel & Alloy Utility Pdts Inc .... E 330 530-2220
Mc Donald *(G-13348)*

Steelial Wldg Met Fbrction Inc .... E 740 669-5300
Vinton *(G-19383)*

Steve Vore Welding and Steel .... F 419 375-4087
Fort Recovery *(G-9959)*

Suburban Metal Products Inc .... F 740 474-4237
Circleville *(G-4644)*

Sulecki Precision Products .... F 440 255-5454
Mentor *(G-13740)*

Super Sheet Metal .... G 330 482-9045
Leetonia *(G-11866)*

Swanton Wldg Machining Co Inc .... D 419 826-4816
Swanton *(G-18091)*

Systech Handling Inc .... F 419 445-8226
Archbold *(G-696)*

Tangent Air Inc .... E 740 474-1114
Circleville *(G-4645)*

▼ Tectum Inc .... C 740 345-9691
Newark *(G-15063)*

Tendon Manufacturing Inc .... E 216 663-3200
Cleveland *(G-6305)*

Tex-Tyler Corporation .... E 419 729-4951
Toledo *(G-18720)*

▲ Thermo Vent Manufacturing Inc .... F 330 239-0239
Medina *(G-13487)*

Thompson Culvert Company LLC .... F 513 645-7000
West Chester *(G-19956)*

Tkr Metal Fabricating LLC .... G 440 221-2770
Willoughby *(G-20617)*

TL Industries Inc .... C 419 666-8144
Northwood *(G-15490)*

Toledo Window & Awning Inc .... G 419 474-3396
Toledo *(G-18748)*

Tool & Die Systems Inc .... E 440 327-5800
North Ridgeville *(G-15406)*

Torok Supply Company .... G 330 799-6677
Youngstown *(G-21224)*

Tower Tool & Manufacturing Co .... F 330 425-1623
Twinsburg *(G-19028)*

Transtar Holding Company .... G 800 359-3339
Cleveland *(G-6349)*

Tri-Fab Inc .... E 330 337-3425
Salem *(G-16931)*

Tri-Mac Mfg & Svcs Co .... F 513 896-4445
Hamilton *(G-10749)*

Tri-State Fabricators Inc .... E 513 752-5005
Amelia *(G-587)*

Triangle Precision Industries .... D 937 299-6776
Dayton *(G-8723)*

▲ Tricor Industrial Inc .... D 330 264-3299
Wooster *(G-20841)*

Tru Form Metal Products Inc .... G 216 252-3700
Cleveland *(G-6368)*

Unison Industries LLC .... F 937 426-4676
Alpha *(G-555)*

▲ United McGill Corporation .... E 614 829-1200
Groveport *(G-10648)*

▲ Universal Steel Company .... D 216 883-4972
Cleveland *(G-6392)*

Upside Innovations LLC .... G 513 889-2492
West Chester *(G-20065)*

V & S Schuler Engineering Inc .... E 330 452-5200
Canton *(G-2893)*

V M Systems Inc .... D 419 535-1044
Toledo *(G-18763)*

Valley Metal Works Inc .... F 513 554-1022
Cincinnati *(G-4553)*

Varmland Inc .... F 216 741-1510
Cleveland *(G-6408)*

Verhoff Machine & Welding Inc .... C 419 596-3202
Continental *(G-7829)*

Vicart Prcsion Fabricators Inc .... E 614 771-0080
Hilliard *(G-10992)*

Visual Information Institute .... F 937 376-4361
Xenia *(G-20985)*

▲ Vortex Metals Ltd .... G 216 365-2300
Warrensville Heights *(G-19636)*

W & W Custom Fabrication Inc .... G 513 353-4617
Hamilton *(G-10755)*

▼ W J Egli Company Inc .... F 330 823-3666
Alliance *(G-551)*

Waino Sheet Metal Inc .... E 330 945-4226
Stow *(G-17816)*

Warner Fabricating Inc .... F 330 848-3191
Wadsworth *(G-19443)*

◆ Warren Fabricating Corporation .... D 330 847-0596
Warren *(G-19621)*

Waterville Sheet Metal Company .... E 419 878-5050
Waterville *(G-19670)*

Weber Technologies Inc .... E 440 946-8833
Eastlake *(G-9297)*

Wheeler Sheet Metal Inc .... G 419 668-0481
Norwalk *(G-15566)*

▲ Will-Burt Company .... B 330 682-7015
Orrville *(G-15770)*

William Weber .... G 440 350-9397
Painesville *(G-15941)*

Wolf Metals Inc .... G 614 461-6361
Columbus *(G-7768)*

Worthington Steel Company .... G 513 702-0130
Middletown *(G-14100)*

▲ Ysd Industries Inc .... D 330 792-6521
Youngstown *(G-21260)*

Z Line Kitchen and Bath LLC .... G 614 777-5004
Marysville *(G-12977)*

3446 Architectural & Ornamental Metal Work

A & E Butscha Co .... G 513 761-1919
Cincinnati *(G-3329)*

▲ A & G Manufacturing Co Inc .... E 419 468-7433
Galion *(G-10250)*

A & T Ornamental Iron Company .... G 937 859-6006
Miamisburg *(G-13778)*

▲ Agratronix LLC .... E 330 562-2222
Streetsboro *(G-17834)*

Akron Products Company .... F 330 576-1750
Wadsworth *(G-19391)*

All Ohio Companies Inc .... F 216 420-9274
Cleveland *(G-4756)*

Alumina Rling Cstm Ir Wrks Inc .... E 513 353-1116
Cleves *(G-6506)*

Annin & Co .... D 740 622-4447
Coshocton *(G-7878)*

Architect Louvers .... G 513 541-5364
Cincinnati *(G-3411)*

▲ Armor Consolidated Inc .... E 513 923-5260
Mason *(G-12982)*

▲ Armor Metal Group Mason Inc .... C 513 769-0700
Mason *(G-12983)*

Art Fremont Iron Co .... G 419 332-5554
Fremont *(G-10125)*

▲ AT&f Advanced Metals LLC .... E 330 684-1122
Cleveland *(G-4851)*

Autogate Inc .... E 419 588-2796
Berlin Heights *(G-1660)*

Bauer Corporation .... E 800 321-4760
Wooster *(G-20746)*

Beacon Metal Fabricators Inc .... F 216 391-7444
Cleveland *(G-4900)*

Beauty Cft Met Fabricators Inc .... F 440 439-0710
Bedford *(G-1405)*

Blevins Metal Fabrication Inc .... E 419 522-6082
Mansfield *(G-12567)*

Brown-Campbell Company .... E 513 860-3564
Fairfield *(G-9647)*

Brown-Campbell Company .... F 216 332-0101
Maple Heights *(G-12729)*

Chc Manufacturing Inc .... E 513 821-7757
Cincinnati *(G-3525)*

Chc Manufacturing Inc .... G 614 527-1606
Columbus *(G-6923)*

City Iron LLC .... E 513 721-5678
Cincinnati *(G-3580)*

Courtad Inc .... G 330 274-3100
Aurora *(G-913)*

Cozmyk Enterprises Inc .... F 614 231-1370
Columbus *(G-6994)*

Cramers Inc .... E 330 477-4571
Canton *(G-2670)*

Debra-Kuempel Inc .... D 513 271-6500
Cincinnati *(G-3645)*

Decor Architectural Products .... G 419 537-9493
Toledo *(G-18432)*

Dover Tank and Plate Company .... E 330 343-4443
Dover *(G-8982)*

E B P Inc .... E 216 241-2550
Cleveland *(G-5230)*

E C S Corp .... F 440 323-1707
Elyria *(G-9409)*

Elwers Fence .... G 419 221-2511
Lima *(G-12009)*

Federal Iron Works Company .... E 330 482-5910
Columbiana *(G-6616)*

Final Touch Metal Fabricating .... G 216 348-1750
Cleveland *(G-5345)*

Finelli Ornamental Iron Co .... F 440 248-0050
Cleveland *(G-5347)*

Fortin Welding & Mfg Inc .... E 614 291-4342
Columbus *(G-7094)*

Friends Ornamental Iron Co .... G 216 431-6710
Cleveland *(G-5382)*

Geist Co Inc .... F 216 771-2200
Cleveland *(G-5406)*

Gem City Metal Tech LLC .... E 937 252-8998
Dayton *(G-8362)*

Gem Ornamental Iron Co .... G 216 661-6965
Cleveland *(G-5408)*

GL Nause Co Inc .... E 513 722-9500
Loveland *(G-12353)*

Glas Ornamental Metals Inc .... G 330 753-0215
Barberton *(G-1118)*

Graber Metal Works Inc .... E 440 237-8422
North Royalton *(G-15422)*

◆ Granite Industries Inc .... D 419 445-4733
Archbold *(G-679)*

▲ Gwp Holdings Inc .... D 513 860-4050
Fairfield *(G-9662)*

Hansen Scaffolding LLC .... F 513 574-9000
West Chester *(G-20012)*

Harsco Corporation .... E 740 387-1150
Marion *(G-12873)*

Hart & Cooley Inc .... C 937 832-7800
Englewood *(G-9522)*

Hayes Bros Ornamental Ir Works .... F 419 531-1491
Toledo *(G-18498)*

Hrh Door Corp .... C 330 828-2291
Dalton *(G-8070)*

Indian Creek Fabricators Inc .... E 937 667-7214
Tipp City *(G-18283)*

J N Linrose Mfg LLC .... E 513 867-5500
Hamilton *(G-10709)*

J S Stairs .... G 440 632-5680
Middlefield *(G-13946)*

James C Denier Co Inc .... G 513 385-6272
Cincinnati *(G-3939)*

James L Wereb .... G 440 942-2405
Willoughby *(G-20515)*

Jason Incorporated .... F 513 860-3400
Hamilton *(G-10711)*

Jerry Harolds Doors Unlimited .... G 740 635-4949
Bridgeport *(G-2090)*

Jim Denigris & Sons Ldscpg .... G 440 449-5548
Cleveland *(G-5615)*

John A & William J Wiechart .... G 419 647-4617
Spencerville *(G-17461)*

Joyce Manufacturing Co .... D 440 239-9100
Berea *(G-1624)*

L & L Ornamental Iron Co .... F 513 353-1930
Cleves *(G-6520)*

Lakeway Mfg Inc .... E 419 433-3030
Huron *(G-11232)*

▲ Langdon Inc .... E 513 733-5955
Cincinnati *(G-4011)*

Lifetime Ironworks LLC .... G 419 443-0567
Tiffin *(G-18227)*

M F Y Inc .... F 330 747-1334
Youngstown *(G-21137)*

M M I Services Inc .... F 440 259-2939
Perry *(G-16053)*

Mack Iron Works Company .... E 419 626-3712
Sandusky *(G-16984)*

▲ Mataco .... G 440 546-8355
Broadview Heights *(G-2114)*

Metal Craft Docks Inc .... G 440 286-7135
Mentor *(G-13653)*

Metal Maintenance Inc .... F 513 661-3300
Cleves *(G-6521)*

Michaels Pre-Cast Con Pdts .... F 513 683-1292
Loveland *(G-12374)*

Modern Builders Supply Inc .... C 330 729-2690
Youngstown *(G-21147)*

◆ Momentive Prfmce Mtls Qrtz Inc .... C 440 878-5700
Strongsville *(G-17941)*

National Stair Corp .... E 937 325-1347
Springfield *(G-17611)*

Newman Brothers Inc ....E 513 242-0011
Cincinnati (G-4151)

▼ Ohio Gratings Inc ....B 330 477-6707
Canton (G-2799)

One Wish LLC ....F 800 505-6883
Beachwood (G-1289)

P & L Metalcrafts LLC ....F 330 793-2178
Youngstown (G-21160)

Phase II Enterprises Inc ....G 330 484-2113
Canton (G-2812)

Quality Architectural and Fabr ......F 937 743-2923
Franklin (G-10046)

Quality Security Door & Mfg Co ......G 440 246-0770
Lorain (G-12269)

Randy Lewis Inc ....F 330 784-0456
Akron (G-365)

Rezmann Karoly ....G 216 441-4357
Cleveland (G-6110)

Royalton Archtctral Fbrication ......F 440 582-0400
North Royalton (G-15447)

▲ Sausser Steel Company Inc ......F 419 422-9632
Findlay (G-9888)

Schwab Welding Inc ....G 513 353-4262
Cincinnati (G-4390)

Security Fence Group Inc ....E 513 681-3700
Cincinnati (G-4395)

Sewah Studios Inc ....F 740 373-2087
Marietta (G-12827)

Sine Wall LLC ....G 919 453-2011
West Chester (G-19946)

◆ Sky Climber LLC......................E 740 203-3900
Delaware (G-8888)

Sky Climber Wind Solutions LLC ......F 740 203-3900
Delaware (G-8890)

Southern Ornamental Iron Co........G 937 278-4319
Dayton (G-8663)

◆ Spallinger Millwright Svc Co ......D 419 225-5830
Lima (G-12094)

◆ Spillman Company ....E 614 444-2184
Columbus (G-7644)

Stephens Pipe & Steel LLC ....C 740 869-2257
Mount Sterling (G-14604)

Swanton Wldg Machining Co Inc ......D 419 826-4816
Swanton (G-18091)

T E Martindale Enterprises ....G 614 253-6826
Columbus (G-7673)

Taflan Steel & Welding Inc ....G 740 635-0841
Bridgeport (G-2093)

Tarrier Steel Company Inc............E 614 444-4000
Columbus (G-7679)

Tim Calvin Access Controls ....G 740 494-4200
Radnor (G-16508)

Triangle Precision Industries ....D 937 299-6776
Dayton (G-8723)

Upright Steel LLC ....E 216 923-0852
Cleveland (G-6396)

Upside Innovations LLC ....G 513 889-2492
West Chester (G-20065)

Van Dyke Custom Iron Inc............G 614 860-9300
Columbus (G-7732)

Viking Fabricators Inc ....E 740 374-5246
Marietta (G-12848)

Wanner Metal Worx Inc ....F 740 369-4034
Delaware (G-8894)

Wendell August Gift Sp & Forge ......F 330 893-3713
Berlin (G-1653)

▼ Wooster Products Inc ....D 330 264-2844
Wooster (G-20850)

Wooster Products Inc ....G 330 264-2854
Wooster (G-20851)

Worthington Cnstr Group Inc ....G 216 472-1511
Cleveland (G-6481)

Worthington Mid-Rise Cnstr Inc ......E 216 472-1511
Cleveland (G-6482)

Wright Brothers Inc ....F 513 731-2222
Cincinnati (G-4606)

3448 Prefabricated Metal Buildings & Cmpnts

Affordable Barn Co Ltd ....F 330 674-3001
Millersburg (G-14190)

American Steel Carports Inc ....F 419 737-1331
Pioneer (G-16232)

Amto Acquisition Corp ....F 419 347-1185
Shelby (G-17131)

Barncraft Storage Buildings ....G 513 738-5654
Hamilton (G-10672)

▲ Benchmark Archtectural Systems ....E 614 444-0110
Columbus (G-6821)

▼ Benko Products Inc ....E 440 934-2180
Sheffield Village (G-17121)

Better Built Barns ....G 606 348-6146
Winchester (G-20690)

Better Living Sunrooms NW Ohio ......G 419 692-4526
Delphos (G-8902)

C Green & Sons Incorporated ....F 740 745-2998
Saint Louisville (G-16826)

Commercial Dock & Door Inc ....E 440 951-1210
Mentor (G-13550)

Consoldted Grnhse Slutions LLC ......G 330 844-8598
Strongsville (G-17907)

Consolidatd Analytical Sys Inc ......F 513 542-1200
Cleves (G-6511)

Cover Up Building Systems ....G 740 668-8985
Martinsburg (G-12929)

◆ Cropking Incorporated ....F 330 302-4203
Lodi (G-12159)

▲ Enclosure Suppliers LLC ....E 513 782-3900
Cincinnati (G-3701)

Golden Giant Inc ....G 419 674-4038
Kenton (G-11547)

Great Day Improvements LLC ....G 330 468-0700
Macedonia (G-12456)

Haz-Safe LLC ....F 330 793-0900
Austintown (G-974)

▲ Hoge Lumber Company ....E 419 753-2263
New Knoxville (G-14836)

Homecare Mattress Inc ....F 937 746-2556
Franklin (G-10027)

Jack Walters & Sons Corp ....F 937 653-8986
Urbana (G-19164)

▼ Jet Dock Systems Inc ....E 216 750-2264
Cleveland (G-5613)

Jh Industries Inc ....E 330 963-4105
Twinsburg (G-18961)

Joyce Manufacturing Co ....D 440 239-9100
Berea (G-1624)

Lab-Pro Inc ....G 937 434-9600
Dayton (G-8450)

Ludy Greenhouse Mfg Corp ....D 800 255-5839
New Madison (G-14870)

Metal Craft Docks Inc ....G 440 286-7135
Mentor (G-13653)

▼ Metal Seal Precision Ltd ....C 440 205-0016
Mentor (G-13654)

Mobile Mini Inc ....E 303 305-9515
Canton (G-2783)

Mobile Mini Inc ....E 513 353-9800
Fairfield (G-9686)

Mobile Mini Inc ....F 614 449-8655
Columbus (G-7360)

Morton Buildings Inc ....F 330 345-6188
Wooster (G-20812)

Morton Buildings Inc ....F 740 783-2331
Caldwell (G-2430)

Morton Buildings Inc ....E 419 673-0741
Kenton (G-11560)

Morton Buildings Inc ....D 419 675-2311
Kenton (G-11561)

Nci Building Systems Inc ....C 937 584-3300
Middletown (G-14069)

ONeals Tarpaulin & Awning Co ....F 330 788-6504
Youngstown (G-21157)

Otter Group LLC ....F 937 315-1199
Dayton (G-8554)

Overhead Door Corporation ....F 419 294-3874
Upper Sandusky (G-19138)

Patton Aluminum Products Inc ....F 937 845-9404
New Carlisle (G-14811)

Pei Liquidation Company ....E 615 781-5020
Macedonia (G-12471)

▲ Pei Liquidation Company ....G 330 467-4267
Macedonia (G-12470)

R L Torbeck Industries Inc ....D 513 367-0080
Harrison (G-10800)

Rayhaven Group Inc ....F 330 659-3183
Richfield (G-16634)

Rebsco Inc ....F 937 548-2246
Greenville (G-10517)

◆ Rough Brothers Mfg Inc ....D 513 242-0310
Cincinnati (G-4360)

Rupcol Inc ....F 419 924-5215
West Unity (G-20135)

Shrock Prefab LLC ....F 740 599-9401
Danville (G-8091)

Skyline Corporation ....C 330 852-2483
Sugarcreek (G-18039)

Sorta 4 U LLC ....G 440 365-0091
Elyria (G-9495)

St Marys Iron Works Inc ....F 419 300-6300
Saint Marys (G-16857)

Storage Buildings Unlimited ....G 216 731-0010
Doylestown (G-9030)

Superior Structures Inc ....F 513 942-5954
Harrison (G-10807)

Upside Innovations LLC ....G 513 889-2492
West Chester (G-20065)

Vinyl Tech Storage Barn ....G 330 674-5670
Millersburg (G-14278)

Will-Burt Advnced Cmpsites Inc......F 330 684-5286
Orrville (G-15769)

Wyse Industrial Carts Inc ....F 419 923-7353
Wauseon (G-19702)

3449 Misc Structural Metal Work

Action Group Inc ....D 614 868-8868
Blacklick (G-1686)

Advance Industrial Mfg Inc ....E 614 871-3333
Grove City (G-10539)

Akron Rebar Co ....E 330 745-7100
Akron (G-54)

Alpha Control LLC ....F 740 377-3400
South Point (G-17431)

American Roll Formed Pdts Corp .....C 440 352-0753
Painesville (G-15851)

Arcelormittal USA LLC ....F 740 375-2299
Marion (G-12856)

Architctral Rfuse Slutions LLC ....G 330 733-3996
Akron (G-72)

Arrow Tru-Line Inc ....D 419 636-7013
Bryan (G-2279)

Austintown Metal Works Inc ....F 330 259-4673
Youngstown (G-21028)

BMA Metals Group Inc ....G 513 874-5152
West Chester (G-19819)

Bridge Components Incorporated ......G 614 873-0777
Columbus (G-6858)

Buckeye Stamping Company ....D 614 445-0059
Columbus (G-6875)

Burghardt Metal Fabg Inc ....F 330 794-1830
Akron (G-104)

CMF Custom Metal Finishers ....G 513 821-8145
Cincinnati (G-3592)

▲ Concast Birmingham Inc ....D 440 965-4455
Wakeman (G-19446)

Custom Manufacturing Solutions ......E 937 372-0777
Dayton (G-8259)

Dan Novak ....G 440 269-1741
Willoughby (G-20469)

Ej Usa Inc ....F 330 782-3900
Youngstown (G-21076)

Fabrication Group LLC ....E 216 251-1125
Cleveland (G-5318)

Falcon Fab and Finishes LLC ....G 740 820-4458
Lucasville (G-12420)

Formasters Corporation ....F 440 639-9206
Mentor (G-13580)

Fortin Welding & Mfg Inc ....G 614 291-4342
Columbus (G-7094)

▲ Foundation Systems Anchors Inc ....E 330 454-1700
Canton (G-2707)

Friesingers Inc ....G 740 452-9480
Zanesville (G-21312)

Gateway Concrete Forming Svcs ......D 513 353-2000
Miamitown (G-13887)

Hartford Steel Sales ....G 513 275-1744
Hamilton (G-10703)

Harvey Brothers Inc ....F 513 541-2622
Cincinnati (G-3868)

▲ Hynes Industries Inc ....C 330 799-3221
Youngstown (G-21111)

J & L Welding Fabricating Inc.........F 330 393-9353
Warren (G-19561)

L B Steel Plate ....G 440 893-0680
Chagrin Falls (G-3062)

Lion Industries LLC ....E 740 699-0012
Saint Clairsville (G-16794)

Lwr Enterprises Inc ....G 740 984-0036
Waterford (G-19650)

▲ Markley Enterprises LLC ....E 513 771-1290
Cincinnati (G-4061)

Matteo Aluminum Inc ....E 440 585-5213
Wickliffe (G-20372)

Meibuhr Co Inc ....G 440 942-9375
Willoughby (G-20543)

Melinz-Rebar Inc ....E 216 531-8988
Cleveland (G-5781)

Metal Sales Manufacturing Corp ......F 440 576-9070
Jefferson (G-11367)

Metrodeck Inc .... F 513 541-4370
Cincinnati *(G-4095)*

Midwest Curtainwalls Inc .... D 216 641-7900
Cleveland *(G-5809)*

Mk Metal Products Inc .... E 419 756-3644
Mansfield *(G-12650)*

Mound Steel Corp .... E 937 748-2937
Springboro *(G-17490)*

Mound Technologies Inc .... E 937 748-2937
Springboro *(G-17491)*

▼ Ohio Bridge Corporation .... C 740 432-6334
Cambridge *(G-2470)*

Omco Holdings Inc .... E 440 944-2100
Wickliffe *(G-20375)*

Ontario Mechanical LLC .... E 419 529-2578
Ontario *(G-15691)*

Sarka Shtmtl & Fabrication Inc .... E 419 447-4377
Tiffin *(G-18242)*

Scs Construction Services Inc .... E 513 929-0260
Cincinnati *(G-4393)*

Simcote Inc .... E 740 382-5000
Marion *(G-12902)*

Skinner Sales Group Inc .... E 440 572-8455
Strongsville *(G-17966)*

Smith Brothers Erection Inc .... E 740 373-3575
Marietta *(G-12832)*

Steel Structures of Ohio LLC .... E 330 374-9900
Akron *(G-417)*

Steel Warehouse Company LLC .... E 216 206-2800
Cleveland *(G-6245)*

Steelcon Inc .... F 330 457-2419
New Waterford *(G-14974)*

Superior Steel Service LLC .... F 513 724-0437
Batavia *(G-1227)*

Tallmadge Spinning & Metal Co .... F 330 794-2277
Akron *(G-427)*

Trulite GL Alum Solutions LLC .... D 614 876-1057
Columbus *(G-7712)*

Ventari Corporation .... E 937 278-4269
Miamisburg *(G-13874)*

▲ Ver-Mac Industries Inc .... F 740 397-6511
Mount Vernon *(G-14654)*

Veterans Steel Inc .... F 216 938-7476
Cleveland *(G-6412)*

◆ Watteredge LLC .... D 440 933-6110
Avon Lake *(G-1055)*

Will-Burt Company .... E 330 682-7015
Orrville *(G-15772)*

▲ Will-Burt Company .... B 330 682-7015
Orrville *(G-15770)*

Worthington Industries Inc .... C 614 438-3210
Worthington *(G-20896)*

Wt Acquisition Company Ltd .... E 513 577-7980
Cincinnati *(G-4610)*

YKK AP America Inc .... F 513 942-7200
West Chester *(G-20071)*

Zelcor Group LLC .... G 419 592-0803
Napoleon *(G-14702)*

3451 Screw Machine Prdts

Abco Bar & Tube Cutting Svc .... E 513 697-9487
Maineville *(G-12520)*

Abel Fbrction Prcsion Pdts Inc .... F 513 681-5000
Cincinnati *(G-3344)*

Abel Manufacturing Company .... F 513 681-5000
Cincinnati *(G-3345)*

Accuracy Products Inc .... F 937 454-2240
Dayton *(G-8132)*

Adams Automatic Inc .... F 440 235-4416
Olmsted Falls *(G-15672)*

Alco Manufacturing .... G 440 322-9166
Amherst *(G-590)*

All-Craft Wellman Products .... F 440 946-9646
Willoughby *(G-20428)*

Amco Products Inc .... F 937 433-7982
Kettering *(G-11575)*

Amerascrew Inc .... E 419 522-2232
Mansfield *(G-12559)*

American Aero Components LLC .... G 937 367-5068
Dayton *(G-8150)*

Amt Machine Systems Limited .... F 740 965-2693
Columbus *(G-6747)*

▲ Ashley F Ward Inc .... C 513 398-1414
Mason *(G-12984)*

Atlas Machine Products Co .... G 216 228-3688
Cleveland *(G-4855)*

▲ Automatic Screw Products Co .... G 216 241-7896
Cleveland *(G-4868)*

Blc Precision Machine Co Inc .... F 937 783-1406
Blanchester *(G-1710)*

Bronco Machine Inc .... F 440 951-5015
Willoughby *(G-20446)*

Bront Machining Inc .... E 937 228-4551
Moraine *(G-14470)*

Chardon Metal Products Co .... E 440 285-2147
Chardon *(G-3144)*

Clear Creek Screw Machine Corp .... G 740 969-2113
Amanda *(G-562)*

Condo Inc .... G 330 505-0485
Niles *(G-15148)*

Condo Incorporated .... D 330 609-6021
Warren *(G-19537)*

CT Ferry Screw Products I .... G 440 871-1617
Cleveland *(G-5145)*

D L Salkil LLC .... G 419 841-3341
Toledo *(G-18424)*

▲ Day-Hio Products Inc .... E 937 445-0782
Dayton *(G-8267)*

Dove Machine Inc .... F 440 864-2645
Columbia Station *(G-6589)*

Dunham Products Inc .... F 440 232-0885
Walton Hills *(G-19473)*

Eastlake Machine Products Inc .... F 440 953-1014
Willoughby *(G-20479)*

Efficient Machine Pdts Corp .... F 440 268-0205
Strongsville *(G-17915)*

Elgin Fastener Group LLC .... E 216 481-4400
Cleveland *(G-5271)*

Elliott Oren Products Inc .... F 419 298-0015
Edgerton *(G-9328)*

Elliott Oren Products Inc .... F 419 298-2306
Edgerton *(G-9329)*

▲ Elyria Manufacturing Corp .... D 440 365-4171
Elyria *(G-9413)*

Engels Machining LLC .... G 419 485-1500
Montpelier *(G-14445)*

Engstrom Manufacturing Inc .... E 513 573-0010
Mason *(G-13017)*

Eureka Screw Machine Pdts Co .... G 216 883-1715
Cleveland *(G-5304)*

Fair Field Machine Products .... F 740 756-4409
Carroll *(G-2941)*

Fairfield Machined Products .... F 740 756-4409
Carroll *(G-2942)*

Fairfield Screw Products Co .... G 740 653-7627
Lancaster *(G-11714)*

Falmer Screw Pdts & Mfg Inc .... F 330 758-0593
Youngstown *(G-21082)*

▲ Flash Industrial Tech Ltd .... G 440 786-8979
Cleveland *(G-5353)*

Forrest Machine Pdts Co Ltd .... F 419 589-3774
Mansfield *(G-12607)*

Fostoria Machine Products .... G 419 435-4262
Fostoria *(G-9977)*

Gent Machine Company .... F 216 481-2334
Cleveland *(G-5423)*

Global Precision Parts Inc .... D 419 453-0010
Ottoville *(G-15821)*

Global Precision Parts Inc .... G 260 563-9030
Van Wert *(G-19258)*

Great Lakes Defense Svcs LLC .... G 216 272-3450
University Heights *(G-19109)*

Gtd Machine Inc .... G 440 812-6877
Mentor *(G-13597)*

H & E Machine Company .... F 614 443-7635
Columbus *(G-7133)*

H & S Precision Screw Pdts Inc .... E 937 437-0316
New Paris *(G-14880)*

H & W Screw Products Inc .... F 937 866-2577
Franklin *(G-10026)*

Hamco Manufacturing Inc .... G 440 774-1637
Oberlin *(G-15643)*

Harding Machine Acquisition Co .... D 937 666-3031
East Liberty *(G-9201)*

Hebco Products Inc .... A 419 562-7987
Bucyrus *(G-2347)*

Heller Machine Products Inc .... G 216 281-2951
Cleveland *(G-5496)*

Hept Machine Inc .... G 937 890-5633
Vandalia *(G-19294)*

Hi-Tech Solutions LLC .... G 216 331-3050
Cleveland *(G-5511)*

Houston Machine Products Inc .... E 937 322-8022
Springfield *(G-17577)*

▲ Hy-Production Inc .... C 330 273-2400
Valley City *(G-19206)*

▲ Hyland Machine Company .... E 937 233-8600
Dayton *(G-8399)*

Ilsco Corporation .... E 513 367-9100
Harrison *(G-10785)*

Integrity Manufacturing Corp .... E 937 233-6792
Dayton *(G-8413)*

J & M Cutting Tools Inc .... G 440 622-3900
Mentor *(G-13615)*

JAD Machine Company Inc .... F 419 256-6332
Malinta *(G-12535)*

Karma Metal Products Inc .... F 419 524-4371
Mansfield *(G-12632)*

▲ Kernells Autmtc Machining Inc .... E 419 588-2164
Berlin Heights *(G-1662)*

Kohut Enterprises Inc .... G 440 366-6666
Independence *(G-11263)*

Krausher Machining Inc .... G 440 839-2828
Wakeman *(G-19449)*

Krist Krenz Machine Inc .... D 440 237-1800
North Royalton *(G-15431)*

Kts-Met Bar Products Inc .... G 440 288-9308
Lorain *(G-12252)*

▲ Lake Erie Industries LLC .... G 216 255-1867
Lakewood *(G-11671)*

Lear Manufacturing Inc .... G 440 327-4545
North Ridgeville *(G-15387)*

Lehner Screw Machine LLC .... E 330 688-6616
Munroe Falls *(G-14662)*

Lenco Industries Inc .... E 937 277-9364
Dayton *(G-8455)*

Machine Tek Systems Inc .... E 330 527-4450
Garrettsville *(G-10329)*

Magnetic Screw Machine Pdts .... G 937 348-2807
Marysville *(G-12956)*

Mansfield Screw Mch Pdts Co .... D 419 884-1511
Mansfield *(G-12644)*

Maumee Machine & Tool Corp .... E 419 385-2501
Toledo *(G-18578)*

McDaniel Products Inc .... F 440 967-5630
Vermilion *(G-19333)*

McDaniel Products Inc .... E 419 524-5841
Mansfield *(G-12645)*

Meistermatic Inc .... D 216 481-7773
Chesterland *(G-3214)*

Mettlr-Tledo Globl Hldings LLC .... G 614 438-4511
Columbus *(G-6655)*

Midwest Precision LLC .... D 440 951-2333
Eastlake *(G-9282)*

▲ Morgal Machine Tool Co .... D 937 325-5561
Springfield *(G-17607)*

Mosher Machine & Tool Co Inc .... E 937 258-8070
Dayton *(G-8511)*

Murray Machine & Tool Inc .... G 216 267-1126
Cleveland *(G-5841)*

▲ Nook Industries Inc .... C 216 271-7900
Cleveland *(G-5887)*

Obars Machine and Tool Company ...... E 419 535-6307
Toledo *(G-18613)*

Ohio Machined Products Inc .... F 419 264-2400
Holgate *(G-11038)*

Ohio Metal Products Company .... E 937 228-6101
Dayton *(G-8545)*

Ohio Screw Products Inc .... D 440 322-6341
Elyria *(G-9472)*

Paramont Machine Company LLC .... E 330 339-3489
New Philadelphia *(G-14921)*

Parker-Hannifin Corporation .... D 218 534-3148
Wickliffe *(G-20380)*

▲ Pfi Precision Inc .... E 937 845-3563
New Carlisle *(G-14812)*

Phoenix Tool & Thread Grindng .... G 216 433-7008
Cleveland *(G-6004)*

Pike Machine Products Co .... E 216 731-1880
Euclid *(G-9597)*

Port Clinton Manufacturing LLC .... E 419 734-2141
Port Clinton *(G-16409)*

▲ Precision Fittings LLC .... E 440 647-4143
Wellington *(G-19752)*

Profile Grinding Inc .... E 216 351-0600
Cleveland *(G-6055)*

Qcsm LLC .... G 216 531-5960
Euclid *(G-9602)*

R T & T Machining Co Inc .... F 440 974-8479
Mentor *(G-13714)*

R W Screw Products Inc .... C 330 837-9211
Massillon *(G-13198)*

Raka Corporation .... D 419 476-6572
Toledo *(G-18671)*

Richland Screw Mch Pdts Inc .... E 419 524-1272
Mansfield *(G-12672)*

Rite Machine Inc .... G 216 267-6911
Cleveland *(G-6114)*

Roehlers Machine Products .... G 937 354-4401
Mount Victory *(G-14659)*

Rtsi LLC ....G....440 542-3066 Solon *(G-17373)*
Rural Products Inc ....G....419 298-2677 Edgerton *(G-9335)*
S & S Machining Ltd ....F....419 524-9525 Mansfield *(G-12675)*
▲ **Semtorq Inc** ....F....330 487-0600 Twinsburg *(G-19019)*
Shanafelt Manufacturing Co ....E....330 455-0315 Canton *(G-2847)*
▲ **Slabe Machine Products Co** ....D....440 946-6555 Willoughby *(G-20599)*
Southern Adhsives Coatings Inc ....G....513 561-8440 Cincinnati *(G-4438)*
Stadco Inc ....E....937 878-0911 Fairborn *(G-9630)*
▲ **Standby Screw Machine Pdts Co** ....B....440 243-8200 Berea *(G-1635)*
Star Screw Machine Products ....G....216 361-0307 Cleveland *(G-6238)*
State Machine Co Inc ....G....440 248-1050 Cleveland *(G-6240)*
▲ **Summit Machine Ltd** ....E....330 628-2663 Mogadore *(G-14386)*
Superior Bar Products Inc ....G....419 784-2590 Defiance *(G-8811)*
▼ **Superior Products Llc** ....D....216 651-9400 Cleveland *(G-6269)*
Supply Technologies LLC ....D....740 363-1971 Delaware *(G-8891)*
Swagelok Hy-Level Company ....C....440 238-1260 Strongsville *(G-17975)*
Swivel-Tek Industries LLC ....G....419 636-7770 Bryan *(G-2322)*
Toledo Automatic Screw Co ....G....419 726-3441 Toledo *(G-18729)*
Toledo Screw Products Inc ....G....419 841-3341 Toledo *(G-18741)*
Tri-K Enterprises Inc ....G....330 832-7380 Canton *(G-2882)*
Triangle Machine Products Co ....E....216 524-5872 Cleveland *(G-6361)*
Trojon Gear Inc ....F....937 254-1737 Dayton *(G-8729)*
Troy Manufacturing Co ....E....440 834-8262 Burton *(G-2388)*
Twin Valley Metalcraft Asm LLC ....G....937 787-4634 West Alexandria *(G-19784)*
United Auto Worker AFL CIO ....F....419 592-0434 Napoleon *(G-14701)*
Valley Tool & Die Inc ....D....440 237-0160 North Royalton *(G-15458)*
Vanamatic Company ....D....419 692-6085 Delphos *(G-8927)*
Vinco Machine Products Inc ....G....216 475-6708 Cleveland *(G-6420)*
Vulcan Products Co Inc ....F....419 468-1039 Galion *(G-10290)*
Warren Screw Machine Inc ....E....330 609-6020 Warren *(G-19623)*
Watters Manufacturing Co Inc ....G....216 281-8600 Cleveland *(G-6451)*
▲ **Whirlaway Corporation** ....C....440 647-4711 Wellington *(G-19758)*
Whirlaway Corporation ....C....440 647-4711 Wellington *(G-19759)*
Whirlaway Corporation ....E....440 647-4711 Wellington *(G-19760)*
Whiteford Industries Inc ....F....419 381-1155 Toledo *(G-18774)*
Wood-Sebring Corporation ....G....216 267-3191 Cleveland *(G-6475)*
Z and M Screw Machine Products ....G....330 467-5822 Garrettsville *(G-10337)*

3452 Bolts, Nuts, Screws, Rivets & Washers

Abco Bar & Tube Cutting Svc ....E....513 697-9487 Maineville *(G-12520)*
Airfasco Inc ....E....330 430-6190 Canton *(G-2591)*
Airfasco Inds Fstner Group LLC ....E....330 430-6190 Canton *(G-2592)*
▲ **Akko Fastener Inc** ....E....513 489-8300 Blue Ash *(G-1738)*
▲ **Altenloh Brinck & Co Inc** ....C....419 636-6715 Bryan *(G-2276)*
▲ **Altenloh Brinck & Co US Inc** ....D....419 636-6715 Bryan *(G-2277)*
▲ **Amanda Manufacturing** ....C....740 385-6893 Logan *(G-12171)*
Ampex Metal Products Company ....E....216 267-9242 Brookpark *(G-2151)*
Andre Corporation ....E....574 293-0207 Mason *(G-12981)*
▲ **Atlas Bolt & Screw Company LLC** ....C....419 289-6171 Ashland *(G-709)*
Auto Bolt Company ....E....216 881-3913 Cleveland *(G-4862)*
Bowes Manufacturing Inc ....F....216 378-2110 Solon *(G-17271)*
Brainard Rivet Company ....E....330 545-4931 Girard *(G-10383)*
Buck Eye Pressure Wash ....G....419 385-9274 Toledo *(G-18384)*
Capitol City Mfg Co Inc ....G....614 491-1192 Obetz *(G-15650)*
▲ **Cold Headed Fas Assemblies Inc** ....F....330 833-0800 Massillon *(G-13120)*
Cold Heading Co ....D....216 581-3000 Cleveland *(G-5097)*
Connell Limited Partnership ....D....877 534-8986 Northfield *(G-15464)*
Consolidated Metal Pdts Inc ....C....513 251-2624 Cincinnati *(G-3604)*
Core Manufacturing LLC ....G....440 946-8002 Mentor *(G-13552)*
▲ **Crawford Products Inc** ....E....614 890-1822 Columbus *(G-6999)*
Curtiss-Wright Flow Ctrl Corp ....D....216 267-3200 Cleveland *(G-5148)*
▲ **Dayton Superior Corporation** ....C....937 866-0711 Miamisburg *(G-13798)*
Die-Cut Products Co ....E....216 771-6994 Cleveland *(G-5193)*
▲ **Dimcogray Corporation** ....D....937 433-7600 Centerville *(G-3039)*
▲ **Dph Discount Pin Inc** ....G....740 264-2450 Steubenville *(G-17692)*
Edward W Daniel LLC ....E....440 647-1960 Wellington *(G-19742)*
Efg Holdings Inc ....G....812 717-2544 Brecksville *(G-2044)*
Elgin Fastener Group LLC ....E....440 717-7650 Brecksville *(G-2045)*
Elgin Fastener Group LLC ....E....216 481-4400 Cleveland *(G-5271)*
Elgin Fastener Group LLC ....F....812 717-2544 Brecksville *(G-2046)*
Emerson Electric Co ....E....513 631-6112 Cincinnati *(G-3697)*
Engstrom Manufacturing Inc ....F....513 573-0010 Mason *(G-13017)*
Express Trading Pins ....G....419 394-2550 Saint Marys *(G-16838)*
◆ **Facil North America Inc** ....C....330 487-2500 Twinsburg *(G-18934)*
Fastener Industries Inc ....E....440 891-2031 Berea *(G-1615)*
▲ **Ferry Cap & Set Screw Company** ....C....216 649-7400 Lakewood *(G-11664)*
Gauntlet Awards & Engraving ....G....937 890-5811 Dayton *(G-8357)*
General Plastex Inc ....E....330 745-7775 Barberton *(G-1117)*
Grntwrx LLC ....G....440 478-6160 Garrettsville *(G-10322)*
▲ **Group Industries Inc** ....E....216 271-0702 Cleveland *(G-5461)*
H G Schneider Company ....G....614 882-6944 Westerville *(G-20216)*
Hargis Industries LP ....E....513 874-5905 West Chester *(G-20013)*
▲ **Hexagon Industries Inc** ....E....216 249-0200 Cleveland *(G-5506)*
Hl Tecmetal Group Inc ....F....216 881-8100 Cleveland *(G-5510)*
Hudson Fasteners Inc ....G....330 270-9500 Youngstown *(G-21110)*
▲ **Industrial Nut Corp** ....D....419 625-8543 Sandusky *(G-16973)*
Ivan Extruders Co Inc ....G....330 644-7400 Akron *(G-237)*
Iwata Bolt USA Inc ....F....513 942-5050 Fairfield *(G-9669)*
◆ **Jacobson Mfg LLC** ....C....330 725-8853 Medina *(G-13429)*
Jacobson Mfg LLC ....G....740 467-3199 Millersport *(G-14295)*
Jacobson Mfg - Tiffin LLC ....D....419 447-2221 Tiffin *(G-18224)*
Jacodar Inc ....F....330 832-9557 Massillon *(G-13159)*
Jenco Manufacturing Inc ....E....216 898-9682 Independence *(G-11261)*
▲ **Jergens Inc** ....C....216 486-5540 Cleveland *(G-5610)*
Jerry Tools Inc ....F....513 242-3211 Cincinnati *(G-3944)*
▲ **Keystone Bolt & Nut Company** ....D....216 524-9626 Cleveland *(G-5652)*
Kre Inc ....F....216 883-1600 Twinsburg *(G-18967)*
Lapel Pins Unlimited LLC ....G....614 562-3218 Lewis Center *(G-11904)*
Lear Mfg Co Inc ....F....440 324-1111 Elyria *(G-9451)*
Long-Lok Fasteners Corporation ....E....513 772-1880 Cincinnati *(G-4032)*
M C Industries Inc ....F....440 355-4040 Lagrange *(G-11631)*
Master Products Company ....D....216 341-1740 Cleveland *(G-5760)*
▲ **Matdan Corporation** ....E....513 794-0500 Blue Ash *(G-1834)*
Microform Inc ....G....440 899-6339 Cleveland *(G-5799)*
Mid-West Fabricating Co ....G....740 681-4411 Lancaster *(G-11729)*
◆ **Mid-West Fabricating Co** ....C....740 969-4411 Amanda *(G-563)*
▲ **Miller Studio Inc** ....D....330 339-1100 New Philadelphia *(G-14916)*
◆ **Nelson Stud Welding Inc** ....B....440 329-0400 Elyria *(G-9467)*
North Coast Rivet Inc ....F....440 366-6829 Elyria *(G-9468)*
▲ **Nova Machine Products Inc** ....C....216 267-3200 Middleburg Heights *(G-13907)*
▲ **Ohashi Technica USA Inc** ....E....740 965-5115 Sunbury *(G-18070)*
Paine Falls Centerpin LLC ....G....440 298-3202 Thompson *(G-18189)*
Patchwork People Pins Etc ....G....937 725-2981 Clarksville *(G-4652)*
▲ **Paulin Industries Inc** ....E....216 433-7633 Parma *(G-15965)*
Pin Oak Development LLC ....G....440 933-9862 Avon Lake *(G-1043)*
Pin Oak Estates Ltd ....G....330 657-2727 Akron *(G-339)*
Pin Point Marketing LLC ....G....330 336-5863 Wadsworth *(G-19428)*
▲ **Precision Fittings LLC** ....E....440 647-4143 Wellington *(G-19752)*
Pressure Washer Mfrs Assn ....G....216 241-7333 Cleveland *(G-6045)*
Pro Roof Washers ....G....440 521-2622 Cleveland *(G-6051)*
Quality Concepts Telecom ....E....740 385-2003 Logan *(G-12191)*
R S Manufacturing Inc ....F....440 946-8002 Mentor *(G-13713)*
▲ **Ramco Specialties Inc** ....D....330 653-5135 Hudson *(G-11195)*
RB&w Manufacturing LLC ....G....740 363-1971 Delaware *(G-8881)*
▲ **RB&w Manufacturing LLC** ....F....234 380-8540 Streetsboro *(G-17870)*
Roehlers Machine Products ....G....937 354-4401 Mount Victory *(G-14659)*
Ronson Manufacturing Inc ....G....440 256-1463 Willoughby *(G-20590)*
Sabre Enterprises Inc ....G....216 941-9700 Cleveland *(G-6153)*
Saf-Holland Inc ....G....513 874-7888 West Chester *(G-20046)*
Senco Holdings Inc ....G....800 543-4596 Cincinnati *(G-3316)*
Simpson Strong-Tie Company Inc ....C....614 876-8060 Columbus *(G-7624)*
▲ **Smw Manufacturing** ....G....937 781-4945 Kettering *(G-11586)*
▲ **Solon Manufacturing Company** ....E....440 286-7149 Chardon *(G-3180)*
▲ **Stafast Products Inc** ....E....440 357-5546 Painesville *(G-15922)*
▲ **Stanley Industrial & Auto LLC** ....D....614 755-7000 Westerville *(G-20188)*
Steeramerica Inc ....F....330 563-4407 Uniontown *(G-19100)*

S I C

▲ Stelfast Inc ....E 440 879-0077
  Strongsville *(G-17974)*

Supply Technologies LLC ....F 614 759-9939
  Columbus *(G-7670)*

▲ Supply Technologies LLC ....C 440 947-2100
  Cleveland *(G-6274)*

▲ Telefast Industries Inc ....D 440 826-0011
  Berea *(G-1638)*

Tessec Manufacturing Svcs LLC .....E 937 985-3552
  Dayton *(G-8710)*

▲ Tinnerman Palnut Engineered PR ....E 330 220-5100
  Brunswick *(G-2263)*

Twin Ventures Inc ....F 330 405-3838
  Twinsburg *(G-19031)*

▲ United Titanium Inc ....C 330 264-2111
  Wooster *(G-20842)*

Valley Tool & Die Inc ....D 440 237-0160
  North Royalton *(G-15458)*

W-J Inc ....E 440 248-8282
  Solon *(G-17412)*

▲ Wallace Forge Company ....D 330 488-1203
  Canton *(G-2900)*

Wecall Inc ....G 440 437-8202
  Orwell *(G-15780)*

Wheel Group Holdings LLC ....G 614 253-6247
  Columbus *(G-7760)*

Wodin Inc ....E 440 439-4222
  Cleveland *(G-6474)*

3462 Iron & Steel Forgings

Akron Gear & Engineering Inc ....E 330 773-6608
  Akron *(G-45)*

Alliance Forging Group LLC ....F 330 680-4861
  Alliance *(G-494)*

Alta Mira Corporation ....D 330 648-2461
  Spencer *(G-17455)*

Anchor Flange Company ....F 513 527-4444
  Cincinnati *(G-3401)*

▲ Anchor Industries Incorporated ....E 440 473-1414
  Cleveland *(G-4803)*

Brooker Bros Forging Co Inc ....E 419 668-2535
  Norwalk *(G-15528)*

Buckeye Gear Co ....F 216 292-7998
  Chagrin Falls *(G-3078)*

Bula Forge & Machine Inc ....E 216 252-7600
  Cleveland *(G-4947)*

Cailin Dev Ltd Lblty Co ....F 216 408-6261
  Cleveland *(G-4962)*

◆ Canton Drop Forge Inc ....B 330 477-4511
  Canton *(G-2638)*

Carbo Forge Inc ....E 419 334-9788
  Fremont *(G-10134)*

Cincinnati Gearing Systems Inc ......C 513 527-8634
  Cincinnati *(G-3553)*

▲ Cleveland Hdwr & Forging Co ....E 216 641-5200
  Cleveland *(G-5064)*

Cleveland Hollow Boring Inc ....G 216 883-1926
  Cleveland *(G-5065)*

Cliffs High Performance ....G 740 397-2921
  Mount Vernon *(G-14616)*

▲ Colfor Manufacturing Inc ....B 330 863-0404
  Malvern *(G-12541)*

Colfor Manufacturing Inc ....C 330 863-0404
  Minerva *(G-14319)*

Cordier Group Holdings Inc ....G 330 477-4511
  Canton *(G-2669)*

Crum Manufacturing Inc ....E 419 878-9779
  Waterville *(G-19654)*

Dayton Forging Heat Treating ....D 937 253-4126
  Dayton *(G-8273)*

▲ Dayton Superior Corporation ....C 937 866-0711
  Miamisburg *(G-13798)*

Dependable Gear Corp ....G 440 942-4969
  Eastlake *(G-9264)*

Edgerton Forge Inc ....D 419 298-2333
  Edgerton *(G-9327)*

Edward W Daniel LLC ....E 440 647-1960
  Wellington *(G-19742)*

Engineered Metal Products ....G 740 446-9211
  Gallipolis *(G-10296)*

▲ Ferrotherm Corporation ....C 216 883-9350
  Cleveland *(G-5339)*

For Call Inc ....B 330 863-0404
  Malvern *(G-12544)*

Forge Products Corporation ....E 216 231-2600
  Cleveland *(G-5370)*

Forging Eqp Solutions Inc ....G 330 239-2222
  Medina *(G-13411)*

▼ Gam ....G 330 427-6470
  Leetonia *(G-11860)*

Gear Company of America Inc ....D 216 671-5400
  Cleveland *(G-5404)*

Geneva Gear & Machine Inc ....F 937 866-0318
  Dayton *(G-8363)*

GKN Sinter Metals LLC ....C 740 441-3203
  Gallipolis *(G-10298)*

Hand Screw Machine Co ....G 216 475-0220
  Stow *(G-17761)*

Ken Forging Inc ....C 440 993-8091
  Jefferson *(G-11364)*

King Forge and Machine Company ....F 330 963-0600
  Twinsburg *(G-18964)*

King-Indiana Forge Inc ....F 330 425-4250
  Twinsburg *(G-18965)*

Landerman Industries Inc ....E 440 233-4234
  Willoughby *(G-20525)*

Lange Precision Inc ....F 513 530-9500
  Blue Ash *(G-1824)*

Lextech Industries Ltd ....G 216 883-7900
  Cleveland *(G-5694)*

Martin Sprocket & Gear Inc ....D 419 485-5515
  Montpelier *(G-14448)*

▲ Master Bolt & Mfg Inc ....E 440 323-5529
  Elyria *(G-9459)*

Metal Forming & Coining Corp ....D 419 897-9530
  Maumee *(G-13281)*

Mid-West Forge Corporation ....C 216 481-3030
  Cleveland *(G-5806)*

▲ Ohio Metal Technologies Inc ....E 740 928-8288
  Hebron *(G-10879)*

Omnisource Corporation ....F 419 784-5669
  Defiance *(G-8808)*

◆ Park-Ohio Holdings Corp ....F 440 947-2000
  Cleveland *(G-5966)*

◆ Park-Ohio Industries Inc ....C 440 947-2000
  Cleveland *(G-5967)*

Park-Ohio Industries Inc ....E 216 431-2900
  Cleveland *(G-5968)*

Penn Machine Company ....F 814 288-1547
  Twinsburg *(G-18996)*

Performance Motorsports ....F 513 931-9999
  Cincinnati *(G-4226)*

Powers and Sons LLC ....D 419 737-2373
  Pioneer *(G-16240)*

Presrite Corporation ....B 216 441-5990
  Cleveland *(G-6043)*

Presrite Corporation ....C 440 576-0015
  Jefferson *(G-11369)*

Queen City Forging Company ....F 513 321-2003
  Cincinnati *(G-4316)*

▲ Romark Industries Inc ....G 440 333-5480
  Westlake *(G-20304)*

Rose Metal Industries LLC ....F 216 881-3355
  Cleveland *(G-6132)*

▲ Rotek Incorporated ....C 330 562-4000
  Aurora *(G-945)*

Rudd Equipment Company Inc ....E 513 321-7833
  Cincinnati *(G-4365)*

Satellite Gear Inc ....F 216 514-8668
  Cleveland *(G-6162)*

▲ Schaefer Equipment Inc ....D 330 372-4006
  Warren *(G-19598)*

Shot-Force Pro LLC ....G 740 753-3927
  Nelsonville *(G-14739)*

◆ Sifco Industries Inc ....B 216 881-8600
  Cleveland *(G-6201)*

Solmet Technologies Inc ....E 330 915-4160
  Canton *(G-2852)*

Stahl Gear & Machine Co ....E 216 431-2820
  Cleveland *(G-6231)*

◆ Summa Holdings Inc ....G 440 838-4700
  Cleveland *(G-6261)*

T & S Discount Tires Inc ....G 440 951-9084
  Willoughby *(G-20607)*

▲ T & W Forge LLC ....E 216 881-8600
  Alliance *(G-543)*

Tek Group International Inc ....E 330 706-0000
  Canal Fulton *(G-2515)*

▲ Tekfor Inc ....B 330 202-7420
  Wooster *(G-20840)*

▲ Tfo Tech Co Ltd ....C 740 426-6381
  Jeffersonville *(G-11382)*

TRM Manufacturing Inc ....E 330 769-2600
  Cuyahoga Falls *(G-8057)*

US Tsubaki Power Transm LLC ....D 419 626-4560
  Sandusky *(G-17019)*

▲ Wallace Forge Company ....D 330 488-1203
  Canton *(G-2900)*

Wendell August Gift Sp & Forge ....F 330 893-3713
  Berlin *(G-1653)*

Western Reserve Mfg Co ....G 216 641-0500
  Cleveland *(G-6459)*

Wodin Inc ....E 440 439-4222
  Cleveland *(G-6474)*

▲ Wright Tool Company ....C 330 848-0600
  Barberton *(G-1157)*

Wyman-Gordon Company ....E 216 341-0085
  Cleveland *(G-6485)*

3463 Nonferrous Forgings

Alcoa Inc ....A 216 641-3600
  Newburgh Heights *(G-15067)*

Arconic Inc ....A 216 641-3600
  Newburgh Heights *(G-15069)*

◆ Canton Drop Forge Inc ....B 330 477-4511
  Canton *(G-2638)*

Clarke Power Services Inc ....E 513 771-2200
  Cincinnati *(G-3583)*

▲ Cleveland Hdwr & Forging Co ....E 216 641-5200
  Cleveland *(G-5064)*

▲ Colfor Manufacturing Inc ....B 330 863-0404
  Malvern *(G-12541)*

Edward W Daniel LLC ....E 440 647-1960
  Wellington *(G-19742)*

Forge Products Corporation ....E 216 231-2600
  Cleveland *(G-5370)*

▼ Gateway Industries ....G 330 633-3700
  Akron *(G-199)*

▲ Guarantee Specialties Inc ....D 216 451-9744
  Strongsville *(G-17923)*

◆ Mansfield Plumbing Pdts LLC ....A 419 938-5211
  Perrysville *(G-16173)*

Ohio Conveyor and Supply Inc ....E 419 422-3825
  Findlay *(G-9870)*

▲ Ohio Star Forge Co ....E 330 847-6360
  Warren *(G-19583)*

Powers and Sons LLC ....D 419 737-2373
  Pioneer *(G-16240)*

▲ Rotek Incorporated ....C 330 562-4000
  Aurora *(G-945)*

▲ Showa Aluminum Corp America ......F 740 869-3333
  Mount Sterling *(G-14603)*

Turbine Eng Cmpnents Tech Corp .....E 216 692-6173
  Cleveland *(G-6374)*

▲ Wallace Forge Company ....D 330 488-1203
  Canton *(G-2900)*

Wendell August Gift Sp & Forge ....F 330 893-3713
  Berlin *(G-1653)*

Wodin Inc ....E 440 439-4222
  Cleveland *(G-6474)*

3465 Automotive Stampings

A J Rose Mfgco ....C 216 631-4645
  Cleveland *(G-4675)*

◆ A J Rose Mfgco ....C 216 631-4645
  Avon *(G-978)*

American Quality Molds LLC ....G 513 276-7345
  Hamilton *(G-10665)*

American Trim LLC ....A 419 228-1145
  Sidney *(G-17167)*

AMG Industries LLC ....D 740 397-4044
  Mount Vernon *(G-14605)*

▲ Anchor Tool & Die Co ....B 216 362-1850
  Cleveland *(G-4806)*

▲ Angell-Demmel North Amer Corp ....D 937 461-5800
  Dayton *(G-8158)*

Antique Auto Sheet Metal Inc ....E 937 833-4422
  Brookville *(G-2174)*

Arcelormittal Tailored Blanks ....D 419 737-3180
  Pioneer *(G-16233)*

▲ Artiflex Manufacturing LLC ....A 330 262-2015
  Wooster *(G-20741)*

Artiflex Manufacturing LLC ....F 419 547-9211
  Clyde *(G-6537)*

Blackburn Hubcaps & Wheels LLC ....G 330 467-0236
  Macedonia *(G-12438)*

Buyers Products Company ....G 440 974-8888
  Mentor *(G-13541)*

Cleveland Die & Mfg Co ....D 440 243-3404
  Cleveland *(G-5059)*

Cleveland Metal Processing Inc ....C 440 243-3404
  Cleveland *(G-5070)*

Cole Tool & Die Company ....E 419 522-1272
  Ontario *(G-15686)*

Custom Floaters LLC ....G 216 337-9118
  Brookpark *(G-2155)*

Decoma Systems Integration Gro ......D 419 324-3387
  Toledo *(G-18431)*

▲ Defiance Metal Products Co ....B 419 784-5332
  Defiance *(G-8785)*

Defiance Metal Products Co ....B 419 784-5332
Defiance (G-8786)

▲ Defiance Stamping Co ....D 419 782-5781
Napoleon (G-14677)

▲ E & W Enterprises Powell Inc ....D 937 346-0800
Springfield (G-17549)

Elyria Spring & Specialty Inc ....E 440 323-5502
Elyria (G-9417)

Emerson Electric Co ....E 513 631-6112
Cincinnati (G-3697)

Exact-Tool & Die Inc ....E 216 676-9140
Cleveland (G-5311)

Falls Stamping & Welding Co ....C 330 928-1191
Cuyahoga Falls (G-7996)

Falls Stamping & Welding Co ....F 216 771-9635
Cleveland (G-5323)

Falls Tool & Die Incorporated ....G 330 633-4884
Akron (G-179)

▲ Feintool Cincinnati Inc ....C 513 247-0110
Blue Ash (G-1793)

▲ Feintool US Operations Inc ....C 513 247-4061
Blue Ash (G-1794)

Fiberglass Link Inc ....G 216 531-5515
Cleveland (G-5343)

▲ Findlay Products Corporation ....C 419 423-3324
Findlay (G-9825)

Florida Production Engrg Inc ....D 937 996-4361
New Madison (G-14869)

Ford Motor Company ....A 216 587-7700
Bedford (G-1424)

Ford Motor Company ....A 216 587-7700
Cleveland (G-5368)

▲ Fuserashi Intl Tech Inc ....E 330 273-0140
Valley City (G-19204)

Gamco Componets Group LLC ....G 440 593-1500
Conneaut (G-7804)

General Motors LLC ....B 330 824-5840
Warren (G-19554)

General Motors LLC ....A 216 265-5000
Cleveland (G-5419)

Gt Technologies Inc ....D 419 324-7300
Toledo (G-18489)

▲ Guarantee Specialties Inc ....D 216 451-9744
Strongsville (G-17923)

Hayford Technologies ....D 419 524-7627
Mansfield (G-12622)

Hercules Acquisition Corp ....E 419 287-3223
Pemberville (G-16027)

Honda of America Mfg Inc ....C 937 644-0724
Marysville (G-12951)

Jatdco LLC ....G 440 238-6570
Strongsville (G-17933)

Ksi Distribution Inc ....G 440 256-2500
Mentor (G-13624)

L & W Inc ....D 734 397-6300
Avon (G-999)

Lakepark Industries Inc ....C 419 752-4471
Greenwich (G-10533)

Langenau Manufacturing Company ......F 216 651-3400
Cleveland (G-5680)

Liber Limited LLC ....G 440 427-0647
Olmsted Twp (G-15680)

Ltf Acquisition LLC ....F 330 533-0111
Canfield (G-2563)

Lwb/ISE LP ....F 937 778-3828
Piqua (G-16288)

M-Tek Inc ....A 419 209-0399
Upper Sandusky (G-19130)

Mahle Behr USA Inc ....G 937 356-2001
Vandalia (G-19302)

▲ Matsu Ohio Inc ....C 419 298-2394
Edgerton (G-9332)

Merrick Manufacturing II LLC ....G 937 222-7164
Dayton (G-8485)

Metal Products Company ....E 330 652-2558
Niles (G-15168)

▲ Murotech Ohio Corporation ....D 419 394-6529
Saint Marys (G-16844)

N N Metal Stampings Inc ....E 419 737-2311
Pioneer (G-16235)

Nasg Ohio LLC ....F 419 634-3125
Ada (G-6)

Navistar Inc ....D 937 390-2800
Springfield (G-17613)

Nebraska Industries Corp ....E 419 335-6010
Wauseon (G-19691)

◆ Northern Stamping Co ....C 216 883-8888
Cleveland (G-5912)

Northern Stamping Co ....C 216 642-8081
Cleveland (G-5913)

Oerlikon Friction Systems ....E 937 233-7002
Dayton (G-8539)

Oerlikon Friction Systems ....E 937 233-9191
Dayton (G-8541)

Ohio Stamping & Machine LLC ....C 937 322-3880
Springfield (G-17619)

P & A Industries Inc ....C 419 422-7070
Findlay (G-9875)

▲ Parts Channel Inc ....F 614 497-9199
Groveport (G-10638)

Pennant Companies ....B 614 451-1782
Columbus (G-7476)

◆ Progressive Stamping Inc ....C 419 453-1111
Ottoville (G-15825)

▲ Quaker Mfg Corp ....C 330 332-4631
Salem (G-16922)

▲ R K Industries Inc ....D 419 523-5001
Ottawa (G-15806)

Sapa Extrusions North Amer LLC ......C 888 935-5759
Sidney (G-17221)

Select International Corp ....G 937 233-9191
Dayton (G-8653)

Shiloh Industries Inc ....E 330 558-2300
Valley City (G-19232)

Shiloh Industries Inc ....A 440 647-2100
Wellington (G-19755)

Shiloh Industries Inc ....A 330 558-2000
Valley City (G-19233)

◆ Shiloh Industries Inc ....G 330 558-2600
Valley City (G-19234)

Shiloh Industries Inc ....A 330 558-2600
Valley City (G-19235)

▲ SSP Industrial Group Inc ....G 330 665-2900
Fairlawn (G-9761)

▲ Stamco Industries Inc ....E 216 731-9333
Cleveland (G-6233)

▲ Stripmatic Products Inc ....E 216 241-7143
Cleveland (G-6255)

Styner+bienz US Inc ....G 216 362-1850
Cleveland (G-6258)

Sulzer Transmission Tech ....G 937 449-4000
Dayton (G-8688)

Sunrise Cooperative Inc ....E 419 683-4600
Crestline (G-7936)

Synergy Alliance ....G 330 253-9475
Akron (G-424)

▲ T A Bacon Co ....F 216 851-1404
Chesterland (G-3220)

▲ Taylor Metal Products Co ....C 419 522-3471
Mansfield (G-12693)

▲ Tfo Tech Co Ltd ....C 740 426-6381
Jeffersonville (G-11382)

Tower Automotive Operations I ....B 419 358-8966
Bluffton (G-1918)

Trellborg Sling Prfiles US Inc ....G 330 995-9725
Aurora (G-951)

▲ Trucut Incorporated ....D 330 938-9806
Sebring (G-17055)

TS Trim Industries Inc ....G 614 837-4114
Canal Winchester (G-2539)

TS Trim Trimold Inc ....G 614 920-1927
Canal Winchester (G-2540)

Valco Industries Inc ....E 937 399-7400
Springfield (G-17672)

Valley Tool & Die Inc ....D 440 237-0160
North Royalton (G-15458)

◆ Vehtek Systems Inc ....A 419 373-8741
Bowling Green (G-2019)

▲ Vr Waverly Inc ....D 740 947-7763
Waverly (G-19720)

Wrena LLC ....E 937 667-4403
Tipp City (G-18312)

▲ Yachiyo of America Inc ....D 614 876-3220
Columbus (G-7781)

Zip Tool & Die Inc ....F 216 267-1117
Cleveland (G-6496)

3466 Crowns & Closures

American Flange & Mfg Co Inc ....G 740 549-6073
Delaware (G-8820)

▲ Boardman Molded Products Inc ......D 330 788-2401
Youngstown (G-21032)

Crown Cork & Seal Usa Inc ....D 740 681-3000
Lancaster (G-11702)

3469 Metal Stampings, NEC

A J Rose Mfgco ....C 216 631-4645
Cleveland (G-4675)

◆ A J Rose Mfgco ....C 216 631-4645
Avon (G-978)

A-1 Manufacturing Corp ....G 216 475-6084
Maple Heights (G-12726)

▲ A-Stamp Industries LLC ....D 419 633-0451
Bryan (G-2273)

AAA Stamping Inc ....E 216 749-4494
Cleveland (G-4681)

Abbott Tool Inc ....E 419 476-6742
Toledo (G-18318)

Abl Products Inc ....F 216 281-2400
Cleveland (G-4684)

Accurate Tool Co Inc ....G 330 332-9448
Salem (G-16868)

▲ Acro Tool & Die Company ....D 330 773-5173
Akron (G-29)

▲ Advanced Technology Corp ....C 440 293-4064
Andover (G-611)

Agb LLC ....G 419 924-5216
West Unity (G-20126)

AJD Holding Co ....D 330 405-4477
Twinsburg (G-18895)

Allied Tool & Die Inc ....F 216 941-6196
Cleveland (G-4766)

Amaroq Inc ....G 419 747-2110
Mansfield (G-12558)

Amclo Group Inc ....C 216 791-8400
Cleveland (G-4776)

▼ Amcraft Inc ....G 419 729-7900
Toledo (G-18335)

▲ American Guard Co Inc ....F 440 354-1400
Geneva (G-10342)

◆ American Pan Company ....G 937 652-3232
Urbana (G-19146)

American Rugged Enclosures ....F 513 942-3004
Hamilton (G-10666)

American Tool & Mfg Co ....F 419 522-2452
Mansfield (G-12561)

American Tool and Die Inc ....F 419 726-5394
Toledo (G-18346)

American Trim LLC ....A 419 228-1145
Sidney (G-17167)

American Trim LLC ....G 419 996-4703
Lima (G-11989)

American Trim LLC ....D 419 739-4349
Wapakoneta (G-19476)

American Trim LLC ....D 419 738-9664
Wapakoneta (G-19477)

American Trim LLC ....D 419 996-4729
Lima (G-11990)

American Trim LLC ....D 419 996-4703
Lima (G-11991)

▲ American Trim LLC ....E 419 228-1145
Lima (G-11992)

Ampex Metal Products Company ....E 216 267-9242
Brookpark (G-2151)

Amtekco Industries Inc ....D 614 228-6590
Columbus (G-6749)

Amtekco Industries Inc ....G 614 228-6525
Columbus (G-6750)

Anchor Fabricators Inc ....E 937 836-5117
Clayton (G-4656)

Anchor Tool & Die Co ....C 216 362-1850
Cleveland (G-4807)

▲ Anchor Tool & Die Co ....B 216 362-1850
Cleveland (G-4806)

Anderson Industries Inc ....F 216 941-7766
Cleveland (G-4810)

Andre Corporation ....E 574 293-0207
Mason (G-12981)

▲ Angell-Demmel North Amer Corp ....D 937 461-5800
Dayton (G-8158)

◆ Anomatic Corporation ....B 740 522-2203
New Albany (G-14745)

Arrow Tru-Line Inc ....D 419 636-7013
Bryan (G-2279)

▲ Artiflex Manufacturing LLC ....B 330 262-2015
Wooster (G-20741)

Artisan Equipment Inc ....F 740 756-9135
Carroll (G-2936)

▼ Artisan Tool & Die Corp ....E 216 883-2769
Cleveland (G-4838)

Artistic Metal Spinning Inc ....G 216 961-3336
Cleveland (G-4839)

▲ Atlantic Durant Technology Inc ......G 440 238-6931
Strongsville (G-17890)

◆ Atlantic Tool & Die Company ....C 440 238-6931
Strongsville (G-17891)

Atlantic Tool & Die Company ....C 330 769-4500
Seville (G-17068)

Atlantic Tool & Die Company ....C 330 239-3700
Sharon Center (G-17101)

SIC

Atra Metal Spinning Inc	F	440 354-9525	
Painesville (G-15853)			
Automatic Stamp Products Inc	F	216 781-7933	
Cleveland (G-4869)			
Avion Manufacturing Company	G	330 220-1989	
Brunswick (G-2207)			
Ayling and Reichert Co Consent	E	419 898-2471	
Oak Harbor (G-15586)			
Banner Metals Group Inc	D	614 291-3105	
Columbus (G-6805)			
Barbara A Lieurance	G	937 382-2864	
Wilmington (G-20656)			
Barnes Group Inc	G	440 526-5900	
Brecksville (G-2035)			
Bates Metal Products Inc	D	740 498-8371	
Port Washington (G-16422)			
Bayloff Stmped Pdts Knsman Inc	D	330 876-4511	
Kinsman (G-11608)			
Bellevue Manufacturing Company	G	419 483-3190	
Bellevue (G-1546)			
Boehm Pressed Steel Company	E	330 220-8000	
Valley City (G-19200)			
Brainerd Industries Inc	E	937 228-0488	
Miamisburg (G-13786)			
Brainin-Advance Industries LLC	E	513 874-9760	
West Chester (G-19821)			
Breitinger Company	C	419 526-4255	
Mansfield (G-12569)			
Brooks Utility Products Group	E	330 455-0301	
Canton (G-2629)			
Brw Tool Inc	F	419 394-3371	
Saint Marys (G-16835)			
Buckeye Metals Industries Inc	F	216 663-4300	
Cleveland (G-4943)			
Buckeye Stamping Company	D	614 445-0059	
Columbus (G-6875)			
Buckley Manufacturing Company	F	513 821-4444	
Cincinnati (G-3485)			
▲ Bud Industries Inc	G	440 946-3200	
Willoughby (G-20447)			
C & C Fabrication Inc	G	419 354-3535	
Bowling Green (G-1975)			
▲ CA Picard Surface Engrg Inc	F	440 366-5400	
Elyria (G-9386)			
Camelot Manufacturing Inc	F	419 678-2603	
Coldwater (G-6554)			
▲ Case Industries Inc	G	330 963-7717	
Twinsburg (G-18908)			
▲ Catania Medallic Specialty	E	440 933-9595	
Avon Lake (G-1026)			
Central Ohio Metal Stampi	E	614 861-3332	
Columbus (G-6918)			
Clemens License Agency	G	614 288-8007	
Pickerington (G-16188)			
▲ Cleveland Die & Mfg Co	D	440 243-3404	
Middleburg Heights (G-13904)			
Cleveland Hollow Boring Inc	G	216 883-1926	
Cleveland (G-5065)			
Cleveland Metal Stamping Co	F	440 234-0010	
Berea (G-1607)			
Cole Tool & Die Company	E	419 522-1272	
Ontario (G-15686)			
◆ Com-Corp Industries Inc	D	216 431-6266	
Cleveland (G-5101)			
Commercial Vehicle Group Inc	C	740 676-6542	
Shadyside (G-17080)			
Compco Industries Incorporated	D	330 482-6488	
Columbiana (G-6614)			
Compressor Technologies Inc	E	937 492-3711	
Sidney (G-17172)			
Connaughton Wldg & Fence LLC	G	513 867-0230	
Hamilton (G-10680)			
Continental Business Entps Inc	F	440 439-4400	
Cleveland (G-5123)			
Contour Forming Inc	E	740 345-9777	
Newark (G-14996)			
Coreworth Holdings LLC	G	419 468-7100	
Iberia (G-11242)			
Counts Container Corporation	E	216 433-4336	
Cleveland (G-5135)			
Cqt Kennedy LLC	D	419 238-2442	
Van Wert (G-19252)			
Cubbison Company	D	330 793-2481	
Youngstown (G-21059)			
Customformed Products Inc	F	937 388-0480	
Miamisburg (G-13795)			
D & L Manufacturing	G	440 428-1627	
Madison (G-12503)			
D J Klinger Inc	F	513 891-2284	
Cincinnati (G-3632)			

Dayton Tool Co Inc	E	937 222-5501	
Dayton (G-8288)			
Dayton Tractor & Crane	G	937 317-5014	
Xenia (G-20946)			
Dayton United Metal Spinners	F	937 222-6732	
Tipp City (G-18275)			
Deerfield Manufacturing Inc	E	513 398-2010	
Mason (G-13008)			
Delafoil Pennsylvania Inc	G	610 327-9565	
Perrysburg (G-16083)			
Delta Tool & Die Stl Block Inc	F	419 822-5939	
Delta (G-8930)			
Dependable Stamping Company	E	216 486-5522	
Cleveland (G-5184)			
Deshler Metal Working Co Inc	E	419 278-0472	
Deshler (G-8949)			
▼ Destiny Manufacturing Inc	E	330 273-9000	
Brunswick (G-2220)			
▲ Die Co Inc	E	440 942-8856	
Eastlake (G-9265)			
▲ Die-Matic Corporation	D	216 749-4656	
Brooklyn Heights (G-2138)			
▼ Die-Mension Corporation	F	330 273-5872	
Brunswick (G-2221)			
Doan Machinery & Eqp Co Inc	E	216 932-6243	
University Heights (G-19108)			
Dove Die and Stamping Company	E	216 267-3720	
Cleveland (G-5211)			
Durivage Pattern & Mfg Co	E	419 836-8655	
Williston (G-20420)			
▲ Duro Dyne Midwest Corp	B	513 870-6000	
Hamilton (G-10685)			
Dyco Manufacturing Inc	F	419 485-5525	
Montpelier (G-14444)			
E C Shaw Co	E	513 721-6334	
Cincinnati (G-3677)			
Eagle Precision Products LLC	G	440 582-9393	
North Royalton (G-15418)			
▲ Ecp Corporation	E	440 934-0444	
Avon (G-994)			
Eisenhauer Manufacturing Co	E	419 238-0081	
Van Wert (G-19256)			
Electrical Control Systems	G	937 859-7136	
Dayton (G-8321)			
Elliott Oren Products Inc	E	419 298-2306	
Edgerton (G-9329)			
Elyria Mtal Spnning Fbrication	G	440 323-8068	
Elyria (G-9414)			
Elyria Spring & Specialty Inc	E	440 323-5502	
Elyria (G-9417)			
Emerson Electric Co	E	513 631-6112	
Cincinnati (G-3697)			
▲ Ernie Green Industries Inc	G	614 219-1423	
Columbus (G-7064)			
▲ Ernst Metal Technologies LLC	E	937 434-3133	
Moraine (G-14485)			
Eurocase Architectural Cabinet	F	330 674-0681	
Millersburg (G-14214)			
▲ Even Heat Mfg Ltd	F	330 695-9351	
Fredericksburg (G-10085)			
Everyware Global Inc	D	740 687-2500	
Lancaster (G-11711)			
Exact-Tool & Die Inc	E	216 676-9140	
Cleveland (G-5311)			
Exline Manufacturing Co Inc	G	937 866-1515	
Miamisburg (G-13808)			
F & G Tool and Die Co	E	937 746-3658	
Franklin (G-10019)			
F C Brengman and Assoc LLC	E	740 756-4308	
Carroll (G-2940)			
Fairfield License Center Inc	G	513 829-6224	
Hamilton (G-10691)			
Falls Stamping & Welding Co	C	330 928-1191	
Cuyahoga Falls (G-7996)			
Falls Tool & Die Incorporated	G	330 633-4884	
Akron (G-179)			
Famous Industries Inc	D	740 685-2592	
Byesville (G-2401)			
Faull & Son LLC	F	330 652-4341	
Niles (G-15152)			
Federal-Mogul Valve Train Inte	G	330 628-6700	
Brunswick (G-2224)			
Feinblanking Limited Inc	G	513 860-2100	
West Chester (G-19863)			
▲ Feintool US Operations Inc	C	513 247-4061	
Blue Ash (G-1794)			
▲ Findlay Products Corporation	C	419 423-3324	
Findlay (G-9825)			
Five Star Machine & Tool	E	937 420-2170	
Fort Loramie (G-9930)			

Flood Heliarc Inc	F	614 835-3929	
Groveport (G-10621)			
Formasters Corporation	F	440 639-9206	
Mentor (G-13580)			
Formed Metal Products Inc	F	440 775-0819	
Oberlin (G-15639)			
Formetal Inc	F	419 898-2211	
Oak Harbor (G-15591)			
Fremont Plastic Products Inc	E	419 332-6407	
Fremont (G-10150)			
Frepeg Industries Inc	F	440 255-8595	
Mentor (G-13585)			
Fulton Industries Inc	D	419 335-3015	
Wauseon (G-19678)			
Fulton Manufacturing Inds LLC	E	440 546-1435	
Brecksville (G-2050)			
G & M Metal Products Inc	G	513 863-3353	
Hamilton (G-10695)			
▲ G & W Products LLC	C	513 860-4050	
Fairfield (G-9660)			
Gb Fabrication Company	E	419 347-1835	
Shelby (G-17136)			
Gb Fabrication Company	E	419 896-3191	
Shiloh (G-17148)			
▲ Gb Manufacturing Company	D	419 822-5323	
Delta (G-8934)			
Gem City Metal Tech LLC	G	937 252-8998	
Dayton (G-8395)			
▲ General Technologies Inc	E	419 747-1800	
Mansfield (G-12612)			
Gentzler Tool & Die Corp	E	330 896-1941	
Akron (G-205)			
Global Manufacturing Tech LLC	G	440 205-1001	
Mentor (G-13594)			
Gottschall Tool & Die Inc	E	330 332-1544	
Salem (G-16895)			
Gt Technologies Inc	D	419 324-7300	
Toledo (G-18489)			
▲ Guarantee Specialties Inc	E	216 451-9744	
Strongsville (G-17923)			
Guardian Engineering & Mfg Co	E	419 335-1784	
Wauseon (G-19680)			
▲ Gwp Holdings Inc	B	513 860-4050	
Fairfield (G-9662)			
H&M Mtal Stamping Assembly Inc	F	216 898-9030	
Brookpark (G-2163)			
Hamlin Newco LLC	D	330 753-7791	
Akron (G-212)			
Hamlin Steel Products LLC	D	330 753-7791	
Akron (G-213)			
Hawthorne Caravan & Assoc LLC	F	440 366-9065	
Elyria (G-9428)			
Hayford Technologies	D	419 524-7627	
Mansfield (G-12622)			
Heatherdowns License Bureau	G	419 381-1109	
Toledo (G-18501)			
Hercules Acquisition Corp	E	419 287-3223	
Pemberville (G-16027)			
Herd Manufacturing Inc	E	216 651-4221	
Cleveland (G-5503)			
▲ Hidaka Usa Inc	E	614 889-8611	
Dublin (G-9084)			
▲ Hill Manufacturing Inc	E	419 335-5006	
Wauseon (G-19682)			
Howland Machine Corp	E	330 544-4029	
Niles (G-15158)			
Hpl Stampings Inc	F	440 582-9794	
Cleveland (G-5531)			
Huber Heights License Bureau	F	937 233-7560	
Dayton (G-8395)			
Hukon Manufacturing Company	E	513 721-5562	
Cincinnati (G-3901)			
Hynes Modern Pattern Co Inc	G	937 322-3451	
Springfield (G-17579)			
Ice Industries Inc	E	513 398-2010	
Mason (G-13040)			
▲ Ice Industries Inc	E	419 842-3612	
Sylvania (G-18110)			
Ice Industries Columbus Inc	E	419 842-3600	
Sylvania (G-18111)			
Impact Industries Inc	E	440 327-2360	
North Ridgeville (G-15380)			
Imperial Die & Mfg Co	F	440 268-9080	
Strongsville (G-17929)			
Imperial Metal Spinning Co	E	216 524-5020	
Cleveland (G-5557)			
Independent Power Consultants	G	419 476-8383	
Toledo (G-18520)			
Independent Stamping Inc	E	216 251-3500	
Cleveland (G-5563)			

Interlake Industries Inc ....G....... 440 942-0800
  Willoughby (G-20512)

Interlake Stamping Ohio Inc ....E....... 440 942-0800
  Willoughby (G-20513)

International Trade Group Inc ....G....... 614 486-4634
  Columbus (G-7207)

J B Stamping Inc ....E....... 216 631-0013
  Cleveland (G-5597)

▼ J R Machining Inc ....G....... 330 528-3406
  Hudson (G-11184)

J Schrader Co ....F....... 216 961-2890
  Cleveland (G-5601)

J Williams & Associates Inc ....G....... 330 887-1392
  Westfield Center (G-20244)

JD Norman Industries Inc ....D....... 216 671-8000
  Brooklyn (G-2129)

Jebco Machine Company Inc ....G....... 330 452-2909
  Canton (G-2747)

▲ Jet Stream International Inc ....E....... 330 505-9988
  Niles (G-15164)

Jones Metal Products Company ....D....... 740 545-6381
  West Lafayette (G-20087)

K & B Stamping & Manufacturing ....G....... 937 778-8875
  Piqua (G-16284)

K & H Industries LLC ....F....... 513 921-6770
  Cincinnati (G-3964)

K & L Die & Manufacturing ....G....... 419 895-1301
  Greenwich (G-10532)

Kelch Manufacturing Corp ....G....... 440 366-5060
  Elyria (G-9446)

Knight Manufacturing Co Inc ....F....... 740 676-9532
  Shadyside (G-17081)

Knight Manufacturing Co Inc ....E....... 740 676-5516
  Shadyside (G-17082)

Knowlton Manufacturing Co Inc ....F....... 513 631-7353
  Cincinnati (G-3999)

Kreider Corp ....D....... 937 325-8787
  Springfield (G-17592)

L & W Inc ....D....... 734 397-6300
  Avon (G-999)

▼ L C G Machine & Tool Inc ....G....... 614 261-1651
  Columbus (G-7276)

L C I Inc ....G....... 330 948-1922
  Lodi (G-12163)

La Ganke & Sons Stamping Co ....F....... 216 451-0278
  Columbia Station (G-6590)

Lakepark Industries Inc ....C....... 419 752-4471
  Greenwich (G-10533)

Langenau Manufacturing Company .....F....... 216 651-3400
  Cleveland (G-5680)

Larosa Die Engineering Inc ....G....... 513 284-9195
  Cincinnati (G-4012)

Lewark Metal Spinning Inc ....E....... 937 275-3303
  Dayton (G-8457)

Lextech Industries Ltd ....G....... 216 883-7900
  Cleveland (G-5694)

Liberty Steel Industries Inc ....D....... 330 372-6363
  Warren (G-19570)

Liberty Steel Industries Inc ....E....... 330 372-6363
  Warren (G-19571)

▲ Logan Machine Company ....D....... 330 633-6163
  Akron (G-275)

▲ Long-Stanton Mfg Company ....E....... 513 874-8020
  West Chester (G-19895)

Lowery Industries ....G....... 740 745-5045
  Saint Louisville (G-16828)

M S C Industries Inc ....G....... 440 474-8788
  Rome (G-16717)

Mahoning Valley Manufacturing ....E....... 330 537-4492
  Beloit (G-1584)

Malin Wire Co ....E....... 216 267-9080
  Cleveland (G-5735)

▲ Malin Wire Co ....G....... 216 267-9080
  Cleveland (G-5734)

Mallory Pattern Works Inc ....G....... 419 726-8001
  Toledo (G-18572)

Mansfield Industries Inc ....E....... 419 524-1300
  Mansfield (G-12643)

▼ Marc V Concepts Inc ....F....... 419 782-6505
  Defiance (G-8801)

Mark True Engraving Co ....G....... 216 651-7700
  Cleveland (G-5745)

Master Products Company ....D....... 216 341-1740
  Cleveland (G-5760)

▲ Matco Tools Corporation 1 ....B....... 330 929-4949
  Stow (G-17773)

Maumee Assembly & Stamping LLC .....D....... 419 304-2887
  Maumee (G-13278)

McAfee Tool & Die Inc ....E....... 330 896-9555
  Uniontown (G-19092)

McGlennon Metal Products Inc ....F....... 614 252-7114
  Columbus (G-7335)

Medina Blanking Inc ....C....... 330 558-2300
  Valley City (G-19217)

Merrick Manufacturing II LLC ....G....... 937 222-7164
  Dayton (G-8485)

Metal & Wire Products Company ....E....... 330 332-9448
  Salem (G-16914)

Metal Fabricating Corporation ....D....... 216 631-8121
  Cleveland (G-5787)

Metal Products Company ....C....... 330 652-6201
  Niles (G-15169)

Metal Stampings Unlimited ....F....... 937 328-0206
  Springfield (G-17603)

Mic-Ray Metal Products Inc ....F....... 216 791-2206
  Cleveland (G-5796)

Mid-America Steel Corp ....E....... 800 282-3466
  Cleveland (G-5805)

Middletown License Agency Inc ....F....... 513 422-7225
  Middletown (G-14062)

Modern Engineering ....G....... 440 593-5414
  Conneaut (G-7816)

Modern Pipe Supports Corp ....E....... 216 361-1666
  Cleveland (G-5828)

Monode Steel Stamp Inc ....G....... 419 929-3501
  New London (G-14862)

Monode Steel Stamp Inc ....F....... 440 975-8802
  Mentor (G-13661)

▲ Morgal Machine Tool Co ....D....... 937 325-5561
  Springfield (G-17607)

Msd Products Inc ....G....... 440 946-0040
  Mentor (G-13662)

◆ Mtd Holdings Inc ....B....... 330 225-2600
  Valley City (G-19220)

N N Metal Stampings Inc ....E....... 419 737-2311
  Pioneer (G-16235)

Nebraska Industries Corp ....E....... 419 335-6010
  Wauseon (G-19691)

New Bremen Machine & Tool Co ....E....... 419 629-3295
  New Bremen (G-14790)

New Holland Engineering Inc ....G....... 740 495-5200
  New Holland (G-14835)

Neway Stamping & Mfg Inc ....D....... 440 951-8500
  Willoughby (G-20554)

Nicholas Press Sales LLC ....G....... 440 652-6604
  Brunswick (G-2239)

Niles Manufacturing & Finshg ....C....... 330 544-0402
  Niles (G-15171)

◆ Norplas Industries Inc ....B....... 419 662-3317
  Northwood (G-15485)

◆ Northern Stamping Co ....C....... 216 883-8888
  Cleveland (G-5912)

Northwind Industries Inc ....E....... 216 433-0666
  Cleveland (G-5916)

Northwood Industries Inc ....F....... 419 666-2100
  Perrysburg (G-16128)

Norwood Medical ....G....... 937 228-4101
  Dayton (G-8530)

Norwood Medical ....C....... 937 228-4101
  Dayton (G-8531)

Norwood Tool Company ....D....... 937 228-4101
  Dayton (G-8532)

Ohi-TEC Manufacturing Inc ....E....... 937 882-6144
  Dayton (G-8542)

Ohio Associated Entps LLC ....E....... 440 354-3148
  Painesville (G-15908)

▲ Ohio Gasket and Shim Co Inc ....E....... 330 630-0626
  Akron (G-323)

Ohio Valley Manufacturing Inc ....D....... 419 522-5818
  Mansfield (G-12662)

Omni Manufacturing Inc ....D....... 419 394-7424
  Saint Marys (G-16846)

Omni Manufacturing Inc ....F....... 419 394-7424
  Saint Marys (G-16847)

Orick Stamping ....D....... 419 331-0600
  Elida (G-9353)

Ottawa Products Co ....E....... 419 836-5115
  Curtice (G-7958)

P & A Industries Inc ....C....... 419 422-7070
  Findlay (G-9875)

P M Motor Company ....F....... 440 327-9999
  North Ridgeville (G-15393)

▲ Pacific Manufacturing Ohio Inc .....B....... 513 860-3900
  Fairfield (G-9696)

Pacific Manufacturing Tenn Inc ....E....... 513 900-7862
  Jackson (G-11324)

Paramount Stamping & Wldg Co ....D....... 216 631-1755
  Cleveland (G-5964)

Parker-Hannifin Corporation ....F....... 330 336-3511
  Wadsworth (G-19427)

Parma Heights License Bureau ....G....... 440 888-0388
  Cleveland (G-5978)

▼ Pax Machine Works Inc ....C....... 419 586-2337
  Celina (G-3012)

PDQ Technologies Inc ....F....... 937 274-4958
  Dayton (G-8568)

Peerless Metal Products Inc ....E....... 216 431-6905
  Cleveland (G-5988)

Pennant Moldings Inc ....C....... 937 584-5411
  Sabina (G-16775)

◆ Pentaflex Inc ....C....... 937 325-5551
  Springfield (G-17626)

Perry Welding Service Inc ....F....... 330 425-2211
  Twinsburg (G-19001)

Pettit W T & Sons Co Inc ....G....... 330 539-6100
  Girard (G-10392)

Pfahl Gauge & Manufacturing Co ....G....... 330 633-8402
  Akron (G-337)

Phillips Mch & Stamping Corp ....G....... 330 882-6714
  New Franklin (G-14829)

Pilot-Run Stamping Company ....E....... 440 255-8821
  Mentor (G-13687)

▲ Plating Technology Inc ....D....... 937 268-6882
  Dayton (G-8578)

Precision Fabg & Stamping ....G....... 740 453-7310
  Zanesville (G-21345)

Precision Metal Products Inc ....F....... 216 447-1900
  Cleveland (G-6036)

Precision Pressed Powdered Met ......G....... 937 433-6802
  Dayton (G-8588)

Premier Stamping and Assembly ....G....... 440 293-8961
  Williamsfield (G-20416)

▼ Production Products Inc ....D....... 419 659-2978
  Columbus Grove (G-7797)

Progress Tool & Stamping Inc ....E....... 419 628-2384
  Minster (G-14360)

Progressive Machine Die Inc ....E....... 330 405-6600
  Macedonia (G-12478)

Project Engineering Company ....F....... 937 743-9114
  Miamisburg (G-13849)

Public Safety Ohio Department ....G....... 216 283-4000
  Cleveland (G-6060)

Public Safety Ohio Department ....G....... 440 943-5545
  Willowick (G-20650)

Q Model Inc ....E....... 330 673-0473
  Barberton (G-1144)

▲ Quaker Mfg Corp ....C....... 330 332-4631
  Salem (G-16922)

Quality Fabricated Metals Inc ....E....... 330 332-7008
  Salem (G-16923)

Quality Metal Products Inc ....G....... 440 355-6165
  Lagrange (G-11636)

Quality Stamping Products Co ....F....... 216 441-2700
  Cleveland (G-6075)

Quality Tool Company ....E....... 419 476-8228
  Toledo (G-18663)

R K Metals Ltd ....E....... 513 874-6055
  Fairfield (G-9708)

R L Rush Tool & Pattern Inc ....G....... 419 562-9849
  Bucyrus (G-2356)

Racelite South Coast Inc ....F....... 216 581-4600
  Maple Heights (G-12739)

▲ Range Kleen Mfg Inc ....B....... 419 331-8000
  Elida (G-9356)

Rapid Machine Inc ....F....... 419 737-2377
  Pioneer (G-16243)

RB&w Manufacturing LLC ....G....... 740 363-1971
  Delaware (G-8881)

▲ RB&w Manufacturing LLC ....F....... 234 380-8540
  Streetsboro (G-17870)

Regal Metal Products Co ....E....... 330 868-6343
  Minerva (G-14339)

Regal Metal Products Co ....F....... 330 868-6343
  Minerva (G-14340)

Rezmann Karoly ....G....... 216 441-4357
  Cleveland (G-6110)

Ridge Tool Manufacturing Co ....A....... 440 323-5581
  Elyria (G-9488)

Rittal Corp ....C....... 440 572-4999
  Strongsville (G-17958)

Rittal Corp ....C....... 937 399-0500
  Urbana (G-19176)

Rittal Corp ....F....... 937 399-0500
  Springfield (G-17639)

Rjm Stamping Co ....F....... 614 443-1191
  Columbus (G-7565)

Roemer Industries Inc ....D....... 330 448-2000
  Masury (G-13216)

Ronfeldt Associates Inc ....D....... 419 382-5641
  Toledo (G-18680)

S I C

Ronfeldt Manufacturing LLC ....E 419 382-5641
Toledo (G-18681)

Ronlen Industries Inc ....E 330 273-6468
Brunswick (G-2255)

Roper Lockbox LLC ....G 330 656-5148
Hudson (G-11197)

S-P Company Inc ....F 330 482-0200
Columbiana (G-6631)

Saco Lowell Parts LLC ....E 330 794-1535
Akron (G-393)

Sadler Corporation ....G 330 688-7400
Stow (G-17796)

Sakas Incorporated ....E 740 862-4114
Baltimore (G-1087)

Schoen Industries Inc ....G 330 533-6659
Canfield (G-2573)

Schott Metal Products Company ....D 330 773-7873
Akron (G-397)

Scott Fetzer Company ....C 216 267-9000
Cleveland (G-6168)

Sectional Stamping Inc ....B 440 647-2100
Wellington (G-19754)

Seilkop Industries Inc ....E 513 761-1035
Cincinnati (G-4398)

◆ Select Industries Corporation ....C 937 233-9191
Dayton (G-8652)

Service Stampings Inc ....E 440 946-2330
Willoughby (G-20593)

Seven Ranges Mfg Corp ....E 330 627-7155
Carrollton (G-2965)

Shiloh Automotive Inc ....E 330 558-2600
Valley City (G-19230)

Shiloh Corporation ....B 330 558-2600
Valley City (G-19231)

◆ Shiloh Industries Inc ....G 330 558-2600
Valley City (G-19234)

Shiloh Industries Inc ....A 330 558-2600
Valley City (G-19235)

Smithville Manufacturing Co ....E 330 345-5818
Wooster (G-20836)

Spectrum Machine Inc ....E 330 626-3666
Streetsboro (G-17877)

SPR Machine Inc ....G 513 737-8040
Indian Spgs (G-11286)

Stamped Steel Products Inc ....F 330 538-3951
North Jackson (G-15299)

Stanley Industrial & Auto LLC ....C 614 755-7089
Westerville (G-20187)

▲ Steel Forming Inc ....C 714 532-6321
Youngstown (G-21212)

Stolle Machinery Company LLC ....C 937 497-5400
Sidney (G-17230)

Stolle Properties Inc ....A 513 932-8664
Blue Ash (G-1875)

▲ Stripmatic Products Inc ....E 216 241-7143
Cleveland (G-6255)

Stuebing Automatic Machine Co ....E 513 771-8028
Cincinnati (G-4473)

Suburban Manufacturing Co ....D 440 953-2024
Eastlake (G-9290)

▲ Sunfield Inc ....D 740 928-0404
Hebron (G-10887)

◆ Superior Metal Products Inc ....E 419 228-1145
Lima (G-12099)

Superior Steel Stamp Co ....G 216 431-6460
Cleveland (G-6271)

▲ Supply Technologies LLC ....C 440 947-2100
Cleveland (G-6274)

T & D Fabricating Inc ....E 440 951-5646
Eastlake (G-9292)

T & W Stamping Inc ....G 330 270-0891
Youngstown (G-21216)

▲ Takk Industries Inc ....F 513 353-4306
Cincinnati (G-4491)

▲ Talan Products Inc ....D 216 458-0170
Cleveland (G-6292)

▲ Talent Tool & Die Inc ....E 440 239-8777
Berea (G-1637)

▲ Taylor Metal Products Co ....C 419 522-3471
Mansfield (G-12693)

TEC Design & Manufacturing Inc ....F 937 435-2147
Dayton (G-8707)

Tech-Med Inc ....F 216 486-0900
Euclid (G-9608)

Tenacity Manufacturing Company ....E 513 821-0201
West Chester (G-19955)

The Reliable Spring Wire Frms ....E 440 365-7400
Elyria (G-9501)

The W L Jenkins Company ....F 330 477-3407
Canton (G-2869)

▲ Thk Manufacturing America Inc ....C 740 928-1415
Hebron (G-10889)

▼ Toledo Metal Spinning Company ....E 419 535-5931
Toledo (G-18733)

▲ Toledo Tool and Die Co Inc ....E 419 476-4422
Toledo (G-18747)

Tool & Die Systems Inc ....E 440 327-5800
North Ridgeville (G-15406)

Torr Metal Products Inc ....E 216 671-1616
Cleveland (G-6339)

Transportation Ohio Department ....E 740 927-2285
Pataskala (G-15987)

▲ Transue & Williams Stampg Corp ....D 330 821-5777
Alliance (G-546)

Transue Williams Stamping Inc ....G 330 270-0891
Austintown (G-976)

▲ Transue Williams Stamping Inc ....G 330 829-5007
Alliance (G-547)

Treaty City Industries Inc ....F 937 548-9000
Greenville (G-10525)

▲ Triad Metal Products Company ....D 216 676-6505
Chagrin Falls (G-3128)

▲ Trucut Incorporated ....D 330 938-9806
Sebring (G-17055)

True Turn Industries ....G 440 355-6256
Lagrange (G-11640)

TRW Automotive US LLC ....E 216 750-2400
Cleveland (G-6372)

TRW Automotive US LLC ....E 419 726-5599
Toledo (G-18758)

TRW Automotive US LLC ....E 216 332-7100
Cleveland (G-6373)

▲ Twist Inc ....C 937 675-9581
Jamestown (G-11353)

Twist Inc ....C 937 675-9581
Jamestown (G-11354)

United Die & Mfg Co ....E 330 938-6141
Sebring (G-17056)

United Tool and Machine Inc ....F 937 843-5603
Lakeview (G-11650)

▲ Universal Industrial Pdts Inc ....F 419 737-9584
Pioneer (G-16245)

▲ Universal Metal Products Inc ....C 440 943-3040
Wickliffe (G-20391)

Universal Metal Products Inc ....E 419 287-3223
Pemberville (G-16031)

V K C Inc ....F 440 951-9634
Mentor (G-13764)

Valley Tool & Die Inc ....D 440 237-0160
North Royalton (G-15458)

▼ Varbros LLC ....E 216 267-5200
Cleveland (G-6406)

Veeders Mailbox Inc ....E 513 984-8749
Cincinnati (G-4557)

Verhoff Machine & Welding Inc ....C 419 596-3202
Continental (G-7829)

▲ Voss Industries Inc ....E 216 771-0870
Cleveland (G-6429)

W H Heimkreiter Manufacturing ....G 513 681-9192
Cincinnati (G-4574)

W M Inc ....E 330 427-6115
Washingtonville (G-19644)

Washington Products Inc ....F 330 837-5101
Massillon (G-13211)

Weber Technologies Inc ....E 440 946-8833
Eastlake (G-9297)

▲ Wedge Products Inc ....B 330 405-4477
Twinsburg (G-19038)

Weiss Industries Inc ....E 419 526-2480
Mansfield (G-12704)

Welage Corporation ....F 513 681-2300
Cincinnati (G-4583)

Wellington Industries ....D 734 942-1060
Maumee (G-13308)

Westlake Tool & Die Mfg Co ....D 440 934-5305
Avon (G-1019)

▲ Whirlaway Corporation ....C 440 647-4711
Wellington (G-19758)

Willow Hill Industries LLC ....D 440 942-3003
Willoughby (G-20631)

Winco Stamping Inc ....G 937 859-5522
Miamisburg (G-13881)

Winzeler Stamping Co ....D 419 485-3147
Montpelier (G-14458)

Wire Products Company Inc ....C 216 267-0777
Cleveland (G-6469)

▼ Witt Industries Inc ....D 513 871-5700
Mason (G-13103)

▲ WLS Fabricating Co ....E 440 449-0543
Cleveland (G-6471)

▲ WLS Stamping Co ....D 216 271-5100
Cleveland (G-6472)

▲ Ysk Corporation ....B 740 774-7315
Chillicothe (G-3284)

Zip Tool & Die Inc ....F 216 267-1117
Cleveland (G-6496)

3471 Electroplating, Plating, Polishing, Anodizing & Coloring

A & B Deburring Company ....F 513 723-0777
Cincinnati (G-3328)

▲ A J Oster Foils LLC ....D 330 823-1700
Alliance (G-486)

A-Brite LP ....D 216 252-2995
Cleveland (G-4680)

Abel Metal Processing Inc ....F 216 881-4156
Cleveland (G-4683)

Acme Industrial Group Inc ....F 330 821-3900
Alliance (G-488)

Aetna Plating Co ....F 216 341-9111
Cleveland (G-4726)

Aircraft Plating Corp ....E 216 781-5845
Cleveland (G-4737)

Ak-Isg Steel Coating Company ....D 216 429-6901
Cleveland (G-4739)

Akron Plating Co Inc ....F 330 773-6878
Akron (G-51)

Allegheny Ludlum LLC ....E 330 875-2244
Louisville (G-12308)

Allen Aircraft Products Inc ....E 330 296-1531
Ravenna (G-16515)

Allen Aircraft Products Inc ....E 330 296-9621
Ravenna (G-16514)

Als Polishing Shop Inc ....G 419 476-8857
Toledo (G-18332)

Aluminum Color Industries Inc ....E 330 536-6295
Lowellville (G-12404)

Aluminum Extruded Shapes Inc ....C 513 563-2205
Cincinnati (G-3383)

Amac Enterprises Inc ....D 216 362-1880
Cleveland (G-4775)

Amac Enterprises Inc ....C 216 362-1880
Parma (G-15954)

American Indus Maintanence ....G 937 254-3400
Dayton (G-8154)

American Metal Cleaning Inc ....G 419 255-1828
Toledo (G-18341)

American Metal Coatings Inc ....E 216 451-3131
Cleveland (G-4788)

American Mtal Clg Cncnnati Inc ....G 513 825-1171
Cincinnati (G-3392)

American Quality Stripping ....E 419 625-6288
Sandusky (G-16946)

Anchor Fabricators Inc ....E 937 836-5117
Clayton (G-4656)

Anodizing Specialists Inc ....F 440 951-0257
Mentor (G-13523)

◆ Anomatic Corporation ....B 740 522-2203
New Albany (G-14745)

▲ Arcelormittal Columbus LLC ....C 614 492-6800
Columbus (G-6768)

Arem Co ....F 440 974-6740
Mentor (G-13526)

Areway Acquisition Inc ....D 216 651-9022
Brooklyn (G-2127)

▲ Atom Blasting & Finishing Inc ....G 440 235-4765
Columbia Station (G-6580)

Auto Core Systems ....G 740 362-5599
Delaware (G-8824)

Autocoat ....G 419 636-3830
Bryan (G-2280)

◆ Automated Wheel LLC ....D 216 651-9022
Cleveland (G-4867)

Automation Finishing Inc ....E 216 251-8805
Cleveland (G-4870)

B & R Custom Chrome ....G 419 536-7215
Toledo (G-18362)

▲ Badboy Blasters Incorporated ....F 330 454-2699
Canton (G-2614)

Bar Processing Corporation ....D 330 872-0914
Newton Falls (G-15129)

▲ Barker Products Company ....E 216 249-0900
Cleveland (G-4891)

Bedford Anodizing Co ....E 330 650-6052
Hudson (G-11160)

Beringer Plating Inc ....G 330 633-8409
Akron (G-88)

Best Plating Rack Corp ....F 440 944-3270
   Wickliffe (G-20358)

Bill J Jernigan Inc ....D 937 264-1598
   Vandalia (G-19283)

Bmd Blasting ....G 614 580-9468
   Columbus (G-6841)

Boville Indus Coatings Inc ....E 330 669-8558
   Smithville (G-17238)

Bricker Plating Inc ....E 419 636-1990
   Bryan (G-2285)

Bron-Shoe Company ....E 614 252-0967
   Columbus (G-6867)

Buffex Metal Finishing Inc ....F 216 631-2202
   Cleveland (G-4946)

Canton Plating Co Inc ....G 330 452-7808
   Canton (G-2646)

Carboline Company ....G 800 848-4645
   University Heights (G-19107)

Carlisle and Finch Company ....E 513 681-6080
   Cincinnati (G-3502)

Carter Machine Company Inc ....E 419 468-3530
   Galion (G-10256)

Cascade Plating Inc ....G 440 366-4931
   Elyria (G-9389)

Case Plating Inc ....G 440 288-8304
   Lorain (G-12237)

Century Plating Inc ....G 216 531-4131
   Cleveland (G-5007)

Charles J Meyers ....G 513 922-2866
   Cincinnati (G-3523)

Chemical Methods Inc ....E 216 476-8400
   Strongsville (G-17901)

▲ Chemical Solvents Inc ....E 216 741-9310
   Cleveland (G-5025)

Chromatic Inc ....F 216 881-2228
   Cleveland (G-5031)

Chrome & Speed Cycle LLC ....G 937 429-5656
   Beavercreek (G-1323)

Chrome Deposit Corporation ....E 513 539-8486
   Monroe (G-14395)

Chrome Deposit Corporation ....E 513 539-8486
   Monroe (G-14396)

Chrome Industries Inc ....G 216 771-2266
   Cleveland (G-5032)

Cincinnati Gearing Systems Inc .....D 513 527-8600
   Cincinnati (G-3552)

City Plating and Polishing LLC ....G 216 267-8158
   Cleveland (G-5038)

Classic Evolution Inc ....G 216 440-0559
   Medina (G-13388)

Cleveland Finishing Inc ....G 440 572-5475
   Strongsville (G-17904)

Cleveland Plating ....G 216 249-0300
   Cleveland (G-5072)

CMF Custom Metal Finishers ....G 513 821-8145
   Cincinnati (G-3592)

Colonial Surface Solutions Inc ....E 419 358-0129
   Bluffton (G-1910)

Colonial Surface Solutions Inc ....D 419 659-5639
   Columbus Grove (G-7793)

Columbus Coatings Company ....D 614 492-6800
   Columbus (G-6949)

Commercial Anodizing Co ....E 440 942-8384
   Willoughby (G-20460)

▲ Commercial Honing LLC ....D 330 343-8896
   Dover (G-8971)

Commercial Steel Treating Co ....F 216 431-8204
   Cleveland (G-5105)

Crystal Koch Finishing Inc ....G 440 366-7526
   Elyria (G-9399)

Custom Brass Finishing Inc ....G 330 453-0888
   Canton (G-2673)

Custom Nickel LLC ....G 937 222-1995
   Dayton (G-8261)

Custom Polishing ....G 937 596-0430
   Sidney (G-17173)

Customchrome Plating Inc ....F 440 926-3116
   Grafton (G-10423)

D-G Custom Chrome LLC ....D 513 531-1881
   Cincinnati (G-3634)

Davro Ltd ....G 216 258-0057
   Cleveland (G-5171)

Dayton United Metal Spinners ....F 937 222-6732
   Tipp City (G-18275)

Delta Plating Inc ....E 330 452-2300
   Canton (G-2684)

Derrick Company Inc ....E 513 321-8122
   Cincinnati (G-3648)

Diamond Hard Chrome Co Inc ....F 216 391-3618
   Cleveland (G-5188)

▲ Die Co Inc ....E 440 942-8856
   Eastlake (G-9265)

Durable Plating Co ....G 216 391-2132
   Cleveland (G-5223)

Duray Plating Company Inc ....E 216 941-5540
   Cleveland (G-5224)

E L Stone Company ....E 330 825-4565
   Norton (G-15510)

Electro Polish Company Inc ....E 937 222-3611
   Dayton (G-8322)

▲ Electro Prime Group LLC ....D 419 476-0100
   Toledo (G-18453)

Electro Prime Group LLC ....D 419 666-5000
   Rossford (G-16739)

Electro-Metallics Co ....G 513 423-8091
   Middletown (G-14039)

Electrolizing Corporation Ohio ....E 216 451-3153
   Cleveland (G-5267)

Electrolizing Corporation Ohio ....F 216 451-8653
   Cleveland (G-5268)

Elyria Plating Corporation ....E 440 365-8300
   Elyria (G-9416)

Emerson Electric Co ....E 513 631-6112
   Cincinnati (G-3697)

Engineering Coatings LLC ....G 419 485-0077
   Montpelier (G-14446)

Epd Enterprises Inc ....D 216 961-1200
   Cleveland (G-5289)

Equinox Enterprises LLC ....F 419 627-0022
   Sandusky (G-16964)

Erieview Metal Treating Co ....E 216 663-1780
   Cleveland (G-5298)

▲ Ernie Green Industries Inc ....G 614 219-1423
   Columbus (G-7064)

▲ Etched Metal Company ....E 440 248-0240
   Solon (G-17290)

Euclid Refinishing Compnay Inc .....F 440 275-3356
   Austinburg (G-960)

Faithful Mold Polishing Ex ....G 330 678-8006
   Kent (G-11458)

Fastenal Company ....E 330 745-2996
   Akron (G-182)

Finishers Inc ....G 937 773-3177
   Piqua (G-16264)

Foundry Support Operation ....F 440 951-4142
   Mentor (G-13581)

Future Finishes Inc ....E 513 860-0020
   Hamilton (G-10693)

Gateway Metal Finishing Inc ....G 216 267-2580
   Cleveland (G-5401)

Gei of Columbiana Inc ....D 330 783-0270
   Youngstown (G-21094)

General Extrusions Inc ....D 330 783-0270
   Youngstown (G-21096)

GRB Holdings Inc ....C 937 236-3250
   Dayton (G-8377)

▲ Guaranteed Fnshg Unlimited Inc ....E 216 252-8200
   Cleveland (G-5463)

H & R Metal Finishing Inc ....E 440 942-6656
   Willoughby (G-20502)

Hadronics Inc ....G 513 321-9350
   Cincinnati (G-3861)

Hale Performance Coatings Inc ....E 419 244-6451
   Toledo (G-18494)

Hall Company ....E 937 652-1376
   Urbana (G-19160)

Hartzell Manufacturing Co Inc ....F 937 859-5955
   Miamisburg (G-13815)

Hayes Metalfinishing Inc ....E 937 228-7550
   Dayton (G-8386)

Hearn Plating Co Ltd ....F 419 473-9773
   Toledo (G-18499)

Heatstar ....G 440 701-1031
   Mentor (G-13600)

Hercules Polishing & Plating ....F 330 455-8871
   Canton (G-2726)

Highland Precision Plating ....G 937 393-9501
   Hillsboro (G-11002)

Hy-Blast Inc ....F 513 424-0704
   Middletown (G-14045)

I P S Treatments Inc ....E 419 241-5955
   Toledo (G-18514)

Indigo 48 LLC ....G 419 551-6931
   Bryan (G-2304)

Industrial Mill Maintenance ....E 330 746-1155
   Youngstown (G-21115)

J Horst Manufacturing Co ....D 330 828-2216
   Dalton (G-8072)

J M Hamilton Group Inc ....F 419 229-4010
   Lima (G-12032)

Jason Incorporated ....F 513 860-3400
   Hamilton (G-10711)

Jotco Inc ....G 513 721-4943
   Mansfield (G-12630)

K-B Plating Inc ....F 216 341-1115
   Cleveland (G-5630)

Kel-Mar Inc ....E 419 806-4600
   Bowling Green (G-1994)

Kelly Plating Co ....E 216 961-1080
   Cleveland (G-5643)

Kellys Polishing Metal Finshg ....G 440 232-8800
   Bedford (G-1436)

Krendl Rack Co Inc ....E 419 667-4800
   Venedocia (G-19321)

Kyron Plating Corp ....F 216 221-7275
   Cleveland (G-5668)

L & N Olde Car Co ....G 440 564-7204
   Newbury (G-15099)

Lake City Plating LLC ....F 440 964-3555
   Ashtabula (G-817)

Lake County Plating Corp ....E 440 255-8835
   Mentor (G-13627)

Lakeside Custom Plating Inc ....G 440 599-2035
   Conneaut (G-7812)

Leonhardt Plating Company ....E 513 242-1410
   Cincinnati (G-4020)

Lima Sandblasting & Pntg Co ....G 419 331-2939
   Lima (G-12044)

◆ Luke Engineering & Mfg Corp .....E 330 335-1501
   Wadsworth (G-19418)

Luke Engineering & Mfg Corp ....E 330 925-3344
   Rittman (G-16679)

Lustrous Metal Coatings Inc ....E 330 478-4653
   Canton (G-2760)

M I P Inc ....F 330 744-0215
   Youngstown (G-21138)

M&L Plating Works LLC ....G 419 255-7701
   Toledo (G-18568)

Master Chrome Service Inc ....E 216 961-2012
   Cleveland (G-5756)

▲ McCrary Metal Polishing Inc ....E 937 492-1979
   Port Jefferson (G-16420)

McGean-Rohco Inc ....D 216 441-4900
   Newburgh Heights (G-15076)

Mechanical Finishers Inc LLC ....E 513 641-5419
   Cincinnati (G-4074)

Mechanical Finishing Inc ....E 513 641-5419
   Cincinnati (G-4075)

▲ Mechanical Galv-Plating Corp .....E 937 492-3143
   Sidney (G-17200)

Medina Plating Corp ....E 330 725-4155
   Medina (G-13443)

Metal Brite Polishing ....F 937 278-9739
   Dayton (G-8486)

Metal Finishers Inc ....F 937 492-9175
   Sidney (G-17201)

Metal Finishing Needs Ltd ....G 216 561-6334
   Cleveland (G-5788)

Metal Improvement Company LLC ....E 330 425-1490
   Twinsburg (G-18985)

Metal Improvement Company LLC ....E 513 489-6484
   Blue Ash (G-1838)

Metokote Corporation ....D 440 934-4686
   Sheffield Village (G-17127)

Metokote Corporation ....C 419 221-2754
   Lima (G-12057)

Miami Valley Polishing ....F 937 615-9353
   Piqua (G-16292)

Miami Valley Polishing LL ....G 937 498-1634
   Sidney (G-17203)

Micro Lapping & Grinding Co ....E 216 267-6500
   Cleveland (G-5798)

Micro Metal Finishing LLC ....D 513 541-3095
   Cincinnati (G-4100)

Micro Products Co Inc ....D 440 943-0258
   Willoughby Hills (G-20641)

Microsheen Corporation ....F 216 481-5610
   Cleveland (G-5801)

▲ Microtek Finishing LLC ....E 513 766-5600
   West Chester (G-20029)

Milestone Services Corp ....G 330 374-9988
   Akron (G-298)

Mmf Incorporated ....F 614 252-2522
   Columbus (G-7358)

Mmf Incorporated ....F 614 252-2522
   Columbus (G-7359)

Moore Chrome Products Co ....E 419 843-3510
   Sylvania (G-18119)

MPC Plastics Inc ....D 216 881-7220
   Cleveland (G-5835)

S I C

▲ MPC Plating Inc ....E 216 881-7220
Cleveland (G-5836)

MPC Plating Inc ....E 216 881-7220
Cleveland (G-5837)

National Plating Corporation ....E 216 341-6707
Cleveland (G-5858)

National Polishing Systems Inc ....E 330 659-6547
Richfield (G-16629)

Newsome & Work Metalizing Co ....F 330 376-7144
Akron (G-313)

Nicks Plating Co Inc ....F 937 773-3175
Piqua (G-16294)

Niles Manufacturing & Finshg ....C 330 544-0402
Niles (G-15171)

Noble Anodizing Inc ....G 216 268-1263
Cleveland (G-5884)

Northeast Coatings Inc ....F 330 784-7773
Tallmadge (G-18159)

▲ Novavision Inc ....D 419 354-1427
Bowling Green (G-2003)

Nuclear Plating Service Inc ....E 216 641-1109
Brecksville (G-2068)

Oerlikon Blzers Cating USA Inc ....E 330 220-7716
Brunswick (G-2240)

Ohio Anodizing Company Inc ....F 614 252-7855
Columbus (G-7414)

◆ Ohio Decorative Products LLC ....C 419 647-9033
Spencerville (G-17463)

Ohio Electro-Polishing Co Inc ....G 419 667-2281
Venedocia (G-19322)

Ohio Metal Products Company ....E 937 228-6101
Dayton (G-8545)

Ohio Metalizing LLC ....G 330 830-1092
Massillon (G-13185)

Ohio Roll Grinding Inc ....E 330 453-1884
Louisville (G-12322)

Oliver Chemical Co Inc ....G 513 541-4540
Cincinnati (G-4185)

P & C Metal Polishing Inc ....E 513 771-9143
Cincinnati (G-4206)

▼ P & J Industries Inc ....C 419 726-2675
Toledo (G-18629)

P & J Manufacturing Inc ....F 419 241-7369
Toledo (G-18630)

P & L Heat Trting Grinding Inc ....G 330 746-1339
Youngstown (G-21159)

Parker Rst-Proof Cleveland Inc ....E 216 481-6680
Cleveland (G-5972)

Parker Trutec Incorporated ....D 937 653-8500
Urbana (G-19172)

Paxos Plating Inc ....E 330 479-0022
Canton (G-2810)

Phoenix Technologies Inc ....G 330 630-5888
Akron (G-338)

Piedmont Chemical Co Inc ....G 937 428-6640
Dayton (G-8575)

Pki Inc ....G 859 291-8680
Cincinnati (G-4241)

Plastic Platers LLC ....C 216 961-1200
Cleveland (G-6013)

Plate-All Metal Company Inc ....G 330 633-6166
Akron (G-342)

Plating Perceptions Inc ....G 330 425-4180
Twinsburg (G-19002)

Plating Resources Supply ....G 330 908-3949
Macedonia (G-12475)

Plating Solutions ....G 513 771-1941
Cincinnati (G-4244)

▲ Plating Technology Inc ....D 937 268-6882
Dayton (G-8578)

Plating Technology Inc ....E 937 268-6788
Dayton (G-8579)

Porter-Guertin Co Inc ....F 513 241-7663
Cincinnati (G-4251)

Precious Metal Plating Co ....E 440 585-7117
Wickliffe (G-20384)

Precision Finishing Systems ....F 937 415-5794
Dayton (G-8583)

Prince Plating Inc ....D 216 881-7523
Cleveland (G-6048)

▲ Quality Plating Co ....E 216 361-0151
Cleveland (G-6072)

R A Heller Company ....F 513 771-6100
Cincinnati (G-4322)

Rack Processing Company Inc ....E 937 294-1911
Moraine (G-14522)

Rack Processing Company Inc ....E 937 294-1911
Moraine (G-14521)

Raf Acquisition Co ....F 440 572-5999
Valley City (G-19227)

Rawac Plating Company ....E 937 322-7491
Springfield (G-17635)

REA Polishing Inc ....D 419 470-0216
Toledo (G-18672)

▲ Reifel Industries Inc ....D 419 737-2138
Pioneer (G-16244)

Reliable Buffing Co Inc ....E 419 647-4432
Spencerville (G-17464)

Rite Way Black & Deburr Inc ....G 937 224-7762
Dayton (G-8632)

Roberts Demand No 3 Corp ....F 216 641-0660
Cleveland (G-6121)

Roberts-Demand Corp ....E 216 581-1300
Cleveland (G-6122)

Russell Products Co Inc ....C 330 535-3391
Akron (G-386)

Russell Products Co Inc ....E 330 633-5252
Akron (G-385)

Rykon Plating Inc ....G 440 933-3273
Avon Lake (G-1049)

S & K Metal Polsg & Buffing ....F 513 732-6662
Batavia (G-1221)

Samuel Steel Pickling Company ....E 330 963-3777
Twinsburg (G-19016)

▲ Sawyer Technical Materials LLC ....E 440 951-8770
Willoughby (G-20591)

Scot Industries Inc ....E 330 262-7585
Wooster (G-20832)

Sebring Industrial Plating ....G 330 938-6666
Sebring (G-17054)

Shalmet Corporation ....C 440 236-8840
Elyria (G-9492)

Shur Clean Usa LLC ....G 513 341-5486
Liberty Township (G-11968)

Sifco Applied Srfc Cncepts LLC ....E 216 524-0099
Cleveland (G-6200)

◆ Sifco Industries Inc ....B 216 881-8600
Cleveland (G-6201)

Smith Electro Chemical Co ....E 513 351-7227
Cincinnati (G-4430)

Springco Metal Coatings Inc ....E 216 251-7023
Cleveland (G-6228)

Springfield Metal Finishing ....G 937 324-2353
Springfield (G-17652)

Stricker Refinishing Inc ....G 216 696-2906
Cleveland (G-6253)

Sun Polishing Corp ....G 440 237-5525
Cleveland (G-6263)

Super Fine Shine Inc ....G 740 774-1700
Chillicothe (G-3279)

Superfinishers Inc ....G 330 467-2125
Macedonia (G-12492)

▲ Swagelok ....G 440 349-5657
Solon (G-17389)

Tablox Inc ....G 440 953-1951
Willoughby (G-20608)

Tatham Schulz Incorporated ....E 216 861-4431
Cleveland (G-6295)

Techniplate Inc ....F 216 486-8825
Cleveland (G-6301)

Teikuro Corporation ....D 937 327-3955
Springfield (G-17662)

Toledo Metal Finishing Inc ....G 419 661-1422
Northwood (G-15491)

Trans-Acc Inc ....E 513 793-6410
Blue Ash (G-1883)

Tri-State Fabricators Inc ....E 513 752-5005
Amelia (G-587)

Tubetech Inc ....G 330 426-9476
East Palestine (G-9247)

Tuckers Mold Polishing ....G 937 339-3063
Troy (G-18883)

▲ Twist Inc ....C 937 675-9581
Jamestown (G-11353)

U S Chrome Corporation Ohio ....F 937 224-0548
Dayton (G-8736)

United Hard Chrome Corporation ....F 330 453-2786
Canton (G-2887)

United State Pltg Bumper Svc ....G 614 403-4666
Worthington (G-20892)

United Surface Finishing Inc ....G 330 453-2786
Canton (G-2889)

Vacuum Finishing Company ....F 440 286-4386
Chardon (G-3182)

Vectron Inc ....D 440 323-3369
Elyria (G-9507)

Wall Polishing LLC ....G 937 698-1330
Ludlow Falls (G-12429)

Weber Technologies Inc ....E 440 946-8833
Eastlake (G-9297)

▲ Whitaker Finishing LLC ....E 419 666-7746
Northwood (G-15496)

Whitaker Surface Systems ....E 419 874-1211
Northwood (G-15497)

Witt Enterprises Inc ....E 440 992-8333
Ashtabula (G-845)

Woodhill Plating Works Company ....E 216 883-1344
Cleveland (G-6476)

Worthington Industries Inc ....C 513 539-9291
Monroe (G-14420)

Worthington Steel Company ....C 614 438-3210
Worthington (G-20900)

Worthngton Stl Cmpny-Baltimore ....C 410 574-5835
Worthington (G-20901)

Yoder Industries Inc ....C 937 278-5769
Dayton (G-8766)

Youngstown Hard Chrome Plating ....E 330 758-9721
Youngstown (G-21252)

3479 Coating & Engraving, NEC

A Class Coatings Inc ....F 440 960-6869
Lorain (G-12229)

A Plus Powder Coaters Inc ....F 330 482-4389
Columbiana (G-6604)

AAA Galvanizing - Joliet Inc ....E 513 871-5700
Cincinnati (G-3341)

Advance Paint Technology Inc ....G 216 676-8770
Cleveland (G-4710)

▲ Advanced Coatings Intl ....G 330 794-6361
Akron (G-31)

Advanced Technical Pdts Sup Co ....F 513 851-6858
Cincinnati (G-3360)

Advantage Powder Coating Inc ....D 419 782-2363
Defiance (G-8775)

Aesthetic Finishers Inc ....E 937 778-8777
Piqua (G-16246)

Ak-Isg Steel Coating Company ....D 216 429-6901
Cleveland (G-4739)

Akron Metal Etching Co ....G 330 762-7687
Akron (G-48)

Akron Steel Treating Co ....E 330 773-8211
Akron (G-58)

Allied Coating Co ....F 937 615-0391
Piqua (G-16247)

Alpha Coatings Inc ....C 419 435-5111
Fostoria (G-9964)

◆ Alsco Metals Corporation ....E 740 983-2571
Dennison (G-8942)

American Tchnical Coatings Inc ....G 440 401-2270
Westlake (G-20253)

American Utility Proc LLC ....G 330 535-3000
Akron (G-69)

▲ Anest Iwata Usa Inc ....G 513 755-3100
Hamilton (G-10670)

Anotex Industries Inc ....G 513 860-1165
West Chester (G-19805)

▲ Aps-Materials Inc ....D 937 278-6547
Dayton (G-8161)

Aps-Materials Inc ....E 937 278-6547
Dayton (G-8162)

▲ Arcelormittal Columbus LLC ....C 614 492-6800
Columbus (G-6768)

Architectural and Industrial ....F 440 963-0410
Vermilion (G-19323)

ARE Inc ....C 330 830-7800
Massillon (G-13112)

Armoloy of Ohio Inc ....F 937 323-8702
Springfield (G-17519)

Art Galvanizing Works Inc ....F 216 749-0020
Cleveland (G-4835)

Astro-Coatings Inc ....E 330 755-1414
Struthers (G-17990)

Auld Company ....F 614 454-1010
Columbus (G-6786)

Austin Finishing Co Inc ....G 216 883-0326
Cleveland (G-4859)

Azz Incorporated ....E 330 445-2170
Canton (G-2612)

Balser Inc ....G 567 444-4737
Archbold (G-667)

Bekaert Corporation ....C 330 683-5060
Orrville (G-15729)

Benco Industries Inc ....G 440 572-3555
Strongsville (G-17896)

Boville Indus Coatings Inc ....E 330 669-8558
Smithville (G-17238)

Brilliant Colorworks LLC ....G 800 566-4162
Columbus (G-6862)

Bta of Motorcars Inc ....G 440 716-1000
North Olmsted (G-15328)

Bundy Baking Solutions ....F 740 965-3008
Sunbury *(G-18057)*

C L S Finishing Inc ....F 330 784-4134
Tallmadge *(G-18136)*

Canfield Coating LLC ....C 330 533-3311
Canfield *(G-2550)*

Canfield Metal Coating Corp ....D 330 702-3876
Canfield *(G-2551)*

Carboline Company ....G 513 896-1919
Fairfield *(G-9650)*

▲ Cardinal Rubber Company Inc ......E 330 745-2191
Barberton *(G-1113)*

Carlisle Plastics Company Inc ....G 937 845-9411
New Carlisle *(G-14798)*

Carved Stone LLC ....G 614 778-9855
Radnor *(G-16505)*

Cast Plus Inc ....E 937 743-7278
Franklin *(G-10011)*

Central Aluminum Company LLC ......E 614 491-5700
Obetz *(G-15652)*

Cincinnati Thermal Spray Inc ....C 513 793-1037
Blue Ash *(G-1765)*

Coat All ....G 419 659-2757
Columbus Grove *(G-7792)*

Coating Systems Inc ....F 513 367-5600
Harrison *(G-10774)*

Colonial Surface Solutions Inc ....D 419 659-5639
Columbus Grove *(G-7793)*

Colonial Surface Solutions Inc ....E 419 358-0129
Bluffton *(G-1910)*

Columbus Coatings Company ....D 614 492-6800
Columbus *(G-6949)*

Corrotec Inc ....E 937 325-3585
Springfield *(G-17536)*

Creative Powder Coatings ....G 440 322-8197
Elyria *(G-9398)*

Cto Inc ....G 330 785-1130
Akron *(G-134)*

Cubbison Company ....D 330 793-2481
Youngstown *(G-21059)*

Custom Color Match and Spc ....G 419 868-5882
Holland *(G-11050)*

Dayton Coating Tech LLC ....G 937 278-2060
Dayton *(G-8272)*

▲ De Nora North America Inc ....F 440 357-4000
Painesville *(G-15874)*

De Vore Engraving Co ....G 330 454-6820
Canton *(G-2681)*

Doak Laser ....G 740 374-0090
Marietta *(G-12781)*

Duffee Finishing Inc ....G 740 965-4848
Sunbury *(G-18059)*

E L Stone Company ....E 330 825-4565
Norton *(G-15510)*

Ellison Group Inc ....F 513 770-4900
Mason *(G-13013)*

Ellison Surface Tech - W LLC ....G 513 770-4900
Mason *(G-13015)*

Ellison Surface Tech Inc ....F 513 770-4922
Mason *(G-13016)*

▲ Enerfab Inc ....B 513 641-0500
Cincinnati *(G-3704)*

Epco Extrusion Painting Co ....F 330 781-6100
Youngstown *(G-21078)*

Erie Ceramic Arts Company LLC ......G 419 228-1145
Lima *(G-12010)*

▲ Etched Metal Company ....E 440 248-0240
Solon *(G-17290)*

F & K Concepts Inc ....G 937 426-6843
Beavercreek *(G-1337)*

Fayette Industrial Coatings ....E 419 636-1773
Bryan *(G-2295)*

◆ Ferro Corporation ....D 216 875-5600
Mayfield Heights *(G-13313)*

Final Finish Corp ....G 440 439-3303
Macedonia *(G-12450)*

Five Handicap Inc ....F 419 525-2511
Mansfield *(G-12603)*

Gem Coatings Ltd ....E 740 589-2998
Athens *(G-868)*

George Manufacturing Inc ....E 513 932-1067
Lebanon *(G-11801)*

Georgia Metal Coatings Company ....F 770 446-3930
Chardon *(G-3155)*

▲ Godfrey & Wing Inc ....E 330 562-1440
Aurora *(G-922)*

Great Lakes Etching Finshg Co ....F 440 439-3624
Cleveland *(G-5449)*

Greber Machine Tool Inc ....G 440 322-3685
Elyria *(G-9427)*

◆ Greenkote Usa Inc ....G 440 243-2865
Brookpark *(G-2162)*

Gs Wood & Metal Coating LLC ....G 419 375-7708
Fort Recovery *(G-9953)*

▲ Gwp Holdings Inc ....D 513 860-4050
Fairfield *(G-9662)*

Hadronics Inc ....D 513 321-9350
Cincinnati *(G-3861)*

Hardcoating Technologies Ltd ....E 330 686-2136
Munroe Falls *(G-14660)*

Hardline International Inc ....F 419 924-9556
West Unity *(G-20129)*

Hartzell Manufacturing Co Inc ....E 937 859-5955
Miamisburg *(G-13815)*

Harwood Rubber Products Inc ....E 330 923-3256
Cuyahoga Falls *(G-8008)*

Hathaway Stamp & Ident Co of C ......F 513 621-1052
Cincinnati *(G-3870)*

Herbert E Orr Company ....C 419 399-4866
Paulding *(G-16005)*

Heritage Industrial Finshg Inc ....D 330 798-9840
Akron *(G-222)*

▲ High Tech Elastomers Inc ....E 937 236-6575
Vandalia *(G-19296)*

Highway Safety Corp ....F 740 387-6991
Marion *(G-12874)*

◆ Howmet Corporation ....E 800 242-9898
Newburgh Heights *(G-15074)*

Imperial Metal Solutions LLC ....F 216 781-4094
Cleveland *(G-5556)*

Industrial and Mar Eng Svc Co ....F 740 694-0791
Fredericktown *(G-10104)*

Industrial Finishers Inc ....G 330 343-7797
Dover *(G-8993)*

Industrial Metal Finishing ....G 440 232-2400
Solon *(G-17314)*

Industrial Thermoset Plas Inc ....F 440 975-0411
Mentor *(G-13608)*

Inter-Ion Inc ....E 330 928-9655
Cuyahoga Falls *(G-8011)*

Interntnal Tchncal Catings Inc ....D 614 449-6669
Columbus *(G-7208)*

Ionbond LLC ....F 216 831-0880
Cleveland *(G-5586)*

Ivac Technologies Corp ....F 216 662-4987
Cleveland *(G-5592)*

J M Hamilton Group Inc ....F 419 229-4010
Lima *(G-12032)*

Kars Ohio LLC ....G 614 655-1099
Pataskala *(G-15973)*

Kecamm LLC ....G 330 527-2918
Garrettsville *(G-10326)*

Laserdealer Inc ....G 440 357-8419
Mentor *(G-13630)*

Lima Sandblasting & Pntg Co ....G 419 331-2939
Lima *(G-12044)*

Logan Coatings LLC ....G 740 380-0047
Logan *(G-12184)*

◆ Loroco Industries Inc ....E 513 891-9544
Blue Ash *(G-1828)*

M & M Engraving ....G 216 749-7166
Cleveland *(G-5716)*

Mark True Engraving Company ....G 216 252-7422
Cleveland *(G-5746)*

Master Marking Company Inc ....F 330 688-6797
Stow *(G-17772)*

Master Vac Incorporated ....G 419 335-7796
Wauseon *(G-19689)*

▲ Materials Science Intl Inc ....E 614 870-0400
Columbus *(G-7323)*

▲ Mesocoat Inc ....F 216 453-0866
Euclid *(G-9593)*

Metokote Corporation ....D 440 934-4686
Sheffield Village *(G-17127)*

▲ Metokote Corporation ....B 419 996-7800
Lima *(G-12054)*

Metokote Corporation ....D 419 227-1100
Lima *(G-12055)*

Metokote Corporation ....D 319 232-6994
Lima *(G-12056)*

Metokote Corporation ....C 419 221-2754
Lima *(G-12057)*

Metokote Corporation ....C 937 235-2811
Dayton *(G-8487)*

Miamisburg Coating ....F 937 866-1323
Miamisburg *(G-13834)*

Momentive Performance Mtls Inc ......C 740 928-7010
Hebron *(G-10874)*

Momentive Performance Mtls Inc ......A 440 878-5705
Richmond Heights *(G-16655)*

◆ Momentive Prfmce Mtls Qrtz Inc ....C 440 878-5700
Strongsville *(G-17941)*

MSC Walbridge Coatings Inc ....C 419 666-6130
Walbridge *(G-19461)*

Nation Coating Systems Inc ....G 937 746-7632
Franklin *(G-10038)*

Newsome & Work Metalizing Co ....F 330 376-7144
Akron *(G-313)*

Newtons Paint & Body ....G 740 352-9334
Lucasville *(G-12423)*

Niles Manufacturing & Finshg ....C 330 544-0402
Niles *(G-15171)*

Oerlikon Blzers Cating USA Inc ....E 330 220-7716
Brunswick *(G-2240)*

Office Magic Inc ....F 510 782-6100
Medina *(G-13452)*

Ohio Coatings Company ....D 740 859-5500
Yorkville *(G-21007)*

Ohio Galvanizing Corp ....E 740 387-6474
Marion *(G-12891)*

Omni Manufacturing Inc ....D 419 394-7424
Saint Marys *(G-16846)*

Omni Manufacturing Inc ....F 419 394-7424
Saint Marys *(G-16847)*

Parker Rst-Proof Cleveland Inc ....E 216 481-6680
Cleveland *(G-5972)*

Parker Trutec Incorporated ....D 937 653-8500
Urbana *(G-19172)*

▲ Parker Trutec Incorporated ....D 937 323-8833
Springfield *(G-17625)*

Perfection Finishers Inc ....E 419 337-8015
Wauseon *(G-19693)*

Pioneer Custom Coating LLC ....E 419 737-3152
Pioneer *(G-16236)*

Pki Inc ....G 859 291-8680
Cincinnati *(G-4241)*

Play All LLC ....G 440 992-7529
Ashtabula *(G-833)*

Poly-Met Inc ....F 330 630-9006
Akron *(G-343)*

▲ Precision Applied Coatings ....G 614 252-8711
Columbus *(G-7513)*

Precision Coatings Inc ....F 216 441-0805
Cleveland *(G-6034)*

Precision Coatings Systems ....G 937 642-4727
Marysville *(G-12963)*

▲ Pro-TEC Coating Company Inc .....C 419 943-1211
Leipsic *(G-11875)*

Procoat Painting Inc ....G 513 735-2500
Batavia *(G-1218)*

Production Paint Finishers Inc ....D 937 448-2627
Bradford *(G-2026)*

Progressive Manufacturing Co ....G 330 784-4717
Akron *(G-354)*

Progressive Powder Coating Inc ....E 440 974-3478
Mentor *(G-13701)*

Rack Coating Service Inc ....E 330 854-2869
Canal Fulton *(G-2512)*

Rack Processing Company Inc ....E 937 294-1911
Moraine *(G-14522)*

Raf Acquisition Co ....F 440 572-5999
Valley City *(G-19227)*

▲ Reifel Industries Inc ....D 419 737-2138
Pioneer *(G-16244)*

Rite Way Black & Deburr Inc ....G 937 224-7762
Dayton *(G-8632)*

Roban Inc ....G 330 794-1059
Lakemore *(G-11645)*

Roemer Industries Inc ....D 330 448-2000
Masury *(G-13216)*

Russell Products Co Inc ....E 330 633-5252
Akron *(G-385)*

Russell Products Co Inc ....G 330 434-9163
Akron *(G-387)*

Russell Products Co Inc ....G 216 267-0880
Akron *(G-388)*

Russell T Bundy Associates Inc ....E 419 526-4454
Mansfield *(G-12674)*

Ryder Engraving Inc ....G 740 927-7193
Pataskala *(G-15982)*

Sapa Extrusions North Amer LLC .....C 888 935-5759
Sidney *(G-17221)*

Scholz & Ey Engravers Inc ....F 614 444-8052
Columbus *(G-7597)*

Seacor Painting Corporation ....G 330 755-6361
Campbell *(G-2491)*

Semper Quality Industry Inc ....G 440 352-8111
Mentor *(G-13719)*

SH Bell Company ....E 412 963-9910
East Liverpool *(G-9227)*

SIC

Signa Stortech Systems Inc ....E 214 357-0411
  Canton *(G-2849)*

▲ Signature Partners Inc ....D 419 678-1400
  Coldwater *(G-6571)*

Simcote Inc ....E 740 382-5000
  Marion *(G-12902)*

▼ Spectrum Metal Finishing Inc ....D 330 758-8358
  Youngstown *(G-21211)*

Springco Metal Coatings Inc ....C 216 251-7023
  Cleveland *(G-6228)*

▲ Star Fab Inc ....C 330 533-9863
  Canfield *(G-2576)*

Sterling Coating ....G 513 942-4900
  West Chester *(G-19949)*

Surftech Inc ....G 440 275-3356
  Austinburg *(G-967)*

Syscom Advanced Materials Inc .....F 614 487-3626
  Columbus *(G-7672)*

T&K Laser Works Inc ....G 937 693-3783
  Botkins *(G-1956)*

▼ Tce International Ltd ....G 800 962-2376
  Perry *(G-16059)*

▲ Techneglas Inc ....G 419 873-2000
  Perrysburg *(G-16154)*

Tendon Manufacturing Inc ....E 216 663-3200
  Cleveland *(G-6305)*

Tennessee Coatings Inc ....F 513 770-4900
  Mason *(G-13096)*

Terra Coat LLC ....G 216 254-8157
  Northfield *(G-15475)*

Thornton Powder Coatings Inc ....F 419 522-7183
  Mansfield *(G-12698)*

Tool & Die Systems Inc ....E 440 327-5800
  North Ridgeville *(G-15406)*

Trans-Acc Inc ....E 513 793-6410
  Blue Ash *(G-1883)*

Treemen Industries Inc ....E 330 965-3777
  Boardman *(G-1925)*

Tri-State Fabricators Inc ....E 513 752-5005
  Amelia *(G-587)*

Tsp Inc ....E 513 732-8900
  Batavia *(G-1229)*

Universal Rack & Equipment Co ......E 330 963-6776
  Twinsburg *(G-19033)*

V & S Columbus Galanizing LLC .....D 614 449-8281
  Columbus *(G-7730)*

▲ Vacono America LLC ....E 216 938-7428
  Cleveland *(G-6405)*

Vacuum Finishing Company ....F 440 286-4386
  Chardon *(G-3182)*

▼ Venus Trading LLC ....G 513 374-0066
  Loveland *(G-12398)*

Visimax Technologies Inc ....F 330 405-8330
  Twinsburg *(G-19037)*

Visionmark Nameplate Co LLC ....E 419 977-3131
  New Bremen *(G-14796)*

▲ Voigt & Schweitzer LLC ....F 614 449-8281
  Columbus *(G-7744)*

W C J Corp ....G 216 523-1135
  Cleveland *(G-6434)*

▼ Witt Industries Inc ....D 513 871-5700
  Mason *(G-13103)*

Woodrow Manufacturing Co ....E 937 399-9333
  Springfield *(G-17682)*

Worldclass Processing Corp ....E 724 251-9000
  Twinsburg *(G-19040)*

X-Treme Finishes Inc ....F 330 474-0614
  Medina *(G-13498)*

3482 Small Arms Ammunition

Ares Inc ....D 419 635-2175
  Port Clinton *(G-16393)*

Big Iron Guns Inc ....G 740 464-0852
  Portsmouth *(G-16432)*

Center Mass Ammo LLC ....G 440 796-6207
  Madison *(G-12498)*

Galion LLC ....C 419 468-5214
  Galion *(G-10268)*

Grindel Sales Corp ....G 740 382-1528
  Marion *(G-12870)*

Jmr Enterprises LLC ....G 937 618-1736
  Maineville *(G-12525)*

Johndavid D Jones ....G 740 264-0176
  Wintersville *(G-20711)*

Mons Meg Cartridges Inc ....G 937 849-9646
  Medway *(G-13500)*

National Bullet Co ....G 800 317-9506
  Eastlake *(G-9284)*

▲ Premier Shot Company Inc ....G 330 405-0583
  Twinsburg *(G-19005)*

R & S Monitions Inc ....G 614 846-0597
  Columbus *(G-7542)*

3483 Ammunition, Large

Center Mass Ammo LLC ....G 440 796-6207
  Madison *(G-12498)*

▼ Ithaca Gun Company ....E 419 294-4113
  Upper Sandusky *(G-19126)*

L-3 Fuzing and Ord Systems Inc ......A 513 943-2000
  Cincinnati *(G-3310)*

▲ Marine Jet Power Inc ....G 614 759-9000
  Blacklick *(G-1701)*

Vergeline LLC ....G 419 730-0300
  Toledo *(G-18767)*

3484 Small Arms

762mm Firearms LLC ....G 440 655-8572
  Wadsworth *(G-19384)*

▲ American Apex Corporation ....F 614 652-2000
  Plain City *(G-16319)*

Ares Inc ....D 419 635-2175
  Port Clinton *(G-16393)*

Beech Armament LLC ....G 330 962-4694
  Cuyahoga Falls *(G-7974)*

Faxon Firearms LLC ....G 513 674-2580
  Cincinnati *(G-3744)*

Global Precision Parts Inc ....D 419 453-0010
  Ottoville *(G-15821)*

Highpoint Firearms ....E 419 747-9444
  Mansfield *(G-12625)*

Iberia Firearms Inc ....G 419 468-3746
  Galion *(G-10276)*

Inland Manufacturing LLC ....G 937 835-0220
  Dayton *(G-8403)*

Jmr Enterprises LLC ....G 937 618-1736
  Maineville *(G-12525)*

Kelblys Rifle Range Inc ....G 330 683-0070
  North Lawrence *(G-15306)*

Nicana Consulting Inc ....G 419 615-9703
  Kalida *(G-11415)*

◆ Ohio Ordnance Works Inc ....G 440 285-3481
  Chardon *(G-3170)*

Parabellum Armament Co LLC ....G 614 557-5987
  Grove City *(G-10582)*

▲ Quality Replacement Parts Inc .....G 216 674-0200
  Cleveland *(G-6073)*

Reloading Supplies Corp ....G 440 228-0367
  Ashtabula *(G-836)*

Smokin Guns LLC ....G 440 324-4003
  Elyria *(G-9494)*

X-Treme Shooting Products LLC ......G 513 313-3464
  Batavia *(G-1234)*

Zshot Inc ....G 800 385-8581
  Lewis Center *(G-11930)*

3489 Ordnance & Access, NEC

Advanced Innovation & Mfg Inc ....G 330 308-6360
  New Philadelphia *(G-14882)*

▲ American Apex Corporation ....F 614 652-2000
  Plain City *(G-16319)*

Ares Inc ....D 419 635-2175
  Port Clinton *(G-16393)*

Excelitas Technologies Corp ....C 937 865-4621
  Miamisburg *(G-13807)*

Expert Outfitters ....G 330 965-9620
  North Lima *(G-15316)*

General Dynamics-Ots Inc ....C 937 746-8500
  Springboro *(G-17481)*

Hi-Tech Solutions LLC ....G 216 331-3050
  Cleveland *(G-5511)*

Ordnance Cleaning Systems LLC ......G 440 205-0677
  Mentor *(G-13674)*

3491 Industrial Valves

Akron Steel Fabricators Co ....E 330 644-0616
  Akron *(G-57)*

▲ Alkon Corporation ....D 419 355-9111
  Fremont *(G-10124)*

Alkon Corporation ....E 614 799-6650
  Dublin *(G-9039)*

Bosch Rexroth Corporation ....B 330 263-3300
  Wooster *(G-20751)*

Canfield Industries Inc ....G 800 554-5071
  Youngstown *(G-21042)*

Cfrc Wtr & Enrgy Solutions Inc ....G 216 479-0290
  Cleveland *(G-5011)*

Clark-Reliance Corporation ....G 440 572-7408
  Strongsville *(G-17903)*

◆ Clark-Reliance Corporation ....C 440 572-1500
  Strongsville *(G-17902)*

Cleveland Valve & Gauge Co LLC ....G 216 362-1702
  Cleveland *(G-5084)*

Curtiss-Wright Flow Control ....D 513 735-2538
  Batavia *(G-1175)*

Curtiss-Wright Flow Control ....D 513 528-7900
  Cincinnati *(G-3296)*

Curtiss-Wright Flow Control ....D 513 528-7900
  Cincinnati *(G-3297)*

Dayton Air Control Pdts LLC ....G 937 254-4441
  Moraine *(G-14476)*

Digital Automation Associates ....G 419 352-6977
  Bowling Green *(G-1986)*

Emerson Network Power System ......G 614 841-6309
  Westerville *(G-20150)*

Fisher Controls Intl LLC ....G 513 285-6000
  West Chester *(G-19864)*

Flow Technology Inc ....C 513 745-6000
  Cincinnati *(G-3764)*

▲ Hearth Products Controls Co ....F 937 436-9800
  Dayton *(G-8108)*

Honeywell International Inc ....A 937 484-2000
  Urbana *(G-19162)*

Hunt Valve Company Inc ....E 330 337-9535
  Salem *(G-16901)*

Hunt Valve Company Inc ....G 330 337-9535
  Salem *(G-16902)*

Kaman Industrial Tech Corp ....G 740 779-9201
  Chillicothe *(G-3248)*

Keen Manufacturing Inc ....G 330 427-0045
  Washingtonville *(G-19642)*

Maass Midwest Mfg Inc ....G 419 894-6424
  Arcadia *(G-654)*

Machine Component Mfg ....F 330 454-4566
  Canton *(G-2765)*

Manico Inc ....G 440 946-5333
  Willoughby *(G-20534)*

Nupro Company ....C 440 951-9729
  Willoughby *(G-20559)*

Parker-Hannifin Corporation ....C 419 542-6611
  Hicksville *(G-10905)*

Parker-Hannifin Corporation ....C 937 644-3915
  Marysville *(G-12962)*

Phoenix Partners LLC ....E 734 654-2201
  Ottawa Hills *(G-15817)*

Precision Q Systems LLC ....E 614 286-5142
  Westerville *(G-20229)*

▲ Richards Industries Inc ....C 513 533-7340
  Cincinnati *(G-4344)*

▲ Rogers Industrial Products Inc .....E 330 535-3331
  Akron *(G-378)*

Russments Inc ....G 513 602-5035
  Cincinnati *(G-4368)*

Ruthman Pump and Engineering ....E 937 783-2411
  Blanchester *(G-1716)*

Seawin Inc ....D 419 355-9111
  Fremont *(G-10182)*

Shan-Rod Inc ....E 419 588-2066
  Berlin Heights *(G-1663)*

Sherwood Valve LLC ....D 216 264-5028
  Cleveland *(G-6194)*

Swagelok Company ....G 440 248-4600
  Willoughby Hills *(G-20644)*

◆ Swagelok Company ....A 440 248-4600
  Solon *(G-17390)*

Swagelok Company ....D 440 349-5652
  Solon *(G-17391)*

Swagelok Company ....E 440 349-5836
  Solon *(G-17393)*

Transdigm Inc ....G 216 706-2939
  Cleveland *(G-6347)*

▲ Tylok International Inc ....D 216 261-7310
  Cleveland *(G-6377)*

Vickers International Inc ....E 419 867-2200
  Maumee *(G-13307)*

Viking Group Inc ....G 937 443-0433
  Dayton *(G-8743)*

▲ Waxman Industries Inc ....C 440 439-1830
  Cleveland *(G-6452)*

▲ William Powell Company ....E 513 852-2000
  Cincinnati *(G-4596)*

Xomox Corporation ....E 513 947-1200
  Batavia *(G-1235)*

Xomox Corporation ....E 936 271-6500
  Cincinnati *(G-4614)*

Xomox Corporation ....G 513 745-6000
  Blue Ash *(G-1903)*

Zal Air Products Inc ....G 440 237-7155
  Cleveland *(G-6492)*

3492 Fluid Power Valves & Hose Fittings

▲ Ace Manufacturing Company ....E 513 541-2490
West Chester (G-19976)

Aerocontrolex Group Inc ....D 440 352-6182
Cleveland (G-4719)

Aeroquip-Vickers Inc ....G 216 523-5000
Cleveland (G-4722)

Air-Way Manufacturing Company ....C 419 298-2366
Edgerton (G-9325)

Aj Fluid Power Sales & Sup Inc ......G 440 255-7960
Mentor (G-13514)

▲ Alkon Corporation ....D 419 355-9111
Fremont (G-10124)

Canfield Industries Inc ....C 800 554-5071
Youngstown (G-21042)

Cfrc Wtr & Enrgy Solutions Inc ....G 216 479-0290
Cleveland (G-5011)

Commercial Honing Ohio Inc ....D 330 343-8896
Dover (G-8972)

Custom Cltch Jint Hydrlics Inc ....F 216 431-1630
Cleveland (G-5149)

Dana Incorporated ....B 419 887-3000
Maumee (G-13246)

▲ Dana Limited ....B 630 697-3783
Maumee (G-13249)

Dixon Valve & Coupling Co Inc ......F 330 425-3000
Twinsburg (G-18926)

DNC Hydraulics LLC ....F 419 963-2800
Rawson (G-16573)

▲ Dyna-Flex Inc ....F 440 946-9424
Mentor (G-13567)

Eaton Hydraulics LLC ....E 419 232-7777
Van Wert (G-19254)

Eaton-Aeroquip Inc ....G 419 891-7775
Maumee (G-13258)

▲ Eaton-Aeroquip Llc ....C 216 523-5000
Cleveland (G-5254)

Eaton-Aeroquip Llc ....D 419 238-1190
Van Wert (G-19255)

Encore Distributing Inc ....G 513 948-1242
Cincinnati (G-3702)

Fluid Line Products Inc ....C 440 946-9470
Willoughby (G-20491)

Freudenberg-Nok General Partnr 419 427-5221
Findlay (G-9827)

▲ Hy-Production Inc ....C 330 273-2400
Valley City (G-19206)

Hydraulic Parts Store Inc ....E 330 364-6667
New Philadelphia (G-14902)

▼ Industrial Connections Inc ....G 330 274-2155
Mantua (G-12713)

Integrated Aircraft Systems ....G 330 686-2982
Stow (G-17764)

Kaman Fluid Power LLC ....C 330 315-3100
Akron (G-248)

◆ Kirtland Capital Partners LP ....E 216 593-0100
Beachwood (G-1276)

▲ Malone Specialty Inc ....F 440 255-4200
Mentor (G-13645)

Maverick Industries Inc ....F 440 838-5335
Brecksville (G-2064)

Mid-State Sales Inc ....G 330 744-2158
Youngstown (G-21145)

National Aviation Products Inc ....D 330 688-6494
Stow (G-17779)

▲ National Machine Company ....C 330 688-6494
Stow (G-17780)

Netherland Rubber Company ....F 513 733-0883
Cincinnati (G-4146)

Ohio Hydraulics Inc ....E 513 771-2590
Cincinnati (G-4178)

Parker-Hannifin Corporation ....C 419 542-6611
Hicksville (G-10905)

Parker-Hannifin Corporation ....B 440 366-5100
Elyria (G-9475)

Parker-Hannifin Corporation ....E 440 943-5700
Wickliffe (G-20381)

Parker-Hannifin Corporation ....C 937 962-5566
Lewisburg (G-11939)

Parker-Hannifin Corporation ....B 440 943-5700
Wickliffe (G-20379)

Parker-Hannifin Corporation ....D 218 534-3148
Wickliffe (G-20380)

◆ Parker-Hannifin Corporation ....B 216 896-3000
Cleveland (G-5973)

Parker-Hannifin Corporation ....F 216 896-3000
Cleveland (G-5976)

Parker-Hannifin Corporation ....B 937 456-5571
Eaton (G-9320)

Quality Machining and Mfg Inc ....E 419 899-2543
Sherwood (G-17147)

▲ Ruthman Pump and Engineering ....G 513 559-1901
Cincinnati (G-4369)

SMC Corporation of America ....E 330 659-2006
Richfield (G-16638)

▲ SSP Fittings Corp ....D 330 425-4250
Twinsburg (G-19022)

State Metal Hose Inc ....G 614 527-4700
Hilliard (G-10982)

Summers Acquisition Corp ....G 740 373-0303
Marietta (G-12839)

Superior Holding LLC ....G 216 651-9400
Cleveland (G-6265)

Superior Products LLC ....D 216 651-9400
Cleveland (G-6270)

▼ Superior Products Llc ....G 216 651-9400
Cleveland (G-6269)

▲ Swagelok ....G 440 349-5657
Solon (G-17389)

Swagelok Company ....E 440 349-5836
Solon (G-17393)

T D Group Holdings LLC ....G 216 706-2939
Cleveland (G-6289)

▲ Taiyo America Inc ....F 419 300-8811
Saint Marys (G-16858)

▲ Thogus Products Company ....D 440 933-8850
Avon Lake (G-1053)

Transdigm Inc ....F 216 291-6025
Cleveland (G-6346)

Transdigm Inc ....G 216 706-2939
Cleveland (G-6347)

▲ Tylok International Inc ....D 216 261-7310
Cleveland (G-6377)

United States Controls Inc ....G 330 758-1147
Poland (G-16386)

Valv-Trol Company ....F 330 686-2800
Stow (G-17814)

Valveco Inc ....D 330 337-9535
Salem (G-16933)

Valvole America LLC ....G 330 464-8872
Medina (G-13495)

Winzeler Stamping Co ....G 419 485-3147
Montpelier (G-14458)

Zaytran Corporation ....E 440 324-2814
Elyria (G-9512)

3493 Steel Springs, Except Wire

Accurate Tool Co Inc ....G 330 332-9448
Salem (G-16868)

Crawford Manufacturing Company .....F 330 897-1060
Baltic (G-1068)

▲ Dayton Progress Corporation ....A 937 859-5111
Dayton (G-8284)

E & L Spring Shop ....G 440 632-1439
Middlefield (G-13933)

Elyria Spring & Specialty Inc ....E 440 323-5502
Elyria (G-9417)

Euclid Spring Co ....E 440 943-3213
Wickliffe (G-20365)

Formed Metal Products Inc ....F 440 775-0819
Oberlin (G-15639)

Golden Spring Co Inc ....F 937 848-2513
Bellbrook (G-1509)

Hendrickson International Corp ....D 740 929-5600
Hebron (G-10870)

Jamestown Industries Inc ....D 330 779-0670
Youngstown (G-21125)

▲ Kern-Liebers Usa Inc ....D 419 865-2437
Holland (G-11070)

▲ Liteflex LLC ....E 937 836-7025
Englewood (G-9530)

Marik Spring Inc ....G 330 564-0617
Tallmadge (G-18152)

Matthew Warren Inc ....E 614 418-0250
Columbus (G-7326)

▼ Napoleon Spring Works Inc ....C 419 445-1010
Archbold (G-688)

Precision Products Group Inc ....D 330 698-4711
Apple Creek (G-647)

Rassini Chassis Systems LLC ....D 419 485-1524
Montpelier (G-14452)

▼ Service Spring Corp ....D 419 838-6081
Maumee (G-13292)

▲ Solon Manufacturing Company ......C 440 286-7149
Chardon (G-3180)

Tadd Spring Co Inc ....E 440 572-1313
Strongsville (G-17976)

Timac Manufacturing Company ....F 937 372-3305
Xenia (G-20980)

Torsion Control Product ....G 248 597-9997
Dayton (G-8721)

Tremac Corporation ....E 937 372-8662
Xenia (G-20982)

3494 Valves & Pipe Fittings, NEC

Adaptall America Inc ....F 330 425-4114
Twinsburg (G-18894)

Air Tool Service Company ....F 440 701-1021
Mentor (G-13513)

◆ Alloy Bllows Prcision Wldg Inc ......D 440 684-3000
Cleveland (G-4767)

Amaltech Inc ....G 440 248-7500
Solon (G-17256)

Auto-Valve Inc ....E 937 854-3037
Dayton (G-8172)

Bosch Rexroth Corporation ....B 330 263-3300
Wooster (G-20751)

Bowes Manufacturing Inc ....G 216 378-2110
Solon (G-17271)

Calvin J Magsig ....G 419 862-3311
Elmore (G-9361)

Crane Pumps & Systems Inc ....B 937 773-2442
Piqua (G-16256)

Cylinders & Valves Inc ....G 440 238-7343
Strongsville (G-17910)

Drainage Pipe & Fitting ....G 419 538-6337
Ottawa (G-15793)

Eaton Corporation ....C 440 826-1115
Berea (G-1613)

Eaton Corporation ....C 330 274-0743
Aurora (G-916)

Edward W Daniel LLC ....E 440 647-1960
Wellington (G-19742)

▲ Fcx Performance Inc ....E 614 324-6050
Columbus (G-7078)

Fulflo Specialties Company ....E 937 783-2411
Blanchester (G-1713)

General Aluminum Mfg Company ......C 419 739-9300
Wapakoneta (G-19487)

▲ General Plug and Mfg Co ....C 440 926-2411
Grafton (G-10426)

Greater Cleve Pipe Ftting Fund ......F 216 524-8334
Cleveland (G-5458)

Grip Force LLC ....G 440 497-7014
Eastlake (G-9272)

H P E Inc ....F 330 833-3161
Massillon (G-13145)

Hydro-Aire Inc ....G 440 323-3211
Elyria (G-9431)

Ill Williams LLC ....G 440 721-8191
Chardon (G-3158)

Impaction Co ....G 440 349-5652
Solon (G-17313)

Insulpro Inc ....F 614 262-3768
Columbus (G-7200)

◆ Kirtland Capital Partners LP ....E 216 593-0100
Beachwood (G-1276)

Lsq Manufacturing Inc ....F 330 725-4905
Medina (G-13437)

Machine Component Mfg ....G 330 454-4566
Canton (G-2765)

Mack Iron Works Company ....E 419 626-3712
Sandusky (G-16984)

Mih Marketing Group Inc ....F 740 942-0411
Cadiz (G-2420)

Northcoast Valve and Gate Inc ....G 440 392-9910
Mentor (G-13669)

Nupro Company ....C 440 951-9729
Willoughby (G-20559)

O E M Hydraulics Inc ....G 740 454-1201
Zanesville (G-21335)

Oceco Inc ....F 419 447-0916
Tiffin (G-18235)

▲ Opw Engineered Systems Inc ....D 888 771-9438
Lebanon (G-11824)

Parker-Hannifin Corporation ....B 937 456-5571
Eaton (G-9320)

Parker-Hannifin Corporation ....C 614 279-7070
Columbus (G-7462)

Parker-Hannifin Corporation ....C 937 962-5301
Lewisburg (G-11938)

Parker-Hannifin Corporation ....C 216 531-3000
Cleveland (G-5974)

PHD Manufacturing Inc ....C 330 482-9256
Columbiana (G-6628)

Piersante and Associates ....G 330 533-9904
Canfield (G-2569)

Pipelines Inc ....G 330 448-0000
Masury (G-13215)

SIC

▲ Precision Fittings LLC ....E 440 647-4143
Wellington (G-19752)
▲ Richards Industries Inc ....C 513 533-7340
Cincinnati (G-4344)
Robbins & Myers Inc ....B 937 327-3111
Springfield (G-17642)
▲ Robeck Fluid Power Co ....D 330 562-1140
Aurora (G-944)
Ruthman Pump and Engineering ....E 937 783-2411
Blanchester (G-1716)
Simplex Time Recorder LLC ....D 419 861-0661
Maumee (G-13293)
Siteone Landscape Supply LLC ....G 330 220-8691
Brunswick (G-2257)
Spirax Sarco Inc ....G 803 714-2023
Worthington (G-20889)
▲ SSP Fittings Corp ....D 330 425-4250
Twinsburg (G-19022)
Stelter and Brinck Inc ....E 513 367-9300
Harrison (G-10805)
Stephens Pipe & Steel LLC ....C 740 869-2257
Mount Sterling (G-14604)
Steven L Lones ....G 740 452-8851
Zanesville (G-21357)
Superior Holding LLC ....E 216 651-9400
Cleveland (G-6265)
Superior Products LLC ....D 216 651-9400
Cleveland (G-6270)
▼ Superior Products Llc ....G 216 651-9400
Cleveland (G-6269)
▲ Swagelok ....E 440 349-5657
Solon (G-17389)
◆ Swagelok Company ....A 440 248-4600
Solon (G-17390)
Swagelok Company ....D 440 349-5652
Solon (G-17391)
Swagelok Company ....E 440 944-8988
Willoughby Hills (G-20645)
Swagelok Company ....E 440 473-1050
Cleveland (G-6278)
Swagelok Company ....E 440 349-5836
Solon (G-17393)
Swagelok Company ....E 440 542-1250
Solon (G-17394)
Swagelok Company ....F 440 442-6611
Cleveland (G-6277)
Swagelok Company ....D 440 349-5934
Solon (G-17392)
▲ Tech Tool Inc ....F 330 674-1176
Millersburg (G-14267)
▲ Thogus Products Company ....D 440 933-8850
Avon Lake (G-1053)
▲ Tylok International Inc ....D 216 261-7310
Cleveland (G-6377)
US Fittings Inc ....F 234 212-9420
Twinsburg (G-19034)
▲ Waxman Industries Inc ....C 440 439-1830
Cleveland (G-6452)
Wells Inc ....F 419 457-2611
Risingsun (G-16673)
▲ William Powell Company ....E 513 852-2000
Cincinnati (G-4596)
Xomox Corporation ....G 936 271-6500
Cincinnati (G-4614)
Zeiger Industries ....E 330 484-4413
Canton (G-2906)

3495 Wire Springs

A & W Spring Co Inc ....G 937 222-7284
Dayton (G-8126)
B & P Spring Production Co ....F 216 486-4260
Cleveland (G-4881)
Barnes Group Inc ....G 440 526-5900
Brecksville (G-2035)
Barnes Group Inc ....E 419 891-9292
Maumee (G-13229)
▲ Bloomingburg Spring & Wire For .....E 740 437-7614
Bloomingburg (G-1720)
▲ Dayton Progress Corporation ....A 937 859-5111
Dayton (G-8284)
Elyria Spring & Specialty Inc ....E 440 323-5502
Elyria (G-9417)
Kern-Liebers Texas Inc ....E 419 865-2437
Holland (G-11069)
▲ Kern-Liebers Usa Inc ....D 419 865-2437
Holland (G-11070)
Matthew Warren Inc ....E 614 418-0250
Columbus (G-7326)
Ohio Wire Form & Spring Co ....F 614 444-3676
Columbus (G-7436)

Precision Products Group Inc ....D 330 698-4711
Apple Creek (G-647)
Protech Electric LLC ....F 937 427-0813
Beavercreek (G-1357)
Regal Spring Co ....G 614 278-7761
Columbus (G-7552)
▲ Solon Manufacturing Company ....E 440 286-7149
Chardon (G-3180)
▼ Spring Team Inc ....D 440 275-5981
Austinburg (G-966)
Spring Works Inc ....E 614 351-9345
Columbus (G-7646)
Springtime Manufacturing ....G 419 697-3720
Toledo (G-18702)
▲ Stalder Spring Works Inc ....F 937 322-6120
Springfield (G-17656)
▲ Supro Spring & Wire Forms Inc ....E 330 722-5628
Medina (G-13485)
Tadd Spring Co Inc ....E 440 572-1313
Strongsville (G-17976)
The Reliable Spring Wire Frms ....E 440 365-7400
Elyria (G-9501)
Trupoint Products ....F 330 204-3302
Sugarcreek (G-18046)
▲ Twist Inc ....E 937 675-9581
Jamestown (G-11353)
Twist Inc ....E 937 675-9581
Jamestown (G-11354)
Wire Products Company Inc ....C 216 267-0777
Cleveland (G-6469)
▼ Yost Superior Co ....E 937 323-7591
Springfield (G-17683)

3496 Misc Fabricated Wire Prdts

4-Sure Wire Products Inc ....G 440 563-9263
Rock Creek (G-16684)
Able Fence of Columbus Inc ....G 614 253-8587
Columbus (G-6679)
◆ Alcan Corporation ....E 440 460-3307
Cleveland (G-4741)
▲ Amanda Manufacturing ....C 740 385-6893
Logan (G-12171)
American Pennekamp Mfg Inc ....G 740 687-0096
Lancaster (G-11685)
Apache Hose & Belting Co Inc ....D 513 587-8313
West Chester (G-19981)
Assembly Specialty Pdts Inc ....E 216 676-5600
Cleveland (G-4848)
Blacco Splcing Rgging Loft Inc ....G 614 444-2888
Columbus (G-6836)
▲ Bloomingburg Spring & Wire For .....D 740 437-7614
Bloomingburg (G-1720)
Busch & Thiem Inc ....E 419 625-7515
Sandusky (G-16952)
C & F Fabrications Inc ....E 937 666-3234
East Liberty (G-9199)
Cable and Ctrl Solutions LLC ....G 937 254-2227
Dayton (G-8097)
▲ Cable Mfg & Assembly Inc ....C 330 874-2900
Bolivar (G-1929)
Canron Manufacturing Inc ....F 330 497-1131
Greentown (G-10485)
Clamps Inc ....E 419 729-2141
Toledo (G-18398)
▲ Cleveland Wire Cloth & Mfg Co ....E 216 341-1832
Cleveland (G-5087)
Columbus McKinnon Corporation ....D 330 424-7248
Lisbon (G-12118)
Con-Belt Inc ....F 330 273-2003
Valley City (G-19201)
Contitech Usa Inc ....E 937 644-8900
Marysville (G-12937)
Darryl Smith ....G 216 991-5468
Cleveland (G-5169)
Dayton Wire Products Inc ....E 937 236-8000
Dayton (G-8291)
▲ Die Co Inc ....E 440 942-8856
Eastlake (G-9265)
Dolin Supply Co ....E 304 529-4171
South Point (G-17436)
Eagle Wire Works Inc ....F 216 341-8550
Cleveland (G-5238)
Efco Corp ....E 614 876-1226
Columbus (G-7048)
Elyria Spring & Specialty Inc ....E 440 323-5502
Elyria (G-9417)
▲ Engineered Wire Products Inc ....C 419 294-3817
Upper Sandusky (G-19121)
▲ Ever Roll Specialties Co ....E 937 964-1302
Springfield (G-17555)

Falcon Fab and Finishes LLC ....G 740 820-4458
Lucasville (G-12420)
Fastener Industries Inc ....F 216 267-2240
Cleveland (G-5326)
Fence One Inc ....F 216 441-2600
Cleveland (G-5334)
Friends Ornamental Iron Co ....F 216 431-6710
Cleveland (G-5382)
Gateway Concrete Forming Svcs ....D 513 353-2000
Miamitown (G-13887)
General Chain & Mfg Corp ....E 513 541-6005
Cincinnati (G-3812)
General Electric Company ....D 330 343-8841
Dover (G-8987)
Gr Group Sales Inc ....G 216 961-3773
Cleveland (G-5441)
◆ Industrial Wire Rope Sup Inc ....E 513 941-2443
Cincinnati (G-3919)
Interntnal Tchncal Catings Inc ....D 614 449-6669
Columbus (G-7208)
J B Kepple Sheet Metal ....F 740 393-2971
Mount Vernon (G-14624)
JD Norman Industries Inc ....D 216 671-8000
Brooklyn (G-2129)
John A & William J Wiechart ....G 419 647-4617
Spencerville (G-17461)
K Effs Inc ....F 614 443-0586
Columbus (G-7250)
Kadee Industries Newco Inc ....F 440 439-8650
Bedford (G-1435)
Kimmatt Corp ....G 937 228-3811
Dayton (G-8441)
▲ Malin Wire Co ....G 216 267-9080
Cleveland (G-5734)
▲ Manufacturers Equipment Co ....F 513 424-3573
Middletown (G-14059)
Marik Spring Inc ....F 330 564-0617
Tallmadge (G-18152)
Mason Company LLC ....E 937 780-2321
Leesburg (G-11855)
▲ May Conveyor Inc ....F 440 237-8012
North Royalton (G-15435)
▲ Mazzella Lifting Tech Inc ....D 440 239-7000
Cleveland (G-5765)
Mazzella Lifting Tech Inc ....F 513 772-4466
Cincinnati (G-4069)
◆ McM Ind Co Inc ....E 216 292-4506
Beachwood (G-1278)
McM Ind Co Inc ....E 216 641-6300
Cleveland (G-5770)
Meese Inc ....D 440 998-1202
Ashtabula (G-819)
Microplex Inc ....G 330 498-0600
North Canton (G-15249)
▼ Midwestern Industries Inc ....C 330 837-4203
Massillon (G-13180)
Mueller Electric Company Inc ....E 216 771-5225
Akron (G-307)
▲ Ofco Inc ....D 740 622-5922
Coshocton (G-7904)
Ohio Wire Form & Spring Co ....F 614 444-3676
Columbus (G-7436)
▼ Options Plus Incorporated ....F 740 694-9811
Fredericktown (G-10108)
▲ Organized Living Inc ....E 513 489-9300
Cincinnati (G-4194)
◆ Panacea Products Corporation ....E 614 850-7000
Columbus (G-7456)
Panacea Products Corporation ....D 614 429-6320
Columbus (G-7457)
Parker-Hannifin Corporation ....F 330 336-3511
Wadsworth (G-19427)
▲ Polymet Corporation ....E 513 874-3586
West Chester (G-20038)
Precision Wire Products Inc ....G 216 265-7580
Cleveland (G-6038)
◆ Premier Manufacturing Corp ....D 216 941-9700
Cleveland (G-6041)
Production Plus Corp ....G 614 492-8811
Obetz (G-15658)
Providence Rees Inc ....E 614 833-6231
Columbus (G-7525)
▲ Pwp Inc ....G 216 251-2181
Cleveland (G-6064)
▲ Qualtek Electronics Corp ....C 440 951-3300
Mentor (G-13710)
Range One Products & Fabg ....F 330 533-1151
Canfield (G-2571)
RFS Fabrication ....G 419 547-0650
Clyde (G-6546)

Roy I Kaufman Inc ... G ... 740 382-0643
Marion *(G-12896)*
▲ Royal Wire Products Inc ... D ... 440 237-8787
North Royalton *(G-15446)*
▲ Saxon Products Inc ... G ... 419 241-6771
Toledo *(G-18685)*
Schweizer Dipple Inc ... D ... 440 786-8090
Cleveland *(G-6167)*
Seven-Ogun International LLC ... G ... 614 888-8939
Worthington *(G-20887)*
▼ Spring Team Inc ... D ... 440 275-5981
Austinburg *(G-966)*
Starr Fabricating Inc ... D ... 330 394-9891
Vienna *(G-19376)*
Stephens Pipe & Steel LLC ... C ... 740 869-2257
Mount Sterling *(G-14604)*
Stolle Machinery Company LLC ... E ... 937 859-4644
Dayton *(G-8684)*
▼ T & R Welding Systems Inc ... F ... 937 228-7517
Dayton *(G-8696)*
▲ Therm-O-Link Inc ... D ... 330 527-2124
Garrettsville *(G-10334)*
Tom Thumb Clip Co Inc ... F ... 440 953-9606
Willoughby *(G-20619)*
Tri-State Belting Ltd ... G ... 800 330-2358
Cincinnati *(G-4522)*
▲ Tyler Haver Inc ... E ... 440 974-1047
Mentor *(G-13756)*
Unified Scrn & Crush-Oh Inc ... G ... 937 836-3201
Englewood *(G-9541)*
▲ US Screen Co ... G ... 419 736-2400
Sullivan *(G-18055)*
Utility Wire Products Inc ... F ... 216 441-2180
Cleveland *(G-6403)*
▲ Ver-Mac Industries Inc ... E ... 740 397-6511
Mount Vernon *(G-14654)*
▼ W J Egli Company Inc ... F ... 330 823-3666
Alliance *(G-551)*
West Equipment Company Inc ... F ... 419 698-1601
Toledo *(G-18772)*
Wire Products Company Inc ... D ... 216 267-0777
Cleveland *(G-6468)*
Wrwp LLC ... F ... 330 425-3421
Twinsburg *(G-19041)*
Yankee Wire Cloth Products Inc ... E ... 740 545-9129
West Lafayette *(G-20090)*
▼ Yost Superior Co ... E ... 937 323-7591
Springfield *(G-17683)*

3497 Metal Foil & Leaf

▲ A J Oster Foils LLC ... D ... 330 823-1700
Alliance *(G-486)*
CC Investors Management Co LLC ... G ... 740 374-8129
Marietta *(G-12772)*
CCL Label Inc ... C ... 216 676-2703
Cleveland *(G-4998)*
CCL Label Inc ... E ... 440 878-7000
Brunswick *(G-2215)*
◆ Gould Electronics Inc ... C ... 440 953-5000
Eastlake *(G-9271)*
Nestle R&D Center Inc ... G ... 440 349-5757
Solon *(G-17346)*
▲ Quaker Mfg Corp ... C ... 330 332-4631
Salem *(G-16922)*
United Ultra Violet Inc ... F ... 614 875-8088
Grove City *(G-10609)*
▲ USA Foils Inc ... G ... 440 975-1145
Willoughby *(G-20626)*

3498 Fabricated Pipe & Pipe Fittings

◆ Alloy Bllows Prcision Wldg Inc ... D ... 440 684-3000
Cleveland *(G-4767)*
American Roll Formed Pdts Corp ... C ... 440 352-0753
Painesville *(G-15851)*
▲ Appian Manufacturing Corp ... E ... 614 445-2230
Columbus *(G-6762)*
Arem Co ... F ... 440 974-6740
Mentor *(G-13526)*
Atlas Industrial Contrs LLC ... B ... 614 841-4500
Columbus *(G-6784)*
B S F Inc ... F ... 937 890-6121
Dayton *(G-8179)*
B S F Inc ... F ... 937 890-6121
Tipp City *(G-18264)*
Beaverson Machine Inc ... G ... 419 923-8064
Delta *(G-8929)*
Benjamin Steel Company Inc ... E ... 937 233-1212
Springfield *(G-17522)*
Carter Machine Company Inc ... G ... 419 468-3530
Galion *(G-10256)*
Chardon Metal Products Co ... E ... 440 285-2147
Chardon *(G-3144)*
Cleveland Coppersmithing Works ... G ... 330 607-3998
Richfield *(G-16618)*
Cleveland Plastic Fabricat ... F ... 216 797-7300
Euclid *(G-9572)*
Contractors Steel Company ... E ... 330 425-3050
Twinsburg *(G-18919)*
Crest Bending Inc ... E ... 419 492-2108
New Washington *(G-14959)*
Defiance Metal Products WI Inc ... C ... 920 426-9207
Defiance *(G-8787)*
Dekay Fabricators Inc ... G ... 330 793-0826
Youngstown *(G-21066)*
▲ Duro Dyne Midwest Corp ... B ... 513 870-6000
Hamilton *(G-10685)*
Eaton Corporation ... C ... 440 826-1115
Berea *(G-1613)*
▲ Ebner Furnaces Inc ... D ... 330 335-2311
Wadsworth *(G-19404)*
Elliott Tool Technologies Ltd ... D ... 937 253-6133
Dayton *(G-8324)*
◆ Elster Perfection Corporation ... D ... 440 428-1171
Geneva *(G-10346)*
Esterle Mold & Machine Co Inc ... E ... 330 686-1685
Stow *(G-17748)*
▲ Ever Roll Specialties Co ... E ... 937 964-1302
Springfield *(G-17555)*
Excel Loading Systems LLC ... G ... 513 265-2936
Blue Ash *(G-1790)*
Fabcraft Inc ... G ... 440 286-6700
Chardon *(G-3152)*
Famous Industries Inc ... D ... 740 685-2592
Byesville *(G-2401)*
Faull & Son LLC ... F ... 330 652-4341
Niles *(G-15152)*
Franklin Frames and Cycles ... G ... 740 763-3838
Newark *(G-15008)*
H-P Products Inc ... E ... 330 875-7193
Louisville *(G-12313)*
▼ Hollaender Manufacturing Co ... D ... 513 772-8800
Cincinnati *(G-3887)*
Hycom Inc ... E ... 330 753-2330
Barberton *(G-1120)*
Hydra-TEC Inc ... G ... 330 225-8797
Brunswick *(G-2232)*
▲ Hydro Tube Enterprises Inc ... D ... 440 774-1022
Oberlin *(G-15644)*
Industrial Quartz Corp ... F ... 440 942-0909
Mentor *(G-13606)*
Ipsco Tubulars Inc ... G ... 330 448-6772
Brookfield *(G-2125)*
Jan Squires Inc ... G ... 440 988-7859
Amherst *(G-599)*
John H Hosking Inc ... G ... 513 821-1080
Middletown *(G-14052)*
John Maneely Company ... E ... 724 342-6851
Niles *(G-15165)*
Kenley Enterprises LLC ... E ... 419 630-0921
Bryan *(G-2308)*
Kings Welding and Fabg Inc ... E ... 330 738-3592
Mechanicstown *(G-13359)*
◆ Kirtland Capital Partners LP ... E ... 216 593-0100
Beachwood *(G-1276)*
▲ Kottler Metal Products Co Inc ... E ... 440 946-7473
Willoughby *(G-20523)*
Lakewood Steel Inc ... F ... 440 965-4226
Wakeman *(G-19450)*
Lim Services LLC ... F ... 513 217-0801
Middletown *(G-14054)*
Machine Dynamics & Engrg Inc ... D ... 330 868-5603
Minerva *(G-14331)*
McJunkn Redman ... F ... 330 686-4988
Stow *(G-17774)*
Mitchell Piping LLC ... E ... 330 245-0258
Hartville *(G-10830)*
Moss Vale Inc ... F ... 513 939-1970
Fairfield *(G-9687)*
Normandy Products Company ... D ... 440 632-5050
Middlefield *(G-13976)*
Parker-Hannifin Corporation ... B ... 937 456-5571
Eaton *(G-9320)*
Phillips Mfg and Tower Co ... D ... 419 347-1720
Shelby *(G-17140)*
Phoenix Forge Group LLC ... C ... 800 848-6125
West Jefferson *(G-20082)*
Pines Manufacturing Inc ... E ... 440 835-5553
Westlake *(G-20294)*
▲ Pioneer Pipe Inc ... B ... 740 376-2400
Marietta *(G-12816)*
▲ Pipe Line Development Company ... D ... 440 871-5700
Westlake *(G-20296)*
▲ Pipe Products Inc ... D ... 513 587-7532
West Chester *(G-19915)*
Precise Tube Forming Inc ... G ... 440 237-3956
North Royalton *(G-15445)*
Precision Cutoff LLC ... C ... 419 866-8000
Holland *(G-11078)*
▲ Precision Fittings LLC ... E ... 440 647-4143
Wellington *(G-19752)*
Propipe Technologies Inc ... E ... 513 424-5311
Middletown *(G-14079)*
▼ Qual-Fab Inc ... E ... 440 327-5000
Avon *(G-1005)*
Quality Mechanicals Inc ... E ... 513 559-0998
Cincinnati *(G-4307)*
Quality Tube Service Inc ... F ... 419 237-3014
Fayette *(G-9778)*
Rafter Equipment Corporation ... E ... 440 572-3700
Strongsville *(G-17956)*
Rbm Environmental and Cnstr ... E ... 419 693-5840
Oregon *(G-15715)*
▼ Rexarc International Inc ... E ... 937 839-4604
West Alexandria *(G-19781)*
▲ Rhenium Alloys Inc ... D ... 440 365-7388
North Ridgeville *(G-15401)*
▼ Riker Products Inc ... C ... 419 729-1626
Toledo *(G-18676)*
Rocks General Maintenance LLC ... G ... 740 323-4711
Thornville *(G-18195)*
S-P Company Inc ... F ... 330 482-0200
Columbiana *(G-6631)*
▲ Sanoh America Inc ... D ... 419 425-2600
Findlay *(G-9887)*
Scot Industries Inc ... E ... 330 262-7585
Wooster *(G-20832)*
▲ Scott Process Systems Inc ... C ... 330 877-2350
Hartville *(G-10834)*
Seal Tite LLC ... D ... 937 393-4268
Hillsboro *(G-11014)*
▲ Sroka Industries Inc ... E ... 440 572-2811
Strongsville *(G-17972)*
▲ SSP Fittings Corp ... D ... 330 425-4250
Twinsburg *(G-19022)*
Stam Inc ... E ... 440 974-2500
Mentor *(G-13729)*
▲ Stripmatic Products Inc ... E ... 216 241-7143
Cleveland *(G-6255)*
Summers Acquisition Corp ... G ... 419 423-5800
Findlay *(G-9898)*
Swagelok Company ... D ... 440 349-5934
Solon *(G-17392)*
Swagelok Company ... D ... 440 349-5652
Solon *(G-17391)*
T & D Fabricating Inc ... E ... 440 951-5646
Eastlake *(G-9292)*
▲ Tech Tool Inc ... F ... 330 674-1176
Millersburg *(G-14267)*
Thompson Culvert Company LLC ... F ... 513 645-7000
West Chester *(G-19956)*
TI Group Auto Systems LLC ... C ... 740 929-2049
Hebron *(G-10890)*
Tomco Machining Inc ... E ... 937 264-1943
Dayton *(G-8718)*
Transit Sittings of NA ... G ... 330 797-2516
Youngstown *(G-21227)*
Tri-America Contractors Inc ... E ... 740 574-0148
Wheelersburg *(G-20335)*
Tri-America Contractors Inc ... E ... 740 574-0148
Wheelersburg *(G-20336)*
Tri-State Fabricators Inc ... E ... 513 752-5005
Amelia *(G-587)*
Tristate Tubular Inc ... G ... 330 339-5240
New Philadelphia *(G-14937)*
U S Weatherford L P ... C ... 330 746-2502
Youngstown *(G-21233)*
Unison Industries LLC ... D ... 937 426-4676
Alpha *(G-555)*
Unison Industries LLC ... A ... 937 426-0621
Dayton *(G-8122)*
Unison Industries LLC ... B ... 937 426-0621
Dayton *(G-8121)*
United Group Services Inc ... C ... 800 633-9690
West Chester *(G-20063)*
United Metal Fabricators Inc ... E ... 216 662-2000
Maple Heights *(G-12742)*
Unity Tube Inc ... F ... 330 426-4282
East Palestine *(G-9248)*
US Tubular Products Inc ... D ... 330 832-1734
North Lawrence *(G-15307)*

S I C

Vortec Corporation ....E 513 686-8210
Blue Ash (G-1891)

▼ W J Egli Company Inc ....F 330 823-3666
Alliance (G-551)

Welded Tubes Inc ....F 440 437-5144
Orwell (G-15782)

Woodsage Corporation ....D 419 476-3553
Holland (G-11097)

Zekelman Industries Inc ....C 740 432-2146
Cambridge (G-2483)

3499 Fabricated Metal Prdts, NEC

A&E Machine & Fabrication Inc ....F 740 820-4701
Beaver (G-1309)

Accurate Mechanical Inc ....E 740 654-5898
Lancaster (G-11683)

Ace Plastics Co ....G 330 928-7720
Stow (G-17728)

Alacriant Inc ....D 330 562-7191
Streetsboro (G-17835)

Alacriant Inc ....E 330 562-7191
Streetsboro (G-17836)

Alchemical Transmutation ....C 216 313-8674
Cleveland (G-4742)

▲ Alert Stamping & Mfg Co Inc ....E 440 232-5020
Bedford Heights (G-1476)

Alex Products Inc ....C 419 399-4500
Paulding (G-15999)

All-Craft Wellman Products ....F 440 946-9646
Willoughby (G-20428)

American Scaffolding Inc ....G 216 524-7733
Cleveland (G-4795)

Arete Innovative Solutions LLC ....G 513 503-2712
Morrow (G-14543)

▲ Automatic Equipment Corp ....F 513 771-3833
West Chester (G-19983)

Avenue Fabricating Inc ....E 513 752-1911
Batavia (G-1165)

Axis Corporation ....F 937 592-1958
Bellefontaine (G-1520)

B C Composites Corporation ....F 330 262-3070
Medina (G-13376)

B K Fabrication & Machine Shop ....G 740 695-4164
Saint Clairsville (G-16781)

Bauer Corporation ....E 800 321-4760
Wooster (G-20746)

Bc Investment Corporation ....G 330 262-3070
Wooster (G-20747)

Ben James Enterprises Inc ....G 330 477-9353
Canton (G-2620)

Blue Chip Machine & Tool Ltd ....G 419 626-9559
Sandusky (G-16949)

Buckeye Metals ....G 740 446-9590
Bidwell (G-1675)

Byer Steel Rebar Inc ....E 513 821-6400
Cincinnati (G-3492)

Camaco LLC ....A 440 288-4444
Lorain (G-12236)

Candle Cottage ....G 937 526-4041
Versailles (G-19343)

Cctm Inc ....G 513 934-3533
Lebanon (G-11788)

CDI ....G 440 249-4178
Avon (G-988)

Cincy Safe Company ....E 513 900-9152
Milford (G-14130)

Company Front Awards ....G 440 636-5493
Middlefield (G-13924)

COW Industries Inc ....E 614 443-6537
Columbus (G-6992)

Cpmg ....G 440 263-2780
North Royalton (G-15415)

Crest Craft Company ....F 513 271-4858
Blue Ash (G-1770)

Custom Fabrication By Fisher ....G 513 738-4600
Okeana (G-15664)

Dayton Safe Company ....G 937 461-3900
Dayton (G-8286)

Deltec Incorporated ....E 513 732-0800
Batavia (G-1177)

▲ Dern Trophies Corp ....F 614 895-3260
Westerville (G-20145)

Detrick Design Fabrication LLC ....G 937 620-6736
Troy (G-18820)

Die-Cut Products Co ....E 216 771-6994
Cleveland (G-5193)

Diebold Nixdorf Incorporated ....A 330 490-4000
North Canton (G-15228)

Dimensional Fabricating Inc ....G 513 482-7440
Cincinnati (G-3655)

Donald E Didion II ....E 419 483-2226
Bellevue (G-1550)

Drawn Metals Corp ....F 937 433-6151
Dayton (G-8311)

▲ Dura Magnetics Inc ....F 419 882-0591
Sylvania (G-18106)

Eastern Automated Piping ....G 740 535-8184
Mingo Junction (G-14348)

Elite Enclosure Company LLC ....E 937 492-3548
Sidney (G-17185)

Exair Corporation ....E 513 671-3322
Cincinnati (G-3729)

Extreme Marine ....G 330 963-7800
Twinsburg (G-18932)

EZ Grout Corporation Inc ....E 740 962-2024
Malta (G-12536)

Fabricating Solutions Inc ....F 330 486-0998
Twinsburg (G-18933)

Fenix Magnetics Inc ....G 415 308-0134
Lakewood (G-11663)

Fisher Metal Fabricating ....F 419 838-7200
Walbridge (G-19457)

▲ Flexmag Industries Inc ....D 740 373-3492
Marietta (G-12784)

Fountain Specialists Inc ....E 513 831-5717
Milford (G-14142)

◆ Frame USA ....E 513 577-7107
Cincinnati (G-3776)

Frame Warehouse ....G 614 861-4582
Reynoldsburg (G-16591)

G & M Metal Products Inc ....E 513 863-3353
Hamilton (G-10695)

General Metals Powder Co ....D 330 633-1226
Akron (G-203)

◆ Gregory Industries Inc ....D 330 477-4800
Canton (G-2719)

Hamilton Fabricators Inc ....E 513 735-7773
Batavia (G-1190)

Hamilton Safe Amelia ....F 513 753-5694
Amelia (G-576)

▲ Hamilton Safe Co ....F 513 874-3733
Cincinnati (G-3863)

▲ Hamilton Security Products Co ....E 513 874-3733
Cincinnati (G-3864)

Heim Sheet Metal Inc ....G 330 424-7820
Lisbon (G-12121)

Hit Trophy Inc ....E 419 445-5356
Archbold (G-681)

Hoffman Machining & Repair LLC ....G 419 547-9204
Clyde (G-6540)

Humble Construction Co ....E 614 888-8960
Columbus (G-7169)

Hykon Manufacturing Company ....G 330 821-8889
Alliance (G-517)

Ibi Brake Products Inc ....G 440 543-7962
Chagrin Falls (G-3094)

Industrial Fabricators Inc ....E 614 882-7423
Westerville (G-20218)

Inspiring Kind LLC ....E 513 321-1705
Cincinnati (G-3924)

J & J Performance Inc ....F 330 567-2455
Shreve (G-17159)

J Feldkamp Design Build Ltd ....E 513 870-0601
Fairfield (G-9670)

Jaguar Medical Supplies Inc ....G 440 263-2780
North Royalton (G-15428)

Johnson Machining Services LLC ....G 937 866-4744
Miamisburg (G-13823)

K C Creations ....G 937 748-8181
Troy (G-18850)

Kard Welding Inc ....E 419 628-2598
Minster (G-14356)

Karyall-Telday Inc ....E 216 281-4063
Cleveland (G-5633)

Labcraft Inc ....F 419 878-4400
Waterville (G-19662)

Lewark Metal Spinning Inc ....E 937 275-3303
Dayton (G-8457)

Linsalata Capital Partners Fun ....G 440 684-1400
Cleveland (G-5703)

M A K Fabricating Inc ....F 330 747-0040
Youngstown (G-21136)

Mab Fabrication Inc ....G 855 622-3221
Harrison (G-10788)

Mad Metal Wldg Fabrication LLC ....G 614 256-4163
Columbus (G-7313)

▼ Magnum Magnetics Corporation ....D 740 373-7770
Marietta (G-12801)

Mansfield Welding Services LLC ....G 419 594-2738
Oakwood (G-15617)

Manufacturing Futures Inc ....G 216 903-7993
Shaker Heights (G-17092)

Mast Farm Service Ltd ....E 330 893-2972
Walnut Creek (G-19470)

Mid Ohio Trophy & Awards ....G 419 756-2266
Mansfield (G-12647)

Midwest Metals & Supply LLC ....G 513 489-1666
Maineville (G-12529)

Mills Aluminum Fab ....G 330 821-4108
Alliance (G-527)

Miscellnous Mtals Fbrction Inc ....G 740 779-3071
Chillicothe (G-3252)

Mk Trempe Corporation ....G 937 492-3548
Sidney (G-17204)

MTS Enterprises LLC ....G 937 324-7510
Springfield (G-17609)

National Security Products ....G 216 566-9962
Cleveland (G-5860)

▲ New American Reel Company LLC ....G 419 258-2900
Antwerp (G-631)

North American Steel Company ....E 216 475-7300
Cleveland (G-5890)

▲ North Shore Strapping Inc ....G 216 661-5200
Brooklyn Heights (G-2144)

▲ Nostalgic Images Inc ....E 419 784-1728
Defiance (G-8807)

▲ Ohio Gasket and Shim Co Inc ....E 330 630-0626
Akron (G-323)

Ohio Laser LLC ....E 614 873-7030
Plain City (G-16352)

▲ Ohio Magnetics Inc ....G 216 662-8484
Maple Heights (G-12736)

Olwin Metal Fabrication LLC ....G 937 277-4501
Dayton (G-8547)

P S Superior Inc ....F 216 587-1000
Cleveland (G-5958)

Paulg Corporation ....E 914 662-9837
Columbus (G-7470)

▲ Peter Graham Dunn Inc ....E 330 816-0035
Dalton (G-8077)

Pucel Enterprises Inc ....D 216 881-4604
Cleveland (G-6061)

Quest Technologies Inc ....E 937 743-1200
Franklin (G-10047)

R L Torbeck Industries Inc ....D 513 367-0080
Harrison (G-10800)

Ratliff Metal Spinning Co Inc ....E 937 836-3900
Englewood (G-9538)

Ray Rieser Trophy Co ....G 614 279-1128
Columbus (G-7549)

Rift Lake Aquatics ....G 216 221-1437
Cleveland (G-6113)

▼ Riverside Steel Inc ....F 330 856-5299
Vienna (G-19375)

Rti International Metals Inc ....D 330 455-4010
Canton (G-2844)

Sharonco Inc ....G 419 882-3443
Sylvania (G-18124)

Shipping Room Products Inc ....G 216 531-4422
Cleveland (G-6195)

▲ Specialty Magnetics LLC ....G 330 468-8834
Macedonia (G-12484)

Spirol International Corp ....D 330 920-3655
Stow (G-17802)

▲ Sulo Enterprises Inc ....F 440 926-3322
Grafton (G-10437)

Systems Jay LLC Nanogate ....B 419 747-4161
Mansfield (G-12691)

Systems Jay LLC Nanogate ....B 419 747-4161
Mansfield (G-12692)

Target Holdings Inc ....E 513 474-4409
Cincinnati (G-4493)

Thieman Quality Metal Fab Inc ....D 419 629-2612
New Bremen (G-14795)

Titan Metal Fabricators ....F 513 755-3394
Liberty Township (G-11969)

Tosoh SMD Inc ....G 614 875-7912
Grove City (G-10605)

▲ Tosoh SMD Inc ....G 614 875-7912
Grove City (G-10606)

Tribco Incorporated ....E 216 486-2000
Cleveland (G-6363)

US Powder Coating Inc ....G 440 255-3090
Mentor (G-13763)

Vortec Corporation ....E 513 686-8210
Blue Ash (G-1891)

▲ Voss Industries Inc ....C 216 771-0870
Cleveland (G-6429)

Voyale Minority Enterprise LLC ....E 216 271-3661
Cleveland (G-6431)

Walker Magnetics Group Inc...............E........614 492-1614
Columbus *(G-7747)*

◆ Walker National Inc.........................E........614 492-1614
Columbus *(G-7748)*

Warren Steel Specialties Corp...........F........330 399-8360
Warren *(G-19624)*

Weldcraft Products Co.......................F........937 233-6141
Dayton *(G-8750)*

Williamson Safe Inc...........................E........937 393-9919
Hillsboro *(G-11019)*

▲ Winkle Industries Inc.....................D........330 823-9730
Alliance *(G-554)*

Yarder Manufacturing Company........D........419 476-3933
Toledo *(G-18778)*

Yarder Manufacturing Company........G........419 269-3474
Toledo *(G-18779)*

Youngstown Specialty Mtls Inc.........G........330 259-1110
Youngstown *(G-21256)*

Zimmerman Steel & Sup Co LLC........F........330 828-1010
Dalton *(G-8082)*

35 INDUSTRIAL AND COMMERCIAL MACHINERY AND COMPUTER EQUIPMENT

3511 Steam, Gas & Hydraulic Turbines & Engines

Aero Propulsion Support Inc..............E........513 367-9452
Harrison *(G-10766)*

Alin Machining Company Inc..............E........740 223-0200
Marion *(G-12853)*

Arete Innovative Solutions LLC..........G........513 503-2712
Morrow *(G-14543)*

▲ Argosy Wind Power Ltd.................G........440 539-1345
Aurora *(G-906)*

Camfil USA Inc..................................G........937 773-0866
Piqua *(G-16255)*

Eaton Leasing Corporation.................G........216 382-2292
Beachwood *(G-1270)*

Fluid System Service Inc....................G........216 651-2450
Cleveland *(G-5361)*

Fluidpower Assembly Inc....................G........419 394-7486
Saint Marys *(G-16839)*

▲ Fusion Incorporated.......................E........440 946-3300
Willoughby *(G-20494)*

▲ GE Aviation Systems LLC..............C........937 898-9600
Dayton *(G-8358)*

General Electric Company..................F........513 243-9317
West Chester *(G-19874)*

Kw River Hydroelectric I LLC............G........513 673-2251
Cincinnati *(G-4007)*

▲ Metalex Manufacturing Inc............C........513 489-0507
Blue Ash *(G-1839)*

Muller Engine & Machine Co..............G........937 322-1861
Springfield *(G-17610)*

Northel Usa LLC...............................G........740 973-0309
Newark *(G-15040)*

On-Power Inc....................................E........513 228-2100
Lebanon *(G-11823)*

Parker Triad Store............................D........937 293-4080
Moraine *(G-14511)*

Pfpc Enterprises Inc.........................B........513 941-6200
Cincinnati *(G-4233)*

R H Industries Inc............................E........216 281-5210
Cleveland *(G-6083)*

Siemens Energy Inc..........................B........740 393-8897
Mount Vernon *(G-14648)*

Steam Engine Works LLC..................G........513 813-3690
Cincinnati *(G-4461)*

Steam Turb Alte Reso.......................E........740 387-5535
Marion *(G-12903)*

Td Power Systems (usa) Inc..............G........330 247-5264
Richfield *(G-16642)*

Teledyne Technologies Inc ....D........419 470-3000
Toledo *(G-18717)*

3519 Internal Combustion Engines, NEC

▲ American Fine Sinter Co Ltd...........C........419 443-8880
Tiffin *(G-18202)*

B A Malcuit Racing Inc......................G........330 878-7111
Strasburg *(G-17820)*

Brinkley Technology Group LLC.........F........330 830-2498
Massillon *(G-13115)*

Cameron International Corp...............G........740 397-4888
Mount Vernon *(G-14611)*

Chemequip Sales Inc........................E........330 724-8300
Akron *(G-120)*

▲ Clarke Fire Prtection Pdts Inc.........D........513 771-2200
Cincinnati *(G-3582)*

Clarke Fire Prtection Pdts Inc...........G........513 771-2200
West Chester *(G-19989)*

Cummins - Allison Corp.....................G........614 529-1940
Hilliard *(G-10945)*

Cummins - Allison Corp.....................G........513 469-2924
Blue Ash *(G-1772)*

Cummins - Allison Corp.....................G........440 824-5050
Cleveland *(G-5146)*

Cummins Bridgeway LLC...................E........513 563-6670
West Chester *(G-19850)*

Cummins Bridgeway LLC...................E........614 604-6000
Grove City *(G-10552)*

Cummins Bridgeway LLC...................E........614 771-1000
Hilliard *(G-10946)*

Cummins Bridgeway Columbus LLC...D........614 771-1000
Hilliard *(G-10947)*

Cummins Bridgeway Toledo LLC........F........419 893-8711
Maumee *(G-13235)*

Debolt Machine Inc...........................G........740 454-8082
Zanesville *(G-21298)*

Detroit Desl Rmnfacturing Corp.........F........740 439-7701
Cambridge *(G-2454)*

◆ Detroit Desl Rmnfctrng-Ast Inc......B........740 439-7701
Byesville *(G-2398)*

◆ Dmax Ltd......................................D........937 425-9700
Moraine *(G-14479)*

Draime Enterprises Inc.....................G........330 837-2254
Massillon *(G-13126)*

▲ DW Hercules LLC...........................E........330 830-2498
Massillon *(G-13127)*

Enginetics Corporation......................C........937 878-3800
Huber Heights *(G-11146)*

Ford Motor Company.........................A........419 226-7000
Lima *(G-12014)*

GE Honda Aero Engines LLC.............F........513 552-4322
West Chester *(G-19873)*

GE Rolls Royce Fighter.....................G........513 243-2787
Cincinnati *(G-3811)*

Gellner Engineering Inc.....................G........216 398-8500
Cleveland *(G-5407)*

▲ General Engine Products LLC.........D........937 704-0160
Franklin *(G-10024)*

Graham Ford Power Products............G........614 801-0049
Columbus *(G-7127)*

Great Lakes Diesel............................G........419 433-9898
Vermilion *(G-19327)*

▲ Hemco Inc.....................................G........419 499-4602
Milan *(G-14112)*

▲ HK Engine Components LLC...........G........330 830-3500
Massillon *(G-13151)*

▲ Hy-Production Inc..........................C........330 273-2400
Valley City *(G-19206)*

Industrial Parts Depot LLC................G........440 237-9164
North Royalton *(G-15427)*

▼ Jatrodiesel Inc..............................F........937 847-8050
Miamisburg *(G-13821)*

Jjb Engineer....................................G........330 807-0671
Cuyahoga Falls *(G-8014)*

Kenworth of Dayton..........................F........937 235-2589
Dayton *(G-8438)*

Maags Automotive & Machine............G........419 626-1539
Sandusky *(G-16982)*

Mantapart...G........330 549-2389
New Springfield *(G-14951)*

Metaldyne Pwrtrain Cmpnnts Inc.......C........330 486-3200
Twinsburg *(G-18986)*

Navistar Inc......................................E........937 390-5704
Springfield *(G-17616)*

Performace Diesel Inc.......................F........740 392-3693
Mount Vernon *(G-14637)*

Performance Research Inc.................G........614 475-8300
Columbus *(G-7479)*

▼ Rozevink Engines LLC...................G........419 789-1159
Holgate *(G-11041)*

Western Branch Diesel Inc................E........330 454-8800
Canton *(G-2902)*

3523 Farm Machinery & Eqpt

Afs Technology LLC...........................F........937 669-3548
Tipp City *(G-18262)*

American Baler Co.............................D........419 483-5790
Bellevue *(G-1543)*

Andrews Farms Inc...........................G........419 594-2111
Oakwood *(G-15614)*

Baker Built Products Inc....................G........419 965-2646
Ohio City *(G-15660)*

Beth Otto Independent Case Exa........G........513 868-0484
Fairfield *(G-9645)*

Birds Eye Foods Inc..........................E........330 854-0818
Canal Fulton *(G-2499)*

▼ Buckeye Tractor Company Corp.....G........419 659-2162
Columbus Grove *(G-7791)*

Cailin Dev Ltd Lblty Co......................F........216 408-6261
Cleveland *(G-4962)*

Case Western Reserve Univ ....G........216 368-2574
Cleveland *(G-4988)*

◆ Chick Master Incubator Company ...C........330 722-5591
Medina *(G-13386)*

Creamer Metal Products Inc ....F........740 852-1752
London *(G-12207)*

Empire Plow Company Inc.................E........216 641-2290
Cleveland *(G-5278)*

END Separation LLC.........................G........419 438-0879
Oakwood *(G-15616)*

Field Gymmy Inc...............................G........419 538-6511
Glandorf *(G-10397)*

Flying Dutchman Inc..........................G........740 694-1734
Smithville *(G-17239)*

◆ Fort Recovery Equipment Inc.........G........419 375-1006
Fort Recovery *(G-9949)*

Fremont Plastic Products Inc ....C........419 332-6407
Fremont *(G-10150)*

Gerald Grain Center Inc....................F........419 445-2451
Archbold *(G-678)*

Gilbert Geiser...................................G........330 237-7901
Canton *(G-2714)*

H & S Company Inc...........................F........419 394-4444
Celina *(G-2999)*

▲ Hawkline Nevada LLC....................G........937 444-4295
Mount Orab *(G-14579)*

Hawthorne Systems Inc.....................F........419 643-5861
Beaverdam *(G-1393)*

▼ Healthpro Brands Inc.....................G........513 492-7512
Loveland *(G-12357)*

Hershberger & Sons LLC...................G........937 588-2195
Hillsboro *(G-11000)*

Hershy Way Ltd.................................G........330 893-2809
Millersburg *(G-14223)*

Hollmann Inc.....................................G........513 522-1800
Cincinnati *(G-3889)*

Hord Elevator LLC.............................F........419 562-5934
Bucyrus *(G-2349)*

◆ Intertec Corporation......................B........419 537-9711
Toledo *(G-18527)*

◆ J & M Manufacturing Co Inc...........E........419 375-2376
Fort Recovery *(G-9955)*

Keynes Brothers Inc..........................G........740 426-6332
Jeffersonville *(G-11381)*

Knief Farms A Partnership.................G........937 585-4810
Lewistown *(G-11945)*

◆ Komar Industries Inc......................E........614 836-2366
Groveport *(G-10629)*

Kriss Kreations.................................G........330 405-6102
Twinsburg *(G-18968)*

Landscape Group LLC.......................G........614 302-4537
Mount Sterling *(G-14600)*

Ley Equipment Co ....G........419 238-6742
Van Wert *(G-19264)*

Ley Industries Inc.............................G........419 238-6742
Van Wert *(G-19265)*

Marion Caldwell................................G........740 446-1042
Gallipolis *(G-10304)*

Motrin Corporation............................G........740 439-2725
Cambridge *(G-2469)*

Ntech Industries Inc..........................F........707 467-3747
Dayton *(G-8534)*

Ohio Windmill & Pump Co Inc............G........330 547-6300
Berlin Center *(G-1658)*

◆ Pioneer Equipment Company.........F........330 857-6340
Dalton *(G-8078)*

▲ R L Parsons & Son Equipment Co ...G........614 879-7601
West Jefferson *(G-20083)*

Randall Richard & Moore LLC ....F........330 455-8873
Canton *(G-2835)*

▲ Remlinger Manufacturing Co Inc.....E........419 532-3647
Kalida *(G-11416)*

Rhinestahl Corporation......................D........513 229-5300
Mason *(G-13083)*

▲ S I Distributing Inc.........................F........419 647-4909
Spencerville *(G-17465)*

Safe-Grain Inc...................................G........513 398-2500
Wapakoneta *(G-19506)*

Shearer Farm Inc.............................E........330 345-9023
Wooster *(G-20834)*

Stein-Way Equipment.......................F........330 857-8700
Apple Creek *(G-649)*

Stephens Pipe & Steel LLC...............C........740 869-2257
Mount Sterling *(G-14604)*

◆ Sweet Manufacturing Company ....E 937 325-1511
Springfield *(G-17659)*
TD Landscape Inc ....F 740 694-0244
Fredericktown *(G-10110)*
Toolco Inc ....G 419 667-3462
Van Wert *(G-19273)*
Universal Equipment Mfg ....G 614 586-1780
Columbus *(G-7722)*
◆ Unverferth Mfg Co Inc ....C 419 532-3121
Kalida *(G-11418)*
Unverferth Mfg Co Inc ....D 419 695-2060
Delphos *(G-8923)*
▲ Val-Co Pax Inc ....D 717 354-4586
Coldwater *(G-6573)*
Warren Zachman Contracting ......G 740 389-4503
Marion *(G-12911)*
Wiley Farms ....G 937 537-0676
Richwood *(G-16661)*
Woodbury Welding Inc ....G 937 968-3573
Union City *(G-19073)*
Yocom Brothers ....G 937 653-8767
Cable *(G-2414)*
Yoder & Frey Inc ....G 419 445-2070
Archbold *(G-700)*

3524 Garden, Lawn Tractors & Eqpt

Albright Saw Company Inc ....G 740 887-2107
Londonderry *(G-12225)*
Bortnick Tractor Sales Inc ....F 330 924-2555
Cortland *(G-7862)*
California Grounds Care LLC ....G 513 207-0244
Cincinnati *(G-3494)*
Cannon Salt & Supply Inc ....G 440 232-1700
Bedford *(G-1410)*
Commercial Turf Products Ltd ....C 330 995-7000
Streetsboro *(G-17846)*
Country Manufacturing Inc ....F 740 694-9926
Fredericktown *(G-10097)*
Dinsmore Inc ....G 937 544-3332
West Union *(G-20120)*
Elan Designs Inc ....G 614 985-5600
Westerville *(G-20212)*
Extrudex Limited Partnership ....E 440 352-7101
Painesville *(G-15879)*
Franklin Equipment LLC ....E 614 228-2014
Groveport *(G-10623)*
Friesen Fab and Equipment ....G 614 873-4354
Plain City *(G-16340)*
Gececo Inc ....E 614 861-4479
Columbus *(G-7106)*
Johnson Tool Distributors ....G 740 653-6959
Lancaster *(G-11724)*
Klawhorn Industries Inc ....G 330 335-8191
Wadsworth *(G-19414)*
Koenig Equipment Inc ....F 937 653-5281
Urbana *(G-19167)*
◆ Mid-West Fabricating Co ....C 740 969-4411
Amanda *(G-563)*
Mm Service ....G 330 474-3098
Streetsboro *(G-17863)*
Mo-Trim Inc ....E 740 432-2098
Cambridge *(G-2467)*
▼ Mtd Consumer Group Inc ....F 330 225-2600
Valley City *(G-19219)*
◆ Mtd Holdings Inc ....B 330 225-2600
Valley City *(G-19220)*
Mtd LLC ....G 800 269-6215
Valley City *(G-19221)*
◆ Mtd Products Inc ....B 330 225-2600
Valley City *(G-19222)*
Mtd Products Inc ....A 419 935-6611
Willard *(G-20397)*
Mtd Products Inc ....B 330 225-9127
Valley City *(G-19223)*
Mtd Products Inc ....C 419 342-6455
Shelby *(G-17139)*
Mtd Products Inc ....B 330 225-1940
Valley City *(G-19224)*
Outback Tree Works ....G 937 332-7300
Troy *(G-18860)*
◆ Park-Ohio Holdings Corp ....F 440 947-2000
Cleveland *(G-5966)*
◆ Park-Ohio Industries Inc ....C 440 947-2000
Cleveland *(G-5967)*
R J Engineering Company Inc ....G 419 843-8651
Toledo *(G-18667)*
Rotoline USA LLC ....G 330 677-3223
Kent *(G-11520)*
Russell Hunt ....F 740 264-1196
Steubenville *(G-17711)*

Schomaker Natural Resource ....G 513 741-1370
Cincinnati *(G-4389)*
◆ Scotts Company LLC ....A 937 644-3729
Marysville *(G-12967)*
Smg Growing Media Inc ....G 937 644-0011
Marysville *(G-12971)*
◆ Speed North America Inc ....G 330 202-7775
Wooster *(G-20838)*
Tierra-Derco International LLC ....G 419 929-2240
New London *(G-14868)*
Tri-Tech Mfg LLC ....G 419 238-0140
Delphos *(G-8921)*
Village Outdoors ....G 440 256-1172
Kirtland *(G-11618)*
Westerville Lawn & Garden ....G 740 936-8452
Westerville *(G-20195)*
WH Fetzer & Sons Mfg Inc ....E 419 687-8237
Plymouth *(G-16380)*

3531 Construction Machinery & Eqpt

A Reed Excavating LLC ....G 740 391-4985
Beallsville *(G-1306)*
Adairs Pavers ....G 937 454-9302
Vandalia *(G-19277)*
▼ Aim Attachments ....E 614 539-3030
Grove City *(G-10540)*
Allied Consolidated Industries ......C 330 744-0808
Youngstown *(G-21020)*
▲ Allied Construction Pdts LLC .....E 216 431-2600
Cleveland *(G-4764)*
Allied Construction Pdts LLC ....E 216 431-2600
Cleveland *(G-4765)*
American Highway Products Ltd .....F 330 874-3270
Bolivar *(G-1927)*
▲ American Power Pull Corp ....G 419 335-7050
Wauseon *(G-19671)*
▲ ARM Opco Inc ....G 330 868-7724
Canton *(G-2605)*
Ballinger Industries Inc ....F 419 422-4533
Findlay *(G-9794)*
▲ Barbco Inc ....G 330 488-9400
East Canton *(G-9190)*
Basetek LLC ....F 877 712-2273
Middlefield *(G-13916)*
Basetek LLC ....E 877 712-2273
Dayton *(G-8182)*
Belden Brick Company ....G 330 852-2411
Sugarcreek *(G-18016)*
Black Lab LLC ....G 815 313-0400
Chardon *(G-3142)*
Brewpro Inc ....G 513 577-7200
Cincinnati *(G-3472)*
Brovig Engineering Inc ....G 419 426-1333
Attica *(G-893)*
▲ Buck Equipment Inc ....E 614 539-3039
Grove City *(G-10548)*
▲ Bucyrus Blades Inc ....D 419 562-6015
Bucyrus *(G-2332)*
City of Oxford ....F 513 523-8412
Oxford *(G-15834)*
Cityscapes International Inc ....E 614 850-2540
Hilliard *(G-10938)*
Coe Manufacturing Company ....D 440 352-9381
Painesville *(G-15865)*
Concord Road Equipment Mfg Inc ...E 440 357-5344
Painesville *(G-15867)*
Concrete Cnstr McHy Co LLC ....G 330 638-1515
Cortland *(G-7863)*
Concrete Leveling Systems Inc ......G 330 966-8120
Canton *(G-2666)*
Connor Electric Inc ....G 513 932-5798
Lebanon *(G-11790)*
▲ Construction Polymers Co ....G 440 591-9018
Chagrin Falls *(G-3081)*
Custom Machining Solutions LLC ...G 330 221-1523
Rootstown *(G-16720)*
CW Machine Worx Ltd ....F 740 654-5304
Carroll *(G-2939)*
D & D Landscaping Inc ....G 330 507-6647
Brookfield *(G-2122)*
D & L Excavating Ltd ....G 419 271-0635
Port Clinton *(G-16398)*
Dandy Products Inc ....G 800 591-2284
Mount Vernon *(G-14618)*
▲ David Round Company Inc ....E 330 656-1600
Streetsboro *(G-17847)*
Desco Corporation ....G 614 888-8855
New Albany *(G-14757)*
Dimensional Metals Inc ....D 740 927-3633
Reynoldsburg *(G-16586)*

Donald E Dornon ....G 740 926-9144
Beallsville *(G-1308)*
Dover Corporation ....G 513 696-1790
Mason *(G-13010)*
Duplex Mill & Manufacturing Co ....E 937 325-5555
Springfield *(G-17548)*
◆ Duramax Marine LLC ....D 440 834-5400
Hiram *(G-11034)*
Dynamic Plastics Inc ....G 937 437-7261
New Paris *(G-14879)*
◆ E R Advanced Ceramics Inc ......E 330 426-9433
East Palestine *(G-9237)*
◆ Eagle Crusher Co Inc ....D 419 468-2288
Galion *(G-10266)*
Ers Industries Inc ....E 419 562-6010
Bucyrus *(G-2342)*
◆ Fabco Inc ....E 419 421-4740
Findlay *(G-9820)*
Field Gymmy Inc ....G 419 538-6511
Glandorf *(G-10397)*
▲ Forge Industries Inc ....A 330 782-8301
Youngstown *(G-21089)*
G & D Leasing Services Inc ....G 303 457-9189
Columbus *(G-7103)*
G & J Asphalt & Material Inc ....F 740 773-6358
Chillicothe *(G-3238)*
G & T Manufacturing Co ....F 440 639-7777
Mentor *(G-13588)*
Gibson Machinery LLC ....G 440 439-4000
Cleveland *(G-5429)*
Gledhill Road Machinery Co ....E 419 468-4400
Galion *(G-10273)*
◆ Gradall Industries Inc ....C 330 339-2211
New Philadelphia *(G-14901)*
Gradeworks ....G 440 487-4201
Willoughby *(G-20501)*
Grand Harbor Yacht Sales & Svc ...G 440 442-2919
Cleveland *(G-5445)*
▼ Grasan Equipment Company Inc ...D 419 526-4440
Mansfield *(G-12620)*
Great Lakes Machine and Tool ....G 419 836-2346
Curtice *(G-7957)*
H Y O Inc ....F 614 488-2861
Columbus *(G-7136)*
Harsco Corporation ....E 740 387-1150
Marion *(G-12873)*
◆ Haulotte US Inc ....E 419 445-8915
Archbold *(G-680)*
Howard & Blake Excavating LLC ....G 740 701-7938
Richmond Dale *(G-16650)*
◆ Hudco Manufacturing Inc ....G 440 951-4040
Willoughby *(G-20505)*
Hug Manufacturing Corporation .....G 419 668-5086
Norwalk *(G-15546)*
▲ Indy Eqp Indpndence Recycl Inc ...C 216 524-0999
Independence *(G-11260)*
Jbw Systems Inc ....F 614 882-5008
Westerville *(G-20162)*
JC Roofing Supply ....G 937 258-9999
Dayton *(G-8424)*
Jcl Equipment Co Inc ....G 937 374-1010
Xenia *(G-20958)*
Jennmar McSweeney LLC ....C 740 377-3354
South Point *(G-17439)*
Jlg Industries Inc ....C 330 684-0132
Orrville *(G-15743)*
Jlg Industries Inc ....C 330 684-0200
Orrville *(G-15744)*
▲ Jrb Attachments LLC ....C 330 734-3000
Akron *(G-243)*
Kaffenberger Truck Eqp Co ....E 513 772-6800
Cincinnati *(G-3967)*
◆ Komar Industries Inc ....E 614 836-2366
Groveport *(G-10629)*
Koski Construction Co ....G 440 964-8171
Ashtabula *(G-816)*
Kubota Tractor Corporation ....F 614 835-3800
Groveport *(G-10631)*
Lake Township Trustees ....G 419 836-1143
Millbury *(G-14184)*
Liebrecht Manufacturing ....G 419 596-3501
Continental *(G-7827)*
Liverpool Township ....G 330 483-4747
Valley City *(G-19211)*
M S K Partnership ....G 419 394-4444
Celina *(G-3005)*
Magna Group LLC ....G 513 388-9463
Cincinnati *(G-4051)*
Mazzella Lifting Tech Inc ....D 440 239-5700
Cleveland *(G-5766)*

McNeilus Truck and Mfg Inc ... E ... 513 874-2022
Fairfield *(G-9683)*
McTech Corp ... F ... 216 391-7700
Cleveland *(G-5773)*
Mead Paving ... G ... 937 322-7414
Springfield *(G-17602)*
◆ **Mesa Industries Inc** ... E ... 513 321-2950
Cincinnati *(G-4087)*
Metro Mech Inc ... G ... 216 641-6262
Cleveland *(G-5792)*
◆ **Meyer Products LLC** ... D ... 216 486-1313
Cleveland *(G-5794)*
▲ **Miller Curber Company LLC** ... F ... 330 782-8081
Youngstown *(G-21146)*
▲ **Minnich Manufacturing Co Inc** ... E ... 419 903-0010
Mansfield *(G-12649)*
Msk Trencher Mfg Inc ... F ... 419 394-4444
Celina *(G-3010)*
Murphy Tractor & Eqp Co Inc ... G ... 614 876-1141
Columbus *(G-7374)*
Murphy Tractor & Eqp Co Inc ... G ... 937 898-4198
Vandalia *(G-19306)*
Murphy Tractor & Eqp Co Inc ... G ... 419 221-3666
Lima *(G-12061)*
Murphy Tractor & Eqp Co Inc ... G ... 330 477-9304
Canton *(G-2785)*
Murphy Tractor & Eqp Co Inc ... G ... 330 220-4999
Brunswick *(G-2238)*
National Oilwell Varco LP ... E ... 978 687-0101
Dayton *(G-8519)*
New River Equipment Corp ... G ... 330 669-0040
North Canton *(G-15255)*
◆ **Npk Construction Equipment Inc** ... D ... 440 232-7900
Bedford *(G-1449)*
Ohio Valley Trackwork Inc ... F ... 740 446-0181
Bidwell *(G-1677)*
◆ **Pace Consolidated Inc** ... D ... 440 942-1234
Willoughby *(G-20564)*
Pace Engineering Inc ... C ... 440 942-1234
Willoughby *(G-20565)*
Power-Pack Conveyor Company ... E ... 440 975-9955
Willoughby *(G-20576)*
Precision Engineered Tech LLC ... G ... 330 335-3300
Wadsworth *(G-19430)*
Pro-Hoe Utility LLC ... G ... 740 892-4765
Johnstown *(G-11403)*
◆ **Pubco Corporation** ... D ... 216 881-5300
Cleveland *(G-6059)*
Quikstir Inc ... F ... 419 732-2601
Port Clinton *(G-16410)*
Richland Twp Garage ... G ... 419 358-4897
Bluffton *(G-1915)*
Rls Parts & Equipment LLC ... G ... 440 498-1843
Solon *(G-17369)*
▲ **Rnm Holdings Inc** ... E ... 937 704-9900
Franklin *(G-10050)*
Roadsafe Traffic Systems Inc ... G ... 614 274-9782
Columbus *(G-7567)*
◆ **Robbins Company** ... C ... 440 248-3303
Solon *(G-17370)*
Rogue Manufacturing Inc ... G ... 937 839-4026
West Alexandria *(G-19782)*
Ryman Grinders Inc ... F ... 330 652-5080
Niles *(G-15183)*
Safesmart USA ... G ... 404 703-1008
Medina *(G-13473)*
Schwieterman Cy Inc ... G ... 937 548-3965
Arcanum *(G-660)*
▲ **Scott Port-A-Fold Inc** ... E ... 419 748-8880
Napoleon *(G-14698)*
Screen Machine Industries LLC ... G ... 740 927-3464
Pataskala *(G-15984)*
▼ **Shaffer Manufacturing Corp** ... E ... 937 652-2151
Urbana *(G-19180)*
Shatzels Backhoe Service LLC ... G ... 937 289-9630
Clarksville *(G-4653)*
▲ **Sk Machinery Corporation** ... G ... 330 733-7325
Akron *(G-403)*
Stillwell Equipment Co Inc ... G ... 330 650-1029
Peninsula *(G-16042)*
Stony Point Metals LLC ... G ... 330 852-7100
Sugarcreek *(G-18041)*
Terex Utilities Inc ... D ... 513 539-9770
Monroe *(G-14416)*
▼ **Tgs Industries Inc** ... E ... 330 339-2211
New Philadelphia *(G-14933)*
◆ **Thorworks Industries Inc** ... E ... 419 626-4375
Sandusky *(G-17015)*
▲ **Toku America Inc** ... F ... 440 954-9923
Willoughby *(G-20618)*
Tri County Asphalt Materials ... G ... 330 549-2852
Youngstown *(G-21229)*
Tri-Way Rebar Inc ... G ... 330 296-9662
Ravenna *(G-16568)*
Turn-Key Tunneling Inc ... E ... 614 275-4832
Columbus *(G-7715)*
▲ **Werk-Brau Company** ... D ... 419 422-2912
Findlay *(G-9907)*
Wilkett Enterprises LLC ... G ... 740 384-2890
Wellston *(G-19773)*
Workpros ... G ... 740 512-8512
Brilliant *(G-2096)*
◆ **Wyeth-Scott Company** ... G ... 740 345-4528
Newark *(G-15066)*
Youngstown Bending Rolling ... F ... 330 799-2227
Youngstown *(G-21246)*

3532 Mining Machinery & Eqpt

▲ **2828 Clinton Inc** ... E ... 216 241-7157
Leetonia *(G-11857)*
80 Acres Urban Agriculture LLC ... G ... 513 218-4387
Cincinnati *(G-3327)*
Belden Brick Company ... E ... 330 852-2411
Sugarcreek *(G-18016)*
▲ **Belle Center Air Tool Co Inc** ... G ... 937 464-7474
Belle Center *(G-1511)*
Bowdil Company ... F ... 800 356-8663
Canton *(G-2626)*
Breaker Technology Inc ... E ... 440 248-7168
Solon *(G-17274)*
▼ **Brydet Development Corporation** ... E ... 740 623-0455
Coshocton *(G-7883)*
Buzz N Shuttle Service ... G ... 740 223-0567
Marion *(G-12860)*
Cailin Dev Ltd Lblty Co ... F ... 216 408-6261
Cleveland *(G-4962)*
Carr Tool Company ... E ... 513 825-2900
Fairfield *(G-9651)*
Cool Machines Inc ... F ... 419 232-4871
Van Wert *(G-19249)*
▲ **Davey Kent Inc** ... E ... 330 673-5400
Kent *(G-11446)*
▲ **Deep Springs Technology LLC** ... G ... 419 536-5741
Toledo *(G-18434)*
Dover Conveyor Inc ... E ... 740 922-9390
Midvale *(G-14106)*
Eagle Crusher Co Inc ... E ... 419 562-1183
Bucyrus *(G-2340)*
◆ **Eagle Crusher Co Inc** ... D ... 419 468-2288
Galion *(G-10266)*
Enercon Systems Inc ... G ... 305 213-3997
Elyria *(G-9419)*
Engines Inc of Ohio ... D ... 740 377-9874
South Point *(G-17437)*
Esco Corporation ... E ... 419 562-6015
Bucyrus *(G-2343)*
▲ **Furukawa Rock Drill** ... G ... 330 673-5821
Kent *(G-11461)*
▼ **Grasan Equipment Company Inc** ... D ... 419 526-4440
Mansfield *(G-12620)*
Horizontal Eqp Manufacturing ... G ... 330 264-2229
Wooster *(G-20784)*
▲ **Irock Crushers LLC** ... G ... 866 240-0201
Cleveland *(G-5587)*
Jennmar McSweeney LLC ... C ... 740 377-3354
South Point *(G-17439)*
Joy Global Inc ... G ... 216 503-5029
Independence *(G-11262)*
▲ **Joy Mining Machinery** ... C ... 440 248-7970
Solon *(G-17323)*
Kaffenbarger Truck Eqp Co ... E ... 513 772-6800
Cincinnati *(G-3967)*
Kennametal Inc ... C ... 440 349-5151
Solon *(G-17329)*
Kilgore Manufacturing Mch Co ... G ... 330 491-1915
Canton *(G-2752)*
Mike Suponcic ... G ... 740 635-0654
Bridgeport *(G-2092)*
Nolan Company ... G ... 330 453-7922
Canton *(G-2789)*
Nolan Company ... G ... 740 269-1512
Bowerston *(G-1959)*
◆ **Npk Construction Equipment Inc** ... D ... 440 232-7900
Bedford *(G-1449)*
Penn Machine Company ... E ... 814 288-1547
Twinsburg *(G-18996)*
Pneumatic Parts Co ... F ... 330 923-6063
Stow *(G-17788)*
◆ **Reduction Engineering Inc** ... E ... 330 677-2225
Kent *(G-11514)*
Riverrock Recycl Crushing LLC ... G ... 937 325-2052
Springfield *(G-17640)*
◆ **SMI Holdings Inc** ... D ... 740 927-3464
Pataskala *(G-15985)*
▲ **Tema Systems Inc** ... E ... 513 489-7811
Cincinnati *(G-4501)*
Terrasource Global Corporation ... D ... 330 923-5254
Cuyahoga Falls *(G-8054)*
Underground Professionals ... G ... 419 282-6400
Ashland *(G-783)*
◆ **Warren Fabricating Corporation** ... D ... 330 847-0596
Warren *(G-19621)*
Zen Industries Inc ... E ... 216 432-3240
Cleveland *(G-6493)*

3533 Oil Field Machinery & Eqpt

Allied Machine Works Inc ... G ... 740 454-2534
Zanesville *(G-21270)*
Appalachian Equipment Co LLC ... G ... 330 345-2251
Wooster *(G-20739)*
Arete Innovative Solutions LLC ... G ... 513 503-2712
Morrow *(G-14543)*
Baker Hughes C/O Tangoe Inc ... G ... 304 884-6442
Hubbard *(G-11127)*
Buckeye Companies ... E ... 740 452-3641
Zanesville *(G-21282)*
Cameron International Corp ... G ... 740 654-4260
Lancaster *(G-11695)*
Condition Monitoring Supplies ... G ... 216 941-6868
Strongsville *(G-17906)*
Cyclone Supply Company Inc ... G ... 330 204-0313
Dover *(G-8974)*
D & L Gas Energy Ltd ... C ... 330 792-9524
Youngstown *(G-21062)*
Dynamic Leasing Ltd ... G ... 330 892-0164
New Waterford *(G-14970)*
Electrnic Dsign For Indust Inc ... E ... 740 401-4000
Belpre *(G-1586)*
Enercon Systems Inc ... G ... 305 213-3997
Elyria *(G-9419)*
◆ **Gougler Industries Inc** ... F ... 330 673-5826
Kent *(G-11463)*
H & S Company Inc ... F ... 419 394-4444
Celina *(G-2999)*
H P E Inc ... F ... 330 833-3161
Massillon *(G-13145)*
Hughes Christensen ... G ... 330 455-2140
Canton *(G-2731)*
Jet Rubber Company ... E ... 330 325-1821
Rootstown *(G-16723)*
Kelley Brothers Roofing Inc ... F ... 330 273-3700
Medina *(G-13432)*
Midflow Services LLC ... E ... 330 674-2399
Millersburg *(G-14246)*
Midflow Services LLC ... G ... 330 567-3108
Shreve *(G-17161)*
Monroe Drilling Operations ... G ... 740 472-0866
Woodsfield *(G-20721)*
▲ **Multi Products Company** ... E ... 330 674-5981
Millersburg *(G-14252)*
N & N Oil ... G ... 740 743-2848
Somerset *(G-17417)*
National Oilwell Varco Inc ... E ... 440 577-1225
Pierpont *(G-16213)*
Ohio Energy Assets Inc ... G ... 740 332-9511
Laurelville *(G-11771)*
Oil Skimmers Inc ... E ... 440 237-4600
North Royalton *(G-15440)*
Pride of Hills Mfg Inc ... D ... 330 567-3108
Big Prairie *(G-1683)*
Pride of Hills Mfg Inc ... E ... 800 345-1744
Killbuck *(G-11598)*
Rampp Company ... E ... 740 373-7886
Marietta *(G-12822)*
▲ **Reberland Equipment Inc** ... F ... 330 698-5883
Apple Creek *(G-648)*
▼ **Rmi Titanium Company LLC** ... E ... 330 652-9952
Niles *(G-15176)*
Robbins & Myers Inc ... F ... 937 454-3200
Dayton *(G-8636)*
◆ **Saint-Gobain Norpro Corp** ... C ... 330 673-5860
Stow *(G-17798)*
Smith International Inc ... F ... 570 368-2130
Strasburg *(G-17829)*
Smith International Inc ... G ... 330 497-2999
Uniontown *(G-19098)*
▲ **Tech Tool Inc** ... F ... 330 674-1176
Millersburg *(G-14267)*
◆ **Terra Sonic International LLC** ... E ... 740 374-6608
Marietta *(G-12840)*

Employee Codes: A=Over 500 employees, B=251-500
C=101-250, D=51-100, E=20-50, F=10-19, G=3-9
2017 Harris Ohio
Industrial Directory
1011

Tiger General LLC ....D... 330 239-4949
Medina (G-13489)

Timco Inc ....F... 740 685-2594
Byesville (G-2410)

Under Hill Water Well ....G... 740 852-0858
London (G-12221)

Westerman Inc ....D... 330 262-6946
Wooster (G-20846)

3534 Elevators & Moving Stairways

Aimco Mfg Inc ....G... 419 476-6572
Toledo (G-18324)

▼ Benko Products Inc ....E... 440 934-2180
Sheffield Village (G-17121)

▲ Canton Elevator Inc ....D... 330 833-3600
North Canton (G-15224)

Edmonds Elevator Company ....F... 216 781-9135
Thompson (G-18188)

▲ Elevator Cncepts By Wurtec LLC ....F... 734 246-4700
Toledo (G-18455)

▲ Federal Equipment Company ....D... 513 621-5260
Cincinnati (G-3747)

▲ Fujitec America Inc ....C... 513 755-6100
Mason (G-13024)

Gray-Eering Ltd ....G... 740 498-8816
Tippecanoe (G-18314)

Heartland Stairways Inc ....F... 330 279-2554
Holmesville (G-11102)

Heartland Stairways Inc ....G... 330 279-2554
Holmesville (G-11103)

Holmes Stair Parts Ltd ....E... 330 279-2797
Holmesville (G-11104)

Otis Elevator Company ....F... 419 867-7758
Toledo (G-18623)

Otis Elevator Company ....D... 216 573-2333
Cleveland (G-5951)

Schindler Elevator Corporation ....E... 513 341-2600
West Chester (G-20047)

Schindler Elevator Corporation ....E... 419 861-5900
Holland (G-11084)

▲ Sematic Usa Inc ....E... 330 405-3004
Twinsburg (G-19018)

◆ Sweet Manufacturing Company ....E... 937 325-1511
Springfield (G-17659)

Thyssenkrupp Elevator Corp ....D... 513 241-0222
Cincinnati (G-4508)

Versalift East Inc ....G... 610 866-1400
Canton (G-2897)

3535 Conveyors & Eqpt

Advanced Equipment Systems LLC ....G... 216 289-6505
Euclid (G-9564)

◆ Air Technical Industries Inc ....E... 440 951-5191
Mentor (G-13512)

Alba Manufacturing Inc ....D... 513 874-0551
Fairfield (G-9640)

Allied Consolidated Industries ....C... 330 744-0808
Youngstown (G-21020)

Allied Fabricating & Wldg Co ....E... 614 751-6664
Columbus (G-6725)

Alloy Welding & Fabricating ....F... 440 914-0650
Solon (G-17254)

▲ Almo Process Technology Inc ....G... 513 402-2566
West Chester (G-19804)

◆ Ambaflex Inc ....E... 330 478-1858
Canton (G-2601)

▲ American Solving Inc ....G... 440 234-7373
Brookpark (G-2150)

Ashtech Corporation ....G... 440 646-9911
Cleveland (G-4847)

Automation Systems Designs Inc ....E... 937 387-0351
Dayton (G-8173)

▲ Barth Industries Co LP ....D... 216 267-0531
Cleveland (G-4893)

Belden Brick Company ....E... 330 852-2411
Sugarcreek (G-18016)

◆ Blair Rubber Company ....D... 330 769-5583
Seville (G-17070)

Bobco Enterprises Inc ....F... 419 867-3560
Toledo (G-18374)

▲ Bry-Air Inc ....E... 740 965-2974
Sunbury (G-18056)

Building & Conveyer Maint LLC ....G... 303 882-0912
Ravenna (G-16520)

Bulk Handling Equipment Co ....G... 330 468-5703
Northfield (G-15462)

C S Bell Co ....F... 419 448-0791
Tiffin (G-18213)

▲ CA Litzler Co Inc ....E... 216 267-8020
Cleveland (G-4958)

Ccw Group Pacesetter Inc ....C... 740 474-0122
Circleville (G-4624)

▲ Cincinnati Mine Machinery Co ....D... 513 522-7777
Cincinnati (G-3560)

Conveyor Metal Works Inc ....E... 740 477-8700
Frankfort (G-9998)

Conveyor Solutions LLC ....E... 513 367-4845
Cleves (G-6512)

Conveyor Technologies Ltd ....G... 513 248-0663
Milford (G-14134)

▲ Conveyors Inc ....C... 740 490-0300
London (G-12206)

Decision Systems Inc ....E... 330 456-7600
Canton (G-2682)

Dillin Engineered Systems Corp ....E... 419 666-6789
Perrysburg (G-16085)

Dover Conveyor Inc ....E... 740 922-9390
Midvale (G-14106)

Duplex Mill & Manufacturing Co ....E... 937 325-5555
Springfield (G-17548)

E S Industries Inc ....E... 419 643-2625
Lima (G-12008)

◆ Eagle Crusher Co Inc ....E... 419 468-2288
Galion (G-10266)

Ethos Corp ....C... 513 242-6336
Cincinnati (G-3720)

Fabacraft Inc ....E... 513 677-0500
Maineville (G-12524)

▲ Fabco Inc ....E... 419 421-4740
Findlay (G-9820)

Falcon Industries Inc ....E... 330 723-0099
Medina (G-13409)

▲ Federal Equipment Company ....D... 513 621-5260
Cincinnati (G-3747)

Feedall Inc ....F... 440 942-8100
Willoughby (G-20486)

◆ Fenner Dunlop Port Clinton Inc ....E... 419 635-2191
Port Clinton (G-16399)

Formtek Inc ....D... 216 292-6300
Cleveland (G-5371)

▲ Formtek Inc ....D... 216 292-4460
Cleveland (G-5372)

Fred D Pfening Company ....E... 614 294-5361
Columbus (G-7099)

◆ Glassline Corporation ....E... 419 666-9712
Perrysburg (G-16102)

▼ Grasan Equipment Company Inc ....D... 419 526-4440
Mansfield (G-12620)

Gray-Eering Ltd ....G... 740 498-8816
Tippecanoe (G-18314)

◆ Grob Systems Inc ....C... 419 358-9015
Bluffton (G-1912)

Hamilton Air Products Inc ....G... 513 874-4030
Fairfield (G-9664)

Harsco Corporation ....E... 740 387-1150
Marion (G-12873)

Hawthorne-Seving Inc ....E... 419 643-5531
Cridersville (G-7945)

Hoist Equipment Co Inc ....E... 440 232-0300
Bedford Heights (G-1486)

Hostar International Inc ....F... 440 564-5362
Newbury (G-15095)

Hostar International Inc ....F... 440 564-5362
Newbury (G-15096)

Ibiza Holdings Inc ....E... 513 701-7300
Mason (G-13039)

Innovative Controls Corp ....D... 419 691-6684
Toledo (G-18524)

Innovative Hdlg & Metalfab LLC ....E... 419 882-7480
Sylvania (G-18112)

Ins Robotics Inc ....G... 888 293-5325
Hilliard (G-10953)

▲ Intelligrated Inc ....E... 866 936-7300
Mason (G-13042)

Intelligrated Inc ....E... 513 874-0788
West Chester (G-20016)

Intelligrated Headquarters LLC ....E... 866 936-7300
Mason (G-13043)

▲ Intelligrated Products LLC ....E... 740 490-0300
London (G-12212)

Intelligrated Sub Holdings Inc ....E... 513 701-7300
Mason (G-13044)

Intelligrated Systems Inc ....A... 866 936-7300
Mason (G-13045)

Intelligrated Systems LLC ....A... 513 701-7300
Mason (G-13046)

◆ Intelligrated Systems Ohio LLC ....A... 513 701-7300
Mason (G-13047)

Joy Global Underground Min LLC ....F... 440 248-7970
Cleveland (G-5624)

K F T Inc ....D... 513 241-5910
Cincinnati (G-3965)

Ka Wanner Inc ....E... 740 251-4636
Marion (G-12878)

King Conveyor LLC ....F... 740 332-6200
Laurelville (G-11770)

Kolinahr Systems Inc ....F... 513 745-9401
Blue Ash (G-1823)

Laser Automation Inc ....F... 440 543-9291
Chagrin Falls (G-3099)

Ledow Company Inc ....G... 330 657-2837
Peninsula (G-16038)

◆ Lewco Inc ....C... 419 625-4014
Sandusky (G-16979)

▲ Logitech Inc ....E... 614 871-2822
Grove City (G-10569)

▲ Manufacturers Equipment Co ....F... 513 424-3573
Middletown (G-14059)

Martin Rubber Company ....F... 330 336-6604
Seville (G-17078)

Martin Sprocket & Gear Inc ....D... 419 485-5515
Montpelier (G-14448)

▲ Mayfran International Inc ....E... 440 461-4100
Cleveland (G-5764)

Met Fab Fabrication and Mch ....G... 513 724-3715
Batavia (G-1203)

Mfh Partners Inc ....F... 440 461-4100
Cleveland (G-5795)

Midwest Conveyor Products Inc ....E... 419 281-1235
Ashland (G-754)

Midwest Industrial Rubber Inc ....F... 614 876-3110
Hilliard (G-10963)

Miller Products Inc ....E... 330 308-5934
New Philadelphia (G-14915)

Mine Equipment Services LLC ....E... 740 936-5427
Sunbury (G-18067)

Mountaineer Mining Corp ....G... 740 418-1817
Jackson (G-11322)

Mulhern Belting Inc ....E... 201 337-5700
Fairfield (G-9689)

◆ Nesco Inc ....E... 440 461-6000
Cleveland (G-5871)

Nkc of America Inc ....G... 937 642-4033
Marysville (G-12961)

▲ Ocs Intellitrak Inc ....F... 513 742-5600
Fairfield (G-9693)

▲ Ohio Magnetics Inc ....E... 216 662-8484
Maple Heights (G-12736)

▲ Opw Engineered Systems Inc ....D... 888 771-9438
Lebanon (G-11824)

P B Fabrication Mech Contr ....F... 419 478-4869
Toledo (G-18631)

Parker-Hannifin Corporation ....D... 330 336-3511
Wadsworth (G-19427)

Pfpc Enterprises Inc ....B... 513 941-6200
Cincinnati (G-4233)

◆ Pneumatic Scale Corporation ....C... 330 923-0491
Cuyahoga Falls (G-8033)

Pomacon Inc ....F... 330 273-1576
Brunswick (G-2244)

Power-Pack Conveyor Company ....E... 440 975-9955
Willoughby (G-20576)

Precision Conveyor Technology ....F... 440 352-3601
Perry (G-16056)

Quickdraft Inc ....E... 330 477-4574
Canton (G-2832)

Rhino Robotics Ltd ....G... 513 353-9772
Miamitown (G-13891)

Richmond Machine Co ....E... 419 485-5740
Montpelier (G-14454)

◆ Robbins Company ....C... 440 248-3303
Solon (G-17370)

Rolcon Inc ....F... 513 821-7259
Cincinnati (G-4358)

Sandusky Fabricating & Sls Inc ....E... 419 626-4465
Sandusky (G-17001)

Schenck Process LLC ....E... 513 576-9200
Milford (G-14173)

Scott-Randall Systems Inc ....F... 937 446-2293
Sardinia (G-17033)

Siemens Industry Inc ....E... 440 526-2770
Brecksville (G-2073)

▲ Sst Conveyor Components Inc ....E... 513 583-5500
Loveland (G-12389)

▲ Stock Equipment Company Inc ....C... 440 543-6000
Chagrin Falls (G-3121)

Stock Fairfield Corporation ....C... 440 543-6000
Chagrin Falls (G-3122)

◆ Sweet Manufacturing Company ....E... 937 325-1511
Springfield (G-17659)

T J Davies Company Inc ....G 440 248-5510
  Solon (G-17396)
◆ Transcon Inc ....E 440 255-7600
  Mentor (G-13754)
▲ Trico Belting & Supply Company ...E 513 860-8400
  West Chester (G-20061)
Ulterior Products LLC ....G 614 519-3210
  Hilliard (G-10990)
▲ Webb-Stiles Company ....D 330 225-7761
  Valley City (G-19237)
◆ Webster Industries Inc ....B 419 447-8232
  Tiffin (G-18253)

3536 Hoists, Cranes & Monorails

ACC Automation Co Inc ....E 330 928-3821
  Akron (G-25)
Acme Lifting Products Inc ....G 440 838-4430
  Cleveland (G-4693)
◆ Air Technical Industries Inc ....E 440 951-5191
  Mentor (G-13512)
American Climber & Mch Corp ....G 330 420-0019
  Lisbon (G-12117)
American Power Hoist Inc ....G 740 964-2035
  Pataskala (G-15967)
▲ American Power Pull Corp ....G 419 335-7050
  Wauseon (G-19671)
ARI Phoenix Inc ....E 513 229-3750
  Lebanon (G-11781)
Belden Brick Company ....E 330 852-2411
  Sugarcreek (G-18016)
Bobco Enterprises Inc ....F 419 867-3560
  Toledo (G-18374)
Cincinnati Crane & Hoist LLC ....F 513 202-1408
  Harrison (G-10772)
Cincinnati Recreation Comm ....G 513 921-5657
  Cincinnati (G-3564)
Columbus McKinnon Corporation ....D 330 332-5769
  Salem (G-16884)
Columbus McKinnon Corporation ....D 330 424-7248
  Lisbon (G-12118)
Crane Training USA Inc ....G 513 755-2177
  West Chester (G-19848)
▲ David Round Company Inc ....E 330 656-1600
  Streetsboro (G-17847)
Delta Crane Systems Inc ....F 937 324-7425
  Springfield (G-17542)
◆ Emh Inc ....E 330 220-8600
  Valley City (G-19203)
▲ Federal Equipment Company ....E 513 621-5260
  Cincinnati (G-3747)
Galion-Godwin Truck Bdy Co LLC ......D 330 359-5495
  Millersburg (G-14217)
Gray-Eering Ltd ....G 740 498-8816
  Tippecanoe (G-18314)
Harsco Corporation ....E 740 387-1150
  Marion (G-12873)
◆ Hiab USA Inc ....D 419 482-6000
  Perrysburg (G-16106)
Hoist Equipment Co Inc ....E 440 232-0300
  Bedford Heights (G-1486)
Ibi Brake Products Inc ....G 440 543-7962
  Chagrin Falls (G-3094)
Indian Lake Boat Lift ....G 937 539-2868
  Russells Point (G-16755)
Ingersoll-Rand Company ....E 419 633-6800
  Bryan (G-2306)
◆ Kci Holding USA Inc ....C 937 525-5533
  Springfield (G-17585)
Konecranes Inc ....E 937 328-5100
  Springfield (G-17589)
◆ Konecranes Inc ....B 937 525-5533
  Springfield (G-17590)
Konecranes Inc ....F 440 461-8400
  Highland Heights (G-10916)
Laird Controls Holdings Inc ....E 234 806-0018
  Warren (G-19567)
Lisbon Hoist Inc ....F 330 424-7283
  Lisbon (G-12127)
Mmh Americas Inc ....G 414 764-6200
  Springfield (G-17605)
◆ Mmh Holdings Inc ....G 937 525-5533
  Springfield (G-17606)
Morgan Engineering Systems Inc ......E 330 821-4721
  Alliance (G-528)
Morgan Engineering Systems Inc ......E 330 823-6120
  Alliance (G-529)
Ohio Mechanical Handling Co ....F 330 773-5165
  Akron (G-325)
Radocy Inc ....F 419 666-4400
  Rossford (G-16747)

Replacment Prts Spcialists Inc ....G 440 248-0731
  Solon (G-17367)
Rnm Holdings Inc ....E 419 867-8712
  Holland (G-11082)
Rnm Holdings Inc ....F 614 444-5556
  Columbus (G-7566)
Stahl Cranesystems Inc ....G 843 767-1951
  Springfield (G-17655)
Terex Mhps Corp ....G 440 349-8235
  Solon (G-17403)
Terex Utilities Inc ....D 513 539-9770
  Monroe (G-14416)
Terex Utilities Inc ....F 440 262-3200
  Brecksville (G-2076)
▲ Webb-Stiles Company ....D 330 225-7761
  Valley City (G-19237)
Westerman Inc ....D 330 262-6946
  Wooster (G-20846)

3537 Indl Trucks, Tractors, Trailers & Stackers

◆ Air Technical Industries Inc ....E 440 951-5191
  Mentor (G-13512)
AJD Holding Co ....D 330 405-4477
  Twinsburg (G-18895)
Belden Brick Company ....E 330 852-2411
  Sugarcreek (G-18016)
Boltech Incorporated ....G 330 746-6881
  Youngstown (G-21033)
Bpr-Rico Elc Trck Spcalist Inc ....D 330 723-4050
  Medina (G-13381)
▲ Bpr-Rico Manufacturing Inc ....D 330 723-4050
  Medina (G-13382)
▲ Canton Elevator Inc ....D 330 833-3600
  North Canton (G-15224)
Cascade Corporation ....C 937 327-0300
  Springfield (G-17527)
Chemtrans Logistics Inc ....G 419 447-8041
  Tiffin (G-18215)
City Machine Technologies Inc ....F 330 747-2639
  Youngstown (G-21047)
▲ Crescent Metal Products Inc ....C 440 350-1100
  Mentor (G-13555)
Crown Credit Company ....F 419 629-2311
  New Bremen (G-14782)
Crown Equipment Corporation ....D 937 295-4062
  Fort Loramie (G-9927)
Crown Equipment Corporation ....A 419 586-1100
  Celina (G-2991)
Crown Equipment Corporation ....G 419 629-9201
  New Bremen (G-14783)
Crown Equipment Corporation ....D 937 454-7545
  Vandalia (G-19288)
Crown Equipment Corporation ....E 440 232-7772
  Oakwood Village (G-15623)
Crown Equipment Corporation ....D 419 629-2311
  New Bremen (G-14784)
Crown Equipment Corporation ....D 419 629-2311
  New Bremen (G-14786)
Crown Equipment Corporation ....D 614 274-7700
  Grove City (G-10551)
Crown Equipment Corporation ....D 513 874-2600
  Cincinnati (G-3622)
Crown Equipment Corporation ....D 419 629-2311
  New Bremen (G-14785)
Dale Lute Logging ....G 740 352-1779
  Mc Dermott (G-13341)
Elliott Machine Works Inc ....E 419 468-4709
  Galion (G-10267)
Fairborn Services Inc ....F 513 492-9422
  Lebanon (G-11799)
Fairway Carts Parts & More LLC ....G 234 209-9008
  North Canton (G-15229)
▲ Falls Welding & Fabg Inc ....G 330 253-3437
  Akron (G-180)
Fame Tool & Mfg Co Inc ....E 513 271-6387
  Cincinnati (G-3737)
Fives St Corp ....F 419 522-1080
  Mansfield (G-12604)
▲ Fives St Corp ....F 419 522-1080
  Mansfield (G-12605)
Foerster Instruments Inc ....F 330 332-9100
  Salem (G-16891)
Foerster Systems Inc ....F 330 332-9100
  Salem (G-16892)
Forklifts of Americas LLC ....G 440 821-5143
  Highland Heights (G-10912)
Forte Indus Eqp Systems Inc ....E 513 398-2800
  Mason (G-13022)

G & T Manufacturing Co ....F 440 639-7777
  Mentor (G-13588)
G P Manufacturing Inc ....G 937 544-3190
  Peebles (G-16020)
General Electric Company ....B 513 977-1500
  Cincinnati (G-3813)
Global Trucking LLC ....F 614 598-6264
  Columbus (G-7121)
◆ Gradall Industries Inc ....C 330 339-2211
  New Philadelphia (G-14901)
Grand Aire Inc ....E 419 861-6700
  Swanton (G-18084)
Grand Harbor Yacht Sales & Svc ......G 440 442-2919
  Cleveland (G-5445)
Gvs Inc ....G 330 310-8275
  Fairlawn (G-9751)
Harsco Corporation ....E 740 387-1150
  Marion (G-12873)
Hendrickson Usa LLC ....C 330 456-7288
  Canton (G-2725)
◆ Hobart Brothers Company ....A 937 332-5439
  Troy (G-18836)
Hoist Equipment Co Inc ....E 440 232-0300
  Bedford Heights (G-1486)
Hunter Lift Ltd ....F 330 549-3347
  North Lima (G-15317)
Hyster-Yale Materials Hdlg Inc ....C 440 449-9600
  Cleveland (G-5544)
Integrity Industrial Eqp Inc ....G 937 238-9275
  Huber Heights (G-11149)
◆ Intelligrated Systems Ohio LLC ....A 513 701-7300
  Mason (G-13047)
Jh Industries Inc ....E 330 963-4105
  Twinsburg (G-18961)
Kay Capital Company ....G 216 531-1010
  Cleveland (G-5638)
Kinetic Technologies Inc ....F 440 943-4111
  Wickliffe (G-20369)
Lange Precision Inc ....E 513 530-9500
  Blue Ash (G-1824)
Leebaw Manufacturing Company ....F 330 533-3368
  Canfield (G-2561)
Machine Tool Corporation ....G 513 863-4920
  Hamilton (G-10722)
Marlow-2000 Inc ....E 216 362-8500
  Cleveland (G-5751)
Martin Sheet Metal Inc ....D 216 377-8200
  Cleveland (G-5753)
Martin Sprocket & Gear Inc ....D 419 485-5515
  Montpelier (G-14448)
McCullough Industries Inc ....E 800 245-9490
  Kenton (G-11556)
Medrano Usa Inc ....C 614 272-5856
  Columbus (G-7341)
MH Logistics Corp ....D 513 681-2200
  West Chester (G-20028)
Miller Products Inc ....E 330 308-5934
  New Philadelphia (G-14915)
Miners Tractor Sales Inc ....F 330 325-9914
  Rootstown (G-16725)
Mitchs Welding & Hitches ....G 419 893-3117
  Maumee (G-13286)
Newsafe Transport Service Inc ....F 740 387-1679
  Marion (G-12890)
Parker Elwell Ltd ....G 216 881-5042
  Cleveland (G-5970)
Parobek Trucking Co ....G 419 869-7500
  West Salem (G-20116)
Perfecto Industries Inc ....E 937 778-1900
  Piqua (G-16299)
Pollock Research & Design Inc ....E 330 332-3300
  Salem (G-16920)
Precision Equipment Llc ....G 330 220-7600
  Brunswick (G-2246)
Products Innovators ....E 216 932-5269
  Cleveland (G-6053)
Pucel Enterprises Inc ....D 216 881-4604
  Cleveland (G-6061)
▲ R B Mfg Co ....F 419 626-9464
  Sandusky (G-16999)
Saf-Holland Inc ....G 513 874-7888
  West Chester (G-20046)
Saunders Trucking Lcc ....G 419 210-0551
  Marengo (G-12753)
Scott-Randall Systems Inc ....F 937 446-2293
  Sardinia (G-17033)
Shanafelt Manufacturing Co ....E 330 455-0315
  Canton (G-2847)
Skylift Inc ....G 440 960-2100
  Lorain (G-12277)

Snair Co .... F 614 873-7020
Plain City (G-16360)

▲ Sroka Inc .... E 440 572-2811
Strongsville (G-17971)

St Marys Iron Works Inc .... F 419 300-6300
Saint Marys (G-16857)

Stock Fairfield Corporation .... C 440 543-6000
Chagrin Falls (G-3122)

Surplus Freight Inc .... G 614 235-7660
Gahanna (G-10237)

Suspension Technology Inc .... F 330 458-3058
Canton (G-2865)

◆ Sweet Manufacturing Company .... E 937 325-1511
Springfield (G-17659)

Tarpco Inc .... F 330 677-8277
Kent (G-11535)

Thieman Tailgates Inc .... D 419 586-7727
Celina (G-3022)

Tilt-Or-Lift Inc .... G 419 893-6944
Maumee (G-13302)

▲ Trailer Component Mfg Inc .... E 440 255-2888
Mentor (G-13753)

Transco Railway Products Inc .... E 419 726-3383
Toledo (G-18756)

Triumphant Enterprises Inc .... F 513 617-1668
Goshen (G-10417)

Venturo Manufacturing Inc .... E 513 772-8448
Cincinnati (G-4562)

▲ Waltco Lift Corp .... C 330 633-9191
Tallmadge (G-18175)

▲ Webb-Stiles Company .... D 330 225-7761
Valley City (G-19237)

▲ Whiteside Manufacturing Co .... E 740 363-1179
Delaware (G-8896)

Yemaneh Musie .... G 614 506-3687
Columbus (G-7783)

Youngstown-Kenworth Inc .... E 330 534-9761
Hubbard (G-11143)

3541 Machine Tools: Cutting

3 Brothers Torching Inc .... G 419 339-9985
Lima (G-11979)

A & P Tool Inc .... E 419 542-6681
Hicksville (G-10897)

Accu-Grind & Mfg Co Inc .... E 937 224-3303
Dayton (G-8130)

Accurate Machining & Welding .... G 937 584-4518
Sabina (G-16772)

Accurate Plasma Cutting Inc .... F 440 943-1655
Wickliffe (G-20350)

▲ Acro Tool & Die Company .... D 330 773-5173
Akron (G-29)

Advanced Innovative Mfg Inc .... G 440 759-2034
Aurora (G-905)

Advetech Inc .... E 330 533-2227
Canfield (G-2543)

▼ Alcon Tool Company .... D 330 773-9171
Akron (G-62)

Ald Group LLC .... G 440 942-9800
Willoughby (G-20427)

Alien Products LLC .... E 440 946-9100
Mentor (G-13517)

Alliance Drilling Inc .... F 330 584-2781
North Benton (G-15211)

◆ Alliance Knife Inc .... E 513 367-9000
Harrison (G-10768)

▲ AM Industrial Group LLC .... G 216 433-7171
Brookpark (G-2149)

Applied Automation Enterprise .... F 419 929-2428
New London (G-14858)

Applied Metals Technologies .... E 216 741-2440
Brooklyn Heights (G-2130)

▲ Areway LLC .... D 216 651-9022
Brooklyn (G-2128)

Automatic Parts .... E 419 524-5841
Mansfield (G-12564)

B V Grinding Machining Inc .... G 440 918-1884
Willoughby (G-20442)

Bar Tech Service Inc .... G 440 943-5286
Wickliffe (G-20356)

▲ Barbco Inc .... E 330 488-9400
East Canton (G-9190)

▲ Bardons & Oliver Inc .... C 440 498-5800
Solon (G-17264)

▲ Barth Industries Co LP .... D 216 267-0531
Cleveland (G-4893)

Blairs Cnc Turning Inc .... F 937 461-1100
Dayton (G-8189)

▼ Bor-It Manufacturing Inc .... E 419 289-6639
Ashland (G-714)

Bortnick Tractor Sales Inc .... F 330 924-2555
Cortland (G-7862)

Boye & Emmes Machine Tool Co .... F 513 541-2520
Cincinnati (G-3464)

Bud May Inc .... F 216 676-8850
Cleveland (G-4945)

C M M S - Re LLC .... F 513 489-5111
Blue Ash (G-1760)

C S Bell Co .... F 419 448-0791
Tiffin (G-18213)

▲ Cammann Inc .... E 440 965-4051
Birmingham (G-1685)

Cardinal Builders Inc .... E 614 237-1000
Columbus (G-6905)

Carlton Natco .... G 216 451-5588
Cleveland (G-4978)

Carter Manufacturing Co Inc .... G 513 398-7303
Mason (G-12991)

Center Line Machining LLC .... G 216 289-6828
Euclid (G-9571)

▲ Channel Products Inc .... D 440 423-0113
Chesterland (G-3199)

Chart Tech Tool Inc .... G 937 667-3543
Tipp City (G-18272)

Cincinnati Electrical Tool .... F 513 941-5000
Cleves (G-6509)

▲ Cincinnati Gilbert Mch Tl LLC .... E 513 541-4815
Cincinnati (G-3555)

▲ Cincinnati Mine Machinery Co .... D 513 522-7777
Cincinnati (G-3560)

Cleveland Deburring Machine Co .... G 216 472-0200
Cleveland (G-5057)

◆ Cleveland Tool and Machine Inc .... F 216 267-6010
Cleveland (G-5081)

▼ Coil Technology Inc .... G 330 601-1350
Wooster (G-20759)

Commercial Grinding Services .... G 330 273-5040
Medina (G-13390)

▲ Competetive Carbide Inc .... E 440 350-9393
Mentor (G-13551)

Criterion Tool & Die Inc .... G 216 267-1733
Brookpark (G-2154)

▲ Cutting Systems Inc .... F 216 928-0500
Cleveland (G-5155)

Dan Wilzynski .... G 800 531-3343
Columbus (G-7010)

Dbcr Inc .... E 330 920-1900
Cuyahoga Falls (G-7986)

Dexport Tool Manufacturing Co .... G 513 625-1600
Loveland (G-12348)

Diversified Honing Inc .... G 330 874-4663
Bolivar (G-1932)

Dixie Machinery Inc .... F 513 360-0091
Monroe (G-14400)

▲ Drake Manufacturing Svcs Co .... D 330 847-7291
Warren (G-19545)

E D M Electrofying Inc .... G 440 322-8900
Elyria (G-9410)

▲ Eagle Machinery & Supply Inc .... E 330 852-1300
Sugarcreek (G-18023)

Elliott Tool Technologies Ltd .... D 937 253-6133
Dayton (G-8324)

Falcon Industries Inc .... E 330 723-0099
Medina (G-13409)

Falcon Tool & Machine Inc .... G 937 534-9999
Moraine (G-14487)

▲ Faxon Machining Inc .... C 513 851-4644
Cincinnati (G-3745)

Fischer Special Tooling Corp .... F 440 951-8411
Mentor (G-13578)

Fives Landis Corp .... D 440 709-0700
Painesville (G-15882)

Frazier Machine and Prod Inc .... E 419 661-1656
Perrysburg (G-16098)

▼ Fredon Corporation .... D 440 951-5200
Mentor (G-13584)

▲ Gbi Cincinnati Inc .... G 513 841-8684
Cincinnati (G-3801)

Genex Tool & Die Inc .... F 330 788-2466
Youngstown (G-21098)

▼ George A Mitchell Company .... G 330 758-5777
Youngstown (G-21099)

◆ Glassline Corporation .... E 419 666-9712
Perrysburg (G-16102)

▲ Global Specialty Machines LLC .... F 513 701-0452
Mason (G-13030)

◆ Glt Inc .... F 937 237-0055
Dayton (G-8372)

Grind-All Corporation .... E 330 220-1600
Brunswick (G-2230)

◆ Grt Utilicorp Inc .... E 330 264-8444
Wooster (G-20780)

▲ H & D Steel Service Inc .... E 440 237-3390
North Royalton (G-15423)

Hawk Manufacturing LLC .... D 330 784-3151
Akron (G-218)

Hawk Manufacturing LLC .... F 330 784-4815
Akron (G-219)

Hdi Rock Drilling Group Ltd .... G 740 369-2968
Delaware (G-8858)

Hesler Machine Tool .... G 937 299-3833
Moraine (G-14496)

Houston Machine Products Inc .... E 937 322-8022
Springfield (G-17577)

Hyper Tool Company .... F 440 543-5151
Chagrin Falls (G-3093)

Interstate Tool Corporation .... E 216 671-1077
Cleveland (G-5583)

J and S Tool Incorporated .... E 216 676-8330
Cleveland (G-5595)

▲ J-C-R Tech Inc .... E 937 783-2296
Blanchester (G-1714)

Jacp Inc .... G 513 353-3660
Miamitown (G-13888)

Jeb Modern Machines Ltd .... G 419 639-3937
Republic (G-16579)

K L M Manufacturing Company .... G 740 666-5171
Ostrander (G-15787)

Kay Capital Company .... G 216 531-1010
Cleveland (G-5638)

Ken Emerick Machine Products .... G 440 834-4501
Burton (G-2380)

Kilroy Company .... D 440 951-8700
Eastlake (G-9278)

Klawhorn Industries Inc .... G 330 335-8191
Wadsworth (G-19414)

Kmi Processing LLC .... G 330 862-2185
Minerva (G-14328)

Kmi Processing LLC .... F 330 862-2185
Minerva (G-14329)

L M Equipment & Design Inc .... E 330 332-9951
Salem (G-16907)

Lahm-Trosper Inc .... F 937 252-8791
Dayton (G-8451)

Lawrence Industries Inc .... D 216 518-1400
Cleveland (G-5686)

◆ Lawrence Industries Inc .... E 216 518-7000
Cleveland (G-5687)

Lees Machinery .... G 440 259-2222
Perry (G-16052)

Leland-Gifford Inc .... G 330 785-9730
Akron (G-269)

Levan Enterprises Inc .... E 330 923-9797
Stow (G-17769)

Machine Component Mfg .... F 330 454-4566
Canton (G-2765)

Machine Tl Sltons Unlmited LLC .... F 513 761-0709
Cincinnati (G-4046)

▲ Makino Inc .... B 513 573-7200
Mason (G-13058)

Mansfield Screw Mch Pdts Co .... D 419 884-1511
Mansfield (G-12644)

Martin & Marianne Tools Inc .... G 440 255-5107
Mentor (G-13646)

Martindale Electric Company .... E 216 521-8567
Cleveland (G-5754)

Masheen Specialties .... E 330 652-7535
Mineral Ridge (G-14308)

Master Grinding Company Inc .... F 440 944-3680
Wickliffe (G-20371)

Masters Prcision Machining Inc .... F 330 419-1933
Kent (G-11487)

▲ Mataco .... G 440 546-8355
Broadview Heights (G-2114)

Max Pro Tools Inc .... F 440 885-9522
Cleveland (G-5762)

Melin Tool Company Inc .... D 216 362-4200
Cleveland (G-5780)

Metal Cutting Technology LLC .... G 419 733-1236
Celina (G-3008)

Micron Manufacturing Inc .... D 440 355-4200
Lagrange (G-11633)

Midwest Knife Grinding Inc .... F 330 854-1030
Canal Fulton (G-2508)

Midwest Specialties Inc .... F 419 738-8147
Wapakoneta (G-19501)

◆ Milacron Marketing Company LLC ..... E 513 536-2000
Batavia (G-1207)

▲ Milan Tool Corp .... E 216 661-1078
Cleveland (G-5813)

Mk Global Enterprises LLC ....G...... 440 823-0081
  Beachwood (G-1282)
Molding Machine Services Inc ....G...... 330 461-2270
  Medina (G-13448)
Monaghan & Associates Inc ....E...... 937 253-7706
  Dayton (G-8506)
▲ Monarch Lathes LP ....E...... 937 492-4111
  Sidney (G-17205)
More Manufacturing LLC ....F...... 937 233-3898
  Tipp City (G-18289)
Mrd Solutions LLC ....G...... 440 942-6969
  Eastlake (G-9283)
My Catered Table LLC 614 882-7323
  Columbus (G-7376)
National Machine Tool Company ....G...... 513 541-6682
  Cincinnati (G-4140)
◆ Nesco Inc ....E...... 440 461-6000
  Cleveland (G-5871)
New Holland Engineering Inc ....G...... 740 495-5200
  New Holland (G-14835)
Nmgg Ctg LLC 419 447-5211
  Tiffin (G-18234)
North East Technologies Inc ....G...... 440 327-9278
  North Ridgeville (G-15392)
Northwood Industries Inc ....F...... 419 666-2100
  Perrysburg (G-16128)
Obars Machine and Tool Company ....E...... 419 535-6307
  Toledo (G-18613)
Oceco Inc ....F...... 419 447-0916
  Tiffin (G-18235)
▼ Ohio Broach & Machine Company ....E...... 440 946-1040
  Willoughby (G-20560)
Ohio CAM & Tool Co ....G...... 216 531-7900
  Cleveland (G-5932)
Ohio Screw Products Inc ....D...... 440 322-6341
  Elyria (G-9472)
P M R Inc ....G...... 440 937-6241
  Avon (G-1001)
P R Racing Engines 419 472-2277
  Toledo (G-18632)
Page Slotting Saw Co Inc ....F...... 419 476-7475
  Toledo (G-18633)
Parkn Manufacturing LLC ....F...... 330 723-8172
  Litchfield (G-12139)
▲ Peerless Saw Company ....E...... 614 836-5790
  Groveport (G-10640)
Phillips Manufacturing Co ....G...... 330 652-4335
  Niles (G-15173)
▲ Pilgrim-Harp Co ....G...... 440 249-4185
  Avon (G-1003)
Pinnacle Precision Pdts LLC ....G...... 440 786-0248
  Bedford (G-1453)
Power Engineering LLC ....G...... 513 793-5800
  Cincinnati (G-4255)
Precision Honing Inc ....G...... 440 942-7339
  Willoughby (G-20578)
Rafter Equipment Corporation ....E...... 440 572-3700
  Strongsville (G-17956)
Raka Corporation ....D...... 419 476-6572
  Toledo (G-18671)
Rapid Machine Inc ....F...... 419 737-2377
  Pioneer (G-16243)
Ravana Industries Inc ....G...... 330 536-4015
  Lowellville (G-12411)
▲ Raymath Company ....C...... 937 335-1860
  Troy (G-18867)
Reliable Products Co Inc ....E...... 419 394-5854
  Saint Marys (G-16853)
Republic EDM Services Inc ....G...... 937 278-7070
  Dayton (G-8626)
▲ Rex International USA Inc ....E...... 800 321-7950
  Ashtabula (G-837)
◆ Ridge Tool Company ....A...... 440 323-5581
  Elyria (G-9486)
Ridge Tool Company ....D...... 740 432-8782
  Cambridge (G-2474)
Ridge Tool Manufacturing Co ....A...... 440 323-5581
  Elyria (G-9488)
Rimrock Holdings Corporation ....E...... 614 471-5926
  Columbus (G-7564)
◆ Robbins Company ....C...... 440 248-3303
  Solon (G-17370)
▼ Roll-In Saw Inc ....F...... 216 459-9001
  Brookpark (G-2169)
Rossi Machinery Services Inc ....G...... 419 281-4488
  Ashland (G-773)
Sharp Industrial Tools Inc ....G...... 513 741-9562
  Cincinnati (G-4413)
Shumaker Racing Components ....G...... 419 238-0801
  Van Wert (G-19270)

Sonic Drilling ....G...... 330 359-0079
  Dundee (G-9180)
▲ Specialty Metals Processing ....E...... 330 656-2767
  Hudson (G-11201)
Stadco Inc ....E...... 937 878-0911
  Fairborn (G-9630)
STC International Co Ltd ....G...... 561 308-6002
  Lebanon (G-11842)
Stevenson Mfg Co ....G...... 330 532-1581
  Wellsville (G-19775)
Strouse Industries Inc ....G...... 440 257-2520
  Mentor (G-13739)
Sumitomo Elc Carbide Mfg Inc ....F...... 440 354-0600
  Grand River (G-10453)
▲ Superion Inc ....E...... 937 374-0033
  Xenia (G-20977)
Superior Machining Inc ....E...... 937 236-9619
  Dayton (G-8689)
Supply Dynamics LLC ....F...... 513 965-2000
  Loveland (G-12392)
Swagelok Hy-Level Company ....C...... 440 238-1260
  Strongsville (G-17975)
Synergy Grinding Inc ....F...... 216 447-4000
  Cleveland (G-6282)
Systematic Machine Corp ....G...... 440 877-9884
  North Royalton (G-15455)
Tailored Systems Inc ....G...... 937 299-3900
  Moraine (G-14534)
Taper Tool & Broach Inc ....G...... 216 486-4435
  Cleveland (G-6294)
Technidrill Systems Inc ....E...... 330 678-9980
  Kent (G-11536)
Tessec Manufacturing Svcs LLC ....G...... 937 985-3552
  Dayton (G-8710)
Tool Service Co Inc ....G...... 937 254-4000
  Dayton (G-8119)
Tooling Connection Inc ....G...... 419 594-3339
  Oakwood (G-15620)
Tri-State Tool Grinding Inc ....E...... 513 347-0100
  Cincinnati (G-4524)
TSR Machinery Services Inc ....E...... 513 874-9697
  Fairfield (G-9726)
Twin Tool LLC ....E...... 937 435-8946
  Dayton (G-8735)
Tykma Inc ....E...... 877 318-9562
  Chillicothe (G-3283)
U S Alloy Die Corp ....F...... 216 749-9700
  Cleveland (G-6379)
U S Electrical Tool Inc ....G...... 513 353-3660
  Miamitown (G-13893)
U-Sonico ....F...... 423 348-7117
  Springfield (G-17669)
▲ Union Process Inc ....E...... 330 929-3333
  Akron (G-454)
United Wire Edm Inc ....G...... 440 239-8777
  Berea (G-1639)
Updike Supply Company ....E...... 937 482-4000
  Huber Heights (G-11152)
Usm Acquisition Corporation ....F...... 440 975-8600
  Willoughby (G-20627)
▲ Vulcan Tool Company ....G...... 937 253-6194
  Dayton (G-8744)
Walter Grinders Inc ....G...... 937 859-1975
  Miamisburg (G-13877)
Warner Vess Inc ....G...... 740 585-2481
  Lower Salem (G-12416)
West Ohio Tool & Mfg LLC ....G...... 419 678-4745
  Saint Henry (G-16825)
West Ohio Tool Company ....F...... 937 842-6688
  Russells Point (G-16758)
Whole Solutions ....G...... 330 652-1725
  Mineral Ridge (G-14315)
Willow Tool & Machining Ltd ....G...... 440 572-2288
  Strongsville (G-17984)
Wonder Machine Services Inc ....E...... 440 937-7500
  Avon (G-1020)
◆ Zagar Inc ....E...... 216 731-0500
  Cleveland (G-6490)

3542 Machine Tools: Forming

Accurate Manufacturing Company ....E...... 614 878-6510
  Columbus (G-6685)
▲ Addisonmckee Inc ....C...... 513 228-7000
  Lebanon (G-11774)
Advanced Tech Utilization Co ....F...... 440 238-3770
  Strongsville (G-17884)
▲ Ajax Manufacturing Company ....E...... 440 295-0244
  Wickliffe (G-20351)
Ajax Tocco Magnethermic Corp ....C...... 440 278-7200
  Wickliffe (G-20352)

Akron Specialized Products ....G...... 330 762-9269
  Akron (G-56)
Alco Manufacturing Corp LLC ....E...... 440 458-5165
  Elyria (G-9367)
Alien Products LLC ....E...... 440 946-9100
  Mentor (G-13517)
Alliance Die Design & Mfg ....G...... 330 821-2440
  Alliance (G-492)
Allied Mask and Tooling Inc ....G...... 419 470-2555
  Toledo (G-18329)
American Fluid Power Inc ....G...... 877 223-8742
  Elyria (G-9371)
American Laser and Machine LLC ....G...... 419 214-0880
  Toledo (G-18339)
American Metal Tech LLC ....D...... 937 347-1111
  Xenia (G-20936)
Anderson & Vreeland Inc ....D...... 419 636-5002
  Bryan (G-2278)
Apeks LLC ....E...... 740 809-1160
  Johnstown (G-11389)
Asb Industries Inc ....E...... 330 753-8458
  Barberton (G-1099)
Ata Tools Inc ....G...... 330 928-7744
  Cuyahoga Falls (G-7973)
BAC Technologies Ltd ....G...... 937 465-2228
  West Liberty (G-20091)
Barclay Machine Inc ....F...... 330 337-9541
  Salem (G-16874)
▲ Barth Industries Co LP ....D...... 216 267-0531
  Cleveland (G-4893)
Bendco Machine & Tool Co Inc ....F...... 419 628-3802
  Minster (G-14350)
Bintzler Inc 513 677-1164
  Loveland (G-12343)
Brilex Industries Inc ....D...... 330 744-1114
  Youngstown (G-21036)
▲ Brilex Industries Inc ....C...... 330 744-1114
  Youngstown (G-21037)
Columbia Stamping Inc ....F...... 440 236-6677
  Columbia Station (G-6585)
Columbus Jack Corporation ....D...... 614 228-0185
  Columbus (G-6958)
▼ Compass Systems & Sales LLC ....D...... 330 733-2111
  Norton (G-15508)
Connell Limited Partnership ....D...... 877 534-8986
  Northfield (G-15464)
Diamond America Corporation ....G...... 330 535-3330
  Akron (G-149)
Diverse Mfg Solutions LLC ....F...... 740 363-3600
  Delaware (G-8838)
Dover Corporation ....G...... 513 696-1790
  Mason (G-13010)
▲ DRG Hydraulics Inc ....E...... 216 663-9747
  Cleveland (G-5216)
E Systems Design & Automtn Inc ....G...... 419 443-0220
  Tiffin (G-18219)
Eae Logistics Company LLC ....G...... 440 417-4788
  Madison (G-12505)
Eaton Corporation ....C...... 216 281-2211
  Cleveland (G-5247)
Eaton Hydraulics LLC ....E...... 419 232-7777
  Van Wert (G-19254)
Ebo Group Inc ....D...... 330 239-4933
  Sharon Center (G-17105)
Edwards Machine Service Inc ....F...... 937 295-2929
  Fort Loramie (G-9929)
Elliott Tool Technologies Ltd ....D...... 937 253-6133
  Dayton (G-8324)
Exito Manufacturing ....G...... 937 291-9871
  Dayton (G-8337)
F & G Tool and Die Co ....E...... 937 746-3658
  Franklin (G-10019)
Fabriweld Corporation ....G...... 419 668-3358
  Norwalk (G-15539)
Falls Metal Fabricators Ind ....F...... 330 253-7181
  Akron (G-178)
First Tool Corp ....E...... 937 254-6197
  Dayton (G-8342)
Fluidpower Assembly Inc ....G...... 419 394-7486
  Saint Marys (G-16839)
▲ French Oil Mill Machinery Co ....D...... 937 773-3420
  Piqua (G-16266)
Gadjets Inc ....G...... 937 274-2111
  Dayton (G-8356)
Gem City Metal Tech LLC ....E...... 937 252-8998
  Dayton (G-8362)
▼ George A Mitchell Company ....E...... 330 758-5777
  Youngstown (G-21099)
▲ Green Corp Magnetic Inc ....E...... 614 801-4000
  Grove City (G-10560)

S
I
C

Hawk Manufacturing LLC ....D...... 330 784-3151
Akron (G-218)

Heimann Manufacturing Co ....G...... 937 652-1865
Urbana (G-19161)

Hendricks Vacuum Forming Inc ....G...... 330 833-8913
Massillon (G-13148)

Henry & Wright Corporation ....F...... 216 851-3750
Cleveland (G-5500)

High Production Technology LLC ....F...... 419 591-7000
Napoleon (G-14680)

High Production Technology LLC ....G...... 419 599-1511
Napoleon (G-14681)

Hill & Griffith Company ....G...... 513 921-1075
Cincinnati (G-3882)

◆ Howmet Corporation ....E...... 800 242-9898
Newburgh Heights (G-15074)

▲ HPM North America Corp ....E...... 740 382-5600
Marion (G-12876)

Hunter Hydraulics Inc ....G...... 330 455-3983
Canton (G-2732)

Industrial Machine Tool Svc ....G...... 216 651-1122
Cleveland (G-5564)

J and S Tool Incorporated ....E...... 216 676-8330
Cleveland (G-5595)

K & L Tool Inc ....F...... 419 258-2086
Antwerp (G-630)

Kay Capital Company ....G...... 216 531-1010
Cleveland (G-5638)

Kiraly Tool and Die Inc ....F...... 330 744-5773
Youngstown (G-21129)

L B Machine & Mfg Co Inc ....G...... 513 471-6137
Cincinnati (G-4008)

Levan Enterprises Inc ....E...... 330 923-9797
Stow (G-17769)

▲ Machine Concepts Inc ....E...... 419 628-3498
Minster (G-14357)

▲ Machine Tool Rebuilders Inc.............G...... 614 228-1070
Columbus (G-7311)

◆ McNeil & Nrm Inc ....D...... 330 761-1855
Akron (G-291)

Meadors Machine Inc ....G...... 937 452-5571
Camden (G-2485)

Metal & Wire Products Company ....E...... 330 332-9448
Salem (G-16914)

Meyer Machine Tool Company ....G...... 614 235-0039
Columbus (G-7344)

Monode Marking Products Inc...............E...... 440 975-8802
Mentor (G-13660)

Monode Marking Products Inc...............G...... 419 929-0346
New London (G-14861)

Monode Steel Stamp Inc ....G...... 419 929-3501
New London (G-14862)

Monode Steel Stamp Inc ....F...... 440 975-8802
Mentor (G-13661)

Multipress Inc ....G...... 614 228-0185
Columbus (G-7373)

◆ National Machinery LLC ....B...... 419 447-5211
Tiffin (G-18232)

NM Group Global LLC ....G...... 419 447-5211
Tiffin (G-18233)

Nu-Tool Industries Inc ....F...... 440 237-9240
North Royalton (G-15438)

Ohio Metal Fabricating Inc ....G...... 937 233-2400
Dayton (G-8544)

Omni Technical Products Inc ....F...... 216 433-1970
Cleveland (G-5942)

Parker-Hannifin Corporation ....C...... 419 394-9600
Saint Marys (G-16848)

Parker-Hannifin Corporation ....C...... 419 644-4311
Metamora (G-13776)

Phoenix Hydraulic Presses Inc ....F...... 614 850-8940
Hilliard (G-10970)

▲ Pines Manufacturing Inc ....E...... 440 835-5553
Westlake (G-20293)

Pyramid Rebuild and Mch LLC ....F...... 330 633-4452
Tallmadge (G-18166)

Qpi Multipress Inc...................................G...... 614 228-0185
Columbus (G-7530)

Quality Products Inc ....D...... 614 228-0185
Columbus (G-7535)

R & B Machining Inc ....E...... 937 382-6710
Wilmington (G-20677)

Rafter Equipment Corporation ....E...... 440 572-3700
Strongsville (G-17956)

Ram Products Inc ....F...... 614 443-4634
Columbus (G-7547)

Ready Technology Inc ....F...... 937 228-8181
Dayton (G-8618)

▲ Ready Technology Inc ....F...... 937 866-7200
Dayton (G-8619)

▼ Recycling Eqp Solutions Corp ....G...... 330 920-1500
Cuyahoga Falls (G-8040)

Ritime Incorporated ....F...... 330 273-3443
Cleveland (G-6115)

▲ Rogers Industrial Products Inc.........E...... 330 535-3331
Akron (G-378)

Rossi Machinery Services Inc ....G...... 419 281-4488
Ashland (G-773)

S & H Automation & Eqp Co ....E...... 419 636-0020
Bryan (G-2320)

▲ Sakamura USA Inc ....F...... 740 223-7777
Marion (G-12897)

◆ Scotts Miracle-Gro Company ....B...... 937 644-0011
Marysville (G-12968)

▲ Semtorq Inc ....F...... 330 487-0600
Twinsburg (G-19019)

Slade Gardner ....G...... 440 355-8015
Lagrange (G-11637)

Snair Co ....F...... 614 873-7020
Plain City (G-16360)

Spencer Manufacturing Company ....D...... 330 648-2461
Spencer (G-17457)

▲ Standard Engineering Group Inc........G...... 330 494-4300
North Canton (G-15267)

Starkey Machinery Inc ....G...... 419 468-2560
Galion (G-10289)

Stolle Machinery Company LLC ....C...... 937 497-5400
Sidney (G-17230)

Stutzman Manufacturing Ltd ....G...... 330 674-4359
Millersburg (G-14265)

▼ Taylor - Winfield Corporation ....D...... 330 259-8500
Hubbard (G-11140)

TEC Design & Manufacturing Inc ....F...... 937 435-2147
Dayton (G-8707)

▲ Technical Machine Products Inc.........F...... 216 281-9500
Cleveland (G-6300)

Terminal Equipment Industries ....G...... 330 468-0322
Northfield (G-15474)

▲ THT Presses Inc ....E...... 937 898-2012
Dayton (G-8715)

Tri-K Enterprises Inc ....G...... 330 832-7380
Canton (G-2882)

▲ Trucut Incorporated ....D...... 330 938-9806
Sebring (G-17055)

Turner Machine Co ....F...... 330 332-5821
Salem (G-16932)

▲ Twist Inc ....C...... 937 675-9581
Jamestown (G-11353)

Twist Inc ....E...... 937 675-9581
Jamestown (G-11354)

Uhrichsville Carbide Inc ....F...... 740 922-9197
Uhrichsville (G-19064)

Valley Tool & Die Inc ....D...... 440 237-0160
North Royalton (G-15458)

Van Burens Welding & Machine ....G...... 740 787-2636
Glenford (G-10401)

Vmaxx Inc ....F...... 419 738-4044
Wapakoneta (G-19511)

▲ Vulcan Tool Company ....F...... 937 253-6194
Dayton (G-8744)

W G Machine Tool Service Co ....G...... 330 723-3428
Medina (G-13496)

3543 Industrial Patterns

7 Rowe Court Properties LLC ....G...... 513 874-7236
Hamilton (G-10659)

Accuform Manufacturing Inc ....E...... 330 797-9291
Youngstown (G-21014)

Aero Pattern Works ....G...... 937 890-3720
Dayton (G-8139)

Air Power Dynamics LLC ....G...... 440 701-2100
Mentor (G-13511)

Anger Pattern Company Inc....................G...... 330 882-6519
Clinton (G-6533)

API Pattern Works Inc ....G...... 440 269-1766
Willoughby (G-20433)

Boko Patterns Models & Molds ....G...... 937 426-9667
Beavercreek (G-1371)

Cascade Pattern Company Inc ....E...... 440 323-4300
Elyria (G-9388)

Case Pattern Co Inc ....G...... 216 531-0744
Cleveland (G-4987)

Cincinnati Pattern Company ....F...... 513 241-9872
Cincinnati (G-3562)

Clinton Pattern Works Inc ....G...... 419 243-0855
Toledo (G-18402)

▲ Colonial Patterns Inc ....E...... 330 673-6475
Kent (G-11440)

Consolidated Pattern Works Inc............G...... 330 434-6060
Akron (G-127)

Dayton Pattern Inc ....G...... 937 277-0761
Dayton (G-8281)

Design Pattern Works Inc ....G...... 937 252-0797
Dayton (G-8300)

Design Tech Inc ....G...... 937 254-7000
Dayton (G-8301)

Elyria Pattern Co Inc ....G...... 440 323-1526
Elyria (G-9415)

Exochem Corporation ....D...... 440 277-6116
Lorain (G-12246)

Feiner Pattern Works Inc ....F...... 513 851-9800
Cincinnati (G-3748)

Foster Pattern Works Inc ....G...... 330 482-3612
Columbiana (G-6617)

Founder Service & Mfg Co ....G...... 330 584-7759
Deerfield (G-8773)

Freeman Manufacturing & Sup Co ....E...... 440 934-1902
Avon (G-996)

Geotech Pattern & Mold Inc ....G...... 513 683-2600
Loveland (G-12352)

Glazier Pattern & Coach ....G...... 937 492-7355
Houston (G-11121)

H&M Machine & Tool LLC ....E...... 419 776-9220
Toledo (G-18491)

Humtown Pattern Company ....D...... 330 482-5555
Columbiana (G-6621)

Hynes Modern Pattern Co Inc ....G...... 937 322-3451
Springfield (G-17579)

Industrial Pattern & Mfg Co ....F...... 614 252-0934
Columbus (G-7185)

Industrial Technologies Inc ....G...... 330 434-2033
Akron (G-232)

▲ J-Lenco Inc ....D...... 740 499-2260
Morral (G-14540)

Jack R Stiner Models & Pattern ....G...... 330 494-1730
Canton (G-2744)

Ketco Inc ....E...... 937 426-9331
Beavercreek (G-1346)

Kohl Patterns ....G...... 513 353-3831
Cleves (G-6519)

Lesleys Patterns Ltd ....G...... 937 554-4674
Vandalia (G-19300)

Liberty Pattern and Mold Inc ....G...... 330 788-9463
Youngstown (G-21134)

Lisbon Pattern Limited ....G...... 330 424-7676
Lisbon (G-12128)

Lorain Modern Pattern Inc ....F...... 440 365-6780
Elyria (G-9455)

Maumee Pattern Company Inc ....E...... 419 693-4968
Toledo (G-18579)

Model Engineering Company ....G...... 330 644-3450
Barberton (G-1132)

Morcast Precision Inc.............................G...... 614 258-5071
Columbus (G-7368)

Mount Union Pattern Works Inc ....G...... 330 821-2274
Alliance (G-530)

National Pattern Mfg Co ....F...... 330 682-6871
Orrville (G-15750)

North Coast Pattern Inc ....G...... 440 322-5064
Strongsville (G-17946)

PCC Airfoils LLC ....G...... 216 692-7900
Cleveland (G-5983)

Plas-Mac Corp ....D...... 440 349-3222
Solon (G-17361)

R L Rush Tool & Pattern Inc...................G...... 419 562-9849
Bucyrus (G-2356)

▲ Ross Aluminum Castings LLC...........C...... 937 492-4134
Sidney (G-17218)

Seaport Mold & Casting Company ....F...... 419 243-1422
Toledo (G-18688)

Seaway Pattern Mfg Inc ....G...... 419 865-5724
Toledo (G-18689)

Seilkop Industries Inc ....F...... 513 679-5680
Cincinnati (G-4399)

Shells Inc ....G...... 330 808-5558
Wadsworth (G-19440)

Sherwood Rtm Corp ....G...... 330 875-7151
Louisville (G-12328)

Spectracam Ltd ....G...... 937 223-3805
Dayton (G-8667)

Standard Pattern Works Inc ....G...... 330 745-2295
Akron (G-414)

Tempcraft Corporation ....C...... 216 391-3885
Cleveland (G-6303)

Th Manufacturing Inc ....G...... 330 893-3572
Millersburg (G-14269)

◆ Transducers Direct Llc ....F...... 513 247-0601
Cincinnati (G-4519)

United States Drill Head Co ....E...... 513 941-0300
Cincinnati (G-4540)

Wendling Patterns Inc ....G 937 233-7770
Dayton (G-8752)

Wright Way Patterns ....G 513 574-5776
Cincinnati (G-4608)

XI Pattern Shop Inc ....G 330 682-2981
Orrville (G-15773)

3544 Dies, Tools, Jigs, Fixtures & Indl Molds

5me LLC ....E 513 719-1600
Cincinnati (G-3285)

5me Holdings LLC ....G 859 534-4872
Cincinnati (G-3286)

A & B Tool & Manufacturing ....G 419 382-0215
Toledo (G-18316)

A G Industries Inc ....F 330 220-0050
Brunswick (G-2200)

Absolute Grinding Co Inc ....F 440 974-4030
Mentor (G-13504)

Accu Tool Inc ....G 937 667-5878
Tipp City (G-18257)

Accu-Rite Tool & Die Co Corp ......G 330 497-9959
Canton (G-2586)

Accu-Tek Tool & Die Inc ....G 330 726-1946
Salem (G-16867)

Accuform Manufacturing Inc ....E 330 797-9291
Youngstown (G-21014)

Accurate Machining & Welding ....G 937 584-4518
Sabina (G-16772)

Accurate Tool Co Inc ....G 330 332-9448
Salem (G-16868)

Ace American Wire Die Co ....G 330 425-7269
Twinsburg (G-18890)

▲ Acro Tool & Die Company ....D 330 773-5173
Akron (G-29)

▲ Addisonmckee Inc ....C 513 228-7000
Lebanon (G-11774)

▲ Adena Tool Corporation ....D 937 890-8428
Dayton (G-8136)

Adept Manufacturing Corp ....F 937 222-7110
Dayton (G-8137)

▲ Advanced Engrg Solutions Inc ..D 937 743-6900
Springboro (G-17470)

▲ Advanced Intr Solutions Inc ......E 937 550-0065
Springboro (G-17471)

AJD Holding Co ....D 330 405-4477
Twinsburg (G-18895)

Akro Tool Co Inc ....G 513 858-1555
Fairfield (G-9639)

Akron Centl Engrv Mold Mch Inc ..E 330 794-8704
Akron (G-37)

Allen Mold & Die Inc ....G 440 944-1819
Willowick (G-20646)

Allen Tool Co Inc ....G 937 987-2037
New Vienna (G-14954)

Allied Tool & Die Inc ....F 216 941-6196
Cleveland (G-4766)

Alpha Tool & Mold Inc ....F 440 473-2343
Cleveland (G-4769)

Alternative Flash Inc ....E 330 334-6111
Wadsworth (G-19393)

Aluminum Fence & Mfg Co ....G 330 755-3323
Burton (G-2372)

Amaroq Inc ....G 419 747-2110
Mansfield (G-12558)

▼ Amcraft Inc ....G 419 729-7900
Toledo (G-18335)

American Cube Mold Inc ....G 330 558-0044
Hinckley (G-11022)

American Extrusion Svcs Inc ....G 937 743-1210
Springboro (G-17473)

American Punch Co Inc ....E 216 731-4501
Euclid (G-9566)

American Tool and Die Inc ....F 419 726-5394
Toledo (G-18346)

Amerimold Inc ....G 330 628-2190
Mogadore (G-14367)

Amex Dies Inc ....F 330 545-9766
Girard (G-10382)

Ampex Metal Products Company ....E 216 267-9242
Brookpark (G-2151)

Amtech Tool and Machine Inc ....F 330 758-8215
Youngstown (G-21024)

Anchor Foundry & Machine Inc ....G 330 453-3441
Canton (G-2603)

Anchor Glass Container Corp ....C 740 452-2743
Zanesville (G-21272)

▲ Anchor Tool & Die Co ....B 216 362-1850
Cleveland (G-4806)

Antwerp Tool & Die Inc ....F 419 258-5271
Antwerp (G-628)

Apollo Plastics Inc ....F 440 951-7774
Mentor (G-13525)

Apollo Products Inc ....F 440 269-8551
Willoughby (G-20434)

Apr Tool Inc ....G 440 946-0393
Willoughby (G-20437)

Arete Innovative Solutions LLC ....G 513 503-2712
Morrow (G-14543)

Argo Tool Corporation ....F 330 425-2407
Twinsburg (G-18901)

Arken Manufacturing Inc ....G 216 883-6628
Cleveland (G-4830)

Artisan Equipment Inc ....F 740 756-9135
Carroll (G-2936)

▼ Artisan Tool & Die Corp ....E 216 883-2769
Cleveland (G-4838)

Aspec Inc ....E 513 561-9922
Cincinnati (G-3420)

Athens Mold and Machine Inc ......D 740 593-6613
Akron (G-76)

◆ Atlantic Tool & Die Company .....C 440 238-6931
Strongsville (G-17891)

Atlantic Tool & Die Company ....C 330 769-4500
Seville (G-17068)

Aukerman J F Steel Rule Die ....G 937 456-4498
Eaton (G-9299)

Automation Plastics Corp ....D 330 562-5148
Aurora (G-908)

Automation Tool & Die Inc ....D 330 225-8336
Valley City (G-19199)

Autotec Engineering Company ......E 419 885-2529
Toledo (G-18360)

B C Wilson Co ....G 937 439-1866
Dayton (G-8178)

B V Mfg Inc ....F 330 549-5331
New Springfield (G-14949)

Balancing Company Inc ....E 937 898-9111
Vandalia (G-19282)

Banco Die Inc ....F 330 821-8511
Alliance (G-497)

Banner Metals Group Inc ....D 614 291-3105
Columbus (G-6805)

Barberton Mold & Machine Co ......G 330 745-8559
Barberton (G-1108)

▲ Basilius Inc ....E 419 536-5810
Toledo (G-18364)

Bk Tool Company Inc ....F 513 870-9622
Fairfield (G-9646)

Blick Tool & Die Inc ....G 330 343-1277
Dover (G-8969)

Blitz Tool & Die Inc ....G 440 237-1177
Cleveland (G-4917)

Bloom Industries Inc ....D 330 898-3878
Warren (G-19529)

Blue Ash Tool & Die Co Inc ....F 513 793-4530
Blue Ash (G-1752)

Bollinger Tool & Die Inc ....G 419 866-5180
Holland (G-11046)

Borke Mold Specialist Inc ....F 513 870-8000
West Chester (G-19820)

Brainin-Advance Industries LLC ...E 513 874-9760
West Chester (G-19821)

▲ Brinkman Tool & Die Inc ....E 937 222-1161
Dayton (G-8196)

Broadway Companies Inc ....E 937 890-1888
Dayton (G-8197)

Brothers Tool and Mfg Ltd ....F 513 353-9700
Miamitown (G-13885)

Browder Tool Co Inc ....G 937 233-6731
Dayton (G-8199)

Bruck Manufacturing Co Inc ....G 440 327-6619
North Ridgeville (G-15363)

Brw Tool Inc ....F 419 394-3371
Saint Marys (G-16835)

C & D Tool Inc ....G 440 942-8463
Eastlake (G-9260)

C-H Tool & Die ....G 740 397-7214
Mount Vernon (G-14610)

Caliber Mold and Machine Inc ......E 330 633-8171
Akron (G-107)

California Ceramic Supply Co ....G 216 531-9185
Euclid (G-9569)

CAM-Lem Inc ....E 216 391-7750
Cleveland (G-4963)

▼ Camden Concrete Products ....G 937 456-1229
Eaton (G-9302)

Canton Pattern & Mold Inc ....G 330 455-4316
Canton (G-2645)

Capital Precision Machine & Tl .....F 937 258-1176
Dayton (G-8098)

Capital Tool Company ....E 216 661-5750
Cleveland (G-4971)

Carbide Specialist Inc ....F 440 951-4027
Willoughby (G-20452)

Carter Manufacturing Co Inc ....E 513 398-7303
Mason (G-12991)

Case Pattern Co Inc ....G 216 531-0744
Cleveland (G-4987)

Cctm Inc ....G 513 934-3533
Lebanon (G-11788)

Centaur Tool & Die Inc ....F 419 352-7704
Bowling Green (G-1976)

Centerline Tool & Machine ....G 937 222-3600
Dayton (G-8221)

Central Machinery Company LLC ...F 740 387-1289
Marion (G-12862)

Century Die Company LLC ....D 419 332-2693
Fremont (G-10136)

Chart Tech Tool Inc ....E 937 667-3543
Tipp City (G-18272)

Chipmatic Tool & Machine Inc ......D 419 862-2737
Elmore (G-9362)

Chippewa Tool & Mfg Co ....F 419 849-2790
Woodville (G-20724)

Cincinnati Mold Incorporated ....G 513 922-1888
Cincinnati (G-3561)

Cinn Wire E D M Inc ....G 513 741-5402
Cincinnati (G-3576)

Circle Mold Incorporated ....G 330 633-7017
Tallmadge (G-18138)

Claridon Tool & Die Inc ....G 740 389-1944
Caledonia (G-2435)

Classic Tool Inc ....G 330 922-1933
Stow (G-17740)

Cleveland Die & Mfg Co ....E 216 941-7268
Cleveland (G-5058)

▲ Cleveland Die & Mfg Co ....D 440 243-3404
Middleburg Heights (G-13904)

Cleveland Metal Processing Inc ....C 440 243-3404
Cleveland (G-5070)

Cleveland Roll Forming Co ....G 216 281-0202
Cleveland (G-5077)

◆ Cleveland Steel Tool Company ...E 216 681-7400
Cleveland (G-5080)

Cliffco Stands Inc ....E 937 382-3700
Wilmington (G-20659)

Clyde Tool & Die Inc ....G 419 547-9574
Clyde (G-6538)

CMI Technology Inc ....F 937 832-2000
Englewood (G-9513)

Cmt Machining & Fabg LLC ....F 937 652-3740
Urbana (G-19151)

Coach Tool & Die Inc ....G 937 890-4716
Dayton (G-8234)

Cobb Industries Inc ....G 440 946-4695
Mentor (G-13549)

Cole Tool & Die Company ....E 419 522-1272
Ontario (G-15686)

Colonial Machine Company Inc .....D 330 673-5859
Kent (G-11439)

▲ Colonial Patterns Inc ....E 330 673-6475
Kent (G-11440)

Columbia Stamping Inc ....F 440 236-6677
Columbia Station (G-6585)

Companies of North Coast LLC .....G 216 398-8550
Cleveland (G-5109)

Concord Design Inc ....D 330 722-5133
Medina (G-13391)

Conforming Matrix Corporation ....E 419 729-3777
Toledo (G-18409)

Connell Limited Partnership ....D 877 534-8986
Northfield (G-15464)

Container Graphics Corp ....E 937 746-5666
Franklin (G-10013)

Conti Tool & Die Inc ....G 330 633-1414
Akron (G-128)

Continental Business Entps Inc .....F 440 439-4400
Cleveland (G-5123)

Contour Tool Inc ....E 440 365-7333
North Ridgeville (G-15364)

Cornerstone Manufacturing Inc ....G 937 456-5930
Eaton (G-9303)

▲ CP Technologies Company ....E 614 866-9200
Blacklick (G-1693)

Creative Foam Dayton Mold ....G 937 279-9987
Dayton (G-8249)

Criterion Tool & Die Inc ....E 216 267-1733
Brookpark (G-2154)

Crowe Manufacturing Services ......D 800 831-1893
Troy (G-18813)

SIC

Crum Manufacturing Inc .... E 419 878-9779
  Waterville (G-19654)

Csw of Ny Inc .... F 413 589-1311
  Sylvania (G-18102)

Cubic Blue Inc .... G 330 638-2999
  Cortland (G-7866)

Custom Design & Tool .... G 419 865-9773
  Holland (G-11051)

Custom Machine Inc .... E 419 986-5122
  Tiffin (G-18217)

Custom Tooling Company Inc .... F 513 733-5790
  Cincinnati (G-3627)

Customformed Products Inc .... F 937 388-0480
  Miamisburg (G-13795)

D A Fitzgerald Co Inc .... G 937 548-0511
  Greenville (G-10497)

D A Stirling Inc .... G 330 923-3195
  Cuyahoga Falls (G-7985)

D J Metro Mold & Die Inc .... G 440 237-1130
  North Royalton (G-15416)

Darke Precision Inc .... F 937 548-2232
  Piqua (G-16260)

Data Mold and Tool Inc .... G 419 878-9861
  Waterville (G-19655)

Dayton Lamina Corporation .... G 937 859-5111
  Dayton (G-8277)

▲ Dayton Progress Corporation .... A 937 859-5111
  Dayton (G-8284)

Dayton Progress Intl Corp .... G 937 859-5111
  Dayton (G-8285)

Dayton Stencil Works Company .... E 937 223-3233
  Dayton (G-8287)

Dayton Tool Co Inc .... E 937 222-5501
  Dayton (G-8288)

Dcd Technologies Inc .... E 216 481-0056
  Cleveland (G-5177)

De-Lux Mold & Machine Inc .... G 330 678-1030
  Kent (G-11447)

Deca Manufacturing Co Inc .... D 419 884-0071
  Mansfield (G-12594)

Deepwood Roll Tooling .... G 440 946-5640
  Mentor (G-13560)

▲ Defiance Metal Products Co .... B 419 784-5332
  Defiance (G-8785)

Delco Corporation .... E 330 896-4220
  Akron (G-145)

Delta Machine & Tool Co .... F 216 524-2477
  Cleveland (G-5183)

Delta Tool & Die Stl Block Inc .... F 419 822-5939
  Delta (G-8930)

▲ Deuer Developments Inc .... F 937 299-1213
  Moraine (G-14478)

Diamond Mold & Die Co .... F 330 633-5682
  Tallmadge (G-18141)

Die Cast Division .... G 330 769-2013
  Seville (G-17074)

Die Cast Tool LLC .... G 419 874-1211
  Perrysburg (G-16084)

Die Guys Inc .... E 330 948-1984
  Medina (G-13402)

▲ Die-Matic Corporation .... D 216 749-4656
  Brooklyn Heights (G-2138)

▼ Die-Mension Corporation .... F 330 273-5872
  Brunswick (G-2221)

Die-Namic Tool & Die Inc .... G 330 296-6923
  Ravenna (G-16525)

Diemaster Tool & Mold Inc .... F 330 467-4281
  Macedonia (G-12445)

Disciple Tool & Machine .... G 330 503-7879
  Lake Milton (G-11642)

Diversified Mold Castings LLC .... E 216 663-1814
  Cleveland (G-5199)

Diversified Tool Systems .... G 419 845-2143
  Caledonia (G-2436)

Dove Die and Stamping Company ...... E 216 267-3720
  Cleveland (G-5211)

Dover Machine Co .... G 330 343-4123
  Dover (G-8981)

Doyle Manufacturing Inc .... D 419 865-2548
  Holland (G-11055)

Dreier Tool & Die Corp .... F 513 521-8200
  Cincinnati (G-3671)

◆ Drt Mfg Co .... G 937 297-6670
  Dayton (G-8313)

Duco Tool & Die Inc .... F 419 628-2031
  Minster (G-14351)

▲ Duncan Tool Inc .... F 937 667-9364
  Tipp City (G-18276)

Durivage Pattern & Mfg Co .... G 419 836-8655
  Williston (G-20420)

Dyco Manufacturing Inc .... F 419 485-5525
  Montpelier (G-14444)

Dynamic Tool & Mold Inc .... G 440 237-8665
  Cleveland (G-5227)

Dynamic Tool Die .... G 440 834-0007
  Middlefield (G-13932)

E & E Mold & Die Inc .... G 216 898-5853
  Cleveland (G-5228)

E D M Electrofying Inc .... G 440 322-8900
  Elyria (G-9410)

E D M Fastar Inc .... E 216 676-0100
  Cleveland (G-5231)

▲ E D M Services Inc .... E 216 486-2068
  Euclid (G-9575)

Eagle Precision Products LLC .... G 440 582-9393
  North Royalton (G-15418)

Eagle Tool & Die Inc .... E 216 671-5055
  Cleveland (G-5237)

◆ Edco Inc .... E 419 726-1595
  Toledo (G-18450)

Edge-Rite Tools Inc .... F 216 642-0966
  Cleveland (G-5258)

Eger Products Inc .... D 513 753-4200
  Amelia (G-575)

Elliott Mfg Co .... F 937 833-4430
  Brookville (G-2182)

▲ EMI Corp .... D 937 596-5511
  Jackson Center (G-11341)

Endura Plastics Inc .... D 440 951-4466
  Kirtland (G-11613)

Engineered Mfg & Eqp Co .... F 937 642-7776
  Marysville (G-12942)

▲ Enterprise Plastics Inc .... E 330 346-0496
  Kent (G-11456)

Enterprise Tool & Die Company .... F 216 351-1300
  Cleveland (G-5285)

Equipment Concepts .... G 937 291-9734
  Dayton (G-8329)

Erickson-Huff Tool and Die .... G 740 596-4036
  Mc Arthur (G-13331)

Estee Mold & Die Inc .... E 937 224-7853
  Dayton (G-8332)

Esterle Mold & Machine Co Inc .... F 330 686-1685
  Stow (G-17749)

Esterle Mold & Machine Co Inc .... E 330 686-1685
  Stow (G-17748)

Euclid Design & Manufacturing .... F 440 942-0066
  Willoughby (G-20481)

Event Inc .... F 440 951-4477
  Mentor (G-13575)

Exact-Tool & Die Inc .... E 216 676-9140
  Cleveland (G-5311)

Exito Manufacturing .... G 937 291-9871
  Dayton (G-8337)

Exodus Mold & Machine Inc .... G 330 854-0282
  Canal Fulton (G-2501)

Expert Regrind Service Inc .... G 937 526-5662
  Versailles (G-19347)

F & G Tool and Die Co .... E 937 294-1405
  Moraine (G-14486)

Fabrication Shop Inc .... F 419 435-7934
  Fostoria (G-9970)

Faith Tool & Manufacturing .... G 440 951-5934
  Willoughby (G-20485)

Falls Stamping & Welding Co .... C 330 928-1191
  Cuyahoga Falls (G-7996)

Falls Tool & Die Incorporated .... G 330 633-4884
  Akron (G-179)

Fame Tool & Mfg Co Inc .... E 513 271-6387
  Cincinnati (G-3737)

Fargo Toolite Incorporated .... F 440 997-2442
  Ashtabula (G-806)

Faull & Son LLC .... F 330 652-4341
  Niles (G-15152)

Feller Tool Co Inc .... F 440 324-6277
  Elyria (G-9423)

Fenton Manufacturing Inc .... G 440 969-1128
  Ashtabula (G-807)

▲ Ferriot Inc .... C 330 786-3000
  Akron (G-185)

Fine Line Tool and Die Inc .... F 330 782-8139
  Warren (G-19550)

First Machine & Tool Corp .... F 440 269-8644
  Willoughby (G-20489)

First Tool Corp .... E 937 254-6197
  Dayton (G-8342)

Fischer Special Tooling Corp .... F 440 951-8411
  Mentor (G-13578)

Fostoria Machine Products .... G 419 435-4262
  Fostoria (G-9977)

Founder Service & Mfg Co .... F 330 584-7759
  Deerfield (G-8773)

▲ Frecon Technologies Inc .... F 513 874-8981
  West Chester (G-19868)

▼ Fremar Industries Inc .... E 330 220-3700
  Brunswick (G-2227)

Fremont Cutting Dies Inc .... G 419 334-5153
  Fremont (G-10148)

G & G Header Die Inc .... G 330 468-3458
  Macedonia (G-12453)

G & S Custom Tooling LLC .... G 419 286-2888
  Fort Jennings (G-9926)

Galaxy Products Inc .... G 419 843-7337
  Sylvania (G-18107)

Garvin Tool & Die Inc .... G 419 334-2392
  Fremont (G-10153)

Gasdorf Tool and Mch Co Inc .... E 419 227-0103
  Lima (G-12017)

Gem City Engineering Co .... C 937 223-5544
  Dayton (G-8361)

General Die Casters .... G 330 678-2528
  Cuyahoga Falls (G-8002)

▲ General Die Casters Inc .... E 330 678-2528
  Twinsburg (G-18942)

▲ General Tool Company .... C 513 733-5500
  Cincinnati (G-3820)

Gentzler Tool & Die Corp .... F 330 896-1941
  Akron (G-205)

Gilson Machine & Tool Co Inc .... E 419 592-2911
  Napoleon (G-14678)

Glendale Machine Inc .... G 440 248-8646
  Solon (G-17298)

▲ Gokoh Corporation .... F 937 339-4977
  Troy (G-18832)

Gordon Tool Inc .... F 419 263-3151
  Payne (G-16015)

Gottschall Tool & Die Inc .... F 330 332-1544
  Salem (G-16895)

Green Machine Tool Inc .... F 937 253-0771
  Dayton (G-8106)

H & R Tool & Machine Co Inc .... G 740 452-0784
  Zanesville (G-21316)

H Machining Inc .... F 419 636-6890
  Bryan (G-2298)

H R Machine .... G 937 838-6289
  Beavercreek (G-1343)

H&M Machine & Tool LLC .... E 419 776-9220
  Toledo (G-18491)

Hale Performance Coatings Inc .... E 419 244-6451
  Toledo (G-18494)

Hamilton Custom Molding Inc .... G 513 844-6643
  Hamilton (G-10702)

Hamilton Mold & Machine Co .... E 216 732-8200
  Cleveland (G-5474)

Hardin Creek Machine & Tool .... F 419 678-4913
  Coldwater (G-6561)

Hawthorne Tool LLC .... F 440 516-1891
  Wickliffe (G-20367)

Hedalloy Die Corp .... F 216 341-3768
  Cleveland (G-5493)

Hedges Selective Tool & Prod .... F 419 478-8670
  Toledo (G-18504)

Heimann Manufacturing Co .... G 937 652-1865
  Urbana (G-19161)

▲ Herbert Machine Works Inc .... D 330 929-4297
  Akron (G-221)

Herd Manufacturing Inc .... E 216 651-4221
  Cleveland (G-5503)

Hess Industries Ltd .... F 419 525-4000
  Mansfield (G-12624)

Hi-Tek Manufacturing Inc .... C 513 459-1094
  Mason (G-13037)

High Card Industries LLC .... F 330 547-3381
  Berlin Center (G-1655)

High Tech Mold & Machine Co .... G 330 896-4466
  Uniontown (G-19087)

Hofacker Prcsion Machining LLC .... F 937 832-7712
  Clayton (G-4659)

Holland Engraving Company .... F 419 865-2765
  Toledo (G-18509)

Homeworth Fabrications & Mchs .... F 330 525-5459
  Homeworth (G-11116)

▲ Honda Engineering N Amer Inc ...... B 937 642-5000
  Marysville (G-12948)

Honda Engineering NA Inc .... G 937 707-5357
  Marysville (G-12949)

Horizon Industries Corp .... G 937 323-0801
  Springfield (G-17575)

Hudak Machine & Tool Inc .... G 440 366-8955
  Elyria (G-9429)

Hunt Products Inc....E....440 667-2457
Newburgh Heights (G-15075)
Hunter Tool and Die Company....G....937 256-9798
Dayton (G-8397)
I-Dee-X Inc....G....330 788-2186
Youngstown (G-21112)
Ibycorp....G....330 425-8226
Twinsburg (G-18957)
Impact Industries Inc....E....440 327-2360
North Ridgeville (G-15380)
Imperial Die & Mfg Co....F....440 268-9080
Strongsville (G-17929)
Independent Stamping Inc....E....216 251-3500
Cleveland (G-5563)
Industrial Automation Service....G....740 747-2222
Ashley (G-789)
Industrial Machining Services....E....937 295-2022
Fort Loramie (G-9932)
Industrial Mold Inc....E....330 425-7374
Twinsburg (G-18959)
Industry Products Co....B....937 778-0585
Piqua (G-16279)
Innovative Plastic Molders LLC....E....937 898-3775
Dayton (G-8405)
Innovative Tool & Die Inc....G....419 599-0492
Napoleon (G-14684)
International Dies Co Inc....G....330 744-7951
Youngstown (G-21119)
▲ Ishmael Precision Tool Corp....E....937 335-8070
Troy (G-18846)
IV M Tool & Die....G....513 625-6464
Williamsburg (G-20409)
J & H Corporation....G....440 357-5982
Painesville (G-15893)
J & J Tool & Die Inc....G....330 343-4721
Dover (G-8994)
J and S Tool Incorporated....E....216 676-8330
Cleveland (G-5595)
J M Mold Inc....G....937 778-0077
Piqua (G-16281)
J P Tool Inc....G....419 354-8696
Bowling Green (G-1993)
J Tek Tool & Mold Inc....F....419 547-9476
Clyde (G-6541)
J W Harwood Co....F....216 531-6230
Cleveland (G-5602)
▲ J-C-R Tech Inc....E....937 783-2296
Blanchester (G-1714)
Jamen Tool & Die Co....F....330 788-6521
Youngstown (G-21123)
Jamen Tool & Die Co....E....330 782-6731
Youngstown (G-21124)
JB Products Co....G....330 342-0223
Streetsboro (G-17859)
JBI Corporation....F....419 855-3389
Genoa (G-10361)
Jena Tool Inc....D....937 296-1122
Moraine (G-14497)
▲ Jergens Inc....C....216 486-5540
Cleveland (G-5610)
Jet Tool and Prototype Co....G....419 666-1199
Walbridge (G-19459)
John F Kilfoil Co....G....513 791-6150
Cincinnati (G-3951)
Johnston Manufacturing Inc....G....440 269-1420
Mentor (G-13621)
Justin P Straub LLC....G....513 761-0282
Cincinnati (G-3963)
K & L Die & Manufacturing....G....419 895-1301
Greenwich (G-10532)
K & L Tool Inc....F....419 258-2086
Antwerp (G-630)
K B Machine & Tool Inc....G....937 773-1624
Piqua (G-16285)
K P Precision Tool and Mch Co....G....419 237-2596
Fayette (G-9775)
▲ Kalt Manufacturing Company....D....440 327-2102
North Ridgeville (G-15384)
Kastler & Reichlin Inc....E....440 322-0970
Elyria (G-9445)
Kelch Manufacturing Corp....G....440 366-5060
Elyria (G-9446)
Ken Forging Inc....C....440 993-8091
Jefferson (G-11364)
Kent Mold and Manufacturing Co....E....330 673-3469
Kent (G-11480)
KG Tool Company....G....440 428-8633
Madison (G-12508)
Kilroy Company....D....440 951-8700
Eastlake (G-9278)

▲ King Machine and Tool Co....F....330 833-7217
Massillon (G-13164)
King Machine of Akron Inc....E....330 762-7116
Akron (G-258)
Kinninger Prod Wldg Co Inc....D....419 629-3491
New Bremen (G-14788)
Kiraly Tool and Die Inc....F....330 744-5773
Youngstown (G-21129)
Knoble Tool Corp....E....937 461-4040
Dayton (G-8443)
Knous Tool & Machine Inc....G....419 394-3541
Saint Marys (G-16841)
Knowlton Manufacturing Co Inc....F....513 631-7353
Cincinnati (G-3999)
Kramer & Kiefer Inc....G....330 336-8742
Wadsworth (G-19416)
Krdc Inc....G....937 222-2332
Dayton (G-8446)
Kreider Corp....D....937 325-8787
Springfield (G-17592)
Krisdale Industries Inc....G....330 225-2392
Valley City (G-19209)
Kurtz Tool & Die Co Inc....G....330 755-7723
Struthers (G-17993)
L B Machine & Mfg Co Inc....G....513 471-6137
Cincinnati (G-4008)
La Ganke & Sons Stamping Co....F....216 451-0278
Columbia Station (G-6590)
Lab Quality Machining Inc....G....513 625-0219
Goshen (G-10416)
Lahm-Trosper Inc....F....937 252-8791
Dayton (G-8451)
▲ Lako Tool & Mfg....F....419 662-5256
Perrysburg (G-16118)
Lange Precision Inc....F....513 530-9500
Blue Ash (G-1824)
Langenau Manufacturing Company....F....216 651-3400
Cleveland (G-5680)
Lanko Industries Inc....G....440 269-1641
Mentor (G-13629)
Larosa Die Engineering Inc....G....513 284-9195
Cincinnati (G-4012)
Laspina Tool & Die Inc....F....330 923-9996
Stow (G-17767)
▲ Laszeray Technology LLC....D....440 582-8430
North Royalton (G-15432)
Levan Enterprises Inc....E....330 923-9797
Stow (G-17769)
Liberty Die Cast Molds Inc....F....740 666-7492
Ostrander (G-15788)
Liberty Mold & Machine Company....G....330 278-7825
Hinckley (G-11027)
Lideco LLC....G....330 539-9333
Vienna (G-19367)
Lightning Mold & Machine Inc....F....440 593-6460
Conneaut (G-7813)
Line Tool & Die Inc....G....419 332-2931
Fremont (G-10165)
Liqui-Box Corporation....C....419 209-9085
Upper Sandusky (G-19129)
▲ Logan Machine Company....D....330 633-6163
Akron (G-275)
Lomar Enterprises Inc....F....614 409-9104
Groveport (G-10633)
▲ Long-Stanton Mfg Company....E....513 874-8020
West Chester (G-19895)
Lorain Ruled Die Products Inc....G....440 281-8607
North Ridgeville (G-15389)
◆ Loroco Industries Inc....E....513 891-9544
Blue Ash (G-1828)
Lostcreek Tool & Machine Inc....F....937 773-6022
Piqua (G-16287)
Louis G Freeman Co....E....419 334-9709
Fremont (G-10167)
Lowry Tool & Die Inc....F....330 332-1722
Salem (G-16908)
Lrb Tool & Die Ltd....F....330 898-5783
Warren (G-19574)
Lukens Inc....D....937 440-2500
Troy (G-18854)
Lunar Tool & Mold Inc....F....440 237-2141
North Royalton (G-15434)
M & M Dies Inc....G....216 883-6628
Cleveland (G-5715)
M S K Tool & Die Inc....G....440 930-8100
Avon Lake (G-1038)
Macek Industries....G....440 205-8711
Mentor (G-13641)
Machine Tek Systems Inc....E....330 527-4450
Garrettsville (G-10329)

Machine Tool Corporation....G....513 863-4920
Hamilton (G-10722)
Machine Tool Design & Fab LLC....F....419 435-7676
Fostoria (G-9984)
Madsco Inc....F....513 242-4200
Cincinnati (G-4049)
Magna Exteriors America Inc....A....419 662-3256
Northwood (G-15484)
Magnum Molding Inc....G....937 368-3040
Conover (G-7824)
◆ Magnum Tool Corp....G....937 228-0900
Dayton (G-8469)
Majestic Tool and Machine Inc....E....440 248-5058
Solon (G-17331)
Mallory Pattern Works Inc....G....419 726-8001
Toledo (G-18572)
Mar-Metal Mfg Inc....E....419 447-1102
Upper Sandusky (G-19131)
Mar-Vel Tool Co Inc....E....937 223-2137
Dayton (G-8476)
Marsh Technologies Inc....F....330 545-0085
Girard (G-10391)
Martin Machine & Tool Inc....F....419 373-1711
Bowling Green (G-2000)
Martin Pultrusion Group Inc....G....440 439-9130
Cleveland (G-5752)
Martz Mold & Machine Inc....G....330 928-2159
Cuyahoga Falls (G-8024)
Master Craft Products Inc....F....216 281-5910
Cleveland (G-5757)
Master Marking Company Inc....F....330 688-6797
Stow (G-17772)
Match Mold & Machine Inc....E....330 830-5503
Massillon (G-13176)
Maumee Pattern Company Inc....E....419 693-4968
Toledo (G-18579)
Maxtool Company Limited....G....937 415-5776
Dayton (G-8479)
McAfee Tool & Die Inc....E....330 896-9555
Uniontown (G-19092)
MD Tool & Die Inc....G....440 647-6456
Wellington (G-19750)
Mdf Enterprises LLC....G....937 640-3436
Dayton (G-8481)
Mdf Tool Corporation....F....440 237-2277
North Royalton (G-15436)
Medway Tool Corp....E....937 335-7717
Troy (G-18857)
Meese Inc....D....440 998-1202
Ashtabula (G-819)
Meggitt (erlanger) LLC....D....513 851-5550
Cincinnati (G-4080)
Mercury Machine Co....D....440 349-3222
Solon (G-17335)
Metal & Wire Products Company....E....330 332-9448
Salem (G-16914)
▲ Metalex Manufacturing Inc....C....513 489-0507
Blue Ash (G-1839)
Metro Mech Inc....G....216 641-6262
Cleveland (G-5792)
Metro Tool & Die Co Inc....G....937 836-8242
Englewood (G-9531)
Meyer Machine Tool Company....G....614 235-0039
Columbus (G-7344)
Miami Valley Punch & Mfg....E....937 237-0533
Dayton (G-8491)
Micro Mold Co Inc....G....330 325-2373
Ravenna (G-16540)
▲ Mid-Ohio Products Inc....D....614 771-2795
Hilliard (G-10962)
Midwest Industrial Specialties....G....740 815-0541
Galena (G-10248)
▲ Midwest Mold & Texture Corp....E....513 732-1300
Batavia (G-1205)
Midwest Tool & Engineering Co....E....937 224-0756
Dayton (G-8498)
Mikan Die and Tool LLC....G....216 265-2811
Cleveland (G-5812)
Milacron Holdings Corp....E....513 487-5000
Blue Ash (G-1841)
▲ Milacron Plas Tech Group LLC....C....513 536-2000
Batavia (G-1208)
Milacron Plas Tech Group LLC....C....937 444-2532
Mount Orab (G-14583)
Misumi Investment USA Corp....G....937 859-5111
Dayton (G-8504)
Modern Manufacturing Inc....F....513 251-3600
Cincinnati (G-4116)
Mold Crafters Inc....G....937 426-3179
Dayton (G-8505)

SIC

Employee Codes: A=Over 500 employees, B=251-500
C=101-250, D=51-100, E=20-50, F=10-19, G=3-9

Mold Shop Inc	F	419 829-2041	
Sylvania (G-18118)			
Mold Solutions	G	800 948-4947	
Oberlin (G-15645)			
Moldmakers Inc	F	419 673-0902	
Kenton (G-11559)			
MOM Tools LLC	G	216 283-4014	
Cleveland (G-5829)			
Monarch Products Co	E	330 868-7717	
Minerva (G-14336)			
Monroe Die & Stamping Co	G	216 883-6390	
Cleveland (G-5831)			
Moran Tool Inc	G	937 526-5210	
Versailles (G-19354)			
▲ Morgal Machine Tool Co	D	937 325-5561	
Springfield (G-17607)			
Mosbro Machine and Tool Inc	G	330 467-0913	
Northfield (G-15468)			
◆ Mtd Holdings Inc	B	330 225-2600	
Valley City (G-19220)			
Multi Form Mfg	G	330 922-1933	
Stow (G-17778)			
Mutual Tool LLC	D	937 667-5818	
Tipp City (G-18290)			
N N Metal Stampings Inc	E	419 737-2311	
Pioneer (G-16235)			
National Mold Remediation	G	614 231-6653	
Columbus (G-7384)			
National Pattern Mfg Co	F	330 682-6871	
Orrville (G-15750)			
National Roller Die Inc	F	440 951-3850	
Willoughby (G-20552)			
NBC Industries Inc	F	216 651-9800	
Cleveland (G-5863)			
Nelson Tool Corporation	F	740 965-1894	
Sunbury (G-18068)			
◆ Nesco Inc	E	440 461-6000	
Cleveland (G-5871)			
New Bremen Machine & Tool Co	E	419 629-3295	
New Bremen (G-14790)			
New Die Inc	E	419 726-7581	
Toledo (G-18601)			
Neway Stamping & Mfg Inc	D	440 951-8500	
Willoughby (G-20554)			
Nichols Mold Inc	G	330 297-9719	
Ravenna (G-16544)			
▲ Northeast Tire Molds Inc	G	330 376-6107	
Akron (G-319)			
Norwalk Precast Molds Inc	F	419 668-1639	
Norwalk (G-15557)			
Numerics Unlimited Inc	F	937 849-0100	
New Carlisle (G-14810)			
▲ Oakley Die & Mold Co	E	513 754-8500	
Mason (G-13070)			
Ogs Tool & Manufacturing	G	419 524-6200	
Mansfield (G-12660)			
Ohio Associated Entps LLC	E	440 354-3148	
Painesville (G-15900)			
Ohio Tool & Jig Grind Inc	G	937 415-0692	
Dayton (G-8546)			
Omega Tool & Die Inc	F	937 890-2350	
Dayton (G-8550)			
Omni Manufacturing	G	419 394-7424	
Saint Marys (G-16845)			
Omni Manufacturing Inc	D	419 394-7424	
Saint Marys (G-16846)			
Omni Manufacturing Inc	F	419 394-7424	
Saint Marys (G-16847)			
Omnimold LLC	G	419 332-4466	
Fremont (G-10172)			
Opti Mold Inc	G	440 248-9179	
Solon (G-17356)			
Orick Stamping	D	419 331-0600	
Elida (G-9353)			
OSG Usa Inc	G	513 755-3360	
Mason (G-13071)			
P J Tool Company Inc	G	937 254-2817	
Dayton (G-8558)			
P O McIntire Company	E	440 269-1848	
Wickliffe (G-20376)			
PA MA Inc	G	440 846-3799	
Strongsville (G-17950)			
Pace Mold & Machine LLC	G	330 879-1777	
Massillon (G-13192)			
Pacific Tool & Die Co	F	330 273-7363	
Brunswick (G-2241)			
Paradise Mold & Die LLC	G	216 362-1945	
Cleveland (G-5961)			
Paramount Stamping & Wldg Co	D	216 631-1755	
Cleveland (G-5964)			

Part Rite Inc	G	216 362-4100	
North Royalton (G-15443)			
Penco Tool LLC	G	440 998-1116	
Ashtabula (G-829)			
Pendleton Mold & Machine LLC	G	440 998-0041	
Ashtabula (G-830)			
Perfection Mold & Machine Co	F	330 784-5435	
Twinsburg (G-19000)			
Perry Welding Service Inc	F	330 425-2211	
Twinsburg (G-19001)			
Phillips Mch & Stamping Corp	G	330 882-6714	
New Franklin (G-14829)			
Pier Tool & Die Inc	F	440 236-3188	
Columbia Station (G-6594)			
Pines Manufacturing Inc	F	440 835-5553	
Westlake (G-20294)			
Pioneer Precision Tool Inc	G	513 932-8805	
Lebanon (G-11827)			
Pitco Products Inc	F	513 228-7245	
Dayton (G-8577)			
Plastic Enterprises Inc	E	440 324-3240	
Elyria (G-9478)			
Plastic Mold Technology Inc	G	330 848-4921	
Barberton (G-1139)			
Porter Precision Products Co	G	513 385-1569	
Cincinnati (G-4250)			
Positool Technologies Inc	G	330 220-4002	
Brunswick (G-2245)			
Precise Tool Inc	G	937 778-3441	
Piqua (G-16307)			
Precision Component Inds LLC	E	330 477-1052	
Canton (G-2820)			
Precision Details Inc	F	937 596-0068	
Jackson Center (G-11346)			
Precision Die Masters	F	440 255-1204	
Mentor (G-13695)			
Premiere Mold and Machine Co	G	330 874-3000	
Bolivar (G-1942)			
Preuss Mold & Die	F	419 729-9100	
Toledo (G-18656)			
Prime Industries Inc	E	440 288-3626	
Lorain (G-12268)			
Prime Time Machine Inc	F	440 942-7410	
Willoughby (G-20579)			
Product Tooling Inc	G	740 524-2061	
Sunbury (G-18075)			
Production Design Services Inc	D	937 866-3377	
Dayton (G-8598)			
Producto Dieco Corporation	F	440 542-0000	
Solon (G-17364)			
Progress Tool & Stamping Inc	E	419 628-2384	
Minster (G-14360)			
Progressive Machine Die Inc	E	330 405-6600	
Macedonia (G-12478)			
Progrssive Molding Bolivar Inc	C	330 874-3000	
Bolivar (G-1944)			
Promac Inc	E	937 864-1961	
Enon (G-9548)			
Promold Inc	F	330 633-3532	
Tallmadge (G-18165)			
▲ Prospect Mold & Die Company	D	330 929-3311	
Cuyahoga Falls (G-8037)			
▲ Proto Plastics Inc	E	937 667-8416	
Tipp City (G-18295)			
▲ PSK Steel Corp	G	330 759-1251	
Hubbard (G-11139)			
Puehler Tool Co	G	216 447-0101	
Cleveland (G-6062)			
Pyramid Mold Inc	F	330 673-5200	
Kent (G-11509)			
▲ Quaker Mfg Corp	C	330 332-4631	
Salem (G-16922)			
Qualiform Inc	E	330 336-6777	
Wadsworth (G-19432)			
Quality Mfg Company Inc	G	513 921-4500	
Cincinnati (G-4308)			
▲ Quality Mold Inc	D	330 645-6653	
Akron (G-357)			
Quality Mold Inc	D	419 752-4511	
Greenwich (G-10534)			
Quality Specialists Inc	G	440 946-9129	
Willoughby (G-20584)			
Quality Tooling Systems Inc	F	330 722-5025	
Medina (G-13466)			
Queen City Tool Works Inc	G	513 874-0111	
Fairfield (G-9707)			
Quest Tool & Machine Ltd	E	937 969-8782	
Urbana (G-19174)			
R & R Machine & Tool Co	G	216 281-7609	
Cleveland (G-6079)			

R K S Tool & Die Inc	G	513 870-0225	
Fairfield (G-9709)			
R M Tool & Die Inc	F	440 238-6459	
Strongsville (G-17955)			
R T & T Machining Co Inc	F	440 974-8479	
Mentor (G-13714)			
▲ Rage Corporation	D	614 771-4771	
Hilliard (G-10974)			
Ram Tool Inc	G	937 277-0717	
Dayton (G-8615)			
Rapid Machine Inc	F	419 737-2377	
Pioneer (G-16243)			
Rapid Mold Repair & Machine	G	330 253-1000	
Akron (G-366)			
▲ Raymath Company	C	937 335-1860	
Troy (G-18867)			
Raymonds Tool & Gauge LLC	G	419 485-8340	
Montpelier (G-14453)			
▲ Ready Technology Inc	E	937 866-7200	
Dayton (G-8619)			
Regal Metal Products Co	E	330 868-6343	
Minerva (G-14339)			
Regal Metal Products Co	E	330 868-6343	
Minerva (G-14340)			
Regal Tool & Die Inc	G	330 746-6644	
Youngstown (G-21187)			
Renco Mold Inc	G	937 233-3233	
Dayton (G-8625)			
Reserve Industries Inc	E	440 871-2796	
Bay Village (G-1243)			
Retco Mold & Machine	F	330 633-5725	
Tallmadge (G-18167)			
Reuther Mold & Mfg Co Inc	D	330 923-5266	
Cuyahoga Falls (G-8041)			
▲ Reymond Products Intl Inc	E	330 339-3583	
New Philadelphia (G-14923)			
Rhinestahl Corporation	E	513 229-5300	
Mason (G-13084)			
Richard Paskiet Machinists	G	330 854-4160	
Canal Fulton (G-2513)			
Rme Machining Co	G	513 541-3328	
Cincinnati (G-4351)			
Rmt Corporation	F	513 942-8308	
Dayton (G-8635)			
Rockstedt Tool & Die Inc	F	330 273-9000	
Brunswick (G-2254)			
Romarc Enterprises Inc	G	419 287-4837	
Pemberville (G-16030)			
Ron-Al Mold & Machine Inc	F	330 673-7919	
Kent (G-11519)			
Ronfeldt Associates Inc	D	419 382-5641	
Toledo (G-18680)			
Ronlen Industries Inc	G	330 273-6468	
Brunswick (G-2255)			
Ross Special Products Inc	F	937 335-8406	
Troy (G-18869)			
Rotocast Technologies Inc	E	330 798-9091	
Akron (G-379)			
▲ Royer Technologies Inc	G	937 743-6114	
Springboro (G-17506)			
RPM Carbide Die Inc	F	419 894-6426	
Arcadia (G-655)			
Runner Tool & Die Inc	G	330 794-8843	
Akron (G-382)			
Rural Products Inc	G	419 298-2677	
Edgerton (G-9335)			
S & R Tool & Die Services Inc	G	937 584-4691	
Sabina (G-16777)			
S-K Mold & Tool Company	E	937 339-0299	
Tipp City (G-18298)			
S-K Mold & Tool Company	E	937 339-0299	
Troy (G-18870)			
Saint-Gobain Ceramics Plas Inc	A	330 673-5860	
Stow (G-17797)			
Sanborn Plastics Corp	D	440 286-4122	
Chardon (G-3177)			
Schmitmeyer Inc	G	937 295-2091	
Fort Loramie (G-9937)			
Schuster Manufacturing Inc	G	419 476-5800	
Toledo (G-18687)			
Seaway Pattern Mfg Inc	E	419 865-5724	
Toledo (G-18689)			
Seilkop Industries Inc	E	513 761-1035	
Cincinnati (G-4398)			
Seilkop Industries Inc	E	513 353-3090	
Miamitown (G-13892)			
▼ Sekely Industries Inc	C	248 844-9201	
Salem (G-16927)			
Select Machine Co Inc	F	330 678-7676	
Kent (G-11526)			

Selzer Tool & Die Inc..........G....... 440 365-4124
Elyria *(G-9491)*
Shalix Inc..........F....... 216 941-3546
Cleveland *(G-6183)*
Sharp Industrial Tools Inc..........G....... 513 741-9562
Cincinnati *(G-4413)*
Shelburne Corp..........G....... 216 321-9177
Shaker Heights *(G-17094)*
Shiloh Automotive Inc..........E....... 330 558-2600
Valley City *(G-19230)*
Shiloh Corporation..........B....... 330 558-2600
Valley City *(G-19231)*
◆ **Shiloh Industries Inc**..........G....... 330 558-2600
Valley City *(G-19234)*
Shiloh Industries Inc..........A....... 330 558-2600
Valley City *(G-19235)*
Shook Tool Inc..........G....... 937 337-6471
Ansonia *(G-626)*
Short Run Machine Products Inc..........F....... 440 969-1313
Ashtabula *(G-838)*
Sivon Mfr Co..........G....... 440 259-5505
Perry *(G-16057)*
Skribs Tool and Die Inc..........E....... 440 951-7774
Mentor *(G-13724)*
Skrl Die Casting Inc..........D....... 440 946-7200
Willoughby *(G-20598)*
Slabe Tool Company..........G....... 740 439-1647
Cambridge *(G-2476)*
Smithville Manufacturing Co..........E....... 330 345-5818
Wooster *(G-20836)*
Sni Inc..........G....... 937 427-9447
Beavercreek *(G-1380)*
Snyders Tool & Die Inc..........G....... 614 878-2205
Galloway *(G-10315)*
Space Age Coatings LLC..........G....... 937 275-5117
Dayton *(G-8665)*
Spectracam Ltd..........G....... 937 223-3805
Dayton *(G-8667)*
Spintech LLC..........F....... 937 912-3250
Xenia *(G-20974)*
▲ **Sroka Industries Inc**..........E....... 440 572-2811
Strongsville *(G-17972)*
▲ **Stanco Precision Manufacturing**..........G....... 937 274-1785
Dayton *(G-8675)*
Starkey Machinery Inc..........E....... 419 468-2560
Galion *(G-10289)*
Stolle Machinery Company LLC..........E....... 937 859-4644
Dayton *(G-8684)*
Straight 72 Inc..........D....... 740 943-5730
Marysville *(G-12973)*
Styner+bienz US Inc..........G....... 216 362-1850
Cleveland *(G-6258)*
Suburban Metal Products Inc..........F....... 740 474-4237
Circleville *(G-4644)*
Sulecki Precision Products..........F....... 440 255-5454
Mentor *(G-13740)*
Sumitomo Elc Carbide Mfg Inc..........F....... 440 354-0600
Grand River *(G-10453)*
Sup-R-Die Inc..........G....... 330 688-7600
Stow *(G-17807)*
▲ **Superb Industries Inc**..........D....... 330 852-0500
Sugarcreek *(G-18045)*
Superior Mold & Die Co..........E....... 330 688-8251
Munroe Falls *(G-14666)*
Supply Dynamics LLC..........F....... 513 965-2000
Loveland *(G-12392)*
Sure Tool & Manufacturing Co..........E....... 937 253-9111
Dayton *(G-8691)*
Sutterlin Machine & Tool Co..........F....... 440 357-0817
Mentor *(G-13742)*
Symbol Tool & Die Inc..........G....... 440 582-5989
North Royalton *(G-15454)*
T & W Tool & Machine Inc..........G....... 937 667-2039
Tipp City *(G-18302)*
Taft Tool & Production Co..........F....... 419 385-2576
Toledo *(G-18715)*
▲ **Talent Tool & Die Inc**..........E....... 440 239-8777
Berea *(G-1637)*
Tater Tool & Die Inc..........G....... 330 648-1148
Spencer *(G-17458)*
Taylor Tool & Die Inc..........G....... 937 845-1491
New Carlisle *(G-14813)*
▲ **Te-Co Manufacturing LLC**..........D....... 937 836-0961
Union *(G-19068)*
Tech Industries Inc..........E....... 216 861-7337
Cleveland *(G-6298)*
Tech Mold & Tool Co Inc..........G....... 937 667-8851
Tipp City *(G-18304)*
▲ **Technology House The Ltd**..........D....... 440 248-3025
Solon *(G-17400)*

Tempcraft Corporation..........C....... 216 391-3885
Cleveland *(G-6303)*
Tessec Manufacturing Svcs LLC..........E....... 937 985-3552
Dayton *(G-8710)*
Tetra Mold & Tool Inc..........E....... 937 845-1651
New Carlisle *(G-14814)*
Thomas Tool & Mold Company..........F....... 614 890-4978
Westerville *(G-20237)*
Tig Wood & Die Inc..........F....... 937 849-6741
New Carlisle *(G-14815)*
Tipco Punch Inc..........E....... 513 874-9140
Hamilton *(G-10748)*
Tipp Machine & Tool Inc..........C....... 937 890-8428
Dayton *(G-8716)*
Tm Machine & Tool Inc..........G....... 419 478-0310
Toledo *(G-18727)*
◆ **Toledo Molding & Die Inc**..........D....... 419 470-3950
Toledo *(G-18736)*
Toledo Molding & Die Inc..........C....... 419 476-0581
Toledo *(G-18737)*
▲ **Toledo Tool and Die Co Inc**..........E....... 419 476-4422
Toledo *(G-18747)*
▲ **Tom Smith Industries Inc**..........C....... 937 832-1555
Clayton *(G-4663)*
Tomahawk Tool Supply..........G....... 419 485-8737
Montpelier *(G-14455)*
Tomco Industries..........G....... 330 652-7531
Mineral Ridge *(G-14313)*
Tomco Tool Inc..........G....... 937 322-5768
Springfield *(G-17665)*
Tool Technologies Van Dyke..........F....... 937 349-4900
Marysville *(G-12975)*
Toolcraft Products Inc..........D....... 937 223-8271
Dayton *(G-8719)*
Tooling & Components Corp..........F....... 419 478-9122
Toledo *(G-18750)*
Tooling Connection Inc..........G....... 419 594-3339
Oakwood *(G-15620)*
Tooling Technology LLC..........D....... 937 295-3672
Fort Loramie *(G-9943)*
Tooling Zone Inc..........E....... 937 550-4180
Springboro *(G-17510)*
Toolrite Manufacturing Inc..........F....... 937 278-1962
Dayton *(G-8720)*
Top Tool & Die Inc..........F....... 216 267-5878
Cleveland *(G-6337)*
Torr Metal Products Inc..........E....... 216 671-1616
Cleveland *(G-6339)*
Tower Tool & Manufacturing Co..........F....... 330 425-1623
Twinsburg *(G-19028)*
Tracker Machine Inc..........G....... 330 482-4086
Columbiana *(G-6635)*
Tradye Machine & Tool Inc..........G....... 740 625-7550
Centerburg *(G-3031)*
Tree City Mold & Machine Co..........G....... 330 673-9807
Kent *(G-11538)*
Trexler Rubber Co Inc..........E....... 330 296-9677
Ravenna *(G-16567)*
Tri-Craft Inc..........E....... 440 826-1050
Cleveland *(G-6358)*
Tri-R Dies Inc..........E....... 330 758-8050
Youngstown *(G-21230)*
Trico Machine Products Corp..........F....... 216 662-4194
Cleveland *(G-6365)*
▲ **Trim Parts Inc**..........E....... 513 934-0815
Lebanon *(G-11845)*
Trim Tool & Machine Inc..........E....... 216 889-1916
Cleveland *(G-6366)*
Trimline Die Corporation..........E....... 440 355-6900
Lagrange *(G-11639)*
◆ **Troy West LLC**..........G....... 937 339-2192
Troy *(G-18882)*
Tru-Tex International Corp..........E....... 513 825-8844
Cincinnati *(G-4530)*
▲ **Trucut Incorporated**..........D....... 330 938-9806
Sebring *(G-17055)*
True Industries Inc..........E....... 330 296-4342
Ravenna *(G-16569)*
True Kote Inc..........G....... 419 334-8813
Fremont *(G-10188)*
Turbo Machine & Tool Inc..........G....... 216 651-1940
Cleveland *(G-6375)*
Turbo-Mold Inc..........G....... 440 352-2530
Painesville *(G-15934)*
Tyler Mold & Machine Inc..........E....... 330 645-6653
Akron *(G-452)*
U S Alloy Die Corp..........F....... 216 749-9700
Cleveland *(G-6379)*
Umat LLC..........E....... 937 224-3303
Dayton *(G-8737)*

United Extrusion Dies Inc..........F....... 330 533-2915
Canfield *(G-2581)*
United Finshg & Die Cutng Inc..........F....... 216 881-0239
Cleveland *(G-6384)*
▲ **Universal Tire Molds Inc**..........E....... 330 253-5101
Akron *(G-458)*
Universal Tool Technology LLC..........E....... 937 222-4608
Dayton *(G-8739)*
Unlimited Machine and Tool LLC..........F....... 419 269-1730
Toledo *(G-18761)*
Valley Tool & Die Inc..........D....... 440 237-0160
North Royalton *(G-15458)*
Van Wert Machine Inc..........F....... 419 692-6836
Delphos *(G-8926)*
Varbros Tool and Die Company..........D....... 216 267-5200
Cleveland *(G-6407)*
Velocity Concept Dev Group LLC..........G....... 740 685-2637
Byesville *(G-2412)*
Village Plastics Co..........G....... 330 753-0100
Barberton *(G-1156)*
Vinyl Tool & Die Company Inc..........F....... 330 782-0254
Youngstown *(G-21241)*
Vinyltech Inc..........E....... 330 538-0369
North Jackson *(G-15302)*
▲ **Vmi Americas Inc**..........E....... 330 929-6800
Stow *(G-17815)*
Voisard Tool Service..........E....... 937 526-5451
Russia *(G-16771)*
▲ **Vulcan Tool Company**..........G....... 937 253-6194
Dayton *(G-8744)*
W H Heimkreiter Manufacturing..........G....... 513 681-9192
Cincinnati *(G-4574)*
Walest Incorporated..........G....... 216 362-8110
Cleveland *(G-6443)*
Walker Tool & Machine Co..........F....... 419 661-8000
Perrysburg *(G-16167)*
Wapak Tool & Die Inc..........G....... 419 738-6215
Wapakoneta *(G-19512)*
Ward Mold & Machine..........G....... 740 472-5303
Woodsfield *(G-20722)*
▲ **Wauseon Machine & Mfg Inc**..........D....... 419 337-0940
Wauseon *(G-19700)*
Waverly Tool Co Ltd..........G....... 740 988-4831
Beaver *(G-1312)*
Wayne Trail Technologies Inc..........D....... 937 295-2120
Fort Loramie *(G-9944)*
Weiss Industries Inc..........E....... 419 526-2480
Mansfield *(G-12704)*
Welage Corporation..........F....... 513 681-2300
Cincinnati *(G-4583)*
▲ **Wentworth Mold Inc Electra**..........D....... 937 898-8460
Vandalia *(G-19317)*
White Machine Inc..........G....... 440 237-3282
North Royalton *(G-15460)*
Williams Steel Rule Die Co..........F....... 216 431-3232
Cleveland *(G-6464)*
Windsor Tool Inc..........F....... 216 671-1900
Cleveland *(G-6466)*
Wire Shop Inc..........E....... 440 354-6842
Mentor *(G-13771)*
▲ **WLS Stamping Co**..........D....... 216 271-5100
Cleveland *(G-6472)*
Wrena LLC..........E....... 937 667-4403
Tipp City *(G-18312)*
Wt Tool & Die Inc..........G....... 330 332-2254
Salem *(G-16936)*
▲ **Wurtec Manufacturing Service**..........E....... 419 726-1066
Toledo *(G-18777)*
XCEL Mold and Machine Inc..........F....... 330 499-8450
Canton *(G-2905)*
Youngstown Die Development..........G....... 330 755-0722
Struthers *(G-18000)*
Youngstown Tool & Die Company..........D....... 330 747-4464
Youngstown *(G-21257)*
Ypf Corporation..........G....... 330 743-6404
Petersburg *(G-16180)*
Yugo Mold Inc..........F....... 330 606-0710
Akron *(G-479)*

3545 Machine Tool Access

A & B Machine Inc..........E....... 937 492-8662
Sidney *(G-17164)*
Able Tool Corporation..........E....... 513 733-8989
Cincinnati *(G-3346)*
Abrasive Technology Lapidary..........C....... 740 548-4855
Lewis Center *(G-11881)*
Accu Jet Corp..........E....... 937 252-9931
Dayton *(G-8129)*
Advanced Holding Designs Inc..........F....... 330 928-4456
Cuyahoga Falls *(G-7962)*

SIC

Employee Codes: A=Over 500 employees, B=251-500
C=101-250, D=51-100, E=20-50, F=10-19, G=3-9

Advantage Tool Supply Inc ....G...... 330 896-8869
Uniontown (G-19074)

Aeroll Engineering Corp ....G...... 216 481-2266
Cleveland (G-4720)

▲ Ajax Industries Inc ....E...... 614 272-6944
Columbus (G-6707)

Akron Gear & Engineering Inc..........E...... 330 773-6608
Akron (G-45)

◆ Alliance Knife Inc ....E...... 513 367-9000
Harrison (G-10768)

▲ Allied Machine & Engrg Corp..........C...... 330 343-4283
Dover (G-8963)

Anchor Lamina America Inc ....E...... 330 952-1595
Medina (G-13370)

Angstrom Corp ....G...... 330 405-0524
Twinsburg (G-18899)

▲ Angstrom Precision Metals LLC......D...... 440 255-6700
Mentor (G-13522)

Antwerp Tool & Die Inc ....F...... 419 258-5271
Antwerp (G-628)

Apollo Manufacturing Co LLC............E...... 440 951-9972
Mentor (G-13524)

Apollo Products Inc ....F...... 440 269-8551
Willoughby (G-20434)

Atlantic Tool & Die Company ....C...... 330 769-4500
Seville (G-17068)

B & R Machine Co Inc ....F...... 216 961-7370
Cleveland (G-4882)

BAP Manufacturing Inc ....E...... 419 332-5041
Fremont (G-10127)

Bee Jax Inc ....G...... 330 373-0500
Warren (G-19527)

Bendel Inc ....G...... 614 478-9013
Columbus (G-6822)

Bender Engineering Company ....G...... 330 938-2355
Beloit (G-1581)

▲ Big Chief Manufacturing Ltd ....E...... 513 934-3888
Lebanon (G-11784)

Blue Ash Tool & Die Co Inc ....F...... 513 793-4530
Blue Ash (G-1752)

Bully Tools Inc ....E...... 740 282-5834
Steubenville (G-17690)

Capital Tool Company ....E...... 216 661-5750
Cleveland (G-4971)

Carbide Probes Inc ....E...... 937 490-2994
Beavercreek (G-1322)

Carlton Natco ....G...... 216 451-5588
Cleveland (G-4978)

Certified Comparator Products ....G...... 937 426-9677
Beavercreek (G-1372)

▲ Certified Tool & Grinding Inc ....G...... 937 865-5934
Miamisburg (G-13791)

Chardon Tool & Supply Co Inc ....E...... 440 286-6440
Chardon (G-3146)

Chart Tech Tool Inc ....E...... 937 667-3543
Tipp City (G-18272)

Chippewa Tool & Mfg Co ....F...... 419 849-2790
Woodville (G-20724)

Clapp & Haney Brazed Tool Co ....E...... 740 922-3515
Dennison (G-8944)

Cleveland Carbide Tool Co ....E...... 440 974-1155
Mentor (G-13545)

Cleveland Specialty Insptn Svc ....F...... 440 578-1046
Mentor (G-13546)

Cnc Indexing Feeding Tech LLC ....G...... 513 770-4200
Mason (G-13004)

Coleys Inc ....F...... 440 967-5630
Vermilion (G-19325)

Commercial Grinding Services...........E...... 330 273-5040
Medina (G-13390)

Connell Limited Partnership ....D...... 877 534-8986
Northfield (G-15464)

Contour Tool Inc ....E...... 440 365-7333
North Ridgeville (G-15364)

▲ Covert Manufacturing Inc ....C...... 419 468-1761
Galion (G-10261)

Cowles Industrial Tool Co LLC ....E...... 330 799-9100
Austintown (G-972)

Cowles Tool Company LLC ....G...... 330 799-9100
Austintown (G-973)

Cr Supply LLC ....G...... 440 759-5408
Mentor (G-13554)

Custom Carbide Cutter Inc ....F...... 513 851-6363
West Chester (G-19996)

Cyber Tech Tooling ....G...... 937 320-2298
Dayton (G-8262)

Dark Diamond Tools Inc ....G...... 440 701-6424
Chardon (G-3148)

Dayton Precision Punch.....................G...... 937 275-8700
Dayton (G-8283)

▲ Dayton Progress Corporation...........A...... 937 859-5111
Dayton (G-8284)

Delta Machine & Tool Co ....F...... 216 524-2477
Cleveland (G-5183)

Diamond Products Limited ....F...... 440 323-4616
Elyria (G-9402)

Diamond Reserve Inc ....F...... 440 892-7877
Westlake (G-20263)

▲ Diamonds Products LLC..................G...... 440 323-4616
Elyria (G-9403)

Dillon Manufacturing Inc ....F...... 937 325-8482
Springfield (G-17544)

Diversified Mch Components LLC ....E...... 440 942-5701
Eastlake (G-9266)

◆ Drt Mfg Co ....C...... 937 297-6670
Dayton (G-8313)

E & J Demark Inc ....F...... 419 337-5866
Wauseon (G-19675)

E & J Demark Inc ....F...... 419 337-5866
Wauseon (G-19676)

Edge-Rite Tools Inc ....F...... 216 642-0966
Cleveland (G-5258)

Electrofuel Industries Inc ....G...... 937 783-2846
Batavia (G-1181)

Ellison Technologies Inc ....E...... 513 874-2736
Hamilton (G-10687)

Evandy Co Inc ....G...... 216 518-9713
Cleveland (G-5305)

Eversharpe Deburring Tool Co ....G...... 513 988-6240
Trenton (G-18791)

Expert Regrind Service Inc ....G...... 937 526-5662
Versailles (G-19347)

Feedall Inc ....F...... 440 942-8100
Willoughby (G-20486)

Ferguson Tools Inc ....E...... 419 298-2327
Edgerton (G-9330)

Firstar Precision Corporation ....E...... 216 362-7888
Cleveland (G-5350)

Fischer Special Tooling Corp ....F...... 440 951-8411
Mentor (G-13578)

Flex-E-On Inc ....G...... 330 928-4496
Cuyahoga Falls (G-7997)

Formed Metal Products Inc ....F...... 440 775-0819
Oberlin (G-15639)

Fox Tool Co Inc ....E...... 330 928-3402
Cuyahoga Falls (G-7998)

Frecon Engineering ....G...... 513 874-8981
West Chester (G-19867)

▼ Furukawa Rock Drill USA Co Ltd......E...... 330 673-5826
Kent (G-11462)

Galaxy Products Inc ....G...... 419 843-7337
Sylvania (G-18107)

Gem Tool LLC ....G...... 216 771-8444
Cleveland (G-5409)

George Whalley Company ....E...... 216 453-0099
Fairport Harbor (G-9765)

◆ Glassline Corporation ....E...... 419 666-9712
Perrysburg (G-16102)

◆ Gleason Metrology Systems Corp ....E...... 937 384-8901
Dayton (G-8365)

◆ Global Trade Network Inc ....G...... 513 701-0411
Mason (G-13031)

H & S Tool Inc ....F...... 330 335-1536
Wadsworth (G-19409)

H Duane Leis Acquisitions ....E...... 937 835-5621
New Lebanon (G-14842)

H E Long Company ....F...... 513 899-2610
Morrow (G-14547)

H Machining Inc ....F...... 419 636-6890
Bryan (G-2298)

H3d Tool Corporation ....G...... 740 498-5181
Newcomerstown (G-15114)

Hammill Manufacturing Co ....D...... 419 476-0789
Maumee (G-13264)

◆ Hapco Inc ....F...... 330 678-9353
Kent (G-11469)

Herco Inc ....E...... 740 498-5181
Newcomerstown (G-15115)

HI Carb Corp ....F...... 216 486-5000
Cleveland (G-5507)

HI Tech Tool Corporation ....G...... 513 346-4061
Monroe (G-14404)

▲ High Quality Tools Inc ....F...... 440 975-9684
Eastlake (G-9273)

Hilti Inc ....F...... 614 258-8384
Columbus (G-7158)

▲ Hudson Supply Company Inc ....G...... 216 518-3000
Cleveland (G-5535)

Hydra Air Equipment Inc ....G...... 330 274-2222
Mantua (G-12712)

Hykon Manufacturing Company ....G...... 330 821-8889
Alliance (G-517)

Hyper Tool Company ....F...... 440 543-5151
Chagrin Falls (G-3093)

Imco Carbide Tool Inc ....D...... 419 661-6313
Perrysburg (G-16110)

Independent Die & Mfg Co ....F...... 216 362-6778
Cleveland (G-5562)

Interstate Tool Corporation ....E...... 216 671-1077
Cleveland (G-5583)

J and L Manufacturing Inc ....G...... 937 492-0008
Sidney (G-17197)

▲ Jergens Inc ....C...... 216 486-5540
Cleveland (G-5610)

Jerry Tools Inc ....F...... 513 242-3211
Cincinnati (G-3944)

JM Performance Products Inc ....F...... 440 357-1234
Fairport Harbor (G-9766)

Johnson Bros Rubber Co Inc ....E...... 419 752-4814
Greenwich (G-10531)

Jones Industrial Service LLC ....G...... 419 287-4553
Pemberville (G-16029)

Jump N Sales LLC ....G...... 513 509-7661
Hamilton (G-10713)

Kaeper Machine Inc ....G...... 440 974-1010
Mentor (G-13622)

▲ Kalt Manufacturing Company ....D...... 440 327-2102
North Ridgeville (G-15384)

Karma Metal Products Inc ....F...... 419 524-4371
Mansfield (G-12632)

Kaskell Manufacturing Inc ....F...... 937 704-9700
Springboro (G-17485)

Keb Industries Inc ....G...... 440 953-4623
Willoughby (G-20519)

Kennametal Inc ....C...... 440 437-5131
Orwell (G-15777)

Kennametal Inc ....C...... 216 898-6120
Cleveland (G-5644)

Kennametal Inc ....C...... 440 349-5151
Solon (G-17329)

Kennametal Inc ....C...... 419 877-5358
Whitehouse (G-20341)

Kilroy Company ....D...... 440 951-8700
Eastlake (G-9278)

▲ Knb Tools of America Inc ....F...... 614 733-0400
Plain City (G-16347)

Knoble Tool Corp ....E...... 937 461-4040
Dayton (G-8443)

Knox Machinery Inc ....C...... 937 743-2641
Franklin (G-10031)

Kyocera SGS Precision Tools............E...... 330 688-6667
Munroe Falls (G-14661)

Kyocera SGS Precision Tools............E...... 330 688-6667
Cuyahoga Falls (G-8019)

L C Smith Co ....G...... 440 327-1251
Elyria (G-9448)

Lange Precision Inc ....F...... 513 530-9500
Blue Ash (G-1824)

Lear Manufacturing Inc ....C...... 440 327-4545
North Ridgeville (G-15387)

Levan Enterprises Inc ....E...... 330 923-9797
Stow (G-17769)

Lord Corporation ....C...... 937 278-9431
Dayton (G-8459)

LS Starrett Company ....D...... 440 835-0005
Westlake (G-20282)

M A Harrison Mfg Co Inc ....E...... 440 965-4306
Wakeman (G-19451)

M S C Industries Inc..........................C...... 440 474-8788
Rome (G-16717)

▲ Machining Technologies Inc ....E...... 419 862-3110
Elmore (G-9363)

Master Carbide Tools Company ....F...... 440 352-1112
Mentor (G-13647)

Matrix Tool & Machine Inc ....E...... 440 255-0300
Mentor (G-13648)

Matvest Inc ....E...... 614 487-8720
Columbus (G-7327)

McRill Service LLC ....F...... 419 408-3113
Kenton (G-11557)

Mdf Tool Corporation ....F...... 440 237-2277
North Royalton (G-15436)

Medina Blanking Inc ....C...... 330 558-2300
Valley City (G-19217)

Medway Tool Corp ....E...... 937 335-7717
Troy (G-18857)

Melin Tool Company Inc ....D...... 216 362-4200
Cleveland (G-5780)

▲ Metalex Manufacturing Inc ....C...... 513 489-0507
Blue Ash (G-1839)

Midwest Ohio Tool Co ....G....... 419 294-1987
Upper Sandusky (G-19132)
Midwest Tool & Engineering Co ....E....... 937 224-0756
Dayton (G-8498)
Mikan Die and Tool LLC ....G....... 216 265-2811
Cleveland (G-5812)
Monaghan & Associates Inc ....E....... 937 253-7706
Dayton (G-8506)
Morgan Precision Instrs LLC ....G....... 330 896-0846
Akron (G-303)
Myers Precision Grinding Co ....F....... 216 365-2630
Cleveland (G-5844)
National Machine Company ....E....... 330 688-2584
Stow (G-17781)
National Rolled Thread Die Co ....F....... 440 232-8101
Cleveland (G-5859)
▲ Nook Industries Inc ....C....... 216 271-7900
Cleveland (G-5887)
North-West Tool Co ....G....... 937 278-7995
Dayton (G-8527)
Northeast Broach & Tool ....G....... 440 918-0048
Willoughby (G-20556)
Numatx Inc ....G....... 937 435-8178
Dayton (G-8536)
▲ Oakley Die & Mold Co ....G....... 513 754-8500
Mason (G-13070)
Obars Machine and Tool Company ......E....... 419 535-6307
Toledo (G-18613)
▼ Ohio Broach & Machine Company ....E....... 440 946-1040
Willoughby (G-20560)
Ohio Drill & Tool Co ....G....... 330 525-7717
Homeworth (G-11117)
Omwp Company ....E....... 330 453-8438
Canton (G-2804)
OReilly Precision Pdts Inc ....G....... 937 526-4677
Russia (G-16766)
▲ Osg-Sterling Die Inc ....D....... 216 267-1300
Parma (G-15964)
Ovase Manufacturing LLC ....G....... 937 275-0617
Dayton (G-8557)
P F S Incorporated ....E....... 440 582-1620
Cleveland (G-5954)
P O McIntire Company ....E....... 440 269-1848
Wickliffe (G-20376)
Pakk Systems LLC ....G....... 440 839-9999
Wakeman (G-19452)
Patriot Mfg Group Inc ....D....... 937 746-2117
Carlisle (G-2934)
Pemco Inc ....G....... 216 524-2990
Cleveland (G-5989)
Performance Superabrasives LLC ....G....... 440 946-7171
Mentor (G-13685)
▲ Pfi Precision Inc ....E....... 937 845-3563
New Carlisle (G-14812)
Pike Tool & Manufacturing Co ....G....... 740 947-7462
Waverly (G-19718)
PMC Gage Inc ....E....... 440 953-1672
Willoughby (G-20572)
PMC Mercury ....G....... 440 953-3300
Willoughby (G-20573)
Polhe Tool Inc ....G....... 419 476-2433
Toledo (G-18648)
Positrol Inc ....E....... 513 272-0500
Cincinnati (G-4252)
Precise Tool & Mfg Corp ....F....... 216 524-1500
Cleveland (G-6033)
Precision Component Inds LLC ....E....... 330 477-1052
Canton (G-2820)
Precision Gage & Tool Company ....E....... 937 866-9666
Dayton (G-8584)
Preston ....F....... 740 788-8208
Newark (G-15048)
Production Design Services Inc ....D....... 937 866-3377
Dayton (G-8598)
Productive Carbides Inc ....G....... 513 771-7092
Cincinnati (G-4293)
Quality Cutter Grinding Co ....F....... 216 362-6444
Cleveland (G-6070)
R & J Tool Inc ....F....... 937 833-3200
Brookville (G-2198)
R A Heller Company ....F....... 513 771-6100
Cincinnati (G-4322)
R Dunn Mold Inc ....G....... 937 773-3388
Piqua (G-16309)
R T & T Machining Co Inc ....F....... 440 974-8479
Mentor (G-13714)
Reed Machinery Inc ....G....... 330 220-6668
Brunswick (G-2253)
▼ Regal Diamond Products Corp ......E....... 440 944-7700
Wickliffe (G-20385)

Retention Knob Supply & Mfg Co ....F....... 937 686-6405
Huntsville (G-11215)
▲ Rex International USA Inc ....E....... 800 321-7950
Ashtabula (G-837)
Ridge Tool Manufacturing Co ....A....... 440 323-5581
Elyria (G-9488)
Riten Industries Incorporated ....E....... 740 335-5353
Wshngtn CT Hs (G-20925)
Roehlers Machine Products ....G....... 937 354-4401
Mount Victory (G-14659)
▲ Rol - Tech Inc ....C....... 214 905-8050
Fort Loramie (G-9936)
Rossi Machinery Services Inc ....G....... 419 281-4488
Ashland (G-773)
▲ Royer Technologies Inc ....G....... 937 743-6114
Springboro (G-17506)
▲ Schober USA Inc ....G....... 513 489-7393
Fairfield (G-9714)
Schumann Enterprises Inc ....E....... 216 267-6850
Cleveland (G-6166)
Seco Machine Inc ....E....... 330 499-2150
North Canton (G-15263)
▲ Setco Sales Company ....D....... 513 941-5110
Cincinnati (G-4409)
Sharp Tool Service Inc ....E....... 330 273-4144
Cleveland (G-6184)
Sharper Tooling ....G....... 330 667-2960
Litchfield (G-12140)
▲ Shook Manufactured Pdts Inc ......G....... 330 848-9780
Akron (G-401)
Shook Manufactured Pdts Inc ....G....... 440 247-9130
Chagrin Falls (G-3069)
Silver Tool Inc ....E....... 937 865-0012
Miamisburg (G-13860)
▲ Skidmore-Wilhelm Mfg Company ....E....... 216 481-4774
Solon (G-17381)
Sorbothane Inc ....E....... 330 678-9444
Kent (G-11530)
Sp3 Cutting Tools Inc ....G....... 937 667-4476
Tipp City (G-18301)
Spectrum Machine Inc ....E....... 330 626-3666
Streetsboro (G-17877)
Stanley Bittinger ....G....... 740 942-4302
Cadiz (G-2422)
Star Metal Products Co Inc ....D....... 440 899-7000
Westlake (G-20311)
▼ Stark Industrial LLC ....E....... 330 493-9773
North Canton (G-15269)
STC International Co Ltd ....G....... 561 308-6002
Lebanon (G-11842)
Sumitomo Elc Carbide Mfg Inc ....F....... 440 354-0600
Grand River (G-10453)
▲ Superion Inc ....E....... 937 374-0033
Xenia (G-20977)
Supplier Inspection Svcs Inc ....E....... 937 263-7097
Dayton (G-8690)
T M Industries Inc ....G....... 330 627-4410
Carrollton (G-2967)
Taft Tool & Production Co ....F....... 419 385-2576
Toledo (G-18715)
▲ Te-Co Manufacturing LLC ....D....... 937 836-0961
Union (G-19068)
Technidrill Systems Inc ....E....... 330 678-9980
Kent (G-11536)
Thaler Machine Company ....G....... 937 550-2400
Springboro (G-17509)
Tomco Tool Inc ....G....... 937 322-5768
Springfield (G-17665)
Tool Systems Inc ....F....... 440 461-6363
Cleveland (G-6333)
Tormaxx Co ....G....... 513 721-6299
Cincinnati (G-4513)
Trison Tool Inc ....G....... 440 352-1055
Painesville (G-15933)
Troyke Manufacturing Company ....F....... 513 769-4242
Cincinnati (G-4529)
Uhrichsville Carbide Inc ....F....... 740 922-9197
Uhrichsville (G-19064)
◆ Ultra-Met Company ....D....... 937 653-7133
Urbana (G-19186)
United States Drill Head Co ....E....... 513 941-0300
Cincinnati (G-4540)
Voisard Tool Service ....E....... 937 526-5451
Russia (G-16771)
Whip Guide Co ....F....... 440 543-5151
Chagrin Falls (G-3133)
Whitworth Knife Company ....G....... 513 321-9177
Cincinnati (G-4592)
William Darling Company Inc ....G....... 614 878-0085
Columbus (G-7764)

WMI Group LLC ....F....... 330 535-8848
Akron (G-474)
World Automtn Measurement Tech ......F....... 216 651-1883
Cleveland (G-6478)
◆ Worldwide Machine Tool LLC ....G....... 614 496-9414
Lewis Center (G-11928)
Wright Buffing Wheel Company ....G....... 330 424-7887
Lisbon (G-12136)
X-Press Tool Inc ....E....... 330 225-8748
Brunswick (G-2271)

3546 Power Hand Tools

Air Tool Service Company ....F....... 440 701-1021
Mentor (G-13513)
Aircraft Dynamics Corporation ....F....... 419 331-0371
Elida (G-9350)
Airmachinescom Inc ....G....... 330 759-1620
Youngstown (G-21019)
Alvords Yard & Garden Eqp ....G....... 440 286-2315
Chardon (G-3140)
Apex Tool Group LLC ....G....... 937 222-7871
Dayton (G-8160)
Black & Decker (us) Inc ....G....... 513 772-3111
Cincinnati (G-3452)
Black & Decker (us) Inc ....G....... 614 895-3112
Columbus (G-6837)
Black & Decker Corporation ....E....... 440 842-9100
Cleveland (G-4913)
▼ Campbell Hausfeld LLC ....C....... 513 367-4811
Harrison (G-10770)
Corbett R Caudill Chipping Inc ....F....... 740 596-5984
Hamden (G-10656)
▼ Furukawa Rock Drill USA Co Ltd.....E....... 330 673-5826
Kent (G-11462)
Galaxy Products Inc ....G....... 419 843-7337
Sylvania (G-18107)
◆ Gougler Industries Inc ....F....... 330 673-5826
Kent (G-11463)
Hall-Toledo Inc ....F....... 419 893-4334
Maumee (G-13263)
Huron Cement Products Company ......F....... 419 433-4161
Huron (G-11224)
Ingersoll-Rand Company ....E....... 419 633-6800
Bryan (G-2306)
Michabo Inc ....G....... 419 893-4334
Maumee (G-13282)
◆ Npk Construction Equipment Inc.....D....... 440 232-7900
Bedford (G-1449)
Ohio Drill & Tool Co ....E....... 330 525-7717
Homeworth (G-11117)
Rboog Industries LLC ....G....... 330 350-0396
Brunswick (G-2252)
▲ Rex International USA Inc ....E....... 800 321-7950
Ashtabula (G-837)
◆ Ridge Tool Company ....A....... 440 323-5581
Elyria (G-9486)
Ridge Tool Manufacturing Co ....A....... 440 323-5581
Elyria (G-9488)
Selbro Inc ....F....... 419 483-9918
Bellevue (G-1558)
Senco Brands Inc ....E....... 513 388-2833
Cincinnati (G-4403)
▲ Senco Brands Inc ....D....... 513 388-2000
Cincinnati (G-3315)
▲ Sensource Global Sourcing LLC .....E....... 513 659-8283
Cincinnati (G-3317)
Sewer Rodding Equipment Co ....E....... 419 991-2065
Lima (G-12089)
Stanley Access Tech LLC ....C....... 440 461-5500
Cleveland (G-6235)
Stanley Bittinger ....G....... 740 942-4302
Cadiz (G-2422)
▲ Stanley Industrial & Auto LLC ......D....... 614 755-7000
Westerville (G-20188)
Stevens Auto Parts & Towng ....G....... 740 988-2260
Jackson (G-11325)
Suburban Manufacturing Co ....D....... 440 953-2024
Eastlake (G-9290)
Sumitomo Elc Carbide Mfg Inc ....F....... 440 354-0600
Grand River (G-10453)
Superior Pneumatic & Mfg Inc ....F....... 440 871-8780
Cleveland (G-6266)
TC Service Co ....E....... 440 954-7500
Willoughby (G-20609)
Technidrill Systems Inc ....E....... 330 678-9980
Kent (G-11536)
Triad Capital Aat LLC ....G....... 440 236-4163
Columbia Station (G-6603)
Uhrichsville Carbide Inc ....F....... 740 922-9197
Uhrichsville (G-19064)

White Industrial Tool Inc ....F 330 773-6889
Akron (G-471)

Wolf Machine Company ....E 513 791-5194
Blue Ash (G-1897)

◆ Wyeth-Scott Company ....G 740 345-4528
Newark (G-15066)

X-Press Tool Inc ....E 330 225-8748
Brunswick (G-2271)

◆ Zagar Inc ....E 216 731-0500
Cleveland (G-6490)

3547 Rolling Mill Machinery & Eqpt

▲ Addisonmckee Inc ....C 513 228-7000
Lebanon (G-11774)

ADS Machinery Corp ....D 330 399-3601
Warren (G-19515)

Atkore Plastic Pipe Corp ....D 330 627-8002
Carrollton (G-2952)

▲ Bardons & Oliver Inc ....C 440 498-5800
Solon (G-17264)

Bendco Machine & Tool Co Inc ....F 419 628-3802
Minster (G-14350)

▲ Circle Machine Rolls Inc ....E 330 938-9010
Sebring (G-17044)

◆ E R Advanced Ceramics Inc ....E 330 426-9433
East Palestine (G-9237)

Element Machinery LLC ....G 855 447-7648
Toledo (G-18454)

▲ Enprotech Industrial Tech LLC ......C 216 883-3220
Cleveland (G-5283)

◆ Fives Bronx Inc ....D 330 277-1366
North Canton (G-15231)

Formtek Inc ....D 216 292-6300
Cleveland (G-5371)

▲ Formtek Inc ....D 216 292-4460
Cleveland (G-5372)

▲ Foseco Inc ....G 440 826-4548
Cleveland (G-5374)

▼ George A Mitchell Company ....E 330 758-5777
Youngstown (G-21099)

▲ Graebener Group Tech Ltd ....G 419 591-7033
Napoleon (G-14679)

Grinding Equipment & McHy LLC ......F 330 747-2313
Youngstown (G-21105)

H P E Inc ....F 330 833-3161
Massillon (G-13145)

Hydranamics Inc ....D 419 468-3530
Galion (G-10275)

J Horst Manufacturing Co ....D 330 828-2216
Dalton (G-8072)

▲ Kottler Metal Products Co Inc ......E 440 946-7473
Willoughby (G-20523)

▲ Leadar Roll Inc ....E 419 227-2200
Lima (G-12037)

Multi Galvanizing LLC ....G 330 453-1441
Canton (G-2784)

North Coast Profile Inc ....G 330 823-7777
Alliance (G-531)

◆ Park Corporation ....B 216 267-4870
Cleveland (G-5965)

Perfecto Industries Inc ....E 937 778-1900
Piqua (G-16299)

Pines Manufacturing Inc ....E 440 835-5553
Westlake (G-20294)

▲ Pines Manufacturing Inc ....E 440 835-5553
Westlake (G-20293)

Pipeline Automation Syste Inc ......F 419 462-8833
Galion (G-10282)

Rafter Equipment Corporation ....E 440 572-3700
Strongsville (G-17956)

◆ Ridge Tool Company ....A 440 323-5581
Elyria (G-9486)

Ridge Tool Manufacturing Co ....A 440 323-5581
Elyria (G-9488)

Rki Inc ....C 888 953-9400
Mentor (G-13715)

Sentek Corporation ....G 614 586-1123
Columbus (G-7608)

Steel Eqp Specialists Inc ....E 330 829-2626
Alliance (G-539)

▲ Steel Eqp Specialists Inc ....E 330 823-8260
Alliance (G-540)

Sticker Corporation ....F 440 946-2100
Willoughby (G-20606)

Turner Machine Co ....F 330 332-5821
Salem (G-16932)

◆ United Rolls Inc ....C 330 456-2761
Canton (G-2888)

◆ Warren Fabricating Corporation ....D 330 847-0596
Warren (G-19621)

▲ Wauseon Machine & Mfg Inc ....D 419 337-0940
Wauseon (G-19700)

◆ Xtek Inc ....B 513 733-7800
Cincinnati (G-4616)

3548 Welding Apparatus

Accurate Machining & Welding ......G 937 584-4518
Sabina (G-16772)

Accurate Manufacturing Company ....E 614 878-6510
Columbus (G-6685)

Aerowave Inc ....G 440 731-8464
North Ridgeville (G-15355)

Airgas ....G 330 345-1257
Wooster (G-20732)

AK Fabrication Inc ....F 330 458-1037
Canton (G-2595)

American Weldquip Inc ....F 330 239-0317
Sharon Center (G-17100)

Buckeye State Welding & Fabg ....E 440 322-0344
Elyria (G-9385)

▼ Campbell Hausfeld LLC ....C 513 367-4811
Harrison (G-10770)

Dennis Corso Co Inc ....G 330 673-2411
Kent (G-11448)

Fanuc America Corporation ....E 513 754-2400
Mason (G-13020)

Firelands Manufacturing LLC ....F 419 687-8237
Plymouth (G-16376)

Fusion Automation Inc ....G 440 602-5595
Willoughby (G-20493)

Fusion Incorporated ....E 440 946-3300
Willoughby (G-20495)

Halls Welding & Supplies Inc ....G 330 385-9353
East Liverpool (G-9217)

◆ Hobart Brothers Company ....A 937 332-5439
Troy (G-18836)

Hobart Brothers Company ....A 937 773-5869
Piqua (G-16276)

Hobart Brothers Company ....G 937 332-5338
Troy (G-18837)

Hobart Brothers Company ....G 937 332-5023
Troy (G-18838)

Imax Industries Inc ....F 440 639-0242
Painesville (G-15889)

J T E Corp ....G 937 454-1112
Dayton (G-8418)

▲ Lima Equipment Co ....G 419 222-4181
Lima (G-12040)

◆ Lincoln Electric Company ....A 216 481-8100
Euclid (G-9589)

Lincoln Electric Company ....E 216 481-8100
Cleveland (G-5697)

Lincoln Electric Holdings Inc ....C 216 481-8100
Cleveland (G-5698)

Lincoln Electric Holdings Inc ....A 440 255-7696
Mentor (G-13634)

▲ Lincoln Electric Intl Holdg Co ......E 216 481-8100
Euclid (G-9590)

▲ Luvata Ohio Inc ....D 740 363-1981
Delaware (G-8870)

M B Industries Inc ....A 419 738-4769
Wapakoneta (G-19496)

▲ Midwest Fasteners Inc ....D 937 866-0463
Miamisburg (G-13835)

◆ Miller Weldmaster Corporation .....D 330 833-6739
Navarre (G-14719)

◆ Nelson Stud Welding Inc ....B 440 329-0400
Elyria (G-9467)

O E Meyer Co ....G 419 332-6931
Fremont (G-10171)

Otto Konigslow Mfg Co ....F 216 851-7900
Cleveland (G-5952)

Owen & Sons ....G 513 726-5406
Seven Mile (G-17066)

Peco Holdings Corp ....F 937 667-4451
Tipp City (G-18292)

▲ Polymet Corporation ....E 513 874-3586
West Chester (G-20038)

▲ Postle Industries Inc ....E 216 265-9000
Cleveland (G-6022)

Process Development Corp ....E 937 890-3388
Dayton (G-8597)

▲ Process Equipment Co Tipp City ....D 937 667-7105
Tipp City (G-18294)

▼ Production Products Inc ....D 419 659-2978
Columbus Grove (G-7797)

PWS Welding & Mtg ....F 330 385-6922
East Liverpool (G-9226)

Quality Components Inc ....F 440 255-0606
Mentor (G-13706)

Retek Inc ....G 440 937-6282
Avon (G-1008)

▼ Rexarc International Inc ....E 937 839-4604
West Alexandria (G-19781)

◆ Select-Arc Inc ....C 937 295-5215
Fort Loramie (G-9938)

▲ Semtorq Inc ....F 330 487-0600
Twinsburg (G-19019)

Sherbrooke Metals ....E 440 942-3520
Willoughby (G-20596)

Spiegelberg Manufacturing Inc ......E 440 324-3042
Strongsville (G-17970)

Stryver Mfg Inc ....E 937 854-3048
Trotwood (G-18799)

▼ Taylor - Winfield Corporation ......D 330 259-8500
Hubbard (G-11140)

Taylor-Winfield Tech Inc ....E 330 259-8500
Youngstown (G-21218)

Tech-Sonic Inc ....F 614 792-3117
Columbus (G-7683)

▲ Techalloy Inc ....E 410 633-9300
Euclid (G-9609)

Tokin America Corporation ....G 513 644-9743
West Chester (G-19959)

Weld-Action Company Inc ....G 330 372-1063
Warren (G-19626)

▲ Weldparts Inc ....F 513 530-0064
Blue Ash (G-1892)

Westside Supply Co Inc ....G 216 267-9353
Brookpark (G-2172)

Wiederhold Wldg & Fabrication ......G 513 875-3755
Fayetteville (G-9785)

Wonder Weld Inc ....G 614 875-1447
Orient (G-15726)

3549 Metalworking Machinery, NEC

Added Edge Assembly Inc ....F 216 464-4305
Cleveland (G-4703)

▲ Addisonmckee Inc ....C 513 228-7000
Lebanon (G-11774)

ADS Machinery Corp ....D 330 399-3601
Warren (G-19515)

Advance Manufacturing Corp ....E 216 333-1684
Cleveland (G-4708)

▲ Arku Coil-Systems Inc ....E 513 985-0500
Blue Ash (G-1745)

Armature Coil Equipment Inc ....E 216 267-6366
Cleveland (G-4831)

Automated Machinery Solutions ......F 419 727-1772
Toledo (G-18359)

▲ Automatic Feed Co ....D 419 592-0050
Napoleon (G-14671)

▲ Bardons & Oliver Inc ....C 440 498-5800
Solon (G-17264)

▲ Barth Industries Co LP ....D 216 267-0531
Cleveland (G-4893)

Berran Industrial Group Inc ....E 330 253-5800
Akron (G-89)

Binns Machinery Company ....G 513 242-3388
Cincinnati (G-3449)

Bison USA Corp ....G 513 713-0513
West Chester (G-19818)

Brilex Industries Inc ....G 330 744-1114
Youngstown (G-21036)

▲ Brilex Industries Inc ....C 330 744-1114
Youngstown (G-21037)

▲ CA Litzler Co Inc ....E 216 267-8020
Cleveland (G-4958)

▲ Cammann Inc ....F 440 965-4051
Birmingham (G-1685)

Cauffiel Corporation ....G 419 843-7262
Toledo (G-18390)

Coating Control Inc ....G 330 453-9136
Canton (G-2663)

Combined Tech Group Inc ....E 937 274-4866
Dayton (G-8237)

Ctm Integration Incorporated ....E 330 332-1800
Salem (G-16887)

Dallas Design & Technology Inc ......G 419 884-9750
Mansfield (G-12592)

Dango & Dienenthal Inc ....G 330 829-0277
Alliance (G-504)

Design Technologies & Mfg Co ....F 937 335-0757
Troy (G-18818)

Econ-O-Machine Products Inc ....E 937 882-6307
Donnelsville (G-8961)

Elite Mfg Solutions LLC ....G 330 612-7434
Macedonia (G-12447)

EZ Grout Corporation Inc ....E 740 962-2024
Malta (G-12536)

F L Enterprises ....G...... 216 898-5551
  Cleveland (G-5317)
Fabriweld Corporation ....G...... 419 668-3358
  Norwalk (G-15539)
Filmtec Inc ....E...... 419 435-1819
  Fostoria (G-9972)
Flexomation LLC ....F...... 513 825-0555
  Cincinnati (G-3759)
Fmt Repair Service Co ....G...... 330 347-7374
  Mentor (G-13579)
▲ Formtek Inc ....D...... 216 292-4460
  Cleveland (G-5372)
Forrest Machine Pdts Co Ltd ....E...... 419 589-3774
  Mansfield (G-12607)
Ged Holdings Inc ....C...... 330 963-5401
  Twinsburg (G-18941)
Gem City Engineering Co ....C...... 937 223-5544
  Dayton (G-8361)
Generic Systems Inc ....F...... 419 841-8460
  Holland (G-11062)
Gilson Machine & Tool Co Inc ....E...... 419 592-2911
  Napoleon (G-14678)
▲ Glunt Industries Inc ....C...... 330 399-7585
  Warren (G-19555)
▲ Guild International Inc ....E...... 440 232-5887
  Bedford (G-1426)
Hahn Manufacturing Company ....G...... 216 391-9300
  Cleveland (G-5472)
Heisler Tool Company ....F...... 440 951-2424
  Willoughby (G-20503)
Holdren Brothers Inc ....F...... 937 465-7050
  West Liberty (G-20092)
Hoppel Fabrication Specialties ....F...... 330 823-5700
  Louisville (G-12315)
▼ Hunter Defense Tech Inc ....E...... 216 438-6111
  Solon (G-17312)
I C Consultants Inc ....F...... 216 731-9992
  Cleveland (G-5545)
J Horst Manufacturing Co ....D...... 330 828-2216
  Dalton (G-8072)
▲ Kalt Manufacturing Company ....D...... 440 327-2102
  North Ridgeville (G-15384)
Kay Capital Company ....G...... 216 531-1010
  Cleveland (G-5638)
Kenley Enterprises LLC ....E...... 419 630-0921
  Bryan (G-2308)
▲ Kent Corporation ....E...... 440 582-3400
  North Royalton (G-15430)
Kilroy Company ....D...... 440 951-8700
  Eastlake (G-9278)
▲ Louis Leasing LLC ....E...... 440 243-3810
  Medina (G-13436)
Manufctring Sltons Brbrton Inc ....G...... 330 745-4539
  Barberton (G-1128)
Master Marking Company Inc ....F...... 330 688-6797
  Stow (G-17772)
Mathew Odonnell ....G...... 440 969-4054
  Andover (G-618)
Midwest Laser Systems Inc ....E...... 419 424-0062
  Findlay (G-9861)
◆ Milacron LLC ....E...... 513 487-5000
  Blue Ash (G-1842)
Motion Industries Inc ....F...... 419 224-1988
  Lima (G-12060)
Nova Industrial Machine Co ....E...... 419 535-0800
  Whitehouse (G-20342)
▲ Oma USA Inc ....G...... 330 487-0602
  Twinsburg (G-18991)
Omega Automation Inc ....D...... 937 890-2350
  Dayton (G-8548)
Omega International Inc ....E...... 937 890-2350
  Dayton (G-8549)
Peco Holdings Corp ....F...... 937 667-4451
  Tipp City (G-18292)
Perfecto Industries Inc ....E...... 937 778-1900
  Piqua (G-16299)
▲ Pines Manufacturing Inc ....E...... 440 835-5553
  Westlake (G-20293)
▲ Pipe Coil Technology Inc ....F...... 330 256-6070
  Burbank (G-2367)
▲ Portage Machine Concepts Inc ......F...... 330 628-2343
  Akron (G-344)
Pre-Melt Systems Inc ....F...... 330 818-8088
  Canton (G-2819)
Precision Cnc LLC ....E...... 740 689-9009
  Lancaster (G-11740)
Precision Metal Products Inc ....F...... 216 447-1900
  Cleveland (G-6036)
▲ Process Equipment Co Tipp City ....D...... 937 667-7105
  Tipp City (G-18294)

Rafter Equipment Corporation ....E...... 440 572-3700
  Strongsville (G-17956)
Richard A Limbacher ....G...... 330 897-4515
  Stone Creek (G-17726)
Riverside Mch & Automtn Inc ....G...... 419 855-8308
  Walbridge (G-19463)
Riverside Mch & Automtn Inc ....D...... 419 855-8308
  Genoa (G-10363)
Scott Systems International ....G...... 740 383-8383
  Marion (G-12898)
▲ Semtorq Inc ....F...... 330 487-0600
  Twinsburg (G-19019)
Shadetree Machine ....G...... 513 727-8771
  Middletown (G-14082)
Simon De Young Corporation ....G...... 440 834-3000
  Middlefield (G-13991)
Sir Steak Machinery Inc ....E...... 419 526-9181
  Mansfield (G-12678)
South Shore Controls Inc ....E...... 440 259-2500
  Perry (G-16058)
Stainless Automation ....G...... 216 961-4550
  Cleveland (G-6232)
Standard Car Truck Company ....D...... 740 775-6450
  Chillicothe (G-3276)
Stein Inc ....D...... 216 883-7444
  Cleveland (G-6249)
Steinbarger Precision Cnc Inc ....G...... 937 376-0322
  Xenia (G-20975)
Sticker Corporation ....E...... 440 946-2100
  Willoughby (G-20606)
Tdm LLC ....G...... 440 969-1442
  Ashtabula (G-840)
Todd Industries Inc ....E...... 440 439-2900
  Cleveland (G-6330)
Tri-Mac Mfg & Svcs Co ....F...... 513 896-4445
  Hamilton (G-10749)
Universal Precision Products ....E...... 330 633-6128
  Akron (G-457)

3552 Textile Machinery

Alley Cat Designs Inc ....G...... 937 885-7950
  Dayton (G-8145)
American Precision Spindles ....G...... 267 436-6000
  Cleveland (G-4792)
▲ Barudan America Inc ....F...... 440 248-8770
  Solon (G-17265)
▲ CA Litzler Co Inc ....E...... 216 267-8020
  Cleveland (G-4958)
Impact Sports Wear Inc ....E...... 513 922-7406
  North Bend (G-15205)
Karg Corporation ....F...... 330 633-4916
  Tallmadge (G-18149)
Knitting Machinery Corp ....G...... 216 851-9900
  Cleveland (G-5661)
Knitting Machinery Corp ....F...... 937 548-2338
  Greenville (G-10509)
Leesburg Looms Incorporated ....G...... 419 238-2738
  Van Wert (G-19263)
▲ Oma USA Inc ....G...... 330 487-0602
  Twinsburg (G-18991)
Professional Grinding Inc ....G...... 330 628-3001
  Akron (G-353)
Protofab Manufacturing Inc ....G...... 937 849-4983
  Medway (G-13501)
R Sportswear LLC ....G...... 937 748-3507
  Springboro (G-17504)
Randy Gray ....G...... 513 533-3200
  Cincinnati (G-4330)
Schilling Graphics Inc ....E...... 419 468-1037
  Galion (G-10286)
Simon De Young Corporation ....G...... 440 834-3000
  Middlefield (G-13991)
Solid Light Company Inc ....E...... 740 548-1219
  Lewis Center (G-11920)
Truck Stop Embroidery ....G...... 419 257-2860
  North Baltimore (G-15199)
Wayne Sporting Goods ....G...... 937 236-6665
  Dayton (G-8748)
Wolf Machine Company ....E...... 513 791-5194
  Blue Ash (G-1897)
Xpressions LLC ....G...... 330 898-8591
  Warren (G-19627)

3553 Woodworking Machinery

Bent Wood Solutions LLC ....G...... 330 674-1454
  Millersburg (G-14199)
Boko Patterns Models & Molds ....G...... 937 426-9667
  Beavercreek (G-1371)
Closettec of North East Ohio ....G...... 216 464-0042
  Bedford (G-1416)

Coe Manufacturing Company ....D...... 440 352-9381
  Painesville (G-15865)
▲ Dayton Hawker Corporation ....F...... 937 293-8147
  Dayton (G-8276)
General Intl Pwr Pdts LLC ....G...... 419 877-5234
  Whitehouse (G-20340)
ITR Manufacturing LLC ....F...... 419 852-8574
  Saint Henry (G-16819)
McFeelys Inc ....F...... 800 443-7937
  Harrison (G-10790)
Midwest Timber & Land Co Inc ....E...... 740 493-2400
  Piketon (G-16224)
Northcoast Woodcraft Inc ....G...... 330 677-1189
  Kent (G-11497)
▲ Rlfshop LLC ....G...... 937 898-6070
  Dayton (G-8634)
Seilkop Industries Inc ....E...... 513 761-1035
  Cincinnati (G-4398)
Senco Holdings Inc ....G...... 800 543-4596
  Cincinnati (G-3316)
Trico Enterprises LLC ....E...... 330 674-1157
  Millersburg (G-14272)
Trico Enterprises LLC ....G...... 330 674-1157
  Millersburg (G-14273)

3554 Paper Inds Machinery

Aleris Recycling Inc ....G...... 216 910-3400
  Beachwood (G-1254)
▲ Baumfolder Corporation ....D...... 937 492-1281
  Sidney (G-17169)
▲ Coater Services Inc ....E...... 330 499-1407
  Canton (G-2662)
Comco Machinery Inc ....C...... 513 248-8000
  Milford (G-14132)
Custom Threading Systems LLC ....G...... 937 846-1405
  New Carlisle (G-14799)
Elite Mill Service & Cnstr ....E...... 513 422-4234
  Trenton (G-18790)
▲ Fluid Quip Inc ....E...... 937 324-0352
  Springfield (G-17561)
▲ French Oil Mill Machinery Co ....D...... 937 773-3420
  Piqua (G-16266)
G Fordyce Co ....G...... 937 393-3241
  Hillsboro (G-10998)
Grandon Mfg Co Inc ....G...... 614 294-2694
  Columbus (G-7128)
▲ J E Doyle Company ....E...... 330 564-0743
  Norton (G-15515)
▲ Kadant Black Clawson Inc ....D...... 513 229-8100
  Mason (G-13052)
L B Folding Co Inc ....G...... 216 961-0888
  Cleveland (G-5670)
Loroco Industries Inc ....E...... 513 554-0356
  Cincinnati (G-4033)
▼ Magna Machine Co ....C...... 513 851-6900
  Cincinnati (G-4052)
Mc Kinley Machinery Inc ....E...... 440 937-6300
  Avon (G-1000)
▲ Miami Machine Corporation ....F...... 513 863-6707
  Overpeck (G-15832)
▼ Mtr Martco LLC ....D...... 513 424-5307
  Middletown (G-14065)
National Oilwell Varco LP ....E...... 937 454-3200
  Dayton (G-8520)
◆ Nilpeter Usa Inc ....C...... 513 489-4400
  Cincinnati (G-4156)
Pearce Inc ....F...... 216 252-0550
  Cleveland (G-5986)
▲ Press Technology & Mfg Inc ....G...... 937 327-0755
  Springfield (G-17631)
Rebiltco Inc ....G...... 513 424-2024
  Middletown (G-14081)
Rumford Paper Company ....G...... 937 242-9230
  Miamisburg (G-13856)
Sso Inc ....F...... 440 235-3500
  Olmsted Twp (G-15683)
Tri-Mac Mfg & Svcs Co ....F...... 513 896-4445
  Hamilton (G-10749)
Universal Precision Products ....E...... 330 633-6128
  Akron (G-457)
Vail Rubber Works Inc ....F...... 513 705-2060
  Middletown (G-14093)

3555 Printing Trades Machinery & Eqpt

1st Choice Web Solution Inc ....G...... 330 503-1591
  Youngstown (G-21008)
A/C Laser Technologies Inc ....F...... 330 784-3355
  Akron (G-23)
Advanced Web Corporation ....G...... 740 662-6323
  Stewart (G-17721)

S I C

Aleris Ohio Management Inc ....F 216 910-3400
  Cleveland *(G-4747)*
Allen Green Enterprises LLC ....G 330 339-0200
  New Philadelphia *(G-14883)*
Anderson & Vreeland Inc ....D 419 636-5002
  Bryan *(G-2278)*
▼ Boggs Graphic Equipment LLC ....G 440 564-9675
  Maple Heights *(G-12728)*
Capital Track Company Inc ....G 614 595-5088
  Columbus *(G-6902)*
Comco Machinery Inc ....C 513 248-8000
  Milford *(G-14132)*
Commonwealth Aluminum Mtls LLC ....G 216 910-3400
  Beachwood *(G-1263)*
▲ Desco Equipment Corp ....E 330 405-1581
  Twinsburg *(G-18923)*
E C Shaw Co ....E 513 721-6334
  Cincinnati *(G-3677)*
▲ Flexodie ....G 513 489-0433
  Middletown *(G-14042)*
Flexoplate Inc ....E 513 489-0433
  Blue Ash *(G-1796)*
Flexotech Graphics Inc ....F 330 929-4743
  Stow *(G-17754)*
FT Group Inc ....E 937 746-6439
  Cincinnati *(G-3786)*
Gedico International Inc ....G 937 274-2167
  Dayton *(G-8360)*
▲ Gew Inc ....G 440 237-4439
  Cleveland *(G-5427)*
Graphic Systems Services Inc ....E 937 746-0708
  Springboro *(G-17482)*
Great Lakes Graphics Inc ....E 216 391-0077
  Cleveland *(G-5450)*
Hadronics Inc ....D 513 321-9350
  Cincinnati *(G-3861)*
Hays Fabricating & Welding ....E 937 325-0031
  Springfield *(G-17568)*
Hotend Works Inc ....G 440 787-3181
  Grafton *(G-10430)*
Incorporated Trustees Gospel W ....D 216 749-1428
  Cleveland *(G-5561)*
▲ Kase Equipment ....D 216 642-9040
  Cleveland *(G-5634)*
Key Blue Prints Inc ....G 614 899-6180
  Columbus *(G-7259)*
Klebaum Machinery Inc ....G 330 455-2046
  Canton *(G-2753)*
Lyle Printing & Publishing Co ....F 330 337-7172
  Salem *(G-16910)*
Moments To Remember USA LLC ......G 330 830-0839
  Massillon *(G-13181)*
◆ Nilpeter Usa Inc ....C 513 489-4400
  Cincinnati *(G-4156)*
Ohio Graphic Supply Inc ....G 937 433-7537
  Dayton *(G-8543)*
Pearce Inc ....F 216 252-0550
  Cleveland *(G-5986)*
▲ R & D Equipment Inc ....F 419 668-8439
  Norwalk *(G-15561)*
Resource Graphics ....G 513 205-2686
  Cincinnati *(G-4339)*
Roconex Corporation ....F 937 339-2616
  Troy *(G-18868)*
Roessner Holdings Inc ....G 419 356-2123
  Fort Recovery *(G-9958)*
Rotation Dynamics Corporation ....F 937 746-4069
  Franklin *(G-10051)*
Schilling Graphics Inc ....E 419 468-1037
  Galion *(G-10286)*
Springfield Engraving Company ....G 937 390-0011
  Springfield *(G-17651)*
Suspension Feeder Corporation ....F 419 763-1377
  Fort Recovery *(G-9960)*
▲ Tinker Omega Manufacturing LLC ...E 937 322-2272
  Springfield *(G-17664)*
Tykma Inc ....E 877 318-9562
  Chillicothe *(G-3283)*
◆ Wood Graphics Inc ....E 513 771-6300
  Cincinnati *(G-4603)*

3556 Food Prdts Machinery

5 Axis Grinding Inc ....G 937 312-9797
  Dayton *(G-8124)*
Abj Equipfix ....E 419 684-5236
  Castalia *(G-2972)*
Acreo Inc ....G 513 734-3327
  Amelia *(G-565)*
▼ Anderson International Corp ....D 216 641-1112
  Stow *(G-17730)*

Armour-Eckrich Meats LLC ....G 614 539-9600
  Grove City *(G-10544)*
Ashco ....G 330 385-2400
  East Liverpool *(G-9203)*
Avure Technologies Inc ....D 513 433-2500
  Middletown *(G-14022)*
Big Drum Usa Ltd ....G 614 626-0843
  Columbus *(G-6827)*
◆ Biro Manufacturing Company ....D 419 798-4451
  Lakeside Marblehead *(G-11647)*
C M Slicechief Co ....G 419 241-7647
  Toledo *(G-18386)*
Christy Machine Company ....F 419 332-6451
  Fremont *(G-10137)*
▼ Cleveland Gas Systems LLC ....G 216 391-7780
  Streetsboro *(G-17844)*
▲ Cleveland Range LLC ....G 216 481-4900
  Cleveland *(G-5074)*
▲ Cleveland Range LLC ....G 216 481-4900
  Cleveland *(G-5075)*
Country Freezer Units LLC ....G 740 623-8658
  Baltic *(G-1067)*
▲ Crescent Metal Products Inc ....C 440 350-1100
  Mentor *(G-13555)*
E S Industries Inc ....E 419 643-2625
  Lima *(G-12008)*
Ford Piping and Brewry Svc LLC ......G 614 284-2409
  Columbus *(G-7092)*
Fred D Pfening Company ....G 614 294-5361
  Columbus *(G-7100)*
Fred D Pfening Company ....E 614 294-5361
  Columbus *(G-7099)*
▲ French Oil Mill Machinery Co ....D 937 773-3420
  Piqua *(G-16266)*
Frost Engineering Inc ....E 513 541-6330
  Cincinnati *(G-3785)*
G F Frank and Sons Inc ....F 513 870-9075
  West Chester *(G-19871)*
▲ Harry C Lobalzo & Sons Inc ....E 330 666-6758
  Akron *(G-216)*
Hawthorne-Seving Inc ....G 419 643-5531
  Cridersville *(G-7945)*
Hobart Corporation ....E 937 332-3000
  Troy *(G-18840)*
Hobart Corporation ....C 937 332-2797
  Piqua *(G-16277)*
Hobart International Holdings ....G 937 332-3000
  Troy *(G-18842)*
Home City Ice ....G 859 441-1700
  Aberdeen *(G-1)*
Innovative Controls Corp ....D 419 691-6684
  Toledo *(G-18524)*
ITW Food Equipment Group LLC ....G 937 332-3000
  Troy *(G-18847)*
◆ ITW Food Equipment Group LLC .....A 937 332-2396
  Troy *(G-18848)*
◆ JE Grote Company Inc ....G 614 868-8414
  Columbus *(G-7229)*
John Bean Technologies Corp ....E 419 627-4349
  Sandusky *(G-16975)*
Kasel Engineering LLC ....G 937 854-8875
  Trotwood *(G-18798)*
Kraft Heinz Foods Company ....E 419 332-7357
  Fremont *(G-10162)*
▲ Lem Products Holding LLC ....E 513 202-1188
  West Chester *(G-19892)*
Lima Sheet Metal Machine & Mfg ......E 419 229-1161
  Lima *(G-12045)*
◆ Lincoln Foodservice Pdts LLC ....E 260 459-8200
  Cleveland *(G-5699)*
Listermann Mfg Co Inc ....G 513 731-1130
  Cincinnati *(G-4027)*
▼ Magna Machine Co ....C 513 851-6900
  Cincinnati *(G-4052)*
Maverick Corp Partners LLC ....G 330 669-2631
  Smithville *(G-17241)*
▲ Maverick Innvtive Slutions LLC ......E 419 281-7944
  Ashland *(G-751)*
◆ Meyer Company ....C 216 587-3400
  Cleveland *(G-5793)*
Mojonnier Usa LLC ....G 844 665-6664
  Streetsboro *(G-17864)*
◆ N Wasserstrom & Sons Inc ....G 614 228-5550
  Columbus *(G-7377)*
National Oilwell Varco LP ....E 937 454-3200
  Dayton *(G-8520)*
◆ Nemco Food Equipment Ltd ....D 419 542-7751
  Hicksville *(G-10904)*
▼ Norse Dairy Systems LP ....B 614 421-5297
  Columbus *(G-7398)*

Omar Associates LLC ....G 419 426-0610
  Attica *(G-894)*
◆ Peerless Foods Inc ....C 937 492-4158
  Sidney *(G-17207)*
Piece of Cake ....G 614 421-0399
  Columbus *(G-7485)*
Premier Industries Inc ....E 513 271-2550
  Cincinnati *(G-4266)*
◆ Prime Equipment Group Inc ....D 614 253-8590
  Columbus *(G-7517)*
R and J Corporation ....E 440 871-6009
  Westlake *(G-20299)*
Railroad Brewing Company ....G 440 723-8234
  Avon *(G-1006)*
Richard B Linneman ....G 513 922-5537
  Cincinnati *(G-4342)*
Royalton Food Service Eqp Co ....E 440 237-0806
  North Royalton *(G-15448)*
RS Industries Inc ....G 216 524-2998
  Brooklyn Heights *(G-2146)*
Sarka Bros Machining Inc ....G 419 532-2393
  Kalida *(G-11417)*
▲ Security Systems Eqp Corp ....G 513 758-1070
  Cincinnati *(G-4396)*
▼ Shaffer Manufacturing Corp ....E 937 652-2151
  Urbana *(G-19180)*
▼ Sidney Manufacturing Company ....G 937 492-4154
  Sidney *(G-17227)*
▲ Tomlinson Industries Co ....C 216 332-1595
  Cleveland *(G-6332)*
Tpsc Inc ....F 440 439-9320
  Bedford Heights *(G-1495)*
Wolf Machine Company ....E 513 791-5194
  Blue Ash *(G-1897)*

3559 Special Ind Machinery, NEC

A & M Kiln Dry Ltd ....G 330 473-8634
  Millersburg *(G-14188)*
A & M Kiln Dry Ltd ....F 330 852-0505
  Dundee *(G-9170)*
Acb Three Inc ....G 614 873-4680
  Plain City *(G-16317)*
Affinity Information Managemet ....G 419 517-2055
  Sylvania *(G-18098)*
Agmet Metals Inc ....E 440 439-7400
  Oakwood Village *(G-15621)*
Alstart Enterprises LLC ....F 330 533-3222
  Canfield *(G-2547)*
Altera Corporation ....G 330 650-5200
  Hudson *(G-11155)*
Amano Cincinnati Incorporated ....D 513 697-9000
  Loveland *(G-12338)*
American Manufacturing & Eqp ....E 513 829-2248
  Fairfield *(G-9642)*
▲ American Plastic Tech Inc ....D 440 632-5203
  Middlefield *(G-13914)*
▼ Anderson International Corp ....D 216 641-1112
  Stow *(G-17730)*
Aot Inc ....E 937 323-9669
  Springfield *(G-17517)*
Aquila Pharmatech LLC ....G 419 386-2527
  Waterville *(G-19652)*
ARS Recycling Systems LLC ....F 330 536-8210
  Lowellville *(G-12405)*
Auto-Tap Inc ....E 216 671-1043
  Cleveland *(G-4864)*
Automated Mfg Solutions Inc ....G 440 878-3711
  Strongsville *(G-17893)*
Autotool Inc ....E 614 733-0222
  Plain City *(G-16322)*
Beam Machines Inc ....G 513 745-4510
  Blue Ash *(G-1747)*
Bethel Engineering and Eqp Inc ....E 419 568-1100
  New Hampshire *(G-14833)*
Bethel Engineering and Eqp Inc ....E 419 568-7976
  New Hampshire *(G-14834)*
Bradford Neal Machinery Inc ....G 440 632-1393
  Middlefield *(G-13918)*
Broco Products Inc ....G 216 531-0880
  Cleveland *(G-4933)*
▲ Buddy Backyard Inc ....E 330 393-9353
  Warren *(G-19532)*
Budget Molders Supply Inc ....E 216 367-7050
  Macedonia *(G-12439)*
Burton Metal Finishing Inc ....E 614 252-9523
  Columbus *(G-6876)*
CAM-Lem Inc ....G 216 391-7750
  Cleveland *(G-4963)*
▲ Cammann Inc ....F 440 965-4051
  Birmingham *(G-1685)*

Camton Mechanical Inc ... G ... 614 864-7620
Columbus *(G-6892)*
Cantrell Rfinery Sls Trnsp Inc ... F ... 937 695-0318
Winchester *(G-20691)*
Cbg Biotech Ltd Co ... E ... 440 786-7667
Bedford *(G-1413)*
Chardon Plastics Machinery ... G ... 440 564-5360
Chardon *(G-3145)*
Chart Industries Inc ... E ... 440 753-1490
Cleveland *(G-5020)*
Chart International Inc ... D ... 440 753-1490
Cleveland *(G-5021)*
City of Cleveland ... G ... 216 664-2711
Cleveland *(G-5036)*
Cohesant Inc ... E ... 216 910-1700
Beachwood *(G-1262)*
◆ Cold Jet LLC ... D ... 513 831-3211
Loveland *(G-12346)*
Component Mfg & Design ... F ... 330 225-8080
Brunswick *(G-2218)*
Conforming Matrix Corporation ... E ... 419 729-3777
Toledo *(G-18409)*
Continental Turf Systems Inc ... G ... 419 596-4409
Continental *(G-7825)*
Conviber Inc ... F ... 330 723-6006
Medina *(G-13393)*
Corrotec Inc ... E ... 937 325-3585
Springfield *(G-17536)*
Crowne Group LLC ... D ... 216 589-0198
Cleveland *(G-5143)*
Customers Car Care Center ... G ... 419 841-6646
Toledo *(G-18419)*
Day-TEC Tool & Mfg Inc ... F ... 937 847-0022
Miamisburg *(G-13797)*
Decision Systems Inc ... E ... 330 456-7600
Canton *(G-2682)*
▲ Dengensha America Corporation ... F ... 440 439-8081
Bedford *(G-1418)*
Design Fabricators of Mantua ... G ... 330 274-5353
Mantua *(G-12709)*
Designetics Inc ... D ... 419 866-0700
Holland *(G-11054)*
Devilbiss Ransburg ... F ... 419 470-2000
Toledo *(G-18437)*
Diptech Systems Inc ... G ... 330 673-4400
Kent *(G-11449)*
Dover High Prfmce Plas Inc ... E ... 330 343-3477
Dover *(G-8980)*
▲ DRG Hydraulics Inc ... E ... 216 663-9747
Cleveland *(G-5216)*
Dura Temp Corporation ... F ... 419 866-4348
Holland *(G-11058)*
◆ Eaton Corporation ... B ... 216 523-5000
Cleveland *(G-5245)*
Eaton Corporation ... C ... 216 416-2500
Cleveland *(G-5246)*
Eaton Electrical Inc ... F ... 216 433-0616
Beachwood *(G-1269)*
▲ Eden Cryogenics LLC ... E ... 614 873-3949
Plain City *(G-16339)*
Emhart Glass Manufacturing Inc ... D ... 567 336-7733
Perrysburg *(G-16090)*
Emhart Glass Manufacturing Inc ... G ... 567 336-8784
Perrysburg *(G-16091)*
▲ Encore Plastics Corporation ... F ... 419 626-8000
Sandusky *(G-16962)*
Enerfab Inc ... G ... 513 771-2300
Cincinnati *(G-3705)*
▲ Equipment Manufacturers Intl ... E ... 216 651-6700
Cleveland *(G-5291)*
Fanuc America Corporation ... E ... 513 754-2400
Mason *(G-13020)*
Fawcett Co Inc ... G ... 330 659-4187
Richfield *(G-16623)*
File 13 Inc ... F ... 937 642-4855
Marysville *(G-12943)*
Findlay Machine & Tool Inc ... E ... 419 434-3100
Findlay *(G-9823)*
Florida Production Engrg Inc ... C ... 740 420-5252
Circleville *(G-4629)*
▲ Freeman Schwabe Machinery LLC ... E ... 513 947-2888
Batavia *(G-1188)*
Fremont Flask Co ... F ... 419 332-2231
Fremont *(G-10149)*
▲ French Oil Mill Machinery Co ... D ... 937 773-3420
Piqua *(G-16266)*
▼ Gam ... G ... 330 427-6470
Leetonia *(G-11860)*
◆ Ganzcorp Investments Inc ... D ... 330 963-5400
Twinsburg *(G-18939)*

Gary Compton ... G ... 937 339-6829
Troy *(G-18830)*
Ged Holdings Inc ... C ... 330 963-5401
Twinsburg *(G-18941)*
General Fabrications Corp ... E ... 419 625-6055
Sandusky *(G-16970)*
Girard Machine Company Inc ... E ... 330 545-9731
Girard *(G-10390)*
▼ Glenn Hunter & Associates Inc ... D ... 419 822-3744
Delta *(G-8935)*
▲ Gokoh Corporation ... F ... 937 339-4977
Troy *(G-18832)*
▼ Grasan Equipment Company Inc ... D ... 419 526-4440
Mansfield *(G-12620)*
Guild Associates Inc ... E ... 614 798-8215
Dublin *(G-9081)*
Guild Associates Inc ... G ... 843 573-0095
Dublin *(G-9082)*
▲ Haeco Inc ... F ... 513 722-1030
Loveland *(G-12356)*
Halifax Industries Inc ... G ... 216 990-8951
Hudson *(G-11177)*
Handle Light Inc ... G ... 330 772-8901
Kinsman *(G-11609)*
Heartland Group Holdings LLC ... E ... 614 441-4001
Columbus *(G-7147)*
Heil Engneered Process Eqp Inc ... F ... 440 327-6051
North Ridgeville *(G-15378)*
◆ Heintz Manufacturers Inc ... G ... 724 274-6300
Medina *(G-13420)*
▲ Herschal Products Inc ... G ... 330 659-2165
Richfield *(G-16627)*
Hess Technologies Inc ... G ... 513 228-0909
Lebanon *(G-11808)*
▲ High Temperature Systems Inc ... G ... 440 543-8271
Chagrin Falls *(G-3091)*
House Silva-Strongsville Inc ... G ... 330 464-6419
Strongsville *(G-17927)*
Hydratecs Injection Eqp Co ... G ... 330 773-0491
Akron *(G-226)*
I G Brenner Inc ... F ... 740 345-8845
Newark *(G-15022)*
I T W Automotive Finishing ... G ... 419 470-2000
Toledo *(G-18515)*
◆ Industrial Thermal Systems Inc ... F ... 513 561-2100
Cincinnati *(G-3918)*
▼ Ingredient Masters Inc ... G ... 513 231-7432
Cincinnati *(G-3920)*
Innovative Plastic Machinery ... G ... 330 478-1825
Canton *(G-2737)*
Innovative Recycling Systems ... G ... 440 498-9200
Solon *(G-17317)*
Inpower LLC ... F ... 740 548-0965
Lewis Center *(G-11901)*
Intelliworks Ht ... G ... 419 660-9050
Norwalk *(G-15547)*
International Finishing LLC ... G ... 937 293-3340
Dayton *(G-8416)*
◆ Intertec Corporation ... B ... 419 537-9711
Toledo *(G-18527)*
J & S Industrial Mch Pdts Inc ... D ... 419 691-1380
Toledo *(G-18531)*
J M Hamilton Group Inc ... F ... 419 229-4010
Lima *(G-12032)*
J McCaman Enterprises Inc ... F ... 330 825-2401
New Franklin *(G-14825)*
Jaco Manufacturing Company ... F ... 440 234-4000
Berea *(G-1622)*
Jbf Repair Service LLC ... G ... 740 550-0089
Proctorville *(G-16490)*
Jbw Systems Inc ... F ... 614 882-5008
Westerville *(G-20162)*
▲ JC Carter LLC ... G ... 949 764-6465
Richmond Heights *(G-16654)*
▲ Johndow Industries Inc ... E ... 330 753-6895
Barberton *(G-1122)*
Kiln ... G ... 440 717-1880
Brecksville *(G-2058)*
▲ Kobelco Stewart Bolling Inc ... D ... 330 655-3111
Hudson *(G-11187)*
◆ Koch Knight LLC ... D ... 330 488-1651
East Canton *(G-9194)*
Lam Research Corporation ... C ... 937 472-3311
Eaton *(G-9314)*
Lange Equipment ... G ... 440 953-1621
Eastlake *(G-9281)*
Life Formations Inc ... F ... 419 352-2101
Bowling Green *(G-1996)*
Lifeformations Inc ... E ... 419 352-2101
Bowling Green *(G-1997)*

Linden Industries Inc ... E ... 330 928-4064
Cuyahoga Falls *(G-8020)*
▲ Liquid Development Company ... G ... 216 641-9366
Independence *(G-11265)*
Lube Depot ... G ... 330 758-0570
Youngstown *(G-21135)*
◆ Luke Engineering & Mfg Corp ... E ... 330 335-1501
Wadsworth *(G-19418)*
M M Industries Inc ... E ... 330 332-5947
Salem *(G-16912)*
M W Solutions LLC ... F ... 419 782-1611
Defiance *(G-8800)*
Mactek Corporation ... F ... 330 487-5477
Twinsburg *(G-18976)*
▼ Manifold & Phalor Inc ... E ... 614 920-1200
Canal Winchester *(G-2531)*
Manufctring Bus Dev Sltons LLC ... E ... 419 294-1313
Findlay *(G-9853)*
Mark Carpenter Industries Inc ... G ... 419 294-4568
Fremont *(G-10169)*
◆ Master Chemical Corporation ... D ... 419 874-7902
Perrysburg *(G-16121)*
▲ McFlusion Inc ... G ... 800 341-8616
Twinsburg *(G-18982)*
◆ McNeil & Nrm Inc ... D ... 330 761-1855
Akron *(G-291)*
McNeil & Nrm Intl Inc ... D ... 330 253-2525
Akron *(G-292)*
Measurement Specialties Inc ... F ... 937 885-0800
Dayton *(G-8482)*
MI 2009 Inc ... A ... 513 536-2000
Batavia *(G-1204)*
◆ Micro-Pise Msrment Systems LLC ... C ... 330 541-9100
Streetsboro *(G-17861)*
▼ Midwestern Industries Inc ... C ... 330 837-4203
Massillon *(G-13180)*
Military Resources LLC ... E ... 330 263-1040
Wooster *(G-20809)*
Military Resources LLC ... G ... 330 309-9970
Wooster *(G-20810)*
Mirion Technologies Ist Corp ... G ... 614 367-2050
Pickerington *(G-16198)*
Modular Assembly Innovations ... F ... 614 389-4860
Dublin *(G-9104)*
Mosbro Machine and Tool Inc ... G ... 330 467-0913
Northfield *(G-15468)*
Nalco Company LLC ... F ... 432 528-5214
Louisville *(G-12320)*
Nutro Corporation ... D ... 440 572-3800
Cleveland *(G-5923)*
Nutro Inc ... E ... 440 572-3800
Strongsville *(G-17947)*
▲ Ohio Magnetics Inc ... E ... 216 662-8484
Maple Heights *(G-12736)*
Omar McDowell Co ... G ... 440 808-2280
Westlake *(G-20289)*
Palmer Klein Inc ... G ... 937 323-6339
Springfield *(G-17623)*
◆ Palmer Mfg and Supply Inc ... E ... 937 323-6339
Springfield *(G-17624)*
Patientss Consumers Phrm Inc ... G ... 937 813-7800
Dayton *(G-8565)*
▲ Peerless-Winsmith Inc ... G ... 614 526-7000
Dublin *(G-9122)*
Pfaudler Inc ... G ... 585 464-4872
Beavercreek *(G-1378)*
Plastic Partners LLC ... G ... 425 765-2416
Salem *(G-16919)*
◆ Plastic Process Equipment Inc ... E ... 216 367-7000
Macedonia *(G-12474)*
Poly Products Inc ... G ... 216 391-7659
Cleveland *(G-6020)*
▲ Pro Quip Inc ... D ... 330 468-1850
Macedonia *(G-12477)*
Process Development Corp ... E ... 937 890-3388
Dayton *(G-8597)*
Prodeva Inc ... F ... 937 596-6713
Jackson Center *(G-11347)*
R A K Machine Inc ... F ... 216 631-7750
Cleveland *(G-6080)*
▲ R R R Development Co ... D ... 330 966-8855
North Canton *(G-15260)*
Ratech ... G ... 513 742-2111
Cincinnati *(G-4331)*
Rda Group LLC ... G ... 440 724-4347
Avon *(G-1007)*
Rebuilding & Fabricating Inc ... G ... 440 322-0844
Elyria *(G-9484)*
Regal Industries Inc ... G ... 440 352-9600
Painesville *(G-15917)*

SIC

Employee Codes: A=Over 500 employees, B=251-500
C=101-250, D=51-100, E=20-50, F=10-19, G=3-9

▲ Rhino Rubber LLC ....F 877 744-6603
North Canton *(G-15262)*

Riceland Dry Kiln ....G..... 330 683-9151
Orrville *(G-15758)*

▲ RMS Equipment LLC ....E 330 564-1360
Cuyahoga Falls *(G-8042)*

◆ RP Gatta Inc ....E 330 562-2288
Aurora *(G-946)*

▼ RSI Company ....F 216 360-9800
Beachwood *(G-1297)*

▲ Rubber City Machinery Corp ....E 330 434-3500
Akron *(G-380)*

SDS National LLC ....G..... 330 759-8066
Youngstown *(G-21198)*

◆ Segna Inc ....F 937 335-6700
Troy *(G-18874)*

Service Station Equipment Co..........F 216 431-6100
Cleveland *(G-6181)*

Shred Away ....G..... 740 363-6327
Delaware *(G-8887)*

Silver Tool Inc ....E 937 865-0012
Miamisburg *(G-13860)*

▼ Singleton Corporation ....F 216 651-7800
Cleveland *(G-6205)*

Sizetec Inc ....G..... 330 492-9682
Canton *(G-2850)*

Stainless Automation ....E 216 961-4550
Cleveland *(G-6232)*

Starkey Machinery Inc ....E 419 468-2560
Galion *(G-10289)*

▲ Steelastic Company LLC ....E 330 633-0505
Cuyahoga Falls *(G-8050)*

Steinert Industries Inc ....F 330 678-0028
Kent *(G-11533)*

Stevens Auto Glaze and SEC LL ....G..... 440 953-2900
Eastlake *(G-9288)*

Stoneworkd ....F 740 920-4099
Newark *(G-15058)*

Storetek Engineering Inc ....E 330 294-0678
Tallmadge *(G-18170)*

▲ Technical Glass Products Inc ....F 440 639-6399
Painesville *(G-15925)*

▲ Technical Machine Products Inc.....F 216 281-9500
Cleveland *(G-6300)*

Tegratek ....G..... 513 742-5100
Cincinnati *(G-4499)*

Tex-Vent Co ....G..... 614 299-1902
Columbus *(G-7686)*

Time Is Money ....G..... 419 701-6098
Fostoria *(G-9997)*

Tks Industrial Company ....G..... 614 444-5602
Columbus *(G-7696)*

▲ Toledo Engineering Co Inc ....D..... 419 537-9711
Toledo *(G-18731)*

▲ Tom Richards Inc ....C..... 440 974-1300
Mentor *(G-13748)*

Tooltex Inc ....F 614 539-3222
Grove City *(G-10603)*

Tri Technologies Inc ....F 513 422-1300
Middletown *(G-14090)*

Universal Rack & Equipment Co ....E 330 963-6776
Twinsburg *(G-19033)*

US Machine Prcsion Grnding LLC ......G..... 440 284-0711
Elyria *(G-9506)*

Velocys Inc ....D..... 614 733-3300
Plain City *(G-16363)*

Vulcan Machinery Corporation ....E 330 376-6025
Akron *(G-465)*

▲ Wauseon Machine & Mfg Inc ....D..... 419 337-0940
Wauseon *(G-19700)*

▼ Wentworth Mold Inc Electra ....D..... 937 898-8460
Vandalia *(G-19317)*

Wesco Machine Inc ....F 330 688-6973
Munroe Falls *(G-14668)*

Wolfe Oil Company LLC ....G..... 513 732-6220
Williamsburg *(G-20414)*

◆ Woodman Agitator Inc ....F 440 937-9865
Avon *(G-1021)*

Yost & Son Inc ....G..... 440 779-8025
North Olmsted *(G-15353)*

Youngstown Plastic Tooling ....E 330 782-7222
Youngstown *(G-21254)*

Zed Industries Inc ....D..... 937 667-8407
Vandalia *(G-19318)*

Zeeco Equipment Commodity ....G..... 440 838-1102
Brecksville *(G-2078)*

▲ Zook Enterprises LLC ....E 440 543-1010
Chagrin Falls *(G-3137)*

3561 Pumps & Pumping Eqpt

A & F Machine Products Co...............E 440 826-0959
Berea *(G-1599)*

A P O Holdings Inc ....E 330 455-8925
Canton *(G-2585)*

▼ Advanced Fuel Systems Inc ....G..... 614 252-8422
Columbus *(G-6697)*

▲ All - Flo Pump Company ....G..... 440 354-1700
Mentor *(G-13518)*

Ayling and Reichert Co Consent ....E 419 898-2471
Oak Harbor *(G-15586)*

Belden Brick Company ....E 330 852-2411
Sugarcreek *(G-18016)*

Bergstrom Company Ltd Partnr ....E 440 232-2282
Cleveland *(G-4905)*

Blue Chip Pump Inc ....G..... 513 871-7867
Cincinnati *(G-3453)*

Certified Labs & Service Inc ....E 419 289-7462
Ashland *(G-718)*

▲ Champion Pump Company Inc ....G..... 419 281-4500
Ashland *(G-719)*

Chaos Entertainment ....G..... 937 520-5260
Dayton *(G-8225)*

▲ Cima Inc ....E 513 682-5900
Fairfield *(G-9653)*

City of Newark ....F 740 349-6765
Newark *(G-14993)*

Cleveland Plastic Fabricat ....F 216 797-7300
Euclid *(G-9572)*

Crane Co ....C..... 330 337-7861
Salem *(G-16886)*

▲ Crane Pumps & Systems Inc ....B..... 937 773-2442
Piqua *(G-16257)*

Curtiss-Wright Flow Ctrl Corp ....E 440 838-7690
Brecksville *(G-2042)*

Custom Cltch Jint Hydrlics Inc...........F 216 431-1630
Cleveland *(G-5149)*

▲ Dreison International Inc ....C..... 216 362-0755
Cleveland *(G-5215)*

◆ E R Advanced Ceramics Inc ....E 330 426-9433
East Palestine *(G-9237)*

Eaton-Aeroquip Inc ....D..... 419 891-7775
Maumee *(G-13258)*

Eco-Flo Products Inc ....F 877 326-3561
Ashland *(G-730)*

Electro-Mechanical Mfg Co Inc ....G..... 330 864-0717
Akron *(G-161)*

Eric Allshouse LLC ....G..... 330 533-4258
Canfield *(G-2554)*

▲ F E Myers Co ....G..... 419 289-1144
Ashland *(G-731)*

▲ Fischer Global Enterprises LLC ......E 513 583-4900
Loveland *(G-12349)*

Flow Control US Holding Corp ....G..... 800 843-5628
Cincinnati *(G-3763)*

Flow Control US Holding Corp ....G..... 419 289-1144
Ashland *(G-733)*

Flowserve Corporation ....G..... 513 874-6990
Loveland *(G-12350)*

Flowserve Corporation ....D..... 937 226-4568
Dayton *(G-8346)*

Fluid Automation Inc ....E 248 912-1970
North Canton *(G-15232)*

Frantz Medical Development Ltd.........D..... 440 205-9026
Mentor *(G-13583)*

General Electric Company ....D..... 216 883-1000
Cleveland *(G-5412)*

General Electric Intl Inc ....E 330 963-2066
Twinsburg *(G-18944)*

Gerow Equipment Company Inc ....E 216 383-8800
Cleveland *(G-5426)*

▲ Giant Industries Inc ....E 419 531-4600
Toledo *(G-18480)*

Gorman-Rupp Company ....E 419 886-3001
Bellville *(G-1570)*

Gorman-Rupp Company ....B..... 419 755-1011
Mansfield *(G-12614)*

Gorman-Rupp Company ....B..... 419 755-1011
Mansfield *(G-12615)*

Gorman-Rupp Company ....G..... 419 755-1245
Mansfield *(G-12616)*

▲ Graphite Equipment Mfg Co ....G..... 216 271-9500
Solon *(G-17303)*

Hpc Manufacturing Inc ....G..... 440 322-8334
Lorain *(G-12249)*

▼ Hr Parts N Stuff ....G..... 330 947-2433
Atwater *(G-898)*

▲ Hugo Vglsang Maschinenbau GMBH..............E
330 296-3820
Ravenna *(G-16532)*

▲ Hurst Auto-Truck Electric ....G..... 216 961-1800
Cleveland *(G-5538)*

▼ Hydromatic Pumps Inc ....A..... 419 289-1144
Ashland *(G-741)*

Ingersoll-Rand Company ....E 419 633-6800
Bryan *(G-2306)*

▲ Keen Pump Company Inc ....G..... 419 207-9400
Ashland *(G-745)*

Lakecraft Inc ....G..... 419 734-2828
Port Clinton *(G-16402)*

M T Systems Inc ....G..... 330 453-4646
Canton *(G-2763)*

Magnum Piering Inc ....E 513 759-3348
West Chester *(G-20022)*

▲ Molten Mtal Eqp Innvations LLC .....E 440 632-9119
Middlefield *(G-13968)*

Neptune Chemical Pump Company .....G..... 513 870-3239
West Chester *(G-19905)*

Pckd Enterprises Inc ....E 440 632-9119
Middlefield *(G-13980)*

◆ Pentair Flow Technologies LLC ....B..... 419 289-1144
Ashland *(G-764)*

▲ Preferred Global Equipment LLC .....D..... 513 530-5800
Cincinnati *(G-4265)*

Pyrotek Incorporated ....C..... 440 349-8800
Aurora *(G-942)*

Quikstir Inc ....F 419 732-2601
Port Clinton *(G-16410)*

▲ Replica Engineering Inc ....F 216 252-2204
Cleveland *(G-6103)*

Robbins & Myers Inc ....C..... 937 327-3023
Springfield *(G-17643)*

Rolcon Inc ....E 513 821-7259
Cincinnati *(G-4358)*

Rumpke Transportation Co LLC ....F 513 851-0122
Cincinnati *(G-4366)*

▲ Ruthman Pump and Engineering ....G..... 513 559-1901
Cincinnati *(G-4369)*

◆ Seepex Inc ....C..... 937 864-7150
Enon *(G-9549)*

Stahl Gear & Machine Co ....E 216 431-2820
Cleveland *(G-6231)*

Suburban Manufacturing Co ....D..... 440 953-2024
Eastlake *(G-9290)*

Swanson Industries Inc ....D..... 304 284-5199
New Philadelphia *(G-14931)*

Systecon Inc ....D..... 513 777-7722
West Chester *(G-19953)*

T D Group Holdings LLC ....G..... 216 706-2939
Cleveland *(G-6289)*

Tark Inc ....E 937 434-6766
Dayton *(G-8702)*

Tat Pumps Inc ....G..... 740 385-0008
Nelsonville *(G-14742)*

▲ Tolco Corporation ....E 419 241-1113
Toledo *(G-18728)*

Transdigm Inc ....F 216 291-6025
Cleveland *(G-6346)*

Transdigm Inc ....E 440 352-6182
Painesville *(G-15931)*

▲ Valco Cincinnati Inc ....C..... 513 874-6550
West Chester *(G-20067)*

Vertiflo Pump Company ....F 513 530-0888
Cincinnati *(G-4566)*

Vickers International Inc ....E 419 867-2200
Maumee *(G-13307)*

▲ Warren Rupp Inc ....E 419 524-8388
Mansfield *(G-12703)*

Waterpro ....F 330 372-3565
Warren *(G-19625)*

▲ Wayne/Scott Fetzer Company ....C..... 800 237-0987
Harrison *(G-10811)*

▲ Wepuko Pahnke Engineering LP .....F 937 390-2100
Springfield *(G-17676)*

Westerman Inc ....D..... 330 262-6946
Wooster *(G-20846)*

3562 Ball & Roller Bearings

Ashland Precision Tooling LLC............D..... 419 289-1736
Ashland *(G-707)*

Bearings Manufacturing Company .....E 440 846-5517
Strongsville *(G-17895)*

Extreme Caster Services Inc ....G..... 330 637-9030
Cortland *(G-7868)*

FAg Bearings Corporation ....C..... 513 398-1139
Mason *(G-13019)*

Federal-Mogul Corporation ....C..... 740 432-2393
Cambridge *(G-2457)*

Gemini Advertising Associates ....D..... 513 896-3541
Hamilton *(G-10698)*

Gt Technologies Inc ....C...... 419 782-8955
 Defiance (G-8792)
▲ HMS Industries LLC ....G...... 440 899-0001
 Westlake (G-20277)
▲ Jay Dee Service Corporation ....G...... 330 425-1546
 Macedonia (G-12463)
▲ Jtekt North America Corp ....C...... 440 835-1000
 Westlake (G-20279)
Miller Bearing Company Inc ....E...... 330 678-8844
 Kent (G-11493)
Nn Inc ....G...... 440 647-4711
 Wellington (G-19751)
Randolph Research Co ....G...... 330 666-1667
 Akron (G-364)
▲ Rotek Incorporated ....A...... 330 562-4000
 Aurora (G-945)
Schaeffler Group USA Inc ....B...... 330 273-4383
 Valley City (G-19229)
◆ Timken Company ....A...... 234 262-3000
 North Canton (G-15273)
Timken Company ....A...... 419 563-2200
 Bucyrus (G-2360)
Timken Company ....C...... 330 339-1151
 New Philadelphia (G-14934)
Timken Company ....G...... 330 471-4300
 Canton (G-2871)
Timken Company ....G...... 614 476-3934
 Gahanna (G-10239)
Timken Company ....F...... 614 836-3337
 Groveport (G-10646)
Timken Company ....G...... 330 471-5028
 Canton (G-2872)
Timken Company ....G...... 234 262-3000
 North Canton (G-15274)
Timken Company ....G...... 330 471-2121
 Canton (G-2873)
Timken Company ....D...... 234 262-3000
 Niles (G-15185)
Timken Company ....G...... 330 471-4791
 Alliance (G-545)
Timken Company ....A...... 330 471-5043
 Canton (G-2874)
▲ Tsk America Co Ltd ....F...... 513 942-4002
 West Chester (G-20062)
Western Reserve Mfg Co ....G...... 216 641-0500
 Cleveland (G-6459)

3563 Air & Gas Compressors

Aci Services Inc ....E...... 740 435-0240
 Cambridge (G-2442)
Airtx International Ltd...........................F...... 513 631-0660
 Cincinnati (G-3372)
▲ Anest Iwata Air Engrg Inc ....F...... 513 755-3100
 Hamilton (G-10669)
Arete Innovative Solutions LLC ....G...... 513 503-2712
 Morrow (G-14543)
Ariel Corporation ....F...... 740 397-0311
 Mount Vernon (G-14606)
Ariel Corporation ....F...... 740 397-0311
 Mount Vernon (G-14607)
▲ Armour Spray Systems Inc ....F...... 216 398-3838
 Cleveland (G-4833)
Atlas Machine and Supply Inc ....G...... 614 351-1603
 Hilliard (G-10928)
▼ Ats Ohio Inc ....C...... 614 888-2344
 Lewis Center (G-11884)
▼ Campbell Hausfeld LLC ....C...... 513 367-4811
 Harrison (G-10770)
Carlisle Fluid Tech Inc ....C...... 419 470-2000
 Toledo (G-18389)
Cipar Inc ....G...... 216 910-1700
 Beachwood (G-1260)
Cohesant Inc ....E...... 216 910-1700
 Beachwood (G-1262)
Coulson Cmprssion Msrement Ltd ....F...... 740 697-0220
 Roseville (G-16730)
Deco Tools Inc ....E...... 419 476-9321
 Toledo (G-18430)
◆ Eaton Comprsr Fabrication Inc...........E...... 877 283-7614
 Englewood (G-9518)
Ecowise LLC ....G...... 216 692-3700
 Cleveland (G-5257)
Ernest Industries Inc ....F...... 937 325-9851
 Springfield (G-17553)
Field Gymmy Inc ....G...... 419 538-6511
 Glandorf (G-10397)
Finishmaster Inc ....D...... 614 228-4328
 Columbus (G-7086)
General Fabrications Corp ....E...... 419 625-6055
 Sandusky (G-16970)

Giti Tech Group Ltd ....G...... 866 381-7955
 West Carrollton (G-19793)
Glascraft Inc ....D...... 330 966-3000
 North Canton (G-15234)
Kingsly Compression Inc ....G...... 740 439-0772
 Cambridge (G-2462)
Lsq Manufacturing Inc ....F...... 330 725-4905
 Medina (G-13437)
Mack Industrial LLC ....G...... 800 918-9986
 Perrysburg (G-16119)
National Compressor Svcs LLC ....E...... 419 865-3126
 Holland (G-11073)
◆ Nordson Corporation ....D...... 440 892-1580
 Westlake (G-20285)
Nordson Corporation ....B...... 440 985-4000
 Amherst (G-601)
Nordson Corporation ....B...... 440 988-9411
 Amherst (G-602)
Nordson Corporation ....B...... 440 985-4496
 Amherst (G-603)
Optimair Ltd..G...... 419 661-9568
 Perrysburg (G-16137)
Optime Air MSP Ltd ....G...... 419 661-9568
 Perrysburg (G-16138)
Paratus Supply Inc..............................G...... 330 745-3600
 Barberton (G-1137)
Potemkin Industries Inc ....E...... 740 397-4888
 Mount Vernon (G-14638)
Powerex-Iwata Air Tech Inc ....D...... 888 769-7979
 Harrison (G-10795)
Quikstir Inc ....F...... 419 732-2601
 Port Clinton (G-16410)
Rimrock Holdings Corporation ....E...... 614 471-5926
 Columbus (G-7564)
Rotary Compression Tech Inc ....E...... 937 498-2555
 Sidney (G-17220)
Rubberset Company ....G...... 800 345-4939
 Cleveland (G-6142)
T D Group Holdings LLC ....G...... 216 706-2939
 Cleveland (G-6289)
▲ Tolco Corporation ....D...... 419 241-1113
 Toledo (G-18728)
Transdigm Inc ....G...... 216 706-2939
 Cleveland (G-6347)
Transdigm Inc ....F...... 216 291-6025
 Cleveland (G-6346)
Tri State Equipment Company ....G...... 513 738-7227
 Shandon (G-17098)
◆ United Air Specialists Inc ....C...... 513 891-0400
 Blue Ash (G-1886)
▲ Wiwa LLC ....F...... 419 757-0141
 Alger (G-482)
Wiwa LP ....F...... 419 757-0141
 Alger (G-483)

3564 Blowers & Fans

A A S Amels Sheet Meta L Inc................E...... 330 793-9326
 Youngstown (G-21010)
Adwest Technologies Inc ....G...... 513 458-2600
 Cincinnati (G-3362)
Air Cleaning Solutions ....G...... 937 832-3600
 Dayton (G-8141)
Air Plastics Inc ....E...... 513 469-1074
 Blue Ash (G-1737)
▼ Air-Rite Inc ....E...... 216 228-8200
 Cleveland (G-4735)
▲ Airecon Manufacturing Corp ....E...... 513 561-5522
 Cincinnati (G-3370)
American Manufacturing & Eqp ....G...... 513 829-2248
 Fairfield (G-9642)
Americraft Mfg Co Inc ....F...... 513 489-1047
 Cincinnati (G-3395)
ARI Phoenix Inc...................................E...... 513 229-3750
 Lebanon (G-11781)
Automtve Cmpnnts Holdings LLC ....A...... 419 627-3600
 Sandusky (G-16947)
Babcock & Wilcox Megtec ....C...... 614 258-9501
 Columbus (G-6799)
▲ Beckett Air Incorporated ....D...... 440 327-9999
 North Ridgeville (G-15359)
▲ Bry-Air Inc ....E...... 740 965-2974
 Sunbury (G-18056)
Buckeye BOP LLC ....G...... 740 498-9898
 Newcomerstown (G-15110)
Burt Manufacturing Company Inc ....C...... 330 762-0061
 Akron (G-105)
Camfil USA Inc ....G...... 937 773-0866
 Piqua (G-16255)
Ceco Environmental Corp ....G...... 513 458-2606
 Blue Ash (G-1763)

Ceco Environmental Corp ....G...... 513 458-2600
 Cincinnati (G-3509)
Ceco Group Inc ....G...... 513 458-2600
 Cincinnati (G-3510)
Cincinnati A Flter Sls Svc Inc ....E...... 513 242-3400
 Cincinnati (G-3536)
Clearflite Inc ....G...... 440 281-7368
 Sheffield Lake (G-17118)
Complete Filter Media LLC ....E...... 740 438-0929
 Lancaster (G-11698)
Criticalaire LLC ....F...... 513 475-3800
 Columbus (G-7000)
Criticalaire LLC ....G...... 614 499-7744
 Cincinnati (G-3620)
◆ Diamond Power Intl Inc ....B...... 740 687-6500
 Lancaster (G-11708)
▲ Dreison International Inc ....C...... 216 362-0755
 Cleveland (G-5215)
▲ Duro Dyne Midwest Corp ....B...... 513 870-6000
 Hamilton (G-10685)
▲ Ellis & Watts Intl LLC ....G...... 513 752-9000
 Batavia (G-1183)
Envirofab Inc ....F...... 216 651-1767
 Cleveland (G-5286)
Famous Industries Inc ....D...... 740 685-2592
 Byesville (G-2401)
First Filter LLC ....G...... 419 666-5260
 Perrysburg (G-16095)
Flex Technologies Inc ....D...... 330 359-5415
 Mount Eaton (G-14555)
Glasfloss Industries Inc ....C...... 740 687-1100
 Lancaster (G-11721)
▲ Guardian Technologies LLC ....E...... 216 706-2250
 Euclid (G-9582)
◆ Hartzell Fan Inc ....C...... 937 773-7411
 Piqua (G-16271)
Hdt Ep Inc ....C...... 216 438-6111
 Solon (G-17307)
Hdt Expeditionary Systems Inc ....F...... 440 466-6640
 Geneva (G-10350)
Herman Manufacturing LLC ....F...... 216 251-6400
 Cleveland (G-5504)
▲ Howden American Fan Company...........C...... 513 773-0103
 Fairfield (G-9667)
Howden North America Inc ....D...... 330 867-8540
 Akron (G-224)
Howden North America Inc ....E...... 330 723-0492
 Medina (G-13423)
Illinois Tool Works Inc ....C...... 262 248-8277
 Bryan (G-2303)
Jacp Inc ....G...... 513 353-3660
 Miamitown (G-13888)
JD Enterprises ....G...... 937 764-1611
 Hillsboro (G-11005)
Kirk Williams Company Inc ....D...... 614 875-9023
 Grove City (G-10568)
▲ Langdon Inc ....E...... 513 733-5955
 Cincinnati (G-4011)
▼ Lau Industries Inc ....C...... 937 476-6500
 Dayton (G-8110)
◆ McGill Airclean LLC ....D...... 614 829-1200
 Columbus (G-7330)
◆ McGill Corporation ....F...... 614 829-1200
 Groveport (G-10635)
Mestek Inc ....D...... 419 288-2703
 Bradner (G-2029)
▼ Midwestern Industries Inc ....C...... 330 837-4203
 Massillon (G-13180)
▲ Multi-Wing America Inc ....E...... 440 834-9400
 Middlefield (G-13969)
Neundorfer Inc ....E...... 440 942-8990
 Willoughby (G-20553)
Nupro Company ....C...... 440 951-9729
 Willoughby (G-20559)
▼ OEM Corporation ....F...... 937 859-7492
 Miamisburg (G-13845)
Ohio Blow Pipe Company ....E...... 216 681-7379
 Cleveland (G-5930)
Oil Skimmers Inc ....E...... 440 237-4600
 North Royalton (G-15440)
Orica Ground Support Inc ....D...... 740 377-9146
 South Point (G-17443)
Pcy Enterprises Inc..............................E...... 513 241-5566
 Cincinnati (G-4219)
Plas-Tanks Industries Inc ....E...... 513 942-3800
 Hamilton (G-10730)
Process Automation Specialists ....G...... 330 247-1384
 Canal Fulton (G-2510)
▲ Qualtek Electronics Corp ....C...... 440 951-3300
 Mentor (G-13710)

S I C

Quickdraft Inc ....E 330 477-4574
Canton (G-2832)

Radon Be Gone Inc ....G 614 268-4440
Columbus (G-7545)

Schenck Process LLC ....F 513 576-9200
Milford (G-14173)

▲ Selas Heat Technology Co LLC ....E 800 523-6500
Streetsboro (G-17875)

◆ Skuttle Mfg Co ....F 740 373-9169
Marietta (G-12831)

Sly Inc ....F 440 891-3200
Strongsville (G-17967)

Starr Fabricating Inc ....D 330 394-9891
Vienna (G-19376)

Std Specialty Filters Inc ....F 216 881-3727
Cleveland (G-6243)

Stelter and Brinck Inc ....E 513 367-9300
Harrison (G-10805)

▲ Thermo Vent Manufacturing Inc .....F 330 239-0239
Medina (G-13487)

Thompson Culvert Company LLC .....F 513 645-7000
West Chester (G-19956)

▲ Tisch Environmental Inc ....F 513 467-9000
Cleves (G-6529)

Tlt-Turbo Inc ....G 330 776-5115
Akron (G-443)

▲ Tosoh America Inc ....B 614 539-8622
Grove City (G-10604)

◆ United Air Specialists Inc ....C 513 891-0400
Blue Ash (G-1886)

▲ United McGill Corporation ....E 614 829-1200
Groveport (G-10648)

Usui International Corporation ....E 513 448-0410
Cincinnati (G-4548)

▼ Verantis Corporation ....E 440 243-0700
Middleburg Heights (G-13909)

Vortec and Paxton Products ....F 513 891-7474
Blue Ash (G-1890)

3565 Packaging Machinery

Able Tool Corporation ....E 513 733-8989
Cincinnati (G-3346)

Accu Pak Mfg Inc ....G 330 644-3015
Akron (G-26)

Advanced Poly-Packaging Inc ....E 330 785-4000
Akron (G-33)

Andy Pac Inc ....G 440 748-8800
Columbia Station (G-6578)

▲ Atlas Vac Machine Co LLC ....G 513 407-3513
Cincinnati (G-3426)

▲ Audion Automation Ltd ....E 216 267-1911
Berea (G-1602)

Audion Automation Ltd ....E 216 267-1911
Berea (G-1603)

Automated Packg Systems Inc ....D 330 342-2000
Bedford (G-1401)

Automated Packg Systems Inc ....C 330 626-2313
Streetsboro (G-17842)

Automation Solutions Inc ....G 614 235-4060
Columbus (G-6790)

Beckermills Inc ....G 419 738-3450
Wapakoneta (G-19481)

▼ Boggs Graphic Equipment LLC .....G 440 564-9675
Maple Heights (G-12728)

◆ Combi Packaging Systems Llc ......D 330 456-9333
Canton (G-2664)

▲ Crown Closures Machinery ....E 740 681-6593
Lancaster (G-11701)

Ctm Integration Incorporated ....E 330 332-1800
Salem (G-16887)

D&D Design Concepts Inc ....F 513 752-2191
Batavia (G-1176)

▲ Darifill Inc ....F 614 890-3274
Westerville (G-20208)

Dayton Systems Group Inc ....D 937 885-5665
Miamisburg (G-13799)

Dover Corporation ....G 513 696-1790
Mason (G-13010)

Dynamic Bar Code Systems Inc ....G 330 220-5451
Brunswick (G-2222)

Euclid Products Co Inc ....G 440 942-7310
Willoughby (G-20482)

Exact Equipment Corporation ....F 215 295-2000
Columbus (G-6645)

Food Equipment Mfg Corp ....E 216 672-5859
Bedford Heights (G-1484)

G L Industries Inc ....E 513 874-1233
Hamilton (G-10696)

◆ Glassline Corporation ....E 419 666-9712
Perrysburg (G-16102)

Gunnison Associates LLC ....G 330 562-5230
Aurora (G-923)

Hadsell Chemical Proc LLC ....E 740 941-1792
Waverly (G-19710)

Heat Seal LLC ....C 216 341-2022
Cleveland (G-5491)

Hill & Griffith Company ....G 513 921-1075
Cincinnati (G-3882)

Huhtamaki Inc ....B 513 201-1525
Batavia (G-1192)

Huhtamaki Inc ....B 937 746-9700
Franklin (G-10028)

Hunkar Technologies Inc ....C 513 272-1010
Cincinnati (G-3902)

Impackt ....G 513 559-1488
Cincinnati (G-3913)

Kaufman Engineered Systems Inc ....D 419 878-9727
Waterville (G-19661)

Kaws Inc ....E 513 521-8292
Cincinnati (G-3973)

▲ Kennedy Group Incorporated ....D 440 951-7660
Willoughby (G-20520)

Kolinahr Systems Inc ....F 513 745-9401
Blue Ash (G-1823)

Labeldata ....G 614 891-5858
Westerville (G-20222)

M PI Label Systems ....G 330 938-2134
Sebring (G-17047)

Madgar Genis Corp ....G 330 848-6950
Barberton (G-1125)

◆ Miconvi Properties Inc ....E 440 954-3500
Willoughby (G-20548)

Millwood Inc ....E 614 717-9099
Powell (G-16479)

Millwood Inc ....F 513 860-4567
West Chester (G-19901)

◆ Millwood Inc ....E 330 393-4400
Vienna (G-19370)

Millwood Natural LLC ....D 330 393-4400
Vienna (G-19371)

◆ Morgan Adhesives Company LLC ..B 330 688-1111
Stow (G-17775)

Mpi Labels of Baltimore Inc ....E 330 938-2134
Sebring (G-17049)

MTS Medication Tech Inc ....G 440 238-0840
Strongsville (G-17943)

◆ Nilpeter Usa Inc ....C 513 489-4400
Cincinnati (G-4156)

◆ OKL Can Line Inc ....E 513 825-1655
Cincinnati (G-4183)

▲ Pack Line Corp ....F 212 564-0664
Cleveland (G-5960)

◆ Pneumatic Scale Corporation ....C 330 923-0491
Cuyahoga Falls (G-8033)

Precision Replacement LLC ....G 330 908-0410
Macedonia (G-12476)

◆ Quadrel Inc ....E 440 602-4700
Mentor (G-13705)

▲ Reactive Resin Products Co ....E 419 666-6119
Perrysburg (G-16146)

Rpmi Packaging Inc ....F 513 398-4040
Lebanon (G-11835)

S A Langmack Company ....F 216 541-0500
Cleveland (G-6149)

Samuel Strapping Systems Inc ....D 740 522-2500
Heath (G-10855)

▲ Scanacon Incorporated ....G 330 877-7600
Hartville (G-10833)

Superior Label Systems Inc ....B 513 336-0825
Mason (G-13092)

Switchback Group Inc ....E 330 523-5200
Richfield (G-16641)

System Packaging of Glassline ....C 419 666-9712
Perrysburg (G-16151)

Universal Packg Systems Inc ....B 513 674-9400
Cincinnati (G-4542)

Universal Packg Systems Inc ....B 513 732-2000
Batavia (G-1231)

Universal Packg Systems Inc ....E 513 735-4777
Batavia (G-1232)

Vistech Mfg Solutions LLC ....F 513 933-9300
Lebanon (G-11848)

▲ Vmi Americas Inc ....E 330 929-6800
Stow (G-17815)

W/S Packaging Group Inc ....C 513 459-2400
Mason (G-13102)

3566 Speed Changers, Drives & Gears

Accurate Gear Manufacturing Co ......G 513 761-3220
Cincinnati (G-3347)

Aerotorque Corporation ....G 330 590-8105
Sharon Center (G-17099)

Akron Gear & Engineering Inc ....E 330 773-6608
Akron (G-45)

Ametek Technical & Indus Pdts ....D 330 677-3754
Kent (G-11429)

Avotronics Powertrain Inc ....G 614 537-0261
Columbus (G-6793)

B & B Gear & Machine Co Inc ....F 937 687-1771
New Lebanon (G-14840)

Bluffton Motor Works LLC ....E 419 885-3769
Sylvania (G-18100)

Buckeye Gear Co ....F 216 292-7998
Chagrin Falls (G-3078)

▲ Bunting Bearings LLC ....D 419 866-7000
Holland (G-11047)

Cage Gear & Machine LLC ....G 330 452-1532
Canton (G-2633)

Canton Gear Mfg Design Co Inc ....F 330 455-2771
Canton (G-2640)

▲ Cleveland Gear Company Inc ....C 216 641-9000
Cleveland (G-5062)

Dayton Gear & Tool Co Inc ....F 937 866-4327
Dayton (G-8275)

Dependable Gear Corp ....G 440 942-4969
Eastlake (G-9264)

Eaton Leasing Corporation ....E 216 382-2292
Beachwood (G-1270)

Ebo Group Inc ....D 330 239-4933
Sharon Center (G-17105)

◆ Force Control Industries Inc ....D 513 868-0900
Fairfield (G-9659)

▲ Forge Industries Inc ....A 330 782-8301
Youngstown (G-21089)

Gear Company of America Inc ....D 216 671-5400
Cleveland (G-5404)

Gearing Solutions Inc ....G 440 498-9538
Solon (G-17295)

Geneva Gear & Machine Inc ....F 937 866-0318
Dayton (G-8363)

▲ Great Lakes Power Products Inc ....G 440 951-5111
Mentor (G-13596)

▲ Hefty Hoist Inc ....E 740 467-2515
Millersport (G-14294)

▲ Horsburgh & Scott Co ....C 216 432-5858
Cleveland (G-5526)

Horsburgh & Scott Co ....C 216 383-2909
Cleveland (G-5527)

◆ Industrial Mfg Co LLC ....F 440 838-4700
Brecksville (G-2055)

▲ Jamtek Enterprises Inc ....G 513 738-4700
Harrison (G-10786)

Jonmar Gear and Machine Inc ....G 330 854-6500
Canal Fulton (G-2503)

▲ Joseph Industries Inc ....D 330 528-0091
Streetsboro (G-17860)

▲ Julie Maynard Inc ....F 937 443-0408
Dayton (G-8429)

Kenmore Gear & Machine Co Inc ......G 330 753-6671
Akron (G-254)

Lincoln Electric Company ....C 216 524-8800
Cleveland (G-5696)

▲ Linde Hydraulics Corporation ....E 330 533-6801
Canfield (G-2562)

▲ Luk Clutch Systems LLC ....E 330 264-4383
Wooster (G-20798)

◆ Luk Transmission Systems LLC ....A 330 264-4383
Wooster (G-20799)

Martin Sprocket & Gear Inc ....D 419 485-5515
Montpelier (G-14448)

Matlock Electric Co Inc ....E 513 731-9600
Cincinnati (G-4066)

Nidec Indus Automtn USA LLC ....E 216 901-2400
Cleveland (G-5882)

▲ Peerless-Winsmith Inc ....G 614 526-7000
Dublin (G-9122)

Pentagear Products LLC ....G 937 660-8182
Dayton (G-8569)

Petro Gear Corporation ....F 216 431-2820
Cleveland (G-5998)

Radocy Inc ....F 419 666-4400
Rossford (G-16747)

Rhino Gear Manufacturing Inc ....G 440 639-1125
Painesville (G-15918)

Richard A Scott ....G 937 898-1592
Dayton (G-8631)

Right Track Corp ....G 937 663-0366
Saint Paris (G-16863)

Robertson Manufacturing Co ....F 216 531-8222
Cleveland (G-6123)

▲ Satco Inc .... G 330 630-8866
  Tallmadge (G-18168)

Sew-Eurodrive Inc .... D 937 335-0036
  Troy (G-18875)

Sika Corporation .... G 740 375-3020
  Marion (G-12900)

Sika Corporation .... D 740 387-9224
  Marion (G-12901)

▲ Skidmore-Wilhelm Mfg Company ... E 216 481-4774
  Solon (G-17381)

Spang & Company .... E 440 350-6108
  Mentor (G-13727)

Speed Selector Inc .... F 440 543-8233
  Chagrin Falls (G-3120)

Stahl Gear & Machine Co .... E 216 431-2820
  Cleveland (G-6231)

Titanium Metals Corporation .... A 740 537-1571
  Toronto (G-18785)

Trojon Gear Inc .... F 937 254-1737
  Dayton (G-8729)

Tymoca Partners LLC .... F 440 946-4327
  Eastlake (G-9294)

◆ Wasserstrom Company .... B 614 737-8472
  Columbus (G-7750)

◆ Westerman Inc .... C 740 569-4143
  Bremen (G-2081)

Westerman Inc .... D 330 262-6946
  Wooster (G-20846)

3567 Indl Process Furnaces & Ovens

A E F Inc .... D 216 360-9800
  Cleveland (G-4670)

▲ A Jacks Manufacturing Co .... E 216 531-1010
  Cleveland (G-4676)

Abp Induction LLC .... F 330 830-6252
  Massillon (G-13106)

Agridry LLC .... E 419 459-4399
  Edon (G-9339)

◆ Ajax Tocco Magnethermic Corp ... C 330 372-8511
  Warren (G-19517)

Ajax Tocco Magnethermic Corp ..... D 330 818-8080
  Canton (G-2594)

Allstates Refr Contrs LLC .... F 419 878-4691
  Waterville (G-19651)

Armature Coil Equipment Inc .... F 216 267-6366
  Cleveland (G-4831)

▼ Benko Products Inc .... E 440 934-2180
  Sheffield Village (G-17121)

Briskheat Corporation .... D 614 429-3232
  Columbus (G-6864)

▲ CA Litzler Co Inc .... E 216 267-8020
  Cleveland (G-4958)

▲ CA Litzler Holding Company ...... D 216 267-8020
  Cleveland (G-4959)

▲ CMI Industry Americas Inc .... D 330 332-4661
  Salem (G-16883)

▲ Crescent Metal Products Inc ...... C 440 350-1100
  Mentor (G-13555)

Custom Coils .... G 330 426-3797
  Negley (G-14729)

Delta H Technologies LLC .... G 614 561-8860
  Pickerington (G-16190)

▲ Ebner Furnaces Inc .... D 330 335-2311
  Wadsworth (G-19404)

Euclid Products Co Inc .... G 440 942-7310
  Willoughby (G-20482)

▲ Facultatieve Tech Americas Inc ... E 330 723-6339
  Medina (G-13408)

▲ Fives N Amercn Combustn Inc ... C 216 271-6000
  Cleveland (G-5352)

Furnace Technologies Inc .... D 419 878-2100
  Waterville (G-19658)

Glenro Inc .... E 937 392-0111
  Ripley (G-16667)

Glo-Quartz Electric Heater Co .... E 440 255-9701
  Mentor (G-13593)

Hannon Company .... D 330 456-4728
  Canton (G-2723)

Haynn Construction Co Inc .... G 419 853-4747
  West Salem (G-20113)

▲ Heat and Sensor Tech LLC .... D 513 228-0481
  Lebanon (G-11807)

I Cerco Inc .... D 304 387-0178
  East Liverpool (G-9218)

▲ I Cerco Inc .... C 330 567-2145
  Shreve (G-17158)

I Cerco Inc .... D 740 982-2050
  Crooksville (G-7950)

Induction Services Inc .... G 330 652-4494
  Niles (G-15159)

Induction Tooling Inc .... E 440 237-0711
  North Royalton (G-15426)

Inter-Power Corporation .... G 330 652-4494
  Niles (G-15160)

James Thomas Shiveley .... G 330 468-2601
  Macedonia (G-12462)

Kaufman Engineered Systems Inc ... D 419 878-9727
  Waterville (G-19661)

◆ Komar Industries Inc .... E 614 836-2366
  Groveport (G-10629)

L Haberny Co Inc .... F 440 543-5999
  Chagrin Falls (G-3098)

Lakeway Mfg Inc .... E 419 433-3030
  Huron (G-11232)

Lanly Company .... E 216 731-1115
  Cleveland (G-5682)

◆ Lewco Inc .... C 419 625-4014
  Sandusky (G-16979)

Magneforce Inc .... F 330 856-9300
  Warren (G-19577)

McGill Airpressure LLC .... G 614 882-5455
  Columbus (G-7332)

▲ Micropyretics Heaters Intl Inc .... F 513 772-0404
  Cincinnati (G-4103)

Miller Core 2 Inc .... G 330 359-0500
  Beach City (G-1249)

▲ P S C Inc .... G 216 531-3375
  Cleveland (G-5957)

◆ Park-Ohio Holdings Corp .... F 440 947-2000
  Cleveland (G-5966)

◆ Park-Ohio Industries Inc .... C 440 947-2000
  Cleveland (G-5967)

RAD-Con Inc .... E 440 871-5720
  Lakewood (G-11678)

Resilience Fund III LP .... G 216 292-0200
  Cleveland (G-6106)

Robbins Furnace Works Inc .... F 440 949-2292
  Sheffield Village (G-17129)

▲ Selas Heat Technology Co LLC ... E 800 523-6500
  Streetsboro (G-17875)

Sivon Mfr Co .... G 440 259-5505
  Perry (G-16057)

Specialties Mds Induction Ltd .... G 330 394-3338
  Warren (G-19601)

STA-Warm Electric Company .... F 330 296-6461
  Ravenna (G-16561)

Star Engineering Inc .... E 740 342-3514
  New Lexington (G-14855)

Stelter and Brinck Inc .... E 513 367-9300
  Harrison (G-10805)

Stricodynarad Corp .... F 330 239-0005
  Hinckley (G-11029)

▲ Strohecker Incorporated .... D 330 426-9496
  East Palestine (G-9245)

▲ Surface Combustion Inc .... C 419 891-7150
  Maumee (G-13300)

▼ Taylor - Winfield Corporation ..... D 330 259-8500
  Hubbard (G-11140)

Tegratek .... E 513 742-5100
  Cincinnati (G-4499)

Thermo Systems Technology .... E 216 292-8250
  Cleveland (G-6320)

▲ United McGill Corporation .... E 614 829-1200
  Groveport (G-10648)

Williams Industrial Svc Inc .... E 419 353-2120
  Bowling Green (G-2020)

3568 Mechanical Power Transmission Eqpt, NEC

A J Rose Mfgco .... C 216 631-4645
  Cleveland (G-4675)

◆ A J Rose Mfgco .... C 216 631-4645
  Avon (G-978)

Abl Products Inc .... F 216 281-2400
  Cleveland (G-4684)

▲ Advance Bronze Inc .... D 330 948-1231
  Lodi (G-12155)

Advanced Pneumatics Inc .... D 440 953-0700
  Mentor (G-13510)

Akron Gear & Engineering Inc ...... E 330 773-6608
  Akron (G-45)

▲ Art Metals Group Inc .... D 513 942-8800
  Hamilton (G-10671)

B S F Inc .... F 937 890-6121
  Dayton (G-8179)

B S F Inc .... F 937 890-6121
  Tipp City (G-18264)

Ban-Fam Industries Inc .... G 216 265-9588
  Cleveland (G-4888)

Bdi Inc .... F 330 498-4980
  Canton (G-2617)

Bearings Manufacturing Company ... E 440 846-5517
  Strongsville (G-17895)

Bowes Manufacturing Inc .... F 216 378-2110
  Solon (G-17271)

▲ Bucyrus Precision Tech Inc .... C 419 563-9950
  Bucyrus (G-2334)

Bunting Bearings LLC .... E 419 522-3323
  Mansfield (G-12572)

City Machine Technologies Inc ...... E 330 740-8186
  Youngstown (G-21048)

Cleveland Rebabbitting Service ..... G 216 433-0123
  Cleveland (G-5076)

▲ Climax Metal Products Company ... D 440 943-8898
  Mentor (G-13547)

Columbus McKinnon Corporation ... D 330 424-7248
  Lisbon (G-12118)

Connell Limited Partnership .... D 877 534-8986
  Northfield (G-15464)

Custom Cltch Jint Hydrlics Inc ...... F 216 431-1630
  Cleveland (G-5149)

Dependable Gear Corp .... G 440 942-4969
  Eastlake (G-9264)

▲ Drive Components .... G 440 234-6200
  Brookpark (G-2157)

E I Du Pont De Nemours & Co ..... G 216 901-3600
  Cleveland (G-5232)

Eaton Corporation .... C 440 826-1115
  Berea (G-1613)

Eaton Corporation .... G 216 281-2211
  Cleveland (G-5247)

Eaton Hydraulics LLC .... E 419 232-7777
  Van Wert (G-19254)

Ebo Group Inc .... G 330 239-4933
  Sharon Center (G-17105)

Eicom Corporation .... E 937 294-5692
  Moraine (G-14483)

Equipment Concepts .... G 937 291-9734
  Dayton (G-8329)

Erie Shore Industrial Svc Co .... G 440 933-4301
  Avon Lake (G-1028)

▲ Euclid Universal Corporation ...... G 440 542-0960
  Cleveland (G-5302)

▲ Force Control Industries Inc ...... D 513 868-0900
  Fairfield (G-9659)

General Electric Company .... D 216 883-1000
  Cleveland (G-5412)

General Metals Powder Co .... D 330 633-1226
  Akron (G-203)

Geneva Gear & Machine Inc .... F 937 866-0318
  Dayton (G-8363)

GKN Sinter Metals LLC .... C 740 441-3203
  Gallipolis (G-10298)

Hite Parts Exchange Inc .... G 614 272-5115
  Columbus (G-7160)

▲ Holmbury Inc .... G 440 578-1070
  Eastlake (G-9274)

J L R Products Inc .... F 330 832-9557
  Massillon (G-13158)

Lextech Industries Ltd .... G 216 883-7900
  Cleveland (G-5694)

▲ Logan Clutch Corporation .... E 440 808-4258
  Cleveland (G-5707)

▲ Luk Clutch Systems LLC .... E 330 264-4383
  Wooster (G-20798)

Martin Sprocket & Gear Inc .... D 419 485-5515
  Montpelier (G-14448)

Master Products Company .... D 216 341-1740
  Cleveland (G-5760)

Mechanical Dynamics Analis Ltd .... E 440 946-0082
  Euclid (G-9592)

Metro Mech Inc .... G 216 641-6262
  Cleveland (G-5792)

Mfh Partners Inc .... F 440 461-4100
  Cleveland (G-5795)

▲ Morgal Machine Tool Co .... D 937 325-5561
  Springfield (G-17607)

▲ Nook Industries Inc .... C 216 271-7900
  Cleveland (G-5887)

▲ Opw Engineered Systems Inc .... D 888 771-9438
  Lebanon (G-11824)

Penn Machine Company .... E 814 288-1547
  Twinsburg (G-18996)

Poly Products Inc .... G 216 391-7659
  Cleveland (G-6020)

Rampe Manufacturing Company ..... F 440 352-8995
  Fairport Harbor (G-9771)

▲ Randall Bearings Inc .... D 419 223-1075
  Lima (G-12080)

Randall Bearings Inc .... F 419 678-2486
Coldwater (G-6570)

Regal Industries Inc .... G 440 352-9600
Painesville (G-15917)

Rexnord Industries LLC .... D 614 675-1800
Grove City (G-10588)

Robertson Manufacturing Co .... F 216 531-8222
Cleveland (G-6123)

Saf-Holland Inc .... G 513 874-7888
West Chester (G-20046)

Sintered Metal Industries Inc .... F 330 650-4000
Hudson (G-11199)

Southeastern Shafting Mfg .... F 740 342-4629
New Lexington (G-14854)

Stevenson Machine Inc .... F 513 761-4121
Cincinnati (G-4467)

▲ Stripmatic Products Inc .... E 216 241-7143
Cleveland (G-6255)

◆ Taiho Corporation of America .... C 419 443-1645
Tiffin (G-18246)

▲ Tsk America Co Ltd .... F 513 942-4002
West Chester (G-20062)

US Tsubaki Power Transm LLC ..... C 419 626-4560
Sandusky (G-17019)

◆ Webb-Stiles Company .... D 330 225-7761
Valley City (G-19237)

Western Branch Diesel Inc .... E 330 454-8800
Canton (G-2902)

◆ Xtek Inc .... B 513 733-7800
Cincinnati (G-4616)

3569 Indl Machinery & Eqpt, NEC

A S Manufacturing Inc .... G 216 476-0656
Cleveland (G-4677)

A-1 Sprinkler Company Inc .... D 937 859-6198
Miamisburg (G-13779)

▲ Abanaki Corporation .... F 440 543-7400
Chagrin Falls (G-3075)

▲ Action Coupling & Eqp Inc .... D 330 279-4242
Holmesville (G-11099)

▲ Advanced Design Industries Inc ... E 440 277-4141
Sheffield Village (G-17120)

◆ Air Technical Industries Inc .... E 440 951-5191
Mentor (G-13512)

Akron Brass Company .... E 309 444-4440
Wooster (G-20733)

Akron Brass Company .... B 330 264-5678
Wooster (G-20734)

American Baler Co .... D 419 483-5790
Bellevue (G-1543)

▲ American Rescue Technology ..... F 937 293-6240
Dayton (G-8155)

▲ Applied Marketing Services .... E 440 716-9962
Westlake (G-20255)

Aronit Machine LLC .... F 419 782-4740
Defiance (G-8778)

Ats Assembly and Test Inc .... B 937 222-3030
Dayton (G-8169)

▲ Ats Systems Oregon Inc .... B 541 738-0932
Lewis Center (G-11885)

◆ Automation Tooling Systems ...... C 614 781-8063
Lewis Center (G-11887)

◆ Barney Corporation Inc .... G 614 274-9069
Hilliard (G-10930)

Cae Ransohoff Inc .... G 513 870-0100
West Chester (G-19986)

Chart Industries Inc .... E 440 753-1490
Cleveland (G-5020)

Chart International Inc .... E 440 753-1490
Cleveland (G-5021)

City of Mansfield .... F 419 884-3310
Mansfield (G-12580)

Cleaning Tech Group LLC .... E 513 870-0100
West Chester (G-19991)

▲ Cleveland Gear Company Inc ..... C 216 641-9000
Cleveland (G-5062)

◆ Columbus Industries Inc .... D 740 983-2552
Ashville (G-849)

Computer Allied Technology Co ..... G 614 457-2292
Columbus (G-6973)

D C Filter & Chemical Inc .... G 419 626-3967
Sandusky (G-16955)

Diamondback Filters .... G 419 494-1156
Bowling Green (G-1985)

Digilube Systems Inc .... F 937 748-2209
Springboro (G-17479)

▲ Dosmatic USA Inc .... F 972 245-9765
Cincinnati (G-3667)

◆ E R Advanced Ceramics Inc ...... G 330 426-9433
East Palestine (G-9237)

E S H Inc .... G 330 345-1010
Wooster (G-20768)

Eco Mechanical LLC .... G 440 610-9253
Wellington (G-19741)

Edjean Technical Services Inc .... G 440 647-3300
Sullivan (G-18054)

Elite Fire Services LLC .... F 614 586-4255
Columbus (G-7053)

Evoqua Water Technologies LLC .... E 614 861-5440
Pickerington (G-16192)

Falls Filtration Tech Inc .... E 330 928-4100
Stow (G-17752)

Fanuc America Corporation .... G 513 754-2400
Mason (G-13020)

Filter Factory-Ttn Inc .... E 440 963-2034
Vermilion (G-19326)

Fire & Marine Inc .... E 937 323-2770
Springfield (G-17559)

Fire Fab Inc .... G 330 759-9834
Girard (G-10386)

Fire Foe Corp .... E 330 759-9834
Girard (G-10387)

Fluid Automation Inc .... E 248 912-1970
North Canton (G-15232)

▲ Foseco Inc .... G 440 826-4548
Cleveland (G-5374)

Gem City Engineering Co .... C 937 223-5544
Dayton (G-8361)

▲ Globe Pipe Hanger Products Inc ... E 216 362-6300
Cleveland (G-5434)

Gould Fire Protection Inc .... E 419 957-2416
Findlay (G-9832)

▲ Groeneveld Atlantic South .... F 330 225-4949
Brunswick (G-2231)

H P E Inc .... F 330 833-3161
Massillon (G-13145)

Hdt Expeditionary Systems Inc ..... G 216 438-6111
Solon (G-17308)

▲ Hellan Strainer Company .... E 216 206-4200
Cleveland (G-5495)

▼ Hunter Defense Tech Inc .... E 216 438-6111
Solon (G-17312)

Innovative Assembly Svcs LLC ...... F 419 399-3886
Paulding (G-16006)

Joseph B Stinson Co .... G 419 334-4151
Fremont (G-10160)

▲ Joyce/Dayton Corp .... E 937 294-6261
Dayton (G-8428)

◆ Kc Robotics Inc .... E 513 860-4442
West Chester (G-19887)

◆ Keltec Inc .... D 330 425-3100
Twinsburg (G-18962)

▲ Koehler Rubber & Supply Co ..... F 216 749-5100
Cleveland (G-5662)

Koester Corporation .... D 419 599-0291
Napoleon (G-14687)

▲ Kuss Filtration Inc .... B 419 423-9040
Findlay (G-9849)

La Mfg Inc .... G 513 577-7200
Cincinnati (G-4009)

▲ Laureate Machine & Automtn LLC ... G 419 615-4601
Leipsic (G-11871)

▲ Lawrence Technologies Inc .... G 937 274-7771
Dayton (G-8454)

Mac Ltt Inc .... E 330 474-3795
Kent (G-11486)

Marmac Co .... G 937 372-8093
Xenia (G-20963)

Membrane Specialists LLC .... G 513 860-9490
Hamilton (G-10724)

▲ Met-Chem Inc .... E 216 881-7900
Cleveland (G-5786)

▲ Midwest Filtration LLC .... E 513 874-6510
West Chester (G-20030)

Motionsource International LLC ..... F 440 287-7037
Solon (G-17339)

Motor Systems Incorporated .... E 513 576-1725
Milford (G-14164)

National Oilwell Varco LP .... E 978 687-0101
Dayton (G-8519)

Nmgg Ctg LLC .... G 419 447-5211
Tiffin (G-18234)

Nupro Company .... C 440 951-9729
Willoughby (G-20559)

Nutro Corporation .... D 440 572-3800
Cleveland (G-5923)

Ogden Hydraulics LLC .... G 419 686-1108
Portage (G-16426)

Oil Skimmers Inc .... E 440 237-4600
North Royalton (G-15440)

Omega Automation Inc .... D 937 890-2350
Dayton (G-8548)

Omega International Inc .... E 937 890-2350
Dayton (G-8549)

Osair Inc .... G 440 255-8238
Mentor (G-13676)

Parker-Hannifin Corporation .... E 330 335-6740
Wadsworth (G-19426)

◆ Parker-Hannifin Corporation ..... B 216 896-3000
Cleveland (G-5973)

Parker-Hannifin Corporation .... F 216 896-3000
Cleveland (G-5976)

Pax Products Inc .... F 419 586-2337
Celina (G-3013)

Petro Ware Inc .... D 740 982-1302
Crooksville (G-7953)

Phoenix Safety Outfitters LLC .... G 614 361-0544
Springfield (G-17627)

◆ Pneumatic Scale Corporation ..... C 330 923-0491
Cuyahoga Falls (G-8033)

Process Innovations Inc .... G 330 856-5192
Vienna (G-19373)

Process Machinery Inc .... F 614 278-1055
Columbus (G-7522)

Production Design Services Inc ..... G 937 866-3377
Dayton (G-8598)

Programmable Control Service ...... F 740 927-0744
Pataskala (G-15978)

Pyrotek Incorporated .... C 440 349-8800
Aurora (G-942)

Quality Products Inc .... D 614 228-0185
Columbus (G-7535)

Radco Fire Protection Inc .... G 419 476-0102
Toledo (G-18668)

Raymond W Reisiger .... G 740 400-4090
Baltimore (G-1086)

Recognition Robotics Inc .... F 440 590-0499
Elyria (G-9485)

Remtec Corp .... G 513 860-4299
Mason (G-13081)

Remtec Engineering .... G 513 860-4299
Mason (G-13082)

Renite Company .... F 614 253-5509
Columbus (G-7554)

Rennco Automation Systems Inc ... E 419 861-2340
Holland (G-11080)

▼ Rexarc International Inc .... E 937 839-4604
West Alexandria (G-19781)

▲ Rhba Acquisitions LLC .... D 330 567-2903
Shreve (G-17162)

Rimrock Holdings Corporation ...... G 614 471-5926
Columbus (G-7564)

Rixan Associates Inc .... E 937 438-3005
Dayton (G-8633)

◆ Rotex Global Lcc .... C 513 541-1236
Cincinnati (G-4359)

Russell E Coy .... G 419 658-2366
Ney (G-15143)

S A Langmack Company .... F 216 541-0500
Cleveland (G-6149)

Sas Automation LLC .... G 937 372-5255
Xenia (G-20972)

Selecteon Corporation .... G 614 228-8008
Columbus (G-7607)

Stateline Power Corp .... F 937 547-1006
Greenville (G-10524)

▼ Steel & Alloy Utility Pdts Inc ..... E 330 530-2220
Mc Donald (G-13348)

Steven Douglas Corp .... E 440 564-5200
Newbury (G-15105)

◆ Summa Holdings Inc .... G 440 838-4700
Cleveland (G-6261)

Swift Filters Inc .... E 440 735-0995
Oakwood Village (G-15628)

Titan Fire Protection Inc .... G 740 451-0838
Chesapeake (G-3191)

▲ Total Lubrication MGT Co .... E 888 478-6996
Canton (G-2880)

Two M Precision Co Inc .... E 440 946-2120
Willoughby (G-20623)

Tyler Haver Inc .... F 800 255-1259
Mentor (G-13757)

United Fire Apparatus Corp .... G 419 645-4083
Cridersville (G-7947)

▲ Versatile Automation Tech Ltd ... G 330 220-2600
Brunswick (G-2265)

Viking Group Inc .... G 937 443-0433
Dayton (G-8743)

Warren Fire Equipment Inc .... G 937 866-8918
Miamisburg (G-13878)

▲ Weiss North America Inc..........F...... 440 269-8031
   Willoughby (G-20629)

Winston Oil Co Inc.................G...... 740 373-9664
   Marietta (G-12850)

Xigent Automation Systems Inc...........D...... 740 548-3700
   Lewis Center (G-11929)

Yaskawa America Inc..............C...... 937 847-6200
   Miamisburg (G-13883)

Zephyr Industries Inc..............G...... 419 281-4485
   Ashland (G-787)

Zhao Hui Filters (us) Inc...........G...... 440 519-9300
   Chagrin Falls (G-3136)

3571 Electronic Computers

3d Systems Inc..................C...... 215 757-9611
   Columbus (G-6664)

Advance Products................F...... 419 882-8117
   Sylvania (G-18097)

Analog Bridge Inc................G...... 937 901-4832
   Beavercreek (G-1317)

Apple Inc......................G...... 614 478-5592
   Columbus (G-6763)

Applied Imagination Inc............G...... 419 352-8373
   Bowling Green (G-1968)

Ascendtech Inc..................E...... 216 458-1101
   Willoughby (G-20441)

AT&T Corp......................C...... 513 792-9300
   Cincinnati (G-3423)

Cardinal Health Tech LLC..........G...... 614 757-5000
   Dublin (G-9059)

Chaos Matrix Ltd.................G...... 614 638-4748
   Oberlin (G-15636)

◆ Codonics Inc..................C...... 216 226-1066
   Cleveland (G-5096)

Computer Zoo Inc................G...... 937 310-1474
   Bellbrook (G-1504)

Dapsco........................F...... 937 294-5331
   Moraine (G-14475)

Davis Laser Products.............G...... 614 252-7711
   Columbus (G-7015)

Delohio Tech...................F...... 740 816-5628
   Delaware (G-8837)

Dupont Electronic Polymers LP.......D...... 937 268-3411
   Dayton (G-8314)

Eaj Services LLC.................F...... 513 792-3400
   Blue Ash (G-1780)

◆ Eaton Corporation..............B...... 216 523-5000
   Cleveland (G-5245)

Eaton Corporation................C...... 216 416-2500
   Cleveland (G-5246)

Falcon Ridge Technologies LLC........G...... 216 674-1649
   Cleveland (G-5322)

Fleet Graphics Inc................G...... 937 252-2552
   Dayton (G-8345)

Freedom Usa Inc.................F...... 216 503-6374
   Twinsburg (G-18937)

▲ Golubitsky Corporation..........G...... 800 552-4204
   Cleveland (G-5436)

Hardware Exchange Inc............G...... 440 449-8006
   Solon (G-17306)

HP Inc........................E...... 513 956-4253
   Blue Ash (G-1810)

International Products.............G...... 614 334-1500
   Columbus (G-7206)

▲ International Products...........F...... 614 850-3000
   Hilliard (G-10954)

Journey Systems LLC.............F...... 513 831-6200
   Milford (G-14157)

Kenneth Hickman Co..............F...... 513 348-0016
   Batavia (G-1197)

Lab Electronics Inc...............G...... 330 674-9818
   Millersburg (G-14238)

Magnum Computers Inc............F...... 216 781-1757
   Cleveland (G-5730)

Mbenztech.....................G...... 937 291-1527
   Centerville (G-3044)

Micro Center Corporation..........G...... 614 326-8500
   Columbus (G-7346)

Oracle America Inc...............F...... 513 381-0125
   Blue Ash (G-1848)

Parker-Hannifin Corporation........D...... 513 831-2340
   Milford (G-14166)

PC Systems....................G...... 330 825-7966
   Akron (G-333)

Sense Labs LLC.................G...... 740 590-0009
   Athens (G-883)

Site Tech......................G...... 740 522-0019
   Heath (G-10857)

Smartronix Inc..................F...... 216 378-3300
   Northfield (G-15472)

▲ Systemax Manufacturing Inc........C...... 937 368-2300
   Dayton (G-8694)

Teradata Corporation.............B...... 866 548-8348
   Miamisburg (G-13870)

Teradata Operations Inc...........G...... 937 866-0032
   Miamisburg (G-13871)

Teradata Operations Inc...........D...... 937 242-4030
   Miamisburg (G-13872)

Terra Comp Technology............G...... 330 745-8912
   Barberton (G-1154)

Thomas Ross Associates Inc.........G...... 330 723-1110
   Medina (G-13488)

Tracewell Systems Inc.............D...... 614 846-6175
   Lewis Center (G-11927)

You52.........................F...... 440 477-7704
   Ashtabula (G-846)

3572 Computer Storage Devices

Capsa Solutions LLC..............D...... 614 864-9966
   Canal Winchester (G-2521)

CHI Corporation.................F...... 440 498-2300
   Cleveland (G-5026)

EMC Corporation................D...... 614 865-4200
   Westerville (G-20149)

EMC Corporation................D...... 513 794-9624
   Blue Ash (G-1783)

EMC Corporation................E...... 216 606-2000
   Independence (G-11254)

Enviroscape EMC................G...... 419 278-2000
   Deshler (G-8950)

Expansion Programs Intl...........G...... 216 631-8544
   Cleveland (G-5314)

Magnext Ltd....................G...... 614 406-4136
   Columbus (G-7314)

▲ Pinnacle Data Systems Inc.........C...... 614 748-1150
   Groveport (G-10641)

Quantem Fbo Services.............G...... 603 647-6763
   Cincinnati (G-4310)

Quantum.......................G...... 740 328-2548
   Newark (G-15050)

Quantum Athletics LLC............G...... 513 248-2966
   Terrace Park (G-18182)

Quantum Commerce LLC...........G...... 513 777-0737
   West Chester (G-19926)

Quantum Integration Llc...........G...... 330 609-0355
   Cortland (G-7874)

Quantum Sails..................G...... 567 283-5335
   Sandusky (G-16998)

Quantum Technologies Inc..........G...... 330 645-2762
   Akron (G-359)

Quantum Techonology & Services......G...... 937 642-2929
   Marysville (G-12964)

Quantum World Technologies.........G...... 937 747-3018
   Zanesfield (G-21262)

Service Storage Intl Inc...........G...... 440 951-7579
   Willoughby (G-20594)

Solsys Inc.....................G...... 419 886-4683
   Mansfield (G-12682)

Teradata Corporation.............B...... 866 548-8348
   Miamisburg (G-13870)

Tracewell Systems Inc.............D...... 614 846-6175
   Lewis Center (G-11927)

Western Digital Corporation.........G...... 440 684-1331
   Cleveland (G-6458)

3575 Computer Terminals

Bluelevel Technologies Inc..........G...... 330 523-5215
   Richfield (G-16616)

Copier Resources Inc.............G...... 614 268-1100
   Columbus (G-6981)

Discount Computer Parts...........G...... 216 228-4949
   Lakewood (G-11662)

Fivepoint LLC...................F...... 937 374-3193
   Xenia (G-20952)

Ftk Manufacturing LLC.............G...... 513 218-7237
   Williamsburg (G-20407)

Parker-Hannifin Corporation........D...... 513 831-2340
   Milford (G-14166)

▲ Pinnacle Data Systems Inc.........C...... 614 748-1150
   Groveport (G-10641)

R J Silvia......................G...... 740 400-4066
   Lancaster (G-11744)

Thames Company Ltd.............G...... 614 228-4869
   Columbus (G-7687)

▲ Yutec LLC....................G...... 440 725-5353
   Chagrin Falls (G-3074)

3577 Computer Peripheral Eqpt, NEC

Abstract Displays Inc.............G...... 513 985-9700
   Blue Ash (G-1732)

Adaptive Data Inc................F...... 937 436-2343
   Centerville (G-3032)

Advanced Microbeam Inc...........G...... 330 394-1255
   Vienna (G-19362)

AGE Graphics LLC...............F...... 740 989-0006
   Long Bottom (G-12228)

Airwave Communications Cons.......G...... 419 331-1526
   Lima (G-11984)

Applied Vision Corporation.........D...... 330 926-2222
   Cuyahoga Falls (G-7969)

AT&T Corp.....................G...... 513 792-9300
   Cincinnati (G-3423)

Ava Graphix....................G...... 216 409-8646
   Brunswick (G-2206)

Black Box Corporation............F...... 937 438-8660
   Brecksville (G-2037)

Black Box Corporation............E...... 614 825-7400
   Lewis Center (G-11890)

Cisco Systems Inc...............A...... 419 977-2404
   New Bremen (G-14781)

Cisco Systems Inc...............G...... 937 427-4264
   Beavercreek (G-1325)

Computer Zoo Inc................G...... 937 310-1474
   Bellbrook (G-1504)

▼ Data Processing Sciences Corp......D...... 513 791-7100
   Cincinnati (G-3640)

Dataq Instruments...............F...... 330 668-1444
   Akron (G-141)

Eastman Kodak Company...........G...... 937 259-3000
   Dayton (G-8317)

Electrodynamics Inc..............C...... 847 259-0740
   Cincinnati (G-3300)

Electronic Vision Inc..............E...... 740 592-2433
   Athens (G-864)

Embedded Planet Inc..............F...... 216 245-4180
   Warrensville Heights (G-19632)

Enterasys Networks Inc............B...... 330 245-0240
   Akron (G-169)

Epic Technologies LLC.............D...... 513 683-5455
   Mason (G-13018)

Eprintworksplus.................G...... 513 731-3797
   Cincinnati (G-3713)

Esterline Georgia US LLC...........E...... 937 372-7579
   Xenia (G-20949)

Fitne Inc.......................F...... 740 592-2433
   Athens (G-865)

Gameday Vision.................F...... 330 830-4550
   Massillon (G-13137)

◆ Gleason Metrology Systems Corp....E...... 937 384-8901
   Dayton (G-8365)

Government Acquisitions Inc.........E...... 513 721-8700
   Cincinnati (G-3842)

Harris Mackessy & Brennan........C...... 614 221-6831
   Westerville (G-20157)

Hunkar Technologies Inc...........C...... 513 272-1010
   Cincinnati (G-3902)

ID Images Inc...................G...... 330 220-7300
   Brunswick (G-2233)

Intermec Inc....................F...... 513 874-5882
   West Chester (G-19883)

Intermec Technologies Corp.........F...... 513 874-5882
   West Chester (G-19884)

▲ Kern Inc......................E...... 614 317-2600
   Grove City (G-10567)

Kern Inc.......................G...... 440 930-7315
   Cleveland (G-5649)

Lazer Action Inc.................G...... 330 630-9200
   Akron (G-268)

M C Systems Inc.................G...... 513 336-6007
   Mason (G-13056)

▲ Microcom Corporation............E...... 740 548-6262
   Lewis Center (G-11907)

Parker-Hannifin Corporation........D...... 513 831-2340
   Milford (G-14166)

Penca Design Group Ltd...........G...... 440 210-4422
   Painesville (G-15910)

Perfection Packaging Inc...........G...... 614 866-8558
   Gahanna (G-10226)

Prentke Romich Company..........C...... 330 202-5800
   Wooster (G-20825)

▲ Qualtek Electronics Corp..........C...... 440 951-3300
   Mentor (G-13710)

Royal Specialty Products Inc.........G...... 513 841-1267
   Cincinnati (G-4362)

▲ Scriptel Corporation.............F...... 614 276-8402
   Columbus (G-7604)

Signature Technologies Inc..........E...... 937 859-6323
   Miamisburg (G-13859)

Small Business Products...........G...... 800 553-6485
   Cincinnati (G-4427)

Star City Art Co ....F 937 865-9792
Miamisburg *(G-13864)*

Stellar Systems Inc ....G 513 921-8748
Cincinnati *(G-4464)*

Superior Label Systems Inc ....B 513 336-0825
Mason *(G-13092)*

▲ Systemax Manufacturing Inc .....C 937 368-2300
Dayton *(G-8694)*

T E Hubler Inc ....G 419 476-2552
Toledo *(G-18714)*

▲ Tech Pro Inc ....E 330 923-3546
Akron *(G-430)*

Timekeeping Systems Inc ....F 216 595-0890
Solon *(G-17406)*

Ucr LLC ....F 937 253-8898
Dayton *(G-8120)*

United Ultra Violet Inc ....F 614 875-8088
Grove City *(G-10609)*

▲ University Accessories Inc ....G 440 327-4151
North Ridgeville *(G-15407)*

Video Products Inc ....D 330 562-2622
Aurora *(G-955)*

▲ Vmetro Inc ....G 281 584-0728
Fairborn *(G-9633)*

Xerox Corporation ....D 740 592-5609
Athens *(G-890)*

Xerox Corporation ....D 513 539-4858
Monroe *(G-14421)*

Xerox Corporation ....G 513 539-4808
Monroe *(G-14422)*

Xerox Corporation ....D 614 409-6527
Groveport *(G-10650)*

Xponet Inc ....G 440 354-6617
Painesville *(G-15943)*

Yonezawa USA Inc ....G 614 799-2210
Plain City *(G-16367)*

3578 Calculating & Accounting Eqpt

A & M Creative Group Inc ....E 330 452-8940
Canton *(G-2584)*

Allied Retail Solutions ....G 330 332-8141
Salem *(G-16870)*

American Merchant Servic ....G 216 598-3100
Westlake *(G-20251)*

Bartek Systems ....G 614 759-6014
Columbus *(G-6810)*

Cambridge Ohio Production & As ......F 740 432-6383
Cambridge *(G-2448)*

Cme Federal Credit Union ....F 614 876-1382
Hilliard *(G-10940)*

Diebold Incorporated ....D 330 899-0097
Uniontown *(G-19082)*

Diebold Incorporated ....D 330 490-4000
North Canton *(G-15227)*

Diebold Incorporated ....B 330 490-4000
Canton *(G-2688)*

Diebold Nixdorf Incorporated ....A 330 490-4000
North Canton *(G-15228)*

▲ Diebold Self Service Systems ......A 330 490-5099
Canton *(G-2689)*

Ganymede Technologies Corp ....G 419 562-5522
Bucyrus *(G-2344)*

Garda CL Technical Svcs Inc ....E 937 294-4099
Moraine *(G-14490)*

Ginko Voting Systems LLC ....G 937 291-4060
Dayton *(G-8364)*

Glenn Michael Brick ....F 740 391-5735
Flushing *(G-9916)*

J3 Systems Ltd ....G 419 562-5522
Bucyrus *(G-2351)*

Jpmorgan Chase Bank Nat Assn ......G 937 443-6260
Vandalia *(G-19299)*

Jpmorgan Chase Bank Nat Assn ......G 330 287-5102
Wooster *(G-20792)*

Outta Box Dispensers LLC ....G 937 221-7106
Dayton *(G-8556)*

Peoples Bancorp Inc ....E 740 685-1500
Byesville *(G-2408)*

◆ Puddle Shark Studios Inc ....G 440 286-2811
Chardon *(G-3173)*

Testlink USA ....F 513 272-1081
Cincinnati *(G-4502)*

3579 Office Machines, NEC

Advanced Time Systems ....G 440 466-2689
Geneva *(G-10340)*

Baumer HHS Corp. ....E 937 886-3160
Dayton *(G-8183)*

▲ Baumfolder Corporation ....D 937 492-1281
Sidney *(G-17169)*

Buynix ....G 216 551-3485
Cleveland *(G-4954)*

Cap Data Supply Inc ....G 216 252-2280
Cleveland *(G-4969)*

Central Business Products Inc ....G 513 385-5899
Cincinnati *(G-3513)*

Collated Products Corp ....F 440 946-1950
Willoughby *(G-20459)*

Industrial Electronic Service ....F 937 746-9750
Carlisle *(G-2931)*

▲ Kern Inc ....E 614 317-2600
Grove City *(G-10567)*

Kern Inc ....G 440 930-7315
Cleveland *(G-5649)*

Parallel Solutions ....G 440 498-9920
Cleveland *(G-5962)*

Pitney Bowes Inc ....D 203 426-7025
Brecksville *(G-2069)*

Pitney Bowes Inc ....D 740 374-5535
Marietta *(G-12817)*

R T Industries Inc ....G 937 335-5784
Troy *(G-18865)*

Signa Stortech Systems Inc ....E 214 357-0411
Canton *(G-2849)*

Simplex Time Recorder LLC ....D 937 291-0355
Miamisburg *(G-13861)*

Symatic Inc ....E 330 225-1510
Brunswick *(G-2260)*

3581 Automatic Vending Machines

AVI Food Systems Inc ....E 513 860-4191
Fairfield *(G-9644)*

AVI Food Systems Inc ....E 440 327-1944
North Ridgeville *(G-15358)*

▲ Giant Industries Inc ....E 419 531-4600
Toledo *(G-18480)*

Innovative Vend Solutions LLC ....G 866 931-9413
Dayton *(G-8407)*

Michele Mellen ....G 740 369-1422
Powell *(G-16478)*

Reeces Las Vegas Supplies ....G 937 274-5000
Dayton *(G-8620)*

Tranzonic Companies ....B 216 535-4300
Richmond Heights *(G-16657)*

▲ Ve Global Vending Inc ....F 216 785-2611
Cleveland *(G-6409)*

3582 Commercial Laundry, Dry Clean & Pressing Mchs

Ellis Laundry & Linen Supply ....G 330 339-4941
New Philadelphia *(G-14897)*

Ha-International LLC ....E 419 537-0096
Toledo *(G-18492)*

▲ Husqvarna US Holding Inc ....D 216 898-1800
Cleveland *(G-5539)*

Linen Care Plus Inc ....F 614 224-1791
Columbus *(G-7299)*

Process Development Corp ....E 937 890-3388
Dayton *(G-8597)*

Swisher Hygiene Inc ....G 513 870-4830
West Chester *(G-20057)*

Thompson Distributing Co Inc ....D 513 422-9011
Middletown *(G-14088)*

Whirlpool Corporation ....B 419 547-7711
Clyde *(G-6548)*

3585 Air Conditioning & Heating Eqpt

A A S Amels Sheet Meta L Inc ....E 330 793-9326
Youngstown *(G-21010)*

▲ Adams Manufacturing Company ......E 216 662-1600
Cleveland *(G-4700)*

Aeroquip-Vickers Inc ....B 216 523-5000
Cleveland *(G-4722)*

Airtex Manufacturing Lllp ....G 614 436-9693
Columbus *(G-6705)*

Albin Sales Inc ....G 740 927-7210
Pataskala *(G-15966)*

All About House ....G 614 725-3595
Columbus *(G-6718)*

Aquapro Systems LLC ....F 877 278-2797
West Chester *(G-19808)*

Arthurs Refrigeration ....G 740 532-0206
Ironton *(G-11290)*

▼ Bard Manufacturing Company Inc ......D 419 636-1194
Bryan *(G-2281)*

▲ Beckett Air Incorporated ....D 440 327-9999
North Ridgeville *(G-15359)*

Beverage Engineering Inc ....G 216 641-6678
Brooklyn Heights *(G-2131)*

BMC Holdings Inc ....G 419 636-1194
Bryan *(G-2283)*

Boston Beer Company ....F 267 240-4429
Cincinnati *(G-3463)*

▲ Briskheat Corporation ....C 614 294-3376
Columbus *(G-6863)*

Brookpark Laboratories Inc ....G 216 267-7140
Cleveland *(G-4935)*

▲ Bry-Air Inc ....E 740 965-2974
Sunbury *(G-18056)*

▲ Budzar Industries Inc ....D 440 530-1000
Willoughby *(G-20448)*

▼ C Nelson Manufacturing Co ....G 419 898-3305
Oak Harbor *(G-15587)*

Carrier Corporation ....E 937 275-0645
Dayton *(G-8212)*

Cartwright Construction Inc ....G 330 929-3020
Cuyahoga Falls *(G-7976)*

Central Heating & Cooling Inc ....G 330 782-7100
Youngstown *(G-21045)*

Certified Service Inc ....G 937 643-0393
Dayton *(G-8223)*

CFC Startec LLC ....G 330 688-8316
Stow *(G-17737)*

Chilltex LLC ....F 937 710-3308
Anna *(G-621)*

Cleveland Smacna ....G 440 877-3500
Cleveland *(G-5078)*

Climateright LLC ....G 800 725-4628
Columbus *(G-6939)*

Columbus Heating & Vent Co ....C 614 274-1177
Columbus *(G-6954)*

▲ Cryogenic Equipment & Svcs Inc ......F 513 761-4200
Cincinnati *(G-3623)*

▲ Csafe LLC ....G 937 312-0114
Moraine *(G-14473)*

Daikin Applied Americas Inc ....G 614 351-9862
Columbus *(G-7007)*

▲ Dj Beverage Innovations Inc ....G 614 769-1569
Plain City *(G-16336)*

Dmtco LLC ....G 937 324-0061
Springfield *(G-17545)*

DTE Cool Co ....G 513 579-0160
Cincinnati *(G-3672)*

▲ Duro Dyne Midwest Corp ....B 513 870-6000
Hamilton *(G-10685)*

▲ Eaton-Aeroquip Llc ....C 216 523-5000
Cleveland *(G-5254)*

◆ Ecu Corporation ....E 513 898-9294
Cincinnati *(G-3690)*

Edison Solar Inc ....F 419 499-0000
Milan *(G-14111)*

◆ Electrolux Professional Inc ....E 216 898-1800
Cleveland *(G-5269)*

Ellis & Watts Global Inds Inc ....F 513 752-9000
Batavia *(G-1182)*

▲ Ellis & Watts Intl LLC ....G 513 752-9000
Batavia *(G-1183)*

◆ Emerson Climate Tech Inc ....A 937 498-3011
Sidney *(G-17186)*

Emerson Climate Tech Inc ....C 937 498-3011
Sidney *(G-17187)*

Emerson Climate Tech Inc ....C 937 498-3587
Sidney *(G-17188)*

Emerson Electric Co ....C 513 731-2020
Cincinnati *(G-3698)*

Famous Industries Inc ....D 740 685-2592
Byesville *(G-2401)*

Famous Industries Inc ....G 740 397-8842
Mount Vernon *(G-14622)*

Famous Realty Cleveland Inc ....F 740 685-2533
Byesville *(G-2402)*

▲ Fire From Ice Ventures LLC ....F 419 944-6705
Solon *(G-17293)*

Florline Display Products Corp ....G 440 975-9449
Willoughby *(G-20490)*

Fred D Pfening Company ....E 614 294-5361
Columbus *(G-7099)*

Goodman Distribution Inc ....G 440 324-4071
Elyria *(G-9426)*

Gould Group LLC ....G 740 807-4294
Hilliard *(G-10949)*

▲ Guardian Technologies LLC ....E 216 706-2250
Euclid *(G-9582)*

Hanon Systems Usa LLC ....C 313 920-0583
Carey *(G-2919)*

Hatfield Industries LLC ....G 513 225-0456
West Chester *(G-19880)*

Hbb Pro Sales ....G 216 901-7900
Cleveland *(G-5486)*

Hdt Ep Inc C 216 438-6111
Solon *(G-17307)*

Hdt Expeditionary Systems Inc F 440 466-6640
Geneva *(G-10350)*

Heat Exchange Applied Tech F 330 682-4328
Orrville *(G-15740)*

Hobart Corporation E 937 332-3000
Troy *(G-18840)*

Hobart Corporation C 937 332-2797
Piqua *(G-16277)*

▲ Hydro-Dyne Inc E 330 832-5076
Massillon *(G-13153)*

▼ Hydro-Thrift Corporation E 330 837-5141
Massillon *(G-13154)*

Insource Tech Inc F 419 399-3600
Paulding *(G-16007)*

International Beverage Works G 614 798-5398
Columbus *(G-7205)*

IV J Telecommunications LLC G 606 694-1762
South Point *(G-17438)*

J D Indoor Comfort Inc F 440 949-8758
Sheffield Village *(G-17123)*

J E M Industries Inc F 440 951-4884
Willoughby *(G-20514)*

▲ Jbar A/C Inc F 216 447-4294
Cleveland *(G-5609)*

Jnp Group LLC G 800 735-9645
Wooster *(G-20791)*

Keith Chrissinger G 740 549-0683
Lewis Center *(G-11903)*

Lfg Specialties LLC E 419 424-4999
Findlay *(G-9852)*

◆ Liebert Corporation A 614 888-0246
Columbus *(G-7292)*

Liebert North America Inc A 614 888-0246
Columbus *(G-7293)*

▲ Lintern Corporation E 440 255-9333
Mentor *(G-13635)*

◆ Liqui-Box Corporation D 614 888-9280
Columbus *(G-7300)*

Lockes Heating & Cooling Llc F 513 793-1900
Blue Ash *(G-1827)*

▲ Lvd Acquisition LLC E 614 861-1350
Columbus *(G-7306)*

Mahle Behr USA Inc A 937 369-2000
Dayton *(G-8472)*

Martinov Home Solutions LLC G 330 926-3059
Akron *(G-288)*

▲ Maverick Innvtive Slutions LLC E 419 281-7944
Ashland *(G-751)*

Midwest Compressor Co Inc G 216 941-9200
Cleveland *(G-5808)*

Mv Group Inc G 419 776-1133
Toledo *(G-18594)*

Northeastern Rfrgn Corp E 440 942-7676
Willoughby *(G-20557)*

NRC Inc E 440 975-9449
Willoughby *(G-20558)*

Prime Manufacturing Corp G 937 496-3900
Dayton *(G-8593)*

Professional Supply Inc F 419 332-7373
Fremont *(G-10177)*

R & R Comfort Experts LLC G 216 475-3995
Cleveland *(G-6078)*

Rack Draft Service Inc F 513 353-5520
North Bend *(G-15207)*

Red DOT Corporation G 216 447-4294
Cleveland *(G-6094)*

Refrigeration Industries Corp F 740 377-9166
South Point *(G-17446)*

Rs Pro Sales LLC G 513 699-5329
Cincinnati *(G-4364)*

▼ RSI Company F 216 360-9800
Beachwood *(G-1297)*

Snap Rite Manufacturing Inc E 910 897-4080
Cleveland *(G-6214)*

So-Low Environmental Eqp Co E 513 772-9410
Cincinnati *(G-4431)*

Space Dynamics Corp E 513 792-9800
Blue Ash *(G-1871)*

Sticker Corporation F 440 946-2100
Willoughby *(G-20606)*

T J F Inc F 419 878-4400
Waterville *(G-19668)*

Tactical Envmtl Systems Inc G 513 831-2663
Milford *(G-14176)*

◆ Taiho Corporation of America C 419 443-1645
Tiffin *(G-18246)*

Taylor & Moore Co F 513 733-5530
Cincinnati *(G-4495)*

Thermo King Corporation B 478 625-7241
Chagrin Falls *(G-3071)*

Thermo King Corporation F 478 625-7241
Chagrin Falls *(G-3072)*

Throck Supply Co LLC G 937 393-9276
Hillsboro *(G-11015)*

Trane Company F 419 491-2278
Holland *(G-11091)*

Trane US Inc E 513 771-8884
Cincinnati *(G-4517)*

Trane US Inc C 614 473-3131
Columbus *(G-7703)*

Trane US Inc C 614 497-6300
Groveport *(G-10647)*

Trane US Inc D 614 473-8701
Columbus *(G-7704)*

U Haul Neighborhood Dealer G 740 445-4125
Vincent *(G-19381)*

United Technologies Corp B 330 784-5477
North Canton *(G-15279)*

Variflow Equipment Inc G 513 245-0420
Cincinnati *(G-4556)*

Vertiv Group Corporation A 614 888-0246
Columbus *(G-7735)*

Virginia Air Distributors Inc G 614 262-1129
Columbus *(G-7741)*

Vortec Corporation E 513 686-8210
Blue Ash *(G-1891)*

Whirlpool Corporation C 614 409-4340
Lockbourne *(G-12153)*

3586 Measuring & Dispensing Pumps

Bergstrom Company Ltd Partnr E 440 232-2282
Cleveland *(G-4905)*

Cohesant Inc E 216 910-1700
Beachwood *(G-1262)*

Energy Manufacturing Ltd G 419 355-9304
Fremont *(G-10143)*

▲ Field Stone Inc D 937 898-3236
Tipp City *(G-18277)*

◆ Gojo Industries Inc C 330 255-6000
Akron *(G-206)*

Gojo Industries Inc C 330 255-6525
Stow *(G-17760)*

Gojo Industries Inc C 330 922-4522
Cuyahoga Falls *(G-8005)*

▲ Graco Ohio Inc D 330 494-1313
North Canton *(G-15235)*

Hydro Systems Company G 513 271-8800
Milford *(G-14151)*

◆ Hydro Systems Company E 513 271-8800
Cincinnati *(G-3905)*

Neptune Chemical Pump Company G 513 870-3239
West Chester *(G-19905)*

Porto Pump Inc G 740 454-2576
Zanesville *(G-21343)*

Precision Conveyor Technology F 440 352-3601
Perry *(G-16056)*

◆ Seepex Inc C 937 864-7150
Enon *(G-9549)*

▲ Tolco Corporation D 419 241-1113
Toledo *(G-18728)*

Tranzonic Companies B 216 535-4300
Richmond Heights *(G-16657)*

▲ Valco Cincinnati Inc C 513 874-6550
West Chester *(G-20067)*

Valco Cincinnati Inc G 513 874-6550
West Chester *(G-20068)*

3589 Service Ind Machines, NEC

Accushred LLC F 419 244-7473
Toledo *(G-18319)*

▲ Ameriwater LLC E 937 461-8833
Dayton *(G-8157)*

Amsoil Inc G 614 274-9851
Columbus *(G-6746)*

Applied Biomimetic Inc G 513 558-6090
Cincinnati *(G-3409)*

Aqua Pennsylvania Inc G 440 257-6190
Mentor On The Lake *(G-13773)*

Askia Inc G 513 828-7443
Cincinnati *(G-3419)*

Aurand Manufacturing & Eqp Co G 513 541-7200
Cincinnati *(G-3429)*

B L Anderson Co Inc G 765 463-1518
West Chester *(G-19812)*

▲ Baleco International Inc E 513 353-3000
North Bend *(G-15202)*

Beckman Environmental Svcs Inc F 513 752-3570
Batavia *(G-1168)*

Best Equipment Co Inc E 440 237-3515
North Royalton *(G-15411)*

Bleachtech LLC D 330 421-2134
Medina *(G-13378)*

Buckeye Field Supply Ltd G 513 312-2343
Cincinnati *(G-3484)*

C J Smith Machinery Service G 614 348-1376
Columbus *(G-6883)*

Car-Nation Inc G 330 862-9001
Paris *(G-15949)*

Chiefs Manufacturing & Eqp Co G 216 291-3200
Cleveland *(G-5027)*

Cintas Corporation No 2 G 937 236-1506
Dayton *(G-8230)*

City of Ashland G 419 289-8728
Ashland *(G-722)*

City of Athens E 740 592-3344
Athens *(G-858)*

City of Chardon F 440 286-2657
Chardon *(G-3147)*

City of Marietta E 740 374-6864
Marietta *(G-12774)*

City of Middletown F 513 425-7781
Middletown *(G-14030)*

City of Ravenna G 330 296-5214
Ravenna *(G-16522)*

City of Troy F 937 339-4826
Troy *(G-18809)*

City of Xenia E 937 376-7269
Xenia *(G-20943)*

Clark Auto Machine Shop G 216 939-0768
Cleveland *(G-5041)*

Clean Water Conditioning G 614 475-4532
Columbus *(G-6935)*

Clearwater Systems Inc F 330 262-5515
Wooster *(G-20758)*

▲ Cleveland Range LLC C 216 481-4900
Cleveland *(G-5075)*

Coldwell Wilcox Tech LLC G 513 758-1010
Cincinnati *(G-3596)*

Comp-U-Chem Inc G 740 345-3332
Newark *(G-14995)*

Complete Dry Flood G 513 200-9274
Cincinnati *(G-3601)*

County of Lake F 440 428-1794
Madison *(G-12502)*

County of Lawrence F 740 867-8700
Chesapeake *(G-3186)*

CST Zero Discharged Car Wash S G 740 947-5480
Waverly *(G-19706)*

De Nora Holdings Us Inc B 440 710-5300
Painesville *(G-15873)*

◆ De Nora Tech Inc D 440 710-5300
Painesville *(G-15875)*

Dinkmar Inc G 419 468-8516
Galion *(G-10263)*

▲ E - I Corp F 614 899-2282
Westerville *(G-20146)*

◆ Eagle Crusher Co Inc D 419 468-2288
Galion *(G-10266)*

Eagle Engineering Wtr Tech LLC G 419 345-4688
Perrysburg *(G-16087)*

Eastern Ohio Investments Inc G 740 266-2228
Steubenville *(G-17693)*

▲ Electric Eel Mfg Co Inc E 937 323-4644
Springfield *(G-17552)*

▲ Enting Water Conditioning Inc E 937 294-5100
Moraine *(G-14484)*

Environmental Closure Systems F 614 759-9186
Reynoldsburg *(G-16588)*

Eps Wastewater LLC G 859 689-4300
Milford *(G-14139)*

Erichar Inc G 216 402-2628
Cleveland *(G-5293)*

Evers Enterprises Inc G 513 541-7200
Cincinnati *(G-3722)*

Evoqua Water Technologies LLC G 262 521-8352
Milford *(G-14140)*

Evoqua Water Technologies LLC E 614 491-4000
Groveport *(G-10620)*

EZ Wall LLC G 800 424-8251
Winchester *(G-20692)*

Fimco Services LLC E 330 830-1413
Massillon *(G-13132)*

Flexcart LLC G 614 348-2517
New Albany *(G-14759)*

Flow-Liner Systems Ltd E 800 348-0020
Zanesville *(G-21309)*

Friess Equipment Inc G 330 945-9440
Akron *(G-194)*

S I C

Employee Codes: A=Over 500 employees, B=251-500
C=101-250, D=51-100, E=20-50, F=10-19, G=3-9

2017 Harris Ohio
Industrial Directory

1035

▼ Frontline International Inc ....F 330 861-1100
Cuyahoga Falls (G-8000)

▲ Giant Industries Inc ....E 419 531-4600
Toledo (G-18480)

Greene County ....G 937 429-0127
Dayton (G-8107)

Hempy Water Conditioning Inc ....G 419 273-2531
Forest (G-9921)

Hempy Water Conditioning Inc ....G 419 448-8885
Tiffin (G-18222)

Hempy Water Conditioning Inc ....G 419 529-4002
Ontario (G-15688)

◆ Henny Penny Corporation ....A 937 456-8400
Eaton (G-9309)

Hi-Vac Corporation ....G 740 374-2306
Marietta (G-12790)

High-TEC Industrial Services.............C 937 667-1772
Tipp City (G-18281)

Hilo Tech Inc ....E 440 979-1155
North Olmsted (G-15339)

Hirons Memorial Works Inc ....G 937 444-2917
Mount Orab (G-14581)

Hobart Corporation ....E 937 332-3000
Troy (G-18840)

Hobart Corporation ....G 937 335-7171
Troy (G-18841)

Hobart Corporation ....C 937 332-2797
Piqua (G-16277)

Holdren Brothers Inc ....G 937 465-7050
West Liberty (G-20092)

Homer G Waller Jr ....G 330 788-4023
Youngstown (G-21108)

J & K Wade Ltd............................G 419 352-6163
Bowling Green (G-1992)

◆ JE Grote Company Inc ....D 614 868-8414
Columbus (G-7229)

K S W C Inc................................G 440 577-1114
Pierpont (G-16212)

◆ Kaivac Inc ....E 513 887-4600
Hamilton (G-10714)

Kinetico Incorporated ....G 440 564-7167
Newbury (G-15098)

Knight Manufacturing Co Inc.............G 740 676-5516
Shadyside (G-17082)

◆ Komar Industries Inc ....G 614 836-2366
Groveport (G-10629)

L A Express ....G 513 752-6999
Batavia (G-1201)

L N Brut Manufacturing Co ....G 330 833-9045
Navarre (G-14717)

Larrys Water Conditioning ....G 419 887-0290
Maumee (G-13275)

Layne Heavy Civil Inc ....E 513 424-7287
Middletown (G-14053)

Lima Sheet Metal Machine & Mfg ....E 419 229-1161
Lima (G-12045)

Mack Industries PA Inc ....F 330 638-7680
Vienna (G-19369)

Majic Touch ....G 330 923-8259
Cuyahoga Falls (G-8023)

Master Disposers Inc ....F 513 553-2289
New Richmond (G-14942)

McNish Corporation ....G 614 899-2282
Westerville (G-20171)

Metropolitan Envmtl Svcs Inc ....D 614 771-1881
Hilliard (G-10961)

Monarch Water Systems Inc ....F 937 426-5773
Beavercreek (G-1353)

▲ Mork Process Inc ....E 330 928-3700
Worthington (G-20881)

Mountain Filtration Systems ....G 419 395-2526
Defiance (G-8806)

MPW Industrial Svcs Group Inc...........C 740 927-8790
Hebron (G-10875)

Mt Vernon Cy Wastewater Trtmnt........G 740 393-9502
Mount Vernon (G-14633)

N-Viro International Corp ....G 419 535-6374
Toledo (G-18597)

National Pride Equipment Inc ....G 419 289-2886
Ashland (G-756)

Neil Barton ....G 614 889-9933
Dublin (G-9111)

Nestle R&D Center Inc ....G 440 349-5757
Solon (G-17346)

◆ Norwalk Wastewater Eqp Co ....G 419 668-4471
Norwalk (G-15558)

◆ Nss Enterprises Inc ....G 419 531-2121
Toledo (G-18610)

Oceco Inc ....G 419 447-0916
Tiffin (G-18235)

Oh-LI Commercial Cleaning LLC ....G 614 390-3628
Grove City (G-10579)

▲ Or-Tec Inc ....G 216 475-5225
Maple Heights (G-12737)

Peerless Stove & Mfg Co Inc ....F 419 625-4514
Sandusky (G-16994)

Pelton Environmental Pdts Inc ....G 440 838-1221
Lewis Center (G-11909)

Powerbuff Inc ....F 419 241-2156
Toledo (G-18650)

Powerwash of Ohio ....G 614 260-2756
Lewis Center (G-11911)

R D Baker Enterprises Inc ....G 937 461-5225
Dayton (G-8609)

R Houston Son Sndblst Spclsts ....E 513 367-5252
Harrison (G-10799)

Reid Asset Management Company ....G 216 642-3223
Cleveland (G-6097)

Reynolds & Co Inc ....G 937 592-8300
Bellefontaine (G-1538)

Samco Technologies Inc ....G 216 641-5288
Newburgh Heights (G-15079)

Sammy S Auto Detail ....F 614 263-2728
Columbus (G-7589)

Shred Devil LLC ....G 740 776-1400
Portsmouth (G-16452)

Shred-It USA LLC ....G 614 231-7470
Columbus (G-7618)

Shred-It USA LLC ....E 513 699-0845
Blue Ash (G-1869)

Smart Sonic Corporation ....G 818 610-7900
Cleveland (G-6211)

Staley & Sons Powerwashing LLC........G 937 843-2713
Russells Point (G-16757)

▲ Tema Systems Inc ....E 513 489-7811
Cincinnati (G-4501)

The Mahoning Valley Sani Dst ....D 330 799-6315
Mineral Ridge (G-14312)

Tipton Environmental Intl Inc ....F 513 735-2777
Batavia (G-1228)

Tri County Quality Wtr Systems ....G 740 751-4764
Marion (G-12909)

Trionetics Inc ....G 216 812-3570
Brooklyn Heights (G-2148)

Under Pressure Systems Inc ....G 330 602-4466
New Philadelphia (G-14938)

United McGill ....G 614 829-1226
Columbus (G-7720)

Veolia Water Technologies Inc............D 937 890-4075
Vandalia (G-19316)

Village of Somerset ....G 740 743-1986
Somerset (G-17420)

Village of West Alexandria ....G 937 839-4168
West Alexandria (G-19785)

W3 Ultrasonics LLC ....G 330 284-3667
North Canton (G-15283)

Waste Water Pollution Control ....F 330 263-5290
Wooster (G-20844)

Water & Waste Water Eqp Co ....G 440 542-0972
Solon (G-17413)

Water Poll Control ....E 740 383-4446
Marion (G-12912)

Water Systems Services ....G 513 523-6766
Oxford (G-15845)

Water Treatment Dept ....G 937 498-8180
Sidney (G-17234)

Wb Industries Inc ....G 440 708-0309
Burton (G-2390)

◆ Western Rserve Wtr Systems Inc .....D 216 341-9797
Newburgh Heights (G-15080)

◆ William R Hague Inc ....G 614 836-2115
Groveport (G-10649)

Willow Water Treatment Inc ....G 440 254-6313
Painesville (G-15942)

X-3-5 LLC ....G 513 489-5477
Cincinnati (G-4613)

3592 Carburetors, Pistons, Rings & Valves

Ad Piston Ring Company LLC.............F 216 781-5200
Cleveland (G-4699)

Air Conversion Technology Inc ....G 419 841-1720
Sylvania (G-18099)

Brooks Manufacturing ....G 419 244-1777
Toledo (G-18382)

Buckeye BOP LLC ....G 740 498-9898
Newcomerstown (G-15110)

▲ Celina Alum Precision Tech Inc ....B 419 586-2278
Celina (G-2989)

Dover Corporation ....G 440 951-6600
Mentor (G-13563)

Eaton Usev Holding Company ....G 216 523-5000
Cleveland (G-5253)

Federal-Mogul Corporation ....C 740 432-2393
Cambridge (G-2457)

▲ Group Industries Inc ....E 216 271-0702
Cleveland (G-5461)

Hite Parts Exchange Inc ....E 614 272-5115
Columbus (G-7160)

Manufacturing Division Inc ....G 330 533-6835
Canfield (G-2564)

Michael N Wheeler ....F 740 377-9777
South Point (G-17442)

Northcoast Process Contrls Inc ....G 440 498-0542
Cleveland (G-5901)

Oylair Specialty ....G 614 873-3968
Plain City (G-16353)

▲ PMI Operating Company Inc ....B 440 951-6600
Mentor (G-13690)

Tiffin Foundry & Machine Inc..............G 419 447-3991
Tiffin (G-18247)

3593 Fluid Power Cylinders & Actuators

B & H Machine Inc ....E 330 868-6425
Minerva (G-14317)

Carter Machine Company Inc ....G 419 468-3530
Galion (G-10256)

Cascade Corporation ....C 937 327-0300
Springfield (G-17527)

Commercial Honing Ohio Inc..............G 330 343-8896
Dover (G-8973)

▲ Control Line Equipment Inc ....F 216 433-7766
Cleveland (G-5127)

▲ Custom Hoists Inc ....C 419 368-4721
Ashland (G-727)

Cylinders & Valves Inc ....G 440 238-7343
Strongsville (G-17910)

Dana Incorporated ....B 419 887-3000
Maumee (G-13246)

▲ Dana Limited ....B 630 697-3783
Maumee (G-13249)

Eaton Leasing Corporation ....G 216 382-2292
Beachwood (G-1270)

Eaton-Aeroquip Inc ....D 419 891-7775
Maumee (G-13258)

Emerson Process Management ....E 419 529-4311
Ontario (G-15687)

▲ Hunger Hydraulics CC Ltd ....F 419 666-4510
Rossford (G-16741)

Hydranamics Inc ....D 419 468-3530
Galion (G-10275)

Hydraulic Parts Store Inc ....E 330 364-6667
New Philadelphia (G-14902)

▲ Hydraulic Products Inc ....G 440 946-4575
Willoughby (G-20506)

Hydraulic Specialists Inc ....E 740 922-3343
Midvale (G-14108)

J D Hydraulic Inc ....F 419 686-5234
Portage (G-16424)

Kyntrol Holdings Inc ....G 440 220-5990
Eastlake (G-9279)

Kyntrol LLC ....G 440 951-2333
Eastlake (G-9280)

Malcolm Hydraulics ....G 330 819-2033
Atwater (G-900)

Mrf Machine and Hydraulics Inc...........F 330 673-0135
Kent (G-11495)

▲ Nook Industries Inc ....C 216 271-7900
Cleveland (G-5887)

North Coast Instruments Inc ....E 216 251-2353
Cleveland (G-5896)

Parker-Hannifin Corporation ....F 330 743-6893
Youngstown (G-21166)

◆ Parker-Hannifin Corporation ....B 216 896-3000
Cleveland (G-5973)

Parker-Hannifin Corporation ....G 216 896-3000
Cleveland (G-5976)

Parker-Hannifin Corporation ....C 419 394-9600
Saint Marys (G-16848)

Parker-Hannifin Corporation ....G 330 336-3511
Wadsworth (G-19425)

Qcsm LLC ....G 216 531-5960
Euclid (G-9602)

R & J Cylinder & Machine Inc ....G 330 364-8263
Dover (G-8382)

R & M Fluid Power Inc ....E 330 758-2766
Youngstown (G-21182)

▲ Robeck Fluid Power Co ....D 330 562-1140
Aurora (G-944)

Rosenboom Machine & Tool Inc...........E 419 352-9484
Bowling Green (G-2015)

Sebring Fluid Power Corp .... G 330 938-9984
Sebring *(G-17053)*

▲ Skidmore-Wilhelm Mfg Company .....E 216 481-4774
Solon *(G-17381)*

Steel Eqp Specialists Inc .... E 330 829-2626
Alliance *(G-539)*

▲ Steel Eqp Specialists Inc .... D 330 823-8260
Alliance *(G-540)*

Suburban Manufacturing Co .... D 440 953-2024
Eastlake *(G-9290)*

Swagelok Company .... D 440 349-5934
Solon *(G-17392)*

United Hydraulics .... F 440 585-0906
Wickliffe *(G-20390)*

V & P Hydraulic Products LLC .... D 740 203-3600
Delaware *(G-8893)*

▲ Waltco Lift Corp .... C 330 633-9191
Tallmadge *(G-18175)*

Xomox Corporation .... G 936 271-6500
Cincinnati *(G-4614)*

Zaytran Corporation .... E 440 324-2814
Elyria *(G-9512)*

3594 Fluid Power Pumps & Motors

Aerocontrolex Group Inc .... D 440 352-6182
Cleveland *(G-4719)*

Alkid Corporation .... G 216 896-3000
Cleveland *(G-4754)*

▲ All - Flo Pump Company .... E 440 354-1700
Mentor *(G-13518)*

Ban-Fam Industries Inc .... G 216 265-9588
Cleveland *(G-4888)*

Bergstrom Company Ltd Partnr .... G 440 232-2282
Cleveland *(G-4905)*

Bosch Rexroth Corporation .... B 330 263-3300
Wooster *(G-20751)*

Crown Elec Svcs & Automtn Inc ...... G 330 270-9890
Youngstown *(G-21058)*

Custom Cltch Jint Hydrlics Inc .... F 216 431-1630
Cleveland *(G-5149)*

Cylinders & Valves Inc .... G 440 238-7343
Strongsville *(G-17910)*

◆ Eaton Corporation .... B 216 523-5000
Cleveland *(G-5245)*

Eaton Corporation .... C 216 416-2500
Cleveland *(G-5246)*

Eaton Hydraulics LLC .... E 419 232-7777
Van Wert *(G-19254)*

Eaton Leasing Corporation .... G 216 382-2292
Beachwood *(G-1270)*

Eaton-Aeroquip Inc .... D 419 891-7775
Maumee *(G-13258)*

Emerson Process Management .... E 419 529-4311
Ontario *(G-15687)*

▲ Force Control Industries Inc .... D 513 868-0900
Fairfield *(G-9659)*

▼ Furukawa Rock Drill USA Co Ltd .....E 330 673-5826
Kent *(G-11462)*

▼ George A Mitchell Company .... E 330 758-5777
Youngstown *(G-21099)*

▲ Giant Industries Inc .... E 419 531-4600
Toledo *(G-18480)*

Gorman-Rupp Company .... G 419 755-1011
Mansfield *(G-12617)*

Gorman-Rupp Company .... B 419 755-1011
Mansfield *(G-12614)*

H Y O Inc .... F 614 488-2861
Columbus *(G-7136)*

Hite Parts Exchange Inc .... E 614 272-5115
Columbus *(G-7160)*

▲ Hy-Production Inc .... G 330 273-2400
Valley City *(G-19206)*

Hydraulic Parts Store Inc .... E 330 364-6667
New Philadelphia *(G-14902)*

▲ Hydraulic Products Inc .... G 440 946-4575
Willoughby *(G-20506)*

Ingersoll-Rand Company .... E 419 633-6800
Bryan *(G-2306)*

▲ Linde Hydraulics Corporation .... E 330 533-6801
Canfield *(G-2562)*

Midwest Tool & Engineering Co .... E 937 224-0756
Dayton *(G-8498)*

▲ Opw Inc .... A 800 422-2525
West Chester *(G-19910)*

Parker Royalty Partnership .... D 216 896-3000
Cleveland *(G-5971)*

◆ Parker-Hannifin Corporation .... B 216 896-3000
Cleveland *(G-5973)*

Parker-Hannifin Corporation .... C 330 963-0601
Macedonia *(G-12468)*

Parker-Hannifin Corporation .... C 330 740-8366
Youngstown *(G-21165)*

Parker-Hannifin Corporation .... C 513 847-1758
West Chester *(G-19912)*

Parker-Hannifin Corporation .... F 216 896-3000
Macedonia *(G-12469)*

Parker-Hannifin Corporation .... E 440 266-2300
Mentor *(G-13681)*

Parker-Hannifin Corporation .... C 937 644-3915
Marysville *(G-12962)*

Parker-Hannifin Corporation .... F 216 896-3000
Cleveland *(G-5976)*

Parker-Hannifin Corporation .... C 419 394-9600
Saint Marys *(G-16848)*

Pfpc Enterprises Inc .... B 513 941-6200
Cincinnati *(G-4233)*

Quad Fluid Dynamics Inc .... F 330 220-3005
Brunswick *(G-2250)*

R & L Hydraulics Inc .... G 937 399-3407
Springfield *(G-17632)*

Radocy Inc .... F 419 666-4400
Rossford *(G-16747)*

▲ Robeck Fluid Power Co .... D 330 562-1140
Aurora *(G-944)*

▲ Semtorq Inc .... F 330 487-0600
Twinsburg *(G-19019)*

Stanley Proctor & Company Inc .... F 330 425-7814
Twinsburg *(G-19023)*

Starkey Machinery Inc .... E 419 468-2560
Galion *(G-10289)*

Suburban Manufacturing Co .... D 440 953-2024
Eastlake *(G-9290)*

Sunset Industries Inc .... E 216 731-8131
Euclid *(G-9607)*

Swagelok Company .... E 440 349-5836
Solon *(G-17393)*

Swanson Industries Inc .... D 304 284-5199
New Philadelphia *(G-14931)*

Toth Industries Inc .... D 419 729-4669
Toledo *(G-18752)*

Vertiflo Pump Company .... F 513 530-0888
Cincinnati *(G-4566)*

Vickers International Inc .... D 419 867-2200
Maumee *(G-13307)*

3596 Scales & Balances, Exc Laboratory

Advance Weight System Inc .... F 440 926-3691
Grafton *(G-10418)*

▲ Etched Metal Company .... E 440 248-0240
Solon *(G-17290)*

Exact Equipment Corporation .... F 215 295-2000
Columbus *(G-6645)*

Hobart Corporation .... C 937 332-3000
Troy *(G-18840)*

Hobart Corporation .... C 937 332-2797
Piqua *(G-16277)*

▲ Holtgreven Scale & Elec Corp .... F 419 422-4779
Findlay *(G-9840)*

Interface Logic Systems Inc .... G 614 236-8388
Columbus *(G-7202)*

Kanawha Scales & Systems Inc .... F 513 576-0700
Milford *(G-14158)*

▲ LTS Metrology LLC .... E 330 425-3092
Twinsburg *(G-18975)*

Mettler-Toledo LLC .... D 614 438-4511
Worthington *(G-20878)*

Mettler-Toledo LLC .... C 614 438-4390
Worthington *(G-20879)*

Mettler-Toledo LLC .... C 614 841-7300
Columbus *(G-7343)*

Mettler-Toledo Intl Fin Inc .... G 614 438-4511
Columbus *(G-6653)*

◆ Mettler-Toledo Intl Inc .... B 614 438-4511
Columbus *(G-6654)*

Roth Transit Inc .... G 937 773-5051
Piqua *(G-16311)*

Scale Tech Ltd .... E 419 729-5240
Toledo *(G-18686)*

T & S Enterprises .... E 419 424-1122
Findlay *(G-9899)*

3599 Machinery & Eqpt, Indl & Commercial, NEC

2-M Manufacturing Company .... E 440 269-1270
Eastlake *(G-9256)*

3way Machine and Tool Company ...... G 419 925-7222
Maria Stein *(G-12756)*

5s Inc .... G 440 968-0212
Montville *(G-14459)*

8888 Butler Investments Inc .... G 440 748-0810
North Ridgeville *(G-15354)*

▲ A & G Manufacturing Co Inc .... E 419 468-7433
Galion *(G-10250)*

A & G Manufacturing Co Inc .... D 419 468-7433
Galion *(G-10251)*

A & L Industries .... E 419 698-3733
Oregon *(G-15698)*

A & L Machine Tool .... G 513 863-2662
Hamilton *(G-10660)*

A & R Machine Co Inc .... G 330 832-4631
Massillon *(G-13105)*

A and V Grinding Inc .... G 937 444-4141
Cincinnati *(G-3330)*

A B & J Machining & Fabg .... G 513 769-5900
Cincinnati *(G-3331)*

A E Ruston Electric LLC .... G 740 286-3022
Jackson *(G-11306)*

A S T Machine Co .... G 740 494-2013
Prospect *(G-16495)*

A&S Machine .... G 440 946-3976
Willoughby *(G-20423)*

A+ Engineering Fabrication Inc .... F 419 832-0748
Grand Rapids *(G-10439)*

A-A1 Machine and Supply Co .... G 440 346-0698
Tallmadge *(G-18131)*

Abbey Machine Products Co .... G 216 481-0080
Cleveland *(G-4682)*

Abco Bar & Tube Cutting Svc .... E 513 697-9487
Maineville *(G-12520)*

Able Grinding Co Inc .... G 216 961-6555
Cleveland *(G-4686)*

Able Tool Corporation .... E 513 733-8989
Cincinnati *(G-3346)*

Absolute Cnc Machining LLC .... G 937 855-0406
Germantown *(G-10368)*

Accu Tool Inc .... G 937 667-5878
Tipp City *(G-18257)*

Accu-Tech Mfg & Support .... F 440 205-8882
Mentor *(G-13505)*

Accuform Manufacturing Inc .... E 330 797-9291
Youngstown *(G-21014)*

Accurate Machining & Welding .... G 937 584-4518
Sabina *(G-16772)*

Accurate Manufacturing Company .....E 614 878-6510
Columbus *(G-6685)*

Accurate Metal Machining Inc .... C 440 350-8225
Painesville *(G-15847)*

Accurate Tech Inc .... G 440 951-9153
Mentor *(G-13506)*

Ace Boiler & Welding Co Inc .... G 330 745-4443
Barberton *(G-1092)*

▲ Ace Manufacturing Company .... E 513 541-2490
West Chester *(G-19976)*

▲ Ace Precision Industries Inc .... E 330 633-8523
Akron *(G-28)*

Acme Machine Technology LLC .... E 419 594-3349
Oakwood *(G-15613)*

Acrodyne Mfg Co .... G 614 443-5517
Columbus *(G-6690)*

Action Machine & Manufacturing ..... G 513 899-3889
Morrow *(G-14542)*

Action Mechanical Repair Inc .... E 513 353-1046
Cincinnati *(G-3351)*

Action Precision Products Inc .... E 419 737-2348
Pioneer *(G-16231)*

Active Roads LLC .... G 937 242-6555
West Chester *(G-19797)*

▲ Addisonmckee Inc .... C 513 228-7000
Lebanon *(G-11774)*

ADI Machining Inc .... F 440 277-4141
Sheffield Village *(G-17119)*

Adisco Inc .... F 937 296-5070
Kettering *(G-11574)*

▲ Advance Apex Inc .... E 614 539-3000
Grove City *(G-10538)*

Advance Manufacturing Corp .... E 216 333-1684
Cleveland *(G-4708)*

Advanced Cylinder Repair Inc .... G 419 289-0538
Ashland *(G-701)*

▲ Advanced Design Industries Inc .....E 440 277-4141
Sheffield Village *(G-17120)*

Advanced Engrg & Mfg Co Inc .... F 330 686-9911
Stow *(G-17729)*

Advanced Indus Machining Inc .... F 614 596-4183
Powell *(G-16461)*

Advanced Welding Co .... G 937 746-6800
Franklin *(G-10005)*

Advantage Machine Shop .... G 330 337-8377
Salem *(G-16869)*

Advetech Inc ....E 330 533-2227
Canfield (G-2543)

Aero-Med Industries Inc ....G 216 459-0004
Cleveland (G-4718)

Aeroserv ....F 513 932-9227
Lebanon (G-11777)

Aerotech Enterprise ....F 440 729-2616
Chesterland (G-3195)

Aircraft and Auto Fittings Co ....G 216 486-0047
Cleveland (G-4736)

Aisco Metallizing Corp ....F 216 441-7244
Cleveland (G-4738)

▲ Aja Industries LLC ....G 614 216-9566
Gahanna (G-10203)

Akri Tool Corporation ....F 440 237-3050
Brunswick (G-2203)

▼ Akron Equipment Company ....G 330 645-3780
Akron (G-42)

Akron Gear & Engineering Inc ....E 330 773-6608
Akron (G-45)

▼ Akron Special Machinery Inc ......E 330 753-1077
Akron (G-55)

Albright Machine ....G 419 483-1088
Monroeville (G-14424)

Aleco Machine LLC ....E 513 894-6400
Hamilton (G-10664)

▲ Alex Products Inc ....B 419 267-5240
Ridgeville Corners (G-16662)

▲ Alfons Haar Inc ....E 937 560-2031
Springboro (G-17472)

Alfred Machine Co ....D 440 248-4600
Cleveland (G-4753)

All Craft Manufacturing Co ....F 513 661-3383
Cincinnati (G-3377)

All-Tech Manufacturing Ltd ....G 330 633-1095
Akron (G-63)

All-Type Welding & Fabrication ....E 440 439-3990
Cleveland (G-4761)

Allen Randall Enterprises Inc ....F 330 374-9850
Akron (G-64)

Alliance Automation LLC ....F 419 238-2520
Van Wert (G-19243)

Allied Machine Works Inc ....G 740 454-2534
Zanesville (G-21270)

Allied Mask and Tooling Inc ....F 419 470-2555
Toledo (G-18329)

◆ Alloy Bllows Prcision Wldg Inc ....D 440 684-3000
Cleveland (G-4767)

Alloy Machining and Fabg ....E 330 482-5543
Columbiana (G-6605)

Alpha Machining LLC ....G 330 889-2207
West Farmington (G-20074)

Alpha Omega Dev & Mch Co ....G 440 352-9915
Painesville (G-15848)

Alton Products Inc ....F 419 893-0201
Maumee (G-13221)

Aluminum Fence & Mfg Co ....G 330 755-3323
Burton (G-2372)

Amcan Productions Ltd ....G 330 332-9129
Salem (G-16871)

American Aero Components LLC .....G 937 367-5068
Dayton (G-8150)

American Punch Co Inc ....E 216 731-4501
Euclid (G-9566)

American Tool Works Inc ....F 513 844-6363
Hamilton (G-10667)

American Tool Works Inc ....F 513 844-6363
Hamilton (G-10668)

Amerimold Inc ....G 330 628-2190
Mogadore (G-14367)

Amon Inc ....F 513 734-1700
Amelia (G-567)

AMP-Tech Inc ....F 419 652-3444
Nova (G-15575)

Ampsco Division ....G 614 444-2181
Columbus (G-6745)

▲ Amt Machine Systems Ltd ....G 614 635-8050
Columbus (G-6748)

Amtech Tool and Machine Inc ....F 330 758-8215
Youngstown (G-21024)

Anchor Fabricators Inc ....E 937 836-5117
Clayton (G-4656)

Anchor Metal Processing Inc ....F 216 362-6463
Cleveland (G-4804)

Anchor Metal Processing Inc ....F 216 362-1850
Cleveland (G-4805)

Andersons Inc ....F 419 891-2930
Maumee (G-13225)

Andrew & Sons Inc ....G 419 693-0292
Toledo (G-18350)

Andrew Tool Co Inc ....G 440 237-4340
North Royalton (G-15409)

▲ Ansco Machine Company ....E 330 929-8181
Peninsula (G-16034)

Anstine Machining Corp ....G 330 821-4365
Alliance (G-496)

Anvil Products Co ....E 216 883-3740
Cleveland (G-4817)

Apex Bolt & Machine Company ....E 419 729-3741
Toledo (G-18351)

Apex Specialty Co Inc ....G 330 725-6663
Medina (G-13371)

Apollo Welding & Fabg Inc ....E 440 942-0227
Willoughby (G-20435)

Applied Experience LLC ....G 614 943-2970
Columbus (G-6765)

Apr Tool Inc ....G 440 946-0393
Willoughby (G-20437)

Arabian Tools Inc ....G 440 286-3600
Chardon (G-3141)

ARC Drilling Inc ....F 216 525-0920
Cleveland (G-4822)

Ardar Co Inc ....G 440 582-3371
Cleveland (G-4828)

Arlington Prcsion Grinding LLC ....G 937 833-1553
Brookville (G-2175)

◆ ARM (usa) Inc ....E 740 264-6599
Steubenville (G-17688)

Arnold Machine Inc ....F 419 443-1818
Tiffin (G-18205)

Arnolds Repair Shop ....E 740 373-5313
Marietta (G-12762)

Artisan Equipment Inc ....F 740 756-9135
Carroll (G-2936)

Asb Industries Inc ....E 330 753-8458
Barberton (G-1099)

Ash Machine Corporation ....E 740 927-0506
Pataskala (G-15968)

Ashcraft Machine & Supply Inc ....F 740 349-8110
Newark (G-14984)

Ashta Forge & Machine Inc ....E 216 252-7000
Cleveland (G-4846)

Assembly Machining Wire Pdts ....G 614 443-1110
Columbus (G-6779)

Associated Press Repair Inc ....G 216 881-2288
Cleveland (G-4849)

Astro Technical Services Inc ....E 330 394-7350
Warren (G-19525)

Athens Mold and Machine Inc ....D 740 593-6613
Akron (G-76)

Atlas Gear and Machine Co ....G 614 272-6944
Columbus (G-6783)

▲ Atlas Industries Inc ....G 419 355-1000
Fremont (G-10126)

Atlas Industries Inc ....D 419 447-4730
Tiffin (G-18206)

Atlas Industries Inc ....B 419 637-2117
Tiffin (G-18207)

Atlas Machine and Supply Inc ....G 614 351-1603
Hilliard (G-10928)

Atlas Machine and Supply Inc ....G 502 584-7262
West Chester (G-19982)

Atlas Precision Machining Inc ....G 937 615-9585
Piqua (G-16251)

▲ Ats Assembly and Test Inc ....B 937 222-3030
Dayton (G-8170)

Ats Machine & Tool Co Inc ....F 440 255-1120
Mentor (G-13528)

Auglaize Erie Machine Company ....E 419 629-2068
New Bremen (G-14780)

Austinburg Machine Inc ....G 440 275-2001
Austinburg (G-958)

Austins Machine Shop ....E 614 855-2525
Blacklick (G-1689)

Autotec Engineering Company ....E 419 885-2529
Toledo (G-18360)

Avs Oil Recovery LLC ....G 937 645-4600
Marysville (G-12932)

Axis Tool & Grinding LLC ....G 330 535-4713
Akron (G-79)

B & B Gear & Machine Co Inc ....F 937 687-1771
New Lebanon (G-14840)

▲ B & C Research Inc ....B 330 848-4000
Barberton (G-1101)

B & D Machinists Inc ....F 513 831-8588
Milford (G-14123)

B & F Manufacturing Co ....F 216 518-0333
Warrensville Heights (G-19629)

B & G Machine Company Inc ....G 440 946-8787
Mentor (G-13533)

B & G Tool Company ....G 614 451-2538
Columbus (G-6795)

B & H Machine Inc ....E 330 868-6425
Minerva (G-14317)

B & R Machine Co Inc ....F 216 961-7370
Cleveland (G-4882)

B & T Welding and Machine Co ....G 740 687-1908
Lancaster (G-11690)

B B & H Tool Company ....G 614 868-8634
Reynoldsburg (G-16581)

B C Machining Inc ....G 440 593-4763
Conneaut (G-7800)

B C Metals Inc ....G 513 732-9644
Batavia (G-1166)

B M C Inc ....G 216 581-9595
Cleveland (G-4883)

B N Machine Inc ....G 440 255-5200
Mentor (G-13534)

B S F Inc ....F 937 890-6121
Tipp City (G-18264)

B Y G Industries Inc ....G 216 961-5436
Cleveland (G-4884)

B&C Machine Co LLC ....B 330 745-4013
Barberton (G-1103)

Baco Manufacturing Corp ....G 440 585-5858
Wickliffe (G-20355)

Bainter Machining Company ....F 740 756-4598
Carroll (G-2937)

Bainter Machining Company ....G 740 653-2422
Lancaster (G-11691)

Balancing Company Inc ....E 937 898-9111
Vandalia (G-19282)

Ban-Fam Industries Inc ....G 216 265-9588
Cleveland (G-4888)

▲ Bardons & Oliver Inc ....C 440 498-5800
Solon (G-17264)

Barile Precision Grinding Inc ....E 216 267-6500
Cleveland (G-4890)

Bartley Offie ....G 614 235-9050
Columbus (G-6811)

Bay West Products ....G 440 835-1991
Bay Village (G-1242)

Beacon Metal Fabricators Inc ....F 216 391-7444
Cleveland (G-4900)

Beckman Machine LLC ....E 513 242-2700
Cincinnati (G-3443)

Bedford Precision Products Inc ....G 440 786-7277
Bedford (G-1406)

Beemer Machine Company Inc ....G 330 678-3822
Kent (G-11434)

Bender Cycle & Machine Corp ....G 440 946-0681
Willoughby (G-20443)

▲ Berea Manufacturing Inc ....F 440 260-0590
Berea (G-1604)

Bergman Tool & Machine Co ....G 419 925-4963
Maria Stein (G-12757)

Berran Industrial Group Inc ....G 330 253-5800
Akron (G-89)

Best Inc ....G 419 394-2745
Saint Marys (G-16833)

Best Mold & Manufacturing Inc ....E 330 896-4084
Akron (G-90)

Best Performance Inc ....E 419 394-2299
Saint Marys (G-16834)

Beta Industries Inc ....E 937 299-7385
Dayton (G-8186)

Beta Machine Company Inc ....F 216 383-0000
Cleveland (G-4909)

Beverage Machine & Fabricators ....F 216 252-5100
Cleveland (G-4911)

▲ Bexley Pen Company Inc ....G 614 351-9988
Columbus (G-6826)

Bic Manufacturing Inc ....E 216 531-9393
Euclid (G-9567)

Bickett Machine and Supply Inc ....G 740 353-5710
Portsmouth (G-16431)

Bishop Machine Tool & Die ....F 740 453-8818
Zanesville (G-21280)

Bits & Chips Machining Company ......G 513 539-0800
Monroe (G-14394)

Black Machining & Technology ....F 513 752-8625
Batavia (G-1169)

Blacklick Machine Co Inc ....G 614 866-9300
Blacklick (G-1691)

Bleil Chan ....G 440 352-6012
Mentor (G-13536)

Blue Chip Machine & Tool Ltd ....G 419 626-9559
Sandusky (G-16949)

Blue Chip Tool Inc ....F 513 489-3561
Cincinnati (G-3454)

Bmi Machine Inc ....G 614 785-7020
   Columbus (G-6842)

Bobs Grinding Inc ....G 440 946-6179
   Mentor (G-13537)

Boggs & Associates Inc ....G 614 237-0600
   Columbus (G-6844)

Bollari/Davis Inc ....F 330 296-4445
   Ravenna (G-16519)

Bomen Marking Products Inc ....G 440 582-0053
   Cleveland (G-4922)

Bond Machine Company Inc ....F 937 746-4941
   Franklin (G-10009)

▼ Bonnot Company ....E 330 896-6544
   Akron (G-96)

Borman Enterprises Inc ....F 216 459-9292
   Cleveland (G-4926)

Bowdil Company ....F 800 356-8663
   Canton (G-2626)

Boyce Machine Inc ....G 330 678-3210
   Kent (G-11436)

Boyds Machine and Met Finshg ......F 937 698-5623
   West Milton (G-20105)

Brandts Custom Machining LLC ......G 419 566-3192
   Mansfield (G-12568)

Brinkley Technology Group LLC ......F 330 830-2498
   Massillon (G-13115)

Brocker Machine Inc ....F 330 744-5858
   Youngstown (G-21038)

Brockman Jig Grinding Service ......G 937 220-9780
   Dayton (G-8198)

Brogan Machine Shop ....G 513 683-9054
   Loveland (G-12345)

Bront Machining Inc ....E 937 228-4551
   Moraine (G-14470)

Brooklyn Machine & Mfg Co Inc ....G 216 341-1846
   Cleveland (G-4934)

Brown Cnc Machinery Inc ....E 937 865-9191
   Miamisburg (G-13787)

Brown Machine Co ....G 216 631-1255
   Cleveland (G-4939)

Brown Precision Machine ....G 937 675-6585
   Jamestown (G-11350)

Bruck Manufacturing Co Inc ....G 440 327-6619
   North Ridgeville (G-15363)

Bsm Columbus Llp ....G 740 755-2380
   Johnstown (G-11392)

Buckeye Field Machining Inc ....G 330 336-7036
   Norton (G-15507)

Buckeye Mch Fabricators Inc ....E 419 273-2521
   Forest (G-9918)

Buckeye State Welding & Fabg ....G 440 322-0319
   Elyria (G-9384)

Buckys Machine and Fab Ltd ....G 419 981-5050
   Mc Cutchenville (G-13340)

▲ Bullen Ultrasonics Inc ....D 937 456-7133
   Eaton (G-9301)

Bullseye Machines LLC ....G 419 485-5951
   Montpelier (G-14439)

Burdens Machine & Welding ....E 740 345-9246
   Newark (G-14989)

▲ Burke Products Inc ....E 937 372-3516
   Xenia (G-20940)

Burton Industries Inc ....F 440 974-1700
   Mentor (G-13539)

C & C Machine Co ....G 330 633-4485
   Silver Lake (G-17237)

C & D Manufacturing Inc ....G 330 828-8357
   Dalton (G-8064)

C & K Machine Co Inc ....G 419 237-3203
   Fayette (G-9774)

C A Joseph Co ....F 330 532-4646
   Irondale (G-11287)

▲ C A Joseph Co ....G 330 385-6869
   East Liverpool (G-9204)

C A M Machine Inc ....E 937 663-5000
   Saint Paris (G-16860)

C A T-Wood Metal Works Inc ....E 937 866-4917
   Moraine (G-14471)

C and J Machine Inc ....G 330 935-2170
   Hartville (G-10817)

C G Egli Inc ....G 937 254-8898
   Dayton (G-8204)

C G Manufacturing Company Inc ....E 440 951-8555
   Willoughby (G-20450)

C M M S - Re Inc ....F 513 489-5111
   Blue Ash (G-1759)

C N C Precision Machine Inc ....D 440 548-3880
   Parkman (G-15950)

C RC Automotive ....G 513 422-4775
   Middletown (G-14025)

C-N-D Industries Inc ....E 330 478-8811
   Massillon (G-13118)

Cage Gear & Machine LLC ....F 330 452-1532
   Canton (G-2633)

Calvin J Magsig ....G 419 862-3311
   Elmore (G-9361)

CAM Machine Inc ....G 937 663-0680
   Saint Paris (G-16861)

Capital Machine & Fabrication ....G 740 773-4976
   Chillicothe (G-3231)

Cardinal Machine Company ....F 440 238-7050
   Strongsville (G-17899)

Carl Hucke ....G 419 396-6078
   Carey (G-2916)

Carnation Machine & Tool Inc ....G 330 823-5352
   Alliance (G-502)

Carousel Magic LLC ....G 419 522-6456
   Mansfield (G-12575)

Carousel Works Inc ....E 419 522-7558
   Mansfield (G-12576)

Cascade Unlimited LLC ....G 440 352-7995
   Painesville (G-15863)

▲ Case-Maul Manufacturing Co .....F 419 524-1061
   Mansfield (G-12577)

Caskeys Inc ....G 330 683-0249
   Orrville (G-15733)

Cave Tool & Manufacturing Inc ....F 937 324-0662
   Springfield (G-17528)

CBs Boring and Mch Co Inc ....E 419 784-9500
   Defiance (G-8783)

CC Ironworks LLC ....G 330 542-0500
   New Middletown (G-14874)

Cctm Inc ....G 513 934-3533
   Lebanon (G-11788)

Ceemco Incorporated ....D 513 563-8822
   Cincinnati (G-3511)

Cen-Trol Machine Co ....G 216 524-1932
   Cleveland (G-5002)

Center Automotive Parts Co ....G 330 434-2174
   Akron (G-117)

Center Line Drilling Inc ....G 440 951-5920
   Willoughby (G-20454)

Centerless Grinding Service ....G 216 251-4100
   Cleveland (G-5003)

Centerless Grinding Solutions ....G 216 520-4612
   Cleveland (G-5004)

Centerline Tool & Machine ....G 937 222-3600
   Dayton (G-8221)

Central State Enterprises Inc ....E 419 468-8191
   Galion (G-10258)

Century Tool & Stamping Inc ....F 216 241-2032
   Cleveland (G-5008)

Certified Welding Co ....F 216 961-5410
   Cleveland (G-5009)

Chandler Machine Co Inc ....G 330 688-7615
   Stow (G-17738)

Chandler Machine Prod Gear ....G 330 688-5585
   Stow (G-17739)

Chardon Metal Products Co ....G 440 285-2147
   Chardon (G-3144)

Charles Costa Inc ....F 330 376-3636
   Akron (G-119)

Chelsea Machine Service Inc ....G 937 233-6330
   Dayton (G-8227)

▼ Chickasaw Machine & Tl Co Inc ..F 419 925-4325
   Chickasaw (G-3225)

Chipman Machining Co Inc ....G 513 681-8515
   Cincinnati (G-3529)

Chipmatic Tool & Machine Inc ....D 419 862-2737
   Elmore (G-9362)

Chips Manufacturing Inc ....G 440 946-3666
   Willoughby (G-20456)

Christopher Tool & Mfg Co ....C 440 248-8080
   Cleveland (G-5030)

▲ Cincinnati Babbitt Inc ....F 513 942-5088
   Fairfield (G-9654)

Cinex Inc ....D 513 921-2825
   Cincinnati (G-3574)

▲ Circle Machine Rolls Inc ....G 330 938-9010
   Sebring (G-17044)

City Machine Technologies Inc ....E 330 740-8186
   Youngstown (G-21048)

City Machine Technologies Inc ....G 330 747-2639
   Youngstown (G-21049)

City Machine Technologies Inc ....G 330 747-2639
   Youngstown (G-21050)

City Machine Technologies Inc ....F 330 747-2639
   Youngstown (G-21047)

Clapp & Haney Brazed Tool Co ....E 740 922-3515
   Dennison (G-8944)

Clark Machine Service ....G 740 887-2396
   Londonderry (G-12226)

Cleaning Tech Group LLC ....E 513 870-0100
   West Chester (G-19991)

Clear Creek Screw Machine Corp .....G 740 969-2113
   Amanda (G-562)

Cleveland Plastic Fabricat ....F 216 797-7300
   Euclid (G-9572)

Cleveland Special Tool Inc ....F 440 944-1600
   Wickliffe (G-20362)

Clipsons Metal Working Inc ....G 513 772-6393
   Cincinnati (G-3588)

CMI Technology Inc ....F 937 832-2000
   Englewood (G-9513)

Cmt Machining & Fabg LLC ....F 937 652-3740
   Urbana (G-19151)

Coit Tool Company Inc ....G 440 946-3377
   Willoughby (G-20458)

▲ Cold Headed Fas Assemblies Inc ..F 330 833-0800
   Massillon (G-13120)

Coleman Machine Inc ....G 740 695-3006
   Saint Clairsville (G-16787)

Coleys Inc ....E 440 967-5630
   Vermilion (G-19324)

▲ Colfor Manufacturing Inc ....B 330 863-0404
   Malvern (G-12541)

Columbia Machine Company ....G 740 452-1736
   Zanesville (G-21292)

Columbus Advanced Mfg Sftwr ....G 614 433-0415
   Powell (G-16467)

Columbus Machine Works Inc ....F 614 409-0244
   Columbus (G-6960)

Combine Grinding Co Inc ....G 440 439-6148
   Bedford (G-1417)

Combined Industrial Solutions ....G 513 659-3091
   Milford (G-14131)

▲ Commercial Honing LLC ....D 330 343-8896
   Dover (G-8971)

Compton Metal Products Inc ....D 937 382-2403
   Wilmington (G-20660)

Comptons Precision Machine ....F 937 325-9139
   Springfield (G-17535)

Conison Tool and Die Inc ....G 330 758-1574
   Youngstown (G-21056)

Copen Machine Inc ....F 330 678-4598
   Kent (G-11441)

Core-Tech Inc ....G 440 946-8324
   Mentor (G-13553)

Coshocton Industries Inc ....G 330 339-4744
   New Philadelphia (G-14893)

Coshocton Industries Inc ....G 740 622-4734
   Coshocton (G-7886)

Craig Bros Machine Co Inc ....G 740 756-9280
   Carroll (G-2938)

Creative Mold and Machine Inc ....E 440 338-5146
   Newbury (G-15087)

Creative Processing Inc ....F 440 834-4070
   Mantua (G-12708)

Creative Tool & Die ....G 614 836-0080
   Groveport (G-10619)

Crissman Tool & Machine Inc ....G 330 872-1412
   Newton Falls (G-15131)

Crists Machining Inc ....G 740 653-0041
   Lancaster (G-11700)

Criterion Tool & Die Inc ....E 216 267-1733
   Brookpark (G-2154)

Croft & Son Mfg Inc ....G 740 859-2200
   Tiltonsville (G-18254)

Crowe Manufacturing Services ....D 800 831-1893
   Troy (G-18813)

Crum Manufacturing Inc ....E 419 878-9779
   Waterville (G-19654)

Ctek Tool & Machine Company ....G 513 742-0423
   Cincinnati (G-3624)

Curtiss-Wright Flow Control ....D 513 528-7900
   Cincinnati (G-3296)

Curtiss-Wright Flow Control ....D 513 735-2538
   Batavia (G-1175)

Custom Crankshaft Inc ....E 330 382-1200
   East Liverpool (G-9209)

Custom Machine Inc ....E 419 986-5122
   Tiffin (G-18217)

Custom Metal Works Inc ....F 419 668-7831
   Norwalk (G-15531)

▲ Cutting Dynamics Inc ....C 440 249-4662
   Avon (G-993)

Cutting Edge Manufacturing LLC ....G 419 547-9204
   Clyde (G-6539)

Cuyahoga Mch Co Ltd Lblty Co ....G 216 267-3560
   Cleveland (G-5158)

S I C

D & B Industries Inc..........G.... 937 253-8658
Dayton (G-8100)

D & B Machine Welding Inc..........G.... 740 922-4930
Uhrichsville (G-19048)

D & D Quality Machining Co Inc..........F.... 440 942-2772
Willoughby (G-20466)

D & E Machine Co..........G.... 513 932-2184
Lebanon (G-11793)

D & J Machine Shop..........G.... 937 256-2730
Dayton (G-8263)

D & L Machine Co Inc..........E.... 330 785-0781
Akron (G-140)

D & L Machining LLC..........G.... 419 253-1351
Marengo (G-12749)

D 4 Industries Inc..........G.... 419 523-9555
Ottawa (G-15792)

D M Tool & Plastics Inc..........F.... 937 962-4140
Brookville (G-2180)

D M Tool & Plastics Inc..........F.... 937 962-4140
Lewisburg (G-11932)

D O Technologies Inc..........F.... 330 725-4561
Medina (G-13399)

D S H Machine Co..........G.... 440 946-4311
Willoughby (G-20467)

Dalton Stryker McHining Fcilty..........D.... 419 682-6328
Stryker (G-18002)

Dana Off Highway Products LLC..........E.... 614 864-1116
Blacklick (G-1695)

Dana White Machining Wldg Inc..........G.... 419 652-3444
Nova (G-15577)

Daugherty Machine Company Inc..........F.... 614 834-4010
Canal Winchester (G-2522)

▲ David Price Metal Services Inc..........C.... 419 668-3358
Norwalk (G-15533)

Davis Machine Products Inc..........G.... 440 474-0247
Streetsboro (G-17849)

Davis Machining Service..........G.... 513 528-4917
Cincinnati (G-3642)

Dearborn Inc..........E.... 440 234-1353
Berea (G-1610)

Dee Lee Machine Inc..........G.... 440 259-2245
Madison (G-12504)

▲ Deimling/Jeliho Plastics Inc..........D.... 513 752-6653
Amelia (G-572)

Del-Ter Precision Machine Inc..........G.... 330 724-9167
Akron (G-144)

Delco LLC..........E.... 330 896-4220
Akron (G-146)

Delta Machine & Tool Co..........F.... 216 524-2477
Cleveland (G-5183)

Delta Manufacturing Inc..........F.... 330 386-1270
East Liverpool (G-9213)

Des Machine Services Inc..........G.... 330 633-6897
Tallmadge (G-18140)

Design & Fabrication Inc..........G.... 419 294-2414
Upper Sandusky (G-19119)

Design Tech Inc..........G.... 937 254-7000
Dayton (G-8301)

Detailed Machining Inc..........E.... 937 492-1264
Sidney (G-17178)

▲ Detroit Diesl Specialty TI Inc..........E.... 740 435-4452
Byesville (G-2399)

Deuce Machining LLC..........G.... 513 875-2291
Fayetteville (G-9781)

Devault Machine & Mould Co LLC..........G.... 740 654-5925
Lancaster (G-11705)

Dex-Cut Tools..........G.... 513 248-9898
Milford (G-14136)

Dg Custom Machine..........G.... 419 636-8059
Bryan (G-2294)

Die-Tech Machine Inc..........G.... 740 264-2426
Bloomingdale (G-1722)

Dilco Industries Inc..........E.... 330 337-6732
Salem (G-16888)

◆ Dilworth Machine..........F.... 330 427-1706
East Palestine (G-9233)

Dimension Industries Inc..........F.... 440 236-3265
Columbia Station (G-6587)

Dimension Machine Company Inc..........G.... 513 242-9996
Cincinnati (G-3654)

Direct Wire Service LLP..........G.... 937 526-4447
Versailles (G-19345)

▲ Diversified Fittings Inc..........F.... 440 259-0093
Perry (G-16048)

Dollman Technical Services..........G.... 419 877-9404
Toledo (G-18442)

Donaldson Company Inc..........D.... 330 928-4100
Stow (G-17743)

Dover Machine Co..........F.... 330 343-4123
Dover (G-8981)

Drabik Manufacturing Inc..........F.... 216 267-1616
Cleveland (G-5214)

▲ Duke Manufacturing Inc..........E.... 440 951-1879
Willoughby (G-20476)

Dunaway Inc..........E.... 330 533-7753
Canfield (G-2552)

▲ Duncan Tool Inc..........F.... 937 667-9364
Tipp City (G-18276)

Dunham Machine Inc..........E.... 216 398-4500
Independence (G-11253)

Duray Machine Co Inc..........F.... 440 277-4119
Amherst (G-597)

Dynamic Industries Inc..........E.... 513 861-6767
Cincinnati (G-3675)

Dynapoint Technologies Inc..........E.... 937 859-5193
Dayton (G-8315)

E & E Machine & Tool Inc..........G.... 937 492-3447
Sidney (G-17182)

E & J Demark Inc..........G.... 419 337-5866
Wauseon (G-19675)

E & K Products Co Inc..........G.... 216 631-2510
Cleveland (G-5229)

▲ E D M Services Inc..........G.... 216 486-2068
Euclid (G-9575)

Eagle Machine and Welding Inc..........G.... 740 345-5210
Newark (G-15001)

Eagle Manufacturing Inc..........G.... 419 738-3491
Uniopolis (G-19106)

Eagle Mfg Solutions LLC..........F.... 937 865-0366
Miamisburg (G-13803)

▲ East End Welding Company..........G.... 330 677-6000
Kent (G-11452)

East Fork Precision Machine LL..........G.... 513 753-4157
Amelia (G-574)

Eastlake Machine Products Inc..........E.... 440 953-1014
Willoughby (G-20479)

▲ Eaton Fabricating Company Inc..........E.... 440 926-3121
Grafton (G-10425)

Econ-O-Machine Products Inc..........G.... 937 882-6307
Donnelsville (G-8961)

Edinburg Fixture & Machine..........F.... 330 947-1700
Rootstown (G-16721)

Ellwood Group Inc..........G.... 216 862-6341
Cleveland (G-5274)

Eltool Corporation..........E.... 513 723-1772
Mansfield (G-12599)

Elyria Mtal Spnning Fbrication..........G.... 440 323-8068
Elyria (G-9414)

EMC Precision Machining II LLC..........E.... 440 365-4171
Elyria (G-9418)

Emrick Machine & Tool..........G.... 937 692-5901
Arcanum (G-656)

▲ Energy Machine Inc..........E.... 740 397-1155
Mount Vernon (G-14621)

Engine Machine Service Inc..........G.... 330 505-1804
Niles (G-15151)

▲ Enprotech Industrial Tech LLC..........C.... 216 883-3220
Cleveland (G-5283)

Enterprise C N C Inc..........G.... 440 354-3868
Mentor (G-13573)

Eos Technology Inc..........E.... 216 281-2999
Cleveland (G-5288)

Erie Shore Machine Co Inc..........G.... 216 692-1484
Cleveland (G-5290)

Esterle Mold & Machine Co Inc..........E.... 330 686-1685
Stow (G-17748)

▲ Esterline & Sons Mfg Co LLC..........E.... 937 265-5278
Springfield (G-17554)

Eti Tech Inc..........F.... 937 832-4200
Englewood (G-9519)

Etko Machine Inc..........G.... 330 745-4033
Norton (G-15511)

Euclid Precision Grinding Co..........G.... 440 946-8888
Eastlake (G-9270)

Evolutions North America..........F.... 330 688-2630
Stow (G-17750)

Exact Cutting Service Inc..........E.... 440 546-1319
Brecksville (G-2048)

Excel Machine & Tool Inc..........F.... 419 678-3318
Coldwater (G-6559)

Excellent Tool & Die Inc..........G.... 216 671-9222
Cleveland (G-5312)

Exline Manufacturing Co Inc..........G.... 937 866-1515
Miamisburg (G-13808)

EZ Machine Inc..........G.... 330 784-3363
Akron (G-176)

F & G Tool and Die Co..........E.... 937 294-1405
Moraine (G-14486)

F & J Grinding Inc..........G.... 440 942-4430
Willoughby (G-20483)

F & W Auto Supply..........G.... 419 445-3350
Archbold (G-671)

F A Tech Corp..........E.... 513 942-1920
West Chester (G-19861)

F M Machine Co..........E.... 330 773-8237
Akron (G-177)

F3 Defense Systems LLC..........G.... 419 982-2020
Lima (G-12012)

Fab-Tech Machine Inc..........G.... 937 473-5572
Covington (G-7922)

Fair Field Machine Products..........F.... 740 756-4409
Carroll (G-2941)

Falcon Innovations Inc..........G.... 216 252-0676
Cleveland (G-5321)

Falcon Tool & Machine Inc..........G.... 937 534-9999
Moraine (G-14487)

Falmer Screw Pdts & Mfg Inc..........F.... 330 758-0593
Youngstown (G-21082)

Fargo Toolite Incorporated..........F.... 440 997-2442
Ashtabula (G-806)

▲ Farmerstown Axle Co..........G.... 330 897-2711
Baltic (G-1070)

Farnsworth Engineering..........G.... 330 385-1745
East Liverpool (G-9215)

Farr Automation Inc..........G.... 419 289-1883
Ashland (G-732)

▼ FAS Machinery LLC..........G.... 216 472-3800
Cleveland (G-5325)

Fasco Machine Products Inc..........G.... 440 437-6242
Orwell (G-15775)

Fast Fab and Laser LLC..........G.... 937 224-3048
Dayton (G-8338)

Fate Industries Inc..........G.... 440 327-1770
North Ridgeville (G-15372)

Feilhauers Machine Shop Inc..........G.... 513 202-0545
Harrison (G-10778)

Feller Tool Co Inc..........F.... 440 324-6277
Elyria (G-9423)

▲ Ferralloy Inc..........E.... 440 250-1900
Cleveland (G-5335)

▲ Ferry Industries Inc..........D.... 330 920-9200
Stow (G-17753)

Fetzer Machining Co Inc..........G.... 937 962-4019
Lewisburg (G-11933)

Final Machine..........G.... 330 966-1744
Canton (G-2702)

Fincom Corporation..........G.... 330 456-8341
Canton (G-2703)

Finishing Machine Inc..........E.... 419 491-0197
Holland (G-11060)

First Francis Company Inc..........F.... 440 352-8927
Painesville (G-15881)

Fleetline Tool & Die Co..........G.... 216 441-4949
Cleveland (G-5354)

Flohr Machine Company Inc..........F.... 330 745-3030
Barberton (G-1114)

◆ Floturn Inc..........C.... 513 860-8040
West Chester (G-19865)

Fluid Conservation Systems..........F.... 513 831-9335
Milford (G-14141)

Focus Manufacturing Inc..........F.... 440 946-8766
Willoughby (G-20492)

Foltz Machine LLC..........E.... 330 453-9235
Canton (G-2705)

▲ Forge Industries Inc..........A.... 330 782-8301
Youngstown (G-21089)

Forrest Machine Shop..........G.... 419 822-5847
Delta (G-8932)

Forward Technologies Inc..........F.... 513 489-5111
Blue Ash (G-1800)

Frazier Machine and Prod Inc..........E.... 419 661-1656
Perrysburg (G-16098)

Fred W Hanks Company..........G.... 216 731-1774
Cleveland (G-5380)

▼ Fredon Corporation..........D.... 440 951-5200
Mentor (G-13584)

Fredrick Welding & Machining..........F.... 614 866-9650
Reynoldsburg (G-16592)

Friend Engrg & Mch Co Inc..........G.... 419 589-5066
Mansfield (G-12608)

Fries Machine & Tool Inc..........F.... 937 898-6432
Dayton (G-8353)

Friess Equipment Inc..........G.... 330 945-9440
Akron (G-194)

Frisbie Engine & Machine Co..........F.... 513 542-1770
Cincinnati (G-3784)

G & L Machining Inc..........G.... 513 724-2600
Williamsburg (G-20408)

G & M Precision Machining Inc..........G.... 937 667-1443
Tipp City (G-18278)

G F Frank and Sons Inc ....F 513 870-9075
West Chester (G-19871)

G Grafton Machine & Rubber ....F 330 297-1062
Ravenna (G-16530)

G H Cutter Services Inc ....G 419 476-0476
Toledo (G-18476)

G L Heller Co Inc ....F 419 877-5122
Whitehouse (G-20339)

▲ G L T Inc ....E 937 395-4817
Moraine (G-14489)

G T M Associates Inc ....G 440 951-0006
Mentor (G-13589)

G-N Sales & Manufacturing Inc ....G 440 237-9014
Cleveland (G-5390)

Galactic Precision Mfg LLC ....G 937 540-1800
Englewood (G-9521)

Garber Machine Co ....G 330 399-4181
Warren (G-19552)

Garner Industries Inc ....G 740 349-0238
Newark (G-15011)

Garvey Corporation ....E 330 779-0700
Youngstown (G-21090)

Gasdorf Tool and Mch Co Inc ....F 419 227-0103
Lima (G-12017)

Gaydash Enterprises Inc ....E 330 896-4811
Uniontown (G-19085)

Gb Image Machine Incorporated ....G 419 628-4150
Minster (G-14353)

Gearhart Machine Company ....G 330 253-1880
Akron (G-201)

Gedico International Inc ....G 937 274-2167
Dayton (G-8360)

Gemco Machine & Tool Inc ....F 740 344-3111
Newark (G-15013)

General Machine & Supply Co ....G 740 453-4804
Zanesville (G-21315)

General Parts Inc ....G 614 891-6014
Westerville (G-20215)

▲ General Plug and Mfg Co ....C 440 926-2411
Grafton (G-10426)

General Sheave Company Inc ....G 216 781-8120
Cleveland (G-5420)

▲ General Tool Company ....C 513 733-5500
Cincinnati (G-3820)

George Steel Fabricating Inc ....E 513 932-2887
Lebanon (G-11802)

Gerald Rose ....G 937 866-6339
Miamisburg (G-13813)

Gillam Machine Company ....G 330 457-2557
New Waterford (G-14971)

Gilson Machine & Tool Co Inc ....E 419 592-2911
Napoleon (G-14678)

Girard Machine Company Inc ....E 330 545-9731
Girard (G-10390)

Gisco Inc ....G 937 773-7601
Piqua (G-16267)

▲ GKN Aerospace Cincinnati Inc ....C 513 489-9800
Blue Ash (G-1804)

Glendale Machine Inc ....G 440 248-8646
Solon (G-17298)

▲ Glenridge Machine Co ....E 440 975-1055
Willoughby (G-20499)

Global Body & Equipment Co ....D 330 264-6640
Wooster (G-20777)

▲ Global Sourcing & Support Svcs .....G 513 321-0957
Cincinnati (G-3838)

◆ Global Trade Network Inc ....G 513 701-0411
Mason (G-13031)

▲ Globe Products Inc ....E 937 233-0233
Dayton (G-8371)

▲ Glunt Industries Inc ....C 330 399-7585
Warren (G-19555)

▼ Gmd Industries LLC ....D 937 252-3643
Dayton (G-8373)

Gold Metal Machining Inc ....F 614 873-5031
Plain City (G-16343)

Goodwin Farms ....G 513 877-2636
Pleasant Plain (G-16371)

◆ Gougler Industries Inc ....F 330 673-5826
Kent (G-11463)

▲ Goyal Industries Inc ....E 419 522-7099
Mansfield (G-12618)

Graber Metal Works Inc ....E 440 237-8422
North Royalton (G-15422)

Grand Harbor Yacht Sales & Svc ....G 440 442-2919
Cleveland (G-5445)

Grandview Grind ....G 614 485-9005
Columbus (G-7129)

Graphel Corporation ....C 513 779-6166
West Chester (G-19879)

Green Machine Tool Inc ....F 937 253-0771
Dayton (G-8106)

Grenga Machine & Welding ....F 330 743-1113
Youngstown (G-21104)

Gt Technologies Inc ....C 419 782-8955
Defiance (G-8792)

Guardian Engineering & Mfg Co ....G 419 335-1784
Wauseon (G-19680)

Guyer Precision Inc ....F 440 354-8024
Painesville (G-15886)

H & B Machine & Tool Inc ....F 216 431-3254
Cleveland (G-5466)

H & H Machine Shop Akron Inc ....E 330 773-3327
Akron (G-209)

H & H Quick Machine Inc ....F 330 935-0944
Louisville (G-12312)

H & M Machine Shop Inc ....F 419 453-3414
Ottoville (G-15822)

H & R Tool & Machine Co Inc ....G 740 452-0784
Zanesville (G-21316)

H K K Machining Co ....E 419 924-5116
West Unity (G-20128)

H-W Machine Inc ....G 330 477-7231
Canton (G-2721)

Habco Tool and Dev Co Inc ....E 440 946-5546
Mentor (G-13598)

Hafco-Case Inc ....G 216 267-4644
Cleveland (G-5471)

Hahn Manufacturing Company ....E 216 391-9300
Cleveland (G-5472)

Haiss Fabripart LLC ....E 330 821-2028
Alliance (G-512)

Hale Manufacturing LLC ....F 937 382-2127
Wilmington (G-20667)

Hannon Company ....F 330 343-7758
Dover (G-8990)

Hardin Creek Machine & Tool ....F 419 678-4913
Coldwater (G-6561)

Harris Welding and Machine Co ....G 419 281-9623
Ashland (G-737)

Harris Welding and Machine Co ....F 419 281-8351
Ashland (G-736)

Hartley Machine Inc ....G 330 821-0343
Alliance (G-513)

Hashier & Hashier Mfg ....G 440 933-4883
Avon Lake (G-1031)

Haulette Manufacturing Inc ....D 419 586-1717
Celina (G-3000)

Hawk Engine & Machine ....G 440 582-0900
North Royalton (G-15424)

Hawk Manufacturing LLC ....F 330 784-6234
Akron (G-217)

Hawk Manufacturing LLC ....F 330 784-4815
Akron (G-219)

Hawk Manufacturing LLC ....S 330 784-3151
Akron (G-218)

▲ Hazenstab Machine Inc ....F 330 337-1865
Salem (G-16900)

Hbe Machine ....G 419 668-9426
Monroeville (G-14426)

Heisler Tool Company ....F 440 951-2424
Willoughby (G-20503)

Henderson Fabricating Co Inc ....F 216 432-0404
Cleveland (G-5497)

Hennacy Machine Company Inc ....G 330 785-2940
Akron (G-220)

Hephaestus Technologies LLC ....F 216 252-0430
Cleveland (G-5502)

Herd Manufacturing Inc ....E 216 651-4221
Cleveland (G-5503)

Hergatt Machine Inc ....G 419 589-2931
Mansfield (G-12623)

Heritage Tool ....F 513 753-7300
Loveland (G-12358)

Herman Machine Inc ....F 330 633-3261
Tallmadge (G-18145)

Hesler Machine Tool ....G 937 299-3833
Moraine (G-14496)

Hi-Tek Manufacturing Inc ....C 513 459-1094
Mason (G-13037)

High Tech Metal Products LLC ....G 419 227-9414
Lima (G-12024)

High Tech Mold & Machine Co ....F 330 896-4466
Uniontown (G-19087)

Highland Products Corp ....F 440 352-4777
Mentor (G-13602)

Hillman Precision Inc ....F 419 289-1557
Ashland (G-740)

Hocker Tool and Die Inc ....F 937 274-3443
Dayton (G-8390)

Hofacker Prcsion Machining LLC ....F 937 832-7712
Clayton (G-4659)

Hoffman Machining & Repair LLC ....G 419 547-9204
Clyde (G-6540)

Holdren Brothers Inc ....F 937 465-7050
West Liberty (G-20092)

Hollow Boring Inc ....G 440 951-2929
Mentor (G-13604)

Houston Machine Products Inc ....F 937 322-8022
Springfield (G-17577)

▼ Hr Parts N Stuff ....G 330 947-2433
Atwater (G-898)

Htec Systems Inc ....F 937 438-3010
Dayton (G-8394)

Hubbell Machine Tooling Inc ....F 216 524-1797
Cleveland (G-5533)

Hudak Machine & Tool Inc ....G 440 366-8955
Elyria (G-9429)

Hutnik Company ....G 330 336-9700
Wadsworth (G-19411)

Hutter Racing Engines Ltd ....F 440 285-2175
Chardon (G-3157)

▲ Hy-Production Inc ....C 330 273-2400
Valley City (G-19206)

Hydro Supply Co ....F 740 454-3842
Zanesville (G-21320)

Hylun Machine Co Inc ....G 440 256-8755
Willoughby (G-20507)

Hyneks Machine and Welding ....G 419 281-7966
Ashland (G-742)

Hyprolap Finishing Co ....G 440 352-0270
Mentor (G-13605)

I R B F Company ....G 330 633-5100
Tallmadge (G-18147)

Iberia Machine Shop Inc ....G 419 468-7100
Iberia (G-11244)

Imds Corporation ....F 330 747-4637
Youngstown (G-21113)

Impac Hi-Performance Machining ....G 419 726-7100
Toledo (G-18517)

Independent Machine & Wldg Inc ....G 937 339-7330
Troy (G-18845)

Industrial Grinders Co Inc ....F 440 237-2600
Brookpark (G-2164)

Industrial Hanger Conveyor Co ....G 419 332-2661
Fremont (G-10158)

Industrial Metal Products ....G 440 237-3506
Cleveland (G-5566)

Industrial Shaft and Mfg Inc ....G 440 942-9104
Eastlake (G-9275)

Innovative Tool & Die Inc ....G 419 599-0492
Napoleon (G-14684)

Inovent Engineering Inc ....G 330 468-0005
Macedonia (G-12459)

Integrity Crane Services Ltd ....G 330 479-2003
Massillon (G-13157)

Integrity Manufacturing Corp ....E 937 233-6792
Dayton (G-8413)

International Bellows ....F 937 832-4501
Englewood (G-9526)

International Grinding Inc ....G 330 659-0220
Akron (G-235)

International Machining Inc ....E 330 225-1963
Brunswick (G-2235)

◆ Interscope Manufacturing Inc ....E 513 423-8866
Middletown (G-14050)

Intertek Machining & Wldg Inc ....F 440 323-3325
Elyria (G-9433)

Invotec Engineering Inc ....D 937 886-3232
Miamisburg (G-13820)

Isco Inc ....F 614 792-2206
Columbus (G-7212)

IV M Tool & Die ....G 513 625-6464
Williamsburg (G-20409)

Ivan Extruders Co Inc ....G 330 644-7400
Akron (G-237)

Izit Cain Sheet Metal Corp ....G 937 667-6521
Tipp City (G-18284)

J & A Auto Service ....G 614 837-6820
Pickerington (G-16193)

J & C Industries Inc ....F 216 362-8867
Cleveland (G-5593)

J & P Products Inc ....E 440 974-2830
Mentor (G-13616)

J B M Machine Co Inc ....G 440 446-0819
Cleveland (G-5596)

J B Manufacturing Inc ....E 330 676-9744
Kent (G-11472)

J Horst Manufacturing Co ....D 330 828-2216
Dalton (G-8072)

J P Dennis Machine Inc ....G..... 440 474-0247
Rome (G-16716)

J S Company ....G..... 440 632-0052
Middlefield (G-13945)

J T E Corp ....G..... 937 454-1112
Dayton (G-8418)

Jackson Machine & Fabrication ....G..... 740 682-3994
Oak Hill (G-15598)

Jade Products Inc ....F..... 440 352-1700
Mentor (G-13618)

Jade Tool Co Inc ....G..... 937 376-4740
Xenia (G-20957)

Jamar Precision Grinding Co ....E..... 330 220-0099
Hinckley (G-11026)

James Eastwood ....G..... 614 444-1340
Columbus (G-7224)

James L Wereb ....G..... 440 942-2405
Willoughby (G-20515)

Jamison Manufacturing Co ....G..... 440 237-8085
Cleveland (G-5607)

Jay-Em Aerospace Corporation ....E..... 330 923-0333
Cuyahoga Falls (G-8013)

Jayna Inc ....E..... 937 335-8922
Troy (G-18849)

JB Industries Ltd ....F..... 330 856-4587
Warren (G-19563)

Jbj Technologies Inc ....F..... 216 469-7297
Euclid (G-9588)

▲ Jbk Manufacturing LLC ....E..... 937 233-8300
Dayton (G-8423)

Jed Industries Inc ....E..... 440 639-9973
Grand River (G-10451)

Jed Tool Company ....G..... 937 857-9222
Casstown (G-2970)

Jenkins Motor Parts ....G..... 330 525-4011
Beloit (G-1583)

Jerl Machine Inc ....D..... 419 873-0270
Perrysburg (G-16114)

Jerpbak-Bayless Co ....E..... 440 248-5387
Solon (G-17322)

Jesco Products Inc ....G..... 440 233-5828
Grafton (G-10431)

Jett Industries Inc ....G..... 740 344-4140
Newark (G-15024)

JF Martt and Associates Inc ....F..... 330 938-4000
Sebring (G-17046)

Jh Industries Inc ....E..... 330 963-4105
Twinsburg (G-18961)

Jilco Precision Mold & Mch Co ....G..... 330 633-9645
Akron (G-239)

Jit Company Inc ....F..... 614 529-8010
Hilliard (G-10956)

Jj Sleeves Inc ....G..... 440 205-1055
Mentor (G-13619)

Johnson Engine & Machine ....G..... 614 876-0724
Hilliard (G-10957)

Johnson Machining Services LLC ....G..... 937 866-4744
Miamisburg (G-13823)

Johnson Precision Machining ....G..... 513 353-4252
Cleves (G-6517)

Jonashtons ....G..... 419 488-2363
Cloverdale (G-6536)

Jotco Inc ....G..... 513 721-4943
Mansfield (G-12630)

Jrg Performance Technologies ....G..... 216 408-5974
Cleveland (G-5625)

Jrs Hydraulic & Welding ....G..... 614 497-1100
Columbus (G-7246)

K & G Machine Co ....E..... 216 732-7115
Cleveland (G-5628)

K & J Machine Inc ....F..... 740 425-3282
Barnesville (G-1160)

K & K Precision Inc ....E..... 513 336-0032
Mason (G-13051)

K & M Tool & Machine Co Inc ....G..... 440 572-5130
Strongsville (G-17934)

K P Precision Tool and Mch Co ....G..... 419 237-2596
Fayette (G-9775)

K S Machine Inc ....F..... 216 687-0459
Cleveland (G-5629)

K-M-S Industries Inc ....E..... 440 243-6680
Brookpark (G-2165)

▲ Kalt Manufacturing Company ....D..... 440 327-2102
North Ridgeville (G-15384)

Karder Machine Co ....E..... 330 253-3377
Akron (G-250)

Kastler & Reichlin Inc ....E..... 440 322-0970
Elyria (G-9445)

Keban Industries Inc ....G..... 216 446-0159
Cleveland (G-5639)

Keck Engineering Inc ....G..... 440 355-9855
Lagrange (G-11629)

Kelly Machine Ltd ....G..... 419 825-2006
Swanton (G-18085)

▲ Ken-Dal Corporation ....F..... 330 644-7118
Akron (G-252)

Kenmore Development & Mch Co ....F..... 330 753-2274
Akron (G-253)

Kennedy Repair Services ....G..... 937 332-9118
Troy (G-18851)

Kent Automation Inc ....G..... 330 678-6343
Kent (G-11476)

Kent Swigart ....G..... 937 836-5292
Englewood (G-9528)

Kerek Industries Ltd Lblty Co ....F..... 440 461-1450
Cleveland (G-5648)

Kerf Waterjet Ltd ....G..... 937 254-9711
Dayton (G-8439)

Kern Machine Tool Inc ....G..... 419 470-1206
Toledo (G-18543)

Kiefer Tool & Mold Inc ....F..... 216 251-0076
Cleveland (G-5653)

Kiley Machine Company Inc ....G..... 513 875-3223
Fayetteville (G-9783)

Kimble Machines Inc ....F..... 419 485-8449
Montpelier (G-14447)

Kings Welding and Fabg Inc ....E..... 330 738-3592
Mechanicstown (G-13359)

Kj Machining Systems Inc ....G..... 440 975-8624
Willoughby (G-20521)

Knape Industries Inc ....E..... 614 885-3016
Worthington (G-20875)

Knight Manufacturing Co Inc ....F..... 740 676-9532
Shadyside (G-17081)

Knous Tool & Machine Inc ....G..... 419 394-3541
Saint Marys (G-16841)

Knowlton Machine Inc ....G..... 419 281-6802
Ashland (G-748)

Knox Machine & Tool ....G..... 740 392-3133
Mount Vernon (G-14627)

Koester Machined Products Co ....F..... 419 782-0291
Defiance (G-8799)

Kole Specialties Inc ....G..... 513 829-1111
Fairfield (G-9675)

Komatec Tool & Die Inc ....G..... 937 252-1133
Dayton (G-8445)

Kopachko Machining Inc ....G..... 440 953-3988
Willoughby (G-20522)

Korff Machine LLC ....G..... 330 332-1566
Salem (G-16906)

Krafft and Associates Inc ....G..... 937 325-4671
Springfield (G-17591)

▲ Kram Precision Machining Inc ....G..... 937 849-1301
New Carlisle (G-14805)

Kramer Power Equipment Co ....F..... 937 456-2232
Eaton (G-9313)

Krdc Inc ....G..... 937 222-2332
Dayton (G-8446)

▼ Krendl Machine Company ....D..... 419 692-3060
Delphos (G-8910)

Kyron Tool and Machine Co Inc ....F..... 614 231-6000
Columbus (G-7274)

L & L Machine Inc ....F..... 419 272-5000
Edon (G-9341)

L & P Machine Company ....G..... 330 527-2753
Garrettsville (G-10328)

L A Machine ....G..... 216 651-1712
Cleveland (G-5669)

L C I Inc ....G..... 330 948-1922
Lodi (G-12163)

L J Manufacturing Inc ....G..... 440 352-1979
Mentor (G-13626)

Lake Erie Machine ....G..... 440 353-9191
North Ridgeville (G-15386)

Lakecraft Inc ....G..... 419 734-2828
Port Clinton (G-16402)

Lambert Bros Inc ....G..... 513 541-1042
Cincinnati (G-4010)

Langa Tool & Machine Inc ....E..... 440 953-1138
Willoughby (G-20526)

Lange Precision Inc ....F..... 513 530-9500
Blue Ash (G-1824)

Larcom & Mitchell LLC ....F..... 740 595-3750
Delaware (G-8867)

Lariat Machine Inc ....G..... 330 297-5765
Ravenna (G-16538)

Las Motor Sports ....G..... 937 456-2441
Eaton (G-9315)

Laserflex Corporation ....D..... 614 850-9600
Hilliard (G-10958)

Laspina Tool & Die Inc ....F..... 330 923-9996
Stow (G-17767)

Latanick Equipment Inc ....E..... 419 433-2200
Huron (G-11233)

Lawrence Industries Inc ....D..... 216 518-1400
Cleveland (G-5686)

◆ Lawrence Industries Inc ....E..... 216 518-7000
Cleveland (G-5687)

Lawson Precision Machining Inc ....G..... 419 562-1543
Bucyrus (G-2352)

Leader Engnrng-Fabrication Inc ....G..... 419 592-0008
Napoleon (G-14688)

Leader Engnrng-Fabrication Inc ....G..... 419 636-1731
Bryan (G-2311)

Lees Grinding Inc ....E..... 440 572-4610
Strongsville (G-17938)

Lees Machinery ....G..... 440 259-2222
Perry (G-16052)

Lehner Screw Machine LLC ....E..... 330 688-6616
Munroe Falls (G-14662)

Lem Incorporated ....G..... 330 535-6422
Munroe Falls (G-14663)

Lennox Machine Inc ....G..... 419 525-1020
Mansfield (G-12635)

Leon Newswanger ....F..... 419 896-3336
Shiloh (G-17151)

Lesage Machine Inc ....G..... 419 687-0131
Plymouth (G-16377)

Lewis Unlimited Inc ....G..... 216 514-8282
Chagrin Falls (G-3063)

Lightning Mold & Machine Inc ....F..... 440 593-6460
Conneaut (G-7813)

Lima Sheet Metal Machine & Mfg ....E..... 419 229-1161
Lima (G-12045)

Line Tool & Die Inc ....G..... 419 332-2931
Fremont (G-10165)

Lion Mold & Machine Inc ....G..... 330 688-4248
Stow (G-17770)

Lmp Machine LLC ....G..... 740 596-4559
Zaleski (G-21261)

Loecy Precision Manufacturing ....F..... 440 358-0551
Mentor (G-13636)

▲ Logan Machine Company ....D..... 330 633-6163
Akron (G-275)

Lostcreek Tool & Machine Inc ....F..... 937 773-6022
Piqua (G-16287)

Lous Machine Company Inc ....F..... 513 856-9199
Hamilton (G-10718)

Lowell Marcum ....G..... 330 948-2353
Lodi (G-12165)

Lukens Blacksmith Shop ....G..... 513 821-2308
Cincinnati (G-4038)

M & B Machine Inc ....F..... 419 476-8836
Toledo (G-18565)

M & J Machine Shop Inc ....F..... 330 645-0042
Akron (G-278)

M & L Machine ....G..... 937 386-2604
Seaman (G-17041)

M A C Machine ....G..... 410 944-6171
Canton (G-2761)

M C D Plastics & Manufacturing ....G..... 937 778-1850
Piqua (G-16289)

M L C Technologies Inc ....G..... 513 874-7792
Hamilton (G-10720)

M L Grinding Co ....G..... 440 975-9111
Willoughby (G-20531)

M P Machine Inc ....G..... 440 255-8355
Mentor (G-13639)

M S B Machine Inc ....G..... 330 686-7740
Munroe Falls (G-14664)

Machine Component Mfg ....F..... 330 454-4566
Canton (G-2765)

Machine Development Corp ....G..... 513 825-5885
Cincinnati (G-4044)

Machine Industries Inc ....G..... 216 881-8555
Cleveland (G-5724)

Machine Parts International ....G..... 216 251-4334
Cleveland (G-5725)

Machine Products Company ....G..... 937 890-6600
Dayton (G-8466)

Machine Shop ....G..... 330 494-1251
Canton (G-2766)

Machine Tek Systems Inc ....E..... 330 527-4450
Garrettsville (G-10329)

Machine Tool & Fab Corp ....F..... 419 435-7676
Fostoria (G-9983)

Machine Works Inc ....G..... 513 771-4600
Cincinnati (G-4047)

▲ Machine-Pro Technologies Inc ....D..... 419 584-0086
Celina (G-3006)

Machinex of Dayton Inc .... G 937 252-7021
Dayton *(G-8467)*

▲ Machintek Co .... D 513 551-1000
Fairfield *(G-9678)*

Macpro Inc .... F 513 575-3000
Loveland *(G-12372)*

Mader Automotive Center Inc .... F 937 339-2681
Troy *(G-18855)*

Madison Tool & Die Inc .... G 440 354-8642
Painesville *(G-15899)*

Mag Machine Inc .... G 440 946-3381
Mentor *(G-13642)*

Magic City Machine Inc .... F 330 825-0048
Barberton *(G-1127)*

▼ Magna Machine Co .... C 513 851-6900
Cincinnati *(G-4052)*

Magnolia Machine & Repair Inc .... G 330 866-4200
Magnolia *(G-12516)*

Magnum Machine Works LLC .... G 614 231-4880
Columbus *(G-7315)*

Mahoning Valley Fabricators .... F 330 793-8995
Austintown *(G-975)*

Main Street Machine Inc .... G 330 427-9828
Leetonia *(G-11862)*

Majestic Engineering & Tl LLC .... G 937 845-1079
New Carlisle *(G-14807)*

▲ Majestic Manufacturing Inc .... E 330 457-2447
New Waterford *(G-14972)*

Majestic Tool and Machine Inc .... E 440 248-5058
Solon *(G-17331)*

▼ Manifold & Phalor Inc .... E 614 920-1200
Canal Winchester *(G-2531)*

Manitowoc Company Inc .... G 920 746-3332
Cleveland *(G-5739)*

Mantych Metalworking Inc .... E 937 258-1373
Dayton *(G-8111)*

Mar-Con Tool Company .... E 937 299-2244
Moraine *(G-14504)*

Margo Tool Technology Inc .... F 740 653-8115
Lancaster *(G-11727)*

Marich Machine & Tool Co Inc .... G 216 391-5502
Cleveland *(G-5743)*

Mark Cottle .... G 937 787-4791
Eaton *(G-9317)*

Mark J Myers .... G 513 753-7300
Amelia *(G-579)*

Markham Machine Company Inc .... F 330 762-7676
Akron *(G-286)*

▲ Markley Enterprises LLC .... E 513 771-1290
Cincinnati *(G-4061)*

Markwith Tool Company Inc .... F 937 548-6808
Greenville *(G-10510)*

Marmax Machine Co .... G 937 698-9900
Ludlow Falls *(G-12427)*

Marsch Machine Products .... G 440 298-3932
Madison *(G-12510)*

Martin Machine & Tool Inc .... F 419 373-1711
Bowling Green *(G-2000)*

Martin Machine Co Inc .... G 440 946-5174
Willoughby *(G-20539)*

Master Swaging Inc .... G 937 596-6171
Jackson Center *(G-11343)*

Matrix Tool & Machine Inc .... E 440 255-0300
Mentor *(G-13648)*

Max Daetwyler Corp .... F 937 428-1781
Miamisburg *(G-13828)*

May Thread Grinding Co .... G 440 953-0678
Willoughby *(G-20540)*

Mc Brown Industries Inc .... F 419 963-2800
Findlay *(G-9859)*

McAttack Machine LLC .... G 440 946-3855
Willoughby *(G-20541)*

McCann Tool & Die Inc .... F 330 264-8820
Wooster *(G-20803)*

▲ McCrary Metal Polishing Inc .... E 937 492-1979
Port Jefferson *(G-16420)*

McDannald Welding & Machining .... G 937 644-0300
Marysville *(G-12960)*

McGuire Machine LLC .... G 330 868-3072
Minerva *(G-14333)*

McIntosh Machine .... G 937 687-3936
New Lebanon *(G-14844)*

◆ McNeil & Nrm Inc .... D 330 761-1855
Akron *(G-291)*

McNeil & Nrm Intl Inc .... D 330 253-2525
Akron *(G-292)*

McPherson Wire Cut Inc .... G 330 896-0267
Canton *(G-2777)*

◆ McSwain Manufacturing LLC .... C 513 671-6130
Cincinnati *(G-4072)*

McTt Machine Tool Inc .... G 440 946-9559
Willoughby *(G-20542)*

Medway Tool Corp .... E 937 335-7717
Troy *(G-18857)*

Meldrum Mechanical Services .... F 419 535-3500
Toledo *(G-18583)*

Melinz Industries Inc .... F 440 946-3512
Willoughby *(G-20545)*

Mellott Bronze Inc .... F 330 435-6304
Creston *(G-7941)*

Memac Industries Inc .... G 740 653-4815
Lancaster *(G-11728)*

Mentor Tool Inc .... G 440 942-5273
Willoughby *(G-20546)*

Meridian Machine Inc .... G 330 308-0296
New Philadelphia *(G-14913)*

Meridian Manufacturing Company .... G 330 793-9632
Youngstown *(G-21144)*

Merit Mold & Tool Products .... G 937 435-0932
Dayton *(G-8484)*

Mes Material Hdlg Systems LLC .... G 740 477-8920
Circleville *(G-4633)*

Messerman Corp .... G 419 782-1136
Defiance *(G-8804)*

Met Fab Fabrication and Mch .... G 513 724-3715
Batavia *(G-1203)*

Meta Manufacturing Corporation .... E 513 793-6382
Blue Ash *(G-1837)*

Metal Quality Products Co Inc .... G 440 942-0787
Willoughby *(G-20547)*

▲ Metalex Manufacturing Inc .... C 513 489-0507
Blue Ash *(G-1839)*

Metals Crankshaft Grinding .... G 216 431-5778
Cleveland *(G-5791)*

Metcut Research Associates Inc .... D 513 271-5100
Cincinnati *(G-4092)*

Metro Design Inc .... F 440 458-4200
Elyria *(G-9462)*

Metzger Machine Co .... F 513 241-3360
Cincinnati *(G-4096)*

◆ Meyer Tool Inc .... A 513 681-7362
Cincinnati *(G-4097)*

Mh & Son Machining & Wldg Co .... G 419 621-0690
Sandusky *(G-16988)*

Miami Valley Precision Inc .... E 937 866-1804
Miamisburg *(G-13832)*

Miami Vly Mfg & Assembly Inc .... F 937 254-6665
Dayton *(G-8113)*

Michaels Tool Service Co Inc .... G 330 772-1119
Burghill *(G-2368)*

Mickes Quality Machining .... G 614 746-6639
Columbus *(G-7345)*

Micro Lapping & Grinding Co .... E 216 267-6500
Cleveland *(G-5798)*

Micro Machine Ltd .... G 330 438-7078
Brewster *(G-2086)*

Micro Machine Works Inc .... F 740 678-8471
Vincent *(G-19380)*

Midway Machining Inc .... F 740 373-8976
Marietta *(G-12808)*

Midway Swiss Turn Inc .... G 330 264-4300
Wooster *(G-20808)*

Midwest Laser Systems Inc .... E 419 424-0062
Findlay *(G-9861)*

Midwest Production Machining .... G 419 924-5616
West Unity *(G-20133)*

Midwest Specialties Inc .... F 419 738-8147
Wapakoneta *(G-19501)*

Mike Loppe .... F 937 969-8102
Tremont City *(G-18789)*

▲ Mil-Mar Century Corporation .... F 937 275-4860
Miamisburg *(G-13836)*

Mill & Motion Inc .... F 216 524-4000
Cleveland *(G-5816)*

Mill Craft Mch & Fabrication .... G 419 422-6346
Findlay *(G-9862)*

▲ Millat Industries Corp .... D 937 434-6666
Dayton *(G-8501)*

Millennium Mch Techlonlogy LLC .... F 440 269-8080
Willoughby *(G-20550)*

Miller Machine & Mfg LLC .... G 740 439-2283
Cambridge *(G-2466)*

Miller Tool and Machine Co .... G 330 297-9657
Ravenna *(G-16541)*

Minerva Welding and Fabg Inc .... E 330 868-7731
Minerva *(G-14335)*

Miracle Welding Inc .... G 513 746-9977
Franklin *(G-10037)*

Mirmat Cnc Machining Inc .... G 440 951-2410
Willoughby *(G-20551)*

Mission Industrial Group LLC .... F 740 387-2287
Marion *(G-12886)*

Modern Design Stamping Div .... G 216 382-6318
Cleveland *(G-5826)*

Modern Engineering .... G 440 593-5414
Conneaut *(G-7816)*

Modern Industries Inc .... G 216 432-2855
Cleveland *(G-5827)*

Modern Mold and Tool .... G 440 236-9600
Columbia Station *(G-6591)*

Monovision Machine .... G 330 833-2146
Massillon *(G-13182)*

Monroe Die & Stamping Co .... G 216 883-6390
Cleveland *(G-5831)*

Monroe Tool and Mfg Co .... F 216 883-7360
Cleveland *(G-5832)*

Montgomery Mch & Fabrication .... E 740 286-2863
Jackson *(G-11321)*

▲ Monti Incorporated .... D 513 761-7775
Cincinnati *(G-4120)*

Morning Glory Technologies .... F 440 796-5076
Chesterland *(G-3216)*

Morris Technologies Inc .... C 513 733-1611
Cincinnati *(G-4123)*

Mosher Machine & Tool Co Inc .... E 937 258-8070
Dayton *(G-8511)*

Mossing Machine and Tool .... G 419 476-5657
Toledo *(G-18592)*

Mound Manufacturing Center Inc .... F 937 236-8387
Dayton *(G-8512)*

Muller Engine & Machine Co .... G 937 322-1861
Springfield *(G-17610)*

Munson Machine Company Inc .... G 740 967-6867
Johnstown *(G-11402)*

Munson Sales & Engineering .... G 216 496-5436
Chardon *(G-3167)*

Murray Brothers Shows Inc .... F 513 941-6500
Cincinnati *(G-4133)*

Murray Machine & Tool Inc .... G 216 267-1126
Cleveland *(G-5841)*

Muskingum Grinding & Mch Co .... F 740 622-4741
Coshocton *(G-7899)*

Mutual Tool LLC .... D 937 667-5818
Tipp City *(G-18290)*

Myers Machining Inc .... F 330 874-3005
Bolivar *(G-1938)*

Mysta Equipment Co .... G 330 879-5353
Navarre *(G-14720)*

N & W Machining & Fabricating .... G 937 695-5582
Winchester *(G-20696)*

N C Tool & Die Company .... F 440 354-4152
Mentor *(G-13664)*

Narrow Way Custom Technology .... E 937 743-1611
Carlisle *(G-2933)*

National Aviation Products Inc .... D 330 688-6494
Stow *(G-17779)*

▲ National Machine Company .... C 330 688-6494
Stow *(G-17780)*

National Machine Company .... E 330 688-2584
Stow *(G-17781)*

Nauvod Machine Co .... G 440 632-1990
Middlefield *(G-13973)*

NCM Corp .... G 440 786-9870
Cleveland *(G-5865)*

Neff Machinery and Supplies .... E 740 454-0128
Zanesville *(G-21331)*

Neidert Fabricating Inc .... G 330 753-3331
Barberton *(G-1133)*

Neil R Scholl Inc .... F 740 653-6593
Lancaster *(G-11733)*

Nevels Precision Machining LLC .... G 937 387-6037
Dayton *(G-8523)*

New Cut Tool and Mfg Corp .... F 740 676-1666
Shadyside *(G-17083)*

New Pme Inc .... E 513 671-1717
Cincinnati *(G-4148)*

New Tech .... G 330 494-8338
Canton *(G-2787)*

▲ Nfm/Welding Engineers Inc .... C 330 837-3868
Massillon *(G-13184)*

Nichols Manufacturing Inc .... F 440 255-0188
Mentor *(G-13666)*

Nichols Mold Inc .... G 330 297-9719
Ravenna *(G-16544)*

Nicklaus Machine Co .... G 614 262-7223
Columbus *(G-7392)*

Nippon Stl Smkin Crnkshaft LLC .... F 419 435-0411
Fostoria *(G-9988)*

Nk Machine Inc .... G 513 737-8035
Hamilton *(G-10727)*

Employee Codes: A=Over 500 employees, B=251-500
C=101-250, D=51-100, E=20-50, F=10-19, G=3-9

NM Group Global LLC ....G...... 419 447-5211
Tiffin (G-18233)
Nobal Enterprises Inc ....G...... 440 748-0522
Columbia Station (G-6592)
Noble Tool Corp ....E...... 937 461-4040
Dayton (G-8524)
Norman Noble Inc ....C...... 216 761-5387
Highland Heights (G-10917)
Norman Noble Inc ....D...... 216 761-5387
Cleveland (G-5888)
Norman Noble Inc ....C...... 216 761-2133
Cleveland (G-5889)
Norman Noble Inc ....B...... 216 761-5387
Highland Heights (G-10918)
North Canton Tool Co ....G...... 330 452-0545
Canton (G-2793)
Northcoast Prfmce & Mch Co .....G...... 330 753-7333
Barberton (G-1134)
Northeast Machine Tool Corp .....G...... 216 641-0141
Cleveland (G-5904)
Northend Gear & Machine Inc .....F...... 513 860-4334
Fairfield (G-9690)
Northern Machine Tool Co ....G...... 216 961-0444
Cleveland (G-5911)
Northern Precision Inc ....F...... 513 860-4701
Fairfield (G-9691)
Northmont Tool and Gage Inc ....G...... 937 836-9879
Clayton (G-4661)
Northshore Mold Inc ....G...... 440 838-8212
Cleveland (G-5915)
Northwind Industries Inc ....E...... 216 433-0666
Cleveland (G-5916)
Norwood Medical ....G...... 937 228-4101
Dayton (G-8530)
Norwood Tool Company ....D...... 937 228-4101
Dayton (G-8532)
◆ Npk Construction Equipment Inc..D...... 440 232-7900
Bedford (G-1449)
Nt Machine Inc ....G...... 440 968-3506
Montville (G-14460)
Oak Industrial Inc ....G...... 440 263-2780
North Royalton (G-15439)
▲ Oakley Die & Mold Co ....E...... 513 754-8500
Mason (G-13070)
Oaks Welding Inc ....G...... 330 482-4216
Columbiana (G-6627)
Oceco Inc ....F...... 419 447-0916
Tiffin (G-18235)
▲ Odawara Automation Inc ....E...... 937 667-8433
Tipp City (G-18291)
Odyssey Machine Company Ltd ..G...... 419 455-6621
Perrysburg (G-16129)
of Machining LLC ....G...... 419 396-7870
Carey (G-2922)
▼ Ohio Broach & Machine Company ..E.. 440 946-1040
Willoughby (G-20560)
Ohio Engineering and Mfg Sls ...G...... 937 855-6971
Germantown (G-10371)
▲ Ohio Gasket and Shim Co Inc ....E...... 330 630-0626
Akron (G-323)
Ohio Hydraulics Inc ....E...... 513 771-2590
Cincinnati (G-4178)
Ohio Metalizing LLC ....G...... 330 830-1092
Massillon (G-13185)
Ohio Precision Inc ....G...... 330 453-9710
Canton (G-2803)
Ohio Roll Grinding Inc ....E...... 330 453-1884
Louisville (G-12322)
Ohio Tool Works LLC ....D...... 419 281-3700
Ashland (G-761)
Ohio Transitional Machine & Tl ..G...... 419 476-0820
Toledo (G-18618)
Ojim Inc ....F...... 330 832-9557
Massillon (G-13187)
◆ OKL Can Line Inc ....E...... 513 825-1655
Cincinnati (G-4183)
Omega International Inc ....E...... 937 890-2350
Dayton (G-8549)
Omega Machine & Tool Inc ....F...... 440 946-6846
Mentor (G-13672)
Omega Tool & Die Inc ....E...... 937 890-2350
Dayton (G-8550)
Omnimold LLC ....D...... 419 332-4466
Fremont (G-10172)
Outlook Tool Inc ....G...... 937 235-6330
Dayton (G-8555)
Owen S Precision Grinding ....G...... 513 745-9335
Cincinnati (G-4204)
P & G Precision LLC ....G...... 513 738-3500
Fairfield (G-9694)

P & L Heat Trting Grinding Inc ....E...... 330 746-1339
Youngstown (G-21159)
P & P Machine Tool Inc ....G...... 440 232-7404
Cleveland (G-5953)
P & P Mold & Die Inc ....F...... 330 784-8333
Tallmadge (G-18164)
P F S Incorporated ....G...... 440 582-1620
Cleveland (G-5954)
P J Tool Company Inc ....G...... 937 254-2817
Dayton (G-8558)
▲ P R Machine Works Inc ....D...... 419 529-5748
Ontario (G-15693)
P R W Tool Inc ....G...... 440 585-3373
Wickliffe (G-20377)
Palmer Industries Inc ....G...... 330 630-9397
Akron (G-332)
Paramont Machine Company LLC ......E...... 330 339-3489
New Philadelphia (G-14921)
Parco Inc ....F...... 937 296-0356
Dayton (G-8563)
Parker Precision Inc ....G...... 440 951-6501
Mentor (G-13680)
Parker-Hannifin Corporation ....F...... 330 336-3511
Wadsworth (G-19427)
Part Rite Inc ....G...... 216 362-4100
North Royalton (G-15443)
Parts Unlimited ....G...... 937 558-1527
Dayton (G-8564)
Patriot Precision Products ....D...... 330 966-7177
Canton (G-2807)
Patton Industries Inc ....G...... 419 331-5658
Elida (G-9354)
Pattons Truck & Heavy Eqp Svc ..F...... 740 385-4067
Logan (G-12189)
Paul Popov ....G...... 440 582-6677
North Royalton (G-15444)
Paul Wilke & Son Inc ....F...... 513 921-3163
Cincinnati (G-4217)
▲ Pdi Communication Systems Inc ...D...... 937 743-6010
Springboro (G-17495)
Pearce Inc ....F...... 216 252-0550
Cleveland (G-5986)
Peco Holdings Corp ....F...... 937 667-4451
Tipp City (G-18292)
Pemco Inc ....G...... 216 524-2990
Cleveland (G-5989)
Penco Tool LLC ....E...... 440 998-1116
Ashtabula (G-829)
Perfect Prcision Machining Ltd ....G...... 330 475-0324
Akron (G-335)
Perfection Metal Co ....G...... 216 641-0949
Cleveland (G-5992)
Perfecto Industries Inc ....E...... 937 778-1900
Piqua (G-16299)
Perform Metals Inc ....G...... 440 286-1951
Chardon (G-3172)
Performance Point Grinding ....G...... 330 220-0871
Hinckley (G-11028)
Performance Services ....G...... 419 385-1236
Toledo (G-18640)
Perry Welding Service Inc ....F...... 330 425-2211
Twinsburg (G-19001)
◆ Phase Array Company LLC ....G...... 513 785-0801
West Chester (G-19914)
PHI Werkes LLC ....G...... 419 586-9222
Celina (G-3014)
Phil Matic Screw Products Inc ....F...... 440 942-7290
Willoughby (G-20568)
Phillips Mfg & Mch Corp ....G...... 330 823-9178
Alliance (G-533)
Phoenix Tool Co Inc ....G...... 330 372-4627
Warren (G-19586)
Pierce-Wright Precision Inc ....G...... 216 362-2870
Cleveland (G-6005)
Pike Machine Products Co ....E...... 216 731-1880
Euclid (G-9597)
▲ Pioneer Industrial Systems LLC ...F...... 419 737-9506
Alvordton (G-559)
Pioneer Machine Inc ....G...... 330 948-6500
Lodi (G-12168)
Plas-Mac Corp ....D...... 440 349-3222
Solon (G-17361)
PME of Ohio Inc ....E...... 513 671-1717
Cincinnati (G-4248)
Pohl Machining Inc ....G...... 513 353-2929
Cleves (G-6522)
Polytech Component Corp ....E...... 330 726-3235
Youngstown (G-21173)
▲ Positech Corp ....F...... 513 942-7411
Blue Ash (G-1853)

Post Products Inc ....G...... 330 678-0048
Kent (G-11505)
▲ Precise Tool & Die Company ....E...... 440 951-9173
Willoughby (G-20577)
Precision Component Inds LLC ...E...... 330 477-1052
Canton (G-2820)
Precision Dynamics Inc ....G...... 330 697-0611
Akron (G-347)
Precision Hydraulic Connectors ...F...... 440 953-3778
Euclid (G-9601)
Precision Inc ....G...... 330 897-8860
Fresno (G-10198)
Precision Machine & Tool Co ....G...... 419 334-8405
Fremont (G-10176)
Precision Machining Corp ....G...... 419 433-3520
Huron (G-11240)
Precision McHning Srfacing Inc ...G...... 440 439-9850
Cleveland (G-6035)
▲ Precision Production Inc ....E...... 216 252-0372
Strongsville (G-17952)
Precision Reflex Inc ....F...... 419 629-2603
New Bremen (G-14792)
Premier Prod Svc Inds Inc ....G...... 330 527-0333
Garrettsville (G-10332)
Premier Tool Inc ....G...... 937 332-0996
Troy (G-18864)
▲ Pride Cast Metals Inc ....D...... 513 541-1295
Cincinnati (G-4268)
Pride Tool Co Inc ....F...... 513 563-0070
Cincinnati (G-4269)
Pro-Tech Manufacturing Inc ....F...... 937 444-6484
Mount Orab (G-14586)
Process Development Corp ....E...... 937 890-3388
Dayton (G-8597)
▲ Process Equipment Co Tipp City ..G...... 937 667-7105
Tipp City (G-18294)
Prodeva Inc ....F...... 937 596-6713
Jackson Center (G-11347)
Product Tooling Inc ....G...... 740 524-2061
Sunbury (G-18075)
Proficient Machining Co ....E...... 440 942-4942
Mentor (G-13699)
Profile Grinding Inc ....E...... 216 351-0600
Cleveland (G-6055)
Progressive Manufacturing Co .....G...... 330 784-4717
Akron (G-354)
Prohos Inc ....G...... 419 877-0153
Whitehouse (G-20343)
Prohos Manufacturing Co Inc ......G...... 419 877-0153
Whitehouse (G-20344)
▼ Projects Designed & Built ....E...... 419 726-7400
Toledo (G-18659)
Promac Inc ....F...... 937 864-1961
Enon (G-9548)
Prostar Machine & Tool Co ....G...... 937 223-1997
Dayton (G-8602)
Proto Machine & Mfg Inc ....F...... 330 677-1700
Kent (G-11508)
Pumphrey Machine Corp ....G...... 440 417-0481
Madison (G-12511)
Puritas Metal Products Inc ....F...... 440 353-1917
North Ridgeville (G-15397)
Pvm Incorporated ....G...... 614 871-0302
Grove City (G-10587)
Q M C Pleasants Inc ....G...... 937 278-7302
Dayton (G-8605)
Qcsm LLC ....G...... 216 531-5960
Euclid (G-9602)
Qp Manufacturing Co Inc ....G...... 440 946-2120
Chardon (G-3174)
Qpmr Inc ....G...... 330 723-1739
Medina (G-13465)
▲ Quaker Mfg Corp ....C...... 330 332-4631
Salem (G-16922)
Qualiturn ....E...... 513 868-3333
West Chester (G-19925)
Quality CNC Machining Inc ....F...... 440 942-0542
Willoughby (G-20581)
Quality Craft Machine Inc ....F...... 330 928-4064
Cuyahoga Falls (G-8038)
Quality Design Machining Inc ....G...... 440 352-7290
Mentor (G-13707)
Quality Industries Inc ....G...... 216 961-5566
Cleveland (G-6071)
Quality Machine ....G...... 330 877-6163
Hartville (G-10831)
Quality Machine Systems LLC .....G...... 440 223-2217
Mentor (G-13708)
Quality Metal Products Inc ....G...... 440 355-6165
Lagrange (G-11636)

Quality Mold Inc ....D 419 752-4511
  Greenwich (G-10534)
Quality Screw Products Inc ....G 440 975-1828
  Willoughby (G-20583)
Quality Specialists Inc ....G 440 946-9129
  Willoughby (G-20584)
Queen City Tool Company Inc ......G 513 752-4200
  Amelia (G-582)
Queen City Tool Works Inc ....G 513 874-0111
  Fairfield (G-9707)
Quest Technologies Inc ....F 937 743-1200
  Franklin (G-10047)
Quick Service Welding & Mch Co ....F 330 673-3818
  Kent (G-11511)
R & B Machining Inc ....G 937 698-3528
  Wilmington (G-20676)
R & B Machining Inc ....G 937 382-6710
  Wilmington (G-20677)
R & D Custom Machine & Tool .....E 419 727-1700
  Toledo (G-18666)
R & J Cylinder & Machine Inc ....D 330 364-8263
  Dover (G-9007)
R & M Grinding Inc ....G 513 732-3330
  Owensville (G-15833)
R A Heller Company ....F 513 771-6100
  Cincinnati (G-4322)
R and S Technologies Inc ....F 419 483-3691
  Bellevue (G-1555)
R H Industries Inc ....E 216 281-5210
  Cleveland (G-6083)
R J K Enterprises Inc ....F 440 257-6018
  Mentor (G-13712)
R L Craig Inc ....F 330 424-1525
  Lisbon (G-12133)
R T & T Machining Co Inc ....F 440 974-8479
  Mentor (G-13714)
R T R Slotting & Machine Inc ....G 330 929-2608
  Cuyahoga Falls (G-8039)
R Vandewalle Inc ....G 513 921-2657
  Cincinnati (G-4327)
▲ R W Machine & Tool Inc ....E 330 296-5211
  Ravenna (G-16552)
▲ Radco Industries Inc ....F 419 531-4731
  Toledo (G-18669)
Ram Machining Inc ....G 740 333-5522
  Wshngtn CT Hs (G-20923)
▲ Ram Precision Industries Inc ......D 937 885-7700
  Dayton (G-8614)
Randolph Tool Company Inc ....F 330 877-4923
  Hartville (G-10832)
Range One Products & Fabg ....F 330 533-1151
  Canfield (G-2571)
Rapid Mold Repair & Machine ....G 330 253-1000
  Akron (G-366)
Ray Townsend ....G 440 968-3617
  Montville (G-14461)
Reeces Las Vegas Supplies ....G 937 274-5000
  Dayton (G-8620)
Reese Machine Company Inc ....F 440 992-3942
  Ashtabula (G-835)
Reesers Machine Inc ....G 937 548-5847
  Greenville (G-10518)
Reichard Industries LLC ....G 330 482-5511
  Columbiana (G-6630)
Reliance Design Inc ....F 216 267-5450
  Rocky River (G-16707)
Rely-On Manufacturing Inc ....G 937 254-0118
  Dayton (G-8623)
Remington Engrg Machining Inc .....G 513 965-8999
  Milford (G-14170)
Repko Machine Inc ....G 216 267-1144
  Cleveland (G-6102)
Reuther Mold & Mfg Co Inc ....D 330 923-5266
  Cuyahoga Falls (G-8041)
▲ Reymond Products Intl Inc ....E 330 339-3583
  New Philadelphia (G-14923)
Rezmann Karoly ....G 216 441-4357
  Cleveland (G-6110)
RI Alto Mfg Inc ....F 740 914-4230
  Marion (G-12895)
Richard Paskiet Machinists ....G 330 854-4160
  Canal Fulton (G-2513)
Richard Pauley ....G 740 965-6897
  Sunbury (G-18076)
Richards Grinding Co Inc ....F 216 631-7675
  Cleveland (G-6112)
Richmond Machine Co ....E 419 485-5740
  Montpelier (G-14454)
Ridge Enterprises Inc ....G 740 867-3456
  Chesapeake (G-3190)

Ridge Machine & Welding Co ....G 740 537-2821
  Toronto (G-18784)
Riffle Machine Works Inc ....F 740 775-2838
  Chillicothe (G-3271)
Rimeco Products Inc ....G 440 918-1220
  Willoughby (G-20588)
Rinaldi and Packard Industries ....G 330 395-4942
  Warren (G-19596)
Risher & Co ....F 216 732-8351
  Euclid (G-9604)
Ritime Incorporated ....F 330 273-3443
  Cleveland (G-6115)
Riverside Mch & Automtn Inc ....D 419 855-8308
  Genoa (G-10363)
Rj S Machine Shop Service ....G 937 927-0137
  Seaman (G-17042)
Rjm Tool ....G 419 355-0900
  Fremont (G-10179)
RL Best Company ....E 330 758-8601
  Boardman (G-1924)
Rme Machining Co ....G 513 541-3328
  Cincinnati (G-4351)
Robert Alten Inc ....G 740 653-2640
  Lancaster (G-11747)
Robert J & Cindy K Hartz ....G 513 521-6215
  Cincinnati (G-4354)
Robert Long Manufacturing Inc ......G 330 678-0911
  Kent (G-11518)
Robert Smart Inc ....F 330 454-8881
  Canton (G-2841)
▲ Roberts Manufacturing Co Inc ....E 419 594-2712
  Oakwood (G-15618)
Robertson EDM LLC ....G 419 658-2219
  Edgerton (G-9334)
Robey Tool & Machine ....G 614 251-0412
  Columbus (G-7570)
Rochester Manufacturing Inc ....F 440 647-2463
  Wellington (G-19753)
Roerig Machine ....G 440 647-4718
  New London (G-14864)
Rogar International Inc ....F 419 476-5500
  Toledo (G-18679)
Roof Die Tool & Machine Inc ....G 614 444-6253
  Columbus (G-7572)
Rosenboom Machine & Tool Inc .....E 419 352-9484
  Bowling Green (G-2015)
Rotary Tech Inc ....G 440 862-8568
  Burton (G-2383)
Rowtac Inc ....G 419 994-4777
  Loudonville (G-12304)
Royal Tool and Machine LLC ....G 419 836-7781
  Northwood (G-15489)
Royalton Industries Inc ....F 440 748-9900
  Columbia Station (G-6597)
Royalton Manufacturing Inc ....F 440 237-2233
  North Royalton (G-15449)
Royce Co ....G 513 933-0344
  Lebanon (G-11834)
Rpg Industries Inc ....G 937 698-9801
  Tipp City (G-18297)
RTZ Manufacturing Co ....G 614 848-8366
  Columbus (G-7577)
Runner Tool & Die Inc ....G 330 794-8843
  Akron (G-382)
Ruth Leinasars ....G 937 484-8542
  Urbana (G-19178)
S & N Engineering Svcs Corp ....G 216 433-1700
  Cleveland (G-6147)
S & R Tool & Die Services Inc ....G 937 584-4691
  Sabina (G-16777)
S & V Automatics ....G 216 429-2228
  Cleveland (G-6148)
S A E Manufacturing ....G 440 322-9026
  Elyria (G-9490)
S and S Tool Inc ....G 440 593-4000
  Conneaut (G-7818)
S C Machine ....G 419 752-6961
  Greenwich (G-10536)
S J Cox Tool Inc ....G 740 756-1100
  Carroll (G-2946)
S J K Metalworking Inc ....G 440 564-7877
  Newbury (G-15104)
S K S Manufacturing Corp ....G 330 669-9133
  Smithville (G-17244)
S P Z Machine Co ....G 330 848-3286
  Barberton (G-1148)
S R P M Inc ....E 440 248-8440
  Cleveland (G-6151)
S T Tool & Design Inc ....F 440 357-1250
  Mentor (G-13718)

S-K Mold & Tool Company ....E 937 339-0299
  Tipp City (G-18298)
S-K Mold & Tool Company ....G 937 339-0299
  Troy (G-18870)
S-P Company Inc ....F 330 482-0200
  Columbiana (G-6631)
Sadler Corporation ....G 330 688-7400
  Stow (G-17796)
Safar Machine Company ....F 330 644-0155
  Akron (G-394)
Saint Paris Tool and Grinding ....F 937 526-9800
  Russia (G-16770)
Salco Machine Inc ....F 330 456-8281
  Louisville (G-12326)
Salley Tool & Die Co ....F 937 258-3333
  Dayton (G-8116)
Sample Machining Inc ....E 937 258-3338
  Dayton (G-8645)
Sandusky Machine & Tool Inc ....F 419 626-8359
  Sandusky (G-17003)
Santos Industrial Ltd ....G 937 299-7333
  Moraine (G-14526)
▲ Sattler Companies Inc ....E 330 239-2552
  Wadsworth (G-19439)
Sauder Machine Ltd ....G 419 896-3722
  Plymouth (G-16379)
Savanna Tool and Manufacturing ....G 440 327-8330
  North Ridgeville (G-15403)
Schaffer Grinding Co Inc ....F 323 724-4476
  Twinsburg (G-19017)
Schmidt Machine Company ....E 419 294-3814
  Upper Sandusky (G-19139)
Schmitmeyer Inc ....G 937 295-2091
  Fort Loramie (G-9937)
Schuster Manufacturing Inc ....G 419 476-5800
  Toledo (G-18687)
Schwab Machine Co Inc ....G 419 626-0245
  Sandusky (G-17006)
Scott A Zurbrugg ....G 330 821-9814
  Alliance (G-537)
Sebring Fluid Power Corp ....G 330 938-9984
  Sebring (G-17053)
Secondary Machining Services ....G 440 593-1272
  Conneaut (G-7819)
Seeb Industrial Inc ....G 216 896-9016
  Bedford (G-1461)
Seebach Inc ....F 937 275-3565
  Dayton (G-8651)
Select Machine Co Inc ....F 330 678-7676
  Kent (G-11526)
Selzer Tool & Die Inc ....G 440 365-4124
  Elyria (G-9491)
▲ Semco ....D 800 848-5764
  Marion (G-12899)
Seme & Son Automotive Inc ....G 216 261-0066
  Euclid (G-9606)
Shannon Tool Inc ....G 513 563-2300
  Cincinnati (G-4412)
Shoreline Machine Products Co ......F 216 481-8033
  Cleveland (G-6196)
Short Run Machine Products Inc .....F 440 969-1313
  Ashtabula (G-838)
Sierra Precision Components ....G 440 230-9570
  Cleveland (G-6198)
Sietins Plastics Incorporated ....G 440 232-8515
  Cleveland (G-6199)
Silver Tool Inc ....E 937 865-0012
  Miamisburg (G-13860)
Simpson Brothers Machine Works ....G 740 353-6870
  Portsmouth (G-16453)
Sivon Mfr Co ....G 440 259-5505
  Perry (G-16057)
Skinner Machining Co ....G 216 486-6636
  Cleveland (G-6207)
Slimline Surgical Devices LLC ....G 937 335-0496
  Troy (G-18876)
Sluterbeck Tool & Die Inc ....F 937 836-5736
  Clayton (G-4662)
Smith Machine Inc ....G 330 821-9898
  Alliance (G-538)
Smolic Machine Co ....G 440 946-1747
  Willoughby (G-20601)
Sni Inc ....G 937 427-9447
  Beavercreek (G-1380)
Snyder Fabrication LLC ....G 419 946-6616
  Mount Gilead (G-14569)
Snyder Machine Co Inc ....G 419 526-1527
  Mansfield (G-12681)
Sonoma Grinding ....G 440 918-7990
  Willoughby (G-20602)

Southeastern Shafting Mfg ....F 740 342-4629
New Lexington (G-14854)
Southern Ohio Mfg Inc ....E 513 943-2555
Batavia (G-1224)
Southstern Machining Field Svc ....E 740 689-1147
Lancaster (G-11754)
Sp Acquisitions LLC ....E 440 205-0143
Mentor (G-13726)
Spartan Fabrication ....G 330 758-3512
Youngstown (G-21208)
Special Machined Components ....G 513 459-1113
Mason (G-13089)
Specialty Hose Aerospace Corp ....F 330 497-9650
Canton (G-2854)
Specialty Hose Corporation ....F 330 497-9650
North Canton (G-15266)
Spectre EDM ....G 513 469-7700
Blue Ash (G-1872)
Spectrum Dynamics Inc ....G 614 486-3223
Columbus (G-7641)
Spectrum Machine Inc ....E 330 626-3666
Streetsboro (G-17877)
Spectrum Mfg & Sls Inc ....G 614 486-3223
Columbus (G-7642)
Spence Technologies Inc ....F 440 946-3035
Willoughby (G-20603)
Spinks Machine Products Co ....G 440 951-5814
Willoughby (G-20604)
Sponseller Group Inc ....E 419 861-3000
Holland (G-11087)
Sponseller Group Inc ....G 937 492-9949
Sidney (G-17229)
▲ Sroka Industries Inc ....E 440 572-2811
Strongsville (G-17972)
SRS Manufacturing Corp ....F 937 746-3086
Franklin (G-10054)
Ss Automotive Service ....G 419 859-2885
Benton Ridge (G-1598)
Sst Precision Manufacturing ....F 513 583-5500
Loveland (G-12390)
Stafford Gage & Tool Inc ....F 937 277-9944
Dayton (G-8674)
Stainless Machine Engineering ....G 330 501-1992
Leetonia (G-11865)
▲ Stanco Precision Manufacturing ....G 937 274-1785
Dayton (G-8675)
▲ Standard Jig Boring Svc LLC ....E 330 896-9530
Akron (G-412)
Standard Jig Boring Svc LLC ....G 330 644-5405
Akron (G-413)
Standard Machine Inc ....E 216 631-4440
Cleveland (G-6234)
▼ Stanley Industries Inc ....E 216 475-4000
Cleveland (G-6236)
Starr Machine Inc ....E 740 753-0009
Nelsonville (G-14740)
Starwin Industries Inc ....E 937 293-8568
Dayton (G-8681)
▲ Steck Manufacturing Co Inc ....F 937 222-0062
Dayton (G-8683)
Steel Eqp Specialists Inc ....E 330 829-2626
Alliance (G-539)
▲ Steel Eqp Specialists Inc ....D 330 823-8260
Alliance (G-540)
Steel Products Corp Akron ....E 330 688-6633
Stow (G-17803)
Stefra Inc ....G 440 846-8240
Strongsville (G-17973)
Stegemeyer Machine ....G 513 321-5651
Cincinnati (G-4463)
Steinbarger Precision Cnc Inc ....G 937 252-0322
Dayton (G-8117)
Steinert Industries Inc ....F 330 678-0028
Kent (G-11533)
Sterling Grinding Company Inc ....F 614 836-3412
Carroll (G-2947)
Stevenson Machine Inc ....F 513 761-4121
Cincinnati (G-4467)
Stevenson Mfg Co ....G 330 532-1581
Wellsville (G-19775)
Stewarts Machining Inc ....G 513 422-5000
Monroe (G-14415)
Strassells Machine Inc ....F 419 747-1088
Mansfield (G-12685)
Stryver Mfg Inc ....E 937 854-3048
Trotwood (G-18799)
Suburban Manufacturing Co ....D 440 953-2024
Eastlake (G-9290)
Suburban Metal Products Inc ....F 740 474-4237
Circleville (G-4644)
Sulecki Precision Products ....F 440 255-5454
Mentor (G-13740)
Summer Global Systems LLC ....G 330 397-1653
Campbell (G-2492)
Sunset Industries Inc ....E 216 731-8131
Euclid (G-9607)
Superfinishers Inc ....G 330 467-2125
Macedonia (G-12492)
Superior Machine and Tool ....G 937 308-5771
De Graff (G-8770)
Superior Machine Tool Inc ....F 419 675-2363
Kenton (G-11571)
Superior Mold & Die Co ....E 330 688-8251
Munroe Falls (G-14666)
Superior Precision Products ....G 216 881-3696
Cleveland (G-6267)
▲ Superior Quality Machine Co ....E 330 527-7146
Garrettsville (G-10333)
Swagelok Company ....C 440 461-7714
Cleveland (G-6279)
Swagelok Company ....D 440 248-4600
Willoughby Hills (G-20644)
◆ Swagelok Company ....A 440 248-4600
Solon (G-17390)
Swagelok Company ....D 440 349-5652
Solon (G-17391)
Swagelok Company ....E 440 349-5836
Solon (G-17393)
▲ Swagelok Manufacturing Co LLC ....E 440 248-4600
Solon (G-17395)
Swanton Wldg Machining Co Inc ....D 419 826-4816
Swanton (G-18091)
Swartz Manufacturing Inc ....G 440 284-0297
Elyria (G-9497)
Swift Tool Inc ....G 330 945-6973
Cuyahoga Falls (G-8052)
Systech Handling Inc ....F 419 445-8226
Archbold (G-696)
Szpak Manufacturing Co Inc ....G 440 236-5233
Columbia Station (G-6602)
T & K Welding Co Inc ....G 216 432-0221
Cleveland (G-6287)
T & M Machine Products Inc ....G 740 753-2960
Nelsonville (G-14741)
T & S Machine Inc ....F 419 453-2101
Wapakoneta (G-19509)
T & T Machine Inc ....F 440 354-0605
Painesville (G-15924)
T & W Tool & Machine Inc ....G 937 667-2039
Tipp City (G-18302)
T E Martindale Enterprises ....G 614 253-6826
Columbus (G-7673)
T J Automation Inc ....E 419 267-5687
Archbold (G-697)
T J Karg Company Inc ....G 330 836-0921
Akron (G-425)
T N T Technologies Inc ....G 330 448-4744
Masury (G-13217)
Tailored Systems Inc ....G 937 299-3900
Moraine (G-14534)
Tat Machine and Tool Ltd ....G 419 836-7706
Curtice (G-7959)
Tc Precision Machine Inc ....G 937 278-3334
Dayton (G-8705)
Tdl Tool Inc ....E 937 374-0055
Xenia (G-20978)
▲ Te-Co Manufacturing LLC ....D 937 836-0961
Union (G-19068)
Technical Tool & Gauge Inc ....F 330 273-1778
Brunswick (G-2261)
Techniform Industries Inc ....E 419 332-8484
Fremont (G-10186)
Tegratek ....G 513 742-5100
Cincinnati (G-4499)
Tek Gear & Machine Inc ....G 330 455-3331
Canton (G-2868)
Tekraft Industries Inc ....G 440 352-8321
Painesville (G-15926)
Telcon LLC ....D 330 562-5566
Streetsboro (G-17881)
▲ Tema Systems Inc ....E 513 489-7811
Cincinnati (G-4501)
Tenan Machine & Fabricating ....G 440 997-5100
Ashtabula (G-841)
Tendon Manufacturing Inc ....E 216 663-3200
Cleveland (G-6305)
Tenex Tool Co ....G 440 354-5979
Painesville (G-15927)
Tenney Tool & Supply Co ....F 330 666-2807
Barberton (G-1153)
Terydon Inc ....F 330 879-2448
Navarre (G-14728)
Tessa Precision Product Inc ....E 440 392-3470
Painesville (G-15928)
▲ The Ewart-Ohlson Machine Co ....E 330 928-2171
Cuyahoga Falls (G-8055)
Thees Machine & Tool Co ....G 419 586-4766
Celina (G-3021)
Thieman Machine ....G 419 628-2474
Minster (G-14364)
Thomas Entps of Georgetown ....G 937 378-6300
Georgetown (G-10366)
Thread-Rite Tool & Mfg Inc ....G 937 222-2836
Dayton (G-8712)
Tiffin Foundry & Machine Inc ....E 419 447-3991
Tiffin (G-18247)
Tig Welding Specialties Inc ....G 216 621-1763
Cleveland (G-6324)
Timar Enterprises Inc ....G 440 942-4001
Willoughby (G-20615)
Timekap Inc ....G 330 747-2122
Youngstown (G-21222)
Timon J Reinhart ....G 419 476-1990
Toledo (G-18725)
Tipp Machine & Tool Inc ....C 937 890-8428
Dayton (G-8716)
Titan Manufacturing LLC ....G 440 942-2258
Willoughby (G-20616)
Tj Bell Inc ....G 330 633-3644
Akron (G-442)
Tm Machine & Tool Inc ....G 419 478-0310
Toledo (G-18727)
Tmac Machine Inc ....G 330 673-0621
Kent (G-11537)
Todd Industries Inc ....E 440 439-2900
Cleveland (G-6330)
Tom Barbour Auto Parts Inc ....F 740 354-4654
Portsmouth (G-16457)
Tool & Die Systems Inc ....E 440 327-5800
North Ridgeville (G-15406)
Toolbold Corporation ....G 216 676-9840
Cleveland (G-6334)
Toolco Inc ....G 419 667-3462
Van Wert (G-19273)
Tooling & Components Corp ....F 419 478-9122
Toledo (G-18750)
Total Manufacturing Co Inc ....E 440 205-9700
Mentor (G-13750)
Total Quality Machining Inc ....F 937 746-7765
Franklin (G-10059)
Total Repair Express Mich LLC ....G 248 690-9410
Stow (G-17809)
Toth Industries Inc ....D 419 729-4669
Toledo (G-18752)
Tower Tool & Manufacturing Co ....F 330 425-1623
Twinsburg (G-19028)
Tq Manufacturing Company Inc ....F 440 255-9000
Mentor (G-13752)
Tracer Specialties Inc ....G 216 696-2363
Cleveland (G-6344)
Tradye Machine & Tool Inc ....G 740 625-7550
Centerburg (G-3031)
▲ Trailer Component Mfg Inc ....E 440 255-2888
Mentor (G-13753)
Trec Industries Inc ....E 216 741-4114
Cleveland (G-6353)
Tri R Tooling Inc ....F 419 522-8665
Mansfield (G-12699)
Tri-State Machining LLC ....G 513 257-9442
Cleves (G-6530)
▲ Tri-State Tool & Die Inc ....G 330 655-2536
Stow (G-17812)
Triangle Precision Industries ....D 937 299-6776
Dayton (G-8723)
Triaxis Machine & Tool LLC ....G 440 230-0303
North Royalton (G-15457)
Trinel Inc ....F 216 265-9190
Cleveland (G-6367)
Triumph Tool LLC ....G 937 222-6885
Dayton (G-8728)
Trojon Gear Inc ....F 937 254-1737
Dayton (G-8729)
Trotwood Corporation ....E 937 854-3047
Trotwood (G-18800)
Troy Precision Carbide Die ....F 440 834-4477
Burton (G-2389)
Trs Engineering LLC ....G 419 714-7034
Perrysburg (G-16163)
Tru-Fab Technology Inc ....F 440 954-9760
Willoughby (G-20620)

Trucast Inc ....D...... 440 942-4923
　Willoughby (G-20621)

True Grinding ....G...... 440 786-7608
　Bedford (G-1469)

Trumbull Engrg Assembly & Mch ....G...... 330 394-6628
　Warren (G-19613)

Trv Incorporated ....E...... 440 951-7722
　Willoughby (G-20622)

▲ TSS Technologies Inc ....C...... 513 772-7000
　West Chester (G-19962)

TSS Technologies Inc ....G...... 513 772-7000
　Cincinnati (G-4532)

TSS Technologies Inc ....G...... 513 772-7000
　West Chester (G-19963)

TSS Technologies Inc ....G...... 513 772-7000
　Cincinnati (G-4533)

▲ Tsw Industries Inc ....E...... 440 572-7200
　Strongsville (G-17979)

Tubular Techniques Inc ....G...... 614 529-4130
　Hilliard (G-10989)

Turbo Machine & Tool Inc ....G...... 216 651-1940
　Cleveland (G-6375)

Turn-All Machine & Gear Co ....F...... 937 342-8710
　Springfield (G-17668)

Turner Machine Co.............................F...... 330 332-5821
　Salem (G-16932)

Twin Valley Metalcraft Asm LLC ....G...... 937 787-4634
　West Alexandria (G-19784)

Two M Precision Co Inc ....E...... 440 946-2120
　Willoughby (G-20623)

U S Alloy Die Corp ....F...... 216 749-9700
　Cleveland (G-6379)

Ultra Machine Inc ....G...... 440 323-7632
　Elyria (G-9504)

▲ Ultra Tech Machinery Inc ....E...... 330 929-5544
　Cuyahoga Falls (G-8059)

Umat LLC ....E...... 937 224-3303
　Dayton (G-8737)

▲ United Grinding and Machine Co ......D...... 330 453-7402
　Canton (G-2886)

United Machine and Tool Inc ....G...... 440 946-7677
　Eastlake (G-9295)

United Tool & Gage Co ....G...... 216 676-1000
　Cleveland (G-6389)

▲ Universal Fabg Cnstr Svcs Inc ....D...... 614 274-1128
　Columbus (G-7723)

Universal J&Z Machine LLC ....E...... 216 486-2220
　Willoughby (G-20624)

Universal Machine Products ....G...... 513 860-4530
　West Chester (G-19968)

Universal Prototype Product Co...........G...... 440 953-3550
　Eastlake (G-9296)

▲ Universal Tire Molds Inc ....E...... 330 253-5101
　Akron (G-458)

Universal Tool Technology LLC ....E...... 937 222-4608
　Dayton (G-8739)

Updegraff Inc ....G...... 216 621-7600
　Cleveland (G-6395)

Upm Inc ....G...... 419 595-2600
　Alvada (G-557)

Usm Acquisition Corporation ....F...... 440 975-8600
　Willoughby (G-20627)

Usm Precision Products Inc ....D...... 440 975-8600
　Willoughby (G-20628)

V M Machine Co Inc ....G...... 216 281-4569
　Cleveland (G-6404)

V-Ash Machine Company ....G...... 216 267-3400
　Cuyahoga Falls (G-8061)

Valley Machine Tool Co Inc ....E...... 513 899-2737
　Morrow (G-14553)

Vandalia Machining Inc ....G...... 937 264-9155
　Vandalia (G-19314)

Vanguard Die & Machine Inc ....E...... 330 394-4170
　Warren (G-19617)

Vectron Inc ....D...... 440 323-3369
　Elyria (G-9507)

▲ Ver-Mac Industries Inc ....E...... 740 397-6511
　Mount Vernon (G-14654)

Verhoff Machine & Welding Inc ....C...... 419 596-3202
　Continental (G-7829)

Versatile Machine..............................G...... 330 618-9895
　Tallmadge (G-18174)

Vic Mar Manufacturing Inc ....G...... 740 687-5434
　Lancaster (G-11761)

Vicas Manufacturing Co Inc ....E...... 513 791-7741
　Cincinnati (G-4568)

Vics Turning Co Inc ....G...... 216 531-5016
　Cleveland (G-6415)

Vision Projects Inc ....G...... 937 667-8648
　Tipp City (G-18309)

Vorlage Special Tool ....G...... 419 697-1201
　Oregon (G-15721)

Vrc Inc ....D...... 440 243-6666
　Berea (G-1640)

Vtd Systems Inc ....E...... 440 323-4122
　Elyria (G-9508)

Wade Dynamics Inc ....G...... 216 431-8484
　Cleveland (G-6439)

▲ Wagner Machine Inc ....E...... 330 706-0700
　Norton (G-15523)

Wakeman Auto and Tractor Parts ....G...... 440 839-2835
　Wakeman (G-19454)

Walest Incorporated ....G...... 216 362-8110
　Cleveland (G-6443)

Walt Myers ....G...... 937 325-0313
　Springfield (G-17675)

◆ Warren Fabricating Corporation ....D...... 330 847-0596
　Warren (G-19621)

Warrior Technologies Inc ....G...... 937 438-0279
　Dayton (G-8745)

Watkins Grinding Inc ....G...... 937 461-4487
　Dayton (G-8746)

▲ Wauseon Machine & Mfg Inc ....G...... 419 337-0940
　Wauseon (G-19700)

Waxler Machine Tool Company ....G...... 419 422-1240
　Findlay (G-9906)

Wayne Trail Technologies Inc ....G...... 937 295-2120
　Fort Loramie (G-9944)

Waynes Precision Machine Inc............G...... 330 426-4626
　East Palestine (G-9249)

Wc Sales Inc ....G...... 419 836-2300
　Northwood (G-15494)

Webb Machine & Fab Inc....................G...... 330 717-5745
　Berlin Center (G-1659)

Weber Tool & Mfg Inc ....G...... 440 786-0221
　Oakwood Village (G-15632)

Wedgeworks Mch Tl & Boring Co.........G...... 216 441-1200
　Cleveland (G-6453)

Welker Machine & Grinding Co ....G...... 216 481-1360
　Cleveland (G-6457)

Wendell Machine Shop ....G...... 330 627-3480
　Carrollton (G-2969)

Wenrick Machine and Tool Corp ....F...... 937 667-7307
　Tipp City (G-18311)

Wesco Machine Inc ....F...... 330 688-6973
　Munroe Falls (G-14668)

Westerman Acquisition Co LLC ....E...... 330 264-2447
　Wooster (G-20847)

Westgate Machine Co Inc ....G...... 216 889-9745
　North Royalton (G-15459)

White Machine & Mfg Co ....F...... 740 453-3444
　Zanesville (G-21362)

White Machine Inc ....G...... 440 237-3282
　North Royalton (G-15460)

Whitt Machine Inc ....F...... 513 423-7624
　Middletown (G-14098)

Wilguss Automotive Machine ....G...... 937 465-0043
　West Liberty (G-20095)

▲ Will-Burt Company ....B...... 330 682-7015
　Orrville (G-15770)

Will-Burt Company ....G...... 330 683-9991
　Orrville (G-15771)

Will-Burt Company ....E...... 330 682-7015
　Orrville (G-15772)

William Weber ....G...... 440 350-9397
　Painesville (G-15941)

Williams Machine Co Inc ....G...... 330 534-3058
　Hubbard (G-11141)

Williams Precision Tool Inc ....F...... 937 384-0608
　Miamisburg (G-13880)

Willmac Enterprises Inc ....G...... 740 967-1979
　Johnstown (G-11410)

Willow Tool & Machining Ltd ....F...... 440 572-2288
　Strongsville (G-17984)

Winans Manufacturing Co Inc ....G...... 440 338-8599
　Novelty (G-15585)

Wipe Out Enterprises ....G...... 937 497-9473
　Sidney (G-17236)

Wire Shop Inc ....E...... 440 354-6842
　Mentor (G-13771)

Wise Enterprises Inc..........................G...... 330 568-7095
　Hubbard (G-11142)

Wm Plotz Machine and Forge Co ....F...... 216 861-0441
　Cleveland (G-6473)

Wodin Inc ....E...... 440 439-4222
　Cleveland (G-6474)

Wolfe Grinding Inc ....G...... 330 929-6677
　Stow (G-17817)

Wonder Machine Services Inc ....E...... 440 937-7500
　Avon (G-1020)

Workshop Wire Cut and Mch Inc.........G...... 330 995-6404
　Aurora (G-957)

Worleys Machine & Fab Inc ....G...... 740 532-3337
　Hanging Rock (G-10762)

Wray Precision Products Inc ....G...... 513 228-5000
　Lebanon (G-11849)

Wt Tool & Die Inc ....G...... 330 332-2254
　Salem (G-16936)

Wulco Inc ....D...... 513 679-2600
　Cincinnati (G-4611)

▲ Wulco Inc ....D...... 513 679-2600
　Cincinnati (G-4612)

X-Mil Inc ....E...... 937 444-1323
　Mount Orab (G-14589)

Xact Spec Industires LLC ....G...... 440 543-8157
　Chagrin Falls (G-3134)

Xact Spec Industries LLC ....G...... 440 543-8157
　Chagrin Falls (G-3135)

Xorb Corporation ....G...... 419 354-6021
　Bowling Green (G-2023)

York Fabrication & Machine ....G...... 419 483-6275
　Bellevue (G-1567)

Youngstown Hard Chrome Plating ....E...... 330 758-9721
　Youngstown (G-21252)

Z & Z Manufacturing Inc ....F...... 440 953-2800
　Willoughby (G-20634)

Zanesville Tool Grinding ....G...... 740 453-9356
　Zanesville (G-21368)

Zaromet Inc ....E...... 513 891-0773
　Blue Ash (G-1904)

Zephyr Industries Inc ....G...... 419 281-4485
　Ashland (G-787)

Ziegler Bros Tool & Mch Inc ....G...... 419 738-6048
　Wapakoneta (G-19514)

Zitnik Enterprises Inc ....G...... 440 951-0089
　Willoughby (G-20635)

36 ELECTRONIC AND OTHER ELECTRICAL EQUIPMENT AND COMPONENTS, EXCEPT COMPUTER

3612 Power, Distribution & Specialty Transformers

ABB Inc ....D...... 440 585-8500
　Wickliffe (G-20347)

ABB Inc ....D...... 513 874-4730
　West Chester (G-19795)

Acuity Brands Lighting Inc ....B...... 740 349-4343
　Newark (G-14979)

◆ Ajax Tocco Magnethermic Corp ....C...... 330 372-8511
　Warren (G-19517)

Alfred J Buescher Jr ....G...... 216 752-3676
　Cleveland (G-4752)

Arisdyne Systems Inc ....F...... 216 458-1991
　Cleveland (G-4829)

Clark Substations LLC ....E...... 330 452-5200
　Canton (G-2659)

Contact Industries Inc ....E...... 419 884-9788
　Lexington (G-11949)

▲ Control Transformer Inc ....E...... 330 637-6015
　Cortland (G-7864)

Custom Coil & Transformer Co ....E...... 740 452-5211
　Zanesville (G-21297)

Darrah Electric Company ....E...... 216 631-0912
　Cleveland (G-5168)

Delta Transformer Inc ....G...... 513 242-9400
　Cincinnati (G-3647)

Eaton Leasing Corporation ....G...... 216 382-2292
　Beachwood (G-1270)

Energy Developments Inc ....G...... 440 774-6816
　Oberlin (G-15638)

Fishel Company ....D...... 614 850-4400
　Columbus (G-7089)

▲ Fostoria Bshngs Inslators Corp ....E...... 419 435-7514
　Fostoria (G-9973)

▲ Fostoria Bushings Inc ....G...... 419 435-7514
　Fostoria (G-9974)

General Electric Company ....D...... 216 883-1000
　Cleveland (G-5412)

H Left Company ....G...... 216 361-6348
　Cleveland (G-5468)

Hannon Company ....D...... 330 456-4728
　Canton (G-2723)

▲ Japlar Group Inc ....F...... 513 791-7192
　Cincinnati (G-3942)

Karrier Company Inc ....G...... 330 823-9597
　Alliance (G-520)

◆ Lake Shore Electric Corp ....E 440 232-0200
Bedford *(G-1438)*

▼ LTI Power Systems ....E 440 327-5050
Elyria *(G-9457)*

Matlock Electric Co Inc ....E 513 731-9600
Cincinnati *(G-4066)*

▼ Morlan & Associates Inc ....E 614 889-6152
Hilliard *(G-10964)*

Nautilus Hyosung America Inc ....G 937 203-4900
Miamisburg *(G-13839)*

▼ Norlake Manufacturing Company ....D 440 353-3200
North Ridgeville *(G-15391)*

◆ Ohio Semitronics Inc ....D 614 777-1005
Hilliard *(G-10967)*

▲ Otc Services Inc ....D 330 871-2444
Louisville *(G-12323)*

▲ Pioneer Transformer Company ....G 419 737-2304
Pioneer *(G-16239)*

Power House Electric Sup LLC ....G 419 523-6614
Ottawa *(G-15805)*

Precision Switching Inc ....G 800 800-8143
Mansfield *(G-12667)*

▲ Qualtek Electronics Corp ....C 440 951-3300
Mentor *(G-13710)*

Schneider Electric Usa Inc ....C 513 755-4231
West Chester *(G-19942)*

Schneider Electric Usa Inc ....D 513 755-5000
West Chester *(G-19943)*

Schneider Electric Usa Inc ....B 513 523-4171
Oxford *(G-15843)*

▲ SGB Usa Inc ....G 720 897-7090
Louisville *(G-12327)*

Siemens Industry Inc ....D 937 593-6010
Bellefontaine *(G-1539)*

Spectre Sensors Inc ....G 440 250-0372
Westlake *(G-20309)*

Spectre Sensors Inc ....G 440 250-0616
Westlake *(G-20310)*

◆ Staco Energy Products Co ....G 937 253-1191
Miamisburg *(G-13863)*

Tesa Inc ....G 614 847-8200
Lewis Center *(G-11925)*

Transcontinental Electric LLC ....G 614 496-4379
Columbus *(G-7705)*

Transformer Associates Limited ....G 330 430-0750
Canton *(G-2881)*

Unity Cable Technologies Inc ....G 419 322-4118
Toledo *(G-18759)*

Vida Ve Corp ....G 614 203-2607
Dublin *(G-9162)*

▼ Voltage Regulator Sales & Svcs ....G 937 878-0673
Fairborn *(G-9634)*

3613 Switchgear & Switchboard Apparatus

Acorn Technology Corporation ....E 216 663-1244
Cleveland *(G-4697)*

Adgo Incorporated ....E 513 752-6880
Cincinnati *(G-3292)*

Advanced Controls Inc ....G 440 354-5413
Eastlake *(G-9257)*

Agent Technologies Inc ....G 513 942-9444
West Chester *(G-19800)*

All Pack Services LLC ....F 614 935-0964
Grove City *(G-10541)*

▲ Altronic LLC ....C 330 545-9768
Girard *(G-10381)*

▲ American Controls Inc ....G 440 944-9735
Wickliffe *(G-20353)*

Apex Circuits Inc ....G 513 942-4400
West Chester *(G-19806)*

Asco Power Technologies LP ....E 216 573-7600
Cleveland *(G-4841)*

Asco Power Technologies LP ....G 973 966-2161
Cleveland *(G-4842)*

Assembly Works Inc ....G 419 433-5010
Huron *(G-11217)*

Auto-Tronic Control Co ....F 419 666-5100
Northwood *(G-15477)*

Bentronix Corp ....G 440 632-0606
Middlefield *(G-13917)*

▲ Bud Industries Inc ....E 440 946-3200
Willoughby *(G-20447)*

CDI Industries Inc ....E 440 243-1100
Cleveland *(G-4999)*

City Machine Technologies Inc ....G 330 747-2639
Youngstown *(G-21049)*

City Machine Technologies Inc ....G 330 747-2639
Youngstown *(G-21050)*

Control Craft LLC ....F 513 674-0056
Cincinnati *(G-3606)*

▲ Control Interface Inc ....G 513 874-2062
West Chester *(G-19843)*

Control Works Inc ....E 513 831-9959
Milford *(G-14133)*

Custom Craft Controls Inc ....F 330 630-9599
Akron *(G-136)*

Cutler Richard DBA Ohio Contro ....G 440 892-1858
Cleveland *(G-5153)*

▲ Delta Systems Inc ....C 330 626-2811
Streetsboro *(G-17850)*

DRDC Realty Inc ....G 419 478-7091
Toledo *(G-18444)*

Dynamics Research & Dev ....G 419 478-7091
Toledo *(G-18446)*

Electrical Control Systems ....G 937 859-7136
Dayton *(G-8321)*

Electro Controls Inc ....E 866 497-1717
Sidney *(G-17184)*

Emerson Network Power ....F 740 833-8630
Delaware *(G-8842)*

Empire Power Systems Co ....G 440 796-4401
Madison *(G-12506)*

Emt Inc ....G 330 399-6939
Warren *(G-19547)*

▲ Etched Metal Company ....E 440 248-0240
Solon *(G-17290)*

Fabriweld Corporation ....G 419 668-3358
Norwalk *(G-15539)*

Filnor Inc ....F 330 821-7667
Alliance *(G-508)*

Flood Heliarc Inc ....F 614 835-3929
Groveport *(G-10621)*

General Electric Company ....D 216 883-1000
Cleveland *(G-5412)*

◆ Gould Electronics Inc ....C 440 953-5000
Eastlake *(G-9271)*

Hosler Maps Inc ....G 937 855-4173
Germantown *(G-10369)*

◆ Hyundai Ideal Electric Co ....G 419 520-3314
Mansfield *(G-12626)*

Ida Controls ....G 440 785-8457
Willoughby *(G-20508)*

Industrial and Mar Eng Svc Co ....F 740 694-0791
Fredericktown *(G-10104)*

Industrial Ctrl Dsign Mint Inc ....F 330 785-9840
Tallmadge *(G-18148)*

Industrial Solutions Inc ....E 614 431-8118
Lewis Center *(G-11900)*

◆ Industrial Thermal Systems Inc ....F 513 561-2100
Cincinnati *(G-3918)*

Innovative Control Systems ....G 513 894-3712
Hamilton *(G-10705)*

Innovative Controls Corp ....D 419 691-6684
Toledo *(G-18524)*

Instrmntation Ctrl Systems Inc ....E 513 662-2600
Cincinnati *(G-3925)*

International Bus Mchs Corp ....B 513 826-1001
Blue Ash *(G-1816)*

Jeff Bonham Electric Inc ....E 937 233-7662
Dayton *(G-8425)*

Koester Corporation ....D 419 599-0291
Napoleon *(G-14687)*

◆ Lake Shore Electric Corp ....E 440 232-0200
Bedford *(G-1438)*

Layerzero Power Systems Inc ....E 440 399-9000
Aurora *(G-932)*

◆ Liebert Corporation ....A 614 888-0246
Columbus *(G-7292)*

Matrix Cable and Mould ....G 513 832-2577
Cincinnati *(G-4067)*

Mercury Iron & Steel ....F 440 349-1500
Solon *(G-17334)*

▲ Myers Controlled Power LLC ....C 330 834-3200
North Canton *(G-15253)*

Nolan Manufacturing LLC ....G 614 859-2302
Westerville *(G-20173)*

◆ Osborne Coinage Company ....D 513 681-5424
Cincinnati *(G-4197)*

Otr Controls LLC ....G 513 621-2197
Cincinnati *(G-4200)*

Panel Control Inc ....G 937 394-2201
Anna *(G-624)*

Panel Master LLC ....E 440 355-4442
Lagrange *(G-11635)*

Panel-Fab Inc ....D 513 771-1462
Cincinnati *(G-4210)*

Panelmatic Inc ....G 513 829-3666
Fairfield *(G-9698)*

Panelmatic Inc ....E 330 782-8007
Youngstown *(G-21162)*

Panelmatic Cincinnati Inc ....E 513 829-1960
Fairfield *(G-9699)*

▼ Panelmatic Youngstown Inc ....E 330 782-8007
Youngstown *(G-21163)*

Precision Switching Inc ....G 800 800-8143
Mansfield *(G-12667)*

Regal Beloit America Inc ....C 419 352-8441
Bowling Green *(G-2013)*

Roemer Industries Inc ....D 330 448-2000
Masury *(G-13216)*

Schneider Electric Usa Inc ....C 513 755-5503
Liberty Township *(G-11967)*

Schneider Electric Usa Inc ....C 513 755-4231
West Chester *(G-19942)*

Schneider Electric Usa Inc ....D 513 755-5000
West Chester *(G-19943)*

Scott Fetzer Company ....C 216 267-9000
Cleveland *(G-6168)*

Siemens Industry Inc ....G 937 593-6010
Bellefontaine *(G-1539)*

Spb Global LLC ....G 419 931-6559
Perrysburg *(G-16150)*

▲ Spectra-Tech Manufacturing Inc ....E 513 735-9300
Batavia *(G-1225)*

System Controls Inc ....G 216 351-9121
Cleveland *(G-6283)*

Systems Specialty Ctrl Co Inc ....E 419 478-4156
Toledo *(G-18713)*

Te Connectivity Corporation ....C 419 521-9500
Mansfield *(G-12694)*

Technology Products Inc ....G 937 652-3412
Urbana *(G-19184)*

Toledo Transducers Inc ....E 419 724-4170
Holland *(G-11090)*

▲ Trucut Incorporated ....D 330 938-9806
Sebring *(G-17055)*

◆ United Rolls Inc ....D 330 456-2761
Canton *(G-2888)*

Vacuum Electric Switch Co Inc ....G 330 374-5156
Akron *(G-461)*

3621 Motors & Generators

Aadco Instruments Inc ....G 513 467-1477
Cleves *(G-6505)*

▲ ABM Drives Inc ....G 513 576-1300
Loveland *(G-12336)*

Accurate Electronics Inc ....C 330 682-7015
Orrville *(G-15727)*

AEP Resources Inc ....E 614 716-1000
Columbus *(G-6700)*

Alliance Torque Converters Inc ....G 937 222-3394
Dayton *(G-8147)*

American Mitsuba Corporation ....G 989 779-4962
Dublin *(G-9042)*

American Mitsuba Corporation ....G 989 779-4962
Dublin *(G-9043)*

Ametek Inc ....G 302 636-5401
Worthington *(G-20857)*

Ametek Florcare Specialty Mtrs ....F 330 677-3786
Kent *(G-11428)*

Ametek Technical & Indus Pdts ....D 330 677-3754
Kent *(G-11429)*

Ares Inc ....G 419 635-2175
Port Clinton *(G-16393)*

Brinkley Technology Group LLC ....F 330 830-2498
Massillon *(G-13115)*

Charger Connection ....G 888 427-5829
Cincinnati *(G-3522)*

Charles Auto Electric Co Inc ....G 330 535-6269
Akron *(G-118)*

Chemequip Sales Inc ....E 330 724-8300
Akron *(G-120)*

City Machine Technologies Inc ....D 330 747-2639
Youngstown *(G-21047)*

City Machine Technologies Inc ....E 330 740-8186
Youngstown *(G-21048)*

Custom Coil & Transformer Co ....E 740 452-5211
Zanesville *(G-21297)*

◆ Dayton-Phoenix Group Inc ....C 937 496-3900
Dayton *(G-8293)*

◆ Dcm Manufacturing Inc ....E 216 265-8006
Cleveland *(G-5178)*

Design Flux Technologies LLC ....G 216 543-6066
Akron *(G-147)*

▲ Dreison International Inc ....C 216 362-0755
Cleveland *(G-5215)*

Econ-O-Machine Products Inc ....G 937 882-6307
Donnelsville *(G-8961)*

Electric Service Co Inc ....E 513 271-6387
Cincinnati *(G-3692)*

▲ Electrocraft Arkansas Inc ....D.... 501 268-4203
  Gallipolis (G-10294)
Energy Technologies Inc ....D.... 419 522-4444
  Mansfield (G-12600)
Franklin Electric Co Inc ....A.... 614 794-2266
  Dublin (G-9077)
Freeman Enclosure Systems LLC ......C.... 877 441-8555
  Batavia (G-1187)
GE Aviation Systems LLC ....B.... 937 898-5881
  Vandalia (G-19293)
General Electric Company ....E.... 740 498-5151
  Newcomerstown (G-15113)
General Electric Company ....D.... 216 883-1000
  Cleveland (G-5412)
◆ Gleason Metrology Systems Corp ...E.... 937 384-8901
  Dayton (G-8365)
▲ Globe Motors Inc ....C.... 334 983-3542
  Dayton (G-8368)
Globe Motors Inc ....C.... 937 228-3171
  Dayton (G-8369)
Globe Motors Inc ....C.... 937 228-3171
  Dayton (G-8370)
▲ Grand-Rock Company Inc ....E.... 440 639-2000
  Painesville (G-15884)
Gunter Electric LLC ....G.... 304 253-4671
  Athens (G-871)
H W Fairway International Inc ....E.... 330 678-2540
  Kent (G-11467)
Hannon Company ....D.... 330 456-4728
  Canton (G-2723)
High Performance Servo LLC ....G.... 440 541-3529
  Westlake (G-20276)
Home Resolver ....G.... 440 886-6758
  Cleveland (G-5520)
▲ Hurst Auto-Truck Electric ....E.... 216 961-1800
  Cleveland (G-5538)
◆ Hyundai Ideal Electric Co ....C.... 419 520-3314
  Mansfield (G-12626)
Industrial and Mar Eng Svc Co ....F.... 740 694-0791
  Fredericktown (G-10104)
Intellitronix Corporation ....E.... 440 210-7645
  Eastlake (G-9276)
JD Power Systems LLC ....F.... 614 317-9394
  Hilliard (G-10955)
Kirkwood Holding Inc ....G.... 216 267-6200
  Cleveland (G-5659)
◆ Lake Shore Electric Corp ....E.... 440 232-0200
  Bedford (G-1438)
Lesch Btry & Pwr Solution LLC ....G.... 419 884-0219
  Mansfield (G-12636)
▲ Linde Hydraulics Corporation ....E.... 330 533-6801
  Canfield (G-2562)
Martin Diesel Inc ....E.... 419 782-9911
  Defiance (G-8802)
Michael Bradley Apparatus LLC ....F.... 740 374-6255
  Marietta (G-12807)
Micropower LLC ....F.... 513 382-0100
  Cincinnati (G-4101)
Mv Designlabs LLC ....G.... 724 355-7986
  Cleveland (G-5842)
Nidec Motor Corporation ....C.... 575 434-0633
  Akron (G-315)
Ohio Generator Remanufacturing ....G.... 330 875-6677
  Louisville (G-12321)
▲ Ohio Magnetics Inc ....E.... 216 662-8484
  Maple Heights (G-12736)
◆ Ohio Semitronics Inc ....D.... 614 777-1005
  Hilliard (G-10967)
Pace Converting Eqp Co Inc ....F.... 216 631-4555
  Cleveland (G-5959)
Palesh & Associates Inc ....G.... 440 942-9168
  Willoughby (G-20566)
Parker-Hannifin Corporation ....C.... 330 336-3511
  Wadsworth (G-19425)
Peerless-Winsmith Inc ....B.... 330 399-3651
  Dublin (G-9121)
▲ Peerless-Winsmith Inc ....G.... 614 526-7000
  Dublin (G-9122)
Precision Design Inc ....G.... 419 289-1553
  Ashland (G-767)
R E Smith Inc ....F.... 513 771-0645
  Cincinnati (G-4325)
R Gordon Jones Inc ....G.... 740 986-8381
  Williamsport (G-20418)
Ramco Electric Motors Inc ....D.... 937 548-2525
  Greenville (G-10516)
Regal Beloit America Inc ....C.... 937 667-2431
  Tipp City (G-18296)
Reuland Electric Co ....G.... 513 825-7314
  Cincinnati (G-4340)

Siemens Industry Inc ....C.... 513 841-3100
  Cincinnati (G-4417)
Stateline Power Corp ....F.... 937 547-1006
  Greenville (G-10524)
▲ Surenergy LLC ....F.... 419 626-8000
  Sandusky (G-17011)
▲ Swiger Coil Systems Ltd ....C.... 216 362-7500
  Cleveland (G-6280)
Td Power Systems (usa) Inc ....G.... 330 247-5264
  Richfield (G-16642)
Thermelectricity LLC ....G.... 330 972-8054
  Akron (G-438)
▲ Tigerpoly Manufacturing Inc ....B.... 614 871-0045
  Grove City (G-10601)
Tremont Electric Incorporated ....G.... 888 214-3137
  Cleveland (G-6355)
▲ Turk+hillinger Usa Inc ....G.... 440 781-1900
  Brecksville (G-2077)
Turtlecreek Township ....F.... 513 932-4080
  Lebanon (G-11846)
◆ Vanner Holdings Inc ....D.... 614 771-2718
  Hilliard (G-10991)
Visiontech Automation LLC ....G.... 614 554-2013
  Dublin (G-9164)
Wabtec Corporation ....G.... 216 362-7500
  Cleveland (G-6437)
Waibel Electric Co Inc ....F.... 740 964-2956
  Etna (G-9553)
▲ Yamada North America Inc ....B.... 937 462-7111
  South Charleston (G-17428)

3624 Carbon & Graphite Prdts

Advanced Energy Tech LLC ....E.... 216 676-2259
  Lakewood (G-11654)
Albemarle Corporation ....G.... 330 425-2354
  Twinsburg (G-18897)
Algie Composites Inc ....G.... 614 529-0477
  Columbus (G-6715)
▲ American Spring Wire Corp ....C.... 216 292-4620
  Bedford Heights (G-1478)
▲ Americarb Inc ....D.... 419 281-5800
  Ashland (G-703)
Americarb International Corp ....D.... 419 281-5800
  Ashland (G-704)
Angstron Materials Inc ....G.... 937 331-9884
  Dayton (G-8159)
Applied Sciences Inc ....E.... 937 766-2020
  Cedarville (G-2980)
Babcock & Wilcox Megtec ....C.... 614 258-9501
  Columbus (G-6799)
Buckeye Molded Products Ltd ....F.... 440 323-2244
  Elyria (G-9383)
▲ Cammann Inc ....F.... 440 965-4051
  Birmingham (G-1685)
◆ De Nora Tech Inc ....D.... 440 710-5300
  Painesville (G-15875)
GE Aviation Systems LLC ....B.... 937 898-5881
  Vandalia (G-19293)
Graftech Advanced Graphite ....E.... 216 676-2259
  Parma (G-15960)
Graftech Holdings Inc ....A.... 216 676-2000
  Independence (G-11256)
◆ Graftech International Ltd ....E.... 216 676-2000
  Independence (G-11257)
Graftech Intl Holdings Inc ....E.... 216 529-3777
  Cleveland (G-5443)
Graftech Intl Holdings Inc ....C.... 330 239-3023
  Parma (G-15961)
◆ Graftech Intl Holdings Inc ....C.... 216 676-2000
  Independence (G-11258)
Graphel Corporation ....C.... 513 779-6166
  West Chester (G-19879)
▲ Graphite Sales Inc ....F.... 440 543-8221
  Chagrin Falls (G-3090)
Graphite Sales Inc ....E.... 419 652-3388
  Nova (G-15578)
▲ Mill-Rose Company ....C.... 440 255-9171
  Mentor (G-13657)
National Elec Carbn Pdts Inc ....D.... 419 435-8182
  Fostoria (G-9986)
Ohio Carbon Blank Inc ....G.... 440 953-9302
  Willoughby (G-20561)
Ohio Carbon Industries Inc ....E.... 419 496-2530
  Ashland (G-759)
Ohio Power Tool Brush Co ....G.... 419 736-3010
  Ashland (G-760)
Pyrograf Products Inc ....F.... 937 766-2020
  Cedarville (G-2983)
Pyrotek Incorporated ....C.... 440 349-8800
  Aurora (G-942)

▼ R&S Carbon Trading LLC ....G.... 614 264-3083
  Gahanna (G-10227)
▲ Randall Bearings Inc ....D.... 419 223-1075
  Lima (G-12080)
Randall Bearings Inc ....F.... 419 678-2486
  Coldwater (G-6570)
▲ Sangraf International Inc ....F.... 216 543-3288
  Independence (G-11273)
Sentinel Management Inc ....E.... 440 821-7372
  Lorain (G-12274)
Sherbrooke Metals ....F.... 440 942-3520
  Willoughby (G-20596)
▲ Spectramed Inc ....F.... 740 263-3059
  Gahanna (G-10235)
▲ Timcal America Inc ....F.... 440 871-7504
  Westlake (G-20316)
▼ Wolfden Products Inc ....G.... 614 219-6990
  Columbus (G-7769)
Wolfden Products LLC ....G.... 614 219-6990
  Columbus (G-7770)
Xperion E&E USA LLC ....E.... 740 788-9560
  Heath (G-10858)
Zyvex Performance Mtls Inc ....E.... 614 481-2222
  Columbus (G-7789)

3625 Relays & Indl Controls

Acon Inc ....G.... 513 276-2111
  Tipp City (G-18258)
▲ Altronic LLC ....C.... 330 545-9768
  Girard (G-10381)
Amano Cincinnati Incorporated ....D.... 513 697-9000
  Loveland (G-12338)
Apex Circuits Inc ....G.... 513 942-4400
  West Chester (G-19806)
Asco Power Technologies LP ....B.... 216 573-7600
  Cleveland (G-4841)
Asco Power Technologies LP ....C.... 973 966-2161
  Cleveland (G-4842)
Asco Valve Inc ....F.... 216 360-0366
  Cleveland (G-4843)
Automatic Timing & Contrls Inc ....D.... 614 888-8855
  New Albany (G-14747)
Automation Technology Inc ....E.... 937 233-6084
  Dayton (G-8174)
Autoneum North America Inc ....B.... 419 693-0511
  Oregon (G-15703)
Avtron Holdings LLC ....B.... 216 642-1230
  Cleveland (G-4876)
▼ Axel Austin LLC ....G.... 440 237-1610
  North Royalton (G-15410)
Barry Brothers Electric ....G.... 614 299-8187
  Columbus (G-6809)
▼ Bay Controls LLC ....E.... 419 891-4390
  Maumee (G-13231)
Beckworth Industries Inc ....G.... 216 268-5557
  Cleveland (G-4902)
▲ C-Tech Industries LLC ....F.... 877 755-7311
  West Chester (G-19822)
Central Systems & Control ....G.... 440 835-0015
  Cleveland (G-5005)
▲ Chandler Systems Incorporated ......D.... 419 281-5767
  Ashland (G-721)
▲ Channel Products Inc ....G.... 440 423-0113
  Chesterland (G-3199)
Cincinnati Ctrl Dynamics Inc ....E.... 513 242-7300
  Cincinnati (G-3547)
Clark Substations LLC ....E.... 330 452-5200
  Canton (G-2659)
▲ Cleveland Hdwr & Forging Co ....E.... 216 641-5200
  Cleveland (G-5064)
Command Alkon Incorporated ....D.... 614 799-0600
  Dublin (G-9064)
Comtec Incorporated ....F.... 330 425-8102
  Twinsburg (G-18918)
Contact Industries Inc ....E.... 419 884-9788
  Lexington (G-11949)
Control Associates Inc ....G.... 440 708-1770
  Chagrin Falls (G-3082)
Control Electric Co ....E.... 216 671-8010
  Columbia Station (G-6586)
Control Works Inc ....E.... 513 831-9959
  Milford (G-14133)
Controllix Corporation ....F.... 440 232-8757
  Walton Hills (G-19472)
Controls Inc ....G.... 330 239-4345
  Medina (G-13392)
Cook Bonding & Mfg Co Inc ....G.... 216 661-1698
  Cleveland (G-5129)
Corrotec Inc ....E.... 937 325-3585
  Springfield (G-17536)

SIC

Creative Electronic Design ....G...... 937 256-5106
　　Beavercreek (G-1327)
Curtiss-Wright Controls ....E...... 937 252-5601
　　Fairborn (G-9618)
Dalton Corporation ....D...... 419 682-6328
　　Stryker (G-18001)
Davis Technologies Inc ....F...... 330 823-2544
　　Alliance (G-505)
Delta Control Inc ....G...... 937 277-3444
　　Dayton (G-8297)
▲ Delta Systems Inc ....C...... 330 626-2811
　　Streetsboro (G-17850)
▲ Dimcogray Corporation ....D...... 937 433-7600
　　Centerville (G-3039)
Divelbiss Corporation ....E...... 800 245-2327
　　Fredericktown (G-10100)
◆ Eaton Corporation ....B...... 216 523-5000
　　Cleveland (G-5245)
Eaton Corporation ....C...... 216 416-2500
　　Cleveland (G-5246)
Eaton Corporation ....C...... 888 328-6677
　　Cleveland (G-5248)
Eaton Corporation ....C...... 440 826-1115
　　Cleveland (G-5250)
Eaton Corporation ....C...... 440 748-2236
　　Grafton (G-10424)
Eaton Corporation ....C...... 216 281-2211
　　Cleveland (G-5247)
Electrical Control Design Inc ....G...... 419 443-9290
　　Perrysburg (G-16088)
▲ Electrocraft Ohio Inc ....C...... 740 441-6200
　　Gallipolis (G-10295)
Electrodynamics Inc ....G...... 847 259-0740
　　Cincinnati (G-3300)
▲ Ellis & Watts Intl LLC ....G...... 513 752-9000
　　Batavia (G-1183)
Energy Technologies Inc ....D...... 419 522-4444
　　Mansfield (G-12600)
Fabriweld Corporation ....G...... 419 668-3358
　　Norwalk (G-15539)
▲ Filnor Inc ....F...... 330 821-8731
　　Alliance (G-506)
Filnor Inc ....G...... 330 829-3180
　　Alliance (G-507)
Filnor Inc ....F...... 330 821-7667
　　Alliance (G-508)
▼ Fuse Chicken Llc ....G...... 330 338-7108
　　Cuyahoga Falls (G-8001)
Future Controls Corporation ....E...... 440 275-3191
　　Austinburg (G-962)
Gc Controls Inc ....G...... 440 779-4777
　　North Olmsted (G-15337)
GE Aviation Systems LLC ....B...... 937 898-5881
　　Vandalia (G-19293)
GE Intelligent Platforms Inc ....G...... 937 459-5404
　　Greenville (G-10502)
Grill ....G...... 937 673-6768
　　Eaton (G-9307)
Harris Instrument Corporation ......G...... 740 369-3580
　　Delaware (G-8857)
Helm Instrument Company Inc ....E...... 419 893-4356
　　Maumee (G-13265)
Hite Parts Exchange Inc ....E...... 614 272-5115
　　Columbus (G-7160)
Hueston Industries Inc ....G...... 937 264-8163
　　Dayton (G-8396)
▲ Hurst Auto-Truck Electric ....G...... 216 961-1800
　　Cleveland (G-5538)
▲ Hyde Park Electronics LLC ....D...... 937 252-2121
　　Dayton (G-8398)
◆ Hyundai Ideal Electric Co ....C...... 419 520-3314
　　Mansfield (G-12626)
Ignio Systems LLC ....F...... 419 708-0503
　　Toledo (G-18516)
Independent Digital Consulting .....G...... 330 753-0777
　　Norton (G-15514)
Inductive Components Mfg ....E...... 513 752-4731
　　Amelia (G-577)
Industrial and Mar Eng Svc Co ....F...... 740 694-0791
　　Fredericktown (G-10104)
Innovative Controls Corp ....D...... 419 691-6684
　　Toledo (G-18524)
Innovative Integrations Inc ....G...... 216 533-5353
　　Mesopotamia (G-13775)
ITT Corporation ....D...... 937 256-1705
　　Dayton (G-8109)
James R Eaton ....G...... 937 435-7767
　　Dayton (G-8421)
Jay Instruments ....G...... 513 733-5200
　　Cincinnati (G-3943)

Job One Control Services ....G...... 216 347-0133
　　Cleveland (G-5617)
Kahle Technologies Inc ....G...... 419 523-3951
　　Ottawa (G-15799)
Konecranes Inc ....G...... 937 328-5123
　　Springfield (G-17588)
Kz Solutions Inc ....G...... 513 942-9378
　　West Chester (G-19889)
Laird Controls Holdings Inc ....E...... 234 806-0018
　　Warren (G-19567)
◆ Laird Controls North Amer Inc ....F...... 234 806-0018
　　Warren (G-19568)
◆ Lake Shore Electric Corp ....E...... 440 232-0200
　　Bedford (G-1438)
Lincoln Electric Company ....C...... 216 524-8800
　　Cleveland (G-5696)
M Technologies ....F...... 330 477-9009
　　Canton (G-2764)
MA Flynn Associates LLC ....G...... 513 893-7873
　　Hamilton (G-10721)
Maags Automotive & Machine ....G...... 419 626-1539
　　Sandusky (G-16982)
McGill Airsilence LLC ....F...... 614 443-0192
　　Columbus (G-7333)
Miami Control Systems Inc ....G...... 937 698-5725
　　West Milton (G-20107)
Midwest Minicranes Inc ....G...... 330 332-3700
　　Salem (G-16915)
Mission Control Systems Inc ....G...... 419 472-3791
　　Toledo (G-18587)
Moog Inc ....D...... 330 682-0010
　　Orrville (G-15748)
◆ Morris Material Handling Inc ....G...... 937 525-5520
　　Springfield (G-17608)
New ERA Controls Inc ....G...... 216 641-8683
　　Cleveland (G-5877)
Noise Suppression Technologies ....F...... 614 275-1818
　　Columbus (G-7395)
Norgren Inc ....C...... 937 833-4033
　　Brookville (G-2194)
Northcoast Process Contrls Inc ....G...... 440 498-0542
　　Cleveland (G-5901)
▲ Ohio Magnetics Inc ....E...... 216 662-8484
　　Maple Heights (G-12736)
◆ Ohio Semitronics Inc ....D...... 614 777-1005
　　Hilliard (G-10967)
Omega Tek Inc ....G...... 419 756-9580
　　Mansfield (G-12664)
▲ Opw Engineered Systems Inc ....D...... 888 771-9438
　　Lebanon (G-11824)
Orion Control Panels Inc ....G...... 513 615-6534
　　Cincinnati (G-4195)
Panel Master LLC ....E...... 440 355-4442
　　Lagrange (G-11635)
Parkside & Eaton Estate ....G...... 330 467-2995
　　Northfield (G-15469)
Peco II Inc ....D...... 614 431-0694
　　Columbus (G-7473)
▲ Peloton Manufacturing Corp ....F...... 440 205-1600
　　Mentor (G-13684)
▲ Pepperl + Fuchs Inc ....C...... 330 425-3555
　　Twinsburg (G-18997)
PMC Systems Limited ....E...... 330 538-2268
　　North Jackson (G-15297)
Positive Safety Mfr Co ....F...... 440 951-2130
　　Willoughby (G-20575)
Precision Switching Inc ....G...... 800 800-8143
　　Mansfield (G-12667)
Prime Controls Inc ....G...... 937 435-8659
　　Dayton (G-8592)
Quality Controls Inc ....F...... 513 272-3900
　　Cincinnati (G-4306)
▲ R-K Electronics Inc ....C...... 513 204-6060
　　Mason (G-13079)
Ramco Electric Motors Inc ....D...... 937 548-2525
　　Greenville (G-10516)
Rbb Systems Inc ....D...... 330 263-4502
　　Wooster (G-20827)
Rbb Systems Inc ....D...... 330 263-4502
　　Wooster (G-20828)
Resinoid Engineering Corp ....E...... 740 928-2220
　　Heath (G-10854)
Retek Inc ....G...... 440 937-6282
　　Avon (G-1008)
Rex Automation Inc ....G...... 614 766-4672
　　Columbus (G-7559)
Robert C Bost Associates Inc ....F...... 301 206-9466
　　Columbus (G-7568)
Rockwell Automation Inc ....D...... 513 942-9828
　　West Chester (G-19936)

Rockwell Automation Inc ....E...... 440 604-8410
　　Cleveland (G-6127)
Rockwell Automation Inc ....B...... 330 425-3211
　　Twinsburg (G-19011)
Rockwell Automation Inc ....E...... 513 943-1145
　　Batavia (G-1219)
Rockwell Automation Inc ....D...... 440 646-5000
　　Cleveland (G-6128)
Rockwell Automation Inc ....D...... 614 776-3021
　　Westerville (G-20184)
Rockwell Automation Inc ....F...... 440 646-7900
　　Cleveland (G-6129)
▲ Rogers Industrial Products Inc .....E...... 330 535-3331
　　Akron (G-378)
▲ Satco Inc ....G...... 330 630-8866
　　Tallmadge (G-18168)
SCC Instruments ....E...... 513 856-8444
　　Hamilton (G-10735)
Schneider Electric Usa Inc ....C...... 513 755-4231
　　West Chester (G-19942)
Schneider Electric Usa Inc ....D...... 513 755-5000
　　West Chester (G-19943)
Sieb & Meyer America Inc ....F...... 513 563-0860
　　Fairfield (G-9717)
SMC Corporation of America ....E...... 330 659-2006
　　Richfield (G-16638)
Spang & Company ....E...... 440 350-6108
　　Mentor (G-13727)
Stambaugh Engineering Inc ....G...... 330 666-0088
　　Akron (G-411)
Stock Fairfield Corporation ....C...... 440 543-6000
　　Chagrin Falls (G-3122)
T D Group Holdings LLC ....G...... 216 706-2939
　　Cleveland (G-6289)
Tabtronics Inc ....F...... 937 222-9969
　　Dayton (G-8697)
Te Connectivity Corporation ....G...... 419 521-9500
　　Mansfield (G-12694)
Tech Products Corporation ....E...... 937 438-1100
　　Miamisburg (G-13867)
Technology Products Inc ....G...... 937 652-3412
　　Urbana (G-19184)
Tekworx LLC ....G...... 513 533-4777
　　Blue Ash (G-1881)
Temple Israel ....G...... 330 762-8617
　　Akron (G-434)
Thermotion Corp ....F...... 440 639-8325
　　Mentor (G-13746)
Toledo Electromotive Inc ....G...... 419 874-7751
　　Perrysburg (G-16162)
Toledo Transducers Inc ....E...... 419 724-4170
　　Holland (G-11090)
Transdigm Inc ....G...... 216 706-2939
　　Cleveland (G-6347)
Transdigm Inc ....F...... 216 291-6025
　　Cleveland (G-6346)
Tri-Tech Research LLC ....G...... 440 946-6122
　　Eastlake (G-9293)
Turvey Engineering ....G...... 330 427-0125
　　Washingtonville (G-19643)
Tvh Parts Co ....F...... 877 755-7311
　　West Chester (G-19965)
United States Controls Inc ....G...... 330 758-1147
　　Poland (G-16386)
Utility Relay Co Ltd ....E...... 440 708-1000
　　Chagrin Falls (G-3131)
▲ Valve Related Controls Inc ....F...... 513 677-8724
　　Loveland (G-12397)
Vintage Electric Ltd Inc ....G...... 419 472-9349
　　Toledo (G-18770)
Wes-Garde Components Group Inc ...G...... 614 885-0319
　　Westerville (G-20240)

3629 Electrical Indl Apparatus, NEC

10155 Broadview Business ....G...... 440 546-1901
　　Broadview Heights (G-2101)
Amplified Solar Inc ....G...... 216 236-4225
　　Lakewood (G-11656)
Avtron Inc ....E...... 216 642-1230
　　Independence (G-11249)
▲ Brookwood Group Inc ....F...... 513 791-3030
　　Cincinnati (G-3481)
Cable and Ctrl Solutions LLC ....G...... 937 254-2227
　　Dayton (G-8097)
▲ Core Technology Inc ....F...... 440 934-9935
　　Avon (G-991)
Cvc Limited 1 LLC ....G...... 740 605-3853
　　Lebanon (G-11792)
D C Systems Inc ....F...... 330 273-3030
　　Brunswick (G-2219)

Dan-Mar Company Inc ....E 419 660-8830
   Norwalk (G-15532)
Dishtronix Inc ....G 937 292-7981
   Bellefontaine (G-1528)
▲ Ecotec Ltd LLC ....G 937 606-2793
   Troy (G-18821)
Energy Technologies Inc ....D 419 522-4444
   Mansfield (G-12600)
Eti Tech Inc ....F 937 832-4200
   Englewood (G-9519)
Industrial Application Svs ....G 419 875-5093
   Grand Rapids (G-10440)
▲ Japlar Group Inc ....F 513 791-7192
   Cincinnati (G-3942)
◆ Lubrizol Advanced Mtls Inc .....F 216 447-5000
   Brecksville (G-2061)
McGregor-Surmount Corporation ...C 937 833-6768
   Brookville (G-2193)
Myers Controlled Power LLC ....F 909 923-1800
   Canton (G-2786)
Proteus Electronics Inc ....G 419 886-2296
   Bellville (G-1575)
Sarica Manufacturing Company ....G 937 484-4030
   Urbana (G-19179)
▲ Smartshopper Electronics Inc ...G 440 349-5119
   Solon (G-17382)
Spirit Avionics Ltd ....F 614 358-0333
   Columbus (G-7645)
Superior Packaging ....F 419 380-3335
   Toledo (G-18710)
▲ Takk Industries Inc ....F 513 353-4306
   Cincinnati (G-4491)
Tasi Holdings Inc ....E 513 202-5182
   Harrison (G-10809)
▲ Tecmark Corporation ....D 440 205-7600
   Mentor (G-13743)
TL Industries Inc ....C 419 666-8144
   Northwood (G-15490)
◆ Vanner Holdings Inc ....D 614 771-2718
   Hilliard (G-10991)
Waterloo Manufacturing Co Inc ....G 330 947-2917
   Atwater (G-904)
Wired Inc ....G 440 567-8379
   Willoughby (G-20632)
▲ Xenotronix/Tli Inc ....G 407 331-4793
   Northwood (G-15498)

3631 Household Cooking Eqpt

Lapa Lowe Enterprises LLC ....G 440 944-9410
   Willoughby (G-20527)
Nacco Industries Inc ....E 440 229-5151
   Cleveland (G-5848)
Royalton Food Service Eqp Co ......E 440 237-0806
   North Royalton (G-15448)

3632 Household Refrigerators & Freezers

Liebrecht Manufacturing ....G 419 596-3501
   Continental (G-7827)
◆ Norcold Inc ....B 937 497-3080
   Sidney (G-17206)
Norcold Inc ....C 937 447-2241
   Gettysburg (G-10375)
Whirlpool Corporation ....B 419 547-7711
   Clyde (G-6548)
Whirlpool Corporation ....D 419 423-8123
   Findlay (G-9908)
Whirlpool Corporation ....C 419 523-5100
   Ottawa (G-15815)
Whirlpool Corporation ....C 740 383-7122
   Marion (G-12913)
Whirlpool Corporation ....C 614 409-4340
   Lockbourne (G-12153)

3633 Household Laundry Eqpt

Carly Co LLC ....G 937 477-6411
   Centerville (G-3038)
Junebugs Wash N Dry ....G 513 988-5863
   Trenton (G-18794)
▲ Staber Industries Inc ....E 614 836-5995
   Groveport (G-10645)
Whirlpool Corporation ....C 740 383-7122
   Marion (G-12913)
Whirlpool Corporation ....B 419 547-7711
   Clyde (G-6548)
Whirlpool Corporation ....C 937 547-0773
   Greenville (G-10528)
Whirlpool Corporation ....C 614 409-4340
   Lockbourne (G-12153)
Whirlpool Corporation ....C 419 523-5100
   Ottawa (G-15815)

3634 Electric Household Appliances

Acorn Technology Corporation ....E 216 663-1244
   Cleveland (G-4697)
Aitken Products Inc ....G 440 466-5711
   Geneva (G-10341)
Anson Co ....G 216 524-8838
   Bedford (G-1397)
Broan-Nutone LLC ....G 888 336-3948
   Blue Ash (G-1755)
▲ Budzar Industries Inc ....D 440 530-1000
   Willoughby (G-20448)
Ces Nationwide ....G 937 322-0771
   Springfield (G-17530)
▲ Cleveland Range LLC ....C 216 481-4900
   Cleveland (G-5075)
Didonato Products Inc ....G 330 535-1119
   Akron (G-151)
Driven Innovations LLC ....G 330 818-7681
   Englewood (G-9517)
▲ Fhi Heat Inc ....G 216 456-0353
   Solon (G-17291)
Glo-Quartz Electric Heater Co ....E 440 255-9701
   Mentor (G-13593)
◆ Hmi Industries Inc ....G 440 846-7800
   Strongsville (G-17926)
Johnson Bros Rubber Co Inc ....E 419 752-4814
   Greenwich (G-10531)
Klawhorn Industries Inc ....G 330 335-8191
   Wadsworth (G-19414)
Nacco Industries Inc ....E 440 229-5151
   Cleveland (G-5848)
Ohio Valley Vapor Station ....G 740 449-2288
   Saint Clairsville (G-16804)
▲ Peerless-Winsmith Inc ....G 614 526-7000
   Dublin (G-9122)
▲ Qualtek Electronics Corp ....C 440 951-3300
   Mentor (G-13710)
▲ Skuttle Mfg Co ....F 740 373-9169
   Marietta (G-12831)
Ventilation Systems Jsc ....G 513 348-3853
   Blue Ash (G-1889)
Whirlpool Corporation ....B 937 548-4126
   Greenville (G-10527)

3635 Household Vacuum Cleaners

Edwards Vacuum LLC ....G 440 248-4453
   Solon (G-17284)
▲ GMI Holdings Inc ....B 330 821-5360
   Mount Hope (G-14571)
H-P Products Inc ....E 330 875-7193
   Louisville (G-12313)
Hoover Inc ....F 330 499-9200
   Canton (G-2730)
J K Plastics Co ....G 440 632-1482
   Middlefield (G-13944)
◆ Kirby Sales Company Inc ....B 216 228-2400
   Cleveland (G-5657)
Powerclean Equipment Company ......G 513 202-0001
   Cleves (G-6524)
Rent A Mom Inc ....F 216 901-9599
   Seven Hills (G-17063)
Scott Fetzer Company ....B 216 228-2403
   Cleveland (G-6169)
Scott Fetzer Company ....D 216 252-1190
   Cleveland (G-6170)
Scott Fetzer Company ....B 440 871-2160
   Cleveland (G-6171)
Scott Fetzer Company ....C 440 439-1616
   Cleveland (G-6172)
Scott Fetzer Company ....D 216 281-1100
   Cleveland (G-6173)
Scott Fetzer Company ....C 216 433-7797
   Cleveland (G-6174)
Scott Fetzer Company ....C 440 871-2160
   Avon Lake (G-1050)
Scott Fetzer Company ....E 216 228-2400
   Chagrin Falls (G-3119)
▲ Stanley Steemer Intl Inc ....C 614 764-2007
   Dublin (G-9149)
Western/Scott Fetzer Company ....C 440 871-2160
   Westlake (G-20319)
◆ Western/Scott Fetzer Company ...E 440 892-3000
   Westlake (G-20320)

3639 Household Appliances, NEC

ABC Appliance Inc ....E 419 693-4414
   Oregon (G-15699)
▲ Anaheim Manufacturing Company ...E 800 767-6293
   North Olmsted (G-15326)

JC and Associates Sylvania LLC ......G 419 824-0011
   Sylvania (G-18114)
▲ New Path International LLC ....E 614 410-3974
   Powell (G-16481)
RAD Technologies Incorporated ....F 513 641-0523
   Cincinnati (G-4328)
U S Thermal Inc ....G 513 777-7763
   West Chester (G-19966)
Whirlpool Corporation ....D 419 423-8123
   Findlay (G-9908)
Whirlpool Corporation ....B 419 547-7711
   Clyde (G-6548)
Whirlpool Corporation ....C 419 523-5100
   Ottawa (G-15815)

3641 Electric Lamps

Acuity Brands Lighting Inc ....C 740 349-4409
   Newark (G-14980)
▲ Advanced Lighting Tech Inc ....D 440 519-0500
   Solon (G-17249)
▲ Alert Stamping & Mfg Co Inc ......E 440 232-5020
   Bedford Heights (G-1476)
Carlisle and Finch Company ....E 513 681-6080
   Cincinnati (G-3502)
Drs Milburn-Medina Inc ....G 330 725-4680
   Medina (G-13404)
Emitted Energy Inc ....E 513 752-9999
   Cincinnati (G-3302)
Energy Focus Inc ....C 440 715-1300
   Solon (G-17286)
▲ Eye Lighting Intl N Amer Inc ....C 440 350-7000
   Mentor (G-13576)
▲ Eye Lightning International ....D 440 354-2938
   Mentor (G-13577)
◆ GE Lighting LLC ....B 216 266-2000
   Cleveland (G-5402)
General Electric Company ....C 440 593-1156
   Conneaut (G-7806)
General Electric Company ....B 419 563-1200
   Bucyrus (G-2345)
General Electric Company ....C 330 793-3911
   Youngstown (G-21095)
General Electric Company ....A 330 297-0861
   Niles (G-15154)
General Electric Company ....A 330 373-1400
   Niles (G-15155)
General Electric Company ....B 216 391-8741
   Cleveland (G-5415)
General Electric Company ....B 740 477-5200
   Circleville (G-4630)
Johnsons Lamp Shop & Antq Co ......G 937 568-4551
   South Vienna (G-17450)
◆ L D Kichler Co ....B 866 558-5706
   Cleveland (G-5671)
Lumitex Inc ....G 949 250-8557
   Strongsville (G-17940)
▲ Lumitex Inc ....D 440 243-8401
   Strongsville (G-17939)
Magenta Incorporated ....E 216 571-4094
   Cleveland (G-5728)
◆ Medallion Lighting Corporation ...E 440 255-8383
   Mentor (G-13650)
Pure Light Technology LLC ....G 513 779-7474
   West Chester (G-20042)
Resource Exchange Company Inc ......G 440 773-8915
   Akron (G-372)
Sunburst Light Corp America ....G 419 886-3786
   Bellville (G-1576)
◆ Venture Lighting Intl Inc ....D 800 451-2606
   Twinsburg (G-19035)
Venture Lighting Intl Inc ....F 440 248-3510
   Twinsburg (G-19036)

3643 Current-Carrying Wiring Devices

Accurate Electronics Inc ....C 330 682-7015
   Orrville (G-15727)
Alcon Inc ....E 513 722-1037
   Loveland (G-12337)
Alert Safety Lite Products Co ....F 440 232-5020
   Cleveland (G-4750)
Amidac Wind Corporation ....G 213 973-4000
   Elyria (G-9372)
Aviation Technologies Inc ....G 216 706-2960
   Cleveland (G-4872)
▲ Bardes Corporation ....B 513 533-6200
   Cincinnati (G-3436)
Brooks Utility Products Group ....E 330 455-0301
   Canton (G-2629)
▲ Brumall Mfg Corporation ....E 440 974-2622
   Mentor (G-13538)

▲ Bud Industries Inc ....G....... 440 946-3200
  Willoughby (G-20447)
Burkett Industries Inc ....G....... 419 332-4391
  Fremont (G-10132)
Cambridge Ohio Production & As ......F....... 740 432-6383
  Cambridge (G-2448)
▼ Chalfant Manufacturing Company ...G....... 330 273-3510
  Brunswick (G-2216)
Chalfant Manufacturing Company ......F....... 440 323-9870
  Elyria (G-9392)
▲ Channel Products Inc ....D....... 440 423-0113
  Chesterland (G-3199)
▲ Connector Manufacturing Co ......C....... 513 860-4455
  Hamilton (G-10681)
Connectronics Corp ....D....... 419 537-0020
  Toledo (G-18410)
Cooper Interconnect Inc ....G....... 800 386-1911
  Cleveland (G-5130)
▲ Crown Electric Engrg & Mfg LLC ......E....... 513 539-7394
  Middletown (G-14035)
D & E Electric Inc ....F....... 513 738-1172
  Okeana (G-15665)
Da-Lite Screen Company LLC ......E....... 574 267-8101
  Blue Ash (G-1774)
Deals ....G....... 937 293-7429
  Dayton (G-8294)
Desco Corporation ....G....... 614 888-8855
  New Albany (G-14757)
▲ Dreison International Inc ....C....... 216 362-0755
  Cleveland (G-5215)
▲ Electric Cord Sets Inc ....G....... 216 261-1000
  Cleveland (G-5263)
Empire Power Systems Co ....G....... 440 796-4401
  Madison (G-12506)
◆ Ericson Manufacturing Co ....D....... 440 951-8000
  Willoughby (G-20480)
Erie Copper Works Inc ....G....... 330 725-5590
  Medina (G-13406)
Filnor Inc ....F....... 330 821-7667
  Alliance (G-508)
Formed Metal Products Inc ....F....... 440 775-0819
  Oberlin (G-15639)
GE Aviation Systems LLC ....B....... 937 898-5881
  Vandalia (G-19292)
GE Aviation Systems LLC ....B....... 937 898-5881
  Vandalia (G-19293)
▲ General Plug and Mfg Co ....C....... 440 926-2411
  Grafton (G-10426)
Hermetic Seal Technology Inc ......F....... 513 851-4899
  Cincinnati (G-3880)
Hubbell Incorporated ....E....... 330 335-2361
  Wadsworth (G-19410)
▲ I Sq R Power Cable Co ....F....... 330 588-3000
  Canton (G-2736)
▲ International Hydraulics Inc ......E....... 440 951-1781
  Mentor (G-13610)
J & S Products Inc ....G....... 330 686-5840
  Stow (G-17766)
Kathom Manufacturing Co Inc ......E....... 513 868-8890
  Hamilton (G-10715)
◆ Lake Shore Electric Corp ....E....... 440 232-0200
  Bedford (G-1438)
Legrand North America LLC ....B....... 937 224-0639
  Moraine (G-14503)
▲ MJM Industries Inc ....D....... 440 350-1230
  Fairport Harbor (G-9768)
Mueller Electric Company Inc ......E....... 216 771-5225
  Akron (G-307)
Newact Inc ....F....... 513 321-5177
  Batavia (G-1213)
Ohio Associated Entps LLC ....C....... 440 354-3148
  Painesville (G-15907)
Ohio Vly Lightning Protection ....G....... 937 987-0245
  New Vienna (G-14956)
Omnithruster Inc ....F....... 330 963-6310
  Twinsburg (G-18992)
P C Power Inc ....G....... 440 779-4080
  North Olmsted (G-15342)
Parker-Hannifin Corporation ....C....... 330 336-3511
  Wadsworth (G-19425)
▲ Pave Technology Co ....F....... 937 890-1592
  Dayton (G-8566)
▲ Power Grounding Solutions LLC ......G....... 440 926-3219
  Grafton (G-10435)
▲ Qualtek Electronics Corp ....G....... 440 951-3300
  Mentor (G-13710)
▲ Rogers Industrial Products Inc......E....... 330 535-3331
  Akron (G-378)
▲ Royal Plastics Inc ....C....... 440 352-1357
  Mentor (G-13717)

Ruegg Mfg LLC ....G....... 330 418-5617
  Navarre (G-14727)
▲ Saia-Burgess Lcc ....D....... 937 898-3621
  Vandalia (G-19310)
Schneider Electric Usa Inc ....B....... 513 523-4171
  Oxford (G-15843)
Schneider Electric Usa Inc ....C....... 513 755-4231
  West Chester (G-19942)
Schneider Electric Usa Inc ....D....... 513 755-5000
  West Chester (G-19943)
Siemens Industry Inc ....D....... 937 593-6010
  Bellefontaine (G-1539)
Simpson Strong-Tie Company Inc ......G....... 614 876-8060
  Columbus (G-7624)
SMH Manufacturing Inc ....F....... 419 884-0071
  Lexington (G-11952)
▲ Solon Manufacturing Company ......E....... 440 286-7149
  Chardon (G-3180)
T & S Enterprises ....G....... 419 424-1122
  Findlay (G-9899)
▲ Tecmark Corporation ....E....... 440 205-7600
  Mentor (G-13743)
Tip Products Inc ....E....... 216 252-2535
  Cleveland (G-6326)
▲ Torq Corporation ....E....... 440 232-4100
  Bedford (G-1468)
Turner Lightning Protection Co ....G....... 614 738-6225
  Dublin (G-9157)
Vital Connections Incorporated ......E....... 937 667-3880
  Tipp City (G-18310)
▲ Vulcan Tool Company ....G....... 937 253-6194
  Dayton (G-8744)
◆ Watteredge LLC ....D....... 440 933-6110
  Avon Lake (G-1055)
▲ Wedge Products Inc ....B....... 330 405-4477
  Twinsburg (G-19038)
Wiremax Ltd ....G....... 419 531-9500
  Toledo (G-18776)
Xponet Inc ....E....... 440 354-6617
  Painesville (G-15943)

3644 Noncurrent-Carrying Wiring Devices

Akron Foundry Co ....E....... 330 745-3101
  Barberton (G-1095)
Allied Tube & Conduit Corp ....F....... 740 928-1018
  Hebron (G-10860)
▲ Arnco Corporation ....C....... 800 847-7661
  Elyria (G-9375)
Barracuda Technologies Inc ....F....... 216 469-1566
  Aurora (G-910)
Bourbon Plastics Inc ....E....... 574 342-0893
  Cuyahoga Falls (G-7975)
Buckeye Raceway LLC ....Sg....... 614 272-7888
  Columbus (G-6874)
▲ Bud Industries Inc ....G....... 440 946-3200
  Willoughby (G-20447)
Cornerstone Indus Holdings ....G....... 440 893-9144
  Chagrin Falls (G-3054)
Eger Products Inc ....G....... 513 753-4200
  Amelia (G-575)
▲ Emco Electric International ....G....... 440 878-1199
  Strongsville (G-17917)
◆ Erico Inc ....G....... 440 248-0100
  Solon (G-17287)
Glt Fabricators Inc ....G....... 440 914-1122
  Solon (G-17299)
▼ Helical Line Products Co ....E....... 440 933-9263
  Avon Lake (G-1032)
Highline Raceway LLC ....G....... 419 883-2042
  Butler (G-2391)
Hollywood Gaming At Dayton RAC ......G....... 937 235-7800
  Dayton (G-8391)
Indian Lake Raceway LLC ....G....... 937 837-7533
  Clayton (G-4660)
M & W Electric Mfg Co LLC ....G....... 330 332-9553
  Salem (G-16911)
◆ Madison Electric Products Inc ......E....... 216 391-7776
  Bedford Heights (G-1488)
Merrico Inc ....G....... 419 525-2711
  Mansfield (G-12646)
▲ Monti Incorporated ....D....... 513 761-7775
  Cincinnati (G-4120)
Mueller Electric Company Inc ....E....... 216 771-5225
  Akron (G-307)
▲ Osborne Coinage Company ....D....... 513 681-5424
  Cincinnati (G-4197)
Power Shelf LLC ....G....... 419 775-6125
  Plymouth (G-16378)
Preformed Line Products Co ....G....... 440 461-5200
  Mayfield Village (G-13324)

Raceway Beverage LLC ....G....... 513 932-2214
  Lebanon (G-11831)
Raceway Petroleum Inc ....G....... 440 989-2660
  Lorain (G-12270)
▲ Red Seal Electric Co ....E....... 216 941-3900
  Cleveland (G-6095)
Regal Beloit America Inc ....C....... 419 352-8441
  Bowling Green (G-2013)
Resource Mechanical Insul LLC ......E....... 248 577-0200
  Walbridge (G-19462)
◆ Rochling Glastic Composites LP ......C....... 216 486-0100
  Cleveland (G-6125)
Saylor Products Corporation ....F....... 419 832-2125
  Grand Rapids (G-10445)
State of Ohio Dayton Raceway ....G....... 937 237-7802
  Dayton (G-8682)
Tri-Fab Inc ....E....... 330 337-3425
  Salem (G-16931)
United Fiberglass America Inc ......F....... 937 325-7305
  Springfield (G-17670)
Vertiv Co ....E....... 440 288-1122
  Lorain (G-12290)
Von Roll Usa Inc ....E....... 216 433-7474
  Cleveland (G-6428)
Weidmann Electrical Tech Inc ......D....... 937 652-1220
  Urbana (G-19187)
Zekelman Industries Inc ....C....... 740 432-2146
  Cambridge (G-2483)

3645 Residential Lighting Fixtures

Acuity Brands Lighting Inc ....C....... 740 349-4409
  Newark (G-14980)
Acuity Brands Lighting Inc ....B....... 740 349-4343
  Newark (G-14979)
▲ Advanced Lighting Tech Inc ......D....... 440 519-0500
  Solon (G-17249)
Aladdinslights Inc ....G....... 330 963-6997
  Twinsburg (G-18896)
▲ Alert Stamping & Mfg Co Inc ......E....... 440 232-5020
  Bedford Heights (G-1476)
American Superior Lighting ....G....... 740 266-2959
  Steubenville (G-17687)
▲ Besa Lighting Co Inc ....E....... 614 475-7046
  Blacklick (G-1690)
Contract Lighting Inc ....E....... 614 746-7022
  Columbus (G-6978)
Country Tin ....G....... 937 746-7229
  Franklin (G-10015)
Degaetano Sales ....G....... 440 729-8877
  Chesterland (G-3202)
E L Ostendorf Inc ....G....... 440 247-7631
  Chagrin Falls (G-3056)
◆ Hinkley Lighting Inc ....E....... 216 671-3132
  Avon Lake (G-1033)
J Schrader Co ....F....... 216 961-2890
  Cleveland (G-5601)
JB Machining Concepts LLC ....G....... 419 523-0096
  Ottawa (G-15797)
◆ L D Kichler Co ....B....... 866 558-5706
  Cleveland (G-5671)
Lighting Concepts & Controls ....E....... 513 761-6360
  West Chester (G-19894)
LSI Industries Inc ....E....... 513 793-3200
  Blue Ash (G-1829)
Manairco Inc ....G....... 419 524-2121
  Mansfield (G-12640)
◆ Medallion Lighting Corporation ......E....... 440 255-8383
  Mentor (G-13650)
Mega Bright LLC ....F....... 330 577-8859
  Cuyahoga Falls (G-8026)
Microsun Lamps LLC ....G....... 888 328-8701
  Dayton (G-8494)
Night Lightscapes ....G....... 419 304-2486
  Sylvania (G-18121)
Palette Studios Inc ....G....... 513 961-1316
  Cincinnati (G-4209)
Pike Machine Products Co ....E....... 216 731-1880
  Euclid (G-9597)
▲ Tresco International Ltd Co ....G....... 330 757-8131
  Youngstown (G-21228)

3646 Commercial, Indl & Institutional Lighting Fixtures

Acuity Brands Lighting Inc ....B....... 740 349-4343
  Newark (G-14979)
Acuity Brands Lighting Inc ....C....... 740 349-4409
  Newark (G-14980)
▲ Advanced Lighting Tech Inc ....D....... 440 519-0500
  Solon (G-17249)

▲ Besa Lighting Co Inc ....E 614 475-7046
Blacklick *(G-1690)*

◆ Best Lighting Products Inc ....D 740 964-0063
Etna *(G-9555)*

▲ Bock Company LLC ....G 216 912-7050
Solon *(G-17270)*

Eaton Electric Holdings LLC ....E 440 523-5000
Cleveland *(G-5251)*

Evp International LLC ....G 513 761-7614
Cincinnati *(G-3727)*

General Electric Company ....B 740 477-5200
Circleville *(G-4630)*

General Electric Company ....A 216 266-2121
Cleveland *(G-5413)*

General Electric Company ....E 330 458-3200
Canton *(G-2712)*

▲ Genesis Lamp Corp ....F 440 354-0095
Painesville *(G-15883)*

Holophane Corporation ....F 740 349-4194
Newark *(G-15018)*

◆ Holophane Corporation ....C 866 759-1577
Granville *(G-10459)*

Holophane Lighting ....G 330 823-5535
Alliance *(G-515)*

Importers Direct LLC ....E 330 436-3260
Akron *(G-230)*

J Schrader Co ....F 216 961-2890
Cleveland *(G-5601)*

JB Machining Concepts LLC ....G 419 523-0096
Ottawa *(G-15797)*

▲ King Luminaire Company Inc ....E 440 576-9073
Jefferson *(G-11365)*

Less Cost Lighting Inc ....F 866 633-6883
Etna *(G-9559)*

▲ Light Craft Manufacturing Inc ....F 419 332-0536
Fremont *(G-10164)*

LSI Industries Inc ....E 513 793-3200
Blue Ash *(G-1829)*

▲ Lumitex Inc ....D 440 243-8401
Strongsville *(G-17939)*

M-Boss Inc ....E 216 441-6080
Cleveland *(G-5719)*

Mega Bright LLC ....F 330 577-8859
Cuyahoga Falls *(G-8026)*

Mills Led LLC ....G 800 690-6403
Columbus *(G-7353)*

Mills Led LLC ....G 800 690-6403
Columbus *(G-7354)*

Nordic Light America Inc ....F 614 981-9497
Columbus *(G-7397)*

Norton Industries Inc ....F 888 357-2345
Lakewood *(G-11676)*

Patriot Consulting LLC ....G 614 554-6455
Columbus *(G-7465)*

SMS Technologies Inc ....F 419 465-4175
Monroeville *(G-14429)*

Stress-Crete Company ....F 440 576-9073
Jefferson *(G-11372)*

Sunburst Light Corp America ....G 419 886-3786
Bellville *(G-1576)*

Techbrite LLC ....E 800 246-9977
Cincinnati *(G-4498)*

▲ Teron Lighting Inc ....E 513 858-6004
Fairfield *(G-9724)*

Treemen Industries Inc ....E 330 965-3777
Boardman *(G-1925)*

3647 Vehicular Lighting Eqpt

▲ Advanced Technology Corp ....C 440 293-4064
Andover *(G-611)*

Akron Brass Company ....E 614 529-7230
Columbus *(G-6708)*

Akron Brass Company ....B 330 264-5678
Wooster *(G-20734)*

▲ Akron Brass Company ....B 330 264-5678
Wooster *(G-20735)*

Akron Brass Holding Corp ....G 330 264-5678
Wooster *(G-20736)*

▲ Atc Group Inc ....D 440 293-4064
Andover *(G-612)*

▲ Atc Lighting & Plastics Inc ....C 440 466-7670
Andover *(G-613)*

Automtive Cmpnnts Holdings LLC ....A 419 627-3600
Sandusky *(G-16947)*

Automtive Cmpnnts Holdings LLC ....F 419 483-5622
Bellevue *(G-1544)*

Federal-Mogul Corporation ....C 740 432-2393
Cambridge *(G-2457)*

Grimes Aerospace Company ....B 937 484-2001
Urbana *(G-19158)*

▲ K D Lamp Company ....E 440 293-4064
Andover *(G-616)*

Lighting Products Inc ....D 440 293-4064
Andover *(G-617)*

▲ Stanley Electric US Co Inc ....B 740 852-5200
London *(G-12219)*

Treemen Industries Inc ....E 330 965-3777
Boardman *(G-1925)*

Washington Products Inc ....F 330 837-5101
Massillon *(G-13211)*

3648 Lighting Eqpt, NEC

Acuity Brands Lighting Inc ....B 740 349-4343
Newark *(G-14979)*

◆ ADB Safegate Americas LLC ....B 614 861-1304
Columbus *(G-6694)*

▲ Advanced Lighting Tech Inc ....D 440 519-0500
Solon *(G-17249)*

Akron Brass Company ....E 614 529-7230
Columbus *(G-6708)*

Architectural Busstrut Corp ....G 614 933-8695
New Albany *(G-14746)*

▲ Atc Lighting & Plastics Inc ....C 440 466-7670
Andover *(G-613)*

ATI Irrigation LLC ....G 937 750-2976
Troy *(G-18806)*

Aviation Technologies Inc ....G 216 706-2960
Cleveland *(G-4872)*

Broadview Heights Spotlights ....G 440 526-4404
Broadview Heights *(G-2105)*

Carlisle and Finch Company ....E 513 681-6080
Cincinnati *(G-3502)*

Cinti Tan Company ....E 513 874-8267
Fairfield *(G-9655)*

Energy Focus Inc ....C 440 715-1300
Solon *(G-17286)*

◆ Ericson Manufacturing Co ....D 440 951-8000
Willoughby *(G-20480)*

Fulton Industries Inc ....D 419 335-3015
Wauseon *(G-19678)*

◆ GE Lighting Solutions LLC ....E 216 266-4800
Cleveland *(G-5403)*

General Electric Company ....A 330 373-1400
Niles *(G-15155)*

▲ Genesis Lamp Corp ....F 440 354-0095
Painesville *(G-15883)*

Global E-Lumenation Tech ....G 513 821-8687
Cincinnati *(G-3836)*

▲ Global Lighting Tech Inc ....E 440 922-4584
Brecksville *(G-2052)*

◆ Holophane Corporation ....C 866 759-1577
Granville *(G-10459)*

Hot Spot ....G 740 947-8888
Waverly *(G-19711)*

Hughey & Phillips LLC ....E 937 652-3500
Urbana *(G-19163)*

Iacono Production Services Inc ....F 513 469-5095
Blue Ash *(G-1811)*

Importers Direct LLC ....E 330 436-3260
Akron *(G-230)*

Jeff Katz ....G 614 834-0404
Pickerington *(G-16195)*

◆ L D Kichler Co ....B 866 558-5706
Cleveland *(G-5671)*

▲ Lighting Solutions Group LLC ....F 614 868-5337
Columbus *(G-7295)*

▲ Lintern Corporation ....E 440 255-9333
Mentor *(G-13635)*

LSI Industries Inc ....E 513 793-3200
Blue Ash *(G-1829)*

LSI Industries Inc ....B 513 793-3200
Blue Ash *(G-1830)*

▲ Lumitex Inc ....D 440 243-8401
Strongsville *(G-17939)*

Manairco Inc ....G 419 524-2121
Mansfield *(G-12640)*

Medina Lighting Inc ....G 330 721-1441
Medina *(G-13442)*

Miami Valley Lighting LLC ....G 937 224-6000
Dayton *(G-8112)*

◆ Midmark Corporation ....A 937 526-3662
Versailles *(G-19352)*

Midmark Corporation ....A 937 526-8387
Versailles *(G-19353)*

Moonlighting ....G 330 533-3324
Canfield *(G-2567)*

▲ National Biological Corp ....E 216 831-0600
Beachwood *(G-1283)*

Premier Office ....G 419 329-9692
Mansfield *(G-12668)*

Pro Lighting LLC ....G 614 561-0089
Hilliard *(G-10973)*

Shelly Company ....G 330 666-1125
Copley *(G-7854)*

Specialty Systems Electric LLC ....G 304 529-3861
Proctorville *(G-16492)*

Sunburst Light Corp America ....G 419 886-3786
Bellville *(G-1576)*

▲ Sunless Inc ....C 440 836-0199
Macedonia *(G-12491)*

UIC Energy LLC ....G 614 839-0250
Columbus *(G-7718)*

◆ Union Metal Corporation ....C 330 456-7653
Canton *(G-2884)*

Uv Doctor Systems LLC ....G 513 553-9000
Amelia *(G-588)*

◆ Vanner Holdings Inc ....D 614 771-2718
Hilliard *(G-10991)*

▲ Will-Burt Company ....B 330 682-7015
Orrville *(G-15770)*

3651 Household Audio & Video Eqpt

Advanced Custom Sound ....G 330 372-9900
Warren *(G-19516)*

Andersound PA Service ....G 216 561-2636
Cleveland *(G-4811)*

Array Telepresence Inc ....G 800 779-7480
West Chester *(G-19809)*

▲ Avtek International Inc ....G 330 633-7500
Tallmadge *(G-18134)*

Background Music & Sound Inc ....G 937 898-9871
Dayton *(G-8180)*

Beacon Audio Video Systems Inc ....G 937 723-9587
Centerville *(G-3037)*

Bose Corporation ....G 614 475-8565
Columbus *(G-6850)*

Bose Corporation ....G 513 891-4384
Cincinnati *(G-3462)*

C T I Audio Inc ....D 440 593-1111
Brooklyn Heights *(G-2133)*

▲ Cad Audio LLC ....F 440 349-4900
Solon *(G-17275)*

China Enterprises Inc ....G 419 885-1485
Toledo *(G-18396)*

Custom Automation Technologies ....G 614 939-4228
New Albany *(G-14755)*

▲ Daca Vending Wholesale LLC ....G 513 753-1600
Amelia *(G-571)*

Dare Electronics Inc ....E 937 335-0031
Troy *(G-18814)*

Dayton Audio LLC ....G 937 743-3000
Springboro *(G-17478)*

Digital Media Integration LLC ....G 937 305-5582
Dayton *(G-8303)*

Dlng Products ....G 440 442-7777
Cleveland *(G-5195)*

Dr Z Amps Inc ....F 216 475-1444
Maple Heights *(G-12733)*

Dream Space ....G 440 945-6596
Bedford *(G-1421)*

E3 Diagnostics Inc ....G 937 435-2250
Dayton *(G-8316)*

Electrimotion Inc ....G 740 362-0251
Delaware *(G-8840)*

Eprad Inc ....G 419 666-3266
Perrysburg *(G-16093)*

Eq Technologies LLC ....G 216 548-3684
Cleveland *(G-5290)*

Gadgets Manufacturing Co ....G 937 686-5371
Huntsville *(G-11214)*

Greyfield Industries Inc ....F 513 860-1785
Trenton *(G-18793)*

House of Hindenach ....G 419 422-0392
Findlay *(G-9843)*

Hudson Access Group II ....G 330 283-6214
Hudson *(G-11179)*

Janszen Loudspeaker Ltd ....G 614 448-1811
Columbus *(G-7227)*

▲ Knukonceptzcom Ltd ....G 216 310-6555
Windham *(G-20698)*

▼ Lightyearmusiccom ....G 216 929-1022
Cleveland *(G-5695)*

Markeys Audio/Visual Inc ....G 419 244-8844
Toledo *(G-18573)*

◆ Mitsubishi Elc Auto Amer Inc ....B 513 573-6614
Mason *(G-13065)*

◆ Phantom Sound ....F 513 759-4477
Mason *(G-13072)*

▲ Pioneer Automotive Tech Inc ....C 937 746-2293
Springboro *(G-17497)*

S I C

Pioneer North America Inc .... B 937 746-6600
Springdale *(G-17498)*

Pro Audio .... G 513 752-7500
Cincinnati *(G-3314)*

Pro Audio Innovations .... G 330 705-5069
Canton *(G-2824)*

Q Music USA LLC .... G 239 995-5888
North Olmsted *(G-15343)*

R L Drake Company .... D 937 746-4556
Franklin *(G-10048)*

Rs Pro Sales LLC .... G 513 699-5329
Cincinnati *(G-4364)*

◆ Snyder Electronics .... G 513 738-7200
Harrison *(G-10803)*

Soundproof .... G 440 864-8864
Grafton *(G-10436)*

South Side Audio LLC .... G 614 453-0757
Columbus *(G-7632)*

Tech Products Corporation .... E 937 438-1100
Miamisburg *(G-13867)*

Technical Artistry Inc .... G 614 299-7777
Columbus *(G-7684)*

Technicolor Usa Inc .... A 614 474-8821
Circleville *(G-4646)*

Thomas David Design .... G 614 595-0379
Cleveland *(G-6321)*

◆ Tls Corp .... E 216 574-4759
Cleveland *(G-6327)*

Tune Town Car Audio .... G 419 627-1100
Sandusky *(G-17017)*

Undiscovered Radio Network .... G 740 533-1032
Ironton *(G-11303)*

▲ UNI Corp .... E 330 489-6500
Canton *(G-2883)*

Universal Electronics Inc .... D 330 487-1110
Twinsburg *(G-19032)*

3652 Phonograph Records & Magnetic Tape

Belkin Production .... E 440 247-2722
Chagrin Falls *(G-3049)*

Beverly Snider .... G 614 837-5817
Columbus *(G-6824)*

Jk Digital Publishing LLC .... E 937 299-0185
Springboro *(G-17484)*

News Reel Inc .... G 614 469-0700
Columbus *(G-7390)*

Q C A Inc .... F 513 681-8400
Cincinnati *(G-4304)*

3661 Telephone & Telegraph Apparatus

7signal Solutions Inc .... E 330 761-3515
Akron *(G-15)*

Alcatel Co .... G 818 878-4485
Westerville *(G-20197)*

▲ Arnco Corporation .... C 800 847-7661
Elyria *(G-9375)*

AT&T Corp .... G 513 792-9300
Cincinnati *(G-3423)*

Black Box Corporation .... E 614 825-7400
Lewis Center *(G-11890)*

C Dcap Modem Line .... G 419 748-7409
Mc Clure *(G-13334)*

C Dcap Modem Line .... G 440 685-4302
North Bloomfield *(G-15215)*

Commercial Electric Pdts Corp .... E 216 241-2886
Cleveland *(G-5104)*

Commtech Solutions Inc .... G 440 458-4870
Grafton *(G-10421)*

Cotsworks LLC .... E 440 446-8800
Highland Heights *(G-10911)*

Crase Communications Inc .... F 419 468-1173
Galion *(G-10262)*

Cutting Edge Technologies Inc .... E 216 574-4759
Cleveland *(G-5154)*

DTE Inc .... E 419 522-3428
Mansfield *(G-12597)*

Electrodata Inc .... F 216 663-3333
Bedford Heights *(G-1483)*

Fremont Plastic Products Inc .... E 419 332-6407
Fremont *(G-10150)*

Greyfield Industries Inc .... F 513 860-1785
Trenton *(G-18793)*

Interline Brands Inc .... G 614 527-9475
Columbus *(G-7204)*

▲ Kentrox Inc .... D 614 798-2000
Dublin *(G-9096)*

Lisa Modem .... G 216 551-3365
Cleveland *(G-5706)*

Minor Corporation .... G 216 291-8723
Cleveland *(G-5822)*

Mitel (delaware) Inc .... E 513 733-8000
West Chester *(G-19902)*

Ocs Telecom LLC .... F 740 503-5939
Hilliard *(G-10965)*

Peco II Inc .... D 614 431-0694
Columbus *(G-7473)*

Preformed Line Products Co .... C 440 461-5200
Mayfield Village *(G-13324)*

Prentke Romich Company .... C 330 202-5800
Wooster *(G-20825)*

Pro Oncall Technologies LLC .... F 614 761-1400
Dublin *(G-9126)*

Procomsol Ltd .... G 216 221-1550
Lakewood *(G-11677)*

Siemens Energy Inc .... G 740 393-8464
Mount Vernon *(G-14649)*

◆ Tls Corp .... E 216 574-4759
Cleveland *(G-6327)*

Vertiv Co .... G 440 288-1122
Lorain *(G-12290)*

Vertiv Co .... G 440 460-3600
Cleveland *(G-6410)*

Viasat Inc .... D 216 706-7800
Independence *(G-11282)*

3663 Radio & T V Communications, Systs & Eqpt, Broadcast/Studio

Accurate Electronics Inc .... C 330 682-7015
Orrville *(G-15727)*

Advanced Telemetrics Intl .... F 937 862-6948
Spring Valley *(G-17466)*

AG Antenna Group LLC .... F 513 289-6521
Cincinnati *(G-3366)*

Always Better Communications .... F 330 445-2220
Canton *(G-2600)*

◆ Analynk Wireless LLC .... G 614 755-5091
Columbus *(G-6752)*

Armada Power LLC .... G 614 204-9341
Columbus *(G-6772)*

CDI Industries .... E 440 243-1100
Cleveland *(G-4999)*

Central USA Wireless LLC .... E 513 469-1500
Cincinnati *(G-3518)*

Circle Prime Manufacturing .... E 330 923-0019
Cuyahoga Falls *(G-7980)*

Commscope Technologies LLC .... C 216 272-0055
Cleveland *(G-5107)*

Control Industries Inc .... G 937 653-7694
Findlay *(G-9810)*

Diamond Electronics Inc .... C 740 652-9222
Lancaster *(G-11706)*

Douglas J Hall .... E 614 261-8871
Columbus *(G-7035)*

Eei Acquisition Corp .... E 440 564-5484
Newbury *(G-15089)*

Electro-Magwave Inc .... G 216 453-1160
Cleveland *(G-5266)*

Envision Radio MII .... F 216 831-3761
Beachwood *(G-1271)*

Essential Pathways Ohio LLC .... G 330 518-3091
Youngstown *(G-21079)*

G2 Digital Solutions .... F 937 241-6003
Xenia *(G-20953)*

Gatesair Inc .... E 513 459-3400
Mason *(G-13025)*

Globecom Technologies Inc .... G 330 408-7008
Canal Fulton *(G-2502)*

Grace Automation Services Inc .... G 330 567-3108
Big Prairie *(G-1681)*

Great Lakes Telcom Ltd .... G 330 629-8848
Youngstown *(G-21103)*

Greyfield Industries Inc .... F 513 860-1785
Trenton *(G-18793)*

Harris Broadcast Communication .... E 513 459-3400
Mason *(G-13035)*

Hyq Technologies LLC .... G 513 225-6911
Oxford *(G-15837)*

Iheartcommunications Inc .... C 513 241-1550
Cincinnati *(G-3911)*

Imagine Communications Corp .... D 513 459-3400
Mason *(G-13041)*

Intwine Energy Networks LLC .... G 216 970-5908
Chagrin Falls *(G-3096)*

L-3 Cmmncations Nova Engrg Inc .... C 877 282-1168
Mason *(G-13054)*

Liquid Image Corp of America .... G 216 458-9800
Cleveland *(G-5705)*

LSI Industries Inc .... B 513 793-3200
Blue Ash *(G-1830)*

Manchik Engineering & Co .... G 740 927-4454
Dublin *(G-9101)*

▲ Maranatha Industries Inc .... E 419 263-2013
Payne *(G-16016)*

Marrik Dish Company LLC .... E 419 475-6538
Toledo *(G-18574)*

McClaflin Mobile Media LLC .... G 419 575-9367
Bradner *(G-2028)*

Mentor Radio LLC .... G 216 265-2315
Elyria *(G-9460)*

Musair Ohio .... G 330 455-2800
Massillon *(G-13183)*

▲ Nissin Precision N Amer Inc .... D 937 836-1910
Englewood *(G-9536)*

Northrop Grumman Systems Corp .... B 513 881-3296
West Chester *(G-20032)*

◆ Ohio Semitronics Inc .... D 614 777-1005
Hilliard *(G-10967)*

▲ Pdi Communication Systems Inc .... D 937 743-6010
Springboro *(G-17495)*

Peterson Radio Inc .... G 937 549-3731
Manchester *(G-12551)*

Pole/Zero Acquisition Inc .... C 513 870-9060
West Chester *(G-19917)*

Prentke Romich Company .... C 330 202-5800
Wooster *(G-20825)*

Punch Components Inc .... E 419 224-1242
Lima *(G-12077)*

Quasonix Inc .... E 513 942-1287
West Chester *(G-19927)*

R L Drake Company .... D 937 746-4556
Franklin *(G-10048)*

▲ R L Drake Holdings LLC .... F 937 746-4556
Springboro *(G-17503)*

Radio Hospital .... G 419 679-1103
Kenton *(G-11565)*

Rev38 LLC .... G 937 572-4000
West Chester *(G-19932)*

▲ Rf Linx Inc .... G 513 777-2774
Lebanon *(G-11833)*

Sagequest LLC .... D 216 896-7243
Solon *(G-17374)*

Shenet LLC .... E 614 563-9600
Columbus *(G-7615)*

Solar Con Inc .... E 419 865-5877
Holland *(G-11086)*

Sourcepoint Logistics LLC .... E 937 604-8209
Tipp City *(G-18300)*

T V Specialties Inc .... F 330 364-6678
Dover *(G-9020)*

◆ Tls Corp .... E 216 574-4759
Cleveland *(G-6327)*

Total Supply Solutions LLC .... G 614 989-6665
Dublin *(G-9155)*

Touba Satellite R US .... G 513 853-0700
Cincinnati *(G-4514)*

Track-It Systems .... G 513 522-0083
Cincinnati *(G-4516)*

Transel Corporation .... G 513 897-3442
Harveysburg *(G-10835)*

Trimble Inc .... D 937 245-5951
Dayton *(G-8727)*

▲ Valco Melton Inc .... E 513 874-6550
West Chester *(G-20069)*

Wirenet Inc .... F 513 774-7759
Loveland *(G-12400)*

3669 Communications Eqpt, NEC

Alert Safety Products Inc .... G 513 791-4790
Blue Ash *(G-1739)*

Area Wide Protective Inc .... E 330 644-0655
Kent *(G-11431)*

Area Wide Protective Inc .... G 419 221-2997
Lima *(G-11993)*

Area Wide Protective Inc .... E 513 321-9889
Fairfield *(G-9643)*

▲ Athens Technical Specialists .... F 740 592-2874
Athens *(G-857)*

Bird Technologies Group Inc .... G 440 248-1200
Solon *(G-17269)*

▲ Ceia Usa Ltd .... G 330 405-3190
Twinsburg *(G-18909)*

Cincinnati Bell Any Dstnce Inc .... A 513 397-9900
Cincinnati *(G-3540)*

City Elyria Communication .... G 440 322-3329
Elyria *(G-9394)*

City of Canton .... E 330 489-3370
Canton *(G-2656)*

▼ Data Processing Sciences Corp .... D 513 791-7100
Cincinnati *(G-3640)*

David Boswell ....E 614 441-2497
  Columbus (G-7014)
Ds Express Carriers Inc ....G 419 433-6200
  Norwalk (G-15534)
▲ Findaway World LLC ....D 440 893-0808
  Solon (G-17292)
General Dynmcs Mssion Systems ......E 513 253-4770
  Beavercreek (G-1340)
Honeywell International Inc ....D 937 754-4134
  Fairborn (G-9625)
Honeywell International Inc ....A 937 484-2000
  Urbana (G-19162)
Hyq Technologies LLC ....G 513 225-6911
  Oxford (G-15837)
Intelligent Signal Tech ....G 614 530-4784
  Loveland (G-12361)
Jhs Toyz LLC ....F 440 946-6600
  Willowick (G-20648)
K-Hill Signal Co Inc ....G 740 922-0421
  Uhrichsville (G-19054)
Lightle Enterprises Ohio LLC ....G 740 998-5363
  Frankfort (G-10000)
Lightle Enterprises Ohio LLC ....G 740 998-5363
  Frankfort (G-10001)
▲ MD Solutions Inc ....G 866 637-6588
  Plain City (G-16348)
Milicom LLC ....G 216 765-8875
  Beachwood (G-1280)
Musair Ohio ....G 330 455-2800
  Massillon (G-13183)
Ohio Department Transportation .....E 614 351-2898
  Columbus (G-7418)
▲ Ohio Magnetics Inc ....E 216 662-8484
  Maple Heights (G-12736)
Paul Peterson Company ....E 614 486-4375
  Columbus (G-7467)
Public Safety Concepts LLC ....G 614 733-0200
  Plain City (G-16355)
Quasonix Inc ....E 513 942-1287
  West Chester (G-19927)
Robert F Sams ....G 330 990-0477
  Akron (G-376)
Safe Systems Inc ....G 216 661-1166
  Cleveland (G-6154)
▲ Saltillo Corporation ....G 330 674-6722
  Millersburg (G-14261)
Security Fence Group Inc ....E 513 681-3700
  Cincinnati (G-4395)
Signature Technologies Inc ....E 937 859-6323
  Miamisburg (G-13859)
Simplexgrinnell LP ....G 419 861-0662
  Maumee (G-13294)
▲ Slap N Tickle LLC ....G 419 349-3226
  Toledo (G-18698)
Sound Communications Inc ....F 614 875-8500
  Grove City (G-10597)
Special Way 2 ....G 740 282-8281
  Steubenville (G-17713)
Storecom Equipment LLC ....G 800 356-0368
  Dayton (G-8685)
UTC Fire SEC Americas Corp Inc ....E 513 821-7945
  Cincinnati (G-4549)
Viking Group Inc ....G 937 443-0433
  Dayton (G-8743)
Voice Products Inc ....F 216 360-0433
  Cleveland (G-6426)

3671 Radio & T V Receiving Electron Tubes

Fripro Energy LLC ....G 419 865-0002
  Maumee (G-13259)

3672 Printed Circuit Boards

Accurate Electronics Inc ....C 330 682-7015
  Orrville (G-15727)
Adonai Technologies LLC ....G 513 560-9020
  Middletown (G-14012)
Airborn Flxble Circuits NH Inc ......G 603 537-9500
  Akron (G-36)
Alektronics Inc ....F 937 429-2118
  Beavercreek (G-1368)
Avcom Smt Inc ....F 614 882-8176
  Westerville (G-20200)
▲ Bud Industries Inc ....G 440 946-3200
  Willoughby (G-20447)
C E Electronics Inc ....D 419 636-6705
  Bryan (G-2289)
▼ Cartessa Corporation ....F 513 738-4477
  Shandon (G-17096)
Central Systems & Control ....G 440 835-0015
  Cleveland (G-5005)

Chaffin Electronics Inc ....G 740 354-9896
  Franklin Furnace (G-10068)
Circle Prime Manufacturing ....E 330 923-0019
  Cuyahoga Falls (G-7980)
Circuit Center ....G 513 435-2131
  Dayton (G-8231)
Co- Ax Technology Inc ....C 440 914-9200
  Solon (G-17279)
Community RE Group-Comvet ....G 440 319-6714
  Ashtabula (G-798)
Debra Harbour ....G 937 440-9618
  Troy (G-18816)
Deca Manufacturing Co Inc ....D 419 884-0071
  Mansfield (G-12594)
Flextronics International Usa ....A 513 755-2500
  Liberty Township (G-11961)
Interactive Engineering Corp ....E 330 239-6888
  Medina (G-13427)
International Trade Group Inc ....G 614 486-4634
  Columbus (G-7207)
Journey Electronics Corp ....G 513 539-9836
  Monroe (G-14406)
L3 Technologies Inc ....E 513 943-2000
  Cincinnati (G-3311)
Lad Technology Inc ....E 440 461-8002
  Cleveland (G-5675)
Levison Enterprises LLC ....E 419 838-7365
  Millbury (G-14185)
Libra Industries Inc ....E 440 974-7770
  Mentor (G-13632)
McGregor-Surmount Corporation ....C 937 833-6768
  Brookville (G-2193)
Philway Products Inc ....C 419 281-7777
  Ashland (G-765)
Precision Switching Inc ....G 800 800-8143
  Mansfield (G-12667)
▲ Qualtech Technologies Inc ....E 440 946-8081
  Willoughby (G-20585)
▲ R-K Electronics Inc ....F 513 204-6060
  Mason (G-13079)
S Wj Llcred ....G 330 938-6173
  Sebring (G-17051)
▲ Staci Corp ....F 440 355-5102
  Lagrange (G-11638)
▲ Techtron Systems Inc ....G 440 505-2990
  Solon (G-17401)
Tetrad Electronics Inc ....D 440 946-6443
  Willoughby (G-20614)
Thomas Enterprises ....G 330 394-4483
  Warren (G-19607)
United Circuits Inc ....F 440 926-1000
  Grafton (G-10438)
Viasystems Tech Corp LLC ....C 330 538-3900
  North Jackson (G-15300)
Visual Information Institute ....F 937 376-4361
  Xenia (G-20985)
▲ Vmetro Inc ....G 281 584-0728
  Fairborn (G-9633)
Wurth Electronics Ics Inc ....F 937 415-7700
  Dayton (G-8765)

3674 Semiconductors

A M D ....G 440 918-8930
  Willoughby (G-20422)
Advanced Dstrbted Gnration LLC ...G 419 530-3792
  Maumee (G-13219)
▲ AEG Photoconductor Corporation ...D 513 874-4939
  West Chester (G-19799)
Altera Corporation ....G 513 444-2021
  Cincinnati (G-3381)
AT&T Corp ....G 513 792-9300
  Cincinnati (G-3423)
Babcock & Wilcox Megtec ....C 614 258-9501
  Columbus (G-6799)
Biometric Information MGT LLC ......G 614 456-1296
  Dublin (G-9054)
Bright Focus Sales Inc ....F 216 751-8384
  Cleveland (G-4931)
▲ Burke Products Inc ....E 937 372-3516
  Xenia (G-20940)
Ceso Inc ....D 937 435-8584
  Dayton (G-8224)
Communication Concepts Inc ....C 937 426-8600
  Beavercreek (G-1326)
CPC Logistics Inc ....D 513 874-5787
  Fairfield (G-9657)
Crishtronics Inc ....G 440 572-8318
  Strongsville (G-17908)
D F Electronics Inc ....D 513 772-7792
  Cincinnati (G-3631)

Dan-Mar Company Inc ....E 419 660-8830
  Norwalk (G-15532)
Darrah Electric Company ....E 216 631-0912
  Cleveland (G-5168)
Energy Focus Inc ....C 440 715-1300
  Solon (G-17286)
First Solar Inc ....B 419 661-1478
  Perrysburg (G-16096)
Firstfuelcellscom LLC ....G 440 884-2503
  Cleveland (G-5351)
General Nano LLC ....G 513 309-5947
  Cincinnati (G-3819)
◆ Gould Electronics Inc ....C 440 953-5000
  Eastlake (G-9271)
Greenfield Solar Inc ....E 216 535-9200
  Oberlin (G-15642)
Heraeus Electro-Nite Co LLC ....G 330 725-1419
  Medina (G-13421)
Honeywell International Inc ....C 614 850-5000
  Columbus (G-7163)
Honeywell International Inc ....D 614 850-5000
  Columbus (G-7164)
Hunters Hightech Energy Systm .....G 614 275-4777
  Columbus (G-7171)
Hydrogen 411 Technology LLC ......G 440 941-6760
  Cleveland (G-5543)
Hyper Tech Research Inc ....F 614 481-8050
  Columbus (G-7173)
Integrated Sensors LLC ....G 419 536-3212
  Ottawa Hills (G-15816)
Intel Industries LLC ....G 614 551-5702
  Cincinnati (G-3926)
▲ Isofoton North America Inc ....F 419 591-4330
  Napoleon (G-14685)
John B Allen ....G 614 488-7122
  Columbus (G-7238)
Ki Intel LLC ....G 740 200-9000
  Sunbury (G-18065)
Leidos Inc ....D 937 431-2400
  Beavercreek (G-1348)
Linear Asics Inc ....G 330 474-3920
  Tallmadge (G-18150)
Madison Electric (mepco) Inc ....G 440 279-0521
  Chardon (G-3165)
▲ Materion Brush Inc ....D 216 486-4200
  Mayfield Heights (G-13317)
◆ Materion Corporation ....C 216 486-4200
  Mayfield Heights (G-13318)
Measurement Specialties Inc ....F 937 427-1231
  Beavercreek (G-1374)
◆ Melcor Corporation ....C 609 393-4178
  Cleveland (G-5779)
Micro Industries Corporation ....F 740 548-7878
  Columbus (G-7347)
Micro Industries Corporation ....D 740 548-7878
  Westerville (G-20224)
Mok Industries LLC ....G 614 934-1734
  Columbus (G-7363)
◆ Ohio Semitronics Inc ....D 614 777-1005
  Hilliard (G-10967)
▲ Pepperl + Fuchs Inc ....C 330 425-3555
  Twinsburg (G-18997)
Philips Medical Systems Mr ....C 440 483-2499
  Highland Heights (G-10919)
Precision Energy & Tech LLC ....G 937 558-2708
  Dayton (G-8582)
Rbs Technologies LLC ....G 937 320-8189
  Xenia (G-20970)
Redhawk Energy Systems LLC ....G 740 927-8244
  Pataskala (G-15979)
Rexon Components Inc ....F 440 585-7086
  Cleveland (G-6109)
Salient Systems Inc ....E 614 792-5800
  Dublin (G-9138)
SCI Engineered Materials Inc ....E 614 486-0261
  Columbus (G-7599)
Selectronics Incorporated ....G 440 546-5595
  Brecksville (G-2072)
Sideline Tech Inc ....G 440 331-0560
  Rocky River (G-16710)
Signature Technologies Inc ....E 937 859-6323
  Miamisburg (G-13859)
▲ Silfex Inc ....C 937 472-3311
  Eaton (G-9323)
Smart Microsystems Ltd ....F 440 366-4257
  Elyria (G-9493)
Solar Integrated Resources LLC .....G 937 608-4498
  Moraine (G-14530)
Spang & Company ....E 440 350-6108
  Mentor (G-13727)

Spb Global LLC ....G 419 931-6559
　Perrysburg (G-16150)
Special Mtls RES & Tech Inc ....G 440 777-4024
　North Olmsted (G-15347)
▲ Techneglas Inc ....G 419 873-2000
　Perrysburg (G-16154)
Transducers Direct Llc ....G 513 583-7597
　Loveland (G-12395)
Tri-Tech Led Systems ....G 614 593-2868
　Baltimore (G-1090)
▲ Tytek Industries Inc ....G 513 874-7326
　Blue Ash (G-1884)
UIC Energy LLC ....G 614 839-0250
　Columbus (G-7718)
▲ Ustek Incorporated ....G 614 538-8000
　Columbus (G-7728)
Vega Technology Group LLC ....G 216 772-1434
　North Canton (G-15281)

3675 Electronic Capacitors

CPI Group Limited ....G 216 525-0046
　Cleveland (G-5138)
Elliott Oren Products Inc ....E 419 298-2306
　Edgerton (G-9329)

3676 Electronic Resistors

Filnor Inc ....F 330 821-7667
　Alliance (G-508)
Measurement Specialties Inc ....F 937 427-1231
　Beavercreek (G-1374)

3677 Electronic Coils & Transformers

Adkel Corp ....G 740 452-6973
　Zanesville (G-21266)
Barnes International Inc ....D 419 352-7501
　Bowling Green (G-1970)
Canfield Industries Inc ....G 800 554-5071
　Youngstown (G-21042)
Captor Corporation ....D 937 667-8484
　Tipp City (G-18270)
Chicopee Engineering Assoc Inc ....E 413 592-2273
　Twinsburg (G-18911)
▼ Cletronics Inc ....F 330 239-2002
　Medina (G-13389)
Contech Strmwter Solutions LLC ....G 513 645-7000
　West Chester (G-19842)
Crawford Resources Inc ....G 419 624-8400
　Sandusky (G-16954)
Custom Coil & Transformer Co ....E 740 452-5211
　Zanesville (G-21297)
Electric Service Co Inc ....E 513 271-6387
　Cincinnati (G-3692)
Electromotive Inc ....G 330 688-6494
　Stow (G-17746)
Enviro Crest Services Inc ....G 330 932-0345
　East Liverpool (G-9214)
GE Healthcare Fincl Svcs Inc ....C 312 697-3999
　Aurora (G-921)
General Electric Company ....E 740 498-5151
　Newcomerstown (G-15113)
Illinois Tool Works Inc ....C 262 248-8277
　Bryan (G-2303)
Industrial Quartz Corp ....F 440 942-0909
　Mentor (G-13606)
▲ Kurz-Kasch Inc ....C 740 498-8343
　Newcomerstown (G-15118)
M2m Imaging Corporation ....F 440 684-9690
　Cleveland (G-5720)
Media Matrix LLC 888 833-8681
　Mount Vernon (G-14630)
▲ Micropure Filtration Inc ....F 952 472-2323
　Cleveland (G-5800)
▼ Norlake Manufacturing Company ..D 440 353-3200
　North Ridgeville (G-15391)
North Dixie Parts & Service ....G 937 275-0933
　Dayton (G-8526)
PCC Airfoils LLC ....C 216 692-7900
　Cleveland (G-5983)
Precision Switching Inc ....G 800 800-8143
　Mansfield (G-12667)
Rapid Mr International LLC ....G 614 486-6300
　Columbus (G-7548)
Schneider Electric Usa Inc ....B 513 523-4171
　Oxford (G-15843)
◆ Staco Energy Products Co ....G 937 253-1191
　Miamisburg (G-13863)
Standard Car Truck Company ....D 740 775-6450
　Chillicothe (G-3276)
▲ Standex Electronics Inc ....E 513 871-3777
　Cincinnati (G-4456)

▲ Swiger Coil Systems Ltd ....C 216 362-7500
　Cleveland (G-6280)
Wabtec Corporation ....G 216 362-7500
　Cleveland (G-6437)
Wonder Weld Inc ....G 614 875-1447
　Orient (G-15726)

3678 Electronic Connectors

Ankim Enterprises Incorporated ....E 937 599-1121
　Bellefontaine (G-1518)
Astro Industries Inc ....E 937 429-5900
　Beavercreek (G-1319)
Aviation Technologies Inc ....E 216 706-2960
　Cleveland (G-4872)
Canadus Power Systems LLC ....E 216 831-6600
　Twinsburg (G-18907)
Canfield Industries Inc ....G 800 554-5071
　Youngstown (G-21042)
Connective Design Incorporated ....F 937 746-8252
　Miamisburg (G-13793)
▲ Connectors Unlimited Inc ....E 440 357-1161
　Painesville (G-15868)
Connectronics Corp ....D 419 537-0020
　Toledo (G-18410)
Cooper Interconnect Inc ....E 800 386-1911
　Cleveland (G-5130)
D C M Industries Inc ....E 937 254-8500
　Dayton (G-8264)
HCC/Sealtron ....E 513 733-8400
　Cincinnati (G-3873)
▲ Lastar Inc ....G 937 224-0639
　Moraine (G-14502)
Mueller Electric Company Inc ....E 614 888-8855
　New Albany (G-14765)
▲ Ohio Associated Entps LLC ....E 440 354-2106
　Painesville (G-15906)
Ohio Associated Entps LLC ....E 440 354-3148
　Painesville (G-15908)
◆ Plcc2 LLC ....G 614 279-1796
　Columbus (G-7499)
Powell Electrical Systems Inc ....D 330 966-1750
　Canton (G-2816)
Servo Systems Inc ....G 440 779-2780
　North Olmsted (G-15345)
▲ Spi Inc ....E 937 374-2700
　Xenia (G-20973)
▲ Superb Industries Inc ....D 330 852-0500
　Sugarcreek (G-18045)
U S Terminals Inc ....G 513 561-8145
　Cincinnati (G-4534)
Xponet Inc ....E 440 354-6617
　Painesville (G-15943)

3679 Electronic Components, NEC

Accurate Electronics Inc ....C 330 682-7015
　Orrville (G-15727)
Adco Products Inc ....D 937 339-6267
　Tipp City (G-18261)
Advanced Cryogenic Entps LLC ....F 330 922-0750
　Akron (G-32)
Advantage Circuits Ltd ....G 330 256-7768
　Rootstown (G-16719)
▲ Aeroseal LLC ....E 937 428-9300
　Centerville (G-3034)
Alphabet Inc ....D 330 856-3366
　Warren (G-19519)
American Advnced Assmblies LLC .....E 937 339-6267
　Troy (G-18802)
Ankim Enterprises Incorporated ....E 937 599-1121
　Bellefontaine (G-1518)
Artificial Neural Systems Inc ....G 740 593-7675
　Athens (G-856)
Astro Industries Inc ....E 937 429-5900
　Beavercreek (G-1319)
Autosyte ....G 440 858-3226
　Painesville (G-15854)
Aviation Technologies Inc ....E 216 706-2960
　Cleveland (G-4872)
B5 Systems Inc ....G 937 372-4768
　Xenia (G-20937)
Bennett & Bennett Inc ....F 937 324-1100
　Springfield (G-17523)
Berry Investments Inc ....G 937 293-0398
　Moraine (G-14469)
Black Box Corporation ....E 614 825-7400
　Lewis Center (G-11890)
C E Electronics Inc ....D 419 636-6705
　Bryan (G-2289)
CEC Electronics Corp ....G 330 916-8100
　Akron (G-115)

▲ Channel Products Inc ....D 440 423-0113
　Chesterland (G-3199)
Circuits Alive LLC ....G 937 427-4141
　Beavercreek (G-1324)
▲ Cks Solution Incorporated ....E 513 947-1277
　Fairfield (G-9656)
▲ Cleanlife Energy LLC ....F 216 661-7872
　Cleveland (G-5044)
Cleveland Circuits Corp ....E 216 267-9020
　Cleveland (G-5051)
CMC Electronics Cincinn ....G 513 573-6316
　Mason (G-13003)
Co- Ax Technology Inc ....C 440 914-9200
　Solon (G-17279)
Connective Design Incorporated ....F 937 746-8252
　Miamisburg (G-13793)
Cutting Edge Technologies Inc ....E 216 574-4759
　Cleveland (G-5154)
D C M Industries Inc ....F 937 254-8500
　Dayton (G-8264)
Dare Electronics Inc ....E 937 335-0031
　Troy (G-18814)
Darrah Electric Company ....E 216 631-0912
　Cleveland (G-5168)
Deca Manufacturing Co Inc ....D 419 884-0071
　Mansfield (G-12594)
Don-Ell Corporation ....E 419 841-7114
　Sylvania (G-18103)
Drivetrain USA Inc ....F 614 733-0940
　Plain City (G-16337)
▲ Dynalab Ems Inc ....C 614 866-9999
　Reynoldsburg (G-16587)
Educational Electronics Inc ....G 234 301-9077
　Millersburg (G-14213)
Electro-Line Inc ....F 937 461-5683
　Dayton (G-8323)
Electromotive Inc ....G 330 688-6494
　Stow (G-17746)
Electronic Solutions Inc ....F 419 666-4700
　Perrysburg (G-16089)
Empire Power Systems Co ....G 440 796-4401
　Madison (G-12506)
Epic Technologies LLC ....D 513 683-5455
　Mason (G-13018)
Eti Tech Inc ....F 937 832-4200
　Englewood (G-9519)
Evension ....G 330 634-1430
　Akron (G-172)
Ewh Spectrum LLC ....D 937 593-8010
　Bellefontaine (G-1530)
Fischer-Backus Corp ....F 740 362-2100
　Lewis Center (G-11898)
Gmelectric Inc ....G 330 477-3392
　Canton (G-2715)
▲ Guitammer Company ....G 614 898-9370
　Westerville (G-20156)
Hall Company ....F 937 652-1376
　Urbana (G-19160)
Idcomm LLC ....G 661 250-4081
　Willoughby Hills (G-20639)
▲ Ingram Products Inc ....F 904 778-1010
　Ashland (G-743)
Innocomp ....G 440 248-5104
　Solon (G-17316)
▲ Inservco Inc ....D 847 855-9600
　Lagrange (G-11627)
▲ J & C Group Inc of Ohio ....C 440 205-9658
　Mentor (G-13613)
John B Allen ....G 614 488-7122
　Columbus (G-7238)
▲ Kent Displays Inc ....C 330 673-8784
　Kent (G-11477)
Kirby Electronics Inc ....G 614 395-8926
　Pickerington (G-16196)
▲ L & J Cable Inc ....E 937 526-9445
　Russia (G-16765)
La Grange Elec Assemblies Co ....F 440 355-5388
　Lagrange (G-11630)
Lake Shore Cryotronics Inc ....C 614 891-2243
　Westerville (G-20165)
Leidos Inc ....D 937 431-2400
　Beavercreek (G-1348)
Lintech Electronics LLC ....F 513 528-6190
　Cincinnati (G-3312)
◆ Liquid Crystal Tech LLC ....G 440 232-8590
　Cleveland (G-5704)
Madison Manufacturing LLC ....G 440 428-4630
　Madison (G-12509)
▲ Mc Gregor & Associates Inc ....C 937 833-6768
　Brookville (G-2192)

Microplex Inc ....E 330 498-0600
North Canton (G-15249)

Mitchell Electronics Inc ....G 740 594-8532
Athens (G-879)

Mk Enterprises Inc ....E 440 632-0121
Middlefield (G-13967)

Ms Squared Inc ....G 330 666-0255
Akron (G-306)

Mssl Wiring System Inc ....D 330 856-3344
Warren (G-19579)

Mueller Electric Company Inc ....E 614 888-8855
New Albany (G-14765)

▲ Nexergy Inc ....C 614 351-2191
Dublin (G-9114)

▼ Niktec LLC ....G 513 282-3747
Franklin (G-10040)

Ogc Industries Inc ....F 330 456-1500
Canton (G-2797)

◆ Ohio Semitronics Inc ....D 614 777-1005
Hilliard (G-10967)

Omega Engineering Inc ....E 740 965-9340
Sunbury (G-18072)

Ops Wireless ....G 419 396-4041
Carey (G-2923)

Otr Controls LLC ....G 513 621-2197
Cincinnati (G-4200)

Parker-Hannifin Corporation ....C 937 644-3915
Marysville (G-12962)

Per-Tech Inc ....E 330 833-8824
Massillon (G-13193)

Performance Electronics Ltd ....G 513 777-5233
Cincinnati (G-4225)

Philips Medical Systems Mr ....C 440 483-2499
Highland Heights (G-10919)

Precision Manufacturing Co Inc ....D 937 236-2170
Dayton (G-8585)

Qlog Corp ....G 513 874-1211
Hamilton (G-10732)

◆ Quality Quartz Engineering Inc ....D 937 236-3250
Dayton (G-8606)

Quality Quartz of America Inc ....G 440 352-2851
Mentor (G-13709)

Quality Switch Inc ....E 330 872-5707
Newton Falls (G-15138)

Quartz Scientific Inc ....E 360 574-6254
Fairport Harbor (G-9770)

Ra Consultants LLC ....E 513 469-6600
Blue Ash (G-1861)

Rct Industries Inc ....F 937 602-1100
Springboro (G-17505)

Rpa Electronic Distrs Inc ....G 937 223-7001
Dayton (G-8639)

RTD Electronics Inc ....F 330 487-0716
Twinsburg (G-19014)

Saint-Gobain Ceramics Plas Inc ....A 330 673-5860
Stow (G-17797)

Sawyer Research Product ....G 440 951-8770
Eastlake (G-9286)

▲ Sawyer Technical Materials LLC ....E 440 951-8770
Willoughby (G-20591)

Schupp Advanced Materials LLC ....G 440 488-6416
Willoughby (G-20592)

Shiloh Industries Inc ....F 937 236-5100
Dayton (G-8655)

Showplace Inc ....G 419 468-7368
Galion (G-10287)

Siglent Technologies Amer Inc ....G 440 398-5800
Solon (G-17380)

Sinbon Usa LLC ....G 937 667-8999
Tipp City (G-18299)

SMH Manufacturing Inc ....F 419 884-0071
Lexington (G-11952)

Sol-Fly Technologies LLC ....G 330 465-8883
Wooster (G-20837)

Solar Con Inc ....E 419 865-5877
Holland (G-11086)

Sovereign Circuits Inc ....F 330 538-3900
North Jackson (G-15298)

Specialty Switch Co ....F 330 427-3000
Youngstown (G-21210)

Spectron Inc ....G 937 461-5590
Dayton (G-8668)

▲ Spi Inc ....G 937 374-2700
Xenia (G-20973)

Suburban Electronics Assembly ....G 330 483-4077
Valley City (G-19236)

The W L Jenkins Company ....F 330 477-3407
Canton (G-2869)

◆ Thermtrol Corporation ....E 330 497-4148
North Canton (G-15272)

TL Industries Inc ....C 419 666-8144
Northwood (G-15490)

◆ Tls Corp ....E 216 574-4759
Cleveland (G-6327)

▲ Total Cable Solutions Inc ....G 513 457-7013
Springboro (G-17511)

Tracewell Power Inc ....E 614 846-6175
Westerville (G-20239)

▲ Twin Point Inc ....F 419 923-7525
Delta (G-8940)

U S Terminals Inc ....G 513 561-8145
Cincinnati (G-4534)

Valtronic Technology Inc ....D 440 349-1239
Solon (G-17411)

Vertiv Group Corporation ....A 614 888-0246
Columbus (G-7735)

Weldon ....G 330 263-9533
Columbus (G-7757)

Wetsu Group Inc ....F 937 324-9353
Springfield (G-17678)

Wifi-Plus Inc ....G 877 838-4195
Brunswick (G-2268)

Zeus Electronics LLC ....G 330 220-1571
Brunswick (G-2272)

3691 Storage Batteries

All Power Battery Inc ....G 330 453-5236
Canton (G-2597)

B W T Inc ....G 330 928-9107
Akron (G-81)

◆ Crown Battery Manufacturing Co ....B 419 332-0563
Fremont (G-10139)

Dynalite Corp ....G 419 873-1706
Perrysburg (G-16086)

◆ Energizer Manufacturing Inc ....D 440 835-7866
Westlake (G-20267)

Enersys ....D 513 737-2268
West Chester (G-19858)

Enersys Delaware Inc ....G 216 252-4242
Cleveland (G-5282)

◆ Gould Electronics Inc ....C 440 953-5000
Eastlake (G-9271)

Graywacke Engineering Inc ....F 419 884-7014
Mansfield (G-12621)

Innovative Weld Solutions Ltd ....G 937 545-7695
Dayton (G-8408)

Interstate Batteries Inc ....G 740 968-2211
Saint Clairsville (G-16792)

Johnson Contrls Btry Group Inc ....A 419 865-0542
Holland (G-11068)

Lithchem Intl Toxco Inc ....G 740 653-6290
Lancaster (G-11726)

Megajoule Storage Inc ....G 216 496-8302
Cleveland (G-5778)

Ovonic Energy Products Inc ....C 937 743-1001
Springboro (G-17493)

Retriev Technologies Inc ....D 740 653-6290
Lancaster (G-11746)

Toxco Inc ....G 740 653-6290
Lancaster (G-11757)

Transdigm Inc ....F 216 291-6025
Cleveland (G-6346)

Transdigm Inc ....G 216 706-2939
Cleveland (G-6347)

3692 Primary Batteries: Dry & Wet

D C Systems Inc ....F 330 273-3030
Brunswick (G-2219)

N S T Battery ....G 937 433-9222
Bellbrook (G-1510)

Spectrum Brands Inc ....D 513 231-0952
Anderson Township (G-610)

Toyo System Usa Inc ....G 614 414-0515
Columbus (G-7702)

3694 Electrical Eqpt For Internal Combustion Engines

▲ Altronic LLC ....C 330 545-9768
Girard (G-10381)

Brinkley Technology Group LLC ....F 330 830-2498
Massillon (G-13115)

Charles Auto Electric Co Inc ....G 330 535-6269
Akron (G-118)

Cuyahoga Rebuilders Inc ....G 440 846-0532
Cleveland (G-5159)

Cycle Electric Inc ....F 937 884-7300
Brookville (G-2179)

Design Flux Technologies LLC ....G 216 543-6066
Akron (G-147)

Egr Products Company Inc ....F 330 833-6554
Dalton (G-8068)

Elcor Inc ....E 440 365-5941
Elyria (G-9411)

Electra Sound Inc ....D 216 433-9600
Parma (G-15957)

◆ Electripack Inc ....E 937 433-2602
Miamisburg (G-13804)

Empire Power Systems Co ....G 440 796-4401
Madison (G-12506)

Ewh Spectrum LLC ....D 937 593-8010
Bellefontaine (G-1530)

Exact-Tool & Die Inc ....E 216 676-9140
Cleveland (G-5311)

▲ Ferrotherm Corporation ....C 216 883-9350
Cleveland (G-5339)

Flex Technologies Inc ....D 330 359-5415
Mount Eaton (G-14555)

Fram Group Operations LLC ....G 419 661-6700
Perrysburg (G-16097)

Gmelectric Inc ....G 330 477-3392
Canton (G-2715)

▲ GSW Manufacturing Inc ....B 419 423-7111
Findlay (G-9834)

▲ Hurst Auto-Truck Electric ....G 216 961-1800
Cleveland (G-5538)

Industrial Systems & Solutions ....G 440 205-1658
Mentor (G-13607)

Legacy Supplies Inc ....F 330 405-4565
Twinsburg (G-18971)

M W Solutions LLC ....F 419 782-1611
Defiance (G-8800)

Machine Products Company ....C 937 890-6600
Dayton (G-8466)

◆ Mitsubishi Elc Auto Amer Inc ....B 513 573-6614
Mason (G-13065)

Mueller Electric Company Inc ....E 216 771-5225
Akron (G-307)

▲ Noco Company ....B 216 464-8131
Solon (G-17350)

Ohio Generator Remanufacturing ....G 330 875-6677
Louisville (G-12321)

Per-Tech Inc ....E 330 833-8824
Massillon (G-13193)

Power Acquisition LLC ....G 614 228-5000
Columbus (G-7506)

▲ Satco Inc ....G 330 630-8866
Tallmadge (G-18168)

▲ Sk Tech Inc ....C 937 836-3535
Englewood (G-9539)

▲ Stanley Electric US Co Inc ....B 740 852-5200
London (G-12219)

Stellar Industrial Tech Co ....G 740 654-7052
Lancaster (G-11756)

Sumitomo Elc Wirg Systems Inc ....E 937 642-7579
Marysville (G-12974)

Td Power Systems (usa) Inc ....G 330 247-5264
Richfield (G-16642)

Thirion Brothers Eqp Co LLC ....G 440 357-8004
Painesville (G-15930)

▲ Towing Electrical Systems ....G 330 793-3887
Youngstown (G-21225)

Unison Industries LLC ....C 937 426-0621
Beavercreek (G-1364)

United Controls Group Inc ....G 740 936-0005
Columbus (G-6659)

United Controls Group Inc ....G 740 936-0005
Columbus (G-6660)

▲ United Ignition Wire Corp ....G 216 898-1112
Cleveland (G-6385)

Unity Cable Technologies Inc ....G 419 322-4118
Toledo (G-18759)

Vintage Electric Ltd Inc ....F 419 472-9349
Toledo (G-18770)

W W Williams Company LLC ....D 614 228-5000
Columbus (G-7746)

Weldon Pump Acquition LLC ....E 440 232-2282
Oakwood Village (G-15633)

3695 Recording Media

CD Solutions Inc ....G 937 676-2376
Pleasant Hill (G-16369)

Characteristic Solutions LLC ....G 614 360-2424
Columbus (G-6922)

Folio Photonics LLC ....G 440 420-4500
Solon (G-17294)

Future Pos Ohio Inc ....F 330 645-6623
Akron (G-196)

Ginko Voting Systems LLC ....G 937 291-4060
Dayton (G-8364)

▲ Magnet Technology Inc ....G...... 513 932-4416
  Lebanon (G-11814)

Magnetnotes Ltd ....G...... 419 593-0060
  Toledo (G-18571)

Medical Soft Inc ....G...... 937 293-2575
  Oakwood (G-15609)

Paragon Robotics LLC ....G...... 216 313-9299
  Bedford Heights (G-1492)

Procomsol Ltd ....G...... 216 221-1550
  Lakewood (G-11677)

Signalysis Inc ....F...... 513 528-6164
  Cincinnati (G-4420)

US Video ....G...... 440 734-6463
  North Olmsted (G-15350)

Wm Software Inc ....F...... 330 558-0501
  Brunswick (G-2270)

3699 Electrical Machinery, Eqpt & Splys, NEC

1 A Lifesafer Inc ....G...... 513 651-9560
  Blue Ash (G-1729)

A L Callahan Door Sales ....G...... 419 884-3667
  Mansfield (G-12554)

Aaron Smith ....G...... 330 285-1360
  Akron (G-24)

Access 2 Communications Inc ....G...... 800 561-1110
  Steubenville (G-17686)

▲ Action Industries Ltd ....F...... 216 252-7800
  Cleveland (G-4698)

▲ AEG Photoconductor Corporation ...D...... 513 874-4939
  West Chester (G-19799)

▲ Agratronix LLC ....E...... 330 562-2222
  Streetsboro (G-17834)

Akron Brass Company ....E...... 614 529-7230
  Columbus (G-6708)

▲ Akron Brass Company ....B...... 330 264-5678
  Wooster (G-20735)

Akron Brass Holding Corp ....G...... 330 264-5678
  Wooster (G-20736)

Akron Foundry Co ....E...... 330 745-3101
  Barberton (G-1095)

Alert Safety Lite Products Co ....F...... 440 232-5020
  Cleveland (G-4750)

▲ Alert Stamping & Mfg Co Inc ....E...... 440 232-5020
  Bedford Heights (G-1476)

Allen Fields Assoc Inc ....G...... 513 228-1010
  Lebanon (G-11778)

▲ Allied Moulded Products Inc ....B...... 419 636-4217
  Bryan (G-2275)

Ametek Inc ....F...... 937 440-0800
  Troy (G-18804)

ARC Elec ....F...... 440 774-2800
  Wellington (G-19737)

Asco Power Technologies LP ....C...... 937 748-8884
  Springboro (G-17474)

▼ Automation Metrology Intl LLC ....G...... 440 354-6436
  Mentor (G-13529)

Azz Inc ....E...... 330 456-3241
  Canton (G-2611)

▲ Barth Industries Co LP ....D...... 216 267-0531
  Cleveland (G-4893)

Bert Radebaugh ....G...... 740 382-8134
  Marion (G-12857)

Beta Industries Inc ....E...... 937 299-7385
  Dayton (G-8186)

Bonham Enterprsises ....G...... 740 333-0501
  Wshngtn CT Hs (G-20902)

Buckeye Electrical Products ....E...... 937 693-7519
  Botkins (G-1952)

C L S Inc ....E...... 216 251-5011
  Cleveland (G-4956)

▲ Cecil C Peck Co ....F...... 330 785-0781
  Akron (G-116)

Ces Nationwide ....G...... 937 322-0771
  Springfield (G-17530)

Chandler Systems Incorporated .....G...... 419 281-6829
  Ashland (G-720)

Checkpoint Systems Inc ....C...... 937 281-1304
  Dayton (G-8226)

Christmas Ranch LLC ....E...... 513 505-3865
  Morrow (G-14545)

Ci Disposition Co ....E...... 216 587-5200
  Brooklyn Heights (G-2135)

Cincinnati Gate Systems Inc ....G...... 513 769-5200
  Cincinnati (G-3551)

Cincinnati Laser Cutting LLC ....E...... 513 772-6999
  Cincinnati (G-3556)

Circle Prime Manufacturing ....E...... 330 923-0019
  Cuyahoga Falls (G-7980)

Clark Substations LLC ....E...... 330 452-5200
  Canton (G-2659)

◆ Cleaning Tech Group LLC ....C...... 513 870-0100
  West Chester (G-19990)

Commercial Electric Pdts Corp ....E...... 216 241-2886
  Cleveland (G-5104)

Control System Manufacturing ....E...... 330 542-0000
  New Middletown (G-14876)

Control Works Inc ....G...... 513 831-9959
  Milford (G-14133)

▼ Corrpro Companies Inc ....G...... 330 723-5082
  Medina (G-13394)

Corrpro Companies Inc ....F...... 330 725-6681
  Medina (G-13395)

Corrpro Companies Intl Inc ....G...... 330 723-5082
  Medina (G-13396)

Cv Electric ....G...... 419 630-0800
  Bryan (G-2292)

D&M Fencing LLC ....G...... 419 604-0698
  Spencerville (G-17459)

Daskal Enterprise LLC ....G...... 614 848-5700
  Columbus (G-7012)

Debra Harbour ....G...... 937 440-9618
  Troy (G-18816)

Diebold Nixdorf Incorporated ....A...... 330 490-4000
  North Canton (G-15228)

E-Beam Services Inc ....E...... 513 933-0031
  Lebanon (G-11795)

E-One Electric ....G...... 937 296-4420
  Moraine (G-14481)

Eagle Wldg & Fabrication Inc ....E...... 440 946-0692
  Willoughby (G-20478)

Elcor Inc ....E...... 440 365-5941
  Elyria (G-9411)

▲ Electra - Cord Inc ....D...... 330 832-8124
  Massillon (G-13129)

▲ Electrowarmth Products LLC ....G...... 740 599-7222
  Danville (G-8088)

Emega Technologies LLC ....G...... 740 407-3712
  Zanesville (G-21307)

▲ Emx Industries Inc ....E...... 216 518-9888
  Cleveland (G-5279)

Engineered Mfg & Eqp Co ....G...... 937 642-7776
  Marysville (G-12942)

Everykey Inc ....G...... 866 798-5577
  Cleveland (G-5309)

Executive Security Systems Inc ....G...... 513 895-2783
  Cincinnati (G-3730)

▲ Federal Equipment Company ....D...... 513 621-5260
  Cincinnati (G-3747)

▲ Fernandes Enterprises LLC ....F...... 937 890-6444
  Dayton (G-8340)

Fire-End & Croker Corp ....G...... 513 870-0517
  West Chester (G-20001)

FM Manufacturing Inc ....E...... 419 445-0700
  Archbold (G-673)

Fortec Medical Lithotripsy LLC ....E...... 330 656-4301
  Streetsboro (G-17854)

General Electric Company ....C...... 216 266-2357
  Cleveland (G-5416)

Global Laser Tek ....E...... 513 701-0452
  Mason (G-13029)

▲ GMI Holdings Inc ....B...... 330 821-5360
  Mount Hope (G-14571)

GMI Holdings Inc ....C...... 330 897-4424
  Baltic (G-1073)

Great Lakes Power Service Co ....F...... 440 259-0025
  Perry (G-16050)

H W Fairway International Inc ....E...... 330 678-2540
  Kent (G-11467)

Habitec SEC Diversfd Alarm ....G...... 419 636-1155
  Bryan (G-2299)

▲ Halex/Scott Fetzer Company ....D...... 440 439-1616
  Bedford Heights (G-1485)

Halls Welding & Supplies Inc ....G...... 330 385-9353
  East Liverpool (G-9217)

Hannon Company ....D...... 330 456-4728
  Canton (G-2723)

Hanon Systems Usa LLC ....C...... 313 920-0583
  Carey (G-2919)

Heat Exchange Institute Inc ....G...... 216 241-7333
  Cleveland (G-5490)

Henderson Partners LLC ....G...... 614 883-1310
  Columbus (G-7149)

Hess Advanced Solutions Llc ....G...... 937 829-4794
  Dayton (G-8389)

Holland Assocts LLC DBA Archou ...F...... 513 891-0006
  Cincinnati (G-3888)

Honeywell International Inc ....A...... 937 484-2000
  Urbana (G-19162)

▲ I T Verdin Co ....E...... 513 241-4010
  Cincinnati (G-3906)

I T Verdin Co ....E...... 513 241-4010
  Cincinnati (G-3907)

I T Verdin Co ....E...... 513 559-3947
  Cincinnati (G-3908)

Innovar Systems Limited ....F...... 330 538-3942
  North Jackson (G-15292)

▲ Insource Technologies Inc ....C...... 419 399-3600
  Paulding (G-16008)

Intelligent Biometric Controls ....G...... 513 239-6322
  Milford (G-14152)

▼ Invue Security Products Inc ....C...... 330 456-7776
  Canton (G-2740)

Izit Cain Sheet Metal Corp ....G...... 937 667-6521
  Tipp City (G-18284)

J Beischel Electric ....G...... 513 860-3290
  West Chester (G-20018)

J II Fire Systems Inc ....G...... 513 574-0609
  Cincinnati (G-3935)

JC Electric ....E...... 330 760-2915
  Garrettsville (G-10325)

Jech Technologies Inc ....G...... 740 927-3495
  Pickerington (G-16194)

▲ Jobap Assembly Inc ....F...... 440 632-5393
  Middlefield (G-13947)

Kiemle-Hankins Company ....G...... 419 661-2430
  Perrysburg (G-16117)

Kraft Electrical Contg Inc ....E...... 614 836-9300
  Groveport (G-10630)

Laser Automation Inc ....E...... 440 543-9291
  Chagrin Falls (G-3099)

Levans Electric & Hvac ....G...... 937 468-2269
  Rushsylvania (G-16752)

Libra Industries Inc ....E...... 440 974-7770
  Mentor (G-13631)

Liebert North America Inc ....A...... 614 888-0246
  Columbus (G-7293)

▼ Lindsay Precast Inc ....E...... 330 854-6282
  Canal Fulton (G-2505)

Linear Dynamics ....E...... 419 806-6689
  Risingsun (G-16672)

Linear Technology Corporation ....G...... 440 239-0817
  Cleveland (G-5701)

Lockheed Martin Corporation ....B...... 330 796-7000
  Akron (G-272)

Lockheed Martin Integ ....D...... 330 796-2800
  Akron (G-274)

Lucky Thirteen Inc ....G...... 216 631-0013
  Cleveland (G-5712)

◆ Mace Security Intl Inc ....F...... 440 424-5321
  Cleveland (G-5723)

Magnus Engineered Eqp LLC ....E...... 440 942-8488
  Willoughby (G-20533)

MAI Media Group Llc ....G...... 513 779-0604
  West Chester (G-20023)

Matlock Electric Co Inc ....E...... 513 731-9600
  Cincinnati (G-4066)

Mixed Logic LLC ....G...... 440 826-1676
  Valley City (G-19218)

▼ Modular Security Systems Inc ....G...... 740 532-7822
  Ironton (G-11297)

Mr Electric ....G...... 419 289-7474
  Mansfield (G-12654)

Mueller Electric Company Inc ....E...... 216 771-5225
  Akron (G-307)

Mv Innovative Technologies LLC .....G...... 937 221-7639
  Dayton (G-8515)

Niftech Inc ....F...... 440 257-6018
  Mentor (G-13667)

▲ Nook Industries Inc ....C...... 216 271-7900
  Cleveland (G-5887)

Northeast Laser Inc ....G...... 330 633-2897
  Tallmadge (G-18160)

Oakes Door Serv ....G...... 937 323-6188
  Springfield (G-17618)

Ohio Electric Motor Svc LLC ....G...... 419 525-2225
  Mansfield (G-12661)

Oldaker Manufacturing Corp ....G...... 419 759-3551
  Dunkirk (G-9189)

Overhead Door of Salem Inc ....G...... 330 332-9530
  Salem (G-16918)

▲ Overly Hautz Motor Base Co ....E...... 513 932-0025
  Lebanon (G-11825)

P & B Electric ....G...... 937 754-4695
  Fairborn (G-9628)

Peerless Laser Processors Inc ....E...... 614 836-5790
  Groveport (G-10639)

Pentagon Protection Usa LLC ....F...... 614 734-7240
  Dublin (G-9123)

◆ Philips Medical Systems Clevel ......B...... 440 247-2652
  Cleveland (G-6001)

Powell Electrical Systems Inc ....D 330 966-1750
Canton (G-2816)

PWS Welding & Mtg ....F 330 385-6922
East Liverpool (G-9226)

▲ Qualtech Technologies Inc ....E 440 946-8081
Willoughby (G-20585)

Rent-A-Center Inc ....G 740 373-1342
Marietta (G-12823)

Residential Electronic Svcs ....G 740 681-9150
Lancaster (G-11745)

Resonance Group Ltd ....G 419 509-2245
Toledo (G-18675)

Resonetics LLC ....D 937 865-4070
Kettering (G-11585)

▲ Riverside Drives Inc ....E 216 362-1211
Cleveland (G-6118)

Romanoff Elc Residential LLC ....E 614 755-4500
Gahanna (G-10230)

RPS America Inc ....G 937 231-9339
West Chester (G-19937)

▲ S R Technologies LLC ....G 330 523-7184
Akron (G-392)

Schneider Electric Usa Inc ....B 513 523-4171
Oxford (G-15843)

Securcom Inc ....G 419 628-1049
Minster (G-14361)

Sew-Eurodrive Inc ....D 937 335-0036
Troy (G-18875)

Smart Sonic Corporation ....G 818 610-7900
Cleveland (G-6211)

Spang & Company ....E 440 350-6108
Mentor (G-13727)

State Electric Supply Company ....F 330 308-0659
New Philadelphia (G-14929)

Tech-Sonic Inc ....E 614 792-3117
Columbus (G-7683)

▲ Technibus Inc ....D 330 479-4202
Canton (G-2867)

Technical Sales & Solution ....G 614 793-9612
Dublin (G-9154)

Technlogy Install Partners LLC ....E 888 586-7040
Cleveland (G-6302)

Technology Products Inc ....G 937 652-3412
Urbana (G-19184)

The W L Jenkins Company ....F 330 477-3407
Canton (G-2869)

Tip Products Inc ....E 216 252-2535
Cleveland (G-6326)

▲ Transdermal Inc ....F 440 241-1846
Gates Mills (G-10338)

Trinity Door Systems ....G 877 603-2018
New Springfield (G-14953)

TSS Technologies Inc ....E 513 772-7000
West Chester (G-19964)

◆ Vanner Holdings Inc ....D 614 771-2718
Hilliard (G-10991)

Vero Security Group Ltd ....G 513 731-8376
Cincinnati (G-4564)

Vigilant Defense ....E 513 214-1635
Mason (G-13101)

Villers Enterprises Limited ....G 330 818-9838
North Canton (G-15282)

Viotec LLC ....G 614 596-2054
Dublin (G-9163)

Vortec Corporation ....E 513 686-8210
Blue Ash (G-1891)

Vti Instruments Corporation ....G 216 447-8950
Cleveland (G-6432)

Wesco Distribution Inc ....E 419 666-1670
Northwood (G-15495)

Yaskawa America Inc ....F 614 733-3200
Plain City (G-16365)

37 TRANSPORTATION EQUIPMENT

3711 Motor Vehicles & Car Bodies

Accubuilt Inc ....C 419 224-3910
Lima (G-11980)

Accubuilt Inc ....C 419 224-3910
Lima (G-11981)

Aftermarket Parts Company LLC ....B 740 369-1056
Delaware (G-8818)

◆ Airstream Inc ....B 937 596-6111
Jackson Center (G-11337)

Allen Morgan Trucking & Repair ....G 330 336-5192
Norton (G-15506)

AM General LLC ....G 937 704-0160
Franklin (G-10006)

American Honda Motor Co Inc ....C 937 332-6100
Troy (G-18803)

American Race Cars ....G 419 836-5070
Millbury (G-14182)

AMP Electric Vehicles Inc ....F 513 360-4704
Loveland (G-12339)

Antique Auto Sheet Metal Inc ....E 937 833-4422
Brookville (G-2174)

Antram Fire Equipment ....G 330 525-7171
North Georgetown (G-15286)

Auto Expo USA of Cleveland ....G 216 889-3000
Cleveland (G-4863)

Autowax Inc ....G 440 334-4417
Strongsville (G-17894)

Bartley Lawn Service LLC ....G 937 435-8884
West Carrollton (G-19791)

Bethlehem Fire and Rescue Inc ....G 330 879-5800
Navarre (G-14710)

Biggys Auto Buffet ....G 740 455-4663
Zanesville (G-21278)

Bobbart Industries Inc ....E 419 350-5477
Sylvania (G-18101)

Braun Industries Inc ....G 419 232-7020
Van Wert (G-19246)

Brookville Roadster Inc ....G 937 833-4605
Brookville (G-2176)

Buses International ....F 440 233-4091
Lorain (G-12235)

Columbus Fire Fighters Union ....G 614 481-8900
Columbus (G-6951)

Comprehensive Logistics Co Inc ....E 330 793-0504
Youngstown (G-21055)

Copley Fire & Rescue Assn ....E 330 666-6464
Copley (G-7843)

▲ Custom Chassis Inc ....G 440 839-5574
Wakeman (G-19447)

D & D Classic Auto Restoration ....E 937 473-2229
Covington (G-7921)

Dakkota Integrated Systems LLC ....E 517 694-6500
Toledo (G-18425)

Dave Foreign Cars ....G 419 727-0685
Toledo (G-18428)

Eagle Coach Inc ....D 513 797-4100
Amelia (G-573)

Eldorado National Kansas Inc ....G 937 596-6849
Jackson Center (G-11340)

Electro Prime Assembly Inc ....F 419 476-0100
Rossford (G-16738)

Falls Stamping & Welding Co ....C 330 928-1191
Cuyahoga Falls (G-7996)

▼ Farber Specialty Vehicles Inc ....C 614 863-6470
Reynoldsburg (G-16589)

Ford Motor Company ....A 440 933-1215
Avon Lake (G-1029)

Ford Motor Company ....A 216 587-7700
Cleveland (G-5368)

Galion-Godwin Truck Bdy Co LLC ....D 330 359-5495
Millersburg (G-14217)

General Motors LLC ....A 330 824-5000
Warren (G-19553)

General Motors LLC ....A 216 265-5000
Cleveland (G-5419)

◆ Gerling and Associates Inc ....D 740 965-6200
Sunbury (G-18060)

Great Lakes Assemblies LLC ....D 937 645-3900
East Liberty (G-9200)

◆ Honda of America Mfg Inc ....A 937 642-5000
Marysville (G-12950)

Honda of America Mfg Inc ....B 937 642-5000
Marysville (G-12952)

Honda of America Mfg Inc ....C 937 644-0724
Marysville (G-12951)

Horton Enterprises Inc ....G 614 539-8181
Grove City (G-10563)

Hyq Technologies LLC ....G 513 225-6911
Oxford (G-15837)

▲ Jefferson Industries Corp ....C 614 879-5300
West Jefferson (G-20079)

JLW - TW Corp ....G 216 361-5940
Avon (G-998)

Johns Body Shop ....G 419 358-1200
Bluffton (G-1913)

K K Racing Chassis ....G 330 628-2930
Akron (G-247)

Kps NAPA ....F 740 522-9445
Heath (G-10849)

La Boit Specialty Vehicles ....E 614 231-7640
Gahanna (G-10216)

Lawsons Towing & Auto Wrckg ....F 216 883-9050
Cleveland (G-5688)

Magic Dragon Machine Inc ....G 614 539-8004
Grove City (G-10570)

Marc Industries Inc ....G 440 944-9305
Willoughby (G-20536)

Mbm Industries Ltd ....G 937 522-0719
Beavercreek Township (G-1385)

Mobile Solutions LLC ....F 614 286-3944
Columbus (G-7361)

Mobis North America LLC ....E 419 729-6700
Toledo (G-18589)

Monarch Plastic Inc ....F 330 683-0822
Orrville (G-15747)

▲ Myers Motors LLC ....G 330 630-7000
Tallmadge (G-18157)

Navistar Inc ....C 937 390-5848
Springfield (G-17612)

Navistar Inc ....D 937 390-2800
Springfield (G-17613)

Navistar Inc ....D 937 390-5653
Springfield (G-17614)

Navistar Inc ....D 937 390-4774
Springfield (G-17615)

Navistar Inc ....D 937 390-5704
Springfield (G-17616)

Navistar Inc ....B 513 733-8500
Cincinnati (G-4142)

▲ Obs Inc ....F 330 453-3725
Canton (G-2796)

▲ Ogara Hess Eisenhardt ....G 513 346-1300
West Chester (G-19907)

P C Workshop Inc ....D 419 399-4805
Paulding (G-16012)

Paccar Inc ....A 740 774-5111
Chillicothe (G-3257)

Petermann ....G 419 925-5404
Maria Stein (G-12760)

Pittsburgh Glass Works LLC ....C 419 569-7521
Crestline (G-7934)

Progressive Automotive Inc ....G 740 862-4696
Baltimore (G-1085)

▲ Reberland Equipment Inc ....F 330 698-5883
Apple Creek (G-648)

▲ Rikenkaki America Corporation ....G 614 336-2744
Dublin (G-9133)

Scottrods LLC ....G 419 499-2705
Monroeville (G-14428)

Star Fab Inc ....G 330 482-1601
Columbiana (G-6634)

◆ Sutphen Corporation ....C 800 726-7030
Dublin (G-9150)

Sutphen Corporation ....D 937 969-8851
Springfield (G-17658)

Svm America Ltd ....E 937 218-7591
Maineville (G-12532)

Thor Industries Inc ....E 937 596-6111
Jackson Center (G-11349)

Toledo Molding & Die Inc ....D 419 720-3500
Toledo (G-18735)

Toledo Pro Fiberglass Inc ....G 419 241-9390
Toledo (G-18740)

United Fire Apparatus Corp ....G 419 645-4083
Cridersville (G-7947)

Universal Composite LLC ....E 614 507-1646
Sunbury (G-18077)

W&W Automotive & Towing Inc ....F 937 429-1699
Beavercreek Township (G-1391)

Weastec Incorporated ....G 614 734-9645
Dublin (G-9165)

Weiss Motors ....G 330 678-5585
Kent (G-11542)

Workhorse Group Inc ....F 513 297-3640
Loveland (G-12401)

Wyatt Specialties Inc ....G 614 989-5362
Circleville (G-4650)

3713 Truck & Bus Bodies

Able Industries Inc ....G 614 252-1050
Columbus (G-6680)

Ace Truck Equipment Co ....E 740 453-0551
Zanesville (G-21264)

◆ Airstream Inc ....B 937 596-6111
Jackson Center (G-11337)

Alterntive Spport Appratus LLC ....G 740 922-2727
Midvale (G-14103)

▲ ARE Accessories LLC ....A 330 830-7800
Massillon (G-13110)

ARE Inc ....B 330 830-7800
Massillon (G-13111)

ARE Inc ....C 330 830-7800
Massillon (G-13112)

Arts Rolloffs & Refuse Inc ....G 419 991-3730
Lima (G-11994)

▲ Atc Lighting & Plastics Inc ....C 440 466-7670
   Andover (G-613)
Bair Bodies & Trailers Inc ....G 330 343-4853
   Dover (G-8966)
Bloomdale Plastics Co ....E 419 454-5135
   Bloomdale (G-1719)
Bores Manufacturing Co Inc ....F 419 465-2606
   Monroeville (G-14425)
Bosserman Automotive Engrg LLC ......G 419 722-2879
   Findlay (G-9800)
▲ Brothers Body and Eqp LLC ....F 419 462-1975
   Galion (G-10255)
Brown Industrial Inc ....G 937 693-3838
   Botkins (G-1951)
Bush Specialty Vehicles Inc ....G 937 382-5502
   Wilmington (G-20657)
Cascade Corporation ....C 937 327-0300
   Springfield (G-17527)
Cipted Corp ....D 412 829-2120
   Monroe (G-14397)
▲ Cleveland Hdwr & Forging Co ....E 216 641-5200
   Cleveland (G-5064)
Columbus McKinnon Corporation ....D 330 424-7248
   Lisbon (G-12118)
Columbus Mobility Specialist ....G 614 825-8996
   Worthington (G-20861)
▲ Cota International Inc ....F 937 526-5520
   Versailles (G-19344)
Crosco ....G 330 477-1999
   Canton (G-2671)
Daniel Wagner ....G 740 942-2928
   Cadiz (G-2416)
Elliott Machine Works Inc ....E 419 468-4709
   Galion (G-10267)
▲ Ellis & Watts Intl LLC ....G 513 752-9000
   Batavia (G-1183)
Field Gymmy Inc ....G 419 538-6511
   Glandorf (G-10397)
Ford Motor Company ....A 440 933-1215
   Avon Lake (G-1029)
Friesen Transfer Ltd ....G 614 873-5672
   Plain City (G-16341)
Galion-Godwin Truck Bdy Co LLC ....D 330 359-5495
   Millersburg (G-14217)
Gerich Fiberglass Inc ....E 419 362-4591
   Mount Gilead (G-14560)
H & H Truck Parts LLC ....G 216 642-4540
   Cleveland (G-5467)
▼ Halcore Group Inc ....C 614 539-8181
   Grove City (G-10561)
Hendrickson International Corp ....D 740 929-5600
   Hebron (G-10870)
Johnny On The Spot Inc ....E 614 497-1776
   Columbus (G-7239)
Johns Body Shop ....G 419 358-1200
   Bluffton (G-1913)
▲ Joseph Industries Inc ....D 330 528-0091
   Streetsboro (G-17860)
Kaffenbarger Truck Eqp Co ....G 937 845-3804
   New Carlisle (G-14804)
Kaffenbarger Truck Eqp Co ....E 513 772-6800
   Cincinnati (G-3967)
Kilar Manufacturing Inc ....E 330 534-8961
   Hubbard (G-11133)
▲ Kimble Custom Chassis Company ..D 877 546-2537
   New Philadelphia (G-14906)
▲ Kimble Mixer Company ....D 330 308-6700
   New Philadelphia (G-14907)
▲ King Kutter II Inc ....E 740 446-0351
   Gallipolis (G-10302)
Kruz Inc ....E 330 878-5595
   Dover (G-8996)
Kuka Toledo Production ....C 419 727-5500
   Toledo (G-18550)
La Boit Specialty Vehicles ....E 614 231-7640
   Gahanna (G-10216)
▲ Leyman Manufacturing Corp ....D 513 891-6210
   Cincinnati (G-4021)
Life Star Rescue Inc ....E 419 238-2507
   Van Wert (G-19266)
Mancor Ohio Inc ....G 937 228-6141
   Dayton (G-8474)
Mancor Ohio Inc ....G 937 228-6141
   Dayton (G-8475)
Marengo Fabricated Steel Ltd ....F 419 253-2119
   Marengo (G-12752)
Martin Sheet Metal Inc ....D 216 377-8200
   Cleveland (G-5753)
McNeilus Truck and Mfg Inc ....G 614 868-0760
   Gahanna (G-10218)

McNeilus Truck and Mfg Inc ....E 513 874-2022
   Fairfield (G-9683)
Meritor Inc ....C 740 348-3498
   Granville (G-10461)
Miller Industries Inc ....G 937 293-2223
   Dayton (G-8503)
Navistar Inc ....D 937 390-2800
   Springfield (G-17613)
Neiss Body & Equipment Corp ....G 330 828-2409
   Dalton (G-8075)
Paccar Inc ....A 740 774-5111
   Chillicothe (G-3257)
Proform Group Inc ....D 614 332-9654
   Columbus (G-7524)
Q T Columbus LLC ....G 800 758-2410
   Columbus (G-7528)
▼ QT Equipment Company ....E 330 724-3055
   Akron (G-355)
▲ Reberland Equipment Inc ....F 330 698-5883
   Apple Creek (G-648)
River City Body Company ....E 513 772-9317
   Cincinnati (G-4347)
Rke Trucking Co ....F 614 891-1786
   Westerville (G-20183)
Schodorf Truck Body & Eqp Co ....E 614 228-6793
   Columbus (G-7596)
Silverado Trucks & Accessories ....G 937 492-8862
   Sidney (G-17228)
▲ Tarpstop LLC ....E 419 873-7867
   Perrysburg (G-16152)
▲ Tremcar USA Inc ....C 330 878-7708
   Strasburg (G-17831)
Trim Systems Operating Corp ....C 614 289-5360
   New Albany (G-14774)
Unlimited Rcovery Solutions LLC ....E 419 868-4888
   Wauseon (G-19699)
Valco Industries Inc ....E 937 399-7400
   Springfield (G-17672)
▲ Venco Venturo Industries LLC ....E 513 772-8448
   Cincinnati (G-4561)
▲ Wallace Forge Company ....D 330 488-1203
   Canton (G-2900)
Willard Machine & Welding Inc ....F 330 467-0642
   Macedonia (G-12495)
Wilson Seat Company Inc ....E 513 732-2460
   Batavia (G-1233)
Youngstown-Kenworth Inc ....G 330 534-9761
   Hubbard (G-11143)
Zie Bart Rhino Linings Toledo ....G 419 841-2886
   Toledo (G-18780)

3714 Motor Vehicle Parts & Access

1 A Lifesafer Hawaii Inc ....F 513 651-9560
   Blue Ash (G-1730)
◆ 31 Inc ....D 740 498-8324
   Newcomerstown (G-15107)
A & H Automotive Industries ....G 614 235-1759
   Columbus (G-6666)
A G Parts Inc ....F 937 596-6448
   Jackson Center (G-11336)
▲ Aap St Marys Corp ....A 419 394-7840
   Saint Marys (G-16830)
◆ Accel Performance Group LLC ....C 216 658-6413
   Independence (G-11245)
Access 2 Communications Inc ....G 800 561-1110
   Steubenville (G-17686)
Ach LLC ....G 419 621-5748
   Sandusky (G-16943)
Actuation Kongsberg Systems II ....F 440 639-8778
   Grand River (G-10447)
▲ Ada Technologies Inc ....C 419 634-7000
   Ada (G-3)
◆ Adelmans Truck Parts Corp ....E 330 456-0206
   Canton (G-2587)
Adelmans Truck Parts Corp ....F 216 362-0500
   Canton (G-2588)
▲ Advics Manufacturing Ohio Inc ....A 513 934-0023
   Lebanon (G-11776)
Aerotech Styling Inc ....G 419 923-6970
   Lyons (G-12430)
◆ Airstream Inc ....B 937 596-6111
   Jackson Center (G-11337)
Albright Radiator Inc ....G 330 264-8886
   Wooster (G-20738)
▲ Alegre Inc ....F 937 885-6786
   Miamisburg (G-13782)
Alex Products Inc ....C 419 399-4500
   Paulding (G-15999)
All Pro Alum Cylinder Heads ....G 740 967-7761
   Johnstown (G-11387)

All Wright Enterprises LLC ....G 440 259-5656
   Perry (G-16047)
Alpha Coatins Inc ....G 419 436-6144
   Fostoria (G-9965)
Alta Mira Corporation ....D 330 648-2461
   Spencer (G-17455)
AM General LLC ....G 937 704-0160
   Franklin (G-10006)
American Manufacturing & Eqp ....G 513 829-2248
   Fairfield (G-9642)
American Showa Inc ....A 937 783-4961
   Blanchester (G-1709)
AMP Electric Vehicles Inc ....F 513 360-4704
   Loveland (G-12339)
Amsoil Inc ....G 614 274-9851
   Columbus (G-6746)
Amsted Industries Incorporated ....G 614 836-2323
   Groveport (G-10612)
Angstrom Automotive Group LLC ....G 440 255-6700
   Mentor (G-13521)
ARE Inc ....B 330 830-7800
   Massillon (G-13111)
▲ Areway LLC ....G 216 651-9022
   Brooklyn (G-2128)
Arlington Rack & Packaging Co ....G 419 476-7700
   Toledo (G-18355)
▲ ASC Holdco Inc ....G 330 899-0340
   Canton (G-2607)
◆ ASC Industries Inc ....G 330 899-0340
   North Canton (G-15220)
▲ Atc Lighting & Plastics Inc ....G 440 466-7670
   Andover (G-613)
Atlas Industries Inc ....G 419 447-4730
   Tiffin (G-18206)
Atlas Industries Inc ....B 419 637-2117
   Tiffin (G-18207)
Atwood Mobile Products LLC ....G 419 258-5531
   Antwerp (G-629)
Auto-Seat Tec LLC ....E 419 267-5240
   Ridgeville Corners (G-16664)
Autoliv Nissin Brake ....B 419 425-6725
   Findlay (G-9791)
Automtive Cmpnnts Holdings LLC ....A 419 627-3600
   Sandusky (G-16947)
Automtive Cmpnnts Holdings LLC ....F 419 483-5622
   Bellevue (G-1544)
Autoneum North America Inc ....B 419 693-0511
   Oregon (G-15703)
Axle Surgeons of NW Ohio ....G 419 822-5775
   Delta (G-8928)
B A Malcuit Racing Inc ....G 330 878-7111
   Strasburg (G-17820)
B&C Machine Co LLC ....G 330 745-4013
   Barberton (G-1103)
Bandon Corp ....G 614 766-7243
   Dublin (G-9053)
Beach Manufacturing Co ....G 937 882-6372
   Donnelsville (G-8960)
Beasley Fiberglass Inc ....G 440 357-6644
   Painesville (G-15861)
Bellevue Manufacturing Company ....D 419 483-3190
   Bellevue (G-1545)
Bellevue Manufacturing Company ....G 419 483-3190
   Bellevue (G-1546)
▲ Bendix Spcer Fndtion Brake LLC ....C 440 329-9709
   Elyria (G-9380)
Bergstrom Company Ltd Partnr ....E 440 232-2282
   Cleveland (G-4905)
Bloomdale Plastics Co ....E 419 454-5135
   Bloomdale (G-1719)
Bobbart Industries Inc ....E 419 350-5477
   Sylvania (G-18101)
Bores Manufacturing Co Inc ....F 419 465-2606
   Monroeville (G-14425)
Buckeye Brake Manufacturing ....F 740 782-1379
   Morristown (G-14541)
Buckley Manufacturing Company ....F 513 821-4444
   Cincinnati (G-3485)
▲ Bucyrus Precision Tech Inc ....F 419 563-9950
   Bucyrus (G-2334)
Bug-Barrier Screen Corp ....G 330 723-2551
   Medina (G-13384)
▲ Buyers Products Company ....C 440 974-8888
   Mentor (G-13540)
Buyers Products Company ....G 440 974-8888
   Mentor (G-13542)
Bwi North America Inc ....C 937 455-5190
   Kettering (G-11576)
▲ Bwi North America Inc ....E 937 253-1130
   Kettering (G-11577)

Cadillac Products Inc	E	248 813-8255	
Lebanon (G-11786)			
Capital Core Inc	G	800 223-1884	
Dayton (G-8209)			
▲ Cardington Yutaka Tech Inc	A	419 864-8777	
Cardington (G-2909)			
Carlisle Brake & Friction Inc	F	440 528-4000	
Solon (G-17276)			
Carlton-Bates Company	G	937 384-0426	
Miamisburg (G-13789)			
Chantilly Development Corp	F	419 243-8109	
Toledo (G-18393)			
▲ Chestnut Holdings Inc	G	330 849-6503	
Akron (G-122)			
Cincinnati Drveline Hydraulics	G	513 651-2406	
Cincinnati (G-3548)			
Cincinnati Gearing Systems Inc	C	513 527-8600	
Cincinnati (G-3554)			
Classic Exhaust	G	440 466-5460	
Geneva (G-10344)			
Classic Reproductions	G	937 548-9839	
Greenville (G-10493)			
Commercial Vehicle Group Inc	A	614 289-5360	
New Albany (G-14753)			
Comprehensive Logistics Co Inc	E	440 934-3517	
Avon (G-990)			
Comprehensive Logistics Co Inc	E	330 793-0504	
Youngstown (G-21055)			
Connective Design Incorporated	F	937 746-8252	
Miamisburg (G-13793)			
Continental Strl Plas Inc	B	419 396-1980	
Carey (G-2917)			
Continental Strl Plas Inc	B	419 238-4628	
Van Wert (G-19248)			
Continental Strl Plas Inc	C	419 257-2231	
North Baltimore (G-15192)			
Cooper-Standard Automotive Inc	B	740 342-3523	
New Lexington (G-14846)			
Core Automotive Tech LLC	G	614 870-5000	
Columbus (G-6982)			
Coupled Products LLC	C	419 294-3827	
Wharton (G-20328)			
CR Laurence Co Inc	G	440 248-0003	
Cleveland (G-5139)			
▲ Custer Products Limited	F	330 490-3158	
North Canton (G-15225)			
Custom Cltch Jjnt Hydrlics Inc	F	216 431-1630	
Cleveland (G-5149)			
Custom Fab	G	330 825-3586	
Norton (G-15509)			
Custom Speed Parts Inc	F	440 238-3260	
Strongsville (G-17909)			
◆ Dana Auto Systems Group LLC	D	419 887-3000	
Maumee (G-13237)			
Dana Brazil Holdings I LLC	G	419 887-3000	
Maumee (G-13238)			
◆ Dana Commercial Vhcl Mfg LLC	D	419 887-3000	
Maumee (G-13239)			
◆ Dana Commercial Vhcl Pdts LLC	C	419 887-3000	
Maumee (G-13240)			
Dana Corporation	E	419 887-3000	
Toledo (G-18426)			
Dana Driveshaft Mfg LLC	C	419 222-9708	
Lima (G-12004)			
▲ Dana Driveshaft Mfg LLC	G	419 887-3000	
Maumee (G-13241)			
▲ Dana Driveshaft Products LLC	E	419 887-3000	
Maumee (G-13242)			
Dana Global Products Inc	G	419 887-3000	
Maumee (G-13243)			
◆ Dana Global Products Inc	G	419 887-3000	
Maumee (G-13244)			
◆ Dana Heavy Vehicle Systems	E	419 887-3000	
Maumee (G-13245)			
Dana Incorporated	B	419 887-3000	
Maumee (G-13246)			
Dana Light Axle Mfg LLC	B	419 887-3000	
Toledo (G-18427)			
▲ Dana Light Axle Mfg LLC	F	419 887-3000	
Maumee (G-13247)			
Dana Limited	D	419 482-2000	
Maumee (G-13248)			
▲ Dana Limited	B	630 697-3783	
Maumee (G-13249)			
Dana Off Highway Products LLC	E	614 864-1116	
Blacklick (G-1695)			
Dana Off Highway Products LLC	C	740 694-2055	
Fredericktown (G-10098)			
◆ Dana Off Highway Products LLC	E	419 887-3000	
Maumee (G-13250)			

▲ Dana Sealing Manufacturing LLC	D	419 887-3000	
Maumee (G-13251)			
Dana Sealing Products LLC	E	419 887-3000	
Maumee (G-13252)			
Dana Structural Products LLC	G	419 887-3000	
Maumee (G-13253)			
▲ Dana Thermal Products LLC	F	419 887-3000	
Maumee (G-13254)			
Dana World Trade Corp	G	419 887-3000	
Maumee (G-13255)			
David Boswell	E	614 441-2497	
Columbus (G-7014)			
Dayton Air Control Pdts LLC	G	937 254-4441	
Moraine (G-14476)			
Dayton Clutch & Joint Inc	F	937 236-9770	
Dayton (G-8271)			
Dayton Superior Pdts Co Inc	G	937 332-1930	
Troy (G-18815)			
▲ Dayton Wheel Concepts Inc	E	937 438-0100	
Dayton (G-8290)			
◆ Dcm Manufacturing Inc	E	216 265-8006	
Cleveland (G-5178)			
Delphi Automotive Systems LLC	B	330 306-1000	
Warren (G-19542)			
Delphi Automotive Systems LLC	C	330 367-6000	
Vienna (G-19364)			
Designed Harness Systems Inc	F	937 599-2485	
Bellefontaine (G-1527)			
Detroit Toledo Fiber LLC	F	248 647-0400	
Toledo (G-18436)			
▼ Dexol Industries Inc	G	330 633-4477	
Akron (G-148)			
Done Right Engine & Machine	G	440 582-1366	
Cleveland (G-5206)			
Doran Mfg LLC	F	513 681-5424	
Cincinnati (G-3664)			
Doug Marine Motors Inc	E	740 335-3700	
Wshngtn CT Hs (G-20907)			
Dove Machine Inc	F	440 864-2645	
Columbia Station (G-6589)			
▲ Dreison International Inc	C	216 362-0755	
Cleveland (G-5215)			
Dti Molded Products Inc	F	937 492-5008	
Sidney (G-17181)			
Eaton Corporation	A	440 523-5000	
Beachwood (G-1267)			
Eaton Corporation	C	216 281-2211	
Cleveland (G-5247)			
Eaton Corporation	B	216 523-5000	
Beachwood (G-1268)			
Eaton Corporation	B	216 920-2000	
Cleveland (G-5249)			
◆ Eaton Corporation	B	216 523-5000	
Cleveland (G-5245)			
Eaton Corporation	C	216 416-2500	
Cleveland (G-5246)			
Ebo Group Inc	D	330 239-4933	
Sharon Center (G-17105)			
Edgerton Forge Inc	D	419 298-2333	
Edgerton (G-9327)			
Egr Products Company Inc	F	330 833-6554	
Dalton (G-8068)			
Enhanced Mfg Solutions LLC	D	440 476-1244	
Brecksville (G-2047)			
Entratech Systems LLC	C	419 433-7683	
Sandusky (G-16963)			
▲ Ernie Green Industries Inc	C	614 219-1423	
Columbus (G-7064)			
Exito Manufacturing	G	937 291-9871	
Dayton (G-8337)			
▲ F&P America Mfg Inc	C	937 339-0212	
Troy (G-18825)			
Falls Stamping & Welding Co	C	330 928-1191	
Cuyahoga Falls (G-7996)			
▲ Faurecia Automotive Holdings	A	419 727-5000	
Toledo (G-18461)			
Faurecia Exhaust Systems Inc	E	419 727-5000	
Toledo (G-18462)			
Faurecia Exhaust Systems Inc	B	937 339-0551	
Troy (G-18826)			
▲ Faurecia Exhaust Systems LLC	C	419 727-5000	
Toledo (G-18463)			
Faurecia Exhaust Systems LLC	C	330 824-2807	
Warren (G-19549)			
Faurecia Exhaust Systems Inc	B	937 743-0551	
Franklin (G-10021)			
Faurecia USA Holdings Inc	A	419 727-5000	
Toledo (G-18464)			
FCA US LLC	A	419 661-3500	
Perrysburg (G-16094)			

Federal-Mogul Corporation	C	740 432-2393	
Cambridge (G-2457)			
Fetters Racing Engine Inc	G	937 698-6411	
Union (G-19066)			
▲ First Place Auto Products	G	330 493-1420	
Canton (G-2704)			
▲ Flaming River Industries Inc	F	440 826-4488	
Berea (G-1616)			
Flex Technologies Inc	D	330 359-5415	
Mount Eaton (G-14555)			
Florence Alloys Inc	G	330 745-9141	
Barberton (G-1115)			
Florida Production Engrg Inc	D	937 996-4361	
New Madison (G-14869)			
◆ Force Control Industries Inc	D	513 868-0900	
Fairfield (G-9659)			
Ford Motor Company	A	419 226-7000	
Lima (G-12014)			
Ford Motor Company	A	216 676-3989	
Brookpark (G-2160)			
Ford Motor Company	A	216 587-7700	
Cleveland (G-5368)			
Forgeline Inc	F	937 299-0298	
Moraine (G-14488)			
Fram Group Operations LLC	G	937 316-3000	
Greenville (G-10499)			
Fram Group Operations LLC	A	419 436-5827	
Fostoria (G-9979)			
Fram Group Operations LLC	D	419 661-6700	
Perrysburg (G-16097)			
Fremont Plastic Products Inc	E	419 332-6407	
Fremont (G-10150)			
◆ Friction Products Co	B	330 725-4941	
Medina (G-13413)			
Frontier Tank Center Inc	E	330 659-3888	
Richfield (G-16624)			
▲ FT Precision Inc	A	740 694-1500	
Fredericktown (G-10103)			
Ftd Investments LLC	C	937 833-2161	
Brookville (G-2184)			
Ftech R&D North America Inc	D	937 339-2777	
Troy (G-18829)			
▲ G S Wiring Systems Inc	G	419 423-7111	
Findlay (G-9829)			
Gear Company of America Inc	D	216 671-5400	
Cleveland (G-5404)			
◆ Gear Star American Performance	G	330 434-5216	
Akron (G-200)			
▲ Geartec Inc	G	440 953-3900	
Willoughby (G-20497)			
Gellner Engineering Inc	G	216 398-8500	
Cleveland (G-5407)			
General Aluminum Mfg Company	C	419 739-9300	
Wapakoneta (G-19487)			
General Metals Powder Co	D	330 633-1226	
Akron (G-203)			
General Motors LLC	B	330 824-5840	
Warren (G-19554)			
General Motors LLC	A	216 265-5000	
Cleveland (G-5419)			
Gerich Fiberglass Inc	E	419 362-4591	
Mount Gilead (G-14560)			
Goodale Auto-Truck Parts Inc	E	614 294-4777	
Columbus (G-7125)			
Goodrich Corporation	A	937 339-3811	
Troy (G-18833)			
▲ Grand-Rock Company Inc	E	440 639-2000	
Painesville (G-15884)			
Green Acquisition LLC	E	440 930-7600	
Avon (G-997)			
Green Rdced Emssons Netwrk LLC	G	330 340-0941	
Strasburg (G-17823)			
Green Tokai Co Ltd	G	937 237-1630	
Dayton (G-8379)			
◆ Green Tokai Co Ltd	A	937 833-5444	
Brookville (G-2185)			
Gregory Auto Service	G	513 248-0423	
Loveland (G-12355)			
▲ GSW Manufacturing Inc	B	419 423-7111	
Findlay (G-9834)			
Gt Technologies Inc	C	419 782-8955	
Defiance (G-8792)			
Gt Technologies Inc	D	419 324-7300	
Toledo (G-18489)			
H O Fibertrends	G	740 983-3864	
Ashville (G-851)			
Hall-Toledo Inc	F	419 893-4334	
Maumee (G-13263)			
◆ Haltec Corporation	D	330 222-1501	
Salem (G-16898)			

Hanon Systems Usa LLC	C	313 920-0583
Carey (G-2919)		
▲ Harco Industries Inc	F	937 832-9697
Moraine (G-14493)		
▲ Harco Manufacturing Group LLC	C	937 528-5000
Moraine (G-14494)		
Harco Manufacturing Group LLC	C	937 528-5000
Moraine (G-14495)		
Hdt Expeditionary Systems Inc	G	216 438-6111
Solon (G-17308)		
Hebco Products Inc	A	419 562-7987
Bucyrus (G-2347)		
Hendrickson International Corp	D	740 929-5600
Hebron (G-10870)		
▲ Hfi LLC	B	614 491-0700
Canal Winchester (G-2525)		
Hfi Manufacturing Holdings LLC	G	614 491-0700
Canal Winchester (G-2528)		
Hi-Tek Manufacturing Inc	C	513 459-1094
Mason (G-13037)		
◆ Hirschvogel Incorporated	C	614 340-5657
Columbus (G-7159)		
Hite Parts Exchange Inc	E	614 272-5115
Columbus (G-7160)		
Hmf Engineering Inc	G	216 631-6980
Cleveland (G-5518)		
Honda of America Mfg Inc	C	937 644-0724
Marysville (G-12951)		
▲ Honda Transm Mfg Amer Inc	A	937 843-5555
Russells Point (G-16754)		
Horizon Global Americas Inc	D	440 498-0001
Solon (G-17311)		
Hot Shot Motor Works M LLC	G	419 294-1997
Upper Sandusky (G-19125)		
Hp2g LLC	E	419 906-1525
Napoleon (G-14683)		
▲ Hurst Auto-Truck Electric	G	216 961-1800
Cleveland (G-5538)		
◆ Hytec Automotive Ind LLC	F	614 527-9370
Columbus (G-7175)		
▲ Hytec-Debartolo LLC	F	614 527-9370
Columbus (G-7176)		
Ig Watteeuw Usa LLC	F	740 588-1722
Zanesville (G-21321)		
Illinois Tool Works Inc	C	513 489-7600
Blue Ash (G-1812)		
Illinois Tool Works Inc	C	262 248-8277
Bryan (G-2303)		
◆ Imasen Bucyrus Technology Inc	C	419 563-9590
Bucyrus (G-2350)		
Industrial Steering Pdts Inc	G	419 636-3300
Bryan (G-2305)		
Industry Products Co	B	937 778-0585
Piqua (G-16279)		
International Automotive	A	419 335-1000
Wauseon (G-19684)		
International Automotive	B	937 492-1225
Sidney (G-17195)		
International Automotive	A	419 433-5653
Huron (G-11228)		
▲ Interstate Diesel Service Inc	C	216 881-0015
Cleveland (G-5582)		
◆ Interstate-Mcbee LLC	G	800 321-4234
Cleveland (G-5584)		
Inteva Products LLC	F	937 280-8500
Vandalia (G-19297)		
Ishikawa Gasket America Inc	C	419 353-7300
Bowling Green (G-1991)		
Jae Tech Inc	D	330 698-2000
Apple Creek (G-640)		
▲ Jbar A/C Inc	F	216 447-4294
Cleveland (G-5609)		
Jeff Wyler Chevrolet Inc	B	513 752-3447
Batavia (G-1194)		
▼ Johnson Welded Products Inc	C	937 652-1242
Urbana (G-19166)		
▲ Joseph Industries Inc	D	330 528-0091
Streetsboro (G-17860)		
Josh L Derksen	G	937 548-0080
Greenville (G-10507)		
◆ Jr Engineering Inc	C	330 848-0960
Barberton (G-1123)		
▲ Julie Maynard Inc	F	937 443-0408
Dayton (G-8429)		
K Wm Beach Mfg Co Inc	C	937 399-3838
Springfield (G-17584)		
▲ Kalida Manufacturing Inc	C	419 532-2026
Kalida (G-11414)		
Karg Fiberglass Inc	G	330 494-2611
Middlebranch (G-13901)		

Kasai North America Inc	F	614 356-1494
Dublin (G-9094)		
◆ Keihin Thermal Tech Amer Inc	B	740 869-3000
Mount Sterling (G-14599)		
Kenley Enterprises LLC	E	419 630-0921
Bryan (G-2308)		
Kerr Friction Products Inc	E	330 455-3983
Canton (G-2751)		
Kilar Manufacturing Inc	E	330 534-8961
Hubbard (G-11133)		
▲ Knippen Chrysler Dodge Jeep	E	419 695-4976
Delphos (G-8909)		
▲ Kth Parts Industries Inc	A	937 663-5941
Saint Paris (G-16862)		
Ktsdi LLC	G	330 783-2000
North Lima (G-15318)		
Kurts Auto Parts LLC	G	330 723-0166
Medina (G-13435)		
▲ Kyklos Bearing Intl LLC	B	419 627-7000
Sandusky (G-16977)		
Lacal Equipment Inc	E	800 543-6161
Jackson Center (G-11342)		
Lakota Racing	G	330 627-7255
Carrollton (G-2959)		
▲ Lawrence Technologies Inc	G	937 274-7771
Dayton (G-8454)		
▲ Leadec Corp	E	513 731-3590
Blue Ash (G-1826)		
Lear Corporation	E	740 928-4358
Hebron (G-10872)		
▲ Leggett & Platt Incorporated	E	330 262-6010
Apple Creek (G-643)		
▲ Linde Hydraulics Corporation	E	330 533-6801
Canfield (G-2562)		
▲ Lintern Corporation	E	440 255-9333
Mentor (G-13635)		
Lorain County Auto Systems Inc	D	248 442-6800
Elyria (G-9454)		
▲ Lorain County Auto Systems Inc	E	440 960-7470
Lorain (G-12256)		
▲ Luk Clutch Systems LLC	E	330 264-4383
Wooster (G-20798)		
▲ Luk Transmission Systems LLC	A	330 264-4383
Wooster (G-20799)		
▲ Luk USA LLC	B	330 264-4383
Wooster (G-20800)		
Lynn Truck Parts & Service	G	330 966-1470
North Canton (G-15248)		
M-Tek Inc	A	419 209-0399
Upper Sandusky (G-19130)		
Maags Automotive & Machine	G	419 626-1539
Sandusky (G-16982)		
Maca Plastics Inc	F	937 544-8618
Winchester (G-20695)		
▲ Magna Modular Systems Inc	D	419 324-3387
Toledo (G-18570)		
Magna Seating America Inc	C	330 824-3101
Warren (G-19576)		
Magnaco Industries Inc	E	216 961-3636
Lodi (G-12166)		
Mahle Behr Dayton LLC	B	937 356-2001
Vandalia (G-19301)		
Mahle Behr Dayton LLC	B	937 369-2900
Dayton (G-8470)		
◆ Mahle Behr Dayton LLC	D	937 369-2900
Dayton (G-8471)		
Mahle Behr Service America LLC	G	937 369-2610
Xenia (G-20962)		
Mahle Industries Incorporated	C	740 962-2040
McConnelsville (G-13353)		
Mahle Industries Incorporated	E	937 890-2739
Dayton (G-8473)		
Majestic Trailers Inc	F	330 798-1698
Akron (G-280)		
Manuel Tamargo	G	330 456-3080
Akron (G-282)		
Marion Industries Inc	A	740 223-0075
Marion (G-12883)		
Marmon Highway Tech LLC	E	330 878-5595
Dover (G-9000)		
▲ Martin Wheel Co Inc	D	330 633-3278
Tallmadge (G-18153)		
Matrix Cable and Mould	G	513 832-2577
Cincinnati (G-4067)		
▲ Maval Industries LLC	C	330 405-1600
Twinsburg (G-18981)		
▲ Maxion Wheels Akron LLC	E	330 794-2310
Akron (G-289)		
Meritor Inc	C	740 348-3498
Granville (G-10461)		

Metro Mech Inc	G	216 641-6262
Cleveland (G-5792)		
◆ Mid-West Fabricating Co	C	740 969-4411
Amanda (G-563)		
Mid-West Fabricating Co	G	740 681-4411
Lancaster (G-11729)		
Millat Industries Corp	E	937 535-1500
Dayton (G-8502)		
▲ Millat Industries Corp	D	937 434-6666
Dayton (G-8501)		
▲ Mitec Powertrain Inc	E	567 525-5606
Findlay (G-9864)		
◆ Mitsubishi Elc Auto Amer Inc	B	513 573-6614
Mason (G-13065)		
Monarch Plastic Inc	F	330 683-0822
Orrville (G-15747)		
Mrs Electronic Inc	F	937 660-6767
Dayton (G-8513)		
Mueller Gas Products	D	513 424-5311
Middletown (G-14066)		
Multi-Design Inc	G	440 275-2255
Austinburg (G-963)		
Navistar Inc	D	937 390-5653
Springfield (G-17614)		
Navistar Inc	E	937 390-5704
Springfield (G-17616)		
▲ Neaton Auto Products Mfg Inc	B	937 456-7103
Eaton (G-9319)		
Nebraska Industries Corp	E	419 335-6010
Wauseon (G-19691)		
▲ New Sabina Industries Inc	B	937 584-2433
Sabina (G-16774)		
▲ Newman Technology Inc	C	419 525-1856
Mansfield (G-12656)		
Nippon Stl Smkin Crnkshaft LLC	F	419 435-0411
Fostoria (G-9988)		
▲ Nissin Brake Ohio Inc	A	419 420-3800
Findlay (G-9868)		
Nissin Brake Ohio Inc	G	937 642-7556
East Liberty (G-9202)		
▲ Noco Company	B	216 464-8131
Solon (G-17350)		
▼ Norlake Manufacturing Company	D	440 353-3200
North Ridgeville (G-15391)		
North Coast Camshaft Inc	G	216 671-3700
Cleveland (G-5892)		
North Coast Exotics Inc	G	216 651-5512
Cleveland (G-5895)		
Northern Stamping Co	C	216 642-8081
Cleveland (G-5913)		
Oakley Industries Sub Assembly	E	419 661-8888
Northwood (G-15486)		
Oe Exchange LLC	G	440 266-1639
Mentor (G-13671)		
◆ Oerlikon Friction Systems	C	937 449-4000
Dayton (G-8540)		
Ohio Auto Supply Company	E	330 454-5105
Canton (G-2798)		
▲ Ohio Classic Street Rods Inc	G	440 543-6593
Chagrin Falls (G-3108)		
Ohio Harness LLC	E	937 292-7355
Bellefontaine (G-1537)		
▲ Ohta Press US Inc	F	937 374-3382
Xenia (G-20966)		
▲ Omsi Transmissions Inc	G	330 405-7350
Twinsburg (G-18993)		
Onix Corporation	E	800 844-0076
Perrysburg (G-16136)		
OReilly Equipment LLC	G	440 564-1234
Newbury (G-15101)		
◆ Pacific Industries USA Inc	E	513 860-3900
Fairfield (G-9695)		
▲ Pacific Manufacturing Ohio Inc	B	513 860-3900
Fairfield (G-9696)		
Pako Inc	C	440 946-8030
Mentor (G-13678)		
Park-Ohio Industries Inc	C	216 341-2300
Newburgh Heights (G-15077)		
Parker-Hannifin Corporation	B	440 943-5700
Wickliffe (G-20379)		
Parker-Hannifin Corporation	A	216 531-3000
Cleveland (G-5975)		
▲ Pdi Ground Support Systems Inc	D	216 271-7344
Solon (G-17360)		
▲ Pioneer Automotive Tech Inc	C	937 746-2293
Springboro (G-17497)		
Piston Automotive LLC	D	419 464-0250
Toledo (G-18645)		
▲ PMI Operating Company Inc	B	440 951-6600
Mentor (G-13690)		

▲ Powers and Sons LLC ....C...... 419 485-3151
Montpelier (G-14450)

Powers and Sons LLC ....D...... 419 737-2373
Pioneer (G-16240)

Pro Gram Engineering Corp ....G...... 330 745-1004
Barberton (G-1143)

Production Turning LLC ....G...... 937 424-0034
Moraine (G-14520)

Pt Tech Inc ....D...... 330 239-4933
Sharon Center (G-17108)

Pullman Company ....C...... 419 592-2055
Napoleon (G-14693)

Pullman Company ....E...... 419 499-2541
Milan (G-14115)

▲ Qualitor Inc ....G...... 248 204-8600
Lima (G-12078)

Quality Reproductions Inc ....G...... 330 335-5000
Wadsworth (G-19433)

▲ Ramco Specialties Inc ....D...... 330 653-5135
Hudson (G-11195)

▲ Reactive Resin Products Co ....E...... 419 666-6119
Perrysburg (G-16146)

Recon Systems LLC ....G...... 330 484-8444
East Canton (G-9196)

Reineke Company LLC ....F...... 419 281-5800
Ashland (G-772)

Resinoid Engineering Corp ....E...... 740 928-2220
Heath (G-10854)

▼ Riker Products Inc ....C...... 419 729-1626
Toledo (G-18676)

Riverside Engines Inc ....G...... 419 927-6838
Tiffin (G-18239)

Rochling Automotive USA LLP ....D...... 330 400-5785
Akron (G-377)

▲ Roki America Co Ltd ....B...... 419 424-9713
Findlay (G-9883)

Rubberduck 4x4 ....G...... 513 889-1735
Hamilton (G-10734)

▼ S & A Precision Bearing Inc ....G...... 440 930-7600
Avon (G-1010)

Saf-Holland Inc ....G...... 513 874-7888
West Chester (G-20046)

▲ Saia-Burgess Lcc ....D...... 937 898-3621
Vandalia (G-19310)

Sanoh America Inc ....C...... 740 392-9200
Mount Vernon (G-14643)

▲ Satco Inc ....G...... 330 630-8866
Tallmadge (G-18168)

Schafer Driveline LLC ....G...... 614 864-1116
Blacklick (G-1706)

▲ Schafer Driveline LLC ....E...... 740 694-0462
Fredericktown (G-10109)

Schott Metal Products Company ....D...... 330 773-7873
Akron (G-397)

Scott Emerson ....G...... 330 372-1040
Warren (G-19599)

Scs Gearbox Inc ....F...... 419 483-7278
Bellevue (G-1557)

Senneco Glass Inc ....G...... 330 825-7717
Cuyahoga Falls (G-8043)

Sew-Eurodrive Inc ....D...... 937 335-0036
Troy (G-18875)

Sheet Angle Bar Met Fbrication ....G...... 513 829-8600
Fairfield (G-9716)

◆ Showa Aluminum Corp America ....B...... 740 869-3333
Mount Sterling (G-14602)

SMH Manufacturing Inc ....F...... 419 884-0071
Lexington (G-11952)

Soundwich Inc ....D...... 216 486-2666
Cleveland (G-6221)

Spectrum Brands Inc ....F...... 440 357-2600
Painesville (G-15921)

Spencer Manufacturing Company ....D...... 330 648-2461
Spencer (G-17457)

SPS International Inc ....G...... 216 671-9911
Cleveland (G-6229)

Std Specialty Filters Inc ....F...... 216 881-3727
Cleveland (G-6243)

▲ Steck Manufacturing Co Inc ....F...... 937 222-0062
Dayton (G-8683)

Steer & Gear Inc ....E...... 614 231-4064
Columbus (G-7655)

Stoneridge Inc ....A...... 419 884-1219
Lexington (G-11953)

◆ Sumiriko Ohio Inc ....C...... 419 358-2121
Bluffton (G-1916)

Sumitomo Elc Wirg Systems Inc ....E...... 937 642-7579
Marysville (G-12974)

Supercharger Systems Inc ....G...... 216 676-5800
Brookpark (G-2170)

▼ Superior Energy Systems LLC ....F...... 440 236-6009
Columbia Station (G-6601)

▲ Supertrapp Industries Inc ....D...... 216 265-8400
Cleveland (G-6273)

Supplier Park Industries LLC ....D...... 440 476-1244
Brecksville (G-2074)

Sutphen Corporation ....D...... 937 969-8851
Springfield (G-17658)

▲ Switzer Performance Engrg ....F...... 440 774-4219
Oberlin (G-15648)

Systems Jay LLC Nanogate ....C...... 419 522-7745
Mansfield (G-12690)

T L H Windshield Repair ....G......
Botkins (G-1955)

◆ Taiho Corporation of America ....C...... 419 443-1645
Tiffin (G-18246)

Tenneco Automotive Oper Co Inc ....D...... 937 781-4940
Kettering (G-11587)

Tetra Mold & Tool Inc ....E...... 937 845-1651
New Carlisle (G-14814)

▲ Tfo Tech Co Ltd ....C...... 740 426-6381
Jeffersonville (G-11382)

▲ Thyssenkrupp Bilstein Amer Inc ....C...... 513 881-7600
Hamilton (G-10747)

Thyssenkrupp Bilstein Amer Inc ....C...... 513 881-7600
West Chester (G-19958)

TI Group Auto Systems LLC ....C...... 740 929-2049
Hebron (G-10890)

▲ Tigerpoly Manufacturing Inc ....B...... 614 871-0045
Grove City (G-10601)

Tko Mfg Services Inc ....E...... 937 299-1637
Moraine (G-14535)

Toledo Molding & Die Inc ....C...... 419 692-6022
Delphos (G-8919)

Toledo Molding & Die Inc ....C...... 419 692-6022
Delphos (G-8920)

Toledo Pro Fiberglass Inc ....G...... 419 241-9390
Toledo (G-18740)

▲ Tom Smith Industries Inc ....C...... 937 832-1555
Clayton (G-4663)

Tower Automotive Operations I ....C...... 419 483-1500
Bellevue (G-1564)

▲ Trailer Component Mfg Inc ....E...... 440 255-2888
Mentor (G-13753)

Tri-Mac Mfg & Svcs Co ....F...... 513 896-4445
Hamilton (G-10749)

▲ Trim Parts Inc ....E...... 513 934-0815
Lebanon (G-11845)

▲ Trim Systems Operating Corp ....D...... 614 289-5360
New Albany (G-14773)

Trojon Gear Inc ....F...... 937 254-1737
Dayton (G-8729)

TRW Automotive Inc ....C...... 419 237-2511
Fayette (G-9780)

TRW Automotive Inc ....E...... 216 750-2400
Cleveland (G-6371)

▲ TS Tech USA Corporation ....C...... 614 577-1088
Reynoldsburg (G-16610)

TS Trim Industries Inc ....B...... 740 593-5958
Athens (G-888)

Ugn Inc ....C...... 513 360-3500
Lebanon (G-11847)

▲ Undercar Express LLC ....E...... 216 531-7004
Cleveland (G-6381)

Unique-Chardan Inc ....E...... 419 636-6900
Bryan (G-2325)

Unison Industries LLC ....B...... 937 426-0621
Dayton (G-8121)

US Tsubaki Power Transm LLC ....C...... 419 626-4560
Sandusky (G-17019)

Usui International Corporation ....G...... 513 448-0410
Sharonville (G-17115)

Utv Hitchworks LLC ....G...... 513 615-8568
Maineville (G-12533)

Vanderpool Motor Sports ....G...... 513 424-2166
Middletown (G-14094)

▼ Varbros LLC ....C...... 216 267-5200
Cleveland (G-6406)

▲ Vari-Wall Tube Specialists Inc ....D...... 330 482-0000
Columbiana (G-6637)

Vehicle Systems Inc ....G...... 330 854-0535
Massillon (G-13210)

▲ Venco Manufacturing Inc ....F...... 513 772-8448
Cincinnati (G-4560)

▲ Venco Venturo Industries LLC ....E...... 513 772-8448
Cincinnati (G-4561)

▲ Ventra Sandusky LLC ....D...... 419 627-3600
Sandusky (G-17020)

Visible Solutions Inc ....G...... 440 925-2810
Westlake (G-20317)

Vivid Wraps LLC ....G...... 513 515-8386
Cincinnati (G-4569)

W W Williams Company LLC ....F...... 330 659-3084
Richfield (G-16645)

Walther Engrg & Mfg Co Inc ....F...... 937 743-8125
Franklin (G-10064)

▲ Weastec Incorporated ....C...... 937 393-6800
Hillsboro (G-11018)

West & Barker Inc ....E...... 330 652-9923
Niles (G-15189)

Western Branch Diesel Inc ....E...... 330 454-8800
Canton (G-2902)

Westfield Steel Inc ....D...... 937 322-2414
Springfield (G-17677)

Wheel Group Holdings LLC ....G...... 614 253-6247
Columbus (G-7760)

▲ Whirlaway Corporation ....C...... 440 647-4711
Wellington (G-19758)

Whirlaway Corporation ....C...... 440 647-4711
Wellington (G-19759)

Whirlaway Corporation ....C...... 440 647-4711
Wellington (G-19760)

White Mule Company ....E...... 740 382-9008
Ontario (G-15697)

Woodbridge Group ....C...... 419 334-3666
Fremont (G-10195)

Workhorse Group Inc ....F...... 513 297-3640
Loveland (G-12401)

▲ Yachiyo of America Inc ....D...... 614 876-3220
Columbus (G-7781)

▲ Yamada North America Inc ....G...... 937 462-7111
South Charleston (G-17428)

3715 Truck Trailers

4w Services ....F...... 614 554-5427
Hebron (G-10859)

▼ All A Cart Manufacturing Inc ....F...... 614 443-5544
Columbus (G-6717)

American Mnfcturing Operations ....G...... 419 269-1560
Toledo (G-18342)

Appalachian Trailer Inc ....E...... 330 277-4140
Salem (G-16872)

ATW Ohio LLC ....C...... 937 444-4295
Mount Orab (G-14575)

Bell Logistics Co ....E...... 740 702-9830
Chillicothe (G-3229)

Brothers Equipment Inc ....G...... 216 458-0180
Cleveland (G-4937)

Bruce High Performance Tran ....E...... 440 357-8964
Painesville (G-15862)

▲ Containerport Group Inc ....D...... 440 333-2009
Cleveland (G-5122)

David Ogilbee ....G...... 740 929-2638
Hebron (G-10864)

Diamond Trailers Inc ....E...... 513 738-4500
Shandon (G-17097)

Diverse Logistics & Trnsp Inc ....G...... 513 305-1460
Cincinnati (G-3656)

Ds Express Carriers Inc ....G...... 419 433-6200
Norwalk (G-15534)

▼ East Manufacturing Corporation ....B...... 330 325-9921
Randolph (G-16509)

East Manufacturing Corporation ....F...... 330 325-9921
Randolph (G-16510)

Engineered MBL Solutions Inc ....F...... 513 724-0247
Batavia (G-1184)

Extreme Trailers LLC ....G...... 330 440-0026
Dover (G-8985)

Gerich Fiberglass Inc ....E...... 419 362-4591
Mount Gilead (G-14560)

H & H Equipment Inc ....G...... 330 264-5400
Wooster (G-20781)

Haulette Manufacturing Inc ....D...... 419 586-1717
Celina (G-3000)

Heritage Manufacturing Inc ....G...... 217 854-2513
Akron (G-223)

High Tech Prfmce Trlrs Inc ....G...... 440 357-8964
Painesville (G-15888)

J & L Body Inc ....F...... 216 661-2323
Brooklyn Heights (G-2141)

J W Devers & Son Inc ....F...... 937 854-3040
Trotwood (G-18797)

Jerry Tadlock ....G...... 937 544-2851
West Union (G-20122)

Kenan Advantage Group Inc ....E...... 614 878-4050
Columbus (G-7254)

L C Smith Co ....G...... 440 327-1251
Elyria (G-9448)

Larry Moore ....G...... 740 697-7085
Roseville (G-16731)

Longriders Trucking Company ....G..... 740 975-7863
  Mount Vernon *(G-14629)*
Lyons ....G..... 440 224-0676
  Kingsville *(G-11605)*
M & W Trailers Inc ....F..... 419 453-3331
  Ottoville *(G-15824)*
▲ Mac Manufacturing Inc ....A..... 330 823-9900
  Alliance *(G-523)*
Mac Manufacturing Inc ....C..... 330 829-1680
  Salem *(G-16913)*
Mac Steel Trailer Ltd ....E..... 330 823-9900
  Alliance *(G-524)*
▲ Mac Trailer Manufacturing Inc .....C..... 330 823-9900
  Alliance *(G-525)*
Majestic Trailers Inc ....F..... 330 798-1698
  Akron *(G-280)*
Monarch Trailers Co ....F..... 419 747-2848
  Shelby *(G-17138)*
Moritz International Inc ....E..... 419 526-5222
  Mansfield *(G-12653)*
Mr Trailer Sales Inc ....G..... 330 339-7701
  Dover *(G-9004)*
Navarre Trailer Sales Inc ....G..... 330 879-2406
  Navarre *(G-14722)*
▼ Nelson Manufacturing Company .....D..... 419 523-5321
  Ottawa *(G-15802)*
Paccar Inc ....A..... 740 774-5111
  Chillicothe *(G-3257)*
▲ Pdi Ground Support Systems Inc ..D...... 216 271-7344
  Solon *(G-17360)*
Pegasus Vans & Trailers Inc ....E..... 419 625-8953
  Sandusky *(G-16995)*
Pleasant Vly Tardrop Trlrs LLC ....E..... 330 752-4425
  Sugarcreek *(G-18033)*
Quick Loadz Delivery Sys LLC ....G..... 888 304-3946
  Nelsonville *(G-14735)*
R J Cox Co ....G..... 937 548-4699
  Arcanum *(G-658)*
Saf-Holland Inc ....G..... 513 874-7888
  West Chester *(G-20046)*
Shilling Transport ....G..... 330 948-1105
  Lodi *(G-12169)*
Stahl/Scott Fetzer Company ....C..... 800 277-8245
  Wooster *(G-20839)*
Trailer One Inc ....G..... 330 723-7474
  Medina *(G-13490)*
▼ Trailex Inc ....F..... 330 533-6814
  Canfield *(G-2580)*
Tri County Wheel and Rim Ltd ....G..... 419 666-1760
  Northwood *(G-15492)*
Wabash National Corporation ....C..... 419 434-9409
  Findlay *(G-9905)*
William Minnier ....G..... 614 562-8080
  Canal Winchester *(G-2541)*

3716 Motor Homes

Advanced Rv LLC ....G..... 440 283-0405
  Willoughby *(G-20425)*
◆ Airstream Inc ....B..... 937 596-6111
  Jackson Center *(G-11337)*

3721 Aircraft

Aero Composites Inc ....G..... 937 849-0244
  Medway *(G-13499)*
Aerovation Tech Holdings LLC ....G..... 567 208-5525
  Forest *(G-9917)*
Air One Jet Center ....G..... 513 867-9500
  Hamilton *(G-10663)*
American Aero Components LLC ....G..... 937 367-5068
  Dayton *(G-8150)*
Capital City Aviation Inc ....F..... 614 459-2541
  Columbus *(G-6896)*
Carlson Aircraft Inc ....G..... 330 426-3934
  East Palestine *(G-9230)*
Clm Marketing Inc ....G..... 440 526-8613
  Brecksville *(G-2041)*
E Star Aerospace Corporation ....G..... 614 396-6868
  Westerville *(G-20147)*
Edward S Eveland ....G..... 937 233-6568
  Dayton *(G-8320)*
Executive Wings Inc ....G..... 440 254-1812
  Painesville *(G-15878)*
Flightlogix LLC ....G..... 513 321-1200
  Cincinnati *(G-3760)*
Goodrich Corporation ....A..... 937 339-3811
  Troy *(G-18833)*
Jetoptera Inc ....G..... 516 456-7609
  Mason *(G-13050)*
Lockheed Martin Corporation ....B..... 330 796-2800
  Akron *(G-273)*

Mercury Air Services LLC ....E..... 216 898-4800
  Cleveland *(G-5783)*
Nextant Aerospace Holdings LLC .....D..... 216 261-9000
  Cleveland *(G-5881)*
Ruhe Sales Inc ....F..... 419 943-3357
  Leipsic *(G-11876)*
Sea Air Spc McG and Mld LLC ....F..... 440 248-3025
  Solon *(G-17377)*
Sky Riders Inc ....G..... 440 310-6819
  Lorain *(G-12276)*
Snow Aviation Intl Inc ....C..... 614 588-2452
  Gahanna *(G-10234)*
Star Jet LLC ....F..... 614 338-4379
  Columbus *(G-7651)*
Stark Airways ....G..... 330 526-6416
  North Canton *(G-15268)*
Steel Aviation Aircraft Sales ....G..... 937 332-7587
  Casstown *(G-2971)*
Summit Aerospace Products ....G..... 330 612-7341
  Northfield *(G-15473)*
Tdc Systems Inc ....G..... 440 953-5918
  Willoughby *(G-20610)*
Tessec LLC ....E..... 937 985-3552
  Dayton *(G-8709)*
Tessec Manufacturing Svcs LLC ......E..... 937 985-3552
  Dayton *(G-8710)*
Textron Inc ....C..... 330 626-7800
  Streetsboro *(G-17882)*
Theiss Uav Solutions LLC ....G..... 330 584-2070
  North Benton *(G-15214)*
Toledo Jet Center LLC ....F..... 419 866-9050
  Swanton *(G-18092)*
Tri-State Model Flyers Inc ....D..... 740 886-8429
  Proctorville *(G-16494)*
Unmanned Solutions Tech LLC ....G..... 937 771-7023
  Beavercreek *(G-1382)*
Wanashab Inc ....G..... 330 606-6675
  Cleveland *(G-6445)*

3724 Aircraft Engines & Engine Parts

Advanced Ground Systems ....F..... 513 402-7226
  Monroe *(G-14390)*
Aero Jet Wash Llc ....F..... 866 381-7955
  West Carrollton *(G-19789)*
Aerospace Co Inc ....D..... 413 998-1637
  Cleveland *(G-4724)*
American Aero Components LLC ....G..... 937 367-5068
  Dayton *(G-8150)*
At Holdings Corporation ....G..... 216 692-6000
  Cleveland *(G-4850)*
Avion Tool Corporation ....F..... 937 278-0779
  Dayton *(G-8175)*
Barnes Group Inc ....A..... 513 759-3528
  West Chester *(G-19814)*
Barnes Group Inc ....A..... 513 779-6888
  West Chester *(G-19815)*
Certech Inc ....G..... 330 405-1033
  Twinsburg *(G-18910)*
CFM International Inc ....E..... 513 552-2787
  West Chester *(G-19825)*
CFM International Inc ....E..... 513 563-4180
  Cincinnati *(G-3519)*
Challenger Aviation Products ....G..... 937 387-6500
  Vandalia *(G-19285)*
Eaton Industrial Corporation ....B..... 216 692-5456
  Cleveland *(G-5252)*
Enginetics Corporation ....C..... 937 878-3800
  Huber Heights *(G-11146)*
▲ Ferrotherm Corporation ....C..... 216 883-9350
  Cleveland *(G-5339)*
GE Aircraft Engines ....E..... 513 243-2000
  Cincinnati *(G-3803)*
▲ GE Aviation Systems LLC ....C..... 937 898-9600
  Dayton *(G-8358)*
GE Military Systems ....A..... 513 243-2000
  Cincinnati *(G-3810)*
General Electric Company ....G..... 513 948-4170
  Cincinnati *(G-3814)*
General Electric Company ....G..... 513 552-5364
  West Chester *(G-19875)*
General Electric Company ....A..... 513 552-2000
  Cincinnati *(G-3815)*
▲ Henry Tools Inc ....G..... 216 291-1011
  Cleveland *(G-5501)*
Hi-Tek Manufacturing Inc ....C..... 513 459-1094
  Mason *(G-13037)*
Honeywell ....G..... 614 850-8228
  Columbus *(G-7162)*
Honeywell International Inc ....A..... 216 459-6048
  Independence *(G-11259)*

Honeywell International Inc ....A..... 440 349-7330
  Solon *(G-17310)*
Honeywell International Inc ....G..... 216 682-1600
  Cleveland *(G-5523)*
Lsp Technologies Inc ....E..... 614 718-3000
  Dublin *(G-9100)*
Magellan Arospc Middletown Inc .....D..... 513 422-2751
  Middletown *(G-14058)*
Metro Mech Inc ....G..... 216 641-6262
  Cleveland *(G-5792)*
◆ Meyer Tool Inc ....A..... 513 681-7362
  Cincinnati *(G-4097)*
Otto Konigslow Mfg Co ....F..... 216 851-7900
  Cleveland *(G-5952)*
Parker Aircraft Sales ....G..... 937 833-4820
  Brookville *(G-2195)*
Parker-Hannifin Corporation ....C..... 440 284-6277
  Elyria *(G-9476)*
Pas Technologies Inc ....D..... 937 840-1000
  Hillsboro *(G-11012)*
PCC Airfoils LLC ....C..... 440 255-9770
  Mentor *(G-13683)*
Pierce-Spafford Metals Co Inc ....G..... 800 421-3778
  Niles *(G-15174)*
Polycraft Products Inc ....G..... 513 353-3334
  Cleves *(G-6523)*
Scis Aerospace LLC ....G..... 216 533-8533
  Medina *(G-13476)*
◆ Sifco Industries Inc ....B..... 216 881-8600
  Cleveland *(G-6201)*
Snow Aviation Intl Inc ....C..... 614 588-2452
  Gahanna *(G-10234)*
Spirit Avionics Ltd ....F..... 614 358-0333
  Columbus *(G-7645)*
Stofiel Aerospace LLC ....G..... 216 389-0084
  Cleveland *(G-6250)*
Trojon Gear Inc ....F..... 937 254-1737
  Dayton *(G-8729)*
Turbine Eng Cmpnents Tech Corp ....E..... 216 692-6173
  Cleveland *(G-6374)*
▲ Turbine Standard Ltd ....F..... 419 865-0355
  Holland *(G-11094)*
US Aeroteam Inc ....E..... 937 458-0344
  Dayton *(G-8740)*
▲ Welded Ring Products Co ....D..... 216 961-3800
  Cleveland *(G-6455)*

3728 Aircraft Parts & Eqpt, NEC

8888 Butler Investments Inc ....G..... 440 748-0810
  North Ridgeville *(G-15354)*
Ace Products Co of Toledo Inc ....G..... 419 472-1247
  Toledo *(G-18320)*
Achilles Aerospace Pdts Inc ....E..... 330 425-8444
  Twinsburg *(G-18892)*
▼ Advanced Fuel Systems Inc ....G..... 614 252-8422
  Columbus *(G-6697)*
Aero Tube & Connector Company .....G..... 614 885-2514
  Worthington *(G-20853)*
Aeroquip-Vickers Inc ....G..... 216 523-5000
  Cleveland *(G-4722)*
Airtug LLC ....G..... 440 829-2167
  Avon *(G-983)*
Airwolf Aerospace LLC ....G..... 440 632-1687
  Middlefield *(G-13913)*
Allen Aircraft Products Inc ....E..... 330 296-9621
  Ravenna *(G-16514)*
American Aero Components LLC ....G..... 937 367-5068
  Dayton *(G-8150)*
At Holdings Corporation ....G..... 216 692-6000
  Cleveland *(G-4850)*
Auto-Valve Inc ....E..... 937 854-3037
  Dayton *(G-8172)*
Aviation Cmpnent Solutions Inc ......F..... 440 295-6590
  Richmond Heights *(G-16652)*
Aviation Technologies Inc ....G..... 216 706-2960
  Cleveland *(G-4872)*
Avtron Aerospace Inc ....C..... 216 750-5152
  Cleveland *(G-4875)*
Aws Industries Inc ....E..... 513 932-7941
  Lebanon *(G-11782)*
Cleveland Instrument Corp ....G..... 440 826-1800
  Brookpark *(G-2153)*
Columbus Jack Corporation ....D..... 614 228-0185
  Columbus *(G-6958)*
Ctl-Aerospace Inc ....C..... 513 874-1118
  West Chester *(G-19994)*
Ctl-Aerospace Inc ....D..... 513 874-7900
  West Chester *(G-19995)*
Cuda Composites LLC ....G..... 937 499-0360
  Dayton *(G-8256)*

Dirksen and Associates Inc ....G..... 614 238-0413
  Columbus *(G-7027)*

Drt Power Systems LLC - Sidney ....C....... 937 492-6121
  Sidney *(G-17180)*

Eaton Hydraulics LLC.........................E...... 419 232-7777
  Van Wert *(G-19254)*

Eaton Industrial Corporation ....B...... 216 692-5456
  Cleveland *(G-5252)*

▲ Eaton-Aeroquip Llc ....C...... 216 523-5000
  Cleveland *(G-5254)*

Electronic Concepts Engrg Inc ....F...... 419 861-9000
  Holland *(G-11059)*

Enginetics Corporation ....C...... 937 878-3800
  Huber Heights *(G-11146)*

Eti Tech Inc ....F....... 937 832-4200
  Englewood *(G-9519)*

Exito Manufacturing ....G...... 937 291-9871
  Dayton *(G-8337)*

▲ Federal Equipment Company ....D...... 513 621-5260
  Cincinnati *(G-3747)*

Ferco Tech LLC ....C...... 937 746-6696
  Franklin *(G-10022)*

Fgc Plasma Solutions LLC ....Gc.... 954 591-1429
  Cleveland *(G-5342)*

Field Aviation Inc ....G...... 513 792-2282
  Cincinnati *(G-3753)*

Fluid Power Inc ....F....... 330 653-5107
  Hudson *(G-11171)*

◆ Friction Products Co ....C...... 330 725-4941
  Medina *(G-13413)*

Garsite/Progress LLC ....F....... 419 424-1100
  Findlay *(G-9830)*

General Electric Company ....B...... 513 977-1500
  Cincinnati *(G-3813)*

Goodrich Corporation ....A...... 937 339-3811
  Troy *(G-18833)*

Goodrich Corporation ....B...... 216 429-4018
  Independence *(G-11255)*

Grimes Aerospace Company ....G...... 937 484-2000
  Urbana *(G-19159)*

Hartzell Propeller Inc ....F....... 937 778-4200
  Piqua *(G-16274)*

◆ Hartzell Propeller Inc......................C...... 937 778-4200
  Piqua *(G-16275)*

Hdi Landing Gear Usa Inc ....C...... 513 619-1203
  Springfield *(G-17569)*

Hdi Landing Gear Usa Inc ....E...... 440 783-5255
  Strongsville *(G-17924)*

Heico Aerospace Parts Corp ....B...... 954 987-6101
  Highland Heights *(G-10915)*

Heller Machine Products Inc ....G...... 216 281-2951
  Cleveland *(G-5496)*

◆ Industrial Mfg Co LLC ....F....... 440 838-4700
  Brecksville *(G-2055)*

Jay-Em Aerospace Corporation ....E...... 330 923-0333
  Cuyahoga Falls *(G-8013)*

JCB Arrowhead Products Inc ....G...... 440 546-4288
  Brecksville *(G-2057)*

Jeff Cales Customer AVI LLC..............G...... 330 298-9479
  Ravenna *(G-16534)*

Jo-Bar Manufacturing Corp ....F....... 440 232-5555
  Chagrin Falls *(G-3097)*

Jonathan Bishop ....G...... 330 836-6947
  Akron *(G-241)*

▲ Lawrence Technologies Inc ....G...... 937 274-7771
  Dayton *(G-8454)*

Lockheed Martin Integ ....D...... 330 796-2800
  Akron *(G-274)*

▲ Logan Machine Company ....D...... 330 633-6163
  Akron *(G-275)*

M & L Machine ....G...... 937 386-2604
  Seaman *(G-17041)*

Magellan Arospc Middletown Inc ....D...... 513 422-2751
  Middletown *(G-14058)*

Master Swaging Inc ....G...... 937 596-6171
  Jackson Center *(G-11343)*

▲ Maverick Molding Co ....F....... 513 469-9919
  Blue Ash *(G-1836)*

▲ Meggitt Aircraft Braking ....A...... 330 796-4400
  Akron *(G-294)*

Microweld Engineering Inc ....F....... 614 847-9410
  Worthington *(G-20880)*

▼ Midwest Aircraft Products Co ....F....... 419 884-2164
  Mansfield *(G-12648)*

▲ Milan Tool Corp ....E...... 216 661-1078
  Cleveland *(G-5813)*

Nona Composites LLC ....G...... 937 490-4814
  Beavercreek *(G-1376)*

Orbital Atk Inc ....C...... 937 429-9261
  Beavercreek *(G-1377)*

Pako Inc ....C....... 440 946-8030
  Mentor *(G-13678)*

Parker-Hannifin Corporation.............C....... 440 937-6211
  Avon *(G-1002)*

Parker-Hannifin Corporation.............C....... 440 284-6277
  Elyria *(G-9476)*

Parker-Hannifin Corporation.............C....... 440 205-8230
  Mentor *(G-13682)*

PCC Airfoils LLC ....B...... 740 982-6025
  Crooksville *(G-7952)*

Pitco Products Inc ....F....... 513 228-7245
  Dayton *(G-8577)*

Precision Aircraft Components ....E...... 937 278-0264
  Dayton *(G-8581)*

Proflo Industries LLC ....E...... 419 436-6008
  Alvada *(G-556)*

Salley Tool & Die Co ....F....... 937 258-3333
  Dayton *(G-8116)*

Schneller LLC ....D...... 330 673-1299
  Kent *(G-11523)*

Scis Aerospace LLC ....G...... 216 533-8533
  Medina *(G-13476)*

▲ Skidmore-Wilhelm Mfg Company ....E...... 216 481-4774
  Solon *(G-17381)*

Snow Aviation Intl Inc ....C...... 614 588-2452
  Gahanna *(G-10234)*

◆ Summa Holdings Inc ....G...... 440 838-4700
  Cleveland *(G-6261)*

Summit Avionics Inc ....F....... 330 425-1440
  Twinsburg *(G-19025)*

Taylor Manufacturing Company ....E...... 937 322-8622
  Springfield *(G-17660)*

Tracewell Systems Inc.......................D...... 614 846-6175
  Lewis Center *(G-11927)*

Transdigm Inc ....D...... 440 352-6182
  Painesville *(G-15932)*

Transdigm Group Incorporated ....D...... 216 706-2960
  Cleveland *(G-6348)*

Triaxis Machine & Tool LLC ....G...... 440 230-0303
  North Royalton *(G-15457)*

Triumph Thermal Systems LLC ....C...... 419 273-2511
  Forest *(G-9923)*

◆ Tronair Inc ....D...... 419 866-6301
  Holland *(G-11092)*

Tronair Parent Inc ....D...... 419 866-6301
  Holland *(G-11093)*

Truline Industries Inc ....D...... 440 729-0140
  Chesterland *(G-3222)*

Turbine Eng Cmpnents Tech Corp ......E...... 216 692-6173
  Cleveland *(G-6374)*

Unison Industries LLC.......................B...... 937 426-0621
  Dayton *(G-8121)*

Unison Industries LLC.......................B...... 937 427-0550
  Beavercreek *(G-1363)*

Unison Industries LLC.......................B...... 937 426-4676
  Alpha *(G-555)*

US Aeroteam Inc ....E...... 937 458-0344
  Dayton *(G-8740)*

◆ US Technology Corporation ....E...... 330 455-1181
  Canton *(G-2891)*

UTC Aerospace Systems ....F....... 216 341-1700
  Cleveland *(G-6402)*

Wayne Trail Technologies Inc ....D...... 937 295-2120
  Fort Loramie *(G-9944)*

Weldon Pump Acquition LLC................E...... 440 232-2282
  Oakwood Village *(G-15633)*

White Machine Inc..............................G...... 440 237-3282
  North Royalton *(G-15460)*

3731 Shipbuilding & Repairing

Great Lakes Group.............................C....... 216 621-4854
  Cleveland *(G-5451)*

Ironhead Marine Inc ....E...... 419 690-0001
  Toledo *(G-18529)*

Lake Erie Ship Repair ....F....... 440 624-0025
  Jefferson *(G-11366)*

Lighthouse Youth Services Inc ....F....... 513 961-4080
  Cincinnati *(G-4024)*

Manitowoc Company Inc ....G...... 920 746-3332
  Cleveland *(G-5739)*

McGinnis Inc ....C...... 740 377-4391
  South Point *(G-17440)*

McNational Inc....................................E...... 740 377-4391
  South Point *(G-17441)*

O-Kan Marine Repair Inc.....................E...... 740 446-4686
  Gallipolis *(G-10306)*

▲ Oneseal Inc ....G...... 973 599-1155
  Perrysburg *(G-16134)*

◆ Pinney Dock & Transport LLC...........E...... 440 964-7186
  Ashtabula *(G-832)*

Services Acquisition Co LLC ....G...... 330 479-9267
  Dennison *(G-8946)*

Superior Marine Ways Inc ....G...... 740 894-6224
  South Point *(G-17448)*

Superior Marine Ways Inc ....G...... 740 894-6224
  Proctorville *(G-16493)*

Tack-Anew Inc ....E...... 419 734-4212
  Port Clinton *(G-16417)*

V&P Group International LLC ....F....... 703 349-6432
  Cincinnati *(G-4550)*

WH Fetzer & Sons Mfg Inc ....E...... 419 687-8237
  Plymouth *(G-16380)*

3732 Boat Building & Repairing

Brewster Sugarcreek Twp Histo ....F....... 330 767-0045
  Brewster *(G-2084)*

Checkmate Marine Inc ....F....... 419 562-3881
  Bucyrus *(G-2335)*

Don Wartko Construction Co...............D...... 330 673-5252
  Kent *(G-11450)*

Doyle Sailmaker ....G...... 216 486-5732
  Cleveland *(G-5213)*

Dynamic Plastics Inc ....G...... 937 437-7261
  New Paris *(G-14879)*

Gallagher Wood & Crafts ....G...... 513 523-2748
  Oxford *(G-15836)*

Great Midwest Yacht Co ....G...... 740 965-4511
  Sunbury *(G-18061)*

Healthcare Benefits Inc ....G...... 419 433-4499
  Huron *(G-11223)*

Jacks Marine Inc ....G...... 440 997-5060
  Ashtabula *(G-814)*

Marinemax Inc ....C...... 918 782-3277
  Port Clinton *(G-16405)*

Mariners Landing Inc ....F....... 513 941-3625
  Cincinnati *(G-4060)*

▲ Mentor Inc ....G...... 440 255-1250
  Mentor On The Lake *(G-13774)*

▲ Nauticus Inc.....................................G...... 440 746-1290
  Brecksville *(G-2066)*

O-Kan Marine Repair Inc.....................E...... 740 446-4686
  Gallipolis *(G-10306)*

Racelite South Coast Inc.....................F....... 216 581-4600
  Maple Heights *(G-12739)*

William Thompson ....G...... 440 232-4363
  Aurora *(G-956)*

Www Boat Services Inc.......................G...... 419 626-0883
  Sandusky *(G-17022)*

3743 Railroad Eqpt

A Stucki Company ....G...... 412 424-0560
  North Canton *(G-15218)*

▲ Alliance Castings Company LLC .....E...... 330 829-5600
  Alliance *(G-491)*

Amsted Industries Incorporated ....C...... 614 836-2323
  Groveport *(G-10612)*

Amsted Rail Company Inc....................F....... 614 836-2323
  Groveport *(G-10613)*

B&C Machine Co LLC ....B...... 330 745-4013
  Barberton *(G-1103)*

▲ Buck Equipment Inc ....E...... 614 539-3039
  Grove City *(G-10548)*

◆ Dayton-Phoenix Group Inc ....C...... 937 496-3900
  Dayton *(G-8293)*

Dennis Lavender ....G...... 740 344-3336
  Newark *(G-14999)*

Engines Inc of Ohio ....D...... 740 377-9874
  South Point *(G-17437)*

George R Silcott Railway Equip ....G...... 614 885-7224
  Worthington *(G-20867)*

Good Day Tools LLC ....G...... 513 578-2050
  Cincinnati *(G-3840)*

Gunderson Rail Services LLC ....E...... 330 792-6521
  Youngstown *(G-21106)*

▼ Jk-Co LLC ....E...... 419 422-5240
  Findlay *(G-9846)*

Johnson Bros Rubber Co Inc ....E...... 419 752-4814
  Greenwich *(G-10531)*

K & G Machine Co ....E...... 216 732-7115
  Cleveland *(G-5628)*

L B Foster Company ....E...... 330 652-1461
  Mineral Ridge *(G-14307)*

Nolan Company ....G...... 330 453-7922
  Canton *(G-2789)*

Nolan Company ....G...... 740 269-1512
  Bowerston *(G-1959)*

Norfolk Southern Corporation ....E...... 419 697-5070
  Oregon *(G-15712)*

Plymouth Locomotive Svc LLC............G...... 419 896-2854
  Shiloh *(G-17153)*

S I C.

Precision Runners LLC ....E 330 240-5988
   Burghill *(G-2369)*
Prime Manufacturing Corp ....G 937 496-3900
   Dayton *(G-8593)*
R H Little Co ....G 330 477-3455
   Canton *(G-2833)*
Rail Road Corporation ....G 614 771-2102
   Columbus *(G-7546)*
Rescar Industries Inc ....F 630 963-1114
   Minerva *(G-14341)*
Sperling Railway Services Inc ....F 330 479-2004
   Canton *(G-2855)*
Standard Car Truck Company ....D 740 775-6450
   Chillicothe *(G-3276)*
Transco Railway Products Inc ....D 330 872-0934
   Newton Falls *(G-15140)*
Trinity Highway Products Llc ....E 419 227-1296
   Lima *(G-12105)*
Westinghouse A Brake Tech Corp ....D 419 526-5323
   Mansfield *(G-12705)*

3751 Motorcycles, Bicycles & Parts

B&D Truck Parts Sls & Svcs LLC ....G 419 701-7041
   Fostoria *(G-9968)*
Beasley Fiberglass Inc ....G 440 357-6644
   Painesville *(G-15861)*
Behlke Dalene ....G 330 399-6780
   Warren *(G-19528)*
Carlisle Brake & Friction Inc ....E 330 725-4941
   Medina *(G-13385)*
▲ Carlisle Brake & Friction Inc ....G 440 528-4000
   Solon *(G-17277)*
Cherhire Choppers ....G 740 362-0695
   Delaware *(G-8834)*
▲ Cobra Motorcycles Mfg ....E 330 207-3844
   North Lima *(G-15312)*
Custom Assembly Inc ....E 419 622-3040
   Haviland *(G-10837)*
◆ Dana Companies LLC ....G 419 931-9086
   Perrysburg *(G-16082)*
Farin Industries Inc ....F 440 275-2755
   Austinburg *(G-961)*
Franklin Frames and Cycles ....G 740 763-3838
   Newark *(G-15008)*
Heritage Tool ....F 513 753-7300
   Loveland *(G-12358)*
▲ Huffy Corporation ....G 937 865-2800
   Centerville *(G-3043)*
▲ Ktm North America Inc ....D 440 985-3553
   Amherst *(G-600)*
Multi-Design Inc ....G 440 275-2255
   Austinburg *(G-963)*
▲ Newman Technology Inc ....C 419 525-1856
   Mansfield *(G-12656)*
Nikola Innovation LLC ....G 216 496-3022
   Cleveland *(G-5883)*
Old Mill Power Equipment ....G 740 982-3246
   Crooksville *(G-7951)*
Outback Cycle Shack LLC ....G 513 554-1048
   Cincinnati *(G-4203)*
Shumaker Racing Components ....G 419 238-0801
   Van Wert *(G-19270)*
Sinners N Saints LLC ....G 614 231-7467
   Columbus *(G-7625)*
▲ Spiegler Brake Systems USA LLC ....G 937 291-1735
   Dayton *(G-8670)*
Sunstar Engrg Americas Inc ....F 937 743-9049
   Franklin *(G-10056)*
▲ Sunstar Engrg Americas Inc ....E 937 746-8575
   Springboro *(G-17508)*
◆ Tarantula Performance Racg LLC .....G 330 273-3456
   Hinckley *(G-11030)*
▲ Tc Bros Choppers LLC ....G 419 265-9399
   Wauseon *(G-19695)*
Thomas D Epperson ....G 937 855-3300
   Germantown *(G-10374)*
▲ Vari-Wall Tube Specialists Inc ....D 330 482-0000
   Columbiana *(G-6637)*
Warrior Trikes Inc ....G 419 264-6008
   Holgate *(G-11042)*

3761 Guided Missiles & Space Vehicles

Boeing Company ....A 740 788-4000
   Newark *(G-14985)*
Lockheed Martin Corporation ....B 330 796-2800
   Akron *(G-273)*
Tessec Manufacturing Svcs LLC ....E 937 985-3552
   Dayton *(G-8710)*

3764 Guided Missile/Space Vehicle Propulsion Units & parts

Morton International LLC ....G 937 222-3860
   Dayton *(G-8510)*

3769 Guided Missile/Space Vehicle Parts & Eqpt, NEC

Curtiss-Wright Controls ....E 937 252-5601
   Fairborn *(G-9618)*
Defense Co Inc ....D 413 998-1637
   Cleveland *(G-5181)*
General Electric Company ....B 513 977-1500
   Cincinnati *(G-3813)*
◆ Gleason Metrology Systems Corp ....E 937 384-8901
   Dayton *(G-8365)*
Grimes Aerospace Company ....B 937 484-2001
   Urbana *(G-19158)*
Industrial Quartz Corp ....F 440 942-0909
   Mentor *(G-13606)*
L-3 Communications Cincinnati ....A 513 573-6100
   Mason *(G-13055)*
Lockheed Martin Integ ....D 330 796-2800
   Akron *(G-274)*
Lord Corporation ....G 937 278-9431
   Dayton *(G-8459)*
▲ Metalex Manufacturing Inc ....E 513 489-0507
   Blue Ash *(G-1839)*
▲ Millat Industries Corp ....D 937 434-6666
   Dayton *(G-8501)*
Morris Bean & Company ....C 937 767-7301
   Yellow Springs *(G-20996)*
Shelburne Corp ....G 216 321-9177
   Shaker Heights *(G-17094)*
Sunpower Inc ....D 740 594-2221
   Athens *(G-887)*
Tdm Fuelcell LLC Tdm LLC ....G 440 969-1442
   Chesterland *(G-3221)*
Te Connectivity Corporation ....C 419 521-9500
   Mansfield *(G-12694)*
US Aeroteam Inc ....E 937 458-0344
   Dayton *(G-8740)*

3792 Travel Trailers & Campers

◆ Airstream Inc ....B 937 596-6111
   Jackson Center *(G-11337)*
ARE Inc ....C 330 830-7800
   Massillon *(G-13112)*
ARE Inc ....B 330 830-7800
   Massillon *(G-13111)*
Berlin Truck Caps Ltd ....F 330 893-2811
   Millersburg *(G-14201)*
C&C Trailer Park ....G 330 823-7733
   Salem *(G-16877)*
Capitol City Trailers Inc ....D 614 491-2616
   Obetz *(G-15651)*
Cecil Caudill Trailer Sls Inc ....F 740 574-0704
   Franklin Furnace *(G-10067)*
D W Truax Enterprise Inc ....G 740 695-2596
   Saint Clairsville *(G-16789)*
Gerich Fiberglass Inc ....E 419 362-4591
   Mount Gilead *(G-14560)*
Hybrid Trailer Co LLC ....G 419 433-3022
   Huron *(G-11227)*
Isaacs Jr Floyd Thomas ....F 513 899-2342
   Morrow *(G-14548)*
Jeff Couchs Campers LLC ....G 513 863-7000
   Hamilton *(G-10712)*

3795 Tanks & Tank Components

▲ American Apex Corporation ....F 614 652-2000
   Plain City *(G-16319)*
General Dynamics Land ....B 419 221-7000
   Lima *(G-12018)*
▲ Joint Systems Mfg Ctr ....G 419 221-9580
   Lima *(G-12034)*
Sugartree Square Mercantile ....G 740 345-3882
   Newark *(G-15060)*
▲ Tencate Advanced Armor USA Inc ....D 740 928-0326
   Hebron *(G-10888)*
Tessec Manufacturing Svcs LLC ....E 937 985-3552
   Dayton *(G-8710)*
United States Dept of Army ....D 419 221-9500
   Lima *(G-12108)*
▲ US Yachiyo Inc ....C 740 223-3134
   Marion *(G-12910)*
Weldon Pump Acquition LLC ....E 440 232-2282
   Oakwood Village *(G-15633)*

3799 Transportation Eqpt, NEC

Acorn Products Inc ....B 614 222-4400
   Columbus *(G-6689)*
Aerodynamic Systems ....G 440 463-8820
   Chagrin Falls *(G-3076)*
All Power Equipment LLC ....F 740 593-3279
   Athens *(G-855)*
Belshe Industries Inc ....F 937 526-4460
   Versailles *(G-19340)*
Besl Specialized Carrier ....G 740 599-6305
   Danville *(G-8084)*
Blue Ribbon Trailers Ltd ....E 330 538-4114
   North Jackson *(G-15288)*
Branham Motorsports LLC ....G 937 428-6040
   Dayton *(G-8193)*
Burkholder Buggy Shop ....G 330 674-5891
   Millersburg *(G-14208)*
▲ Cleveland Hdwr & Forging Co ....E 216 641-5200
   Cleveland *(G-5064)*
Cleveland Wheels ....D 440 937-6211
   Avon *(G-989)*
D & A Custom Trailer Inc ....G 740 922-2205
   Uhrichsville *(G-19047)*
▲ Farmerstown Axle Co ....G 330 897-2711
   Baltic *(G-1070)*
Fitchville East Corp ....E 419 929-1510
   New London *(G-14859)*
Geyer Transport & Mfg ....F 740 382-9008
   Marion *(G-12868)*
▲ Hawkline Nevada LLC ....E 937 444-4295
   Mount Orab *(G-14579)*
Hitch-Hiker Mfg Inc ....F 330 542-3052
   New Middletown *(G-14877)*
Independent Trailer Services ....G 937 667-8900
   Tipp City *(G-18282)*
Interstate Truckway Inc ....E 614 771-1220
   Columbus *(G-7209)*
Johnny On The Spot Inc ....E 614 497-1776
   Columbus *(G-7239)*
Kedar D Army ....G 419 238-6929
   Van Wert *(G-19262)*
Kmj Leasing Ltd ....E 614 871-3883
   Orient *(G-15723)*
Kolpin Outdoors Corporation ....G 330 328-0772
   Cuyahoga Falls *(G-8018)*
Liebrecht Manufacturing ....G 419 596-3501
   Continental *(G-7827)*
Loadmaster Trailer Company ....F 419 732-3434
   Port Clinton *(G-16403)*
London Coach Shop ....G 419 347-4803
   Shelby *(G-17137)*
▲ Lux Corporation ....G 419 562-7978
   Bucyrus *(G-2353)*
M Manufacturing Inc ....G 330 793-6806
   Youngstown *(G-21139)*
▲ Miba Bearings US LLC ....B 740 962-4242
   McConnelsville *(G-13354)*
Midway Trailer Sales LLC ....G 419 394-4408
   Saint Marys *(G-16843)*
Mohawk Manufacturing Inc ....G 860 632-2345
   Mount Vernon *(G-14631)*
Mx Spring Inc ....G 330 426-4600
   East Palestine *(G-9242)*
Polaris Industries Inc ....E 937 283-1200
   Wilmington *(G-20673)*
Premier Uv Products LLC ....G 330 715-2452
   Cuyahoga Falls *(G-8035)*
R V Spa LLC ....G 440 284-4800
   Elyria *(G-9482)*
Rv Xpress Inc ....G 937 418-0127
   Piqua *(G-16312)*
Shiloh Carriage Shop LLC ....G 419 896-3869
   Shiloh *(G-17155)*
Swartz Audie ....G 740 820-2341
   Minford *(G-14346)*
Thor Industries Inc ....E 937 596-6111
   Jackson Center *(G-11349)*
Transglobal Inc ....G 419 396-9079
   Carey *(G-2927)*
Victorian Farms ....G 330 628-9188
   Atwater *(G-903)*
Walnut Creek Cart Shop ....G 330 893-1097
   Millersburg *(G-14280)*
▼ Wholecycle Inc ....G 330 929-8123
   Peninsula *(G-16045)*

38 MEASURING, ANALYZING AND CONTROLLING INSTRUMENTS; PHOTOGRAPHIC, MEDICAL AN

3812 Search, Detection, Navigation & Guidance Systs & Instrs

3gc LLC ....G....740 703-0580
Cardington *(G-2907)*

Accurate Electronics Inc ....C....330 682-7015
Orrville *(G-15727)*

◆ **ADB Safegate Americas LLC** ....B....614 861-1304
Columbus *(G-6694)*

Atlantic Inertial Systems Inc ....E....740 788-3800
Heath *(G-10845)*

Aviation Technologies Inc ....G....216 706-2960
Cleveland *(G-4872)*

Ball Aerospace & Tech Corp ....C....937 429-5005
Beavercreek *(G-1321)*

Boeing Company ....A....740 788-5805
Newark *(G-14987)*

Boeing Company ....E....740 788-4000
Newark *(G-14986)*

Brookpark Laboratories Inc ....G....216 267-7140
Cleveland *(G-4935)*

Btc Inc ....E....740 549-2722
Lewis Center *(G-11892)*

Cedar Elec Holdings Corp ....G....513 870-8500
West Chester *(G-19824)*

▲ **Ceia Usa Ltd** ....E....330 405-3190
Twinsburg *(G-18909)*

Circle Prime Manufacturing ....E....330 923-0019
Cuyahoga Falls *(G-7980)*

David Boswell ....E....614 441-2497
Columbus *(G-7014)*

Decibel Research Inc ....D....256 705-3341
Beavercreek *(G-1329)*

Dragoon Technologies Inc ....G....937 439-9223
Dayton *(G-8310)*

Drs Advanced Isr LLC ....C....937 429-7408
Beavercreek *(G-1330)*

Drs Advanced Isr LLC ....E....603 429-0111
Beavercreek *(G-1331)*

Drs Icas LLC ....E....937 429-7408
Beavercreek *(G-1332)*

Drs Mobile Environmntl Svc ....G....513 943-1111
Cincinnati *(G-3299)*

Dynamic Sensor Systems LLC ....G....614 430-2888
Worthington *(G-20865)*

▲ **Eaton Aerospace LLC** ....F....216 523-5000
Cleveland *(G-5243)*

Eaton Aerospace LLC ....E....216 523-5000
Cleveland *(G-5244)*

Electrodynamics Inc ....C....847 259-0740
Cincinnati *(G-3300)*

Enginetics Corporation ....C....937 878-3800
Huber Heights *(G-11146)*

▲ **Escort Inc** ....D....513 870-8500
West Chester *(G-19859)*

Eti Tech Inc ....F....937 832-4200
Englewood *(G-9519)*

Fame Tool & Mfg Co Inc ....E....513 271-6387
Cincinnati *(G-3737)*

▲ **Ferrotherm Corporation** ....C....216 883-9350
Cleveland *(G-5339)*

Fluid Conservation Systems ....F....513 831-9335
Milford *(G-14141)*

GE Aviation Systems LLC ....G....513 470-2889
Cincinnati *(G-3804)*

GE Aviation Systems LLC ....C....513 977-1500
Cincinnati *(G-3806)*

▲ **GE Aviation Systems LLC** ....G....513 243-2000
Cincinnati *(G-3808)*

GE Aviation Systems LLC ....C....937 898-9600
Dayton *(G-8359)*

General Dynmics Mssion Systems ....E....513 253-4770
Beavercreek *(G-1340)*

Goodrich Corporation ....D....330 374-2882
Uniontown *(G-19086)*

Grimes Aerospace Company ....B....937 484-2001
Urbana *(G-19158)*

Harris Corporation ....C....973 284-2866
Beavercreek *(G-1344)*

Heller Machine Products Inc ....G....216 281-2951
Cleveland *(G-5496)*

Hept Machine Inc ....G....937 890-5633
Vandalia *(G-19294)*

HI Tech Aero Spares ....G....513 942-4150
West Chester *(G-19882)*

Honeywell International Inc ....A....937 484-2000
Urbana *(G-19162)*

IMT Defense Corp ....G....614 891-8812
Westerville *(G-20159)*

John Wolf & Co Inc ....G....440 942-0083
Willoughby *(G-20516)*

L-3 Communications Cincinnati ....A....513 573-6100
Mason *(G-13055)*

L3 Aviation Products Inc ....D....614 825-2001
Columbus *(G-7278)*

L3 Technologies Inc ....G....937 223-3285
Dayton *(G-8449)*

Lake Shore Cryotronics Inc ....C....614 891-2243
Westerville *(G-20165)*

Lockheed Martin Integ ....D....330 796-2800
Akron *(G-274)*

MCO Solutions Inc ....G....937 205-9512
Dayton *(G-8480)*

Nhvs International Inc ....B....440 527-8610
Mentor *(G-13665)*

PCC Airfoils LLC ....C....216 692-7900
Cleveland *(G-5983)*

▲ **Peerless-Winsmith Inc** ....G....614 526-7000
Dublin *(G-9122)*

Quasonix Inc ....E....513 942-1287
West Chester *(G-19927)*

Raytheon Company ....F....937 429-5429
Beavercreek *(G-1359)*

Redco Instrument ....G....440 232-2132
Cleveland *(G-6096)*

◆ **Reuter-Stokes Inc** ....B....330 425-3755
Twinsburg *(G-19008)*

Saircorp Ltd ....G....330 669-9099
Smithville *(G-17245)*

Sextant Group Inc ....G....614 429-3606
Columbus *(G-7613)*

▲ **Star Dynamics Corporation** ....D....614 334-4510
Hilliard *(G-10981)*

Sunset Industries Inc ....E....216 731-8131
Euclid *(G-9607)*

Te Connectivity Corporation ....C....419 521-9500
Mansfield *(G-12694)*

Tmw Systems Inc ....F....615 986-1900
Cleveland *(G-6328)*

Tri-State Jet Mfg LLC ....G....513 896-4538
Hamilton *(G-10750)*

Trimble Inc ....F....937 233-8921
Dayton *(G-8726)*

U S Army Corps of Engineers ....F....740 537-2571
Toronto *(G-18786)*

Unmanned Science Inc ....G....614 581-9893
Dublin *(G-9159)*

Valentine Research Inc ....E....513 984-8900
Blue Ash *(G-1888)*

Vector Electromagnetics LLC ....G....937 478-5904
Beavercreek *(G-1383)*

Wall Colmonoy Corporation ....D....513 842-4200
Cincinnati *(G-4577)*

Yost Labs Inc ....F....740 876-4936
Portsmouth *(G-16459)*

3821 Laboratory Apparatus & Furniture

4r Enterprises Incorporated ....G....330 923-9799
Cuyahoga Falls *(G-7960)*

Accuscan Instruments Inc ....F....614 878-6644
Columbus *(G-6686)*

▲ **American Isostatic Presses Inc** ....F....614 445-9081
Columbus *(G-6739)*

Amteco Inc ....G....513 217-4430
Middletown *(G-14020)*

Asbeka Custom Products LLC ....F....440 352-0839
Painesville *(G-15852)*

Ashton Pumpmatic Inc ....G....937 424-1380
Dayton *(G-8165)*

▲ **Caron Products and Svcs Inc** ....E....740 373-6809
Marietta *(G-12770)*

Cellular Technology Limited ....E....216 791-5084
Shaker Heights *(G-17088)*

Center For Excptonal Practices ....G....330 523-5240
Richfield *(G-16617)*

▲ **Cheminstruments Inc** ....G....513 860-1598
West Chester *(G-19827)*

Cheminstruments Inc ....G....513 860-1598
West Chester *(G-19828)*

Chemsultants International Inc ....G....513 860-1598
West Chester *(G-19829)*

Chemsultants International Inc ....G....440 974-3080
Mentor *(G-13543)*

Continental Hydrodyne Systems ....F....330 494-2740
Canton *(G-2667)*

Cortest Inc ....F....440 942-1235
Willoughby *(G-20463)*

Denton Atd Inc ....E....567 265-5200
Huron *(G-11220)*

Dentronix Inc ....E....330 916-7300
Cuyahoga Falls *(G-7987)*

◆ **E R Advanced Ceramics Inc** ....E....330 426-9433
East Palestine *(G-9237)*

Gdj Inc ....G....440 975-0258
Mentor *(G-13590)*

◆ **Global Cooling Inc** ....E....740 274-7900
Athens *(G-869)*

H & N Instruments Inc ....G....740 344-4351
Newark *(G-15017)*

Ies Systems Inc ....E....330 533-6683
Canfield *(G-2558)*

Ignio Systems LLC ....F....419 708-0503
Toledo *(G-18516)*

Mettler-Toledo Intl Fin Inc ....G....614 438-4511
Columbus *(G-6653)*

◆ **Mettler-Toledo Intl Inc** ....B....614 438-4511
Columbus *(G-6654)*

▼ **Nanotech Innovations LLC** ....G....440 926-4888
Oberlin *(G-15646)*

◆ **Philips Medical Systems Clevel** ....B....440 247-2652
Cleveland *(G-6001)*

Poi Holdings Inc ....F....937 253-7377
Dayton *(G-8115)*

Powdermet Powder Production ....F....216 404-0053
Euclid *(G-9599)*

Qualitech Associates Inc ....G....216 265-8702
Cleveland *(G-6068)*

Regal Industries Inc ....G....440 352-9600
Painesville *(G-15917)*

So-Low Environmental Eqp Co ....E....513 772-9410
Cincinnati *(G-4431)*

Strategic Technology Entp ....E....440 354-2600
Mentor *(G-13738)*

▲ **Tech Pro Inc** ....E....330 923-3546
Akron *(G-430)*

Teledyne Instruments Inc ....E....513 229-7000
Mason *(G-13094)*

Teledyne Tekmar Company ....E....513 229-7000
Mason *(G-13095)*

Thermo Fisher Scientific ....A....740 373-4763
Marietta *(G-12841)*

Tri-Tech Machining LLC ....G....513 575-3959
Milford *(G-14179)*

Universal Scientific Inc ....G....440 428-1777
Madison *(G-12513)*

Waller Brothers Stone Company ....E....740 858-1948
Mc Dermott *(G-13345)*

3822 Automatic Temperature Controls

A & P Tool Inc ....E....419 542-6681
Hicksville *(G-10897)*

ABB Automation Inc ....B....440 347-9668
Wickliffe *(G-20346)*

Action Air & Hydraulics Inc ....G....937 372-8614
Xenia *(G-20933)*

Acutemp Thermal Systems ....F....937 312-0114
Moraine *(G-14464)*

▲ **Alan Manufacturing Inc** ....E....330 262-1555
Wooster *(G-20737)*

◆ **Babcock & Wilcox Company** ....A....330 753-4511
Barberton *(G-1104)*

Balta Technology Inc ....G....513 724-0247
Batavia *(G-1167)*

Blue Wolfe Air Systems Inc ....G....937 295-3632
Houston *(G-11120)*

▲ **Bry-Air Inc** ....E....740 965-2974
Sunbury *(G-18056)*

▲ **Budzar Industries Inc** ....D....440 530-1000
Willoughby *(G-20448)*

Building Ctrl Integrators LLC ....E....614 334-3300
Powell *(G-16464)*

Building Ctrl Integrators LLC ....G....513 247-6154
Cincinnati *(G-3486)*

Building Ctrl Integrators LLC ....G....440 526-6660
Broadview Heights *(G-2106)*

Building Ctrl Integrators LLC ....G....513 860-9600
West Chester *(G-19985)*

Certified Labs & Service Inc ....G....419 289-7462
Ashland *(G-718)*

Cfrc Wtr & Enrgy Solutions Inc ....G....216 479-0290
Cleveland *(G-5011)*

▲ **Channel Products Inc** ....D....440 423-0113
Chesterland *(G-3199)*

Cincinnati Air Conditioning Co ....D....513 721-5622
Cincinnati *(G-3538)*

SIC

▲ Conery Manufacturing Inc ....F 419 289-1444
  Ashland (G-724)

Cool Times ....G 513 608-5201
  Cincinnati (G-3608)

Data Analysis Technologies ....G 614 873-0710
  Plain City (G-16333)

▼ Estabrook Assembly Svcs Inc .....F 440 243-3350
  Berea (G-1614)

Etc Enterprises LLC ....G 417 262-6382
  Delphos (G-8908)

Fes-Ohio Inc ....G 513 772-8566
  Cincinnati (G-3750)

Follow River Designs LLC ....G 614 325-9954
  McConnelsville (G-13350)

Furnace Control Corp ....E 513 772-1000
  West Chester (G-19870)

Future Controls Corporation ....E 440 275-3191
  Austinburg (G-962)

Great Lakes Management Inc ....G 216 883-6500
  Cleveland (G-5454)

Grid Sentry LLC ....F 937 490-2101
  Beavercreek (G-1342)

Helm Instrument Company Inc .....E 419 893-4356
  Maumee (G-13265)

Honeywell International Inc ....D 937 754-4134
  Fairborn (G-9625)

Honeywell International Inc ....A 937 484-2000
  Urbana (G-19162)

Howden North America Inc ....D 330 867-8540
  Akron (G-224)

Hunter Defense Tech Inc ....C 513 943-7880
  Cincinnati (G-3309)

▼ Hunter Defense Tech Inc ....E 216 438-6111
  Solon (G-17312)

Ignio Systems LLC ....F 419 708-0503
  Toledo (G-18516)

Integrated Development & Mfg .....F 440 247-5100
  Chagrin Falls (G-3060)

Integrated Development & Mfg .....F 440 543-2423
  Chagrin Falls (G-3095)

Kanawha Scales & Systems Inc ....F 513 576-0700
  Milford (G-14158)

Karman Rubber Company ....E 330 864-2161
  Akron (G-251)

Mader Machine Co Inc ....E 440 355-4505
  Lagrange (G-11632)

Melink Corporation ....F 513 685-0958
  Milford (G-14161)

Mestek Inc ....D 419 288-2703
  Bradner (G-2029)

Mestek Inc ....D 419 288-2703
  Holland (G-11072)

Midwest Energy Emissions Corp ....F 614 505-6115
  Lewis Center (G-11908)

Norcold Inc ....C 937 447-2241
  Gettysburg (G-10375)

Ohio Coatings Company ....D 740 859-5500
  Yorkville (G-21007)

Peco II Inc ....D 614 431-0694
  Columbus (G-7473)

▲ Pepperl + Fuchs Inc ....C 330 425-3555
  Twinsburg (G-18997)

▲ Portage Electric Products Inc ....C 330 499-2727
  North Canton (G-15259)

Prentke Romich Company ....C 330 202-5800
  Wooster (G-20825)

Providence Group Inc ....F 440 350-4615
  Mentor (G-13703)

Qleanair Scandinavia Inc ....G 614 323-1272
  Columbus (G-7529)

▲ Sasha Electronics Inc ....F 419 662-8100
  Rossford (G-16749)

Schneder Elc Bldngs Amrcas Inc ....D 513 398-9800
  Lebanon (G-11838)

Siemens Industry Inc ....G 614 846-9540
  Worthington (G-20888)

Siemens Industry Inc ....G 937 748-1726
  Springboro (G-17507)

Siemens Industry Inc ....D 513 336-2267
  Lebanon (G-11839)

Siemens Industry Inc ....D 614 573-8212
  Columbus (G-7619)

▲ Skuttle Mfg Co ....F 740 373-9169
  Marietta (G-12831)

Tecmark Corporation ....E 440 205-9188
  Mentor (G-13744)

Tetra Tech Inc ....F 330 286-3683
  Canfield (G-2578)

▲ Therm-O-Disc Incorporated ....A 419 525-8500
  Mansfield (G-12697)

Thermo King Corporation ....B 478 625-7241
  Chagrin Falls (G-3071)

◆ Thermtrol Corporation ....E 330 497-4148
  North Canton (G-15272)

Thomas Enterprises ....G 330 394-4483
  Warren (G-19607)

Tier Environmental ....F 440 232-9400
  Bedford (G-1466)

Turner Pressure ....G 614 871-7775
  Grove City (G-10608)

Twinsource LLC ....G 440 248-6800
  Solon (G-17410)

▲ Ventra Sandusky LLC ....D 419 627-3600
  Sandusky (G-17020)

Vortec Corporation ....E 513 686-8210
  Blue Ash (G-1891)

Young Regulator Company Inc ......E 440 232-9452
  Bedford (G-1474)

Zenith Energy Group LLC ....F 216 587-9510
  Cleveland (G-6494)

3823 Indl Instruments For Meas, Display & Control

ABB Inc ....C 440 585-8500
  Wickliffe (G-20348)

ABB Inc ....G 440 585-8500
  Wickliffe (G-20349)

Air Logic Power Systems LLC ......G 513 202-5130
  Harrison (G-10767)

▲ Airmate Company ....D 419 636-3184
  Bryan (G-2274)

◆ Alpha Technologies Svcs LLC ....D 330 745-1641
  Akron (G-65)

▲ Altronic LLC ....C 330 545-9768
  Girard (G-10381)

American Water Services Inc ....G 440 243-9840
  Strongsville (G-17887)

Appleton Grp LLC ....C 330 689-1904
  Cuyahoga Falls (G-7968)

Aqua Technology Group LLC ....G 513 298-1183
  West Chester (G-19807)

Aquacalc LLC ....G 916 372-0534
  Columbus (G-6767)

▼ Arzel Technology Inc ....E 216 831-6068
  Cleveland (G-4840)

Ascon Tecnologic N Amer LLC ......G 216 485-8350
  Cleveland (G-4844)

Automatic Timing & Contrls Inc .....D 614 888-8855
  New Albany (G-14747)

Automation and Ctrl Tech Inc ....E 614 495-1120
  Dublin (G-9050)

▼ Automation Metrology Intl LLC ....G 440 354-6436
  Mentor (G-13529)

Automation Technology Inc ....E 937 233-6084
  Dayton (G-8174)

◆ Avure Autoclave Systems Inc ....E 614 891-2732
  Columbus (G-6794)

Avure Technologies Inc ....E 614 891-2732
  Lewis Center (G-11888)

Beaumont Machine LLC ....F 513 701-0421
  Mason (G-12988)

Brighton Technologies LLC ....F 513 469-1800
  Saint Bernard (G-16779)

▲ Bry-Air Inc ....E 740 965-2974
  Sunbury (G-18056)

BSK Industries Inc ....G 440 230-9299
  North Royalton (G-15412)

▲ Budzar Industries Inc ....D 440 530-1000
  Willoughby (G-20448)

Burner Technology Unlimited ....G 440 232-6181
  Cleveland (G-4949)

C H Washington Water Plan ....G 740 636-2382
  Wshngtn CT Hs (G-20904)

▲ Cammann Inc ....F 440 965-4051
  Birmingham (G-1685)

▲ Caron Products and Svcs Inc .....E 740 373-6809
  Marietta (G-12770)

▲ Chandler Systems Incorporated ....D 419 281-5767
  Ashland (G-721)

Cincinnati Test Systems Inc ....C 800 850-3189
  Harrison (G-10773)

◆ Clark-Reliance Corporation ....C 440 572-1500
  Strongsville (G-17902)

Cleveland Controls Inc ....D 216 398-0330
  Cleveland (G-5053)

Cleveland Electric Labs Co ....E 800 447-2207
  Twinsburg (G-18915)

Cleveland Instrument Corp ....G 440 826-1800
  Brookpark (G-2153)

Command Alkon Incorporated ....D 614 799-0600
  Dublin (G-9064)

Computer Aided Solutions LLC .....E 440 729-2570
  Chesterland (G-3201)

Comtec Incorporated ....F 330 425-8102
  Twinsburg (G-18918)

Consolidatd Analytical Sys Inc ......F 513 542-1200
  Cleves (G-6511)

Control Associates Inc ....G 440 708-1770
  Chagrin Falls (G-3082)

Control Works Inc ....E 513 831-9959
  Milford (G-14133)

Corro-Tech Equipment Corp ....G 216 941-1552
  Cleveland (G-5133)

Crown Elec Svcs & Automtn Inc ....G 330 270-9890
  Youngstown (G-21058)

Danaher Corporation ....C 440 995-3003
  Cleveland (G-5164)

Danaher Corporation ....C 440 995-3025
  Mentor (G-13558)

Deban Enterprises Inc ....G 937 426-4235
  Dayton (G-8295)

Diamond Power Intl Inc ....F 740 687-4001
  Lancaster (G-11707)

▲ Doubleday Acquisitions LLC ......C 937 242-6768
  Moraine (G-14480)

▲ Dynamic Temperature Sups LLC ....G 216 767-5799
  Parma (G-15956)

Dynetech LLC ....E 419 690-4281
  Toledo (G-18447)

E E Controls Inc ....G 440 585-5554
  Willowick (G-20647)

Electrodynamics Inc ....C 847 259-0740
  Cincinnati (G-3300)

Elpro Services Inc ....G 740 568-9900
  Marietta (G-12783)

Emerson Electric Co ....E 513 631-6112
  Cincinnati (G-3697)

Emerson Electric Co ....E 440 288-1122
  Lorain (G-12244)

Emerson Electric Co ....E 440 248-9400
  Solon (G-17285)

Emerson Electric Co ....E 513 942-1118
  West Chester (G-19856)

Emerson Network Power System ....G 614 841-6309
  Westerville (G-20150)

Encompass Automation & ....F 419 873-0000
  Perrysburg (G-16092)

Ernst Flow Industries LLC ....F 732 938-5641
  Strongsville (G-17918)

Ets Solution NA LLC ....G 330 666-8696
  Bath (G-1236)

Facts Inc ....E 330 928-2332
  Cuyahoga Falls (G-7995)

Fluid Equipment Corp ....G 419 636-0777
  Bryan (G-2296)

Fondriest Environmental Inc ....F 937 426-2151
  Fairborn (G-9621)

▲ Furnace Parts LLC ....E 216 916-9601
  Cleveland (G-5384)

Future Controls Corporation ....E 440 275-3191
  Austinburg (G-962)

GE Infrastructure Sensing Inc ....B 740 928-7010
  Hebron (G-10866)

Gem Instrument Co ....F 330 273-6117
  Brunswick (G-2229)

Geocorp Inc ....E 419 433-1101
  Huron (G-11222)

Gilbarco Catlow LLC ....G 937 898-3236
  Tipp City (G-18279)

◆ Gleason Metrology Systems Corp ....E 937 384-8901
  Dayton (G-8365)

Glo-Quartz Electric Heater Co ....E 440 255-9701
  Mentor (G-13593)

Godfrey & Wing Inc ....F 419 980-4616
  Defiance (G-8791)

Gooch & Housego (ohio) LLC ......D 216 486-6100
  Highland Heights (G-10914)

H W Fairway International Inc ....E 330 678-2540
  Kent (G-11467)

Harris Corporation ....C 973 284-2866
  Beavercreek (G-1344)

Harris Instrument Corporation ......G 740 369-3580
  Delaware (G-8857)

Helm Instrument Company Inc .....E 419 893-4356
  Maumee (G-13265)

Henry & Wright Corporation ....F 216 851-3750
  Cleveland (G-5500)

Hickok Incorporated ....D 216 541-8060
  Cleveland (G-5513)

Homeworth Fabrications & Mchs ....F 330 525-5459
Homeworth (G-11116)

Honeywell Inc ....C 513 272-1111
Cincinnati (G-3896)

Honeywell International Inc ....A 937 484-2000
Urbana (G-19162)

Hunkar Technologies Inc ....C 513 272-1010
Cincinnati (G-3902)

Huntington Instruments Inc ....G 937 767-7001
Yellow Springs (G-20993)

Infrared Imaging Systems Inc ....G 614 989-1148
Marysville (G-12954)

Ingersoll-Rand Company ....E 419 633-6800
Bryan (G-2306)

Innovative Controls Corp ....D 419 691-6684
Toledo (G-18524)

▼ Intek Inc ....E 614 895-0301
Westerville (G-20160)

John McHael Priester Assoc Inc ....G 513 761-8605
Wyoming (G-20932)

Journey Electronics Corp ....G 513 539-9836
Monroe (G-14406)

Jual Corporation ....E 614 430-0683
Worthington (G-20874)

▲ Keithley Instruments LLC ....C 440 248-0400
Solon (G-17328)

Koester Corporation ....D 419 599-0291
Napoleon (G-14687)

Kuhlman Instrument Company ....G 419 668-9533
Norwalk (G-15548)

▲ L J Star Incorporated ....E 330 405-3040
Twinsburg (G-18969)

L-3 Communications Cincinnati ....A 513 573-6100
Mason (G-13055)

Lake Shore Cryotronics Inc ....C 614 891-2243
Westerville (G-20165)

Liebert Corporation ....B 740 547-5100
Ironton (G-11296)

Lincoln Electric Company ....A 216 524-8800
Cleveland (G-5696)

Logan Enterprises Inc ....G 937 465-8170
West Liberty (G-20093)

LS Starrett Company ....D 440 835-0005
Westlake (G-20282)

M T Systems Inc ....G 330 453-4646
Canton (G-2763)

Machine Applications Corp ....G 419 621-2322
Sandusky (G-16983)

Manico Inc ....G 440 946-5333
Willoughby (G-20534)

▲ Marlin Manufacturing Corp ....D 216 676-1340
Cleveland (G-5749)

Maxon Corporation ....A 216 459-6056
Independence (G-11267)

Measurement Computing Corp ....E 440 439-4091
Cleveland (G-5774)

▲ Meech Sttic Elminators USA Inc ....F 330 564-2000
Barberton (G-1130)

Mercury Iron & Steel ....F 440 349-1500
Solon (G-17334)

Mettler-Toledo Intl Fin Inc ....G 614 438-4511
Columbus (G-6653)

◆ Mettler-Toledo Intl Inc ....B 614 438-4511
Columbus (G-6654)

Monitor Mapboard Systems LLC ....G 614 761-9985
Dublin (G-9105)

Monitortech Corp ....G 614 231-0500
Columbus (G-7366)

▲ MR&e Ltd ....G 419 872-8180
Toledo (G-18593)

Nanostatics Corporation ....F 740 477-5900
Circleville (G-4635)

NDC Technologies Inc ....C 937 233-9935
Dayton (G-8522)

Newtech Materials & Analytical ....G 330 329-1080
Copley (G-7851)

Nidec Indus Automtn USA LLC ....E 216 901-2400
Cleveland (G-5882)

Nidec Motor Corporation ....G 216 642-1230
Independence (G-11268)

Noramar Company Inc ....G 440 338-5740
Novelty (G-15583)

Northern Instruments Corp LLC ....G 216 450-5073
Cleveland (G-5910)

▲ Noshok Inc ....E 440 243-0888
Berea (G-1630)

Onevision Corporation ....G 614 794-1144
Westerville (G-20174)

Overhoff Technology Corp ....F 513 248-2400
Milford (G-14165)

Parker-Hannifin Corporation ....A 216 531-3000
Cleveland (G-5975)

Poi Holdings Inc ....F 937 253-7377
Dayton (G-8115)

Pride Gage Associates LLC ....G 419 318-3793
Toledo (G-18657)

Process Pigging Systems LLC ....G 513 731-6005
Cincinnati (G-4276)

▼ Production Control Units Inc ....D 937 299-5594
Moraine (G-14519)

Production Design Services Inc ....G 937 866-3377
Dayton (G-8598)

▲ Q-Lab Corporation ....D 440 835-8700
Westlake (G-20298)

Quad/Graphics Inc ....A 513 932-1064
Lebanon (G-11830)

Quality Mtrlogy Stym Solutions ....G 937 431-1800
Beavercreek (G-1358)

Ralph A Felice Inc ....G 330 468-0482
Macedonia (G-12479)

Ram Sensors Inc ....F 440 835-3540
Cleveland (G-6089)

▲ Refractory Specialties Inc ....E 330 938-2101
Sebring (G-17050)

◆ Reuter-Stokes Inc ....B 330 425-3755
Twinsburg (G-19008)

▲ Richards Industries Inc ....C 513 533-7340
Cincinnati (G-4344)

Rickly Hydrological Co ....E 614 297-9877
Columbus (G-7562)

Ridge Tool Company ....E 440 329-4737
Elyria (G-9487)

Rsa Controls Inc ....G 513 476-6277
West Chester (G-19940)

▲ Rsw Technologies LLC ....F 419 662-8100
Rossford (G-16748)

Sansei Showa Co Ltd ....E 440 248-4440
Cleveland (G-6158)

Scadatech LLC ....G 614 552-7726
Reynoldsburg (G-16604)

Schneider Electric Usa Inc ....C 513 755-4231
West Chester (G-19942)

Schneider Electric Usa Inc ....D 513 755-5000
West Chester (G-19943)

Seekirk Inc ....F 614 278-9200
Columbus (G-7606)

Seelaus Instrument Co ....G 513 733-8222
Miamisburg (G-13857)

▲ Selas Heat Technology Co LLC ....E 800 523-6500
Streetsboro (G-17875)

Selective Med Components Inc ....E 740 397-7838
Mount Vernon (G-14645)

Shelburne Corp ....E 216 321-9177
Shaker Heights (G-17094)

Sherbrooke Metals ....E 440 942-3520
Willoughby (G-20596)

Snappskin Inc ....G 440 318-4879
Chagrin Falls (G-3070)

▲ Solon Manufacturing Company ....E 440 286-7149
Chardon (G-3180)

Stancorp Inc ....G 330 545-6615
Girard (G-10396)

Star Combustion Systems LLC ....G 513 282-0810
Mason (G-13090)

Stewart Manufacturing Corp ....E 937 390-3333
Springfield (G-17657)

Stock Fairfield Corporation ....E 440 543-6000
Chagrin Falls (G-3122)

T P F Inc ....E 513 761-9968
Cincinnati (G-4490)

Tasi Holdings Inc ....E 513 202-5182
Harrison (G-10809)

TE Brown LLC ....G 937 223-2241
Dayton (G-8706)

Technology Resources Inc ....G 419 241-9248
Toledo (G-18716)

▲ Tecmark Corporation ....D 440 205-7600
Mentor (G-13743)

Tecsis LP ....E 614 430-0683
Worthington (G-20891)

Tegron Holding LLC ....G 330 836-2004
Akron (G-431)

Tempest Inc ....F 216 883-6500
Cleveland (G-6304)

▲ Therm-O-Disc Incorporated ....A 419 525-8500
Mansfield (G-12697)

Thermacal Inc ....G 440 498-1005
Solon (G-17405)

▲ Thk Manufacturing America Inc ....C 740 928-1415
Hebron (G-10889)

◆ Tls Corp ....E 216 574-4759
Cleveland (G-6327)

Toledo Transducers Inc ....E 419 724-4170
Holland (G-11090)

▲ Unicontrol Inc ....D 216 398-0330
Cleveland (G-6382)

United Tool Supply Inc ....G 513 752-6000
Cincinnati (G-3320)

◆ Vanner Holdings Inc ....D 614 771-2718
Hilliard (G-10991)

◆ Vega Americas Inc ....C 513 272-0131
Cincinnati (G-4558)

Vertiv Co ....G 614 888-0246
Columbus (G-7734)

Visi-Trak Worldwide LLC ....F 216 524-2363
Cleveland (G-6421)

Vitec Inc ....F 216 464-4670
Bedford (G-1471)

Wabash River Conservancy ....G 419 375-2577
Fort Recovery (G-9962)

Weed Instrument Company Inc ....E 216 676-5005
Independence (G-11283)

Westerman Inc ....D 330 262-6946
Wooster (G-20846)

Wild Fire Systems ....G 440 442-8999
Cleveland (G-6462)

World Automtn Measurement Tech ....F 216 651-1883
Cleveland (G-6478)

Ysi Environmental Inc ....G 937 767-7241
Yellow Springs (G-21004)

◆ Ysi Incorporated ....D 937 767-7241
Yellow Springs (G-21005)

3824 Fluid Meters & Counters

Aclara Technologies LLC ....C 440 528-7200
Solon (G-17248)

Aqua Technology Group LLC ....G 513 298-1183
West Chester (G-19807)

Automatic Timing & Contrls Inc ....D 614 888-8855
New Albany (G-14747)

Bif Co LLC ....F 330 564-0941
Akron (G-92)

Brooks Manufacturing ....G 419 244-1777
Toledo (G-18382)

CNG Fueling LLC ....G 330 772-2403
Brookfield (G-2121)

Commercial Electric Pdts Corp ....E 216 241-2886
Cleveland (G-5104)

Eaton Corporation ....B 440 523-5000
Beachwood (G-1267)

Electrodynamics Inc ....C 847 259-0740
Cincinnati (G-3300)

Ernst Flow Industries LLC ....F 732 938-5641
Strongsville (G-17918)

Exact Equipment Corporation ....F 215 295-2000
Columbus (G-6645)

Flow Line Options Corp ....G 330 331-7331
Wadsworth (G-19407)

Fred W Hanks Company ....G 216 731-1774
Cleveland (G-5380)

Gilbarco Catlow LLC ....G 937 898-3236
Tipp City (G-18279)

▲ Graco Ohio Inc ....D 330 494-1313
North Canton (G-15235)

Hanger Prsthetcs & Ortho Inc ....G 440 892-6665
Westlake (G-20274)

Harris Instrument Corporation ....G 740 369-3580
Delaware (G-8857)

K-Hill Signal Co Inc ....G 740 922-0421
Uhrichsville (G-19054)

Lake Shore Cryotronics Inc ....C 614 891-2243
Westerville (G-20165)

Parking & Traffic Control SEC ....F 440 243-7565
Cleveland (G-5977)

▲ Triplett Bluffton Corporation ....G 419 358-8750
Bluffton (G-1919)

▼ United Process Controls Inc ....E 414 462-8200
West Chester (G-19967)

Westmont Inc ....G 330 862-3080
Minerva (G-14345)

3825 Instrs For Measuring & Testing Electricity

Accu-Feed Engineering ....F 419 668-7990
Norwalk (G-15524)

Aclara Technologies LLC ....C 440 528-7200
Solon (G-17248)

Advanced Kiffer Systems Inc ....F 216 267-8181
Cleveland (G-4714)

Alpine Gage Inc ....G....... 937 669-8665
Tipp City (G-18263)

Andeen-Hagerling Inc ....F....... 440 349-0370
Cleveland (G-4808)

Andromeda Research ....G....... 513 831-9708
Cincinnati (G-3403)

Aqua Technology Group LLC ....G....... 513 298-1183
West Chester (G-19807)

Ats Assembly and Test Inc ....B....... 937 222-3030
Dayton (G-8169)

Automation Technology Inc ....E....... 937 233-6084
Dayton (G-8174)

Automtiq Msurement Systems LLC ....G....... 614 431-2667
Columbus (G-6791)

Avtron Holdings LLC ....B....... 216 642-1230
Cleveland (G-4876)

Battery Unlimited ....G....... 740 452-5030
Zanesville (G-21276)

▲ Bird Electronic Corporation ....C....... 440 248-1200
Solon (G-17268)

Bird Technologies Group Inc ....G....... 440 248-1200
Solon (G-17269)

CDI Industries Inc ....E....... 440 243-1100
Cleveland (G-4999)

Community Care Network Inc ....E....... 216 671-0977
Cleveland (G-5108)

Complete Network Solutions Inc ....G....... 330 328-2596
Stow (G-17742)

Contact Industries Inc ....E....... 419 884-9788
Lexington (G-11949)

County of Medina ....F....... 330 723-3641
Medina (G-13397)

Data Power Solutions ....G....... 614 471-1911
Columbus (G-7013)

Desco Corporation ....G....... 614 888-8855
New Albany (G-14757)

Drs Signal Technologies Inc ....E....... 937 429-7470
Beavercreek (G-1333)

▲ Dynamp LLC ....E....... 614 871-6900
Grove City (G-10555)

F Squared Inc ....G....... 419 752-7273
Greenwich (G-10530)

Field Apparatus Service & Tstg ....G....... 513 353-9399
Cincinnati (G-3752)

Fisher Testers LLC ....G....... 937 416-6554
Huber Heights (G-11147)

FT Group Inc ....E....... 937 746-6439
Cincinnati (G-3786)

◆ Gould Electronics Inc ....C....... 440 953-5000
Eastlake (G-9271)

▲ Hana Microdisplay Tech Inc ....G....... 330 405-4600
Twinsburg (G-18954)

Hannon Company ....D....... 330 456-4728
Canton (G-2723)

Harris Instrument Corporation ....G....... 740 369-3580
Delaware (G-8857)

Helm Instrument Company Inc ....E....... 419 893-4356
Maumee (G-13265)

Hughes Corporation ....E....... 440 238-2550
Strongsville (G-17928)

Infinity Plus ....G....... 937 828-1350
Mechanicsburg (G-13357)

▲ Japlar Group Inc ....F....... 513 791-7192
Cincinnati (G-3942)

▲ Keithley Instruments LLC ....C....... 440 248-0400
Solon (G-17328)

Keithley Instruments Intl Corp ....B....... 440 248-0400
Cleveland (G-5642)

Key Principal Partners Corp ....F....... 888 539-3322
Cleveland (G-5651)

Lake Shore Cryotronics Inc ....C....... 614 891-2243
Westerville (G-20165)

Lawhorn Machine & Tool Inc ....G....... 937 884-5674
Phillipsburg (G-16184)

Lomar Enterprises Inc ....F....... 614 409-9104
Groveport (G-10633)

Machine Products Company ....G....... 937 890-6600
Dayton (G-8466)

Midwest Metrology LLC ....G....... 937 832-0965
Englewood (G-9533)

Midwest Telemetry Inc ....G....... 440 725-5718
Chesterland (G-3215)

Mueller Electric Company Inc ....E....... 614 888-8855
New Albany (G-14765)

National Safety Tech LLC ....E....... 419 727-0552
Toledo (G-18598)

Nebulatronics Inc ....E....... 440 243-2370
Olmsted Twp (G-15681)

Neptune Equipment Company ....F....... 513 851-8008
Cincinnati (G-4145)

Nu-Di Products Co Inc ....D....... 216 251-9070
Cleveland (G-5922)

O H Technologies Inc ....G....... 440 354-8780
Mentor (G-13670)

Omega Engineering Inc ....E....... 740 965-9340
Sunbury (G-18072)

▲ Opw Engineered Systems Inc ....D....... 888 771-9438
Lebanon (G-11824)

▼ Orton Edward Jr Crmic Fndation ....E....... 614 895-2663
Westerville (G-20176)

P G M Diversified Industries ....G....... 440 885-3500
Cleveland (G-5955)

P P M Inc ....F....... 216 701-0419
Chagrin Falls (G-3066)

Palstar Inc ....F....... 937 773-6255
Piqua (G-16298)

Paneltech LLC ....F....... 440 516-1300
Wickliffe (G-20378)

▲ Pile Dynamics Inc ....E....... 216 831-6131
Cleveland (G-6007)

▲ Pressco Technology Inc ....D....... 440 498-2600
Cleveland (G-6044)

▲ Prime Instruments Inc ....D....... 216 651-0400
Cleveland (G-6047)

Rosemount Analytical Inc ....C....... 440 914-1261
Solon (G-17372)

Simplex-It LLC ....G....... 234 380-1277
Stow (G-17800)

▲ Skidmore-Wilhelm Mfg Company ....E....... 216 481-4774
Solon (G-17381)

Speelman Electric Inc ....D....... 330 633-1410
Tallmadge (G-18169)

Strong M Llc ....F....... 614 329-8025
Columbus (G-7661)

▲ Tech Pro Inc ....E....... 330 923-3546
Akron (G-430)

Tektronix Inc ....E....... 513 870-4729
West Chester (G-20058)

Tektronix Inc ....E....... 440 248-0400
Solon (G-17402)

◆ Tmsi LLC ....F....... 888 867-4872
North Canton (G-15276)

▲ Triplett Bluffton Corporation ....G....... 419 358-8750
Bluffton (G-1919)

▲ TTI Floor Care North Amer Inc ......B....... 440 996-2000
Solon (G-17409)

Val-Con Inc ....G....... 440 357-1898
Painesville (G-15936)

Visual Information Institute ....F....... 937 376-4361
Xenia (G-20985)

▲ Vmetro Inc ....G....... 281 584-0728
Fairborn (G-9633)

▲ Zts Inc ....F....... 513 271-2557
Cincinnati (G-4620)

3826 Analytical Instruments

4r Enterprises Incorporated ....G....... 330 923-9799
Cuyahoga Falls (G-7960)

Acense LLC ....G....... 330 242-0046
Twinsburg (G-18891)

Affymetrix Inc ....C....... 216 765-5000
Cleveland (G-4729)

Affymetrix Inc ....F....... 419 887-1233
Maumee (G-13220)

Akron Council of Engineering ....G....... 330 535-8835
Akron (G-39)

Alliance Healthcare Svcs Inc ....D....... 330 493-6747
Canton (G-2598)

▲ Astro Instrumentation LLC ....D....... 440 238-2005
Strongsville (G-17889)

Auto Technology Company ....F....... 440 572-7800
Strongsville (G-17892)

Blue Water Satellite Inc ....G....... 419 372-0160
Toledo (G-18373)

▲ Bry-Air Inc ....E....... 740 965-2974
Sunbury (G-18056)

C D C At Cityview ....E....... 216 426-2020
Cleveland (G-4955)

◆ Columbus Instruments Intl Corp ....E....... 614 276-0593
Columbus (G-6956)

Compliant Healthcare Tech LLC ....F....... 216 255-9607
Cleveland (G-5111)

Compliant Healthcare Tech LLC ....E....... 216 255-9607
Cleveland (G-5112)

Consolidatd Analytical Sys Inc ....F....... 513 542-1200
Cleves (G-6511)

CST Zero Discharged Car Wash S ....G....... 740 947-5480
Waverly (G-19706)

Dentronix Inc ....E....... 330 916-7300
Cuyahoga Falls (G-7987)

Diascopic LLC ....G....... 312 282-1800
Cleveland (G-5191)

Doncasters Group Ltd ....G....... 440 329-0400
Elyria (G-9406)

Environ International Cor ....G....... 440 834-1460
Burton (G-2374)

Fertility Solutions Inc ....G....... 216 491-0030
Cleveland (G-5340)

Filament LLC ....G....... 614 732-0754
Columbus (G-7083)

Health Bridge Imaging LLC ....G....... 740 423-3300
Belpre (G-1587)

▲ HEF USA Corporation ....F....... 937 323-2556
Springfield (G-17572)

IEC Infrared Systems LLC ....G....... 440 234-8000
Middleburg Heights (G-13906)

Innovative Lab Services LLC ....G....... 614 554-6446
Pataskala (G-15972)

Isotopx Inc ....G....... 508 337-8467
Hudson (G-11183)

Koster Crop Tester Inc ....G....... 330 220-2116
Brunswick (G-2236)

▲ Laserlinc Inc ....E....... 937 318-2440
Fairborn (G-9626)

Mansfield Imaging Center LLC ....F....... 419 756-8899
Mansfield (G-12642)

Markes International Inc ....D....... 513 745-0241
Blue Ash (G-1832)

Measurenet Technology Ltd ....F....... 513 396-6765
Cincinnati (G-4073)

Metron Instruments Inc ....E....... 216 332-0592
Bedford Heights (G-1489)

Mettler-Toledo Intl Fin Inc ....G....... 614 438-4511
Columbus (G-6653)

◆ Mettler-Toledo Intl Inc ....B....... 614 438-4511
Columbus (G-6654)

Mettlr-Tledo Globl Hldings LLC ....G....... 614 438-4511
Columbus (G-6655)

Nanotronics Imaging Inc ....G....... 330 926-9809
Cuyahoga Falls (G-8028)

National Safety Tech LLC ....E....... 419 727-0552
Toledo (G-18598)

Nordson Uv Inc ....F....... 440 985-4573
Amherst (G-604)

Northcoast Environmental Labs ....G....... 330 342-3377
Streetsboro (G-17865)

Nvision Technology Inc ....F....... 412 254-4668
Norton (G-15519)

Ohio Lumex Co Inc ....G....... 440 264-2500
Solon (G-17355)

Omnitech Electronics Inc ....F....... 800 822-1344
Columbus (G-7442)

▼ Orton Edward Jr Crmic Fndation ....E....... 614 895-2663
Westerville (G-20176)

PMC Gage Inc ....E....... 440 953-1672
Willoughby (G-20572)

Precision Anlytical Instrs Inc ....D....... 513 984-1600
Blue Ash (G-1854)

▲ Q-Lab Corporation ....D....... 440 835-8700
Westlake (G-20298)

Quaker Chemical Corporation ....G....... 216 265-5079
Cleveland (G-6066)

Reid Asset Management Company ....E....... 216 642-3223
Cleveland (G-6098)

◆ Reuter-Stokes Inc ....B....... 330 425-3755
Twinsburg (G-19008)

◆ Rotex Global Lcc ....C....... 513 541-1236
Cincinnati (G-4359)

Spirit Solutions Inc ....G....... 937 431-8041
Moraine (G-14532)

Summit Diagnostic Imaging LLC ....E....... 513 233-3320
Cincinnati (G-4475)

Targeted Cmpund Monitoring LLC ....G....... 513 461-3535
Dayton (G-8701)

Teledyne Instruments Inc ....E....... 513 229-7000
Mason (G-13094)

Teledyne Tekmar Company ....E....... 513 229-7000
Mason (G-13095)

Thermo Fisher Scientific Inc ....G....... 440 703-1400
Bedford (G-1465)

◆ Ysi Incorporated ....D....... 937 767-7241
Yellow Springs (G-21005)

3827 Optical Instruments

Bright Eyes Inc ....G....... 937 277-9991
Dayton (G-8195)

Bsa Industries Inc ....D....... 614 846-5515
Columbus (G-6869)

▲ Cleveland Hoya Corp ....D....... 440 234-5703
Berea (G-1606)

FT Group Inc .... E 937 746-6439
Cincinnati **(G-3786)**

Genvac Aerospace Corp .... F 440 646-9986
Cleveland **(G-5424)**

Gooch & Housego (florida) LLC .... D 321 242-7818
Cleveland **(G-5437)**

Gooch & Housego (ohio) LLC .... D 216 486-6100
Highland Heights **(G-10914)**

Greenlight Optics LLC .... E 513 247-9777
Loveland **(G-12354)**

Harris Instrument Corporation .... G 740 369-3580
Delaware **(G-8857)**

Holte Eyeware .... G 513 321-4000
Cincinnati **(G-3890)**

Hoya Optical Labs .... G 440 239-1924
Berea **(G-1619)**

▼ Krendl Machine Company .... D 419 692-3060
Delphos **(G-8910)**

Lear Engineering Corp .... F 937 429-0534
Beavercreek **(G-1347)**

▲ Lens AC .... E 888 248-5367
Columbus **(G-7291)**

Mbm Industries Ltd .... G 937 522-0719
Beavercreek Township **(G-1385)**

Mercury Iron & Steel .... F 440 349-1500
Solon **(G-17334)**

Ncrx Optical Solutions Inc .... F 330 239-5353
Hudson **(G-11189)**

Point Source Inc .... F 937 855-6020
Germantown **(G-10373)**

Punch Components Inc .... E 419 224-1242
Lima **(G-12077)**

▲ Trevi Technology Inc .... G 614 754-7175
Columbus **(G-7708)**

Uvisir Inc .... G 216 374-9376
Beachwood **(G-1304)**

▲ Vampire Optical Coatings Inc ..... G 740 919-4596
Pataskala **(G-15989)**

Vance Adams .... G 330 424-9670
Lisbon **(G-12134)**

▲ Volk Optical Inc .... D 440 942-6161
Mentor **(G-13768)**

Vsp Lab Columbus .... E 614 409-8900
Lockbourne **(G-12152)**

Welded Tube Pros LLC .... G 330 854-2966
Canal Fulton **(G-2517)**

Wilson Optical Laboratory Inc .... F 440 357-7000
Mentor **(G-13769)**

3829 Measuring & Controlling Devices, NEC

1 A Lifesafer Hawaii Inc .... F 513 651-9560
Blue Ash **(G-1730)**

Aclara Technologies LLC .... C 440 528-7200
Solon **(G-17248)**

Acuren Inspection Inc .... G 419 698-5040
Oregon **(G-15700)**

▲ Advanced Industrial Measuremnt ... E 937 320-4930
Miamisburg **(G-13780)**

Advanced OEM Solutions LLC .... G 513 846-5755
Liberty Township **(G-11957)**

Amano Cincinnati Incorporated ..... D 513 697-9000
Loveland **(G-12338)**

American Cube Mold Inc .... G 330 558-0044
Hinckley **(G-11022)**

American Ndt Incorporated .... F 740 687-1321
Lancaster **(G-11684)**

Amron LLC .... G 330 457-8570
New Waterford **(G-14968)**

ARC Drilling Inc .... F 216 525-0920
Cleveland **(G-4822)**

▲ Arnco Corporation .... C 800 847-7661
Elyria **(G-9375)**

AT&T Government Solutions Inc ..... D 937 306-3030
Beavercreek **(G-1320)**

Automation and Ctrl Tech Inc .... E 614 495-1120
Dublin **(G-9050)**

Automation Technology Inc .... E 937 233-6084
Dayton **(G-8174)**

Balmac Inc .... F 614 873-8222
Plain City **(G-16324)**

▲ Bilz Vibration Technology Inc ...... F 330 468-2459
Macedonia **(G-12437)**

▲ Bionix Development Corporation ... E 419 727-8421
Toledo **(G-18368)**

Blaze Technical Services Inc .... E 330 923-0409
Stow **(G-17736)**

▲ Ceia Usa Ltd .... G 330 405-3190
Twinsburg **(G-18909)**

Certified Pressure Testing LLC .... G 740 374-2071
Marietta **(G-12773)**

Cincinnati Ctrl Dynamics Inc .... G 513 242-7300
Cincinnati **(G-3547)**

Continental Testing Inc .... F 937 832-3322
Union **(G-19065)**

Control Measurement Inc .... G 440 639-0020
Painesville **(G-15869)**

▲ Controlled Access Inc .... F 330 273-6185
Hinckley **(G-11023)**

Corcadence Inc .... G 216 702-6371
Beachwood **(G-1265)**

David Boswell .... E 614 441-2497
Columbus **(G-7014)**

Daytronic Corporation .... F 937 866-3300
Miamisburg **(G-13800)**

Denton Atd Inc .... E 567 265-5200
Huron **(G-11220)**

Electric Speed Indicator Co .... F 216 251-2540
Cleveland **(G-5265)**

▲ Ets Solutions Usa LLC .... G 330 666-8696
Bath **(G-1237)**

Euclid Products Co Inc .... G 440 942-7310
Willoughby **(G-20482)**

Excelitas Technologies Corp .... C 937 865-4621
Miamisburg **(G-13807)**

▲ Ferry Industries Inc .... D 330 920-9200
Stow **(G-17753)**

Fiomet LLC .... G 513 519-7622
Cincinnati **(G-3757)**

Fischer Engineering Company .... G 937 754-1750
Dayton **(G-8343)**

▲ Fluke Biomedical LLC .... C 440 248-9300
Cleveland **(G-5362)**

▲ Fowler Products Inc .... F 419 683-4057
Crestline **(G-7929)**

Furnace Control Corp .... E 513 772-1000
West Chester **(G-19870)**

Gem Instrument Co .... G 330 273-6117
Brunswick **(G-2229)**

Gilson Screen Incorporated .... E 419 256-7711
Malinta **(G-12534)**

Glass Sensors LLC .... G 330 234-7999
Wooster **(G-20776)**

GLC Biotechnology Inc .... G 440 349-2193
Hudson **(G-11173)**

◆ Gleason Metrology Systems Corp ... E 937 384-8901
Dayton **(G-8365)**

Global Gauge Corporation .... F 937 222-0797
Moraine **(G-14491)**

Grale Technologies Inc .... G 724 683-8141
Youngstown **(G-21102)**

Halliday Technologies Inc .... G 614 504-4150
Plain City **(G-16345)**

Harris Instrument Corporation .... G 740 369-3580
Delaware **(G-8857)**

Helm Instrument Company Inc .... E 419 893-4356
Maumee **(G-13265)**

Henry & Wright Corporation .... F 216 851-3750
Cleveland **(G-5500)**

Heraeus Electro-Nite Co LLC .... G 330 725-1419
Medina **(G-13421)**

Hickok Incorporated .... D 216 541-8060
Cleveland **(G-5513)**

Honeywell International Inc .... C 614 850-5000
Columbus **(G-7163)**

Honeywell International Inc .... C 614 850-5000
Columbus **(G-7164)**

▲ Honeywell Lebow Products .... C 614 850-5000
Columbus **(G-7165)**

Indicator Shop .... G 513 897-0055
Waynesville **(G-19730)**

Industrial Masurement Ctrl Inc .... G 440 877-1140
Cleveland **(G-5565)**

Instrumentors Inc .... G 440 238-3430
Strongsville **(G-17931)**

J C Equipment Sales & Lsg .... G 513 772-7612
Cincinnati **(G-3934)**

Karman Rubber Company .... E 330 864-2161
Akron **(G-251)**

Krumor Inc .... F 216 328-9802
Cleveland **(G-5667)**

L H Marshall Co .... F 614 294-6433
Columbus **(G-7277)**

Lake Shore Cryotronics Inc .... C 614 891-2243
Westerville **(G-20165)**

Lawhorn Machine & Tool Inc .... G 937 884-5674
Phillipsburg **(G-16184)**

Low Stress Grind Inc .... G 513 771-7977
Cincinnati **(G-4034)**

LS Starrett Company .... D 440 835-0005
Westlake **(G-20282)**

Magnetic Analysis Corporation ...... F 330 758-1367
Youngstown **(G-21140)**

Matrix Measuring System .... G 330 718-2804
Newton Falls **(G-15136)**

Matrix Research Inc .... E 937 427-8433
Beavercreek **(G-1350)**

MB Dynamics Inc .... E 216 292-5850
Cleveland **(G-5768)**

Measurement Specialties Inc .... G 330 659-3312
Akron **(G-293)**

Micro Laboratories Inc .... G 440 918-0001
Mentor **(G-13655)**

Micro Systems Development Inc ..... G 937 438-3567
Dayton **(G-8493)**

Multi Lapping Service Inc .... F 440 944-7592
Wickliffe **(G-20373)**

▲ Multilink Inc .... C 440 366-6966
Elyria **(G-9465)**

Nanologix Inc .... G 330 534-0800
Hubbard **(G-11135)**

National Patent Analytical Sys .... E 419 526-6727
Mansfield **(G-12655)**

National Safety Tech LLC .... E 419 727-0552
Toledo **(G-18598)**

Nebulatronics Inc .... E 440 243-2370
Olmsted Twp **(G-15681)**

▲ Newall Electronics Inc .... F 614 771-0213
Columbus **(G-7388)**

Nidec Motor Corporation .... C 216 642-1230
Independence **(G-11268)**

Novitran LLC .... G 513 792-2727
Cincinnati **(G-4166)**

Nuclear Physicians Limited .... G 330 920-3770
Stow **(G-17785)**

▲ Nucon International Inc .... F 614 846-5710
Columbus **(G-7405)**

Omega Automation Inc .... D 937 890-2350
Dayton **(G-8548)**

Omega Engineering Inc .... E 740 965-9340
Sunbury **(G-18072)**

Omega International Inc .... E 937 890-2350
Dayton **(G-8549)**

Overhoff Technology Corp .... F 513 248-2400
Milford **(G-14165)**

P H Glatfelter Company .... F 740 289-5100
Piketon **(G-16226)**

◆ Parker-Hannifin Corporation .... B 216 896-3000
Cleveland **(G-5973)**

Parker-Hannifin Corporation .... F 216 896-3000
Cleveland **(G-5976)**

▲ Perfect Measuring Tape Company ... G 419 243-6811
Toledo **(G-18639)**

Plating Test Cell Supply Co .... G 216 486-8400
Cleveland **(G-6017)**

PMC Gage Inc .... E 440 953-1672
Willoughby **(G-20572)**

▲ Portage Electric Products Inc .... C 330 499-2727
North Canton **(G-15259)**

Precision Environments Inc .... E 513 847-1510
West Chester **(G-19919)**

Prentke Romich Company .... C 330 202-5800
Wooster **(G-20825)**

▲ Pressco Technology Inc .... D 440 498-2600
Cleveland **(G-6044)**

▼ Production Control Units Inc .... D 937 299-5594
Moraine **(G-14519)**

▲ Q-Lab Corporation .... D 440 835-8700
Westlake **(G-20298)**

Quality Controls Inc .... F 513 272-3900
Cincinnati **(G-4306)**

R J Engineering Company Inc .... G 419 843-8651
Toledo **(G-18667)**

Ralston Instruments LLC .... E 440 564-1430
Newbury **(G-15103)**

◆ Reuter-Stokes Inc .... B 330 425-3755
Twinsburg **(G-19008)**

Rickly Hydrological Company .... G 614 297-9877
Columbus **(G-7563)**

Roberts Group Inc .... G 614 486-0497
Columbus **(G-7569)**

Rosemount Analytical Inc .... C 440 914-1261
Solon **(G-17372)**

Safe-Grain Inc .... G 513 398-2500
Loveland **(G-12383)**

◆ Saginomiya America Inc .... F 614 766-7390
Dublin **(G-9136)**

Schneider Instrument Co .... F 513 561-6803
Cincinnati **(G-4388)**

Science/Electronics Inc .... F 937 224-4444
Dayton **(G-8648)**

S
I
C

Sensotec LLC ....G....... 614 481-8616
Hilliard *(G-10978)*

▲ Skidmore-Wilhelm Mfg Company ....E....... 216 481-4774
Solon *(G-17381)*

▲ Standards Testing Labs Inc ....E....... 330 833-8548
Massillon *(G-13203)*

◆ Struers Inc ....D....... 440 871-0071
Westlake *(G-20313)*

◆ Sumiriko Ohio Inc ....C....... 419 358-2121
Bluffton *(G-1916)*

Super Systems Inc ....E....... 513 772-0060
Cincinnati *(G-4483)*

▲ Te-Co Manufacturing LLC ....D....... 937 836-0961
Union *(G-19068)*

▲ Tech Pro Inc ....E....... 330 923-3546
Akron *(G-430)*

Tech Products Corporation ....G....... 937 438-1100
Miamisburg *(G-13867)*

Tegam Inc ....E....... 440 466-6100
Geneva *(G-10357)*

Teledyne Instruments Inc ....E....... 513 229-7000
Mason *(G-13094)*

Teledyne Tekmar Company ....E....... 513 229-7000
Mason *(G-13095)*

Test Mark Industries Inc ....F....... 330 426-2200
East Palestine *(G-9246)*

Thermo Eberline LLC ....C....... 440 703-1400
Oakwood Village *(G-15629)*

Tmw Systems Inc ....F....... 615 986-1900
Cleveland *(G-6328)*

Toledo Transducers Inc ....E....... 419 724-4170
Holland *(G-11090)*

Tool Technologies Van Dyke ....F....... 937 349-4900
Marysville *(G-12975)*

Tripoint Instruments Inc ....E....... 513 702-9217
Cincinnati *(G-4527)*

Tuppas Software Corporation ....C....... 419 897-7902
Maumee *(G-13304)*

◆ UPA Technology Inc ....F....... 513 755-1380
West Chester *(G-19969)*

Vibration Test Systems Inc ....G....... 330 562-5729
Aurora *(G-954)*

Welding Consultants Inc ....G....... 614 258-7018
Columbus *(G-7756)*

Womens Imaging Center LLC ....E....... 614 457-7660
Columbus *(G-7772)*

Xcite Systems Corporation ....G....... 513 965-0300
Cincinnati *(G-3321)*

3841 Surgical & Medical Instrs & Apparatus

3d Systems Inc ....D....... 216 229-2040
Cleveland *(G-4665)*

3M Company ....B....... 513 248-1749
Milford *(G-14118)*

Acela Biomedical ....F....... 937 544-8618
Winchester *(G-20689)*

Acouflow Therapeutics LLC ....G....... 513 558-0073
Cincinnati *(G-3350)*

Advanced Med Interfaces LLC ....G....... 937 361-8385
Lebanon *(G-11775)*

Advanced Medical Solutions Inc .....G....... 937 291-0069
Centerville *(G-3033)*

Aeiou Scientific LLC ....G....... 614 325-2103
Columbus *(G-6699)*

Altitude Medical Inc ....G....... 440 799-7701
Chardon *(G-3139)*

Applied Medical Technology Inc .....E....... 440 717-4000
Brecksville *(G-2034)*

Apto Orthopaedics Corporation ......E....... 330 572-7544
Akron *(G-70)*

▲ Atc Group Inc ....D....... 440 293-4064
Andover *(G-612)*

Atricure Inc ....E....... 513 755-4100
Mason *(G-12985)*

Avalign Technologies Inc ....F....... 419 542-7743
Hicksville *(G-10900)*

Aws Industries Inc ....E....... 513 932-7941
Lebanon *(G-11782)*

Axon Medical LLC ....E....... 216 276-0262
Medina *(G-13374)*

Baby Love Prenatal Imaging LLC .....G....... 419 905-7935
Delphos *(G-8901)*

Beam Technologies Inc ....G....... 800 648-1179
Columbus *(G-6815)*

▲ Bionix Development Corporation ....E....... 419 727-8421
Toledo *(G-18368)*

Blue Bell Bio-Medical Inc ....G....... 419 238-4442
Van Wert *(G-19245)*

Boston Scntfc Nrmdlation Corp ....G....... 419 720-9510
Toledo *(G-18377)*

Broad Street Imaging ....G....... 614 621-9100
Columbus *(G-6643)*

Buckeye Medical Tech LLC ....G....... 330 719-9868
Warren *(G-19531)*

Bulk Molding Compounds Inc ....D....... 419 874-7941
Perrysburg *(G-16071)*

▲ Casco Mfg Solutions Inc ....D....... 513 681-0003
Cincinnati *(G-3504)*

Clevex Inc ....G....... 614 675-3757
Columbus *(G-6938)*

Collaborative For Adaptive Lif ....G....... 216 513-0572
Fairlawn *(G-9746)*

Cqt Kennedy LLC ....D....... 419 238-2442
Van Wert *(G-19252)*

▼ Daavlin Distributing Co ....E....... 419 636-6304
Bryan *(G-2293)*

▲ Dayton Hawker Corporation ....F....... 937 293-8147
Dayton *(G-8276)*

Dentronix Inc ....G....... 330 916-7300
Cuyahoga Falls *(G-7987)*

Devicor Med Pdts Holdings Inc ....A....... 513 864-9000
Cincinnati *(G-3652)*

Devicor Medical Products Inc ....G....... 513 864-9000
Cincinnati *(G-3653)*

Diagnostic Hybrids Inc ....C....... 740 593-1784
Athens *(G-861)*

Drt Medical LLC ....G....... 937 298-7391
Dayton *(G-8312)*

Ebisyn Medical Inc ....G....... 609 759-1101
Dublin *(G-9071)*

Elite Biomedical Solutions LLC ....F....... 513 207-0602
Cincinnati *(G-3301)*

Ellen L Ellsworth ....G....... 440 352-8031
Mentor *(G-13571)*

▲ Em Innovations Inc ....G....... 614 853-1504
Galloway *(G-10313)*

▲ Encore Plastics Corporation ....F....... 419 626-8000
Sandusky *(G-16962)*

Ennovea Medical LLC ....G....... 855 997-2273
Columbus *(G-7060)*

▼ Eoi Inc ....F....... 740 201-3300
Lewis Center *(G-11897)*

Estech Inc ....G....... 805 895-1263
West Chester *(G-19860)*

Ethicon Endo-Surgery Inc ....A....... 513 337-7000
Blue Ash *(G-1786)*

Ethicon US LLC ....E....... 513 337-7000
Blue Ash *(G-1788)*

Eye Center ....E....... 614 228-3937
Columbus *(G-7074)*

▲ Falls Welding & Fabg Inc ....G....... 330 253-3437
Akron *(G-180)*

Filament LLC ....G....... 614 732-0754
Columbus *(G-7083)*

Findlay American Prosthetic & ....G....... 419 424-1622
Findlay *(G-9822)*

Flotbi Inc ....G....... 216 619-5928
Cleveland *(G-5359)*

Fountain of Youth ....G....... 937 723-9743
Centerville *(G-3042)*

Frantz Medical Development Ltd ......G....... 212 308-4860
Mentor *(G-13582)*

Frantz Medical Development Ltd ......D....... 440 205-9026
Mentor *(G-13583)*

Fresenius Med Care Hldings Inc ......G....... 216 661-1627
Cleveland *(G-5381)*

General Data Company Inc ....E....... 919 384-0037
Cincinnati *(G-3306)*

▲ General Data Company Inc ....C....... 513 752-7978
Cincinnati *(G-3304)*

Goal Medical LLC ....E....... 541 654-5951
Mentor *(G-13595)*

Gqi Inc ....G....... 330 830-9805
Massillon *(G-13141)*

Grimm Scientific Industries ....F....... 740 374-3412
Marietta *(G-12787)*

Gyrus Acmi LP ....C....... 419 668-8201
Norwalk *(G-15542)*

Haag-Streit Holding Us Inc ....E....... 513 336-7255
Mason *(G-13033)*

Hill-Rom Holdings Inc ....G....... 937 604-6019
Lima *(G-12025)*

I D X Medical Ltd ....G....... 513 583-9081
Loveland *(G-12359)*

Immersus Health Company LLC ......G....... 855 994-4325
Cincinnati *(G-3912)*

Immersus Health Company LLC ......G....... 855 994-4325
Blue Ash *(G-1814)*

▲ Innovative Medical Eqp LLC ....G....... 440 646-1286
Cleveland *(G-5572)*

Integrated Med Solutions Inc ....D....... 440 269-6984
Mentor *(G-13609)*

Integrted Med Systems Intl Inc ....E....... 800 783-9251
Stow *(G-17765)*

Intellirod Spine Inc ....G....... 234 678-8965
Akron *(G-234)*

▲ Invacare Holdings Corporation ......G....... 440 329-6000
Elyria *(G-9438)*

Invacare International Corp ....G....... 440 329-6000
Elyria *(G-9439)*

▲ Invacare Respiratory Corp ....E....... 440 329-6000
Elyria *(G-9440)*

Klarity Medical Products LLC ....F....... 740 788-8107
Newark *(G-15027)*

Lababidi Enterprises Inc ....E....... 330 733-2907
Akron *(G-266)*

Lifes Products Inc ....G....... 740 965-9711
Sunbury *(G-18066)*

Liquid Logic LLC ....G....... 937 865-3068
Miamisburg *(G-13826)*

M & S Acquistion Co LLC ....E....... 440 951-8700
Mentor *(G-13638)*

Mac Dhui Probe of America Inc ....G....... 440 942-5597
Mentor *(G-13640)*

Majors Wholesale Med Sup LLC ......G....... 800 376-7263
Cleveland *(G-5733)*

Medinvent LLC ....G....... 330 247-0921
Medina *(G-13446)*

◆ Midmark Corporation ....A....... 937 526-3662
Versailles *(G-19352)*

▲ Mill-Rose Company ....C....... 440 255-9171
Mentor *(G-13657)*

Minimally Invasive Devices Inc ....E....... 614 484-5036
Columbus *(G-7356)*

▲ Mobility Revolution LLC ....G....... 909 980-2259
Cleveland *(G-5825)*

Morris Technologies Inc ....C....... 513 733-1611
Cincinnati *(G-4123)*

Morrison Medical ....E....... 614 461-4400
Columbus *(G-7370)*

▲ National Biological Corp ....E....... 216 831-0600
Beachwood *(G-1283)*

Neptune Aquatic Systems Inc ....G....... 513 575-2989
Loveland *(G-12375)*

Nervive Inc ....F....... 847 274-1790
Akron *(G-312)*

New Leaf Medical Inc ....G....... 216 391-7749
Cleveland *(G-5878)*

North Coast Medi-Tek Inc ....F....... 440 974-0750
Mentor *(G-13668)*

Office Bsed Ansthesia Svcs LLC .....G....... 513 582-5170
Montgomery *(G-14435)*

Olentangy Eye and Laser A ....G....... 614 267-4122
Columbus *(G-7441)*

Optoquest Inc ....G....... 216 445-3637
Cleveland *(G-5944)*

Patriot Products Inc ....F....... 419 865-9712
Holland *(G-11076)*

Pediavascular Inc ....F....... 216 236-5533
Chagrin Falls *(G-3111)*

Pemco Inc ....G....... 216 524-2990
Cleveland *(G-5989)*

Percuvision LLC ....F....... 614 891-4800
Columbus *(G-7478)*

Perfusion Solutions Inc ....G....... 216 848-1610
Cleveland *(G-5993)*

Philips Medical Systems Clevel ......E....... 440 473-3001
Mentor *(G-13686)*

Prentke Romich Company ....C....... 330 202-5800
Wooster *(G-20825)*

Quality Electrodynamics LLC ....C....... 440 638-5106
Mayfield Village *(G-13326)*

▲ R-Med Inc ....G....... 419 693-7481
Oregon *(G-15714)*

REA Incorporated ....G....... 330 666-7414
Akron *(G-369)*

◆ Reliance Medical Products Inc ....D....... 513 398-3937
Mason *(G-13080)*

Resonetics LLC ....D....... 937 865-4070
Kettering *(G-11585)*

Rhinosystems Inc ....F....... 216 351-6262
Independence *(G-11272)*

RJR Surgical Inc ....G....... 216 241-2804
Cleveland *(G-6119)*

Rockdale Systems LLC ....G....... 513 379-3577
Cincinnati *(G-4355)*

Rsb Spine LLC ....F....... 216 241-2804
Cleveland *(G-6141)*

Rultract Inc ....G....... 216 524-2990
Cleveland *(G-6144)*

Scottcare Corporation .... E 216 362-0550
Cleveland *(G-6175)*

Secqure Surgical Corp .... G 513 769-1916
Blue Ash *(G-1867)*

Securus Medical Group Inc .... G 216 445-4683
Cleveland *(G-6178)*

Sense Diagnostics LLC .... G 513 515-3853
Cincinnati *(G-4405)*

Smiths Medical Asd Inc .... C 614 889-2220
Dublin *(G-9145)*

Smiths Medical North America .... G 614 210-7300
Dublin *(G-9146)*

◆ Smiths Medical Pm Inc .... F 614 210-7300
Dublin *(G-9147)*

Sonogage Inc .... F 216 464-1119
Cleveland *(G-6220)*

Sparton Medical Systems Inc .... G 440 878-4630
Strongsville *(G-17969)*

◆ Steris Corporation .... F 440 354-2600
Mentor *(G-13733)*

Suarez Corporation Industries .... E 330 494-4282
Canton *(G-2861)*

Summit Online Products LLC .... G 800 326-1972
Powell *(G-16485)*

▼ Surgical Theater LLC .... G 216 452-2177
Mayfield Village *(G-13327)*

Surgical Theater LLC .... G 216 496-7884
Cleveland *(G-6276)*

Surgrx Inc .... F 650 482-2400
Blue Ash *(G-1878)*

Synergy Health North Amer Inc .... D 513 398-6406
Mason *(G-13093)*

Theken Companies LLC .... E 330 733-7600
Akron *(G-437)*

Thermo Fisher Scientific Inc .... C 800 871-8909
Oakwood Village *(G-15630)*

Thompson Partners Inc .... G 866 475-2500
Gahanna *(G-10238)*

Torbot Group Inc .... E 419 724-1475
Toledo *(G-18751)*

▲ Transdermal Inc .... F 440 241-1846
Gates Mills *(G-10338)*

◆ Tri-Tech Medical Inc .... F 800 253-8692
Avon *(G-1017)*

Triatrix LLC .... G 440 263-8936
Cleveland *(G-6362)*

Troy Innovative Instrs Inc .... E 440 834-9567
Middlefield *(G-13996)*

United States Endoscopy .... G 440 639-4494
Mentor *(G-13760)*

▲ United States Endoscopy .... F 440 639-4494
Mentor *(G-13761)*

Venturemedgroup Ltd .... G 567 661-0768
Toledo *(G-18766)*

Vertebration Inc .... G 614 395-3346
Powell *(G-16487)*

Vesco Medical LLC .... G 614 914-5991
Columbus *(G-7736)*

World Wide Medical Physics Inc .... G 419 266-7530
Perrysburg *(G-16172)*

◆ Ysi Incorporated .... D 937 767-7241
Yellow Springs *(G-21005)*

3842 Orthopedic, Prosthetic & Surgical Appliances/Splys

ABI Orthtc/Prosthetic Labs Ltd .... E 330 758-1143
Youngstown *(G-21013)*

Ace Prosthetics Inc .... G 614 291-8325
Columbus *(G-6687)*

Acela Biomedical .... F 937 544-8618
Winchester *(G-20689)*

▲ Acor Orthopaedic Inc .... D 216 662-4500
Cleveland *(G-4695)*

Acor Orthopaedic Inc .... G 440 532-0117
Cleveland *(G-4696)*

Action Prosthetics LLC .... G 937 548-9100
Greenville *(G-10487)*

Advanced Arm Dynamics .... G 440 617-6601
Westlake *(G-20245)*

Akron Ent Hearing Services Inc .... G 330 762-8959
Akron *(G-41)*

Akron Orthotic Solutions Inc .... G 330 253-3002
Akron *(G-49)*

American Orthopedics Inc .... E 614 291-6454
Columbus *(G-6741)*

American Ride Wheelchair Coach .... G 216 276-1700
Cleveland *(G-4794)*

Anatomical Concepts Inc .... F 330 757-3569
Youngstown *(G-21026)*

Anderson Cosmetic & Vein Inst .... G 513 624-7900
Cincinnati *(G-3402)*

Ansell Healthcare Products LLC .... D 740 622-4311
Coshocton *(G-7879)*

Ansell Healthcare Products LLC .... C 740 295-5414
Coshocton *(G-7880)*

Apex Fire Services LLC .... G 614 274-6400
Columbus *(G-6761)*

Arthur W Guilford III Inc .... G 216 362-1350
Cleveland *(G-4837)*

Avalign Technologies Inc .... F 419 542-7743
Hicksville *(G-10900)*

Axon Medical LLC .... E 216 276-0262
Medina *(G-13374)*

Bahler Medical Inc .... E 614 873-7600
Plain City *(G-16323)*

Barton-Carey Medical Products .... E 419 887-1285
Maumee *(G-13230)*

▲ Beaufort Rfd Inc .... F 330 239-4331
Sharon Center *(G-17102)*

Beeline Purchasing LLC .... G 513 703-3733
Mason *(G-12989)*

Beiersdorf Inc .... C 513 682-7300
West Chester *(G-19984)*

Bills Sports Center .... G 419 335-2405
Wauseon *(G-19672)*

Biocare Orthopedic .... G 614 754-7514
Canal Winchester *(G-2520)*

Boston Scntfic Nrmdlation Corp .... C 330 372-2652
Warren *(G-19530)*

Brace Sp Prsthtic Orthtic Ctrs .... F 513 421-5653
Cincinnati *(G-3465)*

Bracemart LLC .... G 440 353-2830
North Ridgeville *(G-15362)*

Bulk Molding Compounds Inc .... D 419 874-7941
Perrysburg *(G-16071)*

Canton Orthotic Laboratory .... G 330 833-0955
Canton *(G-2644)*

Capital Prosthetic & .... F 614 451-0446
Columbus *(G-6899)*

Capital Prosthetic & .... G 567 560-2051
Mansfield *(G-12574)*

Capital Prosthetic & .... G 740 453-9545
Zanesville *(G-21286)*

Capital Prosthetic & .... G 614 451-0446
Columbus *(G-6900)*

Capital Prosthetic & .... G 740 522-3331
Newark *(G-14991)*

Cardinal Health Inc .... A 614 757-5000
Dublin *(G-9057)*

Catech Inc .... E 937 439-0432
Dayton *(G-8215)*

Central Ohio Orthtic Prsthetic .... G 614 659-1580
Dublin *(G-9060)*

▲ Chester West Holdings Inc .... C 800 647-1900
Sharonville *(G-17113)*

Cleveland Medical Devices Inc .... E 216 426-0365
Cleveland *(G-5068)*

Cole Orthotics Prosthetic Ctr .... G 419 476-4248
Toledo *(G-18405)*

Columbus Prescr Rehabilitation .... G 614 294-1600
Westerville *(G-20204)*

Communications Aid Inc .... F 513 475-8453
Cincinnati *(G-3599)*

Comprhnsive Brace Limb Ctr LLC ...... G 330 337-8333
Salem *(G-16885)*

▲ Daishin Industrial Co .... G 614 766-9535
Dublin *(G-9067)*

Deco Tools Inc .... E 419 476-9321
Toledo *(G-18430)*

Dentronix Inc .... E 330 916-7300
Cuyahoga Falls *(G-7987)*

Depuy Orthopaedics Inc .... E 937 274-5850
Dayton *(G-8299)*

Doling & Associates Dental Lab .... E 937 254-0075
Dayton *(G-8307)*

DPM Orthodontics Inc .... G 330 673-0334
Kent *(G-11451)*

Dynamic Control North Amer Inc .... G 440 979-0657
North Olmsted *(G-15330)*

Ear Medical Center Inc .... F 812 537-0031
Cincinnati *(G-3684)*

Earthwalk Orthotic .... G 330 837-6569
Massillon *(G-13128)*

Ent Physicians Inc .... F 419 698-4505
Oregon *(G-15708)*

Ethicon Inc .... C 513 786-7000
Blue Ash *(G-1787)*

Evanko Wm/Barringer Richd DDS ...... G 330 336-6693
Wadsworth *(G-19405)*

▲ Faretec Inc .... F 440 350-9510
Painesville *(G-15880)*

Fidelity Orthopedic Inc .... G 937 228-0682
Dayton *(G-8341)*

Findlay American Prosthetic & .... G 419 424-1622
Findlay *(G-9822)*

Foot Logic Inc .... G 330 699-0123
Uniontown *(G-19084)*

Forbes Rehab Services Inc .... G 419 589-7688
Mansfield *(G-12606)*

Forceone LLC .... E 513 939-1018
Hebron *(G-10865)*

Francisco Jaume .... G 740 622-1200
Coshocton *(G-7891)*

▲ Frohock-Stewart Inc .... E 440 329-6000
North Ridgeville *(G-15375)*

Gaitwell Orthotics Pedorthics .... G 513 829-2217
Cincinnati *(G-3793)*

◆ Gelok International Corp .... F 419 352-1482
Dunbridge *(G-9169)*

Gendron Wheel LLC .... G 419 445-6060
Archbold *(G-677)*

Gottfried Medical Inc .... G 419 474-2973
Toledo *(G-18484)*

▲ Guardian Manufacturing Co LLC ... G 419 933-2711
Willard *(G-20395)*

Hall Safety Apparel Inc .... F 740 922-3671
Uhrichsville *(G-19051)*

Hammill Manufacturing Co .... G 419 476-0789
Maumee *(G-13264)*

Hanger Prosthetics & Orthotics .... D 614 436-3516
Columbus *(G-6648)*

Hanger Prsthetcs & Ortho Inc .... G 440 605-0232
Mayfield Heights *(G-13316)*

Hanger Prsthetcs & Ortho Inc .... G 330 670-8263
Akron *(G-214)*

Hanger Prsthetcs & Ortho Inc .... G 614 471-8210
Gahanna *(G-10208)*

Hanger Prsthetcs & Ortho Inc .... G 440 842-4251
Cleveland *(G-5477)*

Hanger Prsthetcs & Ortho Inc .... F 419 841-9852
Toledo *(G-18495)*

Hanger Prsthetcs & Ortho Inc .... G 330 374-9544
Akron *(G-215)*

Hanger Prsthetcs & Ortho Inc .... G 330 856-6990
Warren *(G-19556)*

Hanger Prsthetcs & Ortho Inc .... G 937 773-2441
Piqua *(G-16269)*

Hanger Prsthetcs & Ortho Inc .... F 937 228-5462
Dayton *(G-8384)*

Hanger Prsthetcs & Ortho Inc .... G 740 383-2163
Marion *(G-12872)*

Hanger Prsthetcs & Ortho Inc .... G 740 266-6400
Steubenville *(G-17697)*

Hanger Prsthetcs & Ortho Inc .... G 740 446-6879
Gallipolis *(G-10299)*

Hanger Prsthetcs & Ortho Inc .... F 614 481-8338
Columbus *(G-7142)*

Hanger Prsthetcs & Ortho Inc .... G 740 369-2424
Marysville *(G-12947)*

Hanger Prsthetcs & Ortho Inc .... G 419 522-0055
Marion *(G-12871)*

Hanger Prsthetcs & Ortho Inc .... G 740 354-4775
Portsmouth *(G-16437)*

Hanger Prsthetcs & Ortho Inc .... G 740 654-1884
Lancaster *(G-11722)*

Hanger Prsthetcs & Ortho Inc .... G 740 454-6215
Zanesville *(G-21317)*

Healthwares Manufacturing .... F 513 353-3691
Cincinnati *(G-3874)*

Hearing Aid Center of NW Ohio .... G 419 636-8959
Bryan *(G-2301)*

Integrated Med Solutions Inc .... D 440 269-6984
Mentor *(G-13609)*

Interplex Medical LLC .... E 513 248-5120
Milford *(G-14154)*

Invacare Canadian Holdings LLC .... G 440 329-6000
Elyria *(G-9434)*

◆ Invacare Corporation .... A 440 329-6000
Elyria *(G-9435)*

Invacare Corporation .... D 800 333-6900
Elyria *(G-9436)*

Invacare Corporation .... F 440 329-6000
Elyria *(G-9437)*

Invacare Corporation .... F 440 329-6000
North Ridgeville *(G-15381)*

◆ Invacare Corporation (tw) .... E 440 329-6000
North Ridgeville *(G-15382)*

▲ Invacare Holdings Corporation ...... G 440 329-6000
Elyria *(G-9438)*

Invacare International Corp ....G..... 440 329-6000
Elyria *(G-9439)*

▲ Isomedix Inc ....F..... 440 354-2600
Mentor *(G-13612)*

▲ JI Safety LLC ....G..... 440 582-5866
Broadview Heights *(G-2112)*

Jobskin Div of Torbot Group ....E..... 419 724-1475
Toledo *(G-18535)*

Joint Vue LLC ....G..... 614 640-3350
Columbus *(G-7243)*

Jones Metal Products Company ......D..... 740 545-6381
West Lafayette *(G-20087)*

Jones Metal Products Company ......E..... 740 545-6341
West Lafayette *(G-20088)*

▲ Julius Zorn Inc ....D..... 330 923-4999
Cuyahoga Falls *(G-8015)*

Kempf Surgical Appliances Inc .....E..... 513 984-5758
Montgomery *(G-14433)*

Kufbag Inc ....G..... 614 589-8687
Westerville *(G-20221)*

Kuhlmanns Fabrication ....G..... 513 967-4617
Hamilton *(G-10717)*

Leimkuehler Inc ....E..... 440 899-7842
Cleveland *(G-5693)*

Lexington Prosthetic Ortotics ....G..... 803 939-0097
Galena *(G-10246)*

Lifes Products Inc ....G..... 740 965-9711
Sunbury *(G-18066)*

Lower Limb Centers LLC ....G..... 440 365-2502
Elyria *(G-9456)*

Luminaud Inc ....G..... 440 255-9082
Mentor *(G-13637)*

M & S Acquistion Co LLC ....E..... 440 951-8700
Mentor *(G-13638)*

M-Co Welling ....G..... 330 897-1374
Stone Creek *(G-17724)*

▲ Marlen Manufacturing & Dev Co......G..... 216 292-7060
Bedford *(G-1441)*

Marlen Manufacturing & Dev Co......E..... 216 292-7546
Bedford *(G-1442)*

Materials Engineering & Dev ....G..... 937 884-5118
Brookville *(G-2191)*

▲ Matplus Ltd ....G..... 440 352-7201
Painesville *(G-15900)*

Medco Labs Inc ....F..... 216 292-7546
Cleveland *(G-5775)*

Meridian Industries Inc ....D..... 330 673-1011
Kent *(G-11488)*

◆ Meridienne International Inc ....G..... 330 274-8317
Mantua *(G-12717)*

◆ Midmark Corporation ....A..... 937 526-3662
Versailles *(G-19352)*

Miller Prsthtics Orthotics LLC ....G..... 740 421-4211
Belpre *(G-1591)*

▲ Morning Pride Mfg LLC ....A..... 937 264-2662
Dayton *(G-8508)*

Morning Pride Mfg LLC ....G..... 937 264-1726
Dayton *(G-8509)*

Morris Maico Hearing Aid Svc ......G..... 419 232-6200
Van Wert *(G-19267)*

Mosher Medical Inc ....G..... 330 668-2252
Akron *(G-305)*

Motion Mobility & Design Inc ....F..... 330 244-9723
North Canton *(G-15251)*

MST Inc ....G..... 419 542-6645
Hicksville *(G-10903)*

Mt Pleasant Pharmacy LLC ....G..... 216 672-4377
Bedford *(G-1446)*

Neu Prosthetics & Orthotics ....G..... 740 363-3522
Delaware *(G-8874)*

North Cast Orthtics Prsthetics ....F..... 440 233-4314
Lorain *(G-12263)*

Northestrn OH Foot & Ankl Asoc ......G..... 330 633-3445
Tallmadge *(G-18161)*

Novacare Inc ....G..... 216 704-4817
Beachwood *(G-1285)*

O & P Options LLC ....G..... 513 791-7767
Montgomery *(G-14434)*

Ohio State University ....G..... 614 293-3600
Columbus *(G-7433)*

▲ Ohio Willow Wood Company ....C..... 740 869-3377
Mount Sterling *(G-14601)*

Opc Inc ....G..... 419 531-2222
Toledo *(G-18620)*

Optimus LLC ....G..... 513 918-2320
Cincinnati *(G-4191)*

Optimus LLC ....G..... 937 454-1900
Dayton *(G-8551)*

▲ Orion Holdings LLC ....G..... 513 871-4344
Cincinnati *(G-4196)*

Ortho Prosthetic Center ....G..... 419 352-8161
Bowling Green *(G-2005)*

Orthotic and Prostetic Spc ....F..... 216 531-2773
Euclid *(G-9596)*

Orthotic and Prosthetics Svc ....G..... 330 723-6679
Medina *(G-13454)*

Orthotic Prosthetic Center ....G..... 419 531-2222
Toledo *(G-18621)*

Orthotics & Prosthetics Rehab ......F..... 330 856-2553
Warren *(G-19585)*

Osteo Solution ....G..... 614 485-9790
Westerville *(G-20177)*

Osteonovus Inc ....G..... 617 717-8867
Toledo *(G-18622)*

Osteosymbionics LLC ....F..... 216 881-8500
Cleveland *(G-5950)*

Out On A Limb ....G..... 513 432-5091
Cincinnati *(G-4202)*

◆ Philips Medical Systems Clevel ......B..... 440 247-2652
Cleveland *(G-6001)*

Phonak LLC ....G..... 513 420-4568
Middletown *(G-14074)*

▲ Prosthetic Design Inc ....G..... 937 836-1464
Englewood *(G-9537)*

Pure Light Technology LLC ....G..... 513 779-7474
West Chester *(G-20042)*

Rees Wheelchair Mobility Svc ....G..... 330 923-2345
Akron *(G-370)*

Reliable Wheelchair Trans ....G..... 216 390-3999
Beachwood *(G-1296)*

Rowley J F Prosth & Orth Lab ....G..... 513 861-3705
Cincinnati *(G-4361)*

S K M L Inc ....G..... 330 220-7565
Valley City *(G-19228)*

S R T Prosthetics & Orthotics ....G..... 419 272-3102
Edon *(G-9345)*

▲ Schaerer Medical Usa Inc ....F..... 513 561-2241
Cincinnati *(G-4386)*

Sentinel Consumer Products Inc ......D..... 801 825-5671
Mentor *(G-13720)*

Serena Safety ....G..... 440 572-4481
Columbia Station *(G-6599)*

Sfl Enterprises Inc ....G..... 513 239-6822
Loveland *(G-12385)*

Smith & Nephew Inc ....E..... 513 821-5888
Cincinnati *(G-4429)*

Smiths Medical Asd Inc ....E..... 800 796-8701
Dublin *(G-9144)*

Sonus-Usa Inc ....E..... 419 474-9324
Toledo *(G-18701)*

Sonus-Usa Inc ....G..... 513 475-8400
Cincinnati *(G-4437)*

▼ Southpaw Enterprises Inc ....E..... 937 252-7676
Moraine *(G-14531)*

▲ Sroufe Healthcare Products LLC ......E..... 260 894-4171
Wadsworth *(G-19442)*

Stable Step LLC ....E..... 513 825-1888
West Chester *(G-19948)*

Steris Corporation ....C..... 440 352-8724
Mentor *(G-13731)*

Steris Corporation ....C..... 440 354-2600
Mentor *(G-13732)*

Steris Corporation ....G..... 330 686-4550
Stow *(G-17804)*

Steris Corporation ....C..... 440 354-2600
Mentor *(G-13734)*

Steris Corporation ....G..... 440 354-2600
Mentor *(G-13735)*

Steris Corporation ....D..... 440 354-2600
Mentor *(G-13736)*

Steris Corporation ....G..... 440 354-2600
Mentor *(G-13737)*

◆ Steris Corporation ....A..... 440 354-2600
Mentor *(G-13733)*

▲ Surgical Appliance Inds Inc ....C..... 513 271-4594
Cincinnati *(G-4488)*

Surgical Appliance Inds Inc ....E..... 937 392-4301
Ripley *(G-16671)*

Swanson Orthotic & Prosthetic ......G..... 419 690-0026
Oregon *(G-15719)*

Synthetic Body Parts Inc ....G..... 440 838-0985
Brecksville *(G-2075)*

Targeting Customer Safety Inc ......G..... 330 865-9593
Akron *(G-429)*

Thomas Products Co Inc ....E..... 513 756-9009
Cincinnati *(G-4507)*

▲ Tilt 15 Inc ....D..... 330 239-4192
Sharon Center *(G-17112)*

Touch Life Centers LLC ....G..... 614 388-8075
Hilliard *(G-10988)*

▲ Tradex International Inc ....D..... 216 651-4788
Cleveland *(G-6345)*

Tranzonic Companies ....B..... 216 535-4300
Richmond Heights *(G-16657)*

Tytek Medical Inc ....G..... 513 247-2002
Blue Ash *(G-1885)*

Visualy Imp Exp Wm Isues Fr Gr ......G..... 216 561-6864
Cleveland *(G-6422)*

▲ Washington Laboratories Inc ....G..... 330 452-4928
Canton *(G-2901)*

▲ Wcm Holdings Inc ....G..... 513 705-2100
Cincinnati *(G-4581)*

Weber Orthopedic Inc ....G..... 440 934-1812
Avon *(G-1018)*

Western Reserve Orthodontics & ......F..... 330 792-6826
Austintown *(G-977)*

Whiteford Industries Inc ....F..... 419 381-1155
Toledo *(G-18774)*

Wilson Mobility LLC ....G..... 216 921-9457
Cleveland *(G-6465)*

▲ World Prep Inc ....G..... 419 843-3869
Sylvania *(G-18130)*

X-Spine Systems Inc ....D..... 937 847-8400
Miamisburg *(G-13882)*

Yanke Bionics Inc ....E..... 330 762-6411
Akron *(G-475)*

Yanke Bionics Inc ....G..... 330 833-0955
Massillon *(G-13212)*

Yanke Bionics Inc ....G..... 330 668-4070
Akron *(G-476)*

▲ Zimme Ortho Surgi Produ Inc ......D..... 800 321-5533
Dover *(G-9025)*

Zimmer Inc ....C..... 614 508-6000
Columbus *(G-7788)*

3843 Dental Eqpt & Splys

Absolute Smile LLC ....G..... 937 293-9866
Dayton *(G-8128)*

Asch-Klaassen Sonics LLC ....G..... 513 671-3226
Cincinnati *(G-3417)*

Branam Oral Health Tech Inc ....G..... 248 670-0040
Oregon *(G-15704)*

Chewrite Co ....D..... 937 746-5509
Springboro *(G-17476)*

▲ Chicago Dental Supply Inc ....G..... 800 571-5211
Harrison *(G-10771)*

▲ Coltene/Whaledent Inc ....C..... 330 916-8800
Cuyahoga Falls *(G-7981)*

Dental Ceramics Inc ....E..... 330 523-5240
Richfield *(G-16620)*

Dentronix Inc ....E..... 330 916-7300
Cuyahoga Falls *(G-7987)*

Dentsply International Inc ....D..... 419 865-9497
Maumee *(G-13256)*

Dentsply Sirona Inc ....E..... 419 893-5672
Maumee *(G-13257)*

Dresch Tolson Dental Labs ....D..... 419 842-6730
Sylvania *(G-18105)*

Duncan Dental Lab LLC ....G..... 614 793-0330
Dublin *(G-9070)*

Endodent Inc ....E..... 626 359-5715
Cuyahoga Falls *(G-7991)*

Mark Dental Laboratory ....G..... 216 464-6424
Cleveland *(G-5744)*

◆ Midmark Corporation ....A..... 937 526-3662
Versailles *(G-19352)*

Obsidian Biodent ....G..... 937 938-9244
Oakwood *(G-15610)*

Precision Swiss LLC ....G..... 513 716-7000
Cincinnati *(G-4264)*

Smile Brands Inc ....G..... 440 471-6133
North Olmsted *(G-15346)*

Sportsguard Laboratories Inc ....G..... 330 673-3932
Kent *(G-11531)*

Thomas J Raffa DDS Inc ....G..... 440 997-5208
Ashtabula *(G-842)*

United Dental Laboratories ....E..... 330 253-1810
Akron *(G-455)*

▲ Vacalon Company Inc ....G..... 614 577-1945
Pickerington *(G-16209)*

▲ Wbc Group LLC ....C..... 866 528-2144
Hudson *(G-11207)*

3844 X-ray Apparatus & Tubes

Comet Technologies USA Inc ....F..... 234 284-7849
Hudson *(G-11165)*

Dentsply International Inc ....D..... 419 865-9497
Maumee *(G-13256)*

General Electric Company ....D..... 216 663-2110
Cleveland *(G-5414)*

Metro Design Inc ....F 440 458-4200
Elyria (G-9462)

North Coast Medical Eqp Inc ....F 440 243-2722
Berea (G-1629)

◆ Philips Medical Systems Clevel ....B 440 247-2652
Cleveland (G-6001)

Trionix Research Laboratory ....G 330 425-9055
Twinsburg (G-19030)

Yxlon ....G 234 284-7862
Hudson (G-11211)

3845 Electromedical & Electrotherapeutic Apparatus

Acela Biomedical ....F 937 544-8618
Winchester (G-20689)

▼ Alltech Med Systems Amer Inc ....E 440 424-2240
Solon (G-17255)

Axiomed Spine Corp ....F 216 587-5566
Cleveland (G-4879)

Brainmaster Technologies Inc ....G 440 232-6000
Bedford (G-1409)

Cardiac Analytics LLC ....F 614 314-1332
Powell (G-16466)

Cardiac Arrhythmia Associates ....G 330 759-8169
Youngstown (G-21043)

Cardioinsight Technologies Inc ....G 216 274-2221
Cleveland (G-4976)

Century Biotech Partners Inc ....G 614 746-6998
Dublin (G-9061)

Checkpoint Surgical Inc ....G 216 378-9107
Cleveland (G-5023)

▲ Clear Image Technology LLC ....G 440 366-4330
Westlake (G-20260)

Cleveland Medical Devices Inc ....E 216 426-0365
Cleveland (G-5068)

Cri Inc ....G 513 266-0882
Blue Ash (G-1771)

▲ Critical Patient Care Inc ....G 937 434-5455
Dayton (G-8252)

Ctl Analyzers LLC ....G 216 791-5084
Shaker Heights (G-17089)

Daniel M Beyerbach ....G 513 206-1180
Cincinnati (G-3639)

Deerfield Medical Imaging LLC ....G 513 271-5717
Mason (G-13009)

E3 Diagnostics Inc ....G 330 926-0594
Cuyahoga Falls (G-7988)

E3 Diagnostics Inc ....G 937 435-2250
Dayton (G-8316)

Elastance Imaging LLC ....G 614 579-9520
Columbus (G-7049)

▼ Eoi Inc ....F 740 201-3300
Lewis Center (G-11897)

Ep Technologies LLC ....F 234 208-8967
Akron (G-171)

Flocel Inc ....G 216 619-5903
Cleveland (G-5358)

Furniss Corporation Ltd ....F 614 871-1470
Mount Sterling (G-14598)

GE Medical Systems Information ....G 216 663-2110
Warrensville Heights (G-19633)

Great Lkes Nrotechnologies Inc ....E 216 520-1537
Cleveland (G-5456)

Gvi Medical Devices Corp ....F 330 963-4083
Twinsburg (G-18951)

Gvi Neuro Inc ....G 330 963-4083
Twinsburg (G-18952)

Gyrus Acmi LP ....C 419 668-8201
Norwalk (G-15542)

Hair Science Systems LLC ....G 513 231-8284
Cincinnati (G-3862)

Health Care Solutions Inc ....G 419 636-4189
Bryan (G-2300)

Imageiq Inc ....F 855 462-4347
Cleveland (G-5551)

Imaging Center East Main ....G 614 566-8120
Columbus (G-7183)

Imalux Corporation ....F 216 502-0755
Cleveland (G-5553)

Infinity Trichology Center ....G 937 281-0555
Kettering (G-11581)

Kamala K Tamirisa MD ....G 419 842-3000
Toledo (G-18538)

Keyghobad Ventures LLC ....G 440 366-3278
Elyria (G-9447)

▲ Lumitex Inc ....D 440 243-8401
Strongsville (G-17939)

Magnetic Resonance Tech ....G 440 942-2922
Willoughby (G-20532)

Medforall LLC ....G 614 947-0791
Columbus (G-7340)

Medical Equipment Provider ....G 937 778-2190
Piqua (G-16291)

Medical Quant USA Inc ....F 440 542-0761
Solon (G-17333)

Medinvent LLC ....G 330 247-0921
Medina (G-13446)

Medtronic Inc ....F 216 642-1977
Cleveland (G-5777)

Mercury Biomed LLC ....G 216 777-1492
Cleveland (G-5784)

Monitored Therapeutics Inc ....G 614 761-3555
Dublin (G-9106)

N K H Safety Inc ....G 513 771-3839
Cincinnati (G-4134)

Nano Mark LLC ....G 216 409-3104
Cleveland (G-5850)

◆ Ndi Medical LLC ....G 216 378-9106
Cleveland (G-5866)

Neuros Medical Inc ....G 440 951-2565
Willoughby Hills (G-20642)

Neurowave Systems Inc ....G 216 361-1591
Cleveland (G-5875)

Nkh Life Safety LLC ....F 513 688-7100
Cincinnati (G-4159)

Nuvasive Manufacturing LLC ....E 937 343-0400
Fairborn (G-9627)

Nxstage Medical Inc ....G 513 712-1300
Cincinnati (G-4170)

Open Sided Mri Cleveland LLC ....G 804 217-7114
Westlake (G-20290)

Osteodynamics ....G 405 921-9271
Cincinnati (G-4198)

Pemco Inc ....E 216 524-2990
Cleveland (G-5989)

Philips Medical Systems Mr ....C 440 483-2499
Highland Heights (G-10919)

Rapiscan Systems High Energy I ....G 937 879-4200
Fairborn (G-9629)

Relevium Labs Inc ....G 614 568-7000
Oxford (G-15842)

Sail Medical Inc ....G 513 961-3144
Cincinnati (G-4376)

Scallywag Tag ....G 513 922-4999
Cincinnati (G-4383)

Sensetronics LLC ....G 614 292-2833
Dublin (G-9142)

◆ Steris Corporation ....A 440 354-2600
Mentor (G-13733)

Synsei Medical ....G 609 759-1101
Dublin (G-9152)

University Crdc & Thrc Grp ....F 216 844-3053
Cleveland (G-6393)

Valued Relationships Inc ....B 800 860-4230
Franklin (G-10061)

▲ Viewray Incorporated ....D 440 703-3210
Oakwood Village (G-15631)

Westerville Endoscopy Ctr LLC ....F 614 568-1666
Westerville (G-20194)

3851 Ophthalmic Goods

Albright Albright & Schn ....G 614 825-4829
Worthington (G-20855)

Brunswick Eye & Contact Lens C ....G 419 439-3381
Defiance (G-8782)

Bsa Industries Inc ....D 614 846-5515
Columbus (G-6869)

Bulk Molding Compounds Inc ....D 419 874-7941
Perrysburg (G-16071)

▲ Central Optical Inc ....E 330 783-9660
Youngstown (G-21046)

▲ Classic Optical Labs Inc ....C 330 759-8245
Youngstown (G-21052)

▲ Cleveland Hoya Corp ....D 440 234-5703
Berea (G-1606)

Di Walt Optical Inc ....F 330 453-8427
Canton (G-2686)

DMV Corporation ....G 740 452-4787
Zanesville (G-21299)

Essilor Laboratories Amer Inc ....G 330 425-3003
Twinsburg (G-18931)

Essilor Laboratories Amer Inc ....E 614 274-0840
Columbus (G-7066)

Fresh Look Laser Eye Ctrs LLC ....G 614 885-2745
Cuyahoga Falls (G-7999)

Hollywood Family Eye Care ....G 740 264-1220
Steubenville (G-17699)

Jerold Optical Inc ....G 216 781-4279
Cleveland (G-5611)

Lake Cable Optical Lab ....G 330 497-3022
Canton (G-2758)

Libbey Inc ....F 419 244-5697
Toledo (G-18560)

Luxottica Retail N Amer Inc ....C 614 409-9381
Lockbourne (G-12149)

Mileti Optical Inc ....G 440 884-6333
Cleveland (G-5815)

▲ Nexus Vision Group LLC ....E 866 492-6499
Grove City (G-10578)

Oakley Inc ....D 949 672-6560
Dayton (G-8537)

Opti Vision Inc ....G 330 650-0919
Hudson (G-11191)

▲ Optical Distribution Corp ....F 937 405-7280
Columbus (G-7444)

Rooney Optical Inc ....E 216 267-5600
Twinsburg (G-19012)

Rx Frames N Lenses Ltd ....G 513 557-2970
Cincinnati (G-4370)

Safeway Contact Lens Inc ....G 330 536-6469
Lowellville (G-12413)

Soderberg Inc ....F 937 298-0223
Moraine (G-14529)

Steiner Eoptics Inc ....G 937 426-2341
Miamisburg (G-13865)

Sunforest Vision Center Inc ....G 419 475-4646
Toledo (G-18707)

Terminal Optical Lab ....G 216 289-7722
Euclid (G-9610)

Toledo Optical Laboratory Inc ....G 419 248-3384
Toledo (G-18738)

Usv Optical Inc ....G 614 717-0238
Dublin (G-9160)

▲ Volk Optical Inc ....D 440 942-6161
Mentor (G-13768)

Wilson Optical Laboratory Inc ....E 440 357-7000
Mentor (G-13769)

3861 Photographic Eqpt & Splys

Advanced Litho Systems ....G 419 865-2652
Monclova (G-14388)

▲ AEG Photoconductor Corporation ...D 513 874-4939
West Chester (G-19799)

AGFA Corporation ....C 513 829-6292
Fairfield (G-9638)

Anderson Industries Inc ....F 216 941-7766
Cleveland (G-4810)

Da-Lite Screen Company LLC ....E 574 267-8101
Blue Ash (G-1774)

E I Du Pont De Nemours & Co ....E 740 474-0220
Circleville (G-4627)

E-Waste Systems (ohio) Inc ....G 614 824-3057
Columbus (G-7044)

Eprad Inc ....G 419 666-3266
Perrysburg (G-16093)

Gvs Industries Inc ....G 513 887-8660
Hamilton (G-10699)

Horizons Inc Camcode Division ....E 216 714-0020
Cleveland (G-5524)

▲ Horizons Incorporated ....C 216 475-0555
Cleveland (G-5525)

Ink Again ....G 419 232-4465
Van Wert (G-19260)

Jay Tackett ....G 740 779-1715
Frankfort (G-9999)

Kay Zee Inc ....G 330 339-1268
New Philadelphia (G-14905)

Plastigraphics Inc ....F 513 771-8848
Cincinnati (G-4243)

Rightway Fab & Machine Inc ....G 937 295-2200
Russia (G-16769)

Sensopart USA Inc ....G 419 931-7696
Perrysburg (G-16149)

Smartcopy Inc ....G 740 392-6162
Mount Vernon (G-14651)

Stewart Filmscreen Corp ....E 513 753-0800
Amelia (G-584)

▲ Stretchtape Inc ....E 216 486-9400
Cleveland (G-6251)

Tameran Inc ....E 440 349-7100
Solon (G-17397)

Tbh International ....G 440 323-4651
Elyria (G-9499)

Transimage Inc ....G 937 293-0261
Oakwood (G-15611)

Xerox Corporation ....F 513 860-8600
West Chester (G-20070)

Xerox Corporation ....B 513 554-3200
Blue Ash (G-1902)

▲ Xerox Corporation C/O Genco ....G 503 582-6059
  Groveport *(G-10651)*

3873 Watch & Clock Devices & Parts

Amano Cincinnati Incorporated ....D 513 697-9000
  Loveland *(G-12338)*
▲ Dimcogray Corporation ....D 937 433-7600
  Centerville *(G-3039)*
▲ I T Verdin Co ....E 513 241-4010
  Cincinnati *(G-3906)*
I T Verdin Co ....E 513 559-3947
  Cincinnati *(G-3908)*
▲ R & M Imports ....G 513 897-5015
  Waynesville *(G-19734)*
Sgi Matrix LLC ....D 937 438-9033
  Miamisburg *(G-13858)*

39 MISCELLANEOUS MANUFACTURING INDUSTRIES

3911 Jewelry: Precious Metal

A R Jester Co ....G 513 241-1465
  Cincinnati *(G-3335)*
Auld Crafters Inc ....G 614 221-6825
  Columbus *(G-6787)*
Baldwin B AA Design ....G 740 374-5844
  Marietta *(G-12766)*
Barany Jewelry Inc ....G 330 220-4367
  Brunswick *(G-2211)*
Benchworks Jewelers Inc ....G 937 439-4243
  Dayton *(G-8185)*
Bensan Jewelers Inc ....G 216 221-1434
  Lakewood *(G-11657)*
Boos Make & Take ....G 440 647-0000
  Wellington *(G-19738)*
C & J Jewelers Inc ....G 614 221-8588
  Columbus *(G-6881)*
C M Stephanoff Jewelers Inc ....G 440 526-5890
  Brecksville *(G-2039)*
Cambridge Mfg Jewelers ....G 330 528-0207
  Hudson *(G-11162)*
Cigs N Such ....G 614 389-6115
  Columbus *(G-6929)*
Crest Craft Company ....F 513 271-4858
  Blue Ash *(G-1770)*
Davidson Jewelers Inc ....G 513 932-3936
  Lebanon *(G-11794)*
Diamond Designs Inc ....G 330 434-6776
  Akron *(G-150)*
Dimensional Works of Art ....G 330 657-2681
  Peninsula *(G-16036)*
Don Basch Jewelers Inc ....F 330 467-2116
  Macedonia *(G-12446)*
Farah Jewelers Inc ....F 614 438-6140
  Columbus *(G-6646)*
▲ Ginos Awards Inc ....E 216 831-5653
  Cleveland *(G-5431)*
Gold Mine Inc ....G 614 378-8308
  Dublin *(G-9079)*
Gold Pro Inc ....G 216 241-5143
  Cleveland *(G-5435)*
Goyal Enterprises Inc ....F 513 874-9303
  West Chester *(G-20010)*
Gustave Julian Jewelers Inc ....G 440 888-1100
  Cleveland *(G-5465)*
H P Nielsen Inc ....G 440 244-4255
  Lorain *(G-12248)*
Heather B Moore Inc ....G 216 932-5430
  Cleveland *(G-5492)*
J and L Jewelry Manufacturing ....G 440 546-9988
  Cleveland *(G-5594)*
Jaffe & Gross Jewelry Company ......G 937 461-9450
  Dayton *(G-8419)*
▲ James C Free Inc ....E 937 298-0171
  Dayton *(G-8420)*
James C Free Inc ....G 513 793-0133
  Cincinnati *(G-3940)*
Jensen & Sons Inc ....F 419 471-1000
  Toledo *(G-18534)*
Jewels By Img Inc ....F 440 461-4464
  Cleveland *(G-5614)*
Jostens Inc ....G 513 615-3281
  Cincinnati *(G-3959)*
Jostens Inc ....G 419 794-7343
  Maumee *(G-13272)*
Jostens Inc ....G 513 731-5900
  Cincinnati *(G-3960)*
Jostens Inc ....E 419 874-5835
  Perrysburg *(G-16116)*

Koop Diamond Cutters Inc..............F 513 621-2838
  Cincinnati *(G-4002)*
La Gra Jewelers Inc ....G 440 439-5869
  Cleveland *(G-5673)*
Levit Jewelers Inc ....G 440 985-1685
  Lorain *(G-12255)*
M & M Tobacco ....G 330 573-8543
  Carrollton *(G-2961)*
M B Saxon Co Inc ....F 440 229-5006
  Cleveland *(G-5717)*
M S Abbott Jewelers ....G 614 430-8800
  Worthington *(G-20877)*
Marcus Jewelers ....G 513 474-4950
  Cincinnati *(G-4058)*
Marfo Company ....G 614 276-3352
  Columbus *(G-7318)*
Michael W Hyes Desgr Goldsmith........G 440 519-0889
  Solon *(G-17338)*
Mr 14k Inc ....G 440 234-6661
  Berea *(G-1628)*
Ms Barkin Company ....G 216 761-9500
  Cleveland *(G-5839)*
N J Thomas Fine Jewelry Inc...........G 440 892-0656
  Cleveland *(G-5847)*
O C Tanner Company ....G 513 583-1100
  Mason *(G-13069)*
Ohio Silver Co ....G 937 767-8261
  Yellow Springs *(G-20997)*
Old Village ....F 614 791-8467
  Delaware *(G-8877)*
Puppy Paws Inc ....G 440 461-9667
  Cleveland *(G-6063)*
Rego Manufacturing Co Inc ....D 419 562-0466
  Bucyrus *(G-2357)*
Rita Caz Jwly Studio & Gallery ....G 937 767-7713
  Yellow Springs *(G-20998)*
Robert W Johnson Inc ....D 614 336-4545
  Dublin *(G-9134)*
Rosenfeld Jewelry Inc ....G 440 446-0099
  Cleveland *(G-6134)*
Roulet Company ....G 419 241-2988
  Toledo *(G-18682)*
Sands Co Jewelers ....G 216 261-8270
  Cleveland *(G-6157)*
Sheiban Jewelry Inc ....F 440 238-0616
  Strongsville *(G-17964)*
Stephen R White ....G 740 522-1512
  Newark *(G-15057)*
Timothy Allen Jewelers Inc ....G 440 974-8885
  Mentor *(G-13747)*
Val Casting Inc ....E 419 562-2499
  Bucyrus *(G-2361)*
Vy Inc ....F 513 421-8100
  Cincinnati *(G-4572)*
Weber Jewelers Incorporated ....G 937 643-9200
  Dayton *(G-8749)*
White Jewelers ....G 330 264-3324
  Wooster *(G-20848)*
Whitehouse Bros Inc ....G 513 621-2259
  Blue Ash *(G-1894)*
William A Weidinger Jewelry ....G 614 481-8866
  Columbus *(G-7763)*
Your Personal Jeweler Inc ....G 330 836-2446
  Akron *(G-478)*

3914 Silverware, Plated & Stainless Steel Ware

Ahner Fabricating & Shtmtl Inc ....E 419 626-6641
  Sandusky *(G-16945)*
All American Trophy ....G 614 231-8824
  Columbus *(G-6719)*
B & B Trophies & Awards ....G 330 225-6193
  Brunswick *(G-2209)*
Behrco Inc ....G 419 394-1612
  Saint Marys *(G-16832)*
▲ Ginos Awards Inc ....E 216 831-5653
  Cleveland *(G-5431)*
Hr Machine LLC ....G 937 222-7644
  Beavercreek *(G-1345)*
Lawnview Industries Inc ....G 937 653-5217
  Urbana *(G-19168)*
▼ Online Engineering Corporation ....G 513 561-8878
  Amelia *(G-581)*
Professional Award Service ....G 513 389-3600
  Cincinnati *(G-4294)*
Quantum Jewelry Dist ....E 330 678-2222
  Kent *(G-11510)*
Regal Trophy & Awards Company .....G 877 492-7531
  Sidney *(G-17214)*

Tempo Manufacturing Company ....G 937 773-6613
  Piqua *(G-16314)*

3915 Jewelers Findings & Lapidary Work

▲ Dayton Hawker Corporation ....F 937 293-8147
  Dayton *(G-8276)*
Dentsply International Inc ....D 419 865-9497
  Maumee *(G-13256)*
Koop Diamond Cutters Inc..............F 513 621-2838
  Cincinnati *(G-4002)*
Lapcraft Inc.................................G 614 764-8993
  Powell *(G-16477)*
Sunshine Products ....G 303 478-4913
  Toledo *(G-18708)*
The-Fischer-Group..........................E 513 285-1281
  Fairfield *(G-9725)*
Zero-D Products Inc ....G 440 417-1843
  Madison *(G-12514)*

3931 Musical Instruments

▲ A R Schopps Sons Inc ....E 330 821-8406
  Alliance *(G-487)*
Bbb Music LLC ....G 740 772-2262
  Chillicothe *(G-3228)*
Belco Works Inc ....B 740 695-0500
  Saint Clairsville *(G-16782)*
Bell Industries ....F 513 353-2355
  Harrison *(G-10769)*
Belmont County of Ohio ....G 740 699-2140
  Saint Clairsville *(G-16783)*
Brooks Manufacturing ....G 419 244-1777
  Toledo *(G-18382)*
C E Kegg Inc ....G 330 877-8800
  Hartville *(G-10818)*
▼ Commercial Music Service Co........G 740 746-8500
  Sugar Grove *(G-18011)*
Conn-Selmer Inc ....B 440 946-6100
  Willoughby *(G-20462)*
Conn-Selmer Inc ....E 216 391-7723
  Cleveland *(G-5115)*
D C Ramey Piano Co ....G 708 602-3961
  Marysville *(G-12940)*
D Picking & Co ....G 419 562-5016
  Bucyrus *(G-2337)*
DC Music ....G 330 385-0468
  East Liverpool *(G-9211)*
Earthquaker Devices LLC ....F 330 252-9220
  Akron *(G-160)*
Engels Machining LLC ....G 419 485-1500
  Montpelier *(G-14445)*
Fifth Avenue Fret Shop LLC ....G 614 481-8300
  Columbus *(G-7082)*
Garys Classic Guitars ....G 513 891-0555
  Loveland *(G-12351)*
Hisey Bells ....G 740 333-7669
  Greenfield *(G-10480)*
▲ I T Verdin Co ....E 513 241-4010
  Cincinnati *(G-3906)*
I T Verdin Co ....E 513 241-4010
  Cincinnati *(G-3907)*
I T Verdin Co ....E 513 559-3947
  Cincinnati *(G-3908)*
J Zamberlan & Co ....G 740 765-9028
  Steubenville *(G-17700)*
Lima Pipe Organ Co Inc ....G 419 331-5461
  Elida *(G-9352)*
Loft Violin Shop ....F 614 267-7221
  Columbus *(G-7303)*
McHael D Goronok String Instrs ....G 216 421-4227
  Cleveland *(G-5769)*
▲ New Cleveland Group Inc ....G 216 932-9310
  Cleveland *(G-5876)*
▲ Paul Bartel ....G 513 541-2000
  Cincinnati *(G-4216)*
Peebles - Herzog Inc ....G 614 279-2211
  Columbus *(G-7474)*
Peter Zaret & Sons Violins ....G 440 461-1411
  Cleveland *(G-5995)*
S I T Strings Co Inc ....E 330 434-8010
  Akron *(G-391)*
Schantz Organ Company ....G 330 682-6065
  Orrville *(G-15762)*
Sperzel Inc ....E 216 281-6868
  Cleveland *(G-6225)*
▲ Stewart-Macdonald Mfg Co ....E 740 592-3021
  Athens *(G-885)*
The Holtkamp Organ Co ....F 216 741-5180
  Cleveland *(G-6314)*
The W L Jenkins Company ....F 330 477-3407
  Canton *(G-2869)*

Tremelo ....G.....330 823-6359
  Alliance (G-548)

▲ Universal Percussion Inc ....F.....330 482-5750
  Columbiana (G-6636)

Victor Organ Company ....G.....330 792-1321
  Youngstown (G-21238)

Waits Instruments LLC ....G.....513 600-5996
  Cincinnati (G-4575)

Watson Meeks and Company ....G.....937 378-2355
  Georgetown (G-10367)

3942 Dolls & Stuffed Toys

Alice Beougher ....G.....740 927-2470
  Etna (G-9551)

▲ Classic Toy Company Inc ....G.....216 851-2000
  Cleveland (G-5043)

Datatex Media Dolls ....G.....216 598-1000
  Cleveland (G-5170)

Gail J Shumaker Originals ....G.....330 659-0680
  Richfield (G-16625)

Huston Gifts Dolls and Flowers ....G.....740 775-9141
  Chillicothe (G-3244)

Middleton Llyd Dolls Inc ....G.....740 989-2082
  Coolville (G-7835)

▲ Middleton Lee Original Dolls ....F
  Columbus (G-7350)

3944 Games, Toys & Children's Vehicles

Advance Novelty Incorporated ....G.....419 424-0363
  Findlay (G-9787)

▲ Ajj Enterprises LLC ....F.....513 755-9562
  West Chester (G-19979)

▲ American Traditions Basket Co ....E.....330 854-0900
  Canal Fulton (G-2496)

Applied Concepts Inc ....F.....440 229-5033
  Willoughby (G-20436)

◆ Arrow International Inc ....B.....216 961-3500
  Cleveland (G-4834)

▲ AW Faber-Castell Usa Inc ....D.....216 643-4660
  Cleveland (G-4877)

Berlin Wood Products Inc ....E.....330 893-3281
  Berlin (G-1646)

Brown Dave Products Inc ....F.....513 738-1576
  Hamilton (G-10677)

Brp Inc ....G.....440 988-4398
  Amherst (G-593)

Cornpentry ....G.....513 741-0594
  Cincinnati (G-3612)

Cowells - Arrow Bingo Company ....G.....216 961-3500
  Cleveland (G-5137)

D L H Locomotive Works ....G.....937 629-0321
  Springfield (G-17538)

▲ Dunecraft Inc ....G.....800 306-4168
  Cleveland (G-5222)

Evenflo Company Inc ....D.....937 773-3971
  Troy (G-18823)

◆ Evenflo Company Inc ....C.....937 415-3300
  Miamisburg (G-13806)

First Merit ....G.....330 849-8750
  Akron (G-188)

◆ Foundations Worldwide Inc ....E.....330 722-5033
  Medina (G-13412)

Fremont Plastic Products Inc ....F.....419 332-6407
  Fremont (G-10150)

Gingerbread N Bows ....G.....740 945-1027
  Scio (G-17037)

Hershberger Lawn Structures ....F.....330 674-3900
  Millersburg (G-14221)

Ink Factory Inc ....G.....330 799-0888
  Youngstown (G-21116)

Iron Wind Metals Co LLC ....G.....513 870-0606
  Cincinnati (G-3932)

Jackpot Festival & Gaming ....G.....216 531-3500
  Cleveland (G-5604)

Larose Industries LLC ....E.....419 237-1600
  Fayette (G-9776)

▲ Late For Sky Production Co ....E.....513 531-4400
  Cincinnati (G-4013)

Lawbre Co ....G.....330 637-3363
  Cortland (G-7871)

Little Cottage Company ....G.....330 893-4212
  Dundee (G-9174)

M G 3d ....F.....614 262-0956
  Columbus (G-7308)

▲ Mag-Nif Inc ....D.....440 946-4308
  Mentor (G-13643)

Mahoning Valley Manufacturing ....E.....330 537-4492
  Beloit (G-1584)

Michaels Stores Inc ....E.....330 505-1168
  Niles (G-15170)

Moonstruck Games Inc ....G.....513 721-3900
  Cincinnati (G-4121)

▲ Parma International Inc ....E.....440 237-8650
  North Royalton (G-15442)

▲ Pioneer National Latex Inc ....D.....419 289-3300
  Ashland (G-766)

Premier Kites & Designs Inc ....G.....888 416-0174
  Portsmouth (G-16449)

Ramon Robinson ....G.....330 883-3244
  Vienna (G-19374)

Rbs Citizens NA ....G.....330 468-1600
  Sagamore Hills (G-16778)

▲ Ready Made Rc LLC ....G.....740 936-4500
  Lewis Center (G-11913)

Resaurus Company Inc ....F.....614 751-9352
  Columbus (G-7555)

Rockys Hinge Co ....G.....330 539-6296
  Girard (G-10393)

RPM Consumer Holding Company ....G.....330 273-5090
  Medina (G-13470)

Scrambl-Gram Inc ....F.....419 635-2321
  Port Clinton (G-16414)

◆ Step2 Company Inc ....B.....866 429-5200
  Streetsboro (G-17879)

Step2 Company LLC ....B.....419 938-6343
  Perrysville (G-16176)

◆ Step2 Holdings LLC ....A.....330 656-0440
  Streetsboro (G-17880)

The Guardtower Inc ....F.....614 488-4311
  Columbus (G-7689)

▲ Todd Smith Products ....G.....216 529-0525
  Lakewood (G-11680)

Unique-Chardan Inc ....G.....419 636-6900
  Bryan (G-2325)

Vacuum Finishing Company ....F.....440 286-4386
  Chardon (G-3182)

▲ Watch-Us Inc ....E.....513 829-8870
  Fairfield (G-9731)

Weenk Labs LLC ....G.....614 448-0160
  Columbus (G-7754)

Wells Manufacturing Co Llc ....F.....937 987-2481
  New Vienna (G-14957)

3949 Sporting & Athletic Goods, NEC

▲ 1 Iron Golf Inc ....G.....419 662-9336
  Celina (G-2984)

AC Shiners Inc ....G.....513 738-1573
  Okeana (G-15662)

Achilles Running Shop LLC ....G.....440 942-2059
  Mentor (G-13507)

Advanced Fitness Inc ....G.....513 563-1000
  Cincinnati (G-3358)

Adventurous Child Inc ....G.....513 531-7700
  Cincinnati (G-3361)

Al-Co Products Inc ....F.....419 399-3867
  Latty (G-11767)

All Sport Services Corporation ....G.....216 361-1965
  Cleveland (G-4759)

◆ American Heritage Billd LLC ....D.....330 626-3710
  Streetsboro (G-17838)

American Heritage Billiards ....G.....330 626-3710
  Streetsboro (G-17839)

American Sports Design Company ....D.....937 865-5431
  Centerville (G-3035)

American Whistle Corporation ....F.....614 846-2918
  Columbus (G-6742)

Apex Target Systems LLC ....G.....877 224-6692
  Tiffin (G-18204)

Arem Co ....F.....440 974-6740
  Mentor (G-13526)

Argrov Box Co ....G.....513 217-5900
  Middletown (G-14021)

Backyard Scoreboards LLC ....G.....513 702-6561
  Middletown (G-14023)

Balbo Industries Inc ....G.....440 333-0630
  Rocky River (G-16695)

Barnett Spouting Inc ....G.....330 644-0853
  Akron (G-85)

Baseball Card Corner ....G.....513 677-0464
  Loveland (G-12340)

Bay Area Products Inc ....G.....419 732-2147
  Port Clinton (G-16394)

Bay Island Company Inc ....G.....513 248-0356
  Loveland (G-12341)

Black Wing Shooting Center LLC ....G.....740 363-7555
  Delaware (G-8825)

Board of Park Commissioners ....G.....216 635-3200
  Cleveland (G-4920)

Boatfun Sports Inc ....G.....513 379-0506
  Liberty Township (G-11958)

Bracemart LLC ....G.....440 353-2830
  North Ridgeville (G-15362)

Bradley Enterprises Inc ....G.....330 875-1444
  Louisville (G-12311)

▲ Bullseye Dart Shoppe Inc ....G.....440 951-9277
  Willoughby (G-20449)

Cabin Creek Golf ....G.....330 852-4879
  Sugarcreek (G-18018)

Careless Heart Enterprises ....G.....740 654-9999
  Lancaster (G-11696)

Challenge Targets ....G.....859 462-5851
  Batavia (G-1170)

Charles V Snider & Assoc Inc ....F.....440 877-9151
  North Royalton (G-15414)

Clark & Son Pool Table Company ....G.....330 454-9153
  Canton (G-2657)

▼ Coulter Ventures Llc ....E.....614 358-6190
  Columbus (G-6990)

Creighton Sports Center Inc ....G.....740 865-2521
  New Matamoras (G-14873)

Daisys Pillows LLC ....G.....937 776-6968
  Dayton (G-8265)

Dayton Stencil Works Company ....G.....937 223-3233
  Dayton (G-8287)

▲ Done-Rite Bowling Service Co ....G.....440 232-3280
  Bedford (G-1420)

Drop Zone Ltd ....G.....234 806-4604
  Warren (G-19546)

Drowned Lure ....G.....330 548-5873
  Tallmadge (G-18144)

Duff Farm ....G.....740 742-2182
  Langsville (G-11764)

Ebsco Industries Inc ....F.....513 398-2149
  Mason (G-13012)

Equipment Guys Inc ....F.....614 871-9220
  Newark (G-15004)

Europa Sports Products Inc ....F.....440 846-9571
  Strongsville (G-17919)

Field Specialties ....G.....440 635-0064
  Chardon (G-3153)

Foot Locker Retail Inc ....G.....513 671-4085
  Cincinnati (G-3767)

Forrest Enterprises Inc ....G.....937 773-1714
  Piqua (G-16265)

Foster Manufacturing ....G.....513 735-9770
  Batavia (G-1185)

Fowl Foolers LLC ....G.....419 797-2412
  Port Clinton (G-16400)

Funtown Playgrounds Inc ....E.....513 871-8585
  Cincinnati (G-3303)

▲ Galaxy Balloons Incorporated ....C.....216 476-3360
  Cleveland (G-5392)

▲ Gayston Corporation ....G.....937 743-6050
  Miamisburg (G-13812)

▲ Ghostblind Industries Inc ....G.....740 374-6766
  Marietta (G-12785)

▲ GL International LLC ....C.....330 744-8812
  Youngstown (G-21101)

Golf Car Company Inc ....F.....614 873-1055
  Plain City (G-16344)

Golf Dome ....G.....440 543-1211
  Chagrin Falls (G-3089)

▲ Golf Galaxy Golfworks Inc ....C.....740 328-4193
  Newark (G-15014)

Grey Hawk Golf Club ....E.....440 355-4844
  Lagrange (G-11626)

Gym Pro LLC ....G.....740 984-4143
  Waterford (G-19648)

▲ H & H of Milford Ohio LLC ....G.....513 576-9004
  Milford (G-14149)

Hibbett Sporting Goods Inc ....G.....330 837-9272
  Massillon (G-13149)

Hofmanns Lures Inc ....G.....937 684-0338
  Ansonia (G-625)

Hoistech LLC ....G.....440 327-5379
  North Ridgeville (G-15379)

Hole Hunter Golf Inc ....G.....937 339-5833
  Piqua (G-16278)

House of Awards and Sports ....G.....419 422-7877
  Findlay (G-9842)

▲ Huffy Corporation ....D.....937 865-2800
  Centerville (G-3043)

▲ Hunters Manufacturing Co Inc ....E.....330 628-9245
  Mogadore (G-14377)

Imperial On-Pece Fibrgls Pools ....F.....740 747-2971
  Ashley (G-788)

Imperial Pools Inc ....D.....513 771-1506
  Cincinnati (G-3915)

Jason Stuller Pro Shop LLC ....G.....419 882-3197
  Sylvania (G-18113)

S
I
C

JPb Lures Manufacturing LLC ....G..... 419 734-9488
Marblehead *(G-12745)*

Just Basic Sports Inc ....G..... 330 264-7771
Wooster *(G-20793)*

Kabler Farms ....G..... 513 732-0501
Batavia *(G-1195)*

▲ Kent Sporting Goods Co Inc ....D..... 419 929-7021
New London *(G-14860)*

Konkrete City Skateboards ....G..... 513 231-0399
Cincinnati *(G-4001)*

L A Productions Co LLC ....G..... 330 666-4230
Akron *(G-264)*

Lakota Industries Inc ....G..... 937 532-6394
Xenia *(G-20960)*

Lasermark LLC ....G..... 513 312-9889
Dayton *(G-8452)*

▲ Lem Products Holding LLC ....E..... 513 202-1188
West Chester *(G-19892)*

Line Drive Sportz-Lcrc LLC ....G..... 419 794-7150
Maumee *(G-13276)*

Lure Inc ....E..... 440 951-8862
Willoughby *(G-20530)*

M C Sports ....F..... 419 874-2990
Rossford *(G-16742)*

▼ M&M Great Adventures LLC ....G..... 937 344-1415
Westerville *(G-20169)*

Martini Skate & Snow ....G..... 216 371-0155
Cleveland Heights *(G-6500)*

Mc Alarney Pool Spas and Billd ......E..... 740 373-6698
Marietta *(G-12806)*

McSports ....G..... 419 586-5555
Celina *(G-3007)*

Meridian Industries Inc ....D..... 330 359-5447
Winesburg *(G-20706)*

Meyer Design Inc ....E..... 330 434-9176
Akron *(G-296)*

Mudbrook Golf Center ....G..... 419 433-2945
Huron *(G-11234)*

N Bass Bait Co ....G..... 419 647-4501
Spencerville *(G-17462)*

Nemire Lures LLC ....G..... 419 729-1280
Toledo *(G-18599)*

Ohio Sporting Goods LLC ....G..... 330 548-5911
Cuyahoga Falls *(G-8030)*

▲ Ohio Table Pad Company ....F..... 419 872-6400
Perrysburg *(G-16130)*

▲ Otomik Products Inc ....G..... 877 776-5358
Cincinnati *(G-4199)*

Ouchless Lures Inc ....G..... 330 653-3867
Hudson *(G-11192)*

Packaging Plus Inc ....G..... 304 429-5900
Dayton *(G-8562)*

▲ Phoenix Bat Company ....G..... 614 873-7776
Plain City *(G-16354)*

Playground Equipment Service ....G..... 513 481-3776
Cincinnati *(G-4245)*

R L Y Inc ....G..... 513 385-1950
Cincinnati *(G-4326)*

◆ Rain Drop Products Llc ....E..... 419 207-1229
Ashland *(G-771)*

Raven Concealment Systems LLC ....G..... 440 508-9000
North Ridgeville *(G-15399)*

Ready To Haul Columbus LLC ....F..... 614 329-5161
Streetsboro *(G-17871)*

Red Barakuda LLC ....G..... 614 596-5432
Columbus *(G-7550)*

Reef Runner Tackle Co Inc ....G..... 419 798-9125
Marblehead *(G-12746)*

Reelflyrodcom ....G..... 937 434-8472
Dayton *(G-8622)*

Rockbridge Outfitters ....G..... 740 654-1956
Lancaster *(G-11748)*

Rockys Gym ....G..... 330 965-0464
Youngstown *(G-21192)*

Royal Spa Columbus ....G..... 614 529-8569
Lewis Center *(G-11915)*

Sabrecat Bat Company Inc ....G..... 330 327-1532
Louisville *(G-12325)*

Shoot A Way Inc ....F..... 419 294-4654
Upper Sandusky *(G-19140)*

Shoot-A-Way Inc ....F..... 419 294-4654
Upper Sandusky *(G-19141)*

Shooting Range Supply LLC ....G..... 440 576-7711
Jefferson *(G-11370)*

Smart 3d Solutions LLC ....G..... 330 972-7840
Akron *(G-405)*

Soccer Centre Owners Ltd ....G..... 419 893-5425
Maumee *(G-13296)*

Soccer First Inc ....G..... 614 889-1115
Dublin *(G-9148)*

Soccer Village Inc ....G..... 513 451-8500
Cincinnati *(G-4432)*

▲ Sunset Golf LLC ....E..... 419 994-5563
Tallmadge *(G-18171)*

Target Thompson Technology ....G..... 330 699-8000
Uniontown *(G-19102)*

The Salem Golf Club ....G..... 330 332-0346
Salem *(G-16930)*

Total Tennis Inc ....G..... 614 488-5004
Columbus *(G-7701)*

Toy & Sport Trends Inc ....G..... 419 748-8880
Napoleon *(G-14700)*

Tri County Vking Warriors ....E..... 330 646-4632
Warren *(G-19610)*

▲ Trilo Inc ....F..... 937 276-4288
Dayton *(G-8725)*

Tuffy Pad Company Inc ....G..... 330 688-0043
Stow *(G-17813)*

U S Development Corp ....E..... 570 966-5990
Kent *(G-11540)*

Ultrabuilt Play Systems Inc ....F..... 419 652-2294
Nova *(G-15580)*

Unique-Chardan Inc ....E..... 419 636-6900
Bryan *(G-2325)*

Uniwall Manufacturing Co ....F..... 330 875-1444
Louisville *(G-12332)*

Vf Outdoor LLC ....G..... 614 337-1147
Columbus *(G-7738)*

Victory Athletics Inc ....G..... 330 274-2854
Mantua *(G-12724)*

Voll Hockey Inc ....G..... 216 521-4625
Lakewood *(G-11681)*

▲ Wake Nation ....F..... 513 887-9253
Fairfield *(G-9730)*

Wholesale Bait Co Inc ....F..... 513 863-2380
Fairfield *(G-9732)*

Wilson Sporting Goods Co ....C..... 419 634-9901
Ada *(G-7)*

Wooden Horse Corporation ....G..... 419 663-1472
Norwalk *(G-15568)*

▲ Zebec of North America Inc ....E..... 513 829-5533
Fairfield *(G-9735)*

Zwf Golf LLC ....E..... 937 767-5621
Fairborn *(G-9636)*

3951 Pens & Mechanical Pencils

▲ Berea Hardwood Co Inc ....G..... 216 898-8956
Cleveland *(G-4904)*

▲ Bexley Pen Company Inc ....G..... 614 351-9988
Columbus *(G-6826)*

3952 Lead Pencils, Crayons & Artist's Mtrls

Clay Logan Products Company ....D..... 740 385-2184
Logan *(G-12172)*

Modern Ink Technology LLC ....F..... 419 738-9664
Lima *(G-12059)*

▲ North Shore Strapping Inc ....E..... 216 661-5200
Brooklyn Heights *(G-2144)*

Pen Pal LLC ....G..... 614 348-2517
New Albany *(G-14768)*

Ramon Robinson ....G..... 330 883-3244
Vienna *(G-19374)*

RPM Consumer Holding Company .....G..... 330 273-5090
Medina *(G-13470)*

Whitten Studios ....G..... 419 368-8366
Ashland *(G-785)*

3953 Marking Devices

Ace Rubber Stamp & Off Sup Co ....E..... 216 771-8483
Cleveland *(G-4690)*

◆ Akron Paint & Varnish Inc ....D..... 330 773-8911
Akron *(G-50)*

All-Craft Wellman Products ....F..... 440 946-9646
Willoughby *(G-20428)*

Bishop Machine Tool & Die ....F..... 740 453-8818
Zanesville *(G-21280)*

Boehm Inc ....E..... 614 875-9010
Grove City *(G-10546)*

Ccsi Inc ....G..... 800 742-8535
Akron *(G-114)*

Dayton Stencil Works Company ....G..... 937 223-3233
Dayton *(G-8287)*

Desmond Engraving Co Inc ....G..... 216 265-8338
Cleveland *(G-5186)*

E C Shaw Co ....E..... 513 721-6334
Cincinnati *(G-3677)*

East Cleveland Rubber Stamp ....G..... 216 851-5050
Cleveland *(G-5239)*

▲ Garvey Products Inc ....E..... 513 771-8710
West Chester *(G-20009)*

Global Partners USA Co Inc ....G..... 513 276-4981
West Chester *(G-19878)*

Greg G Wright & Sons LLC ....E..... 513 721-3310
Cincinnati *(G-3852)*

Hathaway Stamp & Ident Co of C ......F..... 513 621-1052
Cincinnati *(G-3870)*

Hathaway Stamp Co ....F..... 513 621-1052
Cincinnati *(G-3871)*

Identity Holding Company LLC ....C..... 216 514-1277
Cleveland *(G-5548)*

▲ Infosight Corporation ....D..... 740 642-3600
Chillicothe *(G-3245)*

Inner Products Sales Inc ....G..... 216 581-4141
Bedford *(G-1431)*

Innovative Ceramic Corp ....G..... 330 385-6515
East Liverpool *(G-9219)*

Jerry Pulfer ....G..... 937 778-1861
Piqua *(G-16283)*

◆ Lectroetch Co ....F..... 440 934-1249
Sheffield Village *(G-17125)*

Marathon Mfg & Sup Co ....D..... 330 343-2656
New Philadelphia *(G-14911)*

Mark Rite Co ....G..... 330 757-7229
Youngstown *(G-21141)*

Mark-All Enterprises LLC ....E..... 800 433-3615
Akron *(G-284)*

Marking Devices Inc ....E..... 216 861-4498
Cleveland *(G-5748)*

Master Marking Company Inc ....F..... 330 688-6797
Stow *(G-17772)*

▲ Microcom Corporation ....E..... 740 548-6262
Lewis Center *(G-11907)*

Monode Marking Products Inc ....F..... 419 929-0346
New London *(G-14861)*

Monode Steel Stamp Inc ....G..... 419 929-3501
New London *(G-14862)*

Quality Rubber Stamp Inc ....G..... 614 235-2700
Columbus *(G-7536)*

Quick As A Wink Printing Co ....F..... 419 224-9786
Lima *(G-12079)*

Raschke Engraving Inc ....G..... 330 677-5544
Kent *(G-11512)*

▲ REA Elektronik Inc ....F..... 440 232-0555
Bedford *(G-1456)*

▲ Royal Acme Corporation ....E..... 216 241-1477
Cleveland *(G-6136)*

Sprinter Marking Inc ....F..... 740 453-1000
Zanesville *(G-21356)*

Stencilsmith Inc ....G..... 614 876-4350
Hilliard *(G-10983)*

Superior Steel Stamp Co ....G..... 216 431-6460
Cleveland *(G-6271)*

▲ System Seals Inc ....D..... 440 735-0200
Cleveland *(G-6284)*

Taradon Rubber Co Inc ....F..... 330 896-3143
Akron *(G-428)*

▼ Technology and Services Inc ....G..... 740 626-2020
Chillicothe *(G-3280)*

▲ Telesis Technologies Inc ....C..... 740 477-5000
Circleville *(G-4647)*

The Metal Marker Mfg Co ....F..... 440 327-2300
North Ridgeville *(G-15405)*

Ulrich Rubber Stamp Company ....G..... 419 339-9939
Elida *(G-9359)*

Volk Corporation ....G..... 513 621-1052
Cincinnati *(G-4570)*

Williams Steel Rule Die Co ....F..... 216 431-3232
Cleveland *(G-6464)*

3955 Carbon Paper & Inked Ribbons

Adaptive Data Inc ....F..... 937 436-2343
Centerville *(G-3032)*

▲ All Write Ribbon Inc ....E..... 513 753-8300
Amelia *(G-566)*

Eco-Print Solutions LLC ....G..... 513 731-3106
Cincinnati *(G-3689)*

Jay Tackett ....G..... 740 779-1715
Frankfort *(G-9999)*

Kehler Enterprises Inc ....G..... 614 889-8488
Dublin *(G-9095)*

▲ Kroy LLC ....C..... 216 426-5600
Cleveland *(G-5666)*

Nanotechlabs Inc ....F..... 937 297-9518
Kettering *(G-11584)*

Progressive Ribbon Inc ....E..... 513 705-9319
Middletown *(G-14078)*

◆ Pubco Corporation ....D..... 216 881-5300
Cleveland *(G-6059)*

Wood County Ohio ....G..... 419 353-1227
Bowling Green *(G-2022)*

3961 Costume Jewelry & Novelties

Benzle Porcelain Company Inc .... G 614 876-2159
Hilliard (G-10931)
Cult Couture LLC .... G 330 801-9475
Akron (G-135)
Gardella Jewelry LLC .... G 440 877-9261
North Royalton (G-15420)
Johnstons Banks Inc .... G 614 499-4374
Westerville (G-20163)
Polarx Ornaments LLC .... F 866 298-0433
North Ridgeville (G-15395)
Prosperity On Payne Inc .... G 216 431-7677
Cleveland (G-6057)
Pughs Designer Jewelers Inc .... G 740 344-9259
Newark (G-15049)
Swarovski US Holding Limited .... G 330 867-2201
Fairlawn (G-9763)

3965 Fasteners, Buttons, Needles & Pins

A Raymond Tinnerman Mfg Inc .... E 330 220-5179
Brunswick (G-2202)
Cailin Dev Ltd Lblty Co .... F 216 408-6261
Cleveland (G-4962)
▲ Cardinal Fstener Specialty Inc .... E 216 831-3800
Bedford Heights (G-1479)
▲ Catania Medallic Specialty .... E 440 933-9595
Avon Lake (G-1026)
▲ Dimcogray Corporation .... D 937 433-7600
Centerville (G-3039)
Dubose Energy Fasteners & Mach .... F 216 362-1700
Middleburg Heights (G-13905)
Eaglehead Manufacturing Co .... E 216 692-1240
Euclid (G-9576)
Erico International Corp .... B 440 248-0100
Solon (G-17289)
Heads & Threads Intl LLC .... F 216 433-1660
North Olmsted (G-15338)
▼ Hillman Fastener .... F 513 851-6200
Cincinnati (G-3883)
Interfast Inc .... G 216 581-3000
Cleveland (G-5577)
▲ Midwest Motor Supply Co .... C 800 233-1294
Columbus (G-7351)
Ohashi Technica USA Mfg Inc .... E 740 965-9002
Sunbury (G-18071)
Optimas Oe Solutions LLC .... G 740 774-4553
Chillicothe (G-3254)
Phillips Contractors Sup LLC .... F 216 861-5730
Cleveland (G-6002)
▲ Puttmann Industries Inc .... F 513 202-9444
Harrison (G-10797)
R L Technologies Inc .... G 937 321-5544
Dayton (G-8610)
▲ Ramco Specialties Inc .... D 330 653-5135
Hudson (G-11195)
▲ Silicon USA Inc .... G 330 928-6217
Cuyahoga Falls (G-8044)
Solution Industries LLC .... E 440 816-9500
Middleburg Heights (G-13908)
Tri-State Fasteners LLC .... G 937 442-1904
Sardinia (G-17034)
▲ Triangle Fastener Corporation .... F 734 458-1700
Cleveland (G-6360)
W W Cross Industries Inc .... F 330 588-8400
Canton (G-2898)
Wodin Inc .... E 440 439-4222
Cleveland (G-6474)
Youngstown Bolt & Supply Co .... G 330 799-3201
Youngstown (G-21247)
Zipper Manufacturing LLC .... G 937 444-0904
Williamsburg (G-20415)

3991 Brooms & Brushes

Brushes Inc .... E 216 267-8084
Cleveland (G-4941)
D A L E S Corporation .... F 419 255-5335
Toledo (G-18423)
Deco Tools Inc .... E 419 476-9321
Toledo (G-18430)
▲ Demel Enterprises Inc .... G 740 592-5800
Athens (G-860)
Designetics Inc .... D 419 866-0700
Holland (G-11054)
Enercon Systems Inc .... G 305 213-3997
Elyria (G-9419)
◆ Fimm USA Inc .... F 253 243-1522
Columbus (G-7084)
Hoge Lumber Company .... F 419 753-2351
New Knoxville (G-14837)
◆ Malish Corporation .... C 440 951-5356
Mentor (G-13644)
▲ Mill Rose Laboratories Inc .... E 440 974-6730
Mentor (G-13656)
▲ Mill-Rose Company .... C 440 255-9171
Mentor (G-13657)
Ohio Brush Company .... F 216 791-3265
Cleveland (G-5931)
Ohio Carbon Company .... G 216 251-7274
Ashland (G-758)
Precision Brush Co .... F 440 542-9600
Solon (G-17363)
Public Works Dept Street Div .... E 740 283-6013
Steubenville (G-17710)
▲ Spiral Brushes Inc .... E 330 686-2861
Stow (G-17801)
▲ Stephen M Trudick .... E 440 834-1891
Burton (G-2385)
Taupe Holdings Co .... G 614 330-4600
Dublin (G-9153)
Tod Thin Brushes Inc .... F 440 576-6859
Jefferson (G-11375)
Trent Manufacturing Company .... F 216 391-1551
Cleveland (G-6356)
Unique Packaging & Printing .... F 440 785-6730
Mentor (G-13759)
United Rotary Brush Inc .... D 937 644-3515
Plain City (G-16362)
◆ Venture Plas Middlefield LLC .... E 440 834-0704
Middlefield (G-14002)
Wooster Brush Company .... G 440 322-8081
Elyria (G-9511)

3993 Signs & Advertising Displays

1 Day Sign .... G 419 475-6060
Toledo (G-18315)
A & A Safety Inc .... E 513 943-6100
Amelia (G-564)
A B C Sign Inc .... F 513 241-8884
Cincinnati (G-3332)
A M Scheffer Signs Fab .... G 330 666-6674
Copley (G-7837)
A Plus Signs & Graphix .... G 330 848-4800
Akron (G-18)
A Sign Above Inc .... F 330 723-3650
Twinsburg (G-18889)
A Sign For The Times Inc .... G 216 297-2977
Cleveland (G-4678)
Abbot Image Solutions LLC .... G 937 382-6677
Wilmington (G-20652)
Abbott Signs .... G 937 393-6600
Hillsboro (G-10995)
Accu-Sign .... G 216 544-2059
Broadview Heights (G-2102)
Accutech Sign Shop .... G 513 385-3595
Cincinnati (G-3348)
Action Enterprise .... G 740 522-1678
Newark (G-14978)
Action Sign Inc .... G 330 966-0390
Greentown (G-10484)
Ad-Pro Signs I LLC .... G 513 922-5046
Cincinnati (G-3354)
Adcraft Decals Inc .... E 216 524-2934
Cleveland (G-4702)
Advance Sign Group LLC .... E 614 429-2111
Columbus (G-6696)
Advertising Ideas of Ohio Inc .... G 330 745-6555
Barberton (G-1094)
▲ Affinity Disp Expositions Inc .... D 513 771-2339
Cincinnati (G-3363)
Affinity Disp Expositions Inc .... D 513 771-2339
Cincinnati (G-3364)
AG Designs LLC .... G 614 506-2849
Delaware (G-8819)
Agile Sign & Ltg Maint Inc .... F 440 918-1311
Eastlake (G-9258)
Akers Identity LLC .... G 330 493-0055
Canton (G-2596)
▲ Alberts Screen Print Inc .... C 330 753-7559
Norton (G-15505)
All Signs and Designs LLC .... G 216 267-8588
Cleveland (G-4758)
All Signs Express Inc .... F 513 489-7744
Blue Ash (G-1741)
All Signs of Chillicothe Inc .... G 740 773-5016
Chillicothe (G-3227)
All Star Sign Company .... E 614 461-9052
Columbus (G-6722)
Alvin L Roepke .... F 419 862-3891
Elmore (G-9360)
Am Graphics .... G 330 799-7319
Youngstown (G-21022)
American Awards Inc .... F 614 875-1850
Grove City (G-10542)
American Executive Gifts Inc .... F 330 645-4396
Akron (G-66)
▲ American Led-Gible Inc .... F 614 851-1100
Columbus (G-6740)
American Metal Sign .... G 267 521-2670
Ada (G-4)
Aq Productions Inc .... G 614 486-7700
Dublin (G-9046)
Archer Corporation .... E 330 455-9995
Canton (G-2604)
Architctral Identification Inc .... E 614 868-8400
Gahanna (G-10204)
Art & Sign Corporation .... G 419 865-3336
Toledo (G-18356)
Art Tees Inc .... G 614 338-8337
Columbus (G-6774)
Atchley Signs & Graphics .... G 614 421-7446
Columbus (G-6781)
Atlantic Sign Company Inc .... F 513 383-1504
Cincinnati (G-3425)
Auld Company .... E 614 454-1010
Columbus (G-6786)
Auld Lang Signs Inc .... G 513 792-5555
Blue Ash (G-1746)
Auld Technologies LLC .... F 614 755-2853
Columbus (G-6788)
Auto Dealer Designs Inc .... E 330 374-7666
Akron (G-78)
Baker Plastics Inc .... G 330 743-3142
Youngstown (G-21031)
Bambeck Inc .... G 614 766-1000
Dublin (G-9052)
Barnes Advertising Corp .... F 740 453-6836
Zanesville (G-21275)
Bates Metal Products Inc .... D 740 498-8371
Port Washington (G-16422)
BDS Packaging Inc .... D 937 643-0530
Moraine (G-14468)
Becker Signs Inc .... G 330 659-4504
Richfield (G-16615)
Beebe Worldwide Graphics Sign .... G 513 241-2726
Blue Ash (G-1748)
Beesign Signs Inc .... G 614 449-3233
Columbus (G-6819)
Behrco Inc .... G 419 394-1612
Saint Marys (G-16832)
Belco Works Inc .... B 740 695-0500
Saint Clairsville (G-16782)
Bench Billboard Company Inc .... G 513 271-2222
Cincinnati (G-3444)
Benchmark Craftsman Inc .... E 330 975-4214
Seville (G-17069)
Bernard R Doyles Inc .... G 216 523-2288
Cleveland (G-4906)
Bird Corporation .... G 419 424-3095
Findlay (G-9795)
Blang Acquisition LLC .... F 937 223-2155
Dayton (G-8190)
Bob King Sign Company Inc .... G 330 753-2679
Akron (G-94)
Boyer Signs & Graphics Inc .... E 216 383-7242
Euclid (G-9568)
Brainerd Industries Inc .... E 937 228-0488
Miamisburg (G-13786)
Brandon Screen Printing .... F 419 229-9837
Lima (G-11996)
Breibach Association .... G 614 876-6480
Hilliard (G-10936)
Brent Bleh Company .... G 513 721-1100
Cincinnati (G-3467)
Brilliant Electric Sign Co Ltd .... D 216 741-3800
Brooklyn Heights (G-2132)
Brockmans Signs Inc .... G 513 574-6163
Cincinnati (G-3478)
Brown Cnty Bd Mntal Rtardation .... E 937 378-4891
Georgetown (G-10364)
▲ Buckeye Boxes Inc .... D 614 274-8484
Columbus (G-6870)
Buds Sign Shop Inc .... F 330 744-5555
Youngstown (G-21039)
Busch & Thiem Inc .... E 419 625-7515
Sandusky (G-16952)
Business Idntification Systems .... G 614 841-1255
Columbus (G-6879)
Byers Sign Co .... G 614 561-1224
Columbus (G-6880)

S I C

C A Kustoms ..... G 419 332-4395
Fremont (G-10133)
C JS Signs ..... G 330 821-7446
Alliance (G-500)
Campbell Signs & Apparel LLC ..... F 330 386-4768
East Liverpool (G-9205)
Canton Sign Co ..... G 330 456-7151
Canton (G-2647)
▲ Casad Company Inc ..... F 419 586-9457
Coldwater (G-6555)
▲ Catalog Merchandiser Inc ..... F 888 325-9677
Cincinnati (G-3505)
Central Graphics Inc ..... G 330 928-7080
Cuyahoga Falls (G-7977)
Century Signs ..... G 419 352-2666
Bowling Green (G-1979)
▲ Cgs Signs LLC ..... F 419 897-3000
Maumee (G-13233)
Chas J Steven Inc ..... G 440 954-9191
Painesville (G-15864)
Chatelain Plastics Inc ..... G 419 422-4323
Findlay (G-9807)
Cicogna Electric and Sign Co ..... D 440 998-2637
Ashtabula (G-797)
Classic Sign Company Inc ..... G 419 420-0058
Findlay (G-9809)
Cline Signs LLC ..... G 513 396-7446
Cincinnati (G-3586)
▲ Co Pac Services Inc ..... F 216 688-1780
Cleveland (G-5095)
Columbus Graphics Inc ..... F 614 577-9360
Reynoldsburg (G-16584)
Columbus Sign Company ..... E 614 252-3133
Columbus (G-6966)
Creative Blast Co ..... G 513 251-4177
Cincinnati (G-3618)
CTS Signs & Sales ..... G 419 407-5534
Oregon (G-15707)
Cubbison Company ..... D 330 793-2481
Youngstown (G-21059)
Custom Engraving & Screen Prtg ..... G 440 933-2902
Avon Lake (G-1027)
Custom Neon & Commercial Signs ..... G 440 327-0225
North Ridgeville (G-15367)
Custom Retail Group LLC ..... G 614 409-9720
Columbus (G-7004)
Custom Sign Center Inc ..... E 614 279-6700
Columbus (G-7005)
D & D Next Day Signs Inc ..... G 419 537-9595
Toledo (G-18422)
Dana Signs LLC ..... G 937 653-3917
Urbana (G-19155)
Danite Holdings Ltd ..... E 614 444-3333
Columbus (G-7011)
David Esrati ..... G 937 228-4433
Dayton (G-8266)
Dayton Wire Products Inc ..... E 937 236-8000
Dayton (G-8291)
▼ Dee Sign Co ..... E 513 779-3333
West Chester (G-19852)
Dee Sign Usa LLC ..... G 513 779-3333
West Chester (G-19853)
▲ Dern Trophies Corp ..... F 614 895-3260
Westerville (G-20145)
Design Masters Inc ..... G 513 772-7175
Cincinnati (G-3649)
Design Sign Inc ..... G 216 398-9900
Cleveland (G-5185)
Devries & Associates Inc ..... F 614 890-3821
Westerville (G-20209)
Devries & Associates Inc ..... G 614 860-0103
Westerville (G-20210)
Devries & Associates Inc ..... G 614 860-0103
Columbus (G-7023)
Digimatics Inc ..... G 419 478-0804
Toledo (G-18438)
Digimax Signs ..... G 513 576-0747
Milford (G-14137)
Direct Image Signs Inc ..... G 440 327-5575
North Ridgeville (G-15369)
Discount Signs Awnings ..... G 740 373-3556
Marietta (G-12780)
DJ Signs MD LLC ..... G 330 344-6643
Akron (G-153)
Donald Marlo ..... G 937 836-4880
Dayton (G-8308)
▲ Downing Displays Inc ..... D 513 248-9800
Milford (G-14138)
▲ Downing Enterprises Inc ..... D 330 666-3888
Copley (G-7845)

Dyverse Entertainment LLC ..... G 513 225-3301
Blue Ash (G-1779)
E S Sign & Design LLC ..... G 330 405-4799
Twinsburg (G-18927)
▲ Eighth Floor Promotions ..... C 419 586-6433
Celina (G-2994)
Ellet Neon Sales & Service Inc ..... E 330 628-9907
Akron (G-162)
Engravers Gallery & Sign Co ..... G 330 830-1271
Massillon (G-13130)
Enlarging Arts Inc ..... G 330 434-3433
Akron (G-168)
▲ Etched Metal Company ..... E 440 248-0240
Solon (G-17290)
Ew Publishing Company ..... G 440 887-0131
North Olmsted (G-15333)
Exchange Signs ..... G 330 644-4552
Akron (G-174)
F J Designs Inc ..... E 330 264-1377
Wooster (G-20771)
Fair Publishing House Inc ..... E 419 668-3746
Norwalk (G-15540)
Fastsigns ..... G 513 489-8989
Cincinnati (G-3741)
Fdi Cabinetry LLC ..... G 513 353-4500
Cleves (G-6514)
Federal Heath Sign Company LLC ..... D 740 369-0999
Delaware (G-8844)
Fetters and Son Sign Company ..... G 614 299-6947
Mount Gilead (G-14559)
Ffr-DSI Company ..... E 330 998-7800
Twinsburg (G-18936)
Fineline Imprints Inc ..... E 740 453-1083
Zanesville (G-21308)
Finn Graphics Inc ..... E 513 941-6161
Cincinnati (G-3756)
Firehouse Sign Co Inc ..... G 216 267-5300
Brookpark (G-2159)
First Stop Signs and Decals ..... G 330 343-1859
New Philadelphia (G-14899)
Folks Creative Printers Inc ..... E 740 383-6326
Marion (G-12865)
Forty Nine Degrees LLC ..... F 419 678-0100
Coldwater (G-6560)
Fourteen Ventures Group LLC ..... G 937 866-2341
West Carrollton (G-19792)
Fried Daddy ..... G 937 854-4542
Dayton (G-8351)
Frontier Signs & Displays Inc ..... G 513 367-0813
Harrison (G-10779)
Fultz Sign Co Inc ..... G 419 225-6000
Lima (G-12016)
Gail Berner ..... G 937 322-0314
Springfield (G-17563)
▲ Galaxy Balloons Incorporated ..... C 216 476-3360
Cleveland (G-5392)
◆ Gallo Displays Inc ..... E 216 431-9500
Cleveland (G-5393)
Gardner Signs Inc ..... F 419 385-6669
Toledo (G-18477)
Gary Krinn ..... G 740 344-3695
Newark (G-15012)
Gary Lawrence Enterprises Inc ..... F 330 833-7181
Massillon (G-13138)
Gauntlet Awards & Engraving ..... G 937 890-5811
Dayton (G-8357)
Gedco Inc ..... G 330 828-2044
Dalton (G-8069)
Genesis Display Systems Inc ..... G 513 561-1440
Cincinnati (G-3821)
Geoffrey Smith ..... G 614 793-1996
Dublin (G-9078)
Geograph Industries Inc ..... E 513 202-9200
Harrison (G-10780)
Gerber Wood Products Inc ..... G 330 857-3901
Kidron (G-11591)
▲ Ginos Awards Inc ..... E 216 831-5653
Cleveland (G-5431)
Glavin Industries Inc ..... E 440 349-0049
Solon (G-17297)
▲ Global Lighting Tech Inc ..... E 440 922-4584
Brecksville (G-2052)
Global Signs and Graphics Inc ..... G 440 230-2100
North Royalton (G-15421)
Golden Signs and Lighting LLC ..... G 513 248-0895
Milford (G-14144)
▲ Golf Marketing Group Inc ..... G 330 963-5155
Twinsburg (G-18950)
Grady McCauley Incorporated ..... D 330 494-9444
North Canton (G-15236)

◆ Granite Industries Inc ..... D 419 445-4733
Archbold (G-679)
Greg G Wright & Sons LLC ..... E 513 721-3310
Cincinnati (G-3852)
Gus Holthaus Signs Inc ..... E 513 861-0060
Cincinnati (G-3858)
Hall Company ..... E 937 652-1376
Urbana (G-19160)
Ham Signs LLC ..... G 937 454-9111
Dayton (G-8383)
Hart Advertising Inc ..... F 419 668-1194
Norwalk (G-15543)
Hendricks Vacuum Forming Inc ..... E 330 837-2040
Massillon (G-13147)
Hill John ..... F 419 727-8666
Toledo (G-18508)
Hollingsworth Signs Inc ..... G 614 875-2825
Grove City (G-10562)
HP Manufacturing Company Inc ..... D 216 361-6500
Cleveland (G-5530)
HPM Business Systems Inc ..... G 216 520-1330
Cleveland (G-5532)
Identitek Systems Inc ..... D 330 832-9844
Massillon (G-13155)
Impressions To Go LLC ..... G 614 760-0600
Dublin (G-9088)
Industrial and Mar Eng Svc Co ..... F 740 694-0791
Fredericktown (G-10104)
Industrial Electronic Service ..... F 937 746-9750
Carlisle (G-2931)
Industrial Image ..... G 419 547-1417
Bellevue (G-1551)
Inner Products Sales Inc ..... G 216 581-4141
Bedford (G-1431)
Innersource Inc ..... F 330 799-7619
Youngstown (G-21117)
Innovation Exhibits Inc ..... G 330 726-1324
Youngstown (G-21118)
Insignia Signs Inc ..... G 937 866-2341
Dayton (G-8409)
Insta Plak Inc ..... F 419 537-1555
Toledo (G-18525)
Integral Design Inc ..... F 216 524-0555
Cleveland (G-5574)
Interior Graphic Systems LLC ..... G 330 244-0100
Canton (G-2738)
Interstate Sign Products Inc ..... G 419 683-1962
Crestline (G-7930)
J & D Berdine Signs Inc ..... G 330 468-0556
Macedonia (G-12461)
Jacqueline L Vandyke ..... G 740 593-6779
Athens (G-874)
Janeway Signs Inc ..... G 937 237-8433
Dayton (G-8422)
JCP Signs & Graphix Inc ..... G 740 965-3058
Galena (G-10244)
Jeffrey A Clark ..... G 419 866-8775
Holland (G-11067)
Jeffrey L Becht Inc ..... G 937 264-2070
Dayton (G-8426)
Jerry Pulfer ..... G 937 778-1861
Piqua (G-16283)
Jfm Industries ..... G 330 550-6009
Struthers (G-17992)
Joe Paxton ..... G 614 424-9000
Columbus (G-7237)
Jones & Assoc Advg & Design ..... G 330 799-6876
Youngstown (G-21127)
Jones Old Rustic Sign ..... E 937 643-1695
Moraine (G-14498)
Joseph A Panico & Sons Inc ..... G 614 235-3188
Columbus (G-7244)
Judco Inc ..... G 440 322-6604
Elyria (G-9444)
Judith C Zell ..... G 740 385-0386
Logan (G-12180)
Kane Sign Co ..... G 330 253-5263
Akron (G-249)
Kasper Enterprises Inc ..... G 419 829-2121
Toledo (G-18540)
Kdm Signs Inc ..... C 513 769-1932
Cincinnati (G-3975)
Kenneth J Moore ..... G 330 923-8313
Cuyahoga Falls (G-8016)
Kessler Sign Company ..... E 740 453-0668
Zanesville (G-21326)
Kessler Sign Company ..... G 937 898-0633
Dayton (G-8440)
Kief Signs ..... G 513 941-8800
Addyston (G-11)

Kim Phillips Sign Co LLC ....G...... 330 364-4280
Dover (G-8995)
King Retail Solutions Inc ....F...... 513 729-5858
Hamilton (G-10716)
Kingsway Art & Sign ....G...... 330 877-6241
Hartville (G-10826)
Kmgrafx Inc ....G...... 513 248-4100
Loveland (G-12367)
Koebbeco Signs LLC ....G...... 513 923-2974
Cincinnati (G-4000)
Krigbaum Inc ....E...... 614 478-6472
Columbus (G-7267)
Laad Sign & Lighting Inc ....F...... 330 379-2297
Akron (G-265)
Lapat Signs ....G...... 440 277-6291
Sheffield Village (G-17124)
Ledge Hill Signs Limited ....G...... 440 461-4445
Cleveland (G-5690)
Letter Graphics Sign Co Inc ....G...... 330 683-3903
Orrville (G-15746)
Long Sign Co ....G...... 614 294-1057
Columbus (G-7304)
LSI Industries Inc ....E...... 513 793-3200
Blue Ash (G-1829)
LSI Industries Inc ....B...... 513 793-3200
Blue Ash (G-1830)
Macray Co LLC ....G...... 937 325-1726
Springfield (G-17596)
Magnetic Mktg Solutions LLC ....G...... 513 721-3801
Cincinnati (G-4053)
Maines Inc ....G...... 937 322-2084
Springfield (G-17601)
Massillon-Cleveland-Akron Sign ....C...... 330 833-3165
Massillon (G-13175)
Mayfair Granite Co Inc ....G...... 216 382-8150
Cleveland (G-5763)
Mc Sign Company ....C...... 440 209-6200
Mentor (G-13649)
McQueen Advertising Inc ....G...... 440 967-1137
Vermilion (G-19334)
McRd Enterprises LLC ....F...... 740 775-2377
Chillicothe (G-3250)
ME Signs Inc ....G...... 419 222-7446
Lima (G-12052)
Media Sign Company ....G...... 513 564-9500
Cincinnati (G-4078)
Medina Signs Post Inc ....G...... 330 723-2484
Medina (G-13444)
Meka Signs Enterprises Inc ....G...... 513 942-5494
West Chester (G-20027)
Mel Wacker Sign Inc ....G...... 330 832-1726
Massillon (G-13178)
Mentor Signs & Graphics Inc ....G...... 440 951-7446
Mentor (G-13652)
Metalphoto of Cincinnati Inc ....E...... 513 772-8281
Cincinnati (G-4090)
Metromedia Technologies Inc ....D...... 330 264-2501
Wooster (G-20807)
Middlefield Sign Co ....G...... 440 632-0708
Middlefield (G-13963)
Midwest Sign Ctr ....F...... 330 493-7330
Canton (G-2781)
Mike B Crawford ....G...... 330 673-7944
Kent (G-11492)
Mike Closterman ....G...... 513 245-9593
Cincinnati (G-4107)
Mitchell Plastics Inc ....E...... 330 825-2461
Barberton (G-1131)
Moments To Remember USA LLC ....G...... 330 830-0839
Massillon (G-13181)
Moonlight Specialties ....G...... 216 464-6444
Cleveland (G-5833)
Moonshine Screen Printing Inc ....F...... 513 523-7775
Oxford (G-15840)
Morrison Sign Company Inc ....E...... 614 276-1181
Columbus (G-7371)
Municipal Signs and Sales Inc ....G...... 330 457-2421
Columbiana (G-6625)
Myers and Lasch Inc ....G...... 440 235-2050
Cleveland (G-5843)
Names Unlimited Corp ....G...... 419 845-2005
Caledonia (G-2440)
National Illmination Sign Corp ....G...... 419 866-1666
Holland (G-11074)
Nauman Communications Inc ....G...... 740 654-0084
Lancaster (G-11732)
Neon Beach Tanning Inc ....G...... 440 333-3050
Rocky River (G-16702)
Neon Nights ....F...... 330 345-9907
Wooster (G-20815)

Next Day Sign ....G...... 419 537-9595
Toledo (G-18605)
Next Day Signs LLC ....G...... 614 764-7446
Columbus (G-7391)
Norcal Signs Inc ....G...... 513 779-6982
West Chester (G-19906)
North Coast Theatrical Inc ....G...... 330 762-1768
Akron (G-317)
North Hill Marble & Granite Co ....F...... 330 253-2179
Akron (G-318)
Northmont Sign Co Inc ....G...... 937 890-0372
Dayton (G-8528)
Norton Outdoor Advertising ....E...... 513 631-4864
Cincinnati (G-4164)
Off The Wall Signs ....G...... 740 264-7759
Steubenville (G-17707)
▲ Ohio Awning & Manufacturing Co ....E...... 216 861-2400
Cleveland (G-5928)
Ohio Displays Inc ....F...... 216 961-5600
Elyria (G-9470)
Ohio Logos Inc ....G...... 614 717-0833
Dublin (G-9115)
Ohio Plastics & Safety Pdts ....G...... 330 882-6764
New Franklin (G-14827)
Ohio Shelterall Inc ....F...... 614 882-1110
Westerville (G-20227)
Oliver Signs & Graphics ....G...... 330 460-2996
Valley City (G-19226)
Omni Media ....G...... 216 687-0077
Cleveland (G-5941)
Orange Barrel Media LLC ....E...... 614 294-4898
Columbus (G-7445)
Painted Hill Inv Group Inc ....F...... 937 339-1756
Troy (G-18861)
Paul Peterson Safety Div Inc ....E...... 614 486-4375
Columbus (G-7468)
Penca Design Group Ltd ....G...... 440 210-4422
Painesville (G-15910)
Pfi Displays Inc ....E...... 330 925-9015
Rittman (G-16681)
Plastigraphics Inc ....F...... 513 771-8848
Cincinnati (G-4243)
Platinum Productions Inc ....E...... 614 888-7771
Columbus (G-7496)
Power Corp Sign Products Inc ....G...... 740 344-0468
Newark (G-15047)
Power Media Inc ....G...... 330 475-0500
Akron (G-345)
PR Signs & Service ....G...... 614 252-7090
Columbus (G-7511)
Pro Companies Inc ....G...... 614 738-1222
Pickerington (G-16201)
Pro-Decal Inc ....G...... 330 484-0089
Canton (G-2825)
Quality Channel Letters ....G...... 859 866-6500
Miamisburg (G-13850)
▲ Quikey Manufacturing Co Inc ....C...... 330 633-8106
Akron (G-360)
R & H Signs Unlimited Inc ....E...... 937 293-3834
Dayton (G-8608)
R M Davis Inc ....G...... 419 756-6719
Mansfield (G-12669)
R Weir Inc ....G...... 937 438-5730
Dayton (G-8613)
Ram Z Neon ....G...... 330 788-5121
Youngstown (G-21185)
Rapid Signs & More Inc ....G...... 513 553-4040
New Richmond (G-14944)
Red Hot Studios ....G...... 330 609-7446
Warren (G-19592)
Redi-Quik Signs Inc ....G...... 614 228-6641
Columbus (G-7551)
Renoir Visions LLC ....F...... 419 586-5679
Celina (G-3016)
Ricks Graphic Accents Inc ....G...... 330 644-4455
Akron (G-374)
Rise N Shine Yard Signs ....G...... 330 745-5868
Barberton (G-1147)
▲ Rocal Inc ....D...... 740 998-2122
Frankfort (G-10002)
Roderer Enterprises Inc ....G...... 513 942-3000
Fairfield (G-9712)
Roemer Industries Inc ....D...... 330 448-2000
Masury (G-13216)
Rossi Concept Arts ....G...... 330 453-6366
Canton (G-2843)
▲ Royal Acme Corporation ....E...... 216 241-1477
Cleveland (G-6136)
Ruff Neon & Lighting Maint Inc ....F...... 440 350-6267
Painesville (G-15920)

▲ Ruthie Ann Inc ....F...... 800 231-3567
New Paris (G-14881)
S & S Sign Co ....G...... 614 837-1511
Canal Winchester (G-2536)
S T Custom Signs ....G...... 513 733-4227
Cincinnati (G-4375)
S&S Sign Service ....G...... 614 279-9722
Columbus (G-7582)
Sa-Mor Signs ....G...... 937 441-4950
Wapakoneta (G-19505)
▲ Sabco Industries Inc ....E...... 419 531-5347
Toledo (G-18683)
Safety Sign Company ....E...... 440 238-7722
Strongsville (G-17960)
Scioto Sign Co Inc ....E...... 419 673-1261
Kenton (G-11568)
Screen Images Inc ....G...... 440 779-7356
North Olmsted (G-15344)
Screen Works Inc ....E...... 937 264-9111
Dayton (G-8650)
▲ Sensical Inc ....D...... 216 641-1141
Solon (G-17378)
Sign A Rama ....G...... 330 499-4653
North Canton (G-15265)
Sign A Rama ....G...... 614 337-6000
Gahanna (G-10232)
Sign A Rama Inc ....G...... 440 442-5002
Cleveland (G-6202)
Sign A Rama Inc ....G...... 513 671-2213
Cincinnati (G-4419)
Sign America Incorporated ....E...... 740 765-5555
Richmond (G-16649)
Sign City Inc ....G...... 614 486-6700
Mount Gilead (G-14568)
Sign Connection Inc ....G...... 937 435-4070
Dayton (G-8657)
Sign Design Wooster Inc ....G...... 330 262-8838
Wooster (G-20835)
Sign Graphics & Design ....G...... 513 576-1639
Milford (G-14174)
Sign Pro of Lima ....G...... 419 222-7767
Lima (G-12091)
Sign Shop ....G...... 740 474-1499
Circleville (G-4643)
Sign Smith LLC ....G...... 614 519-9144
Marengo (G-12755)
Sign Source USA Inc ....D...... 419 224-1130
Lima (G-12092)
Sign Write ....G...... 937 559-4388
Beavercreek (G-1361)
Sign-Lite Corporation ....D...... 216 851-1000
Cleveland (G-6203)
Signaffects Limited LLC ....G...... 614 504-5324
Plain City (G-16358)
Signage Consultants Inc ....G...... 614 297-7446
Columbus (G-7620)
Signcom Incorporated ....E...... 614 228-9999
Columbus (G-7621)
Signed By Josette LLC ....G...... 419 796-9632
Findlay (G-9889)
Signery ....G...... 513 932-1938
Lebanon (G-11840)
Signery2 LLC ....G...... 513 738-3048
Hamilton (G-10739)
Significant Impressions Inc ....G...... 513 874-5223
Fairfield (G-9718)
Signline Graphics & Lettering ....G...... 740 397-5806
Mount Vernon (G-14650)
Signmaster Inc ....G...... 614 777-0670
Lewis Center (G-11918)
Signs 2 Graphics ....G...... 740 493-2049
Piketon (G-16228)
Signs By George ....G...... 216 394-2095
Brookfield (G-2126)
Signs Limited LLC ....G...... 740 282-7715
Steubenville (G-17712)
Signs N Stuff Inc ....G...... 440 974-3151
Mentor (G-13723)
Signs PDQ Inc ....G...... 440 951-6651
Willoughby (G-20597)
Signs Unlimited ....G...... 614 836-7446
Logan (G-12193)
Skyline Exhibits Grtr Cncnt ....G...... 513 671-4460
Cincinnati (G-4426)
Specialty Nameplate Corp ....F...... 614 444-6876
Columbus (G-7636)
Spotted Horse Studio Inc ....G...... 330 533-2391
Greenford (G-10483)
Standard Signs Incorporated ....F...... 330 467-2030
Macedonia (G-12489)

S
I
C

Steel Valley Sign ....G... 330 755-7446
　Struthers *(G-17999)*
Sterling Associates Inc ....G... 330 630-3500
　Akron *(G-418)*
Steven Mercer Inc ....G... 740 623-0033
　Coshocton *(G-7911)*
Stine Consulting Inc ....G... 513 723-4800
　Cincinnati *(G-4469)*
Summco Inc ....G... 330 965-7446
　Youngstown *(G-21215)*
Super Sign Guys LLC ....G... 330 477-3887
　Canton *(G-2864)*
Super Signs Inc ....E... 480 968-2200
　North Bend *(G-15209)*
Superior Label Systems Inc ....B... 513 336-0825
　Mason *(G-13092)*
T-Top Shoppe ....G... 330 343-3481
　New Philadelphia *(G-14932)*
Tamblingson Inc ....G... 419 221-3437
　Lima *(G-12101)*
▼ Tce International Ltd ....F... 800 962-2376
　Perry *(G-16059)*
◆ Ternion Inc ....E... 216 642-6180
　Cleveland *(G-6307)*
Terry & Jack Neon Sign Co ....E... 419 229-0674
　Lima *(G-12103)*
Thatcher Enterprises Co Ltd ....G... 614 228-2013
　Columbus *(G-7688)*
The Hartman Corp ....G... 614 475-5035
　Columbus *(G-7690)*
Tillmans Entp -Signs Ship LLC ....G... 440 281-9340
　Elyria *(G-9502)*
Tim Boutwell ....G... 419 358-4653
　Bluffton *(G-1917)*
▲ To A T ....G... 216 621-3322
　Cleveland *(G-6329)*
Toledo Mobile Media LLC ....G... 419 389-0687
　Toledo *(G-18734)*
Traffic Cntrl Sgnls Signs & MA ....G... 740 670-7763
　Newark *(G-15064)*
Traffic Detectors & Signs Inc ....G... 330 707-9060
　Youngstown *(G-21226)*
Triangle Sign Co ....G... 513 863-2578
　Hamilton *(G-10751)*
Tridico Silk Screen & Sign Co ....G... 419 526-1695
　Mansfield *(G-12700)*
Triumph Signs & Consulting Inc ....E... 513 576-8090
　Milford *(G-14180)*
Ultimate Signs and Graphics ....G... 740 633-8928
　Martins Ferry *(G-12926)*
Unionville Center Sign Co ....G... 614 873-5834
　Unionville Center *(G-19105)*
Unique Straight Line & Sfety S ....G... 740 452-2724
　Zanesville *(G-21359)*
United-Maier Signs Inc ....D... 513 681-6600
　Cincinnati *(G-4541)*
▲ Vgu Industries Inc ....E... 216 676-9093
　Cleveland *(G-6414)*
Visionary Signs LLC ....G... 614 504-5899
　Columbus *(G-7742)*
Visual Advantage LLC ....G... 714 671-0988
　Perrysburg *(G-16166)*
Visual Expressions Sign Co ....G... 440 245-6660
　Lorain *(G-12291)*
Vital Signs & Advertising LLC ....G... 937 292-7967
　Bellefontaine *(G-1540)*
▲ Vmi Liquidating Inc ....E... 937 492-3100
　Sidney *(G-17232)*
Vsl Signs ....G... 740 441-7578
　Gallipolis *(G-10311)*
Warren Enterprises ....G... 330 836-6119
　Akron *(G-468)*
Waterford Signs Inc ....G... 740 362-7446
　Delaware *(G-8895)*
Westrock Cp LLC ....B... 513 745-2400
　Blue Ash *(G-1893)*
Wettle Corporation ....G... 419 865-6923
　Holland *(G-11096)*
WH Fetzer & Sons Mfg Inc ....E... 419 687-8237
　Plymouth *(G-16380)*
Wholesale Channel Letters ....G... 440 256-3200
　Kirtland *(G-11619)*
Wide Area Media LLC ....G... 440 356-3133
　Westlake *(G-20321)*
Williams Steel Rule Die Co ....F... 216 431-3232
　Cleveland *(G-6464)*
Wilson Seat Company Inc ....E... 513 732-2460
　Batavia *(G-1233)*
Wilson Sign Co Inc ....F... 937 253-2246
　Dayton *(G-8760)*

Woodrow Corp ....G... 937 322-7696
　Springfield *(G-17681)*
Wright John ....G... 937 653-4570
　Urbana *(G-19188)*
▲ Wurtec Manufacturing Service .....E... 419 726-1066
　Toledo *(G-18777)*
Yes Management Inc ....G... 330 747-8593
　Columbiana *(G-6638)*

3995 Burial Caskets

American Steel Grave Vault Co ....F... 419 468-6715
　Galion *(G-10253)*
Case Ohio Burial Co ....F... 440 779-1992
　Cleveland *(G-4986)*
Clark Grave Vault Company ....C... 614 294-3761
　Columbus *(G-6933)*
McCord Products Inc ....F... 419 352-3691
　Bowling Green *(G-2001)*
Milso Midwest ....G... 513 745-0760
　West Chester *(G-20031)*
Youngstown Casket Co Inc ....F... 330 758-2008
　Youngstown *(G-21249)*
Zane Casket Company Inc ....E... 740 452-4680
　Zanesville *(G-21365)*

3996 Linoleum & Hard Surface Floor Coverings, NEC

Armstrong World Industries Inc ....D... 614 771-9307
　Hilliard *(G-10927)*
Prints & Paints Flr Cvg Co Inc ....E... 419 462-5663
　Galion *(G-10283)*
Quality Drble Indus Floors Inc ....E... 937 696-2833
　Farmersville *(G-9773)*
Schlabach Woodworks Ltd ....E... 330 674-7488
　Millersburg *(G-14262)*

3999 Manufacturing Industries, NEC

3-D Technical Services Inc ....E... 937 746-2901
　Franklin *(G-10004)*
4S Company ....F... 330 792-5518
　Youngstown *(G-21009)*
A-Buck Manufacturing Inc ....G... 937 687-3738
　New Lebanon *(G-14839)*
Abby Industries LLC ....G... 513 502-9865
　Eaton *(G-9298)*
Access Manufacturing Svcs LLC ......G... 330 659-9893
　Richfield *(G-16612)*
Access To Independence Inc ....G... 330 296-8111
　Ravenna *(G-16512)*
Accu Pak Mfg Inc ....G... 330 644-3015
　Akron *(G-26)*
Accurate Automatic Mfg Ltd ....G... 330 435-4575
　Creston *(G-7937)*
Ace Assembly Packaging Inc ....E... 330 866-9117
　Waynesburg *(G-19722)*
Ace Grinding Co ....G... 440 951-6760
　Willoughby *(G-20424)*
Actual Industries LLC ....G... 614 379-2739
　Columbus *(G-6693)*
Advance Products ....F... 419 882-8117
　Sylvania *(G-18097)*
Advanced Livescan Technologies .....G... 440 759-7028
　Cleveland *(G-4715)*
Aerovent Inc ....G... 937 473-3789
　Covington *(G-7917)*
▲ Al Root Company ....C... 330 723-4359
　Medina *(G-13364)*
Al Root Company ....C... 330 725-6677
　Medina *(G-13365)*
AK Mansfield ....B... 419 755-3011
　Mansfield *(G-12556)*
Alligator Cmpt Systems Corp ....F... 513 542-1000
　Cincinnati *(G-3380)*
Alt Fuel LLC ....G... 419 865-4196
　Toledo *(G-18334)*
Altec Industries ....G... 419 289-6066
　Ashland *(G-702)*
◆ Aluminum Line Products Company .D... 440 835-8880
　Westlake *(G-20249)*
Ambrosia Inc ....G... 419 825-1151
　Swanton *(G-18079)*
American Inks and Coatings Co ....F... 513 552-7200
　Fairfield *(G-9641)*
American Pioneer Manufacturing ......G... 330 457-1400
　New Waterford *(G-14967)*
Amish Lights Candles ....G... 330 546-3900
　North Canton *(G-15219)*
▲ Anza Inc ....G... 513 542-7337
　Cincinnati *(G-3406)*

API Machining Fabrication Inc ....G... 740 369-0455
　Delaware *(G-8821)*
◆ Aquatic Technology ....F... 440 236-8330
　Columbia Station *(G-6579)*
Arrowhead Industries ....G... 440 349-2846
　Solon *(G-17261)*
Aster Industries Inc ....F... 330 762-7965
　Akron *(G-75)*
AT&f Nuclear Inc ....G... 216 252-1500
　Cleveland *(G-4852)*
Autograph Inc ....E... 216 881-1911
　Cleveland *(G-4865)*
Bay Industries Incorporated ....F... 740 549-2305
　Lewis Center *(G-11889)*
Bead Shoppe At Home ....G... 330 479-9598
　Canton *(G-2618)*
Beauty Systems Group LLC ....G... 740 456-5434
　New Boston *(G-14779)*
Beck Studios Inc ....E... 513 831-6650
　Milford *(G-14125)*
Bird Loft ....G... 440 988-2473
　Amherst *(G-592)*
Birge Heavy Industries Ltd ....E... 440 821-3249
　Elyria *(G-9382)*
Bison USA Corp ....G... 513 713-0513
　West Chester *(G-19818)*
Blackhawk Industries ....F... 918 610-4719
　Brunswick *(G-2213)*
Blue Creek Renewables LLC ....G... 419 576-7855
　Paulding *(G-16001)*
BMC of Barfield Inc ....G... 513 860-4455
　Hamilton *(G-10676)*
Bomb Mfg LLC ....G... 419 559-9689
　Fremont *(G-10131)*
▲ Boss Pet Products Inc ....F... 216 332-0832
　Bedford *(G-1408)*
Buckbuilt Manufacturing Co ....F... 330 764-3363
　Medina *(G-13383)*
Burton Bottling Company Inc ....E... 216 681-0025
　Cleveland *(G-4950)*
C P R Drain Cleaning Inc ....F... 614 279-3445
　Columbus *(G-6884)*
C&H Industries ....G... 330 899-0001
　Canton *(G-2632)*
Candle Cottage ....G... 937 526-4041
　Versailles *(G-19343)*
Candle-Lite Company LLC ....E... 937 780-2711
　Leesburg *(G-11850)*
Candle-Lite Company LLC ....D... 513 563-1113
　Blue Ash *(G-1762)*
Candles By Joyce ....G... 740 886-6355
　Proctorville *(G-16489)*
Canine Creations ....G... 937 667-8576
　Tipp City *(G-18269)*
Carroll Hills Industries Inc ....D... 330 627-5524
　Carrollton *(G-2953)*
▲ Centaur Inc ....G... 419 469-8000
　Toledo *(G-18392)*
Centerless Grinding Service ....G... 216 251-4100
　Cleveland *(G-5003)*
City Dog ....G... 614 228-3647
　Columbus *(G-6931)*
▲ CK Technologies LLC ....C... 419 485-1110
　Montpelier *(G-14441)*
Cleveland Plant and Flower Co ....E... 614 478-9900
　Columbus *(G-6937)*
◆ CM Paula Company ....E... 513 759-7473
　Mason *(G-13002)*
CNB Machining and Mfg LLC ....G... 330 877-7920
　Hartville *(G-10819)*
Colby Properties LLC ....G... 937 390-0816
　Springfield *(G-17534)*
Columbus Industries Inc ....F... 937 544-6896
　West Union *(G-20119)*
Condos and Trees LLC ....G... 419 691-2287
　Northwood *(G-15479)*
Connelly Industries LLC ....G... 330 468-0675
　Macedonia *(G-12443)*
Connies Candles ....G... 740 574-1224
　Wheelersburg *(G-20329)*
Consolidated Pattern Works Inc ....G... 330 434-6060
　Akron *(G-127)*
Continental Fan Mfg ....G... 937 233-5524
　Huber Heights *(G-11144)*
Country Clippins ....G... 740 472-5228
　Woodsfield *(G-20716)*
Cr Brands Inc ....D... 513 860-5039
　West Chester *(G-19846)*
Creation Industries LLC ....G... 440 554-6286
　Middlefield *(G-13925)*

◆ Cropking Incorporated...............F.......330 302-4203
Lodi (G-12159)
Custom Made Palm Trees LLC.............G.......330 633-0063
Akron (G-138)
▲ Daca Vending Wholesale LLC...........G.......513 753-1600
Amelia (G-571)
Dano Jr LLC...............................G.......440 781-5774
Cleveland (G-5165)
Datco Mfg Company Inc..................E.......330 787-1127
Youngstown (G-21064)
Dcc Corp..................................G.......330 494-0494
Canton (G-2680)
Debolt Machine Inc.......................G.......740 454-8082
Zanesville (G-21298)
▲ Dem Manufacturing LLC...............F.......440 564-7160
Newbury (G-15088)
Dem Technology LLC....................G.......937 223-1317
Dayton (G-8298)
Denton Atd Inc..........................E.......567 265-5200
Huron (G-11220)
Devault Industries LLC...................G.......330 456-6070
Canton (G-2685)
Dmi Products Inc........................G.......440 951-1828
Mentor (G-13561)
Duraflow Industries Inc..................G.......440 965-5047
Wakeman (G-19448)
Duramax Marine Industries..............G.......419 668-3728
Norwalk (G-15536)
Dynamic Manufacturing..................G.......419 564-8738
Shelby (G-17135)
Eagle Burgmann Industries..............G.......513 563-7325
Cincinnati (G-3681)
Eaglehead Manufacturing Co.............G.......440 951-0400
Eastlake (G-9267)
Elaire Corporation.......................G.......419 843-2192
Toledo (G-18451)
Energizer Battery Mfg Inc................G.......330 527-2191
Garrettsville (G-10321)
Erichar Inc...............................G.......216 402-2628
Cleveland (G-5293)
Exikon Industries LLC....................F.......216 485-2947
Cleveland (G-5313)
▲ Faith Guiding Cafe LLC...............F.......614 245-8451
New Albany (G-14758)
Fallen Oak Candles Inc...................G.......419 204-8162
Celina (G-2997)
Faw Industries...........................G.......216 651-9595
Cleveland (G-5327)
Fbr Industries Inc........................G.......330 701-7425
Mineral Ridge (G-14304)
Ferguson Fire Fabrication Inc............F.......614 299-2070
Columbus (G-7081)
Fin Feather Fur..........................G.......330 493-8300
Canton (G-2701)
Fire Safety Services Inc..................F.......937 686-2000
Huntsville (G-11213)
Firelands Manufacturing LLC............F.......419 687-8237
Plymouth (G-16376)
Fleig Enterprises Inc.....................G.......216 361-8020
Cleveland (G-5355)
Frugal Systems..........................G.......419 957-7863
Carey (G-2918)
▲ Gayston Corporation.................C.......937 743-6050
Miamisburg (G-13812)
Gececo Inc...............................E.......614 861-4479
Columbus (G-7106)
Gen Two Industries LLC..................G.......419 624-8803
Sandusky (G-16969)
Gerber Wood Products Inc...............G.......330 857-3901
Kidron (G-11591)
Gibraltar Industries Inc..................G.......440 617-9230
Westlake (G-20272)
Gibson Greetings Inc....................G.......216 252-7300
Cleveland (G-5428)
▲ GKN Driveline Bowl Green Inc.........G.......419 354-3955
Bowling Green (G-1989)
Glass Mirror Awards Inc..................G.......419 638-2221
Helena (G-10896)
Glasslight Candles LLC...................G.......443 509-5505
Mason (G-13028)
Global Manufacturing Inds................G.......513 271-2180
Cincinnati (G-3837)
Goodwill Idstrs Grtr Clvlnd L.............E.......330 456-8020
Canton (G-2716)
Goodwill Inds NW Ohio Inc...............E.......419 255-0070
Toledo (G-18483)
Gorant Chocolatier LLC..................C.......330 726-8821
Boardman (G-1921)
Grant Solutions.........................G.......937 344-5558
Tipp City (G-18280)

Green Door Industries LLC................G.......614 558-1663
Blacklick (G-1696)
Groff Industries..........................F.......216 634-9100
Cleveland (G-5460)
Gumbys LLC.............................D.......740 671-0818
Bellaire (G-1498)
H Rosen Usa LLC........................C.......614 354-6707
Columbus (G-7135)
Hafner Hardwood Connection LLC.........G.......419 726-4828
Toledo (G-18493)
Hartz Mountain Corporation..............D.......513 877-2131
Pleasant Plain (G-16372)
HCC Industries...........................G.......513 334-5585
Cincinnati (G-3872)
Heart Warming Candles..................G.......937 456-2720
Eaton (G-9308)
▲ Henry-Griffitts Limited...............G.......419 482-9095
Maumee (G-13266)
Highland Technologies LLC...............G.......513 739-3510
Mount Orab (G-14580)
HK Technologies.........................G.......330 337-9710
Cleveland (G-5515)
Housing & Emrgncy Lgstcs Plnnr..........E.......209 201-7511
Lisbon (G-12122)
Hung Pham...............................G.......614 850-9695
Columbus (G-7170)
ID Card Systems Inc.....................G.......330 963-7446
Twinsburg (G-18958)
Idx Corporation..........................C.......937 401-3225
Dayton (G-8400)
J S Manufacturing LLC....................G.......330 815-2136
Kent (G-11473)
J-Fab.....................................G.......740 384-2649
Wellston (G-19764)
Jack R Stiner Models & Pattern...........G.......330 494-1730
Canton (G-2744)
James J Fairbanks Company Inc...........G.......330 534-1374
Hubbard (G-11132)
Janson Industries........................D.......330 455-7029
Canton (G-2745)
Jrf Industries Ltd........................G.......330 665-3130
Copley (G-7849)
Jrw Manufacturing.......................G.......330 628-2994
Akron (G-244)
JW Manufacturing........................G.......419 375-5536
Fort Recovery (G-9957)
Kendee Candles LLC......................G.......330 899-9898
Uniontown (G-19088)
Kenton Industries Ltd....................G.......915 603-2139
Cleveland (G-5647)
Key Mobility Services Ltd................G.......937 374-3226
Xenia (G-20959)
King Model Company.....................E.......330 633-0491
Akron (G-259)
Kiser Industries llc.......................G.......937 332-6723
Troy (G-18853)
L & L Fabricating LLC.....................G.......440 647-6649
Wellington (G-19749)
L E P D Industries Ltd....................G.......614 985-1470
Powell (G-16476)
Lawnview Industries Inc.................C.......937 653-5217
Urbana (G-19168)
Leyshon Miller Industries LLC............F.......740 432-2969
Cambridge (G-2463)
Lincoln Candle Company Inc..............G.......419 749-4224
Convoy (G-7832)
Linebacker Inc...........................G.......614 340-1446
Columbus (G-7298)
▲ Lumi-Lite Candle Company............D.......740 872-3248
Norwich (G-15569)
M & R Industries Inc......................G.......440 897-7950
Brecksville (G-2062)
Mab Fabrication Inc......................G.......855 622-3221
Harrison (G-10788)
Maca Mold & Machine Co Inc.............G.......330 854-0292
Canal Fulton (G-1131)
◆ Mace Personal Def & SEC Inc.........E.......440 424-5321
Cleveland (G-5722)
◆ Mace Security Intl Inc................F.......440 424-5321
Cleveland (G-5723)
Makergear LLC..........................E.......216 765-0030
Beachwood (G-1277)
Manufacturing Company LLC.............G.......414 708-7583
Cincinnati (G-4056)
Marcy Industries Company LLC...........E.......740 387-1213
Marion (G-12881)
Mark-All Enterprises LLC.................E.......800 433-3615
Akron (G-284)
Markethatch Co Inc.....................F.......330 376-6363
Akron (G-285)

MCS Mfg LLC.............................G.......419 923-7535
Lyons (G-12432)
▲ MD Solutions Inc....................G.......866 637-6588
Plain City (G-16348)
Medline Industries Inc....................G.......330 484-1450
Canton (G-2778)
Mels Life Like Hair.......................G.......937 278-9486
Dayton (G-8483)
Melvin Grain Co..........................G.......937 382-1249
Wilmington (G-20670)
Mibtach Enterprises Inc..................G.......513 941-0387
Cincinnati (G-4098)
Midwest Stamping & Mfg Co..............G.......419 298-2394
Edgerton (G-9333)
◆ Miraclecorp Products.................D.......937 293-9994
Moraine (G-14509)
Model Engineering Company.............G.......330 644-3450
Barberton (G-1132)
Morris Technologies.....................G.......330 384-3084
Akron (G-304)
Morris Technologies Inc..................C.......513 733-1611
Cincinnati (G-4123)
My Major Family LLP.....................G.......567 218-1206
Toledo (G-18595)
N2y LLC..................................E.......419 433-9800
Huron (G-11235)
Nail Art..................................G.......614 899-7155
Westerville (G-20225)
Nail Secret..............................G.......513 459-3373
Maineville (G-12530)
Natural Beauty Hc Express...............G.......440 459-1776
Mayfield Heights (G-13319)
New Can Company Inc....................G.......937 547-9050
Greenville (G-10512)
▲ NI Mfg & Distribution Sys In...........G.......513 422-5216
Middletown (G-14102)
Norris North Manufacturing..............G.......330 691-0449
Canton (G-2791)
Norton Manufacturing Co Inc.............F.......419 435-0411
Fostoria (G-9990)
Octsys Security Corp.....................G.......614 470-4510
Columbus (G-7412)
Ohio Candle Co Inc......................G.......740 289-8000
Waverly (G-19715)
▲ Ohio Feather Company Inc............G.......513 921-3373
Cincinnati (G-4176)
Ohio Manufacturing EXT Partnr...........G.......614 644-8788
Columbus (G-7422)
▲ Ohio Model Planes...................G.......937 372-0603
Xenia (G-20965)
On Display LLC...........................E.......513 841-1600
Batavia (G-1214)
▲ Osborne Coinage Company............D.......513 681-5424
Cincinnati (G-4197)
▲ Otomik Products Inc................G.......877 776-5358
Cincinnati (G-4199)
▲ Ourpets Company....................D.......440 354-6500
Fairport Harbor (G-9769)
Oveco Industries Electrica................G.......740 381-3326
Richmond (G-16648)
Parrot University LLC....................G.......740 965-1965
Sunbury (G-18073)
◆ Partners In Recognition Inc..........E.......937 420-2150
Fort Loramie (G-9934)
Pdi Constellation LLC.....................G.......216 271-7344
Solon (G-17359)
Pegasus Industries.......................G.......740 772-1049
Chillicothe (G-3259)
Phoenix Trinity Mfg Inc...................G.......937 619-0172
Dayton (G-8574)
Pinnacle Sales Inc.......................G.......440 777-2544
Westlake (G-20295)
Plx Industries Inc........................G.......330 896-7373
Uniontown (G-19095)
Power Media Inc.........................G.......330 475-0500
Akron (G-345)
Powersonic Industries LLC................F.......513 429-2339
Cincinnati (G-4257)
PPG Industries...........................G.......419 433-0567
Huron (G-11239)
PPG Industries Inc.......................G.......330 825-6328
Barberton (G-1141)
Precise Models Inc.......................G.......440 365-5701
Elyria (G-9480)
▼ Premier Seals Mfg....................G.......330 861-1060
Akron (G-349)
Priority Vending Inc......................G.......216 361-4100
Cleveland (G-6050)
Procter & Gamble Distrg LLC.............C.......937 387-5189
Union (G-19067)

Puritan Systems Inc ....E 330 686-0527
Stow *(G-17794)*

Quality Compound Mfg ....G 440 353-0150
North Ridgeville *(G-15398)*

Quick Tech Business Forms Inc ....E 937 743-5952
Springboro *(G-17501)*

R and D Industries Unlimited ....G 937 502-1374
Xenia *(G-20969)*

R M Industries Inc ....G 419 529-8970
Mansfield *(G-12670)*

Rays Whistle Stop ....G 740 965-2085
New Albany *(G-14771)*

Rbs Mfg Inc ....F 330 426-9486
East Palestine *(G-9243)*

Reiser Manufacturing ....G 330 846-8003
New Waterford *(G-14973)*

Reliable Fur Co ....G 513 288-5093
New Richmond *(G-14945)*

Resource Recycling Inc ....F 419 222-2702
Lima *(G-12081)*

Restless Noggins Mfg LLC ....G 330 526-6908
North Canton *(G-15261)*

Rmw Industries Inc ....G 440 439-1971
Bedford Heights *(G-1493)*

Rose of Sharon Enterprises ....G 937 862-4543
Waynesville *(G-19735)*

Rowend Industries Inc ....G 419 333-8300
Fremont *(G-10181)*

Royal Mfg ....G 419 902-8222
Findlay *(G-9886)*

RPM Industries ....G 440 268-8077
Elyria *(G-9489)*

▲ S & H Industries Inc ....G 216 831-0550
Cleveland *(G-6146)*

Safe 4 People Inc ....G 419 797-4087
Port Clinton *(G-16412)*

▲ Salon Styling Concepts Ltd ....E 216 539-0437
Maple Heights *(G-12740)*

Scarefactory Inc ....F 614 252-8000
Columbus *(G-7594)*

Schell Scenic Studio Inc ....G 614 444-9550
Columbus *(G-7595)*

Schreiner Manufacturing ....G 419 937-0300
New Riegel *(G-14948)*

Scott Models Inc ....F 513 771-8005
Cincinnati *(G-4391)*

Sdi Industries ....G 513 561-4032
Cincinnati *(G-4394)*

Seavival LLC ....G 330 252-1151
Akron *(G-398)*

Serving Veterans Mobility Inc ....G 937 746-4788
Franklin *(G-10052)*

Shafts Mfg ....G 440 942-6012
Willoughby *(G-20595)*

Sharc Industries ....G 216 272-0668
Columbia Station *(G-6600)*

Shaw Industries Inc ....G 513 942-3692
West Chester *(G-19945)*

Sheridan Mfg of Ohio LLC ....G 419 825-2950
Swanton *(G-18090)*

Shermco Industries Inc ....G 614 836-8556
Groveport *(G-10643)*

Skr Enterprises LLC ....G 419 891-1112
Maumee *(G-13295)*

Smith & Mills Shapers Inc ....F 513 541-4031
Cincinnati *(G-4428)*

Smokeheal Inc ....G 216 255-5119
Cleveland *(G-6213)*

Softpoint Industries ....G 330 668-2645
Copley *(G-7855)*

Soldier Tech & Armor RES LLC ....G 330 896-5217
Akron *(G-407)*

Solomon Industries LLC ....G 937 558-5334
Troy *(G-18877)*

◆ Staco Energy Products Co ....G 937 253-1191
Miamisburg *(G-13863)*

Sterling Collectables Inc ....G 419 892-5708
Mansfield *(G-12684)*

Steves Vans & Accessories LLC ....G 740 374-3154
Marietta *(G-12836)*

Stone & Sullivan Industries ....F 513 896-1976
Hamilton *(G-10742)*

◆ Sun Drenched Art Studios ....G 513 375-9612
Cincinnati *(G-4482)*

▲ Sunbright Usa Inc ....G 440 205-0600
Mentor *(G-13741)*

Superfine Manufacturing Inc ....F 330 897-9024
Fresno *(G-10199)*

Sword Furs ....G 440 249-5001
Westlake *(G-20314)*

Tango Echo Bravo Mfg Inc ....G 440 937-3800
North Ridgeville *(G-15404)*

Tanner Industries Inc ....F 419 221-1576
Lima *(G-12102)*

Texstone Industries ....G 419 722-4664
Findlay *(G-9900)*

Thapa Industries ....G 419 234-3498
Lima *(G-12104)*

Thomas Mfg ....G 330 758-2384
Youngstown *(G-21220)*

▲ Thoroughbred Gt Mfg LLC ....F 330 533-0048
Canfield *(G-2579)*

Tiffin Scenic Studios Inc ....E 800 445-1546
Tiffin *(G-18249)*

Tiger Cat Furniture ....G 330 220-7232
Brunswick *(G-2262)*

Tmb Enterprises LLC ....F 419 243-2189
Holland *(G-11089)*

Tmt Inc ....C 419 592-1041
Perrysburg *(G-16161)*

Toledo Mobile Media LLC ....G 419 389-0687
Toledo *(G-18734)*

Tommy B Manufacturing Inc ....G 330 745-4539
Barberton *(G-1155)*

Trademark Designs Inc ....E 419 628-3897
Minster *(G-14365)*

▲ Tradex International Inc ....D 216 651-4788
Cleveland *(G-6345)*

Treadway Manufacturing LLC ....G 937 264-8447
Dayton *(G-8722)*

Trumbull Inc ....G 419 849-3561
Woodville *(G-20727)*

Ttr Manufacturing ....G 440 366-5005
Elyria *(G-9503)*

Tuffy Manufacturing ....G 330 940-2356
Cuyahoga Falls *(G-8058)*

Twin Oaks Barn ....F 330 893-3126
Dundee *(G-9184)*

U S Hair Inc ....G 614 235-5190
Columbus *(G-7717)*

▲ Utopia Products Inc ....G 330 666-2602
Akron *(G-460)*

V Mast Manufacturing Inc ....G 330 409-8116
Canton *(G-2894)*

Vacca Inc ....G 513 697-0270
Loveland *(G-12396)*

Valentino Industries LLC ....G 330 523-7216
Richfield *(G-16644)*

Vandalia Massage Therapy ....G 937 890-8660
Vandalia *(G-19315)*

Vandiley Industries Ltd ....G 419 618-1970
Tiffin *(G-18251)*

Velocity Concept Dev Group LLC ....G 513 204-2100
Mason *(G-13100)*

Vermilion Dock Masters ....G 440 244-5370
Vermilion *(G-19337)*

Vic Maroscher ....F 330 332-4958
Salem *(G-16934)*

Visual Education Association ....G 937 325-5503
Springfield *(G-17673)*

▲ Voodoo Industries ....G 440 653-5333
Avon Lake *(G-1054)*

Vulcan International Corp ....G 513 621-2850
Cincinnati *(G-4571)*

Waterloo Industries Inc ....G 800 833-8851
Cleveland *(G-6449)*

Wellington Manufacturing ....G 440 647-1162
Wellington *(G-19757)*

Wheeler Embroidery ....G 740 550-9751
Ironton *(G-11305)*

▼ Wholesale Supplies Plus Inc ....E 440 526-6556
Independence *(G-11285)*

Willoughby Manufacturing Inc ....G 330 402-8217
New Waterford *(G-14976)*

Woodson Distribution LLC ....G 937 864-9013
Xenia *(G-20989)*

Yankee Candle Company Inc ....G 419 223-0073
Lima *(G-12113)*

Yoder Manufacturing ....G 740 504-5028
Howard *(G-11125)*

73 BUSINESS SERVICES

7372 Prepackaged Software

252 Tattoo ....G 440 235-6699
Columbia Station *(G-6577)*

360water Inc ....G 614 294-3600
Columbus *(G-6663)*

4me Group LLC ....G 513 898-1083
Cincinnati *(G-3326)*

About Time Software Inc ....F 614 759-6295
Pickerington *(G-16185)*

Acclaimd Inc ....G 614 219-9519
Columbus *(G-6684)*

Accumulus Software ....G 937 435-0861
Dayton *(G-8131)*

Actipro Software LLC ....G 888 922-8477
Broadview Heights *(G-2103)*

Acu-Serve Corp ....G 330 923-5258
Cuyahoga Falls *(G-7961)*

Advanced Prgrm Resources Inc ....E 614 761-9994
Dublin *(G-9037)*

Advant-E Corporation ....F 937 429-4288
Beavercreek *(G-1316)*

Agile Global Solutions Inc ....G 916 655-7745
Independence *(G-11246)*

Air Force US Dept of ....B 937 656-2354
Dayton *(G-8095)*

Alanax Technologies Inc ....G 216 469-1545
Belmont *(G-1577)*

Alltel Communications Corp ....G 419 784-3808
Defiance *(G-8777)*

Alpps Ltd ....G 614 804-3772
Dublin *(G-9040)*

American Dreams Inc ....G 740 385-4444
Thornville *(G-18191)*

American Grphcal Sftwr Systems ......G 440 729-0018
Chesterland *(G-3198)*

Ames Development Group Ltd ....G 419 704-7812
Toledo *(G-18347)*

Ampersand International Inc ....G 216 831-3500
Beachwood *(G-1257)*

Apex Solutions Inc ....G 419 843-3434
Toledo *(G-18352)*

Apostrophe Apps LLC ....G 513 608-4399
Liberty Twp *(G-11970)*

Application Link Inc ....F 614 934-1735
Columbus *(G-6764)*

Applied Systems Inc ....E 513 943-0000
Milford *(G-14121)*

Arges ....G 440 574-1305
Oberlin *(G-15634)*

Assisted Patrol LLC ....G 937 369-0080
Beavercreek *(G-1318)*

Associated Software Cons Inc ....E 440 826-1010
Middleburg Heights *(G-13902)*

Asterena Corporation ....G 937 605-6470
Dayton *(G-8167)*

Atr Distributing Company ....F 513 353-1800
Cincinnati *(G-3427)*

Auto Des Sys Inc ....E 614 488-7984
Upper Arlington *(G-19110)*

Autorentalsystemscom LLC ....G 513 334-1040
Norwood *(G-15570)*

Avasax Ltd ....G 937 694-0807
Beavercreek *(G-1369)*

Aver Inc ....G 877 841-2775
Columbus *(G-6792)*

Bass International Sftwr LLC ....G 877 227-0155
Columbus *(G-6814)*

Besttransportcom Inc ....E 614 888-2378
Worthington *(G-20858)*

Bjond Inc ....G 614 537-7246
Columbus *(G-6835)*

Butler Tech Career Dev Schools ....F 513 867-1028
Hamilton *(G-10679)*

Cake LLC ....G 614 592-7681
Dublin *(G-9056)*

Callcopy Inc ....G 614 340-3346
Columbus *(G-6890)*

Capitol Citicom Inc ....G 614 472-2679
Columbus *(G-6903)*

Carenection LLC ....G 614 468-6045
Columbus *(G-6907)*

Caring Things Inc ....G 614 749-9084
Columbus *(G-6908)*

Casentric LLC ....G 216 233-6300
Shaker Heights *(G-17087)*

Check Yourself LLC ....G 513 685-0868
Blue Ash *(G-1764)*

Cimx LLC ....E 513 248-7700
Cincinnati *(G-3534)*

Cincom Systems Inc ....C 513 459-1470
Mason *(G-12996)*

Citynet Ohio LLC ....E 614 364-7881
Columbus *(G-6932)*

Cleveland Business Supply LLC ....G 888 831-0088
Broadview Heights *(G-2108)*

Click It Connect Corp ....G 440 247-4998
Chagrin Falls *(G-3053)*

Clientrax Technology Solutions ....F 614 875-2245
Grove City *(G-10549)*
Clinical Computing Inc ....F 513 651-3803
Cincinnati *(G-3587)*
Clinicl Otcms Mngmnt Syst LLC ....D 330 650-9900
Broadview Heights *(G-2109)*
Cluster Software Inc ....F 614 760-9380
Columbus *(G-6940)*
Coffing Corporation ....E 513 919-2813
Liberty Twp *(G-11972)*
Columbus International Corp ....F 614 323-1086
Columbus *(G-6957)*
Commercial Transportation Svcs ....G 216 267-2000
Cleveland *(G-5106)*
Computer System Enhancement ....G 513 251-6791
Cincinnati *(G-3603)*
Computer Zoo Inc ....G 937 310-1474
Bellbrook *(G-1504)*
Compuware Corporation ....D 614 847-8212
Columbus *(G-6975)*
Concept Xxi Inc ....F 216 831-2121
Beachwood *(G-1264)*
Contractor Tools Online LLC ....G 614 264-9392
New Albany *(G-14754)*
Corillian Payment Solutions ....F 419 244-8048
Toledo *(G-18413)*
Corporate Elevator LLC ....F 614 288-1847
Columbus *(G-6985)*
Crabware Ltd ....G 330 699-2305
Uniontown *(G-19081)*
Creative Microsystems Inc ....D 937 836-4499
Englewood *(G-9515)*
Crimson Gate Consulting Co ....G 614 805-0897
Dublin *(G-9066)*
D+h USA Corporation ....C 513 381-9400
Cincinnati *(G-3633)*
D+h USA Corporation ....E 937 435-2335
Miamisburg *(G-13796)*
Dante Solutions Inc ....G 440 234-8477
Cleveland *(G-5166)*
Datatrak International Inc ....E 440 443-0082
Mayfield Heights *(G-13312)*
Deadbolt Software ....G 614 679-2093
Columbus *(G-7016)*
Delphia Consulting LLC ....G 614 421-2000
Columbus *(G-7021)*
Delta Media Group Inc ....E 330 493-0350
Canton *(G-2683)*
Digionyx LLC ....G 614 594-9897
London *(G-12209)*
Digisoft Systems Corporation ....G 937 833-5016
Brookville *(G-2181)*
Digital Controls Corporation ....D 513 746-8118
Miamisburg *(G-13801)*
Drb Systems LLC ....D 330 645-3299
Akron *(G-157)*
Dwllr Inc ....G 513 400-5544
West Chester *(G-19854)*
Echo Mobile Solutions LLC ....G 614 282-3756
Pickerington *(G-16191)*
Edict Systems Inc ....E 937 429-4288
Beavercreek *(G-1334)*
Efab Technologies LLC ....G 937 429-1401
Beavercreek *(G-1335)*
Eighty Six Inc ....G 800 760-0722
Huber Heights *(G-11145)*
Einstruction Corp ....G 940 565-0004
Youngstown *(G-21074)*
▲ Einstruction Corporation ....D 330 746-3015
Youngstown *(G-21075)*
Ela Holding Corporation ....G 513 200-1374
Cincinnati *(G-3691)*
Electronic Vision Inc ....E 740 592-2433
Athens *(G-864)*
Elynx Holdings LLC ....G 513 612-5969
Cincinnati *(G-3693)*
Elytus Ltd ....F 614 824-4985
Columbus *(G-7054)*
EMC Corporation ....D 513 794-9624
Blue Ash *(G-1783)*
EMC Corporation ....E 216 606-2000
Independence *(G-11254)*
Emerge Health Solutions ....G 513 204-5600
Cincinnati *(G-3696)*
Empyracom Inc ....E 330 744-5570
Canfield *(G-2553)*
Engineering Methods Inc ....E 513 563-0400
Cincinnati *(G-3706)*
Equipsync LLC ....G 216 367-6640
Cleveland *(G-5292)*

▲ Esko-Graphics Inc ....D 937 454-1721
Miamisburg *(G-13805)*
Estreamz Inc ....E 513 278-7836
Cincinnati *(G-3719)*
Exact Software North Amer LLC ....C 978 539-6186
Dublin *(G-9075)*
Explorys Inc ....D 216 767-4700
Cleveland *(G-5315)*
Exponentia US Inc ....E 614 944-5103
Columbus *(G-7073)*
Ezshred LLC ....G 440 256-7640
Kirtland *(G-11614)*
Facilities Management Ex LLC ....F 844 664-4400
Columbus *(G-7075)*
Field Dailies LLC ....G 859 379-2120
Cincinnati *(G-3754)*
Flexnova Inc ....E 216 288-6961
Cleveland *(G-5356)*
Flypaper Studio Inc ....E 602 801-2208
Cincinnati *(G-3765)*
Forcam Inc ....F 513 878-2780
Cincinnati *(G-3768)*
Foundation Software Inc ....D 330 220-8383
Strongsville *(G-17920)*
Fusionstorm ....G 614 431-8000
Columbus *(G-6647)*
Gain LLC ....G 440 396-6613
Westerville *(G-20153)*
Gis Dynamics LLC ....G 513 847-4931
Blue Ash *(G-1803)*
Gracie Plum Investments Inc ....E 740 355-9029
Portsmouth *(G-16436)*
Hardmagic ....F 415 390-6232
Marietta *(G-12789)*
Health Nuts Media LLC ....G 818 802-5222
Cleveland *(G-5489)*
Healthedge Software Inc ....G 614 431-3711
Powell *(G-16473)*
Honeywell International Inc ....D 513 745-7200
Cincinnati *(G-3897)*
Hyland Software Inc ....A 440 788-5000
Westlake *(G-20278)*
ICC Systems Inc ....G 614 524-0299
Sunbury *(G-18063)*
Idialogs LLC ....G 937 372-2890
Xenia *(G-20956)*
Igc Software ....F 614 759-9148
Reynoldsburg *(G-16595)*
Image Integrations Systems ....F 419 872-0003
Perrysburg *(G-16109)*
Incessant Software Inc ....G 614 206-2211
Lancaster *(G-11723)*
Infinite Synergy LLC ....G 330 892-8777
Poland *(G-16383)*
Infoaccessnet LLC ....E 216 328-0100
Cleveland *(G-5568)*
Innerapps LLC ....G 419 467-3110
Perrysburg *(G-16112)*
Innovative Apps Ltd ....G 330 687-2888
New Albany *(G-14761)*
Innovative Bus Cmpt Solutions ....G 937 832-3969
Englewood *(G-9525)*
Intelligent Mobile Support Inc ....F 440 600-7343
Solon *(G-17318)*
Intellinetics Inc ....F 614 388-8908
Columbus *(G-7201)*
Interactive Fincl Solutions ....F 419 335-1280
Wauseon *(G-19683)*
Intermec Technologies Corp ....F 513 874-5882
West Chester *(G-19884)*
Intersoft Group Inc ....F 216 765-7351
Cleveland *(G-5581)*
Investment Systems Company ....G 440 247-2865
Chagrin Falls *(G-3061)*
Iq Solutions Group LLC ....F 855 367-4774
Westerville *(G-20161)*
Jack A Byte Mltmdia Gaming LLC ....G 937 321-1716
Englewood *(G-9527)*
Jack C Keir Inc ....F 513 422-4860
Middletown *(G-14051)*
Janova LLC ....F 614 638-6785
New Albany *(G-14763)*
Jasstek Inc ....F 614 808-3600
Dublin *(G-9091)*
Jehm Technologies Inc ....G 440 355-5558
Lagrange *(G-11628)*
Jst LLC ....G 614 423-7815
Westerville *(G-20164)*
Kapios LLC ....G 567 661-0772
Toledo *(G-18539)*

King Software Systems ....G 330 562-1135
Aurora *(G-931)*
Kronos Incorporated ....F 614 528-2200
Columbus *(G-7273)*
Kronos Incorporated ....G 216 867-5609
Independence *(G-11264)*
Learning Egg LLC ....G 330 207-8663
North Jackson *(G-15293)*
Linestream Technologies ....G 216 862-7874
Cleveland *(G-5702)*
Liquid Shock Games LLC ....G 386 627-0840
Elyria *(G-9453)*
List Media Inc ....G 330 995-0864
Aurora *(G-934)*
Lockheed Martin Corporation ....G 614 418-1930
Columbus *(G-7302)*
Lost Technology LLP ....G 513 685-0054
West Chester *(G-19896)*
Lync Corp ....E 513 655-7286
Cincinnati *(G-4041)*
Mae Consulting ....G 513 531-8100
Cincinnati *(G-4050)*
Magic Interface Ltd ....G 440 498-3700
Solon *(G-17330)*
Mainstream Software Inc ....F 330 963-0103
Twinsburg *(G-18977)*
Mamsys Consulting Services ....G 440 287-6824
Solon *(G-17332)*
Mapsys Inc ....E 614 255-7258
Columbus *(G-7316)*
Marxware Computing Services ....F 216 661-5263
Cleveland *(G-5755)*
Mathematical Business Systems ....G 440 237-2345
Broadview Heights *(G-2115)*
Matrix Management Solutions ....C 330 470-3700
Canton *(G-2773)*
McGaw Technology Inc ....G 216 521-3490
Lakewood *(G-11675)*
Merkur Group Inc ....G 937 429-4288
Beavercreek *(G-1351)*
Miami Valley Eductl Cmpt Assn ....F 937 767-1468
Yellow Springs *(G-20995)*
Microsoft Corporation ....E 614 719-5900
Columbus *(G-6656)*
Microsoft Corporation ....E 216 986-1440
Cleveland *(G-5802)*
Microsoft Corporation ....D 513 339-2800
Mason *(G-13062)*
Microstrategy Incorporated ....G 513 792-2253
Cincinnati *(G-4104)*
Mim Software Inc ....E 216 896-9798
Beachwood *(G-1281)*
Mindcrafted Systems Inc ....G 440 821-2245
Cleveland *(G-5819)*
Mirus Adapted Tech LLC ....E 614 402-4585
Dublin *(G-9103)*
Monitored Therapeutics Inc ....G 614 761-3555
Dublin *(G-9106)*
Netpark LLC ....F 614 866-2495
Gahanna *(G-10222)*
Netsmart Technologies Inc ....E 440 942-4040
Solon *(G-17349)*
Network Savvy Ltd ....G 419 843-1122
Toledo *(G-18600)*
Neural Holdings LLC ....G 734 512-8865
Cincinnati *(G-4147)*
Nextmed Systems Inc ....E 216 674-0511
Cincinnati *(G-4153)*
No Surprises Software Inc ....G 855 462-6448
Columbus *(G-7394)*
Noggin LLC ....G 440 305-6188
Cleveland *(G-5886)*
North Coast Security Group LLC ....G 614 887-7255
Columbus *(G-7399)*
Northrop Grmmn Spce & Mssn Sys ....D 937 259-4956
Dayton *(G-8529)*
Now Software Inc ....G 614 783-4517
New Albany *(G-14767)*
Nsa Technologies LLC ....C 330 576-4600
Akron *(G-321)*
▲ Ohio Cllbrtive Lrng Sltons Inc ....E 216 595-5289
Beachwood *(G-1286)*
Ohio Distinctive Enterprises ....E 614 459-0453
Columbus *(G-7420)*
One Cloud Services LLC ....G 513 231-9500
Cincinnati *(G-4187)*
Onx Holdings LLC ....G 800 559-2497
Mayfield Heights *(G-13320)*
Onx USA LLC ....D 440 569-2300
Cleveland *(G-5943)*

Open Text Inc ....E 614 658-3588
Hilliard *(G-10968)*
Optimal Office Solutions LLC ....G 201 257-8516
Cincinnati *(G-4190)*
Optimzed Prdctvity Sltions LLC ....G 513 444-2156
Cincinnati *(G-4192)*
Oracle Corporation ....C 513 826-5632
Beavercreek *(G-1355)*
Oracle Corporation ....G 440 264-1620
Cleveland *(G-5945)*
Oracle Systems Corporation ....E 513 826-6000
Blue Ash *(G-1849)*
Oracle Systems Corporation ....G 937 427-5495
Beavercreek *(G-1356)*
Pakra LLC ....F 614 477-6965
Columbus *(G-7455)*
Parallel Technologies Inc ....D 614 798-9700
Dublin *(G-9117)*
Parthenon Global LLC ....G 888 332-5303
Cleveland *(G-5979)*
Pathfinder Computer Systems ....G 330 928-1961
Barberton *(G-1138)*
Pathos LLC ....G 440 497-7278
Chesterland *(G-3219)*
Patient Focus Systems ....G 330 655-7222
Hudson *(G-11193)*
Patrick J Burke & Co ....E 513 455-8200
Cincinnati *(G-4215)*
Patriot Software Inc ....F 877 968-7147
Canton *(G-2808)*
Patterson Colburne ....G 419 866-5544
Holland *(G-11077)*
Paul/Jay Associates ....G 740 676-8770
Bellaire *(G-1500)*
Pdmb Inc ....G 513 522-7362
Cincinnati *(G-4220)*
Pearl Tech Corporation ....G 614 284-8357
Dublin *(G-9119)*
Peco II Inc ....D 614 431-0694
Columbus *(G-7473)*
Perennial Software Inc ....F 440 247-5602
Chagrin Falls *(G-3067)*
Perfect Probate ....G 513 791-4100
Cincinnati *(G-4223)*
Pkg Technologies Inc ....G 513 967-2783
Lebanon *(G-11828)*
Pmj Partners LLC ....G 201 360-1914
Columbus *(G-7501)*
Polygon Spaceship ....G 440 506-0403
Amherst *(G-606)*
Posm Software LLC ....G 859 274-0041
Columbus *(G-7505)*
Precision Castparts Corp ....G 330 868-7376
Minerva *(G-14338)*
Preemptive Solutions LLC ....E 216 732-5895
Cleveland *(G-6040)*
Proepo Software Ltd ....G 937 243-3825
Wshngtn CT Hs *(G-20921)*
Profile Imaging Columbus LLC ....G 614 222-2888
Columbus *(G-7523)*
Profound Logic Software Inc ....G 937 439-7925
Dayton *(G-8600)*
Protel Systems and Svcs LLC ....G 419 893-2440
Maumee *(G-13289)*
Protel Systems and Svcs LLC ....G 419 913-0825
Toledo *(G-18661)*
Ptc Inc ....F 513 791-0330
Cincinnati *(G-4303)*
Pwi Inc ....F 732 212-8110
New Albany *(G-14770)*
Qm Scientific LLP ....G 513 250-2397
Cincinnati *(G-4305)*
◆ Quayle Consulting Inc ....G 614 868-1363
Pickerington *(G-16202)*
Queen City Software Inc ....G 513 469-1424
Cincinnati *(G-4321)*
Queen City Technologies ....F 513 253-1312
West Chester *(G-20044)*
R & L Software LLC ....G 513 847-4942
Monroe *(G-14412)*
R&D Software Services Inc ....G 513 755-8851
Liberty Twp *(G-11978)*
Racedirector LLC ....G 440 940-6675
Willoughby *(G-20586)*
Rawhide Software Inc ....G 419 878-0857
Bowling Green *(G-2010)*
Reichard Software Corp ....G 614 537-8598
Dublin *(G-9130)*
Research Metrics LLC ....G 419 464-3333
Norwalk *(G-15562)*

Retail Management Products ....F 740 548-1725
Lewis Center *(G-11914)*
Retalix Inc ....C 937 384-2277
Miamisburg *(G-13855)*
Revolution Group Inc ....D 614 212-1111
Westerville *(G-20182)*
Reynolds and Reynolds Company ....F 937 485-2805
Beavercreek *(G-1379)*
Rhino Tech Software LLC ....G 614 456-9321
Pickerington *(G-16204)*
Rockware Corp ....G 419 483-5649
Bellevue *(G-1556)*
S L C Software Services ....G 513 922-4303
Cincinnati *(G-4374)*
Sanctuary Software Studio Inc ....E 330 666-9690
Fairlawn *(G-9759)*
Sark Technologies LLC ....G 216 932-3171
Cleveland *(G-6160)*
Sas Institute Inc ....F 216 643-6719
Cleveland *(G-6161)*
SC Elearning LLC ....D 513 852-6841
Cincinnati *(G-4382)*
Seapine Software Inc ....E 513 754-1655
Mason *(G-13087)*
Secure Medical Mail LLC ....G 216 269-1971
Cleveland *(G-6177)*
Sest Inc ....F 440 777-9777
Westlake *(G-20307)*
Sherwin Software Solutions ....G 440 498-8010
Solon *(G-17379)*
Showroom Tracker LLC ....G 888 407-0094
Canton *(G-2848)*
Sigmatek Systems LLC ....D 513 674-0005
Cincinnati *(G-4418)*
Simple Vms LLC ....G 888 255-8918
Cincinnati *(G-4421)*
Simplex-It LLC ....G 234 380-1277
Stow *(G-17800)*
Skillsoft Corporation ....E 216 524-5200
Independence *(G-11275)*
Socialpay LLC ....G 513 721-3900
Cincinnati *(G-4433)*
Soda Pig LLC ....G 646 241-7126
Columbus *(G-7627)*
Softchoice Corporation ....E 614 224-4123
Columbus *(G-7628)*
Softura Legal Solutions LLC ....G 614 220-5611
Columbus *(G-7629)*
Software Authority Inc ....E 216 236-0200
Cleveland *(G-6217)*
Software Management Group ....E 513 618-2165
Cincinnati *(G-4434)*
Software Solutions Inc ....E 513 932-6667
Lebanon *(G-11841)*
Software To Systems Inc ....G 513 893-4367
Fairfield *(G-9720)*
Southwestern Ohio Instruction ....F 937 746-6333
Dayton *(G-8664)*
Spearfysh Inc ....F 330 487-0300
Twinsburg *(G-19021)*
Specialized Business Sftwr Inc ....E 440 542-9145
Solon *(G-17385)*
Spitfire Technologies LLC ....G 937 463-7729
Dayton *(G-8671)*
Splicenet Inc ....G 513 563-3533
West Chester *(G-20053)*
Starwin Industries Inc ....E 937 293-8568
Dayton *(G-8681)*
Step It Up LLC ....G 720 289-1520
Columbus *(G-7656)*
Steve Schaefer ....G 513 792-9911
Cincinnati *(G-4465)*
Streamsavvy LLC ....G 614 256-7955
Columbus *(G-7660)*
Strongbasics LLC ....G 716 903-6151
Columbus *(G-7662)*
Sunday School Software ....G 614 527-8776
Hilliard *(G-10984)*
Symantec Corporation ....G 614 793-3060
Dublin *(G-9151)*
Symantec Corporation ....D 216 643-6700
Independence *(G-11276)*
Tahoe Interactive Systems Inc ....F 614 891-2323
Westerville *(G-20235)*
Tarigma Corporation ....F 614 436-3734
Columbus *(G-7677)*
Tata America Intl Corp ....B 513 677-6500
Milford *(G-14177)*
Tech Solutions LLC ....G 419 852-7190
Celina *(G-3020)*

Tech-E-Z LLC ....G 419 692-1700
Delphos *(G-8918)*
Technosoft Inc ....F 513 985-9877
Blue Ash *(G-1880)*
Tekdog Inc ....G 614 737-3743
Columbus *(G-7685)*
Teradata Corporation ....B 866 548-8348
Miamisburg *(G-13870)*
Terrene Labs ....G 404 408-2241
Mason *(G-13097)*
Thinkware Incorporated ....E 513 598-3300
Cincinnati *(G-4506)*
Timekeeping Systems Inc ....F 216 595-0890
Solon *(G-17406)*
Tmw Systems Inc ....E 216 831-6606
Mayfield Heights *(G-13322)*
To Scale Software LLC ....E 513 253-0053
Mason *(G-13099)*
Torah Tech Inc ....G 614 570-6298
Columbus *(G-7699)*
Trapeze Software Group Inc ....G 905 629-8727
Beachwood *(G-1302)*
Triad Governmental Systems ....E 937 376-5446
Xenia *(G-20983)*
Trivantis Corporation ....D 513 929-0188
Cincinnati *(G-4528)*
Turning Technologies LLC ....C 330 746-3015
Youngstown *(G-21231)*
Turning Technologies LLC ....G 330 746-3015
Youngstown *(G-21232)*
Uninterrupted LLC ....F 216 771-2323
Akron *(G-453)*
United Computer Group Inc ....G 216 520-1333
Independence *(G-11280)*
Veeam Software Corporation ....G 678 353-2140
Columbus *(G-6661)*
Vertex Computer Systems Inc ....F 513 662-6888
Cincinnati *(G-4565)*
Vertical Data LLC ....F 330 289-0313
Akron *(G-463)*
Virtual Boss Inc ....G 419 872-7686
Perrysburg *(G-16165)*
Virtual Hold Technology LLC ....D 330 666-1181
Akron *(G-464)*
Vitalrock LLC ....G 888 596-8892
Rocky River *(G-16713)*
W L Arehart Computing Systems ....G 937 383-4710
Wilmington *(G-20681)*
Web3box Software LLC ....G 330 794-7397
Tallmadge *(G-18176)*
Wentworth Solutions ....F 440 212-7696
Brunswick *(G-2266)*
Wentworth Technologies LLC ....F 440 212-7696
Brunswick *(G-2267)*
Westmount Technology Inc ....G 216 328-2011
Independence *(G-11284)*
Wififace LLC ....G 419 754-4816
Toledo *(G-18775)*
Willow Frog LLC ....G 513 861-4834
Cincinnati *(G-4598)*
Wissman & Wood Incorporated ....G 513 793-6222
Cincinnati *(G-4600)*
Wonderful Failure LLC ....G 440 666-0919
Lakewood *(G-11682)*
Workflex Solutions LLC ....G 513 257-0215
Cincinnati *(G-4604)*
Workspeed Management LLC ....E 917 369-9025
Solon *(G-17415)*
Zebu Compliance Solutions Inc ....E 740 355-9029
Portsmouth *(G-16460)*
Zipscene LLC ....D 513 201-5174
Cincinnati *(G-4619)*
Znode Inc ....F 614 468-7900
Columbus *(G-6662)*

76 MISCELLANEOUS REPAIR SERVICES

7692 *Welding Repair*

A & C Welding Inc ....E 330 762-4777
Peninsula *(G-16032)*
▲ A & G Manufacturing Co Inc ....E 419 468-7433
Galion *(G-10250)*
A Metalcraft Associates Inc ....G 937 693-4008
Botkins *(G-1949)*
Abbott Tool Inc ....E 419 476-6742
Toledo *(G-18318)*
Advanced Onsight Welding Svcs ....G 513 924-1400
Cincinnati *(G-3359)*

Advanced Welding Co ....E 937 746-6800
Franklin *(G-10005)*
Aetna Welding Co Inc ....G 216 883-1801
Cleveland *(G-4727)*
Aircraft Welding Inc ....G 440 951-3863
Willoughby *(G-20426)*
Albright Radiator Inc ....G 330 264-8886
Wooster *(G-20738)*
All American Welding Co ....G 614 224-7752
Columbus *(G-6720)*
All Do Weld & Fab LLC ....G 740 477-2133
Circleville *(G-4622)*
All-Type Welding & Fabrication ....E 440 439-3990
Cleveland *(G-4761)*
Allied Fabricating & Wldg Co ....E 614 751-6664
Columbus *(G-6725)*
Alloy Unlimited Weld ....G 330 506-8375
Canfield *(G-2546)*
Amptech Machining & Welding ....G 419 652-3444
Nova *(G-15576)*
ARC Solutions Inc ....F 419 542-9272
Hicksville *(G-10899)*
Arctech Fabricating Inc ....E 937 525-9353
Springfield *(G-17518)*
Arnolds Repair Shop ....G 740 373-5313
Marietta *(G-12762)*
Artiflex Manufacturing LLC ....F 419 547-9211
Clyde *(G-6537)*
Athens Mold and Machine Inc ....D 740 593-6613
Akron *(G-76)*
Auglaize Welding Company Inc ....G 419 738-4422
Wapakoneta *(G-19480)*
Auto-Tap Inc ....E 216 671-1043
Cleveland *(G-4864)*
Automation Welding System ....G 330 263-1176
Wooster *(G-20744)*
B & B Welding ....G 419 968-2743
Middle Point *(G-13898)*
Baker Built Products Inc ....G 419 965-2646
Ohio City *(G-15660)*
Baker Welding Llc ....G 614 252-6100
Columbus *(G-6803)*
Baughmans Machine & Weld Shop ....G 330 866-9243
Waynesburg *(G-19723)*
Bayloff Stmped Pdts Knsman Inc ....D 330 876-4511
Kinsman *(G-11608)*
Bear Welding Services LLC ....F 740 630-7538
Caldwell *(G-2424)*
Bens Welding Service Inc ....G 937 878-4052
Fairborn *(G-9615)*
Blackwood Sheet Metal Inc ....G 614 291-3115
Columbus *(G-6839)*
Blevins Metal Fabrication Inc ....E 419 522-6082
Mansfield *(G-12567)*
Bob Lanes Welding Inc ....F 740 373-3567
Marietta *(G-12767)*
Breitinger Company ....C 419 526-4255
Mansfield *(G-12569)*
Bridgetown Welders LLC ....G 513 574-4851
Cincinnati *(G-3473)*
Broadway Welding & Fabrication ....G 513 821-0004
Cincinnati *(G-3476)*
Brock RAD & Wldg Fabrication ....G 740 773-2540
Chillicothe *(G-3230)*
Brocks Welding & Repair Svc ....G 740 453-3943
Zanesville *(G-21281)*
Brown Industrial Inc ....E 937 693-3838
Botkins *(G-1951)*
Bse Welding & Fabricating LLC ....F 419 547-1043
Vickery *(G-19361)*
Buckeye Welding ....G 330 674-0944
Millersburg *(G-14206)*
C & M Welding Services LLC ....G 419 584-0008
Celina *(G-2987)*
C & R Inc ....E 614 497-1130
Groveport *(G-10617)*
C O Welding & Fabrication Inc ....G 419 394-3293
Saint Marys *(G-16836)*
C Stoneman Corporation ....G 440 942-3325
Eastlake *(G-9261)*
C-N-D Industries Inc ....E 330 478-8811
Massillon *(G-13118)*
Camelot Manufacturing Inc ....F 419 678-2603
Coldwater *(G-6554)*
Cardinal Welding Inc ....G 330 426-2404
East Palestine *(G-9229)*
Carol J Guiler ....G 614 252-6920
Columbus *(G-6910)*
Carter Manufacturing Co Inc ....E 513 398-7303
Mason *(G-12991)*
▲ Case-Maul Manufacturing Co ....F 419 524-1061
Mansfield *(G-12577)*
Central Ohio Fabrication LLC ....G 740 969-2976
Amanda *(G-561)*
Certified Welding Co ....F 216 961-5410
Cleveland *(G-5009)*
Chipmatic Tool & Machine Inc ....D 419 862-2737
Elmore *(G-9362)*
Chore Anden ....G 330 695-2300
Fredericksburg *(G-10080)*
City Machine Technologies Inc ....F 330 747-2639
Youngstown *(G-21047)*
Cleveland Welding & Fabg LLC ....G 440 364-5137
Cleveland *(G-5085)*
Clipsons Metal Working Inc ....G 513 772-6393
Cincinnati *(G-3588)*
Cmt Machining & Fabg LLC ....F 937 652-3740
Urbana *(G-19151)*
Columbus Mobile Welding ....G 614 352-6052
Centerburg *(G-3029)*
Columbus Pipe and Equipment Co ....F 614 444-7871
Columbus *(G-6962)*
Compton Metal Products Inc ....D 937 382-2403
Wilmington *(G-20660)*
Comptons Precision Machine ....F 937 325-9139
Springfield *(G-17535)*
Connaughton Wldg & Fence LLC ....G 513 867-0230
Hamilton *(G-10680)*
County Wide Welding LLC ....G 440 564-1333
Newbury *(G-15086)*
Creative Fab & Welding LLC ....E 937 780-5000
Leesburg *(G-11851)*
Creative Fabrication Ltd ....G 740 262-5789
Richwood *(G-16659)*
Creative Mold and Machine Inc ....E 440 338-5146
Newbury *(G-15087)*
Crest Bending Inc ....E 419 492-2108
New Washington *(G-14959)*
Custom Machine Inc ....E 419 986-5122
Tiffin *(G-18217)*
Custom Way Welding Inc ....F 937 845-9469
New Carlisle *(G-14800)*
D & G Welding Inc ....G 419 445-5751
Archbold *(G-670)*
D & M Welding & Radiator ....G 740 947-9032
Waverly *(G-19707)*
Dalin Auto Service ....G 440 997-3301
Ashtabula *(G-801)*
Davenport Service Group Inc ....G 440 487-9353
Mentor *(G-13559)*
David Cox ....G 740 254-4858
Gnadenhutten *(G-10405)*
Dayton Brick Company Inc ....F 937 293-4189
Moraine *(G-14477)*
Dayton United Metal Spinners ....F 937 222-6732
Tipp City *(G-18275)*
Dbcr Inc ....E 330 920-1900
Cuyahoga Falls *(G-7986)*
Delta Machine & Tool Co ....F 216 524-2477
Cleveland *(G-5183)*
Des Eck Welding ....G 330 698-7271
Apple Creek *(G-636)*
Diamond Welding Co Inc ....G 216 251-1679
Cleveland *(G-5190)*
Diversified Welding Services ....G 419 382-1433
Toledo *(G-18440)*
Dover Fabrication and Burn Inc ....G 330 339-1057
New Philadelphia *(G-14895)*
Dover Machine Co ....F 330 343-4123
Dover *(G-8981)*
Drabik Manufacturing Inc ....F 216 267-1616
Cleveland *(G-5214)*
Duco Tool & Die Inc ....F 419 628-2031
Minster *(G-14351)*
Duray Machine Co Inc ....F 440 277-4119
Amherst *(G-597)*
Durisek Enterprises Inc ....G 216 281-3898
Cleveland *(G-5225)*
Dynamic Specialties Inc ....G 440 946-2838
Mentor *(G-13568)*
Dynamic Weld Corporation ....E 419 582-2900
Osgood *(G-15785)*
E & M Liberty Welding Inc ....G 330 866-2338
Waynesburg *(G-19724)*
E & R Welding Inc ....F 440 329-9387
Berlin Heights *(G-1661)*
E L Davis Inc ....G 419 268-2004
Celina *(G-2993)*
E W Welding & Fabricating ....G 440 826-9038
Berea *(G-1612)*
Eagle Machine and Welding Inc ....G 740 345-5210
Newark *(G-15001)*
Eagle Wldg & Fabrication Inc ....E 440 946-0692
Willoughby *(G-20478)*
▲ East End Welding Company ....C 330 677-6000
Kent *(G-11452)*
Euclid Welding Co Inc ....G 216 289-0714
Cleveland *(G-5303)*
Fab-Tech Machine Inc ....G 937 473-5572
Covington *(G-7922)*
Fabrication Shop Inc ....F 419 435-7934
Fostoria *(G-9970)*
Fabrication Unlimited LLC ....G 937 492-3166
Sidney *(G-17189)*
Falls Stamping & Welding Co ....C 330 928-1191
Cuyahoga Falls *(G-7996)*
Farnsworth Engineering ....F 330 385-1745
East Liverpool *(G-9215)*
◆ Fosbel Inc ....C 216 362-3900
Brookpark *(G-2161)*
Fosbel Holding Inc ....E 216 362-3900
Cleveland *(G-5373)*
Fred Winner ....G 419 582-2421
New Weston *(G-14977)*
Fredrick Welding & Machining ....F 614 866-9650
Reynoldsburg *(G-16592)*
Friess Welding Inc ....F 330 644-8160
Akron *(G-195)*
G B Welding & Metal Fabg Co ....G 937 444-2091
Fayetteville *(G-9782)*
G M P Welding and Fabricating ....F 513 825-7861
Cincinnati *(G-3792)*
Garland Welding Co Inc ....F 330 536-6506
Lowellville *(G-12408)*
Gaspar Inc ....D 330 477-2222
Canton *(G-2711)*
▲ General Technologies Inc ....E 419 747-1800
Mansfield *(G-12612)*
▲ General Tool Company ....C 513 733-5500
Cincinnati *(G-3820)*
George Steel Fabricating Inc ....E 513 932-2887
Lebanon *(G-11802)*
Gilson Machine & Tool Co Inc ....E 419 592-2911
Napoleon *(G-14678)*
▲ Glenridge Machine Co ....E 440 975-1055
Willoughby *(G-20499)*
Greber Machine Tool Inc ....G 440 322-3685
Elyria *(G-9427)*
Greggs Specialty Services ....F 419 478-0803
Toledo *(G-18488)*
▲ Grodhaus & Young Inc ....F 330 866-3321
Waynesburg *(G-19725)*
Gurina Company ....G 614 279-3891
Columbus *(G-7132)*
H & H Machine Shop Akron Inc ....E 330 773-3327
Akron *(G-209)*
H & K Fabricating ....G 330 767-4279
Navarre *(G-14715)*
H & L Welding Service Inc ....G 740 862-3520
Columbus *(G-7134)*
Habco Tool and Dev Co Inc ....E 440 946-5546
Mentor *(G-13598)*
Hackworth Electric Motors Inc ....G 330 345-6049
Wooster *(G-20782)*
Harris Welding and Machine Co ....F 419 281-8351
Ashland *(G-736)*
Harris Welding and Machine Co ....G 419 281-9623
Ashland *(G-737)*
Hartley Machine Inc ....G 330 821-0343
Alliance *(G-513)*
HI Tecmetal Group Inc ....E 216 881-8100
Cleveland *(G-5508)*
HI Tecmetal Group Inc ....E 440 373-5101
Wickliffe *(G-20368)*
HI Tecmetal Group Inc ....E 440 946-2280
Willoughby *(G-20504)*
Hi-Tek Manufacturing Inc ....C 513 459-1094
Mason *(G-13037)*
Highs Welding Inc ....G 937 464-3029
Belle Center *(G-1513)*
Hobart Bros Stick Electrode ....C 937 332-5375
Troy *(G-18835)*
Hoffman Machining & Repair LLC ....G 419 547-9204
Clyde *(G-6540)*
Holdren Brothers Inc ....F 937 465-7050
West Liberty *(G-20092)*
Holdsworth Industrial Fabg ....G 330 874-3945
Bolivar *(G-1936)*
Hyneks Machine and Welding ....G 419 281-7966
Ashland *(G-742)*

SIC

Independent Machine & Wldg Inc......G..... 937 339-7330	Marsam Metalfab Inc......E..... 330 405-1520	Quality Welding Inc......E..... 419 483-6067
Troy *(G-18845)*	Twinsburg *(G-18978)*	Bellevue *(G-1554)*
Industry Products Co......B..... 937 778-0585	Martin Welding LLC......F..... 937 687-3602	Quick Service Welding & Mch Co......F..... 330 673-3818
Piqua *(G-16279)*	New Lebanon *(G-14843)*	Kent *(G-11511)*
Innovative Wldg & Design LLC......G..... 330 581-1316	Matheson Tri-Gas Inc......E..... 440 365-1741	R & M Welding Co......G..... 330 264-4788
Alliance *(G-518)*	Twinsburg *(G-18980)*	Wooster *(G-20826)*
J & A Machine......G..... 330 424-5235	Mc Elwain Industries Inc......E..... 419 532-3126	▲ R K Industries Inc......D..... 419 523-5001
Lisbon *(G-12123)*	Ottawa *(G-15800)*	Ottawa *(G-15806)*
J & L Welding Fabricating Inc......F..... 330 393-9353	McDannald Welding & Machining......G..... 937 644-0300	R M Welding Products......G..... 937 260-4510
Warren *(G-19561)*	Marysville *(G-12960)*	Dayton *(G-8611)*
J & S Industrial Mch Pdts Inc......D..... 419 691-1380	McIntosh Machine......G..... 937 687-3936	R S V Wldg Fbrcation Machining......F..... 419 592-0993
Toledo *(G-18531)*	New Lebanon *(G-14844)*	Napoleon *(G-14694)*
J A B Welding Service Inc......F..... 740 453-5868	Mecca Rebuilding & Welding Co......G..... 419 476-8133	Ray Townsend......G..... 440 968-3617
Zanesville *(G-21322)*	Toledo *(G-18581)*	Montville *(G-14461)*
J P Suggins Mobile Welding......E..... 216 566-7131	Mercers Welding Inc......G..... 330 533-3373	Rbm Environmental and Cnstr......E..... 419 693-5840
Cleveland *(G-5599)*	Canfield *(G-2565)*	Oregon *(G-15715)*
James G Morehouse......G..... 513 752-2236	Meta Manufacturing Corporation......E..... 513 793-6382	RI Alto Mfg Inc......G..... 740 914-4230
Milford *(G-14155)*	Blue Ash *(G-1837)*	Marion *(G-12895)*
Jatdco LLC......G..... 440 238-6570	Microweld Engineering Inc......F..... 614 847-9410	Ridge Engineering Inc......G..... 513 681-5500
Strongsville *(G-17933)*	Worthington *(G-20880)*	Cincinnati *(G-4346)*
Jerl Machine Inc......D..... 419 873-0270	Mike Loppe......F..... 937 969-8102	Ridge Enterprises Inc......G..... 740 867-3456
Perrysburg *(G-16114)*	Tremont City *(G-18789)*	Chesapeake *(G-3190)*
Jerrys Welding Supply Inc......G..... 937 364-1500	Mikes Automotive LLC......G..... 937 233-1433	Ridge Machine & Welding Co......G..... 740 537-2821
Hillsboro *(G-11006)*	Dayton *(G-8500)*	Toronto *(G-18784)*
JJ Delong & Associates Inc......G..... 216 861-4727	Mikes Welding......G..... 937 675-6587	RJR & Associates Inc......G..... 419 237-2220
Cleveland *(G-5616)*	Jamestown *(G-11352)*	Fayette *(G-9779)*
JMw Welding and Mfg......E..... 330 484-2428	Miller Welding Inc......G..... 330 364-6173	Robert Alten Inc......G..... 740 653-2640
Canton *(G-2748)*	Dover *(G-9002)*	Lancaster *(G-11747)*
Johns Welding & Towing Inc......F..... 419 447-8937	Millwrght Wldg Fbrication Svcs......F..... 740 533-1510	Robert E Moore......G..... 513 367-0006
Tiffin *(G-18225)*	Kitts Hill *(G-11621)*	Harrison *(G-10801)*
Jrs Hydraulic & Welding......G..... 614 497-1100	Mitchell Welding LLC......G..... 740 259-2211	Romar Metal Fabricating Inc......G..... 740 682-7731
Columbus *(G-7246)*	Lucasville *(G-12422)*	Oak Hill *(G-15606)*
K & J Machine Inc......F..... 740 425-3282	Monnig Welding Co......G..... 513 241-5156	▲ Rose City Manufacturing Inc......D..... 937 325-5561
Barnesville *(G-1160)*	Cincinnati *(G-4119)*	Springfield *(G-17645)*
K & M Tool & Machine Co Inc......G..... 440 572-5130	Montgomery & Montgomery LLC......G..... 330 858-9533	Rose Metal Industries LLC......F..... 216 881-3355
Strongsville *(G-17934)*	Akron *(G-301)*	Cleveland *(G-6132)*
K-M-S Industries Inc......E..... 440 243-6680	National Welding & Tanker Repr......G..... 614 875-3399	Rosie S Welding......G..... 614 506-2475
Brookpark *(G-2165)*	Grove City *(G-10576)*	Reynoldsburg *(G-16603)*
Kedar D Army......G..... 419 238-6929	National Welding & Tanker Repr......G..... 614 875-3399	Rush Welding & Machine Inc......G..... 740 354-7874
Van Wert *(G-19262)*	Grove City *(G-10577)*	Portsmouth *(G-16450)*
Kellys Welding & Fabricating......G..... 440 593-6040	New Tech Welding Inc......G..... 937 426-4801	S & S Spring Shop......G..... 800 619-4652
Conneaut *(G-7811)*	Beavercreek *(G-1354)*	Mount Perry *(G-14594)*
Kendel Welding & Fabrication......G..... 330 834-2429	Norman Noble Inc......C..... 216 761-2133	Salem Welding & Supply Company......G..... 330 332-4517
Massillon *(G-13161)*	Cleveland *(G-5889)*	Salem *(G-16925)*
Kings Welding and Fabg Inc......E..... 330 738-3592	Northwind Industries Inc......E..... 216 433-0666	Sammartino Welding & Auto Sls......G..... 330 782-6086
Mechanicstown *(G-13359)*	Cleveland *(G-5916)*	Youngstown *(G-21196)*
Kirbys Auto & Truck Repair......G..... 513 934-3999	Oaks Welding Inc......G..... 330 482-4216	Sauerwein Welding......G..... 513 563-2979
Lebanon *(G-11812)*	Columbiana *(G-6627)*	Cincinnati *(G-4380)*
Kirk Welding & Fabricating......G..... 216 961-6403	Oceco Inc......E..... 419 447-0916	Schmidt Machine Company......E..... 419 294-3814
Cleveland *(G-5658)*	Tiffin *(G-18235)*	Upper Sandusky *(G-19139)*
▲ Kottler Metal Products Co Inc......E..... 440 946-7473	Ohio Hydraulics Inc......E..... 513 771-2590	Schwab Welding Inc......G..... 513 353-4262
Willoughby *(G-20523)*	Cincinnati *(G-4178)*	Cincinnati *(G-4390)*
Kramer Power Equipment Co......F..... 937 456-2232	Ohio State University......E..... 614 292-4139	Selinick Co......G..... 440 632-1788
Eaton *(G-9313)*	Columbus *(G-7432)*	Middlefield *(G-13988)*
Kys Welding & Fabrication......G..... 513 702-9081	Ohio Trailer Inc......F..... 330 392-4444	Selzer Tool & Die Inc......G..... 440 365-4124
Loveland *(G-12368)*	Warren *(G-19584)*	Elyria *(G-9491)*
L B Industries Inc......G..... 330 750-1002	Ohio Trailer Supply Inc......G..... 614 471-9121	▲ Semtorq Inc......F..... 330 487-0600
Struthers *(G-17994)*	Columbus *(G-7435)*	Twinsburg *(G-19019)*
Lakecraft Inc......G..... 419 734-2828	Paul Wilke & Son Inc......F..... 513 921-3163	Sheet Angle Bar Met Fbrication......G..... 513 829-8600
Port Clinton *(G-16402)*	Cincinnati *(G-4217)*	Fairfield *(G-9716)*
Lanes Welding & Repair......G..... 740 397-2525	Paulo Products Company......E..... 440 942-0153	Simpson & Sons Inc......F..... 513 367-0152
Mount Vernon *(G-14628)*	Willoughby *(G-20567)*	Harrison *(G-10802)*
Laserflex Corporation......D..... 614 850-9600	Penco Tool LLC......E..... 440 998-1116	Slabe Tool Company......G..... 740 439-1647
Hilliard *(G-10958)*	Ashtabula *(G-829)*	Cambridge *(G-2476)*
Liberty Casting Company LLC......D..... 740 363-1941	◆ Pentaflex Inc......C..... 937 325-5551	Slade Gardner......G..... 440 355-8015
Delaware *(G-8869)*	Springfield *(G-17626)*	Lagrange *(G-11637)*
Lima Sheet Metal Machine & Mfg......E..... 419 229-1161	Perkins Motor Service Ltd......F..... 440 277-1256	Smith Springs Inc......G..... 800 619-4652
Lima *(G-12045)*	Lorain *(G-12267)*	Mount Perry *(G-14595)*
Logan Welding Inc......G..... 740 385-9651	Perry Welding Service Inc......F..... 330 425-2211	Smp Welding LLC......G..... 440 205-9353
Logan *(G-12186)*	Twinsburg *(G-19001)*	Mentor *(G-13725)*
▲ Long-Stanton Mfg Company......E..... 513 874-8020	Phillips & Sons Welding & Fabg......G..... 440 428-1625	Somerville Manufacturing Inc......E..... 740 336-7847
West Chester *(G-19895)*	Geneva *(G-10355)*	Marietta *(G-12834)*
Lostcreek Tool & Machine Inc......F..... 937 773-6022	Phillips Mfg and Tower Co......D..... 419 347-1720	Spradlin Bros Welding Co......F..... 800 219-2182
Piqua *(G-16287)*	Shelby *(G-17140)*	Springfield *(G-17650)*
Lukens Blacksmith Shop......G..... 513 821-2308	Phoenix Industries & Apparatus......F..... 513 722-1085	Steubenville Truck Center Inc......E..... 740 282-2711
Cincinnati *(G-4038)*	Loveland *(G-12377)*	Steubenville *(G-17715)*
Lunar Tool & Mold Inc......F..... 440 237-2141	Precision Mtal Fabrication Inc......D..... 937 235-9261	Steve Vore Welding and Steel......F..... 419 375-4087
North Royalton *(G-15434)*	Dayton *(G-8587)*	Fort Recovery *(G-9959)*
M & M Concepts Inc......G..... 937 355-1115	Precision Reflex Inc......F..... 419 629-2603	Stryker Welding......G..... 419 682-2301
West Mansfield *(G-20100)*	New Bremen *(G-14792)*	Stryker *(G-18009)*
M & W Welding Inc......G..... 614 224-0501	Precision Welding Corporation......E..... 216 524-6110	Suburban Metal Products Inc......F..... 740 474-4237
Columbus *(G-7307)*	Cleveland *(G-6037)*	Circleville *(G-4644)*
M S Welding......G..... 419 925-4141	Prestons Repair & Welding......G..... 937 947-1883	Superior Weld and Fabg Co Inc......G..... 216 249-5122
Maria Stein *(G-12758)*	Laura *(G-11768)*	Cleveland *(G-6272)*
Maintenance and Repair Fabg Co......G..... 330 478-1149	Pro Fab Welding Service LLC......G..... 937 272-2142	Systech Handling Inc......F..... 419 445-8226
Massillon *(G-13171)*	Moraine *(G-14518)*	Archbold *(G-696)*
Majestic Tool and Machine Inc......E..... 440 248-5058	Product Tooling Inc......G..... 740 524-2061	Systems Jay LLC Nanogate......B..... 419 747-4161
Solon *(G-17331)*	Sunbury *(G-18075)*	Mansfield *(G-12691)*
Manufacturing Concepts......F..... 330 784-9054	Prout Boiler Htg & Wldg Inc......E..... 330 744-0293	T & L Welding LLC......G..... 937 498-9170
Tallmadge *(G-18151)*	Youngstown *(G-21180)*	Sidney *(G-17231)*

▼ T & R Welding Systems Inc ....F 937 228-7517
Dayton *(G-8696)*

T&T Welding ....G 513 615-1156
Loveland *(G-12393)*

Tbone Sales LLC ....E 330 897-6131
Baltic *(G-1077)*

Temperature Controls Company ......F 330 773-6633
Akron *(G-433)*

Tendon Manufacturing Inc ....E 216 663-3200
Cleveland *(G-6305)*

Thomas Entps of Georgetown ....G 937 378-6300
Georgetown *(G-10366)*

Tig Welding Specialties Inc ....G 216 621-1763
Cleveland *(G-6324)*

Timothy Sasser ....G 740 260-9499
Byesville *(G-2411)*

Top Notch Fleet Services LLC ....E 419 260-4057
Maumee *(G-13303)*

Tri-Weld Inc ....F 216 281-6009
Cleveland *(G-6359)*

Triangle Precision Industries ....D 937 299-6776
Dayton *(G-8723)*

Tru-Fab Technology Inc ....F 440 954-9760
Willoughby *(G-20620)*

Turn-Key Industrial Svcs LLC ....D 614 274-1128
Columbus *(G-7714)*

TW Tank LLC ....G 419 334-2664
Fremont *(G-10190)*

Two M Precision Co Inc ....E 440 946-2120
Willoughby *(G-20623)*

Valley Machine Tool Co Inc ....E 513 899-2737
Morrow *(G-14553)*

Van Burens Welding & Machine ....G 740 787-2636
Glenford *(G-10401)*

Viking Fabricators Inc ....E 740 374-5246
Marietta *(G-12848)*

Waldock Eqp Sls & Svc Inc ....G 419 426-7771
Attica *(G-897)*

Warlock Inc ....G 614 471-4055
Columbus *(G-7749)*

Waxler Machine Tool Company ....G 419 422-1240
Findlay *(G-9906)*

Wayne Trail Technologies Inc ....D 937 295-2120
Fort Loramie *(G-9944)*

Webers Body & Frame ....G 937 839-5946
West Alexandria *(G-19786)*

Weldcraft Products Co ....F 937 233-6141
Dayton *(G-8750)*

Weldfab Inc ....G 440 563-3310
Rock Creek *(G-16687)*

Welding Consultants Inc ....G 614 258-7018
Columbus *(G-7756)*

Welding Equipment Repair Co ....G 330 536-2125
Lowellville *(G-12414)*

Weldments Inc ....F 937 235-9261
Dayton *(G-8751)*

Wenrick Machine and Tool Corp ......F 937 667-7307
Tipp City *(G-18311)*

Westerman Acquisition Co LLC ....E 330 264-2447
Wooster *(G-20847)*

Wg Mobile Welding LLC ....G 440 720-1940
Highland Heights *(G-10921)*

Whitt Machine Inc ....F 513 423-7624
Middletown *(G-14098)*

Wonder Weld Inc ....G 614 875-1447
Orient *(G-15726)*

Worleys Machine & Fab Inc ....G 740 532-3337
Hanging Rock *(G-10762)*

7694 Armature Rewinding Shops

▲ 3-D Service Ltd ....C 330 830-3500
Massillon *(G-13104)*

A E Ruston Electric LLC ....G 740 286-3022
Jackson *(G-11306)*

Akron Industrial Motor Service ....G 330 753-7624
Norton *(G-15504)*

Al Bradshaw Jr ....G 513 422-8870
Middletown *(G-14018)*

Allan A Irish ....G 419 394-3284
Saint Marys *(G-16831)*

Als High Tech Inc ....F 440 232-7090
Bedford *(G-1395)*

American Electric Motor Svc ....G 614 297-1600
Columbus *(G-6737)*

B W Electrical & Maint Svc ....G 330 534-7870
Hubbard *(G-11126)*

Bar1 Motorsports ....F 614 284-3732
Marysville *(G-12933)*

Barry Brothers Electric ....G 614 299-8187
Columbus *(G-6809)*

Bay Electric Co ....G 419 625-1046
Sandusky *(G-16948)*

Bennett Electric Inc ....F 800 874-5405
Norwalk *(G-15527)*

Big River Electric Inc ....G 740 446-4360
Gallipolis *(G-10292)*

Bornhorst Motor Service Inc ....G 937 773-0426
Piqua *(G-16253)*

Brian Franks Electric Inc ....G 330 821-5457
Alliance *(G-499)*

C and O Electric Motor Service ....G 614 491-6387
Columbus *(G-6882)*

C P Electric Motor Repair Inc ....G 330 425-9593
Twinsburg *(G-18906)*

Campton Electric Sales & Svc ....G 740 826-4429
New Concord *(G-14816)*

Carnation Elc Mtr Repr Sls Inc ....G 330 823-7116
Alliance *(G-501)*

City Machine Technologies Inc ....F 330 747-2639
Youngstown *(G-21047)*

City Machine Technologies Inc ....E 330 740-8186
Youngstown *(G-21048)*

Clark-Fowler Enterprises Inc ....G 330 262-0906
Wooster *(G-20757)*

Columbus Electrical Works Co ....F 614 294-4651
Columbus *(G-6950)*

D & J Electric Motor Repair Co ....F 330 336-4343
Wadsworth *(G-19401)*

Diversified Air Systems Inc ....E 216 741-1700
Brooklyn Heights *(G-2139)*

Dolin Supply Co ....E 304 529-4171
South Point *(G-17436)*

E-Z Electric Motor Svc Corp ....F 216 581-8820
Cleveland *(G-5235)*

Econ-O-Machine Products Inc ....G 937 882-6307
Donnelsville *(G-8961)*

Electric Ctrl & Mtr Repr Svc ....G 216 881-3143
Cleveland *(G-5264)*

Electric Motor Svc of Athens ....F 740 592-1682
The Plains *(G-18186)*

Fenton Bros Electric Co ....G 330 343-0093
New Philadelphia *(G-14898)*

Fmh Electric Inc ....F 419 782-0671
Lima *(G-12013)*

Franks Electric Inc ....G 513 542-0342
Cincinnati *(G-3781)*

General Electric Intl Inc ....G 410 737-7228
Cincinnati *(G-3816)*

Gunter Electric LLC ....G 304 253-4671
Athens *(G-871)*

Hackworth Electric Motors Inc ....G 330 345-6049
Wooster *(G-20782)*

Hannon Company ....E 740 453-0527
Zanesville *(G-21318)*

Hannon Company ....F 330 343-7758
Dover *(G-8990)*

Hennings Quality Service Inc ....F 216 941-9120
Cleveland *(G-5499)*

Home Service Station Inc ....G 419 678-2612
Coldwater *(G-6565)*

Horner Industrial Services Inc ....G 513 874-8722
West Chester *(G-20014)*

Horner Industrial Services Inc ....E 937 390-6667
Springfield *(G-17576)*

Hunnell Electric Co Inc ....G 330 773-8278
Akron *(G-225)*

Integrated Power Services LLC ....E 216 433-7808
Cleveland *(G-5575)*

Integrated Power Services LLC ....E 513 863-8816
Hamilton *(G-10707)*

James W Cunningham ....F 419 639-2111
Green Springs *(G-10471)*

▲ Joe Baker Equipment Sales ....G 513 451-1327
Cincinnati *(G-3948)*

K B Electric Motor Service ....G 740 537-1346
Toronto *(G-18783)*

K C N Technologies LLC ....G 440 439-4219
Bedford *(G-1434)*

Kaman Automation Inc ....G 216 663-0072
Cleveland *(G-5632)*

Kent Swigart ....G 937 836-5292
Englewood *(G-9528)*

Kiemle-Hankins Company ....E 419 661-2430
Perrysburg *(G-16117)*

Kw Services LLC ....G 419 636-3438
Bryan *(G-2309)*

Kw Services LLC ....G 419 228-1325
Lima *(G-12036)*

Lebanon Electric Motor Svc LLC ......G 513 932-2889
Lebanon *(G-11813)*

Lemsco Inc ....G 419 242-4005
Toledo *(G-18557)*

Lima Armature Works Inc ....G 419 222-4010
Lima *(G-12039)*

Lorain Armature & Mtr Repr Inc ....G 440 967-2620
Vermilion *(G-19332)*

M & R Electric Motor Svc Inc ....E 937 222-6282
Dayton *(G-8461)*

Mac Electric Inc ....G 419 782-0671
Lima *(G-12050)*

Machine Doctors Inc ....G 513 422-3060
Cincinnati *(G-4045)*

Mader Electr Motor & Power Tra ....G 937 325-5576
Springfield *(G-17599)*

Magnetech Industrial Svcs Inc ....C 330 830-3500
Massillon *(G-13170)*

Matlock Electric Co Inc ....E 513 731-9600
Cincinnati *(G-4066)*

Mid-Ohio Electric Co ....E 614 274-8000
Columbus *(G-7349)*

Moto-Electric Inc ....G 419 668-7894
Norwalk *(G-15552)*

◆ National Electric Coil Inc ....B 614 488-1151
Columbus *(G-7382)*

Ohio Electric Motor Svc LLC ....G 419 525-2225
Mansfield *(G-12661)*

Oliver Pool and Spa Inc ....G 740 264-5368
Steubenville *(G-17709)*

Phillips Electric Co ....F 216 361-0014
Cleveland *(G-6003)*

▲ Setco Sales Company ....D 513 941-5110
Cincinnati *(G-4409)*

Sheldon On Site Inc ....G 419 339-1381
Elida *(G-9357)*

▲ Shoemaker Electric Company ....E 614 294-5626
Columbus *(G-7617)*

Southwest Electric Co ....F 330 875-7000
Louisville *(G-12330)*

T & J Nickum Inc ....G 216 881-2565
Cleveland *(G-6286)*

Total Maintenance Management ....G 513 228-2345
Lebanon *(G-11844)*

Tyler Electric Motor Repair ....G 330 836-5537
Akron *(G-451)*

Watson Electric Motor Svc Inc ....F 614 836-9904
Columbus *(G-7753)*

Wheatley Electric Service Co ....G 513 531-4951
Cincinnati *(G-4590)*

Whelco Industrial Ltd ....F 419 385-4627
Perrysburg *(G-16169)*

Wyse Electric Motor Repair ....G 419 445-5921
Archbold *(G-699)*

S
I
C

ALPHABETIC SECTION

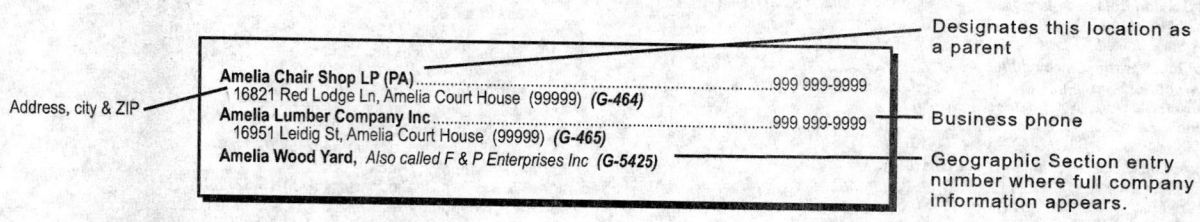

Amelia Chair Shop LP (PA) 999 999-9999
  16821 Red Lodge Ln, Amelia Court House (99999) *(G-464)*
Amelia Lumber Company Inc 999 999-9999
  16951 Leidig St, Amelia Court House (99999) *(G-465)*
Amelia Wood Yard, *Also called F & P Enterprises Inc (G-5425)*

Designates this location as a parent

Address, city & ZIP

Business phone

Geographic Section entry number where full company information appears.

See footnotes for symbols and codes identification.

* Companies listed alphabetically.

* Complete physical or mailing address.

---

1 888 U Pitch It 440 796-9028
  7176 Fillmore Ct Mentor (44060) *(G-13503)*
1 A Lifesafer Inc (PA) 513 651-9560
  4290 Glendale Milford Rd Blue Ash (45242) *(G-1729)*
1 A Lifesafer Hawaii Inc 513 651-9560
  4290 Glendale Milford Rd Blue Ash (45242) *(G-1730)*
1 Day Sign 419 475-6060
  4236 Secor Rd Toledo (43623) *(G-18315)*
1 Iron Golf Inc 419 662-9336
  504 Maplewood Ln Celina (45822) *(G-2984)*
1 Stop Graphics, Barberton *Also called Advertising Ideas of Ohio Inc (G-1094)*
1-2-3 Gluten Free Inc 216 378-9233
  125 Orange Tree Dr Chagrin Falls (44022) *(G-3046)*
10155 Broadview Business 440 546-1901
  10155 Broadview Rd Broadview Heights (44147) *(G-2101)*
11 92 Holdings LLC 216 920-7790
  8 E Washington St Ste 200 Chagrin Falls (44022) *(G-3047)*
119c Landis Display Co 937 307-9499
  346 Beam Dr Franklin (45005) *(G-10003)*
1455 Group LLC 330 494-9074
  6116 Market Ave N Canton (44721) *(G-2583)*
1923 W 25th St Inc 216 696-7529
  1923 W 25th St Cleveland (44113) *(G-4664)*
1999 Pvc Partner Inc 440 930-1000
  33587 Walker Rd Avon Lake (44012) *(G-1022)*
1st Choice Web Solution Inc 330 503-1591
  3000 Belmont Ave Youngstown (44505) *(G-21008)*
2-M Manufacturing Company 440 269-1270
  34560 Lakeland Blvd Eastlake (44095) *(G-9256)*
20/20 Custom Molded Plast 419 485-2020
  14620 Selwyn Dr Montpelier (43543) *(G-14437)*
201 E Liberty St. 234 249-0145
  201 E Liberty St Wooster (44691) *(G-20728)*
21st Century Printers Inc 513 771-4150
  326 Northland Blvd Cincinnati (45246) *(G-3322)*
252 Tattoo (PA) 440 235-6699
  24525 Sprague Rd Columbia Station (44028) *(G-6577)*
2828 Clinton Inc (PA) 216 241-7157
  600 Cherry Fork Ave Leetonia (44431) *(G-11857)*
2cravealloys, Dalton *Also called J Horst Manufacturing Co (G-8072)*
2nd Roe LLC 419 499-3031
  12014 Thomas Rd Monroeville (44847) *(G-14423)*
3 Brothers Torching Inc 419 339-9985
  4915 Dutch Hollow Rd Lima (45807) *(G-11979)*
3 Dips 937 247-5914
  33 S Main St Miamisburg (45342) *(G-13777)*
3 Sigma Corporation 937 440-3400
  1985 W Stanfield Rd Troy (45373) *(G-18801)*
3-D Service Ltd (PA) 330 830-3500
  800 Nave Rd Se Massillon (44646) *(G-13104)*
3-D Technical Services Inc 937 746-2901
  255 Industrial Dr Franklin (45005) *(G-10004)*
3-Dmed, Franklin *Also called 3-D Technical Services Inc (G-10004)*
3-G Incorporated (PA) 513 921-4515
  4122 Spring Grove Ave Cincinnati (45223) *(G-3323)*
31 Inc 740 498-8324
  100 Enterprise Dr Newcomerstown (43832) *(G-15107)*
360 Communications LLC 330 329-2013
  826 Minota Ave Akron (44306) *(G-12)*
360water Inc 614 294-3600
  965 W 3rd Ave Columbus (43212) *(G-6663)*
3d Systems, Barberton *Also called Village Plastics Co (G-1156)*
3d Systems Inc 215 757-9611
  950 Taylor Station Rd K Columbus (43230) *(G-6664)*
3d Systems Inc 216 229-2040
  7100 Euclid Ave Cleveland (44103) *(G-4665)*
3dlt LLC 513 452-3358
  8 Peasenhall Ln Cincinnati (45208) *(G-3324)*

3gc LLC 740 703-0580
  5600 Sw Us 42 Cardington (43315) *(G-2907)*
3jd Inc 513 324-9655
  2823 Northlawn Ave Moraine (45439) *(G-14462)*
3M Company 513 248-1749
  910 Lila Ave Milford (45150) *(G-14118)*
3M Company 330 725-1444
  1030 Lake Rd Medina (44256) *(G-13361)*
3M Company 440 323-6161
  1301 Lowell St Elyria (44035) *(G-9366)*
3n1 Mens Fashion 513 851-3610
  481 E Kemper Rd Cincinnati (45246) *(G-3325)*
3way Machine and Tool Company 419 925-7222
  2411 Cssella Montezuma Rd Maria Stein (45860) *(G-12756)*
4 Him Sales, Morrow *Also called Isaacs Jr Floyd Thomas (G-14548)*
4 Over LLC 937 610-0629
  7801 Technology Blvd Dayton (45424) *(G-8123)*
4 Walls Com LLC 216 432-1400
  4700 Lakeside Ave E 173a Cleveland (44114) *(G-4666)*
4-B Wood Custom Cabinets, Seville *Also called 4-B Wood Specialties Inc (G-17067)*
4-B Wood Specialties Inc 330 769-2188
  255 W Greenwich Rd Seville (44273) *(G-17067)*
4-Sure Wire Products Inc 440 563-9263
  2589 Forman Rd Rock Creek (44084) *(G-16684)*
48 Hr Books Inc 330 374-6917
  2249 14th St Sw Akron (44314) *(G-13)*
48hourprint.com, Cleveland *Also called Advanced Mdia Publications Inc (G-4716)*
48hr Books, Akron *Also called Printing System Inc (G-351)*
4d Screenprinting Ltd 513 353-1070
  5833 Hamilton Cleves Rd Cleves (45002) *(G-6504)*
4everready, Dayton *Also called P3 Secure LLC (G-8559)*
4me Group LLC 513 898-1083
  6740 Clough Pike Ste 207 Cincinnati (45244) *(G-3326)*
4r Enterprises Incorporated 330 923-9799
  700 Portage Trl Cuyahoga Falls (44221) *(G-7960)*
4S Company 330 792-5518
  3730 Mahoning Ave Youngstown (44515) *(G-21009)*
4w Services 614 554-5427
  7901 Minecaster Rd Hebron (43025) *(G-10859)*
5 Axis Grinding Inc 937 312-9797
  86 Westpark Rd Dayton (45459) *(G-8124)*
5 BS Inc (PA) 740 454-8453
  1000 5 Bs Dr Zanesville (43701) *(G-21263)*
5-Acre Mill, Hicksville *Also called Adroit Thinking Inc (G-10898)*
5me LLC 513 719-1600
  4270 Ivy Pointe Blvd # 100 Cincinnati (45245) *(G-3285)*
5me Holdings LLC (PA) 859 534-4872
  4270 Ivy Pointe Blvd # 100 Cincinnati (45245) *(G-3286)*
5s Inc 440 968-0212
  9755 Plank Rd Montville (44064) *(G-14459)*
6062 Holdings LLC 216 359-9005
  23366 Commerce Park 100b Beachwood (44122) *(G-1252)*
614 Cupcakes LLC. 614 245-8800
  4045 Chelsea Grn W New Albany (43054) *(G-14744)*
614 Magazine, Columbus *Also called 614 Media Group LLC (G-6665)*
614 Media Group LLC 614 488-4400
  458 E Main St Columbus (43215) *(G-6665)*
64 Metals, Saint Louisville *Also called C Green & Sons Incorporated (G-16826)*
69 Taps 330 253-4554
  374 Paul Williams St Akron (44311) *(G-14)*
6s Products LLC 937 394-7440
  12800 Wenger Rd Anna (45302) *(G-619)*
7 Little Cupcakes 419 252-0858
  1021 Sandusky St Ste C Perrysburg (43551) *(G-16060)*
7 Rowe Court Properties LLC 513 874-7236
  7 Rowe Ct Hamilton (45015) *(G-10659)*
7 Up / R C/Canada Dry Btlg Co, Columbus *Also called American Bottling Company (G-6731)*

A
L
P
H
A
B
E
T
I
C

(PA)=Parent Co (HQ)=Headquarters (DH)=Div Headquarters

7 Up Bottling Co, Midvale *Also called American Bottling Company* ***(G-14104)***
7 Up Bottling Co, Lima *Also called American Bottling Company* ***(G-11988)***
7 Up of Marietta Inc 740 423-9230
871 State Route 618 Little Hocking (45742) ***(G-12141)***
7 Up/ Royal Crown, Cincinnati *Also called American Bottling Company* ***(G-3385)***
7&7 Woodworking 330 347-6574
11080 Ashland Rd Wooster (44691) ***(G-20729)***
717 Inc 440 925-0402
13000 Athens Ave Ste 110 Lakewood (44107) ***(G-11652)***
717 Ink, Lakewood *Also called 717 Inc* ***(G-11652)***
762mm Firearms LLC 440 655-8572
224 High St Wadsworth (44281) ***(G-19384)***
77 Coach Supply Ltd 330 674-1454
7426 County Road 77 Millersburg (44654) ***(G-14187)***
7d Marketing Inc 330 721-8822
345 N State Rd Medina (44256) ***(G-13362)***
7signal Solutions Inc (PA) 330 761-3515
526 S Main St Ste 601g Akron (44311) ***(G-15)***
80 Acres Urban Agriculture LLC (PA) 513 218-4387
4535 Este Ave Cincinnati (45232) ***(G-3327)***
8888 Butler Investments Inc 440 748-0810
8888 Riverwood Dr North Ridgeville (44039) ***(G-15354)***
9444 Ohio Holding Co 330 359-6291
1658 Us Route 62 E Winesburg (44690) ***(G-20701)***
A A S Amels Sheet Meta L Inc 330 793-9326
222 Steel St Youngstown (44509) ***(G-21010)***
A & A Discount Tire 330 863-1936
5125 Canton Rd Nw Carrollton (44615) ***(G-2950)***
A & A Safety Inc (PA) 513 943-6100
1126 Ferris Rd Bldg A Amelia (45102) ***(G-564)***
A & B Deburring Company 513 723-0777
525 Carr St Cincinnati (45203) ***(G-3328)***
A & B Interiors Shine A Blind (PA) 937 371-4731
4407 Rudy Rd Tipp City (45371) ***(G-18256)***
A & B Iron & Metal Company 937 228-1561
329 Washington St Dayton (45402) ***(G-8125)***
A & B Machine Inc 937 492-8662
2040 Commerce Dr Sidney (45365) ***(G-17164)***
A & B Printing, Fort Loramie *Also called Sharp Enterprises Inc* ***(G-9939)***
A & B Tool & Manufacturing 419 382-0215
2921 South Ave Toledo (43609) ***(G-18316)***
A & B Wood Design Assoc Inc 330 721-2789
3193 Greenwich Rd Wadsworth (44281) ***(G-19385)***
A & C Welding Inc 330 762-4777
80 Cuyhoga Fls Indus Pkwy Peninsula (44264) ***(G-16032)***
A & D Printing Co 440 975-8001
38287 Airport Pkwy Ste A Willoughby (44094) ***(G-20421)***
A & D Wood Products Inc (PA) 419 331-8859
4220 Sherrick Rd Elida (45807) ***(G-9349)***
A & E Butscha Co 513 761-1919
110 E Seymour Ave Cincinnati (45216) ***(G-3329)***
A & F Machine Products Co 440 826-0959
454 Geiger St Berea (44017) ***(G-1599)***
A & G Manufacturing Co Inc (PA) 419 468-7433
280 Gelsanliter Rd Galion (44833) ***(G-10250)***
A & G Manufacturing Co Inc 419 468-7433
165 Gelsanliter Rd Galion (44833) ***(G-10251)***
A & H Automotive Industries 614 235-1759
701 Hadley Dr Columbus (43228) ***(G-6666)***
A & H Truck Parts, Columbus *Also called A & H Automotive Industries* ***(G-6666)***
A & I Metal Finishing, Vermilion *Also called Architectural and Industrial* ***(G-19323)***
A & J Woodworking 888 572-9561
4012 Winklepleck Rd Nw Sugarcreek (44681) ***(G-18014)***
A & J Woodworking Inc 419 695-5655
808 Ohio St Delphos (45833) ***(G-8898)***
A & L Inds Machining & Repr, Oregon *Also called A & L Industries* ***(G-15698)***
A & L Industries 419 698-3733
2054 Grange St Oregon (43616) ***(G-15698)***
A & L Machine Tool 513 863-2662
3080 Darrtown Rd Hamilton (45013) ***(G-10660)***
A & L Metal Processing, Sandusky *Also called Equinox Enterprises LLC* ***(G-16964)***
A & M Cheese Co 419 476-8369
253 Waggoner Blvd Toledo (43612) ***(G-18317)***
A & M Creative Group Inc 330 452-8940
1704 Ira Turpin Way Ne Canton (44705) ***(G-2584)***
A & M Hardwoods, Millersburg *Also called Andy A Raber* ***(G-14194)***
A & M Kiln Dry Ltd 330 473-8634
3570 County Road 135 Millersburg (44654) ***(G-14188)***
A & M Kiln Dry Ltd 330 852-0505
10836 Lower Trail Rd Nw Dundee (44624) ***(G-9170)***
A & M Logging 740 543-3171
8633 Township Road 289 Salineville (43945) ***(G-16939)***
A & M Ornamental Mfg Co, Columbus *Also called T E Martindale Enterprises* ***(G-7673)***
A & M Pallet 937 295-3093
3860 Rangeline Rd Russia (45363) ***(G-16760)***
A & M Pallet Shop Inc 440 632-1941
14550 Madison Rd Middlefield (44062) ***(G-13911)***
A & M Products 419 595-2092
3060 S County Road 591 Tiffin (44883) ***(G-18201)***
A & M Refractories Inc 740 456-8020
202 West Ave New Boston (45662) ***(G-14778)***
A & M Woodworking 330 893-1331
6440 State Route 515 Millersburg (44654) ***(G-14189)***
A & P Tech Services Inc 330 535-1700
856 Home Ave Akron (44310) ***(G-16)***
A & P Technology Inc 513 688-3200
4599 E Tech Dr Cincinnati (45245) ***(G-3287)***
A & P Technology Inc 513 688-3200
4622 E Tech Dr Cincinnati (45245) ***(G-3288)***
A & P Technology Inc 513 688-3200
4578 E Tech Dr Cincinnati (45245) ***(G-3289)***
A & P Technology Inc 513 688-3200
4624 E Tech Dr Cincinnati (45245) ***(G-3290)***
A & P Technology Inc (PA) 513 688-3200
4595 E Tech Dr Cincinnati (45245) ***(G-3291)***
A & P Tool Inc 419 542-6681
801 Industrial Dr Hicksville (43526) ***(G-10897)***
A & P Wood Products Inc 419 673-1196
15790 State Route 31 Kenton (43326) ***(G-11543)***
A & R Machine Co Inc 330 832-4631
13212 Vega St Sw Massillon (44647) ***(G-13105)***
A & T Ornamental Iron Company 937 859-6006
415 E Sycamore St Miamisburg (45342) ***(G-13778)***
A & W Spring Co Inc 937 222-7284
1000 E 2nd St Ste 8 Dayton (45402) ***(G-8126)***
A & W Table Pad Co 800 541-0271
6520 Carnegie Ave Cleveland (44103) ***(G-4667)***
A A A Professional Htg & Coolg 513 933-0564
535 N Broadway St Lebanon (45036) ***(G-11773)***
A A E, Canton *Also called American Aluminum Extrusions* ***(G-2602)***
A Aabaco Plastics Inc 216 663-9494
9520 Midwest Ave Cleveland (44125) ***(G-4668)***
A and V Grinding Inc 937 444-4141
1115 Straight St 17 Cincinnati (45214) ***(G-3330)***
A B & J Machining & Fabg 513 769-5900
10330 Wayne Ave Cincinnati (45215) ***(G-3331)***
A B C Sign Inc 513 241-8884
38 W Mcmicken Ave Cincinnati (45202) ***(G-3332)***
A B Siemer Inc 614 888-8855
150 E Campus View Blvd # 250 Columbus (43235) ***(G-6667)***
A Best Trmt & Pest Ctrl Sups 330 434-5555
891 Gorge Blvd Akron (44310) ***(G-17)***
A Bun In Oven 419 559-3056
1011 Hayes Ave Fremont (43420) ***(G-10121)***
A C F, Lima *Also called Allen County Fabrication Inc* ***(G-11986)***
A C Hadley - Printing Inc 937 426-0952
1530 Marsetta Dr Beavercreek (45432) ***(G-1314)***
A C Knox Inc 513 921-5028
525 Purcell Ave Cincinnati (45205) ***(G-3333)***
A C Products Co 330 698-1105
4299 S Apple Creek Rd Apple Creek (44606) ***(G-633)***
A C Shutters Inc 216 429-2424
8119 Mansfield Ave Cleveland (44105) ***(G-4669)***
A C Williams Co Inc (PA) 330 296-6110
700 N Walnut St Ravenna (44266) ***(G-16511)***
A Class Coatings Inc 440 960-6869
4481 Oakhill Blvd Lorain (44053) ***(G-12229)***
A Cupcake A Day LLC 330 389-1247
115 W Liberty St Stow (44224) ***(G-17727)***
A Designers Workroom 513 251-7396
3066 Madison Rd 3 Cincinnati (45209) ***(G-3334)***
A E F Inc 216 360-9800
24050 Commerce Park Fl 2 Cleveland (44122) ***(G-4670)***
A E Ruston Electric LLC 740 286-3022
121 N David Ave Jackson (45640) ***(G-11306)***
A E T, Maumee *Also called Applied Energy Tech Inc* ***(G-13227)***
A E T, Bellbrook *Also called Advanced Engine Tech LLC* ***(G-1503)***
A E Wilson Holdings Inc 330 405-0316
2307 E Aurora Rd Twinsburg (44087) ***(G-18888)***
A F Krainz Co 216 431-4341
1364 E 47th St Cleveland (44103) ***(G-4671)***
A F P Ohio, Columbus *Also called Austin Foam Plastics Inc* ***(G-6789)***
A G Industries Inc 330 220-0050
2963 Interstate Pkwy Brunswick (44212) ***(G-2200)***
A G Mercury, Galion *Also called A & G Manufacturing Co Inc* ***(G-10250)***
A G Parts Inc 937 596-6448
500 N Linden St Jackson Center (45334) ***(G-11336)***
A G Ruff Paper Specialties Co 513 891-7990
4320 Indeco Ct Blue Ash (45241) ***(G-1731)***
A G S Ohio, Macedonia *Also called AGS Custom Graphics Inc* ***(G-12433)***
A Grade Notes Inc (PA) 614 766-9999
6385 Shier Rings Rd Ste 1 Dublin (43016) ***(G-9034)***
A Graphic Solution 216 228-7223
14900 Detroit Ave Ste 205 Cleveland (44107) ***(G-4672)***
A H Marty Co Ltd 216 641-8950
6900 Union Ave Cleveland (44105) ***(G-4673)***
A H Pelz Co 216 861-1882
2498 Superior Ave E Cleveland (44114) ***(G-4674)***

A I M Specialists, Toledo *Also called Print All Inc (G-18658)*

A I P, Columbus *Also called American Isostatic Presses Inc (G-6739)*

A J Construction Co 330 539-9544
870 Shannon Rd Girard (44420) *(G-10380)*

A J Oster Foils LLC 330 823-1700
2081 Mccrea St Alliance (44601) *(G-486)*

A J Rose Mfgco 216 631-4645
3115 W 38th St Cleveland (44109) *(G-4675)*

A J Rose Mfgco (PA) 216 631-4645
38000 Chester Rd Avon (44011) *(G-978)*

A Jack' S Industries, Columbus *Also called Atlas Gear and Machine Co (G-6783)*

A Jacks Manufacturing Co 216 531-1010
1441 Chardon Rd Cleveland (44117) *(G-4676)*

A K Athletic Equipment Inc 614 920-3069
8015 Howe Industrial Pkwy Canal Winchester (43110) *(G-2518)*

A K Ready Mix LLC 740 286-8900
441 Dixon Run Rd Jackson (45640) *(G-11307)*

A L Callahan Door Sales 419 884-3667
35 Industrial Dr Mansfield (44904) *(G-12554)*

A M C P, Greenfield *Also called American Made Corrugated Packg (G-10473)*

A M Castle & Co 330 425-7000
26800 Miles Rd Bedford (44146) *(G-1394)*

A M D 440 918-8930
4580 Beidler Rd Willoughby (44094) *(G-20422)*

A M Scheffer Signs Fab 330 666-6674
1089 S Clvland Mssllon Rd Copley (44321) *(G-7837)*

A M W, Columbus *Also called Assembly Machining Wire Pdts (G-6779)*

A Metalcraft Associates Inc 937 693-4008
18965 State Route 219 Botkins (45306) *(G-1949)*

A P, Salem *Also called Absolute Polymers Inc (G-16866)*

A P O Holdings Inc 330 455-8925
1405 Timken Pl Sw Canton (44706) *(G-2585)*

A P Production & Service 740 745-5317
12546 Pleasant Valley Rd Utica (43080) *(G-19191)*

A P S, Dayton *Also called Aps-Materials Inc (G-8161)*

A P T, Middlefield *Also called American Plastic Tech Inc (G-13914)*

A Park Ohio Company, Wickliffe *Also called PMC Industries Corp (G-20383)*

A Plus Machining & Tooling, New Carlisle *Also called Custom Threading Systems LLC (G-14799)*

A Plus Powder Coaters Inc 330 482-4389
1384 Kauffman Ave Columbiana (44408) *(G-6604)*

A Plus Propane LLC 419 399-4445
8622 Us Route 127 Paulding (45879) *(G-15998)*

A Plus Signs & Graphix 330 848-4800
833 E Waterloo Rd Akron (44306) *(G-18)*

A Pop of Elegance LLC 330 225-4724
4955 Neura Pkwy Brunswick (44212) *(G-2201)*

A Printed Impression, Newark *Also called Crain-Tharp Printing Inc (G-14998)*

A Quick Copy Center, Cleveland *Also called T H E B Inc (G-6290)*

A R C, Troy *Also called ARC Abrasives Inc (G-18805)*

A R C of Dayton, Dayton *Also called Hayes Reconditioning Group (G-8387)*

A R Harding Publishing Company 614 231-5735
2878 E Main St Columbus (43209) *(G-6668)*

A R J, Wickliffe *Also called Andy Russo Jr Inc (G-20354)*

A R Jester Co 513 241-1465
6781 Harrison Ave Cincinnati (45247) *(G-3335)*

A R Schopps Sons Inc 330 821-8406
14536 Oyster Rd Alliance (44601) *(G-487)*

A Raymond Tinnerman Mfg Inc (HQ) 330 220-5179
1060 W 130th St Brunswick (44212) *(G-2202)*

A Reed Excavating LLC 740 391-4985
52912 State Route 145 Beallsville (43716) *(G-1306)*

A S C, Middleburg Heights *Also called Associated Software Cons Inc (G-13902)*

A S D, Dayton *Also called Automation Systems Designs Inc (G-8173)*

A S Manufacturing Inc 216 476-0656
4412 W 130th St Cleveland (44135) *(G-4677)*

A S Nf Producing Inc 330 933-0622
10539 Schlabach Ave Ne Hartville (44632) *(G-10815)*

A S T Machine Co 740 494-2013
1 N 4th St Prospect (43342) *(G-16495)*

A S W, Bedford Heights *Also called American Spring Wire Corp (G-1478)*

A Schulman Inc (PA) 330 666-3751
3637 Ridgewood Rd Fairlawn (44333) *(G-9736)*

A Schulman Inc 330 498-4840
8562 Port Jackson Ave Nw North Canton (44720) *(G-15217)*

A Schulman Inc 330 773-2700
1353 Exeter Rd Akron (44306) *(G-19)*

A Schulman Inc 330 630-3315
1183 Home Ave Akron (44310) *(G-20)*

A Schulman Inc 330 630-0308
790 E Tallmadge Ave Akron (44310) *(G-21)*

A Screen Printed Products 419 352-1535
17715 N Dixie Hwy Bowling Green (43402) *(G-1961)*

A Service Glass Inc 937 426-4920
1363 N Fairfield Rd Beavercreek (45432) *(G-1315)*

A Sign Above Inc 330 723-3650
8982 Dutton Dr Twinsburg (44087) *(G-18889)*

A Sign For The Times Inc 216 297-2977
4100 Mayfield Rd Cleveland (44121) *(G-4678)*

A Special Touch Embroidery LLC 740 858-2241
22326 State Route 73 Portsmouth (45663) *(G-16429)*

A Spoon Fulla Sugar LLC 513 683-0444
11916 Montgomery Rd Cincinnati (45249) *(G-3336)*

A Stucki Company 412 424-0560
7376 Whipple Ave Nw North Canton (44720) *(G-15218)*

A T & F Co, Cleveland *Also called American Tank & Fabricating Co (G-4796)*

A T C, Westlake *Also called American Tchnical Coatings Inc (G-20253)*

A T E C Diversifed, Wilmington *Also called Atec Diversfd Wldg Fabrication (G-20655)*

A T I, Spring Valley *Also called Advanced Telemetrics Intl (G-17466)*

A T Tube Company Inc 330 336-8706
188 S Lyman St Wadsworth (44281) *(G-19386)*

A To Z Paper Box Co 330 325-8722
4477 Tallmadge Rd Rootstown (44272) *(G-16718)*

A To Z Portion Ctrl Meats Inc 419 358-2926
201 N Main St Bluffton (45817) *(G-1906)*

A To Z Wear Ltd 513 923-4662
5647 Cheviot Rd Cincinnati (45247) *(G-3337)*

A United 330 782-6005
5234 Southern Blvd Ste D Youngstown (44512) *(G-21011)*

A V C, Canton *Also called Assocted Vsual Cmmncations Inc (G-2608)*

A W C Inc (PA) 216 831-0550
5200 Richmond Rd Cleveland (44146) *(G-4679)*

A W S C O, Dayton *Also called American Woodwork Specialty Co (G-8156)*

A W S Incorporated 419 352-5397
520 Hankey Ave Bowling Green (43402) *(G-1962)*

A W Taylor Lumber Incorporated 440 577-1889
1114 State Route 7 S Pierpont (44082) *(G-16210)*

A W Tipka Oil & Gas Inc 330 364-4333
2421 Johnstown Rd Ne Dover (44622) *(G-8962)*

A Z Printing Inc (PA) 513 733-3900
10122 Reading Rd Cincinnati (45241) *(G-3338)*

A Z Printing Inc 513 745-0700
4077 E Galbraith Rd Cincinnati (45236) *(G-3339)*

A&B Interiors, Tipp City *Also called A & B Interiors Shine A Blind (G-18256)*

A&E Machine & Fabrication Inc (PA) 740 820-4701
384 State Route 335 Beaver (45613) *(G-1309)*

A&S Machine 440 946-3976
38363 Western Pkwy Unit 1 Willoughby (44094) *(G-20423)*

A+ Engineering Fabrication Inc 419 832-0748
17562 Beech St Grand Rapids (43522) *(G-10439)*

A-1 Fabricators Finishers LLC 513 724-0383
4220 Curliss Ln Batavia (45103) *(G-1163)*

A-1 Manufacturing Corp 216 475-6084
5446 Dunham Rd Maple Heights (44137) *(G-12726)*

A-1 Printing Inc (PA) 419 562-3111
825 S Sandusky Ave Bucyrus (44820) *(G-2330)*

A-1 Sprinkler Company Inc 937 859-6198
2383 Northpointe Dr Miamisburg (45342) *(G-13779)*

A-1 Welding & Fabricating Inc 440 233-8474
1005 E 32nd St Lorain (44055) *(G-12230)*

A-1 Welding & Sandblasting, Columbus *Also called Carol J Guiler (G-6910)*

A-B Blueprint Co Inc 330 794-8803
2757 Gilchrist Rd Akron (44305) *(G-22)*

A-A1 Machine and Supply Co 440 346-0698
3130 Klages Blvd Tallmadge (44278) *(G-18131)*

A-Best Termite and Pest Ctrl, Akron *Also called A Best Trmt & Pest Ctrl Sups (G-17)*

A-Brite LP 216 252-2995
3000 W 121st St Cleveland (44111) *(G-4680)*

A-Buck Manufacturing Inc 937 687-3738
12251 Eagle Rd New Lebanon (45345) *(G-14839)*

A-D Machine, Euclid *Also called Bic Manufacturing Inc (G-9567)*

A-Display Service Corp 614 469-1230
541 Dana Ave Columbus (43223) *(G-6669)*

A-Door Lock Shop, Dayton *Also called Dayton Safe Company (G-8286)*

A-Kobak Container Company 330 225-7791
1701 W 130th St Hinckley (44233) *(G-11020)*

A-Stamp Industries LLC 419 633-0451
633 Commerce Dr Bryan (43506) *(G-2273)*

A-Wall, Cleveland *Also called Component Systems Inc (G-5113)*

A-Z Discount Printing, Cincinnati *Also called A Z Printing Inc (G-3338)*

A-Z Packaging Company 614 444-8441
1221 Harmon Ave Columbus (43223) *(G-6670)*

A.I.M., Aurora *Also called Advanced Innovative Mfg Inc (G-905)*

A/C Laser Technologies Inc 330 784-3355
867 Moe Dr Ste F Akron (44310) *(G-23)*

A2z Pallets LLC 513 652-9026
1292 Glendale Milford Rd Cincinnati (45215) *(G-3340)*

AA1 Tool and Tech Supply, Tallmadge *Also called A-A1 Machine and Supply Co (G-18131)*

AAA, Perrysburg *Also called Industrial Hardwood Inc (G-16111)*

AAA Galvanizing - Joliet Inc 513 871-5700
4454 Steel Pl Cincinnati (45209) *(G-3341)*

AAA Laminating & Bindery 513 860-2680
7209 Dixie Hwy Fairfield (45014) *(G-9637)*

AAA Plastics and Pallets Ltd 330 844-2556
13943 Sousa St North Lawrence (44666) *(G-15305)*

AAA Stamping Inc 216 749-4494
4001 Pearl Rd Uppr Cleveland (44109) *(G-4681)*

Aabel Plumbing Inc 937 434-4343
440 Congress Park Dr Dayton (45459) *(G-8127)*

Aadco Instruments Inc 513 467-1477
145 S Miami Ave Cleves (45002) *(G-6505)*

Aak Kings Mills LLC 513 598-4460
5250 Courseview Dr Mason (45040) *(G-12978)*

Aap St Marys Corp 419 394-7840
1100 Mckinley Rd Saint Marys (45885) *(G-16830)*

Aardvark Graphic Enterprises L 419 352-3197
123 S Main St Bowling Green (43402) *(G-1963)*

Aardvark Screen Prtg & EMB LLC 419 354-6686
123 S Main St Bowling Green (43402) *(G-1964)*

Aardvark Sportswear Inc 330 793-9428
5329 Mahoning Ave Youngstown (44515) *(G-21012)*

Aaron Smith 330 285-1360
385 Rutland Ave Akron (44305) *(G-24)*

Aaronyx Design, Mansfield *Also called Aaronyx Publishing (G-12555)*

Aaronyx Publishing 419 747-2400
1924 Springmill Rd Mansfield (44903) *(G-12555)*

AB Bonded Locksmiths Inc 513 531-7334
4344 Montgomery Rd Cincinnati (45212) *(G-3342)*

AB Plastics Inc 513 576-6333
1287 Us Route 50 Milford (45150) *(G-14119)*

AB Resources LLC 440 922-1098
6802 W Snowville Rd Ste E Brecksville (44141) *(G-2031)*

AB&j Machng Fabrictn, Cincinnati *Also called A B & J Machining & Fabg (G-3331)*

Aba Gutters Inc 440 729-2177
13046 Cherry Ln Chesterland (44026) *(G-3193)*

Abacus Biodiesel Complex, Columbus *Also called Citi 2 Citi Logistics (G-6930)*

Abanaki Corporation (PA) 440 543-7400
17387 Munn Rd Chagrin Falls (44023) *(G-3075)*

ABB Autoclave Systems, Columbus *Also called Avure Autoclave Systems Inc (G-6794)*

ABB Automation Inc 440 347-9668
29801 Euclid Ave Wickliffe (44092) *(G-20346)*

ABB Electric Systems, Wickliffe *Also called ABB Inc (G-20347)*

ABB Inc 440 585-8500
29801 Euclid Ave Wickliffe (44092) *(G-20347)*

ABB Inc 440 585-8500
1400 Worden Rd Wickliffe (44092) *(G-20348)*

ABB Inc 513 874-4730
7759 Lakota Springs Dr West Chester (45069) *(G-19795)*

ABB Inc 440 585-8500
29801 Euclid Ave Wickliffe (44092) *(G-20349)*

Abbey Carpet, Canton *Also called Shaheen Oriental Rug Co Inc (G-2846)*

Abbey Machine Products Co 216 481-0080
1100 E 222nd St Ste 4 Cleveland (44117) *(G-4682)*

Abbot Bindery, Cleveland *Also called Irvin Oslin Inc (G-5588)*

Abbot Image Solutions LLC 937 382-6677
185 Park Dr Wilmington (45177) *(G-20652)*

Abbott Laboratories 614 624-3191
585 Cleveland Ave Columbus (43215) *(G-6671)*

Abbott Laboratories 614 624-7677
3300 Stelzer Rd Columbus (43219) *(G-6672)*

Abbott Laboratories 614 624-6627
1033 Kingsmill Pkwy Columbus (43229) *(G-6673)*

Abbott Laboratories 614 624-3078
350 N 5th St Columbus (43215) *(G-6674)*

Abbott Laboratories 614 624-6627
6550 Singletree Dr Columbus (43229) *(G-6675)*

Abbott Laboratories 614 624-6088
6 Cleveland Ave Columbus (43215) *(G-6676)*

Abbott Nutrition, Columbus *Also called Abbott Laboratories (G-6671)*

Abbott Nutrition Mfg Inc 614 624-7485
625 Cleveland Ave Columbus (43215) *(G-6677)*

Abbott Signs (PA) 937 393-6600
251 John St Hillsboro (45133) *(G-10995)*

Abbott Tool Inc 419 476-6742
405 Dura Ave Toledo (43612) *(G-18318)*

Abby Girl Sweets Cupcakery 513 335-0898
41 W 5th St Cincinnati (45202) *(G-3343)*

Abby Industries LLC 513 502-9865
346 Frizzell Ave Eaton (45320) *(G-9298)*

ABC, Canton *Also called Always Better Communications (G-2600)*

ABC Appliance Inc 419 693-4414
3012 Navarre Ave Oregon (43616) *(G-15699)*

ABC Countertops, Toledo *Also called Brad Snoderly (G-18380)*

ABC Inoac Exterior Systems LLC 419 334-8951
1410 Motor Ave Fremont (43420) *(G-10122)*

ABC Lettering & Embroidery 216 321-8338
13727 Madison Ave Lakewood (44107) *(G-11653)*

ABC Packaging Direct LLC 440 934-1477
2162 Clifton Way Avon (44011) *(G-979)*

ABC Plastics Inc 330 948-3322
140 West Dr Lodi (44254) *(G-12154)*

ABC Refreshments LLC 866 382-5575
19541 Roseland Ave Euclid (44117) *(G-9563)*

Abco Bar & Tube Cutting Svc 513 697-9487
7685 S State Route 48 # 1 Maineville (45039) *(G-12520)*

Abel Fabrication & Precision, Cincinnati *Also called Abel Fbrction Prcsion Pdts Inc (G-3344)*

Abel Fbrction Prcsion Pdts Inc 513 681-5000
3260 Beekman St Cincinnati (45223) *(G-3344)*

Abel Manufacturing Company 513 681-5000
3474 Beekman St Cincinnati (45223) *(G-3345)*

Abel Metal Processing Inc 216 881-4156
2105 E 77th St Cleveland (44103) *(G-4683)*

Abeon Medical Corporation 440 262-6000
8006 Katherine Blvd Brecksville (44141) *(G-2032)*

Abhushan LLC 614 789-0632
2815 Festival Ln Dublin (43017) *(G-9035)*

ABI, Bedford *Also called Automatic Bacterial Injection (G-1402)*

ABI Orthtc/Prosthetic Labs Ltd (HQ) 330 758-1143
930 Trailwood Dr Youngstown (44512) *(G-21013)*

Abitec Corporation (HQ) 614 429-6464
501 W 1st Ave Columbus (43215) *(G-6678)*

Abj Equipfix 419 684-5236
202 Lucas St W Castalia (44824) *(G-2972)*

Abl Lighting Service, Akron *Also called Bob King Sign Company Inc (G-94)*

Abl Products Inc 216 281-2400
3726 Ridge Rd Cleveland (44144) *(G-4684)*

Abl Screen Printing 440 914-0093
30300 Solon Indus Pkwy Solon (44139) *(G-17247)*

Able Alloy Inc 216 251-6110
3500 W 140th St Cleveland (44111) *(G-4685)*

Able Fence of Columbus Inc 614 253-8587
2779 E 4th Ave Columbus (43219) *(G-6679)*

Able Grinding Co Inc 216 961-6555
10015 Walford Ave Cleveland (44102) *(G-4686)*

Able Industries Inc 614 252-1050
870 N 20th St Columbus (43219) *(G-6680)*

Able Manufacturing, Columbus *Also called Able Industries Inc (G-6680)*

Able One's Moving Company, Cleveland *Also called C P S Enterprises Inc (G-4957)*

Able Pallet Mfg & Repr 614 444-2115
1271 Harmon Ave Columbus (43223) *(G-6681)*

Able Printing Company 614 294-4547
1325 Holly Ave Columbus (43212) *(G-6682)*

Able Tool Corporation 513 733-8989
617 N Wayne Ave Cincinnati (45215) *(G-3346)*

ABM Drives Inc 513 576-1300
394 Wards Corner Rd # 110 Loveland (45140) *(G-12336)*

About and Dogs LLC 440 263-8989
7600 Olde Eight Rd Hudson (44236) *(G-11153)*

About Golf, Maumee *Also called Henry-Griffitts Limited (G-13266)*

About Time Software Inc 614 759-6295
12790 Pickerington Rd Pickerington (43147) *(G-16185)*

Abp Induction LLC 330 830-6252
607 1st St Sw Massillon (44646) *(G-13106)*

Abrasive Leaders & Innovators, Fairborn *Also called Ali Industries Inc (G-9613)*

Abrasive Source Inc 937 526-9753
211 W Main St Russia (45363) *(G-16761)*

Abrasive Technology Inc (PA) 740 548-4100
8400 Green Meadows Dr N Lewis Center (43035) *(G-11880)*

Abrasive Technology Lapidary 740 548-4855
8400 Green Meadows Dr N Lewis Center (43035) *(G-11881)*

Abraxus Salt Inc 440 743-7669
5595 Ridge Rd Cleveland (44129) *(G-4687)*

ABS Materials Inc 330 234-7999
1909 Old Mansfield Rd Wooster (44691) *(G-20730)*

Absolute Cnc Machining LLC 937 855-0406
2643 Dyton Grmantown Pike Germantown (45327) *(G-10368)*

Absolute Grinding Co Inc 440 974-4030
7007 Spinach Dr Mentor (44060) *(G-13504)*

Absolute Impressions Inc (PA) 614 840-0599
281 Enterprise Dr Lewis Center (43035) *(G-11882)*

Absolute Polymers Inc 888 850-0455
2789 E State St Unit 10s Salem (44460) *(G-16866)*

Absolute Smile LLC 937 293-9866
4469 Far Hills Ave Dayton (45429) *(G-8128)*

Absolutely Paper Established 216 932-4822
14000 Mont Ave Cleveland (44118) *(G-4688)*

Absorbcore LLC 440 614-0457
30275 Lorain Rd North Olmsted (44070) *(G-15324)*

Absorbent Products Company Inc 419 352-5353
2121 S Woodland Cir Bowling Green (43402) *(G-1965)*

Abstract Displays Inc 513 985-9700
6465 Creek Rd Blue Ash (45242) *(G-1732)*

AC Shiners Inc 513 738-1573
5747 Jenkins Rd Okeana (45053) *(G-15662)*

Academy Graphic Comm Inc 216 661-2550
1000 Brookpark Rd Cleveland (44109) *(G-4689)*

Acb Three Inc 614 873-4680
9341 Industrial Pkwy Plain City (43064) *(G-16317)*

ACC Automation Co Inc 330 928-3821
475 Wolf Ledges Pkwy Akron (44311) *(G-25)*

Accel Color, Avon *Also called Accel Corporation (G-980)*

Accel Color, Avon *Also called Accel Corporation (G-981)*

Accel Corporation...440 327-7418
 38620 Chester Rd Avon (44011) *(G-980)*

Accel Corporation (HQ)..440 934-7711
 38620 Chester Rd Avon (44011) *(G-981)*

Accel Group Inc (PA)..330 336-0317
 325 Quadral Dr Wadsworth (44281) *(G-19387)*

Accel Performance Group LLC (HQ).................................216 658-6413
 6100 Oak Tree Blvd # 200 Independence (44131) *(G-11245)*

Accent Drapery Co Inc...614 488-0741
 1180 Goodale Blvd Columbus (43212) *(G-6683)*

Accent Drapery Supply Co, Columbus *Also called Accent Drapery Co Inc (G-6683)*

Accent Manufacturing Inc (PA)....................................330 724-7704
 1026 Gardner Blvd Norton (44203) *(G-15500)*

Accent Showroom & Design Ctr, Norton *Also called Accent Manufacturing Inc (G-15500)*

Accent Signs and Graphics, Blue Ash *Also called All Signs Express Inc (G-1741)*

Accents By Renoir, Celina *Also called Renoir Visions LLC (G-3016)*

Accesories Tools, Painesville *Also called Alpha Omega Dev & Mch Co (G-15848)*

Access 2 Communications Inc......................................800 561-1110
 225 Technology Way Steubenville (43952) *(G-17686)*

Access Manufacturing Svcs LLC....................................330 659-9893
 4807 Hawkins Rd Richfield (44286) *(G-16612)*

Access To Independence Inc.......................................330 296-8111
 4960 S Prospect St Ravenna (44266) *(G-16512)*

Acclaimd Inc...614 219-9519
 1275 Kinnear Rd Columbus (43212) *(G-6684)*

Acco & Burley Clay Products Co, Roseville *Also called Valley Clay Mining Co (G-16734)*

Acco Brands Corporation..937 495-5723
 4751 Hempstead Station Dr Kettering (45429) *(G-11572)*

Acco Brands USA LLC..937 495-6323
 4751 Hempstead Station Dr Kettering (45429) *(G-11573)*

Accounting Software Solutions, Solon *Also called Sherwin Software Solutions (G-17379)*

Accounts Payable Department, Cleveland *Also called Cuyahoga Community College (G-5157)*

Accu Grind, Kent *Also called Reduction Engineering Inc (G-11514)*

Accu Jet Corp..937 252-9931
 612 Linden Ave Dayton (45403) *(G-8129)*

Accu Pak Mfg Inc...330 644-3015
 2422 Pickle Rd Akron (44312) *(G-26)*

Accu Tool Inc..937 667-5878
 9765 Julie Ct Tipp City (45371) *(G-18257)*

Accu-Feed Engineering..419 668-7990
 50 Newton St Norwalk (44857) *(G-15524)*

Accu-Grind & Mfg Co Inc..937 224-3303
 272 Leo St Dayton (45404) *(G-8130)*

Accu-Jet Div of First Tool, Dayton *Also called Accu Jet Corp (G-8129)*

Accu-Rite Tool & Die Co Corp.....................................330 497-9959
 7295 Sunset Strip Ave Nw Canton (44720) *(G-2586)*

Accu-Sign..216 544-2059
 3652 Elm Brook Dr Broadview Heights (44147) *(G-2102)*

Accu-Tech Manufacturing Co.......................................330 848-8100
 2691 Wingate Ave Akron (44314) *(G-27)*

Accu-Tech Mfg & Support..440 205-8882
 8875 East Ave Mentor (44060) *(G-13505)*

Accu-Tek Tool & Die Inc..330 726-1946
 1390 Allen Rd Bldg 1 Salem (44460) *(G-16867)*

Accubuilt Inc (PA)...419 224-3910
 2550 Cent Point Pkwy Lima (45804) *(G-11980)*

Accubuilt Inc..419 224-3910
 2550 Central Point Pkwy Lima (45804) *(G-11981)*

Accufab Inc..513 942-1929
 9059 Sutton Pl West Chester (45011) *(G-19796)*

Accufilm, Hebron *Also called Virgail Industries Inc (G-10894)*

Accuform Manufacturing Inc.......................................330 797-9291
 2750 Intertech Dr Youngstown (44509) *(G-21014)*

Accumulus Software...937 435-0861
 6708 Innsbruck Dr Dayton (45459) *(G-8131)*

Accuphase Metal Treating LLC.....................................937 610-5934
 2490 Arbor Blvd Moraine (45439) *(G-14463)*

Accuracy Products Inc..937 454-2240
 2551 Thunderhawk Ct Dayton (45414) *(G-8132)*

Accurate Automatic Mfg Ltd.......................................330 435-4575
 141 Factory St Creston (44217) *(G-7937)*

Accurate Electronics Inc...330 682-7015
 169 S Main St Orrville (44667) *(G-15727)*

Accurate Fab LLC...330 562-0566
 1760 Miller Pkwy Streetsboro (44241) *(G-17833)*

Accurate Fabricating, Painesville *Also called William Weber (G-15941)*

Accurate Gear Manufacturing Co...................................513 761-3220
 16 E 73rd St Cincinnati (45216) *(G-3347)*

Accurate Machining & Welding.....................................937 584-4518
 764 N State Route 729 Sabina (45169) *(G-16772)*

Accurate Mail, Findlay *Also called Kennedy Printing Co (G-9847)*

Accurate Manufacturing Company...................................614 878-6510
 1940 Lone Eagle St Columbus (43228) *(G-6685)*

Accurate Mechanical Inc..740 654-5898
 2257 W Fair Ave Lancaster (43130) *(G-11683)*

Accurate Metal Machining Inc.....................................440 350-8225
 882 Callendar Blvd Painesville (44077) *(G-15847)*

Accurate Plasma Cutting Inc......................................440 943-1655
 1271 E 289th St Wickliffe (44092) *(G-20350)*

Accurate Plastics LLC..330 346-0048
 4430 Crystal Pkwy Kent (44240) *(G-11422)*

Accurate Products Company..740 498-7202
 98 Elizabeth St Newcomerstown (43832) *(G-15108)*

Accurate Tech Inc..440 951-9153
 7230 Industrial Park Blvd Mentor (44060) *(G-13506)*

Accurate Tool Co Inc...330 332-9448
 1065 Salem Pkwy Salem (44460) *(G-16868)*

Accuscan Instruments Inc...614 878-6644
 5098 Trabue Rd Columbus (43228) *(G-6686)*

Accushred LLC..419 244-7473
 1114 W Central Ave Toledo (43610) *(G-18319)*

Accutech Films Inc (HQ)..419 678-8700
 620 Hardin St Coldwater (45828) *(G-6549)*

Accutech Plastic Molding Inc.....................................937 233-0017
 5015 Kitridge Rd Dayton (45424) *(G-8133)*

Accutech Sign Shop...513 385-3595
 9316 Colerain Ave Cincinnati (45251) *(G-3348)*

Ace, Cleveland *Also called Brothers Equipment Inc (G-4937)*

Ace American Wire Die Co...330 425-7269
 9041 Dutton Dr Twinsburg (44087) *(G-18890)*

Ace Assembly Packaging Inc.......................................330 866-9117
 133 N Mill St Waynesburg (44688) *(G-19722)*

Ace Boiler & Welding Co Inc......................................330 745-4443
 2891 Newpark Dr Barberton (44203) *(G-1092)*

Ace Equipment Company, Cleveland *Also called Armature Coil Equipment Inc (G-4831)*

Ace Gasket Manufacturing Co......................................513 271-6321
 7873 Main St Cincinnati (45244) *(G-3349)*

Ace Grinding Co..440 951-6760
 37518 N Industrial Pkwy Willoughby (44094) *(G-20424)*

Ace Hydraulics, Bedford *Also called K C N Technologies LLC (G-1434)*

Ace Lumber Company...330 744-3167
 1039 Poland Ave Youngstown (44502) *(G-21015)*

Ace Manufacturing Company..513 541-2490
 5452 Spellmire Dr West Chester (45246) *(G-19976)*

Ace Metal Stamping Company, Cleveland *Also called Continental Business Entps Inc (G-5123)*

Ace Plastics Co..330 928-7720
 122 E Tuscarawas Ave Stow (44224) *(G-17728)*

Ace Precision Industries Inc.....................................330 633-8523
 925 Moe Dr Akron (44310) *(G-28)*

Ace Products Co of Toledo Inc....................................419 472-1247
 4902 Douglas Rd Toledo (43613) *(G-18320)*

Ace Prosthetics Inc..614 291-8325
 4971 Arlington Centre Blvd Columbus (43220) *(G-6687)*

ACE Ready Mix Company Inc..330 745-8125
 3826 Summit Rd Norton (44203) *(G-15501)*

Ace Ready Mix Concrete Co Inc....................................330 745-8125
 3826 Summit Rd Norton (44203) *(G-15502)*

Ace Rubber Products Division, Akron *Also called Garro Tread Corporation (G-198)*

Ace Rubber Stamp & Off Sup Co....................................216 771-8483
 3110 Payne Ave Cleveland (44114) *(G-4690)*

Ace Sanitary, West Chester *Also called Ace Manufacturing Company (G-19976)*

Ace Transfer Company...937 398-1103
 1017 Hometown St Springfield (45504) *(G-17514)*

Ace Truck Equipment Co...740 453-0551
 1130 Newark Rd Zanesville (43701) *(G-21264)*

Ace-Tex Enterprises Inc..513 829-8899
 4981 Factory Dr Hamilton (45014) *(G-10661)*

Acela Biomedical...937 544-8618
 3455 Cross Rd Winchester (45697) *(G-20689)*

Acense LLC...330 242-0046
 8941 Dutton Dr Twinsburg (44087) *(G-18891)*

Acer Contracting LLC...702 236-5917
 3840 N High St Ste B Columbus (43214) *(G-6688)*

Ach LLC..419 621-5748
 3020 Tiffin Ave Sandusky (44870) *(G-16943)*

Ach Sandusky Plastics, Sandusky *Also called Ach LLC (G-16943)*

Achill Island Composites LLC.....................................440 838-1746
 6981 Chapel Hill Dr Brecksville (44141) *(G-2033)*

Achilles Aerospace Pdts Inc......................................330 425-8444
 2100 Enterprise Pkwy Twinsburg (44087) *(G-18892)*

Achilles Running Shop LLC (PA)...................................440 942-2059
 7439 Mentor Ave Mentor (44060) *(G-13507)*

Aci Industries Ltd (PA)..740 368-4160
 970 Pittsburgh Dr Delaware (43015) *(G-8815)*

Aci Industries Converting Ltd (HQ)...............................740 368-4160
 970 Pittsburgh Dr Delaware (43015) *(G-8816)*

Aci Services Inc (PA)..740 435-0240
 125 Steubenville Ave Cambridge (43725) *(G-2442)*

Aclara Technologies LLC..440 528-7200
 30400 Solon Rd Solon (44139) *(G-17248)*

Acm, Hinckley *Also called American Cube Mold Inc (G-11022)*

Acm Ohio, Waverly *Also called News Watchman & Paper (G-19713)*

Acm Ohio LLC...740 286-2187
 1 Acy Ave Ste D Jackson (45640) *(G-11308)*

Acme, Stow *Also called Fred W Albrecht Grocery Co (G-17757)*

A
L
P
H
A
B
E
T
I
C

Acme Boiler Co Inc 216 961-2471
3718 Ridge Rd Cleveland (44144) *(G-4691)*
Acme Company 330 758-2313
9495 Harvard Blvd Poland (44514) *(G-16381)*
Acme Duplicating Co 216 241-1241
800 Saint Clair Ave Ne Cleveland (44114) *(G-4692)*
Acme Fence & Lumber, Akron *Also called Randy Lewis Inc (G-365)*
Acme Industrial Group Inc 330 821-3900
540 N Freedom Ave Alliance (44601) *(G-488)*
Acme Label & Tag Inc 440 729-1040
9578 Mulberry Rd Chesterland (44026) *(G-3194)*
Acme Lead Burning Company, Cleveland *Also called Acme Boiler Co Inc (G-4691)*
Acme Lifting Products Inc 440 838-4430
6892 W Snowville Rd Ste 2 Cleveland (44141) *(G-4693)*
Acme Machine Technology LLC 419 594-3349
115 Main St Oakwood (45873) *(G-15613)*
Acme Paper Tube, Cleveland *Also called Acme Spirally Wound Paper Pdts (G-4694)*
Acme Printing, Cleveland *Also called Acme Duplicating Co (G-4692)*
Acme Printing Co Inc 419 626-4426
2143 Sherman St Sandusky (44870) *(G-16944)*
Acme Spirally Wound Paper Pdts 216 267-2950
4810 W 139th St Cleveland (44135) *(G-4694)*
Acme Steak & Seafood Inc 330 270-8000
31 Bissell Ave Youngstown (44505) *(G-21016)*
Acme Turret Lathe, Cincinnati *Also called Boye & Emmes Machine Tool Co (G-3464)*
Aco Polymer Products Inc (HQ) 440 285-7000
9470 Pinecone Dr Mentor (44060) *(G-13508)*
Acon Inc 513 276-2111
11408 Dogleg Rd Tipp City (45371) *(G-18258)*
Acor Orthopaedic Inc 216 662-4500
18530 S Miles Rd Cleveland (44128) *(G-4695)*
Acor Orthopaedic Inc 440 532-0117
18700 S Miles Rd Cleveland (44128) *(G-4696)*
Acorn Products Inc 614 222-4400
390 W Nationwide Blvd Columbus (43215) *(G-6689)*
Acorn Technology Corporation 216 663-1244
23103 Miles Rd Cleveland (44128) *(G-4697)*
Acouflow Therapeutics LLC 513 558-0073
6914 Copperglow Ct Cincinnati (45244) *(G-3350)*
Acoustical Publications Inc 440 835-0101
27101 E Oviatt Rd Bay Village (44140) *(G-1241)*
Acreo Inc 513 734-3327
3209 Marshall Dr Amelia (45102) *(G-565)*
Acro Tool & Die Company 330 773-5173
325 Morgan Ave Akron (44311) *(G-29)*
Acrodyne Mfg Co 614 443-5517
41 Kingston Ave Columbus (43207) *(G-6690)*
Acromet Metal Fabricators, Cleveland *Also called G T Metal Fabricators Inc (G-5388)*
Acrylic Arts 440 537-0300
3698 G P Easterly Rd West Farmington (44491) *(G-20073)*
Acrylicon Inc 614 263-2086
1976 Britains Ln Columbus (43224) *(G-6691)*
ACS, Cincinnati *Also called Alligator Cmpt Systems Corp (G-3380)*
ACS, Mentor *Also called Al Chem Specialties LLC (G-13515)*
ACS Commercial Graphics, Columbus *Also called American Colorscans Inc (G-6732)*
Act, Dublin *Also called Automation and Ctrl Tech Inc (G-9050)*
Actega North America Inc 513 489-5691
11264 Grooms Rd Ste A Blue Ash (45242) *(G-1733)*
Action Air & Hydraulics Inc 937 372-8614
1087 Bellbrook Ave Xenia (45385) *(G-20933)*
Action Blacktop Sealcoating & 937 667-4769
340 E Shoop Rd Bldg B Tipp City (45371) *(G-18259)*
Action Coupling & Eqp Inc 330 279-4242
8248 County Road 245 Holmesville (44633) *(G-11099)*
Action Door, Mentor On The Lake *Also called Mentor Inc (G-13774)*
Action Enterprise 740 522-1678
416 W Main St Newark (43055) *(G-14978)*
Action Group Inc 614 868-8868
411 Reynoldsburg New Blacklick (43004) *(G-1686)*
Action Industries Ltd (PA) 216 252-7800
12625 Berea Rd Cleveland (44111) *(G-4698)*
Action Machine & Manufacturing 513 899-3889
6788 E Us Highway 22 & 3 Morrow (45152) *(G-14542)*
Action Mechanical Repair Inc 513 353-1046
7760 Harrison Ave Cincinnati (45247) *(G-3351)*
Action Precision Products Inc 419 737-2348
100 E North Ave Pioneer (43554) *(G-16231)*
Action Printing & Photography 419 332-9615
626 Grant St Fremont (43420) *(G-10123)*
Action Printing Inc 330 963-7772
2307 E Aurora Rd Ste 8 Twinsburg (44087) *(G-18893)*
Action Prosthetics LLC 937 548-9100
1498 N Broadway St Ste 3 Greenville (45331) *(G-10487)*
Action Rubber Co Inc 937 866-5975
601 Fame Rd Dayton (45449) *(G-8134)*
Action Sign Inc 330 966-0390
3140 Stage St Greentown (44630) *(G-10484)*
Action Signs, Newark *Also called Action Enterprise (G-14978)*

Action Sports Apparel Inc 330 848-9300
3070 Wadsworth Rd Norton (44203) *(G-15503)*
Action Super Abrasive Pdts Inc 330 673-7333
945 Greenbriar Pkwy Kent (44240) *(G-11423)*
Actipro Software LLC 888 922-8477
8576 Somerset Dr Broadview Heights (44147) *(G-2103)*
Active Daily Living LLC 513 607-6769
3308 Bishop St Cincinnati (45220) *(G-3352)*
Active Roads LLC 937 242-6555
7641 Kirkwood Dr West Chester (45069) *(G-19797)*
Activewares 419 994-5932
431 E Haskell St Loudonville (44842) *(G-12295)*
Activities Press Inc 440 953-1200
7181 Industrial Park Blvd Mentor (44060) *(G-13509)*
Actual Brewing 614 636-3825
655 N James Rd Columbus (43219) *(G-6692)*
Actual Industries LLC 614 379-2739
655 N James Rd Columbus (43219) *(G-6693)*
Actuation Kongsberg Systems II 440 639-8778
301 Olive St Grand River (44045) *(G-10447)*
Acu-Serve Corp 330 923-5258
2020 Front St Ste 205 Cuyahoga Falls (44221) *(G-7961)*
Acuity Brands Lighting Inc 740 349-4343
214 Oakwood Ave Newark (43055) *(G-14979)*
Acuity Brands Lighting Inc 740 349-4409
465 Mckinley Ave Newark (43055) *(G-14980)*
ACUITY BRANDS LIGHTING, INC., Newark *Also called Acuity Brands Lighting Inc (G-14979)*
Acuren Inspection Inc 419 698-5040
205 N Lallendorf Rd Ste B Oregon (43616) *(G-15700)*
Acuren Inspection Inc 937 228-9729
705 Albany St Dayton (45417) *(G-8135)*
Acuren Inspection Inc 330 733-8160
535 Kennedy Rd Ste D Akron (44305) *(G-30)*
Acuren Inspection Inc 513 671-7073
502 W Crescentville Rd Cincinnati (45246) *(G-3353)*
Acutemp, Moraine *Also called Doubleday Acquisitions LLC (G-14480)*
Acutemp Thermal Systems 937 312-0114
2900 Dryden Rd Moraine (45439) *(G-14464)*
Ad Piston Ring Company LLC 216 781-5200
3145 Superior Ave E Cleveland (44114) *(G-4699)*
Ad Source Inc 330 468-2934
1816 Main St Peninsula (44264) *(G-16033)*
Ad-Pro Signs I LLC 513 922-5046
11336 Dallas Blvd Cincinnati (45231) *(G-3354)*
Ada Solutions Inc 440 576-0423
901 Ftville Richmond Rd E Jefferson (44047) *(G-11355)*
Ada Technologies Inc 419 634-7000
805 E North Ave Ada (45810) *(G-3)*
Adairs Pavers 937 454-9302
50 Lakin Ct Vandalia (45377) *(G-19277)*
Adam Printing, West Chester *Also called Cornerstone Industries Lcc (G-19845)*
Adams Automatic Inc 440 235-4416
26070 N Depot St Olmsted Falls (44138) *(G-15672)*
Adams Brothers Inc 740 819-0323
1501 Woodlawn Ave Zanesville (43701) *(G-21265)*
Adams County Lumber, Manchester *Also called Vances Department Store (G-12553)*
Adams Custom Woodworking 513 761-1395
324 W Wyoming Ave Cincinnati (45215) *(G-3355)*
Adams Fabricating Inc 330 866-2986
10125 Sandyville Ave East Sparta (44626) *(G-9253)*
Adams Manufacturing Company (PA) 216 662-1600
9790 Midwest Ave Cleveland (44125) *(G-4700)*
Adams Publishing Group LLC (HQ) 740 592-6612
9300 Johnson Hollow Rd Athens (45701) *(G-854)*
Adams Signs, Massillon *Also called Identitek Systems Inc (G-13155)*
Adams Street Publishing Co 419 244-9859
1120 Adams St Toledo (43604) *(G-18321)*
Adapt-A-Pak Inc 937 845-0386
9215 State Route 201 Tipp City (45371) *(G-18260)*
Adaptall America Inc 330 425-4114
9047 Dutton Dr Twinsburg (44087) *(G-18894)*
Adaptive Data Inc 937 436-2343
93 W Franklin St Centerville (45459) *(G-3032)*
Adare Pharmaceuticals Inc (HQ) 937 898-9669
845 Center Dr Vandalia (45377) *(G-19278)*
ADB Safegate Americas LLC 614 861-1304
977 Gahanna Pkwy Columbus (43230) *(G-6694)*
Adchem Adhesives Inc 440 526-1976
4111 E Royalton Rd Cleveland (44147) *(G-4701)*
Adco Products Inc 937 339-6267
65 W Kssler Cwlesville Rd Tipp City (45371) *(G-18261)*
Adcraft Decals Inc 216 524-2934
7708 Commerce Park Oval Cleveland (44131) *(G-4702)*
Adcura Mfg, Springboro *Also called Rct Industries Inc (G-17505)*
Add-A-Trap LLC 330 750-0417
488 Como St Struthers (44471) *(G-17988)*
Added Edge Assembly Inc 216 464-4305
26800 Fargo Ave Ste A Cleveland (44146) *(G-4703)*
Added Touch Decorating Gallery 419 747-3146
1162 Cobblefield Dr Ontario (44903) *(G-15684)*

Addis Glass Fabricating Inc 513 860-3340
9418 Sutton Pl West Chester (45011) *(G-19798)*

Addisonmckee Inc (PA) 513 228-7000
1637 Kingsview Dr Lebanon (45036) *(G-11774)*

Additive Metal Alloys Ltd 800 687-6110
1421 Holloway Rd Ste B Holland (43528) *(G-11043)*

Additive Technology Inc 419 968-2777
404 W Railroad St Middle Point (45863) *(G-13896)*

Adelman's Truck Sales, Canton Also called Adelmans Truck Parts Corp *(G-2587)*

Adelmans Truck Parts Corp (PA) 330 456-0206
2000 Waynesburg Dr Se Canton (44707) *(G-2587)*

Adelmans Truck Parts Corp 216 362-0500
2000 Waynesburg Dr Se Canton (44707) *(G-2588)*

Adelphi Enterprises 937 372-3791
1340 Gultice Rd Xenia (45385) *(G-20934)*

Adelphia, Wellington Also called Forest City Technologies Inc *(G-19746)*

Adena Tool Corporation 937 890-8428
4201 Little York Rd Dayton (45414) *(G-8136)*

Adept Manufacturing Corp 937 222-7110
511 N Findlay St Dayton (45404) *(G-8137)*

Adex International, Cincinnati Also called Affinity Disp Expositions Inc *(G-3363)*

Adex International, Cincinnati Also called Affinity Disp Expositions Inc *(G-3364)*

Adexis, Columbus Also called Fusionstorm *(G-6647)*

Adgo Incorporated 513 752-6880
3988 Mcmann Rd Cincinnati (45245) *(G-3292)*

Adhesves Sealants Coatings Div, Blue Ash Also called HB Fuller Company *(G-1806)*

ADI, Sheffield Village Also called Advanced Design Industries Inc *(G-17120)*

ADI Machining Inc 440 277-4141
4686 French Creek Rd Sheffield Village (44054) *(G-17119)*

Adidas North America Inc 513 360-2979
937 Premium Outlets Dr Monroe (45050) *(G-14389)*

Adient US LLC 937 383-5200
1147 N Washington St Greenfield (45123) *(G-10472)*

Adisco Inc 937 296-5070
2000 Composite Dr Kettering (45420) *(G-11574)*

Adjustable Kicker LLC 740 362-9170
45 River St Delaware (43015) *(G-8817)*

Adkel Corp (PA) 740 452-6973
2920 Newark Rd Zanesville (43701) *(G-21266)*

Adkins Marlena 216 704-2751
4729 W 157th St Cleveland (44135) *(G-4704)*

Adkins & Co Inc 216 521-6323
14541 Madison Ave Cleveland (44107) *(G-4705)*

Adkins & Sons, Oak Hill Also called Denver Adkins *(G-15595)*

Adkins Printing, Cleveland Also called Adkins & Co Inc *(G-4705)*

Adler & Company Inc 513 248-1500
6801 Shawnee Run Rd Cincinnati (45243) *(G-3356)*

Adler Team Sports, Euclid Also called R & A Sports Inc *(G-9603)*

ADM, Fostoria Also called Archer-Daniels-Midland Company *(G-9966)*

ADM Animal Nutrition, Sugarcreek Also called Archer-Daniels-Midland Company *(G-18015)*

ADM Grain Company, Toledo Also called Archer-Daniels-Midland Company *(G-18353)*

Adma Products, Hudson Also called Advanced Materials Products *(G-11154)*

Admail.net, Aurora Also called List Media Inc *(G-934)*

Admark Printing Inc 937 833-5111
310 Sycamore St Brookville (45309) *(G-2173)*

Admaster Supply, New Paris Also called Ruthie Ann Inc *(G-14881)*

Admiral Products Company Inc 216 671-0600
4101 W 150th St Cleveland (44135) *(G-4706)*

Admiral Products Company Inc 216 671-0600
4101 W 150th St Cleveland (44135) *(G-4706)*

Adna Inc 614 397-4974
6866 Mcdougal Ct Dublin (43017) *(G-9036)*

Adohio, Columbus Also called Ohio Newspaper Services Inc *(G-7424)*

Adonai Technologies LLC 513 560-9020
1223 Hook Dr Middletown (45042) *(G-14012)*

Adr Fuel Inc 419 872-2178
353 Elm St Perrysburg (43551) *(G-16061)*

Adria Scientific GL Works Co 440 474-6691
2683 State Route 534 S Geneva (44041) *(G-10339)*

Adrians Place 513 651-2154
1801 Race St Ste 10 Cincinnati (45202) *(G-3357)*

Adroit Thinking Inc 419 542-9363
10860 State Route 2 Hicksville (43526) *(G-10898)*

ADS, London Also called Advanced Drainage Systems Inc *(G-12199)*

ADS Machinery Corp 330 399-3601
1201 Vine Ave Ne Ste 1 Warren (44483) *(G-19515)*

ADS Ventures Inc (HQ) 614 658-0050
4640 Trueman Blvd Hilliard (43026) *(G-10922)*

ADS Worldwide Inc (PA) 614 658-0050
4640 Trueman Blvd Hilliard (43026) *(G-10923)*

Adsetting Service, Cleveland Also called Royal Acme Corporation *(G-6136)*

Adtec, Middle Point Also called Additive Technology Inc *(G-13896)*

Adult Daily Living LLC 330 612-7941
3603 Highspire Dr Barberton (44203) *(G-1093)*

Advanatage Print Solut 614 519-2392
79 Acton Rd Columbus (43214) *(G-6695)*

Advance Apex Inc (PA) 614 539-3000
2375 Harrisburg Pike Grove City (43123) *(G-10538)*

Advance Bronze Inc (PA) 330 948-1231
139 Ohio St Lodi (44254) *(G-12155)*

Advance Cnc Machining, Grove City Also called Advance Apex Inc *(G-10538)*

Advance Graphics, Columbus Also called Hoster Graphics Company Inc *(G-7168)*

Advance Industrial Mfg Inc 614 871-3333
1996 Longwood Ave Grove City (43123) *(G-10539)*

Advance Industries Group LLC 216 741-1800
3636 W 58th St Cleveland (44102) *(G-4707)*

Advance Lens Labs, Berea Also called Cleveland Hoya Corp *(G-1606)*

Advance Manufacturing Corp 216 333-1684
6800 Madison Ave Cleveland (44102) *(G-4708)*

Advance Metal Products Inc 216 741-1800
3636 W 58th St Cleveland (44102) *(G-4709)*

Advance Novelty Incorporated 419 424-0363
101 Stanford Pkwy Findlay (45840) *(G-9787)*

Advance Paint Technology Inc 216 676-8770
4650 W 160th St Ste 600 Cleveland (44135) *(G-4710)*

Advance Pierre Foods, Blue Ash Also called Advancepierre Foods Inc *(G-1734)*

Advance Printing Company, Cincinnati Also called J & P Investments Inc *(G-3933)*

Advance Products 419 882-8117
6041 Angleview Dr Sylvania (43560) *(G-18097)*

Advance Reporter (PA) 419 485-4851
115 Broad St Montpelier (43543) *(G-14438)*

Advance Sign Group LLC 614 429-2111
5150 Walcutt Ct Columbus (43228) *(G-6696)*

Advance Weight System Inc 440 926-3691
409 Main St Grafton (44044) *(G-10418)*

Advance Wire Forming Inc 216 432-3250
3636 W 58th St Cleveland (44102) *(G-4711)*

Advanced Arm Dynamics 440 617-6601
30701 Clemens Rd Ste C Westlake (44145) *(G-20245)*

Advanced Bar Technology, Canton Also called Gerdau Macsteel Atmosphere Ann *(G-2713)*

Advanced Biological Mktg Inc 419 232-2461
375 Bonnewitz Ave Van Wert (45891) *(G-19241)*

Advanced Chem Solutions Inc 216 692-3005
150 Allen Ave Orrville (44667) *(G-15728)*

Advanced Chem Solutions Inc (PA) 330 283-5157
1114 N Court St 196 Medina (44256) *(G-13363)*

Advanced Cleaning Tech LLC 614 504-5433
7533 Merchant Rd Plain City (43064) *(G-16318)*

Advanced Coatings Intl 330 794-6361
2990 Gilchrist Rd # 1100 Akron (44305) *(G-31)*

Advanced Composites Inc (HQ) 937 575-9800
1062 S 4th Ave Sidney (45365) *(G-17165)*

Advanced Controls Inc 440 354-5413
34300 Lakeland Blvd Frnt Eastlake (44095) *(G-9257)*

Advanced Cryogenic Entps LLC 330 922-0750
1034 Home Ave Akron (44310) *(G-32)*

Advanced Custom Sound 330 372-9900
1894 Elm Rd Ne Warren (44483) *(G-19516)*

Advanced Cylinder Repair Inc 419 289-0538
942 State Route 302 Ashland (44805) *(G-701)*

Advanced Design Industries, Sheffield Village Also called ADI Machining Inc *(G-17119)*

Advanced Design Industries Inc 440 277-4141
4686 French Creek Rd Sheffield Village (44054) *(G-17120)*

Advanced Display Systems, Kent Also called Mike B Crawford *(G-11492)*

Advanced Drainage of Ohio Inc 614 658-0050
4640 Trueman Blvd Hilliard (43026) *(G-10924)*

Advanced Drainage Systems Inc 740 852-9554
288 Lafayette St London (43140) *(G-12198)*

Advanced Drainage Systems Inc 513 863-1384
2650 Hamilton Eaton Rd Hamilton (45011) *(G-10662)*

Advanced Drainage Systems Inc 419 384-3140
501 Basinger Rd Pandora (45877) *(G-15947)*

Advanced Drainage Systems Inc 330 264-4949
3113 W Old Lincoln Way Wooster (44691) *(G-20731)*

Advanced Drainage Systems Inc (PA) 614 658-0050
4640 Trueman Blvd Hilliard (43026) *(G-10925)*

Advanced Drainage Systems Inc 419 599-9565
1075 Independence Dr Napoleon (43545) *(G-14669)*

Advanced Drainage Systems Inc 740 852-2980
400 E High St London (43140) *(G-12199)*

Advanced Drainage Systems Inc 419 424-8324
401 Olive St Findlay (45840) *(G-9788)*

Advanced Dstrbted Gnration LLC 419 530-3792
1331 Conant St Ste 107 Maumee (43537) *(G-13219)*

Advanced Elastomer Systems LP 330 336-7641
1000 Seville Rd Wadsworth (44281) *(G-19389)*

Advanced Energy Tech LLC 216 676-2259
11709 Madison Ave Lakewood (44107) *(G-11654)*

Advanced Engine Tech LLC 937 439-0224
3192 Bugle Bluff Dr Bellbrook (45305) *(G-1503)*

Advanced Engrg & Mfg Co Inc 330 686-9911
5026 Hudson Dr Ste D Stow (44224) *(G-17729)*

Advanced Engrg Solutions Inc 937 743-6900
250 Advanced Dr Springboro (45066) *(G-17470)*

Advanced Equipment Systems LLC 216 289-6505
22800 Lakeland Blvd Euclid (44132) *(G-9564)*

Advanced F.M.e Products, Mentor *Also called Advanced Pneumatics Inc (G-13510)*

Advanced Fiber Technology Inc 513 860-4446
100 Crossroads Blvd Bucyrus (44820) *(G-2331)*

Advanced Fitness Inc 513 563-1000
11875 Reading Rd Cincinnati (45241) *(G-3358)*

Advanced Flame Hardening Inc 216 431-0370
1209 Marquette St Cleveland (44114) *(G-4712)*

Advanced Fluids Inc 216 692-3050
18127 Roseland Rd Cleveland (44112) *(G-4713)*

Advanced Fuel Systems Inc 614 252-8422
841 Alton Ave Columbus (43219) *(G-6697)*

Advanced Graphic Solutions, Cleveland *Also called A Graphic Solution (G-4672)*

Advanced Graphics of Dayton 937 228-2221
207 Air St Dayton (45404) *(G-8138)*

Advanced Ground Systems 513 402-7226
441 Breaden Dr Monroe (45050) *(G-14390)*

Advanced Holding Designs Inc 330 928-4456
3332 Cavalier Trl Cuyahoga Falls (44224) *(G-7962)*

Advanced Indus Machining Inc (PA) 614 596-4183
3982 Powell Rd 218 Powell (43065) *(G-16461)*

Advanced Industrial Measuremnt 937 320-4930
2580 Kohnle Dr Miamisburg (45342) *(G-13780)*

Advanced Innovation & Mfg Inc 330 308-6360
326 Pearl Ave Ne New Philadelphia (44663) *(G-14882)*

Advanced Innovative Mfg Inc 440 759-2034
116 Lena Dr Aurora (44202) *(G-905)*

Advanced Intr Solutions Inc 937 550-0065
250 Advanced Dr Springboro (45066) *(G-17471)*

Advanced Kiffer Systems Inc 216 267-8181
4905 Rocky River Dr Cleveland (44135) *(G-4714)*

Advanced Lighting Tech Inc (HQ) 440 519-0500
7905 Cochran Rd Ste 300 Solon (44139) *(G-17249)*

Advanced Litho Systems 419 865-2652
4429 Weckerly Rd Monclova (43542) *(G-14388)*

Advanced Livescan Technologies 440 759-7028
3575 W 132nd St Cleveland (44111) *(G-4715)*

Advanced Marking Systems Inc (PA) 330 792-8239
6000 Mahoning Ave Ste 50 Youngstown (44515) *(G-21017)*

Advanced Materials Products 330 650-4000
1890 Georgetown Rd Hudson (44236) *(G-11154)*

Advanced Mdia Publications Inc 440 260-9910
6410 Eastland Rd Ste F Cleveland (44142) *(G-4716)*

Advanced Med Interfaces LLC 937 361-8385
950 Mulford Rd Lebanon (45036) *(G-11775)*

Advanced Medical Solutions Inc 937 291-0069
7026 Corp Way Ste 116 Centerville (45459) *(G-3033)*

Advanced Metals Group LLC 937 492-4134
815 Oak Ave Sidney (45365) *(G-17166)*

Advanced Microbeam Inc 330 394-1255
4217 King Graves Rd Ste C Vienna (44473) *(G-19362)*

Advanced OEM Solutions LLC 513 846-5755
6655 Woodsedge Dr Liberty Township (45044) *(G-11957)*

Advanced Onsight Welding Svcs 513 924-1400
5220 Globe Ave Cincinnati (45212) *(G-3359)*

Advanced Paper Tube Inc 216 281-5691
1951 W 90th St Cleveland (44102) *(G-4717)*

Advanced Plastic Systems Inc 614 759-6550
990 Gahanna Pkwy Gahanna (43230) *(G-10202)*

Advanced Plastics Inc 330 336-6681
307 Water St Wadsworth (44281) *(G-19390)*

Advanced Pneumatics Inc 440 953-0700
9413 Hamilton Dr Mentor (44060) *(G-13510)*

Advanced Poly-Packaging Inc 330 785-4000
1360 Exeter Rd Akron (44306) *(G-33)*

Advanced Polymer Coatings Ltd 440 937-6218
951 Jaycox Rd Avon (44011) *(G-982)*

Advanced Prgrm Resources Inc (PA) 614 761-9994
2715 Tuller Pkwy Dublin (43017) *(G-9037)*

Advanced Printing, Youngstown *Also called Advanced Marking Systems Inc (G-21017)*

Advanced Propeller Systems 937 409-1038
1297 Windsor Dr Dayton (45434) *(G-8094)*

Advanced Quartz Fabrication 440 350-4567
11920 Quail Woods Dr Chardon (44024) *(G-3138)*

Advanced Recycling Systems,, Lowellville *Also called ARS Recycling Systems LLC (G-12405)*

Advanced Rv LLC 440 283-0405
4590 Hamann Pkwy Willoughby (44094) *(G-20425)*

Advanced Specialty Products 419 882-6528
428 Clough St Bowling Green (43402) *(G-1966)*

Advanced Tech Utilization Co 440 238-3770
12005 Prospect Rd Unit 1 Strongsville (44149) *(G-17884)*

Advanced Technical Pdts Sup Co 513 851-6858
508 Northland Blvd Cincinnati (45240) *(G-3360)*

Advanced Technology Corp 440 293-4064
101 Parker Dr Andover (44003) *(G-611)*

Advanced Telemetrics Intl 937 862-6948
2361 Darnell Dr Spring Valley (45370) *(G-17466)*

Advanced Time Systems 440 466-2689
4591 Cork Cold Springs Rd Geneva (44041) *(G-10340)*

Advanced Translation/Cnsltng 440 716-0820
3751 Willow Run Westlake (44145) *(G-20246)*

Advanced Vehicles, Cleveland *Also called Kay Capital Company (G-5638)*

Advanced Web Corporation 740 662-6323
10999 E Copeland Rd Stewart (45778) *(G-17721)*

Advanced Welding Co 937 746-6800
901 N Main St Franklin (45005) *(G-10005)*

Advanced Wire and Cable, Spring Valley *Also called Max Mighty Inc (G-17468)*

Advancepierre Foods Inc (HQ) 513 874-8741
9987 Carver Rd Ste 500 Blue Ash (45242) *(G-1734)*

Advancepierre Foods Inc 513 874-8741
9990 Prnceton Glendale Rd West Chester (45246) *(G-19977)*

Advancing Eco-Agriculture LLC 800 495-6603
4551 Parks West Rd Middlefield (44062) *(G-13912)*

Advancpperre Foods Holdings Inc (PA) 800 969-2747
9987 Carver Rd Blue Ash (45242) *(G-1735)*

Advanstar Art Group, North Olmsted *Also called Advanstar Communications Inc (G-15325)*

Advanstar Communications Inc 440 243-8100
24950 Country Club Blvd # 200 North Olmsted (44070) *(G-15325)*

Advant-E Corporation (PA) 937 429-4288
2434 Esquire Dr Beavercreek (45431) *(G-1316)*

Advantage Circuits Ltd 330 256-7768
3512 Industry Rd Rootstown (44272) *(G-16719)*

Advantage Machine Shop 330 337-8377
777 S Ellsworth Ave Salem (44460) *(G-16869)*

Advantage Mold Inc 419 691-5676
525 N Wheeling St Toledo (43605) *(G-18322)*

Advantage Powder Coating Inc (PA) 419 782-2363
2090 E 2nd St Ste 102 Defiance (43512) *(G-8775)*

Advantage Printing Inc 614 272-8259
1369 Royston Dr Columbus (43204) *(G-6698)*

Advantage Products Corporation (PA) 513 489-2283
11559 Grooms Rd Blue Ash (45242) *(G-1736)*

Advantage Tent Fittings Inc 740 773-3015
11661 Pleasant Valley Rd Chillicothe (45601) *(G-3226)*

Advantage Tool Supply Inc 330 896-8869
3666 Avanti Ln Uniontown (44685) *(G-19074)*

Advantage Truck Trailers, Columbus *Also called Kenan Advantage Group Inc (G-7254)*

Advent Designs, Logan *Also called Signs Unlimited (G-12193)*

Advent Drilling Inc 330 497-2533
366 Rose Lane St Sw Canton (44720) *(G-2589)*

Adventurous Child Inc 513 531-7700
4781 Duck Creek Rd Cincinnati (45227) *(G-3361)*

Advertising Ideas of Ohio Inc 330 745-6555
833 Wooster Rd N Barberton (44203) *(G-1094)*

Advertising Tribune, Tiffin *Also called Ogden Newspapers of Ohio Inc (G-18236)*

Advetech Inc (PA) 330 533-2227
445 W Main St Canfield (44406) *(G-2543)*

Advetech Inc 330 533-2227
451 W Main St Canfield (44406) *(G-2544)*

Advics Manufacturing Ohio Inc 513 934-0023
1650 Kingsview Dr Lebanon (45036) *(G-11776)*

Adwest Technologies Inc 513 458-2600
4625 Red Bank Rd Ste 200 Cincinnati (45227) *(G-3362)*

Adyl Inc 330 797-8700
6000 Mahoning Ave Ste 230 Austintown (44515) *(G-968)*

AEC Brews LLC DBA Old Frhuse B 513 536-9071
237 W Main St Williamsburg (45176) *(G-20406)*

AEC Magnetics, West Chester *Also called Automatic Equipment Corp (G-19983)*

Aecom Energy & Cnstr Inc 419 698-6277
4001 Cedar Point Rd Oregon (43616) *(G-15701)*

AEG Photoconductor Corporation 513 874-4939
6929 Tylersville Rd # 18 West Chester (45069) *(G-19799)*

Aeiou Diagnostics, Columbus *Also called Aeiou Scientific LLC (G-6699)*

Aeiou Scientific LLC 614 325-2103
311 Kendall Pl Columbus (43205) *(G-6699)*

AEP Resources Inc 614 716-1000
1 Riverside Plz Columbus (43215) *(G-6700)*

Aero Composites Inc 937 849-0244
3400 Spangler Rd Medway (45341) *(G-13499)*

Aero Fluid Products, Painesville *Also called Transdigm Inc (G-15932)*

Aero Fulfillment Services Corp (PA) 800 225-7145
3900 Aero Dr Mason (45040) *(G-12979)*

Aero Jet Wash Llc 866 381-7955
440 Fame Rd West Carrollton (45449) *(G-19789)*

Aero Pattern Works 937 890-3720
2725 Stonequarry Rd Dayton (45414) *(G-8139)*

Aero Printing Inc 419 695-2931
710 Elida Ave Delphos (45833) *(G-8899)*

Aero Propulsion Support Inc 513 367-9452
108 May Dr Ste A Harrison (45030) *(G-10766)*

Aero Propulsion Support Group, Harrison *Also called Aero Propulsion Support Inc (G-10766)*

Aero Refining, Painesville *Also called Panama Jewelers LLC (G-15909)*

Aero Tube & Connector Company 614 885-2514
7100 N High St Worthington (43085) *(G-20853)*

Aero-Med Industries Inc.................................216 459-0004
1205 Brookpark Rd Cleveland (44109) *(G-4718)*

Aerocase Incorporated.................................440 617-9294
1061 Bradley Rd Westlake (44145) *(G-20247)*

Aerocontrolex, Cleveland *Also called Transdigm Inc* *(G-6346)*

Aerocontrolex, Cleveland *Also called Transdigm Inc* *(G-6347)*

Aerocontrolex Group Inc (HQ).........................440 352-6182
4223 Monticello Blvd Cleveland (44121) *(G-4719)*

Aerodynamic Systems....................................440 463-8820
19020 Brookfield Rd Chagrin Falls (44023) *(G-3076)*

Aerodyne, Chagrin Falls *Also called Abanaki Corporation* *(G-3075)*

Aeroflex Powell, Hilliard *Also called Star Dynamics Corporation* *(G-10981)*

Aerolite Extrusion Company...........................330 782-1127
4605 Lake Park Rd Youngstown (44512) *(G-21018)*

Aeroll Engineering Corp...............................216 481-2266
18511 Euclid Ave Rear Cleveland (44112) *(G-4720)*

Aeromics Inc...216 772-1004
11000 Cedar Ave Ste 270 Cleveland (44106) *(G-4721)*

Aeroquip Corp...419 238-1190
1225 W Main St Van Wert (45891) *(G-19242)*

Aeroquip-Vickers Inc (HQ)............................216 523-5000
1111 Superior Ave E Cleveland (44114) *(G-4722)*

Aeroscena LLC...800 671-1890
10000 Cedar Ave Cleveland (44106) *(G-4723)*

Aeroseal LLC (PA).....................................937 428-9300
7989 S Suburban Rd Centerville (45458) *(G-3034)*

Aeroserv...513 932-9227
603 Norgal Dr Ste B Lebanon (45036) *(G-11777)*

Aerospace Co Inc......................................413 998-1637
600 Superior Ave E Cleveland (44114) *(G-4724)*

Aerospace Lubricants Inc..............................614 878-3600
1600 Georgesville Rd Columbus (43228) *(G-6701)*

Aerospace Mfg Group-Ohio, Blue Ash *Also called GKN Aerospace Cincinnati Inc* *(G-1804)*

Aerotech Enterprise...................................440 729-2616
8511 Mulberry Rd Chesterland (44026) *(G-3195)*

Aerotech Industries Inc...............................216 881-6660
1435 E 49th St Cleveland (44103) *(G-4725)*

Aerotech Styling Inc..................................419 923-6970
14181 County Road 10 2 Lyons (43533) *(G-12430)*

Aerotorque Corporation................................330 590-8105
1441 Wolf Creek Trl Sharon Center (44274) *(G-17099)*

Aerovation Tech Holdings LLC..........................567 208-5525
11651 Township Rd 81 Forest (45843) *(G-9917)*

Aerovent Inc..937 473-3789
800 S High St Covington (45318) *(G-7917)*

Aerowave Inc..440 731-8464
37190 Sugar Ridge Rd North Ridgeville (44039) *(G-15355)*

AES, Cincinnati *Also called Aluminum Extruded Shapes Inc* *(G-3383)*

Aesi, Springboro *Also called Advanced Engrg Solutions Inc* *(G-17470)*

Aesthetic Finishers Inc...............................937 778-8777
1502 S Main St Piqua (45356) *(G-16246)*

Aetna Plastics Corp...................................330 274-2855
4466 Orchard St Mantua (44255) *(G-12706)*

Aetna Plating Co......................................216 341-9111
6511 Morgan Ave Cleveland (44127) *(G-4726)*

Aetna Welding Co Inc..................................216 883-1801
4613 Broadway Ave Cleveland (44127) *(G-4727)*

Afc Company...330 533-5581
5183 W Western Reserve Rd Canfield (44406) *(G-2545)*

Affinity Disp Expositions Inc (PA)....................513 771-2339
1301 Glendale Milford Rd Cincinnati (45215) *(G-3363)*

Affinity Disp Expositions Inc.........................513 771-2339
1375 Spring Park Walk Cincinnati (45215) *(G-3364)*

Affinity Information Managemet........................419 517-2055
3359 Silica Rd Sylvania (43560) *(G-18098)*

Affinity Therapeutics LLC.............................216 224-9364
11000 Cedar Ave Cleveland (44106) *(G-4728)*

Affordable Barn Co Ltd................................330 674-3001
4260 Township Road 617 Millersburg (44654) *(G-14190)*

Affordable Cabinet Doors..............................513 734-9663
205 S Main St Bethel (45106) *(G-1664)*

Affordable Med Scrubs LLC (PA)........................419 222-1088
2190 Allentown Rd Lima (45805) *(G-11982)*

Affordable Stump Removal LLC..........................419 841-8331
2624 Heysler Rd Toledo (43617) *(G-18323)*

Affymetrix Inc..216 765-5000
26111 Miles Rd Cleveland (44128) *(G-4729)*

Affymetrix Inc..419 887-1233
434 W Dussel Dr Maumee (43537) *(G-13220)*

Afi Brands LLC..614 999-6426
5575 Hayden Run Blvd Dublin (43016) *(G-9038)*

Afs Technology LLC....................................937 669-3548
4060 Gibson Dr Tipp City (45371) *(G-18262)*

After Werk..513 661-9375
3095 Glenmore Ave Cincinnati (45238) *(G-3365)*

Aftermarket Parts Company LLC.........................740 369-1056
2338 Us Highway 42 S Delaware (43015) *(G-8818)*

Afv, Macedonia *Also called Insightfuel LLC* *(G-12460)*

AG Antenna Group LLC..................................513 289-6521
11931 Montgomery Rd Cincinnati (45249) *(G-3366)*

AG Designs LLC..614 506-2849
1165 Dunham Rd Delaware (43015) *(G-8819)*

AG Industries Inc.....................................216 252-7300
1 American Rd Cleveland (44144) *(G-4730)*

Agb LLC...419 924-5216
15188 Us Highway 127 West Unity (43570) *(G-20126)*

AGC Automotive Americas...............................937 599-3131
1465 W Sandusky Ave Bellefontaine (43311) *(G-1515)*

AGC Flat Glass North Amer Inc.........................937 292-7784
31 Hunter Pl Bellefontaine (43311) *(G-1516)*

AGC Flat Glass North Amer Inc.........................937 599-3131
1465 W Sandusky Ave Bellefontaine (43311) *(G-1517)*

AGE Graphics LLC (PA).................................740 989-0006
52231 State Route 248 Long Bottom (45743) *(G-12228)*

Agean Marble Manufacturing............................513 874-1475
9756 Prnceton Glendale Rd West Chester (45246) *(G-19978)*

Agent Technologies Inc (PA)...........................513 942-9444
8216 Princeton Glendale West Chester (45069) *(G-19800)*

AGFA Corporation......................................513 829-6292
6104 Monastery Dr Fairfield (45014) *(G-9638)*

Aggregate Tersornance LLC.............................330 418-4751
455 Navarre Rd Sw Unit H Canton (44707) *(G-2590)*

Agile Global Solutions Inc............................916 655-7745
5755 Granger Rd Ste 610 Independence (44131) *(G-11246)*

Agile Sign & Ltg Maint Inc............................440 918-1311
35280 Lakeland Blvd Eastlake (44095) *(G-9258)*

Agmet LLC...216 663-8200
5533 Dunham Rd Cleveland (44137) *(G-4731)*

Agmet Metals Inc......................................440 439-7400
7800 Medusa Rd Oakwood Village (44146) *(G-15621)*

Agnone-Kelly Enterprises Inc..........................800 634-6503
11658 Baen Rd Cincinnati (45242) *(G-3367)*

Agrana Fruit Us Inc...................................937 693-3821
16197 County Road 25a Anna (45302) *(G-620)*

Agratronix LLC..330 562-2222
10375 State Route 43 Streetsboro (44241) *(G-17834)*

Agri Communicators Inc................................614 273-0465
1625 Bethel Rd Ste 203 Columbus (43220) *(G-6702)*

Agri-Products Inc.....................................216 831-5890
29326 Bolingbrook Rd Cleveland (44124) *(G-4732)*

Agridry LLC...419 459-4399
3460 Us Highway 20 Edon (43518) *(G-9339)*

Agrium Advanced Tech US Inc...........................614 276-5103
701 Kaderly Dr Columbus (43228) *(G-6703)*

Agrium US Inc...513 941-4100
10743 Brower Rd North Bend (45052) *(G-15201)*

AGS Custom Graphics Inc...............................330 963-7770
8107 Bavaria Dr E Macedonia (44056) *(G-12433)*

Ahd, Cuyahoga Falls *Also called Advanced Holding Designs Inc* *(G-7962)*

Ahemco LLC..513 385-0555
5313 Robert Ave Cincinnati (45248) *(G-3368)*

Ahlstrom West Carrollton LLC..........................937 859-3621
1 S Elm St Dayton (45449) *(G-8140)*

Ahmf Inc (PA)...614 921-1223
2245 Wilson Rd Columbus (43228) *(G-6704)*

Ahner Fabricating & Shtmtl Inc........................419 626-6641
2001 E Perkins Ave Sandusky (44870) *(G-16945)*

Ahresty Wilmington Corporation........................937 382-6112
2627 S South St Wilmington (45177) *(G-20653)*

AI Root Company (PA)..................................330 723-4359
623 W Liberty St Medina (44256) *(G-13364)*

AI Root Company.......................................330 725-6677
234 S State Rd Medina (44256) *(G-13365)*

Aida Embroidery & Printing............................440 498-8981
33800 Sherbrook Park Dr Solon (44139) *(G-17250)*

Ailes Millwork Inc....................................330 678-4300
1520 Enterprise Way Kent (44240) *(G-11424)*

Aim Attachments.......................................614 539-3030
1720 Feddern Ave Grove City (43123) *(G-10540)*

Aimco Mfg Inc...419 476-6572
203 Matzinger Rd Toledo (43612) *(G-18324)*

AIN Industries Inc....................................440 781-0950
13901 Aspinwall Ave Cleveland (44110) *(G-4733)*

Air Cleaning Solutions................................937 832-3600
8613 N Main St Dayton (45415) *(G-8141)*

Air Compressor Exchange, Perrysburg *Also called Optimair Ltd* *(G-16137)*

Air Conversion Technology Inc.........................419 841-1720
3485 Silica Rd Unit A Sylvania (43560) *(G-18099)*

Air Craft Wheels LLC..................................440 937-7903
700 N Walnut St Ravenna (44266) *(G-16513)*

Air Enterprises LLC...................................330 794-9770
735 Glaser Pkwy Akron (44306) *(G-34)*

Air Entrprises Acquisition LLC........................330 794-9770
735 Glaser Pkwy Akron (44306) *(G-35)*

Air Force US Dept of..................................937 656-2354
4225 Logistics Ave Dayton (45433) *(G-8095)*

Air Heater Seal Company Inc...........................740 984-2146
15710 Waterford Rd Waterford (45786) *(G-19645)*

A
L
P
H
A
B
E
T
I
C

Air Locke Dock Seal Division, Youngstown *Also called ONeals Tarpaulin & Awning Co* **(G-21157)**

Air Logic Power Systems LLC 513 202-5130
10100 Progress Way Harrison (45030) **(G-10767)**

Air One Jet Center 513 867-9500
2808 Bobmeyer Rd Hamilton (45015) **(G-10663)**

Air Plastics Inc 513 469-1074
4468 Classic Dr Blue Ash (45241) **(G-1737)**

Air Power Dynamics LLC 440 701-2100
7350 Corporate Blvd Mentor (44060) **(G-13511)**

Air Power of Ohio, Canton *Also called A P O Holdings Inc* **(G-2585)**

Air Products and Chemicals Inc 513 420-3663
2500 Yankee Rd Middletown (45044) **(G-14013)**

Air Products and Chemicals Inc 216 781-2801
2820 Quigley Rd Cleveland (44113) **(G-4734)**

Air Products and Chemicals Inc 513 242-9215
4900 Este Ave Cincinnati (45232) **(G-3369)**

AIR RITE SERVICE SUPPLY, Cleveland *Also called Air-Rite Inc* **(G-4735)**

Air Services, Cleveland *Also called Mercury Air Services LLC* **(G-5783)**

Air Shop, The, Loveland *Also called Paul Miracle* **(G-12376)**

Air Technical Industries Inc 440 951-5191
7501 Clover Ave Mentor (44060) **(G-13512)**

Air Tool Service Company (PA) 440 701-1021
7722 Metric Dr Mentor (44060) **(G-13513)**

Air Waves Inc 740 548-1200
7750 Green Meadows Dr A Lewis Center (43035) **(G-11883)**

Air-Rite Inc 216 228-8200
1290 W 117th St Cleveland (44107) **(G-4735)**

Air-Way Manufacturing Company 419 298-2366
303 W River St Edgerton (43517) **(G-9325)**

Airborn Flxble Circuits NH Inc 603 537-9500
2230 Picton Pkwy Akron (44312) **(G-36)**

Airborne, Centerville *Also called American Sports Design Company* **(G-3035)**

Aircraft and Auto Fittings Co 216 486-0047
17120 Saint Clair Ave Cleveland (44110) **(G-4736)**

Aircraft Dynamics Corporation 419 331-0371
418 E Kiracofe Ave Elida (45807) **(G-9350)**

Aircraft Plating Corp 216 781-5845
1106 Clark Ave Cleveland (44109) **(G-4737)**

Aircraft Welding Inc 440 951-3863
38335 Apollo Pkwy Unit 1 Willoughby (44094) **(G-20426)**

Aircraft Wheels and Breaks, Avon *Also called Cleveland Wheels* **(G-989)**

Aircraft-Refuelers.com, Findlay *Also called Bosserman Automotive Engrg LLC* **(G-9800)**

Airecon Manufacturing Corp 513 561-5522
5271 Brotherton Rd Cincinnati (45227) **(G-3370)**

Airfasco Inc 330 430-6190
2655 Harrison Ave Sw Canton (44706) **(G-2591)**

Airfasco Inds Fstner Group LLC 330 430-6190
2655 Harrison Ave Sw Canton (44706) **(G-2592)**

Airgas 330 345-1257
115 N Smyser Rd Wooster (44691) **(G-20732)**

Airgas Inc 419 695-7085
11713b Delphs Spncrvle Rd Delphos (45833) **(G-8900)**

Airgas Merchant Gases LLC 330 454-1330
2505 Shepler Ave Sw Canton (44706) **(G-2593)**

Airgas Usa LLC 419 228-2828
1590 Mcclain Rd Lima (45804) **(G-11983)**

Airgas Usa LLC 440 232-6397
21610 Alexander Rd Oakwood Village (44146) **(G-15622)**

Airgas USA LLC 937 228-8594
1223 Mccook Ave Dayton (45404) **(G-8142)**

Airgas USA LLC 513 563-9400
10031 Cncnnati Dyton Pike Cincinnati (45241) **(G-3371)**

Airgas USA LLC 419 726-2719
526 Dura Ave Toledo (43612) **(G-18325)**

Airmachinescom Inc 330 759-1620
4705 Belmont Ave Youngstown (44505) **(G-21019)**

Airmate Company 419 636-3184
16280 County Road D Bryan (43506) **(G-2274)**

Airplaco Equipment Company, Cincinnati *Also called Mesa Industries Inc* **(G-4087)**

Airplane Plastics, Tipp City *Also called J & B Rogers Inc* **(G-18285)**

Airstream Inc (HQ) 937 596-6111
419 W Pike St Jackson Center (45334) **(G-11337)**

Airtech Mechanical Inc 419 292-0074
4444 Monroe St Toledo (43613) **(G-18326)**

Airtex Manufacturing Lllp 614 436-9693
991 Schrock Rd Ste B Columbus (43229) **(G-6705)**

Airtug LLC 440 829-2167
1350 Chester Indus Pkwy Avon (44011) **(G-983)**

Airtx International Ltd 513 631-0660
6320 Wiehe Rd Cincinnati (45237) **(G-3372)**

Airwave Communications Cons 419 331-1526
1209 Allentown Rd Lima (45805) **(G-11984)**

Airwaves, Lewis Center *Also called Solid Light Company Inc* **(G-11920)**

AIRWAY, Cincinnati *Also called Surgical Appliance Inds Inc* **(G-4488)**

Airwolf Aerospace LLC 440 632-1687
15369 Madison Rd Middlefield (44062) **(G-13913)**

Aisco Metallizing Corp 216 441-7244
2996 Eggers Ave Cleveland (44105) **(G-4738)**

Aitken Products Inc 440 466-5711
566 N Eagle St Geneva (44041) **(G-10341)**

Aj Fluid Power Sales & Sup Inc 440 255-7960
8766 Tyler Blvd Mentor (44060) **(G-13514)**

Aj Stineburg Wdwkg Studio LLC 614 526-9480
4651 Tatersall Ct Columbus (43230) **(G-6706)**

Aja Industries LLC 614 216-9566
3857 Wintergreen Blvd Gahanna (43230) **(G-10203)**

Ajami Holdings Group LLC 216 396-6089
5247 Wilson Mills Rd # 311 Richmond Heights (44143) **(G-16651)**

Ajax - Ceco Manufacturing Co, Wickliffe *Also called Ajax Manufacturing Company* **(G-20351)**

Ajax Industries Inc 614 272-6944
575 N Hague Ave Columbus (43204) **(G-6707)**

Ajax Jaws, Columbus *Also called Ajax Industries Inc* **(G-6707)**

Ajax Manufacturing Company 440 295-0244
29100 Lakeland Blvd Wickliffe (44092) **(G-20351)**

Ajax Tocco Magnethermic Corp (HQ) 330 372-8511
1745 Overland Ave Ne Warren (44483) **(G-19517)**

Ajax Tocco Magnethermic Corp 440 278-7200
29100 Lakeland Blvd Wickliffe (44092) **(G-20352)**

Ajax Tocco Magnethermic Corp 330 818-8080
8984 Meridian Cir Nw Canton (44720) **(G-2594)**

AJD Holding Co (PA) 330 405-4477
2181 Enterprise Pkwy Twinsburg (44087) **(G-18895)**

Ajeh & Company Unlimited 440 729-2367
12497 Bentbrook Dr Chesterland (44026) **(G-3196)**

Ajj Enterprises LLC 513 755-9562
4636 Interstate Dr West Chester (45246) **(G-19979)**

AK Fabrication Inc 330 458-1037
1500 Allen Ave Se Canton (44707) **(G-2595)**

AK Mansfield 419 755-3011
913 Bowman St Mansfield (44903) **(G-12556)**

AK Steel Corp Copy Center, West Chester *Also called AK Steel Corporation* **(G-19801)**

AK Steel Corporation 419 755-3011
913 Bowman St Mansfield (44903) **(G-12557)**

AK Steel Corporation 740 450-5600
1724 Linden Ave Zanesville (43701) **(G-21267)**

AK Steel Corporation 740 829-2206
17400 State Route 16 Coshocton (43812) **(G-7877)**

AK Steel Corporation 513 425-3694
801 Crawford St Middletown (45044) **(G-14014)**

AK Steel Corporation 513 425-3593
622 Box Middletown (45042) **(G-14015)**

AK Steel Corporation 513 425-5000
9227 Centre Pointe Dr West Chester (45069) **(G-19801)**

AK Steel Corporation 513 231-2552
1080 Nimitzview Dr Cincinnati (45230) **(G-3373)**

AK Steel Corporation (HQ) 513 425-4200
9227 Centre Pointe Dr West Chester (45069) **(G-19802)**

AK Steel Door 360, Middletown *Also called Matheson Tri-Gas Inc* **(G-14060)**

AK Steel Holding Corporation (PA) 513 425-5000
9227 Centre Pointe Dr West Chester (45069) **(G-19803)**

AK Tube LLC (HQ) 419 661-4150
30400 E Broadway St Walbridge (43465) **(G-19456)**

Ak-Isg Steel Coating Company 216 429-6901
3531 Campbell Rd Cleveland (44105) **(G-4739)**

Akers America Inc 330 757-4100
58 S Main St Poland (44514) **(G-16382)**

Akers Identity LLC 330 493-0055
4150 Belden Village St Nw # 503 Canton (44718) **(G-2596)**

Akers Packaging Service Inc (PA) 513 422-6312
2820 Lefferson Rd Middletown (45044) **(G-14016)**

Akers Packaging Service Group, Middletown *Also called Akers Packaging Service Inc* **(G-14016)**

Akers Packaging Service Group, Middletown *Also called Akers Packaging Solutions Inc* **(G-14017)**

Akers Packaging Solutions Inc (PA) 513 422-6312
2820 Lefferson Rd Middletown (45044) **(G-14017)**

Akers Sign, Canton *Also called Akers Identity LLC* **(G-2596)**

Akko Fastener Inc 513 489-8300
6855 Cornell Rd Blue Ash (45242) **(G-1738)**

Akland Printing, Macedonia *Also called Gaspar Services LLC* **(G-12455)**

Akos Promotions Inc 513 398-6324
668 Reading Rd Ste C Mason (45040) **(G-12980)**

Akri Tool Corporation 440 237-3050
2927 Nationwide Pkwy Brunswick (44212) **(G-2203)**

Akro Polychem Inc 330 864-0360
150 N Miller Rd Ste 300b Fairlawn (44333) **(G-9737)**

Akro Tool Co Inc 513 858-1555
240 Donald Dr Fairfield (45014) **(G-9639)**

Akro-Mils, Sandusky *Also called R B Mfg Co* **(G-16999)**

Akro-Plastics, Kent *Also called U S Development Corp* **(G-11541)**

Akron Anodizing & Coating Div, Akron *Also called Russell Products Co Inc* **(G-386)**

Akron Beacon Journal, Akron *Also called Sound Publishing Holding Inc* **(G-408)**

Akron Beacon Journal, Akron *Also called The Beacon Journal Pubg Co* **(G-435)**

Akron Brass Company 309 444-4440
343 Venture Blvd Wooster (44691) *(G-20733)*

Akron Brass Company 614 529-7230
3656 Paragon Dr Columbus (43228) *(G-6708)*

Akron Brass Company 330 264-5678
1615 Old Mansfield Rd Wooster (44691) *(G-20734)*

Akron Brass Company (HQ) 330 264-5678
343 Venture Blvd Wooster (44691) *(G-20735)*

Akron Brass Holding Corp (HQ) 330 264-5678
343 Venture Blvd Wooster (44691) *(G-20736)*

Akron Centl Engrv Mold Mch Inc 330 794-8704
1625 Massillon Rd Akron (44312) *(G-37)*

Akron Cotton Products Inc 330 434-7171
437 W Cedar St Akron (44307) *(G-38)*

Akron Council of Engineering (PA) 330 535-8835
411 Wolf Ledges Pkwy # 105 Akron (44311) *(G-39)*

Akron Crate and Pallet LLC 330 524-8955
1545 Mogadore Rd Kent (44240) *(G-11425)*

Akron Crematory, Akron *Also called Akron Vault Company Inc (G-60)*

Akron Cultured Marble Pdts LLC 330 628-6757
3992 Mogadore Rd Mogadore (44260) *(G-14366)*

Akron Design & Costume Co 330 644-4849
3425 Manchester Rd Akron (44319) *(G-40)*

Akron Dispersions Inc 330 666-0045
3291 Sawmill Rd Copley (44321) *(G-7838)*

Akron E N T Associates, Akron *Also called Akron Ent Hearing Services Inc (G-41)*

Akron Electric, Barberton *Also called Akron Foundry Co (G-1095)*

Akron Ent Hearing Services Inc 330 762-8959
395 E Market St Akron (44304) *(G-41)*

Akron Equipment Company (PA) 330 645-3780
3522 Manchester Rd Ste B Akron (44319) *(G-42)*

Akron Felt & Chenille Mfg Co 330 733-7778
1205 George Wash Blvd Akron (44312) *(G-43)*

Akron Foundry Co (PA) 330 745-3101
2728 Wingate Ave Akron (44314) *(G-44)*

Akron Foundry Co 330 745-3101
1025 Eagon St Barberton (44203) *(G-1095)*

Akron Gasket & Packg Entps Inc 330 633-3742
445 Northeast Ave Tallmadge (44278) *(G-18132)*

Akron Gear & Engineering Inc 330 773-6608
501 Morgan Ave Akron (44311) *(G-45)*

Akron Industrial Motor Service 330 753-7624
3041 Barber Rd Norton (44203) *(G-15504)*

Akron Jewelry Rubber, Madison *Also called Zero-D Products Inc (G-12514)*

Akron Legal News Inc 330 296-7578
60 S Summit St Akron (44308) *(G-46)*

Akron Life, Akron *Also called Baker Media Group LLC (G-83)*

Akron Litho-Print Company Inc 330 434-3145
1026 S Main St Akron (44311) *(G-47)*

Akron Metal Etching Co 330 762-7687
463 Locust St Akron (44307) *(G-48)*

Akron Orthotic Solutions Inc 330 253-3002
582 W Market St Akron (44303) *(G-49)*

Akron Paint & Varnish Inc 330 773-8911
1390 Firestone Pkwy Akron (44301) *(G-50)*

Akron Plating Co Inc 330 773-6878
1774 Hackberry St Akron (44301) *(G-51)*

Akron Polymer Products Inc 330 628-5551
571 Kennedy Rd Akron (44305) *(G-52)*

Akron Porcelain & Plastic Co, Akron *Also called Akron Porcelain & Plastics Co (G-53)*

Akron Porcelain & Plastics Co (PA) 330 745-2159
2739 Cory Ave Akron (44314) *(G-53)*

Akron Products Company 330 576-1750
6600 Ridge Rd Wadsworth (44281) *(G-19391)*

Akron Rebar Co (PA) 330 745-7100
809 W Waterloo Rd Akron (44314) *(G-54)*

Akron Rebar Co 216 433-0000
16216 Brookpark Rd Cleveland (44135) *(G-4740)*

Akron Special Machinery Inc (PA) 330 753-1077
2740 Cory Ave Akron (44314) *(G-55)*

Akron Specialized Products (PA) 330 762-9269
96 E Miller Ave Akron (44301) *(G-56)*

Akron Steel Fabricators Co 330 644-0616
3291 Manchester Rd Akron (44319) *(G-57)*

Akron Steel Treating Co 330 773-8211
336 Morgan Ave Akron (44311) *(G-58)*

Akron Thermography Inc 330 896-9712
3406 Fortuna Dr Akron (44312) *(G-59)*

Akron Vault Company Inc 330 784-5475
2399 Gilchrist Rd Akron (44305) *(G-60)*

Akzo Nobel Chemicals LLC 419 229-0088
1747 Fort Amanda Rd Lima (45804) *(G-11985)*

Akzo Nobel Coatings Inc 614 294-3361
1313 Windsor Ave Ste 1313 Columbus (43211) *(G-6709)*

Akzo Nobel Coatings Inc 614 294-3361
1313 Windsor Ave Columbus (43211) *(G-6710)*

Akzo Nobel Coatings Inc 937 322-2671
1550 Progress Rd Springfield (45505) *(G-17515)*

Akzo Nobel Coatings Inc 614 294-3361
1313 Windsor Ave Columbus (43211) *(G-6711)*

Akzo Nobel Inc 205 323-5201
1313 Windsor Ave Columbus (43211) *(G-6712)*

Akzo Nobel Paints LLC 513 242-0530
1754 Tennessee Ave Cincinnati (45229) *(G-3374)*

Al Bradshaw Jr 513 422-8870
5009 Oxford Middleton Rd Middletown (45042) *(G-14018)*

Al Chem Specialties LLC 440 255-2826
7284 Justin Way Mentor (44060) *(G-13515)*

Al Fe Heat Treating-Ohio Inc 330 336-0211
979 Seville Rd Wadsworth (44281) *(G-19392)*

Al Meda Chocolates Inc 419 446-2676
23050 Fulton County Rd E Archbold (43502) *(G-661)*

Al Yoder Construction Company 330 359-5726
3375 County Road 160 Millersburg (44654) *(G-14191)*

Al's Electric Motor Service, Bedford *Also called Als High Tech Inc (G-1395)*

Al's Polsg Pltg Powdr Coating, Toledo *Also called Als Polishing Shop Inc (G-18332)*

Al-Co Products Inc 419 399-3867
485 2nd St Latty (45855) *(G-11767)*

Al-Fe Heat Treating Defiance, Defiance *Also called Al-Fe Heat Treating Inc (G-8776)*

Al-Fe Heat Treating Inc 419 782-7200
2066 E 2nd St Defiance (43512) *(G-8776)*

Alacriant Inc (PA) 330 562-7191
1760 Miller Pkwy Streetsboro (44241) *(G-17835)*

Alacriant Inc 330 562-7191
1760 Miller Pkwy Streetsboro (44241) *(G-17836)*

Alacwin Nutrition Corporation 614 961-6479
3706 Kimberly Pkwy N Columbus (43232) *(G-6713)*

Aladdinslights Inc 330 963-6997
2201a Pinnacle Pkwy Twinsburg (44087) *(G-18896)*

Alamarra Inc 800 336-3007
8788 Tyler Blvd Mentor (44060) *(G-13516)*

Alan BJ Company 330 372-1201
3566 Larchmont Ave Ne Warren (44483) *(G-19518)*

Alan Manufacturing Inc 330 262-1555
3927 E Lincoln Way Wooster (44691) *(G-20737)*

Alanax Technologies Inc 216 469-1545
40714 Cherrywood Dr Belmont (43718) *(G-1577)*

Alanod Westlake Metal Ind Inc 440 327-8184
36696 Sugar Ridge Rd North Ridgeville (44039) *(G-15356)*

Alaskan Falls Bottling Company 614 888-9280
6950 Wrthington Galena Rd Worthington (43085) *(G-20854)*

Alba Manufacturing Inc 513 874-0551
8950 Seward Rd Fairfield (45011) *(G-9640)*

Albeco, Cleveland *Also called Aluminum Bearing Co of America (G-4773)*

Albemarle Corporation 330 425-2354
1664 Highland Rd Twinsburg (44087) *(G-18897)*

Albemarle Sorbent Technologies, Twinsburg *Also called Albemarle Corporation (G-18897)*

Albert Bickel 513 530-5700
7116 Leibel Rd Cincinnati (45248) *(G-3375)*

Albert Bramkamp Printing Co 513 641-1069
4501 Greenlee Ave Cincinnati (45217) *(G-3376)*

Albert Freytag Inc 419 628-2018
306 Executive Dr Minster (45865) *(G-14349)*

Albert Screenprint, Norton *Also called Alberts Screen Print Inc (G-15505)*

Alberts Screen Print Inc 330 753-7559
3704 Summit Rd Norton (44203) *(G-15505)*

Albin Sales Inc 740 927-7210
81 Brandon Dr Pataskala (43062) *(G-15966)*

Albion Industries Inc 440 238-1955
20246 Progress Dr Strongsville (44149) *(G-17885)*

Albright Albright & Schn 614 825-4829
89 E Wilson Bridge Rd D Worthington (43085) *(G-20855)*

Albright Machine 419 483-1088
4296 Us Highway 20 W Monroeville (44847) *(G-14424)*

Albright Radiator Inc 330 264-8886
331 N Hillcrest Dr Wooster (44691) *(G-20738)*

Albright Saw Company Inc 740 887-2107
33535 Us Highway 50 Londonderry (45647) *(G-12225)*

Albright Supply Company, Londonderry *Also called Albright Saw Company Inc (G-12225)*

ALC Holdings Inc 740 452-2500
4005 All American Way Zanesville (43701) *(G-21268)*

Alcan Corporation (HQ) 440 460-3307
6060 Parkland Blvd Cleveland (44124) *(G-4741)*

Alcan Primary Products Corp 440 460-3300
6055 Rockside Woods Blvd Independence (44131) *(G-11247)*

Alcatel Co 818 878-4485
4571 Cautela Dr Westerville (43081) *(G-20197)*

Alchem Corporation 330 725-2436
525 W Liberty St Medina (44256) *(G-13366)*

Alchemical Transmutation 216 313-8674
314 E 195th St Cleveland (44119) *(G-4742)*

Alcm, Cleveland *Also called Aluminum Coating Manufacturers (G-4774)*

Alco Manufacturing 440 322-9166
105 Middle Ave Amherst (44001) *(G-590)*

Alco Manufacturing Corp LLC (PA) 440 458-5165
10584 Middle Ave Elyria (44035) *(G-9367)*

Alco-Chem Inc (PA) 330 253-3535
45 N Summit St Akron (44308) *(G-61)*

Alcoa, Mogadore *Also called Arconic Inc (G-14368)*

(PA)=Parent Co (HQ)=Headquarters (DH)=Div Headquarters

Alcoa, Newburgh Heights *Also called Arconic Inc* ***(G-15069)***
Alcoa Inc......216 391-3885
3960 S Marginal Rd Cleveland (44114) ***(G-4743)***
Alcoa Inc......216 641-3600
1600 Harvard Ave Newburgh Heights (44105) ***(G-15067)***
Alcoa Inc......330 848-4000
842 Norton Ave Barberton (44203) ***(G-1096)***
Alcoa Inc......608 363-5214
1616 Harvard Ave Newburgh Heights (44105) ***(G-15068)***
Alcoa Power & Propulsion, Newburgh Heights *Also called Howmet Corporation* ***(G-15074)***
Alcohol & Drug Addiction Svcs......216 348-4830
2012 W 25th St Ste 600 Cleveland (44113) ***(G-4744)***
ALCOHOLICS ANONYMOUS, Cuyahoga Falls *Also called Paradise Inc* ***(G-8031)***
Alcon Inc (PA)......513 722-1037
6522 Snider Rd Loveland (45140) ***(G-12337)***
Alcon Industries Inc......216 961-1100
7990 Baker Ave Cleveland (44102) ***(G-4745)***
Alcon Tool Company......330 773-9171
565 Lafollette St Akron (44311) ***(G-62)***
Ald Group LLC......440 942-9800
34201 Melinz Pkwy Unit A Willoughby (44095) ***(G-20427)***
Ald Precast Corp (PA)......614 449-3366
400 Frank Rd Columbus (43207) ***(G-6714)***
Alden Excavating, Cuyahoga Falls *Also called Alden Sand & Gravel Co Inc* ***(G-7963)***
Alden Sand & Gravel Co Inc......330 928-3249
2486 Northampton Rd Cuyahoga Falls (44223) ***(G-7963)***
Aldrich Chemical......937 859-1808
3858 Benner Rd Miamisburg (45342) ***(G-13781)***
Aldridge Folders, Wadsworth *Also called Keeler Enterprises Inc* ***(G-19412)***
Aldridge Folders, Wadsworth *Also called Deshea Printing Company* ***(G-19402)***
Aleco Machine LLC......513 894-6400
233 N Martin L King Blvd Hamilton (45011) ***(G-10664)***
Alegre Inc......937 885-6786
3101 W Tech Blvd Miamisburg (45342) ***(G-13782)***
Alegre Global Supply Solutions, Miamisburg *Also called Alegre Inc* ***(G-13782)***
Alektronics Inc......937 429-2118
4095 Executive Dr Beavercreek (45430) ***(G-1368)***
Aleris Corporation (PA)......216 910-3400
25825 Science Park Dr # 400 Cleveland (44122) ***(G-4746)***
Aleris International Inc (HQ)......216 910-3400
25825 Science Park Dr # 400 Beachwood (44122) ***(G-1253)***
Aleris Ohio Management Inc (HQ)......216 910-3400
25825 Science Park Dr # 400 Cleveland (44122) ***(G-4747)***
Aleris Recycling Inc......216 910-3400
25825 Science Park Dr # 400 Beachwood (44122) ***(G-1254)***
Aleris Rm Inc......216 910-3400
25825 Science Park Dr # 400 Beachwood (44122) ***(G-1255)***
Aleris Rolled Pdts Sls Corp......216 910-3400
25825 Science Park Dr Cleveland (44122) ***(G-4748)***
Aleris Rolled Products Inc (HQ)......216 910-3400
25825 Science Park Dr # 400 Beachwood (44122) ***(G-1256)***
Aleris Rolled Products Inc......740 983-2571
1 Reynolds Rd Ashville (43103) ***(G-848)***
Aleris Rolled Products Inc......740 922-2540
7319 Newport Rd Se Uhrichsville (44683) ***(G-19044)***
Aleris Rolled Products LLC (HQ)......216 910-3400
25825 Science Park Dr # 400 Cleveland (44122) ***(G-4749)***
Alert Safety Lite Products Co......440 232-5020
24500 Solon Rd Cleveland (44146) ***(G-4750)***
Alert Safety Products Inc......513 791-4790
11435 Williamson Rd Ste C Blue Ash (45241) ***(G-1739)***
Alert Stamping & Mfg Co Inc......440 232-5020
24500 Solon Rd Bedford Heights (44146) ***(G-1476)***
Alex Products Inc......419 399-4500
810 W Gasser Rd Paulding (45879) ***(G-15999)***
Alex Products Inc (PA)......419 267-5240
19911 County Rd T Ridgeville Corners (43555) ***(G-16662)***
Alexander Wilbert Vault Co (PA)......419 468-3477
134 Harding Way W Galion (44833) ***(G-10252)***
Alexis Concrete Enterprise Inc......440 366-0031
672 Sugar Ln Elyria (44035) ***(G-9368)***
ALFA GREEN SUPREME, Ottawa *Also called Verhoff Alfalfa Mills Inc* ***(G-15813)***
Alfacomp Inc......216 459-1790
4485 Broadview Rd Cleveland (44109) ***(G-4751)***
Alfagreen Supreme, Toledo *Also called Ohio Blenders Inc* ***(G-18615)***
Alfman Logging LLC......740 982-6227
4499 Township Road 448 Ne Crooksville (43731) ***(G-7948)***
Alfons Haar Inc......937 560-2031
150 Advanced Dr Springboro (45066) ***(G-17472)***
Alfred J Buescher Jr......216 752-3676
17001 Shaker Blvd Cleveland (44120) ***(G-4752)***
Alfred Machine Co (HQ)......440 248-4600
29500 Solon Rd Cleveland (44139) ***(G-4753)***
Alfred Nickles Bakery Inc (PA)......330 879-5635
26 Main St N Navarre (44662) ***(G-14708)***
Alfred Nickles Bakery Inc......740 453-6522
1147 Newark Rd Zanesville (43701) ***(G-21269)***
Alfred Nickles Bakery Inc......937 256-3762
201 Pritz Ave Dayton (45403) ***(G-8143)***
Algie Composites Inc......614 529-0477
2755 Westbelt Dr Columbus (43228) ***(G-6715)***
Ali Industries Inc......937 878-3946
747 E Xenia Dr Fairborn (45324) ***(G-9613)***
Alice Beougher......740 927-2470
13255 National Rd Sw Etna (43068) ***(G-9551)***
Alien Products LLC......440 946-9100
7123 Industrial Park Blvd Mentor (44060) ***(G-13517)***
Alien Workshop, Dayton *Also called Trilo Inc* ***(G-8725)***
Alifet USA Inc......513 793-8033
3714 Fallentree Ln Blue Ash (45236) ***(G-1740)***
Align Assess Achieve LLC......614 505-6820
900 Michigan Ave Columbus (43215) ***(G-6716)***
Alin Machining Company Inc......740 223-0200
875 E Mark St Marion (43302) ***(G-12853)***
Alkermes Inc......937 382-5642
265 Olinger Cir Wilmington (45177) ***(G-20654)***
Alkid Corporation......216 896-3000
6035 Parkland Blvd Cleveland (44124) ***(G-4754)***
Alkon Corporation (PA)......419 355-9111
728 Graham Dr Fremont (43420) ***(G-10124)***
Alkon Corporation......614 799-6650
6750 Crosby Ct Dublin (43016) ***(G-9039)***
All - Flo Pump Company......440 354-1700
7750 Tyler Blvd Mentor (44060) ***(G-13518)***
All A Cart Manufacturing Inc......614 443-5544
2001 Courtright Rd Columbus (43232) ***(G-6717)***
All About House......614 725-3595
1071 Afton Rd Columbus (43221) ***(G-6718)***
All American Screen Printing......419 475-0696
2607 W Central Ave Toledo (43606) ***(G-18327)***
All American Trophy......614 231-8824
3055 Templeton Rd Ste M Columbus (43209) ***(G-6719)***
All American Welding Co......614 224-7752
185 Mcdowell St Columbus (43215) ***(G-6720)***
All Around Garage Door Inc......440 759-5079
33434 Liberty Pkwy North Ridgeville (44039) ***(G-15357)***
All Coatings Co Inc......330 821-3806
510 W Ely St Alliance (44601) ***(G-489)***
All County Phone Directories......419 865-2464
7056 Wexford Hill Ln Holland (43528) ***(G-11044)***
All County Phone Directory, Holland *Also called All County Phone Directories* ***(G-11044)***
All Craft Manufacturing Co......513 661-3383
6500 Glenway Ave Side 2 Cincinnati (45211) ***(G-3377)***
All Cstom Fabricators Erectors, Cleveland *Also called Varmland Inc* ***(G-6408)***
All Do Weld & Fab LLC......740 477-2133
28155 River Dr Circleville (43113) ***(G-4622)***
All Fired Up Pnt Your Own Pot......330 865-5858
30 Rothrock Loop Copley (44321) ***(G-7839)***
All For Show Inc......440 729-7186
9321 Winchester Vly Chesterland (44026) ***(G-3197)***
All Metal Fabricators Inc......216 267-0033
15400 Commerce Park Dr Cleveland (44142) ***(G-4755)***
All Ohio Companies Inc......216 420-9274
2735 Scranton Rd Cleveland (44113) ***(G-4756)***
All Ohio Ready Mix Concrete......419 841-3838
622 Eckel Rd Perrysburg (43551) ***(G-16062)***
All Ohio Threaded Rod Co Inc......216 426-1800
5349 Saint Clair Ave Cleveland (44103) ***(G-4757)***
All Pack Services LLC......614 935-0964
3442 Grant Ave Grove City (43123) ***(G-10541)***
All Power Battery Inc......330 453-5236
1387 Clarendon Ave Sw # 6 Canton (44710) ***(G-2597)***
All Power Equipment LLC (PA)......740 593-3279
8880 United Ln Athens (45701) ***(G-855)***
All Prem Cleaners Inc......440 349-3649
33640 Aurora Rd Solon (44139) ***(G-17251)***
All Premium Cleaners, Solon *Also called All Prem Cleaners Inc* ***(G-17251)***
All Print Ltd......440 349-6868
38415 Flanders Dr Solon (44139) ***(G-17252)***
All Pro Alum Cylinder Heads......740 967-7761
5370 Jhnstown Alxndria Rd Johnstown (43031) ***(G-11387)***
All Pro Ovrhd Door Systems LLC......614 444-3667
1985 Oakland Park Ave Columbus (43224) ***(G-6721)***
All Signs and Designs LLC......216 267-8588
5101 W 161st St Cleveland (44142) ***(G-4758)***
All Signs Express Inc (PA)......513 489-7744
6610 Corporate Dr Blue Ash (45242) ***(G-1741)***
All Signs of Chillicothe Inc......740 773-5016
559 N High St Chillicothe (45601) ***(G-3227)***
All Sport Printwear Inc......330 887-6505
8606 N Leroy Rd Westfield Center (44251) ***(G-20243)***
All Sport Services Corporation......216 361-1965
3635 Perkins Ave Ste 1e Cleveland (44114) ***(G-4759)***
All Srvice Plastic Molding Inc......937 415-3674
611 Yllow Sprng Frfeld Rd Fairborn (45324) ***(G-9614)***
All Srvice Plastic Molding Inc......937 890-0322
900 Falls Creek Dr Vandalia (45377) ***(G-19279)***
All Srvice Plastic Molding Inc (PA)......937 890-0322
900 Fall Creek Dr Vandalia (45377) ***(G-19280)***

All Star Sign Company...614 461-9052
  112 S Glenwood Ave Columbus (43222) *(G-6722)*

All State GL Block Fctry Inc...440 205-8410
  8781 East Ave Mentor (44060) *(G-13519)*

All Steel Structures Inc...330 312-3131
  755 N Lisbon St Carrollton (44615) *(G-2951)*

All Systems Colour Inc...937 859-9701
  2032 S Alex Rd Ste A Dayton (45449) *(G-8144)*

All Ways Green Lawn & Turf LLC..................................937 763-4766
  1856 Greenbrier Rd Seaman (45679) *(G-17040)*

All Wright Enterprises LLC..440 259-5656
  4285 Main St Perry (44081) *(G-16047)*

All Write Ribbon Inc...513 753-8300
  3916 Bach Buxton Rd Amelia (45102) *(G-566)*

All-Bilt Uniform Corp..513 793-5400
  4545 Malsbary Rd Blue Ash (45242) *(G-1742)*

All-Craft Wellman Products...440 946-9646
  4839 E 345th St Willoughby (44094) *(G-20428)*

All-Line Truck Sales, Hubbard *Also called Youngstown-Kenworth Inc* *(G-11143)*

All-Plant Liquid Plant Food, Ashland *Also called R & J AG Manufacturing Inc* *(G-770)*

All-Seasons Paper Company...440 826-1700
  6346 Eastland Rd Cleveland (44142) *(G-4760)*

All-Tech Manufacturing Ltd..330 633-1095
  1477 Industrial Pkwy Akron (44310) *(G-63)*

All-Tra Rubber Processing...330 630-1945
  154 Potomac Ave Ste B Tallmadge (44278) *(G-18133)*

All-Type Welding & Fabrication.....................................440 439-3990
  7690 Bond St Cleveland (44139) *(G-4761)*

Allan A Irish...419 394-3284
  1600 Celina Rd Saint Marys (45885) *(G-16831)*

Allega Concrete Corp...216 447-0814
  5585 Canal Rd Cleveland (44125) *(G-4762)*

Allega Slag Recovery Inc..216 447-0814
  5585 Canal Rd Cleveland (44125) *(G-4763)*

Allegheny Ludlum LLC...330 875-2244
  1500 W Main St Louisville (44641) *(G-12308)*

Allegra Marketing & Printing, Cambridge *Also called H&An LLC* *(G-2460)*

Allegra Marketing Print Mail, Blue Ash *Also called Dsk Imaging LLC* *(G-1777)*

Allegra Print & Imaging, Columbus *Also called Rutobo Inc* *(G-7579)*

Allegra Print & Imaging, Westlake *Also called Allegra Printing & Imaging LLC* *(G-20248)*

Allegra Print & Imaging...419 427-8095
  701 W Sandusky St Findlay (45840) *(G-9789)*

Allegra Printing & Imaging LLC....................................440 449-6989
  1486 Barclay Blvd Westlake (44145) *(G-20248)*

Allen Aircraft Products Inc..330 296-9621
  312 E Lake St Ravenna (44266) *(G-16514)*

Allen Aircraft Products Inc..330 296-1531
  4879 Newton Falls Rd Ravenna (44266) *(G-16515)*

Allen Alloys..330 422-1814
  8693 State Route 14 Streetsboro (44241) *(G-17837)*

Allen County Fabrication Inc..419 227-7447
  999 Industry Ave Lima (45804) *(G-11986)*

Allen Drain Service Inc...330 253-4206
  1008 Mogadore Rd Kent (44240) *(G-11426)*

Allen Enterprises Inc...740 532-5913
  2900 S 9th St Ironton (45638) *(G-11288)*

Allen Fields Assoc Inc...513 228-1010
  3525 Grant Ave Ste D Lebanon (45036) *(G-11778)*

Allen Graphics Inc..440 349-4100
  27100 Richmond Rd Ste 6 Solon (44139) *(G-17253)*

Allen Green Enterprises LLC.......................................330 339-0200
  513 Mill Ave Se New Philadelphia (44663) *(G-14883)*

Allen Harper..740 543-3919
  1654 Township Road 266 Amsterdam (43903) *(G-609)*

Allen Kenard Printing Inc..440 323-7405
  501 Clark St Elyria (44035) *(G-9369)*

Allen Milk Division, Columbus *Also called Tmarzetti Company* *(G-7697)*

Allen Mold & Die Inc..440 944-1819
  850 Charles St Willowick (44095) *(G-20646)*

Allen Morgan Trucking & Repair....................................330 336-5192
  4162 Greenwich Rd Norton (44203) *(G-15506)*

Allen Press...614 891-4413
  6132 Batavia Rd Westerville (43081) *(G-20198)*

Allen Randall Enterprises Inc.......................................330 374-9850
  70 E Miller Ave Akron (44301) *(G-64)*

Allen Tool Co Inc..937 987-2037
  300 S 2nd St New Vienna (45159) *(G-14954)*

Allen Zahradnik Inc (PA)..419 729-1201
  5902 Edgewater Dr Toledo (43611) *(G-18328)*

Allenbaugh Foods LLC...216 952-3984
  14305 Bayes Ave Lakewood (44107) *(G-11655)*

Allergan Inc..614 623-8140
  4321 Scioto Pkwy Powell (43065) *(G-16462)*

Allermuir, Maumee *Also called Senator International Inc* *(G-13291)*

Alley Cat Designs Inc..937 885-7950
  919 Senate Dr Dayton (45459) *(G-8145)*

Allfab Inc...614 491-4944
  2273 Williams Rd Columbus (43207) *(G-6723)*

Allfasteners Usa LLC (HQ)..440 232-6060
  959 Laker Rd Medina (44256) *(G-13367)*

Allgeier & Son Inc (PA)..513 574-3735
  6386 Bridgetown Rd Cincinnati (45248) *(G-3378)*

Alliance Abrasives LLC...330 823-7957
  23649 State Route 62 Alliance (44601) *(G-490)*

Alliance Automation LLC...419 238-2520
  560 Bonnewitz Ave Van Wert (45891) *(G-19243)*

Alliance Carpet Cushion Co...740 966-5001
  143 Commerce Blvd Johnstown (43031) *(G-11388)*

Alliance Castings Company LLC....................................330 829-5600
  1001 E Broadway St Alliance (44601) *(G-491)*

Alliance Die Design & Mfg...330 821-2440
  230 Buckeye Ave Alliance (44601) *(G-492)*

Alliance Drilling Inc...330 584-2781
  20388 N Benton West Rd North Benton (44449) *(G-15211)*

Alliance Equipment Company Inc...................................330 821-2291
  1000 N Union Ave Alliance (44601) *(G-493)*

Alliance Forging Group LLC...330 680-4861
  12240 Rockhill Ave Ne Alliance (44601) *(G-494)*

Alliance Healthcare Svcs Inc.......................................330 493-6747
  5005 Whipple Ave Nw Canton (44718) *(G-2598)*

Alliance Indus Masking Inc..937 681-5569
  204 S Ludlow St Ste 201 Dayton (45402) *(G-8146)*

Alliance Knife Inc...513 367-9000
  124 May Dr Harrison (45030) *(G-10768)*

Alliance Petroleum, Canton *Also called Ohio L & M Company Inc* *(G-2800)*

Alliance Petroleum Corporation (PA)..............................330 493-0440
  4150 Belden Village Mall Canton (44718) *(G-2599)*

Alliance Printing & Publishing.......................................513 422-7611
  2520 Atco Ave Middletown (45042) *(G-14019)*

Alliance Publishing Co Inc (HQ)....................................330 453-1304
  40 S Linden Ave Alliance (44601) *(G-495)*

Alliance Publishing Co Inc...330 868-5222
  177 Curry St Minerva (44657) *(G-14316)*

Alliance Torque Converters Inc.....................................937 222-3394
  5915 Wolf Creek Pike Dayton (45426) *(G-8147)*

Allied Coating Co...937 615-0391
  387 Fox Dr Piqua (45356) *(G-16247)*

Allied Consolidated Industries (PA).................................330 744-0808
  2100 Poland Ave Youngstown (44502) *(G-21020)*

Allied Construction Pdts LLC (HQ).................................216 431-2600
  3900 Kelley Ave Cleveland (44114) *(G-4764)*

Allied Construction Pdts LLC..216 431-2600
  1840 E 40th St Cleveland (44103) *(G-4765)*

Allied Corporation Inc (HQ)...330 425-7861
  8920 Canyon Falls Blvd # 120 Twinsburg (44087) *(G-18898)*

Allied Custom Molded Products....................................614 291-0629
  1240 Essex Ave Columbus (43201) *(G-6724)*

Allied Fabricating & Wldg Co..614 751-6664
  5699 Chantry Dr Columbus (43232) *(G-6725)*

Allied Machine & Engrg Corp (PA)..................................330 343-4283
  120 Deeds Dr Dover (44622) *(G-8963)*

Allied Machine Works Inc..740 454-2534
  120 Graham St Zanesville (43701) *(G-21270)*

Allied Mask and Tooling Inc...419 470-2555
  6051 Telegraph Rd Ste 6 Toledo (43612) *(G-18329)*

Allied Mineral Products Inc (PA)....................................614 876-0244
  2700 Scioto Pkwy Columbus (43221) *(G-6726)*

Allied Moulded Products Inc...419 636-4217
  222 N Union St Bryan (43506) *(G-2275)*

Allied Plastic Co Inc..419 389-1688
  3203 South Ave Toledo (43609) *(G-18330)*

Allied Retail Solutions..330 332-8141
  1960 S Lincoln Ave Unit 4 Salem (44460) *(G-16870)*

Allied Silk Screen Inc...937 223-4921
  2740 Thunderhawk Ct Dayton (45414) *(G-8148)*

Allied Tool & Die Inc..216 941-6196
  16146 Puritas Ave Cleveland (44135) *(G-4766)*

Allied Tube & Conduit Corp...740 928-1018
  250 Capital Dr Hebron (43025) *(G-10860)*

Allied Window Inc...513 559-1212
  11111 Canal Rd Cincinnati (45241) *(G-3379)*

Alligator Cmpt Systems Corp.......................................513 542-1000
  2060 Waycross Rd Cincinnati (45240) *(G-3380)*

Alloy Bllows Prcision Wldg Inc......................................440 684-3000
  653 Miner Rd Cleveland (44143) *(G-4767)*

Alloy Engineering Company (PA)...................................440 243-6800
  844 Thacker St Berea (44017) *(G-1600)*

Alloy Extrusion Company..330 677-4946
  4211 Karg Indl Pkwy Kent (44240) *(G-11427)*

Alloy Fabricators Inc..330 948-3535
  700 Wooster St Lodi (44254) *(G-12156)*

Alloy Machining and Fabg...330 482-5543
  1028 Lower Elkton Rd Columbiana (44408) *(G-6605)*

Alloy Metal Exchange LLC...216 478-0200
  26000 Corbin Dr Bedford Heights (44128) *(G-1477)*

Alloy Polymers, Gahanna *Also called Pahuja Inc* *(G-10225)*

Alloy Unlimited Weld..330 506-8375
  4200 W Middletown Rd Canfield (44406) *(G-2546)*

Alloy Welding & Fabricating 440 914-0650
30340 Solon Indtl Pky B Solon (44139) ***(G-17254)***

Allpass Corporation 440 998-6300
2605 Crane Ave Ashtabula (44004) ***(G-792)***

Allstates Refr Contrs LLC 419 878-4691
218 Mechanic St B Waterville (43566) ***(G-19651)***

Alltech Med Systems Amer Inc 440 424-2240
28900 Fountain Pkwy Solon (44139) ***(G-17255)***

Alltel Communications Corp 419 784-3808
1007 N Clinton St Ste 1 Defiance (43512) ***(G-8777)***

Allyn Corp (PA) 614 442-3900
1491 Clairmonte Rd Columbus (43221) ***(G-6727)***

Almo Process Technology Inc 513 402-2566
8849 Brookside Ave # 101 West Chester (45069) ***(G-19804)***

Almondina Brand Biscuits, Maumee *Also called Y Z Enterprises Inc* ***(G-13310)***

Alms Company, Blue Ash *Also called Markes International Inc* ***(G-1832)***

Alpco, Westlake *Also called Aluminum Line Products Company* ***(G-20249)***

Alpha Bus Forms & Prtg LLC 419 999-5138
4330 East Rd Lima (45807) ***(G-11987)***

Alpha Coatings Inc 419 435-5111
622 S Corporate Dr W Fostoria (44830) ***(G-9964)***

Alpha Coatins Inc 419 436-6144
431 E North St Fostoria (44830) ***(G-9965)***

Alpha Container Co Inc 937 644-5511
16789 Square Dr Marysville (43040) ***(G-12931)***

Alpha Control LLC 740 377-3400
1042 County Road 60 South Point (45680) ***(G-17431)***

Alpha Control Fabg & Mfg, South Point *Also called Alpha Control LLC* ***(G-17431)***

Alpha Machining LLC 330 889-2207
394 E Main St West Farmington (44491) ***(G-20074)***

Alpha Omega Bioremediation LLC 614 287-2600
2824 Fisher Rd Ste E Columbus (43204) ***(G-6728)***

Alpha Omega Dev & Mch Co 440 352-9915
10395 Squires Ct Painesville (44077) ***(G-15848)***

Alpha Packaging Holdings Inc 216 252-5595
14801 Emery Ave Cleveland (44135) ***(G-4768)***

Alpha Print Specialties 440 282-1150
3330 Oberlin Ave Lorain (44053) ***(G-12231)***

Alpha Sintered Metals LLC 330 220-5800
1126 Industrial Pkwy N Brunswick (44212) ***(G-2204)***

Alpha Strike, Kent *Also called Primal Screen Inc* ***(G-11507)***

Alpha Technologies Svcs LLC (HQ) 330 745-1641
3030 Gilchrist Rd Akron (44305) ***(G-65)***

Alpha Tool & Mold Inc 440 473-2343
83 Alpha Park Cleveland (44143) ***(G-4769)***

Alpha Water Conditioning Co, Dayton *Also called R D Baker Enterprises Inc* ***(G-8609)***

Alpha Zeta Holdings Inc (PA) 216 271-1601
2981 Independence Rd Cleveland (44115) ***(G-4770)***

Alphabet Inc (HQ) 330 856-3366
8640 E Market St Warren (44484) ***(G-19519)***

Alphabet Embroidery Studios 937 372-6557
1291 Bellbrook Ave Xenia (45385) ***(G-20935)***

Alphabet Soup Inc 330 467-4418
981 Cessna Dr Macedonia (44056) ***(G-12434)***

AlphaGraphics, Strongsville *Also called Blue Crescent Enterprises Inc* ***(G-17897)***

AlphaGraphics, Columbus *Also called Headlee Enterprises Ltd* ***(G-6649)***

AlphaGraphics, Cleveland *Also called Swimmer Printing Inc* ***(G-6281)***

AlphaGraphics 507 Inc 440 878-9700
14765 Pearl Rd Strongsville (44136) ***(G-17886)***

AlphaGraphics Cincinnati, Mason *Also called Morse Enterprises Inc* ***(G-13066)***

AlphaGraphics Valley View, Cleveland *Also called Image Concepts Inc* ***(G-5550)***

AlphaGraphics Westlake, Westlake *Also called Vision Graphix Inc* ***(G-20318)***

Alpine Cabinets Inc 330 273-2131
1515 W 130th St Ste E Hinckley (44233) ***(G-11021)***

Alpine Gage Inc 937 669-8665
4325 Lisa Dr Tipp City (45371) ***(G-18263)***

Alpla Inc 419 991-9484
3320 Fort Shwnee Indus Dr Lima (45806) ***(G-12114)***

Alpps Ltd 614 804-3772
8226 Glencullen Ct Dublin (43017) ***(G-9040)***

Alro Steel Corporation 419 720-5300
3003 Airport Hwy Toledo (43609) ***(G-18331)***

Alro Steel Corporation 937 253-6121
821 Springfield St Dayton (45403) ***(G-8149)***

Alron 330 477-3405
805 Margo Dr Sw Strasburg (44680) ***(G-17819)***

Als High Tech Inc (PA) 440 232-7090
135 Northfield Rd Bedford (44146) ***(G-1395)***

Als Polishing Shop Inc 419 476-8857
1615 W Laskey Rd Toledo (43612) ***(G-18332)***

Alsco Metals Corporation (HQ) 740 983-2571
1309 Deer Hill Rd Dennison (44621) ***(G-8942)***

Alside Supply Center, Dayton *Also called Associated Materials LLC* ***(G-8166)***

Alstart Enterprises LLC 330 533-3222
451 W Main St Canfield (44406) ***(G-2547)***

Alsteel Fabricators Inc 330 652-4344
3500 Union St Mineral Ridge (44440) ***(G-14302)***

Alt Control Print 419 841-2467
6906 Milrose Ln Toledo (43617) ***(G-18333)***

Alt Fuel LLC 419 865-4196
1100 King Rd Toledo (43617) ***(G-18334)***

Alta Mira Corporation 330 648-2461
225 N Main St Spencer (44275) ***(G-17455)***

Altana 440 954-7600
830 E Erie St Painesville (44077) ***(G-15849)***

Altec Industries 419 289-6066
1236 Township Road 1175 Ashland (44805) ***(G-702)***

Alteirs Oil Inc 740 347-4335
140 W Main St Corning (43730) ***(G-7858)***

Altenloh Brinck & Co Inc 419 636-6715
2105 County Road 12c Bryan (43506) ***(G-2276)***

Altenloh Brinck & Co US Inc (HQ) 419 636-6715
2105 Williams Co Rd 12 C Bryan (43506) ***(G-2277)***

Altera Corporation 513 444-2021
9435 Waterstone Blvd # 140 Cincinnati (45249) ***(G-3381)***

Altera Corporation 330 650-5200
591 Boston Mills Rd # 600 Hudson (44236) ***(G-11155)***

Altera Polymers LLC 864 973-7000
222 S Sycamore St Jefferson (44047) ***(G-11356)***

Alternative Flash Inc 330 334-6111
1734 Wall Rd Ste B Wadsworth (44281) ***(G-19393)***

Alternative Press Magazine Inc 216 631-1510
1305 W 80th St Ste 214 Cleveland (44102) ***(G-4771)***

Alternative Surface Grinding 330 273-3443
1093 Industrial Pkwy N Brunswick (44212) ***(G-2205)***

Alterntive Spport Appratus LLC 740 922-2727
5609 Gundy Dr Midvale (44653) ***(G-14103)***

Altheirs Oil Inc 740 347-4335
140 E Main St Corning (43730) ***(G-7859)***

Altier Brothers Inc 740 347-4329
155 Walnut St Corning (43730) ***(G-7860)***

Altitude Medical Inc 440 799-7701
Po Box 770 Chardon (44024) ***(G-3139)***

Altivia Petrochemicals LLC 740 532-3420
1019 Haverhill Ohio Haverhill (45636) ***(G-10836)***

Altivity Packaging, Middletown *Also called Graphic Packaging Intl Inc* ***(G-14044)***

Altivity Packaging, Solon *Also called Graphic Packaging Intl Inc* ***(G-17301)***

Altivity Packaging, Cincinnati *Also called Multi-Color Corporation* ***(G-4131)***

Alton Products Inc 419 893-0201
425 W Sophia St Maumee (43537) ***(G-13221)***

Altraserv LLC 614 889-2500
6365 Old Avery Rd Ste 3 Dublin (43016) ***(G-9041)***

Altronic LLC (HQ) 330 545-9768
712 Trumbull Ave Girard (44420) ***(G-10381)***

Aluchem Inc (PA) 513 733-8519
1 Landy Ln Ste 1 Cincinnati (45215) ***(G-3382)***

Aluchem of Jackson Inc 740 286-2455
14782 Beaver Pike Jackson (45640) ***(G-11309)***

Alufab Inc 513 528-7281
1018 Seabrook Way Cincinnati (45245) ***(G-3293)***

Alumacast LLC 419 584-1473
300 N Brandon Ave Celina (45822) ***(G-2985)***

Alumalloy Metalcasting Company 440 930-2222
33665 Walker Rd Avon Lake (44012) ***(G-1023)***

Alumetal Manufacturing Company 419 268-2311
4555 Sr 127 Coldwater (45828) ***(G-6550)***

Alumin Nu Corp 216 421-2116
9513 Woodland Ave Cleveland (44104) ***(G-4772)***

ALUMINA RAILING PRODUCTS, Cleves *Also called Alumina Rling Cstm Ir Wrks Inc* ***(G-6506)***

Alumina Rling Cstm Ir Wrks Inc 513 353-1116
8301 Strimple Rd Cleves (45002) ***(G-6506)***

Aluminum Bearing Co of America 216 267-8560
4775 W 139th St Cleveland (44135) ***(G-4773)***

Aluminum Coating Manufacturers 216 341-2000
7301 Bessemer Ave Cleveland (44127) ***(G-4774)***

Aluminum Color Industries Inc (PA) 330 536-6295
369 W Wood St Lowellville (44436) ***(G-12404)***

Aluminum Extruded Shapes Inc 513 563-2205
10549 Reading Rd Cincinnati (45241) ***(G-3383)***

Aluminum Extrusion Tech LLC 330 533-3994
6155 State Route 446 Canfield (44406) ***(G-2548)***

Aluminum Fence & Mfg Co 330 755-3323
15600 Main Market Rd Burton (44021) ***(G-2372)***

Aluminum Line Products Company (PA) 440 835-8880
24460 Sperry Cir Westlake (44145) ***(G-20249)***

Alumo Extrusions & Mfr Company 330 779-3333
3749 Mahoning Ave Ste 2 Youngstown (44515) ***(G-21021)***

Alutrim North America, Dayton *Also called Angell-Demmel North Amer Corp* ***(G-8158)***

Alvin L Roepke 419 862-3891
329 Rice St Elmore (43416) ***(G-9360)***

Alvio, Cleveland *Also called Golubitsky Corporation* ***(G-5436)***

Alvito Custom Imprints 614 846-8986
7469 Wrthington Galena Rd Worthington (43085) ***(G-20856)***

Alvords Yard & Garden Eqp 440 286-2315
12089 Ravenna Rd Chardon (44024) ***(G-3140)***

Always Better Communications 330 445-2220
4641 Dueber Ave Sw Canton (44706) ***(G-2600)***

Always Promoting Co., Maumee *Also called Skr Enterprises LLC (G-13295)*

AM & PM United, Youngstown *Also called A United (G-21011)*

AM General LLC 937 704-0160
2000 Watkins Glen Dr Franklin (45005) *(G-10006)*

Am Graphics 330 799-7319
20 S Maryland Ave Youngstown (44509) *(G-21022)*

AM Industrial Group LLC (PA) 216 433-7171
16000 Commerce Park Dr Brookpark (44142) *(G-2149)*

AM Retail Group Inc 513 539-7837
628 Premium Outlets Dr Monroe (45050) *(G-14391)*

AM Warren LLC 330 841-2800
2234 Main Ave Sw Warren (44481) *(G-19520)*

AMA Fuel Services LLC 513 836-3800
3053 Hart Rd Lebanon (45036) *(G-11779)*

Amac Enterprises Inc (PA) 216 362-1880
5909 W 130th St Parma (44130) *(G-15954)*

Amac Enterprises Inc 216 362-1880
5925 W 130th St Cleveland (44130) *(G-4775)*

Amaltech Inc 440 248-7500
30670 Bainbridge Rd Solon (44139) *(G-17256)*

Aman & Co Inc 330 854-1122
231 Locust St S Canal Fulton (44614) *(G-2495)*

Amanda Manufacturing 740 385-6893
1120 C I C Dr Logan (43138) *(G-12171)*

Amano Cincinnati Incorporated 513 697-9000
130 Commerce Dr Loveland (45140) *(G-12338)*

Amaroq Inc 419 747-2110
648 N Trimble Rd Mansfield (44906) *(G-12558)*

Amarr Company 216 573-7100
800 Resource Dr Ste 3 Independence (44131) *(G-11248)*

Amarr Garage Doors, Independence *Also called Amarr Company (G-11248)*

Amatech Inc 614 252-2506
1633 Woodland Ave Columbus (43219) *(G-6729)*

Amatech Polycell, Columbus *Also called Polycel Incorporated (G-7503)*

Ambaflex Inc 330 478-1858
1530 Raff Rd Sw Canton (44710) *(G-2601)*

Ambassador Heat Transfer, Blue Ash *Also called Space Dynamics Corp (G-1871)*

Ambassador Steel Corporation 740 382-9969
850 Barks Rd W Marion (43302) *(G-12854)*

Ambrosia Inc (PA) 419 825-1151
395 W Airport Hwy Swanton (43558) *(G-18079)*

AMC, Wooster *Also called ABS Materials Inc (G-20730)*

Amcan Productions Ltd 330 332-9129
3735 Mccracken Rd Salem (44460) *(G-16871)*

Amcan Stair & Rail LLC 937 781-3084
20 Zischler St Springfield (45504) *(G-17516)*

Amclo Group Inc 216 791-8400
2750 Grand Ave Cleveland (44104) *(G-4776)*

Amco Products Inc 937 433-7982
4800 Hempstead Station Dr Kettering (45429) *(G-11575)*

Amcor, Medina *Also called American Metal Chemical Corp (G-13369)*

Amcor Marine, Lorain *Also called American Metal Chemical Corp (G-12232)*

Amcor Rigid Plastics Usa LLC 419 483-4343
975 W Main St Bellevue (44811) *(G-1541)*

Amcor Rigid Plastics Usa LLC 419 592-1998
12993 State Route 110 Napoleon (43545) *(G-14670)*

Amcor Rigid Plastics Usa LLC 419 483-4343
975 W Main St Bellevue (44811) *(G-1542)*

Amcraft Inc 419 729-7900
5144 Enterprise Blvd Toledo (43612) *(G-18335)*

Amcraft Manufacturing, Toledo *Also called Amcraft Inc (G-18335)*

AMD Fabricators Inc 440 946-8855
4580 Beidler Rd Willoughby (44094) *(G-20429)*

AMD Plastics LLC (PA) 216 289-4862
27600 Lakeland Blvd Euclid (44132) *(G-9565)*

Ameco USA Metal Fabrication 440 899-9400
4600 W 160th St Cleveland (44135) *(G-4777)*

Amerascrew Inc 419 522-2232
653 Lida St Mansfield (44903) *(G-12559)*

Ameri-Cal Corporation 330 725-7735
1001 Lake Rd Medina (44256) *(G-13368)*

American Academic Press 216 906-2518
550 Turney Rd Apt C Bedford (44146) *(G-1396)*

American Advnced Assmblies LLC 937 339-6267
37 Harolds Way Troy (45373) *(G-18802)*

American Aero Components LLC 937 367-5068
2601 W Stroop Rd Unit 60 Dayton (45439) *(G-8150)*

American Airless Inc 614 552-0146
7095 Americana Pkwy Reynoldsburg (43068) *(G-16580)*

American Aluminum Extrusions 330 458-0300
4416 Louisville St Ne Canton (44705) *(G-2602)*

American Apex Corporation 614 652-2000
8515 Rausch Dr Plain City (43064) *(G-16319)*

American Assembly Tools, Columbia Station *Also called Triad Capital Aat LLC (G-6603)*

American Awards Inc 614 875-1850
2380 Harrisburg Pike Grove City (43123) *(G-10542)*

American Baler Co 419 483-5790
800 E Center St Bellevue (44811) *(G-1543)*

American Band Saw Co 740 452-8168
4049 Newark Rd Zanesville (43701) *(G-21271)*

American Barricade, Dalton *Also called Gedco Inc (G-8069)*

American Book Screening, Cleveland *Also called Betley Printing Co (G-4910)*

American Bottling Company 614 237-4201
960 Stelzer Rd Columbus (43219) *(G-6730)*

American Bottling Company 937 236-0333
3131 Transportation Rd Dayton (45404) *(G-8151)*

American Bottling Company 740 922-5253
Old Rte 250 Midvale (44653) *(G-14104)*

American Bottling Company 740 377-4371
2531 County Road 1 South Point (45680) *(G-17432)*

American Bottling Company 740 423-9230
871 State Route 618 Little Hocking (45742) *(G-12142)*

American Bottling Company 614 237-4201
950 Stelzer Rd Columbus (43219) *(G-6731)*

American Bottling Company 419 229-7777
2350 Central Point Pkwy Lima (45804) *(G-11988)*

American Bottling Company 419 535-0777
224 N Byrne Rd Toledo (43607) *(G-18336)*

American Bottling Company 513 381-4891
125 E Court St Ste 820 Cincinnati (45202) *(G-3384)*

American Bottling Company 419 529-6773
1115 National Pkwy Mansfield (44906) *(G-12560)*

American Bottling Company 513 242-5151
5151 Fischer Ave Cincinnati (45217) *(G-3385)*

American Brass, Cleveland *Also called Empire Brass Co (G-5276)*

American Brass Manufacturing 216 431-6565
5000 Superior Ave Cleveland (44103) *(G-4778)*

American Brick & Block, Dayton *Also called American Concrete Products (G-8153)*

American Bronze Corporation 216 341-7800
2941 Broadway Ave Cleveland (44115) *(G-4779)*

American Bronzing Company, Columbus *Also called Bron-Shoe Company (G-6867)*

American Brzing Div Paulo Pdts, Willoughby *Also called Paulo Products Company (G-20567)*

American Buffing, Carlisle *Also called Qibco Buffing Pads Inc (G-2935)*

American Built Custom Pallets 330 532-4780
42120 Glasgow Rd Lisbon (44432) *(G-12116)*

American Canvas Products Inc 419 382-8450
2925 South Ave Toledo (43609) *(G-18337)*

American Carbide Tool Company, Canton *Also called Ohio Metal Working Products (G-2801)*

American Carved Crystal, Cleveland *Also called R M Yates Co Inc (G-6084)*

American Centrifuge Plant, Piketon *Also called Centrus Energy Corp (G-16217)*

American Ceramic Society (PA) 614 890-4700
600 N Cleveland Ave # 210 Westerville (43082) *(G-20137)*

American Chemical Products 216 267-7722
5041 W 161st St Cleveland (44142) *(G-4780)*

American City Bus Journals Inc 513 337-9450
120 E 4th St Ste 230 Cincinnati (45202) *(G-3386)*

American City Bus Journals Inc 937 528-4400
40 N Main St Ste 800 Dayton (45423) *(G-8152)*

American Climber & Mch Corp 330 420-0019
38294 Industrial Park Rd Lisbon (44432) *(G-12117)*

American Coal Co 740 926-1372
56854 Pleasant Ridge Rd Alledonia (43902) *(G-484)*

American Colloid Company 419 445-9085
809 Myers St Archbold (43502) *(G-662)*

American Colorscans Inc 614 895-0233
5178 Sinclair Rd Columbus (43229) *(G-6732)*

American Commodore Tuxedos 440 324-2889
3433 Midway Mall Elyria (44035) *(G-9370)*

American Community Newspapers 614 888-4567
5255 Sinclair Rd Columbus (43229) *(G-6733)*

American Concrete Products 937 224-1433
1433 S Euclid Ave Dayton (45417) *(G-8153)*

American Confections Co LLC 614 888-8838
6291 Busch Blvd Columbus (43229) *(G-6734)*

American Controls Inc 440 944-9735
1340 Lloyd Rd Wickliffe (44092) *(G-20353)*

American Corrugated Michigan, Columbus *Also called American Corrugated Pdts Inc (G-6736)*

American Corrugated Pdts Inc (PA) 614 870-2000
4700 Alkire Rd Columbus (43228) *(G-6735)*

American Corrugated Pdts Inc 800 248-6840
4700 Alkire Rd Columbus (43228) *(G-6736)*

American Craft Brewery LLC 513 412-3200
1625 Central Pkwy Cincinnati (45214) *(G-3387)*

American Cube Mold Inc 330 558-0044
1515 W 130th St Ste C Hinckley (44233) *(G-11022)*

American Culvert & Fabg Co 740 432-6334
201 Wheeling Ave Cambridge (43725) *(G-2443)*

American Custom Industries, Sylvania *Also called Bobbart Industries Inc (G-18101)*

American Custom Polishing, Cincinnati *Also called Charles J Meyers (G-3523)*

American Doll Accessories 740 590-8458
24924 Brimstone Rd Coolville (45723) *(G-7833)*

American Dreams Inc 740 385-4444
1 Shoreline Dr Thornville (43076) *(G-18191)*

American Electric Furnace Co, Cleveland *Also called A E F Inc (G-4670)*

American Electric Motor Svc................................614 297-1600
  900 Gray St Columbus (43201) (G-6737)
American Electric Power, Columbus Also called AEP Resources Inc (G-6700)
American Energy Corporation................................740 926-2430
  43521 Mayhugh Hill Rd Beallsville (43716) (G-1307)
American Energy Pdts Inc Ind, Mount Vernon Also called Capital City Oil Inc (G-14612)
American Envmtl Group Ltd................................330 659-5930
  3600 Brecksville Rd # 100 Richfield (44286) (G-16613)
American Executive Gifts Inc................................330 645-4396
  2098 Sypher Rd Unit C Akron (44306) (G-66)
American Extrusion Svcs Inc (HQ)................................937 743-1210
  235 Advanced Dr Springboro (45066) (G-17473)
American Fine Sinter Co Ltd................................419 443-8880
  957 N County Road 11 Tiffin (44883) (G-18202)
American Fireworks Company Inc................................330 650-1776
  7041 Darrow Rd Hudson (44236) (G-11156)
American Flange & Mfg Co Inc................................740 549-6073
  425 Winter Rd Delaware (43015) (G-8820)
American Fluid Power Inc................................877 223-8742
  144 Reaser Ct Elyria (44035) (G-9371)
American Foam Products Inc................................440 352-3434
  753 Liberty St Painesville (44077) (G-15850)
American Foods Dist Co LLC................................614 218-4049
  7884 Dolmen Dr Blacklick (43004) (G-1687)
American Foods Group LLC................................513 733-8898
  3480 E Kemper Rd Cincinnati (45241) (G-3388)
American Frame Corporation................................419 893-5595
  400 Tomahawk Dr Maumee (43537) (G-13222)
American Friction Tech LLC................................216 823-0861
  9300 Midwest Ave Cleveland (44125) (G-4781)
American Future Systems Inc................................330 758-0277
  970 Windham Ct Ste 1b Youngstown (44512) (G-21023)
American Greetings Corporation (HQ)................................216 252-7300
  1 American Rd Cleveland (44144) (G-4782)
American Greetings Corporation................................216 685-9167
  230 W Huron Rd Ste 7228 Cleveland (44113) (G-4783)
American Grphcal Sftwr Systems, Chesterland Also called American Grphcal Sftwr
Systems (G-3198)
American Grphcal Sftwr Systems................................440 729-0018
  8000 Wedgewood Dr Chesterland (44026) (G-3198)
American Guard Co Inc................................440 354-1400
  150 D Termination Ave Geneva (44041) (G-10342)
American Guild of English Hand................................937 438-0085
  201 E 5th St 19001025 Cincinnati (45202) (G-3389)
American Health Packaging................................614 492-8177
  2550 John Glenn Ave Ste A Columbus (43217) (G-6738)
American Heart Association Inc................................419 740-6180
  4331 Keystone Dr Ste D Maumee (43537) (G-13223)
American Heat Treating, Dayton Also called Pride Investments LLC (G-8591)
American Heritage Blld LLC................................330 626-3710
  630 Mondial Pkwy Streetsboro (44241) (G-17838)
American Heritage Billiards................................330 626-3710
  630 Mondial Pkwy Streetsboro (44241) (G-17839)
American Highway Products Ltd................................330 874-3270
  11723 Strasburg Bolivar Bolivar (44612) (G-1927)
American Home Products LLC (HQ)................................800 684-3434
  25201 Chagrin Blvd # 350 Cleveland (44122) (G-4784)
American Honda Motor Co Inc................................937 332-6100
  101 S Stanfield Rd Troy (45373) (G-18803)
American Imprssions Sportswear, Worthington Also called Robert Midkiff (G-20885)
American Indus Maintenance................................937 254-3400
  605 Springfield St Dayton (45403) (G-8154)
American Inks and Coatings Co................................513 552-7200
  575 Quality Blvd Fairfield (45014) (G-9641)
American Insulation Tech LLC................................513 733-4248
  6071 Branch Hill Guinea P Milford (45150) (G-14120)
American Interior Design Inc................................216 663-0606
  19561 Miles Rd Cleveland (44128) (G-4785)
American Interiors Inc (PA)................................419 324-0365
  302 S Byrne Rd Bldg 100 Toledo (43615) (G-18338)
American Ir Met Cleveland LLC................................216 266-0518
  1240 Marquette St Cleveland (44114) (G-4786)
American Isostatic Presses Inc................................614 445-9081
  1205 S Columbus Arprt Rd Columbus (43207) (G-6739)
American Israelite Co................................513 621-3145
  18 W 9th St Ste 2 Cincinnati (45202) (G-3390)
American Israelite Newspaper, Cincinnati Also called American Israelite Co (G-3390)
American Jrnl of Drmtpathology................................440 542-0041
  6554 Dorset Ln Solon (44139) (G-17257)
American Laser and Machine LLC................................419 214-0880
  501 Weston St Toledo (43609) (G-18339)
American Lawyers Co Inc (PA)................................440 333-5190
  853 Westpoint Pkwy # 710 Westlake (44145) (G-20250)
American Lawyers Quarterly, Westlake Also called American Lawyers Co Inc (G-20250)
American Led-Gible Inc................................614 851-1100
  1776 Lone Eagle St Columbus (43228) (G-6740)
American Legal Publishing Corp................................513 421-4248
  1 W 4th St 300 Cincinnati (45202) (G-3391)

American Light Metals LLC................................330 467-0750
  635 Highland Rd E Macedonia (44056) (G-12435)
American Lithuanian Press................................216 531-8150
  19807 Cherokee Ave Cleveland (44119) (G-4787)
American Made Corrugated Packg................................937 981-2111
  1100 N 5th St Greenfield (45123) (G-10473)
American Manufacturing Inc (PA)................................419 531-9471
  2375 Dorr St Ste F Toledo (43607) (G-18340)
American Manufacturing & Eqp................................513 829-2248
  4990 Factory Dr Fairfield (45014) (G-9642)
American Merchant Servic................................216 598-3100
  3076 Waterfall Way Westlake (44145) (G-20251)
American Metal Chemical Corp (PA)................................330 725-4501
  835 W Smith Rd Medina (44256) (G-13369)
American Metal Chemical Corp................................440 244-1800
  200 E 9th St Lorain (44052) (G-12232)
American Metal Cleaning Inc................................419 255-1828
  2512 Albion St Toledo (43610) (G-18341)
American Metal Coatings Inc................................216 451-3131
  1088 Ivanhoe Rd Cleveland (44110) (G-4788)
American Metal Proc Co LLC................................216 486-4600
  17001 Saranac Rd Cleveland (44110) (G-4789)
American Metal Sign................................267 521-2670
  4750 State Route 309 Ada (45810) (G-4)
American Metal Tech LLC................................937 347-1111
  851 Bellbrook Ave Xenia (45385) (G-20936)
American Metal Treating Co................................216 431-4492
  1043 E 62nd St Cleveland (44103) (G-4790)
American Mfg & Engrg Co................................440 899-9400
  7500 Grand Division Ave Cleveland (44125) (G-4791)
American Mine Door, Cleveland Also called Zen Industries Inc (G-6493)
American Mitsuba Corporation................................989 779-4962
  4140 Tuller Rd Ste 106 Dublin (43017) (G-9042)
American Mitsuba Corporation................................989 779-4962
  4140 Tuller Rd Ste 106 Dublin (43017) (G-9043)
American Mnfcturing Operations................................419 269-1560
  1931 E Manhattan Blvd Toledo (43608) (G-18342)
American Molded Plastics Inc................................330 872-3838
  3876 Newton Fls Bailey Rd Newton Falls (44444) (G-15128)
American Molding Company Inc................................330 620-6799
  711 Wooster Rd W Barberton (44203) (G-1097)
American Mtal Clg Cncnnati Inc................................513 825-1171
  475 Northland Blvd Cincinnati (45240) (G-3392)
American Ndt Incorporated................................740 687-1321
  671 E Walnut St Lancaster (43130) (G-11684)
American Office Services Inc................................440 899-6888
  30257 Clemens Rd Unit C Westlake (44145) (G-20252)
American Ohio Locomotive Crane, Bucyrus Also called Ers Industries Inc (G-2342)
American Orginal Bldg Pdts LLC................................330 786-3000
  1000 Arlington Cir Akron (44306) (G-67)
American Orthopedics Inc (PA)................................614 291-6454
  1151 W 5th Ave Columbus (43212) (G-6741)
American Paint Recyclers, Lima Also called Brinkman LLC (G-11997)
American Paint Recyclers LLC................................888 978-6558
  4664 Mddle Pint Wetzel Rd Middle Point (45863) (G-13897)
American Pan Company, Sunbury Also called Bundy Baking Solutions (G-18057)
American Pan Company (PA)................................937 652-3232
  417 E Water St Ste 2 Urbana (43078) (G-19146)
American Paper Converting LLC................................419 729-4782
  6142 American Rd Toledo (43612) (G-18343)
American Pennekamp Mfg Inc................................740 687-0096
  1495 Longwood Dr Ne Lancaster (43130) (G-11685)
American Pioneer Manufacturing................................330 457-1400
  3672 Silliman St New Waterford (44445) (G-14967)
American Plastic Tech Inc (PA)................................440 632-5203
  15229 S State Ave Middlefield (44062) (G-13914)
American Polymer Standards................................440 255-2211
  8680 Tyler Blvd Mentor (44060) (G-13520)
American Posts LLC................................419 720-0652
  810 Chicago St Toledo (43611) (G-18344)
American Power Hoist Inc................................740 964-2035
  63 E Mill St Pataskala (43062) (G-15967)
American Power Pull Corp................................419 335-7050
  115 E Linfoot St Wauseon (43567) (G-19671)
American Precision Spindles (HQ)................................267 436-6000
  670 Alpha Dr Cleveland (44143) (G-4792)
American Printing Inc................................330 630-1121
  1121 Tower Dr Akron (44305) (G-68)
American Pro-Mold Inc................................330 336-4111
  350 State St 7 Wadsworth (44281) (G-19394)
American Processing LLC................................216 486-4600
  17001 Saranac Rd Cleveland (44110) (G-4793)
American Products, Waterville Also called Duvall Woodworking Inc (G-19656)
American Punch Co Inc................................216 731-4501
  1655 Century Corners Pkwy Euclid (44132) (G-9566)
American Quality Door, Marion Also called Bert Radebaugh (G-12857)
American Quality Molds LLC................................513 276-7345
  2275 Millville Ave Ste E Hamilton (45013) (G-10665)
American Quality Stripping................................419 625-6288
  1750 5th St Sandusky (44870) (G-16946)

American Quicksilver Co 513 871-4517
646 Rushton Rd Cincinnati (45226) *(G-3393)*

American Qulty Fabrication Inc 937 667-2861
849 Scholz Dr Vandalia (45377) *(G-19281)*

American Race Cars 419 836-5070
29724 Pemberville Rd Millbury (43447) *(G-14182)*

American Rescue Technology 937 293-6240
2780 Culver Ave Dayton (45429) *(G-8155)*

American Ride Wheelchair Coach 216 276-1700
1368 W 65th St Cleveland (44102) *(G-4794)*

American Road Machinery, Canton Also called ARM Opco Inc *(G-2605)*

American Rodpump Ltd 440 987-9457
5201 Indian Hill Rd Dublin (43017) *(G-9044)*

American Roll Formed Pdts Corp (HQ) 440 352-0753
141 W Walnut Ave Painesville (44077) *(G-15851)*

American Rubber Products Co 440 461-0900
30775 Solon Indus Pkwy Solon (44139) *(G-17258)*

American Rugged Enclosures (PA) 513 942-3004
4 Standen Dr Hamilton (45015) *(G-10666)*

American Sand & Gravel Div, Massillon Also called Kenmore Construction Co Inc *(G-13162)*

American Scaffolding Inc 216 524-7733
7600 Wall St Ste 200 Cleveland (44125) *(G-4795)*

American Showa Inc 937 783-4961
960 Cherry St Blanchester (45107) *(G-1709)*

American Solving Inc 440 234-7373
6519 Eastland Rd Ste 5 Brookpark (44142) *(G-2150)*

American Speedy Printing, Zanesville Also called T & K Heins Corporation *(G-21358)*

American Speedy Printing, North Olmsted Also called E T & K Inc *(G-15331)*

American Speedy Printing, Cleveland Also called E T & K Inc *(G-5234)*

American Sports Center, Dayton Also called Fried Daddy *(G-8351)*

American Sports Design Company 937 865-5431
6551 Centervl Bus Pkwy Centerville (45459) *(G-3035)*

American Spring Wire Corp (PA) 216 292-4620
26300 Miles Rd Bedford Heights (44146) *(G-1478)*

American Standard Brands, Groveport Also called As America Inc *(G-10614)*

American Standard Brands, Mansfield Also called As America Inc *(G-12563)*

American Steel & Alloys LLC 330 847-0487
4000 Mahoning Ave Nw Warren (44483) *(G-19521)*

American Steel Assod Pdts Inc 419 531-9471
2375 Dorr St Ste F Toledo (43607) *(G-18345)*

American Steel Carports Inc 419 737-1331
200 Industrial Ave Pioneer (43554) *(G-16232)*

American Steel Grave Vault Co 419 468-6715
799 Newberry Dr Galion (44833) *(G-10253)*

American Steel Treating Inc 419 662-5500
525 W 6th St Perrysburg (43551) *(G-16063)*

American Steel Treating Inc (PA) 419 874-2044
525 W 6th St Perrysburg (43551) *(G-16064)*

American Stirrup, Holmesville Also called Holmes Wheel Shop Inc *(G-11106)*

American Superior Lighting 740 266-2959
1506 Fernwood Rd Steubenville (43953) *(G-17687)*

American Sweet Bean Co LLC 888 995-0007
8133 N Township Road 72a Tiffin (44883) *(G-18203)*

American Tank & Fabricating Co (PA) 216 252-1500
12314 Elmwood Ave Cleveland (44111) *(G-4796)*

American Tchnical Coatings Inc 440 401-2270
28045 Ranney Pkwy Ste H Westlake (44145) *(G-20253)*

American Tool & Manufacturing, Mansfield Also called American Tool & Mfg Co *(G-12561)*

American Tool & Mfg Co 419 522-2452
211 Newman St Mansfield (44902) *(G-12561)*

American Tool and Die Inc 419 726-5394
2024 Champlain St Toledo (43611) *(G-18346)*

American Tool Works Inc 513 844-6363
1691 Thall Dr Hamilton (45013) *(G-10667)*

American Tool Works Inc (PA) 513 844-6363
160 Hancock Ave Hamilton (45011) *(G-10668)*

American Tower, Shelby Also called Amto Acquisition Corp *(G-17131)*

American Traditions Basket Co 330 854-0900
722 Tell Dr Canal Fulton (44614) *(G-2496)*

American Trim, Lima Also called Superior Metal Products Inc *(G-12099)*

American Trim LLC 419 228-1145
1501 Michigan St Ste 1 Sidney (45365) *(G-17167)*

American Trim LLC 419 996-4703
999 W Grand Ave Lima (45801) *(G-11989)*

American Trim LLC 419 739-4349
217 Krein Ave Wapakoneta (45895) *(G-19476)*

American Trim LLC 419 738-9664
713 Maple St Wapakoneta (45895) *(G-19477)*

American Trim LLC 419 996-4729
651 N Baxter St Lima (45801) *(G-11990)*

American Trim LLC 419 996-4703
625 Victory Ave Lima (45801) *(G-11991)*

American Trim LLC (HQ) 419 228-1145
1005 W Grand Ave Lima (45801) *(G-11992)*

American Ultra Specialties Inc 330 656-5000
6855 Industrial Pkwy Hudson (44236) *(G-11157)*

American Utility Proc LLC 330 535-3000
1246 Princeton St Akron (44301) *(G-69)*

American Veneer Edgebanding 740 928-0266
1700 James Pkwy Newark (43056) *(G-14981)*

American Water Services Inc 440 243-9840
17449 W Sprague Rd Strongsville (44136) *(G-17887)*

American Way Manufacturing Inc 330 824-2353
1871 Henn Pkwy Sw Warren (44481) *(G-19522)*

American Weldquip Inc 330 239-0317
1375 Wolf Creek Trl Sharon Center (44274) *(G-17100)*

American Western Inc 513 662-8802
2575 Queen City Ave Cincinnati (45238) *(G-3394)*

American Western Cigar Company, Cincinnati Also called American Western Inc *(G-3394)*

American Whistle Corporation 614 846-2918
6540 Huntley Rd Ste B Columbus (43229) *(G-6742)*

American Window Pdts of Ohio 330 830-0274
1200 Cleveland St Sw D Massillon (44647) *(G-13107)*

American Wire & Cable Company (PA) 440 235-1140
7951 Bronson Rd Olmsted Twp (44138) *(G-15678)*

American Wood Fibers Inc 740 420-3233
2500 Owens Rd Circleville (43113) *(G-4623)*

American Woodwork Specialty Co 937 263-1053
4301 N James H Mcgee Blvd Dayton (45417) *(G-8156)*

Americarb Inc 419 281-5800
1025 Faultless Dr Ashland (44805) *(G-703)*

Americarb International Corp 419 281-5800
1025 Faultless Dr Ashland (44805) *(G-704)*

Americas Best Cstm Digitizing, Xenia Also called Alphabet Embroidery Studios *(G-20935)*

Americas Best Siding Co 419 589-5900
1395 W Longview Ave Mansfield (44906) *(G-12562)*

Americas Components, Springfield Also called Konecranes Inc *(G-17589)*

Americas Styrenics LLC 740 533-4017
925 County Road 1a Hanging Rock (45638) *(G-10761)*

Americhem Inc 330 926-3185
155 E Steels Corners Rd Cuyahoga Falls (44224) *(G-7964)*

Americhem Inc (PA) 330 929-4213
2000 Americhem Way Cuyahoga Falls (44221) *(G-7965)*

Americraft Bronze Co, Waterville Also called Maumee Valley Memorials Inc *(G-19663)*

Americraft Carton Inc 419 668-1006
209 Republic St Norwalk (44857) *(G-15525)*

Americraft Mfg Co Inc 513 489-1047
7937 School Rd Cincinnati (45249) *(G-3395)*

Americraft Stor Buildings Ltd 330 877-6900
1147 W Maple St Hartville (44632) *(G-10816)*

Ameridian Specialty Services 513 769-0150
11520 Rockfield Ct Cincinnati (45241) *(G-3396)*

Amerigraph Llc 614 278-8000
2727 Harrison Rd Columbus (43204) *(G-6743)*

Amerilam Laminating 440 235-4687
4651 W 130th St Cleveland (44135) *(G-4797)*

Amerimold Inc 330 628-2190
595a Waterloo Rd Ste A Mogadore (44260) *(G-14367)*

Amerimulch, Twinsburg Also called Chromascape Inc *(G-18912)*

Ameriprint 440 235-6094
8119 Columbia Rd Olmsted Falls (44138) *(G-15673)*

Amerisourcebergen Corporation 614 497-3665
6305 Lasalle Dr Lockbourne (43137) *(G-12145)*

Ameritech Publishing Inc 614 895-6123
2550 Corp Exchange Dr # 310 Columbus (43231) *(G-6744)*

Ameritech Publishing Inc 330 896-6037
1530 Corp Woods Pkwy # 100 Uniontown (44685) *(G-19075)*

Ameritest, Solon Also called Ohio Lumex Co Inc *(G-17355)*

Ameriwater LLC 937 461-8833
3345 Stop 8 Rd Dayton (45414) *(G-8157)*

Ameriwood, Steubenville Also called Express Care *(G-17694)*

Ames Companies Inc 740 783-2535
21460 Ames Ln Dexter City (45727) *(G-8953)*

Ames Development Group Ltd 419 704-7812
2339 Drummond Rd Toledo (43606) *(G-18347)*

Ames Lock Specialties Inc 419 474-2995
2121 W Sylvania Ave Toledo (43613) *(G-18348)*

Ames Locksmith, Toledo Also called Ames Lock Specialties Inc *(G-18348)*

Ametco Manufacturing Corp 440 951-4300
4326 Hamann Pkwy Willoughby (44094) *(G-20430)*

Ametek Inc 937 440-0800
66 Industry Ct Ste F Troy (45373) *(G-18804)*

Ametek Inc 302 636-5401
530 Lakeview Plaza Blvd C Worthington (43085) *(G-20857)*

Ametek Electromechanical Group, Kent Also called Ametek Technical & Indus Pdts *(G-11429)*

Ametek Florcare Specialty Mtrs 330 677-3786
100 E Erie St Ste 200 Kent (44240) *(G-11428)*

Ametek Presto Light Power, Troy Also called Ametek Inc *(G-18804)*

Ametek Technical & Indus Pdts (HQ) 330 677-3754
100 E Erie St Ste 130 Kent (44240) *(G-11429)*

Ametek Westchester Plastics 419 739-3200
14101 Cemetery Rd Wapakoneta (45895) *(G-19478)*

Amex Dies Inc 330 545-9766
932 N State St Girard (44420) *(G-10382)*

AMF Bruns America Lp 877 506-3770
1797 Georgetown Rd Hudson (44236) *(G-11158)*

AMF Bruns of America, Hudson *Also called AMF Bruns America Lp* ***(G-11158)***
Amfm Inc 440 953-4545
38373 Pelton Rd Willoughby (44094) ***(G-20431)***
AMG Industries LLC 740 397-4044
200 Commerce Dr Mount Vernon (43050) ***(G-14605)***
AMG Vanadium LLC 740 435-4600
60790 Southgate Rd Cambridge (43725) ***(G-2444)***
Amh Holdings LLC 330 929-1811
3773 State Rd Cuyahoga Falls (44223) ***(G-7966)***
Amh Holdings II Inc 330 929-1811
3773 State Rd Cuyahoga Falls (44223) ***(G-7967)***
Amherst Party Shop, Amherst *Also called Currier Richard & James* ***(G-596)***
Amidac Wind Corporation 213 973-4000
151 Innovation Dr Elyria (44035) ***(G-9372)***
Amir International Foods Inc 614 332-1742
3504 Broadway Grove City (43123) ***(G-10543)***
Amish Country Essentials LLC 330 674-3088
1817 State Route 83 # 353 Millersburg (44654) ***(G-14192)***
Amish Door Inc (PA) 330 359-5464
1210 Winesburg St Wilmot (44689) ***(G-20683)***
Amish Door Restaurant, Wilmot *Also called Amish Door Inc* ***(G-20683)***
Amish Heritg WD Floors & Furn, Middlefield *Also called Cherokee Hardwoods Inc* ***(G-13922)***
Amish Lights Candles 330 546-3900
8748 Woodlore Cir Nw North Canton (44720) ***(G-15219)***
Amish Timber Framers 330 658-5699
11627 Hametown Rd Doylestown (44230) ***(G-9026)***
Amish Wedding Foods, Millersburg *Also called Troyer Cheese Inc* ***(G-14274)***
Amish Wedding Foods Inc 330 674-9199
316 S Mad Anthony St Millersburg (44654) ***(G-14193)***
Amko Service Company, Midvale *Also called Fiba Technologies Inc* ***(G-14107)***
Amko Service Company (HQ) 330 364-8857
3211 Brightwood Rd Midvale (44653) ***(G-14105)***
Aml Industries Inc 330 399-5000
520 Pine Ave Se Ste 1 Warren (44483) ***(G-19523)***
Amon Inc 513 734-1700
3214 Marshall Dr Amelia (45102) ***(G-567)***
Amoney Train Music, Cuyahoga Falls *Also called Thickemz Entertainment LLC* ***(G-8056)***
Amos Press Inc (PA) 937 498-2111
911 S Vandemark Rd Sidney (45365) ***(G-17168)***
AMP Electric Vehicles Inc 513 360-4704
100 Commerce Dr Loveland (45140) ***(G-12339)***
AMP-Tech Inc 419 652-3444
910 County Road 40 Nova (44859) ***(G-15575)***
Ampac Holdings LLC (HQ) 513 671-1777
12025 Tricon Rd Cincinnati (45246) ***(G-3397)***
Ampac Packaging LLC (HQ) 513 671-1777
12025 Tricon Rd Cincinnati (45246) ***(G-3398)***
Ampac Plastics LLC 513 671-1777
12025 Tricon Rd Cincinnati (45246) ***(G-3399)***
Ampacet Corporation 740 929-5521
1855 James Pkwy Newark (43056) ***(G-14982)***
Ampacet Corporation 513 247-5400
4705 Duke Dr 400 Cincinnati (45249) ***(G-3400)***
Ampak, Cleveland *Also called Heat Seal LLC* ***(G-5491)***
Ampersand International Inc 216 831-3500
23775 Commerce Park Beachwood (44122) ***(G-1257)***
Ampex Metal Products Company (PA) 216 267-9242
5581 W 164th St Brookpark (44142) ***(G-2151)***
Ample Industries Inc 937 746-9700
4000 Commerce Center Dr Franklin (45005) ***(G-10007)***
Amplified Solar Inc 216 236-4225
1453 Wayne Ave Lakewood (44107) ***(G-11656)***
Ampp Incorporated 419 666-4747
28271 Cedar Park Blvd # 5 Perrysburg (43551) ***(G-16065)***
Ampsco Division 614 444-2181
2301 Fairwood Ave Columbus (43207) ***(G-6745)***
Amptech Machining & Welding 419 652-3444
910 County Road 40 Nova (44859) ***(G-15576)***
Amresco LLC 440 349-2805
6681 Cochran Rd Solon (44139) ***(G-17259)***
Amresco LLC 440 349-2805
29999 Solon Indus Pkwy Cleveland (44139) ***(G-4798)***
Amrex Inc 330 678-7050
431 W Elm St Kent (44240) ***(G-11430)***
Amrod Bridge & Iron LLC 330 530-8230
105 Ohio Ave Mc Donald (44437) ***(G-13346)***
Amron LLC 330 457-8570
47287 State Route 558 New Waterford (44445) ***(G-14968)***
Amron Testing, New Waterford *Also called Amron LLC* ***(G-14968)***
Amros Industries Inc 216 433-0010
14701 Industrial Pkwy Cleveland (44135) ***(G-4799)***
AMS, Strongsville *Also called Automated Mfg Solutions Inc* ***(G-17893)***
AMS Global Ltd 937 620-1036
119 E Dayton St West Alexandria (45381) ***(G-19778)***
AMS Uniforms, Lima *Also called Affordable Med Scrubs LLC* ***(G-11982)***
Amsoil Inc 614 274-9851
707 Hadley Dr Columbus (43228) ***(G-6746)***
Amsted Industries Incorporated 614 836-2323
3900 Bixby Rd Groveport (43125) ***(G-10612)***
Amsted Rail Company Inc 614 836-2323
3900 Bixby Rd Groveport (43125) ***(G-10613)***
Amt, Brecksville *Also called Applied Medical Technology Inc* ***(G-2034)***
Amt Machine Systems Limited 740 965-2693
1760 Zollinger Rd Ste 2 Columbus (43221) ***(G-6747)***
Amt Machine Systems Ltd 614 635-8050
50 W Broad St Ste 1200 Columbus (43215) ***(G-6748)***
Amtank Armor LLC 216 252-1500
12314 Elmwood Ave Cleveland (44111) ***(G-4800)***
Amtech Inc 440 238-2141
11925 Pearl Rd Ste 207 Strongsville (44136) ***(G-17888)***
Amtech Laminating Equipment, Strongsville *Also called Amtech Inc* ***(G-17888)***
Amtech Tool and Machine Inc 330 758-8215
100 Mcclurg Rd Youngstown (44512) ***(G-21024)***
Amteco Inc 513 217-4430
5773 Elk Creek Rd Middletown (45042) ***(G-14020)***
Amtekco Industries Inc (HQ) 614 228-6590
1205 Refugee Rd Columbus (43207) ***(G-6749)***
Amtekco Industries Inc 614 228-6525
33 W Hinman Ave Columbus (43207) ***(G-6750)***
Amthor Steel Inc 330 759-0200
5019 Belmont Ave Youngstown (44505) ***(G-21025)***
Amto Acquisition Corp 419 347-1185
5085 State Route 39 W Shelby (44875) ***(G-17131)***
An Baiceir Bakery 740 739-0501
116 Reader Ct Etna (43062) ***(G-9554)***
An Environmental Inks 513 870-0288
5150 Duff Dr West Chester (45246) ***(G-19980)***
Anadem Inc 614 262-2539
3620 N High St Ste 201 Columbus (43214) ***(G-6751)***
Anaheim Manufacturing Company 800 767-6293
25300 Al Moen Dr North Olmsted (44070) ***(G-15326)***
Analiza Inc (PA) 216 432-9050
3615 Superior Ave E 4407b Cleveland (44114) ***(G-4801)***
Analog Bridge Inc 937 901-4832
2897 Kant Pl Beavercreek (45431) ***(G-1317)***
Analynk Wireless LLC 614 755-5091
790 Cross Pointe Rd Columbus (43230) ***(G-6752)***
Analytic Stress Relieving Inc 804 271-7198
6944 Mcnerney Dr Northwood (43619) ***(G-15476)***
Anatomical Concepts Inc 330 757-3569
1399 E Western Reserve Rd Youngstown (44514) ***(G-21026)***
Anchi Inc 740 653-2527
1115 W 5th Ave Lancaster (43130) ***(G-11686)***
Anchor Bronze and Metals Inc 440 549-5653
11470 Euclid Ave Ste 509 Cleveland (44106) ***(G-4802)***
Anchor Chemical Co Inc (PA) 440 871-1660
777 Canterbury Rd Westlake (44145) ***(G-20254)***
Anchor Corporation 614 836-9590
2160 Cloverleaf St E Columbus (43232) ***(G-6753)***
Anchor Fabricators Inc 937 836-5117
386 Talmadge Rd Clayton (45315) ***(G-4656)***
Anchor Flange Company 513 527-4444
3959 Virginia Ave Cincinnati (45227) ***(G-3401)***
Anchor Fluid Power, Cincinnati *Also called Anchor Flange Company* ***(G-3401)***
Anchor Foundry & Machine Inc 330 453-3441
4411 Louisville St Ne Canton (44705) ***(G-2603)***
Anchor Glass Container Corp 740 452-2743
1555 Fairview Rd Zanesville (43701) ***(G-21272)***
Anchor Hocking, Lancaster *Also called Anchi Inc* ***(G-11686)***
Anchor Hocking LLC (HQ) 740 681-6478
519 N Pierce Ave Lancaster (43130) ***(G-11687)***
Anchor Hocking Company, The, Lancaster *Also called Anchor Hocking LLC* ***(G-11687)***
Anchor Hocking Consmr GL Corp 740 653-2527
1115 W 5th Ave Lancaster (43130) ***(G-11688)***
Anchor Hocking Corporation 740 681-6461
1115 W 5th Ave Lancaster (43130) ***(G-11689)***
Anchor Hocking Indus GL Div, Lancaster *Also called Ghp II LLC* ***(G-11719)***
Anchor Industries Incorporated 440 473-1414
30775 Solon Indus Pkwy Cleveland (44139) ***(G-4803)***
Anchor Lamina America, Dayton *Also called Dayton Lamina Corporation* ***(G-8277)***
Anchor Lamina America Inc 330 952-1595
445 W Liberty St Medina (44256) ***(G-13370)***
Anchor Manufacturing Group, Cleveland *Also called Anchor Tool & Die Co* ***(G-4806)***
Anchor Manufacturing Group, Cleveland *Also called Anchor Tool & Die Co* ***(G-4807)***
Anchor Metal Processing Inc 216 362-6463
12200 Brookpark Rd Cleveland (44130) ***(G-4804)***
Anchor Metal Processing Inc (PA) 216 362-1850
11830 Brookpark Rd Cleveland (44130) ***(G-4805)***
Anchor Pattern Company 614 443-2221
748 Frebis Ave Columbus (43206) ***(G-6754)***
Anchor Template Die Div, Cleveland *Also called Paramount Stamping & Wldg Co* ***(G-5964)***
Anchor Tool & Die Co (PA) 216 362-1850
12200 Brookpark Rd Cleveland (44130) ***(G-4806)***
Anchor Tool & Die Co 216 362-1850
12200 Brookpark Rd Cleveland (44130) ***(G-4807)***
Ancom Business Products, Brunswick *Also called Symatic Inc* ***(G-2260)***

Andal Woodworking..330 897-8059
1411 Township Road 151 Baltic (43804) *(G-1064)*

Andeen-Hagerling Inc...440 349-0370
31200 Bainbridge Rd Ste 2 Cleveland (44139) *(G-4808)*

Anderson & Vreeland Inc..419 636-5002
15348 State Rte 127 E Bryan (43506) *(G-2278)*

Anderson Brothers Entps Inc..................................440 269-3920
38180 Airport Pkwy Willoughby (44094) *(G-20432)*

Anderson Co (PA)...419 396-7056
415 W North St Carey (43316) *(G-2914)*

Anderson Concrete Corp (PA).................................614 443-0123
400 Frank Rd Columbus (43207) *(G-6755)*

Anderson Cosmetic & Vein Inst..............................513 624-7900
7794 5 Mile Rd Ste 270 Cincinnati (45230) *(G-3402)*

Anderson Door Co..216 475-5700
18090 Miles Rd Cleveland (44128) *(G-4809)*

Anderson Energy Inc..740 678-8608
12959 State Route 550 Fleming (45729) *(G-9909)*

Anderson Glass Co Inc...614 476-4877
2816 Morse Rd Columbus (43231) *(G-6756)*

Anderson Graphics Inc..330 745-2165
711 Wooster Rd W Barberton (44203) *(G-1098)*

Anderson Industries Inc...216 941-7766
15501 Chatfield Ave Cleveland (44111) *(G-4810)*

Anderson International Corp....................................216 641-1112
4545 Boyce Pkwy Stow (44224) *(G-17730)*

Anderson Pallet & Packg Inc..................................937 962-2614
210 Western Ave Lewisburg (45338) *(G-11931)*

Anderson Pallet Service, Lewisburg *Also called Anderson Pallet & Packg Inc (G-11931)*

Anderson Printing & Supply LLC.............................614 891-1100
237 E Broadway Ave Westerville (43081) *(G-20199)*

Anderson Publishing Co (PA).................................513 474-9305
9443 Springboro Pike Miamisburg (45342) *(G-13783)*

Anderson Vreeland Midwest, Bryan *Also called Anderson & Vreeland Inc (G-2278)*

Andersons Inc (PA)..419 893-5050
1947 Briarfield Blvd Maumee (43537) *(G-13224)*

Andersons Inc...419 536-0460
801 S Reynolds Rd Toledo (43615) *(G-18349)*

Andersons Inc...419 891-2930
415 Illinois Ave Maumee (43537) *(G-13225)*

Andersons Lawn Fert Div Inc..................................419 893-5050
480 W Dussel Dr Ste A Maumee (43537) *(G-13226)*

Andersons Marathon Ethanol LLC...........................937 316-3700
5728 Sebring Warner Rd N Greenville (45331) *(G-10488)*

Andersound PA Service..216 561-2636
15911 Harvard Ave Cleveland (44128) *(G-4811)*

Andras Corp..440 323-2528
840 Infirmary Rd Elyria (44035) *(G-9373)*

Andre Corporation...574 293-0207
4600 N Masn Montgomery Rd Mason (45040) *(G-12981)*

Andre Kitchens, Brice *Also called Carl C Andre Inc (G-2087)*

Andrew & Sons Inc..419 693-0292
2401 Consaul St Toledo (43605) *(G-18350)*

Andrew Tool Co Inc...440 237-4340
12146 York Rd Unit 2 North Royalton (44133) *(G-15409)*

Andrews Farms Inc..419 594-2111
12878 Road 209 Oakwood (45873) *(G-15614)*

Andromeda Research...513 831-9708
648 Quail Run Cincinnati (45244) *(G-3403)*

Andy A Raber..330 893-0400
3497 County Road 135 Millersburg (44654) *(G-14194)*

Andy Pac Inc...440 748-8800
11600 Hawke Rd Columbia Station (44028) *(G-6578)*

Andy Russo Jr Inc...440 585-1456
29200 Anderson Rd Wickliffe (44092) *(G-20354)*

Andys Mdterranean Fd Pdts LLC............................513 281-9791
906 Nassau St Cincinnati (45206) *(G-3404)*

Anest Iwata Air Engrg Inc......................................513 755-3100
5325 Muhlhauser Rd Hamilton (45011) *(G-10669)*

Anest Iwata Usa Inc..513 755-3100
5325 Muhlhauser Rd Hamilton (45011) *(G-10670)*

Angel Glass Lost...419 353-2831
122 Meeker St Bowling Green (43402) *(G-1967)*

Angel Prtg & Reproduction Co................................216 631-5225
1400 W 57th St Cleveland (44102) *(G-4812)*

Angel Window Mfg Corp...440 891-1006
237 Depot St Berea (44017) *(G-1601)*

Angelina Stone & Marble Ltd..................................740 633-3360
55341 W Center St Bridgeport (43912) *(G-2088)*

Angell-Demmel North Amer Corp (PA)....................937 461-5800
1516 Stanley Ave Dayton (45404) *(G-8158)*

Angels Landing Inc..513 687-3681
3430 S Dixie Dr Ste 301 Moraine (45439) *(G-14465)*

Anger Pattern Company Inc....................................330 882-6519
2999 S 1st St Clinton (44216) *(G-6533)*

Angleboard, Loveland *Also called Signode Industrial Group LLC (G-12387)*

Angry Cupcakes Productions LLC...........................216 229-2394
2300 E 95th St Cleveland (44106) *(G-4813)*

Angstrom Automotive Group LLC............................440 255-6700
8229 Tyler Blvd Mentor (44060) *(G-13521)*

Angstrom Corp..330 405-0524
9221 Ravenna Rd Ste 1 Twinsburg (44087) *(G-18899)*

Angstrom Graphics Inc (PA)...................................216 271-5300
4437 E 49th St Cleveland (44125) *(G-4814)*

Angstrom Graphics Inc Midwest (HQ).....................216 271-5300
4437 E 49th St Cleveland (44125) *(G-4815)*

Angstrom Graphics Southeast (HQ)........................216 271-5300
4437 E 49th St Cleveland (44125) *(G-4816)*

Angstrom Precision Metals LLC..............................440 255-6700
8229 Tyler Blvd Mentor (44060) *(G-13522)*

Angstron Materials Inc...937 331-9884
1240 Mccook Ave Dayton (45404) *(G-8159)*

Anheuser-Busch LLC...614 847-6213
700 Schrock Rd Columbus (43229) *(G-6757)*

Anita Plastics Inc..216 831-5773
38790 Glenlivet Ct Solon (44139) *(G-17260)*

Ankim Enterprises Incorporated..............................937 599-1121
1221 W Sandusky Ave Bellefontaine (43311) *(G-1518)*

Ann Printing & Promotions.....................................330 399-6564
269 E Market St Warren (44481) *(G-19524)*

Annals of Pharmaco Therapy, Cincinnati *Also called Harvey Whitney Books Company (G-3869)*

Annes Auntie Pretzels...614 418-7021
125 Easton Town Ctr Columbus (43219) *(G-6758)*

Annies Mud Pie Shop LLC.....................................513 871-2529
3130 Wasson Rd Unit 4 Cincinnati (45209) *(G-3405)*

Annin & Co..740 622-4447
700 S 3rd St Coshocton (43812) *(G-7878)*

Anodizing Specialists Inc.......................................440 951-0257
7547 Tyler Blvd Mentor (44060) *(G-13523)*

Anointed Design & Technologies.............................330 826-1493
1766 Huron Rd Se Massillon (44646) *(G-13108)*

Anomatic Corporation (HQ)....................................740 522-2203
8880 Innovation Campus Ct New Albany (43054) *(G-14745)*

Anotex Industries Inc..513 860-1165
4914 Rialto Rd West Chester (45069) *(G-19805)*

Anro Logistics Inc...614 428-7490
7473 Bentley Pl Westerville (43082) *(G-20138)*

Ansco Machine Company..330 929-8181
60 Cuyhoga Fls Indus Pkwy Peninsula (44264) *(G-16034)*

Ansell Healthcare Products LLC.............................740 622-4311
925 Chestnut St Coshocton (43812) *(G-7879)*

Ansell Healthcare Products LLC.............................740 295-5414
925 Chestnut St Coshocton (43812) *(G-7880)*

Anson Co..216 524-8838
18679 Orchard Hill Dr Bedford (44146) *(G-1397)*

Anstine Machining Corp...330 821-4365
15835 Armour St Ne Alliance (44601) *(G-496)*

Antero Resources Corporation................................303 357-7310
44510 Marietta Rd Caldwell (43724) *(G-2423)*

Anthony Business Forms Inc...................................937 253-0072
3160 Plainfield Rd Dayton (45432) *(G-8096)*

Anthony Decorative Fabrics and.............................937 299-4637
2701 Lance Dr Moraine (45409) *(G-14466)*

Anthony Mining Co Inc...740 266-8100
72 Airport Rd Wintersville (43953) *(G-20710)*

Anthony Thomas Candy Shoppes, Columbus *Also called Anthony-Thomas Candy Company (G-6760)*

Anthony's Fabric, Moraine *Also called Anthony Decorative Fabrics and (G-14466)*

Anthony-Lee Screen Prtg Inc.................................419 683-1861
401 S Thoman St Crestline (44827) *(G-7928)*

Anthony-Thomas Candy Company (PA)....................614 274-8405
1777 Arlingate Ln Columbus (43228) *(G-6759)*

Anthony-Thomas Candy Company...........................614 870-8899
4636 W Broad St Columbus (43228) *(G-6760)*

Anthony-Thomas Candy Shoppes, Columbus *Also called Anthony-Thomas Candy Company (G-6759)*

Antique Auto Sheet Metal Inc................................937 833-4422
718 Albert Rd Brookville (45309) *(G-2174)*

Antram Fire Equipment..330 525-7171
27970 Winona Rd North Georgetown (44665) *(G-15286)*

Antwerp Bee-Argus...419 258-8161
113 N Main St Antwerp (45813) *(G-627)*

Antwerp Tool & Die Inc..419 258-5271
3167 County Road 424 Antwerp (45813) *(G-628)*

Anvil Products Co..216 883-3740
4535 E 71st St Cleveland (44105) *(G-4817)*

Anything Personalized..330 655-0723
9261 Ravenna Rd Ste 10 Twinsburg (44087) *(G-18900)*

Anza Inc...513 542-7337
3265 Colerain Ave Ste 2 Cincinnati (45225) *(G-3406)*

Aot Inc...937 323-9669
4800 Gateway Blvd Springfield (45502) *(G-17517)*

AP Direct, Mentor *Also called Activities Press Inc (G-13509)*

AP Tech Group Inc...513 761-8111
11411 Williamson Rd Blue Ash (45241) *(G-1743)*

Ap-Alternatives LLC..419 267-5280
20 345 County Road X Ridgeville Corners (43555) *(G-16663)*

Apache Hose & Belting Co Inc 513 587-8313
9965 Farr Ct West Chester (45246) **(G-19981)**

Apartment Finder Magazine, Gahanna *Also called Network Communications Inc* **(G-10223)**

Apeks LLC 740 809-1160
150 Commerce Blvd Johnstown (43031) **(G-11389)**

Apeks Super Critical, Johnstown *Also called Apeks LLC* **(G-11389)**

Apex Advanced Technologies LLC 216 898-1595
4857a W 130th St Cleveland (44135) **(G-4818)**

Apex Aluminum Die Cast Co Inc 937 773-0432
8877 Sherry Dr Piqua (45356) **(G-16248)**

Apex Bolt & Machine Company 419 729-3741
5324 Enterprise Blvd Toledo (43612) **(G-18351)**

Apex Bulk Handlers, Bedford *Also called Apex Welding Incorporated* **(G-1398)**

Apex Circuits Inc 513 942-4400
5100 Excello Ct West Chester (45069) **(G-19806)**

Apex Crcits Elctrnic Dsign Man, West Chester *Also called Apex Circuits Inc* **(G-19806)**

Apex Fire Services LLC 614 274-6400
449 Industry Dr Columbus (43204) **(G-6761)**

Apex Metal Fabricating & Mch, Toledo *Also called Apex Bolt & Machine Company* **(G-18351)**

Apex Metals, Cleveland *Also called Erieview Metal Treating Co* **(G-5298)**

Apex Property Management, Richmond Heights *Also called Ajami Holdings Group LLC* **(G-16651)**

Apex Services, Akron *Also called Aaron Smith* **(G-24)**

Apex Solutions Inc 419 843-3434
2620 Centennial Rd Ste P Toledo (43617) **(G-18352)**

Apex Specialty Co Inc 330 725-6663
620 E Smith Rd Ste E7 Medina (44256) **(G-13371)**

Apex Target Systems LLC 877 224-6692
37 Heilman St Tiffin (44883) **(G-18204)**

Apex Tool Group LLC 937 222-7871
762 W Stewart St Dayton (45417) **(G-8160)**

Apex Welding Incorporated 440 232-6770
1 Industry Dr Bedford (44146) **(G-1398)**

Apg Media of Ohio, Athens *Also called Adams Publishing Group LLC* **(G-854)**

API Machining Fabrication Inc 740 369-0455
377 London Rd Delaware (43015) **(G-8821)**

API Pattern Works Inc 440 269-1766
4456 Hamann Pkwy Willoughby (44094) **(G-20433)**

Apollo GL Mirror Win Screen Co, Cincinnati *Also called Dale Kestler* **(G-3637)**

Apollo Manufacturing Co LLC 440 951-9972
7911 Enterprise Dr Mentor (44060) **(G-13524)**

Apollo Medical Devices LLC 440 935-5027
11000 Cedar Ave Ste 146 Cleveland (44106) **(G-4819)**

Apollo Plastic, Mentor *Also called Skribs Tool and Die Inc* **(G-13724)**

Apollo Plastics Inc 440 951-7774
7555 Tyler Blvd Ste 11 Mentor (44060) **(G-13525)**

Apollo Products Inc 440 269-8551
4456 Hamann Pkwy Willoughby (44094) **(G-20434)**

Apollo Welding & Fabg Inc (PA) 440 942-0227
35600 Curtis Blvd Willoughby (44095) **(G-20435)**

Apostrophe Apps LLC 513 608-4399
4452 Millikin Rd Liberty Twp (45011) **(G-11970)**

Appal Energy 740 448-4605
15383 E Kasler Creek Rd Amesville (45711) **(G-589)**

Appalachia Wood Inc (PA) 740 596-2551
31310 State Route 93 Mc Arthur (45651) **(G-13328)**

Appalachian Equipment Co LLC 330 345-2251
2054 Great Trails Dr Wooster (44691) **(G-20739)**

Appalachian Fuels LLC (PA) 606 928-0460
6375 Riverside Dr Ste 200 Dublin (43017) **(G-9045)**

Appalachian Oilfield Svcs LLC 337 216-0066
34602 State Route 7 Sardis (43946) **(G-17035)**

Appalachian Solvents LLC 740 680-3649
5041 Skyline Dr Cambridge (43725) **(G-2445)**

Appalachian Trailer Inc 330 277-4140
5409 Newgarden Rd Salem (44460) **(G-16872)**

Appalachian Well Surveys Inc 740 255-7652
10291 Ohio Ave Cambridge (43725) **(G-2446)**

Appalachian Wood Floors Inc 740 354-4572
838 Campbell Ave Portsmouth (45662) **(G-16430)**

Apparel Impressions Inc 513 247-0555
11410 Gideon Ln Cincinnati (45249) **(G-3407)**

Apparel Screen Printing Inc 513 733-9495
11255 Reading Rd Ste 1 Cincinnati (45241) **(G-3408)**

Appc Plumbing Co 330 722-7754
3247 Pearl Rd Medina (44256) **(G-13372)**

Appian Manufacturing Corp 614 445-2230
2025 Camaro Ave Columbus (43207) **(G-6762)**

Apple Inc 614 478-5592
4070 The Strand E Columbus (43219) **(G-6763)**

Appleheart 937 384-0430
2240 E Central Ave Miamisburg (45342) **(G-13784)**

Applelane Press LLC 440 543-6747
37 Forest Dr Chagrin Falls (44022) **(G-3048)**

Appleton Grp LLC 330 689-1904
4441 Hickory Trl Cuyahoga Falls (44224) **(G-7968)**

Application Link Inc 614 934-1735
4449 Easton Way Fl 2 Columbus (43219) **(G-6764)**

Applied Automation Enterprise 419 929-2428
24 Cedar St New London (44851) **(G-14858)**

Applied Bingo Mate, Willoughby *Also called Applied Concepts Inc* **(G-20436)**

Applied Biomimetic 513 558-6090
2180 E Galbraith Rd D Cincinnati (45237) **(G-3409)**

Applied Concepts Inc 440 229-5033
36445 Biltmore Pl Ste E Willoughby (44094) **(G-20436)**

Applied Energy Tech Inc 419 537-9052
1720 Indian Wood Cir E Maumee (43537) **(G-13227)**

Applied Engineered Surface, Elyria *Also called Lauren Yoakam* **(G-9450)**

Applied Engneered Surfaces Inc 440 366-0440
535 Ternes Ln Elyria (44035) **(G-9374)**

Applied Experience LLC 614 943-2970
1003 Kinnear Rd Columbus (43212) **(G-6765)**

Applied Imagination Inc 419 352-8373
128 W Wooster St Ofc Ofc Bowling Green (43402) **(G-1968)**

Applied Innovations 330 837-5694
1245 Cleveland St Sw Massillon (44647) **(G-13109)**

Applied Marketing Services 440 716-9962
28825 Ranney Pkwy Westlake (44145) **(G-20255)**

Applied Materials Finishing 330 336-5645
901 Seville Rd Wadsworth (44281) **(G-19395)**

Applied Medical Technology Inc 440 717-4000
8006 Katherine Blvd Brecksville (44141) **(G-2034)**

Applied Metals Technologies 216 741-2440
1040 Valley Belt Rd Brooklyn Heights (44131) **(G-2130)**

Applied Sciences Inc (PA) 937 766-2020
141 W Xenia Ave Cedarville (45314) **(G-2980)**

Applied Systems Inc 513 943-0000
100 Techne Center Dr # 125 Milford (45150) **(G-14121)**

Applied Vision Corporation (PA) 330 926-2222
2020 Vision Ln Cuyahoga Falls (44223) **(G-7969)**

Approved Plbg & Sewer Clg Co, Cleveland *Also called Approved Plumbing Co* **(G-4820)**

Approved Plumbing Co 216 663-5063
770 Ken Mar Indus Pkwy Cleveland (44147) **(G-4820)**

Appvion Inc 937 859-8261
1030 W Alex Bell Rd West Carrollton (45449) **(G-19790)**

Apr Tool Inc 440 946-0393
4712 Beidler Rd Ste A Willoughby (44094) **(G-20437)**

Aprecia Pharmaceuticals Co 513 204-1369
10901 Kenwood Rd Blue Ash (45242) **(G-1744)**

Aps-Materials Inc (PA) 937 278-6547
4011 Riverside Dr Dayton (45405) **(G-8161)**

Aps-Materials Inc 937 278-6547
153 Walbrook Ave Dayton (45405) **(G-8162)**

APT Manufacturing Solutions, Hicksville *Also called A & P Tool Inc* **(G-10897)**

Apto Orthopaedics Corporation 330 572-7544
47 N Main St Akron (44308) **(G-70)**

APV Engineered Coatings, Akron *Also called Akron Paint & Varnish Inc* **(G-50)**

Aq Productions Inc 614 486-7700
5945 Wilcox Pl Ste B Dublin (43016) **(G-9046)**

Aqua Lily Products LLC 480 588-6731
4485 Glenbrook Rd Willoughby (44094) **(G-20438)**

Aqua Lily Products LLC (PA) 951 246-9610
4485 Glenbrook Rd Willoughby (44094) **(G-20439)**

Aqua Marine Supply, Millersport *Also called Hefty Hoist Inc* **(G-14294)**

Aqua Ohio, Mentor On The Lake *Also called Aqua Pennsylvania Inc* **(G-13773)**

Aqua Pennsylvania Inc 440 257-6190
7748 Twilight Dr Mentor On The Lake (44060) **(G-13773)**

Aqua Science Inc 614 252-5000
1877 E 17th Ave Columbus (43219) **(G-6766)**

Aqua Technology Group LLC 513 298-1183
8104 Beckett Center Dr West Chester (45069) **(G-19807)**

Aquablok Ltd 419 402-4170
230 W Airport Hwy Swanton (43558) **(G-18080)**

Aquablue Inc 330 343-0220
1776 Tech Park Dr Ne New Philadelphia (44663) **(G-14884)**

Aquacalc LLC 916 372-0534
1700 Joyce Ave Columbus (43219) **(G-6767)**

Aquanaut Lounge, Hammondsville *Also called Sam Abdallah* **(G-10760)**

Aquapro Systems LLC 877 278-2797
4438 Muhlhauser Rd # 500 West Chester (45011) **(G-19808)**

Aquatic Lighting Systems, Pickerington *Also called Jeff Katz* **(G-16195)**

Aquatic Technology 440 236-8330
26966 Royalton Rd Columbia Station (44028) **(G-6579)**

Aquila Pharmatech LLC 419 386-2527
8225 Farnsworth Rd Ste A7 Waterville (43566) **(G-19652)**

Arabian Tools Inc 440 286-3600
9632 Brakeman Rd Chardon (44024) **(G-3141)**

Aracor, Fairborn *Also called Rapiscan Systems High Energy I* **(G-9629)**

Aran Inc 216 464-1508
23500 Mercantile Rd Ste F Cleveland (44122) **(G-4821)**

Aratinabox Companies Inc 330 699-3421
12910 Cleveland Ave Nw Uniontown (44685) **(G-19076)**

Arboris LLC 740 522-9350
1780 Tamarack Rd Newark (43055) **(G-14983)**

Arbortech, Wooster *Also called Stahl/Scott Fetzer Company* **(G-20839)**

ARC Abrasives Inc 800 888-4885
2131 Corporate Dr Troy (45373) **(G-18805)**

ARC Blinds Inc 513 889-4864
  4889 Mercedes Dr Liberty Twp (45011) *(G-11971)*

ARC Drilling Inc (PA) 216 525-0920
  9551 Corporate Cir Cleveland (44125) *(G-4822)*

ARC Elec 440 774-2800
  18637 State Route 511 Wellington (44090) *(G-19737)*

ARC Rubber Inc 440 466-4555
  100 Water St Geneva (44041) *(G-10343)*

ARC Solutions Inc 419 542-9272
  605 Industrial Dr Hicksville (43526) *(G-10899)*

Arcadian Ohio, Lima *Also called Pcs Nitrogen Inc (G-12066)*

Arcalloy Metal Fabrication 800 822-9402
  39 E Market St Ste 403 Akron (44308) *(G-71)*

Arcelormittal Cleveland LLC (HQ) 216 429-6000
  3060 Eggers Ave Cleveland (44105) *(G-4823)*

Arcelormittal Cleveland LLC 216 429-6000
  3060 Eggers Ave Cleveland (44105) *(G-4824)*

Arcelormittal Columbus LLC 614 492-6800
  1800 Watkins Rd Columbus (43207) *(G-6768)*

Arcelormittal Obetz LLC 614 492-8287
  4300 Alum Creek Dr Columbus (43207) *(G-6769)*

Arcelormittal Tailored Blanks 419 737-3180
  2 Kexon Dr Pioneer (43554) *(G-16233)*

Arcelormittal Tubular 740 382-3979
  686 W Fairground St Marion (43302) *(G-12855)*

Arcelormittal Tubular 419 347-2424
  132 W Main St Shelby (44875) *(G-17132)*

Arcelormittal USA LLC 740 375-2299
  686 W Fairground St Marion (43302) *(G-12856)*

Arcelormittal USA LLC 419 347-2424
  132 W Main St Shelby (44875) *(G-17133)*

Arcelormittal USA LLC 330 659-9100
  4020 Kinross Lakes Pkwy Richfield (44286) *(G-16614)*

Arcelormittal Warren, Warren *Also called AM Warren LLC (G-19520)*

Arch Angle Window and Door, Medina *Also called Bug-Barrier Screen Corp (G-13384)*

Arch Polymers, Marysville *Also called Triple Arrow Industries Inc (G-12976)*

Archbold Buckeye Inc 419 445-4466
  207 N Defiance St Archbold (43502) *(G-663)*

Archbold Container Corp 800 446-2520
  800 W Barre Rd Archbold (43502) *(G-664)*

Archbold Furniture Co 567 444-4666
  733 W Barre Rd Archbold (43502) *(G-665)*

Archday, Medina *Also called Architectural Daylighting LLC (G-13373)*

Arched Casings Inc 614 873-1196
  8490 Carters Mill Rd Plain City (43064) *(G-16320)*

Archer Corporation 330 455-9995
  1917 Henry Ave Sw Canton (44706) *(G-2604)*

Archer Counter Design Inc 513 396-7526
  4433 Verne Ave Cincinnati (45209) *(G-3410)*

Archer Sign, Canton *Also called Archer Corporation (G-2604)*

Archer-Daniels-Midland Company 419 705-3292
  1308 Miami St Toledo (43605) *(G-18353)*

Archer-Daniels-Midland Company 419 435-6633
  608 Findlay St Fostoria (44830) *(G-9966)*

Archer-Daniels-Midland Company 330 852-3025
  554 Pleasant Valley Rd Nw Sugarcreek (44681) *(G-18015)*

Archies Too 419 427-2663
  2145 S Lake Ct Findlay (45840) *(G-9790)*

Architctral Identification Inc (PA) 614 868-8400
  1170 Claycraft Rd Gahanna (43230) *(G-10204)*

Architctral Rfuse Slutions LLC 330 733-3996
  525 Kennedy Rd Akron (44305) *(G-72)*

Architechual Etc, Cortland *Also called Lawbre Co (G-7871)*

Architect Louvers 513 541-5364
  266 W Mitchell Ave Cincinnati (45232) *(G-3411)*

Architectural and Industrial 440 963-0410
  1091 Sunnyside Rd Vermilion (44089) *(G-19323)*

Architectural Art Glass Studio 513 731-7336
  5 Water St Milford (45150) *(G-14122)*

Architectural Arts, Toledo *Also called Digimatics Inc (G-18438)*

Architectural Busstrut Corp 614 933-8695
  4311 Brompton St New Albany (43054) *(G-14746)*

Architectural Daylighting LLC 330 460-5000
  879 S Progress Dr Ste C Medina (44256) *(G-13373)*

Architectural Door Systems LLC 513 808-9900
  2810 Highland Ave Lebanon (45036) *(G-11780)*

Architectural Fiberglass Inc 216 641-8300
  8300 Bessemer Ave Cleveland (44127) *(G-4825)*

Architectural Metal Maint, Cleves *Also called Metal Maintenance Inc (G-6521)*

Architectural Products Dev 216 631-6260
  6605 Clark Ave Rear 1 Cleveland (44102) *(G-4826)*

Architectural Sheet Metals LLC 216 361-9952
  1457 E 39th St Cleveland (44114) *(G-4827)*

Archival Conservation Center 513 861-3268
  772 Crooked Stone Rd Cincinnati (45220) *(G-3412)*

Archival Conservatn Cntr, Cincinnati *Also called Archival Conservation Center (G-3412)*

Arclin 877 689-9145
  7230 Lilac Ct Holland (43528) *(G-11045)*

Arclin USA LLC 419 726-5013
  6175 American Rd Toledo (43612) *(G-18354)*

Arconic Inc 330 835-6000
  3340 Gilchrist Rd Mogadore (44260) *(G-14368)*

Arconic Inc 216 641-3600
  1600 Harvard Ave Newburgh Heights (44105) *(G-15069)*

Arctech Fabricating Inc (PA) 937 525-9353
  1317 Lagonda Ave Springfield (45503) *(G-17518)*

Ardar Co Inc 440 582-3371
  12955 York Delta Dr Ste A Cleveland (44133) *(G-4828)*

Arden J Neer Sr 937 585-6733
  4859 Township Road 45 Bellefontaine (43311) *(G-1519)*

Ardent Mills LLC 419 994-4181
  945 Mill Rd Loudonville (44842) *(G-12296)*

Ardent Mills LLC 614 274-2545
  4200 Sullivant Ave Columbus (43228) *(G-6770)*

Are, Massillon *Also called ARE Accessories LLC (G-13110)*

ARE Accessories LLC 330 830-7800
  400 Nave Rd Se Massillon (44646) *(G-13110)*

ARE Inc (PA) 330 830-7800
  400 Nave Rd Sw Massillon (44646) *(G-13111)*

ARE Inc 330 830-7800
  400 Nave Rd Se Massillon (44646) *(G-13112)*

Area Wide Protective Inc (HQ) 330 644-0655
  826 Overholt Rd Kent (44240) *(G-11431)*

Area Wide Protective Inc 419 221-2997
  413 Flanders Ave Lima (45801) *(G-11993)*

Area Wide Protective Inc 513 321-9889
  9500 Le Saint Dr Fairfield (45014) *(G-9643)*

Arem Co 440 974-6740
  8200 Tyler Blvd Ste L Mentor (44060) *(G-13526)*

Arens Corporation (PA) 937 473-2028
  395 S High St Covington (45318) *(G-7918)*

Arens Corporation 937 473-2028
  22 N High St Covington (45318) *(G-7919)*

Arens Publications & Printing, Covington *Also called Arens Corporation (G-7919)*

Ares Inc 419 635-2175
  818 Front St Port Clinton (43452) *(G-16393)*

Ares Sportswear Ltd 614 767-1950
  3704 Lacon Rd Hilliard (43026) *(G-10926)*

Aresgear 518 966-2737
  1807 Obrien Rd Columbus (43228) *(G-6771)*

Arete Innovative Solutions LLC 513 503-2712
  3050 Shawhan Rd Morrow (45152) *(G-14543)*

Areway Acquisition Inc 216 651-9022
  8525 Clinton Rd Brooklyn (44144) *(G-2127)*

Areway LLC 216 651-9022
  8525 Clinton Rd Brooklyn (44144) *(G-2128)*

Arf, Painesville *Also called American Roll Formed Pdts Corp (G-15851)*

Arges 440 574-1305
  275 N Pleasant St Oberlin (44074) *(G-15634)*

Argo Tool Corporation 330 425-2407
  1962 Case Pkwy Twinsburg (44087) *(G-18901)*

Argo-Tech, Cleveland *Also called Eaton Industrial Corporation (G-5252)*

Argosy Wind Power Ltd 440 539-1345
  70 Aurora Industrial Pkwy Aurora (44202) *(G-906)*

Argrov Box Co 513 217-5900
  1500 S University Blvd Middletown (45044) *(G-14021)*

Argrov Box Co 937 898-1700
  6030 Webster St Dayton (45414) *(G-8163)*

ARI Phoenix Inc (PA) 513 229-3750
  4119 Binion Way Lebanon (45036) *(G-11781)*

Ariel Corporation 740 397-0311
  8585 Blackjack Road Ext Mount Vernon (43050) *(G-14606)*

Ariel Corporation 740 397-0311
  35 Blackjack Road Ext Mount Vernon (43050) *(G-14607)*

Ariel's Oak, Sherrodsville *Also called Ariels Oak Inc (G-17145)*

Ariels Oak Inc 330 343-7453
  9486 Cutler Rd Ne Sherrodsville (44675) *(G-17145)*

Arisdyne Systems Inc 216 458-1991
  17909 Cleveland Pkwy Dr # 100 Cleveland (44135) *(G-4829)*

Aristocrat Industries Inc 740 694-2752
  7555 Sharp Rd Mount Vernon (43050) *(G-14608)*

Arizona Beverage Company LLC 516 837-1999
  644 Linn St Ste 318 Cincinnati (45203) *(G-3413)*

Arizona Beverages, Cincinnati *Also called Hornell Brewing Co Inc (G-3899)*

Arizona Chemical Company LLC 330 343-7701
  875 Harger St Dover (44622) *(G-8964)*

Arkansas Face Veneer Co Inc (HQ) 937 773-6295
  1025 S Roosevelt Ave Piqua (45356) *(G-16249)*

Arkay Industries Inc (PA) 513 360-0390
  240 American Way Monroe (45050) *(G-14392)*

Arkay Plastics Alabama Inc (HQ) 513 360-0390
  220 American Way Monroe (45050) *(G-14393)*

Arken Manufacturing Inc 216 883-6628
  3502 Beyerle Rd Cleveland (44105) *(G-4830)*

Arku Coil-Systems Inc 513 985-0500
  11405 Grooms Rd Blue Ash (45242) *(G-1745)*

Arlington Prcsion Grinding LLC 937 833-1553
  8909 Arlington Rd Brookville (45309) *(G-2175)*

A
L
P
H
A
B
E
T
I
C

Arlington Rack & Packaging Co...419 476-7700
6120 N Detroit Ave Toledo (43612) ***(G-18355)***
Arlington-Blaine Lumber Co, Delaware *Also called Khempco Bldg Sup Co Ltd Partnr* ***(G-8865)***
Arlo Aluminum & Steel, Dayton *Also called Alro Steel Corporation* ***(G-8149)***
Arm & Hammer, London *Also called Church & Dwight Co Inc* ***(G-12204)***
ARM (usa) Inc...740 264-6599
1506 Fernwood Rd Steubenville (43953) ***(G-17688)***
ARM Opco Inc...330 868-7724
3026 Saratoga Ave Sw Canton (44706) ***(G-2605)***
Armada Fortress LLC...330 953-2185
6971 Southern Blvd Ste B Youngstown (44512) ***(G-21027)***
Armada Power LLC...614 204-9341
230 West St Ste 150 Columbus (43215) ***(G-6772)***
Armaly Brands, London *Also called Armaly LLC* ***(G-12200)***
Armaly LLC...740 852-3621
110 W 1st St London (43140) ***(G-12200)***
Armature Coil Equipment Inc...216 267-6366
4725 Manufacturing Ave Cleveland (44135) ***(G-4831)***
Armbrust Concrete, Wshngtn CT Hs *Also called Philip Armbrust* ***(G-20919)***
Armeton US Co...419 554-1866
205 Republic St Norwalk (44857) ***(G-15526)***
Armin R Jewett...419 647-6644
607 N Water St Wapakoneta (45895) ***(G-19479)***
Armoloy of Ohio Inc...937 323-8702
1950 E Leffel Ln Springfield (45505) ***(G-17519)***
Armor Consolidated Inc (PA)...513 923-5260
4600 N Masn Montgomery Rd Mason (45040) ***(G-12982)***
Armor Group, The, Mason *Also called Armor Consolidated Inc* ***(G-12982)***
Armor Metal Group Mason Inc (HQ)...513 769-0700
4600 N Masn Montgomery Rd Mason (45040) ***(G-12983)***
Armormetal, Mason *Also called Armor Metal Group Mason Inc* ***(G-12983)***
Armorsource LLC...740 928-0070
3600 Hebron Rd Hebron (43025) ***(G-10861)***
Armotec Materials Corporation...216 476-2766
3825 W 150th St Cleveland (44111) ***(G-4832)***
Armour Spray Systems Inc...216 398-3838
210 Hayes Dr Ste I Cleveland (44131) ***(G-4833)***
Armour-Eckrich Meats LLC...614 539-9600
6130 Enterprise Pkwy Grove City (43123) ***(G-10544)***
Armstrong Custom Moulding Inc...740 922-5931
6408 State Route 800 Se Uhrichsville (44683) ***(G-19045)***
Armstrong Printing, Springfield *Also called Graphic Paper Products Corp* ***(G-17566)***
Armstrong S Printing Ex LLC...937 276-7794
8810 Grovecreek Ct Dayton (45458) ***(G-8164)***
Armstrong World Industries Inc...614 771-9307
4241 Leap Rd Bldg A Hilliard (43026) ***(G-10927)***
Arnco Corporation...800 847-7661
860 Garden St Elyria (44035) ***(G-9375)***
Arnold Machine Inc...419 443-1818
19 Heritage Dr Tiffin (44883) ***(G-18205)***
Arnold Printing Inc...330 494-1191
5772 West Blvd Nw Canton (44718) ***(G-2606)***
Arnolds Candies Inc...330 733-4022
931 High Grove Blvd Akron (44312) ***(G-73)***
Arnolds Repair Shop...740 373-5313
101 Simpson St Marietta (45750) ***(G-12762)***
Aronit Machine LLC...419 782-4740
2018 Baltimore St Defiance (43512) ***(G-8778)***
Arps Dairy Inc...419 782-9116
220 N Clinton St Defiance (43512) ***(G-8779)***
Array Telepresence Inc...800 779-7480
9480 Meridian Way West Chester (45069) ***(G-19809)***
Arrow Coal Grove Inc...740 532-6143
300 Marion Pike Ironton (45638) ***(G-11289)***
Arrow Fabricating Co...216 641-0490
7355 Calley Ln Novelty (44072) ***(G-15581)***
Arrow International Inc (PA)...216 961-3500
9900 Clinton Rd Cleveland (44144) ***(G-4834)***
Arrow Print & Copy, Sylvania *Also called Kevin K Tidd* ***(G-18115)***
Arrow Tru-Line Inc...419 636-7013
720 E Perry St Bryan (43506) ***(G-2279)***
Arrow Tru-Line Inc (PA)...419 446-2785
2211 S Defiance St Archbold (43502) ***(G-666)***
Arrowhead Energy, Newark *Also called Flint Ridge Energy* ***(G-15007)***
Arrowhead Industries...440 349-2846
33891 Canterbury Rd Solon (44139) ***(G-17261)***
Arrowhead Pallets LLC...440 693-4241
7851 Parkman Mespo Rd Middlefield (44062) ***(G-13915)***
Arrowstrip Inc...740 633-2609
1st & Locust St S Martins Ferry (43935) ***(G-12921)***
ARS Recycling Systems LLC...330 536-8210
4000 Mccartney Rd Lowellville (44436) ***(G-12405)***
Arsco Manufacturing Company, Cincinnati *Also called Ahemco LLC* ***(G-3368)***
Art & Sign Corporation...419 865-3336
5458 Angola Rd Toledo (43615) ***(G-18356)***
Art Brands LLC...614 755-4278
225 Business Center Dr Blacklick (43004) ***(G-1688)***
Art Columbus Memorial Inc...614 221-9333
606 W Broad St Columbus (43215) ***(G-6773)***
Art Fremont Iron Co...419 332-5554
307 E State St Fremont (43420) ***(G-10125)***
Art Galvanizing Works Inc...216 749-0020
3935 Valley Rd Cleveland (44109) ***(G-4835)***
Art Guild Binders Inc...513 242-3000
1068 Meta Dr Cincinnati (45237) ***(G-3414)***
Art Metals Group Inc...513 942-8800
3795 Symmes Rd Hamilton (45015) ***(G-10671)***
Art of Beauty Company Inc (PA)...216 438-6363
200 Egbert Rd Bedford (44146) ***(G-1399)***
Art Printing Co Inc...419 281-4371
147 E 2nd St Ashland (44805) ***(G-705)***
Art Pro Graphics...216 236-6465
7279 Summitview Dr Seven Hills (44131) ***(G-17060)***
Art Saylor Logging...740 682-6188
343 Slab Hill Rd Oak Hill (45656) ***(G-15594)***
Art Tech, Chillicothe *Also called McRd Enterprises LLC* ***(G-3250)***
Art Tees Inc...614 338-8337
39 S Yearling Rd Columbus (43213) ***(G-6774)***
Art Woodworking & Mfg Co...513 681-2986
4238 Dane Ave Cincinnati (45223) ***(G-3415)***
Art Works...740 425-5765
119 E Pike St Barnesville (43713) ***(G-1158)***
Art-American Printing Plates...216 241-4420
1138 W 9th St Fl 4 Cleveland (44113) ***(G-4836)***
Arte Limited, Cleveland *Also called Lawrence Industries Inc* ***(G-5686)***
Artesian Tan, Toledo *Also called Kahuna Bay Spray Tan LLC* ***(G-18537)***
Artex Oil Company, Marietta *Also called James Engineering Inc* ***(G-12794)***
Artex Oil Company...740 373-3313
2337 State Route 821 Marietta (45750) ***(G-12763)***
Artfind Tile, Wooster *Also called Artfinders* ***(G-20740)***
Artfinders...330 264-7706
143 S Market St Wooster (44691) ***(G-20740)***
Arthur Corporation...419 433-7202
1305 Huron Avery Rd Huron (44839) ***(G-11216)***
Arthur W Guilford III Inc...216 362-1350
13515 Brookpark Rd Cleveland (44142) ***(G-4837)***
Arthurs Refrigeration...740 532-0206
2156 State Route 93 Ironton (45638) ***(G-11290)***
Artic Diamond, Cincinnati *Also called Brady A Lantz Enterprises Inc* ***(G-3466)***
Artic Diamond...513 742-4921
11242 Sebring Dr Cincinnati (45240) ***(G-3416)***
Artificial Neural Systems Inc...740 593-7675
352 Carroll Rd Athens (45701) ***(G-856)***
Artiflex Manufacturing LLC (HQ)...330 262-2015
1425 E Bowman St Wooster (44691) ***(G-20741)***
Artiflex Manufacturing LLC...419 547-9211
550 Premier Dr Clyde (43410) ***(G-6537)***
Artisan Equipment Inc...740 756-9135
5943 Clmbus Lncster Rd Nw Carroll (43112) ***(G-2936)***
Artisan Mold Co Inc...440 926-4511
1021 Commerce Dr 219 Grafton (44044) ***(G-10419)***
Artisan Tool & Die Corp...216 883-2769
4911 Grant Ave Cleveland (44125) ***(G-4838)***
Artistic Composite & Mold Co...330 352-6632
9225 Stone Rd Litchfield (44253) ***(G-12137)***
Artistic Finishes Inc...440 951-7850
38357 Apollo Pkwy Willoughby (44094) ***(G-20440)***
Artistic Foods Incorporated...330 401-1313
355 Elyria St Lodi (44254) ***(G-12157)***
Artistic Memorials Ltd...419 873-0433
12551 Jefferson St Perrysburg (43551) ***(G-16066)***
Artistic Metal Spinning Inc...216 961-3336
4700 Lorain Ave Cleveland (44102) ***(G-4839)***
Arts Rolloffs & Refuse Inc...419 991-3730
108 Cheshire Cir Lima (45804) ***(G-11994)***
Artsinheaven.com, Millersburg *Also called Educational Electronics Inc* ***(G-14213)***
Arvinmrtor Commerical Vhcl Sys, Granville *Also called Meritor Inc* ***(G-10461)***
Arzel Technology Inc...216 831-6068
4801 Commerce Pkwy Cleveland (44128) ***(G-4840)***
Arzel Zoning Technology, Cleveland *Also called Arzel Technology Inc* ***(G-4840)***
As America Inc...614 497-9384
6600 Port Rd Ste 200 Groveport (43125) ***(G-10614)***
As America Inc...330 337-2219
605 S Ellsworth Ave Salem (44460) ***(G-16873)***
As America Inc...615 873-2410
41 Cairns Rd Mansfield (44903) ***(G-12563)***
ASAP Ready Mix Inc...513 797-1774
250 Mount Holly Rd Amelia (45102) ***(G-568)***
Asb Industries Inc...330 753-8458
1031 Lambert St Barberton (44203) ***(G-1099)***
Asbeka Custom Products LLC...440 352-0839
11288 Saint Andrews Way Painesville (44077) ***(G-15852)***
ASC Holdco Inc (HQ)...330 899-0340
2100 International Pkwy Canton (44720) ***(G-2607)***
ASC Industries Inc...330 899-0340
2100 International Pkwy North Canton (44720) ***(G-15220)***

Ascendtech Inc 216 458-1101
  4772 E 355th St Willoughby (44094) *(G-20441)*

Ascents, Cleveland *Also called Aeroscena LLC (G-4723)*

Asch-Klaassen Sonics LLC 513 671-3226
  11711 Princeton Pike # 943 Cincinnati (45246) *(G-3417)*

Asco Power Technologies LP 216 573-7600
  8400 E Pleasant Valley Rd Cleveland (44131) *(G-4841)*

Asco Power Technologies LP 973 966-2161
  6255 Halle Dr Cleveland (44125) *(G-4842)*

Asco Power Technologies LP 937 748-8884
  2715 Factory Rd Springboro (45066) *(G-17474)*

Asco Valve Inc 216 360-0366
  26401 Emery St Ste 105 Cleveland (44128) *(G-4843)*

Ascon Tecnologic N Amer LLC 216 485-8350
  1111 Brookpark Rd Cleveland (44109) *(G-4844)*

Ascot Valley Foods LLC (PA) 330 376-9411
  205 Ascot Pkwy Cuyahoga Falls (44223) *(G-7970)*

ASG 216 486-6163
  15700 S Waterloo Rd Cleveland (44110) *(G-4845)*

Ash Machine Corporation 740 927-0506
  10795 Morse Rd Sw Pataskala (43062) *(G-15968)*

Ash Sewer & Drain Service 330 376-9714
  451 E North St Akron (44304) *(G-74)*

Ashco 330 385-2400
  1250 Saint George St # 3 East Liverpool (43920) *(G-9203)*

Ashco Manufacturing Inc 419 838-7157
  5234 Tulane Ave Toledo (43611) *(G-18357)*

Ashcraft Machine & Supply Inc 740 349-8110
  185 Wilson St Newark (43055) *(G-14984)*

Ashland Conveyor Products, Ashland *Also called Midwest Conveyor Products Inc (G-754)*

Ashland Distribution, Dublin *Also called Ashland LLC (G-9047)*

Ashland Inc 800 283-4823
  1979 Atlas St Columbus (43228) *(G-6775)*

Ashland Inc Valvoline Instant 330 653-3926
  1691 Georgetown Rd Unit C Hudson (44236) *(G-11159)*

Ashland LLC 614 790-3333
  5200 Blazer Pkwy Dublin (43017) *(G-9047)*

Ashland LLC 513 682-2405
  9451 Meridian Way West Chester (45069) *(G-19810)*

Ashland LLC 419 998-8728
  1220 S Metcalf St Lima (45804) *(G-11995)*

Ashland LLC 513 557-3100
  3901 River Rd Cincinnati (45204) *(G-3418)*

Ashland Monument Company Inc 419 281-2688
  34 E 2nd St Ashland (44805) *(G-706)*

Ashland Precision Tooling LLC 419 289-1736
  1750 Baney Rd S Ashland (44805) *(G-707)*

Ashland Publishing Co 419 281-0581
  40 E 2nd St Ashland (44805) *(G-708)*

Ashland R Crawford Knox, Mansfield *Also called Child Evngelism Fellowship Inc (G-12579)*

Ashland Spcalty Ingredients GP, Dublin *Also called Ashland Specialty Ingredients (G-9048)*

Ashland Specialty Ingredients (PA) 302 594-5000
  5200 Laser Pkwy Dublin (43017) *(G-9048)*

Ashland Specialty Ingredients 614 529-3311
  1979 Atlas St Columbus (43228) *(G-6776)*

Ashland Times Gazette, Ashland *Also called Ashland Publishing Co (G-708)*

Ashley F Ward Inc (PA) 513 398-1414
  7490 Easy St Mason (45040) *(G-12984)*

Ashta Chemicals Inc 440 997-5221
  3509 Middle Rd Ashtabula (44004) *(G-793)*

Ashta Forge & Machine Inc 216 252-7000
  3001 W 121st St Cleveland (44111) *(G-4846)*

Ashtabula Rubber Co 440 992-2195
  2751 West Ave Ashtabula (44004) *(G-794)*

Ashtabula Star Beacon, Ashtabula *Also called Newspaper Holding Inc (G-826)*

Ashtech Corporation 440 646-9911
  5875 Landerbrook Dr # 140 Cleveland (44124) *(G-4847)*

Ashton LLC 614 833-4165
  145 W Columbus St Pickerington (43147) *(G-16186)*

Ashton Pumpmatic Inc 937 424-1380
  7670 Mcewen Rd Dayton (45459) *(G-8165)*

Asi Investment Holding Co 330 666-3751
  3550 W Market St Fairlawn (44333) *(G-9738)*

Asi Investments Holding Co, Fairlawn *Also called Sunprene Company (G-9762)*

Asi Sign Systems, Loveland *Also called Kmgrafx Inc (G-12367)*

Asia For Kids, Blue Ash *Also called Master Communications Inc (G-1833)*

Asist Inc 614 451-6744
  4891 Sawmill Rd Ste 200 Columbus (43235) *(G-6777)*

Asist Translation Services, Columbus *Also called Asist Inc (G-6777)*

Ask Chemicals LP 614 763-0384
  495 Metro Pl S Ste 250 Dublin (43017) *(G-9049)*

Askia Inc 513 828-7443
  4303 Williamsburg Rd N Cincinnati (45215) *(G-3419)*

Aslan Worldwide 513 671-0671
  8583 Rupp Farm Dr West Chester (45069) *(G-19811)*

Asm International 440 338-5151
  9639 Kinsman Rd Novelty (44073) *(G-15582)*

Aspec Inc 513 561-9922
  5810 Carothers St Cincinnati (45227) *(G-3420)*

Aspen Machine and Plastics 937 526-4644
  257 Baker Rd Versailles (45380) *(G-19339)*

Aspen Mulling Company 970 925-5027
  5111 Richmond Rd Bedford (44146) *(G-1400)*

Aspen Mulling Spices, Bedford *Also called Aspen Mulling Company (G-1400)*

Aspery Farms, Streetsboro *Also called Microbiological Labs Inc (G-17862)*

Asphalt Fabrics & Specialties 440 786-1077
  7710 Bond St Solon (44139) *(G-17262)*

Asphalt Materials Inc 740 373-3040
  505 River Ln Marietta (45750) *(G-12764)*

Asphalt Materials Inc 419 693-0626
  940 N Wynn Rd Oregon (43616) *(G-15702)*

Asphalt Materials Inc 740 374-5100
  13925 State Route 7 Marietta (45750) *(G-12765)*

Asphalt Services & Cnstr 330 995-6044
  114 Barrington Town Sq Dr Aurora (44202) *(G-907)*

Asphalt Services Ohio Inc 614 864-4600
  4579 Poth Rd Columbus (43213) *(G-6778)*

Assembly Division, Walbridge *Also called Riverside Mch & Automtn Inc (G-19463)*

Assembly Machining Wire Pdts 614 443-1110
  2375 Refugee Park Columbus (43207) *(G-6779)*

Assembly Specialty Pdts Inc 216 676-5600
  14700 Brookpark Rd Cleveland (44135) *(G-4848)*

Assembly Works Inc 419 433-5010
  1705 Sawmill Pkwy Huron (44839) *(G-11217)*

Assembly Works Matrix Automtn, Huron *Also called Assembly Works Inc (G-11217)*

Assisted Patrol LLC 937 369-0080
  2130 Hedge Gate Blvd Beavercreek (45431) *(G-1318)*

Assistive Technology of Ohio, Columbus *Also called Ohio State University (G-7433)*

Assoc Talents Inc 440 716-1265
  3700 Greenbriar Cir Westlake (44145) *(G-20256)*

Associated Assoc Rdymx Con, Akron *Also called Carbros (G-110)*

Associated Associates Inc 330 626-3300
  9551 Elliman Rd Mantua (44255) *(G-12707)*

Associated Graphics Inc 614 873-1273
  9021 Heritage Dr Ste I Plain City (43064) *(G-16321)*

Associated Hygienic Pdts LLC 770 497-9800
  2332 Us Highway 42 S Delaware (43015) *(G-8822)*

Associated Materials LLC (HQ) 330 929-1811
  3773 State Rd Cuyahoga Falls (44223) *(G-7971)*

Associated Materials LLC 937 236-5679
  3361 Needmore Rd Dayton (45414) *(G-8166)*

Associated Mtls Holdings LLC 330 929-1811
  3773 State Rd Cuyahoga Falls (44223) *(G-7972)*

Associated Plastics Corp 419 634-3910
  502 Eric Wolber Dr Ada (45810) *(G-5)*

Associated Press Repair Inc 216 881-2288
  5321 Saint Clair Ave Cleveland (44103) *(G-4849)*

Associated Ready Mix Concrete, Mantua *Also called Associated Associates Inc (G-12707)*

Associated Software Cons Inc 440 826-1010
  7251 Engle Rd Ste 300 Middleburg Heights (44130) *(G-13902)*

Associated Technical Sales, Dayton *Also called Gadjets Inc (G-8356)*

Assocted Vsual Cmmncations Inc 330 452-4449
  200 Cherry Ave Ne Canton (44702) *(G-2608)*

Astellas Pharma Us Inc 614 409-2953
  5650 Green Pointe Dr N Groveport (43125) *(G-10615)*

Aster Elements Inc 440 942-2799
  7657 Saint Clair Ave Mentor (44060) *(G-13527)*

Aster Industries Inc 330 762-7965
  275 N Arlington St Ste B Akron (44305) *(G-75)*

Asterena Corporation 937 605-6470
  1413 Verna Ct Dayton (45458) *(G-8167)*

Astra Products of Ohio Ltd (PA) 330 296-0112
  7154 State Route 88 Ravenna (44266) *(G-16516)*

Astro Industries Inc 937 429-5900
  4403 Dayton Xenia Rd Beavercreek (45432) *(G-1319)*

Astro Instrumentation LLC 440 238-2005
  22740 Lunn Rd Strongsville (44149) *(G-17889)*

Astro Met Inc (PA) 513 772-1242
  9974 Springfield Pike Cincinnati (45215) *(G-3421)*

Astro Qcb Inc 513 921-8811
  1937 South St Cincinnati (45204) *(G-3422)*

Astro Shapes LLC (PA) 330 755-1414
  65 Main St Struthers (44471) *(G-17989)*

Astro Technical Services Inc 330 394-7350
  2401 Parkman Rd Nw Warren (44485) *(G-19525)*

Astro-Coatings Inc 330 755-1414
  65 Main St Struthers (44471) *(G-17990)*

Astro-TEC Mfg Inc 330 854-2209
  550 Elm Ridge Ave Canal Fulton (44614) *(G-2497)*

At Holdings Corporation (HQ) 216 692-6000
  23555 Euclid Ave Cleveland (44117) *(G-4850)*

At Pallet 330 264-3903
  4224 E Messner Rd Wooster (44691) *(G-20742)*

AT&f Advanced Metals LLC (PA) 330 684-1122
  12314 Elmwood Ave Cleveland (44111) *(G-4851)*

AT&f Nuclear Inc (HQ) 216 252-1500
  12314 Elmwood Ave Cleveland (44111) *(G-4852)*

A L P H A B E T I C

AT&T Corp..614 223-8236
  150 E Gay St Ste 4a Columbus (43215) *(G-6780)*

AT&T Corp..513 792-9300
  7875 Montgomery Rd Ofc Cincinnati (45236) *(G-3423)*

AT&T Government Solutions Inc.........................937 306-3030
  2940 Presidential Dr # 390 Beavercreek (45324) *(G-1320)*

Ata Tools Inc..330 928-7744
  238 Marc Dr Cuyahoga Falls (44223) *(G-7973)*

Atc Group Inc (PA)...440 293-4064
  101 Parker Dr Andover (44003) *(G-612)*

Atc Lighting & Plastics, Andover Also called Atc Group Inc *(G-612)*

Atc Lighting & Plastics Inc (HQ).....................440 466-7670
  101 Parker Dr Andover (44003) *(G-613)*

Atc Nymold Corporation....................................440 293-4064
  101 Parker Dr Andover (44003) *(G-614)*

Atc Nymold Corporation (HQ)...........................440 293-4064
  101 Parker Dr Andover (44003) *(G-615)*

Atchley Signs & Graphics..................................614 421-7446
  1616 Transamerica Ct Columbus (43228) *(G-6781)*

Atd, Strongsville Also called Atlantic Durant Technology Inc *(G-17890)*

Atec Diversfd Wldg Fabrication..........................937 546-4399
  466 Dehan Rd Wilmington (45177) *(G-20655)*

Athens Foods Inc...216 676-8500
  13600 Snow Rd Cleveland (44142) *(G-4853)*

Athens Messenger, The, Athens Also called Messenger Publishing Company *(G-876)*

Athens Mold and Machine Inc............................740 593-6613
  1461 Industrial Pkwy Akron (44310) *(G-76)*

Athens Technical Specialists.............................740 592-2874
  8157 Us Highway 50 Athens (45701) *(G-857)*

Athersys Inc (PA)...216 431-9900
  3201 Carnegie Ave Cleveland (44115) *(G-4854)*

ATI, Toledo Also called Abbott Tool Inc *(G-18318)*

ATI, Batavia Also called Auto Temp Inc *(G-1164)*

ATI Allegheny Ludlum, Louisville Also called Allegheny Ludlum LLC *(G-12308)*

ATI Irrigation LLC...937 750-2976
  4746 W State Route 55 Troy (45373) *(G-18806)*

Atk2 Inc...513 661-5869
  3111 Harrison Ave Cincinnati (45211) *(G-3424)*

Atkinson Printing Inc...330 669-3515
  2876 N Applecreek Rd Wooster (44691) *(G-20743)*

Atkore Plastic Pipe Corp...................................330 627-8002
  861 N Lisbon St Carrollton (44615) *(G-2952)*

Atlantic and Prfmce Rigging, Tiffin Also called Tiffin Scenic Studios Inc *(G-18249)*

Atlantic Co..440 944-8988
  26651 Curtiss Wright Pkwy Willoughby Hills (44092) *(G-20637)*

Atlantic Durant Technology Inc (HQ).................440 238-6931
  19963 Progress Dr Strongsville (44149) *(G-17890)*

Atlantic Inertial Systems Inc.............................740 788-3800
  781 Irving Wick Dr W Heath (43056) *(G-10845)*

Atlantic Investment...440 567-5054
  6117 Antler Xing Lorain (44053) *(G-12233)*

Atlantic Sign Company Inc.................................513 383-1504
  2328 Florence Ave Cincinnati (45206) *(G-3425)*

Atlantic Tool & Die Company (PA).....................440 238-6931
  19963 Progress Dr Strongsville (44149) *(G-17891)*

Atlantic Tool & Die Company.............................330 769-4500
  4995 Atlantic Dr Seville (44273) *(G-17068)*

Atlantic Tool & Die Company.............................330 239-3700
  6965 Ridge Rd Sharon Center (44274) *(G-17101)*

Atlantic Water Gardens, Mantua Also called Meridienne International Inc *(G-12717)*

Atlantis Sportswear Inc.....................................937 773-0680
  344 Fox Dr Piqua (45356) *(G-16250)*

Atlapac Corp...614 252-2121
  2901 E 4th Ave Ste 5 Columbus (43219) *(G-6782)*

Atlas America Inc...330 339-3155
  1026a Cookson Ave Se New Philadelphia (44663) *(G-14885)*

Atlas Bolt & Screw Company LLC (HQ).............419 289-6171
  1628 Troy Rd Ashland (44805) *(G-709)*

Atlas Dowel & Wood Products Co, Harrison Also called Puttmann Industries Inc *(G-10797)*

Atlas Fasteners For Cnstr, Ashland Also called Atlas Bolt & Screw Company LLC *(G-709)*

Atlas Gear and Machine Co................................614 272-6944
  575 N Hague Ave Columbus (43204) *(G-6783)*

Atlas Industrial Contrs LLC (HQ).......................614 841-4500
  5275 Sinclair Rd Columbus (43229) *(G-6784)*

Atlas Industries Inc (PA)..................................419 355-1000
  1750 E State St Fremont (43420) *(G-10126)*

Atlas Industries Inc..419 447-4730
  401 Wall St Tiffin (44883) *(G-18206)*

Atlas Industries Inc..419 637-2117
  401 Wall St Tiffin (44883) *(G-18207)*

Atlas Machine and Supply Inc............................502 584-7262
  4985 Provident Dr West Chester (45246) *(G-19982)*

Atlas Machine and Supply Inc............................614 351-1603
  5040 Nike Dr Hilliard (43026) *(G-10928)*

Atlas Machine Products Co................................216 228-3688
  12507 Plover St Cleveland (44107) *(G-4855)*

Atlas Portable Space Solutions, Cleveland Also called Atlas Machine Products Co *(G-4855)*

Atlas Precision Machining Inc............................937 615-9585
  8899 Sherry Dr Piqua (45356) *(G-16251)*

Atlas Printing and Embroidery...........................440 882-3537
  7632 Pleasant View Dr Cleveland (44134) *(G-4856)*

Atlas Produce LLC...937 223-1446
  104 Salem Ave Dayton (45406) *(G-8168)*

Atlas Roofing Corporation.................................937 746-9941
  675 Oxford Rd Franklin (45005) *(G-10008)*

Atlas Vac Machine Co LLC...............................513 407-3513
  9150 Reading Rd Cincinnati (45215) *(G-3426)*

Atlasbooks, Ashland Also called Bookmasters Inc *(G-713)*

Atmosphere Annealing LLC..............................330 478-0314
  1501 Raff Rd Sw Kenton (43326) *(G-11544)*

Atom Blasting & Finishing Inc............................440 235-4765
  24933 Sprague Rd Columbia Station (44028) *(G-6580)*

Atotech USA Inc...216 398-0550
  1000 Harvard Ave Cleveland (44109) *(G-4857)*

Atr Distributing Company..................................513 353-1800
  11857 Tamper Springs Dr Cincinnati (45240) *(G-3427)*

Atra Metal Spinning Inc....................................440 354-9525
  572 S Saint Clair St Painesville (44077) *(G-15853)*

Atricure Inc (PA)...513 755-4100
  7555 Innovation Way Mason (45040) *(G-12985)*

Atrium Corp...740 966-8200
  188 Commerce Blvd Johnstown (43031) *(G-11390)*

Ats Assembly and Test Inc................................937 222-3030
  313 Mound St Dayton (45402) *(G-8169)*

Ats Assembly and Test Inc (HQ)........................937 222-3030
  313 Mound St Dayton (45402) *(G-8170)*

Ats Machine & Tool Co Inc................................440 255-1120
  7750 Division Dr Mentor (44060) *(G-13528)*

Ats Ohio, Lewis Center Also called Automation Tooling Systems *(G-11887)*

Ats Ohio Inc...614 888-2344
  425 Enterprise Dr Lewis Center (43035) *(G-11884)*

Ats Systems Oregon Inc....................................541 738-0932
  425 Enterprise Dr Lewis Center (43035) *(G-11885)*

Atsi, Athens Also called Athens Technical Specialists *(G-857)*

Attia Applied Sciences Inc...............................740 369-1891
  548 W Central Ave Delaware (43015) *(G-8823)*

Attica Hub Office, Attica Also called Bloomville Gazette Inc *(G-892)*

Attractive Kitchens & Flrg LLC..........................440 406-9299
  536 Cleveland St Elyria (44035) *(G-9376)*

ATW, Hamilton Also called American Tool Works Inc *(G-10668)*

ATW Ohio LLC..937 444-4295
  200 Front St Mount Orab (45154) *(G-14575)*

Atwood Mobile Products LLC............................419 258-5531
  5406 Us 24 Antwerp (45813) *(G-629)*

Aubrey Rose Apparel LLC................................513 728-2681
  3862 Race Rd Cincinnati (45211) *(G-3428)*

Auburn Dairy Products Inc.................................614 488-2536
  2200 Cardigan Ave Columbus (43215) *(G-6785)*

Auburn Metal Processing LLC (PA)...................315 253-2565
  1831 Highland Rd Twinsburg (44087) *(G-18902)*

Audimute Soundproofing & Medic, Beachwood Also called One Wish LLC *(G-1289)*

Audion Automation Ltd (PA).............................216 267-1911
  775 Berea Industrial Pkwy Berea (44017) *(G-1602)*

Audion Automation Ltd.....................................216 267-1911
  775 Berea Industrial Pkwy Berea (44017) *(G-1603)*

Audit Forms, Cleveland Also called Foote Printing Company *(G-5367)*

Aufbackgroundscreeningcom............................216 831-4113
  26101 Village Ln Beachwood (44122) *(G-1258)*

Auglaize Embroidery Co, Wapakoneta Also called Judy Dubois *(G-19493)*

Auglaize Erie Machine Company.........................419 629-2068
  07148 Quellhorst Rd New Bremen (45869) *(G-14780)*

Auglaize Farmers, New Bremen Also called Sunrise Cooperative Inc *(G-14794)*

Auglaize Welding Company Inc...........................419 738-4422
  106 N Water St Wapakoneta (45895) *(G-19480)*

August Graphics Inc..216 381-5503
  834 Haywood Dr Cleveland (44121) *(G-4858)*

August Incorporated...937 434-2520
  354 Congress Park Dr Dayton (45459) *(G-8171)*

August Nine Enterprises, Troy Also called Debra Harbour *(G-18816)*

Aukerman J F Steel Rule Die.............................937 456-4498
  5582 Ozias Rd Eaton (45320) *(G-9299)*

Auld Company...614 454-1010
  1003 Kinnear Rd Columbus (43212) *(G-6786)*

Auld Crafters Inc..614 221-6825
  175 Cleveland Ave Rear Columbus (43215) *(G-6787)*

Auld Lang Signs Inc...513 792-5555
  11109 Kenwood Rd Blue Ash (45242) *(G-1746)*

Auld Technologies LLC......................................614 755-2853
  2030 Dividend Dr Columbus (43228) *(G-6788)*

Aultwrks Occupational Medicine........................330 491-9675
  4650 Hills And Dales Rd N Canton (44708) *(G-2609)*

Aunt Minnies Food Services Inc.........................419 872-4396
  702 Searles Rd Toledo (43607) *(G-18358)*

Auntie Annes...330 652-1939
  5555 Youngstown Warren Rd # 637 Niles (44446) *(G-15144)*

Aunties Attic...740 548-5059
  1550 Lewis Center Rd G Lewis Center (43035) *(G-11886)*

Aurand Manufacturing & Eqp Co 513 541-7200
1210 Ellis St Cincinnati (45223) *(G-3429)*

Auris Noble LLC (PA) 330 321-6649
3045 Smith Rd Ste 700 Fairlawn (44333) *(G-9739)*

Auris Noble LLC 330 685-3748
130 E Voris St Ste C Akron (44311) *(G-77)*

Aurora Balloon Company, Malvern *Also called Perfect Products Company (G-12548)*

Aurora Plastics Inc (PA) 330 422-0700
9280 Jefferson St Streetsboro (44241) *(G-17840)*

Austin Engineering Group, Barberton *Also called Austin Engineering Inc (G-1100)*

Austin Engineering Inc 330 848-0815
834 Promenade Cir Barberton (44203) *(G-1100)*

Austin Finishing Co Inc 216 883-0326
3805 E 91st St Cleveland (44105) *(G-4859)*

Austin Foam Plastics Inc 614 921-0824
2200 International St Columbus (43228) *(G-6789)*

Austin Powder Company (HQ) 216 464-2400
25800 Science Park Dr # 300 Cleveland (44122) *(G-4860)*

Austin Powder Company 740 596-5286
430 Powder Plant Rd Mc Arthur (45651) *(G-13329)*

Austin Powder Company 740 968-1555
74200 Edwards Rd Saint Clairsville (43950) *(G-16780)*

Austin Powder Holdings Company (HQ) 216 464-2400
25800 Science Park Dr # 300 Cleveland (44122) *(G-4861)*

Austin Tape and Label Inc 330 928-7999
3350 Cavalier Trl Stow (44224) *(G-17731)*

Austinburg Machine Inc 440 275-2001
2899 Industrial Park Dr Austinburg (44010) *(G-958)*

Austins Machine Shop 614 855-2525
4295 N Waggoner Rd Blacklick (43004) *(G-1689)*

Austintown Metal Works Inc 330 259-4673
45 Victoria Rd Youngstown (44515) *(G-21028)*

Austintown Printing Inc 330 797-0099
5015 Mahoning Ave Ste 3 Youngstown (44515) *(G-21029)*

Auto Bolt Company 216 881-3913
4740 Manufacturing Ave Cleveland (44135) *(G-4862)*

Auto Core Systems 740 362-5599
2097 London Rd Unit A Delaware (43015) *(G-8824)*

Auto Dealer Designs Inc 330 374-7666
303 W Bartges St Akron (44307) *(G-78)*

Auto Des Sys Inc 614 488-7984
3518 Riverside Dr Upper Arlington (43221) *(G-19110)*

Auto Expo USA of Cleveland 216 889-3000
3250 W 117th St Cleveland (44111) *(G-4863)*

Auto Magic Systems, Steubenville *Also called Eastern Ohio Investments Inc (G-17693)*

Auto Technology Company 440 572-7800
20026 Progress Dr Strongsville (44149) *(G-17892)*

Auto Temp Inc 513 732-6969
950 Kent Rd Batavia (45103) *(G-1164)*

Auto-Seat Tec LLC 419 267-5240
19911 County Rd T Ridgeville Corners (43555) *(G-16664)*

Auto-Tap Inc 216 671-1043
3317 W 140th St Cleveland (44111) *(G-4864)*

Auto-Tronic Control Co 419 666-5100
240 W Andrus Rd Northwood (43619) *(G-15477)*

Auto-Valve Inc 937 854-3037
1707 Guenther Rd Dayton (45417) *(G-8172)*

Autobody Supply Company, Columbus *Also called Finishmaster Inc (G-7086)*

Autocoat 419 636-3830
1900 Progress Dr Bryan (43506) *(G-2280)*

Autogate Inc 419 588-2796
7306 Driver Rd Berlin Heights (44814) *(G-1660)*

Autograph Inc 216 881-1911
4419 Perkins Ave Cleveland (44103) *(G-4865)*

Autograph Foliages, Cleveland *Also called Autograph Inc (G-4865)*

Autoliv Nissin Brake 419 425-6725
2001 Industrial Dr Findlay (45840) *(G-9791)*

Automated Bldg Components Inc (PA) 419 257-2152
2359 Grant Rd North Baltimore (45872) *(G-15191)*

Automated Machinery Solutions 419 727-1772
6010 N Summit St Toledo (43611) *(G-18359)*

Automated Mfg Solutions Inc 440 878-3711
19706 Progress Dr Strongsville (44149) *(G-17893)*

Automated Packaging Systems 330 342-0205
10320 Philipp Pkwy Streetsboro (44241) *(G-17841)*

Automated Packg Systems Inc 330 342-2000
25900 Solon Rd Bedford (44146) *(G-1401)*

Automated Packg Systems Inc 330 626-2313
600 Mondial Pkwy Streetsboro (44241) *(G-17842)*

Automated Packg Systems Inc 216 663-2000
13555 Mccracken Rd Cleveland (44125) *(G-4866)*

Automated Systems Div, Painesville *Also called Coe Manufacturing Company (G-15865)*

Automated Wheel LLC 216 651-9022
8525 Clinton Rd Cleveland (44144) *(G-4867)*

Automatic Bacterial Injection 216 378-1336
26000 Richmond Rd Ste 4 Bedford (44146) *(G-1402)*

Automatic Equipment Corp 513 771-3833
4699 Interstate Dr West Chester (45246) *(G-19983)*

Automatic Feed Co (PA) 419 592-0050
476 E Riverview Ave Napoleon (43545) *(G-14671)*

Automatic Feed Company, Napoleon *Also called Automatic Feed Co (G-14671)*

Automatic Parts, Vermilion *Also called McDaniel Products Inc (G-19333)*

Automatic Parts, Mansfield *Also called McDaniel Products Inc (G-12645)*

Automatic Parts 419 524-5841
433 Springmill St Mansfield (44903) *(G-12564)*

Automatic Screw Products Co 216 241-7896
2070 W 7th St Cleveland (44113) *(G-4868)*

Automatic Stamp Products Inc 216 781-7933
1822 Columbus Rd Cleveland (44113) *(G-4869)*

Automatic Timing & Contrls Div, New Albany *Also called Automatic Timing & Contrls Inc (G-14747)*

Automatic Timing & Contrls Inc (PA) 614 888-8855
7795 Walton Pkwy Ste 175 New Albany (43054) *(G-14747)*

Automation and Ctrl Tech Inc 614 495-1120
6141 Avery Rd Dublin (43016) *(G-9050)*

Automation Etc, Cincinnati *Also called Justin P Straub LLC (G-3963)*

Automation Finishing Inc 216 251-8805
3206 W 121st St Cleveland (44111) *(G-4870)*

Automation Metrology Intl LLC (PA) 440 354-6436
8808 Tyler Blvd Mentor (44060) *(G-13529)*

Automation Plastics Corp 330 562-5148
150 Lena Dr Aurora (44202) *(G-908)*

Automation Solutions Inc 614 235-4060
505 S Parkview Ave # 206 Columbus (43209) *(G-6790)*

Automation Systems Designs Inc 937 387-0351
6222 Webster St Dayton (45414) *(G-8173)*

Automation Technology Inc 937 233-6084
1900 Troy St Dayton (45404) *(G-8174)*

Automation Tool & Die Inc 330 225-8336
5576 Innovation Dr Valley City (44280) *(G-19199)*

Automation Tooling Systems, Lewis Center *Also called Ats Ohio Inc (G-11884)*

Automation Tooling Systems (HQ) 614 781-8063
425 Enterprise Dr Lewis Center (43035) *(G-11887)*

Automation Welding System 330 263-1176
3132 E Lincoln Way Wooster (44691) *(G-20744)*

Automotive Industries Division, Huron *Also called International Automotive (G-11228)*

Automtiq Msurement Systems LLC 614 431-2667
797 Gatehouse Ln Columbus (43235) *(G-6791)*

Automtive Cmpnnts Holdings LLC 419 627-3600
3020 Tiffin Ave Sandusky (44870) *(G-16947)*

Automtive Cmpnnts Holdings LLC 419 483-5622
111 Hirt Dr Bellevue (44811) *(G-1544)*

Autoneum North America Inc 419 693-0511
645 N Lallendorf Rd Oregon (43616) *(G-15703)*

Autoplas Division, Bellevue *Also called Windsor Mold USA Inc (G-1566)*

Autorentalsystemscom LLC 513 334-1040
1776 Mentor Ave Ste 427 Norwood (45212) *(G-15570)*

Autosyte 440 858-3226
829 Callendar Blvd Painesville (44077) *(G-15854)*

Autotec Engineering Company 419 885-2529
6155 Brent Dr Toledo (43611) *(G-18360)*

Autotool Inc 614 733-0222
7875 Corporate Blvd Plain City (43064) *(G-16322)*

Autowax Inc 440 334-4417
15015 Foltz Pkwy Strongsville (44149) *(G-17894)*

Ava Graphix 216 409-8646
3693 Walters Dr Brunswick (44212) *(G-2206)*

Avadirect.com, Twinsburg *Also called Freedom Usa Inc (G-18937)*

Avail Vapor LLC 440 716-6027
26429 Grt Nthrn Shop Ctr North Olmsted (44070) *(G-15327)*

Avail Vapor LLC 440 365-5440
641 Chestnut Commons Dr Elyria (44035) *(G-9377)*

Avalign Technologies Inc (HQ) 419 542-7743
801 Industrial Dr Hicksville (43526) *(G-10900)*

Avalon, Cleveland *Also called Xapc Co (G-6486)*

Avasax Data Recovery, Beavercreek *Also called Avasax Ltd (G-1369)*

Avasax Ltd 937 694-0807
3895 Oakview Dr Beavercreek (45430) *(G-1369)*

Avcom Smt Inc 614 882-8176
213 E Broadway Ave Westerville (43081) *(G-20200)*

Avenue Fabricating Inc 513 752-1911
1281 Clough Pike Batavia (45103) *(G-1165)*

Aver Inc 877 841-2775
41 S High St Ste 1400 Columbus (43215) *(G-6792)*

Avery Dennison Corporation 440 358-3466
670 Hardy Rd Painesville (44077) *(G-15855)*

Avery Dennison Corporation 440 358-4691
7600 Auburn Rd Bldg 18 Painesville (44077) *(G-15856)*

Avery Dennison Corporation 440 358-3700
250 Chester St Painesville (44077) *(G-15857)*

Avery Dennison Corporation 216 267-8700
15939 Industrial Pkwy Cleveland (44135) *(G-4871)*

Avery Dennison Corporation 800 282-8379
250 Chester St Painesville (44077) *(G-15858)*

Avery Dennison Corporation 440 358-3408
250 Chester St Bldg 11 Painesville (44077) *(G-15859)*

Avery Dennison Corporation 614 418-7740
7795 Walton Pkwy Ste 370 New Albany (43054) *(G-14748)*

A
L
P
H
A
B
E
T
I
C

Avery Dennison Corporation............440 358-2828
7100 Lindsay Dr Mentor (44060) *(G-13530)*

Avery Dennison Corporation............440 266-2500
7236 Justin Way Mentor (44060) *(G-13531)*

Avery Dennison Corporation............440 358-2930
7070 Spinach Dr Bldg 19 Mentor (44060) *(G-13532)*

Avery Dennison Corporation............513 682-7500
11101 Mosteller Rd Ste 2 Cincinnati (45241) *(G-3430)*

Avetec Products Group, North Ridgeville *Also called University Accessories Inc* *(G-15407)*

AVI Food Systems Inc............513 860-4191
4175 Port Union Rd Ste B Fairfield (45014) *(G-9644)*

AVI Food Systems Inc............440 327-1944
4937 Mills Indus Pkwy North Ridgeville (44039) *(G-15358)*

AVI Staging Technology, Blue Ash *Also called Iacono Production Services Inc* *(G-1811)*

Aviation Cmpnent Solutions Inc............440 295-6590
26451 Curtiss Wright Pkwy # 106 Richmond Heights (44143) *(G-16652)*

Aviation Technologies Inc (HQ)............216 706-2960
1301 E 9th St Ste 3000 Cleveland (44114) *(G-4872)*

Aviles Construction Company............216 939-1084
7011 Clark Ave Cleveland (44102) *(G-4873)*

Avina Specialties Inc............419 592-5646
116 W Washington St Napoleon (43545) *(G-14672)*

Avion Manufacturing Company............330 220-1989
2950 Westway Dr Ste 106 Brunswick (44212) *(G-2207)*

Avion Tool Corporation............937 278-0779
2624 Keenan Ave Dayton (45414) *(G-8175)*

Avitae USA LLC............216 416-3461
1660 W 2nd St Ste 1100 Cleveland (44113) *(G-4874)*

Avon, Cleveland *Also called Wallseye Concrete Corp* *(G-6444)*

Avon Concrete, Elyria *Also called Westview Concrete Corp* *(G-9510)*

Avon Concrete Corporation............440 937-6264
930 Miller Rd Avon (44011) *(G-984)*

Avon Lake Printing............440 933-2078
227 Miller Rd Avon Lake (44012) *(G-1024)*

Avon Lake Sheet Metal Co............440 933-3505
33574 Pin Oak Pkwy Avon Lake (44012) *(G-1025)*

Avondale Printing Inc............330 477-1180
2820 Whipple Ave Nw Canton (44708) *(G-2610)*

Avotronics Powertrain Inc............614 537-0261
4200 Regent St Columbus (43219) *(G-6793)*

Avs Oil Recovery LLC............937 645-4600
13311 Industrial Pkwy Marysville (43040) *(G-12932)*

Avtek International Inc............330 633-7500
382 Commerce St Tallmadge (44278) *(G-18134)*

Avtron Inc............216 642-1230
7900 E Pleasant Valley Rd Independence (44131) *(G-11249)*

Avtron Aerospace Inc (PA)............216 750-5152
7900 E Pleasant Valley Rd Cleveland (44131) *(G-4875)*

Avtron Holdings LLC............216 642-1230
7900 E Pleasant Valley Rd Cleveland (44131) *(G-4876)*

Avtron Loadbank, Cleveland *Also called Asco Power Technologies LP* *(G-4842)*

Avure Autoclave Systems Inc (HQ)............614 891-2732
3721 Corp Dr Columbus (43231) *(G-6794)*

Avure Technologies Inc............614 891-2732
8270 Green Meadows Dr N Lewis Center (43035) *(G-11888)*

Avure Technologies Inc............513 433-2500
2601 S Verity Pkwy # 13 Middletown (45044) *(G-14022)*

AW Faber-Castell Usa Inc............216 643-4660
9450 Allen Dr Ste B Cleveland (44125) *(G-4877)*

Award One, Troy *Also called Designer Awards Inc* *(G-18819)*

Awardcraft, Celina *Also called Eighth Floor Promotions* *(G-2994)*

Awesome Yogurt LLC............937 643-0879
3337 Lenox Dr Dayton (45429) *(G-8176)*

Awning Fabri Caters Inc............216 476-4888
10237 Lorain Ave Cleveland (44111) *(G-4878)*

Awp, Kent *Also called Area Wide Protective Inc* *(G-11431)*

Aws Industries Inc............513 932-7941
2600 Henkle Dr Lebanon (45036) *(G-11782)*

Axalt Powde Coati Syste Usa I............614 600-4104
4130 Lyman Dr Hilliard (43026) *(G-10929)*

Axalta Coating Systems LLC............419 478-1211
1930 Tremainsville Rd Toledo (43613) *(G-18361)*

Axel Austin LLC............440 237-1610
10147 Royalton Rd Ste I North Royalton (44133) *(G-15410)*

Axent Graphics LLC............216 362-7560
6270 Engle Rd Brookpark (44142) *(G-2152)*

Axess International LLC............330 460-4840
4641 Stag Thicket Ln Brunswick (44212) *(G-2208)*

Axiomed Spine Corp (PA)............216 587-5566
5350 Trnsp Blvd Ste 18 Cleveland (44125) *(G-4879)*

Axion Strl Innovations LLC (PA)............740 452-2500
1100 Brandywine Blvd H Zanesville (43701) *(G-21273)*

Axis Corporation............937 592-1958
314 Water Ave Bellefontaine (43311) *(G-1520)*

Axis Led Group LLC............614 633-7955
6810 Avery Rd Dublin (43017) *(G-9051)*

Axis Tool & Grinding LLC............330 535-4713
895 Home Ave Akron (44310) *(G-79)*

Axle Surgeons of NW Ohio............419 822-5775
811 Helvetia St Delta (43515) *(G-8928)*

Axon Medical LLC............216 276-0262
1484 Medina Rd Ste 117 Medina (44256) *(G-13374)*

Ayling and Reichert Co Consent............419 898-2471
411 S Railroad St Oak Harbor (43449) *(G-15586)*

Aza Enterprises LLC............740 678-8482
1149 Fisher Ridge Rd Fleming (45729) *(G-9910)*

Aztec Manufacturing Inc............330 783-9747
4325 Simon Rd Youngstown (44512) *(G-21030)*

Aztlan Communications, Toledo *Also called Laprensa Publications Inc* *(G-18554)*

Azz Galvanizing - Cincinnati, Cincinnati *Also called AAA Galvanizing - Joliet Inc* *(G-3341)*

Azz Inc............330 456-3241
1723 Cleveland Ave Sw Canton (44707) *(G-2611)*

Azz Incorporated............330 445-2170
1723 Cleveland Ave Sw Canton (44707) *(G-2612)*

B & B Bindery Inc............330 722-5430
4381 Pine Lake Dr Medina (44256) *(G-13375)*

B & B Box Company Inc............419 872-5600
26490 Southpoint Rd Perrysburg (43551) *(G-16067)*

B & B Cast Stone Co Inc............740 697-0008
7790 Ransbottom Rd Roseville (43777) *(G-16726)*

B & B Gear & Machine Co Inc............937 687-1771
440 W Main St New Lebanon (45345) *(G-14840)*

B & B Industries, Orient *Also called Kmj Leasing Ltd* *(G-15723)*

B & B Molded Products Inc............419 592-8700
600 Fillmore St Napoleon (43545) *(G-14673)*

B & B Necessities............330 995-0489
1004 Old Barn Rd Aurora (44202) *(G-909)*

B & B Pallet Co............419 435-4530
885 S State Route 587 Fostoria (44830) *(G-9967)*

B & B Paper Converters Inc............216 941-8100
12500 Elmwood Ave Frnt Cleveland (44111) *(G-4880)*

B & B Printing Graphics Inc............419 893-7068
1689 Lance Pointe Rd Maumee (43537) *(G-13228)*

B & B Trophies & Awards............330 225-6193
1317 Pearl Rd Brunswick (44212) *(G-2209)*

B & B Welding............419 968-2743
6647 Middle Pt Wetzel Rd Middle Point (45863) *(G-13898)*

B & C Research Inc............330 848-4000
842 Norton Ave Barberton (44203) *(G-1101)*

B & D Commissary LLC............740 743-3890
5705 State Route 204 Ne Mount Perry (43760) *(G-14590)*

B & D Graphics Inc............513 641-0855
300 Township Ave Cincinnati (45216) *(G-3431)*

B & D Machinists Inc............513 831-8588
1350 Us Route 50 Milford (45150) *(G-14123)*

B & F Manufacturing Co............216 518-0333
19050 Cranwood Pkwy Warrensville Heights (44128) *(G-19629)*

B & G Machine Company Inc............440 946-8787
7205 Commerce Dr Mentor (44060) *(G-13533)*

B & G Tool Company............614 451-2538
4832 Kenny Rd Columbus (43220) *(G-6795)*

B & H Machine Inc............330 868-6425
15001 Lincoln St Se Minerva (44657) *(G-14317)*

B & J Baking Company Inc............513 541-2386
4056 Colerain Ave Cincinnati (45223) *(G-3432)*

B & J Drilling Company Inc............740 599-6700
13911 Millersburg Rd Danville (43014) *(G-8083)*

B & L Labels and Packg Co Inc............937 773-9080
421 Fox Dr Piqua (45356) *(G-16252)*

B & P Company Inc............937 298-0265
97 Compark Rd Dayton (45459) *(G-8177)*

B & P Polishing Inc............330 753-4202
123 9th St Nw Barberton (44203) *(G-1102)*

B & P Spring Production Co............216 486-4260
19520 Nottingham Rd Cleveland (44110) *(G-4881)*

B & R Custom Chrome............419 536-7215
469 Dearborn Ave Toledo (43605) *(G-18362)*

B & R Machine Co Inc............216 961-7370
2216 W 65th St Cleveland (44102) *(G-4882)*

B & S Blacktop Co............513 797-5759
1704 Lndale Nchlsville Rd New Richmond (45157) *(G-14940)*

B & S Transport Inc (PA)............330 767-4319
11325 Lawndell Rd Sw Navarre (44662) *(G-14709)*

B & T Welding and Machine Co............740 687-1908
423 S Mount Pleasant Ave Lancaster (43130) *(G-11690)*

B A Malcuit Racing Inc............330 878-7111
707 S Wooster Ave Strasburg (44680) *(G-17820)*

B and L Sales Inc (PA)............330 279-2007
3149 State Rte Ste 39 Millersburg (44654) *(G-14195)*

B B & H Tool Company............614 868-8634
7719 Taylor Rd Sw Reynoldsburg (43068) *(G-16581)*

B B Bradley Company Inc (PA)............440 354-2005
7755 Crile Rd Painesville (44077) *(G-15860)*

B B Bradley Company Inc.............614 777-5600
2699 Scioto Pkwy Columbus (43221) *(G-6796)*

B C Composites Corporation............330 262-3070
777 W Smith Rd Medina (44256) *(G-13376)*

B C I, Fairlawn *Also called Buckeye Corrugated Inc* *(G-9744)*

B C I, Powell Also called Building Ctrl Integrators LLC (G-16464)
B C Machining Inc 440 593-4763
502 E Main Rd Conneaut (44030) (G-7800)
B C Metals Inc 513 732-9644
4484 Hartman Ln Batavia (45103) (G-1166)
B C Wilson Inc 937 439-1866
85 Compark Rd Dayton (45459) (G-8178)
B D G Wrap-Tite Inc 440 349-5400
6200 Cochran Rd Solon (44139) (G-17263)
B D P Services Inc 740 828-9685
8255 Blackrun Rd Nashport (43830) (G-14703)
B F, Cleveland Also called Bula Forge & Machine Inc (G-4947)
B G News 419 372-2601
214 W Hall Bgsu Bowling Green (43403) (G-1969)
B Hogenkamp & R Harlamert 419 925-0526
3145 Hartke Rd Celina (45822) (G-2986)
B J Pallett 419 447-9665
525 Wall St Tiffin (44883) (G-18208)
B K Fabrication & Machine Shop 740 695-4164
70300 Kagg Hill Rd Saint Clairsville (43950) (G-16781)
B K Plastics Inc 937 473-2087
1400 Mote Dr Covington (45318) (G-7920)
B L Anderson Co Inc 765 463-1518
8887 Eagle Ridge Ct West Chester (45069) (G-19812)
B L F Enterprises Inc 937 642-6425
445 S State St Westerville (43081) (G-20201)
B M C Inc 216 581-9595
17209 S Miles Rd Cleveland (44128) (G-4883)
B M DS Fish N More LLC 419 238-2722
121 South Ave Van Wert (45891) (G-19244)
B M Pallets 740 634-2659
5837 Dry Bone Rd Hillsboro (45133) (G-10996)
B N Machine Inc 440 255-5200
8853 East Ave Mentor (44060) (G-13534)
B O K Inc 937 322-9588
508 W Main St Springfield (45504) (G-17520)
B P Exploration, Dayton Also called BP Products North America Inc (G-8192)
B P Exploration, Bryan Also called BP Products North America Inc (G-2284)
B P Oil Company 513 671-4107
1201 Omniplex Dr Cincinnati (45240) (G-3433)
B P T, Bucyrus Also called Bucyrus Precision Tech Inc (G-2334)
B Richardson Inc 330 724-2122
25 Elinor Ave Akron (44305) (G-80)
B S F Inc (PA) 937 890-6121
8895 N Dixie Dr Dayton (45414) (G-8179)
B S F Inc 937 890-6121
320b S 5th St Tipp City (45371) (G-18264)
B T C, Dayton Also called Browder Tool Co Inc (G-8199)
B V Grinding Machining Inc 440 918-1884
1438 E 363rd St Willoughby (44095) (G-20442)
B V Mfg Inc 330 549-5331
13426 Woodworth Rd New Springfield (44443) (G-14949)
B W Electrical & Maint Svc 330 534-7870
6204 Yungstown Hubbard Rd Hubbard (44425) (G-11126)
B W Grinding Co 419 923-1376
15048 County Road 10 3 Lyons (43533) (G-12431)
B W T Inc 330 928-9107
353 E Cuyahoga Falls Ave Akron (44310) (G-81)
B Y G Industries Inc 216 961-5436
8003 Clinton Rd Cleveland (44144) (G-4884)
B&A Holstic Food and Herbs 614 747-2885
6031 E Main St Columbus (43213) (G-6797)
B&B Distributors LLC 440 324-1293
150 Keep Ct Ste A Elyria (44035) (G-9378)
B&C Machine Co LLC 330 745-4013
401 Newell St Barberton (44203) (G-1103)
B&D Productions Inc 216 961-0310
2223 Willowdale Ave Cleveland (44109) (G-4885)
B&D Truck Parts Sls & Svcs LLC 419 701-7041
1498 Perrysburg Rd Fostoria (44830) (G-9968)
B&N Coal Inc 740 783-3575
38455 Marietta Rte Dexter City (45727) (G-8954)
B-F Processing Corporation, Columbus Also called B-F Processing LLC (G-6798)
B-F Processing LLC 614 225-4000
180 E Broad St Lbby Columbus (43215) (G-6798)
B-K Tool & Design Inc 419 532-3890
480 W Main St Kalida (45853) (G-11412)
B-R-O-T Incorporated 216 267-5335
4730 Briar Rd Cleveland (44135) (G-4886)
B-Squared Prtg Mktg Solutions, North Canton Also called B2 Incorporated (G-15221)
B-Tek Scales LLC 330 471-8900
1510 Metric Ave Sw Canton (44706) (G-2613)
B-Wear Sportswear, Zanesville Also called 5 BS Inc (G-21263)
B2 Incorporated (PA) 330 244-9510
8324c Cleveland Ave Nw North Canton (44720) (G-15221)
B5 Systems Inc 937 372-4768
1463 Bellbrook Ave Xenia (45385) (G-20937)
Baaron Abrasives Inc 330 263-7737
2015 Great Trails Dr Wooster (44691) (G-20745)

Babbert Real Estate Inv Co Ltd (PA) 614 837-8444
7415 Diley Rd Canal Winchester (43110) (G-2519)
Babcock & Wilcox Company (HQ) 330 753-4511
20 S Van Buren Ave Barberton (44203) (G-1104)
Babcock & Wilcox Megtec 614 258-9501
835 N Cassady Ave Columbus (43219) (G-6799)
Babcock & Wilcox Megtec 614 340-4154
2120 Citygate Dr Columbus (43219) (G-6800)
Babcock & Wilcox Nuclr Oprtns 330 860-1010
91 Stirling Ave Barberton (44203) (G-1105)
Babcock & Wilcox Powr Generatn 330 753-4511
91 Stirling Ave Barberton (44203) (G-1106)
Babcox Media Inc (PA) 330 670-1234
3550 Embassy Pkwy Akron (44333) (G-82)
Baby Love Prenatal Imaging LLC 419 905-7935
727 W 2nd St Delphos (45833) (G-8901)
BAC Technologies Ltd 937 465-2228
8115 Calland Rd West Liberty (43357) (G-20091)
Bacconis Lickety Split 330 924-0418
4194 Greenville Rd Cortland (44410) (G-7861)
Back Development LLC 937 671-7896
3700 Northfield Rd Ste 11 Cleveland (44122) (G-4887)
Background Music & Sound Inc 937 898-9871
8529 N Dixie Dr Ste 325 Dayton (45414) (G-8180)
Backyard Scoreboards LLC 513 702-6561
431 Kenridge Dr Middletown (45042) (G-14023)
Baco Manufacturing Corp 440 585-5858
29175 Anderson Rd Wickliffe (44092) (G-20355)
Bad Brush Design, Holland Also called Jeffrey A Clark (G-11067)
Badboy Blasters Incorporated 330 454-2699
1720 Wallace Ave Ne Canton (44705) (G-2614)
Badizo LLC 844 344-3833
4466 Darrow Rd Ste 3 Stow (44224) (G-17732)
Badurik Butcher Block 330 652-2333
3761 Main St Mineral Ridge (44440) (G-14303)
Baerlocher Production LLC 513 482-6300
5890 Highland Ridge Dr Cincinnati (45232) (G-3434)
Baerlocher USA LLC (HQ) 330 364-6000
3676 Davis Rd Nw Dover (44622) (G-8965)
Bag-Pack Inc 513 346-3900
9486 Sutton Pl West Chester (45011) (G-19813)
Bagpack, West Chester Also called Bag-Pack Inc (G-19813)
Bahler Medical Inc 614 873-7600
8910 Warner Rd Plain City (43064) (G-16323)
Bailey & Jensen Inc 937 272-1784
442 Yankee Trace Dr Centerville (45458) (G-3036)
Bailey Controls, Wickliffe Also called ABB Inc (G-20348)
Baileys Asphalt Sealing 740 453-9409
2092 Newark Rd South Zanesville (43701) (G-17453)
Baillie Lumber Co LP 419 462-2000
3953 County Road 51 Galion (44833) (G-10254)
Bainter Machining Company (PA) 740 653-2422
1230 Rainbow Dr Ne Lancaster (43130) (G-11691)
Bainter Machining Company 740 756-4598
2945 Carroll Eastern Rd Carroll (43112) (G-2937)
Bair Bodies & Trailers Inc 330 343-4853
4562 Bair Rd Nw Dover (44622) (G-8966)
Baird Brothers Sawmill Inc 330 533-3122
7060 Crory Rd Canfield (44406) (G-2549)
Baird Cabinet Shop Inc 330 837-9075
2330 Tiffin Cir Se Massillon (44646) (G-13113)
Baird Concrete Products Inc 740 623-8600
15 Locust St Coshocton (43812) (G-7881)
Baird Furniture Repair, Massillon Also called Baird Cabinet Shop Inc (G-13113)
Baise Enterprises Inc 614 444-3171
695 Koebel Ave Frnt Columbus (43207) (G-6801)
Baise Quality Printing, Columbus Also called Baise Enterprises Inc (G-6801)
Bake ME Happy LLC 614 477-3642
116 E Moler St Columbus (43207) (G-6802)
Baked & More LLC 330 324-4981
5194 California Ave Louisville (44641) (G-12309)
Bakehouse Bread and Cookie Co, Troy Also called Bakehouse Bread Co Inc (G-18807)
Bakehouse Bread Co Inc 937 339-8100
317 Public Sq Troy (45373) (G-18807)
Bakelite N Sumitomo Amer Inc 419 675-1282
13717 Us Highway 68 Kenton (43326) (G-11545)
Baker Built Products Inc 419 965-2646
11877 Walnut Grove Ch Rd Ohio City (45874) (G-15660)
Baker Hughes C/O Tangoe Inc 304 884-6442
8008 Truck World Blvd Hubbard (44425) (G-11127)
Baker Logging 740 686-2817
62683 Ok Rd Belmont (43718) (G-1578)
Baker McMillen Co (PA) 330 923-8300
3688 Wyoga Lake Rd Stow (44224) (G-17733)
Baker McMillen Co 330 923-3303
3688 Wyoga Lake Rd Stow (44224) (G-17734)
Baker Media Group LLC 330 253-0056
1653 Merriman Rd Ste 116 Akron (44313) (G-83)
Baker Plastics Inc 330 743-3142
900 Mahoning Ave Youngstown (44502) (G-21031)

Baker Store Equipment Company 216 475-5900
23449 Laureldale Rd Shaker Heights (44122) *(G-17084)*

Baker Welding Llc 614 252-6100
2901 Eastport Ave Bldg 95 Columbus (43219) *(G-6803)*

Baker-Shindler Builders Sup Co, Defiance *Also called Baker-Shindler Contracting Co (G-8780)*

Baker-Shindler Contracting Co (PA) 419 782-5080
525 Cleveland Ave Defiance (43512) *(G-8780)*

Baker-Shindler Contracting Co 419 399-4841
121 German St Cecil (45821) *(G-2979)*

Baker-Shindler Ready Mix, Cecil *Also called Baker-Shindler Contracting Co (G-2979)*

Bakers Choice Distributing 330 273-5745
4794 Whiteoaks Dr Brunswick (44212) *(G-2210)*

Bakers Print Shop 740 423-1717
23 Wood Dr Little Hocking (45742) *(G-12143)*

Bakers Welding, Zanesville *Also called J A B Welding Service Inc (G-21322)*

Bakerwell Inc (PA) 330 276-2161
10420 County Road 620 Killbuck (44637) *(G-11592)*

Bakerwell Inc 614 898-7590
6295 Maxtown Rd Ste 300 Westerville (43082) *(G-20139)*

Bakerwell Service Rigs Inc (HQ) 330 276-2161
10420 County Road 620 Killbuck (44637) *(G-11593)*

Balance Disorder Institute, Cincinnati *Also called Ear Medical Center Inc (G-3684)*

Balancing Company Inc (PA) 937 898-9111
898 Center Dr Vandalia (45377) *(G-19282)*

Balbo Industries Inc (PA) 440 333-0630
20630 Center Ridge Rd Rocky River (44116) *(G-16695)*

Baldie Import and Export Corp 513 503-0953
4520 Lucerne Ave Cincinnati (45227) *(G-3435)*

Baldwin, Hilliard *Also called Merry X-Ray Chemical Corp (G-10960)*

Baldwin B AA Design 740 374-5844
256 Front St Marietta (45750) *(G-12766)*

Baleco International Inc 513 353-3000
3200 State Line Rd North Bend (45052) *(G-15202)*

Ball Bounce and Sport Inc (PA) 419 289-9310
1 Hedstrom Dr Ashland (44805) *(G-710)*

Ball Aerospace & Tech Corp 937 429-5005
2875 Presidential Dr # 180 Beavercreek (45324) *(G-1321)*

Ball Arosol Specialty Cont Inc 330 534-9273
644 Myon St Hubbard (44425) *(G-11128)*

Ball Corporation 419 423-3071
1800 Production Dr Findlay (45840) *(G-9792)*

Ball Corporation 330 244-2313
3075 Brookline Rd North Canton (44720) *(G-15222)*

Ball Corporation 614 771-9112
2690 Charter St Columbus (43228) *(G-6804)*

Ball Corporation 330 534-7418
644 Myron St Hubbard (44425) *(G-11129)*

Ball Corporation 330 244-2800
2121 Warner Rd Se Canton (44707) *(G-2615)*

Ball Metal Beverage Cont Corp 419 423-3071
12340 Township Rd 99 E Findlay (45840) *(G-9793)*

Ball Metal Beverage Cont Div, Findlay *Also called Ball Metal Beverage Cont Corp (G-9793)*

Ball Plastic Container Div, Bellevue *Also called Amcor Rigid Plastics Usa LLC (G-1542)*

Ballas Egg Products, Zanesville *Also called BE Products Inc (G-21277)*

Ballas Egg Products Corp 614 453-0386
40 N 2nd St Zanesville (43701) *(G-21274)*

Ballinger Industries Inc (PA) 419 422-4533
2500 Fostoria Ave Findlay (45840) *(G-9794)*

Ballreich Bros Inc 419 447-1814
186 Ohio Ave Tiffin (44883) *(G-18209)*

Ballreichs Potato Chips Snacks, Tiffin *Also called Ballreich Bros Inc (G-18209)*

Balmac Inc 614 873-8222
8205 Estates Pkwy Ste N Plain City (43064) *(G-16324)*

Balser Inc 567 444-4737
502 Jackson St Archbold (43502) *(G-667)*

Balta Technology Inc 513 724-0247
4350 Batavia Rd Batavia (45103) *(G-1167)*

Baltic Country Meats 330 897-7025
3320 State Route 557 Baltic (43804) *(G-1065)*

Baltic Meats, Baltic *Also called Baltic Country Meats (G-1065)*

Baltimore Fabricators Inc 740 862-6016
9420 Lancaster Krkersvlle Baltimore (43105) *(G-1080)*

Balzer's Tool Coating Co, Brunswick *Also called Oerlikon Blzers Cating USA Inc (G-2240)*

Bam Fuel Inc 740 397-6674
21191 Floralwood Dr Howard (43028) *(G-11122)*

Bambeck Inc 614 766-1000
4362 Tuller Rd Dublin (43017) *(G-9052)*

Ban-Fam Industries Inc 216 265-9588
4740 Briar Rd Cleveland (44135) *(G-4888)*

Bancequity Petroleum Corp 330 468-5935
8821 Freeway Dr Macedonia (44056) *(G-12436)*

Banco Die Inc 330 821-8511
11322 Union Ave Ne Alliance (44601) *(G-497)*

Bandon Corp 614 766-7243
8420 Kilbirnie Ct Dublin (43017) *(G-9053)*

Bands Company Inc 330 674-0446
164 E Jackson St Millersburg (44654) *(G-14196)*

Bang Printing of Ohio Inc 800 678-1222
3765 Sunnybrook Rd Kent (44240) *(G-11432)*

Banks Manufacturing Company 440 458-8661
40259 Banks Rd Grafton (44044) *(G-10420)*

Banner Mattress & Furniture Co, Toledo *Also called Banner Mattress Co Inc (G-18363)*

Banner Mattress Co Inc (PA) 419 324-7181
2544 N Reynolds Rd Toledo (43615) *(G-18363)*

Banner Metals Group Inc 614 291-3105
1308 Holly Ave Columbus (43212) *(G-6805)*

Bansal Enterprises Inc 330 633-9355
1538 Home Ave Akron (44310) *(G-84)*

BAP Manufacturing Inc 419 332-5041
601 N Stone St Ste 1 Fremont (43420) *(G-10127)*

Bar Codes Unlimited Inc 937 434-2633
683 Miamisburg Ctrvl 21 Ste Dayton (45459) *(G-8181)*

Bar Processing Corporation 330 872-0914
1000 Windham Rd Newton Falls (44444) *(G-15129)*

Bar Tech Service Inc 440 943-5286
30012 Lakeland Blvd Wickliffe (44092) *(G-20356)*

Bar1 Motorsports 614 284-3732
1757 Creekview Dr Marysville (43040) *(G-12933)*

Barany Jewelry Inc 330 220-4367
3702 Center Rd Brunswick (44212) *(G-2211)*

Barbara A Eisenhardt 614 436-9690
7726 Cloister Dr Columbus (43235) *(G-6806)*

Barbara A Lieurance 937 382-2864
180 E Sugartree St Wilmington (45177) *(G-20656)*

Barbasol LLC 419 903-0738
2011 Ford Dr Ashland (44805) *(G-711)*

Barbco Inc 330 488-9400
315 Pekin Dr Se East Canton (44730) *(G-9190)*

Barbeque Integrated Inc 614 430-0572
1481 Polaris Pkwy Columbus (43240) *(G-6640)*

Barber Spring Ohio, Chillicothe *Also called Standard Car Truck Company (G-3276)*

Barberton Herald, Barberton *Also called Richardson Publishing Company (G-1146)*

Barberton Magic Press Printing 330 753-9578
699 Wooster Rd N Barberton (44203) *(G-1107)*

Barberton Mold & Machine Co 330 745-8559
465 5th St Ne Barberton (44203) *(G-1108)*

Barberton Printcraft 330 848-3000
520 Wooster Rd W Barberton (44203) *(G-1109)*

Barberton Steel Industries Inc 330 745-6837
240 E Huston St Barberton (44203) *(G-1110)*

Barbs Custom Embroidery 419 393-2226
14845 State Route 111 Defiance (43512) *(G-8781)*

Barbs Embroidery 614 875-9933
2700 Brunswick Dr Grove City (43123) *(G-10545)*

Barbs Graffiti Inc (PA) 216 881-5550
3111 Carnegie Ave Cleveland (44115) *(G-4889)*

Barclay Machine Inc 330 337-9541
650 S Broadway Ave Salem (44460) *(G-16874)*

Barclay Petroleum Inc 740 569-4327
7400 Marietta Rd Se Bremen (43107) *(G-2079)*

Barclay Rolls, Salem *Also called Barclay Machine Inc (G-16874)*

Bard Manufacturing Company Inc (PA) 419 636-1194
1914 Randolph Dr Bryan (43506) *(G-2281)*

Bardes Corporation (PA) 513 533-6200
4730 Madison Rd Cincinnati (45227) *(G-3436)*

Bardons & Oliver Inc (PA) 440 498-5800
5800 Harper Rd Solon (44139) *(G-17264)*

Bardwell Winery, Mount Orab *Also called Wedco LLC (G-14587)*

Bargain Hunter, Millersburg *Also called Graphic Publications Inc (G-14218)*

Barile Precision Grinding Inc 216 267-6500
12320 Plaza Dr Cleveland (44130) *(G-4890)*

Baring Distributors, Cleveland *Also called Bdi Inc (G-4898)*

Barker Lumber 740 289-2424
103 Lewis Rd Piketon (45661) *(G-16215)*

Barker Products Company 216 249-0900
1028 E 134th St Cleveland (44110) *(G-4891)*

Barkett Fruit Co Inc (PA) 330 364-6645
1213 E 3rd St Dover (44622) *(G-8967)*

Barkman Products LLC 330 893-2520
2550 Township Road 121 Millersburg (44654) *(G-14197)*

Barlamy Supply, Wapakoneta *Also called Jewett Supply (G-19492)*

Barley's Brewing Company, Columbus *Also called Brewpub Restaurant Corp (G-6857)*

Barncraft Storage Buildings 513 738-5654
2527 Millville Shandon Rd Hamilton (45013) *(G-10672)*

Barnes Advertising Corp 740 453-6836
1580 Fairview Rd Zanesville (43701) *(G-21275)*

Barnes Group Inc 513 759-3528
9826 Crescent Park Dr West Chester (45069) *(G-19814)*

Barnes Group Inc 513 779-6888
9826 Crescent Park Dr West Chester (45069) *(G-19815)*

Barnes Group Inc 440 526-5900
10367 Brecksville Rd Brecksville (44141) *(G-2035)*

Barnes Group Inc 419 891-9292
370 W Dussel Dr Ste A Maumee (43537) *(G-13229)*

Barnes International Inc 419 352-7501
555 Van Camp Rd Bowling Green (43402) *(G-1970)*

Barnes Services LLC...440 319-2088
    20677 Centuryway Rd Maple Heights (44137) *(G-12727)*
Barnett Spouting Inc...330 644-0853
    204 E Ralston Ave Akron (44301) *(G-85)*
Barney Corporation Inc (PA)....................................614 274-9069
    4089 Leap Rd Hilliard (43026) *(G-10930)*
Barney Schoolers, Akron Also called Barnett Spouting Inc *(G-85)*
Barnhart Printing Corp..330 456-2279
    1107 Melchoir Pl Sw Canton (44707) *(G-2616)*
Barnhart Publishing, Canton Also called Barnhart Printing Corp *(G-2616)*
Barnstorm Brewing Company LLC..............................419 852-9366
    706 N 2nd St Coldwater (45828) *(G-6551)*
Baroque Violin Shop, Cincinnati Also called Paul Bartel *(G-4216)*
Barr Engineering Incorporated..................................614 892-0162
    5710 Westbourne Ave Columbus (43213) *(G-6807)*
Barr Engineering Incorporated (PA)...........................614 714-0299
    2800 Corp Exchange Dr # 240 Columbus (43231) *(G-6808)*
Barr Laboratories Inc..513 731-9900
    5040 Duramed Rd Cincinnati (45213) *(G-3437)*
Barracuda Technologies Inc.....................................216 469-1566
    2900 State Route 82 Aurora (44202) *(G-910)*
Barrett & Sons Pallet & Lbr Co, East Liverpool Also called Joe Barrett *(G-9220)*
Barrett Paving Materials Inc.....................................513 271-6200
    3751 Commerce Dr Middletown (45005) *(G-14101)*
Barrette Outdoor Living Inc (HQ).............................440 891-0790
    7830 Freeway Cir Middleburg Heights (44130) *(G-13903)*
Barry Brothers Electric...614 299-8187
    1100 Leona Ave Columbus (43201) *(G-6809)*
Barta Viorel...440 735-1699
    26245 Broadway Ave Bedford (44146) *(G-1403)*
Bartan Design Inc..216 267-6474
    13100 Enterprise Ave Cleveland (44135) *(G-4892)*
Bartek Systems...614 759-6014
    6155 Chinaberry Dr Columbus (43213) *(G-6810)*
Bartells Cupcakery..330 957-1793
    4555 Norquest Blvd Austintown (44515) *(G-969)*
Barth Industries Co LP (PA)...................................216 267-0531
    12650 Brookpark Rd Cleveland (44130) *(G-4893)*
Bartley Lawn Service LLC.......................................937 435-8884
    69 W Alex Bell Rd West Carrollton (45449) *(G-19791)*
Bartley Offie..614 235-9050
    3760 E 5th Ave Columbus (43219) *(G-6811)*
Bartleys Lawn Services, West Carrollton Also called Bartley Lawn Service LLC *(G-19791)*
Barton-Carey Medical Products (PA).........................419 887-1285
    1331 Conant St Ste 102 Maumee (43537) *(G-13230)*
Bartter & Sons..419 651-0374
    1761 Township Road 85 Jeromesville (44840) *(G-11383)*
Barudan America Inc (HQ)......................................440 248-8770
    30901 Carter St Frnt A Solon (44139) *(G-17265)*
Basco Manufacturing Company (PA)..........................513 573-1900
    7201 Snider Rd Mason (45040) *(G-12986)*
Basco Shower Enclosures, Mason Also called Basco Manufacturing Company *(G-12986)*
Baseball Card Corner...513 677-0464
    1812 Arrowhead Trl Loveland (45140) *(G-12340)*
Baseline Printing Inc...330 369-3204
    1262 Youngstown Rd Se Warren (44484) *(G-19526)*
Basetek LLC (PA)..877 712-2273
    14975 White Rd Middlefield (44062) *(G-13916)*
Basetek LLC...877 712-2273
    35 Irongate Park Dr Dayton (45459) *(G-8182)*
BASF Battery Materials, Independence Also called BASF Catalysts LLC *(G-11250)*
BASF Catalysts LLC...440 322-3741
    120 Pine St Elyria (44035) *(G-9379)*
BASF Catalysts LLC...216 867-1047
    8001 E Pleasant Valley Rd Independence (44131) *(G-11250)*
BASF Catalysts LLC...216 360-5005
    23800 Mercantile Rd Cleveland (44122) *(G-4894)*
BASF Construction Chem LLC (HQ)............................216 831-5500
    23700 Chagrin Blvd Cleveland (44122) *(G-4895)*
BASF Corporation..937 547-6700
    1175 Martin St Greenville (45331) *(G-10489)*
BASF Corporation..419 877-0876
    6125 Industrial Pkwy Whitehouse (43571) *(G-20337)*
BASF Corporation..513 482-3000
    4900 Este Ave Cincinnati (45232) *(G-3438)*
BASF Corporation..614 662-5682
    9565 Logistics Ct Columbus (43217) *(G-6812)*
BASF Corporation..216 867-1040
    8001 E Pleasant Vly Independence (44131) *(G-11251)*
BASF Corporation..513 482-3000
    4900 Este Ave Cincinnati (45232) *(G-3439)*
Basic Cases Inc...216 662-3900
    19561 Miles Rd Cleveland (44128) *(G-4896)*
Basic Coatings LLC...419 241-2156
    400 Van Camp Rd Bowling Green (43402) *(G-1971)*
Basic Grain Products Inc..614 408-3091
    300 E Vine St Coldwater (45828) *(G-6552)*
Basic Grain Products Inc (PA)..................................419 678-2304
    300310 E Vine St Coldwater (45828) *(G-6553)*

Basic Packaging Ltd...330 634-9665
    65 Carmen Rd Tallmadge (44278) *(G-18135)*
Basilius Inc..419 536-5810
    4338 South Ave Toledo (43615) *(G-18364)*
Basinger Inc...614 771-8300
    2222 Wilson Rd Columbus (43228) *(G-6813)*
Bass International Sftwr LLC (PA)..............................877 227-0155
    4449 Easton Way Ste 200 Columbus (43219) *(G-6814)*
Baswa Acoustics North Amer LLC..............................216 475-7197
    21863 Aurora Rd Bedford (44146) *(G-1404)*
Bates Metal Products Inc..740 498-8371
    403 E Mn St Port Washington (43837) *(G-16422)*
Bates Printing Inc...330 833-5830
    150 23rd St Se Massillon (44646) *(G-13114)*
Bath & Body Works LLC (HQ)...................................614 856-6000
    7 Limited Pkwy E Reynoldsburg (43068) *(G-16582)*
Bath & Brass Emporium The, Columbus Also called Savko Plastic Pipe & Fittings *(G-7591)*
Battershell Cabinets..419 542-6448
    312 Defiance Ave Hicksville (43526) *(G-10901)*
Battery Unlimited..740 452-5030
    2350 Adamsville Rd Zanesville (43701) *(G-21276)*
Bauer Corporation (PA)...800 321-4760
    2540 Progress Dr Wooster (44691) *(G-20746)*
Bauer Ladder, Wooster Also called Bauer Corporation *(G-20746)*
Baughman Tile Company...800 837-3160
    8516 Road 137 Paulding (45879) *(G-16000)*
Baughmans Machine & Weld Shop.............................330 866-9243
    6498 June Rd Nw Waynesburg (44688) *(G-19723)*
Bauman Custom Woodworking LLC............................330 482-4330
    13650 Green Beaver Rd Salem (44460) *(G-16875)*
Baumer HHS Corp..937 886-3160
    10570 Success Ln Dayton (45458) *(G-8183)*
Baumfolder Corporation..937 492-1281
    1660 Campbell Rd Sidney (45365) *(G-17169)*
Bautec N Technoform Amer Inc................................330 487-6600
    1755 Entp Pkwy Ste 300 Twinsburg (44087) *(G-18903)*
Bawls Acquisition LLC..888 731-9708
    8840 Commons Blvd Ste 101 Twinsburg (44087) *(G-18904)*
Baxter Burial Vault Service......................................513 641-1010
    909 E Ross Ave Cincinnati (45217) *(G-3440)*
Baxter Holdings Inc..513 860-3593
    3370 Port Union Rd Hamilton (45014) *(G-10673)*
Baxter-Wilbert Burial Vault, Cincinnati Also called Baxter Burial Vault Service *(G-3440)*
Bay Area Products Inc..419 732-2147
    4942 W Fremont Rd Port Clinton (43452) *(G-16394)*
Bay Business Forms Inc..937 322-3000
    1803 W Columbia St Springfield (45504) *(G-17521)*
Bay Controls LLC..419 891-4390
    6528 Weatherfield Ct Maumee (43537) *(G-13231)*
Bay Electric Co...419 625-1046
    2612 Columbus Ave Sandusky (44870) *(G-16948)*
Bay Industries Incorporated....................................740 549-2305
    3390 Woodstone Dr Lewis Center (43035) *(G-11889)*
Bay Island Company Inc..513 248-0356
    585 Ibold Rd Loveland (45140) *(G-12341)*
Bay Manufacturing, Milan Also called Hemco Inc *(G-14112)*
Bay Packing, Lancaster Also called C J Kraft Enterprises Inc *(G-11694)*
Bay Village Printing Inc..440 892-2005
    27209 Wolf Rd Cleveland (44140) *(G-4897)*
Bay West Products...440 835-1991
    31008 Walker Rd Bay Village (44140) *(G-1242)*
Bay World International Inc......................................419 525-2222
    395 Reed St Mansfield (44903) *(G-12565)*
Bayard Inc..937 293-1415
    2621 Dryden Rd Ste 300 Moraine (45439) *(G-14467)*
Bayberry Co, Canal Fulton Also called American Traditions Basket Co *(G-2496)*
Bayes, Roy Products, Columbus Also called Roy L Bayes *(G-7575)*
Bayley Envelope Inc..330 821-2150
    119 E State St Alliance (44601) *(G-498)*
Bayloff Stmped Pdts Knsman Inc...............................330 876-4511
    8091 State Route 5 Kinsman (44428) *(G-11608)*
Bayswater Beverages LLC.......................................312 224-8012
    705 Wakefield Dr Cincinnati (45226) *(G-3441)*
Bbb Music LLC...740 772-2262
    20 E Water St Chillicothe (45601) *(G-3228)*
Bbi Well Service, Dellroy Also called Beucler Brothers Inc *(G-8897)*
Bc Investment Corporation (PA)................................330 262-3070
    1505 E Bowman St Wooster (44691) *(G-20747)*
Bcast Stainless Products LLC...................................614 873-3945
    9000 Heritage Dr Plain City (43064) *(G-16325)*
Bcfab Inc (PA)..419 532-2899
    15751 Road 19 Fort Jennings (45844) *(G-9925)*
BCI, Toledo Also called Block Communications Inc *(G-18372)*
BCi and V Investments Inc.......................................330 538-0660
    11675 Mahoning Ave North Jackson (44451) *(G-15287)*
BCI International, Dublin Also called Smiths Medical Pm Inc *(G-9147)*
Bcmr Publications LLC...740 441-7778
    1140 2nd Ave Gallipolis (45631) *(G-10291)*

A
L
P
H
A
B
E
T
I
C

Bcs Metal Prep LLC..440 663-1100
31000 Solon Rd Solon (44139) *(G-17266)*

BCT, Akron *Also called Akron Thermography Inc (G-59)*

BCT Alarm Services Inc....................................440 669-8153
103 Milan Ave Ste 4 Amherst (44001) *(G-591)*

Bdi Inc (PA)..216 642-9100
8000 Hub Pkwy Cleveland (44125) *(G-4898)*

Bdi Inc..330 498-4980
417 Applegrove St Nw Canton (44720) *(G-2617)*

BDS Packaging Inc...937 643-0530
3155 Elbee Rd Ste 201 Moraine (45439) *(G-14468)*

BE Products Inc..740 453-0386
40 N 2nd St Zanesville (43701) *(G-21277)*

Bea-Ecc Apparels Inc.......................................216 650-6336
1287 W 76th St Cleveland (44102) *(G-4899)*

Beach City Lumber LLC....................................330 878-4097
5177 Austin Ln Nw Strasburg (44680) *(G-17821)*

Beach Company...740 622-0905
240 Browns Ln Coshocton (43812) *(G-7882)*

Beach Manufacturing Co...................................937 882-6372
118 N Hampton Rd Donnelsville (45319) *(G-8960)*

Beach Mfg Plastic Molding Div...........................937 882-6400
7816 W National Rd New Carlisle (45344) *(G-14797)*

Beachs Trees Selective Harvest..........................513 289-5976
915 Wilma Cir Cincinnati (45245) *(G-3294)*

Beacon Audio Video Systems Inc.........................937 723-9587
155 N Main St Centerville (45459) *(G-3037)*

Beacon Metal Fabricators Inc............................216 391-7444
5425 Hamilton Ave Ste D Cleveland (44114) *(G-4900)*

Bead Shoppe At Home.......................................330 479-9598
2872 Whipple Ave Nw Canton (44708) *(G-2618)*

Beam Machines Inc...513 745-4510
5101 Creek Rd Blue Ash (45242) *(G-1747)*

Beam Technologies Inc.....................................800 648-1179
629 N High St Fl 6 Columbus (43215) *(G-6815)*

Bean Bag City, Spring Valley *Also called Sailors Tailor Inc (G-17469)*

Bean Counter LLC..419 636-0705
1210 W High St Ste C Bryan (43506) *(G-2282)*

Bear Worlding Services LLC...............................740 630-7538
18210 Myrtle Ake Rd Caldwell (43724) *(G-2424)*

Bearcat Construction Inc...................................513 314-0867
4457 Bethany Rd Mason (45040) *(G-12987)*

Bearing & Transm Sup Co Div, Macedonia *Also called Jay Dee Service Corporation (G-12463)*

Bearing Precious Seed (PA)...............................513 575-1706
1369 Woodville Pike B Milford (45150) *(G-14124)*

Bearings Manufacturing Company (PA).................440 846-5517
15157 Foltz Pkwy Strongsville (44149) *(G-17895)*

Beasley Fiberglass Inc......................................440 357-6644
799 Lakeshore Blvd Painesville (44077) *(G-15861)*

Beatty Foods LLC...330 327-2442
1117 Brant Ave Nw Canton (44708) *(G-2619)*

Beaufort Rfd Inc..330 239-4331
1420 Wolfcreek Trl Sharon Center (44274) *(G-17102)*

Beaumont Brothers Pottery, Crooksville *Also called Beaumont Brothers Stoneware (G-7949)*

Beaumont Brothers Stoneware (PA).....................740 982-0055
410 Keystone St Crooksville (43731) *(G-7949)*

Beaumont Machine LLC....................................513 701-0421
7697 Innovation Way Mason (45040) *(G-12988)*

Beautiful Bites..937 397-4225
609 S Columbus St Xenia (45385) *(G-20938)*

Beauty Cft Met Fabricators Inc...........................440 439-0710
5439 Perkins Rd Bedford (44146) *(G-1405)*

Beauty Systems Group LLC................................740 456-5434
3606 Rhodes Ave New Boston (45662) *(G-14779)*

Beaver Productions..330 352-4603
2251 Cooledge Ave Akron (44305) *(G-86)*

Beaver Wood Products......................................740 226-6211
190 Buck Hollow Rd Beaver (45613) *(G-1310)*

Beaverson Machine Inc......................................419 923-8064
11600 County Road 10 2 Delta (43515) *(G-8929)*

Bechem Lubrication Tech LLC.............................440 543-9845
8401 Chagrin Rd Ste 5a Chagrin Falls (44023) *(G-3077)*

Beck & Orr Inc..614 276-8809
3097 W Broad St Columbus (43204) *(G-6816)*

Beck Aluminum Alloys Ltd................................216 861-4455
6150 Parkland Blvd Mayfield Heights (44124) *(G-13311)*

Beck Energy Corp..330 297-6891
160 N Chestnut St Ravenna (44266) *(G-16517)*

Beck Flavors Inc (PA).......................................513 889-1268
1301 Mattec Dr Loveland (45140) *(G-12342)*

Beck Sand & Gravel Inc.....................................330 626-3863
2820 Webb Rd Ravenna (44266) *(G-16518)*

Beck Studios Inc...513 831-6650
1001 Tech Dr Milford (45150) *(G-14125)*

Beckenhorst Press Inc......................................614 451-6461
960 Old Henderson Rd Columbus (43220) *(G-6817)*

Becker Gallagher Legal Pubg..............................513 677-5044
8790 Governors Hill Dr # 102 Cincinnati (45249) *(G-3442)*

Becker Signs Inc...330 659-4504
4762 Black Rd Richfield (44286) *(G-16615)*

Beckermills Inc..419 738-3450
15286 State Route 67 Wapakoneta (45895) *(G-19481)*

Beckers Bakeshop Inc.......................................216 752-4161
13510 Miles Ave Cleveland (44105) *(G-4901)*

Beckett Air Incorporated (PA)...........................440 327-9999
37850 Taylor Pkwy North Ridgeville (44039) *(G-15359)*

Beckett Gas Inc (PA).......................................440 327-3141
38000 Taylor Pkwy North Ridgeville (44039) *(G-15360)*

Beckman & Gast Co Inc.....................................419 678-4195
282 W Kremer Hoying Rd Saint Henry (45883) *(G-16814)*

Beckman & Gast Company (PA)...........................419 678-4195
282 W Kremer Hoying Rd Saint Henry (45883) *(G-16815)*

Beckman Environmental Svcs Inc........................513 752-3570
4259 Armstrong Blvd Batavia (45103) *(G-1168)*

Beckman Machine LLC......................................513 242-2700
4684 Paddock Rd Cincinnati (45229) *(G-3443)*

Beckman Xmo, Columbus *Also called S Beckman Print & G (G-7581)*

Beckman Xmo...614 864-3305
376 Morrison Rd Ste D Columbus (43213) *(G-6818)*

Beckwith Orchards Inc.....................................330 673-6433
1617 Lake Rockwell Rd Kent (44240) *(G-11433)*

Beckworth Industries Inc...................................216 268-5557
14511 Saranac Rd Cleveland (44110) *(G-4902)*

Becky Knapp..330 854-4400
136 N Canal St Canal Fulton (44614) *(G-2498)*

Bedell-Kraus Flexographic and...........................330 688-4881
1350 Commerce Dr Stow (44224) *(G-17735)*

Bedford Anodizing Co (PA)................................330 650-6052
82 Aurora St Hudson (44236) *(G-11160)*

Bedford Cabinet Inc..440 439-4830
21891 Forbes Rd Ste 102 Cleveland (44146) *(G-4903)*

Bedford Gear, Solon *Also called Joy Mining Machinery (G-17323)*

Bedford Precision Products Inc...........................440 786-7277
339 Northfield Rd 339 Bedford (44146) *(G-1406)*

Bee Jax Inc...330 373-0500
156 Vermont Ave Sw Warren (44485) *(G-19527)*

Beebe Worldwide Graphics Sign.........................513 241-2726
9933 Alliance Rd Ste 2 Blue Ash (45242) *(G-1748)*

Beech Armament LLC..330 962-4694
105 Marc Dr Cuyahoga Falls (44223) *(G-7974)*

Beech Engineering & Mfg, New Philadelphia *Also called Miller Products Inc (G-14915)*

Beechvale Laminating..330 674-2804
7241 Township Road 572 Millersburg (44654) *(G-14198)*

Beekman Logging...740 493-2763
204 Wyckoff Rd Piketon (45661) *(G-16216)*

Beeline Purchasing LLC....................................513 703-3733
4454 N Mallard Cv Mason (45040) *(G-12989)*

Beemer Machine Company Inc.............................330 678-3822
1530 Enterprise Way Kent (44240) *(G-11434)*

Beer Communications Inc...................................419 756-6882
1717 Mccarrick Pkwy Mansfield (44903) *(G-12566)*

Beertubes.com, Plain City *Also called Dj Beverage Innovations Inc (G-16336)*

Beesign Signs Inc..614 449-3233
3079 W Broad St Ste 2 Columbus (43204) *(G-6819)*

Beevinwood Inc...937 678-9910
5748 Clark Rd West Manchester (45382) *(G-20096)*

Begashaw & Associates.....................................614 329-1630
33 S James Rd Ste 203 Columbus (43213) *(G-6820)*

Behlke Dalene...330 399-6780
958 Tod Ave Nw Warren (44485) *(G-19528)*

Behr Dayton Thermal Products, Dayton *Also called Mahle Behr USA Inc (G-8472)*

Behrco Inc..419 394-1612
1865 Celina Rd Saint Marys (45885) *(G-16832)*

Beiersdorf Inc...513 682-7300
5232 E Provident Dr West Chester (45246) *(G-19984)*

Beiting Farms..740 384-5127
5941 State Route 327 Jackson (45640) *(G-11310)*

Bekaert Corporation...330 683-5060
322 E Pine St Orrville (44667) *(G-15729)*

Bekaert Corporation...330 683-5060
510 Collins Blvd Orrville (44667) *(G-15730)*

Bekaert Corporation...330 835-5124
3200 W Market St Ste 303 Fairlawn (44333) *(G-9740)*

Bekaert Corporation...330 867-3325
3200 W Market St Ste 303 Fairlawn (44333) *(G-9741)*

Bekaert North America MGT Corp (HQ).................330 867-3325
3200 W Market St Ste 303 Fairlawn (44333) *(G-9742)*

Belco Works Inc...740 695-0500
68425 Hammond Rd Saint Clairsville (43950) *(G-16782)*

Belden & Blake Corporation...............................330 602-5551
1748 Saltwell Rd Nw Dover (44622) *(G-8968)*

Belden Brick Company.......................................330 852-2411
750 Edelweiss Dr Ne Sugarcreek (44681) *(G-18016)*

Belden Brick Company LLC.................................330 456-0031
700 Edelweiss Dr Ne Sugarcreek (44681) *(G-18017)*

Beldex Land Company LLC (PA)..........................740 783-3575
38455 State Rte 821 S Dexter City (45727) *(G-8955)*

Belkin Production 440 247-2722
44 N Main St Chagrin Falls (44022) *(G-3049)*

Bell Binders LLC 419 242-3201
320 21st St Toledo (43604) *(G-18365)*

Bell Burial Vault Co 513 896-9044
804 Belle Ave Hamilton (45015) *(G-10674)*

Bell Incorporated, Groveport *Also called Bell Ohio Inc (G-10616)*

Bell Industries 513 353-2355
9843 New Haven Rd Harrison (45030) *(G-10769)*

Bell Logistics Co 740 702-9830
27311 Old Route 35 Chillicothe (45601) *(G-3229)*

Bell Ohio Inc 605 332-6721
Ste 100 Groveport (43125) *(G-10616)*

Bell Optical, Twinsburg *Also called Essilor Laboratories Amer Inc (G-18931)*

Bell Vault & Monument Works 937 866-2444
1019 S Main St Miamisburg (45342) *(G-13785)*

Belle Center Air Tool Co Inc 937 464-7474
202 N Elizabeth St Belle Center (43310) *(G-1511)*

Belle Printing 937 592-5161
118 S Main St Bellefontaine (43311) *(G-1521)*

Bellefontaine Examiner 937 592-3060
127 E Chillicothe Ave Bellefontaine (43311) *(G-1522)*

Bellevue Gazette, Oberlin *Also called Gazette Publishing Company (G-15640)*

Bellevue Manufacturing Company (PA) 419 483-3190
520 Goodrich Rd Bellevue (44811) *(G-1545)*

Bellevue Manufacturing Company 419 483-3190
300 Ashford Ave Bellevue (44811) *(G-1546)*

Bellisio Foods Inc 740 286-5505
100 E Broadway St Jackson (45640) *(G-11311)*

Bellville Flowers and Gifts, Bellville *Also called Colleen D Turner (G-1568)*

Bellwyck Clinical Services, West Chester *Also called Bellwyck Packg Solutions Inc (G-19816)*

Bellwyck Packg Solutions Inc 513 874-1200
8946 Global Way West Chester (45069) *(G-19816)*

Belmon Coutn Recoder's Office, Saint Clairsville *Also called Belmont County of Ohio (G-16783)*

Belmont Community Health Ctr, Bellaire *Also called Belmont Community Hospital (G-1496)*

Belmont Community Hospital 740 671-1216
4697 Harrison St Bellaire (43906) *(G-1496)*

Belmont County of Ohio 740 699-2140
101 W Main St Ste 205 Saint Clairsville (43950) *(G-16783)*

Belmont Stamping, Shadyside *Also called Knight Manufacturing Co Inc (G-17082)*

Beloit Fuel LLC 330 584-1915
9379 First East St North Benton (44449) *(G-15212)*

Belot Concrete Block, Tiltonsville *Also called Walden Industries Inc (G-18255)*

Belpre Sand and Gravel Company, Dexter City *Also called Beldex Land Company LLC (G-8955)*

Belshe Industries Inc 937 526-4460
11465 Mangen Rd Versailles (45380) *(G-19340)*

Belton Foods 937 890-7768
2701 Thunderhawk Ct Dayton (45414) *(G-8184)*

Bemis Company Inc 330 923-5281
1972 Akron Peninsula Rd Akron (44313) *(G-87)*

Bemis Company Inc 419 334-9465
730 Industrial Dr Fremont (43420) *(G-10128)*

Bemis North America, Akron *Also called Bemis Company Inc (G-87)*

Ben James Enterprises Inc 330 477-9353
4110 Southway St Sw Canton (44706) *(G-2620)*

Ben Logging, Sarahsville *Also called Ned A Shreve (G-17025)*

Bena Inc 419 299-3313
1390 Township Road 229 Van Buren (45889) *(G-19239)*

Bench Billboard Company Inc 513 271-2222
6805 Cambridge Ave Cincinnati (45227) *(G-3444)*

Benchmark Archtectural Systems 614 444-0110
720 Marion Rd Columbus (43207) *(G-6821)*

Benchmark Cabinets 740 397-4615
17239 Sycamore Rd Mount Vernon (43050) *(G-14609)*

Benchmark Cabinets 740 694-1144
97 Mount Vernon Ave Fredericktown (43019) *(G-10096)*

Benchmark Craftsman Inc 330 975-4214
4700 Greenwich Rd Seville (44273) *(G-17069)*

Benchmark Craftsmen, Seville *Also called Benchmark Craftsman Inc (G-17069)*

Benchmark Prints 419 332-7640
2252 W State St Fremont (43420) *(G-10129)*

Benchworks Jewelers Inc 937 439-4243
133 E Franklin St Dayton (45459) *(G-8185)*

Benco Industries Inc 440 572-3555
19231 Royalton Rd Strongsville (44149) *(G-17896)*

Bendco Machine & Tool Co Inc 419 628-3802
283 W 1st St Minster (45865) *(G-14350)*

Bendel Inc (PA) 614 478-9013
4120 The Strand Columbus (43219) *(G-6822)*

Bender Cycle & Machine Corp 440 946-0681
1476 E 359th St Willoughby (44095) *(G-20443)*

Bender Engineering Company 330 938-2355
17934 Mill St Beloit (44609) *(G-1581)*

Bendix Spcer Fndtion Brake LLC (HQ) 440 329-9709
901 Cleveland St Elyria (44035) *(G-9380)*

Bendon Inc (PA) 419 207-3600
1840 Baney Rd S Ashland (44805) *(G-712)*

Benjamin Media Inc 330 467-7588
10050 Brecksville Rd Brecksville (44141) *(G-2036)*

Benjamin P Forbes Company 440 838-4400
800 Ken Mar Indus Pkwy Broadview Heights (44147) *(G-2104)*

Benjamin Steel Company Inc 937 233-1212
777 Benjamin Dr Springfield (45502) *(G-17522)*

Benko Products Inc 440 934-2180
5350 Evergreen Pkwy Sheffield Village (44054) *(G-17121)*

Benmit Division, North Lawrence *Also called US Tubular Products Inc (G-15307)*

Benners Custom Woodworking (PA) 513 932-9159
1004 W Main St Lebanon (45036) *(G-11783)*

Bennett & Bennett Inc (PA) 937 324-1100
1318 Kenton St Springfield (45505) *(G-17523)*

Bennett Displays, Geneva *Also called Dwayne Bennett Industries (G-10345)*

Bennett Electric Inc 800 874-5405
211 Republic St Norwalk (44857) *(G-15527)*

Bennett Plastics Inc 740 432-2209
197 N 2nd St Cambridge (43725) *(G-2447)*

Bens Welding Service Inc 937 878-4052
605 Middle St Fairborn (45324) *(G-9615)*

Bensan Jewelers Inc 216 221-1434
14410 Madison Ave Lakewood (44107) *(G-11657)*

Bent Nail Millwork, Lodi *Also called Oak Front Inc (G-12167)*

Bent Wood Solutions LLC 330 674-1454
7426 County Road 77 Millersburg (44654) *(G-14199)*

Bentley World-Packaging Ltd 440 232-1100
19800 Alexander Rd Bedford (44146) *(G-1407)*

Bentronix Corp 440 632-0606
14999 Madison Rd Middlefield (44062) *(G-13917)*

Benzle Porcelain Company Inc 614 876-2159
6100 Hayden Run Rd Hilliard (43026) *(G-10931)*

Berea Hardwood Co Inc 216 898-8956
18745 Sheldon Rd Cleveland (44130) *(G-4904)*

Berea Manufacturing Inc 440 260-0590
480 Geiger St Berea (44017) *(G-1604)*

Berea Printing Company 440 243-1080
1060 W Bagley Rd Ste 102 Berea (44017) *(G-1605)*

Bergen, W J & Co, Solon *Also called William J Bergen & Co (G-17414)*

Berghausen Corporation 513 541-5631
4524 Este Ave Cincinnati (45232) *(G-3445)*

Bergholz 7, Bergholz *Also called Rosebud Mining Company (G-1642)*

Bergman Safety Spanner Co Inc 419 691-1462
3002 Woodville Rd Ste B Northwood (43619) *(G-15478)*

Bergman Tool & Machine Co 419 925-4963
8066 Industrial Dr Maria Stein (45860) *(G-12757)*

Bergstein Oil & Gas Partnr 513 771-6220
11464 Lippelman Rd # 200 Cincinnati (45246) *(G-3446)*

Bergstrom Company Ltd Partnr 440 232-2282
640 Golden Oak Pkwy Cleveland (44146) *(G-4905)*

Beringer Plating Inc 330 633-8409
1211 Devalera St Akron (44310) *(G-88)*

Berlekamp Plastics Inc 419 334-4481
2587 County Road 99 Fremont (43420) *(G-10130)*

Berlin Boat Covers 330 547-7600
17740 W Akron Canfield Rd Berlin Center (44401) *(G-1654)*

Berlin Boat Covers Ulphostery, Berlin Center *Also called Berlin Boat Covers (G-1654)*

Berlin Custom Leather Ltd 330 674-3768
5085 Township Road 353 Millersburg (44654) *(G-14200)*

Berlin Gardens Gazebos Ltd 330 893-3411
5045 State Rte 39 Berlin (44610) *(G-1644)*

Berlin Inds Protector Pdts, North Lima *Also called Berlin Industries Inc (G-15310)*

Berlin Industries Inc (HQ) 330 549-2100
131 W South Range Rd North Lima (44452) *(G-15310)*

Berlin Natural Bakery Inc 330 893-2734
5126 County Rd 120 Berlin (44610) *(G-1645)*

Berlin Parts, Millersburg *Also called Berlin Truck Caps Ltd (G-14201)*

Berlin Truck Caps Ltd 330 893-2811
4560 State Route 39 Millersburg (44654) *(G-14201)*

Berlin Wood Products Inc 330 893-3281
5039 County Rd 120 Berlin (44610) *(G-1646)*

Berlin Woodworking 330 893-3234
4575 Township Road 366 Millersburg (44654) *(G-14202)*

Berman Industries Inc 513 874-7477
10999 Reed Hartman Hwy # 204 Blue Ash (45242) *(G-1749)*

Bermex, Columbus *Also called Matvest Inc (G-7327)*

Bernard Laboratories Inc 513 681-7373
1738 Townsend St Cincinnati (45223) *(G-3447)*

Bernard R Doyles Inc 216 523-2288
2102 Saint Clair Ave Ne Cleveland (44114) *(G-4906)*

Bernard Specialty Co 216 881-2200
2800 E 55th St Frnt Cleveland (44104) *(G-4907)*

Berner Screen Print, Springfield *Also called Gail Berner (G-17563)*

Berran Industrial Group Inc 330 253-5800
570 Wolf Ledges Pkwy Akron (44311) *(G-89)*

Berry Co (PA) 877 742-3779
571 Boston Mills Rd # 300 Hudson (44236) *(G-11161)*

(PA)=Parent Co (HQ)=Headquarters (DH)=Div Headquarters

Berry Company 513 768-7800
  312 Plum St Ste 600 Cincinnati (45202) **(G-3448)**

Berry Investments Inc 937 293-0398
  3055 Kettering Blvd # 418 Moraine (45439) **(G-14469)**

Berry Plas Technical Svcs Inc 330 995-3459
  4175 Karg Industrial Pkwy Kent (44240) **(G-11435)**

Berry Plastics Corporation 330 896-6700
  1275 Ethan Ave Streetsboro (44241) **(G-17843)**

Berry Plastics Filmco Inc 330 562-6111
  1450 S Chillicothe Rd Aurora (44202) **(G-911)**

Berry Woodworking 513 734-6133
  2244 Berry Rd Amelia (45102) **(G-569)**

Bert Radebaugh 740 382-8134
  1544 Marion Marysville Rd Marion (43302) **(G-12857)**

Bertin Steel Processing Inc 440 943-0094
  1271 E 289th St Ste 1 Wickliffe (44092) **(G-20357)**

Bertsherm Products Inc 440 268-8389
  1417 E 94th St Cleveland (44106) **(G-4908)**

Besa Lighting Co Inc 614 475-7046
  6695 Taylor Rd Blacklick (43004) **(G-1690)**

Bescast Inc 440 946-5300
  4600 E 355th St Willoughby (44094) **(G-20444)**

Besco, Batavia Also called Beckman Environmental Svcs Inc **(G-1168)**

Besi Manufacturing Inc (PA) 513 874-0232
  9087 Sutton Pl West Chester (45011) **(G-19817)**

Besl Specialized Carrier 740 599-6305
  16559 Skyline Dr Danville (43014) **(G-8084)**

Best Bite Grill LLC 419 344-7462
  22 N Center St Versailles (45380) **(G-19341)**

Best Equipment Co Inc 440 237-3515
  12359 Abbey Rd Ste A North Royalton (44133) **(G-15411)**

Best Fab Co 440 328-3254
  936 Taylor St Elyria (44035) **(G-9381)**

Best Glass, Dayton Also called Kimmatt Corp **(G-8441)**

Best Inc 419 394-2745
  Hc 116 Saint Marys (45885) **(G-16833)**

Best Lighting Products Inc (HQ) 740 964-0063
  1213 Etna Pkwy Etna (43062) **(G-9555)**

Best Logging, Stockport Also called Roger L Best **(G-17723)**

Best Mold & Manufacturing Inc 330 896-4084
  1546 E Turkeyfoot Lake Rd Akron (44312) **(G-90)**

Best Performance Inc 419 394-2299
  14381 State Route 116 Saint Marys (45885) **(G-16834)**

Best Plating Rack Corp 440 944-3270
  1321 E 289th St Wickliffe (44092) **(G-20358)**

Best Process Solutions Inc 330 220-1440
  1071 Industrial Pkwy N Brunswick (44212) **(G-2212)**

Best Snow Plow, Willoughby Also called Marc Industries Inc **(G-20536)**

Besten Equipment Inc 216 581-1166
  6680 Parkland Blvd Solon (44139) **(G-17267)**

Besttransportcom Inc 614 888-2378
  400 W Wilson Bridge Rd Worthington (43085) **(G-20858)**

Bestway Cabinets LLC 614 306-3518
  3525 Ridgewood Dr Hilliard (43026) **(G-10932)**

Beta Industries Inc (PA) 937 299-7385
  2860 Culver Ave Dayton (45429) **(G-8186)**

Beta Machine Company Inc 216 383-0000
  17702 S Waterloo Rd Cleveland (44119) **(G-4909)**

Betco Corporation Ltd (HQ) 419 241-2156
  400 Van Camp Rd Bowling Green (43402) **(G-1972)**

Betco Corporation Ltd 419 241-2156
  1001 Brown Ave Toledo (43607) **(G-18366)**

Beth Otto Independent Case Exa 513 868-0484
  544 Walter Ave Fairfield (45014) **(G-9645)**

Bethart Enterprises Inc (PA) 513 863-6161
  531 Main St Hamilton (45013) **(G-10675)**

Bethart Printing Services, Hamilton Also called Bethart Enterprises Inc **(G-10675)**

Bethel Engineering and Eqp Inc (PA) 419 568-1100
  13830 Mcbeth Rd New Hampshire (45870) **(G-14833)**

Bethel Engineering and Eqp Inc 419 568-7976
  13830 Mcbeth Rd New Hampshire (45870) **(G-14834)**

Bethlehem Fire and Rescue Inc 330 879-5800
  34 Main St S Navarre (44662) **(G-14710)**

Betley Printing Co 216 206-5600
  3816 Cullen Dr Cleveland (44105) **(G-4910)**

Better Built Barns (PA) 606 348-6146
  10628 Russellville Winchs Winchester (45697) **(G-20690)**

Better Foam Insulation, South Point Also called Pyro-Chem Corporation **(G-17445)**

Better Living Concepts Inc 330 494-2213
  7233 Freedom Ave Nw Canton (44720) **(G-2621)**

Better Living Sunrooms NW Ohio 419 692-4526
  205 S Pierce St Delphos (45833) **(G-8902)**

Better Than Sex Ice Cream LLC 614 444-5505
  1352 Parsons Ave Columbus (43206) **(G-6823)**

Betula USA, Cincinnati Also called NTS Enterprises Ltd **(G-4167)**

Beucler Brothers Inc 330 735-2267
  7237 Flint Rd Sw Dellroy (44620) **(G-8897)**

Bevclean Products Inc 937 233-5000
  3975 Dayton Park Dr Dayton (45414) **(G-8187)**

Bevcorp Properties, Willoughby Also called Miconvi Properties Inc **(G-20548)**

Beverage Dock, Dayton Also called Csv Inc **(G-8254)**

Beverage Engineering Inc 216 641-6678
  4705 Van Epps Rd Brooklyn Heights (44131) **(G-2131)**

Beverage Machine & Fabricators 216 252-5100
  13301 Lakewood Hts Blvd Cleveland (44107) **(G-4911)**

Beverages Holdings LLC (PA) 513 483-3300
  10300 Alliance Rd Ste 500 Blue Ash (45242) **(G-1750)**

Beverly Snider 614 837-5817
  3900 Noe Bixby Rd Columbus (43232) **(G-6824)**

Bexley Fabrics Inc 614 231-7272
  2476 E Main St Columbus (43209) **(G-6825)**

Bexley Pen Company Inc 614 351-9988
  2840 Fisher Rd Ste B Columbus (43204) **(G-6826)**

BF Diversified Svcs 330 869-5203
  1516 W Exchange St Akron (44313) **(G-91)**

Bfs Supply, Cincinnati Also called Frederick Steel Company LLC **(G-3782)**

Bg News, Bowling Green Also called B G News **(G-1969)**

Bharat Trading, West Chester Also called Goyal Enterprises Inc **(G-20010)**

Biaginis Draperies 614 876-1706
  3082 Alton Darby Creek Rd Hilliard (43026) **(G-10933)**

Bic Manufacturing Inc 216 531-9393
  26420 Cntury Corners Pkwy Euclid (44132) **(G-9567)**

Blc Precision Machine Co Inc 937 783-1406
  3004 Cherry St Blanchester (45107) **(G-1710)**

Bickers Metal Products Inc 513 353-4000
  5825 State Rte128 Miamitown (45041) **(G-13884)**

Bickett Machine and Supply Inc 740 353-5710
  1411 Robinson Ave Portsmouth (45662) **(G-16431)**

Bickford Flavors, Wickliffe Also called Bickford Laboratories Inc **(G-20359)**

Bickford Laboratories Inc 440 354-7747
  1197 E 305th St Wickliffe (44092) **(G-20359)**

Bico Akron Inc 330 794-1716
  3100 Gilchrist Rd Mogadore (44260) **(G-14369)**

Bico Steel Service Centers, Mogadore Also called Bico Akron Inc **(G-14369)**

Biedenbach Logging 740 732-6477
  48443 Seneca Lake Rd Sarahsville (43779) **(G-17024)**

Biery Cheese Co (PA) 330 875-3381
  6544 Paris Ave Louisville (44641) **(G-12310)**

Bif Co LLC 330 564-0941
  1405 Home Ave Akron (44310) **(G-92)**

Bif, LLC, Akron Also called Bif Co LLC **(G-92)**

Big Bills Trucking LLC 614 850-0626
  6023 Homestead Ct Hilliard (43026) **(G-10934)**

Big Chief Manufacturing Ltd 513 934-3888
  250 Harmon Ave Lebanon (45036) **(G-11784)**

Big Drum Usa Ltd 614 626-0843
  5706 Westbourne Ave Columbus (43213) **(G-6827)**

Big Gus Onion Rings Inc 216 883-9045
  4500 Turney Rd Cleveland (44105) **(G-4912)**

Big Heart Pet Brands 412 222-2200
  1 Strawberry Ln Orrville (44667) **(G-15731)**

Big Iron Guns Inc 740 464-0852
  1712 11th St Portsmouth (45662) **(G-16432)**

Big Kahuna Graphics Inc 330 455-2625
  1255 Prospect Ave Sw Canton (44706) **(G-2622)**

Big Noodle LLC 614 558-7170
  687 Kenwick Rd Columbus (43209) **(G-6828)**

Big Productions Inc 440 775-0015
  45300b Us Highway 20 Oberlin (44074) **(G-15635)**

Big River Electric Inc 740 446-4360
  299 Upper River Rd Gallipolis (45631) **(G-10292)**

Big Sky Petroleum, New Concord Also called Robert Barr **(G-14821)**

Biggys Auto Buffet 740 455-4663
  806 W Main St Zanesville (43701) **(G-21278)**

Bigmar Inc 740 966-5800
  9711 Sportsman Club Rd Johnstown (43031) **(G-11391)**

Bil-Jac Foods Inc (PA) 330 722-7888
  3337 Medina Rd Medina (44256) **(G-13377)**

Bil-Jax, Archbold Also called Haulotte US Inc **(G-680)**

Bilco Company 740 455-9020
  3400 Jim Granger Dr Zanesville (43701) **(G-21279)**

Bill Hall Well Service 330 695-4671
  10180 James Rd Fredericksburg (44627) **(G-10078)**

Bill J Jernigan Inc 937 264-1598
  865 Scholz Dr Vandalia (45377) **(G-19283)**

Bill Wyatt Inc 330 535-1113
  8857 Lake Shore Blvd Mentor (44060) **(G-13535)**

Bill's Counter Tops, Saint Clairsville Also called D Lewis Inc **(G-16788)**

Bill's Kenwood Pool & Hot Tub, Cincinnati Also called Kenwood Pool Distributors Inc **(G-3984)**

Billock, John N Cpo, Warren Also called Orthotics & Prosthetics Rehab **(G-19585)**

Bills Sports Center 419 335-2405
  1495 N Shoop Ave Wauseon (43567) **(G-19672)**

Bilz Vibration Technology Inc 330 468-2459
  895 Highland Rd E Ste F Macedonia (44056) **(G-12437)**

Bimac, Moraine Also called Santos Industrial Ltd **(G-14525)**

Bimac Machine, Moraine Also called Santos Industrial Ltd **(G-14526)**

Bimbo Bakeries Usa Inc 419 726-6183
5915 Jason St Toledo (43611) **(G-18367)**
Bimbo Bakeries Usa Inc 740 797-4449
33 N Plains Rd The Plains (45780) **(G-18183)**
Bimbo Bakeries Usa Inc 740 797-4449
33 Plains Rd The Plains (45780) **(G-18184)**
Binder Oil Field Construction 330 484-3680
5100 Battlesburg St Se Magnolia (44643) **(G-12515)**
Bindery & Spc Pressworks Inc 614 873-4623
351 W Bigelow Ave Plain City (43064) **(G-16326)**
Bindery Tech Inc 440 934-3247
1260 Moore Rd Ste I Avon (44011) **(G-985)**
Bindusa 513 247-3000
6819 Ashfield Dr Blue Ash (45242) **(G-1751)**
Binns Machinery Company 513 242-3388
330 Railroad Ave Cincinnati (45217) **(G-3449)**
Bintzler Inc 513 677-1164
9570 S State Route 48 Loveland (45140) **(G-12343)**
Bio Fit Engineered Procucts 419 823-1089
15500 Bio Fit Way Bowling Green (43402) **(G-1973)**
Bio Lum, Twinsburg *Also called Gvi Neuro Inc* **(G-18952)**
Bio-Blood Components Inc 614 294-3183
1393 N High St Columbus (43201) **(G-6829)**
Biobent Holdings LLC 513 658-5560
1275 Kinnear Rd Ste 239 Columbus (43212) **(G-6830)**
Biobent Holdings LLC 513 658-5560
1275 Kinnear Rd Ste 239 Columbus (43212) **(G-6831)**
Biobent Polymers, Columbus *Also called Biobent Holdings LLC* **(G-6830)**
Biobent Polymers, Columbus *Also called Biobent Holdings LLC* **(G-6831)**
Biocare Orthopedic 614 754-7514
8889 Basil Western Rd Nw Canal Winchester (43110) **(G-2520)**
Biocurv Medical Instruments 330 451-1628
245 Dryden Ct Sw Canton (44706) **(G-2623)**
Biofocus Inc (PA) 937 890-3068
3345 Old Salem Rd Dayton (45415) **(G-8188)**
Biometric Information MGT LLC 614 456-1296
6059 Frantz Rd Ste 102 Dublin (43017) **(G-9054)**
Bionix Development Corporation (PA) 419 727-8421
5154 Enterprise Blvd Toledo (43612) **(G-18368)**
Bionix Radiation Therapy, Toledo *Also called Bionix Development Corporation* **(G-18368)**
Biorx LLC (HQ) 866 442-4679
7167 E Kemper Rd Cincinnati (45249) **(G-3450)**
Biothane Coated Webbing Corp 440 327-0485
34655 Mills Rd North Ridgeville (44039) **(G-15361)**
Biowish Technologies Inc 312 572-6700
2724 Erie Ave Ste B Cincinnati (45208) **(G-3451)**
Bip Printing Solutions LLC 216 832-5673
23645 Mercantile Rd Ste C Beachwood (44122) **(G-1259)**
Bird Control International 330 425-2377
1393 Highland Rd Twinsburg (44087) **(G-18905)**
Bird Corporation 419 424-3095
100 Stanford Pkwy Findlay (45840) **(G-9795)**
Bird Electronic Corporation 440 248-1200
30303 Aurora Rd Solon (44139) **(G-17268)**
Bird Equipment LLC 330 549-1004
11950 South Ave North Lima (44452) **(G-15311)**
Bird Loft 440 988-2473
141 N Leavitt Rd Amherst (44001) **(G-592)**
Bird Technologies Group Inc (PA) 440 248-1200
30303 Aurora Rd Solon (44139) **(G-17269)**
Bird Watcher's Digest, Marietta *Also called Pardson Inc* **(G-12813)**
Birdfish Brewing Company LLC 330 397-4010
16 S Main St Columbiana (44408) **(G-6606)**
Birds Eye Foods Inc 330 854-0818
611 Elm Ridge Ave Canal Fulton (44614) **(G-2499)**
Birge Heavy Industries Ltd 440 821-3249
322 Furnace St Elyria (44035) **(G-9382)**
Biro Manufacturing Company (PA) 419 798-4451
1114 W Main St Lakeside Marblehead (43440) **(G-11647)**
Bishop International, Akron *Also called Jonathan Bishop* **(G-241)**
Bishop Machine Shop, Zanesville *Also called Bishop Machine Tool & Die* **(G-21280)**
Bishop Machine Tool & Die 740 453-8818
2304 Hoge Ave Zanesville (43701) **(G-21280)**
Bishop Well Service Corp 330 264-2023
416 N Bauer Rd Wooster (44691) **(G-20748)**
Bison Builders LLC 614 636-0365
6999 Huntley Rd Ste M Columbus (43229) **(G-6832)**
Bison Leather Co 419 517-1737
7409 W Central Ave Toledo (43617) **(G-18369)**
Bison USA Corp 513 713-0513
5225 Muhlhauser Rd West Chester (45011) **(G-19818)**
Bison Wldg & Fabrication Inc 440 944-4770
29301 Clayton Ave Wickliffe (44092) **(G-20360)**
Bisson Custom Plastic 937 653-4966
238 Logan St Urbana (43078) **(G-19147)**
Bitec, Dayton *Also called Sample Machining Inc* **(G-8645)**
Bites Baking Company LLC 614 457-6092
8090 Summerhouse Dr W Dublin (43016) **(G-9055)**

Bits & Chips Machining Company 513 539-0800
730 Lebanon St Monroe (45050) **(G-14394)**
Bittersweet Farms, Whitehouse *Also called Bittersweet Inc* **(G-20338)**
Bittersweet Inc (PA) 419 875-6986
12660 Archbold Whthuse Rd Whitehouse (43571) **(G-20338)**
Bittinger Carbide, Cadiz *Also called Stanley Bittinger* **(G-2422)**
Bituminous Products Company 419 693-3933
352 George Hardy Dr Toledo (43605) **(G-18370)**
Bizzy Bee, Columbus *Also called K B Printing* **(G-7249)**
Bizzy Bee Printing Inc 614 771-1222
1500 W 3rd Ave Ste 106 Columbus (43212) **(G-6833)**
BJ Equipment Ltd 614 497-1776
4522 Lockbourne Rd Columbus (43207) **(G-6834)**
BJ Oilfield Services Ltd 419 768-2408
2944 County Road 186 Cardington (43315) **(G-2908)**
Bjond Inc 614 537-7246
1463 Briarmeadow Dr Columbus (43235) **(G-6835)**
Bk Graphics, Canton *Also called Big Kahuna Graphics Inc* **(G-2622)**
Bk Tool Company Inc 513 870-9622
300 Security Dr Fairfield (45014) **(G-9646)**
Bkhn Inc 513 831-4402
55 W Techne Center Dr Milford (45150) **(G-14126)**
Bkt USA Inc 330 836-1090
2660 W Market St Ste 100 Fairlawn (44333) **(G-9743)**
Blacco Splcing Rgging Loft Inc (PA) 614 444-2888
1976 Alum Creek Dr Columbus (43207) **(G-6836)**
Black & Decker (us) Inc 513 772-3111
2310 E Sharon Rd Cincinnati (45241) **(G-3452)**
Black & Decker (us) Inc 614 895-3112
1948 Schrock Rd Columbus (43229) **(G-6837)**
Black & Decker Corporation 440 842-9100
12100 Snow Rd Ste 1 Cleveland (44130) **(G-4913)**
Black Box Columbus, Lewis Center *Also called Black Box Corporation* **(G-11890)**
Black Box Corporation 937 438-8660
6650 W Snowville Rd Ste R Brecksville (44141) **(G-2037)**
Black Box Corporation 614 825-7400
255 Enterprise Dr Lewis Center (43035) **(G-11890)**
Black Cloister Brewing Co LLC 419 481-3891
619 Monroe St Toledo (43604) **(G-18371)**
Black Diamnd Eco Solutions LLC 877 892-3370
34355 Melinz Pkwy Eastlake (44095) **(G-9259)**
Black Lab Custom Products, Chardon *Also called Kona Blackbird Inc* **(G-3160)**
Black Lab LLC 815 313-0400
11730 Ravenna Rd Chardon (44024) **(G-3142)**
Black Machining & Technology 513 752-8625
4020 Bach Buxton Rd Batavia (45103) **(G-1169)**
Black Radish Creamery Ltd 614 323-6016
7064 Cunningham Dr New Albany (43054) **(G-14749)**
Black River Display Group, Mansfield *Also called D & S Crtive Cmmunications Inc* **(G-12591)**
Black Wing Shooting Center LLC 740 363-7555
3722 Marysville Rd Delaware (43015) **(G-8825)**
Blackburn Hubcaps & Wheels LLC 330 467-0236
1001 Paster Ct Macedonia (44056) **(G-12438)**
Blackburns Fabrication Inc 614 875-0784
2467 Jackson Pike Columbus (43223) **(G-6838)**
Blackhawk Industries 918 610-4719
2845 Interstate Pkwy Brunswick (44212) **(G-2213)**
Blacklick Machine Co Inc 614 866-9300
265 North St Blacklick (43004) **(G-1691)**
Blackstone Mining, Dennison *Also called Kenneth Mc Beth* **(G-8945)**
Blackthorn LLC 937 836-9296
6113 Brookville Salem Rd Clayton (45315) **(G-4657)**
Blackwood Sheet Metal Inc 614 291-3115
844 Kerr St Columbus (43215) **(G-6839)**
Blade Manufacturing Co Inc 614 294-1649
915 Distribution Dr Ste A Columbus (43228) **(G-6840)**
Blade Manufacturing Co, The, Columbus *Also called Callahan Cutting Tools Inc* **(G-6889)**
Blains Folding Service Inc 216 631-4700
4103 Detroit Ave Cleveland (44113) **(G-4914)**
Blair Logging 740 934-2730
30530 Lebanon Rd Lower Salem (45745) **(G-12415)**
Blair Rubber Company 330 769-5583
5020 Enterprise Pkwy Seville (44273) **(G-17070)**
Blairs Cnc Turning Inc 937 461-1100
245 Leo St Dayton (45404) **(G-8189)**
Blako Industries Inc 419 246-6172
10850 Middleton Pike Dunbridge (43414) **(G-9168)**
Blanchard Pipe Line Co LLC 419 422-2121
539 S Main St Findlay (45840) **(G-9796)**
Blanchard Refining Company LLC 419 422-2121
539 S Main St Findlay (45840) **(G-9797)**
Blanchard Terminal Company LLC 419 422-2121
539 S Main St Findlay (45840) **(G-9798)**
Blanchester Foundry Co Inc 937 783-2091
214 Cherry St Blanchester (45107) **(G-1711)**
Blaney Hardwoods Ohio Inc (PA) 740 678-8288
425 Timberline Dr Vincent (45784) **(G-19378)**
Blang Acquisition LLC 937 223-2155
1608 Kuntz Rd Dayton (45404) **(G-8190)**

ALPHABETIC

Blankenship Logging LLC 740 372-3833
433 Curtis Smith Rd Otway (45657) **(G-15826)**

Blankenship Lumber Inc 740 372-0191
5356 State Route 348 Otway (45657) **(G-15827)**

Blaster Chemical Co Inc 216 901-5800
8500 Sweet Valley Dr Cleveland (44125) **(G-4915)**

BLaster Corporation 216 901-5800
8500 Sweet Valley Dr Cleveland (44125) **(G-4916)**

Blaze Oil & Gas Inc 330 345-6700
1699 Nupp Dr Wooster (44691) **(G-20749)**

Blaze Technical Services Inc 330 923-0409
1445 Commerce Dr Stow (44224) **(G-17736)**

Bleachtech LLC 330 421-2134
4231 Weymouth Rd Medina (44256) **(G-13378)**

Bleachtech LLC 216 921-1980
320 Ryan Rd Seville (44273) **(G-17071)**

Bleil Chan 440 352-6012
9451 Jackson St Mentor (44060) **(G-13536)**

Bleil Manufacturing Company, Mentor Also called Bleil Chan **(G-13536)**

Blend of Seven Winery, Delaware Also called Sandra Weddington **(G-8885)**

Blendzall Inc 740 633-1333
310 S 1st St Martins Ferry (43935) **(G-12922)**

Blesco Services 614 871-4900
8905 Mckendree Rd Mount Sterling (43143) **(G-14596)**

Blevins Fabrication, Mansfield Also called Blevins Metal Fabrication Inc **(G-12567)**

Blevins Metal Fabrication Inc 419 522-6082
288 Illinois Ave S Mansfield (44905) **(G-12567)**

Blick Tool & Die Inc 330 343-1277
117 E Front St Dover (44622) **(G-8969)**

Blind Factory Showroom 614 771-6549
3670 Parkway Ln Ste M Hilliard (43026) **(G-10935)**

Blind Outlet (PA) 614 895-2002
574 W Schrock Rd Westerville (43081) **(G-20202)**

Blinds Plus and More, Mason Also called Cincinnati Window Shade Inc **(G-12995)**

Blitz Tool & Die Inc 440 237-1177
11941 Abbey Rd Ste I Cleveland (44133) **(G-4917)**

Bloch Printing Company 330 576-6760
3569 Copley Rd Copley (44321) **(G-7840)**

Block Communications Inc (PA) 419 724-6212
405 Madison Ave Ste 2100 Toledo (43604) **(G-18372)**

Bloom Center Biodiesel LLC 937 585-6412
4974 Township Road 79 Lewistown (43333) **(G-11943)**

Bloom Industries Inc 330 898-3878
1052 Mahoney Ave Nw Warren (44483) **(G-19529)**

Bloom Lake Iron Ore Mine Ltd 216 694-5700
200 Public Sq Cleveland (44114) **(G-4918)**

Bloomdale Plastics Co 419 454-5135
305 Walnut St Bloomdale (44817) **(G-1719)**

Bloomingburg Spring & Wire For 740 437-7614
83 Main St Bloomingburg (43106) **(G-1720)**

Bloomville Gazette Inc 419 426-3491
26 N Main St Attica (44807) **(G-892)**

Blt Inc 513 631-5050
2834 Highland Ave Norwood (45212) **(G-15571)**

Blue Ash Tool & Die Co Inc 513 793-4530
4245 Creek Rd Blue Ash (45241) **(G-1752)**

Blue Bell Bio-Medical Inc 419 238-4442
1260 Industrial Dr Van Wert (45891) **(G-19245)**

Blue Chip Machine & Tool Ltd 419 626-9559
4211 Venice Rd Sandusky (44870) **(G-16949)**

Blue Chip Pump Inc 513 871-7867
1045 Meta Dr Cincinnati (45237) **(G-3453)**

Blue Chip Tool Inc 513 489-3561
11511 Goldcoast Dr Cincinnati (45249) **(G-3454)**

Blue Cottage Bakery LLC 216 221-9733
15612 Lake Ave Lakewood (44107) **(G-11658)**

Blue Creek Renewables LLC 419 576-7855
7909 Broughton Pike Paulding (45879) **(G-16001)**

Blue Crescent Enterprises Inc 440 878-9700
19645 Progress Dr Strongsville (44149) **(G-17897)**

Blue Fox Group, The, Mount Vernon Also called Smartcopy Inc **(G-14651)**

Blue Grass Cooperage - Jackson, Wellston Also called Brown-Forman Corporation **(G-19761)**

Blue Jay Entps of Tscrwas Cnty 330 874-2048
9852 Hess Mill Rd Ne Bolivar (44612) **(G-1928)**

Blue Line Painting LLC 440 951-2583
19520 Nottingham Rd Cleveland (44110) **(G-4919)**

Blue Machine, Cincinnati Also called Power Engineering LLC **(G-4255)**

Blue Pawn, Cuyahoga Falls Also called Simon & Simon Blue Pond Inc **(G-8046)**

Blue Ribbon Screen Graphics 216 226-6200
1473 Hollow Wood Ln Avon (44011) **(G-986)**

Blue Ribbon Trailers Ltd 330 538-4114
12800 Leonard Pkwy North Jackson (44451) **(G-15288)**

Blue Ridge Paper Products Inc 440 235-7200
7920 Mapleway Dr Olmsted Falls (44138) **(G-15674)**

Blue Target Firearms, Cuyahoga Falls Also called Ohio Sporting Goods LLC **(G-8030)**

Blue Water Satellite Inc 419 372-0160
1510 N Westwood Ave Toledo (43606) **(G-18373)**

Blue Wolfe Air Systems Inc 937 295-3632
5611 Houston Rd Houston (45333) **(G-11120)**

Bluefoot Energy Services, Steubenville Also called Bluefoot Industrial LLC **(G-17689)**

Bluefoot Industrial LLC 740 314-5299
224 N 3rd St Steubenville (43952) **(G-17689)**

Bluelevel Technologies Inc 330 523-5215
3778 Timberlake Dr Richfield (44286) **(G-16616)**

Bluelogos Inc 614 898-9971
130 Graphic Way Westerville (43081) **(G-20203)**

Blueserv Reprograhics LLC 937 426-6410
3313 Seajay Dr Beavercreek (45430) **(G-1370)**

Bluffton Motor Works LLC 419 885-3769
5439 Roan Rd Sylvania (43560) **(G-18100)**

Bluffton News Pubg & Prtg Co (PA) 419 358-8010
101 S Main St Bluffton (45817) **(G-1907)**

Bluffton News, The, Bluffton Also called Bluffton News Pubg & Prtg Co **(G-1907)**

Bluffton Precast Concrete Co 419 358-6946
8950 Dixie Hwy Bluffton (45817) **(G-1908)**

Bluffton Stone Co 419 358-6941
310 Quarry Dr Bluffton (45817) **(G-1909)**

BMA Metals Group Inc 513 874-5152
7770 W Chester Rd Ste 120 West Chester (45069) **(G-19819)**

BMC, Perrysburg Also called Bulk Molding Compounds Inc **(G-16071)**

BMC, Strongsville Also called Bearings Manufacturing Company **(G-17895)**

BMC Holdings Inc (PA) 419 636-1194
1914 Randolph Dr Bryan (43506) **(G-2283)**

BMC of Barfield Inc 513 860-4455
3501 Symmes Rd Hamilton (45015) **(G-10676)**

Bmd Blasting 614 580-9468
1840 Federal Pkwy Columbus (43207) **(G-6841)**

Bmi Machine Inc 614 785-7020
8354 Fairway Dr Columbus (43235) **(G-6842)**

Bnoat Oncology 330 285-2537
411 Wolf Ledges Pkwy Akron (44311) **(G-93)**

Board of Park Commissioners 216 635-3200
4101 Fulton Pkwy Cleveland (44144) **(G-4920)**

Boardman Molded Products Inc 330 788-2401
1110 Thalia Ave Youngstown (44512) **(G-21032)**

Boardman News 330 758-6397
8302 Southern Blvd Ste 2 Boardman (44512) **(G-1920)**

Boardman Printing, Youngstown Also called Nomis Publications Inc **(G-21150)**

Boardman Steel Inc 330 758-0951
156 Nulf Dr Columbiana (44408) **(G-6607)**

Boatfun Sports Inc 513 379-0506
6548 Westminster Ct Liberty Township (45044) **(G-11958)**

Bob Evans Farms Inc 937 372-4493
640 Birch Rd Xenia (45385) **(G-20939)**

Bob Evans Farms Inc (PA) 614 491-2225
8111 Smiths Mill Rd New Albany (43054) **(G-14750)**

Bob Evans Farms Inc 740 245-5305
791 Farmview Rd Bidwell (45614) **(G-1673)**

Bob King Sign Company Inc 330 753-2679
1631 East Ave Akron (44314) **(G-94)**

Bob Lanes Welding Inc 740 373-3567
545 Rummer Rd Marietta (45750) **(G-12767)**

Bobbart Industries Inc 419 350-5477
5035 Alexis Rd Ste 1 Sylvania (43560) **(G-18101)**

Bobco Enterprises Inc 419 867-3560
2910 Glanzman Rd Toledo (43614) **(G-18374)**

Bobit Business Media Inc 330 899-2200
3515 Massillon Rd Ste 350 Uniontown (44685) **(G-19077)**

Bobs Custom Str Interiors LLC 567 316-7490
5333 Secor Rd Ste 19 Toledo (43623) **(G-18375)**

Bobs Grinding Inc 440 946-6179
7564 Tyler Blvd Ste D Mentor (44060) **(G-13537)**

Bocchi Laboraties Ohio LLC 661 673-8500
9200 Smiths Mill Rd N New Albany (43054) **(G-14751)**

Bock & Pierce Enterprises 513 474-9500
8550 Beechmont Ave # 800 Cincinnati (45255) **(G-3455)**

Bock Company LLC 216 912-7050
30901 Carter St Ste B Solon (44139) **(G-17270)**

Bock Lighting, Solon Also called Bock Company LLC **(G-17270)**

Bocor Holdings LLC 330 494-1221
7793 Pittsburg Ave Nw Canton (44720) **(G-2624)**

Bocor Producing, Canton Also called Bocor Holdings LLC **(G-2624)**

Bodnar Printing Co Inc 440 277-8295
3480 Colorado Ave Lorain (44052) **(G-12234)**

Bodycote Imt Inc 740 852-5000
443 E High St London (43140) **(G-12201)**

Bodycote Kolsterising, London Also called Bodycote Thermal Proc Inc **(G-12202)**

Bodycote Thermal Proc Inc 614 444-1181
1515 Universal Rd Columbus (43207) **(G-6843)**

Bodycote Thermal Proc Inc 440 473-2020
5475 Avion Park Dr Cleveland (44143) **(G-4921)**

Bodycote Thermal Proc Inc 513 921-2300
710 Burns St Cincinnati (45204) **(G-3456)**

Bodycote Thermal Proc Inc 740 852-4955
443 E High St London (43140) **(G-12202)**

Boehm Inc (PA) 614 875-9010
   2050 Hardy Parkway St Grove City (43123) *(G-10546)*

Boehm Pressed Steel Company 330 220-8000
   5440 Wegman Dr Valley City (44280) *(G-19200)*

Boehr Print 419 358-1350
   2703 N Main St Ste 1 Findlay (45840) *(G-9799)*

Boeing Company 740 788-4000
   801 Irving Wick Dr W Newark (43056) *(G-14985)*

Boeing Company 740 788-4000
   801 Irving Wick Dr W Newark (43056) *(G-14986)*

Boeing Company 740 788-5805
   801 Irving Wick Dr W Newark (43056) *(G-14987)*

Boes, Wilbert J, New Riegel *Also called New Riegel Cafe Inc* *(G-14947)*

Bogart Imprinting 419 659-2840
   303 Taft St Columbus Grove (45830) *(G-7790)*

Boggs & Associates Inc 614 237-0600
   3555 E Fulton St Columbus (43227) *(G-6844)*

Boggs Graphic Equipment LLC 440 564-9675
   14901 Broadway Ave Maple Heights (44137) *(G-12728)*

Boggs Recycling Inc 800 837-8101
   12355 Kinsman Rd Unit J Newbury (44065) *(G-15082)*

Bogie Industries Inc Ltd 330 745-3105
   1100 Home Ave Akron (44310) *(G-95)*

Bohlender Engravg, Cincinnati *Also called Bohlender Engraving Company* *(G-3457)*

Bohlender Engraving Company 513 621-4095
   2410 Gilbert Ave Cincinnati (45206) *(G-3457)*

Boich Companies LLC 614 221-0101
   41 S High St Ste 3750s Columbus (43215) *(G-6845)*

Bojos Cream 330 270-3332
   1412 S Raccoon Rd Austintown (44515) *(G-970)*

Boko Patterns Models & Molds 937 426-9667
   4130 Industrial Ln Beavercreek (45430) *(G-1371)*

Boldman Printing LLC 937 653-3431
   1333 N Main St Urbana (43078) *(G-19148)*

Bollari/Davis Inc 330 296-4445
   5292 S Prospect St Ravenna (44266) *(G-16519)*

Bollin & Sons Inc 419 693-6573
   6001 Brent Dr Toledo (43611) *(G-18376)*

Bollin Label Systems, Toledo *Also called Bollin & Sons Inc* *(G-18376)*

Bollinger Tool & Die Inc 419 866-5180
   959 Hamilton Dr Holland (43528) *(G-11046)*

Bolon Timber LLC 740 567-4102
   45436 Smithberger Rd Lewisville (43754) *(G-11947)*

Bolons Custom Kitchens Inc 330 499-0092
   6287 Promler St Nw Canton (44720) *(G-2625)*

Boltaron Inc 740 498-5900
   1 General St Newcomerstown (43832) *(G-15109)*

Boltech Incorporated 330 746-6881
   1201 Crescent St Youngstown (44502) *(G-21033)*

Bomb Mfg LLC 419 559-9689
   530 S Taft Ave Fremont (43420) *(G-10131)*

Bomba S Custom Woodworking 330 699-9075
   3748 Dogwood St Nw Uniontown (44685) *(G-19078)*

Bomen Marking Products Inc 440 582-0053
   12905 York Delta Dr Ste A Cleveland (44133) *(G-4922)*

Bonbonneri Bakery, Cincinnati *Also called Bonbonneri Inc* *(G-3458)*

Bonbonneri Inc 513 321-3399
   2030 Madison Rd Ste 1 Cincinnati (45208) *(G-3458)*

Bond Chemicals Inc 330 725-5935
   1154 W Smith Rd Medina (44256) *(G-13379)*

Bond Distributing Inc 440 461-7920
   701 Beta Dr Ste 8 Cleveland (44143) *(G-4923)*

Bond Machine Company Inc 937 746-4941
   921 N Main St Franklin (45005) *(G-10009)*

Bond Quarters Horses 614 354-4028
   23574 Cadiz Rd Freeport (43973) *(G-10117)*

Bonded Chemicals Inc 330 723-4570
   909 W Smith Rd Medina (44256) *(G-13380)*

Bonded Pallets 513 541-1855
   1801 John St Cincinnati (45214) *(G-3459)*

Bonfoey Co 216 621-0178
   1710 Euclid Ave Cleveland (44115) *(G-4924)*

Bonham Doors & Openers, Wshngtn CT Hs *Also called Bonham Enterprsises* *(G-20902)*

Bonham Enterprsises 740 333-0501
   2555 Us Highway 62 Ne Wshngtn CT Hs (43160) *(G-20902)*

Bonne Bell LLC (PA) 440 835-2440
   1006 Crocker Rd Westlake (44145) *(G-20257)*

Bonnot Company 330 896-6544
   1301 Home Ave Akron (44310) *(G-96)*

Bonsal American Inc 513 398-7300
   5155 Fischer Ave Cincinnati (45217) *(G-3460)*

Boochers Inc 937 667-3414
   320 S 5th St Tipp City (45371) *(G-18265)*

Boogie Wipes, Cincinnati *Also called Little Busy Bodies LLC* *(G-4029)*

Book Store, Columbus *Also called US Government Publishing Off* *(G-7727)*

Bookbinders Incorporated 330 848-4980
   90 16th St Sw Ste C Barberton (44203) *(G-1111)*

Bookcolor Bindery Services 614 252-2941
   1685 Woodland Ave Columbus (43219) *(G-6846)*

Bookfactory LLC 937 226-7100
   2302 S Edwin C Moses Blvd Dayton (45417) *(G-8191)*

Bookman & Son Fine Jewelry, Cleveland *Also called J and L Jewelry Manufacturing* *(G-5594)*

Bookmasters Inc (PA) 419 281-1802
   30 Amberwood Pkwy Ashland (44805) *(G-713)*

Bookmyer LLP 419 447-3883
   144 S Washington St Tiffin (44883) *(G-18210)*

Boomerang Rubber Inc 937 693-4611
   215 S Mill St Botkins (45306) *(G-1950)*

Boos Make & Take 440 647-0000
   676 N Main St Wellington (44090) *(G-19738)*

Bor-It Manufacturing Inc 419 289-6639
   1687 Cleveland Rd Ashland (44805) *(G-714)*

Boral Bricks Inc 937 294-1548
   250 Industrial Dr Franklin (45005) *(G-10010)*

BORAL BRICKS INC., Franklin *Also called Boral Bricks Inc* *(G-10010)*

Borchers Americas Inc (HQ) 440 899-2950
   811 Sharon Dr Westlake (44145) *(G-20258)*

Borden Bakers Inc 614 457-9800
   4723 Reed Rd Columbus (43220) *(G-6847)*

Borden Chemical Inc 614 225-4000
   180 E Broad St Columbus (43215) *(G-6848)*

Borden Chemical Foundry LLC 614 225-4000
   180 E Broad St Fl 24 Columbus (43215) *(G-6849)*

Borden Dairy Co Cincinnati LLC 513 948-8811
   415 John St Cincinnati (45215) *(G-3461)*

Borden Dairy Company Ohio LLC 216 671-2300
   3068 W 106th St Cleveland (44111) *(G-4925)*

Boreman Hardwoods Inc 330 262-0403
   4470 W Old Lincoln Way Wooster (44691) *(G-20750)*

Bores Manufacturing Co Inc 419 465-2606
   300 Sandusky St Monroeville (44847) *(G-14425)*

Bores, J F Mfg, Monroeville *Also called Bores Manufacturing Co Inc* *(G-14425)*

Borke Mold Specialist Inc 513 870-8000
   9541 Glades Dr West Chester (45011) *(G-19820)*

Borman Enterprises Inc 216 459-9292
   1311 Brookpark Rd Cleveland (44109) *(G-4926)*

Bornhorst Motor Service Inc 937 773-0426
   8270 N Dixie Dr Piqua (45356) *(G-16253)*

Bornhorst Printing Company Inc 419 738-5901
   10139 County Road 25a Wapakoneta (45895) *(G-19482)*

Bortnick Tractor Sales Inc 330 924-2555
   6192 Warren Rd Cortland (44410) *(G-7862)*

Bosca Accesories, Springfield *Also called Hugo Bosca Company Inc* *(G-17578)*

Bosch Rexroth Corporation 330 263-3300
   1683 Enterprise Pkwy Wooster (44691) *(G-20751)*

Bosco Pup Co LLC 614 833-0349
   290 Parkwood Ave Pickerington (43147) *(G-16187)*

Boscott Metals Inc 937 448-2018
   138 S Miami Ave Bradford (45308) *(G-2024)*

Bose Corporation 614 475-8565
   155 Easton Town Ctr Fl 1 Columbus (43219) *(G-6850)*

Bose Corporation 513 891-4384
   7875 Montgomery Rd # 2422 Cincinnati (45236) *(G-3462)*

Bose Showcase Store, Columbus *Also called Bose Corporation* *(G-6850)*

Bose Showcase Store, Cincinnati *Also called Bose Corporation* *(G-3462)*

Boss Pet Products Inc (HQ) 216 332-0832
   7730 First Pl Ste E Bedford (44146) *(G-1408)*

Bossa Nova Beverage Group Inc 513 483-3300
   10300 Alliance Rd Ste 500 Blue Ash (45242) *(G-1753)*

Bosserman Automotive Engrg LLC 419 722-2879
   18919 Olympic Dr Findlay (45840) *(G-9800)*

Boston Beer Company 267 240-4429
   1625 Central Pkwy Cincinnati (45214) *(G-3463)*

Boston Scntfic Nrmdlation Corp 419 720-9510
   3130 Executive Pkwy Toledo (43606) *(G-18377)*

Boston Scntfic Nrmdlation Corp 330 372-2652
   2174 Sarkies Dr Ne Warren (44483) *(G-19530)*

Boston Stoker Inc (PA) 937 890-6401
   10855 Engle Rd Vandalia (45377) *(G-19284)*

Bottomline Ink Corporation 419 897-8000
   7829 Ponderosa Rd Perrysburg (43551) *(G-16068)*

Boulder Daily Camera, Cincinnati *Also called Brv Inc* *(G-3483)*

Bourbon Plastics Inc (PA) 574 342-0893
   111 Stow Ave Ste 100 Cuyahoga Falls (44221) *(G-7975)*

Boville Indus Coatings Inc 330 669-8558
   7459 Leichty Rd Smithville (44677) *(G-17238)*

Bowdil Company 800 356-8663
   2030 Industrial Pl Se Canton (44707) *(G-2626)*

Bowerston Shale Company 740 763-3921
   1329 Seven Hills Rd Newark (43055) *(G-14988)*

Bowerston Shale Company (PA) 740 269-2921
   515 Main St Bowerston (44695) *(G-1957)*

Bowes Manufacturing Inc 216 378-2110
   30340 Solon Industrial Solon (44139) *(G-17271)*

Bowes Mill and Cabinet LLC 440 236-3255
   33549 E Royalton Rd # 7 Columbia Station (44028) *(G-6581)*

Bowne of Columbus, Columbus *Also called RR Donnelley & Sons Company* *(G-7576)*

A L P H A B E T I C

Bows Barrettes & Baubles 440 247-2697
4180 Chagrin River Rd Moreland Hills (44022) *(G-14537)*

Box King LLC 937 322-8117
1125 N Bechtle Ave Springfield (45504) *(G-17524)*

Boxes & Such 440 237-7122
1118 Mindy Ln Wooster (44691) *(G-20752)*

Boxit Corporation (HQ) 216 631-6900
5555 Walworth Ave Cleveland (44102) *(G-4927)*

Boxit Corporation 216 416-9475
3000 Quigley Rd B Cleveland (44113) *(G-4928)*

Boyce Ltd 614 236-8901
2173 S James Rd Columbus (43232) *(G-6851)*

Boyce Machine Inc 330 678-3210
3609 Mogadore Rd Kent (44240) *(G-11436)*

Boyd Sanitation 740 697-7940
5525 4th St Roseville (43777) *(G-16727)*

Boyds Machine and Met Finshg 937 698-5623
7650 S Kssler Frderick Rd West Milton (45383) *(G-20105)*

Boye & Emmes Machine, Cincinnati *Also called Enterprise Machine Inc (G-3709)*

Boye & Emmes Machine Tool Co 513 541-2520
3640 Llewellyn Ave Cincinnati (45223) *(G-3464)*

Boyer Signs & Graphics Inc 216 383-7242
21611 Tungsten Rd Euclid (44117) *(G-9568)*

BP, Cincinnati *Also called B P Oil Company (G-3433)*

BP, Cincinnati *Also called N M R Inc (G-4135)*

BP Products North America Inc 937 461-3621
621 Brandt St Dayton (45404) *(G-8192)*

BP Products North America Inc 419 537-9540
2450 Hill Ave Toledo (43607) *(G-18378)*

BP Products North America Inc 419 636-2249
710 E Wilson St Bryan (43506) *(G-2284)*

Bpi Energy Holdings Inc 281 556-6200
30775 Bnbridge Rd Ste 280 Solon (44139) *(G-17272)*

Bpm Realty Inc 614 221-6811
195 N Grant Ave Fl 2a Columbus (43215) *(G-6852)*

Bpr-Rico Elc Trck Spcalist Inc 330 723-4050
691 W Liberty St Medina (44256) *(G-13381)*

Bpr-Rico Manufacturing Inc 330 723-4050
691 W Liberty St Medina (44256) *(G-13382)*

Bpr/Rico, Medina *Also called Bpr-Rico Manufacturing Inc (G-13382)*

Bprex Closures LLC 812 424-2904
1695 Indian Cir Ste 116 Maumee (43537) *(G-13232)*

Bprex Halthcare Brookville Inc (HQ) 847 541-9700
1899 N Wilkinson Way Perrysburg (43551) *(G-16069)*

Bprex Plastic Packaging Inc (HQ) 419 247-5000
1 Seagate Ste 10 Toledo (43604) *(G-18379)*

BR Mulch Inc 937 667-8288
620 Ginghamsburg Rd Tipp City (45371) *(G-18266)*

Brace Sp Prsthtic Orthtic Ctrs (HQ) 513 421-5653
111 Wellington Pl Ste 8 Cincinnati (45219) *(G-3465)*

Bracemart LLC 440 353-2830
36097 Westminister Ave North Ridgeville (44039) *(G-15362)*

Brad Snoderly 419 476-0184
444 W Laskey Rd Ste K Toledo (43612) *(G-18380)*

Braden-Sutphin Ink Company (PA) 216 271-2300
3650 E 93rd St Cleveland (44105) *(G-4929)*

Braden-Sutphin Ink Company 614 443-9100
2272 S High St Columbus (43207) *(G-6853)*

Braden-Sutphin Ink Company 937 704-9047
400 Industry Dr Carlisle (45005) *(G-2928)*

Bradford Neal Machinery Inc 440 632-1393
14503 Old State Rd Middlefield (44062) *(G-13918)*

Bradley Enterprises Inc (PA) 330 875-1444
3750 Beck Ave Louisville (44641) *(G-12311)*

Bradley Metal Fabrication 216 881-7400
3451 Helen Rd Shaker Heights (44122) *(G-17085)*

Bradley Metal Fabrication Llc 216 881-7400
17600 S Waterloo Rd Cleveland (44119) *(G-4930)*

Bradley Stone Industries LLC 440 519-3277
30801 Carter St Solon (44139) *(G-17273)*

Bradleys Beacons Ltd 419 447-7560
296 Hedges St Tiffin (44883) *(G-18211)*

Bradner Oil Company Inc 419 288-2945
Wayne Rd Wayne (43466) *(G-19721)*

Bradshaw Manufacturing, Cleveland *Also called Hutchinson-Stevens Inc (G-5540)*

Brady A Lantz Enterprises Inc 513 742-4921
11242 Sebring Dr Cincinnati (45240) *(G-3466)*

Brahler Inc 330 966-7730
4041 Batton St Nw Ste 104 Canton (44720) *(G-2627)*

Brain Child Products LLC 419 698-4020
146 Main St Toledo (43605) *(G-18381)*

Brainard Rivet Company 330 545-4931
222 Harry St Girard (44420) *(G-10383)*

Brainerd Industries Inc (PA) 937 228-0488
680 Precision Ct Miamisburg (45342) *(G-13786)*

Brainin-Advance Industries LLC 513 874-9760
4348 Le Saint Ct West Chester (45014) *(G-19821)*

Brainmaster Technologies Inc 440 232-6000
195 Willis St 3 Bedford (44146) *(G-1409)*

Brakers Publishing & Prtg Svc 440 576-0136
166 W Cedar St Jefferson (44047) *(G-11357)*

Bramhi Inc 740 367-0467
10282 Bulaville Pike Bidwell (45614) *(G-1674)*

Bramkamp Printing Company Inc 513 241-1865
9933 Alliance Rd Ste 2 Blue Ash (45242) *(G-1754)*

Branam Oral Health Tech Inc (PA) 248 670-0040
3140 Dustin Rd Oregon (43616) *(G-15704)*

Branch 300, Groveport *Also called Kurtz Bros Inc (G-10632)*

Branch 49, Columbus *Also called Laird Plastics Inc (G-7280)*

Brandon Screen Printing 419 229-9837
326 S West St Lima (45801) *(G-11996)*

Brands' Marina, Port Clinton *Also called Tack-Anew Inc (G-16417)*

Brandts Candies 440 942-1016
1238 Lost Nation Rd Willoughby (44094) *(G-20445)*

Brandts Custom Machining LLC 419 566-3192
1183 Stewart Rd N Mansfield (44905) *(G-12568)*

Branham Motorsports LLC 937 428-6040
1690 Thomas Paine Pkwy Dayton (45459) *(G-8193)*

Brass & Bronze Ingot Division, Cincinnati *Also called G A Avril Company (G-3790)*

Brass Accents Inc 330 332-9500
1693 Salem Pkwy W Salem (44460) *(G-16876)*

Brass Lantern Antiques, Waynesville *Also called John Purdum (G-19731)*

Brasspack Packing Supply, Mansfield *Also called Skybox Investments Inc (G-12679)*

Brat Printing, Cincinnati *Also called Randy Gray (G-4330)*

Braun Industries Inc 419 232-7020
1170 Production Dr Van Wert (45891) *(G-19246)*

Braun Machine Technologies LLC 330 777-5433
4175 Warren Sharon Rd Vienna (44473) *(G-19363)*

Brazing Service Inc 440 871-1120
24480 Sperry Cir Westlake (44145) *(G-20259)*

Bread Kneads Inc 419 422-3863
510 S Blanchard St Findlay (45840) *(G-9801)*

Breaker Technology Inc 440 248-7168
30625 Solon Ind Pkwy Solon (44139) *(G-17274)*

Breaking Bread Pizza Company 614 754-4777
9042 Cotter St Lewis Center (43035) *(G-11891)*

Breakthrough Media Ministries, Canal Winchester *Also called World Harvest Church Inc (G-2542)*

Breckenridge Paper & Packaging, Groveport *Also called Central Ohio Paper & Packg Inc (G-10618)*

Breckenridge Paper & Packaging, Huron *Also called Central Ohio Paper & Packg Inc (G-11219)*

Brecksville Broadview Gazette 440 526-7977
7014 Mill Rd Brecksville (44141) *(G-2038)*

Breibach & Associates, Hilliard *Also called Breibach Association (G-10936)*

Breibach Association 614 876-6480
5117 Grandon Dr Hilliard (43026) *(G-10936)*

Breitenbach Bed & Breakfast, Dover *Also called Breitenbach Wine Cellar Inc (G-8970)*

Breitenbach Wine Cellar Inc 330 343-3603
5934 Old Route 39 Nw Dover (44622) *(G-8970)*

Breitinger Company 419 526-4255
595 Oakenwaldt St Mansfield (44905) *(G-12569)*

Bren-Ko Patterns, Hamilton *Also called 7 Rowe Court Properties LLC (G-10659)*

Brendel Producing Company 330 854-4151
8215 Arlington Ave Nw Canton (44720) *(G-2628)*

Brendons Fiber Works 614 353-6599
306 E Jeffrey Pl Columbus (43214) *(G-6854)*

Brenmar Construction Inc 740 286-2151
900 Morton St Jackson (45640) *(G-11312)*

Brenner International, Newark *Also called I G Brenner Inc (G-15022)*

Brent Bleh Company 513 721-1100
917 Vine St Cincinnati (45202) *(G-3467)*

Brent Carter Enterprises Inc 513 731-1440
4404 Forest Ave Cincinnati (45212) *(G-3468)*

Brentmoor Hams LLC 513 677-0813
10367 Brentmoor Dr Loveland (45140) *(G-12344)*

Brentwood Originals Inc 330 793-2255
1309 N Meridian Rd Youngstown (44509) *(G-21034)*

Brentwood Printing & Sty 513 522-2679
8630 Winton Rd Cincinnati (45231) *(G-3469)*

Brett Purdum 740 626-2890
10989 Cropp St South Salem (45681) *(G-17449)*

Brew Kettle Inc 440 234-8788
8377 Pearl Rd Strongsville (44136) *(G-17898)*

Brewer Company (PA) 800 394-0017
1354 Us Route 50 Milford (45150) *(G-14127)*

Brewer Company 440 944-3800
30060 Lakeland Blvd Wickliffe (44092) *(G-20361)*

Brewer Company 614 279-8688
472 Brehl Ave Columbus (43223) *(G-6855)*

Brewer Company 513 576-6300
7300 Main St Cincinnati (45244) *(G-3470)*

Brewer Industries LLC 216 469-0808
318 Bentleyville Rd Chagrin Falls (44022) *(G-3050)*

Brewer Products, Cincinnati *Also called La Mfg Inc (G-4009)*

Brewer Products Co, Cincinnati *Also called Brewpro Inc (G-3472)*

Brewercote, Milford *Also called Brewer Company* ***(G-14127)***

Brewery Real Estate Partnr 614 224-9023
467 N High St Columbus (43215) ***(G-6856)***

Brewery X LLC 513 240-3600
417 Warner St Cincinnati (45219) ***(G-3471)***

Brewpro Inc 513 577-7200
9483 Reading Rd Cincinnati (45215) ***(G-3472)***

Brewpub Restaurant Corp 614 228-2537
467 N High St Columbus (43215) ***(G-6857)***

Brewster Cheese Company (PA) 330 767-3492
800 Wabash Ave S Brewster (44613) ***(G-2083)***

BREWSTER HISTORICAL SOCIETY, Brewster *Also called Brewster Sugarcreek Twp Histo* ***(G-2084)***

Brewster Sugarcreek Twp Histo 330 767-0045
45 Wabash Ave S Brewster (44613) ***(G-2084)***

Brian Franks Electric Inc 330 821-5457
11424 Beech St Ne Alliance (44601) ***(G-499)***

Brian Rengh, Cleveland *Also called Atlas Printing and Embroidery* ***(G-4856)***

Briar Hill Furniture 330 223-2109
7061 Bane Rd Ne Kensington (44427) ***(G-11420)***

Briar Hill Stone Company 330 377-5100
12470 State Route 520 Glenmont (44628) ***(G-10402)***

Briarwood Manufacturing, Van Wert *Also called Kedar D Army* ***(G-19262)***

Briarwood Valley Farms 419 736-2298
502 Us Highway 224 Sullivan (44880) ***(G-18053)***

Bricker Plating Inc 419 636-1990
612 E Edgerton St Bryan (43506) ***(G-2285)***

Bricolage Inc 614 853-6789
2989 Lewis Centre Way Grove City (43123) ***(G-10547)***

Bridge Components Incorporated 614 873-0777
3476 Millikin Ct Columbus (43228) ***(G-6858)***

Bridge Components Inds Inc 614 873-0777
3476 Millikin Ct Columbus (43228) ***(G-6859)***

Bridgestone Americas Inc 330 379-7000
10 E Firestone Blvd Akron (44317) ***(G-97)***

Bridgestone APM Company 419 294-6989
235 Commerce Way Upper Sandusky (43351) ***(G-19114)***

Bridgestone APM Company 419 294-6304
245 Commerce Way Upper Sandusky (43351) ***(G-19115)***

Bridgestone Firestone 614 523-2259
8510 Orion Pl Columbus (43240) ***(G-6641)***

Bridgestone Procurement Holdin (HQ) 337 882-1200
381 W Wilbeth Rd Akron (44301) ***(G-98)***

Bridgestone Ret Operations LLC 330 379-6220
1245 Firestone Pkwy Akron (44301) ***(G-99)***

Bridgetek, Dayton *Also called Contech Bridge Solutions LLC* ***(G-8243)***

Bridgetek, West Chester *Also called Contech Bridge Solutions LLC* ***(G-19838)***

Bridgetown Welders LLC 513 574-4851
4489 Bridgetown Rd Cincinnati (45211) ***(G-3473)***

Bridgits Bath LLC 937 259-1960
1226 Pursell Ave Dayton (45420) ***(G-8194)***

Brier Hill Slag Company (PA) 330 743-8170
18 Hogue St Youngstown (44502) ***(G-21035)***

Bright Eyes Inc (PA) 937 277-9991
5135 N Dixie Dr Dayton (45414) ***(G-8195)***

Bright Eyes Optical, Dayton *Also called Bright Eyes Inc* ***(G-8195)***

Bright Focus Sales Inc 216 751-8384
2310 Superior Ave E # 225 Cleveland (44114) ***(G-4931)***

Bright Now Dental, North Olmsted *Also called Smile Brands Inc* ***(G-15346)***

Brighteye Innovations LLC 800 573-0052
1760 Wadsworth Rd Akron (44320) ***(G-100)***

Brighton Collectibles LLC 614 418-7561
217 Easton Town Ctr Columbus (43219) ***(G-6860)***

Brighton Mills, Cincinnati *Also called H Nagel & Son Co* ***(G-3859)***

Brighton Mills, Cincinnati *Also called H Nagel & Son Co* ***(G-3860)***

Brighton Technologies LLC 513 469-1800
5129 Kieley Pl Saint Bernard (45217) ***(G-16779)***

Brighton Truedge 513 771-2300
4955 Spring Grove Ave Cincinnati (45232) ***(G-3474)***

Brightstar Propane & Fuels 614 891-8395
6190 Frost Rd Westerville (43082) ***(G-20140)***

Brilex Industries Inc 330 744-1114
101 Andrews Ave Youngstown (44503) ***(G-21036)***

Brilex Industries Inc (PA) 330 744-1114
1201 Crescent St Youngstown (44502) ***(G-21037)***

Brilista Foods Company Inc (PA) 614 299-4132
1000 Goodale Blvd Columbus (43212) ***(G-6861)***

Brilliant Colorworks LLC 800 566-4162
2940 E 14th Ave Columbus (43219) ***(G-6862)***

Brilliant Electric Sign Co Ltd 216 741-3800
4811 Van Epps Rd Brooklyn Heights (44131) ***(G-2132)***

Brinkley Technology Group LLC 330 830-2498
2770 Erie St S Massillon (44646) ***(G-13115)***

Brinkman LLC 419 204-5934
1524 Adak Ave Lima (45805) ***(G-11997)***

Brinkman Tool & Die Inc 937 222-1161
325 Kiser St Dayton (45404) ***(G-8196)***

Brinkman Turkey Farms Inc (PA) 419 365-5127
16314 State Route 68 Findlay (45840) ***(G-9802)***

Brinkman's Country Corner, Findlay *Also called Brinkman Turkey Farms Inc* ***(G-9802)***

Briskheat Corporation (PA) 614 294-3376
4800 Hilton Corporate Dr Columbus (43232) ***(G-6863)***

Briskheat Corporation 614 429-3232
460 E Starr Ave Columbus (43201) ***(G-6864)***

Bristol-Myers Squibb Company 800 321-1335
999 Polaris Pkwy Ste 100 Columbus (43240) ***(G-6642)***

Brite Brazing, Wickliffe *Also called HI Tecmetal Group Inc* ***(G-20368)***

Broad Street Energy Company 614 228-0326
1515 Lake Shore Dr # 225 Columbus (43204) ***(G-6865)***

Broad Street Financial Company (PA) 614 228-0326
1515 Lake Shore Dr # 225 Columbus (43204) ***(G-6866)***

Broad Street Imaging 614 621-9100
2141 Polaris Pkwy Columbus (43240) ***(G-6643)***

Broadband Hospitality, Youngstown *Also called Great Lakes Telcom Ltd* ***(G-21103)***

Broadstreet Energy Company, Columbus *Also called Broad Street Financial Company* ***(G-6866)***

Broadview Heights Spotlights 440 526-4404
9543 Broadview Rd Bldg 7 Broadview Heights (44147) ***(G-2105)***

Broadview Journal, The, Richfield *Also called Scriptype Publishing Inc* ***(G-16635)***

Broadway Companies Inc (PA) 937 890-1888
6161 Ventnor Ave Dayton (45414) ***(G-8197)***

Broadway Offset Printing Co 216 391-3800
3800 Euclid Ave Cleveland (44115) ***(G-4932)***

Broadway Printing LLC 513 621-3429
530 Reading Rd Cincinnati (45202) ***(G-3475)***

Broadway Welding & Fabrication 513 821-0004
25 E 76th St Cincinnati (45216) ***(G-3476)***

Broan-Nutone LLC 888 336-3948
9825 Kenwood Rd Ste 301 Blue Ash (45242) ***(G-1755)***

Brocar Products Inc 513 922-2888
4335 River Rd Cincinnati (45204) ***(G-3477)***

Brock Burial Vault Inc 740 894-5246
1043 County Road 120 South Point (45680) ***(G-17433)***

Brock RAD & Wldg Fabrication 740 773-2540
370 Douglas Ave Chillicothe (45601) ***(G-3230)***

Brocker Machine Inc 330 744-5858
1530 Poland Ave Youngstown (44502) ***(G-21038)***

Brockman Jig Grinding Service 937 220-9780
1535 Stanley Ave Dayton (45404) ***(G-8198)***

Brockmans Signs Inc 513 574-6163
6041 Harrison Ave Ste 5 Cincinnati (45248) ***(G-3478)***

Brocks Chimney 740 819-2489
4620 Gorsuch Rd Nashport (43830) ***(G-14704)***

Brocks RAD Wldg Fabrication I, Chillicothe *Also called Brock RAD & Wldg Fabrication* ***(G-3230)***

Brocks Welding & Repair Svc 740 453-3943
3985 East Pike Zanesville (43701) ***(G-21281)***

Broco Products Inc 216 531-0880
18624 Syracuse Ave Cleveland (44110) ***(G-4933)***

Brodwill LLC 513 258-2716
3900 Rose Hill Ave Ste C Cincinnati (45229) ***(G-3479)***

Broestl & Wallis Fine Jewelers, Lakewood *Also called Bensan Jewelers Inc* ***(G-11657)***

Brogan Machine Shop 513 683-9054
501 Lovelnd Madera Rd # 2 Loveland (45140) ***(G-12345)***

Broken Spinning Wheel 419 825-1609
14230 Monclova Rd Swanton (43558) ***(G-18081)***

Bron-Shoe Company 614 252-0967
1313 Alum Creek Dr Columbus (43209) ***(G-6867)***

Bronco Machine Inc 440 951-5015
38411 Apollo Pkwy Willoughby (44094) ***(G-20446)***

Bront Machining Inc 937 228-4551
2601 W Dorothy Ln Moraine (45439) ***(G-14470)***

Bronx Taylor Wilson, North Canton *Also called Fives Bronx Inc* ***(G-15231)***

Bronze and Beautiful, Waverly *Also called Hot Spot* ***(G-19711)***

Broodle Brands LLC 855 276-6353
8361 Broadwell Rd Ste 100 Cincinnati (45244) ***(G-3480)***

Brooke Printers Inc 614 235-6800
358 Lincoln Ave Ste C Lancaster (43130) ***(G-11692)***

Brooker Bros Forging Co Inc 419 668-2535
102 Jefferson St Norwalk (44857) ***(G-15528)***

Brookhill Center Industries 419 876-3932
7989 State Route 108 Ottawa (45875) ***(G-15790)***

Brooklyn Machine & Mfg Co Inc 216 341-1846
5180 Grant Ave Cleveland (44125) ***(G-4934)***

Brookpark Laboratories Inc 216 267-7140
4595 Manufacturing Ave Cleveland (44135) ***(G-4935)***

Brooks Manufacturing 419 244-1777
1102 N Summit St Toledo (43604) ***(G-18382)***

Brooks Meter Devices, Canton *Also called Brooks Utility Products Group* ***(G-2629)***

Brooks Utility Products Group 330 455-0301
3359 Bruening Ave Sw Canton (44706) ***(G-2629)***

Brookville Roadster Inc 937 833-4605
718 Albert Rd Brookville (45309) ***(G-2176)***

Brookville Star 937 833-2545
14 Mulberry St Brookville (45309) ***(G-2177)***

Brookwood Group Inc 513 791-3030
3210 Wasson Rd Cincinnati (45209) ***(G-3481)***

Broshco Fabricated Products, Mansfield *Also called Systems Jay LLC Nanogate* *(G-12688)*
Broshco Fabricated Products, Mansfield *Also called Systems Jay LLC Nanogate* *(G-12692)*
Brost Foundry Company (PA) 216 641-1131
2934 E 55th St Cleveland (44127) *(G-4936)*
Brost Foundry Company 419 522-1133
198 Wayne St Mansfield (44902) *(G-12570)*
Brothers Body and Eqp LLC 419 462-1975
352 South St Bldg 24 Galion (44833) *(G-10255)*
Brothers Equipment Inc 216 458-0180
1335 E 171st St Cleveland (44110) *(G-4937)*
Brothers Printing Co Inc 216 621-6050
2000 Euclid Ave Cleveland (44115) *(G-4938)*
Brothers Publishing Co LLC 937 548-3330
5312 Sebring Warner Rd Greenville (45331) *(G-10490)*
Brothers Tool and Mfg Ltd 513 353-9700
8300 Harrison Ave Miamitown (45041) *(G-13885)*
Broty Enterprises Inc (PA) 330 674-6900
88 W Jackson St Millersburg (44654) *(G-14203)*
Broughton Foods Company (HQ) 740 373-4121
1701 Greene St Marietta (45750) *(G-12768)*
Broughton Foods Company 800 598-7545
8099 County Road 1 South Point (45680) *(G-17434)*
Brovig Engineering Inc 419 426-1333
6090 Coder Rd Attica (44807) *(G-893)*
Browder Tool Co Inc 937 233-6731
5924 Executive Blvd Dayton (45424) *(G-8199)*
Brower Products Inc (HQ) 937 563-1111
401 Northland Blvd Cincinnati (45240) *(G-3482)*
Brown Box Company, Findlay *Also called Square One Solutions LLC* *(G-9894)*
Brown Cnc Machinery Inc 937 865-9191
433 E Maple Ave Miamisburg (45342) *(G-13787)*
Brown Cnty Bd Mntal Rtardation 937 378-4891
325 W State St Ste A2 Georgetown (45121) *(G-10364)*
Brown Company of Findlay Ltd 419 425-3002
243 Stanford Pkwy Findlay (45840) *(G-9803)*
Brown Construction & Paving 513 494-0095
4755 Stubbs Mills Rd Morrow (45152) *(G-14544)*
Brown County Press, Mount Orab *Also called Clermont Sun Publishing Co* *(G-14578)*
Brown Dave Products Inc 513 738-1576
4560 Layhigh Rd Hamilton (45013) *(G-10677)*
Brown Fired Heater Div, Elyria *Also called Es Thermal Inc* *(G-9422)*
Brown Forest Products 937 544-1515
652 State Route 348 Otway (45657) *(G-15828)*
Brown Industrial Inc 937 693-3838
311 W South St Botkins (45306) *(G-1951)*
Brown Machine Co 216 631-1255
16151 Puritas Ave Cleveland (44135) *(G-4939)*
Brown Precision Machine 937 675-6585
13 S Buckles Ave Jamestown (45335) *(G-11350)*
Brown Publishing Co 937 544-2391
229 N Cross St West Union (45693) *(G-20118)*
Brown Publishing Co Inc (PA) 740 286-2187
1 Acy Ave Ste D Jackson (45640) *(G-11313)*
Brown Publishing Inc LLC 513 794-5040
4229 Saint Andrews Pl Blue Ash (45236) *(G-1756)*
Brown Wood Products Company 330 339-8000
7783 Crooked Run Rd Sw New Philadelphia (44663) *(G-14886)*
Brown-Campbell Company 513 860-3564
555 Quality Blvd Fairfield (45014) *(G-9647)*
Brown-Campbell Company 216 332-0101
14400 Industrial Ave S Maple Heights (44137) *(G-12729)*
Brown-Campbell Steel, Maple Heights *Also called Brown-Campbell Company* *(G-12729)*
Brown-Forman Corporation 740 384-3027
468 Salem Church Rd Wellston (45692) *(G-19761)*
Brown-Singer Co 513 422-9619
108 Dorset Dr Middletown (45044) *(G-14024)*
Brownie Points Inc 614 860-8470
5712 Westbourne Ave Columbus (43213) *(G-6868)*
Brownlee Engineering & Mfg, Canton *Also called Machine Component Mfg* *(G-2765)*
Brp Inc 440 988-4398
114 Hidden Tree Ln Amherst (44001) *(G-593)*
Brp Manufacturing Company 800 858-0482
637 N Jackson St Lima (45801) *(G-11998)*
BRT Extrusions Inc 330 544-0177
1818 N Main St Unit 1 Niles (44446) *(G-15145)*
Brubaker Metalcrafts Inc 937 456-5834
209 N Franklin St Eaton (45320) *(G-9300)*
Bruce Box Co Inc 740 533-0670
2146 Junior Rd Franklin Furnace (45629) *(G-10066)*
Bruce High Performance Tran 440 357-8964
1 High Tech Ave Painesville (44077) *(G-15862)*
Bruck Manufacturing Co Inc 440 327-6619
33471 Liberty Pkwy North Ridgeville (44039) *(G-15363)*
Bruening Glass Works Inc 440 333-4768
20157 Lake Rd Cleveland (44116) *(G-4940)*
Bruewer Woodwork Mfg Co 513 353-3505
10000 Cilley Rd Cleves (45002) *(G-6507)*
Brufist LLC 330 221-4472
122 1/2 S Maple St Bowling Green (43402) *(G-1974)*

Brumall Mfg Coroporation 440 974-2622
7850 Division Dr Mentor (44060) *(G-13538)*
Brune Printing Co 419 399-2756
310 W Perry St Paulding (45879) *(G-16002)*
Brunswick Eye & Contact Lens C 419 439-3381
2011 S Clinton St Defiance (43512) *(G-8782)*
Brushes Inc 216 267-8084
5400 Smith Rd Cleveland (44142) *(G-4941)*
Brushes Inc 216 267-8084
5400 Smith Rd Cleveland (44142) *(G-4942)*
Brv Inc 513 977-3000
312 Walnut St Ste 2800 Cincinnati (45202) *(G-3483)*
Brw Tool Inc 419 394-3371
502 Scott St Saint Marys (45885) *(G-16835)*
Bry-Air Inc 740 965-2974
10793 E State Route 37 Sunbury (43074) *(G-18056)*
Bryan Metals LLC (HQ) 419 636-4571
1103 S Main St Bryan (43506) *(G-2286)*
Bryan Packaging Inc 419 636-2600
620 E Perry St Bryan (43506) *(G-2287)*
Bryan Publishing Company (PA) 419 636-1111
127 S Walnut St Bryan (43506) *(G-2288)*
Bryce Hill Inc 937 663-4152
8801 State Route 36 Saint Paris (43072) *(G-16859)*
Bryce Hill Inc (PA) 937 325-0651
2301 Sheridan Ave Springfield (45505) *(G-17525)*
Brydet Development Corporation 740 623-0455
16867 State Route 83 Coshocton (43812) *(G-7883)*
Bsa Industries Inc 614 846-5515
6510 Huntley Rd Columbus (43229) *(G-6869)*
Bse Welding & Fabricating LLC 419 547-1043
1787 N State Route 510 Vickery (43464) *(G-19361)*
BSK Industries Inc 440 230-9299
10143 Royalton Rd Ste C North Royalton (44133) *(G-15412)*
Bsm Columbus Llp 740 755-2380
389 Kyber Run Cir Johnstown (43031) *(G-11392)*
BT Energy Corporation (PA) 740 373-6134
1635 Warren Chapel Rd Fleming (45729) *(G-9911)*
BT Investments II Inc 937 434-4321
601 Congress Park Dr Dayton (45459) *(G-8200)*
Bta Enterprises Inc 937 277-0881
4090 Little Richmond Rd Dayton (45417) *(G-8201)*
Bta of Motorcars Inc 440 716-1000
27500 Lorain Rd North Olmsted (44070) *(G-15328)*
Btc Inc 740 549-2722
8595 Columbus Pike 158 Lewis Center (43035) *(G-11892)*
Btg Labs, Saint Bernard *Also called Brighton Technologies LLC* *(G-16779)*
BTS Ice Cream, Columbus *Also called Better Than Sex Ice Cream LLC* *(G-6823)*
Btw LLC 419 382-4443
2226 Greenlawn Dr Toledo (43614) *(G-18383)*
Bu E Comp Inc 419 284-3381
7092 S State Route 19 Bloomville (44818) *(G-1725)*
Bucher Printing, Dayton *Also called Keithley Enterprises Inc* *(G-8434)*
Buchtelite 330 972-6184
303 Carroll St Akron (44325) *(G-101)*
Buck Creek Pallet 937 653-3098
713 Muzzy Rd Urbana (43078) *(G-19149)*
Buck Equipment Inc 614 539-3039
1720 Feddern Ave Grove City (43123) *(G-10548)*
Buck Eye Pressure Wash 419 385-9274
5242 Angola Rd Ste 130 Toledo (43615) *(G-18384)*
Buckbuilt Manufacturing Co 330 764-3363
7007 Wooster Pike Medina (44256) *(G-13383)*
Buckeye Abrasive Inc 330 753-1041
1020 Eagon St Barberton (44203) *(G-1112)*
Buckeye Aluminum Foundry Inc (PA) 440 428-7180
457 N Lake St Madison (44057) *(G-12496)*
Buckeye Asphalt Paving Co, Toledo *Also called Lucas County Asphalt Inc* *(G-18564)*
Buckeye Blow Out Preventer, Newcomerstown *Also called Buckeye BOP LLC* *(G-15110)*
Buckeye BOP LLC 740 498-9898
401 Enterprise Dr Newcomerstown (43832) *(G-15110)*
Buckeye Boxes Inc (PA) 614 274-8484
601 N Hague Ave Columbus (43204) *(G-6870)*
Buckeye Boxes Inc 937 599-2551
1133 W Columbus Ave Bellefontaine (43311) *(G-1523)*
Buckeye Boxes Inc 614 274-8484
601 N Hague Ave Columbus (43204) *(G-6871)*
Buckeye Brake Manufacturing 740 782-1379
40168 National Rd W Morristown (43759) *(G-14541)*
Buckeye Building Products, Reynoldsburg *Also called Buckeye Ready-Mix LLC* *(G-16583)*
Buckeye Business Forms Inc 614 882-1890
7307 Red Bank Rd Westerville (43082) *(G-20141)*
Buckeye Business Products, Cleveland *Also called Kroy LLC* *(G-5666)*
Buckeye Chocolate Co 440 564-8086
15010 Brkshire Indus Pkwy Middlefield (44062) *(G-13919)*
Buckeye Companies Inc 740 452-3641
999 Zane St Zanesville (43701) *(G-21282)*
Buckeye Components LLC (PA) 330 482-5163
1340 State Route 14 Columbiana (44408) *(G-6608)*

Buckeye Composites, Kettering Also called Nanotechlabs Inc (G-11584)

Buckeye Container Division, Wooster Also called Buckeye Corrugated Inc (G-20753)

Buckeye Corrugated Inc (PA) 330 576-0590
822 Kumho Dr Ste 400 Fairlawn (44333) (G-9744)

Buckeye Corrugated Inc 330 264-6336
3350 Long Rd Wooster (44691) (G-20753)

Buckeye Counters 330 682-0902
10207 Ely Rd Orrville (44667) (G-15732)

Buckeye Cstm Screen Print EMB 614 237-0196
3822 Elbern Ave Columbus (43213) (G-6872)

Buckeye Custom Fab, Fort Jennings Also called Bcfab Inc (G-9925)

Buckeye Delivery, Mansfield Also called Buckeye Vault Service Inc (G-12571)

Buckeye Design & Engr Svc LLC 419 375-4241
2600 Wabash Rd Fort Recovery (45846) (G-9945)

Buckeye Diamond Logistics Inc (PA) 937 462-8361
15 Sprague Rd South Charleston (45368) (G-17424)

Buckeye Diamond Logistics Inc 937 644-2194
21963 Northwest Pkwy Marysville (43040) (G-12934)

Buckeye Distillery 937 877-1901
130 W Plum St Tipp City (45371) (G-18267)

Buckeye Electrical Products 937 693-7519
100 Commerce Dr Botkins (45306) (G-1952)

Buckeye Energy Resources Inc 740 452-9506
999 Zane St Zanesville (43701) (G-21283)

Buckeye Engraving, Kent Also called Raschke Engraving Inc (G-11512)

Buckeye Fabricating Co 937 746-9822
245 S Pioneer Blvd Springboro (45066) (G-17475)

BUCKEYE FASTENERS COMPANY, Girard Also called Brainard Rivet Company (G-10383)

BUCKEYE FASTENERS COMPANY, Streetsboro Also called Joseph Industries Inc (G-17860)

Buckeye Fbricators of Leetonia 330 427-0330
38009 Butcher Rd Leetonia (44431) (G-11858)

Buckeye Feed & Grain 937 526-3914
895 E Main St Versailles (45380) (G-19342)

Buckeye Field Machining Inc 330 336-7036
2131 Wadsworth Rd Ste 500 Norton (44203) (G-15507)

Buckeye Field Supply Ltd 513 312-2343
8190 Beechmont Ave 262a Cincinnati (45255) (G-3484)

Buckeye Franklin Co 330 859-2465
3471 New Zoarville Rd Ne Zoarville (44656) (G-21370)

Buckeye Gear Co 216 292-7998
16354 Stone Ridge Rd Chagrin Falls (44023) (G-3078)

Buckeye Lake Beacon, Buckeye Lake Also called Impact Publications (G-2329)

Buckeye Lake Shopper Reporter 740 246-4741
14886 State Route 13 Thornville (43076) (G-18192)

Buckeye Lake Winery 740 246-9890
13750 Rosewood Dr Ne Thornville (43076) (G-18193)

Buckeye Mch Fabricators Inc 419 273-2521
610 E Lima St Forest (45843) (G-9918)

Buckeye Medical Tech LLC 330 719-9868
405 Niles Cortland Rd Se # 202 Warren (44484) (G-19531)

Buckeye Metal Works Inc 614 239-8000
3240 Petzinger Rd Columbus (43232) (G-6873)

Buckeye Metals, Cleveland Also called W R G Inc (G-6436)

Buckeye Metals 740 446-9590
185 Curr Rd Bidwell (45614) (G-1675)

Buckeye Metals Industries Inc 216 663-4300
3238 E 82nd St Cleveland (44104) (G-4943)

Buckeye Molded Products Ltd 440 323-2244
443 Oberlin Elyria Rd Elyria (44035) (G-9383)

Buckeye Oil Producing Co 330 264-8847
544 E Liberty St Wooster (44691) (G-20754)

Buckeye Pallett 330 359-5919
3463 County Road 160 Millersburg (44654) (G-14204)

Buckeye Paper Co Inc 330 477-5925
5233 Southway St Sw # 523 Canton (44706) (G-2630)

Buckeye Polymers Inc (PA) 330 948-3007
104 Lee St Lodi (44254) (G-12158)

Buckeye Post 330 724-2800
1266 Grant St Akron (44301) (G-102)

Buckeye Prep Magazine, New Albany Also called Buckeye Prep Report Magazine (G-14752)

Buckeye Prep Report Magazine 614 855-6977
8599 Swisher Creek Xing New Albany (43054) (G-14752)

Buckeye Products 740 969-4718
6745 Chillicothe Lancster Amanda (43102) (G-560)

Buckeye Raceway LLC 614 272-7888
4050 W Broad St Columbus (43228) (G-6874)

Buckeye Ready Mix, Columbus Also called Anderson Concrete Corp (G-6755)

Buckeye Ready-Mix 419 294-2389
6326 County Highway 61 Upper Sandusky (43351) (G-19116)

Buckeye Ready-Mix 740 967-4801
7720 Jhnstown Alxndria Rd Johnstown (43031) (G-11393)

Buckeye Ready-Mix LLC 614 879-6316
6600 State Route 29 West Jefferson (43162) (G-20076)

Buckeye Ready-Mix LLC 740 387-8846
627 Likens Rd Marion (43302) (G-12858)

Buckeye Ready-Mix LLC (PA) 614 575-2132
7657 Taylor Rd Sw Reynoldsburg (43068) (G-16583)

Buckeye Ready-Mix LLC 937 642-2951
838 N Main St Marysville (43040) (G-12935)

Buckeye Ready-Mix LLC 740 654-4423
1750 Logan Langster Rd Lancaster (43130) (G-11693)

Buckeye Rocker, Millersburg Also called M H Woodworking LLC (G-14243)

Buckeye Rubber Products, Lima Also called Brp Manufacturing Company (G-11998)

Buckeye Sanitary Service, Springfield Also called Reed Elvin Burl II (G-17636)

Buckeye Sauce Corporation (PA) 216 751-0440
12201 Buckeye Rd Cleveland (44120) (G-4944)

Buckeye Sealcoating 330 658-3377
40 W Marion St Doylestown (44230) (G-9027)

Buckeye Seating LLC 330 473-2379
6960 County Road 672 Millersburg (44654) (G-14205)

Buckeye Shapeform, Columbus Also called Buckeye Stamping Company (G-6875)

Buckeye Sports Bulletin, Columbus Also called Columbus-Sports Publications (G-6969)

Buckeye Stamping Company 614 445-0059
555 Marion Rd Columbus (43207) (G-6875)

Buckeye State Welding & Fabg (PA) 440 322-0319
131 Buckeye St Elyria (44035) (G-9384)

Buckeye State Welding & Fabg 440 322-0344
175 Woodford Ave Elyria (44035) (G-9385)

Buckeye Steel Incorporated 740 425-2306
607 Watt Ave Barnesville (43713) (G-1159)

Buckeye Tractor Company Corp 419 659-2162
11313 Slabtown Rd Columbus Grove (45830) (G-7791)

Buckeye Vault Service Inc 419 747-1976
2253 Stiving Rd Mansfield (44903) (G-12571)

Buckeye Veal Services 740 489-5145
1046 N Applecreek Rd Wooster (44691) (G-20755)

Buckeye Volleyball Center LLC 614 764-1075
7824 Maplecreek Ct Powell (43065) (G-16463)

Buckeye Welding 330 674-0944
2507 Township Road 110 Millersburg (44654) (G-14206)

Buckhorn, Milford Also called Bkhn Inc (G-14126)

Buckhorn Inc (HQ) 513 831-4402
55 W Techne Center Dr A Milford (45150) (G-14128)

Buckhorn Material Hdlg Group 513 831-4402
55 W Techne Center Dr A Milford (45150) (G-14129)

Buckingham Coal Company LLC 740 767-2907
11 N 4th St Zanesville (43701) (G-21284)

Buckley Manufacturing Company 513 821-4444
10330 Wayne Ave Ste 1 Cincinnati (45215) (G-3485)

Buckman Machine Works Inc 330 525-7665
24841 Georgetown Rd Homeworth (44634) (G-11115)

Bucktask, Columbus Also called Pmj Partners LLC (G-7501)

Buckys Machine and Fab Ltd 419 981-5050
8376 S County Road 47 Mc Cutchenville (44844) (G-13340)

Bucyrus Blades Inc (HQ) 419 562-6015
260 E Beal Ave Bucyrus (44820) (G-2332)

Bucyrus Extruded Composites, Bloomville Also called Buecomp Inc (G-1726)

Bucyrus Graphics Inc 419 562-2906
214 W Liberty St Bucyrus (44820) (G-2333)

Bucyrus Ice Company, Bucyrus Also called Velvet Ice Cream Company (G-2363)

Bucyrus Precision Tech Inc 419 563-9950
200 Crossroads Blvd Bucyrus (44820) (G-2334)

Bucyrus Telegraph-Forum, Mansfield Also called Gannett Co Inc (G-12610)

Bud Corp 740 967-9992
158 Commerce Blvd Johnstown (43031) (G-11394)

Bud Industries Inc (PA) 440 946-3200
4605 E 355th St Willoughby (44094) (G-20447)

Bud May Inc 216 676-8850
16850 Hummel Rd Cleveland (44142) (G-4945)

Budd Co Plastics Div 419 238-4332
1276 Industrial Dr Van Wert (45891) (G-19247)

Budde Sheet Metal Works Inc (PA) 937 224-0868
305 Leo St Dayton (45404) (G-8202)

Buddy Backyard Inc 330 393-9353
140 Dana St Ne Warren (44483) (G-19532)

Buderer Drug Co (PA) 419 626-3429
633 Hancock St Sandusky (44870) (G-16950)

Buderer Drug Company Inc (PA) 419 627-2800
633 Hancock St Sandusky (44870) (G-16951)

Buderer Drug Company Inc 419 873-2800
26611 Dixie Hwy Ste 119 Perrysburg (43551) (G-16070)

Buderer Drug Company Inc 440 934-3100
38530 Chester Rd Ste 400 Avon (44011) (G-987)

Budget Molders Supply Inc 216 367-7050
8303 Corporate Park Dr Macedonia (44056) (G-12439)

Budget Newspaper, The, Sugarcreek Also called Sugarcreek Budget Publishers (G-18042)

Buds Sign Shop Inc 330 744-5555
892 Mahoning Ave Youngstown (44502) (G-21039)

Budzar Industries Inc 440 530-1000
38241 Willoughby Pkwy Willoughby (44094) (G-20448)

Buecomp Inc 419 284-3840
7016 S State Route 19 Bloomville (44818) (G-1726)

Buffalo Peanuts, Columbus Also called Nuts Are Good Inc (G-7406)

Buffex Metal Finishing Inc 216 631-2202
1935 W 96th St Ste L Cleveland (44102) (G-4946)

Bug-Barrier Screen Corp 330 723-2551
6979 Wooster Pike Medina (44256) *(G-13384)*
Bugh Vinyl Products Inc 330 305-0978
8933 Cleveland Ave Nw Canton (44720) *(G-2631)*
Buhi Imports 440 224-0013
3210 E Center St North Kingsville (44068) *(G-15303)*
Buildcret Concrete, Glenford *Also called James Ryan Soloman (G-10398)*
Builder Tech Wholesale LLC 419 535-7606
2931 South Ave Toledo (43609) *(G-18385)*
Builder Tech Windows, Toledo *Also called Builder Tech Wholesale LLC (G-18385)*
Builders Straight Edge, Elyria *Also called B&B Distributors LLC (G-9378)*
Building & Conveyer Maint LLC 303 882-0912
6803 Cleveland Rd Ravenna (44266) *(G-16520)*
Building Concepts Inc (PA) 419 298-2371
444 N Michigan Ave Edgerton (43517) *(G-9326)*
Building Ctrl Integrators LLC (PA) 614 334-3300
383 N Liberty St Powell (43065) *(G-16464)*
Building Ctrl Integrators LLC 513 247-6154
300 E Bus Way Ste 200 Cincinnati (45241) *(G-3486)*
Building Ctrl Integrators LLC 440 526-6660
325 Treeworth Blvd Broadview Heights (44147) *(G-2106)*
Building Ctrl Integrators LLC 513 860-9600
10174 International Blvd West Chester (45246) *(G-19985)*
Building Maintenance Dept, Willard *Also called Lsc Communications Us LLC (G-20396)*
Building Rlationships Together, Niles *Also called BRT Extrusions Inc (G-15145)*
Built-Rite Box & Crate Inc 330 263-0936
608 Freedlander Rd Wooster (44691) *(G-20756)*
Bula Forge & Machine Inc 216 252-7600
3001 W 121st St Cleveland (44111) *(G-4947)*
Bulk Apothecary, Aurora *Also called Natural Essentials Inc (G-937)*
Bulk Carrier Trnsp Eqp Co 330 339-3333
2743 Brightwood Rd Se New Philadelphia (44663) *(G-14887)*
Bulk Handling Equipment Co 330 468-5703
28 W Aurora Rd Northfield (44067) *(G-15462)*
Bulk Molding Compounds Inc 419 874-7941
12600 Eckel Rd Perrysburg (43551) *(G-16071)*
Bull Moose Tube Company 330 448-4878
1433 Standard Ave Masury (44438) *(G-13213)*
Bulldogsecurity, Steubenville *Also called Access 2 Communications Inc (G-17686)*
Bullen Ultrasonics Inc 937 456-7133
1301 Miller Williams Rd Eaton (45320) *(G-9301)*
Bullseye Activewear Inc 330 220-1720
2947 Nationwide Pkwy Brunswick (44212) *(G-2214)*
Bullseye Dart Shoppe Inc 440 951-9277
950c Erie Rd Willoughby (44095) *(G-20449)*
Bullseye Machines LLC 419 485-5951
13121 County Road 1250 Montpelier (43543) *(G-14439)*
Bully Tools Inc 740 282-5834
14 Technology Way Steubenville (43952) *(G-17690)*
Bundy Baking Solutions 740 965-3008
601 W Cherry St Sunbury (43074) *(G-18057)*
Bunge North America Foundation 740 383-1181
751 E Farming St Marion (43302) *(G-12859)*
Bunge North America Foundation 419 692-6010
234 S Jefferson St Delphos (45833) *(G-8903)*
Bunge North America Foundation 419 483-5340
605 Goodrich Rd Bellevue (44811) *(G-1547)*
Bunge North America Foundation 740 426-6332
12574 State Route 41 Jeffersonville (43128) *(G-11378)*
Bunker Hill Cheese Co Inc 330 893-2131
6005 County Road 77 Millersburg (44654) *(G-14207)*
Bunny B, Cuyahoga Falls *Also called Ascot Valley Foods LLC (G-7970)*
Buns of Delaware Inc 740 363-2867
14 W Winter St Delaware (43015) *(G-8826)*
Buns Restaurant & Bakery, Delaware *Also called Buns of Delaware Inc (G-8826)*
Bunting Bearings LLC 419 522-3323
153 E 5th St Mansfield (44902) *(G-12572)*
Bunting Bearings LLC (PA) 419 866-7000
1001 Holland Park Blvd Holland (43528) *(G-11047)*
Burch Plastics Corp 440 835-2059
30627 Webster Rd Cleveland (44140) *(G-4948)*
Burdens Machine & Welding 740 345-9246
94 S 5th St Newark (43055) *(G-14989)*
Burghardt Manufacturing Inc 330 253-7590
1524 Massillon Rd Akron (44306) *(G-103)*
Burghardt Metal Fabg Inc 330 794-1830
1638 Mcchesney Rd Akron (44306) *(G-104)*
Burgie Brauerei Inc 740 344-1620
860 Village Pkwy Newark (43055) *(G-14990)*
Burial Vaults By Neher, Springfield *Also called Neher Burial Vault Company (G-17617)*
Burke & Company, Cincinnati *Also called Patrick J Burke & Co (G-4215)*
Burke Products Inc 937 372-3516
1355 Enterprise Ln Xenia (45385) *(G-20940)*
Burkett Advnced Composite Tech, West Liberty *Also called BAC Technologies Ltd (G-20091)*
Burkett Industries Inc 419 332-4391
507 Vine St Fremont (43420) *(G-10132)*
Burkettsville Stockyard, Burkettsville *Also called Werling and Sons Inc (G-2370)*
Burkholder Buggy Shop 330 674-5891
7400 County Road 77 Millersburg (44654) *(G-14208)*
Burner Technology Unlimited 440 232-6181
7590 Independence Dr Cleveland (44146) *(G-4949)*
Burns & Rink Enterprises LLC 513 421-7799
2016 Elm St Cincinnati (45202) *(G-3487)*
Burrrows Paper Corroc Div, Franklin *Also called Novolex Holdings Inc (G-10041)*
Burt Manufacturing Company Inc 330 762-0061
44 E South St Akron (44311) *(G-105)*
Burton Bottling Company Inc 216 681-0025
1240 E 9th St R Cleveland (44199) *(G-4950)*
Burton Industries Inc 440 974-1700
7875 Division Dr Mentor (44060) *(G-13539)*
Burton Metal Finishing Inc 614 252-9523
1711 Woodland Ave Columbus (43219) *(G-6876)*
Burton Rubber Processing, Burton *Also called Hexpol Compounding LLC (G-2376)*
Busch & Thiem Inc 419 625-7515
1316 Cleveland Rd Sandusky (44870) *(G-16952)*
Busch Properties Inc 614 888-0946
1103 Schrock Rd Ste 200 Columbus (43229) *(G-6877)*
Buschman Corporation 216 431-6633
4100 Payne Ave Ste 1 Cleveland (44103) *(G-4951)*
Buses International 440 233-4091
702 N Ridge Rd E Lorain (44055) *(G-12235)*
Bush Inc 216 362-6700
15901 Industrial Pkwy Cleveland (44135) *(G-4952)*
Bush Integrated, Cleveland *Also called PJ Bush Associates Inc (G-6009)*
Bush Specialty Vehicles Inc 937 382-5502
80 Park Dr Wilmington (45177) *(G-20657)*
Bushong Auto Service, Troy *Also called Mader Automotive Center Inc (G-18855)*
Bushworks Incorporated 937 767-1713
144 Cliff St Ste A Yellow Springs (45387) *(G-20990)*
Business Courier, Cincinnati *Also called American City Bus Journals Inc (G-3386)*
Business First Columbus Inc (HQ) 614 461-4040
303 W Nationwide Blvd Columbus (43215) *(G-6878)*
Business Fnctnality Forms Svcs 614 557-9420
4367 Grays Market Dr Gahanna (43230) *(G-10205)*
Business Idntification Systems 614 841-1255
6185 Huntley Rd Ste M Columbus (43229) *(G-6879)*
Business Journal 330 744-5023
25 E Boardman St Ste 306 Youngstown (44503) *(G-21040)*
Business Journal, The, Youngstown *Also called Business Journal (G-21040)*
Busken Bakery Inc 513 671-8454
370 W Kemper Rd Cincinnati (45246) *(G-3488)*
Busken Bakery Inc 513 791-6736
7565 Kenwood Rd Ste 104 Cincinnati (45236) *(G-3489)*
Busken Springdale, Cincinnati *Also called Busken Bakery Inc (G-3488)*
Busse Combat Knives, Wauseon *Also called Busse Knife Co (G-19673)*
Busse Knife Co 419 923-6471
11651 County Road 12 Wauseon (43567) *(G-19673)*
Busson Digital Printing Inc 330 753-8373
1061 Eastern Rd Wadsworth (44281) *(G-19396)*
Busy Bee Lumber 330 674-1305
5965 Township Road 355 Millersburg (44654) *(G-14209)*
Butera Manufacturing Inc 440 516-3698
2935 Lynn Dr Willoughby Hills (44092) *(G-20638)*
Butera Manufacturing Inds 216 761-8800
1068 E 134th St Cleveland (44110) *(G-4953)*
Butler Machine, Columbus *Also called Bmi Machine Inc (G-6842)*
Butler Processing Inc 513 874-1400
1326 Stephanie Dr Hamilton (45013) *(G-10678)*
Butler Tech Career Dev Schools 513 867-1028
3611 Hmlton Middletown Rd Hamilton (45011) *(G-10679)*
Butt Hut, Findlay *Also called Smoke Rings Inc (G-9890)*
Butt Hut of America Inc 419 443-1997
1972 W Market St Tiffin (44883) *(G-18212)*
Butt Kickn Creamery Inc 419 482-6610
26383 Carronade Dr Perrysburg (43551) *(G-16072)*
Buttkicker, Westerville *Also called Guitammer Company (G-20156)*
Buy The Pallet LLC 440 521-0073
8183 Twin Oaks Dr Broadview Heights (44147) *(G-2107)*
Buyers Products Company (PA) 440 974-8888
9049 Tyler Blvd Mentor (44060) *(G-13540)*
Buyers Products Company 440 974-8888
8120 Tyler Blvd Mentor (44060) *(G-13541)*
Buyers Products Company 440 974-8888
7700 Tyler Blvd Mentor (44060) *(G-13542)*
Buynix 216 551-3485
2142 W 96th St Cleveland (44102) *(G-4954)*
Buzz N Shuttle Service 740 223-0567
333 Executive Dr Apt I Marion (43302) *(G-12860)*
Buzz Seating Inc (PA) 877 263-5737
623 N Wayne Ave Cincinnati (45215) *(G-3490)*
Bw Supply Co., Lyons *Also called B W Grinding Co (G-12431)*
BWAY Corporation 513 388-2200
8200 Broadwell Rd Cincinnati (45244) *(G-3491)*
Bwaypackaging, Cincinnati *Also called BWAY Corporation (G-3491)*

Bwd Woodwork LLC 740 335-9766
4271 Bush Rd Nw Wshngtn CT Hs (43160) (G-20903)

Bwi Group, Kettering Also called Bwi North America Inc (G-11577)

Bwi North America Inc 937 455-5190
3100 Research Blvd Kettering (45420) (G-11576)

Bwi North America Inc (HQ) 937 253-1130
3100 Res Blvd Ste 240 Kettering (45420) (G-11577)

Byer Steel Rebar Inc 513 821-6400
200 W North Bend Rd Cincinnati (45216) (G-3492)

Byers Sign Co 614 561-1224
2940 E 14th Ave Columbus (43219) (G-6880)

Byler Truss 330 465-5412
1271 State Route 96 Ashland (44805) (G-715)

Byrd Prcurement Specialist Inc 419 936-0019
12150 Monclova Rd Swanton (43558) (G-18082)

Byron Products Inc 513 870-9111
3781 Port Union Rd Fairfield (45014) (G-9648)

C & A Land and Energy LLC 606 434-1420
1243 Monroe St Nw New Philadelphia (44663) (G-14888)

C & B Logging Inc 740 347-4844
9821 State Route 13 Se Glouster (45732) (G-10403)

C & C Fabrication Inc 419 354-3535
18237 N Dixie Hwy Bowling Green (43402) (G-1975)

C & C Machine Co 330 633-4485
3031 S Oak Hill Rd Silver Lake (44224) (G-17237)

C & C Marble & Granite LLC 614 873-1919
4401 Lyman Dr Ste A Hilliard (43026) (G-10937)

C & C Metal Products, Wooster Also called Global Body & Equipment Co (G-20777)

C & C Mobile Homes LLC 740 663-5535
1580 Valley Rd Waverly (45690) (G-19704)

C & C Special Machine, Ney Also called Russell E Coy (G-15143)

C & D Counters 740 259-5529
359b Back St Lucasville (45648) (G-12417)

C & D Manufacturing Inc 330 828-8357
374 Eckard Rd Dalton (44618) (G-8064)

C & D Tool Inc 440 942-8463
35595 Curtis Blvd Unit F Eastlake (44095) (G-9260)

C & F Fabrications Inc 937 666-3234
3100 State St East Liberty (43319) (G-9199)

C & G Associates Inc 419 756-6583
3130 Hastings Newville Rd Mansfield (44903) (G-12573)

C & J Jewelers Inc 614 221-8588
175 Cleveland Ave Frnt Columbus (43215) (G-6881)

C & K Machine Co Inc 419 237-3203
604 N Park St Fayette (43521) (G-9774)

C & L Erectors & Riggers Inc 740 332-7185
16412 Thompson Ridge Rd Laurelville (43135) (G-11769)

C & L Supply, Logan Also called Kilbarger Construction Inc (G-12182)

C & M Rubber Co Inc 937 299-2782
414 Littell Ave Dayton (45419) (G-8203)

C & M Truss LLC 937 446-3400
8319 Ashridge Arnheim Rd Sardinia (45171) (G-17026)

C & M Welding Services LLC 419 584-0008
1405 James Dr Celina (45822) (G-2987)

C & P Metals Inc 724 510-4293
2880 Sferra Ave Nw Warren (44483) (G-19533)

C & R Inc (PA) 614 497-1130
5600 Clyde Moore Dr Groveport (43125) (G-10617)

C & S Associates Inc 440 461-9661
729 Miner Rd Highland Heights (44143) (G-10910)

C & W Custom Wdwkg Co Inc 513 891-6340
6839 Ashfield Dr Blue Ash (45242) (G-1757)

C A I R Ohio 513 281-8200
10999 Reed Hartman Hwy # 207 Blue Ash (45242) (G-1758)

C A Joseph Co (PA) 330 385-6869
13712 Old Frdericktown Rd East Liverpool (43920) (G-9204)

C A Joseph Co 330 532-4646
170 Broadway St Irondale (43932) (G-11287)

C A Kustoms 419 332-4395
524 N Stone St Fremont (43420) (G-10133)

C A M Machine Inc 937 663-5000
513 S Springfield St Saint Paris (43072) (G-16860)

C A P Industries Inc 937 773-1824
543 Staunton St Piqua (45356) (G-16254)

C A T-Wood Metal Works Inc 937 866-4917
2701 Lance Dr Moraine (45409) (G-14471)

C and J Machine Inc 330 935-2170
403 State Route 44 Hartville (44632) (G-10817)

C and O Electric Motor Service 614 491-6387
3105 Hillgate Rd Columbus (43207) (G-6882)

C B & S Spouting Inc 937 866-1600
4609 Slders Hm Mmsburg Rd Miamisburg (45342) (G-13788)

C B C, Marysville Also called Contract Building Components (G-12938)

C D C At Cityview 216 426-2020
6606 Carnegie Ave Cleveland (44103) (G-4955)

C D I, Miamisburg Also called Connective Design Incorporated (G-13793)

C D R Pigments Dispersions Div, Cincinnati Also called Flint Group US LLC (G-3761)

C Dcap Modem Line 419 748-7409
232 S East St Mc Clure (43534) (G-13334)

C Dcap Modem Line 440 685-4302
8829 State Route 45 North Bloomfield (44450) (G-15215)

C E D Process Minerals Inc (PA) 330 666-5500
863 N Clvland Mssillon Rd Akron (44333) (G-106)

C E Electronics Inc 419 636-6705
2107 Industrial Dr Bryan (43506) (G-2289)

C E Kegg Inc (PA) 330 877-8800
1184 Woodland St Sw Hartville (44632) (G-10818)

C E White Co (HQ) 419 492-2157
417 N Kibler St New Washington (44854) (G-14958)

C F Doors, Cleveland Also called Clear Fold Door Inc (G-5045)

C F Poeppelman Inc (PA) 937 448-2191
4755 N State Route 721 Bradford (45308) (G-2025)

C G C Systems Inc 330 678-3261
4763 Sherman Rd Kent (44240) (G-11437)

C G Egli Inc 937 254-8898
515 Springfield St Dayton (45403) (G-8204)

C G Manufacturing Company Inc 440 951-8555
36490 Reading Ave Willoughby (44094) (G-20450)

C G S, Cleveland Also called Centerless Grinding Service (G-5003)

C Green & Sons Incorporated 740 745-2998
9020 Mount Vernon Rd Saint Louisville (43071) (G-16826)

C H T, Cleveland Also called Compliant Healthcare Tech LLC (G-5112)

C H Washington Water Plan 740 636-2382
220 Park Ave Wshngtn CT Hs (43160) (G-20904)

C Imperial Inc 937 669-5620
1322 Commerce Park Dr Tipp City (45371) (G-18268)

C J Kraft Enterprises Inc 740 653-9606
301 S Maple St Lancaster (43130) (G-11694)

C J Krehbiel Company 513 271-6035
3962 Virginia Ave Cincinnati (45227) (G-3493)

C J Smith Machinery Service 614 348-1376
3000 E Main St Ste B Columbus (43209) (G-6883)

C JS Signs 330 821-7446
1670 Charl Ann Dr Alliance (44601) (G-500)

C L D, Franklin Also called 119c Landis Display Co (G-10003)

C L M Associates 440 942-8861
4312 Parklawn Dr Willoughby (44094) (G-20451)

C L S Finishing Inc 330 784-4134
409 Munroe Falls Rd Tallmadge (44278) (G-18136)

C L S Inc 216 251-5011
3812 W 150th St Cleveland (44111) (G-4956)

C L W Inc 740 374-8443
1201 Gilman Ave Marietta (45750) (G-12769)

C M A Supply Company, West Chester Also called CMA Supply Company Inc (G-19992)

C M C, Hamilton Also called Connector Manufacturing Co (G-10681)

C M H A, East Liverpool Also called Columbiana Metro Hsing Auth (G-9207)

C M L Concrete Construction 330 758-8314
482 Garden Valley Ct Youngstown (44512) (G-21041)

C M M S - Re Inc 513 489-5111
6130 Interstate Cir Blue Ash (45242) (G-1759)

C M M S - Re LLC (PA) 513 489-5111
6130 Interstate Cir Blue Ash (45242) (G-1760)

C M Slicechief Co 419 241-7647
3333 Maple St Toledo (43608) (G-18386)

C M Stephanoff Jewelers Inc 440 526-5890
8718 Bradford Ln Brecksville (44141) (G-2039)

C M Tech, Delaware Also called Cast Metals Technology Inc (G-8829)

C Massouh Printing, Canal Fulton Also called C Massouh Printing Co Inc (G-2500)

C Massouh Printing Co Inc 330 408-7330
590 Elm Ridge Ave Canal Fulton (44614) (G-2500)

C Massouh Printing Co Inc 330 832-6334
9589 Portage St Nw Massillon (44646) (G-13116)

C Massouh Printing Services, Massillon Also called C Massouh Printing Co Inc (G-13116)

C N C Precision Machine Inc 440 548-3880
18360 Industrial Cir Parkman (44080) (G-15950)

C N C Wholesale 330 832-9525
1300 Erie St S Massillon (44646) (G-13117)

C Nelson Manufacturing Co 419 898-3305
265 N Lake Winds Pkwy Oak Harbor (43449) (G-15587)

C O Welding & Fabrication Inc 419 394-3293
850 S Main St Saint Marys (45885) (G-16836)

C P D S, West Chester Also called Contract Pckg Dist Specialists (G-19993)

C P Electric Motor Repair Inc 330 425-9593
2212 E Aurora Rd Twinsburg (44087) (G-18906)

C P R Drain Cleaning Inc 614 279-3445
2168 Eakin Rd Columbus (43223) (G-6884)

C P S Enterprises Inc 216 441-7969
9815 Reno Ave Cleveland (44105) (G-4957)

C RC Automotive 513 422-4775
460 N Verity Pkwy Middletown (45042) (G-14025)

C S A Enterprises 740 342-9367
932 S Main St New Lexington (43764) (G-14845)

C S Bell Co 419 448-0791
170 W Davis St Tiffin (44883) (G-18213)

C S I, Toledo Also called Chem-Sales Inc (G-18394)

C S I, Harrison Also called Coating Systems Inc (G-10774)

C S Johns Company, Berea Also called Mr 14k Inc (G-1628)

A
L
P
H
A
B
E
T
I
C

C S T Geometric Forms, Lorain *Also called Custom Sink Top Mfg* *(G-12242)*
C Soltesz Co 614 529-5494
4374 Dublin Rd Columbus (43221) *(G-6885)*
C Square Lumber Products 740 557-3129
1541 S Elliott Rd Stockport (43787) *(G-17722)*
C Stoneman Corporation 440 942-3325
100 E Shore Blvd Eastlake (44095) *(G-9261)*
C T Chemicals Inc 513 336-6160
4110 Columbia Rd Lebanon (45036) *(G-11785)*
C T I Audio Inc 440 593-1111
220 Eastview Dr Ste 1 Brooklyn Heights (44131) *(G-2133)*
C V G, New Albany *Also called National Seating Company* *(G-14766)*
C W Ohio, Conneaut *Also called Cascade Ohio Inc* *(G-7801)*
C&C Trailer Park 330 823-7733
1717 E State St Salem (44460) *(G-16877)*
C&H Industries 330 899-0001
2054 Jaquelyn Dr Canton (44720) *(G-2632)*
C-H Tool & Die 740 397-7214
711 N Sandusky St Mount Vernon (43050) *(G-14610)*
C-Hawk Trailers, Bucyrus *Also called Lux Corporation* *(G-2353)*
C-Link Enterprises LLC 937 222-2829
1825 Webster St Dayton (45404) *(G-8205)*
C-Mold Inc 937 981-7797
175 Industrial Park Dr Greenfield (45123) *(G-10474)*
C-N-D Industries Inc 330 478-8811
359 State Ave Nw Massillon (44647) *(G-13118)*
C-Tech Industries LLC 877 755-7311
8950 Global Way West Chester (45069) *(G-19822)*
C.T.L. Steel Division, Columbus *Also called Clark Grave Vault Company* *(G-6933)*
C2g, Moraine *Also called Legrand North America LLC* *(G-14503)*
CA Litzler Co Inc 216 267-8020
4800 W 160th St Cleveland (44135) *(G-4958)*
CA Litzler Holding Company (PA) 216 267-8020
4800 W 160th St Cleveland (44135) *(G-4959)*
CA Picard Surface Engrg Inc 440 366-5400
1206 E Broad St Elyria (44035) *(G-9386)*
Cabell Huntington 740 867-2665
29 Candy Ln Chesapeake (45619) *(G-3185)*
Cabin Creek Golf 330 852-4879
1361 County Road 108 Sugarcreek (44681) *(G-18018)*
Cabinet 2 Countertops, North Canton *Also called Navigator Construction LLC* *(G-15254)*
Cabinet Concepts Inc 440 232-4644
590 Golden Oak Pkwy B Cleveland (44146) *(G-4960)*
Cabinet Guys, The, Columbus *Also called Bison Builders LLC* *(G-6832)*
Cabinet Restylers, Ashland *Also called Thiels Replacement Systems Inc* *(G-781)*
Cabinet Solutions By Design, Cincinnati *Also called Brower Products Inc* *(G-3482)*
Cabinet Source 330 336-5600
8100 Wadsworth Rd Wadsworth (44281) *(G-19397)*
Cabinet Specialties Inc 330 695-3463
10738 Criswell Rd Fredericksburg (44627) *(G-10079)*
Cabinet Studio, Bedford *Also called Barta Viorel* *(G-1403)*
Cabinet Systems Inc 440 237-1924
9830 York Theta Dr Cleveland (44133) *(G-4961)*
Cabinet Works, Columbus *Also called Cabintpak Kitchens of Columbus* *(G-6886)*
Cabinetry By Ebbing 419 678-2191
5765 State Route 219 Celina (45822) *(G-2988)*
Cabinets Inc 740 377-4629
904 4th St E South Point (45680) *(G-17435)*
Cabintpak Kitchens of Columbus 614 294-4646
899 King Ave Columbus (43212) *(G-6886)*
Cable and Ctrl Solutions LLC 937 254-2227
4726 Springfield St Dayton (45431) *(G-8097)*
Cable Mfg & Assembly Inc (PA) 330 874-2900
10896 Industrial Pkwy Nw Bolivar (44612) *(G-1929)*
Cable Quest, Twinsburg *Also called Go2 Partners Inc* *(G-18949)*
Cabletek Wiring Products Inc 800 562-9378
1150 Taylor St Elyria (44035) *(G-9387)*
Cabot Lumber Inc 740 545-7109
304 E Union Ave West Lafayette (43845) *(G-20085)*
Cac Energy Ltd 937 867-5593
1025 N Main St Dayton (45405) *(G-8206)*
Cad Audio LLC 440 349-4900
6573 Cochran Rd Ste I Solon (44139) *(G-17275)*
Cadbury Schweppes Bottling 614 238-0469
950 Stelzer Rd Columbus (43219) *(G-6887)*
Cadenza Enterprises LLC 937 428-6058
6533 Halberd Ct Dayton (45459) *(G-8207)*
Cadillac Papers, Hamilton *Also called Gvs Industries Inc* *(G-10699)*
Cadillac Products Inc 248 813-8255
265 S West St Lebanon (45036) *(G-11786)*
Cado Door & Design Inc 330 343-4288
5964 Main St Se New Philadelphia (44663) *(G-14889)*
Cado Woodworking, New Philadelphia *Also called Cado Door & Design Inc* *(G-14889)*
Cae Ransohoff Inc 513 870-0100
4933 Provident Dr West Chester (45246) *(G-19986)*
Caesarcreek Pallets Ltd 937 416-4447
4392 Shawnee Trl Jamestown (45335) *(G-11351)*
Cafco Filter, Cincinnati *Also called Cincinnati A Filter Sls Svc Inc* *(G-3536)*

Cage Gear & Machine LLC 330 452-1532
1776 Gateway Blvd Se Canton (44707) *(G-2633)*
Cages By Jim, Cleveland *Also called Precision Wire Products Inc* *(G-6038)*
Cahill Services Inc 216 410-5595
13000 Athens Ave Ste 104e Lakewood (44107) *(G-11659)*
Cailin Dev Ltd Lblty Co 216 408-6261
8960 70th St Cleveland (44102) *(G-4962)*
Cake Arts Supplies 419 472-4959
2858 W Sylvania Ave Toledo (43613) *(G-18387)*
Cake Arts Supplies & Bakery, Toledo *Also called Cake Arts Supplies* *(G-18387)*
Cake LLC 614 592-7681
6724 Perimeter Loop Rd # 254 Dublin (43017) *(G-9056)*
Cal Sales Embroidery 440 236-3820
13975 Station Rd Columbia Station (44028) *(G-6582)*
Cal-Maine Foods Inc 937 337-9576
3078 Washington Rd Rossburg (45362) *(G-16735)*
Cal-Maine Foods Inc 937 968-4874
1039 Zumbrum Rd Union City (45390) *(G-19069)*
Calcol Inc 216 245-6301
23425 Bryden Rd Shaker Heights (44122) *(G-17086)*
Caldwell Lumber & Supply Co 740 732-2306
17990 Woodsfield Rd Caldwell (43724) *(G-2425)*
Caldwell Redi Mix Company (PA) 740 732-2906
45997 Marietta Rd Caldwell (43724) *(G-2426)*
Caldwell Redi Mix Company 740 685-6554
209 Pioneer Rd Byesville (43723) *(G-2395)*
Caldwell Redi-Mix Concrete, Caldwell *Also called Caldwell Redi Mix Company* *(G-2426)*
Calgon Carbon Corporation 614 258-9501
835 N Cassady Ave Columbus (43219) *(G-6888)*
Caliber Mold and Machine Inc 330 633-8171
1461 Industrial Pkwy Akron (44310) *(G-107)*
California Ceramic Supply Co 216 531-9185
19451 Roseland Ave Ste A Euclid (44117) *(G-9569)*
California Grounds Care LLC 513 207-0244
5827 Berte St Cincinnati (45230) *(G-3494)*
Call & Post, Cleveland *Also called King Media Enterprises Inc* *(G-5654)*
Callahan Cutting Tools Inc 614 294-1649
915 Distribution Dr Ste A Columbus (43228) *(G-6889)*
Callcopy Inc (HQ) 614 340-3346
555 S Front St Columbus (43215) *(G-6890)*
Callender Group, The, Mentor *Also called Lake Publishing Inc* *(G-13628)*
Calm, Fairlawn *Also called Collaborative For Adaptive Lif* *(G-9746)*
Calmego Specialized Pdts LLC 937 669-5620
1569 Martindale Rd Greenville (45331) *(G-10491)*
Calphalon Corporation 419 666-8700
3rd St & D St Rossford (43460) *(G-16737)*
Calvary Christian Ch of Ohio 740 828-9000
338 W 3rd St Frazeysburg (43822) *(G-10071)*
Calvary Industries Inc (PA) 513 874-1113
9233 Seward Rd Fairfield (45014) *(G-9649)*
Calvin J Magsig 419 862-3311
343 Clinton St Elmore (43416) *(G-9361)*
Calvin Lanier 937 952-4221
5363 Birdland Ave Dayton (45417) *(G-8208)*
CAM Co Inc (PA) 740 922-4533
6270 Wolf Run Rd Se Dennison (44621) *(G-8943)*
CAM Machine Inc 937 663-0680
3833 State Route 235 N Saint Paris (43072) *(G-16861)*
CAM-Lem Inc 216 391-7750
1768 E 25th St Cleveland (44114) *(G-4963)*
Camaco LLC 440 288-4444
3400 River Indus Pk Rd Lorain (44052) *(G-12236)*
Camaco Lorain, Lorain *Also called Camaco LLC* *(G-12236)*
Camargo Construction, Cincinnati *Also called Adler & Company Inc* *(G-3356)*
Camargo Phrm Svcs LLC (PA) 513 561-3329
9825 Kenwood Rd Ste 203 Blue Ash (45242) *(G-1761)*
Camargo Publications Inc 513 779-7177
7270 N Mingo Ln Cincinnati (45243) *(G-3495)*
Cambridge Box & Gift Shop, Cambridge *Also called Cambridge Packaging Inc* *(G-2449)*
Cambridge Cable Service Co 740 685-5775
58945 Country Club Rd Byesville (43723) *(G-2396)*
Cambridge Jewelers, Hudson *Also called Cambridge Mfg Jewelers* *(G-11162)*
Cambridge Mfg Jewelers 330 528-0207
76 Maple Dr Ste 1 Hudson (44236) *(G-11162)*
Cambridge Mill Products Inc 330 863-1121
6005 Alliance Rd Nw Malvern (44644) *(G-12539)*
Cambridge Ohio Production & As 740 432-6383
1521 Morton Ave Cambridge (43725) *(G-2448)*
Cambridge Packaging Inc 740 432-3351
60794 Southgate Rd Cambridge (43725) *(G-2449)*
Camden Concrete Products 937 456-1229
4952 State Route 732 W Eaton (45320) *(G-9302)*
Camden Ready Mix, West Alexandria *Also called Wysong Gravel Co Inc* *(G-19787)*
Camden Ready Mix Co (PA) 937 456-4539
478 Cmden Cllege Cornr Rd Camden (45311) *(G-2484)*
Cameco Communications 937 840-9490
128 S High St Hillsboro (45133) *(G-10997)*
Camela Nitschke Ribbonry 419 872-0073
119 Louisiana Ave Perrysburg (43551) *(G-16073)*

Camelot Cellars Winery 614 441-8860
  901 Oak St Columbus (43205) *(G-6891)*
Camelot Manufacturing Inc 419 678-2603
  210 Butler St Coldwater (45828) *(G-6554)*
Camelot Printing, Lodi *Also called Stephen Andrews Inc (G-12170)*
Camelot Typesetting Company 216 574-8973
  2570 Superior Ave E # 201 Cleveland (44114) *(G-4964)*
Cameo Countertops Inc (PA) 419 865-6371
  1610 Kieswetter Rd Holland (43528) *(G-11048)*
Cameo Inc 419 661-9611
  995 3rd St Perrysburg (43551) *(G-16074)*
Cameron Drilling Co Inc 740 453-3300
  3636 Adamsville Rd Zanesville (43701) *(G-21285)*
Cameron International Corp 740 397-4888
  8043 Columbus Rd Mount Vernon (43050) *(G-14611)*
Cameron International Corp 740 654-4260
  471 Quarry Rd Se Lancaster (43130) *(G-11695)*
Cameron Packaging Inc 419 222-9404
  250 E Hanthorn Rd Lima (45804) *(G-11999)*
Camfil Farr, Piqua *Also called Camfil USA Inc (G-16255)*
Camfil USA Inc 937 773-0866
  405 Fox Dr Piqua (45356) *(G-16255)*
Cammann Inc 440 965-4051
  7105 State Rte 60 Birmingham (44816) *(G-1685)*
Cammel Saw Company Inc 330 477-3764
  4898 Hills & Dales Rd Nw Canton (44708) *(G-2634)*
Campbell Group, Harrison *Also called Campbell Hausfeld LLC (G-10770)*
Campbell Hausfeld LLC (HQ) 513 367-4811
  100 Production Dr Harrison (45030) *(G-10770)*
Campbell Signs & Apparel LLC 330 386-4768
  47366 Y And O Rd East Liverpool (43920) *(G-9205)*
Campbell Soup Company 419 592-1010
  110 E Maumee Ave Napoleon (43545) *(G-14674)*
Campbells Candies 330 493-1805
  3074 Chaucer Dr Ne Canton (44721) *(G-2635)*
Camphire Drilling Inc 740 599-6928
  8 Ross St Danville (43014) *(G-8085)*
Campton Electric Sales & Svc 740 826-4429
  11615 Norfield Rd New Concord (43762) *(G-14816)*
Cams, Powell *Also called Columbus Advanced Mfg Sftwr (G-16467)*
Camslide South, Ridgeville Corners *Also called Magna International Amer Inc (G-16665)*
Camton Mechanical Inc 614 864-7620
  4531 Ellery Dr Columbus (43227) *(G-6892)*
Canaan Country Meats 330 435-4778
  11970 Canaan Center Rd Creston (44217) *(G-7938)*
Canadus Power Systems LLC 216 831-6600
  9347 Ravenna Rd Ste A Twinsburg (44087) *(G-18907)*
Canal Dover Furniture LLC 330 359-5375
  8211 Township Road 652 Millersburg (44654) *(G-14210)*
Canal Winchester Facility, Canal Winchester *Also called Nifco America Corporation (G-2533)*
Canberra Corporation 419 724-4300
  3610 N Hlland Sylvania Rd Toledo (43615) *(G-18388)*
Candle Cottage 937 526-4041
  732 E Main St Versailles (45380) *(G-19343)*
Candle-Lite Company LLC 937 780-2711
  250 Eastern Ave Leesburg (45135) *(G-11850)*
Candle-Lite Company LLC (HQ) 513 563-1113
  10521 Millington Ct Ste B Blue Ash (45242) *(G-1762)*
Candles By Joyce 740 886-6355
  343 Township Road 1233 Proctorville (45669) *(G-16489)*
Candy Bar, Put In Bay *Also called Gift Cove Inc (G-16498)*
Candy Print Shop 937 390-6458
  4560 Mumper Rd Springfield (45502) *(G-17526)*
Canfield Coating LLC 330 533-3311
  460 W Main St Canfield (44406) *(G-2550)*
Canfield Industrial Park, Canfield *Also called Afc Company (G-2545)*
Canfield Industries Inc (PA) 800 554-5071
  8510 Foxwood Ct Youngstown (44514) *(G-21042)*
Canfield Manufacturing Co Inc 330 533-3333
  489 Rosemont Rd North Jackson (44451) *(G-15289)*
Canfield Metal Coating Corp 330 702-3876
  460 W Main St Canfield (44406) *(G-2551)*
Canine Creations 937 667-8576
  120b W Broadway St A Tipp City (45371) *(G-18269)*
Cannon Salt & Supply Inc 440 232-1700
  26041 Cannon Rd Bedford (44146) *(G-1410)*
Canron Manufacturing Inc 330 497-1131
  3979 State St Nw Greentown (44630) *(G-10485)*
Cansto Coatings Ltd 216 231-6115
  9320 Woodland Ave Cleveland (44104) *(G-4965)*
Cansto Paint and Varnish Co 216 231-6115
  9320 Woodland Ave Cleveland (44104) *(G-4966)*
Cantelli Block and Brick Inc (PA) 419 433-0102
  1001 Sawmill Pkwy Huron (44839) *(G-11218)*
Cantex Inc 330 995-3665
  11444 Chamberlain Rd 1 Aurora (44202) *(G-912)*
Canton Asphalt Co 330 499-6888
  5947 Whipple Ave Nw Canton (44720) *(G-2636)*

Canton Cabinet Co 330 455-2585
  1415 7th St Nw Canton (44703) *(G-2637)*
Canton Cut Stone Co 330 456-8408
  6570 Promway Ave Nw North Canton (44720) *(G-15223)*
Canton Drop Forge Inc 330 477-4511
  4575 Southway St Sw Canton (44706) *(G-2638)*
Canton Elevator Inc 330 833-3600
  2575 Greensburg Rd North Canton (44720) *(G-15224)*
Canton Fuel 330 455-3400
  1600 30th St Ne Canton (44714) *(G-2639)*
Canton Gear Mfg Design Co Inc 330 455-2771
  1600 Tuscarawas St E Canton (44707) *(G-2640)*
Canton Graphic Arts Service 330 456-9868
  800 Cleveland Ave Sw Canton (44702) *(G-2641)*
Canton Hot Rolled Plant, Canton *Also called Republic Steel Inc (G-2837)*
Canton OH Rubber Speclty Prods 330 454-3847
  1387 Clarendon Ave Sw Canton (44710) *(G-2642)*
Canton Oil Well Service Inc 330 494-1221
  7793 Pittsburg Ave Nw Canton (44720) *(G-2643)*
Canton Orthotic Laboratory 330 833-0955
  811 12th St Nw Canton (44703) *(G-2644)*
Canton Pattern & Mold Inc 330 455-4316
  914 Sylvan Ct Ne Canton (44705) *(G-2645)*
Canton Pattern and Mold, Canton *Also called Canton Pattern & Mold Inc (G-2645)*
Canton Plating Co Inc 330 452-7808
  903 9th St Ne Canton (44704) *(G-2646)*
Canton Sign Co 330 456-7151
  222 5th St Ne Canton (44702) *(G-2647)*
Canton Sterilized Wiping Cloth 330 455-5179
  1401 Waynesburg Dr Se Canton (44707) *(G-2648)*
Cantrell Rfinery Sls Trnsp Inc 937 695-0318
  18856 State Route 136 Winchester (45697) *(G-20691)*
Canvas 123 Inc 312 805-0563
  277 Oak Grove Dr Akron (44319) *(G-108)*
Canvas Exchange Inc 216 749-2233
  2330 Denison Ave Cleveland (44109) *(G-4967)*
Canvas Products Co 440 232-8716
  634 Golden Oak Pkwy Bedford (44146) *(G-1411)*
Canvas Salon and Skin Bar 614 336-3942
  3893 Powell Rd Powell (43065) *(G-16465)*
Canvas Specialty Mfg Co 216 881-0647
  4045 Saint Clair Ave Cleveland (44103) *(G-4968)*
Canyon Run Engineering, Troy *Also called Slimline Surgical Devices LLC (G-18876)*
Cap & Associates Incorporated 614 863-3363
  445 Mccormick Blvd Columbus (43213) *(G-6893)*
Cap City Direct LLC 614 252-6245
  3203 E 11th Ave Columbus (43219) *(G-6894)*
Cap Data Supply Inc 216 252-2280
  15227 Triskett Rd Cleveland (44111) *(G-4969)*
Capehart Enterprises LLC 614 769-7746
  1724 Northwest Blvd B1 Columbus (43212) *(G-6895)*
Capital Chemical Co 330 494-9535
  5340 Mayfair Rd Canton (44720) *(G-2649)*
Capital City Aviation Inc 614 459-2541
  2160 West Case Rd Unit 15 Columbus (43235) *(G-6896)*
Capital City Awning Company 614 221-5404
  577 N 4th St Columbus (43215) *(G-6897)*
Capital City Energy Group Inc 614 485-3110
  1335 Dublin Rd Ste 122d Columbus (43215) *(G-6898)*
Capital City Oil Inc 740 397-4483
  375 Columbus Rd Mount Vernon (43050) *(G-14612)*
Capital Connection Cabling 330 620-6311
  1368 Crestview Ave Akron (44320) *(G-109)*
Capital Core Inc 800 223-1884
  1025 N Keowee St Dayton (45404) *(G-8209)*
Capital Engraving Company 440 237-7760
  11963 Abbey Rd Cleveland (44133) *(G-4970)*
Capital Machine & Fabrication 740 773-4976
  162 Commercial Cir Chillicothe (45601) *(G-3231)*
Capital Office Supply, Columbus *Also called Dewitt Group Inc (G-7024)*
Capital Oil & Gas Inc 330 533-1828
  6075 Silica Rd Austintown (44515) *(G-971)*
Capital Precision Machine & Tl 937 258-1176
  1865 Radio Rd Dayton (45431) *(G-8098)*
Capital Prosthetic & (PA) 614 451-0446
  4678 Larwell Dr Columbus (43220) *(G-6899)*
Capital Prosthetic & 567 560-2051
  271 Cline Ave Ste 3 Mansfield (44907) *(G-12574)*
Capital Prosthetic & 740 453-9545
  4035 Northpointe Dr A Zanesville (43701) *(G-21286)*
Capital Prosthetic & 614 451-0446
  4678 Larwell Dr Columbus (43220) *(G-6900)*
Capital Prosthetic & 740 522-3331
  55 S Terrace Ave Newark (43055) *(G-14991)*
Capital Prsthetic Orthotic Ctr, Newark *Also called Capital Prosthetic & (G-14991)*
Capital Resin Corporation 614 445-7177
  324 Dering Ave Columbus (43207) *(G-6901)*
Capital Spring, Columbus *Also called Matthew Warren Inc (G-7326)*
Capital Toe Grinding, Columbus *Also called HI Lite Plastic Products (G-7154)*

A
L
P
H
A
B
E
T
I
C

Capital Tool Company.....216 661-5750
1110 Brookpark Rd Cleveland (44109) ***(G-4971)***
Capital Tool Grinding Co, Columbus *Also called Bartley Offie* ***(G-6811)***
Capital Track Company Inc.....614 595-5088
1364 Cardwell Sq S Columbus (43229) ***(G-6902)***
Capitol Aluminum & Glass Corp.....800 331-8268
1276 W Main St Bellevue (44811) ***(G-1548)***
Capitol Citicom Inc.....614 472-2679
2225 Citygate Dr Ste A Columbus (43219) ***(G-6903)***
Capitol City Mfg Co Inc.....614 491-1192
3881 Groveport Rd Obetz (43207) ***(G-15650)***
Capitol City Trailers Inc.....614 491-2616
3960 Groveport Rd Obetz (43207) ***(G-15651)***
Capozzolo Printers Inc.....513 542-7874
4000 Hamilton Ave Cincinnati (45223) ***(G-3496)***
Caps.....216 524-0418
8300 Sweet Valley Dr # 301 Cleveland (44125) ***(G-4972)***
Capsa Solutions LLC.....614 864-9966
8170 Dove Pkwy Canal Winchester (43110) ***(G-2521)***
Capt, Celina *Also called Celina Alum Precision Tech Inc* ***(G-2989)***
Captor Corporation.....937 667-8484
5040 S County Road 25a Tipp City (45371) ***(G-18270)***
Car-Nation Inc.....330 862-9001
1216 Fox Ave Se Paris (44669) ***(G-15949)***
Carat Patch, The, Newark *Also called Stephen R White* ***(G-15057)***
Caraustar Industrial and Con.....330 868-4111
460 Knox Ct Minerva (44657) ***(G-14318)***
Caraustar Industries Inc.....216 961-5060
3400 Vega Ave Cleveland (44113) ***(G-4973)***
Caraustar Industries Inc.....513 871-7112
5500 Wooster Pike Cincinnati (45226) ***(G-3497)***
Caraustar Industries Inc.....330 665-7700
202 Montrose West Ave # 315 Copley (44321) ***(G-7841)***
Caraustar Industries Inc.....740 862-4167
310 W Water St Baltimore (43105) ***(G-1081)***
Caravan Packaging Inc (PA).....440 243-4100
6427 Eastland Rd Cleveland (44142) ***(G-4974)***
Caravan Protective Cases, Elyria *Also called Hawthorne Caravan & Assoc LLC* ***(G-9428)***
Carbide Probes Inc.....937 490-2994
1328 Research Park Dr Beavercreek (45432) ***(G-1322)***
Carbide Specialist Inc.....440 951-4027
36430 Reading Ave Ste 10 Willoughby (44094) ***(G-20452)***
Carbo Forge Inc.....419 334-9788
150 State Route 523 Fremont (43420) ***(G-10134)***
Carbogene USA LLC.....215 378-4306
2252 Sedgwick Dr Columbus (43220) ***(G-6904)***
Carboline Company.....513 896-1919
3905 Port Union Rd Ste B Fairfield (45014) ***(G-9650)***
Carboline Company.....800 848-4645
2379 Miramar Blvd University Heights (44118) ***(G-19107)***
Carbon Group, The, Solon *Also called Carlisle Brake & Friction Inc* ***(G-17276)***
Carbon Products, West Chester *Also called Graphel Corporation* ***(G-19879)***
Carbonless & Cut Sheet Forms.....740 826-1700
1948 John Glenn Hwy New Concord (43762) ***(G-14817)***
Carbonless On Demandcom.....330 837-8611
332 Erie St S Massillon (44646) ***(G-13119)***
Carbros.....330 375-5000
101 W Emerling Ave Akron (44301) ***(G-110)***
Carden Door Company LLC.....513 459-2233
1224 Castle Dr Mason (45040) ***(G-12990)***
Cardiac Analytics LLC.....614 314-1332
5683 Liberty Rd N Powell (43065) ***(G-16466)***
Cardiac Arrhythmia Associates.....330 759-8169
3622 Belmont Ave Ste 1112 Youngstown (44505) ***(G-21043)***
Cardinal Aggregate.....419 872-4380
8026 Fremont Pike Perrysburg (43551) ***(G-16075)***
Cardinal Builders Inc.....614 237-1000
4409 E Main St Columbus (43213) ***(G-6905)***
Cardinal CT Company.....740 892-2324
140 Carey St Utica (43080) ***(G-19192)***
Cardinal Custom Cabinets Ltd.....216 281-1570
8201 Almira Ave Ste 10 Cleveland (44102) ***(G-4975)***
Cardinal Energy Group Inc (PA).....325 762-2112
2665 Fairfax Dr Upper Arlington (43220) ***(G-19111)***
Cardinal Fstener Specialty Inc.....216 831-3800
5185 Richmond Rd Bedford Heights (44146) ***(G-1479)***
Cardinal Health Inc (PA).....614 757-5000
7000 Cardinal Pl Dublin (43017) ***(G-9057)***
Cardinal Health 414 LLC (HQ).....614 757-5000
7000 Cardinal Pl Dublin (43017) ***(G-9058)***
Cardinal Health 414 LLC.....614 473-0786
2215 Citygate Dr Ste D Columbus (43219) ***(G-6906)***
Cardinal Health 414 LLC.....513 759-1900
9866 Windisch Rd Bldg 3 West Chester (45069) ***(G-19823)***
Cardinal Health Tech LLC (HQ).....614 757-5000
7000 Cardinal Pl Dublin (43017) ***(G-9059)***
Cardinal Machine Company.....440 238-7050
14459 Foltz Pkwy Strongsville (44149) ***(G-17899)***
Cardinal Printing Inc.....330 773-7300
112 W Wilbeth Rd Akron (44301) ***(G-111)***
Cardinal Products Inc.....440 237-8280
11929 Abbey Rd Ste D North Royalton (44133) ***(G-15413)***
Cardinal Pumps Exchangers Inc (HQ).....330 332-8558
1425 Quaker Ct Salem (44460) ***(G-16878)***
Cardinal Rubber Company Inc.....330 745-2191
939 Wooster Rd N Barberton (44203) ***(G-1113)***
Cardinal Truss & Components, Edgerton *Also called Building Concepts Inc* ***(G-9326)***
Cardinal Welding Inc.....330 426-2404
895 E Taggart St East Palestine (44413) ***(G-9229)***
Cardington Yutaka Tech Inc (HQ).....419 864-8777
575 W Main St Cardington (43315) ***(G-2909)***
Cardioinsight Technologies Inc.....216 274-2221
11000 Cedar Ave Ste 210 Cleveland (44106) ***(G-4976)***
Cardpak, Solon *Also called Rohrer Corporation* ***(G-17371)***
Care Cabinetry Inc.....216 481-7445
1410 Chardon Rd Frnt Euclid (44117) ***(G-9570)***
Careless Heart Enterprises (PA).....740 654-9999
600 N Columbus St Lancaster (43130) ***(G-11696)***
Carenection LLC.....614 468-6045
1103 Schrock Rd Ste 205 Columbus (43229) ***(G-6907)***
Carepoint Partners, Canfield *Also called Molorokalin Inc* ***(G-2566)***
Carey Color Inc.....330 239-1835
6835 Ridge Rd Sharon Center (44274) ***(G-17103)***
Carey Color Inc /cincinnati.....513 241-5210
1718 Central Pkwy Cincinnati (45214) ***(G-3498)***
Carey Color Llc/Cincinnati.....513 241-5210
1718 Central Pkwy Cincinnati (45214) ***(G-3499)***
Carey Precast Concrete Company.....419 396-7142
3420 Township Highway 98 Carey (43316) ***(G-2915)***
Cargill Incorporated.....330 745-0031
2065 Manchester Rd Akron (44314) ***(G-112)***
Cargill Incorporated.....937 236-1971
3201 Needmore Rd Dayton (45414) ***(G-8210)***
Cargill Incorporated.....513 941-7400
5204 River Rd Cincinnati (45233) ***(G-3500)***
Cargill Incorporated.....937 498-4555
2400 Industrial Dr Sidney (45365) ***(G-17170)***
Cargill Incorporated.....216 651-7200
2400 Ships Channel Cleveland (44113) ***(G-4977)***
Cargill Incorporated.....513 625-2863
1976 Woodville Pike Goshen (45122) ***(G-10413)***
Carhartt Inc.....513 657-7130
2685 Edmondson Rd Cincinnati (45209) ***(G-3501)***
Carhoff, Cleveland *Also called L-Mor Inc* ***(G-5672)***
Caring Things Inc.....614 749-9084
435 W State St Columbus (43215) ***(G-6908)***
Carl C Andre Inc.....614 864-0123
2894 Brice Rd Brice (43109) ***(G-2087)***
Carl E Oeder Sons Sand & Grav.....513 494-1555
1000 Mason Morrow Rd Lebanon (45036) ***(G-11787)***
Carl Graphics Company.....740 382-6583
600 Bellefontaine Ave Marion (43302) ***(G-12861)***
Carl Graphics Printing, Marion *Also called Carl Graphics Company* ***(G-12861)***
Carl Hucke.....419 396-6078
5239 State Highway 199 Carey (43316) ***(G-2916)***
Carl Rittberger Sr Inc.....740 452-2767
1900 Lutz Ln Zanesville (43701) ***(G-21287)***
Carlas Cake Pops Cnfctions LLC.....614 321-9280
1561 Old Leonard Ave Columbus (43219) ***(G-6909)***
Carlisle and Finch Company.....513 681-6080
4562 W Mitchell Ave Cincinnati (45232) ***(G-3502)***
Carlisle Brake & Friction Inc.....440 528-4000
29001 Solon Rd Solon (44139) ***(G-17276)***
Carlisle Brake & Friction Inc.....330 725-4941
920 Lake Rd Medina (44256) ***(G-13385)***
Carlisle Brake & Friction Inc (HQ).....440 528-4000
6180 Cochran Rd Solon (44139) ***(G-17277)***
Carlisle Fluid Tech Inc.....419 470-2000
320 Phillips Ave Toledo (43612) ***(G-18389)***
Carlisle Oak.....330 852-8734
3872 Township Road 162 Sugarcreek (44681) ***(G-18019)***
Carlisle Plastics Company Inc.....937 845-9411
320 Ohio St New Carlisle (45344) ***(G-14798)***
Carlisle Prtg Walnut Creek Ltd.....330 852-9922
2673 Township Road 421 Sugarcreek (44681) ***(G-18020)***
Carlson Aircraft Inc.....330 426-3934
51028 State Route 14 East Palestine (44413) ***(G-9230)***
Carlton Natco.....216 451-5588
13020 Saint Clair Ave Cleveland (44108) ***(G-4978)***
Carlton Oil Corp.....740 473-2629
961 Greene St Newport (45768) ***(G-15126)***
Carlton-Bates Company.....937 384-0426
4900 Lyons Rd Unit B Miamisburg (45342) ***(G-13789)***
Carly Co LLC.....937 477-6411
235 N Main St Centerville (45459) ***(G-3038)***
Carmel Trader Publishing Inc.....330 478-9200
4501 Hills & Dales Rd Nw Canton (44708) ***(G-2650)***
Carmens Cstm Wndows Treatments, Cleveland *Also called Carmens Installation Co* ***(G-4979)***

Carmens Installation Co 216 371-5633
2865 Mayfield Rd Cleveland (44118) *(G-4979)*
Carmeuse Lime Inc....216 961-1010
5400 Whiskey Is Cleveland (44102) *(G-4980)*
Carmeuse Lime Inc....419 638-2511
3964 County Road 41 Millersville (43435) *(G-14300)*
Carmeuse Lime Inc....419 986-2000
1967 W County Rd 42 Tiffin (44883) *(G-18214)*
Carmeuse Lime Inc....419 986-5200
1967 W County Rd 42 Bettsville (44815) *(G-1668)*
Carmeuse Lime & Stone, Millersville *Also called Carmeuse Lime Inc (G-14300)*
Carmeuse Natural Chemicals, Bettsville *Also called Carmeuse Lime Inc (G-1668)*
Carnation Elc Mtr Repr Sls Inc 330 823-7116
232 N Lincoln Ave Alliance (44601) *(G-501)*
Carnation Machine & Tool Inc 330 823-5352
14632 Oyster Rd Alliance (44601) *(G-502)*
Carnegie Plas Cabinetry Inc....216 451-3300
1755 Coit Ave Cleveland (44112) *(G-4981)*
Carnegie Promotions Inc....440 442-2099
697 Davidson Dr Cleveland (44143) *(G-4982)*
Carney Plastics Inc....330 746-8273
1010 W Rayen Ave Youngstown (44502) *(G-21044)*
Carol J Guiler....614 252-6920
1359 E 5th Ave Columbus (43219) *(G-6910)*
Carol Mickley (PA) 740 599-7870
2 Richard St Danville (43014) *(G-8086)*
Carolex Company Inc....330 386-9529
761 Dresden Ave East Liverpool (43920) *(G-9206)*
Carolina Color Corp Ohio 740 363-6622
100 Colomet Dr Delaware (43015) *(G-8827)*
Carolina Color Corporation 740 363-6622
100 Colomet Dr Delaware (43015) *(G-8828)*
Carolina Stair Supply Inc (PA)....740 922-3333
316 Herrick St Uhrichsville (44683) *(G-19046)*
Carols Ultra Stitch & Variety....419 935-8991
122 S Myrtle Ave Willard (44890) *(G-20393)*
Carolyn Chemical Company....614 252-5000
1601 Woodland Ave Columbus (43219) *(G-6911)*
Caron Products and Svcs Inc....740 373-6809
27640 State Route 7 Marietta (45750) *(G-12770)*
Carousel Carvings, Marion *Also called Todd W Goings (G-12907)*
Carousel Magic LLC....419 522-6456
44 W 4th St Mansfield (44902) *(G-12575)*
Carousel Works Inc....419 522-7558
1285 Pollock Pkwy Mansfield (44905) *(G-12576)*
Carper Well Service Inc....740 374-2567
30745 State Route 7 Marietta (45750) *(G-12771)*
Carquest Auto Parts, Beloit *Also called Jenkins Motor Parts (G-1583)*
Carquest Auto Parts, Westerville *Also called General Parts Inc (G-20215)*
Carr Bros Inc....440 232-3700
7177 Northfield Rd Bedford (44146) *(G-1412)*
Carr Bros Bldrs Sup & Coal Co....440 232-3700
7177 Northfield Rd Cleveland (44146) *(G-4983)*
Carr Supply Co 937 316-6300
900 Sater St Greenville (45331) *(G-10492)*
Carr Supply Co 937 276-2555
4800 Webster St Dayton (45414) *(G-8211)*
Carr Tool Company 513 825-2900
575 Security Dr Fairfield (45014) *(G-9651)*
Carrera Holdings Inc 216 687-1311
101 W Prospect Ave Cleveland (44115) *(G-4984)*
Carrier Corporation 937 275-0645
6050 Milo Rd Dayton (45414) *(G-8212)*
Carrillo Pallets LLC 513 942-2210
1292 Glendale Milford Rd Cincinnati (45215) *(G-3503)*
Carrizo Oil & Gas Inc....740 432-5463
647 Wheeling Ave Cambridge (43725) *(G-2450)*
Carroll Distrg & Cnstr Sup Inc....513 422-3327
6688 Georgetown Ln Middletown (45042) *(G-14026)*
Carroll Distrg & Cnstr Sup Inc....614 564-9799
2929 E 14th Ave Columbus (43219) *(G-6912)*
Carroll Exhibit and Print Svcs....216 361-2325
5150 Prospect Ave Cleveland (44103) *(G-4985)*
Carroll Graphic, Cleveland *Also called Carroll Exhibit and Print Svcs (G-4985)*
Carroll Hills Industries Inc....330 627-5524
540 High St Nw Carrollton (44615) *(G-2953)*
Carrollton Publishing Company....330 627-5591
43 E Main St Carrollton (44615) *(G-2954)*
Carruth Studio Inc (PA)....419 878-3060
1178 Farnsworth Rd Waterville (43566) *(G-19653)*
Carry Grandview Out....614 487-0305
710 Neil Ave Columbus (43215) *(G-6913)*
Cars and Parts Magazine....937 498-0803
911 S Vandemark Rd Sidney (45365) *(G-17171)*
Carson Industries LLC....419 592-2309
1675 Industrial Dr Napoleon (43545) *(G-14675)*
Carson-Saeks Inc (PA) 937 278-5311
2601 Timber Ln Dayton (45414) *(G-8213)*
Carter Drapery Service Inc 419 289-2530
1301 County Road 1356 Ashland (44805) *(G-716)*
Carter Evans Enterprises Inc 614 920-2276
3354 Battee Rd Granville (43023) *(G-10455)*
Carter Machine Company Inc (PA)....419 468-3530
820 Edward St Galion (44833) *(G-10256)*
Carter Manufacturing Co Inc 513 398-7303
4220 State Route 42 Mason (45040) *(G-12991)*
Carter Scott-Browne....513 398-3970
4220 State Route 42 Mason (45040) *(G-12992)*
Carter Woodcraft Center....330 872-6474
3747 State Route 5 Newton Falls (44444) *(G-15130)*
Carter-Jones Lumber Company....330 674-9060
6139 State Route 39 Millersburg (44654) *(G-14211)*
Carter-Jones Lumber Company....440 834-8164
14601 Kinsman Rd Middlefield (44062) *(G-13920)*
Cartessa Corporation....513 738-4477
4825 Cncnnati Brkville Rd Shandon (45063) *(G-17096)*
Carton Service Incorporated (PA) 419 342-5010
101 First Quality Dr Shelby (44875) *(G-17134)*
Cartoon Books Inc....614 224-4487
523 S 4th St Columbus (43206) *(G-6914)*
Cartwright Cnstr H B A C, Cuyahoga Falls *Also called Cartwright Construction Inc (G-7976)*
Cartwright Construction Inc....330 929-3020
4898 Wild Lake Rd Cuyahoga Falls (44224) *(G-7976)*
Caruso Coffee, Brecksville *Also called Pmd Enterprises Inc (G-2070)*
Carved N Stone, Radnor *Also called Carved Stone LLC (G-16505)*
Carved Stone LLC 614 778-9855
3238 N Section Line Rd B7 Radnor (43066) *(G-16505)*
Caryns Cuisine 614 237-4143
155 N Remington Rd Columbus (43209) *(G-6915)*
Cas, Cleves *Also called Consolidatd Analytical Sys Inc (G-6511)*
Cas Data Loggers, Chesterland *Also called Computer Aided Solutions LLC (G-3201)*
Casad Company Inc 419 586-9457
450 S 2nd St Coldwater (45828) *(G-6555)*
Cascade Corporation....937 327-0300
2501 Sheridan Ave Springfield (45505) *(G-17527)*
Cascade Cut Stone....419 422-4341
41 Township Highway 87 Findlay (45839) *(G-9804)*
Cascade Ohio Inc 440 593-5800
1209 Maple Ave Conneaut (44030) *(G-7801)*
Cascade Pattern Company Inc....440 323-4300
519 Ternes Ln Elyria (44035) *(G-9388)*
Cascade Plating Inc....440 366-4931
210 Abbe Rd S Elyria (44035) *(G-9389)*
Cascade Unlimited LLC 440 352-7995
2510 Hale Rd Painesville (44077) *(G-15863)*
Casco Mfg Solutions Inc....513 681-0003
3107 Spring Grove Ave Cincinnati (45225) *(G-3504)*
Case Crafters Inc....937 667-9473
211 S 1st St Tipp City (45371) *(G-18271)*
Case Farms Chicken, Winesburg *Also called Case Farms of Ohio Inc (G-20702)*
Case Farms of Ohio Inc (HQ)....330 359-7141
1818 County Rd 160 Winesburg (44690) *(G-20702)*
Case Farms of Ohio Inc....330 878-7118
1225 Hensel Ave Ne Strasburg (44680) *(G-17822)*
Case Industries Inc....330 963-7717
9043 Dutton Dr Twinsburg (44087) *(G-18908)*
Case Ohio Burial Co (PA)....440 779-1992
1720 Columbus Rd Cleveland (44113) *(G-4986)*
Case Pattern Co Inc....216 531-0744
21691 Tungsten Rd Cleveland (44117) *(G-4987)*
Case Plating Inc....440 288-8304
736 Idaho Ave Lorain (44052) *(G-12237)*
Case Western Reserve Univ 216 368-2574
10900 Euclid Ave Cleveland (44106) *(G-4988)*
Case-Maul Clamps Inc 419 668-6563
69 Northwest St Norwalk (44857) *(G-15529)*
Case-Maul Manufacturing Co 419 524-1061
30 Harker St Mansfield (44903) *(G-12577)*
Casentric LLC....216 233-6300
23700 Fairmount Blvd Shaker Heights (44122) *(G-17087)*
Cashen Builders Supply, Madison *Also called Cashen Inc (G-12497)*
Cashen Inc....440 428-1148
1225 Dock Rd Madison (44057) *(G-12497)*
Caskey's Recreation, Orrville *Also called Caskeys Inc (G-15733)*
Caskeys Inc....330 683-0249
14847 Fosnight Rd Orrville (44667) *(G-15733)*
Caspa Home Page Inc....216 781-0748
1501 N Marginal Rd # 166 Cleveland (44114) *(G-4989)*
Cass Frames Inc....419 468-2863
6052 State Route 19 Galion (44833) *(G-10257)*
Cassady Woodworks Inc....937 256-7948
446 N Smithville Rd Dayton (45431) *(G-8099)*
Casselberry Clinic Inc....440 995-0555
5555 Mayfield Rd Cleveland (44124) *(G-4990)*
Cassis Packaging Co 937 223-8563
1235 Mccook Ave Dayton (45404) *(G-8214)*
Cast Metals Incorporated....419 278-2010
104 W North St Deshler (43516) *(G-8948)*

(PA)=Parent Co (HQ)=Headquarters (DH)=Div Headquarters

Cast Metals Technology Inc (PA) 740 363-1690
550 Liberty Rd Delaware (43015) *(G-8829)*

Cast Plus Inc 937 743-7278
415 Oxford Rd Franklin (45005) *(G-10011)*

Cast Specialties Inc 216 292-7393
26711 Miles Rd Cleveland (44128) *(G-4991)*

Castalia Trenching & Ready Mix 419 684-5502
4814 State Route 269 S Castalia (44824) *(G-2973)*

Castalloy Inc 216 961-7990
7990 Baker Ave Cleveland (44102) *(G-4992)*

Castco Inc 440 365-2333
527 Ternes Ln Elyria (44035) *(G-9390)*

Castek Aluminum Inc 440 365-2333
527 Ternes Ln Elyria (44035) *(G-9391)*

Castelli Marble Inc (PA) 216 361-2410
1521 E 47th St Cleveland (44103) *(G-4993)*

Casting Solutions LLC 740 452-9371
2345 Licking Rd Zanesville (43701) *(G-21288)*

Castings Usa Inc 330 339-3611
2061 Brightwood Rd Se New Philadelphia (44663) *(G-14890)*

Castle Blinds and Draperies, Dayton Also called Custom Blind Corporation *(G-8257)*

Castlebar Corporation 330 451-6511
406 15th St Sw Canton (44707) *(G-2651)*

Castmor Products Inc 440 953-1103
4708 Beidler Rd Willoughby (44094) *(G-20453)*

Castruction Company Inc 330 332-9622
1588 Salem Pkwy Salem (44460) *(G-16879)*

Cat's Meow Village, The, Wooster Also called F J Designs Inc *(G-20771)*

Catalina Tempering - Ohio Inc 740 892-2324
140 Carey St Utica (43080) *(G-19193)*

Catalog Merchandiser Inc 888 325-9677
10525 Chester Rd Ste A Cincinnati (45215) *(G-3505)*

Catania Medallic Specialities, Avon Lake Also called Catania Medallic Specialty *(G-1026)*

Catania Medallic Specialty 440 933-9595
668 Moore Rd Avon Lake (44012) *(G-1026)*

Catawba Canvas Company LLC 419 797-2050
255 Se Catawba Rd Port Clinton (43452) *(G-16395)*

Catawba Island Brewing Co 419 960-7764
2330 East Harbor Rd Port Clinton (43452) *(G-16396)*

Catech Inc 937 439-0432
80 Westpark Rd A Dayton (45459) *(G-8215)*

Cateringstone 513 410-1064
6119 Kenwood Rd Cincinnati (45243) *(G-3506)*

Cathie D Hubbard 937 593-0316
305 E Williams Ave Bellefontaine (43311) *(G-1524)*

Catholic Charity Hispanic Off 216 696-2197
2012 W 25th St Ste 507 Cleveland (44113) *(G-4994)*

Catholic Diocese of Columbus 614 224-5195
197 E Gay St Ste 4 Columbus (43215) *(G-6916)*

Catholic Exponent, Youngstown Also called Roman Cthlic Docese Youngstown *(G-21193)*

Catholic Times, Columbus Also called Catholic Diocese of Columbus *(G-6916)*

Catress LLC 740 695-0918
50482 National Rd E Saint Clairsville (43950) *(G-16784)*

Cats Printing Inc 216 381-8181
3980 Mayfield Rd Cleveland (44121) *(G-4995)*

Cauffiel Corporation (PA) 419 843-7262
3171 N Repub Blvd Ste 102 Toledo (43615) *(G-18390)*

Cavalon Drapery Cleaners, Dayton Also called Willet Enterprises *(G-8758)*

Cave Tool & Manufacturing Inc 937 324-0662
20 Walnut St Springfield (45505) *(G-17528)*

Caven and Sons Meat Packing Co 937 368-3841
7850 E Us Rte 36 Conover (45317) *(G-7822)*

Caxton New Stand 216 861-1600
812 Huron Rd E Fl 1 Cleveland (44115) *(G-4996)*

CB Manufacturing & Sls Co Inc (PA) 937 866-5986
4455 Infirmary Rd Miamisburg (45342) *(G-13790)*

CB Manufacturing & Sls Co Inc. 937 866-5986
4475 Infirmary Rd Dayton (45449) *(G-8216)*

Cbd Media Holdings LLC (HQ) 513 217-9483
312 Plum St Ste 900 Cincinnati (45202) *(G-3507)*

Cbf, Solon Also called Carlisle Brake & Friction Inc *(G-17277)*

Cbg Biotech Ltd Co 440 786-7667
26400 Broadway Ave Ste A Bedford (44146) *(G-1413)*

CBI, West Salem Also called Commodity Blenders Inc *(G-20112)*

Cbl Products 216 321-2599
1661 Cumberland Rd Cleveland (44118) *(G-4997)*

Cbr Industrial Llc 419 645-6447
20086 Wapakoneta Cridersv Wapakoneta (45895) *(G-19483)*

CBs Boring and Mch Co Inc 419 784-9500
2064 E 2nd St Defiance (43512) *(G-8783)*

CBS Pharmacy 740 366-9082
955 N 21st St Newark (43055) *(G-14992)*

CC & Sj of Ohio Inc 614 878-7291
4764 W Broad St Columbus (43228) *(G-6917)*

CC Investors Management Co LLC 740 374-8129
30765 State Route 7 Marietta (45750) *(G-12772)*

CC Ironworks LLC 330 542-0500
10613 Main St New Middletown (44442) *(G-14874)*

CC Pallets LLC 513 442-8766
212 Cambridge Ave Terrace Park (45174) *(G-18179)*

Ccdi, Cincinnati Also called Cincinnati Ctrl Dynamics Inc *(G-3547)*

CCI, Cincinnati Also called Albert Bickel *(G-3375)*

CCL Design, Brunswick Also called CCL Label Inc *(G-2215)*

CCL Design Electronics, Strongsville Also called CCL Label Inc *(G-17900)*

CCL Label Inc 216 676-2703
15939 Industrial Pkwy Cleveland (44135) *(G-4998)*

CCL Label Inc 440 878-7000
2845 Center Rd Brunswick (44212) *(G-2215)*

CCL Label Inc 440 878-7277
17700 Foltz Pkwy Strongsville (44149) *(G-17900)*

CCM Welding Inc 330 630-2521
895 Moe Dr Ste D11 Akron (44310) *(G-113)*

Cconly Inc 614 607-2288
320 London Rd Ste 414 Delaware (43015) *(G-8830)*

Ccp Industries, Richmond Heights Also called Tranzonic Companies *(G-16656)*

Ccsi Inc 800 742-8535
221 Beaver St Akron (44304) *(G-114)*

Cctm Inc 513 934-3533
838 Carson Dr Lebanon (45036) *(G-11788)*

Ccw Group Pacesetter Inc 740 474-0122
Us Highway 23 Circleville (43113) *(G-4624)*

CD / Dvd Distribution, Dayton Also called Chaos Entertainment *(G-8225)*

CD Solutions Inc 937 676-2376
100 W Monument St Pleasant Hill (45359) *(G-16369)*

CDI, Avon Also called Cutting Dynamics Inc *(G-993)*

CDI, Canton Also called Castlebar Corporation *(G-2651)*

CDI 440 249-4178
980 Jaycox Rd Avon (44011) *(G-988)*

CDI Industries Inc 440 243-1100
6800 Lake Abrams Dr Cleveland (44130) *(G-4999)*

Cdmc, Cleveland Also called Cleveland Deburring Machine Co *(G-5057)*

Cdracks.com, Xenia Also called The Wood Shed *(G-20979)*

Cds Signs 513 563-7446
11024 Reading Rd Cincinnati (45241) *(G-3508)*

CEC Electronics Corp 330 916-8100
1739 Akron Peninsula Rd Akron (44313) *(G-115)*

Cecil C Peck Co 330 785-0781
1029 Arlington Cir Akron (44306) *(G-116)*

Cecil Caudill Trailer Sls Inc 740 574-0704
6679 Gallia Pike Franklin Furnace (45629) *(G-10067)*

Ceco Environmental Corp 513 458-2606
6245 Creek Rd Blue Ash (45242) *(G-1763)*

Ceco Environmental Corp 513 874-8915
9759 Inter Ocean Dr West Chester (45246) *(G-19987)*

Ceco Environmental Corp (PA) 513 458-2600
4625 Red Bank Rd Ste 200 Cincinnati (45227) *(G-3509)*

Ceco Equipment Company, Akron Also called Custom Enclosures Corp *(G-137)*

Ceco Group Inc (HQ) 513 458-2600
4625 Red Bank Rd Ste 200 Cincinnati (45227) *(G-3510)*

Ceco Machine & Tool 937 264-3047
5727 Webster St Dayton (45414) *(G-8217)*

Cedar America, Grove City Also called Woodcor America Inc *(G-10610)*

Cedar Chest 937 878-9097
405 W Main St Fairborn (45324) *(G-9616)*

Cedar Craft Products Inc 614 759-1600
776 Reynldsbrg New Albany Blacklick (43004) *(G-1692)*

Cedar Elec Holdings Corp (PA) 513 870-8500
5440 W Chester Rd West Chester (45069) *(G-19824)*

Cedar Outdoor Furniture Inc 330 863-2580
8229 Old Canal Ln Nw Malvern (44644) *(G-12540)*

Cedar Point Laundry 419 627-2274
1 Cedar Point Dr Sandusky (44870) *(G-16953)*

Cedar Woodworking, Delaware Also called Cedee Cedar Inc *(G-8831)*

Cedarville Quarry, Cedarville Also called Martin Marietta Materials Inc *(G-2982)*

Cedee Cedar Inc (PA) 740 363-3148
3903 Us Highway 42 S Delaware (43015) *(G-8831)*

Ceemco Incorporated 513 563-8822
3330 E Kemper Rd Cincinnati (45241) *(G-3511)*

Ceen, Toledo Also called Ames Development Group Ltd *(G-18347)*

Ceia Usa Ltd 330 405-3190
9155 Dutton Dr Twinsburg (44087) *(G-18909)*

Ceja Publishing 216 319-0268
3654 Atherstone Rd Cleveland (44121) *(G-5000)*

Celcore Inc (PA) 440 234-7888
7850 Freeway Cir Ste 100 Cleveland (44130) *(G-5001)*

Celebrations 419 381-8088
2910 Glanzman Rd Unit 1 Toledo (43614) *(G-18391)*

Celebrations Monogramming, Cleveland Also called Kathy Simecek *(G-5635)*

Celina Alum Precision Tech Inc 419 586-2278
7059 Staeger Rd Celina (45822) *(G-2989)*

Celina Industries, Celina Also called Celina Tent Inc *(G-2990)*

Celina Tent Inc 419 586-3610
5373 State Route 29 Celina (45822) *(G-2990)*

Cell 4less, Lima Also called Airwave Communications Cons *(G-11984)*

(G-0000) Company's Geographic Section entry number

Cell-O-Core Co 330 239-4370
  6935 Ridge Rd Sharon Center (44274) *(G-17104)*

Cellular Technology Limited 216 791-5084
  20521 Chagrin Blvd # 200 Shaker Heights (44122) *(G-17088)*

Celstar Group Inc (PA) 937 224-1730
  40 N Main St Ste 1730 Dayton (45423) *(G-8218)*

Celsus Laboratories Inc 513 772-8130
  12150 Best Pl Cincinnati (45241) *(G-3512)*

Celtic Forms, Cincinnati *Also called National Adhesives Inc (G-4138)*

Cem - Fairborn Plant, Xenia *Also called Cemex Cnstr Mtls ATL LLC (G-20941)*

Cement Products Inc 419 524-4342
  389 Park Ave E Mansfield (44905) *(G-12578)*

Cemex Cnstr Mtls ATL LLC 937 878-8651
  3250 Linebaugh Rd Xenia (45385) *(G-20941)*

Cemex Materials LLC 937 268-6706
  1504 N Gettysburg Ave Dayton (45417) *(G-8219)*

Cemex Materials LLC 937 268-6706
  4385 N James H Mcgee Blvd Dayton (45417) *(G-8220)*

Cemex USA Inc 937 879-8350
  2600 Paramount Pl Fairborn (45324) *(G-9617)*

Cen-Trol Machine Co 216 524-1932
  7601 Commerce Park Oval Cleveland (44131) *(G-5002)*

Cengage Learning Inc 513 234-5967
  770 Broadway Mason (45040) *(G-12993)*

Censtar Coatings Inc 330 723-8000
  11829 Jeffrey Rd West Salem (44287) *(G-20111)*

Centaur Inc (PA) 419 469-8000
  2401 Front St Toledo (43605) *(G-18392)*

Centaur Tool & Die Inc 419 352-7704
  2019 Wood Bridge Blvd Bowling Green (43402) *(G-1976)*

Centec Cast Metal Products 419 355-1414
  501 Knapp St Fremont (43420) *(G-10135)*

Centennial Screen Printing 419 422-5548
  1785 S Romick Pkwy Findlay (45840) *(G-9805)*

Center Automotive Parts Co 330 434-2174
  274 E South St Akron (44311) *(G-117)*

Center For Excptonal Practices 330 523-5240
  3404 Brecksville Rd Richfield (44286) *(G-16617)*

Center For Inquiry Inc 330 671-7192
  6413 Riverview Rd Peninsula (44264) *(G-16035)*

Center Line Drilling Inc 440 951-5920
  33000 Lakeland Blvd Willoughby (44095) *(G-20454)*

Center Line Machining LLC 216 289-6828
  25700 Lakeland Blvd Euclid (44132) *(G-9571)*

Center Mass Ammo LLC 440 796-6207
  6642 Middle Ridge Rd Madison (44057) *(G-12498)*

Centerless Grinding Service 216 251-4100
  19500 S Miles Rd Cleveland (44128) *(G-5003)*

Centerless Grinding Solutions 216 520-4612
  7670 Hub Pkwy Cleveland (44125) *(G-5004)*

Centerline Machine Inc 937 322-4887
  4949 Urbana Rd Springfield (45502) *(G-17529)*

Centerline Tool & Machine 937 222-3600
  1330 E 2nd St Dayton (45403) *(G-8221)*

Centerra Co-Op (PA) 419 281-2153
  813 Clark Ave Ashland (44805) *(G-717)*

Centerra Co-Op 800 362-9598
  135 E Walnut St Jefferson (44047) *(G-11358)*

Centerra Co-Op 330 769-3469
  16 Market St Seville (44273) *(G-17072)*

Centor Inc (HQ) 800 321-3391
  1899 N Wilkinson Way Perrysburg (43551) *(G-16076)*

Centor Inc 800 321-3391
  5091 County Rd 120 Berlin (44610) *(G-1647)*

Central Allied Enterprises Inc 330 879-2132
  6331 Blough Ave Sw Navarre (44662) *(G-14711)*

Central Aluminum Company LLC 614 491-5700
  2045 Broehm Rd Obetz (43207) *(G-15652)*

Central Business Products Inc 513 385-5899
  3722 Vernier Dr Cincinnati (45251) *(G-3513)*

Central Coated Products Inc 330 821-9830
  2025 Mccrea St Alliance (44601) *(G-503)*

Central Design Services 513 829-7027
  5417 Dixie Hwy Fairfield (45014) *(G-9652)*

Central Fabricators Inc 513 621-1240
  408 Poplar St Cincinnati (45214) *(G-3514)*

Central Graphics Inc 330 928-7080
  1658 State Rd Cuyahoga Falls (44223) *(G-7977)*

Central Heating & Cooling Inc 330 782-7100
  5626 South Ave Ste 1 Youngstown (44512) *(G-21045)*

Central Machinery Company LLC 740 387-1289
  1339 E Fairground Rd Marion (43302) *(G-12862)*

Central Market Specialty Meats, Columbus *Also called Karn Meats Inc (G-7251)*

Central Ohio Asphalt LLC 419 768-4211
  7250a W State Rt 95 E Chesterville (43317) *(G-3224)*

Central Ohio Bldg Components, Newark *Also called Columbus Roof Trusses Inc (G-14994)*

Central Ohio Fabrication LLC 740 969-2976
  8143 Bowers Rd Sw Amanda (43102) *(G-561)*

Central Ohio Fabricators LLC 740 393-3892
  105 Progress Dr Mount Vernon (43050) *(G-14613)*

Central Ohio Mat Company 740 627-7261
  1025 Harcourt Rd Ste 500 Mount Vernon (43050) *(G-14614)*

Central Ohio Metal Stampi 614 861-3332
  1055 Claycraft Rd Columbus (43230) *(G-6918)*

Central Ohio Orthtic Prsthetic 614 659-1580
  248 Bradenton Ave Dublin (43017) *(G-9060)*

Central Ohio Paper & Packg Inc 614 492-8956
  5885 Green Pointe Dr S C Groveport (43125) *(G-10618)*

Central Ohio Paper & Packg Inc (PA) 419 621-9239
  2350 University Dr E Huron (44839) *(G-11219)*

Central Ohio Printing Corp 740 852-1616
  55 W High St London (43140) *(G-12203)*

Central Ohio Rtrctable Screens 614 868-5080
  6737 Thomas Rd Radnor (43066) *(G-16506)*

Central Ohio Welding, Columbus *Also called COW Industries Inc (G-6992)*

Central Oil Asphalt Corp (PA) 614 224-8111
  8 E Long St Ste 400 Columbus (43215) *(G-6919)*

Central Optical Inc 330 783-9660
  6981 Southern Blvd Ste B Youngstown (44512) *(G-21046)*

Central Ready Mix LLC (PA) 513 402-5001
  6310 E Kemper Rd Ste 125 Cincinnati (45241) *(G-3515)*

Central Ready Mix LLC 513 367-1939
  7340 Dry Fork Rd Cleves (45002) *(G-6508)*

Central Ready-Mix of Ohio LLC 614 252-3452
  6310 E Kemper Rd Ste 125 Cincinnati (45241) *(G-3516)*

Central Ready-Mix Ohio LLC 614 252-3452
  6310 E Kemper Rd Ste 125 Cincinnati (45241) *(G-3517)*

Central State Enterprises Inc 419 468-8191
  1331 Freese Works Pl Galion (44833) *(G-10258)*

Central Systems & Control 440 835-0015
  26933 Westwood Rd Ste 400 Cleveland (44145) *(G-5005)*

Central USA Wireless LLC 513 469-1500
  11210 Montgomery Rd Cincinnati (45249) *(G-3518)*

Centrex Plastics LLC (PA) 419 423-1213
  814 W Lima St Findlay (45840) *(G-9806)*

Centria Inc 740 432-7351
  530 N 2nd St Cambridge (43725) *(G-2451)*

Centria Coil Coating Services, Cambridge *Also called Centria Inc (G-2451)*

Centrus Energy Corp 740 897-2457
  3930 Us Rt 23 S Piketon (45661) *(G-16217)*

Century Biotech Partners Inc 614 746-6998
  7765 Dublin Rd Dublin (43017) *(G-9061)*

Century Container LLC (HQ) 330 457-2367
  5331 State Route 7 New Waterford (44445) *(G-14969)*

Century Container LLC 330 457-2367
  32 W Railroad St Columbiana (44408) *(G-6609)*

Century Die Company LLC 419 332-2693
  215 N Stone St Fremont (43420) *(G-10136)*

Century Graphics Inc 614 895-7698
  9101 Hawthorne Pt Westerville (43082) *(G-20142)*

Century Intermediate Holdg Co (PA) 216 252-7300
  1 American Rd Cleveland (44144) *(G-5006)*

Century Marketing Corporation 419 354-2591
  1145 Fairview Ave Bowling Green (43402) *(G-1977)*

Century Marketing Corporation (HQ) 419 354-2591
  12836 S Dixie Hwy Bowling Green (43402) *(G-1978)*

Century Mold Company Inc 513 539-9283
  55 Wright Dr Middletown (45044) *(G-14027)*

Century Plating Inc 216 531-4131
  18006 S Waterloo Rd Cleveland (44119) *(G-5007)*

Century Signs 419 352-2666
  169 S Main St Bowling Green (43402) *(G-1979)*

Century Tool & Stamping Inc 216 241-2032
  1510 University Rd Cleveland (44113) *(G-5008)*

Centurylabel, Bowling Green *Also called Century Marketing Corporation (G-1978)*

Cep Holdings LLC 330 665-2900
  3560 W Market St Ste 340 Fairlawn (44333) *(G-9745)*

Ceramitec, Columbus *Also called Wk Brick Company (G-7767)*

Ceranode Division, Dayton *Also called Aps-Materials Inc (G-8162)*

Cermet Technologies, Cleveland *Also called Postle Industries Inc (G-6022)*

Certainteed Corporation 419 499-2581
  11519 Us Highway 250 N Milan (44846) *(G-14110)*

Certech Inc 330 405-1033
  2181 Pinnacle Pkwy Twinsburg (44087) *(G-18910)*

Certified Comparator Products 937 426-9677
  1174 Grange Hall Rd Beavercreek (45430) *(G-1372)*

Certified Heat Treating Inc (PA) 937 866-0245
  4475 Infirmary Rd Dayton (45449) *(G-8222)*

Certified Labs & Service Inc 419 289-7462
  535 E 7th St Ashland (44805) *(G-718)*

Certified Oil Company Inc 614 421-7500
  949 King Ave Columbus (43212) *(G-6920)*

Certified Pressure Testing LLC (PA) 740 374-2071
  27515 State Route 7 Marietta (45750) *(G-12773)*

Certified Service Inc 937 643-0393
  2876 Culver Ave Dayton (45429) *(G-8223)*

Certified Tool & Grinding Inc 937 865-5934
  4455 Infirmary Rd Miamisburg (45342) *(G-13791)*

Certified Walk In Tubs 614 436-4848
  926 Freeway Dr N Columbus (43229) *(G-6921)*

Certified Welding Co 216 961-5410
9603 Clinton Rd Cleveland (44144) *(G-5009)*

Certon Technologies Inc (PA) 440 786-7185
60 S Park St Bedford (44146) *(G-1414)*

Ces Nationwide 937 322-0771
567 E Leffel Ln Springfield (45505) *(G-17530)*

Ceso Inc (PA) 937 435-8584
8534 Yankee St Ste 2b Dayton (45458) *(G-8224)*

Cetek, Brookpark *Also called Fosbel Inc (G-2161)*

Cetek Ltd 216 362-3900
20600 Sheldon Rd Cleveland (44142) *(G-5010)*

CFC Startec LLC 330 688-8316
2213 Arndale Rd Stow (44224) *(G-17737)*

CFM International Inc (PA) 513 552-2787
6440 Aviation Way West Chester (45069) *(G-19825)*

CFM International Inc 513 563-4180
1 Neumann Way Cincinnati (45215) *(G-3519)*

CFM Religion Pubg Group LLC (PA) 513 931-4050
8805 Governors Hill Dr # 400 Cincinnati (45249) *(G-3520)*

Cfrc Wtr & Enrgy Solutions Inc 216 479-0290
850 Euclid Ave Ste 1314 Cleveland (44114) *(G-5011)*

Cft Systems, Fairport Harbor *Also called George Whalley Company (G-9765)*

Cgas Exploration Inc (HQ) 614 436-4631
110 E Wilson Bridge Rd # 250 Worthington (43085) *(G-20859)*

Cgas Inc (PA) 614 975-4697
110 E Wilson Bridge Rd # 250 Worthington (43085) *(G-20860)*

Cgs, Medina *Also called Commercial Grinding Services (G-13390)*

Cgs Aviation, Brecksville *Also called Clm Marketing Inc (G-2041)*

Cgs Imaging, Maumee *Also called Cgs Signs LLC (G-13233)*

Cgs Signs LLC 419 897-3000
385 Osage St Maumee (43537) *(G-13233)*

Ch Enterprises, Toledo *Also called Greggs Specialty Services (G-18488)*

Ch Tool & Die, Mount Vernon *Also called C-H Tool & Die (G-14610)*

Chaffin Electronics Inc 740 354-9896
4170 Gallia Pike Franklin Furnace (45629) *(G-10068)*

Chagrin Metal Fabricating Inc 440 946-6342
34201 Melinz Pkwy Unit B Eastlake (44095) *(G-9262)*

Chagrin Valley Publishing Co. 440 247-5335
525 Washington St Chagrin Falls (44022) *(G-3051)*

Chagrin Valley Times, Chagrin Falls *Also called Chagrin Valley Publishing Co (G-3051)*

Chagrin Vly Stl Erectors Inc 440 975-1556
4500 Hamann Pkwy Willoughby (44094) *(G-20455)*

Chalet Debonne Vineyards Inc 440 466-3485
7840 Doty Rd Madison (44057) *(G-12499)*

Chalet In The Valley, Millersburg *Also called Guggisberg Cheese Inc (G-14219)*

Chalfant Loading Dock Eqp, Cleveland *Also called Chalfant Sew Fabricators Inc (G-5012)*

Chalfant Manufacturing Company (HQ) 330 273-3510
50 Pearl Rd Ste 212 Brunswick (44212) *(G-2216)*

Chalfant Manufacturing Company 440 323-9870
7005 W River Rd S Elyria (44035) *(G-9392)*

Chalfant Sew Fabricators Inc 216 521-7922
11525 Madison Ave Cleveland (44102) *(G-5012)*

Chalk Outline Pictures 216 291-3944
4773 Hillary Ln Cleveland (44143) *(G-5013)*

Challenge Targets 859 462-5851
4101 Founders Blvd Batavia (45103) *(G-1170)*

Challenger Aviation Products 937 387-6500
4433 Old Springfield Rd Vandalia (45377) *(G-19285)*

Challenger Hardware Company 216 591-1141
220 Eastview Dr Ste 102 Brooklyn Heights (44131) *(G-2134)*

Cham Cor Industries Inc 740 967-9015
117 W Coshocton St Johnstown (43031) *(G-11395)*

Champa Ventures LLC 614 726-1801
6314 Belvedere Green Blvd Dublin (43016) *(G-9062)*

Champion, Cincinnati *Also called Enclosure Suppliers LLC (G-3701)*

Champion Bridge Company 937 382-2521
261 E Sugartree St Wilmington (45177) *(G-20658)*

Champion Company (PA) 937 324-5681
400 Harrison St Springfield (45505) *(G-17531)*

Champion Company 937 324-5681
1100 Kenton St Springfield (45505) *(G-17532)*

Champion Directories Inc 419 668-1280
100 Old State Rd S Norwalk (44857) *(G-15530)*

CHAMPION INDUSTRIES DIV, Troy *Also called R T Industries Inc (G-18865)*

Champion Manufacturing Inc 419 253-7930
4025 Bennington Way Marengo (43334) *(G-12747)*

Champion Opco LLC (PA) 513 924-4858
12121 Champion Way Cincinnati (45241) *(G-3521)*

Champion Opco LLC 419 740-5193
6214 Monclova Rd Maumee (43537) *(G-13234)*

Champion Pump Company Inc 419 281-4500
1102 Myers Pkwy Ashland (44805) *(G-719)*

Champion Rivet Company, Twinsburg *Also called Kre Inc (G-18967)*

Champion Webbing Company Inc 330 920-1007
2748 2nd St Cuyahoga Falls (44221) *(G-7978)*

Champion Win Co Cleveland LLC 440 899-2562
9011 Freeway Dr Ste 1 Macedonia (44056) *(G-12440)*

Champion Window Co of Akron 330 474-3024
9011 Freeway Dr Ste 1 Macedonia (44056) *(G-12441)*

Champion Window Co of Toledo 419 841-0154
7546 Ponderosa Rd Ste A Perrysburg (43551) *(G-16077)*

Champion Windows, Macedonia *Also called Champion Window Co of Akron (G-12441)*

Champion Windows Manufacturing, Cincinnati *Also called Champion Opco LLC (G-3521)*

Championpages, Norwalk *Also called Champion Directories Inc (G-15530)*

Chandler Machine Co Inc 330 688-7615
4960 Hudson Dr Stow (44224) *(G-17738)*

Chandler Machine Prod Gear 330 688-5585
4960 Hudson Dr Stow (44224) *(G-17739)*

Chandler Mch & Prod Gear & Bro, Stow *Also called Chandler Machine Co Inc (G-17738)*

Chandler Systems Incorporated 419 281-6829
710 Orange St Ashland (44805) *(G-720)*

Chandler Systems Incorporated 419 281-5767
220 Ohio St Ashland (44805) *(G-721)*

Chang Audio, Toledo *Also called China Enterprises Inc (G-18396)*

Channel Products Inc (PA) 440 423-0113
7100 Wilson Mills Rd Chesterland (44026) *(G-3199)*

Chantilly Development Corp 419 243-8109
3101 Monroe St Toledo (43606) *(G-18393)*

Chaos Entertainment 937 520-5260
7570 Mount Whitney St Dayton (45424) *(G-8225)*

Chaos Matrix Ltd 614 638-4748
44451 Kipton Nickle Plate Oberlin (44074) *(G-15636)*

Chaplet & Chill Division, Canton *Also called The W L Jenkins Company (G-2869)*

Chappell Door Company, Washington Court Hou *Also called Courthouse Manufacturing LLC (G-19638)*

Chappell-Zimmerman Inc 330 337-8711
641 Olive St Salem (44460) *(G-16880)*

Characteristic Solutions LLC 614 360-2424
829 Bethel Rd Ste 105 Columbus (43214) *(G-6922)*

Characters Inc 937 335-1976
190 Peters Ave Ste A Troy (45373) *(G-18808)*

Chardon Custom Polymers LLC 440 285-2161
373 Washington St Chardon (44024) *(G-3143)*

Chardon Metal Products Co 440 285-2147
206 5th Ave Chardon (44024) *(G-3144)*

Chardon Plastics Machinery 440 564-5360
11680 Butternut Rd Chardon (44024) *(G-3145)*

Chardon Tool & Supply Co Inc 440 286-6440
115 Parker Ct Chardon (44024) *(G-3146)*

Charger Connection 888 427-5829
7779 Meadowcreek Dr Cincinnati (45244) *(G-3522)*

Charger Press Inc 513 542-3113
6088 Rte128 Miamitown (45041) *(G-13886)*

Charisma Products Inc 614 846-8888
6342 Worthington Rd Westerville (43082) *(G-20143)*

Charizma Corp 216 621-2220
1400 E 30th St Ste 201 Cleveland (44114) *(G-5014)*

Charles Auto Electric Co Inc 330 535-6269
600 Grant St Akron (44311) *(G-118)*

Charles C Lewis Company 440 439-3150
1 W Interstate St Ste 200 Cleveland (44146) *(G-5015)*

Charles Costa Inc 330 376-3636
924 Home Ave Akron (44310) *(G-119)*

Charles Daniel Young 937 968-3423
1324 Wasson Rd Union City (45390) *(G-19070)*

Charles Huffman & Associates 216 295-0850
19214 Gladstone Rd Warrensville Heights (44122) *(G-19630)*

Charles J Meyers 513 922-2866
866 Suncreek Ct Cincinnati (45238) *(G-3523)*

Charles Messina 216 663-3344
16645 Granite Rd Cleveland (44137) *(G-5016)*

Charles Mfg Co 330 395-3490
3021 Sferra Ave Nw Warren (44483) *(G-19534)*

Charles Ray Evans 740 967-3669
451 E Coshocton St Ste B Johnstown (43031) *(G-11396)*

Charles Rewinding Div, Canton *Also called Hannon Company (G-2723)*

Charles Svec Inc (PA) 216 662-5200
5470 Dunham Rd Maple Heights (44137) *(G-12730)*

Charles V Snider & Assoc Inc 440 877-9151
10139 Royalton Rd Ste K North Royalton (44133) *(G-15414)*

Charles Wisvari 740 671-9960
3266 Guernsey St Bellaire (43906) *(G-1497)*

Charlotte M Peters 216 798-8997
3452 W 126th St Cleveland (44111) *(G-5017)*

Charm Harness and Boot Ltd 330 893-0402
4432 County Road 70 Charm (44617) *(G-3183)*

Chart Asia Inc 440 753-1490
1 Infinity Corp Ctr Dr Cleveland (44125) *(G-5018)*

Chart Industries Inc 440 753-1490
5885 Landerbrook Dr # 150 Cleveland (44124) *(G-5019)*

Chart Industries Inc (PA) 440 753-1490
1 Infinity Corp Ctr Dr # 300 Cleveland (44125) *(G-5020)*

Chart International Inc (HQ) 440 753-1490
1 Infinity Corp Ctr Dr Cleveland (44125) *(G-5021)*

Chart Tech Tool Inc 937 667-3543
4060 Lisa Dr Tipp City (45371) *(G-18272)*

Charter Manufacturing Co Inc 216 883-3800
4300 E 49th St Cleveland (44125) *(G-5022)*

Charter Nex Films - Delaware 740 369-2770
1188 S Houk Rd Delaware (43015) *(G-8832)*

Charter Nex Holding Company 740 369-2770
1188 S Houk Rd Delaware (43015) *(G-8833)*

Charter One, Sagamore Hills *Also called Rbs Citizens NA (G-16778)*

Chas J Steven Inc 440 954-9191
7251 S Meadow Dr Painesville (44077) *(G-15864)*

Chase Brass and Copper Co LLC (HQ) 419 485-3193
14212 Selwyn Dr Montpelier (43543) *(G-14440)*

Chase Doors, West Chester *Also called Chase Industries Inc (G-19988)*

Chase Industries Inc (PA) 513 860-5565
10021 Commerce Park Dr West Chester (45246) *(G-19988)*

Chasing Fireflies LLC 206 574-4500
5568 W Chester Rd West Chester (45069) *(G-19826)*

Chassis Division, Springfield *Also called Sutphen Corporation (G-17658)*

Chatelain Plastics Inc 419 422-4323
413 N Main St Findlay (45840) *(G-9807)*

Chattanooga Laser Cutting LLC 513 779-7200
891 Redna Ter Cincinnati (45215) *(G-3524)*

Chautauqua Fiberglass & Plasti 513 423-8840
2601 S Verity Pkwy Middletown (45044) *(G-14028)*

Chc Manufacturing Inc (PA) 513 821-7757
10270 Wayne Ave Cincinnati (45215) *(G-3525)*

Chc Manufacturing Inc 614 527-1606
2343 Glass Brook Dr Columbus (43228) *(G-6923)*

Check Yourself LLC 513 685-0868
4422 Carver Woods Dr # 110 Blue Ash (45242) *(G-1764)*

Checkered Express Inc 330 530-8169
2501 W Liberty St Girard (44420) *(G-10384)*

Checkmate Marine Inc 419 562-3881
3691 State Route 4 Bucyrus (44820) *(G-2335)*

Checkpoint Surgical Inc 216 378-9107
22901 Millcreek Blvd # 110 Cleveland (44122) *(G-5023)*

Checkpoint Systems Inc 937 281-1304
7620 Mcewen Rd Dayton (45459) *(G-8226)*

Checkpoint Systems Inc 330 456-7776
1510 4th St Se Canton (44707) *(G-2652)*

Chef 2 Chef Foods 216 696-0080
1893 E 55th St Cleveland (44103) *(G-5024)*

Chefs Pantry Inc (HQ) 440 288-0146
1833 Cooper Foster Pk Rd Amherst (44001) *(G-594)*

Chelsea House Fabrics, Columbus *Also called Style-Line Incorporated (G-7664)*

Chelsea Machine Service Inc 937 233-6330
2401 Valley Pike Ste 1 Dayton (45404) *(G-8227)*

Chem 1 Inc 216 475-7443
19220 Miles Rd Warrensville Heights (44128) *(G-19631)*

Chem Instruments, West Chester *Also called Chemsultants International Inc (G-19829)*

Chem Masters 440 428-2105
300 Edwards St Madison (44057) *(G-12500)*

Chem Technologies Ltd 440 632-9311
14875 Bonner Dr Middlefield (44062) *(G-13921)*

Chem-Sales Inc 419 531-4292
3860 Dorr St Toledo (43607) *(G-18394)*

Chemcore Inc 937 228-6118
20 Madison St Dayton (45402) *(G-8228)*

Chemequip Sales Inc 330 724-8300
1004 Swartz Rd Akron (44319) *(G-120)*

Chemical Instruments, West Chester *Also called Cheminstruments Inc (G-19828)*

Chemical Methods Inc 216 476-8400
20338 Progress Dr Strongsville (44149) *(G-17901)*

Chemical Solvents Inc (PA) 216 741-9310
3751 Jennings Rd Cleveland (44109) *(G-5025)*

Chemical Systems, Cleveland *Also called Sports Care Products Inc (G-6227)*

Chemigon LLC 330 592-1875
520 S Main St Ste 2511-6 Akron (44311) *(G-121)*

Chemineer, Dayton *Also called National Oilwell Varco LP (G-8519)*

Chemineer, Dayton *Also called National Oilwell Varco LP (G-8520)*

Cheminstruments Inc (PA) 513 860-1598
510 Commercial Dr West Chester (45014) *(G-19827)*

Cheminstruments Inc 513 860-1598
510 Commercial Dr West Chester (45014) *(G-19828)*

Chemionics Corporation 330 733-8834
390 Munroe Falls Rd Tallmadge (44278) *(G-18137)*

Chemmasters Inc 440 428-2105
300 Edwards St Madison (44057) *(G-12501)*

Chemours Company Fc LLC 513 941-4121
11215 Brower Rd North Bend (45052) *(G-15203)*

Chemours Company Fc LLC 740 989-5202
251 Arrowhead Rd Little Hocking (45742) *(G-12144)*

Chempace Corporation 419 535-0101
339 Arco Dr Toledo (43607) *(G-18395)*

Chempak International LLC (PA) 440 543-8511
10175 Queens Way Ste 8 Chagrin Falls (44023) *(G-3079)*

Chempure Products Corporation 330 874-4300
148 Central Ave Bolivar (44612) *(G-1930)*

Chemspec Ltd 330 896-0355
1559 Corporate Woods Pkwy Uniontown (44685) *(G-19079)*

Chemspec Polymer Additives, Uniontown *Also called Chemspec Ltd (G-19079)*

Chemsultants International Inc 513 860-1598
510 Commercial Dr West Chester (45014) *(G-19829)*

Chemsultants International Inc (PA) 440 974-3080
9079 Tyler Blvd Mentor (44060) *(G-13543)*

Chemtech Inc 330 454-2127
1712 Ira Turpin Way Ne Canton (44705) *(G-2653)*

Chemtrade Chemicals US LLC 513 422-6319
305 Richmond St Middletown (45044) *(G-14029)*

Chemtrans Logistics Inc 419 447-8041
281 Hancock St Tiffin (44883) *(G-18215)*

Chemtura Corporation 440 324-6060
110 Liberty Ct Elyria (44035) *(G-9393)*

Cheney Pulp and Paper Company 937 746-9991
1000 Anderson St Franklin (45005) *(G-10012)*

Chep (usa) Inc 614 497-9448
2130 New World Dr Columbus (43207) *(G-6924)*

Cherhire Choppers 740 362-0695
4059 State Route 37 E A Delaware (43015) *(G-8834)*

Cherokee Hardwoods Inc (PA) 440 632-0322
16741 Newcomb Rd Middlefield (44062) *(G-13922)*

Cheryl & Co (HQ) 614 776-1500
646 Mccorkle Blvd Westerville (43082) *(G-20144)*

Cheryl & Co 614 776-1500
4465 Industrial Center Dr Obetz (43207) *(G-15653)*

Cheryl A Lucas 614 755-2100
388 Morrison Rd Columbus (43213) *(G-6925)*

Chesapeake Energy Corporation 740 695-1623
156 Woodrow Ave Ste 2 Saint Clairsville (43950) *(G-16785)*

Chester F Hale 740 379-2437
60 Dry Ridge Rd Patriot (45658) *(G-15993)*

Chester Hoist, Salem *Also called Columbus McKinnon Corporation (G-16884)*

Chester Labs Inc 513 458-3871
900 Section Rd Ste A Cincinnati (45237) *(G-3526)*

Chester Packaging LLC 513 458-3840
1900 Section Rd Ste A Cincinnati (45237) *(G-3527)*

Chester West Holdings Inc 800 647-1900
11500 Canal Rd Sharonville (45241) *(G-17113)*

Chesterhill Stone Co 740 849-2338
6305 Saltillo Rd East Fultonham (43735) *(G-9198)*

Chesterland Cabinet Company 440 564-1157
10389 Kinsman Rd Newbury (44065) *(G-15083)*

Chesterland News Inc 440 729-7667
8389 Mayfield Rd Ste B-4 Chesterland (44026) *(G-3200)*

Chestnut Holdings Inc (PA) 330 849-6503
670 W Market St Akron (44303) *(G-122)*

Chevron Ae Resources LLC 330 896-8510
3500 Massillon Rd Ste 100 Uniontown (44685) *(G-19080)*

Chevron Ae Resources LLC 330 654-4343
1823 State Route 14 Deerfield (44411) *(G-8771)*

Chewrite Co 937 746-5509
265 S Pioneer Blvd Springboro (45066) *(G-17476)*

Chez Rama Restaurant 614 237-9315
3669 E Livingston Ave Columbus (43227) *(G-6926)*

CHI Corporation (PA) 440 498-2300
5265 Naiman Pkwy Ste H Cleveland (44139) *(G-5026)*

Chica Bands LLC 513 871-4300
6216 Madison Rd Cincinnati (45227) *(G-3528)*

Chicago Dental Supply Inc 800 571-5211
10051 Simonson Rd Unit 9 Harrison (45030) *(G-10771)*

Chick Master Incubator Company (PA) 330 722-5591
945 Lafayette Rd Medina (44256) *(G-13386)*

Chickasaw Machine & TI Co Inc 419 925-4325
3050 Chickasaw Rd Chickasaw (45826) *(G-3225)*

Chicopee Engineering Assoc Inc 413 592-2273
2300 E Enterprise Pkwy Twinsburg (44087) *(G-18911)*

Chief General Office 419 782-0950
1340 W High St Ste E Defiance (43512) *(G-8784)*

Chieffos Frozen Foods Inc 330 652-1222
406 S Main St Niles (44446) *(G-15146)*

Chiefs Manufacturing & Eqp Co 216 291-3200
4325 Monticello Blvd Cleveland (44121) *(G-5027)*

Chilcote Company (PA) 216 781-6000
2160 Superior Ave E Cleveland (44114) *(G-5028)*

Child Evngelism Fellowship Inc 440 218-4982
641 Acorn Pl Cuyahoga Falls (44221) *(G-7979)*

Child Evngelism Fellowship Inc 419 756-7799
827 Lexington Ave Mansfield (44907) *(G-12579)*

Chili Logging Ltd 740 545-9502
30240 County Road 10 Fresno (43824) *(G-10196)*

Chillicothe Facility, Chillicothe *Also called P H Glatfelter Company (G-3256)*

Chillicothe Gazette, Chillicothe *Also called Gannett Co Inc (G-3240)*

Chillicothe Packaging Corp 740 773-5800
4168 State Route 159 Chillicothe (45601) *(G-3232)*

Chillicothe Packing, Chillicothe *Also called Churmac Industries Inc (G-3234)*

Chilltex LLC 937 710-3308
7440 Hoying Rd Anna (45302) *(G-621)*

Chime Master Systems, Sugar Grove *Also called Commercial Music Service Co (G-18011)*

China Enterprises Inc 419 885-1485
5151 Monroe St Toledo (43623) *(G-18396)*

Chipman Machining Co Inc 513 681-8515
  2900 Spring Grove Ave Cincinnati (45225) (G-3529)
Chipmatic Tool & Machine Inc 419 862-2737
  212 Ottawa St Elmore (43416) (G-9362)
Chipmunk Logging & Lumber LLC 440 834-4660
  15750 Chipmunk Ln Middlefield (44062) (G-13923)
Chippewa Tool & Mfg Co 419 849-2790
  1101 Oak St Woodville (43469) (G-20724)
Chips Manufacturing Inc 440 946-3666
  35720 Lakeland Blvd Willoughby (44095) (G-20456)
Chocolate Pig Inc (PA) 440 461-4511
  5338 Mayfield Rd Cleveland (44124) (G-5029)
Choice Brands 740 598-4121
  2680 Commercial Ave Mingo Junction (43938) (G-14347)
Choice Brands Adhesives Ltd 513 772-1234
  666 Redna Ter Ste 500 Cincinnati (45215) (G-3530)
Chore Anden 330 695-2300
  11461 Salt Creek Rd Fredericksburg (44627) (G-10080)
Chris Erhart Foundry & Mch Co 513 421-6550
  1240 Mehring Way Cincinnati (45203) (G-3531)
Chris Haughey 937 652-3338
  1463 S Us Highway 68 Urbana (43078) (G-19150)
Chris Nckel Cstm Ltherwork LLC 614 262-2672
  80 E Kelso Rd Columbus (43202) (G-6927)
Chrisnik Inc 513 738-2920
  7461 Cncnnati Brkville Rd Okeana (45053) (G-15663)
Chrissinger Co, Lewis Center Also called Keith Chrissinger (G-11903)
Christian Blue Pages (PA) 937 847-2583
  521 Byers Rd Ste 102 Miamisburg (45342) (G-13792)
Christian Citizen USA, Vandalia Also called Cross Communications Inc (G-19287)
Christian Happenings Magazine, Columbus Also called Wordcross Enterprises Inc (G-7773)
Christies Candies & Mints (PA) 419 382-7313
  2002 Glendale Ave Toledo (43614) (G-18397)
Christman Fabricators Inc 330 477-8077
  4668 Navarre Rd Sw Canton (44706) (G-2654)
Christman Quarry, Lewisville Also called Gerald Christman (G-11948)
Christman Supply Co Inc 740 472-0046
  239 Oaklawn Ave Woodsfield (43793) (G-20715)
Christmas Ranch LLC 513 505-3865
  3205 S Waynesville Rd Morrow (45152) (G-14545)
Christopher Tool & Mfg Co 440 248-8080
  30500 Carter St Frnt Cleveland (44139) (G-5030)
Christy Machine Company 419 332-6451
  118 Birchard Ave Fremont (43420) (G-10137)
Chromaflo Technologies Corp (PA) 440 997-0081
  2600 Michigan Ave Ashtabula (44004) (G-795)
Chromaflo Technologies Corp 513 733-5111
  620 Shepherd Dr Cincinnati (45215) (G-3532)
Chromaflo Technologies Corp 440 997-5137
  1603 W 29th St Ashtabula (44004) (G-796)
Chromascape Inc (PA) 330 998-7574
  2055 Enterprise Pkwy Twinsburg (44087) (G-18912)
Chromatic Inc 216 881-2228
  839 E 63rd St Cleveland (44103) (G-5031)
Chrome & Speed Cycle LLC 937 429-5656
  3490 Dayton Xenia Rd C Beavercreek (45432) (G-1323)
Chrome Deposit Corporation 513 539-8486
  341 Lawton Ave Monroe (45050) (G-14395)
Chrome Deposit Corporation 513 539-8486
  341 Lawton Ave Monroe (45050) (G-14396)
Chrome Industries Inc 216 771-2266
  3041 Perkins Ave Cleveland (44114) (G-5032)
Chronicle Telegram 330 725-4166
  885 W Liberty St Medina (44256) (G-13387)
Chronicle Your Life Story 614 456-7576
  123 S Virginialee Rd Columbus (43209) (G-6928)
Chub Gibsons Logging 740 884-4079
  391 Fyffe Hollow Rd Chillicothe (45601) (G-3233)
Chuck Meadors Plastics Co 440 813-4466
  150 S Cucumber St Jefferson (44047) (G-11359)
Church & Dwight Co Inc 740 852-3621
  110 W 1st St London (43140) (G-12204)
Church & Dwight Co Inc 419 992-4244
  2501 E County Rd 34 Old Fort (44861) (G-15670)
Church Budget Monthly Inc 330 337-1122
  157 W Pershing St Salem (44460) (G-16881)
Church-Budget Envelope Company 800 446-9780
  271 S Ellsworth Ave Salem (44460) (G-16882)
Churchill Steel Plate Ltd 330 425-9000
  7851 Bavaria Rd Twinsburg (44087) (G-18913)
Churmac Industries, Chillicothe Also called Chillicothe Packaging Corp (G-3232)
Churmac Industries Inc 740 773-5800
  4168 State Route 159 Chillicothe (45601) (G-3234)
Chute Source LLC 330 475-0377
  525 Kennedy Rd Akron (44305) (G-123)
Ci Disposition Co 216 587-5200
  1000 Valley Belt Rd Brooklyn Heights (44131) (G-2135)
Cicogna Electric and Sign Co (PA) 440 998-2637
  4330 N Bend Rd Ashtabula (44004) (G-797)

Cigars of Cincy 513 931-5926
  1467 Larann Ln Cincinnati (45231) (G-3533)
Cigs N Such 614 389-6115
  1864 Hard Rd Columbus (43235) (G-6929)
Cil Isotope Separations LLC 937 376-5413
  1689 Burnett Dr Xenia (45385) (G-20942)
Cima Inc 513 682-5900
  4416 Dixie Hwy Fairfield (45014) (G-9653)
Cima Plastics Group, Twinsburg Also called Stewart Acquisition LLC (G-19024)
Cimbar Performance Mnrl WV LLC 330 532-2034
  2400 Clark Ave Wellsville (43968) (G-19774)
Cimino Box & Pallet Company, Cleveland Also called Cimino Box Inc (G-5033)
Cimino Box Inc 216 961-7377
  8500 Clinton Rd Ste 6 Cleveland (44144) (G-5033)
Cimx LLC 513 248-7700
  4625 Red Bank Rd Ste 200 Cincinnati (45227) (G-3534)
Cimx Software, Cincinnati Also called Cimx LLC (G-3534)
Cinchempro Inc 513 724-6111
  458 W Main St Batavia (45103) (G-1171)
Cincinnati Book Publicsher, Cincinnati Also called Psa Consulting Inc (G-4302)
Cincinnati - Vulcan Company 513 242-5300
  5353 Spring Grove Ave Cincinnati (45217) (G-3535)
Cincinnati A Flter Sls Svc Inc (PA) 513 242-3400
  4815 Para Dr Cincinnati (45237) (G-3536)
Cincinnati Advg Pdts LLC (HQ) 513 346-7310
  12150 Northwest Blvd Cincinnati (45246) (G-3537)
Cincinnati Air Conditioning Co 513 721-5622
  2080 Northwest Dr Cincinnati (45231) (G-3538)
Cincinnati Assn For The Blind 513 221-8558
  2045 Gilbert Ave Cincinnati (45202) (G-3539)
Cincinnati Babbitt Inc 513 942-5088
  9217 Seward Rd Fairfield (45014) (G-9654)
Cincinnati Bell Any Dstnce Inc 513 397-9900
  221 E 4th St Ste 700 Cincinnati (45202) (G-3540)
Cincinnati Bell Inc 513 565-2210
  201 E 4th St Cincinnati (45202) (G-3541)
Cincinnati Bindery & Packg Inc 859 816-0282
  2838 Spring Grove Ave Cincinnati (45225) (G-3542)
Cincinnati Biorefining Corp (HQ) 513 482-8800
  470 Este Ave Cincinnati (45232) (G-3543)
Cincinnati Blacktop Company 513 681-0952
  4992 Gray Rd Cincinnati (45232) (G-3544)
Cincinnati Chemical Processing, Batavia Also called Cinchempro Inc (G-1171)
Cincinnati City Boat Ramp, Cincinnati Also called Cincinnati Recreation Comm (G-3564)
Cincinnati Cold Drawn Inc 513 874-3296
  9108 Sutton Pl West Chester (45011) (G-19830)
Cincinnati Convertors Inc 513 731-6600
  1730 Cleneay Ave Cincinnati (45212) (G-3545)
Cincinnati Crane & Hoist LLC 513 202-1408
  10860 Paddys Run Rd Harrison (45030) (G-10772)
Cincinnati Crt Index Press Inc 513 241-1450
  119 W Central Pkwy Cincinnati (45202) (G-3546)
Cincinnati Ctrl Dynamics Inc 513 242-7300
  4924 Para Dr Cincinnati (45237) (G-3547)
Cincinnati Division, Monroe Also called Terex Utilities Inc (G-14416)
Cincinnati Dowel & WD Pdts Co 937 444-2502
  135 Oak St Mount Orab (45154) (G-14576)
Cincinnati Drveline Hydraulics 513 651-2406
  1220 W 8th St Cincinnati (45203) (G-3548)
Cincinnati Electrical Tool 513 941-5000
  5928 Hamilton Cleves Rd Cleves (45002) (G-6509)
Cincinnati Enquirer 513 721-2700
  312 Elm St Fl 18 Cincinnati (45202) (G-3549)
Cincinnati Enquirer, The, Cincinnati Also called Gannett Co Inc (G-3795)
Cincinnati Flame Hardening Co, Fairfield Also called Detroit Flame Hardening Co (G-9658)
Cincinnati Gasket & Indus GL, Cincinnati Also called Cincinnati Gasket Pkg Mfg Inc (G-3550)
Cincinnati Gasket Pkg Mfg Inc 513 761-3458
  40 Illinois Ave Cincinnati (45215) (G-3550)
Cincinnati Gate Systems Inc 513 769-5200
  675 Redna Ter Cincinnati (45215) (G-3551)
Cincinnati Gearing Systems Inc (PA) 513 527-8600
  5757 Mariemont Ave Cincinnati (45227) (G-3552)
Cincinnati Gearing Systems Inc 513 527-8634
  301 Milford Pkwy Cincinnati (45227) (G-3553)
Cincinnati Gearing Systems Inc 513 527-8600
  5757 Mariemont Ave Cincinnati (45227) (G-3554)
Cincinnati Gilbert Mch TI LLC 513 541-4815
  3366 Beekman St Cincinnati (45223) (G-3555)
Cincinnati Gutter Supply Inc 513 825-0500
  9345 Prnceton Glendale Rd West Chester (45011) (G-19831)
Cincinnati Industrial McHy Inc 513 923-5600
  4600 N Masn Montgomery Rd Mason (45040) (G-12994)
Cincinnati Laser Cutting LLC 513 772-6999
  891 Redna Ter Cincinnati (45215) (G-3556)
Cincinnati Machines Inc 513 536-2432
  4165 Half Acre Rd Batavia (45103) (G-1172)
Cincinnati Magazine 513 421-4300
  441 Vine St Ste 200 Cincinnati (45202) (G-3557)

Cincinnati Marlins Inc 513 761-3320
  616 W North Bend Rd Cincinnati (45224) *(G-3558)*
Cincinnati Meat Processing Inc 513 682-6000
  3640 Muddy Creek Rd Cincinnati (45238) *(G-3559)*
Cincinnati Metal Fabricating, Cincinnati *Also called Cincinnati Laser Cutting LLC (G-3556)*
Cincinnati Mine Machinery Co 513 522-7777
  2950 Jonrose Ave Cincinnati (45239) *(G-3560)*
Cincinnati Mold Incorporated 513 922-1888
  225 Stille Dr Cincinnati (45233) *(G-3561)*
Cincinnati Paperboard, Cincinnati *Also called Caraustar Industries Inc (G-3497)*
Cincinnati Pattern Company 513 241-9872
  2405 Spring Grove Ave Cincinnati (45214) *(G-3562)*
Cincinnati Preserving Company 513 771-2000
  3015 E Kemper Rd Cincinnati (45241) *(G-3563)*
Cincinnati Print Solutions LLC 513 943-9500
  4007 Bach Buxton Rd Amelia (45102) *(G-570)*
Cincinnati Printers Co Inc 513 860-9053
  9053 Le Saint Dr West Chester (45014) *(G-19832)*
Cincinnati Prof Door Sls Div, Cincinnati *Also called Division Overhead Door Inc (G-3659)*
Cincinnati Recreation Comm 513 921-5657
  3540 Southside Ave Cincinnati (45204) *(G-3564)*
Cincinnati Renewable Fuels LLC 513 482-8800
  4700 Este Ave Cincinnati (45232) *(G-3565)*
Cincinnati Retread Systems, Fairfield *Also called American Manufacturing & Eqp (G-9642)*
Cincinnati Specialties LLC 513 242-3300
  501 Murray Rd Cincinnati (45217) *(G-3566)*
Cincinnati Stair, Loveland *Also called Jaco Inc (G-12364)*
Cincinnati Test Systems Inc (PA) 800 850-3189
  10100 Progress Way Harrison (45030) *(G-10773)*
Cincinnati Thermal Spray Inc 513 793-1037
  5901 Creek Rd Blue Ash (45242) *(G-1765)*
Cincinnati Valve Company 513 471-8258
  1519 Tremont St Cincinnati (45214) *(G-3567)*
Cincinnati Window Decor, Cincinnati *Also called Cincinnati Window Shade Inc (G-3568)*
Cincinnati Window Shade Inc 513 398-8510
  5633 Tylersville Rd Ste 1 Mason (45040) *(G-12995)*
Cincinnati Window Shade Inc (PA) 513 631-7200
  3004 Harris Ave Cincinnati (45212) *(G-3568)*
Cincinnati Wood Products Co 513 542-0569
  2644 Colerain Ave Cincinnati (45214) *(G-3569)*
Cincinnati Woodworks Inc 513 241-6412
  2161 Elysian Pl Cincinnati (45219) *(G-3570)*
Cincinnatti Premier Candy LLC 513 253-0079
  5141 Fischer Ave Cincinnati (45217) *(G-3571)*
Cincinnati Processing, West Chester *Also called Empire Packing Company LP (G-20000)*
Cincom Systems Inc 513 459-1470
  4605 Duke Dr Mason (45040) *(G-12996)*
Cincy Cupcakes LLC 513 985-4440
  6646 Salem Rd Cincinnati (45230) *(G-3572)*
Cincy Deli & Carryout, Cincinnati *Also called Zygo Inc (G-4621)*
Cincy Glass Inc 513 241-0455
  3249 Fredonia Ave Cincinnati (45229) *(G-3573)*
Cincy Safe Company 513 900-9152
  1607 State Route 131 Milford (45150) *(G-14130)*
Cinderella 937 312-9969
  2700 Mmsburg Cntrville Rd Dayton (45459) *(G-8229)*
Cindoco Wood Products Co 937 444-2504
  410 Mount Clifton Dr Mount Orab (45154) *(G-14577)*
Cineen Inc 440 236-3658
  25011 Royalton Rd Columbia Station (44028) *(G-6583)*
Cinex Inc. 513 921-2825
  2641 Cummins St Cincinnati (45225) *(G-3574)*
Cinfab LLC 513 396-6100
  5240 Lester Rd Cincinnati (45213) *(G-3575)*
Cinn Wire E D M Inc 513 741-5402
  6850 Colerain Ave Cincinnati (45239) *(G-3576)*
Cinncinati Bindery, Cincinnati *Also called Spring Grove Manufacturing (G-4445)*
Cintas Corporation 513 336-6300
  6847 Cintas Blvd Ste 120 Mason (45040) *(G-12997)*
Cintas Corporation (PA) 513 459-1200
  6800 Cintas Blvd Cincinnati (45262) *(G-3577)*
Cintas Corporation 513 631-5750
  5570 Ridge Ave Cincinnati (45213) *(G-3578)*
Cintas Corporation No 2 ....937 236-1506
  903 Brandt St Bldg A Dayton (45404) *(G-8230)*
Cintas Corporation No 2 ....330 966-7800
  3865 Highland Park Nw Canton (44720) *(G-2655)*
Cintas Sales Corporation (HQ) 513 459-1200
  6800 Cintas Blvd Cincinnati (45262) *(G-3579)*
Cintas Uniforms AP Fcilty Svcs, Cincinnati *Also called Cintas Corporation (G-3578)*
Cinti Tan Company 513 874-8267
  6600 Dixie Hwy Ste N Fairfield (45014) *(G-9655)*
CIP International Inc 513 874-9925
  9575 Le Saint Dr West Chester (45014) *(G-19833)*
Cipar Inc (HQ) 216 910-1700
  3601 Green Rd Ste 308 Beachwood (44122) *(G-1260)*
Cipted Corp 412 829-2120
  301 Lawton Ave Monroe (45050) *(G-14397)*

Circle Machine Rolls Inc 330 938-9010
  245 W Kentucky Ave Sebring (44672) *(G-17044)*
Circle Mold & Machine Co, Tallmadge *Also called Circle Mold Incorporated (G-18138)*
Circle Mold Incorporated 330 633-7017
  85 S Thomas Rd Tallmadge (44278) *(G-18138)*
Circle Prime Manufacturing 330 923-0019
  2114 Front St Cuyahoga Falls (44221) *(G-7980)*
Circleville Glass Operations, Circleville *Also called Technicolor Usa Inc (G-4646)*
Circleville Oil Co 740 477-3341
  224 Lancaster Pike Circleville (43113) *(G-4625)*
Circuit Center 513 435-2131
  4738 Gateway Cir Dayton (45440) *(G-8231)*
Circuits Alive LLC 937 427-4141
  2408 Pine Knott Dr Beavercreek (45431) *(G-1324)*
Cirjak Furniture and Design 330 296-8035
  3416 State Route 59 Ravenna (44266) *(G-16521)*
Cirjak's Furntr & Design, Ravenna *Also called Cirjak Furniture and Design (G-16521)*
Cisco Systems Inc 419 977-2404
  130 S Washington St New Bremen (45869) *(G-14781)*
Cisco Systems Inc 937 427-4264
  2661 Commons Blvd Ste 133 Beavercreek (45431) *(G-1325)*
Citco Diamond & Cbn Products, Painesville *Also called Fives Landis Corp (G-15882)*
Citgo Petroleum Corporation 419 698-8055
  1840 Otter Creek Rd Oregon (43616) *(G-15705)*
Citi 2 Citi Logistics 614 306-4109
  6031 E Main St Columbus (43213) *(G-6930)*
Citizens USA 937 280-2001
  3651 Wright Way Rd Dayton (45424) *(G-8232)*
City Dog 614 228-3647
  510 E Main St Columbus (43215) *(G-6931)*
City Elyria Communication 440 322-3329
  851 Garden St Elyria (44035) *(G-9394)*
City Girl Magazine LLC 216 481-4110
  801 E 212th St Cleveland (44119) *(G-5034)*
City Iron LLC 513 721-5678
  4136 Colerain Ave Cincinnati (45223) *(G-3580)*
City Machine Technologies Inc (PA) 330 747-2639
  773 W Rayen Ave Youngstown (44502) *(G-21047)*
City Machine Technologies Inc 330 740-8186
  825 Martin Luther King Jr Youngstown (44502) *(G-21048)*
City Machine Technologies Inc 330 747-2639
  773 W Rayen Ave Youngstown (44502) *(G-21049)*
City Machine Technologies Inc 330 747-2639
  448 Andrews Ave Youngstown (44505) *(G-21050)*
City of Ashland 419 289-8728
  310 W 12th St Ashland (44805) *(G-722)*
City of Athens 740 592-3344
  395 W State St Athens (45701) *(G-858)*
City of Canton 330 489-3370
  2436 30th St Ne Canton (44705) *(G-2656)*
City of Chardon 440 286-2657
  201 N Hambden St Chardon (44024) *(G-3147)*
City of Cleveland 216 664-3013
  1735 Lakeside Ave E Cleveland (44114) *(G-5035)*
City of Cleveland 216 664-2711
  500 Lakeside Ave E Cleveland (44114) *(G-5036)*
City of Columbus 614 645-3152
  7000 State Route 104 Lockbourne (43137) *(G-12146)*
City of Conneaut 440 599-7071
  480 Lake Rd Conneaut (44030) *(G-7802)*
City of Kent 330 673-8897
  497 Middlebury Rd Kent (44240) *(G-11438)*
City of Lancaster 740 687-6670
  1424 Campground Rd Lancaster (43130) *(G-11697)*
City of Mansfield 419 884-3310
  2010 S Lexngtn Sprngml Rd Mansfield (44904) *(G-12580)*
City of Marietta 740 374-6864
  2000 4th St Marietta (45750) *(G-12774)*
City of Middletown 513 425-7781
  805 Columbia Ave Middletown (45042) *(G-14030)*
City of Mount Vernon 740 393-9508
  1550 Old Delaware Rd Mount Vernon (43050) *(G-14615)*
City of Newark, Newark *Also called Traffic Cntrl Sgnls Signs & MA (G-15064)*
City of Newark 740 349-6765
  164 Waterworks Rd Newark (43055) *(G-14993)*
City of Oxford 513 523-8412
  945 Collins Run Rd Oxford (45056) *(G-15834)*
City of Parma 440 885-8816
  6611 Ridge Rd Fl 2 Cleveland (44129) *(G-5037)*
City of Ravenna 330 296-5214
  3722 Hommon Rd Ravenna (44266) *(G-16522)*
City of Troy 937 339-4826
  300 E Staunton Rd Troy (45373) *(G-18809)*
City of Xenia 937 376-7269
  1831 Us Route 68 N Xenia (45385) *(G-20943)*
City Plating and Polishing LLC 216 267-8158
  4821 W 130th St Cleveland (44135) *(G-5038)*
City Printing Co Inc 330 747-5691
  122 Oak Hill Ave Youngstown (44502) *(G-21051)*

City Scrap & Salvage Co......330 753-5051
760 Flora Ave Akron (44314) *(G-124)*

City Visitor Inc......216 661-6666
5755 Granger Rd Ste 600 Cleveland (44131) *(G-5039)*

City Visitor Publications, Cleveland Also called City Visitor Inc *(G-5039)*

Citynet Ohio LLC......614 364-7881
343 N Front St Ste 400 Columbus (43215) *(G-6932)*

Cityscapes International Inc......614 850-2540
4200 Lyman Ct Hilliard (43026) *(G-10938)*

Citywide Materials Inc......513 533-1111
5263 Wooster Pike Cincinnati (45226) *(G-3581)*

Citywide Ready Mix, Cincinnati Also called Citywide Materials Inc *(G-3581)*

Civica CMI, Englewood Also called Creative Microsystems Inc *(G-9515)*

Civitas Media, Miamisburg Also called Heartland Publications LLC *(G-13816)*

Cjk USA Print Possibilities, Cincinnati Also called C J Krehbiel Company *(G-3493)*

Cjt's, Ironton Also called Wheeler Embroidery *(G-11305)*

CK Technologies LLC (HQ)......419 485-1110
1701 Magda Dr Montpelier (43543) *(G-14441)*

Ckm Ventures LLC (PA)......216 623-0370
2635 Payne Ave Cleveland (44114) *(G-5040)*

Cks Solution Incorporated (PA)......513 947-1277
4293 Muhlhauser Rd Fairfield (45014) *(G-9656)*

Claflin Company Inc......330 650-0582
5270 Hudson Dr Hudson (44236) *(G-11163)*

Clampco Products Inc (PA)......330 336-8857
1743 Wall Rd Wadsworth (44281) *(G-19398)*

Clamps Inc......419 729-2141
5960 American Rd E Toledo (43612) *(G-18398)*

Clancys Cabinet Shop......419 445-4455
3751 County Road 26 Archbold (43502) *(G-668)*

Clapp & Haney Brazed Tool Co......740 922-3515
901 Race St Dennison (44621) *(G-8944)*

Clarence Tussel Jr......440 576-3415
141 E Jefferson St Jefferson (44047) *(G-11360)*

Clariant Corporation......513 791-2964
10999 Reed Hartman Hwy # 201 Blue Ash (45242) *(G-1766)*

Claridon Tool & Die Inc......740 389-1944
4985 Marion Mt Gilead Rd Caledonia (43314) *(G-2435)*

Clark & Son Billiard Supply, Canton Also called Clark & Son Pool Table Company *(G-2657)*

Clark & Son Pool Table Company......330 454-9153
2737 Cleveland Ave Nw Canton (44709) *(G-2657)*

Clark Associates Inc......419 334-3838
702 W State St Ste A Fremont (43420) *(G-10138)*

Clark Auto Machine Shop......216 939-0768
2597 W 41st St Cleveland (44113) *(G-5041)*

Clark Dietrich Building, Warren Also called Clarkwestern Dietrich Building *(G-19535)*

Clark Grave Vault Company (PA)......614 294-3761
375 E 5th Ave Columbus (43201) *(G-6933)*

Clark Machine Service......740 887-2396
33926 Us Highway 50 Londonderry (45647) *(G-12226)*

Clark Optimization LLC......330 417-2164
1222 Easton St Ne Canton (44721) *(G-2658)*

Clark Rbr Plastic Intl Sls Inc (PA)......440 953-9514
8888 East Ave Mentor (44060) *(G-13544)*

Clark Rm Inc......419 425-9889
400 Crystal Ave Findlay (45840) *(G-9808)*

Clark Son Actn Liquidation Inc......330 866-9330
10233 Sandyville Ave Se East Sparta (44626) *(G-9254)*

Clark Substations LLC......330 452-5200
2240 Allen Ave Se Canton (44707) *(G-2659)*

Clark Township Garage......330 897-4844
2863 State Route 557 Baltic (43804) *(G-1066)*

Clark Wood Specialties Inc......330 499-8711
9235 Shadybrook St Nw Clinton (44216) *(G-6534)*

Clark-Fowler Elc Mtr & Sups, Wooster Also called Clark-Fowler Enterprises Inc *(G-20757)*

Clark-Fowler Enterprises Inc......330 262-0906
510 W Henry St Wooster (44691) *(G-20757)*

Clark-Reliance Corporation (PA)......440 572-1500
16633 Foltz Pkwy Strongsville (44149) *(G-17902)*

Clark-Reliance Corporation......440 572-7408
16633 Foltz Pkwy Strongsville (44149) *(G-17903)*

Clarkdietrich Bldg Systems LLC......513 870-1100
9100 Centre Pointe Dr # 210 West Chester (45069) *(G-19834)*

Clarke Fire Protection Product, Cincinnati Also called Clarke Power Services Inc *(G-3583)*

Clarke Fire Prtection Pdts Inc (HQ)......513 771-2200
3133 E Kemper Rd Cincinnati (45241) *(G-3582)*

Clarke Fire Prtection Pdts Inc......513 771-2200
133 Circle Freeway Dr West Chester (45246) *(G-19989)*

Clarke Power Services Inc......513 771-2200
3133 E Kemper Rd Cincinnati (45241) *(G-3583)*

Clarksville Stave & Lumber Co......937 376-4618
2808 Jasper Rd Xenia (45385) *(G-20944)*

Clarkwestern Dietrich Building......330 372-5564
1985 N River Rd Ne Warren (44483) *(G-19535)*

Clarkwestern Dietrich Building (HQ)......513 870-1100
9100 Centre Pointe Dr # 210 West Chester (45069) *(G-19835)*

Classic Countertops LLC......330 882-4220
1519 Kenmore Blvd Akron (44314) *(G-125)*

Classic Evolution Inc......216 440-0559
910 Lake Rd Medina (44256) *(G-13388)*

Classic Exhaust......440 466-5460
805 Pro Gram Pkwy Geneva (44041) *(G-10344)*

Classic Laminations Inc......440 735-1333
7703 First Pl Ste B Cleveland (44146) *(G-5042)*

Classic Metal Roofing Systems, Piqua Also called Isaiah Industries Inc *(G-16280)*

Classic Metals Ltd......330 763-1162
7051 State Route 83 Holmesville (44633) *(G-11100)*

Classic Monuments, Piqua Also called Piqua Granite & Marble Co Inc *(G-16304)*

Classic Optical Labs Inc......330 759-8245
3710 Belmont Ave Youngstown (44505) *(G-21052)*

Classic Recipe Chili Inc......513 771-1441
10592 Taconic Ter Cincinnati (45215) *(G-3584)*

Classic Reproductions......937 548-9839
5315 Meeker Rd Greenville (45331) *(G-10493)*

Classic Sign Company Inc......419 420-0058
112 Lagrange St Findlay (45840) *(G-9809)*

Classic Stone Company Inc......614 833-3946
4090 Janitrol Rd Columbus (43228) *(G-6934)*

Classic Tool Inc......330 922-1933
4278 Hudson Dr Stow (44224) *(G-17740)*

Classic Toy Company Inc......216 851-2000
12825 Taft Ave Cleveland (44108) *(G-5043)*

Clay Burley Products Co (PA)......740 452-3633
455 Gordon St Roseville (43777) *(G-16728)*

Clay Burley Products Co......740 697-0221
451 Gordon St Roseville (43777) *(G-16729)*

Clay LBC Co......740 492-5055
59260 County Road 9 Newcomerstown (43832) *(G-15111)*

Clay Logan Products Company......740 385-2184
201 S Walnut St Logan (43138) *(G-12172)*

Claycor Inc......419 318-7290
5924 American Rd E Toledo (43612) *(G-18399)*

Clayton Manufacturing Company......513 563-1300
3051 Exon Ave Cincinnati (45241) *(G-3585)*

Clayton Mfg Co, Cincinnati Also called Clayton Manufacturing Company *(G-3585)*

Clean Harbors Envmtl Svcs Inc......330 425-3825
1672 Highland Rd Twinsburg (44087) *(G-18914)*

Clean Jeans Laundry Room, Mansfield Also called Premier Office *(G-12668)*

Clean Water Conditioning......614 475-4532
305 Sumption Dr Columbus (43230) *(G-6935)*

Cleancut, West Chester Also called Safeway Safety Step Llc *(G-19941)*

Cleaning By Sndra Msters Touch......216 524-6827
6516 Gale Dr Seven Hills (44131) *(G-17061)*

Cleaning Lady Inc......419 589-5566
190 Stewart Rd N Mansfield (44905) *(G-12581)*

Cleaning Tech Group LLC (HQ)......513 870-0100
4933 Provident Dr West Chester (45246) *(G-19990)*

Cleaning Tech Group LLC......513 870-0100
4933 Provident Dr West Chester (45246) *(G-19991)*

Cleaning Technologies Grp, Tiffin Also called Nmgg Ctg LLC *(G-18234)*

Cleanlife Energy LLC......216 661-7872
2400 Superior Ave E LI Cleveland (44114) *(G-5044)*

Cleanlife Products, Springboro Also called No Rinse Laboratories LLC *(G-17492)*

Clear Channel, Lima Also called Iheartcommunications Inc *(G-12026)*

Clear Creek Screw Machine Corp......740 969-2113
4900 Julian Rd Sw Amanda (43102) *(G-562)*

Clear Fold Door Inc......440 735-1351
7703 First Pl Ste A Cleveland (44146) *(G-5045)*

Clear Image Technology LLC......440 366-4330
26202 Detroit Rd Ste 340 Westlake (44145) *(G-20260)*

Clear Images LLC......419 241-9347
121 11th St Toledo (43604) *(G-18400)*

Clear Packaging Films Inc......513 860-9053
9053 Le Saint Dr West Chester (45014) *(G-19836)*

Clear Run Lumber Co......740 747-2665
2830 State Route 229 Marengo (43334) *(G-12748)*

Clearbrook Farms, Cincinnati Also called Cincinnati Preserving Company *(G-3563)*

Clearfield Ohio Holdings Inc......740 947-5121
300 E 2nd St Waverly (45690) *(G-19705)*

Clearflite Inc......440 281-7368
5445 E Lake Rd Sheffield Lake (44054) *(G-17118)*

Clearly Visible Mobile Wash......440 543-9299
8473 Tulip Ln Chagrin Falls (44023) *(G-3080)*

Clearpath Utlity Solutions LLC......740 661-4240
8155 Ridge Rd Zanesville (43701) *(G-21289)*

Clearsonic Manufacturing Inc......330 650-1420
1223 Norton Rd Hudson (44236) *(G-11164)*

Clearwater One LLC......216 554-4747
21400 Lorain Rd Cleveland (44126) *(G-5046)*

Clearwater Systems Inc......330 262-5515
1799 Akron Rd Wooster (44691) *(G-20758)*

Clearwater Wood Group LLC......567 644-9951
4401 Hunts Landing Rd Hebron (43025) *(G-10862)*

Clecorr Inc......216 961-5500
10610 Berea Rd Rear Cleveland (44102) *(G-5047)*

Clecorr Packaging, Cleveland Also called Clecorr Inc *(G-5047)*

Clemens License Agency 614 288-8007
12825 Wheaton Ave Pickerington (43147) **(G-16188)**
Cleobrothers & Company LLC 614 985-3639
200 E Campus View Blvd Columbus (43235) **(G-6936)**
Clermont Steel Fabricators LLC 513 732-6033
2565 Old State Route 32 Batavia (45103) **(G-1173)**
Clermont Sun Publishing Co 937 444-3441
219 S High St Mount Orab (45154) **(G-14578)**
Cletronics Inc 330 239-2002
2262 Port Centre Dr Medina (44256) **(G-13389)**
Cleveland Bagel Company LLC 216 385-7723
4309 Larrain Ave Cleveland (44113) **(G-5048)**
Cleveland Bagel Company, The, Cleveland *Also called Cleveland Bagel Company LLC* **(G-5048)**
Cleveland Bean Sprout Inc 216 881-2112
2675 E 40th St Cleveland (44115) **(G-5049)**
Cleveland Black Oxide, Cleveland *Also called Tatham Schulz Incorporated* **(G-6295)**
Cleveland Black Pages, Cleveland *Also called Lanier & Associates Inc* **(G-5681)**
Cleveland Bulk Terminal, Cleveland *Also called Erie Sand & Gravel Co Inc* **(G-5296)**
Cleveland Business Supply LLC 888 831-0088
8193 Avery Rd Ste 200 Broadview Heights (44147) **(G-2108)**
Cleveland Canvas Goods Mfg Co 216 361-4567
1960 E 57th St Cleveland (44103) **(G-5050)**
Cleveland Carbide Tool Co 440 974-1155
7755 Division Dr Mentor (44060) **(G-13545)**
Cleveland Church Supply, Cleveland *Also called Novak J F Manufacturing Co LLC* **(G-5918)**
Cleveland Circuits Corp 216 267-9020
15516 Industrial Pkwy Cleveland (44135) **(G-5051)**
Cleveland Citizen Pubg Co 216 861-4283
2012 W 25th St Ste 900 Cleveland (44113) **(G-5052)**
Cleveland City Forge Inc 440 647-5400
46950 State Route 18 Wellington (44090) **(G-19739)**
Cleveland Coca-Cola Btlg Inc 216 690-2653
25000 Miles Rd Bedford Heights (44146) **(G-1480)**
Cleveland Controls Inc 216 398-0330
1111 Brookpark Rd Cleveland (44109) **(G-5053)**
Cleveland Coppersmithing Works 330 607-3998
4830 Hawkins Rd Richfield (44286) **(G-16618)**
Cleveland Copy & Prtg Svc LLC (PA) 216 861-0324
1835 E 30th St Fl 3 Cleveland (44114) **(G-5054)**
Cleveland Cstm Pllet Crate Inc 216 881-1414
4201 Lakeside Ave E Cleveland (44114) **(G-5055)**
Cleveland Custom Cabinets LLC 213 663-0606
19561 Miles Rd Cleveland (44128) **(G-5056)**
Cleveland Deburring Machine Co 216 472-0200
3370 W 140th St Cleveland (44111) **(G-5057)**
Cleveland Die & Mfg Co 216 941-7268
14735 Lorain Ave Cleveland (44111) **(G-5058)**
Cleveland Die & Mfg Co (PA) 440 243-3404
20303 1st Ave Middleburg Heights (44130) **(G-13904)**
Cleveland Die & Mfg Co 440 243-3404
20303 1st Ave Cleveland (44130) **(G-5059)**
Cleveland Division, Brecksville *Also called Terex Utilities Inc* **(G-2076)**
Cleveland Drapery Stitch Inc 216 252-3857
12890 Berea Rd Cleveland (44111) **(G-5060)**
Cleveland Electric Labs Co (PA) 800 447-2207
1776 Enterprise Pkwy Twinsburg (44087) **(G-18915)**
Cleveland Finishing Inc 440 572-5475
16979 Falmouth Dr Strongsville (44136) **(G-17904)**
Cleveland Flame Hardening, Euclid *Also called Detroit Flame Hardening Co* **(G-9574)**
Cleveland FP Inc (PA) 216 249-4900
12819 Coit Rd Cleveland (44108) **(G-5061)**
Cleveland Gas Systems LLC 216 391-7780
10325 State Route 43 N Streetsboro (44241) **(G-17844)**
Cleveland Gear Company Inc (HQ) 216 641-9000
3249 E 80th St Cleveland (44104) **(G-5062)**
Cleveland Granite & Marble LLC 216 291-7637
4121 Carnegie Ave Cleveland (44103) **(G-5063)**
Cleveland Hdwr & Forging Co (PA) 216 641-5200
3270 E 79th St Cleveland (44104) **(G-5064)**
Cleveland Hollow Boring Inc 216 883-1926
4501 Lakeside Ave E Cleveland (44114) **(G-5065)**
Cleveland Hoya Corp 440 234-5703
94 Pelret Industrial Pkwy Berea (44017) **(G-1606)**
Cleveland Indus Training Ctr, Cleveland *Also called Borman Enterprises Inc* **(G-4926)**
Cleveland Instrument Corp 440 826-1800
6430 Eastland Rd Ste 2 Brookpark (44142) **(G-2153)**
Cleveland Iron Workers Members 216 687-2290
2121 Euclid Ave Mm304 Cleveland (44115) **(G-5066)**
Cleveland Jewish News, Cleveland *Also called Cleveland Jewish Publ Co* **(G-5067)**
Cleveland Jewish Publ Co 216 454-8300
23880 Commerce Park Ste 1 Cleveland (44122) **(G-5067)**
Cleveland Jewish Publ Co Fdn 216 454-8300
23800 Commerce Park Beachwood (44122) **(G-1261)**
Cleveland Letter Service Inc 216 781-8300
8351 Clover Ln Chagrin Falls (44022) **(G-3052)**
Cleveland Magazine, Cleveland *Also called Great Lakes Publishing Company* **(G-5455)**
Cleveland Medical Devices Inc 216 426-0365
4415 Euclid Ave Ste 400 Cleveland (44103) **(G-5068)**
Cleveland Menu Printing Inc 216 241-5256
1441 E 17th St Cleveland (44114) **(G-5069)**
Cleveland Metal Processing Inc (PA) 440 243-3404
20303 1st Ave Cleveland (44130) **(G-5070)**
Cleveland Metal Stamping Co 440 234-0010
1231 W Bagley Rd Ste 1 Berea (44017) **(G-1607)**
Cleveland Offset Press Co Inc 440 845-9137
1378 E 17th St Cleveland (44114) **(G-5071)**
Cleveland Pigment Blending LLC 330 794-6960
1732 E Market St Akron (44305) **(G-126)**
Cleveland Plant and Flower Co 614 478-9900
2370 Marilyn Ln Columbus (43219) **(G-6937)**
Cleveland Plastic Fabricat 216 797-7300
25861 Tungsten Rd Euclid (44132) **(G-9572)**
Cleveland Plating 216 249-0300
1028 E 134th St Cleveland (44110) **(G-5072)**
Cleveland Printwear Inc 216 521-5500
13300 Madison Ave Cleveland (44107) **(G-5073)**
Cleveland Prosthetic Center, Cleveland *Also called Acor Orthopaedic Inc* **(G-4696)**
Cleveland Punch and Die Co, Ravenna *Also called True Industries Inc* **(G-16569)**
Cleveland Quarries, Vermilion *Also called Irg Operating LLC* **(G-19329)**
Cleveland Range LLC 216 481-4900
18901 Euclid Ave Cleveland (44117) **(G-5074)**
Cleveland Range LLC (HQ) 216 481-4900
18301 Saint Clair Ave Cleveland (44110) **(G-5075)**
Cleveland Rebabbitting Service 216 433-0123
15593 Brookpark Rd Cleveland (44142) **(G-5076)**
Cleveland Rebar, Akron *Also called Akron Rebar Co* **(G-54)**
Cleveland Reclaim Inds Inc 440 282-4917
7400 Industrial Pkwy Dr Lorain (44053) **(G-12238)**
Cleveland Recycling Plant, Cleveland *Also called Caraustar Industries Inc* **(G-4973)**
Cleveland Roll Forming Co 216 281-0202
3170 W 32nd St Cleveland (44109) **(G-5077)**
Cleveland Rubber Products LLC 440 564-7100
9988 Kinsman Rd Newbury (44065) **(G-15084)**
Cleveland Safe Co, Cleveland *Also called National Security Products* **(G-5860)**
Cleveland Scene, Cleveland *Also called Voice Media Group Inc* **(G-6425)**
Cleveland Shiprepair Company, Cleveland *Also called Manitowoc Company Inc* **(G-5739)**
Cleveland Smacna 440 877-3500
6060 Royalton Rd Cleveland (44133) **(G-5078)**
Cleveland Special Tool Inc 440 944-1600
1351 E 286th St Wickliffe (44092) **(G-20362)**
Cleveland Specialty Insptn Svc 440 578-1046
8562 East Ave Mentor (44060) **(G-13546)**
Cleveland Specialty Pdts Inc 216 281-8300
2130 W 110th St Cleveland (44102) **(G-5079)**
Cleveland Steel Container Corp 330 656-5600
10048 Aurora Hudson Rd Streetsboro (44241) **(G-17845)**
Cleveland Steel Container Corp 330 544-2271
412 Mason St Niles (44446) **(G-15147)**
Cleveland Steel Specialty Co 216 464-9400
26001 Richmond Rd Bedford Heights (44146) **(G-1481)**
Cleveland Steel Tool Company 216 681-7400
474 E 105th St Cleveland (44108) **(G-5080)**
Cleveland Syrup Corp (PA) 330 963-1900
2200 Highland Rd Twinsburg (44087) **(G-18916)**
Cleveland Tool and Machine Inc 216 267-6010
5240 Smith Rd Ste 3 Cleveland (44142) **(G-5081)**
Cleveland Track Material Inc (HQ) 216 641-4000
6917 Bessemer Ave Cleveland (44127) **(G-5082)**
Cleveland Track Material Inc 216 641-4000
6917 Bessemer Ave Cleveland (44127) **(G-5083)**
Cleveland Tungsten Inc 440 786-0800
7650 First Pl Ste E Bedford (44146) **(G-1415)**
Cleveland Valve & Gauge Co LLC 216 362-1702
4755 W 150th St Ste H Cleveland (44135) **(G-5084)**
Cleveland Vibrator Company, Leetonia *Also called 2828 Clinton Inc* **(G-11857)**
Cleveland Welding & Fabg LLC 440 364-5137
2175 Columbus Rd Cleveland (44113) **(G-5085)**
Cleveland Wheels 440 937-6211
1160 Center Rd Avon (44011) **(G-989)**
Cleveland Whiskey LLC 216 881-8481
1768 E 25th St Cleveland (44114) **(G-5086)**
Cleveland Wire Cloth & Mfg Co 216 341-1832
3573 E 78th St Cleveland (44105) **(G-5087)**
Clevelandcrystals, Highland Heights *Also called Gooch & Housego (ohio) LLC* **(G-10914)**
Clevemed, Cleveland *Also called Cleveland Medical Devices Inc* **(G-5068)**
Clevex Inc (PA) 614 675-3757
1275 Kinnear Rd Ste 223 Columbus (43212) **(G-6938)**
Clevland Valve & Gauge Co, Ottawa Hills *Also called Phoenix Partners LLC* **(G-15817)**
Click Burial Vault and Mfg Co 330 343-1143
1118 Lakeview Rd Nw New Philadelphia (44663) **(G-14891)**
Click It Connect Corp (PA) 440 247-4998
16 S Main St Chagrin Falls (44022) **(G-3053)**
Clickit, Chagrin Falls *Also called Click It Connect Corp* **(G-3053)**
Clicks Document Management, Cleveland *Also called Marcus Uppe Inc* **(G-5742)**
Clientrax Software, Grove City *Also called Clientrax Technology Solutions* **(G-10549)**

ALPHABETIC

Clientrax Technology Solutions 614 875-2245
3347 Mcdowell Rd Grove City (43123) *(G-10549)*

Cliffco Stands Inc 937 382-3700
397 Starbuck Rd Wilmington (45177) *(G-20659)*

Cliffs, Cleveland *Also called Northshore Mining Company (G-5914)*

Cliffs & Associates Ltd 216 694-5700
1100 Superior Ave E # 1500 Cleveland (44114) *(G-5088)*

Cliffs High Performance 740 397-2921
20579 Berry Rd Mount Vernon (43050) *(G-14616)*

Cliffs Logan County Coal LLC 216 694-5700
200 Public Sq Ste 3300 Cleveland (44114) *(G-5089)*

Cliffs Michigan Operation 216 694-5303
District 1072 Ste 1500 Cleveland (44114) *(G-5090)*

Cliffs Mining Company (HQ) 216 694-5700
200 Public Sq Ste 3300 Cleveland (44114) *(G-5091)*

Cliffs Minnesota Minerals Co 216 694-5700
1100 Superior Ave E Cleveland (44114) *(G-5092)*

Cliffs Natural Resources Inc (PA) 216 694-5700
200 Public Sq Ste 3300 Cleveland (44114) *(G-5093)*

Clifton Steel Company (PA) 216 662-6111
16500 Rockside Rd Maple Heights (44137) *(G-12731)*

Climateright Air, Columbus *Also called Climateright LLC (G-6939)*

Climateright LLC 800 725-4628
777 Manor Park Dr Columbus (43228) *(G-6939)*

Climax Metal Products Company 440 943-8898
8141 Tyler Blvd Mentor (44060) *(G-13547)*

Climax Packaging Machinery, Hamilton *Also called G L Industries Inc (G-10696)*

Cline Signs LLC 513 396-7446
3272 Highland Ave Cincinnati (45213) *(G-3586)*

Clinical Computing Inc 513 651-3803
205 W 4th St Ste 810 Cincinnati (45202) *(G-3587)*

Clinical Specialties Inc (PA) 888 873-7888
6955 Treeline Dr Ste A Brecksville (44141) *(G-2040)*

Clinicl Otcms Mngmnt Syst LLC 330 650-9900
9200 S Hills Blvd Ste 200 Broadview Heights (44147) *(G-2109)*

Clint's Prntng, Beavercreek *Also called Clints Printing Inc (G-1373)*

Clinton Foundry Ltd 419 243-6885
1202 W Bancroft St Toledo (43606) *(G-18401)*

Clinton Machine Co Inc 330 882-6743
6270 Van Buren Rd New Franklin (44216) *(G-14823)*

Clinton Pattern Works Inc 419 243-0855
1215 W Bancroft St Toledo (43606) *(G-18402)*

Clinton Supply, Ravenna *Also called Tri-Way Rebar Inc (G-16568)*

Clinton Supply, Akron *Also called Tri-Way Rebar Inc (G-447)*

Clints Printing Inc 937 426-2771
3963 Rockfield Dr Beavercreek (45430) *(G-1373)*

Clipper Magazine LLC 937 534-0470
2360 W Dorothy Ln Ste 101 Moraine (45439) *(G-14472)*

Clipper Products Inc 513 688-7300
675 Cncnnati Batavia Pike Cincinnati (45245) *(G-3295)*

Clipson S Metalworking, Cincinnati *Also called Clipsons Metal Working Inc (G-3588)*

Clipsons Metal Working Inc 513 772-6393
127 Novner Dr Cincinnati (45215) *(G-3588)*

Clm Marketing Inc 440 526-8613
4200 Royalton Rd Brecksville (44141) *(G-2041)*

Clondalkin Group 440 324-2222
41740 Schadden Rd Elyria (44035) *(G-9395)*

Clopay Building Pdts Co Inc (HQ) 513 770-4800
8585 Duke Blvd Mason (45040) *(G-12998)*

Clopay Building Pdts Co Inc 937 526-4301
101 N Liberty St Russia (45363) *(G-16762)*

Clopay Building Pdts Co Inc 937 440-6403
1400 W Market St Troy (45373) *(G-18810)*

Clopay Corporation (HQ) 800 282-2260
8585 Duke Blvd Mason (45040) *(G-12999)*

Clopay Corporation 440 542-9215
7905 Cochran Rd Ste 500 Solon (44139) *(G-17278)*

Clopay Corporation 513 742-1984
1260 W Sharon Rd Cincinnati (45240) *(G-3589)*

Clopay Plastic Products Co Inc (HQ) 513 770-4800
8585 Duke Blvd Mason (45040) *(G-13000)*

Clorox Company 513 445-1840
5181 Natorp Blvd Ste 610 Mason (45040) *(G-13001)*

Clorox Sales Company 440 892-1700
24500 Center Ridge Rd # 240 Westlake (44145) *(G-20261)*

Closet Factory, The, Cleveland *Also called Home Stor & Off Solutions Inc (G-5521)*

Closets By Mike 740 607-2212
517 Winton Ave Zanesville (43701) *(G-21290)*

Closettec of North East Ohio 216 464-0042
5222 Richmond Rd Bedford (44146) *(G-1416)*

Clover Pallet LLC 330 454-5592
5219 Violet Knoll Ave Ne Canton (44705) *(G-2660)*

Cloverdale Food Processing, Amherst *Also called Chefs Pantry Inc (G-594)*

Cloverleaf Office Slutions LLC 614 219-9050
5394 Old Creek Ln Hilliard (43026) *(G-10939)*

Clovernook Center For The Bli (PA) 513 522-3860
7000 Hamilton Ave Cincinnati (45231) *(G-3590)*

Clovervale Farms Inc (HQ) 440 960-0146
8133 Cooper Foster Pk Rd Amherst (44001) *(G-595)*

Clovervale Foods, Amherst *Also called Clovervale Farms Inc (G-595)*

CLS FABRICATING, INC., Canton *Also called Concrete Leveling Systems Inc (G-2666)*

Club 513 LLC 800 530-2574
201 E 5th St Fl 19 Cincinnati (45202) *(G-3591)*

Cluster Software Inc 614 760-9380
2674 Billingsley Rd Columbus (43235) *(G-6940)*

Clyde Ferenbaugh 740 397-0287
Allen Rd Mount Vernon (43050) *(G-14617)*

Clyde Foam, Clyde *Also called Clyde Tool & Die Inc (G-6538)*

Clyde Tool & Die Inc (PA) 419 547-9574
524 S Church St Clyde (43410) *(G-6538)*

CM Paula Company (PA) 513 759-7473
6049 Hi Tek Ct Mason (45040) *(G-13002)*

CM Printing, Columbus *Also called Dispatch Printing Company (G-7030)*

CMA, Bolivar *Also called Cable Mfg & Assembly Inc (G-1929)*

CMA Supply Company Inc 513 942-6663
9984 Commerce Park Dr West Chester (45246) *(G-19992)*

CMC Consulting, Cleveland *Also called CMC Pharmaceuticals Inc (G-5094)*

CMC Daymark Corporation 419 354-2591
12830 S Dixie Hwy Bowling Green (43402) *(G-1980)*

CMC Electronics Cincin 513 573-6316
7500 Innovation Way Mason (45040) *(G-13003)*

CMC Group Inc (PA) 419 352-9567
12836 S Dixie Hwy Bowling Green (43402) *(G-1981)*

CMC Pharmaceuticals Inc (PA) 216 600-9430
7100 Euclid Ave Ste 152 Cleveland (44103) *(G-5094)*

Cme Federal Credit Union 614 876-1382
4099 Trueman Blvd Hilliard (43026) *(G-10940)*

CMF Custom Metal Finishers 513 821-8145
7616 Anthony Wayne Ave Cincinnati (45216) *(G-3592)*

Cmg Company Plant 2, West Mansfield *Also called M & M Concepts Inc (G-20100)*

CMI, Lancaster *Also called Crists Machining Inc (G-11700)*

CMI Holding Company Crawford 419 468-9122
1310 Freese Works Pl Galion (44833) *(G-10259)*

CMI Industry Americas Inc (HQ) 330 332-4661
435 W Wilson St Salem (44460) *(G-16883)*

CMI Technology Inc 937 832-2000
65 Haas Dr Englewood (45322) *(G-9513)*

CMS, Strongsville *Also called Condition Monitoring Supplies (G-17906)*

Cmt Machining & Fabg LLC 937 652-3740
1411 Knnard Kingscreek Rd Urbana (43078) *(G-19151)*

Cnb LLC 419 528-3109
84 Briggs Dr Ontario (44906) *(G-15685)*

CNB Machining and Mfg LLC 330 877-7920
1052 Manning Rd Nw Hartville (44632) *(G-10819)*

Cnc Indexing Feeding Tech LLC (PA) 513 770-4200
7944 Innovation Way Ste B Mason (45040) *(G-13004)*

Cnc Machine Shop, Cleveland *Also called Firstar Precision Corporation (G-5350)*

Cnd Machine, Massillon *Also called C-N-D Industries Inc (G-13118)*

CNG Business Group 614 771-0877
4974 Scioto Darby Rd A Hilliard (43026) *(G-10941)*

CNG Fueling LLC 330 772-2403
1266 State Route 7 Ne F Brookfield (44403) *(G-2121)*

Cnr Marketing Ltd 937 293-1030
3149 Far Hills Ave Dayton (45429) *(G-8233)*

Cns Inc (PA) 513 631-7073
3716 Montgomery Rd Cincinnati (45207) *(G-3593)*

Co Pac Services Inc 216 688-1780
3113 W 110th St Cleveland (44111) *(G-5095)*

Co- Ax Technology Inc 440 914-9200
30301 Emerald Valley Pkwy Solon (44139) *(G-17279)*

Coach Inc 330 491-8658
4205 Belden Village Mall Canton (44718) *(G-2661)*

Coach Inc 513 539-8087
849 Premium Outlets Dr Monroe (45050) *(G-14398)*

Coach Inc 614 885-6184
1500 Polaris Pkwy # 1198 Columbus (43240) *(G-6644)*

Coach Inc 419 471-9033
5001 Monroe St Ste 1743 Toledo (43623) *(G-18403)*

Coach Inc 440 871-0103
183 Main St Westlake (44145) *(G-20262)*

Coach Tool & Die Inc 937 890-4716
5728 Webster St Dayton (45414) *(G-8234)*

Coal Resources Inc 740 338-3100
46226 National Rd W Saint Clairsville (43950) *(G-16786)*

Coal Services Inc 740 795-5220
155 Highway 7 S Powhatan Point (43942) *(G-16488)*

Coal Services Group, Powhatan Point *Also called Coal Services Inc (G-16488)*

Coalescence LLC 614 861-3639
3455 Millennium Ct Columbus (43219) *(G-6941)*

Coastal Diamond, Mentor *Also called Performance Superabrasives LLC (G-13685)*

Coastal Diamond Incorporated 440 946-7171
7255 Industrial Park Blvd A Mentor (44060) *(G-13548)*

Coat All 419 659-2757
4599 Campbell Rd Columbus Grove (45830) *(G-7792)*

Coate Concrete Products Inc (PA) 937 698-4181
7330 W State Route 571 West Milton (45383) *(G-20106)*

Coater Services Inc 330 499-1407
  1205 5th St Sw Canton (44707) *(G-2662)*

Coating Applications Intl LLC 513 956-5222
  2860 Cooper Rd Ste 200 Cincinnati (45241) *(G-3594)*

Coating Control Inc 330 453-9136
  825 Navarre Rd Sw Canton (44707) *(G-2663)*

Coating Systems Inc 513 367-5600
  150 Sales Ave Harrison (45030) *(G-10774)*

Coatings & Colorants, Cincinnati *Also called Evonik Corporation* *(G-3726)*

Coaxial Dynamics, Cleveland *Also called CDI Industries Inc* *(G-4999)*

Cobb Industries Inc 440 946-4695
  7605 Saint Clair Ave Mentor (44060) *(G-13549)*

Cobblers Corner LLC 330 482-4005
  1115 Village Plz Columbiana (44408) *(G-6610)*

Coblentz Brothers Inc 330 857-7211
  7101 S Kohler Rd Apple Creek (44606) *(G-634)*

Coblentz Chocolate Co, Walnut Creek *Also called Walnut Creek Chocolate Company* *(G-19471)*

Cobra Motorcycles Mfg 330 207-3844
  11511 Springfield Rd North Lima (44452) *(G-15312)*

Cobra Plastics Inc 330 425-3669
  1244 Highland Rd E Macedonia (44056) *(G-12442)*

Coburn Inc (PA) 419 368-4051
  636 Ashland Cnty Rd 30 A Hayesville (44838) *(G-10843)*

Coca-Cola, Circleville *Also called Scioto Coca Cola* *(G-4641)*

Coca-Cola 937 446-4644
  136 Fairview Ave Sardinia (45171) *(G-17027)*

Coca-Cola Bottling Co Cnsld 419 422-3743
  201 N Shore Dr Lima (45801) *(G-12000)*

Coca-Cola Bottling Co Cnsld 740 353-3133
  5050 Old Scioto Trl Portsmouth (45662) *(G-16433)*

Coca-Cola Bottling Co Cnsld 419 229-2000
  201 N Shore Dr Lima (45801) *(G-12001)*

Coca-Cola Bottling Co Cnsld 937 878-5000
  1000 Coca Cola Blvd Dayton (45424) *(G-8235)*

Coca-Cola Bottling Co Cnsld 513 527-6600
  5100 Duck Creek Rd Cincinnati (45227) *(G-3595)*

Coca-Cola Company 614 491-6305
  2455 Watkins Rd Columbus (43207) *(G-6942)*

Coca-Cola Company 614 863-7200
  4500 Groves Rd Columbus (43232) *(G-6943)*

Coca-Cola Company 330 783-1982
  531 E Indianola Ave Youngstown (44502) *(G-21053)*

Coca-Cola Company 419 522-2653
  100 Industrial Pkwy Mansfield (44903) *(G-12582)*

Coca-Cola Company 937 446-4644
  7906 Yochum Rd Sardinia (45171) *(G-17028)*

Coca-Cola Company 440 324-3335
  1410 Lake Ave Elyria (44035) *(G-9396)*

Coca-Cola Company 740 452-3608
  154 S 7th St Zanesville (43701) *(G-21291)*

Coca-Cola Company 513 898-7800
  10151 Carver Rd Ste 500 Blue Ash (45242) *(G-1767)*

Coca-Cola Company 440 269-1433
  4800 E 355th St Willoughby (44094) *(G-20457)*

Coca-Cola Refreshments USA Inc 419 476-6622
  3970 Catawba St Toledo (43612) *(G-18404)*

Coca-Cola Refreshments USA Inc 330 425-4401
  1882 Highland Rd Twinsburg (44087) *(G-18917)*

Codonics Inc (PA) 216 226-1066
  17991 Englewood Dr Ste D Cleveland (44130) *(G-5096)*

Coe Manufacturing Company (HQ) 440 352-9381
  70 W Erie St Ste 150 Painesville (44077) *(G-15865)*

Coffee News 330 688-0952
  4305 Cheval Cir Stow (44224) *(G-17741)*

Coffelt Candy Inc (PA) 937 399-8772
  6050 Urbana Rd Springfield (45502) *(G-17533)*

Coffey and Associates, West Chester *Also called DC Controls LLC* *(G-19997)*

Coffing Corporation (PA) 513 919-2813
  5336 Lesourdsville Rd Liberty Twp (45011) *(G-11972)*

Cohen Brothers Inc (PA) 513 422-3696
  1723 Woodlawn Ave Middletown (45044) *(G-14031)*

Cohesant Inc (PA) 216 910-1700
  3601 Green Rd Ste 308 Beachwood (44122) *(G-1262)*

Coil Specialty Chemicals LLC 740 236-2407
  2375 Glendale Rd Marietta (45750) *(G-12775)*

Coil Technology Inc 330 601-1350
  2109 Great Trails Dr Wooster (44691) *(G-20759)*

Coil Tek, Wooster *Also called Coil Technology Inc* *(G-20759)*

Coin World, Sidney *Also called Amos Press Inc* *(G-17168)*

Coit Tool Company Inc 440 946-3377
  38134 Western Pkwy Unit 3 Willoughby (44094) *(G-20458)*

Col-Pump Company Inc 330 482-1029
  131 E Railroad St Columbiana (44408) *(G-6611)*

Colburn Dairy, Waverly *Also called C & C Mobile Homes LLC* *(G-19704)*

Colby Properties LLC 937 390-0816
  2071 N Bechtle Ave Springfield (45504) *(G-17534)*

Colby Woodworking Inc 937 224-7676
  1912 Lucille Dr Dayton (45404) *(G-8236)*

Cold Duck Screen Prtg & EMB Co 330 426-1900
  540 Sugar Camp Dr East Palestine (44413) *(G-9231)*

Cold Headed Fas Assemblies Inc 330 833-0800
  1875 Harsh Ave Se Massillon (44646) *(G-13120)*

Cold Heading Co 216 581-3000
  4444 Lee Rd Cleveland (44128) *(G-5097)*

Cold Jet LLC (PA) 513 831-3211
  455 Wards Corner Rd # 100 Loveland (45140) *(G-12346)*

Coldstone Creamery, Powell *Also called Stella Lou LLC* *(G-16483)*

Coldwell Family Tree Farm 330 506-9012
  33320 Hull Rd Salineville (43945) *(G-16940)*

Coldwell Wilcox Tech LLC 513 758-1010
  3040 Forrer St Cincinnati (45209) *(G-3596)*

Cole Orthotics Prosthetic Ctr 419 476-4248
  723 Phillips Ave Bldg F Toledo (43612) *(G-18405)*

Cole Pak Inc 937 652-3910
  1138 Phoenix Dr Urbana (43078) *(G-19152)*

Cole Tool & Die Company 419 522-1272
  466 State Route 314 N Ontario (44903) *(G-15686)*

Coleman Machine Inc 740 695-3006
  49381 Firpoint Maynard Rd Saint Clairsville (43950) *(G-16787)*

Coleman Machine Company, Saint Clairsville *Also called Coleman Machine Inc* *(G-16787)*

Coleys Inc 440 967-5630
  1775 Liberty Ave Vermilion (44089) *(G-19324)*

Coleys Inc 440 967-5630
  1775 Liberty Ave Vermilion (44089) *(G-19325)*

Colfor Manufacturing Inc (HQ) 330 863-0404
  3255 Alliance Rd Nw Malvern (44644) *(G-12541)*

Colfor Manufacturing Inc 330 863-0404
  461 Knox Ct Minerva (44657) *(G-14319)*

Colgate-Palmolive Company 212 310-2000
  8800 Guernsey Indus Blvd Cambridge (43725) *(G-2452)*

Collaborative For Adaptive Lif 216 513-0572
  3250 W Market St Ste 205 Fairlawn (44333) *(G-9746)*

Collated Products Corp 440 946-1950
  35595 Curtis Blvd Unit D Willoughby (44095) *(G-20459)*

Colleen D Turner 419 886-4810
  72 Main St Bellville (44813) *(G-1568)*

College Issue, Piqua *Also called Atlantis Sportswear Inc* *(G-16250)*

Collegiate Connection 419 352-8333
  1420 E Wooster St Bowling Green (43402) *(G-1982)*

Collegiate Directories Inc 440 835-1172
  30205 Clemens Rd Ste C Cleveland (44145) *(G-5098)*

Collier Well Eqp & Sup Inc (PA) 330 345-3968
  3310 Columbus Rd Wooster (44691) *(G-20760)*

Colliers Cstmizing Fabrication 937 523-0420
  1675 W County Line Rd Urbana (43078) *(G-19153)*

Collins & Venco Venturo, Cincinnati *Also called Venco Manufacturing Inc* *(G-4560)*

Colonial Cabinets Inc 440 355-9663
  337 S Center St Lagrange (44050) *(G-11624)*

Colonial Fireworks Company 419 478-4945
  5225 Telegraph Rd Toledo (43612) *(G-18406)*

Colonial Machine Company Inc 330 673-5859
  1041 Mogadore Rd Kent (44240) *(G-11439)*

Colonial Patterns Inc 330 673-6475
  920 Overholt Rd Kent (44240) *(G-11440)*

Colonial Rubber Company (PA) 330 296-2831
  706 Oakwood St Ravenna (44266) *(G-16523)*

Colonial Surface Solutions Inc (PA) 419 659-5639
  4599 Campbell Rd Columbus Grove (45830) *(G-7793)*

Colonial Surface Solutions Inc 419 358-0129
  505 E Jefferson St Bluffton (45817) *(G-1910)*

Colonial Woodcraft Inc 513 779-8088
  1004 W Main St Lebanon (45036) *(G-11789)*

Colony Hardware, Cleveland *Also called Phillips Contractors Sup LLC* *(G-6002)*

Color 3 Embroidery Inc 330 652-9495
  387 Chestnut Ave Ne Warren (44483) *(G-19536)*

Color Bar Printing Centers Inc 216 595-3939
  4576 Renaissance Pkwy Cleveland (44128) *(G-5099)*

Color Brite Company Inc 216 441-4117
  5209 Grant Ave Cleveland (44125) *(G-5100)*

Color Process Inc 440 268-7100
  13900 Prospect Rd Strongsville (44149) *(G-17905)*

Coloramic Process Inc 440 275-1199
  2883 Industrial Park Dr Austinburg (44010) *(G-959)*

Coloramics LLC 614 876-1171
  4077 Weaver Ct S Hilliard (43026) *(G-10942)*

Coloring Book Solutions LLC 419 281-9641
  426 E 8th St Ashland (44805) *(G-723)*

Colormatrix Group Inc (HQ) 216 622-0100
  680 N Rocky River Dr Berea (44017) *(G-1608)*

Colormatrix Holdings Inc 440 930-3162
  680 N Rocky River Dr Berea (44017) *(G-1609)*

Colors, North Canton *Also called Jane Valentine* *(G-15244)*

Colortech Graphics & Printing (PA) 614 766-2400
  4000 Business Park Dr Columbus (43204) *(G-6944)*

Colortrend USA LLC 513 733-5111
  620 Shepherd Dr Cincinnati (45215) *(G-3597)*

Colossal Cupcakes 216 322-7656
  1060 Abbieshire Ave Lakewood (44107) *(G-11660)*

A L P H A B E T I C

Coltene/Whaledent Inc (HQ) 330 916-8800
235 Ascot Pkwy Cuyahoga Falls (44223) *(G-7981)*

Columbia, Vandalia Also called Datwyler Sling Sltions USA Inc *(G-19289)*

Columbia Cabinets Inc 440 748-1010
33549 E Royalton Rd 4-5 Columbia Station (44028) *(G-6584)*

Columbia Chemical Corporation 330 225-3200
1000 Western Dr Brunswick (44212) *(G-2217)*

Columbia Energy Group 614 460-4683
200 Civic Center Dr Columbus (43215) *(G-6945)*

Columbia Gas Meter Shop 614 460-5519
5315 Fisher Rd Columbus (43228) *(G-6946)*

Columbia Industries, Solon Also called Skidmore-Wilhelm Mfg Company *(G-17381)*

Columbia Industries, Euclid Also called Qcsm LLC *(G-9602)*

Columbia Machine Company 740 452-1736
961 Hughes St Zanesville (43701) *(G-21292)*

Columbia Midstream Group LLC 330 542-1095
10846 Stateline Rd New Middletown (44442) *(G-14875)*

Columbia Stamping Inc 440 236-6677
13676 Station Rd Columbia Station (44028) *(G-6585)*

Columbia Steel and Wire Inc 330 468-2709
30 W Aurora Rd Northfield (44067) *(G-15463)*

Columbiana Boiler Company LLC 330 482-3373
200 W Railroad St Columbiana (44408) *(G-6612)*

Columbiana Holding Co Inc (PA) 330 482-3373
200 W Railroad St Columbiana (44408) *(G-6613)*

Columbiana Metro Hsing Auth 330 385-6662
325 Moore St East Liverpool (43920) *(G-9207)*

Columbus Advanced Mfg Sftwr 614 433-0415
495 Village Park Dr Powell (43065) *(G-16467)*

Columbus Alive Inc 614 221-2449
34 S 3rd St Columbus (43215) *(G-6947)*

Columbus Bakery, Columbus Also called Kroger Co *(G-7270)*

Columbus Brewing Co, Columbus Also called District Brewing Co Inc *(G-7032)*

Columbus Bride 614 888-4567
34 S 3rd St Columbus (43215) *(G-6948)*

Columbus Castings, Columbus Also called Columbus Steel Castings Co *(G-6967)*

Columbus Coatings Company 614 492-6800
1800 Watkins Rd Columbus (43207) *(G-6949)*

Columbus Dispatch, Lewis Center Also called Dispatch Printing Company *(G-11895)*

Columbus Electrical Works Co 614 294-4651
777 N 4th St Columbus (43215) *(G-6950)*

Columbus Equipment Company 740 455-4036
818 Lee St Zanesville (43701) *(G-21293)*

Columbus Fire Fighters Union 614 481-8900
379 W Broad St Columbus (43215) *(G-6951)*

Columbus Gasket & Supply, Columbus Also called Columbus Gasket Co Inc *(G-6953)*

Columbus Gasket and Sup Co LLC 614 878-6041
1875 Lone Eagle St Columbus (43228) *(G-6952)*

Columbus Gasket Co Inc 614 878-6041
1875 Lone Eagle St Columbus (43228) *(G-6953)*

Columbus Graphics Inc 614 577-9360
7295 Rickly St Reynoldsburg (43068) *(G-16584)*

Columbus Heating & Vent Co 614 274-1177
182 N Yale Ave Columbus (43222) *(G-6954)*

Columbus Humungous Apparel LLC 614 824-2657
2913 Manola Dr Ste 100 Columbus (43209) *(G-6955)*

Columbus Industries Inc (PA) 740 983-2552
2938 State Route 752 Ashville (43103) *(G-849)*

Columbus Industries Inc 937 544-6896
11545 State Route 41 West Union (45693) *(G-20119)*

Columbus Instruments Intl Corp 614 276-0593
950 N Hague Ave Columbus (43204) *(G-6956)*

Columbus International Corp 614 323-1086
200 E Campus View Blvd # 200 Columbus (43235) *(G-6957)*

Columbus Jack Corporation 614 228-0185
2222 S 3rd St Columbus (43207) *(G-6958)*

Columbus Kombucha Company LLC 614 262-0000
930 Freeway Dr N Columbus (43229) *(G-6959)*

Columbus Machine Works Inc 614 409-0244
2491 Fairwood Ave Columbus (43207) *(G-6960)*

Columbus Marble Products Inc 614 766-2786
6843 Bowles Ct Dublin (43017) *(G-9063)*

Columbus McKinnon Corporation 330 332-5769
240 Pennsylvania Ave Salem (44460) *(G-16884)*

Columbus McKinnon Corporation 330 424-7248
7573 State Route 45 Lisbon (44432) *(G-12118)*

Columbus Messenger Company (PA) 614 272-5422
3500 Sullivant Ave Columbus (43204) *(G-6961)*

Columbus Messenger Company 740 852-0809
78 S Main St London (43140) *(G-12205)*

Columbus Mobile Welding 614 352-6052
110 S Preston St Centerburg (43011) *(G-3029)*

Columbus Mobility Specialist 614 825-8996
6330 Proprietors Rd Ste F Worthington (43085) *(G-20861)*

Columbus Oil Field Exploration, Powell Also called Columbus Oilfield Exploration *(G-16468)*

Columbus Oilfield Exploration 614 895-9520
80 Grace Dr Ste G Powell (43065) *(G-16468)*

Columbus Pipe and Equipment Co 614 444-7871
763 E Markison Ave Columbus (43207) *(G-6962)*

Columbus Prescr Rehabilitation 614 294-1600
975 Eastwind Dr Ste 155 Westerville (43081) *(G-20204)*

Columbus Processing Co LLC 614 492-8287
4300 Alum Creek Dr Columbus (43207) *(G-6963)*

Columbus Qcb, Inc., Blacklick Also called Cqcb Inc *(G-1694)*

Columbus Roof Trusses Inc (PA) 614 272-6464
2525 Fisher Rd Columbus (43204) *(G-6964)*

Columbus Roof Trusses Inc 740 763-3000
400 Marne Dr Newark (43055) *(G-14994)*

Columbus Serum Co 614 793-0615
7570 Donora Ln Columbus (43235) *(G-6965)*

Columbus Sign Company (PA) 614 252-3133
1515 E 5th Ave Columbus (43219) *(G-6966)*

Columbus Steel Castings Co 614 444-2121
2211 Parsons Ave Columbus (43207) *(G-6967)*

Columbus Steelmasters Inc 614 231-2141
660 Concrea Rd Columbus (43219) *(G-6968)*

Columbus Underground, Columbus Also called Evans Creative Group LLC *(G-7072)*

Columbus Washboard Company Ltd 740 380-3828
14 Gallagher Ave Logan (43138) *(G-12173)*

Columbus-Sports Publications 614 486-2202
1350 W 5th Ave Ste 30 Columbus (43212) *(G-6969)*

Com-Corp Industries Inc 216 431-6266
7601 Bittern Ave Cleveland (44103) *(G-5101)*

Com-Fab Inc 740 857-1107
4657 Price Hilliards Rd Plain City (43064) *(G-16327)*

Com-Net Software Specialists, Miamisburg Also called Signature Technologies
Inc *(G-13859)*

Combi Packaging Systems Llc 330 456-9333
5365 E Center Dr Ne Canton (44721) *(G-2664)*

Combine Grinding Co Inc 440 439-6148
7005 Krick Rd Bedford (44146) *(G-1417)*

Combined Container Board 513 530-5700
7741 School Rd Cincinnati (45249) *(G-3598)*

Combined Industrial Solutions 513 659-3091
944 Klondyke Rd Milford (45150) *(G-14131)*

Combined Tech Group Inc 937 274-4866
6061 Milo Rd Dayton (45414) *(G-8237)*

Comco Machinery Inc 513 248-8000
910 Lila Ave Milford (45150) *(G-14132)*

Comco Machnry, Milford Also called Comco Machinery Inc *(G-14132)*

Comcorp Inc. 718 981-1234
1801 Superior Ave E Cleveland (44114) *(G-5102)*

Comdess Company Inc 330 769-2094
8733 Wooster Pike Rd Seville (44273) *(G-17073)*

Comdoc Inc 330 899-8000
330 W Spring St Ste 100 Columbus (43215) *(G-6970)*

Comet Technologies USA Inc 234 284-7849
5675 Hudson Indus Pkwy Hudson (44236) *(G-11165)*

Comex Group, Cleveland Also called Comex North America Inc *(G-5103)*

Comex North America Inc (HQ) 303 307-2100
101 W Prospect Ave # 1020 Cleveland (44115) *(G-5103)*

Comfort Line Ltd 419 729-8520
5500 Enterprise Blvd Toledo (43612) *(G-18407)*

Command Alkon Incorporated 614 799-0600
6750 Crosby Ct Dublin (43016) *(G-9064)*

Command Plastic Corporation 800 321-8001
124 West Ave Tallmadge (44278) *(G-18139)*

Commconnect 937 414-0505
915 E Central Ave Dayton (45449) *(G-8238)*

Commercial Anodizing Co 440 942-8384
38387 Apollo Pkwy Willoughby (44094) *(G-20460)*

Commercial Bar & Cabinetry 330 743-1420
12 S Worthington St Youngstown (44502) *(G-21054)*

Commercial Bindery Inc 419 517-9914
2738 Shetland Rd Toledo (43617) *(G-18408)*

Commercial Cabinets, Youngstown Also called Commercial Bar & Cabinetry *(G-21054)*

Commercial Cutng Graphics LLC 419 526-4800
208 Central Ave Mansfield (44905) *(G-12583)*

Commercial Decal of Ohio Inc 330 385-7178
46686 Y And O Rd East Liverpool (43920) *(G-9208)*

Commercial Dock & Door Inc 440 951-1210
7653 Saint Clair Ave Mentor (44060) *(G-13550)*

Commercial Electric Pdts Corp (PA) 216 241-2886
1821 E 40th St Cleveland (44103) *(G-5104)*

Commercial Fluid Power, Dover Also called Commercial Honing LLC *(G-8971)*

Commercial Grinding Services 330 273-5040
1155 Industrial Pkwy # 1 Medina (44256) *(G-13390)*

Commercial Honing LLC (PA) 330 343-8896
2997 Progress St Dover (44622) *(G-8971)*

Commercial Honing Ohio Inc (PA) 330 343-8896
2997 Progress St Dover (44622) *(G-8972)*

Commercial Honing Ohio Inc 330 343-8896
2997 Progress St Dover (44622) *(G-8973)*

Commercial Interior Products, West Chester Also called CIP International Inc *(G-19833)*

Commercial Lubricants Inc 614 475-5952
2854 Johnstown Rd Columbus (43219) *(G-6971)*

Commercial Metal Forming, Youngstown Also called Steel Forming Inc *(G-21212)*

Commercial Minerals Inc 330 549-2165
  10900 South Ave North Lima (44452) *(G-15313)*

Commercial Mtal Fbricators Inc 937 233-4911
  150 Commerce Park Dr Dayton (45404) *(G-8239)*

Commercial Music Service Co 740 746-8500
  6312 Goss Rd Sugar Grove (43155) *(G-18011)*

Commercial Prtg of Greenvill 937 548-3835
  314 S Broadway St Greenville (45331) *(G-10494)*

Commercial Steel Treating Co 216 431-8204
  1394 E 39th St Cleveland (44114) *(G-5105)*

Commercial Transportation Svcs 216 267-2000
  12487 Plaza Dr Cleveland (44130) *(G-5106)*

Commercial Turf Products Ltd 330 995-7000
  1777 Miller Pkwy Streetsboro (44241) *(G-17846)*

Commercial Vehicle Group Inc (PA) 614 289-5360
  7800 Walton Pkwy New Albany (43054) *(G-14753)*

Commercial Vehicle Group Inc 740 676-6542
  60581 State Route 7 Shadyside (43947) *(G-17080)*

Commissary Brewing 614 636-3164
  1400 Dublin Rd Columbus (43215) *(G-6972)*

Commodity Blenders Inc 419 846-3155
  10510 Myers Rd West Salem (44287) *(G-20112)*

Commonwealth Aluminum Mtls LLC 216 910-3400
  25825 Science Park Dr # 400 Beachwood (44122) *(G-1263)*

Commscope Technologies LLC 216 272-0055
  1668 Sunview Rd Cleveland (44124) *(G-5107)*

Commtech Solutions Inc 440 458-4870
  38900 Arbor Ct Grafton (44044) *(G-10421)*

Communication Concepts Inc 937 426-8600
  508 Mill Stone Dr Beavercreek (45434) *(G-1326)*

Communication Resources Inc 800 992-2144
  4786 Dressler Rd Nw Ste 3 Canton (44718) *(G-2665)*

Communications Aid Inc 513 475-8453
  222 Piedmont Ave Ste 5200 Cincinnati (45219) *(G-3599)*

Community Action Program Corp 740 374-8501
  696 Wayne St Marietta (45750) *(G-12776)*

Community Action Wic Hlth Svc, Marietta Also called Community Action Program
Corp *(G-12776)*

Community Care Network Inc (PA) 216 671-0977
  1400 W 25th St Fl 2 Cleveland (44113) *(G-5108)*

Community Care On Wheels 330 882-5506
  2 Kauffmans Crk Clinton (44216) *(G-6535)*

Community Mirror, The, Maumee Also called Mirror *(G-13284)*

Community Post, Minster Also called Horizon Publications Inc *(G-14355)*

Community RE Group-Comvet 440 319-6714
  3220 Station Ave Ashtabula (44004) *(G-798)*

Comp-U-Chem Inc 740 345-3332
  195 Dayton Rd Ne Newark (43055) *(G-14995)*

Companies of North Coast LLC (HQ) 216 398-8550
  4605 Spring Rd Cleveland (44131) *(G-5109)*

Company Front Awards 440 636-5493
  12653 Madison Rd Middlefield (44062) *(G-13924)*

Compass, Moraine Also called Angels Landing Inc *(G-14465)*

Compass Energy LLC 866 665-2225
  17877 Saint Clair Ave # 1 Cleveland (44110) *(G-5110)*

Compass Systems & Sales LLC 330 733-2111
  5185 New Haven Cir Norton (44203) *(G-15508)*

Compco Industries Incorporated (HQ) 330 482-6488
  400 W Railroad St Ste 1 Columbiana (44408) *(G-6614)*

Competetive Carbide Inc 440 350-9393
  9332 Pinecone Dr Mentor (44060) *(G-13551)*

Competitive Carbide, Mentor Also called Competetive Carbide Inc *(G-13551)*

Competitive Press Inc 330 289-1968
  144 Scenic View Dr Copley (44321) *(G-7842)*

Complements Lighting, Mentor Also called Medallion Lighting Corporation *(G-13650)*

Complete Cylinder Service Inc 513 772-1500
  1240 Glendale Milford Rd Cincinnati (45215) *(G-3600)*

Complete Dry Flood 513 200-9274
  6006 Madison Rd Cincinnati (45227) *(G-3601)*

Complete Energy Services Inc 440 577-1070
  7338 Us Route 6 Pierpont (44082) *(G-16211)*

Complete Filter Media LLC 740 438-0929
  1000 Mcgrery Rd Se Lancaster (43130) *(G-11698)*

Complete Network Solutions Inc 330 328-2596
  3766 Fishcreek Rd Ste 287 Stow (44224) *(G-17742)*

Compliance Elements LLC 419 217-1793
  8017 State Route 269 Bellevue (44811) *(G-1549)*

Compliant Access Products LLC 513 518-4525
  5885 Hamilton Cleves Rd Cleves (45002) *(G-6510)*

Compliant Healthcare Tech LLC 216 255-9607
  7123 Pearl Rd Ste 305 Cleveland (44130) *(G-5111)*

Compliant Healthcare Tech LLC (PA) 216 255-9607
  7123 Pearl Rd Ste 305 Cleveland (44130) *(G-5112)*

Component Mfg & Design 330 225-8080
  3121 Interstate Pkwy Brunswick (44212) *(G-2218)*

Component Systems Inc 216 252-9292
  2245 W 114th St Cleveland (44102) *(G-5113)*

Composite Advantage LLC 937 723-9031
  401 Kiser St Dayton (45404) *(G-8240)*

Composite Concepts Inc 440 247-3844
  615 Bunker Ln Mason (45040) *(G-13005)*

Composite Group, The, Fairlawn Also called Hpc Holdings LLC *(G-9753)*

Composite Technical Svcs LLC 937 660-3783
  2000 Composite Dr Kettering (45420) *(G-11578)*

Composite Technologies Co LLC 937 228-2880
  401 N Keowee St Dayton (45404) *(G-8241)*

Compost Cincy 513 278-8178
  5800 Este Ave Cincinnati (45232) *(G-3602)*

Compost Facility, Lockbourne Also called City of Columbus *(G-12146)*

Comprehensive Logistics Co Inc 440 934-3517
  1200 A Chester Indus Pkwy Avon (44011) *(G-990)*

Comprehensive Logistics Co Inc 330 793-0504
  365 Victoria Rd Youngstown (44515) *(G-21055)*

Compressor Technologies Inc 937 492-3711
  211 E Russell Rd Sidney (45365) *(G-17172)*

Comprhnsive Brace Limb Ctr LLC (PA) 330 337-8333
  2235 E Pershing St Salem (44460) *(G-16885)*

Compton Metal Products Inc 937 382-2403
  416 Steele Rd Wilmington (45177) *(G-20660)*

Comptons Precision Machine 937 325-9139
  224 Dayton Ave Springfield (45506) *(G-17535)*

Comptroll, Eastlake Also called Kyntrol LLC *(G-9280)*

Compu-Print, Canton Also called Better Living Concepts Inc *(G-2621)*

Computational Engineering Svcs 513 745-0313
  10979 Reed Hartman Hwy # 210 Blue Ash (45242) *(G-1768)*

Computer Aided Solutions LLC 440 729-2570
  8437 Mayfield Rd Ste 104a Chesterland (44026) *(G-3201)*

Computer Allied Technology Co 614 457-2292
  3385 Somerford Rd Columbus (43221) *(G-6973)*

Computer Forms Printing, Westerville Also called Jeffrey Reedy *(G-20219)*

Computer System Enhancement 513 251-6791
  927 Kreis Ln Cincinnati (45205) *(G-3603)*

Computer Workshop Inc (PA) 614 798-9505
  5131 Post Rd Ste 102 Dublin (43017) *(G-9065)*

Computer Workshop Inc 216 901-0106
  6100 Rockside Woods Blvd Cleveland (44131) *(G-5114)*

Computer Zoo Inc 937 310-1474
  1930 N Lakeman Dr Ste 106 Bellbrook (45305) *(G-1504)*

Computercrafts 614 231-7559
  2936 Brownlee Ave Columbus (43209) *(G-6974)*

Compuware Corporation 614 847-8212
  8351 N High St Ste 200 Columbus (43235) *(G-6975)*

Coms Interactive, Broadview Heights Also called Clinicl Otcms Mngmnt Syst LLC *(G-2109)*

Comtec Incorporated 330 425-8102
  1800 Enterprise Pkwy Twinsburg (44087) *(G-18918)*

Con-AG, Saint Marys Also called Conag Inc *(G-16837)*

Con-Belt Inc 330 273-2003
  5656 Innovation Dr Valley City (44280) *(G-19201)*

Conag Inc 419 394-8870
  16672 County Road 66a Saint Marys (45885) *(G-16837)*

Conagra Brands Inc 513 229-0305
  7308 Central Parke Blvd Mason (45040) *(G-13006)*

Conagra Brands Inc 419 445-8015
  901 Stryker St Archbold (43502) *(G-669)*

Conagra Brands Inc 740 465-3912
  2970 County Highway 74 Morral (43337) *(G-14539)*

Conagra Brands Inc 937 440-2800
  801 Dye Mill Rd Troy (45373) *(G-18811)*

Conagra Foods, Loudonville Also called Ardent Mills LLC *(G-12296)*

Concast Birmingham Inc 440 965-4455
  14315 State Route 113 Wakeman (44889) *(G-19446)*

Concast Metal Products, Wakeman Also called Concast Birmingham Inc *(G-19446)*

Concept 9 Inc 614 294-3743
  1604 Clara St Columbus (43211) *(G-6976)*

Concept Printing of Wauseon 419 335-6627
  775 N Shoop Ave Wauseon (43567) *(G-19674)*

Concept Wear, Columbus Also called Srm Graphics Inc *(G-7648)*

Concept Xxi Inc 216 831-2121
  23600 Merc Rd Ste 101 Beachwood (44122) *(G-1264)*

Concord Design Inc 330 722-5133
  3382 S Weymouth Rd Medina (44256) *(G-13391)*

Concord Fabricators Inc 614 875-2500
  6511 Seeds Rd Grove City (43123) *(G-10550)*

Concord Paving Co 440 354-8580
  500a Lakeshore Blvd Painesville (44077) *(G-15866)*

Concord Road Equipment Mfg Inc 440 357-5344
  348 Chester St Painesville (44077) *(G-15867)*

Concorde Castings Inc 440 953-0053
  34000 Lakeland Blvd Willoughby (44095) *(G-20461)*

Concrete Cnstr McHy Co LLC 330 638-1515
  5210 State Route 46 Cortland (44410) *(G-7863)*

Concrete Fealants Inc 937 339-0549
  515 W Water St Troy (45373) *(G-18812)*

Concrete Leveling Systems Inc 330 966-8120
  5046 East Blvd Nw Canton (44718) *(G-2666)*

Concrete Material Supply LLC 419 261-6404
  875 E Main St Woodville (43469) *(G-20725)*

A
L
P
H
A
B
E
T
I
C

Concrete Sealants Inc 937 845-8776
9325 State Route 201 Tipp City (45371) *(G-18273)*

Condition Monitoring Supplies 216 941-6868
20338 Progress Dr Strongsville (44149) *(G-17906)*

Condo Inc 330 505-0485
49 W Federal St Niles (44446) *(G-15148)*

Condo Incorporated 330 609-6021
3869 Niles Rd Se Warren (44484) *(G-19537)*

Condos and Trees LLC 419 691-2287
2674 Woodville Rd Northwood (43619) *(G-15479)*

Conduit Pipe Products Company 614 879-9114
1501 W Main St West Jefferson (43162) *(G-20077)*

Cone of West Chester 513 779-7040
6855 Tylersville Rd West Chester (45069) *(G-19837)*

Conery Manufacturing Inc 419 289-1444
1380 Township Road 743 Ashland (44805) *(G-724)*

Conform Automotive, Sidney *Also called Dti Molded Products Inc (G-17181)*

Conforming Matrix Corporation 419 729-3777
6255 Suder Ave Toledo (43611) *(G-18409)*

Conison Tool and Die Inc 330 758-1574
8100 Southern Blvd Youngstown (44512) *(G-21056)*

Conn-Selmer Inc 440 946-6100
34199 Curtis Blvd Willoughby (44095) *(G-20462)*

Conn-Selmer Inc 216 391-7723
1440 E 36th St Ste 501 Cleveland (44114) *(G-5115)*

Connaughton Wldg & Fence LLC 513 867-0230
440 Hensel Pl Hamilton (45011) *(G-10680)*

Conneaut Township Park, Conneaut *Also called City of Conneaut (G-7802)*

Connect Television 614 876-4402
4811 Northwest Pkwy Hilliard (43026) *(G-10943)*

Connective Design Incorporated 937 746-8252
3010 S Tech Blvd Miamisburg (45342) *(G-13793)*

Connector Manufacturing Co (HQ) 513 860-4455
3501 Symmes Rd Hamilton (45015) *(G-10681)*

Connectors Unlimited Inc (PA) 440 357-1161
1359 W Jackson St Painesville (44077) *(G-15868)*

Connectronics Corp (HQ) 419 537-0020
2745 Avondale Ave Toledo (43607) *(G-18410)*

Connell Limited Partnership 877 534-8986
154 E Aurora Rd Pmb 186 Northfield (44067) *(G-15464)*

Connelly Industries LLC 330 468-0675
9651 N Bedford Rd Macedonia (44056) *(G-12443)*

Connies Candles 740 574-1224
9103 Ohio River Rd Wheelersburg (45694) *(G-20329)*

Connolly Construction Co Inc 937 644-8831
179 Emmaus Rd Marysville (43040) *(G-12936)*

Connor Electric Inc 513 932-5798
605 N Liberty Keuter Rd Lebanon (45036) *(G-11790)*

Conns Potato Chip Co Inc (PA) 740 452-4615
1805 Kemper Ct Zanesville (43701) *(G-21294)*

Conover Lumber Company Inc 937 368-3010
7960 N Alcony Conover Rd Conover (45317) *(G-7823)*

Conseal, Tipp City *Also called Concrete Sealants Inc (G-18273)*

Consol Coal Company 740 942-4353
79285 Cadiz New Athens Rd Cadiz (43907) *(G-2415)*

Consolidated Graphics Group Inc 216 881-9191
1614 E 40th St Cleveland (44103) *(G-5116)*

Consoldted Grnhse Slutions LLC 330 844-8598
14800 Foltz Pkwy Strongsville (44149) *(G-17907)*

Consoldted Precision Pdts Corp (HQ) 909 595-2252
1621 Euclid Ave Ste 1850 Cleveland (44115) *(G-5117)*

Consoldted Precision Pdts Corp 440 953-0053
34000 Lakeland Blvd Eastlake (44095) *(G-9263)*

Consolidatd Analytical Sys Inc 513 542-1200
201 S Miami Ave Cleves (45002) *(G-6511)*

Consolidated Biscuit Company, Mc Comb *Also called Hearthside Food Solutions LLC (G-13338)*

Consolidated Biscuit Company 419 293-2911
312 Rader Rd Mc Comb (45858) *(G-13336)*

Consolidated Coatings Corp 216 514-7596
3735 Green Rd Cleveland (44122) *(G-5118)*

Consolidated Gas Coop Inc 419 946-6600
5255 State Route 95 Mount Gilead (43338) *(G-14557)*

Consolidated Graphics Inc 740 654-2112
3950 Lancaster New Lxngtn Lancaster (43130) *(G-11699)*

Consolidated Metal Pdts Inc 513 251-2624
1028 Depot St Cincinnati (45204) *(G-3604)*

Consolidated Pattern Works Inc 330 434-6060
754 E Glenwood Ave Akron (44310) *(G-127)*

Consolidated Solutions, Cleveland *Also called Consolidated Web (G-5119)*

Consolidated Solutions, Cleveland *Also called Consoldated Graphics Group Inc (G-5116)*

Consolidated Vehicle Converter, Dayton *Also called Julie Maynard Inc (G-8429)*

Consolidated Web 216 881-7816
3831 Kelley Ave Cleveland (44114) *(G-5119)*

Constar International, Hebron *Also called Plastipak Packaging Inc (G-10880)*

Construction Bulletin Inc 330 782-3733
4178 Market St Lowr Youngstown (44512) *(G-21057)*

Construction Journal Ltd 440 826-4700
7261 Engle Rd Ste 101 Cleveland (44130) *(G-5120)*

Construction Polymers Co 440 591-9018
8160 Devon Ct Chagrin Falls (44023) *(G-3081)*

Construction Techniques Inc (HQ) 216 267-7310
15887 Snow Rd Ste 100 Cleveland (44142) *(G-5121)*

Consuetudo Abscisum Inc 419 281-8002
921 Jacobson Ave Ashland (44805) *(G-725)*

Consumer Guild Foods Inc 419 726-3406
5035 Enterprise Blvd Toledo (43612) *(G-18411)*

Consumer Source Inc 513 621-7300
431 Elliott Ave Cincinnati (45215) *(G-3605)*

Consumeracq Inc (PA) 440 277-9305
2509 N Ridge Rd E Lorain (44055) *(G-12239)*

Consumers Builders Supply Co (PA) 440 277-9306
2509 N Ridge Rd E Lorain (44055) *(G-12240)*

Consumers News Services Inc (HQ) 740 888-6000
7801 N Central Dr Lewis Center (43035) *(G-11893)*

Consun Food Industries Inc 440 322-6301
123 Gateway Blvd N Elyria (44035) *(G-9397)*

Contact Industries Inc 419 884-9788
25 Industrial Dr Lexington (44904) *(G-11949)*

Container Graphics Corp 937 746-5666
1 Miller St Franklin (45005) *(G-10013)*

Container King Inc 937 652-3087
955 Lippincott Rd Urbana (43078) *(G-19154)*

Container Manufacturing Ltd 937 264-2370
6450 Poe Ave Ste 511 Dayton (45414) *(G-8242)*

Containercraft Inc 419 884-2414
144 Plymouth St Mansfield (44904) *(G-12584)*

Containerport Group Inc (HQ) 440 333-2009
1340 Depot St Ste 103 Cleveland (44116) *(G-5122)*

Containment Solutions Inc 419 874-8765
103 Secor Woods Ln Perrysburg (43551) *(G-16078)*

Contech Bridge Solutions LLC 937 878-2170
7941 New Carlisle Pike Dayton (45424) *(G-8243)*

Contech Bridge Solutions LLC (HQ) 513 645-7000
9025 Cntrpinte Dr Ste 400 West Chester (45069) *(G-19838)*

Contech Cnstr Pdts Hldings Inc 513 645-7000
9025 Centre Pointe Dr # 400 West Chester (45069) *(G-19839)*

Contech Engnered Solutions Inc 513 645-7000
9025 Centre Pointe Dr # 400 West Chester (45069) *(G-19840)*

Contech Engnered Solutions LLC 513 645-7000
1001 Grove St Middletown (45044) *(G-14032)*

Contech Engnered Solutions LLC 614 477-1171
1103 Schrock Rd Ste 105 Columbus (43229) *(G-6977)*

Contech Engnered Solutions LLC 513 425-5337
1001 Grove St Middletown (45044) *(G-14033)*

Contech Engnered Solutions LLC (HQ) 513 645-7000
9025 Ctr Pinte Dr Ste 400 West Chester (45069) *(G-19841)*

Contech Strmwter Solutions LLC 513 645-7000
9025 Centre Pointe Dr # 400 West Chester (45069) *(G-19842)*

Contemporary Cabinets Inc 937 833-1135
175 Carr Dr Brookville (45309) *(G-2178)*

Contemprary Image Labeling Inc 513 583-5699
2034 Mckinley Blvd Lebanon (45036) *(G-11791)*

Conti Tool & Die Inc 330 633-1414
1333 Devalera St Akron (44310) *(G-128)*

Continental Business Entps Inc (PA) 440 439-4400
7311 Northfield Rd Cleveland (44146) *(G-5123)*

Continental Carbonic Pdts Inc 614 491-4327
4852 Frusta Dr Obetz (43207) *(G-15654)*

Continental Carbonic Pdts Inc 937 316-6160
198 Continental Dr Greenville (45331) *(G-10495)*

Continental Coml Pdts LLC 419 447-5000
1780 S County Road 1 Tiffin (44883) *(G-18216)*

Continental Contitech, Marysville *Also called Contitech Usa Inc (G-12937)*

Continental Contitech, Fairlawn *Also called Contitech Usa Inc (G-9748)*

Continental Fan Mfg 937 233-5524
6274 Executive Blvd Huber Heights (45424) *(G-11144)*

Continental GL Sls & Inv Group 614 679-1201
315 Ashmoore Ct Powell (43065) *(G-16469)*

Continental Group, Powell *Also called Continental GL Sls & Inv Group (G-16469)*

Continental Hydrodyne Systems 330 494-2740
2216 Glenmont Dr Nw Canton (44708) *(G-2667)*

Continental Jwly Replacement, Columbus *Also called C & J Jewelers Inc (G-6881)*

Continental Metal Proc Co (PA) 216 268-0000
18711 Cleveland Ave Cleveland (44110) *(G-5124)*

Continental Metal Proc Co 216 268-0000
14919 Saranac Rd Cleveland (44110) *(G-5125)*

Continental Products Company (PA) 216 383-3932
1150 E 222nd St Euclid (44117) *(G-9573)*

Continental Products Company 216 531-0710
1150 E 222nd St Cleveland (44117) *(G-5126)*

Continental Strl Plas Inc 440 945-4800
333 Gore Rd Conneaut (44030) *(G-7803)*

Continental Strl Plas Inc 419 396-1980
2915 County Rd 96 Carey (43316) *(G-2917)*

Continental Strl Plas Inc 419 238-4628
1276 Industrial Dr Van Wert (45891) *(G-19248)*

Continental Strl Plas Inc 419 257-2231
100 S Poe Rd North Baltimore (45872) *(G-15192)*

Continental Testing Inc 937 832-3322
104 S Main St Union (45322) *(G-19065)*

Continental Tire Americas LLC 419 633-4221
927 S Union Bryan Bryan (43506) *(G-2290)*

Continental Turf Systems Inc 419 596-4409
21801 Road E16 Continental (45831) *(G-7825)*

Contingncy Prcrments Group LLC 513 204-9590
2800 Millbank Row Maineville (45039) *(G-12521)*

Contitech North America Inc 440 225-5363
1144 E Market St Ste 543 Akron (44316) *(G-129)*

Contitech North America Inc (HQ) 330 664-7180
703 S Clvlnd Massillon Rd Fairlawn (44333) *(G-9747)*

Contitech Usa Inc 937 644-8900
13601 Industrial Pkwy Marysville (43040) *(G-12937)*

Contitech Usa Inc (HQ) 330 664-7000
703 S Clvlnd Mssillon Rd Fairlawn (44333) *(G-9748)*

Contour Forming Inc 740 345-9777
215 Oakwood Ave Newark (43055) *(G-14996)*

Contour Tool Inc 440 365-7333
38830 Taylor Pkwy North Ridgeville (44035) *(G-15364)*

Contours, Orrville Also called Bekaert Corporation *(G-15729)*

Contract Building Components 937 644-0739
14540 Industrial Pkwy Marysville (43040) *(G-12938)*

Contract Lighting Inc 614 746-7022
1207 Grandview Ave Columbus (43212) *(G-6978)*

Contract Pckg Dist Specialists 513 942-0300
236 Circle Freeway Dr West Chester (45246) *(G-19993)*

Contractor Tools Online LLC 614 264-9392
Uknown New Albany (43054) *(G-14754)*

Contractors Steel Company 330 425-3050
8383 Boyle Pkwy Twinsburg (44087) *(G-18919)*

Contreras Pallets 567 277-2447
1734 Balkan Pl Toledo (43613) *(G-18412)*

Control Associates Inc 440 708-1770
10205 Queens Way Chagrin Falls (44023) *(G-3082)*

Control Craft LLC 513 674-0056
2130 Schappelle Ln Cincinnati (45240) *(G-3606)*

Control Electric Co 216 671-8010
12130 Eaton Commerce Pkwy Columbia Station (44028) *(G-6586)*

Control Industries Inc 937 653-7694
1700 Fostoria Ave Ste 300 Findlay (45840) *(G-9810)*

Control Interface Inc 513 874-2062
517 Commercial Dr West Chester (45014) *(G-19843)*

Control Line Equipment Inc 216 433-7766
14750 Industrial Pkwy Cleveland (44135) *(G-5127)*

Control Measurement Inc 440 639-0020
1400 Mentor Ave Ste 5 Painesville (44077) *(G-15869)*

Control System Manufacturing 330 542-0000
10725 Struthers Rd New Middletown (44442) *(G-14876)*

Control System Upgrades, Cincinnati Also called Magna Group LLC *(G-4051)*

Control Transformer Inc 330 637-6015
3701 Warren Meadville Rd Cortland (44410) *(G-7864)*

Control Works Inc 513 831-9959
400 Techne Center Dr # 104 Milford (45150) *(G-14133)*

Controlled Access Inc 330 273-6185
1515 W 130th St Ste A Hinckley (44233) *(G-11023)*

Controllix Corporation 440 232-8757
21415 Alexander Rd Walton Hills (44146) *(G-19472)*

Controls and Sheet Metal Inc (PA) 513 721-3610
1051 Sargent St Cincinnati (45203) *(G-3607)*

Controls Inc 330 239-4345
5204 Portside Dr Medina (44256) *(G-13392)*

Convault of Ohio Inc 614 252-8422
841 Alton Ave Columbus (43219) *(G-6979)*

Converge Group Inc 419 281-0000
1850 Baney Rd S Ashland (44805) *(G-726)*

Conversion Tech Intl Inc 419 924-5566
700 Oak St West Unity (43570) *(G-20127)*

Convertapax, Midvale Also called Maintenance Repair Supply Inc *(G-14109)*

Converters/Prepress Inc 937 743-0935
301 Industry Dr Carlisle (45005) *(G-2929)*

Conveyor Metal Works Inc 740 477-8700
2717 Bush Mill Rd Frankfort (45628) *(G-9998)*

Conveyor Solutions LLC 513 367-4845
6705 Dry Fork Rd Cleves (45002) *(G-6512)*

Conveyor Technologies Ltd 513 248-0663
501 Techne Center Dr B Milford (45150) *(G-14134)*

Conveyors Ltd 740 490-0300
475 E High St London (43140) *(G-12206)*

Conviber, Medina Also called Heintz Manufacturers Inc *(G-13420)*

Conviber Inc 330 723-6006
1066 Industrial Pkwy Medina (44256) *(G-13393)*

Conway Greene Co Inc 216 619-8091
1400 E 30th St Ste 402 Cleveland (44114) *(G-5128)*

Cook Bonding & Mfg Co Inc 216 661-1698
701 W Schaaf Rd Cleveland (44109) *(G-5129)*

Cook, R D Company, Columbus Also called R D Cook Company LLC *(G-7543)*

Cooked Foods, Fairfield Also called Koch Meat Co Inc *(G-9674)*

Cookie Bouquets Inc 614 888-2171
6665 Huntley Rd Ste F Columbus (43229) *(G-6980)*

Cookie Cupboard, Cleveland Also called Mid American Ventures Inc *(G-5804)*

Cool Machines Inc 419 232-4871
740 Fox Rd Van Wert (45891) *(G-19249)*

Cool Seal Usa LLC 419 666-1111
232 J St Perrysburg (43551) *(G-16079)*

Cool Times 513 608-5201
6127 Fairway Dr Cincinnati (45212) *(G-3608)*

Coolant Control Inc (PA) 513 471-8770
5353 Spring Grove Ave Cincinnati (45217) *(G-3609)*

Coomercial Forg Heat Treatment, Cleveland Also called Cleveland Hollow Boring Inc *(G-5065)*

Coons Homemade Candies 740 496-4141
16451 County Highway 113 Harpster (43323) *(G-10765)*

Cooper, Orwell Also called CT Hydraulics Inc *(G-15774)*

Cooper - Eaton Center, Cleveland Also called Cooper Interconnect Inc *(G-5130)*

Cooper Energy Services, Mount Vernon Also called Cameron International Corp *(G-14611)*

Cooper Farms, Oakwood Also called Cooper Hatchery Inc *(G-15615)*

Cooper Farms, Saint Henry Also called V H Cooper & Co Inc *(G-16824)*

Cooper Farms Inc (PA) 419 375-4116
2321 State Route 49 Fort Recovery (45846) *(G-9946)*

Cooper Farms Inc 419 375-4119
2351 Wabash Rd Fort Recovery (45846) *(G-9947)*

Cooper Farms Inc 419 375-4619
3310 State Route 49 Fort Recovery (45846) *(G-9948)*

Cooper Farms Cooked Meat, Van Wert Also called Cooper Foods *(G-19250)*

Cooper Farms Cooked Meats, Van Wert Also called Cooper Hatchery Inc *(G-19251)*

Cooper Farms East Mill, Fort Recovery Also called Cooper Farms Inc *(G-9947)*

Cooper Foods, Fort Recovery Also called V H Cooper & Co Inc *(G-9961)*

Cooper Foods 419 232-2440
6893 Us Route 127 Van Wert (45891) *(G-19250)*

Cooper Hatchery Inc (PA) 419 594-3325
22348 Road 140 Oakwood (45873) *(G-15615)*

Cooper Hatchery Inc 419 238-4869
6793 Us Route 127 Van Wert (45891) *(G-19251)*

Cooper Interconnect Inc 800 386-1911
1000 Eaton Blvd Cleveland (44122) *(G-5130)*

Cooper Tire & Rubber Company (PA) 419 423-1321
701 Lima Ave Findlay (45840) *(G-9811)*

Cooper Tire & Rubber Company 419 424-4202
900 Lima Ave Findlay (45840) *(G-9812)*

Cooper Tire & Rubber Company 419 424-4384
1625 Lake Casscade Pkwy Findlay (45840) *(G-9813)*

Cooper Tire Vhcl Test Ctr Inc (HQ) 419 423-1321
701 Lima Ave Findlay (45840) *(G-9814)*

Cooper-Standard Automotive Inc 740 342-3523
2378 State Route 345 Ne New Lexington (43764) *(G-14846)*

Cooper-Standard Automotive Inc 419 352-3533
1175 N Main St Bowling Green (43402) *(G-1983)*

Coopers Mill 419 562-4215
1414 N Sandusky Ave Bucyrus (44820) *(G-2336)*

Copac, Cambridge Also called Cambridge Ohio Production & As *(G-2448)*

Copen Machine Inc 330 678-4598
501 Dodge St Kent (44240) *(G-11441)*

Copernicus Therapeutics Inc 216 707-1776
11000 Cedar Ave Ste 145 Cleveland (44106) *(G-5131)*

Copier Resources Inc 614 268-1100
4800 Evanswood Dr Columbus (43229) *(G-6981)*

Copley Fire & Rescue Assn 330 666-6464
1540 S Clvlnd Mssllon Rd Copley (44321) *(G-7843)*

Copley Ohio Newspapers Inc (HQ) 585 598-0030
500 Market Ave S Canton (44702) *(G-2668)*

Copley Ohio Newspapers Inc 330 364-5577
629 Wabash Ave Nw New Philadelphia (44663) *(G-14892)*

Copley Ohio Newspapers Inc 330 833-2631
729 Lincoln Way E Massillon (44646) *(G-13121)*

COPLEY TOWNSHIP FIRE DEPT, Copley Also called Copley Fire & Rescue Assn *(G-7843)*

Copper Mountain Beverages LLC 513 484-9550
1776 Mentor Ave Ste 250 Cincinnati (45212) *(G-3610)*

Copperloy, Twinsburg Also called Jh Industries Inc *(G-18961)*

Copy Cat Printing, Portsmouth Also called Keystone Printing & Copy Cat *(G-16439)*

Copy Cats Printing LLC 440 345-5966
6659 Pearl Rd Ste 101 Cleveland (44130) *(G-5132)*

Copy Center West Printing Co, Berea Also called George D Kanaan & Associates *(G-1617)*

Copy Print, Kent Also called Rhoads Printing Center Inc *(G-11516)*

Copy Quick Instant Printing, Strongsville Also called J & J Bechke Inc *(G-17932)*

Copy Right of Ohio LLC 614 431-1303
7445 Montgomery Rd B Plain City (43064) *(G-16328)*

Copy Source Inc 937 642-7140
105 S Main St Marysville (43040) *(G-12939)*

Copyrite Printing, Wheelersburg Also called Greg Blume *(G-20332)*

Cora Cupcakes 440 227-7145
95 Park Rd Painesville (44077) *(G-15870)*

Corbett R Caudill Chipping Inc 740 596-5984
35887 State Route 324 Hamden (45634) *(G-10656)*

Corcadence Inc 216 702-6371
26701 Bernwood Rd Beachwood (44122) *(G-1265)*

Cordier Group Holdings Inc (PA)..........................330 477-4511
　4575 Southway St Sw Canton (44706) *(G-2669)*
Core Automotive Tech LLC (HQ)..........................614 870-5000
　800 Manor Park Dr Columbus (43228) *(G-6982)*
Core Composites Cincinnati LLC..........................513 724-6111
　4174 Half Acre Rd Batavia (45103) *(G-1174)*
Core Manufacturing LLC..........................440 946-8002
　8878 East Ave Mentor (44060) *(G-13552)*
Core Molding Technologies Inc (PA)..........................614 870-5000
　800 Manor Park Dr Columbus (43228) *(G-6983)*
Core Quantum Technologies Inc..........................614 214-7210
　1275 Kinnear Rd Columbus (43212) *(G-6984)*
Core Technology Inc..........................440 934-9935
　1260 Moore Rd Ste E Avon (44011) *(G-991)*
Core-Tech Inc..........................440 946-8324
　7850 Enterprise Dr Mentor (44060) *(G-13553)*
Corell's Potato Chips, Beach City *Also called Daniel Meenan (G-1247)*
Coreworth Holdings LLC..........................419 468-7100
　8402 County Rd Iberia (43325) *(G-11242)*
Corillian Payment Solutions..........................419 244-8048
　1946 N 13th St Ste 392 Toledo (43604) *(G-18413)*
Cornerstone Brands Inc..........................866 668-5962
　5568 W Chester Rd West Chester (45069) *(G-19844)*
Cornerstone Indus Holdings (PA)..........................440 893-9144
　100 Park Pl Chagrin Falls (44022) *(G-3054)*
Cornerstone Industries Lcc..........................513 871-4546
　10132 Mosteller Ln West Chester (45069) *(G-19845)*
Cornerstone Manufacturing Inc..........................937 456-5930
　861 Us Route 35 Eaton (45320) *(G-9303)*
Cornerstone Printing Inc..........................614 861-2138
　443 Knob Ave Reynoldsburg (43068) *(G-16585)*
Cornerstone Spclty WD Pdts LLC..........................513 772-5560
　12020 Tramway Dr Cincinnati (45241) *(G-3611)*
Cornpentry..........................513 741-0594
　2122 Schappelle Ln Cincinnati (45240) *(G-3612)*
Corns Quality Woodworking LLC..........................419 589-4899
　1525 Chew Rd Mansfield (44903) *(G-12585)*
CORNWELL QUALITY TOOLS, Van Wert *Also called Cqt Kennedy LLC (G-19252)*
Cornwell Quality Tools Company..........................330 628-2627
　200 N Cleveland Ave Mogadore (44260) *(G-14370)*
Corpad Company Inc..........................419 522-7818
　555 Park Ave E Mansfield (44905) *(G-12586)*
Corporate Dcment Solutions Inc..........................513 595-8200
　11120 Ashburn Rd Cincinnati (45240) *(G-3613)*
Corporate Elevator LLC..........................614 288-1847
　35 E Gay St Ste 218 Columbus (43215) *(G-6985)*
Corporate Image Makers, Springfield *Also called Ed Thomas (G-17551)*
Corporate Printing, Cincinnati *Also called Newhouse & Faulkner Inc (G-4150)*
Corporate Printing, Liberty Twp *Also called Kuwatch Printing LLC (G-11976)*
Corporate Supply LLC..........................614 876-8400
　3608 Sugar Loaf Ct Columbus (43221) *(G-6986)*
Corporation Lord, Ashtabula *Also called Lord Corporation (G-818)*
Corrchoice Inc (HQ)..........................330 833-5705
　777 3rd St Nw Massillon (44647) *(G-13122)*
Corro-Tech Equipment Corp..........................216 941-1552
　4034 W 163rd St Cleveland (44135) *(G-5133)*
Corrosion Resistant Technology..........................440 543-1320
　11345 Saybrook Ln Chagrin Falls (44023) *(G-3083)*
Corrotec Inc..........................937 325-3585
　1125 W North St Springfield (45504) *(G-17536)*
Corrpro Companies Inc (HQ)..........................330 723-5082
　1055 W Smith Rd Medina (44256) *(G-13394)*
Corrpro Companies Inc..........................330 725-6681
　1055 W Smith Rd Medina (44256) *(G-13395)*
Corrpro Companies Intl Inc..........................330 723-5082
　1055 W Smith Rd Medina (44256) *(G-13396)*
Corrpro Waterworks, Medina *Also called Corrpro Companies Inc (G-13395)*
Corrugated Chemicals Inc..........................513 561-7773
　3865 Virginia Ave Cincinnati (45227) *(G-3614)*
Cors Products, Canton *Also called Canton OH Rubber Speclty Prods (G-2642)*
Cortape Inc..........................330 929-6700
　60 Marc Dr Cuyahoga Falls (44223) *(G-7982)*
Cortes NP Acquisition Corp, Columbus *Also called Vertiv Group Corporation (G-7735)*
Cortest Inc..........................440 942-1235
　38322 Apollo Pkwy Willoughby (44094) *(G-20463)*
Cortland Hardwood Products LLC..........................330 638-3232
　234 N Mecca St Cortland (44410) *(G-7865)*
Corvac Composites LLC..........................248 807-0969
　1025 N Washington St Greenfield (45123) *(G-10475)*
COS Blueprint Inc (PA)..........................330 376-0022
　590 N Main St Akron (44310) *(G-130)*
Coshocton County Advertiser..........................740 295-3435
　550 Main St Coshocton (43812) *(G-7884)*
Coshocton Ethanol LLC..........................740 623-3046
　18137 County Road 271 Coshocton (43812) *(G-7885)*
Coshocton Industries Inc..........................330 339-4744
　1040 Commercial Ave Se New Philadelphia (44663) *(G-14893)*
Coshocton Industries Inc (PA)..........................740 622-4734
　605 N 15th St Coshocton (43812) *(G-7886)*

Coshocton Orthopedic Center, Coshocton *Also called Francisco Jaume (G-7891)*
Coshocton Pallet & Door Co, Coshocton *Also called Thomas J Weaver Inc (G-7913)*
Coshocton Stainless, Coshocton *Also called AK Steel Corporation (G-7877)*
Coshocton Tribune, Coshocton *Also called Gannett Co Inc (G-7892)*
Cosmo Corporation..........................330 359-5429
　211 N Winesburg Rd Wilmot (44689) *(G-20684)*
Cosmo Plastics Co, Wilmot *Also called Cosmo Corporation (G-20684)*
Coso Media LLC..........................330 904-5889
　5603 Darrow Rd Ste 500 Hudson (44236) *(G-11166)*
Costa Machine, Akron *Also called Charles Costa Inc (G-119)*
Costume Specialists Inc (PA)..........................614 464-2115
　211 N 5th St Ste 100 Columbus (43215) *(G-6987)*
Costume Specialists Inc..........................614 464-2115
　211 N 5th St Ste 100 Columbus (43215) *(G-6988)*
Cota International Inc..........................937 526-5520
　67 Industrial Pkwy Versailles (45380) *(G-19344)*
Cotsworks LLC..........................440 446-8800
　749 Miner Rd Highland Heights (44143) *(G-10911)*
Cott Systems Inc..........................614 847-4405
　2800 Corp Exchange Dr # 300 Columbus (43231) *(G-6989)*
Cotton Fabrics Company Inc..........................419 389-9904
　3647 Marine Rd Toledo (43609) *(G-18414)*
Cotton Pickin Tees & Caps..........................419 636-3595
　215 W Bryan St Bryan (43506) *(G-2291)*
Cotton Wood Pallet Co, Galion *Also called Cottonwood Pallet Inc (G-10260)*
Cottonwood Pallet Inc..........................419 468-9703
　9541 Mrral Krkptrick Rd E Galion (44833) *(G-10260)*
Couch Business Development Inc..........................937 253-1099
　32 Bates St Dayton (45402) *(G-8244)*
Coulson Cmprssion Msrement Ltd..........................740 697-0220
　7280 Rose Hill Rd Roseville (43777) *(G-16730)*
Coulter Ventures Llc (PA)..........................614 358-6190
　1080 Steelwood Rd Columbus (43212) *(G-6990)*
Coulton Chemical..........................419 698-8181
　1400 Otter Creek Rd Oregon (43616) *(G-15706)*
Counter Concepts Inc..........................330 848-4848
　15535 Portage St Doylestown (44230) *(G-9028)*
Counter Creation Plus L L C..........................419 826-7449
　106 Church St Swanton (43558) *(G-18083)*
Counter Method Inc..........................614 206-3192
　13767 E State Route 37 Sunbury (43074) *(G-18058)*
Counter Rhythm Group..........................513 379-6587
　397 Lombardy St Cincinnati (45216) *(G-3615)*
Counter- Advice Inc..........................937 291-1600
　7002 State Route 123 Franklin (45005) *(G-10014)*
Countertop Sales..........................614 626-4476
　5767 Westbourne Ave Columbus (43213) *(G-6991)*
Countertop Xpress..........................440 358-0500
　381 Fountain Ave Painesville (44077) *(G-15871)*
Countertops Helmart, Cincinnati *Also called Helmart Company Inc (G-3876)*
Country Caterers Inc (PA)..........................740 389-1013
　409 Mrion Cardington Rd W Marion (43302) *(G-12863)*
Country Clippins..........................740 472-5228
　237 S Main St Woodsfield (43793) *(G-20716)*
Country Comfort Woodworking..........................330 695-4408
　2 Mi Sw Of Mt Eaton Fredericksburg (44627) *(G-10081)*
Country Crust Bakery..........................888 860-2940
　4918 State Route 41 S Bainbridge (45612) *(G-1057)*
Country Freezer Units LLC..........................740 623-8658
　50938 Township Road 220 Baltic (43804) *(G-1067)*
Country Ice Cream Freezer, Baltic *Also called Country Freezer Units LLC (G-1067)*
Country Maid Ice Cream Inc..........................330 659-6830
　3252 W Streetsboro Rd Richfield (44286) *(G-16619)*
Country Manufacturing Inc..........................740 694-9926
　333 Salem Ave Ext Fredericktown (43019) *(G-10097)*
Country Molding..........................440 564-5235
　12375 Kinsman Rd Newbury (44065) *(G-15085)*
Country Parlour Ice Cream Co..........................440 237-4040
　12905 York Delta Dr Ste C Cleveland (44133) *(G-5134)*
Country Pure Foods Inc (HQ)..........................330 848-6875
　222 W Main St Ste 401 Akron (44308) *(G-131)*
Country Savings Magazine, Burton *Also called Fontanelle Group Inc (G-2375)*
Country Tin..........................937 746-7229
　228 S Main St Franklin (45005) *(G-10015)*
Countryside Pumping Inc..........................330 628-0058
　1496 Martin Rd Mogadore (44260) *(G-14371)*
Counts Container Corporation..........................216 433-4336
　5137 W 161st St Cleveland (44142) *(G-5135)*
County Classifieds..........................937 592-8847
　117 E Patterson Ave Bellefontaine (43311) *(G-1525)*
County Line, Bryan *Also called Bryan Publishing Company (G-2288)*
County of Lake..........................440 428-1794
　7815 Cashen Rd Madison (44057) *(G-12502)*
County of Lake..........................440 269-2193
　2100 Joseph Lloyd Pkwy Willoughby (44094) *(G-20464)*
County of Lawrence..........................740 867-8700
　11100 Private Dr Chesapeake (45619) *(G-3186)*
County of Medina..........................330 723-3641
　144 N Broadway St Ste 117 Medina (44256) *(G-13397)*

(G-0000) Company's Geographic Section entry number

County of Summit...330 865-8065
  1828 Smith Rd Akron (44313) **(G-132)**
County Wide Welding LLC..440 564-1333
  14999 Cross Creek Pkwy Newbury (44065) **(G-15086)**
Countyline Co-Op Inc (PA)......................................419 287-3241
  425 E Front St Pemberville (43450) **(G-16026)**
Coupled Products LLC...419 294-3827
  200 E Wyandotte St Wharton (43359) **(G-20328)**
Courtad Inc..330 274-3100
  510 Cobblestone Rd Aurora (44202) **(G-913)**
Courthouse Manufacturing LLC...................................740 335-2727
  1730 Wash Ave Solar Ln Washington Court Hou (43160) **(G-19638)**
Covap Inc..513 793-1855
  10829 Millington Ct Ste 1 Blue Ash (45242) **(G-1769)**
Coventry Steel Services Inc....................................216 883-4477
  4200 E 71st St Ste 1 Cleveland (44105) **(G-5136)**
Coventya Inc (HQ)..216 351-1500
  4639 Van Epps Rd Brooklyn Heights (44131) **(G-2136)**
Cover Up Building Systems......................................740 668-8985
  101 N Market St Martinsburg (43037) **(G-12929)**
Covert Manufacturing Inc (PA)..................................419 468-1761
  328 S East St Galion (44833) **(G-10261)**
Covestro LLC...740 929-2015
  Newark Industrial Park Hebron (43025) **(G-10863)**
COW Industries Inc (PA)..614 443-6537
  1875 Progress Ave Columbus (43207) **(G-6992)**
Cowells - Arrow Bingo Company..................................216 961-3500
  9900 Clinton Rd Cleveland (44144) **(G-5137)**
Cowgill Printing Co..216 741-2076
  4427 Brookpark Rd Parma (44134) **(G-15955)**
Cowles Industrial Tool Co LLC..................................330 799-9100
  185 N Four Mile Run Rd Austintown (44515) **(G-972)**
Cowles Tool Company LLC..330 799-9100
  185 N Four Mile Run Rd Austintown (44515) **(G-973)**
Cox Inc..740 858-4400
  11201 State Route 104 Lucasville (45648) **(G-12418)**
Cox Interior Inc...614 473-9169
  2220 Citygate Dr Columbus (43219) **(G-6993)**
Cox Machine & Fabrication, Carroll Also called S J Cox Tool Inc **(G-2946)**
Cox Media Group Ohio Inc (HQ)..................................937 225-2000
  1611 S Main St Dayton (45409) **(G-8245)**
Cox Media Group Ohio Inc.......................................937 743-6700
  5000 Commerce Center Dr Franklin (45005) **(G-10016)**
Cox Newspapers LLC...513 696-4500
  200 Harmon Ave Liberty Township (45044) **(G-11959)**
Cox Newspapers LLC...937 866-3331
  230 S 2nd St Miamisburg (45342) **(G-13794)**
Cox Newspapers LLC...937 225-2000
  1611 S Main St Dayton (45409) **(G-8246)**
Cox Newspapers LLC...513 863-8200
  7320 Yankee Rd Liberty Township (45044) **(G-11960)**
Cox Newspapers LLC...513 523-4139
  30 W Park Pl Uppr Uppr Oxford (45056) **(G-15835)**
Cox Painting, Wilmington Also called Cox Printing Co **(G-20661)**
Cox Precast, Lucasville Also called Cox Inc **(G-12418)**
Cox Printing Co..937 382-2312
  1087 Wayne Rd Wilmington (45177) **(G-20661)**
Cox Publishing Hq..937 225-2000
  1611 S Main St Dayton (45409) **(G-8247)**
Cox Trailer, Arcanum Also called R J Cox Co **(G-658)**
Cox Wood Product Inc...740 372-4735
  5715 State Route 348 Otway (45657) **(G-15829)**
Cox's Interior Supply, Columbus Also called Cox Interior Inc **(G-6993)**
Cozmyk Enterprises Inc...614 231-1370
  3757 Courtright Ct Columbus (43227) **(G-6994)**
CP Chemicals Group LP..440 833-3000
  28960 Lakeland Blvd Wickliffe (44092) **(G-20363)**
CP Industries Inc..740 763-2886
  11047 Lambs Ln Newark (43055) **(G-14997)**
CP Technologies Company..614 866-9200
  6615 Taylor Rd Blacklick (43004) **(G-1693)**
CP Trading Group, Wickliffe Also called CP Chemicals Group LP **(G-20363)**
CPC Logistics Inc..513 874-5787
  8695 Seward Rd Fairfield (45011) **(G-9657)**
Cpd Chemical Products Division, Wapakoneta Also called Ametek Westchester
Plastics **(G-19478)**
Cpg - Ohio LLC (PA)..513 825-4800
  470 Northland Blvd Cincinnati (45240) **(G-3616)**
Cpg Printing & Graphics, Toledo Also called Culaine Inc **(G-18417)**
CPI, Holland Also called Creative Products Inc **(G-11049)**
CPI Group Limited..216 525-0046
  13858 Tinkers Creek Rd Cleveland (44125) **(G-5138)**
CPI Industrial Co..614 445-0800
  2300 Parsons Ave Columbus (43207) **(G-6995)**
Cpic Automotive Inc..740 587-3262
  1226 Weaver Dr Granville (43023) **(G-10456)**
Cpmg...440 263-2780
  12955 York Delta Dr Ste G North Royalton (44133) **(G-15415)**

Cpmm Services Group Inc..614 447-0165
  3785 Indianola Ave Columbus (43214) **(G-6996)**
Cpp, Coshocton Also called Ansell Healthcare Products LLC **(G-7880)**
Cpp Cleveland, Eastlake Also called Consoldted Precision Pdts Corp **(G-9263)**
Cpp Pomona, Cleveland Also called Consoldted Precision Pdts Corp **(G-5117)**
Cpu Satellite Systems, Lakewood Also called Discount Computer Parts **(G-11662)**
Cqcb Inc...614 864-1900
  1385 Blatt Blvd Blacklick (43004) **(G-1694)**
Cqt Kennedy LLC..419 238-2442
  1260 Industrial Dr Van Wert (45891) **(G-19252)**
Cr Brands Inc (HQ)...513 860-5039
  8790 Beckett Rd West Chester (45069) **(G-19846)**
Cr Holding Inc (HQ)..513 860-5039
  9100 Centre Pointe Dr West Chester (45069) **(G-19847)**
CR Laurence Co Inc...440 248-0003
  31600 Carter St Cleveland (44139) **(G-5139)**
Cr Supply LLC..440 759-5408
  7661 Ohio St Mentor (44060) **(G-13554)**
CRA-Z-Art, Palmer Paint, Fayette Also called Larose Industries LLC **(G-9776)**
Crabar Business Systems, Leipsic Also called Crabar/Gbf Inc **(G-11868)**
Crabar/Gbf Inc...419 269-1720
  4444 N Detroit Ave Toledo (43612) **(G-18415)**
Crabar/Gbf Inc (HQ)..419 943-2141
  68 Vine St Leipsic (45856) **(G-11867)**
Crabar/Gbf Inc...740 622-0222
  24170 Hangar Ct Coshocton (43812) **(G-7887)**
Crabar/Gbf Inc...419 943-2141
  68 Vine St Leipsic (45856) **(G-11868)**
Crabar/Gbf Inc., Leipsic Also called Crabar/Gbf Inc **(G-11867)**
Crabro Printing Inc..740 533-3404
  314 Chestnut St Ironton (45638) **(G-11291)**
Crabware Ltd...330 699-2305
  3842 Park Ridge Dr Uniontown (44685) **(G-19081)**
Craco Embroidery Inc...513 563-6999
  37 Techview Dr Cincinnati (45215) **(G-3617)**
Crafts For Kids, Solon Also called Katherine A Stull Inc **(G-17327)**
Craftwood, Mount Orab Also called Cindoco Wood Products Co **(G-14577)**
Craig Bros Machine Co Inc......................................740 756-9280
  5869 Clmbus Lncster Rd Nw Carroll (43112) **(G-2938)**
Craig Industries, Canton Also called Pritt Enterprises Inc **(G-2823)**
Crain Communications Inc.......................................216 522-1383
  700 W Saint Clair Ave # 310 Cleveland (44113) **(G-5140)**
Crain Communications Inc.......................................330 836-9180
  1725 Merriman Rd Ste 300 Akron (44313) **(G-133)**
Crain's Cleveland Business, Cleveland Also called Crain Communications Inc **(G-5140)**
Crain-Tharp Printing Inc.......................................740 345-9823
  11 W Main St Newark (43055) **(G-14998)**
Cramers Inc..330 477-4571
  4944 Southway St Sw Canton (44706) **(G-2670)**
Crane Blending Center..614 542-1199
  2141 Fairwood Ave Columbus (43207) **(G-6997)**
Crane Chempharma & Energy, Cincinnati Also called Xomox Corporation **(G-4614)**
Crane Co...330 337-7861
  1453 Allen Rd Salem (44460) **(G-16886)**
Crane Consumables LLC..513 539-9980
  155 Westheimer Dr Middletown (45044) **(G-14034)**
Crane Plastics, Columbus Also called Engineered Profiles LLC **(G-7058)**
Crane Plastics Mfg Ltd...614 754-3700
  2141 Fairwood Ave Columbus (43207) **(G-6998)**
Crane Plumbing LLC...419 522-4211
  41 Cairns Rd Mansfield (44903) **(G-12587)**
Crane Plumbing LLC (PA)..419 522-4211
  41 Cairns Rd Mansfield (44903) **(G-12588)**
Crane Plumbing LLC...419 522-0321
  41 Cairns Rd Mansfield (44903) **(G-12589)**
Crane Plumbing Products, Mansfield Also called Crane Plumbing LLC **(G-12587)**
Crane Pro Services, Highland Heights Also called Konecranes Inc **(G-10916)**
Crane Pumps & Systems Inc......................................937 773-2442
  420 3rd St Piqua (45356) **(G-16256)**
Crane Pumps & Systems Inc (HQ).................................937 773-2442
  420 3rd St Piqua (45356) **(G-16257)**
Crane Training USA Inc...513 755-2177
  7908 Cincinnati Dayton Rd H West Chester (45069) **(G-19848)**
Crane Xomox, Blue Ash Also called Xomox Corporation **(G-1903)**
Crase Communications Inc.......................................419 468-1173
  120 Harding Way E Ste 104 Galion (44833) **(G-10262)**
Crawford Acquisition Corp......................................216 486-0702
  16130 Saint Clair Ave Cleveland (44110) **(G-5141)**
Crawford Computer Center, Solon Also called Swagelok Company **(G-17393)**
Crawford Manufacturing Company.................................330 897-1060
  52496 State Route 651 Baltic (43804) **(G-1068)**
Crawford Products Inc..614 890-1822
  3637 Corporate Dr Columbus (43231) **(G-6999)**
Crawford Resources Inc...419 624-8400
  105 W Market St Ste 100 Sandusky (44870) **(G-16954)**
CRC Metal Products...740 966-0475
  29 Greenscapes Ct Johnstown (43031) **(G-11397)**

A L P H A B E T I C

Creamer Metal Products Inc (PA).................740 852-1752
　77 S Madison Rd London (43140) *(G-12207)*
Creatia Inc.................937 368-3100
　7990 Sodom Ballou Rd Fletcher (45326) *(G-9915)*
Creation Industries LLC.................440 554-6286
　15236 Shedd Rd Middlefield (44062) *(G-13925)*
Creation Sew Clever, Chillicothe Also called Rita Fishel Inc *(G-3272)*
Creative Blast Co.................513 251-4177
　3627 Spring Grove Ave Cincinnati (45223) *(G-3618)*
Creative Commercial Finishing.................513 722-9393
　1298 State Route 28 Ste B Loveland (45140) *(G-12347)*
Creative Concepts.................216 513-6463
　620 E Smith Rd Ste W1 Medina (44256) *(G-13398)*
Creative Countertops Ohio LLC.................937 540-9450
　477 E Wenger Rd Englewood (45322) *(G-9514)*
Creative Curbing America LLC.................419 738-7668
　1634 Springfield Ave Wapakoneta (45895) *(G-19484)*
Creative Design Marble Inc.................937 434-8892
　7901 S Suburban Rd Dayton (45458) *(G-8248)*
Creative Documents Solutions.................740 389-4252
　1629 Marion Waldo Rd Marion (43302) *(G-12864)*
Creative Electronic Design.................937 256-5106
　2565 Celia Dr Beavercreek (45434) *(G-1327)*
Creative Elements Studio.................330 606-2068
　1717 Trares Rd Mogadore (44260) *(G-14372)*
Creative Extruded Products Inc.................937 667-1618
　3510 Lightner Rd Vandalia (45377) *(G-19286)*
Creative Fab & Welding LLC.................937 780-5000
　9691 Stafford Rd Leesburg (45135) *(G-11851)*
Creative Fabrication Ltd.................740 262-5789
　20110 Predmore Rd Richwood (43344) *(G-16659)*
Creative Foam Dayton Mold.................937 279-9987
　3337 N Dixie Dr Dayton (45414) *(G-8249)*
Creative Fuels LLC.................330 923-2222
　1093 Foxglove Cir Cuyahoga Falls (44223) *(G-7983)*
Creative Impressions Inc.................937 435-5296
　4611 Gateway Cir Dayton (45440) *(G-8250)*
Creative Microsystems Inc.................937 836-4499
　52 Hillside Ct Englewood (45322) *(G-9515)*
Creative Millwork Ohio Inc.................440 992-3566
　1801 W 47th St Ashtabula (44004) *(G-799)*
Creative Mold and Machine Inc.................440 338-5146
　10385 Kinsman Rd Newbury (44065) *(G-15087)*
Creative Packaging LLC.................740 452-8497
　1781 Kemper Ct Zanesville (43701) *(G-21295)*
Creative Plastic Concepts LLC (PA).................419 927-9588
　206 S Griffith St Sycamore (44882) *(G-18096)*
Creative Plastics Intl.................937 596-6769
　18163 Snider Rd Jackson Center (45334) *(G-11338)*
Creative Powder Coatings.................440 322-8197
　6412 Gateway Blvd S Elyria (44035) *(G-9398)*
Creative Print Solutions LLC.................614 989-1747
　71 Granby Pl W Westerville (43081) *(G-20205)*
Creative Processing Inc.................440 834-4070
　17540 Rapids Rd Mantua (44255) *(G-12708)*
Creative Products Inc.................419 866-5501
　1430 Kieswetter Rd Holland (43528) *(G-11049)*
Creative Tool & Die.................614 836-0080
　244 Main St Groveport (43125) *(G-10619)*
Creative Woodworks.................330 897-1432
　5209 Evans Creek Rd Sw Sugarcreek (44681) *(G-18021)*
Creatia Woodworks.................440 355-8155
　16940 Indian Hollow Rd Grafton (44044) *(G-10422)*
Creativity For Kids, Cleveland Also called AW Faber-Castell Usa Inc *(G-4877)*
Creek Smoothies LLC.................937 429-1519
　3195 Dayton Xenia Rd Beavercreek (45434) *(G-1328)*
Creekside Springs LLC.................330 679-1010
　32 Washington St Salineville (43945) *(G-16941)*
Creighton Sports Center Inc (PA).................740 865-2521
　205 Broadway Ave New Matamoras (45767) *(G-14873)*
Cremeans Concrete and Sup Co.................740 446-1142
　161 Georges Creek Rd Gallipolis (45631) *(G-10293)*
Cres Cor, Mentor Also called Crescent Metal Products Inc *(G-13555)*
Crescent Metal Products Inc (PA).................440 350-1100
　5925 Heisley Rd Mentor (44060) *(G-13555)*
Crescent Services LLC.................405 603-1200
　11137 E Pike Rd Cambridge (43725) *(G-2453)*
Cresset Chemical Co Inc (PA).................419 669-2041
　13255 Main St Weston (43569) *(G-20324)*
Cresset Chemical Co Inc.................419 669-2041
　13490 Silver St Weston (43569) *(G-20325)*
Crest Aluminum Products, Mentor Also called Crest Products Inc *(G-13556)*
Crest Awning & Home Imprv Co.................440 942-3092
　1571 E 361st St Bldg 1 Willoughby (44095) *(G-20465)*
Crest Bending Inc.................419 492-2108
　108 John St New Washington (44854) *(G-14959)*
Crest Craft Company.................513 271-4858
　4460 Lake Forest Dr # 232 Blue Ash (45242) *(G-1770)*
Crest Graphics Inc.................513 271-2200
　1871 Summit Rd Cincinnati (45237) *(G-3619)*

Crest Products Inc.................440 942-5770
　8287 Tyler Blvd Mentor (44060) *(G-13556)*
Crestar Crusts Inc.................740 335-4813
　1104 Clinton Ave Wshngtn CT Hs (43160) *(G-20905)*
Crestar Foods, Wshngtn CT Hs Also called Crestar Crusts Inc *(G-20905)*
Crg Plastics Inc.................937 298-2025
　2661 Culver Ave Dayton (45429) *(G-8251)*
Crg Worldwide, Columbus Also called Custom Retail Group LLC *(G-7004)*
Cri Digital, Columbus Also called Copier Resources Inc *(G-6981)*
Cri Inc.................513 266-0882
　11060 Kenwood Rd Ste D Blue Ash (45242) *(G-1771)*
Crimson Gate Consulting Co (PA).................614 805-0897
　3274 Heatherstone Ct Dublin (43017) *(G-9066)*
Crisenbery Logging LLC.................740 256-1439
　7818 Lincoln Pike Patriot (45658) *(G-15994)*
Crishtronics Llc.................440 572-8318
　15249 Sassafras Dr Strongsville (44136) *(G-17908)*
Crispie Creme of Chillicothe.................740 774-3770
　47 N Bridge St Chillicothe (45601) *(G-3235)*
Criss Cross Directories, North Canton Also called Haines & Company Inc *(G-15237)*
Crissman Tool & Machine Inc.................330 872-1412
　3877 Hallock Sook Rd Newton Falls (44444) *(G-15131)*
Cristal USA Inc.................440 994-1400
　2900 Middle Rd Ashtabula (44004) *(G-800)*
Crists Machining Inc.................740 653-0041
　1910 Hamburg Rd Sw Lancaster (43130) *(G-11700)*
Criswell Furniture.................330 695-2082
　8139 Criswell Rd Fredericksburg (44627) *(G-10082)*
Criterion Instrument, Brookpark Also called Criterion Tool & Die Inc *(G-2154)*
Criterion Tool & Die Inc.................216 267-1733
　5349 W 161st St Brookpark (44142) *(G-2154)*
Critical Patient Care Inc.................937 434-5455
　4738 Gateway Cir Ste B Dayton (45440) *(G-8252)*
Criticalaire LLC.................513 475-3800
　6155 Huntley Rd Ste A Columbus (43229) *(G-7000)*
Criticalaire LLC (PA).................614 499-7744
　11325 R Hartman Hwy 100 Cincinnati (45241) *(G-3620)*
Crocs Inc.................330 954-1963
　549 S Chilcthe Rd Ste 240 Aurora (44202) *(G-914)*
Croft & Son Mfg Inc.................740 859-2200
　509 Highland Ave Tiltonsville (43963) *(G-18254)*
Cromwell Aleene.................937 547-2281
　101 W Main St Greenville (45331) *(G-10496)*
Crook Miller Company, Stow Also called Baker McMillen Co *(G-17733)*
Crooked Handle Brewing Co LLC.................937 241-5965
　760 N Main St Springboro (45066) *(G-17477)*
Crooked River Coffee Co.................440 442-8330
　761 Beta Dr Ste E Cleveland (44143) *(G-5142)*
Crop Production Services Inc.................614 873-4253
　9972 State Route 38 Milford Center (43045) *(G-14181)*
Crop Production Services Inc.................513 941-4100
　10743 Brower Rd North Bend (45052) *(G-15204)*
Crop Production Services Inc.................419 274-2701
　8767 County Road F Hamler (43524) *(G-10759)*
Crop Production Services Inc.................740 869-3369
　249 Chestnut St Mount Sterling (43143) *(G-14597)*
Cropking Incorporated.................330 302-4203
　134 West Dr Lodi (44254) *(G-12159)*
Crosco.................330 477-1999
　5246 18th St Sw Canton (44706) *(G-2671)*
Crosco Wood Products, Fredericksburg Also called Miller Crist *(G-10088)*
Crosco Wood Products.................330 857-0228
　1543 Zuercher Rd Dalton (44618) *(G-8065)*
Cross Communications Inc.................937 304-0010
　250 N Cassel Rd Vandalia (45377) *(G-19287)*
Crosscreek Pallet Co.................440 632-1940
　14530 Madison Rd Middlefield (44062) *(G-13926)*
Crosstown Bindery, Cincinnati Also called Patricia Lee Burd *(G-4214)*
Crowe Manufacturing Services.................800 831-1893
　2731 Walnut Ridge Dr Troy (45373) *(G-18813)*
Crowes Cabinets Inc.................330 536-2545
　725 S Hubbard Rd Lowellville (44436) *(G-12406)*
Crown Auto Top Mfg Co, Columbus Also called Crown Dielectric Inds Inc *(G-7001)*
Crown Battery Manufacturing Co (PA).................419 332-0563
　1445 Majestic Dr Fremont (43420) *(G-10139)*
Crown Closures Machinery.................740 681-6593
　1765 W Fair Ave Lancaster (43130) *(G-11701)*
Crown Cork & Seal Usa Inc.................419 727-8201
　5201 Enterprise Blvd Toledo (43612) *(G-18416)*
Crown Cork & Seal Usa Inc.................330 833-1011
　700 16th St Se Massillon (44646) *(G-13123)*
Crown Cork & Seal Usa Inc.................740 681-3000
　940 Mill Park Dr Lancaster (43130) *(G-11702)*
Crown Cork & Seal Usa Inc.................740 681-6593
　1765 W Fair Ave Lancaster (43130) *(G-11703)*
Crown Credit Company.................419 629-2311
　44 S Washington St New Bremen (45869) *(G-14782)*
Crown Dielectric Inds Inc.................614 224-5161
　830 W Broad St Columbus (43222) *(G-7001)*

Crown Elec Svcs & Automtn Inc 330 270-9890
102 Javit Ct Youngstown (44515) *(G-21058)*
Crown Electric Engrg & Mfg LLC 513 539-7394
175 Edison Dr Middletown (45044) *(G-14035)*
Crown Envelope LLC 513 771-5070
3249 E Kemper Rd Ste 1 Cincinnati (45241) *(G-3621)*
Crown Equipment Corporation 937 295-4062
300 S Tower St Fort Loramie (45845) *(G-9927)*
Crown Equipment Corporation 419 586-1100
410 Grand Lake Rd Celina (45822) *(G-2991)*
Crown Equipment Corporation 419 629-9201
120 W Monroe St New Bremen (45869) *(G-14783)*
Crown Equipment Corporation 937 454-7545
750 Center Dr Vandalia (45377) *(G-19288)*
Crown Equipment Corporation 440 232-7772
26400 Broadway Ave Ste B Oakwood Village (44146) *(G-15623)*
Crown Equipment Corporation 419 629-2311
624 W Monroe St New Bremen (45869) *(G-14784)*
Crown Equipment Corporation 419 629-2311
40 S Washington St New Bremen (45869) *(G-14785)*
Crown Equipment Corporation 419 629-2311
510 W Monroe St New Bremen (45869) *(G-14786)*
Crown Equipment Corporation 614 274-7700
2100 Southwest Blvd Grove City (43123) *(G-10551)*
Crown Equipment Corporation 513 874-2600
10685 Medallion Dr Cincinnati (45241) *(G-3622)*
Crown Lift Trucks, Fort Loramie *Also called Crown Equipment Corporation (G-9927)*
Crown Lift Trucks, Celina *Also called Crown Equipment Corporation (G-2991)*
Crown Lift Trucks, New Bremen *Also called Crown Equipment Corporation (G-14783)*
Crown Lift Trucks, Vandalia *Also called Crown Equipment Corporation (G-19288)*
Crown Lift Trucks, Oakwood Village *Also called Crown Equipment Corporation (G-15623)*
Crown Lift Trucks, New Bremen *Also called Crown Equipment Corporation (G-14784)*
Crown Lift Trucks, New Bremen *Also called Crown Equipment Corporation (G-14786)*
Crown Lift Trucks, Grove City *Also called Crown Equipment Corporation (G-10551)*
Crown Lift Trucks, Cincinnati *Also called Crown Equipment Corporation (G-3622)*
Crown Mats & Mating, Fremont *Also called Ludlow Composites Corporation (G-10168)*
Crown North America, Apple Creek *Also called Leggett & Platt Incorporated (G-643)*
Crown Plastics Co 513 367-0238
116 May Dr Harrison (45030) *(G-10775)*
Crown Printing Inc 740 477-2511
118 S Scioto St Circleville (43113) *(G-4626)*
Crowne Group LLC (PA) 216 589-0198
127 Public Sq Ste 5110 Cleveland (44114) *(G-5143)*
Crownover Lumber Co Inc (PA) 740 596-5229
501 Fairview Ave Mc Arthur (45651) *(G-13330)*
Crude Oil Buyer, Gnadenhutten *Also called Echo Drilling Inc (G-10406)*
Crude Oil Company 740 452-3335
1819 Newark Rd Zanesville (43701) *(G-21296)*
Cruise Quarters 614 777-6022
4013 Main St Hilliard (43026) *(G-10944)*
Cruise Quarters and Tours 614 891-6089
730 Mohican Way Westerville (43081) *(G-20206)*
Cruisin Times Magazine 440 331-4615
20545 Center Ridge Rd Ll40 Rocky River (44116) *(G-16696)*
Crum Manufacturing Inc 419 878-9779
1265 Wtrville Monclova Rd Waterville (43566) *(G-19654)*
Crumbs Bakery, Athens *Also called Crumbs Inc (G-859)*
Crumbs Inc 740 592-3803
94 Columbus Rd Athens (45701) *(G-859)*
Crummitt & Son Vault Corp (PA) 304 281-2420
329 N 2nd St Martins Ferry (43935) *(G-12923)*
Crushproof Tubing Co 419 293-2111
100 North St Mc Comb (45858) *(G-13337)*
Cryogenic Equipment & Svcs Inc 513 761-4200
11959 Tramway Dr Ste 1 Cincinnati (45241) *(G-3623)*
Cryogenic Technical Services, Plain City *Also called Drivetrain USA Inc (G-16337)*
Cryoplus Inc 330 683-3375
2429 N Millborne Rd Wooster (44691) *(G-20761)*
Cryovac Inc 513 771-7770
7410 Union Centre Blvd West Chester (45014) *(G-19849)*
Crystal Art Imports Inc (PA) 614 505-6001
6185 Huntley Rd Ste K Columbus (43229) *(G-7002)*
Crystal Carvers Inc 800 365-9782
4040 Essex Ct Powell (43065) *(G-16470)*
Crystal Classics, Columbus *Also called Crystal Art Imports Inc (G-7002)*
Crystal Koch Finishing Inc 440 366-7526
630 Sugar Ln Elyria (44035) *(G-9399)*
Crystal Spirits LLC 937 228-0201
827 S Patterson Blvd Dayton (45402) *(G-8253)*
Crystal Water Company, Dayton *Also called Rambasek Realty Inc (G-8616)*
Crystalite, Lewis Center *Also called Abrasive Technology Lapidary (G-11881)*
Cs Products 330 452-8566
1307 Gross Ave Ne Canton (44705) *(G-2672)*
Csafe LLC 937 312-0114
2900 Dryden Rd Moraine (45439) *(G-14473)*
Csc Ltd 330 841-6011
4000 Mahoning Ave Nw Warren (44483) *(G-19538)*
Cse-Industrial Products Group, Cincinnati *Also called Computer System Enhancement (G-3603)*
Csi Controls, Ashland *Also called Chandler Systems Incorporated (G-721)*
Csi Infusion Services, Brecksville *Also called Clinical Specialties Inc (G-2040)*
Csl Plasma Inc 937 325-4200
435 E Columbia St Springfield (45503) *(G-17537)*
CSM Horvath Ledgebrook 419 522-1133
198 Wayne St Mansfield (44902) *(G-12590)*
CSP Carey, Carey *Also called Continental Strl Plas Inc (G-2917)*
CSP Graphics Inc 216 426-2660
1538 E 41st St Cleveland (44103) *(G-5144)*
CSP North Baltimore, North Baltimore *Also called Continental Strl Plas Inc (G-15192)*
CSP Van Wert, Van Wert *Also called Continental Strl Plas Inc (G-19248)*
Csqp Quick Printing, North Olmsted *Also called Whiskey Fox Corporation (G-15352)*
CSS Publishing Co Inc 419 227-1818
5450 N Dixie Hwy Lima (45807) *(G-12002)*
Cssi & Quality Printing, Kent *Also called Customer Service Systems Inc (G-11442)*
CST Zero Discharged Car Wash S 740 947-5480
223 Virginia Ln Waverly (45690) *(G-19706)*
Csv Inc 937 438-1142
2080 E Rahn Rd Dayton (45440) *(G-8254)*
Csw of Ny Inc 413 589-1311
3545 Silica Rd Unit E Sylvania (43560) *(G-18102)*
CT Ferry Screw Products I 440 871-1617
1660 Queen Annes Gate Cleveland (44145) *(G-5145)*
CT Hydraulics Inc 440 437-2101
243 Staley Rd Ste A Orwell (44076) *(G-15774)*
CTB Consulting LLC 216 712-7764
19056 Old Detroit Rd Rocky River (44116) *(G-16697)*
Ctc Plastics 937 228-9184
401 N Keowee St Dayton (45404) *(G-8255)*
Ctek Tool & Machine Company 513 742-0423
11310 Southland Rd Cincinnati (45240) *(G-3624)*
Ctg, Miamisburg *Also called Certified Tool & Grinding Inc (G-13791)*
Ctl Analyzers, Shaker Heights *Also called Cellular Technology Limited (G-17088)*
Ctl Analyzers LLC (PA) 216 791-5084
20521 Chagrin Blvd # 200 Shaker Heights (44122) *(G-17089)*
Ctl-Aerospace Inc (PA) 513 874-1118
5616 Spellmire Dr West Chester (45246) *(G-19994)*
Ctl-Aerospace Inc 513 874-7900
9970 International Blvd West Chester (45246) *(G-19995)*
Ctm Integration Incorporated 330 332-1800
1318 Quaker Cir Salem (44460) *(G-16887)*
Ctna Tire Plant, Bryan *Also called Continental Tire Americas LLC (G-2290)*
Cto Inc 330 785-1130
2035 S Main St Akron (44301) *(G-134)*
CTS, Kettering *Also called Composite Technical Svcs LLC (G-11578)*
CTS Signs & Sales 419 407-5534
1030 Cresceus Rd Oregon (43616) *(G-15707)*
Cubbison Company (PA) 330 793-2481
380 Victoria Rd Youngstown (44515) *(G-21059)*
Cubic Blue Inc 330 638-2999
2934 Warren Meadville Rd Cortland (44410) *(G-7866)*
Cuda Composites LLC 937 499-0360
1788 S Metro Pkwy Dayton (45459) *(G-8256)*
Culaine Inc 419 345-4984
1036 W Laskey Rd Toledo (43612) *(G-18417)*
Culinary Standards, Blue Ash *Also called Rsw Distributors LLC (G-1863)*
Culligan, Zanesville *Also called US Water Company LLC (G-21360)*
Cult Couture LLC 330 801-9475
835 Berwin St Akron (44310) *(G-135)*
Cultured Marble Inc 330 549-2282
11331 South Ave North Lima (44452) *(G-15314)*
Cummins - Allison Corp 614 529-1940
3970 Brown Park Dr Ste C Hilliard (43026) *(G-10945)*
Cummins - Allison Corp 440 824-5050
6777 Engle Rd Ste H Cleveland (44130) *(G-5146)*
Cummins - Allison Corp 513 469-2924
11256 Cornell Park Dr Blue Ash (45242) *(G-1772)*
Cummins Bridgeway LLC 614 604-6000
2297 Southwest Blvd Ste K Grove City (43123) *(G-10552)*
Cummins Bridgeway LLC 614 771-1000
4000 Lyman Dr Hilliard (43026) *(G-10946)*
Cummins Bridgeway LLC 513 563-6670
5400 Rialto Rd West Chester (45069) *(G-19850)*
Cummins Bridgeway Columbus LLC 614 771-1000
4000 Lyman Dr Hilliard (43026) *(G-10947)*
Cummins Bridgeway Toledo LLC 419 893-8711
801 Illinois Ave Maumee (43537) *(G-13235)*
Cummins-Allison, Hilliard *Also called Cummins - Allison Corp (G-10945)*
Cupboard Distributing, Urbana *Also called Chris Haughey (G-19150)*
Cupcake Divaz 216 509-3850
5480 Autumn Ln North Ridgeville (44039) *(G-15365)*
Cupcake Wishes 440 315-3856
34340 Bainbridge Rd North Ridgeville (44039) *(G-15366)*
Cupcake Wishes Ltd 440 934-5550
37000 Detroit Rd Avon (44011) *(G-992)*

ALPHABETIC

Cupcakes For A Cure 419 764-1719
26595 Woodmont Dr Perrysburg (43551) *(G-16080)*

Curless Printing Company 937 783-2403
202 E Main St Unit 1 Blanchester (45107) *(G-1712)*

Current Inc 330 392-5151
455 N River Rd Nw Warren (44483) *(G-19539)*

Current Technology, Columbus *Also called Data Power Solutions (G-7013)*

Currier Richard & James 440 988-4132
540 Mcintosh Ln Amherst (44001) *(G-596)*

Curry Copy Center of Lakewood 216 521-5775
14528 Detroit Ave Lakewood (44107) *(G-11661)*

Curt Harler Inc 440 238-4556
12936 Falling Water Rd Cleveland (44136) *(G-5147)*

Curtis Chemical Inc 330 656-2514
6020 Ogilby Dr Hudson (44236) *(G-11167)*

Curtiss-Wright Controls 937 252-5601
2600 Paramount Pl Ste 200 Fairborn (45324) *(G-9618)*

Curtiss-Wright Flow Control 513 735-2538
750 Kent Rd Batavia (45103) *(G-1175)*

Curtiss-Wright Flow Control 513 528-7900
4600 E Tech Dr Cincinnati (45245) *(G-3296)*

Curtiss-Wright Flow Control 513 528-7900
4600 E Tech Dr Cincinnati (45245) *(G-3297)*

Curtiss-Wright Flow Ctrl Corp 440 838-7690
10195 Brecksville Rd Brecksville (44141) *(G-2042)*

Curtiss-Wright Flow Ctrl Corp 216 267-3200
18001 Sheldon Rd Cleveland (44130) *(G-5148)*

Curtiss-Wright Flow Ctrl Corp 513 528-7900
4600 E Tech Dr Cincinnati (45245) *(G-3298)*

Curv Imaging LLC 614 890-2878
841 Green Crest Dr Westerville (43081) *(G-20207)*

Curves and More Woodworking 614 239-7837
2002 Zettler Rd Columbus (43232) *(G-7003)*

Cusc International Ltd 513 881-2000
3 Standen Dr Hamilton (45015) *(G-10682)*

Cushman Foundry LLC 513 984-5570
5300 Creek Rd Blue Ash (45242) *(G-1773)*

Cushman Foundry Div, Cincinnati *Also called Sawbrook Steel Castings Co (G-4381)*

Custar Stone Co 419 669-4327
9072 County Road 424 Napoleon (43545) *(G-14676)*

Custer Products Limited 330 490-3158
4101 Shuffel St Nw # 100 North Canton (44720) *(G-15225)*

Custom Aerosol Packaging, Piqua *Also called C A P Industries Inc (G-16254)*

Custom Aluminum Boxes 440 864-2664
330 10th St Elyria (44035) *(G-9400)*

Custom Assembly Inc 419 622-3040
2952 Road 107 Haviland (45851) *(G-10837)*

Custom Automation Technologies 614 939-4228
1267 Bayboro Dr New Albany (43054) *(G-14755)*

Custom Blast & Coat Inc 419 225-6024
1511 S Dixie Hwy Lima (45804) *(G-12003)*

Custom Blind Corporation 937 643-2907
2895 Culver Ave Dayton (45429) *(G-8257)*

Custom Boat Covers, Aurora *Also called William Thompson (G-956)*

Custom Bobbin Winding, Zanesville *Also called Adkel Corp (G-21266)*

Custom Brackets, Cleveland *Also called J B M Machine Co Inc (G-5596)*

Custom Brass Finishing Inc 330 453-0888
1541 Raff Rd Sw Canton (44710) *(G-2673)*

Custom Built Crates Inc 513 248-4422
1700 Victory Park Dr Milford (45150) *(G-14135)*

Custom Canvas & Boat Repair 419 732-3314
29 S Bridge Rd Lakeside (43440) *(G-11646)*

Custom Canvas & Upholstery, Lakeside *Also called Custom Canvas & Boat Repair (G-11646)*

Custom Carbide Cutter Inc 513 851-6363
133 Circle Freeway Dr West Chester (45246) *(G-19996)*

Custom Cases For Collectibles, Hamilton *Also called Specialty Plas Fabrications (G-10740)*

Custom Cast Marbleworks Inc 513 769-6505
3154 Exon Ave Cincinnati (45241) *(G-3625)*

Custom Chassis Inc 440 839-5574
52826 State Route 303 Wakeman (44889) *(G-19447)*

Custom Chemical Packaging LLC 330 331-7416
303 Water St Wadsworth (44281) *(G-19399)*

Custom Chrome Plating, Grafton *Also called Customchrome Plating Inc (G-10423)*

Custom Cltch Jint Hydrlcs Inc (PA) 216 431-1630
3417 Saint Clair Ave Ne Cleveland (44114) *(G-5149)*

Custom Cntrwght Plate Proc Inc 330 448-2347
7799 Locust St Masury (44438) *(G-13214)*

Custom Coil & Transformer Co 740 452-5211
2900 Newark Rd Zanesville (43701) *(G-21297)*

Custom Coils 330 426-3797
51305 Carmel Achor Rd Negley (44441) *(G-14729)*

Custom Color Match and Spc 419 868-5882
8930 Airport Hwy Holland (43528) *(G-11050)*

Custom Counter Tops & Spc Co 330 637-4856
161 W Main St Cortland (44410) *(G-7867)*

Custom Craft Controls Inc 330 630-9599
1620 Triplett Blvd Akron (44306) *(G-136)*

Custom Craft Drap Inc 330 929-5728
1924 Portage Trl Cuyahoga Falls (44223) *(G-7984)*

Custom Crankshaft Inc 330 382-1200
1730 Annesley Rd East Liverpool (43920) *(G-9209)*

Custom Crete 740 726-2433
6928 Gillette Rd Waldo (43356) *(G-19465)*

Custom Cut UPS Scapbooking 330 698-5164
131 Apple Ridge Dr Apple Creek (44606) *(G-635)*

Custom Cutting Company, Ashland *Also called Consuetudo Abscism Inc (G-725)*

Custom Deco South Inc 419 698-2900
1343 Miami St Toledo (43605) *(G-18418)*

Custom Design & Tool 419 865-9773
8900 Geiser Rd Holland (43528) *(G-11051)*

Custom Design Cabinets & Tops 440 639-9900
379 Fountain Ave Painesville (44077) *(G-15872)*

Custom Design Kitchen & Bath, Painesville *Also called Custom Design Cabinets & Tops (G-15872)*

Custom Displays LLC 330 454-8850
9838 Bimeler St Ne Bolivar (44612) *(G-1931)*

Custom Duct & Supply Co Inc 937 228-2058
912 Cincinnati St Dayton (45417) *(G-8258)*

Custom Enclosures Corp 330 786-9000
1951 S Main St Akron (44301) *(G-137)*

Custom Engraving & Screen Prtg 440 933-2902
690 Avon Belden Rd Ste 1b Avon Lake (44012) *(G-1027)*

Custom Fab 330 825-3586
5281 S Hametown Rd Norton (44203) *(G-15509)*

Custom Fabrication By Fisher 513 738-4600
100 Weaver Rd Okeana (45053) *(G-15664)*

Custom Floaters LLC 216 337-9118
5161 W 161st St Brookpark (44142) *(G-2155)*

Custom Foam Products Inc (PA) 937 295-2700
900 Tower Dr Fort Loramie (45845) *(G-9928)*

Custom Formed Products, Miamisburg *Also called Customformed Products Inc (G-13795)*

Custom Fountains Inc 513 398-1447
4300 State Route 42 Mason (45040) *(G-13007)*

Custom GL Sltons Millbury Corp 419 855-7706
24145 W Moline Martin Rd Millbury (43447) *(G-14183)*

Custom Glass Solutions Corp 614 987-1390
600 Lkview Plz Blvd Ste A Worthington (43085) *(G-20862)*

Custom Glass Solutions Upr Snd 419 294-4921
12688 State Highway 67 Upper Sandusky (43351) *(G-19117)*

Custom Hitch & Trailer, Piketon *Also called Custom Hitch and Trailer/ Over (G-16218)*

Custom Hitch and Trailer/ Over 740 289-3925
4237 Us Highway 23 Piketon (45661) *(G-16218)*

Custom Hoists Inc (HQ) 419 368-4721
771 County Road 30a Ashland (44805) *(G-727)*

Custom Industries Inc 216 251-2804
10701 Briggs Rd Cleveland (44111) *(G-5150)*

Custom Machine Inc 419 986-5122
3315 W Township Road 158 Tiffin (44883) *(G-18217)*

Custom Machining Solutions LLC 330 221-1523
5605 Tallmadge Rd Rootstown (44272) *(G-16720)*

Custom Made Palm Trees & Tiki, Akron *Also called Custom Made Palm Trees LLC (G-138)*

Custom Made Palm Trees LLC 330 633-0063
1201 Devalera St Akron (44310) *(G-138)*

Custom Manufacturing Solutions (PA) 937 372-0777
1129 Miamisburg Centervil Dayton (45449) *(G-8259)*

Custom Marine Canvas Training 419 732-8362
250 Se Catawba Rd Ste C Port Clinton (43452) *(G-16397)*

Custom Material Hdlg Eqp LLC 513 235-5336
9089 Fontainebleau Ter Cincinnati (45231) *(G-3626)*

Custom Metal Products Inc 614 855-2263
5037 Babbitt Rd New Albany (43054) *(G-14756)*

Custom Metal Shearing Inc 937 233-6950
80 Commerce Park Dr Dayton (45404) *(G-8260)*

Custom Metal Works Inc (PA) 419 668-7831
193 State Route 18 Norwalk (44857) *(G-15531)*

Custom Millcraft Corp 513 874-7080
9092 Le Saint Dr West Chester (45014) *(G-19851)*

Custom Millwork Designs, Cleveland *Also called Cabinet Concepts Inc (G-4960)*

Custom Molded Foam Products 440 288-8951
1821 Iowa Ave Lorain (44052) *(G-12241)*

Custom Molded Products LLC 937 382-1070
92 Grant St Wilmington (45177) *(G-20662)*

Custom Neon & Commercial Signs 440 327-0225
7820 Maddock Rd North Ridgeville (44039) *(G-15367)*

Custom Nickel LLC 937 222-1995
45 N Clinton St Dayton (45402) *(G-8261)*

Custom Palet Manufacturing 440 693-4603
9291 N Girdle Rd Middlefield (44062) *(G-13927)*

Custom Polishing 937 596-0430
559 Plum Ridge Trl Sidney (45365) *(G-17173)*

Custom Powdr Coating By Greber, Elyria *Also called Greber Machine Tool Inc (G-9427)*

Custom Products Corporation (PA) 440 528-7100
7100 Cochran Rd Solon (44139) *(G-17280)*

Custom Pultrusions Inc (HQ) 330 562-5201
1331 S Chillicothe Rd Aurora (44202) *(G-915)*

ALPHABETIC SECTION
D A L E S Corporation

Custom Retail Group LLC 614 409-9720
6311 Busch Blvd Columbus (43229) ***(G-7004)***
Custom Rubber Corporation 216 391-2928
1274 E 55th St Cleveland (44103) ***(G-5151)***
Custom Screen Printing (PA) 330 963-3131
1869 E Aurora Rd Ste 100 Twinsburg (44087) ***(G-18920)***
Custom Seal Inc 419 334-1020
708 Graham Dr Fremont (43420) ***(G-10140)***
Custom Seal Roofing, Fremont *Also called Custom Seal Inc* ***(G-10140)***
Custom Sign Center Inc 614 279-6700
3200 Valleyview Dr Columbus (43204) ***(G-7005)***
Custom Sink Top Mfg 440 245-6220
302 W 12th St Lorain (44052) ***(G-12242)***
Custom Speed Parts Inc 440 238-3260
19769 Progress Dr Strongsville (44149) ***(G-17909)***
Custom Sporstwear Imprints LLC 330 335-8326
238 High St Wadsworth (44281) ***(G-19400)***
Custom Stamp Makers Inc 216 351-1470
4901 Brookpark Rd Cleveland (44134) ***(G-5152)***
Custom Surroundings Inc 330 483-9020
6450 Grafton Rd Valley City (44280) ***(G-19202)***
Custom Tarpaulin Products Inc 330 758-1801
8095 Southern Blvd Youngstown (44512) ***(G-21060)***
Custom Threading Systems LLC 937 846-1405
1833 N Dayton Lakeview Rd New Carlisle (45344) ***(G-14799)***
Custom Tooling Company Inc 513 733-5790
603 Wayne Park Dr Cincinnati (45215) ***(G-3627)***
Custom Way Welding Inc 937 845-9469
2217 N Dayton Lakeview Rd New Carlisle (45344) ***(G-14800)***
Custom Welding, Columbus *Also called Warlock Inc* ***(G-7749)***
Custom Woodworking Inc 419 456-3330
214 S Main St Ottawa (45875) ***(G-15791)***
Customchrome Plating Inc 440 926-3116
963 Mechanic St Grafton (44044) ***(G-10423)***
Customer Printing Inc 330 629-8676
592 Industrial Rd Youngstown (44509) ***(G-21061)***
Customer Service Systems Inc 330 677-2877
1250 W Main St Ste A Kent (44240) ***(G-11442)***
Customers Car Care Center 419 841-6646
5299 Monroe St Toledo (43623) ***(G-18419)***
Customformed Products Inc 937 388-0480
645 Precision Ct Miamisburg (45342) ***(G-13795)***
Customized Girl, Columbus *Also called E Retailing Associates LLC* ***(G-7043)***
Customized Vinyl Sales 330 518-3238
50814 Hadley Rd East Palestine (44413) ***(G-9232)***
Cut Off Blades Inc 440 543-2947
426 Chipping Ln Chagrin Falls (44023) ***(G-3084)***
Cutler Richard DBA Ohio Contro 440 892-1858
21506 Ellen Dr Cleveland (44126) ***(G-5153)***
Cutter Equipment Company, Canton *Also called Randall Richard & Moore LLC* ***(G-2835)***
Cutting Dynamics Inc (PA) 440 249-4662
980 Jaycox Rd Avon (44011) ***(G-993)***
Cutting Edge , The, Perry *Also called Tce International Ltd* ***(G-16059)***
Cutting Edge Cnverted Pdts Inc 888 720-3343
330 Ryder Rd Toledo (43607) ***(G-18420)***
Cutting Edge Countertops Inc 419 873-9500
1300 Flagship Dr Perrysburg (43551) ***(G-16081)***
Cutting Edge Manufacturing LLC 419 547-9204
1744 W Mcpherson Hwy Clyde (43410) ***(G-6539)***
Cutting Edge Packaging Pdts, Toledo *Also called Cutting Edge Cnverted Pdts Inc* ***(G-18420)***
Cutting Edge Technologies Inc 216 574-4759
1241 Superior Ave E Cleveland (44114) ***(G-5154)***
Cutting Systems Inc 216 928-0500
15593 Brookpark Rd Cleveland (44142) ***(G-5155)***
Cuyahoga Co Med Examiner S Off 216 721-5610
11001 Cedar Ave Cleveland (44106) ***(G-5156)***
Cuyahoga Community College 216 987-4744
700 Carnegie Ave Cleveland (44115) ***(G-5157)***
Cuyahoga Concrete Products, Cleveland *Also called Osborne Inc* ***(G-5949)***
Cuyahoga Falls Plant, Cuyahoga Falls *Also called Terrasource Global Corporation* ***(G-8054)***
Cuyahoga Group, The, North Ridgeville *Also called Cuyahoga Vending Co Inc* ***(G-15368)***
Cuyahoga Mch Co Ltd Lblty Co 216 267-3560
12301 Sprecher Ave Cleveland (44135) ***(G-5158)***
Cuyahoga Rebuilders Inc 440 846-0532
5111 Brookpark Rd Cleveland (44134) ***(G-5159)***
Cuyahoga Vending Co Inc 440 353-9595
39405 Taylor Pkwy North Ridgeville (44035) ***(G-15368)***
Cv Electric 419 630-0800
241 Baker St Bryan (43506) ***(G-2292)***
Cvc Limited 1 LLC 740 605-3853
568 S Liberty Keuter Rd Lebanon (45036) ***(G-11792)***
Cvg, New Albany *Also called Commercial Vehicle Group Inc* ***(G-14753)***
Cvg Trim Systems, New Albany *Also called Trim Systems Operating Corp* ***(G-14773)***
CW Machine Worx Ltd 740 654-5304
4805 Scooby Ln Carroll (43112) ***(G-2939)***
CWC Partners LLC 567 208-1573
228 Stadium Dr Findlay (45840) ***(G-9815)***
Cwh Graphics LLC 866 241-8515
23196 Miles Rd Ste A Bedford Heights (44128) ***(G-1482)***
Cwm Smoothie LLC 419 283-6387
2859 N Hiland Sylvania Rd Toledo (43615) ***(G-18421)***
Cwru Irland Cncer Ctr Cellular 216 368-1007
2103 Cornell Rd Rm 6-303 Cleveland (44106) ***(G-5160)***
Cyber Tech Tooling 937 320-2298
9378 Taylorsville Rd Dayton (45424) ***(G-8262)***
Cyberutility LLC 216 291-8723
1599 Maywood Rd Cleveland (44121) ***(G-5161)***
Cycle Electric Inc 937 884-7300
8734 Dyton Grenville Pike Brookville (45309) ***(G-2179)***
Cyclone Supply Company Inc (PA) 330 204-0313
524 River St Dover (44622) ***(G-8974)***
Cylinders & Valves Inc 440 238-7343
20811 Westwood Dr Strongsville (44149) ***(G-17910)***
Cylindrical Fabrications, Cleveland *Also called Cleveland Track Material Inc* ***(G-5082)***
Cypress Valley Log Homes, Marietta *Also called Gillard Construction Inc* ***(G-12786)***
Cyril-Scott Company The, Lancaster *Also called Consolidated Graphics Inc* ***(G-11699)***
Cytec Industries Inc 740 374-7171
1405 Greene St Marietta (45750) ***(G-12777)***
D & A Custom Trailer Inc 740 922-2205
6700 Moores Ridge Rd Se Uhrichsville (44683) ***(G-19047)***
D & A Rofael Enterprises Inc 513 751-4929
3026 Burnet Ave Cincinnati (45219) ***(G-3628)***
D & B Industries Inc 937 253-8658
5031 Linden Ave Ste B Dayton (45432) ***(G-8100)***
D & B Machine Welding Inc 740 922-4930
1128 N Main St Uhrichsville (44683) ***(G-19048)***
D & D Classic Auto Restoration 937 473-2229
2300 Mote Dr Covington (45318) ***(G-7921)***
D & D Energy Co 330 495-1631
6033 Marelis Ave Ne Canton (44721) ***(G-2674)***
D & D Landscaping Inc 330 507-6647
7012 Warren Sharon Rd Brookfield (44403) ***(G-2122)***
D & D Metal Supply Inc 513 272-1246
3717 Jonlen Dr Cincinnati (45227) ***(G-3629)***
D & D Mining Co Inc 330 549-3127
3379 E Garfield Rd New Springfield (44443) ***(G-14950)***
D & D Next Day Signs Inc 419 537-9595
2112 N Reynolds Rd Toledo (43615) ***(G-18422)***
D & D Plastics Inc 330 376-0668
581 E Tallmadge Ave Akron (44310) ***(G-139)***
D & D Quality Machining Co Inc 440 942-2772
36495 Reading Ave Willoughby (44094) ***(G-20466)***
D & E Electric Inc 513 738-1172
7055 Okana Drewersburg Rd Okeana (45053) ***(G-15665)***
D & E Machine Co 513 932-2184
962 S Us Route 42 Lebanon (45036) ***(G-11793)***
D & G Welding Inc 419 445-5751
302 W Barre Rd Archbold (43502) ***(G-670)***
D & H Meats Inc 419 387-7767
400 S Blanchard Vanlue (45890) ***(G-19319)***
D & J Distributing & Mfg 419 865-2552
1302 Holloway Rd Holland (43528) ***(G-11052)***
D & J Electric Motor Repair Co 330 336-4343
1734 Wall Rd Unit Office Wadsworth (44281) ***(G-19401)***
D & J Machine Shop 937 256-2730
442 Todd St Dayton (45403) ***(G-8263)***
D & J Printing Inc 330 678-5868
3765 Sunnybrook Rd Kent (44240) ***(G-11443)***
D & K Designs, Millersburg *Also called Lamar D Steiner* ***(G-14239)***
D & L Energy Inc 330 270-1201
3930 Fulton Dr Nw Ste 200 Canton (44718) ***(G-2675)***
D & L Excavating Ltd 419 271-0635
969 N Rymers Rd Port Clinton (43452) ***(G-16398)***
D & L Gas Energy Ltd 330 792-9524
2761 Salt Springs Rd Youngstown (44509) ***(G-21062)***
D & L Machine Co Inc 330 785-0781
1029 Arlington Cir Akron (44306) ***(G-140)***
D & L Machining LLC 419 253-1351
4621 Township Road 21 Marengo (43334) ***(G-12749)***
D & L Manufacturing 440 428-1627
2715 Bennett Rd Madison (44057) ***(G-12503)***
D & L Overhead Door Co Ltd 440 255-9720
9118 Tyler Blvd Mentor (44060) ***(G-13557)***
D & M Printing, Massillon *Also called David A and Mary A Mathis* ***(G-13124)***
D & M Saw & Tool Inc 513 871-5433
2974 P G Graves Ln Cincinnati (45241) ***(G-3630)***
D & M Welding, Moraine *Also called Dayton Brick Company Inc* ***(G-14477)***
D & M Welding & Radiator 740 947-9032
9093 State Route 220 Waverly (45690) ***(G-19707)***
D & R Supply Inc 330 855-3781
18228 Fulton Rd Marshallville (44645) ***(G-12917)***
D & S Crtive Cmmunications Inc (PA) 419 524-6699
140 Park Ave E Mansfield (44902) ***(G-12591)***
D 4 Industries Inc 419 523-9555
685 Woodland Dr Ottawa (45875) ***(G-15792)***
D A Fitzgerald Co Inc 937 548-0511
1045 Sater St Greenville (45331) ***(G-10497)***
D A L E S Corporation 419 255-5335
1402 Jackson St Toledo (43604) ***(G-18423)***

A L P H A B E T I C

D A Stirling Inc 330 923-3195
  2740 Hudson Dr Cuyahoga Falls (44221) *(G-7985)*

D and D Asp Sealcoating LLC 614 288-3597
  13199 E Crosset Hill Dr Pickerington (43147) *(G-16189)*

D Anderson Corp 330 433-0606
  6872 Glengarry Ave Nw Canton (44718) *(G-2676)*

D B Hess Company (HQ) 330 678-5868
  3765 Sunnybrook Rd Kent (44240) *(G-11444)*

D B Hess Company 330 676-2006
  3765 Sunnybrook Rd Kent (44240) *(G-11445)*

D B S Stinless Stl Fabricators 513 856-9600
  21 Standen Dr Hamilton (45015) *(G-10683)*

D C, Cleveland Also called Die-Cut Products Co *(G-5193)*

D C, Norwalk Also called Durable Corporation *(G-15535)*

D C Filter & Chemical Inc 419 626-3967
  1517 5th St Sandusky (44870) *(G-16955)*

D C G, Cleveland Also called Directconnectgroup Ltd *(G-5196)*

D C I, Akron Also called Digital Color Intl LLC *(G-152)*

D C M Industries Inc 937 254-8500
  1901 E 5th St Dayton (45403) *(G-8264)*

D C Ramey Piano Co 708 602-3961
  17768 Woodview Dr Marysville (43040) *(G-12940)*

D C S Specialty Packaging Inc 937 615-0100
  9700 Looney Rd Piqua (45356) *(G-16258)*

D C Systems Inc 330 273-3030
  1251 Industrial Pkwy N Brunswick (44212) *(G-2219)*

D D D Hams Inc 440 487-9572
  34234 Aurora Rd Solon (44139) *(G-17281)*

D F Electronics Inc 513 772-7792
  200 Novner Dr Cincinnati (45215) *(G-3631)*

D I, Canfield Also called Dunaway Inc *(G-2552)*

D J Decorative Stone Inc 937 848-6462
  3180 Ferry Rd Bellbrook (45305) *(G-1505)*

D J Klingler Inc 513 891-2284
  9999 Montgomery Rd Cincinnati (45242) *(G-3632)*

D J Metro Mold & Die Inc 440 237-1130
  9841 York Alpha Dr Ste J North Royalton (44133) *(G-15416)*

D Johnson Services 330 386-4588
  50579 Fisher Ave East Liverpool (43920) *(G-9210)*

D K Manufacturing 740 654-5566
  2118 Commerce St Lancaster (43130) *(G-11704)*

D L H Locomotive Works 937 629-0321
  1528 Mitchell Blvd Springfield (45503) *(G-17538)*

D L Salkil LLC 419 841-3341
  8261 W Bancroft St Toledo (43617) *(G-18424)*

D L T, Cincinnati Also called Dominion Liquid Tech LLC *(G-3663)*

D Lewis Inc 740 695-2615
  52235 National Rd E Saint Clairsville (43950) *(G-16788)*

D M I, Reynoldsburg Also called Dimensional Metals Inc *(G-16586)*

D M J F Inc 440 845-1155
  6571 Pearl Rd Cleveland (44130) *(G-5162)*

D M L Steel Tech 513 737-9911
  6974 Zenith Ct Liberty Twp (45011) *(G-11973)*

D M Pallet Service Inc 614 491-0881
  2019 Rathmell Rd Columbus (43207) *(G-7006)*

D M Tool & Plastics Inc 937 962-4140
  11150 Baltimore Brookville (45309) *(G-2180)*

D M Tool & Plastics Inc (PA) 937 962-4140
  4140 Us Route 40 E Lewisburg (45338) *(G-11932)*

D M U, Dayton Also called Dayton Molded Urethanes LLC *(G-8280)*

D M V Supply Corporation 330 847-0450
  3047 Anderson Anthony Warren (44481) *(G-19540)*

D M Z Machine Co, Willoughby Also called Zitnik Enterprises Inc *(G-20635)*

D Martone Industries Inc 440 632-5800
  15060 Madison Rd Middlefield (44062) *(G-13928)*

D N A, Plain City Also called Daily Needs Assistance *(G-16330)*

D O Technologies Inc 330 725-4561
  667 Lafayette Rd Medina (44256) *(G-13399)*

D P I, Toledo Also called Decorative Panels Intl Inc *(G-18433)*

D P Products Inc 440 834-9663
  14790 Brkshire Ind Pkwy Middlefield (44062) *(G-13929)*

D Picking & Co 419 562-5016
  119 S Walnut St Bucyrus (44820) *(G-2337)*

D S H Machine Co 440 946-4311
  36255 Reading Ave Ste A Willoughby (44094) *(G-20467)*

D T Kothera Inc 440 632-1651
  15422 Georgia Rd Middlefield (44062) *(G-13930)*

D W Dickey, Lisbon Also called D W Dickey and Son Inc *(G-12119)*

D W Dickey and Son Inc (PA) 330 424-1441
  7896 Dickey Dr Lisbon (44432) *(G-12119)*

D W Truax Enterprise Inc 740 695-2596
  52499 National Rd E Saint Clairsville (43950) *(G-16789)*

D&D Classic Restoration, Covington Also called D & D Classic Auto Restoration *(G-7921)*

D&D Design Concepts Inc 513 752-2191
  4360 Winding Creek Blvd Batavia (45103) *(G-1176)*

D&D Logging 740 679-2573
  52759 State Route 379 Woodsfield (43793) *(G-20717)*

D&M Fencing LLC 419 604-0698
  08656 Deep Cut Rd Spencerville (45887) *(G-17459)*

D'Ing Meeting Room Products, Cleveland Also called DIng Products *(G-5195)*

D+h USA Corporation 513 381-9400
  312 Plum St Ste 500 Cincinnati (45202) *(G-3633)*

D+h USA Corporation 937 435-2335
  8555 Gander Creek Dr Miamisburg (45342) *(G-13796)*

D-Flite Mfg LLC 419 485-3081
  705 Shawanoe St Montpelier (43543) *(G-14442)*

D-G Custom Chrome LLC 513 531-1881
  5200 Lester Rd Cincinnati (45213) *(G-3634)*

D.B.G. Cleaners, Mansfield Also called Our Detergent Inc *(G-12665)*

D.O.V.E.S., Clarington Also called Diversifd OH Vlly Eqpt & Srvcs *(G-4651)*

Da-Lite Screen Company LLC 574 267-8101
  11500 Williamson Rd Blue Ash (45241) *(G-1774)*

Daavlin Distributing Co 419 636-6304
  205 W Bement St Bryan (43506) *(G-2293)*

Dabar Industries LLC 614 873-3949
  8475 Rausch Dr Plain City (43064) *(G-16329)*

Dac, Dover Also called Direct Action Co Inc *(G-8976)*

Daca Vending Wholesale LLC 513 753-1600
  1105b W Ohio Pike Amelia (45102) *(G-571)*

Dacon Industries Co 330 298-9491
  4839 Washington Ave Ravenna (44266) *(G-16524)*

Dacraft, Miamisburg Also called Waxco International Inc *(G-13879)*

Dadco Inc (PA) 513 489-2244
  7365 E Kemper Rd Ste D Cincinnati (45249) *(G-3635)*

Dadco Inc 513 489-2244
  12151 Best Pl Cincinnati (45241) *(G-3636)*

Daddy Katz LLC 937 296-0347
  3250 Kettering Blvd Moraine (45439) *(G-14474)*

Daffin Candies, Girard Also called Daffins Candies *(G-10385)*

Daffins Candies (PA) 330 545-0325
  39 W Liberty St Girard (44420) *(G-10385)*

Daffy Dan's, Cleveland Also called To A T *(G-6329)*

Dai Ceramics Inc 440 946-6964
  38240 Airport Pkwy Willoughby (44094) *(G-20468)*

Daido Metal Bellefontaine LLC 937 592-5010
  1215 S Greenwood St Bellefontaine (43311) *(G-1526)*

Daikin Applied Americas Inc 614 351-9862
  739 N Wilson Rd Columbus (43204) *(G-7007)*

Daily Agency Inc 937 456-9808
  309 N Barron St Eaton (45320) *(G-9304)*

Daily Chief Union 419 294-2331
  111 W Wyandot Ave Upper Sandusky (43351) *(G-19118)*

Daily Dog 419 708-4923
  8325 Hill Ave Holland (43528) *(G-11053)*

Daily Fostoria Review Co 419 435-6641
  113 E Center St Fostoria (44830) *(G-9969)*

Daily Gazette 937 372-4444
  1836 W Park Sq Xenia (45385) *(G-20945)*

Daily Globe, Shelby Also called Shelby Daily Globe Inc *(G-17142)*

Daily Growler Inc 614 656-2337
  2812 Fishinger Rd Upper Arlington (43221) *(G-19112)*

Daily Kent Stater, Kent Also called Kent State University *(G-11482)*

Daily Legal News, Cleveland Also called Legal News Publishing Co *(G-5692)*

Daily Legal News Inc 330 747-7777
  100 E Federal St Ste 126 Youngstown (44503) *(G-21063)*

Daily Needs Assistance 614 824-8340
  340 W Main St Plain City (43064) *(G-16330)*

Daily Needs Personal Care LLC 614 598-8383
  11560 State Route 104 Ashville (43103) *(G-850)*

Daily Record, The, Millersburg Also called Holmes County Hub Inc *(G-14230)*

Daily Reporter 614 224-4835
  580 S High St Ste 316 Columbus (43215) *(G-7008)*

Daily Squawk LLC 937 426-6247
  3214 Bob White Pl Dayton (45431) *(G-8101)*

Daily Standard The, Celina Also called Standard Printing Co Inc *(G-3019)*

Dairy Clean, Delaware Also called Frischco Inc *(G-8846)*

Dairy Farmers America Inc 330 670-7800
  1035 Medina Rd Ste 300 Medina (44256) *(G-13400)*

Dairy Pak Div, Olmsted Falls Also called Blue Ridge Paper Products Inc *(G-15674)*

Dairy Shed 937 848-3504
  55 Bellbrook Plz Bellbrook (45305) *(G-1506)*

Dairymens, Cleveland Also called Borden Dairy Company Ohio LLC *(G-4925)*

Daishin Industrial Co 614 766-9535
  6490 Shier Rings Rd Ste E Dublin (43016) *(G-9067)*

Daisy Brand LLC 330 202-4376
  3600 N Geyers Chapel Rd Wooster (44691) *(G-20762)*

Daisys Pillows LLC 937 776-6968
  4694 Free Pike Dayton (45416) *(G-8265)*

Dak Enterprises Inc (PA) 740 828-3291
  18062 Timber Trails Rd Marysville (43040) *(G-12941)*

Dakkota Integrated Systems LLC 517 694-6500
  315 Matzinger Rd Unit G Toledo (43612) *(G-18425)*

Dal-Little Fabricating Inc 216 883-3323
  11707 Putnam Ave Cleveland (44105) *(G-5163)*

Dalaco Materials LLC 513 893-5483
4805 Hamilton Middltwn Liberty Twp (45011) *(G-11974)*

Dale Kestler 513 871-9000
3667 Paxton Ave Cincinnati (45208) *(G-3637)*

Dale Lute Logging 740 352-1779
2696 Henley Deemer Rd Mc Dermott (45652) *(G-13341)*

Dalin Auto Service 440 997-3301
3041 S Ridge Rd W Ashtabula (44004) *(G-801)*

Dallas Design & Technology Inc 419 884-9750
184 Industrial Dr Mansfield (44904) *(G-12592)*

Dallas Instantwhip Inc 614 488-2536
2200 Cardigan Ave Columbus (43215) *(G-7009)*

Dalmatian Press LLC 419 207-3600
605 Westlake Dr Ashland (44805) *(G-728)*

Dalton Corporation 419 682-6328
310 Ellis St Stryker (43557) *(G-18001)*

Dalton Stryker McHining Fcilty 419 682-6328
310 Ellis St Stryker (43557) *(G-18002)*

Dalton Veal 330 828-8337
14978 Arnold Rd Dalton (44618) *(G-8066)*

Dalton Wood Products Inc 330 682-0727
101 N Swinehart Rd Orrville (44667) *(G-15734)*

Damar Products Inc (PA) 937 492-9023
17222 State Route 47 E Sidney (45365) *(G-17174)*

Damar Products Inc 937 492-9023
516 Park St Sidney (45365) *(G-17175)*

Dan K Williams Inc 419 893-3251
1350 Ford St Maumee (43537) *(G-13236)*

Dan Nemes American Racing 216 749-4203
4770 Van Epps Rd Ste 200b Brooklyn Heights (44131) *(G-2137)*

Dan Novak 440 269-1741
1455 E 328th St Willoughby (44095) *(G-20469)*

Dan S Miller & David S Miller 937 464-9061
9216 County Road 97 Belle Center (43310) *(G-1512)*

Dan Shrock Cement 440 548-2498
9344 Pritchard Rd Parkman (44080) *(G-15951)*

Dan Wilzynski 800 531-3343
2000 Fairwood Ave Columbus (43207) *(G-7010)*

Dan-Loc LLC 937 778-0485
294 Fox Dr Piqua (45356) *(G-16259)*

Dan-Loc Express, Piqua *Also called Dan-Loc LLC (G-16259)*

Dan-Mar Company Inc 419 660-8830
200 Bluegrass Dr E Norwalk (44857) *(G-15532)*

Dana Auto Systems Group LLC (HQ) 419 887-3000
3939 Technology Dr Maumee (43537) *(G-13237)*

Dana Brazil Holdings I LLC (HQ) 419 887-3000
3939 Technology Dr Maumee (43537) *(G-13238)*

Dana Commercial Vehicle Pdts, Maumee *Also called Dana Commercial Vhcl Mfg LLC (G-13239)*

Dana Commercial Vhcl Mfg LLC (HQ) 419 887-3000
3939 Technology Dr Maumee (43537) *(G-13239)*

Dana Commercial Vhcl Pdts LLC (HQ) 419 887-3000
3939 Technology Dr Maumee (43537) *(G-13240)*

Dana Companies LLC (HQ) 419 931-9086
900 Ws Boundary Ste 8a Perrysburg (43551) *(G-16082)*

Dana Corporation 419 887-3000
4500 Dorr St Toledo (43615) *(G-18426)*

Dana Driveshaft Mfg LLC 419 222-9708
777 Bible Rd Lima (45801) *(G-12004)*

Dana Driveshaft Mfg LLC (HQ) 419 887-3000
3939 Technology Dr Maumee (43537) *(G-13241)*

Dana Driveshaft Products, Lima *Also called Dana Driveshaft Mfg LLC (G-12004)*

Dana Driveshaft Products, Maumee *Also called Dana Driveshaft Mfg LLC (G-13241)*

Dana Driveshaft Products LLC (HQ) 419 887-3000
3939 Technology Dr Maumee (43537) *(G-13242)*

Dana Global Products Inc 419 887-3000
3939 Technology Dr Maumee (43537) *(G-13243)*

Dana Global Products Inc (HQ) 419 887-3000
3939 Technology Dr Maumee (43537) *(G-13244)*

Dana Graphics Inc 513 351-4400
2200 Dana Ave Fl 2 Cincinnati (45208) *(G-3638)*

Dana Heavy Vehicle Systems (HQ) 419 887-3000
3939 Technology Dr Maumee (43537) *(G-13245)*

Dana Heavy Vhcl Systems Group, Maumee *Also called Dana Heavy Vehicle Systems (G-13245)*

Dana Incorporated (PA) 419 887-3000
3939 Technology Dr Maumee (43537) *(G-13246)*

Dana Information Technology, Maumee *Also called Dana Limited (G-13248)*

Dana Light Axle Mfg LLC 419 887-3000
3044 Jeep Parkway Toledo (43657) *(G-18427)*

Dana Light Axle Mfg LLC (HQ) 419 887-3000
3939 Technology Dr Maumee (43537) *(G-13247)*

Dana Light Axle Products, Maumee *Also called Dana Light Axle Mfg LLC (G-13247)*

Dana Limited 419 482-2000
580 Longbow Dr Maumee (43537) *(G-13248)*

Dana Limited (HQ) 630 697-3783
3939 Technology Dr Maumee (43537) *(G-13249)*

Dana Off Highway Products LLC 614 864-1116
6635 Taylor Rd Blacklick (43004) *(G-1695)*

Dana Off Highway Products LLC 740 694-2055
123 Phoenix Pl Fredericktown (43019) *(G-10098)*

Dana Off Highway Products LLC (HQ) 419 887-3000
3939 Technology Dr Maumee (43537) *(G-13250)*

Dana Sealing Manufacturing LLC (HQ) 419 887-3000
3939 Technology Dr Maumee (43537) *(G-13251)*

Dana Sealing Products, Maumee *Also called Dana Sealing Manufacturing LLC (G-13251)*

Dana Sealing Products LLC (HQ) 419 887-3000
3939 Technology Dr Maumee (43537) *(G-13252)*

Dana Signs LLC 937 653-3917
1052 S Main St Frnt Frnt Urbana (43078) *(G-19155)*

Dana Structural Products LLC (HQ) 419 887-3000
3939 Technology Dr Maumee (43537) *(G-13253)*

Dana Thermal Products LLC (HQ) 419 887-3000
3939 Technology Dr Maumee (43537) *(G-13254)*

Dana White Machining Wldg Inc 419 652-3444
910 County Road 40 Nova (44859) *(G-15577)*

Dana World Trade Corp (HQ) 419 887-3000
3939 Technology Dr Maumee (43537) *(G-13255)*

Danaher Corporation 440 995-3003
6095 Parkland Blvd # 310 Cleveland (44124) *(G-5164)*

Danaher Corporation 440 995-3025
7171 Industrial Park Blvd Mentor (44060) *(G-13558)*

Dandi Enterprises Inc 419 516-9070
6353 Som Center Rd Solon (44139) *(G-17282)*

Dandy Products Inc 800 591-2284
1095 Harcourt Rd Ste C Mount Vernon (43050) *(G-14618)*

Dandy Products Inc 513 625-3000
3314 State Route 131 Goshen (45122) *(G-10414)*

Dango & Dienenthal Inc 330 829-0277
21 E Chestnut St Alliance (44601) *(G-504)*

Daniel M Beyerbach 513 206-1180
2123 Auburn Ave Cincinnati (45219) *(G-3639)*

Daniel Meenan 330 756-2818
614 Pine St Nw Beach City (44608) *(G-1247)*

Daniel Wagner 740 942-2928
39110 Welsh Rd Cadiz (43907) *(G-2416)*

Daniels Amish Collection LLC 330 276-0110
100 Straits Ln Killbuck (44637) *(G-11594)*

Daniels Amish Collection LLC (PA) 330 359-0400
9190 Massillon Rd Dundee (44624) *(G-9171)*

Daniels Brothers Fuel Co 440 942-1800
38700 Pelton Rd Willoughby (44094) *(G-20470)*

Danis Sweet Cupcakes 614 581-8978
283 N Clayton St Centerburg (43011) *(G-3030)*

Danite Holdings Ltd 614 444-3333
1640 Harmon Ave Columbus (43223) *(G-7011)*

Danite Sign Co, Columbus *Also called Danite Holdings Ltd (G-7011)*

Danmarco, Norwalk *Also called Dan-Mar Company Inc (G-15532)*

Danner Press Corp 330 454-5692
1411 Navarre Rd Sw Canton (44706) *(G-2677)*

Dano Jr LLC 440 781-5774
6185 Ridgebury Blvd Cleveland (44124) *(G-5165)*

Danroc Corp 330 262-0712
326 N Hillcrest Dr Wooster (44691) *(G-20763)*

Dansco Mfg & Pmpg Unit Svc LP 330 452-3677
2149 Moore Ave Se Canton (44707) *(G-2678)*

Dansizen Printing Co Inc 330 966-4962
4525 Aultman Ave Nw North Canton (44720) *(G-15226)*

Dante Solutions Inc 440 234-8477
7261 Engle Rd Ste 105 Cleveland (44130) *(G-5166)*

Dap Products Inc 937 667-4461
875 N 3rd St Tipp City (45371) *(G-18274)*

Dapsco 937 294-5331
3110 Kettering Blvd Moraine (45439) *(G-14475)*

Darby Creek Millwork Co 614 873-3267
10001 Plain Cy Grgesville Plain City (43064) *(G-16331)*

Darby Creek Publishing 614 873-7958
7858 Industrial Pkwy Plain City (43064) *(G-16332)*

Dare Electronics Inc 937 335-0031
3245 S County Road 25a Troy (45373) *(G-18814)*

Dari Freeze 937 678-6171
414 N Main St West Manchester (45382) *(G-20097)*

Darifill Inc 614 890-3274
750 Green Crest Dr Westerville (43081) *(G-20208)*

Dark Continent 330 454-7804
817 High Ave Nw Canton (44703) *(G-2679)*

Dark Diamond Tools Inc 440 701-6424
10319 Sawmill Dr Chardon (44024) *(G-3148)*

Darke Precision Inc 937 548-2232
291 Fox Dr Piqua (45356) *(G-16260)*

Darko Inc 330 425-9805
2026 Summit Commerce Park Twinsburg (44087) *(G-18921)*

Darling International Inc 216 651-9300
1002 Peltnine Ave Cleveland (44109) *(G-5167)*

Daron Coal Company LLC 614 643-0337
40580 Cadiz Piedmont Rd Cadiz (43907) *(G-2417)*

Darrah Electric Company (PA) 216 631-0912
5914 Merrill Ave Cleveland (44102) *(G-5168)*

A
L
P
H
A
B
E
T
I
C

Darryl Smith 216 991-5468
3571 E 147th St Cleveland (44120) ***(G-5169)***
Darusta Woodlife Division, Tipp City *Also called Dap Products Inc* ***(G-18274)***
Das Deutsch Cheese, Middlefield *Also called Middlfeld Original Cheese Coop* ***(G-13964)***
Daskal Enterprise LLC (PA) 614 848-5700
6522 Singletree Dr Columbus (43229) ***(G-7012)***
Data Analysis Technologies 614 873-0710
7715 Corporate Blvd Plain City (43064) ***(G-16333)***
Data Image 740 763-7017
2345 Gratiot Rd Se Heath (43056) ***(G-10846)***
Data Mold and Tool Inc 419 878-9861
160 Concord St Waterville (43566) ***(G-19655)***
Data Power Solutions 614 471-1911
804 Hedley Pl Columbus (43230) ***(G-7013)***
Data Processing Sciences Corp (HQ) 513 791-7100
2 Camargo Cyn Cincinnati (45243) ***(G-3640)***
Dataq Instruments 330 668-1444
241 Springside Dr Akron (44333) ***(G-141)***
Datatex Media Dolls 216 598-1000
7027 Columbia Rd Cleveland (44138) ***(G-5170)***
Datatrak International Inc 440 443-0082
5900 Landerbrook Dr # 170 Mayfield Heights (44124) ***(G-13312)***
Datco Mfg Company Inc 330 787-1127
4605 Lake Park Rd Youngstown (44512) ***(G-21064)***
Datco Mfg Company Inc (PA) 330 781-6100
4605 Lake Park Rd Youngstown (44512) ***(G-21065)***
Datono Products, Dayton *Also called Dayton Stencil Works Company* ***(G-8287)***
Datwyler Sling Sltions USA Inc 937 387-2800
875 Center Dr Vandalia (45377) ***(G-19289)***
Daubenmires Printing 513 425-7223
1527 Central Ave Middletown (45044) ***(G-14036)***
Daugherty Machine Company Inc 614 834-4010
8215 Dove Pkwy Canal Winchester (43110) ***(G-2522)***
Dave Foreign Cars 419 727-0685
6151 American Rd Toledo (43612) ***(G-18428)***
Dave's Welding & Excavation, Gnadenhutten *Also called David Cox* ***(G-10405)***
Davenport Service Group Inc 440 487-9353
7561 Tyler Blvd Ste 9 Mentor (44060) ***(G-13559)***
Daves Pallets 740 525-4938
710 Thomas St Belpre (45714) ***(G-1585)***
Daves Printing 513 221-0182
614 Riddle Rd Cincinnati (45220) ***(G-3641)***
Davey Drill, Kent *Also called Davey Kent Inc* ***(G-11446)***
Davey Kent Inc 330 673-5400
200 W Williams St Kent (44240) ***(G-11446)***
David A and Mary A Mathis 330 837-8611
332 Erie St S Massillon (44646) ***(G-13124)***
David A Waldron & Associates (PA) 330 264-7275
2285 Eagle Pass A Wooster (44691) ***(G-20764)***
David Adkins Logging 740 533-0297
1260 Township Road 256 Kitts Hill (45645) ***(G-11620)***
David Boswell 614 441-2497
1777 Franklin Park S Columbus (43205) ***(G-7014)***
David Brandeberry 937 653-4680
703 Miami St Urbana (43078) ***(G-19156)***
David Butler Tax Service 419 626-8086
415 Tiffin Ave Sandusky (44870) ***(G-16956)***
David Cox 740 254-4858
9664 Gilmore Rd Se Gnadenhutten (44629) ***(G-10405)***
David E Easterday and Co Inc 330 359-0700
1225c Us Route 62 Wilmot (44689) ***(G-20685)***
David Esrati 937 228-4433
100 Bonner St Dayton (45410) ***(G-8266)***
David Ogilbee 740 929-2638
1881 Beaver Run Rd Se Hebron (43025) ***(G-10864)***
David Price Metal Services Inc 419 668-3358
360 Eastpark Dr Norwalk (44857) ***(G-15533)***
David R Hill Inc 740 685-5168
132 S 2nd St Byesville (43723) ***(G-2397)***
David Round Company Inc 330 656-1600
10200 Wellman Rd Streetsboro (44241) ***(G-17847)***
David S Rodgers 740 490-5843
8168 Business Way Plain City (43064) ***(G-16334)***
David Wolfe Design Inc 330 633-6124
829 Moe Dr Akron (44310) ***(G-142)***
Davidson Converting Inc 330 626-2118
1611 Frost Rd Streetsboro (44241) ***(G-17848)***
Davidson Jewelers Inc 513 932-3936
726 E Main St Lebanon (45036) ***(G-11794)***
Davidson Meat Processing Plant, Waynesville *Also called Patrick M Davidson* ***(G-19733)***
Davies Interiors, Mansfield *Also called Davies Since 1900* ***(G-12593)***
Davies Since 1900 ....419 756-4212
913 S Main St Mansfield (44907) ***(G-12593)***
Davis Caulking & Sealant LLC 740 286-3825
199 Garfield Rd Wellston (45692) ***(G-19762)***
Davis Fabricators Inc 419 898-5297
15765 W State Route 2 Oak Harbor (43449) ***(G-15588)***
Davis Laser Products 614 252-7711
2700 E 6th Ave Columbus (43219) ***(G-7015)***
Davis Machine Products Inc 440 474-0247
74 Sapphire Ln Streetsboro (44241) ***(G-17849)***
Davis Machining Service 513 528-4917
602 Comet Dr Cincinnati (45244) ***(G-3642)***
Davis Technologies Inc 330 823-2544
837 W Main St Alliance (44601) ***(G-505)***
Davis Welding Company, Celina *Also called E L Davis Inc* ***(G-2993)***
Davro Ltd 216 258-0057
1200 E 152nd St Cleveland (44110) ***(G-5171)***
Dawn Enterprises Inc (PA) 216 642-5506
9155 Sweet Valley Dr Cleveland (44125) ***(G-5172)***
Day Pre-Cast Products Co 419 536-2909
801 N Westwood Ave Toledo (43607) ***(G-18429)***
Day-Glo Color Corp (HQ) 216 391-7070
4515 Saint Clair Ave Cleveland (44103) ***(G-5173)***
Day-Glo Color Corp 216 391-7070
4518 Hamilton Ave Cleveland (44114) ***(G-5174)***
Day-Glo Color Corp 216 391-7070
1570 Highland Rd Twinsburg (44087) ***(G-18922)***
Day-Hio Products Inc 937 445-0782
709 Webster St Dayton (45404) ***(G-8267)***
Day-TEC Tool & Mfg Inc 937 847-0022
4900 Lyons Rd Unit A Miamisburg (45342) ***(G-13797)***
Daymark Security Systems, Bowling Green *Also called CMC Daymark Corporation* ***(G-1980)***
Dayton Air Control Pdts LLC 937 254-4441
2785 Lance Dr Moraine (45409) ***(G-14476)***
Dayton Audio LLC 937 743-3000
725 Pleasant Valley Dr Springboro (45066) ***(G-17478)***
Dayton Bag & Burlap Co 937 253-1722
448 Huffman Ave Dayton (45403) ***(G-8268)***
Dayton Bindery Service Inc 937 235-3111
3757 Inpark Dr Dayton (45414) ***(G-8269)***
Dayton Brick Company Inc 937 293-4189
2300 Arbor Blvd Moraine (45439) ***(G-14477)***
Dayton Business Journal, Dayton *Also called American City Bus Journals Inc* ***(G-8152)***
Dayton City Paper New LLC 937 222-8855
126 N Main St Ste 240 Dayton (45402) ***(G-8270)***
Dayton Clutch & Joint Inc (PA) 937 236-9770
2005 Troy St 1 Dayton (45404) ***(G-8271)***
Dayton Coating Tech LLC 937 278-2060
1926 E Siebenthaler Ave Dayton (45414) ***(G-8272)***
Dayton Dailey News 937 743-2387
5000 Commerce Center Dr Franklin (45005) ***(G-10017)***
Dayton Daily News, Dayton *Also called Cox Newspapers LLC* ***(G-8246)***
Dayton Environmental 937 478-1536
1621 Pence Pl Dayton (45432) ***(G-8102)***
Dayton Forging Heat Treating 937 253-4126
215 N Findlay St Dayton (45403) ***(G-8273)***
Dayton Fruit Tree Label Co 937 223-4650
1225 Ray St Dayton (45404) ***(G-8274)***
Dayton Garden Labels, Dayton *Also called Dayton Fruit Tree Label Co* ***(G-8274)***
Dayton Gear & Tool Co Inc 937 866-4327
500 Fame Rd Dayton (45449) ***(G-8275)***
Dayton Hawker Corporation 937 293-8147
2844 Culver Ave Dayton (45429) ***(G-8276)***
Dayton Heidelberg Distrg Co 440 989-1027
5901 Baumhart Rd Lorain (44053) ***(G-12243)***
Dayton Industrial Drum Inc 937 253-8933
1880 Radio Rd Dayton (45431) ***(G-8103)***
Dayton Lamina Corporation (HQ) 937 859-5111
500 Progress Rd Dayton (45449) ***(G-8277)***
Dayton Laser & Aesthetic Medic 937 208-8282
6611 Clyo Rd Ste E Dayton (45459) ***(G-8278)***
Dayton Mailing Services Inc 937 222-5056
100 S Keowee St Dayton (45402) ***(G-8279)***
Dayton Manufacturing Company, Dayton *Also called Delma Corp* ***(G-8296)***
Dayton Metal Products Company 937 849-0071
8296 Tidewater Ct Cincinnati (45255) ***(G-3643)***
Dayton Mixing Center, Union *Also called Procter & Gamble Distrg LLC* ***(G-19067)***
Dayton Molded Urethanes LLC 937 279-9987
3337 N Dixie Dr Dayton (45414) ***(G-8280)***
Dayton Pattern Inc 937 277-0761
5591 Wadsworth Rd Dayton (45414) ***(G-8281)***
Dayton Polymeric Products Inc 937 279-9987
3337 N Dixie Dr Dayton (45414) ***(G-8282)***
Dayton Precision Punch 937 275-8700
4900 Webster St Dayton (45414) ***(G-8283)***
Dayton Progress Corporation (HQ) 937 859-5111
500 Progress Rd Dayton (45449) ***(G-8284)***
Dayton Progress Intl Corp 937 859-5111
500 Progress Rd Dayton (45449) ***(G-8285)***
Dayton Safe Company 937 461-3900
1803 Webster St Ste A Dayton (45404) ***(G-8286)***
Dayton Stencil Works Company 937 223-3233
113 E 2nd St Dayton (45402) ***(G-8287)***
Dayton Superior Corporation (HQ) 937 866-0711
1125 Byers Rd Miamisburg (45342) ***(G-13798)***
Dayton Superior Corporation 937 682-4015
270 Rush St Rushsylvania (43347) ***(G-16751)***

Dayton Superior Pdts Co Inc 937 332-1930
1370 Lytle Rd Troy (45373) *(G-18815)*
Dayton Systems Group Inc 937 885-5665
3003 S Tech Blvd Miamisburg (45342) *(G-13799)*
Dayton Tool Co Inc 937 222-5501
1825 E 1st St Dayton (45403) *(G-8288)*
Dayton Tractor & Crane 937 317-5014
1861 Us Route 42 S Xenia (45385) *(G-20946)*
Dayton United Metal Spinners 937 222-6732
933 York Meadows Dr Tipp City (45371) *(G-18275)*
Dayton Weekly News 937 223-8060
118 Salem Ave Dayton (45406) *(G-8289)*
Dayton Wheel Concepts Inc 937 438-0100
115 Compark Rd Dayton (45459) *(G-8290)*
Dayton Wire Products Inc 937 236-8000
7 Dayton Wire Pkwy Dayton (45404) *(G-8291)*
Dayton Wire Wheel, Dayton *Also called Dayton Wheel Concepts Inc (G-8290)*
Dayton Wright Composite 937 469-3962
3251 Mccall St Dayton (45417) *(G-8292)*
Dayton-Phoenix Group Inc (PA) 937 496-3900
1619 Kuntz Rd Dayton (45404) *(G-8293)*
Daytronic Corporation (HQ) 937 866-3300
2566 Kohnle Dr Miamisburg (45342) *(G-13800)*
Db Parent Inc 513 475-3265
3630 E Kemper Rd Cincinnati (45241) *(G-3644)*
Db Rediheat Inc 216 361-0530
4516 Saint Clair Ave Cleveland (44103) *(G-5175)*
Dbcr Inc 330 920-1900
3400 Cavalier Trl Cuyahoga Falls (44224) *(G-7986)*
Dbd, Akron *Also called 360 Communications LLC (G-12)*
Dbhl Inc (HQ) 216 267-7100
4700 W 160th St Cleveland (44135) *(G-5176)*
DC Controls LLC 513 225-0813
4836 Duff Dr Ste E West Chester (45246) *(G-19997)*
DC Music 330 385-0468
15765 State Route 170 # 9 East Liverpool (43920) *(G-9211)*
Dc- Digital, Carlisle *Also called Industrial Electronic Service (G-2931)*
Dcc Corp (PA) 330 494-0494
5757 Mayfair Rd Canton (44720) *(G-2680)*
Dcd Technologies Inc 216 481-0056
17920 S Waterloo Rd Cleveland (44119) *(G-5177)*
Dcm Manufacturing Inc (HQ) 216 265-8006
4540 W 160th St Cleveland (44135) *(G-5178)*
DCS Technologies Corporation (PA) 937 743-4060
6501 State Route 123 Franklin (45005) *(G-10018)*
DCW Acquisition Inc 216 451-0666
10646 Leuer Ave Cleveland (44108) *(G-5179)*
Dd Foundry Inc (PA) 216 362-4100
15583 Brookpark Rd Brookpark (44142) *(G-2156)*
De Bra - Kuempel, Cincinnati *Also called Debra-Kuempel Inc (G-3645)*
De Milta Sand and Gravel 440 942-2015
921 Erie Rd Willoughby (44095) *(G-20471)*
De Nora Holdings Us Inc (HQ) 440 710-5300
7590 Discovery Ln Painesville (44077) *(G-15873)*
De Nora North America Inc (HQ) 440 357-4000
7590 Discovery Ln Painesville (44077) *(G-15874)*
De Nora Tech Inc (HQ) 440 710-5300
7590 Discovery Ln Painesville (44077) *(G-15875)*
De Vore Engraving Co 330 454-6820
1017 Tuscarawas St E Canton (44707) *(G-2681)*
De-Ko Inc 440 951-2585
38334 Willoughby Pkwy Willoughby (44094) *(G-20472)*
De-Lux Mold & Machine Inc 330 678-1030
6523 Pleasant Ave Kent (44240) *(G-11447)*
Deadbolt Software 614 679-2093
43 Amazon Pl Columbus (43214) *(G-7016)*
Deaks Form Tools Inc 440 286-2353
9954a Cutts Rd Chardon (44024) *(G-3149)*
Dealer Communications, Twinsburg *Also called Horizon Communications Inc (G-18955)*
Deals 937 293-7429
5522 Springboro Pike Dayton (45449) *(G-8294)*
Dearborn Inc 440 234-1353
678 Front St Berea (44017) *(G-1610)*
Dearth Resources Inc (PA) 937 325-0651
2301 Sheridan Ave Springfield (45505) *(G-17539)*
Dearth Resources Inc 937 663-4171
8801 State Route 36 Springfield (45501) *(G-17540)*
Deban Enterprises Inc 937 426-4235
611 Congress Park Dr Dayton (45459) *(G-8295)*
Debandale Printing Inc 330 725-5122
2785 Sharon Copley Rd Medina (44256) *(G-13401)*
Debolt Machine Inc 740 454-8082
4208 West Pike Zanesville (43701) *(G-21298)*
Debra Harbour 937 440-9618
251 S Mulberry St # 220 Troy (45373) *(G-18816)*
Debra-Kuempel Inc (HQ) 513 271-6500
3976 Southern Ave Cincinnati (45227) *(G-3645)*
Debs Welding & Fabrication 330 376-2242
950 Rhodes Ave Akron (44307) *(G-143)*
Deca Manufacturing, Lexington *Also called SMH Manufacturing Inc (G-11952)*
Deca Manufacturing Co Inc 419 884-0071
300 S Mill St Mansfield (44904) *(G-12594)*
Decal Impressions, Cincinnati *Also called Magnetic Mktg Solutions LLC (G-4053)*
Decaplus, Middletown *Also called Natural Beauty Products Inc (G-14068)*
Decaria Brothers Inc 330 385-0825
104 E 5th St East Liverpool (43920) *(G-9212)*
Decent Hill Press, Hilliard *Also called Decent Hill Publishers LLC (G-10948)*
Decent Hill Publishers LLC 216 548-1255
2825 Wynneleaf St Hilliard (43026) *(G-10948)*
Deceuninck North America LLC (PA) 513 539-5466
351 N Garver Rd Monroe (45050) *(G-14399)*
Decibel Research Inc 256 705-3341
2661 Commons Blvd Ste 136 Beavercreek (45431) *(G-1329)*
Decision Systems Inc 330 456-7600
2935 Woodcliff Dr Nw Canton (44718) *(G-2682)*
Deck & Fence Revivers, Springfield *Also called US Pro Painters (G-17671)*
Decker Custom Wood Llc 419 332-3464
505 W Mcgormley Rd Fremont (43420) *(G-10141)*
Decker Custom Wood Working, Fremont *Also called Decker Custom Wood Llc (G-10141)*
Decker Drilling Inc 740 749-3939
11565 State Route 676 Vincent (45784) *(G-19379)*
Decker Well Service LLC 740 678-2970
14165 State Route 550 Fleming (45729) *(G-9912)*
Decko Products Inc 419 626-5757
2105 Superior St Sandusky (44870) *(G-16957)*
Deco Plas Properties LLC 419 485-0632
700 Randolph St Montpelier (43543) *(G-14443)*
Deco Tools Inc 419 476-9321
1541 Coining Dr Toledo (43612) *(G-18430)*
Decoma Systems Integration Gro 419 324-3387
1800 Nathan Dr Toledo (43611) *(G-18431)*
Decor Architectural Products 419 537-9493
2375 Dorr St Ste E Toledo (43607) *(G-18432)*
Decor At 124 ....260 319-4213
7944 Kings Church Rd Convoy (45832) *(G-7831)*
Decorative Panels Intl Inc (HQ) 419 535-5921
2900 Hill Ave Toledo (43607) *(G-18433)*
Decorative Veneer Inc (PA) 216 741-5511
2121 Saint Clair Ave Ne Cleveland (44114) *(G-5180)*
Dee Lee Machine Inc 440 259-2245
3921 Townline Rd Madison (44057) *(G-12504)*
Dee Printing Inc 614 777-8700
4999 Transamerica Dr Columbus (43228) *(G-7017)*
Dee Sign Co (PA) 513 779-3333
6163 Allen Rd West Chester (45069) *(G-19852)*
Dee Sign Usa LLC 513 779-3333
6163 Allen Rd West Chester (45069) *(G-19853)*
Dee-Jays Cstm Butchering Proc 740 694-7492
17460 Ankneytown Rd Fredericktown (43019) *(G-10099)*
Deemsys Inc 614 322-9928
800 Cross Pointe Rd Ste A Gahanna (43230) *(G-10206)*
Deep Resources LLC 419 869-7441
120 State Route 302 Polk (44866) *(G-16388)*
Deep Springs Technology LLC 419 536-5741
4750 W Bancroft St Ste 1 Toledo (43615) *(G-18434)*
Deepwood Roll Tooling 440 946-5640
7591 Tyler Blvd Ste 3 Mentor (44060) *(G-13560)*
Deer Creek Honey Farms Ltd 740 852-0899
551 E High St London (43140) *(G-12208)*
Deer Valley Woodworking, Fresno *Also called Thomas Hora (G-10200)*
Deerfield Digital, Cincinnati *Also called Laurenee Ltd LLC (G-4015)*
Deerfield Farms Service Inc 800 589-8606
9041 U S Route 224 Deerfield (44411) *(G-8772)*
Deerfield Manufacturing Inc 513 398-2010
320 N Mason Montgomery Rd Mason (45040) *(G-13008)*
Deerfield Medical Imaging LLC 513 271-5717
9311 S Masn Montgomery Rd Mason (45040) *(G-13009)*
Deerfield Ventures Inc 614 875-0688
2224 Stringtown Rd Grove City (43123) *(G-10553)*
Defense Co Inc 413 998-1637
600 Superior Ave E Cleveland (44114) *(G-5181)*
Defiance Crescent News, The, Defiance *Also called Defiance Publishing Co (G-8788)*
Defiance Metal Products Co (PA) 419 784-5332
21 Seneca St Defiance (43512) *(G-8785)*
Defiance Metal Products Co 419 784-5332
6728 N State Route 66 Defiance (43512) *(G-8786)*
Defiance Metal Products Wl Inc 920 426-9207
21 Seneca St Defiance (43512) *(G-8787)*
Defiance Operations, Defiance *Also called Gt Technologies Inc (G-8792)*
Defiance Publishing Co 419 784-5441
624 W 2nd St Defiance (43512) *(G-8788)*
Defiance Stamping Co 419 782-5781
800 Independence Dr Napoleon (43545) *(G-14677)*
Deflecto LLC 330 602-0840
303 Oxford St Ste A Dover (44622) *(G-8975)*
Degaetano Sales 440 729-8877
8408 Mayfield Rd Chesterland (44026) *(G-3202)*
Degussa Construction, Cleveland *Also called BASF Construction Chem LLC (G-4895)*

ALPHABETIC

Degussa Incorporated 513 733-5111
    620 Shepherd Dr Cincinnati (45215) *(G-3646)*

Dei Fratelli, Northwood Also called Hirzel Canning Company *(G-15482)*

Deibel Manufacturing LLC 330 482-3351
    41659 Esterly Dr Leetonia (44431) *(G-11859)*

Deimling/Jeliho Plastics Inc 513 752-6653
    4010 Bach Buxton Rd Amelia (45102) *(G-572)*

Dejak Machine Tool Company, Euclid Also called Eaglehead Manufacturing Co *(G-9576)*

Dekay Fabricators Inc 330 793-0826
    295 S Meridian Rd Youngstown (44509) *(G-21066)*

Del Holdash 440 427-0611
    29891 Westminster Dr North Olmsted (44070) *(G-15329)*

Del-Ter Precision Machine Inc. 330 724-9167
    1038 Triplett Blvd Akron (44306) *(G-144)*

Dela-Glassware Ltd LLC 740 369-6737
    130 N Liberty St Delaware (43015) *(G-8835)*

Delafoil Pennsylvania Inc 610 327-9565
    1775 Progress Dr Perrysburg (43551) *(G-16083)*

Delano Foods, Canton Also called Hiland Group Incorporated *(G-2728)*

Delaware Company, Cleveland Also called Tremont Electric Incorporated *(G-6355)*

Delaware Gazette Company 740 363-1161
    40 N Sandusky St Ste 202 Delaware (43015) *(G-8836)*

Delco Corporation 330 896-4220
    3300 Massillon Rd Akron (44312) *(G-145)*

Delco LLC 330 896-4220
    3300 Massillon Rd Akron (44312) *(G-146)*

Delhi Welding Co, Cincinnati Also called Ridge Engineering Inc *(G-4346)*

Deliciously Different Candies, Canal Fulton Also called Becky Knapp *(G-2498)*

Delille Oxygen Company (PA) 614 444-1177
    772 Marion Rd Columbus (43207) *(G-7018)*

Delille Oxygen Company 937 325-9595
    1101 W Columbia St Springfield (45504) *(G-17541)*

Delite Fruit Juices 614 470-4333
    185 N Yale Ave Columbus (43222) *(G-7019)*

Dell Fixtures Inc 614 449-1750
    321 Dering Ave Columbus (43207) *(G-7020)*

Delma Corp 937 253-2142
    3327 Elkton Ave Dayton (45403) *(G-8296)*

Delmar E Hicks (PA) 740 354-4333
    2310 A St Portsmouth (45662) *(G-16434)*

Delo Screw Products, Delaware Also called Supply Technologies LLC *(G-8891)*

Delo Screw Products, Delaware Also called RB&w Manufacturing LLC *(G-8881)*

Delohio Tech 740 816-5628
    2061 State Route 521 Delaware (43015) *(G-8837)*

Delores E OBeirn 440 582-3610
    13022 Kingston Way Cleveland (44133) *(G-5182)*

Delphi, Vandalia Also called Mahle Behr USA Inc *(G-19302)*

Delphi Automotive Systems LLC 248 813-2000
    1265 N River Rd Ne Plant11 Warren (44483) *(G-19541)*

Delphi Automotive Systems LLC 330 306-1000
    4551 Research Prwy Warren (44483) *(G-19542)*

Delphi Automotive Systems LLC 330 367-6000
    3400 Aero Park Dr Vienna (44473) *(G-19364)*

Delphi-T - Vandalia Ptc, Dayton Also called Mahle Industries Incorporated *(G-8473)*

Delphia Consulting Inc 614 421-2000
    250 E Broad St Ste 1150 Columbus (43215) *(G-7021)*

Delphia Pckrd Eea-Wrrn Plnt 47, Vienna Also called Delphi Automotive Systems
LLC *(G-19364)*

Delphos Herald Inc (PA) 419 695-0015
    405 N Main St Delphos (45833) *(G-8904)*

Delphos Herald Inc 419 399-4015
    113 S Williams St Paulding (45879) *(G-16003)*

Delphos Herald Inc 419 695-0015
    405 N Main St Delphos (45833) *(G-8905)*

Delphos Plant 2, Delphos Also called Toledo Molding & Die Inc *(G-8920)*

Delta Control Inc (PA) 937 277-3444
    2532 Nordic Rd Dayton (45414) *(G-8297)*

Delta Crane Systems Inc 937 324-7425
    624 Aberfelda Dr Springfield (45504) *(G-17542)*

Delta H Technologies LLC 614 561-8860
    8847 Easton Dr Pickerington (43147) *(G-16190)*

Delta Machine & Tool Co. 216 524-2477
    7575 Wall St Cleveland (44125) *(G-5183)*

Delta Manufacturing Inc. 330 386-1270
    49207 Clctta Smthferry Rd East Liverpool (43920) *(G-9213)*

Delta Media Group Inc. 330 493-0350
    4726 Hills And Dales Rd N Canton (44708) *(G-2683)*

Delta Plating Inc. 330 452-2300
    2125 Harrison Ave Sw Canton (44706) *(G-2684)*

Delta Systems Inc 330 626-2811
    1734 Frost Rd Streetsboro (44241) *(G-17850)*

Delta Tool & Die Stl Block Inc. 419 822-5939
    5226 County Road 6 Delta (43515) *(G-8930)*

Delta Transformer Inc. 513 242-9400
    406 Blade Ave Cincinnati (45216) *(G-3647)*

Deltacraft, Cleveland Also called Millcraft Group LLC *(G-5817)*

Deltec Incorporated 513 732-0800
    4230 Grissom Dr Batavia (45103) *(G-1177)*

Deltech Polymers Corporation 937 339-3150
    1250 S Union St Troy (45373) *(G-18817)*

Deluca Vineyards 440 685-4242
    8954 State Route 45 North Bloomfield (44450) *(G-15216)*

Deluxe Corporation 330 342-1500
    10030 Phillipp Pkwy Hudson (44236) *(G-11168)*

Dem Manufacturing LLC 440 564-7160
    10357 Kinsman Rd Newbury (44065) *(G-15088)*

Dem Technology LLC 937 223-1317
    755 Albany St Dayton (45417) *(G-8298)*

Demel Enterprises Inc 740 592-5800
    10980 Northpoint Dr Athens (45701) *(G-860)*

Demmy Sand and Gravel LLC 937 325-8840
    4324 Fairfield Pike Springfield (45502) *(G-17543)*

Dempsey Industries, Miamisburg Also called Mdi of Ohio Inc *(G-13829)*

Denbro Plastics Company, Toledo Also called Claycor Inc *(G-18399)*

Dendratec Ltd 330 473-4878
    1417 Zuercher Rd Dalton (44618) *(G-8067)*

Dengensha America Corporation 440 439-8081
    7647 First Pl Bedford (44146) *(G-1418)*

Denizen Inc. 937 615-9561
    130 Fox Dr Piqua (45356) *(G-16261)*

Denmac Metalworks, Marion Also called Central Machinery Company LLC *(G-12862)*

Denne Industries Inc 440 365-0600
    650 Sugar Ln Elyria (44035) *(G-9401)*

Denney Plastics Machining LLC 330 308-5300
    149 Stonecreek Rd Nw New Philadelphia (44663) *(G-14894)*

Dennis Constuction Sanitation 419 332-8301
    1201 Siler St Fremont (43420) *(G-10142)*

Dennis Corso Co Inc 330 673-2411
    266 Martinel Dr Ste A Kent (44240) *(G-11448)*

Dennis Lavender 740 344-3336
    200 Maholm St Newark (43055) *(G-14999)*

Denoon Lumber Company LLC (PA) 740 768-2220
    571 County Highway 52 Bergholz (43908) *(G-1641)*

Dental Ceramics Inc 330 523-5240
    3404 Brecksville Rd Richfield (44286) *(G-16620)*

Dental Sealants 440 582-3466
    7029 Royalton Rd North Royalton (44133) *(G-15417)*

Denton & Anderson Mktg Div, Hubbard Also called Taylor - Winfield Corporation *(G-11140)*

Denton Atd Inc (PA) 567 265-5200
    900 Denton Dr Huron (44839) *(G-11220)*

Dentronix Inc 330 916-7300
    235 Ascot Pkwy Cuyahoga Falls (44223) *(G-7987)*

Dentsply International Inc 419 865-9497
    3535 Briarfield Blvd Maumee (43537) *(G-13256)*

Dentsply Sirona Inc 419 893-5672
    520 Illinois Ave Maumee (43537) *(G-13257)*

Denver Adkins 740 682-3123
    642 Phillip Kuhn Rd Oak Hill (45656) *(G-15595)*

Dependable Gear Corp 440 942-4969
    1422 E 363rd St Eastlake (44095) *(G-9264)*

Dependable Stamping Company 216 486-5522
    1160 E 222nd St Cleveland (44117) *(G-5184)*

Depuy Orthopaedics Inc 937 274-5850
    2747 Armstrong Ln Dayton (45414) *(G-8299)*

Derby Fabg Solutions LLC 937 498-4054
    570 Lester Ave Sidney (45365) *(G-17176)*

Derby Print and Copy Shop, Beavercreek Also called Flowers Print Inc *(G-1338)*

Dern Trophies Corp 614 895-3260
    6225 Frost Rd Westerville (43082) *(G-20145)*

Dern Trophy Mfg, Westerville Also called Dern Trophies Corp *(G-20145)*

Derrick Company Inc 513 321-8122
    4560 Kellogg Ave Cincinnati (45226) *(G-3648)*

Derrick Petroleum Inc. 740 668-5711
    Market St Bladensburg (43005) *(G-1707)*

Deruijter Intl USA Inc 419 678-3909
    120 Harvest Dr Coldwater (45828) *(G-6556)*

Des Eck Welding 330 698-7271
    10777 E Moreland Rd Apple Creek (44606) *(G-636)*

Des Machine Services Inc 330 633-6897
    351 Tacoma Ave Tallmadge (44278) *(G-18140)*

Des Tech, Troy Also called Design Technologies & Mfg Co *(G-18818)*

Desco Corporation (PA) 614 888-8855
    7795 Walton Pkwy Ste 175 New Albany (43054) *(G-14757)*

Desco Equipment Corp 330 405-1581
    1903 Case Pkwy Twinsburg (44087) *(G-18923)*

Deshea Printing Company 330 336-7601
    924 Seville Rd Wadsworth (44281) *(G-19402)*

Deshler Flag, Liberty Center Also called Mickens Inc *(G-11955)*

Deshler Metal Working Co Inc 419 278-0472
    140 S East Ave Deshler (43516) *(G-8949)*

Design & Fabrication Inc 419 294-2414
    400 Malabar Dr Upper Sandusky (43351) *(G-19119)*

Design Avenue Inc 330 487-5280
    1710 Enterprise Pkwy Twinsburg (44087) *(G-18924)*

Design Concrete Surfaces, Kent Also called Don Wartko Construction Co *(G-11450)*

Design Fabricators of Mantua 330 274-5353
    10612 Main St Mantua (44255) *(G-12709)*

Design Farm, Millersburg *Also called Simple Products LLC (G-14263)*

Design Flux Technologies LLC 216 543-6066
526 S Main St Ste 108 Akron (44311) *(G-147)*

Design Graphics Group Inc 419 354-8717
333 Van Camp Rd Bowling Green (43402) *(G-1984)*

Design Magnetics Ltd 234 380-5500
7941 Valley View Rd Hudson (44236) *(G-11169)*

Design Masters Inc 513 772-7175
800 Redna Ter Cincinnati (45215) *(G-3649)*

Design Molded Plastics Inc 330 963-4400
8220 Bavaria Rd Macedonia (44056) *(G-12444)*

Design Original Inc 937 596-5121
402 Jackson St Jackson Center (45334) *(G-11339)*

Design Pattern Works Inc 937 252-0797
2312 E 3rd St Dayton (45403) *(G-8300)*

Design Sign Inc 216 398-9900
1723 Brookpark Rd Cleveland (44109) *(G-5185)*

Design Tech Inc 937 254-7000
1531 Keystone Ave Dayton (45403) *(G-8301)*

Design Technologies & Mfg Co 937 335-0757
2000 Corporate Dr Troy (45373) *(G-18818)*

Design Trac Inc 330 759-3131
4136 Logan Way Youngstown (44505) *(G-21067)*

Design Wheel and Hub, Akron *Also called Schott Metal Products Company (G-397)*

Design-N-Wood LLC 937 419-0479
3700 Michigan St Sidney (45365) *(G-17177)*

Designed Harness Systems Inc 937 599-2485
227 Water Ave Bellefontaine (43311) *(G-1527)*

Designer Awards Inc 937 339-4444
101 S Market St Troy (45373) *(G-18819)*

Designer Cntemporary Laminates 440 946-8207
37105 Code Ave Willoughby (44094) *(G-20473)*

Designer Set 937 382-8000
529 S Walnut St Wilmington (45177) *(G-20663)*

Designer Stone Co 740 492-1300
303 E Main St Port Washington (43837) *(G-16423)*

Designetics Inc (PA) 419 866-0700
1624 Eber Rd Holland (43528) *(G-11054)*

Desmond Engraving Co Inc 216 265-8338
13410 Enterprise Ave D Cleveland (44135) *(G-5186)*

Desmond-Stephan Mfgcompany 937 653-7181
121 W Water St Urbana (43078) *(G-19157)*

Desserts By Sandy LLC 513 385-8755
8071 Redhaven Ct Cincinnati (45247) *(G-3650)*

Destin Die Casting LLC 937 347-1111
851 Bellbrook Ave Xenia (45385) *(G-20947)*

Destin Die Casting, LLC, Xenia *Also called American Metal Tech LLC (G-20936)*

Destination Donuts LLC 614 370-0754
59 Spruce St Columbus (43215) *(G-7022)*

Destiny Manufacturing Inc 330 273-9000
2974 Interstate Pkwy Brunswick (44212) *(G-2220)*

Detailed Athletic Wear Co Inc 513 541-0884
6272 Cleves Warsaw Pike Cincinnati (45233) *(G-3651)*

Detailed Machining Inc 937 492-1264
2490 Ross St Sidney (45365) *(G-17178)*

Detrex Corporation 440 997-6131
1100 State Rd Ashtabula (44004) *(G-802)*

Detrick Design Fabrication LLC 937 620-6736
425 Wisteria Dr Troy (45373) *(G-18820)*

Detroit Desl Rmnfacturing Corp 740 439-7701
8475 Reitler Rd Cambridge (43725) *(G-2454)*

Detroit Desl Rmnfctrng-Ast Inc 740 439-7701
60703 Country Club Rd Byesville (43723) *(G-2398)*

Detroit Diesl Specialty TI Inc 740 435-4452
60703 Country Club Rd Byesville (43723) *(G-2399)*

Detroit Flame Hardening Co 216 531-4273
24951 Tungsten Rd Euclid (44117) *(G-9574)*

Detroit Flame Hardening Co 513 942-1400
375 Security Dr Fairfield (45014) *(G-9658)*

Detroit Technologies Inc 937 492-2708
1630 Ferguson Ct Sidney (45365) *(G-17179)*

Detroit Technologies Inc 248 647-0400
2959 Nebraska Ave Toledo (43607) *(G-18435)*

Detroit Toledo Fiber LLC 248 647-0400
1245 E Manhattan Blvd Toledo (43608) *(G-18436)*

Deuce Machining LLC 513 875-2291
3088 Us Highway 50 Fayetteville (45118) *(G-9781)*

Deuer Developments Inc 937 299-1213
3434 Encrete Ln Moraine (45439) *(G-14478)*

Devault Industries LLC 330 456-6070
3500 12th St Nw Canton (44708) *(G-2685)*

Devault Machine & Mould Co LLC 740 654-5925
2294 Commerce St Lancaster (43130) *(G-11705)*

Devicor Med Pdts Holdings Inc 513 864-9000
300 E Business Way Fl 5 Cincinnati (45241) *(G-3652)*

Devicor Medical Products Inc (HQ) 513 864-9000
300 E Business Way Fl 5 Cincinnati (45241) *(G-3653)*

Devilbiss Ransburg 419 470-2000
320 Phillips Ave Toledo (43612) *(G-18437)*

Devries & Associates Inc 614 890-3821
654 Brooksedge Blvd Ste A Westerville (43081) *(G-20209)*

Devries & Associates Inc (PA) 614 860-0103
5117 E Main St Westerville (43081) *(G-20210)*

Devries & Associates Inc 614 860-0103
5117 E Main St Columbus (43213) *(G-7023)*

Dewalt Factory Service, Cincinnati *Also called Black & Decker (us) Inc (G-3452)*

Deward Publishing Co Ltd 800 300-9778
278 Scott Rd Chillicothe (45601) *(G-3236)*

Dewitt Group Inc 614 847-5919
777 Dearborn Park Ln E Columbus (43085) *(G-7024)*

Dewitt Inc 216 662-0800
14450 Industrial Ave N Maple Heights (44137) *(G-12732)*

Dex-Cut Tools 513 248-9898
71 Powhatton Dr Milford (45150) *(G-14136)*

Dexol Industries Inc 330 633-4477
844 E Tallmadge Ave Akron (44310) *(G-148)*

Dexport Tool Manufacturing Co 513 625-1600
855 Carpenter Rd Loveland (45140) *(G-12348)*

Dexter Hardwoods Inc 740 783-4141
145 Jefferson St Dexter City (45727) *(G-8956)*

Df Consumer Products 440 239-4795
1220 W Bagley Rd Berea (44017) *(G-1611)*

Dg Custom Machine 419 636-8059
840 E Edgerton St Bryan (43506) *(G-2294)*

Dgl Woodworking Inc 937 837-7091
5931 Wolf Creek Pike Dayton (45426) *(G-8302)*

DH, Cincinnati *Also called D+h USA Corporation (G-3633)*

Dhpp, Dover *Also called Dover High Prfmce Plas Inc (G-8980)*

Dhs Innovations, Bellefontaine *Also called Designed Harness Systems Inc (G-1527)*

Di Lorio Sheet Metal Inc 216 961-3703
5002 Clark Ave Cleveland (44102) *(G-5187)*

Di Walt Optical Inc 330 453-8427
1112 12th St Ne Canton (44705) *(G-2686)*

DIA Enterprises Inc 740 802-7075
731 Decliff Rd N New Bloomington (43341) *(G-14777)*

Diagnostic Hybrids Inc 740 593-1784
2005 E State St Ste 100 Athens (45701) *(G-861)*

Dialogue House Associates Inc 216 342-5170
23400 Mercantile Rd Ste 2 Beachwood (44122) *(G-1266)*

Diamond Aluminum Co, Middletown *Also called John H Hosking Inc (G-14052)*

Diamond America Corporation 330 535-3330
520 S Main St Ste 2456 Akron (44311) *(G-149)*

Diamond Cellar, The, Dublin *Also called Robert W Johnson Inc (G-9134)*

Diamond Designs Inc 330 434-6776
333 S Main St Ste B100 Akron (44308) *(G-150)*

Diamond Electronics, Lancaster *Also called Diamond Power Intl Inc (G-11707)*

Diamond Electronics Inc 740 652-9222
1858 Cedar Hill Rd Lancaster (43130) *(G-11706)*

Diamond Hard Chrome Co Inc 216 391-3618
6110 Grand Ave Cleveland (44104) *(G-5188)*

Diamond Heavy Haul, Shandon *Also called Diamond Trailers Inc (G-17097)*

Diamond Innovations Inc (HQ) 614 438-2000
6325 Huntley Rd Columbus (43229) *(G-7025)*

Diamond Machine and Mfg, Bluffton *Also called Colonial Surface Solutions Inc (G-1910)*

Diamond Metals Dist Inc 216 898-7900
4635 W 160th St Cleveland (44135) *(G-5189)*

Diamond Mfg Bluffton Ltd 419 358-0129
505 E Jefferson St Bluffton (45817) *(G-1911)*

Diamond Mold & Die Co 330 633-5682
109 E Garwood Dr Tallmadge (44278) *(G-18141)*

Diamond Oilfield Tech LLC 234 806-4185
4494 Warren Sharon Rd Vienna (44473) *(G-19365)*

Diamond Plastics Inc 419 759-3838
211 W Geneva St Dunkirk (45836) *(G-9187)*

Diamond Power Intl Inc 740 687-4001
2530 E Main St Lancaster (43130) *(G-11707)*

Diamond Power Intl Inc (HQ) 740 687-6500
2600 E Main St Lancaster (43130) *(G-11708)*

Diamond Power Specialty, Lancaster *Also called Diamond Power Intl Inc (G-11708)*

Diamond Products Limited 440 323-4616
1111 Taylor St Elyria (44035) *(G-9402)*

Diamond Reserve Inc 440 892-7877
801 Sharon Dr Westlake (44145) *(G-20263)*

Diamond Roll-Up Door Inc 419 294-3373
295 Commerce Way Upper Sandusky (43351) *(G-19120)*

Diamond Sparkler Mfg Co (PA) 330 746-1064
555 Martin Luther King Jr Youngstown (44502) *(G-21068)*

Diamond Trailers Inc 513 738-4500
5045 Cncnnt Brookville Rd Shandon (45063) *(G-17097)*

Diamond Welding Co Inc 216 251-1679
11030 Briggs Rd Cleveland (44111) *(G-5190)*

Diamond Wipes Intl Inc 419 562-3575
1375 Isaac Beal Rd Bucyrus (44820) *(G-2338)*

Diamondback Filters 419 494-1156
11602 Sugar Ridge Rd Bowling Green (43402) *(G-1985)*

Diamonds Products LLC 440 323-4616
1250 E Broad St Elyria (44035) *(G-9403)*

Diamonite Plant, Shreve *Also called I Cerco Inc (G-17158)*

Diano Construction and Sup Co....................330 456-7229
1000 Warner Rd Se Canton (44707) ***(G-2687)***
Diano Supply Co, Canton *Also called Diano Construction and Sup Co* ***(G-2687)***
Diascopic LLC....................312 282-1800
16173 Cleviden Rd Cleveland (44112) ***(G-5191)***
Dickens Foundry, Arcadia *Also called Maass Midwest Mfg Inc* ***(G-654)***
Dickman Directories Inc....................740 548-6130
6145 Columbus Pike Lewis Center (43035) ***(G-11894)***
Dicks Counter D M....................440 322-3312
275 Warden Ave Elyria (44035) ***(G-9404)***
Didion's Mechanical, Bellevue *Also called Donald E Didion II* ***(G-1550)***
Didonato Products Inc....................330 535-1119
1145 Highbrook St Ste 507 Akron (44301) ***(G-151)***
Die Cast Division....................330 769-2013
5151 Greenwich Rd Seville (44273) ***(G-17074)***
Die Cast Tool LLC....................419 874-1211
26437 Southpoint Rd Perrysburg (43551) ***(G-16084)***
Die Co Inc....................440 942-8856
1889 E 337th St Eastlake (44095) ***(G-9265)***
Die Craft Division, Cincinnati *Also called Markley Enterprises LLC* ***(G-4061)***
Die Guys Inc....................330 948-1984
5238 Portside Dr Medina (44256) ***(G-13402)***
Die Services Ltd....................216 883-5800
9200 Inman Ave Cleveland (44105) ***(G-5192)***
Die-Cut Products Co....................216 771-6994
1801 E 30th St Cleveland (44114) ***(G-5193)***
Die-Matic Corporation....................216 749-4656
201 Eastview Dr Brooklyn Heights (44131) ***(G-2138)***
Die-Mension Corporation....................330 273-5872
3020 Nationwide Pkwy Brunswick (44212) ***(G-2221)***
Die-Namic Tool & Die Inc....................330 296-6923
100 Romito St Ste D Ravenna (44266) ***(G-16525)***
Die-Tech Machine Inc....................740 264-2426
1650 County Road 22a Bloomingdale (43910) ***(G-1722)***
Diebold Incorporated....................330 899-0097
3800 Tabs Dr Uniontown (44685) ***(G-19082)***
Diebold Incorporated....................330 490-4000
5995 Mayfair Rd North Canton (44720) ***(G-15227)***
Diebold Incorporated....................330 490-4000
5571 Global Gtwy Canton (44720) ***(G-2688)***
Diebold Nixdorf Incorporated (PA)....................330 490-4000
5995 Mayfair Rd North Canton (44720) ***(G-15228)***
Diebold Self Service Systems (PA)....................330 490-5099
5995 Mayfair Rd Canton (44720) ***(G-2689)***
Diemaster Tool & Mold Inc....................330 467-4281
895 Highland Rd E 5 Macedonia (44056) ***(G-12445)***
Diesel Fltrtion Spcialists LLC....................740 698-0255
5475 Ste Rte 681 New Marshfield (45766) ***(G-14871)***
Diesel Recon Service Inc....................513 625-1887
2641 State Route 28 Pleasant Plain (45162) ***(G-16370)***
Dietrich Industries Inc....................330 372-4014
1300 Phoenix Rd Ne Warren (44483) ***(G-19543)***
Dietrich Industries Inc....................614 438-3210
200 W Old Wlson Bridge Rd Worthington (43085) ***(G-20863)***
Dietrich Industries Inc....................330 372-2868
1985 N River Rd Ne Warren (44483) ***(G-19544)***
Dietrich Industries Inc....................216 472-1511
818 E 73rd St Cleveland (44103) ***(G-5194)***
Dietrich Industries Inc....................614 438-3210
200 W Old Wlson Bridge Rd Worthington (43085) ***(G-20864)***
Dietrich Metal Framing, Warren *Also called Dietrich Industries Inc* ***(G-19543)***
Dietrich Von Hildebrand Legacy....................703 496-7821
1235 University Blvd Steubenville (43952) ***(G-17691)***
Dietsch Brothers Incorporated (PA)....................419 422-4474
400 W Main Cross St Findlay (45840) ***(G-9816)***
Digicom Inc....................216 642-3838
6916 Daisy Ave Independence (44131) ***(G-11252)***
Digilube Systems Inc....................937 748-2209
216 E Mill St Springboro (45066) ***(G-17479)***
Digimatics Inc....................419 478-0804
4011 Vermaas Ave Toledo (43612) ***(G-18438)***
Digimax Signs....................513 576-0747
759 Us Route 50 Milford (45150) ***(G-14137)***
Digionyx LLC....................614 594-9897
8420 Opossum Run Rd London (43140) ***(G-12209)***
Digisoft Systems Corporation....................937 833-5016
4520 Clayton Rd Brookville (45309) ***(G-2181)***
Digital & Analog Design, Dublin *Also called Pro Oncall Technologies LLC* ***(G-9126)***
Digital Automation Associates....................419 352-6977
310 W Gypsy Lane Rd Bowling Green (43402) ***(G-1986)***
Digital Color Intl LLC....................330 762-6959
1653 Merriman Rd Ste 211 Akron (44313) ***(G-152)***
Digital Controls Corporation (PA)....................513 746-8118
444 Alexandersville Rd Miamisburg (45342) ***(G-13801)***
Digital Graphics, Cleveland *Also called Alfacomp Inc* ***(G-4751)***
Digital Graphics....................330 707-1720
4589 Dobbins Rd Youngstown (44514) ***(G-21069)***
Digital Media Integration LLC....................937 305-5582
9090 State Route 48 B Dayton (45458) ***(G-8303)***
Digital Shorts Inc....................937 228-1700
136 N Saint Clair St # 100 Dayton (45402) ***(G-8304)***
Digital Solutions, Bellaire *Also called Paul/Jay Associates* ***(G-1500)***
Digital Technologies, Rossford *Also called Sasha Electronics Inc* ***(G-16749)***
Digital Visuals Inc....................513 420-9466
15 N Clinton St Middletown (45042) ***(G-14037)***
Digitek Corp....................513 794-3190
5665 Creek Rd Blue Ash (45242) ***(G-1775)***
Dik Jaxon Products Co....................937 890-7350
6195 Webster St Dayton (45414) ***(G-8305)***
Dilco Industries Inc....................330 337-6732
300 Benton Rd Salem (44460) ***(G-16888)***
Dillen Products, Middlefield *Also called Myers Industries Inc* ***(G-13971)***
Diller Metals Inc....................419 943-3364
507 S Eastom St Leipsic (45856) ***(G-11869)***
Dillin Engineered Systems Corp....................419 666-6789
8030 Broadstone Rd Perrysburg (43551) ***(G-16085)***
Dillon Manufacturing Inc....................937 325-8482
2115 Progress Rd Springfield (45505) ***(G-17544)***
Dilworth Machine....................330 427-1706
51552 Chain School Rd East Palestine (44413) ***(G-9233)***
Dimco-Gray Company, Centerville *Also called Dimcogray Corporation* ***(G-3039)***
Dimcogray Corporation (PA)....................937 433-7600
900 Dimco Way Centerville (45458) ***(G-3039)***
Dimension Hardwood Veneers Inc....................419 272-2245
509 Woodville St Edon (43518) ***(G-9340)***
Dimension Industries Inc....................440 236-3265
27335 Royalton Rd Columbia Station (44028) ***(G-6587)***
Dimension Machine Company Inc....................513 242-9996
6614 Lebanon St Cincinnati (45216) ***(G-3654)***
Dimensional Equipment Div, Elida *Also called Patton Industries Inc* ***(G-9354)***
Dimensional Fabricating Inc....................513 482-7440
6230 Wiehe Rd Unit 1 Cincinnati (45237) ***(G-3655)***
Dimensional Metals Inc (PA)....................740 927-3633
58 Klema Dr N Reynoldsburg (43068) ***(G-16586)***
Dimensional Works of Art....................330 657-2681
2355 Main St Peninsula (44264) ***(G-16036)***
Dimensions Three Inc....................614 539-5180
6157 Enterprise Pkwy Grove City (43123) ***(G-10554)***
Dimex LLC....................740 374-3100
28305 State Route 7 Marietta (45750) ***(G-12778)***
Dinesol Plastics Inc....................330 544-7171
195 E Park Ave Niles (44446) ***(G-15149)***
Dlng Products....................440 442-7777
5695 Cherokee Dr Cleveland (44124) ***(G-5195)***
Dinkmar Inc....................419 468-8516
9357 Township Road 48 Galion (44833) ***(G-10263)***
Dinos Drive Thru LLC....................330 263-1111
1541 Jones Ave Wooster (44691) ***(G-20765)***
Dinsmore Inc....................937 544-3332
11780 State Route 41 West Union (45693) ***(G-20120)***
Diocesan Publications Inc Ohio (PA)....................614 718-9500
6161 Wilcox Rd Dublin (43016) ***(G-9068)***
Dip It Good Foods Inc....................330 219-3137
325 S Milton Blvd Newton Falls (44444) ***(G-15132)***
Diptech Systems Inc (PA)....................330 673-4400
4485 Crystal Pkwy Ste 100 Kent (44240) ***(G-11449)***
Diramed LLC....................614 487-3660
1275 Kinnear Rd Columbus (43212) ***(G-7026)***
Dircksen and Associates Inc....................614 238-0413
3452 E Livingston Ave Columbus (43227) ***(G-7027)***
Direct Action Co Inc....................330 364-3219
6668 Old State Rte 39 Nw Dover (44622) ***(G-8976)***
Direct Digital Graphics Inc....................330 405-3770
1716 Enterprise Pkwy Twinsburg (44087) ***(G-18925)***
Direct Disposables LLC....................440 717-3335
10605 Snowville Rd Brecksville (44141) ***(G-2043)***
Direct Image Signs Inc....................440 327-5575
7820 Maddock Rd North Ridgeville (44039) ***(G-15369)***
Direct Mailbox, Huron *Also called Gdm Mailbox Company LLC* ***(G-11221)***
Direct Wire Service LLP....................937 526-4447
100 Subler Dr Versailles (45380) ***(G-19345)***
Directconnectgroup Ltd....................216 281-2866
5501 Cass Ave Cleveland (44102) ***(G-5196)***
Directional One Svcs Inc USA....................740 371-5031
2163a-1 Gwb Complex Marietta (45750) ***(G-12779)***
Dirt Works Excavating, Wellston *Also called Wilkett Enterprises LLC* ***(G-19773)***
Dirussos Sausage Inc....................330 744-1208
1035 W Rayen Ave Youngstown (44502) ***(G-21070)***
DIRVA LITHUANIAN NEWSPAPER, Cleveland *Also called American Lithuanian Press* ***(G-4787)***
Disalvo Deli & Italian Store, Dayton *Also called Disalvos Deli & Italian Store* ***(G-8306)***
Disalvos Deli & Italian Store....................937 298-5053
1383 E Stroop Rd Dayton (45429) ***(G-8306)***
Disante Socks....................614 481-3243
1540 Westwood Ave Columbus (43212) ***(G-7028)***
Dischem Inc....................330 494-5210
4252 Strausser St Nw Canton (44720) ***(G-2690)***

Disciple Tool & Machine 330 503-7879
189 Se River Rd Lake Milton (44429) *(G-11642)*

Discount Computer Parts 216 228-4949
16500 Detroit Ave Lakewood (44107) *(G-11662)*

Discount Dring Sups Cincinnati, Cincinnati Also called G & C Drainage Supplies
Inc *(G-3788)*

Discount Signs Awnings 740 373-3556
114 Greene St Marietta (45750) *(G-12780)*

Discover Publications 614 785-1111
6427 Busch Blvd Columbus (43229) *(G-7029)*

Discus Sofware, Columbus Also called Characteristic Solutions LLC *(G-6922)*

Dishtronix Inc 937 292-7981
2497 Township Road 55 Bellefontaine (43311) *(G-1528)*

Dismat Corporation 419 531-8963
336 N Westwood Ave Toledo (43607) *(G-18439)*

DISPATCH PRINTING, Columbus Also called Wolfe Associates Inc *(G-7771)*

Dispatch Printing Company 740 548-5331
7801 N Central Dr Lewis Center (43035) *(G-11895)*

Dispatch Printing Company 614 885-6020
5253 Sinclair Rd Columbus (43229) *(G-7030)*

Display Dynamics Inc 937 832-2830
1 Display Point Dr Englewood (45315) *(G-9516)*

Distillata Company (PA) 216 771-2900
1608 E 24th St Cleveland (44114) *(G-5197)*

Distinct Advantage Cabinetry, Toledo Also called Online Mega Sellers Corp *(G-18619)*

Distinctive Marble & Gran Inc 614 760-0003
7635 Commerce Pl Plain City (43064) *(G-16335)*

Distinctive Surfaces LLC 614 431-0898
5158 Sinclair Rd Columbus (43229) *(G-7031)*

Distribution Center, West Chester Also called Martin-Brower Company LLC *(G-19898)*

Distributor Graphics Inc 440 260-0024
6909 Engle Rd Ste 13 Cleveland (44130) *(G-5198)*

District Brewing Co Inc 614 224-3626
2555 Harrison Rd Columbus (43204) *(G-7032)*

Dittmar Sales and Service 740 653-7933
132 W 6th Ave Lancaster (43130) *(G-11709)*

Ditz Designs, Norwalk Also called Hen House Inc *(G-15544)*

Divelbiss Corporation 800 245-2327
9778 Mount Gilead Rd Fredericktown (43019) *(G-10100)*

Diverse Acquisitions Group LLC 888 232-1546
5021 Lausanne Dr Centerville (45458) *(G-3040)*

Diverse Logistics & Trnsp Inc 513 305-1460
313 Glensford Ct Cincinnati (45246) *(G-3656)*

Diverse Mfg Solutions LLC 740 363-3600
970 Pittsburgh Dr Ste 22 Delaware (43015) *(G-8838)*

Diversey Inc 513 326-8300
200 Crowne Point Pl Cincinnati (45241) *(G-3657)*

Diversifed Mch Pdts Gnsvlle GA, Columbus Also called Prime Equipment Group
Inc *(G-7517)*

Diversifd OH Vlly Eqpt & Srvcs 740 458-9881
50817 State Route 556 Clarington (43915) *(G-4651)*

Diversified Air Systems Inc (PA) 216 741-1700
4760 Van Epps Rd Brooklyn Heights (44131) *(G-2139)*

Diversified Brands 216 595-8777
26300 Fargo Ave Bedford (44146) *(G-1419)*

Diversified Fittings Inc 440 259-0093
3450 Blackmore Rd Perry (44081) *(G-16048)*

Diversified Honing Inc 330 874-4663
11064 Industrial Pkwy Nw Bolivar (44612) *(G-1932)*

Diversified Mch Components LLC 440 942-5701
34099 Melinz Pkwy Unit D Eastlake (44095) *(G-9266)*

Diversified Mold & Castings Co, Cleveland Also called Diversified Mold Castings
LLC *(G-5199)*

Diversified Mold and Castings, Cleveland Also called Plaster Process Castings Co *(G-6012)*

Diversified Mold Castings LLC 216 663-1814
19800 Miles Rd Cleveland (44128) *(G-5199)*

Diversified Products & Svcs 740 393-6202
1250 Vernonview Dr Mount Vernon (43050) *(G-14619)*

Diversified Ready Mix Ltd 330 628-3355
1680 Southeast Ave Tallmadge (44278) *(G-18142)*

Diversified Sign, West Chester Also called Dee Sign Co *(G-19852)*

Diversified Technology Inc 330 722-4995
650 W Smith Rd Ste 10 Medina (44256) *(G-13403)*

Diversified Tool Systems 419 845-2143
5357 Mrion Wllmsport Rd E Caledonia (43314) *(G-2436)*

Diversified Welding Services 419 382-1433
3541 Marine Rd Toledo (43609) *(G-18440)*

Diversified Woodworking, Findlay Also called Old Mill Custom Cabinetry Co *(G-9871)*

Diversipak Inc (PA) 513 321-7884
838 Reedy St Cincinnati (45202) *(G-3658)*

Divine Prtg T-Shirts & More 419 241-8208
3433 Monroe St Toledo (43606) *(G-18441)*

Division Gorman-Rupp Company, Bellville Also called Gorman-Rupp Company *(G-1570)*

Division of Selling Materials, Dover Also called Smith Concrete Co *(G-9015)*

Division Overhead Door Inc (PA) 513 872-0888
861 Dellway St Cincinnati (45229) *(G-3659)*

Dixie Flyer & Printing Co 937 687-0088
424 Rosetta St New Lebanon (45345) *(G-14841)*

Dixie Machinery Inc 513 360-0091
845 Todhunter Rd Monroe (45050) *(G-14400)*

Dixitech Cnc, Monroe Also called Dixie Machinery Inc *(G-14400)*

Dixon Valve & Coupling Co Inc 330 425-3000
1900 Enterprise Pkwy Twinsburg (44087) *(G-18926)*

Diy Holster LLC 419 921-2168
7836 Oberlin Rd Elyria (44035) *(G-9405)*

Dj & Woodies Vinyl Frontier 740 623-2818
2339 County Road 16 Coshocton (43812) *(G-7888)*

Dj Beverage Innovations Inc 614 769-1569
8400 Indl Pkwy Bldg 2 Plain City (43064) *(G-16336)*

Dj Pallets 216 701-9183
23845 Royalton Rd Columbia Station (44028) *(G-6588)*

Dj S Weld 330 432-2206
424 N Main St Uhrichsville (44683) *(G-19049)*

DJ Signs MD LLC 330 344-6643
224 W Exchange St Ste 290 Akron (44302) *(G-153)*

Djc Holdings, Huron Also called N2y LLC *(G-11235)*

DJM Plastics Ltd 419 424-5250
1530 Harvard Ave Findlay (45840) *(G-9817)*

DK & J Inc 216 357-3090
2331 Superior Ave E R Cleveland (44114) *(G-5200)*

DK Manfcturing Frazeysburg Inc (HQ) 740 828-3291
119 W 2nd St Frazeysburg (43822) *(G-10072)*

DK Manufacturing Lancaster Inc 740 654-5566
2118 Commerce St Lancaster (43130) *(G-11710)*

Dla Document Services 216 522-3535
1240 E 9th St Rm B31 Cleveland (44199) *(G-5201)*

Dla Document Services 937 257-6014
4165 Communications Blvd Dayton (45433) *(G-8104)*

Dlhbowles Inc (PA) 330 478-2503
2422 Leo Ave Sw Canton (44706) *(G-2691)*

Dlhbowles Inc 330 478-2503
2422 Leo Ave Sw Canton (44706) *(G-2692)*

Dlhbowles Inc 330 479-7595
2410 Leo Ave Sw Canton (44706) *(G-2693)*

Dlhbowles Inc 330 488-0716
336 Wood St S East Canton (44730) *(G-9191)*

DLM Plastics, Findlay Also called DJM Plastics Ltd *(G-9817)*

Dlwoodworking 740 927-2693
9330 Hollow Rd Sw Pataskala (43062) *(G-15969)*

Dlz Ohio Inc (HQ) 614 888-0040
6121 Huntley Rd Columbus (43229) *(G-7033)*

Dm Pallet Service, Columbus Also called Ohio Wood Recycling Inc *(G-7437)*

Dmax Ltd (HQ) 937 425-9700
3100 Dryden Rd Moraine (45439) *(G-14479)*

DMC Welding Incorporated 330 877-1935
9975 Market Ave N Hartville (44632) *(G-10820)*

DMG Tool & Die LLC 937 407-0810
1215 S Greenwood St Bellefontaine (43311) *(G-1529)*

Dmi Products Inc 440 951-1828
7177 Industrial Park Blvd Mentor (44060) *(G-13561)*

Dmi Products Inc (PA) 440 975-8645
7177 Industrial Park Blvd Mentor (44060) *(G-13562)*

Dmk Industries Inc 513 727-4549
1801 Made Dr Middletown (45044) *(G-14038)*

Dmtco LLC 937 324-0061
302 S Center St Springfield (45506) *(G-17545)*

DMV Corporation 740 452-4787
1024 Military Rd Zanesville (43701) *(G-21299)*

DNC Hydraulics LLC 419 963-2800
5219 County Road 313 Rawson (45881) *(G-16573)*

Dnd Emulsions Inc 419 525-4988
270 Park Ave E Mansfield (44902) *(G-12595)*

Dnd Products Inc 440 286-7275
13262 Chardon Windsor Rd Chardon (44024) *(G-3150)*

Dnl Oil Corp 740 342-4970
7913 State Route 37 E New Lexington (43764) *(G-14847)*

Dno Inc 614 231-3601
3650 E 5th Ave Columbus (43219) *(G-7034)*

Do All Sheet Metal, New Albany Also called Samuel Clark *(G-14772)*

Do All Sheet Metal, New Albany Also called Custom Metal Products Inc *(G-14756)*

Do It Best, Cincinnati Also called Hyde Park Lumber Company *(G-3903)*

Do It Best, Caldwell Also called Caldwell Lumber & Supply Co *(G-2425)*

Doak Laser 740 374-0090
2801 Waterford Rd Marietta (45750) *(G-12781)*

Doan Machinery & Eqp Co Inc 216 932-6243
2636 S Belvoir Blvd University Heights (44118) *(G-19108)*

Docmann Printing & Assoc Inc 440 975-1775
4889 E 345th St Willoughby (44094) *(G-20474)*

Docupros 513 242-7700
9933 Alliance Rd Blue Ash (45242) *(G-1776)*

Docustar, Cincinnati Also called Vya Inc *(G-4573)*

Dodds Monument Inc (PA) 937 372-2736
123 W Main St Xenia (45385) *(G-20948)*

Dodge Company, Dayton Also called Ronald T Dodge Co *(G-8638)*

Dodge Data & Analytics LLC 513 345-8200
7265 Kenwood Rd Ste 200 Cincinnati (45236) *(G-3660)*

Dog Daily 216 624-0735
  1180 Blanchester Rd Cleveland (44124) *(G-5202)*

Dog Depot 513 771-9274
  950 S Troy Ave Cincinnati (45246) *(G-3661)*

Doglok Inc 440 223-1836
  3512 River Rd Perry (44081) *(G-16049)*

Dole Fresh Vegetables Inc 937 525-4300
  600 Benjamin Dr Springfield (45502) *(G-17546)*

Dolgencorp LLC 740 289-4790
  7095 Us Highway 23 Piketon (45661) *(G-16219)*

Dolin Supply Co 304 529-4171
  702 Solida Rd South Point (45680) *(G-17436)*

Doling & Associates Dental Lab 937 254-0075
  3318 Successful Way Dayton (45414) *(G-8307)*

Doll Inc 419 586-7880
  1901 Havemann Rd Celina (45822) *(G-2992)*

Doll Printing, Celina *Also called Doll Inc (G-2992)*

Dollar General, Piketon *Also called Dolgencorp LLC (G-16219)*

Dollman Technical Services 419 877-9404
  2910 Glanzman Rd Toledo (43614) *(G-18442)*

Domair Transmore Inc 513 771-1516
  130 Novner Dr Cincinnati (45215) *(G-3662)*

Dome Drilling Co (PA) 440 892-9434
  2001 Crocker Rd Ste 420 Westlake (44145) *(G-20264)*

Dome Drilling Co. 330 262-5113
  4489 E Lincoln Way Wooster (44691) *(G-20766)*

Dome Energicorp 440 892-4900
  2001 Crocker Rd Ste 420 Westlake (44145) *(G-20265)*

Dome Resources, Westlake *Also called Dome Drilling Co (G-20264)*

Domestic Casting Company LLC 717 532-6615
  620 Liberty Rd Delaware (43015) *(G-8839)*

Domestic Oil & Gas Co Inc 440 232-3150
  19600 Rockside Rd Cleveland (44146) *(G-5203)*

Dometic Sanitation Corporation 330 439-5550
  13128 State Route 226 Big Prairie (44611) *(G-1680)*

Domicone Printing Inc 937 878-3080
  854 Kauffman Ave Fairborn (45324) *(G-9619)*

Dominion East Ohio, Byesville *Also called East Ohio Gas Company (G-2400)*

Dominion Enterprises 216 472-1870
  26301 Curtiss Wright Pkwy Cleveland (44143) *(G-5204)*

Dominion Labels & Forms 419 784-1041
  232 Adams St Defiance (43512) *(G-8789)*

Dominion Liquid Tech LLC 513 272-2824
  3965 Virginia Ave Cincinnati (45227) *(G-3663)*

Domino Foods Inc 216 432-3222
  2075 E 65th St Cleveland (44103) *(G-5205)*

Domino Sugar, Cleveland *Also called Domino Foods Inc (G-5205)*

Domtar Paper Company LLC 740 333-0003
  1803 Lowes Blvd Wshngtn CT Hs (43160) *(G-20906)*

Don Basch Jewelers Inc 330 467-2116
  8210 Mcidonia Comm Blvd36 Macedonia (44056) *(G-12446)*

Don Gamertsfelder 740 797-4495
  10416 State Route 682 The Plains (45780) *(G-18185)*

Don Puckett Lumber Inc 740 887-4191
  31263 Beech Grove Rd Londonderry (45647) *(G-12227)*

Don Walter Kitchen Distrs Inc 330 793-9338
  260 Victoria Rd Youngstown (44515) *(G-21071)*

Don Wartko Construction Co (PA) 330 673-5252
  975 Tallmadge Rd Kent (44240) *(G-11450)*

Don-Ell Corporation (PA) 419 841-7114
  8450 Central Ave Sylvania (43560) *(G-18103)*

Don-Ell Corporation 419 841-7114
  8456 Central Ave Sylvania (43560) *(G-18104)*

Donahue's Hilltop Supply, Cambridge *Also called Donahues Hilltop Ice Company (G-2455)*

Donahues Hilltop Ice Company 740 432-3348
  1112 Highland Ave Cambridge (43725) *(G-2455)*

Donald E Didion II 419 483-2226
  1027b County Road 308 Bellevue (44811) *(G-1550)*

Donald E Dornon 740 926-9144
  44592 Game Ridge Rd Beallsville (43716) *(G-1308)*

Donald Marlo 937 836-4880
  5003 Brock Ln Dayton (45415) *(G-8308)*

Donald Schloemer 419 933-2002
  2441 Niver Rd Willard (44890) *(G-20394)*

Donaldson Company Inc 330 928-4100
  115 E Steels Corners Rd Stow (44224) *(G-17743)*

Doncasters Group Ltd 440 329-0400
  7900 W Ridge Rd Elyria (44035) *(G-9406)*

Done Right Engine & Machine 440 582-1366
  12955 York Delta Dr Ste J Cleveland (44133) *(G-5206)*

Done-Rite Bowling Service Co (PA) 440 232-3280
  20434 Krick Rd Bedford (44146) *(G-1420)*

Donegal Bay Ltd 216 360-9966
  26055 Emery Rd Ste F Cleveland (44128) *(G-5207)*

Dongan Electric Mfg Co, Pioneer *Also called Pioneer Transformer Company (G-16239)*

Donisi Mirror Company, Loveland *Also called R G C Inc (G-12380)*

Donkey Coffee & Espresso 740 594-7353
  17 1/2 W Washington St Athens (45701) *(G-862)*

Donnelley Financial LLC 216 621-8384
  1300 E 9th St Ste 1200 Cleveland (44114) *(G-5208)*

Donprint Inc 847 573-7777
  17700 Foltz Pkwy Strongsville (44149) *(G-17911)*

Donze Enterprises, Grafton *Also called Great Works Publishing Inc (G-10428)*

Door Fabrication Services Inc 937 454-9207
  3250 Old Springfield Rd # 1 Vandalia (45377) *(G-19290)*

Door Guys Inc 419 562-3376
  113 W Rensselaer St Bucyrus (44820) *(G-2339)*

Doran Manufacturing Co., Cincinnati *Also called Osborne Coinage Company (G-4197)*

Doran Mfg LLC 513 681-5424
  2851 Massachusetts Ave Cincinnati (45225) *(G-3664)*

Dorel Home Furnishings Inc 419 447-7448
  458 2nd Ave Tiffin (44883) *(G-18218)*

Doris Kimble 330 343-1226
  3596 State Route 39 Nw Dover (44622) *(G-8977)*

Dornback Furnace Division, Cleveland *Also called Adams Manufacturing Company (G-4700)*

Dorothy Crooker 513 385-0888
  5984 Cheviot Rd Cincinnati (45247) *(G-3665)*

Dorum Color Co Inc 330 773-1900
  2229 Stahl Rd Akron (44319) *(G-154)*

Doschers Candies Inc 513 381-8656
  24 W Court St Cincinnati (45202) *(G-3666)*

Dosmatic USA Inc (PA) 972 245-9765
  3798 Round Bottom Rd Cincinnati (45244) *(G-3667)*

DOT-2-Dot Inc 440 891-9388
  6909 Engle Rd Ste 16 Cleveland (44130) *(G-5209)*

Double b Printing LLC 740 593-7393
  17 W Washington St Athens (45701) *(G-863)*

Double Dippin Inc 937 847-2572
  949 Blanche Dr Miamisburg (45342) *(G-13802)*

Double Eagle, Lima *Also called Lima Armature Works Inc (G-12039)*

Doubleday Acquisitions LLC 937 242-6768
  2900 Dryden Rd Moraine (45439) *(G-14480)*

Doug Hall Electric, Columbus *Also called Douglas J Hall (G-7035)*

Doug Marine Motors Inc 740 335-3700
  1120 Clinton Ave Wshngtn CT Hs (43160) *(G-20907)*

Doug Smith 740 345-1398
  55 W Church St Newark (43055) *(G-15000)*

Douglas Industries LLC 740 775-2400
  379 Douglas Ave Chillicothe (45601) *(G-3237)*

Douglas J Hall 614 261-8871
  815 E Hudson St Columbus (43211) *(G-7035)*

Douglas Michalske 216 631-0567
  5808 Clark Ave Cleveland (44102) *(G-5210)*

Douglas S Kutz 440 238-8426
  19395 Knowlton Pkwy # 103 Strongsville (44149) *(G-17912)*

Douglas W & B C Richardson 440 247-5262
  62 Wychwood Dr Chagrin Falls (44022) *(G-3055)*

Douthit Communications Inc (PA) 419 625-5825
  520 Warren St Sandusky (44870) *(G-16958)*

Douthit Communications Inc 419 621-2142
  165 Jackson St Sandusky (44870) *(G-16959)*

DOV Graphics Inc 513 241-5150
  2230 Gilbert Ave Cincinnati (45206) *(G-3668)*

Dove Cds Inc 330 928-3430
  290 West Ave Ste J Tallmadge (44278) *(G-18143)*

Dove Die and Stamping Company 216 267-3720
  15665 Brookpark Rd Cleveland (44142) *(G-5211)*

Dove Graphics Inc 440 238-1800
  13500 Pearl Rd Cleveland (44136) *(G-5212)*

Dove Machine Inc 440 864-2645
  27100 Royalton Rd Columbia Station (44028) *(G-6589)*

Dover Atwood Corp 330 809-0630
  1875 Harsh Ave Se Ste 1 Massillon (44646) *(G-13125)*

Dover Cabinet Inc 330 343-9074
  1568 State Route 39 Nw Dover (44622) *(G-8978)*

Dover Chemical Corporation (HQ) 330 343-7711
  3676 Davis Rd Nw Dover (44622) *(G-8979)*

Dover Conveyor Inc 740 922-9390
  3323 Brightwood Rd Midvale (44653) *(G-14106)*

Dover Corporation 440 951-6600
  7201 Industrial Park Blvd Mentor (44060) *(G-13563)*

Dover Corporation 513 696-1790
  4680 Parkway Dr Ste 203 Mason (45040) *(G-13010)*

Dover Cryogenics, Midvale *Also called Amko Service Company (G-14105)*

Dover Fabrication and Burn Inc (HQ) 330 339-1057
  1106 Commercial Ave Se New Philadelphia (44663) *(G-14895)*

Dover High Prfmce Plas Inc 330 343-3477
  140 Williams Dr Nw Dover (44622) *(G-8980)*

Dover Machine Co 330 343-4123
  2208 State Route 516 Nw Dover (44622) *(G-8981)*

Dover Phila Heating & Cooling, Dover *Also called Hvac Inc (G-8991)*

Dover Tank and Plate Company 330 343-4443
  5725 Crown Rd Nw Dover (44622) *(G-8982)*

Dover Tower Company, The, Dover *Also called T V Specialties Inc (G-9020)*

Dover Wipes Company 513 983-1100
  1 Procter And Gamble Plz Cincinnati (45202) *(G-3669)*

Dovetail Dimensions 330 674-9533
  6534 Township Road 603 Millersburg (44654) *(G-14212)*

Dow Bar Roman Hosue, Cincinnati *Also called Rohm and Haas Chemicals LLC (G-4356)*

Dow Cameron Oil & Gas LLC 740 452-1568
  5555 Eden Park Dr Zanesville (43701) *(G-21300)*

Dow Chemical, Hebron *Also called Transcendia Inc (G-10891)*

Dow Chemical Company 740 533-4000
  925 County Road 1a Ironton (45638) *(G-11292)*

Dow Chemical Company 419 423-6500
  3441 N Main St Findlay (45840) *(G-9818)*

Dow Chemical Company 937 839-4612
  10 Electric St West Alexandria (45381) *(G-19779)*

Dow Chemical Company 937 254-1550
  555 Gaddis Blvd Dayton (45403) *(G-8309)*

Dow Corning Corporation 330 319-1127
  3835 Copley Rd Copley (44321) *(G-7844)*

Dow Jones & Company Inc 419 352-4696
  1201 Brim Rd Bowling Green (43402) *(G-1987)*

Dowa Tht America Inc 419 354-4144
  2130 S Woodland Cir Bowling Green (43402) *(G-1988)*

Dowco LLC 330 773-6654
  1374 Markle St Akron (44306) *(G-155)*

Down Decor, Cincinnati *Also called Downhome Inc (G-3670)*

Down Home 740 393-1186
  9 N Main St Mount Vernon (43050) *(G-14620)*

Down Home Leather, Mount Vernon *Also called Down Home (G-14620)*

Down-Lite International Inc (PA) 513 229-3696
  8153 Duke Blvd Mason (45040) *(G-13011)*

Downey Enterprises Inc 740 587-4258
  2087 Jones Rd Granville (43023) *(G-10457)*

Downhome Inc 513 921-3373
  1 Kovach Dr Cincinnati (45215) *(G-3670)*

Downing Displays Inc (PA) 513 248-9800
  550 Techne Center Dr Milford (45150) *(G-14138)*

Downing Enterprises Inc 330 666-3888
  1287 Centerview Cir Copley (44321) *(G-7845)*

Downing Exhibits, Copley *Also called Downing Enterprises Inc (G-7845)*

Downlite, Mason *Also called Down-Lite International Inc (G-13011)*

Downtown Print Shop 419 242-9164
  500 Madison Ave Fl 1 Toledo (43604) *(G-18443)*

Doyle Manufacturing Inc 419 865-2548
  1440 Holloway Rd Holland (43528) *(G-11055)*

Doyle Sailmaker 216 486-5732
  805 E 185th St Cleveland (44119) *(G-5213)*

Doyle Systems, Norton *Also called J E Doyle Company (G-15515)*

Dp Operating Company Inc 330 938-2172
  19220 State Route 62 Beloit (44609) *(G-1582)*

Dp Products LLC 440 834-9663
  14395 Aquilla Rd Burton (44021) *(G-2373)*

Dp2 Energy LLC 330 376-5068
  697 W Market St Akron (44303) *(G-156)*

Dpa Investments Inc. 440 992-3377
  3050 Lake Rd E Ashtabula (44004) *(G-803)*

Dpa Investments Inc. 440 992-7039
  1741 W 47th St Ashtabula (44004) *(G-804)*

Dph Discount Pin Inc 740 264-2450
  30 Snug Hbr Steubenville (43953) *(G-17692)*

Dpi Inc. 419 273-1400
  110 N Davis St Forest (45843) *(G-9919)*

DPM Orthodontics Inc 330 673-0334
  1519 Enterprise Way Ste H Kent (44240) *(G-11451)*

Dpsciences, Cincinnati *Also called Data Processing Sciences Corp (G-3640)*

Dr Hess Products LLC 800 718-8022
  1000 Hedstrom Dr Ste B Ashland (44805) *(G-729)*

Dr Pepper Bottlers Associates 330 746-7651
  500 Pepsi Pl Youngstown (44502) *(G-21072)*

Dr Pepper Bottling Company 740 452-2721
  335 N 6th St Zanesville (43701) *(G-21301)*

Dr Pepper Snapple Group 419 529-6773
  1115 National Pkwy Mansfield (44906) *(G-12596)*

Dr Pepper Snapple Group Inc 614 237-4201
  950 Stelzer Rd Columbus (43219) *(G-7036)*

Dr Pepper Snapple Group Inc 614 237-4201
  960 Stelzer Rd Columbus (43219) *(G-7037)*

Dr Pepper/Seven Up Inc 419 229-7777
  2350 Central Point Pkwy Lima (45804) *(G-12005)*

Dr Z Amplification, Maple Heights *Also called Dr Z Amps Inc (G-12733)*

Dr Z Amps Inc 216 475-1444
  17011 Broadway Ave Maple Heights (44137) *(G-12733)*

Dr. Pepper 7 Up Columbus, Columbus *Also called American Bottling Company (G-6730)*

Drabik Manufacturing Inc 216 267-1616
  15601 Commerce Park Dr Cleveland (44142) *(G-5214)*

Dracool-Usa Inc (PA) 937 743-5899
  30 Eagle Ct Carlisle (45005) *(G-2930)*

Dragon Beverage Inc. 614 506-5592
  1945 Judwick Dr Columbus (43229) *(G-7038)*

Dragon Products Ltd 330 345-3968
  3310 Columbus Rd Wooster (44691) *(G-20767)*

Dragon Racing Service, Loveland *Also called Gregory Auto Service (G-12355)*

Dragoon Technologies Inc (PA) 937 439-9223
  900 Senate Dr Dayton (45459) *(G-8310)*

Dragoonitcn, Dayton *Also called Dragoon Technologies Inc (G-8310)*

Draime Enterprises Inc 330 837-2254
  1300 Erie St S Unit C Massillon (44646) *(G-13126)*

Drain Products LLC (PA) 419 230-4549
  13051 County Road 301 Lakeview (43331) *(G-11649)*

Drainage Pipe & Fitting 419 538-6337
  450 Tile Company St Ottawa (45875) *(G-15793)*

Drainage Products Inc 419 622-6951
  100 W Main St Haviland (45851) *(G-10838)*

Drake Brothers Ltd 415 819-4941
  1215 Forsythe Ave Columbus (43201) *(G-7039)*

Drake Manufacturing Svcs Co 330 847-7291
  4371 N Leavitt Rd Nw Warren (44485) *(G-19545)*

Drake Monument Company 937 399-7941
  524 W Mccreight Ave Springfield (45504) *(G-17547)*

Drapery Stitch of Delphos 419 692-3921
  50 Summers Ln Delphos (45833) *(G-8906)*

Drawn Metals Corp 937 433-6151
  331 Congress Park Dr Dayton (45459) *(G-8311)*

Drb Systems LLC 330 645-3299
  3245 Pickle Rd Akron (44312) *(G-157)*

DRDC Realty Inc (PA) 419 478-7091
  4401 Jackman Rd Toledo (43612) *(G-18444)*

Dream Space 440 945-6596
  25405 Broadway Ave Bedford (44146) *(G-1421)*

Dreamscape Media LLC (PA) 877 983-7326
  1417 Timber Wolf Dr Holland (43528) *(G-11056)*

Dreco Inc 440 327-6021
  7887 Root Rd North Ridgeville (44039) *(G-15370)*

Dreier Tool & Die Corp 513 521-8200
  2865 Compton Rd Cincinnati (45251) *(G-3671)*

Dreison International Inc (PA) 216 362-0755
  4540 W 160th St Cleveland (44135) *(G-5215)*

Dresch Tolson Dental Labs 419 842-6730
  8730 Resource Park Dr Sylvania (43560) *(G-18105)*

Dresden Specialties Inc (PA) 740 754-2451
  305 Main St Dresden (43821) *(G-9032)*

Dresden Specialties Inc 740 452-7100
  710 Main St Zanesville (43701) *(G-21302)*

DRG Hydraulics Inc 216 663-9747
  18200 S Miles Rd Cleveland (44128) *(G-5216)*

Drillex Inc (PA) 440 255-7500
  8100 Deepwood Blvd Mentor (44060) *(G-13564)*

Drive Components 440 234-6200
  6519 Eastland Rd Ste 106 Brookpark (44142) *(G-2157)*

Driven Innovations LLC 330 818-7681
  140 Harrisburg Dr Englewood (45322) *(G-9517)*

Drivetrain USA Inc 614 733-0940
  8445 Rausch Dr Plain City (43064) *(G-16337)*

Drop Zone Ltd 234 806-4604
  3680 N River Rd Ne Warren (44484) *(G-19546)*

Drowned Lure 330 548-5873
  3295 Klages Blvd Tallmadge (44278) *(G-18144)*

Drs Advanced Isr LLC (HQ) 937 429-7408
  2601 Mission Point Blvd Beavercreek (45431) *(G-1330)*

Drs Advanced Isr LLC. 603 429-0111
  2601 Mission Point Blvd Beavercreek (45431) *(G-1331)*

Drs Icas LLC. 937 429-7408
  2601 Miohion Point Blvd Ste 250 Beavercreek (45431) *(G-1332)*

Drs Industries Inc 419 861-0334
  1067 Hamilton Dr Holland (43528) *(G-11057)*

Drs Milburn-Medina Inc. 330 725-4680
  409 N Court St Medina (44256) *(G-13404)*

Drs Mobile Environmntl Svc 513 943-1111
  4043 Mcmann Rd Cincinnati (45245) *(G-3299)*

Drs Signal Technologies Inc. 937 429-7470
  4393 Dayton Xenia Rd Beavercreek (45432) *(G-1333)*

Drt Medical LLC 937 298-7391
  618 Greenmount Blvd Dayton (45419) *(G-8312)*

Drt Mfg Co (HQ) 937 297-6670
  618 Greenmount Blvd Dayton (45419) *(G-8313)*

Drt Power Systems LLC - Sidney 937 492-6121
  1950 Campbell Rd Sidney (45365) *(G-17180)*

Drum Parts, Cleveland *Also called Group Industries Inc (G-5461)*

Drum Runner, Marion *Also called Mission Industrial Group LLC (G-12886)*

Drummond Corp 440 834-9660
  14990 Brkshire Indus Pkwy Middlefield (44062) *(G-13931)*

Drummond Dolomite Inc 440 942-7000
  7954 Reynolds Rd Mentor (44060) *(G-13565)*

Drummond Dolomite Quarry, Mentor *Also called Drummond Dolomite Inc (G-13565)*

Drycal Inc 440 974-1999
  7355 Production Dr Mentor (44060) *(G-13566)*

Ds Express Carriers Inc (PA) 419 433-6200
  203 Republic St Norwalk (44857) *(G-15534)*

Ds Technologies Group Ltd 419 841-5388
  2537 Wimbledon Park Blvd Toledo (43617) *(G-18445)*

DSC Supply Company LLC 614 891-1100
  237 E Broadway Ave Ste A Westerville (43081) *(G-20211)*

Dsg-Canusa, Loveland Also called Shawcor Inc **(G-12386)**

Dsk Imaging LLC 513 554-1797
6839 Ashfield Dr Blue Ash (45242) **(G-1777)**

DSM Industries Inc 440 585-1100
1340 E 289th St Wickliffe (44092) **(G-20364)**

DTE Cool Co 513 579-0160
105 E 4th Ste G100 Cincinnati (45202) **(G-3672)**

DTE Inc 419 522-3428
110 Baird Pkwy Mansfield (44903) **(G-12597)**

Dti, Alliance Also called Davis Technologies Inc **(G-505)**

Dti Molded Products Inc 937 492-5008
250 Stolle Ave Sidney (45365) **(G-17181)**

DTR Equipment Inc 419 692-3000
1430 N Main St Delphos (45833) **(G-8907)**

Dts, Parma Also called Dynamic Temperature Sups LLC **(G-15956)**

Du Pont E I De Nemours and Co, Little Hocking Also called Chemours Company Fc LLC **(G-12144)**

Dublin Millwork Co Inc 614 889-7776
7575 Fishel Dr S Dublin (43016) **(G-9069)**

Dublin Plastics Inc 216 641-5904
9202 Reno Ave Cleveland (44105) **(G-5217)**

Dubois Chemicals Inc 513 868-9662
2550 Bobmeyer Rd Hamilton (45015) **(G-10684)**

Dubois Chemicals Inc (PA) 513 731-6350
3630 E Kemper Rd Cincinnati (45241) **(G-3673)**

Dubose Energy Fasteners & Mach 216 362-1700
18737 Sheldon Rd Middleburg Heights (44130) **(G-13905)**

Dubro Oil Corporation 216 696-2646
2400 Mulberry Ave Cleveland (44113) **(G-5218)**

Duck Tape, Avon Also called Shurtech Brands LLC **(G-1012)**

Duco Tool & Die Inc 419 628-2031
19 S Main St Minster (45865) **(G-14351)**

Duct Fabricators Inc 216 391-2400
883 Addison Rd Cleveland (44103) **(G-5219)**

Ducts Inc 216 391-2400
883 Addison Rd Cleveland (44103) **(G-5220)**

Dudick Inc 330 562-1970
1818 Miller Pkwy Streetsboro (44241) **(G-17851)**

Dues Jersey Farm 419 678-2102
4131 Philothea Rd Coldwater (45828) **(G-6557)**

Dues Lumbermill, Coldwater Also called Dues Jersey Farm **(G-6557)**

Duff Farm 740 742-2182
30762 Old Dexter Rd Langsville (45741) **(G-11764)**

Duff Quarry Inc (PA) 937 686-2811
9042 State Route 117 Huntsville (43324) **(G-11212)**

Duff Quarry Inc 419 273-2518
3798 State Route 53 Forest (45843) **(G-9920)**

Duffee Finishing Inc 740 965-4848
4860 N County Line Rd Sunbury (43074) **(G-18059)**

Dugan Drilling Incorporated 740 668-3811
27238 New Guilford Rd Walhonding (43843) **(G-19468)**

Duke Graphics Inc 440 946-0606
33212 Lakeland Blvd Willoughby (44095) **(G-20475)**

Duke Manufacturing Inc 440 951-1879
38205 Western Pkwy Willoughby (44094) **(G-20476)**

Duke Printing, Willoughby Also called Duke Graphics Inc **(G-20475)**

Dulcelicious Cupcakes and More 440 385-7706
22368 Lorain Rd Cleveland (44126) **(G-5221)**

Dulle Associates 513 723-9600
5960 Glenway Ave Cincinnati (45238) **(G-3674)**

Dulle Printing, Cincinnati Also called Dulle Associates **(G-3674)**

Dumas Meats Inc 330 628-3438
857 Randolph Rd Mogadore (44260) **(G-14373)**

Dunagan Logging 740 599-9368
16844 Pritchard Rd Danville (43014) **(G-8087)**

Dunaway Inc 330 533-7753
5959 Leffingwell Rd Canfield (44406) **(G-2552)**

Duncan Brothers Drilling Inc (PA) 330 426-9507
1264 Howell Ave East Palestine (44413) **(G-9234)**

Duncan Brothers Drilling Inc 330 426-9507
1264 Howell Ave East Palestine (44413) **(G-9235)**

Duncan Dental Lab LLC 614 793-0330
6175 Shamrock Ct Ste A Dublin (43016) **(G-9070)**

Duncan Press Corporation 330 477-4529
5049 Yukon St Nw Canton (44708) **(G-2694)**

Duncan Tool Inc 937 667-9364
9790 Julie Ct Tipp City (45371) **(G-18276)**

Dunecraft Inc 800 306-4168
19201 Cranwood Pkwy Cleveland (44128) **(G-5222)**

Dunham Machine Inc 216 398-4500
1311 E Schaaf Rd Bldg A Independence (44131) **(G-11253)**

Dunham Products Inc 440 232-0885
7400 Northfield Rd Walton Hills (44146) **(G-19473)**

Dunhams Sports 330 334-3257
180 Great Oaks Trl Wadsworth (44281) **(G-19403)**

Dunkin' Donuts, Solon Also called Dandi Enterprises Inc **(G-17282)**

Dunn S Tank Service Inc 330 863-2200
6036 Alliance Rd Nw Malvern (44644) **(G-12542)**

Duo-Corp 330 549-2149
280 Miley Rd North Lima (44452) **(G-15315)**

Duplex Mill & Manufacturing Co 937 325-5555
415 Sigler St Springfield (45506) **(G-17548)**

Dupli-Systems Inc 440 234-9415
8260 Dow Cir Strongsville (44136) **(G-17913)**

Dupont, Circleville Also called E I Du Pont De Nemours & Co **(G-4627)**

Dupont, Stow Also called E I Du Pont De Nemours & Co **(G-17745)**

Dupont Electronic Polymers LP 937 268-3411
1515 Nicholas Rd Dayton (45417) **(G-8314)**

Dupont Prfmce Elastomers LLC 330 929-6934
4330 Allen Rd Stow (44224) **(G-17744)**

Dupont Prfmce Elastomers LLC 330 929-6934
820 Flora Ave Akron (44314) **(G-158)**

Dupont Vespel Parts and Shapes, Cleveland Also called E I Du Pont De Nemours & Co **(G-5232)**

Dupont Vespel Parts and Shapes, Circleville Also called E I Du Pont De Nemours & Co **(G-4628)**

Dupps Printing and Supply Co, Port Clinton Also called William J Dupps **(G-16419)**

Dura Bilt Drapery & Upholstery 440 269-8438
4041 Erie St Willoughby (44094) **(G-20477)**

Dura Magnetics Inc 419 882-0591
5500 Schultz Dr Sylvania (43560) **(G-18106)**

Dura Temp Corporation 419 866-4348
949 S Mccord Rd Holland (43528) **(G-11058)**

Dura-Line Corporation 440 322-1000
860 Garden St Elyria (44035) **(G-9407)**

Durable Corporation 419 668-8138
75 N Pleasant St Norwalk (44857) **(G-15535)**

Durable Plating Co 216 391-2132
4404 Saint Clair Ave Cleveland (44103) **(G-5223)**

Duracorp LLC 740 549-3336
7787 Graphics Way Lewis Center (43035) **(G-11896)**

Duracote Corporation 330 296-9600
350 N Diamond St Ravenna (44266) **(G-16526)**

Duraflow Industries Inc 440 965-5047
15706 Garfield Rd Wakeman (44889) **(G-19448)**

Duramax Global Corp 440 834-5400
17990 Great Lakes Pkwy Hiram (44234) **(G-11033)**

Duramax Marine, Hiram Also called Duramax Global Corp **(G-11033)**

Duramax Marine LLC 440 834-5400
17990 Great Lakes Pkwy Hiram (44234) **(G-11034)**

Duramax Marine Industries 419 668-3728
53 Saint Marys St Norwalk (44857) **(G-15536)**

Durashield, Urbana Also called American Pan Company **(G-19146)**

Duray Machine Co Inc 440 277-4119
400 Ravenglass Blvd Amherst (44001) **(G-597)**

Duray Plating Company Inc 216 941-5540
13701 Triskett Rd Cleveland (44111) **(G-5224)**

Durbin Minuteman Press 513 791-9171
11130 Kenwood Rd Blue Ash (45242) **(G-1778)**

Dure Foods Us LLC 614 409-9030
6967 Alum Creek Dr Columbus (43217) **(G-7040)**

Durez Corporation 567 295-6400
13717 State Route 68 Kenton (43326) **(G-11546)**

Durisek Enterprises Inc 216 281-3898
5200 Train Ave Cleveland (44102) **(G-5225)**

Durivage Pattern & Mfg Co 419 836-8655
20522 State Route 579 W Williston (43468) **(G-20420)**

Duro Dyne Midwest Corp 513 870-6000
3825 Symmes Rd Hamilton (45015) **(G-10685)**

Durox Company 440 238-5350
12312 Alameda Dr Strongsville (44149) **(G-17914)**

DUrso Bakery Inc 330 652-4741
212 S Cedar Ave Niles (44446) **(G-15150)**

Dusty's Salvage & Supply, New Lexington Also called Dnl Oil Corp **(G-14847)**

Dutch Barn Builders, Old Washington Also called Hershbergers Dutch Market LLLP **(G-15671)**

Dutch Cntry Apple Dmplings Inc 330 683-0646
229 W Market St Orrville (44667) **(G-15735)**

Dutch Design Products LLC 330 674-1167
8216 State Route 241 Fredericksburg (44627) **(G-10083)**

Dutch Heritage Woodcraft 330 893-2211
4363 State Route 39 Berlin (44610) **(G-1648)**

Dutch Legacy LLC 330 359-0270
2425 Us Route 62 Dundee (44624) **(G-9172)**

Dutch Valley Woodcraft Ltd 330 695-2364
5833 Township Road 610 Fredericksburg (44627) **(G-10084)**

Dutch Valley Woodworking Inc 330 852-4319
Hc 39 Sugarcreek (44681) **(G-18022)**

Dutchcraft Truss Component Inc 330 862-2220
2212 Fox Ave Se Minerva (44657) **(G-14320)**

Duvall Woodworking Inc 419 878-9581
7551 Dutch Rd Waterville (43566) **(G-19656)**

Dvi Retal, Middletown Also called Digital Visuals Inc **(G-14037)**

Dvuv LLC (PA) 216 741-5511
4641 Hinckley Indus Pkwy Cleveland (44109) **(G-5226)**

DW Hercules LLC 330 830-2498
2770 Erie St S Massillon (44646) **(G-13127)**

Dwayne Bennett Industries 440 466-5724
  6708 N Ridge Rd W Geneva (44041) *(G-10345)*

Dwayne Hall 740 685-5270
  57501 Cherry Hill Rd Senecaville (43780) *(G-17058)*

Dwllr Inc 513 400-5544
  6556 Lakeside Dr West Chester (45069) *(G-19854)*

Dwllr Labs, West Chester *Also called Dwllr Inc (G-19854)*

Dyco Manufacturing Inc 419 485-5525
  12708 State Route 576 Montpelier (43543) *(G-14444)*

Dyenamo Distributing 419 462-9474
  6124 State Route 19 Galion (44833) *(G-10264)*

Dyna Floor, Solon *Also called Dynafloor Systems Inc (G-17283)*

Dyna Tech Molding & Beta 330 296-2315
  367 N Freedom St Ravenna (44266) *(G-16527)*

Dyna Vac Plastics Inc 937 773-0092
  921 S Downing St Piqua (45356) *(G-16262)*

Dyna-Flex Inc 440 946-9424
  7300 Industrial Park Blvd Mentor (44060) *(G-13567)*

Dynaco Usa Inc 419 227-3000
  1075 Prosperity Rd Lima (45801) *(G-12006)*

Dynafloor Systems Inc 330 467-6005
  35079 Quartermane Cir Solon (44139) *(G-17283)*

Dynalab Ems Inc 614 866-9999
  555 Lancaster Ave Reynoldsburg (43068) *(G-16587)*

Dynalite Corp 419 873-1706
  26040a Glenwood Rd Ste A Perrysburg (43551) *(G-16086)*

Dynamic Bar Code Systems Inc 330 220-5451
  3139 Ipswich Ct Brunswick (44212) *(G-2222)*

Dynamic Control North Amer Inc 440 979-0657
  31335 Industrial Pkwy # 2 North Olmsted (44070) *(G-15330)*

Dynamic Control North Amer Inc (PA) 513 860-5094
  3042 Symmes Rd Hamilton (45015) *(G-10686)*

Dynamic Design & Systems Inc 440 708-1010
  7639 Washington St Chagrin Falls (44023) *(G-3085)*

Dynamic Industries Inc 513 861-6767
  3611 Woodburn Ave Cincinnati (45207) *(G-3675)*

Dynamic Leasing Ltd 330 892-0164
  3790 State Route 7 New Waterford (44445) *(G-14970)*

Dynamic Manufacturing 419 564-8738
  3351 State Route 39 Shelby (44875) *(G-17135)*

Dynamic Metal Services, Bedford Heights *Also called Alloy Metal Exchange LLC (G-1477)*

Dynamic Plastics Inc 937 437-7261
  8207 H W Rd New Paris (45347) *(G-14879)*

Dynamic Polymers LLC 614 575-1222
  950 Taylor Station Rd M Columbus (43230) *(G-7041)*

Dynamic Sensor Systems LLC 614 430-2888
  510 E Wilson Bridge Rd Worthington (43085) *(G-20865)*

Dynamic Specialties Inc 440 946-2838
  7471 Tyler Blvd Ste E Mentor (44060) *(G-13568)*

Dynamic Temperature Sups LLC 216 767-5799
  12448 Plaza Dr Parma (44130) *(G-15956)*

Dynamic Tool & Mold Inc 440 237-8665
  12126 York Rd Unit N Cleveland (44133) *(G-5227)*

Dynamic Tool Die 440 834-0007
  14925 White Rd Middlefield (44062) *(G-13932)*

Dynamic Weld Corporation 419 582-2900
  242 N St Osgood (45351) *(G-15785)*

Dynamics Manufacturing, Toledo *Also called Dynamics Research & Dev (G-18446)*

Dynamics Research & Dev 419 478-7091
  4401 Jackman Rd Toledo (43612) *(G-18446)*

Dynamp LLC 614 871-6900
  3735 Gantz Rd Ste D Grove City (43123) *(G-10555)*

Dynapoint Technologies Inc 937 859-5193
  475 Progress Rd Dayton (45449) *(G-8315)*

Dynatech Systems Inc 440 365-1774
  161 Reaser Ct Elyria (44035) *(G-9408)*

Dyneon LLC 859 334-4500
  2165 Cablecar Ct Cincinnati (45244) *(G-3676)*

Dynetech LLC 419 690-4281
  916 N Summit St Toledo (43604) *(G-18447)*

Dyverse Entertainment LLC 513 225-3301
  10979 Reed Hartman Hwy Blue Ash (45242) *(G-1779)*

Dyverse Marketing Solutions, Blue Ash *Also called Dyverse Entertainment LLC (G-1779)*

E & E Machine & Tool Inc 937 492-3447
  2423 Michigan St Sidney (45365) *(G-17182)*

E & E Mold & Die Inc 216 898-5853
  4605 Manufacturing Ave Cleveland (44135) *(G-5228)*

E & E Nameplates Inc 419 468-3617
  760 E Walnut St Galion (44833) *(G-10265)*

E & E Parts Machining, Strongsville *Also called Stefra Inc (G-17973)*

E & E Ready Rooms, Saint Clairsville *Also called D W Truax Enterprise Inc (G-16789)*

E & E Screen Prtg & Cstm EMB 614 235-2177
  901 Robinwood Ave Ste G Columbus (43213) *(G-7042)*

E & I, Westerville *Also called McNish Corporation (G-20171)*

E & J Demark Inc (PA) 419 337-5866
  1115 N Ottokee St Wauseon (43567) *(G-19675)*

E & J Demark Inc 419 337-5866
  1115 N Ottokee St Wauseon (43567) *(G-19676)*

E & K Products Co Inc 216 631-2510
  3520 Cesko Ave Cleveland (44109) *(G-5229)*

E & L Spring Shop 440 632-1439
  16035 Nauvoo Rd Middlefield (44062) *(G-13933)*

E & M Liberty Welding Inc 330 866-2338
  141 James St Waynesburg (44688) *(G-19724)*

E & R Welding Inc 440 329-9387
  32 South St Berlin Heights (44814) *(G-1661)*

E & W Enterprises Powell Inc (HQ) 937 346-0800
  2020 Progress Rd Springfield (45505) *(G-17549)*

E - I Corp. 614 899-2282
  214 Hoff Rd Unit M Westerville (43082) *(G-20146)*

E A Cox Inc. 740 858-4400
  11201 State Route 104 Lucasville (45648) *(G-12419)*

E B P Inc. 216 241-2550
  2041 W 17th St Cleveland (44113) *(G-5230)*

E C Babbert Inc 614 837-8444
  7415 Diley Rd Canal Winchester (43110) *(G-2523)*

E C E, Holland *Also called Electronic Concepts Engrg Inc (G-11059)*

E C S, Dayton *Also called Electrical Control Systems (G-8321)*

E C S, Reynoldsburg *Also called Environmental Closure Systems (G-16588)*

E C S, East Liverpool *Also called Enviro Crest Services Inc (G-9214)*

E C S Corp. 440 323-1707
  8015 Murray Ridge Rd Elyria (44035) *(G-9409)*

E C Shaw Co 513 721-6334
  1242 Mehring Way Cincinnati (45203) *(G-3677)*

E D I, Belpre *Also called Electric Dsign For Indust Inc (G-1586)*

E D M Electrofying Inc. 440 322-8900
  34 Artemas Ct Elyria (44035) *(G-9410)*

E D M Fastar Inc. 216 676-0100
  13410 Enterprise Ave Cleveland (44135) *(G-5231)*

E D M Services LLC. 216 486-2068
  21724 Saint Clair Ave Euclid (44117) *(G-9575)*

E D M Star-One Inc. 440 647-0600
  745 Shiloh Ave Wellington (44090) *(G-19740)*

E E Controls Inc. 440 585-5554
  30301 Fairway Blvd Willowick (44095) *(G-20647)*

E E M C O, Cleveland *Also called Eaton Aerospace LLC (G-5243)*

E H T Company, Euclid *Also called Euclid Heat Treating Co (G-9579)*

E I Ceramics Inc. 513 772-7001
  2600 Commerce Blvd Cincinnati (45241) *(G-3678)*

E I Du Pont De Nemours & Co. 740 474-0220
  S Dupont Rd Rr 23 Circleville (43113) *(G-4627)*

E I Du Pont De Nemours & Co. 330 929-2961
  4330 Allen Rd Stow (44224) *(G-17745)*

E I Du Pont De Nemours & Co. 216 901-3600
  6200 Hillcrest Dr Cleveland (44125) *(G-5232)*

E I Du Pont De Nemours & Co. 330 364-6002
  1929 Tremont St Dover (44622) *(G-8983)*

E I Du Pont De Nemours & Co. 740 474-0635
  800 Dupont Rd Circleville (43113) *(G-4628)*

E J Bognar Inc. 330 426-9292
  51887 E Taggart St East Palestine (44413) *(G-9236)*

E J Skok Industries (PA) 216 292-7533
  26901 Richmond Rd Bedford (44146) *(G-1422)*

E L Davis Inc. 419 268-2004
  6032 State Route 219 Celina (45822) *(G-2993)*

E L Frueh Inc. 419 222-9741
  232 N Union St Lima (45801) *(G-12007)*

E L Mustee & Sons Inc (PA) 216 267-3100
  5431 W 164th St Brookpark (44142) *(G-2158)*

E L Ostendorf Inc. 440 247-7631
  3425 Roundwood Rd Chagrin Falls (44022) *(G-3056)*

E L Stone Company 330 825-4565
  2998 Eastern Rd Norton (44203) *(G-15510)*

E M E C, Marysville *Also called Engineered Mfg & Eqp Co (G-12942)*

E M I, Cleveland *Also called Equipment Manufacturers Intl (G-5291)*

E M I Plastic Equipment, Jackson Center *Also called EMI Corp (G-11341)*

E M S, Delaware *Also called Engineered Mtls Systems Inc (G-8843)*

E M S, Batavia *Also called Engineered MBL Solutions Inc (G-1184)*

E M Wave, Cleveland *Also called Electro-Magwave Inc (G-5266)*

E P S Specialists Ltd Inc 513 489-3676
  7875 School Rd Cincinnati (45249) *(G-3679)*

E Pompili & Sons Inc. 216 581-8080
  12307 Broadway Ave Cleveland (44125) *(G-5233)*

E R Advanced Ceramics Inc. 330 426-9433
  600 E Clark St East Palestine (44413) *(G-9237)*

E R B Enterprises Inc. 740 948-9174
  8205 Factory Shops Blvd Jeffersonville (43128) *(G-11379)*

E Retailing Associates LLC 614 300-5785
  2282 Westbrooke Dr Columbus (43228) *(G-7043)*

E S C, Akron *Also called Ellet Neon Sales & Service Inc (G-162)*

E S H Inc. 330 345-1010
  390 W South St Wooster (44691) *(G-20768)*

E S Industries Inc (PA) 419 643-2625
  110 Brookview Ct Lima (45801) *(G-12008)*

E S Sign & Design LLC 330 405-4799
  9478 Ravenna Rd Twinsburg (44087) *(G-18927)*

E Star Aerospace Corporation 614 396-6868
470 Olde Worthington Rd # 200 Westerville (43082) *(G-20147)*

E Systems Design & Automtn Inc 419 443-0220
226 Heritage Dr Tiffin (44883) *(G-18219)*

E T & K Inc 440 777-7375
23545 Lorain Rd North Olmsted (44070) *(G-15331)*

E T & K Inc 440 888-4780
9809 Running Brook Dr Cleveland (44130) *(G-5234)*

E T I, Mansfield *Also called Energy Technologies Inc (G-12600)*

E W Perry Service Co Inc 419 473-1231
4216 W Alexis Rd Toledo (43623) *(G-18448)*

E W Welding & Fabricating 440 826-9038
336 Wyleswood Dr Berea (44017) *(G-1612)*

E Z Binderys 513 733-0005
10122 Reading Rd Cincinnati (45241) *(G-3680)*

E Z Grout Corporation 740 749-3512
405 Watertown Rd Waterford (45786) *(G-19646)*

E Z Rout Inc 330 467-4814
102 E Aurora Rd Northfield (44067) *(G-15465)*

E-Beam Services Inc 513 933-0031
2775 Henkle Dr Unit B Lebanon (45036) *(G-11795)*

E-Narratives, Sandusky *Also called Douthit Communications Inc (G-16959)*

E-One Electric 937 296-4420
2754 Viking Ln Moraine (45439) *(G-14481)*

E-Pak Manufacturing LLC 800 235-1632
1109 Pittsburg Ave Wooster (44691) *(G-20769)*

E-Waste Systems (ohio) Inc 614 824-3057
1033 Brentnell Ave # 300 Columbus (43219) *(G-7044)*

E-Z Electric Motor Svc Corp 216 581-8820
8510 Bessemer Ave Cleveland (44127) *(G-5235)*

E-Z Grader Company 440 247-7511
300 Industrial Pkwy Ste A Chagrin Falls (44022) *(G-3057)*

E-Z Label Co, Brookfield *Also called E-Z Stop Service Center (G-2123)*

E-Z Pack, Cincinnati *Also called Wayne Signer Enterprises Inc (G-4580)*

E-Z Stop Service Center 330 448-2236
354 Bedford Rd Se Brookfield (44403) *(G-2123)*

E.C. Kitzel & Sons, Cleveland *Also called Schumann Enterprises Inc (G-6166)*

E2 Merchandising Inc 513 860-5444
9706 Inter Ocean Dr West Chester (45246) *(G-19998)*

E3 Diagnostics Inc 330 926-0594
3420 Cavalier Trl Ste C Cuyahoga Falls (44224) *(G-7988)*

E3 Diagnostics Inc 937 435-2250
74 Marco Ln Dayton (45458) *(G-8316)*

E3 Gordon Stowe, Dayton *Also called E3 Diagnostics Inc (G-8316)*

E3 Materials LLC 330 972-6457
411 Wolf Ledges Pkwy Akron (44311) *(G-159)*

Eae Logistics Company LLC 440 417-4788
5907 S Ridge Rd Madison (44057) *(G-12505)*

Eagle Advertising 216 881-0800
4101 Commerce Ave Cleveland (44103) *(G-5236)*

Eagle Burgmann Industries 513 563-7325
3478 Hauck Rd Cincinnati (45241) *(G-3681)*

Eagle Chemicals, Hamilton *Also called Dubois Chemicals Inc (G-10684)*

Eagle Coach Inc 513 797-4100
3344 State Route 132 Amelia (45102) *(G-573)*

Eagle Coach Company, Amelia *Also called Eagle Coach Inc (G-573)*

Eagle Creek Inc 513 385-4442
9799 Prechtel Rd Cincinnati (45252) *(G-3682)*

Eagle Crusher Co Inc (PA) 419 468-2288
525 S Market St Galion (44833) *(G-10266)*

Eagle Crusher Co Inc 419 562-1183
521 E Southern Ave Bucyrus (44820) *(G-2340)*

Eagle Elastomer Inc 330 923-7070
70 Cuyhoga Fls Indus Pkwy Peninsula (44264) *(G-16037)*

Eagle Engineering Wtr Tech LLC 419 345-4688
10211 White Oak Dr Perrysburg (43551) *(G-16087)*

Eagle Family Foods Group LLC (PA) 330 382-3725
4020 Kinross Lakes Pkwy Richfield (44286) *(G-16621)*

Eagle Fireworks Co (PA) 740 373-3357
26400 State Route 7 Marietta (45750) *(G-12782)*

Eagle Fireworks Co 740 758-5649
21860 Bridgewater Rd Quaker City (43773) *(G-16499)*

Eagle Hardwoods, Windsor *Also called Hershberger Manufacturing (G-20699)*

Eagle Image Inc 513 662-3000
4742 Blue Rock Rd Cincinnati (45247) *(G-3683)*

Eagle Machine and Welding Inc 740 345-5210
18 W Walnut St Newark (43055) *(G-15001)*

Eagle Machinery & Supply Inc 330 852-1300
422 Dutch Valley Dr Ne Sugarcreek (44681) *(G-18023)*

Eagle Manufacturing Inc 419 738-3491
88 High St Uniopolis (45888) *(G-19106)*

Eagle Mfg Solutions LLC 937 865-0366
2585 Belvo Rd Miamisburg (45342) *(G-13803)*

Eagle Precision Products LLC 440 582-9393
13800 Progress Pkwy Ste J North Royalton (44133) *(G-15418)*

Eagle Printing & Graphics LLC 937 773-7900
318 N Wayne St Piqua (45356) *(G-16263)*

Eagle Rock Brand Cons LLC 614 403-4802
10370 Summersweet Way Plain City (43064) *(G-16338)*

Eagle Tool & Die Inc 216 671-5055
10805 Briggs Rd Cleveland (44111) *(G-5237)*

Eagle Wire Works Inc 216 341-8550
3173 E 66th St Fl 3 Cleveland (44127) *(G-5238)*

Eagle Wldg & Fabrication 440 946-0692
1766 Joseph Lloyd Pkwy Willoughby (44094) *(G-20478)*

Eagle Wright Innovations Inc 937 640-8093
2591 Lance Dr Moraine (45409) *(G-14482)*

Eaglehead Manufacturing Co 216 692-1240
23555 Euclid Ave Euclid (44117) *(G-9576)*

Eaglehead Manufacturing Co 440 951-0400
35280 Lakeland Blvd Eastlake (44095) *(G-9267)*

Eagles Club 740 962-6490
407 W Riverside Dr McConnelsville (43756) *(G-13349)*

Eaj Services LLC 513 792-3400
4350 Glendale Milford Rd # 170 Blue Ash (45242) *(G-1780)*

Ear Medical Center Inc (PA) 812 537-0031
2121 Alpine Pl Apt 1101 Cincinnati (45206) *(G-3684)*

Earl D Arnold Printing Company 513 533-6900
630 Lunken Park Dr Cincinnati (45226) *(G-3685)*

Early Bird, The, Greenville *Also called Brothers Publishing Co LLC (G-10490)*

Earth and Atmospheric Sciences, Dayton *Also called Science/Electronics Inc (G-8648)*

Earth Dreams Jewelry, North Royalton *Also called Gardella Jewelry LLC (G-15420)*

Earth Safe Chemical LLC 419 648-7801
8122 Faulkner Rd Harrod (45850) *(G-10813)*

Earthquaker Devices LLC 330 252-9220
350 W Bowery St Akron (44307) *(G-160)*

Earthwalk Orthotic 330 837-6569
500 Vista Ave Se Massillon (44646) *(G-13128)*

Easi, Berea *Also called Estabrook Assembly Svcs Inc (G-1614)*

East Balt Ohio LLC (HQ) 740 454-6876
3005 E Pointe Dr Zanesville (43701) *(G-21303)*

East Balt Ohio LLC 740 454-6876
3005 E Pointe Dr Zanesville (43701) *(G-21304)*

East Balt Us LLC 740 454-6876
750 Airport Rd Zanesville (43701) *(G-21305)*

East Chemical Plant, Marysville *Also called Scotts Miracle-Gro Company (G-12969)*

East Cleveland Rubber Stamp 216 851-5050
16501 Euclid Ave Cleveland (44112) *(G-5239)*

East End Welding Company 330 677-6000
357 Tallmadge Rd Kent (44240) *(G-11452)*

East Fairfield Coal Co 330 542-1010
13699 Youngstown Pittsbur Petersburg (44454) *(G-16177)*

East Fork Precision Machine LL 513 753-4157
3874 Gordon Dr Amelia (45102) *(G-574)*

East Manufacturing Corporation (PA) 330 325-9921
1871 State Rte 44 Randolph (44265) *(G-16509)*

East Manufacturing Corporation 330 325-9921
3865 Waterloo Rd Randolph (44265) *(G-16510)*

East Oberlin Cabinets 440 775-1166
13184 Hale Rd Oberlin (44074) *(G-15637)*

East Ohio Gas Company 740 439-2721
60755 Country Club Rd Byesville (43723) *(G-2400)*

East Palestine Decorating LLC 330 426-9600
870 W Main St East Palestine (44413) *(G-9238)*

East Side Fuel Plus Operations 419 563-0777
1505 N Sandusky Ave Bucyrus (44820) *(G-2341)*

East Woodworking Company 216 791-5950
2044 Random Rd Cleveland (44106) *(G-5240)*

Easterday & Co, Wilmot *Also called David E Easterday and Co Inc (G-20685)*

Easterdays Printing Center 330 726-1182
86 Boardman Poland Rd Youngstown (44512) *(G-21073)*

Eastern Automated Piping 740 535-8184
424 State St Mingo Junction (43938) *(G-14348)*

Eastern Enterprise, Springfield *Also called Comptons Precision Machine (G-17535)*

Eastern Graphic Arts 419 994-5815
214 N Jefferson St Loudonville (44842) *(G-12297)*

Eastern Lawrnce Cty Watr Reclm, Chesapeake *Also called County of Lawrence (G-3186)*

Eastern Ohio Investments Inc 740 266-2228
213 Braybarton Blvd Steubenville (43952) *(G-17693)*

Eastern Ohio Newspapers Inc 740 633-1131
200 S 4th St Martins Ferry (43935) *(G-12924)*

Eastern Reserve Development 614 319-3179
3888 Stonewater Dr Columbus (43221) *(G-7045)*

Eastern Sheet Metal Inc (HQ) 513 793-3440
8959 Blue Ash Rd Blue Ash (45242) *(G-1781)*

Eastern Slipcover Company Inc 440 951-2310
6399 Cumberland Dr Mentor (44060) *(G-13569)*

Eastgate Custom Graphics Ltd 513 528-7922
4459 Mt Carmel Tobasco Rd Cincinnati (45244) *(G-3686)*

Eastlake Machine Products Inc 440 953-1014
1956 Joseph Lloyd Pkwy Willoughby (44094) *(G-20479)*

Eastlake Mfg Facility, Willoughby *Also called Conn-Selmer Inc (G-20462)*

Eastman Kodak Company 937 259-3000
3100 Research Blvd # 250 Kettering (45420) *(G-11579)*

Eastman Kodak Company 937 259-3000
3000 Research Blvd Dayton (45420) *(G-8317)*

Easton-Mccarthy Division, Wooster *Also called Baaron Abrasives Inc (G-20745)*

Eastside Daily News, Cleveland *Also called Easy Side Publishing Co Inc (G-5242)*

Eastword Publications Dev 216 781-9594
812 Huron Rd E Ste 401 Cleveland (44115) *(G-5241)*
Easy Board Inc....440 205-8836
8621 Station St Mentor (44060) *(G-13570)*
Easy Care Products Inc 330 405-1380
8870 Darrow Rd Ste F106 Twinsburg (44087) *(G-18928)*
Easy Side Publishing Co Inc 216 721-1674
11400 Woodland Ave Cleveland (44104) *(G-5242)*
Easy Way Leisure Corporation (PA) 513 731-5640
8950 Rossash Rd Cincinnati (45236) *(G-3687)*
Easy Way Products, Cincinnati *Also called Easy Way Leisure Corporation (G-3687)*
Eat Moore Cupcakes 513 713-8139
1212 Forest Run Dr Batavia (45103) *(G-1178)*
Eaton Aerospace LLC (HQ)....216 523-5000
1000 Eaton Blvd Cleveland (44122) *(G-5243)*
Eaton Aerospace LLC 216 523-5000
2000 Apollo Dr Cleveland (44142) *(G-5244)*
Eaton Comprsr Fabrication Inc....877 283-7614
1000 Cass Dr Englewood (45315) *(G-9518)*
Eaton Corporation (HQ) 216 523-5000
1000 Eaton Blvd Cleveland (44122) *(G-5245)*
Eaton Corporation 440 523-5000
1000 Eaton Blvd Beachwood (44122) *(G-1267)*
Eaton Corporation 419 238-1190
1225 W Main St Van Wert (45891) *(G-19253)*
Eaton Corporation 216 416-2500
2000 Apollo Dr Cleveland (44142) *(G-5246)*
Eaton Corporation....330 274-0743
115 Lena Dr Aurora (44202) *(G-916)*
Eaton Corporation 216 281-2211
9919 Clinton Rd Cleveland (44144) *(G-5247)*
Eaton Corporation 888 328-6677
6055 Rckside Woods Blvd N Cleveland (44131) *(G-5248)*
Eaton Corporation....440 826-1115
1000 W Bagley Rd Berea (44017) *(G-1613)*
Eaton Corporation 216 523-5000
1000 Eaton Blvd Beachwood (44122) *(G-1268)*
Eaton Corporation 216 920-2000
333 Babbitt Rd Ste 100 Cleveland (44123) *(G-5249)*
Eaton Corporation....330 562-9111
115 Lena Dr Aurora (44202) *(G-917)*
Eaton Corporation....440 826-1115
6055 Rckside Woods Blvd N Cleveland (44131) *(G-5250)*
Eaton Corporation 440 748-2236
12043 Avon Belden Rd Grafton (44044) *(G-10424)*
Eaton Electric Holdings LLC (HQ) 440 523-5000
1000 Eaton Blvd Cleveland (44122) *(G-5251)*
Eaton Electrical Inc 216 433-0616
1000 Eaton Blvd Beachwood (44122) *(G-1269)*
Eaton Fabricating Company Inc....440 926-3121
1009 Mcalpin Ct Grafton (44044) *(G-10425)*
Eaton Global Hose, Cleveland *Also called Eaton-Aeroquip Llc (G-5254)*
Eaton Global Hose, Van Wert *Also called Eaton-Aeroquip Llc (G-19255)*
Eaton Hydraulics LLC 419 232-7777
1225 W Main St Van Wert (45891) *(G-19254)*
Eaton Industrial Corporation (HQ) 216 692-5456
23555 Euclid Ave Cleveland (44117) *(G-5252)*
Eaton Leasing Corporation (HQ)....216 382-2292
1000 Eaton Blvd Beachwood (44122) *(G-1270)*
Eaton Township, Grafton *Also called Eaton Corporation (G-10424)*
Eaton Usev Holding Company (HQ) 216 523-5000
1111 Suprr Eatn Ctr 173 Cleveland (44114) *(G-5253)*
Eaton-Aeroquip Inc....419 891-7775
1660 Indian Wood Cir Maumee (43537) *(G-13258)*
Eaton-Aeroquip Llc (HQ)....216 523-5000
1000 Eaton Blvd Cleveland (44122) *(G-5254)*
Eaton-Aeroquip Llc....419 238-1190
1225 W Main St Van Wert (45891) *(G-19255)*
Ebel Tape & Label, Cincinnati *Also called Ebel-Binder Printing Co (G-3688)*
Ebel-Binder Printing Co....513 471-1067
1630 Dalton Ave 1 Cincinnati (45214) *(G-3688)*
Ebisyn Medical Inc....609 759-1101
6474 Weston Cir W Dublin (43016) *(G-9071)*
Ebner Furnaces Inc 330 335-2311
224 Quadral Dr Wadsworth (44281) *(G-19404)*
Ebnerfab, Wadsworth *Also called Ebner Furnaces Inc (G-19404)*
Ebo Group Inc (PA)....330 239-4933
1441 Wolf Creek Trl Sharon Center (44274) *(G-17105)*
Ebsco Industries Inc 513 398-2149
1111 Western Row Rd Mason (45040) *(G-13012)*
Ecc Company, Groveport *Also called Lomar Enterprises Inc (G-10633)*
Eccles Saw & Tool, Cincinnati *Also called D & M Saw & Tool Inc (G-3630)*
Echo Drilling Inc (PA)....740 498-8560
11 Crestview Mnr Newcomerstown (43832) *(G-15112)*
Echo Drilling Inc 740 254-4127
367 Echo Rd Se Gnadenhutten (44629) *(G-10406)*
Echo EMR Inc....937 322-4972
2755 Columbus Rd Springfield (45503) *(G-17550)*
Echo Environmental Waverly LLC 740 286-2810
479 Indl Pk Dr Waverly (45690) *(G-19708)*
Echo Mobile Solutions LLC 614 282-3756
108 Leasure Dr Pickerington (43147) *(G-16191)*
Echographics Inc....440 846-2330
9454 Grist Mill Dr North Ridgeville (44039) *(G-15371)*
Eci....419 483-2738
8802 Portland Rd Castalia (44824) *(G-2974)*
Ecil Met TEC, Avon Lake *Also called Reliacheck Manufacturing Inc (G-1048)*
Eckart Aluminum, Painesville *Also called Eckart America Corporation (G-15876)*
Eckart America, Painesville *Also called Obron Atlantic Corporation (G-15905)*
Eckart America Corporation (HQ) 440 954-7600
830 E Erie St Painesville (44077) *(G-15876)*
Eckel Industries Inc....978 772-0480
10021 Commerce Park Dr West Chester (45246) *(G-19999)*
Eclipse Blind Systems Inc 330 296-0112
7154 State Route 88 Ravenna (44266) *(G-16528)*
Eclipse Resources - Ohio LLC 740 452-4503
4900 Boggs Rd Zanesville (43701) *(G-21306)*
Ecm Biofilms Inc....440 350-1400
1 Victoria Pl Ste 304 Painesville (44077) *(G-15877)*
Eco Chem Alternative Fuels LLC 614 764-3835
565 Metro Pl S Ste 300 Dublin (43017) *(G-9072)*
Eco Fuel Solution LLC 440 282-8592
779 Sunrise Dr Amherst (44001) *(G-598)*
Eco Mechanical LLC....440 610-9253
47559 Hughes Rd Wellington (44090) *(G-19741)*
Eco Waste Solutions USA, Elyria *Also called Enercon Systems Inc (G-9419)*
Eco-Flo Products Inc (PA) 877 326-3561
1899 Cottage St Ashland (44805) *(G-730)*
Eco-Groupe Inc (PA)....937 898-2603
6161 Ventnor Ave Dayton (45414) *(G-8318)*
Eco-Print Solutions LLC 513 731-3106
6893 High Meadows Dr Cincinnati (45230) *(G-3689)*
Ecolab Inc....513 932-0830
726 E Main St Ste F Lebanon (45036) *(G-11796)*
Ecologic Fdsrvice Slutions LLC....419 467-8758
3901 Hill Ave Toledo (43607) *(G-18449)*
Econ-O-Machine Products Inc 937 882-6307
160 E Main St Donnelsville (45319) *(G-8961)*
Econo Products Inc....330 923-4101
101 Ascot Pkwy Cuyahoga Falls (44223) *(G-7989)*
Economy Flame Hardening Inc....216 431-9333
896 E 70th St Cleveland (44103) *(G-5255)*
Economy Forms, Columbus *Also called Efco Corp (G-7048)*
Economy Straightening Service 216 432-4410
896 E 70th St Cleveland (44103) *(G-5256)*
Ecoponics Group LLC....330 819-1233
964 Kevin Dr Kent (44240) *(G-11453)*
Ecotec Ltd LLC 937 606-2793
150 Marybill Dr S Troy (45373) *(G-18821)*
Ecowise LLC....216 692-3700
17000 Saint Clair Ave Cleveland (44110) *(G-5257)*
Ecp, Akron *Also called Enzyme Catalyzed Polymers LLC (G-170)*
Ecp Corporation 440 934-0444
1305 Chester Indus Pkwy Avon (44011) *(G-994)*
Ecu Corporation (PA) 513 898-9294
7209 E Kemper Rd Cincinnati (45249) *(G-3690)*
Ed Thomas 937 325-4300
819 Cedar St Springfield (45504) *(G-17551)*
Edac Composites, Cincinnati *Also called Meggitt (erlanger) LLC (G-4080)*
Edco Inc....419 726-1595
5244 Enterprise Blvd # 5 Toledo (43612) *(G-18450)*
Edco Producing....419 947-2515
869 Meadow Dr Mount Gilead (43338) *(G-14558)*
Edco Tool & Die, Toledo *Also called Edco Inc (G-18450)*
Edelmann Provision Company....513 881-5800
10000 Martins Way Harrison (45030) *(G-10776)*
Eden Cryogenics LLC 614 873-3949
8475 Rausch Dr Plain City (43064) *(G-16339)*
Edge Adhesives-Oh, Grove City *Also called Rubex Inc (G-10590)*
Edge Makers, Columbus *Also called Dan Wilzynski (G-7010)*
Edge Plastics Inc (PA)....419 522-6696
449 Newman St Mansfield (44902) *(G-12598)*
Edge-Rite Tools Inc 216 642-0966
7700 Exchange St Cleveland (44125) *(G-5258)*
Edgerton Forge Inc (HQ)....419 298-2333
257 E Morrison St Edgerton (43517) *(G-9327)*
Edgewater Canvas Co, Toledo *Also called Allen Zahradnik Inc (G-18328)*
Edgewell Per Care Brands LLC....937 228-0105
973 S Perry St Dayton (45402) *(G-8319)*
Edgewell Per Care Brands LLC....440 835-7500
25225 Detroit Rd Westlake (44145) *(G-20266)*
Edgewell Per Care Brands LLC....330 527-2191
10545 Freedom St Garrettsville (44231) *(G-10320)*
Edgewell Per Care Brands LLC....440 572-1336
17120 Hawks Lookout Ln Cleveland (44136) *(G-5259)*
Edgewell Personal Care LLC....937 492-1057
1810 Progress Way Sidney (45365) *(G-17183)*

ALPHABETIC

(PA)=Parent Co (HQ)=Headquarters (DH)=Div Headquarters

Edible Arrangement, Twinsburg *Also called Kriss Kreations* *(G-18968)*
Edible Arrangements, Dayton *Also called PA & Jjs Fruity Smiles Inc* *(G-8560)*
Edict Systems Inc 937 429-4288
  2434 Esquire Dr Beavercreek (45431) *(G-1334)*
Edinburg Fixture & Machine 330 947-1700
  3101 State Route 14 Rootstown (44272) *(G-16721)*
Edison Solar Inc 419 499-0000
  3809 State Route 113 E Milan (44846) *(G-14111)*
Edjean Technical Services Inc 440 647-3300
  246 Us Highway 224 Ste A Sullivan (44880) *(G-18054)*
Edjetech Services, Sullivan *Also called Edjean Technical Services Inc* *(G-18054)*
Edmar Chemical Company 440 247-9560
  539 Washington St Chagrin Falls (44022) *(G-3058)*
Edmonds Elevator Company 216 781-9135
  6777 Sidley Rd Thompson (44086) *(G-18188)*
Edsal Sandusky Corporation 419 626-5465
  117 E Washington Row Sandusky (44870) *(G-16960)*
Educational Electronics Inc 234 301-9077
  101 Lakeview Dr Apt 28 Millersburg (44654) *(G-14213)*
Educational Equipment, Kent *Also called Michael Kaufman Companies Inc* *(G-11490)*
Educational Equipment, Kent *Also called Michael Kaufman Companies Inc* *(G-11491)*
Educational Publisher Inc 614 485-0721
  1091 W 1st Ave Columbus (43212) *(G-7046)*
Edw C Levy Co. 330 484-6328
  3715 Whipple Ave Sw Canton (44706) *(G-2695)*
Edw C Levy Co. 419 822-8286
  6565 County Road 9 Delta (43515) *(G-8931)*
Edward Keiter & Sons 937 382-3249
  1235 Stone Rd Wilmington (45177) *(G-20664)*
Edward Orton Jr Crmic Fndation 614 895-2663
  6991 S Old 3c Hwy Westerville (43082) *(G-20148)*
Edward S Eveland 937 233-6568
  6175 Falkland Dr Dayton (45424) *(G-8320)*
Edward W Daniel LLC 440 647-1960
  46950 State Route 18 S Wellington (44090) *(G-19742)*
Edwards Auger Mining Inc 330 339-7318
  1010 Hummel Valley Rd Sw New Philadelphia (44663) *(G-14896)*
Edwards Culvert Co, Fredericktown *Also called Edwards Sheet Metal Works Inc* *(G-10101)*
Edwards Electrical & Mech 614 485-2003
  685 Grandview Ave Columbus (43215) *(G-7047)*
Edwards Machine Service Inc 937 295-2929
  8800 State Route 66 Fort Loramie (45845) *(G-9929)*
Edwards Sheet Metal Works Inc 740 694-0010
  10439 Sparta Rd Fredericktown (43019) *(G-10101)*
Edwards Vacuum LLC 440 248-4453
  7905 Cochran Rd Ste 100 Solon (44139) *(G-17284)*
Edzplace 216 289-4834
  400 E 255th St Euclid (44132) *(G-9577)*
Eei Acquisition Corp 440 564-5484
  10975 Kinsman Rd Newbury (44065) *(G-15089)*
Effective Air, Bedford *Also called Anson Co* *(G-1397)*
Efficient Machine Pdts Corp 440 268-0205
  12133 Alameda Dr Strongsville (44149) *(G-17915)*
Efg Holdings Inc (PA) 812 717-2544
  10217 Brecksville Rd Brecksville (44141) *(G-2044)*
Eg Enterprise Services Inc 216 431-3300
  5000 Euclid Ave Ste 100 Cleveland (44103) *(G-5260)*
Eg Industries, Columbus *Also called Ernie Green Industries Inc* *(G-7064)*
Eg Industries, Circleville *Also called Florida Production Engrg Inc* *(G-4629)*
Egc Enterprises Inc 440 285-5835
  140 Parker Ct Chardon (44024) *(G-3151)*
Eger Products Inc (PA) 513 753-4200
  1132 Ferris Rd Amelia (45102) *(G-575)*
Eger Products Inc 513 735-1400
  4226 Grissom Dr Batavia (45103) *(G-1179)*
Egr Products Company Inc (PA) 330 833-6554
  55 Eckard Rd Dalton (44618) *(G-8068)*
Egypt Structural Steel Proc 419 628-2375
  480 Osterloh Rd Minster (45865) *(G-14352)*
Eia, Cleveland *Also called Everything In America* *(G-5310)*
Eicom Corporation 937 294-5692
  3249 Dryden Rd Moraine (45439) *(G-14483)*
Eighth Floor Promotions 419 586-6433
  1 Visions Pkwy Celina (45822) *(G-2994)*
Eighty Six Inc 800 760-0722
  8823 Salon Cir Huber Heights (45424) *(G-11145)*
Einstruction Corp 940 565-0004
  255 W Federal St Youngstown (44503) *(G-21074)*
Einstruction Corporation (HQ) 330 746-3015
  255 W Federal St Youngstown (44503) *(G-21075)*
Eisenhauer Manufacturing Co. 419 238-0081
  409 Center St Van Wert (45891) *(G-19256)*
Ej Usa Inc 216 692-3001
  4160 Glenridge Rd Cleveland (44121) *(G-5261)*

Ej Usa Inc 330 782-3900
  4150 Simon Rd Youngstown (44512) *(G-21076)*
Ej Usa Inc 614 871-2436
  1855 Feddern Ave Grove City (43123) *(G-10556)*
El Nuevo Naranjo 614 863-4212
  6142 Glenworth Ct Galloway (43119) *(G-10312)*
Ela Holding Corporation 513 200-1374
  5403 Haft Rd Cincinnati (45247) *(G-3691)*
Elaire Corporation 419 843-2192
  7944 W Central Ave Ste 10 Toledo (43617) *(G-18451)*
Elan Designs Inc 614 985-5600
  10 E Schrock Rd 110 Westerville (43081) *(G-20212)*
Elano Div, Dayton *Also called Unison Industries LLC* *(G-8122)*
Elano Div, Beavercreek *Also called Unison Industries LLC* *(G-1363)*
Elano Machine Operations, Alpha *Also called Unison Industries LLC* *(G-555)*
Elastance Imaging LLC 614 579-9520
  226 E Beechwold Blvd Columbus (43214) *(G-7049)*
Elaston Company 330 863-2865
  448 E Mohawk Dr Malvern (44644) *(G-12543)*
Elastostar Rubber Corp 614 841-4400
  7030 Huntley Rd Ste B Columbus (43229) *(G-7050)*
Elations Company 513 483-3300
  10300 Alliance Rd Ste 500 Blue Ash (45242) *(G-1782)*
Elbern Publications 614 235-2643
  3120 Elbern Ave Columbus (43209) *(G-7051)*
Elbex Corporation 330 673-3233
  300 Martinel Dr Kent (44240) *(G-11454)*
Elco Corporation 440 997-6131
  1100 State Rd Ashtabula (44004) *(G-805)*
Elco Corporation (HQ) 800 321-0467
  1000 Belt Line Ave Cleveland (44109) *(G-5262)*
Elcor Inc 440 365-5941
  640 Sugar Ln Elyria (44035) *(G-9411)*
Elden Draperies of Toledo Inc 419 535-1909
  1845 N Reynolds Rd Toledo (43615) *(G-18452)*
Eldorado National Kansas Inc 937 596-6849
  419 W Pike St Jackson Center (45334) *(G-11340)*
Electr-Gnral Plas Corp Clumbus 614 871-2915
  6200 Enterprise Pkwy Grove City (43123) *(G-10557)*
Electra - Cord Inc 330 832-8124
  1320 Sanders Ave Sw Massillon (44647) *(G-13129)*
Electra Sound Inc (PA) 216 433-9600
  5260 Commerce Pkwy W Parma (44130) *(G-15957)*
Electra Tarp Inc 330 477-7168
  2900 Perry Dr Sw Canton (44706) *(G-2696)*
Electraform Industries Div, Vandalia *Also called Wentworth Mold Inc Electra* *(G-19317)*
Electrasound TV & Appl Svc, Parma *Also called Electra Sound Inc* *(G-15957)*
Electric Cord Sets Inc (PA) 216 261-1000
  4700 Manufacturing Ave Cleveland (44135) *(G-5263)*
Electric Ctrl & Mtr Repr Svc 216 881-3143
  6717 Saint Clair Ave Cleveland (44103) *(G-5264)*
Electric Eel Mfg Co Inc 937 323-4644
  501 W Leffel Ln Springfield (45506) *(G-17552)*
Electric Motor Service, Piqua *Also called Bornhorst Motor Service Inc* *(G-16253)*
Electric Motor Svc of Athens 740 592-1682
  6 E 4th St The Plains (45780) *(G-18186)*
Electric Service Co Inc 513 271-6387
  5331 Hetzell St Cincinnati (45227) *(G-3692)*
Electric Speed Indicator Co 216 251-2540
  12234 Triskett Rd Cleveland (44111) *(G-5265)*
Electrical Control Design Inc 419 443-9290
  25571 Fort Meigs Rd Ste D Perrysburg (43551) *(G-16088)*
Electrical Control Systems 937 859-7136
  3731 W Alex Bell Rd Dayton (45449) *(G-8321)*
Electrical Machinery & Repair, Green Springs *Also called James W Cunningham* *(G-10471)*
Electrimotion Inc 740 362-0251
  1484 Dale Ford Rd Delaware (43015) *(G-8840)*
Electripack Inc 937 433-2602
  2064 Byers Rd Miamisburg (45342) *(G-13804)*
Electrnic Dsign For Indust Inc 740 401-4000
  100 Ayers Blvd Belpre (45714) *(G-1586)*
Electro Controls Inc 866 497-1717
  1625 Ferguson Ct Sidney (45365) *(G-17184)*
Electro Polish Company Inc 937 222-3611
  332 Vermont Ave Dayton (45404) *(G-8322)*
Electro Prime Assembly Inc 419 476-0100
  63 Dixie Hwy Ste 7 Rossford (43460) *(G-16738)*
Electro Prime Group LLC (PA) 419 476-0100
  4510 Lint Ave Ste B Toledo (43612) *(G-18453)*
Electro Prime Group LLC 419 666-5000
  63 Dixie Hwy Ste 7 Rossford (43460) *(G-16739)*
Electro-Cap International Inc 937 456-6099
  1011 W Lexington Rd Eaton (45320) *(G-9305)*
Electro-Line Inc 937 461-5683
  118 S Terry St Dayton (45403) *(G-8323)*
Electro-Magwave Inc 216 453-1160
  6111 Carey Dr Ste 1 Cleveland (44125) *(G-5266)*
Electro-Mechanical Mfg Co Inc 330 864-0717
  1351 S Clvlnd Mhlln Rd Ste 6 Akron (44321) *(G-161)*

Electro-Metallics Co 513 423-8091
   3004 Lefferson Rd Middletown (45044) *(G-14039)*

Electro-Plating & Fabricating, Cleveland *Also called Roberts Demand No 3 Corp* *(G-6121)*

ELECTROBURR, Wellington *Also called Rochester Manufacturing Inc* *(G-19753)*

Electrocoat, Medina *Also called Office Magic Inc* *(G-13452)*

Electrocraft Arkansas Inc 501 268-4203
   250 Mccormick Rd Gallipolis (45631) *(G-10294)*

Electrocraft Ohio Inc 740 441-6200
   250 Mccormick Rd Gallipolis (45631) *(G-10295)*

Electrodata Inc 216 663-3333
   23400 Aurora Rd Ste E Bedford Heights (44146) *(G-1483)*

Electroduct LLC 330 220-9300
   1126 Industrial Pkwy N Brunswick (44212) *(G-2223)*

Electrodynamics Inc 847 259-0740
   3975 Mcmann Rd Cincinnati (45245) *(G-3300)*

Electrodyne Company Inc 513 732-2822
   4188 Taylor Rd Batavia (45103) *(G-1180)*

Electrofuel Industries Inc 937 783-2846
   77 N Depot Rd Batavia (45103) *(G-1181)*

Electrolizing Corporation Ohio (PA) 216 451-3153
   1325 E 152nd St Cleveland (44112) *(G-5267)*

Electrolizing Corporation Ohio 216 451-8653
   1655 Collamer Ave Cleveland (44110) *(G-5268)*

Electrolux Professional Inc (HQ) 216 898-1800
   20445 Emerald Pkwy Cleveland (44135) *(G-5269)*

Electromech Technologies LLC (HQ) 216 706-2960
   1301 E 9th St Ste 3000 Cleveland (44114) *(G-5270)*

Electromechanical North Amer, Milford *Also called Parker-Hannifin Corporation* *(G-14166)*

Electromechanical North Amer, Wadsworth *Also called Parker-Hannifin Corporation* *(G-19427)*

Electromotive Inc (PA) 330 688-6494
   4880 Hudson Dr Stow (44224) *(G-17746)*

Electronic Concepts Engrg Inc 419 861-9000
   1465 Timber Wolf Dr Holland (43528) *(G-11059)*

Electronic Services, Fairborn *Also called Voltage Regulator Sales & Svcs* *(G-9634)*

Electronic Solutions Inc 419 666-4700
   28271 Cedar Park Blvd Perrysburg (43551) *(G-16089)*

Electronic Vision Inc 740 592-2433
   5 Depot St Athens (45701) *(G-864)*

Electrovations Inc 330 274-3558
   350 Harris Dr Aurora (44202) *(G-918)*

Electrowarmth Products LLC 740 599-7222
   513 Market St Danville (43014) *(G-8088)*

Eleet Cryogenics Inc 330 874-4009
   11132 Industrial Pkwy Nw Bolivar (44612) *(G-1933)*

Elegant Embroidery Llc 440 878-0904
   11053 Prospect Rd Strongsville (44149) *(G-17916)*

Elektro Kopy, Columbus *Also called Instant Impressions Inc* *(G-7191)*

Elektron N Magnesium Amer Inc 419 424-8878
   115 Stanford Pkwy Findlay (45840) *(G-9819)*

Element Machinery LLC 855 447-7648
   4801 Bennett Rd Toledo (43612) *(G-18454)*

Element14 US Holdings Inc (HQ) 330 523-4280
   4180 Highlander Pkwy Richfield (44286) *(G-16622)*

Elevator Brewing Company LLC 614 679-2337
   165 N 4th St Columbus (43215) *(G-7052)*

Elevator Cncepts By Wurtec LLC 734 246-4700
   6200 Brent Dr Toledo (43611) *(G-18455)*

Elf Atochem NA OH 740 363-1351
   421 London Rd Delaware (43015) *(G-8841)*

Elg Inc 216 518-0476
   14600 Industrial Ave S Maple Heights (44137) *(G-12734)*

Elgin Fastener Group LLC 440 717-7650
   10147 Brecksville Rd Brecksville (44141) *(G-2045)*

Elgin Fastener Group LLC (HQ) 812 717-2544
   10217 Brecksville Rd Brecksville (44141) *(G-2046)*

Elgin Fastener Group LLC 216 481-4400
   1491 Chardon Rd Cleveland (44117) *(G-5271)*

Eliokem Inc 330 734-1100
   175 Ghent Rd Fairlawn (44333) *(G-9749)*

Eliokem Materials and Concepts, Fairlawn *Also called Eliokem Inc* *(G-9749)*

Elite Biomedical Solutions LLC 513 207-0602
   756 Old State Route 74 C Cincinnati (45245) *(G-3301)*

Elite Enclosure Company, Sidney *Also called Mk Trempe Corporation* *(G-17204)*

Elite Enclosure Company LLC 937 492-3548
   2349 Industrial Dr Sidney (45365) *(G-17185)*

Elite Fire Services LLC 614 586-4255
   1520 Harmon Ave Ste 667 Columbus (43223) *(G-7053)*

Elite Mfg Solutions LLC 330 612-7434
   7792 Capital Blvd Ste 6 Macedonia (44056) *(G-12447)*

Elite Mill Service & Cnstr 513 422-4234
   5757 Cottonrun Rd Trenton (45067) *(G-18790)*

Elite Property Group LLC 216 316-8222
   3281 W 86th St Cleveland (44102) *(G-5272)*

Elite Ship Packaging System 216 502-6798
   4535 Big Met Pl Cleveland (44135) *(G-5273)*

Elite Tactical Supply, Wadsworth *Also called 762mm Firearms LLC* *(G-19384)*

Elizabeths Closet 513 646-5025
   8847 Dover Dr Maineville (45039) *(G-12522)*

Elken Co 513 459-7207
   2905 Afton Valley Ct Maineville (45039) *(G-12523)*

Elkham Plastics, Ohio City *Also called Elkhart Plastics* *(G-15661)*

Elkhart Plastics 419 965-2103
   106 S Ball Rd Ohio City (45874) *(G-15661)*

Elkhead Gas & Oil Co 740 763-3966
   12163 Marne Rd Newark (43055) *(G-15002)*

Ellen L Ellsworth 440 352-8031
   9930 Johnnycake Ridge Rd 4b Mentor (44060) *(G-13571)*

Ellet Neon Sales & Service Inc 330 628-9907
   3041 E Waterloo Rd Akron (44312) *(G-162)*

Ellinger Monument Inc 740 385-3687
   27841 Fairview Cmtry Rd Rockbridge (43149) *(G-16688)*

Elliott Machine Works Inc 419 468-4709
   1351 Freese Works Pl Galion (44833) *(G-10267)*

Elliott Mfg Co 937 833-4430
   407 Albert Rd Brookville (45309) *(G-2182)*

Elliott Oren Products Inc 419 298-0015
   113 Industrial Dr Edgerton (43517) *(G-9328)*

Elliott Oren Products Inc (PA) 419 298-2306
   128 W Vine St Edgerton (43517) *(G-9329)*

Elliott Tool Technologies Ltd (PA) 937 253-6133
   1760 Tuttle Ave Dayton (45403) *(G-8324)*

Ellis & Watts Global Inds Inc 513 752-9000
   4400 Glen Willow Lake Ln Batavia (45103) *(G-1182)*

Ellis & Watts Intl LLC 513 752-9000
   4400 Glen Willow Lake Ln Batavia (45103) *(G-1183)*

Ellis Laundry & Linen Supply 330 339-4941
   213 8th Street Ext Sw New Philadelphia (44663) *(G-14897)*

Ellison Group Inc (PA) 513 770-4900
   8118 Corp Way Ste 201 Mason (45040) *(G-13013)*

Ellison Srfc Tech - Mexico LLC 513 770-4900
   8093 Columbia Rd Ste 201 Mason (45040) *(G-13014)*

Ellison Surface Tech - W LLC 513 770-4900
   8093 Columbia Rd Ste 201 Mason (45040) *(G-13015)*

Ellison Surface Tech Inc (HQ) 513 770-4922
   8118 Corp Way Ste 201 Mason (45040) *(G-13016)*

Ellison Surfc Technologies-Tn, Mason *Also called Tennessee Coatings Inc* *(G-13096)*

Ellison Technologies Inc 513 874-2736
   5333 Muhlhauser Rd Hamilton (45011) *(G-10687)*

Elloras Cave Publishing Inc 330 253-3521
   1056 Home Ave Akron (44310) *(G-163)*

Ellwood Engineered Castings Co 330 568-3000
   7158 Hubbard Masury Rd Hubbard (44425) *(G-11130)*

Ellwood Group Inc 216 862-6341
   777 E 79th St Cleveland (44103) *(G-5274)*

Elmore Mfg Co, Elmore *Also called Calvin J Magsig* *(G-9361)*

Elpro Services Inc 740 568-9900
   210 Mill Creek Rd Marietta (45750) *(G-12783)*

Elra Industries Inc 513 868-6228
   550 S Erie Hwy Hamilton (45011) *(G-10688)*

Elsaan Energy LLC 740 294-9399
   26100 Township Road 52 Walhonding (43843) *(G-19469)*

Elsass Fabricating Ltd 937 394-7169
   11385 Amsterdam Rd Anna (45302) *(G-622)*

Elsevier Inc 513 942-5070
   8080 Beckett Center Dr # 225 West Chester (45069) *(G-19855)*

Elsons International, Cleveland *Also called International Cont Systems LLC* *(G-5580)*

Elster Perfection Corporation (HQ) 440 428-1171
   436 N Eagle St Geneva (44041) *(G-10346)*

Eltool Corporation 513 723-1772
   1400 Park Ave E Mansfield (44905) *(G-12599)*

Elwer Fence, Lima *Also called Elwers Fence* *(G-12009)*

Elwers Fence 419 221-2511
   367 Fraunfelter Rd N Lima (45807) *(G-12009)*

Elwood Crankshaft Group, Cleveland *Also called Ellwood Group Inc* *(G-5274)*

Ely Road Reel Company Ltd 330 683-1818
   9081 Ely Rd Apple Creek (44606) *(G-637)*

Elynx Holdings LLC (HQ) 513 612-5969
   11500 Northlake Dr # 200 Cincinnati (45249) *(G-3693)*

Elyria Concrete Step Company, Elyria *Also called E C S Corp* *(G-9409)*

Elyria Copy Center Inc 440 323-4145
   325 Lake Ave Elyria (44035) *(G-9412)*

Elyria Manufacturing Corp (PA) 440 365-4171
   145 Northrup St Elyria (44035) *(G-9413)*

Elyria Mtal Spnning Fbrication 440 323-8068
   7511 W River Rd S Elyria (44035) *(G-9414)*

Elyria Pattern Co Inc 440 323-1526
   6785 W River Rd S Elyria (44035) *(G-9415)*

Elyria Plastic Products, Elyria *Also called P P E Inc* *(G-9473)*

Elyria Plating Corporation 440 365-8300
   118 Olive St Elyria (44035) *(G-9416)*

Elyria Spring & Specialty Inc 440 323-5502
   123 Elbe St Elyria (44035) *(G-9417)*

Elytus Ltd 614 824-4985
   40 E Columbus St Columbus (43206) *(G-7054)*

Em Innovations Inc 614 853-1504
   6106 Bausch Rd Galloway (43119) *(G-10313)*

EMB Designs, Coldwater *Also called K Ventures Inc* *(G-6566)*

Embedded Planet Inc 216 245-4180
  4760 Richmond Rd Ste 400 Warrensville Heights (44128) *(G-19632)*

Embedee LLC 419 678-7007
  625 Cron St Coldwater (45828) *(G-6558)*

Embroid ME 216 459-9250
  4311 Ridge Rd Cleveland (44144) *(G-5275)*

Embroidered ID Inc 440 974-8113
  7845 Hidden Hollow Dr Mentor (44060) *(G-13572)*

Embroidered Identity, Mentor *Also called Embroidered ID Inc (G-13572)*

Embroidery Design Group LLC 614 798-8152
  2564 Billingsley Rd Columbus (43235) *(G-7055)*

Embroidme 330 484-8484
  3611 Cleveland Ave S Canton (44707) *(G-2697)*

Embroidme Co 614 933-9194
  950 Taylor Station Rd U Columbus (43230) *(G-7056)*

EMC Corporation 614 865-4200
  9200 Worthington Rd # 200 Westerville (43082) *(G-20149)*

EMC Corporation 513 794-9624
  9825 Kenwood Rd Ste 300 Blue Ash (45242) *(G-1783)*

EMC Corporation 216 606-2000
  6480 Rcksde Wds Blvd S # 330 Independence (44131) *(G-11254)*

EMC Precision Machining, Elyria *Also called Elyria Manufacturing Corp (G-9413)*

EMC Precision Machining II LLC (PA) 440 365-4171
  145 Northrup St Elyria (44035) *(G-9418)*

Emc2, Westerville *Also called EMC Corporation (G-20149)*

Emc2, Independence *Also called EMC Corporation (G-11254)*

Emco Electric International 440 878-1199
  19449 Progress Dr Strongsville (44149) *(G-17917)*

EMD Millipore Corporation 513 631-0445
  2909 Highland Ave Norwood (45212) *(G-15572)*

Emega Technologies LLC 740 407-3712
  205 N 5th St Zanesville (43701) *(G-21307)*

Emerald Hilton Davis, Cincinnati *Also called Emerald Performance Mtls LLC (G-3695)*

Emerald Hilton Davis LLC 513 841-0057
  2235 Langdon Farm Rd Cincinnati (45237) *(G-3694)*

Emerald Performance Mtls LLC 513 841-4000
  2235 Langdon Farm Rd Cincinnati (45237) *(G-3695)*

Emerald Performance Mtls LLC (PA) 330 916-6700
  2020 Front St Ste 100 Cuyahoga Falls (44221) *(G-7990)*

Emerald Performance Mtls LLC 330 374-2418
  240 W Emerling Ave Akron (44301) *(G-164)*

Emerald Polymer Additives LLC (HQ) 330 374-2424
  240 W Emerling Ave Akron (44301) *(G-165)*

Emerald Specialties Group, Cincinnati *Also called Emerald Hilton Davis LLC (G-3694)*

Emerald Specialty Polymers LLC 330 374-2424
  240 W Emerling Ave Akron (44301) *(G-166)*

Emerge Health Solutions 513 204-5600
  2925 Vernon Pl Ste 100 Cincinnati (45219) *(G-3696)*

Emergency Products & RES Inc 330 673-5003
  890 W Main St Kent (44240) *(G-11455)*

Emerson Climate Tech Inc (HQ) 937 498-3011
  1675 Campbell Rd Sidney (45365) *(G-17186)*

Emerson Climate Tech Inc 937 498-3011
  756 Brooklyn Ave Sidney (45365) *(G-17187)*

Emerson Climate Tech Inc 937 498-3587
  1351 N Vandemark Rd Sidney (45365) *(G-17188)*

Emerson Electric Co 513 631-6112
  6265 Wiehe Rd Cincinnati (45237) *(G-3697)*

Emerson Electric Co 513 731-2020
  6000 Fernview Ave Cincinnati (45212) *(G-3698)*

Emerson Electric Co. 440 288-1122
  1509 Iowa Ave Lorain (44052) *(G-12244)*

Emerson Electric Co 440 248-9400
  31100 Bainbridge Rd Solon (44139) *(G-17285)*

Emerson Electric Co 513 942-1118
  4400 Muhlhauser Rd West Chester (45011) *(G-19856)*

Emerson Network Power 740 833-8630
  975 Pittsburgh Dr Delaware (43015) *(G-8842)*

Emerson Network Power System 614 841-6309
  610 Executive Campus Dr Westerville (43082) *(G-20150)*

Emerson Process Management 419 529-4311
  2500 Park Ave W Ontario (44906) *(G-15687)*

Emery Oleochemicals LLC (HQ) 513 762-2500
  4900 Este Ave Cincinnati (45232) *(G-3699)*

Emh Inc (PA) 330 220-8600
  550 Crane Dr Valley City (44280) *(G-19203)*

Emhart Glass Manufacturing Inc 567 336-7733
  1899 N Wilkinson Way Perrysburg (43551) *(G-16090)*

Emhart Glass Manufacturing Inc 567 336-8784
  7401 Fremont Pike 6 Perrysburg (43551) *(G-16091)*

EMI Corp (PA) 937 596-5511
  801 W Pike St Jackson Center (45334) *(G-11341)*

Emitted Energy Inc 513 752-9999
  754 Cincinnati Batavia Pi Cincinnati (45245) *(G-3302)*

Emmco, Akron *Also called Electro-Mechanical Mfg Co Inc (G-161)*

Empire Bakery Commissary LLC 513 793-6241
  11243 Cornell Park Dr Blue Ash (45242) *(G-1784)*

Empire Brass Co 216 431-6565
  5000 Superior Ave Cleveland (44103) *(G-5276)*

Empire Die Casting Company, Macedonia *Also called American Light Metals LLC (G-12435)*

Empire Iron Mining Partnership (PA) 216 694-5700
  1100 Superior Ave E Fl 15 Cleveland (44114) *(G-5277)*

Empire Packing Company LP 513 942-5400
  113 Circle Freeway Dr West Chester (45246) *(G-20000)*

Empire Plastics, Newcomerstown *Also called Boltaron Inc (G-15109)*

Empire Plow Company Inc (HQ) 216 641-2290
  3140 E 65th St Cleveland (44127) *(G-5278)*

Empire Power Systems Co 440 796-4401
  6211 Shore Dr Madison (44057) *(G-12506)*

Empire Printing Inc 513 242-3900
  5877 Highland Ridge Dr Cincinnati (45232) *(G-3700)*

Empress Chili, Cincinnati *Also called Classic Recipe Chili Inc (G-3584)*

Empress Chili 513 312-9589
  9266 Hunters Creek Dr B Blue Ash (45242) *(G-1785)*

Empyracom Inc 330 744-5570
  6550 Seville Dr Canfield (44406) *(G-2553)*

Emrick Machine & Tool 937 692-5901
  211 S Sycamore St Arcanum (45304) *(G-656)*

Ems/Hooptech (PA) 513 829-7768
  9185 Le Saint Dr West Chester (45014) *(G-19857)*

Emt Inc 330 399-6939
  1201 Vine Ave Ne Ste 2 Warren (44483) *(G-19547)*

Emta Inc 440 734-6464
  28875 Lorain Rd North Olmsted (44070) *(G-15332)*

Emx Industries Inc 216 518-9888
  4564 Johnston Pkwy Cleveland (44128) *(G-5279)*

En-Hanced Products Inc 614 882-7400
  229 E Broadway Ave Westerville (43081) *(G-20213)*

Enclosure Suppliers LLC 513 782-3900
  12119 Champion Way Cincinnati (45241) *(G-3701)*

Encompass Automation & 419 873-0000
  622 Eckel Rd Perrysburg (43551) *(G-16092)*

Encon Inc (HQ) 937 898-2603
  6161 Ventnor Ave Dayton (45414) *(G-8325)*

Encon Inc 937 890-6239
  3435 Stop Eight Rd 8rd Vandalia (45377) *(G-19291)*

Encore Distributing Inc 513 948-1242
  8060 Reading Rd Ste 6 Cincinnati (45237) *(G-3702)*

Encore Industries Inc (PA) 419 626-8000
  319 Howard Dr Sandusky (44870) *(G-16961)*

Encore Plastics, Sandusky *Also called Encore Industries Inc (G-16961)*

Encore Plastics Corporation 740 432-1652
  725 Water St Cambridge (43725) *(G-2456)*

Encore Plastics Corporation (HQ) 419 626-8000
  319 Howard Dr Sandusky (44870) *(G-16962)*

Encore Precast LLC 513 726-5678
  416 W Ritter Seven Mile (45062) *(G-17065)*

END Separation LLC 419 438-0879
  12742 Road 191 Oakwood (45873) *(G-15616)*

Endodent Inc 626 359-5715
  235 Ascot Pkwy Cuyahoga Falls (44223) *(G-7991)*

Endoglobe, Oregon *Also called R-Med Inc (G-15714)*

Endura Plastics, Kirtland *Also called Stewart Acquisition LLC (G-11617)*

Endura Plastics Inc 440 951-4466
  7955 Euclid Chardon Rd Kirtland (44094) *(G-11613)*

Endurance Manufacturing Inc 330 628-2600
  213 Randolph Rd Mogadore (44260) *(G-14374)*

Enduro Rubber Company 330 296-9603
  685 S Chestnut St Ravenna (44266) *(G-16529)*

Enerchem Incorporated 513 745-0580
  8373 Squirrelridge Dr Cincinnati (45243) *(G-3703)*

Enerco Group Inc (PA) 216 916-3000
  4560 W 160th St Cleveland (44135) *(G-5280)*

Enerco Technical Products Inc 216 916-3000
  4560 W 160th St Cleveland (44135) *(G-5281)*

Enercon Systems Inc 305 213-3997
  300 Huron St Elyria (44035) *(G-9419)*

Enerfab Inc (PA) 513 641-0500
  4955 Spring Grove Ave Cincinnati (45232) *(G-3704)*

Enerfab Inc 513 771-2300
  11861 Mosteller Rd Cincinnati (45241) *(G-3705)*

Energizer Battery Mfg Inc 330 527-2191
  10545 Freedom St Garrettsville (44231) *(G-10321)*

Energizer Manufacturing Inc 440 835-7866
  25225 Detroit Rd Westlake (44145) *(G-20267)*

Energy Corportive, Coshocton *Also called Ngo Development Corporation (G-7901)*

Energy Developments Inc 440 774-6816
  43550 Oberlin Elyria Rd Oberlin (44074) *(G-15638)*

Energy Focus Inc (PA) 440 715-1300
  32000 Aurora Rd Ste B Solon (44139) *(G-17286)*

Energy Machine Inc 740 397-1155
  100 Commerce Dr Mount Vernon (43050) *(G-14621)*

Energy Manufacturing Ltd 419 355-9304
  1830 Old Oak Harbour Rd Fremont (43420) *(G-10143)*

Energy Products, Lorain *Also called Exochem Corporation (G-12246)*

Energy Resources of America In 330 953-1813
  6075 Silica Rd Ste B Youngstown (44515) *(G-21077)*

Energy Storage Technologies 937 312-0114
7610 Mcewen Rd Dayton (45459) *(G-8326)*

Energy Technologies Inc 419 522-4444
219 Park Ave E Mansfield (44902) *(G-12600)*

Energy Transfer, Minerva *Also called Machine Dynamics & Engrg Inc* *(G-14331)*

Enersys 513 737-2268
9436 Meridian Way West Chester (45069) *(G-19858)*

Enersys Delaware Inc 216 252-4242
12690 Elmwood Ave Cleveland (44111) *(G-5282)*

Engelhard Corp 440 322-3741
120 Pine St Elyria (44035) *(G-9420)*

Engels Machining LLC 419 485-1500
13299 State Route 107 Montpelier (43543) *(G-14445)*

Engine Machine Service Inc 330 505-1804
865 Summit Ave Unit 2 Niles (44446) *(G-15151)*

Engineered Air, Columbus *Also called Airtex Manufacturing Lllp* *(G-6705)*

Engineered Endeavors, Newbury *Also called Eei Acquisition Corp* *(G-15089)*

Engineered Films Division (HQ) 419 884-8150
230 Industrial Dr Lexington (44904) *(G-11950)*

Engineered Films Division 419 884-8150
215 Industrial Dr Mansfield (44904) *(G-12601)*

Engineered Marble Inc 614 308-0041
4064 Fisher Rd Columbus (43228) *(G-7057)*

Engineered Material Handling, Valley City *Also called Emh Inc* *(G-19203)*

Engineered MBL Solutions Inc 513 724-0247
4350 Batavia Rd Batavia (45103) *(G-1184)*

Engineered Metal Products 740 446-9211
2160 Eastern Ave Gallipolis (45631) *(G-10296)*

Engineered Mfg & Eqp Co 937 642-7776
11611 Industrial Pkwy Marysville (43040) *(G-12942)*

Engineered Mtls Systems Inc 740 362-4444
100 Innovation Ct Delaware (43015) *(G-8843)*

Engineered Plastics Corp 330 376-7700
420 Kenmore Blvd Akron (44301) *(G-167)*

Engineered Products, Twinsburg *Also called EPI of Cleveland Inc* *(G-18929)*

Engineered Profiles LLC 614 754-3700
2141 Fairwood Ave Columbus (43207) *(G-7058)*

Engineered Wire Products Inc (HQ) 419 294-3817
1200 N Warpole St Upper Sandusky (43351) *(G-19121)*

Engineering Coatings LLC 419 485-0077
1826 Magda Dr Montpelier (43543) *(G-14446)*

Engineering Dept, Troy *Also called Hobart Corporation* *(G-18840)*

Engineering Methods Inc 513 563-0400
9352 Main St Unit 2 Cincinnati (45242) *(G-3706)*

Engines Inc of Ohio 740 377-9874
101 Commerce Dr South Point (45680) *(G-17437)*

Enginetics, Huber Heights *Also called Mpe Aeroengines Inc* *(G-11150)*

Enginetics Aero Space, Huber Heights *Also called Enginetics Corporation* *(G-11146)*

Enginetics Corporation (HQ) 937 878-3800
7700 New Carlisle Pike Huber Heights (45424) *(G-11146)*

Enginred Plstic Components Inc 513 228-0298
315 S West St Lebanon (45036) *(G-11797)*

Engler Printing Co 419 332-2181
808 W State St Fremont (43420) *(G-10144)*

Engravers Gallery & Sign Co 330 830-1271
10 Lincoln Way E Massillon (44646) *(G-13130)*

Engstrom Manufacturing Inc 513 573-0010
4503b State Route 42 Mason (45040) *(G-13017)*

Enhanced Mfg Solutions LLC 440 476-1244
2890 Boston Mills Rd Brecksville (44141) *(G-2047)*

ENI USA R & M CO. INC., Medina *Also called Eni USA R & M Co Inc* *(G-13405)*

Eni USA R & M Co Inc 330 723-6457
740 S Progress Dr Medina (44256) *(G-13405)*

Enk Tenofour LLC 419 661-1465
6964 Mcnerney Dr Northwood (43619) *(G-15480)*

Enkon LLC 937 898-2603
6161 Ventnor Ave Dayton (45414) *(G-8327)*

Enlarging Arts Inc 330 434-3433
2280 Tinkham Rd Akron (44313) *(G-168)*

Enlyton Ltd 614 888-9220
1216 Kinnear Rd Columbus (43212) *(G-7059)*

Ennis Business Forms of Ohio, Coshocton *Also called Crabar/Gbf Inc* *(G-7887)*

Ennovea Medical LLC 855 997-2273
2030 Dividend Dr Columbus (43228) *(G-7060)*

Enpac LLC 440 975-0070
34355 Melinz Pkwy Eastlake (44095) *(G-9268)*

Enpress LLC 440 510-0108
34899 Curtis Blvd Eastlake (44095) *(G-9269)*

Enprotech Industrial Tech LLC (HQ) 216 883-3220
4259 E 49th St Cleveland (44125) *(G-5283)*

Enquirer Printing Co Inc 513 241-1956
7188 Main St Cincinnati (45244) *(G-3707)*

Enquirer Printing Company 513 241-1956
7188 Main St Cincinnati (45244) *(G-3708)*

Enquirer, The, Milford *Also called Gannett Stllite Info Ntwrk Inc* *(G-14143)*

Enrevo Pyro LLC 203 517-5002
6874 Strimbu Dr Brookfield (44403) *(G-2124)*

Ensign Product Company Inc 216 341-5911
3528 E 76th St Cleveland (44105) *(G-5284)*

Enso Vapors, Columbus *Also called Ev Liquids LLC* *(G-7069)*

Ent Physicians Inc (PA) 419 698-4505
1050 Isaac Streets Dr # 137 Oregon (43616) *(G-15708)*

Entec International Systems, Lakewood *Also called RAD-Con Inc* *(G-11678)*

Enterasys Networks Inc 330 245-0240
1093 Corsham Cir Akron (44312) *(G-169)*

Enterprise / Ameriseal Inc 937 284-3003
6800 S Charleston Rd South Charleston (45368) *(G-17425)*

Enterprise C N C Inc 440 354-3868
9280 Pineneedle Dr Mentor (44060) *(G-13573)*

Enterprise Machine Inc 513 541-4031
3640 Llewellyn Ave Cincinnati (45223) *(G-3709)*

Enterprise Plastics Inc 330 346-0496
1500 Enterprise Way Kent (44240) *(G-11456)*

Enterprise Tool & Die Company 216 351-1300
4940 Schaaf Ln Cleveland (44131) *(G-5285)*

Enterprise Welding & Fabg Inc 440 354-4128
6257 Heisley Rd Mentor (44060) *(G-13574)*

Entertainment Junction 513 326-1100
2721 E Sharon Rd Cincinnati (45241) *(G-3710)*

Enting Water Conditioning Inc (PA) 937 294-5100
3211 Dryden Rd Frnt Frnt Moraine (45439) *(G-14484)*

Entratech Systems LLC (PA) 419 433-7683
202 Fox Rd Sandusky (44870) *(G-16963)*

Entrochem Inc 614 946-7602
1245 Kinnear Rd Columbus (43212) *(G-7061)*

Entrotech Inc 614 946-7602
1245 Kinnear Rd Columbus (43212) *(G-7062)*

Envelope 1 Inc (PA) 330 482-3900
41969 State Route 344 Columbiana (44408) *(G-6615)*

Envelope Mart of Ohio Inc 440 365-8177
1540 Lowell St Elyria (44035) *(G-9421)*

Envirnmental Archtctral Signage, Findlay *Also called Bird Corporation* *(G-9795)*

Envirnmntal Prtctive Ctngs LLC 740 363-6180
5999 Houseman Rd Ostrander (43061) *(G-15786)*

Enviro Crest Services Inc 330 932-0345
16977 Park Way East Liverpool (43920) *(G-9214)*

Enviro Polymers & Chemicals 937 427-1315
3045 Rodenbeck Dr Ste D Beavercreek (45432) *(G-1336)*

Envirofab Inc 216 651-1767
7914 Lake Ave Cleveland (44102) *(G-5286)*

Environ International Cor 440 834-1460
13801 W Center St Burton (44021) *(G-2374)*

Environment Chemical Corp 330 453-5200
2167 Crestwick Dr Uniontown (44685) *(G-19083)*

Environmental Closure Systems 614 759-9186
536 Killin Ct Reynoldsburg (43068) *(G-16588)*

Environmental Growth Chambers, Chagrin Falls *Also called Integrated Development & Mfg* *(G-3060)*

Environmental Products Div, Sheffield Village *Also called Benko Products Inc* *(G-17121)*

Environmental Wall Systems 440 542-6600
77 Milford Dr Ste 283 Hudson (44236) *(G-11170)*

Environmental Water Engrg, Bowling Green *Also called J & K Wade Ltd* *(G-1992)*

Enviroscape EMC 419 278-2000
300 S Chestnut St Deshler (43516) *(G-8950)*

Envision Radio MII 216 831-3761
3733 Park East Dr Ste 222 Beachwood (44122) *(G-1271)*

Envoi Design Inc 513 651-4229
1332 Main St Frnt Cincinnati (45202) *(G-3711)*

Enzyme Catalyzed Polymers LLC 330 310-1072
2295 W Market St Ste D Akron (44313) *(G-170)*

Enzyme Industries of The U S A 740 929-4975
2090 James Pkwy Newark (43056) *(G-15003)*

Eoi Inc 740 201-3300
8377 C Gree Meado Dr N St Lewis Center (43035) *(G-11897)*

Eomg Harko Holdings LLC 216 781-0083
1500 Key Tower 127 Pub Sq Cleveland (44114) *(G-5287)*

Eos Technology Inc 216 281-2999
8525 Clinton Rd Cleveland (44144) *(G-5288)*

Ep Bollinger LLC 513 941-1101
2664 Saint Georges Ct Cincinnati (45233) *(G-3712)*

EP Ferris & Associates Inc 614 299-2999
880 King Ave Columbus (43212) *(G-7063)*

Ep Technologies LLC 234 208-8967
520 S Main St Ste 2455 Akron (44311) *(G-171)*

Epco, Germantown *Also called Thomas D Epperson* *(G-10374)*

Epco Extrusion Painting Co 330 781-6100
4605 Lake Park Rd Youngstown (44512) *(G-21078)*

Epcor Foundries, Cincinnati *Also called Seilkop Industries Inc* *(G-4398)*

Epd Enterprises Inc 216 961-1200
9921 Clinton Rd Cleveland (44144) *(G-5289)*

Epg Inc 330 995-5125
500 Lena Dr Aurora (44202) *(G-919)*

Epg Inc (HQ) 330 995-9725
1780 Miller Pkwy Streetsboro (44241) *(G-17852)*

Epi Global, Millbury *Also called Levison Enterprises LLC* *(G-14185)*

EPI of Cleveland Inc 330 468-2872
2224 E Enterprise Pkwy Twinsburg (44087) *(G-18929)*

Epic Steel, Cleveland *Also called E B P Inc* *(G-5230)*

A
L
P
H
A
B
E
T
I
C

Epic Technologies LLC 513 683-5455
4240 Irwin Simpson Rd Mason (45040) *(G-13018)*

Epix Tube Co Inc (PA) 937 529-4858
5800 Wolf Creek Pike Dayton (45426) *(G-8328)*

Epoxy Chemicals, Cleveland *Also called The Euclid Chemical Company (G-6309)*

Epoxy Systems Blstg Cating Inc 513 924-1800
5640 Morgan Rd Cleves (45002) *(G-6513)*

Epr, Kent *Also called Emergency Products & RES Inc (G-11455)*

Eprad Inc 419 666-3266
28271 Cedar Park Blvd # 1 Perrysburg (43551) *(G-16093)*

Eprintworksplus 513 731-3797
5846 Hamilton Ave Cincinnati (45224) *(G-3713)*

Epro Inc 419 426-5053
10890 E County Road 6 Bloomville (44818) *(G-1727)*

Eps Specialties Ltd Inc 513 489-3676
7875 School Rd 77 Cincinnati (45249) *(G-3714)*

Eps Wastewater LLC 859 689-4300
601 Brooklyn Ave Ste B Milford (45150) *(G-14139)*

Eq Technologies LLC 216 548-3684
11601 Wade Park Ave Cleveland (44106) *(G-5290)*

Eqm Technologies & Energy Inc (PA) 513 825-7500
1800 Carillion Blvd Cincinnati (45240) *(G-3715)*

Equinox Enterprises LLC 419 627-0022
1920 George St Sandusky (44870) *(G-16964)*

Equipment Concepts 937 291-9734
400 Linden Ave Ste 14 Dayton (45403) *(G-8329)*

Equipment Guys Inc 614 871-9220
185 Westgate Dr Newark (43055) *(G-15004)*

Equipment Manufacturers Intl 216 651-6700
16151 Puritas Ave Cleveland (44135) *(G-5291)*

Equipment Spcalists Dayton LLC 937 415-2151
5595 Webster St Dayton (45414) *(G-8330)*

Equipsync LLC 216 367-6640
4755 W 150th St Cleveland (44135) *(G-5292)*

Equistar Chemicals LP 513 530-4000
11530 Northlake Dr Cincinnati (45249) *(G-3716)*

Equity Oil & Gas Funds Inc (PA) 234 231-1004
4704 Barrow Ste 1 Stow (44224) *(G-17747)*

Erath Veneer Corp Virginia 540 483-5223
2825 Hallie Ln B Granville (43023) *(G-10458)*

Erd Specialty Graphics Inc 419 242-9545
3250 Monroe St Toledo (43606) *(G-18456)*

Erdie Industries Inc 440 288-0166
1205 Colorado Ave Lorain (44052) *(G-12245)*

Ergo Desktop LLC 567 890-3746
457 Grand Lake Rd Celina (45822) *(G-2995)*

Ergocan, Toledo *Also called Mon-Say Corp (G-18590)*

Eric Allshouse LLC 330 533-4258
9666 Lisbon Rd Canfield (44406) *(G-2554)*

Eric Mondene 740 965-2842
4278 Harlem Rd Galena (43021) *(G-10241)*

Eric Nickel 614 818-2488
5563 Covington Meadows Ct Westerville (43082) *(G-20151)*

Erichar Inc 216 402-2628
2051 W Ridgewood Dr Cleveland (44134) *(G-5293)*

Erickson-Huff Tool and Die 740 596-4036
61698 Locker Plant Rd Mc Arthur (45651) *(G-13331)*

Erico Inc 440 248-0100
34600 Solon Rd Solon (44139) *(G-17287)*

Erico International Corp (HQ) 440 349-2630
31700 Solon Rd Solon (44139) *(G-17288)*

Erico International Corp 440 248-0100
34600 Solon Rd Solon (44139) *(G-17289)*

Ericson Manufacturing Co 440 951-8000
4323 Hamann Pkwy Willoughby (44094) *(G-20480)*

Erie Black Top, Castalia *Also called Erie Materials Inc (G-2975)*

Erie Ceramic Arts Company LLC 419 228-1145
1005 W Grand Ave Lima (45801) *(G-12010)*

Erie Chinese Journal 216 324-2959
9810 Ravenna Rd Ste 1 Twinsburg (44087) *(G-18930)*

Erie Container Corporation 216 631-1650
4700 Lorain Ave Cleveland (44102) *(G-5294)*

Erie Copper Works Inc 330 725-5590
230 N State Rd Medina (44256) *(G-13406)*

Erie Lake Plastic Inc 440 333-4880
19940 Ingersoll Dr Cleveland (44116) *(G-5295)*

Erie Laser Ink LLC 419 346-0600
911 Jefferson Ave Toledo (43604) *(G-18457)*

Erie Materials Inc 419 483-4648
9200 Portland Rd Castalia (44824) *(G-2975)*

Erie Sand & Gravel Co Inc 216 961-1010
5400 Wiskey Is Cleveland (44102) *(G-5296)*

Erie Shore Industrial Svc Co 440 933-4301
683 Moore Rd Ste A Avon Lake (44012) *(G-1028)*

Erie Shore Machine Co Inc 216 692-1484
18602 Syracuse Ave Cleveland (44110) *(G-5297)*

Erie Steel Ltd 419 478-3743
5540 Jackman Rd Toledo (43613) *(G-18458)*

Erieview Metal Treating Co 216 663-1780
4465 Johnston Pkwy Cleveland (44128) *(G-5298)*

Erik V Lamb 330 962-1540
1638 S Clvland Msslon Rd Copley (44321) *(G-7846)*

Ernest Industries Inc 937 325-9851
1221 Groop Rd Springfield (45504) *(G-17553)*

Ernest Warther and Sons Inc 330 343-7513
327 Karl Ave Dover (44622) *(G-8984)*

Ernie Green Industries Inc (PA) 614 219-1423
2030 Dividend Dr Columbus (43228) *(G-7064)*

Ernst Concrete, Dayton *Also called Ernst Enterprises Inc (G-8331)*

Ernst Custom Cabinets LLC 513 376-9554
4686 Paddock Rd Ste 99 Cincinnati (45229) *(G-3717)*

Ernst Enterprises Inc 937 878-9378
5325 Medway Rd Fairborn (45324) *(G-9620)*

Ernst Enterprises Inc (PA) 937 233-5555
3361 Successful Way Dayton (45414) *(G-8331)*

Ernst Enterprises Inc 513 874-8300
4250 Columbia Rd Lebanon (45036) *(G-11798)*

Ernst Enterprises Inc 937 848-6811
2181 Ferry Rd Bellbrook (45305) *(G-1507)*

Ernst Enterprises Inc 614 443-9456
711 Stimmel Rd Columbus (43223) *(G-7065)*

Ernst Enterprises Inc 937 866-9441
4710 Soldiers Home Rd Carrollton (44615) *(G-2955)*

Ernst Enterprises Inc 419 222-2015
377 S Central Ave Lima (45804) *(G-12011)*

Ernst Enterprises Inc 937 339-6249
805 S Union St Troy (45373) *(G-18822)*

Ernst Flow Industries LLC 732 938-5641
16633 Foltz Pkwy Strongsville (44149) *(G-17918)*

Ernst Metal Technologies LLC 937 434-3133
2920 Kreitzer Rd Moraine (45439) *(G-14485)*

Ernst Ready Mix Division, Lima *Also called Ernst Enterprises Inc (G-12011)*

Ernst Sporting Gds Minster LLC 937 526-9822
32 E Main St Versailles (45380) *(G-19346)*

Erodetech Inc 330 725-9181
4986 Gateway Dr Medina (44256) *(G-13407)*

Ers Industries Inc 419 562-6010
811 Hopley Ave Bucyrus (44820) *(G-2342)*

Ervan Guttman Co 513 791-0767
8208 Blue Ash Rd Rear Cincinnati (45236) *(G-3718)*

Ervin Lee Logging 330 771-0039
8555 Stump Rd Minerva (44657) *(G-14321)*

Ervin Yoder 330 359-5862
7700 County Rd 77 Mount Hope (44660) *(G-14570)*

Es Manufacturing Inc 888 331-3443
55 Builders Dr Newark (43055) *(G-15005)*

Es Sign and Design, Twinsburg *Also called E S Sign & Design LLC (G-18927)*

Es Steiner Dairy, Baltic *Also called Tri State Dairy LLC (G-1078)*

Es Steiner Dairy LLC 330 897-5555
115 S Mill St Baltic (43804) *(G-1069)*

Es Thermal Inc 440 323-3291
300 Ceran Elyria (44035) *(G-9422)*

ES&w, Euclid *Also called Euclid Steel & Wire Inc (G-9580)*

Escher Division, Toledo *Also called Maumee Valley Fabricators Inc (G-18580)*

Esco Bucyrus Inc., Bucyrus *Also called Bucyrus Blades Inc (G-2332)*

Esco Corporation 419 562-6015
260 E Beal Ave Bucyrus (44820) *(G-2343)*

Escort Inc (HQ) 513 870-8500
5440 W Chester Rd West Chester (45069) *(G-19859)*

Esko-Graphics Inc (HQ) 937 454-1721
8535 Gander Creek Dr Miamisburg (45342) *(G-13805)*

Eskoartwork, Miamisburg *Also called Esko-Graphics Inc (G-13805)*

Esm Products Inc 937 492-4644
5445 Behm Rd Lot 5 Celina (45822) *(G-2996)*

Esperia Holdings LLC (PA) 714 249-7888
8035 W Lake Winds Dr Oak Harbor (43449) *(G-15589)*

Essco Aircraft, Barberton *Also called Stadvec Inc (G-1150)*

Essence Maker 440 729-3894
12819 Opalocka Dr Chesterland (44026) *(G-3203)*

Essential Learning Products, Hilliard *Also called Teachers Publishing Group (G-10985)*

Essential Pathways Ohio LLC 330 518-3091
726 E Boston Ave Youngstown (44502) *(G-21079)*

Essential Sealing Products Inc (PA) 440 543-8108
10145 Queens Way Chagrin Falls (44023) *(G-3086)*

Essential Wonders Inc 888 525-5282
2926 State Rd Ste 202 Cuyahoga Falls (44223) *(G-7992)*

Essilor Laboratories Amer Inc 330 425-3003
9221 Ravenna Rd # 3 Twinsburg (44087) *(G-18931)*

Essilor Laboratories Amer Inc 614 274-0840
3671 Interchange Rd Columbus (43204) *(G-7066)*

Essroc Cement Corp 330 499-9100
8282 Middlebranch Ave Ne Middlebranch (44652) *(G-13900)*

Essroc Cement Corp 614 497-2001
1550 Williams Rd Columbus (43207) *(G-7067)*

Est, Bedford *Also called Intigral Inc (G-1432)*

Estabrook Assembly Svcs LLC 440 243-3350
700 W Bagley Rd Berea (44017) *(G-1614)*

Estech Inc 805 895-1263
6217 Centre Park Dr West Chester (45069) *(G-19860)*

ALPHABETIC SECTION

EW Scripps Company (PA)

Estee Mold & Die Inc 937 224-7853
1467 Stanley Ave Dayton (45404) *(G-8332)*
Esterle Mold & Machine Co Inc (PA) 330 686-1685
1539 Commerce Dr Stow (44224) *(G-17748)*
Esterle Mold & Machine Co Inc 330 686-1685
1567 Commerce Dr Stow (44224) *(G-17749)*
Esterline & Sons Mfg Co LLC 937 265-5278
6508 Old Clifton Rd Springfield (45502) *(G-17554)*
Esterline Georgia US LLC (HQ) 937 372-7579
600 Bellbrook Ave Xenia (45385) *(G-20949)*
Esterman Printing Services, Cincinnati *Also called Robert Esterman (G-4353)*
Estreamz Inc 513 278-7836
1311 Vine St Cincinnati (45202) *(G-3719)*
Etc Enterprises LLC 417 262-6382
330 Sunderland Rd S Delphos (45833) *(G-8908)*
Etched Metal Company 440 248-0240
30200 Solon Indus Pkwy Solon (44139) *(G-17290)*
Etching Concepts 419 691-9086
621 Bruns Dr Rossford (43460) *(G-16740)*
Ethicon Endo - Surgery, Blue Ash *Also called Ethicon Inc (G-1787)*
Ethicon Endo-Surgery Inc (HQ) 513 337-7000
4545 Creek Rd Blue Ash (45242) *(G-1786)*
Ethicon Inc 513 786-7000
10123 Alliance Rd Blue Ash (45242) *(G-1787)*
Ethicon US LLC (HQ) 513 337-7000
4545 Creek Rd 3 Blue Ash (45242) *(G-1788)*
Ethos Corp 513 242-6336
1045 Meta Dr Cincinnati (45237) *(G-3720)*
Eti Tech Inc 937 832-4200
75 Holiday Dr Englewood (45322) *(G-9519)*
Etko Machine Inc 330 745-4033
2796 Barber Rd Norton (44203) *(G-15511)*
Etna Products Incorporated (PA) 440 543-9845
16824 Park Circle Dr Chagrin Falls (44023) *(G-3087)*
Ets Schaefer LLC 330 468-6600
8050 Highland Pointe Pkwy Macedonia (44056) *(G-12448)*
Ets Solution NA LLC 330 666-8696
3900 Ira Rd Bath (44210) *(G-1236)*
Ets Solutions Usa LLC 330 666-8696
3900 Ira Rd Bath (44210) *(G-1237)*
Euclid Beach Popcorn, Cleveland *Also called Humphrey Company (G-5537)*
Euclid Brewing Company LLC 216 289-5100
22408 Lake Shore Blvd Euclid (44123) *(G-9578)*
Euclid Coffee Co Inc 216 481-3330
17230 S Waterloo Rd Cleveland (44110) *(G-5299)*
Euclid Design & Manufacturing 440 942-0066
38333 Willoughby Pkwy Willoughby (44094) *(G-20481)*
Euclid Heat Treating Co 216 481-8444
1408 E 222nd St Euclid (44117) *(G-9579)*
Euclid Jalousies Inc 440 953-1112
490 E 200th St Cleveland (44119) *(G-5300)*
Euclid Media Group LLC (PA) 216 241-7550
737 Bolivar Rd Cleveland (44115) *(G-5301)*
Euclid Precision Grinding Co 440 946-8888
35400 Lakeland Blvd Eastlake (44095) *(G-9270)*
Euclid Products Co Inc 440 942-7310
3625 Lost Nation Rd Willoughby (44094) *(G-20482)*
Euclid Refinishing Compnay Inc (PA) 440 275-3356
2937 Industrial Park Dr Austinburg (44010) *(G-960)*
Euclid Spring Co 440 943-3213
30006 Lakeland Blvd Wickliffe (44092) *(G-20365)*
Euclid Steel & Wire Inc 216 731-6744
25030 Lakeland Blvd Euclid (44132) *(G-9580)*
Euclid Universal Corporation 440 542-0960
30500 Bruce Industrial B Cleveland (44139) *(G-5302)*
Euclid Vidaro Manufacturing Co (PA) 330 673-7413
333 Martinel Dr Kent (44240) *(G-11457)*
Euclid Vidaro Mfg. Co., Kent *Also called Euclid Vidaro Manufacturing Co (G-11457)*
Euclid Welding Co Inc 216 289-0714
26670 Lakeland Blvd Cleveland (44132) *(G-5303)*
Eugene Stewart 937 898-1117
5671 Webster St Dayton (45414) *(G-8333)*
Eureeka, Lima *Also called Accubuilt Inc (G-11981)*
Eureka Screw Machine Co, Cleveland *Also called Eureka Screw Machine Pdts Co (G-5304)*
Eureka Screw Machine Pdts Co 216 883-1715
3960 E 91st St Cleveland (44105) *(G-5304)*
Eurocase Architectural Cabinet 330 674-0681
7488 State Route 241 Millersburg (44654) *(G-14214)*
Europa Sports Products Inc 440 846-9571
13675 Darice Pkwy Strongsville (44149) *(G-17919)*
Europia Gourmet Foods LLC 614 460-3000
672 N High St Columbus (43215) *(G-7068)*
Eurostampa North America Inc (HQ) 513 821-2275
1440 Seymour Ave Cincinnati (45237) *(G-3721)*
Eurotherm, North Olmsted *Also called Gc Controls Inc (G-15337)*
Ev Liquids LLC 614 622-9617
192 Oak St Columbus (43235) *(G-7069)*
Evan Ragouzis Co 513 242-5900
4 Standen Dr Hamilton (45015) *(G-10689)*
Evandy Co Inc 216 518-9713
5450 Dunham Rd Cleveland (44137) *(G-5305)*
Evanko Wm/Barringer Richd DDS 330 336-6693
185 Wadsworth Rd Ste K Wadsworth (44281) *(G-19405)*
Evans Adhesive Corporation Ltd (PA) 614 451-2665
925 Old Henderson Rd Columbus (43220) *(G-7070)*
Evans Adhesive Corporation Ltd 614 451-2665
925 Old Henderson Rd Columbus (43220) *(G-7071)*
Evans Bakery Inc 937 228-4151
700 Troy St Dayton (45404) *(G-8334)*
Evans Creative Group LLC 614 657-9439
11 E Gay St Columbus (43215) *(G-7072)*
Evans Industries Inc 330 453-1122
606 Walnut Ave Ne Canton (44702) *(G-2698)*
Even Heat Mfg Ltd 330 695-9351
8241 Tr 601 Fredericksburg (44627) *(G-10085)*
Even-Cut Abrasive Company 216 881-9595
850 E 72nd St Cleveland (44103) *(G-5306)*
Evenflo Company Inc 937 773-3971
1801 W Main St Troy (45373) *(G-18823)*
Evenflo Company Inc (HQ) 937 415-3300
225 Byers Rd Miamisburg (45342) *(G-13806)*
Evening Leader, The, Saint Marys *Also called Horizon Ohio Publications Inc (G-16840)*
Evension 330 634-1430
899 Moe Dr Ste 21 Akron (44310) *(G-172)*
Event Inc 440 951-4477
7555 Tyler Blvd Ste 6 Mentor (44060) *(G-13575)*
Ever Roll Specialties Co 937 964-1302
3988 Lawrenceville Dr Springfield (45504) *(G-17555)*
Eveready Printing Inc 216 587-2389
20700 Miles Pkwy Cleveland (44128) *(G-5307)*
Eveready Products Corporation 216 661-2755
1101 Belt Line Ave Cleveland (44109) *(G-5308)*
Everett Industries Inc 330 372-3700
3601 Larchmont Ave Ne Warren (44483) *(G-19548)*
Everflow Eastern Partners LP 330 537-3863
29093 Salem Alliance Rd Salem (44460) *(G-16889)*
Everflow Eastern Partners LP (PA) 330 533-2692
585 W Main St Canfield (44406) *(G-2555)*
Evergreen Packaging Inc 440 235-7200
7920 Mapleway Dr Olmsted Falls (44138) *(G-15675)*
Evergreen Plastics, Clyde *Also called Polychem Corporation (G-6543)*
Everhard Products Inc (PA) 330 453-7786
1016 9th St Sw Canton (44707) *(G-2699)*
Everly Concrete Products 740 635-1415
53620 Farmington Rd Bridgeport (43912) *(G-2089)*
Everris NA Inc (HQ) 800 492-8255
4950 Blaver Pkwy Dublin (43017) *(G-9073)*
Everris NA Inc (HQ) 614 726-7100
4950 Blazer Pkwy Dublin (43017) *(G-9074)*
Evers Enterprises Inc 513 541-7200
1210 Ellis St Cincinnati (45223) *(G-3722)*
Evers Welding Co Inc 513 385-7352
4849 Blue Rock Rd Cincinnati (45247) *(G-3723)*
Eversharpe Deburring Tool Co 513 988-6240
10 Baltimore Ave Trenton (45067) *(G-18791)*
Evertz Technology Service Usa 513 422-8400
2601 S Verity Pkwy # 102 Middletown (45044) *(G-14040)*
Everykey Inc 866 798-5577
1988 Ford Dr Cleveland (44106) *(G-5309)*
Everything In America 347 871-6872
4141 Stilmore Rd Cleveland (44121) *(G-5310)*
Everythings Image Inc 513 469-6727
9933 Alliance Rd Ste 2 Blue Ash (45242) *(G-1789)*
Everyware Global Inc (PA) 740 687-2500
519 N Pierce Ave Lancaster (43130) *(G-11711)*
Evil Corporation Corporation 937 902-5921
116 Front St Dayton (45402) *(G-8335)*
Evolution Crtive Solutions Inc 513 681-4450
7107 Shona Dr Cincinnati (45237) *(G-3724)*
Evolution Crtive Solutions LLC 513 681-4450
7107 Shona Dr Ste 110 Cincinnati (45237) *(G-3725)*
Evolution Resources LLC 937 438-2390
480 Congress Park Dr Centerville (45459) *(G-3041)*
Evolutions North America 330 688-2630
1699 Commerce Dr Stow (44224) *(G-17750)*
Evonik Corporation 513 554-8969
620 Shepherd Dr Cincinnati (45215) *(G-3726)*
Evoqua Water Technologies LLC 614 861-5440
1154 Hill Rd N Pickerington (43147) *(G-16192)*
Evoqua Water Technologies LLC 262 521-8352
2002 Ford Cir Ste F Milford (45150) *(G-14140)*
Evoqua Water Technologies LLC 614 491-4000
6300 Commerce Center Dr Groveport (43125) *(G-10620)*
Evp International LLC 513 761-7614
10179 Wayne Ave Cincinnati (45215) *(G-3727)*
Ew Publishing Company 440 887-0131
24181 Lorain Rd North Olmsted (44070) *(G-15333)*
EW Scripps Company (PA) 513 977-3000
312 Walnut St Ste 2800 Cincinnati (45202) *(G-3728)*

ALPHABETIC

Ewh Spectrum LLC 937 593-8010
  221 W Chillicothe Ave Bellefontaine (43311) *(G-1530)*

Exact Cutting Service Inc 440 546-1319
  6892 W Snwvlle Rd Ste 108 Brecksville (44141) *(G-2048)*

Exact Equipment Corporation (HQ) 215 295-2000
  1900 Polaris Pkwy Columbus (43240) *(G-6645)*

Exact Pipe Tools 330 922-8150
  141 Broad Blvd Ste 201 Cuyahoga Falls (44221) *(G-7993)*

Exact Software North Amer LLC (HQ) 978 539-6186
  5455 Rings Rd Ste 100 Dublin (43017) *(G-9075)*

Exact-Tool & Die Inc 216 676-9140
  5425 W 140th St Cleveland (44142) *(G-5311)*

Exair Corporation (PA) 513 671-3322
  11510 Goldcoast Dr Cincinnati (45249) *(G-3729)*

Exal Corporation (PA) 330 744-9505
  1 Performance Pl Youngstown (44502) *(G-21080)*

Excalibur Exploration Inc 330 966-7003
  9720 Cleveland Ave Nw Greentown (44630) *(G-10486)*

Excel Loading Systems LLC 513 265-2936
  675 N Deis Dr Ste 276 Blue Ash (45242) *(G-1790)*

Excel Machine & Tool Inc 419 678-3318
  212 Butler St Coldwater (45828) *(G-6559)*

Excel Printing & Graphics, Chagrin Falls Also called R B Robinson Inc *(G-3116)*

Excelitas Technologies Corp 937 865-4621
  1100 Vanguard Blvd Miamisburg (45342) *(G-13807)*

Excellent Tool & Die Inc 216 671-9222
  10921 Briggs Rd Cleveland (44111) *(G-5312)*

Excello Fabric Finishers Inc 740 622-7444
  802 S 2nd St Coshocton (43812) *(G-7889)*

Excelsior Marking, Akron Also called Mark-All Enterprises LLC *(G-284)*

Excelsior Printing Co 740 927-2934
  1014 Putnam Rd Sw Pataskala (43062) *(G-15970)*

Excelsior Solutions 937 848-2569
  1742 River Ridge Dr Spring Valley (45370) *(G-17467)*

Exchange Printing Company 330 773-7842
  969 Grant St Akron (44311) *(G-173)*

Exchange Signs 330 644-4552
  3152 Manchester Rd Akron (44319) *(G-174)*

Exciton Inc 937 252-2989
  5271 Split Rail Dayton (45429) *(G-8336)*

Exec-U-Print Inc 440 333-6484
  19930 Detroit Rd Rocky River (44116) *(G-16698)*

Executive Security Systems Inc 513 895-2783
  332 Cherry St Cincinnati (45246) *(G-3730)*

Executive Wings Inc 440 254-1812
  13550 Carter Rd Painesville (44077) *(G-15878)*

Exelon Energy Company 614 797-4377
  470 Olde Worthington Rd # 375 Westerville (43082) *(G-20152)*

Exikon Industries LLC 216 485-2947
  15215 Chatfield Ave Cleveland (44111) *(G-5313)*

Exito Manufacturing 937 291-9871
  4738 Gateway Cir Ste E Dayton (45440) *(G-8337)*

Exline Manufacturing Co Inc 937 866-1515
  4352 Slders Hm Mmsburg Rd Miamisburg (45342) *(G-13808)*

Exochem Corporation 440 277-6116
  2421 E 28th St Lorain (44055) *(G-12246)*

Exochem Corporation (PA) 800 807-7464
  2421 E 28th St Lorain (44055) *(G-12247)*

Exochem Corporation 330 426-9898
  90 Kemple Dr East Palestine (44413) *(G-9239)*

Exodus Mold & Machine Inc 330 854-0282
  960 Milan St N Canal Fulton (44614) *(G-2501)*

Exothermics Inc 419 729-9726
  5040 Enterprise Blvd Toledo (43612) *(G-18459)*

Exotica Fresheners Co, Holland Also called D & J Distributing & Mfg *(G-11052)*

Exp Fuels Inc 419 382-7713
  3070 Airport Hwy Toledo (43609) *(G-18460)*

Expansion Programs Intl 216 631-8544
  11115 Edgewater Dr Cleveland (44102) *(G-5314)*

Experimental Machine, Brecksville Also called Exact Cutting Service Inc *(G-2048)*

Expert Outfitters 330 965-9620
  9074 Market St North Lima (44452) *(G-15316)*

Expert Regrind Service Inc 937 526-5662
  20 S Pearl St Versailles (45380) *(G-19347)*

Expert TS 330 263-4588
  221 Beall Ave Wooster (44691) *(G-20770)*

Expertise, Wooster Also called Expert TS *(G-20770)*

Explorys Inc 216 767-4700
  1111 Superior Ave E Cleveland (44114) *(G-5315)*

Exponentia US Inc 614 944-5103
  424 Beecher Rd Ste A Columbus (43230) *(G-7073)*

Express Care 740 266-2501
  197 Main St Steubenville (43953) *(G-17694)*

Express Energy Svcs Oper LP 740 337-4530
  1515 Franklin St Toronto (43964) *(G-18781)*

Express Graphic Prtg & Design 513 728-3344
  9695 Hamilton Ave Cincinnati (45231) *(G-3731)*

Express Lube, Massillon Also called Melanda Inc *(G-13179)*

Express Trading Pins 419 394-2550
  105 Marbello Ct Saint Marys (45885) *(G-16838)*

Expressive Scents By A 513 254-5399
  1336 Behles Ave Cincinnati (45215) *(G-3732)*

Extendit Company 330 743-4343
  601 Jones St Youngstown (44502) *(G-21081)*

Extol of Ohio Inc (PA) 419 668-2072
  208 Republic St Norwalk (44857) *(G-15537)*

Extol of Ohio Inc 419 668-2072
  208 Republic St Norwalk (44857) *(G-15538)*

Extra Seal, Newcomerstown Also called 31 Inc *(G-15107)*

Extreme Caster Services Inc 330 637-9030
  3333 Niles Cortland Rd Ne Cortland (44410) *(G-7868)*

Extreme Custom Spools 330 533-6936
  3711 Starrs Centre Dr Canfield (44406) *(G-2556)*

Extreme Elements 330 325-2807
  1016 Morse St Akron (44320) *(G-175)*

Extreme Marine 330 963-7800
  2057 E Aurora Rd Ste Lm Twinsburg (44087) *(G-18932)*

Extreme Trailers LLC 330 440-0026
  317 E Broadway St Dover (44622) *(G-8985)*

Extruded Silicon Products Inc 330 733-0101
  3300 Gilchrist Rd Mogadore (44260) *(G-14375)*

Extrudex Aluminum Inc 330 538-4444
  12051 Mahoning Ave North Jackson (44451) *(G-15290)*

Extrudex Limited Partnership (PA) 440 352-7101
  310 Figgie Dr Painesville (44077) *(G-15879)*

Exxcite Marketing Inc 513 271-4550
  7949 Graves Rd Cincinnati (45243) *(G-3733)*

Exxcite Marketing Products, Cincinnati Also called Exxcite Marketing Inc *(G-3733)*

Exxon, Wadsworth Also called Advanced Elastomer Systems LP *(G-19389)*

Eye Center (PA) 614 228-3937
  262 Neil Ave Columbus (43215) *(G-7074)*

Eye Lighting Intl N Amer Inc 440 350-7000
  9150 Hendricks Rd Mentor (44060) *(G-13576)*

Eye Lightning International 440 354-2938
  8150 Hendricks Rd Mentor (44060) *(G-13577)*

Eye3data, West Chester Also called MAI Media Group Llc *(G-20023)*

Eyescience Labs LLC 614 885-7100
  493 Village Park Dr Powell (43065) *(G-16471)*

EZ Brite Brands Inc 440 871-7817
  806 Sharon Dr Ste C Cleveland (44145) *(G-5316)*

EZ Grout Corporation Inc 740 962-2024
  1833 N Riverview Rd Malta (43758) *(G-12536)*

EZ Machine Inc 330 784-3363
  2359 Triplett Blvd Akron (44312) *(G-176)*

EZ Wall LLC 800 424-8251
  3455 Cross Rd Winchester (45697) *(G-20692)*

Ezg Manufacturing, Malta Also called EZ Grout Corporation Inc *(G-12536)*

Ezg Manufacturing, Waterford Also called E Z Grout Corporation *(G-19646)*

Ezshred LLC (PA) 440 256-7640
  7621 Euclid Chardon Rd Kirtland (44094) *(G-11614)*

F & B Engraving Tls & Sup LLC 937 332-7994
  701 W Water St A Troy (45373) *(G-18824)*

F & G Tool and Die Co (PA) 937 294-1405
  3024 Dryden Rd Moraine (45439) *(G-14486)*

F & G Tool and Die Co. 937 746-3658
  130 Industrial Dr Franklin (45005) *(G-10019)*

F & J Grinding Inc. 440 942-4430
  36495 Reading Ave Willoughby (44094) *(G-20483)*

F & J Manufacturing, Dayton Also called Weber Jewelers Incorporated *(G-8749)*

F & K Concepts Inc. 937 426-6843
  462 Carthage Dr Beavercreek (45434) *(G-1337)*

F & M Coal Company 740 544-5203
  3925 County Road 56 Toronto (43964) *(G-18782)*

F & W Auto Supply 419 445-3350
  111 Depot St Archbold (43502) *(G-671)*

F A S T, Cincinnati Also called Field Apparatus Service & Tstg *(G-3752)*

F A Tech Corp 513 942-1920
  9065 Sutton Pl West Chester (45011) *(G-19861)*

F and W Publications Inc 513 531-2690
  4700 E Galbraith Rd Cincinnati (45236) *(G-3734)*

F C Brengman and Assoc LLC 740 756-4308
  86 High St Carroll (43112) *(G-2940)*

F E Myers Co 419 289-1144
  740 E 9th St Ashland (44805) *(G-731)*

F H Bonn Co Inc. 937 323-7024
  4300 Gateway Blvd Springfield (45502) *(G-17556)*

F I C, Akron Also called Foundation Industries Inc *(G-193)*

F I T, Valley City Also called Fuserashi Intl Tech Inc *(G-19204)*

F J Designs Inc 330 264-1377
  2163 Great Trails Dr Wooster (44691) *(G-20771)*

F K Holding Inc (PA) 513 641-1400
  2100 Section Rd Cincinnati (45237) *(G-3735)*

F L Distributors, Cleveland Also called F L Enterprises *(G-5317)*

F L Enterprises 216 898-5551
  4740 Briar Rd Cleveland (44135) *(G-5317)*

F M Machine Co 330 773-8237
  1114 Triplett Blvd Akron (44306) *(G-177)*

F M P Enterprises Inc 330 920-8059
  1871 12th St Cuyahoga Falls (44223) *(G-7994)*

F M Sheet Metal Fabrication...937 362-4357
13019 Shanley Rd Quincy (43343) **(G-16503)**
F P C Printing Inc...937 743-8136
119 Art Ave Franklin (45005) **(G-10020)**
F P M, Lancaster *Also called Fabricated Packaging Mtls Inc* **(G-11713)**
F S, Batavia *Also called Freeman Schwabe Machinery LLC* **(G-1188)**
F S A, Canton *Also called Foundation Systems Anchors Inc* **(G-2707)**
F Squared Inc...419 752-7273
9 Sunset Dr Greenwich (44837) **(G-10530)**
F W Dodge, Cincinnati *Also called Dodge Data & Analytics LLC* **(G-3660)**
F&P America Mfg Inc (HQ)...937 339-0212
2101 Corporate Dr Troy (45373) **(G-18825)**
F+w Media Inc (HQ)...513 531-2690
10151 Carver Rd Ste 200 Blue Ash (45242) **(G-1791)**
F3 Defense Systems LLC...419 982-2020
1601 S Dixie Hwy Lima (45804) **(G-12012)**
FA Siberling Naturelm Mtro Prk, Akron *Also called County of Summit* **(G-132)**
Fab Form, Mentor *Also called V K C Inc* **(G-13764)**
Fab Shop Inc...513 860-1332
1520 Bender Ave Hamilton (45011) **(G-10690)**
Fab Steel Co Inc...419 666-5100
240 W Andrus Rd Northwood (43619) **(G-15481)**
Fab Tech Inc...330 926-9556
6500 W Snowville Rd Brecksville (44141) **(G-2049)**
Fab-Tech Machine Inc...937 473-5572
2 W Spring St Covington (45318) **(G-7922)**
Fab3 Group, Cleveland *Also called Duct Fabricators Inc* **(G-5219)**
Fabacraft Inc...513 677-0500
201 Grandin Rd Maineville (45039) **(G-12524)**
Fabacraft Co, Maineville *Also called Fabacraft Inc* **(G-12524)**
Fabco Inc (HQ)...419 421-4740
616 N Blanchard St Findlay (45840) **(G-9820)**
Fabco Tool and Machine, Warren *Also called Fine Line Tool and Die Inc* **(G-19550)**
Fabcon Companies LLC...614 875-8601
3400 Jackson Pike Grove City (43123) **(G-10558)**
Fabcraft Inc...440 286-6700
344 Center St Chardon (44024) **(G-3152)**
Fabohio Inc...740 922-4233
521 E 7th St Uhrichsville (44683) **(G-19050)**
Fabri-Form Company (HQ)...740 826-5000
200 S Friendship Dr New Concord (43762) **(G-14818)**
Fabric Square Shop...330 752-3044
2091 Liberty Rd Stow (44224) **(G-17751)**
Fabricated Packaging Mtls Inc...740 681-1750
296 Quarry Rd Se Lancaster (43130) **(G-11712)**
Fabricated Packaging Mtls Inc (PA)...740 654-3492
2109 Commerce St Lancaster (43130) **(G-11713)**
Fabricating Solutions Inc...330 486-0998
7920 Bavaria Rd Twinsburg (44087) **(G-18933)**
Fabrication Division, Maumee *Also called Andersons Inc* **(G-13225)**
Fabrication Group LLC...216 251-1125
3453 W 140th St Cleveland (44111) **(G-5318)**
Fabrication Shop Inc...419 435-7934
1395 Buckley St Fostoria (44830) **(G-9970)**
Fabrication Unlimited LLC...937 492-3166
4343 State Route 29 E Sidney (45365) **(G-17189)**
Fabriweld Corporation...419 668-3358
360 Eastpark Dr Norwalk (44857) **(G-15539)**
Fabstar Tanks Inc...419 587-3639
20302 Road 48 Grover Hill (45849) **(G-10652)**
Fabtech Machine, Covington *Also called Fab-Tech Machine Inc* **(G-7922)**
Fabtech Ohio...440 942-0811
38311 Apollo Pkwy Ste 3 Willoughby (44094) **(G-20484)**
Facemyer Forest Products Inc...740 992-7425
Hc 7 Middleport (45760) **(G-14010)**
Facemyer Lumber Co Inc (PA)...740 992-5965
31940 Bailey Run Rd Pomeroy (45769) **(G-16389)**
Facial Sensation Products...937 293-2280
12 Beverly Pl Oakwood (45419) **(G-15607)**
Facil North America Inc (HQ)...330 487-2500
2242 Pinnacle Pkwy # 100 Twinsburg (44087) **(G-18934)**
Facilities Management Ex LLC...844 664-4400
1515 Lake Shore Dr # 100 Columbus (43204) **(G-7075)**
Factory Direct International...419 425-9636
337 S Main St Ste 400 Findlay (45840) **(G-9821)**
Facts Inc...330 928-2332
2737 Front St Cuyahoga Falls (44221) **(G-7995)**
Facultatieve Tech Americas Inc...330 723-6339
940 Lake Rd Medina (44256) **(G-13408)**
FAg Bearings Corporation...513 398-1139
4035 N Ascot Pl Mason (45040) **(G-13019)**
Fair Field Machine Products...740 756-4409
6215 Clmbus Lncster Rd Nw Carroll (43112) **(G-2941)**
Fair Publishing, Norwalk *Also called Rotary Printing Company* **(G-15563)**
Fair Publishing House Inc...419 668-3746
15 Schauss Ave Norwalk (44857) **(G-15540)**
Fairborn Cement Company LLC...937 879-8393
3250 Linebaugh Rd Xenia (45385) **(G-20950)**
Fairborn Herald, Xenia *Also called Suburban Newpapers of Dayton* **(G-20976)**
Fairborn Services Inc...513 492-9422
3816 Welden Dr Lebanon (45036) **(G-11799)**
Fairchild Labs LLC...614 235-7040
2243 S James Rd Columbus (43232) **(G-7076)**
Fairchild Printing Co...216 641-4192
5807 Fleet Ave Cleveland (44105) **(G-5319)**
Faircrest Steel Plant, Canton *Also called Timkensteel Corporation* **(G-2879)**
Fairfield License Center Inc...513 829-6224
530 Wessel Dr Ste L Hamilton (45014) **(G-10691)**
Fairfield Machined Products...740 756-4409
6215 Clmbus Lncster Rd Nw Carroll (43112) **(G-2942)**
Fairfield Screw Products Co...740 653-7627
505 Slocum St Lancaster (43130) **(G-11714)**
Fairfield Woodworks Ltd...740 689-1953
1612 E Main St Lancaster (43130) **(G-11715)**
Fairmont Creamery LLC...216 357-2560
1720 Willey Ave Cleveland (44113) **(G-5320)**
Fairmount Minerals, Chesterland *Also called Fairmount Santrol Inc* **(G-3206)**
Fairmount Minerals LLC...269 926-9450
8834 Mayfield Rd Ste A Chesterland (44026) **(G-3204)**
Fairmount Santrol, Chesterland *Also called Fairmount Minerals LLC* **(G-3204)**
Fairmount Santrol Holdings Inc (PA)...800 255-7263
8834 Mayfield Rd Ste A Chesterland (44026) **(G-3205)**
Fairmount Santrol Inc (HQ)...440 214-3200
8834 Mayfield Rd Ste A Chesterland (44026) **(G-3206)**
Fairmount Water Solutions LLC...440 285-3132
10975 Kinsman Rd Newbury (44065) **(G-15090)**
Fairview Log Homes, Millersburg *Also called Al Yoder Construction Company* **(G-14191)**
Fairway Carts Parts & More LLC...234 209-9008
6944 Wales Ave Nw North Canton (44720) **(G-15229)**
Fairway Pines Golf Course, Mentor *Also called Drillex Inc* **(G-13564)**
Fairy Dust Ltd Inc...513 251-0065
3528 Warsaw Ave Cincinnati (45205) **(G-3736)**
Faith Guiding Cafe LLC...614 245-8451
5195 Hampsted Vlg Ctr Way New Albany (43054) **(G-14758)**
Faith Tool & Manufacturing...440 951-5934
36575 Reading Ave Willoughby (44094) **(G-20485)**
Faithful Mold Polishing Ex...330 678-8006
4485 Crystal Pkwy Kent (44240) **(G-11458)**
Falcon Fab and Finishes LLC...740 820-4458
3368 Piketon Rd Lucasville (45648) **(G-12420)**
Falcon Fabrication, Lucasville *Also called Falcon Fab and Finishes LLC* **(G-12420)**
Falcon Foundry Company...330 536-6221
96 6th St Lowellville (44436) **(G-12407)**
Falcon Industries Inc (PA)...330 723-0099
180 Commerce Dr Medina (44256) **(G-13409)**
Falcon Innovations Inc...216 252-0676
3316 W 118th St Cleveland (44111) **(G-5321)**
Falcon Ridge Technologies LLC...216 674-1649
5055 Corbin Dr Ste 200 Cleveland (44128) **(G-5322)**
Falcon Tool & Machine Inc...937 534-9999
2795 Lance Dr Moraine (45409) **(G-14487)**
Fallen Oak Candles Inc...419 204-8162
917 Lilac St Celina (45822) **(G-2997)**
Falls Filtration Tech Inc...330 928-4100
115 E Steels Corners Rd Stow (44224) **(G-17752)**
Falls Metal Fabricators Ind...330 253-7181
760 Home Ave Akron (44310) **(G-178)**
Falls Stamping & Welding Co (PA)...330 928-1191
2900 Vincent St Cuyahoga Falls (44221) **(G-7996)**
Falls Stamping & Welding Co...216 771-9635
1720 Fall St Cleveland (44113) **(G-5323)**
Falls Tool & Die Incorporated...330 633-4884
1416 Piedmont Ave Akron (44310) **(G-179)**
Falls Welding & Fabg Inc...330 253-3437
608 Grant St Akron (44311) **(G-180)**
Falmer Screw Pdts & Mfg Inc...330 758-0593
690 Mcclurg Rd Youngstown (44512) **(G-21082)**
Fame Tool & Mfg Co Inc...513 271-6387
5340 Hetzell St Cincinnati (45227) **(G-3737)**
Family Fun, Louisville *Also called Bradley Enterprises Inc* **(G-12311)**
Family Medical Clinic & Laser...740 345-2767
44 S 29th St Newark (43055) **(G-15006)**
Family Memorials...330 477-4900
1325 Whipple Ave Nw Canton (44708) **(G-2700)**
Family Motor Coach Assn Inc (PA)...513 474-3622
8291 Clough Pike Cincinnati (45244) **(G-3738)**
Family Motor Coaching Inc...513 474-3622
8291 Clough Pike Cincinnati (45244) **(G-3739)**
Family Packaging Inc (PA)...937 325-4106
504 W Euclid Ave Springfield (45506) **(G-17557)**
Family Values Magazine...419 566-1102
3027 Fox Rd Mansfield (44904) **(G-12602)**
Family Woodworks LLC...740 289-4071
286 Taylor Hollow Rd Piketon (45661) **(G-16220)**
Famous Industries Inc (HQ)...330 535-1811
2620 Ridgewood Rd Ste 200 Akron (44313) **(G-181)**

Famous Industries Inc 740 685-2592
  356 W Main St Byesville (43723) *(G-2401)*

Famous Industries Inc 740 397-8842
  325 Commerce Dr Mount Vernon (43050) *(G-14622)*

Famous Kiss-N-Korn Shop, Cleveland *Also called Crawford Acquisition Corp* *(G-5141)*

Famous Realty Cleveland Inc 740 685-2533
  354 W Main St Byesville (43723) *(G-2402)*

Famous Supply, Byesville *Also called Famous Realty Cleveland Inc* *(G-2402)*

Fanci Forms, Upper Sandusky *Also called Mar-Metal Mfg Inc* *(G-19131)*

Fannie May Cnfctons Brands Inc 330 494-0833
  5353 Lauby Rd North Canton (44720) *(G-15230)*

Fantastic Sams Hair Care Salon 740 456-4296
  4490 Gallia St Portsmouth (45662) *(G-16435)*

Fantasy Candies, Cleveland *Also called Chocolate Pig Inc* *(G-5029)*

Fanuc America Corporation 513 754-2400
  7700 Innovation Way Mason (45040) *(G-13020)*

Fanz Stop 937 310-1436
  63 Bellbrook Plz Bellbrook (45305) *(G-1508)*

Far Associates, Macedonia *Also called Ralph A Felice Inc* *(G-12479)*

Far Corner 330 767-3734
  13189 Mount Eaton St Sw Navarre (44662) *(G-14712)*

Farah Jewelers Inc 614 438-6140
  1500 Polaris Pkwy # 2156 Columbus (43240) *(G-6646)*

Farasey Steel Fabricators Inc 216 641-1853
  4000 Iron Ct Cleveland (44115) *(G-5324)*

Farber Specialty Vehicles Inc 614 863-6470
  7052 Americana Pkwy Reynoldsburg (43068) *(G-16589)*

Faretec Inc 440 350-9510
  1610 W Jackson St Unit 6 Painesville (44077) *(G-15880)*

Fargo Toolite Incorporated 440 997-2442
  998 Stevenson Rd Ashtabula (44004) *(G-806)*

Farin Industries Inc 440 275-2755
  2844 Industrial Park Dr Austinburg (44010) *(G-961)*

Farm & Dairy, Salem *Also called Lyle Printing & Publishing Co* *(G-16909)*

Farm Centers, Maumee *Also called Andersons Lawn Fert Div Inc* *(G-13226)*

Farm Products Division, Dayton *Also called Putnam Plastics Inc* *(G-8603)*

Farmed Materials Inc 513 680-4046
  300 E Business Way # 200 Cincinnati (45241) *(G-3740)*

Farmer Hub, Wooster *Also called Wooster Daily Record Inc* *(G-20849)*

Farmer Smiths Market, Dover *Also called Barkett Fruit Co Inc* *(G-8967)*

Farmers Commission Company (HQ) 419 294-2371
  520 W Wyandot Ave Upper Sandusky (43351) *(G-19122)*

Farmers National Banc Corp 330 726-8896
  102 W Western Reserve Rd Youngstown (44514) *(G-21083)*

Farmerstown Axle Co 330 897-2711
  2816 State Route 557 Baltic (43804) *(G-1070)*

Farmland News LLC 419 445-9456
  104 Depot St Archbold (43502) *(G-672)*

Farmstead Acres Woodworking 330 695-6492
  9106 County Road 201 Fredericksburg (44627) *(G-10086)*

Farnsworth Engineering 330 385-1745
  313 Smith St East Liverpool (43920) *(G-9215)*

Farquhar Heating and Air, Dayton *Also called BT Investments II Inc* *(G-8200)*

Farr Automation Inc 419 289-1883
  58 Sugarbush Ct Ashland (44805) *(G-732)*

Farrell Services, Twinsburg *Also called Lasting Impressions Printing* *(G-18970)*

FAS Machinery LLC 216 472-3800
  9916 Broadway Ave Cleveland (44125) *(G-5325)*

Fasco Machine Products Inc 440 437-6242
  554 E Main St Orwell (44076) *(G-15775)*

Fast Blast, Gibsonburg *Also called Universal Ground Cullet Inc* *(G-10378)*

Fast Fab and Laser LLC 937 224-3048
  401 Kiser St Dayton (45404) *(G-8338)*

Fastenal Company 419 629-3024
  575 W Monroe St New Bremen (45869) *(G-14787)*

Fastenal Company 330 745-2996
  2465 Romig Rd Akron (44320) *(G-182)*

Fastener Industries Inc 440 891-2031
  33 Lou Groza Blvd Berea (44017) *(G-1615)*

Fastener Industries Inc 216 267-2240
  5250 W 164th St Cleveland (44142) *(G-5326)*

Fastfeed Corp 330 948-7333
  124 S Academy St Lodi (44254) *(G-12160)*

Fastformingcom LLC 330 927-3277
  300 Morning Star Dr Rittman (44270) *(G-16674)*

Fastpatch Ltd 513 367-1838
  10774 Carolina Trace Rd Harrison (45030) *(G-10777)*

Fastsigns, Cleveland *Also called Ledge Hill Signs Limited* *(G-5690)*

Fastsigns, Lima *Also called ME Signs Inc* *(G-12052)*

Fastsigns, Youngstown *Also called Summco Inc* *(G-21215)*

Fastsigns, Akron *Also called Sterling Associates Inc* *(G-418)*

Fastsigns, Dayton *Also called Janeway Signs Inc* *(G-8422)*

Fastsigns, Cincinnati *Also called Stine Consulting Inc* *(G-4469)*

Fastsigns, Cincinnati *Also called Cline Signs LLC* *(G-3586)*

Fastsigns, Cleveland *Also called Bernard R Doyles Inc* *(G-4906)*

Fastsigns, Bedford *Also called Inner Products Sales Inc* *(G-1431)*

Fastsigns, Westerville *Also called Devries & Associates Inc* *(G-20210)*

Fastsigns, Dublin *Also called Geoffrey Smith* *(G-9078)*

Fastsigns, Westerville *Also called Devries & Associates Inc* *(G-20209)*

Fastsigns, Dayton *Also called R Weir Inc* *(G-8613)*

Fastsigns, Columbus *Also called Devries & Associates Inc* *(G-7023)*

Fastsigns, Columbus *Also called Thatcher Enterprises Co Ltd* *(G-7688)*

Fastsigns, Fairfield *Also called Roderer Enterprises Inc* *(G-9712)*

Fastsigns, Blue Ash *Also called Auld Lang Signs Inc* *(G-1746)*

Fastsigns, North Olmsted *Also called Ew Publishing Company* *(G-15333)*

Fastsigns, Painesville *Also called Chas J Steven Inc* *(G-15864)*

Fastsigns 513 489-8989
  12125 Montgomery Rd Cincinnati (45249) *(G-3741)*

Fate Industries Inc 440 327-1770
  36682 Sugar Ridge Rd North Ridgeville (44039) *(G-15372)*

Faull & Son LLC 330 652-4341
  515 Holford Ave Niles (44446) *(G-15152)*

Faurecia Automotive Holdings 419 727-5000
  543 Matzinger Rd Toledo (43612) *(G-18461)*

Faurecia Exhaust Systems Inc 419 727-5000
  5225 Telegraph Rd Toledo (43612) *(G-18462)*

Faurecia Exhaust Systems Inc 937 339-0551
  1255 Archer Dr Troy (45373) *(G-18826)*

Faurecia Exhaust Systems LLC (HQ) 419 727-5000
  543 Matzinger Rd Toledo (43612) *(G-18463)*

Faurecia Exhaust Systems LLC 330 824-2807
  1849 Ellsworth Bailey Rd Warren (44481) *(G-19549)*

Faurecia Exhaust Systems Inc 937 743-0551
  2301 Commerce Center Dr Franklin (45005) *(G-10021)*

Faurecia Exhaust Systems, Inc., Toledo *Also called Faurecia Exhaust Systems LLC* *(G-18463)*

Faurecia USA Holdings Inc 419 727-5000
  543 Matzinger Rd Toledo (43612) *(G-18464)*

Faw Industries 216 651-9595
  14837 Detroit Ave 207 Cleveland (44107) *(G-5327)*

Fawcett Co Inc 330 659-4187
  3863 Congress Pkwy Richfield (44286) *(G-16623)*

Fawn Confectionery (PA) 513 574-9612
  4271 Harrison Ave Cincinnati (45211) *(G-3742)*

Fax Medley Group Inc 513 272-1932
  7754 Camargo Rd Ste 18 Cincinnati (45243) *(G-3743)*

Faxon Firearms LLC 513 674-2580
  11101 Adwood Dr Cincinnati (45240) *(G-3744)*

Faxon Machining Inc 513 851-4644
  11101 Adwood Dr Cincinnati (45240) *(G-3745)*

Fayette Industrial Coatings 419 636-1773
  533 Commerce Dr Ste A Bryan (43506) *(G-2295)*

FB Ins, Fostoria *Also called Fostoria Bushings Inc* *(G-9974)*

FBC Chemical Corporation 216 341-2000
  7301 Bessemer Ave Cleveland (44127) *(G-5328)*

Fbf Limited 513 541-6300
  2980 Spring Grove Ave Cincinnati (45225) *(G-3746)*

Fbg Bottling Group LLC 614 554-4646
  1523 Alum Creek Dr Columbus (43209) *(G-7077)*

Fbr Industries Inc 330 701-7425
  1336 Seaborn St Ste 7 Mineral Ridge (44440) *(G-14304)*

Fca LLC 309 644-2424
  6611 Hoke Rd Clayton (45315) *(G-4658)*

FCA US LLC 419 661-3500
  8000 Chrysler Dr Perrysburg (43551) *(G-16094)*

Fci Inc 216 251-5200
  4661 Giles Rd Cleveland (44135) *(G-5329)*

Fcr Suspension, East Palestine *Also called Mx Spring Inc* *(G-9242)*

Fcs, Milford *Also called Fluid Conservation Systems* *(G-14141)*

Fcs Graphics Inc 216 771-5177
  2169 Saint Clair Ave Ne Cleveland (44114) *(G-5330)*

Fcx Performance Inc (PA) 614 324-6050
  3000 E 14th Ave Columbus (43219) *(G-7078)*

Fdi Cabinetry LLC 513 353-4500
  5555 Dry Fork Rd Cleves (45002) *(G-6514)*

Feather Lite Innovations Inc (PA) 937 743-9008
  650 Pleasant Valley Dr Springboro (45066) *(G-17480)*

Featherweight Turf Inc 920 452-4861
  2250 Kenskill Ave Wshngtn CT Hs (43160) *(G-20908)*

Fechheimer Brothers Company (HQ) 513 793-7819
  4545 Malsbary Rd Blue Ash (45242) *(G-1792)*

Federal Barcode Label Systems 440 748-8060
  33438 Liberty Pkwy North Ridgeville (44039) *(G-15373)*

Federal Equipment Company (PA) 513 621-5260
  5298 River Rd Cincinnati (45233) *(G-3747)*

Federal Gear, Eastlake *Also called Tymoca Partners LLC* *(G-9294)*

Federal Heath Sign Company LLC 740 369-0999
  1020 Pittsburgh Dr Ste B Delaware (43015) *(G-8844)*

Federal Hose Manufacturing, Painesville *Also called First Francis Company Inc* *(G-15881)*

Federal Iron Works Company 330 482-5910
  42082 State Route 344 Columbiana (44408) *(G-6616)*

Federal Metal Co, Bedford *Also called Oakwood Industries Inc* *(G-1450)*

Federal Metal Company...440 232-8700
7250 Division St Cleveland (44146) **(G-5331)**
Federal Process Corporation (PA)...216 464-6440
4520 Richmond Rd Cleveland (44128) **(G-5332)**
Federal-Mogul Corporation...740 432-2393
6420 Glenn Hwy Cambridge (43725) **(G-2457)**
Federal-Mogul Corporation...419 238-1053
150 Fisher Ave Van Wert (45891) **(G-19257)**
Federal-Mogul Valve Train Inte...330 628-6700
1035 Western Dr Brunswick (44212) **(G-2224)**
Fedex Corporation...740 687-0334
1612 N Memorial Dr Lancaster (43130) **(G-11716)**
Fedex Office & Print Svcs Inc...513 777-1079
7785 Cox Ln West Chester (45069) **(G-19862)**
Fedex Office & Print Svcs Inc...614 356-1639
6735 Avery Muirfield Dr Dublin (43016) **(G-9076)**
Fedex Office & Print Svcs Inc...937 335-3816
1886 W Main St Troy (45373) **(G-18827)**
Fedex Office & Print Svcs Inc...419 841-2756
7007 W Central Ave Unit C Toledo (43617) **(G-18465)**
Fedex Office & Print Svcs Inc...614 478-1180
4157 Morse Xing Columbus (43219) **(G-7079)**
Fedex Office & Print Svcs Inc...937 436-0677
1189 Mmsburg Cntrville Rd Dayton (45459) **(G-8339)**
Fedex Office & Print Svcs Inc...330 376-6002
322 E Exchange St Akron (44304) **(G-183)**
Fedex Office & Print Svcs Inc...614 621-1100
180 N High St Columbus (43215) **(G-7080)**
Fedex Office & Print Svcs Inc...419 866-5464
2306 S Reynolds Rd Toledo (43614) **(G-18466)**
Fedex Office & Print Svcs Inc...614 898-0000
604 W Schrock Rd Westerville (43081) **(G-20214)**
Fedex Office & Print Svcs Inc...614 575-0800
2668 Brice Rd Reynoldsburg (43068) **(G-16590)**
Fedex Office & Print Svcs Inc...513 754-1482
8463 S Mason Montgomery R Mason (45040) **(G-13021)**
Fedex Office & Print Svcs Inc...216 573-1511
6901 Rockside Rd Cleveland (44131) **(G-5333)**
Fedex Office & Print Svcs Inc...440 605-0191
5138 Wilson Mills Rd Richmond Heights (44143) **(G-16653)**
Feedall Inc...440 942-8100
38379 Pelton Rd Willoughby (44094) **(G-20486)**
Feikert Concrete, Millersburg *Also called Feikert Sand & Gravel Co Inc* **(G-14215)**
Feikert Sand & Gravel Co Inc...330 674-0038
6971 County Road 189 Millersburg (44654) **(G-14215)**
Feilhauers Machine Shop Inc (PA)...513 202-0545
421 Industrial Dr Harrison (45030) **(G-10778)**
Feinblanking Limited Inc...513 860-2100
9461 Le Saint Dr West Chester (45014) **(G-19863)**
Feiner Pattern Works Inc...513 851-9800
11335 Sebring Dr Cincinnati (45240) **(G-3748)**
Feinkost Ingredient Co U S A...330 948-3006
103 Billman St Lodi (44254) **(G-12161)**
Feinkost Ingredients, Lodi *Also called Feinkost Ingredient Co U S A* **(G-12161)**
Feintool Cincinnati Inc (HQ)...513 247-0110
11280 Cornell Park Dr Blue Ash (45242) **(G-1793)**
Feintool US Operations Inc (HQ)...513 247-4061
11280 Cornell Park Dr Blue Ash (45242) **(G-1794)**
Feld Printing Co...513 271-6806
6806 Main St Cincinnati (45244) **(G-3749)**
Feller Tool Co Inc...440 324-6277
194 Morgan Ave Elyria (44035) **(G-9423)**
Fellow's, Willoughby *Also called Fionas Fineries* **(G-20487)**
Femc, Bedford Heights *Also called Food Equipment Mfg Corp* **(G-1484)**
Fence One Inc...216 441-2600
11111 Broadway Ave Cleveland (44125) **(G-5334)**
Fenix LLC (HQ)...419 739-3400
319 S Vine St Fostoria (44830) **(G-9971)**
Fenix Fabrication Inc...330 745-8731
2689 Wingate Ave Akron (44314) **(G-184)**
Fenix Magnetics Inc...415 308-0134
1360 W Clifton Blvd Lakewood (44107) **(G-11663)**
Fenner Dunlop (toledo) LLC...419 531-5300
146 S Westwood Ave Toledo (43607) **(G-18467)**
Fenner Dunlop Port Clinton Inc...419 635-2191
5225 W Lakeshore Dr Port Clinton (43452) **(G-16399)**
Fenner Enterprises Inc...937 698-7048
7131 Fenner Rd Ludlow Falls (45339) **(G-12426)**
Fenner Sand & Gravel, Ludlow Falls *Also called Fenner Enterprises Inc* **(G-12426)**
Fenton Bros Electric Co...330 343-0093
235 Ray Ave Ne New Philadelphia (44663) **(G-14898)**
Fenton Manufacturing Inc...440 969-1128
6600 Depot Rd Ashtabula (44004) **(G-807)**
Fenton's Festival of Lights, New Philadelphia *Also called Fenton Bros Electric Co* **(G-14898)**
Fenwick Frame Shppe Art Gllery, Toledo *Also called Fenwick Gallery of Fine Arts* **(G-18468)**
Fenwick Gallery of Fine Arts (PA)...419 475-1651
3433 W Alexis Rd Frnt Toledo (43623) **(G-18468)**
Ferco Tech LLC...937 746-6696
291 Conover Dr Franklin (45005) **(G-10022)**
Ferguson Fire Fabrication Inc...614 299-2070
1640 Clara St Columbus (43211) **(G-7081)**
Ferguson Tools Inc...419 298-2327
103 Industrial Dr Edgerton (43517) **(G-9330)**
Fergusons Cut Glass Works...419 734-0808
5890 East Harbor Rd Marblehead (43440) **(G-12744)**
Fergusons Finishing Inc...419 241-9123
126 N Ontario St Toledo (43604) **(G-18469)**
Fernandes Enterprises LLC (PA)...937 890-6444
2801 Ontario Ave Dayton (45414) **(G-8340)**
Ferralloy Inc...440 250-1900
28001 Ranney Pkwy Cleveland (44145) **(G-5335)**
Ferrante Wine Farm Inc...440 466-8466
558 Rte 307 Geneva (44041) **(G-10347)**
Ferriot Inc...330 786-3000
1000 Arlington Cir Akron (44306) **(G-185)**
Ferro Corporation...216 577-7144
7050 Krick Rd Bedford (44146) **(G-1423)**
Ferro Corporation (PA)...216 875-5600
6060 Parkland Blvd # 250 Mayfield Heights (44124) **(G-13313)**
Ferro Corporation...216 875-5600
6060 Parkland Blvd # 250 Cleveland (44124) **(G-5336)**
Ferro Corporation...216 875-6178
4150 E 56th St Ste 1 Cleveland (44105) **(G-5337)**
Ferro Corporation...330 682-8015
1560 N Main St Orrville (44667) **(G-15736)**
Ferro Corporation...216 481-0238
1636 Wayside Rd Cleveland (44112) **(G-5338)**
Ferro International Svcs Inc...216 875-5600
6060 Parkland Blvd # 250 Mayfield Heights (44124) **(G-13314)**
Ferrolux Metals Co Ohio LLC...216 671-6161
8055a Hghland Pointe Pkwy Macedonia (44056) **(G-12449)**
Ferrotherm Corporation...216 883-9350
4758 Warner Rd Cleveland (44125) **(G-5339)**
Ferrous Processing and Trading, Cleveland *Also called Fpt Cleveland LLC* **(G-5376)**
Ferrum Industries Inc (HQ)...440 519-1768
1831 Highland Rd Twinsburg (44087) **(G-18935)**
Ferry & Quintax, Stow *Also called Ferry Industries Inc* **(G-17753)**
Ferry Cap & Set Screw Company (HQ)...216 649-7400
13300 Bramley Ave Lakewood (44107) **(G-11664)**
Ferry Industries Inc (PA)...330 920-9200
4445 Allen Rd Ste A Stow (44224) **(G-17753)**
Fertility Solutions Inc...216 491-0030
11811 Shaker Blvd Ste 330 Cleveland (44120) **(G-5340)**
Fes Incorprated, Cincinnati *Also called Fes-Ohio Inc* **(G-3750)**
Fes-Ohio Inc...513 772-8566
4030 Mt Carml Tbsc Rd # 227 Cincinnati (45255) **(G-3750)**
Feslers Refinishing...740 622-4849
315 Main St Coshocton (43812) **(G-7890)**
Fetters and Son Sign Company...614 299-6947
4305 State Route 314 Mount Gilead (43338) **(G-14559)**
Fetters Racing Engine Inc...937 698-6411
7245 S Rangeline Rd Union (45322) **(G-19066)**
Fetzer Machining Co Inc...937 962-4019
5192 Pyrmont Rd Lewisburg (45338) **(G-11933)**
Few Atmtive GL Applcations Inc...234 249-1880
1660 Enterprise Pkwy Wooster (44691) **(G-20772)**
Ffr-DSI Company...330 998-7800
8181 Darrow Rd Twinsburg (44087) **(G-18936)**
Fgb International LLC (PA)...440 359-0000
7670 First Pl Cleveland (44146) **(G-5341)**
Fgc Plasma Solutions LLC...954 591-1429
11201 Cedar Ave Cleveland (44106) **(G-5342)**
Fgm Media Inc...440 376-0487
13981 Stoney Creek Dr North Royalton (44133) **(G-15419)**
Fhi Heat Inc (PA)...216 456-0353
31875 Solon Rd Ste 6 Solon (44139) **(G-17291)**
Fiba Technologies Inc...330 602-7300
3211 Brightwood Rd Midvale (44653) **(G-14107)**
Fiber Sales & Development, Urbana *Also called Solvaira Specialties Inc* **(G-19181)**
Fiber Systems, Dayton *Also called Industrial Fiberglass Spc Inc* **(G-8402)**
Fiber Tech Industries Inc...740 636-3232
2000 Kenskill Ave Wshngtn CT Hs (43160) **(G-20909)**
Fibercorr Mills LLC...330 837-5151
670 17th St Nw Massillon (44647) **(G-13131)**
Fiberglass Engineering Co, Cleveland *Also called Hanlon Industries Inc* **(G-5479)**
Fiberglass Link Inc...216 531-5515
18607 Saint Clair Ave Cleveland (44110) **(G-5343)**
Fibreboard Corporation (HQ)...419 248-8000
1 Owens Corning Pkwy Toledo (43659) **(G-18470)**
Fidelity Orthopedic Inc (PA)...937 228-0682
8514 N Main St Dayton (45415) **(G-8341)**
Fiedeldey Stl Fabricators Inc...513 353-3300
8487 E Miami River Rd Cincinnati (45247) **(G-3751)**
Field Apparatus Service & Tstg...513 353-9399
4040 Rev Dr Cincinnati (45232) **(G-3752)**
Field Aviation Inc (PA)...513 792-2282
8044 Montgomery Rd # 530 Cincinnati (45236) **(G-3753)**
Field Dailies LLC...859 379-2120
323 W 5th St Apt 3 Cincinnati (45202) **(G-3754)**

ALPHABETIC

(PA)=Parent Co (HQ)=Headquarters (DH)=Div Headquarters

Field Gymmy Inc 419 538-6511
138-143 S Main St Glandorf (45848) *(G-10397)*

Field Specialties 440 635-0064
11609 Claridon Troy Rd Chardon (44024) *(G-3153)*

Field Stone Inc 937 898-3236
2750 Us Route 40 Tipp City (45371) *(G-18277)*

Fields Associates Inc 513 426-8652
2134 Hatmaker St Ste 3 Cincinnati (45204) *(G-3755)*

Fiery Chillcom 800 575-4180
515 E Turkeyfoot Lake Rd Akron (44319) *(G-186)*

Fifth Avenue Fret Shop LLC 614 481-8300
1597 W 5th Ave Columbus (43212) *(G-7082)*

Fifth Avenue Lumber Co 614 833-6655
5200 Winchester Pike Canal Winchester (43110) *(G-2524)*

Figleaf Brewing Company, Middletown *Also called Unbridled Brewing Company LLC (G-14091)*

Figley Stamping Company, Defiance *Also called Marc V Concepts Inc (G-8801)*

Filament LLC 614 732-0754
1507 Chambers Rd Fl 1 Columbus (43212) *(G-7083)*

File 13 Inc 937 642-4855
232 N Main St Ste K Marysville (43040) *(G-12943)*

File Sharpening Company Inc 937 376-8268
360 W Church St Xenia (45385) *(G-20951)*

Fillous & Ruppel Inc 216 431-0470
7411 Cedar Ave Cleveland (44103) *(G-5344)*

Filmco, Aurora *Also called Kapstone Container Corporation (G-928)*

Filmtec Inc 419 435-1819
1120 Sandusky St Fostoria (44830) *(G-9972)*

Filnor Inc (PA) 330 821-8731
227 N Freedom Ave Alliance (44601) *(G-506)*

Filnor Inc 330 829-3180
181 N Arch Ave Alliance (44601) *(G-507)*

Filnor Inc 330 821-7667
227 N Freedom Ave Alliance (44601) *(G-508)*

Filter Factory-Ttn Inc 440 963-2034
3409 Liberty Ave Ste 100 Vermilion (44089) *(G-19326)*

Filters.com, Hilliard *Also called Barney Corporation Inc (G-10930)*

Fimco Services LLC 330 830-1413
11771 Barrs Rd Sw Massillon (44647) *(G-13132)*

Fimm USA Inc 253 243-1522
5454 Alkire Rd Columbus (43228) *(G-7084)*

Fin Feather Fur 330 493-8300
4080 Belden Village St Nw Canton (44718) *(G-2701)*

Fin Pan Inc (PA) 513 870-9200
3255 Symmes Rd Hamilton (45015) *(G-10692)*

Fin Tube Products Inc 330 334-3736
188 S Lyman St Ste 100 Wadsworth (44281) *(G-19406)*

Final Finish Corp 440 439-3303
596 Highland Rd E Macedonia (44056) *(G-12450)*

Final Machine 330 966-1744
8397 Cleveland Ave Nw Canton (44720) *(G-2702)*

Final Touch Metal Fabricating 216 348-1750
2290 Scranton Rd Cleveland (44113) *(G-5345)*

Fincom Corporation (PA) 330 456-8341
220 Market Ave S Ste 612 Canton (44702) *(G-2703)*

Findaway World LLC 440 893-0808
31999 Aurora Rd Solon (44139) *(G-17292)*

Findlay American Prosthetic & 419 424-1622
12474 County Road 99 Findlay (45840) *(G-9822)*

Findlay Machine & Tool Inc 419 434-3100
2000 Industrial Dr Findlay (45840) *(G-9823)*

Findlay Pallet Inc 419 423-0511
300 Bell Ave Findlay (45840) *(G-9824)*

Findlay Party Mart, Findlay *Also called Ottawa Oil Co Inc (G-9874)*

Findlay Products Corporation 419 423-3324
2045 Industrial Dr Findlay (45840) *(G-9825)*

Findlay Terminal, Findlay *Also called Michigan Sugar Company (G-9860)*

Fine Line Embroidery Company 330 788-9070
4660 Lake Park Rd Youngstown (44512) *(G-21084)*

Fine Line Embroidery Company (PA) 440 331-7030
20525 Detroit Rd Ste 9 Rocky River (44116) *(G-16699)*

Fine Line Graphics Corp (PA) 614 486-0276
1481 Goodale Blvd Columbus (43212) *(G-7085)*

Fine Line Tool and Die Inc 330 782-8139
1804 Roberts Ln Ne Warren (44483) *(G-19550)*

Fine Lines, Wadsworth *Also called Quality Reproductions Inc (G-19433)*

Fine Lines Laser Engraving 419 337-6313
12825 County Road 14 Wauseon (43567) *(G-19677)*

Fine Points Inc 216 229-6644
12620 Larchmere Blvd Cleveland (44120) *(G-5346)*

Fine Print LLC 419 702-7087
508 Oak Ave Lakeside Marblehead (43440) *(G-11648)*

Fine Wood Design Inc 440 327-0751
35535 Center Ridge Rd North Ridgeville (44039) *(G-15374)*

Fineline Imprints Inc 740 453-1083
516 State St Zanesville (43701) *(G-21308)*

Finelli Architectural Iron Co, Cleveland *Also called Finelli Ornamental Iron Co (G-5347)*

Finelli Ornamental Iron Co 440 248-0050
30815 Solon Rd Cleveland (44139) *(G-5347)*

Finishers Inc 937 773-3177
1718 Commerce Dr Piqua (45356) *(G-16264)*

Finishing Brands, Toledo *Also called Carlisle Fluid Tech Inc (G-18389)*

Finishing Machine Inc 419 491-0197
707 Lost Lakes Dr Holland (43528) *(G-11060)*

Finishing Touch 440 263-9264
22084 Lorain Rd Cleveland (44126) *(G-5348)*

Finishmaster Inc 614 228-4328
212 N Grant Ave Columbus (43215) *(G-7086)*

Finite Fibers, Akron *Also called Dowco LLC (G-155)*

Fink Meat Company Inc 937 390-2750
2475 Troy Rd Springfield (45504) *(G-17558)*

Finn Graphics Inc 513 941-6161
220 Stille Dr Cincinnati (45233) *(G-3756)*

Fiomet LLC 513 519-7622
2717 Erie Ave Cincinnati (45208) *(G-3757)*

Fionas Fineries 440 796-7426
9077 Billings Rd Willoughby (44094) *(G-20487)*

Fire & Marine Inc 937 323-2770
5325 Prosperity Dr Springfield (45502) *(G-17559)*

Fire Ball Press 614 280-0100
27 E 5th Ave Columbus (43201) *(G-7087)*

Fire Fab Corporation 330 759-9834
999 Trumbull Ave Girard (44420) *(G-10386)*

Fire Foe Corp 330 759-9834
999 Trumbull Ave Girard (44420) *(G-10387)*

Fire From Ice Ventures LLC 419 944-6705
30333 Emerald Valley Pkwy Solon (44139) *(G-17293)*

Fire Nation Glassline Stud, Holland *Also called Fire Nation Ltd (G-11061)*

Fire Nation Ltd 419 866-6288
7166 Front St Holland (43528) *(G-11061)*

Fire Pit Gallery, The, Bristolville *Also called Strutt Products LLC (G-2100)*

Fire Safety Services Inc 937 686-2000
6228 Township Road 95 Huntsville (43324) *(G-11213)*

Fire Tetrahedron Journal 567 220-6477
3110 E County Road 50 C Tiffin (44883) *(G-18220)*

Fire-Dex LLC 330 723-0000
780 S Progress Dr Medina (44256) *(G-13410)*

Fire-End & Croker Corp 513 870-0517
4690 Interstate Dr Ste P West Chester (45246) *(G-20001)*

Firehouse Foods 614 592-8115
917 E Whittier St Columbus (43206) *(G-7088)*

Firehouse Sign Co Inc 216 267-5300
5241 W 161st St Brookpark (44142) *(G-2159)*

Firelands Farmer, The, New London *Also called Sdg News Group Inc (G-14865)*

Firelands Fas-Print LLC 419 668-3045
59 Benedict Ave Norwalk (44857) *(G-15541)*

Firelands Manufacturing LLC 419 687-8237
500 Industrial Park Dr Plymouth (44865) *(G-16376)*

Firelands Winery 419 625-5474
917 Bardshar Rd Sandusky (44870) *(G-16965)*

Fireline Inc 330 259-0647
8560 Foxwood Ct Youngstown (44514) *(G-21085)*

Fireline Inc (PA) 330 743-1164
300 Andrews Ave Youngstown (44505) *(G-21086)*

Fireline Tcon, Youngstown *Also called Fireline Inc (G-21086)*

Firenza Stone Inc 440 953-8883
36420 Biltmore Pl Ste 4 Willoughby (44094) *(G-20488)*

Fireside Hearth & Homes, Cincinnati *Also called Hearth & Home Technologies LLC (G-3875)*

Firestone, Akron *Also called Bridgestone Ret Operations LLC (G-99)*

Firestone Polymers LLC (HQ) 330 379-7000
381 W Wilbeth Rd Akron (44301) *(G-187)*

Firestone Sheet Metal Inc 330 337-9551
949 S Broadway Ave Salem (44460) *(G-16890)*

Firovac, Apple Creek *Also called Reberland Equipment Inc (G-648)*

First Catholc Slovak Union U S (PA) 216 642-9406
6611 Rockside Rd Cleveland (44131) *(G-5349)*

First Choice Packaging Inc (PA) 419 333-4100
1501 W State St Fremont (43420) *(G-10145)*

First Choice Packg Solutions, Fremont *Also called First Choice Packaging Inc (G-10145)*

First Filter LLC 419 666-5260
620 1st St Ampoint Perrysburg (43551) *(G-16095)*

First Francis Company Inc (HQ) 440 352-8927
25 Florence Ave Painesville (44077) *(G-15881)*

First Impression Wear 937 456-3900
120 E Main St Eaton (45320) *(G-9306)*

First Impressions Printing, Lancaster *Also called Brooke Printers Inc (G-11692)*

First Machine & Tool Corp 440 269-8644
38181 Airport Pkwy Willoughby (44094) *(G-20489)*

First Merit 330 849-8750
106 S Main St Fl 6 Akron (44308) *(G-188)*

First Place Auto Products 330 493-1420
6495 Chesham Ave Ne Canton (44721) *(G-2704)*

First Solar Inc 419 661-1478
28101 Cedar Park Blvd Perrysburg (43551) *(G-16096)*

First Solar Electric, Perrysburg *Also called First Solar Inc (G-16096)*

First Stop Signs and Decals 330 343-1859
138 E High Ave New Philadelphia (44663) *(G-14899)*

First Tool Corp 937 254-6197
612 Linden Ave Dayton (45403) **(G-8342)**

Firstar Precision Corporation 216 362-7888
12340 Plaza Dr Cleveland (44130) **(G-5350)**

Firstenergy Corp 419 321-7114
5501 N State Route 2 Oak Harbor (43449) **(G-15590)**

Firstfuelcellscom LLC 440 884-2503
11163 Blossom Ave Cleveland (44130) **(G-5351)**

Firstnrgy Nclear Gnration Corp 330 761-4370
76 S Main St Bsmt Akron (44308) **(G-189)**

Fischer Engineering Company 937 754-1750
8220 Expansion Way Dayton (45424) **(G-8343)**

Fischer Global Enterprises LLC 513 583-4900
155 Commerce Dr Loveland (45140) **(G-12349)**

Fischer Special Tooling Corp 440 951-8411
7219 Commerce Dr Mentor (44060) **(G-13578)**

Fischer-Backus Corp 740 362-2100
8919 Whitney Dr Lewis Center (43035) **(G-11898)**

Fish Express 513 661-3000
2463 Harrison Ave Cincinnati (45211) **(G-3758)**

Fishburn Tank Truck Service 419 253-6031
5012 State Route 229 Marengo (43334) **(G-12750)**

Fishel Company 614 850-4400
1600 Walcutt Rd Columbus (43228) **(G-7089)**

Fisher Cast Steel Products Inc (PA) 614 879-8325
6 W Town St West Jefferson (43162) **(G-20078)**

Fisher Controls Intl LLC 513 285-6000
5453 W Chester Rd West Chester (45069) **(G-19864)**

Fisher Drug, Sandusky Also called Buderer Drug Co **(G-16950)**

Fisher Metal Fabricating 419 838-7200
27953 E Broadway St Walbridge (43465) **(G-19457)**

Fisher Pallet 440 632-0863
8496 Bundysburg Rd Middlefield (44062) **(G-13934)**

Fisher Sand & Gravel Inc 330 745-9239
3322 Clark Mill Rd Norton (44203) **(G-15512)**

Fisher Testers LLC 937 416-6554
5079 Kerridge Rd Huber Heights (45424) **(G-11147)**

Fiske Brothers Refining Co 419 691-2491
1500 Oakdale Ave Toledo (43605) **(G-18471)**

Fitchville East Corp 419 929-1510
1732 Us Highway 250 S New London (44851) **(G-14859)**

Fitchville East Storage, New London Also called Fitchville East Corp **(G-14859)**

Fithian-Wilbert Burial Vlt Co 330 758-2327
6234 Market St Youngstown (44512) **(G-21087)**

Fitne Inc 740 592-2433
5 Depot St Athens (45701) **(G-865)**

Fitness Serve, Rocky River Also called Balbo Industries Inc **(G-16695)**

Five Handicap Inc (PA) 419 525-2511
127 N Walnut St Mansfield (44902) **(G-12603)**

Five Points Distillery LLC 937 776-4634
122 Van Buren St Dayton (45402) **(G-8344)**

Five Star Graphics Inc 330 545-5077
201 W Liberty St Girard (44420) **(G-10388)**

Five Star Machine & Tool 937 420-2170
403 S Main St Fort Loramie (45845) **(G-9930)**

Fivecoat Lumber Inc 740 254-4681
2400 Larson Rd Se Gnadenhutten (44629) **(G-10407)**

Fivepoint LLC 937 374-3193
825 Bellbrook Ave Unit B Xenia (45385) **(G-20952)**

Fives Bronx Inc 330 277-1366
8817 Pleasantwood Ave Nw North Canton (44720) **(G-15231)**

Fives Landis Corp 440 709-0700
7605 Discovery Ln Painesville (44077) **(G-15882)**

Fives N Amercn Combustn Inc (HQ) 216 271-6000
4455 E 71st St Cleveland (44105) **(G-5352)**

Fives St Corp 419 522-1080
1485 Lexington Ave Mansfield (44907) **(G-12604)**

Fives St Corp (HQ) 419 522-1080
1485 Lexington Ave Mansfield (44907) **(G-12605)**

Fixture Dimensions Inc 513 360-7512
4355 Salzman Rd Middletown (45044) **(G-14041)**

Fkci, Beavercreek Also called F & K Concepts Inc **(G-1337)**

Flag Lady Inc 614 263-1776
4567 N High St Columbus (43214) **(G-7090)**

Flag Lady's Flag Store, The, Columbus Also called Flag Lady Inc **(G-7090)**

Flambeau Inc 440 632-3752
15981 Valplast St Middlefield (44062) **(G-13935)**

Flambeau Inc 440 632-1631
15981 Valplast St Middlefield (44062) **(G-13936)**

Flambeau Inc 330 239-0202
1468 Wolfe Creek Trl Sharon Center (44274) **(G-17106)**

Flame Safe of Northern Ohio 419 626-6204
1202 Stone St Sandusky (44870) **(G-16966)**

Flaming River Industries Inc 440 826-4488
800 Poertner Dr Berea (44017) **(G-1616)**

Flash Industrial Tech Ltd 440 786-8979
30 Industry Dr Cleveland (44146) **(G-5353)**

Flashions Sportswear Ltd 937 323-5885
1002 N Bechtle Ave Springfield (45504) **(G-17560)**

Flavor Systems International 513 870-0420
9930 Commerce Park Dr West Chester (45246) **(G-20002)**

Flavor Systems Intl Inc (HQ) 513 870-4900
5404 Duff Dr West Chester (45246) **(G-20003)**

Flavorseal LLC 440 937-3900
35179 Avon Commerce Pkwy Avon (44011) **(G-995)**

Fleet Graphics Inc 937 252-2552
1701 Thomas Paine Pkwy Dayton (45459) **(G-8345)**

Fleetchem LLC 513 539-1111
651 N Garver Rd Monroe (45050) **(G-14401)**

Fleetline Tool & Die Co 216 441-4949
7803 Harvard Ave Cleveland (44105) **(G-5354)**

Fleetmaster Express Inc 419 425-0666
5250 Distribution Dr Findlay (45840) **(G-9826)**

Fleetwood Craftsman, Johnstown Also called Fleetwood Custom Countertops **(G-11398)**

Fleetwood Custom Countertops (PA) 740 965-9833
15710 Center Village Rd Johnstown (43031) **(G-11398)**

Flegal Brothers Inc 419 298-3539
104 Industrial Dr Edgerton (43517) **(G-9331)**

Fleig Enterprises Inc 216 361-8020
940 E 67th St Cleveland (44103) **(G-5355)**

Fleming Construction Co 740 494-2177
5298 Marion Marysville Rd Prospect (43342) **(G-16496)**

Flemish Investments Inc 419 625-4073
1005 Cleveland Rd Sandusky (44870) **(G-16967)**

Flesher Sand & Gravel, Norton Also called Fisher Sand & Gravel Inc **(G-15512)**

Flex Pro Label Inc 513 489-4417
11465 Deerfield Rd Blue Ash (45242) **(G-1795)**

Flex Technologies Inc 330 359-5415
16183 E Main St Mount Eaton (44659) **(G-14555)**

Flex Technologies Inc 330 897-6311
3430 State Route 93 Baltic (43804) **(G-1071)**

Flex-Core Division, Hilliard Also called Morlan & Associates Inc **(G-10964)**

Flex-E-On Inc 330 928-4496
3332 Cavalier Trl Cuyahoga Falls (44224) **(G-7997)**

Flex-Strut Inc 330 372-9999
2900 Commonwealth Ave Ne Warren (44483) **(G-19551)**

Flexarm, Wapakoneta Also called Midwest Specialties Inc **(G-19501)**

Flexcart LLC 614 348-2517
5868 Kitzmiller Rd New Albany (43054) **(G-14759)**

Flexmag Industries Inc (HQ) 740 373-3492
107 Industry Rd Marietta (45750) **(G-12784)**

Flexnova Inc 216 288-6961
6100 Oak Tree Blvd Cleveland (44131) **(G-5356)**

Flexodie (HQ) 513 489-0433
1310 Hook Dr Middletown (45042) **(G-14042)**

Flexomation LLC 513 825-0555
11701 Chesterdale Rd Cincinnati (45246) **(G-3759)**

Flexoplate Inc 513 489-0433
6504 Corporate Dr Blue Ash (45242) **(G-1796)**

Flexotech Graphics Inc (PA) 330 929-4743
4830 Hudson Dr Stow (44224) **(G-17754)**

Flexsys America LP (HQ) 330 666-4111
260 Springside Dr Akron (44333) **(G-190)**

Flextronics International Usa 513 755-2500
6224 Windham Ct Liberty Township (45044) **(G-11961)**

Flight Operations, Cleveland Also called Swagelok Company **(G-6277)**

Flight Specialties Components, Highland Heights Also called Heico Aerospace Parts Corp **(G-10915)**

Flightlogix LLC 513 321-1200
4510 Airport Rd Cincinnati (45226) **(G-3760)**

Flint Group Global Packaging, Lebanon Also called Flint Group US LLC **(G-11800)**

Flint Group US LLC 513 771-1900
410 Glendale Milford Rd Cincinnati (45215) **(G-3761)**

Flint Group US LLC 513 934-6500
2675 Henkle Dr Lebanon (45036) **(G-11800)**

Flint Group US LLC 216 267-1927
4801 W 160th St Cleveland (44135) **(G-5357)**

Flint Ridge Energy 740 344-1351
581 Country Club Dr Ste B Newark (43055) **(G-15007)**

Flipside Inc (PA) 440 600-7274
44 N Main St Chagrin Falls (44022) **(G-3059)**

Flocel Inc 216 619-5903
4415 Euclid Ave Ste 421 Cleveland (44103) **(G-5358)**

Flohr Machine Company Inc 330 745-3030
1028 Coventry Rd Barberton (44203) **(G-1114)**

Flohrmachine.com, Barberton Also called Flohr Machine Company Inc **(G-1114)**

Flood Heliarc Inc 614 835-3929
4181 Venture Pl Groveport (43125) **(G-10621)**

Floorcraft Designs, Toledo Also called Property Assist Inc **(G-18660)**

Florence Alloys Inc 330 745-9141
121 Snyder Ave Barberton (44203) **(G-1115)**

Florida Production Engrg Inc 937 996-4361
1855 State Route 121 N New Madison (45346) **(G-14869)**

Florida Production Engrg Inc 740 420-5252
30627 Orr Rd Circleville (43113) **(G-4629)**

Florida Tile Inc 513 891-1122
10840 Millington Ct Blue Ash (45242) **(G-1797)**

Florida Tile Inc 614 436-2511
  7029 Huntley Rd Ste B Columbus (43229) *(G-7091)*
Florida Tile Inc 937 293-5151
  2105 Lyons Rd Miamisburg (45342) *(G-13809)*
Florline Display Products Corp 440 975-9449
  38160 Western Pkwy Willoughby (44094) *(G-20490)*
Flory Cabinetry, Covington *Also called Harold Flory (G-7924)*
Flotbi Inc 216 619-5928
  4415 Euclid Ave Ste 421 Cleveland (44103) *(G-5359)*
Flottemesch Anthony & Son 513 561-1212
  8201 Camargo Rd Ste 1 Cincinnati (45243) *(G-3762)*
Floturn Inc (PA) 513 860-8040
  4236 Thunderbird Ln West Chester (45014) *(G-19865)*
Flow Control US Holding Corp 800 843-5628
  4030 Mount Carmel Tobasco Cincinnati (45255) *(G-3763)*
Flow Control US Holding Corp 419 289-1144
  1430 George Rd 1101 Ashland (44805) *(G-733)*
Flow Dry Technology Inc (HQ) 937 833-2161
  379 Albert Rd Brookville (45309) *(G-2183)*
Flow Dry Technology, LLC, Brookville *Also called Ftd Investments LLC (G-2184)*
Flow Line Options Corp 330 331-7331
  471 E Bergey St Wadsworth (44281) *(G-19407)*
Flow Polymers LLC 216 249-4900
  12819 Coit Rd Cleveland (44108) *(G-5360)*
Flow Technology Inc 513 745-6000
  4444 Cooper Rd Cincinnati (45242) *(G-3764)*
Flow-Liner Systems Ltd 800 348-0020
  4830 Northpointe Dr Zanesville (43701) *(G-21309)*
Flowers Bakeries LLC 330 724-1604
  1500 Firestone Pkwy Akron (44301) *(G-191)*
Flowers Print Inc 937 429-3823
  3783 Dayton Xenia Rd Beavercreek (45432) *(G-1338)*
Flowserve Corporation 513 874-6990
  422 Wards Corner Rd F Loveland (45140) *(G-12350)*
Flowserve Corporation 937 226-4568
  2200 E Monument Ave Dayton (45402) *(G-8346)*
Fluence Therapeutics 216 780-5220
  526 S Main St Ste 608c Akron (44311) *(G-192)*
Fluid Automation Inc 248 912-1970
  8400 Port Jackson Ave Nw North Canton (44720) *(G-15232)*
Fluid Conservation Systems (HQ) 513 831-9335
  502 Techne Center Dr B Milford (45150) *(G-14141)*
Fluid Equipment Corp 419 636-0777
  7671 County Road E 7g Bryan (43506) *(G-2296)*
Fluid Line Products Inc 440 946-9470
  38273 Western Pkwy Willoughby (44094) *(G-20491)*
Fluid Power Inc 330 653-5107
  1300 Hudson Gate Dr Hudson (44236) *(G-11171)*
Fluid Power Plant, Beachwood *Also called Eaton Corporation (G-1267)*
Fluid Quip Inc (PA) 937 324-0352
  1940 S Yellow Spring St # 2 Springfield (45506) *(G-17561)*
Fluid System Connectors Div, Kent *Also called Parker-Hannifin Corporation (G-11499)*
Fluid System Service Inc 216 651-2450
  13825 Triskett Rd Cleveland (44111) *(G-5361)*
Fluid-Bag LLC 513 310-9550
  4555 Lake Forest Dr # 650 Blue Ash (45242) *(G-1798)*
Fluidpower Assembly Inc 419 394-7486
  313 S Park Dr Saint Marys (45885) *(G-16839)*
Fluke Biomedical LLC (HQ) 440 248-9300
  6045 Cochran Rd Cleveland (44139) *(G-5362)*
Fly Race Fuels LLC 419 744-9402
  1905 Maple Ridge Rd North Fairfield (44855) *(G-15285)*
Flying Dutchman Inc 740 694-1734
  6631 Egypt Rd Smithville (44677) *(G-17239)*
Flynn Inc 419 478-3743
  5540 Jackman Rd Toledo (43613) *(G-18472)*
Flynn Metering, Hamilton *Also called MA Flynn Associates LLC (G-10721)*
Flypaper Studio Inc 602 801-2208
  311 Elm St Ste 200 Cincinnati (45202) *(G-3765)*
FM, Cleveland *Also called Federal Metal Company (G-5331)*
FM Manufacturing Inc 419 445-0700
  300 E Mechanic St Archbold (43502) *(G-673)*
Fmh Electric Inc 419 782-0671
  1240 Fairgreen Ave Lima (45805) *(G-12013)*
FML Resin LLC 440 214-3200
  8834 Mayfield Rd Chesterland (44026) *(G-3207)*
FML Sand LLC 440 214-3200
  8834 Mayfield Rd Chesterland (44026) *(G-3208)*
FML Terminal Logistics LLC 440 214-3200
  8834 Mayfield Rd Chesterland (44026) *(G-3209)*
Fmt, Findlay *Also called Findlay Machine & Tool Inc (G-9823)*
Fmt Repair Service Co 330 347-7374
  6374 Dawson Blvd Mentor (44060) *(G-13579)*
Fmx, Columbus *Also called Facilities Management Ex LLC (G-7075)*
Foam Concepts & Design Inc 513 860-5589
  4602 Muhlhauser Rd West Chester (45011) *(G-19866)*
Foam Pac Materials Company, West Chester *Also called Storopack Inc (G-20056)*
Foam Seal Inc 216 881-8111
  5109 Hamilton Ave Cleveland (44114) *(G-5363)*

Foam-Tex Solutions Corp 216 889-2702
  13981 W Parkway Rd Cleveland (44135) *(G-5364)*
Focke Rubber Products Div, Dayton *Also called Miami Valley Gasket Co Inc (G-8490)*
Focus Manufacturing Inc 440 946-8766
  38127 Willoughby Pkwy Willoughby (44094) *(G-20492)*
Foerster Instruments Inc 330 332-9100
  1484 Quaker Cir Salem (44460) *(G-16891)*
Foerster Systems Inc 330 332-9100
  1484 Quaker Cir Salem (44460) *(G-16892)*
Folding Carton Service Inc 419 281-4099
  608 Westlake Dr Ashland (44805) *(G-734)*
Folger Coffee Company (HQ) 800 937-9745
  1 Strawberry Ln Orrville (44667) *(G-15737)*
Folgers, Orrville *Also called Folger Coffee Company (G-15737)*
Folio Photonics LLC 440 420-4500
  6864 Cochran Rd Solon (44139) *(G-17294)*
Folks Creative Printers Inc 740 383-6326
  101 E George St Marion (43302) *(G-12865)*
Follow Print Club On Facebook 216 707-2579
  11150 East Blvd Cleveland (44106) *(G-5365)*
Follow River Designs LLC 614 325-9954
  4330 E Hppole Ridge Rd Ne McConnelsville (43756) *(G-13350)*
Foltz & Foltz Ltd Partnership 330 488-1898
  4700 Ravenna Ave Se East Canton (44730) *(G-9192)*
Foltz Machine LLC 330 453-9235
  2030 Allen Ave Se Canton (44707) *(G-2705)*
Fomerly Daniels Printing Den, Waverly *Also called Printex Incorporated (G-19719)*
Fomo Products, Norton *Also called ICP Adhesives and Sealants Inc (G-15513)*
Fondriest Environmental Inc 937 426-2151
  2091 Exchange Ct Fairborn (45324) *(G-9621)*
Fontanelle Group Inc 440 834-8900
  13199 Longwood Ave Burton (44021) *(G-2375)*
Fontova Mexican Foods, Loveland *Also called Lifo Enterprises Inc (G-12371)*
Food 4 Your Soul 330 402-4073
  3957 S Schenley Ave Youngstown (44511) *(G-21088)*
Food Designs Inc 216 651-9221
  5299 Crayton Ave Cleveland (44104) *(G-5366)*
Food Equipment Mfg Corp 216 672-5859
  22201 Aurora Rd Bedford Heights (44146) *(G-1484)*
Food Furniture, Lebanon *Also called Schmidt Progressive LLC (G-11837)*
Food Specialties Co (PA) 513 761-1242
  12 Sunnybrook Dr Cincinnati (45237) *(G-3766)*
Foot Locker Retail Inc 513 671-4085
  11700 Princeton Pike D215 Cincinnati (45246) *(G-3767)*
Foot Logic Inc 330 699-0123
  2824 Sweitzer Rd Uniontown (44685) *(G-19084)*
Foot Wings, Ohio City *Also called Baker Built Products Inc (G-15660)*
Foote Foundry LLC 740 694-1595
  283 N Main St Fredericktown (43019) *(G-10102)*
Foote Printing Company 216 431-1757
  2800 E 55th St Cleveland (44104) *(G-5367)*
For Call Inc 330 863-0404
  3255 Alliance Rd Nw Malvern (44644) *(G-12544)*
For Every Home 740 710-1253
  10381 Chillicothe Pike Jackson (45640) *(G-11314)*
For Rent Magazine, Cincinnati *Also called United Advg Publications Inc (G-4537)*
Forbes Chocolate, Broadview Heights *Also called Benjamin P Forbes Company (G-2104)*
Forbes Rehab Services Inc (PA) 419 589-7688
  49 Illinois Ave S Mansfield (44905) *(G-12606)*
Forcam Inc 513 878-2780
  250 E 5th St Fl 15 Cincinnati (45202) *(G-3768)*
Force Control Industries Inc 513 868-0900
  3660 Dixie Hwy Fairfield (45014) *(G-9659)*
Forceone LLC 513 939-1018
  3600 Hebron Rd Hebron (43025) *(G-10865)*
Ford Motor Company 419 226-7000
  1155 Bible Rd Lima (45801) *(G-12014)*
Ford Motor Company 216 676-3989
  17601 Brookpark Rd Brookpark (44142) *(G-2160)*
Ford Motor Company 440 933-1215
  650 Miller Rd Avon Lake (44012) *(G-1029)*
Ford Motor Company 216 587-7700
  7845 Northfield Rd Bedford (44146) *(G-1424)*
Ford Motor Company 216 587-7700
  7845 Northfield Rd Cleveland (44146) *(G-5368)*
Ford Piping and Brewry Svc LLC 614 284-2409
  1742 Kenny Rd Columbus (43212) *(G-7092)*
Fordyce Custom Finishing, Dayton *Also called Couch Business Development Inc (G-8244)*
Forepleasure 330 821-1293
  14461 Gaskill Dr Ne Alliance (44601) *(G-509)*
Forest City Companies Inc 216 586-5279
  3607 W 56th St Cleveland (44102) *(G-5369)*
Forest City Packaging, Cleveland *Also called Forest City Companies Inc (G-5369)*
Forest City Specialties, Cleveland *Also called Fcs Graphics Inc (G-5330)*
Forest City Tech, Wellington *Also called Tite Seal Case Company Inc (G-19756)*
Forest City Tech Plant 4, Wellington *Also called Forest City Technologies Inc (G-19745)*
Forest City Technologies Inc (PA) 440 647-2115
  299 Clay St Wellington (44090) *(G-19743)*

Forest City Technologies Inc 440 647-2115
  232 Maple St Wellington (44090) *(G-19744)*
Forest City Technologies Inc 440 647-2115
  401 Magyar St Wellington (44090) *(G-19745)*
Forest City Technologies Inc 440 647-2115
  299 Clay St Wellington (44090) *(G-19746)*
Forest City Technologies Inc 440 647-2115
  234 Maple St Wellington (44090) *(G-19747)*
Forest Converting Company Inc 513 631-4190
  4701 Forest Ave Cincinnati (45212) *(G-3769)*
Forest Pharmaceuticals Inc 513 271-6800
  3941 Brotherton Rd Cincinnati (45209) *(G-3770)*
Forest Pharmaceuticals Inc 513 271-6800
  5000 Brotherton Rd Cincinnati (45209) *(G-3771)*
Forge Industries Inc (PA) 330 782-8301
  4450 Market St Youngstown (44512) *(G-21089)*
Forge Products Corporation 216 231-2600
  9503 Woodland Ave Cleveland (44104) *(G-5370)*
Forged Products, Cleveland *Also called Forge Products Corporation* *(G-5370)*
Forgeline Inc 937 299-0298
  3522 Kettering Blvd Ste B Moraine (45439) *(G-14488)*
Forging Eqp Solutions Inc 330 239-2222
  1486 Medina Rd Ste 209 Medina (44256) *(G-13411)*
Forklifts of Americas LLC 440 821-5143
  28 Alpha Park Highland Heights (44143) *(G-10912)*
Form-A-Chip Inc 937 223-4135
  2069 Webster St Dayton (45404) *(G-8347)*
Form-A-Top Products Inc 440 779-9452
  25044 Chase Dr North Olmsted (44070) *(G-15334)*
Formasters Corporation 440 639-9206
  5959 Pinecone Dr Mentor (44060) *(G-13580)*
Formatech Inc 330 273-2800
  3024 Interstate Pkwy Brunswick (44212) *(G-2225)*
Formation Cementing Inc 740 453-6926
  1800 Timber Port Dr Zanesville (43701) *(G-21310)*
Formco Inc 330 966-2111
  5175 Stoneham Rd Canton (44720) *(G-2706)*
Formed Metal Products Inc 440 775-0819
  185 Oberlin Rd Oberlin (44074) *(G-15639)*
Formetal Inc 419 898-2211
  220 Houghton St Ste 36 Oak Harbor (43449) *(G-15591)*
Formica Corporation (HQ) 513 786-3400
  10155 Reading Rd Cincinnati (45241) *(G-3772)*
Formtech Enterprises Inc (PA) 330 688-2171
  3924 Clock Pointe Trl # 101 Stow (44224) *(G-17755)*
Formtek Inc 216 292-6300
  4899 Commerce Pkwy Cleveland (44128) *(G-5371)*
Formtek Inc (HQ) 216 292-4460
  4899 Commerce Pkwy Cleveland (44128) *(G-5372)*
Formware Inc 614 231-9387
  3441 Winchester Pike Columbus (43232) *(G-7093)*
Forrest Enterprises Inc 937 773-1714
  510 W Statler Rd Piqua (45356) *(G-16265)*
Forrest Machine Pdts Co Ltd 419 589-3774
  139 Illinois Ave S Mansfield (44905) *(G-12607)*
Forrest Machine Shop 419 822-5847
  204 Main St Delta (43515) *(G-8932)*
Forrest Pharmaceuticals 513 791-1701
  10901 Kenwood Rd Blue Ash (45242) *(G-1799)*
Forrest Rawlins 740 778-3366
  902 Great Meadow Rd Wheelersburg (45694) *(G-20330)*
Forrest Scrw Machine, Mansfield *Also called Forrest Machine Pdts Co Ltd* *(G-12607)*
Fort Amanda Specialties LLC 419 229-0088
  1747 Fort Amanda Rd Lima (45804) *(G-12015)*
Fort Loramie Cast Stone Pdts 937 420-2257
  120 S Main St Fort Loramie (45845) *(G-9931)*
Fort Recovery Equipment Inc 419 375-1006
  1201 Industrial Dr Fort Recovery (45846) *(G-9949)*
Fort Recovery Equity Inc (PA) 419 375-4119
  2351 Wabash Rd Fort Recovery (45846) *(G-9950)*
Fort Recovery Equity Exchange 937 338-8901
  13243 Cochran Rd Rossburg (45362) *(G-16736)*
Fort Recovery Industries Inc (PA) 419 375-4121
  2440 State Route 49 Fort Recovery (45846) *(G-9951)*
Fort Recovery Industries Inc 419 375-3005
  1200 Industrial Park Dr Fort Recovery (45846) *(G-9952)*
Fort Stben Burial Estates Assn 740 266-6101
  801 Canton Rd Steubenville (43953) *(G-17695)*
Forte Indus Eqp Systems Inc 513 398-2800
  6037 Commerce Ct Mason (45040) *(G-13022)*
Forte Industries, Mason *Also called Forte Indus Eqp Systems Inc* *(G-13022)*
Fortec Litho Central LLC 330 463-1265
  10125 Wellman Rd Streetsboro (44241) *(G-17853)*
Fortec Medical Lithotripsy LLC 330 656-4301
  10125 Wellman Rd Streetsboro (44241) *(G-17854)*
Forterra Pipe & Precast LLC 330 467-7890
  7925 Empire Pkwy Macedonia (44056) *(G-12451)*
Forterra Pipe & Precast LLC 937 268-6707
  1504 N Gettysburg Ave Dayton (45417) *(G-8348)*

Forterra Pipe & Precast LLC 937 268-6707
  1504 N Gettysburg Ave Dayton (45417) *(G-8349)*
Fortin Ironworks, Columbus *Also called Fortin Welding & Mfg Inc* *(G-7094)*
Fortin Welding & Mfg Inc 614 291-4342
  944 W 5th Ave Columbus (43212) *(G-7094)*
Fortner Upholstering Inc 614 475-8282
  2624 Johnstown Rd Columbus (43219) *(G-7095)*
Forty Nine Degrees LLC 419 678-0100
  149 Harvest Dr Coldwater (45828) *(G-6560)*
Forum III Inc 513 961-5123
  436 Mcgregor Ave Cincinnati (45206) *(G-3773)*
Forward Day By Day, Cincinnati *Also called Forward Movement Publications* *(G-3774)*
Forward Movement Publications 513 721-6659
  412 Sycamore St Fl 2 Cincinnati (45202) *(G-3774)*
Forward Technologies, Blue Ash *Also called C M M S - Re LLC* *(G-1760)*
Forward Technologies, Blue Ash *Also called C M M S - Re Inc* *(G-1759)*
Forward Technologies Inc 513 489-5111
  6130 Interstate Cir Blue Ash (45242) *(G-1800)*
Fosbel Inc (HQ) 216 362-3900
  20600 Sheldon Rd Brookpark (44142) *(G-2161)*
Fosbel Holding Inc (PA) 216 362-3900
  20600 Sheldon Rd Cleveland (44142) *(G-5373)*
Foseco Inc (HQ) 440 826-4548
  20200 Sheldon Rd Cleveland (44142) *(G-5374)*
Foseco Metallurgical, Conneaut *Also called Vesuvius U S A Corporation* *(G-7821)*
Foster Manufacturing 513 735-9770
  4283 Armstrong Blvd Batavia (45103) *(G-1185)*
Foster Pattern Works Inc 330 482-3612
  1371 Kauffman Ave Columbiana (44408) *(G-6617)*
Foster Products Inc 513 735-9770
  4283 Armstrong Blvd Batavia (45103) *(G-1186)*
Fostoria Bshngs Inslators Corp 419 435-7514
  602 S Corporate Dr W D Fostoria (44830) *(G-9973)*
Fostoria Bushings Inc 419 435-7514
  602 S Corporate Dr W Fostoria (44830) *(G-9974)*
Fostoria Concrete, Bowling Green *Also called Palmer Bros Transit Mix Con* *(G-2006)*
Fostoria Ethanol LLC 419 436-0954
  2111 Sandusky St Fostoria (44830) *(G-9975)*
Fostoria Focus Inc 419 435-6397
  112 N Main St Fostoria (44830) *(G-9976)*
Fostoria Machine Products 419 435-4262
  425 S Union St Fostoria (44830) *(G-9977)*
Fostoria Monument Co (PA) 419 435-0373
  701 Van Buren St Fostoria (44830) *(G-9978)*
Foundatia Technologies, Cleveland *Also called Falcon Ridge Technologies LLC* *(G-5322)*
Foundation Industries Inc (PA) 330 564-1250
  880 W Waterloo Rd Ste B Akron (44314) *(G-193)*
Foundation Software Inc 330 220-8383
  17999 Foltz Pkwy Strongsville (44149) *(G-17920)*
Foundation Systems Anchors Inc 330 454-1700
  2300 Allen Ave Se Canton (44707) *(G-2707)*
Foundations Worldwide Inc (PA) 330 722-5033
  5216 Portside Dr Medina (44256) *(G-13412)*
Founder Service & Mfg Co 330 584-7759
  879 State Route 14 Deerfield (44411) *(G-8773)*
Founder's Service Co, Deerfield *Also called Founder Service & Mfg Co* *(G-8773)*
Foundry Artist Inc 216 391-9030
  4404 Perkins Ave Cleveland (44103) *(G-5375)*
Foundry Sand Service LLC 330 823-6152
  20455 Lake Park Blvd Sebring (44672) *(G-17045)*
Foundry Support Operation 440 951-4142
  7849 Enterprise Dr Mentor (44060) *(G-13581)*
Fountain of Youth 937 723-9743
  450 N Main St Ste 100 Centerville (45459) *(G-3042)*
Fountain Pk Inn Upper Sandusky 419 209-1100
  101 Westbrook Blvd Upper Sandusky (43351) *(G-19123)*
Fountain Specialists Inc 513 831-5717
  226 Main St Milford (45150) *(G-14142)*
Four Generations Inc 330 784-2243
  1320 Main St Lakemore (44250) *(G-11644)*
Four Js Bldg Components LLC 740 886-6112
  16435 State Route 217 Scottown (45678) *(G-17039)*
Four Natures Keepers Inc 740 363-8007
  4651 Marysville Rd Delaware (43015) *(G-8845)*
Fouremans Sand & Gravel Inc 937 547-1005
  2791 Wildcat Rd Greenville (45331) *(G-10498)*
Fourjay Industries, Dayton *Also called Fernandes Enterprises LLC* *(G-8340)*
Fourjays Inc 216 741-8258
  5341 Broadview Rd Parma (44134) *(G-15958)*
Fourteen Ventures Group LLC 937 866-2341
  3131 W Alex Bell Rd West Carrollton (45449) *(G-19792)*
Fouty & Company Inc 419 693-0017
  5003 Bayshore Rd Oregon (43616) *(G-15709)*
Fowl Foolers LLC 419 797-2412
  2268 Nw Catawba Rd Port Clinton (43452) *(G-16400)*
Fowler Products Inc 419 683-4057
  810 Colby Rd Crestline (44827) *(G-7929)*
Fowlers Milling Co Inc 440 286-2024
  12500 Fowlers Mill Rd Chardon (44024) *(G-3154)*

Fox Hollow Pallet, Winchester *Also called Leroy Yutzy (G-20694)*

Fox Hollow Pallet..937 386-2872
   3519 Graces Run Rd Winchester (45697) *(G-20693)*

Fox Lite Inc..937 864-1966
   8300 Dayton Rd Fairborn (45324) *(G-9622)*

Fox Tool Co Inc...330 928-3402
   1471 Main St Cuyahoga Falls (44221) *(G-7998)*

Fox Valley Forge, Cleveland *Also called Cleveland Hdwr & Forging Co (G-5064)*

Foxtail Foods, Fairfield *Also called Perkins & Marie Callenders LLC (G-9702)*

Foxtronix Inc..937 866-2112
   2240 E Central Ave Ste 4 Miamisburg (45342) *(G-13810)*

Fpt Cleveland LLC (HQ).....................................216 441-3800
   8550 Aetna Rd Cleveland (44105) *(G-5376)*

Fragapane Bakeries Inc (PA)...............................440 779-6050
   28625 Lorain Rd North Olmsted (44070) *(G-15335)*

Fragapane Bakery & Deli, North Olmsted *Also called Fragapane Bakeries Inc (G-15335)*

Fram Group Operations LLC................................937 316-3000
   851 Jackson St Greenville (45331) *(G-10499)*

Fram Group Operations LLC................................419 436-5827
   1600 N Union St Fostoria (44830) *(G-9979)*

Fram Group Operations LLC................................419 661-6700
   28399 Cedar Park Blvd Perrysburg (43551) *(G-16097)*

Frame Depot Inc..330 652-7865
   1043 Youngstown Warren Rd Niles (44446) *(G-15153)*

Frame Shoppe..513 232-3970
   7750 Beechmont Ave Cincinnati (45255) *(G-3775)*

Frame USA...513 577-7107
   225 Northland Blvd Cincinnati (45246) *(G-3776)*

Frame Warehouse...614 861-4582
   7502 E Main St Reynoldsburg (43068) *(G-16591)*

Franchise Services Inc.....................................513 731-1440
   4404 Forest Ave Cincinnati (45212) *(G-3777)*

Francis Manufacturing Company...........................937 526-4551
   500 E Mn St Russia (45363) *(G-16763)*

Francis-Schulze Co...937 295-3941
   3880 Rangeline Rd Russia (45363) *(G-16764)*

Francisco Jaume...740 622-1200
   311 S 15th St Ste 206 Coshocton (43812) *(G-7891)*

Franck and Fric Incorporated.............................216 524-4451
   7919 Old Rockside Rd Cleveland (44131) *(G-5377)*

Franjinhas Inc...440 463-1523
   17656 Fairfax Ln Strongsville (44136) *(G-17921)*

Frank Brunckhorst Company LLC..........................614 662-5300
   2225 Spiegel Dr Groveport (43125) *(G-10622)*

Frank Csapo..330 435-4458
   157 Myers St Creston (44217) *(G-7939)*

Frank Csapo Oil & Gas Producer, Creston *Also called Frank Csapo (G-7939)*

Frank J Prucha & Associates...............................216 642-3838
   6916 Daisy Ave Cleveland (44131) *(G-5378)*

Frank L Harter & Son Inc....................................513 574-1330
   3778 Frondorf Ave Cincinnati (45211) *(G-3778)*

Frank W Schaefer, Perrysburg *Also called Schaefer Group Inc (G-16147)*

Frankes Wood Products LLC................................937 642-0706
   825 Collins Ave Marysville (43040) *(G-12944)*

Frankie Tatum...614 216-1556
   3604 Watt Rd Gahanna (43230) *(G-10207)*

Frankies Graphics Inc.......................................440 979-0824
   3770 Windsong Ct Westlake (44145) *(G-20268)*

Franklin...419 699-5757
   747 Michigan Ave Waterville (43566) *(G-19657)*

Franklin Art Glass Studios..................................614 221-2972
   222 E Sycamore St Columbus (43206) *(G-7096)*

Franklin Brazing Met Treating, Lebanon *Also called Kando of Cincinnati Inc (G-11811)*

Franklin Cabinet Company Inc..............................937 743-9606
   2500 Commerce Center Dr Franklin (45005) *(G-10023)*

Franklin Communications Inc...............................614 459-9769
   4401 Carriage Hill Ln Columbus (43220) *(G-7097)*

Franklin Covey Co...513 792-0099
   7875 Montgomery Rd # 1202 Cincinnati (45236) *(G-3779)*

Franklin Electric Co Inc......................................614 794-2266
   555 Metro Pl N Dublin (43017) *(G-9077)*

Franklin Equipment LLC (PA)...............................614 228-2014
   4141 Hamilton Square Blvd Groveport (43125) *(G-10623)*

Franklin Field Service.......................................614 885-1779
   7065 Huntley Rd Columbus (43229) *(G-7098)*

Franklin Frames and Cycles................................740 763-3838
   7179 Reform Rd Newark (43055) *(G-15008)*

Franklin Fueling Systems...................................513 231-7840
   2715 Turpin Knoll Ct Cincinnati (45244) *(G-3780)*

Franklin Gas & Oil Company LLC...........................330 264-8739
   1615 W Old Lincoln Way Wooster (44691) *(G-20773)*

Franklin Graphics, North Canton *Also called Paul Stipkovich (G-15258)*

Franklin Iron & Metal Corp..................................937 253-8184
   1939 E 1st St Dayton (45403) *(G-8350)*

Franklin Mfg Div, Franklin *Also called Faurecia Exhaust Systems Inc (G-10021)*

Franklin's Printing, Franklin *Also called F P C Printing Inc (G-10020)*

Franklins Printing Company................................740 452-6375
   984 Beverly Ave Zanesville (43701) *(G-21311)*

Franks Casing...330 236-4264
   607 1st St Sw Massillon (44646) *(G-13133)*

Franks Electric Inc..513 542-0342
   2640 Colerain Ave Cincinnati (45214) *(G-3781)*

Franks Electric Motor Repair, Cincinnati *Also called Franks Electric Inc (G-3781)*

Franks Sawmill Inc..419 682-3831
   Rr 195 Stryker (43557) *(G-18003)*

Frantz Medical Development Ltd (PA).....................212 308-4860
   7740 Metric Dr Mentor (44060) *(G-13582)*

Frantz Medical Development Ltd...........................440 205-9026
   7740 Metric Dr Mentor (44060) *(G-13583)*

Frasernet Inc..216 691-6686
   2940 Noble Rd Ste 1 Cleveland (44121) *(G-5379)*

Frazeysburg Restaurant & Bky, Frazeysburg *Also called Calvary Christian Ch of Ohio (G-10071)*

Frazier Machine and Prod Inc..............................419 661-1656
   26489 Southpoint Rd Perrysburg (43551) *(G-16098)*

Frd, Kent *Also called Furukawa Rock Drill USA Co Ltd (G-11462)*

Freak-N-Fries Inc..440 453-1877
   204 Taylor Blvd Lagrange (44050) *(G-11625)*

Frecon Engineering..513 874-8981
   9319 Prnceton Glendale Rd West Chester (45011) *(G-19867)*

Frecon Technologies, West Chester *Also called Frecon Engineering (G-19867)*

Frecon Technologies Inc....................................513 874-8981
   9319 Prnceton Glendale Rd West Chester (45011) *(G-19868)*

Fred D Pfening Company (PA)..............................614 294-5361
   1075 W 5th Ave Columbus (43212) *(G-7099)*

Fred D Pfening Company....................................614 294-5361
   1075 W 5th Ave Columbus (43212) *(G-7100)*

Fred Marvin and Associates Inc............................330 784-9211
   4484 Allen Rd Stow (44224) *(G-17756)*

Fred Marvin Associates, Stow *Also called Fred Marvin and Associates Inc (G-17756)*

Fred W Albrecht Grocery Co................................330 922-4057
   4302 Allen Rd Ste 110 Stow (44224) *(G-17757)*

Fred W Hanks Company.....................................216 731-1774
   25018 Lakeland Blvd Cleveland (44132) *(G-5380)*

Fred Winner...419 582-2421
   7860 Cohn Rd New Weston (45348) *(G-14977)*

Fredebaugh Well Drilling Co................................440 357-6924
   714 Lakeshore Blvd Grand River (44045) *(G-10448)*

Frederick Steel Company LLC..............................513 821-6400
   630 Glendale Milford Rd Cincinnati (45215) *(G-3782)*

Fredericksburg Facility, Fredericksburg *Also called Robin Industries Inc (G-10092)*

Fredon Corporation..440 951-5200
   8990 Tyler Blvd Mentor (44060) *(G-13584)*

Fredrick Ramond, Avon Lake *Also called Hinkley Lighting Inc (G-1033)*

Fredrick Welding & Machining..............................614 866-9650
   6840 Americana Pkwy Reynoldsburg (43068) *(G-16592)*

Free Bird Publications Ltd...................................216 673-0229
   1410 S Carptr Rd Apt 238 Brunswick (44212) *(G-2226)*

Free Press Standard, Carrollton *Also called Carrollton Publishing Company (G-2954)*

Freedom Asphalt Sealant & Line..........................937 416-1053
   1241 Stephens St Miamisburg (45342) *(G-13811)*

Freedom Health LLC..330 562-0888
   65 Aurora Industrial Pkwy Aurora (44202) *(G-920)*

Freedom Usa Inc..216 503-6374
   1750 Highland Rd Ste 4 Twinsburg (44087) *(G-18937)*

Freeman Enclosure Systems LLC..........................877 441-8555
   4160 Half Acre Rd Batavia (45103) *(G-1187)*

Freeman Manufacturing & Sup Co (PA)...................440 934-1902
   1101 Moore Rd Avon (44011) *(G-996)*

Freeman Schwabe Machinery LLC.........................513 947-2888
   4064 Clough Woods Dr Batavia (45103) *(G-1188)*

Freeport Press Inc (PA).....................................740 658-3315
   121 E Main St Freeport (43973) *(G-10118)*

Fremar Industries Inc.......................................330 220-3700
   2808 Westway Dr Brunswick (44212) *(G-2227)*

Fremont Company (PA)......................................419 334-8995
   802 N Front St Fremont (43420) *(G-10146)*

Fremont Company...419 334-8995
   802 N Front St Fremont (43420) *(G-10147)*

Fremont Company...419 363-2924
   150 Hickory St Rockford (45882) *(G-16691)*

Fremont Cutting Dies Inc...................................419 334-5153
   3179 Us 20 E Fremont (43420) *(G-10148)*

Fremont Flask Co..419 332-2231
   1000 Wolfe Ave Fremont (43420) *(G-10149)*

Fremont Plastic Molds, Fremont *Also called Omnimold LLC (G-10172)*

Fremont Plastic Products, Fremont *Also called Plastics Group Inc (G-10175)*

Fremont Plastic Products Inc................................419 332-6407
   2101 Cedar St Fremont (43420) *(G-10150)*

Fremont Quick Print...419 334-8808
   2870 W Us Highway 6 Helena (43435) *(G-10895)*

French Oil Mill Machinery Co (PA)..........................937 773-3420
   1035 W Greene St Piqua (45356) *(G-16266)*

French Quarter LLC..614 781-0588
   6210 Busch Blvd Columbus (43229) *(G-7101)*

French USA, Piqua *Also called French Oil Mill Machinery Co (G-16266)*

Frenchtown Trailers SL & Sups, Versailles *Also called Belshe Industries Inc* *(G-19340)*
Frepeg Industries Inc 440 255-8595
 8624 East Ave Mentor (44060) *(G-13585)*
Fresenius Med Care Hldings Inc 216 661-1627
 3764 Pearl Rd Cleveland (44109) *(G-5381)*
Fresenius Medical Care, North Olmsted *Also called Fresenius Usa Inc* *(G-15336)*
Fresenius Usa Inc 330 837-2575
 2474 Lincoln Way E Massillon (44646) *(G-13134)*
Fresenius Usa Inc 440 734-7474
 25050 Country Club Blvd # 250 North Olmsted (44070) *(G-15336)*
Fresh Aire Farms, Union City *Also called Charles Daniel Young* *(G-19070)*
Fresh and Limited, Sidney *Also called Freshway Foods Inc* *(G-17190)*
Fresh Health, Columbus *Also called Dno Inc* *(G-7034)*
Fresh Look Laser Eye Ctrs LLC 614 885-2745
 789 Graham Rd Cuyahoga Falls (44221) *(G-7999)*
Fresh Mark Inc (PA) 330 834-3669
 1888 Southway St Se Massillon (44646) *(G-13135)*
Fresh Mark Inc 330 832-7491
 1888 Southway St Sw Massillon (44646) *(G-13136)*
Fresh Mark Inc 330 332-8508
 1735 S Lincoln Ave Salem (44460) *(G-16893)*
Fresh Mark Sugardale, Massillon *Also called Fresh Mark Inc* *(G-13136)*
Fresh Products LLC 419 531-9741
 30600 Oregon Rd Perrysburg (43551) *(G-16099)*
Fresh Sausage Specialists, Harrison *Also called Edelmann Provision Company* *(G-10776)*
Fresh Table LLC 513 381-3774
 1801 Race St Ste 2 Cincinnati (45202) *(G-3783)*
Fresh Vegetable Technology, Columbus *Also called National Fruit Vegetable Tech* *(G-7383)*
Freshway Foods Inc (PA) 937 498-4664
 601 Stolle Ave Sidney (45365) *(G-17190)*
Freudenberg-Nok General Partnr 937 335-3306
 1275 Archer Dr Troy (45373) *(G-18828)*
Freudenberg-Nok General Partnr 419 427-5221
 555 Marathon Blvd Findlay (45840) *(G-9827)*
Frickco Inc 740 887-2017
 54660 Pretty Run Rd South Bloomingville (43152) *(G-17422)*
Friction Products Co 330 725-4941
 920 Lake Rd Medina (44256) *(G-13413)*
Friday's Creations, Hilliard *Also called CNG Business Group* *(G-10941)*
Fried Daddy 937 854-4542
 448 N Union Rd Dayton (45417) *(G-8351)*
Friend Engrg & Mch Co Inc 419 589-5066
 67 Illinois Ave S Mansfield (44905) *(G-12608)*
Friends Business Source, Findlay *Also called Friends Service Co Inc* *(G-9828)*
Friends of Bears Mill Inc 937 548-5112
 6450 Arcanum Bearsmill Rd Greenville (45331) *(G-10500)*
Friends Ornamental Iron Co 216 431-6710
 1593 E 41st St Cleveland (44103) *(G-5382)*
Friends Service Co Inc 800 427-1704
 4604 Salem Ave Dayton (45416) *(G-8352)*
Friends Service Co Inc 800 427-1704
 948 Cherry St Kent (44240) *(G-11459)*
Friends Service Co Inc (PA) 419 427-1704
 2300 Bright Rd Findlay (45840) *(G-9828)*
Fries Machine & Tool Inc 937 898-6432
 5729 Webster St Dayton (45414) *(G-8353)*
Friesen Fab & Equipment, Plain City *Also called Friesen Fab and Equipment* *(G-16340)*
Friesen Fab and Equipment 614 873-4354
 10030 Smith Calhoun Rd Plain City (43064) *(G-16340)*
Friesen Transfer Ltd 614 873-5672
 9280 Iams Rd Plain City (43064) *(G-16341)*
Friesingers Inc 740 452-9480
 120 Graham St Zanesville (43701) *(G-21312)*
Friess Equipment Inc 330 945-9440
 2222 Akron Peninsula Rd Akron (44313) *(G-194)*
Friess Welding Inc 330 644-8160
 3342 S Main St Akron (44319) *(G-195)*
Frigid Units Inc 419 478-4000
 5072 Lewis Ave Toledo (43612) *(G-18473)*
Fripro Energy LLC 419 865-0002
 7008 Garden Rd Maumee (43537) *(G-13259)*
Frisbie Engine & Machine Co (PA) 513 542-1770
 2635 Spring Grove Ave Cincinnati (45214) *(G-3784)*
Frisby Printing Company 330 665-4565
 3571 Brookwall Dr Unit C Fairlawn (44333) *(G-9750)*
Frischco Inc 740 363-7537
 715 Sunbury Rd Delaware (43015) *(G-8846)*
Frito-Lay North America Inc 972 334-7000
 1626 Old Mansfield Rd Wooster (44691) *(G-20774)*
Frito-Lay North America Inc 513 759-1000
 7781 Service Center Dr West Chester (45069) *(G-19869)*
Frito-Lay North America Inc 330 477-7009
 4030 16th St Sw Canton (44710) *(G-2708)*
Frito-Lay North America Inc 419 595-2338
 6661 State Route 587 New Riegel (44853) *(G-14946)*
Frito-Lay North America Inc 513 229-3000
 5181 Natorp Blvd Ste 400 Mason (45040) *(G-13023)*
Fritzie Freeze Inc 419 727-0818
 5137 N Summit St Unit 1 Toledo (43611) *(G-18474)*

Frog Ranch Foods Ltd 740 767-3705
 5 S High St Glouster (45732) *(G-10404)*
Frogs In Bloom 330 678-9508
 1112 Delores Ave Kent (44240) *(G-11460)*
Frohock-Stewart Inc 440 329-6000
 39400 Taylor Pkwy North Ridgeville (44035) *(G-15375)*
Frontier Signs & Displays Inc 513 367-0813
 525 New Biddinger Rd Harrison (45030) *(G-10779)*
Frontier Tank Center Inc 330 659-3888
 3800 Congress Pkwy Richfield (44286) *(G-16624)*
Frontiers Unlimited, Lisbon *Also called Vance Adams* *(G-12134)*
Frontline International Inc 330 861-1100
 187 Ascot Pkwy Cuyahoga Falls (44223) *(G-8000)*
Frost Engineering Inc (PA) 513 541-6330
 3408 Beekman St Cincinnati (45223) *(G-3785)*
Frostop, Columbus *Also called Fbg Bottling Group LLC* *(G-7077)*
Frosty Twins 330 359-0708
 2236 Main St Winesburg (44690) *(G-20703)*
Froyo Twist 440 974-1001
 7267 Center St Mentor (44060) *(G-13586)*
Frozen Specialties Inc 419 445-9015
 720 W Barre Rd Archbold (43502) *(G-674)*
Frozen Specialties Inc (PA) 419 445-9015
 8600 S Wilkinson Way G Perrysburg (43551) *(G-16100)*
Frsteam By Sun Cleaners, Carroll *Also called Sun Cleaners & Laundry Inc* *(G-2948)*
Frugal Systems 419 957-7863
 21250 County Road 26 Carey (43316) *(G-2918)*
Frutarom USA Holding Inc (HQ) 201 861-9500
 5404 Duff Dr West Chester (45246) *(G-20004)*
Frutarom USA Inc (HQ) 513 870-4900
 5404 Duff Dr West Chester (45246) *(G-20005)*
Frutarom USA Inc 513 870-4900
 9950 Commerce Park Dr West Chester (45246) *(G-20006)*
Frutarom USA Inc 513 870-4900
 9930 Commerce Park Dr West Chester (45246) *(G-20007)*
Frutarom USA Inc 513 870-4900
 10139 Commerce Park Dr West Chester (45246) *(G-20008)*
Fry Foods Inc 419 448-0831
 99 Maule Rd Tiffin (44883) *(G-18221)*
Fryes Soccer Shoppe 937 832-2230
 709 Taywood Rd Englewood (45322) *(G-9520)*
FSI, Perrysburg *Also called Frozen Specialties Inc* *(G-16100)*
FSI/Mfp Inc 419 445-9015
 720 W Barre Rd Archbold (43502) *(G-675)*
FSRc Tanks Inc 234 221-2015
 11029 Industrial Pkwy Nw Bolivar (44612) *(G-1934)*
FT Group Inc 937 746-6439
 4710 Madison Rd Cincinnati (45227) *(G-3786)*
FT Precision Inc 740 694-1500
 9731 Mount Gilead Rd Fredericktown (43019) *(G-10103)*
Ftd Investments LLC 937 833-2161
 379 Albert Rd Brookville (45309) *(G-2184)*
Ftech R&D North America Inc (HQ) 937 339-2777
 1191 Horizon West Ct Troy (45373) *(G-18829)*
Ftk Manufacturing LLC 513 218-7237
 1514 Lost Lake Ct Williamsburg (45176) *(G-20407)*
Ftp, Fredericktown *Also called FT Precision Inc* *(G-10103)*
Fts International Inc 330 754-2375
 1520 Wood Ave Se East Canton (44730) *(G-9193)*
Fuchs Franklin Div, Twinsburg *Also called Fuchs Lubricants Co* *(G-18938)*
Fuchs Lubricants Co 330 963-0400
 8036 Bavaria Rd Twinsburg (44087) *(G-18938)*
Fuel America 419 586-5609
 204 E Market St Celina (45822) *(G-2998)*
Fuel G USA LLC 440 617-0950
 1457 Mendelssohn Dr Westlake (44145) *(G-20269)*
Fuhrmann Orchards LLC 740 776-6406
 510 Hansgen Morgan Rd Wheelersburg (45694) *(G-20331)*
Fujitec America Inc (HQ) 513 755-6100
 7258 Innovation Way Mason (45040) *(G-13024)*
Fukuvi Usa Inc 937 236-7288
 7631 Progress Ct Dayton (45424) *(G-8354)*
Fulflo Specialties Company, Cincinnati *Also called Ruthman Pump and Engineering* *(G-4369)*
Fulflo Specialties Company 937 783-2411
 459 E Fancy St Blanchester (45107) *(G-1713)*
Full Circle Technologies LLC 216 650-0007
 33199 Fairmount Blvd Pepper Pike (44124) *(G-16046)*
Full Gospel Baptist Times 614 279-3307
 3415 El Paso Dr Columbus (43204) *(G-7102)*
Fullton Mill Services, Delta *Also called Edw C Levy Co* *(G-8931)*
Fulton County Expositor, Wauseon *Also called Gazette Publishing Company* *(G-19679)*
Fulton County Processing Ltd 419 822-9266
 7800 State Route 109 Delta (43515) *(G-8933)*
Fulton Equipment Co (PA) 419 290-5393
 823 Hamilton St Toledo (43607) *(G-18475)*
Fulton Industries Inc (PA) 419 335-3015
 135 E Linfoot St Wauseon (43567) *(G-19678)*

A
L
P
H
A
B
E
T
I
C

Fulton Manufacturing Inds LLC 440 546-1435
6600 W Snowville Rd # 6500 Brecksville (44141) *(G-2050)*

Fulton Sign & Decal Inc 440 951-1515
7144 Industrial Park Blvd Mentor (44060) *(G-13587)*

Fultz Sign Co Inc 419 225-6000
3350 Slabtown Rd Lima (45801) *(G-12016)*

Functional Imaging Ltd 740 689-2466
2368 Pine Crest Dr Lancaster (43130) *(G-11717)*

Functional Products Inc 330 963-3060
8282 Bavaria Dr E Macedonia (44056) *(G-12452)*

Funke Signature Holdings, Cincinnati *Also called Annies Mud Pie Shop LLC (G-3405)*

Funny Times Inc 216 371-8600
2176 Lee Rd Cleveland (44118) *(G-5383)*

FUNSPORTS BRANDS, Liberty Township *Also called Boatfun Sports Inc (G-11958)*

Funtown Playgrounds Inc 513 871-8585
839 Cypresspoint Ct Cincinnati (45245) *(G-3303)*

Fur-Fish-Game, Columbus *Also called A R Harding Publishing Company (G-6668)*

Furn Tech, Waterville *Also called Furnace Technologies Inc (G-19658)*

Furnace Control Corp 513 772-1000
8904 Beckett Rd West Chester (45069) *(G-19870)*

Furnace Parts, Independence *Also called Weed Instrument Company Inc (G-11283)*

Furnace Parts LLC 216 916-9601
4755 W 150th St Ste C Cleveland (44135) *(G-5384)*

Furnace Technologies Inc 419 878-2100
1070 Disher Dr Waterville (43566) *(G-19658)*

Furniss Corporation Ltd 614 871-1470
15812 State Route 56 W Mount Sterling (43143) *(G-14598)*

Furniture By Otmar Inc (PA) 937 435-2039
301 Mmsburg Cnterville Rd Dayton (45459) *(G-8355)*

Furniture By Otmar Inc 513 891-5141
9500 Montgomery Rd Cincinnati (45242) *(G-3787)*

Furniture Concepts Inc 216 292-9100
4925 Galaxy Pkwy Ste G Cleveland (44128) *(G-5385)*

Furukawa Rock Drill, Kent *Also called Gougler Industries Inc (G-11463)*

Furukawa Rock Drill 330 673-5821
805 Lake St Kent (44240) *(G-11461)*

Furukawa Rock Drill USA Co Ltd (PA) 330 673-5826
711 Lake St Kent (44240) *(G-11462)*

Fuse Chicken Llc 330 338-7108
1127 Portage Trl Cuyahoga Falls (44223) *(G-8001)*

Fuserashi Intl Tech Inc 330 273-0140
5401 Innovation Dr Valley City (44280) *(G-19204)*

Fusion Automation Inc (HQ) 440 602-5595
4658 E 355th St Willoughby (44094) *(G-20493)*

Fusion Ceramics Inc (PA) 330 627-5821
160 Scio Rd Se Carrollton (44615) *(G-2956)*

Fusion Incorporated 440 946-3300
4658 E 355th St Willoughby (44094) *(G-20494)*

Fusion Incorporated 440 946-3300
4711 Topps Indus Pkwy Willoughby (44094) *(G-20495)*

Fusion Noodle Co 740 589-5511
30 E Union St Athens (45701) *(G-866)*

Fusionstorm 614 431-8000
1900 Polaris Pkwy Ste 385 Columbus (43240) *(G-6647)*

Future Controls Corporation 440 275-3191
1419 State Route 45 Austinburg (44010) *(G-962)*

Future Finishes, Inc 513 860-0020
40 Standen Dr Hamilton (45015) *(G-10693)*

Future Polytech Inc 419 763-1352
393 N Eastern Ave Saint Henry (45883) *(G-16816)*

Future Pos Ohio Inc 330 645-6623
2561 S Arlington Rd Akron (44319) *(G-196)*

Future Productions Inc 330 478-0477
4601 11th St Nw Canton (44708) *(G-2709)*

Future Screen Inc 440 838-5055
9009 Broadview Rd Unit B Cleveland (44147) *(G-5386)*

Fwt LLC 419 542-1420
761 W High St Hicksville (43526) *(G-10902)*

Fww, Canton *Also called Super Sign Guys LLC (G-2864)*

Fx Digital Media Inc 216 241-4040
2400 Superior Ave E # 100 Cleveland (44114) *(G-5387)*

Fypon Ltd 800 446-3040
1750 Indian Wood Cir Maumee (43537) *(G-13260)*

G & C Drainage Supplies Inc 513 563-8616
200 Cavett Dr Cincinnati (45215) *(G-3788)*

G & C Raw LLC 937 827-0010
225 N West St Versailles (45380) *(G-19348)*

G & C Raw Dog Food, Versailles *Also called G & C Raw LLC (G-19348)*

G & D Leasing Services Inc 303 457-9189
870 N 20th St Columbus (43219) *(G-7103)*

G & D Twinsburg, Twinsburg *Also called Giesecke & Devrient Amer Inc (G-18947)*

G & G Header Die Inc 330 468-3458
1200 Saybrook Dr Macedonia (44056) *(G-12453)*

G & G Originals, Cleveland *Also called Glauners Wholesale Inc (G-5432)*

G & H Drilling Inc 330 674-4868
5550 County Road 314 Millersburg (44654) *(G-14216)*

G & J, Toledo *Also called Mecca Rebuilding & Welding Co (G-18581)*

G & J Asphalt & Material Inc 740 773-6358
379 Seney Rd Chillicothe (45601) *(G-3238)*

G & J Extrusions Inc 330 753-0162
1580 Turkeyfoot Lake Rd New Franklin (44203) *(G-14824)*

G & J Pepsi-Cola Bottlers Inc 740 354-9191
4587 Gallia Pike Franklin Furnace (45629) *(G-10069)*

G & J Pepsi-Cola Bottlers Inc 740 774-2148
400 E 7th St Chillicothe (45601) *(G-3239)*

G & J Pepsi-Cola Bottlers Inc (PA) 513 785-6060
9435 Waterstone Blvd # 390 Cincinnati (45249) *(G-3789)*

G & J Pepsi-Cola Bottlers Inc 937 392-4937
1111 S 2nd St Ripley (45167) *(G-16666)*

G & J Pepsi-Cola Bottlers Inc 513 896-3700
2580 Bobmeyer Rd Hamilton (45015) *(G-10694)*

G & J Pepsi-Cola Bottlers Inc 740 593-3366
2001 E State St Athens (45701) *(G-867)*

G & J Pepsi-Cola Bottlers Inc 614 253-8771
1241 Gibbard Ave Columbus (43219) *(G-7104)*

G & J Pepsi-Cola Bottlers Inc 740 452-2721
335 N 6th St Zanesville (43701) *(G-21313)*

G & L Machining Inc 513 724-2600
299 N 3rd St Williamsburg (45176) *(G-20408)*

G & M Metal Products Inc 513 863-3353
1001 Fairview Ave Hamilton (45015) *(G-10695)*

G & M Precision Machining Inc 937 667-1443
9785 Wildcat Rd Tipp City (45371) *(G-18278)*

G & R Welding & Machining 937 323-9353
4690 E National Rd Springfield (45505) *(G-17562)*

G & S Custom Tooling LLC 419 286-2888
18406 Road 20 Fort Jennings (45844) *(G-9926)*

G & T Manufacturing Co 440 639-7777
6085 Pinecone Dr Mentor (44060) *(G-13588)*

G & W Products LLC 513 860-4050
8675 Seward Rd Fairfield (45011) *(G-9660)*

G A Avril Company (PA) 513 641-0566
4445 Kings Run Dr Cincinnati (45232) *(G-3790)*

G A Avril Company 513 731-5133
2108 Eagle Ct Cincinnati (45237) *(G-3791)*

G A Guilford & Sons, Cleveland *Also called Arthur W Guilford III Inc (G-4837)*

G A Spring Advertising 330 343-9030
2101 N Wooster Ave Dover (44622) *(G-8986)*

G A Wintzer and Son Company 419 739-4913
12279 S Dixey Hwy Wapakoneta (45895) *(G-19485)*

G B Welding & Metal Fabg Co 937 444-2091
3288 Mcmullen Rd Fayetteville (45118) *(G-9782)*

G Big Inc (PA) 740 867-5758
441 Rockwood Ave Chesapeake (45619) *(G-3187)*

G Big Inc 740 532-9123
300 Marion Pike Ironton (45638) *(G-11293)*

G F Frank and Sons Inc 513 870-9075
9075 Le Saint Dr West Chester (45014) *(G-19871)*

G Fordyce Co 937 393-3241
210 Hobart Dr Hillsboro (45133) *(G-10998)*

G Grafton Machine & Rubber 330 297-1062
640 Cleveland Rd Ravenna (44266) *(G-16530)*

G H Cutter Services Inc 419 476-0476
6203 N Detroit Ave Toledo (43612) *(G-18476)*

G I Plastek Inc 440 230-1942
24700 Center Ridge Rd # 8 Westlake (44145) *(G-20270)*

G Keener & Co 937 846-1210
2936 Liberty Rd New Carlisle (45344) *(G-14801)*

G L Heller Co Inc 419 877-5122
6246 Industrial Pkwy Whitehouse (43571) *(G-20339)*

G L Industries Inc 513 874-1233
25 Standen Dr Hamilton (45015) *(G-10696)*

G L T Inc 937 395-4817
2691 Lance Dr Moraine (45409) *(G-14489)*

G M P Welding and Fabricating 513 825-7861
11175 Adwood Dr Cincinnati (45240) *(G-3792)*

G M R Technology Inc 440 992-6003
2131 Aetna Rd Ashtabula (44004) *(G-808)*

G Metal, Stow *Also called Glebus Alloys LLC (G-17759)*

G P Manufacturing Inc 937 544-3190
376 Buckeye St Peebles (45660) *(G-16020)*

G Q Business Products 513 792-4750
11380 Grooms Rd Blue Ash (45242) *(G-1801)*

G R K Manufacturing Co Inc 513 863-3131
1200 Dayton St Hamilton (45011) *(G-10697)*

G S K Inc 937 547-1611
915 Front St Greenville (45331) *(G-10501)*

G S Link & Associates 513 722-2457
1881 Main St Goshen (45122) *(G-10415)*

G S S, Barberton *Also called Glass Surface Systems Inc (G-1119)*

G S S, Springboro *Also called Graphic Systems Services Inc (G-17482)*

G S Wiring Systems Inc (HQ) 419 423-7111
1801 Production Dr Findlay (45840) *(G-9829)*

G T M Associates Inc 440 951-0006
7112 Industrial Park Blvd Mentor (44060) *(G-13589)*

G T Metal Fabricators Inc 440 237-8745
12126 York Rd Unit E Cleveland (44133) *(G-5388)*

G W Cobb Co 216 341-0100
3914 Broadway Ave 16 Cleveland (44115) *(G-5389)*

(G-0000) Company's Geographic Section entry number

G W Smith and Sons Inc 937 253-5114
1700 Spaulding Rd Dayton (45432) ***(G-8105)***
G W Steffen Bookbinders Inc 330 963-0300
8212 Bavaria Dr E Macedonia (44056) ***(G-12454)***
G W Tool & Die Co, Fort Loramie *Also called Schmitmeyer Inc* ***(G-9937)***
G&M Media Packaging Inc 419 636-5461
1 Toy St Bryan (43506) ***(G-2297)***
G-M-I Inc 440 953-8811
4822 E 355th St Willoughby (44094) ***(G-20496)***
G-N Sales & Manufacturing Inc 440 237-9014
12166 York Rd Unit 3&4 Cleveland (44133) ***(G-5390)***
G.S. Steel Company, Cuyahoga Falls *Also called Dbcr Inc* ***(G-7986)***
G2 Digital Solutions 937 241-6003
1841 Trebein Rd Xenia (45385) ***(G-20953)***
G2 Print Plus 614 276-0500
3787 Interchange Rd Columbus (43204) ***(G-7105)***
Gabriel Logan LLC (PA) 740 380-6809
1689 E Front St Logan (43138) ***(G-12174)***
Gabriel Performance Pdts LLC (HQ) 440 992-3200
388 S Main St Akron (44311) ***(G-197)***
Gabriel Performance Pdts LLC 440 992-3200
725 State Rd Ashtabula (44004) ***(G-809)***
Gadd Logging 513 312-3941
823 E Jameson Ct Trenton (45067) ***(G-18792)***
Gadgets Manufacturing Co 937 686-5371
9366 State Route 117 Huntsville (43324) ***(G-11214)***
Gadjets Inc 937 274-2111
3629 N Dixie Dr Dayton (45414) ***(G-8356)***
Gail Berner 937 322-0314
514 W Columbia St Springfield (45504) ***(G-17563)***
Gail J Shumaker Originals 330 659-0680
3999 Brush Rd Richfield (44286) ***(G-16625)***
Gail Zeilmann 440 888-4858
3560 W 105th St Cleveland (44111) ***(G-5391)***
Gain LLC 440 396-6613
8475 Fallgold Ln Westerville (43082) ***(G-20153)***
Gaitwell Orthotics Pedorthics 513 829-2217
1 N Commerce Park Dr # 306 Cincinnati (45215) ***(G-3793)***
Galactic Precision Mfg LLC 937 540-1800
345 Huls Dr Englewood (45315) ***(G-9521)***
Galaxy Balloons Incorporated 216 476-3360
11750 Berea Rd Ste 3 Cleveland (44111) ***(G-5392)***
Galaxy Products Inc 419 843-7337
3403 Silica Rd Sylvania (43560) ***(G-18107)***
Galena Vault Ltd 740 965-2200
4909 Harlem Rd Galena (43021) ***(G-10242)***
Galion LLC 419 468-5214
515 N East St Galion (44833) ***(G-10268)***
Galion Canvas Products Co (PA) 419 468-5333
385 S Market St Galion (44833) ***(G-10269)***
Galion Dump Bodies, Millersburg *Also called Galion-Godwin Truck Bdy Co LLC* ***(G-14217)***
Galion Packaging Co Inc 419 468-2548
340 S East St Galion (44833) ***(G-10270)***
Galion-Godwin Truck Bdy Co LLC 330 359-5495
7415 Peabody Kent Rd Millersburg (44654) ***(G-14217)***
Gallagher Lumber Co 330 274-2333
10272 Vaughn Rd Mantua (44255) ***(G-12710)***
Gallagher Wood & Crafts 513 523-2748
2715 Scott Rd Oxford (45056) ***(G-15836)***
Galleria Co 513 983-1490
1 Procter And Gamble Plz Cincinnati (45202) ***(G-3794)***
Galley Printing Inc 330 220-5577
2892 Westway Dr Brunswick (44212) ***(G-2228)***
Galley Printing Company, Brunswick *Also called Galley Printing Inc* ***(G-2228)***
Gallipolis Vault Co Inc 740 446-3357
1050 State Route 141 Gallipolis (45631) ***(G-10297)***
Gallo Displays Inc (PA) 216 431-9500
4922 E 49th St Cleveland (44125) ***(G-5393)***
Galt Alloys, Canton *Also called Rti International Metals Inc* ***(G-2845)***
Galt Alloys Inc Main Ofc 330 453-4678
122 Central Plz N Canton (44702) ***(G-2710)***
Gam 330 427-6470
142 Chestnut St Leetonia (44431) ***(G-11860)***
Gamco, Cleveland *Also called General Aluminum Mfg Company* ***(G-5410)***
Gamco Componets Group LLC 440 593-1500
1370 Chamberlain Blvd Conneaut (44030) ***(G-7804)***
Gameday Vision 330 830-4550
1147 Oberlin Ave Sw Massillon (44647) ***(G-13137)***
Ganeden Biotech Inc 440 229-5200
5800 Landerbrook Dr # 300 Mayfield Heights (44124) ***(G-13315)***
Ganger Enterprises Inc 614 776-3985
214 Hoff Rd Unit D Westerville (43082) ***(G-20154)***
Gannett Co Inc 740 345-4053
22 N 1st St Newark (43055) ***(G-15009)***
Gannett Co Inc 513 721-2700
312 Elm St Ste 1400 Cincinnati (45202) ***(G-3795)***
Gannett Co Inc 740 654-1321
138 W Chestnut St Lancaster (43130) ***(G-11718)***
Gannett Co Inc 740 773-2111
50 W Main St Chillicothe (45601) ***(G-3240)***
Gannett Co Inc 419 521-7341
163 E Center St Marion (43302) ***(G-12866)***
Gannett Co Inc 740 295-3435
550 Main St Coshocton (43812) ***(G-7892)***
Gannett Co Inc 740 452-4561
3871 Gorsky Dr Zanesville (43701) ***(G-21314)***
Gannett Co Inc 419 332-5511
1700 Cedar St Fremont (43420) ***(G-10151)***
Gannett Co Inc 419 522-3311
70 W 4th St Mansfield (44903) ***(G-12609)***
Gannett Co Inc 740 349-1100
2 N 1st St Newark (43055) ***(G-15010)***
Gannett Co Inc 419 562-3333
70 W 4th St Mansfield (44903) ***(G-12610)***
Gannett Publishing Svcs LLC 419 522-3311
70 W 4th St Mansfield (44903) ***(G-12611)***
Gannett Stllite Info Ntwrk Inc 513 721-2700
312 Elm St Ste 1400 Cincinnati (45202) ***(G-3796)***
Gannett Stllite Info Ntwrk Inc 513 576-1800
200 Techne Center Dr # 206 Milford (45150) ***(G-14143)***
Gannett Stllite Info Ntwrk LLC 419 334-1012
1800 E State St Ste B Fremont (43420) ***(G-10152)***
Gannons Discount Blinds 216 398-2761
2725 Ralph Ave Cleveland (44109) ***(G-5394)***
Ganymede Technologies Corp 419 562-5522
1685 Marion Rd Bucyrus (44820) ***(G-2344)***
Ganymede Technology, Bucyrus *Also called J3 Systems Ltd* ***(G-2351)***
Ganzcorp Investments Inc 330 963-5400
2300 Pinnacle Pkwy Twinsburg (44087) ***(G-18939)***
Gar-Nays Winery 419 668-6802
1846 Wells Rd Collins (44826) ***(G-6575)***
Garber Farms, Greenville *Also called Russell L Garber* ***(G-10521)***
Garber Machine Co 330 399-4181
1788 Drexel Ave Nw Warren (44485) ***(G-19552)***
Garda Arch Fab LLC 216 431-6300
1873 E 55th St Cleveland (44103) ***(G-5395)***
Garda Architectural Fabrication, Cleveland *Also called Garda Arch Fab LLC* ***(G-5395)***
Garda CL Technical Svcs Inc 937 294-4099
2690 Lance Dr Moraine (45409) ***(G-14490)***
Gardella Jewelry LLC 440 877-9261
7432 Julia Dr North Royalton (44133) ***(G-15420)***
Garden Art Innovations LLC 330 697-0007
30 2nd St Sw Barberton (44203) ***(G-1116)***
Garden of Delight LLC 513 300-7205
5540 Chandler St Cincinnati (45227) ***(G-3797)***
Garden of Flavor LLC 216 702-7991
7501 Carnegie Ave Cleveland (44103) ***(G-5396)***
Garden Street Iron & Metal (PA) 513 853-3700
2885 Spring Grove Ave Cincinnati (45225) ***(G-3798)***
Gardenscape 419 445-6561
56 State Rte 66 Archbold (43502) ***(G-676)***
Gardner Business Media Inc 513 527-8800
6925 Valley Ave Cincinnati (45244) ***(G-3799)***
Gardner Lumber Co Inc 740 254-4664
5805 Laurel Creek Rd Se Tippecanoe (44699) ***(G-18313)***
Gardner Metal Craft Inc 513 539-4538
490 S Main St Monroe (45050) ***(G-14402)***
Gardner Signs Inc (PA) 419 385-6669
3800 Airport Hwy Toledo (43615) ***(G-18477)***
Gareth Stevens Publishing LP 800 542-2595
23221 Morgan Ct Strongsville (44149) ***(G-17922)***
Garfield Alloys Inc (PA) 216 587-4843
4878 Chaincraft Rd Cleveland (44125) ***(G-5397)***
Garick LLC (PA) 216 581-0100
13600 Broadway Ave Ste 1 Cleveland (44125) ***(G-5398)***
Garland Industries Inc (PA) 216 641-7500
3800 E 91st St Cleveland (44105) ***(G-5399)***
Garland Welding Co Inc 330 536-6506
804 E Liberty St Lowellville (44436) ***(G-12408)***
Garland/Dbs Inc 216 641-7500
3800 E 91st St Cleveland (44105) ***(G-5400)***
Garment Specialties Inc 330 425-2928
1885 E Aurora Rd Twinsburg (44087) ***(G-18940)***
Garner Industries Inc 740 349-0238
767 Country Club Dr Newark (43055) ***(G-15011)***
Garro Tread Corporation (PA) 330 376-3125
100 Beech St Akron (44308) ***(G-198)***
Garsite/Progress LLC 419 424-1100
1005 Lima Ave Findlay (45840) ***(G-9830)***
Garvey Corporation 330 779-0700
1019 Ohio Works Dr Youngstown (44510) ***(G-21090)***
Garvey Products Inc (HQ) 513 771-8710
5428 Duff Dr West Chester (45246) ***(G-20009)***
Garvin Industries Div, Strongsville *Also called Guarantee Specialties Inc* ***(G-17923)***
Garvin Tool & Die Inc 419 334-2392
3000 State Route 412 Fremont (43420) ***(G-10153)***
Gary Brown Farm & Sawmill 740 372-5022
3575 State Route 348 Otway (45657) ***(G-15830)***
Gary Compton 937 339-6829
3245 Piqua Troy Rd Troy (45373) ***(G-18830)***

ALPHABETIC

Gary I Teach Jr 614 582-7483
  4855 Rsdale Mlford Ctr Rd London (43140) *(G-12210)*

Gary Krinn 740 344-3695
  951 Buckeye Ave Ste D Newark (43055) *(G-15012)*

Gary L Gast 419 626-5915
  2024 Campbell St Sandusky (44870) *(G-16968)*

Gary Lawrence Enterprises Inc 330 833-7181
  21 Charles Ave Sw Massillon (44646) *(G-13138)*

Garys Chesecakes Fine Desserts 513 574-1700
  5285 Crookshank Rd Side Cincinnati (45238) *(G-3800)*

Garys Classic Guitars 513 891-0555
  6692 Sandy Shores Dr Loveland (45140) *(G-12351)*

Garys Pallet Sales 330 569-7676
  12680 Herr Dr Hiram (44234) *(G-11035)*

Gas & Grills, Willoughby Also called Lapa Lowe Enterprises LLC *(G-20527)*

Gas Analytical Services Inc 330 539-4267
  1688 Shannon Rd Girard (44420) *(G-10389)*

Gas Enterprise Company, Wingett Run Also called James L Williams *(G-20709)*

Gas Products, Cambridge Also called Aci Services Inc *(G-2442)*

Gas Tran Systems, Streetsboro Also called Cleveland Gas Systems LLC *(G-17844)*

Gas Turbine Fuel Systems, Mentor Also called Parker-Hannifin Corporation *(G-13681)*

Gas Turbine Fuel Systems Div, Cleveland Also called Parker-Hannifin Corporation *(G-5974)*

Gasdorf Tool and Mch Co Inc 419 227-0103
  445 N Mcdonel St Lima (45801) *(G-12017)*

Gasflux Company 440 365-1941
  32 Hawthorne St Elyria (44035) *(G-9424)*

Gasko Fabricated Products LLC (HQ) 330 239-1781
  4049 Ridge Rd Medina (44256) *(G-13414)*

Gasoila Thred-Taper, Cleveland Also called Federal Process Corporation *(G-5332)*

Gaspar Inc 330 477-2222
  1545 Whipple Ave Sw Canton (44710) *(G-2711)*

Gaspar Services LLC 330 467-8292
  9009 Freeway Dr 4 Macedonia (44056) *(G-12455)*

Gasser Chair Co Inc (PA) 330 534-2234
  4136 Logan Way Youngstown (44505) *(G-21091)*

Gasser Chair Co Inc 330 534-2234
  4136 Logan Way Youngstown (44505) *(G-21092)*

Gasser Chair Co Inc 330 759-2234
  2457 Logan Ave Youngstown (44505) *(G-21093)*

Gate Way News Stands, Cleveland Also called Shree Krupa Inc *(G-6197)*

Gate West Coast Ventures LLC 513 891-1000
  4412 Carver Woods Dr # 200 Blue Ash (45242) *(G-1802)*

Gatesair Inc (HQ) 513 459-3400
  5300 Kings Island Dr. Mason (45040) *(G-13025)*

Gateway Biotechnology Inc 314 747-7199
  4209 State Route 44 D-148 Rootstown (44272) *(G-16722)*

Gateway Concrete Forming Svcs 513 353-2000
  5938 Hamilton Cleves Rd Miamitown (45041) *(G-13887)*

Gateway Industrial Pdts Inc 440 324-4112
  160 Freedom Ct Elyria (44035) *(G-9425)*

Gateway Industries 330 633-3700
  1236 Brittain Rd Akron (44310) *(G-199)*

Gateway Metal Finishing Inc 216 267-2580
  5310 W 161st St Ste J Cleveland (44142) *(G-5401)*

Gateway Packaging Company 419 738-5126
  253 Industrial Dr Wapakoneta (45895) *(G-19486)*

Gateway Printing, Wadsworth Also called Rohrer Corporation *(G-19438)*

Gathering Place, Galion Also called Ginnys Custom Framing Gallery *(G-10272)*

Gatton Packaging Inc 419 886-2577
  99 East St Bellville (44813) *(G-1569)*

Gauntlet Awards & Engraving 937 890-5811
  9153 N Dixie Dr Dayton (45414) *(G-8357)*

Gaydash Enterprises Inc 330 896-4811
  3640 Tabs Dr Uniontown (44685) *(G-19085)*

Gaydash Industries, Uniontown Also called Gaydash Enterprises Inc *(G-19085)*

Gayston Corporation 937 743-6050
  721 Richard St Miamisburg (45342) *(G-13812)*

Gazette Editorial Department 330 725-6220
  885 W Liberty St Medina (44256) *(G-13415)*

Gazette Publishing, Conneaut Also called The Gazette Printing Co Inc *(G-7820)*

Gazette Publishing Company (PA) 419 483-4190
  42 S Main St Oberlin (44074) *(G-15640)*

Gazette Publishing Company 419 335-2010
  1270 N Shoop Ave Ste A Wauseon (43567) *(G-19679)*

Gb Fabrication Company 419 347-1835
  2510 Taylortown Rd Shelby (44875) *(G-17136)*

Gb Fabrication Company (HQ) 419 896-3191
  60 Scott St Shiloh (44878) *(G-17148)*

Gb Image Machine Incorporated (PA) 419 628-4150
  179 N Ohio St Minster (45865) *(G-14353)*

Gb Manufacturing Company (PA) 419 822-5323
  1120 E Main St Delta (43515) *(G-8934)*

Gbc Metals LLC 330 823-1700
  2081 Mccrea St Alliance (44601) *(G-510)*

Gbi Cincinnati Inc 513 841-8684
  7700 Shawnee Run Rd Cincinnati (45243) *(G-3801)*

GBS Computer Solutions, North Canton Also called GBS Corp *(G-15233)*

GBS Corp (PA) 330 494-5330
  7233 Freedom Ave Nw North Canton (44720) *(G-15233)*

GBS Corp 330 929-8050
  3658 Wyoga Lake Rd Stow (44224) *(G-17758)*

GBS Corp 330 863-1828
  224 Morges Rd Malvern (44644) *(G-12545)*

GBS Filing Solutions, Malvern Also called GBS Corp *(G-12545)*

Gc Controls Inc 440 779-4777
  3926 Pine Cir North Olmsted (44070) *(G-15337)*

GCI Digital Imaging Inc 513 521-7446
  5031 Winton Rd Cincinnati (45232) *(G-3802)*

Gdc Inc 574 533-3128
  1700 Old Mansfield Rd Wooster (44691) *(G-20775)*

Gdc Industries LLC 937 367-7229
  1423 Research Park Dr Beavercreek (45432) *(G-1339)*

Gdj Inc 440 975-0258
  7585 Tyler Blvd Mentor (44060) *(G-13590)*

Gdm Mailbox Company LLC 419 433-3022
  912 University Dr S Huron (44839) *(G-11221)*

Gdw Woodworking LLC 513 494-3041
  120 Vista Ridge Dr South Lebanon (45065) *(G-17429)*

Gdy Installations Inc 419 467-0036
  302 Arco Dr Toledo (43607) *(G-18478)*

GE, Beavercreek Also called Unison Industries LLC *(G-1364)*

GE Aircraft Engines 513 243-2000
  1 Neumann Way Cincinnati (45215) *(G-3803)*

GE Aviation Services, Cincinnati Also called GE Aviation Systems LLC *(G-3806)*

GE Aviation Systems LLC 937 898-5881
  740 E National Rd Vandalia (45377) *(G-19292)*

GE Aviation Systems LLC 937 898-9600
  6800 Poe Ave Dayton (45414) *(G-8358)*

GE Aviation Systems LLC 513 470-2889
  10270 Saint Rita Ln Cincinnati (45215) *(G-3804)*

GE Aviation Systems LLC 513 552-5663
  123 Merchant St Cincinnati (45246) *(G-3805)*

GE Aviation Systems LLC 513 977-1500
  201 W Crescentville Rd Cincinnati (45246) *(G-3806)*

GE Aviation Systems LLC 513 733-1611
  11988 Tramway Dr Cincinnati (45241) *(G-3807)*

GE Aviation Systems LLC 513 889-5150
  5223 Muhlhauser Rd West Chester (45011) *(G-19872)*

GE Aviation Systems LLC (HQ) 513 243-2000
  1 Neumann Way Cincinnati (45215) *(G-3808)*

GE Aviation Systems LLC 937 898-5881
  740 E National Rd Vandalia (45377) *(G-19293)*

GE Aviation Systems LLC 937 898-9600
  6800 Poe Ave Dayton (45414) *(G-8359)*

GE Betz Inc 330 339-2292
  2118 Reiser Ave Se New Philadelphia (44663) *(G-14900)*

GE Energy Oilfield Technology, Twinsburg Also called Reuter-Stokes Inc *(G-19008)*

GE Health 513 241-5955
  346 Gest St Cincinnati (45203) *(G-3809)*

GE Healthcare Fincl Svcs Inc 312 697-3999
  1515 Danner Dr Aurora (44202) *(G-921)*

GE Honda Aero Engines LLC 513 552-4322
  9050 Centre Pointe Dr West Chester (45069) *(G-19873)*

GE Infrastructure Sensing Inc 740 928-7010
  611 O Neill Dr Hebron (43025) *(G-10866)*

GE Intelligent Platforms Inc 937 459-5404
  5438 S State Route 49 Greenville (45331) *(G-10502)*

GE Lighting LLC (PA) 216 266-2000
  1975 Noble Rd Ste 338e Cleveland (44112) *(G-5402)*

GE Lighting Solutions LLC (HQ) 216 266-4800
  1975 Noble Rd Ste 338e Cleveland (44112) *(G-5403)*

GE Medical Systems Information 216 663-2110
  18683 S Miles Rd Warrensville Heights (44128) *(G-19633)*

GE Military Systems 513 243-2000
  1 Neumann Way Cincinnati (45215) *(G-3810)*

GE Rolls Royce Fighter 513 243-2787
  1 Neumann Way 318a Cincinnati (45215) *(G-3811)*

GE Water & Process Tech, New Philadelphia Also called GE Betz Inc *(G-14900)*

Gear Company of America Inc 216 671-5400
  14300 Lorain Ave Cleveland (44111) *(G-5404)*

Gear Products Co, Willoughby Also called T & S Discount Tires Inc *(G-20607)*

Gear Star American Performance 330 434-5216
  132 N Howard St Akron (44308) *(G-200)*

Gearhart Machine Company 330 253-1880
  1145 Highbrook St Ste 508 Akron (44301) *(G-201)*

Gearing Solutions Inc 440 498-9538
  5905 Harper Rd Ste A Solon (44139) *(G-17295)*

Geartec Inc 440 953-3900
  4245 Hamann Pkwy Willoughby (44094) *(G-20497)*

Geauga Concrete Inc 440 338-4915
  10509 Kinsman Rd Newbury (44065) *(G-15091)*

Geauga Feed and Grain Supply 440 564-5000
  11030 Kinsman Rd Newbury (44065) *(G-15092)*

Geauga Machine and Tool, Newbury Also called Cleveland Rubber Products LLC *(G-15084)*

Geauge Decal, Grove City Also called Boehm Inc *(G-10546)*

Gebauer Company 216 581-3030
4444 E 153rd St Cleveland (44128) *(G-5405)*

Gececo Inc 614 861-4479
6416 Plankton Dr Columbus (43213) *(G-7106)*

Ged Holdings Inc 330 963-5401
9280 Dutton Dr Twinsburg (44087) *(G-18941)*

Gedco Inc 330 828-2044
130 Briarwood Dr Dalton (44618) *(G-8069)*

Gedico International Inc 937 274-2167
4050 Grafix Blvd Dayton (45417) *(G-8360)*

Gehm & Sons Limited (PA) 330 724-8423
825 S Arlington St Akron (44306) *(G-202)*

Gei, Youngstown *Also called General Extrusions Inc (G-21096)*

Gei of Columbiana Inc 330 783-0270
4040 Lake Park Rd Youngstown (44512) *(G-21094)*

Geist Co Inc 216 771-2200
1814 W 30th St Cleveland (44113) *(G-5406)*

Gellner Engineering Inc 216 398-8500
2827 Brookpark Rd Cleveland (44134) *(G-5407)*

Gelok International Corp 419 352-1482
Pine Lake Rd Pn Lk In Par Dunbridge (43414) *(G-9169)*

Gem Beverages Inc 740 384-2411
106 E 11th St Wellston (45692) *(G-19763)*

Gem City Engineering & Mfg, Dayton *Also called Gem City Engineering Co (G-8361)*

Gem City Engineering Co (PA) 937 223-5544
401 Leo St Dayton (45404) *(G-8361)*

Gem City Golf Club, Fairborn *Also called Zwf Golf LLC (G-9636)*

Gem City Metal Tech LLC 937 252-8998
1825 E 1st St Dayton (45403) *(G-8362)*

Gem Coatings Ltd 740 589-2998
5840 Industrial Park Rd Athens (45701) *(G-868)*

Gem Instrument Co 330 273-6117
2832 Nationwide Pkwy Brunswick (44212) *(G-2229)*

Gem Ornamental Iron Co 216 661-6965
4681 Broadview Rd Cleveland (44109) *(G-5408)*

Gem Tool LLC 216 771-8444
127 Public Sq Cleveland (44114) *(G-5409)*

Gemco Machine & Tool Inc 740 344-3111
88 Decrow Ave Newark (43055) *(G-15013)*

Gemini Advertising Associates 513 896-3541
1637 Dixie Hwy Hamilton (45011) *(G-10698)*

Gemini Fiber Corporation 330 874-4131
11145 Industrial Pkwy Nw Bolivar (44612) *(G-1935)*

Gemini Products, Brecksville *Also called Knight Ergonomics Inc (G-2059)*

Gempco, Akron *Also called General Metals Powder Co (G-203)*

Gen III 614 737-8744
2300 Lockbourne Rd Columbus (43207) *(G-7107)*

Gen Two Industries LLC 419 624-8803
413 Industrial Pkwy Sandusky (44870) *(G-16969)*

Gendron Wheel LLC 419 445-6060
400 E Lugbill Rd Archbold (43502) *(G-677)*

General Aluminum Mfg Company (HQ) 440 947-2000
6065 Parkland Blvd Cleveland (44124) *(G-5410)*

General Aluminum Mfg Company 330 297-1020
5159 S Prospect St Ravenna (44266) *(G-16531)*

General Aluminum Mfg Company 419 739-9300
13663 Short Rd Wapakoneta (45895) *(G-19487)*

General Aluminum Mfg Company 440 593-6225
1370 Chamberlain Blvd Conneaut (44030) *(G-7805)*

General Aquatics, Cincinnati *Also called Flow Control US Holding Corp (G-3763)*

General Awning Company Inc 216 749-0110
1350 E Granger Rd Cleveland (44131) *(G-5411)*

General Bar Inc 440 835-2000
25000 Center Ridge Rd # 3 Westlake (44145) *(G-20271)*

General Book Binding, Chesterland *Also called Hf Group LLC (G-3212)*

General Chain & Mfg Corp 513 541-6005
3182 Beekman St Cincinnati (45223) *(G-3812)*

General Color Investments Inc 330 868-4161
250 Bridge St Minerva (44657) *(G-14322)*

General Cutlery Inc (PA) 419 332-2316
1918 N County Road 232 Fremont (43420) *(G-10154)*

General Data Company Inc (PA) 513 752-7978
4354 Ferguson Dr Cincinnati (45245) *(G-3304)*

General Data Company Inc 513 752-7978
1004 Seabrook Way Cincinnati (45245) *(G-3305)*

General Data Company Inc 919 384-0037
1004 Seabrook Way Cincinnati (45245) *(G-3306)*

General Die Casters 330 678-2528
4607 Dresher Trl Cuyahoga Falls (44224) *(G-8002)*

General Die Casters 330 467-6700
6212 Akron Peninsula Rd Northfield (44067) *(G-15466)*

General Die Casters Inc (PA) 330 678-2528
2150 Highland Rd Twinsburg (44087) *(G-18942)*

General Dynamics Land 419 221-7000
1161 Buckeye Rd Lima (45804) *(G-12018)*

General Dynamics Lima Army Tan, Lima *Also called General Dynamics Land (G-12018)*

General Dynamics-Ots Inc 937 746-8500
200 S Pioneer Blvd Springboro (45066) *(G-17481)*

General Dynmics Mssion Systems 513 253-4770
2673 Commons Blvd Ste 200 Beavercreek (45431) *(G-1340)*

General Electric Company 440 593-1156
880 Maple Ave Conneaut (44030) *(G-7806)*

General Electric Company 330 343-8841
200 W Broadway St Dover (44622) *(G-8987)*

General Electric Company 419 563-1200
1250 S Walnut St Bucyrus (44820) *(G-2345)*

General Electric Company 740 477-5200
559 E Ohio St Circleville (43113) *(G-4630)*

General Electric Company 216 883-1000
4477 E 49th St Cleveland (44125) *(G-5412)*

General Electric Company 216 266-2121
1975 Noble Rd Cleveland (44112) *(G-5413)*

General Electric Company 740 623-5366
1350 S 2nd St Coshocton (43812) *(G-7893)*

General Electric Company 513 977-1500
201 W Crescentville Rd Cincinnati (45246) *(G-3813)*

General Electric Company 513 243-9317
9050 Centre Pointe Dr West Chester (45069) *(G-19874)*

General Electric Company 740 385-2114
Hc 93 Box N Logan (43138) *(G-12175)*

General Electric Company 330 425-3755
8499 Darrow Rd Twinsburg (44087) *(G-18943)*

General Electric Company 216 663-2110
18683 S Miles Rd Cleveland (44128) *(G-5414)*

General Electric Company 330 793-3911
280 N Meridian Rd Youngstown (44509) *(G-21095)*

General Electric Company 513 948-4170
445 S Cooper Ave Cincinnati (45215) *(G-3814)*

General Electric Company 740 928-7010
611 O Neill Dr Hebron (43025) *(G-10867)*

General Electric Company 330 297-0861
403 N Main St Niles (44446) *(G-15154)*

General Electric Company 330 373-1400
403 N Main St Niles (44446) *(G-15155)*

General Electric Company 740 498-5151
700 Newport St Newcomerstown (43832) *(G-15113)*

General Electric Company 216 391-8741
1814 E 45th St Cleveland (44103) *(G-5415)*

General Electric Company 513 552-5364
9100 Centre Pointe Dr # 4 West Chester (45069) *(G-19875)*

General Electric Company 216 266-2357
21800 Tungsten Rd Cleveland (44117) *(G-5416)*

General Electric Company 216 268-3846
1099 Ivanhoe Rd Cleveland (44110) *(G-5417)*

General Electric Company 330 458-3200
5555 Massillon Rd Bldg D Canton (44720) *(G-2712)*

General Electric Company 513 552-2000
1 Neumann Way Cincinnati (45215) *(G-3815)*

General Electric Intl Inc 410 737-7228
191 Rosa Parks St Cincinnati (45202) *(G-3816)*

General Electric Intl Inc 330 963-2066
8941 Dutton Dr Twinsburg (44087) *(G-18944)*

General Engine Products LLC 937 704-0160
2000 Watkins Glen Dr Franklin (45005) *(G-10024)*

General Envmtl Science Corp 216 464-0680
26000 Richmond Rd Cleveland (44146) *(G-5418)*

General Equipped Products, Columbus *Also called U S Fuel Development Co (G-7716)*

General Extrusions Inc 330 783-0270
4040 Lake Park Rd Youngstown (44512) *(G-21096)*

General Fabrications Corp 419 625-6055
7777 Milan Rd Sandusky (44870) *(G-16970)*

General Films Inc 888 436-3456
645 S High St Covington (45318) *(G-7923)*

General Glass & Screen Inc 440 350-9033
6095 Pinecone Dr Mentor (44060) *(G-13591)*

General Industrial Supply, Piqua *Also called Gisco Inc (G-16267)*

General Intl Pwr Pdts LLC 419 877-5234
6243 Industrial Pkwy Whitehouse (43571) *(G-20340)*

General Machine & Saw Company 740 375-5730
305 Davis St Marion (43302) *(G-12867)*

General Machine & Supply Co 740 453-4804
3135 Lookout Dr Zanesville (43701) *(G-21315)*

General Machine and Mould Co, Lancaster *Also called Devault Machine & Mould Co LLC (G-11705)*

General Metals Powder Co (PA) 330 633-1226
1195 Home Ave Akron (44310) *(G-203)*

General Mills Inc 513 771-8200
11301 Mosteller Rd Cincinnati (45241) *(G-3817)*

General Mills Inc 419 269-3100
1250 W Laskey Rd Toledo (43612) *(G-18479)*

General Mills Inc 513 770-0558
5181 Natorp Blvd Ste 540 Mason (45040) *(G-13026)*

General Mills Inc 513 563-8866
4100 Executive Park Dr # 11 Cincinnati (45241) *(G-3818)*

General Motors LLC 419 782-2244
26427 State Route 281 Defiance (43512) *(G-8790)*

General Motors LLC 330 824-5000
2300 Hallock Young Rd Sw Warren (44481) *(G-19553)*

General Motors LLC 216 265-5000
5400 Chevrolet Blvd Cleveland (44130) *(G-5419)*

General Motors LLC 330 824-5840
2369 Ellsworth Bailey Rd Warren (44481) *(G-19554)*

General Nano LLC 513 309-5947
1776 Mentor Ave Ste 170 Cincinnati (45212) *(G-3819)*

General Packaging Products 330 725-7731
1030 Industrial Pkwy Medina (44256) *(G-13416)*

General Parts Inc 614 891-6014
24 E Schrock Rd Westerville (43081) *(G-20215)*

General Plastex Inc 330 745-7775
35 Stuver Pl Barberton (44203) *(G-1117)*

General Plug and Mfg Co (PA) 440 926-2411
455 Main St Grafton (44044) *(G-10426)*

General Precision Corporation 440 951-9380
4553 Beidler Rd Willoughby (44094) *(G-20498)*

General Sheave Company Inc 216 781-8120
1335 Main Ave Cleveland (44113) *(G-5420)*

General Steel Corporation 216 883-4200
3344 E 80th St Cleveland (44127) *(G-5421)*

General Technologies Inc 419 747-1800
855 W Longview Ave Mansfield (44906) *(G-12612)*

General Theming Contrs LLC 614 252-6342
3750 Courtright Ct Columbus (43227) *(G-7108)*

General Tool Company (PA) 513 733-5500
101 Landy Ln Cincinnati (45215) *(G-3820)*

Generals Books 614 870-1861
522 Norton Rd Columbus (43228) *(G-7109)*

Generations Coffee Company LLC 440 546-0901
60100 W Snowell Brecksville (44141) *(G-2051)*

Generic Systems Inc 419 841-8460
10560 Geiser Rd Holland (43528) *(G-11062)*

Genesco Inc 330 633-8179
2000 Brittain Rd Ste 681 Akron (44310) *(G-204)*

Genesco Inc 513 947-1200
4601 Estgate Blvd Ste 564 Cincinnati (45245) *(G-3307)*

Genesis Display Systems Inc 513 561-1440
4004 Erie Ct Cincinnati (45227) *(G-3821)*

Genesis Graphics 937 335-5332
14 N Walnut St Ste 2 Troy (45373) *(G-18831)*

Genesis Lamp Corp 440 354-0095
375 N Saint Clair St Painesville (44077) *(G-15883)*

Genesis Plastic Tech LLC 440 542-0722
27200 Tinkers Ct Solon (44139) *(G-17296)*

Genesis Quality Printing Inc 440 975-5700
7250 Commerce Dr Ste G Mentor (44060) *(G-13592)*

Genesis Steel Corp 740 282-2300
6th & Adams St Steubenville (43952) *(G-17696)*

Geneva Gear & Machine Inc 937 866-0318
339 Progress Rd Dayton (45449) *(G-8363)*

Geneva Liberty Steel Ltd (PA) 330 740-0103
947 Martin Luther King Jr Youngstown (44502) *(G-21097)*

Geneva Rubber Company, Cortland Also called *Control Transformer Inc* *(G-7864)*

Genex Mold, Canton Also called *Dlhbowles Inc* *(G-2692)*

Genex Tool & Die Inc 330 788-2466
4000 Lake Park Rd Youngstown (44512) *(G-21098)*

Genie Company, The, Mount Hope Also called *GMI Holdings Inc* *(G-14571)*

Genie Company, The, Baltic Also called *GMI Holdings Inc* *(G-1073)*

Genie Repros Inc 216 965-0213
2211 Hamilton Ave Cleveland (44114) *(G-5422)*

Genmak Geneva Liberty, Youngstown Also called *Geneva Liberty Steel Ltd* *(G-21097)*

Gennaro Pavers 330 536-6825
6065 Arrel Smith Rd Lowellville (44436) *(G-12409)*

Gent Machine Company 216 481-2334
445 S Green Rd Cleveland (44121) *(G-5423)*

Gentek Building Products Inc (HQ) 800 548-4542
3773 State Rd Cuyahoga Falls (44223) *(G-8003)*

Gentzler Tool & Die Corp (PA) 330 896-1941
3903 Massillon Rd Akron (44312) *(G-205)*

Genvac Aerospace Corp (PA) 440 646-9986
110 Alpha Park Cleveland (44143) *(G-5424)*

Geo Specialty Chemical 330 650-0237
2685 Blue Heron Dr Hudson (44236) *(G-11172)*

Geo-Tech Polymers LLC 614 797-2300
423 Hopewell Rd Waverly (45690) *(G-19709)*

Geocentral, Mason Also called *CM Paula Company* *(G-13002)*

Geocore Drilling Inc 419 864-4011
2918 Us Highway 42 Cardington (43315) *(G-2910)*

Geocorp Inc 419 433-1101
9010 River Rd Huron (44839) *(G-11222)*

Geodyne One, Columbus Also called *Mori Shuji* *(G-7369)*

Geoffrey Smith 614 793-1996
2829 Festival Ln Dublin (43017) *(G-9078)*

Geograph Industries Inc 513 202-9200
475 Industrial Dr Harrison (45030) *(G-10780)*

Geopetro LLC 614 885-9350
7100 N High St Ste 303 Worthington (43085) *(G-20866)*

George A Mitchell Company 330 758-5777
557 Mcclurg Rd Youngstown (44512) *(G-21099)*

George Biniker Wooden Pallets 419 666-3185
28961 Oregon Rd Perrysburg (43551) *(G-16101)*

George D Kanaan & Associates 440 243-6410
9 N Rocky River Dr Berea (44017) *(G-1617)*

George Manufacturing Inc 513 932-1067
160 Harmon Ave Lebanon (45036) *(G-11801)*

George R Klein News, Cleveland Also called *Ckm Ventures LLC* *(G-5040)*

George R Silcott Railway Equip 614 885-7224
564 E Dublin Granville Rd Worthington (43085) *(G-20867)*

George Steel Fabricating Inc 513 932-2887
1207 S Us Route 42 Lebanon (45036) *(G-11802)*

George Weston Co 614 868-7565
1020 Claycraft Rd Ste D Columbus (43230) *(G-7110)*

George Whalley Company 216 453-0099
1180 High St Ste 1 Fairport Harbor (44077) *(G-9765)*

Georges Donuts Inc 330 963-9902
7995 Darrow Rd Twinsburg (44087) *(G-18945)*

Georgetown Vineyards LLC 740 435-3222
62920 Georgetown Rd Cambridge (43725) *(G-2458)*

Georgia Boot LLC 740 753-1951
39 E Canal St Nelsonville (45764) *(G-14734)*

Georgia Metal Coatings Company 770 446-3930
275 Industrial Pkwy Chardon (44024) *(G-3155)*

Georgia-Pacific LLC 330 794-4444
3265 Gilchrist Rd Mogadore (44260) *(G-14376)*

Georgia-Pacific LLC 740 477-3347
2850 Owens Rd Circleville (43113) *(G-4631)*

Georgia-Pacific LLC 513 336-4200
5181 Natorp Blvd Ste 520 Mason (45040) *(G-13027)*

Georgia-Pacific LLC 614 491-9100
1975 Watkins Rd Columbus (43207) *(G-7111)*

Geotech Pattern & Mold Inc 513 683-2600
272 E Kemper Rd Loveland (45140) *(G-12352)*

Gerald Christman 740 838-2475
47278 Swazey Rd Lewisville (43754) *(G-11948)*

Gerald D Damron 740 894-3680
197 Township Road 1156 Chesapeake (45619) *(G-3188)*

Gerald Grain Center Inc 419 445-2451
3265 County Road 24 Archbold (43502) *(G-678)*

Gerald H Smith 740 446-3455
670 Buck Ridge Rd Bidwell (45614) *(G-1676)*

Gerald L Hermann Co Inc 513 661-1818
3325 Harrison Ave Cincinnati (45211) *(G-3822)*

Gerald Rose 937 866-6339
9600 Byers Rd Miamisburg (45342) *(G-13813)*

Gerber & Sons Inc (PA) 330 897-6201
201 E Main St Baltic (43804) *(G-1072)*

Gerber Farm Division Inc 800 362-7381
5889 Kidron Rd Kidron (44636) *(G-11590)*

Gerber Wood Products Inc 330 857-3901
6075 Kidron Rd Kidron (44636) *(G-11591)*

Gerdau Macsteel Atmosphere Ann 330 478-0314
1501 Raff Rd Sw Canton (44710) *(G-2713)*

Gergel-Kellem Company Inc 216 398-2000
4544 Hinckley Indus Pkwy Cleveland (44109) *(G-5425)*

Gerich Fiberglass Inc 419 362-4591
7004 Us Highway 42 Mount Gilead (43338) *(G-14560)*

Gerling and Associates Inc 740 965-6200
138 Stelzer Ct Sunbury (43074) *(G-18060)*

Germ Guardian, Euclid Also called *Guardian Technologies LLC* *(G-9582)*

Gerow Equipment Company Inc 216 383-8800
706 E 163rd St Cleveland (44110) *(G-5426)*

Gerstco Division, Wooster Also called *Artiflex Manufacturing LLC* *(G-20741)*

Gerstco Division, Clyde Also called *Artiflex Manufacturing LLC* *(G-6537)*

Gerstenslager Construction 330 832-3604
343 16th St Se Massillon (44646) *(G-13139)*

Gerstenslager Hardwood Pdts, Massillon Also called *Gerstenslager Construction* *(G-13139)*

Gerstner International, Dayton Also called *H Gerstner & Sons Inc* *(G-8382)*

Gew Inc 440 237-4439
11941 Abbey Rd Ste X Cleveland (44133) *(G-5427)*

Geyer Transport & Mfg 740 382-9008
1443 N Main St Marion (43302) *(G-12868)*

Geyers Markets Inc 419 468-9477
230 Portland Way N Galion (44833) *(G-10271)*

Geygan Enterprises Inc 513 932-4222
101 Dave Ave Ste E Lebanon (45036) *(G-11803)*

GFS Chemicals Inc (PA) 740 881-5501
3041 Home Rd Powell (43065) *(G-16472)*

GFS Chemicals Inc 614 224-5345
851 Mckinley Ave Columbus (43222) *(G-7112)*

GFS Chemicals Inc 740 881-5501
800 Mckinley Ave Columbus (43222) *(G-7113)*

GFS Chemicals Inc 614 351-5347
800 Kaderly Dr Columbus (43228) *(G-7114)*

Ghent Manufacturing, Lebanon Also called *GMI Companies Inc* *(G-11804)*

Ghostblind Industries Inc 740 374-6766
2347a State Route 821 Marietta (45750) *(G-12785)*

Ghp II LLC (HQ) 740 687-2500
1115 W 5th Ave Lancaster (43130) *(G-11719)*

Ghp II LLC 740 681-6825
  2893 W Fair Ave Lancaster (43130) *(G-11720)*

Gia Russa (PA) 330 743-6050
  574 Mcclurg Rd Youngstown (44512) *(G-21100)*

Giannios Candy Co Inc (PA) 330 755-7000
  430 Youngstown Poland Rd Struthers (44471) *(G-17991)*

Giant Eagle, Tallmadge *Also called Tamarkin Company (G-18172)*

Giant Industries Inc 419 531-4600
  900 N Westwood Ave Toledo (43607) *(G-18480)*

Giant Lemonade Cup, Westerville *Also called Paradise Lemonade (G-20178)*

Gibbco, Cincinnati *Also called Trans Ash Inc (G-4518)*

Gibbs E & Associates 614 939-1672
  7386 Hampsted Sq S New Albany (43054) *(G-14760)*

Gibraltar Industries Inc 440 617-9230
  26314 Center Ridge Rd Westlake (44145) *(G-20272)*

Gibson Bakery, Oberlin *Also called Gibson Bros Inc (G-15641)*

Gibson Bros Inc 440 774-2401
  23 W College St Oberlin (44074) *(G-15641)*

Gibson Greetings Inc (HQ) 216 252-7300
  1 American Rd Cleveland (44144) *(G-5428)*

Gibson Machinery LLC 440 439-4000
  181 Oak Leaf Oval Cleveland (44146) *(G-5429)*

Gibson, Jo K, Marietta *Also called Rockbottom Oil & Gas (G-12825)*

Gie Media Inc (PA) 800 456-0707
  5811 Canal Rd Cleveland (44125) *(G-5430)*

Giesecke & Devrient Amer Inc 330 405-8442
  1960 Enterprise Pkwy Twinsburg (44087) *(G-18946)*

Giesecke & Devrient Amer Inc 330 425-1515
  2020 Enterprise Pkwy Twinsburg (44087) *(G-18947)*

Giesecke & Devrient Can 330 425-1515
  2020 Enterprise Pkwy Twinsburg (44087) *(G-18948)*

Gift Cove Inc 419 285-2920
  170 Delaware St Put In Bay (43456) *(G-16498)*

Gifted Nutrition, Stow *Also called Badizo LLC (G-17732)*

Gigis Cupcakes of Kenwood 513 985-4440
  7940 Hosbrook Rd Cincinnati (45243) *(G-3823)*

Gilbarco Catlow LLC 937 898-3236
  2750 Us Route 40 Tipp City (45371) *(G-18279)*

Gilbert Geiser 330 237-7901
  3301 Longview Pl Nw Canton (44720) *(G-2714)*

Gilkey Window Company Inc 513 769-9663
  3528 Hauck Rd Cincinnati (45241) *(G-3824)*

Gilkey Window Company Inc (PA) 513 769-4527
  3625 Hauck Rd Cincinnati (45241) *(G-3825)*

Gillam Machine Company 330 457-2557
  1888 Macklin Rd New Waterford (44445) *(G-14971)*

Gillard Construction Inc 740 376-9744
  1308 Greene St Marietta (45750) *(G-12786)*

Gillig Custom Winery Inc 419 202-6057
  1720 Northridge Rd Findlay (45840) *(G-9831)*

Gilson Machine & Tool Co Inc 419 592-2911
  529 Freedom Dr Napoleon (43545) *(G-14678)*

Gilson Screen Incorporated 419 256-7711
  8-810 K 2 Rd Malinta (43535) *(G-12534)*

Giminetti Baking Company 513 751-7655
  2900 Gilbert Ave Cincinnati (45206) *(G-3826)*

Gingerbread N Bows 740 945-1027
  202 W Main St Scio (43988) *(G-17037)*

Ginko Systems, Dayton *Also called Ginko Voting Systems LLC (G-8364)*

Ginko Voting Systems LLC (PA) 937 291-4060
  600 Progress Rd Dayton (45449) *(G-8364)*

Ginnys Custom Framing Gallery 419 468-7240
  1135 Cherington Dr Galion (44833) *(G-10272)*

Gino's Jewelers & Trophy Mfrs, Cleveland *Also called Ginos Awards Inc (G-5431)*

Ginos Awards Inc 216 831-5653
  4701 Richmond Rd Ste 300 Cleveland (44128) *(G-5431)*

Girard Machine Company Inc 330 545-9731
  700 Dot St Girard (44420) *(G-10390)*

Gis Dynamics LLC 513 847-4931
  11315 Williamson Rd Blue Ash (45241) *(G-1803)*

Gisco Inc 937 773-7601
  308 W Statler Rd Piqua (45356) *(G-16267)*

Giti Tech Group Ltd 866 381-7955
  440 Fame Rd West Carrollton (45449) *(G-19793)*

Givaudan 513 482-2536
  110 E 69th St Cincinnati (45216) *(G-3827)*

Givaudan Flavors Corporation 513 948-8000
  100 E 69th St Cincinnati (45216) *(G-3828)*

Givaudan Flavors Corporation 513 948-8000
  110 E 70th St Cincinnati (45216) *(G-3829)*

Givaudan Flvors Fragrances Inc (HQ) 513 948-8000
  1199 Edison Dr Cincinnati (45216) *(G-3830)*

Givaudan Fragrances Corp (HQ) 513 948-3428
  1199 Edison Dr Ste 1-2 Cincinnati (45216) *(G-3831)*

Givaudan Fragrances Corp 513 948-3428
  100 E 69th St Cincinnati (45216) *(G-3832)*

Givaudan Roure US Inc (HQ) 513 948-8000
  1199 Edison Dr Cincinnati (45216) *(G-3833)*

Givaudan US, Cincinnati *Also called Givaudan Roure US Inc (G-3833)*

Gizmo, Chagrin Falls *Also called Whip Guide Co (G-3133)*

GK Packaging Inc (PA) 614 873-3900
  7680 Commerce Pl Plain City (43064) *(G-16342)*

GKN Aerospace Cincinnati Inc (HQ) 513 489-9800
  11230 Deerfield Rd Blue Ash (45242) *(G-1804)*

GKN Driveline Bowl Green Inc 419 354-3955
  2223 Wood Bridge Blvd Bowling Green (43402) *(G-1989)*

GKN Sinter Metals LLC 740 441-3203
  2160 Eastern Ave Gallipolis (45631) *(G-10298)*

GL International LLC 330 744-8812
  215 Sinter Ct Youngstown (44510) *(G-21101)*

GL Nause Co Inc 513 722-9500
  1971 Phoenix Dr Loveland (45140) *(G-12353)*

Glas Ornamental Metals Inc 330 753-0215
  1559 Waterloo Rd Barberton (44203) *(G-1118)*

Glascraft Inc 330 966-3000
  8400 Port Jackson Ave Nw North Canton (44720) *(G-15234)*

Glasfloss Industries Inc (PA) 740 687-1100
  2168 Commerce St Lancaster (43130) *(G-11721)*

Glass Axis 614 291-4250
  610 W Town St Columbus (43215) *(G-7115)*

Glass Coatings & Concepts LLC 513 539-5300
  300 Lawton Ave Monroe (45050) *(G-14403)*

Glass Fabricators Inc 216 529-1919
  2160 Halstead Ave Lakewood (44107) *(G-11665)*

Glass Medic America, Westerville *Also called Glass Medic Inc (G-20155)*

Glass Medic Inc 800 356-4009
  6996 Four Seasons Dr Westerville (43082) *(G-20155)*

Glass Mirror Awards Inc 419 638-2221
  703 County Road 26 Helena (43435) *(G-10896)*

Glass Seale Ltd 513 733-1464
  1700 Hunt Rd Cincinnati (45215) *(G-3834)*

Glass Sensors LLC 330 234-7999
  770 Spruce St Wooster (44691) *(G-20776)*

Glass Specialties, Fredericksburg *Also called Yoder Window & Siding Ltd (G-10094)*

Glass Surface Systems Inc 330 745-8500
  24 Brown St Barberton (44203) *(G-1119)*

Glasslight Candles LLC 443 509-5505
  8706 Charleston Ridge Dr Mason (45040) *(G-13028)*

Glassline Corporation (PA) 419 666-9712
  28905 Glenwood Rd Perrysburg (43551) *(G-16102)*

Glassrock Plant, Glenford *Also called Premier Silica LLC (G-10400)*

Glasstastic, South Point *Also called Cabinets Inc (G-17435)*

Glasstech Inc (PA) 419 661-9500
  995 4th St Perrysburg (43551) *(G-16103)*

Glauners Wholesale Inc 216 398-7088
  5011 Brookpark Rd Cleveland (44134) *(G-5432)*

Glavin Industries Inc 440 349-0049
  6835 Cochran Rd Ste A Solon (44139) *(G-17297)*

Glavin Specialty Co, Solon *Also called Glavin Industries Inc (G-17297)*

Glawe Awnings, Fairborn *Also called Glawe Manufacturing Co Inc (G-9623)*

Glawe Manufacturing Co Inc 937 754-0064
  851 Zapata Dr Fairborn (45324) *(G-9623)*

Glaxosmithkline LLC 937 623-2680
  741 Chaffin Rdg Columbus (43214) *(G-7116)*

Glaxosmithkline LLC 440 552-2895
  37381 Stone Creek Dr North Ridgeville (44039) *(G-15376)*

Glaxosmithkline LLC 330 608-2365
  4273 Ridge Crest Dr Copley (44321) *(G-7847)*

Glaxosmithkline LLC 614 570-5970
  359 Garden Rd Columbus (43214) *(G-7117)*

Glaxosmithkline LLC 330 241-4447
  6250 Highland Meadows Dr Medina (44256) *(G-13417)*

Glazier Pattern & Coach 937 492-7355
  3720 Loramie Wash Rd Houston (45333) *(G-11121)*

GLC Biotechnology Inc 440 349-2193
  7925 Megan Meadow Dr Hudson (44236) *(G-11173)*

Gleason M & M Precision, Dayton *Also called Gleason Metrology Systems Corp (G-8365)*

Gleason Metrology Systems Corp (HQ) 937 384-8901
  300 Progress Rd Dayton (45449) *(G-8365)*

Glebus Alloys LLC 330 867-9999
  883 Hampshire Rd Ste E Stow (44224) *(G-17759)*

Gledhill Road Machinery Co 419 468-4400
  765 Portland Way S Galion (44833) *(G-10273)*

Glen D Lala 937 274-7770
  2610 Willowburn Ave Dayton (45417) *(G-8366)*

Glen-Gery Caledonia Plant, Caledonia *Also called Glen-Gery Corporation (G-2437)*

Glen-Gery Corporation 419 845-3321
  5692 Rinker Rd Caledonia (43314) *(G-2437)*

Glen-Gery Corporation 419 468-4890
  3785 Cardington Iberia Rd Galion (44833) *(G-10274)*

Glen-Gery Corporation 419 468-5002
  County Rd 9 Iberia (43325) *(G-11243)*

Glendale Machine Inc 440 248-8646
  30625 Solon Industrial # 1 Solon (44139) *(G-17298)*

Glenn Hunter & Associates Inc 419 822-3744
  1222 County Road 6 Delta (43515) *(G-8935)*

Glenn Michael Brick 740 391-5735
  108 Wood St Flushing (43977) *(G-9916)*

Glenn Ravens Winery 740 545-1000
56183 County Road 143 West Lafayette (43845) *(G-20086)*

Glenridge Machine Co 440 975-1055
4610 Beidler Rd Willoughby (44094) *(G-20499)*

Glenro Inc 937 392-0111
330 N Front St Ripley (45167) *(G-16667)*

Glenwood Erectors Inc 330 652-9616
905 Summit Ave Niles (44446) *(G-15156)*

Gli, Cleveland *Also called Great Lakes Integrated Inc (G-5452)*

Gli Pool Products, Youngstown *Also called GL International LLC (G-21101)*

Glidden Professional Paint Ctr, Youngstown *Also called PPG Architectural Finishes Inc (G-21174)*

Glidden Professional Paint Ctr, Mentor *Also called PPG Architectural Finishes Inc (G-13694)*

Glidden Professional Paint Ctr, Cincinnati *Also called Akzo Nobel Paints LLC (G-3374)*

Glidden Professional Paint Ctr, Columbus *Also called PPG Architectural Finishes Inc (G-7508)*

Glidden Professional Paint Ctr, Cleveland *Also called PPG Architectural Finishes Inc (G-6025)*

Glidden Professional Paint Ctr, Canton *Also called PPG Architectural Finishes Inc (G-2817)*

Glister Inc 614 252-6400
3065 Switzer Ave Columbus (43219) *(G-7118)*

Glo-Quartz Electric Heater Co 440 255-9701
7084 Maple St Mentor (44060) *(G-13593)*

Global Biochem 513 792-2218
8044 Montgomery Rd Cincinnati (45236) *(G-3835)*

Global Body & Equipment Co 330 264-6640
2061 Sylvan Rd Wooster (44691) *(G-20777)*

Global Chemical Inc 419 242-1004
1925 Nebraska Ave Toledo (43607) *(G-18481)*

Global Clean and Go, Berea *Also called Df Consumer Products (G-1611)*

Global Coal Sales Group LLC (HQ) 614 221-0101
41 S High St Ste 3750s Columbus (43215) *(G-7119)*

Global Cooling Inc 740 274-7900
6000 Poston Rd Athens (45701) *(G-869)*

Global Design Factory LLC 330 322-8775
1227 Norton Rd 3b Hudson (44236) *(G-11174)*

Global E-Lumenation Tech 513 821-8687
3289 Spring Grove Ave Cincinnati (45225) *(G-3836)*

Global Furnishings Inc 216 595-0901
3659 Green Rd Ste 203 Beachwood (44122) *(G-1272)*

Global Gauge Corporation 937 222-0797
3200 Kettering Blvd Moraine (45439) *(G-14491)*

Global Gear LLC 941 830-0531
8336 W Craig Dr Chagrin Falls (44023) *(G-3088)*

Global Glass Block Inc 216 731-2333
23570 Lakeland Blvd Euclid (44132) *(G-9581)*

Global Health Services Inc 513 777-8111
8087 Cincinnati Dayton Rd B West Chester (45069) *(G-19876)*

Global Laser Tek 513 701-0452
7697 Innovation Way # 700 Mason (45040) *(G-13029)*

Global Lighting Tech Inc 440 922-4584
55 Andrews Cir Ste 1 Brecksville (44141) *(G-2052)*

Global Manufacturing Inds (PA) 513 271-2180
7710 Shawnee Run Rd Cincinnati (45243) *(G-3837)*

Global Manufacturing Solutions 937 236-8315
2001 Kuntz Rd Dayton (45404) *(G-8367)*

Global Manufacturing Tech LLC 440 205-1001
8671 Tyler Blvd Unit F Mentor (44060) *(G-13594)*

Global Mining Holding Co LLC (PA) 614 221-0101
41 S High St Columbus (43215) *(G-7120)*

Global Oilfield Services LLC 419 756-8027
3401 State Route 13 Mansfield (44904) *(G-12613)*

Global Packaging & Exports Inc (PA) 513 454-2020
9166 Sutton Pl West Chester (45011) *(G-19877)*

Global Partners USA Co Inc 513 276-4981
7544 Bermuda Trce West Chester (45069) *(G-19878)*

Global Payments Inc 440 356-0325
21320 Hillsdale Ave Cleveland (44126) *(G-5433)*

Global Plastic Tech Inc 330 963-6830
7762 Sunstone Dr Brecksville (44141) *(G-2053)*

Global Precision Parts, East Liberty *Also called Harding Machine Acquisition Co (G-9201)*

Global Precision Parts Inc 419 453-0010
111 Progressive Dr Ottoville (45876) *(G-15821)*

Global Precision Parts Inc 260 563-9030
7600 Us Route 127 Van Wert (45891) *(G-19258)*

Global Signs and Graphics Inc 440 230-2100
10147 Royalton Rd Ste M North Royalton (44133) *(G-15421)*

Global Sourcing & Support Svcs 513 321-0957
260 E University Ave Cincinnati (45219) *(G-3838)*

Global Specialty Machines LLC (PA) 513 701-0452
7697 Innovation Way # 700 Mason (45040) *(G-13030)*

Global Technology Center, Holland *Also called Tekni-Plex Inc (G-11088)*

Global Tool, Dayton *Also called Ovase Manufacturing LLC (G-8557)*

Global Trade Network Inc 513 701-0411
7697 Innovation Way # 200 Mason (45040) *(G-13031)*

Global Trucking LLC 614 598-6264
3723 Ellerdale Dr Columbus (43230) *(G-7121)*

Global Wood Products LLC 440 442-5859
734 Alpha Dr Ste J Highland Heights (44143) *(G-10913)*

Globe Metallurgical Inc (HQ) 740 984-2361
County Road 32 Waterford (45786) *(G-19647)*

Globe Motors Inc (HQ) 334 983-3542
2275 Stanley Ave Dayton (45404) *(G-8368)*

Globe Motors Inc 937 228-3171
1944 Troy St Dayton (45404) *(G-8369)*

Globe Motors Inc 937 228-3171
2275 Stanley Ave Dayton (45404) *(G-8370)*

Globe Pipe Hanger Products Inc 216 362-6300
14601 Industrial Pkwy Cleveland (44135) *(G-5434)*

Globe Products Inc (PA) 937 233-0233
5051 Kitridge Rd Dayton (45424) *(G-8371)*

Globe Specialty Metals, Waterford *Also called Globe Metallurgical Inc (G-19647)*

Globecom Technologies Inc 330 408-7008
8542 Kepler Ave Nw Canal Fulton (44614) *(G-2502)*

Globus Printing & Packg Co Inc (PA) 419 628-2381
1 Executive Pkwy Minster (45865) *(G-14354)*

Glorias 330 264-8963
2023 Portage Rd Wooster (44691) *(G-20778)*

Glorious Cupcakes 216 544-2325
3132 Sterling Lake Dr Medina (44256) *(G-13418)*

Glt Inc (PA) 937 237-0055
3341 Successful Way Dayton (45414) *(G-8372)*

Glt Fabricators Inc (PA) 440 914-1122
6810 Cochran Rd Solon (44139) *(G-17299)*

Glt Products, Solon *Also called Great Lakes Textiles Inc (G-17304)*

Glunt Industries Inc 330 399-7585
319 N River Rd Nw Warren (44483) *(G-19555)*

Gluten-Free Expressions 740 928-0338
520 E Main St Hebron (43025) *(G-10868)*

GM Logging 740 501-0819
204 Cole Dr Johnstown (43031) *(G-11399)*

GM Management, Zanesville *Also called General Machine & Supply Co (G-21315)*

Gmd Industries LLC 937 252-3643
1414 E 2nd St Dayton (45403) *(G-8373)*

Gmelectric Inc 330 477-3392
4606 Southway St Sw Canton (44706) *(G-2715)*

Gmerecords, Reynoldsburg *Also called Swagg Productions2015llc (G-16608)*

GMI Companies Inc (PA) 513 932-3445
2999 Henkle Dr Lebanon (45036) *(G-11804)*

GMI Companies Inc 937 981-0244
512 S Washington St Greenfield (45123) *(G-10476)*

GMI Companies Inc 937 981-7724
512 S Washington St Greenfield (45123) *(G-10477)*

GMI Holdings Inc (HQ) 330 821-5360
1 Door Dr Mount Hope (44660) *(G-14571)*

GMI Holdings Inc 330 897-4424
606 N Ray St Baltic (43804) *(G-1073)*

GMR Furniture Services Ltd 216 244-5072
7403 Dorothy Ave Parma (44129) *(G-15959)*

GNI Erectors 614 465-7260
8907 Stillwater Dr Galloway (43119) *(G-10314)*

Gnrl Chemical L 419 255-0193
1661 Campbell St Toledo (43607) *(G-18482)*

Gns, Danville *Also called Besl Specialized Carrier (G-8084)*

Gnw Aluminum Inc 330 821-7955
1356 Beeson St Ne Alliance (44601) *(G-511)*

Go Calendars 513 755-1555
7100 Foundry Row Liberty Township (45069) *(G-11962)*

Go Cupcake 937 299-4985
5017 Rolling Woods Trl Dayton (45429) *(G-8374)*

Go For Broke Amusement, Flushing *Also called Glenn Michael Brick (G-9916)*

Go2 Partners Inc 330 650-5300
2265 E Entp Pkwy A Twinsburg (44087) *(G-18949)*

Goal Medical LLC 541 654-5951
7555 Tyler Blvd Mentor (44060) *(G-13595)*

Godfrey & Wing Inc (PA) 330 562-1440
220 Campus Dr Aurora (44202) *(G-922)*

Godfrey & Wing Inc 419 980-4616
2066 E 2nd St Defiance (43512) *(G-8791)*

Godiva Chocolatier Inc 216 831-9414
26300 Cedar Rd Ste 1035 Beachwood (44122) *(G-1273)*

Gofast LLC 419 562-8027
963 Hopley Ave Bucyrus (44820) *(G-2346)*

Gofs, Mansfield *Also called Global Oilfield Services LLC (G-12613)*

Gojo Industries Inc (PA) 330 255-6000
1 Gojo Plz Ste 500 Akron (44311) *(G-206)*

Gojo Industries Inc 330 255-6000
3783 State Rd Cuyahoga Falls (44223) *(G-8004)*

Gojo Industries Inc 330 255-6525
1366 Commerce Dr Stow (44224) *(G-17760)*

Gojo Industries Inc 330 922-4522
3901 Lippman Pkwy Cuyahoga Falls (44224) *(G-8005)*

Gokoh Corporation (HQ) 937 339-4977
1280 Archer Dr Troy (45373) *(G-18832)*

Gold Key Processing Inc 440 632-0901
14910 Madison Rd Middlefield (44062) *(G-13937)*

Gold Metal Machining Inc 614 873-5031
216 W Bigelow Ave Plain City (43064) (G-16343)

Gold Mine Inc 614 378-8308
4951 Gillingham Way Dublin (43017) (G-9079)

Gold N Krisp Chips & Pretzels 330 832-8395
1900 Erie Ave Nw Massillon (44646) (G-13140)

Gold Pro Inc 216 241-5143
850 Euclid Ave Ste 518 Cleveland (44114) (G-5435)

Gold Rush Jerky, Litchfield Also called Medina Foods Inc (G-12138)

Gold Star Chili Inc 513 631-1990
5420 Ridge Ave Cincinnati (45213) (G-3839)

Gold Star Chili-Burnet, Cincinnati Also called D & A Rofael Enterprises Inc (G-3628)

Gold Star Met Fabg & Repr Inc 440 353-3233
4940 Mills Indus Pkwy North Ridgeville (44039) (G-15377)

Gold Toe Moretz Holdings Corp 740 948-0004
8512 Factory Shops Blvd Jeffersonville (43128) (G-11380)

Golden Dynamic Inc 614 575-1222
950 Taylor Station Rd M Columbus (43230) (G-7122)

Golden Eagle, Upper Sandusky Also called New Eezy-Gro Inc (G-19136)

Golden Giant Inc 419 674-4038
13300 S Vision Dr Kenton (43326) (G-11547)

Golden Giants Building System, Kenton Also called Golden Giant Inc (G-11547)

Golden Graphics Ltd 419 673-6260
314 W Franklin St Kenton (43326) (G-11548)

Golden Jersey Inn, Yellow Springs Also called Youngs Jersey Dairy Inc (G-21003)

Golden Signs and Lighting LLC 513 248-0895
120-150 Olympic Rd Milford (45150) (G-14144)

Golden Spring Co Inc 937 848-2513
2143 Ferry Rd Bellbrook (45305) (G-1509)

Golden Turtle Chocolate Fctry 513 932-1990
120 S Broadway St Ste 1 Lebanon (45036) (G-11805)

Goldsmith & Eggleton LLC 203 855-6000
300 1st St Wadsworth (44281) (G-19408)

Golf Car Company Inc 614 873-1055
8899 Memorial Dr Plain City (43064) (G-16344)

Golf Dome 440 543-1211
8198 Washington St Chagrin Falls (44023) (G-3089)

Golf Dsign Screcards Unlimited, Columbus Also called Scorecards Unlimited LLC (G-7602)

Golf Galaxy Golfworks Inc 740 328-4193
4820 Jacksontown Rd Newark (43056) (G-15014)

Golf Graphics, Bluffton Also called Tim Boutwell (G-1917)

Golf Marketing Group Inc 330 963-5155
9221 Ravenna Rd Ste 7 Twinsburg (44087) (G-18950)

Golfpremiums.com, Columbus Also called Corporate Supply LLC (G-6986)

Golubitsky Corporation 800 552-4204
4364 Cranwood Pkwy Cleveland (44128) (G-5436)

Gomech Ltd 419 419-4446
355 Tomahawk Dr Unit 2 Maumee (43537) (G-13261)

Gonda Wood Products, Elyria Also called Joe Gonda Company Inc (G-9443)

Gongwer News Service Inc (PA) 614 221-1992
17 S High St Ste 630 Columbus (43215) (G-7123)

Gongwer News Service Inc (HQ) 614 221-1992
17 S High St Ste 630 Columbus (43215) (G-7124)

Gooch & Housego (florida) LLC (HQ) 321 242-7818
676 Alpha Dr Cleveland (44143) (G-5437)

Gooch & Housego (ohio) LLC 216 486-6100
676 Alpha Dr Highland Heights (44143) (G-10914)

Good Beans Coffee Roasters LLC 513 310-9516
1381 Cottonwood Dr Milford (45150) (G-14145)

Good Day Tools LLC 513 578-2050
4603 Carter Ave Cincinnati (45212) (G-3840)

Good Fortunes Inc 440 942-2888
1486 E 361st St Willoughby (44095) (G-20500)

Good Greens, Oakwood Village Also called Good Nutrition LLC (G-15624)

Good JP 419 207-8484
854 Willow Ln Ashland (44805) (G-735)

Good News, Middlefield Also called Suburban Communications Inc (G-13993)

Good Nutrition LLC 216 534-6617
7710 First Pl Oakwood Village (44146) (G-15624)

Good Wood Inc (PA) 740 484-1500
42591 Bina Rd Belmont (43718) (G-1579)

Goodale Auto-Truck Parts Inc 614 294-4777
1100 E 5th Ave Columbus (43201) (G-7125)

Goodell Farms 330 274-2161
5212 Goodell Rd Mantua (44255) (G-12711)

Goodman Distribution Inc 440 324-4071
160 Liberty Ct Elyria (44035) (G-9426)

Goodrich Avionics, Columbus Also called L3 Aviation Products Inc (G-7278)

Goodrich Corporation 937 339-3811
101 Waco St Troy (45373) (G-18833)

Goodrich Corporation 216 429-4018
6225 Oak Tree Blvd Independence (44131) (G-11255)

Goodrich Corporation 330 374-2882
1555 Corporate Woods Pkwy Uniontown (44685) (G-19086)

Goodrich Corporation 216 429-4655
925 Keynote Cir Ste 300 Brooklyn Heights (44131) (G-2140)

Goodrich Landing Gear Division, Independence Also called Goodrich Corporation (G-11255)

Goodwill Idstrs Grtr Clvlnd L 330 456-8020
2630 Atlantic Blvd Ne Canton (44705) (G-2716)

Goodwill Inds NW Ohio Inc 419 255-0070
525 Cherry St Toledo (43604) (G-18483)

Goodwin Farms 513 877-2636
10092 State Route 132 Pleasant Plain (45162) (G-16371)

Goodyear, Shelby Also called Sumitomo Rubber Usa LLC (G-17144)

Goodyear Tire & Rubber Company (PA) 330 796-2121
200 E Innovation Way Akron (44316) (G-207)

Goodyear Tire & Rubber Company 216 265-1800
18901 Snow Rd Cleveland (44142) (G-5438)

Goosefoot Acres Inc (PA) 330 225-7184
5879 Center Rd Valley City (44280) (G-19205)

Goosefoot Acres Cntr For, Valley City Also called Goosefoot Acres Inc (G-19205)

Gorant Chocolatier LLC (PA) 330 726-8821
8301 Market St Boardman (44512) (G-1921)

Gorant's Yum Yum Tree, Boardman Also called Gorant Chocolatier LLC (G-1921)

Gordon Bernard Co Inc 513 248-7600
22 Whitney Dr Milford (45150) (G-14146)

Gordon Bernard Company LLC 513 248-7600
22 Whitney Dr Milford (45150) (G-14147)

Gordon Brothers Btlg Group Inc 330 337-8754
776 N Ellsworth Ave Salem (44460) (G-16894)

Gordon Tool Inc 419 263-3151
1301 State Route 49 Payne (45880) (G-16015)

Gordons Graphics Inc 330 863-2322
123 S Reed Ave Malvern (44644) (G-12546)

Gorell Enterprises Inc (PA) 724 465-1800
10250 Philipp Pkwy Streetsboro (44241) (G-17855)

Gorell Windows & Doors, Streetsboro Also called Gorell Enterprises Inc (G-17855)

Gorey Construction, Medina Also called Robert Gorey (G-13468)

Gorman-Rupp Company 419 886-3001
180 Hines Ave Bellville (44813) (G-1570)

Gorman-Rupp Company (PA) 419 755-1011
600 S Airport Rd Mansfield (44903) (G-12614)

Gorman-Rupp Company 419 755-1011
305 Bowman St Mansfield (44903) (G-12615)

Gorman-Rupp Company 419 755-1245
100 Rump Rd Mansfield (44903) (G-12616)

Gorman-Rupp Company 419 755-1011
100 Rupp Rd Mansfield (44903) (G-12617)

Gortons Inc 216 362-1050
13525 Hummel Rd Cleveland (44142) (G-5439)

Gospel Trumpet Publishing 937 548-9876
5065 S State Route 49 Greenville (45331) (G-10503)

Gosun Inc 513 709-2519
1217 Ellis St Cincinnati (45223) (G-3841)

Gotcha Covered 513 829-7555
4854 Factory Dr Fairfield (45014) (G-9661)

Gotta Groove Records Inc 216 431-7373
3615 Superior Ave E 4201a Cleveland (44114) (G-5440)

Gottfried Medical Inc 419 474-2973
2920 Centennial Rd Toledo (43617) (G-18484)

Gottschall Tool & Die Inc 330 332-1544
14028 W Middletown Rd Salem (44460) (G-16895)

Gougler Industries Inc (HQ) 330 673-5826
705 Lake St Kent (44240) (G-11463)

Gould Electronics Inc (PA) 440 953-5000
34929 Curtis Blvd Ste 100 Eastlake (44095) (G-9271)

Gould Fire Protection Inc 419 957-2416
633 Bristol Dr Findlay (45840) (G-9832)

Gould Group LLC 740 807-4294
4653 Trueman Blvd Ste 120 Hilliard (43026) (G-10949)

Government Acquisitions Inc 513 721-8700
720 E Pete Rose Way # 360 Cincinnati (45202) (G-3842)

Government Specialty Pdts LLC (PA) 937 672-9473
9588 Quailwood Trl Dayton (45458) (G-8375)

Goyal Enterprises Inc 513 874-9303
4836 Business Center Way West Chester (45246) (G-20010)

Goyal Industries Inc 419 522-7099
382 Park Ave E Mansfield (44905) (G-12618)

GPM, Franklin Also called Green Point Metals Inc (G-10025)

Gqi Inc 330 830-9805
2650 Richville Dr Sw # 105 Massillon (44646) (G-13141)

Gr Golf, New Washington Also called Wurms Woodworking Company (G-14966)

Gr Group Sales Inc 216 961-3773
9400 Maywood Ave Cleveland (44102) (G-5441)

Gra-Mag Truck Intr Systems LLC (HQ) 740 490-1000
470 E High St London (43140) (G-12211)

Graber Metal Works Inc 440 237-8422
9664 Akins Rd Ste 1 North Royalton (44133) (G-15422)

Grabo Interiors Inc 216 391-6677
3605 Perkins Ave Cleveland (44114) (G-5442)

Grace Automation Services Inc 330 567-3108
8140 State Route 514 Big Prairie (44611) (G-1681)

Grace Imaging LLC 419 874-2127
28400 Cedar Park Blvd C Perrysburg (43551) (G-16104)

Grace Metals Ltd 234 380-1433
685 Ashbrooke Way Hudson (44236) (G-11175)

A
L
P
H
A
B
E
T
I
C

Grace Petroleum Inc...330 484-0709
5506 Keiffer Ave Nw Canton (44706) (G-2717)

Gracie Plum Investments Inc..740 355-9029
609 2nd St Unit 2 Portsmouth (45662) (G-16436)

Graco Ohio Inc (HQ)..330 494-1313
8400 Port Jackson Ave Nw North Canton (44720) (G-15235)

Gradall Industries Inc (HQ)..330 339-2211
406 Mill Ave Sw New Philadelphia (44663) (G-14901)

Gradeworks..440 487-4201
10655 Hickory Hill Ct Willoughby (44094) (G-20501)

Grady McCauley Incorporated.......................................330 494-9444
9260 Pleasantwood Ave Nw North Canton (44720) (G-15236)

Graebener Group Tech Ltd..419 591-7033
476 E Riverview Ave Napoleon (43545) (G-14679)

Graeter's Ice Cream, Columbus Also called Superior Tasting Products Inc (G-7668)

Graeter's Ice Cream, Cincinnati Also called International Brand Services (G-3930)

Graeters Manufacturing Co (PA)....................................513 721-3323
1175 Regina Graeter Way Cincinnati (45216) (G-3843)

Graffiti Co, Cleveland Also called Barbs Graffiti Inc (G-4889)

Graffiti Foods Limited..614 759-1921
333 Outerbelt St Columbus (43213) (G-7126)

Grafix, Cleveland Also called Graphic Art Systems Inc (G-5446)

Graftech Advanced Graphite..216 676-2259
12300 Snow Rd Parma (44130) (G-15960)

Graftech Holdings Inc...216 676-2000
6100 Oak Tree Blvd # 300 Independence (44131) (G-11256)

Graftech International Ltd (HQ)...................................216 676-2000
6100 Oak Tree Blvd # 300 Independence (44131) (G-11257)

Graftech Intl Holdings Inc..216 529-3777
11709 Madison Ave Cleveland (44107) (G-5443)

Graftech Intl Holdings Inc..330 239-3023
12300 Snow Rd Parma (44130) (G-15961)

Graftech Intl Holdings Inc (HQ)..................................216 676-2000
6100 Oak Tree Blvd # 300 Independence (44131) (G-11258)

Grafton Ready Mix Concret Inc.....................................440 926-2911
1155 Elm St Grafton (44044) (G-10427)

Graham Ford Power Products..614 801-0049
850 Harmon Ave Columbus (43223) (G-7127)

Graham Packaging Co Europe LLC....................................513 398-5000
1225 Castle Dr Mason (45040) (G-13032)

Graham Packaging Company LP.......................................740 439-4242
8800 Guernsey Industrial Cambridge (43725) (G-2459)

Graham Packaging Company LP.......................................513 874-1770
290 Circle Freeway Dr West Chester (45246) (G-20011)

Graham Packaging Company LP.......................................419 334-4197
725 Industrial Dr Fremont (43420) (G-10155)

Graham Packaging Pet Tech Inc.....................................419 334-4197
725 Industrial Dr Fremont (43420) (G-10156)

Graham Packg Plastic Pdts Inc (HQ)................................717 849-8500
1 Seagate Ste 10 Toledo (43604) (G-18485)

Graham Packg Plastic Pdts Inc.....................................419 421-8037
170 Stanford Pkwy 7 Findlay (45840) (G-9833)

Grain Craft Inc...216 621-3206
1635 Merwin Ave Cleveland (44113) (G-5444)

Grale Technologies Inc..724 683-8141
1019 Ohio Works Dr Youngstown (44510) (G-21102)

Gramag LLC..614 875-8435
2999 Lewis Centre Way Grove City (43123) (G-10559)

Graminex LLC..419 278-1023
2 300 County Rd C Deshler (43516) (G-8951)

Grand Aire Inc (PA)...419 861-6700
11777 W Airport Svc Rd Swanton (43558) (G-18084)

Grand Harbor Yacht Sales & Svc....................................440 442-2919
706 Alpha Dr Cleveland (44143) (G-5445)

Grand Rapids Printing Ink Co......................................859 261-4530
95 Glendale Milford Rd Cincinnati (45215) (G-3844)

Grand River Asphalt...440 352-2254
6 Coast Guard Rd Grand River (44045) (G-10449)

Grand Slam Acres, Celina Also called B Hogenkamp & R Harlamert (G-2986)

Grand Unification Press Inc.......................................330 683-1187
2380 Wayne St Orrville (44667) (G-15738)

Grand-Rock Company Inc..440 639-2000
395 Fountain Ave Painesville (44077) (G-15884)

Grandinroad Catalog, West Chester Also called Cornerstone Brands Inc (G-19844)

Grandmas Fruit Cakes..614 761-1118
45 N High St Dublin (43017) (G-9080)

Grandon Mfg Co Inc..614 294-2694
530 Dow Ave Columbus (43211) (G-7128)

Grandpa Jack's, Chillicothe Also called Crispie Creme of Chillicothe (G-3235)

Grandpas Pottery..937 382-6442
3558 W State Route 73 Wilmington (45177) (G-20665)

Grandview Grind...614 485-9005
1423 Grandview Ave Columbus (43212) (G-7129)

Grandview Materials Inc...614 488-6998
8598 Cotter St Lewis Center (43035) (G-11899)

Granex Industries Inc (PA)..440 248-4915
32400 Aurora Rd Ste 4 Solon (44139) (G-17300)

Granger Pipeline Corporation......................................330 454-8095
111 2nd St Nw Ste 202 Canton (44702) (G-2718)

Granger Plastic Company...513 424-1955
1600 M A D E Indus Dr Middletown (45044) (G-14043)

Granite Industries Inc..419 445-4733
595 E Lugbill Rd Archbold (43502) (G-679)

Grant John...937 298-0633
2715 Culver Ave Dayton (45429) (G-8376)

Grant Solutions...937 344-5558
7745 Winding Way N Tipp City (45371) (G-18280)

Grant Street Pallet Inc...330 424-0355
39196 Grant St Lisbon (44432) (G-12120)

Granville Milling Co..740 345-1305
145 N Cedar St Newark (43055) (G-15015)

Granville Milling Drive-Thru, Newark Also called Granville Milling Co (G-15015)

Graphel Corporation...513 779-6166
6115 Centre Park Dr West Chester (45069) (G-19879)

Graphic Art Systems Inc...216 581-9050
5800 Pennsylvania Ave Cleveland (44137) (G-5446)

Graphic Arts Rubber, Cuyahoga Falls Also called Econo Products Inc (G-7989)

Graphic Awards, Columbus Also called Joe Paxton (G-7237)

Graphic Expressions Signs...330 422-7446
8540 State Route 14 Ste D Streetsboro (44241) (G-17856)

Graphic Image..937 320-0302
2210 Shumway Ct Beavercreek (45431) (G-1341)

Graphic Packaging Intl Inc..513 424-4200
407 Charles St Middletown (45042) (G-14044)

Graphic Packaging Intl Inc..440 248-4370
6385 Cochran Rd Solon (44139) (G-17301)

Graphic Packaging Intl Inc..740 387-6543
1171 W Center St Marion (43302) (G-12869)

Graphic Paper..419 526-4123
1111 N Main St Mansfield (44903) (G-12619)

Graphic Paper Products Corp (HQ)..................................937 325-5503
581 W Leffel Ln Springfield (45506) (G-17564)

Graphic Paper Products Corp.......................................937 322-7711
581 W Leffel Ln Springfield (45506) (G-17565)

Graphic Paper Products Corp.......................................937 325-3912
222 E Main St Springfield (45503) (G-17566)

Graphic Plus..740 701-1860
712 Overlook Heights Ln Chillicothe (45601) (G-3241)

Graphic Publications Inc..330 674-2300
7368 County Road 623 Millersburg (44654) (G-14218)

Graphic Publications Inc..330 343-4377
123 W 3rd St Dover (44622) (G-8988)

Graphic Solutions Company...513 484-3067
3438 Middleton Ave Cincinnati (45220) (G-3845)

Graphic Stitch Inc..937 642-6707
169 Grove St Rm A Marysville (43040) (G-12945)

Graphic Systems Services Inc......................................937 746-0708
400 S Pioneer Blvd Springboro (45066) (G-17482)

Graphic Touch Inc...330 337-3341
451 E Pershing St Salem (44460) (G-16896)

Graphic TS..614 836-2613
532 Main St Rear Bldg Groveport (43125) (G-10624)

Graphicom Press Inc...937 767-1916
302 Orton Rd Yellow Springs (45387) (G-20991)

Graphics By Design Avenue, Twinsburg Also called Design Avenue Inc (G-18924)

Graphics To Go LLC..937 382-4100
761 S Nelson Ave Wilmington (45177) (G-20666)

Graphicsource Inc...440 248-9200
30405 Solon Rd Ste 12 Solon (44139) (G-17302)

Graphite Equipment Mfg Co...216 271-9500
5577 Valley Ln Solon (44139) (G-17303)

Graphite Sales Inc (PA)...440 543-8221
16710 W Park Circle Dr Chagrin Falls (44023) (G-3090)

Graphite Sales Inc..419 652-3388
220 Township Road 791 Nova (44859) (G-15578)

Graphix Junction..234 284-8392
5170 Hudson Dr Ste B Hudson (44236) (G-11176)

Graphtech Communications Inc......................................216 676-1020
4724 W 150th St Cleveland (44135) (G-5447)

Grasan Equipment Company Inc......................................419 526-4440
440 S Illinois Ave Mansfield (44907) (G-12620)

Gravel Doctor of Ohio LLC...844 472-8353
2985 Canal Dr Millersport (43046) (G-14293)

Gravel Doctor of Ohio, The, Millersport Also called Gravel Doctor of Ohio LLC (G-14293)

Gravel-Tech...513 703-3672
4005 E Fster Mineville Rd Morrow (45152) (G-14546)

Gray & Company Publishers...216 431-2665
1588 E 40th St Ste 1b Cleveland (44103) (G-5448)

Gray Tech International, Cleveland Also called Hephaestus Technologies LLC (G-5502)

Gray-Eering Ltd...740 498-8816
3158 Sandy Ridge Rd Se Tippecanoe (44699) (G-18314)

Graymont Dolime (oh) Inc..419 855-8682
21880 W State Route 163 Genoa (43430) (G-10360)

Grayson Graphics Inc..740 927-7080
910 Villas Dr Pataskala (43062) (G-15971)

Graywacke Engineering Inc...419 884-7014
300 S Mill St Mansfield (44904) (G-12621)

GRB Holdings Inc..937 236-3250
131 Janney Rd Dayton (45404) (G-8377)

Gre'n Disc, Strasburg *Also called Green Rdced Emssons Netwrk LLC* ***(G-17823)***
Great American Cookie Company..............419 474-9417
5001 Monroe St Ste Fc13 Toledo (43623) ***(G-18486)***
Great Day Improvements LLC (HQ)..............330 468-0700
700 Highland Rd E Macedonia (44056) ***(G-12456)***
Great Gatherings, Streetsboro *Also called American Heritage Billiards* ***(G-17839)***
Great Harvest Bread, Westerville *Also called B L F Enterprises Inc* ***(G-20201)***
Great Lake Fence, Cleveland *Also called Fence One Inc* ***(G-5334)***
Great Lakes Assemblies LLC..............937 645-3900
11590 Tr 298 East Liberty (43319) ***(G-9200)***
Great Lakes Center Excellence, Westlake *Also called Advanced Arm Dynamics* ***(G-20245)***
Great Lakes Cheese Co Inc (PA)..............440 834-2500
17825 Great Lakes Pkwy Hiram (44234) ***(G-11036)***
Great Lakes Crushing Ltd..............440 944-5500
30831 Euclid Ave Wickliffe (44092) ***(G-20366)***
Great Lakes Defense Svcs LLC..............216 272-3450
2319 Miramar Blvd University Heights (44118) ***(G-19109)***
Great Lakes Diesel..............419 433-9898
5148 Concord Dr Vermilion (44089) ***(G-19327)***
Great Lakes Embroidery, Chardon *Also called Screen Craft Plastics* ***(G-3178)***
Great Lakes Engraving Corp..............419 867-1607
1736 Henthorne Dr Maumee (43537) ***(G-13262)***
Great Lakes Etching Finshg Co..............440 439-3624
7010 Krick Rd Ste 3 Cleveland (44146) ***(G-5449)***
Great Lakes Glasswerks Inc..............440 358-0460
360 W Prospect St Painesville (44077) ***(G-15885)***
Great Lakes Graphics Inc..............216 391-0077
3354 Superior Ave E Cleveland (44114) ***(G-5450)***
Great Lakes Group..............216 621-4854
4500 Division Ave Cleveland (44102) ***(G-5451)***
Great Lakes Integrated Inc (PA)..............216 651-1500
4005 Clark Ave Cleveland (44109) ***(G-5452)***
Great Lakes Integrated Inc..............440 892-7760
33625 Pin Oak Pkwy Avon Lake (44012) ***(G-1030)***
Great Lakes Lithograph..............216 651-1500
4005 Clark Ave Cleveland (44109) ***(G-5453)***
Great Lakes Machine and Tool..............419 836-2346
10705 Jerusalem Rd Curtice (43412) ***(G-7957)***
Great Lakes Management Inc (PA)..............216 883-6500
8510 Bessemer Ave Cleveland (44127) ***(G-5454)***
Great Lakes Popcorn Company..............419 732-3080
60 Madison St Port Clinton (43452) ***(G-16401)***
Great Lakes Power Products Inc (PA)..............440 951-5111
7455 Tyler Blvd Mentor (44060) ***(G-13596)***
Great Lakes Power Service Co..............440 259-0025
3691 Shepard Rd Perry (44081) ***(G-16050)***
Great Lakes Printing Inc..............440 993-8781
2926 Lake Ave Ashtabula (44004) ***(G-810)***
Great Lakes Publishing Company (PA)..............216 771-2833
1422 Euclid Ave Ste 730 Cleveland (44115) ***(G-5455)***
Great Lakes Reprographic, Maumee *Also called Great Lakes Engraving Corp* ***(G-13262)***
Great Lakes Stair & Mllwk Co..............330 225-2005
1545 W 130th St Ste A1 Hinckley (44233) ***(G-11024)***
Great Lakes Telcom Ltd..............330 629-8848
590 E Western Reserve Rd Youngstown (44514) ***(G-21103)***
Great Lakes Textiles Inc (PA)..............440 439-1300
6810 Cochran Rd Solon (44139) ***(G-17304)***
Great Lakes Textiles Inc..............440 201-1300
11 Industry Dr Bedford (44146) ***(G-1425)***
Great Lakes Towing, Cleveland *Also called Great Lakes Group* ***(G-5451)***
Great Lakes Window Inc..............419 666-5555
30499 Tracy Rd Walbridge (43465) ***(G-19458)***
Great Lkes Nrotechnologies Inc..............216 520-1537
10055 Sweet Valley Dr # 5 Cleveland (44125) ***(G-5456)***
Great Midwest Tobacco Inc..............513 745-0450
10825 Medallion Dr Cincinnati (45241) ***(G-3846)***
Great Midwest Yacht Co..............740 965-4511
140 E Granville St Sunbury (43074) ***(G-18061)***
Great Oppurtunities Inc..............614 868-1899
1750 Idlewild Dr Columbus (43232) ***(G-7130)***
Great Western Juice Company..............216 475-5770
16153 Libby Rd Cleveland (44137) ***(G-5457)***
Great Works Publishing Inc..............440 926-1100
1080 Cleveland St Grafton (44044) ***(G-10428)***
Greater Cincinnati Bowl Assn..............513 761-7387
611 Mercury Dr Cincinnati (45244) ***(G-3847)***
Greater Cleve Pipe Ftting Fund..............216 524-8334
6305 Halle Dr Cleveland (44125) ***(G-5458)***
Greater Ohio Ethanol LLC (PA)..............567 940-9500
7227 Harding Hwy Lima (45801) ***(G-12019)***
Greber Machine Tool Inc..............440 322-3685
313 Clark St Elyria (44035) ***(G-9427)***
Green Acquisition LLC..............440 930-7600
1141 Jaycox Rd Avon (44011) ***(G-997)***
Green Acres Furniture Ltd..............330 359-6251
7412 Massillon Rd Sw Navarre (44662) ***(G-14713)***
Green Bay Packaging Inc..............419 332-5593
2323 Commerce Dr Fremont (43420) ***(G-10157)***
Green Bay Packaging Inc..............513 228-5560
760 Kingsview Dr Lebanon (45036) ***(G-11806)***
Green Bearing Co, Avon *Also called Green Acquisition LLC* ***(G-997)***
Green Brothers Enterprises..............937 444-3323
516 Sicily Rd Sardinia (45171) ***(G-17029)***
Green Corp Magnetic Inc..............614 801-4000
4342 Mcdowell Rd Grove City (43123) ***(G-10560)***
Green County Wtr Sup & Trtmnt, Dayton *Also called Greene County* ***(G-8107)***
Green Door Industries LLC..............614 558-1663
7844 Waggoner Trace Dr Blacklick (43004) ***(G-1696)***
Green Energy Inc..............330 262-5112
4489 E Lincoln Way Wooster (44691) ***(G-20779)***
Green Forward Technologies LLC..............513 607-9639
180 Linden Dr Cincinnati (45215) ***(G-3848)***
Green Fuel Today..............440 925-7820
11 April Hill Dr Grafton (44044) ***(G-10429)***
Green Gourmet Foods LLC..............740 400-4212
515 N Main St Baltimore (43105) ***(G-1082)***
Green Harvest Energy LLC..............330 716-3068
1340 State Route 14 Columbiana (44408) ***(G-6618)***
Green Leaf Printing and Design..............937 222-3634
1001 E 2nd St Ste 2485 Dayton (45402) ***(G-8378)***
Green Machine Tool Inc..............937 253-0771
1865 Radio Rd Dayton (45431) ***(G-8106)***
Green Point Metals Inc (PA)..............937 743-4075
301 Shotwell Dr Franklin (45005) ***(G-10025)***
Green Rdced Emssons Netwrk LLC..............330 340-0941
5029 Hilltop Dr Nw Strasburg (44680) ***(G-17823)***
Green Recycling Works LLC..............513 278-7111
1530 Tremont St Cincinnati (45214) ***(G-3849)***
Green Room Brewing LLC..............614 596-3655
1101 N 4th St Columbus (43201) ***(G-7131)***
Green Tokai Co Ltd..............937 237-1630
3700 Inpark Dr Dayton (45414) ***(G-8379)***
Green Tokai Co Ltd (HQ)..............937 833-5444
55 Robert Wright Dr Brookville (45309) ***(G-2185)***
Green Vision Materials Inc..............440 564-5500
11220 Kinsman Rd Newbury (44065) ***(G-15093)***
Greenbrier Rail Services, Youngstown *Also called Gunderson Rail Services LLC* ***(G-21106)***
Greencore USA Inc..............513 645-1985
3465 Hauck Rd Cincinnati (45241) ***(G-3850)***
Greene County..............937 429-0127
1122 Beaver Valley Rd Dayton (45434) ***(G-8107)***
Greene Fuel Plaza Inc..............937 532-4826
3151 E Dorothy Ln Kettering (45420) ***(G-11580)***
Greenes Fence, Solon *Also called Mi-Lar Fence Co Inc* ***(G-17337)***
Greenes Fence Co Inc..............216 464-3160
5250 Naiman Pkwy Ste B Solon (44139) ***(G-17305)***
Greenfield Research Inc (PA)..............937 981-7763
347 Edgewood Ave Greenfield (45123) ***(G-10478)***
Greenfield Research Inc..............937 876-9224
324 S Washington St Greenfield (45123) ***(G-10479)***
Greenfield Solar Inc..............216 535-9200
126 Artino St Oberlin (44074) ***(G-15642)***
Greenhills Journal..............513 825-2525
22 Endicott St Cincinnati (45218) ***(G-3851)***
Greenkote Usa Inc..............440 243-2865
6435 Eastland Rd Brookpark (44142) ***(G-2162)***
Greenlight Optics LLC..............513 247-9777
8940 Glendale Milford Rd Loveland (45140) ***(G-12354)***
Greeno Company, Cincinnati *Also called Tri-State Belting Ltd* ***(G-4522)***
Greenville Techniology Inc..............937 642-6744
15000 Industrial Pkwy Marysville (43040) ***(G-12946)***
Greenville Technology Inc (HQ)..............937 548-3217
5755 State Route 571 Greenville (45331) ***(G-10504)***
Greenway Home Products Inc..............419 874-6770
1270 Flagship Dr Perrysburg (43551) ***(G-16105)***
Greenwood Printing & Graphics..............419 727-3275
3615 Stickney Ave Toledo (43608) ***(G-18487)***
Greer & Whitehead Cnstr Inc..............513 202-1757
510 S State St Ste D Harrison (45030) ***(G-10781)***
Greer Steel Company..............330 343-8811
624 Boulevard St Dover (44622) ***(G-8989)***
Greg Blume..............740 574-2308
7459 Ohio River Rd Wheelersburg (45694) ***(G-20332)***
Greg G Wright & Sons LLC..............513 721-3310
10200 Springfield Pike Cincinnati (45215) ***(G-3852)***
Gregg Macmillan..............513 248-2121
2002 Ford Cir Ste A Milford (45150) ***(G-14148)***
Greggs Specialty Services..............419 478-0803
306 Dura Ave Toledo (43612) ***(G-18488)***
Gregoire Moulin..............614 861-4582
7502 E Main St Reynoldsburg (43068) ***(G-16593)***
Gregory Auto Service..............513 248-0423
224 Beech Rd Loveland (45140) ***(G-12355)***
Gregory Industries Inc (PA)..............330 477-4800
4100 13th St Sw Canton (44710) ***(G-2719)***
Gregory Roll Form Inc..............330 477-4800
4100 13th St Sw Canton (44710) ***(G-2720)***

ALPHABETIC

Gregory Stone Co Inc....937 275-7455
1860 N Gettysburg Ave Dayton (45417) ***(G-8380)***
Gregs Eagle Tire Co Inc....330 837-1983
3425 Lincoln Way E Massillon (44646) ***(G-13142)***
Greif Inc (PA)....740 549-6000
425 Winter Rd Delaware (43015) ***(G-8847)***
Greif Inc....740 657-6500
366 Greif Pkwy Delaware (43015) ***(G-8848)***
Greif Inc....740 657-6500
366 Greif Pkwy Delaware (43015) ***(G-8849)***
Greif Inc....419 238-0565
975 Glenn St Van Wert (45891) ***(G-19259)***
Greif Inc....740 549-6000
425 Winter Rd Delaware (43015) ***(G-8850)***
Greif Inc....740 549-6000
425 Winter Rd Delaware (43015) ***(G-8851)***
Greif Inc....330 879-2101
9420 Warmington St Sw Navarre (44662) ***(G-14714)***
Greif Inc....937 548-4111
366 Greif Pkwy Delaware (43015) ***(G-8852)***
Greif Inc....330 879-2936
787 Warmington Rd Se Massillon (44646) ***(G-13143)***
Greif Bros Corp Ohio Inc....740 549-6000
425 Winter Rd Delaware (43015) ***(G-8853)***
Greif Packaging LLC....330 879-2101
787 Warmington Rd Sw Massillon (44646) ***(G-13144)***
Greif Packaging LLC (HQ)....740 549-6000
366 Greif Pkwy Delaware (43015) ***(G-8854)***
Greif Paper Packg & Svcs LLC....740 549-6000
425 Winter Rd Delaware (43015) ***(G-8855)***
Greif U S Holdings Inc....740 549-6000
425 Winter Rd Delaware (43015) ***(G-8856)***
Grenga Machine & Welding....330 743-1113
56 Wayne Ave Youngstown (44502) ***(G-21104)***
Grey Hawk Golf Club....440 355-4844
665 U S Grant St Lagrange (44050) ***(G-11626)***
Greyden Press, Springboro *Also called Jk Digital Publishing LLC* ***(G-17484)***
Greyfield Industries Inc....513 860-1785
3104 Wayne Madison Rd Trenton (45067) ***(G-18793)***
Grid Industrial Heating Inc....330 332-9931
1108 Salem Pkwy Salem (44460) ***(G-16897)***
Grid Sentry LLC....937 490-2101
3915 Germany Ln Beavercreek (45431) ***(G-1342)***
Grief Brothers, Delaware *Also called Greif Inc* ***(G-8848)***
Griffin Cider Works LLC....440 785-7418
2165 Elmwood Dr Westlake (44145) ***(G-20273)***
Griffin Fisher Co Inc....513 961-2110
1126 Wlliam Hward Taft Rd Cincinnati (45206) ***(G-3853)***
Griffin Industries LLC....216 696-2588
2254 Hamilton Ave Cleveland (44114) ***(G-5459)***
Grill....937 673-6768
100 Morton Rd Eaton (45320) ***(G-9307)***
Grimes Aerospace Company....937 484-2001
550 State Route 55 Urbana (43078) ***(G-19158)***
Grimes Aerospace Company....937 484-2000
515 N Russell St Urbana (43078) ***(G-19159)***
Grimm Scientific Industries....740 374-3412
1403 Pike St Marietta (45750) ***(G-12787)***
Grind-All Corporation....330 220-1600
1113 Industrial Pkwy N Brunswick (44212) ***(G-2230)***
Grindel Sales Corp....740 382-1528
1645 Cascade Dr Marion (43302) ***(G-12870)***
Grinding Equipment & McHy LLC....330 747-2313
15 S Worthington St Youngstown (44502) ***(G-21105)***
Grip Force LLC....440 497-7014
990 Quentin Rd Eastlake (44095) ***(G-9272)***
Grippo Potato Chip Co Inc....513 923-1900
6750 Colerain Ave Cincinnati (45239) ***(G-3854)***
Grit Guard Inc....937 592-9003
3690 County Road 10 Bellefontaine (43311) ***(G-1531)***
Grntwrx LLC....440 478-6160
8205 Clover Ln Garrettsville (44231) ***(G-10322)***
Gro2 Bags & Accessories LLC....740 622-0928
1760 Buena Vista Dr Coshocton (43812) ***(G-7894)***
Grob Systems Inc....419 358-9015
1070 Navajo Dr Bluffton (45817) ***(G-1912)***
Grodhaus & Young Inc....330 866-3321
144 Niles Ave Waynesburg (44688) ***(G-19725)***
Groeneveld Atlantic South....330 225-4949
1130 Industrial Pkwy N # 7 Brunswick (44212) ***(G-2231)***
Groff Industries....216 634-9100
2201 W 110th St Cleveland (44102) ***(G-5460)***
Groovemaster Music, Perrysburg *Also called Tiny Lion Music Groups* ***(G-16160)***
Gross & Sons Custom Millwork....419 227-0214
1219 Grant St Lima (45801) ***(G-12020)***
Gross Lumber Inc....330 683-2055
8848 Ely Rd Apple Creek (44606) ***(G-638)***
Groundhogs 2000 LLC....440 653-1647
6070 Richmond Rd Oakwood Village (44146) ***(G-15625)***
Group Industries Inc (PA)....216 271-0702
7580 Garfield Blvd Cleveland (44125) ***(G-5461)***
Grove Engineered Products Inc....419 659-5939
201 E Cross St Columbus Grove (45830) ***(G-7794)***
Grow With ME Bibs, Hartville *Also called Grow With Me- Creations* ***(G-10821)***
Grow With Me- Creations....800 850-1889
14236 Wade Ave Ne Hartville (44632) ***(G-10821)***
Growers Choice Ltd....330 262-8754
5505 S Elyria Rd Shreve (44676) ***(G-17156)***
Growmark Fs LLC....330 386-7626
1080 Elmwood St East Liverpool (43920) ***(G-9216)***
Grt Utilicorp Inc....330 264-8444
9268 Ashland Rd Wooster (44691) ***(G-20780)***
Gruppo Mossi & Ghisolfi, Sharon Center *Also called M & G Polymers Usa LLC* ***(G-17107)***
Gs Wood & Metal Coating LLC....419 375-7708
2096 Saint Joe Rd Fort Recovery (45846) ***(G-9953)***
Gsf Energy LLC....513 825-0504
10795 Hughes Rd Cincinnati (45251) ***(G-3855)***
Gsi of Ohio LLC....216 431-3344
3820 Lakeside Ave E Cleveland (44114) ***(G-5462)***
GSW Manufacturing Inc....419 423-7111
1801 Production Dr Findlay (45840) ***(G-9834)***
Gt Industrial Supply Inc....513 771-7000
2315 Crowne Point Dr Cincinnati (45241) ***(G-3856)***
Gt Technologies Inc....419 782-8955
1125 Precision Way Defiance (43512) ***(G-8792)***
Gt Technologies Inc....419 324-7300
99 N Fearing Blvd Toledo (43607) ***(G-18489)***
GTC, Brookville *Also called Green Tokai Co Ltd* ***(G-2185)***
GTC Artist With Machines, Columbus *Also called General Theming Contrs LLC* ***(G-7108)***
Gtd Machine Inc....440 812-6877
7875 Enterprise Dr Mentor (44060) ***(G-13597)***
Gtlp Holdings LLC (PA)....513 489-6700
7911 School Rd Cincinnati (45249) ***(G-3857)***
Guadalupe Publishing Inc....614 450-2474
60 Dellenbaugh Loop Etna (43062) ***(G-9556)***
Guarantee Specialties Inc....216 451-9744
21693 Drake Rd Strongsville (44149) ***(G-17923)***
Guaranteed Fnshg Unlimited Inc....216 252-8200
3200 W 121st St Cleveland (44111) ***(G-5463)***
Guardian Co Inc....216 721-2262
2754 Woodhill Rd Cleveland (44104) ***(G-5464)***
Guardian Engineering & Mfg Co....419 335-1784
965 Fairway Ln Wauseon (43567) ***(G-19680)***
Guardian Gloves, Willard *Also called Guardian Manufacturing Co LLC* ***(G-20395)***
Guardian Industries Corp....614 431-6309
600 Lkview Plz Blvd Ste A Worthington (43085) ***(G-20868)***
Guardian Lima LLC....567 940-9500
2485 Houx Pkwy Lima (45804) ***(G-12021)***
Guardian Manufacturing Co LLC....419 933-2711
302 S Conwell Ave Willard (44890) ***(G-20395)***
Guardian Mfg., Hudson *Also called Fluid Power Inc* ***(G-11171)***
Guardian Millbury, Millbury *Also called Custom GL Sltons Millbury Corp* ***(G-14183)***
Guardian Technologies LLC....216 706-2250
26251 Bluestone Blvd # 7 Euclid (44132) ***(G-9582)***
Guari Inc....330 733-4005
2215 E Waterloo Rd # 101 Akron (44312) ***(G-208)***
Guerin-Zimmerman Co, Cleveland *Also called B Y G Industries Inc* ***(G-4884)***
GUERNSEY INDUSTRIES, Byesville *Also called Ken Harper* ***(G-2406)***
Guetle Die & Stamping, Mansfield *Also called Amaroq Inc* ***(G-12558)***
Guggisberg Cheese Inc (PA)....330 893-2550
5060 State Route 557 Millersburg (44654) ***(G-14219)***
Guild Associates Inc (PA)....614 798-8215
5750 Shier Rings Rd Dublin (43016) ***(G-9081)***
Guild Associates Inc....843 573-0095
4412 Tuller Rd Dublin (43017) ***(G-9082)***
Guild Biosciences, Dublin *Also called Guild Associates Inc* ***(G-9081)***
Guild Biosciences, Dublin *Also called Guild Associates Inc* ***(G-9082)***
Guild International Inc....440 232-5887
7273 Division St Bedford (44146) ***(G-1426)***
Guitammer Company....614 898-9370
6117 Maxtown Rd Westerville (43082) ***(G-20156)***
Guitar Digest Inc....740 592-4614
23 Curtis St Athens (45701) ***(G-870)***
Gulfport Energy Corporation....740 251-0407
67185 Executive Dr Saint Clairsville (43950) ***(G-16790)***
Gumbys LLC....740 671-0818
2300 Belmont St Bellaire (43906) ***(G-1498)***
Gunderson Rail Services LLC....330 792-6521
3710 Hendricks Rd Bldg 2a Youngstown (44515) ***(G-21106)***
Gundlach, Cincinnati *Also called Rotex Global Lcc* ***(G-4359)***
Gundlach Sheet Metal Works Inc (PA)....419 626-4525
910 Columbus Ave Sandusky (44870) ***(G-16971)***
Gunnison Associates LLC....330 562-5230
114 Barrngton Twn Sq 11 Aurora (44202) ***(G-923)***
Gunter Electric LLC....304 253-4671
237 W State St Athens (45701) ***(G-871)***

Gurina Company..614 279-3891
1379 River St Columbus (43222) *(G-7132)*

Gus Holthaus Signs Inc...513 861-0060
817 Ridgeway Ave Cincinnati (45229) *(G-3858)*

Gustave Julian Jewelers Inc..440 888-1100
7432 State Rd Cleveland (44134) *(G-5465)*

Gutter Shutter Manufacturing, Cincinnati *Also called Mid-America Gutters Inc* *(G-4105)*

Gutter Topper Ltd...513 797-5800
4111 Founders Blvd Batavia (45103) *(G-1189)*

Guttman Oil, Westerville *Also called Brightstar Propane & Fuels* *(G-20140)*

Guy's Award Winning Barbeque, Newton Falls *Also called Guys Barbeque Inc* *(G-15133)*

Guyer Precision Inc..440 354-8024
280 W Prospect St Painesville (44077) *(G-15886)*

Guys Barbeque Inc...330 872-7256
4498 W Oakland St Sw Newton Falls (44444) *(G-15133)*

Guys Brewing Gear...330 554-9362
1325 Chelton Dr Kent (44240) *(G-11464)*

Gvc Plastics & Metals LLC...440 232-9360
7051 Krick Rd Bedford (44146) *(G-1427)*

Gvi Medical Devices Corp..330 963-4083
1470 Enterprise Pkwy Twinsburg (44087) *(G-18951)*

Gvi Neuro Inc...330 963-4083
1470 Enterprise Pkwy Twinsburg (44087) *(G-18952)*

Gvimd, Twinsburg *Also called Gvi Medical Devices Corp* *(G-18951)*

Gvs Inc...330 310-8275
3406 S Smith Rd Fairlawn (44333) *(G-9751)*

Gvs Industries Inc..513 887-8660
1030 Beissinger Rd Hamilton (45013) *(G-10699)*

Gwen Rosenberg Enterprises LLC................................330 678-1893
175 E Erie St Ste 201 Kent (44240) *(G-11465)*

Gwp Holdings Inc...513 860-4050
8675 Seward Rd Fairfield (45011) *(G-9662)*

Gym Pro LLC...740 984-4143
50 Washington St Waterford (45786) *(G-19648)*

Gyrus Acmi LP..419 668-8201
93 N Pleasant St Norwalk (44857) *(G-15542)*

H & A Drilling..740 763-2575
4780 Tavener Rd Newark (43056) *(G-15016)*

H & B Machine & Tool Inc...216 431-3254
1390 E 40th St Cleveland (44103) *(G-5466)*

H & C Building Supplies, Huron *Also called Huron Cement Products Company* *(G-11224)*

H & D Drilling Co Inc...740 745-2236
11183 Pleasant Valley Rd Frazeysburg (43822) *(G-10073)*

H & D Steel Service Inc..440 237-3390
9960 York Alpha Dr North Royalton (44133) *(G-15423)*

H & D Steel Service Center, North Royalton *Also called H & D Steel Service Inc* *(G-15423)*

H & E Machine Company...614 443-7635
1646 Fairwood Ave Columbus (43206) *(G-7133)*

H & H Engineered Molded Pdts....................................440 415-1814
436 N Eagle St Geneva (44041) *(G-10348)*

H & H Equipment Inc...330 264-5400
6247 Ashland Rd Wooster (44691) *(G-20781)*

H & H Industries Inc..740 682-7721
5400 State Route 93 Oak Hill (45656) *(G-15596)*

H & H Machine Shop Akron Inc.....................................330 773-3327
955 Grant St Akron (44311) *(G-209)*

H & H of Milford Ohio LLC..513 576-9004
1194 Wintercrest Cir Milford (45150) *(G-14149)*

H & H Quick Machine Inc..330 935-0944
7816 Edison St Louisville (44641) *(G-12312)*

H & H Sailcraft, New Paris *Also called Dynamic Plastics Inc* *(G-14879)*

H & H Screen Process Inc..937 253-7520
1220 Wyoming St Dayton (45410) *(G-8381)*

H & H Tooling, Westlake *Also called Pines Manufacturing Inc* *(G-20294)*

H & H Tree Service LLC...440 632-0551
15530 Old State Rd Middlefield (44062) *(G-13938)*

H & H Truck Parts LLC..216 642-4540
5500s Cloverleaf Pkwy Cleveland (44125) *(G-5467)*

H & K Fabricating...330 767-4279
13415 Baughman St Sw Navarre (44662) *(G-14715)*

H & K Pallet Services...937 608-1140
1039 Jasper Ave Xenia (45385) *(G-20954)*

H & K Products Inc...419 659-5110
10246 Road P Columbus Grove (45830) *(G-7795)*

H & L Welding Service Inc...740 862-3520
3756 Agler Rd Columbus (43219) *(G-7134)*

H & M Machine Shop Inc..419 453-3414
290 State Route 189 Ottoville (45876) *(G-15822)*

H & M Metal Processing Co..330 745-3075
1414 Kenmore Blvd Akron (44314) *(G-210)*

H & N Instruments Inc...740 344-4351
219 N Westmoor Ave Newark (43055) *(G-15017)*

H & R Metal Finishing Inc...440 942-6656
1650 E 361st St Unit L Willoughby (44095) *(G-20502)*

H & R Tool & Machine Co Inc..740 452-0784
18 Jefferson St Zanesville (43701) *(G-21316)*

H & S Company Inc...419 394-4444
7219 Harris Rd Celina (45822) *(G-2999)*

H & S Drilling Co Inc...740 828-2411
101 E 3rd St Frazeysburg (43822) *(G-10074)*

H & S Operating Company Inc......................................330 830-8178
2581 County Rd 160 Winesburg (44690) *(G-20704)*

H & S Precision Screw Pdts Inc....................................937 437-0316
8205 H W Rd New Paris (45347) *(G-14880)*

H & S Steel Treating Inc...330 678-5245
4142 Mogadore Rd Kent (44240) *(G-11466)*

H & S Tool Inc..330 335-1536
715 Weber Dr Wadsworth (44281) *(G-19409)*

H & W Screw Products Inc..937 866-2577
335 Industrial Dr Franklin (45005) *(G-10026)*

H B Products Inc..937 492-7031
1661 Saint Marys Rd Sidney (45365) *(G-17191)*

H C Starck Inc..216 692-6990
1250 E 222nd St Euclid (44117) *(G-9583)*

H C Starck Inc..216 692-3990
21801 Tungsten Rd Euclid (44117) *(G-9584)*

H D C, Miamisburg *Also called Hooven - Dayton Corp* *(G-13818)*

H Duane Leis Acquisitions..937 835-5621
443 S Diamond Mill Rd New Lebanon (45345) *(G-14842)*

H E Long Company..513 899-2610
3910 Anderson Rd Morrow (45152) *(G-14547)*

H F I, Canal Winchester *Also called Hfi Manufacturing Holdings LLC* *(G-2528)*

H G Schneider Company...614 882-6944
291 Broad St Westerville (43081) *(G-20216)*

H Gerstner & Sons Inc..937 228-1662
20 Gerstner Way Dayton (45402) *(G-8382)*

H Goodman Inc...216 341-0200
3201 Harvard Ave Newburgh Heights (44105) *(G-15070)*

H I Smith Oil & Gas Inc...330 279-2361
8255 County Road 192 Holmesville (44633) *(G-11101)*

H I T, Painesville *Also called Hardy Industrial Tech LLC* *(G-15887)*

H K K Machining Co...419 924-5116
1201 Oak St West Unity (43570) *(G-20128)*

H K M, Cleveland *Also called Hkm Drect Mkt Cmmnications Inc* *(G-5516)*

H K M Drect Mktg Cmmunications, Sheffield Village *Also called Hkm Drect Mkt Cmmnications Inc* *(G-17122)*

H Left Company..216 361-6348
4700 Spring Rd Cleveland (44131) *(G-5468)*

H Machining Inc..419 636-6890
720 Commerce Dr Bryan (43506) *(G-2298)*

H Nagel & Son Co..513 665-4550
2641 Spring Grove Ave Cincinnati (45214) *(G-3859)*

H Nagel & Son Co (PA)..513 665-4550
2428 Central Pkwy Cincinnati (45214) *(G-3860)*

H O Fibertrends...740 983-3864
235 State Route 674 S Ashville (43103) *(G-851)*

H P E Inc...330 833-3161
2025 Harsh Ave Se Massillon (44646) *(G-13145)*

H P I, Richfield *Also called Herschal Products Inc* *(G-16627)*

H P Manufacturing Co...216 361-6500
3740 Prospect Ave E Cleveland (44115) *(G-5469)*

H P Nielsen Inc...440 244-4255
753 Broadway Lorain (44052) *(G-12248)*

H P Streicher Inc (PA)...419 841-4715
2955 Gradwohl Rd Toledo (43617) *(G-18490)*

H R Machine..937 838-6289
2972 Homeway Dr Beavercreek (45434) *(G-1343)*

H Rosen Usa LLC...614 354-6707
1195 Technology Dr Columbus (43230) *(G-7135)*

H S Morgan Limited Partnership (PA)...........................513 870-4400
3158 Production Dr Fairfield (45014) *(G-9663)*

H S Processing LP..216 641-6995
4600 Heidtman Pkwy Cleveland (44105) *(G-5470)*

H W Chair Co, Millersburg *Also called Hochstetler Wood* *(G-14226)*

H W Fairway International Inc..330 678-2540
716 N Mantua St Kent (44240) *(G-11467)*

H Y O Inc..614 488-2861
2550 W 5th Ave Columbus (43204) *(G-7136)*

H&An LLC..740 435-0200
1224 Southgate Pkwy Cambridge (43725) *(G-2460)*

H&H Custom Homes, Loudonville *Also called Mohican Log Homes Inc* *(G-12299)*

H&M Machine & Tool LLC..419 776-9220
3823 Seiss Ave Toledo (43612) *(G-18491)*

H&M Mtal Stamping Assembly Inc.................................216 898-9030
5325 W 140th St Brookpark (44142) *(G-2163)*

H-P Products Inc...330 875-7193
2000 W Main St Louisville (44641) *(G-12313)*

H-W Machine Inc...330 477-7231
4028 Southway St Sw Canton (44706) *(G-2721)*

H. Meyer Dairy, Cincinnati *Also called Borden Dairy Co Cincinnati LLC* *(G-3461)*

H3d Tool Corporation..740 498-5181
295 Enterprise Dr Newcomerstown (43832) *(G-15114)*

Ha-International LLC...419 537-0096
4243 South Ave Toledo (43615) *(G-18492)*

Ha-Ste Manufacturing Co Inc.......................................937 968-4858
119 E Elm St Union City (45390) *(G-19071)*

A
L
P
H
A
B
E
T
I
C

Haag-Streit Holding Us Inc (HQ) 513 336-7255
3535 Kings Mills Rd Mason (45040) *(G-13033)*

Haas Door Company 419 337-9900
320 Sycamore St Wauseon (43567) *(G-19681)*

Haas Doors, Wauseon *Also called Nofziger Door Sales Inc (G-19692)*

Haas Jordan Company, Holland *Also called Tmb Enterprises LLC (G-11089)*

Habco Tool and Dev Co Inc 440 946-5546
7725 Metric Dr Mentor (44060) *(G-13598)*

Habitec SEC Diversfd Alarm 419 636-1155
115 N Lynn St Bryan (43506) *(G-2299)*

Hacienda Publications LLC 216 202-5440
20970 Wilmore Ave Euclid (44123) *(G-9585)*

Hacker Wood Products Inc 513 737-4462
2144 Jackson Rd Hamilton (45011) *(G-10700)*

Hackman Frames LLC 614 841-0007
502 Schrock Rd Columbus (43229) *(G-7137)*

Hackworth Electric Motors Inc 330 345-6049
4952 Cleveland Rd Wooster (44691) *(G-20782)*

Hackworth Electrical Contrs In, Wooster *Also called Hackworth Oil Field Electric (G-20783)*

Hackworth Oil Field Electric 330 345-6504
4931 Cleveland Rd Wooster (44691) *(G-20783)*

Hadley Printing, Beavercreek *Also called A C Hadley - Printing Inc (G-1314)*

Hadlock Plastics LLC 440 466-4876
110 N Eagle St Geneva (44041) *(G-10349)*

Hadronics Inc 513 321-9350
4570 Steel Pl Cincinnati (45209) *(G-3861)*

Hadsell Chemical Proc LLC 740 941-1792
9329 State Route 220 Waverly (45690) *(G-19710)*

Haeco Inc (PA) 513 722-1030
6504 Snider Rd Loveland (45140) *(G-12356)*

Haessly Lumber Sales Co (PA) 740 373-6681
25 Sheets Run Rd Marietta (45750) *(G-12788)*

Hafco-Case Inc 216 267-4644
12212 Sprecher Ave Cleveland (44135) *(G-5471)*

Hafner Hardwood Connection LLC 419 726-4828
2845 111th St Toledo (43611) *(G-18493)*

Hague Quality Water Intl, Groveport *Also called William R Hague Inc (G-10649)*

Hahn Manufacturing Company 216 391-9300
5332 Hamilton Ave Cleveland (44114) *(G-5472)*

Hahs Factory Outlet 330 405-4227
1993 Case Pkwy Twinsburg (44087) *(G-18953)*

Haines & Company Inc (PA) 330 494-9111
8050 Freedom Ave Nw North Canton (44720) *(G-15237)*

Haines Criss Cross (PA) 330 494-9111
8050 Freedom Ave Nw North Canton (44720) *(G-15238)*

Haines Publishing Inc 330 494-9111
8050 Freedom Ave Nw Canton (44720) *(G-2722)*

Hair & Nail Impressions 937 399-0221
2330 Northmoor Dr Springfield (45503) *(G-17567)*

Hair Science Systems LLC 513 231-8284
445 Bishopsbridge Dr Cincinnati (45255) *(G-3862)*

Haiss Fabripart LLC 330 821-2028
22421 Lake Park Blvd Alliance (44601) *(G-512)*

Hake Head LLC 614 291-2244
1855 E 17th Ave Columbus (43219) *(G-7138)*

Hal Mar Printing, Warren *Also called Mackland Co Inc (G-19575)*

Halcore Group Inc (HQ) 614 539-8181
3800 Mcdowell Rd Grove City (43123) *(G-10561)*

Hale Logging, Patriot *Also called Chester F Hale (G-15993)*

Hale Manufacturing Inc 937 382-2127
1065 Wayne Rd Wilmington (45177) *(G-20667)*

Hale Performance Coatings Inc 419 244-6451
2282 Albion St Toledo (43606) *(G-18494)*

Halex, Cleveland *Also called Scott Fetzer Company (G-6172)*

Halex, A Scott Fetzer Company, Bedford Heights *Also called Halex/Scott Fetzer Company (G-1485)*

Halex/Scott Fetzer Company (HQ) 440 439-1616
23901 Aurora Rd Bedford Heights (44146) *(G-1485)*

Half Price Bks Rec Mgzines Inc 614 776-5551
561 S State St Westerville (43081) *(G-20217)*

Half Price Bks Rec Mgzines Inc 440 255-2581
9383 Mentor Ave Mentor (44060) *(G-13599)*

Halifax Industries Inc 216 990-8951
2060 Garden Ln Hudson (44236) *(G-11177)*

Hall Company 937 652-1376
420 E Water St Urbana (43078) *(G-19160)*

Hall Creations 330 357-2428
705 Silver Meadows Blvd Kent (44240) *(G-11468)*

Hall Safety Apparel Inc 740 922-3671
1020 W 1st St Uhrichsville (44683) *(G-19051)*

Hall Trencher Service, South Webster *Also called Roger Hall (G-17451)*

Hall's Sheet Metal Fabricating, Galena *Also called Halls Sheet Metal Fabrication (G-10243)*

Hall-Toledo Inc 419 893-4334
525 W Sophia St Maumee (43537) *(G-13263)*

Haller Enterprises Inc 330 733-9693
1621 E Market St Akron (44305) *(G-211)*

Halliday Holdings Inc 740 335-1430
1544 Old Us 35 Se Wshngtn CT Hs (43160) *(G-20910)*

Halliday Technologies Inc 614 504-4150
8525 Rausch Dr Unit B Plain City (43064) *(G-16345)*

Hallmark Industries Inc (PA) 937 864-7378
6711 Dyton Springfield Rd Enon (45323) *(G-9545)*

Hallmark Industries Inc 937 864-7378
6711 Dyton Springfield Rd Enon (45323) *(G-9546)*

Hallmark Manufacturing, Enon *Also called Hallmark Industries Inc (G-9546)*

Halls Sheet Metal Fabrication 740 965-9264
10001 Center Village Rd Galena (43021) *(G-10243)*

Halls Welding & Supplies Inc 330 385-9353
49037 Clctta Smthferry Rd East Liverpool (43920) *(G-9217)*

Halman Inc 440 992-4239
3901 N Bend Rd Ashtabula (44004) *(G-811)*

Haltec Corporation 330 222-1501
32585 N Price Rd Salem (44460) *(G-16898)*

Halvey Quarter Horses 614 648-0483
6230 Havens Corners Rd Blacklick (43004) *(G-1697)*

Halvorsen Company 216 341-7500
7500 Grand Division Ave Cleveland (44125) *(G-5473)*

Ham Signs LLC 937 454-9111
6020 N Dixie Dr Dayton (45414) *(G-8383)*

Haman Enterprises Inc 614 888-7574
7525 Pingue Dr Worthington (43085) *(G-20869)*

Haman Midwest, Worthington *Also called Haman Enterprises Inc (G-20869)*

Hamco Manufacturing Inc 440 774-1637
48882 State Route 511 Oberlin (44074) *(G-15643)*

Hamilton Air Products Inc 513 874-4030
3143 Production Dr Fairfield (45014) *(G-9664)*

Hamilton Animal Products LLC 937 293-9994
2425 W Dorothy Ln Moraine (45439) *(G-14492)*

Hamilton Arts Inc 937 767-1834
750 Union St Yellow Springs (45387) *(G-20992)*

Hamilton Brass & Alum Castings 513 867-0400
706 S 8th St Hamilton (45011) *(G-10701)*

Hamilton Custom Molding Inc 513 844-6643
1365 Shuler Ave Hamilton (45011) *(G-10702)*

Hamilton Fabricators Inc 513 735-7773
4008 Borman Dr Batavia (45103) *(G-1190)*

Hamilton Journal News Inc 513 863-8200
7320 Yankee Rd Liberty Township (45044) *(G-11963)*

Hamilton Journalnews, Liberty Township *Also called Cox Newspapers LLC (G-11960)*

Hamilton Manufacturing Corp 419 867-4858
1026 Hamilton Dr Holland (43528) *(G-11063)*

Hamilton Mold & Machine Co 216 732-8200
25016 Lakeland Blvd Cleveland (44132) *(G-5474)*

Hamilton Rti Inc 330 652-9951
1000 Warren Ave Niles (44446) *(G-15157)*

Hamilton Safe, Cincinnati *Also called Hamilton Security Products Co (G-3864)*

Hamilton Safe Amelia 513 753-5694
3997 Bach Buxton Rd Amelia (45102) *(G-576)*

Hamilton Safe Co (PA) 513 874-3733
7775 Cooper Rd Cincinnati (45242) *(G-3863)*

Hamilton Security Products Co (PA) 513 874-3733
7775 Cooper Rd Cincinnati (45242) *(G-3864)*

Hamilton Sorter, Fairfield *Also called Workstream Inc (G-9733)*

Hamilton Tanks LLC 614 445-8446
2200 Refugee Rd Columbus (43207) *(G-7139)*

Hamilton Whiting Cloth, Hamilton *Also called Ace-Tex Enterprises Inc (G-10661)*

Hamlet Protein Inc 567 525-5627
5289 Hamlet Dr Findlay (45840) *(G-9835)*

Hamlin Newco LLC 330 753-7791
2741 Wingate Ave Akron (44314) *(G-212)*

Hamlin Steel Products LLC 330 753-7791
2741 Wingate Ave Akron (44314) *(G-213)*

Hammelmann Corporation (HQ) 937 859-8777
436 Southpointe Dr Miamisburg (45342) *(G-13814)*

Hammill Manufacturing Co (PA) 419 476-0789
360 Tomahawk Dr Maumee (43537) *(G-13264)*

Hampshire Co 937 773-3493
9225 State Route 66 Piqua (45356) *(G-16268)*

Hampton Publishing Company 513 777-9543
7739 Derbyshire Ct Liberty Township (45044) *(G-11964)*

Hana Microdisplay Tech Inc 330 405-4600
2061 Case Pkwy S Twinsburg (44087) *(G-18954)*

Hanby Farms Inc 740 763-3554
10790 Newark Rd Nashport (43830) *(G-14705)*

Hanchett Paper Company 513 782-4440
12121 Best Pl Cincinnati (45241) *(G-3865)*

Hancor Holding Corporation (HQ) 419 422-6521
401 Olive St Findlay (45840) *(G-9836)*

Hancor Inc (HQ) 614 658-0050
4640 Trueman Blvd Hilliard (43026) *(G-10950)*

Hancor Inc 419 424-8225
433 Olive St Findlay (45840) *(G-9837)*

Hancor Inc 419 424-8222
12370 Jackson Township Rd Findlay (45839) *(G-9838)*

Hand Screw Machine Co 216 475-0220
883 Hampshire Rd Ste A Stow (44224) *(G-17761)*

Handcrafted Jewelry Inc 330 650-9011
116 N Main St Hudson (44236) *(G-11178)*

(G-0000) Company's Geographic Section entry number

Handicraft LLC............216 295-1950
3407 Saint Clair Ave Ne Cleveland (44114) *(G-5475)*

Handkerchief House, The, Hudson *Also called Thompson Assoc Hudson Ohio* *(G-11204)*

Handle Light Inc............330 772-8901
5533 State Route 7 Kinsman (44428) *(G-11609)*

Hands On International LLC............513 502-9000
8541 Charleston Ridge Dr Mason (45040) *(G-13034)*

Handy Twine Knife Co............419 294-3424
5676 County Highway 330 Upper Sandusky (43351) *(G-19124)*

Hang Time Group Inc............216 771-5885
5340 Hamilton Ave Ste 107 Cleveland (44114) *(G-5476)*

Hang-It-All Curtain System LLC............614 275-0954
89 S Burgess Ave Columbus (43204) *(G-7140)*

Hang-UPS Instllation Group Inc............614 239-7004
3751 April Ln Columbus (43227) *(G-7141)*

Hanger Clinic, Columbus *Also called Hanger Prosthetics & Orthotics (G-6648)*

Hanger Clinic, Gallipolis *Also called Hanger Prsthetcs & Ortho Inc (G-10299)*

Hanger Orthopedic, Marysville *Also called Hanger Prsthetcs & Ortho Inc (G-12947)*

Hanger Prosthetics & Orthotics............614 436-3516
1210 Gemini Pl Ste 101 Columbus (43240) *(G-6648)*

Hanger Prsthetcs & Ortho Inc............440 605-0232
6001 Landerhaven Dr Ste A Mayfield Heights (44124) *(G-13316)*

Hanger Prsthetcs & Ortho Inc............330 670-8263
61 N Clvlnd Msslln Rd C Akron (44333) *(G-214)*

Hanger Prsthetcs & Ortho Inc............614 471-8210
471 Morrison Rd Ste E Gahanna (43230) *(G-10208)*

Hanger Prsthetcs & Ortho Inc............440 842-4251
6789 Ridge Rd Ste 104 Cleveland (44129) *(G-5477)*

Hanger Prsthetcs & Ortho Inc............419 841-9852
3435 N Hlland Sylvania Rd Toledo (43615) *(G-18495)*

Hanger Prsthetcs & Ortho Inc............740 454-6215
930 Orchard Hill Rd Zanesville (43701) *(G-21317)*

Hanger Prsthetcs & Ortho Inc............440 892-6665
29101 Health Campus Dr # 104 Westlake (44145) *(G-20274)*

Hanger Prsthetcs & Ortho Inc............330 374-9544
388 S Main St Ste 205 Akron (44311) *(G-215)*

Hanger Prsthetcs & Ortho Inc............330 856-6990
8029 E Market St Warren (44484) *(G-19556)*

Hanger Prsthetcs & Ortho Inc............937 773-2441
9179 N County Road 25a 2b Piqua (45356) *(G-16269)*

Hanger Prsthetcs & Ortho Inc............937 228-5462
1 Elizabeth Pl Ste 300 Dayton (45417) *(G-8384)*

Hanger Prsthetcs & Ortho Inc............419 522-0055
1136 Independence Ave Marion (43302) *(G-12871)*

Hanger Prsthetcs & Ortho Inc............740 354-4775
1611 27th St Ste 303 Portsmouth (45662) *(G-16437)*

Hanger Prsthetcs & Ortho Inc............740 383-2163
1136 Independence Ave Marion (43302) *(G-12872)*

Hanger Prsthetcs & Ortho Inc............740 266-6400
2605 Sunset Blvd Unit C Steubenville (43952) *(G-17697)*

Hanger Prsthetcs & Ortho Inc............740 446-6879
1168 Jackson Pike Gallipolis (45631) *(G-10299)*

Hanger Prsthetcs & Ortho Inc............614 481-8338
1357 Dublin Rd Columbus (43215) *(G-7142)*

Hanger Prsthetcs & Ortho Inc............740 654-1884
111 N Ewing St Lancaster (43130) *(G-11722)*

Hanger Prsthetcs & Ortho Inc............740 369-2424
211 Stocksdale Dr Ste C Marysville (43040) *(G-12947)*

Hanini Seven Oil............216 857-0172
6501 Denison Ave Cleveland (44102) *(G-5478)*

Hanlon Industries Inc............216 261-7056
1280 E 286th St Cleveland (44132) *(G-5479)*

Hann Box Works............740 962-3752
4678 N State Route 60 Nw McConnelsville (43756) *(G-13351)*

Hann Construction, McConnelsville *Also called Hann Box Works (G-13351)*

Hann Manufacturing Inc............740 962-3752
4678 N State Route 60 Nw McConnelsville (43756) *(G-13352)*

Hannibal Co Inc............614 846-5060
6536 Proprietors Rd Worthington (43085) *(G-20870)*

Hannon Company (PA)............330 456-4728
1605 Waynesburg Dr Se Canton (44707) *(G-2723)*

Hannon Company............330 343-7758
801 Commercial Pkwy Dover (44622) *(G-8990)*

Hannon Company............740 453-0527
218 Adams St Zanesville (43701) *(G-21318)*

Hanon Systems Usa LLC............313 920-0583
581 Arrowhead Dr Carey (43316) *(G-2919)*

Hanover Publishing Co............440 838-0911
7569 Sanctuary Cir Brecksville (44141) *(G-2054)*

Hans Rothenbuhler & Son Inc............440 632-6000
15815 Nauvoo Rd Middlefield (44062) *(G-13939)*

Hansen Coupling Division, Berea *Also called Eaton Corporation (G-1613)*

Hansen Scaffolding LLC (PA)............513 574-9000
193 Circle Freeway Dr West Chester (45246) *(G-20012)*

Hansen-Mueller Co............419 729-5535
1800 N Water St Toledo (43611) *(G-18496)*

Hanson Aggregates, Sandusky *Also called Wagner Quarries Company (G-17021)*

Hanson Aggregates East............513 353-1100
7000 Dry Fork Rd Cleves (45002) *(G-6515)*

Hanson Aggregates East LLC............937 364-2311
4281 Roush Rd Hillsboro (45133) *(G-10999)*

Hanson Aggregates East LLC............937 587-2671
848 Plum Run Rd Peebles (45660) *(G-16021)*

Hanson Aggregates East LLC............740 773-2172
33 Renick Ave Chillicothe (45601) *(G-3242)*

Hanson Aggregates East LLC............330 467-7890
7925 Empire Pkwy Macedonia (44056) *(G-12457)*

Hanson Aggregates East LLC............419 483-4390
9220 Portland Rd Castalia (44824) *(G-2976)*

Hanson Aggregates East LLC............937 382-2557
1481 S Us Highway 68 Wilmington (45177) *(G-20668)*

Hanson Aggregates LLC............419 841-3413
4100 Centennial Rd Sylvania (43560) *(G-18108)*

Hanson Aggregates Mid West, Bloomville *Also called Hanson Aggregates Midwest LLC (G-1728)*

Hanson Aggregates Midwest Inc............419 399-4846
11450 Road 180 Paulding (45879) *(G-16004)*

Hanson Aggregates Midwest LLC............419 882-0123
8130 Brint Rd Sylvania (43560) *(G-18109)*

Hanson Aggregates Midwest LLC............419 983-2211
4575 S County Road 49 Bloomville (44818) *(G-1728)*

Hanson Aggregates Midwest LLC............419 878-2006
600 S River Rd Waterville (43566) *(G-19659)*

Hanson Concrete Products Ohio............614 443-4846
1500 Haul Rd Columbus (43207) *(G-7143)*

Hanson Pipe & Precast Hamburg, Dayton *Also called Forterra Pipe & Precast LLC (G-8349)*

Hanson Pipe & Products, Columbus *Also called Hanson Concrete Products Ohio (G-7143)*

Hantech, Findlay *Also called Hancor Inc (G-9837)*

Hapco Inc............330 678-9353
390 Portage Blvd Kent (44240) *(G-11469)*

Happy Booker, Cincinnati *Also called Art Guild Binders Inc (G-3414)*

Har Adhesive Technologies, Bedford *Also called Certon Technologies Inc (G-1414)*

Har Equipment Sales Inc............440 786-7189
60 S Park St Bedford (44146) *(G-1428)*

Harbisonwalker Intl Inc............740 682-7711
1627 Pyro Rd Oak Hill (45656) *(G-15597)*

Harbisonwalker Intl Inc............330 326-2010
9686 E Center St Windham (44288) *(G-20697)*

Harbisonwalker Intl Inc............513 576-6240
4065a Clough Woods Dr Batavia (45103) *(G-1191)*

Harbisonwalker Intl Inc............330 868-4141
1316 Alliance Rd Nw Minerva (44657) *(G-14323)*

Harbor Castings Inc............231 733-1053
2508 Bailey Rd Cuyahoga Falls (44221) *(G-8006)*

Harbor Castings Inc (PA)............330 499-7178
2508 Bailey Rd Cuyahoga Falls (44221) *(G-8007)*

Harbor Freight Tools Usa Inc............937 415-0770
1941 Needmore Rd Dayton (45414) *(G-8385)*

Harbor Industrial Corp............440 599-8366
859 W Jackson St Conneaut (44030) *(G-7807)*

Harbor Perk LLC............440 964-9277
1025 Bridge St Ashtabula (44004) *(G-812)*

Harbro LLC............810 229-4755
18615 Detroit Ave Ste 203 Lakewood (44107) *(G-11666)*

Harco Industries Inc............937 832-9697
3535 Kettering Blvd Moraine (45439) *(G-14493)*

Harco Manufacturing Group LLC (PA)............937 528-5000
3535 Kettering Blvd Moraine (45439) *(G-14494)*

Harco Manufacturing Group LLC............937 528-5000
3535 Kettering Blvd 200 Moraine (45439) *(G-14495)*

Hard Chrome Plating Consultant............216 631-9090
2196 W 59th St Cleveland (44102) *(G-5480)*

Hard Drive Co, Barberton *Also called Florence Alloys Inc (G-1115)*

Hardcoating Technologies Ltd............330 686-2136
103 S Main St Munroe Falls (44262) *(G-14660)*

Hardcore Offroad Tires, Youngstown *Also called Warrior Imports Inc (G-21243)*

Hardin County Publishing Co (HQ)............419 674-4066
201 E Columbus St Kenton (43326) *(G-11549)*

Hardin Creek Machine & Tool............419 678-4913
200 Hardin St Coldwater (45828) *(G-6561)*

Harding Machine Acquisition Co............937 666-3031
13060 State Route 287 East Liberty (43319) *(G-9201)*

Hardline International Inc............419 924-9556
1107 Oak St West Unity (43570) *(G-20129)*

Hardmagic............415 390-6232
125 Frederick St Marietta (45750) *(G-12789)*

Hardware Exchange Inc............440 449-8006
6573 Cochran Rd Ste F Solon (44139) *(G-17306)*

Hardware Unlimited LLC............419 472-8745
226 S Reynolds Rd Ste A Toledo (43615) *(G-18497)*

Hardwood Connection, The, Toledo *Also called Hafner Hardwood Connection LLC (G-18493)*

Hardwood Flrg & Paneling Inc............440 834-1710
15320 Burton Windsor Rd Middlefield (44062) *(G-13940)*

Hardwood Lumber Co, Burton *Also called Stephen M Trudick (G-2385)*

Hardwood Solutions............330 359-5755
112 E Main St Wilmot (44689) *(G-20686)*

Hardwood Store Inc............937 864-2899
340 Enon Rd Enon (45323) *(G-9547)*

Hardy Industrial Tech LLC 440 350-6300
679 Hardy Rd Painesville (44077) *(G-15887)*

Hargis Industries LP 513 874-5905
9950 Prnceton Glendale Rd West Chester (45246) *(G-20013)*

Harlan Graphic Arts Svcs Inc 513 251-5700
4752 River Rd Cincinnati (45233) *(G-3866)*

Harland Sharp, Strongsville Also called Custom Speed Parts Inc *(G-17909)*

Harmon John 740 934-2032
36300 Greenbrier Rd Graysville (45734) *(G-10469)*

Harmon Sign Company, Toledo Also called Kasper Enterprises Inc *(G-18540)*

Harmon, John K, Graysville Also called Harmon John *(G-10469)*

Harmony Systems and Svc Inc 937 778-1082
1711 Commerce Dr Piqua (45356) *(G-16270)*

Harn Vault Service Inc (PA) 330 832-1995
422 East St Minerva (44657) *(G-14324)*

Harness Shop, Charm Also called Charm Harness and Boot Ltd *(G-3183)*

Harold Flory 937 473-3030
5225 W Myers Rd Covington (45318) *(G-7924)*

Harper Engraving & Printing Co (PA) 614 276-0700
2626 Fisher Rd Columbus (43204) *(G-7144)*

Harray LLC 888 568-8371
266 W Mitchell Ave Cincinnati (45232) *(G-3867)*

Harris Mackessy & Brennan 614 221-6831
570 Polaris Pkwy Ste 125 Westerville (43082) *(G-20157)*

Harris & Company Inc 330 332-4127
980 Salem Pkwy Salem (44460) *(G-16899)*

Harris Broadcast, Mason Also called Imagine Communications Corp *(G-13041)*

Harris Broadcast Communication 513 459-3400
5300 Kings Island Dr Mason (45040) *(G-13035)*

Harris Corporation 973 284-2866
3500 Pentagon Blvd # 300 Beavercreek (45431) *(G-1344)*

Harris Hawk 800 459-4295
306 W Main St Mason (45040) *(G-13036)*

Harris Instrument Corporation 740 369-3580
155 Johnson Dr Delaware (43015) *(G-8857)*

Harris Paper Crafts Inc 614 299-2141
266 E 5th Ave Columbus (43201) *(G-7145)*

Harris Products Group, The, Euclid Also called J W Harris Co Inc *(G-9587)*

Harris Welding and Machine Co (PA) 419 281-8351
2219 Cottage St Ashland (44805) *(G-736)*

Harris Welding and Machine Co. 419 281-9623
2219 Cottage St Ashland (44805) *(G-737)*

Harrison 20 Mtd Borefinery LLC 740 796-4797
9665 Young America Rd Adamsville (43802) *(G-8)*

Harrison County Coal Company (PA) 740 338-3100
46226 National Rd W Saint Clairsville (43950) *(G-16791)*

Harrison Ethanol, Adamsville Also called Harrison 20 Mtd Borefinery LLC *(G-8)*

Harrison Mch & Plastic Corp (PA) 330 569-3128
11614 State Route 88 Garrettsville (44231) *(G-10323)*

Harrison News Herald Inc 740 942-2118
144 S Main St Lowr Cadiz (43907) *(G-2418)*

Harrison Paint Company (PA) 330 455-5120
1329 Harrison Ave Sw Canton (44706) *(G-2724)*

Harrison Steel Plant, Canton Also called Timkensteel Corporation *(G-2878)*

Harry and David LLC 740 929-7100
500 Reliance Dr Hebron (43025) *(G-10869)*

Harry and David's, Hebron Also called Harry and David LLC *(G-10869)*

Harry C Lobalzo & Sons Inc (PA) 330 666-6758
61 N Cleveland Ste A Akron (44333) *(G-216)*

Harry London Candies Inc (HQ) 330 494-0833
5353 Lauby Rd North Canton (44720) *(G-15239)*

Harry London Chocolates, North Canton Also called Harry London Candies Inc *(G-15239)*

Harsco Corporation 740 387-1150
3477 Harding Hwy E Marion (43302) *(G-12873)*

Harsco Corporation 740 367-7322
5486 State Route 7 N Cheshire (45620) *(G-3192)*

Harsco Corporation 216 961-1570
7900 Hub Pkwy Cleveland (44125) *(G-5481)*

Harsco Corporation 330 372-1781
101 Tidewater St Ne Warren (44483) *(G-19557)*

Hart & Cooley Inc 937 832-7800
1 Lau Pkwy Englewood (45315) *(G-9522)*

Hart Advertising Inc 419 668-1194
6975 E Seminary St Norwalk (44857) *(G-15543)*

Hartco Printing Company (PA) 614 761-1292
4106 Delancy Park Dr Dublin (43016) *(G-9083)*

Hartco Products, The, Dublin Also called Hartco Printing Company *(G-9083)*

Hartford Steel Sales 513 275-1744
6 S 2nd St Ste 214 Hamilton (45011) *(G-10703)*

Hartley Machine Inc 330 821-0343
22640 Hartley Rd Alliance (44601) *(G-513)*

Hartline Products Coinc (PA) 216 291-2303
4568 Mayfield Rd Ste 202 Cleveland (44121) *(G-5482)*

Hartline Products Coinc. 216 851-7189
15035 Woodworth Rd Cleveland (44110) *(G-5483)*

Hartman Baseball Cards, Columbus Also called The Hartman Corp *(G-7690)*

Hartman Distributing LLC 740 616-7764
1262 Bluejack Ln Heath (43056) *(G-10847)*

Hartman Printing Co 419 946-2854
425 W Marion St Mount Gilead (43338) *(G-14561)*

Hartmann Incorporated 513 276-7318
4615 Carlynn Dr Blue Ash (45241) *(G-1805)*

Hartville Chocolate Factory, Hartville Also called Hartville Chocolates Inc *(G-10822)*

Hartville Chocolates Inc. 330 877-1999
114 S Prospect Ave Hartville (44632) *(G-10822)*

Hartville Locker Service Inc 330 877-9547
119 Sunnyside St Sw Hartville (44632) *(G-10823)*

Hartville News, Hartville Also called Knowles Press Inc *(G-10827)*

Hartville Plastics Inc. 330 877-9090
322 Lake Ave Ne Hartville (44632) *(G-10824)*

Hartz Mountain Corporation 513 877-2131
5374 Long Spurling Rd Pleasant Plain (45162) *(G-16372)*

Hartzell Fan Inc (PA) 937 773-7411
910 S Downing St Piqua (45356) *(G-16271)*

Hartzell Hardwoods Inc (PA) 937 773-7054
1025 S Roosevelt Ave Piqua (45356) *(G-16272)*

Hartzell Industries Inc (PA) 937 773-6295
1025 S Roosevelt Ave Piqua (45356) *(G-16273)*

Hartzell Manufacturing Co Inc 937 859-5955
2533 Technical Dr Miamisburg (45342) *(G-13815)*

Hartzell Propeller Inc 937 778-4200
1 Propeller Pl Piqua (45356) *(G-16274)*

Hartzell Propeller Inc (HQ) 937 778-4200
1 Propeller Pl Piqua (45356) *(G-16275)*

Hartzell Service Center, Piqua Also called Hartzell Propeller Inc *(G-16274)*

Harvard Coil Processing Inc 216 883-6366
5400 Harvard Ave Cleveland (44105) *(G-5484)*

Harvard Metal Treating Inc 216 271-4424
2819 Harvard Ave Newburgh Heights (44105) *(G-15071)*

Harvest Land Co-Op Inc 937 884-5526
141 S Commerce St Verona (45378) *(G-19338)*

Harvest Sand and Gravel Inc 330 372-4408
522 Perkins Dr Nw Warren (44483) *(G-19558)*

Harvey Brothers Inc (PA) 513 541-2622
3492 Spring Grove Ave Cincinnati (45223) *(G-3868)*

Harvey Whitney Books Company 513 793-3555
8044 Montgomery Rd # 415 Cincinnati (45236) *(G-3869)*

Harwood Rubber Products Inc. 330 923-3256
1365 Orlen Ave Cuyahoga Falls (44221) *(G-8008)*

Hashier & Hashier Mfg 440 933-4883
644 Moore Rd Avon Lake (44012) *(G-1031)*

Hason USA Corp. 513 248-0287
1262 Us Highway 50 Milford (45150) *(G-14150)*

Hatchery, Strasburg Also called Case Farms of Ohio Inc *(G-17822)*

Hatfield Industries LLC 513 225-0456
9717 Flagstone Way West Chester (45069) *(G-19880)*

Hathaway, Cincinnati Also called Volk Corporation *(G-4570)*

Hathaway Stamp & Ident Co of C 513 621-1052
635 Main St Cincinnati (45202) *(G-3870)*

Hathaway Stamp Co. 513 621-1052
635 Main St Ste 1 Cincinnati (45202) *(G-3871)*

Hathaway Stamp Identification, Cincinnati Also called Hathaway Stamp & Ident Co of C *(G-3870)*

Hattenbach Company (PA) 216 881-5200
5309 Hamilton Ave Cleveland (44114) *(G-5485)*

Hattenbach Company 330 744-2732
52 E Myrtle Ave Youngstown (44507) *(G-21107)*

Haueter Construction Co 440 834-8220
15349 Ravenna Rd Newbury (44065) *(G-15094)*

Haul, Mark Sales/Service/Parts, Navarre Also called Navarre Trailer Sales Inc *(G-14722)*

Haul-Away Containers Inc 440 546-1879
3554 Brecksville Rd # 500 Richfield (44286) *(G-16626)*

Haulette Manufacturing Inc 419 586-1717
8271 Us Route 127 Celina (45822) *(G-3000)*

Haulotte US Inc (HQ) 419 445-8915
125 Taylor Pkwy Archbold (43502) *(G-680)*

Haus Cider Mill & Fruit Farm, Canfield Also called Haus Mathias *(G-2557)*

Haus Mathias 330 533-5305
6742 W Calla Rd Canfield (44406) *(G-2557)*

Hauser Landscaping, Middlefield Also called Hauser Services Llc *(G-13941)*

Hauser Services Llc 440 632-5126
15668 Old State Rd Middlefield (44062) *(G-13941)*

Haute Chocolate Inc 513 793-9999
9424 Shelly Ln Montgomery (45242) *(G-14432)*

Haviland Culvert Company 419 622-6951
100 W Main Haviland (45851) *(G-10839)*

Haviland Drainage Products Co (PA) 419 622-4611
100 W Main St Haviland (45851) *(G-10840)*

Haviland Plastic Products Co. 419 622-3110
119 W Main St Haviland (45851) *(G-10841)*

Hawaii Revealed, Lancaster Also called Wizard Publications Inc *(G-11762)*

Hawk Engine & Machine 440 582-0900
12166 York Rd Unit 1 North Royalton (44133) *(G-15424)*

Hawk Manufacturing LLC 330 784-6234
2642 Gilchrist Rd Akron (44305) *(G-217)*

Hawk Manufacturing LLC (HQ) 330 784-3151
380 Kennedy Rd Akron (44305) *(G-218)*

Hawk Manufacturing LLC 330 784-4815
382 Kennedy Rd Akron (44305) *(G-219)*

Hawk Performance, Medina *Also called Friction Products Co (G-13413)*

Hawkline Nevada LLC 937 444-4295
200 Front St Mount Orab (45154) *(G-14579)*

Hawks & Associates Inc 513 752-4311
1029 Seabrook Way Cincinnati (45245) *(G-3308)*

Hawks Tag, Cincinnati *Also called Hawks & Associates Inc (G-3308)*

Hawthorne Bolt Works Corp 330 723-0555
355 Lake Rd Ste A Medina (44256) *(G-13419)*

Hawthorne Caravan & Assoc LLC 440 366-9065
25 Hawthorne St Elyria (44035) *(G-9428)*

Hawthorne Systems Inc 419 643-5861
318 W Main St Beaverdam (45808) *(G-1393)*

Hawthorne Tool LLC 440 516-1891
1340 Lloyd Rd Ste C Wickliffe (44092) *(G-20367)*

Hawthorne Wire Ltd 216 712-4747
13000 Athens Ave Ste 101 Lakewood (44107) *(G-11667)*

Hawthorne Wire Services Ltd 216 712-4747
13000 Athens Ave Ste 101 Lakewood (44107) *(G-11668)*

Hawthorne-Seving Inc 419 643-5531
320 W Main St Cridersville (45806) *(G-7945)*

Hayden Valley Foods Inc 614 539-7233
3150 Urbancrest Indus Urbancrest (43123) *(G-19189)*

Hayes Bros Ornamental Ir Works 419 531-1491
1830 N Reynolds Rd Toledo (43615) *(G-18498)*

Hayes Lemmerz Intl-Commrcl Hwy, Akron *Also called Maxion Wheels Akron LLC (G-289)*

Hayes Metalfinishing Inc 937 228-7550
2617 Stanley Ave Dayton (45404) *(G-8386)*

Hayes Reconditioning Group 937 299-8013
1301 Robert Dickey Pkwy Dayton (45409) *(G-8387)*

Hayes, Michael Designer, Solon *Also called Michael W Hyes Desgr Goldsmith (G-17338)*

Hayford Technologies 419 524-7627
500 S Airport Rd Mansfield (44903) *(G-12622)*

Haynes Manufacturing Company, Westlake *Also called R and J Corporation (G-20299)*

Haynn Construction Co Inc 419 853-4747
14866 N Elyria Rd West Salem (44287) *(G-20113)*

Hays Cleveland, Cleveland *Also called Unicontrol Inc (G-6382)*

Hays Fabricating & Welding 937 325-0031
633 E Leffel Ln Springfield (45505) *(G-17568)*

Hays Orchard & Cider Mill LLC 330 482-2924
3622 Middleton Rd Columbiana (44408) *(G-6619)*

Haz-Safe LLC 330 793-0900
3850 Hendricks Rd Austintown (44515) *(G-974)*

Hazelbaker Industries Inc 614 276-2631
1661 Old Henderson Rd Columbus (43220) *(G-7146)*

Hazenstab Machine Inc 330 337-1865
1575 Salem Pkwy Salem (44460) *(G-16900)*

HB, Sidney *Also called H B Products Inc (G-17191)*

HB Fuller Company 513 719-3600
4450 Malsbary Rd Blue Ash (45242) *(G-1806)*

HB Fuller Company 513 719-3600
4440 Malsbary Rd Blue Ash (45242) *(G-1807)*

Hbb Pro Sales (PA) 216 901-7900
9700 Rockside Rd Ste 120 Cleveland (44125) *(G-5486)*

Hbd/Thermoid Inc 937 593-5010
1301 W Sandusky Ave Bellefontaine (43311) *(G-1532)*

Hbe Machine 419 668-9426
1100 State Route 61 N Monroeville (44847) *(G-14426)*

HBK Stoneworks 740 817-2244
9292 Jhnstown Alxndria Rd Johnstown (43031) *(G-11400)*

Hc 142, Columbus *Also called Hilti Inc (G-7158)*

Hc Apparel, Columbus *Also called Columbus Humungous Apparel LLC (G-6955)*

HC Starck (ohio) Inc 216 692-3990
21801 Tungsten Rd Cleveland (44117) *(G-5487)*

HCC Holdings Inc 800 203-1155
4700 W 160th St Cleveland (44135) *(G-5488)*

HCC Industries 513 334-5585
9705 Reading Rd Cincinnati (45215) *(G-3872)*

HCC/Sealtron (HQ) 513 733-8400
9705 Reading Rd Cincinnati (45215) *(G-3873)*

Hcf of Bowling Green Inc 419 999-2010
1100 Shawnee Rd Lima (45805) *(G-12022)*

Hdi Landing Gear Usa Inc (HQ) 513 619-1203
663 Montgomery Ave Springfield (45506) *(G-17569)*

Hdi Landing Gear Usa Inc 440 783-5255
15900 Foltz Pkwy Strongsville (44149) *(G-17924)*

Hdi Rock Drilling Group Ltd 740 369-2968
3955 Klondike Rd Delaware (43015) *(G-8858)*

Hdt Engineered Technologies, Solon *Also called Hunter Defense Tech Inc (G-17312)*

Hdt Ep Inc 216 438-6111
30500 Aurora Rd Ste 100 Solon (44139) *(G-17307)*

Hdt Expeditionary Systems Inc 216 438-6111
30500 Aurora Rd Ste 100 Solon (44139) *(G-17308)*

Hdt Expeditionary Systems Inc 440 466-6640
5455 Route 307 W Geneva (44041) *(G-10350)*

Hdt Expeditionary Systems Inc (HQ) 216 438-6111
30500 Aurora Rd Ste 100 Solon (44139) *(G-17309)*

Headlee Enterprises Ltd 614 785-0011
9015 Antares Ave Columbus (43240) *(G-6649)*

Heads & Threads Intl LLC 216 433-1660
289070 Lorain Rd Ste 101 North Olmsted (44070) *(G-15338)*

Headwaters Incorporated 989 671-1500
745 Us Route 52 Manchester (45144) *(G-12549)*

Health Bridge Imaging LLC 740 423-3300
809 Farson St Unit 107 Belpre (45714) *(G-1587)*

Health Care Products Inc 419 678-9620
410 Nisco St Coldwater (45828) *(G-6562)*

Health Care Solutions Inc 419 636-4189
5673 State Route 15 Bryan (43506) *(G-2300)*

Health Mor At Home Cbp, Strongsville *Also called Hmi Industries Inc (G-17926)*

Health Nuts Media LLC 818 802-5222
4225 W 229th St Cleveland (44126) *(G-5489)*

Healthcare Benefits Inc 419 433-4499
1212 Cleveland Rd W Huron (44839) *(G-11223)*

Healthedge Software Inc 614 431-3711
50 S Liberty St Ste 200 Powell (43065) *(G-16473)*

Healthpro Brands Inc 513 492-7512
12044 Millstone Ct Loveland (45140) *(G-12357)*

Healthwares Manufacturing 513 353-3691
8649 E Miami River Rd Cincinnati (45247) *(G-3874)*

Healthy Living 937 962-4705
4248 New Market Banta Rd Lewisburg (45338) *(G-11934)*

Hearing Aid Center of NW Ohio 419 636-8959
1318 E High St Ste B Bryan (43506) *(G-2301)*

Hearing Aid Ctr of NW Ohio The, Bryan *Also called Hearing Aid Center of NW Ohio (G-2301)*

Hearn Plating Co Ltd 419 473-9773
3184 Bellevue Rd Toledo (43606) *(G-18499)*

Heart Warming Candles 937 456-2720
6806 Cumbersville St Eaton (45320) *(G-9308)*

Hearth & Home Technologies LLC 513 874-4770
10025 Prncton Glendale Rd Cincinnati (45246) *(G-3875)*

Hearth Products Controls Co 937 436-9800
3050 Plainfield Rd Dayton (45432) *(G-8108)*

Hearthside Food Solutions LLC 419 727-1298
3444 N Summit St Toledo (43611) *(G-18500)*

Hearthside Food Solutions LLC 419 293-2911
312 Rader Rd Mc Comb (45858) *(G-13338)*

Heartland Bread & Roll, Worthington *Also called Hannibal Co Inc (G-20870)*

Heartland Communications, Utica *Also called Utica Herald (G-19197)*

Heartland Communications Div, Pataskala *Also called Pataskala Post (G-15977)*

Heartland Education Community 330 684-3034
200 N Main St Orrville (44667) *(G-15739)*

Heartland Group Holdings LLC (HQ) 614 441-4001
4001 E 5th Ave Columbus (43219) *(G-7147)*

Heartland Home Cabinetry Ltd 740 936-5100
35 S Galena Rd Unit C Sunbury (43074) *(G-18062)*

Heartland Publications LLC (HQ) 860 664-1075
4500 Lyons Rd Miamisburg (45342) *(G-13816)*

Heartland Publications LLC 740 446-2342
825 3rd Ave Gallipolis (45631) *(G-10300)*

Heartland Stairway Ltd 330 279-2554
7080 Township Road 601 Millersburg (44654) *(G-14220)*

Heartland Stairways Inc (PA) 330 279-2554
8230 County Road 245 Holmesville (44633) *(G-11102)*

Heartland Stairways Inc 330 279-2554
Township Road 245 Holmesville (44633) *(G-11103)*

Heartland Steel Inc 740 333-5401
1629 S Fayette St Washington Court Hou (43160) *(G-19639)*

Heartland Thermography, West Chester *Also called Lasting First Impressions Inc (G-20020)*

Heat & Sensor, Lebanon *Also called Heat and Sensor Tech LLC (G-11807)*

Heat and Sensor Tech LLC 513 228-0481
627 Norgal Dr Lebanon (45036) *(G-11807)*

Heat Exchange Applied Tech 330 682-4328
150b Allen Ave Orrville (44667) *(G-15740)*

Heat Exchange Institute Inc 216 241-7333
1300 Sumner Ave Cleveland (44115) *(G-5490)*

Heat Seal LLC 216 341-2022
4922 E 49th St Cleveland (44125) *(G-5491)*

Heat Treating Inc (PA) 937 325-3121
1762 W Pleasant St Springfield (45506) *(G-17570)*

Heat Treating Inc 937 325-3121
1807 W Pleasant St Springfield (45506) *(G-17571)*

Heat Treating Inc 614 759-9963
675 Cross Pointe Rd Gahanna (43230) *(G-10209)*

Heat Treating Technologies 419 224-8324
1799 E 4th St Lima (45804) *(G-12023)*

Heatermeals, Cincinnati *Also called Luxfer Magtech Inc (G-4040)*

Heather B Moore Inc 216 932-5430
4502 Prospect Ave Cleveland (44103) *(G-5492)*

Heather Creek Foods LLC 330 792-8654
12485 Commissioner Dr North Jackson (44451) *(G-15291)*

Heatherdowns License Bureau 419 381-1109
4460 Heatherdowns Blvd Toledo (43614) *(G-18501)*

Heating & Cooling Products, Mount Vernon *Also called Famous Industries Inc (G-14622)*

Heatstar, Cleveland *Also called Mr Heater Inc (G-5838)*

A
L
P
H
A
B
E
T
I
C

Heatstar 440 701-1031
  7547 Mentor Ave Ste 304 Mentor (44060) *(G-13600)*

Hebco Products Inc 419 562-7987
  1232 Whetstone St Bucyrus (44820) *(G-2347)*

Hec Investments Inc 937 278-9123
  4800 Wadsworth Rd Dayton (45414) *(G-8388)*

Heck's Diamond Printing, Toledo Also called Hecks Direct Mail & Prtg Svc *(G-18503)*

Hecks Direct Mail & Prtg Svc (PA) 419 697-3505
  417 Main St Toledo (43605) *(G-18502)*

Hecks Direct Mail & Prtg Svc 419 661-6028
  202 W Florence Ave Toledo (43605) *(G-18503)*

Hedalloy Die Corp 216 341-3768
  3266 E 49th St Cleveland (44127) *(G-5493)*

Hedges Selective Tool & Prod 419 478-8670
  702 W Laskey Rd Toledo (43612) *(G-18504)*

Hedstrom Fitness, Ashland Also called Ball Bounce and Sport Inc *(G-710)*

Hedstrom Injection, Ashland Also called Converge Group Inc *(G-726)*

HEF USA Corporation (PA) 937 323-2556
  2015 Progress Rd Springfield (45505) *(G-17572)*

Heffelfingers Meats Inc 419 368-7131
  469 County Road 30a Jeromesville (44840) *(G-11384)*

Hefty Hoist Inc 740 467-2515
  2397a Refugee Rd Ne Millersport (43046) *(G-14294)*

Heico Aerospace Parts Corp (HQ) 954 987-6101
  375 Alpha Park Highland Heights (44143) *(G-10915)*

Heidtman Steel Products, Toledo Also called Centaur Inc *(G-18392)*

Heidtman Steel Products Inc (HQ) 419 691-4646
  2401 Front St Toledo (43605) *(G-18505)*

Heidtman Steel Products Inc 216 641-6995
  4600 Heidtman Pkwy Cleveland (44105) *(G-5494)*

Heidtman Steel Products Inc 419 385-0636
  135 N Flearing Blvd Toledo (43609) *(G-18506)*

Heidtman Toledo Blank, Toledo Also called Heidtman Steel Products Inc *(G-18506)*

Heil Engneered Process Eqp Inc 440 327-6051
  37000 Center Ridge Rd North Ridgeville (44039) *(G-15378)*

Heim Sheet Metal Inc 330 424-7820
  525 E Chestnut St Lisbon (44432) *(G-12121)*

Heimann Manufacturing Co 937 652-1865
  1140 N Main St Urbana (43078) *(G-19161)*

Heinen's 8, Aurora Also called Heinens Inc *(G-924)*

Heinens Inc 330 562-5297
  115 N Chillicothe Rd Aurora (44202) *(G-924)*

Heinis Cheese Chalet, Millersburg Also called Bunker Hill Cheese Co Inc *(G-14207)*

Heintz Conveying Belt Service, Medina Also called Conviber Inc *(G-13393)*

Heintz Manufacturers Inc 724 274-6300
  1066 Industrial Pkwy Medina (44256) *(G-13420)*

Heinz Foreign Investment Co (HQ) 330 837-8331
  1301 Oberlin Ave Sw Massillon (44647) *(G-13146)*

Heinz Frozen Foods, Massillon Also called HJ Heinz Company LP *(G-13150)*

Heisler Tool Company 440 951-2424
  38228 Western Pkwy Willoughby (44094) *(G-20503)*

Heitkamp & Kremer Printing 419 925-4121
  6184 State Route 274 Celina (45822) *(G-3001)*

Helena Chemical Company 614 275-4200
  800 Distribution Dr Columbus (43228) *(G-7148)*

Helena Chemical Company 419 596-3806
  200 N Main St Continental (45831) *(G-7826)*

Helex Division, Cincinnati Also called A C Knox Inc *(G-3333)*

Helical Line Products Co 440 933-9263
  659 Miller Rd Avon Lake (44012) *(G-1032)*

Hellan Strainer Company 216 206-4200
  3249 E 80th St Cleveland (44104) *(G-5495)*

Heller Acquisitions Inc 937 833-2676
  912 Salem St Brookville (45309) *(G-2186)*

Heller Machine Products Inc 216 281-2951
  1971 W 90th St Cleveland (44102) *(G-5496)*

Heller Sports Center, Montpelier Also called W C Heller & Co Inc *(G-14457)*

Helm Instrument Company Inc 419 893-4356
  361 W Dussel Dr Maumee (43537) *(G-13265)*

Helmart Company Inc 513 941-3095
  4960 Hillside Ave Cincinnati (45233) *(G-3876)*

Hely & Weber Orthopedic, Avon Also called Weber Orthopedic Inc *(G-1018)*

Hemco Inc 419 499-4602
  1413 State Route 113 E Milan (44846) *(G-14112)*

Hemmelgarn & Sons Inc 419 678-2351
  3763 Philothea Rd Coldwater (45828) *(G-6563)*

Hempy Water Conditioning Inc (PA) 419 273-2531
  505 Smith St Forest (45843) *(G-9921)*

Hempy Water Conditioning Inc 419 448-8885
  227 S Washington St Tiffin (44883) *(G-18222)*

Hempy Water Conditioning Inc 419 529-4002
  4148b Park Ave W Ontario (44903) *(G-15688)*

Hempy Water of Tiffin, Tiffin Also called Hempy Water Conditioning Inc *(G-18222)*

Hen House Inc 419 663-3377
  100 Northwest St Norwalk (44857) *(G-15544)*

Hen of Woods LLC 513 833-7357
  1432 Main St Cincinnati (45202) *(G-3877)*

Henderson Builders Inc 419 665-2684
  1610 County Road 90 Gibsonburg (43431) *(G-10377)*

Henderson Fabricating Co Inc 216 432-0404
  6217 Central Ave Cleveland (44104) *(G-5497)*

Henderson Partners LLC 614 883-1310
  4424 N High St Columbus (43214) *(G-7149)*

Henderson Trucking, Delaware Also called Rjw Trucking Company Ltd *(G-8883)*

Hendricks Vacuum Forming Inc (PA) 330 837-2040
  3500 17th St Sw Massillon (44647) *(G-13147)*

Hendricks Vacuum Forming Inc 330 833-8913
  3536 17th St Sw Massillon (44647) *(G-13148)*

Hendrickson Auxiliary Axles, Hebron Also called Hendrickson International Corp *(G-10870)*

Hendrickson International Corp 740 929-5600
  277 N High St Hebron (43025) *(G-10870)*

Hendrickson Trailer, Canton Also called Hendrickson Usa LLC *(G-2725)*

Hendrickson Usa LLC 330 456-7288
  2070 Industrial Pl Se Canton (44707) *(G-2725)*

Henkel Corporation 740 363-1351
  421 London Rd Delaware (43015) *(G-8859)*

Henkel Corporation 216 475-3600
  18731 Cranwood Pkwy Cleveland (44128) *(G-5498)*

Henkel Corporation 440 250-7700
  26235 1st St Westlake (44145) *(G-20275)*

Henkel Corporation 513 830-0260
  9435 Waterstone Blvd Cincinnati (45249) *(G-3878)*

Henkel Surface Technologies, Delaware Also called Henkel Corporation *(G-8859)*

Henly Corporation 419 476-0851
  520 W Laskey Rd Toledo (43612) *(G-18507)*

Hennacy Machine Company Inc 330 785-2940
  1209 Triplett Blvd Akron (44306) *(G-220)*

Hennig Inc 513 247-0838
  11431 Williamson Rd Ste A Blue Ash (45241) *(G-1808)*

Hennings Quality Service Inc 216 941-9120
  3115 Berea Rd Cleveland (44111) *(G-5499)*

Henny Penny Corporation (PA) 937 456-8400
  1219 Us Route 35 Eaton (45320) *(G-9309)*

Henry & Wright Corporation 216 851-3750
  739 E 140th St Ste 1 Cleveland (44110) *(G-5500)*

Henry Bussman 614 224-0417
  70 S 4th St Columbus (43215) *(G-7150)*

Henry Tools Inc 216 291-1011
  498 S Belvoir Blvd Cleveland (44121) *(G-5501)*

Henry-Griffitts Limited (HQ) 419 482-9095
  352 Tomahawk Dr Maumee (43537) *(G-13266)*

Hensel Ready Mix 419 253-9200
  4050 Bennington Way Marengo (43334) *(G-12751)*

Hensel Ready Mix Inc (PA) 419 675-1808
  9925 County Road 265 Kenton (43326) *(G-11550)*

Henty USA 513 984-5590
  7260 Edington Dr Cincinnati (45249) *(G-3879)*

Hephaestus Technologies LLC 216 252-0430
  3811 W 150th St Cleveland (44111) *(G-5502)*

Hept Machine Inc 937 890-5633
  19 E Alkaline Springs Rd Vandalia (45377) *(G-19294)*

Heraeus Electro-Nite Co LLC 330 725-1419
  585 N State Rd Medina (44256) *(G-13421)*

Heraeus Precious Metals North 937 264-1000
  970 Industrial Park Dr Vandalia (45377) *(G-19295)*

Herald Inc 419 492-2133
  625 S Kibler St New Washington (44854) *(G-14960)*

Herald House 740 967-8044
  3121 S County Line Rd Johnstown (43031) *(G-11401)*

Herald Looms 330 948-1080
  118 Lee St Lodi (44254) *(G-12162)*

Herald Reflector Inc (PA) 419 668-3771
  61 E Monroe St Norwalk (44857) *(G-15545)*

Herald Star Newspaper, Steubenville Also called Weirton Daily Times *(G-17720)*

Herbert E Orr Company 419 399-4866
  335 W Wall St Paulding (45879) *(G-16005)*

Herbert Machine Works Inc 330 929-4297
  1480 Industrial Pkwy Akron (44310) *(G-221)*

Herbert Wood Products Inc 440 834-1410
  15089 White Rd Middlefield (44062) *(G-13942)*

Herco Inc 740 498-5181
  295 Enterprise Dr Newcomerstown (43832) *(G-15115)*

Hercules, Wickliffe Also called Universal Metal Products Inc *(G-20391)*

Hercules Acquisition Corp 419 287-3223
  850 W Front St Pemberville (43450) *(G-16027)*

Hercules Engine Components, Massillon Also called Brinkley Technology Group LLC *(G-13115)*

Hercules Engine Components, Massillon Also called DW Hercules LLC *(G-13127)*

Hercules Industries Inc 740 494-2620
  7194 Prospect Delaware Rd Prospect (43342) *(G-16497)*

Hercules Polishing & Plating 330 455-8871
  4883 Southway St Sw Canton (44706) *(G-2726)*

Hercules Stamping Co, Pemberville Also called Hercules Acquisition Corp *(G-16027)*

Herd Manufacturing Inc 216 651-4221
  9227 Clinton Rd Cleveland (44144) *(G-5503)*

Herff Jones LLC 330 678-8138
4468 Berry Hl Stow (44224) *(G-17762)*

Herff Jones Inc 740 821-3109
2470 Orizaba Ln Portsmouth (45662) *(G-16438)*

Hergatt Machine Inc 419 589-2931
2530 Pavonia Rd Mansfield (44903) *(G-12623)*

Heritage Bag Company 513 874-3311
4255 Thunderbird Ln West Chester (45014) *(G-19881)*

Heritage Group Inc 330 875-5566
303 S Chapel St Louisville (44641) *(G-12314)*

Heritage Inc 614 860-1185
2087 State Route 256 T Reynoldsburg (43068) *(G-16594)*

Heritage Industrial Finshg Inc 330 798-9840
1874 Englewood Ave Akron (44312) *(G-222)*

Heritage Lounge, Reynoldsburg Also called Heritage Inc *(G-16594)*

Heritage Manufacturing Inc 217 854-2513
1600 E Waterloo Rd Akron (44306) *(G-223)*

Heritage Marble of Ohio Inc 614 436-1464
7086 Huntley Rd Columbus (43229) *(G-7151)*

Heritage Marbles, Columbus Also called Heritage Marble of Ohio Inc *(G-7151)*

Heritage Plas An Atkore Intl, Carrollton Also called Atkore Plastic Pipe Corp *(G-2952)*

Heritage Press Inc 419 289-9209
651 Sandusky St Ashland (44805) *(G-738)*

Heritage Sleep Products LLC 440 437-4425
243 Staley Rd Orwell (44076) *(G-15776)*

Heritage Stone, Sugarcreek Also called Provia Stone LLC *(G-18035)*

Heritage Tool 513 753-7300
6225 N Shadow Hill Way Loveland (45140) *(G-12358)*

Heritage Tool & Manufacturing, Amelia Also called Mark J Myers *(G-579)*

Herman Machine Inc 330 633-3261
252 Northeast Ave Tallmadge (44278) *(G-18145)*

Herman Manufacturing LLC 216 251-6400
13825 Triskett Rd Cleveland (44111) *(G-5504)*

Hermann Pickle Company (PA) 330 527-2696
11964 State Route 88 Garrettsville (44231) *(G-10324)*

Hermetic Seal Technology Inc 513 851-4899
2150 Schappelle Ln Cincinnati (45240) *(G-3880)*

Herold Salads Inc 216 991-7500
17512 Miles Ave Cleveland (44128) *(G-5505)*

Heroux Devtek Landing Gear Div, Strongsville Also called Hdi Landing Gear Usa Inc *(G-17924)*

Herr Foods Incorporated 740 773-8282
476 E 7th St Chillicothe (45601) *(G-3243)*

Herschal Products Inc 330 659-2165
3778 Timberlake Dr Richfield (44286) *(G-16627)*

Hershberger & Sons LLC 937 588-2195
12439 Turley Ln Hillsboro (45133) *(G-11000)*

Hershberger Lawn Structures 330 674-3900
8990 State Route 39 Millersburg (44654) *(G-14221)*

Hershberger Manufacturing 440 272-5555
7584 Rockwood Rd Windsor (44099) *(G-20699)*

Hershbergers Dutch Market LLP 740 489-5322
228 Old National Rd Old Washington (43768) *(G-15671)*

Hershey Creamery Co 937 374-0688
1065 S Columbus St Xenia (45385) *(G-20955)*

Hershey Machine 330 674-2718
5502 State Route 557 Millersburg (44654) *(G-14222)*

Hershy Way Ltd 330 893-2809
5918 County Road 201 Millersburg (44654) *(G-14223)*

Heskamp Printing Co Inc 513 871-6770
5514 Fair Ln Cincinnati (45227) *(G-3881)*

Hesler Machine Tool 937 299-3833
2651 E River Rd Moraine (45439) *(G-14496)*

Hess & Gault Lumber Co 419 281-3105
707 County Road 1302 Ashland (44805) *(G-739)*

Hess Advanced Solutions Llc 937 829-4794
7415 Chambersburg Rd Dayton (45424) *(G-8389)*

Hess Advanced Technology Inc 937 268-4377
7415 Chambersburg Rd Huber Heights (45424) *(G-11148)*

Hess Corporation 740 346-0581
4525 Sunset Blvd Steubenville (43952) *(G-17698)*

Hess Industries Ltd 419 525-4000
108 Sawyer Pkwy Mansfield (44903) *(G-12624)*

Hess Print Solutions, Kent Also called D B Hess Company *(G-11444)*

Hess Print Solutions, Kent Also called Press of Ohio Inc *(G-11506)*

Hess Print Solutions, Kent Also called D B Hess Company *(G-11445)*

Hess Print Solutions, Kent Also called D & J Printing Inc *(G-11443)*

Hess Technologies Inc 513 228-0909
200 Harmon Ave Lebanon (45036) *(G-11808)*

Hexa Americas Inc 937 497-7900
1150 S Vandemark Rd Sidney (45365) *(G-17192)*

Hexagon Industries Inc 216 249-0200
1135 Ivanhoe Rd Cleveland (44110) *(G-5506)*

Hexion Inc (HQ) 614 225-4000
180 E Broad St Fl 26 Columbus (43215) *(G-7152)*

Hexion Inc 614 759-6227
630 Morrison Rd Ste 300 Gahanna (43230) *(G-10210)*

Hexion LLC (HQ) 614 225-4000
180 E Broad St Fl 26 Columbus (43215) *(G-7153)*

Hexpol Compounding LLC 440 834-4644
14330 Kinsman Rd Burton (44021) *(G-2376)*

Hexpol Compounding LLC (HQ) 440 834-4644
14330 Kinsman Rd Burton (44021) *(G-2377)*

Hexpol Polymers, Burton Also called Hexpol Compounding LLC *(G-2377)*

Hf Group LLC (PA) 440 729-2445
8844 Mayfield Rd Chesterland (44026) *(G-3210)*

Hf Group LLC 440 729-9411
8844 Mayfield Rd Chesterland (44026) *(G-3211)*

Hf Group LLC 440 729-9411
8844 Mayfield Rd Chesterland (44026) *(G-3212)*

Hfi LLC (PA) 614 491-0700
59 Gender Rd Canal Winchester (43110) *(G-2525)*

Hfi LLC 614 491-0700
59 Gender Rd Canal Winchester (43110) *(G-2526)*

Hfi Inc 614 491-0700
59 Gender Rd Canal Winchester (43110) *(G-2527)*

Hfi Manufacturing Holdings LLC 614 491-0700
59 Gender Rd Canal Winchester (43110) *(G-2528)*

Hggc Citadel Plas Holdings Inc (HQ) 330 666-3751
3637 Ridgewood Rd Fairlawn (44333) *(G-9752)*

Hhi, Canton Also called Hunter Hydraulics Inc *(G-2732)*

Hhi Company Inc (PA) 330 455-3983
2512 Columbus Rd Ne Canton (44705) *(G-2727)*

HI Carb Corp 216 486-5000
23610 Saint Clair Ave Cleveland (44117) *(G-5507)*

HI Lite Plastic Products 614 235-9050
3760 E 5th Ave Columbus (43219) *(G-7154)*

HI Tech Aero Spares 513 942-4150
9436 Meridian Way West Chester (45069) *(G-19882)*

HI Tech Graphics, Cincinnati Also called Nickum Enterprises Inc *(G-4154)*

HI Tech Tool Corporation 513 346-4061
415 Breaden Dr Ste 1 Monroe (45050) *(G-14404)*

HI Tecmetal Group Inc (PA) 216 881-8100
1101 E 55th St Cleveland (44103) *(G-5508)*

HI Tecmetal Group Inc 440 373-5101
28910 Lakeland Blvd Wickliffe (44092) *(G-20368)*

HI Tecmetal Group Inc 440 946-2280
34800 Lakeland Blvd Willoughby (44095) *(G-20504)*

HI Tecmetal Group Inc 216 941-0440
10601 Briggs Rd Cleveland (44111) *(G-5509)*

HI Tecmetal Group Inc 216 881-8100
1432 E 47th St Cleveland (44103) *(G-5510)*

HI Tek Mold 440 942-4090
7777 Saint Clair Ave Mentor (44060) *(G-13601)*

Hi-Point Firearms, Mansfield Also called Highpoint Firearms *(G-12625)*

Hi-Stat A Stoneridge Co, Lexington Also called Stoneridge Inc *(G-11953)*

Hi-Tech Extrusions Ltd 440 286-4000
12621 Chardon Windsor Rd Chardon (44024) *(G-3156)*

Hi-Tech Solutions LLC 216 331-3050
510 Karl Dr Cleveland (44143) *(G-5511)*

Hi-Tech Wire Inc 419 678-8376
631 E Washington St Saint Henry (45883) *(G-16817)*

Hi-Tek Manufacturing Inc 513 459-1094
6050 Hi Tek Ct Mason (45040) *(G-13037)*

Hi-Vac Corporation 740 374-2306
27895 State Route 7 Marietta (45750) *(G-12790)*

Hiab USA Inc (HQ) 419 482-6000
12233 Williams Rd Perrysburg (43551) *(G-16106)*

Hibbett Sporting Goods Inc 330 837-9272
2010 Lincoln Way E Ste 1 Massillon (44646) *(G-13149)*

Hibbing Taconite A Joint Ventr (PA) 216 694-5700
200 Public Sq Ste 3300 Cleveland (44114) *(G-5512)*

Hibu Inc 614 468-7900
8415 Pulsar Pl Ste 200 Columbus (43240) *(G-6650)*

Hickok Incorporated (PA) 216 541-8060
10514 Dupont Ave Cleveland (44108) *(G-5513)*

Hickory Harvest Foods, Akron Also called Ohio Hickory Harvest Brand Pro *(G-324)*

Hickory Lane Welding, Fredericksburg Also called Chore Anden *(G-10080)*

Hidaka Usa Inc 614 889-8611
5761 Shier Rings Rd Dublin (43016) *(G-9084)*

Hidden View Woodworking 330 674-5196
7826 State Route 241 Millersburg (44654) *(G-14224)*

Higgins Building Mtls No 2 LLC 740 395-5410
2000 Acy Ave Jackson (45640) *(G-11315)*

High Card Industries LLC 330 547-3381
15439 W Akron Canfield Rd Berlin Center (44401) *(G-1655)*

High Concrete Group LLC 937 748-2412
95 Mound Park Dr Springboro (45066) *(G-17483)*

High Definition Tooling, Newcomerstown Also called H3d Tool Corporation *(G-15114)*

High Lvel Fshion Athletes Foot 614 577-8800
5200 E Main St Columbus (43213) *(G-7155)*

High Performance Servo LLC 440 541-3529
1477 E Crossings Pl Westlake (44145) *(G-20276)*

High Production Technology LLC (HQ) 419 591-7000
476 E Riverview Ave Napoleon (43545) *(G-14680)*

High Production Technology LLC 419 599-1511
13068 County Road R Napoleon (43545) *(G-14681)*

ALPHABETIC

High Quality Plastics....419 422-8290
2000 Fostoria Ave Findlay (45840) ***(G-9839)***
High Quality Tools Inc (PA)....440 975-9684
34940 Lakeland Blvd Eastlake (44095) ***(G-9273)***
High Tech Elastomers Inc (PA)....937 236-6575
885 Scholz Dr Vandalia (45377) ***(G-19296)***
High Tech Metal Products LLC....419 227-9414
2300 Central Point Pkwy Lima (45804) ***(G-12024)***
High Tech Mold & Machine Co....330 896-4466
3771 Tabs Dr Uniontown (44685) ***(G-19087)***
High Tech Prfmce Trlrs Inc....440 357-8964
1 High Tech Ave Painesville (44077) ***(G-15888)***
High Temperature Systems Inc....440 543-8271
16755 Park Circle Dr Chagrin Falls (44023) ***(G-3091)***
High-TEC Industrial Services....937 667-1772
15 Industry Park Ct Tipp City (45371) ***(G-18281)***
Highland Computer Forms Inc (PA)....937 393-4215
1025 W Main St Hillsboro (45133) ***(G-11001)***
Highland County Press, Hillsboro *Also called Cameco Communications* ***(G-10997)***
Highland Precision Plating....937 393-9501
6940 State Route 124 Hillsboro (45133) ***(G-11002)***
Highland Products Corp....440 352-4777
9331 Mercantile Dr Mentor (44060) ***(G-13602)***
Highland Stone....937 364-2311
4281 Roush Rd Hillsboro (45133) ***(G-11003)***
Highland Technologies LLC....513 739-3510
630 Harwood Rd Mount Orab (45154) ***(G-14580)***
Highlights For Children Inc....614 486-0631
4555 Lyman Dr Hilliard (43026) ***(G-10951)***
Highlights Press Inc....614 487-2767
1800 Watermark Dr Columbus (43215) ***(G-7156)***
Highline Raceway LLC....419 883-2042
1766 Cassell Rd Butler (44822) ***(G-2391)***
Highpoint Firearms....419 747-9444
1015 Springmill St Mansfield (44906) ***(G-12625)***
Highs Welding Inc....937 464-3029
3065 County Road 150 Belle Center (43310) ***(G-1513)***
Highschoolball Inc....844 472-2551
10143 Royalton Rd North Royalton (44133) ***(G-15425)***
Hightech Signs, Fairfield *Also called Significant Impressions Inc* ***(G-9718)***
Highway Safety Corp....740 387-6991
473 W Fairground St Marion (43302) ***(G-12874)***
Hiland Group Incorporated (PA)....330 499-8404
7600 Supreme St Nw Canton (44720) ***(G-2728)***
Hildreth Mfg LLC....740 375-5832
1657 Cascade Dr Marion (43302) ***(G-12875)***
Hill James R & Hill Earley W....740 591-4203
41085 Townsend Rd Albany (45710) ***(G-480)***
Hill & Associates Inc....740 685-5168
132 S 6th St Byesville (43723) ***(G-2403)***
Hill & Griffith Company (PA)....513 921-1075
1085 Summer St Cincinnati (45204) ***(G-3882)***
Hill Bryce Concrete, Springfield *Also called Dearth Resources Inc* ***(G-17539)***
Hill John....419 727-8666
3019 E Manhattan Blvd Toledo (43611) ***(G-18508)***
Hill Manufacturing Inc....419 335-5006
318 W Chestnut St Wauseon (43567) ***(G-19682)***
Hill-Rom Holdings Inc....937 604-6019
1273 N Cole St Lima (45801) ***(G-12025)***
Hillcrest....740 824-4849
31580 Township Rd Brinkhaven (43006) ***(G-2097)***
Hillcrest Lumber Ltd....330 359-5721
8669 Zuercher Rd Apple Creek (44606) ***(G-639)***
Hilleary-Whitaker Inc....614 766-4694
2646 Billingsley Rd Columbus (43235) ***(G-7157)***
Hilles Burial Vaults Inc....330 823-2251
2145 S Union Ave Alliance (44601) ***(G-514)***
Hilliard Cat Shack LLC....614 527-9711
5484 Pearson Ct Hilliard (43026) ***(G-10952)***
Hillman Fastener....513 851-6200
10590 Hamilton Ave Cincinnati (45231) ***(G-3883)***
Hillman Group Inc....800 800-4900
12400 Plaza Dr Parma (44130) ***(G-15962)***
Hillman Precision Inc....419 289-1557
462 E 9th St Ste 1 Ashland (44805) ***(G-740)***
Hillside Pallet....440 272-5425
8552 Cox Rd Windsor (44099) ***(G-20700)***
Hillside Winery....419 456-3108
221 Main St Gilboa (45875) ***(G-10379)***
Hillside Wood Ltd....330 359-5991
8413 Township Road 652 Millersburg (44654) ***(G-14225)***
Hilltop Basic Resources Inc (PA)....513 651-5000
1 W 4th St Ste 1100 Cincinnati (45202) ***(G-3884)***
Hilltop Basic Resources Inc....937 878-8631
5325 Medway Rd Fairborn (45324) ***(G-9624)***
Hilltop Basic Resources Inc....937 882-6357
1665 Enon Rd Springfield (45502) ***(G-17573)***
Hilltop Basic Resources Inc....937 859-3616
4710 Soldiers Home W Miamisburg (45342) ***(G-13817)***
Hilltop Basic Resources Inc....513 621-1500
511 W Water St Cincinnati (45202) ***(G-3885)***
Hilltop Concrete, Cincinnati *Also called Hilltop Basic Resources Inc* ***(G-3884)***
Hilltop Concrete, Cincinnati *Also called Hilltop Basic Resources Inc* ***(G-3885)***
Hilltop Energy Inc....330 859-2108
6978 Lindentree Rd Ne Mineral City (44656) ***(G-14301)***
Hilltop Printing....419 782-9898
1815 Baltimore St Defiance (43512) ***(G-8793)***
Hilltop Stone Llc....513 651-5000
1 W 4th St Ste 1100 Cincinnati (45202) ***(G-3886)***
Hilo Tech Inc....440 979-1155
31532 Lorain Rd North Olmsted (44070) ***(G-15339)***
Hilti Inc....614 258-8384
818 N Rose Ave Columbus (43219) ***(G-7158)***
Hinchcliff Lumber Company....440 238-5200
13550 Falling Water Rd # 105 Strongsville (44136) ***(G-17925)***
Hinchcliff Products Co, Strongsville *Also called Hinchcliff Lumber Company* ***(G-17925)***
Hinckley Wood Products....330 220-9999
1545 W 130th St Hinckley (44233) ***(G-11025)***
Hines Builders Inc....937 335-4586
1587 Lytle Rd Troy (45373) ***(G-18834)***
Hines Specialty Vehicle Group, New Philadelphia *Also called Kimble Mixer Company* ***(G-14907)***
Hinkle Fine Foods Inc....937 836-3665
130 Harrisburg Dr Englewood (45322) ***(G-9523)***
Hinkle Manufacturing Inc....419 666-5550
348 5th St Perrysburg (43551) ***(G-16107)***
Hinkley Lighting Inc (PA)....216 671-3132
33000 Pin Oak Pkwy Avon Lake (44012) ***(G-1033)***
Hipsy LLC....513 403-5333
4951 Dixie Hwy Fairfield (45014) ***(G-9665)***
Hirons Memorial Works Inc....937 444-2917
14950 Us Highway 68 Mount Orab (45154) ***(G-14581)***
Hirschvogel Incorporated....614 340-5657
2230 S 3rd St Columbus (43207) ***(G-7159)***
Hirt Publishing Co Inc....419 946-3010
245 Neal Ave Ste A Mount Gilead (43338) ***(G-14562)***
Hirt Publishing Co Inc (PA)....419 523-5709
224 E Main St Ottawa (45875) ***(G-15794)***
Hirt Publishing Co Inc....419 523-5709
224 E Main St Ottawa (45875) ***(G-15795)***
Hirzel Canning Company....419 287-3288
115 Columbus St Pemberville (43450) ***(G-16028)***
Hirzel Canning Company (PA)....419 693-0531
411 Lemoyne Rd Northwood (43619) ***(G-15482)***
Hirzel Canning Company....419 523-3225
325 E Williamstown Rd Ottawa (45875) ***(G-15796)***
Hisey Bells....740 333-7669
581 Capps Rd Greenfield (45123) ***(G-10480)***
Hit Trophy Inc....419 445-5356
4989 State Route 66 Archbold (43502) ***(G-681)***
Hitch-Hiker Mfg Inc....330 542-3052
10065 Rapp Rd New Middletown (44442) ***(G-14877)***
Hite Parts Exchange Inc....614 272-5115
2235 Mckinley Ave Columbus (43204) ***(G-7160)***
Hitech Shapes & Designs, Cincinnati *Also called Seilkop Industries Inc* ***(G-4399)***
Hitti Enterprises Inc....440 243-4100
6427 Eastland Rd Cleveland (44142) ***(G-5514)***
HJ Heinz Company LP....330 837-8331
1301 Oberlin Ave Sw Massillon (44647) ***(G-13150)***
Hj Systems Inc....614 351-9777
230 N Central Ave Columbus (43222) ***(G-7161)***
HK Engine Components LLC (HQ)....330 830-3500
800 Nave Rd Se Massillon (44646) ***(G-13151)***
HK Technologies....330 337-9710
2828 Clinton Ave Cleveland (44113) ***(G-5515)***
Hkm Drect Mkt Cmmnications Inc (PA)....216 651-9500
5501 Cass Ave Cleveland (44102) ***(G-5516)***
Hkm Drect Mkt Cmmnications Inc....440 934-3060
2931 Abbe Rd Sheffield Village (44054) ***(G-17122)***
Hkm Drect Mkt Cmmnications Inc....330 395-9538
5501 Cass Ave Cleveland (44102) ***(G-5517)***
Hl Oilfield Services LLC....740 783-1156
19797 Harl Weiller Rd Caldwell (43724) ***(G-2427)***
HM Wire International Inc....330 244-8501
2125 46th St Nw Canton (44709) ***(G-2729)***
Hmb Information Sys Developers, Westerville *Also called Harris Mackessy & Brennan* ***(G-20157)***
Hmf Engineering Inc....216 631-6980
5111 W 164th St Cleveland (44142) ***(G-5518)***
Hmf Racing, Cleveland *Also called Hmf Engineering Inc* ***(G-5518)***
Hmi Industries Inc (PA)....440 846-7800
13325 Darice Pkwy Unit A Strongsville (44149) ***(G-17926)***
HMS Industries LLC....440 899-0001
27995 Ranney Pkwy Westlake (44145) ***(G-20277)***
Hmt Associates Inc....216 369-0109
335 Treeworth Blvd Broadview Heights (44147) ***(G-2110)***
Hmt Inc (PA)....440 599-7005
360 Commerce St Conneaut (44030) ***(G-7808)***

Hob Enterprises LLC......440 290-8861
8255 Mentor Ave Mentor (44060) *(G-13603)*
Hobart, Hillsboro *Also called Illinois Tool Works Inc (G-11004)*
Hobart, Troy *Also called ITW Food Equipment Group LLC (G-18848)*
Hobart Bros Stick Electrode......937 332-5375
101 Trade Sq E Troy (45373) *(G-18835)*
Hobart Brothers Company (HQ)......937 332-5439
101 Trade Sq E Troy (45373) *(G-18836)*
Hobart Brothers Company......937 773-5869
8585 Industry Park Dr Piqua (45356) *(G-16276)*
Hobart Brothers Company......937 332-5338
400 Trade Sq E Troy (45373) *(G-18837)*
Hobart Brothers Company......937 332-5023
1260 Bruckner Dr Troy (45373) *(G-18838)*
Hobart Cabinet Company......937 335-4666
301 E Water St Troy (45373) *(G-18839)*
Hobart Corporation......937 332-3000
401 S Market St Troy (45373) *(G-18840)*
Hobart Corporation......937 335-7171
701 S Ridge Ave Troy (45374) *(G-18841)*
Hobart Corporation......937 332-2797
8515 Industry Park Dr Piqua (45356) *(G-16277)*
Hobart International Holdings (HQ)......937 332-3000
701 S Ridge Ave Troy (45373) *(G-18842)*
Hobart Sales & Service, Akron *Also called Harry C Lobalzo & Sons Inc (G-216)*
Hobby Printing, Dayton *Also called Oscar Hicks (G-8553)*
Hochstetler Milling LLC......419 368-0004
552 State Route 95 Loudonville (44842) *(G-12298)*
Hochstetler Wood......330 893-2384
6791 County Road 77 Millersburg (44654) *(G-14226)*
Hochstetler Wood Ltd......330 893-1601
6791 County Road 77 Millersburg (44654) *(G-14227)*
Hocker Tool and Die Inc......937 274-3443
5161 Webster St Dayton (45414) *(G-8390)*
Hocking Hills Energy & Well SE......740 385-6690
32919 Logan Horns Mill Rd Logan (43138) *(G-12176)*
Hocking Hills Hardwoods, Laurelville *Also called T & D Thompson Inc (G-11772)*
Hocking Valley Concrete Inc (PA)......740 385-2165
35255 Hocking Dr Logan (43138) *(G-12177)*
Hocking Valley Concrete Inc......740 385-2165
35255 Hocking Dr Logan (43138) *(G-12178)*
Hoehnes Custom Woodworking......937 693-8008
9600 Amsterdam Rd Anna (45302) *(G-623)*
Hofacker Prcsion Machining LLC......937 832-7712
7560 Jacks Ln Clayton (45315) *(G-4659)*
Hoffee John......330 868-3553
207 N Market St Minerva (44657) *(G-14325)*
Hoffman Machining & Repair LLC......419 547-9204
1744 W Mcpherson Hwy Clyde (43410) *(G-6540)*
Hoffman Meat Processing......419 864-3994
157 S 4th St Cardington (43315) *(G-2911)*
Hoffmans Country Market......740 216-0115
685 E Front St Logan (43138) *(G-12179)*
Hofmanns Lures Inc......937 684-0338
5350 State Route 47 Ansonia (45303) *(G-625)*
Hogan Awning Inc......440 352-4033
503 Lake Shore Blvd Grand River (44045) *(G-10450)*
Hoge Brush, New Knoxville *Also called Hoge Lumber Company (G-14836)*
Hoge Lumber Company (PA)......419 753-2263
701 S Main St State New Knoxville (45871) *(G-14836)*
Hoge Lumber Company......419 753-2351
202 E South St New Knoxville (45871) *(G-14837)*
Hoist Equipment Co Inc (PA)......440 232-0300
26161 Cannon Rd Bedford Heights (44146) *(G-1486)*
Hoistech LLC......440 327-5379
5131 Mills Indus Pkwy North Ridgeville (44039) *(G-15379)*
Holdren Brothers Inc......937 465-7050
301 Runkle St West Liberty (43357) *(G-20092)*
Holdsworth Industrial Fabg......330 874-3945
10407 Welton Rd Ne Bolivar (44612) *(G-1936)*
Hole Hunter Golf Driving Range, Piqua *Also called Hole Hunter Golf Inc (G-16278)*
Hole Hunter Golf Inc......937 339-5833
438 S Downing St Piqua (45356) *(G-16278)*
Holes Custom Woodworking......419 586-8171
6875 Nancy Ave Celina (45822) *(G-3002)*
Holgate Metal Fab Inc......419 599-2000
555 Independence Dr Napoleon (43545) *(G-14682)*
Holiday Hmes Rvrview Crossings, Harrison *Also called Holiday Homes Inc (G-10782)*
Holiday Homes Inc......513 353-9777
10620 Sand Run Rd Harrison (45030) *(G-10782)*
Holistic Foods Herbs and Books, Columbus *Also called B&A Holstic Food and Herbs (G-6797)*
Hollaender Manufacturing Co......513 772-8800
10285 Wayne Ave Cincinnati (45215) *(G-3887)*
Holland Assocts LLC DBA Archou......513 891-0006
316 W 4th St Ste 201 Cincinnati (45202) *(G-3888)*
Holland Engineering Co, Toledo *Also called Holland Engraving Company (G-18509)*
Holland Engraving Company......419 865-2765
7340 Dorr St Toledo (43615) *(G-18509)*
Holland Grills Distributing, Spencerville *Also called S I Distributing Inc (G-17465)*
Holland Springfield Journal......419 874-2528
117 E 2nd St Perrysburg (43551) *(G-16108)*
Hollingsworth Signs Inc......614 875-2825
4423 Broadway Grove City (43123) *(G-10562)*
Hollingswrth Otdoor Buying Svc, Grove City *Also called Hollingsworth Signs Inc (G-10562)*
Hollmann Inc......513 522-1800
1617 W Belmar Pl Cincinnati (45224) *(G-3889)*
Hollow Boring Inc......440 951-2929
7832 Enterprise Dr Mentor (44060) *(G-13604)*
Hollphane, Newark *Also called Acuity Brands Lighting Inc (G-14980)*
Hollys Custom Print Inc......740 928-2697
1001 O Neill Dr Hebron (43025) *(G-10871)*
Hollywood Family Eye Care......740 264-1220
276 S Hollywood Blvd Steubenville (43952) *(G-17699)*
Hollywood Gaming At Dayton RAC......937 235-7800
777 Hollywood Blvd Dayton (45414) *(G-8391)*
Hollywood Imprints LLC......614 501-6040
1000 Morrison Rd Ste D Gahanna (43230) *(G-10211)*
Holm Industries Inc......330 562-2900
1300 Danner Dr Aurora (44202) *(G-925)*
Holmbury Inc......440 578-1070
33801 Curtis Blvd Ste 104 Eastlake (44095) *(G-9274)*
Holmco Division, Winesburg *Also called Robin Industries Inc (G-20707)*
Holmes By Products Co......330 893-2322
3175 Township Road 411 Millersburg (44654) *(G-14228)*
Holmes Cheese Co......330 674-6451
9444 State Route 39 Millersburg (44654) *(G-14229)*
Holmes County Hub Inc......330 674-1811
25 N Clay St Millersburg (44654) *(G-14230)*
Holmes Limestone Co (PA)......330 893-2721
4255 State Rte 39 Berlin (44610) *(G-1649)*
Holmes Lumber & Bldg Ctr Inc......330 674-9060
6139 Hc 39 Millersburg (44654) *(G-14231)*
Holmes Lumber & Supply, Millersburg *Also called Holmes Lumber & Bldg Ctr Inc (G-14231)*
Holmes Panel......330 897-5040
3052 State Route 557 Baltic (43804) *(G-1074)*
Holmes Prcut/Troyer Imprinting......330 359-0000
7540 Peabody Kent Rd Dundee (44624) *(G-9173)*
Holmes Printing, Springfield *Also called Holmes W & Sons Printing (G-17574)*
Holmes Printing Solutions LLC......330 234-9699
8757 County Road 77 Fredericksburg (44627) *(G-10087)*
Holmes Stair Parts Ltd......330 279-2797
8614 Township Road 561 Holmesville (44633) *(G-11104)*
Holmes Supply Corp......330 279-2634
7571 State Route 83 Holmesville (44633) *(G-11105)*
Holmes W & Sons Printing......937 325-1509
401 E Columbia St Springfield (45503) *(G-17574)*
Holmes Wheel Shop Inc......330 279-2891
7969 County Road 189 Holmesville (44633) *(G-11106)*
Holophane Corporation......740 349-4194
515 Mckinley Ave Newark (43055) *(G-15018)*
Holophane Corporation (HQ)......866 759-1577
3825 Columbus Rd Bldg A Granville (43023) *(G-10459)*
Holophane Lighting......330 823-5535
12720 Beech St Ne Alliance (44601) *(G-515)*
Holte Eyeware......513 321-4000
2651 Observatory Ave # 1 Cincinnati (45208) *(G-3890)*
Holtgreven Scale & Elec Corp......419 422-4779
420 E Lincoln St Findlay (45840) *(G-9840)*
Holthaus Lackner Signs, Cincinnati *Also called Gus Holthaus Signs Inc (G-3858)*
Homan Metals LLC......513 721-5010
1253 Knowlton St Cincinnati (45223) *(G-3891)*
Home Bakery......419 678-3018
109 W Main St Coldwater (45828) *(G-6564)*
Home Care Products LLC (HQ)......919 693-1002
7160 Chagrin Rd Ste 220 Chagrin Falls (44023) *(G-3092)*
Home City Ice......859 441-1700
701 Us Highway 52 Aberdeen (45101) *(G-1)*
Home City Ice Company (PA)......513 574-1800
6045 Bridgetown Rd Ste 1 Cincinnati (45248) *(G-3892)*
Home City Ice Company......614 836-2877
4505 S Hamilton Rd Groveport (43125) *(G-10625)*
Home City Ice Company......513 851-4040
11920 Kemper Springs Dr Cincinnati (45240) *(G-3893)*
Home City Ice Company......937 461-6028
1020 Gateway Dr Dayton (45404) *(G-8392)*
Home City Ice Company......216 429-0535
10000 Broadway Ave Cleveland (44125) *(G-5519)*
Home City Ice Company......419 562-4953
150 Johnson Dr Delaware (43015) *(G-8860)*
Home City Ice Company......440 439-5001
20282 Hannan Pkwy Bedford (44146) *(G-1429)*
Home Idea Center Inc......419 375-4951
1100 Commerce St Fort Recovery (45846) *(G-9954)*
Home Pro, Columbus *Also called Certified Walk In Tubs (G-6921)*
Home Quarters North Canto......330 806-5336
717 S Main St North Canton (44720) *(G-15240)*

A L P H A B E T I C

(PA)=Parent Co (HQ)=Headquarters (DH)=Div Headquarters

Home Resolver 440 886-6758
   11121 Magdala Dr Cleveland (44130) *(G-5520)*

Home Service Station Inc 419 678-2612
   116 S 1st St Coldwater (45828) *(G-6565)*

Home Sheet Metal & Roofing Co 419 562-7806
   211 W Galen St Bucyrus (44820) *(G-2348)*

Home Stor & Off Solutions Inc 216 362-4660
   5305 Commerce Pkwy W Cleveland (44130) *(G-5521)*

Homecare Mattress Inc 937 746-2556
   303 Conover Dr Franklin (45005) *(G-10027)*

Homeguard Building Products, Baltimore *Also called Homeguard Products Inc (G-1083)*

Homeguard Products Inc (PA) 616 846-0804
   6797 Thoreau Ln Ne Baltimore (43105) *(G-1083)*

Homeland AG Fuels LLC 216 763-1004
   25700 Science Park Dr # 210 Cleveland (44122) *(G-5522)*

Homer G Waller Jr 330 788-4023
   3142 Southern Blvd Youngstown (44507) *(G-21108)*

Homestat Farm Ltd (PA) 614 718-3060
   6065 Frantz Rd Ste 206 Dublin (43017) *(G-9085)*

Homestead Collections 419 422-8286
   11300 Township Rd 99 Findlay (45840) *(G-9841)*

Homestretch Inc 419 738-6604
   203 E Auglaize St Wapakoneta (45895) *(G-19488)*

Homestretch Sportswear Inc 419 678-4282
   491 S Eastern Ave Saint Henry (45883) *(G-16818)*

Homewood Press Inc 419 478-0695
   400 E State Line Rd Toledo (43612) *(G-18510)*

Homeworth Fabrications & Mchs 330 525-5459
   23094 Georgetown Rd Homeworth (44634) *(G-11116)*

Homeworth Sales Service Div, Homeworth *Also called Ohio Drill & Tool Co (G-11117)*

Honda Engineering N Amer Inc 937 642-5000
   24000 Honda Pkwy Marysville (43040) *(G-12948)*

Honda Engineering NA Inc 937 707-5357
   24000 Honda Pkwy Marysville (43040) *(G-12949)*

Honda of America Mfg Inc (HQ) 937 642-5000
   24000 Honda Pkwy Marysville (43040) *(G-12950)*

Honda of America Mfg Inc 937 644-0724
   19900 State Route 739 Marysville (43040) *(G-12951)*

Honda of America Mfg Inc 937 642-5000
   25000 Honda Pkwy Marysville (43040) *(G-12952)*

Honda Support Office, Marysville *Also called Honda of America Mfg Inc (G-12951)*

Honda Transm Mfg Amer Inc 937 843-5555
   6964 State Route 235 N Russells Point (43348) *(G-16754)*

Honey Baked Ham 8401, Cincinnati *Also called Honey Baked Ham Company LLC (G-3894)*

Honey Baked Ham Company LLC 513 474-0022
   8315 Beechmont Ave Ste 41 Cincinnati (45255) *(G-3894)*

Honey Cell Inc Mid West 513 360-0280
   6480 Hamilton Lebanon Rd Monroe (45044) *(G-14405)*

Honey Gold Company 330 688-5502
   152 E Main St Kent (44240) *(G-11470)*

Honeybaked Ham Company (PA) 513 583-9700
   11935 Mason Montgomery Rd # 200 Cincinnati (45249) *(G-3895)*

Honeymoon Paper Products Inc (PA) 513 755-7200
   7100 Dixie Hwy Fairfield (45014) *(G-9666)*

Honeywell, Lancaster *Also called Diamond Electronics Inc (G-11706)*

Honeywell, Urbana *Also called Grimes Aerospace Company (G-19158)*

Honeywell, Perrysburg *Also called Fram Group Operations LLC (G-16097)*

Honeywell 614 850-8228
   2199 Dividend Dr Columbus (43228) *(G-7162)*

Honeywell First Responder Pdts, Dayton *Also called Morning Pride Mfg LLC (G-8508)*

Honeywell Inc 513 272-1111
   3940 Virginia Ave Cincinnati (45227) *(G-3896)*

Honeywell International Inc 216 459-6048
   950 Keynote Cir Ste 90 Independence (44131) *(G-11259)*

Honeywell International Inc 440 349-7330
   5935 Stephanie Ln Solon (44139) *(G-17310)*

Honeywell International Inc 216 682-1600
   6060 Rockside Woods Blvd Cleveland (44131) *(G-5523)*

Honeywell International Inc 614 850-5000
   2080 Arlingate Ln Columbus (43228) *(G-7163)*

Honeywell International Inc 937 484-2000
   550 State Route 55 Urbana (43078) *(G-19162)*

Honeywell International Inc 513 745-7200
   1280 Kemper Meadow Dr Cincinnati (45240) *(G-3897)*

Honeywell International Inc 614 850-5000
   2080 Arlingate Ln Columbus (43228) *(G-7164)*

Honeywell International Inc 937 754-4134
   1232 Dytn Yllow Sprng Rd Fairborn (45324) *(G-9625)*

Honeywell Lebow Products 614 850-5000
   2080 Arlingate Ln Columbus (43228) *(G-7165)*

Honeywell Lightning & Elec, Urbana *Also called Grimes Aerospace Company (G-19159)*

Honeywell Senfopec, Columbus *Also called Honeywell Lebow Products (G-7165)*

Hood Packaging Corporation 937 382-6681
   1961 Rombach Ave Wilmington (45177) *(G-20669)*

Hookah Rush 614 267-6463
   2422 N High St Columbus (43202) *(G-7166)*

Hoopes Fertilizer Works Inc (PA) 330 894-2121
   24104 Us Route 30 East Rochester (44625) *(G-9250)*

Hoopes Fertilizer Works Inc 330 821-3550
   9866 Freshley Ave Ne # 166 Alliance (44601) *(G-516)*

Hoot and Holler,, Cincinnati *Also called Owl Be Sweatin (G-4205)*

Hooven - Dayton Corp (PA) 937 233-4473
   511 Byers Rd Miamisburg (45342) *(G-13818)*

Hoover & Wells Inc 419 691-9220
   2011 Seaman St Toledo (43605) *(G-18511)*

Hoover Group 419 525-3159
   411 Eby Rd Shiloh (44878) *(G-17149)*

Hoover Inc 330 499-9200
   8200 Freedom Ave Nw Canton (44720) *(G-2730)*

Hopco Resources Inc 614 882-8533
   2829 E Dblin Granville Rd Columbus (43231) *(G-7167)*

Hope Timber & Marketing Group (PA) 740 344-1788
   141 Union St Newark (43055) *(G-15019)*

Hope Timber Mulch Inc 740 344-1788
   141 Union St Newark (43055) *(G-15020)*

Hope Timber Pallet Recycl Inc 740 344-1788
   141 Union St Newark (43055) *(G-15021)*

Hopedale Mining LLC 740 937-2225
   86900 Sinfield Rd Hopedale (43976) *(G-11118)*

Hopewell Industries Inc (PA) 740 622-3563
   637 Chestnut St Coshocton (43812) *(G-7895)*

Hopewell Oil & Gas Dev Co 740 452-9326
   1615 W Main St Zanesville (43701) *(G-21319)*

Hopewell Oil and Gas, Zanesville *Also called Zane Petroleum Inc (G-21366)*

Hopewood Inc 330 359-5656
   8087 Township Road 652 Millersburg (44654) *(G-14232)*

Hoppel Fabrication Specialties 330 823-5700
   9481 Columbus Rd Ste 1 Louisville (44641) *(G-12315)*

Hord Elevator LLC 419 562-5934
   1016 State Route 98 Bucyrus (44820) *(G-2349)*

Horizon Communications Inc 330 968-6959
   8870 Darrow Rd Ste F106 Twinsburg (44087) *(G-18955)*

Horizon Global Americas Inc 440 498-0001
   29000 Aurora Rd Ste 2 Solon (44139) *(G-17311)*

Horizon Industries Corp 937 323-0801
   1801 W Columbia St Springfield (45504) *(G-17575)*

Horizon Metals Inc 440 235-3338
   8059 Lewis Rd Ste 102 Berea (44017) *(G-1618)*

Horizon Ohio Publications Inc (HQ) 419 394-7414
   102 E Spring St Saint Marys (45885) *(G-16840)*

Horizon Ohio Publications Inc 419 738-2128
   520 Industrial Dr Wapakoneta (45895) *(G-19489)*

Horizon Publications Inc 419 628-2369
   326 N Main St Ste 200 Minster (45865) *(G-14355)*

Horizon Publications Inc 419 738-2128
   520 Industrial Dr Wapakoneta (45895) *(G-19490)*

Horizons Inc Camcode Division 216 714-0020
   18531 S Miles Rd Cleveland (44128) *(G-5524)*

Horizons Incorporated (PA) 216 475-0555
   18531 S Miles Rd Cleveland (44128) *(G-5525)*

Horizontal Eqp Manufactoring 330 264-2229
   3310 Columbus Rd Wooster (44691) *(G-20784)*

Hormel Foods Corp Svcs LLC 513 563-0211
   4055 Executive Park Dr # 300 Cincinnati (45241) *(G-3898)*

Hornell Brewing Co Inc 516 812-0384
   644 Linn St Ste 318 Cincinnati (45203) *(G-3899)*

Horner Industrial Services Inc 937 390-6667
   5330 Prosperity Dr Springfield (45502) *(G-17576)*

Horner Industrial Services Inc 513 874-8722
   4721 Interstate Dr West Chester (45246) *(G-20014)*

Horning Steel Co 330 633-0028
   167 Southwest Ave Tallmadge (44278) *(G-18146)*

Horsburgh & Scott Co (PA) 216 432-5858
   5114 Hamilton Ave Cleveland (44114) *(G-5526)*

Horsburgh & Scott Co 216 383-2909
   1441 Chardon Rd Cleveland (44117) *(G-5527)*

Horsemens Pride Inc 800 232-7950
   10008 State Route 43 Streetsboro (44241) *(G-17857)*

Horseshoe Drive Thru, Danville *Also called Lynn Lyons (G-8089)*

Horst Packing Inc 330 482-2997
   3535 Renkenberger Rd Columbiana (44408) *(G-6620)*

Horton Emergency Vehicles, Grove City *Also called Halcore Group Inc (G-10561)*

Horton Enterprises Inc 614 539-8181
   3800 Mcdowell Rd Grove City (43123) *(G-10563)*

Horwitz & Pintis Co 419 666-2220
   1604 Tracy St Toledo (43605) *(G-18512)*

Hosler Maps Inc 937 855-4173
   115 N Plum St Germantown (45327) *(G-10369)*

Hospeco, Richmond Heights *Also called Tranzonic Companies (G-16657)*

Hostar International Inc (PA) 440 564-5362
   15000 Cross Creek Pkwy Newbury (44065) *(G-15095)*

Hostar International Inc 440 564-5362
   15000 Cross Creek Pkwy Newbury (44065) *(G-15096)*

Hoster Graphics Company Inc 614 299-9770
   1349 Delashmut Ave Columbus (43212) *(G-7168)*

Hot Cards.com, Cleveland *Also called Fx Digital Media Inc (G-5387)*

HOT Graphic Services Inc 419 242-7000
   2595 Tracy Rd Northwood (43619) *(G-15483)*

Hot Mama Foods Inc 419 474-3402
5839 Secor Rd Toledo (43623) *(G-18513)*

Hot Sauce Williams Barbecue, Cleveland *Also called Buckeye Sauce Corporation (G-4944)*

Hot Shot Motor Works M LLC 419 294-1997
555 S Warpole St Rear Upper Sandusky (43351) *(G-19125)*

Hot Spot 740 947-8888
800 W 2nd St Waverly (45690) *(G-19711)*

Hotcardscom Inc (PA) 216 241-4040
2400 Superior Ave E Cleveland (44114) *(G-5528)*

Hotend Works Inc 440 787-3181
18153 Indian Hollow Rd Grafton (44044) *(G-10430)*

House of 10000 Picture Frames 937 254-5541
2210 Wilmington Pike Dayton (45420) *(G-8393)*

House of Awards and Sports 419 422-7877
419 N Main St Findlay (45840) *(G-9842)*

House of Blinds and More, Mentor *Also called Hob Enterprises LLC (G-13603)*

House of Delara Fragrances 216 651-5803
1810 W 47th St Cleveland (44102) *(G-5529)*

House of Hindenach 419 422-0392
408 N Main St Findlay (45840) *(G-9843)*

House of Plastics, Cleveland *Also called HP Manufacturing Company Inc (G-5530)*

House Silva-Strongsville Inc 330 464-6419
Al156 Southpark Mall Al Strongsville (44136) *(G-17927)*

Housetrends 513 794-4103
4601 Malsbary Rd 104 Blue Ash (45242) *(G-1809)*

Housing & Emrgncy Lgstcs Plnnr 209 201-7511
36905 State Route 30 Lisbon (44432) *(G-12122)*

Houston Machine Products Inc 937 322-8022
1065 W Leffel Ln Springfield (45506) *(G-17577)*

Howard & Blake Excavating LLC 740 701-7938
1030 Main St Richmond Dale (45673) *(G-16650)*

Howard B Claflin Co 330 928-1704
2475 2nd St Cuyahoga Falls (44221) *(G-8009)*

Howard Grant Corporation 330 743-3151
316 Alexander St Youngstown (44502) *(G-21109)*

Howden American Fan Company (HQ) 513 773-0103
2933 Symmes Rd Fairfield (45014) *(G-9667)*

Howden North America Inc 330 867-8540
260 Springside Dr Akron (44333) *(G-224)*

Howden North America Inc 330 721-7374
935 Heritage Dr Medina (44256) *(G-13422)*

Howden North America Inc 330 723-0492
411 Independence Dr Medina (44256) *(G-13423)*

Howland Machine Corp 330 544-4029
947 Summit Ave Niles (44446) *(G-15158)*

Howland Printing Inc 330 637-8255
3117 Niles Cortland Rd Ne Cortland (44410) *(G-7869)*

Howmet Aluminum Casting Inc (HQ) 216 641-4340
1600 Harvard Ave Newburgh Heights (44105) *(G-15072)*

Howmet Castings & Services Inc (HQ) 216 641-4400
1616 Harvard Ave Newburgh Heights (44105) *(G-15073)*

Howmet Corporation (HQ) 800 242-9898
1616 Harvard Ave Newburgh Heights (44105) *(G-15074)*

Hoya Optical Labs 440 239-1924
869 W Bagley Rd Berea (44017) *(G-1619)*

HP Inc 513 956-4253
4440 Lake Forest Dr # 100 Blue Ash (45242) *(G-1810)*

HP Manufacturing Company Inc (PA) 216 361-6500
3705 Carnegie Ave Cleveland (44115) *(G-5530)*

Hp2g LLC 419 906-1525
2611 Scott St Napoleon Napoleon (43545) *(G-14683)*

Hpc Holdings LLC (HQ) 330 666-3751
3637 Ridgewood Rd Fairlawn (44333) *(G-9753)*

Hpc Manufacturing Inc 440 322-8334
7405 Industrial Pkwy Dr Lorain (44053) *(G-12249)*

Hpl Stampings Inc 440 582-9794
4949 Galaxy Pkwy Ste W Cleveland (44128) *(G-5531)*

HPM Business Systems Inc 216 520-1330
21887 Lorain Rd 300 Cleveland (44126) *(G-5532)*

HPM North America Corp 740 382-5600
1193 Pole Lane Rd Marion (43302) *(G-12876)*

Hr Machine LLC 937 222-7644
2972 Homeway Dr Beavercreek (45434) *(G-1345)*

Hr Parts N Stuff 330 947-2433
2002 Industry Rd Atwater (44201) *(G-898)*

Hrh Door Corp (PA) 850 208-3400
1 Door Dr Mount Hope (44660) *(G-14572)*

Hrh Door Corp 513 674-9300
2136 Stapleton Ct Cincinnati (45240) *(G-3900)*

Hrh Door Corp 330 896-2175
4577 Tr 634 Millersburg (44654) *(G-14233)*

Hrh Door Corp 330 828-2291
14512 Lincoln Way E Dalton (44618) *(G-8070)*

Hrh Door Corp 440 593-5226
1001 Chamberlain Blvd Conneaut (44030) *(G-7809)*

Hsm Wire International Inc 330 244-8501
820 S Valley Blvd Nw North Canton (44720) *(G-15241)*

Hst, Cincinnati *Also called Hermetic Seal Technology Inc (G-3880)*

Htci Co 937 845-1204
12170 Milton Carlisle Rd New Carlisle (45344) *(G-14802)*

Htec Systems Inc 937 438-3010
561 Congress Park Dr Dayton (45459) *(G-8394)*

Hub Plastics Inc 614 861-1791
725 Reynoldsburg New Blacklick (43004) *(G-1698)*

Hubbard Company 419 784-4455
612 Clinton St Defiance (43512) *(G-8794)*

Hubbard Feeds, Botkins *Also called Ridley USA Inc (G-1953)*

Hubbard Feeds, Botkins *Also called Ridley USA Inc (G-1954)*

Hubbard Publishing Co 937 592-3060
127 E Chillicothe Ave Bellefontaine (43311) *(G-1533)*

Hubbell Incorporated 330 335-2361
8711 Wadsworth Rd Wadsworth (44281) *(G-19410)*

Hubbell Machine Tooling Inc 216 524-1797
7507 Exchange St Cleveland (44125) *(G-5533)*

Huber Heights Courier, Dayton *Also called Suburban Newpapers of Dayton (G-8686)*

Huber Heights License Bureau 937 233-7560
6134 Chambersburg Rd Dayton (45424) *(G-8395)*

Hubert Enterprises Inc 513 367-8600
9555 Dry Fork Rd Harrison (45030) *(G-10783)*

Hudak Machine & Tool Inc 440 366-8955
144 Eady Ct Elyria (44035) *(G-9429)*

Hudco Manufacturing Inc 440 951-4040
38250 Western Pkwy Willoughby (44094) *(G-20505)*

Hudecek Cement Inc 216 676-0362
6678 Big Creek Pkwy Cleveland (44130) *(G-5534)*

Hudson Access Group II 330 283-6214
2460 Bramfield Way Hudson (44236) *(G-11179)*

Hudson Drilling, Hillsboro *Also called Tom Hudson (G-11016)*

Hudson Extrusions Inc 330 653-6015
1255 Norton Rd Hudson (44236) *(G-11180)*

Hudson Fasteners Inc 330 270-9500
241 W Federal St 512 Youngstown (44503) *(G-21110)*

Hudson Feeds, Okolona *Also called Republic Mills Inc (G-15669)*

Hudson Leather Ltd 419 485-8531
14700 State Route 15 Pioneer (43554) *(G-16234)*

Hudson Leather Co, Pioneer *Also called Hudson Leather Ltd (G-16234)*

Hudson Printing of Medina LLC 330 591-4800
2425 Medina Rd Ste 206 Medina (44256) *(G-13424)*

Hudson Supply Company Inc 216 518-3000
4500 Lee Rd Ste 120 Cleveland (44128) *(G-5535)*

Hudson Village Pizza Inc 330 968-4563
3825 Kay Dr Stow (44224) *(G-17763)*

Hueston Industries Inc 937 264-8163
3020 Production Ct Dayton (45414) *(G-8396)*

Huffy Bicycle Company, Centerville *Also called Huffy Corporation (G-3043)*

Huffy Corporation (PA) 937 865-2800
6551 Centervl Bus Pkwy Centerville (45459) *(G-3043)*

Hug Manufacturing Corporation 419 668-5086
2858 Arcade Rd Norwalk (44857) *(G-15546)*

Hughes Christensen 330 455-2140
1807 Allen Ave Se Canton (44707) *(G-2731)*

Hughes Corporation (PA) 440 238-2550
16900 Foltz Pkwy Strongsville (44149) *(G-17928)*

Hughey & Phillips LLC 937 652-3500
240 W Twain Ave Urbana (43078) *(G-19163)*

Hugo Bosca Company Inc (PA) 937 323-5523
1905 W Jefferson St Springfield (45506) *(G-17578)*

Hugo Boss Usa Inc 216 671-8100
4600 Piderman Rd Cleveland (44144) *(G-5536)*

Hugo Sand Company 216 570-1212
7055 State Route 43 Kent (44240) *(G-11471)*

Hugo Vglsang Maschinenbau GMBH 330 296-3820
7966 State Route 44 Ravenna (44266) *(G-16532)*

Huhtamaki Inc 513 201-1525
1985 James E Sauls Sr Dr Batavia (45103) *(G-1192)*

Huhtamaki Inc 937 746-9700
4000 Commerce Center Dr Franklin (45005) *(G-10028)*

Huhtamaki Inc 937 987-3078
5566 New Vienna Rd New Vienna (45159) *(G-14955)*

Huhtamaki Plastics, New Vienna *Also called Huhtamaki Inc (G-14955)*

Hukon Manufacturing Company 513 721-5562
2111 Freeman Ave Cincinnati (45214) *(G-3901)*

Hull Builders Supply, Sandusky *Also called Hull Ready Mix Concrete Inc (G-16972)*

Hull Builders Supply Inc 440 967-3159
685 Main St Vermilion (44089) *(G-19328)*

Hull Ready Mix Concrete Inc 419 625-8070
4419 Tiffin Ave Sandusky (44870) *(G-16972)*

Humbert Screen Graphix, Canton *Also called Tim L Humbert (G-2870)*

Humble Construction Co 614 888-8960
3441 Morse Rd Columbus (43231) *(G-7169)*

Humphrey Company (PA) 216 662-6629
20810 Miles Pkwy Cleveland (44128) *(G-5537)*

Humtown Pattern Company 330 482-5555
44708 Clmbana Wterford Rd Columbiana (44408) *(G-6621)*

Humtown Products, Columbiana *Also called Humtown Pattern Company (G-6621)*

Hundley Cellars LLC 843 368-5016
6451 N River Rd W Geneva (44041) *(G-10351)*

Hung Pham 614 850-9695
5291 Westpointe Plaza Dr Columbus (43228) *(G-7170)*

A
L
P
H
A
B
E
T
I
C

Hunger Hydraulics CC Ltd....419 666-4510
63 Dixie Hwy Ste 1 Rossford (43460) ***(G-16741)***
Hunger Industrial Complex, Rossford *Also called Hunger Hydraulics CC Ltd* ***(G-16741)***
Hunkar Technologies Inc (PA)....513 272-1010
2368 Victory Pkwy Ste 210 Cincinnati (45206) ***(G-3902)***
Hunnell Electric Co Inc....330 773-8278
950 Grant St Akron (44311) ***(G-225)***
Hunnell Electric Motor Repair, Akron *Also called Hunnell Electric Co Inc* ***(G-225)***
Hunt Imaging LLC (PA)....440 826-0433
210 Sheldon Rd Berea (44017) ***(G-1620)***
Hunt Products Inc....440 667-2457
3982 E 42nd St Newburgh Heights (44105) ***(G-15075)***
Hunt Valve Company Inc....330 337-9535
1913 E State St Salem (44460) ***(G-16901)***
Hunt Valve Company Inc....330 337-9535
1913 E State St Salem (44460) ***(G-16902)***
Hunter Defense Tech Inc....513 943-7880
1032 Seabrook Way Cincinnati (45245) ***(G-3309)***
Hunter Defense Tech Inc (PA)....216 438-6111
30500 Aurora Rd Ste 100 Solon (44139) ***(G-17312)***
Hunter Eureka Pipeline LLC....740 374-2940
125 Putnam St Marietta (45750) ***(G-12791)***
Hunter Hydraulics Inc....330 455-3983
2512 Columbus Rd Ne Canton (44705) ***(G-2732)***
Hunter Lift Ltd....330 549-3347
11233 South Ave North Lima (44452) ***(G-15317)***
Hunter Tool and Die Company....937 256-9798
2104 E 1st St Dayton (45403) ***(G-8397)***
Hunters Hightech Energy Systm....614 275-4777
2059 Big Tree Dr Columbus (43223) ***(G-7171)***
Hunters Manufacturing Co Inc (PA)....330 628-9245
1325 Waterloo Rd Mogadore (44260) ***(G-14377)***
Huntington Hardwood Lbr Co Inc....440 647-2283
28211 Baker Rd Wellington (44090) ***(G-19748)***
Huntington Instruments Inc....937 767-7001
303 N Walnut St Yellow Springs (45387) ***(G-20993)***
Huron Cement Products Company (PA)....419 433-4161
617 Main St Huron (44839) ***(G-11224)***
Huron Hometown News....419 433-1401
304 Williams St Huron (44839) ***(G-11225)***
Huron Lime Inc....419 433-2141
100 Meeker St Huron (44839) ***(G-11226)***
Hurst Auto-Truck Electric....216 961-1800
9004 Madison Ave Cleveland (44102) ***(G-5538)***
Husac Paving....513 200-2818
114 S Walnut St Harrison (45030) ***(G-10784)***
Husky Energy, Dublin *Also called Husky Marketing and Supply Co* ***(G-9087)***
Husky Energy....614 766-5633
5550 Blazer Pkwy Ste 200 Dublin (43017) ***(G-9086)***
Husky Marketing and Supply Co, Dublin *Also called Husky Energy* ***(G-9086)***
Husky Marketing and Supply Co....614 210-2300
5550 Blazer Pkwy Ste 200 Dublin (43017) ***(G-9087)***
Husqvarna US Holding Inc (HQ)....216 898-1800
20445 Emerald Pkwy Cleveland (44135) ***(G-5539)***
Huston Gift Shop, Chillicothe *Also called Huston Gifts Dolls and Flowers* ***(G-3244)***
Huston Gifts Dolls and Flowers....740 775-9141
306 Fairway Ave Chillicothe (45601) ***(G-3244)***
Hutchinson-Stevens Inc....216 281-8585
9627 Clinton Rd Cleveland (44144) ***(G-5540)***
Huth Ready Mix & Supply Co....330 833-4191
501 5th St Nw Massillon (44647) ***(G-13152)***
Huth Ready-Mix & Supply Co, Massillon *Also called Huth Ready Mix & Supply Co* ***(G-13152)***
Hutnik Company....330 336-9700
350 State St Ste 5 Wadsworth (44281) ***(G-19411)***
Hutter Racing Engines Ltd....440 285-2175
12550 Gar Hwy Chardon (44024) ***(G-3157)***
Hvac, Akron *Also called Lowry Furnace Company Inc* ***(G-276)***
Hvac Inc....330 343-5511
133 W 3rd St Dover (44622) ***(G-8991)***
Hw Chair, Brinkhaven *Also called Hillcrest* ***(G-2097)***
Hy-Blast Inc....513 424-0704
70 Enterprise Dr Middletown (45044) ***(G-14045)***
Hy-Grade Corporation (PA)....216 341-7711
3993 E 93rd St Cleveland (44105) ***(G-5541)***
Hy-Production Inc....330 273-2400
6000 Grafton Rd Valley City (44280) ***(G-19206)***
Hy-Tech Products....440 537-1257
125 Abbe Rd S Elyria (44035) ***(G-9430)***
Hybrid Trailer Co LLC....419 433-3022
912 University Dr S Huron (44839) ***(G-11227)***
Hycom Inc....330 753-2330
374 5th St Nw Barberton (44203) ***(G-1120)***
Hycomp LLC....440 234-2002
17960 Englewood Dr Ste A Cleveland (44130) ***(G-5542)***
Hyde Brothers Printing Co, Marietta *Also called Pen-Ann Corporation* ***(G-12815)***
Hyde Brothers Prtg & Mktg LLC (PA)....740 373-2054
101 Rathbone Rd Marietta (45750) ***(G-12792)***
Hyde Park Electronics LLC....937 252-2121
1875 Founders Dr Dayton (45420) ***(G-8398)***
Hyde Park Lumber Company....513 271-1500
3360 Red Bank Rd Cincinnati (45227) ***(G-3903)***
Hydra Air Equipment Inc....330 274-2222
9222 State Route 44 Mantua (44255) ***(G-12712)***
Hydra-TEC Inc....330 225-8797
3027 Nationwide Pkwy Brunswick (44212) ***(G-2232)***
Hydranamics, Galion *Also called Carter Machine Company Inc* ***(G-10256)***
Hydranamics Div Carter Mch Co, Galion *Also called Hydranamics Inc* ***(G-10275)***
Hydranamics Inc....419 468-3530
820 Edward St Galion (44833) ***(G-10275)***
Hydrant Hat LLC....440 224-1007
5759 S Wright St Kingsville (44048) ***(G-11604)***
Hydratech Engineered Pdts LLC....513 827-9169
10448 Chester Rd Cincinnati (45215) ***(G-3904)***
Hydratecs Injection Eqp Co....330 773-0491
430 Morgan Ave Akron (44311) ***(G-226)***
Hydraulic Parts Store Inc....330 364-6667
145 1st Dr Ne New Philadelphia (44663) ***(G-14902)***
Hydraulic Products Inc....440 946-4575
4540 Beidler Rd Willoughby (44094) ***(G-20506)***
Hydraulic Specialists Inc....740 922-3343
5655 Gundy Dr Midvale (44653) ***(G-14108)***
Hydro Aluminum Fayetteville....937 492-9194
401 N Stolle Ave Sidney (45365) ***(G-17193)***
Hydro Supply Co....740 454-3842
3112 East Pike Zanesville (43701) ***(G-21320)***
Hydro Systems Company....513 271-8800
401 Milford Pkwy Milford (45150) ***(G-14151)***
Hydro Systems Company (HQ)....513 271-8800
3798 Round Bottom Rd Cincinnati (45244) ***(G-3905)***
Hydro Tube Enterprises Inc (PA)....440 774-1022
137 Artino St Oberlin (44074) ***(G-15644)***
Hydro-Aire Inc....440 323-3211
241 Abbe Rd S Elyria (44035) ***(G-9431)***
Hydro-Dyne Inc....330 832-5076
225 Wetmore Ave Se Massillon (44646) ***(G-13153)***
Hydro-Thrift Corporation....330 837-5141
1301 Sanders Ave Sw Massillon (44647) ***(G-13154)***
Hydro-Vac, Cleveland *Also called HI Tecmetal Group Inc* ***(G-5508)***
Hydrodec Inc (HQ)....330 454-8202
2021 Steinway Blvd Se Canton (44707) ***(G-2733)***
Hydrodec of North America LLC....330 454-8202
2021 Steinway Blvd Se Canton (44707) ***(G-2734)***
Hydrogen 411 Technology LLC....440 941-6760
7777 W 130th St Cleveland (44130) ***(G-5543)***
Hydrogen Energy Systems LLC....330 236-0358
12 E Exchange St Fl 8 Akron (44308) ***(G-227)***
Hydromatic Pumps Inc....419 289-1144
1101 Myers Pkwy Ashland (44805) ***(G-741)***
Hydromotive Engineering Co....330 425-4266
9261 Ravenna Rd Bldg B1b2 Twinsburg (44087) ***(G-18956)***
Hydrothrift, Massillon *Also called Hydro-Thrift Corporation* ***(G-13154)***
Hygenic Acquisition Co....330 633-8460
1245 Home Ave Akron (44310) ***(G-228)***
Hygenic Corporation (HQ)....330 633-8460
1245 Home Ave Akron (44310) ***(G-229)***
Hykon Manufacturing Company....330 821-8889
163 E State St Alliance (44601) ***(G-517)***
Hyland Machine Company....937 233-8600
1900 Kuntz Rd Dayton (45404) ***(G-8399)***
Hyland Screw Machine Products, Dayton *Also called Hyland Machine Company* ***(G-8399)***
Hyland Software Inc (HQ)....440 788-5000
28500 Clemens Rd Westlake (44145) ***(G-20278)***
Hyload Inc (HQ)....330 336-6604
5020 Enterprise Pkwy Seville (44273) ***(G-17075)***
Hylun Machine Co Inc....440 256-8755
9220 Woods Way Dr Willoughby (44094) ***(G-20507)***
Hyneks Machine & Weld Shop, Ashland *Also called Hyneks Machine and Welding* ***(G-742)***
Hyneks Machine and Welding....419 281-7966
1372 State Route 603 Ashland (44805) ***(G-742)***
Hynes Industries Inc (PA)....330 799-3221
3805 Hericks Rd Youngstown (44515) ***(G-21111)***
Hynes Modern Pattern Co Inc....937 322-3451
2141 Erie Ave Springfield (45505) ***(G-17579)***
Hype Socks....614 506-5248
33 N 3rd St Columbus (43215) ***(G-7172)***
Hyper Tech Research Inc....614 481-8050
539 Industrial Mile Rd Columbus (43228) ***(G-7173)***
Hyper Tool Company....440 543-5151
16829 Park Circle Dr Chagrin Falls (44023) ***(G-3093)***
Hypodermic Designs LLC....614 203-4048
3089 1/2 W Broad St Apt C Columbus (43204) ***(G-7174)***
Hyponex Corporation (HQ)....937 644-0011
14111 Scottslawn Rd Marysville (43040) ***(G-12953)***
Hyponex Corporation....330 262-1300
3875 S Elyria Rd Shreve (44676) ***(G-17157)***
Hyprolap Finishing Co....440 352-0270
9300 Pinecone Dr Mentor (44060) ***(G-13605)***
Hyq Technologies LLC....513 225-6911
2897 Miamiview Ct Apt A Oxford (45056) ***(G-15837)***

Hyq Teq, Oxford *Also called Hyq Technologies LLC* **(G-15837)**

Hyson Products, Brecksville *Also called Barnes Group Inc* **(G-2035)**

Hyster-Yale Materials Hdlg Inc (PA) 440 449-9600
5875 Landerbrook Dr # 300 Cleveland (44124) **(G-5544)**

Hytec Automotive, Columbus *Also called Hytec-Debartolo LLC* **(G-7176)**

Hytec Automotive Ind LLC 614 527-9370
4419 Equity Dr Columbus (43228) **(G-7175)**

Hytec-Debartolo LLC 614 527-9370
4419 Equity Dr Columbus (43228) **(G-7176)**

Hytech Silicone Products Inc 330 297-1888
6112 Knapp Rd Ravenna (44266) **(G-16533)**

Hytek Coatings Inc 513 424-0131
1700 S University Blvd Middletown (45044) **(G-14046)**

Hyundai Ideal Electric Co 419 520-3314
330 E 1st St Mansfield (44902) **(G-12626)**

I A B F Inc 614 279-4498
1890 Mckinley Ave Columbus (43222) **(G-7177)**

I B C S, Englewood *Also called Innovative Bus Cmpt Solutions* **(G-9525)**

I B-Tech, Bucyrus *Also called Imasen Bucyrus Technology Inc* **(G-2350)**

I C Consultants Inc 216 731-9992
23564 Saint Clair Ave Cleveland (44117) **(G-5545)**

I C M I, Amelia *Also called Inductive Components Mfg* **(G-577)**

I C S, Groveport *Also called Innovtive Crtive Solutions LLC* **(G-10626)**

I Cerco Inc 740 982-2050
416 Maple Ave Crooksville (43731) **(G-7950)**

I Cerco Inc 304 387-0178
48400 Huston Rd East Liverpool (43920) **(G-9218)**

I Cerco Inc (PA) 330 567-2145
453 W Mcconkey St Shreve (44676) **(G-17158)**

I D I, Wapakoneta *Also called Ingredia Inc* **(G-19491)**

I D X Medical Ltd 513 583-9081
101 Southbend Ct Loveland (45140) **(G-12359)**

I Dream of Cakes 937 533-6024
995 Camden Rd Eaton (45320) **(G-9310)**

I E C, Bolivar *Also called Inventive Extrusions Corp* **(G-1937)**

I E R Industries, Macedonia *Also called Ier Fujikura Inc* **(G-12458)**

I F C O Systems, Cincinnati *Also called Ifco Systems Us LLC* **(G-3910)**

I G Brenner Inc 740 345-8845
32 E North St Newark (43055) **(G-15022)**

I H Schlezinger Inc 614 252-1188
1041 Joyce Ave Columbus (43219) **(G-7178)**

I Heart Cupcakes 614 787-3896
372 Hanton Way Columbus (43213) **(G-7179)**

I L R Inc 216 587-2212
5240 Greenhurst Ext Cleveland (44137) **(G-5546)**

I L S, Cleveland *Also called Supply Technologies LLC* **(G-6274)**

I L S, Hamilton *Also called Innovtive Lbling Solutions Inc* **(G-10706)**

I P Contractors LLC 330 452-1643
4974 Higbee Ave Nw Ste 11 Canton (44718) **(G-2735)**

I P D, North Royalton *Also called Industrial Parts Depot LLC* **(G-15427)**

I P S Treatments Inc 419 241-5955
3254 Hill Ave Toledo (43607) **(G-18514)**

I P Specrete Inc 216 721-2050
10703 Quebec Ave Cleveland (44106) **(G-5547)**

I R B F Company 330 633-5100
195 Potomac Ave Ste A Tallmadge (44278) **(G-18147)**

I S I, Lewis Center *Also called Industrial Solutions Inc* **(G-11900)**

I Schumann & Co LLC (PA) 440 439-2300
22500 Alexander Rd Bedford (44146) **(G-1430)**

I Sq R Power Cable Co 330 588-3000
4300 Chamber Ave Sw Canton (44706) **(G-2736)**

I T Verdin Co (PA) 513 241-4010
444 Reading Rd Cincinnati (45202) **(G-3906)**

I T Verdin Co. 513 241-4010
3900 Kellogg Ave Cincinnati (45226) **(G-3907)**

I T Verdin Co. 513 559-3947
3900 Kellogg Ave Cincinnati (45226) **(G-3908)**

I T W Automotive Finishing 419 470-2000
320 Phillips Ave Toledo (43612) **(G-18515)**

I-Convert, Caldwell *Also called Interntnal Cnvrter Cldwell Inc* **(G-2428)**

I-Dee-X Inc 330 788-2186
4302 Lake Park Rd Youngstown (44512) **(G-21112)**

I.T. Plastics, Mentor *Also called Industrial Thermoset Plas Inc* **(G-13608)**

I2, Hubbard *Also called Independence 2 LLC* **(G-11131)**

I3, Mesopotamia *Also called Innovative Integrations Inc* **(G-13775)**

IAC Holmesville LLC 330 279-4505
8281 County Road 245 Holmesville (44633) **(G-11107)**

IAC Sidney LLC 937 492-1225
2000 Schlater Dr Sidney (45365) **(G-17194)**

Iacono Production Services Inc 513 469-5095
11420 Deerfield Rd Blue Ash (45242) **(G-1811)**

IAMS Company (HQ) 800 675-3849
8700 S Masn Montgomery Rd Mason (45040) **(G-13038)**

IAMS Company 419 943-4267
3700 State Route 65 Leipsic (45856) **(G-11870)**

IAMS Company 937 962-2624
6571 State Route 503 N Lewisburg (45338) **(G-11935)**

Ibeda Inc Sprflash Gas Equip, Westlake *Also called Applied Marketing Services* **(G-20255)**

Iberia Firearms Inc 419 468-3746
3929 State Route 309 Galion (44833) **(G-10276)**

Iberia Machine Shop Inc 419 468-7100
8402 County Rd 30 Iberia (43325) **(G-11244)**

Ibex Rapid Cooks, Troy *Also called ITW Food Equipment Group LLC* **(G-18847)**

Ibi Brake Products Inc 440 543-7962
16751 Hilltop Park Pl Chagrin Falls (44023) **(G-3094)**

Ibiza Holdings Inc 513 701-7300
7901 Innovation Way Mason (45040) **(G-13039)**

IBM, Blue Ash *Also called International Bus Mchs Corp* **(G-1816)**

Ibsa, Dayton *Also called International Business Solutio* **(G-8415)**

Ibycorp 330 425-8226
8968 Dutton Dr Twinsburg (44087) **(G-18957)**

Ibycorp Tool & Die, Twinsburg *Also called Ibycorp* **(G-18957)**

Ic Roofing, Mason *Also called Interstate Contractors LLC* **(G-13048)**

Ic3d LLC 614 260-5631
421 W State St Columbus (43215) **(G-7180)**

Icandi Graphics LLC 330 723-8337
650 W Smith Rd Ste 3 Medina (44256) **(G-13425)**

ICAOT, Painesville *Also called International Cntr Artfcial or* **(G-15891)**

ICC, Brecksville *Also called Integrated Chem Concepts Inc* **(G-2056)**

ICC Safety Service Inc 614 261-4557
1070 Leona Ave Columbus (43201) **(G-7181)**

ICC Systems Inc 614 524-0299
5665 Blue Church Rd # 202 Sunbury (43074) **(G-18063)**

Icci, Cleveland *Also called I C Consultants Inc* **(G-5545)**

Iccnexergy, Dublin *Also called Nexergy Inc* **(G-9114)**

Ice Industries Inc 513 398-2010
320 N Mason Montgomery Rd Mason (45040) **(G-13040)**

Ice Industries Inc (PA) 419 842-3612
3810 Herr Rd Sylvania (43560) **(G-18110)**

Ice Industries Columbus Inc. 419 842-3600
3810 Herr Rd Sylvania (43560) **(G-18111)**

Ice Industries Deerfield, Mason *Also called Deerfield Manufacturing Inc* **(G-13008)**

Ice Industries Ronfeldt, Toledo *Also called Ronfeldt Manufacturing LLC* **(G-18681)**

ICEE USA 513 771-0630
44 Carnegie Way West Chester (45246) **(G-20015)**

Icgc The Andersons Inc 419 893-5050
1947 Briarfield Blvd Maumee (43537) **(G-13267)**

ICI Binding Corp (PA) 440 729-2445
8834 Mayfield Rd Ste A Chesterland (44026) **(G-3213)**

ICO Products LLC 419 867-3900
6415 Angola Rd Holland (43528) **(G-11064)**

ICO Technology Inc 330 666-3751
3550 W Market St Fairlawn (44333) **(G-9754)**

Icon Energy Systems Inc 937 423-4786
5261 S State Route 49 Greenville (45331) **(G-10505)**

ICP Adhesives and Sealants Inc 330 753-4585
2775 Barber Rd Norton (44203) **(G-15513)**

Ics Electrical Services, Cincinnati *Also called Instrmntation Ctrl Systems Inc* **(G-3925)**

Ics-Cargo Clean, Cincinnati *Also called Industrial Container Svcs LLC* **(G-3916)**

Ics-Cargo Clean, Cincinnati *Also called Industrial Container Svcs LLC* **(G-3917)**

ID Card Systems   Inc 330 963-7446
2248 E Enterprise Pkwy Twinsburg (44087) **(G-18958)**

ID Images Inc 330 220-7300
2991 Interstate Pkwy Brunswick (44212) **(G-2233)**

ID Images LLC (PA) 330 220-7300
2991 Interstate Pkwy Brunswick (44212) **(G-2234)**

ID Plastech Engraving, Cincinnati *Also called Professional Award Service* **(G-4294)**

Ida Controls 440 785-8457
38593 Bell Rd Willoughby (44094) **(G-20508)**

Idcomm LLC 661 250-4081
32315 White Rd Willoughby Hills (44092) **(G-20639)**

Idea Works, Sugarcreek *Also called Middaugh Enterprises Inc* **(G-18026)**

Ideal Baking Co, Lakemore *Also called Four Generations Inc* **(G-11644)**

Ideal Door, Mason *Also called Clopay Building Pdts Co Inc* **(G-12998)**

Ideal Drapery Company Inc 330 745-9873
1024 Wooster Rd N Barberton (44203) **(G-1121)**

Ideal Electric Company, Mansfield *Also called Hyundai Ideal Electric Co* **(G-12626)**

Ideal Steel Inc 937 525-9161
423 York St Springfield (45505) **(G-17580)**

Ideas & Ad Ventures Inc 513 542-7154
2614 Spring Grove Ave Cincinnati (45214) **(G-3909)**

Identitek Systems Inc 330 832-9844
1100 Industrial Ave Sw Massillon (44647) **(G-13155)**

Identity Holding Company LLC 216 514-1277
4944 Commerce Pkwy Cleveland (44128) **(G-5548)**

Identity Syncronizer, Perrysburg *Also called Innerapps LLC* **(G-16112)**

Idialogs LLC 937 372-2890
121 Pawleys Plantation Ct Xenia (45385) **(G-20956)**

Idx Corporation 937 401-3225
2875 Needmore Rd Dayton (45414) **(G-8400)**

Idx Supply Division, Youngstown *Also called I-Dee-X Inc* **(G-21112)**

IEC Infrared Systems LLC 440 234-8000
7803 Freeway Cir Middleburg Heights (44130) **(G-13906)**

A
L
P
H
A
B
E
T
I
C

Ier Fujikura Inc (PA)....330 425-7121
8271 Bavaria Dr E Macedonia (44056) *(G-12458)*
Ies Systems Inc....330 533-6683
464 Lisbon St Canfield (44406) *(G-2558)*
Ifco Systems North America Inc....330 669-2726
179 S Gilbert Dr Smithville (44677) *(G-17240)*
Ifco Systems Us LLC....513 769-0377
10725 Evendale Dr Cincinnati (45241) *(G-3910)*
Ig Watteeuw Usa LLC....740 588-1722
1000 Linden Ave Zanesville (43701) *(G-21321)*
Igc Software....614 759-9148
6432 E Main St Ste 201 Reynoldsburg (43068) *(G-16595)*
Igloo Press LLC....614 787-5528
39 W New England Ave Worthington (43085) *(G-20871)*
Ignio Systems LLC....419 708-0503
444 W Laskey Rd Ste V Toledo (43612) *(G-18516)*
Ignition Interlock, Blue Ash *Also called 1 A Lifesafer Inc (G-1729)*
Igo Home Products, Cleveland *Also called Toolovation LLC (G-6336)*
Iheartcommunications Inc....513 241-1550
8044 Montgomery Rd # 650 Cincinnati (45236) *(G-3911)*
Iheartcommunications Inc....740 335-0941
1535 N North St Wshngtn CT Hs (43160) *(G-20911)*
Iheartcommunications Inc....419 223-2060
667 W Market St Lima (45801) *(G-12026)*
Ihi Connectors R, Mentor *Also called International Hydraulics Inc (G-13610)*
Ihod USA LLC....216 459-7179
127 Public Sq Ste 4120 Cleveland (44114) *(G-5549)*
Ill Williams LLC....440 721-8191
11993 Ravenna Rd Ste 12 Chardon (44024) *(G-3158)*
Iko Production Inc....937 746-4561
1200 S Main St Franklin (45005) *(G-10029)*
Illinois Tool Works Inc....937 332-2839
750 Lincoln Ave Troy (45373) *(G-18843)*
Illinois Tool Works Inc....513 489-7600
6600 Cornell Rd Blue Ash (45242) *(G-1812)*
Illinois Tool Works Inc....419 636-3161
730 E South St Bryan (43506) *(G-2302)*
Illinois Tool Works Inc....937 393-4271
1495 N High St Hillsboro (45133) *(G-11004)*
Illinois Tool Works Inc....262 248-8277
730 E South St Bryan (43506) *(G-2303)*
Illinois Tool Works Inc....519 376-8886
401 W Market St Troy (45373) *(G-18844)*
Illusions Screenprinting....330 263-7770
334 E South St Ste 3 Wooster (44691) *(G-20785)*
Ilpea Industries Inc....330 562-2916
1300 Danner Dr Aurora (44202) *(G-926)*
Ilsco, Cincinnati *Also called Bardes Corporation (G-3436)*
Ilsco Corporation....513 367-9100
119 May Dr Harrison (45030) *(G-10785)*
Image Armor LLC....877 673-4377
220 1st Dr Ne New Philadelphia (44663) *(G-14903)*
Image Concepts Inc....216 524-9000
8200 Sweet Valley Dr # 107 Cleveland (44125) *(G-5550)*
Image Graphics, Columbia Station *Also called Perrons Printing Company (G-6593)*
Image Group Inc....419 866-3300
1255 Corporate Dr Holland (43528) *(G-11065)*
Image Group of Toledo Inc....419 866-3300
1255 Corporate Dr Holland (43528) *(G-11066)*
Image Industries Inc....937 832-7969
305 Smith Dr Englewood (45315) *(G-9524)*
Image Integrations Systems (PA)....419 872-0003
885 Commerce Dr Ste B Perrysburg (43551) *(G-16109)*
Image Pavement Maintenance....937 833-9200
425 Carr Dr Brookville (45309) *(G-2187)*
Image Print Inc....614 776-3985
214 Hoff Rd Unit D Westerville (43082) *(G-20158)*
Image Print Inc....614 430-8470
6417 Busch Blvd Columbus (43229) *(G-7182)*
Imageiq Inc....855 462-4347
26801 Miles Rd Ste 103 Cleveland (44128) *(G-5551)*
Imagemart Inc....216 486-4767
17320 Saint Clair Ave Cleveland (44110) *(G-5552)*
Imageries, Lima *Also called J&D Beck Co Inc (G-12033)*
Imagine Communications Corp....513 459-3400
5300 Kings Island Dr # 101 Mason (45040) *(G-13041)*
Imagine This Renovations....330 833-6739
4220 Alabama Ave Sw Navarre (44662) *(G-14716)*
Imaging Center, Stow *Also called Nuclear Physicians Limited (G-17785)*
Imaging Center East Main....614 566-8120
500 E Main St 2nd Columbus (43215) *(G-7183)*
Imaging Sciences LLC....440 975-9640
38174 Willoughby Pkwy Willoughby (44094) *(G-20509)*
Imalux Corporation....216 502-0755
11000 Cedar Ave Ste 250 Cleveland (44106) *(G-5553)*
Imasen Bucyrus Technology Inc....419 563-9590
260 Crossroads Blvd Bucyrus (44820) *(G-2350)*
Imax Industries Inc....440 639-0242
117 W Walnut Ave Painesville (44077) *(G-15889)*
Imco Carbide Tool Inc (PA)....419 661-6313
28170 Cedar Park Blvd Perrysburg (43551) *(G-16110)*
Imco Recycling of Ohio LLC....740 922-2373
7335 Newport Rd Se Uhrichsville (44683) *(G-19052)*
Imds Corporation....330 747-4637
840 Mcclurg Rd Youngstown (44512) *(G-21113)*
Imds Defense Systems, Youngstown *Also called Imds Corporation (G-21113)*
Imerys Usa Inc....920 687-0872
9987 Carver Rd Ste 300 Blue Ash (45242) *(G-1813)*
Imesco, Fredericktown *Also called Industrial and Mar Eng Svc Co (G-10104)*
IMI Precision, Brookville *Also called Norgren Inc (G-2194)*
IMI-Irving Materials Inc....513 844-8444
600 Augspurger Rd Hamilton (45011) *(G-10704)*
Immersus Health Company LLC (PA)....855 994-4325
2 Hill And Hollow Ln Cincinnati (45208) *(G-3912)*
Immersus Health Company LLC....855 994-4325
4351 Creek Rd Blue Ash (45241) *(G-1814)*
Immigration Law Systems Inc....614 252-3078
1620 E Broad St Ste 107 Columbus (43203) *(G-7184)*
Impac Hi-Performance Machining....419 726-7100
5515 Enterprise Blvd Toledo (43612) *(G-18517)*
Impackt....513 559-1488
3700 Pocahontas Ave Cincinnati (45227) *(G-3913)*
Impact Armor Technologies LLC....216 706-2024
17000 Saint Clair Ave Cleveland (44110) *(G-5554)*
Impact Cutoff Div, Maumee *Also called Hammill Manufacturing Co (G-13264)*
Impact Industries Inc....440 327-2360
5120 Mills Indus Pkwy North Ridgeville (44039) *(G-15380)*
Impact Products LLC (HQ)....419 841-2891
2840 Centennial Rd Toledo (43617) *(G-18518)*
Impact Promotions, North Bend *Also called Impact Sports Wear Inc (G-15205)*
Impact Publications....740 928-5541
4675 Walnut Rd Buckeye Lake (43008) *(G-2329)*
Impact Sports Wear Inc....513 922-7406
99 Saint Annes Ave North Bend (45052) *(G-15205)*
Impact Weekly, Dayton *Also called Dayton City Paper New LLC (G-8270)*
Impaction Co....440 349-5652
6100 Cochran Rd Solon (44139) *(G-17313)*
Imperial Adhesives....513 351-1300
6315 Wiehe Rd Cincinnati (45237) *(G-3914)*
Imperial Alum - Minerva LLC....330 868-7765
217 Roosevelt St Minerva (44657) *(G-14326)*
Imperial Castings, Tipp City *Also called C Imperial Inc (G-18268)*
Imperial Countertops....216 851-0888
10646 Leuer Ave Cleveland (44108) *(G-5555)*
Imperial Die & Mfg Co....440 268-9080
22930 Royalton Rd Strongsville (44149) *(G-17929)*
Imperial Metal Solutions LLC....216 781-4094
2284 Scranton Rd Cleveland (44113) *(G-5556)*
Imperial Metal Spinning Co....216 524-5020
7600 Exchange St Cleveland (44125) *(G-5557)*
Imperial On-Pece Fibrgls Pools....740 747-2971
255 S Franklin St Ashley (43003) *(G-788)*
Imperial Orthodontics, Urbana *Also called Triage Ortho Group (G-19185)*
Imperial Plastics Inc....330 927-5065
80 Industrial St Rittman (44270) *(G-16675)*
Imperial Pools Inc....513 771-1506
12090 Best Pl Cincinnati (45241) *(G-3915)*
Imperial Tent Company, Coldwater *Also called Embedee LLC (G-6558)*
Importers Direct LLC....330 436-3260
1559 S Main St Akron (44301) *(G-230)*
Impressions - A Print Shop....440 449-6966
370 Alpha Park Cleveland (44143) *(G-5558)*
Impressions To Go LLC....614 760-0600
6121 Pirthshire St Dublin (43016) *(G-9088)*
Imprints....330 650-0467
77 Maple Dr Hudson (44236) *(G-11181)*
Improv Electronics, Kent *Also called Kent Displays Inc (G-11477)*
IMS, Shaker Heights *Also called Institute Mthmtical Statistics (G-17090)*
IMT Defense Corp....614 891-8812
5386 Club Dr Westerville (43082) *(G-20159)*
In Box Publications LLC....330 592-4288
977 Hampton Ridge Dr Akron (44313) *(G-231)*
In Good Hlth & Animal Wellness....330 908-1234
9425 Olde 8 Rd Ste 4 Northfield (44067) *(G-15467)*
In Sttches Ctr For Ltrgcal Art, Cleveland *Also called Strictly Stitchery Inc (G-6254)*
In The Mix Dj Service....330 704-2833
5437 Portage St Nw North Canton (44720) *(G-15242)*
In-Touch Corp....440 268-0881
13500 Pearl Rd Ste 139 Cleveland (44136) *(G-5559)*
Inc., K.I.W.I., Twinsburg *Also called Kiwi Promotional AP & Prtg Co (G-18966)*
Inca Presswood-Pallets Ltd (PA)....330 343-3361
3005 Progress St Dover (44622) *(G-8992)*
Inceptor Inc....419 726-8804
1301 Progress Ave Toledo (43612) *(G-18519)*
Incessant Software Inc....614 206-2211
8577 Ohio Wesleyan Ct Nw Lancaster (43130) *(G-11723)*
Incinerator Specialists, Medina *Also called Facultatieve Tech Americas Inc (G-13408)*

Incorporated Trst Gspl Wk Scty 216 749-2100
2000 Brookpark Rd Cleveland (44109) *(G-5560)*

Incorporated Trustees Gospel W 216 749-1428
1980 Brookpark Rd Cleveland (44109) *(G-5561)*

Incredible Plastics, Warren Also called Bloom Industries Inc *(G-19529)*

Incredible Solutions Inc 330 898-3878
1052 Mahoning Ave Nw Warren (44483) *(G-19559)*

Independence 2 LLC 800 414-0545
623 W Liberty St Hubbard (44425) *(G-11131)*

Independent Awning & Canvas Co 937 223-9661
324 Jones St Dayton (45410) *(G-8401)*

Independent Can Company 440 593-5300
1049 Chamberlain Blvd Conneaut (44030) *(G-7810)*

Independent Container, Delaware Also called Greif Inc *(G-8849)*

Independent Die & Mfg Co 216 362-6778
5161 W 161st St Cleveland (44142) *(G-5562)*

Independent Digital Consulting 330 753-0777
2081 Wadsworth Rd Norton (44203) *(G-15514)*

Independent Machine & Wldg Inc 937 339-7330
35 Marybill Dr S Troy (45373) *(G-18845)*

Independent Power Consultants 419 476-8383
6051 Telegraph Rd Ste 19 Toledo (43612) *(G-18520)*

Independent Protection Systems 330 832-7992
2510 Upland Ave Sw Massillon (44647) *(G-13156)*

Independent Restaurateur, Newark Also called Plus Publications Inc *(G-15046)*

Independent Stamping Inc 216 251-3500
12025 Zelis Rd Cleveland (44135) *(G-5563)*

Independent Steel Company LLC 330 225-7741
615 Liverpool Dr Valley City (44280) *(G-19207)*

Independent Trailer Services 937 667-8900
4465 Lisa Dr Tipp City (45371) *(G-18282)*

Independent, The, Massillon Also called Copley Ohio Newspapers Inc *(G-13121)*

Indian Creek Distillery 937 846-1443
7095 Staley Rd New Carlisle (45344) *(G-14803)*

Indian Creek Fabricators Inc 937 667-7214
1350 Commerce Park Dr Tipp City (45371) *(G-18283)*

Indian Lake Boat Lift 937 539-2868
129 Wilgus W Russells Point (43348) *(G-16755)*

Indian Lake Raceway LLC 937 837-7533
6341 Silverbell Ct Clayton (45315) *(G-4660)*

Indian Lake Shoppers Edge 937 843-6600
204 1/2 Lincoln Blvd Russells Point (43348) *(G-16756)*

Indian River Industries 740 965-4377
31 E Granville St Sunbury (43074) *(G-18064)*

Indicator Advisory Corporation 419 726-9000
3061 Shoreland Ave Toledo (43611) *(G-18521)*

Indicator Shop 513 897-0055
8875 Bellbrook Rd Waynesville (45068) *(G-19730)*

Indie-Peasant Enterprises 740 590-8240
88 Columbus Cir Athens (45701) *(G-872)*

Indigo 48 LLC 419 551-6931
125 S Beech St Bryan (43506) *(G-2304)*

Induction Iron Incorporated 330 501-8852
3710 Hendricks Rd Bldg 1 Youngstown (44515) *(G-21114)*

Induction Services Inc 330 652-4494
1713 N Main St Niles (44446) *(G-15159)*

Induction Tooling Inc 440 237-0711
12510 York Delta Dr North Royalton (44133) *(G-15426)*

Inductive Components Mfg 513 752-4731
1200 Ferris Rd Amelia (45102) *(G-577)*

Industrial Aluminum Foundry, Columbus Also called I A B F Inc *(G-7177)*

Industrial and Mar Eng Svc Co 740 694-0791
13843 Armentrout Rd Fredericktown (43019) *(G-10104)*

Industrial Application Svs 419 875-5093
13453 Woodbrier Ln Grand Rapids (43522) *(G-10440)*

Industrial Automation Service 740 747-2222
4590 State Route 229 Ashley (43003) *(G-789)*

Industrial Connections Inc 330 274-2155
11730 Timber Point Trl Mantua (44255) *(G-12713)*

Industrial Container Svcs LLC 513 921-2056
1258 Knowlton St Cincinnati (45223) *(G-3916)*

Industrial Container Svcs LLC 513 921-8811
837 Depot St Cincinnati (45204) *(G-3917)*

Industrial Container Svcs LLC 614 864-1900
1385 Blatt Blvd Gahanna A Indsutrial Blacklick (43004) *(G-1699)*

Industrial Crate & Lumber Div, Zanesville Also called Southeast Ohio Timber Pdts Co *(G-21355)*

Industrial Ctrl Design & Maint, Tallmadge Also called Industrial Ctrl Dsign Mint Inc *(G-18148)*

Industrial Ctrl Dsign Mint Inc 330 785-9840
311 Geneva Ave Tallmadge (44278) *(G-18148)*

Industrial Electronic Service 937 746-9750
325 Industry Dr Carlisle (45005) *(G-2931)*

Industrial Fabricators Inc 614 882-7423
265 E Broadway Ave Westerville (43081) *(G-20218)*

Industrial Farm Tank Inc 937 843-2972
10676 Township Road 80 Lewistown (43333) *(G-11944)*

Industrial Fiberglass Spc Inc 937 222-9000
521 Kiser St Dayton (45404) *(G-8402)*

Industrial Finishers Inc 330 343-7797
3690 State Route 800 Ne Dover (44622) *(G-8993)*

Industrial Graphic, Groveport Also called Graphic TS *(G-10624)*

Industrial Grinders Co Inc 440 237-2600
5261 W 137th St Brookpark (44142) *(G-2164)*

Industrial Grinders Machining, Brookpark Also called Industrial Grinders Co Inc *(G-2164)*

Industrial Hanger Conveyor Co 419 332-2661
886 N County Road 232 Fremont (43420) *(G-10158)*

Industrial Hardwood Inc 419 666-2503
521 F St Perrysburg (43551) *(G-16111)*

Industrial Hose Product Div, Wickliffe Also called Parker-Hannifin Corporation *(G-20381)*

Industrial Image 419 547-1417
5630 State Route 113 Bellevue (44811) *(G-1551)*

Industrial Machine Service, Cardington Also called Jack Gruber *(G-2912)*

Industrial Machine Tool Svc 216 651-1122
3560 Ridge Rd Cleveland (44102) *(G-5564)*

Industrial Machining Services 937 295-2022
700 Tower Dr Fort Loramie (45845) *(G-9932)*

Industrial Masurement Ctrl Inc 440 877-1140
9901 Beechwood Dr Cleveland (44133) *(G-5565)*

Industrial Metal Finishing 440 232-2400
7680 Bond St Solon (44139) *(G-17314)*

Industrial Metal Products 440 237-3506
9921 York Alpha Dr Cleveland (44133) *(G-5566)*

Industrial Mfg Co LLC (HQ) 440 838-4700
8223 Brecksville Rd Ste 1 Brecksville (44141) *(G-2055)*

Industrial Mill Maintenance 330 746-1155
1609 Wilson Ave Ste 2 Youngstown (44506) *(G-21115)*

Industrial Mold Inc 330 425-7374
2057 E Aurora Rd Twinsburg (44087) *(G-18959)*

Industrial Nut Corp 419 625-8543
1425 Tiffin Ave Sandusky (44870) *(G-16973)*

Industrial Packaging Products 440 734-2663
22259 Spencer Ln Cleveland (44126) *(G-5567)*

Industrial Parts Depot LLC 440 237-9164
11266 Royalton Rd North Royalton (44133) *(G-15427)*

Industrial Pattern & Mfg Co 614 252-0934
899 N 20th St Columbus (43219) *(G-7185)*

Industrial Prfctn Mold & Mch, Twinsburg Also called Industrial Mold Inc *(G-18959)*

Industrial Pulley & Machine Co 937 355-4910
E Center St West Mansfield (43358) *(G-20099)*

Industrial Quartz Corp 440 942-0909
7552 Saint Clair Ave D Mentor (44060) *(G-13606)*

Industrial Repair & Mfg Inc (PA) 419 822-4232
1140 E Main St Ste A Delta (43515) *(G-8936)*

Industrial Screen Process (PA) 419 255-4900
17 17th St Toledo (43604) *(G-18522)*

Industrial Shaft and Mfg Inc 440 942-9104
34201 Melinz Pkwy Unit A Eastlake (44095) *(G-9275)*

Industrial Solutions Inc 614 431-8118
8333 Green Meadows Dr N A Lewis Center (43035) *(G-11900)*

Industrial Steering Pdts Inc 419 636-3300
426 N Lewis St Bryan (43506) *(G-2305)*

Industrial Systems & Solutions 440 205-1658
8812 Tyler Blvd Mentor (44060) *(G-13607)*

Industrial Technologies Inc 330 434-2033
1643 Massillon Rd Akron (44312) *(G-232)*

Industrial Thermal Systems Inc 513 561-2100
3914 Virginia Ave Cincinnati (45227) *(G-3918)*

Industrial Thermoset Plas Inc 440 975-0411
7675 Jenther Dr Mentor (44060) *(G-13608)*

Industrial Timber & Lumber Co, Cleveland Also called Itl Corp *(G-5591)*

Industrial Timber and Lbr LLC, Beachwood Also called Itl LLC *(G-1274)*

Industrial WD Prts Fabrication, Archbold Also called Liechty Specialties Inc *(G-683)*

Industrial Wire Rope Sup Inc (PA) 513 941-2443
7390 Harrison Ave Cincinnati (45247) *(G-3919)*

Industry Products Co (PA) 937 778-0585
500 W Statler Rd Piqua (45356) *(G-16279)*

Indy Eqp Indpndence Recycl Inc 216 524-0999
6220 E Schaaf Rd Independence (44131) *(G-11260)*

Ineos LLC (PA) 419 226-1200
1900 Fort Amanda Rd Lima (45804) *(G-12027)*

Ineos ABS (usa) LLC (HQ) 513 467-2400
356 Three Rivers Pkwy Addyston (45001) *(G-10)*

Ineos Americas LLC 419 226-1200
1900 Fort Amanda Rd Lima (45804) *(G-12028)*

Ineos USA LLC 419 226-1200
1900 Fort Amanda Rd Lima (45804) *(G-12029)*

Infant Food Project Inc 614 239-5763
638 S Hampton Rd Columbus (43213) *(G-7186)*

Infinit Nutrition LLC 513 791-3500
11240 Cornell Park Dr # 110 Blue Ash (45242) *(G-1815)*

Infinite Synergy LLC 330 892-8777
7252 Elmland Ave Poland (44514) *(G-16383)*

Infinity Oilfield Services LLC 570 567-7027
311 Adena Dr Newcomerstown (43832) *(G-15116)*

Infinity Plus 937 828-1350
7213 Brigner Rd Mechanicsburg (43044) *(G-13357)*

A
L
P
H
A
B
E
T
I
C

Infinity Trichology Center...........................937 281-0555
  5250 Far Hills Ave Kettering (45429) *(G-11581)*

Infinium Wall Systems Inc...........................440 572-5000
  22555 Ascoa Ct Strongsville (44149) *(G-17930)*

Inflatable Images, Brunswick *Also called Scherba Industries Inc* *(G-2256)*

Info-Graphics Inc...........................440 498-1640
  5960 Liberty Rd Solon (44139) *(G-17315)*

Infoaccessnet LLC...........................216 328-0100
  8801 E Pleasant Valley Rd Cleveland (44131) *(G-5568)*

Infosight Corporation...........................740 642-3600
  20700 Us Highway 23 Chillicothe (45601) *(G-3245)*

Infrared Imaging Systems Inc...........................614 989-1148
  22718 Holycross Epps Rd Marysville (43040) *(G-12954)*

Ingersoll Rand, Holland *Also called Trane Company* *(G-11091)*

Ingersoll-Rand Company...........................419 633-6800
  209 N Main St Bryan (43506) *(G-2306)*

Ingles Logging...........................740 379-2909
  19094 State Route 141 Patriot (45658) *(G-15995)*

Ingles Logging...........................740 379-2760
  17748 State Route 141 Patriot (45658) *(G-15996)*

Ingram Products Inc...........................904 778-1010
  1376 Township Road 743 Ashland (44805) *(G-743)*

Ingredia Inc...........................419 738-4060
  625 Commerce Rd Wapakoneta (45895) *(G-19491)*

Ingredient Innovations Intl Co...........................330 262-4440
  146 S Bever St Wooster (44691) *(G-20786)*

Ingredient Masters Inc...........................513 231-7432
  7529 State Rd Ste A Cincinnati (45255) *(G-3920)*

Ingredient Technology Division, Elyria *Also called Chemtura Corporation* *(G-9393)*

Inhance Technologies LLC...........................614 846-6400
  6575 Huntley Rd Ste D Columbus (43229) *(G-7187)*

Initial Designs Inc...........................419 475-3900
  2453 Tremainsville Rd # 2 Toledo (43613) *(G-18523)*

Initially Yours...........................216 228-4478
  15028 Madison Ave Lakewood (44107) *(G-11669)*

Injection Alloys Incorporated...........................513 422-8819
  1700 Made Industrial Dr Middletown (45044) *(G-14047)*

Injection Molding Specialist...........................440 639-7896
  251 W Prospect St Painesville (44077) *(G-15890)*

Injoy Foods LLC...........................614 798-2033
  4860 Calloway Ct Dublin (43017) *(G-9089)*

Ink Again...........................419 232-4465
  115 N Washington St Van Wert (45891) *(G-19260)*

Ink Factory Inc...........................330 799-0888
  2750 Salt Springs Rd Youngstown (44509) *(G-21116)*

Ink Inc...........................330 875-4789
  200 S Bauman Ct Louisville (44641) *(G-12316)*

Ink Production Services Inc...........................513 733-9338
  9648 Wayne Ave Cincinnati (45215) *(G-3921)*

Ink Technology Corporation (PA)...........................216 486-6720
  18320 Lanken Ave Cleveland (44119) *(G-5569)*

Ink Well, Grove City *Also called Deerfield Ventures Inc* *(G-10553)*

Ink Well, Akron *Also called Bansal Enterprises Inc* *(G-84)*

Ink Well, Bedford Heights *Also called Cwh Graphics LLC* *(G-1482)*

Ink Well...........................614 861-7113
  969 Claycraft Rd Gahanna (43230) *(G-10212)*

Inktastic Inc...........................330 345-0911
  5214 Cleveland Rd Wooster (44691) *(G-20787)*

Inkwell, The, Westerville *Also called Technoprint Inc* *(G-20236)*

Inland Hardwood Corporation...........................740 373-7187
  25 Sheets Run Rd Marietta (45750) *(G-12793)*

Inland Manufacturing LLC...........................937 835-0220
  6785 W 3rd St Dayton (45417) *(G-8403)*

Inland Products Inc (PA)...........................614 443-3425
  599 Frank Rd Columbus (43223) *(G-7188)*

Inland Wood Products, Marietta *Also called Inland Hardwood Corporation* *(G-12793)*

Inline Label Company...........................513 217-5662
  4720 Emerald Way Middletown (45044) *(G-14048)*

Inn Maid Products, Westerville *Also called Tmarzetti Company* *(G-20193)*

Inner City Abrasives LLC...........................216 391-4402
  7209 Saint Clair Ave 101b Cleveland (44103) *(G-5570)*

Inner Fire Sports LLC...........................719 244-6622
  2558 Madison Rd Apt 18 Cincinnati (45208) *(G-3922)*

Inner Products Sales Inc...........................216 581-4141
  5221 Northfield Rd A Bedford (44146) *(G-1431)*

Innerapps LLC...........................419 467-3110
  28350 Kensington Ln # 200 Perrysburg (43551) *(G-16112)*

Innersource Inc...........................330 799-7619
  755 Wick Ave Youngstown (44505) *(G-21117)*

Innerwood & Company...........................513 677-2229
  688 Elizabeth Ln Loveland (45140) *(G-12360)*

Inno-Pak Holding Inc...........................740 363-0090
  1932 Pittsburgh Dr Delaware (43015) *(G-8861)*

Innocomp...........................440 248-5104
  33195 Wagon Wheel Dr Solon (44139) *(G-17316)*

Innocor Foam Tech - Acp Inc...........................419 647-4172
  200 E North St Spencerville (45887) *(G-17460)*

Innmark Communications, Fairfield *Also called Innomark Perm Disply Grp LLC* *(G-9668)*

Innomark Communications LLC...........................513 285-1040
  3005 W Tech Blvd Miamisburg (45342) *(G-13819)*

Innomark Communications LLC...........................937 454-5555
  6700 Homestretch Rd Dayton (45414) *(G-8404)*

Innomark Perm Disply Grp LLC...........................513 285-1040
  420 Distribution Cir Fairfield (45014) *(G-9668)*

Innovar Systems Limited...........................330 538-3942
  12155 Commissioner Dr North Jackson (44451) *(G-15292)*

Innovated Health LLC...........................330 858-0651
  2241 Front St Fl 1 Cuyahoga Falls (44221) *(G-8010)*

Innovation Exhibits Inc...........................330 726-1324
  85 Karago Ave Ste 1&2 Youngstown (44512) *(G-21118)*

Innovation Plastics LLC...........................513 818-1771
  1150 State St Fostoria (44830) *(G-9980)*

Innovation Sales LLC...........................330 239-0400
  784 Medina Rd Ste 103 Medina (44256) *(G-13426)*

Innovations In Plastic Inc...........................216 541-6060
  1643 Eddy Rd Cleveland (44112) *(G-5571)*

Innovative Apps Ltd...........................330 687-2888
  8000 Walton Pkwy Ste 208 New Albany (43054) *(G-14761)*

Innovative Assembly Svcs LLC...........................419 399-3886
  715 N Elm St Paulding (45879) *(G-16006)*

Innovative Bus Cmpt Solutions...........................937 832-3969
  303 Shady Tree Ct Englewood (45315) *(G-9525)*

Innovative Ceramic Corp...........................330 385-6515
  432 Walnut St East Liverpool (43920) *(G-9219)*

Innovative Computer Forms, Columbus *Also called Bizzy Bee Printing Inc* *(G-6833)*

Innovative Control Systems...........................513 894-3712
  5870 Fairham Rd Hamilton (45011) *(G-10705)*

Innovative Controls Corp...........................419 691-6684
  1354 E Broadway St Toledo (43605) *(G-18524)*

Innovative Creations, Dayton *Also called Glen D Lala* *(G-8366)*

Innovative Hdlg & Metalfab LLC...........................419 882-7480
  7755 Sylvania Ave Sylvania (43560) *(G-18112)*

Innovative Industries, Macedonia *Also called James Thomas Shively* *(G-12462)*

Innovative Integrations Inc...........................216 533-5353
  7877 Girdle Rd Mesopotamia (44439) *(G-13775)*

Innovative Lab Services LLC...........................614 554-6446
  7123 National Rd Sw Rear Pataskala (43062) *(G-15972)*

Innovative Medical Eqp LLC...........................440 646-1286
  29001 Cedar Rd Ste 325 Cleveland (44124) *(G-5572)*

Innovative Packaging LLC...........................419 222-6071
  1150 N Cable Rd Ste B Lima (45805) *(G-12030)*

Innovative Plastic Machinery...........................330 478-1825
  5252 Southway St Sw Canton (44706) *(G-2737)*

Innovative Plastic Molders LLC...........................937 898-3775
  7438 Webster St Dayton (45414) *(G-8405)*

Innovative Recycling Systems...........................440 498-9200
  31655 Arthur Rd Solon (44139) *(G-17317)*

Innovative Retail Displays Inc...........................937 237-7708
  2127 Troy St Dayton (45404) *(G-8406)*

Innovative Stiching, North Baltimore *Also called Truck Stop Embroidery* *(G-15200)*

Innovative Tool & Die Inc...........................419 599-0492
  1700 Industrial Dr Napoleon (43545) *(G-14684)*

Innovative Vend Solutions LLC...........................866 931-9413
  2048 S Alex Rd Dayton (45449) *(G-8407)*

Innovative Weld Solutions Ltd...........................937 545-7695
  1701 Farr Dr Dayton (45404) *(G-8408)*

Innovative Wldg & Design LLC...........................330 581-1316
  24946 Hartley Rd Alliance (44601) *(G-518)*

Innovative Woodworking Inc...........................513 531-1940
  1901 Ross Ave Cincinnati (45212) *(G-3923)*

Innovtive Crtive Solutions LLC...........................614 491-9638
  5835 Green Pointe Dr S B Groveport (43125) *(G-10626)*

Innovtive Lbling Solutions Inc...........................513 860-2457
  4000 Hmlton Middletown Rd Hamilton (45011) *(G-10706)*

Inovent Engineering Inc...........................330 468-0005
  8877 Freeway Dr Macedonia (44056) *(G-12459)*

Inpaco Corporation...........................614 888-9288
  6950 Wrthington Galena Rd Worthington (43085) *(G-20872)*

Inpower LLC...........................740 548-0965
  8311 Green Meadows Dr N Lewis Center (43035) *(G-11901)*

Ins Robotics Inc...........................888 293-5325
  3600 Parkway Ln Hilliard (43026) *(G-10953)*

Inservco Inc (HQ)...........................847 855-9600
  110 Commerce Dr Lagrange (44050) *(G-11627)*

Inside Outfitters, Lewis Center *Also called Lumenomics Inc* *(G-11906)*

Insightfuel LLC...........................330 998-7380
  1333 Highland Rd E Ste P Macedonia (44056) *(G-12460)*

Insignia Signs Inc...........................937 866-2341
  300 Gargrave Rd Dayton (45449) *(G-8409)*

Inskeep Brothers Inc...........................614 898-6620
  3193 E Dblin Granville Rd Columbus (43231) *(G-7189)*

Inskeep Brothers Printers, Columbus *Also called Inskeep Brothers Inc* *(G-7189)*

Insley Printing Inc...........................614 885-5973
  666 High St Ste 400 Worthington (43085) *(G-20873)*

Insource Tech Inc...........................419 399-3600
  12124 Road 111 Paulding (45879) *(G-16007)*

Insource Technologies Inc...........................419 399-3600
  12124 Road 111 Paulding (45879) *(G-16008)*

(G-0000) Company's Geographic Section entry number

Inspiring Kind LLC 513 321-1705
7757 5 Mile Rd Cincinnati (45230) *(G-3924)*

Insta Plak Inc (PA) 419 537-1555
5025 Dorr St Toledo (43615) *(G-18525)*

Insta-Gro Manufacturing Inc 419 845-3046
8217 Linn Hipsher Rd Caledonia (43314) *(G-2438)*

Insta-Plak, Toledo *Also called Insta Plak Inc (G-18525)*

Insta-Print Inc 216 741-6500
3101 Brookpark Rd Cleveland (44134) *(G-5573)*

Instacopy, Salem *Also called Sanscan Inc (G-16926)*

Installed Building Pdts LLC 614 308-9900
1320 Mckinley Ave Ste A Columbus (43222) *(G-7190)*

Instant Impressions Inc 614 538-9844
4499 Kenny Rd Columbus (43220) *(G-7191)*

Instant Replay 937 592-0534
334 E Columbus Ave Bellefontaine (43311) *(G-1534)*

Instant Whip Detroit, Columbus *Also called Instantwhip Detroit Inc (G-7194)*

Instantorder, Celina *Also called Tech Solutions LLC (G-3020)*

Instantwhip Connecticut Inc (PA) 614 488-2536
2200 Cardigan Ave Columbus (43215) *(G-7192)*

Instantwhip Detroit Inc (PA) 614 488-2536
2200 Cardigan Ave Columbus (43215) *(G-7193)*

Instantwhip Detroit Inc 800 544-9447
2200 Cardigan Ave Columbus (43215) *(G-7194)*

Instantwhip Foods Inc (PA) 614 488-2536
2200 Cardigan Ave Columbus (43215) *(G-7195)*

Instantwhip National Office, Columbus *Also called Dallas Instantwhip Inc (G-7009)*

Instantwhip of Buffalo Inc (HQ) 614 488-2536
2200 Cardigan Ave Columbus (43215) *(G-7196)*

Instantwhip of Pennsylvania, Columbus *Also called Instantwhip Products Co PA (G-7197)*

Instantwhip Products Co PA (HQ) 614 488-2536
2200 Cardigan Ave Columbus (43215) *(G-7197)*

Instantwhip-Chicago Inc (PA) 614 488-2536
2200 Cardigan Ave Columbus (43215) *(G-7198)*

Instantwhip-Columbus Inc (HQ) 614 871-9447
3855 Marlane Dr Grove City (43123) *(G-10564)*

Instantwhip-Dayton Inc (PA) 937 235-5930
5820 Executive Blvd Dayton (45424) *(G-8410)*

Instantwhip-Dayton Inc 937 435-4371
967 Senate Dr Dayton (45459) *(G-8411)*

Instantwhip-Syracuse Inc (PA) 614 488-2536
2200 Cardigan Ave Columbus (43215) *(G-7199)*

Institute Mthmtical Statistics 216 295-2340
3163 Somerset Dr Shaker Heights (44122) *(G-17090)*

Instrmntation Ctrl Systems Inc 513 662-2600
11355 Sebring Dr Cincinnati (45240) *(G-3925)*

Instruction & Design Concepts 937 439-2698
441 Maple Springs Dr Dayton (45458) *(G-8412)*

Instrumatics, Cleveland *Also called Cleveland Circuits Corp (G-5051)*

Instrumentors Inc 440 238-3430
22077 Drake Rd Strongsville (44149) *(G-17931)*

Insulpro Inc 614 262-3768
4650 Indianola Ave Columbus (43214) *(G-7200)*

Integra Enclosures Inc (PA) 440 269-4966
7750 Pyler Blvd Willoughby (44094) *(G-20510)*

Integral Design Inc 216 524-0555
7670 Hub Pkwy Cleveland (44125) *(G-5574)*

Integrated Aircraft Systems 330 686-2982
1337 Commerce Dr Ste 9 Stow (44224) *(G-17764)*

Integrated Chem Concepts Inc 440 838-5666
6650 W Snowville Rd Ste F Brecksville (44141) *(G-2056)*

Integrated Development & Mfg (PA) 440 247-5100
510 Washington St Chagrin Falls (44022) *(G-3060)*

Integrated Development & Mfg 440 543-2423
8401 Washington St Chagrin Falls (44023) *(G-3095)*

Integrated Med Solutions Inc 440 269-6984
7124 Industrial Park Blvd Mentor (44060) *(G-13609)*

Integrated Power Services LLC 216 433-7808
5325 W 130th St Cleveland (44130) *(G-5575)*

Integrated Power Services LLC 513 863-8816
2175a Schlichter Dr Hamilton (45015) *(G-10707)*

Integrated Sensors LLC 419 536-3212
2403 Evergreen Rd Ottawa Hills (43606) *(G-15816)*

Integrated Systems Professiona 614 875-0104
4110 Demorest Rd Grove City (43123) *(G-10565)*

Integrity Crane Services Ltd 330 479-2003
2100 Venture Cir Se Massillon (44646) *(G-13157)*

Integrity Group Consulting, Reynoldsburg *Also called Igc Software (G-16595)*

Integrity Industrial Eqp Inc 937 238-9275
7401 Bridgewater Rd Huber Heights (45424) *(G-11149)*

Integrity Manufacturing Corp 937 233-6792
3723 Inpark Dr Dayton (45414) *(G-8413)*

Integrity Print Solutions Inc 330 818-0161
567 E Turkeyfoot Lake Rd Akron (44319) *(G-233)*

Integrity Printing 937 331-5390
912 N Main St Dayton (45405) *(G-8414)*

Integrted Med Systems Intl Inc 800 783-9251
4575 Hudson Dr Stow (44224) *(G-17765)*

Intek Inc 614 895-0301
751 Intek Way Westerville (43082) *(G-20160)*

Intel Industries LLC 614 551-5702
773 Laverty Ln Cincinnati (45230) *(G-3926)*

Intelitool Manufacturing Svcs 440 953-1071
36335 Reading Ave Ste 4 Willoughby (44094) *(G-20511)*

Intelligent Biometric Controls 513 239-6322
601 Brooklyn Ave Ste A Milford (45150) *(G-14152)*

Intelligent Mobile Support Inc 440 600-7343
31320 Solon Rd Ste 17 Solon (44139) *(G-17318)*

Intelligent Signal Tech 614 530-4784
6318 Dustywind Ln Loveland (45140) *(G-12361)*

Intelligrated Inc (HQ) 866 936-7300
7901 Innovation Way Mason (45040) *(G-13042)*

Intelligrated Inc 513 874-0788
10045 International Blvd West Chester (45246) *(G-20016)*

Intelligrated Headquarters LLC 866 936-7300
7901 Innovation Way Mason (45040) *(G-13043)*

Intelligrated Products LLC 740 490-0300
475 E High St London (43140) *(G-12212)*

Intelligrated Sub Holdings Inc (PA) 513 701-7300
7901 Innovation Way Mason (45040) *(G-13044)*

Intelligrated Systems Inc (HQ) 866 936-7300
7901 Innovation Way Mason (45040) *(G-13045)*

Intelligrated Systems LLC 513 701-7300
7901 Innovation Way Mason (45040) *(G-13046)*

Intelligrated Systems Ohio LLC (HQ) 513 701-7300
7901 Innovation Way Mason (45040) *(G-13047)*

Intellinetics Inc 614 388-8908
2190 Dividend Dr Columbus (43228) *(G-7201)*

Intellirod Spine Inc 234 678-8965
554 White Pond Dr Ste F Akron (44320) *(G-234)*

Intellitronix Corporation 440 210-7645
34099 Melinz Pkwy Unit E Eastlake (44095) *(G-9276)*

Intelliworks Ht 419 660-9050
61 Saint Marys St Norwalk (44857) *(G-15547)*

Inter American Products Inc (HQ) 800 645-2233
1240 State Ave Cincinnati (45204) *(G-3927)*

Inter Cab Corporation 216 351-0770
8551 Brookpark Rd Cleveland (44129) *(G-5576)*

Inter Tel, West Chester *Also called Mitel (delaware) Inc (G-19902)*

Inter Valley Communication, Greenfield *Also called Hisey Bells (G-10480)*

Inter-Ion Inc 330 928-9655
157 Ascot Pkwy Cuyahoga Falls (44223) *(G-8011)*

Inter-Power Corporation 330 652-4494
1713 N Main St Niles (44446) *(G-15160)*

Interactive Engineering Corp 330 239-6888
884 Medina Rd Medina (44256) *(G-13427)*

Interactive Fincl Solutions 419 335-1280
122 S Fulton St Wauseon (43567) *(G-19683)*

Intercontinental Chemical Corp (PA) 513 541-7100
4660 Spring Grove Ave Cincinnati (45232) *(G-3928)*

Interden Industries Inc 419 368-9011
2377 County Road 175 Lakeville (44638) *(G-11651)*

Interface Logic Systems Inc 614 236-8388
3311 E Livingston Ave Columbus (43227) *(G-7202)*

Interfast Inc 216 581-3000
4444 Lee Rd Cleveland (44128) *(G-5577)*

Intergroup International Ltd 216 965-0257
1111 E 200th St Euclid (44117) *(G-9586)*

Interior Dnnage Spcialites Inc 614 291-0900
470 E Starr Ave Columbus (43201) *(G-7203)*

Interior Graphic Systems LLC 330 244-0100
4550 Aultman Rd Canton (44720) *(G-2738)*

Interior Products Co Inc 216 641-1919
3615 Superior Ave E 3104f Cleveland (44114) *(G-5578)*

Interlake Industries Inc (PA) 440 942-0800
4732 E 355th St Willoughby (44094) *(G-20512)*

Interlake Stamping Ohio Inc 440 942-0800
4732 E 355th St Willoughby (44094) *(G-20513)*

Interline Brands Inc 614 527-9475
2375 International St Columbus (43228) *(G-7204)*

Interlock Industries Inc 440 576-9070
352 E Erie St Jefferson (44047) *(G-11361)*

Interlube Corporation 513 531-1777
4646 Baker St Cincinnati (45212) *(G-3929)*

Intermec Inc 513 874-5882
9290 Le Saint Dr West Chester (45014) *(G-19883)*

Intermec Media Products, West Chester *Also called Intermec Ultra Print Inc (G-19885)*

Intermec Technologies Corp 513 874-5882
9290 Le Saint Dr West Chester (45014) *(G-19884)*

Intermec Ultra Print Inc 513 874-5882
9290 Le Saint Dr West Chester (45014) *(G-19885)*

International Advg Concepts 440 331-4733
4285 W 217th St Cleveland (44126) *(G-5579)*

International Automotive 330 279-6557
8281 County Road 245 Holmesville (44633) *(G-11108)*

International Automotive 419 332-1587
400 S Stone St Fremont (43420) *(G-10159)*

International Automotive 937 492-1225
2000 Schlater Dr Sidney (45365) *(G-17195)*

International Automotive 419 335-1000
555 W Linfoot St Wauseon (43567) *(G-19684)*

International Automotive 419 433-5653
1608 Sawmill Pkwy Huron (44839) *(G-11228)*

International Bellows 937 832-4501
2 Ferrari Ct Englewood (45315) *(G-9526)*

International Beverage Works 614 798-5398
5636 Moorgate Dr Columbus (43235) *(G-7205)*

International Brand Services 513 376-8209
3397 Erie Ave Apt 215 Cincinnati (45208) *(G-3930)*

International Bus Mchs Corp 513 826-1001
4600 Mcauley Pl Ste 200 Blue Ash (45242) *(G-1816)*

International Business Solutio 937 853-0348
432 Windsor Park Dr Dayton (45459) *(G-8415)*

International Cntr Artfcial or 440 358-1102
10 W Erie St Ste 200 Painesville (44077) *(G-15891)*

International Cont Systems LLC 216 481-8219
16601 Saint Clair Ave Cleveland (44110) *(G-5580)*

International Dies Co Inc 330 744-7951
117 S Blaine Ave Youngstown (44506) *(G-21119)*

International Financial Svcs, Cincinnati Also called International Supply Corp *(G-3931)*

International Finishing LLC 937 293-3340
2223 S Dixie Dr Dayton (45409) *(G-8416)*

International Fuel Systems Inc 419 475-5276
2101 W Sylvania Ave Toledo (43613) *(G-18526)*

International Grinding Inc 330 659-0220
1811 Orchard Dr Akron (44333) *(G-235)*

International Hydraulics Inc 440 951-1781
7700 Saint Clair Ave Mentor (44060) *(G-13610)*

International Laminating Corp 937 254-8181
1712 Springfield St Ste 2 Dayton (45403) *(G-8417)*

International Machining Inc 330 225-1963
2885 Nationwide Pkwy Brunswick (44212) *(G-2235)*

International Mill Service, Marion Also called Tms International Corporation *(G-12906)*

International Multifoods Corp (HQ) 330 682-3000
1 Strawberry Ln Orrville (44667) *(G-15741)*

International Multifoods Corp 440 323-5100
6325 Gateway Blvd S Elyria (44035) *(G-9432)*

International Noodle Company 614 888-0665
341 Enterprise Dr Lewis Center (43035) *(G-11902)*

International Paper, Fairfield Also called Veritiv Operating Company *(G-9728)*

International Paper Company 330 264-1322
689 Palmer St Wooster (44691) *(G-20788)*

International Paper Company 937 456-4131
900 State Route 35 W Eaton (45320) *(G-9311)*

International Paper Company 740 397-5215
8800 Granville Rd Mount Vernon (43050) *(G-14623)*

International Paper Company 740 383-4061
1600 Cascade Dr Marion (43302) *(G-12877)*

International Paper Company 800 473-0830
912 Nelbar St Middletown (45042) *(G-14049)*

International Paper Company 877 447-2737
5806 Jeb Stuart Dr Milford (45150) *(G-14153)*

International Paper Company 440 428-5116
3200 County Line Rd Madison (44057) *(G-12507)*

International Paper Company 740 363-9882
865 Pittsburgh Dr Delaware (43015) *(G-8862)*

International Paper Company 513 248-6365
6283 Tri Ridge Blvd Loveland (45140) *(G-12362)*

International Paper Company 740 439-3527
60700 Hope Ave Byesville (43723) *(G-2404)*

International Paper Company 419 675-2534
808 Fontaine St Kenton (43326) *(G-11551)*

International Paper Company 740 369-7691
875 Pittsburgh Dr Delaware (43015) *(G-8863)*

International Paper Company 740 522-3123
1851 Tamarack Rd Newark (43055) *(G-15023)*

International Paper Company 800 422-4657
808 Fontaine St Kenton (43326) *(G-11552)*

International Paper Company 330 626-7300
700 Mondial Pkwy Streetsboro (44241) *(G-17858)*

International Paper Company 419 673-0711
1300 S Main St Kenton (43326) *(G-11553)*

International Paper Company 513 248-6000
6283 Tri Ridge Blvd Loveland (45140) *(G-12363)*

International Products 614 334-1500
2701 Charter St Ste A Columbus (43228) *(G-7206)*

International Products (HQ) 614 850-3000
4119 Leap Rd Hilliard (43026) *(G-10954)*

International Steel Group 330 841-2800
2234 Main Street Ext Sw Warren (44481) *(G-19560)*

International Supply Corp 513 793-0393
3284 E Sharon Rd Cincinnati (45241) *(G-3931)*

International Technical 330 505-1218
852 Ann Ave Niles (44446) *(G-15161)*

International Trade Group Inc 614 486-4634
2920 North Star Rd Columbus (43221) *(G-7207)*

Interntnal Cnvrter Cldwell Inc (HQ) 740 732-5665
17153 Industrial Hwy Caldwell (43724) *(G-2428)*

Interntnal Pckg Pallets Crates, Sidney Also called Wappoo Wood Products Inc *(G-17233)*

Interntnal Plstic Cmpnents Inc 330 744-0625
75 Mccartney Rd Campbell (44405) *(G-2490)*

Interntnal Precision Cast Sups 330 342-0407
1570 Terex Rd Hudson (44236) *(G-11182)*

Interntnal Tchncal Catings Inc 614 449-6669
845 E Markison Ave Columbus (43207) *(G-7208)*

Interpak Inc 440 974-8999
7278 Justin Way Mentor (44060) *(G-13611)*

Interplex Medical LLC 513 248-5120
25 Whitney Dr Ste 114 Milford (45150) *(G-14154)*

Interscope Manufacturing Inc 513 423-8866
2901 Carmody Blvd Middletown (45042) *(G-14050)*

Intersoft Group Inc 216 765-7351
26380 Curtiss Wright Pkwy # 303 Cleveland (44143) *(G-5581)*

Interstate Batteries 740 968-2211
44925 Lafferty Rd Saint Clairsville (43950) *(G-16792)*

Interstate Battery System Amer, Saint Clairsville Also called Interstate Batteries Inc *(G-16792)*

Interstate Contractors LLC 513 372-5393
762 Reading Rd G Mason (45040) *(G-13048)*

Interstate Diesel Service Inc (PA) 216 881-0015
5300 Lakeside Ave E Cleveland (44114) *(G-5582)*

Interstate Gas Supply Inc (PA) 614 659-5000
6100 Emerald Pkwy Dublin (43016) *(G-9090)*

Interstate Sign Products Inc 419 683-1962
432 E Main St Crestline (44827) *(G-7930)*

Interstate Tool Corporation 216 671-1077
4538 W 130th St Cleveland (44135) *(G-5583)*

Interstate Truckway Inc 614 771-1220
5440 Renner Rd Columbus (43228) *(G-7209)*

Interstate-Mcbee, Cleveland Also called Interstate Diesel Service Inc *(G-5582)*

Interstate-Mcbee LLC (PA) 800 321-4234
5300 Lakeside Ave E Cleveland (44114) *(G-5584)*

Intertec Corporation 419 537-9711
3400 Executive Pkwy Toledo (43606) *(G-18527)*

Intertek Machining & Wldg Inc 440 323-3325
6805 W River Rd S Elyria (44035) *(G-9433)*

Intertex World Resources Inc 770 214-5551
4518 Fulton Dr Nw Ste 101 Canton (44718) *(G-2739)*

Interweave Press LLC 513 531-2690
10151 Carver Rd Ste 200 Blue Ash (45242) *(G-1817)*

Inteva - Vandalia Engrg Ctr, Vandalia Also called Inteva Products LLC *(G-19297)*

Inteva Products LLC 937 280-8500
707 Crossroads Ct Vandalia (45377) *(G-19297)*

Intier Sting Systems-Lordstown, Warren Also called Magna Seating America Inc *(G-19576)*

Intigral Inc (PA) 440 439-0980
7850 Northfield Rd Bedford (44146) *(G-1432)*

Intigral Inc 440 439-0980
45 Karago Ave Youngstown (44512) *(G-21120)*

Into Great Brands Inc 888 771-5656
1010 Taylor Station Rd A Gahanna (43230) *(G-10213)*

Intwine Energy Networks LLC 216 970-5908
8401 Chagrin Rd Ste 10a Chagrin Falls (44023) *(G-3096)*

Invacare Canadian Holdings LLC 440 329-6000
1 Invacare Way Elyria (44035) *(G-9434)*

Invacare Corporation (PA) 440 329-6000
1 Invacare Way Elyria (44035) *(G-9435)*

Invacare Corporation 800 333-6900
1320 Taylor St Elyria (44035) *(G-9436)*

Invacare Corporation 440 329-6000
1200 Taylor St Elyria (44035) *(G-9437)*

Invacare Corporation 440 329-6000
38683 Taylor Pkwy North Ridgeville (44035) *(G-15381)*

Invacare Corporation (tw) 440 329-6000
39400 Taylor Pkwy North Ridgeville (44035) *(G-15382)*

Invacare Hme, North Ridgeville Also called Invacare Corporation *(G-15381)*

Invacare Holdings Corporation 440 329-6000
1 Invacare Way Elyria (44035) *(G-9438)*

Invacare Holdings Inc, Elyria Also called Invacare Holdings Corporation *(G-9438)*

Invacare International Corp (HQ) 440 329-6000
1 Invacare Way Elyria (44035) *(G-9439)*

Invacare It & Financial Svcs, Elyria Also called Invacare Corporation *(G-9436)*

Invacare Respiratory Corp 440 329-6000
899 Cleveland St Elyria (44035) *(G-9440)*

Inventive Extrusions Corp 330 874-3000
10882 Fort Laurens Rd Nw Bolivar (44612) *(G-1937)*

Investment Systems Company 440 247-2865
37840 Jackson Rd Chagrin Falls (44022) *(G-3061)*

Invisible Chef, The, Canton Also called Jaz Foods Inc *(G-2746)*

Invisible Repair Products Inc 330 798-0441
1021 Evans Ave Akron (44305) *(G-236)*

Invotec Engineering Inc 937 886-3232
10909 Industry Ln Miamisburg (45342) *(G-13820)*

Invue Security Products Inc 330 456-7776
1510 4th St Se Canton (44707) *(G-2740)*

INX International Ink Co 513 282-2920
350 Homan Rd Lebanon (45036) *(G-11809)*

INX International Ink Co 440 239-1766
18001 Englewood Dr Unit P Cleveland (44130) *(G-5585)*

Ion Vacuum Technologies, Cleveland Also called Ivac Technologies Corp *(G-5592)*

Ionbond LLC 216 831-0880
24700 Highpoint Rd Cleveland (44122) *(G-5586)*

Ioppolo Concrete Corporation 440 439-6606
10 Industry Dr Bedford (44146) *(G-1433)*

Iosil Energy Corporation 614 295-8680
5700 Green Pointe Dr N A Groveport (43125) *(G-10627)*

Iotech, Cleveland Also called Measurement Computing Corp *(G-5774)*

IPA Ltd 614 523-3974
700 Taylor Rd Ste 290 Columbus (43230) *(G-7210)*

Ips, Wadsworth Also called Parker-Hannifin Corporation *(G-19426)*

Ipsco Tubulars Inc 330 448-6772
6880 Parkway Dr Brookfield (44403) *(G-2125)*

Ipsg, Columbus Also called International Products *(G-7206)*

Ipsg / Micro Center, Hilliard Also called International Products *(G-10954)*

Iptc, Troy Also called Ishmael Precision Tool Corp *(G-18846)*

Iq Solutions Group LLC 855 367-4774
570 Polaris Pkwy Ste 110 Westerville (43082) *(G-20161)*

Irg Operating LLC 440 963-4008
850 W River Rd Vermilion (44089) *(G-19329)*

Irish Electric Motor Service, Saint Marys Also called Allan A Irish *(G-16831)*

Irock Crushers LLC 866 240-0201
5531 Canal Rd Cleveland (44125) *(G-5587)*

Iron City Wood Products Inc 330 755-2772
900 Albert St Youngstown (44505) *(G-21121)*

Iron Horse Engineering, Parkman Also called Montville Plastics & Rbr LLC *(G-15952)*

Iron Wind Metals Co LLC 513 870-0606
10488 Chester Rd Cincinnati (45215) *(G-3932)*

Ironfab LLC 614 443-3900
1771 Progress Ave Columbus (43207) *(G-7211)*

Ironhead Fabg & Contg Inc 419 690-0000
2245 Front St Toledo (43605) *(G-18528)*

Ironhead Marine Inc 419 690-0001
2245 Front St Toledo (43605) *(G-18529)*

Ironics Inc 330 652-0583
750 S Main St Niles (44446) *(G-15162)*

Ironman Metalworks LLC 614 907-6629
250 Lowery Ct Ste A Groveport (43125) *(G-10628)*

Ironrock Capital Incorporated 330 484-4887
1201 Millerton St Se Canton (44707) *(G-2741)*

Ironton Publications Inc 740 532-1441
2903 S 5th St Ironton (45638) *(G-11294)*

Ironton Tribune The, Ironton Also called Ironton Publications Inc *(G-11294)*

Irvin Oslin Inc 216 361-7555
2800 E 55th St Frnt Cleveland (44104) *(G-5588)*

Irvine Wood Recovery Inc 513 831-0060
110 Glendale Milford Rd Miamiville (45147) *(G-13894)*

Irving Materials Inc 513 844-8444
600 Augspurger Rd Hamilton (45011) *(G-10708)*

Irving Materials Inc 513 523-7127
6601 Ringwood Rd Oxford (45056) *(G-15838)*

Irwin Engraving & Printing Co 216 391-7300
5318 Saint Clair Ave # 1 Cleveland (44103) *(G-5589)*

Isaacs Jr Floyd Thomas 513 899-2342
3480 E Us Highway 22 & 3 Morrow (45152) *(G-14548)*

Isaiah Industries Inc (PA) 937 773-9840
8510 Industry Park Dr Piqua (45356) *(G-16280)*

Isco Inc 614 792-2206
6360 Fiesta Dr Columbus (43235) *(G-7212)*

Ishikawa Gasket America Inc (HQ) 419 353-7300
828 Van Camp Rd Bowling Green (43402) *(G-1990)*

Ishikawa Gasket America Inc 419 353-7300
828 Van Camp Rd Bowling Green (43402) *(G-1991)*

Ishmael Precision Tool Corp 937 335-8070
55 Industry Ct Troy (45373) *(G-18846)*

Ishos Bros Fuel Ventures Inc 586 634-0187
1289 Conant St Maumee (43537) *(G-13268)*

Ishos Bros Fuel Ventures Inc 419 913-5718
2446 W Alexis Rd Toledo (43613) *(G-18530)*

ISK Americas Incorporated (HQ) 440 357-4600
7474 Auburn Rd Painesville (44077) *(G-15892)*

Island Aseptics LLC 740 685-2548
100 Hope Ave Byesville (43723) *(G-2405)*

Island Castings Inc 231 733-1053
4321 Strasser St Nw North Canton (44720) *(G-15243)*

Isochem Incorporated 614 775-9328
7721 Sutton Pl New Albany (43054) *(G-14762)*

Isofoton North America Inc 419 591-4330
800 Independence Dr Napoleon (43545) *(G-14685)*

Isomedix Inc 440 354-2600
5960 Heisley Rd Mentor (44060) *(G-13612)*

Isostatic Pressing Svcs LLC 614 370-2140
1205 S Columbus Arprt Rd Columbus (43207) *(G-7213)*

Isotopx Inc 508 337-8467
194 Atterbury Blvd Hudson (44236) *(G-11183)*

Isp, Grove City Also called Integrated Systems Professiona *(G-10565)*

Isp Chemicals LLC 614 876-3637
1979 Atlas St Columbus (43228) *(G-7214)*

Isp Lima LLC 419 998-8700
12220 S Metcalf St Lima (45804) *(G-12031)*

Isps, Toledo Also called Industrial Screen Process *(G-18522)*

ISS, Mentor Also called Industrial Systems & Solutions *(G-13607)*

Ist International, Loveland Also called Intelligent Signal Tech *(G-12361)*

It XCEL Consulting LLC 513 847-8261
7112 Office Park Dr West Chester (45069) *(G-19886)*

It's Sew Much More, Columbus Also called Cheryl A Lucas *(G-6925)*

Itc Manufacturing, Columbus Also called Interntnal Tchncal Catings Inc *(G-7208)*

Item North America, Akron Also called Kit MB Systems Inc *(G-260)*

Iten Industries Inc (PA) 440 997-6134
4602 Benefit Ave Ashtabula (44004) *(G-813)*

Itg Brands LLC 614 431-0044
6740 Huntley Rd Columbus (43229) *(G-7215)*

Ithaca Gun Company 419 294-4113
420 N Warpole St Upper Sandusky (43351) *(G-19126)*

Itl LLC 216 831-3140
23925 Commerce Park Beachwood (44122) *(G-1274)*

Itl California LLC 216 831-4734
23925 Commerce Park Cleveland (44122) *(G-5590)*

Itl Corp (HQ) 216 831-3140
23925 Commerce Park Cleveland (44122) *(G-5591)*

Itps, Niles Also called International Technical *(G-15161)*

ITR Manufacturing LLC 419 852-8574
792 Jim Lachey Dr Saint Henry (45883) *(G-16819)*

Itran Electronics Recycling 330 659-0801
4100 Congress Pkwy W Richfield (44286) *(G-16628)*

Its, Tipp City Also called Independent Trailer Services *(G-18282)*

ITT Corporation 937 256-1705
Wright Ptrson A Frce Base Dayton (45433) *(G-8109)*

ITW Filtration Products, Bryan Also called Illinois Tool Works Inc *(G-2303)*

ITW Food Equipment Group LLC 937 332-3000
401 W Market St Troy (45373) *(G-18847)*

ITW Food Equipment Group LLC (HQ) 937 332-2396
701 S Ridge Ave Troy (45374) *(G-18848)*

ITW Hobart Brothers, Troy Also called Hobart Brothers Company *(G-18836)*

Itwfeg, Troy Also called Hobart Corporation *(G-18841)*

IV J Telecommunications LLC 606 694-1762
101 Lea St South Point (45680) *(G-17438)*

IV M Tool & Die 513 625-6464
3227 Us Highway 50 Williamsburg (45176) *(G-20409)*

Ivac Technologies Corp 216 662-4987
18678 Cranwood Pkwy Cleveland (44128) *(G-5592)*

Ivan Extruders Co Inc 330 644-7400
2404 Pickle Rd Akron (44312) *(G-237)*

Ivans Insurance Solutions, Milford Also called Applied Systems Inc *(G-14121)*

IVEX Protective Packaging Inc (HQ) 937 498-9298
456 Stolle Ave Sidney (45365) *(G-17196)*

Ivi Mining Group Ltd 740 418-7745
72116 Grey Rd Vinton (45686) *(G-19382)*

Iwata Bolt USA Inc 513 942-5050
102 Iwata Dr Fairfield (45014) *(G-9669)*

Izit Cain Sheet Metal Corp 937 667-6521
20 N 2nd St Tipp City (45371) *(G-18284)*

J & A Auto Service 614 837-6820
101 E Columbus St Pickerington (43147) *(G-16193)*

J & A Machine 330 424-5235
8362 Thomas Rd Lisbon (44432) *(G-12123)*

J & B Feed Co Inc 419 335-5821
140 S Brunell St Wauseon (43567) *(G-19685)*

J & B Rogers Inc 937 669-2677
9785 Julie Ct Tipp City (45371) *(G-18285)*

J & C Group Inc of Ohio 440 205-9658
6781 Hopkins Rd Mentor (44060) *(G-13613)*

J & C Industries Inc 216 362-8867
4808 W 130th St Cleveland (44135) *(G-5593)*

J & D Berdine Signs Inc 330 468-0556
746 E Aurora Rd Ste 3 Macedonia (44056) *(G-12461)*

J & D Mining Inc 330 339-4935
3497 University Dr Ne New Philadelphia (44663) *(G-14904)*

J & D Printing, Dayton Also called Grant John *(G-8376)*

J & F Furniture Shop 330 852-2478
3521 Township Road 166 Sugarcreek (44681) *(G-18024)*

J & G Sales 740 745-5321
10682 Camp Ohio Rd Utica (43080) *(G-19194)*

J & H Corporation 440 357-5982
444 Newell St Painesville (44077) *(G-15893)*

J & H Manufacturing LLC 330 482-2636
1652 Columbiana Lisbon Rd Columbiana (44408) *(G-6622)*

J & J Bechke Inc (PA) 440 238-1441
12931 Pearl Rd Strongsville (44136) *(G-17932)*

J & J Logging 740 896-2827
7100 Highland Ridge Rd Lowell (45744) *(G-12402)*

J & J Performance Inc 330 567-2455
410 E Wood St Shreve (44676) *(G-17159)*

J & J Performance Paintball, Shreve *Also called J & J Performance Inc* (G-17159)

J & J Snack Foods Corp 440 248-2084
5351 Naiman Pkwy Ste B Solon (44139) (G-17319)

J & J Tool & Die Inc 330 343-4721
203 W 4th St Dover (44622) (G-8994)

J & J Woodcraft, Berlin *Also called J-J Berlin Woodcraft Inc* (G-1650)

J & K Cabinetry Incorporated 513 860-3461
9920 Prnceton Glendale Rd West Chester (45246) (G-20017)

J & K Pallet Inc 937 526-5117
30 Subler Dr Versailles (45380) (G-19349)

J & K Powder Coating 330 540-6145
1336 Seaborn St Mineral Ridge (44440) (G-14305)

J & K Printing 330 456-5306
1728 Navarre Rd Sw Canton (44706) (G-2742)

J & K Wade Ltd 419 352-6163
109 E Wooster St Ste 3-4 Bowling Green (43402) (G-1992)

J & L Body Inc 216 661-2323
4848 Van Epps Rd Brooklyn Heights (44131) (G-2141)

J & L Door 330 684-1496
13505 Bodine Rd Dalton (44618) (G-8071)

J & L Management Corporation 440 205-1199
8634 Station St Mentor (44060) (G-13614)

J & L Specialty Steel Inc 330 875-6200
4055 Beck Ave Louisville (44641) (G-12317)

J & L Steel Bar LLC 440 526-0050
3587 Antony Dr Broadview Heights (44147) (G-2111)

J & L Welding Fabricating Inc 330 393-9353
140 Dana St Ne Warren (44483) (G-19561)

J & L Wood Products Inc (PA) 937 667-4064
910 Ginghamsburg Rd Tipp City (45371) (G-18286)

J & M Construction LLP 740 454-8986
8780 Hopewell National Rd Hopewell (43746) (G-11119)

J & M Cutting Tools Inc 440 622-3900
9401 Hamilton Dr Mentor (44060) (G-13615)

J & M Machine, Fairport Harbor *Also called JM Performance Products Inc* (G-9766)

J & M Manufacturing Co Inc 419 375-2376
284 Railroad St Fort Recovery (45846) (G-9955)

J & M Precision Die Cast Inc 440 365-7388
1329 Taylor St Elyria (44035) (G-9441)

J & M Welding & Fabricating, Rock Creek *Also called Weldfab Inc* (G-16687)

J & O Plastics Inc 330 927-3169
12475 Sheets Rd Rittman (44270) (G-16676)

J & P Investments Inc 513 821-2299
8100 Reading Rd Cincinnati (45237) (G-3933)

J & P Products Inc 440 974-2830
8865 East Ave Mentor (44060) (G-13616)

J & R Woodworking 330 893-0713
4925 Private Road 386 Millersburg (44654) (G-14234)

J & S Industrial Mch Pdts Inc 419 691-1380
123 Oakdale Ave Toledo (43605) (G-18531)

J & S Products Inc 330 686-5840
778 Mccauley Rd Unit 130 Stow (44224) (G-17766)

J & W Canvas Company 330 652-7678
1386 Church St Mineral Ridge (44440) (G-14306)

J A B Welding Service Inc 740 453-5868
2820 S River Rd Zanesville (43701) (G-21322)

J A Donadee Corporation (PA) 330 533-3305
535 N Broad St Ste 5 Canfield (44406) (G-2559)

J A H Woodworking LLC 740 266-6949
39 Belvedere Dr Bloomingdale (43910) (G-1723)

J A McMahon Incorporated 330 652-2588
649 Grant St Niles (44446) (G-15163)

J America LLC 614 914-2091
580 N 4th St Ste 620 Columbus (43215) (G-7216)

J and J Sales, Delaware *Also called Aci Industries Converting Ltd* (G-8816)

J and L Jewelry Manufacturing 440 546-9988
8803 Brecksville Rd # 6 Cleveland (44141) (G-5594)

J and L Manufacturing Inc 937 492-0008
9401 State Route 29 N Sidney (45365) (G-17197)

J and S Tool Incorporated 216 676-8330
15330 Brookpark Rd Cleveland (44135) (G-5595)

J B K Manufacturing & Dev, Dayton *Also called Jbk Manufacturing LLC* (G-8423)

J B Kepple Sheet Metal 740 393-2971
1010 Vernonview Dr Mount Vernon (43050) (G-14624)

J B M Machine Co Inc 440 446-0819
32 Alpha Park Cleveland (44143) (G-5596)

J B Manufacturing Inc 330 676-9744
4465 Crystal Pkwy Kent (44240) (G-11472)

J B Products, Streetsboro *Also called JB Products Co* (G-17859)

J B Stamping Inc 216 631-0013
7413 Associate Ave Cleveland (44144) (G-5597)

J B'S Crafts & Things, Mansfield *Also called Joan B Mailloux* (G-12627)

J Beischel Electric 513 860-3290
10175 International Blvd West Chester (45246) (G-20018)

J C Denier Co, Cincinnati *Also called James C Denier Co Inc* (G-3939)

J C Equipment Sales & Lsg 513 772-7612
2300 E Kemper Rd Unit 11a Cincinnati (45241) (G-3934)

J C L S Enterprises LLC 440 472-0314
742 Lewisville Rd Woodsfield (43793) (G-20718)

J C Penney Optical, Dublin *Also called Usv Optical Inc* (G-9160)

J C Robinson Products, Cincinnati *Also called James C Robinson* (G-3941)

J D Drilling Co 740 949-2512
107 S 3rd St Racine (45771) (G-16504)

J D Hydraulic Inc 419 686-5234
Rr 25 Portage (43451) (G-16424)

J D Indoor Comfort Duct Clg, Sheffield Village *Also called J D Indoor Comfort Inc* (G-17123)

J D Indoor Comfort Inc 440 949-8758
4040 Colorado Ave Sheffield Village (44054) (G-17123)

J D Knisley Logging 740 634-3207
112 W 3rd St Bainbridge (45612) (G-1058)

J D L Hardwoods 440 272-5630
9024 N Girdle Rd Middlefield (44062) (G-13943)

J D'S Pre Cast, Fremont *Also called Dennis Constuction Sanitation* (G-10142)

J Davis Sales and Assoc LLC 330 947-2038
5293 Eberly Rd Atwater (44201) (G-899)

J E Doyle Company 330 564-0743
5186 New Haven Cir Norton (44203) (G-15515)

J E Johnson Pallett Inc 614 424-9663
1465 E 17th Ave Columbus (43219) (G-7217)

J E M Industries Inc 440 951-4884
950 Erie Rd Willoughby (44095) (G-20514)

J Feldkamp Design Build Ltd 513 870-0601
3239 Profit Dr Fairfield (45014) (G-9670)

J G Pads, Akron *Also called Markethatch Co Inc* (G-285)

J H Plastics 419 937-2035
4720 W Us Highway 224 Tiffin (44883) (G-18223)

J Horst Manufacturing Co 330 828-2216
279 E Main St Dalton (44618) (G-8072)

J I C, West Jefferson *Also called Jefferson Industries Corp* (G-20079)

J I T, Lebanon *Also called Jlt Packaging Cincinnati Inc* (G-11810)

J I T Pallets Inc 330 424-0355
39196 Grant St Lisbon (44432) (G-12124)

J Ii Fire Systems Inc 513 574-0609
3628 Harrison Ave Cincinnati (45211) (G-3935)

J J Merlin Systems Inc 330 666-8609
1245 S Cleveland Massillo Copley (44321) (G-7848)

J K Logging & Chipwood Company 330 738-3571
3218 Ogara Rd Ne Salineville (43945) (G-16942)

J K Plastics Co 440 632-1482
14135 Madison Rd Middlefield (44062) (G-13944)

J K Precast, Wshngtn CT Hs *Also called James Kimmey* (G-20913)

J K Precast LLC 740 335-2188
1001 Armbrust Ave Wshngtn CT Hs (43160) (G-20912)

J L R Products Inc 330 832-9557
1212 Oberlin Ave Sw Massillon (44647) (G-13158)

J L Wannemacher Sales & Svc 419 453-3445
26992 Us 224 W Ottoville (45876) (G-15823)

J Liu of Upper Arlington Inc 614 313-1268
7765 Wavetree Ct Columbus (43235) (G-7218)

J M C Rollmasters, Mentor *Also called Johnston Manufacturing Inc* (G-13621)

J M Hamilton Group Inc 419 229-4010
1700 Elida Rd Lima (45805) (G-12032)

J M Machinery, New Franklin *Also called J McCaman Enterprises Inc* (G-14825)

J M Meat Processing 740 259-3030
360 S Zuefle Dr Mc Dermott (45652) (G-13342)

J M Mold Inc 937 778-0077
1707 Commerce Dr Piqua (45356) (G-16281)

J M Smucker, Orrville *Also called International Multifoods Corp* (G-15741)

J M Smucker Company (PA) 330 682-3000
1 Strawberry Ln Orrville (44667) (G-15742)

J M Smucker Company 419 470-7914
1250 W Laskey Rd Toledo (43612) (G-18532)

J M Smucker Company 513 482-8000
5204 Spring Grove Ave Cincinnati (45217) (G-3936)

J M Smucker Company 440 323-5100
6325 Gateway Blvd S Elyria (44035) (G-9442)

J M Smucker Company 330 497-0073
Akron Canton Reg Aprt 7 Canton (44720) (G-2743)

J McCaman Enterprises Inc 330 825-2401
3032 Franks Rd New Franklin (44216) (G-14825)

J McCoy Lumber Co Ltd (PA) 937 587-3423
6 N Main St Peebles (45660) (G-16022)

J McCoy Lumber Co Ltd 937 544-2968
733 Vaughn Ridge Rd West Union (45693) (G-20121)

J N Linrose Mfg LLC 513 867-5500
999 East Ave Hamilton (45011) (G-10709)

J O Y Aluminum Products Inc 513 797-1100
4111 Founders Blvd Batavia (45103) (G-1193)

J P Dennis Machine Inc 440 474-0247
4380 State Route 534 Rome (44085) (G-16716)

J P Industrial Products Inc (PA) 330 424-1110
11988 State Route 45 Lisbon (44432) (G-12125)

J P Industrial Products Inc 330 424-3388
Hc 518 Lisbon (44432) (G-12126)

J P Quality Printing Inc 216 791-6303
12614 Larchmere Blvd Cleveland (44120) (G-5598)

J P Sand & Gravel Company 614 497-0083
5911 Lockbourne Rd Lockbourne (43137) (G-12147)

(G-0000) Company's Geographic Section entry number

J P Suggins Mobile Welding.................................216 566-7131
2020 Saint Clair Ave Ne Cleveland (44114) *(G-5599)*

J P Tool Inc..419 354-8696
2019 Wood Bridge Blvd Bowling Green (43402) *(G-1993)*

J R Custom Unlimited...513 894-9800
2620 Bobmeyer Rd Hamilton (45015) *(G-10710)*

J R Engineering, Barberton *Also called Jr Engineering Inc (G-1123)*

J R Goslee Co...330 723-4904
1154 W Smith Rd Medina (44256) *(G-13428)*

J R M Chemical Inc...216 475-8488
4881 Neo Pkwy Cleveland (44128) *(G-5600)*

J R Machining Inc...330 528-3406
5170 Hudson Dr Ste G Hudson (44236) *(G-11184)*

J R S Hydraulic Welding, Columbus *Also called Jrs Hydraulic & Welding (G-7246)*

J R Tool & Die, Wooster *Also called McCann Tool & Die Inc (G-20803)*

J S C Publishing..614 424-6911
958 King Ave Columbus (43212) *(G-7219)*

J S Company..440 632-0052
16351 Nauvoo Rd Middlefield (44062) *(G-13945)*

J S Manufacturing LLC..330 815-2136
4631 Mogadore Rd Kent (44240) *(G-11473)*

J S Stairs..440 632-5680
16118 Old State Rd Middlefield (44062) *(G-13946)*

J Schrader Co...216 961-2890
4603 Fenwick Ave Cleveland (44102) *(G-5601)*

J Smokin..330 466-7087
9797 Benner Rd Rittman (44270) *(G-16677)*

J Sport, Millersburg *Also called Kent Sporting Goods Co Inc (G-14237)*

J T E Corp..937 454-1112
5675 Webster St Dayton (45414) *(G-8418)*

J T Eaton & Co Inc..330 425-7801
1393 Highland Rd Twinsburg (44087) *(G-18960)*

J T M, Solon *Also called Jtm Products Inc (G-17324)*

J Tek Tool & Mold Inc..419 547-9476
304 Elm St Clyde (43410) *(G-6541)*

J Treharn Co Inc...330 743-8215
1024 Mahoning Ave Ste 5 Youngstown (44502) *(G-21122)*

J Valtier Gas and Oil Co Inc.................................740 342-2839
10416 State Route 37 Malta (43758) *(G-12537)*

J W Devers & Son Inc...937 854-3040
5 N Broadway St Trotwood (45426) *(G-18797)*

J W Goss Co Inc (PA)..330 395-0739
410 South St Sw Warren (44483) *(G-19562)*

J W Harris Co Inc..216 481-8100
22801 Saint Clair Ave Euclid (44117) *(G-9587)*

J W Harwood Co (PA)..216 531-6230
18001 Roseland Rd Cleveland (44112) *(G-5602)*

J W P, Urbana *Also called Johnson Welded Products Inc (G-19166)*

J Williams & Associates Inc.................................330 887-1392
8761 Virginia Dr Westfield Center (44251) *(G-20244)*

J Zamberlan & Co...740 765-9028
100 Keagler Dr Bldg 4 Steubenville (43953) *(G-17700)*

J&D Beck Co Inc...419 224-0027
325 W High St Lima (45801) *(G-12033)*

J&J Precision Fabricators.....................................330 482-4964
1341 Heck Rd Columbiana (44408) *(G-6623)*

J&J Precision Machine Ltd...................................330 923-5783
1474 Main St Cuyahoga Falls (44221) *(G-8012)*

J&R Pallet Ltd..740 226-1112
1100 Travis Rd Waverly (45690) *(G-19712)*

J-C-R Tech Inc..937 783-2296
936 Cherry St Blanchester (45107) *(G-1714)*

J-Fab...740 384-2649
21 N Wisconsin Ave Wellston (45692) *(G-19764)*

J-J Berlin Woodcraft Inc (PA)...............................330 893-9171
4805 State Rt 39 Main St Berlin (44610) *(G-1650)*

J-Lenco Inc (PA)..740 499-2260
664 N High St Morral (43337) *(G-14540)*

J-M Designs LLC..419 794-2114
128 W Wayne St Maumee (43537) *(G-13269)*

J-Mak Industries, Columbus *Also called Panacea Products Corporation (G-7456)*

J-Vac Industries Inc..740 384-2155
202 S Pennsylvania Ave Wellston (45692) *(G-19765)*

J3 Point-Of-Sale, Bucyrus *Also called Ganymede Technologies Corp (G-2344)*

J3 Systems Ltd...419 562-5522
1695 Marion Rd Bucyrus (44820) *(G-2351)*

Jab Sales Inc (PA)..440 446-0606
39 Alpha Park Cleveland (44143) *(G-5603)*

Jabco & Associates Inc.......................................513 752-0600
1188 Ferris Rd Amelia (45102) *(G-578)*

JAC Construction Ohio Llc..................................440 564-5005
14985 Cross Creek Pkwy Newbury (44065) *(G-15097)*

Jack A Byte Mltmdia Gaming LLC.........................937 321-1716
893 S Main St 375 Englewood (45322) *(G-9527)*

Jack C Keir Inc...513 422-4860
4785 Emerald Way Ste A Middletown (45044) *(G-14051)*

Jack G Walker..440 352-4222
9517 Jackson St Mentor (44060) *(G-13617)*

Jack Gruber...740 408-2718
2606 County Rd Ste 184 Cardington (43315) *(G-2912)*

Jack Huffman...740 384-5178
1210 Hiram West Rd Wellston (45692) *(G-19766)*

Jack Pine Studio...614 291-0699
420 1/2 E 5th Ave Columbus (43201) *(G-7220)*

Jack R Stiner Models & Pattern............................330 494-1730
93 Spruce Dr Nw Canton (44720) *(G-2744)*

Jack Walters & Sons Corp...................................937 653-8986
5045 N Us Highway 68 Urbana (43078) *(G-19164)*

Jackabyte, Englewood *Also called Jack A Byte Mltmdia Gaming LLC (G-9527)*

Jackie Os Pub Brewery LLC.................................740 274-0777
25 Campbell St Athens (45701) *(G-873)*

Jackpot Festival & Gaming...................................216 531-3500
650a E 185th St Cleveland (44119) *(G-5604)*

Jacks Marine Inc...440 997-5060
2000 Great Lakes Ave Ashtabula (44004) *(G-814)*

Jackson David Do...419 872-3201
1103 Village Square Dr # 101 Perrysburg (43551) *(G-16113)*

Jackson Deluxe Cleaners Ltd (PA).........................419 592-2826
522 Hobson St Napoleon (43545) *(G-14686)*

Jackson Machine & Fabrication.............................740 682-3994
6679 State Route 93 Oak Hill (45656) *(G-15598)*

Jackson Monument Inc..740 286-1590
14 Fairmount St Jackson (45640) *(G-11316)*

Jackson Tube Service Inc (PA).............................937 773-8550
8210 Industry Park Dr Piqua (45356) *(G-16282)*

Jackson Wells Services.......................................419 886-2017
1201 Mill Rd Bellville (44813) *(G-1571)*

Jacksonlea, Hamilton *Also called Jason Incorporated (G-10711)*

Jaco Inc...513 722-3947
1451 State Route 28 Ste D Loveland (45140) *(G-12364)*

Jaco Manufacturing Company (PA)........................440 234-4000
468 Geiger St Berea (44017) *(G-1621)*

Jaco Manufacturing Company...............................440 234-4000
90 Karl St Berea (44017) *(G-1622)*

Jaco Products, Middlefield *Also called D Martone Industries Inc (G-13928)*

Jacobi Carbons Inc..215 546-3900
432 Mccormick Blvd Columbus (43213) *(G-7221)*

Jacobs & Sons Logging LLC.................................419 678-3802
132 N Sycamore St Saint Henry (45883) *(G-16820)*

Jacobs Mechanical Co...513 681-6800
4500 W Mitchell Ave Cincinnati (45232) *(G-3937)*

Jacobson Mfg LLC (HQ)......................................330 725-8853
941 Lake Rd 955 Medina (44256) *(G-13429)*

Jacobson Mfg LLC...740 467-3199
2140 Refugee Rd Ne Millersport (43046) *(G-14295)*

Jacobson Mfg - Tiffin LLC...................................419 447-2221
1988 S County Road 593 Tiffin (44883) *(G-18224)*

Jacoby Old Smokehouse, West Unity *Also called Jacoby Packing Co (G-20130)*

Jacoby Packing Co..419 924-2684
505 S Main St West Unity (43570) *(G-20130)*

Jacoby Tarbox Co, Strongsville *Also called Clark-Reliance Corporation (G-17903)*

Jacodar Inc..330 832-9557
1212 Oberlin Ave Sw Massillon (44647) *(G-13159)*

Jacp Inc (PA)..513 353-3660
5928 Hamilton Cleves Rd Miamitown (45041) *(G-13888)*

Jacqua's Monogramming & Design, Findlay *Also called Jaquas Monogramming & Design (G-9844)*

Jacqueline L Vandyke..740 593-6779
10414 State Route 550 Athens (45701) *(G-874)*

JAD Machine Company Inc..................................419 256-6332
10620 County Road J Malinta (43535) *(G-12535)*

Jade Products Inc..440 352-1700
9309 Mercantile Dr Mentor (44060) *(G-13618)*

Jade Tool Co Inc...937 376-4740
1280 Burnett Dr Xenia (45385) *(G-20957)*

Jadlyn Inc..330 670-9545
1930 N Clvland Mssllon Rd Akron (44333) *(G-238)*

Jae Tech Inc..330 698-2000
32 Hunter St Apple Creek (44606) *(G-640)*

Jafe Decorating Co Inc..937 547-1888
1250 Martin St Greenville (45331) *(G-10506)*

Jaffe & Gross Jewelry Company............................937 461-9450
3951 Far Hills Ave Dayton (45429) *(G-8419)*

Jagger Cone Company Inc....................................419 682-1816
304 Ellis St Stryker (43557) *(G-18004)*

Jaguar Medical Supplies Inc.................................440 263-2780
12955 York Delta Dr Ste G North Royalton (44133) *(G-15428)*

Jain America Foods Inc (HQ)...............................614 850-9400
1819 Walcutt Rd Ste 1 Columbus (43228) *(G-7222)*

Jain America Holdings Inc.....................................614 850-9400
1819 Walcutt Rd Ste 1 Columbus (43228) *(G-7223)*

Jain Americas, Columbus *Also called Jain America Foods Inc (G-7222)*

Jakes Sportswear Ltd...740 746-8356
112 Elm St Sugar Grove (43155) *(G-18012)*

Jakmar Incorporated...513 631-4303
3280 Hageman Ave Cincinnati (45241) *(G-3938)*

A
L
P
H
A
B
E
T
I
C

Jakprints Inc 877 246-3132
 3133 Chester Ave Cleveland (44114) *(G-5605)*

Jalco Industries Inc 740 286-3808
 330 Athens St Jackson (45640) *(G-11317)*

Jamac Inc 419 625-9790
 422 Buchanan St Sandusky (44870) *(G-16974)*

Jamar Precision Grinding Co 330 220-0099
 2661 Center Rd Hinckley (44233) *(G-11026)*

Jamen Tool & Die Co (PA) 330 788-6521
 4450 Lake Park Rd Youngstown (44512) *(G-21123)*

Jamen Tool & Die Co 330 782-6731
 914 E Indianola Ave Youngstown (44502) *(G-21124)*

James Alexander President, Cincinnati *Also called Baldie Import and Export Corp* *(G-3435)*

James Bunnell Inc 513 353-1100
 7000 Dry Fork Rd Cleves (45002) *(G-6516)*

James C Denier Co Inc 513 385-6272
 3684 Poole Rd Cincinnati (45251) *(G-3939)*

James C Free Inc (PA) 937 298-0171
 3100 Far Hills Ave Dayton (45429) *(G-8420)*

James C Free Inc 513 793-0133
 9555 Main St Ste 1 Cincinnati (45242) *(G-3940)*

James C Robinson 513 969-7482
 442 Chestnut St Apt 1 Cincinnati (45203) *(G-3941)*

James Eastwood 614 444-1340
 663 Harmon Plz Columbus (43223) *(G-7224)*

James Engineering Inc 740 373-9521
 2163 State Route 821 Marietta (45750) *(G-12794)*

James F Seme 440 759-6455
 292 Karl St Berea (44017) *(G-1623)*

James Free Jewelers, Dayton *Also called James C Free Inc* *(G-8420)*

James Free Jewellers, Cincinnati *Also called James C Free Inc* *(G-3940)*

James G Morehouse 513 752-2236
 4814a Woodlawn Dr Milford (45150) *(G-14155)*

James J Fairbanks Company Inc 330 534-1374
 7342 Hubbard Bedford Rd Hubbard (44425) *(G-11132)*

James Kimmey 740 335-5746
 1000 Armbrust Ave Wshngtn CT Hs (43160) *(G-20913)*

James L Wereb 440 942-2405
 38005 Apollo Pkwy Ste 2 Willoughby (44094) *(G-20515)*

James L Williams 740 865-3382
 52 Tr 12 Wingett Run (45789) *(G-20709)*

James Logan Logging, Jackson *Also called For Every Home* *(G-11314)*

James McGuire 614 483-9825
 190 Ziegler Ave Columbus (43207) *(G-7225)*

James O Emert Jr 330 650-6990
 7920 Princewood Dr Hudson (44236) *(G-11185)*

James Oshea 614 262-3188
 326 Richards Rd Columbus (43214) *(G-7226)*

James R Bernhardt Producing 330 345-5306
 6717 Cleveland Rd Wooster (44691) *(G-20789)*

James R Eaton 937 435-7767
 535 Clareridge Ln Dayton (45458) *(G-8421)*

James R Smail Inc 330 264-7500
 2285 Eagle Pass Ste B Wooster (44691) *(G-20790)*

James Ryan Soloman 740 659-2304
 5471 High Point Rd Glenford (43739) *(G-10398)*

James Sorgi 330 653-5180
 7041 Darrow Rd Hudson (44236) *(G-11186)*

James Thomas Shiveley 330 468-2601
 585 Highland Rd E Macedonia (44056) *(G-12462)*

James W Cunningham 419 639-2111
 125 Baker St Green Springs (44836) *(G-10471)*

Jamestown Cont Cleveland Inc 216 831-3700
 4500 Renaissance Pkwy Cleveland (44128) *(G-5606)*

Jamestown Industries Inc 330 779-0670
 650 N Meridian Rd Ste 3 Youngstown (44509) *(G-21125)*

Jamison Manufacturing Co 440 237-8085
 9116 Akins Rd Cleveland (44133) *(G-5607)*

Jamtek Enterprises Inc 513 738-4700
 10845 State Route 128 Harrison (45030) *(G-10786)*

Jan Squires Inc 440 988-7859
 7985 Leavitt Rd Amherst (44001) *(G-599)*

Jane Valentine 330 452-3154
 912 Woodside Ave Se North Canton (44720) *(G-15244)*

Janell Inc 740 532-9111
 1014 S 2nd St Ironton (45638) *(G-11295)*

Janet Sullivan 419 658-2333
 3480 State Route 15 Ney (43549) *(G-15142)*

Janeway Signs Inc 937 237-8433
 7825 Waynetowne Blvd Dayton (45424) *(G-8422)*

Janorpot LLC 330 564-0232
 3175 Gilchrist Rd Mogadore (44260) *(G-14378)*

Janova LLC 614 638-6785
 7570 N Goodrich Sq New Albany (43054) *(G-14763)*

Janson Industries 330 455-7029
 1200 Garfield Ave Sw Canton (44706) *(G-2745)*

Janszen Loudspeaker Ltd 614 448-1811
 480 Trade Rd Columbus (43204) *(G-7227)*

Japlar Group Inc 513 791-7192
 3210 Wasson Rd Cincinnati (45209) *(G-3942)*

Japlar Schauer, Cincinnati *Also called Japlar Group Inc* *(G-3942)*

Jaquas Monogramming & Design 419 422-2244
 1016 Tiffin Ave Ste E Findlay (45840) *(G-9844)*

Jarman Printing Company LLC 330 823-8585
 350 S Union Ave Alliance (44601) *(G-519)*

Jasa Asphalt Russell Standard, Akron *Also called Russell Standard Corporation* *(G-389)*

Jasmine Distributing Ltd 216 251-9420
 12117 Berea Rd Cleveland (44111) *(G-5608)*

Jason C Gibson 740 663-4520
 414 Bethel Rd Chillicothe (45601) *(G-3246)*

Jason Incorporated 513 860-3400
 3440 Symmes Rd Hamilton (45015) *(G-10711)*

Jason Incorporated 419 668-4474
 12406 Us Rte 250 Milan (44846) *(G-14113)*

Jason Stuller Pro Shop LLC (PA) 419 882-3197
 5201 Corey Rd Sylvania (43560) *(G-18113)*

Jasstek Inc 614 808-3600
 555 Metro Pl N Ste 100 Dublin (43017) *(G-9091)*

Jatdco, Seville *Also called Atlantic Tool & Die Company* *(G-17068)*

Jatdco LLC 440 238-6570
 19963 Progress Dr Strongsville (44149) *(G-17933)*

Jatrodiesel Inc 937 847-8050
 845 N Main St Miamisburg (45342) *(G-13821)*

Javanation 419 584-1705
 108 S Main St Celina (45822) *(G-3003)*

Jax Wax Inc 614 476-6769
 3145 E 17th Ave Columbus (43219) *(G-7228)*

Jaxon's, Dayton *Also called Dik Jaxon Products Co* *(G-8305)*

Jay Dee Service Corporation 330 425-1546
 1320 Highland Rd E Macedonia (44056) *(G-12463)*

Jay Instruments 513 733-5200
 11501 Goldcoast Dr Cincinnati (45249) *(G-3943)*

Jay Tackett 740 779-1715
 387 Musselman Station Rd Frankfort (45628) *(G-9999)*

Jay-Em Aerospace Corporation 330 923-0333
 75 Marc Dr Cuyahoga Falls (44223) *(G-8013)*

Jaymac Systems Inc 440 498-0810
 34300 Sherbrook Park Dr Solon (44139) *(G-17320)*

Jayna Inc (PA) 937 335-8922
 15 Marybill Dr S Troy (45373) *(G-18849)*

Jayron Fabrication LLC 740 335-3184
 13140 New Martinsburg Rd Leesburg (45135) *(G-11852)*

Jaytee Division, Mentor *Also called Arem Co* *(G-13526)*

Jaz Foods Inc 800 456-7115
 1818 Hopple Ave Sw Canton (44706) *(G-2746)*

Jazz Textile Impressions 419 242-5940
 1425 Holland Rd Maumee (43537) *(G-13270)*

JB Industries Ltd (PA) 330 856-4587
 160 Clifton Dr Ne Ste 4 Warren (44484) *(G-19563)*

JB Machining Concepts LLC 419 523-0096
 995 Sugar Mill Dr Ottawa (45875) *(G-15797)*

JB Products Co. 330 342-0223
 10299 Wellman Rd Streetsboro (44241) *(G-17859)*

Jbar A/C Inc 216 447-4294
 10221 Sweet Valley Dr Cleveland (44125) *(G-5609)*

Jbc Technologies Inc 440 327-4522
 7887 Bliss Pkwy North Ridgeville (44039) *(G-15383)*

Jbf Repair Service LLC 740 550-0089
 7382 Unit B St Rt 7 Proctorville (45669) *(G-16490)*

JBI Corporation 419 855-3389
 22325 State Route 51 W Genoa (43430) *(G-10361)*

Jbj Technologies Inc 216 469-7297
 185 E 280th St Euclid (44132) *(G-9588)*

Jbk Manufacturing LLC 937 233-8300
 2127 Troy St Dayton (45404) *(G-8423)*

Jbm Enterprises, Powell *Also called Michele Mellen* *(G-16478)*

Jbm Technologies Inc 419 368-4362
 1926 State Rte 179 Hayesville (44838) *(G-10844)*

Jbs Industries, Lebanon *Also called Mix-Masters Inc* *(G-11817)*

Jbs Instruments, Columbus *Also called Aquacalc LLC* *(G-6767)*

Jbt Foodtech, Sandusky *Also called John Bean Technologies Corp* *(G-16975)*

Jbw Systems Inc 614 882-5008
 5840 Chandler Ct Westerville (43082) *(G-20162)*

JC and Associates Sylvania LLC 419 824-0011
 5129 Main St Sylvania (43560) *(G-18114)*

JC Carter LLC 949 764-6465
 26451 Curtiss Wright Pkwy # 106 Richmond Heights (44143) *(G-16654)*

JC Carter Nozzles, Richmond Heights *Also called JC Carter LLC* *(G-16654)*

JC Electric 330 760-2915
 9717 State Route 88 Garrettsville (44231) *(G-10325)*

JC Roofing Supply (PA) 937 258-9999
 1535 Keystone Ave Dayton (45403) *(G-8424)*

JCB Arrowhead Products Inc 440 546-4288
 8223 Brecksville Rd # 100 Brecksville (44141) *(G-2057)*

JCB Payroll Solutions, Cincinnati *Also called Fields Associates Inc* *(G-3755)*

Jci Jones Chemicals Inc 330 825-2531
 2500 Vanderhoof Rd New Franklin (44203) *(G-14826)*

Jck Industries 419 433-6277
 730 River Rd Huron (44839) *(G-11229)*

(G-0000) Company's Geographic Section entry number

Jcl Equipment Co Inc 937 374-1010
  915 Trumbull St Xenia (45385) *(G-20958)*

JCP Signs & Graphix Inc 740 965-3058
  12920 Gorsuch Rd Galena (43021) *(G-10244)*

JD Enterprises 937 764-1611
  8493 State Route 785 Hillsboro (45133) *(G-11005)*

JD Norman Industries Inc 216 671-8000
  4650 Tiedeman Rd Brooklyn (44144) *(G-2129)*

JD Power Systems LLC 614 317-9394
  4079 Lyman Dr Hilliard (43026) *(G-10955)*

JE Grote Company Inc (PA) 614 868-8414
  1160 Gahanna Pkwy Columbus (43230) *(G-7229)*

Jeb Modern Machines Ltd 419 639-3937
  3360 N State Route 19 Republic (44867) *(G-16579)*

Jebco Machine Company Inc 330 452-2909
  1311 Greenfield Ave Sw Canton (44706) *(G-2747)*

Jec Forest & Paper Related Co, Miamisburg *Also called Johnson Energy Company (G-13822)*

Jech Technologies Inc 740 927-3495
  13962 Olde Post Rd Pickerington (43147) *(G-16194)*

Jed Industries Inc 440 639-9973
  320 River St Grand River (44045) *(G-10451)*

Jed Tool Company 937 857-9222
  8058 E Troy Urbana Rd Casstown (45312) *(G-2970)*

Jeff Bonham Electric Inc 937 233-7662
  3647 Wright Way Rd Dayton (45424) *(G-8425)*

Jeff Cales Customer AVI LLC 330 298-9479
  8101 State Route 44 A Ravenna (44266) *(G-16534)*

Jeff Couchs Campers LLC 513 863-7000
  2122 Hamilton Eaton Rd Hamilton (45011) *(G-10712)*

Jeff Couchs Rv Nation, Hamilton *Also called Jeff Couchs Campers LLC (G-10712)*

Jeff Katz (PA) 614 834-0404
  6265 Mamie Dr Pickerington (43147) *(G-16195)*

Jeff Pendergrass 513 575-1226
  6037 Mill Row Ct Milford (45150) *(G-14156)*

Jeff Wyler Chevrolet Inc 513 752-3447
  1117 State Route 32 Batavia (45103) *(G-1194)*

Jeff Wyler Mazda, Batavia *Also called Jeff Wyler Chevrolet Inc (G-1194)*

Jeffco Sheltered Workshop 740 264-4608
  256 John Scott Hwy Steubenville (43952) *(G-17701)*

Jefferson Industries Corp (PA) 614 879-5300
  6670 State Route 29 West Jefferson (43162) *(G-20079)*

Jefferson Landmark Inc (PA) 740 944-1971
  1525 State Route 152 Bloomingdale (43910) *(G-1724)*

Jefferson Smurfit Corporation 440 248-4370
  6385 Cochran Rd Solon (44139) *(G-17321)*

Jeffery A Burns 419 845-2129
  7430 Linn Hipsher Rd Caledonia (43314) *(G-2439)*

Jeffrey A Clark 419 866-8775
  148 N King Rd Holland (43528) *(G-11067)*

Jeffrey Adams Logging Inc 740 634-2286
  3656 Us Highway 50 W Bainbridge (45612) *(G-1059)*

Jeffrey Brandewie 937 726-7765
  30 E Park St Fort Loramie (45845) *(G-9933)*

Jeffrey L Becht Inc 937 264-2070
  2781 Thunderhawk Ct Dayton (45414) *(G-8426)*

Jeffrey Reedy 614 794-9292
  237 E Broadway Ave Ste D Westerville (43081) *(G-20219)*

Jeffrey Weaver, Sharon Center *Also called Sharon Printing Co Inc (G-17110)*

Jeffs Bakery 937 890-9703
  210 Groveview Ave Dayton (45415) *(G-8427)*

Jehm Technologies Inc 440 355-5558
  612 N Center St Ste 201 Lagrange (44050) *(G-11628)*

Jeld-Wen Inc 740 397-1144
  1201 Newark Rd Mount Vernon (43050) *(G-14625)*

Jeld-Wen Inc 740 964-1431
  91 Heritage Dr Etna (43062) *(G-9557)*

Jeld-Wen Inc 740 397-3403
  335 Commerce Dr Mount Vernon (43050) *(G-14626)*

Jeld-Wen Millwork Masters, Etna *Also called Jeld-Wen Inc (G-9557)*

Jeld-Wen Windows, Mount Vernon *Also called Jeld-Wen Inc (G-14625)*

Jena Tool Inc 937 296-1122
  5219 Springboro Pike Moraine (45439) *(G-14497)*

Jenco Manufacturing Inc 216 898-9682
  7682 Valley Vista Rd Independence (44131) *(G-11261)*

Jenkins Motor Parts 330 525-4011
  38 Westville Lake Rd Beloit (44609) *(G-1583)*

Jennmar McSweeney LLC 740 377-3354
  235 Commerce Dr South Point (45680) *(G-17439)*

Jensar Manufacturing LLC 419 727-8320
  1230 S Expressway Dr Toledo (43608) *(G-18533)*

Jensen & Sons Inc 419 471-1000
  4481 Monroe St Toledo (43613) *(G-18534)*

Jergens Inc (PA) 216 486-5540
  15700 S Waterloo Rd Cleveland (44110) *(G-5610)*

Jerguson, Strongsville *Also called Clark-Reliance Corporation (G-17902)*

Jerl Machine Inc 419 873-0270
  11140 Avenue Rd Perrysburg (43551) *(G-16114)*

Jerold Optical Inc 216 781-4279
  800 Huron Rd E Cleveland (44115) *(G-5611)*

Jerpbak-Bayless Co 440 248-5387
  34150 Solon Rd Solon (44139) *(G-17322)*

Jerry Harolds Doors Unlimited (PA) 740 635-4949
  415 Hall St Bridgeport (43912) *(G-2090)*

Jerry Moore Inc (PA) 330 877-1155
  1010 Sunnyside St Sw Hartville (44632) *(G-10825)*

Jerry Pulfer 937 778-1861
  900 S Main St Piqua (45356) *(G-16283)*

Jerry Tadlock 937 544-2851
  5645 State Route 125 West Union (45693) *(G-20122)*

Jerry Tools Inc 513 242-3211
  6200 Vine St Cincinnati (45216) *(G-3944)*

Jerry's Welding Supply ICN, Hillsboro *Also called Jerrys Welding Supply Inc (G-11006)*

Jerrys Welding Supply Inc 937 364-1500
  5367 Us Highway 50 Hillsboro (45133) *(G-11006)*

Jersey West Drilling Inc 513 398-0774
  6715 Irwin Simpson Rd Mason (45040) *(G-13049)*

JES Foods Inc (PA) 216 883-8987
  4733 Broadway Ave Cleveland (44127) *(G-5612)*

JES Foods/Celina Inc 419 586-7446
  1800 Industrial Dr Celina (45822) *(G-3004)*

Jesco Products Inc 440 233-5828
  11811 Robson Rd Grafton (44044) *(G-10431)*

Jet Container Company 614 444-2133
  1033 Brentnell Ave # 100 Columbus (43219) *(G-7230)*

Jet Dock Systems Inc 216 750-2264
  9601 Corporate Cir Cleveland (44125) *(G-5613)*

Jet Electric, Williamsport *Also called R Gordon Jones Inc (G-20418)*

Jet Fuel Tech Inc 614 463-1986
  100 E Broad St Fl 16 Columbus (43215) *(G-7231)*

Jet Machine, Cincinnati *Also called Wulco Inc (G-4611)*

Jet Machine & Manufacturing, Cincinnati *Also called Wulco Inc (G-4612)*

Jet Rubber Company 330 325-1821
  4457 Tallmadge Rd Rootstown (44272) *(G-16723)*

Jet Stream International Inc 330 505-9988
  931 Summit Ave Unit 3 Niles (44446) *(G-15164)*

Jet Tool and Prototype Co 419 666-1199
  230 W Perry St Walbridge (43465) *(G-19459)*

Jetcoat LLC 800 394-0047
  472 Brehl Ave Columbus (43223) *(G-7232)*

Jetoptera Inc 516 456-7609
  3092 Crooked Tree Dr Mason (45040) *(G-13050)*

Jett Industries Inc 740 344-4140
  180 Grant St Newark (43055) *(G-15024)*

Jett's Professional Embroidery, Greenfield *Also called Jetts Embroideries (G-10481)*

Jetts Embroideries 937 981-3716
  1060 Jefferson St Greenfield (45123) *(G-10481)*

Jewelry Art, Hudson *Also called Handcrafted Jewelry Inc (G-11178)*

Jewels By Img Inc 440 461-4464
  5470 Mayfield Rd Cleveland (44124) *(G-5614)*

Jewett Supply 419 738-9882
  607 N Water St Wapakoneta (45895) *(G-19492)*

Jewish Journal Monthly Mag 330 746-3251
  505 Gypsy Ln Youngstown (44504) *(G-21126)*

Jeyes US Holdings Inc 614 984-2896
  8860 Smiths Mill Rd # 500 New Albany (43054) *(G-14764)*

JF Martt and Associates Inc 330 938-4000
  501 N Johnson Rd Sebring (44672) *(G-17046)*

Jfm Industries 330 550-6009
  111 Elm St Struthers (44471) *(G-17992)*

Jh Industries Inc 330 963-4105
  1981 E Aurora Rd Twinsburg (44087) *(G-18961)*

Jh Instruments, Columbus *Also called Fcx Performance Inc (G-7078)*

Jh Woodworking LLC 330 276-7600
  11259 Township Road 71 Killbuck (44637) *(G-11595)*

Jhg Retail Services LLC 216 447-0831
  319 Cooper St Cincinnati (45215) *(G-3945)*

Jhs Toyz LLC 440 946-6600
  35125 Vine St Willowick (44095) *(G-20648)*

Jilco Precision Mold & Mch Co 330 633-9645
  1245 Devalera St Akron (44310) *(G-239)*

Jillians Ltd 740 450-7766
  3935 Northpointe Dr Zanesville (43701) *(G-21323)*

Jim Bumen Construction Company (PA) 740 663-2659
  3218 S Bridge St Chillicothe (45601) *(G-3247)*

Jim Davis 740 335-8030
  1020 Leesburg Ave Wshngtn CT Hs (43160) *(G-20914)*

Jim Denigris & Sons Ldscpg 440 449-5548
  1520 Longwood Dr Cleveland (44124) *(G-5615)*

Jim H Niemeyer 419 422-2465
  1004 W Sandusky St Findlay (45840) *(G-9845)*

Jim Nier Construction Inc 740 289-2629
  3877 Us Highway 23 Piketon (45661) *(G-16221)*

Jim Nier Construction Inc (PA) 740 289-3925
  340 Bailey Chapel Rd Piketon (45661) *(G-16222)*

Jims Donut Shop 937 898-4222
  122 E National Rd Vandalia (45377) *(G-19298)*

A
L
P
H
A
B
E
T
I
C

Jit Company Inc 614 529-8010
  2180 Venus Dr Hilliard (43026) (G-10956)

Jit Milrob, Aurora Also called JIT Packaging Inc (G-927)

JIT Packaging Inc (PA) 330 562-8080
  250 Page Rd Aurora (44202) (G-927)

Jit Packaging Cincinnati Inc (PA) 513 933-0250
  1550 Kingsview Dr Lebanon (45036) (G-11810)

Jj Delong & Associates, Cleveland Also called JJ Delong & Associates Inc (G-5616)

JJ Delong & Associates Inc 216 861-4727
  526 Superior Ave E # 633 Cleveland (44114) (G-5616)

Jj Seville LLC 330 769-2071
  22 Milton St Seville (44273) (G-17076)

Jj Sleeves Inc 440 205-1055
  6850 Patterson Dr Mentor (44060) (G-13619)

Jjb Engineer 330 807-0671
  2695 N Haven Blvd Ste 10 Cuyahoga Falls (44223) (G-8014)

Jjc Plastics Ltd 330 334-3637
  4021 Deerspring Ct Norton (44203) (G-15516)

Jjc Products Inc 330 666-4582
  3670 Forest Oaks Dr Akron (44333) (G-240)

Jjkb Enterprises LLC 513 731-4332
  6125 Montgomery Rd Unit 1 Cincinnati (45213) (G-3946)

Jjs3 Foundation 513 751-3292
  11925 Kemper Springs Dr Cincinnati (45240) (G-3947)

Jk Digital Publishing LLC 937 299-0185
  20 Heatherwoode Cir Springboro (45066) (G-17484)

Jk-Co LLC 419 422-5240
  16960 E State Route 12 Findlay (45840) (G-9846)

Jki Sales 614 581-5498
  3815 Gabrielle Dr Columbus (43234) (G-7233)

Jl Safety LLC 440 582-5866
  2781 Timberwood Dr Broadview Heights (44147) (G-2112)

Jlg Industries Inc 330 684-0132
  2927 Paradise St Orrville (44667) (G-15743)

Jlg Industries Inc 330 684-0200
  600 E Chestnut St Orrville (44667) (G-15744)

Jlm Logging LLC 330 340-4863
  3334 County Road 160 Millersburg (44654) (G-14235)

Jls Funeral Home 614 625-1220
  2322 Randy Ct Columbus (43232) (G-7234)

JLW - TW Corp 216 361-5940
  35350 Chester Rd Avon (44011) (G-998)

JM Gourmet Popcorn, Toledo Also called Celebrations (G-18391)

JM Logging Inc 740 441-0941
  1624 Graham School Rd Gallipolis (45631) (G-10301)

JM Performance Products Inc 440 357-1234
  1234 High St Fairport Harbor (44077) (G-9766)

JM Printing 740 412-8666
  134 W Main St Circleville (43113) (G-4632)

Jmac Inc (PA) 614 436-2418
  200 W Nationwide Blvd # 1 Columbus (43215) (G-7235)

Jmc Steel Group 216 910-3700
  3201 Entp Pkwy Ste 150 Beachwood (44122) (G-1275)

Jmike LLC 740 525-1734
  110 Windy Pt Marietta (45750) (G-12795)

JMJ Paper Inc 216 941-8100
  681 Moore Rd Ste D Avon Lake (44012) (G-1034)

Jmr Enterprises LLC 937 618-1736
  7808 Hyatts Ln Maineville (45039) (G-12525)

JMS Composites, Springfield Also called JMS Industries Inc (G-17581)

JMS Industries Inc 937 325-3502
  3240 E National Rd Springfield (45505) (G-17581)

JMw Welding and Mfg 330 484-2428
  512 45th St Sw Canton (44706) (G-2748)

Jnc,, Piketon Also called Jim Nier Construction Inc (G-16222)

Jnj Distributors, Cincinnati Also called Great Midwest Tobacco Inc (G-3846)

Jnp Group LLC 800 735-9645
  449 Freedlander Rd Wooster (44691) (G-20791)

Jo-Bar Manufacturing Corp 440 232-5555
  17259 Chillicothe Rd Chagrin Falls (44023) (G-3097)

Joan B Mailloux 361 992-5311
  2273 Lakewood Dr Mansfield (44905) (G-12627)

Job News (PA) 513 984-5724
  10250 Alliance Rd Ste 201 Blue Ash (45242) (G-1818)

Job News USA 614 310-1700
  150 E Campus View Blvd # 120 Columbus (43235) (G-7236)

Job One Control Services 216 347-0133
  6893 Lantern Ln Cleveland (44130) (G-5617)

Jobap Assembly Inc 440 632-5393
  16090 Industrial Pkwy # 9 Middlefield (44062) (G-13947)

Jobskin Div of Torbot Group 419 724-1475
  5030 Advantage Dr Ste 101 Toledo (43612) (G-18535)

Jobskin Division, Toledo Also called Torbot Group Inc (G-18751)

Joe Baker Equipment Sales 513 451-1327
  1000 Devils Backbone Rd Cincinnati (45233) (G-3948)

Joe Barrett 216 385-2384
  13583 Old Frdericktown Rd East Liverpool (43920) (G-9220)

Joe Busby 513 821-1716
  439 S Cooper Ave Cincinnati (45215) (G-3949)

Joe D'S Printing, North Olmsted Also called Emta Inc (G-15332)

Joe Gonda Company Inc 440 458-6000
  40196 Butternut Ridge Rd Elyria (44035) (G-9443)

Joe McClelland Inc (PA) 740 452-3036
  98 E La Salle St Zanesville (43701) (G-21324)

Joe P Fischer Woodcraft 513 474-4316
  8455 Greenleaf Dr Cincinnati (45255) (G-3950)

Joe P Fischer Woodcraft 513 530-9600
  4627 Carlynn Dr Blue Ash (45241) (G-1819)

Joe Paxton 614 424-9000
  960 King Ave Columbus (43212) (G-7237)

Joe Rees Welding 937 652-4067
  326 W Twain Ave Urbana (43078) (G-19165)

Joe Sestito 614 871-7778
  5553 Spring Hill Rd Grove City (43123) (G-10566)

Joe The Printer Guy LLC 216 651-3880
  1590 Parkwood Rd Lakewood (44107) (G-11670)

Joes Saw Shop 440 834-1196
  14530 Butternut Rd Burton (44021) (G-2378)

John A & William J Wiechart 419 647-4617
  510 N Saint Marys Rd Spencerville (45887) (G-17461)

John B Allen 614 488-7122
  2346 Brandon Rd Columbus (43221) (G-7238)

John Baird 216 440-3595
  12646 Lovers Lane Rd Spencer (44275) (G-17456)

John Bean Technologies Corp 419 627-4349
  1622 1st St Sandusky (44870) (G-16975)

John Byler 330 627-7635
  5130 Germano Rd Se Carrollton (44615) (G-2957)

John C Meier Grape Juice Co, Cincinnati Also called Meiers Wine Cellars Inc (G-4082)

John C Starr 740 852-5592
  15 S Main St London (43140) (G-12213)

John Christ Winery Inc 440 933-9672
  32421 Walker Rd Avon Lake (44012) (G-1035)

John D Oil and Gas Company 440 255-6325
  7001 Center St Mentor (44060) (G-13620)

John Deere Authorized Dealer, Wooster Also called Shearer Farm Inc (G-20834)

John Deere Authorized Dealer, Urbana Also called Koenig Equipment Inc (G-19167)

John Deere Authorized Dealer, Mentor Also called Great Lakes Power Products Inc (G-13596)

John Deere Authorized Dealer, Hilliard Also called JD Power Systems LLC (G-10955)

John Deere Authorized Dealer, Canton Also called Western Branch Diesel Inc (G-2902)

John Deere Authorized Dealer, Perry Also called Great Lakes Power Service Co (G-16050)

John Deere Authorized Dealer, Columbus Also called Murphy Tractor & Eqp Co Inc (G-7374)

John Deere Authorized Dealer, Vandalia Also called Murphy Tractor & Eqp Co Inc (G-19306)

John Deere Authorized Dealer, Lima Also called Murphy Tractor & Eqp Co Inc (G-12061)

John Deere Authorized Dealer, Canton Also called Murphy Tractor & Eqp Co Inc (G-2785)

John Deere Authorized Dealer, Brunswick Also called Murphy Tractor & Eqp Co Inc (G-2238)

John Downey Company, Granville Also called Downey Enterprises Inc (G-10457)

John F Kilfoil Co 513 791-6150
  3799 Madison Rd Cincinnati (45209) (G-3951)

John Frieda Prof Hair Care Inc (HQ) 800 521-3189
  2535 Spring Grove Ave Cincinnati (45214) (G-3952)

John H Hosking Inc 513 821-1080
  4665 Emerald Way Middletown (45044) (G-14052)

John J Yoder Logging 330 749-6324
  6776 Mount Hope Rd Apple Creek (44606) (G-641)

John Kolesar and Sons Inc 216 221-7117
  13437 Detroit Ave Cleveland (44107) (G-5618)

John Krizay Inc 330 332-5607
  1777 Pennsylvania Ave Salem (44460) (G-16903)

John Krusinski 216 441-0100
  6300 Heisley Ave Cleveland (44105) (G-5619)

John L Garber Materials Corp 419 884-1567
  2745 Gass Rd Mansfield (44904) (G-12628)

John M Hand 937 902-1327
  6417 Enterprise Rd West Alexandria (45381) (G-19780)

John Maneely Company 724 342-6851
  1800 Hunter Ave Niles (44446) (G-15165)

John McHael Priester Assoc Inc 513 761-8605
  266 Elm Ave Wyoming (45215) (G-20932)

John Morrell & Co (HQ) 513 782-3800
  805 E Kemper Rd Cincinnati (45246) (G-3953)

John P Ellis Clinic Podiatry 440 460-0444
  730 Som Center Rd Ste 350 Cleveland (44143) (G-5620)

John Purdum 513 897-9686
  100 S Main St Waynesville (45068) (G-19731)

John R Jurgensen Co 937 293-3112
  1780 Enon Rd Springfield (45502) (G-17582)

John S Swift Company Inc 513 721-4147
  2524 Spring Grove Ave Cincinnati (45214) (G-3954)

John Stehlin & Sons Co Inc 513 385-6164
  10134 Colerain Ave Cincinnati (45251) (G-3955)

John Stieg & Associates 614 889-7954
  8621 Kirkhill Ct Dublin (43017) (G-9092)

John Wolf & Co Inc 440 942-0083
  36420 Biltmore Pl Ste 1 Willoughby (44094) (G-20516)

John Zidian Company, Youngstown Also called Gia Russa (G-21100)

Johndavid D Jones.......740 264-0176
590 Woodvue Ln Wintersville (43953) ***(G-20711)***
Johndow Industries Inc.......330 753-6895
151 Snyder Ave Barberton (44203) ***(G-1122)***
Johnny Chin Insurance Agency.......513 777-8695
9676 Cncnnati Columbus Rd West Chester (45241) ***(G-20019)***
Johnny Johnson Sports, Ontario *Also called Unisport Inc* ***(G-15696)***
Johnny On The Spot Inc (PA).......614 497-1776
4522 Lockbourne Rd Columbus (43207) ***(G-7239)***
Johns Body Shop.......419 358-1200
200 Lake Dr Bluffton (45817) ***(G-1913)***
Johns Jerky & Snack Meats LLC.......937 207-7008
12499 Clmbus Cncinnati Rd South Charleston (45368) ***(G-17426)***
Johns Manville Corporation.......419 499-1400
49 Lockwood Rd Milan (44846) ***(G-14114)***
Johns Manville Corporation.......419 878-8111
7500 Dutch Rd Waterville (43566) ***(G-19660)***
Johns Manville Corporation.......419 784-7000
925 Carpenter Rd Defiance (43512) ***(G-8795)***
Johns Manville Corporation.......419 784-7000
3rd And Perry Defiance (43512) ***(G-8796)***
Johns Manville Corporation.......419 467-8189
1020 Ford St Maumee (43537) ***(G-13271)***
Johns Manville Corporation.......419 878-8111
408 Perry St Plant 02 2 Plant Defiance (43512) ***(G-8797)***
Johns Welding & Towing Inc.......419 447-8937
850 N County Road 11 Tiffin (44883) ***(G-18225)***
Johnson Bros Greenwich, Greenwich *Also called Johnson Bros Rubber Co Inc* ***(G-10531)***
Johnson Bros Rubber Co Inc (PA).......419 853-4122
42 W Buckeye St West Salem (44287) ***(G-20114)***
Johnson Bros Rubber Co Inc.......419 752-4814
41 Center St Greenwich (44837) ***(G-10531)***
Johnson Brothers Holdings LLC.......614 868-5273
717 Oak St Columbus (43205) ***(G-7240)***
Johnson Contrls Authorized Dlr, Akron *Also called Famous Industries Inc* ***(G-181)***
Johnson Contrls Authorized Dlr, Northwood *Also called Yanfeng US Automotive* ***(G-15499)***
Johnson Contrls Btry Group Inc.......419 865-0542
10300 Industrial St Holland (43528) ***(G-11068)***
Johnson Controls, Greenfield *Also called Adient US LLC* ***(G-10472)***
Johnson Controls Inc.......419 636-4211
918 S Union St Bryan (43506) ***(G-2307)***
Johnson Controls Inc.......216 587-0100
9797 Midwest Ave Cleveland (44125) ***(G-5621)***
Johnson Controls Inc.......513 671-6338
11648 Springfield Pike Cincinnati (45246) ***(G-3956)***
Johnson Energy Company.......937 435-5401
1 Prestige Pl Ste 270 Miamisburg (45342) ***(G-13822)***
Johnson Engine & Machine.......614 876-0724
2899 Walcutt Rd Hilliard (43026) ***(G-10957)***
Johnson Machining Services LLC.......937 866-4744
4505 Infirmary Rd Miamisburg (45342) ***(G-13823)***
Johnson Mtthey Prcess Tech Inc.......330 298-7005
785 N Freedom St Ravenna (44266) ***(G-16535)***
Johnson Precision Machining.......513 353-4252
5919 Hamilton Cleves Rd Cleves (45002) ***(G-6517)***
Johnson Printing.......740 922-4821
216 E 5th St Uhrichsville (44683) ***(G-19053)***
Johnson Tool Distributors.......740 653-6959
1059 Rockmill Rd Nw Lancaster (43130) ***(G-11724)***
Johnson Welded Products Inc.......937 652-1242
625 S Edgewood Ave Urbana (43078) ***(G-19166)***
Johnson-Nash Metal Pdts Inc.......513 874-7022
9265 Seward Rd Fairfield (45014) ***(G-9671)***
Johnsonite, Solon *Also called Tarkett USA Inc* ***(G-17399)***
Johnsonite Inc.......440 632-3441
16035 Industrial Pkwy Middlefield (44062) ***(G-13948)***
Johnsonite Rubber Flooring, Middlefield *Also called Johnsonite Inc* ***(G-13948)***
Johnsons Lamp Shop & Antq Co.......937 568-4551
8518 E National Rd South Vienna (45369) ***(G-17450)***
Johnsons Real Ice Cream Co.......614 231-0014
2728 E Main St Columbus (43209) ***(G-7241)***
Johnston Manufacturing Inc.......440 269-1420
7611 Saint Clair Ave Mentor (44060) ***(G-13621)***
Johnston-Morehouse-Dickey Co.......614 866-0452
4647 Poth Rd Columbus (43213) ***(G-7242)***
Johnston-Morehouse-Dickey Co.......330 405-6050
1290 Highland Rd E Macedonia (44056) ***(G-12464)***
Johnstons Banks Inc.......614 499-4374
6927 Sherbrook Dr Westerville (43082) ***(G-20163)***
Joining Metals Inc.......440 259-1790
3314 Blackmore Rd Perry (44081) ***(G-16051)***
Joint Systems Mfg Ctr.......419 221-9580
1155 Buckeye Rd Bldg 147 Lima (45804) ***(G-12034)***
Joint Vue LLC.......614 640-3350
1275 Kinnear Rd Columbus (43212) ***(G-7243)***
Jolly Pats, Streetsboro *Also called Horsemens Pride Inc* ***(G-17857)***
Jomac Ltd.......330 627-7727
182 Scio Rd Se Carrollton (44615) ***(G-2958)***
Jonashtons.......419 488-2363
12485 State Route 634 Cloverdale (45827) ***(G-6536)***
Jonathan Bishop.......330 836-6947
200 Hampshire Rd Akron (44313) ***(G-241)***
Jones & Assoc Advg & Design.......330 799-6876
5015 Mahoning Ave Ste 1 Youngstown (44515) ***(G-21127)***
Jones Industrial Service LLC.......419 287-4553
17221 Eisenhour Rd Pemberville (43450) ***(G-16029)***
Jones Metal Products Company (PA).......740 545-6381
200 N Center St West Lafayette (43845) ***(G-20087)***
Jones Metal Products Company.......740 545-6341
305 N Center St West Lafayette (43845) ***(G-20088)***
Jones Old Rustic Sign.......937 643-1695
2758 Viking Ln Moraine (45439) ***(G-14498)***
Jones Potato Chip Co (PA).......419 529-9424
823 Bowman St Mansfield (44903) ***(G-12629)***
Jones Printing Services Inc.......440 946-7300
1519 E 367th St Ste 1 Eastlake (44095) ***(G-9277)***
Jones Processing.......330 772-2193
Hc 7 Hartford (44424) ***(G-10814)***
Jones Propane Supply, Carrollton *Also called Jomac Ltd* ***(G-2958)***
Jones Signs, Moraine *Also called Jones Old Rustic Sign* ***(G-14498)***
JONES ZYLON COMPANY, West Lafayette *Also called Jones Metal Products Company* ***(G-20087)***
Jones-Hamilton Co (PA).......419 666-9838
30354 Tracy Rd Walbridge (43465) ***(G-19460)***
Joneszylon Company LLC.......740 545-6341
300 N Center St West Lafayette (43845) ***(G-20089)***
Jonmar Gear and Machine Inc.......330 854-6500
13786 Warwick Dr Nw Canal Fulton (44614) ***(G-2503)***
Jordan E Armour.......330 252-0290
1145 Highbrook St Ste 103 Akron (44301) ***(G-242)***
Jordan Young International, London *Also called Textiles Inc* ***(G-12220)***
Jordon Auto Service & Tire Inc.......216 214-6528
5201 Carnegie Ave Cleveland (44103) ***(G-5622)***
Jos-Tech Inc.......330 678-3260
852 W Main St Kent (44240) ***(G-11474)***
Joseph A Panico & Sons Inc (PA).......614 235-3188
4605 E 5th Ave Columbus (43219) ***(G-7244)***
Joseph Adams Corp.......330 225-9125
5740 Grafton Rd Valley City (44280) ***(G-19208)***
Joseph B Stinson Co.......419 334-4151
2300 Napoleon Rd Fremont (43420) ***(G-10160)***
Joseph Berning Printing Co.......513 721-0781
1850 Dalton Ave Cincinnati (45214) ***(G-3957)***
Joseph G Betz & Sons.......513 481-0322
4219 Saint Martins Pl Cincinnati (45211) ***(G-3958)***
Joseph Industries, Cleveland *Also called Charles Messina* ***(G-5016)***
Joseph Industries Inc.......330 528-0091
10039 Aurora Hudson Rd Streetsboro (44241) ***(G-17860)***
Joseph Knapp.......330 832-3515
151 Lennox Ave Sw Massillon (44646) ***(G-13160)***
Joseph Sabatino.......330 332-5879
1834 Depot Rd Salem (44460) ***(G-16904)***
Joseph Scarberry.......740 522-1551
1038 Idlewilde Ave Newark (43055) ***(G-15025)***
Joseph T Ryerson & Son Inc.......513 542-5800
555 N Yearling Rd Columbus (43213) ***(G-7245)***
Joseph T Snyder Industries.......216 883-6900
9210 Loren Ave Cleveland (44105) ***(G-5623)***
Josh L Derksen.......937 548-0080
200 N Broadway St Greenville (45331) ***(G-10507)***
Joshua Enterprises Inc.......419 872-9699
12900 Eckel Junction Rd Perrysburg (43551) ***(G-16115)***
Joshua Label Company, Perrysburg *Also called Joshua Enterprises Inc* ***(G-16115)***
Joshua Leigh Enterprises Inc.......330 244-9200
2191 E Maple St Canton (44720) ***(G-2749)***
Joslyn Manufacturing Company.......330 467-8111
9400 Valley View Rd Macedonia (44056) ***(G-12465)***
Jostens Inc.......513 615-3281
8673 Sarah Bend Dr Cincinnati (45251) ***(G-3959)***
Jostens Inc.......419 794-7343
3455 Briarfield Blvd F Maumee (43537) ***(G-13272)***
Jostens Inc.......513 731-5900
3047 Madison Rd Ste 207 Cincinnati (45209) ***(G-3960)***
Jostens Inc.......419 874-5835
1833 Eaglecrest Rd Perrysburg (43551) ***(G-16116)***
Jotco Inc.......513 721-4943
1400 Park Ave E Mansfield (44905) ***(G-12630)***
Joules Angstrom UV Printing (PA).......740 964-9113
104 Heritage Dr Etna (43062) ***(G-9558)***
Journal Bkr.......440 245-6901
1657 Broadway Lorain (44052) ***(G-12250)***
Journal Leader, Caldwell *Also called Southeast Publications Inc* ***(G-2433)***
Journal Register Company.......440 951-0000
7085 Mentor Ave Willoughby (44094) ***(G-20517)***
Journal Register Company.......440 245-6901
1657 Broadway Lorain (44052) ***(G-12251)***

Journey Electronics Corp..513 539-9836
  902 N Garver Rd Monroe (45050) *(G-14406)*

Journey Systems LLC (PA)..513 831-6200
  25 Whitney Dr Ste 100 Milford (45150) *(G-14157)*

Joy Global Inc..216 503-5029
  981 Keynote Cir Ste 8 Independence (44131) *(G-11262)*

Joy Global Underground Min LLC............................440 248-7970
  6160 Cochran Rd Cleveland (44139) *(G-5624)*

Joy Mining Machinery..440 248-7970
  6160 Cochran Rd Solon (44139) *(G-17323)*

Joyce Manufacturing Co (PA)...................................440 239-9100
  1125 Berea Indus Pkwy Berea (44017) *(G-1624)*

Joyce Windows, Berea *Also called Joyce Manufacturing Co (G-1624)*

Joyce/Dayton Corp (HQ)..937 294-6261
  3300 S Dixie Dr Ste 101 Dayton (45439) *(G-8428)*

JP Good Co, Ashland *Also called Good JP (G-735)*

JP Industrial, Lisbon *Also called J P Industrial Products Inc (G-12125)*

JPb Lures Manufacturing LLC.................................419 734-9488
  7516 E Bayshore Rd Lot 25 Marblehead (43440) *(G-12745)*

Jpmorgan Chase Bank Nat Assn.............................937 443-6260
  806 W National Rd Vandalia (45377) *(G-19299)*

Jpmorgan Chase Bank Nat Assn.............................330 287-5102
  141 N Walnut St Wooster (44691) *(G-20792)*

JPS Technologies Inc (PA).......................................513 984-6400
  11110 Deerfield Rd Blue Ash (45242) *(G-1820)*

JPS Technologies Inc..513 984-6400
  11118 Deerfield Rd Blue Ash (45242) *(G-1821)*

Jr Engineering Inc (PA)..330 848-0960
  123 9th St Nw Barberton (44203) *(G-1123)*

Jr Kennel Mfg..937 780-6104
  12196 Wilmington Ave Leesburg (45135) *(G-11853)*

JR Manufacturing Inc (PA).......................................419 375-8021
  900 Industrial Dr W Fort Recovery (45846) *(G-9956)*

Jrb Attachments LLC (HQ).......................................330 734-3000
  820 Glaser Pkwy Akron (44306) *(G-243)*

Jrf Industries Ltd..330 665-3130
  3675 Copley Rd Copley (44321) *(G-7849)*

Jrg Performance Technologies................................216 408-5974
  340 Balmoral Dr Cleveland (44143) *(G-5625)*

Jroll LLC...330 661-0600
  985 Boardman Aly Medina (44256) *(G-13430)*

Jrs Hydraulic & Welding..614 497-1100
  2774 Groveport Rd Columbus (43207) *(G-7246)*

Jrw Manufacturing..330 628-2994
  667 Killian Rd Akron (44319) *(G-244)*

Js Fabrications Inc..419 333-0323
  1400 E State St Fremont (43420) *(G-10161)*

Jsc Employee Leasing Corp (PA).............................330 773-8971
  1560 Firestone Pkwy Akron (44301) *(G-245)*

Jscs Group Inc..513 563-4900
  690 Northland Blvd Cincinnati (45240) *(G-3961)*

Jst LLC..614 423-7815
  6240 Frost Rd Ste C Westerville (43082) *(G-20164)*

Jtekt North America Corp (HQ)................................440 835-1000
  29570 Clemens Rd Westlake (44145) *(G-20279)*

Jtm Food Group, Harrison *Also called Jtm Provisions Company Inc (G-10787)*

Jtm Products Inc...440 287-2302
  31025 Carter St Solon (44139) *(G-17324)*

Jtm Provisions Company Inc...................................513 367-4900
  200 Sales Ave Harrison (45030) *(G-10787)*

Jual Corporation...614 430-0683
  771 Dearborn Park Ln F Worthington (43085) *(G-20874)*

Juana Williams...614 351-9844
  2850 Fisher Rd Columbus (43204) *(G-7247)*

Judco Inc..440 322-6604
  7501 W River Rd S Elyria (44035) *(G-9444)*

Judith C Zell..740 385-0386
  21313 State Route 93 S Logan (43138) *(G-12180)*

Judith Leiber LLC (PA)...614 449-4217
  4300 E 5th Ave Columbus (43219) *(G-7248)*

Judy Dubois..419 738-6979
  4 N Wood St Wapakoneta (45895) *(G-19493)*

Judy Mills Company Inc (PA)....................................513 271-4241
  3360 Red Bank Rd Cincinnati (45227) *(G-3962)*

Julie Maynard Inc..937 443-0408
  4991 Hempstead Station Dr Dayton (45429) *(G-8429)*

Julius Zorn Inc..330 923-4999
  3690 Zorn Dr Cuyahoga Falls (44223) *(G-8015)*

Jump N Sales LLC..513 509-7661
  6745 Gilmore Rd Ste E Hamilton (45011) *(G-10713)*

Junebugs Cupcaked..937 723-9040
  2423 Mmsburg Cntrville Rd Dayton (45459) *(G-8430)*

Junebugs Wash N Dry...513 988-5863
  6435 E State St Trenton (45067) *(G-18794)*

Just Basic Sports Inc..330 264-7771
  1615 N Geyers Chapel Rd Wooster (44691) *(G-20793)*

Just Business Inc...866 577-3303
  1612 Prosser Ave Ste 100 Dayton (45409) *(G-8431)*

Just Cheking Cash, Fairfield *Also called Southern Glazers Wine & Sprt (G-9721)*

Just Natural Provision Company..............................216 431-7922
  4800 Crayton Ave Cleveland (44104) *(G-5626)*

Just Plastics Inc...419 468-5506
  869 Smith St Galion (44833) *(G-10277)*

Just Quilt It Inc...330 469-6956
  2298 High St Nw Warren (44483) *(G-19564)*

Justin P Straub LLC...513 761-0282
  14 De Camp Ave Cincinnati (45216) *(G-3963)*

Juvenile Furniture Specialties, Sugarcreek *Also called J & F Furniture Shop (G-18024)*

Juzo, Cuyahoga Falls *Also called Julius Zorn Inc (G-8015)*

JW Log and Lumber, Carrollton *Also called John Byler (G-2957)*

JW Manufacturing...419 375-5536
  317 Watkins Rd Fort Recovery (45846) *(G-9957)*

K & B Acquisitions Inc...937 253-1163
  3013 Linden Ave Dayton (45410) *(G-8432)*

K & B Stamping & Manufacturing............................937 778-8875
  9676 Looney Rd Piqua (45356) *(G-16284)*

K & E Chemical Co Inc...216 341-0500
  3960 E 93rd St Cleveland (44105) *(G-5627)*

K & G Machine Co..216 732-7115
  26981 Tungsten Rd Cleveland (44132) *(G-5628)*

K & H Industries LLC...513 921-6770
  1041 Evans St Ste 2 Cincinnati (45204) *(G-3964)*

K & J Machine Inc..740 425-3282
  326 Fairmont Ave Barnesville (43713) *(G-1160)*

K & K Auto & Truck Parts, Logan *Also called Pattons Truck & Heavy Eqp Svc (G-12189)*

K & K Precision Inc..513 336-0032
  5001 N Masn Montgomery Rd Mason (45040) *(G-13051)*

K & L Die & Manufacturing......................................419 895-1301
  7541 Olvsburg Ftchvlle Rd Greenwich (44837) *(G-10532)*

K & L Ready Mix Inc (PA)..419 523-4376
  10391 State Route 15 Ottawa (45875) *(G-15798)*

K & L Ready Mix Inc...419 532-3585
  105 S 6th St Kalida (45853) *(G-11413)*

K & L Ready Mix Inc...419 293-2937
  5511 State Route 613 Mc Comb (45858) *(G-13339)*

K & L Tool Inc...419 258-2086
  5141 Us 24 Antwerp (45813) *(G-630)*

K & M Tool & Machine Co Inc...................................440 572-5130
  17383 Foltz Pkwy Strongsville (44149) *(G-17934)*

K & R Pretzel Co..937 299-2231
  1700 Flesher Ave Dayton (45420) *(G-8433)*

K A P C O, Kent *Also called Kent Adhesive Products Co (G-11475)*

K B Electric Motor Service......................................740 537-1346
  915 Banfield Ave Toronto (43964) *(G-18783)*

K B Electric Service, Toronto *Also called K B Electric Motor Service (G-18783)*

K B I, Sandusky *Also called Kyklos Bearing Intl LLC (G-16977)*

K B Machine & Tool Inc...937 773-1624
  1500 S Main St Piqua (45356) *(G-16285)*

K B Printing...614 771-1222
  1199 Goodale Blvd Columbus (43212) *(G-7249)*

K C Creations...937 748-8181
  218 Riverside Dr Troy (45373) *(G-18850)*

K C N Technologies LLC..440 439-4219
  20637 Krick Rd Bedford (44146) *(G-1434)*

K C P, Beachwood *Also called Kirtland Capital Partners LP (G-1276)*

K Cupcakes..440 576-3464
  222 Elliott Ave Jefferson (44047) *(G-11362)*

K D C, Johnstown *Also called Tri-Tech Laboratories Inc (G-11408)*

K D Hardwoods Inc...440 834-1772
  14195 Kinsman Rd Burton (44021) *(G-2379)*

K D Lamp Company...440 293-4064
  101 Parker Dr Andover (44003) *(G-616)*

K Effs Inc..614 443-0586
  2117 S High St Columbus (43207) *(G-7250)*

K F D Inc...330 773-4300
  39 Alice Dr Unit B Akron (44319) *(G-246)*

K F T Inc...513 241-5910
  726 Mehring Way Cincinnati (45203) *(G-3965)*

K G M, Cincinnati *Also called Knoble Glass & Metal Inc (G-3998)*

K K Racing Chassis...330 628-2930
  485 Taylor Ave Akron (44312) *(G-247)*

K K Tool Co...937 325-1373
  115 S Center St Springfield (45502) *(G-17583)*

K L M Manufacturing Company................................740 666-5171
  56 Houston St Ostrander (43061) *(G-15787)*

K M B Inc..330 889-3451
  1306 State Route 88 Bristolville (44402) *(G-2098)*

K M C, Cleveland *Also called Knitting Machinery Corp (G-5661)*

K P Precision Tool and Mch Co................................419 237-2596
  606 N Park St Fayette (43521) *(G-9775)*

K Petroleum Inc (PA)..614 532-5420
  81 Mill St Ste 205 Gahanna (43230) *(G-10214)*

K S Machine Inc..216 687-0459
  3215 Superior Ave E Cleveland (44114) *(G-5629)*

K S W C Inc...440 577-1114
  697 State Line Rd Pierpont (44082) *(G-16212)*

K Ventures Inc..419 678-2308
  211 E Main St Coldwater (45828) *(G-6566)*

K Wm Beach Mfg Co Inc..................................937 399-3838
  4655 Urbana Rd Springfield (45502) **(G-17584)**
K-B Plating Inc...216 341-1115
  3685 E 78th St Cleveland (44105) **(G-5630)**
K-Hill Signal Co Inc.......................................740 922-0421
  326 W 3rd St Uhrichsville (44683) **(G-19054)**
K-Js Mechanical Service................................419 729-1103
  606 New York Ave Toledo (43611) **(G-18536)**
K-M-S Industries Inc.....................................440 243-6680
  6519 Eastland Rd Ste 1 Brookpark (44142) **(G-2165)**
K-O-K Products Inc.......................................740 548-0526
  700 S 3 Bs And K Rd Galena (43021) **(G-10245)**
K.M.I. Printing, Chardon Also called Key Maneuvers Inc **(G-3159)**
K.M.S., Brookpark Also called K-M-S Industries Inc **(G-2165)**
K2 Petroleum & Supply LLC............................937 503-2614
  11371 Village Brook Dr # 1321 Cincinnati (45249) **(G-3966)**
Ka Molded Products.......................................419 884-3375
  40 Eagle Dr Mansfield (44904) **(G-12631)**
Ka Wanner Inc..740 251-4636
  370 W Fairground St Marion (43302) **(G-12878)**
Kabler Farms..513 732-0501
  4529 Elmwood Rd Batavia (45103) **(G-1195)**
Kacy Architectural Millwork, Howard Also called Kacy Stairs **(G-11123)**
Kacy Stairs..740 599-5201
  19762 Nunda Rd Howard (43028) **(G-11123)**
Kad Holdings Inc...614 792-3399
  5887 Karric Square Dr Dublin (43016) **(G-9093)**
Kadant Black Clawson Inc (HQ).......................513 229-8100
  7312 Central Parke Blvd Mason (45040) **(G-13052)**
Kadee Industries Newco Inc...........................440 439-8650
  7160 Krick Rd Ste A Bedford (44146) **(G-1435)**
Kader Printing LLC.......................................440 668-1579
  12822 Heritage Trl North Royalton (44133) **(G-15429)**
Kaeden Books, Westlake Also called Kaeden Corporation **(G-20280)**
Kaeden Corporation......................................440 617-1400
  806 Sharon Dr Ste F Westlake (44145) **(G-20280)**
Kaeper Machine Inc......................................440 974-1010
  8680 Twinbrook Rd Mentor (44060) **(G-13622)**
Kaffenbarger Truck Eqp Co (PA)......................937 845-3804
  10100 Ballentine Pike New Carlisle (45344) **(G-14804)**
Kaffenbarger Truck Eqp Co............................513 772-6800
  3260 E Kemper Rd Cincinnati (45241) **(G-3967)**
Kahiki Foods Inc...614 322-3180
  1100 Morrison Rd Gahanna (43230) **(G-10215)**
Kahle Technologies Inc..................................419 523-3951
  1204 E 3rd St Ottawa (45875) **(G-15799)**
Kahny Printing Inc...513 251-2911
  4766 River Rd Cincinnati (45233) **(G-3968)**
Kahuna Bay Spray Tan LLC.............................419 386-2387
  757 Warehouse Rd Ste E-F Toledo (43615) **(G-18537)**
Kaiser Aluminum Fab Pdts LLC........................740 522-1151
  600 Kaiser Dr Heath (43056) **(G-10848)**
Kaiser Aluminum Newark Works, Heath Also called Kaiser Aluminum Fab Pdts
LLC **(G-10848)**
Kaiser Foods Inc (PA)....................................513 621-2053
  500 York St Cincinnati (45214) **(G-3969)**
Kaiser Foods Inc...513 241-6833
  2155 Kindel Ave Cincinnati (45214) **(G-3970)**
Kaiser Pickles, Cincinnati Also called Kaiser Foods Inc **(G-3970)**
Kaivac Inc...513 887-4600
  401 S 3rd St Hamilton (45011) **(G-10714)**
Kalcor Coatings Company................................440 946-4700
  37721 Stevens Blvd Willoughby (44094) **(G-20518)**
Kaleidoscope Magazine LLC.............................216 566-5500
  1677 E 40th St Cleveland (44103) **(G-5631)**
Kalida Manufacturing Inc................................419 532-2026
  801 Ottawa St Kalida (45853) **(G-11414)**
Kalinich Fence Company Inc...........................440 238-6127
  12223 Prospect Rd Strongsville (44149) **(G-17935)**
Kalmbach Feeds Inc (PA)...............................419 294-3838
  7148 State Highway 199 Upper Sandusky (43351) **(G-19127)**
Kalt Manufacturing Company............................440 327-2102
  36700 Sugar Ridge Rd North Ridgeville (44039) **(G-15384)**
Kam Manufacturing Inc..................................419 238-6037
  1197 Grill Rd Van Wert (45891) **(G-19261)**
Kam Services, Newark Also called Kathy Edie **(G-15026)**
Kam-Awards Inc...513 631-5553
  7220 Montgomery Rd Cincinnati (45236) **(G-3971)**
Kamala K Tamirisa MD...................................419 842-3000
  2940 N Mccord Rd Toledo (43615) **(G-18538)**
Kaman Automation Inc...................................216 663-0072
  5350 Trnsp Blvd Ste 15 Cleveland (44125) **(G-5632)**
Kaman Fluid Power LLC..................................330 315-3100
  195 S Main St Ste 400 Akron (44308) **(G-248)**
Kaman Industrial Tech Corp...........................740 779-9201
  1404 Delano Rd Chillicothe (45601) **(G-3248)**
Kamco Industries...419 551-9211
  1000 Oak St West Unity (43570) **(G-20131)**

Kamco Industries Inc (HQ).............................419 924-5511
  1001 E Jackson St West Unity (43570) **(G-20132)**
Kamps, Versailles Also called Pallets-Fm-N-plc-packaging Inc **(G-19355)**
Kanan Enterprises Inc (PA)............................440 248-8484
  31900 Solon Rd Solon (44139) **(G-17325)**
Kanan Enterprises Inc....................................440 349-0719
  6401 Davis Indus Pkwy Solon (44139) **(G-17326)**
Kanawha Scales & Systems.............................513 576-0700
  26 Whitney Dr Milford (45150) **(G-14158)**
Kando of Cincinnati Inc..................................513 459-7782
  2025 Mckinley Blvd Lebanon (45036) **(G-11811)**
Kane Sign Co...330 253-5263
  486 E Glenwood Ave Akron (44310) **(G-249)**
Kanel Brothers Church Supplies, Canton Also called Kanel Brothers Supply **(G-2750)**
Kanel Brothers Supply...................................330 499-4802
  8280 Kent Ave Ne Canton (44721) **(G-2750)**
Kangaroo Brand Mops, Union City Also called Ha-Ste Manufacturing Co Inc **(G-19071)**
KAO USA Inc (HQ)...513 421-1400
  2535 Spring Grove Ave Cincinnati (45214) **(G-3972)**
Kap Signs, Dayton Also called Blang Acquisition LLC **(G-8190)**
Kapios LLC...567 661-0772
  2865 N Reynolds Rd 220d Toledo (43615) **(G-18539)**
Kapios Health, Toledo Also called Kapios LLC **(G-18539)**
Kapstone Container Corporation.......................330 562-6111
  1450 S Chillicothe Rd Aurora (44202) **(G-928)**
Kar-Del Plastics Inc......................................419 289-9739
  1177 Faultless Dr Ashland (44805) **(G-744)**
Kard Bridge Products, Minster Also called Kard Welding Inc **(G-14356)**
Kard Welding Inc..419 628-2598
  480 Osterloh Rd Minster (45865) **(G-14356)**
Karder Machine Co (PA).................................330 253-3377
  2680 Waltham Rd Akron (44313) **(G-250)**
Kardol Quality Products LLC (PA).....................513 933-8206
  9933 Alliance Rd Ste 2 Blue Ash (45242) **(G-1822)**
Karen Carson Creations, Dayton Also called Carson-Saeks Inc **(G-8213)**
Karg Corporation..330 633-4916
  241 Southwest Ave Tallmadge (44278) **(G-18149)**
Karg Fiberglass Inc.......................................330 494-2611
  2831 Diamond St Middlebranch (44652) **(G-13901)**
Karl Industries Inc..330 562-4100
  11415 Chamberlain Rd Aurora (44202) **(G-929)**
Karlco Oilfield Services Inc............................440 576-3415
  141 E Jefferson St Jefferson (44047) **(G-11363)**
Karma Metal Products Inc..............................419 524-4371
  556 Caldwell Ave Mansfield (44905) **(G-12632)**
Karman Rubber Company (PA).........................330 864-2161
  2331 Copley Rd Akron (44320) **(G-251)**
Karn Meats Inc...614 252-3712
  922 Taylor Ave Columbus (43219) **(G-7251)**
Karrier Company Inc......................................330 823-9597
  1065 S Liberty Ave Alliance (44601) **(G-520)**
Kars Ohio LLC..614 655-1099
  6359 Summit Rd Sw Pataskala (43062) **(G-15973)**
Karyall-Telday Inc...216 281-4063
  8221 Clinton Rd Cleveland (44144) **(G-5633)**
Kasai North America Inc.................................614 356-1494
  655 Metro Pl S Ste 560 Dublin (43017) **(G-9094)**
Kase Equipment...216 642-9040
  7400 Hub Pkwy Cleveland (44125) **(G-5634)**
Kasel Engineering LLC....................................937 854-8875
  5911 Wolf Creek Pike Trotwood (45426) **(G-18798)**
Kaskell Manufacturing Inc..............................937 704-9700
  240 Hiawatha Trl Springboro (45066) **(G-17485)**
Kasper Enterprises Inc...................................419 829-2121
  7844 W Central Ave Toledo (43617) **(G-18540)**
Kastler & Reichlin Inc....................................440 322-0970
  710 Taylor St Elyria (44035) **(G-9445)**
Katherine A Stull Inc.....................................440 349-3977
  7079 Navajo Trl Solon (44139) **(G-17327)**
Kathom Manufacturing Co Inc.........................513 868-8890
  661 Williams Ave Hamilton (45015) **(G-10715)**
Kathy Edie...740 763-4887
  2737 Licking Valley Rd Newark (43055) **(G-15026)**
Kathy Simecek..440 886-2468
  9119 Running Brook Dr Cleveland (44130) **(G-5635)**
Kathys Krafts and Kollectibles........................423 787-3709
  3303 Hamilton Rd Medina (44256) **(G-13431)**
Katies Light House LLC..................................419 645-5451
  300 Dupler Ave Cridersville (45806) **(G-7946)**
Kaufman Container Company (PA).....................216 898-2000
  1000 Keystone Pkwy # 100 Cleveland (44135) **(G-5636)**
Kaufman Engineered Systems Inc.....................419 878-9727
  1260 Wtrville Monclova Rd Waterville (43566) **(G-19661)**
Kaufman Mulch Inc..330 893-3676
  3988 County Road 135 Millersburg (44654) **(G-14236)**
Kaufman Trucking, Millersburg Also called Kaufman Mulch Inc **(G-14236)**
Kawneer Company Inc....................................216 252-3203
  4536 Industrial Pkwy Cleveland (44135) **(G-5637)**

Kaws Inc 513 521-8292
2680 Civic Center Dr Cincinnati (45231) *(G-3973)*

Kay Capital Company (HQ) 216 531-1010
1441 Chardon Rd Cleveland (44117) *(G-5638)*

Kay Toledo Tag Inc 419 729-5479
6050 Benore Rd Toledo (43612) *(G-18541)*

Kay Zee Inc 330 339-1268
1279 Crestview Ave Sw New Philadelphia (44663) *(G-14905)*

Kay-Dee Air & Elc TI Repr Co, Cleveland *Also called T & J Nickum Inc (G-6286)*

Kaylee Ryan Publishing LLC 937 446-3926
133 Horse Shoe Dr Lake Waynoka (45171) *(G-11643)*

Kbc Services 513 693-3743
9993 Union Cemetery Rd Loveland (45140) *(G-12365)*

Kbi Group Inc 614 873-5825
7370 Merchant Rd Plain City (43064) *(G-16346)*

Kbr, Cincinnati *Also called Kitchens By Rutenschroer Inc (G-3994)*

Kc Robotics Inc 513 860-4442
9000 Le Saint Dr West Chester (45014) *(G-19887)*

Kcg Inc 614 238-9450
3939 E 5th Ave Columbus (43219) *(G-7252)*

Kci Holding USA Inc (HQ) 937 525-5533
4401 Gateway Blvd Springfield (45502) *(G-17585)*

Kcs Cleaning Service 740 418-5479
7550 State Route 93 Oak Hill (45656) *(G-15599)*

Kdlamp Company, Andover *Also called Atc Lighting & Plastics Inc (G-613)*

Kdm Screen Printing, Cincinnati *Also called Kdm Signs Inc (G-3975)*

Kdm Signs Inc 513 769-3900
3000 Exon Ave Cincinnati (45241) *(G-3974)*

Kdm Signs Inc (PA) 513 769-1932
10450 Medallion Dr Cincinnati (45241) *(G-3975)*

Keb Industries Inc 440 953-4623
2166 Joseph Lloyd Pkwy Willoughby (44094) *(G-20519)*

Keban Industries Inc 216 446-0159
7500 Wall St Ste 100 Cleveland (44125) *(G-5639)*

Kecamm LLC 330 527-2918
10404 Industrial Dr Garrettsville (44231) *(G-10326)*

Keck Engineering Inc 440 355-9855
39610 Whitney Rd Lagrange (44050) *(G-11629)*

Keco Plating, Cleveland *Also called Roberts-Demand Corp (G-6122)*

Kecoat LLC 330 527-0215
10610 Freedom St Garrettsville (44231) *(G-10327)*

Kedar D Army 419 238-6929
11373 Van Wert Decatur Rd Van Wert (45891) *(G-19262)*

Kee Printing Inc 937 456-6851
118 W Monfort St Eaton (45320) *(G-9312)*

Keebler Company 513 271-3500
1 Trade St Cincinnati (45227) *(G-3976)*

Keebler Company 614 836-3094
200 E Campus View Blvd # 200 Columbus (43235) *(G-7253)*

Keebler Company 513 671-0880
11490 Mosteller Rd Cincinnati (45241) *(G-3977)*

Keeler Enterprises Inc 330 336-7601
924 Seville Rd Wadsworth (44281) *(G-19412)*

Keen Manufacturing Inc 330 427-0045
240 High St Washingtonville (44490) *(G-19642)*

Keen Pump Company Inc 419 207-9400
471 E State Rte 250 E Ashland (44805) *(G-745)*

Keener Printing Inc 216 531-7595
401 E 200th St Cleveland (44119) *(G-5640)*

Keener Rubber Company 330 821-1880
14700 Commerce St Ne Alliance (44601) *(G-521)*

Keeney Sand & Stone Inc 440 254-4582
13320 Girdled Rd Painesville (44077) *(G-15894)*

Keepsakes Etc 330 559-6716
7320 Akron Canfield Rd B Canfield (44406) *(G-2560)*

Kegg Pipe Organ Builders, Hartville *Also called C E Kegg Inc (G-10818)*

Kehl-Kolor Inc 419 281-3107
824 Us Highway 42 Ashland (44805) *(G-746)*

Kehler Enterprises Inc 614 889-8488
323 W Bridge St Dublin (43017) *(G-9095)*

Kehoe Brothers Printing Inc 216 351-4100
910 W Schaaf Rd Cleveland (44109) *(G-5641)*

Keihin Thermal Tech Amer Inc 740 869-3000
10500 Oday Harrison Rd Mount Sterling (43143) *(G-14599)*

Keir Educational Resources, Middletown *Also called Jack C Keir Inc (G-14051)*

Keith Chrissinger 740 549-0683
2101 Tucker Trl Lewis Center (43035) *(G-11903)*

Keith Grimm 419 899-2725
100 W Pearl St Sherwood (43556) *(G-17146)*

Keithley Enterprises Inc 937 890-1878
3425 Garianne Dr Dayton (45414) *(G-8434)*

Keithley Instruments LLC (HQ) 440 248-0400
28775 Aurora Rd Solon (44139) *(G-17328)*

Keithley Instruments Intl Corp 440 248-0400
28775 Aurora Rd Cleveland (44139) *(G-5642)*

Keito Gas Inc 740 374-5463
101 Wheelbarrow Run Rd Marietta (45750) *(G-12796)*

Kel-Mar Inc 419 806-4600
436 N Enterprise St Bowling Green (43402) *(G-1994)*

Kelblys Rifle Range Inc 330 683-0070
7222 Dalton Fox Lake Rd North Lawrence (44666) *(G-15306)*

Kelch Manufacturing Corp 440 366-5060
626 Sugar Ln Elyria (44035) *(G-9446)*

Kelchner Inc (HQ) 937 704-9890
50 Advanced Dr Springboro (45066) *(G-17486)*

Kelco Hardwood Floors Inc 440 354-0974
10137 Johnnycake Ridge Rd Painesville (44077) *(G-15895)*

Kelic, Waterville *Also called Rimer Enterprises Inc (G-19666)*

Kelley Bible Books, Dayton *Also called Kelley Communication Dev (G-8435)*

Kelley Brothers Roofing Inc 330 273-3700
6867 Wooster Pike Medina (44256) *(G-13432)*

Kelley Communication Dev 937 298-6132
2312 Candlewood Dr Dayton (45419) *(G-8435)*

Kelleys Island Wine Co 419 746-2678
418 Woodford Rd Kelleys Island (43438) *(G-11419)*

Kellogg Cabinets Inc 614 833-9596
7711 Diley Rd Canal Winchester (43110) *(G-2529)*

Kellogg Company 513 271-3500
1 Trade St Cincinnati (45227) *(G-3978)*

Kellogg Company 513 772-8980
11490 Mosteller Rd Cincinnati (45241) *(G-3979)*

Kellogg Company 614 879-9659
125 Enterprise Pkwy West Jefferson (43162) *(G-20080)*

Kellogg Company 330 306-1500
655 N River Rd Nw Warren (44483) *(G-19565)*

Kellogg Company 513 792-2700
8044 Montgomery Rd # 700 Cincinnati (45236) *(G-3980)*

Kellogg Company 614 855-3437
124 Hyatts Rd Delaware (43015) *(G-8864)*

Kellogg Company 740 453-5501
1675 Fairview Rd Zanesville (43701) *(G-21325)*

Kellogg Yard, Cincinnati *Also called Martin Marietta Materials Inc (G-4063)*

Kellstone 419 621-8140
201 Putnam St Sandusky (44870) *(G-16976)*

Kelly Cabinet Company LLC 614 563-2971
525 Thrush Rill Ct Powell (43065) *(G-16474)*

Kelly Duplex, Springfield *Also called Duplex Mill & Manufacturing Co (G-17548)*

Kelly Foods Corporation (PA) 330 722-8855
3337 Medina Rd Medina (44256) *(G-13433)*

Kelly Machine Ltd 419 825-2006
7245 County Road 1 3 Swanton (43558) *(G-18085)*

Kelly Plating Co 216 961-1080
10316 Madison Ave Cleveland (44102) *(G-5643)*

Kelly Printing, Obetz *Also called Michael R Kelly (G-15656)*

Kelly Prints LLC 440 356-6361
24112 Lorain Rd North Olmsted (44070) *(G-15340)*

Kelly-Creswell Company, Springfield *Also called Ernest Industries Inc (G-17553)*

Kellys Polishing Metal Finshg 440 232-8800
7010 Krick Rd Bedford (44146) *(G-1436)*

Kellys Welding & Fabricating 440 593-6040
285 N Amboy Rd Conneaut (44030) *(G-7811)*

Keltec Inc 330 425-3100
2300 E Enterprise Pkwy Twinsburg (44087) *(G-18962)*

Keltec-Technolab, Twinsburg *Also called Keltec Inc (G-18962)*

Kemper Automotive 800 783-8004
1380 E 2nd St Franklin (45005) *(G-10030)*

Kempf Surgical Appliances Inc 513 984-5758
10567 Montgomery Rd Montgomery (45242) *(G-14433)*

Ken AG Inc 419 281-1204
101 E 7th St Ashland (44805) *(G-747)*

Ken Emerick Machine Products 440 834-4501
14504 Main Market Rd Burton (44021) *(G-2380)*

Ken Forging Inc 440 993-8091
1049 Griggs Rd Jefferson (44047) *(G-11364)*

Ken Harper 740 439-4452
60772 Southgate Rd Byesville (43723) *(G-2406)*

Ken Heuser & Gary Gravel 513 752-4159
473 Lenkenann Dr Cincinnati (45255) *(G-3981)*

Ken Veney Industries LLC 330 336-5825
690 Weber Dr Wadsworth (44281) *(G-19413)*

Ken-Dal Corporation 330 644-7118
644 Killian Rd Akron (44319) *(G-252)*

Ken-Tools, Akron *Also called Summit Tool Company (G-422)*

Kenamerican Resources Inc (HQ) 740 338-3100
46226 National Rd W Saint Clairsville (43950) *(G-16793)*

Kenan Advantage Group Inc 614 878-4050
500 Manor Park Dr Columbus (43228) *(G-7254)*

Kencraft Co Inc 419 536-0333
821 N Westwood Ave Toledo (43607) *(G-18542)*

Kendall & Sons Company 937 222-6996
510 Xenia Ave Dayton (45410) *(G-8436)*

Kendall Holdings Ltd (PA) 614 486-4750
2111 Builders Pl Columbus (43204) *(G-7255)*

Kendall Printing, Dayton *Also called Kendall & Sons Company (G-8436)*

Kendall/Hunt Publishing Co 877 275-4725
8805 Governors Hill Dr # 400 Cincinnati (45249) *(G-3982)*

Kendee Candles LLC 330 899-9898
4761 Buhl Blvd Uniontown (44685) *(G-19088)*

(G-0000) Company's Geographic Section entry number

Kendel Welding & Fabrication...................................330 834-2429
1700 Navarre Rd Se Massillon (44646) *(G-13161)*

Kendra Screen Print...440 967-8820
3817 Liberty Ave Vermilion (44089) *(G-19330)*

Kenlake Foods, Cincinnati *Also called Inter American Products Inc (G-3927)*

Kenley Enterprises LLC..419 630-0921
418 N Lynn St Bryan (43506) *(G-2308)*

Kenmore Construction Co Inc...................................330 832-8888
9500 Forty Corners Rd Nw Massillon (44647) *(G-13162)*

Kenmore Development & Mch Co................................330 753-2274
1395 Kenmore Blvd Akron (44314) *(G-253)*

Kenmore Gear & Machine Co Inc...............................330 753-6671
1519 Kenmore Blvd Akron (44314) *(G-254)*

Kennametal Inc..440 437-5131
180 Penniman Rd Orwell (44076) *(G-15777)*

Kennametal Inc..216 898-6120
18105 Cleveland Pkwy Dr Cleveland (44135) *(G-5644)*

Kennametal Inc..440 349-5151
6865 Cochran Rd Solon (44139) *(G-17329)*

Kennametal Inc..419 877-5358
6325 Industrial Pkwy Whitehouse (43571) *(G-20341)*

Kennedy Catalogs LLC..513 753-1518
4177 Knollview Ct Batavia (45103) *(G-1196)*

Kennedy Graphics, Cleveland *Also called Kennedy Mint Inc (G-5645)*

Kennedy Graphics Inc (PA)......................................419 223-9825
1640 N Main St Lima (45801) *(G-12035)*

Kennedy Group Incorporated (PA)..............................440 951-7660
38601 Kennedy Pkwy Willoughby (44094) *(G-20520)*

Kennedy Ink Company Inc (PA).................................513 871-2515
5230 Wooster Pike Cincinnati (45226) *(G-3983)*

Kennedy Ink Company Inc.......................................937 461-5600
110 Vermont Ave Dayton (45404) *(G-8437)*

Kennedy Mint Inc...440 572-3222
12102 Pearl Rd Rear Cleveland (44136) *(G-5645)*

Kennedy Printing Co..419 422-1802
1631 Broad Ave Findlay (45840) *(G-9847)*

Kennedy Repair Services...937 332-9118
221 S Plum St Troy (45373) *(G-18851)*

Kennedys Bakery Inc...740 432-2301
1025 Wheeling Ave Cambridge (43725) *(G-2461)*

Kenneth Hickman Co..513 348-0016
4266 Tranquility Ct Batavia (45103) *(G-1197)*

Kenneth J Moore..330 923-8313
3775 Wyoga Lake Rd Cuyahoga Falls (44224) *(G-8016)*

Kenneth Mc Beth..740 922-9494
514 Stillwater Ave Dennison (44621) *(G-8945)*

Kenneth Schrock..937 544-7566
3735 Wheat Ridge Rd West Union (45693) *(G-20123)*

Kenneth Shannon...513 777-8888
5438 Kyles Station Rd Liberty Twp (45011) *(G-11975)*

Kennewegs Wood Products.......................................330 832-1540
973 Vindell Ave Nw Massillon (44647) *(G-13163)*

Kennick Mold & Die Inc..216 631-3535
3601 Detroit Ave Cleveland (44113) *(G-5646)*

Kenoil Inc..330 262-1144
1537 Blachleyville Rd Wooster (44691) *(G-20794)*

Kenosha Beef International Ltd..................................614 771-1330
1821 Dividend Dr Columbus (43228) *(G-7256)*

Kens His & Hers Shop Inc..330 872-3190
8 W Broad St Newton Falls (44444) *(G-15134)*

Kensington Prep Plant, Carrollton *Also called Rosebud Mining Company (G-2964)*

Kent Adhesive Products Co.......................................330 678-1626
1000 Cherry St Kent (44240) *(G-11475)*

Kent Automation Inc..330 678-6343
449 Dodge St Kent (44240) *(G-11476)*

Kent Corporation..440 582-3400
9601 York Alpha Dr North Royalton (44133) *(G-15430)*

Kent Displays Inc (PA)...330 673-8784
343 Portage Blvd Kent (44240) *(G-11477)*

Kent Elastomer Products, Winesburg *Also called Meridian Industries Inc (G-20706)*

Kent Elastomer Products, Kent *Also called Meridian Industries Inc (G-11488)*

Kent Elastomer Products Inc.....................................800 331-4762
3890 Mogadore Indus Pkwy Mogadore (44260) *(G-14379)*

Kent Elastomer Products Inc (HQ)..............................330 673-1011
1500 Saint Clair Ave Kent (44240) *(G-11478)*

Kent Information Services Inc....................................330 672-2110
6185 2nd Ave Kent (44240) *(G-11479)*

Kent Mold and Manufacturing Co...............................330 673-3469
1190 W Main St Kent (44240) *(G-11480)*

Kent Parks Recreation, Kent *Also called City of Kent (G-11438)*

Kent Paverbrick LLC..330 995-7000
11437 Chamberlain Rd Aurora (44202) *(G-930)*

Kent Sporting Goods Co Inc (PA)...............................419 929-7021
433 Park Ave New London (44851) *(G-14860)*

Kent Sporting Goods Co Inc......................................330 674-2233
374 Railroad St Millersburg (44654) *(G-14237)*

Kent State University...330 672-7913
307 Lwry Hall Terrance Dr Kent (44242) *(G-11481)*

Kent State University...330 672-2586
205 Frlanklin Hall Kent (44242) *(G-11482)*

Kent Stow Screen Printing Inc...................................330 923-5118
1340 Home Ave Ste F Akron (44310) *(G-255)*

Kent Swigart...937 836-5292
301 W Wenger Rd Englewood (45322) *(G-9528)*

Kentak Products Company...330 386-3700
1308 Railroad St East Liverpool (43920) *(G-9221)*

Kentak Products Company (PA)..................................330 382-2000
1230 Railroad St East Liverpool (43920) *(G-9222)*

Kentak Products Company...330 532-6211
795 E Martin St East Palestine (44413) *(G-9240)*

Kenton Industries Ltd...915 603-2139
1278 W 9th St Ph 2 Cleveland (44113) *(G-5647)*

Kenton Iron Products Inc (PA)...................................419 674-4178
347 Vine St Kenton (43326) *(G-11554)*

Kenton Iron Products Inc...419 674-4178
13917 N Vision Dr Kenton (43326) *(G-11555)*

Kenton Times, Kenton *Also called Ray Barnes Newspaper Inc (G-11566)*

Kenton Times, The, Kenton *Also called Hardin County Publishing Co (G-11549)*

Kentrox Inc (HQ)...614 798-2000
5800 Innovation Dr Dublin (43016) *(G-9096)*

Kenway Corp...937 767-1660
504 Xenia Ave Yellow Springs (45387) *(G-20994)*

Kenwel Printers Inc..614 261-1011
4272 Indianola Ave Columbus (43214) *(G-7257)*

Kenwood Pool Distributors Inc...................................513 793-7080
8211 Blue Ash Rd Cincinnati (45236) *(G-3984)*

Kenworth of Dayton..937 235-2589
7740 Center Point 70 Blvd Dayton (45424) *(G-8438)*

Kenyon Co, Coshocton *Also called Novelty Advertising Co Inc (G-7903)*

Kenyon Review..740 427-5208
104 College Dr Fl 2 Gambier (43022) *(G-10316)*

Kepcor Inc...330 868-6434
215 Bridge St Minerva (44657) *(G-14327)*

Kerber Sheetmetal Works Inc....................................937 339-6366
104 Foss Way Troy (45373) *(G-18852)*

Kerek Industries Ltd Lblty Co....................................440 461-1450
750 Beta Dr Ste A Cleveland (44143) *(G-5648)*

Kerf Waterjet Ltd...937 254-9711
313 E Helena St Dayton (45404) *(G-8439)*

Kern Inc (HQ)...614 317-2600
3940 Gantz Rd Ste A Grove City (43123) *(G-10567)*

Kern Inc...440 930-7315
755 Alpha Dr Cleveland (44143) *(G-5649)*

Kern Machine Tool Inc..419 470-1206
367 E State Line Rd Toledo (43612) *(G-18543)*

Kern Manufacturing Inc (PA).....................................216 464-5490
24050 Commerce Park Cleveland (44122) *(G-5650)*

Kern-Liebers Texas Inc...419 865-2437
1510 Albon Rd Holland (43528) *(G-11069)*

Kern-Liebers Usa Inc (HQ).......................................419 865-2437
1510 Albon Rd Holland (43528) *(G-11070)*

Kernells Autmtc Machining Inc...................................419 588-2164
10511 State Rte 61 N Berlin Heights (44814) *(G-1662)*

Kerr Friction Products Inc..330 455-3983
2512 Columbus Rd Ne Canton (44705) *(G-2751)*

Kerry Flavor Systems Us LLC....................................513 771-4682
10261 Chester Rd Cincinnati (45215) *(G-3985)*

Kerry Flavor Systems Us LLC....................................513 539-7373
1055 Reed Dr Monroe (45050) *(G-14407)*

Kerry Ingredients & Flavours, Cincinnati *Also called Kerry Flavor Systems Us LLC (G-3985)*

Kerry Ingredients & Flavours, Monroe *Also called Kerry Flavor Systems Us LLC (G-14407)*

Kes Industries LLC (PA)..330 405-2813
8040 Bavaria Rd Twinsburg (44087) *(G-18963)*

Kessler Outdoor Advertising, Zanesville *Also called Kessler Sign Company (G-21326)*

Kessler Sign Company (PA).......................................740 453-0668
2669 National Rd Zanesville (43701) *(G-21326)*

Kessler Sign Company..937 898-0633
5804 Poe Ave Dayton (45414) *(G-8440)*

Kessler Studios Inc...513 683-7500
273 E Broadway St Loveland (45140) *(G-12366)*

Ketco Inc..937 426-9331
1348 Research Park Dr Beavercreek (45432) *(G-1346)*

Keteli Teamwear LLC...740 373-7969
111 Putnam St Marietta (45750) *(G-12797)*

Ketman Corporation..330 262-1688
205 W Liberty St Wooster (44691) *(G-20795)*

Kettering Monogramming, Dayton *Also called Zimmer Enterprises Inc (G-8768)*

Kettering Roofing & Shtmtl.......................................513 281-6413
3210 Jefferson Ave Ste 1 Cincinnati (45220) *(G-3986)*

Keuchel & Associates Inc...330 945-9455
175 Muffin Ln Cuyahoga Falls (44223) *(G-8017)*

Kever Incorporated...614 552-9000
4581 Poth Rd Columbus (43213) *(G-7258)*

Kever Printing & Promotions, Columbus *Also called Kever Incorporated (G-7258)*

Kevin G Ryba Inc...419 627-2010
3727 Perkins Ave Huron (44839) *(G-11230)*

Kevin K Tidd..419 885-5603
5505 Roan Rd Sylvania (43560) *(G-18115)*

Key Blue Prints Inc 614 899-6180
6180 Cleveland Ave Columbus (43231) *(G-7259)*

Key Finishes LLC 614 351-8393
727 Harrison Dr Columbus (43204) *(G-7260)*

Key Maneuvers Inc (PA) 440 285-0774
510 Center St Chardon (44024) *(G-3159)*

Key Marketing Group 440 748-3479
11185 Arrowhead Dr Grafton (44044) *(G-10432)*

Key Mobility Services Ltd 937 374-3226
1944 Us Route 68 N Xenia (45385) *(G-20959)*

Key Press Inc 513 721-1203
2135 Central Pkwy Cincinnati (45214) *(G-3987)*

Key Principal Investing, Cleveland *Also called Key Principal Partners Corp (G-5651)*

Key Principal Partners Corp (HQ) 888 539-3322
800 Superior Ave E # 1000 Cleveland (44114) *(G-5651)*

Key Resin Company (PA) 513 943-4225
4050 Clough Woods Dr Batavia (45103) *(G-1198)*

Keyah International Trdg LLC (PA) 937 399-3140
4655 Urbana Rd Springfield (45502) *(G-17586)*

Keyghobad Ventures LLC 440 366-3278
141 Innovation Dr Ste 320 Elyria (44035) *(G-9447)*

Keynes Bros Inc (PA) 740 385-6824
1 W Front St Logan (43138) *(G-12181)*

Keynes Brothers Inc 740 426-6332
12574 State Route 41 Jeffersonville (43128) *(G-11381)*

Keysco Tools, Cleveland *Also called S & H Industries Inc (G-6145)*

Keystone Bolt & Nut Company 216 524-9626
7600 Hub Pkwy Cleveland (44125) *(G-5652)*

Keystone Foods LLC 419 257-2341
2208 Grant Rd North Baltimore (45872) *(G-15193)*

Keystone Granite and Tile Inc 614 541-9749
2747 Westbelt Dr Columbus (43228) *(G-7261)*

Keystone Press Inc 419 243-7326
1801 Broadway St Toledo (43609) *(G-18544)*

Keystone Printing & Copy Cat 740 354-6542
842 4th St Portsmouth (45662) *(G-16439)*

Keystone Printing Co 330 385-9519
648 Saint Clair Ave East Liverpool (43920) *(G-9223)*

Keystone Threaded Products, Cleveland *Also called Keystone Bolt & Nut Company (G-5652)*

KG Tool Company 440 428-8633
5640 Middle Ridge Rd Madison (44057) *(G-12508)*

Khempco Bldg Sup Co Ltd Partnr (PA) 740 549-0465
130 Johnson Dr Delaware (43015) *(G-8865)*

Ki Intel LLC 740 200-9000
11720 Kilbourne Rd Sunbury (43074) *(G-18065)*

Kichler Lighting, Cleveland *Also called L D Kichler Co (G-5671)*

Kid Concoctions Company 440 572-1800
18511 Whitemarsh Ln Strongsville (44149) *(G-17936)*

Kiddi Pops, Dalton *Also called Yost Candy Co (G-8081)*

Kief Signs 513 941-8800
3 E Main St Addyston (45001) *(G-11)*

Kiefer Tool & Mold Inc 216 251-0076
3855 W 150th St Cleveland (44111) *(G-5653)*

Kiemle-Hankins Company (PA) 419 661-2430
94 H St Perrysburg (43551) *(G-16117)*

Kiesling-Hess Finishing Co, Cincinnati *Also called Resistflame Acquisition Corp (G-4337)*

Kight Creations, Dayton *Also called Naomi Kight (G-8517)*

Kilar Manufacturing Inc 330 534-8961
2616 N Main St Hubbard (44425) *(G-11133)*

Kilbarger Construction Inc 740 385-5531
450 Gallagher Ave Logan (43138) *(G-12182)*

Kilbarger Investment Co, Logan *Also called Kilbarger Investments Inc (G-12183)*

Kilbarger Investments Inc 740 385-6019
450 Gallagher Ave Logan (43138) *(G-12183)*

Kiley Machine Company Inc 513 875-3223
4196 Anderson State Rd Fayetteville (45118) *(G-9783)*

Kiley Mold Company LLC 513 875-3223
4200 Anderson State Rd Fayetteville (45118) *(G-9784)*

Kilgore Manufacturing Mch Co 330 491-1915
2502 8th St Ne Canton (44704) *(G-2752)*

Killbuck Creek Oil Co 330 601-0921
2538 Columbus Rd Wooster (44691) *(G-20796)*

Killbuck Oilfield Services 330 276-6706
9277 Township Road 92 Killbuck (44637) *(G-11596)*

Killian Latex Inc 330 644-6746
2064 Killian Rd Akron (44312) *(G-256)*

Kiln 440 717-1880
7225 Fitzwater Rd Brecksville (44141) *(G-2058)*

Kiln of Hyde Park Inc 513 321-3307
1286 Herschel Ave Cincinnati (45208) *(G-3988)*

Kilroy Company (PA) 440 951-8700
34929 Curtis Blvd Ste 104 Eastlake (44095) *(G-9278)*

Kiltex Corporation 330 644-6746
2064 Killian Rd Akron (44312) *(G-257)*

Kim Phillips Sign Co LLC 330 364-4280
812 Boulevard St Dover (44622) *(G-8995)*

Kimball Midwest, Columbus *Also called Midwest Motor Supply Co (G-7351)*

Kimberly-Clark Corporation 513 864-3780
209 W 7th St Cincinnati (45202) *(G-3989)*

Kimberly-Clark Corporation 513 794-1005
9277 Centre Pointe Dr # 200 West Chester (45069) *(G-19888)*

Kimble Custom Chassis Company 877 546-2537
1951 Reiser Ave Se New Philadelphia (44663) *(G-14906)*

Kimble Manufacturing Company 419 485-8449
124 S Jonesville St Montpelier (43543) *(G-14447)*

Kimble Manufacturing Company, New Philadelphia *Also called Kimble Custom Chassis Company (G-14906)*

Kimble Mixer Company 330 308-6700
1951 Reiser Ave Se New Philadelphia (44663) *(G-14907)*

Kimmatt Corp 937 228-3811
326 Troy St Dayton (45404) *(G-8441)*

Kimpton Printing & Spc Co 330 467-1640
400 Highland Rd E Macedonia (44056) *(G-12466)*

Kimpton Prtg & Specialities, Macedonia *Also called Kimpton Printing & Spc Co (G-12466)*

Kind Special Alloys Us LLC 330 788-2437
1221 Velma Ct Youngstown (44512) *(G-21128)*

Kinetic Technologies Inc 440 943-4111
1350 Rockefeller Rd Wickliffe (44092) *(G-20369)*

Kinetico Engineered Systems, Newbury *Also called Kinetico Incorporated (G-15098)*

Kinetico Incorporated 440 564-7167
11015 Kinsman Rd Newbury (44065) *(G-15098)*

King Bag and Manufacturing Co (PA) 513 541-5440
1500 Spring Lawn Ave Cincinnati (45223) *(G-3990)*

King Bros Feed & Supply, Bristolville *Also called K M B Inc (G-2098)*

King Castings, Akron *Also called King Model Company (G-259)*

King Conveyor LLC 740 332-6200
21397 State Route 180 Laurelville (43135) *(G-11770)*

King Drilling Co 330 769-3434
24 E Main St Seville (44273) *(G-17077)*

King Energy Inc 330 297-5508
6050 State Route 14 Lot 7 Ravenna (44266) *(G-16536)*

King Force & Machine, Twinsburg *Also called King Forge and Machine Company (G-18964)*

King Forge and Machine Company 330 963-0600
8250 Boyle Pkwy Twinsburg (44087) *(G-18964)*

King Kold Inc 937 836-2731
331 N Main St Englewood (45322) *(G-9529)*

King Kutter II Inc 740 446-0351
2150 Eastern Ave Gallipolis (45631) *(G-10302)*

King Limestone Inc 740 638-3942
53681 Spencer Rd Cumberland (43732) *(G-7956)*

King Luminaire, Jefferson *Also called Stress-Crete Company (G-11372)*

King Luminaire Company Inc (HQ) 440 576-9073
1153 State Route 46 N Jefferson (44047) *(G-11365)*

King Machine and Tool Co 330 833-7217
1237 Sanders Ave Sw Massillon (44647) *(G-13164)*

King Machine of Akron Inc 330 762-7116
365 Kenmore Blvd Akron (44301) *(G-258)*

King Machine of NC, Akron *Also called King Machine of Akron Inc (G-258)*

King Media Enterprises Inc 216 588-6700
11800 Shaker Blvd Cleveland (44120) *(G-5654)*

King Mill's Woodworking, Plain City *Also called Kbi Group Inc (G-16346)*

King Model Company 330 633-0491
365 Kenmore Blvd Akron (44301) *(G-259)*

King Nut Companies, Solon *Also called Kanan Enterprises Inc (G-17325)*

King Nut Companies, Plant 2, Solon *Also called Kanan Enterprises Inc (G-17326)*

King of The Road, Troy *Also called Crowe Manufacturing Services (G-18813)*

King Quarries Inc 740 732-2923
41820 Parrish Ridge Rd Caldwell (43724) *(G-2429)*

King Retail Solutions Inc 513 729-5858
3865 Symmes Rd Hamilton (45015) *(G-10716)*

King Software Systems 330 562-1135
680 Briarcliff Dr Aurora (44202) *(G-931)*

King Vineyards 440 967-4191
5903 Coen Rd Vermilion (44089) *(G-19331)*

King-Indiana Forge Inc 330 425-4250
8250 Boyle Pkwy Twinsburg (44087) *(G-18965)*

Kings Command Foods LLC 937 526-3553
770 N Center St Versailles (45380) *(G-19350)*

Kings Welding and Fabg Inc 330 738-3592
5259 Bane Rd Ne Mechanicstown (44651) *(G-13359)*

Kingscote Chemicals Inc 937 886-9100
3334 S Tech Blvd Miamisburg (45342) *(G-13824)*

Kingscote-Formulabs, Miamisburg *Also called Kingscote Chemicals Inc (G-13824)*

Kingsly Compression Inc 740 439-0772
3956 Glenn Hwy Cambridge (43725) *(G-2462)*

Kingspan Benchmark, Columbus *Also called Benchmark Archtectural Systems (G-6821)*

Kingsway Art & Sign 330 877-6241
1555 Andrews St Ne Hartville (44632) *(G-10826)*

Kingswood Company, The, Columbus *Also called Glister Inc (G-7118)*

Kinnemeyers Cornerstone Cab Co, Cleves *Also called Kinnemyers Cornerstone Cab Inc (G-6518)*

Kinnemyers Cornerstone Cab Inc 513 353-3030
6000 Hamilton Cleves Rd Cleves (45002) *(G-6518)*

Kinninger Prod Wldg Co Inc 419 629-3491
710 Kuenzel Dr New Bremen (45869) *(G-14788)*

2017 Harris Ohio
Industrial Directory

(G-0000) Company's Geographic Section entry number

Kinsella Manufacturing Co Inc 513 561-5285
7880 Camargo Rd Cincinnati (45243) ***(G-3991)***
Kinzua Environmental Inc 216 881-4040
1176 E 38th St Ste 1 Cleveland (44114) ***(G-5655)***
Kip-Craft Incorporated (PA) 216 898-5500
4747 W 160th St Cleveland (44135) ***(G-5656)***
Kipps Gravel Company Inc 513 732-1024
4987 State Route 222 Batavia (45103) ***(G-1199)***
Kiraly Tool and Die Inc 330 744-5773
1250 Crescent St Youngstown (44502) ***(G-21129)***
Kirby and Sons Inc 419 927-2260
4876 County Highway 43 Upper Sandusky (43351) ***(G-19128)***
Kirby Customer Service Center, Cleveland *Also called Scott Fetzer Company* ***(G-6174)***
Kirby Electronics Inc 614 395-8926
13056 Morrison Pl Pickerington (43147) ***(G-16196)***
Kirby Sales Company Inc 216 228-2400
1920 W 114th St Cleveland (44102) ***(G-5657)***
Kirby Sand & Gravel, Upper Sandusky *Also called Kirby and Sons Inc* ***(G-19128)***
Kirbys Auto & Truck Repair 513 934-3999
875 Columbus Ave Lebanon (45036) ***(G-11812)***
Kirk & Blum Manufacturing Co (HQ) 513 458-2600
4625 Red Bank Rd Ste 200 Cincinnati (45227) ***(G-3992)***
Kirk & Blum Manufacturing Co 419 782-9885
24226 Bowman Rd Defiance (43512) ***(G-8798)***
Kirk and Blum, Defiance *Also called Kirk & Blum Manufacturing Co* ***(G-8798)***
Kirk Excavating & Construction 614 444-4008
821 Stimmel Rd Columbus (43223) ***(G-7262)***
Kirk Key Interlock Company LLC 330 833-8223
9048 Meridian Cir Nw North Canton (44720) ***(G-15245)***
Kirk Welding & Fabricating 216 961-6403
10410 Madison Ave Cleveland (44102) ***(G-5658)***
Kirk Williams Company Inc 614 875-9023
2734 Home Rd Grove City (43123) ***(G-10568)***
Kirkwood Holding Inc (PA) 216 267-6200
1239 Rockside Rd Cleveland (44134) ***(G-5659)***
Kirtland Capital Partners LP (PA) 216 593-0100
3201 Entp Pkwy Ste 200 Beachwood (44122) ***(G-1276)***
Kirtland Cpitl Partners III LP (PA) 440 585-9010
2550 Som Center Rd # 105 Willoughby Hills (44094) ***(G-20640)***
Kirwan Industries Inc 513 333-0766
1964 Central Ave Cincinnati (45214) ***(G-3993)***
Kiser Industries llc 937 332-6723
507 Michigan Ave Troy (45373) ***(G-18853)***
Kissicakes - N-Sweets LLC 614 940-2779
7660 Silver Fox Dr Columbus (43235) ***(G-7263)***
Kistler Instrument Corp 937 268-5920
3061 Dorf Dr Dayton (45439) ***(G-8442)***
Kit MB Systems Inc 330 945-4500
925 Glaser Pkwy Akron (44306) ***(G-260)***
Kitchen & Bath Factory Inc 440 510-8111
7170 Hawthorne Dr Mentor (44060) ***(G-13623)***
Kitchen Designs Plus Inc 419 536-6605
2725 N Reynolds Rd Toledo (43615) ***(G-18545)***
Kitchen Works Inc 440 353-0939
34425 Lorain Rd Ste 5 North Ridgeville (44039) ***(G-15385)***
Kitchens By Rutenschroer Inc (PA) 513 251-8333
950 Laidlaw Ave Cincinnati (45237) ***(G-3994)***
Kittyhawk Molding Company Inc 937 746-3663
10 Eagle Ct Carlisle (45005) ***(G-2932)***
Kiwi Promotional AP & Prtg Co 330 487-5115
2170 E Aurora Rd Twinsburg (44087) ***(G-18966)***
Kj Machining Systems Inc 440 975-8624
38254 Airport Pkwy Unit C Willoughby (44094) ***(G-20521)***
Klarity Medical Products LLC 740 788-8107
1987 Coffman Rd Newark (43055) ***(G-15027)***
Klawhorn Industries Inc 330 335-8191
456 South Blvd Wadsworth (44281) ***(G-19414)***
Klb Industries Inc 937 592-9010
Orchard & Elm St Bellefontaine (43311) ***(G-1535)***
Klebaum Machinery Inc 330 455-2046
1303 13th St Se Canton (44707) ***(G-2753)***
Kleen Polymers Inc 330 336-4212
145 Rainbow St Wadsworth (44281) ***(G-19415)***
Kleen Test Products, Beach City *Also called Meridian Industries Inc* ***(G-1248)***
Kleen Test Products Corp 330 878-5586
216 12th St Ne Strasburg (44680) ***(G-17824)***
Kleese Development Associates 330 392-7899
103 W Market St Ste 300 Warren (44481) ***(G-19566)***
Klenk Industries Inc 330 453-7857
1016 9th St Sw Canton (44707) ***(G-2754)***
Klingshirn Winery Inc 440 933-6666
33050 Webber Rd Avon Lake (44012) ***(G-1036)***
Klingstedt Brothers Company 330 456-8319
425 Schroyer Ave Sw Canton (44702) ***(G-2755)***
Klockner Pentaplast Amer Inc 937 548-7272
1671 Martindale Rd Greenville (45331) ***(G-10508)***
Klopfenstein Art Equipment 419 884-2900
25 Walnut St Mansfield (44904) ***(G-12633)***
Klosterman 419 242-3400
660 Sterling St Toledo (43609) ***(G-18546)***
Klosterman Baking Co (PA) 513 242-5667
4760 Paddock Rd Cincinnati (45229) ***(G-3995)***
Klosterman Baking Co 513 398-2707
1130 Reading Rd Mason (45040) ***(G-13053)***
Klosterman Baking Co 614 338-8111
2655 Courtright Rd Columbus (43232) ***(G-7264)***
Klosterman Baking Co 513 242-1004
1000 E Ross Ave Cincinnati (45217) ***(G-3996)***
Klosterman Baking Co Inc 937 322-9588
508 W Main St Springfield (45504) ***(G-17587)***
Klosterman Baking Co Inc 937 743-9021
350 S Pioneer Blvd Springboro (45066) ***(G-17487)***
Klosterman Signs, Cincinnati *Also called Mike Closterman* ***(G-4107)***
Klw Plastics Inc 678 674-2990
930 Deneen Ave Monroe (45050) ***(G-14408)***
Klw Plastics Inc (HQ) 513 539-2673
980 Deneen Ave Monroe (45050) ***(G-14409)***
Kmak Group LLC 937 308-1023
480 E High St London (43140) ***(G-12214)***
Kmart Supercenter 440 974-7300
17840 Bagley Rd Cleveland (44130) ***(G-5660)***
KMC Precision Machine, Canton *Also called Klebaum Machinery Inc* ***(G-2753)***
Kmgrafx Inc 513 248-4100
394 Wards Corner Rd # 100 Loveland (45140) ***(G-12367)***
Kmi Processing LLC (PA) 330 862-2185
15383 Lisbon St Ne Minerva (44657) ***(G-14328)***
Kmi Processing LLC 330 862-2185
15441 Lisbon St Ne Minerva (44657) ***(G-14329)***
Kmj Leasing Ltd 614 871-3883
7001 Harrisburg Pike Orient (43146) ***(G-15723)***
KMS 2000 Inc (PA) 330 454-9444
315 12th St Nw Canton (44703) ***(G-2756)***
Kn Rubber LLC (HQ) 419 739-4200
1400 Lunar Dr Wapakoneta (45895) ***(G-19494)***
Kn8designs LLC 859 380-5926
1716 Madison Rd Cincinnati (45206) ***(G-3997)***
Knape Industries Inc 614 885-3016
6592 Proprietors Rd Worthington (43085) ***(G-20875)***
Knapp Enterprises, Massillon *Also called Joseph Knapp* ***(G-13160)***
Knapp Foundry Co Inc 330 434-0916
1207 Sweitzer Ave Akron (44301) ***(G-261)***
Knauff Bros Logging & Lumber 740 634-2432
494 Houseman Town Rd Bainbridge (45612) ***(G-1060)***
Knauff Logging, Bainbridge *Also called Knauff Bros Logging & Lumber* ***(G-1060)***
Knb Tools of America Inc 614 733-0400
8440 Rausch Dr Plain City (43064) ***(G-16347)***
Kne LLC 859 356-1690
12 Suffolk Ct Fairfield (45014) ***(G-9672)***
Kneiss Saw & Tool Supply, Dayton *Also called Form-A-Chip Inc* ***(G-8347)***
Knief Farms A Partnership 937 585-4810
10532 County Road 13 Lewistown (43333) ***(G-11945)***
Knight Ergonomics Inc 440 746-0044
6650 W Snowville Rd Ste G Brecksville (44141) ***(G-2059)***
Knight Industries Corp 419 478-8550
5949 Telegraph Rd Toledo (43612) ***(G-18547)***
Knight Manufacturing Co Inc (PA) 740 676-9532
399 E 40th St Shadyside (43947) ***(G-17081)***
Knight Manufacturing Co Inc 740 676-5516
E 40th St Shadyside (43947) ***(G-17082)***
Knippen Chrysler Dodge Jeep 419 695-4976
800 W 5th St Delphos (45833) ***(G-8909)***
Knisley Lumber 740 634-2935
160 Potts Hill Rd Bainbridge (45612) ***(G-1061)***
Knitting Machinery Corp (PA) 216 851-9900
15625 Saranac Rd Cleveland (44110) ***(G-5661)***
Knitting Machinery Corp 937 548-2338
607 Riffle Ave Greenville (45331) ***(G-10509)***
Knoble Glass & Metal Inc (PA) 513 753-1246
8650 Green Rd Cincinnati (45255) ***(G-3998)***
Knoble Tool Corp 937 461-4040
1535 Stanley Ave Dayton (45404) ***(G-8443)***
Knous Tool & Machine Inc 419 394-3541
14184 State Route 116 Saint Marys (45885) ***(G-16841)***
Knowles Press Inc 330 877-9345
316 E Maple St Hartville (44632) ***(G-10827)***
Knowlton Machine Inc 419 281-6802
726 Virginia Ave Ashland (44805) ***(G-748)***
Knowlton Manufacturing Co Inc 513 631-7353
2524 Leslie Ave Cincinnati (45212) ***(G-3999)***
Knox County Citizen, Galion *Also called Knox County Printing Co* ***(G-10278)***
Knox County Printing Co 740 848-4032
129 Harding Way E Galion (44833) ***(G-10278)***
Knox Energy Inc (PA) 740 927-6731
11872 Worthington Rd Nw Pataskala (43062) ***(G-15974)***
Knox Energy Inc 740 787-1391
930 Mount Perry Rd Mount Perry (43760) ***(G-14591)***
Knox Machine & Tool 740 392-3133
250 Columbus Rd Mount Vernon (43050) ***(G-14627)***
Knox Machinery Inc 937 743-2641
375 Industrial Dr Franklin (45005) ***(G-10031)***

ALPHABETIC

(PA)=Parent Co (HQ)=Headquarters (DH)=Div Headquarters

Knukonceptzcom Ltd 216 310-6555
7227 Anderson Rd Windham (44288) *(G-20698)*

Kobelco Stewart Bolling Inc 330 655-3111
1600 Terex Rd Hudson (44236) *(G-11187)*

Koch Crystal Finishing, Elyria *Also called Crystal Koch Finishing Inc (G-9399)*

Koch Foods of Cincinnati LLC 513 874-3500
4100 Port Union Rd Fairfield (45014) *(G-9673)*

Koch Knight LLC (HQ) 330 488-1651
5385 Orchardview Dr Se East Canton (44730) *(G-9194)*

Koch Meat Co Inc 513 874-3500
4100 Port Union Rd Fairfield (45014) *(G-9674)*

Kodiak Springs Water Co, Pierpont *Also called K S W C Inc (G-16212)*

Koebbeco Signs LLC 513 923-2974
5683 Springdale Rd Cincinnati (45251) *(G-4000)*

Koehler Rubber & Supply Co 216 749-5100
800 W Resource Dr Cleveland (44131) *(G-5662)*

Koenig Equipment Inc 937 653-5281
3130 E Us Highway 36 Urbana (43078) *(G-19167)*

Koester Corporation (PA) 419 599-0291
813 N Perry St Napoleon (43545) *(G-14687)*

Koester Machined Products Co 419 782-0291
136 Fox Run Dr Defiance (43512) *(G-8799)*

Kofinas Olive Oil, Cincinnati *Also called Lms LLC (G-4031)*

Kohl Patterns 513 353-3831
7983 Morgan Rd Cleves (45002) *(G-6519)*

Kohler Coating, Canton *Also called Coater Services Inc (G-2662)*

Kohut Enterprises 440 366-6666
5281 Butternut Ridge Dr Independence (44131) *(G-11263)*

Koki Laboratories Inc 330 773-7669
1081 Rosemary Blvd Akron (44306) *(G-262)*

Kokosing Materials Inc 419 522-2715
215 Oak St Mansfield (44907) *(G-12634)*

Kokosing Materials Inc 740 745-3341
9134 Mount Vernon Rd Saint Louisville (43071) *(G-16827)*

Kokosing Materials Inc 614 891-5090
6189 Westerville Rd Westerville (43081) *(G-20220)*

Kokosing Materials Inc 614 491-1199
4755 S High St Columbus (43207) *(G-7265)*

Koksing Material Inc 330 721-2775
310 N State Rd Medina (44256) *(G-13434)*

Kol-Cap Manufacturing Co, Cleveland *Also called Walest Incorporated (G-6443)*

Kole Specialties Inc 513 829-1111
4695 Industry Dr Ste A Fairfield (45014) *(G-9675)*

Kolhfab Cstm Plstic Fbrication 937 237-2098
2025 Webster St Dayton (45404) *(G-8444)*

Kolinahr Systems Inc 513 745-9401
6840 Ashfield Dr Blue Ash (45242) *(G-1823)*

Kolpin Outdoors Corporation 330 328-0772
3479 State Rd Cuyahoga Falls (44223) *(G-8018)*

Koltcz Concrete Block Co 440 232-3630
7660 Oak Leaf Rd Bedford (44146) *(G-1437)*

Komar Industries Inc (PA) 614 836-2366
4425 Marketing Pl Groveport (43125) *(G-10629)*

Komatec Tool & Die Inc 937 252-1133
1415 E 2nd St Dayton (45403) *(G-8445)*

Kona Blackbird Inc (PA) 440 285-3189
11730 Ravenna Rd Chardon (44024) *(G-3160)*

Konecranes Inc 937 328-5123
1600 Commerce Rd Springfield (45504) *(G-17588)*

Konecranes Inc 937 328-5100
4505 Gateway Blvd Springfield (45502) *(G-17589)*

Konecranes Inc (HQ) 937 525-5533
4401 Gateway Blvd Springfield (45502) *(G-17590)*

Konecranes Inc 440 461-8400
740 Beta Dr Ste G Highland Heights (44143) *(G-10916)*

Koneta Inc 419 739-4200
1400 Lunar Dr Wapakoneta (45895) *(G-19495)*

Koneta Rubber, Wapakoneta *Also called Kn Rubber LLC (G-19494)*

Kongsberg Automotive, Grand River *Also called Actuation Kongsberg Systems II (G-10447)*

Konkrete City Skateboards 513 231-0399
2109 Beechmont Ave Cincinnati (45230) *(G-4001)*

Konoil Inc 330 499-9811
6477 Frank Ave Nw Canton (44720) *(G-2757)*

Konys, Mark Glass Design, Cleveland *Also called Bruening Glass Works Inc (G-4940)*

Koop Diamond Cutters Inc 513 621-2838
214 E 8th St Fl 4 Cincinnati (45202) *(G-4002)*

Kopachko Machining Inc 440 953-3988
38341 Western Pkwy Willoughby (44094) *(G-20522)*

Koppers Ind Inc 740 776-2149
400 Harding Ave Portsmouth (45662) *(G-16440)*

Koppers Industries Inc 740 776-3238
6501 Pershing Ave Portsmouth (45662) *(G-16441)*

Korda Manufacturing Inc 330 262-1555
3927 E Lincoln Way Wooster (44691) *(G-20797)*

Korff Holdings LLC 330 332-1566
310 E Euclid Ave Salem (44460) *(G-16905)*

Korff Machine LLC 330 332-1566
310 E Euclid Ave Salem (44460) *(G-16906)*

Korkan Granite Co Inc 330 677-1883
4561 Crystal Pkwy Kent (44240) *(G-11483)*

Koroseal Interior Products LLC (PA) 330 668-7600
3875 Embassy Pkwy Ste 110 Fairlawn (44333) *(G-9755)*

Koski Construction Co (PA) 440 997-5337
5841 Woodman Ave Ashtabula (44004) *(G-815)*

Koski Construction Co 440 964-8171
1149 E 5th St Ashtabula (44004) *(G-816)*

Koster Crop Tester Inc 330 220-2116
3077 Nationwide Pkwy Brunswick (44212) *(G-2236)*

Kottler Metal Products Co Inc 440 946-7473
1595 Lost Nation Rd Willoughby (44094) *(G-20523)*

Kountry Pride Enterprises 330 868-3345
10167 Malibu Rd Ne Minerva (44657) *(G-14330)*

Kovacevic Printing Inc 440 887-1000
6886 Pearl Rd Ste A Cleveland (44130) *(G-5663)*

Kovatch Castings Inc 330 896-9944
3743 Tabs Dr Uniontown (44685) *(G-19089)*

Kovels Antiques Inc 216 752-2252
30799 Pinetree Rd 305 Cleveland (44124) *(G-5664)*

Kowalski Heat Treating Co 216 631-4411
3611 Detroit Ave Cleveland (44113) *(G-5665)*

Koyo Bearings, Westlake *Also called Jtekt North America Corp (G-20279)*

Kps NAPA 740 522-9445
441 Hopewell Dr Heath (43056) *(G-10849)*

Krafft and Associates Inc 937 325-4671
991 W Leffel Ln Springfield (45506) *(G-17591)*

Kraft Electrical Contg Inc 614 836-9300
4407 Professional Pkwy Groveport (43125) *(G-10630)*

Kraft Foods, Toledo *Also called Mondelez Global LLC (G-18591)*

Kraft Heinz Company, Massillon *Also called Kraft Heinz Company (G-13165)*

Kraft Heinz Company 330 837-8331
1301 Oberlin Ave Sw Massillon (44647) *(G-13165)*

Kraft Heinz Foods Company 419 332-7357
1200 N 5th St Fremont (43420) *(G-10162)*

Kraft Heinz Foods Company 740 622-0523
1660 S 2nd St Coshocton (43812) *(G-7896)*

Kraft House No 5 ....614 396-9091
5 S Liberty St Powell (43065) *(G-16475)*

Kraft of Writing 614 620-2476
46 Webster Park Ave Columbus (43214) *(G-7266)*

Kraftmaid Cabinetry, Orwell *Also called Masco Cbinetry Middlefield LLC (G-15778)*

Kraftmaid Trucking Inc (PA) 440 632-2531
16052 Industrial Pkwy Middlefield (44062) *(G-13949)*

Krajewski Corp (PA) 740 522-1147
1776 Tamarack Rd Newark (43055) *(G-15028)*

Kram Precision Machining Inc 937 849-1301
1751 Dalton Dr New Carlisle (45344) *(G-14805)*

Kramer & Kiefer Inc 330 336-8742
2662 Valley Side Ave Wadsworth (44281) *(G-19416)*

Kramer Exploration Company 740 362-1805
170 W Lincoln Ave Delaware (43015) *(G-8866)*

Kramer Graphics Inc 937 296-9600
2408 W Dorothy Ln Moraine (45439) *(G-14499)*

Kramer Power Equipment Co 937 456-2232
2388 State Route 726 N Eaton (45320) *(G-9313)*

Kramer Printing, Mentor *Also called J & L Management Corporation (G-13614)*

Krasny Kaplan Division, Cleveland *Also called Formtek Inc (G-5372)*

Kraton Emplyees Recreation CLB 740 423-7571
2419 State Route 618 Belpre (45714) *(G-1588)*

Kraton Polymers US LLC 740 423-7571
2419 State Rd 618 Belpre (45714) *(G-1589)*

Krausher Machining Inc 440 839-2828
4267 Butler Rd Wakeman (44889) *(G-19449)*

Krazy Glue, West Jefferson *Also called Toagosei America Inc (G-20084)*

Krdc Inc 937 222-2332
90 Vermont Ave Dayton (45404) *(G-8446)*

Kre Inc 216 883-1600
2181 Enterprise Pkwy Twinsburg (44087) *(G-18967)*

Kreider Corp 937 325-8787
2000 S Yellow Springs St Springfield (45506) *(G-17592)*

Kreis Sawmill 937 537-1248
728 N Main St Marysville (43040) *(G-12955)*

Krema Nut Co, Columbus *Also called Brilista Foods Company Inc (G-6861)*

Krema Peanut Butter, Dublin *Also called Krema Products Inc (G-9097)*

Krema Products Inc (PA) 614 889-4824
45 N High St Dublin (43017) *(G-9097)*

Krendl Machine Company 419 692-3060
1201 Spencerville Rd Delphos (45833) *(G-8910)*

Krendl Rack Co Inc 419 667-4800
18413 Haver Rd Venedocia (45894) *(G-19321)*

Krigbaum Inc 614 478-6472
76 N Stygler Rd Columbus (43230) *(G-7267)*

Krisdale Industries Inc 330 225-2392
649 Marks Rd Valley City (44280) *(G-19209)*

Krispy Kreme 322, Columbus *Also called Krispy Kreme Doughnut Corp (G-7268)*

Krispy Kreme Doughnut Corp 614 798-0812
3690 W Dblin Granville Rd Columbus (43235) *(G-7268)*

Kriss Kreations 330 405-6102
  9224 Darrow Rd Twinsburg (44087) *(G-18968)*
Krist Krenz Machine Inc 440 237-1800
  9801 York Alpha Dr North Royalton (44133) *(G-15431)*
Kristine Marie's Olfactorium, Cleveland Also called Olfactorium Corp Inc *(G-5938)*
Kroehler Furniture Mfg Co Inc 828 459-9865
  4300 E 5th Ave Columbus (43219) *(G-7269)*
Kroger 00510, Findlay Also called Kroger Co *(G-9848)*
Kroger Co 740 671-5164
  400 28th St Bellaire (43906) *(G-1499)*
Kroger Co 614 462-2000
  457 Cleveland Ave Columbus (43215) *(G-7270)*
Kroger Co 513 671-2790
  11801 Chesterdale Rd Cincinnati (45246) *(G-4003)*
Kroger Co 740 335-4030
  548 Clinton Ave Wshngtn CT Hs (43160) *(G-20915)*
Kroger Co 740 264-5057
  264 S Hollywood Blvd Steubenville (43952) *(G-17702)*
Kroger Co 513 683-4001
  2900 W Us Hwy 22 3 Unit 1 Maineville (45039) *(G-12526)*
Kroger Co 740 374-2523
  40 Acme St Marietta (45750) *(G-12798)*
Kroger Co 513 742-9500
  1212 W Kemper Rd Ste 1 Cincinnati (45240) *(G-4004)*
Kroger Co 419 423-2065
  101 6th St Findlay (45840) *(G-9848)*
Kroger Co 937 277-0950
  1934 Needmore Rd Dayton (45414) *(G-8447)*
Kroger Co 614 263-1766
  3417 N High St Columbus (43214) *(G-7271)*
Kroger Co 937 743-5900
  725 W Central Ave Springboro (45066) *(G-17488)*
Kroger Co 614 575-3742
  7000 E Broad St Columbus (43213) *(G-7272)*
Krok Printing Inc 330 652-8198
  414 W Federal St Niles (44446) *(G-15166)*
Kroner Publications Inc (PA) 330 544-5500
  1123 W Park Ave Niles (44446) *(G-15167)*
Kronos Incorporated 614 528-2200
  1 Easton Oval Ste 350 Columbus (43219) *(G-7273)*
Kronos Incorporated 216 867-5609
  6100 Oak Tree Blvd # 410 Independence (44131) *(G-11264)*
Kroy LLC (HQ) 216 426-5600
  3830 Kelley Ave Cleveland (44114) *(G-5666)*
Krumor Inc 216 328-9802
  7655 Hub Pkwy Ste 206 Cleveland (44125) *(G-5667)*
Krusinski's Meat Market, Cleveland Also called John Krusinski *(G-5619)*
Kruz Inc 330 878-5595
  6332 Columbia Rd Nw Dover (44622) *(G-8996)*
KS Designs Inc 513 241-5953
  3044 Harrison Ave Cincinnati (45211) *(G-4005)*
KSA Limited Partnership 740 776-3238
  6501 Pershing Ave Portsmouth (45662) *(G-16442)*
Ksi Distribution Inc (PA) 440 256-2500
  8724 Tyler Blvd Mentor (44060) *(G-13624)*
Ksm Metal Fabrications, Troy Also called Kerber Sheetmetal Works Inc *(G-18852)*
Ksn Clearing LLC 304 269-3306
  736 2nd Ave Gallipolis (45631) *(G-10303)*
Kth Parts Industries Inc (PA) 937 663-5941
  1111 State Route 235 N Saint Paris (43072) *(G-16862)*
Ktm North America Inc (PA) 440 985-3553
  1119 Milan Ave Amherst (44001) *(G-600)*
Kts Cstm Lgs/Xclsvely You Inc 440 285-9803
  602 South St Ste C-2 Chardon (44024) *(G-3161)*
Kts Custom Logos 440 285-9803
  602 South St Ste C-2 Chardon (44024) *(G-3162)*
Kts-Met Bar Products Inc 440 288-9308
  967 G St Lorain (44052) *(G-12252)*
Ktsdi LLC 330 783-2000
  801 E Middletown Rd North Lima (44452) *(G-15318)*
Kubota Authorized Dealer, Athens Also called All Power Equipment LLC *(G-855)*
Kubota Tractor Corporation 614 835-3800
  6300 At One Kubota Way Groveport (43125) *(G-10631)*
Kufbag Inc 614 589-8687
  1333 Cobblestone Ave Westerville (43081) *(G-20221)*
Kuhlman Construction Products, Maumee Also called Kuhlman Corporation *(G-13273)*
Kuhlman Corporation (PA) 419 897-6000
  1845 Indian Wood Cir Maumee (43537) *(G-13273)*
Kuhlman Corporation 419 321-1670
  444 Kuhlman Dr Toledo (43609) *(G-18548)*
Kuhlman Engineering Co 419 243-2196
  840 Champlain St Toledo (43604) *(G-18549)*
Kuhlman Instrument Company 419 668-9533
  54 Summit St Norwalk (44857) *(G-15548)*
Kuhlmanns Fabrication 513 967-4617
  1753 Millville Oxford Rd Hamilton (45013) *(G-10717)*
Kuhls Hot Sportspot 513 474-2282
  7860 Beechmont Ave Cincinnati (45255) *(G-4006)*
Kuhn Fabricating Inc 440 277-4182
  1637 E 28th St Lorain (44055) *(G-12253)*

Kuka Toledo Production 419 727-5500
  3770 Stickney Ave Toledo (43608) *(G-18550)*
Kurts Auto Parts LLC 330 723-0166
  4093 Watercourse Dr Medina (44256) *(G-13435)*
Kurtz Bros Inc 614 491-0868
  2850 Rohr Rd Groveport (43125) *(G-10632)*
Kurtz Bros Compost Services 330 864-2621
  2677 Riverview Rd Akron (44313) *(G-263)*
Kurtz Tool & Die Co Inc 330 755-7723
  164 State St Struthers (44471) *(G-17993)*
Kurz-Kasch Inc 740 498-8343
  199 E State St Newcomerstown (43832) *(G-15117)*
Kurz-Kasch Inc (HQ) 740 498-8343
  199 E State St Newcomerstown (43832) *(G-15118)*
Kurzkasch Inc Wilm Div 740 498-8345
  199 E State St Newcomerstown (43832) *(G-15119)*
Kuss Filtration Inc (PA) 419 423-9040
  2150 Industrial Dr Findlay (45840) *(G-9849)*
Kustom Cases LLC 240 380-6275
  130 Oxford Ave Dayton (45402) *(G-8448)*
Kutol Products Company Inc 513 527-5500
  100 Partnership Way Sharonville (45241) *(G-17114)*
Kutrite Manufacturing, Tremont City Also called Mike Loppe *(G-18789)*
Kuwatch Printing LLC 513 759-5850
  7163 Ashview Ln Liberty Twp (45011) *(G-11976)*
Kw River Hydroelectric I LLC 513 673-2251
  5667 Krystal Ct Ste 100 Cincinnati (45252) *(G-4007)*
Kw Services LLC 419 636-3438
  527 S Union St Bryan (43506) *(G-2309)*
Kw Services LLC 419 228-1325
  1864 Mccullough St Lima (45801) *(G-12036)*
Kwik Kopy Printing, Blue Ash Also called Larmax Inc *(G-1825)*
Kwik Kopy Printing, Columbus Also called Hilleary-Whitaker Inc *(G-7157)*
Kwik Kopy Printing, Youngstown Also called Austintown Printing Inc *(G-21029)*
Kyklos Bearing Intl LLC (PA) 419 627-7000
  2509 Hayes Ave Sandusky (44870) *(G-16977)*
Kyle Publications Inc 419 754-4234
  2611 Montebello Rd Toledo (43607) *(G-18551)*
Kyntrol Holdings Inc (PA) 440 220-5990
  34700 Lakeland Blvd Eastlake (44095) *(G-9279)*
Kyntrol LLC (HQ) 440 951-2333
  34700 Lakeland Blvd Eastlake (44095) *(G-9280)*
Kyocera SGS Precision Tools (PA) 330 688-6667
  55 S Main St Munroe Falls (44262) *(G-14661)*
Kyocera SGS Precision Tools 330 688-6667
  2824 2nd St Cuyahoga Falls (44221) *(G-8019)*
Kyron Plating Corp 216 221-7275
  1336 W 114th St Cleveland (44102) *(G-5668)*
Kyron Tool and Machine Co Inc 614 231-6000
  2900 Banwick Rd Columbus (43232) *(G-7274)*
Kys Welding & Fabrication 513 702-9081
  154 Shoemaker Dr Loveland (45140) *(G-12368)*
Kz Solutions Inc 513 942-9378
  9440 Sutton Pl West Chester (45011) *(G-19889)*
L & C Plastic Bags Inc 937 473-2968
  500 Dick Minnich Dr Covington (45318) *(G-7925)*
L & F Lauch LLC 513 732-5805
  950 Kent Rd Batavia (45103) *(G-1200)*
L & H Printing 937 855-4512
  34 W Market St Germantown (45327) *(G-10370)*
L & H Printing Co, Germantown Also called L & H Printing *(G-10370)*
L & H Wood Products, Sidney Also called Langston Pallets *(G-17198)*
L & I Natural Resources Inc 513 683-2045
  10369 Cones Rd Loveland (45140) *(G-12369)*
L & J Cable Inc 937 526-9445
  102 Industrial Dr Russia (45363) *(G-16765)*
L & J Drive Thru 330 767-2185
  212 Wabash Ave N Brewster (44613) *(G-2085)*
L & L Fabricating LLC 440 647-6649
  46419 Whitney Rd Wellington (44090) *(G-19749)*
L & L Machine Inc 419 272-5000
  2919 County Road 2I Edon (43518) *(G-9341)*
L & L Ornamental Iron Co 513 353-1930
  6024 Hamilton Cleves Rd Cleves (45002) *(G-6520)*
L & L Plastics, Felicity Also called L C Liming & Sons Inc *(G-9786)*
L & L Railings, Cleves Also called L & L Ornamental Iron Co *(G-6520)*
L & M Mineral Co 330 852-3696
  2010 County Road 144 Sugarcreek (44681) *(G-18025)*
L & N Olde Car Co 440 564-7204
  9992 Kinsman Rd Newbury (44065) *(G-15099)*
L & P Machine Company 330 527-2753
  8488 State Route 305 Garrettsville (44231) *(G-10328)*
L & S Liette Express 419 394-7077
  2286 Celina Rd Saint Marys (45885) *(G-16842)*
L & T Collins Inc 740 345-4494
  44 S 4th St Newark (43055) *(G-15029)*
L & W Inc 734 397-6300
  1190 Jaycox Rd Avon (44011) *(G-999)*

L A Express (PA) 513 752-6999
1148 Marian Dr Batavia (45103) *(G-1201)*

L A Machine 216 651-1712
3818 Trent Ave Cleveland (44109) *(G-5669)*

L A Productions Co LLC (PA) 330 666-4230
1333 Collier Rd Akron (44320) *(G-264)*

L A Products Co, Akron Also called L A Productions Co LLC *(G-264)*

L and S Express Fuel Center 330 549-9566
10125 Market St North Lima (44452) *(G-15319)*

L B Folding Co Inc 216 961-0888
8110 Lake Ave Cleveland (44102) *(G-5670)*

L B Foster Company 330 652-1461
1193 Salt Springs Rd Mineral Ridge (44440) *(G-14307)*

L B Industries Inc 330 750-1002
534 Lowellville Rd Struthers (44471) *(G-17994)*

L B L Lithographers Inc (PA) 440 350-0106
365 W Prospect St Painesville (44077) *(G-15896)*

L B L Printing, Painesville Also called L B L Lithographers Inc *(G-15896)*

L B Machine & Mfg Co Inc 513 471-6137
1640 Lionel Ave Cincinnati (45214) *(G-4008)*

L B Manufacturing, Byesville Also called Famous Industries Inc *(G-2401)*

L B Steel Plate (PA) 440 893-0680
68 Olive St Ste 6 Chagrin Falls (44022) *(G-3062)*

L B Weiss Construction Inc 440 205-1774
8677 Twinbrook Rd Mentor (44060) *(G-13625)*

L Brands Inc 614 479-2000
3 Limited Pkwy Columbus (43230) *(G-7275)*

L C F Inc 330 877-3322
114 S Prospect Ave Hartville (44632) *(G-10828)*

L C G Machine & Tool Inc 614 261-1651
2923 Grasmere Ave Columbus (43224) *(G-7276)*

L C I Inc 330 948-1922
101 West Dr Lodi (44254) *(G-12163)*

L C Liming & Sons Inc 513 876-2555
3200 State Route 756 Felicity (45120) *(G-9786)*

L C Smith Co 440 327-1251
196 Morgan Ave Elyria (44035) *(G-9448)*

L C Systems Inc 614 235-9430
6135 Memorial Dr Ste 106f Dublin (43017) *(G-9098)*

L D C, Independence Also called Liquid Development Company *(G-11265)*

L D Kichler Co (PA) 866 558-5706
7711 E Pleasant Valley Rd Cleveland (44131) *(G-5671)*

L E P D Industries Ltd 614 985-1470
2292 Clairborne Dr Powell (43065) *(G-16476)*

L Garbers Sons Sawmilling LLC 419 335-6362
6444 County Road 12 Wauseon (43567) *(G-19686)*

L H Marshall Co 614 294-6433
1601 Woodland Ave Columbus (43219) *(G-7277)*

L Haberny Co Inc 440 543-5999
10115 Queens Way Chagrin Falls (44023) *(G-3098)*

L J Manufacturing Inc 440 352-1979
9436 Mercantile Dr Mentor (44060) *(G-13626)*

L J Smith Inc (HQ) 740 269-2221
35280 Scio Bowerston Rd Bowerston (44695) *(G-1958)*

L J Star Incorporated 330 405-3040
2396 Edison Blvd Twinsburg (44087) *(G-18969)*

L M Animal Farms, Pleasant Plain Also called Hartz Mountain Corporation *(G-16372)*

L M Berry and Company (PA) 937 296-2121
3170 Kettering Blvd Moraine (45439) *(G-14500)*

L M Engineering Inc 330 270-2400
2720 Intertech Dr Youngstown (44509) *(G-21130)*

L M Equipment & Design Inc 330 332-9951
11000 Youngstown Salem Rd Salem (44460) *(G-16907)*

L N Brut Manufacturing Co 330 833-9045
4680 Alabama Ave Sw Navarre (44662) *(G-14717)*

L N S Pallets 330 936-7507
6144 Smith Rd Sw Navarre (44662) *(G-14718)*

L P S I, Cleveland Also called Laser Printing Solutions Inc *(G-5684)*

L S Manufacturing Inc 614 885-7988
480 E Wilson Bridge Rd C Worthington (43085) *(G-20876)*

L&H Threaded Rods Corp 937 294-6666
3050 Dryden Rd Moraine (45439) *(G-14501)*

L&L Excavating & Land Clearing 740 682-7823
56 Jim Reese Rd Oak Hill (45656) *(G-15600)*

L&M Sheet Metal Ltd 513 858-6173
5010 Factory Dr Fairfield (45014) *(G-9676)*

L&W Cleveland, Avon Also called L & W Inc *(G-999)*

L-3 Cmmncations Nova Engrg Inc 877 282-1168
4393 Digital Way Mason (45040) *(G-13054)*

L-3 Cmmnctions Electrodynamics, Cincinnati Also called Electrodynamics Inc *(G-3300)*

L-3 Communications Cincinnati (HQ) 513 573-6100
7500 Innovation Way Mason (45040) *(G-13055)*

L-3 Fuzing and Ord Systems Inc 513 943-2000
3975 Mcmann Rd Cincinnati (45245) *(G-3310)*

L-K Industry Inc 937 526-3000
176 N West St Versailles (45380) *(G-19351)*

L-Mor Inc 216 541-2224
13404 Saint Clair Ave Cleveland (44110) *(G-5672)*

L.E.M. Products, West Chester Also called Lem Products Holding LLC *(G-19892)*

L3 Aviation Products Inc 614 825-2001
1105 Schrock Rd Ste 800 Columbus (43229) *(G-7278)*

L3 Technologies Inc 513 943-2000
3975 Mcmann Rd Cincinnati (45245) *(G-3311)*

L3 Technologies Inc 937 223-3285
3155 Res Blvd Ste 101 Dayton (45420) *(G-8449)*

La Boit Specialty Vehicles (PA) 614 231-7640
700 Cross Pointe Rd Gahanna (43230) *(G-10216)*

La Dua Inc 440 243-9600
24481 Barrett Rd Olmsted Twp (44138) *(G-15679)*

La Ganke & Sons Stamping Co 216 451-0278
13676 Station Rd Columbia Station (44028) *(G-6590)*

La Gra Jewelers Inc 440 439-5869
674 Broadway Ave Cleveland (44146) *(G-5673)*

La Grange Elec Assemblies Co 440 355-5388
349 S Center St Lagrange (44050) *(G-11630)*

La Mfg Inc 513 577-7200
9483 Reading Rd Cincinnati (45215) *(G-4009)*

La Perla Inc (PA) 419 534-2074
2742 Hill Ave Toledo (43607) *(G-18552)*

La Rose Paving Co Inc 440 632-0330
16590 Nauvoo Rd Middlefield (44062) *(G-13950)*

La Voz Hispania Newspaper 614 274-5505
3552 Sullivant Ave Columbus (43204) *(G-7279)*

Laad Sign & Lighting Inc 330 379-2297
830 Moe Dr Ste B Akron (44310) *(G-265)*

Lab Electronics Inc 330 674-9818
5640 Township Road 353 Millersburg (44654) *(G-14238)*

Lab Quality Machining Inc 513 625-0219
6311 Roudebush Rd Goshen (45122) *(G-10416)*

Lab-Pro Inc 937 434-9600
11019 Cold Spring Dr Dayton (45458) *(G-8450)*

Lababidi Enterprises Inc 330 733-2907
2167 Forest Oak Dr Akron (44312) *(G-266)*

Labcraft Inc 419 878-4400
1070 Disher Dr Waterville (43566) *(G-19662)*

Label Aid Inc 419 433-2888
608 Rye Beach Rd Huron (44839) *(G-11231)*

Label Print Technologies LLC 800 475-4030
3380 Gilchrist Rd Mogadore (44260) *(G-14380)*

Labeldata 614 891-5858
275 Old County Line Rd I Westerville (43081) *(G-20222)*

Labeltek Inc 330 335-3110
985 Seville Rd Wadsworth (44281) *(G-19417)*

Laborie Enterprises LLC 419 686-6245
10892 S Dixie Hwy Portage (43451) *(G-16425)*

Lacal Equipment Inc 800 543-6161
901 W Pike St Jackson Center (45334) *(G-11342)*

Laces For Less, Cincinnati Also called Joe Busby *(G-3949)*

Lachina Publishing Svcs Inc (PA) 216 292-7959
3793 Green Rd Cleveland (44122) *(G-5674)*

Lad Technology Inc 440 461-8002
730 Beta Dr Ste B Cleveland (44143) *(G-5675)*

Lafarge North America Inc 419 399-4861
11435 County Rd 176 Paulding (45879) *(G-16009)*

Lafarge North America Inc 216 781-9330
2500 Elm St Cleveland (44113) *(G-5676)*

Lafarge North America Inc 419 241-5256
840 Water St Toledo (43604) *(G-18553)*

Lafarge North America Inc 419 897-7656
1645 Indian Wood Cir # 201 Maumee (43537) *(G-13274)*

Lafarge North America Inc 740 423-5900
1684 State Route 618 Belpre (45714) *(G-1590)*

Lagc Ltd 419 886-2141
11729 Leedy Rd Fredericktown (43019) *(G-10105)*

Lahm Tool, Dayton Also called Lahm-Trosper Inc *(G-8451)*

Lahm-Trosper Inc 937 252-8791
1030 Springfield St Dayton (45403) *(G-8451)*

Laipplys Prtg Mktg Sltions Inc 740 387-9282
270 E Center St Marion (43302) *(G-12879)*

Laird Controls Holdings Inc (HQ) 234 806-0018
655 N River Rd Nw Ste A Warren (44483) *(G-19567)*

Laird Controls North Amer Inc (HQ) 234 806-0018
655 N River Rd Nw Ste A Warren (44483) *(G-19568)*

Laird Plastics Inc 614 272-0777
2220 International St Columbus (43228) *(G-7280)*

Laird Technologies, Cleveland Also called Thermagon Inc *(G-6315)*

Laird Technologies Inc 234 806-0105
655 N River Rd Nw Warren (44483) *(G-19569)*

Lake Cable Optical Lab 330 497-3022
4837 Frank Ave Nw Canton (44720) *(G-2758)*

Lake Cable Optical Laboratory, Canton Also called Lake Cable Optical Lab *(G-2758)*

Lake City Plating LLC 440 964-3555
1701 Lake Ave Ashtabula (44004) *(G-817)*

Lake Cnty Deptmntl Retrdtn/Dvl, Willoughby Also called County of Lake *(G-20464)*

Lake Community News 440 946-2577
36081 Lake Shore Blvd # 5 Willoughby (44095) *(G-20524)*

Lake County Auto Recyclers 440 428-2886
427 Newell St Painesville (44077) *(G-15897)*

Lake County Plating Corp..440 255-8835
7790 Division Dr Mentor (44060) *(G-13627)*

Lake Erie Asphalt Paving Inc......................................440 526-5191
5510 Oakes Rd Brecksville (44141) *(G-2060)*

Lake Erie Frozen Foods Mfg Co....................................419 289-9204
1830 Orange Rd Ashland (44805) *(G-749)*

Lake Erie Graphics Inc...216 575-1333
5372 W 130th St Brookpark (44142) *(G-2166)*

Lake Erie Industries LLC...216 255-1867
13000 Athens Ave Ste 101 Lakewood (44107) *(G-11671)*

Lake Erie Iron and Metal, Cleveland *Also called Welders Supply Inc (G-6456)*

Lake Erie Machine..440 353-9191
5165 Mills Indus Pkwy North Ridgeville (44039) *(G-15386)*

Lake Erie Rubber Recycling LLC....................................440 570-6027
19940 Echo Dr Strongsville (44149) *(G-17937)*

Lake Erie Ship Repair..440 624-0025
1459 State Route 46 S Jefferson (44047) *(G-11366)*

Lake Metals, Ravenna *Also called A C Williams Co Inc (G-16511)*

Lake Park Tool & Machine LLC.......................................330 788-2437
1221 Velma Ct Youngstown (44512) *(G-21131)*

Lake Plating, Elyria *Also called Cascade Plating Inc (G-9389)*

Lake Publishing Inc..440 299-8500
9853 Johnnycake Ridge Rd # 107 Mentor (44060) *(G-13628)*

Lake Region Oil Inc...330 837-4767
26 N Cochran St Dalton (44618) *(G-8073)*

Lake Screen Printing Inc...440 244-5707
1924 Broadway Lorain (44052) *(G-12254)*

Lake Shore Cryotronics Inc (PA)....................................614 891-2243
575 Mccorkle Blvd Westerville (43082) *(G-20165)*

Lake Shore Electric Corp...440 232-0200
205 Willis St Bedford (44146) *(G-1438)*

Lake Township Trustees..419 836-1143
3800 Ayers Rd Millbury (43447) *(G-14184)*

Lake Wood Product Inc (PA)..419 832-0150
13020 Box Rd Grand Rapids (43522) *(G-10441)*

Lakecraft Inc (PA)...419 734-2828
1010 W Lakeshore Dr Port Clinton (43452) *(G-16402)*

Lakepark Industries Inc..419 752-4471
40 Seminary St Greenwich (44837) *(G-10533)*

Lakeshore Feed & Seed Inc...216 961-5729
5116 Clark Ave Cleveland (44102) *(G-5677)*

Lakeshore Graphic Industries.......................................419 626-8631
617 Hancock St Sandusky (44870) *(G-16978)*

Lakeside Cabins Ltd..419 896-2299
7389 State Route 13 N Shiloh (44878) *(G-17150)*

Lakeside Custom Plating Inc...440 599-2035
373 Commerce St Conneaut (44030) *(G-7812)*

Lakeside Industrial Pdts Corp.......................................440 366-0052
115 Preston St Elyria (44035) *(G-9449)*

Lakeside Sand & Gravel Inc..330 274-2569
3498 Frost Rd Mantua (44255) *(G-12714)*

Lakeside Sport Shop Inc..330 637-2862
2115 Wlson Sharpsville Rd Cortland (44410) *(G-7870)*

Lakeview Farms Inc...419 695-9925
1700 Gressel Dr Delphos (45833) *(G-8911)*

Lakeview Farms LLC...419 695-9925
1600 Gressel Dr Delphos (45833) *(G-8912)*

Lakeview Farms LLC (PA)...419 695-9925
1600 Gressel Dr Delphos (45833) *(G-8913)*

Lakeway Mfg Inc (PA)...419 433-3030
730 River Rd Huron (44839) *(G-11232)*

Lakewood Observer Inc...216 712-7070
14900 Detroit Ave Ste 205 Lakewood (44107) *(G-11672)*

Lakewood Steel Inc..440 965-4226
13616 State Route 113 Wakeman (44889) *(G-19450)*

Lako Tool & Mfg...419 662-5256
7400 Ponderosa Rd Perrysburg (43551) *(G-16118)*

Lakota Archery, Xenia *Also called Lakota Industries Inc (G-20960)*

Lakota Industries Inc...937 532-6394
1463 Bellbrook Ave Xenia (45385) *(G-20960)*

Lakota Printing Inc..513 755-3666
7967 Cincinnati Dayton Rd J West Chester (45069) *(G-19890)*

Lakota Racing...330 627-7255
109 12th St Nw Carrollton (44615) *(G-2959)*

Lally Pipe & Tube, Struthers *Also called L B Industries Inc (G-17994)*

Lam Pro Inc...216 426-0661
4701 Crayton Ave Ste A Cleveland (44104) *(G-5678)*

Lam Research Corporation...937 472-3311
950 S Franklin St Eaton (45320) *(G-9314)*

Lam Tech, Tiffin *Also called Laminate Technologies Inc (G-18226)*

Lamar D Steiner...330 466-1479
6815 State Route 39 Millersburg (44654) *(G-14239)*

Lamar Proforma..440 285-2277
12636 Mayfield Rd Ste 1 Chardon (44024) *(G-3163)*

Lambert Bros Inc..513 541-1042
1337 Bates Ave Cincinnati (45225) *(G-4010)*

Lambert Bros Nutangs, Cincinnati *Also called Lambert Bros Inc (G-4010)*

Lambert Sheet Metal Inc...614 237-0384
3776 E 5th Ave Columbus (43219) *(G-7281)*

Laminate Shop..740 749-3536
1145 Klinger Rd Waterford (45786) *(G-19649)*

Laminate Technologies Inc (PA).....................................419 448-0812
161 Maule Rd Tiffin (44883) *(G-18226)*

Lamont Enterprises Inc...330 677-4400
911 N Mantua St Kent (44240) *(G-11484)*

Lamor Corporation..440 871-8000
841 Hamlet Ln Apt A2 Westlake (44145) *(G-20281)*

Lamports Filter Media Inc..216 881-2050
837 E 79th St Cleveland (44103) *(G-5679)*

Lancaster Colony Corporation (PA).................................614 224-7141
380 Polaris Pkwy Ste 400 Westerville (43082) *(G-20166)*

Lancaster Colony Corporation......................................614 792-9774
380 Polaris Pkwy Ste 400 Westerville (43082) *(G-20167)*

Lancaster Colony Corporation......................................614 224-7141
380 Polaris Pkwy Ste 400 Westerville (43082) *(G-20168)*

Lancaster Colony Design Group, Westerville *Also called Lancaster Colony Corporation (G-20167)*

Lancaster Commercial Pdts LLC....................................740 286-5081
2353 Westbrooke Dr Columbus (43228) *(G-7282)*

Lancaster Eagle Gazette, Lancaster *Also called Gannett Co Inc (G-11718)*

Lancaster Municipal Gas, Lancaster *Also called City of Lancaster (G-11697)*

Lancaster West Side Coal Co (PA)...................................740 862-4713
700 Van Buren Ave Lancaster (43130) *(G-11725)*

Lancio, Bath *Also called Mollard Conducting Batons Inc (G-1239)*

Land & Shore Drilling, Millersburg *Also called G & H Drilling Inc (G-14216)*

Land OLakes Inc..330 879-2158
8485 Navarre Rd Sw Massillon (44646) *(G-13166)*

Land OLakes Inc..330 678-1578
2001 Mogadore Rd Kent (44240) *(G-11485)*

Landec Corporation..419 931-1095
12700 S Dixie Hwy Bowling Green (43402) *(G-1995)*

Landen Desktop Pubg Ctr Inc.......................................513 683-5181
8976 Columbia Rd Loveland (45140) *(G-12370)*

Landen Digital Publishing, Loveland *Also called Landen Desktop Pubg Ctr Inc (G-12370)*

Landerwood Industries Inc...440 233-4234
4245 Hamann Pkwy Willoughby (44094) *(G-20525)*

Landmark Plastic Corporation (PA).................................330 785-2200
1331 Kelly Ave Akron (44306) *(G-267)*

Landon Vault Company..614 443-5505
1477 Frebis Ave Columbus (43206) *(G-7283)*

Landsberg Cincinnati Div 1017, Monroe *Also called Orora North America (G-14411)*

Landscape & Christmas Tree, Akron *Also called Acro Tool & Die Company (G-29)*

Landscape Group LLC...614 302-4537
15740 Scioto Darby Rd Mount Sterling (43143) *(G-14600)*

Lanes Welding & Repair..740 397-2525
9180 Kinney Rd Mount Vernon (43050) *(G-14628)*

Lang Stone Company Inc (PA).......................................614 235-4099
4099 E 5th Ave Columbus (43219) *(G-7284)*

Langa Tool & Machine Inc..440 953-1138
36430 Reading Ave Ste 1 Willoughby (44094) *(G-20526)*

Langdon Inc...513 733-5955
9865 Wayne Ave Cincinnati (45215) *(G-4011)*

Lange Equipment...440 953-1621
1585 E 361st St Unit D Eastlake (44095) *(G-9281)*

Lange Precision Inc...513 530-9500
6971 Cornell Rd Blue Ash (45242) *(G-1824)*

Langenau Manufacturing Company..................................216 651-3400
7306 Madison Ave Cleveland (44102) *(G-5680)*

Langston Pallets...937 492-8769
1650 Miami Conservancy Rd Sidney (45365) *(G-17198)*

Langstons Ultmate Clg Svcs Inc.....................................330 298-9150
3764 Summit Rd Ravenna (44266) *(G-16537)*

Lanier & Associates Inc..216 391-7735
1814 E 40th St Ste 1c Cleveland (44103) *(G-5681)*

Lanko Industries Inc..440 269-1641
7301 Industrial Park Blvd Mentor (44060) *(G-13629)*

Lanly Company..216 731-1115
26201 Tungsten Rd Cleveland (44132) *(G-5682)*

Lansing Bros Sawmill...937 588-4291
897 Chenoweth Fork Rd Piketon (45661) *(G-16223)*

Lantz Lumber & Saw Shop..740 286-5658
637 Industry Dr Jackson (45640) *(G-11318)*

Lanxess Corporation...440 279-2367
145 Parker Ct Chardon (44024) *(G-3164)*

Lanz Printing Co Inc..614 221-1724
257 Cleveland Ave Columbus (43215) *(G-7285)*

Lapa Lowe Enterprises LLC..440 944-9410
5900 Som Center Rd Ste 16 Willoughby (44094) *(G-20527)*

Lapat Signs...440 277-6291
4151 E River Rd Sheffield Village (44054) *(G-17124)*

Lapcraft Inc...614 764-8993
195 W Olentangy St Unit A Powell (43065) *(G-16477)*

Lapel Pins Unlimited LLC..614 562-3218
5649 Ketch St Lewis Center (43035) *(G-11904)*

Lapham-Hickey Steel Corp...614 443-4881
753 Marion Rd Columbus (43207) *(G-7286)*

Laprensa Publications Inc...419 242-7744
616 Adams St Toledo (43604) *(G-18554)*

Larcom & Mitchell LLC......740 595-3750
1800 Pittsburgh Dr Delaware (43015) *(G-8867)*

Largemachining.com, Dayton *Also called Gedico International Inc (G-8360)*

Lariat Machine Inc......330 297-5765
826 Cleveland Rd Ravenna (44266) *(G-16538)*

Lariccias Italian Foods......330 729-0222
7438 Southern Blvd Youngstown (44512) *(G-21132)*

Larmax Inc......513 984-0783
10945 Reed Hartman Hwy # 210 Blue Ash (45242) *(G-1825)*

Larmco Windows Inc (PA)......216 502-2832
8400 Sweet Valley Dr # 404 Cleveland (44125) *(G-5683)*

Larosa Die Engineering Inc......513 284-9195
3320 Robinet Dr Cincinnati (45238) *(G-4012)*

Larose Industries LLC......419 237-1600
40 E Industrial Pkwy Fayette (43521) *(G-9776)*

Larry C White......330 386-3228
101 E 6th St Ste D East Liverpool (43920) *(G-9224)*

Larry Moore......740 697-7085
6680 Ransbottom Rd Roseville (43777) *(G-16731)*

Larrys Drive Thru & Mini Mart......330 953-0512
3305 Center Rd Youngstown (44514) *(G-21133)*

Larrys Water Conditioning......419 887-0290
720 Illinois Ave Ste I Maumee (43537) *(G-13275)*

Larson Manufacturing Co Inc......419 435-9400
616 N Corporate Dr W Fostoria (44830) *(G-9981)*

Las Motor Sports......937 456-2441
1694 Eaton Lewisburg Rd Eaton (45320) *(G-9315)*

Laser Automation Inc......440 543-9291
16771 Hilltop Park Pl Chagrin Falls (44023) *(G-3099)*

Laser Cartridge Express, Bowling Green *Also called Wood County Ohio (G-2022)*

Laser Cutting Shapes, Columbus *Also called Daskal Enterprise LLC (G-7012)*

Laser Horizons......330 208-0575
1879 Caroline Ave Norton (44203) *(G-15517)*

Laser Images Inc......419 668-8348
28 W Main St Norwalk (44857) *(G-15549)*

Laser Printing Solutions Inc......216 351-4444
6040 Hillcrest Dr Cleveland (44125) *(G-5684)*

Lasercap, Gates Mills *Also called Transdermal Inc (G-10338)*

Laserdealer Inc......440 357-8419
9323 Hamilton Dr Mentor (44060) *(G-13630)*

Laserflex Corporation (HQ)......614 850-9600
3649 Parkway Ln Hilliard (43026) *(G-10958)*

Laserlinc Inc......937 318-2440
777 Zapata Dr Fairborn (45324) *(G-9626)*

Lasermark LLC......513 312-9889
530 N Union Rd Dayton (45417) *(G-8452)*

Laspina Tool & Die Inc......330 923-9996
4282 Hudson Dr Stow (44224) *(G-17767)*

Last Word, The, Port Clinton *Also called Scrambl-Gram Inc (G-16414)*

Lastar Inc (HQ)......937 224-0639
3555 Kettering Blvd Moraine (45439) *(G-14502)*

Lasting First Impressions Inc......513 870-6900
36 Carnegie Way West Chester (45246) *(G-20020)*

Lasting Impression Llc......614 806-1186
4415 Berthstone Dr Columbus (43231) *(G-7287)*

Lasting Impressions Printing......216 382-8436
10390 Hanford Ln Twinsburg (44087) *(G-18970)*

Laszeray Technology LLC......440 582-8430
12315 York Delta Dr North Royalton (44133) *(G-15432)*

Latanick Equipment Inc......419 433-2200
720 River Rd Huron (44839) *(G-11233)*

Late For Sky Production Co......513 531-4400
3000 Robertson Ave Cincinnati (45209) *(G-4013)*

LAtelier Custom Woodworking......234 759-3359
11905 Woodworth Rd North Lima (44452) *(G-15320)*

Latham Limestone LLC......740 493-2677
6424 State Route 124 Latham (45646) *(G-11765)*

Latham Lumber & Pallet Co Inc......740 493-2707
9445 Street Rte 124 Latham (45646) *(G-11766)*

Latin Quarter......513 271-5400
6904 Wooster Pike Cincinnati (45227) *(G-4014)*

Latorre Concrete Cnstr Inc......614 257-1401
850 N Cassady Ave Columbus (43219) *(G-7288)*

Latrobe Spcialty Mtls Dist Inc (HQ)......330 609-5137
1551 Vienna Pkwy Vienna (44473) *(G-19366)*

Latrobe Specialty Mtls Co LLC......419 335-8010
14614 County Road H Wauseon (43567) *(G-19687)*

Lattasburg Lumberworks Co LLC......330 202-7671
9399 Lattasburg Rd West Salem (44287) *(G-20115)*

Latte Living......440 364-2201
11005 Johnson Dr Cleveland (44130) *(G-5685)*

Lau Industries Inc (HQ)......937 476-6500
4509 Springfield St Dayton (45431) *(G-8110)*

Lauber Manufacturing Co......419 446-2450
3751 County Road 26 Archbold (43502) *(G-682)*

Laughing Star Montessory......513 683-5682
8725 Davis Rd Maineville (45039) *(G-12527)*

Laura Dawson......513 777-2513
7827 Plantation Dr West Chester (45069) *(G-19891)*

Laureate Machine & Automtn LLC......419 615-4601
100 Laureate Dr Leipsic (45856) *(G-11871)*

Lauren International Ltd (PA)......330 339-3373
2228 Reiser Ave Se New Philadelphia (44663) *(G-14908)*

Lauren Manufacturing, New Philadelphia *Also called Lauren International Ltd (G-14908)*

Lauren Manufacturing LLC......330 339-3373
2228 Reiser Ave Se New Philadelphia (44663) *(G-14909)*

Lauren Yoakam......440 365-3952
591 Ternes Ln Elyria (44035) *(G-9450)*

Laurenee Ltd LLC......513 662-2225
3509 Harrison Ave Cincinnati (45211) *(G-4015)*

Lavander Bridal Salon......330 602-0333
218 W 3rd St Dover (44622) *(G-8997)*

Lavish Lyfe Magazine......937 938-5816
19 Colgate Ave Dayton (45417) *(G-8453)*

Lavy Inc......937 692-8189
1977 Gttysburg Ptsburg Rd Arcanum (45304) *(G-657)*

Lavy's Marathon, Arcanum *Also called Lavy Inc (G-657)*

Lawbre Co......330 637-3363
3311 Warren Meadville Rd Cortland (44410) *(G-7871)*

Lawft (PA)......419 422-5293
1016 N Blanchard St Findlay (45840) *(G-9850)*

Lawhorn Machine & Tool Inc......937 884-5674
25 E Walnut St Phillipsburg (45354) *(G-16184)*

Lawnview Industries Inc......937 653-5217
1250 E Us Highway 36 Urbana (43078) *(G-19168)*

Lawpak Inc......513 831-3900
128 Wrenwood Ln Terrace Park (45174) *(G-18180)*

Lawrence Industries Inc......216 518-1400
4500 Lee Rd Ste 120 Cleveland (44128) *(G-5686)*

Lawrence Industries Inc (PA)......216 518-7000
4500 Lee Rd Ste 120 Cleveland (44128) *(G-5687)*

Lawrence Machine, Massillon *Also called Gary Lawrence Enterprises Inc (G-13138)*

Lawrence Pallets & Solutions......740 259-4283
620 Owensville Rd Lucasville (45648) *(G-12421)*

Lawrence Technologies Inc......937 274-7771
2571 Timber Ln Dayton (45414) *(G-8454)*

Lawson Precision Machining Inc......419 562-1543
3981 Crestline Rd Bucyrus (44820) *(G-2352)*

Lawsons Towing & Auto Wrckg......216 883-9050
14114 Miles Ave Cleveland (44128) *(G-5688)*

Layerzero Power Systems Inc......440 399-9000
1500 Danner Dr Aurora (44202) *(G-932)*

Layne Heavy Civil Inc......513 424-7287
6451 Germantown Rd Middletown (45042) *(G-14053)*

Lazars Art Gllery Crtive Frmng......330 477-8351
2940 Woodlawn Ave Nw Canton (44708) *(G-2759)*

Lazarus Steel LLC......216 391-3245
901 Addison Rd Cleveland (44103) *(G-5689)*

Lazer Action Inc......330 630-9200
1534 Brittain Rd Akron (44310) *(G-268)*

Lazer Systems Inc (PA)......513 641-4002
850 E Ross Ave Cincinnati (45217) *(G-4016)*

LBC Clay Co LLC......330 674-0674
4501 Township Road 307 Millersburg (44654) *(G-14240)*

Lc, Cleveland *Also called Logan Clutch Corporation (G-5707)*

Lcas, Lorain *Also called Lorain County Auto Systems Inc (G-12256)*

Lcmf Inc......513 860-9988
7010 Fairfield Bus Ctr Fairfield (45014) *(G-9677)*

Lcp Tech Inc......513 271-1389
8120 Indian Hill Rd Cincinnati (45243) *(G-4017)*

Le Nurd Mystique LLC, Canal Winchester *Also called Nurdcon LLC (G-2534)*

LE Smith Company (PA)......419 636-4555
1030 E Wilson St Bryan (43506) *(G-2310)*

Le Summer Kidron Inc......330 857-2031
6856 Kidron Rd Apple Creek (44606) *(G-642)*

Leadar Roll Inc (PA)......419 227-2200
893 Shawnee Rd Lima (45805) *(G-12037)*

Leadec Corp (PA)......513 731-3590
9395 Kenwood Rd Ste 200 Blue Ash (45242) *(G-1826)*

Leader Engnrng-Fabrication Inc (PA)......419 592-0008
695 Independence Dr Napoleon (43545) *(G-14688)*

Leader Engnrng-Fabrication Inc......419 636-1731
County Rd D 50 Bryan (43506) *(G-2311)*

Leader Printing, Newark *Also called Ryans Newark Leader Ex Prtg (G-15051)*

Leader Publications Inc......330 665-9595
3075 Smith Rd Ste 204 Fairlawn (44333) *(G-9756)*

Leaf & Thorn Press......614 396-6055
1080 Pebble Brook Dr Columbus (43240) *(G-6651)*

Leaf Lono Earth Alterntv Fuels......614 829-7159
4204 Town Square Dr Canal Winchester (43110) *(G-2530)*

Leafguard, Maple Heights *Also called Elg Inc (G-12734)*

Lean Factory America LLC......513 297-3086
1859 Section Rd Cincinnati (45237) *(G-4018)*

Leap Publishing Services Inc......234 738-0082
4301 Darrow Rd Ste 1200a Stow (44224) *(G-17768)*

Lear Corporation......740 928-4358
180 N High St Hebron (43025) *(G-10872)*

Lear Corporation 419 335-6010
447 E Walnut St Wauseon (43567) *(G-19688)*

Lear Corporation 614 850-8630
2181 International St Columbus (43228) *(G-7289)*

Lear Engineering Corp 937 429-0534
2942 Stauffer Dr Beavercreek (45434) *(G-1347)*

Lear Manufacturing Inc 440 327-4545
7855 Race Rd North Ridgeville (44039) *(G-15387)*

Lear Mfg Co Inc 440 324-1111
147 Freedom Ct Elyria (44035) *(G-9451)*

Lear Romec, Elyria *Also called Hydro-Aire Inc (G-9431)*

Learning Egg LLC 330 207-8663
9332 Silica Rd North Jackson (44451) *(G-15293)*

Learning Egg, The, North Jackson *Also called Learning Egg LLC (G-15293)*

Lebanon Electric Motor Svc LLC 513 932-2889
602 E Main St Lebanon (45036) *(G-11813)*

Lectora, Cincinnati *Also called Trivantis Corporation (G-4528)*

Lectroetch Co 440 934-1249
5342 Evergreen Pkwy Sheffield Village (44054) *(G-17125)*

Ledex & Dormeyer Products, Vandalia *Also called Saia-Burgess Lcc (G-19310)*

Ledge Hill Signs Limited 440 461-4445
5369 Mayfield Rd Cleveland (44124) *(G-5690)*

Ledow Company Inc 330 657-2837
3011 Oak Hill Rd Peninsula (44264) *(G-16038)*

Lee A Williams Jr 419 225-6751
205 W Elm St Lima (45801) *(G-12038)*

Lee Corporation 513 771-3602
12055 Mosteller Rd Cincinnati (45241) *(G-4019)*

Lee Oil & Gas Inc 937 223-8891
326 Spirea Dr Oakwood (45419) *(G-15608)*

Lee Plastic Company LLC 937 456-5720
1100 Us Route 35 Eaton (45320) *(G-9316)*

Lee Printers, Cincinnati *Also called Lee Corporation (G-4019)*

Lee Williams Meats Inc (PA) 419 729-3893
3002 131st St Toledo (43611) *(G-18555)*

Leebaw Manufacturing Company 330 533-3368
3 Industrial Park Dr Canfield (44406) *(G-2561)*

Leeper Printing Co Inc 419 243-2604
710 S Saint Clair St Toledo (43609) *(G-18556)*

Lees Grinding Inc 440 572-4610
15620 Foltz Pkwy Strongsville (44149) *(G-17938)*

Lees Machinery 440 259-2222
4089 N Ridge Rd Perry (44081) *(G-16052)*

Leesburg Loom & Supply, Van Wert *Also called Leesburg Looms Incorporated (G-19263)*

Leesburg Looms Incorporated 419 238-2738
201 N Cherry St Van Wert (45891) *(G-19263)*

Leesburg Modern Sales Inc 937 780-2613
12607 Monroe Rd Leesburg (45135) *(G-11854)*

Leetonia Tool Company 330 427-6944
142 Main St Leetonia (44431) *(G-11861)*

Lefco Worthington LLC 216 432-4422
18451 Euclid Ave Cleveland (44112) *(G-5691)*

Lefeld Supplies Rental, Coldwater *Also called Lefeld Welding & Stl Sups Inc (G-6567)*

Lefeld Welding & Stl Sups Inc (PA) 419 678-2397
600 N 2nd St Coldwater (45828) *(G-6567)*

Legacy Farmers Cooperative (PA) 419 423-2611
6566 County Road 236 Findlay (45840) *(G-9851)*

Legacy Finishing Inc 937 743-7278
415 Oxford Rd Franklin (45005) *(G-10032)*

Legacy Oak and Hardwoods LLC 330 859-2656
7138 Mount Pleasant Rd Ne Zoarville (44656) *(G-21371)*

Legacy Supplies Inc 330 405-4565
8252 Darrow Rd Ste E Twinsburg (44087) *(G-18971)*

Legal News Publishing Co 216 696-3322
2935 Prospect Ave E Cleveland (44115) *(G-5692)*

Legendary Ink Inc 614 766-5101
1559 Granville St Columbus (43203) *(G-7290)*

Leggett & Platt Incorporated 440 322-4865
377 Woodland Ave Elyria (44035) *(G-9452)*

Leggett & Platt Incorporated 330 262-6010
7315 E Lincoln Way Apple Creek (44606) *(G-643)*

Leggett & Platt 0640, Elyria *Also called Leggett & Platt Incorporated (G-9452)*

Legrand North America LLC 937 224-0639
3555 Kettering Blvd Moraine (45439) *(G-14503)*

Lehman & Sons 330 857-7404
3328 S Kohler Rd Orrville (44667) *(G-15745)*

Lehner Screw Machine LLC 330 688-6616
71 S River Rd Munroe Falls (44262) *(G-14662)*

Lehr Awning Co, Mansfield *Also called P C R Restorations Inc (G-12666)*

Leiden Cabinet Company LLC (PA) 330 425-8555
2385 Edison Blvd Twinsburg (44087) *(G-18972)*

Leiden Cabinet Company LLC 330 878-7790
1230 Hensel Ave Ne Strasburg (44680) *(G-17825)*

Leidos Inc 937 431-2400
3745 Pentagon Blvd Beavercreek (45431) *(G-1348)*

Leimkuehler Inc (PA) 440 899-7842
4625 Detroit Ave Cleveland (44102) *(G-5693)*

Leipsic Messenger Newspaper, Leipsic *Also called Mickens Inc (G-11872)*

Leland-Gifford Inc 330 785-9730
1029 Arlington Cir Akron (44306) *(G-269)*

Lem Incorporated 330 535-6422
71 S River Rd Munroe Falls (44262) *(G-14663)*

Lem Products Holding LLC 513 202-1188
4440 Muhlhauser Rd # 300 West Chester (45011) *(G-19892)*

Lemsco Inc 419 242-4005
2056 Canton Ave Toledo (43620) *(G-18557)*

Lemsco-Girkins, Toledo *Also called Lemsco Inc (G-18557)*

Lena Fiore Inc 330 468-3226
2188 Majesty Ct Akron (44333) *(G-270)*

Lenas Amish Granola 330 600-1599
11051 County Road 329 Shreve (44676) *(G-17160)*

Lenco Industries Inc 937 277-9364
3301 Klepinger Rd Dayton (45406) *(G-8455)*

Lennox Machine Inc 419 525-1020
1471 Sprang Pkwy Mansfield (44903) *(G-12635)*

Lennox Machine Shop, Mansfield *Also called Lennox Machine Inc (G-12635)*

Lens AC (PA) 888 248-5367
4265 Diplomacy Dr Columbus (43228) *(G-7291)*

Lenz Inc 937 277-9364
3301 Klepinger Rd Dayton (45406) *(G-8456)*

Lenz Company, Dayton *Also called Lenz Inc (G-8456)*

Leon Newswanger 419 896-3336
7828 Planktown North Rd Shiloh (44878) *(G-17151)*

Leonhardt Plating Company 513 242-1410
5753 Este Ave Cincinnati (45232) *(G-4020)*

Leppert Companies Inc 614 889-2818
8779 Tartan Fields Dr Dublin (43017) *(G-9099)*

Leroi Gas Compressors, Sidney *Also called Rotary Compression Tech Inc (G-17220)*

Leroy Yutzy 937 386-2872
191 Russellville Rd Winchester (45697) *(G-20694)*

Lesage Machine Inc 419 687-0131
5269 State Route 598 Plymouth (44865) *(G-16377)*

Lesch Boat Cover Canvas Co LLC 419 668-6374
43 1/2 Saint Marys St Norwalk (44857) *(G-15550)*

Lesch Btry & Pwr Solution LLC 419 884-0219
2744 Lexington Ave Mansfield (44904) *(G-12636)*

Lesco Inc 740 633-6366
100 Picoma Rd Martins Ferry (43935) *(G-12925)*

Lesco Inc 740 549-2141
729-731 Carle Ave Lewis Center (43035) *(G-11905)*

Lesher Printers Inc 419 332-8253
810 N Wilson Ave Fremont (43420) *(G-10163)*

Lesleys Patterns Ltd 937 554-4674
405 Halifax Dr Vandalia (45377) *(G-19300)*

Less Cost Lighting Inc 866 633-6883
1213 Etna Pkwy Etna (43062) *(G-9559)*

Let's Rage, Cleveland *Also called Rageon Inc (G-6088)*

Lets Golf Daily Inc 330 966-3373
3199 Whitewood St Nw North Canton (44720) *(G-15246)*

Letter Graphics Sign Co Inc 330 683-3903
400 W Market St Orrville (44667) *(G-15746)*

Letter Shop 937 981-3117
247 Jefferson St Greenfield (45123) *(G-10482)*

Letterman Printing Inc 513 523-1111
316 S College Ave Oxford (45056) *(G-15839)*

Levan Enterprises Inc (PA) 330 923-9797
4585 Allen Rd Stow (44224) *(G-17769)*

Levans Electric & Hvac 937 468-2269
275 Mill St W Rushsylvania (43347) *(G-16752)*

Leveck Lighting Products Inc (PA) 937 667-4421
8415 S State Route 202 Tipp City (45371) *(G-18287)*

Levi Strauss & Co 513 539-7822
211 Premium Outlets Dr Monroe (45050) *(G-14410)*

Levison Enterprises LLC 419 838-7365
4470 Moline Martin Rd Millbury (43447) *(G-14185)*

Levit Jewelers Inc 440 985-1685
4274 Oberlin Ave Lorain (44053) *(G-12255)*

Lewark Metal Spinning Inc 937 275-3303
2746 Keenan Ave Dayton (45414) *(G-8457)*

Lewco Inc 419 625-4014
706 Lane St Sandusky (44870) *(G-16979)*

Lewis Unlimited Inc 216 514-8282
165 Jackson Dr Chagrin Falls (44022) *(G-3063)*

Lewisburg Container Company (HQ) 937 962-2681
275 W Clay St Lewisburg (45338) *(G-11936)*

Lexington Abrasives Inc 330 821-1166
16123 Armour St Ne Alliance (44601) *(G-522)*

Lexington Prosthetic Ortotics 803 939-0097
7035 Dustin Rd Galena (43021) *(G-10246)*

Lexington Rubber Group (HQ) 330 425-8472
1700 Highland Rd Twinsburg (44087) *(G-18973)*

Lexis Nexis, Miamisburg *Also called Relx Inc (G-13851)*

Lexisnexis, Miamisburg *Also called Relx Inc (G-13853)*

Lexisnexis Group (HQ) 937 865-6800
9443 Springboro Pike Miamisburg (45342) *(G-13825)*

Lextech Industries Ltd 216 883-7900
6800 Union Ave Cleveland (44105) *(G-5694)*

A
L
P
H
A
B
E
T
I
C

Ley Equipment Co...419 238-6742
121 S Walnut St Van Wert (45891) **(G-19264)**

Ley Industries Inc (PA)..419 238-6742
121 S Walnut St Van Wert (45891) **(G-19265)**

Leyman Liftgates, Cincinnati *Also called Leyman Manufacturing Corp* **(G-4021)**

Leyman Manufacturing Corp..................................513 891-6210
10335 Wayne Ave Cincinnati (45215) **(G-4021)**

Leyshon Miller Industries LLC...............................740 432-2969
534 N 1st St Cambridge (43725) **(G-2463)**

Lfe Instruments, Bluffton *Also called Triplett Bluffton Corporation* **(G-1919)**

Lfg Specialties LLC...419 424-4999
16406 E Us Route 224 Findlay (45840) **(G-9852)**

Libart North America, Hicksville *Also called Stoett Industries Inc* **(G-10907)**

Libbey Glass Factory Outlet, Toledo *Also called Libbey Inc* **(G-18560)**

Libbey Glass Inc (HQ)...419 325-2100
300 Madison Ave Fl 4 Toledo (43604) **(G-18558)**

Libbey Glass Inc...419 729-7272
940 Ash St Toledo (43611) **(G-18559)**

Libbey Inc..419 244-5697
205 S Erie St Toledo (43604) **(G-18560)**

Libbey Inc (PA)..419 325-2100
300 Madison Ave Toledo (43604) **(G-18561)**

Liber Limited LLC..440 427-0647
7162 Windwood Way Olmsted Twp (44138) **(G-15680)**

Liberty Casting Company LLC (PA)...........................740 363-1941
550 Liberty Rd Delaware (43015) **(G-8868)**

Liberty Casting Company LLC.................................740 363-1941
407 Curtis St Delaware (43015) **(G-8869)**

Liberty Die Cast Molds Inc..................................740 666-7492
57 2nd St Ostrander (43061) **(G-15788)**

Liberty Die Casting Company.................................419 636-3971
872 E Trevitt St Bryan (43506) **(G-2312)**

Liberty Fabricating & Steel, Middlefield *Also called D T Kothera Inc* **(G-13930)**

Liberty Mold & Machine Company............................330 278-7825
1369 Ridge Rd Ste B Hinckley (44233) **(G-11027)**

Liberty Ornamental Products, Bryan *Also called Liberty Die Casting Company* **(G-2312)**

Liberty Pattern and Mold Inc................................330 788-9463
1131 Meadowbrook Ave Youngstown (44512) **(G-21134)**

Liberty Plastics LLC (PA)....................................330 627-6677
861 N Lisbon St Carrollton (44615) **(G-2960)**

Liberty Sportswear LLC.......................................513 755-8740
6929 Tylersville Rd Ste 9 West Chester (45069) **(G-19893)**

Liberty Steel Industries Inc (PA)...........................330 372-6363
2207 Larchmont Ave Ne Warren (44483) **(G-19570)**

Liberty Steel Industries Inc................................330 372-6363
900 Dietz Rd Ne Warren (44483) **(G-19571)**

Liberty Steel Pressed Pdts LLC..............................330 538-2236
11650 Mahoning Ave North Jackson (44451) **(G-15294)**

Libido Edge Labs LLC...740 344-1401
26 E Stevens St Newark (43055) **(G-15030)**

Libra Industries, Willoughby *Also called Focus Manufacturing Inc* **(G-20492)**

Libra Industries Inc (PA)....................................440 974-7770
7770 Division Dr Mentor (44060) **(G-13631)**

Libra Industries Inc..440 974-7770
7715 Metric Dr Mentor (44060) **(G-13632)**

Lideco LLC...330 539-9333
972 Yngtn Kngs Rd Se Vienna (44473) **(G-19367)**

Lids, Akron *Also called Genesco Inc* **(G-204)**

Lids, Cincinnati *Also called Genesco Inc* **(G-3307)**

Lids Corporation..419 621-8742
4314 Milan Rd Ste 530 Sandusky (44870) **(G-16980)**

Lids Corporation..440 974-9127
7850 Mentor Ave Ste 542 Mentor (44060) **(G-13633)**

Lids Corporation..440 779-4998
577 Great Nthrn Mall 102 North Olmsted (44070) **(G-15341)**

Liebert Corporation (HQ).....................................614 888-0246
1050 Dearborn Dr Columbus (43085) **(G-7292)**

Liebert Corporation..740 547-5100
3040 S 9th St Ironton (45638) **(G-11296)**

Liebert North America Inc...................................614 888-0246
1050 Dearborn Dr Columbus (43085) **(G-7293)**

Liebrecht Excavating, Continental *Also called Liebrecht Manufacturing* **(G-7827)**

Liebrecht Manufacturing......................................419 596-3501
Rd H 13 Continental (45831) **(G-7827)**

Liechty Specialties Inc......................................419 445-6696
1901 S Defiance St Archbold (43502) **(G-683)**

Life Formations Inc...419 352-2101
2029 Wood Bridge Blvd Bowling Green (43402) **(G-1996)**

Life Star Rescue Inc..419 238-2507
1171 Production Dr Van Wert (45891) **(G-19266)**

Life Support Development Ltd................................614 221-1765
777 Dearborn Park Ln R Columbus (43085) **(G-7294)**

Life Time Embroidery, Brookville *Also called Heller Acquisitions Inc* **(G-2186)**

Lifecubby, Westerville *Also called Jst LLC* **(G-20164)**

Lifeformations Inc...419 352-2101
2029 Wood Bridge Blvd Bowling Green (43402) **(G-1997)**

Lifegas, Columbus *Also called Linde Gas North America LLC* **(G-7297)**

Lifes Products Inc..740 965-9711
3319 N State Route 61 Sunbury (43074) **(G-18066)**

Lifestyle Nutraceuticals Ltd................................513 376-7218
5911 Turpin Hills Dr Cincinnati (45244) **(G-4022)**

Lifetime Fenders, Canfield *Also called Ltf Acquisition LLC* **(G-2563)**

Lifetime Ironworks LLC.......................................419 443-0567
244 Coe St Tiffin (44883) **(G-18227)**

Lifo Enterprises Inc...513 225-8801
810 Carrington Pl Apt 206 Loveland (45140) **(G-12371)**

Light Craft Direct, Fremont *Also called Light Craft Manufacturing Inc* **(G-10164)**

Light Craft Manufacturing Inc...............................419 332-0536
220 Sullivan Rd Fremont (43420) **(G-10164)**

Light Vision...513 351-9444
1776 Mentor Ave Cincinnati (45212) **(G-4023)**

Lighted House Numbers, Circleville *Also called Sign Shop* **(G-4643)**

Lighthouse Youth Services Inc...............................513 961-4080
3330 Jefferson Ave Cincinnati (45220) **(G-4024)**

Lighting Concepts & Controls................................513 761-6360
9753 Crescent Park Dr West Chester (45069) **(G-19894)**

Lighting Products Inc..440 293-4064
101 Parker Dr Andover (44003) **(G-617)**

Lighting Solutions Group LLC................................614 868-5337
153 Outerbelt St Columbus (43213) **(G-7295)**

Lightle Enterprises Ohio LLC (PA)..........................740 998-5363
22 E Springfield St Frankfort (45628) **(G-10000)**

Lightle Enterprises Ohio LLC...............................740 998-5363
23 E Walnut St Frankfort (45628) **(G-10001)**

Lightning Bolt Fastners, Mount Gilead *Also called Lilly Industries Inc* **(G-14563)**

Lightning Mold & Machine Inc...............................440 593-6460
509 W Main Rd Conneaut (44030) **(G-7813)**

Lightstab Ltd Co...216 751-5800
3103 Morley Rd Shaker Heights (44122) **(G-17091)**

Lightyearmusiccom..216 929-1022
5361 Pearl Rd Cleveland (44129) **(G-5695)**

Lilienthal Southeastern Inc...................................740 439-1640
1609 N 11th St Cambridge (43725) **(G-2464)**

Lilleys Fabrication and Design, Morrow *Also called Stephen R Lilley* **(G-14551)**

Lilly Industries Inc (PA).....................................419 946-7908
6437 County Road 20 Mount Gilead (43338) **(G-14563)**

Lily Tiger Press...513 591-0817
1945 Dunham Way Cincinnati (45238) **(G-4025)**

Lim Services LLC...513 217-0801
3351 Cincinnati Dayton Rd Middletown (45044) **(G-14054)**

Lima Armature Works Inc.....................................419 222-4010
142 E Pearl St Lima (45801) **(G-12039)**

Lima Army Tank Plant, Lima *Also called United States Dept of Army* **(G-12108)**

Lima Equipment Co..419 222-4181
895 Shawnee Rd Lima (45805) **(G-12040)**

Lima Millwork Inc..419 331-3303
4251 East Rd Elida (45807) **(G-9351)**

Lima Pallet Company Inc.....................................419 229-5736
1470 Neubrecht Rd Lima (45801) **(G-12041)**

Lima Pipe Organ Co Inc.......................................419 331-5461
408 E Kiracofe Ave Elida (45807) **(G-9352)**

Lima Refining Company (HQ).................................419 226-2300
1150 S Metcalf St Lima (45804) **(G-12042)**

Lima Refining Company..419 226-2300
1150 S Metcalf St Lima (45804) **(G-12043)**

Lima Sandblasting & Pntg Co.................................419 331-2939
4310 East Rd Lima (45807) **(G-12044)**

Lima Sheet Metal Machine & Mfg.............................419 229-1161
1001 Bowman Rd Lima (45804) **(G-12045)**

Lima Sporting Goods Inc.....................................419 222-1036
1404 Allentown Rd Lima (45805) **(G-12046)**

Liming Printing Inc..937 374-2646
1450 S Patton St Xenia (45385) **(G-20961)**

Limited, Sandusky *Also called Lids Corporation* **(G-16980)**

Limited Too 937, Dayton *Also called Tween Brands Inc* **(G-8733)**

Lincoln Candle Company Inc..................................419 749-4224
6588 Pollock Rd Convoy (45832) **(G-7832)**

Lincoln Electric Company (HQ)...............................216 481-8100
22801 Saint Clair Ave Euclid (44117) **(G-9589)**

Lincoln Electric Company.....................................216 524-8800
7550 Hub Pkwy Cleveland (44125) **(G-5696)**

Lincoln Electric Company.....................................216 481-8100
22800 Saint Clair Ave Cleveland (44117) **(G-5697)**

Lincoln Electric Holdings Inc (PA)...........................216 481-8100
22801 Saint Clair Ave Cleveland (44117) **(G-5698)**

Lincoln Electric Holdings Inc................................440 255-7696
6500 Heisley Rd Mentor (44060) **(G-13634)**

Lincoln Electric Intl Holdg Co (HQ)..........................216 481-8100
22801 Saint Clair Ave Euclid (44117) **(G-9590)**

Lincoln Foodservice Pdts LLC (HQ)...........................260 459-8200
1333 E 179th St Cleveland (44110) **(G-5699)**

Lincoln Library Press, Cleveland *Also called Eastword Publications Dev* **(G-5241)**

Lind Stoneworks Ltd...614 866-9733
175 Oberlin Ct N Columbus (43230) **(G-7296)**

Linde Gas North America LLC.................................614 846-7048
7029 Huntley Rd Columbus (43229) **(G-7297)**

Linde Gas North America LLC..........................330 425-3989
  2045 E Aurora Rd Twinsburg (44087) *(G-18974)*
Linde Hydraulics Corporation (HQ)...................330 533-6801
  5089 W Western Reserve Rd Canfield (44406) *(G-2562)*
Linde LLC...330 608-3008
  4179 Meadow Wood Ln Uniontown (44685) *(G-19090)*
Linde LLC...419 435-8153
  405 E Zeller Rd Fostoria (44830) *(G-9982)*
Linde LLC...513 831-4742
  State Road 126160 St State Ro Miamiville (45147) *(G-13895)*
Linde LLC...216 533-7256
  6300 Halle Dr Cleveland (44125) *(G-5700)*
Linde LLC...419 227-9585
  961 Industry Ave Lima (45804) *(G-12047)*
Linde LLC...330 394-4541
  2000 Pine Ave Se Warren (44483) *(G-19572)*
Linde LLC...419 221-5043
  1680 Buckeye Rd Lima (45804) *(G-12048)*
Linde LLC...419 822-3909
  6744 County Road 10 Delta (43515) *(G-8937)*
Linden Industries Inc..................................330 928-4064
  137 Ascot Pkwy Cuyahoga Falls (44223) *(G-8020)*
Linden Monuments......................................419 468-4130
  104 Linden Dr Galion (44833) *(G-10279)*
Lindsay Package Systems Inc...........................330 854-4511
  6845 Erie Ave Nw Canal Fulton (44614) *(G-2504)*
Lindsay Precast Inc (PA)...............................330 854-6282
  6845 Erie Ave Nw Canal Fulton (44614) *(G-2505)*
Lindsey Graphics Inc...................................330 995-9241
  112 Parkview Dr Aurora (44202) *(G-933)*
Line Drive Sportz-Lcrc LLC............................419 794-7150
  2901 Key St Ste 1 Maumee (43537) *(G-13276)*
Line Tool & Die Inc....................................419 332-2931
  933 Napoleon St Fremont (43420) *(G-10165)*
Line-X of Akron/Medina, Medina *Also called X-Treme Finishes Inc (G-13498)*
Linear Asics Inc.......................................330 474-3920
  14 Tallmadge Cir Tallmadge (44278) *(G-18150)*
Linear Dynamics.......................................419 806-6689
  224 Us 23 Risingsun (43457) *(G-16672)*
Linear Technology Corporation.........................440 239-0817
  7550 Lucerne Dr Ste 106 Cleveland (44130) *(G-5701)*
Linebacker Inc...614 340-1446
  1275 Kinnear Rd Columbus (43212) *(G-7298)*
Linen Care Plus Inc....................................614 224-1791
  84 N Glenwood Ave Columbus (43222) *(G-7299)*
Linestream Technologies...............................216 862-7874
  1468 W 9th St Ste 100 Cleveland (44113) *(G-5702)*
Linger Photo Engraving Corp...........................513 579-1380
  2230 Gilbert Ave Cincinnati (45206) *(G-4026)*
Link's Auto, Cleveland *Also called Fiberglass Link Inc (G-5343)*
Links Country Meats...................................419 683-2195
  7252 Leesville Rd Crestline (44827) *(G-7931)*
Linsalata Capital Partners Fun........................440 684-1400
  5900 Landerbrook Dr # 280 Cleveland (44124) *(G-5703)*
Lintech Electronics LLC................................513 528-6190
  4435 Aicholtz Rd Ste 500 Cincinnati (45245) *(G-3312)*
Lintern Corporation (PA)...............................440 255-9333
  8685 Station St Mentor (44060) *(G-13635)*
Lion Apparel Inc (HQ)..................................937 898-1949
  7200 Poe Ave Ste 400 Dayton (45414) *(G-8458)*
Lion Clothing Inc......................................419 692-9981
  206 N Main St Delphos (45833) *(G-8914)*
Lion Helmet Molding...................................937 297-0760
  2000 Composite Dr Kettering (45420) *(G-11582)*
Lion Industries Inc....................................740 699-0012
  49068 Reservoir Rd Saint Clairsville (43950) *(G-16794)*
Lion Mold & Machine Inc...............................330 688-4248
  4510 Darrow Rd Stow (44224) *(G-17770)*
Lion's Den Sport Shop, Minerva *Also called Hoffee John (G-14325)*
Lippincott & Peto Inc..................................330 864-2122
  1741 Akron Peninsula Rd Akron (44313) *(G-271)*
Liqui-Box Corporation (PA).............................614 888-9280
  480 Schrock Rd Ste G Columbus (43229) *(G-7300)*
Liqui-Box Corporation.................................419 289-9696
  1817 Masters Ave Ashland (44805) *(G-750)*
Liqui-Box Corporation.................................419 209-9085
  519 Raybestos Dr Upper Sandusky (43351) *(G-19129)*
Liquid Control, North Canton *Also called Graco Ohio Inc (G-15235)*
Liquid Crystal Tech LLC................................440 232-8590
  24300 Solon Rd Ste 100 Cleveland (44146) *(G-5704)*
Liquid Development Company (PA).......................216 641-9366
  5708 E Schaaf Rd Independence (44131) *(G-11265)*
Liquid Image Corp of America..........................216 458-9800
  3700 Prospect Ave E Cleveland (44115) *(G-5705)*
Liquid Logic LLC.......................................937 865-3068
  720 Mound Rd Ste 250 Miamisburg (45342) *(G-13826)*
Liquid Luggers LLC....................................330 426-2538
  183 Edgeworth Ave East Palestine (44413) *(G-9241)*
Liquid Shock Games LLC...............................386 627-0840
  621 49th St Elyria (44035) *(G-9453)*

Lisa Arters..330 435-1804
  117 Maple Ave Creston (44217) *(G-7940)*
Lisa Modem...216 551-3365
  4195 Zalley Rd Cleveland (44109) *(G-5706)*
Lisbon Hoist Inc.......................................330 424-7283
  321 S Beaver St Lisbon (44432) *(G-12127)*
Lisbon Pattern Limited.................................330 424-7676
  7629 State Route 45 Lisbon (44432) *(G-12128)*
List Media Inc...330 995-0864
  251 W Garfield Rd Ste 284 Aurora (44202) *(G-934)*
Listermann Brewery Supply, Cincinnati *Also called Listermann Mfg Co Inc (G-4027)*
Listermann Mfg Co Inc.................................513 731-1130
  1621 Dana Ave Cincinnati (45207) *(G-4027)*
Litco International Inc (PA).............................330 539-5433
  1 Litco Dr Vienna (44473) *(G-19368)*
Litco Manufacturing LLC...............................330 539-5433
  1512 Phoenix Rd Ne Warren (44483) *(G-19573)*
Litco Wood Products, Apple Creek *Also called Millwood Inc (G-645)*
Lite Metals Company..................................330 296-6110
  700 N Walnut St Ravenna (44266) *(G-16539)*
Liteflex LLC (PA)......................................937 836-7025
  100 Holiday Dr Englewood (45322) *(G-9530)*
Lithchem Intl Toxco Inc................................740 653-6290
  265 Quarry Rd Se Lancaster (43130) *(G-11726)*
Lithium Innovations Co LLC.............................419 725-3525
  3171 N Repub Blvd Ste 101 Toledo (43615) *(G-18562)*
Litho-Craft Lithography Inc............................513 542-6404
  5877 Highland Ridge Dr Cincinnati (45232) *(G-4028)*
Little Busy Bodies LLC.................................513 351-5700
  1130 Findlay St Cincinnati (45214) *(G-4029)*
Little Cottage Company................................330 893-4212
  6673 State Route 515 Dundee (44624) *(G-9174)*
Little Cottage Company................................330 893-4212
  4070 State Route 39 Millersburg (44654) *(G-14241)*
Little Ghost Roasters..................................614 325-2065
  247 1/2 King Ave Columbus (43201) *(G-7301)*
Little Printing Company................................937 773-4595
  4317 W Us Route 36 Piqua (45356) *(G-16286)*
Littlern Corporation...................................330 848-8847
  77 2nd St Sw Barberton (44203) *(G-1124)*
Litzinger Logging.....................................740 743-2245
  314 S Columbus St Somerset (43783) *(G-17416)*
Liverpool Coil Processing Inc..........................330 558-2600
  880 Steel Dr Valley City (44280) *(G-19210)*
Liverpool Manufacturing, Valley City *Also called Shiloh Automotive Inc (G-19230)*
Liverpool Township....................................330 483-4747
  6700 Center Rd Valley City (44280) *(G-19211)*
Liverpool-Coil-Processing, Valley City *Also called Liverpool Coil Processing Inc (G-19210)*
Livingston & Company Ltd..............................513 553-6430
  1103 Ten Mile Rd New Richmond (45157) *(G-14941)*
Lizzie Maes Birdseed & Dg Co..........................330 927-1795
  11315 Steiner Rd Rittman (44270) *(G-16678)*
Lj Woodworking.......................................330 359-3216
  9035 Senff Rd Dundee (44624) *(G-9175)*
LLC Bowman Leather...................................330 893-1954
  6705 Private Road 387 Millersburg (44654) *(G-14242)*
LLC Brand Castle (PA).................................216 292-7700
  5111 Richmond Rd Frnt Bedford Heights (44146) *(G-1487)*
LLC Ring Masters......................................330 832-1511
  240 6th St Nw Massillon (44647) *(G-13167)*
LLC/Owned By Partnership, Cincinnati *Also called Carey Color Llc/Cincinnati (G-3499)*
Lloyd F Helber..740 756-9607
  3820 Clmbus Lncster Rd Nw Carroll (43112) *(G-2943)*
Lloyd Library & Museum................................513 721-3707
  917 Plum St Cincinnati (45202) *(G-4030)*
LMC, Akron *Also called Logan Machine Company (G-275)*
LMI Custom Mixing LLC.................................740 435-0444
  804 Byesville Rd Cambridge (43725) *(G-2465)*
Lmp, Hartville *Also called Louisville Molded Products (G-10829)*
Lmp Machine LLC......................................740 596-4559
  115 E Chestnut St Zaleski (45698) *(G-21261)*
Lms LLC..513 981-1412
  Kofinas Olive Oil Cincinnati (45230) *(G-4031)*
Loadmaster Scale Mfgr, Findlay *Also called Holtgreven Scale & Elec Corp (G-9840)*
Loadmaster Trailer Company............................419 732-3434
  2354 East Harbor Rd Port Clinton (43452) *(G-16403)*
Loadmaster Trailers Mfg, Port Clinton *Also called Loadmaster Trailer Company (G-16403)*
Lobo Awrds Screen Prtg Graphix........................740 972-9087
  627 Bellefontaine Ave Marion (43302) *(G-12880)*
Local Insight Yellow Pages Inc.........................330 650-7100
  100 Executive Pkwy Hudson (44236) *(G-11188)*
Lock-N-Logs Log Homes, Coolville *Also called M & G Truss Rafters (G-7834)*
Lockbourne AG Center Inc.............................614 491-0635
  10 Commerce St Lockbourne (43137) *(G-12148)*
Locke Industrial Maint Svcs, Middletown *Also called Lim Services LLC (G-14054)*
Locker Konnection Services LLC........................419 334-3956
  405 Jackson St Fremont (43420) *(G-10166)*
Locker Room Inc.......................................419 445-9600
  223 N Defiance St Archbold (43502) *(G-684)*

A L P H A B E T I C

Locker Room Lettering Ltd.................................419 359-1761
  7316 Magill Rd Castalia (44824) *(G-2977)*

Lockes Heating & Cooling Llc..........................513 793-1900
  10229 Kenwood Rd Blue Ash (45242) *(G-1827)*

Lockheed Martin Corporation............................614 418-1930
  2720 Airport Dr Ste 100 Columbus (43219) *(G-7302)*

Lockheed Martin Corporation............................330 796-7000
  1210 Massillon Rd Akron (44315) *(G-272)*

Lockheed Martin Corporation............................330 796-2800
  1210 Massillon Rd Akron (44315) *(G-273)*

Lockheed Martin Integ.....................................330 796-2800
  1210 Massillon Rd Akron (44315) *(G-274)*

Lockheed Martin Investments............................937 429-0100
  2940 Presidential Dr # 290 Beavercreek (45324) *(G-1349)*

Lockrey Manufacturing, Toledo Also called Aimco Mfg Inc *(G-18324)*

Lockrey Manufacturing, Toledo Also called Raka Corporation *(G-18671)*

Loctite, Westlake Also called Henkel Corporation *(G-20275)*

Loctote LLC..614 407-0882
  1010 Jackson Hole Dr Blacklick (43004) *(G-1700)*

Lodi Foundry Co Inc...330 948-1516
  106 Billman St Lodi (44254) *(G-12164)*

Loecy Precision Manufacturing..........................440 358-0551
  9180 Hilo Farm Dr Mentor (44060) *(G-13636)*

Loft Violin Shop..614 267-7221
  4604 N High St Columbus (43214) *(G-7303)*

Logan Clutch Corporation.................................440 808-4258
  28855 Ranney Pkwy Cleveland (44145) *(G-5707)*

Logan Coatings LLC..740 380-0047
  2255 E Front St Logan (43138) *(G-12184)*

Logan Enterprises Inc.....................................937 465-8170
  8844 Us Highway 68 N West Liberty (43357) *(G-20093)*

LOGAN FOUNDRY & MACHINE, Logan Also called Clay Logan Products Company *(G-12172)*

Logan Machine Company (PA)............................330 633-6163
  1405 Home Ave Akron (44310) *(G-275)*

Logan Screen Printing......................................740 385-3303
  119 W Main St Logan (43138) *(G-12185)*

Logan Screen Printing & EMB, Logan Also called Logan Screen Printing *(G-12185)*

Logan Welding Inc...740 385-9651
  37062 Hocking Dr Logan (43138) *(G-12186)*

Logitech Inc..614 871-2822
  6423 Seeds Rd Grove City (43123) *(G-10569)*

Logo This...419 445-1355
  301 Ditto St Ste E Archbold (43502) *(G-685)*

Logos On Lee..216 862-5226
  3105 Mayfield Rd Cleveland (44118) *(G-5708)*

Logotec, Cleveland Also called Madison Group Inc *(G-5727)*

Loken Oil Field Services LLC............................740 749-3495
  2190 Olinn Rd Marietta (45750) *(G-12799)*

Lokring Technology LLC..................................440 942-0880
  38376 Apollo Pkwy Willoughby (44094) *(G-20528)*

Loma Lux Laboratories, Solon Also called Plymouth Healthcare Pdts LLC *(G-17362)*

Lomar Enterprises Inc......................................614 409-9104
  5905 Green Pointe Dr S G Groveport (43125) *(G-10633)*

London Coach Shop...419 347-4803
  2962 London East Rd Shelby (44875) *(G-17137)*

Long Sign Co..614 294-1057
  979 E 5th Ave Columbus (43201) *(G-7304)*

Long View Steel Corp.......................................419 747-1108
  1555 W Longview Ave Mansfield (44906) *(G-12637)*

Long-Lok Fasteners Corporation.........................513 772-1880
  10630 Chester Rd Cincinnati (45215) *(G-4032)*

Long-Stanton Mfg Company...............................513 874-8020
  9388 Sutton Pl West Chester (45011) *(G-19895)*

Longaberger Baskets, Frazeysburg Also called Longaberger Company *(G-10075)*

Longaberger Company.......................................740 828-4000
  5563 Raiders Rd Frazeysburg (43822) *(G-10075)*

Longmeier Printing & Advg, Lima Also called E L Frueh Inc *(G-12007)*

Longriders Trucking Company............................740 975-7863
  7 Delano St Mount Vernon (43050) *(G-14629)*

Longs Custom Doors..419 339-2331
  229 S Greenlawn Ave Lima (45807) *(G-12049)*

Longyear Company...740 373-2190
  1010 Greene St Marietta (45750) *(G-12800)*

Lorain Armature & Mtr Repr Inc.........................440 967-2620
  960 Sunnyside Rd Vermilion (44089) *(G-19332)*

Lorain County Auto Systems Inc.........................248 442-6800
  101 Liberty Ct Elyria (44035) *(G-9454)*

Lorain County Auto Systems Inc (HQ)..................440 960-7470
  7470 Industrial Pkwy Dr Lorain (44053) *(G-12256)*

Lorain County Metro Pk Dst..............................440 327-3626
  6195 Otten Rd North Ridgeville (44039) *(G-15388)*

Lorain Journal...440 245-6900
  1657 Broadway Lorain (44052) *(G-12257)*

Lorain Modern Pattern Inc.................................440 365-6780
  159 Woodbury St Elyria (44035) *(G-9455)*

Lorain Printing Company...................................440 288-6000
  1310 Colorado Ave Lorain (44052) *(G-12258)*

Lorain Quickprint, Monroeville Also called Nari Inc *(G-14427)*

Lorain Ruled Die Products Inc............................440 281-8607
  6287 Lear Nagle Rd Ste 4 North Ridgeville (44039) *(G-15389)*

Lord Corporation...440 992-0193
  4212 Ann Ave Ashtabula (44004) *(G-818)*

Lord Corporation...440 333-5750
  19045 Story Rd Rocky River (44116) *(G-16700)*

Lord Corporation...937 278-9431
  4644 Wadsworth Rd Dayton (45414) *(G-8459)*

Lore Inc...513 969-8481
  5526 Garrett Dr Milford (45150) *(G-14159)*

LOreal Usa Inc..440 248-3700
  30601 Carter St Cleveland (44139) *(G-5709)*

Lorenz Corporation (PA)...................................937 228-6118
  501 E 3rd St Dayton (45402) *(G-8460)*

Lori Holding Co (PA)...740 342-3230
  1400 Commerce Dr New Lexington (43764) *(G-14848)*

Loris Printing & Party Center, Sandusky Also called Loris Printing Inc *(G-16981)*

Loris Printing Inc...419 626-6648
  2111 Cleveland Rd Sandusky (44870) *(G-16981)*

Loroco Industries Inc (PA)................................513 891-9544
  5000 Creek Rd Blue Ash (45242) *(G-1828)*

Loroco Industries Inc......................................513 554-0356
  10600 Evendale Dr Cincinnati (45241) *(G-4033)*

Lost Nation Fuel..440 951-9088
  3525 Lost Nation Rd Willoughby (44094) *(G-20529)*

Lost Technology LLP..513 685-0054
  9501 Woodland Hills Dr West Chester (45011) *(G-19896)*

Lostcreek Tool & Machine Inc............................937 773-6022
  1150 S Main St Piqua (45356) *(G-16287)*

Louis Arthur Steel Company (PA).......................440 997-5545
  185 Water St Geneva (44041) *(G-10352)*

Louis Arthur Steel Company..............................440 997-5545
  3700 Massillon Rd Ste 360 Uniontown (44685) *(G-19091)*

Louis G Freeman Co...513 263-1720
  4064 Clough Woods Dr Batavia (45103) *(G-1202)*

Louis G Freeman Co...419 334-9709
  911 Graham Dr Fremont (43420) *(G-10167)*

Louis Instantwhip-St Inc (PA)............................614 488-2536
  2200 Cardigan Ave Columbus (43215) *(G-7305)*

Louis Leasing LLC..440 243-3810
  950 Lake Rd Medina (44256) *(G-13436)*

Louis Trauth Dairy LLC (HQ).............................859 431-7553
  9991 Commerce Park Dr West Chester (45246) *(G-20021)*

Louise Sweet LLC..419 460-5505
  3827 Beechway Blvd Toledo (43614) *(G-18563)*

Louisville Herald Inc...330 875-5610
  308 S Mill St Louisville (44641) *(G-12318)*

Louisville Molded Products................................330 877-9740
  13122 Duquette Ave Ne Hartville (44632) *(G-10829)*

Lous Machine Company Inc................................513 856-9199
  102 Hastings Ave Hamilton (45011) *(G-10718)*

Lous Sausage Ltd..216 752-5060
  14723 Miles Ave Cleveland (44128) *(G-5710)*

Love Chocolate Factory, Hartville Also called L C F Inc *(G-10828)*

Loveman Steel Corporation...............................440 232-6200
  5455 Perkins Rd Bedford (44146) *(G-1439)*

Low Bobs Discount Tobacco..............................513 727-1430
  408 S Breiel Blvd Middletown (45044) *(G-14055)*

Low Stress Grind Inc..513 771-7977
  12077 Mosteller Rd Cincinnati (45241) *(G-4034)*

Lowell Marcum..330 948-2353
  328 Bank St Lodi (44254) *(G-12165)*

Lower Limb Centers LLC...................................440 365-2502
  1100 Abbe Rd N Ste D Elyria (44035) *(G-9456)*

Lowery Industries..740 745-5045
  10975 Houdeshell Rd Saint Louisville (43071) *(G-16828)*

Lowry Furnace Company Inc..............................330 745-4822
  663 Flora Ave Akron (44314) *(G-276)*

Lowry Tool & Die Inc.......................................330 332-1722
  986 Salem Pkwy Salem (44460) *(G-16908)*

Loxcreen Company Inc.....................................513 539-2255
  100 Westheimer Dr Middletown (45044) *(G-14056)*

Lozinak & Sons Inc...440 877-1819
  8695 York Rd North Royalton (44133) *(G-15433)*

LP Propane Gas, Mc Arthur Also called Nimco Inc *(G-13332)*

LPC Publishing Co..216 721-1800
  2026 Murray Hill Rd # 10 Cleveland (44106) *(G-5711)*

Lpi Legacy Plastics LLC..................................270 827-1318
  4425 Appleton St Cincinnati (45209) *(G-4035)*

Lrb Tool & Die Ltd..330 898-5783
  3303 Parkman Rd Nw Warren (44481) *(G-19574)*

LS Bombshelles...513 254-6898
  3940 Vine St Cincinnati (45217) *(G-4036)*

LS Starrett Company...440 835-0005
  24500 Detroit Rd Westlake (44145) *(G-20282)*

Lsc Communications Us LLC.............................419 935-0111
  1145 S Conwell Ave Willard (44890) *(G-20396)*

LSI Graphic Solutions, Blue Ash Also called LSI Industries Inc *(G-1830)*

LSI Graphic Solutions Plus, North Canton Also called Grady McCauley
Incorporated *(G-15236)*

2017 Harris Ohio
Industrial Directory

(G-0000) Company's Geographic Section entry number

LSI Industries Inc...513 793-3200
10000 Alliance Rd Blue Ash (45242) ***(G-1829)***
LSI Industries Inc (PA)...513 793-3200
10000 Alliance Rd Blue Ash (45242) ***(G-1830)***
Lsmi, Columbus *Also called Lambert Sheet Metal Inc* ***(G-7281)***
Lsp Technologies Inc...614 718-3000
6145 Scherers Pl Dublin (43016) ***(G-9100)***
Lsq Manufacturing Inc...330 725-4905
1140 Industrial Pkwy Medina (44256) ***(G-13437)***
Lt Enterprises of Ohio LLC...330 526-6908
334 Orchard Ave Ne North Canton (44720) ***(G-15247)***
Lt Wright Handcrafted Knife Co...740 317-1404
130 Warren Ln Unit B Steubenville (43953) ***(G-17703)***
Ltf Acquisition LLC...330 533-0111
430 W Main St Canfield (44406) ***(G-2563)***
Ltg Polymers Limited...330 854-5609
7612 Onyx Ave Nw Massillon (44646) ***(G-13168)***
LTI Power Systems...440 327-5050
10800 Middle Ave Hngr B Elyria (44035) ***(G-9457)***
LTS Metrology LLC...330 425-3092
1500 Enterprise Pkwy Twinsburg (44087) ***(G-18975)***
LTS Scale Company, Twinsburg *Also called LTS Metrology LLC* ***(G-18975)***
Lube & Chem Products, Cincinnati *Also called Interlube Corporation* ***(G-3929)***
Lube Depot...330 758-0570
6122 Market St Youngstown (44512) ***(G-21135)***
Lube Depot...330 854-6345
2185 Locust St S Canal Fulton (44614) ***(G-2506)***
Lubricant Additives, Wickliffe *Also called Lubrizol Corporation* ***(G-20370)***
Lubrizol Advanced Mtls Inc...440 933-0400
550 Moore Rd Avon Lake (44012) ***(G-1037)***
Lubrizol Advanced Mtls Inc...419 352-5565
1142 N Main St Bowling Green (43402) ***(G-1998)***
Lubrizol Advanced Mtls Inc (HQ)...216 447-5000
9911 Brecksville Rd Brecksville (44141) ***(G-2061)***
Lubrizol Corporation (HQ)...440 943-4200
29400 Lakeland Blvd Wickliffe (44092) ***(G-20370)***
Lubrizol Corporation...440 357-7064
155 Freedom Rd Painesville (44077) ***(G-15898)***
Lubrizol Production Plant, Painesville *Also called Lubrizol Corporation* ***(G-15898)***
Luc Ice Inc...419 734-2201
728 S Railroad St Port Clinton (43452) ***(G-16404)***
Lucas County Asphalt Inc...419 476-0705
7540 Hollow Creek Dr Toledo (43617) ***(G-18564)***
Lucio Vanni LLC...440 823-6103
1545 Wooster Rd Rocky River (44116) ***(G-16701)***
Luckey Farmers Inc...419 287-3275
2320 Bowling Green Rd E Bradner (43406) ***(G-2027)***
Lucky Paws LLC...859 620-2525
5541 Foley Rd Cincinnati (45238) ***(G-4037)***
Lucky Thirteen Inc...216 631-0013
7413 Associate Ave Cleveland (44144) ***(G-5712)***
Lucky Thirteen Laser, Cleveland *Also called Lucky Thirteen Inc* ***(G-5712)***
Ludlow Composites Corporation...419 332-5531
2100 Commerce Dr Fremont (43420) ***(G-10168)***
Ludowici Roof Tile Inc...740 342-1995
4757 Tile Plant Rd Se New Lexington (43764) ***(G-14849)***
Ludwig Music Publishing Co...440 926-1100
1080 Cleveland St Grafton (44044) ***(G-10433)***
Ludy Greenhouse Mfg Corp (PA)...800 255-5839
122 Railroad St New Madison (45346) ***(G-14870)***
Luk Clutch Systems LLC (HQ)...330 264-4383
3401 Old Airport Rd Wooster (44691) ***(G-20798)***
Luk Transmission Systems LLC...330 264-4383
3401 Old Airport Rd Wooster (44691) ***(G-20799)***
Luk USA LLC (HQ)...330 264-4383
3401 Old Airport Rd Wooster (44691) ***(G-20800)***
Luke Engineering & Mfg Corp (PA)...330 335-1501
456 South Blvd Wadsworth (44281) ***(G-19418)***
Luke Engineering & Mfg Corp...330 925-3344
11 Pipestone Rd Rittman (44270) ***(G-16679)***
Lukens Inc...937 440-2500
1040 S Dorset Rd Troy (45373) ***(G-18854)***
Lukens Blacksmith Shop...513 821-2308
30 Compton Rd Cincinnati (45216) ***(G-4038)***
Lukjan Metal Products Inc (PA)...440 599-8127
645 Industry Rd Conneaut (44030) ***(G-7814)***
Luma Electric Company...419 843-7842
3419 Silica Rd Sylvania (43560) ***(G-18116)***
Lumacurve Airfield Signs, Macedonia *Also called Standard Signs Incorporated* ***(G-12489)***
Lumbercraft, Canal Winchester *Also called Strait & Lamp Lumber Co Inc* ***(G-2537)***
Lumberjack Pallet Recycl LLC...513 821-7543
81 Caldwell Dr Cincinnati (45216) ***(G-4039)***
Lumenomics Inc...614 798-3500
8333 Green Meadows Dr N Lewis Center (43035) ***(G-11906)***
Lumi Craft, Norwich *Also called Lumi-Lite Candle Company* ***(G-15569)***
Lumi-Lite Candle Company...740 872-3248
102 Sundale Rd Norwich (43767) ***(G-15569)***
Luminaud Inc...440 255-9082
8688 Tyler Blvd Mentor (44060) ***(G-13637)***
Luminex HD&f Company, Blue Ash *Also called Luminex Home Decor* ***(G-1831)***
Luminex Home Decor (PA)...513 563-1113
10521 Millington Ct Blue Ash (45242) ***(G-1831)***
Lumitex Inc (PA)...440 243-8401
8443 Dow Cir Strongsville (44136) ***(G-17939)***
Lumitex Inc...949 250-8557
8443 Dow Cir Strongsville (44136) ***(G-17940)***
Lunar Tool & Mold Inc...440 237-2141
9860 York Alpha Dr North Royalton (44133) ***(G-15434)***
Lund Equipment Co Inc...330 659-4800
2400 N Clvlnd Mssillon Rd Bath (44210) ***(G-1238)***
Lund Printing Co...330 628-4047
2962 Trenton Rd Akron (44312) ***(G-277)***
Lure Inc...440 951-8862
38040 3rd St Willoughby (44094) ***(G-20530)***
Lustrous Metal Coatings Inc...330 478-4653
1541 Raff Rd Sw Canton (44710) ***(G-2760)***
Luvata Ohio Inc (HQ)...740 363-1981
1376 Pittsburgh Dr Delaware (43015) ***(G-8870)***
Lux Corporation...419 562-7978
4613 Stetzer Rd Bucyrus (44820) ***(G-2353)***
Luxaire Cushion Co...330 872-0995
2410 S Center St Newton Falls (44444) ***(G-15135)***
Luxco Inc...216 671-6300
3116 Berea Rd Cleveland (44111) ***(G-5713)***
Luxfer Magtech Inc (HQ)...513 772-3066
2940 Highland Ave Ste 210 Cincinnati (45212) ***(G-4040)***
Luxottica Optical Mfg, Lockbourne *Also called Luxottica Retail N Amer Inc* ***(G-12149)***
Luxottica Retail N Amer Inc...614 409-9381
2150 Bixby Rd Lockbourne (43137) ***(G-12149)***
Luxus Arms, Mount Orab *Also called Luxus Products LLC* ***(G-14582)***
Luxus Products LLC...937 444-6500
222 Homan Way Mount Orab (45154) ***(G-14582)***
Luxx Ultra-Tech Inc...330 483-6051
7334 Lonesome Pine Trl Medina (44256) ***(G-13438)***
Lvd Acquisition LLC (HQ)...614 861-1350
222 E Campus View Blvd Columbus (43235) ***(G-7306)***
Lwb/ISE LP...937 778-3828
9160 Country Club Rd Piqua (45356) ***(G-16288)***
Lwc, Maumee *Also called Larrys Water Conditioning* ***(G-13275)***
Lwr Enterprises Inc...740 984-0036
4310 Sparling Rd Waterford (45786) ***(G-19650)***
Lyco Corporation...330 534-3330
1089 N Hubbard Rd Lowellville (44436) ***(G-12410)***
Lyle Printing & Publishing Co (PA)...330 337-3419
185 E State St Salem (44460) ***(G-16909)***
Lyle Printing & Publishing Co...330 337-7172
193 S Howard Ave Salem (44460) ***(G-16910)***
Lync Corp...513 655-7286
2963 Commodore Ln Apt 2 Cincinnati (45251) ***(G-4041)***
Lynn James Contracting LLC...419 467-4505
12490 County Road 5 Delta (43515) ***(G-8938)***
Lynn Lyons...740 599-7811
803 Market St Danville (43014) ***(G-8089)***
Lynn Truck Parts & Service...330 966-1470
2690 Missenden St Nw North Canton (44720) ***(G-15248)***
Lynns Logos Inc...440 786-1156
386 Broadway Ave Cleveland (44146) ***(G-5714)***
Lynx Chemical...513 856-9161
370 Industrial Dr Franklin (45005) ***(G-10033)***
Lyondell Chemical Company...440 352-9393
110 3rd St Fairport Harbor (44077) ***(G-9767)***
Lyondell Chemical Company...513 530-4000
11530 Northlake Dr Cincinnati (45249) ***(G-4042)***
Lyons...440 224-0676
5231 State Route 193 Kingsville (44048) ***(G-11605)***
M & B Asphalt Company Inc...419 992-4235
2100 W Senc County Rd 42 Tiffin (44883) ***(G-18228)***
M & B Machine Inc...419 476-8836
4801 Bennett Rd Toledo (43612) ***(G-18565)***
M & D Brink Inc...419 531-6699
2128 Eastedge Dr Toledo (43614) ***(G-18566)***
M & G Polymers Usa LLC...330 239-7400
6951 Ridge Rd Sharon Center (44274) ***(G-17107)***
M & G Truss Rafters...740 667-3166
26077 Congrove St Coolville (45723) ***(G-7834)***
M & H Fabricating Co Inc (PA)...937 325-8708
717 Mound St Springfield (45505) ***(G-17593)***
M & H Fabricating Co Inc...937 325-8708
823 Mound St Springfield (45505) ***(G-17594)***
M & H Screen Printing...740 522-1957
1486 Hebron Rd Newark (43056) ***(G-15031)***
M & J Machine Shop Inc...330 645-0042
2420 Pickle Rd Akron (44312) ***(G-278)***
M & L Machine...937 386-2604
17400 State Route 247 Seaman (45679) ***(G-17041)***
M & M Certified Welding Inc...330 467-1729
556 Highland Rd E Ste 3 Macedonia (44056) ***(G-12467)***
M & M Concepts Inc...937 355-1115
2633 State Route 292 West Mansfield (43358) ***(G-20100)***

ALPHABETIC

M & M Dies Inc 216 883-6628
3502 Beyerle Rd Cleveland (44105) *(G-5715)*

M & M Engraving 216 749-7166
5411 State Rd Cleveland (44134) *(G-5716)*

M & M Fabrication Inc 740 779-3071
18828 Us Highway 50 Chillicothe (45601) *(G-3249)*

M & M Foods, Cleveland Also called Mama Mias Foods Inc *(G-5737)*

M & M Hardwoods, Sugarcreek Also called Tusco Hardwoods LLC *(G-18047)*

M & M Tobacco 330 573-8543
701 Canton Rd Nw Carrollton (44615) *(G-2961)*

M & R Electric Motor Svc Inc 937 222-6282
1516 E 5th St Dayton (45403) *(G-8461)*

M & R Industries Inc 440 897-7950
8651 Dunbar Ln Brecksville (44141) *(G-2062)*

M & R Phillips Enterprises 740 323-0580
6242 Jacksontown Rd Newark (43056) *(G-15032)*

M & R Redi Mix Inc (PA) 419 445-7771
521 Commercial St Pettisville (43553) *(G-16181)*

M & R Redi Mix Inc 419 748-8442
L207 County Road 1c Mc Clure (43534) *(G-13335)*

M & S Acquistion Co LLC 440 951-8700
9470 Pinecone Dr Mentor (44060) *(G-13638)*

M & W Electric Mfg Co LLC 330 332-9553
986 Salem Pkwy Salem (44460) *(G-16911)*

M & W Trailers Inc 419 453-3331
525 E Main St Ottoville (45876) *(G-15824)*

M & W Welding Inc 614 224-0501
72 N Glenwood Ave Columbus (43222) *(G-7307)*

M & Y Marketing 937 322-3423
2651 Danbury Rd Springfield (45505) *(G-17595)*

M A C Machine 410 944-6171
1111 Faircrest St Se Canton (44707) *(G-2761)*

M A Harrison Mfg Co Inc 440 965-4306
14307 State Route 113 Wakeman (44889) *(G-19451)*

M A K Fabricating Inc 330 747-0040
1609 Wilson Ave Youngstown (44506) *(G-21136)*

M A Miller 440 636-5697
16790 Pioneer Rd Middlefield (44062) *(G-13951)*

M B Industries Inc (PA) 419 738-4769
11158 Infirmary Rd Wapakoneta (45895) *(G-19496)*

M B Saxon Co Inc 440 229-5006
47 Alpha Park Cleveland (44143) *(G-5717)*

M B Trucking, Dover Also called Sugarcreek Lime Service *(G-9019)*

M C D Plastics & Manufacturing 937 778-1850
172 Robert M Davis Pkwy Piqua (45356) *(G-16289)*

M C Industries Inc 440 355-4040
111 Commerce Dr Lagrange (44050) *(G-11631)*

M C L Window Coverings Inc 513 868-6000
6741 Gilmore Rd Ste H Hamilton (45011) *(G-10719)*

M C Sports 419 874-2990
27171 Crossroads Pkwy Rossford (43460) *(G-16742)*

M C Systems Inc 513 336-6007
4455 Bethany Rd Unit C Mason (45040) *(G-13056)*

M D Complete Prof Skincare 513 965-3760
614 Wooster Pike Terrace Park (45174) *(G-18181)*

M D Solutions, Plain City Also called MD Solutions Inc *(G-16348)*

M F Y Inc 330 747-1334
1640 Wilson Ave Youngstown (44506) *(G-21137)*

M G 3d 614 262-0956
320 E Weber Rd Columbus (43202) *(G-7308)*

M G Q Inc 419 992-4236
1525 W County Road 42 Tiffin (44883) *(G-18229)*

M Grafix LLC 419 528-8665
384 Gatewood Dr Apt 2 Mansfield (44907) *(G-12638)*

M H EBY Inc 614 879-6901
4435 State Route 29 West Jefferson (43162) *(G-20081)*

M H Logging & Lumber 740 694-1988
14582 Montgomery Rd Fredericktown (43019) *(G-10106)*

M H Woodworking LLC 330 893-3929
2789 County Rd Ste 600 Millersburg (44654) *(G-14243)*

M I P Inc 330 744-0215
701 Jones St Youngstown (44502) *(G-21138)*

M J Coates Construction Co 937 886-9546
9809 Saddle Creek Trl Dayton (45458) *(G-8462)*

M J Coates Construction Co (PA) 937 886-9546
9809 Saddle Creek Trl Dayton (45458) *(G-8463)*

M J S Oil Inc 937 982-3519
23296 Treaty Line Rd West Mansfield (43358) *(G-20101)*

M K Morse Company (PA) 330 453-8187
1101 11th St Se Canton (44707) *(G-2762)*

M L Advertising & Design LLC 419 447-6523
185 Jefferson St Tiffin (44883) *(G-18230)*

M L B Molded Urethane Pdts LLC 419 825-9140
1680 Us Highway 20a Swanton (43558) *(G-18086)*

M L C Technologies Inc 513 874-7792
4 Standen Dr Hamilton (45015) *(G-10720)*

M L Grinding Co 440 975-9111
34620 Lakeland Blvd Willoughby (44095) *(G-20531)*

M M A Authentics LLC 614 274-1141
576 Georgesville Rd Columbus (43228) *(G-7309)*

M M I Services Inc 440 259-2939
3235 Elizabeth Dr Unit 34 Perry (44081) *(G-16053)*

M M Industries Inc 330 332-5947
36135 Salem Grange Rd Salem (44460) *(G-16912)*

M Manufacturing Inc 330 793-6806
75 S Turner Rd Youngstown (44515) *(G-21139)*

M Mazzone & Sons Bakery Inc 216 631-6511
3519 Clark Ave Cleveland (44109) *(G-5718)*

M P G, Maumee Also called Magnesium Products Group Inc *(G-13277)*

M P I Logistics, Massillon Also called Martin Pallet Inc *(G-13172)*

M P Machine Inc 440 255-8355
8743 East Ave Mentor (44060) *(G-13639)*

M Pl Label Systems 330 938-2134
450 Courtney Rd Sebring (44672) *(G-17047)*

M R I Education Foundation 513 281-3400
5400 Kennedy Ave Cincinnati (45213) *(G-4043)*

M R S, Columbus Also called MRS Industrial Inc *(G-7372)*

M Russell & Associates Inc 419 478-8795
3250 Monroe St Toledo (43606) *(G-18567)*

M S Abbott Jewelers 614 430-8800
692 High St Worthington (43085) *(G-20877)*

M S B Machine Inc 330 686-7740
36 Castle Dr Munroe Falls (44262) *(G-14664)*

M S C Industries Inc 440 474-8788
5131 Ireland Rd Rome (44085) *(G-16717)*

M S K Partnership 419 394-4444
7219 Harris Rd Celina (45822) *(G-3005)*

M S K Tool & Die Inc 440 930-8100
685 Moore Rd Ste B Avon Lake (44012) *(G-1038)*

M S Welding 419 925-4141
1729 Hartings Rd Maria Stein (45860) *(G-12758)*

M T, Elmore Also called Machining Technologies Inc *(G-9363)*

M T D Service Division, Shelby Also called Mtd Products Inc *(G-17139)*

M T M Molded Products Company 937 890-7461
3370 Obco Ct Dayton (45414) *(G-8464)*

M T Metals LLC 330 809-6465
240 6th St Nw Massillon (44647) *(G-13169)*

M T O, Saint Marys Also called Murotech Ohio Corporation *(G-16844)*

M T S, Cincinnati Also called Metal Technology Systems Inc *(G-4089)*

M T Systems Inc 330 453-4646
400 Schroyer Ave Sw Canton (44702) *(G-2763)*

M Technologies 330 477-9009
1818 Hopple Ave Sw Canton (44706) *(G-2764)*

M W Solutions LLC 419 782-1611
1802 Baltimore St Ste B Defiance (43512) *(G-8800)*

M Web Type Inc 614 272-8973
3500 Sullivant Ave Columbus (43204) *(G-7310)*

M&L Plating Works LLC (PA) 419 255-7701
425 Jefferson Ave Ste 520 Toledo (43604) *(G-18568)*

M&M Great Adventures LLC 937 344-1415
586 Deer Trl Westerville (43082) *(G-20169)*

M&S Machine and Manufacturing, Cincinnati Also called Modern Manufacturing
Inc *(G-4116)*

M-Boss Inc 216 441-6080
4510 E 71st St Ste 2 Cleveland (44105) *(G-5719)*

M-Co Welling 330 897-1374
10949 Gnther Miller Rd Sw Stone Creek (43840) *(G-17724)*

M-D Building Products Inc 513 539-2255
100 Westheimer Dr Middletown (45044) *(G-14057)*

M-Tek Inc 419 209-0399
1111 N Warpole St Upper Sandusky (43351) *(G-19130)*

M/W International Inc 440 526-6900
10260 Brecksville Rd Brecksville (44141) *(G-2063)*

M21 Industries LLC 937 781-1377
721 Springfield St Dayton (45403) *(G-8465)*

M2m Imaging Corporation 440 684-9690
5427 Wilson Mills Rd Cleveland (44143) *(G-5720)*

M3 Technologies Inc 216 898-9936
13910 Enterprise Ave Cleveland (44135) *(G-5721)*

M7 Technologies, Youngstown Also called Garvey Corporation *(G-21090)*

MA Flynn Associates LLC 513 893-7873
4115 Tonya Trl Hamilton (45011) *(G-10721)*

Maags Automotive & Machine 419 626-1539
1640 Columbus Ave Sandusky (44870) *(G-16982)*

Maan Power Services LLC 740 609-3020
56346 National Rd Bridgeport (43912) *(G-2091)*

Maass Midwest Mfg Inc 419 894-6424
19710 State Route 12 Arcadia (44804) *(G-654)*

Mab Fabrication Inc 855 622-3221
320 N State St Harrison (45030) *(G-10788)*

Mabar Printing Service 419 257-3659
400 N Tarr St North Baltimore (45872) *(G-15194)*

Mabsc, Akron Also called Meggitt Aircraft Braking *(G-294)*

Mac Advertising Co, Dayton Also called Donald Marlo *(G-8308)*

Mac Dhui Probe of America Inc 440 942-5597
7867 Enterprise Dr 9 Mentor (44060) *(G-13640)*

Mac Electric, Lima Also called Fmh Electric Inc *(G-12013)*

Mac Electric Inc 419 782-0671
1240 Fairgreen Ave Lima (45805) *(G-12050)*
Mac Instruments, Sandusky *Also called Machine Applications Corp (G-16983)*
Mac Liquid Tank Trailer, Kent *Also called Mac Ltt Inc (G-11486)*
Mac Ltt Inc 330 474-3795
1400 Fairchild Ave Kent (44240) *(G-11486)*
Mac Manufacturing Inc (PA) 330 823-9900
14599 Commerce St Ne Alliance (44601) *(G-523)*
Mac Manufacturing Inc 330 829-1680
1453 Allen Rd Salem (44460) *(G-16913)*
Mac Oil Field Service Inc 330 674-7371
7861 Township Road 306 Millersburg (44654) *(G-14244)*
Mac Printing Company 937 393-1101
406 N West St Hillsboro (45133) *(G-11007)*
Mac Ritchie Materials Inc 419 288-2790
6126 S Main St West Millgrove (43467) *(G-20104)*
Mac Steel Trailer Ltd 330 823-9900
14599 Commerce St Ne Alliance (44601) *(G-524)*
Mac Trailer Manufacturing Inc (PA) 330 823-9900
14599 Commerce St Ne Alliance (44601) *(G-525)*
Maca Mold & Machine Co Inc 330 854-0292
761 Elm Ridge Ave Canal Fulton (44614) *(G-2507)*
Maca Plastics Inc 937 544-8618
3455 Cross Rd Winchester (45697) *(G-20695)*
Macdivitt Rubber Company LLC 440 259-5937
3291 Center Rd Perry (44081) *(G-16054)*
Mace Personal Def & SEC Inc (HQ) 440 424-5321
4400 Carnegie Ave Cleveland (44103) *(G-5722)*
Mace Security Intl Inc (PA) 440 424-5321
4400 Carnegie Ave Cleveland (44103) *(G-5723)*
Macek Industries 440 205-8711
8830 Tyler Blvd Mentor (44060) *(G-13641)*
Machine & Tool Accessories Co, Broadview Heights *Also called Mataco (G-2114)*
Machine Applications Corp 419 621-2322
3410 Tiffin Ave Sandusky (44870) *(G-16983)*
Machine Component Mfg 330 454-4566
3410 Perry Dr Nw Canton (44708) *(G-2765)*
Machine Concepts Inc 419 628-3498
2167 State Route 66 Minster (45865) *(G-14357)*
Machine Development Corp 513 825-5885
7707 Affinity Dr Cincinnati (45231) *(G-4044)*
Machine Doctors, Middletown *Also called Al Bradshaw Jr (G-14018)*
Machine Doctors Inc 513 422-3060
3490 Mustafa Dr Cincinnati (45241) *(G-4045)*
Machine Dynamics & Engrg Inc 330 868-5603
9312 Arrow Rd Nw Minerva (44657) *(G-14331)*
Machine Industries Inc 216 881-8555
5200 Perkins Ave Cleveland (44103) *(G-5724)*
Machine Parts International 216 251-4334
10925 Briggs Rd Cleveland (44111) *(G-5725)*
Machine Products, Loveland *Also called Macpro Inc (G-12372)*
Machine Products Company 937 890-6600
5660 Webster St Dayton (45414) *(G-8466)*
Machine Shop 330 494-1251
410 Viking St Nw Canton (44720) *(G-2766)*
Machine Tek Systems Inc 330 527-4450
10400 Industrial Dr Garrettsville (44231) *(G-10329)*
Machine Tl Sltons Unlmited LLC 513 761-0709
8711 Reading Rd Cincinnati (45215) *(G-4046)*
Machine Tool & Fab Corp 419 435-7676
1401 Sandusky St Fostoria (44830) *(G-9983)*
Machine Tool Corporation 513 863-4920
102 Hastings Ave Hamilton (45011) *(G-10722)*
Machine Tool Design & Fab LLC 419 435-7676
1401 Sandusky St Fostoria (44830) *(G-9984)*
Machine Tool Division, Bluffton *Also called Grob Systems Inc (G-1912)*
Machine Tool Rebuilders Inc 614 228-1070
2042 Leonard Ave Columbus (43219) *(G-7311)*
Machine Tools Supply, Huber Heights *Also called Updike Supply Company (G-11152)*
Machine Works Inc 513 771-4600
979 Redna Ter Cincinnati (45215) *(G-4047)*
Machine-Pro Technologies Inc 419 584-0086
1321 W Market St Celina (45822) *(G-3006)*
Machined Glass Specialist Inc 937 743-6166
245 Hiawatha Trl Springboro (45066) *(G-17489)*
Machined Seals, Highland Heights *Also called SKF Usa Inc (G-10920)*
Machinex of Dayton Inc 937 252-7021
10 Davis Ave Dayton (45403) *(G-8467)*
Machining Technologies Inc (PA) 419 862-3110
468 Maple St Elmore (43416) *(G-9363)*
Machintek Co 513 551-1000
3721 Port Union Rd Fairfield (45014) *(G-9678)*
Mack Concrete Industries Inc (HQ) 330 483-3111
201 Columbia Rd Valley City (44280) *(G-19212)*
Mack Concrete Industries Inc 330 784-7008
124 Darrow Rd Ste 7 Akron (44305) *(G-279)*
Mack Industrial LLC 800 918-9986
3258 Sterlingwood Ln Perrysburg (43551) *(G-16119)*
Mack Industries 419 353-7081
507 Derby Ave Bowling Green (43402) *(G-1999)*
Mack Industries Inc (PA) 330 460-7005
1321 Industrial Pkwy N # 500 Brunswick (44212) *(G-2237)*
Mack Industries PA Inc (HQ) 330 483-3111
201 Columbia Rd Valley City (44280) *(G-19213)*
Mack Industries PA Inc 330 638-7680
2207 Slem Hutchings Rd Ne Vienna (44473) *(G-19369)*
Mack Iron Works Company 419 626-3712
124 Warren St Sandusky (44870) *(G-16984)*
Mack Ready Mix Concrete Inc 330 483-3111
201 Columbia Rd Valley City (44280) *(G-19214)*
Mack Ready-Mix, Akron *Also called Mack Concrete Industries Inc (G-279)*
Mack Transport, Brunswick *Also called Mack Industries Inc (G-2237)*
Macke Brothers Inc 513 771-7500
10355 Spartan Dr Cincinnati (45215) *(G-4048)*
Mackland Co Inc 330 399-5034
155 North St Nw Warren (44483) *(G-19575)*
Macleod Inc 513 771-9560
5928 Hamilton Cleves Rd Miamitown (45041) *(G-13889)*
Macmillan Graphics, Milford *Also called Gregg Macmillan (G-14148)*
Macpherson & Company, Berea *Also called Macpherson Engineering Inc (G-1625)*
Macpherson Engineering Inc 440 243-6565
95 Pelret Industrial Pkwy Berea (44017) *(G-1625)*
Macpro Inc 513 575-3000
1456 Fay Rd Unit B Loveland (45140) *(G-12372)*
Macray Co LLC 937 325-1726
100 W North St Springfield (45504) *(G-17596)*
Macro Meric, Aurora *Also called Saco Aei Polymers Inc (G-947)*
Mactac, Stow *Also called Morgan Adhesives Company LLC (G-17775)*
Mactac Americas LLC 330 688-1111
4560 Darrow Rd Stow (44224) *(G-17771)*
Mactek Corporation 330 487-5477
2112 Case Pkwy Ste 1 Twinsburg (44087) *(G-18976)*
Macwood Inc 614 279-7676
397 Martha Ave Columbus (43223) *(G-7312)*
Macwood Custom Woodworking, Columbus *Also called Macwood Inc (G-7312)*
Mad Metal Wldg Fabrication LLC 614 256-4163
3435 Polley Rd Columbus (43221) *(G-7313)*
Mad Potter LLC 513 770-5585
6680b Tri Way Dr Mason (45040) *(G-13057)*
Mad River Fabricating Ltd 937 322-6521
2330 Columbus Rd Springfield (45503) *(G-17597)*
Mad River Steel Ltd 937 845-4046
2141 N Dayton Lakeview Rd New Carlisle (45344) *(G-14806)*
Mad River Steel Company, New Carlisle *Also called Mad River Steel Ltd (G-14806)*
Mad River Topsoil Inc 937 882-6115
5625 Lower Valley Pike Springfield (45506) *(G-17598)*
Madaen Natural Products Inc 800 600-1445
141 Broad Blvd Lowr Cuyahoga Falls (44221) *(G-8021)*
Mader Automotive Center Inc (PA) 937 339-2681
225 S Walnut St Troy (45373) *(G-18855)*
Mader Dampers, Lagrange *Also called Mader Machine Co Inc (G-11632)*
Mader Electr Motor & Power Tra 937 325-5576
205 E Main St Springfield (45503) *(G-17599)*
Mader Machine Co Inc 440 355-4505
422 Commerce Dr E Lagrange (44050) *(G-11632)*
Maderite LLC 937 570-1042
6915 Roberta Dr Tipp City (45371) *(G-18288)*
Madgar Genis Corp 330 848-6950
131 Snyder Ave Barberton (44203) *(G-1125)*
Madison Electric (mepco) Inc 440 279-0521
11993 Ravenna Rd Ste 12 Chardon (44024) *(G-3165)*
Madison Electric Products Inc (PA) 216 391-7776
26401 Fargo Ave Bedford Heights (44146) *(G-1488)*
Madison Graphics 216 226-5770
13130 Detroit Ave Cleveland (44107) *(G-5726)*
Madison Group Inc 216 362-9000
15919 Industrial Pkwy Cleveland (44135) *(G-5727)*
Madison Manufacturing LLC 440 428-4630
444 Oak Hollow Dr Madison (44057) *(G-12509)*
Madison Messenger, Columbus *Also called Columbus Messenger Company (G-6961)*
Madison Messenger, London *Also called Columbus Messenger Company (G-12205)*
Madison Press, London *Also called Central Ohio Printing Corp (G-12203)*
Madison Press Inc 216 521-3789
1381 Summit Ave Lakewood (44107) *(G-11673)*
Madison Tool & Die Inc 440 354-8642
147 Elevator Ave Painesville (44077) *(G-15899)*
Madsco Inc 513 242-4200
7015 Mullen Rd Cincinnati (45247) *(G-4049)*
Madsen Wire Products Inc 937 829-6561
101 Madison St Dayton (45402) *(G-8468)*
Mae Consulting 513 531-8100
700 W Pete Rose Way 531b Cincinnati (45203) *(G-4050)*
Mag Machine Inc 440 946-3381
7243 Industrial Park Blvd Mentor (44060) *(G-13642)*
Mag Resources LLC 330 294-0494
90 16th St Sw Ste M Barberton (44203) *(G-1126)*

ALPHABETIC

(PA)=Parent Co (HQ)=Headquarters (DH)=Div Headquarters

Mag-Nif Inc 440 946-4308
 8820 East Ave Mentor (44060) *(G-13643)*

Magellan Arospc Middletown Inc (HQ) 513 422-2751
 2320 Wedekind Dr Middletown (45042) *(G-14058)*

Magenta Incorporated 216 571-4094
 3185a W 33rd St Cleveland (44109) *(G-5728)*

Mageros Candies 330 534-1146
 132 N Main St Hubbard (44425) *(G-11134)*

Magic City Machine Inc 330 825-0048
 21 4th St Nw Barberton (44203) *(G-1127)*

Magic Dragon Machine Inc 614 539-8004
 3451 Grant Ave Grove City (43123) *(G-10570)*

Magic Interface Ltd 440 498-3700
 7295 Popham Pl Solon (44139) *(G-17330)*

Magic Press Printery, Barberton *Also called Barberton Magic Press Printing* *(G-1107)*

Magic Rack, Obetz *Also called Production Plus Corp* *(G-15658)*

Magic Seal Packaging Products, Columbus *Also called The Magic Seal Paper Pdts Co* *(G-7691)*

Magic Wok Enterprises, Toledo *Also called Magic Wok Inc* *(G-18569)*

Magic Wok Inc (PA) 419 531-1818
 3352 W Laskey Rd Toledo (43623) *(G-18569)*

Magna, Northwood *Also called Norplas Industries Inc* *(G-15485)*

Magna Exteriors America Inc 419 662-3256
 7825 Caple Blvd Northwood (43619) *(G-15484)*

Magna Group LLC 513 388-9463
 2340 Clydes Xing Cincinnati (45244) *(G-4051)*

Magna International Amer Inc 905 853-3604
 19911 County Rd Ridgeville Corners (43555) *(G-16665)*

Magna Machine Co (PA) 513 851-6900
 11180 Southland Rd Cincinnati (45240) *(G-4052)*

Magna Modular Systems Inc (HQ) 419 324-3387
 1800 Nathan Dr Toledo (43611) *(G-18570)*

Magna Products, Grafton *Also called Sulo Enterprises Inc* *(G-10437)*

Magna Seating America Inc 330 824-3101
 1702 Henn Pkwy Sw Warren (44481) *(G-19576)*

Magna Seating America Inc 440 846-5680
 3637 Mallard Run Sheffield Village (44054) *(G-17126)*

Magna Team Systems, Toledo *Also called Magna Modular Systems Inc* *(G-18570)*

Magnaco Industries Inc (PA) 216 961-3636
 140 West Dr Lodi (44254) *(G-12166)*

Magneco/Metrel Inc 330 426-9468
 51365 State Route 154 Negley (44441) *(G-14730)*

Magneforce Inc 330 856-9300
 155 Shaffer Dr Ne Warren (44484) *(G-19577)*

Magnesium Products Group Inc 310 971-5799
 3928 Azalea Cir Maumee (43537) *(G-13277)*

Magnesium Refining Tech Inc (PA) 419 483-9199
 29695 Pettibone Rd Cleveland (44139) *(G-5729)*

Magnesium Refining Tech Inc 419 483-9199
 301 County Road 177 Bellevue (44811) *(G-1552)*

Magnesium Technologies Corp (HQ) 330 659-3003
 4807 Rockside Rd Ste 400 Independence (44131) *(G-11266)*

Magnet Technology Inc 513 932-4416
 1599 Kingsview Dr Lebanon (45036) *(G-11814)*

Magnetech, Massillon *Also called 3-D Service Ltd* *(G-13104)*

Magnetech Industrial Svcs Inc 330 830-3500
 800 Nave Rd Se Massillon (44646) *(G-13170)*

Magnetic Analysis Corporation 330 758-1367
 675 Mcclurg Rd Youngstown (44512) *(G-21140)*

Magnetic Mktg Solutions LLC 513 721-3801
 2111 Kindel Ave Cincinnati (45214) *(G-4053)*

Magnetic Resonance Tech 440 942-2922
 4261 Hamann Pkwy Willoughby (44094) *(G-20532)*

Magnetic Screw Machine Pdts 937 348-2807
 23241 State Route 37 Marysville (43040) *(G-12956)*

Magnetic Source, Marietta *Also called Master Magnetics Inc* *(G-12805)*

Magnetnotes Ltd 419 593-0060
 946 Kane St Ste A Toledo (43612) *(G-18571)*

Magnext Ltd 614 406-4136
 7100 Huntley Rd Unit 1 Columbus (43229) *(G-7314)*

Magnode Corporation (PA) 513 988-6351
 400 E State St Trenton (45067) *(G-18795)*

Magnolia Machine & Repair Inc 330 866-4200
 3315 Magnolia Rd Nw Magnolia (44643) *(G-12516)*

Magnum Computers Inc 216 781-1757
 868 Montford Rd Cleveland (44121) *(G-5730)*

Magnum Inks & Coatings, Marietta *Also called Magnum Magnetics Corporation* *(G-12801)*

Magnum Machine Works LLC 614 231-4880
 3680 E 5th Ave Unit D Columbus (43219) *(G-7315)*

Magnum Magnetics Corporation (PA) 740 373-7770
 801 Masonic Park Rd Marietta (45750) *(G-12801)*

Magnum Molding Inc 937 368-3040
 7435 N Bollinger Rd Conover (45317) *(G-7824)*

Magnum Piering Inc 513 759-3348
 156 Circle Freeway Dr West Chester (45246) *(G-20022)*

Magnum Products, Columbus *Also called Kcg Inc* *(G-7252)*

Magnum Tool Corp 937 228-0900
 1407 Stanley Ave Dayton (45404) *(G-8469)*

Magnus Engineered Eqp LLC 440 942-8488
 4500 Beidler Rd Willoughby (44094) *(G-20533)*

Magnus Equipment, Cleveland *Also called Reid Asset Management Company* *(G-6097)*

Magnus Equipment, Willoughby *Also called Reid Asset Management Company* *(G-20587)*

Magnus International Group Inc (PA) 216 592-8355
 16533 Chillicothe Rd Chagrin Falls (44023) *(G-3100)*

Magretech, Bellevue *Also called Magnesium Refining Tech Inc* *(G-1552)*

Mahan Packing Co Inc 330 889-2454
 6540 State Route 45 Bristolville (44402) *(G-2099)*

Mahar Spar Industries Inc 216 249-7143
 341 E 131st St Cleveland (44108) *(G-5731)*

Mahle Behr Dayton LLC 937 356-2001
 250 Northwoods Blvd # 47 Vandalia (45377) *(G-19301)*

Mahle Behr Dayton LLC 937 369-2900
 1720 Webster St Dayton (45404) *(G-8470)*

Mahle Behr Dayton LLC (HQ) 937 369-2900
 1600 Webster St Dayton (45404) *(G-8471)*

Mahle Behr Service America LLC 937 369-2610
 1003 Bellbrook Ave Xenia (45385) *(G-20962)*

Mahle Behr USA Inc 937 356-2001
 250 Northwoods Blvd # 47 Vandalia (45377) *(G-19302)*

Mahle Behr USA Inc 937 369-2000
 1600 Webster St Dayton (45404) *(G-8472)*

Mahle Industries Incorporated 740 962-2040
 5130 N State Route 60 Nw McConnelsville (43756) *(G-13353)*

Mahle Industries Incorporated 937 890-2739
 1600 Webster St Dayton (45404) *(G-8473)*

Mahoning Valley Fabricators 330 793-8995
 3697 Oakwood Ave Austintown (44515) *(G-975)*

Mahoning Valley Manufacturing 330 537-4492
 17796 Rte 62 Beloit (44609) *(G-1584)*

MAI Manufacturing, Marysville *Also called Straight 72 Inc* *(G-12973)*

MAI Media Group Llc 513 779-0604
 9624 Cincinnati Columbus West Chester (45241) *(G-20023)*

MAI-Weave LLC 937 322-1698
 1800 E Pleasant St Springfield (45505) *(G-17600)*

Main Awning & Tent Inc 513 621-6947
 415 W Seymour Ave Cincinnati (45216) *(G-4054)*

Main Fare Box Division, Willoughby *Also called Euclid Products Co Inc* *(G-20482)*

Main Street Cambritt Cookies, Cuyahoga Falls *Also called Main Street Gourmet LLC* *(G-8022)*

Main Street Gourmet LLC 330 929-0000
 170 Muffin Ln Cuyahoga Falls (44223) *(G-8022)*

Main Street Ice Cream Parlor, Van Wert *Also called B M DS Fish N More LLC* *(G-19244)*

Main Street Machine Inc 330 427-9828
 88 W Main St Leetonia (44431) *(G-11862)*

Maine Rubber Preforms LLC 216 210-2094
 16090 Industrial Pkwy # 1 Middlefield (44062) *(G-13952)*

Maine's Sign's & Designs, Springfield *Also called Maines Inc* *(G-17601)*

Maines Brothers Tin Shop 937 393-1633
 121 S West St Hillsboro (45133) *(G-11008)*

Maines Inc 937 322-2084
 1718 E Pleasant St Springfield (45505) *(G-17601)*

Maines, Clyde Sons Tin Shop, Hillsboro *Also called Maines Brothers Tin Shop* *(G-11008)*

Mainstream Software Inc 330 963-0103
 8848 Commons Blvd Ste 103 Twinsburg (44087) *(G-18977)*

Maintenance + Inc 330 264-6262
 1051 W Liberty St Wooster (44691) *(G-20801)*

Maintenance and Repair Fabg Co 330 478-1149
 427 Harding Ave Nw Massillon (44646) *(G-13171)*

Maintenance Building, Oxford *Also called City of Oxford* *(G-15834)*

Maintenance Repair Supply Inc 740 922-3006
 5539 Gundy Dr Midvale (44653) *(G-14109)*

Majestic Engineering & TI LLC 937 845-1079
 107 W Washington St New Carlisle (45344) *(G-14807)*

Majestic Manufacturing Inc 330 457-2447
 4536 State Route 7 New Waterford (44445) *(G-14972)*

Majestic Plastics Inc 937 593-9500
 811 N Main St Bellefontaine (43311) *(G-1536)*

Majestic Sportswear Company 937 773-1144
 2545 Landman Mill Rd Piqua (45356) *(G-16290)*

Majestic Steel Management Co 440 786-2666
 5300 Majestic Pkwy Cleveland (44146) *(G-5732)*

Majestic Tool and Machine Inc 440 248-5058
 30700 Carter St Ste C Solon (44139) *(G-17331)*

Majestic Trailer & Hitch, Akron *Also called Majestic Trailers Inc* *(G-280)*

Majestic Trailers Inc (PA) 330 798-1698
 1750 E Waterloo Rd Akron (44306) *(G-280)*

Majic Touch 330 923-8259
 4133 State Rd Cuyahoga Falls (44223) *(G-8023)*

Major Metals Company 419 886-4600
 844 Kochheiser Rd Mansfield (44904) *(G-12639)*

Majors Wholesale Med Sup LLC 800 376-7263
 6753 Engle Rd Ste A Cleveland (44130) *(G-5733)*

Makergear LLC 216 765-0030
 23632 Merc Rd Unit G Beachwood (44122) *(G-1277)*

Makino Inc (HQ) 513 573-7200
 7680 Innovation Way Mason (45040) *(G-13058)*

Malco Laminated Inc 513 541-8300
   4251 Spring Grove Ave Cincinnati (45223) *(G-4055)*

Malco Products Inc 330 753-0361
   393 W Wilbeth Rd Akron (44301) *(G-281)*

Malcolm Hydraulics 330 819-2033
   6581 Waterloo Rd Atwater (44201) *(G-900)*

Malcuit Racing Engines, Strasburg *Also called B A Malcuit Racing Inc (G-17820)*

Malin Co, Cleveland *Also called Malin Wire Co (G-5735)*

Malin Company, Cleveland *Also called Brushes Inc (G-4942)*

Malin Wire Co (HQ) 216 267-9080
   5400 Smith Rd Cleveland (44142) *(G-5734)*

Malin Wire Co 216 267-9080
   5400 Smith Rd Cleveland (44142) *(G-5735)*

Malish Corporation (PA) 440 951-5356
   7333 Corporate Blvd Mentor (44060) *(G-13644)*

Mall Compan, The, Mansfield *Also called R M Davis Inc (G-12669)*

Malley's Chocolates, Lakewood *Also called Malleys Candies (G-11674)*

Malley's Chocolates, Cleveland *Also called Malleys Candies Inc (G-5736)*

Malleys Candies (PA) 216 362-8700
   1685 Victoria Ave Lakewood (44107) *(G-11674)*

Malleys Candies Inc 216 529-6262
   13400 Brookpark Rd Cleveland (44135) *(G-5736)*

Mallory Pattern Works Inc 419 726-8001
   5340 Enterprise Blvd Toledo (43612) *(G-18572)*

Malone Specialty Inc 440 255-4200
   8900 East Ave Mentor (44060) *(G-13645)*

Mama Mias Foods Inc 216 281-2188
   3270 W 67th Pl Cleveland (44102) *(G-5737)*

Mameco International Inc 216 752-4400
   4475 E 175th St Cleveland (44128) *(G-5738)*

Mammas Mandel 513 827-2457
   7952 Hedgewood Cir Mason (45040) *(G-13059)*

Mammotone, Cincinnati *Also called Devicor Medical Products Inc (G-3653)*

Mamsys Consulting Services 440 287-6824
   35865 Spatterdock Ln Solon (44139) *(G-17332)*

Manairco Inc 419 524-2121
   28 Industrial Pkwy Mansfield (44903) *(G-12640)*

Manchik Engineering & Co 740 927-4454
   7070 Avery Rd Dublin (43017) *(G-9101)*

Manco Inc 937 962-2661
   6531 State Route 503 N Lewisburg (45338) *(G-11937)*

Manco Manufacturing Co 419 925-4152
   2411 Rolfes Rd Maria Stein (45860) *(G-12759)*

Mancor Ohio Inc (HQ) 937 228-6141
   1008 Leonhard St Dayton (45404) *(G-8474)*

Mancor Ohio Inc 937 228-6141
   600 Kiser St Dayton (45404) *(G-8475)*

Mandi A Tripp 740 380-1216
   12691 Ovid Rd Rockbridge (43149) *(G-16689)*

Mane Inc (HQ) 513 248-9876
   2501 Henkle Dr Lebanon (45036) *(G-11815)*

Mane Inc 513 248-9876
   1093 Mane Way Lebanon (45036) *(G-11816)*

Mane Calafornia, Lebanon *Also called Mane Inc (G-11815)*

Manfacturing, Dayton *Also called Daisys Pillows LLC (G-8265)*

Manico Inc 440 946-5333
   37105 Code Ave Willoughby (44094) *(G-20534)*

Manifold & Phalor Inc 614 920-1200
   10385 Busey Rd Nw Canal Winchester (43110) *(G-2531)*

Manitowoc Company Inc 920 746-3332
   1847 Columbus Rd Cleveland (44113) *(G-5739)*

Manitwoc Ovens Advnced Cooking, Cleveland *Also called Cleveland Range LLC (G-5075)*

Mannings Packing Co 937 446-3278
   100 College Ave Sardinia (45171) *(G-17030)*

Manoranjan Shaffer & Heidkamp, Dayton *Also called Watson Haran & Company Inc (G-8747)*

Mansfield Asphalt Paving Inc 740 453-0721
   3570 S River Rd Zanesville (43701) *(G-21327)*

Mansfield Blanking Div, Valley City *Also called Shiloh Corporation (G-19231)*

Mansfield Brass & Alum Corp 419 492-2154
   636 S Center St New Washington (44854) *(G-14961)*

Mansfield Brick & Supply Co (PA) 419 526-1191
   320 N Diamond St Mansfield (44902) *(G-12641)*

Mansfield Castings, New Washington *Also called Mansfield Brass & Alum Corp (G-14961)*

Mansfield Fabricated Products, Mansfield *Also called The Mansfield Strl & Erct Co (G-12695)*

Mansfield Fabricated Products, Mansfield *Also called The Mansfield Strl & Erct Co (G-12696)*

Mansfield Graphics, Mansfield *Also called Five Handicap Inc (G-12603)*

Mansfield Imaging Center LLC 419 756-8899
   536 S Trimble Rd Ste A Mansfield (44906) *(G-12642)*

Mansfield Industries Inc 419 524-1300
   1776 Harrington Mem Rd Mansfield (44903) *(G-12643)*

Mansfield Journal Co 330 364-8641
   629 Wabash Ave Nw New Philadelphia (44663) *(G-14910)*

Mansfield Operations, Mansfield *Also called AK Steel Corporation (G-12557)*

Mansfield Paint Co Inc 330 725-2436
   525 W Liberty St Medina (44256) *(G-13439)*

Mansfield Plumbing Pdts LLC (HQ) 419 938-5211
   150 E 1st St Perrysville (44864) *(G-16173)*

Mansfield Plumbing Pdts LLC 330 496-2301
   13211 State Route 226 Big Prairie (44611) *(G-1682)*

Mansfield Screw Mch Pdts Co 419 884-1511
   145 Industrial Dr Mansfield (44904) *(G-12644)*

Mansfield Welding Services LLC 419 594-2738
   20027 State Route 613 Oakwood (45873) *(G-15617)*

MANSION HOMES, Bryan *Also called Manufactured Housing Entps Inc (G-2313)*

Mantaline Corporation 330 274-2264
   4754 E High St Mantua (44255) *(G-12715)*

Mantapart 330 549-2389
   1161 E Garfield Rd Unit 2 New Springfield (44443) *(G-14951)*

Mantey Vineyards, Sandusky *Also called Firelands Winery (G-16965)*

Mantra Haircare LLC 440 526-3304
   305 Ken Mar Indus Pkwy Broadview Heights (44147) *(G-2113)*

MANTUA BED FRAMES, Bedford *Also called Mantua Manufacturing Co (G-1440)*

Mantua Manufacturing Co (PA) 800 333-8333
   7900 Northfield Rd Bedford (44146) *(G-1440)*

Mantych Metalworking Inc 937 258-1373
   3175 Plainfield Rd Dayton (45432) *(G-8111)*

Manuel Tamargo 330 456-3080
   1004 Swartz Rd Akron (44319) *(G-282)*

Manufactured Housing Entps Inc 419 636-4511
   9302 Us Highway 6 Bryan (43506) *(G-2313)*

Manufacturers Equipment Co 513 424-3573
   35 Enterprise Dr Middletown (45044) *(G-14059)*

Manufacturers Representatives 513 467-6669
   7432 Heathcock Ct West Chester (45241) *(G-20024)*

Manufacturing Company LLC 414 708-7583
   3468 Cornell Pl Cincinnati (45220) *(G-4056)*

Manufacturing Concepts 330 784-9054
   409 Munroe Falls Rd Tallmadge (44278) *(G-18151)*

Manufacturing Division Inc 330 533-6835
   445 W Main St Canfield (44406) *(G-2564)*

Manufacturing Futures Inc (PA) 216 903-7993
   2767 Inverness Rd Shaker Heights (44122) *(G-17092)*

Manufctring Bus Dev Sltons LLC 419 294-1313
   6000 Fostoria Ave Findlay (45840) *(G-9853)*

Manufctring Sltons Brbrton Inc 330 745-4539
   374 5th St Nw Barberton (44203) *(G-1128)*

MAP SYSTEMS AND SOLUTIONS, Columbus *Also called Mapsys Inc (G-7316)*

Mapco, Mansfield *Also called Midwest Aircraft Products Co (G-12648)*

Mapes Concrete Construction 513 245-2631
   5691 Cheviot Rd Apt 3 Cincinnati (45247) *(G-4057)*

Maple City Rubber Company 419 668-8261
   55 Newton St Norwalk (44857) *(G-15551)*

Maple Creek Mining Inc (PA) 740 926-9205
   56854 Pleasant Ridge Rd Alledonia (43902) *(G-485)*

Maple Grove Companies, Tiffin *Also called M G Q Inc (G-18229)*

Maple Grove Materials, Tiffin *Also called M & B Asphalt Company Inc (G-18228)*

Maple Grove Materials Inc 419 992-4235
   1525 W City Rd Ste 42 Tiffin (44883) *(G-18231)*

Maple Hill Woodworking 330 674-2500
   2726 Trl 128 Millersburg (44654) *(G-14245)*

Maple Valley Sug Bush & Farms, Chardon *Also called Dnd Products Inc (G-3150)*

Mapledale Farm Inc 440 286-3389
   12613 Woodin Rd Chardon (44024) *(G-3166)*

Mapledale Landscaping, Chardon *Also called Mapledale Farm Inc (G-3166)*

Mapsys Inc (PA) 614 255-7258
   920 Michigan Ave Columbus (43215) *(G-7316)*

Mar Chele Inc (PA) 937 833-3400
   18 Market St Brookville (45309) *(G-2188)*

Mar Mor Inc 216 961-6900
   3591 W 56th St Cleveland (44102) *(G-5740)*

Mar Zane, Youngstown *Also called Shelly and Sands Inc (G-21201)*

Mar-Bal Inc (PA) 440 543-7526
   10095 Queens Way Chagrin Falls (44023) *(G-3101)*

Mar-Bal Inc 440 543-7526
   16930 Munn Rd Chagrin Falls (44023) *(G-3102)*

Mar-Bal Pultrusion Inc 440 953-0456
   38310 Apollo Pkwy Willoughby (44094) *(G-20535)*

Mar-Con Tool Company 937 299-2244
   2301 Arbor Blvd Moraine (45439) *(G-14504)*

Mar-Metal Mfg Inc 419 447-1102
   420 N Warpole St Upper Sandusky (43351) *(G-19131)*

Mar-Vel Tool Co Inc 937 223-2137
   858 Hall Ave Dayton (45404) *(G-8476)*

Mar-Zane Inc (HQ) 740 453-0721
   3570 S River Rd Zanesville (43701) *(G-21328)*

Mar-Zane Inc 740 782-1240
   38824 National Rd Bethesda (43719) *(G-1666)*

Mar-Zane Inc 740 685-5178
   59903 Vocational Rd Byesville (43723) *(G-2407)*

Mar-Zane Inc 330 626-2079
   9551 Elliman Rd Mantua (44255) *(G-12716)*

Mar-Zane Inc 419 529-2086
1300 W 4th St Ontario (44906) *(G-15689)*

Mar-Zane Materials, Zanesville *Also called Mar-Zane Inc (G-21328)*

Maramor Chocolates, Columbus *Also called Hake Head LLC (G-7138)*

Maranatha Industries Inc 419 263-2013
102 S Main St Payne (45880) *(G-16016)*

Marathon At Sawmill 614 734-0836
7200 Sawmill Rd Columbus (43235) *(G-7317)*

Marathon Industrial Cntrs Inc 440 324-2748
100 Freedom Ct Elyria (44035) *(G-9458)*

Marathon Manufacturing, New Philadelphia *Also called S S T Enterprises Inc (G-14927)*

Marathon Mfg & Sup Co 330 343-2656
5165 Main St Ne New Philadelphia (44663) *(G-14911)*

Marathon Oil Company 419 422-2121
539 S Main St Findlay (45840) *(G-9854)*

Marathon Petroleum Company LP 330 478-5000
2408 Gambrinus Rd Canton (44706) *(G-2767)*

Marathon Petroleum Company LP (HQ) 419 422-2121
539 S Main St Findlay (45840) *(G-9855)*

Marathon Petroleum Corporation (PA) 419 422-2121
539 S Main St Findlay (45840) *(G-9856)*

Marathon Petroleum Supply LLC 419 422-2121
539 S Main St Findlay (45840) *(G-9857)*

Marazita Graphics Inc 330 773-6462
1100 Triplett Blvd Akron (44306) *(G-283)*

Marbee Inc 419 422-9441
2703 N Main St Ste 1 Findlay (45840) *(G-9858)*

Marbee Printing & Graphic Art, Findlay *Also called Marbee Inc (G-9858)*

Marble Arch Products Inc 937 746-8388
263 Industrial Dr Franklin (45005) *(G-10034)*

Marble Cliff Block & Bldrs Sup, Lockbourne *Also called J P Sand & Gravel Company (G-12147)*

Marble Cliff Block & Bldrs Sup, Columbus *Also called Oberfields LLC (G-7409)*

Marble Cliff Limestone Inc 614 488-3030
2650 Old Dublin Rd Hilliard (43026) *(G-10959)*

Marble Works 216 496-7745
17827 Roseland Rd Cleveland (44112) *(G-5741)*

Marblelife of Central Ohio 614 837-6146
8440 Blacklick Eastern Rd Pickerington (43147) *(G-16197)*

Marc Industries Inc 440 944-9305
35140 Lakeland Blvd Willoughby (44095) *(G-20536)*

Marc V Concepts Inc 419 782-6505
401 Agnes St Defiance (43512) *(G-8801)*

Marchione Studio Inc 330 454-7408
1225 Minerva Ct Nw Canton (44703) *(G-2768)*

Marco Printed Products Co 937 433-7030
25 W Whipp Rd Dayton (45459) *(G-8477)*

Marco Printed Products Co Inc (PA) 937 433-5680
14 Marco Ln Dayton (45458) *(G-8478)*

Marco's Paper, Dayton *Also called Marco Printed Products Co Inc (G-8478)*

Marco's Papers, Dayton *Also called Marco Printed Products Co (G-8477)*

Marcum Crew Cut Inc 740 862-3400
6080 Fisher Rd Nw Baltimore (43105) *(G-1084)*

Marcum Development LLC 330 466-8231
2245 Flickinger Hill Rd Wooster (44691) *(G-20802)*

Marcum Machine Shop, Lodi *Also called Lowell Marcum (G-12165)*

Marcus Jewelers 513 474-4950
2022 8 Mile Rd Cincinnati (45244) *(G-4058)*

Marcus Uppe Inc 216 263-4000
815 Superior Ave E # 714 Cleveland (44114) *(G-5742)*

Marcy Industries Company LLC 740 387-1213
1836 Likens Rd Marion (43302) *(G-12881)*

Marengo Fabricated Steel Ltd (PA) 419 253-2119
1089 County Road 26 Marengo (43334) *(G-12752)*

Marfo Company (PA) 614 276-3352
799 N Hague Ave Columbus (43204) *(G-7318)*

Margaret Trentman 513 948-1700
5123 Montgomery Rd Cincinnati (45212) *(G-4059)*

Margo Tool Technology Inc 740 653-8115
2616 Setter Ct Nw Lancaster (43130) *(G-11727)*

Maric Drilling Company Inc 330 830-8178
2581 County Rd 160 Winesburg (44690) *(G-20705)*

Marich Machine & Tool Co Inc 216 391-5502
3815 Lakeside Ave E Cleveland (44114) *(G-5743)*

Marie's Candies, West Liberty *Also called Marrie S Candies LLC (G-20094)*

Marietta Coal Co (PA) 740 695-2197
67705 Friends Church Rd Saint Clairsville (43950) *(G-16795)*

Marietta Eramet Inc 740 374-1000
16705 State Route 7 Marietta (45750) *(G-12802)*

Marietta Martin Materials Inc 937 335-8313
250 Dye Mill Rd Troy (45373) *(G-18856)*

Marietta Martin Materials Inc 919 781-4550
9843 Dyton Grenville Pike Brookville (45309) *(G-2189)*

Marietta Martin Materials Inc 937 766-2351
3744 Turnbull Rd Cedarville (45314) *(G-2981)*

Marietta Martin Materials Inc 937 884-5814
9843 State Route 49 Brookville (45309) *(G-2190)*

Marietta Mobility, Marietta *Also called Steves Vans & Accessories LLC (G-12836)*

Marietta Resources Corporation 740 373-6305
704 Pike St Marietta (45750) *(G-12803)*

Marik Spring Inc 330 564-0617
121 Northeast Ave Tallmadge (44278) *(G-18152)*

Marine Development, Cincinnati *Also called Machine Development Corp (G-4044)*

Marine Jet Power Inc 614 759-9000
6740 Commerce Court Dr Blacklick (43004) *(G-1701)*

Marinemax Inc 918 782-3277
1991 Ne Catawba Rd Port Clinton (43452) *(G-16405)*

Mariner's Landing Marina, Cincinnati *Also called Mariners Landing Inc (G-4060)*

Mariners Landing Inc 513 941-3625
7405 Forbes Rd Cincinnati (45233) *(G-4060)*

Marino Maintenance Co, Canton *Also called Phase II Enterprises Inc (G-2812)*

Marion Caldwell 740 446-1042
1262 Lincoln Pike Rear Gallipolis (45631) *(G-10304)*

Marion Ethanol LLC 740 383-4400
1660 Hillman Ford Rd Marion (43302) *(G-12882)*

Marion Industries Inc 740 223-0075
999 Kellogg Pkwy Marion (43302) *(G-12883)*

Marion Star, Marion *Also called Gannett Co Inc (G-12866)*

Marios Drive Thru 330 452-8793
914 12th St Ne Canton (44704) *(G-2769)*

Mariotti Printing Co LLC 440 245-4120
513 E 28th St Lorain (44055) *(G-12259)*

Mark Advertising Agency Inc 419 626-9000
1600 5th St Sandusky (44870) *(G-16985)*

Mark Carpenter Industries Inc 419 294-4568
2300 Napoleon Rd Fremont (43420) *(G-10169)*

Mark Cottle 937 787-4791
11 Kastrup Dr Eaton (45320) *(G-9317)*

Mark Daily 937 369-5358
807 N Maple St Eaton (45320) *(G-9318)*

Mark Dental Laboratory 216 464-6424
24300 Chagrin Blvd # 310 Cleveland (44122) *(G-5744)*

Mark J Myers (PA) 513 753-7300
80 W Main St Amelia (45102) *(G-579)*

Mark Matthews Glass, Archbold *Also called Matthews Art Glass (G-686)*

Mark Nelson 740 282-5334
980 Lincoln Ave Steubenville (43952) *(G-17704)*

Mark One Manufacturing Ltd 419 628-4405
351 Industrial Dr Ste 9 Minster (45865) *(G-14358)*

Mark Rasche 614 882-1810
6962 Harlem Rd Westerville (43082) *(G-20170)*

Mark Rite Co 330 757-7229
206 Evergreen Dr Youngstown (44514) *(G-21141)*

Mark True Engraving Co 216 651-7700
1250 W 76th St Cleveland (44102) *(G-5745)*

Mark True Engraving Company 216 252-7422
3264 W 105th St Cleveland (44111) *(G-5746)*

Mark West Energy, Cadiz *Also called Markwest Energy Partners LP (G-2419)*

Mark-All Enterprises LLC 800 433-3615
888 W Waterloo Rd Akron (44314) *(G-284)*

Mark-N-Mend Inc 440 951-2003
38151 Airport Pkwy Ste 54 Willoughby (44094) *(G-20537)*

Markers Inc 440 933-5927
33490 Pin Oak Pkwy Avon Lake (44012) *(G-1039)*

Markes International Inc 513 745-0241
11126 Kenwood Rd Ste D Blue Ash (45242) *(G-1832)*

Market Direct, Inc., Cincinnati *Also called Jscs Group Inc (G-3961)*

Market Media Creations, Coshocton *Also called Sprint Print Inc (G-7910)*

Market Ready 513 289-9231
1129 Avalon Dr Maineville (45039) *(G-12528)*

Market-Master, New Richmond *Also called Master Disposers Inc (G-14942)*

Markethatch Co Inc 330 376-6363
91 E Voris St Akron (44311) *(G-285)*

Marketing Comm Resource Inc 440 484-3010
4800 E 345th St Willoughby (44094) *(G-20538)*

Marketing Directions Inc 440 835-5550
28005 Clemens Rd Cleveland (44145) *(G-5747)*

Marketing Essentials LLC 419 629-0080
18 N Washington St New Bremen (45869) *(G-14789)*

Markeys Audio/Visual Inc 419 244-8844
24 S Saint Clair St Toledo (43604) *(G-18573)*

Markham Machine Company Inc 330 762-7676
160 N Union St Akron (44304) *(G-286)*

Marking Devices Inc 216 861-4498
3110 Payne Ave Cleveland (44114) *(G-5748)*

Markko Vineyard 440 593-3197
4500 S Ridge Rd W Conneaut (44030) *(G-7815)*

Markley Enterprises LLC 513 771-1290
1705 Magnolia Dr Cincinnati (45215) *(G-4061)*

Marks Brew Thru 330 699-1755
2455 Canton Rd Akron (44312) *(G-287)*

Markwest Energy Partners LP 740 942-0463
78405 Cadiz New Athens Rd Cadiz (43907) *(G-2419)*

Markwest Utica Emg LLC 740 942-4810
46700 Giacobbi Rd Jewett (43986) *(G-11386)*

Markwith Tool Company Inc 937 548-6808
5261 S State Route 49 Greenville (45331) *(G-10510)*

(G-0000) Company's Geographic Section entry number

Marky Welding, North Bend *Also called Steel Services Inc* ***(G-15208)***
Marlboro Manufacturing Inc 330 935-2221
11750 Marlboro Ave Ne Alliance (44601) ***(G-526)***
Marlen Manufacturing & Dev Co (PA) 216 292-7060
5150 Richmond Rd Bedford (44146) ***(G-1441)***
Marlen Manufacturing & Dev Co 216 292-7546
5156 Richmond Rd Bedford (44146) ***(G-1442)***
Marles Business Systems Inc 440 268-8380
1277 E Schaaf Rd Brooklyn Heights (44131) ***(G-2142)***
Marles Printing Company, Brooklyn Heights *Also called Marles Business Systems Inc* ***(G-2142)***
Marlin Manufacturing Corp (PA) 216 676-1340
12800 Corporate Dr Cleveland (44130) ***(G-5749)***
Marlin Thermocouple Wire Inc 440 835-1950
12800 Corporate Dr Cleveland (44130) ***(G-5750)***
Marlite Inc 330 343-6621
609 S Tuscarawas Ave Dover (44622) ***(G-8998)***
Marlite Inc (HQ) 330 343-6621
1 Marlite Dr Dover (44622) ***(G-8999)***
Marlow-2000 Inc 216 362-8500
13811 Enterprise Ave Cleveland (44135) ***(G-5751)***
Marmac Co 937 372-8093
1231 Bellbrook Ave Xenia (45385) ***(G-20963)***
Marmax Machine Co 937 698-9900
2425 S State Route 48 Ludlow Falls (45339) ***(G-12427)***
Marmon Highway Tech LLC 330 878-5595
6332 Columbia Rd Nw Dover (44622) ***(G-9000)***
Marpro, Cincinnati *Also called Cincinnati Premier Candy LLC* ***(G-3571)***
Marrie S Candies LLC 937 465-3061
311 Zanesfield Rd West Liberty (43357) ***(G-20094)***
Marrik Dish Company LLC 419 475-6538
4102 Monroe St Toledo (43606) ***(G-18574)***
Marrow County Sentinel, Mount Gilead *Also called Hirt Publishing Co Inc* ***(G-14562)***
Marrow County Sentinel 419 946-3010
245 Neal Ave Ste A Mount Gilead (43338) ***(G-14564)***
Mars Petcare Us Inc 614 878-7242
5115 Fisher Rd Columbus (43228) ***(G-7319)***
Marsam Metalfab Inc 330 405-1520
1870 Enterprise Pkwy Twinsburg (44087) ***(G-18978)***
Marsch Machine Products 440 298-3932
16107 Moseley Rd Madison (44057) ***(G-12510)***
Marsh Industries Inc 330 308-8667
1117 Bowers Ave Nw New Philadelphia (44663) ***(G-14912)***
Marsh Technologies Inc 330 545-0085
30 W Main St Ste A Girard (44420) ***(G-10391)***
Marsh Valley Forest Pdts Ltd 440 632-1889
14141 Old State Rd Middlefield (44062) ***(G-13953)***
Marshall Plastics Inc 937 653-4740
590 S Edgewood Ave Urbana (43078) ***(G-19169)***
Marshalls Thrifty Print Inc 513 984-5513
7244 Ohio Ave Cincinnati (45236) ***(G-4062)***
Marshalltown Packaging Inc 641 753-5272
601 N Hague Ave Columbus (43204) ***(G-7320)***
Marshallville Packing Co Inc 330 855-2871
50 E Market St Marshallville (44645) ***(G-12918)***
Marshas Buckeyes LLC 419 872-7666
25631 Fort Meigs Rd Ste E Perrysburg (43551) ***(G-16120)***
Mart Plus Fuel 216 261-0420
21820 Lake Shore Blvd Euclid (44123) ***(G-9591)***
Martans Foods 330 483-9009
6460 Grafton Rd Valley City (44280) ***(G-19215)***
Martin & Marianne Tools Inc 440 255-5107
9335 Kathleen Dr Mentor (44060) ***(G-13646)***
Martin Bauder Woodworking LLC 513 735-0659
1498 Binning Rd Milford (45150) ***(G-14160)***
Martin Block Company 740 286-7507
290 Twin Oaks Dr Jackson (45640) ***(G-11319)***
Martin Cab Div, Cleveland *Also called Martin Sheet Metal Inc* ***(G-5753)***
Martin Diesel Inc 419 782-9911
27809 County Road 424 Defiance (43512) ***(G-8802)***
Martin Industrial Truck, Cleveland *Also called Marlow-2000 Inc* ***(G-5751)***
Martin Industries Inc 419 862-2694
473 Maple St Elmore (43416) ***(G-9364)***
Martin M Hardin 740 282-1234
411 N 7th St Steubenville (43952) ***(G-17705)***
Martin Machine & Tool Inc 419 373-1711
435 W Woodland Cir Bowling Green (43402) ***(G-2000)***
Martin Machine Co Inc 440 946-5174
37151 Ben Hur Ave Ste D Willoughby (44094) ***(G-20539)***
Martin Marietta Aggragate, West Chester *Also called Martin Marietta Materials Inc* ***(G-19897)***
Martin Marietta Aggregates, Harrison *Also called Martin Marietta Materials Inc* ***(G-10789)***
Martin Marietta Aggregates, Cedarville *Also called Marietta Martin Materials Inc* ***(G-2981)***
Martin Marietta Aggregates, Brookville *Also called Marietta Martin Materials Inc* ***(G-2190)***
Martin Marietta Materials Inc 513 701-1120
4900 Parkway Dr Mason (45040) ***(G-13060)***
Martin Marietta Materials Inc 513 353-1400
10905 Us 50 North Bend (45052) ***(G-15206)***
Martin Marietta Materials Inc 513 200-2303
170 Pilot Rd Harrison (45030) ***(G-10789)***
Martin Marietta Materials Inc 513 701-1140
9277 Centre Pointe Dr # 250 West Chester (45069) ***(G-19897)***
Martin Marietta Materials Inc 937 766-2351
3744 Turnbull Rd Cedarville (45314) ***(G-2982)***
Martin Marietta Materials Inc 513 871-7152
4439 Kellogg Ave Cincinnati (45226) ***(G-4063)***
Martin Pallet Inc 330 832-5309
1414 Industrial Ave Sw Massillon (44647) ***(G-13172)***
Martin Paper Products Inc 740 756-9271
5907 Clmbus Lncster Rd Nw Carroll (43112) ***(G-2944)***
Martin Printing Co 419 224-9176
400 N Main St Lima (45801) ***(G-12051)***
Martin Pultrusion Group Inc 440 439-9130
20801 Miles Rd Ste B Cleveland (44128) ***(G-5752)***
Martin Rubber Company 330 336-6604
5020 Panther Pkwy Seville (44273) ***(G-17078)***
Martin Sheet Metal Inc 216 377-8200
7108 Madison Ave Cleveland (44102) ***(G-5753)***
Martin Sprocket & Gear Inc 419 485-5515
350 S Airport Rd Montpelier (43543) ***(G-14448)***
Martin Welding LLC (PA) 937 687-3602
1472 W Main St New Lebanon (45345) ***(G-14843)***
Martin Wheel Co Inc 330 633-3278
342 West Ave Tallmadge (44278) ***(G-18153)***
Martin-Brower Company LLC 513 773-2301
4260 Port Union Rd West Chester (45011) ***(G-19898)***
Martin-Palmer Tl & Die Co Div, Dayton *Also called Krdc Inc* ***(G-8446)***
Martina Metal LLC 614 291-9700
1575 Shawnee Ave Columbus (43211) ***(G-7321)***
Martindale Electric Company 216 521-8567
1375 Hird Ave Cleveland (44107) ***(G-5754)***
Martinez Food Products LLC 419 720-6973
1220 Belmont Ave Toledo (43607) ***(G-18575)***
Martini Skate & Snow 216 371-0155
2122 S Taylor Rd Cleveland Heights (44118) ***(G-6500)***
Martinov Home Solutions LLC 330 926-3059
704 Mentor Rd Akron (44303) ***(G-288)***
Martys Print Shop 740 373-3454
307 3rd St Marietta (45750) ***(G-12804)***
Martz Mold & Machine Inc 330 928-2159
1365 Munroe Falls Ave Cuyahoga Falls (44221) ***(G-8024)***
Martz Well Service 330 323-7417
5101 Rocky Rill Ave Ne Canton (44705) ***(G-2770)***
Marula Publishing LLC 513 549-5218
6539 Harrison Ave Ste 154 Cincinnati (45247) ***(G-4064)***
Marvin Mix 614 774-9337
3113 Kentwood Pl Columbus (43227) ***(G-7322)***
Marwil, Fort Loramie *Also called Rol - Tech Inc* ***(G-9936)***
Marwin Ball Valves Div, Cincinnati *Also called Richards Industries Inc* ***(G-4344)***
Marxware Computing Services 216 661-5263
4963 Schaaf Ln Cleveland (44131) ***(G-5755)***
Mary James Inc 419 599-2941
1025 Clairmont Ave Napoleon (43545) ***(G-14689)***
Marysville Auto Plant, Marysville *Also called Honda of America Mfg Inc* ***(G-12950)***
Marysville Newspaper Inc 740 943-2214
26 S Franklin St Richwood (43344) ***(G-16660)***
Marysville Newspaper Inc (PA) 937 644-9111
207 N Main St Marysville (43040) ***(G-12957)***
Marysville Printing Company 937 644-4959
127 S Main St Marysville (43040) ***(G-12958)***
Marysville Steel Inc 937 642-5971
323 E 8th St Marysville (43040) ***(G-12959)***
Marz Direct, Monroe *Also called R & L Software LLC* ***(G-14412)***
Marzetti Distribution Center, Grove City *Also called Tmarzetti Company* ***(G-10602)***
Masco Cabinetry LLC 740 286-5033
960 E Main St Jackson (45640) ***(G-11320)***
Masco Cabinetry LLC 440 632-2547
15535 S State Ave Middlefield (44062) ***(G-13954)***
Masco Cbinetry Middlefield LLC (HQ) 440 632-5333
15535 S State Ave Middlefield (44062) ***(G-13955)***
Masco Cbinetry Middlefield LLC 440 632-5058
16052 Industrial Pkwy Middlefield (44062) ***(G-13956)***
Masco Cbinetry Middlefield LLC 440 437-8537
150 Grand Valley Ave Orwell (44076) ***(G-15778)***
Mascot Shop, The, Akron *Also called Kent Stow Screen Printing Inc* ***(G-255)***
Masheen Specialties 330 652-7535
3519 Union St Mineral Ridge (44440) ***(G-14308)***
Mason Company LLC 937 780-2321
260 Depot Ln Leesburg (45135) ***(G-11855)***
Mason Producing Inc 740 913-0686
10010 Center Village Rd Galena (43021) ***(G-10247)***
Mason Steel, Walton Hills *Also called Mason Structural Steel Inc* ***(G-19474)***
Mason Structural Steel Inc 440 439-1040
7500 Northfield Rd Walton Hills (44146) ***(G-19474)***
Mason's Century Signs, Bowling Green *Also called Century Signs* ***(G-1979)***
Masonite Corporation 937 454-9207
3250 Old Springfield Rd # 1 Vandalia (45377) ***(G-19303)***
Masonite International Corp 937 454-9308
875 Center Dr Vandalia (45377) ***(G-19304)***

ALPHABETIC

(PA)=Parent Co (HQ)=Headquarters (DH)=Div Headquarters

Masons Sand and Gravel Co 614 491-3611
2385 Rathmell Rd Obetz (43207) *(G-15655)*

Mass-Marketing Inc 513 860-6200
7209 Dixie Hwy Fairfield (45014) *(G-9679)*

Massageblocks.com, Powell *Also called Summit Online Products LLC* *(G-16485)*

Massie Publishing LLC 740 446-4543
460 2nd Ave Gallipolis (45631) *(G-10305)*

Massillon Asphalt Co 330 833-6330
1833 Riverside Dr Nw Massillon (44647) *(G-13173)*

Massillon Machine & Die, Massillon *Also called Hendricks Vacuum Forming Inc* *(G-13148)*

Massillon Materials Inc (PA) 330 837-4767
26 N Cochran St Dalton (44618) *(G-8074)*

Massillon Metaphysics 330 837-1653
912 Amherst Rd Ne Massillon (44646) *(G-13174)*

Massillon Plaque Company 330 494-4199
5757 Mayfair Rd Canton (44720) *(G-2771)*

Massillon Washed Gravel Co, Navarre *Also called Central Allied Enterprises Inc* *(G-14711)*

Massillon-Cleveland-Akron Sign (PA) 330 833-3165
681 1st St Sw Massillon (44646) *(G-13175)*

Mast Farm Service Ltd 330 893-2972
3585 State Rte 39 Walnut Creek (44687) *(G-19470)*

Master Bolt & Mfg Inc 440 323-5529
811 Taylor St Elyria (44035) *(G-9459)*

Master Carbide Tools Company 440 352-1112
9423 Mercantile Dr Mentor (44060) *(G-13647)*

Master Caster Company, Cleveland *Also called Master Mfg Co Inc* *(G-5758)*

Master Chemical Corporation (PA) 419 874-7902
501 W Boundary St Perrysburg (43551) *(G-16121)*

Master Chrome Service Inc 216 961-2012
5709 Herman Ave Cleveland (44102) *(G-5756)*

Master Communications Inc 208 821-3473
4480 Lake Forest Dr # 302 Blue Ash (45242) *(G-1833)*

Master Craft Products Inc 216 281-5910
10621 Briggs Rd Cleveland (44111) *(G-5757)*

Master Disposers Inc 513 553-2289
2128 Idlett Hill Rd New Richmond (45157) *(G-14942)*

Master Draw Lubricants, Chagrin Falls *Also called Etna Products Incorporated* *(G-3087)*

Master Fluid Solutions, Perrysburg *Also called Master Chemical Corporation* *(G-16121)*

Master Grinding Company Inc 440 944-3680
28917 Anderson Rd Wickliffe (44092) *(G-20371)*

Master Label Company Inc 419 625-8095
1048 Cleveland Rd Sandusky (44870) *(G-16986)*

Master Magnetics Inc 740 373-0909
108 Industry Rd Marietta (45750) *(G-12805)*

Master Marking Company Inc 330 688-6797
4830 Hudson Dr Stow (44224) *(G-17772)*

Master Mfg Co Inc 216 641-0500
9200 Inman Ave Cleveland (44105) *(G-5758)*

Master Print Center, Cincinnati *Also called Gerald L Hermann Co Inc* *(G-3822)*

Master Printing Company 216 351-2246
3112 Broadview Rd Cleveland (44109) *(G-5759)*

Master Products Company 216 341-1740
6400 Park Ave Cleveland (44105) *(G-5760)*

Master Street Engineering, Warren *Also called Scott Emerson* *(G-19599)*

Master Swaging Inc 937 596-6171
210 Washington St Jackson Center (45334) *(G-11343)*

Master Tool Div, Grand River *Also called Sumitomo Elc Carbide Mfg Inc* *(G-10453)*

Master Vac Incorporated 419 335-7796
741 Parkview St Wauseon (43567) *(G-19689)*

Master-Halco Inc 513 869-7600
620 Commerce Center Dr Fairfield (45011) *(G-9680)*

Mastercraft Mfg Inc 330 893-3366
6960 Dutch Country Ln Berlin (44610) *(G-1651)*

Masterfoods USA, Columbus *Also called Mars Petcare Us Inc* *(G-7319)*

Masterpiece Publisher L P 513 948-1000
8046 Debonair Ct Cincinnati (45237) *(G-4065)*

Masters Group Inc 440 893-1900
7160 Chagrin Rd Ste 160 Chagrin Falls (44023) *(G-3103)*

Masters Prcision Machining Inc 330 419-1933
4465 Crystal Pkwy Kent (44240) *(G-11487)*

Mastertech Diamond Products Co, Mentor *Also called Master Carbide Tools Company (G-13647)*

Mastic Home Exteriors Inc 937 497-7008
2405 Campbell Rd Sidney (45365) *(G-17199)*

Mastropietro Winery Inc 330 547-2151
14558 Ellsworth Rd Berlin Center (44401) *(G-1656)*

Mataco 440 546-8355
2861 E Royalton Rd Broadview Heights (44147) *(G-2114)*

Matalco (us) Inc 234 806-0600
5120 Tod Ave Sw Warren (44481) *(G-19578)*

Matalco (us) Inc 330 452-4760
4420 Louisville St Ne Canton (44705) *(G-2772)*

Matandy Steel & Metal Pdts LLC 513 844-2277
1200 Central Ave Hamilton (45011) *(G-10723)*

Matandy Steel Sales, Hamilton *Also called Matandy Steel & Metal Pdts LLC* *(G-10723)*

Match Mold & Machine Inc 330 830-5503
1100 Nova Dr Se Massillon (44646) *(G-13176)*

Matco Tools Corporation 1 (HQ) 330 929-4949
4403 Allen Rd Stow (44224) *(G-17773)*

Matdan Corporation 513 794-0500
10855 Millington Ct Blue Ash (45242) *(G-1834)*

Materials Engineering & Dev 937 884-5118
11150 Bltmr Phllpsburg Rd Brookville (45309) *(G-2191)*

Materials Science Intl Inc 614 870-0400
1660 Georgesville Rd Columbus (43228) *(G-7323)*

Materion Brush Inc (HQ) 216 486-4200
6070 Parkland Blvd Ste 1 Mayfield Heights (44124) *(G-13317)*

Materion Brush Inc 419 862-2745
14710 W Prtage River S Rd Elmore (43416) *(G-9365)*

Materion Brush Inc 440 960-5660
7375 Industrial Pkwy Lorain (44053) *(G-12260)*

Materion Corporation (PA) 216 486-4200
6070 Parkland Blvd Ste 1 Mayfield Heights (44124) *(G-13318)*

Materion Technical Mtls Inc 216 486-4200
6070 Parkland Blvd Cleveland (44124) *(G-5761)*

Mathematical Business Systems 440 237-2345
1261 Valley Park Dr Broadview Heights (44147) *(G-2115)*

Matheson Gas Products, Twinsburg *Also called Matheson Tri-Gas Inc* *(G-18979)*

Matheson Tri-Gas Inc 513 727-9638
1801 Crawford St Middletown (45044) *(G-14060)*

Matheson Tri-Gas Inc 330 425-4407
1650 Enterprise Pkwy Twinsburg (44087) *(G-18979)*

Matheson Tri-Gas Inc 419 865-8881
1720 Trade Rd Holland (43528) *(G-11071)*

Matheson Tri-Gas Inc 440 365-1741
1650 Enterprise Pkwy Twinsburg (44087) *(G-18980)*

Mathew Odonnell 440 969-4054
6645 2nd Ave Andover (44003) *(G-618)*

Mathews Printing Company 614 444-1010
1250 S Front St Columbus (43206) *(G-7324)*

Matlock Electric Co Inc (PA) 513 731-9600
2780 Highland Ave Cincinnati (45212) *(G-4066)*

Matly Digital Solutions LLC 513 860-3435
6625 Dixie Hwy Ste E Fairfield (45014) *(G-9681)*

Matplus Ltd 440 352-7201
76 Burton St Painesville (44077) *(G-15900)*

Matrix Cable and Mould 513 832-2577
11785 Highway Dr Ste 900 Cincinnati (45241) *(G-4067)*

Matrix Management Solutions 330 470-3700
5200 Stoneham Rd Canton (44720) *(G-2773)*

Matrix Measuring System 330 718-2804
3877 Hallock Sook Rd Newton Falls (44444) *(G-15136)*

Matrix Plastics Co Inc 330 666-7730
171 Granger Rd Unit 156 Medina (44256) *(G-13440)*

Matrix Research Inc (PA) 937 427-8433
1300 Research Park Dr Beavercreek (45432) *(G-1350)*

Matrix Research & Engineering, Beavercreek *Also called Matrix Research Inc* *(G-1350)*

Matrix Sys Auto Finishes LLC 248 668-8135
600 Nova Dr Se Massillon (44646) *(G-13177)*

Matrix Tool & Machine Inc 440 255-0300
7870 Division Dr Mentor (44060) *(G-13648)*

Matsu Ohio Inc 419 298-2394
228 E Morrison St Edgerton (43517) *(G-9332)*

Matteo Aluminum Inc 440 585-5213
1261 E 289th St Wickliffe (44092) *(G-20372)*

Matterworks 740 200-0071
2135 James Pkwy Heath (43056) *(G-10850)*

Matthew Bender & Company Inc 518 487-3000
9443 Springboro Pike Miamisburg (45342) *(G-13827)*

Matthew Koster 440 887-9000
720 Marks Rd Ste C Valley City (44280) *(G-19216)*

Matthew R Copp (PA) 614 276-8959
2291 Scioto Harper Dr Columbus (43204) *(G-7325)*

Matthew Warren Inc 614 418-0250
2000 Jetway Blvd Columbus (43219) *(G-7326)*

Matthews Art Glass 419 335-2448
22611 State Route 2 Archbold (43502) *(G-686)*

Mattress Mart, Plain City *Also called Quilting Inc* *(G-16356)*

Mattress Mart, Plain City *Also called Midwest Quality Bedding Inc* *(G-16350)*

Mature Living News Magazine 419 241-8880
3601 W Alexis Rd Ste 112 Toledo (43623) *(G-18576)*

Matvest Inc 614 487-8720
1380 Dublin Rd Ste 200 Columbus (43215) *(G-7327)*

Maull Tool & Die Supply Llc 513 646-4229
216 Timber Trl Loveland (45140) *(G-12373)*

Maumee Assembly & Stamping LLC 419 304-2887
920 Illinois Ave Maumee (43537) *(G-13278)*

Maumee Bay Brewing Company 419 243-1253
27 Broadway St Ste A Toledo (43604) *(G-18577)*

Maumee Bay Kitchen & Bath Cent 419 882-4390
5758 Main St Ste 1 Sylvania (43560) *(G-18117)*

Maumee Bay Kitchen & Bath Ctr, Sylvania *Also called Maumee Bay Kitchen & Bath Cent* *(G-18117)*

Maumee Hose & Belting Co, Maumee *Also called Maumee Hose & Fitting Inc* *(G-13279)*

Maumee Hose & Fitting Inc 419 893-7252
720 Illinois Ave Ste H Maumee (43537) *(G-13279)*

Maumee Machine & Tool Corp 419 385-2501
2960 South Ave Toledo (43609) *(G-18578)*
Maumee Pattern Company Inc 419 693-4968
1019 Hazelwood St Toledo (43605) *(G-18579)*
Maumee Quick Print Inc 419 893-4321
219 Conant St Maumee (43537) *(G-13280)*
Maumee Valley Fabricators Inc 419 476-1411
4801 Bennett Rd Toledo (43612) *(G-18580)*
Maumee Valley Memorials Inc (HQ) 419 878-9030
111 Anthony Wayne Trl Waterville (43566) *(G-19663)*
Mauser Usa LLC 614 856-5982
1410 Blatt Blvd Gahanna (43230) *(G-10217)*
Mauser Usa LLC 513 398-1300
1229 Castle Dr Mason (45040) *(G-13061)*
Mauser USA LLC 614 856-5982
1410 Blatt Blvd Columbus (43230) *(G-7328)*
Maval Industries LLC 330 405-1600
1555 Enterprise Pkwy Twinsburg (44087) *(G-18981)*
Maval Manufacturing, Twinsburg *Also called Maval Industries LLC (G-18981)*
Maverick Chocolate Company 513 381-0561
129 W Elder St Cincinnati (45202) *(G-4068)*
Maverick Corp Partners LLC (PA) 330 669-2631
301 W Prospect St Smithville (44677) *(G-17241)*
Maverick Corporation 513 469-9919
11379 Grooms Rd Blue Ash (45242) *(G-1835)*
Maverick Industries Inc 440 838-5335
5945 W Snowville Rd Brecksville (44141) *(G-2064)*
Maverick Innvtive Slutions LLC (PA) 419 281-7944
532 County Road 1600 Ashland (44805) *(G-751)*
Maverick Innvtive Slutions LLC 419 281-7944
532 County Road 1600 Ashland (44805) *(G-752)*
Maverick Molding Co 513 469-9919
11379 Grooms Rd Blue Ash (45242) *(G-1836)*
Mavericks Stainless, Mansfield *Also called Mk Metal Products Inc (G-12650)*
Max Daetwyler Corp 937 428-1781
2133 Lyons Rd Miamisburg (45342) *(G-13828)*
Max Mighty Inc 937 862-9530
2434 Darnell Dr Spring Valley (45370) *(G-17468)*
Max Pro Tools Inc 440 885-9522
8999 W Pleasant Valley Rd Cleveland (44130) *(G-5762)*
Maximum Graphix Inc 440 353-3301
33426 Liberty Pkwy North Ridgeville (44039) *(G-15390)*
Maxion Wheels Akron LLC (HQ) 330 794-2310
428 Seiberling St Akron (44306) *(G-289)*
Maxion Wheels Sedalia LLC 330 794-2300
428 Seiberling St Akron (44306) *(G-290)*
Maxon Corporation 216 459-6056
950 Keynote Cir Ste 113 Independence (44131) *(G-11267)*
Maxtool Company Limited 937 415-5776
2946 Production Ct Dayton (45414) *(G-8479)*
May Conveyor Inc 440 237-8012
9981 York Theta Dr North Royalton (44133) *(G-15435)*
May Lin Silicone Products Inc 330 825-9019
955 Wooster Rd W Barberton (44203) *(G-1129)*
May Thread Grinding Co 440 953-0678
38401 Apollo Pkwy Ste F Willoughby (44094) *(G-20540)*
Mayco Colors, Hilliard *Also called Coloramics LLC (G-10942)*
Mayfair Granite Co Inc 216 382-8150
4202 Mayfield Rd Cleveland (44121) *(G-5763)*
Mayfair Memorial, Cleveland *Also called Mayfair Granite Co Inc (G-5763)*
Mayfran International Inc (HQ) 440 461-4100
6650 Beta Dr Cleveland (44143) *(G-5764)*
Maynard Company, The, Cleveland *Also called Bud May Inc (G-4945)*
Mayo, R A Industries, East Palestine *Also called Robert Mayo Industries (G-9244)*
Maysville Harness Shop Ltd 330 695-9977
8572 Mount Hope Rd Apple Creek (44606) *(G-644)*
Maysville Ready Mix Concr 937 795-2020
8030 Rte 52 Us Aberdeen (45101) *(G-2)*
Mazzella Crane & Hoist Svcs, Cincinnati *Also called Mazzella Lifting Tech Inc (G-4069)*
Mazzella Lifting Tech Inc (HQ) 440 239-7000
21000 Aerospace Pkwy Cleveland (44142) *(G-5765)*
Mazzella Lifting Tech Inc 440 239-5700
21000 Aerospace Pkwy Cleveland (44142) *(G-5766)*
Mazzella Lifting Tech Inc 513 772-4466
10605 Chester Rd Cincinnati (45215) *(G-4069)*
Mazzolini Artcraft Co Inc 216 431-7529
1607 E 41st St Cleveland (44103) *(G-5767)*
Mazzone Bakery, Cleveland *Also called M Mazzone & Sons Bakery Inc (G-5718)*
MB Dynamics Inc 216 292-5850
25865 Richmond Rd Cleveland (44146) *(G-5768)*
MB Manufacturing Corp 513 682-1461
2904 Symmes Rd Fairfield (45014) *(G-9682)*
Mbenztech 937 291-1527
5528 Liberty Bell Cir Centerville (45459) *(G-3044)*
Mbm Industries Ltd 937 522-0719
801 Space Dr Beavercreek Township (45434) *(G-1385)*
Mbm Lumber 937 459-7448
1588 Cox Rd Union City (45390) *(G-19072)*
Mbs Acquisition, Mason *Also called Remtec Engineering (G-13082)*
Mc Alarney Pool Spas and Billd 740 373-6698
908 Pike St Marietta (45750) *(G-12806)*
Mc Brown Industries Inc 419 963-2800
10534 Township Road 128 Findlay (45840) *(G-9859)*
Mc Cartney Industries, Mentor *Also called Semper Quality Industry Inc (G-13719)*
Mc Concepts Llc 330 933-6402
2459 55th St Ne Canton (44721) *(G-2774)*
Mc Connells Market 740 765-4300
2189 State Route 43 Richmond (43944) *(G-16647)*
Mc Cully Supply & Sales Inc 330 497-2211
5559 Fulton Dr Nw Ste A Canton (44718) *(G-2775)*
Mc Elwain Industries Inc 419 532-3126
17941 Road L Ottawa (45875) *(G-15800)*
Mc Graphix Div of Th Newfax, Toledo *Also called Newfax Corporation (G-18604)*
Mc Graw-Hill Educational Pubg, Ashland *Also called McGraw-Hill School Education H (G-753)*
Mc Gregor & Associates Inc 937 833-6768
365 Carr Dr Brookville (45309) *(G-2192)*
Mc Happy's Bake Shoppe, Belpre *Also called Wal-Bon of Ohio Inc (G-1596)*
Mc Happys Donuts, Athens *Also called McHappys Donuts of Parkersburg (G-875)*
Mc Industries, Fremont *Also called Mark Carpenter Industries Inc (G-10169)*
Mc Kay's Food Seasoning, Toledo *Also called Dismat Corporation (G-18439)*
Mc Kinley Machinery Inc 440 937-6300
1265 Lear Industrial Pkwy Avon (44011) *(G-1000)*
Mc Products, Wooster *Also called E S H Inc (G-20768)*
Mc Sign Company (PA) 440 209-6200
8959 Tyler Blvd Mentor (44060) *(G-13649)*
Mc Vay Ventures Inc 614 890-1516
40 W College Ave Westerville (43081) *(G-20223)*
MCA Industries, Massillon *Also called Massillon-Cleveland-Akron Sign (G-13175)*
McAfee Tool & Die Inc 330 896-9555
1717 Boettler Rd Uniontown (44685) *(G-19092)*
McAlarney Pols Spas Billd More, Marietta *Also called Mc Alarney Pool Spas and Billd (G-12806)*
McArthur Lumber and Post, Mc Arthur *Also called Appalachia Wood Inc (G-13328)*
McAttack Machine LLC 440 946-3855
38338 Apollo Pkwy Bldg 2 Willoughby (44094) *(G-20541)*
McCabe's Granola, Cincinnati *Also called Seven Hills Foods Ltd (G-4410)*
McCann Plastics Inc 330 499-1515
5600 Mayfair Rd Canton (44720) *(G-2776)*
McCann Tool & Die Inc 330 264-8820
3230 Columbus Rd Wooster (44691) *(G-20803)*
McCc Sportswear Inc 513 583-9210
9944 Prnceton Glendale Rd West Chester (45246) *(G-20025)*
McClaflin Mobile Media LLC 419 575-9367
106 Caldwell St Bradner (43406) *(G-2028)*
McClellan Rand L 614 462-4782
65 E State St Columbus (43215) *(G-7329)*
McConnell's Farm Market, Richmond *Also called Mc Connells Market (G-16647)*
McCord Monuments, Bowling Green *Also called McCord Products Inc (G-2001)*
McCord Products Inc 419 352-3691
1135 N Main St Bowling Green (43402) *(G-2001)*
McCrary Metal Polishing Inc 937 492-1979
207 Pasco Montra Rd Port Jefferson (45360) *(G-16420)*
McCullough Industries Inc 800 245-9490
13047 County Road 175 Kenton (43326) *(G-11556)*
McDaniel Envelope Co Inc 330 868-5929
1400 Union Ave Se Minerva (44657) *(G-14332)*
McDaniel Products Inc (PA) 440 967-5630
1775 Liberty Ave Vermilion (44089) *(G-19333)*
McDaniel Products Inc 419 524-5841
433 Springmill St Mansfield (44903) *(G-12645)*
McDannald Welding & Machining 937 644-0300
11879 State Route 736 Marysville (43040) *(G-12960)*
McDonald & Woodward Pubg Co 740 321-1140
431b E College St Granville (43023) *(G-10460)*
McDonald Steel Corporation 330 530-9118
100 Ohio Ave Mc Donald (44437) *(G-13347)*
McElroy Contract Packaging 330 262-0855
249 S Bauer Rd Wooster (44691) *(G-20804)*
McFadden Logging 740 599-6902
305 S Mickley St Danville (43014) *(G-8090)*
McFeelys Inc 800 443-7937
320 N State St Harrison (45030) *(G-10790)*
McFlusion Inc 800 341-8616
2112 Case Pkwy Ste 8 Twinsburg (44087) *(G-18982)*
McGaw Technology Inc 216 521-3490
17439 Lake Ave Lakewood (44107) *(G-11675)*
McGean-Rohco Inc 216 441-4900
2910 Harvard Ave Newburgh Heights (44105) *(G-15076)*
McGill Airclean, Columbus *Also called McGill Airpressure LLC (G-7332)*
McGill Airclean LLC 614 829-1200
1777 Refugee Rd Columbus (43207) *(G-7330)*
McGill Airflow LLC 614 829-1200
2400 Fairwood Ave Columbus (43207) *(G-7331)*
McGill Airflow LLC (HQ) 614 829-1200
1 Mission Park Groveport (43125) *(G-10634)*

A L P H A B E T I C

McGill Airpressure LLC 614 882-5455
1777 Refugee Rd Columbus (43207) **(G-7332)**
McGill Airsilence LLC 614 443-0192
2400 Fairwood Ave Columbus (43207) **(G-7333)**
McGill Corporation (PA) 614 829-1200
1 Mission Park Groveport (43125) **(G-10635)**
McGill Septic Tank Co 330 876-2171
8913 State St Kinsman (44428) **(G-11610)**
McGinnis Inc (HQ) 740 377-4391
502 2nd St E South Point (45680) **(G-17440)**
McGlaughln Oil Compny/Fas Lube (PA) 614 231-2518
3750 E Livingston Ave Columbus (43227) **(G-7334)**
McGlennon Metal Products Inc 614 252-7114
940 N 20th St Columbus (43219) **(G-7335)**
McGovney Ready Mix Inc 740 353-4111
55 River Ave Portsmouth (45662) **(G-16443)**
McGovney River Terminal, Portsmouth *Also called McGovney Ready Mix Inc* **(G-16443)**
McGraw Hill Construction Enr, Cleveland *Also called S&P Global Inc* **(G-6152)**
McGraw-Hill Global Educatn LLC 614 755-4151
860 Taylor Station Rd Blacklick (43004) **(G-1702)**
McGraw-Hill School Education H 419 207-7400
1250 George Rd Ashland (44805) **(G-753)**
McGraw-Hill School Education H 614 430-4000
8787 Orion Pl Columbus (43240) **(G-6652)**
McGregor Metalworking, Springfield *Also called Morgal Machine Tool Co* **(G-17607)**
McGregor-Surmount Corporation 937 833-6768
365 Carr Dr Brookville (45309) **(G-2193)**
McGuire Machine LLC 330 868-3072
1400 Union Ave Se Minerva (44657) **(G-14333)**
McHael D Goronok String Instrs 216 421-4227
10823 Magnolia Dr Cleveland (44106) **(G-5769)**
McHappys Donuts of Parkersburg 740 593-8744
384 Richland Ave Athens (45701) **(G-875)**
McHenry Industries Inc 330 799-8930
85 Victoria Rd Youngstown (44515) **(G-21142)**
McIntosh Machine 937 687-3936
11 S Church St New Lebanon (45345) **(G-14844)**
McJak Candy Company LLC 330 722-3531
1087 Branch Rd Medina (44256) **(G-13441)**
McJunkn Redman 330 686-4988
4704 Hudson Dr Stow (44224) **(G-17774)**
McKinley Leather, Marion *Also called Williams Leather Products Inc* **(G-12914)**
McKinleys Meadery LLC 740 928-0229
4412 Keller Rd Hebron (43025) **(G-10873)**
McKinnon A Co, Cuyahoga Falls *Also called McKinnon Printing Inc* **(G-8025)**
McKinnon Printing Inc 330 929-5769
2845 Hickory Cv Cuyahoga Falls (44223) **(G-8025)**
McL Inc 614 861-6259
5240 E Main St Columbus (43213) **(G-7336)**
McL Whitehall, Columbus *Also called McL Inc* **(G-7336)**
McLeod Bar Group LLC 614 299-2099
234 King Ave Columbus (43201) **(G-7337)**
McM Ind Co Inc (PA) 216 292-4506
22901 Millcreek Blvd # 250 Beachwood (44122) **(G-1278)**
McM Ind Co Inc 216 641-6300
7800 Finney Ave Cleveland (44105) **(G-5770)**
McM Industries, Beachwood *Also called McM Ind Co Inc* **(G-1278)**
McM Precision Castings Inc 419 669-3226
13133 Beech St Weston (43569) **(G-20326)**
McMath & Sheets Unlimited Inc 216 381-0010
4427 Mayfield Rd Cleveland (44121) **(G-5771)**
McMillion Lock & Key 937 473-5342
8822 N Rangeline Rd Covington (45318) **(G-7926)**
McNamaras Pub Inc 216 671-8820
3498 W 146th St Cleveland (44111) **(G-5772)**
McNational Inc (PA) 740 377-4391
502 2nd St E South Point (45680) **(G-17441)**
McNeil & Nrm Inc (HQ) 330 761-1855
96 E Crosier St Akron (44311) **(G-291)**
McNeil & Nrm Intl Inc (PA) 330 253-2525
96 E Crosier St Akron (44311) **(G-292)**
McNeil Group Inc 614 298-0300
1701 Woodland Ave Columbus (43219) **(G-7338)**
McNeil Holdings LLC 614 298-0300
1701 Woodland Ave Columbus (43219) **(G-7339)**
McNeil Industries Inc 440 951-7756
835 Richmond Rd Painesville (44077) **(G-15901)**
McNeilus Truck and Mfg Inc 614 868-0760
1130 Morrison Rd Gahanna (43230) **(G-10218)**
McNeilus Truck and Mfg Inc 513 874-2022
8997 Lesaint Dr Fairfield (45014) **(G-9683)**
McNerney & Associates LLC (PA) 513 241-9951
440 Northland Blvd Cincinnati (45240) **(G-4070)**
McNichols Company 877 884-4653
3470 E Kemper Rd Cincinnati (45241) **(G-4071)**
McNish Corporation 614 899-2282
214 Hoff Rd Unit M Westerville (43082) **(G-20171)**
MCO Solutions Inc 937 205-9512
8820 Sugarcreek Pt Dayton (45458) **(G-8480)**

McPc Imaging and Printing LLC 419 627-9872
3911 Venice Rd Sandusky (44870) **(G-16987)**
McPherson Wire Cut Inc 330 896-0267
5208 Mayfair Rd Canton (44720) **(G-2777)**
McPp, Bellevue *Also called Mitsubishi Chls Perf Plyrs Inc* **(G-1553)**
McQueen Advertising Inc 440 967-1137
2010 Vermilion Rd Vermilion (44089) **(G-19334)**
McQueen Sign Co, Vermilion *Also called McQueen Advertising Inc* **(G-19334)**
McRd Enterprises LLC 740 775-2377
337 E Main St Chillicothe (45601) **(G-3250)**
McRill Service LLC 419 408-3113
5304 Us Highway 68 Kenton (43326) **(G-11557)**
MCS Mfg LLC 419 923-7535
15210 County Road 10 3 Lyons (43533) **(G-12432)**
MCS Midwest LLC (PA) 513 217-0805
3876 Hendrickson Rd Franklin (45005) **(G-10035)**
McSports 419 586-5555
1945 Havemann Rd Celina (45822) **(G-3007)**
McSwain Manufacturing LLC 513 671-6130
189 Container Pl Cincinnati (45246) **(G-4072)**
McTech Corp 216 391-7700
5000 Crayton Ave Cleveland (44104) **(G-5773)**
McTt Machine Tool Inc 440 946-9559
38131 Arprt Pkwy Unit 207 Willoughby (44094) **(G-20542)**
McWane Inc 740 622-6651
2266 S 6th St Coshocton (43812) **(G-7897)**
MD Solutions Inc 866 637-6588
8225 Estates Pkwy Plain City (43064) **(G-16348)**
MD Tool & Die Inc 440 647-6456
755 Industrial Ave Wellington (44090) **(G-19750)**
Mdf Enterprises LLC 937 640-3436
821 Hall Ave Dayton (45404) **(G-8481)**
Mdf Tool Corporation 440 237-2277
10166 Royalton Rd North Royalton (44133) **(G-15436)**
Mdi of Ohio Inc 937 866-2345
802 N 4th St Miamisburg (45342) **(G-13829)**
ME Signs Inc 419 222-7446
2155 Elida Rd Lima (45805) **(G-12052)**
Mead Paving 937 322-7414
1023 W Perrin Ave Springfield (45506) **(G-17602)**
Meadors Machine Inc 937 452-5571
7076 N Main St Camden (45311) **(G-2485)**
Meadow Burke Products, West Chester *Also called Merchants Metals LLC* **(G-19900)**
Meadwestvaco, Kettering *Also called Westrock Mwv LLC* **(G-11588)**
Mealey Industrial Lubricants, Cleveland *Also called Mar Mor Inc* **(G-5740)**
Measurement Computing Corp (HQ) 440 439-4091
25971 Cannon Rd Cleveland (44146) **(G-5774)**
Measurement Specialties Inc 330 659-3312
2236 N Cleveland Massillo Akron (44333) **(G-293)**
Measurement Specialties Inc 937 427-1231
2670 Indian Ripple Rd Beavercreek (45440) **(G-1374)**
Measurement Specialties Inc 937 885-0800
10522 Success Ln Dayton (45458) **(G-8482)**
Measurenet Technology Ltd 513 396-6765
4242 Airport Rd Ste 101 Cincinnati (45226) **(G-4073)**
Mecc-Usa LLC (PA) 513 891-0301
9468 Meridian Way West Chester (45069) **(G-19899)**
Mecca Rebuilding & Welding Co 419 476-8133
615 Phillips Ave Toledo (43612) **(G-18581)**
Mecco Inc 513 422-3651
2100 S Main St Middletown (45044) **(G-14061)**
Mechanical Dynamics Analis Ltd 440 946-0082
1250 E 222nd St Euclid (44117) **(G-9592)**
Mechanical Elastomerics Inc 330 863-1014
3266 Coral Rd Nw Malvern (44644) **(G-12547)**
Mechanical Finishers Inc LLC 513 641-5419
6350 Este Ave Cincinnati (45232) **(G-4074)**
Mechanical Finishing Inc 513 641-5419
6350 Este Ave Cincinnati (45232) **(G-4075)**
Mechanical Galv-Plating Corp 937 492-3143
933 Oak Ave Sidney (45365) **(G-17200)**
Mechanicsburg Sand & Gravel 937 834-2606
5734 State Route 4 Mechanicsburg (43044) **(G-13358)**
Meco, Middletown *Also called Manufacturers Equipment Co* **(G-14059)**
Med Center Systems LLC 513 942-6066
10179 Commerce Park Dr West Chester (45246) **(G-20026)**
Medalist Laserfab, Defiance *Also called Defiance Metal Products WI Inc* **(G-8787)**
Medallion Lighting Corporation 440 255-8383
8710 East Ave Mentor (44060) **(G-13650)**
Medco Adhesive Coated Products, Cleveland *Also called Medco Labs Inc* **(G-5775)**
Medco Labs Inc 216 292-7546
5156 Richmond Rd Cleveland (44146) **(G-5775)**
Meders Special Tees 513 921-3800
618 Delhi Ave Cincinnati (45204) **(G-4076)**
Medex, Dublin *Also called Saint-Gobain Prfmce Plas Corp* **(G-9137)**
Medforall LLC 614 947-0791
1500 W 3rd Ave Ste 111 Columbus (43212) **(G-7340)**
Medi Home Health Agency Inc 740 472-3220
117 S Main St Woodsfield (43793) **(G-20719)**

Media Matrix LLC 888 833-8681
  13252 Wooster Rd Mount Vernon (43050) *(G-14630)*

Media Procurement Services Inc 513 977-3000
  312 Walnut St Cincinnati (45202) *(G-4077)*

Media Sign Company 513 564-9500
  2111 Kindel Ave Cincinnati (45214) *(G-4078)*

Medical Elastomer Dev Inc 330 425-8352
  1700 Highland Rd Twinsburg (44087) *(G-18983)*

Medical Equipment Provider 937 778-2190
  102 Fox Dr Piqua (45356) *(G-16291)*

Medical Imaging, Cincinnati *Also called Summit Diagnostic Imaging LLC* *(G-4475)*

Medical Imaging Equipment, Cleveland *Also called Philips Medical Systems Clevel* *(G-6001)*

Medical Quant USA Inc 440 542-0761
  6521 Davis Indus Pkwy Solon (44139) *(G-17333)*

Medical Soft Inc 937 293-2575
  1800 Southwood Ln W Oakwood (45419) *(G-15609)*

Medina Blanking Inc (HQ) 330 558-2300
  5580 Wegman Dr Valley City (44280) *(G-19217)*

Medina County Recorders, Medina *Also called County of Medina* *(G-13397)*

Medina Foods Inc 330 725-1390
  9706 Crow Rd Litchfield (44253) *(G-12138)*

Medina Fuel, Coshocton *Also called MFC Drilling Inc* *(G-7898)*

Medina Lighting Inc 330 721-1441
  3983 Pearl Rd Medina (44256) *(G-13442)*

Medina Plating Corp 330 725-4155
  940 Lafayette Rd Medina (44256) *(G-13443)*

Medina Signs Post Inc 330 723-2484
  411 W Smith Rd Medina (44256) *(G-13444)*

Medina Supply Company (HQ) 330 723-3681
  230 E Smith Rd Medina (44256) *(G-13445)*

Medina Supply Company 440 234-1321
  661 Front St Berea (44017) *(G-1626)*

Medina Supply Company 330 425-0752
  1516 Highland Rd Twinsburg (44087) *(G-18984)*

Medina Tool & Die, Wadsworth *Also called Kramer & Kiefer Inc* *(G-19416)*

Medinvent LLC 330 247-0921
  1133 Medina Rd Ste 500 Medina (44256) *(G-13446)*

Medkeff-Nye, Barberton *Also called Madgar Genis Corp* *(G-1125)*

Medline Industries Inc 330 484-1450
  3800 Commerce St Sw Canton (44706) *(G-2778)*

Medpace Holdings Inc (PA) 513 579-9911
  5375 Medpace Way Cincinnati (45227) *(G-4079)*

Medquest Communications Inc 216 391-9100
  3800 Lkside Ave E Ste 201 Cleveland (44114) *(G-5776)*

Medrano Usa Inc (PA) 614 272-5856
  4311 Janitrol Rd Ste 500 Columbus (43228) *(G-7341)*

Medtrace, Akron *Also called Vertical Data LLC* *(G-463)*

Medtronic Inc 216 642-1977
  5005 Rockside Rd Ste 1160 Cleveland (44131) *(G-5777)*

Medway Tool Corp 937 335-7717
  2100 Corporate Dr Troy (45373) *(G-18857)*

Medwurx, Lewis Center *Also called Eoi Inc* *(G-11897)*

Meech Sttic Eliminators USA Inc 330 564-2000
  2915 Newpark Dr Barberton (44203) *(G-1130)*

Meeks Pastry Shop 419 782-4871
  315 Clinton St Defiance (43512) *(G-8803)*

Meese Inc 440 998-1202
  4920 State Rd Ashtabula (44004) *(G-819)*

Mega Bright LLC 330 577-8859
  2251 Front St Cuyahoga Falls (44221) *(G-8026)*

Mega Plastics Co 330 527-2211
  10610 Freedom St Garrettsville (44231) *(G-10330)*

Megaform Computer Products, Vandalia *Also called Misato Computer Products Inc* *(G-19305)*

Megajoule Storage Inc 216 496-8302
  1768 E 25th St Cleveland (44114) *(G-5778)*

Meggitt (erlanger) LLC 513 851-5550
  10293 Burlington Rd Cincinnati (45231) *(G-4080)*

Meggitt Aircraft Braking (HQ) 330 796-4400
  1204 Massillon Rd Akron (44306) *(G-294)*

Megna Plastics, Cleveland *Also called Dal-Little Fabricating Inc* *(G-5163)*

Mehaffie Pie Company, Dayton *Also called K & B Acquisitions Inc* *(G-8432)*

MEI, Wapakoneta *Also called Midwest Elastomers Inc* *(G-19498)*

MEI, Malvern *Also called Mechanical Elastomerics Inc* *(G-12547)*

Meibuhr Co Inc 440 942-9375
  38301 Apollo Pkwy Ste 1 Willoughby (44094) *(G-20543)*

Meierjohan-Wengler Inc 513 771-6074
  10340 Julian Dr Cincinnati (45215) *(G-4081)*

Meiers Wine Cellars Inc 513 891-2900
  6955 Plainfield Rd Cincinnati (45236) *(G-4082)*

Meiring Precision, Ludlow Falls *Also called Marmax Machine Co* *(G-12427)*

Meister Media Worldwide Inc (PA) 440 942-2000
  37733 Euclid Ave Willoughby (44094) *(G-20544)*

Meistermatic Inc 216 481-7773
  12446 Bentbrook Dr Chesterland (44026) *(G-3214)*

Meka Signs Enterprises Inc 513 942-5494
  10126 Prncton Glendale Rd West Chester (45246) *(G-20027)*

Mel Stevens U-Cart Concrete 419 478-2600
  6151 Telegraph Rd Toledo (43612) *(G-18582)*

Mel Wacker Sign Inc 330 832-1726
  13076 Barrs Rd Sw Massillon (44647) *(G-13178)*

Mel's Lifelike Hair, Dayton *Also called Mels Life Like Hair* *(G-8483)*

Mel-Ba Manufacturing, Independence *Also called Kohut Enterprises Inc* *(G-11263)*

Melanda Inc 330 833-0517
  2646 Lincoln Way Nw Massillon (44647) *(G-13179)*

Melcor Corporation (HQ) 609 393-4178
  4707 Detroit Ave Cleveland (44102) *(G-5779)*

Meldrum Mechanical Services 419 535-3500
  4455 South Ave Toledo (43615) *(G-18583)*

Melin Tool Company Inc 216 362-4200
  5565 Venture Dr Ste C Cleveland (44130) *(G-5780)*

Melink Corporation (PA) 513 685-0958
  5140 River Valley Rd Milford (45150) *(G-14161)*

Melinz Industries Inc (PA) 440 946-3512
  34099 Melinz Pkwy Unit D Willoughby (44095) *(G-20545)*

Melinz-Rebar Inc 216 531-8988
  16226 S Waterloo Rd Ste 3 Cleveland (44110) *(G-5781)*

Mellott Bronze Inc 330 435-6304
  4634 E Sterling Rd Creston (44217) *(G-7941)*

Mels Life Like Hair 937 278-9486
  6140 N Main St Dayton (45415) *(G-8483)*

Melt Inc 330 426-3545
  51621 Darlington Rd Negley (44441) *(G-14731)*

Melvin Grain Co 937 382-1249
  413 Melvin Rd Wilmington (45177) *(G-20670)*

Melvin Stone Co LLC 513 771-0820
  11641 Mosteller Rd Ste 2 Cincinnati (45241) *(G-4083)*

Melvin Stone Company LLC 740 998-5016
  3333 Plano Rd Wshngtn CT Hs (43160) *(G-20916)*

Melvin Stone Company LLC 937 453-2032
  3659 S State Route 72 Sabina (45169) *(G-16773)*

Memac Industries Inc 740 653-4815
  324 Quarry Rd Se Lancaster (43130) *(G-11728)*

Membrane Specialists LLC 513 860-9490
  2 Rowe Ct Hamilton (45015) *(G-10724)*

Memphis Smokehouse Inc 216 351-5321
  8463 Memphis Ave Cleveland (44144) *(G-5782)*

Menard Inc 513 250-4566
  2789 Cunningham Rd Cincinnati (45241) *(G-4084)*

Menard Inc 419 998-4348
  2614 N Eastown Rd Lima (45807) *(G-12053)*

Menasha Packaging Company LLC 740 773-8204
  291 S Mcarthur St Chillicothe (45601) *(G-3251)*

Mennel Milling Company 419 436-5130
  319 S Vine St Fostoria (44830) *(G-9985)*

Mentor Glass Supplies and Repr 440 255-9444
  8985 Osborne Dr Mentor (44060) *(G-13651)*

Mentor Inc 440 255-1250
  5983 Andrews Rd Mentor On The Lake (44060) *(G-13774)*

Mentor Radio LLC 216 265-2315
  151 Innovation Dr Ste 320 Elyria (44035) *(G-9460)*

Mentor Signs & Graphics Inc 440 951-7446
  7522a Tyler Blvd Ste A Mentor (44060) *(G-13652)*

Mentor Tool Inc 440 942-5273
  990 Erie Rd Unit D Willoughby (44095) *(G-20546)*

Mercer Color Corporation 419 678-8273
  425 Hardin St Coldwater (45828) *(G-6568)*

Mercer Landmark Inc 419 363-3391
  450 Strable Rd Rockford (45882) *(G-16692)*

Mercers Welding Inc 330 533-3373
  6336 W Calla Rd Canfield (44406) *(G-2565)*

Merchants Metals LLC 513 942-0268
  8760 Global Way Bldg 1 West Chester (45069) *(G-19900)*

Mercurio Biotec LLC 214 507-8031
  4150 Tuller Rd Ste 23 Dublin (43017) *(G-9102)*

Mercury Air Services LLC 216 898-4800
  5211 Secondary Dr Cleveland (44135) *(G-5783)*

Mercury Biomed LLC 216 777-1492
  29001 Cedar Rd Ste 326 Cleveland (44124) *(G-5784)*

Mercury Iron & Steel 440 349-1500
  6275 Cochran Rd Solon (44139) *(G-17334)*

Mercury Machine Co 440 349-3222
  30250 Carter St Solon (44139) *(G-17335)*

Mercury Plastics Inc 440 632-5281
  15760 Madison Rd Middlefield (44062) *(G-13957)*

Meridian Arts and Graphics 330 759-9099
  16 Belgrade St Youngstown (44505) *(G-21143)*

Meridian Bioscience Inc (PA) 513 271-3700
  3471 River Hills Dr Cincinnati (45244) *(G-4085)*

Meridian Industries Inc 330 359-5447
  7369 Peabody Kent Rd Winesburg (44690) *(G-20706)*

Meridian Industries Inc 330 359-5809
  9901 Chestnut Ridge Rd Nw Beach City (44608) *(G-1248)*

Meridian Industries Inc 330 673-1011
  1500 Saint Clair Ave Kent (44240) *(G-11488)*

Meridian Life Science Inc (HQ) 513 271-3700
  3471 River Hills Dr Cincinnati (45244) *(G-4086)*

Meridian Machine Inc 330 308-0296
  702 Steele Hill Rd Nw New Philadelphia (44663) *(G-14913)*
Meridian Manufacturing Company 330 793-9632
  1191 N Meridian Rd Youngstown (44509) *(G-21144)*
Meridienne International Inc 330 274-8317
  4494 Orchard St Mantua (44255) *(G-12717)*
Merillat Cabinets, Jackson *Also called Masco Cabinetry LLC (G-11320)*
Merit Foundry Co Inc 216 741-4282
  2289 N Saint James Pkwy Cleveland (44106) *(G-5785)*
Merit Mold & Tool Products 937 435-0932
  4648 Gateway Cir Dayton (45440) *(G-8484)*
Meritech, Painesville *Also called Ohio Associated Entps LLC (G-15908)*
Meritor Inc 740 348-3498
  4009 Columbus Rd Ste 111 Granville (43023) *(G-10461)*
Merksteijn, Warren *Also called Reinforcement Systems Ohio LLC (G-19593)*
Merkur Group Inc 937 429-4288
  2434 Esquire Dr Beavercreek (45431) *(G-1351)*
Merrick Manufacturing II LLC 937 222-7164
  844 Hall Ave Dayton (45404) *(G-8485)*
Merrico Inc 419 525-2711
  541 Grant St Mansfield (44903) *(G-12646)*
Merrill Corporation 614 801-4700
  3400 Southpark Pl Ste H Grove City (43123) *(G-10571)*
Merritt Woodwork, Mentor *Also called Profac Inc (G-13698)*
Merry X-Ray Chemical Corp 614 219-2011
  4770 Northwest Pkwy Hilliard (43026) *(G-10960)*
Mes, Sunbury *Also called Mine Equipment Services LLC (G-18067)*
Mes Material Hdlg Systems LLC 740 477-8920
  28196 Scippo Creek Rd Circleville (43113) *(G-4633)*
Mesa Industries Inc (PA) 513 321-2950
  4027 Eastern Ave Cincinnati (45226) *(G-4087)*
Mesocoat Inc 216 453-0866
  24112 Rockwell Dr Euclid (44117) *(G-9593)*
Mesocoat Advanced Coating Tech, Euclid *Also called Mesocoat Inc (G-9593)*
Mespo Woodworking 440 693-4041
  4421 Donley Rd Middlefield (44062) *(G-13958)*
Messenger Press, Celina *Also called Heitkamp & Kremer Printing (G-3001)*
Messenger Publishing Company 740 592-6612
  9300 Johnson Hollow Rd Athens (45701) *(G-876)*
Messerman Corp 419 782-1136
  407 Agnes St Defiance (43512) *(G-8804)*
Messerman Machine Co, Defiance *Also called Messerman Corp (G-8804)*
Messinger Press, Celina *Also called Society of The Precious Blood (G-3018)*
Mestek Inc 419 288-2703
  120 Plin St Bradner (43406) *(G-2029)*
Mestek Inc 419 288-2703
  7301 International Dr Holland (43528) *(G-11072)*
Met Fab Fabrication and Mch 513 724-3715
  2974 Waitensburg Pike Batavia (45103) *(G-1203)*
Met L Fab Inc 513 561-4289
  5313 Robert Ave Cincinnati (45248) *(G-4088)*
Met-All Industries, Canal Fulton *Also called Aman & Co Inc (G-2495)*
Met-Chem Inc 216 881-7900
  837 E 79th St Cleveland (44103) *(G-5786)*
Meta Manufacturing Corporation 513 793-6382
  8901 Blue Ash Rd Ste 1 Blue Ash (45242) *(G-1837)*
Metal & Wire Products Company (PA) 330 332-9448
  1065 Salem Pkwy Salem (44460) *(G-16914)*
Metal Brite Polishing 937 278-9739
  2445 Neff Rd Unit 4 Dayton (45414) *(G-8486)*
Metal Coating Company, Lima *Also called J M Hamilton Group Inc (G-12032)*
Metal Craft Docks Inc 440 286-7135
  6989 Lindsay Dr Mentor (44060) *(G-13653)*
Metal Cutting Technology LLC 419 733-1236
  5410 Golden Pond Rd Celina (45822) *(G-3008)*
Metal Dynamics Co 330 601-0748
  4047 Unit A Lincoln Way Wooster (44691) *(G-20805)*
Metal Fabricating Corporation 216 631-8121
  10408 Berea Rd Cleveland (44102) *(G-5787)*
Metal Finishers Inc 937 492-9175
  2600 Fair Rd Sidney (45365) *(G-17201)*
Metal Finishing Divison, Ravenna *Also called Allen Aircraft Products Inc (G-16515)*
Metal Finishing Needs Ltd 216 561-6334
  16025 Van Aken Blvd Cleveland (44120) *(G-5788)*
Metal Forming & Coining Corp (PA) 419 897-9530
  1007 Illinois Ave Maumee (43537) *(G-13281)*
Metal Forming Lubricants Inc 440 458-5730
  10800 Middle Ave Hngr A Elyria (44035) *(G-9461)*
Metal Improvement Company LLC 513 489-6484
  11131 Luschek Dr Blue Ash (45241) *(G-1838)*
Metal Improvement Company LLC 330 425-1490
  1652 Highland Rd Twinsburg (44087) *(G-18985)*
Metal Maintenance Inc 513 661-3300
  322 N Finley St Cleves (45002) *(G-6521)*
Metal Man Inc 614 830-0968
  4681 Homer Ohio Ln Ste A Groveport (43125) *(G-10636)*
Metal Merchants Usa Inc 330 723-3228
  445 W Liberty St Medina (44256) *(G-13447)*

Metal Product, Akron *Also called Runner Tool & Die Inc (G-382)*
Metal Products Company (PA) 330 652-2558
  112 Erie St Niles (44446) *(G-15168)*
Metal Products Company 330 652-6201
  1818 N Main St Unit 4 Niles (44446) *(G-15169)*
Metal Quality Products Co Inc 440 942-0787
  34640 Lakeland Blvd Willoughby (44095) *(G-20547)*
Metal Sales Manufacturing, Jefferson *Also called Interlock Industries Inc (G-11361)*
Metal Sales Manufacturing Corp 440 576-9070
  352 E Erie St Jefferson (44047) *(G-11367)*
Metal Seal Precision Ltd 440 205-0016
  8687 Tyler Blvd Mentor (44060) *(G-13654)*
Metal Shredders Inc 937 866-0777
  5101 Farmersville W Miamisburg (45342) *(G-13830)*
Metal Stampings Unlimited 937 328-0206
  552 W Johnny Lytle Ave Springfield (45506) *(G-17603)*
Metal Technology Systems Inc 513 563-1882
  675 Redna Ter Cincinnati (45215) *(G-4089)*
Metal-Mation Inc 216 651-1083
  2391 W 38th St Cleveland (44113) *(G-5789)*
Metal-Max Inc 330 673-9926
  1540 Enterprise Way Kent (44240) *(G-11489)*
Metalcrete Industries Inc 440 526-5600
  4133 Payne Ave Cleveland (44103) *(G-5790)*
Metaldyne Pwrtrain Cmpnnts Inc 330 486-3200
  8001 Bavaria Rd Twinsburg (44087) *(G-18986)*
Metaldyne Twinsburg, Twinsburg *Also called Metaldyne Pwrtrain Cmpnnts Inc (G-18986)*
Metalex Manufacturing Inc (PA) 513 489-0507
  5750 Cornell Rd Blue Ash (45242) *(G-1839)*
Metalico Akron Inc (HQ) 330 376-1400
  943 Hazel St Akron (44305) *(G-295)*
Metalico Annaco, Akron *Also called Metalico Akron Inc (G-295)*
Metallic Resources Inc 330 425-3155
  2368 E Enterprise Pkwy Twinsburg (44087) *(G-18987)*
Metallurgical Service Inc 937 294-2681
  2221 Arbor Blvd Moraine (45439) *(G-14505)*
Metalphoto of Cincinnati Inc 513 772-8281
  1080 Skillman Dr Cincinnati (45215) *(G-4090)*
Metals and Additives Corp Inc 740 654-6555
  4850 Elder Rd Ne Pleasantville (43148) *(G-16373)*
Metals Crankshaft Grinding 216 431-5778
  1435 E 45th St Cleveland (44103) *(G-5791)*
Metals Recovery Services LLC 614 870-0364
  1400 Norton Rd Columbus (43228) *(G-7342)*
Metals USA Crbn Flat Rlled Inc 937 882-6354
  5750 Lower Valley Pike Springfield (45502) *(G-17604)*
Metals USA Crbn Flat Rlled Inc (HQ) 330 264-8416
  1070 W Liberty St Wooster (44691) *(G-20806)*
Metalsmiths, Cleveland *Also called Metro Mech Inc (G-5792)*
Metalworking Group Holdings (PA) 513 521-4119
  9070 Pippin Rd Cincinnati (45251) *(G-4091)*
Metalworking Group, The, Cincinnati *Also called Metalworking Group Holdings (G-4091)*
Metcalf Design & Printing Ctr, Gahanna *Also called Sjpm Inc (G-10233)*
Metcut Research Associates Inc (PA) 513 271-5100
  3980 Rosslyn Dr Cincinnati (45209) *(G-4092)*
Meteor Automotive, Dover *Also called Meteor Sealing Systems LLC (G-9001)*
Meteor Sealing Systems LLC 330 343-9595
  400 S Tuscarawas Ave Dover (44622) *(G-9001)*
Metlweb 513 563-8822
  3330 E Kemper Rd Cincinnati (45241) *(G-4093)*
Metokote Corporation 440 934-4686
  5477 Evergreen Pkwy Sheffield Village (44054) *(G-17127)*
Metokote Corporation (HQ) 419 996-7800
  1340 Neubrecht Rd Lima (45801) *(G-12054)*
Metokote Corporation 419 227-1100
  1340 Neubrecht Rd Lima (45801) *(G-12055)*
Metokote Corporation 319 232-6994
  1340 Neubrecht Rd Lima (45801) *(G-12056)*
Metokote Corporation 419 221-2754
  1340 Neubrecht Rd Lima (45801) *(G-12057)*
Metokote Corporation 419 996-7800
  1340 Neubrecht Rd Lima (45801) *(G-12058)*
Metokote Corporation 937 235-2811
  8040 Center Point 70 Blvd Dayton (45424) *(G-8487)*
Metro Design Inc 440 458-4200
  10740 Middle Ave Elyria (44035) *(G-9462)*
Metro Flex Inc 937 299-5360
  3304 Encrete Ln Moraine (45439) *(G-14506)*
Metro Mech Inc 216 641-6262
  3599 E 49th St Cleveland (44105) *(G-5792)*
Metro Recycling Company 513 251-1800
  19 W Vine St Cincinnati (45215) *(G-4094)*
Metro Tool & Die Co Inc 937 836-8242
  11974 Putnam Rd Englewood (45322) *(G-9531)*
Metrodeck Inc 513 541-4370
  4795 Day Rd Cincinnati (45252) *(G-4095)*
Metromedia Technologies Inc 330 264-2501
  1061 Venture Blvd Wooster (44691) *(G-20807)*

Metron Instruments Inc 216 332-0592
5198 Richmond Rd Bedford Heights (44146) ***(G-1489)***
Metropolitan Ceramics Div, Canton *Also called Ironrock Capital Incorporated* ***(G-2741)***
Metropolitan Envmtl Svcs Inc 614 771-1881
5055 Nike Dr Hilliard (43026) ***(G-10961)***
Mettler-Toledo LLC 614 438-4511
720 Dearborn Park Ln Worthington (43085) ***(G-20878)***
Mettler-Toledo LLC 614 438-4390
1150 Dearborn Dr Worthington (43085) ***(G-20879)***
Mettler-Toledo LLC 614 841-7300
6600 Huntley Rd Columbus (43229) ***(G-7343)***
Mettler-Toledo Intl Fin Inc 614 438-4511
1900 Polaris Pkwy Fl 6 Columbus (43240) ***(G-6653)***
Mettler-Toledo Intl Inc (PA) 614 438-4511
1900 Polaris Pkwy Fl 6 Columbus (43240) ***(G-6654)***
Mettlr-Tledo Globl Hldings LLC (HQ) 614 438-4511
1900 Polaris Pkwy Columbus (43240) ***(G-6655)***
Metzger Machine Co 513 241-3360
2165 Spring Grove Ave Cincinnati (45214) ***(G-4096)***
Metzgers 419 861-8611
150 Arco Dr Toledo (43607) ***(G-18584)***
Mexichem Specialty Resins Inc (HQ) 440 930-1435
33653 Walker Rd Avon Lake (44012) ***(G-1040)***
Mexus Holdings Inc 937 832-2307
140 Harrisburg Dr Englewood (45322) ***(G-9532)***
Meyer Company (PA) 216 587-3400
13700 Broadway Ave Cleveland (44125) ***(G-5793)***
Meyer Design Inc 330 434-9176
100 N High St Akron (44308) ***(G-296)***
Meyer Machine Tool Company 614 235-0039
3434 E 7th Ave Columbus (43219) ***(G-7344)***
Meyer Products LLC 216 486-1313
18513 Euclid Ave Cleveland (44112) ***(G-5794)***
Meyer Tool Inc (PA) 513 681-7362
3055 Colerain Ave Cincinnati (45225) ***(G-4097)***
Meyerpt, Hudson *Also called Wbc Group LLC* ***(G-11207)***
Meyers Printing & Design Inc 937 461-6000
254 Leo St Dayton (45404) ***(G-8488)***
MFC, Maumee *Also called Metal Forming & Coining Corp* ***(G-13281)***
MFC Drilling Inc 740 622-5600
46281 Us Highway 36 Coshocton (43812) ***(G-7898)***
Mfg Composite Systems Company 440 997-5851
2925 Mfg Pl Ashtabula (44004) ***(G-820)***
Mfg CSC, Ashtabula *Also called Mfg Composite Systems Company* ***(G-820)***
Mfh Partners Inc (PA) 440 461-4100
6650 Beta Dr Cleveland (44143) ***(G-5795)***
Mfi, Cincinnati *Also called Mechanical Finishers Inc LLC* ***(G-4074)***
Mfs Supply LLC (PA) 440 248-5300
31100 Solon Rd Ste E Solon (44139) ***(G-17336)***
MGM Construction Inc 440 234-7660
1480 W Bagley Rd Ste 1 Berea (44017) ***(G-1627)***
MGM Roofing, Berea *Also called MGM Construction Inc* ***(G-1627)***
Mh & Son Machining & Wldg Co 419 621-0690
210 W Perkins Ave Ste 10 Sandusky (44870) ***(G-16988)***
Mh Equipment, West Chester *Also called MH Logistics Corp* ***(G-20028)***
MH Logistics Corp 513 681-2200
106 Circle Freeway Dr West Chester (45246) ***(G-20028)***
Mhi, Cincinnati *Also called Micropyretics Heaters Intl Inc* ***(G-4103)***
Mhp Flooring, Millersburg *Also called Mount Hope Planing* ***(G-14250)***
MI 2009 Inc 513 536-2000
4165 Half Acre Rd Batavia (45103) ***(G-1204)***
Mi-Lar Fence Co Inc (PA) 216 464-3160
5250 Naiman Pkwy Ste B Solon (44139) ***(G-17337)***
Mia Express Inc 330 896-8180
3238 Robins Trce Akron (44319) ***(G-297)***
Miami Control Systems Inc 937 698-5725
955 S Main St West Milton (45383) ***(G-20107)***
Miami Graphics Services Inc 937 698-4013
225 N Jay St West Milton (45383) ***(G-20108)***
Miami Machine, Cleves *Also called Pohl Machining Inc* ***(G-6522)***
Miami Machine Corporation 513 863-6707
4251 Riverside Dr Overpeck (45055) ***(G-15832)***
Miami River Stone Co 937 492-5412
1556 Miami River Rd Sidney (45365) ***(G-17202)***
Miami Specialties, Piqua *Also called M C D Plastics & Manufacturing* ***(G-16289)***
Miami Steel Fabricators Inc 937 299-5550
1525 Manchester Rd Dayton (45449) ***(G-8489)***
Miami Valley Counters & Spc 937 865-0562
8515 Dyton Cncinnati Pike Miamisburg (45342) ***(G-13831)***
Miami Valley Eductl Cmpt Assn 937 767-1468
330 E Enon Rd Yellow Springs (45387) ***(G-20995)***
Miami Valley Gasket Co Inc 937 228-0781
1222 E 3rd St Dayton (45402) ***(G-8490)***
Miami Valley Lighting LLC 937 224-6000
1065 Woodman Dr Dayton (45432) ***(G-8112)***
Miami Valley Paper LLC 937 746-6451
413 Oxford Rd Franklin (45005) ***(G-10036)***
Miami Valley Pizza Hut Inc 419 586-5900
1152 E Market St Celina (45822) ***(G-3009)***
Miami Valley Plastics Inc 937 273-3200
310 S Main St Eldorado (45321) ***(G-9346)***
Miami Valley Polishing 937 615-9353
220 Fox Dr Piqua (45356) ***(G-16292)***
Miami Valley Polishing LL 937 498-1634
1317 Pinetree Ct Sidney (45365) ***(G-17203)***
Miami Valley Precision Inc 937 866-1804
456 Alexandersville Rd Miamisburg (45342) ***(G-13832)***
Miami Valley Press Inc 937 547-0771
6132 Kruckeburg Rd Greenville (45331) ***(G-10511)***
Miami Valley Punch & Mfg 937 237-0533
3425 Successful Way Dayton (45414) ***(G-8491)***
Miami Valley Ready Mix Inc 513 738-2616
9540 Hamilton Cleves Hwy Harrison (45030) ***(G-10791)***
Miami Vly Mfg & Assembly Inc 937 254-6665
1889 Radio Rd Dayton (45431) ***(G-8113)***
Miami Vly Packg Solutions Inc 937 224-1800
1752 Stanley Ave Dayton (45404) ***(G-8492)***
Miami Wabash, Franklin *Also called Miami Valley Paper LLC* ***(G-10036)***
Miami-Cast Inc 937 866-2951
901 N Main St Miamisburg (45342) ***(G-13833)***
Miamisburg Coating 937 866-1323
925 N Main St Miamisburg (45342) ***(G-13834)***
Miamisburg News, Miamisburg *Also called Cox Newspapers LLC* ***(G-13794)***
Miba Bearings US LLC 740 962-4242
5037 N State Route 60 Nw McConnelsville (43756) ***(G-13354)***
Miba Sinter USA LLC 740 962-4242
5045 N State Route 60 Nw McConnelsville (43756) ***(G-13355)***
Mibtach Enterprises Inc 513 941-0387
2629 Lytham Ct Cincinnati (45233) ***(G-4098)***
Mic-Ray Metal Products Inc 216 791-2206
9016 Manor Ave Cleveland (44104) ***(G-5796)***
Mica Laminates, Columbus *Also called Somerset Galleries Inc* ***(G-7630)***
Miceli Dairy Products Co (PA) 216 791-6222
2721 E 90th St Cleveland (44104) ***(G-5797)***
Michabo Inc (PA) 419 893-4334
525 W Sophia St Maumee (43537) ***(G-13282)***
Michael Bradley Apparatus LLC 740 374-6255
116 Industry Rd Marietta (45750) ***(G-12807)***
Michael D Strickland 740 682-6902
2730 Hickory Grove Rd Oak Hill (45656) ***(G-15601)***
Michael Day Enterprises LLC 330 335-5100
9774 Trease Rd Wadsworth (44281) ***(G-19419)***
Michael Fabricating Inc 330 325-8636
4003 State Route 44 Rootstown (44272) ***(G-16724)***
Michael Kaufman Companies Inc (PA) 330 673-4881
845 Overholt Rd Kent (44240) ***(G-11490)***
Michael Kaufman Companies Inc 330 673-4881
845 Overholt Rd Kent (44240) ***(G-11491)***
Michael N Wheeler 740 377-9777
1004 4th St E South Point (45680) ***(G-17442)***
Michael R Kelly 614 491-1745
1657 Victor Ave Obetz (43207) ***(G-15656)***
Michael W Hyes Desgr Goldsmith 440 519-0889
28200 Miles Rd Unit F Solon (44139) ***(G-17338)***
Michaels 9837, Niles *Also called Michaels Stores Inc* ***(G-15170)***
Michaels Pre-Cast Con Pdts 513 683-1292
1917 Adams Rd Loveland (45140) ***(G-12374)***
Michaels Stores Inc 330 505-1168
5555 Youngstown Warren Rd # 914 Niles (44446) ***(G-15170)***
Michaels Tool Service Co Inc 330 772-1119
8346 Milligan East Rd Burghill (44404) ***(G-2368)***
Michalske Printing Company, Cleveland *Also called Douglas Michalske* ***(G-5210)***
Michele Mellen 740 369-1422
5680 Liberty Rd N Powell (43065) ***(G-16478)***
Michelman Inc 513 793-7766
3023 E Kemper Rd Bldg 2 Cincinnati (45241) ***(G-4099)***
Michigan Report, Columbus *Also called Gongwer News Service Inc* ***(G-7123)***
Michigan Sugar Company 419 332-9931
1101 N Front St Fremont (43420) ***(G-10170)***
Michigan Sugar Company 419 423-1666
1343 Greenwood St Findlay (45840) ***(G-9860)***
Mickens Inc (PA) 419 533-2401
107 East St Ste 1 Liberty Center (43532) ***(G-11955)***
Mickens Inc 419 943-2590
117 E Main St Leipsic (45856) ***(G-11872)***
Mickes Quality Machining 614 746-6639
488 Trade Rd Columbus (43204) ***(G-7345)***
Miconvi Properties Inc 440 954-3500
4711 E 355th St Willoughby (44094) ***(G-20548)***
Micro Center Corporation 614 326-8500
747 Bethel Rd Columbus (43214) ***(G-7346)***
Micro Industries Corporation (PA) 740 548-7878
8399 Green Meadows Dr N Westerville (43081) ***(G-20224)***
Micro Industries Corporation 740 548-7878
2270 Port Rd Columbus (43217) ***(G-7347)***
Micro Laboratories Inc 440 918-0001
7158 Industrial Park Blvd Mentor (44060) ***(G-13655)***
Micro Lapping & Grinding Co 216 267-6500
12320 Plaza Dr Cleveland (44130) ***(G-5798)***

(PA)=Parent Co (HQ)=Headquarters (DH)=Div Headquarters

Micro Machine Ltd 330 438-7078
275 7th St Sw Brewster (44613) *(G-2086)*
Micro Machine Works Inc 740 678-8471
10499 State Route 339 Vincent (45784) *(G-19380)*
Micro Metal Finishing LLC 513 541-3095
3448 Spring Grove Ave Cincinnati (45225) *(G-4100)*
Micro Mold Co Inc 330 325-2373
6671 Cleveland Rd Ravenna (44266) *(G-16540)*
Micro Mower, West Jefferson Also called R L Parsons & Son Equipment Co *(G-20083)*
Micro Products Co Inc 440 943-0258
26653 Curtiss Wright Pkwy Willoughby Hills (44092) *(G-20641)*
Micro Systems Development Inc 937 438-3567
419 E 6th St Dayton (45402) *(G-8493)*
Micro Tool Service, New Lebanon Also called H Duane Leis Acquisitions *(G-14842)*
Micro-Pise Msrment Systems LLC (HQ) 330 541-9100
555 Mondial Pkwy Streetsboro (44241) *(G-17861)*
Microbiological Labs Inc. 330 626-2264
9593 Page Rd Streetsboro (44241) *(G-17862)*
Microcom Corporation 740 548-6262
8220 Green Meadows Dr N Lewis Center (43035) *(G-11907)*
Microfinish, Vandalia Also called Bill J Jernigan Inc *(G-19283)*
Microform Inc 440 899-6339
29529 Goulders Grn Cleveland (44140) *(G-5799)*
Micron Manufacturing Inc 440 355-4200
186 Commerce Dr Lagrange (44050) *(G-11633)*
Microplex Inc 330 498-0600
7568 Whipple Ave Nw North Canton (44720) *(G-15249)*
Microplex Printware Corp 440 374-2424
100 Northfield Rd Bedford (44146) *(G-1443)*
Micropower LLC 513 382-0100
10470 Evendale Dr Cincinnati (45241) *(G-4101)*
Micropress America LLC 513 746-0689
4240 Minmor Dr Cincinnati (45217) *(G-4102)*
Micropure Filtration Inc 952 472-2323
837 E 79th St Cleveland (44103) *(G-5800)*
Micropyretics Heaters Intl Inc 513 772-0404
750 Redna Ter Cincinnati (45215) *(G-4103)*
Microsheen Corporation 216 481-5610
1100 E 222nd St Ste 1 Cleveland (44117) *(G-5801)*
Microsoft Corporation 614 719-5900
8800 Lyra Dr Ste 400 Columbus (43240) *(G-6656)*
Microsoft Corporation 216 986-1440
6050 Oak Tree Blvd # 300 Cleveland (44131) *(G-5802)*
Microsoft Corporation 513 339-2800
4605 Duke Dr Ste 800 Mason (45040) *(G-13062)*
Microsol Inc 330 733-0086
390 Munroe Falls Rd Tallmadge (44278) *(G-18154)*
Microstrategy Incorporated 513 792-2253
8044 Montgomery Rd # 700 Cincinnati (45236) *(G-4104)*
Microsun Lamps LLC 888 328-8701
7890 Center Point 70 Blvd Dayton (45424) *(G-8494)*
Microtek Finishing LLC 513 766-5600
5579 Spellmire Dr West Chester (45246) *(G-20029)*
Microweld Engineering Inc 614 847-9410
7451 Oakmeadows Dr Worthington (43085) *(G-20880)*
Mid, Columbus Also called Minimally Invasive Devices Inc *(G-7356)*
Mid America Chemical Corp 216 749-0100
4701 Spring Rd Cleveland (44131) *(G-5803)*
Mid American Ventures Inc 216 524-0974
7600 Wall St Ste 205 Cleveland (44125) *(G-5804)*
Mid Ohio Net, Delaware Also called Delaware Gazette Company *(G-8836)*
Mid Ohio Packaging LLC 740 383-9200
2135 Innovation Dr Marion (43302) *(G-12884)*
Mid Ohio Screen Print Inc 614 875-1774
4163 Kelnor Dr Grove City (43123) *(G-10572)*
Mid Ohio Trophy & Awards 419 756-2266
131 W Cook Rd Mansfield (44907) *(G-12647)*
Mid Ohio Wood Products Inc 740 323-0427
535 Franklin Ave Newark (43056) *(G-15033)*
Mid Ohio Wood Recycling Inc 419 673-8470
16289 State Route 31 Kenton (43326) *(G-11558)*
Mid West Dry Sift 614 946-3797
3441 Merrydawn Dr Columbus (43221) *(G-7348)*
Mid West Fabricating Co, Amanda Also called Mid-West Fabricating Co *(G-563)*
Mid's Spaghetti Sauce, Navarre Also called RC Industries Inc *(G-14726)*
Mid-America Gutters Inc 513 671-3505
11820 Kemper Springs Dr # 103 Cincinnati (45240) *(G-4105)*
Mid-America Packaging LLC (PA) 330 963-4199
2127 Reiser Ave Se New Philadelphia (44663) *(G-14914)*
Mid-America Stainless, Cleveland Also called Mid-America Steel Corp *(G-5805)*
Mid-America Steel Corp 800 282-3466
20900 Saint Clair Ave Cleveland (44117) *(G-5805)*
Mid-Ohio Electric Co 614 274-8000
1170 Mckinley Ave Columbus (43222) *(G-7349)*
Mid-Ohio Products Inc 614 771-2795
4329 Reynolds Dr Hilliard (43026) *(G-10962)*
Mid-Ohio Tubing LLC (PA) 419 883-2066
145 W Elm St Butler (44822) *(G-2392)*

Mid-Ohio Tubing LLC 419 886-0220
500 Main St Bellville (44813) *(G-1572)*
Mid-State Sales Inc 330 744-2158
854 Mahoning Ave Youngstown (44502) *(G-21145)*
Mid-States Packaging Inc 937 843-3243
12163 State Route 274 Lewistown (43333) *(G-11946)*
Mid-Town Petro Acquisition LLC (PA) 219 728-5149
9395 Kenwood Rd Ste 104 Blue Ash (45242) *(G-1840)*
Mid-West Fabricating Co (PA) 740 969-4411
313 N Johns St Amanda (43102) *(G-563)*
Mid-West Fabricating Co. 740 681-4411
3115 W Fair Ave Lancaster (43130) *(G-11729)*
Mid-West Forge Corporation (PA) 216 481-3030
17301 Saint Clair Ave Cleveland (44110) *(G-5806)*
Mid-West Poly Pak Inc 330 658-2921
89 E Marion St Doylestown (44230) *(G-9029)*
Mid-Wood Inc 419 257-3331
101 E State St North Baltimore (45872) *(G-15195)*
Middaugh Enterprises Inc 330 852-2471
211 Yoder Ave Nw Sugarcreek (44681) *(G-18026)*
Middlefield Glass Incorporated 440 632-5699
17447 Kinsman Rd Middlefield (44062) *(G-13959)*
Middlefield Mix Inc 440 632-0157
15815 Nauvoo Rd Middlefield (44062) *(G-13960)*
Middlefield Pallet Inc 440 632-0553
15940 Burton Windsor Rd Middlefield (44062) *(G-13961)*
Middlefield Plastics Inc 440 834-4638
15235 Burton Windsor Rd Middlefield (44062) *(G-13962)*
Middlefield Sign Co 440 632-0708
14895 N State Ave Unit G Middlefield (44062) *(G-13963)*
Middleton Llyd Dolls Inc (PA) 740 989-2082
23689 Mountain Bell Rd Coolville (45723) *(G-7835)*
Middleton Lee Original Dolls (HQ) ....
2400 Corporate Exch Dr Columbus (43231) *(G-7350)*
Middleton Printing Co Inc 614 294-7277
81 Mill St Ste 300 Gahanna (43230) *(G-10219)*
Middleton License Agency Inc 513 422-7225
3232 Roosevelt Blvd Middletown (45044) *(G-14062)*
Middletown Pharmacy Inc 513 705-6252
4421 Roosevelt Blvd Ste H Middletown (45044) *(G-14063)*
Middletown Tube Works Inc 513 727-0080
2201 Trine St Middletown (45044) *(G-14064)*
Middlfeld Original Cheese Coop 440 632-5567
16942 Kinsman Rd Middlefield (44062) *(G-13964)*
Middlton Lloyd Doll Fctry Outl, Coolville Also called Middleton Llyd Dolls Inc *(G-7835)*
Midflow Services LLC 330 674-2399
812 S Washington St Millersburg (44654) *(G-14246)*
Midflow Services LLC (PA) 330 567-3108
10774 Township Road 506 Shreve (44676) *(G-17161)*
Midlake Products & Mfg Co 330 875-4202
819 N Nickelplate St Louisville (44641) *(G-12319)*
Midland Engineering, Canton Also called Decision Systems Inc *(G-2682)*
Midland Oil Co 740 787-2557
14687 National Rd Se Brownsville (43721) *(G-2199)*
Midlands Millroom Supply Inc 330 453-9100
1911 36th St Ne Canton (44705) *(G-2779)*
Midmark Corporation (PA) 937 526-3662
60 Vista Dr Versailles (45380) *(G-19352)*
Midmark Corporation 937 526-8387
160 Industrial Pkwy Versailles (45380) *(G-19353)*
Midtown Pallet & Recycling 419 241-1311
1987 Hawthorne St Toledo (43606) *(G-18585)*
Midway Machining Inc 740 373-8976
1060 Gravel Bank Rd Marietta (45750) *(G-12808)*
Midway Products Group, Greenwich Also called Lakepark Industries Inc *(G-10533)*
Midway Swiss Turn Inc 330 264-4300
2160 Great Trails Dr Wooster (44691) *(G-20808)*
Midway Trailer Sales LLC 419 394-4408
14275 Glynwood Saint Marys (45885) *(G-16843)*
Midwest Acoust-A-Fiber Inc 740 363-6247
487 London Rd Delaware (43015) *(G-8871)*
Midwest Aircraft Products Co 419 884-2164
125 S Mill St Mansfield (44904) *(G-12648)*
Midwest Box Company 216 281-9021
9801 Walford Ave Ste C Cleveland (44102) *(G-5807)*
Midwest Centerless Grinding, Cincinnati Also called A and V Grinding Inc *(G-3330)*
Midwest Composites LLC 419 738-2431
302 Krein Ave Wapakoneta (45895) *(G-19497)*
Midwest Compost Inc 419 547-7979
6090 State Route 101 E Clyde (43410) *(G-6542)*
Midwest Compressor Co Inc (PA) 216 941-9200
12901 Elmwood Ave Cleveland (44111) *(G-5808)*
Midwest Container Corporation 513 870-3000
375 Northpointe Dr Fairfield (45014) *(G-9684)*
Midwest Conveyor Products Inc 419 281-1235
1919 Cellar Dr Ashland (44805) *(G-754)*
Midwest Curtainwalls Inc 216 641-7900
5171 Grant Ave Cleveland (44125) *(G-5809)*
Midwest Elastomers Inc 419 738-8844
700 Industrial Dr Wapakoneta (45895) *(G-19498)*

Midwest Energy Emissions Corp 614 505-6115
  670 Enterprise Dr Ste D Lewis Center (43035) *(G-11908)*

Midwest Exposure Magazine 937 626-6738
  1509 S Smithville Rd Dayton (45410) *(G-8495)*

Midwest Fabrications Inc 330 633-0191
  516 Commerce St Tallmadge (44278) *(G-18155)*

Midwest Fasteners Inc 937 866-0463
  450 Richard St Miamisburg (45342) *(G-13835)*

Midwest Filtration LLC 513 874-6510
  9775 International Blvd West Chester (45246) *(G-20030)*

Midwest Fireworks Mfg Co II 330 584-7000
  8550 State Route 224 Deerfield (44411) *(G-8774)*

Midwest Granite & Stone, Holland *Also called Schena Company Ltd (G-11083)*

Midwest Graphics, Columbus *Also called Our Nine LLC (G-7449)*

Midwest Industrial Products 216 771-8555
  7424 Bessemer Ave Cleveland (44127) *(G-5810)*

Midwest Industrial Rubber Inc 614 876-3110
  4847 Northwest Pkwy Hilliard (43026) *(G-10963)*

Midwest Industrial Specialties 740 815-0541
  5521 Summer Blvd Galena (43021) *(G-10248)*

Midwest Industrial Supply Inc 330 456-3121
  1101 3rd St Se Canton (44707) *(G-2780)*

Midwest Iron and Metal Co 937 222-5992
  461 Homestead Ave Dayton (45417) *(G-8496)*

Midwest Knife Grinding Inc 330 854-1030
  492 Elm Ridge Ave Ste 4 Canal Fulton (44614) *(G-2508)*

Midwest Laser Systems Inc 419 424-0062
  1101 Commerce Pkwy Findlay (45840) *(G-9861)*

Midwest Machine, West Unity *Also called Midwest Production Machining (G-20133)*

Midwest Metal Fabricators 419 739-7077
  712 Maple St Wapakoneta (45895) *(G-19499)*

Midwest Metal Fabricators 419 739-7077
  712 Maple St Wapakoneta (45895) *(G-19500)*

Midwest Metal Products LLC 614 539-7322
  3945 Brookham Dr Grove City (43123) *(G-10573)*

Midwest Metals & Supply LLC 513 489-1666
  952 Hamlin Dr Maineville (45039) *(G-12529)*

Midwest Metrology LLC 937 832-0965
  341 Smith Dr Englewood (45315) *(G-9533)*

Midwest Minicranes Inc 330 332-3700
  1350 Pennsylvania Ave Salem (44460) *(G-16915)*

Midwest Mold & Texture Corp 513 732-1300
  4270 Armstrong Blvd Batavia (45103) *(G-1205)*

Midwest Molding Inc 614 873-1572
  8245 Estates Pkwy Plain City (43064) *(G-16349)*

Midwest Motor Supply Co (PA) 800 233-1294
  4800 Roberts Rd Columbus (43228) *(G-7351)*

Midwest Ohio Tool Co 419 294-1987
  215 Tarhe Trl Upper Sandusky (43351) *(G-19132)*

Midwest Plastic Systems Inc 513 553-4380
  100 Front St New Richmond (45157) *(G-14943)*

Midwest Plastics, Lima *Also called W T Inc (G-12110)*

Midwest Precision LLC 440 951-2333
  34700 Lakeland Blvd Eastlake (44095) *(G-9282)*

Midwest Precision Products 440 237-9500
  9940 York Alpha Dr Cleveland (44133) *(G-5811)*

Midwest Production Machining 419 924-5616
  10484 State Route 191 West Unity (43570) *(G-20133)*

Midwest Quality Bedding Inc 614 504-5971
  3860 Morse Rd Columbus (43219) *(G-7352)*

Midwest Quality Bedding Inc 614 504-5971
  8400 Industrial Pkwy B Plain City (43064) *(G-16350)*

Midwest Service, Middletown *Also called Vail Rubber Works Inc (G-14093)*

Midwest Sign Center, Canton *Also called Midwest Sign Ctr (G-2781)*

Midwest Sign Ctr 330 493-7330
  4210 Cleveland Ave Nw Canton (44709) *(G-2781)*

Midwest Specialties Inc 419 738-8147
  851 Industrial Dr Wapakoneta (45895) *(G-19501)*

Midwest Specialty Pdts Co Inc 513 874-7070
  280 Northpointe Dr Fairfield (45014) *(G-9685)*

Midwest Spray Booths 937 439-6600
  7672 Mcewen Rd Dayton (45459) *(G-8497)*

Midwest Spray Drying Company 419 294-4221
  422 W Guthrie Dr Upper Sandusky (43351) *(G-19133)*

Midwest Stamping & Mfg Co 419 298-2394
  228 E Morrison St Edgerton (43517) *(G-9333)*

Midwest Telemetry Inc 440 725-5718
  8251 Mayfield Rd Ste 15 Chesterland (44026) *(G-3215)*

Midwest Timber & Land Co Inc 740 493-2400
  88 Jasper Rd Piketon (45661) *(G-16224)*

Midwest Tool & Engineering Co 937 224-0756
  112 Webster St Dayton (45402) *(G-8498)*

Midwest Trmnals Tledo Intl Inc (PA) 419 897-6868
  383 W Dussel Dr Maumee (43537) *(G-13283)*

Midwest Welding & Boiler Co, Cleveland *Also called Durisek Enterprises Inc (G-5225)*

Midwest Woodworking Co Inc 513 631-6684
  4019 Montgomery Rd Cincinnati (45212) *(G-4106)*

Midwestern Bag Co Inc 419 241-3112
  3230 Monroe St Toledo (43606) *(G-18586)*

Midwestern Industries Inc (PA) 330 837-4203
  915 Oberlin Ave Sw Massillon (44647) *(G-13180)*

Mielke Furniture Repair Inc 419 625-4572
  3209 Columbus Ave Sandusky (44870) *(G-16989)*

Mih Marketing Group Inc 740 942-0411
  546 N Main St Cadiz (43907) *(G-2420)*

Mika Metal Fabricating Co 440 951-5500
  4530 Hamann Pkwy Willoughby (44094) *(G-20549)*

Mikan Die and Tool LLC 216 265-2811
  13410 Enterprise Ave Cleveland (44135) *(G-5812)*

Mike B Crawford 330 673-7944
  606 Mogadore Rd Kent (44240) *(G-11492)*

Mike Closterman 513 245-9593
  5620 Cheviot Rd Cincinnati (45247) *(G-4107)*

Mike Loppe 937 969-8102
  2 W Main St Tremont City (45372) *(G-18789)*

Mike Strickland Logging, Oak Hill *Also called Michael D Strickland (G-15601)*

Mike Suponcic 740 635-0654
  68940 Blaine Chermont Rd Bridgeport (43912) *(G-2092)*

Mike-Sells Potato Chip Co (HQ) 937 228-9400
  333 Leo St Dayton (45404) *(G-8499)*

Mikes Automotive LLC 937 233-1433
  7581 Brandt Pike Unit B Dayton (45424) *(G-8500)*

Mikes Mill Shop Inc 419 538-6091
  14768 Road J Ottawa (45875) *(G-15801)*

Mikes Welding 937 675-6587
  5589 Old Us Route 35 E Jamestown (45335) *(G-11352)*

Mil-Mar Century Corporation 937 275-4860
  8641 Washington Church Rd Miamisburg (45342) *(G-13836)*

Milacron Holdings Corp (PA) 513 487-5000
  10200 Alliance Rd Ste 200 Blue Ash (45242) *(G-1841)*

Milacron LLC 513 536-2000
  4165 Half Acre Rd Batavia (45103) *(G-1206)*

Milacron LLC (HQ) 513 487-5000
  10200 Alliance Rd Ste 200 Blue Ash (45242) *(G-1842)*

Milacron Marketing Company LLC (HQ) 513 536-2000
  4165 Half Acre Rd Batavia (45103) *(G-1207)*

Milacron Plas Tech Group LLC (HQ) 513 536-2000
  4165 Half Acre Rd Batavia (45103) *(G-1208)*

Milacron Plas Tech Group LLC 937 444-2532
  418 W Main St Mount Orab (45154) *(G-14583)*

Milan Tool Corp 216 661-1078
  8989 Brookpark Rd Cleveland (44129) *(G-5813)*

Milano Monuments LLC 216 362-1199
  14600 Brookpark Rd Cleveland (44135) *(G-5814)*

Milark Industries, Mansfield *Also called Hayford Technologies (G-12622)*

Milburn Eye Center, Medina *Also called Drs Milburn-Medina Inc (G-13404)*

Miles Folding Box Co Div, Cleveland *Also called Sobel Corrugated Cntrs Inc (G-6216)*

Miles Park Window Treatments, Beachwood *Also called Miles Pk Vntian Blind Shds Mfg (G-1279)*

Miles Pk Vntian Blind Shds Mfg 216 239-0850
  23880 Commerce Park # 100 Beachwood (44122) *(G-1279)*

Miles Rubber & Packing Company (PA) 330 425-3888
  9020 Dutton Dr Twinsburg (44087) *(G-18988)*

Milestone Services Corp 330 374-9988
  551 Beacon St Akron (44311) *(G-298)*

Milestone Veneer, Granville *Also called Milestone Ventures LLC (G-10462)*

Milestone Ventures LLC (PA) 317 908-2093
  2924 Hallie Ln Granville (43023) *(G-10462)*

Mileti Optical & Hearing Ctr, Cleveland *Also called Mileti Optical Inc (G-5815)*

Mileti Optical Inc 440 884-6333
  5957 State Rd Ste 1 Cleveland (44134) *(G-5815)*

Milford Printers (PA) 513 831-6630
  317 Main St Milford (45150) *(G-14162)*

Milford Printers 513 831-6630
  18 Locust St Milford (45150) *(G-14163)*

Milicom LLC 216 765-8875
  23307 Commerce Park Beachwood (44122) *(G-1280)*

Military Resources LLC 330 263-1040
  1036 Burbank Rd Wooster (44691) *(G-20809)*

Military Resources LLC (PA) 330 309-9970
  1834 Cleveland Rd Ste 301 Wooster (44691) *(G-20810)*

Milk & Honey 330 492-5884
  3400 Cleveland Ave Nw # 1 Canton (44709) *(G-2782)*

Mill & Motion Inc 216 524-4000
  5415 E Schaaf Rd Ste 101 Cleveland (44131) *(G-5816)*

Mill Craft Mch & Fabrication 419 422-6346
  1500 Morrical Blvd Findlay (45840) *(G-9862)*

Mill Rose Laboratories Inc 440 974-6730
  7310 Corp Blvd Mentor (44060) *(G-13656)*

Mill-Rose Company (PA) 440 255-9171
  7995 Tyler Blvd Mentor (44060) *(G-13657)*

Millat Industries Corp (PA) 937 434-6666
  4901 Croftshire Dr Dayton (45440) *(G-8501)*

Millat Industries Corp 937 535-1500
  7611 Center Pt I 70 Blvd Dayton (45424) *(G-8502)*

Millcraft Group LLC (PA) 216 441-5500
  6800 Grant Ave Cleveland (44105) *(G-5817)*

Millennium, Ashtabula *Also called Cristal USA Inc (G-800)*

Millennium Adhesive Pdts Inc 440 708-1212
178 E Washington St Ste 1 Chagrin Falls (44022) ***(G-3064)***
Millennium Adhesive Products 440 708-1212
17340 Munn Rd Chagrin Falls (44023) ***(G-3104)***
Millennium Mch Techlonlogy LLC 440 269-8080
38323 Apollo Pkwy Ste 7 Willoughby (44094) ***(G-20550)***
Miller & Son Logging 330 738-2031
8521 Clover Rd Ne Mechanicstown (44651) ***(G-13360)***
Miller and Slay Wdwkg LLC 513 265-3816
8284 Winters Ln Mason (45040) ***(G-13063)***
Miller Bearing Company Inc 330 678-8844
420 Portage Blvd Kent (44240) ***(G-11493)***
Miller Bros Paving Inc (HQ) 419 445-1015
1613 S Defiance St Archbold (43502) ***(G-687)***
Miller Cabinet Company LLC 614 873-4221
6217 Converse Huff Rd Plain City (43064) ***(G-16351)***
Miller Casting Inc 330 482-2923
1634 Lower Elkton Rd Columbiana (44408) ***(G-6624)***
Miller Consolidated Industries (PA) 937 294-2681
2221 Arbor Blvd Moraine (45439) ***(G-14507)***
Miller Core 2 Inc 330 359-0500
9823 Chestnut Ridge Rd Nw Beach City (44608) ***(G-1249)***
Miller Crist 330 359-7877
10258 S Kansas Rd Fredericksburg (44627) ***(G-10088)***
Miller Curber Company LLC 330 782-8081
4020 Simon Rd Youngstown (44512) ***(G-21146)***
Miller Engine & Machine Co, Springfield *Also called Muller Engine & Machine Co* ***(G-17610)***
Miller Enterprises Ohio LLC 330 852-4009
1360 County Road 108 Sugarcreek (44681) ***(G-18027)***
Miller Industries Inc 937 293-2223
139 Auto Club Dr Dayton (45402) ***(G-8503)***
Miller Leasing, Baltic *Also called Crawford Manufacturing Company* ***(G-1068)***
Miller Logging 440 693-4001
5327 Parks West Rd Middlefield (44062) ***(G-13965)***
Miller Logging Inc 330 279-4721
8373 State Route 83 Holmesville (44633) ***(G-11109)***
Miller Lumber Co Inc 330 674-0273
7101 State Route 39 Millersburg (44654) ***(G-14247)***
Miller Machine & Mfg LLC 740 439-2283
62056 Greendale Rd Cambridge (43725) ***(G-2466)***
Miller Manufacturing Inc 330 852-0689
2705 Shetler Rd Nw Sugarcreek (44681) ***(G-18028)***
Miller Pallet Company 937 464-4483
9216 County Road 97 Belle Center (43310) ***(G-1514)***
Miller Printing Co, Springfield *Also called Graphic Paper Products Corp* ***(G-17564)***
Miller Products Inc 330 308-5934
642 Wabash Ave Nw New Philadelphia (44663) ***(G-14915)***
Miller Prsthtics Orthotics LLC 740 421-4211
809 Farson St Unit 108 Belpre (45714) ***(G-1591)***
Miller Publishing Company 937 866-3331
230 S 2nd St Miamisburg (45342) ***(G-13837)***
Miller Studio Inc 330 339-1100
734 Fair Ave Nw New Philadelphia (44663) ***(G-14916)***
Miller Tool and Machine Co 330 297-9657
7888 Cooley Rd Ravenna (44266) ***(G-16541)***
Miller Welding Inc 330 364-6173
2718 Broad Run Dar Rd Nw Dover (44622) ***(G-9002)***
Miller Weldmaster Corporation (PA) 330 833-6739
4220 Alabama Ave Sw Navarre (44662) ***(G-14719)***
Miller Wire & Cable, Cleveland *Also called Marlin Thermocouple Wire Inc* ***(G-5750)***
Miller Wood Design, Sugarcreek *Also called Miller Manufacturing Inc* ***(G-18028)***
Miller, Jim Furniture, Enon *Also called Hallmark Industries Inc* ***(G-9545)***
Millercoors LLC 513 896-9200
2525 Wayne Madison Rd Trenton (45067) ***(G-18796)***
Millers Liniments LLC 440 548-5800
17150 Bundysburg Rd Middlefield (44062) ***(G-13966)***
Millers Mini Barns 937 544-6317
1587 Wheat Ridge Rd West Union (45693) ***(G-20124)***
Millers Storage Barns LLC 330 893-3293
4230 State Route 39 Millersburg (44654) ***(G-14248)***
Millersburg Ice Co 330 674-3016
25 S Grant St Millersburg (44654) ***(G-14249)***
Millersville Lime Inc 3 .... 419 986-2019
1967 County Rd 42 Bettsville (44815) ***(G-1669)***
Milligan Workshops Inc 419 353-0099
420 Industrial Pkwy Bowling Green (43402) ***(G-2002)***
Millinium 3 Inc (PA) 513 770-3122
4660 Duke Dr Ste 390 Mason (45040) ***(G-13064)***
Millmcrawley, Greenville *Also called Markwith Tool Company Inc* ***(G-10510)***
Mills Aluminum Fab 330 821-4108
W 23 Rd St Alliance (44601) ***(G-527)***
Mills Company (HQ) 740 375-0770
3007 Harding Hwy E 4n Marion (43302) ***(G-12885)***
Mills Customs Woodworks 216 407-3600
3950 Prospect Ave E Cleveland (44115) ***(G-5818)***
Mills Led LLC (PA) 800 690-6403
81 S 5th St Ste 201 Columbus (43215) ***(G-7353)***
Mills Led LLC 800 690-6403
655 N Cassady Ave Columbus (43219) ***(G-7354)***
MILLS METAL FINISHING, Columbus *Also called Mmf Incorporated* ***(G-7358)***
Mills Walls, Brecksville *Also called M/W International Inc* ***(G-2063)***
Millstone Coffee Inc (HQ) 513 983-1100
1 Procter And Gamble Plz Cincinnati (45202) ***(G-4108)***
Millstream Press Inc 419 422-9745
1631 Broad Ave Findlay (45840) ***(G-9863)***
Millwood Inc 330 857-3075
8208 S Kohler Rd Apple Creek (44606) ***(G-645)***
Millwood Inc 614 717-9099
9749 Fairway Dr Powell (43065) ***(G-16479)***
Millwood Inc 614 409-9680
1886 Williams Rd Columbus (43207) ***(G-7355)***
Millwood Inc 513 860-4567
4438 Muhlhauser Rd # 100 West Chester (45011) ***(G-19901)***
Millwood Inc (PA) 330 393-4400
3708 International Blvd Vienna (44473) ***(G-19370)***
Millwood Inc 330 359-5220
18279 Dover Rd Dundee (44624) ***(G-9176)***
Millwood Logging, Gnadenhutten *Also called Millwood Lumber Inc* ***(G-10408)***
Millwood Lumber Inc 740 254-4681
2400 Larson Rd Se Gnadenhutten (44629) ***(G-10408)***
Millwood Natural LLC 330 393-4400
3708 International Blvd Vienna (44473) ***(G-19371)***
Millwood Pallet Co, Dundee *Also called Millwood Inc* ***(G-9176)***
Millwood Plant, Howard *Also called Premier Silica LLC* ***(G-11124)***
Millwood Wholesale Inc 330 359-6109
7969 Township Road 662 Dundee (44624) ***(G-9177)***
Millwork Designs Inc 740 335-5203
230 Topaz Ln Wshngtn CT Hs (43160) ***(G-20917)***
Millwork Fabricators Inc 937 299-5452
3176 Kettering Blvd Moraine (45439) ***(G-14508)***
Millwrght Wldg Fbrication Svcs 740 533-1510
1590 County Road 105 Kitts Hill (45645) ***(G-11621)***
Milnot Company 888 656-3245
735 Taylor Rd Ste 200 Gahanna (43230) ***(G-10220)***
Milo Bennett Corp 419 874-1492
12922 Eckel Junction Rd Perrysburg (43551) ***(G-16122)***
Milos Whole World Gourmet LLC 740 589-6456
94 Columbus Rd Athens (45701) ***(G-877)***
Milsek Furniture Polish Inc 330 542-2700
5525 E Pine Lake Rd Petersburg (44454) ***(G-16178)***
Milso Midwest 513 745-0760
4739 Interstate Dr West Chester (45246) ***(G-20031)***
Miltronics & Skye, Mentor *Also called M & S Acquistion Co LLC* ***(G-13638)***
Mim Software Inc (PA) 216 896-9798
25800 Science Park Dr # 180 Beachwood (44122) ***(G-1281)***
Mindcrafted Systems Inc 440 821-2245
1969 Newbury Dr Cleveland (44145) ***(G-5819)***
Minderman Marine Products Inc 419 732-2626
129 Buckeye Blvd Port Clinton (43452) ***(G-16406)***
Mine Equipment Services LLC (PA) 740 936-5427
3958 State Route 3 Sunbury (43074) ***(G-18067)***
Miner's Bishop Tractor Sales, Rootstown *Also called Miners Tractor Sales Inc* ***(G-16725)***
Mineral Met Inc 216 641-3555
7700 Bessemer Ave Cleveland (44127) ***(G-5820)***
Mineral Processing Company 419 396-3501
1855 County Highway 99 Carey (43316) ***(G-2920)***
Mineral Technology Metal Cast, Archbold *Also called American Colloid Company* ***(G-662)***
Miners Tractor Sales Inc (PA) 330 325-9914
6941 Tallmadge Rd Rootstown (44272) ***(G-16725)***
Minerva Dairy Inc 330 868-4196
430 Radloff Ave Minerva (44657) ***(G-14334)***
Minerva Leader, Minerva *Also called Alliance Publishing Co Inc* ***(G-14316)***
Minerva Maid, Minerva *Also called Minerva Dairy Inc* ***(G-14334)***
Minerva Operations, Minerva *Also called Colfor Manufacturing Inc* ***(G-14319)***
Minerva Tube Plant, Minerva *Also called Caraustar Industrial and Con* ***(G-14318)***
Minerva Welding and Fabg Inc 330 868-7731
22133 Us Route 30 Minerva (44657) ***(G-14335)***
Mings Heating & AC 216 721-2007
11902 Larchmere Blvd Cleveland (44120) ***(G-5821)***
Mini-Mix Inc 740 345-3186
746 Maple Grove Ave Newark (43055) ***(G-15034)***
Minimally Invasive Devices Inc 614 484-5036
1275 Kinnear Rd Columbus (43212) ***(G-7356)***
Mining Reclamation Inc 740 327-5555
15953 State Route 60 S Dresden (43821) ***(G-9033)***
Minnich Manufacturing Co Inc 419 903-0010
1444 State Route 42 Mansfield (44903) ***(G-12649)***
Minnicks Drive-Thru 513 868-6126
828 East Ave Hamilton (45011) ***(G-10725)***
Minor Corporation 216 291-8723
1599 Maywood Rd Cleveland (44121) ***(G-5822)***
Minotas Trophies & Awards 440 720-1288
40 Alpha Park Cleveland (44143) ***(G-5823)***
Minster Farmers, Minster *Also called Sunrise Cooperative Inc* ***(G-14362)***
Minteq International Inc 330 343-8821
5864 Crown Street Ext Nw Dover (44622) ***(G-9003)***
Minuteman Distribution, Medina *Also called Jacobson Mfg LLC* ***(G-13429)***

Minuteman Distribution, Millersport *Also called Jacobson Mfg LLC (G-14295)*

Minuteman of Heath, Newark *Also called L & T Collins Inc (G-15029)*

Minuteman Press, Cincinnati *Also called Bock & Pierce Enterprises (G-3455)*

Minuteman Press, Parma *Also called Fourjays Inc (G-15958)*

Minuteman Press, Ontario *Also called Cnb LLC (G-15685)*

Minuteman Press, Columbus *Also called Henry Bussman (G-7150)*

Minuteman Press, Fairlawn *Also called Frisby Printing Company (G-9750)*

Minuteman Press, Athens *Also called Double b Printing LLC (G-863)*

Minuteman Press, Cincinnati *Also called Mmp Printing Inc (G-4112)*

Minuteman Press, Youngstown *Also called Seifert Printing Company (G-21199)*

Minuteman Press, Lebanon *Also called Geygan Enterprises Inc (G-11803)*

Minuteman Press, Medina *Also called Debandale Printing Inc (G-13401)*

Minuteman Press, Troy *Also called Schiffer Group Inc (G-18872)*

Minuteman Press, Toledo *Also called Stepping Stone Enterprises Inc (G-18703)*

Minuteman Press, Columbus *Also called Capehart Enterprises LLC (G-6895)*

Minuteman Press, Middleburg Heights *Also called Williams Executive Entps Inc (G-13910)*

Minuteman Press, Port Clinton *Also called Schaffner Publication Inc (G-16413)*

Minuteman Press, Cleveland *Also called Kovacevic Printing Inc (G-5663)*

Minuteman Press, North Olmsted *Also called Kelly Prints LLC (G-15340)*

Minuteman Press, Dublin *Also called Kad Holdings Inc (G-9093)*

Minuteman Press, Dayton *Also called Premier Printing and Packg Inc (G-8589)*

Minuteman Press, Lewis Center *Also called Shallow Lake Corp (G-11917)*

Minuteman Press 440 946-3311
7450 Mentor Ave Mentor (44060) *(G-13658)*

Minuteman Press 419 782-8002
214 Clinton St Defiance (43512) *(G-8805)*

Minuteman Press 513 772-0500
2312 E Sharon Rd Cincinnati (45241) *(G-4109)*

Minuteman Press 614 337-2334
265 Lincoln Cir Ste C Columbus (43230) *(G-7357)*

Minuteman Press 937 429-8610
2372 Lakeview Dr Beavercreek (45431) *(G-1352)*

Minuteman Press Inc 513 741-9056
9904 Colerain Ave Cincinnati (45251) *(G-4110)*

Minuteman Press of Athens LLC 740 593-7393
17 W Washington St Athens (45701) *(G-878)*

Minuteman Press of Elyria 440 365-9377
631 Abbe Rd S Elyria (44035) *(G-9463)*

Minutman Press Frfeld Cnty LLC 740 689-1992
135 N Columbus St Lancaster (43130) *(G-11730)*

Mir, Hilliard *Also called Midwest Industrial Rubber Inc (G-10963)*

Miracle Air, Franklin *Also called Miracle Welding Inc (G-10037)*

Miracle Core Filters, Sandusky *Also called D C Filter & Chemical Inc (G-16955)*

Miracle Documents 513 651-2222
2300 Montana Ave Ste 301 Cincinnati (45211) *(G-4111)*

Miracle Metal Finishing, Cleveland *Also called Kyron Plating Corp (G-5668)*

Miracle Welding Inc 513 746-9977
141 Industrial Dr Ste 200 Franklin (45005) *(G-10037)*

Miraclecorp Products (PA) 937 293-9994
2425 W Dorothy Ln Moraine (45439) *(G-14509)*

Mirion Technologies Ist Corp 614 367-2050
12954 Stonecreek Dr Ste C Pickerington (43147) *(G-16198)*

Mirmat Cnc Machining Inc 440 951-2410
4550 Hamann Pkwy Willoughby (44094) *(G-20551)*

Mirror 419 893-8135
113 W Wayne St Maumee (43537) *(G-13284)*

Mirror Publishing Co Inc 419 893-8135
113 W Wayne St Maumee (43537) *(G-13285)*

Mirror, The, Maumee *Also called Mirror Publishing Co Inc (G-13285)*

Mirror-Coat, Cincinnati *Also called Southern Adhsives Coatings Inc (G-4438)*

Mirus Adapted Tech LLC 614 402-4585
288 Cramer Creek Ct Dublin (43017) *(G-9103)*

Mis, Ashland *Also called Maverick Innvtive Slutions LLC (G-751)*

Mis Micro Information Services, Cincinnati *Also called Steve Schaefer (G-4465)*

Mis Solutions, Cincinnati *Also called Wissman & Wood Incorporated (G-4600)*

Misato Computer Products Inc 937 890-8410
850 Industrial Park Dr Vandalia (45377) *(G-19305)*

Miscellnous Mtals Fbrction Inc 740 779-3071
18828 Us Highway 50 Chillicothe (45601) *(G-3252)*

Misco Refractometer, Solon *Also called Mercury Iron & Steel (G-17334)*

Mission Control Systems Inc 419 472-3791
3900 Sunforest Ct Ste 119 Toledo (43623) *(G-18587)*

Mission Industrial Group LLC 740 387-2287
3602 Harding Hwy E Marion (43302) *(G-12886)*

Mission Support, Beavercreek *Also called Leidos Inc (G-1348)*

Misumi Investment USA Corp (HQ) 937 859-5111
500 Progress Rd Dayton (45449) *(G-8504)*

Mitchell Bros Ice Cream Inc 216 861-2799
1867 W 25th St Cleveland (44113) *(G-5824)*

Mitchell Electronics Inc 740 594-8532
1005 E State St Ste 5 Athens (45701) *(G-879)*

Mitchell Piping LLC 330 245-0258
1101 Sunnyside St Sw C Hartville (44632) *(G-10830)*

Mitchell Plastics Inc 330 825-2461
130 31st St Nw Barberton (44203) *(G-1131)*

Mitchell Welding LLC 740 259-2211
11761 State Route 104 Lucasville (45648) *(G-12422)*

Mitchellace Inc (PA) 740 354-2813
830 Murray St Portsmouth (45662) *(G-16444)*

Mitchs Welding & Hitches 419 893-3117
802 Kingsbury St Maumee (43537) *(G-13286)*

Mitec Powertrain Inc 567 525-5606
4000 Fostoria Ave Findlay (45840) *(G-9864)*

Mitel (delaware) Inc 513 733-8000
9100 W Chester Towne Ctr West Chester (45069) *(G-19902)*

Mitsubishi Chls Perf Plyrs Inc 419 483-2931
350 N Buckeye St Bellevue (44811) *(G-1553)*

Mitsubishi Elc Auto Amer Inc (HQ) 513 573-6614
4773 Bethany Rd Mason (45040) *(G-13065)*

Mix-Masters Inc 513 228-2800
2550 Henkle Dr Lebanon (45036) *(G-11817)*

Mixed Logic LLC 440 826-1676
5907 E Law Rd Valley City (44280) *(G-19218)*

Mizer Printing & Graphics 740 942-3343
160 Cunningham Ave Cadiz (43907) *(G-2421)*

Mj Coates Homes, Dayton *Also called M J Coates Construction Co (G-8463)*

Mjc Enterprises Inc 330 669-3744
7820 Blough Rd Sterling (44276) *(G-17684)*

MJM Industries Inc 440 350-1230
1200 East St Fairport Harbor (44077) *(G-9768)*

Mk Enterprises Inc 440 632-0121
11162 Industrial Pkwy Middlefield (44062) *(G-13967)*

Mk Global Enterprises LLC 440 823-0081
23980 Chagrin Blvd # 204 Beachwood (44122) *(G-1282)*

Mk Metal Products Inc (PA) 419 756-3644
90 Sawyer Pkwy Mansfield (44903) *(G-12650)*

Mk Trempe Corporation (PA) 937 492-3548
2349 Industrial Dr Sidney (45365) *(G-17204)*

ML Erectors LLC 440 328-3227
827 Walnut St Elyria (44035) *(G-9464)*

Mlad Graphic Design Services, Tiffin *Also called M L Advertising & Design LLC (G-18230)*

MLS Systems, Findlay *Also called Midwest Laser Systems Inc (G-9861)*

Mm Service 330 474-3098
8936 State Route 14 Streetsboro (44241) *(G-17863)*

Mmei, Middlefield *Also called Molten Mtal Eqp Innvations LLC (G-13968)*

Mmf Incorporated (PA) 614 252-2522
1977 Mcallister Ave Columbus (43205) *(G-7358)*

Mmf Incorporated 614 252-2522
1977 Mcallister Ave Columbus (43205) *(G-7359)*

Mmh Americas Inc (HQ) 414 764-6200
4401 Gateway Blvd Springfield (45502) *(G-17605)*

Mmh Holdings Inc (HQ) 937 525-5533
4401 Gateway Blvd Springfield (45502) *(G-17606)*

Mmi Textiles Inc 440 899-8050
29260 Clemens Rd Bldg Ii Westlake (44145) *(G-20283)*

Mmp Printing Inc 513 381-0990
10570 Chester Rd Cincinnati (45215) *(G-4112)*

Mmp Toledo 419 472-0505
5847 Secor Rd Toledo (43623) *(G-18588)*

Mn8-Foxfire, Cincinnati *Also called Evp International LLC (G-3727)*

Mo-Trim Inc 740 432-2098
240 Steubenville Ave Cambridge (43725) *(G-2467)*

Mobile Conversions Inc 513 797-1991
3354 State Route 132 Amelia (45102) *(G-580)*

Mobile Mini Inc 303 305-9515
8045 Dawnwood Ave Ne Canton (44721) *(G-2783)*

Mobile Mini Inc 513 353-9800
4444 Dixie Hwy Fairfield (45014) *(G-9686)*

Mobile Mini Inc. 614 449-8655
871 Buckeye Park Rd Columbus (43207) *(G-7360)*

Mobile Office Solutions, Batavia *Also called Foster Products Inc (G-1186)*

Mobile Operations, Van Wert *Also called Eaton Corporation (G-19253)*

Mobile Solutions LLC 614 286-3944
149 N Hamilton Rd Columbus (43213) *(G-7361)*

Mobility Revolution LLC 909 980-2259
6753 Engle Rd Ste A Cleveland (44130) *(G-5825)*

Mobis North America LLC 419 729-6700
3900 Stickney Ave Toledo (43608) *(G-18589)*

Mock Shoppe, Greenville *Also called Cromwell Aleene (G-10496)*

Mock Woodworking Company LLC 740 452-2701
4400 West Pike Zanesville (43701) *(G-21329)*

Model and Tool Making, Andover *Also called Mathew Odonnell (G-618)*

Model Engineering Company 330 644-3450
610 E State St Barberton (44203) *(G-1132)*

Model Graphics & Media Inc 513 541-2355
2614 Crescentville Rd West Chester (45069) *(G-19903)*

Model Pattern & Foundry Co 513 542-2322
3242 Spring Grove Ave Cincinnati (45225) *(G-4113)*

Modern AG Supply Inc 419 753-3484
302 S Main St New Knoxville (45871) *(G-14838)*

Modern American Design Inc 330 633-0227
491 Tacoma Ave Tallmadge (44278) *(G-18156)*

ALPHABETIC

Modern Builders Supply Inc (PA) 330 729-2690
302 Mcclurg Rd Youngstown (44512) *(G-21147)*
Modern Builders Supply Inc 419 526-0002
85 Smith Ave Mansfield (44905) *(G-12651)*
Modern China Inc (PA) 330 938-6104
550 E Ohio Ave Sebring (44672) *(G-17048)*
Modern Design Stamping Div 216 382-6318
1618 Maple Rd Cleveland (44121) *(G-5826)*
Modern Designs Inc 330 644-1771
310 Killian Rd Akron (44319) *(G-299)*
Modern Displays Inc 513 471-1639
4301 Schulte Dr Cincinnati (45205) *(G-4114)*
Modern Engineering 440 593-5414
527 W Adams St Conneaut (44030) *(G-7816)*
Modern Ice Equipment & Sup Co (PA) 513 367-2101
5709 Harrison Ave Cincinnati (45248) *(G-4115)*
Modern Industries Inc 216 432-2855
6610 Metta Ave Cleveland (44103) *(G-5827)*
Modern Ink Technology LLC 419 738-9664
1005 W Grand Ave Lima (45801) *(G-12059)*
Modern Manufacturing (PA) 513 251-3600
240 Stille Dr Cincinnati (45233) *(G-4116)*
Modern Mold and Tool 440 236-9600
27684 Royalton Rd Columbia Station (44028) *(G-6591)*
Modern Pipe Supports Corp 216 361-1666
4734 Commerce Ave Cleveland (44103) *(G-5828)*
Modern Plastics Recovery Inc 419 622-4611
100 Main St Haviland (45851) *(G-10842)*
Modern Safety Techniques, Hicksville Also called MST Inc *(G-10903)*
Modern Sheet Metal Works Inc 513 353-3666
6037 State Rte 128 Miamitown (45041) *(G-13890)*
Modern Store Fixtures Inc 330 427-6906
10421 Industrial Dr Garrettsville (44231) *(G-10331)*
Modern Time Dealer, Uniontown Also called Bobit Business Media Inc *(G-19077)*
Modern Tour, Cincinnati Also called Modern Ice Equipment & Sup Co *(G-4115)*
Modern Trade Communications 419 849-3109
109 Portage St Woodville (43469) *(G-20726)*
Modern Welding Co Ohio Inc 740 344-9425
1 Modern Way Newark (43055) *(G-15035)*
Modroto 800 772-7659
4920 State Rd Ashtabula (44004) *(G-821)*
Modular Assembly Innovations (PA) 614 389-4860
600 Stonehenge Pkwy # 100 Dublin (43017) *(G-9104)*
Modular Security Systems Inc 740 532-7822
1804 N 2nd St Ironton (45638) *(G-11297)*
Module 21 Bldg Company, Dayton Also called M21 Industries LLC *(G-8465)*
Mohawk Fine Papers Inc 440 969-2000
6800 Center Rd Ashtabula (44004) *(G-822)*
Mohawk Industries Inc 800 837-3812
3565 Urbancrest Indus Dr Grove City (43123) *(G-10574)*
Mohawk Manufacturing Inc 860 632-2345
306 E Gambier St Mount Vernon (43050) *(G-14631)*
Mohican Industries Inc 330 869-0500
1225 W Market St Akron (44313) *(G-300)*
Mohican Log Homes Inc 419 994-4088
2441 State Route 60 Loudonville (44842) *(G-12299)*
Mohican Steel Fabricators Inc 419 994-4802
521 N Spring St Loudonville (44842) *(G-12300)*
Mohican Wood Products 740 599-5655
20460 Nunda Rd Butler (44822) *(G-2393)*
Mohler Lumber Company 330 499-5461
4214 Portage St Nw North Canton (44720) *(G-15250)*
Mojo Sportsgear 614 864-6656
5765 Westbourne Ave Columbus (43213) *(G-7362)*
Mojonnier Usa LLC 844 665-6664
10325 State Route 43 N Streetsboro (44241) *(G-17864)*
Mok Industries LLC 614 934-1734
4449 Easton Way Columbus (43219) *(G-7363)*
Mold Crafters Inc 937 426-3179
1531 Keystone Ave Dayton (45403) *(G-8505)*
Mold Masters Intl Inc 440 953-0220
7500 Clover Ave Mentor (44060) *(G-13659)*
Mold Shop Inc 419 829-2041
8520 Central Ave Sylvania (43560) *(G-18118)*
Mold Solutions 800 948-4947
55 S Main St Ste 131 Oberlin (44074) *(G-15645)*
Mold Surface Textures 330 678-8590
4485 Crystal Pkwy Ste 300 Kent (44240) *(G-11494)*
Mold Tech, Painesville Also called Xponet Inc *(G-15943)*
Molded Extruded 216 475-5491
23940 Miles Rd Bedford Heights (44128) *(G-1490)*
Molded Fiber Glass Companies (PA) 440 997-5851
2925 Mfg Pl Ashtabula (44004) *(G-823)*
Molded Fiber Glass Companies 440 997-5851
4401 Benefit Ave Ashtabula (44004) *(G-824)*
Molded Fiber Glass Research 440 994-5100
1315 W 47th St Ashtabula (44004) *(G-825)*
Molded Parts Division, North Kingsville Also called Premix Inc *(G-15304)*
Molders World Inc 513 469-6653
11471 Deerfield Rd Blue Ash (45242) *(G-1843)*

Molding Dynamics Inc 440 786-8100
7009 Krick Rd Bedford (44146) *(G-1444)*
Molding Machine Services Inc (PA) 330 461-2270
734 N Progress Dr Medina (44256) *(G-13448)*
Molding Technologies, Hebron Also called MTI Acquisition LLC *(G-10876)*
Moldmakers Inc 419 673-0902
13608 Us Highway 68 Kenton (43326) *(G-11559)*
Molecular Research Center (PA) 513 841-0900
5645 Montgomery Rd Cincinnati (45212) *(G-4117)*
Moleman 513 662-3017
1314 Pennsbury Dr Cincinnati (45238) *(G-4118)*
Moleman Mole Trapping, Cincinnati Also called Moleman *(G-4118)*
Mollard Conducting Batons Inc 330 659-7081
2236 N Clvland Mssllon Rd Bath (44210) *(G-1239)*
Molorokalin Inc (HQ) 330 629-1332
4137 Boardman Canfield Rd Ll04 Canfield (44406) *(G-2566)*
Molten Metals, Middlefield Also called Pckd Enterprises Inc *(G-13980)*
Molten Mtal Eqp Innvations LLC 440 632-9119
15510 Old State Rd Middlefield (44062) *(G-13968)*
Molten North America Corp (HQ) 419 425-2700
1835 Industrial Dr Findlay (45840) *(G-9865)*
MOM Tools LLC 216 283-4014
3659 Green Rd Ste 304 Cleveland (44122) *(G-5829)*
Momentive Performance 281 325-3536
180 E Broad St Columbus (43215) *(G-7364)*
Momentive Performance Mtls, Richmond Heights Also called Momentive Performance Mtls Inc *(G-16655)*
Momentive Performance Mtls Inc 740 928-7010
611 O Neill Dr Hebron (43025) *(G-10874)*
Momentive Performance Mtls Inc 440 878-5705
24400 Highland Rd Richmond Heights (44143) *(G-16655)*
Momentive Performance Mtls Inc (PA) 614 986-2495
180 E Broad St Columbus (43215) *(G-7365)*
Momentive Prfmce Mtls Qrtz Inc 440 878-5700
22557 Lunn Rd Strongsville (44149) *(G-17941)*
Momentive Specialty Chem Inc 740 452-5451
2055 Grief Rd Zanesville (43701) *(G-21330)*
Moments To Remember USA LLC 330 830-0839
1250 Sanders Ave Sw Massillon (44647) *(G-13181)*
Mon-Say Corp 419 720-0163
2735 Dorr St Toledo (43607) *(G-18590)*
Monaghan & Associates Inc 937 253-7706
30 N Clinton St Dayton (45402) *(G-8506)*
Monaghan Tooling Group, Dayton Also called Monaghan & Associates Inc *(G-8506)*
Monarch, Cleveland Also called Integrated Power Services LLC *(G-5575)*
Monarch Engraving Inc 440 638-1500
8293 Dow Cir Strongsville (44136) *(G-17942)*
Monarch Ig Inc 330 897-2302
600 N Ray St Baltic (43804) *(G-1075)*
Monarch Lathes LP 937 492-4111
615 Oak Ave Sidney (45365) *(G-17205)*
Monarch Plastic Inc 330 683-0822
516 Jefferson Ave Orrville (44667) *(G-15747)*
Monarch Products Co 330 868-7717
105 Short St Minerva (44657) *(G-14336)*
Monarch Steel Company Inc 216 587-8000
4650 Johnston Pkwy Cleveland (44128) *(G-5830)*
Monarch Trailers Co 419 747-2848
3100 Plymuth Sprngmill Rd Shelby (44875) *(G-17138)*
Monarch Water Systems Inc 937 426-5773
689 Greystone Dr Beavercreek (45434) *(G-1353)*
Monco Enterprises Inc (PA) 937 461-0034
1507 Kuntz Rd Dayton (45404) *(G-8507)*
Mondelez Global LLC 419 691-5200
2221 Front St Toledo (43605) *(G-18591)*
Mondi Akrosil LLC 740 653-4102
3165 Wilson Rd Lancaster (43130) *(G-11731)*
Mondo Polymer Technologies Inc 740 376-9396
27620 State Rte 7 Reno (45773) *(G-16577)*
Money Jewelry Vaults 937 366-6391
236 E Sugartree St Wilmington (45177) *(G-20671)*
Monitor Mapboard Systems LLC 614 761-9985
565 Metro Pl S Ste 300 Dublin (43017) *(G-9105)*
Monitored Therapeutics Inc 614 761-3555
5940 Venture Dr Ste C Dublin (43017) *(G-9106)*
Monitortech Corp 614 231-0500
661 N James Rd Columbus (43219) *(G-7366)*
Monks Copy Shop Inc (PA) 614 885-7228
47 E Gay St Columbus (43215) *(G-7367)*
Monnig Welding Co 513 241-5156
521 Harriet St Cincinnati (45203) *(G-4119)*
Monode Marking Products Inc (PA) 440 975-8802
9200 Tyler Blvd Mentor (44060) *(G-13660)*
Monode Marking Products Inc 419 929-0346
149 High St New London (44851) *(G-14861)*
Monode Steel Stamp Inc (PA) 419 929-3501
149 High St New London (44851) *(G-14862)*
Monode Steel Stamp Inc 440 975-8802
7620 Tyler Blvd Mentor (44060) *(G-13661)*

Monovision Machine 330 833-2146
  125 Walnut Rd Se Massillon (44646) *(G-13182)*

Monroe County Beacon Inc 740 472-0734
  103 E Court St Woodsfield (43793) *(G-20720)*

Monroe Die & Stamping Co 216 883-6390
  3910 E 93rd St Cleveland (44105) *(G-5831)*

Monroe Drilling Operations 740 472-0866
  46886 Moore Ridge Rd Woodsfield (43793) *(G-20721)*

Monroe Tool and Mfg Co 216 883-7360
  3900 E 93rd St Cleveland (44105) *(G-5832)*

Monroe Water Sys Treatmnt Plnt, Sardis Also called Monroe Water System *(G-17036)*

Monroe Water System 740 472-1030
  35100 State Route 7 Sardis (43946) *(G-17036)*

Mons Meg Cartridges Inc 937 849-9646
  20 E Aspen Rd Medway (45341) *(G-13500)*

Montgomery & Montgomery LLC 330 858-9533
  80 N Pershing Ave Akron (44313) *(G-301)*

Montgomery License Bureau, Cincinnati Also called D J Klingler Inc *(G-3632)*

Montgomery Mch & Fabrication 740 286-2863
  206 Watts Blevins Rd Jackson (45640) *(G-11321)*

Montgomerys Pallet Service 330 297-6677
  7937 State Route 44 Ravenna (44266) *(G-16542)*

Monti Incorporated (PA) 513 761-7775
  4510 Reading Rd Cincinnati (45229) *(G-4120)*

Montview Corporation 330 723-3409
  404 W Liberty St Medina (44256) *(G-13449)*

Montville Plastics & Rbr LLC 440 548-3211
  15567 Main Market Rd Parkman (44080) *(G-15952)*

Moo Technologies Inc 513 732-5805
  950 Kent Rd Batavia (45103) *(G-1209)*

Moog Inc 330 682-0010
  1701 N Main St Orrville (44667) *(G-15748)*

Moonlight Specialties 216 464-6444
  4555 Renaissance Pkwy # 105 Cleveland (44128) *(G-5833)*

Moonlighting 330 533-3324
  8627 Gibson Rd Canfield (44406) *(G-2567)*

Moonshine Screen Printing Inc 513 523-7775
  23 N College Ave Oxford (45056) *(G-15840)*

Moonstruck Games Inc 513 721-3900
  312 Walnut St Ste 2275 Cincinnati (45202) *(G-4121)*

Moore Mc Millen Holdings 330 745-3075
  1850 Front St Cuyahoga Falls (44221) *(G-8027)*

Moore Chrome Products Co 419 843-3510
  3525 Silica Rd Sylvania (43560) *(G-18119)*

Moore Industries Inc 419 485-5572
  1317 Henricks Dr Montpelier (43543) *(G-14449)*

Moore Metal Finishing, Sylvania Also called Moore Chrome Products Co *(G-18119)*

Moore Mr Specialty Company 330 332-1229
  1050 Pennsylvania Ave Salem (44460) *(G-16916)*

Moore Outdoor Sign Craftsman, Westerville Also called Ohio Shelterall Inc *(G-20227)*

Moore Well Services Inc 330 650-4443
  246 N Cleveland Ave Mogadore (44260) *(G-14381)*

Mopac, Marion Also called Mid Ohio Packaging LLC *(G-12884)*

Mor-Lite Co Inc 513 661-8587
  2344 Wyoming Ave Cincinnati (45214) *(G-4122)*

Mor-X Plastics, Youngstown Also called Jamen Tool & Die Co *(G-21124)*

Moran Tool Inc 937 526-5210
  261 Baker Rd Versailles (45380) *(G-19354)*

Morcast Precision Inc 614 258-5071
  1615 Woodland Ave Columbus (43219) *(G-7368)*

More Manufacturing LLC 937 233-3898
  4025 Lisa Dr Ste A Tipp City (45371) *(G-18289)*

More Than Gourmet Inc 330 762-6652
  929 Home Ave Akron (44310) *(G-302)*

Morehouse Welding, Milford Also called James G Morehouse *(G-14155)*

Morey Woodworking LLC 937 623-5280
  377 E Loy Rd Piqua (45356) *(G-16293)*

Morgal Machine Tool Co 937 325-5561
  2100 S Yellow Springs St Springfield (45506) *(G-17607)*

Morgan Adhesives Company LLC (HQ) 330 688-1111
  4560 Darrow Rd Stow (44224) *(G-17775)*

Morgan Advanced Ceramics Inc 440 232-8604
  232 Forbes Rd Bedford (44146) *(G-1445)*

Morgan Advanced Materials, Bedford Also called Morgan Advanced Ceramics Inc *(G-1445)*

Morgan County Herald, McConnelsville Also called Morgan County Publishing Co *(G-13356)*

Morgan County Publishing Co 740 962-3377
  89 W Main St McConnelsville (43756) *(G-13356)*

Morgan Engineering Systems Inc 330 821-4721
  1182 E Summit St Alliance (44601) *(G-528)*

Morgan Engineering Systems Inc 330 823-6120
  1049 S Mahoning Ave Alliance (44601) *(G-529)*

Morgan Litho, Cleveland Also called T D Dynamics Inc *(G-6288)*

Morgan Precision Instrs LLC 330 896-0846
  3375 Miller Park Rd Akron (44312) *(G-303)*

Morgan Wood Products Inc 614 336-4000
  9761 Fairway Dr Powell (43065) *(G-16480)*

Morgantown Mch Hydraulics Ohio, New Philadelphia Also called Swanson Industries Inc *(G-14931)*

Mori Shuji 614 459-1296
  3755 Mountview Rd Columbus (43220) *(G-7369)*

Moritz Concrete Inc 419 529-3232
  362 N Trimble Rd Mansfield (44906) *(G-12652)*

Moritz International Inc 419 526-5222
  665 N Main St Mansfield (44902) *(G-12653)*

Moritz Materials Inc (PA) 419 281-0575
  859 Faultless Dr Ashland (44805) *(G-755)*

Mork Process Inc 330 928-3700
  400 W Wilson Bridge Rd # 130 Worthington (43085) *(G-20881)*

Morlan & Associates Inc (PA) 614 889-6152
  4970 Scioto Darby Rd D Hilliard (43026) *(G-10964)*

Morning Glory Technologies 440 796-5076
  12826 Morning Glory Trl Chesterland (44026) *(G-3216)*

Morning Journal, Lisbon Also called Ogden Newspapers Ohio Inc *(G-12129)*

Morning Journal, Lorain Also called Journal Register Company *(G-12251)*

Morning Pride Mfg LLC (HQ) 937 264-2662
  1 Innovation Ct Dayton (45414) *(G-8508)*

Morning Pride Mfg LLC 937 264-1726
  4978 Riverton Dr Dayton (45414) *(G-8509)*

Morning Sun Technologies Inc 513 461-1417
  7191 Morning Sun Rd Oxford (45056) *(G-15841)*

Morris Bean & Company 937 767-7301
  777 E Hyde Rd Yellow Springs (45387) *(G-20996)*

Morris Maico Hearing Aid Svc 419 232-6200
  117 N Washington St Van Wert (45891) *(G-19267)*

Morris Material Handling, Springfield Also called Mmh Holdings Inc *(G-17606)*

Morris Material Handling Inc (HQ) 937 525-5520
  4401 Gateway Blvd Springfield (45502) *(G-17608)*

Morris Paving 740 373-2457
  1470 Killwell Run Rd Marietta (45750) *(G-12809)*

Morris Technologies, Cincinnati Also called GE Aviation Systems LLC *(G-3807)*

Morris Technologies 330 384-3084
  1741 S Main St Akron (44301) *(G-304)*

Morris Technologies Inc 513 733-1611
  11988 Tramway Dr Cincinnati (45241) *(G-4123)*

Morrison Custom Welding Inc 330 264-0626
  1435 S Honeytown Rd Wooster (44691) *(G-20811)*

Morrison Media Group-Cmj LLP 216 973-4005
  11800 Shaker Blvd Cleveland (44120) *(G-5834)*

Morrison Medical 614 461-4400
  3735 Paragon Dr Columbus (43228) *(G-7370)*

Morrison Sign Company Inc 614 276-1181
  2757 Scioto Pkwy Columbus (43221) *(G-7371)*

Morrow Gravel, Morrow Also called Valley Asphalt Corporation *(G-14552)*

Morrow Gravel Company Inc (PA) 513 771-0820
  11641 Mosteller Rd Ste 2 Cincinnati (45241) *(G-4124)*

Morrow Gravel Company Inc 513 899-2000
  4850 Stubbs Mills Rd Morrow (45152) *(G-14549)*

Morse Enterprises Inc 513 229-3600
  6678 Tri Way Dr Mason (45040) *(G-13066)*

Morselicious Cupcakes 216 408-7508
  17341 Independence Ct Brookpark (44142) *(G-2167)*

Morton Buildings Inc 330 345-6188
  1055 Columbus Avenue Ext Wooster (44691) *(G-20812)*

Morton Buildings Inc 740 783-2331
  40800 Marietta Rd Caldwell (43724) *(G-2430)*

Morton Buildings Inc 419 673-0741
  14483 State Route 31 Kenton (43326) *(G-11560)*

Morton Buildings Inc 419 675-2311
  14483 State Route 31 Kenton (43326) *(G-11561)*

Morton Buildings Plant, Kenton Also called Morton Buildings Inc *(G-11561)*

Morton International LLC 513 941-1578
  5340 River Rd Cincinnati (45233) *(G-4125)*

Morton International LLC 937 222-3860
  312 Mound St Dayton (45402) *(G-8510)*

Morton Salt, Cincinnati Also called Morton International LLC *(G-4125)*

Morton Salt Inc 440 354-9901
  570 Headlands Rd Painesville (44077) *(G-15902)*

Morton Salt Inc 330 925-3015
  151 Industrial Ave Rittman (44270) *(G-16680)*

Mos International Inc 330 329-0905
  3213 Peterboro Dr Stow (44224) *(G-17776)*

Mosbro Machine and Tool Inc 330 467-0913
  8135 Crystal Creek Rd Northfield (44067) *(G-15468)*

Moser Leather Company, Hamilton Also called Old West Industries Inc *(G-10728)*

Mosher Machine & Tool Co Inc 937 258-8070
  1420 Springfield St Dayton (45403) *(G-8511)*

Mosher Medical Inc 330 668-2252
  150 Springside Dr 220b Akron (44333) *(G-305)*

Moskowitz Bros Inc 513 242-2100
  5300 Vine St Cincinnati (45217) *(G-4126)*

Moss Vale Inc 513 939-1970
  160 Donald Dr B Fairfield (45014) *(G-9687)*

Mosser Glass Incorporated 740 439-1827
  9279 Cadiz Rd Cambridge (43725) *(G-2468)*

Mossing Machine and Tool 419 476-5657
  5225 Telegraph Rd Toledo (43612) *(G-18592)*

Motion Industries Inc 419 224-1988
  3945 Stewart Rd Lima (45801) *(G-12060)*
Motion Mobility & Design Inc 330 244-9723
  6490 Promler St Nw North Canton (44720) *(G-15251)*
Motionsource International LLC 440 287-7037
  31200 Solon Rd Ste 7 Solon (44139) *(G-17339)*
Moto Photo, Shaker Heights Also called SMS Communications Inc *(G-17095)*
Moto-Electric Inc 419 668-7894
  262 Cleveland Rd Norwalk (44857) *(G-15552)*
Motor Systems Incorporated 513 576-1725
  460 Milford Pkwy Milford (45150) *(G-14164)*
Motorkote & Dura Lube, Gahanna Also called Into Great Brands Inc *(G-10213)*
Motors & Drives Division, Cincinnati Also called Siemens Industry Inc *(G-4417)*
Motrin Corporation 740 439-2725
  1070 Byesville Rd Cambridge (43725) *(G-2469)*
Motz Mobile Containers Inc 513 772-6689
  3153 Madison Rd Apt 1 Cincinnati (45209) *(G-4127)*
Mound Laser Photonics Center, Kettering Also called Resonetics LLC *(G-11585)*
Mound Manufacturing Center Inc 937 236-8387
  33 Commerce Park Dr Dayton (45404) *(G-8512)*
Mound Printing Company Inc 937 866-2872
  2455 Belvo Rd Miamisburg (45342) *(G-13838)*
Mound Steel Corp 937 748-2937
  25 Mound Park Dr Springboro (45066) *(G-17490)*
Mound Technologies Inc 937 748-2937
  25 Mound Park Dr Springboro (45066) *(G-17491)*
Mount Eaton Division, Mount Eaton Also called Flex Technologies Inc *(G-14555)*
Mount Hope Harness & Shoe, Mount Hope Also called Ervin Yoder *(G-14570)*
Mount Hope Planing 330 359-0538
  7598 Tr652 Millersburg (44654) *(G-14250)*
Mount Union Pattern Works Inc 330 821-2274
  920 Auld St Alliance (44601) *(G-530)*
Mount Vernon News, Mount Vernon Also called Progressive Communications *(G-14640)*
Mount Vernon Packaging Inc 740 397-3221
  135 Progress Dr Mount Vernon (43050) *(G-14632)*
Mountain Filtration Systems 419 395-2526
  26705 Blanchard Rd Defiance (43512) *(G-8806)*
Mountain Top Frozen Pies Div, Columbus Also called Quality Bakery Company Inc *(G-7534)*
Mountaineer Mining Corp 740 418-1817
  885 Sternberger Rd Jackson (45640) *(G-11322)*
Moyer Vineyards Inc 937 549-2957
  3859 Us Highway 52 Manchester (45144) *(G-12550)*
Moyer Winery & Restaurant, Manchester Also called Moyer Vineyards Inc *(G-12550)*
Moyno, Springfield Also called Robbins & Myers Inc *(G-17642)*
Moyno, Springfield Also called Robbins & Myers Inc *(G-17643)*
Mp Biomedicals LLC 440 337-1200
  29525 Fountain Pkwy Solon (44139) *(G-17340)*
Mp Printing & Design Inc 740 456-2045
  4302 Gallia St Portsmouth (45662) *(G-16445)*
Mpc Inc 440 835-1405
  835 Canterbury Rd Westlake (44145) *(G-20284)*
MPC Plastics Inc 216 881-7220
  1859 E 63rd St Cleveland (44103) *(G-5835)*
MPC Plating Inc (PA) 216 881-7220
  1859 E 63rd St Cleveland (44103) *(G-5836)*
MPC Plating Inc 216 881-7220
  1859 E 63rd St Cleveland (44103) *(G-5837)*
Mpe Aeroengines Inc (HQ) 937 878-3800
  7700 New Carlisle Pike Huber Heights (45424) *(G-11150)*
Mpi Label Systems., Sebring Also called Mpi Labels of Baltimore Inc *(G-17049)*
Mpi Labels of Baltimore Inc (HQ) 330 938-2134
  450 Courtney Rd Sebring (44672) *(G-17049)*
MPS Manufacturing Company LLC 330 343-1435
  326 Pearl Ave Ne New Philadelphia (44663) *(G-14917)*
MPW Industrial Svcs Group Inc (PA) 740 927-8790
  9711 Lancaster Rd Hebron (43025) *(G-10875)*
Mr 14k Inc 440 234-6661
  370 W Bagley Rd Berea (44017) *(G-1628)*
Mr Box, Mansfield Also called Skybox Packaging LLC *(G-12680)*
Mr Electric 419 289-7474
  24 Bell St Mansfield (44906) *(G-12654)*
Mr Emblem Inc 419 697-1888
  3209 Navarre Ave Oregon (43616) *(G-15710)*
Mr Heater, Cleveland Also called Enerco Group Inc *(G-5280)*
Mr Heater Inc 216 916-3000
  4560 W 160th St Cleveland (44135) *(G-5838)*
Mr Label Inc 513 681-2088
  5018 Gray Rd Cincinnati (45232) *(G-4128)*
Mr Neon Sign, Canton Also called Rossi Concept Arts *(G-2843)*
Mr Trailer Sales Inc 330 339-7701
  1565 Steel Hill Rd Nw Dover (44622) *(G-9004)*
MR&e Ltd 419 872-8180
  3146 W Lincolnshire Blvd Toledo (43606) *(G-18593)*
Mr. Heater, Cleveland Also called Enerco Technical Products Inc *(G-5281)*
MRC, Cincinnati Also called Molecular Research Center *(G-4117)*
MRC Global (us) Inc 614 475-4033
  700 Taylor Rd Gahanna (43230) *(G-10221)*

MRC Global (us) Inc 330 686-4988
  4704 Hudson Dr Stow (44224) *(G-17777)*
Mrd Solutions LLC 440 942-6969
  34201 Melinz Pkwy Unit A Eastlake (44095) *(G-9283)*
Mrdd Solutions, Wauseon Also called Interactive Fincl Solutions *(G-19683)*
Mrf Machine and Hydraulics Inc 330 673-0135
  912 Lock St Kent (44240) *(G-11495)*
Mri, West Chester Also called Manufacturers Representatives *(G-20024)*
Mro Built Inc 330 526-0555
  6410 Promway Ave Nw North Canton (44720) *(G-15252)*
Mrs Electronic Inc 937 660-6767
  2149 Winners Cir Dayton (45404) *(G-8513)*
MRS Industrial Inc 614 308-1070
  2583 Harrison Rd Columbus (43204) *(G-7372)*
Mrs Mllers Hmmade Noodles Ltd 330 694-5814
  9140 County Road 192 Fredericksburg (44627) *(G-10089)*
Ms Barkin Company 216 761-9500
  246 E 131st St Ste 2 Cleveland (44108) *(G-5839)*
Ms Squared Inc 330 666-0255
  2960 W Bath Rd Akron (44333) *(G-306)*
MSC Walbridge Coatings Inc 419 666-6130
  30610 E Broadway St Walbridge (43465) *(G-19461)*
Msd Products Inc 440 946-0040
  7842 Enterprise Dr Mentor (44060) *(G-13662)*
Msg Premier Molded Fiber, Ashtabula Also called Molded Fiber Glass Companies *(G-824)*
MSI, Milford Also called Motor Systems Incorporated *(G-14164)*
Msk Trencher Mfg Inc 419 394-4444
  7219 Harris Rd Celina (45822) *(G-3010)*
Mssi, Ironton Also called Modular Security Systems Inc *(G-11297)*
Mssl Wiring System Inc (HQ) 330 856-3344
  8640 E Market St Warren (44484) *(G-19579)*
MST, Kent Also called Mold Surface Textures *(G-11494)*
MST Inc 419 542-6645
  11370 Breininger Rd Hicksville (43526) *(G-10903)*
Mt Carmel Brewing Company 513 519-7161
  4362 Mt Carmel Tobasco Rd Cincinnati (45244) *(G-4129)*
Mt Eaton Pallet Ltd 330 893-2986
  4761 County Road 207 Millersburg (44654) *(G-14251)*
Mt Perry Foods Inc 740 743-3890
  5705 State Route 204 Ne Mount Perry (43760) *(G-14592)*
Mt Pleasant Blacktopping Inc 513 874-3777
  3199 Production Dr Fairfield (45014) *(G-9688)*
Mt Pleasant Pharmacy LLC 216 672-4377
  631 Lee Rd Apt 1228 Bedford (44146) *(G-1446)*
Mt Vernon Cy Wastewater Trtmnt 740 393-9502
  3 Cougar Dr Unit 3 Mount Vernon (43050) *(G-14633)*
Mtd Consumer Group Inc (HQ) 330 225-2600
  5965 Grafton Rd Valley City (44280) *(G-19219)*
Mtd Consumer Products Supply, Valley City Also called Mtd Products Inc *(G-19224)*
Mtd Holdings Inc (PA) 330 225-2600
  5965 Grafton Rd Valley City (44280) *(G-19220)*
Mtd LLC 800 269-6215
  5903 Grafton Rd Valley City (44280) *(G-19221)*
Mtd Products Inc (HQ) 330 225-2600
  5965 Grafton Rd Valley City (44280) *(G-19222)*
Mtd Products Inc 419 935-6611
  979 S Conwell Ave Willard (44890) *(G-20397)*
Mtd Products Inc 330 225-9127
  680 Liverpool Dr Valley City (44280) *(G-19223)*
Mtd Products Inc 419 342-6455
  305 Mansfield Ave Shelby (44875) *(G-17139)*
Mtd Products Inc 330 225-1940
  5903 Grafton Rd Valley City (44280) *(G-19224)*
MTI Acquisition LLC 740 929-2065
  85 N High St Hebron (43025) *(G-10876)*
Mto Suncoke, Middletown Also called Suncoke Energy Nc *(G-14086)*
Mtr Martco LLC 513 424-5307
  3350 Yankee Rd Middletown (45044) *(G-14065)*
MTS Enterprises LLC 937 324-7510
  1330 Perry St Springfield (45504) *(G-17609)*
MTS Medication Tech Inc 440 238-0840
  21550 Drake Rd Strongsville (44149) *(G-17943)*
Mudbrook Golf Center 419 433-2945
  1609 Mudbrook Rd Huron (44839) *(G-11234)*
Muehlenkamp Properties Inc 513 745-0874
  4317 Kugler Mill Rd Cincinnati (45236) *(G-4130)*
Mueller Art Cover & Binding Co 440 238-3303
  12005 Alameda Dr Strongsville (44149) *(G-17944)*
Mueller Color, Blue Ash Also called Superior Printing Ink Co Inc *(G-1877)*
Mueller Electric Company Inc 216 771-5225
  1208 Massillon Rd G104 Akron (44306) *(G-307)*
Mueller Electric Company Inc 614 888-8855
  7795 Walton Pkwy Ste 175 New Albany (43054) *(G-14765)*
Mueller Gas Products 513 424-5311
  1800 Clayton Ave Middletown (45042) *(G-14066)*
Muir Graphics Inc 309 673-7034
  5454 Alger Dr Ste A Sylvania (43560) *(G-18120)*
Muirfield Wine Company LLC 614 799-9222
  7154 Muirfield Dr Dublin (43017) *(G-9107)*

Mulch Madness LLC 330 920-9900
  8022 S Riverside Dr Aurora (44202) *(G-935)*

Mulch Makers of Ohio Inc 330 753-3090
  3307 Clark Mill Rd Norton (44203) *(G-15518)*

Mulch Man 937 866-5370
  4595 Fairpark Ave Dayton (45431) *(G-8114)*

Mulch Man Greenline Products, Dayton *Also called Mulch Man (G-8114)*

Mulch World 419 873-6852
  8232 Fremont Pike Perrysburg (43551) *(G-16123)*

Mulhern Belting Inc 201 337-5700
  310 Osborne Dr Fairfield (45014) *(G-9689)*

Mull Iron, Rittman *Also called Rittman Inc (G-16682)*

Muller Engine & Machine Co 937 322-1861
  1414 S Yellow Springs St Springfield (45506) *(G-17610)*

Mullet Enterprises Inc (PA) 330 852-4681
  138 2nd St Nw Sugarcreek (44681) *(G-18029)*

Mullet Enterprises Inc 330 897-3911
  28003 Adams Twp Rd 101 Bakersville (43803) *(G-1063)*

Mullin Print Solutions 216 383-2901
  84 E 197th St Euclid (44119) *(G-9594)*

Mullins Rubber Products Inc 937 233-4211
  2949 Valley Pike Dayton (45404) *(G-8514)*

Multi Cast LLC 419 335-0010
  225 E Linfoot St Wauseon (43567) *(G-19690)*

Multi Form Mfg 330 922-1933
  4278 Hudson Dr Stow (44224) *(G-17778)*

Multi Galvanizing LLC 330 453-1441
  825 Navarre Rd Sw Canton (44707) *(G-2784)*

Multi Lapping Service Inc 440 944-7592
  30032 Lakeland Bvld Wickliffe (44092) *(G-20373)*

Multi Products Company 330 674-5981
  7188 State Route 39 Millersburg (44654) *(G-14252)*

Multi Radiance Medical, Solon *Also called Medical Quant USA Inc (G-17333)*

Multi-Color Australia LLC 513 381-1480
  4053 Clough Woods Dr Batavia (45103) *(G-1210)*

Multi-Color Corporation (PA) 513 381-1480
  4053 Clough Woods Dr Batavia (45103) *(G-1211)*

Multi-Color Corporation 513 396-5600
  4500 Beech St Cincinnati (45212) *(G-4131)*

Multi-Color Corporation 513 943-0080
  4053 Clough Woods Dr Batavia (45103) *(G-1212)*

Multi-Design Inc 440 275-2255
  2844 Industrial Park Dr Austinburg (44010) *(G-963)*

Multi-Form Plastics, Batavia *Also called Plastikos Corporation (G-1216)*

Multi-Wing America Inc 440 834-9400
  15030 Brkshire Indus Pkwy Middlefield (44062) *(G-13969)*

Multibase Inc 330 666-0505
  3835 Copley Rd Copley (44321) *(G-7850)*

Multifab, Elyria *Also called Multilink Inc (G-9465)*

Multilink Inc 440 366-6966
  580 Ternes Ln Elyria (44035) *(G-9465)*

Multiplast Systems Inc 440 349-0800
  33355 Station St Solon (44139) *(G-17341)*

Multiple Products Div, Cleveland *Also called Anderson Industries Inc (G-4810)*

Multipress Inc 614 228-0185
  1250 Refugee Ln Columbus (43207) *(G-7373)*

Mum Industries Inc 440 269-4966
  7750 Tyler Blvd Mentor (44060) *(G-13663)*

Mumfords Potato Chips & Deli 937 653-3491
  325 N Main St Urbana (43078) *(G-19170)*

Muncy Co, The, Springfield *Also called E & W Enterprises Powell Inc (G-17549)*

Municipal Signs and Sales Inc 330 457-2421
  1219 Mcclosky Rd Columbiana (44408) *(G-6625)*

Munroe Incorporated 330 755-7216
  25 Union St Struthers (44471) *(G-17995)*

Munson Machine Company Inc 740 967-6867
  80 E College Ave Johnstown (43031) *(G-11402)*

Munson Sales & Engineering 216 496-5436
  13260 Crows Hollow Dr Chardon (44024) *(G-3167)*

Murdock Inc 513 471-7700
  7180 Anderson Woods Dr Cincinnati (45244) *(G-4132)*

Murotech Ohio Corporation 419 394-6529
  550 Mckinley Rd Saint Marys (45885) *(G-16844)*

Murphy Industries Inc 740 387-7890
  1650 Cascade Dr Marion (43302) *(G-12887)*

Murphy James Construction LLC 740 667-3626
  4146 N Torch Rd Coolville (45723) *(G-7836)*

Murphy Tractor & Eqp Co Inc 614 876-1141
  2121 Walcutt Rd Columbus (43228) *(G-7374)*

Murphy Tractor & Eqp Co Inc 937 898-4198
  1015 Industrial Park Dr Vandalia (45377) *(G-19306)*

Murphy Tractor & Eqp Co Inc 419 221-3666
  3550 Saint Johns Rd Lima (45804) *(G-12061)*

Murphy Tractor & Eqp Co Inc 330 477-9304
  1509 Raff Rd Sw Canton (44710) *(G-2785)*

Murphy Tractor & Eqp Co Inc 330 220-4999
  1240 Industrial Rd Pkwy N Brunswick (44212) *(G-2238)*

Murr Corporation 330 264-2223
  201 N Buckeye St Wooster (44691) *(G-20813)*

Murr Printing and Graphics, Wooster *Also called Murr Corporation (G-20813)*

Murray American Energy Inc 740 338-3100
  46226 National Rd W Saint Clairsville (43950) *(G-16796)*

Murray Brothers Shows Inc 513 941-6500
  6282 Ashbourne Pl Cincinnati (45233) *(G-4133)*

Murray Display Fixtures Ltd 614 554-9461
  3721 Thistlewood Dr Ste B Grove City (43123) *(G-10575)*

Murray Energy Corporation (PA) 740 338-3100
  46226 National Rd W Saint Clairsville (43950) *(G-16797)*

Murray Fabrics Inc (PA) 216 881-4041
  837 E 79th St Cleveland (44103) *(G-5840)*

Murray Machine & Tool Inc 216 267-1126
  17801 Sheldon Rd Side Cleveland (44130) *(G-5841)*

Musair Ohio 330 455-2800
  128 North Ave Ne Massillon (44646) *(G-13183)*

Muscle Feast LLC 888 734-3634
  101 Longbow Dr Hebron (43025) *(G-10877)*

Muscle Feast LLC (PA) 740 877-8808
  101 Longbow Dr Hebron (43025) *(G-10878)*

Music Systems, North Olmsted *Also called Q Music USA LLC (G-15343)*

Muskingum Grinding & Mch Co 740 622-4741
  2155 Otsego Ave Coshocton (43812) *(G-7899)*

Mustang Aerial Services Inc 740 373-9262
  27620 State Route 7 Reno (45773) *(G-16578)*

Mustang Dynamometer, Twinsburg *Also called Ganzcorp Investments Inc (G-18939)*

Mustang Multi Graphics, Wauseon *Also called Tomahawk Printing (G-19696)*

Mustang Printing 419 592-2746
  119 W Washington St Napoleon (43545) *(G-14690)*

Mustard Seed Health Fd Mkt Inc 440 519-3663
  6025 Kruse Dr Ste 100 Solon (44139) *(G-17342)*

Mutual Tool LLC 937 667-5818
  1350 Commerce Park Dr Tipp City (45371) *(G-18290)*

Mv Designlabs LLC 724 355-7986
  17138 Lorain Ave Ste 201 Cleveland (44111) *(G-5842)*

Mv Group Inc 419 776-1133
  303 Morris St Toledo (43604) *(G-18594)*

Mv Innovative Technologies LLC 937 221-7639
  711 E Monu Ave Ste 102 Dayton (45402) *(G-8515)*

Mveca, Yellow Springs *Also called Miami Valley Eductl Cmpt Assn (G-20995)*

Mvp Pharmancy 614 449-8000
  1931 Parsons Ave Columbus (43207) *(G-7375)*

Mvp Plastics Inc (PA) 330 872-4451
  15005 Enterprise Way Middlefield (44062) *(G-13970)*

MWC Publishing Co, Dayton *Also called Dayton Weekly News (G-8289)*

Mwe of Ohio 419 777-7192
  146 Rensch Ave Galion (44833) *(G-10280)*

Mx Spring Inc 330 426-4600
  39 Wilderson Ave East Palestine (44413) *(G-9242)*

My Catered Table LLC 614 882-7323
  1871 N High St Columbus (43210) *(G-7376)*

My Floors By Prints and Paints, Galion *Also called Prints & Paints Flr Cvg Co Inc (G-10283)*

My Lady Muffins LLC 937 854-5317
  2475 N Snyder Rd Dayton (45426) *(G-8516)*

My Little Red Wagon, Kent *Also called Honey Gold Company (G-11470)*

My Major Family LLP 567 218-1206
  5001 Monroe St Ste 1505 Toledo (43623) *(G-18595)*

My Pro Apparel, Ontario *Also called Mypro Apparel LLC (G-15690)*

My Scrapbook Paradise LLC 419 584-1393
  202 S Main St Celina (45822) *(G-3011)*

My Way Home Finder Magazine 419 841-6201
  5215 Monroe St Ste 14 Toledo (43623) *(G-18596)*

Myairplane.com, Cardington *Also called 3gc LLC (G-2907)*

Mye Automotive Inc 330 253-5592
  1293 S Main St Akron (44301) *(G-308)*

Myers and Lasch Inc 440 235-2050
  8026 Columbia Rd Cleveland (44138) *(G-5843)*

Myers Controlled Power LLC (HQ) 330 834-3200
  219 E Maple St 100-200e North Canton (44720) *(G-15253)*

Myers Controlled Power LLC 909 923-1800
  133 Taft Ave Ne Canton (44720) *(G-2786)*

Myers Industries Inc (PA) 330 253-5592
  1293 S Main St Akron (44301) *(G-309)*

Myers Industries Inc 440 632-1006
  15150 Madison Rd Middlefield (44062) *(G-13971)*

Myers Industries Inc 330 336-6621
  250 Seville Rd Wadsworth (44281) *(G-19420)*

Myers Industries Inc 440 632-0230
  15150 Madison Rd Middlefield (44062) *(G-13972)*

Myers Machining Inc 330 874-3005
  11789 Strasburg Bolivar Bolivar (44612) *(G-1938)*

Myers Motors LLC 330 630-7000
  180 South Ave Tallmadge (44278) *(G-18157)*

Myers Precision Grinding Co 216 365-2630
  19500 S Miles Rd Cleveland (44128) *(G-5844)*

Myko Industries 216 431-0900
  896 E 70th St Cleveland (44103) *(G-5845)*

Mypro Apparel LLC 419 462-9464
  325 Shelby Ontario Rd Ontario (44906) *(G-15690)*

Myrlen, Cincinnati *Also called Ep Bollinger LLC (G-3712)*

Myron D Budd 330 682-5866
480 S Crown Hill Rd Orrville (44667) **(G-15749)**

Mysta Equipment Co 330 879-5353
6434 Werstler Ave Sw Navarre (44662) **(G-14720)**

Mystic Chemical Products Co 216 251-4416
3561 W 105th St Cleveland (44111) **(G-5846)**

Mytee Products Inc 440 591-4301
1335 S Chillicothe Rd Aurora (44202) **(G-936)**

N & N Oil 740 743-2848
6111 State Route 13 Ne Somerset (43783) **(G-17417)**

N & W Machining & Fabricating 937 695-5582
8 Mathias Rd Winchester (45697) **(G-20696)**

N A C, Findlay Also called Nichidai America Corporation **(G-9867)**

N A D, Cincinnati Also called National Access Design LLC **(G-4137)**

N Bass Bait Co 419 647-4501
08780 Deep Cut Rd Spencerville (45887) **(G-17462)**

N C Tool & Die Company 440 354-4152
9435 Pineneedle Dr Mentor (44060) **(G-13664)**

N E C Columbus, Columbus Also called National Electric Coil Inc **(G-7382)**

N F M, Massillon Also called Nfm/Welding Engineers Inc **(G-13184)**

N G C, North Royalton Also called Next Generation Crimping **(G-15437)**

N J E M A Magazine, Cincinnati Also called Sesh Communications **(G-4408)**

N J Thomas Fine Jewelry Inc 440 892-0656
30191 Detroit Rd Cleveland (44145) **(G-5847)**

N K H Safety Inc 513 771-3839
1375 Kemper Meadow Dr # 12 Cincinnati (45240) **(G-4134)**

N M Hansen Machine and Tool, Toledo Also called Rogar International Inc **(G-18679)**

N M R Inc 513 530-9075
7555 Fields Ertel Rd Cincinnati (45241) **(G-4135)**

N N I, Cleveland Also called Norman Noble Inc **(G-5888)**

N N Metal Stampings Inc (PA) 419 737-2311
510 S Maple St Pioneer (43554) **(G-16235)**

N S T Battery 937 433-9222
4496 W Franklin St Bellbrook (45305) **(G-1510)**

N W P Manufacturing, Waldo Also called Nwp Manufacturing Inc **(G-19466)**

N Wasserstrom & Sons Inc (HQ) 614 228-5550
2300 Lockbourne Rd Columbus (43207) **(G-7377)**

N Wasserstrom & Sons Inc 614 737-5410
862 E Jenkins Ave Columbus (43207) **(G-7378)**

N-Stock Box Inc 513 423-0319
1500 S University Blvd Middletown (45044) **(G-14067)**

N-Viro International Corp 419 535-6374
2254 Centennial Rd Toledo (43617) **(G-18597)**

N2y LLC 419 433-9800
909 University Dr S Huron (44839) **(G-11235)**

N8 Medical Inc 614 537-7246
6000 Memorial Dr Dublin (43017) **(G-9108)**

NA Financial Service Center, Cleveland Also called Eaton Corporation **(G-5250)**

Nacco Industries Inc (PA) 440 229-5151
5875 Landerbrook Dr # 300 Cleveland (44124) **(G-5848)**

Nachurs Alpine Solutions Corp (HQ) 740 382-5701
421 Leader St Marion (43302) **(G-12888)**

Nagele Manufacturing Co Inc 216 433-1100
5201 W 164th St Cleveland (44142) **(G-5849)**

Nail Art 614 899-7155
5470 Westerville Rd Westerville (43081) **(G-20225)**

Nail Artist, Westerville Also called Nail Art **(G-20225)**

Nail Secret 513 459-3373
3187 Wstn Row Rd Ste 105 Maineville (45039) **(G-12530)**

Naked Lime 937 485-1932
2405 County Line Rd Beavercreek (45430) **(G-1375)**

Nalco Company LLC 432 528-5214
3934 Jeffries Cir Louisville (44641) **(G-12320)**

Nalcon Ready Mix Inc 419 422-4341
12484 State Route 701 Kenton (43326) **(G-11562)**

Names Unlimited Corp 419 845-2005
3787 Marion Galion Rd Caledonia (43314) **(G-2440)**

Nanak Bakery 614 882-0882
895 S State St Westerville (43081) **(G-20226)**

Nanbrands LLC 513 313-9581
8405 Indian Hill Rd Cincinnati (45243) **(G-4136)**

Nancys Draperies 330 855-7751
57 S Main St Marshallville (44645) **(G-12919)**

Nano Fabrix, Columbus Also called Nano Innovations LLC **(G-7379)**

Nano Innovations LLC 614 203-5706
2121 Riverside Dr Columbus (43221) **(G-7379)**

Nano Mark LLC 216 409-3104
4415 Euclid Ave Cleveland (44103) **(G-5850)**

Nanobio Systems, Elyria Also called Keyghobad Ventures LLC **(G-9447)**

Nanofiber Solutions Inc 614 559-9065
1275 Kinnear Rd Columbus (43212) **(G-7380)**

Nanofilm Ltd 216 674-1430
6030 Carey Dr Cleveland (44125) **(G-5851)**

Nanolap Technologies LLC 877 658-4949
85 Harrisburg Dr Englewood (45322) **(G-9534)**

Nanologix Inc 330 534-0800
843 N Main St Hubbard (44425) **(G-11135)**

Nanomeld LLC 740 477-5900
18646 Us Rte 23 N Circleville (43113) **(G-4634)**

Nanosperse LLC 937 296-5030
2000 Composite Dr Kettering (45420) **(G-11583)**

Nanostatics Corporation 740 477-5900
18646 Us Rte 23 Circleville (43113) **(G-4635)**

Nanotech Innovations LLC 440 926-4888
132 Artino St Oberlin (44074) **(G-15646)**

Nanotech West Lab 614 688-3055
1381 Kinnear Rd Ste 100 Columbus (43212) **(G-7381)**

Nanotechlabs Inc (PA) 937 297-9518
2000 Composite Dr Kettering (45420) **(G-11584)**

Nanotronics Imaging Inc (PA) 330 926-9809
2251 Front St Ste 109-111 Cuyahoga Falls (44221) **(G-8028)**

Naomi Kight 937 278-0040
132 Marson Dr Dayton (45405) **(G-8517)**

Nap Asset Holdings Ltd 330 633-0599
411 Geneva Ave Tallmadge (44278) **(G-18158)**

Napoleon Inc 419 592-5055
595 E Riverview Ave Napoleon (43545) **(G-14691)**

Napoleon Products Co, Napoleon Also called United Auto Worker AFL CIO **(G-14701)**

Napoleon Spring Works Inc (HQ) 419 445-1010
111 Weires Dr Archbold (43502) **(G-688)**

Napoli's Pizza, Belpre Also called Wal-Bon of Ohio Inc **(G-1595)**

Napolitano Monument, Cincinnati Also called 3-G Incorporated **(G-3323)**

Naptime Productions LLC 419 662-9521
417 Superior St Ste E Rossford (43460) **(G-16743)**

Nari Inc 440 960-2280
5190 State Route 99 N Monroeville (44847) **(G-14427)**

Narrow Way Custom Technology 937 743-1611
100 Industry Dr Carlisle (45005) **(G-2933)**

Nasg Ohio LLC 419 634-3125
605 E Montford Ave Ada (45810) **(G-6)**

Natgascar, Cleveland Also called Ecowise LLC **(G-5257)**

Nation Coating Systems Inc 937 746-7632
501 Shotwell Dr Franklin (45005) **(G-10038)**

National Access Design LLC 513 351-3400
1924 Losantiville Ave Cincinnati (45237) **(G-4137)**

National Adhesives Inc 513 683-8650
9435 Waterstone Blvd # 200 Cincinnati (45249) **(G-4138)**

National Applied Cnstr Pdts 330 644-3117
3200 S Main St Akron (44319) **(G-310)**

National Aviation Products Inc (HQ) 330 688-6494
4880 Hudson Dr Stow (44224) **(G-17779)**

National Bank Note Company (PA) 216 281-7792
9800 Detroit Ave Ste 1 Cleveland (44102) **(G-5852)**

National Bedding Company LLC 513 421-4094
1680 Carolina Ave Cincinnati (45237) **(G-4139)**

National Beverage, Obetz Also called Shasta Beverages Inc **(G-15659)**

National Beverage Corp 614 491-5415
4685 Groveport Rd Obetz (43207) **(G-15657)**

National Bias Fabric Co 216 361-0530
4516 Saint Clair Ave Cleveland (44103) **(G-5853)**

National Biological Corp 216 831-0600
23700 Mercantile Rd Beachwood (44122) **(G-1283)**

National Bios Fabric Company, Cleveland Also called Db Rediheat Inc **(G-5175)**

National Brass Company Inc 216 651-8530
3179 W 33rd St Cleveland (44109) **(G-5854)**

National Bronze and Metals 440 277-1226
5311 W River Rd Lorain (44055) **(G-12261)**

National Bullet Co 800 317-9506
34971 Glen Dr Eastlake (44095) **(G-9284)**

National Carton & Coating Co 937 347-1042
1439 Lavelle Dr Xenia (45385) **(G-20964)**

National Center For Composite 937 297-9450
2000 Composite Dr Dayton (45420) **(G-8518)**

National Colloid Company 740 282-1171
906 Adams St Steubenville (43952) **(G-17706)**

NATIONAL COMPOSITE CENTER, Dayton Also called National Center For
Composite **(G-8518)**

National Compressor Svcs LLC 419 865-3126
10349 Industrial St Holland (43528) **(G-11073)**

National Diamond TI & Coating, Westlake Also called Diamond Reserve Inc **(G-20263)**

National Directories College, Cleveland Also called Collegiate Directories Inc **(G-5098)**

National Directory Morticians 440 247-3561
285 Park Pl Chagrin Falls (44022) **(G-3065)**

National Door and Trim Inc 419 238-9345
1189 Grill Rd Van Wert (45891) **(G-19268)**

National Elec Carbn Pdts Inc 419 435-8182
200 N Town St Fostoria (44830) **(G-9986)**

National Electric Coil Inc (PA) 614 488-1151
800 King Ave Columbus (43212) **(G-7382)**

National Electro-Coatings Inc 216 898-0080
15655 Brookpark Rd Cleveland (44142) **(G-5855)**

National Engrg Archtctral Svcs, Columbus Also called Barr Engineering
Incorporated **(G-6808)**

National Extrusion & Mfg Co, Bellefontaine Also called Klb Industries Inc **(G-1535)**

National Fasteners Inc 216 771-6473
  4581 Spring Rd Brooklyn Heights (44131) *(G-2143)*

National Fleet Svcs Ohio LLC 440 930-5177
  607 Miller Rd Avon Lake (44012) *(G-1041)*

National Foods Packaging Inc 216 415-7102
  8200 Madison Ave Cleveland (44102) *(G-5856)*

National Fruit Vegetable Tech 740 400-4055
  250 Civic Center Dr Columbus (43215) *(G-7383)*

National Gas & Oil Company (PA) 740 344-2102
  1500 Granville Rd Newark (43055) *(G-15036)*

National Gas & Oil Corporation (HQ) 740 344-2102
  1500 Granville Rd Newark (43055) *(G-15037)*

National Glass Service Group 614 652-3699
  5500 Frantz Rd Ste 100 Dublin (43017) *(G-9109)*

National Illmination Sign Corp 419 866-1666
  6525 Angola Rd Holland (43528) *(G-11074)*

National Lien Digest, Highland Heights *Also called C & S Associates Inc* *(G-10910)*

National Lime and Stone Co 419 396-7671
  370 N Patterson St Carey (43316) *(G-2921)*

National Lime and Stone Co 419 657-6745
  18430 Main Street Rd Wapakoneta (45895) *(G-19502)*

National Lime and Stone Co 330 262-1317
  1455 Timken Rd Wooster (44691) *(G-20814)*

National Lime and Stone Co 740 548-4206
  2406 S Section Line Rd Delaware (43015) *(G-8872)*

National Lime and Stone Co 419 562-0771
  4580 Bethel Rd Bucyrus (44820) *(G-2354)*

National Lime and Stone Co 419 228-3434
  1314 Findlay Rd Lima (45801) *(G-12062)*

National Lime and Stone Co 740 387-3485
  700 Likens Rd Marion (43302) *(G-12889)*

National Lime and Stone Co 330 339-2144
  2942 Brightwood Rd Se New Philadelphia (44663) *(G-14918)*

National Lime and Stone Co 419 423-3400
  9860 County Road 313 Findlay (45840) *(G-9866)*

National Lime and Stone Co 419 642-6690
  18264 State Route 189 Columbus Grove (45830) *(G-7796)*

National Lime and Stone Co 614 497-0083
  5911 Lockbourne Rd Lockbourne (43137) *(G-12150)*

National Lime and Stone Co 419 294-3049
  14407 Township Rd 124 Upper Sandusky (43351) *(G-19134)*

National Lime and Stone Co 216 883-9840
  4200 E 71st St Cleveland (44105) *(G-5857)*

National Lime Stone, Wooster *Also called National Lime and Stone Co* *(G-20814)*

National Lime Stone Clmbus Reg, Delaware *Also called National Lime and Stone Co* *(G-8872)*

National Machine Company (HQ) 330 688-6494
  4880 Hudson Dr Stow (44224) *(G-17780)*

National Machine Company 330 688-2584
  1330 Commerce Dr Stow (44224) *(G-17781)*

National Machine Tool Company 513 541-6682
  2013 E Galbraith Rd Cincinnati (45215) *(G-4140)*

National Machinery LLC (HQ) 419 447-5211
  161 Greenfield St Tiffin (44883) *(G-18232)*

National Metal Shapes Inc 740 363-9559
  425 S Sandusky St Ste 1 Delaware (43015) *(G-8873)*

National Mold Remediation 614 231-6653
  3923 E Main St Columbus (43213) *(G-7384)*

National Molded Products Inc 440 365-3400
  147 Kenwood St Elyria (44035) *(G-9466)*

National Mortgage Weekley 330 674-2887
  1817 State Route 83 Millersburg (44654) *(G-14253)*

National Ntwrk EMB Prfssionals 502 212-7500
  3100 Surrey Hill Ln Stow (44224) *(G-17782)*

National Office, Cleveland *Also called National Electro-Coatings Inc* *(G-5855)*

National Oil Products, Hamilton *Also called Wallover Oil Hamilton Inc* *(G-10756)*

National Oilwell Varco Inc 440 577-1225
  7338 N Richmond Rd Pierpont (44082) *(G-16213)*

National Oilwell Varco LP 978 687-0101
  5870 Poe Ave Dayton (45414) *(G-8519)*

National Oilwell Varco LP 937 454-3200
  5870 Poe Ave Dayton (45414) *(G-8520)*

National Pallet & Mulch LLC 937 237-1643
  3550 Intercity Dr Dayton (45424) *(G-8521)*

National Patent Analytical Sys 419 526-6727
  2090 Harrington Mem Rd Mansfield (44903) *(G-12655)*

National Pattern Mfg Co 330 682-6871
  1318 N Main St Orrville (44667) *(G-15750)*

National Peening 216 342-9155
  23800 Corbin Dr Bedford Heights (44128) *(G-1491)*

National Plating Corporation 216 341-6707
  6701 Hubbard Ave Ste 1 Cleveland (44127) *(G-5858)*

National Polishing Systems Inc 330 659-6547
  5145 Brecksville Rd # 101 Richfield (44286) *(G-16629)*

National Polymer Dev Co Inc 440 708-1245
  10200 Gottschalk Pkwy # 4 Chagrin Falls (44023) *(G-3105)*

National Polymer Inc 440 708-1245
  10200 Gottschalk Pkwy Chagrin Falls (44023) *(G-3106)*

National Pride Equipment Inc 419 289-2886
  1266 Middle Rowsburg Rd Ashland (44805) *(G-756)*

National Production, Newark *Also called Ngo Development Corporation* *(G-15039)*

National Psychologist, The, Columbus *Also called Ohio Psychlogy Pblications Inc* *(G-7429)*

National Rolled Thread Die Co 440 232-8101
  7051 Krick Rd Cleveland (44146) *(G-5859)*

National Roller Die Inc 440 951-3850
  4750 Beidler Rd Unit 4 Willoughby (44094) *(G-20552)*

National Safety Tech LLC (HQ) 419 727-0552
  5154 Enterprise Blvd Toledo (43612) *(G-18598)*

National Screen Production, Cleveland *Also called Charizma Corp* *(G-5014)*

National Seating Company 219 872-7295
  7800 Walton Pkwy New Albany (43054) *(G-14766)*

National Security Products 216 566-9962
  1636 Saint Clair Ave Ne Cleveland (44114) *(G-5860)*

National Smallwares, Columbus *Also called Wasserstrom Company* *(G-7750)*

National Stair Corp 937 325-1347
  20 Zischler St Springfield (45504) *(G-17611)*

National Starch Chemical 513 830-0260
  9435 Waterstone Blvd # 200 Cincinnati (45249) *(G-4141)*

National Steel Rule Die LLC 937 667-0967
  3580 Lightner Rd Vandalia (45377) *(G-19307)*

National Super Service Co, Toledo *Also called Nss Enterprises Inc* *(G-18610)*

National Thermoform, Fort Loramie *Also called Jeffrey Brandewie* *(G-9933)*

National Tool & Equipment Inc 330 629-8665
  60 Karago Ave Youngstown (44512) *(G-21148)*

National Welding & Tanker Repr 614 875-3399
  2036 Hendrix Dr Grove City (43123) *(G-10576)*

National Welding & Tanker Repr 614 875-3399
  2036 Hendrix Dr Grove City (43123) *(G-10577)*

Nationwide Chemical Products 419 714-7075
  24851 E Broadway Rd Perrysburg (43551) *(G-16124)*

Natural Beauty Hc Express 440 459-1776
  6809 Mayfield Rd Apt 550 Mayfield Heights (44124) *(G-13319)*

Natural Beauty Products Inc 513 420-9400
  50 S Main St Middletown (45044) *(G-14068)*

Natural Country Farms Inc (HQ) 330 753-2293
  681 W Waterloo Rd Akron (44314) *(G-311)*

Natural Essentials Inc 330 562-8022
  125 Lena Dr Aurora (44202) *(G-937)*

Natural Gas Construction Inc 330 364-9240
  1737 Red Hill Rd Nw Dover (44622) *(G-9005)*

Nature Friendly Products LLC 216 464-5490
  24050 Commerce Park # 101 Cleveland (44122) *(G-5861)*

Nature Pure LLC 937 358-2364
  26560 Storms Rd West Mansfield (43358) *(G-20102)*

Nature Pure LLC (PA) 937 358-2364
  26586 State Route 739 Raymond (43067) *(G-16576)*

Natures Own Source LLC 440 838-5135
  7033 Mill Rd Brecksville (44141) *(G-2065)*

Natures Simple Solution Inc 440 567-6913
  1450 Som Center Rd Ste 2 Cleveland (44124) *(G-5862)*

Nauman Communications Inc 740 654-0084
  743 S Columbus St Lancaster (43130) *(G-11732)*

Nauman Outdoor Advertising Co, Lancaster *Also called Nauman Communications Inc* *(G-11732)*

Nauticus Inc 440 746-1290
  8080 Snowville Rd Brecksville (44141) *(G-2066)*

Nautilus Hyosung America Inc 937 203-4900
  2076 Byers Rd Miamisburg (45342) *(G-13839)*

Nauvod Machine Co 440 632-1990
  16254 Nauvoo Rd Middlefield (44062) *(G-13973)*

Nauvoo Custom Woodworking 440 632-9502
  17231 Nauvoo Rd Middlefield (44062) *(G-13974)*

Navage, Independence *Also called Rhinosystems Inc* *(G-11272)*

Navarre Industries Inc 330 767-3003
  10384 Navarre Rd Sw Navarre (44662) *(G-14721)*

Navarre Trailer Sales Inc 330 879-2406
  4633 Erie Ave Sw Navarre (44662) *(G-14722)*

Navidea Biopharmaceuticals Inc 614 793-7500
  5600 Blazer Pkwy Ste 200 Dublin (43017) *(G-9110)*

Navigator Construction LLC 330 244-0221
  7530 Tim Ave Nw Ste B North Canton (44720) *(G-15254)*

Navistar Inc 937 390-5848
  6125 Urbana Rd Springfield (45502) *(G-17612)*

Navistar Inc 937 390-2800
  6125 Urbana Rd Springfield (45502) *(G-17613)*

Navistar Inc 937 390-5653
  349 W County Line Rd Springfield (45502) *(G-17614)*

Navistar Inc 937 390-4774
  5975 Urbana Rd Springfield (45502) *(G-17615)*

Navistar Inc 937 390-5704
  4949 Urbana Rd Frnt Springfield (45502) *(G-17616)*

Navistar Inc 513 733-8500
  11775 Highway Dr Cincinnati (45241) *(G-4142)*

Navpar Inc 513 738-2230
  11029 State Route 128 Harrison (45030) *(G-10792)*

Naw Petroleum Service 740 464-7988
  80 Cameo Ln Chillicothe (45601) *(G-3253)*

Nbbi 614 888-8320
  1055 Crupper Ave Columbus (43229) *(G-7385)*

NBC Industries Inc 216 651-9800
  4700 Train Ave Ste 3 Cleveland (44102) *(G-5863)*

Nbw Inc 216 377-1700
  4556 Industrial Pkwy Cleveland (44135) *(G-5864)*

NC Tool, Mentor *Also called N C Tool & Die Company (G-13664)*

NC Works Inc 937 514-7781
  3500 Commerce Center Dr Franklin (45005) *(G-10039)*

Ncc, Cleveland *Also called North Coast Container Corp (G-5894)*

Nccd, Wooster *Also called North Central Concrete Design (G-20816)*

Nci Building Systems Inc 937 584-3300
  2400 Yankee Rd Middletown (45044) *(G-14069)*

NCM, Cleveland *Also called North Coast Media LLC (G-5898)*

NCM Corp 440 786-9870
  20437 Hannan Pkwy Ste 3 Cleveland (44146) *(G-5865)*

Ncrx Optical Solutions Inc (PA) 330 239-5353
  105 Executive Pkwy # 401 Hudson (44236) *(G-11189)*

Nct Technologies Group Inc (PA) 937 882-6800
  7867 W National Rd New Carlisle (45344) *(G-14808)*

ND Industries Inc 330 425-3167
  9051 Dutton Dr Twinsburg (44087) *(G-18989)*

NDC Technologies Inc 937 233-9935
  8001 Technology Blvd Dayton (45424) *(G-8522)*

Ndi Medical LLC (PA) 216 378-9106
  22901 Millcreek Blvd # 110 Cleveland (44122) *(G-5866)*

Ndw Textiles, Westlake *Also called Mmi Textiles Inc (G-20283)*

Neal Miller 440 296-5322
  6878 State Route 167 E Pierpont (44082) *(G-16214)*

Neal Publications Inc 419 874-4787
  127 W Indiana Ave Perrysburg (43551) *(G-16125)*

Nease Co LLC (HQ) 513 587-2800
  9774 Windisch Rd West Chester (45069) *(G-19904)*

Nease Co LLC 513 738-1255
  10740 Paddys Run Rd Harrison (45030) *(G-10793)*

Nease Performance Chemicals, West Chester *Also called Nease Co LLC (G-19904)*

Nease Performance Chemicals, Harrison *Also called Nease Co LLC (G-10793)*

Neaton Auto Products Mfg Inc (HQ) 937 456-7103
  975 S Franklin St Eaton (45320) *(G-9319)*

Nebraska Industries Corp 419 335-6010
  447 E Walnut St Wauseon (43567) *(G-19691)*

Nebulatronics Inc 440 243-2370
  24542 Nobottom Rd Olmsted Twp (44138) *(G-15681)*

Necco American, Columbus *Also called Appian Manufacturing Corp (G-6762)*

Necomerstown News, Newcomerstown *Also called The Jeffersonian (G-15125)*

Ned A Shreve 740 732-6465
  48398 Seneca Lake Rd Sarahsville (43779) *(G-17025)*

Neer's Engineering Labs, Bellefontaine *Also called Arden J Neer Sr (G-1519)*

Neff Machinery and Supplies 740 454-0128
  112 S Shawnee Ave Zanesville (43701) *(G-21331)*

Neff Parts, Zanesville *Also called Neff Machinery and Supplies (G-21331)*

Neff-Perkins Company 440 632-1658
  16080 Industrial Pkwy Middlefield (44062) *(G-13975)*

Nehemiah Manufacturing Co LLC 513 351-5700
  1130 Findlay St Cincinnati (45214) *(G-4143)*

Neher Burial Vault Company 937 399-4494
  1903 Saint Paris Pike Springfield (45504) *(G-17617)*

Neidert Fabricating Inc 330 753-3331
  712 Wooster Rd W Barberton (44203) *(G-1133)*

Neighborhood News Pubg Co 216 441-2141
  8613 Garfield Blvd Cleveland (44125) *(G-5867)*

Neil Barton 614 889-9933
  8215 Dublin Rd Dublin (43017) *(G-9111)*

Neil R Scholl Inc 740 653-6593
  54 Snoke Hill Rd Ne Lancaster (43130) *(G-11733)*

Neiss Body & Equipment Corp 330 828-2409
  17485 Old Lincoln Way Dalton (44618) *(G-8075)*

Nel-Ack Sheet Metal Inc 440 357-7844
  546 Hoyt St Ste 18 Painesville (44077) *(G-15903)*

Nelis Printing Co 330 757-4114
  5146 Sterling Ave Youngstown (44515) *(G-21149)*

Nelson Aluminum Foundry Inc 440 543-1941
  17093 Munn Rd Chagrin Falls (44023) *(G-3107)*

Nelson Manufacturing Company 419 523-5321
  6448 State Route 224 Ottawa (45875) *(G-15802)*

Nelson Professional Mktg Inc 513 482-6150
  5353 Spring Grove Ave Cincinnati (45217) *(G-4144)*

Nelson Sand & Gravel Inc 440 224-0198
  5720 State Route 193 Kingsville (44048) *(G-11606)*

Nelson Stud Welding, Elyria *Also called Doncasters Group Ltd (G-9406)*

Nelson Stud Welding Inc (HQ) 440 329-0400
  7900 W Ridge Rd Elyria (44035) *(G-9467)*

Nelson Tool Corporation 740 965-1894
  388 N County Line Rd Sunbury (43074) *(G-18068)*

Nelson's Woodcrafts, Steubenville *Also called Mark Nelson (G-17704)*

Nemco Food Equipment Ltd (PA) 419 542-7751
  301 Meuse Argonne St Hicksville (43526) *(G-10904)*

Nemire Lures LLC 419 729-1280
  2144 Ottawa River Rd Toledo (43611) *(G-18599)*

Neo Tech 937 845-0999
  123 S Main St New Carlisle (45344) *(G-14809)*

Neola Inc (PA) 330 926-0514
  3914 Clk Pnte Trl Ste 103 Stow (44224) *(G-17783)*

Neola Inc 740 622-5341
  632 Main St Coshocton (43812) *(G-7900)*

Neon 216 761-4782
  15201 Euclid Ave Cleveland (44112) *(G-5868)*

Neon Beach Tanning Inc 440 333-3050
  19585 Detroit Rd Rocky River (44116) *(G-16702)*

Neon Health Services Inc 216 231-7700
  4800 Payne Ave Cleveland (44103) *(G-5869)*

Neon Hussy LLC 513 374-7644
  237 E 12th Ave Columbus (43201) *(G-7386)*

Neon Light Manufacturing Co 216 851-1000
  12655 Coit Rd Cleveland (44108) *(G-5870)*

Neon Nights 330 345-9907
  2239 W Smithvl Wstrn Rd Wooster (44691) *(G-20815)*

Neon Paintbrush 419 436-1202
  461 W Lytle St Lot 153 Fostoria (44830) *(G-9987)*

Neptune Aquatic Systems Inc 513 575-2989
  6641 Smith Rd Loveland (45140) *(G-12375)*

Neptune Chemical Pump Company 513 870-3239
  9393 Princetone Glendale West Chester (45011) *(G-19905)*

Neptune Equipment Company 513 851-8008
  11082 Southland Rd Cincinnati (45240) *(G-4145)*

Nervive Inc 847 274-1790
  526 S Main St Ste 801a Akron (44311) *(G-312)*

Nesco Inc (PA) 440 461-6000
  6140 Parkland Blvd # 110 Cleveland (44124) *(G-5871)*

Nesco Resource, Cleveland *Also called Nesco Inc (G-5871)*

Nestier, Milford *Also called Buckhorn Material Hdlg Group (G-14129)*

Nestle Brands Company 440 264-6600
  30000 Bainbridge Rd Solon (44139) *(G-17343)*

Nestle Food Service Factory, Cleveland *Also called Nestle Usa Inc (G-5874)*

Nestle Prepared Foods, Solon *Also called Nestle R&D Center Inc (G-17346)*

Nestle Prepared Foods Company (HQ) 440 248-3600
  30003 Bainbridge Rd Solon (44139) *(G-17344)*

Nestle Prepared Foods Company 440 349-5757
  5750 Harper Rd Solon (44139) *(G-17345)*

Nestle Purina Petcare Company 740 454-8575
  5 N 2nd St Zanesville (43701) *(G-21332)*

Nestle R&D Center Inc 440 349-5757
  5750 Harper Rd Solon (44139) *(G-17346)*

Nestle Usa Inc 216 524-7738
  7645 Granger Rd Cleveland (44125) *(G-5872)*

Nestle Usa Inc 216 524-3397
  7605 Granger Rd Cleveland (44125) *(G-5873)*

Nestle Usa Inc 440 349-5757
  30003 Bainbridge Rd Solon (44139) *(G-17347)*

Nestle Usa Inc 216 861-8350
  2621 W 25th St Cleveland (44113) *(G-5874)*

Netherland Rubber Company (PA) 513 733-0883
  2931 Exon Ave Cincinnati (45241) *(G-4146)*

Netpark LLC 614 866-2495
  1182 Claycraft Rd Gahanna (43230) *(G-10222)*

Netshape Technologies Mim Inc 440 248-5456
  31005 Solon Rd Solon (44139) *(G-17348)*

Netsmart Technologies Inc 440 942-4040
  30775 Bnbridge Rd Ste 200 Solon (44139) *(G-17349)*

Nettleton Steel Treating Div, Cleveland *Also called Thermal Treatment Center Inc (G-6317)*

Nettting Technologies LLC 330 298-0022
  636 S Walnut St Ravenna (44266) *(G-16543)*

Neturen America Corporation 513 863-1900
  2995 Moser Ct Hamilton (45011) *(G-10726)*

Network Communications Inc 614 934-1919
  467 Waterbury Ct Ste B Gahanna (43230) *(G-10223)*

Network Printing & Graphics 614 230-2084
  443 Crestview Rd Columbus (43202) *(G-7387)*

Network Savvy Ltd 419 843-1122
  5217 Monroe St Ste A1 Toledo (43623) *(G-18600)*

Neu Prosthetics & Orthotics 740 363-3522
  2848 Jericho Pl Delaware (43015) *(G-8874)*

Neumeisters Candy Shoppe LLC 419 294-3647
  139 N Sandusky Ave Upper Sandusky (43351) *(G-19135)*

Neundorfer Inc 440 942-8990
  4590 Hamann Pkwy Willoughby (44094) *(G-20553)*

Neundorfer Engineering Service, Willoughby *Also called Neundorfer Inc (G-20553)*

Neural Holdings LLC 734 512-8865
  9867 Beech Dr Cincinnati (45231) *(G-4147)*

Neuros Medical Inc 440 951-2565
  35010 Chardon Rd Ste 210 Willoughby Hills (44094) *(G-20642)*

Neurowave Systems Inc 216 361-1591
  2490 Lee Blvd Ste 300 Cleveland (44118) *(G-5875)*

Neusole Glassworks, Cincinnati *Also called Jjs3 Foundation (G-3947)*

Nevels Precision Machining LLC 937 387-6037
  2770 Thunderhawk Ct Dayton (45414) *(G-8523)*

New Age Design & Tool Inc 440 355-5400
  162 Commerce Dr Lagrange (44050) *(G-11634)*

New American Reel Company LLC 419 258-2900
5278 County Road 424 A Antwerp (45813) *(G-631)*

New Bakery of Zanesville LLC 614 764-3100
1 Dave Thomas Blvd Dublin (43017) *(G-9112)*

New Bremen Machine & Tool Co 419 629-3295
705 Kuenzel Dr New Bremen (45869) *(G-14790)*

New Can Company Inc 937 547-9050
1367 Sater St Greenville (45331) *(G-10512)*

New Century Sales LLC 513 422-3631
2905 Lopane Ave Middletown (45044) *(G-14070)*

New Cleveland Group Inc 216 932-9310
2917 Mayfield Rd Cleveland (44118) *(G-5876)*

New Cumberland Lock & Dam, Toronto *Also called U S Army Corps of Engineers* *(G-18786)*

New Cut Tool and Mfg Corp 740 676-1666
1 New Cut Rd Shadyside (43947) *(G-17083)*

New Die Inc 419 726-7581
2828 E Manhattan Blvd Toledo (43611) *(G-18601)*

New Dimension Metals Corp 937 299-2233
3050 Dryden Rd Moraine (45439) *(G-14510)*

New Eezy-Gro Inc 419 927-6110
9841 County Highway 49 Upper Sandusky (43351) *(G-19136)*

New ERA Controls Inc 216 641-8683
11002 Edgepark Dr Cleveland (44125) *(G-5877)*

New Holland Engineering Inc 740 495-5200
43 E Front St New Holland (43145) *(G-14835)*

New Horizon Baking Company 567 315-8703
1015 New York Ave Toledo (43611) *(G-18602)*

New Horizons Baking Company (PA) 419 668-8226
211 Woodlawn Ave Norwalk (44857) *(G-15553)*

New Image Plastics Mfg Co 330 854-3010
241 Market St W Canal Fulton (44614) *(G-2509)*

New Leaf Medical Inc 216 391-7749
1768 E 25th St Cleveland (44114) *(G-5878)*

New London Foundry Inc 419 929-2073
80 Walnut St New London (44851) *(G-14863)*

New Mansfield Brass & Alum Co 419 492-2166
636 S Center St New Washington (44854) *(G-14962)*

New Mulch In A Bottle Limited 724 290-2341
140 Gross St Ste 116 Marietta (45750) *(G-12810)*

New Path International LLC 614 410-3974
1476 Manning Pkwy Ste A Powell (43065) *(G-16481)*

New Pme Inc 513 671-1717
518 W Crescentville Rd Cincinnati (45246) *(G-4148)*

New Riegel Cafe Inc 419 595-2255
14 N Perry St New Riegel (44853) *(G-14947)*

New River Equipment Corp 330 669-0040
7793 Pittsburg Ave Nw North Canton (44720) *(G-15255)*

New Sabina Industries Inc (HQ) 937 584-2433
12555 Us Highway 22 And 3 Sabina (45169) *(G-16774)*

New Tech 330 494-8338
2751 Wisemill Cir Ne # 3 Canton (44721) *(G-2787)*

New Tech Welding Inc 937 426-4801
2972 Lantz Rd Beavercreek (45434) *(G-1354)*

New Track Media LLC 513 421-6500
10151 Carver Rd Ste 200 Blue Ash (45242) *(G-1844)*

New Urban Distributors LLC 216 373-2349
13940 Cedar Rd Ste 224 Cleveland (44118) *(G-5879)*

New Vulco Mfg & Sales Co LLC 513 242-2672
5353 Spring Grove Ave Cincinnati (45217) *(G-4149)*

New Waste Concepts Inc (PA) 419 872-2190
26624 Glenwood Rd Perrysburg (43551) *(G-16126)*

New Wayne Inc 740 453-3454
1555 Ritchey Pkwy Zanesville (43701) *(G-21333)*

New World Energy Resources (PA) 740 344-4087
1500 Granville Rd Newark (43055) *(G-15038)*

New York Frozen Foods, Bedford *Also called Tmarzetti Company* *(G-1467)*

New York Frozen Foods 614 846-2232
380 Polaris Pkwy Ste 400 Westerville (43082) *(G-20172)*

New York Frozen Foods Inc (HQ) 216 292-5655
25900 Fargo Ave Bedford (44146) *(G-1447)*

Newact Inc 513 321-5177
2084 James E Sauls Sr Dr Batavia (45103) *(G-1213)*

Newall Electronics Inc 614 771-0213
1803 Obrien Rd Columbus (43228) *(G-7388)*

Newark Water Plant, Newark *Also called City of Newark* *(G-14993)*

Neway Stamping & Mfg Inc 440 951-8500
4820 E 345th St Willoughby (44094) *(G-20554)*

Newberry Wood Enterprises Inc (PA) 440 238-6127
12223 Prospect Rd Strongsville (44149) *(G-17945)*

Newbury Sandblasting & Pntg, Newbury *Also called L & N Olde Car Co* *(G-15099)*

Newbury Woodworks 440 564-5273
10958 Kinsman Rd Unit 2 Newbury (44065) *(G-15100)*

Newell Brands Inc 330 733-1184
212 Progress Blvd Kent (44240) *(G-11496)*

Newfax Corporation (PA) 419 241-5157
333 W Woodruff Ave Toledo (43604) *(G-18603)*

Newfax Corporation 419 893-4557
3333 W Wooddrift Toledo (43624) *(G-18604)*

Newhouse & Faulkner Inc 513 721-1660
215 E 9th St Cincinnati (45202) *(G-4150)*

Newhouse Printing Company, Dover *Also called R & J Printing Enterprises Inc* *(G-9008)*

Newkor Inc 216 631-7800
10410 Berea Rd Cleveland (44102) *(G-5880)*

Newman Brothers Inc 513 242-0011
5609 Center Hill Ave Cincinnati (45216) *(G-4151)*

Newman Sanitary Gasket Company 513 932-7379
964 W Main St Lebanon (45036) *(G-11818)*

Newman Technology Inc (HQ) 419 525-1856
100 Cairns Rd Mansfield (44903) *(G-12656)*

Newmast Mktg & Communications 614 837-1200
2060 Integrity Dr N Columbus (43209) *(G-7389)*

Newpage Energy Services LLC 877 855-7243
8540 Gander Creek Dr Miamisburg (45342) *(G-13840)*

Newpage Group Inc (HQ) 937 242-9500
8540 Gander Creek Dr Miamisburg (45342) *(G-13841)*

Newpage Holding Corporation 877 855-7243
8540 Gander Creek Dr Miamisburg (45342) *(G-13842)*

News Democrat 937 378-6161
4500 Lyons Rd Miamisburg (45342) *(G-13843)*

News Gazette Printing Company 419 227-2527
324 W Market St Lima (45801) *(G-12063)*

News Office, Beauro, Warren *Also called Vindicator Printing Company* *(G-19618)*

News Reel Inc 614 469-0700
5 E Long St Ste 1001 Columbus (43215) *(G-7390)*

News Reel Mag By & For Blind, Columbus *Also called News Reel Inc* *(G-7390)*

News Tribune, Hicksville *Also called Tribune Printing Inc* *(G-10909)*

News Watchman & Paper 740 947-2149
860 W Emmitt Ave Ste 5 Waverly (45690) *(G-19713)*

Newsafe Transport Service Inc 740 387-1679
979 Pole Lane Rd Marion (43302) *(G-12890)*

Newsome & Work Metalizing Co 330 376-7144
258 Kenmore Blvd Akron (44301) *(G-313)*

Newspaper Holding Inc 440 998-2323
4626 Park Ave Ashtabula (44004) *(G-826)*

Newspaper Network Central OH 419 524-3545
70 W 4th St Mansfield (44903) *(G-12657)*

Newspaper Network Central Ohio, Newark *Also called Gannett Co Inc* *(G-15010)*

Newspaper Solutions LLC 937 694-9370
116 Old Carriage Dr Englewood (45322) *(G-9535)*

Newswanger Machine, Shiloh *Also called Leon Newswanger* *(G-17151)*

Newtech Materials & Analytical 330 329-1080
618 Tresham Ct Copley (44321) *(G-7851)*

Newton Asphalt Paving Inc 330 878-5648
8344 Central Rd Nw Strasburg (44680) *(G-17826)*

Newton Falls Printing 330 872-3532
27 E Broad St Newton Falls (44444) *(G-15137)*

Newtons Paint & Body 740 352-9334
768 Fairground Rd Lucasville (45648) *(G-12423)*

Nexeo Solutions LLC 800 531-7106
5200 Blazer Pkwy Dublin (43017) *(G-9113)*

Nexergy Inc (HQ) 614 351-2191
5115 Prkcnter Ave Ste 275 Dublin (43017) *(G-9114)*

Nexicor, Cincinnati *Also called Senco Brands Inc* *(G-3315)*

Next, Cincinnati *Also called Nilpeter Usa Inc* *(G-4156)*

Next Day Sign 419 537-9595
2112 N Reynolds Rd Toledo (43615) *(G-18605)*

Next Day Signs LLC 614 764-7446
6403 Nicholas Dr Columbus (43235) *(G-7391)*

Next Design & Build LLC 330 907-3042
3250 Doves Xing Akron (44319) *(G-314)*

Next Dimension Components Inc 440 576-0194
223 S Spruce St Jefferson (44047) *(G-11368)*

Next Generation Bag Inc 419 884-1327
230 Industrial Dr Mansfield (44904) *(G-12658)*

Next Generation Films, Mansfield *Also called Engineered Films Division* *(G-12601)*

Next Generation Films Inc (PA) 419 884-8150
230 Industrial Dr Lexington (44904) *(G-11951)*

Next Gerenation Crimping 440 237-6300
9880 York Alpha Dr North Royalton (44133) *(G-15437)*

Next Sales LLC 330 704-4126
3258 Dogwood Ln Nw Dover (44622) *(G-9006)*

Next Specialty Resins Inc (PA) 517 547-4600
8201 W Central Ave Toledo (43617) *(G-18606)*

Next Step, Centerville *Also called Advanced Medical Solutions Inc* *(G-3033)*

Next Wave Marketing Innovation, Dayton *Also called David Esrati* *(G-8266)*

Nextant Aerospace Holdings LLC 216 261-9000
355 Richmond Rd Ste 8 Cleveland (44143) *(G-5881)*

Nextgen Fiber Optics LLC (PA) 513 549-4691
720 E Pete Rose Way # 410 Cincinnati (45202) *(G-4152)*

Nextmed Systems Inc (PA) 216 674-0511
16 Triangle Park Dr Cincinnati (45246) *(G-4153)*

Nextstep Networking, Blue Ash *Also called Eaj Services LLC* *(G-1780)*

Nexus Vision Group LLC 866 492-6499
2156 Southwest Blvd Grove City (43123) *(G-10578)*

Nfm/Welding Engineers Inc (PA) 330 837-3868
577 Oberlin Ave Sw Massillon (44647) *(G-13184)*

Ngc Red Hill, Dover *Also called Natural Gas Construction Inc* *(G-9005)*

Ngo Development Corporation (HQ)....740 344-3790
1500 Granville Rd Newark (43055) ***(G-15039)***
Ngo Development Corporation....740 622-9560
504 N 3rd St Coshocton (43812) ***(G-7901)***
Ngp Printing Professional, Lima *Also called News Gazette Printing Company* ***(G-12063)***
Nhvs International Inc....440 527-8610
7600 Tyler Blvd Mentor (44060) ***(G-13665)***
Niagara Bottling LLC....614 751-7420
1700 Eastgate Pkwy Gahanna (43230) ***(G-10224)***
Niagara Custombilt Mfg, Cleveland *Also called S A Langmack Company* ***(G-6149)***
Niagara Stamping Co, Cleveland *Also called Robin Industries Inc* ***(G-6124)***
Nibco Inc....513 228-1426
2800 Henkle Dr Lebanon (45036) ***(G-11819)***
Nicana Consulting Inc....419 615-9703
801 Oak Pkwy Kalida (45853) ***(G-11415)***
Nichidai America Corporation....419 423-7511
15630 E State Route 12 # 4 Findlay (45840) ***(G-9867)***
Nicholas Press Sales LLC....440 652-6604
3077 Nationwide Pkwy Brunswick (44212) ***(G-2239)***
Nicholas Ray Enterprises LLC....330 454-4811
3605 Mahoning Rd Ne Canton (44705) ***(G-2788)***
Nichols Aluminum-Alabama LLC....256 353-1550
25825 Science Park Dr # 400 Beachwood (44122) ***(G-1284)***
Nichols Manufacturing Inc....440 255-0188
8980 Osborne Dr Mentor (44060) ***(G-13666)***
Nichols Mold Inc....330 297-9719
222 W Lake St Ravenna (44266) ***(G-16544)***
Nicklaus Machine Co....614 262-7223
3975 Karl Rd Columbus (43224) ***(G-7392)***
Nickles Bakery 45, Zanesville *Also called Alfred Nickles Bakery Inc* ***(G-21269)***
Nicks Plating Co Inc....937 773-3175
6980 Free Rd Piqua (45356) ***(G-16294)***
Nickum Enterprises Inc....513 561-2292
6105 Madison Rd Cincinnati (45227) ***(G-4154)***
Nicofibers Inc....740 394-2491
9702 Iron Point Rd Se Shawnee (43782) ***(G-17116)***
Nidec Avtron, Independence *Also called Nidec Motor Corporation* ***(G-11268)***
Nidec Indus Automtn USA LLC....216 901-2400
7800 Hub Pkwy Cleveland (44125) ***(G-5882)***
Nidec Motor Corporation....216 642-1230
7555 E Pleasant Valley Rd Independence (44131) ***(G-11268)***
Nidec Motor Corporation....575 434-0633
1503 Exeter Rd Akron (44306) ***(G-315)***
Nielsen Jewelers, Lorain *Also called H P Nielsen Inc* ***(G-12248)***
Niese Farms....419 347-1204
7506 Cole Rd Crestline (44827) ***(G-7932)***
Nifco America Corporation (HQ)....614 920-6800
8015 Dove Pkwy Canal Winchester (43110) ***(G-2532)***
Nifco America Corporation....614 836-3808
8015 Dove Pkwy Canal Winchester (43110) ***(G-2533)***
Nifco America Corporation....614 836-8691
4485 S Hamilton Rd Groveport (43125) ***(G-10637)***
Niftech, Mentor *Also called R J K Enterprises Inc* ***(G-13712)***
Niftech Inc....440 257-6018
5565 Wilson Dr Mentor (44060) ***(G-13667)***
Niftech Precision Race Pdts, Mentor *Also called Niftech Inc* ***(G-13667)***
Nifty Promo Products, Middletown *Also called Backyard Scoreboards LLC* ***(G-14023)***
Nigerian Assn Pharmacists & PH....513 861-2329
483 Northland Blvd Cincinnati (45240) ***(G-4155)***
Night Lightscapes....419 304-2486
3303 Herr Rd Sylvania (43560) ***(G-18121)***
Nihon Company, Urbana *Also called Parker Trutec Incorporated* ***(G-19172)***
Niidex Enterprise LLC....614 653-8526
3314 Morse Rd Ste 215 Columbus (43231) ***(G-7393)***
Nikkicakes....330 606-5745
806 Myrtle Ave Cuyahoga Falls (44221) ***(G-8029)***
Niklee Co....440 944-0082
2959 Canterbury Ct Willoughby Hills (44092) ***(G-20643)***
Nikola Innovation LLC....216 496-3022
1768 E 25th St Cleveland (44114) ***(G-5883)***
Niktec LLC....513 282-3747
127 Industrial Dr Franklin (45005) ***(G-10040)***
Niles Manufacturing & Finshg....330 544-0402
465 Walnut St Niles (44446) ***(G-15171)***
Niles Roll Service Inc (PA)....330 544-0026
704 Warren Ave Niles (44446) ***(G-15172)***
Nilodor Inc....800 443-4321
10966 Industrial Pkwy Nw Bolivar (44612) ***(G-1939)***
Nilpeter Usa Inc....513 489-4400
11550 Goldcoast Dr Cincinnati (45249) ***(G-4156)***
Nimco Inc....740 596-4477
33711 State Route 93 Mc Arthur (45651) ***(G-13332)***
Nine Giant Brewing LLC....510 220-5104
3204 Nash Ave Cincinnati (45226) ***(G-4157)***
Nipm, Canal Fulton *Also called New Image Plastics Mfg Co* ***(G-2509)***
Nippon Stl Smkin Crnkshaft LLC....419 435-0411
1815 Sandusky St Fostoria (44830) ***(G-9988)***
Nissen Chemitec America Inc....740 852-3200
350 E High St London (43140) ***(G-12215)***
Nissen Lumber & Coal Co Inc (PA)....419 836-8035
5700 Navarre Ave Oregon (43616) ***(G-15711)***
Nissin Brake Ohio Inc (HQ)....419 420-3800
1901 Industrial Dr Findlay (45840) ***(G-9868)***
Nissin Brake Ohio Inc....937 642-7556
25790 State Route 287 East Liberty (43319) ***(G-9202)***
Nissin Precision N Amer Inc....937 836-1910
375 Union Rd Englewood (45315) ***(G-9536)***
Nitrojection....440 834-8790
8430 Mayfield Rd Chesterland (44026) ***(G-3217)***
Nitto Denko Auto Ohio Inc....937 773-4820
1620 S Main St Piqua (45356) ***(G-16295)***
Nitto Denko Avecia Inc....513 679-3000
8560 Reading Rd Cincinnati (45215) ***(G-4158)***
Njm Furniture Outlet Inc....330 893-3514
6899 County Road 672 Millersburg (44654) ***(G-14254)***
Nk Machine Inc....513 737-8035
1550 Pleasant Ave Hamilton (45015) ***(G-10727)***
Nkc of America Inc....937 642-4033
24000 Honda Pkwy Gate E Marysville (43040) ***(G-12961)***
Nkh Life Safety LLC....513 688-7100
4030 Mount Carmel Tobasco Cincinnati (45255) ***(G-4159)***
Nl Mfg & Distribution Sys In....513 422-5216
6107 Market Ave Middletown (45005) ***(G-14102)***
NM Group Global LLC (PA)....419 447-5211
161 Greenfield St Tiffin (44883) ***(G-18233)***
Nmg Aerospace, Stow *Also called National Machine Company* ***(G-17780)***
Nmgg Ctg LLC (PA)....419 447-5211
161 Greenfield St Tiffin (44883) ***(G-18234)***
Nn Inc....440 647-4711
125 Bennett St Wellington (44090) ***(G-19751)***
Nnodum Pharmaceuticals Corp....513 861-2329
483 Northland Blvd Cincinnati (45240) ***(G-4160)***
No Burn Inc....330 336-1500
1392 High St Ste 211 Wadsworth (44281) ***(G-19421)***
No Burn North America Inc....419 841-6055
2930 Centennial Rd Toledo (43617) ***(G-18607)***
No Rinse Laboratories LLC....937 746-7357
868 Pleasant Valley Dr Springboro (45066) ***(G-17492)***
No Surprises Software Inc....855 462-6448
536 S Wall St Fl 1 Columbus (43215) ***(G-7394)***
Nobal Enterprises Inc....440 748-0522
11470 Hawke Rd Unit 3 Columbia Station (44028) ***(G-6592)***
Noble Anodizing Inc....216 268-1263
1325 E 152nd St Cleveland (44112) ***(G-5884)***
Noble Denim Workshop....513 560-5640
2929 Spring Grove Ave Cincinnati (45225) ***(G-4161)***
Noble Tool Corp....937 461-4040
1535 Stanley Ave Dayton (45404) ***(G-8524)***
Nock and Son Company (PA)....440 871-5525
27320 W Oviatt Rd Cleveland (44140) ***(G-5885)***
Nock and Son Company....740 682-7741
4138 Monroe Hollow Rd Oak Hill (45656) ***(G-15602)***
Noco Company....216 464-8131
30339 Diamond Pkwy # 102 Solon (44139) ***(G-17350)***
Nof Metal Coatings N Amer Inc (HQ)....440 285-2231
275 Industrial Pkwy Chardon (44024) ***(G-3168)***
Nofziger Door Sales Inc (PA)....419 337-9900
320 Sycamore St Wauseon (43567) ***(G-19692)***
Nofziger Door Sales Inc....419 445-2961
111 Taylor Pkwy Archbold (43502) ***(G-689)***
Noggin LLC....440 305-6188
6325 York Rd Ste 208 Cleveland (44130) ***(G-5886)***
Noise Suppression Technologies....614 275-1818
4182 Fisher Rd Columbus (43228) ***(G-7395)***
Nolan Company (PA)....330 453-7922
1016 9th St Sw Canton (44707) ***(G-2789)***
Nolan Company....740 269-1512
300 Boyce Dr Bowerston (44695) ***(G-1959)***
Nolan Manufacturing LLC....614 859-2302
493 Blue Heron Ct Westerville (43082) ***(G-20173)***
Nolan Mfg Co - Electronics Div, Westerville *Also called Nolan Manufacturing LLC* ***(G-20173)***
Nom Nom Nom....614 302-4815
2818 Banwick Rd Columbus (43232) ***(G-7396)***
Nomac Drilling LLC....330 476-7040
1258 Panda Rd Se Carrollton (44615) ***(G-2962)***
Nomac Drilling LLC....724 324-2205
67090 Executive Dr Saint Clairsville (43950) ***(G-16798)***
Nomis Publications Inc....330 965-2380
8570 Foxwood Ct Youngstown (44514) ***(G-21150)***
Non-Ferrous Casting Co....937 228-1162
736 Albany St Dayton (45417) ***(G-8525)***
Non-Ferrous Heat Treating, Maple Heights *Also called Dewitt Inc* ***(G-12732)***
Nona Composites LLC....937 490-4814
2750 Indian Ripple Rd Beavercreek (45440) ***(G-1376)***
None, Curtice *Also called Ottawa Products Co* ***(G-7958)***
Nonnies Goodies LLC....419 435-4685
3352 N County Road 39 Fostoria (44830) ***(G-9989)***
Nook Industries Inc (PA)....216 271-7900
4950 E 49th St Cleveland (44125) ***(G-5887)***

NOOTROPICS CITY DBA, Canton *Also called Aggregate Tersormance LLC* ***(G-2590)***
Noramar Company Inc...440 338-5740
8501 Kinsman Rd Novelty (44072) ***(G-15583)***
Noramco, Euclid *Also called North American Plas Chem Inc* ***(G-9595)***
Norbar Torque Tools Inc...440 953-1175
36400 Biltmore Pl Willoughby (44094) ***(G-20555)***
Norcal Signs Inc...513 779-6982
6163 Allen Rd West Chester (45069) ***(G-19906)***
Norcia Bakery...330 454-1077
624 Belden Ave Ne Canton (44704) ***(G-2790)***
Norcold Inc (HQ)...937 497-3080
600 S Kuther Rd Sidney (45365) ***(G-17206)***
Norcold Inc...937 447-2241
1 Century Dr Gettysburg (45328) ***(G-10375)***
Nordec Inc...330 940-3700
900 Hampshire Rd Stow (44224) ***(G-17784)***
Nordic Light America Inc...614 981-9497
426 Mccormick Blvd Columbus (43213) ***(G-7397)***
Nordson Corporation (PA)...440 892-1580
28601 Clemens Rd Westlake (44145) ***(G-20285)***
Nordson Corporation...440 985-4000
100 Nordson Dr Ms81 Amherst (44001) ***(G-601)***
Nordson Corporation...440 988-9411
555 Jackson St Amherst (44001) ***(G-602)***
Nordson Corporation...440 985-4496
300 Nordson Dr Amherst (44001) ***(G-603)***
Nordson Uv Inc...440 985-4573
555 Jackson St Amherst (44001) ***(G-604)***
Norfolk Southern Corporation...419 697-5070
3830 Corduroy Rd Oregon (43616) ***(G-15712)***
Norgren Inc...937 833-4033
325 Carr Dr Brookville (45309) ***(G-2194)***
Noritake Co Inc...513 234-0770
4990 Alliance Dr Mason (45040) ***(G-13067)***
Norlab Dyes, Lorain *Also called Norlab Inc* ***(G-12262)***
Norlab Inc...440 282-5265
7465 Industrial Pkwy Dr Lorain (44053) ***(G-12262)***
Norlake Manufacturing Company...440 353-3200
39301 Taylor Pkwy North Ridgeville (44035) ***(G-15391)***
Norman Noble Inc (PA)...216 761-5387
5507 Avion Park Dr Highland Heights (44143) ***(G-10917)***
Norman Noble Inc...216 761-5387
5507 Avion Park Dr Cleveland (44143) ***(G-5888)***
Norman Noble Inc...216 761-2133
6120 Parkland Blvd # 306 Cleveland (44124) ***(G-5889)***
Norman Noble Inc...216 761-5387
5340 Avion Park Dr Highland Heights (44143) ***(G-10918)***
Normandy Products Company...440 632-5050
16125 Industrial Pkwy Middlefield (44062) ***(G-13976)***
Normant Candy Co...419 886-4214
1821 Mock Rd Mansfield (44904) ***(G-12659)***
Normant's Salt Water Taffy, Mansfield *Also called Normant Candy Co* ***(G-12659)***
Norplas Industries, Northwood *Also called Magna Exteriors America Inc* ***(G-15484)***
Norplas Industries Inc (HQ)...419 662-3317
7825 Caple Blvd Northwood (43619) ***(G-15485)***
Norris North Manufacturing...330 691-0449
1500 Henry Ave Sw Canton (44706) ***(G-2791)***
Norse Dairy Systems LP...614 421-5297
1740 Joyce Ave Columbus (43219) ***(G-7398)***
Norstar Aluminum Molds Inc...440 632-0853
15986 Valplast St Middlefield (44062) ***(G-13977)***
North Amer Sls & Svc Ret Div, Uniontown *Also called Diebold Incorporated* ***(G-19082)***
North American Auger Mining...740 622-8782
1816 Bayberry Ln Coshocton (43812) ***(G-7902)***
North American Cast Stone Inc...440 286-1999
13271 Bass Lake Rd Chardon (44024) ***(G-3169)***
North American Coating Labs, Mentor *Also called Wilson Optical Laboratory Inc* ***(G-13769)***
North American Dist Ctr, Cambridge *Also called Ridge Tool Company* ***(G-2474)***
North American Fincl Svcs Ctr, Cleveland *Also called Eaton Corporation* ***(G-5246)***
North American Plas Chem Inc (PA)...216 531-3400
1400 E 222nd St Euclid (44117) ***(G-9595)***
North American Stamping Group, Ada *Also called Nasg Ohio LLC* ***(G-6)***
North American Steel Company...216 475-7300
18300 Miles Rd Cleveland (44128) ***(G-5890)***
North Amrcn Sstnable Enrgy Ltd...440 539-7133
1360 Grant Dr Parma (44134) ***(G-15963)***
North Bend Express...513 481-4623
3295 North Bend Rd Cincinnati (45239) ***(G-4162)***
North Canton Plastics Inc...330 497-0071
6658 Promway Ave Nw Canton (44720) ***(G-2792)***
North Canton Tool Co...330 452-0545
1156 Marion Ave Sw Canton (44707) ***(G-2793)***
North Cape Manufacturing, Solon *Also called Technology House The Ltd* ***(G-17400)***
North Cast Orthtics Prsthetics (PA)...440 233-4314
6100 S Broadway Ste 104 Lorain (44053) ***(G-12263)***
North Central Concrete Design...419 606-1908
3331 E Lincoln Way Wooster (44691) ***(G-20816)***
North Central Insulation Inc (PA)...419 886-2030
7539 State Route 13 Bellville (44813) ***(G-1573)***
North Central Processing Inc (PA)...216 623-1090
761 Stones Levee Cleveland (44113) ***(G-5891)***
North Coast Business Journal...419 734-4838
205 Se Catawba Rd Ste G Port Clinton (43452) ***(G-16407)***
North Coast Camshaft Inc...216 671-3700
10910 Briggs Rd Cleveland (44111) ***(G-5892)***
North Coast Composites Inc...216 398-8550
4605 Spring Rd Cleveland (44131) ***(G-5893)***
North Coast Container Corp (PA)...216 441-6214
8806 Crane Ave Cleveland (44105) ***(G-5894)***
North Coast Custom Molding Inc...419 905-6447
211 W Geneva St Dunkirk (45836) ***(G-9188)***
North Coast Exotics Inc...216 651-5512
3159 W 68th St Cleveland (44102) ***(G-5895)***
North Coast Holdings Inc (PA)...330 535-7177
768 E North St Akron (44305) ***(G-316)***
North Coast Instruments Inc...216 251-2353
14615 Lorain Ave Cleveland (44111) ***(G-5896)***
North Coast Litho Inc...216 881-1952
4701 Manufacturing Ave Cleveland (44135) ***(G-5897)***
North Coast Medi-Tek Inc...440 974-0750
8603 East Ave Mentor (44060) ***(G-13668)***
North Coast Media LLC...216 706-3700
1360 E 9th St Ste 1070 Cleveland (44114) ***(G-5898)***
North Coast Medical Eqp Inc...440 243-2722
100 Lincoln Ave Berea (44017) ***(G-1629)***
North Coast Minority Media LLC...216 407-4327
1360 E 9th St Cleveland (44114) ***(G-5899)***
North Coast Pattern Inc...440 322-5064
10587 Scottsdale Dr Strongsville (44136) ***(G-17946)***
North Coast Profile Inc...330 823-7777
255 E Perry St Alliance (44601) ***(G-531)***
North Coast Publications, Cleveland *Also called North Coast Minority Media LLC* ***(G-5899)***
North Coast Rivet Inc...440 366-6829
700 Sugar Ln Elyria (44035) ***(G-9468)***
North Coast Security Group LLC...614 887-7255
750 E Long St Ste 3000 Columbus (43203) ***(G-7399)***
North Coast Theatrical Inc (PA)...330 762-1768
2181 Killian Rd Unit A Akron (44312) ***(G-317)***
North Coast Voice Mag...440 415-0999
143 S Cedar St Geneva (44041) ***(G-10353)***
North Dixie Parts & Service...937 275-0933
3507 N Dixie Dr Dayton (45414) ***(G-8526)***
North East Fuel Inc...330 264-4454
3927 Cleveland Rd Wooster (44691) ***(G-20817)***
North East Technologies Inc...440 327-9278
5127 Mills Indus Pkwy North Ridgeville (44039) ***(G-15392)***
North End Press Incorporated...740 653-6514
235 S Columbus St Lancaster (43130) ***(G-11734)***
North Fork Southern, Columbus *Also called Rail Road Corporation* ***(G-7546)***
North High Brewing LLC...614 407-5278
1125 Cleveland Ave Columbus (43201) ***(G-7400)***
North High Marathon...937 444-1894
570 N High St Mount Orab (45154) ***(G-14584)***
North Hill Marble & Granite Co...330 253-2179
448 N Howard St Akron (44310) ***(G-318)***
North Jckson Specialty Stl LLC...330 538-9621
2058 S Bailey Rd North Jackson (44451) ***(G-15295)***
North Pk Innovations Group Inc...440 247-4600
30333 Emerald Valley Pkwy Solon (44139) ***(G-17351)***
North Sails Toledo LLC...419 726-2933
5556 Edgewater Dr Toledo (43611) ***(G-18608)***
North Shore Safety, Mentor *Also called Tecmark Corporation* ***(G-13744)***
North Shore Stone Inc...614 870-7531
915 Manor Park Dr Columbus (43228) ***(G-7401)***
North Shore Strapping Inc (PA)...216 661-5200
1400 Valley Belt Rd Brooklyn Heights (44131) ***(G-2144)***
North Shore Strapping Inc...216 661-5200
9401 Maywood Ave Cleveland (44102) ***(G-5900)***
North Star Bluescope Steel LLC...419 822-2399
6767 County Road 9 Delta (43515) ***(G-8939)***
North Star Metals Mfg Co...740 254-4567
6850 Edwards Ridge Rd Se Uhrichsville (44683) ***(G-19055)***
North Toledo Graphics LLC...419 476-8808
5225 Telegraph Rd Toledo (43612) ***(G-18609)***
North View Woodworking...330 359-6286
8454 State Route 93 Nw Dundee (44624) ***(G-9178)***
North-West Tool Co...937 278-7995
2725 Kearns Ave Dayton (45414) ***(G-8527)***
Northcoast Advertising, Ashland *Also called Heritage Press Inc* ***(G-738)***
Northcoast Environmental Labs...330 342-3377
10100 Wellman Rd Streetsboro (44241) ***(G-17865)***
Northcoast Prfmce & Mch Co...330 753-7333
1190 Wooster Rd N Barberton (44203) ***(G-1134)***
Northcoast Process Contrls Inc...440 498-0542
6283 Sunnywood Dr Cleveland (44139) ***(G-5901)***
Northcoast Tape & Label Inc...440 439-3200
24300 Solon Rd Ste 7 Cleveland (44146) ***(G-5902)***
Northcoast Valve and Gate Inc...440 392-9910
9437 Mercantile Dr Mentor (44060) ***(G-13669)***

ALPHABETIC

Northcoast Woodcraft Inc 330 677-1189
4259 Karg Industrial Pkwy Kent (44240) *(G-11497)*

Northeast Blueprint & Sup Co 216 261-7500
1230 E 286th St Cleveland (44132) *(G-5903)*

Northeast Box Company 440 992-5500
1726 Griswold Ave Ashtabula (44004) *(G-827)*

Northeast Broach & Tool 440 918-0048
990 Erie Rd Unit H Willoughby (44095) *(G-20556)*

Northeast Cabinet Co LLC 614 759-0800
6063 Taylor Rd Columbus (43230) *(G-7402)*

Northeast Coatings Inc 330 784-7773
415 Munroe Falls Rd Tallmadge (44278) *(G-18159)*

Northeast Laser Inc 330 633-2897
461 Commerce St Tallmadge (44278) *(G-18160)*

Northeast Machine Tool Corp 216 641-0141
6925 Bessemer Ave Ste 1 Cleveland (44127) *(G-5904)*

Northeast OH Neighborhood Heal 216 231-7700
8300 Hough Ave Cleveland (44103) *(G-5905)*

Northeast Ohio Contractors LLC 216 269-7881
1873 E 55th St Cleveland (44103) *(G-5906)*

Northeast Piping Supply, Wooster *Also called Northeast Tubular Service Inc (G-20818)*

Northeast Scene Inc 216 241-7550
737 Bolivar Rd Cleveland (44115) *(G-5907)*

Northeast Tire Molds Inc (HQ) 330 376-6107
159 Opportunity Pkwy Akron (44307) *(G-319)*

Northeast Tubular Service Inc 330 262-1881
6740 E Lincoln Way Wooster (44691) *(G-20818)*

Northeastern Machinery, Warren *Also called Rinaldi and Packard Industries (G-19596)*

Northeastern Oilfield Svcs LLC (PA) 330 581-3304
1537 Waynesburg Dr Se Canton (44707) *(G-2794)*

Northeastern Plastics Inc 330 453-5925
112 Navarre Rd Sw Canton (44707) *(G-2795)*

Northeastern Process Cooling, Willoughby *Also called NRC Inc (G-20558)*

Northeastern Rfrgn Corp 440 942-7676
38274 Western Pkwy Willoughby (44094) *(G-20557)*

Northel Usa LLC 740 973-0309
5772 Bear Hollow Rd Se Newark (43056) *(G-15040)*

Northend Gear & Machine Inc 513 860-4334
475 Security Dr Fairfield (45014) *(G-9690)*

Northern Boiler Company 216 961-3033
3453 W 86th St Cleveland (44102) *(G-5908)*

Northern Chem Blnding Corp Inc 216 781-7799
360 Literary Rd Cleveland (44113) *(G-5909)*

Northern Concrete Pipe Inc 419 841-3361
3756 Centennial Rd Sylvania (43560) *(G-18122)*

Northern Fabricator, Cleveland *Also called Northern Boiler Company (G-5908)*

Northern Instruments Corp LLC (HQ) 216 450-5073
23205 Mercantile Rd Cleveland (44122) *(G-5910)*

Northern Machine Tool Co 216 961-0444
3453 W 86th St Cleveland (44102) *(G-5911)*

Northern Manufacturing Co Inc 419 898-2821
150 N Lake Winds Pkwy Oak Harbor (43449) *(G-15592)*

Northern Mobile Electric, Canton *Also called M Technologies (G-2764)*

Northern Precision Inc 513 860-4701
3245 Production Dr Fairfield (45014) *(G-9691)*

Northern Stamping Co (PA) 216 883-8888
6600 Chapek Pkwy Cleveland (44125) *(G-5912)*

Northern Stamping Co 216 642-8081
7750 Hub Pkwy Cleveland (44125) *(G-5913)*

Northern Stamping Plant 2, Cleveland *Also called Northern Stamping Co (G-5913)*

Northern States Metals Company 860 521-6001
3207 Innovation Pl Youngstown (44509) *(G-21151)*

Northestrn OH Foot & Ankl Asoc 330 633-3445
116 East Ave Ste 4 Tallmadge (44278) *(G-18161)*

Northlake Steel Corporation 330 220-7717
5455 Wegman Dr Valley City (44280) *(G-19225)*

Northmont Sign Co Inc 937 890-0372
8400 N Main St Dayton (45415) *(G-8528)*

Northmont Tool and Gage Inc 937 836-9879
8741 Kimmel Rd Clayton (45315) *(G-4661)*

Northpointe Cabinetry LLC 740 455-4045
4800 Frazeysburg Rd Zanesville (43701) *(G-21334)*

Northrop Grmmn Spce & Mssn Sys 937 259-4956
1900 Founders Dr Ste 202 Dayton (45420) *(G-8529)*

Northrop Grumman Systems Corp 513 881-3296
460 W Crescentville Rd West Chester (45246) *(G-20032)*

Northshore Mining Company (HQ) 216 694-5700
1100 Superior Ave E # 1500 Cleveland (44114) *(G-5914)*

Northshore Mold Inc 440 838-8212
2861 E Royalton Rd Cleveland (44147) *(G-5915)*

Northside Meat Co Inc 513 681-4111
2910 Sidney Ave Cincinnati (45225) *(G-4163)*

Northstar Asphalt, Canton *Also called Stark Materials Inc (G-2856)*

Northstar Publishing 330 721-9126
437 Lafayette Rd Ste 310 Medina (44256) *(G-13450)*

Northwest Installations Inc 419 423-5738
1903 Blanchard Ave Findlay (45840) *(G-9869)*

Northwest Molded Plastics 419 459-4414
14372 County Road 4 Edon (43518) *(G-9342)*

Northwest Print Inc 419 385-3375
12900 Eckel Junction Rd C Perrysburg (43551) *(G-16127)*

Northwest Printing, Westerville *Also called Ganger Enterprises Inc (G-20154)*

NORTHWEST PRODUCTS, Stryker *Also called Quadco Rehabilitation Center (G-18006)*

Northwest Products Div, Archbold *Also called Quadco Rehabilitation Center (G-691)*

Northwest Signal, Napoleon *Also called Napoleon Inc (G-14691)*

Northwind Industries Inc 216 433-0666
15500 Commerce Park Dr Cleveland (44142) *(G-5916)*

Northwood Energy Corporation 614 457-1024
941 Chatham Ln Ste 100 Columbus (43221) *(G-7403)*

Northwood Industries Inc 419 666-2100
7650 Ponderosa Rd Perrysburg (43551) *(G-16128)*

Norton Industries Inc 888 357-2345
1366 W 117th St Lakewood (44107) *(G-11676)*

Norton Manufacturing Co Inc 419 435-0411
455 W 4th St Fostoria (44830) *(G-9990)*

Norton Outdoor Advertising 513 631-4864
5280 Kennedy Ave Cincinnati (45213) *(G-4164)*

Norwalk Concrete Inds Inc (PA) 419 668-8167
80 Commerce Dr Norwalk (44857) *(G-15554)*

Norwalk Concrete Inds Inc 419 668-8167
80 Commerce Dr Norwalk (44857) *(G-15555)*

Norwalk Custom Order Furn LLC 419 744-3200
100 Furniture Pkwy Norwalk (44857) *(G-15556)*

Norwalk Furniture, Norwalk *Also called Norwalk Custom Order Furn LLC (G-15556)*

Norwalk Precast Molds Inc 419 668-1639
205 Industrial Pkwy Norwalk (44857) *(G-15557)*

Norwalk Reflector, Norwalk *Also called Herald Reflector Inc (G-15545)*

Norwalk Wastewater Eqp Co 419 668-4471
220 Republic St Norwalk (44857) *(G-15558)*

Norweco, Norwalk *Also called Norwalk Wastewater Eqp Co (G-15558)*

Norwesco Inc 740 335-6236
2424 Kenskill Ave Wshngtn CT Hs (43160) *(G-20918)*

Norwesco Inc 740 654-6402
3111 Wilson Rd Lancaster (43130) *(G-11735)*

Norwich Overseas Inc (HQ) 513 983-1100
8700 S Masn Montgomery Rd Mason (45040) *(G-13068)*

Norwood Medical, Dayton *Also called Norwood Tool Company (G-8532)*

Norwood Medical 937 228-4101
2055 Winners Cir Dayton (45404) *(G-8530)*

Norwood Medical 937 228-4101
2101 Winners Cir Dayton (45404) *(G-8531)*

Norwood Tool Company (PA) 937 228-4101
2122 Winners Cir Dayton (45404) *(G-8532)*

Noshok Inc (PA) 440 243-0888
1010 W Bagley Rd Berea (44017) *(G-1630)*

Nostalgic Images Inc 419 784-1728
26012 Nostalgic Rd Defiance (43512) *(G-8807)*

Noster Rubber Company Inc 419 299-3387
1481 Township Road 229 Van Buren (45889) *(G-19240)*

Nostrum Laboratories Inc 419 636-1168
705 E Mulberry St Bryan (43506) *(G-2314)*

Noteworthy Woodworking 330 297-0509
6361 Marchinn Dr Ravenna (44266) *(G-16545)*

Noun Research and Dev Svcs, Columbus *Also called David Boswell (G-7014)*

Nova Chemicals Inc 440 352-3381
786 Hardy Rd Painesville (44077) *(G-15904)*

Nova Creative Group Inc 937 291-8653
168 W Franklin St Dayton (45459) *(G-8533)*

Nova Films and Foils Inc 440 201-1300
11 Industry Dr Bedford (44146) *(G-1448)*

Nova Industrial Machine Co 419 535-0800
10843 Little Creek Dr Whitehouse (43571) *(G-20342)*

Nova Machine Products Inc (HQ) 216 267-3200
18001 Sheldon Rd Middleburg Heights (44130) *(G-13907)*

Nova Metal Products, Willoughby *Also called Dan Novak (G-20469)*

Novacare Inc 216 704-4817
24400 Highpoint Rd Ste 10 Beachwood (44122) *(G-1285)*

Novacare Prosthetics Orthotics, Oregon *Also called Swanson Orthotic & Prosthetic (G-15719)*

Novacel Inc 937 335-5611
421 S Union St Troy (45373) *(G-18858)*

Novacel Inc 413 283-3468
421 Union St Troy (45373) *(G-18859)*

Novagard Solutions Inc (PA) 216 881-3890
5109 Hamilton Ave Cleveland (44114) *(G-5917)*

Novak J F Manufacturing Co LLC 216 741-5112
2701 Meyer Ave Cleveland (44109) *(G-5918)*

Novak Supply LLC 216 741-5112
2701 Meyer Ave Cleveland (44109) *(G-5919)*

Novartis Corporation 919 577-5000
1880 Waycross Rd Cincinnati (45240) *(G-4165)*

Novartis Vaccines & Diagnostic, Cincinnati *Also called Novartis Corporation (G-4165)*

Novatex North America Inc 419 282-4264
1070 Faultless Dr Ashland (44805) *(G-757)*

Novavision Inc (PA) 419 354-1427
524 E Wdlnd Cir Ste 2759 Bowling Green (43402) *(G-2003)*

Novel Writing Workshop, Blue Ash *Also called F+w Media Inc (G-1791)*

Novelis Corporation 330 841-3456
390 Griswold St Ne Warren (44483) ***(G-19580)***
Novelty Advertising Co Inc 740 622-3113
1148 Walnut St Coshocton (43812) ***(G-7903)***
Noveon Fcc Inc 440 943-4200
29400 Lakeland Blvd Wickliffe (44092) ***(G-20374)***
Noveon Incorporated 216 447-5000
9921 Brecksville Rd Brecksville (44141) ***(G-2067)***
Novex Inc 330 335-2371
258 Main St Wadsworth (44281) ***(G-19422)***
Novex Products Incorporated 440 244-3330
2707 Toledo Ave Ste A Lorain (44055) ***(G-12264)***
Novex Systems LLC 330 659-3546
2236 N Clvland Msslon Rd Akron (44333) ***(G-320)***
Novitran LLC 513 792-2727
8100 Deer Path Cincinnati (45243) ***(G-4166)***
Novo Foam Products LLC 440 892-3325
1991 Crocker Rd Ste 600 Westlake (44145) ***(G-20286)***
Novolex, Coldwater *Also called Accutech Films Inc* ***(G-6549)***
Novolex Holdings Inc 740 397-2555
101 Commerce Dr Mount Vernon (43050) ***(G-14634)***
Novolex Holdings Inc 937 746-1933
2000 Commerce Center Dr Franklin (45005) ***(G-10041)***
Novolyte Performance, Cleveland *Also called Novolyte Technologies Inc* ***(G-5920)***
Novolyte Technologies, Independence *Also called BASF Corporation* ***(G-11251)***
Novolyte Technologies Inc (HQ) 216 867-1040
8001 E Pleasant Valley Rd Cleveland (44131) ***(G-5920)***
Now Software Inc 614 783-4517
3720 Head Of Pond Rd New Albany (43054) ***(G-14767)***
Noxgear LLC 937 248-1860
2264 Green Island Dr Columbus (43228) ***(G-7404)***
Npa Coatings Inc 216 651-5900
11110 Berea Rd Ste 1 Cleveland (44102) ***(G-5921)***
Npk Construction Equipment Inc (HQ) 440 232-7900
7550 Independence Dr Bedford (44146) ***(G-1449)***
NPS, Richfield *Also called National Polishing Systems Inc* ***(G-16629)***
Nr Lee Restoration Ltd 419 692-2233
7470 Grone Rd Delphos (45833) ***(G-8915)***
NRC Inc 440 975-9449
38160 Western Pkwy Willoughby (44094) ***(G-20558)***
NRG Smoothies LLC 972 800-1002
1887 Youngstown Vienna (44473) ***(G-19372)***
Nsa Technologies LLC 330 576-4600
3867 Medina Rd Ste 256 Akron (44333) ***(G-321)***
Nsi Crankshaft, Fostoria *Also called Nippon Stl Smkin Crnkshaft LLC* ***(G-9988)***
Nss Enterprises Inc (PA) 419 531-2121
3115 Frenchmens Rd Toledo (43607) ***(G-18610)***
Nst, Toledo *Also called National Safety Tech LLC* ***(G-18598)***
Nsti, Columbus *Also called Noise Suppression Technologies* ***(G-7395)***
Nt, Toledo *Also called North Toledo Graphics LLC* ***(G-18609)***
Nt Machine Inc 440 968-3506
10080 Clay St Montville (44064) ***(G-14460)***
Nt Machine Inorp, Montville *Also called Nt Machine Inc* ***(G-14460)***
Nta Graphics Inc 419 476-8808
5225 Telegraph Rd Toledo (43612) ***(G-18611)***
Ntech Industries Inc 707 467-3747
5475 Kellenburger Rd Dayton (45424) ***(G-8534)***
NTS Enterprises Ltd (PA) 513 531-1166
1550 Magnolia Dr Cincinnati (45215) ***(G-4167)***
Nu-Di Products Co Inc 216 251-9070
12730 Triskett Rd Cleveland (44111) ***(G-5922)***
Nu-Tool Industries Inc 440 237-9240
9920 York Alpha Dr North Royalton (44133) ***(G-15438)***
Nucam, Twinsburg *Also called Semtorq Inc* ***(G-19019)***
Nuclear Physicians Limited 330 920-3770
4161 Bridgewater Pkwy Stow (44224) ***(G-17785)***
Nuclear Plating Service Inc 216 641-1109
7935 Orianna St Brecksville (44141) ***(G-2068)***
Nucon International Inc (PA) 614 846-5710
7000 Huntley Rd Columbus (43229) ***(G-7405)***
Nucor Bright Bar Orville LLC 330 682-5555
555 Collins Blvd Orrville (44667) ***(G-15751)***
Nufab Sheet Metal 937 235-2030
4750 Hempstead Station Dr Dayton (45429) ***(G-8535)***
Nuflux LLC 330 399-1122
2395 State Route 5 Cortland (44410) ***(G-7872)***
Numatx Inc 937 435-8178
4668 Gateway Cir Dayton (45440) ***(G-8536)***
Numerics Unlimited Inc 937 849-0100
1700 Dalton Dr New Carlisle (45344) ***(G-14810)***
Numerics Unlimited North, Sidney *Also called Compressor Technologies Inc* ***(G-17172)***
Nupco Inc 419 629-2259
06561 County Road 66a New Bremen (45869) ***(G-14791)***
Nupro Company 440 951-9729
4800 E 345th St Willoughby (44094) ***(G-20559)***
Nurdcon LLC 614 208-5898
6645 Kodiak Dr Canal Winchester (43110) ***(G-2534)***
Nurture Brands LLC 513 307-2338
177 Wyoming Woods Ln Cincinnati (45215) ***(G-4168)***

Nutralab Inc 513 561-0471
5400 Indian Heights Dr Cincinnati (45243) ***(G-4169)***
Nutrifresh Eggs 567 224-7676
342 Plymouth East Rd Willard (44890) ***(G-20398)***
Nutrimir LLC 614 600-2478
408 Tipperary Loop Delaware (43015) ***(G-8875)***
Nutrimir Personalized Wellness, Delaware *Also called Nutrimir LLC* ***(G-8875)***
Nutrition Transportation Svcs, Brookville *Also called Provimi North America Inc* ***(G-2197)***
Nutro Corporation 440 572-3800
11515 Alameda Dr Cleveland (44101) ***(G-5923)***
Nutro Inc 440 572-3800
11515 Alameda Dr Strongsville (44149) ***(G-17947)***
Nutro Machinery, Cleveland *Also called Nutro Corporation* ***(G-5923)***
Nuts Are Good Inc (PA) 586 619-2400
Busch Blvd Columbus (43229) ***(G-7406)***
Nuvasive Manufacturing LLC 937 343-0400
1 Herald Sq Fairborn (45324) ***(G-9627)***
Nuvox 614 232-9115
111 N 4th St Columbus (43215) ***(G-7407)***
Nvision Technology Inc 412 254-4668
2769 Pinegate Dr Norton (44203) ***(G-15519)***
Nwc HUD Corp II 419 228-8400
1404 N West St Lima (45801) ***(G-12064)***
Nwp Manufacturing Inc 419 894-6871
2862 County Road 146 Waldo (43356) ***(G-19466)***
Nxstage Medical Inc 513 712-1300
12065 Montgomery Rd Cincinnati (45249) ***(G-4170)***
NY Logging & Lumber 740 679-2085
61285 Shannon Run Rd Quaker City (43773) ***(G-16500)***
Nyeco Gas Inc 419 447-2712
905 Pierce St Sandusky (44870) ***(G-16990)***
O & P Options LLC 513 791-7767
10547 Montgomery Rd # 600 Montgomery (45242) ***(G-14434)***
O A R Vinyl Window Co, Middlefield *Also called O A R Vinyl Windows & Siding* ***(G-13978)***
O A R Vinyl Windows & Siding 440 636-5573
12880 Clay St Middlefield (44062) ***(G-13978)***
O C Tanner Company 513 583-1100
8569 S Mason Montgomery R Mason (45040) ***(G-13069)***
O Connor Office Pdts & Prtg 740 852-2209
60 W High St London (43140) ***(G-12216)***
O D M, Mason *Also called Oakley Die & Mold Co* ***(G-13070)***
O E M Hydraulics Inc 740 454-1201
1150 Newark Rd Zanesville (43701) ***(G-21335)***
O E M Sales, Germantown *Also called Ohio Engineering and Mfg Sls* ***(G-10371)***
O E Meyer Co 419 332-6931
1005 Everett Rd Fremont (43420) ***(G-10171)***
O G Bell, Avon Lake *Also called Wolff Tool & Manufacturing Co* ***(G-1056)***
O Gauge Railroading, Youngstown *Also called Ogr Publishing Inc* ***(G-21153)***
O H Technologies Inc 440 354-8780
9300 Progress Pkwy Mentor (44060) ***(G-13670)***
O K Brugmann Jr & Sons Inc 330 274-2106
4083 Mennonite Rd Mantua (44255) ***(G-12718)***
O K Coal & Concrete, Zanesville *Also called Joe McClelland Inc* ***(G-21324)***
O S C, Columbus *Also called Octsys Security Corp* ***(G-7412)***
O S U Press, Columbus *Also called Ohio State University* ***(G-7434)***
O T Packaging 330 482-2224
308 Kingwood Dr Columbiana (44408) ***(G-6626)***
O'Beirn Printing Co, Cleveland *Also called Delores E OBeirn* ***(G-5182)***
O-1, Perrysburg *Also called Owens-Illinois General Inc* ***(G-16142)***
O-I, Perrysburg *Also called Owens-Brockway Glass Cont Inc* ***(G-16139)***
O-I, Toledo *Also called Owens-Illinois De Puerto Rico* ***(G-18628)***
O-Kan Marine Repair Inc 740 446-4686
267 Upper River Rd Gallipolis (45631) ***(G-10306)***
O.c Tanner Recognition, Mason *Also called O C Tanner Company* ***(G-13069)***
Oak Chips Inc 740 947-4159
306 W North St Waverly (45690) ***(G-19714)***
Oak Dale Drilling Inc 740 385-5888
149 Ruth Ave Logan (43138) ***(G-12187)***
Oak Front Inc 330 948-4500
830 Bank St Lodi (44254) ***(G-12167)***
Oak Heritage, Yellow Springs *Also called Kenway Corp* ***(G-20994)***
Oak Hill Foundry & Mch Works 740 682-7746
333 S Front St Oak Hill (45656) ***(G-15603)***
Oak Hills Carton Co 513 948-4200
6310 Este Ave Cincinnati (45232) ***(G-4171)***
Oak Industrial Inc 440 263-2780
12955 York Delta Dr Ste G North Royalton (44133) ***(G-15439)***
Oak Pointe Stair Systems Inc 740 498-9820
96 New Pace Rd Newcomerstown (43832) ***(G-15120)***
Oak Printing Company 440 238-3316
19540 Progress Dr Strongsville (44149) ***(G-17948)***
Oak Tree Intl Holdings Inc 702 462-7295
1209 Lowell St Elyria (44035) ***(G-9469)***
Oakbridge Timber Framing 419 994-1052
9001 Township Road 461 Loudonville (44842) ***(G-12301)***
Oakes Door Serv 937 323-6188
5298 Troy Rd Springfield (45502) ***(G-17618)***

Oakes Foundry Inc ... 330 372-4010
700 Bronze Rd Ne Warren (44483) ***(G-19581)***
Oakley Inc ... 949 672-6560
1421 Springfield St # 2 Dayton (45403) ***(G-8537)***
Oakley Die & Mold Co ... 513 754-8500
7595 Innovation Way Mason (45040) ***(G-13070)***
Oakley Full Gospel Baptist Ch, Columbus *Also called Full Gospel Baptist Times* ***(G-7102)***
Oakley Industries Sub Assembly ... 419 661-8888
6317 Fairfield Dr Northwood (43619) ***(G-15486)***
Oakmoor Pallet ... 216 926-1858
795 Sharon Dr Ste 210 Westlake (44145) ***(G-20287)***
Oakmoor Pallet ... 440 385-7340
795 Sharon Dr Westlake (44145) ***(G-20288)***
Oaks Welding Inc ... 330 482-4216
201 Prospect St Columbiana (44408) ***(G-6627)***
Oaktree Wireline LLC ... 330 352-7250
1825 E High Ave New Philadelphia (44663) ***(G-14919)***
Oakvale Farm Cheese Inc ... 740 857-1230
1283 State Route 29 Ne London (43140) ***(G-12217)***
Oakwood Furniture Inc ... 740 896-3162
10105 State Route 60 Lowell (45744) ***(G-12403)***
Oakwood Industries Inc (PA) ... 440 232-8700
7250 Division St Bedford (44146) ***(G-1450)***
Oakwood Laboratories LLC (PA) ... 440 359-0000
7670 First Pl Ste A Oakwood Village (44146) ***(G-15626)***
Oakwood Laboratories LLC ... 440 505-2011
27070 Miles Rd Solon (44139) ***(G-17352)***
Oakwood Register, The, Dayton *Also called Winkler Co Inc* ***(G-8761)***
Oasis Consumer Healthcare LLC ... 216 394-0544
737 Bolivar Rd Ste 4500 Cleveland (44115) ***(G-5924)***
Oasis Embroidery ... 614 785-7266
6663 Huntley Rd Ste R Columbus (43229) ***(G-7408)***
Oasis International, Columbus *Also called Lvd Acquisition LLC* ***(G-7306)***
Oasis Mediterranean Cuisine ... 419 269-1516
1520 W Laskey Rd Toledo (43612) ***(G-18612)***
Obars Machine and Tool Company (PA) ... 419 535-6307
115 N Westwood Ave 125 Toledo (43607) ***(G-18613)***
Obars Welding & Fabg Div, Toledo *Also called Obars Machine and Tool Company* ***(G-18613)***
Oberfields LLC (PA) ... 740 369-7644
528 London Rd Delaware (43015) ***(G-8876)***
Oberfields LLC ... 614 491-7643
4033 Alum Creek Dr Columbus (43207) ***(G-7409)***
Oberfields LLC ... 740 369-7644
471 Kintner Pkwy Sunbury (43074) ***(G-18069)***
Oberfields LLC ... 614 252-0955
1165 Alum Creek Dr Columbus (43209) ***(G-7410)***
Oberfields LLC ... 937 885-3711
10075 Sheehan Rd Dayton (45458) ***(G-8538)***
Obersons Nurs & Landscapes Inc ... 513 894-0669
3951 River Rd Fairfield (45014) ***(G-9692)***
Obersons Snow and Ice MGT, Fairfield *Also called Obersons Nurs & Landscapes Inc* ***(G-9692)***
Obr Cooling Towers Inc ... 419 243-3443
9665 S Compass Dr Rossford (43460) ***(G-16744)***
OBrien Cut Stone Company ... 216 663-7800
19100 Miles Rd Cleveland (44128) ***(G-5925)***
Obron Atlantic Corporation ... 440 954-7600
830 E Erie St Painesville (44077) ***(G-15905)***
Obs Inc ... 330 453-3725
1324 Tuscarawas St W Canton (44702) ***(G-2796)***
OBS SPECIALTY VEHICLES, Canton *Also called Obs Inc* ***(G-2796)***
Obsidian Biodent ... 937 938-9244
260 Ridgewood Ave Oakwood (45409) ***(G-15610)***
OCC, Ashland *Also called Ohio Carbon Company* ***(G-758)***
Occassionaly Yours, Beavercreek *Also called Shops By Todd Inc* ***(G-1360)***
Occidental Chemical Corp ... 513 242-2900
4701 Paddock Rd Cincinnati (45229) ***(G-4172)***
Occidental Chemical Corp ... 330 764-3441
3984 Dogleg Trl Medina (44256) ***(G-13451)***
Occidental Chemical Durez ... 419 675-5300
13717 Us Highway 68 Kenton (43326) ***(G-11563)***
Ocean Providence Columbus LLC ... 614 272-5973
3699 Interchange Rd Columbus (43204) ***(G-7411)***
Oceanside Foods ... 440 554-7810
32859 Lake Rd Avon Lake (44012) ***(G-1042)***
Oceco Co, Tiffin *Also called Oceco Inc* ***(G-18235)***
Oceco Inc ... 419 447-0916
1616 S County Road 1 Tiffin (44883) ***(G-18235)***
Ochc, Cleveland *Also called Oasis Consumer Healthcare LLC* ***(G-5924)***
Ocm LLC (HQ) ... 937 247-2700
4500 Lyons Rd Miamisburg (45342) ***(G-13844)***
Ocs Intellitrak Inc ... 513 742-5600
8660 Seward Rd Fairfield (45011) ***(G-9693)***
Ocs Telecom LLC ... 740 503-5939
4138 Weaver Ct E Hilliard (43026) ***(G-10965)***
Octal Extrusion Corp ... 513 881-6100
5399 E Provident Dr West Chester (45246) ***(G-20033)***
Octapharma Plasma Inc ... 216 518-0322
5398 Northfield Rd Maple Heights (44137) ***(G-12735)***
Octapharma Plasma Inc ... 216 252-6811
10694 Lorain Ave Cleveland (44111) ***(G-5926)***
Octsys Security Corp ... 614 470-4510
341 S 3rd St Ste 100-42 Columbus (43215) ***(G-7412)***
Odacs Inc ... 513 761-0539
8634 Reading Rd Cincinnati (45215) ***(G-4173)***
Odawara Automation Inc ... 937 667-8433
4805 S County Road 25a Tipp City (45371) ***(G-18291)***
Odell Electronic Cleaning Stns, Westlake *Also called Aerocase Incorporated* ***(G-20247)***
Odi, Elyria *Also called Ohio Displays Inc* ***(G-9470)***
Odyssey Canvas Works Inc ... 937 392-4422
6689 Us Highway 52 Ripley (45167) ***(G-16668)***
Odyssey Cellars Inc ... 330 782-0177
4033 Hopkins Rd Youngstown (44511) ***(G-21152)***
Odyssey Machine Company Ltd ... 419 455-6621
26675 Eckel Rd 5 Perrysburg (43551) ***(G-16129)***
Odyssey Press Inc ... 614 410-0356
913 Superior Dr Huron (44839) ***(G-11236)***
Odyssey Printwear, Aurora *Also called Odyssey Spirits Inc* ***(G-938)***
Odyssey Spirits Inc ... 330 562-1523
7286 N Aurora Rd Aurora (44202) ***(G-938)***
Oe Exchange LLC (PA) ... 440 266-1639
8200 Tyler Blvd Mentor (44060) ***(G-13671)***
Oe Plastics LLC ... 513 847-8101
7070 Lindley Way Liberty Twp (45011) ***(G-11977)***
Oeder Carl E Sons Sand & Grav ... 513 494-1238
1000 Mason Mrrow Mlgrv Rd Lebanon (45036) ***(G-11820)***
OEM, West Chester *Also called Ctl-Aerospace Inc* ***(G-19994)***
OEM Corporation ... 937 859-7492
3660 Benner Rd Miamisburg (45342) ***(G-13845)***
Oen Custom Cabinets Inc ... 419 738-8115
8 Willipie St Wapakoneta (45895) ***(G-19503)***
Oen Kitchen & Bath Showroom, Wapakoneta *Also called Oen Custom Cabinets Inc* ***(G-19503)***
Oerlikon Blzers Cating USA Inc ... 330 220-7716
1130 Industrial Pkwy N # 15 Brunswick (44212) ***(G-2240)***
Oerlikon Friction Systems ... 937 233-7002
220 Janney Rd Dayton (45404) ***(G-8539)***
Oerlikon Friction Systems (HQ) ... 937 449-4000
240 Detrick St Dayton (45404) ***(G-8540)***
Oerlikon Friction Systems ... 937 233-9191
240 Detrick St Dayton (45404) ***(G-8541)***
of Machining LLC ... 419 396-7870
2140 State Rd 568 Carey (43316) ***(G-2922)***
OFA Services Inc ... 614 884-1203
2130 Stella Ct Ste 200 Columbus (43215) ***(G-7413)***
Ofco Inc ... 740 622-5922
111 N 14th St Coshocton (43812) ***(G-7904)***
Off Contact Inc ... 419 255-5546
4756 W Bancroft St Toledo (43615) ***(G-18614)***
Off Contact Productions, Toledo *Also called Off Contact Inc* ***(G-18614)***
Off The Wall Signs ... 740 264-7759
1557 Cadiz Rd Steubenville (43953) ***(G-17707)***
Office Bsed Ansthesia Svcs LLC ... 513 582-5170
10296 Gentlewind Dr Montgomery (45242) ***(G-14435)***
Office Graphics, Hamilton *Also called Z P Enterprises Inc* ***(G-10758)***
Office Link Inc ... 440 498-1364
34194 Aurora Rd Ste 242 Solon (44139) ***(G-17353)***
Office Magic Inc (PA) ... 510 782-6100
2290 Wilbur Rd Medina (44256) ***(G-13452)***
Office Print N Copy ... 740 695-3616
104 N Marietta St Saint Clairsville (43950) ***(G-16799)***
Offset Theory, Cleveland *Also called McMath & Sheets Unlimited Inc* ***(G-5771)***
Ogara Hess Eisenhardt ... 513 346-1300
9113 Le Saint Dr West Chester (45014) ***(G-19907)***
Ogc Industries Inc ... 330 456-1500
934 Wells Ave Nw Canton (44703) ***(G-2797)***
Ogden Hydraulics LLC ... 419 686-1108
396 W Main St Portage (43451) ***(G-16426)***
Ogden Newspapers Inc ... 330 332-4601
161 N Lincoln Ave Salem (44460) ***(G-16917)***
Ogden Newspapers Inc ... 740 283-4711
401 Herald Sq Steubenville (43952) ***(G-17708)***
Ogden Newspapers Inc ... 330 841-1600
240 Franklin St Se Warren (44483) ***(G-19582)***
Ogden Newspapers of Ohio Inc ... 419 448-3200
320 Nelson St Tiffin (44883) ***(G-18236)***
Ogden Newspapers Ohio Inc (HQ) ... 330 424-9541
308 Maple St Lisbon (44432) ***(G-12129)***
Ogg Garick, Cleveland *Also called Garick LLC* ***(G-5398)***
Ogr Publishing Inc ... 330 757-3020
33 Sheridan Rd Ste 1 Youngstown (44514) ***(G-21153)***
Ogs Industries, Akron *Also called Ohio Gasket and Shim Co Inc* ***(G-323)***
Ogs Tool & Manufacturing ... 419 524-6200
3520 N Main St Mansfield (44903) ***(G-12660)***
Oh-Ll Commercial Cleaning LLC ... 614 390-3628
1905 Lake Crest Dr Grove City (43123) ***(G-10579)***
Ohashi Technica USA Inc (HQ) ... 740 965-5115
111 Burrer Dr Sunbury (43074) ***(G-18070)***

Ohashi Technica USA Mfg Inc 740 965-9002
99 Burrer Dr Sunbury (43074) *(G-18071)*

Ohi-TEC Manufacturing Inc 937 882-6144
3015 Production Ct Dayton (45414) *(G-8542)*

Ohigro Inc (PA) 740 726-2429
6720 Gillette Rd Waldo (43356) *(G-19467)*

Ohio Aluminum Chemicals LLC 513 860-3842
4544 Muhlhauser Rd West Chester (45011) *(G-19908)*

Ohio Aluminum Industries Inc 216 641-8865
4840 Warner Rd Cleveland (44125) *(G-5927)*

Ohio Anodizing Company Inc 614 252-7855
915 N 20th St Columbus (43219) *(G-7414)*

Ohio Art Company (PA) 419 636-3141
1 Toy St Bryan (43506) *(G-2315)*

Ohio Asphaltic Limestone Corp 937 364-2191
8591 Mad River Rd Hillsboro (45133) *(G-11009)*

Ohio Associated Entps LLC (PA) 440 354-2106
97 Corwin Dr Painesville (44077) *(G-15906)*

Ohio Associated Entps LLC 440 354-3148
1359 W Jackson St Painesville (44077) *(G-15907)*

Ohio Associated Entps LLC 440 354-3148
72 Corwin Dr Painesville (44077) *(G-15908)*

Ohio Association Realtors Inc 614 228-6675
200 E Town St Columbus (43215) *(G-7415)*

Ohio Auto Supply Company 330 454-5105
1128 Tuscarawas St W Canton (44702) *(G-2798)*

Ohio Awning & Manufacturing Co 216 861-2400
5777 Grant Ave Cleveland (44105) *(G-5928)*

Ohio Beauty Cut Stone, Akron *Also called Ohio Beauty Inc (G-322)*

Ohio Beauty Inc 330 644-2241
40 W Turkeyfoot Lake Rd Akron (44319) *(G-322)*

Ohio Belt Control Supply Co, Wadsworth *Also called D & J Electric Motor Repair Co (G-19401)*

Ohio Beverage Systems Inc 216 475-3900
9200 Midwest Ave Cleveland (44125) *(G-5929)*

Ohio Biofuels 614 886-6518
3613 Woodbridge Pl Cincinnati (45226) *(G-4174)*

Ohio Biosystems Coop Inc 419 980-7663
135 N Market St Loudonville (44842) *(G-12302)*

Ohio Blenders Inc (PA) 419 726-2655
2404 N Summit St Toledo (43611) *(G-18615)*

Ohio Blow Pipe Company (PA) 216 681-7379
446 E 131st St Cleveland (44108) *(G-5930)*

Ohio Box & Crate Inc 440 526-3133
16751 Tavern Rd Burton (44021) *(G-2381)*

Ohio Box and Crate Co, Burton *Also called Ohio Box & Crate Inc (G-2381)*

Ohio Bridge Corporation 740 432-6334
201 Wheeling Ave Cambridge (43725) *(G-2470)*

Ohio Broach & Machine Company 440 946-1040
35264 Topps Indus Pkwy Willoughby (44094) *(G-20560)*

Ohio Brush Company 216 791-3265
2680 Lisbon Rd Cleveland (44104) *(G-5931)*

Ohio CAM & Tool Co 216 531-7900
23572 Saint Clair Ave Cleveland (44117) *(G-5932)*

Ohio Candle Co Inc 740 289-8000
7040 Us Rte 23 Waverly (45690) *(G-19715)*

Ohio Carbon Blank Inc (PA) 440 953-9302
38403 Pelton Rd Willoughby (44094) *(G-20561)*

Ohio Carbon Company 216 251-7274
1201 Jacobson Ave Ashland (44805) *(G-758)*

Ohio Carbon Industries Inc 419 496-2530
1201 Jacobson Ave Ashland (44805) *(G-759)*

Ohio Cast Stone Co LLC 614 524-0666
5767 Duvall Rd Ashville (43103) *(G-852)*

Ohio Cast Stone Co LLC 614 444-2278
45 W Barthman Ave Columbus (43207) *(G-7416)*

Ohio Centech 513 477-8779
444 Hidden Valley Ln Cincinnati (45215) *(G-4175)*

Ohio Chemical Two 614 482-8073
8132 Linden Leaf Cir Columbus (43235) *(G-7417)*

Ohio City Pasta, Cleveland *Also called Food Designs Inc (G-5366)*

Ohio Classic Street Rods Inc 440 543-6593
9899 Washington St Chagrin Falls (44023) *(G-3108)*

Ohio Cllbrtive Lrng Sltons Inc (PA) 216 595-5289
24700 Chagrin Blvd # 104 Beachwood (44122) *(G-1286)*

Ohio Coatings Company 740 859-5500
2100 Tin Plate Pl Yorkville (43971) *(G-21007)*

Ohio Community Media, Miamisburg *Also called Ocm LLC (G-13844)*

Ohio Community Media 740 848-4064
59 W College St Fredericktown (43019) *(G-10107)*

Ohio Construction News, Cleveland *Also called Construction Journal Ltd (G-5120)*

Ohio Conveyor and Supply Inc 419 422-3825
1310 N Main St Findlay (45840) *(G-9870)*

OHIO CRAFT MUSEUM, Columbus *Also called Ohio Designer Craftsmen Entps (G-7419)*

Ohio Crankshaft Div, Newburgh Heights *Also called Park-Ohio Industries Inc (G-15077)*

Ohio Cut Sheet, Strongsville *Also called Dupli-Systems Inc (G-17913)*

Ohio Decorative Products LLC (PA) 419 647-9033
220 S Elizabeth St Spencerville (45887) *(G-17463)*

Ohio Department Transportation 614 351-2898
1606 W Broad St Columbus (43223) *(G-7418)*

Ohio Designer Craftsmen Entps (HQ) 614 486-7119
1665 W 5th Ave Columbus (43212) *(G-7419)*

Ohio Displays Inc 216 961-5600
825 Leona St Elyria (44035) *(G-9470)*

Ohio Distinctive Enterprises 614 459-0453
6500 Fiesta Dr Columbus (43235) *(G-7420)*

Ohio Distinctive Software, Columbus *Also called Ohio Distinctive Enterprises (G-7420)*

Ohio Drill & Tool Co (PA) 330 525-7717
23255 Georgetown Rd Homeworth (44634) *(G-11117)*

Ohio Elastomers 440 354-9750
3470 Blackmore Rd Perry (44081) *(G-16055)*

Ohio Electric Control, Ashland *Also called Precision Design Inc (G-767)*

Ohio Electric Motor Svc LLC 419 525-2225
311 E 3rd St Mansfield (44902) *(G-12661)*

Ohio Electric Motors, Dublin *Also called Peerless-Winsmith Inc (G-9122)*

Ohio Electro-Polishing Co Inc 419 667-2281
15085 Main St Venedocia (45894) *(G-19322)*

Ohio Energy Assets Inc 740 332-9511
16276 Long Run Rd Laurelville (43135) *(G-11771)*

Ohio Engineering and Mfg Co, Wadsworth *Also called Hutnik Company (G-19411)*

Ohio Engineering and Mfg Sls 937 855-6971
11610 State Route 725 Germantown (45327) *(G-10371)*

Ohio Envelope Manufacturing Co 216 267-2920
5161 W 164th St Cleveland (44142) *(G-5933)*

Ohio Eye Associates, Columbus *Also called Eye Center (G-7074)*

Ohio Fabricators, Coshocton *Also called Ofco Inc (G-7904)*

Ohio Farms Packing Co Ltd 330 435-6400
2416 E West Salem Rd Creston (44217) *(G-7942)*

Ohio Feather Company Inc 513 921-3373
1 Kovach Dr Cincinnati (45215) *(G-4176)*

Ohio Flame 330 953-0863
7655 Spring Park Dr Youngstown (44512) *(G-21154)*

Ohio Flame Hardening Company (PA) 513 336-6160
4110 Columbia Rd Lebanon (45036) *(G-11821)*

Ohio Flame Hardening Company 513 733-5162
637 N Wayne Ave Cincinnati (45215) *(G-4177)*

Ohio Flexible Packaging Co 513 494-1800
512 S Main St South Lebanon (45065) *(G-17430)*

Ohio Flock-Cote Company Inc 440 498-3877
6810 Cochran Rd Solon (44139) *(G-17354)*

Ohio Foam Corporation 614 252-4877
1513 Alum Creek Dr Columbus (43209) *(G-7421)*

Ohio Foam Corporation (PA) 419 563-0399
820 Plymouth St Bucyrus (44820) *(G-2355)*

Ohio Foam Corporation 330 799-4553
1201 Ameritech Blvd Youngstown (44509) *(G-21155)*

Ohio Foam Corporation 419 492-2151
529 S Kibler St New Washington (44854) *(G-14963)*

Ohio Fresh Eggs LLC (PA) 740 893-7200
11212 Croton Rd Croton (43013) *(G-7955)*

Ohio Fresh Eggs LLC 937 354-2233
20449 County Road 245 Mount Victory (43340) *(G-14657)*

Ohio Galvanizing Corp 740 387-6474
467 W Fairground St Marion (43302) *(G-12891)*

Ohio Gasket and Shim Co Inc (PA) 330 630-0626
976 Evans Ave Akron (44305) *(G-323)*

Ohio Generator Remanufacturing 330 875-6677
134 N Chapel St Louisville (44641) *(G-12321)*

Ohio Graphic Supply Inc 937 433-7537
530 W Whipp Rd Dayton (45459) *(G-8543)*

Ohio Gratings Inc (PA) 330 477-6707
5299 Southway St Sw Canton (44706) *(G-2799)*

Ohio Gravure Technologies Inc 937 439-1582
1241 Byers Rd Miamisburg (45342) *(G-13846)*

Ohio Guns, Ashtabula *Also called Reloading Supplies Corp (G-836)*

Ohio Harness LLC 937 292-7355
227 Water Ave Bellefontaine (43311) *(G-1537)*

Ohio Heat Transfer Ltd 740 695-0635
66721 Executive Dr Saint Clairsville (43950) *(G-16800)*

Ohio Hickory Harvest Brand Pro 330 644-6266
90 Logan Pkwy Akron (44319) *(G-324)*

Ohio Hydraulics Inc 513 771-2590
2510 E Sharon Rd Ste 1 Cincinnati (45241) *(G-4178)*

Ohio Industrial Supply, Dayton *Also called Tool Service Co Inc (G-8119)*

Ohio Knitting Mills, Cleveland *Also called Okm LLC (G-5935)*

Ohio L & M Company Inc 330 493-0440
4150 Belden Village St Nw # 410 Canton (44718) *(G-2800)*

Ohio Laminating & Binding Inc 614 771-4868
4364 Reynolds Dr Hilliard (43026) *(G-10966)*

Ohio Laser LLC 614 873-7030
8260 Estates Pkwy Plain City (43064) *(G-16352)*

Ohio Logos Inc 614 717-0833
4384 Tuller Rd Dublin (43017) *(G-9115)*

Ohio Lumex Co Inc 440 264-2500
30350 Bruce Indus Pkwy Solon (44139) *(G-17355)*

Ohio Machined Products Inc 419 264-2400
503 Joe E Brown Ave Holgate (43527) *(G-11038)*

A
L
P
H
A
B
E
T
I
C

Ohio Magnetics Inc 216 662-8484
  5400 Dunham Rd Maple Heights (44137) *(G-12736)*

Ohio Manufacturing EXT Partnr 614 644-8788
  77 S High St Columbus (43215) *(G-7422)*

Ohio Mattress 740 739-8219
  1408 Ety Rd Nw Lancaster (43130) *(G-11736)*

Ohio Mechanical Handling Co 330 773-5165
  1856 S Main St Akron (44301) *(G-325)*

Ohio Metal Fabricating Inc 937 233-2400
  6057 Milo Rd Dayton (45414) *(G-8544)*

Ohio Metal Products Company 937 228-6101
  35 Bates St Dayton (45402) *(G-8545)*

Ohio Metal Services, Akron Also called WMI Group LLC *(G-474)*

Ohio Metal Technologies Inc 740 928-8288
  470 John Alford Pkwy Hebron (43025) *(G-10879)*

Ohio Metal Working Products 330 455-2009
  3620 Progress St Ne Canton (44705) *(G-2801)*

Ohio Metalizing LLC 330 830-1092
  2519 Erie St S Massillon (44646) *(G-13185)*

Ohio Metallurgical Service Inc 440 365-4104
  1033 Clark St Elyria (44035) *(G-9471)*

Ohio Mill Supply, Cleveland Also called Ohio Mills Corporation *(G-5934)*

Ohio Mills Corporation (PA) 216 431-3979
  1719 E 39th St Cleveland (44114) *(G-5934)*

Ohio Mirror Technologies Inc (PA) 419 399-5903
  114 W Jackson St Paulding (45879) *(G-16010)*

Ohio Mirror Technologies Inc 419 399-5903
  384 W Wall St Paulding (45879) *(G-16011)*

Ohio Model Planes 937 372-0603
  199 Stratford Ln Xenia (45385) *(G-20965)*

Ohio Model Products, Xenia Also called Ohio Model Planes *(G-20965)*

Ohio Natural Gas Services Inc 740 796-3305
  5600 East Pike Zanesville (43701) *(G-21336)*

Ohio News Network 614 460-3700
  770 Twin Rivers Dr Columbus (43215) *(G-7423)*

Ohio News Network, The, Columbus Also called Ohio News Network *(G-7423)*

Ohio Newspaper Services Inc 614 486-6677
  1335 Dublin Rd Ste 216b Columbus (43215) *(G-7424)*

Ohio Newspapers Foundation 614 486-6677
  1335 Dublin Rd Ste 216b Columbus (43215) *(G-7425)*

Ohio Nut & Bolt Company Div, Berea Also called Fastener Industries Inc *(G-1615)*

Ohio Ordnance Works Inc 440 285-3481
  310 Park Dr Chardon (44024) *(G-3170)*

Ohio Oxide Corporation Del 740 654-6555
  4850 Elder Rd Ne Pleasantville (43148) *(G-16374)*

Ohio Packaging (HQ) 330 833-2884
  777 3rd St Nw Massillon (44647) *(G-13186)*

Ohio Packing Company (PA) 614 445-0627
  1306 Harmon Ave Columbus (43223) *(G-7426)*

Ohio Packing Company 614 445-0627
  1306 Harmon Ave Columbus (43223) *(G-7427)*

Ohio Paper Tube Co 330 478-5171
  3422 Navarre Rd Sw Canton (44706) *(G-2802)*

Ohio Pet Foods Inc (PA) 330 424-1431
  38251 Indl Pk Rd Lisbon (44432) *(G-12130)*

Ohio Pickling & Processing LLC 419 241-9601
  1149 Campbell St Toledo (43607) *(G-18616)*

Ohio Plastics & Safety Pdts 330 882-6764
  6140 Manchester Rd New Franklin (44319) *(G-14827)*

Ohio Plastics Belting Co 330 882-6764
  6140 Manchester Rd New Franklin (44319) *(G-14828)*

Ohio Plastics Company 740 828-3291
  3933 Price Rd Ne Newark (43055) *(G-15041)*

Ohio Plywood Box 513 242-9125
  5555 Vine St Cincinnati (45216) *(G-4179)*

Ohio Power Tool Brush Co 419 736-3010
  1201 Jacobson Ave Ashland (44805) *(G-760)*

Ohio Precast Concrete Assoc, Troy Also called Concrete Fealants Inc *(G-18812)*

Ohio Precision Inc 330 453-9710
  1239 Market Ave S Canton (44707) *(G-2803)*

Ohio Precision Molding Inc 330 745-9393
  122 E Tuscarawas Ave Barberton (44203) *(G-1135)*

Ohio Press, Antwerp Also called Antwerp Bee-Argus *(G-627)*

Ohio Print Source, Canton Also called 1455 Group LLC *(G-2583)*

Ohio Printed Products Inc 330 659-0909
  3920 Congress Pkwy Richfield (44286) *(G-16630)*

Ohio Processors Inc (HQ) 740 852-9243
  2200 Cardigan Ave Columbus (43215) *(G-7428)*

Ohio Processors Inc 740 852-9243
  244 E 1st St London (43140) *(G-12218)*

Ohio Psychlogy Pblications Inc 614 861-1999
  620 Taylor Station Rd F Columbus (43230) *(G-7429)*

Ohio Pure Foods Inc (HQ) 330 753-2293
  681 W Waterloo Rd Akron (44314) *(G-326)*

Ohio River Valley Cabinet 740 975-8846
  4 Waterworks Rd Newark (43055) *(G-15042)*

Ohio Roll Grinding Inc 330 453-1884
  5165 Louisville St Louisville (44641) *(G-12322)*

Ohio Screw Products Inc 440 322-6341
  818 Lowell St Elyria (44035) *(G-9472)*

Ohio Select Imprinted Fabrics, Reynoldsburg Also called Ohio State Institute of Fin *(G-16596)*

Ohio Semitronics Inc (PA) 614 777-1005
  4242 Reynolds Dr Hilliard (43026) *(G-10967)*

Ohio Shelterall Inc 614 882-1110
  6060 Westerville Rd Westerville (43081) *(G-20227)*

Ohio Silver Co 937 767-8261
  245 Xenia Ave Yellow Springs (45387) *(G-20997)*

Ohio Slitting & Storage 937 452-1108
  7000 N Main St Camden (45311) *(G-2486)*

Ohio Specialty Mfg Co 419 531-5402
  2008 N Hlland Sylvania Rd Toledo (43615) *(G-18617)*

Ohio Sporting Goods LLC 330 548-5911
  2769 Front St Cuyahoga Falls (44221) *(G-8030)*

Ohio Stamping & Machine LLC 937 322-3880
  2100 S Yellow Springs St Springfield (45506) *(G-17619)*

Ohio Standard Bread, Medina Also called Trogdon Publishing Inc *(G-13491)*

Ohio Star Forge Co 330 847-6360
  4000 Mahoning Ave Nw Warren (44483) *(G-19583)*

Ohio State Institute of Fin 614 861-8811
  7394 E Main St Reynoldsburg (43068) *(G-16596)*

Ohio State Pallet Corp 614 332-3961
  2175 Broehm Rd Homer (43027) *(G-11113)*

Ohio State Plastics 614 299-5618
  1917 Joyce Ave Columbus (43219) *(G-7430)*

Ohio State University 614 292-7656
  1060 Carmack Rd Rm 39 Columbus (43210) *(G-7431)*

Ohio State University 614 292-4139
  1248 Arthur E Adams Dr Columbus (43221) *(G-7432)*

Ohio State University 614 293-3600
  2050 Kenny Rd Fl 9 Columbus (43221) *(G-7433)*

Ohio State University 614 292-6930
  1070 Carmack Rd Rm 180 Columbus (43210) *(G-7434)*

Ohio Steel Industries Inc 740 927-9500
  13792 Broad St Sw Pataskala (43062) *(G-15975)*

Ohio Steel Sheet & Plate Inc 800 827-2401
  7845 Chestnut Ridge Rd Hubbard (44425) *(G-11136)*

Ohio Stoneware LLC 740 450-4415
  34 N 3rd St Zanesville (43701) *(G-21337)*

Ohio Structures Inc 330 547-7705
  6120 S Pricetown Rd Berlin Center (44401) *(G-1657)*

Ohio Structures Inc (HQ) 330 533-0084
  535 N Broad St Ste 5 Canfield (44406) *(G-2568)*

Ohio Table Pad Co Georgia Div, Perrysburg Also called Ohio Table Pad Company *(G-16130)*

Ohio Table Pad Company (PA) 419 872-6400
  350 3 Meadows Dr Perrysburg (43551) *(G-16130)*

Ohio Table Pad Company 419 872-6400
  350 3 Meadows Dr Perrysburg (43551) *(G-16131)*

Ohio Table Pad of Indiana 419 872-6400
  350 3 Meadows Dr Perrysburg (43551) *(G-16132)*

Ohio Tile & Marble Co (PA) 513 541-4211
  3809 Spring Grove Ave Cincinnati (45223) *(G-4180)*

Ohio Timberland Products 419 682-6322
  102 Railroad Ave Stryker (43557) *(G-18005)*

Ohio Tods, Dublin Also called Ohio Logos Inc *(G-9115)*

Ohio Tool & Jig Grind Inc 937 415-0692
  5724 Webster St Dayton (45414) *(G-8546)*

Ohio Tool Works LLC 419 281-3700
  1374 Enterprise Pkwy Ashland (44805) *(G-761)*

Ohio Trailer Inc 330 392-4444
  1899 Tod Ave Sw Warren (44485) *(G-19584)*

Ohio Trailer Supply Inc 614 471-9121
  2966 Westerville Rd Columbus (43224) *(G-7435)*

Ohio Transitional Machine & TI 419 476-0820
  3940 Castener St Toledo (43612) *(G-18618)*

Ohio University 740 593-4010
  28 Union St Ground Fl Athens (45701) *(G-880)*

Ohio Valley Alloy Services Inc 740 373-1900
  100 Westview Ave Marietta (45750) *(G-12811)*

Ohio Valley Coal, Saint Clairsville Also called Ohio Valley Resources Inc *(G-16802)*

Ohio Valley Coal Company (HQ) 740 926-1351
  46226 National Rd W Saint Clairsville (43950) *(G-16801)*

Ohio Valley Energy Systems 330 799-2268
  200 Victoria Rd Bldg 4 Youngstown (44515) *(G-21156)*

Ohio Valley Herbal Products 330 382-1229
  1250 Saint George St # 5 East Liverpool (43920) *(G-9225)*

Ohio Valley Ink, Cincinnati Also called Grand Rapids Printing Ink Co *(G-3844)*

Ohio Valley Manufacturing Inc 419 522-5818
  1501 Harrington Mem Rd Mansfield (44903) *(G-12662)*

Ohio Valley Resources Inc 740 795-5220
  46226 National Rd W Saint Clairsville (43950) *(G-16802)*

Ohio Valley Sand LLC 740 661-4240
  513 Mill Ave Se New Philadelphia (44663) *(G-14920)*

Ohio Valley Specialty Company 740 373-2276
  115 Industry Rd Marietta (45750) *(G-12812)*

Ohio Valley Trackwork Inc 740 446-0181
  39 Fairview Rd Bidwell (45614) *(G-1677)*

Ohio Valley Trading and Exch, Lancaster *Also called Rockbridge Outfitters (G-11748)*

Ohio Valley Transloading Co 740 795-4967
46226 National Rd W Saint Clairsville (43950) *(G-16803)*

Ohio Valley Truss Co (PA) 937 393-3995
6000 Us Highway 50 Hillsboro (45133) *(G-11010)*

Ohio Valley Truss Co 937 393-3995
887 1/2 W Main St Hillsboro (45133) *(G-11011)*

Ohio Valley Vapor Station 740 449-2288
52171 National Rd E Saint Clairsville (43950) *(G-16804)*

Ohio Valley Veneer Inc 740 493-2901
16523 State Route 124 Piketon (45661) *(G-16225)*

Ohio Valley Veneer Co, Piketon *Also called Ohio Valley Veneer Inc (G-16225)*

Ohio Vly Lightning Protection 937 987-0245
520 Leeka Rd New Vienna (45159) *(G-14956)*

Ohio Vly Stmpng-Assemblies Inc 419 522-0983
500 Newman St Mansfield (44902) *(G-12663)*

Ohio Willow Wood Company 740 869-3377
15441 Scioto Darby Rd Mount Sterling (43143) *(G-14601)*

Ohio Windmill & Pump Co Inc 330 547-6300
8389 S Pricetown Rd Berlin Center (44401) *(G-1658)*

Ohio Wire Cloth, Englewood *Also called Unified Scrn & Crush-Oh Inc (G-9541)*

Ohio Wire Form & Spring Co 614 444-3676
2270 S High St Columbus (43207) *(G-7436)*

Ohio Wood Fabrication, Sandusky *Also called Gary L Gast (G-16968)*

Ohio Wood Recycling Inc 614 491-0881
2019 Rathmell Rd Columbus (43207) *(G-7437)*

Ohio Woodlands, Salineville *Also called Coldwell Family Tree Farm (G-16940)*

Ohio Woodworking Co Inc 513 631-0870
5035 Beech St Cincinnati (45212) *(G-4181)*

Ohio's Country Journal, Columbus *Also called Agri Communicators Inc (G-6702)*

Ohiomet, Elyria *Also called Ohio Metallurgical Service Inc (G-9471)*

Ohlinger Publishing Svcs Inc 614 261-5360
28 W Henderson Rd Columbus (43214) *(G-7438)*

Ohmart Vega, Cincinnati *Also called Vega Americas Inc (G-4558)*

Ohmep, Columbus *Also called Ohio Manufacturing EXT Partnr (G-7422)*

Ohta Press US Inc 937 374-3382
1125 S Patton St Xenia (45385) *(G-20966)*

Oi Plastic Products Fts Inc, Toledo *Also called Bprex Plastic Packaging Inc (G-18379)*

Oil Bar LLC (PA) 614 501-9815
2740 Eastland Mall Columbus (43232) *(G-7439)*

Oil Bar LLC 614 880-3950
1500 Polaris Pkwy # 2072 Columbus (43240) *(G-6657)*

Oil Enterprises, Logan *Also called Ralph Robinson Inc (G-12192)*

Oil Etc Inc 513 933-8280
804 Cherry Hill Ln Lebanon (45036) *(G-11822)*

Oil Kraft Div, Cincinnati *Also called US Industrial Lubricants Inc (G-4547)*

Oil Skimmers Inc 440 237-4600
12800 York Rd Ste G North Royalton (44133) *(G-15440)*

Oil Tooling and Stamping, Ontario *Also called Cole Tool & Die Company (G-15686)*

Oiler Processing 740 892-2640
53 S Central Ave Utica (43080) *(G-19195)*

Oiler's Meat Processing, Utica *Also called Oiler Processing (G-19195)*

Oils By Nature Incorporated 330 468-8897
5712 Abbyshire Dr 1a Hudson (44236) *(G-11190)*

Ojim Inc (PA) 330 832-9557
1212 Oberlin Ave Sw Massillon (44647) *(G-13187)*

Okamoto Sandusky Mfg LLC 419 626-1633
3130 W Monroe St Sandusky (44870) *(G-16991)*

Okamoto USA, Sandusky *Also called Okamoto Sandusky Mfg LLC (G-16991)*

OKeefe Casting Co 440 277-5427
2401 E 28th St Lorain (44055) *(G-12265)*

OKeeffes Working Hands Creme 800 275-2718
4550 Red Bank Rd Cincinnati (45227) *(G-4182)*

OKL Can Line Inc 513 825-1655
11235 Sebring Dr Cincinnati (45240) *(G-4183)*

Okm LLC 216 272-6375
4701 Perkins Ave Ste 1 Cleveland (44103) *(G-5935)*

Olan Plastics Inc 614 834-6526
6550 Olan Dr Canal Winchester (43110) *(G-2535)*

Olay LLC 787 535-2191
11530 Reed Hartman Hwy Blue Ash (45241) *(G-1845)*

Old Country Sausage Kitchen 216 662-5988
15711 Libby Rd Cleveland (44137) *(G-5936)*

Old Firehouse Brewery, Williamsburg *Also called AEC Brews LLC DBA Old Frhuse B (G-20406)*

Old Mason Winery Inc 937 698-1122
4199 S Iddings Rd West Milton (45383) *(G-20109)*

Old Mill Custom Cabinetry Co 419 423-8897
310 E Crawford St Findlay (45840) *(G-9871)*

Old Mill Power Equipment 740 982-3246
100 China St Crooksville (43731) *(G-7951)*

Old Mill Winery Inc 440 466-5560
403 S Broadway Geneva (44041) *(G-10354)*

Old Trail Printing Company 614 443-4852
100 Fornoff Rd Columbus (43207) *(G-7440)*

Old Village 614 791-8467
2878 Jericho Pl Delaware (43015) *(G-8877)*

Old West Industries Inc (PA) 513 889-0500
1405 Boyle Rd Hamilton (45013) *(G-10728)*

Old World Foods Inc 216 341-5665
3545 E 76th St Cleveland (44105) *(G-5937)*

Oldaker M F G, Dunkirk *Also called Oldaker Manufacturing Corp (G-9189)*

Oldaker Manufacturing Corp 419 759-3551
301 N Main St Dunkirk (45836) *(G-9189)*

Oldcastle Apg Midwest Inc 440 949-1815
5190 Oster Rd Sheffield Village (44054) *(G-17128)*

Oldcastle Buildingenvelope Inc 419 887-1228
1789 Indian Wood Cir Maumee (43537) *(G-13287)*

Oldcastle Buildingenvelope Inc 419 661-5079
291 M St Perrysburg (43551) *(G-16133)*

Oldcastle Precast Inc 419 592-2309
1675 Industrial Dr Napoleon (43545) *(G-14692)*

Olde Home Market LLC 614 738-3975
2517 Old Home Rd Grove City (43123) *(G-10580)*

Olde Man Granola LLC 419 819-9576
7227 W State Route 12 Findlay (45840) *(G-9872)*

Olde Schlhuse Vnyrd Winery LLC 937 273-6023
8538 State Route 726 Eldorado (45321) *(G-9347)*

Olde Wood Ltd 330 866-1441
7557 Willowdale St Magnolia (44643) *(G-12517)*

Oldforge Tools Inc (HQ) 330 535-7177
768 E North St Akron (44305) *(G-327)*

Olen Corporation 419 294-2611
6326 County Highway 61 Upper Sandusky (43351) *(G-19137)*

Olen Corporation 330 262-6821
3001 Prairie Ln Wooster (44691) *(G-20819)*

Olen Corporation 740 745-5865
9134 Mount Vernon Rd Saint Louisville (43071) *(G-16829)*

Olentangy Eye and Laser A 614 267-4122
3525 Olentngy Rvr Rd # 5310 Columbus (43214) *(G-7441)*

Olfactorium Corp Inc 216 663-8831
12395 Mccracken Rd Cleveland (44125) *(G-5938)*

Olin Brass, Alliance *Also called Gbc Metals LLC (G-510)*

Olivamed Corporation 937 401-0821
401 Shotwell Dr Franklin (45005) *(G-10042)*

Olive Serafino Oils Balsamics 440 773-0200
915 Worton Park Dr Cleveland (44143) *(G-5939)*

Olive Smuckers Oil 513 646-7103
5204 Spring Grove Ave Cincinnati (45217) *(G-4184)*

Olive Tap (PA) 330 721-6500
30 Public Sq Medina (44256) *(G-13453)*

Oliver Chemical Co Inc 513 541-4540
2908 Spring Grove Ave Cincinnati (45225) *(G-4185)*

Oliver Pool and Spa Inc 740 264-5368
512 Main St Steubenville (43953) *(G-17709)*

Oliver Printing & Packg Co LLC 330 425-7890
1760 Enterprise Pkwy Twinsburg (44087) *(G-18990)*

Oliver Products Company 513 860-6880
3840 Symmes Rd Hamilton (45015) *(G-10729)*

Oliver Signs & Graphics 330 460-2996
5880 Myrtle Hill Rd Valley City (44280) *(G-19226)*

Oliver Steel Plate, Bedford *Also called A M Castle & Co (G-1394)*

Oliver-Tolas Healthcare Packg, Hamilton *Also called Oliver Products Company (G-10729)*

Olmsted Falls Plant, Olmsted Falls *Also called Evergreen Packaging Inc (G-15675)*

Olmsted Ice Inc 440 235-8411
8134 Bronson Rd Olmsted Twp (44138) *(G-15682)*

Olmsted Printing Inc 440 234-2600
1060 W Bagley Rd Ste 102 Berea (44017) *(G-1631)*

Olson Sheet Metal Cnstr Co 330 745-8225
465 Glenn St Barberton (44203) *(G-1136)*

Olwin Metal Fabrication LLC 937 277-4501
2514 Nordic Rd Dayton (45414) *(G-8547)*

Olymco, Canton *Also called Delta Plating Inc (G-2684)*

Olympia Candies, Strongsville *Also called Robert E McGrath Inc (G-17959)*

Olympic Enterprises, Canton *Also called Nicholas Ray Enterprises LLC (G-2788)*

Olympic Forest Products Co 216 421-2775
2200 Carnegie Ave Cleveland (44115) *(G-5940)*

Om Group, Westlake *Also called Borchers Americas Inc (G-20258)*

Oma USA Inc 330 487-0602
9329 Ravenna Rd Ste A Twinsburg (44087) *(G-18991)*

Omar Associates LLC 419 426-0610
625 N State Route 4 Attica (44807) *(G-894)*

Omar McDowell Co 440 808-2280
25109 Detroit Rd Ste 320 Westlake (44145) *(G-20289)*

Omative North America, Cincinnati *Also called Optimzed Prdctvity Sltions LLC (G-4192)*

Omco Holdings Inc (PA) 440 944-2100
30396 Lakeland Blvd Wickliffe (44092) *(G-20375)*

Omega Automation Inc 937 890-2350
2850 Needmore Rd Dayton (45414) *(G-8548)*

Omega Cementing Co 330 695-7147
3776 Millborne Rd Apple Creek (44606) *(G-646)*

Omega Engineering Inc 740 965-9340
149 Stelzer Ct Sunbury (43074) *(G-18072)*

Omega International Inc (HQ) 937 890-2350
6192 Webster St Dayton (45414) *(G-8549)*

ALPHABETIC

Omega Logging Inc (PA)..............................330 534-0378
  2550 State Line Rd Hubbard (44425) *(G-11137)*

Omega Machine & Tool Inc..........................440 946-6846
  7590 Jenther Dr Mentor (44060) *(G-13672)*

Omega One, Willoughby *Also called Amfm Inc (G-20431)*

Omega Polymer Technologies Inc (PA)............330 562-5201
  1331 S Chillicothe Rd Aurora (44202) *(G-939)*

Omega Pultrusions Incorporated...................330 562-5201
  1331 S Chillicothe Rd Aurora (44202) *(G-940)*

Omega Tek Inc.......................................419 756-9580
  649 Old Mill Run Rd Mansfield (44906) *(G-12664)*

Omega Tool & Die Inc...............................937 890-2350
  2850 Needmore Rd Dayton (45414) *(G-8550)*

Omega Tool and Die, Dayton *Also called Omega Tool & Die Inc (G-8550)*

Omegadyne, Sunbury *Also called Omega Engineering Inc (G-18072)*

Omer J Smith Inc...................................513 921-4717
  9112 Le Saint Dr West Chester (45014) *(G-19909)*

Ommc, Toledo *Also called Mobis North America LLC (G-18589)*

Omni Die Casting Inc...............................330 830-5500
  1100 Nova Dr Se Massillon (44646) *(G-13188)*

Omni Manufacturing................................419 394-7424
  901 Mckinley Rd Saint Marys (45885) *(G-16845)*

Omni Manufacturing Inc (PA)......................419 394-7424
  901 Mckinley Rd Saint Marys (45885) *(G-16846)*

Omni Manufacturing................................419 394-7424
  220 Cleveland Ave Saint Marys (45885) *(G-16847)*

Omni Media..216 687-0077
  1375 E 9th St Fl 10 Cleveland (44114) *(G-5941)*

Omni Tech Electronics, Columbus *Also called Accuscan Instruments Inc (G-6686)*

Omni Technical Products Inc.......................216 433-1970
  15300 Industrial Pkwy Cleveland (44135) *(G-5942)*

Omni USA Inc..330 830-5500
  1100 Nova Dr Se Massillon (44646) *(G-13189)*

Omnicare Phrm of Midwest LLC (HQ)..............513 719-2600
  201 E 4th St Ste 900 Cincinnati (45202) *(G-4186)*

Omnimold LLC.......................................419 332-4466
  4711 N State Route 19 Fremont (43420) *(G-10172)*

Omnisource Corporation...........................419 784-5669
  880 Linden St Defiance (43512) *(G-8808)*

Omnitec, Painesville *Also called Ohio Associated Entps LLC (G-15907)*

Omnitech Electronics Inc..........................800 822-1344
  5090 Trabue Rd Columbus (43228) *(G-7442)*

Omnithruster Inc....................................330 963-6310
  2201 Pinnacle Pkwy Ste A Twinsburg (44087) *(G-18992)*

Omnova Overseas Inc (HQ).........................330 869-4200
  175 Ghent Rd Fairlawn (44333) *(G-9757)*

Omnova Solutions Inc..............................330 628-6550
  165 S Cleveland Ave Mogadore (44260) *(G-14382)*

Omnova Solutions Inc..............................330 734-1237
  1380 Tech Way Akron (44306) *(G-328)*

Omnova Solutions Inc (PA).........................216 682-7000
  25435 Harvard Rd Beachwood (44122) *(G-1287)*

Omnova Wallcovering USA Inc (HQ)................216 682-7000
  25435 Harvard Rd Beachwood (44122) *(G-1288)*

Omsi Transmissions Inc............................330 405-7350
  9319 Ravenna Rd Ste A Twinsburg (44087) *(G-18993)*

Omwp Company......................................330 453-8438
  3620 Progress St Ne Canton (44705) *(G-2804)*

Omya Distribution LLC (HQ)........................513 387-4600
  9987 Carver Rd Ste 300 Blue Ash (45242) *(G-1846)*

Omya Industries Inc (HQ)..........................513 387-4600
  9987 Carver Rd Ste 300 Blue Ash (45242) *(G-1847)*

On Display LLC......................................513 841-1600
  1250 Clough Pike Batavia (45103) *(G-1214)*

On-Power Inc..513 228-2100
  3525 Grant Ave Ste A Lebanon (45036) *(G-11823)*

One Cloud Services LLC............................513 231-9500
  1080 Nimitzview Dr Cincinnati (45230) *(G-4187)*

One Liberty Street..................................419 352-6298
  813 Hamilton Ct Bowling Green (43402) *(G-2004)*

One Styling, Maple Heights *Also called Salon Styling Concepts Ltd (G-12740)*

One Time, Cleveland *Also called Bond Distributing LLC (G-4923)*

One Universal Brands LLC..........................513 362-4326
  312 Walnut St Ste 1151 Cincinnati (45202) *(G-4188)*

One Wish LLC.......................................800 505-6883
  23945 Mercantile Rd Ste H Beachwood (44122) *(G-1289)*

One With Nature, Cuyahoga Falls *Also called Madaen Natural Products Inc (G-8021)*

One-Write Company.................................740 654-2128
  3750 Lancaster New Lexing Lancaster (43130) *(G-11737)*

ONeals Tarpaulin & Awning Co.....................330 788-6504
  549 W Indianola Ave Youngstown (44511) *(G-21157)*

Oneida Group, The, Lancaster *Also called Everyware Global Inc (G-11711)*

ONeil & Associates Inc (PA)........................937 865-0800
  495 Byers Rd Miamisburg (45342) *(G-13847)*

Oneseal Inc (HQ)...................................973 599-1155
  1300 3rd St Perrysburg (43551) *(G-16134)*

Onetouchpoint East Corp..........................513 421-1600
  1441 Western Ave Cincinnati (45214) *(G-4189)*

Onevision Corporation (PA)........................614 794-1144
  5805 Chandler Ct Ste A Westerville (43082) *(G-20174)*

Onevuex, Columbus *Also called Bass International Sftwr LLC (G-6814)*

Onix Corporation (PA)..............................800 844-0076
  27100 Oakmead Dr Perrysburg (43551) *(G-16135)*

Onix Corporation...................................800 844-0076
  27100 Oakmead Dr Perrysburg (43551) *(G-16136)*

Online Engineering Corporation...................513 561-8878
  3947 Bach Buxton Rd Amelia (45102) *(G-581)*

Online Mega Sellers Corp (PA).....................888 384-6468
  4236 W Alexis Rd Toledo (43623) *(G-18619)*

Onstage Publications, Dayton *Also called Just Business Inc (G-8431)*

Ontario Mechanical LLC............................419 529-2578
  2880 Park Ave W Ontario (44906) *(G-15691)*

Onx Holdings LLC (HQ).............................800 559-2497
  5910 Landerbrook Dr # 250 Mayfield Heights (44124) *(G-13320)*

Onx USA LLC (HQ).................................440 569-2300
  5910 Landerbrook Dr # 250 Cleveland (44124) *(G-5943)*

Oogeep...740 587-0410
  1718 Columbus Rd Granville (43023) *(G-10463)*

Ooteksofpak, Columbus *Also called Tarigma Corporation (G-7677)*

Opal Diamond LLC..................................330 653-5876
  20033 Detroit Rd Rocky River (44116) *(G-16703)*

Opc Inc..419 531-2222
  419 N Reynolds Rd Toledo (43615) *(G-18620)*

OPC Inc, Toledo *Also called Orthotic Prosthetic Center (G-18621)*

Open House Magazine Inc..........................614 523-7775
  1537 Guilford Rd Columbus (43221) *(G-7443)*

Open Sided Mri Cleveland LLC.....................804 217-7114
  30400 Detroit Rd Ste 30 Westlake (44145) *(G-20290)*

Open Text Inc.......................................614 658-3588
  3671 Ridge Mill Dr Hilliard (43026) *(G-10968)*

Operational Support Svcs LLC.....................419 425-0889
  1850 Industrial Dr Findlay (45840) *(G-9873)*

Opm, Barberton *Also called Ohio Precision Molding Inc (G-1135)*

Opp, Toledo *Also called Ohio Pickling & Processing LLC (G-18616)*

Ops Wireless..419 396-4041
  807 E Findlay St Carey (43316) *(G-2923)*

Opt Brush, Ashland *Also called Ohio Power Tool Brush Co (G-760)*

Optem, Medina *Also called Ovation Polymer Technology and (G-13455)*

Opti, Aurora *Also called Omega Polymer Technologies Inc (G-939)*

Opti Mold Inc.......................................440 248-9179
  32400 Aurora Rd Ste 5 Solon (44139) *(G-17356)*

Opti Vision Inc (PA)................................330 650-0919
  5697 Darrow Rd Hudson (44236) *(G-11191)*

Optical Distribution Corp..........................937 405-7280
  401 N Front St Ste 350 Columbus (43215) *(G-7444)*

Optimair Ltd...419 661-9568
  29102 Glenwood Rd Perrysburg (43551) *(G-16137)*

Optimal Office Solutions LLC......................201 257-8516
  25 Merchant St Ste 135 Cincinnati (45246) *(G-4190)*

Optimas Oe Solutions LLC.........................740 774-4553
  101 S Mcarthur St Chillicothe (45601) *(G-3254)*

Optime Air MSP Ltd................................419 661-9568
  29102 Glenwood Rd Perrysburg (43551) *(G-16138)*

Optimum Blinds, Brilliant *Also called Optimun Blinds Inc (G-2094)*

Optimum Graphics, Westerville *Also called Optimum System Products Inc (G-20228)*

Optimum System Products Inc (PA)...............614 885-4464
  921 Eastwind Dr Ste 133 Westerville (43081) *(G-20228)*

Optimun Blinds Inc.................................740 598-5808
  204 Ohio St Brilliant (43913) *(G-2094)*

Optimus LLC.......................................513 918-2320
  4623 Wesley Ave Ste B Cincinnati (45212) *(G-4191)*

Optimus LLC (PA)..................................937 454-1900
  8517 N Dixie Dr Ste 300 Dayton (45414) *(G-8551)*

Optimus Prosthetics, Dayton *Also called Optimus LLC (G-8551)*

Optimzed Prdctvity Sltions LLC....................513 444-2156
  9435 Waterstone Blvd Cincinnati (45249) *(G-4192)*

Options Plus Incorporated.........................740 694-9811
  143 Tuttle Ave Fredericktown (43019) *(G-10108)*

Optonicus, Dayton *Also called Mv Innovative Technologies LLC (G-8515)*

Optoquest Inc......................................216 445-3637
  10000 Cedar Ave Cleveland (44106) *(G-5944)*

Opw Inc...800 422-2525
  9393 Prnceton Glendale Rd West Chester (45011) *(G-19910)*

Opw Engineered Systems, West Chester *Also called Opw Fueling Components Inc (G-19911)*

Opw Engineered Systems Inc.......................888 771-9438
  2726 Henkle Dr Lebanon (45036) *(G-11824)*

Opw Engineering Systems, West Chester *Also called Opw Inc (G-19910)*

Opw Fluid Transfer Group, Mason *Also called Dover Corporation (G-13010)*

Opw Fueling Components Inc (HQ)................800 422-2525
  9393 Prnceton Glendale Rd West Chester (45011) *(G-19911)*

Or-Tec Inc..216 475-5225
  14500 Industrial Ave S Maple Heights (44137) *(G-12737)*

Oracle America Inc.................................513 381-0125
  9987 Carver Rd Ste 250 Blue Ash (45242) *(G-1848)*

Oracle Corporation 513 826-5632
  3610 Pentagon Blvd # 205 Beavercreek (45431) *(G-1355)*

Oracle Corporation 440 264-1620
  30500 Bruce Indus Pkwy Cleveland (44139) *(G-5945)*

Oracle Systems Corporation 513 826-6000
  9987 Carver Rd Ste 250 Blue Ash (45242) *(G-1849)*

Oracle Systems Corporation 937 427-5495
  2661 Commons Blvd Beavercreek (45431) *(G-1356)*

Orange Barrel Media LLC 614 294-4898
  250 N Hartford Ave Columbus (43222) *(G-7445)*

Orange Blossom Press Inc 216 781-8655
  38005 Brown Ave Willoughby (44094) *(G-20562)*

Orange Frazer Press Inc 937 382-3196
  37 1/2 W Main St Wilmington (45177) *(G-20672)*

Orange Leaf 614 898-5323
  750 N State St Westerville (43082) *(G-20175)*

Orbis Corporation 937 652-1361
  200 Elm St Urbana (43078) *(G-19171)*

Orbis Corporation 440 974-3857
  9050 Tyler Blvd Mentor (44060) *(G-13673)*

Orbis Rpm LLC 740 772-6355
  5938 State Route 159 Chillicothe (45601) *(G-3255)*

Orbis Rpm LLC 419 355-8310
  2100 Cedar St Fremont (43420) *(G-10173)*

Orbit Manufacturing Inc 513 732-6097
  4291 Armstrong Blvd Batavia (45103) *(G-1215)*

Orbital Atk Inc 937 429-9261
  1365 Technology Ct Beavercreek (45430) *(G-1377)*

Orbytel Print and Packg Inc 216 267-8734
  4901 Johnston Pkwy Cleveland (44128) *(G-5946)*

Orchem Corporation 513 874-9700
  4927 Beech St Cincinnati (45212) *(G-4193)*

Ordnance Cleaning Systems LLC 440 205-0677
  7895 Division Dr Mentor (44060) *(G-13674)*

Oregon Printing, Dayton *Also called Oregon Village Print Shoppe (G-8552)*

Oregon Village Print Shoppe 937 222-9418
  29 N June St Dayton (45403) *(G-8552)*

OReilly Equipment LLC 440 564-1234
  14555 Ravenna Rd Newbury (44065) *(G-15101)*

OReilly Precision Pdts Inc 937 526-4677
  560 E Main St Russia (45363) *(G-16766)*

OReilly Precision Tool Inc 937 526-4677
  560 E Main St Russia (45363) *(G-16767)*

Organic Coating Products, Lima *Also called Modern Ink Technology LLC (G-12059)*

Organic Roots Horticulture LLC 330 620-1108
  6158 State Route 303 Ravenna (44266) *(G-16546)*

Organic Spa Magazine Ltd (PA) 440 331-5750
  19035 Old Detroit Rd # 201 Rocky River (44116) *(G-16704)*

Organized Lightning LLC 407 965-2730
  5601 Belleview Ave Blue Ash (45242) *(G-1850)*

Organized Living Inc (PA) 513 489-9300
  3100 E Kemper Rd Cincinnati (45241) *(G-4194)*

Organon Inc 440 729-2290
  7407 Cedar Rd Chesterland (44026) *(G-3218)*

Orica Ground Support Inc 740 377-9146
  101 Valley Dr South Point (45680) *(G-17443)*

Orica Ground Support Inc 740 269-8100
  600 Boyce Dr Bowerston (44695) *(G-1960)*

Orick Stamping 419 331-0600
  614 E Kiracofe Ave Elida (45807) *(G-9353)*

Original Mattress Factory, Fairfield *Also called Lcmf Inc (G-9677)*

Original Mattress Factory, Columbus *Also called Ahmf Inc (G-6704)*

Original Mattress Factory Inc 614 291-8085
  851 W 5th Ave Columbus (43212) *(G-7446)*

Original Mattress Factory Inc (PA) 216 661-8388
  4930 State Rd Cleveland (44134) *(G-5947)*

Original Mattress Factory Inc 513 752-6600
  4450 Eastgate Blvd Ste E Cincinnati (45245) *(G-3313)*

Orion Control Panels Inc 513 615-6534
  5012 Calvert St Ste B Cincinnati (45209) *(G-4195)*

Orion Engineered Carbons LLC 740 423-9571
  11135 State Route 7 Belpre (45714) *(G-1592)*

Orion Holdings LLC 513 871-4344
  3802 Ford Cir Cincinnati (45227) *(G-4196)*

Orion Petro Corporation 330 364-8155
  1798 State Route 183 Atwater (44201) *(G-901)*

Orion Safety Systems, Cincinnati *Also called Orion Holdings LLC (G-4196)*

Orlando Baking Company (PA) 216 361-1872
  7777 Grand Ave Cleveland (44104) *(G-5948)*

Ormet Corporation 740 483-1381
  43840 State Rte 7 Hannibal (43931) *(G-10763)*

Orora North America 513 539-8274
  930 Deneen Ave Monroe (45050) *(G-14411)*

Orpro Prosthetics & Orthotics, Piqua *Also called Hanger Prsthetcs & Ortho Inc (G-16269)*

Orpro Prosthetics & Orthotics, Dayton *Also called Hanger Prsthetcs & Ortho Inc (G-8384)*

Orr Felt Company 937 773-0551
  750 S Main St Piqua (45356) *(G-16296)*

Orrcast Aluminum Foundry, Orrville *Also called Myron D Budd (G-15749)*

Orrville Printing Co Inc 330 682-5066
  1645 N Main St Orrville (44667) *(G-15752)*

Orrville Trucking & Grading Co (PA) 330 682-4010
  475 Orr St Orrville (44667) *(G-15753)*

Orrvilon Inc 330 684-9400
  1400 Dairy Ln Orrville (44667) *(G-15754)*

Ortho Prosthetic Center 419 352-8161
  1224 W Wooster St Bowling Green (43402) *(G-2005)*

Orthotic and Prostetic Spc 216 531-2773
  20650 Lakeland Blvd Euclid (44119) *(G-9596)*

Orthotic and Prosthetics Svc 330 723-6679
  132 Highland Dr Medina (44256) *(G-13454)*

Orthotic Prosthetic Center 419 531-2222
  419 N Reynolds Rd Toledo (43615) *(G-18621)*

Orthotics & Prosthetics Rehab 330 856-2553
  700 Howland Wilson Rd Se Warren (44484) *(G-19585)*

Orton Edward Jr Crmic Fndation 614 895-2663
  6991 S Old 3c Hwy Westerville (43082) *(G-20176)*

Orwell Printing 440 285-2233
  510 Center St Chardon (44024) *(G-3171)*

Orzen Extruded Polymers 330 298-9550
  4699 Loomis Pkwy Unit C Ravenna (44266) *(G-16547)*

OS Kelly Corporation (HQ) 937 322-4921
  318 E North St Springfield (45503) *(G-17620)*

OS Power Tong Inc 330 866-3815
  7330 Minerva Rd Se Waynesburg (44688) *(G-19726)*

Osair Inc (PA) 440 974-6500
  7001 Center St Mentor (44060) *(G-13675)*

Osair Inc 440 255-8238
  8649 East Ave Mentor (44060) *(G-13676)*

Osborne Inc (PA) 440 942-7000
  7954 Reynolds Rd Mentor (44060) *(G-13677)*

Osborne Inc 216 771-0010
  2100 Central Furnace Ct Cleveland (44115) *(G-5949)*

Osborne Coinage Company (PA) 513 681-5424
  2851 Massachusetts Ave Cincinnati (45225) *(G-4197)*

Osborne Materials Company (PA) 440 357-7026
  1 Williams St Grand River (44045) *(G-10452)*

Osburn Associates Inc (PA) 740 385-5732
  9383 Vanatta Rd Logan (43138) *(G-12188)*

Oscar Brugmann Sand & Gravel 330 274-8224
  3828 Dudley Rd Mantua (44255) *(G-12719)*

Oscar Hicks 937 435-4350
  9860 Atchison Rd Dayton (45458) *(G-8553)*

Osco Industries Inc (PA) 740 354-3183
  734 11th St Portsmouth (45662) *(G-16446)*

Osco Industries Inc 740 286-5004
  165 Athens St Jackson (45640) *(G-11323)*

OSG Usa Inc 513 755-3360
  3611 Socialvl Fstr Rd # 102 Mason (45040) *(G-13071)*

Osg-Sterling Die Inc 216 267-1300
  12502 Plaza Dr Parma (44130) *(G-15964)*

OSI, Hilliard *Also called Ohio Semitronics Inc (G-10967)*

OSI Global Sourcing LLC 614 471-4800
  2575 Ferris Rd Columbus (43224) *(G-7447)*

Osmans Pies Inc (PA) 330 607-9083
  3678 Elm Rd Stow (44224) *(G-17786)*

Osnaburg Quilt Fibr Art Guild 330 488-2591
  6855 Orchardview Dr Se East Canton (44730) *(G-9195)*

Osteo Solution 614 485-9790
  117 Commerce Park Dr Westerville (43082) *(G-20177)*

Osteodynamics 405 921-9271
  3130 Highland Ave Fl 3 Cincinnati (45219) *(G-4198)*

Osteonovus Inc 617 717-8867
  1510 N Westwood Ave Toledo (43606) *(G-18622)*

Osteosymbionics LLC 216 881-8500
  1768 E 25th St Ste 316 Cleveland (44114) *(G-5950)*

Oster Enterprises, Massillon *Also called Oster Sand and Gravel Inc (G-13190)*

Oster Sand and Gravel Inc (PA) 330 494-5472
  5947 Whipple Ave Nw Canton (44720) *(G-2805)*

Oster Sand and Gravel Inc 330 874-3322
  3467 Dover Zoar Rd Ne Bolivar (44612) *(G-1940)*

Oster Sand and Gravel Inc 330 833-2649
  1955 Riverside Dr Nw Massillon (44647) *(G-13190)*

Osu Arabidopsis Resource, Columbus *Also called Ohio State University (G-7431)*

Osu Industrial Welding Sy, Columbus *Also called Ohio State University (G-7432)*

Otb, Dayton *Also called Outta Box Dispensers LLC (G-8556)*

Otc Services Inc 330 871-2444
  1776 Constitution Ave Louisville (44641) *(G-12323)*

Otis Elevator Company 419 867-7758
  5960 Angola Rd Ste 1 Toledo (43615) *(G-18623)*

Otis Elevator Company 216 573-2333
  9800 Rockside Rd Ste 1200 Cleveland (44125) *(G-5951)*

Otomik Products Inc 877 776-5358
  6919 Silverton Ave Cincinnati (45236) *(G-4199)*

Otr Controls LLC 513 621-2197
  40 E Mcmicken Ave Cincinnati (45202) *(G-4200)*

Ots, Columbus *Also called Ohio Trailer Supply Inc (G-7435)*

Ottawa Oil Co Inc 419 425-3301
  1100 Trenton Ave Findlay (45840) *(G-9874)*

Ottawa Products Co 419 836-5115
1602 N Curtice Rd Ste A Curtice (43412) *(G-7958)*

Ottawa Rubber Company (PA) 419 865-1378
1600 Commerce Rd Holland (43528) *(G-11075)*

Otter Group LLC 937 315-1199
2725 Needmore Rd Dayton (45414) *(G-8554)*

Otto Konigslow Mfg Co 216 851-7900
13300 Coit Rd Cleveland (44110) *(G-5952)*

Ottokee Group Inc 419 636-1932
17768 County Road H50 Bryan (43506) *(G-2316)*

Ouchless Lures Inc 330 653-3867
305 Kilbourne Dr Hudson (44236) *(G-11192)*

Our Daily Bread 513 621-6364
1721 Logan St Cincinnati (45202) *(G-4201)*

Our Detergent Inc 419 589-5571
101 Knight Pkwy Mansfield (44903) *(G-12665)*

Our Heart Health Care Svcs LLC 614 943-5216
1336 E Main St Columbus (43205) *(G-7448)*

Our Nine LLC 614 844-6655
6740 Huntley Rd Ste F Columbus (43229) *(G-7449)*

Ourpets Company (PA) 440 354-6500
1300 East St Fairport Harbor (44077) *(G-9769)*

Out On A Limb 513 432-5091
5311 Springdale Rd Cincinnati (45251) *(G-4202)*

Outback Cycle Shack LLC 513 554-1048
7923 Blue Ash Rd Cincinnati (45236) *(G-4203)*

Outback Tree Works 937 332-7300
808 N Market St Troy (45373) *(G-18860)*

Outdoor & News Service, Port Clinton *Also called Outdoor News Service (G-16408)*

Outdoor Army Navy Stores, Ashtabula *Also called Outdoor Army Store of Ashtbula (G-828)*

Outdoor Army Store of Ashtbula 440 992-8791
4420 Main Ave Ashtabula (44004) *(G-828)*

Outdoor News Service 419 734-5172
127 W Perry St Ste 101 Port Clinton (43452) *(G-16408)*

Outdoor Supply 440 256-3338
7899 Euclid Chardon Rd Kirtland (44094) *(G-11615)*

Outdoorwarehouse, Cleveland *Also called Marble Works (G-5741)*

Outhouse Paper Etc Inc 937 382-2800
319 Collett Rd Waynesville (45068) *(G-19732)*

Outlook Publishing Inc 614 268-8525
815 N High St Ste I Columbus (43215) *(G-7450)*

Outlook Tool Inc 937 235-6330
360 Fame Rd Dayton (45449) *(G-8555)*

Outotec North America, Strongsville *Also called Outotec Oyj (G-17949)*

Outotec Oyj 440 783-3336
11288 Alameda Dr Strongsville (44149) *(G-17949)*

Outsourcing Services Inc 330 963-2710
32503 Jefferson Dr Solon (44139) *(G-17357)*

Outta Box Dispensers LLC 937 221-7106
811 E 4th St Dayton (45402) *(G-8556)*

Ovase Manufacturing LLC 937 275-0617
1990 Berwyck Ave Dayton (45414) *(G-8557)*

Ovation Polymer Technology and 330 723-5686
1030 W Smith Rd Medina (44256) *(G-13455)*

Oveco Industries Electrica 740 381-3326
100 Kragel Rd Ste 4 Richmond (43944) *(G-16648)*

Oven Windows, Saint Henry *Also called West Ohio Tool & Mfg LLC (G-16825)*

Overhead Door Company, Toledo *Also called Overhead Inc (G-18624)*

Overhead Door Corporation 740 383-6376
1332 E Fairground Rd Marion (43302) *(G-12892)*

Overhead Door Corporation 419 294-3874
781 Rt 30w Upper Sandusky (43351) *(G-19138)*

Overhead Door Corporation 330 674-7015
1 Door Dr Mount Hope (44660) *(G-14573)*

Overhead Door Corporation 330 674-7015
4576 County Rd 160 Mount Hope (44660) *(G-14574)*

Overhead Door of Salem Inc 330 332-9530
3864 Mccracken Rd Salem (44460) *(G-16918)*

Overhead Inc 419 476-0300
1621 W Alexis Rd Toledo (43612) *(G-18624)*

Overhoff Technology Corp 513 248-2400
1160 Us Route 50 Milford (45150) *(G-14165)*

Overly Hautz Company, Lebanon *Also called Overly Hautz Motor Base Co (G-11825)*

Overly Hautz Motor Base Co 513 932-0025
215 S West St Lebanon (45036) *(G-11825)*

Overseas Packing LLC 440 232-2917
19800 Alexander Rd Bedford (44146) *(G-1451)*

Ovonic Energy Products Inc 937 743-1001
50 Ovonic Way Springboro (45066) *(G-17493)*

Owen & Sons 513 726-5406
206 S Main St Seven Mile (45062) *(G-17066)*

Owen S Precision Grinding 513 745-9335
8383 Blue Ash Rd Cincinnati (45236) *(G-4204)*

Owens Corning 419 248-8000
9318 Erie Ave Sw Navarre (44662) *(G-14723)*

Owens Corning 740 964-1727
1 Corning Pkwy Pataskala (43062) *(G-15976)*

Owens Corning (PA) 419 248-8000
1 Owens Corning Pkwy Toledo (43659) *(G-18625)*

Owens Corning Sales Inc 740 983-1300
Reynolds Rd Ashville (43103) *(G-853)*

Owens Corning Sales LLC (HQ) 419 248-8000
1 Owens Corning Pkwy Toledo (43659) *(G-18626)*

Owens Corning Sales LLC 740 328-2300
400 Case Ave Newark (43055) *(G-15043)*

Owens Corning Sales LLC 614 399-3915
100 Blackjack Road Ext Mount Vernon (43050) *(G-14635)*

Owens Corning Sales LLC 740 587-3562
2790 Columbus Rd Granville (43023) *(G-10464)*

Owens Corning Sales LLC 330 634-0460
170 South Ave Tallmadge (44278) *(G-18162)*

Owens Corning Sales LLC 330 764-7800
890 W Smith Rd Medina (44256) *(G-13456)*

Owens Corning Sales LLC 330 633-6735
275 Southwest Ave Tallmadge (44278) *(G-18163)*

Owens Corning Sales LLC 614 539-0830
3750 Brookham Dr Ste K Grove City (43123) *(G-10581)*

Owens Precisn Grindg, Cincinnati *Also called Owen S Precision Grinding (G-4204)*

Owens-Brockway Glass Cont Inc (HQ) 567 336-8449
1 Michael Owens Way Perrysburg (43551) *(G-16139)*

Owens-Brockway Glass Cont Inc 740 455-4500
1700 State St Zanesville (43701) *(G-21338)*

Owens-Brockway Packaging (HQ) 567 336-5000
1 Michael Owens Way Perrysburg (43551) *(G-16140)*

Owens-Corning Capital LLC 419 248-8000
1 Owens Corning Pkwy Toledo (43659) *(G-18627)*

Owens-Illinois Inc (PA) 567 336-5000
1 Michael Owens Way Perrysburg (43551) *(G-16141)*

Owens-Illinois De Puerto Rico (PA) 419 874-9708
1 Seagate Toledo (43604) *(G-18628)*

Owens-Illinois General Inc (HQ) 567 336-5000
1 Michael Owens Way Perrysburg (43551) *(G-16142)*

Owens-Illinois Group Inc (HQ) 567 336-5000
1 Michael Owens Way Perrysburg (43551) *(G-16143)*

Owl Be Sweatin 513 260-2026
4914 Ridge Ave Cincinnati (45209) *(G-4205)*

Oxford Min Cmpany-Kentucky LLC 740 622-6302
544 Chestnut St Coshocton (43812) *(G-7905)*

Oxford Mining Company Inc 740 342-7666
2500 Township Rd 205 New Lexington (43764) *(G-14850)*

Oxford Mining Company Inc 330 878-5120
7551 Reed Rd Nw Strasburg (44680) *(G-17827)*

Oxford Mining Company Inc (HQ) 740 622-6302
544 Chestnut St Coshocton (43812) *(G-7906)*

Oxford Mining Company Inc 740 588-0190
1855 Kemper Ct Zanesville (43701) *(G-21339)*

Oxford Mining Company LLC 740 622-6302
544 Chestnut St Coshocton (43812) *(G-7907)*

Oxford Mining Inc 330 339-4546
4371 Rice Rd Sw Stone Creek (43840) *(G-17725)*

Oxford Press, Oxford *Also called Cox Newspapers LLC (G-15835)*

Oxyrase Inc 419 589-8800
3000 Park Ave W Ontario (44906) *(G-15692)*

Oylair Specialty 614 873-3968
9029 Heritage Dr Plain City (43064) *(G-16353)*

Ozone Systems Svcs Group Inc 513 899-4131
6687 State Route 132 Morrow (45152) *(G-14550)*

P & A Industries Inc 419 422-7070
600 Crystal Ave Findlay (45840) *(G-9875)*

P & B Electric 937 754-4695
1835 Successful Dr Fairborn (45324) *(G-9628)*

P & C Metal Polishing Inc 513 771-9143
340 Glendale Milford Rd Cincinnati (45215) *(G-4206)*

P & E Sales Ltd 330 829-0100
1595 W Main St Alliance (44601) *(G-532)*

P & G Precision LLC 513 738-3500
3955 Kraus Ln Fairfield (45014) *(G-9694)*

P & J Industries Inc (PA) 419 726-2675
4934 Lewis Ave Toledo (43612) *(G-18629)*

P & J Manufacturing Inc 419 241-7369
1644 Campbell St Toledo (43607) *(G-18630)*

P & L Heat Treating & Grinding 330 746-8081
948 Poland Ave Youngstown (44502) *(G-21158)*

P & L Heat Trting Grinding Inc 330 746-1339
313 E Wood St Youngstown (44503) *(G-21159)*

P & L Metalcrafts LLC 330 793-2178
1050 Ohio Works Dr Youngstown (44510) *(G-21160)*

P & P Machine Tool Inc 440 232-7404
26189 Broadway Ave Cleveland (44146) *(G-5953)*

P & P Mold & Die Inc 330 784-8333
1034 S Munroe Rd Tallmadge (44278) *(G-18164)*

P & R Hardwoods 937 452-3753
2911 State Route 725 W Camden (45311) *(G-2487)*

P & R Specialty Inc 937 773-0263
1835 W High St Piqua (45356) *(G-16297)*

P & S Energy Inc 330 652-2525
3729 Union St Mineral Ridge (44440) *(G-14309)*

P & S Welding Co 330 274-2850
11611 Mantua Center Rd Mantua (44255) *(G-12720)*

P & T Millwork Inc..440 543-2151
  10090 Queens Way Chagrin Falls (44023) *(G-3109)*

P & T Products Inc..419 621-1966
  472 Industrial Pkwy Sandusky (44870) *(G-16992)*

P A I, Blue Ash *Also called Precision Anlytical Instrs Inc (G-1854)*

P A X, Lebanon *Also called Pax Corrugated Products Inc (G-11826)*

P B Fabrication Mech Contr....................................419 478-4869
  750 W Laskey Rd Toledo (43612) *(G-18631)*

P C M Co (PA)..330 336-8040
  291 W Bergey St Wadsworth (44281) *(G-19423)*

P C Power Inc..440 779-4080
  23792 Lorain Rd Ste 300 North Olmsted (44070) *(G-15342)*

P C R Inc...330 945-7721
  1135 Portage Trail Ext Akron (44313) *(G-329)*

P C R Restorations Inc...419 747-7957
  933 W Longview Ave Mansfield (44906) *(G-12666)*

P C S, Pataskala *Also called Programmable Control Service (G-15978)*

P C T, Burbank *Also called Pipe Coil Technology Inc (G-2367)*

P C Workshop Inc..419 399-4805
  900 W Caroline St Paulding (45879) *(G-16012)*

P D I, Springboro *Also called Pdi Communication Systems Inc (G-17495)*

P E T, Dayton *Also called Precision Energy & Tech LLC (G-8582)*

P F S Incorporated...440 582-1620
  9861 York Alpha Dr Cleveland (44133) *(G-5954)*

P G I, Cleveland *Also called Pinnacle Graphics & Imaging (G-6008)*

P G M Diversified Industries..................................440 885-3500
  6514 Alexandria Dr Cleveland (44130) *(G-5955)*

P Graham Dunn Inc (PA).......................................330 828-2105
  630 Henry St Dalton (44618) *(G-8076)*

P H Glatfelter Company..740 289-5100
  200 Schuster Rd Piketon (45661) *(G-16226)*

P H Glatfelter Company..740 772-3111
  232 E 8th St Chillicothe (45601) *(G-3256)*

P H I, Toledo *Also called Pilkington Holdings Inc (G-18643)*

P J McNerney & Associates, Cincinnati *Also called McNerney & Associates LLC (G-4070)*

P J Tool Company Inc..937 254-2817
  1115 Springfield St Dayton (45403) *(G-8558)*

P L M Corporation..216 341-8008
  7424 Bessemer Ave Cleveland (44127) *(G-5956)*

P M C, Blue Ash *Also called Plastic Moldings Company Llc (G-1851)*

P M I Food Equipment Group, Piqua *Also called Hobart Corporation (G-16277)*

P M Machine Inc...440 942-6537
  38205 Western Pkwy Willoughby (44094) *(G-20563)*

P M Motor -Fan Blade Company, North Ridgeville *Also called P M Motor Company (G-15393)*

P M Motor Company...440 327-9999
  37850 Taylor Pkwy North Ridgeville (44039) *(G-15393)*

P M R Inc...440 937-6241
  4661 Jaycox Rd Avon (44011) *(G-1001)*

P O McIntire Company (PA)....................................440 269-1848
  29191 Anderson Rd Wickliffe (44092) *(G-20376)*

P P C Greatstuff Co, Mansfield *Also called Shelly Fisher (G-12677)*

P P E Inc...440 322-8577
  710 Taylor St Elyria (44035) *(G-9473)*

P P F, Bradford *Also called Production Paint Finishers Inc (G-2026)*

P P G, Milford *Also called PPG Industries Inc (G-14167)*

P P G Chemicals Group, Barberton *Also called PPG Industries Inc (G-1140)*

P P G Regional Support Center, Chillicothe *Also called PPG Industries Inc (G-3266)*

P P I, Cleveland *Also called Plastic Platers LLC (G-6013)*

P P I Graphics, Canton *Also called KMS 2000 Inc (G-2756)*

P P M Inc...216 701-0419
  35 High Ct Chagrin Falls (44022) *(G-3066)*

P R Machine Works Inc...419 529-5748
  1825 Nussbaum Pkwy Ontario (44906) *(G-15693)*

P R Racing Engines...419 472-2277
  1951 W Sylvania Ave Toledo (43613) *(G-18632)*

P R U Industries Inc..937 746-8702
  8401 Claude Thomas Rd Franklin (45005) *(G-10043)*

P R W Tool Inc...440 585-3373
  30036 Lakeland Blvd Wickliffe (44092) *(G-20377)*

P S Awards, Cleveland *Also called P S Superior Inc (G-5958)*

P S C Inc...216 531-3375
  21761 Tungsten Rd Cleveland (44117) *(G-5957)*

P S G, Columbus *Also called Plastic Selection Group Inc (G-7492)*

P S P Inc...330 283-5635
  7337 Westview Rd Kent (44240) *(G-11498)*

P S Plastics Inc...614 262-7070
  2020 Britains Ln Columbus (43224) *(G-7451)*

P S Superior Inc..216 587-1000
  9257 Midwest Ave Cleveland (44125) *(G-5958)*

P T C, Lima *Also called Precision Thrmplstc Componts (G-12115)*

P T X, Cleveland *Also called Plastran Inc (G-6015)*

P W C, Brunswick *Also called Prime Wood Craft Inc (G-2248)*

P&C Pharma, Dayton *Also called Patientss Consumers Phrm (G-8565)*

P&G, Cincinnati *Also called Procter & Gamble Company (G-4277)*

P&M Publishing...740 353-3300
  2225 8th St Portsmouth (45662) *(G-16447)*

P-Americas LLC...740 266-6121
  450 Luray Dr Wintersville (43953) *(G-20712)*

P-Americas LLC...513 948-5100
  2121 Sunnybrook Dr Cincinnati (45237) *(G-4207)*

P-Americas LLC...419 227-3541
  1750 Greely Chapel Rd Lima (45804) *(G-12065)*

P-Americas LLC...614 253-8771
  1241 Gibbard Ave Columbus (43219) *(G-7452)*

P-Americas LLC...440 323-5524
  925 Lorain Blvd Elyria (44035) *(G-9474)*

P-Americas LLC...330 336-3553
  904 Seville Rd Wadsworth (44281) *(G-19424)*

P-Americas LLC...330 837-4224
  815 Oberlin Ave Sw Massillon (44647) *(G-13191)*

P-Americas LLC...937 328-6750
  233 Dayton Ave Springfield (45506) *(G-17621)*

P-Americas LLC...330 963-0090
  2351 Edison Blvd Ste 2 Twinsburg (44087) *(G-18994)*

P-Americas LLC...330 746-7652
  500 Pepsi Pl Youngstown (44502) *(G-21161)*

P3 Secure LLC..937 610-5500
  926 W Fairview Ave Dayton (45406) *(G-8559)*

PA & Jjs Fruity Smiles Inc.....................................937 449-0999
  4015 Far Hills Ave Dayton (45429) *(G-8560)*

PA MA Inc..440 846-3799
  11288 Alameda Dr Strongsville (44149) *(G-17950)*

PA Stratton & Co Inc...419 660-9979
  3768 State Route 20 Collins (44826) *(G-6576)*

Paarlo Plastics Inc...330 494-3798
  7720 Tim Ave Nw North Canton (44720) *(G-15256)*

PAC Drilling O & G LLC..330 874-3781
  1037 Lawnridge St Ne Bolivar (44612) *(G-1941)*

Pac Manufacturing, Middletown *Also called Pac Worldwide Corporation (G-14072)*

Pac Worldwide Corporation...................................513 217-3200
  3131 Cincinnati Dayton Rd Middletown (45044) *(G-14071)*

Pac Worldwide Corporation...................................800 610-9367
  3131 Cincinnati Dayton Rd Middletown (45044) *(G-14072)*

Paccar Inc..740 774-5111
  65 Kenworth Dr Chillicothe (45601) *(G-3257)*

Pace Consolidated Inc (PA)...................................440 942-1234
  4800 Beidler Rd Willoughby (44094) *(G-20564)*

Pace Converting Eqp Co Inc...................................216 631-4555
  8500 Lake Ave Cleveland (44102) *(G-5959)*

Pace Engineering, Willoughby *Also called Pace Consolidated Inc (G-20564)*

Pace Engineering..440 942-1234
  4800 Beidler Rd Willoughby (44094) *(G-20565)*

Pace Mold & Machine LLC......................................330 879-1777
  8225 Navarre Rd Sw Massillon (44646) *(G-13192)*

Pacemaker Plastic Company Inc...............................740 498-4181
  126 New Pace Rd Newcomerstown (43832) *(G-15121)*

Pacer's Embroidery Barn, Granville *Also called Carter Evans Enterprises Inc (G-10455)*

Pacific Industries USA Inc.....................................513 860-3900
  8955 Seward Rd Fairfield (45011) *(G-9695)*

Pacific Manufacturing Ohio Inc...............................513 860-3900
  8955 Seward Rd Fairfield (45011) *(G-9696)*

Pacific Manufacturing Tenn Inc...............................513 900-7862
  555 Smith Ln Jackson (45640) *(G-11324)*

Pacific Tool & Die Co...330 273-7363
  1035 Western Dr Brunswick (44212) *(G-2241)*

Pacific Valve, Piqua *Also called Crane Pumps & Systems Inc (G-16256)*

Pack Line Corp..212 564-0664
  22900 Miles Rd Cleveland (44128) *(G-5960)*

Package Design & Mfg Inc......................................513 874-7364
  4740 Interstate Dr Ste K West Chester (45246) *(G-20034)*

Packages Anything Anywhere...................................937 298-1939
  4085 E Town And Cntry Rd Dayton (45429) *(G-8561)*

Packaging & Labeling Division, Solon *Also called Outsourcing Services Inc (G-17357)*

Packaging Corporation America...............................513 424-3542
  1824 Baltimore St Middletown (45044) *(G-14073)*

Packaging Corporation America...............................419 282-5809
  929 Faultless Dr Ashland (44805) *(G-762)*

Packaging Corporation America...............................513 860-1145
  3840 Port Union Rd Fairfield (45014) *(G-9697)*

Packaging Corporation America...............................513 582-0690
  791 Saint Thomas Ct Cincinnati (45230) *(G-4208)*

Packaging Corporation America...............................740 344-1126
  205 S 21st St Newark (43055) *(G-15044)*

Packaging Corporation America...............................330 644-9542
  708 Killian Rd Ste 1 Akron (44319) *(G-330)*

Packaging Div, Mount Vernon *Also called Novolex Holdings Inc (G-14634)*

Packaging Material Direct Inc..................................989 482-8400
  30405 Solon Rd Ste 9 Solon (44139) *(G-17358)*

Packaging Materials Inc..740 432-6337
  62805 Bennett Ave Cambridge (43725) *(G-2471)*

Packaging Materials Svcs LLC.................................330 745-9722
  3960 Summit Rd Norton (44203) *(G-15520)*

Packaging Plus Inc...304 429-5900
  1235 Mccook Ave Dayton (45404) *(G-8562)*

Packaging Specialties Inc................................330 723-6000
  300 Lake Rd Medina (44256) *(G-13457)*

Pactiv LLC...815 547-1200
  2120 Westbelt Dr Columbus (43228) *(G-7453)*

Pactiv LLC...614 771-5400
  2120 Westbelt Dr Columbus (43228) *(G-7454)*

Pactiv LLC...330 644-9542
  708 Killian Rd Akron (44319) *(G-331)*

Paddock Corporation...................................440 543-0631
  8574 Washington St Chagrin Falls (44023) *(G-3110)*

Paddock Products, Chagrin Falls *Also called Paddock Corporation (G-3110)*

Page One Group..740 397-4240
  10 E Vine St Ste C Mount Vernon (43050) *(G-14636)*

Page Slotting Saw Co Inc..............................419 476-7475
  3820 Lagrange St Toledo (43612) *(G-18633)*

Pahl Ready Mix Concrete Inc (PA)......................419 636-4238
  14586 Us Highway 127 Ew Bryan (43506) *(G-2317)*

Pahl Ready Mix Concrete Inc...........................419 636-4238
  600 S River Rd Waterville (43566) *(G-19664)*

Pahuja Inc..614 864-3989
  1125 Gahanna Pkwy Gahanna (43230) *(G-10225)*

Paine Falls Centerpin LLC.............................440 298-3202
  6342 Ledge Rd Thompson (44086) *(G-18189)*

Painesville Pride, Willoughby *Also called Lake Community News (G-20524)*

Painesville Publishing Co.............................440 354-4142
  2883 Industrial Park Dr Austinburg (44010) *(G-964)*

Painted Hill Inv Group Inc............................937 339-1756
  402 E Main St Troy (45373) *(G-18861)*

Pakk Systems LLC......................................440 839-9999
  39 W Main St Wakeman (44889) *(G-19452)*

Paklab, Cincinnati *Also called Universal Packg Systems Inc (G-4542)*

Paklab, Batavia *Also called Universal Packg Systems Inc (G-1231)*

Pako Inc..440 946-8030
  7615 Jenther Dr Mentor (44060) *(G-13678)*

Pakra LLC...614 477-6965
  449 E Mound St Columbus (43215) *(G-7455)*

Paleomd LLC...248 854-0031
  26245 Broadway Ave Ste B Bedford (44146) *(G-1452)*

Palesh & Associates Inc...............................440 942-9168
  3659 Lost Nation Rd Willoughby (44094) *(G-20566)*

Palette Studios Inc...................................513 961-1316
  2501 Woodburn Ave Cincinnati (45206) *(G-4209)*

Pallet & Cont Corp of Amer............................419 255-1256
  901 Buckingham St Toledo (43607) *(G-18634)*

Pallet Distributors Inc...............................330 852-3531
  10343 Copperhead Rd Nw Sugarcreek (44681) *(G-18030)*

Pallet Guys...440 897-3001
  12720 N Star Dr North Royalton (44133) *(G-15441)*

Pallet Man The, Lisbon *Also called Paul E Cekovich (G-12132)*

Pallet Pros...440 537-9087
  12500 Island Rd Grafton (44044) *(G-10434)*

Pallet Specs Plus LLC.................................513 351-3200
  1701 Mills Ave Norwood (45212) *(G-15573)*

Pallet World Inc......................................419 874-9333
  8272 Fremont Pike Perrysburg (43551) *(G-16144)*

Pallets-Fm-N-plc-packaging Inc........................937 526-9333
  10709 Reed Rd Versailles (45380) *(G-19355)*

Palmer Bros Transit Mix Con...........................419 332-6363
  210 N Stone St Fremont (43420) *(G-10174)*

Palmer Bros Transit Mix Con (PA)......................419 352-4681
  12205 E Gypsy Lane Rd Bowling Green (43402) *(G-2006)*

Palmer Bros Transit Mix Con...........................419 447-2018
  1900 S County Road 1 Tiffin (44883) *(G-18237)*

Palmer Bros Transit Mix Con...........................419 686-2366
  12580 Greensburg Pike Portage (43451) *(G-16427)*

Palmer Engineered Products Inc........................937 322-1481
  1310 W Main St Springfield (45504) *(G-17622)*

Palmer Enterprises, Perrysville *Also called Palmer Properties LLC (G-16174)*

Palmer Industries Inc.................................330 630-9397
  920 Moe Dr Akron (44310) *(G-332)*

Palmer Klein Inc......................................937 323-6339
  18 N Bechtle Ave Springfield (45504) *(G-17623)*

Palmer Mfg and Supply Inc.............................937 323-6339
  18 N Bechtle Ave Springfield (45504) *(G-17624)*

Palmer Products, Akron *Also called Palmer Industries Inc (G-332)*

Palmer Properties LLC.................................419 938-3114
  4688 State Route 95 Perrysville (44864) *(G-16174)*

Palpac Industries Inc.................................419 523-3230
  610 N Agner St Ottawa (45875) *(G-15803)*

Palstar Inc...937 773-6255
  9676 Looney Rd Piqua (45356) *(G-16298)*

Pama Tool & Die, Strongsville *Also called PA MA Inc (G-17950)*

Pan-Glo, Mansfield *Also called Russell T Bundy Associates Inc (G-12674)*

Panacea Products Corporation (PA).....................614 850-7000
  2711 International St Columbus (43228) *(G-7456)*

Panacea Products Corporation..........................614 429-6320
  1825 Joyce Ave Columbus (43219) *(G-7457)*

Panam Imaging Systems, Cleveland *Also called Horizons Incorporated (G-5525)*

Panama Jewelers LLC...................................440 376-6987
  7250 Brakeman Rd Painesville (44077) *(G-15909)*

Panel Control Inc.....................................937 394-2201
  107 Shue Dr Anna (45302) *(G-624)*

Panel Master LLC......................................440 355-4442
  191 Commerce Dr Lagrange (44050) *(G-11635)*

Panel-Fab Inc...513 771-1462
  10520 Taconic Ter Cincinnati (45215) *(G-4210)*

Panelbloc Inc...440 974-8877
  8665 Tyler Blvd Mentor (44060) *(G-13679)*

Panelmatic Inc (PA)...................................513 829-3666
  258 Donald Dr Fairfield (45014) *(G-9698)*

Panelmatic Inc..330 782-8007
  1125 Meadowbrook Ave Youngstown (44512) *(G-21162)*

Panelmatic Cincinnati Inc.............................513 829-1960
  258 Donald Dr Fairfield (45014) *(G-9699)*

Panelmatic Youngstown, Youngstown *Also called Panelmatic Inc (G-21162)*

Panelmatic Youngstown Inc.............................330 782-8007
  1125 Meadowbrook Ave Youngstown (44512) *(G-21163)*

Paneltech LLC...440 516-1300
  1430 Lloyd Rd Wickliffe (44092) *(G-20378)*

Pang Rubber Company, Johnstown *Also called Truflex Rubber Products Co (G-11409)*

Papel Couture...614 848-5700
  6522 Singletree Dr Columbus (43229) *(G-7458)*

Paper Moon Winery.....................................440 967-2500
  2008 State Rd Vermilion (44089) *(G-19335)*

Paper Occasions.......................................614 761-8880
  55 S High St Ste A Dublin (43017) *(G-9116)*

Paper People, Newark *Also called Joseph Scarberry (G-15025)*

Paper Products Company, West Chester *Also called Omer J Smith Inc (G-19909)*

Paper Service Inc.....................................330 227-3546
  12022 Leslie Rd Lisbon (44432) *(G-12131)*

Paper Systems Incorporated (PA).......................937 746-6841
  185 S Pioneer Blvd Springboro (45066) *(G-17494)*

Paper Vault...614 859-5538
  869 Montrose Ave Columbus (43209) *(G-7459)*

Papworth Prints.......................................614 428-6137
  4355 Boulder Creek Dr Columbus (43230) *(G-7460)*

Parabellum Armament Co LLC............................614 557-5987
  3142 Broadway Ste 200 Grove City (43123) *(G-10582)*

Paradise Inc..330 928-3789
  1710 Front St Cuyahoga Falls (44221) *(G-8031)*

Paradise Lemonade.....................................740 816-0771
  12897 Hatch Rd Westerville (43082) *(G-20178)*

Paradise Mold & Die LLC...............................216 362-1945
  10815 Briggs Rd Cleveland (44111) *(G-5961)*

Paragan Tool and Die, Berlin Center *Also called High Card Industries LLC (G-1655)*

Paragon Custom Plastics Inc...........................419 636-6060
  402 N Union St Bryan (43506) *(G-2318)*

Paragon Machine Company, Bedford *Also called Done-Rite Bowling Service Co (G-1420)*

Paragon Metal Fabricators, Cincinnati *Also called Muehlenkamp Properties Inc (G-4130)*

Paragon Plastics......................................330 542-9825
  5551 E Calla Rd New Middletown (44442) *(G-14878)*

Paragon Press...513 281-9911
  2239 Fulton Ave Cincinnati (45206) *(G-4211)*

Paragon Robotics LLC..................................216 313-9299
  5386 Majestic Pkwy Ste 2 Bedford Heights (44146) *(G-1492)*

Paragon Service & Supply Div, Lima *Also called Motion Industries Inc (G-12060)*

Paragon Woodworking LLC...............................614 402-1459
  800 Reynolds Ave Columbus (43201) *(G-7461)*

Paragraphics Inc......................................330 493-1074
  2011 29th St Nw Canton (44709) *(G-2806)*

Parallel Solutions....................................440 498-9920
  5380 Naiman Pkwy Ste B Cleveland (44139) *(G-5962)*

Parallel Technologies Inc.............................614 798-9700
  4868 Blazer Pkwy Dublin (43017) *(G-9117)*

Paramelt Argueso Kindt Inc............................216 252-4122
  12651 Elmwood Ave Cleveland (44111) *(G-5963)*

Paramont Machine Company LLC..........................330 339-3489
  963 Commercial Ave Se New Philadelphia (44663) *(G-14921)*

Paramount Distillers, Cleveland *Also called Luxco Inc (G-5713)*

Paramount Products....................................419 832-0235
  10550 Prov Neap Swan Rd Grand Rapids (43522) *(G-10442)*

Paramount Stamping & Wldg Co..........................216 631-1755
  1200 W 58th St Cleveland (44102) *(G-5964)*

Paratus Supply Inc....................................330 745-3600
  635 Wooster Rd W Barberton (44203) *(G-1137)*

Parco Inc...937 296-0356
  2747 Culver Ave Dayton (45429) *(G-8563)*

Pardson Inc...740 373-5285
  149 Acme St Marietta (45750) *(G-12813)*

Park Corporation (PA).................................216 267-4870
  6200 Riverside Dr Cleveland (44135) *(G-5965)*

Park PLC Prntg Cpyg & Dgtl IMG........................330 799-1739
  3410 Canfield Rd Ste B Youngstown (44511) *(G-21164)*

Park Press Direct.....................................419 626-4426
  2143 Sherman St Sandusky (44870) *(G-16993)*

Park-Ohio Holdings Corp (PA)..........................440 947-2000
  6065 Parkland Blvd Ste 1 Cleveland (44124) *(G-5966)*

(G-0000) Company's Geographic Section entry number

Park-Ohio Industries Inc (HQ)..........440 947-2000
6065 Parkland Blvd Ste 1 Cleveland (44124) *(G-5967)*
Park-Ohio Industries Inc..........216 341-2300
3800 Harvard Ave Newburgh Heights (44105) *(G-15077)*
Park-Ohio Industries Inc..........216 431-2900
777 E 79th St Cleveland (44103) *(G-5968)*
Park-Ohio Products Inc..........216 961-7200
7000 Denison Ave Cleveland (44102) *(G-5969)*
Parker Aircraft Sales..........937 833-4820
212 Church St Brookville (45309) *(G-2195)*
Parker Elwell Ltd..........216 881-5042
4205 Saint Clair Ave Cleveland (44103) *(G-5970)*
Parker Precision Inc..........440 951-6501
8950 Tyler Blvd Mentor (44060) *(G-13680)*
Parker Royalty Partnership..........216 896-3000
6035 Parkland Blvd Cleveland (44124) *(G-5971)*
Parker Rst-Proof Cleveland Inc..........216 481-6680
1688 Arabella Rd Cleveland (44112) *(G-5972)*
Parker Triad Store..........937 293-4080
2402 Springboro Pike Moraine (45439) *(G-14511)*
Parker Trutec Incorporated (HQ)..........937 323-8833
4700 Gateway Blvd Springfield (45502) *(G-17625)*
Parker Trutec Incorporated..........937 653-8500
4795 Upper Valley Pike Urbana (43078) *(G-19172)*
Parker-Hannifin Corporation (PA)..........216 896-3000
6035 Parkland Blvd Cleveland (44124) *(G-5973)*
Parker-Hannifin Corporation..........937 456-5571
725 N Beech St Eaton (45320) *(G-9320)*
Parker-Hannifin Corporation..........440 943-5700
30240 Lakeland Blvd Wickliffe (44092) *(G-20379)*
Parker-Hannifin Corporation..........419 394-9600
1700 E Spring St Saint Marys (45885) *(G-16848)*
Parker-Hannifin Corporation..........330 336-3511
135 Quadral Dr Wadsworth (44281) *(G-19425)*
Parker-Hannifin Corporation..........513 831-2340
50 W Techne Center Dr H Milford (45150) *(G-14166)*
Parker-Hannifin Corporation..........330 963-0601
1390 Highland Rd E Macedonia (44056) *(G-12468)*
Parker-Hannifin Corporation..........614 279-7070
3885 Gateway Blvd Columbus (43228) *(G-7462)*
Parker-Hannifin Corporation..........937 962-5301
700 W Cumberland St Lewisburg (45338) *(G-11938)*
Parker-Hannifin Corporation..........330 673-2700
838 Overholt Rd Kent (44240) *(G-11499)*
Parker-Hannifin Corporation..........218 534-3148
30240 Lakeland Blvd Wickliffe (44092) *(G-20380)*
Parker-Hannifin Corporation..........330 740-8366
1911 Logan Ave Youngstown (44505) *(G-21165)*
Parker-Hannifin Corporation..........216 531-3000
17325 Euclid Ave Cleveland (44112) *(G-5974)*
Parker-Hannifin Corporation..........330 335-6740
135 Quadral Dr Wadsworth (44281) *(G-19426)*
Parker-Hannifin Corporation..........513 847-1758
9050 Centre Pointe Dr # 310 West Chester (45069) *(G-19912)*
Parker-Hannifin Corporation..........419 542-6611
373 Meuse Argonne St Hicksville (43526) *(G-10905)*
Parker-Hannifin Corporation..........440 366-5100
520 Ternes Ln Elyria (44035) *(G-9475)*
Parker-Hannifin Corporation..........419 644-4311
16810 Fulton County Rd 2 Metamora (43540) *(G-13776)*
Parker-Hannifin Corporation..........330 296-2871
1300 N Freedom St Ravenna (44266) *(G-16548)*
Parker-Hannifin Corporation..........216 896-3000
1390 Highland Rd E Macedonia (44056) *(G-12469)*
Parker-Hannifin Corporation..........440 937-6211
1160 Center Rd Avon (44011) *(G-1002)*
Parker-Hannifin Corporation..........440 266-2300
8940 Tyler Blvd Mentor (44060) *(G-13681)*
Parker-Hannifin Corporation..........440 284-6277
711 Taylor St Elyria (44035) *(G-9476)*
Parker-Hannifin Corporation..........440 205-8230
8940 Tyler Blvd Mentor (44060) *(G-13682)*
Parker-Hannifin Corporation..........440 943-5700
30242 Lakeland Blvd Wickliffe (44092) *(G-20381)*
Parker-Hannifin Corporation..........216 531-3000
6035 Parkland Blvd Cleveland (44124) *(G-5975)*
Parker-Hannifin Corporation..........937 962-5566
704 W Cumberland St Lewisburg (45338) *(G-11939)*
Parker-Hannifin Corporation..........937 644-3915
14249 Industrial Pkwy Marysville (43040) *(G-12962)*
Parker-Hannifin Corporation..........330 336-3511
135 Quadral Dr Wadsworth (44281) *(G-19427)*
Parker-Hannifin Corporation..........216 896-3000
6035 Parkland Blvd Cleveland (44124) *(G-5976)*
Parker-Hannifin Corporation..........330 743-6893
58 Hubbard Rd Youngstown (44505) *(G-21166)*
Parker-Hannifin Corporation..........330 296-2871
1300 N Freedom St Ravenna (44266) *(G-16549)*
Parking & Traffic Control SEC..........440 243-7565
13651 Newton Rd Cleveland (44130) *(G-5977)*
Parking Facilities, Cleveland *Also called City of Cleveland (G-5036)*
Parkins Asphalt Sealing..........419 422-2399
1710 Olney Ave Findlay (45840) *(G-9876)*
Parkn Manufacturing LLC..........330 723-8172
8035 Norwalk Rd Ste 107 Litchfield (44253) *(G-12139)*
Parks West Pallet Llc..........440 693-4651
4566 Parks West Rd Middlefield (44062) *(G-13979)*
Parkside & Eaton Estate..........330 467-2995
8689 Parkside Dr Northfield (44067) *(G-15469)*
Parma Heights License Bureau..........440 888-0388
6339 Olde York Rd Cleveland (44130) *(G-5978)*
Parma International Inc..........440 237-8650
13927 Progress Pkwy North Royalton (44133) *(G-15442)*
Parma Seven Hills Gazette, Brecksville *Also called Brecksville Broadview Gazette (G-2038)*
Paro Services Co (PA)..........330 467-1300
1755 Entp Pkwy Ste 100 Twinsburg (44087) *(G-18995)*
Parobek Trucking Co..........419 869-7500
192 State Route 42 West Salem (44287) *(G-20116)*
Parrot Energy Company..........330 637-0151
180 Portal Dr Cortland (44410) *(G-7873)*
Parrot University LLC..........740 965-1965
9000 Cheshire Rd Sunbury (43074) *(G-18073)*
Parry Co..........740 884-4893
33630 Old Route 35 Chillicothe (45601) *(G-3258)*
Part Rite Inc..........216 362-4100
12855 York Delta Dr North Royalton (44133) *(G-15443)*
Parthenon Global LLC..........888 332-5303
3615 Superior Ave E Cleveland (44114) *(G-5979)*
Parthenon Globalsystems LLC, Cleveland *Also called Parthenon Global LLC (G-5979)*
Partitions Plus LLC..........419 422-2600
12517 County Road 99 Findlay (45840) *(G-9877)*
Partners In Recognition Inc..........937 420-2150
405 S Main St Fort Loramie (45845) *(G-9934)*
Partners Manufacturing Group..........419 468-8516
9357 Township Road 48 Galion (44833) *(G-10281)*
Parts Channel Inc..........614 497-9199
5830 Green Pointe Dr S A Groveport (43125) *(G-10638)*
Parts Unlimited..........937 558-1527
5221 Shiloh Springs Rd Dayton (45426) *(G-8564)*
Party Animal Inc..........440 471-1030
909 Crocker Rd Westlake (44145) *(G-20291)*
Party On, Austintown *Also called Adyl Inc (G-968)*
Pas Technologies Inc..........937 840-1000
214 Hobart Dr Hillsboro (45133) *(G-11012)*
Pat's Cleaners, Cleveland *Also called Pats Nu-Style Cleaners Inc (G-5980)*
Pataskala License Bureau, Pataskala *Also called Transportation Ohio Department (G-15987)*
Pataskala Post..........740 964-6226
190 E Broad St Ste 2 Pataskala (43062) *(G-15977)*
Patches LLC..........513 304-4882
1696 Pin Oak Ln Williamsburg (45176) *(G-20410)*
Patchwork People Pins Etc..........937 725-2981
946 Pyle Rd Clarksville (45113) *(G-4652)*
Patent Construction Systems, Marion *Also called Harsco Corporation (G-12873)*
Patenthealth LLC..........330 208-1111
8000 Freedom Ave Nw North Canton (44720) *(G-15257)*
Patheon Pharmaceuticals Inc..........513 948-7942
2110 E Galbraith Rd Cincinnati (45237) *(G-4212)*
Pathfinder Computer Systems..........330 928-1961
345 5th St Ne Barberton (44203) *(G-1138)*
Pathos LLC..........440 497-7278
7948 Mayfield Rd Chesterland (44026) *(G-3219)*
Pathos Printing, Chesterland *Also called Pathos LLC (G-3219)*
Patient Focus Systems..........330 655-7222
1140 Terex Rd Hudson (44236) *(G-11193)*
Patient Medicines, Mount Vernon *Also called Robert Coleman (G-14642)*
Patientss Consumers Phrm Inc..........937 813-7800
955 Congress Park Dr Dayton (45459) *(G-8565)*
Patio Enclosures, Macedonia *Also called Great Day Improvements LLC (G-12456)*
Patio Enclosures (PA)..........513 733-4646
11949 Tramway Dr Cincinnati (45241) *(G-4213)*
Patio Print & Promotions, Columbus *Also called Patio Printing Inc (G-7463)*
Patio Printing Inc..........614 785-9553
6663 Huntley Rd Ste S Columbus (43229) *(G-7463)*
Patio Room Factory Inc..........614 449-7900
2659 Beulah Rd Columbus (43211) *(G-7464)*
Patjim Holdings Company..........419 727-1298
3444 N Summit St Toledo (43611) *(G-18635)*
Patricia Lee Burd..........513 302-4860
310 Culvert St Cincinnati (45202) *(G-4214)*
Patrician Furniture Builders..........330 746-6354
1097 Wick Ave Youngstown (44505) *(G-21167)*
Patrick J Burke & Co..........513 455-8200
901 Adams Crossing Fl 1 Cincinnati (45202) *(G-4215)*
Patrick M Davidson..........513 897-2971
6490 Corwin Ave Waynesville (45068) *(G-19733)*
Patricks, Leipsic *Also called Pretium Packaging LLC (G-11874)*
Patriot..........419 864-8411
217 W Main St Cardington (43315) *(G-2913)*

ALPHABETIC

(PA)=Parent Co (HQ)=Headquarters (DH)=Div Headquarters

Patriot Building Solutions, Wheelersburg Also called Patriot Holdings Unlimited LLC (G-20333)

Patriot Consulting LLC 614 554-6455
20 E Frambes Ave Columbus (43201) (G-7465)

Patriot Distributing, Columbus Also called Patriot Consulting LLC (G-7465)

Patriot Energy LLC 330 923-4442
1574 Main St Cuyahoga Falls (44221) (G-8032)

Patriot Holdings Unlimited LLC 740 574-2112
956 Patriot Ridge Dr Wheelersburg (45694) (G-20333)

Patriot Mfg Group Inc 937 746-2117
512 Linden Ave Carlisle (45005) (G-2934)

Patriot Mobility, Holland Also called Patriot Products Inc (G-11076)

Patriot Precision Products 330 966-7177
8817 Pleasantwood Ave Nw Canton (44720) (G-2807)

Patriot Products Inc 419 865-9712
1133 Corporate Dr Ste B Holland (43528) (G-11076)

Patriot Seating Inc 330 779-0768
1584 Tamarisk Trl Youngstown (44514) (G-21168)

Patriot Software Inc 877 968-7147
4883 Dressler Rd Nw # 301 Canton (44718) (G-2808)

Patriot Special Metals Inc 330 538-9621
2058 S Bailey Rd North Jackson (44451) (G-15296)

Patriot Special Metals Inc 330 580-9600
2201 Harrison Ave Sw Canton (44706) (G-2809)

Patriotic Buildings LLC 740 853-3970
1753 Patriot Rd Patriot (45658) (G-15997)

Patron Graphics, Cincinnati Also called Registered Images Inc (G-4335)

Pats Delicious LLC 614 441-7047
737 Parkwood Ave Columbus (43219) (G-7466)

Pats Nu-Style Cleaners Inc 216 676-4855
5851 Smith Rd Cleveland (44142) (G-5980)

Patterson Colburne (PA) 419 866-5544
1100 S Hiland Sylvania Rd Holland (43528) (G-11077)

Patterson & Sons Inc 419 281-0897
10 Township Road 1031 Nova (44859) (G-15579)

Patterson-Britton Printing 216 781-7997
2165 Lakeside Ave E Cleveland (44114) (G-5981)

Patton Aluminum Products Inc 937 845-9404
65 Quick Rd New Carlisle (45344) (G-14811)

Patton Industries Inc 419 331-5658
1950 Beery Rd Elida (45807) (G-9354)

Pattons Truck & Heavy Eqp Svc 740 385-4067
35640 Hocking Dr Logan (43138) (G-12189)

Paul A Grim Inc 740 385-9637
15104 State Route 328 Logan (43138) (G-12190)

Paul Bartel (PA) 513 541-2000
1038 W North Bend Rd Cincinnati (45224) (G-4216)

Paul Blausey Farms, Genoa Also called Rcr Partnership (G-10362)

Paul E Cekovich 330 424-3213
9403 Black Rd Lisbon (44432) (G-12132)

Paul J Tatulinski Ltd 330 584-8251
1595 W Main St North Benton (44449) (G-15213)

Paul Miracle 513 575-3113
6749 Oakland Rd Loveland (45140) (G-12376)

Paul Peterson Company (PA) 614 486-4375
950 Dublin Rd Columbus (43215) (G-7467)

Paul Peterson Safety Div Inc 614 486-4375
950 Dublin Rd Columbus (43215) (G-7468)

Paul Popov 440 582-6677
13800 Progress Pkwy Ste A North Royalton (44133) (G-15444)

Paul R Lipp & Son Inc 330 227-9614
47563 Pancake Clarkson Rd Rogers (44455) (G-16714)

Paul S Blanch, Bedford Heights Also called Alert Stamping & Mfg Co Inc (G-1476)

Paul Stipkovich 330 499-7391
515 Browning Ave Nw North Canton (44720) (G-15258)

Paul Wilke & Son Inc 513 921-3163
1965 Grand Ave Cincinnati (45214) (G-4217)

Paul Yoder 740 439-5811
13051 Deerfield Rd Senecaville (43780) (G-17059)

Paul/Jay Associates 740 676-8776
3057 Union St Bellaire (43906) (G-1500)

Paula and Julies Cookbooks LLC 614 863-1193
6034 Mcnaughten Grove Ln Columbus (43213) (G-7469)

Pauler Communications Inc (PA) 440 243-1229
3046 Brecksville Rd Ste B Richfield (44286) (G-16631)

Pauley's Machine Shop, Sunbury Also called Richard Pauley (G-18076)

Paulg Corporation 914 662-9837
1601 W 5th Ave Columbus (43212) (G-7470)

Paulin Industries Inc 216 433-7633
12400 Plaza Dr Parma (44130) (G-15965)

Paullin Driveway Sealing 419 289-2228
1306 Wells Rd Ste A Ashland (44805) (G-763)

Paulo Products Company 440 942-0153
4428 Hamann Pkwy Willoughby (44094) (G-20567)

Pave Technology Co 937 890-1592
2751 Thunderhawk Ct Dayton (45414) (G-8566)

Pavestone LLC 513 474-3783
8479 Broadwell Rd Cincinnati (45244) (G-4218)

Pavetech International, Mason Also called Millinium 3 Inc (G-13064)

Pawnee Maintenance Inc 740 373-6861
111 3rd St Marietta (45750) (G-12814)

Pax Corrugated Products Inc 513 932-9855
1899 Kingsview Dr Lebanon (45036) (G-11826)

Pax Machine Works Inc 419 586-2337
5139 Monroe Rd Celina (45822) (G-3012)

Pax Products Inc 419 586-2337
5097 Monroe Rd Celina (45822) (G-3013)

Paxar Corporation 937 681-4541
7801 Technology Blvd Dayton (45424) (G-8567)

Paxos Plating Inc 330 479-0022
4631 Navarre Rd Sw Canton (44706) (G-2810)

Paycard USA Inc 702 216-6801
5854 Whitebark Pine Trl Dublin (43016) (G-9118)

Pazco Inc 216 447-9581
4500 Rockside Rd Ste 420 Cleveland (44131) (G-5982)

PBM Covington LLC 937 473-2050
400 Hazel St Covington (45318) (G-7927)

PC, Columbus Also called Papel Couture (G-7458)

PC Campana Inc (PA) 440 246-6500
6155 Park Square Dr Ste 1 Lorain (44053) (G-12266)

PC Systems 330 825-7966
307 Montrose Ave Akron (44310) (G-333)

PCA, Fairfield Also called Packaging Corporation America (G-9697)

PCA, Cincinnati Also called Packaging Corporation America (G-4208)

PCA/Akron 312, Akron Also called Packaging Corporation America (G-330)

Pca/Ashland 307, Ashland Also called Packaging Corporation America (G-762)

Pca/Middletown 353, Middletown Also called Packaging Corporation America (G-14073)

PCA/Newark 365, Newark Also called Packaging Corporation America (G-15044)

PCC Airfoils LLC 330 868-6441
3860 Union Ave Se Minerva (44657) (G-14337)

PCC Airfoils LLC 740 982-6025
101 China St Crooksville (43731) (G-7952)

PCC Airfoils LLC 216 692-7900
1781 Octavia Rd Cleveland (44112) (G-5983)

PCC Airfoils LLC (HQ) 216 831-3590
3401 Entp Pkwy Ste 200 Cleveland (44122) (G-5984)

PCC Airfoils LLC 440 255-9770
8607 Tyler Blvd Mentor (44060) (G-13683)

PCC Ceramic Group 1 ....440 516-3672
1470 E 289th St Wickliffe (44092) (G-20382)

PCI, West Chester Also called Professional Case Inc (G-20041)

Pckd Enterprises Inc 440 632-9119
15510 Old State Rd Middlefield (44062) (G-13980)

Pcna, Cincinnati Also called Peter Cremer North America LP (G-4231)

Pcs Nitrogen Inc 419 226-1200
1900 Fort Amanda Rd Lima (45804) (G-12066)

Pcs Nitrogen Ohio LP 419 879-8989
2200 Fort Amanda Rd Lima (45804) (G-12067)

Pcs Phosphate Company Inc 513 738-1261
10818 Paddys Run Rd Harrison (45030) (G-10794)

Pct Industries, Perry Also called Precision Conveyor Technology (G-16056)

Pcy Enterprises Inc 513 241-5566
3111 Spring Grove Ave Cincinnati (45225) (G-4219)

PD&b, Toledo Also called Projects Designed & Built (G-18659)

Pdi, Cleveland Also called Pile Dynamics Inc (G-6007)

Pdi, Englewood Also called Prosthetic Design Inc (G-9537)

Pdi Communication Systems Inc (PA) 937 743-6010
40 Greenwood Ln Springboro (45066) (G-17495)

Pdi Constellation LLC 216 271-7344
6225 Cochran Rd Solon (44139) (G-17359)

Pdi Ground Support Systems Inc 216 271-7344
6225 Cochran Rd Solon (44139) (G-17360)

PDI GROUP, THE, Solon Also called Pdi Ground Support Systems Inc (G-17360)

PDM, West Chester Also called Package Design & Mfg Inc (G-20034)

Pdmb Inc 513 522-7362
9600 Colerain Ave Ste 110 Cincinnati (45251) (G-4220)

PDQ Installation Co, Parma Also called GMR Furniture Services Ltd (G-15959)

PDQ Printing Service 216 241-5443
1914 Clark Ave Cleveland (44109) (G-5985)

PDQ Technologies Inc 937 274-4958
2608 Nordic Rd Dayton (45414) (G-8568)

Pds, Fairfield Also called CPC Logistics Inc (G-9657)

Pdsi, Groveport Also called Pinnacle Data Systems Inc (G-10641)

Pdsi Technical Services, Dayton Also called Production Design Services Inc (G-8598)

Peabody Coal Company 740 450-2420
2810 East Pike Apt 3 Zanesville (43701) (G-21340)

Peak Electric Inc 419 726-4848
320 N Byrne Rd Toledo (43607) (G-18636)

Peak Foods Llc 937 440-0707
1903 W Main St Ste B Troy (45373) (G-18862)

Peanut Roaster, The, Sandusky Also called Thorfood LLC (G-17014)

Pearce Inc 216 252-0550
12026 Zelis Rd Cleveland (44135) (G-5986)

Pearl Tech Corporation (PA) 614 284-8357
545 Metro Pl S Ste 100 Dublin (43017) (G-9119)

Pearl Valley Cheese Inc 740 545-6002
54760 Township Road 90 Fresno (43824) (G-10197)
Pearson Education Inc 614 876-0371
4350 Equity Dr Columbus (43228) (G-7471)
Pearson Education Inc 614 841-3700
445 Hutchinson Ave # 400 Columbus (43235) (G-7472)
Pease Industies Inc 513 870-3600
7100 Dixie Hwy Fairfield (45014) (G-9700)
Peck Engraving Co 216 221-1556
14398 Detroit Ave Cleveland (44107) (G-5987)
Peco Holdings Corp (PA) 937 667-4451
6555 S State Route 202 Tipp City (45371) (G-18292)
Peco II Inc 614 431-0694
7060 Huntley Rd Columbus (43229) (G-7473)
Pedestrian Press 419 244-6488
2233 Robinwood Ave Toledo (43620) (G-18637)
Pediavascular Inc 216 236-5533
7181 Chagrin Rd Ste 250 Chagrin Falls (44023) (G-3111)
Peebles - Herzog Inc 614 279-2211
50 Hayden Ave Columbus (43222) (G-7474)
Peebles Creative Group Inc 614 487-2011
4260 Tuller Rd Ste 200 Dublin (43017) (G-9120)
Peebles Messenger Newspaper 937 587-1451
58 S Main St Peebles (45660) (G-16023)
Peer Pantry LLC 216 236-4087
30901 Lake Shore Blvd Willowick (44095) (G-20649)
Peerless Foods Inc 937 492-4158
500 S Vandemark Rd Sidney (45365) (G-17207)
Peerless Group, The, Sidney Also called Peerless Foods Inc (G-17207)
Peerless Laser Processors Inc 614 836-5790
4353 Directors Blvd Groveport (43125) (G-10639)
Peerless Metal Products Inc 216 431-6905
6017 Superior Ave Cleveland (44103) (G-5988)
Peerless Printing Company 513 721-4657
2250 Gilbert Ave Ste 1 Cincinnati (45206) (G-4221)
Peerless Prof Cooking Eqp, Sandusky Also called Peerless Stove & Mfg Co Inc (G-16994)
Peerless Pump Civeland Svc Ctr, Cleveland Also called Wm Plotz Machine and Forge Co (G-6473)
Peerless Saw Company (PA) 614 836-5790
4353 Directors Blvd Groveport (43125) (G-10640)
Peerless Stove & Mfg Co Inc 419 625-4514
334 Harrison St Sandusky (44870) (G-16994)
Peerless-Winsmith Inc 330 399-3651
5200 Upper Metro Pl # 110 Dublin (43017) (G-9121)
Peerless-Winsmith Inc (HQ) 614 526-7000
5200 Upper Metro Pl # 110 Dublin (43017) (G-9122)
Pegasus Industries 740 772-1049
104 S Mcarthur St Chillicothe (45601) (G-3259)
Pegasus Printing Group, Youngstown Also called Customer Printing Inc (G-21061)
Pegasus Products Company Inc 330 677-1123
315 Gougler Ave Kent (44240) (G-11500)
Pegasus Vans & Trailers Inc 419 625-8953
4003 Tiffin Ave Sandusky (44870) (G-16995)
Peggys Pride 614 464-2511
183 E Rich St Columbus (43215) (G-7475)
Pei Liquidation Company (PA) 330 467-4267
700 Highland Rd E Macedonia (44056) (G-12470)
Pei Liquidation Company 615 781-5020
720 Highland Rd E Macedonia (44056) (G-12471)
Pelletier Brothers Mfg 740 774-4704
4000 Sulphur Lick Rd Chillicothe (45601) (G-3260)
Peloton Manufacturing Corp 440 205-1600
8909 East Ave Mentor (44060) (G-13684)
Pelton Environmental Pdts Inc 440 838-1221
8638 Cotter St Lewis Center (43035) (G-11909)
Pelz Lettering Inc 419 625-3567
5003 Milan Rd Sandusky (44870) (G-16996)
Pemco Inc 216 524-2990
5663 Brecksville Rd Cleveland (44131) (G-5989)
Pemco North Canton Division, Canton Also called Powell Electrical Systems Inc (G-2816)
Pemjay Inc 740 254-4591
318 E Tuscarawas Ave Gnadenhutten (44629) (G-10409)
Pen Pal LLC 614 348-2517
5868 Kitzmiller Rd New Albany (43054) (G-14768)
Pen-Ann Corporation 740 373-2054
101 Rathbone Rd Marietta (45750) (G-12815)
Penca Design Group Ltd 440 210-4422
1325 Yale Pl Painesville (44077) (G-15910)
Penco Tool LLC 440 998-1116
2621 West Ave Ashtabula (44004) (G-829)
Pendaform Company (HQ) 740 826-5000
200 S Friendship Dr New Concord (43762) (G-14819)
Pendaform Company 740 826-5000
200 S Friendship Dr New Concord (43762) (G-14820)
Pendant Armor, West Chester Also called Roboworld Molded Products LLC (G-19935)
Pendleton Mold & Machine LLC 440 998-0041
4624 State Rd Ashtabula (44004) (G-830)
Penguin Enterprises Inc 440 899-5110
869 Canterbury Rd Ste 2 Westlake (44145) (G-20292)

Penguin Serv Ice 614 848-6511
530 Lakeview Plaza Blvd Worthington (43085) (G-20882)
Pengywn, Columbus Also called H Y O Inc (G-7136)
Penick Gas & Oil 740 323-3040
1504 Blue Jay Rd Newark (43056) (G-15045)
Peninsula Hardwoods Inc 330 657-2701
1710 Mill St W Peninsula (44264) (G-16039)
Peninsula Publishing LLC 330 524-3359
6138 Riverview Rd Ste B Peninsula (44264) (G-16040)
Penn Machine Company 814 288-1547
2182 E Aurora Rd Twinsburg (44087) (G-18996)
Pennant Companies (PA) 614 451-1782
2000 Bethel Rd Ste D Columbus (43220) (G-7476)
Pennant Moldings Inc 937 584-5411
12381 Route 22 E Sabina (45169) (G-16775)
Pennex Aluminum 330 427-6704
1 Commerce Ave Leetonia (44431) (G-11863)
Pennslyvania Hill, Youngstown Also called Armada Fortress LLC (G-21027)
Penny Fab, Johnstown Also called Charles Ray Evans (G-11396)
Penny Printing Inc 330 645-2955
2957 S Main St Akron (44319) (G-334)
Pennzoil 10 Min Oil Change, Lebanon Also called Oil Etc Inc (G-11822)
Pentaflex Inc 937 325-5551
4981 Gateway Blvd Springfield (45502) (G-17626)
Pentagear Products LLC 937 660-8182
6161 Webster St Dayton (45414) (G-8569)
Pentagon Protection Usa LLC 614 734-7240
5500 Frantz Rd Ste 100 Dublin (43017) (G-9123)
Pentair Flow Technologies LLC (HQ) 419 289-1144
1101 Myers Pkwy Ashland (44805) (G-764)
Pentair Water, Ashland Also called Pentair Flow Technologies LLC (G-764)
Pentair Water Ashland Oper, Ashland Also called Flow Control US Holding Corp (G-733)
Penton Business Media Inc 216 696-7000
1100 Superior Ave E Fl 8 Cleveland (44114) (G-5990)
Penton Media Inc 216 696-7000
1300 E 9th St Ste 300 Cleveland (44114) (G-5991)
People's Defender, West Union Also called Brown Publishing Co (G-20118)
Peoples Bancorp Inc 740 685-1500
221 S 2nd St Byesville (43723) (G-2408)
Pep Brainin Fairfield Division, West Chester Also called Brainin-Advance Industries LLC (G-19821)
Pep Pony Express Printing Inc 513 542-4882
1645 Blue Rock St Cincinnati (45223) (G-4222)
Pepcon Concrete, Bradford Also called C F Poeppelman Inc (G-2025)
Pepi, North Canton Also called Portage Electric Products Inc (G-15259)
Pepperidge Farm Incorporated 419 933-2611
3320 State Route 103 E Willard (44890) (G-20399)
Pepperl + Fuchs (HQ) 330 425-3555
1600 Enterprise Pkwy Twinsburg (44087) (G-18997)
Pepsi-Cola Metro Btlg Co Inc 937 461-4664
526 Milburn Ave Dayton (45404) (G-8570)
Pepsi-Cola Metro Btlg Co Inc 614 261-8193
2553 N High St Columbus (43202) (G-7477)
Pepsi-Cola Metro Btlg Co Inc 330 963-0426
1999 Enterprise Pkwy Twinsburg (44087) (G-18998)
Pepsi-Cola Metro Btlg Co Inc 330 963-5300
1999 Enterprise Pkwy Twinsburg (44087) (G-18999)
Pepsi-Cola Metro Btlg Co Inc 419 534-2186
3245 Hill Ave Toledo (43607) (G-18638)
Pepsico, Franklin Furnace Also called G & J Pepsi-Cola Bottlers Inc (G-10069)
Pepsico, Chillicothe Also called G & J Pepsi-Cola Bottlers Inc (G-3239)
Pepsico, Cincinnati Also called P-Americas LLC (G-4207)
Pepsico, Columbus Also called Pepsi-Cola Metro Btlg Co Inc (G-7477)
Pepsico, Columbus Also called G & J Pepsi-Cola Bottlers Inc (G-7104)
Pepsico, Twinsburg Also called Pepsi-Cola Metro Btlg Co Inc (G-18999)
Pepsico, Toledo Also called Pepsi-Cola Metro Btlg Co Inc (G-18638)
Pepsico, Columbus Also called P-Americas LLC (G-7452)
Pepsico, Elyria Also called P-Americas LLC (G-9474)
Pepsico, Wadsworth Also called P-Americas LLC (G-19424)
Pepsico, Massillon Also called P-Americas LLC (G-13191)
Pepsico, Springfield Also called P-Americas LLC (G-17621)
Pepsico, Zanesville Also called G & J Pepsi-Cola Bottlers Inc (G-21313)
Pepsico, Youngstown Also called P-Americas LLC (G-21161)
Per-Tech Inc 330 833-8824
113 Erie St S Massillon (44646) (G-13193)
Percuvision LLC 614 891-4800
2030 Dividend Dr Columbus (43228) (G-7478)
Perennial Software Inc 440 247-5602
547 Washington St Ste 11 Chagrin Falls (44022) (G-3067)
Perez Foods LLC 419 264-0303
515 Richholt St Holgate (43527) (G-11039)
Perfect Measuring Tape Company 419 243-6811
1116 N Summit St Toledo (43604) (G-18639)
Perfect Packaging 419 662-1700
6959 Wales Rd Northwood (43619) (G-15487)

A
L
P
H
A
B
E
T
I
C

Perfect Prcision Machining Ltd............330 475-0324
920 Clay St Akron (44311) *(G-335)*

Perfect Probate............513 791-4100
2036 8 Mile Rd Cincinnati (45244) *(G-4223)*

Perfect Products Company............330 863-1466
265 Morges Rd Malvern (44644) *(G-12548)*

Perfect Score, The, Bedford Heights Also called Tpsc Inc *(G-1495)*

Perfect Solution, Cleveland Also called Natures Simple Solution Inc *(G-5862)*

Perfection Bakeries Inc............614 866-8171
6720 Commerce Court Dr Blacklick (43004) *(G-1703)*

Perfection Bakeries Inc............419 221-2359
1278 W Robb Ave Lima (45801) *(G-12068)*

Perfection Bakeries Inc............513 942-1442
374 Circle Freeway Dr C West Chester (45246) *(G-20035)*

Perfection Bakeries Inc............937 492-2220
1900 Progress Way Sidney (45365) *(G-17208)*

Perfection Fine Products, Cleveland Also called Great Western Juice Company *(G-5457)*

Perfection Finishers Inc............419 337-8015
1151 N Ottokee St Wauseon (43567) *(G-19693)*

Perfection Glass............614 920-0652
139 Pickerington Ridge Dr Pickerington (43147) *(G-16199)*

Perfection In Carbide, Canfield Also called Advetech Inc *(G-2543)*

Perfection Metal Co............216 641-0949
9416 Richmond Ave Cleveland (44105) *(G-5992)*

Perfection Mold & Machine Co............330 784-5435
2057 E Aurora Rd Ste Hi Twinsburg (44087) *(G-19000)*

Perfection Packaging Inc............614 866-8558
885 Claycraft Rd Gahanna (43230) *(G-10226)*

Perfection Printing............513 874-2173
9560 Le Saint Dr Fairfield (45014) *(G-9701)*

Perfections Fabricators Inc............440 365-5850
680 Sugar Ln Elyria (44035) *(G-9477)*

Perfecto Industries Inc............937 778-1900
1729 W High St Piqua (45356) *(G-16299)*

Perfettes Sausage LLC............330 792-0775
1264 S Schenley Ave Youngstown (44511) *(G-21169)*

Perform Metals Inc............440 286-1951
124 Industrial Pkwy Chardon (44024) *(G-3172)*

Performa La Mar Printing Inc............440 632-9800
15912 W High St Middlefield (44062) *(G-13981)*

Performace Diesel Inc............740 392-3693
16901 Mcvay Rd Mount Vernon (43050) *(G-14637)*

Performance Abrasives Inc............513 733-9283
10330 Wayne Ave Cincinnati (45215) *(G-4224)*

Performance Additives............330 365-9256
906 Cookson Ave Se New Philadelphia (44663) *(G-14922)*

Performance Electronics Ltd............513 777-5233
11529 Goldcoast Dr Cincinnati (45249) *(G-4225)*

Performance Lettering & Signs, Athens Also called Jacqueline L Vandyke *(G-874)*

Performance Motorsports............513 931-9999
2545 W Galbraith Rd Cincinnati (45239) *(G-4226)*

Performance Plastics Ltd............513 321-8404
4435 Brownway Ave Cincinnati (45209) *(G-4227)*

Performance Point Grinding............330 220-0871
1669 W 130th St Ste 302 Hinckley (44233) *(G-11028)*

Performance Research Inc............614 475-8300
3328 Westerville Rd Columbus (43224) *(G-7479)*

Performance Services............419 385-1236
828 Warehouse Rd Ste 8 Toledo (43615) *(G-18640)*

Performance Superabrasives LLC............440 946-7171
7255 Industrial Park Blvd A Mentor (44060) *(G-13685)*

Performance Technologies LLC............330 875-1216
3690 Tulane Ave Louisville (44641) *(G-12324)*

Performanx Specialty Chem LLC (PA)............614 300-7001
300 Westdale Ave Westerville (43082) *(G-20179)*

Performanx Specialty Chem LLC............614 300-7001
423 Hopewell Rd Waverly (45690) *(G-19716)*

Performnce Mtorsports Intl Inc, Mentor Also called PMI Operating Company Inc *(G-13690)*

Performnce Plymr Solutions Inc............937 298-3713
2711 Lance Dr Moraine (45409) *(G-14512)*

Perfume Counter............513 885-5989
11700 Princeton Pike Cincinnati (45246) *(G-4228)*

Perfusion Solutions Inc............216 848-1610
4320 Mayfield Rd Ste 108 Cleveland (44121) *(G-5993)*

Periflo/Px Pumps USA, Loveland Also called Fischer Global Enterprises LLC *(G-12349)*

Perimeter Technologies Inc............513 322-5453
7669 Wooster Pike C Cincinnati (45227) *(G-4229)*

Perkinelmer Hlth Sciences Inc............330 825-4525
520 S Main St Ste 2423 Akron (44311) *(G-336)*

Perkins & Marie Callenders LLC............513 881-7900
6880 Fairfield Bus Ctr Dr Fairfield (45014) *(G-9702)*

Perkins Logging LLC............740 288-7311
361 Perkins Rd Chillicothe (45601) *(G-3261)*

Perkins Motor Service Ltd (PA)............440 277-1256
1864 E 28th St Lorain (44055) *(G-12267)*

Perkins Wood Products............740 884-4046
8686 Limerick Rd Chillicothe (45601) *(G-3262)*

Perma-Fix of Dayton Inc............937 268-6501
300 Cherokee Dr Dayton (45417) *(G-8571)*

Permaguide............330 456-8519
2427 9th St Sw Canton (44710) *(G-2811)*

Permanent Impressions............740 892-3045
12182 Bruce Rd Utica (43080) *(G-19196)*

Permco Inc............330 626-2801
1500 Frost Rd Streetsboro (44241) *(G-17866)*

Permian Oil & Gas Division, Newark Also called National Gas & Oil Corporation *(G-15037)*

Perrons Printing Company............440 236-8870
27500 Royalton Rd Columbia Station (44028) *(G-6593)*

Perry County Tribune............740 342-4121
399 Lincoln Park Dr Ste A New Lexington (43764) *(G-14851)*

Perry Diesel Service, Akron Also called Manuel Tamargo *(G-282)*

Perry Service Co., Toledo Also called E W Perry Service Co Inc *(G-18448)*

Perry Welding Service Inc............330 425-2211
2075 Case Pkwy S Twinsburg (44087) *(G-19001)*

Perrysburg Messenger-Journal, Perrysburg Also called Welch Publishing Co *(G-16168)*

Personal Stitch Monogramming............440 282-7707
924 Amchester Dr Amherst (44001) *(G-605)*

Personnel Selection Services............440 835-3255
31517 Walker Rd Cleveland (44140) *(G-5994)*

Perstorp Polyols Inc............419 729-5448
600 Matzinger Rd Toledo (43612) *(G-18641)*

PES, Cincinnati Also called Burns & Rink Enterprises LLC *(G-3487)*

Pesce Baking Company Ltd............330 746-6537
45 N Hine St Youngstown (44506) *(G-21170)*

Peska Inc (PA)............440 998-4664
3600 N Ridge Rd E Ashtabula (44004) *(G-831)*

Pet Goods Mfg, Columbus Also called Tarahill Inc *(G-7676)*

Pet Processors LLC............440 354-4321
1350 Bacon Rd Painesville (44077) *(G-15911)*

Pet Stop, Cincinnati Also called Perimeter Technologies Inc *(G-4229)*

Pete Emmert Co............740 455-3924
5580 Pleasant Valley Rd Nashport (43830) *(G-14706)*

Pete Gaietto & Associates Inc............513 771-0903
1900 Section Rd Cincinnati (45237) *(G-4230)*

Peter Cremer North America LP (PA)............513 471-7200
3117 Southside Ave Cincinnati (45204) *(G-4231)*

Peter Graham Dunn Inc............330 816-0035
1417 Zuercher Rd Dalton (44618) *(G-8077)*

Peter LI Education Group, Moraine Also called Pjl Enterprise Inc *(G-14513)*

Peter Zaret & Sons Violins............440 461-1411
5767 Mayfield Rd Cleveland (44124) *(G-5995)*

Petermann............419 925-5404
8037 Marion Dr Maria Stein (45860) *(G-12760)*

Peters Cabinetry............937 884-7514
8766 N County Line Rd Brookville (45309) *(G-2196)*

Peters Family Enterprises Inc............419 339-0555
5959 Allentown Rd Elida (45807) *(G-9355)*

Peterson Heat Treating, Kent Also called H & S Steel Treating Inc *(G-11466)*

Peterson Radio Inc............937 549-3731
9711 Us Highway 52 Manchester (45144) *(G-12551)*

Petit Gourmet, Maumee Also called Twenty Second Cntury Foods LLC *(G-13305)*

Petnet Solutions Inc............865 218-2000
2139 Alburn Ave Cincinnati (45219) *(G-4232)*

Petnet Solutions Inc............865 218-2000
11100 Euclid Ave Cleveland (44106) *(G-5996)*

Petnet Solutions Cleveland LLC............865 218-2000
2035 E 86th St Rm Jb-122 Cleveland (44106) *(G-5997)*

Petprojekt, Cincinnati Also called Otomik Products Inc *(G-4199)*

Petro Evaluation Services Inc............330 264-4454
3927 Cleveland Rd Wooster (44691) *(G-20820)*

Petro Gear Corporation (PA)............216 431-2820
3901 Hamilton Ave Cleveland (44114) *(G-5998)*

Petro Quest Inc (PA)............740 593-3800
3 W Stimson Ave Athens (45701) *(G-881)*

Petro Ware Inc............740 982-1302
713 Keystone St Crooksville (43731) *(G-7953)*

Petroliance............614 475-5952
2854 Johnstown Rd Columbus (43219) *(G-7480)*

Petroliance LLC............216 441-7200
8500 Clinton Rd Ste 11 Cleveland (44144) *(G-5999)*

Petros Concrete Inc (PA)............330 868-6130
7105 Lardon Rd Nw Waynesburg (44688) *(G-19727)*

Petrox Inc............330 653-5526
10005 Ellsworth Rd Streetsboro (44241) *(G-17867)*

Petry Power Systems, Kent Also called P S P Inc *(G-11498)*

Pettigrew Pumping Inc............330 297-7900
4171 Sandy Lake Rd Ravenna (44266) *(G-16550)*

Pettisville Grain Co (PA)............419 446-2547
18251 County Road D E Pettisville (43553) *(G-16182)*

Pettisville Meats Inc............419 445-0921
3082 Main St Pettisville (43553) *(G-16183)*

Pettit W T & Sons Co Inc............330 539-6100
1670 Keefer Rd Girard (44420) *(G-10392)*

Pettits Pallets Inc............614 351-4920
11812 London Rd Derby (43117) *(G-8947)*

Pexco Packaging Corp............419 470-5935
795 Berdan Ave Toledo (43610) *(G-18642)*

Pf Management Inc 513 874-8741
  9990 Prnceton Glendale Rd West Chester (45246) *(G-20036)*

Pf Polymers LLC 567 712-7046
  1200 E Kibby St Lima (45804) *(G-12069)*

Pfahl Gauge & Manufacturing Co 330 633-8402
  665 Harden Ave Akron (44310) *(G-337)*

Pfaudler Inc 585 464-4872
  51 Plum St Ste 260 Beavercreek (45440) *(G-1378)*

Pfi Displays Inc (PA) 330 925-9015
  40 Industrial St Rittman (44270) *(G-16681)*

Pfi Precision Inc 937 845-3563
  2011 N Dayton Lakeview Rd New Carlisle (45344) *(G-14812)*

Pfi Precision Machining, New Carlisle *Also called Pfi Precision Inc (G-14812)*

Pfizer Inc 513 342-9056
  9878 Windisch Rd West Chester (45069) *(G-19913)*

Pfizer Inc 614 496-0990
  8192 Bibury Ln Dublin (43016) *(G-9124)*

Pfizer Inc 216 591-0642
  2000 Auburn Dr Ste 200 Beachwood (44122) *(G-1290)*

Pfizer Inc 937 746-3603
  160 Industrial Dr Franklin (45005) *(G-10044)*

Pfmi, West Chester *Also called Pf Management Inc (G-20036)*

Pfpc Enterprises Inc 513 941-6200
  5750 Hillside Ave Cincinnati (45233) *(G-4233)*

Pgc Feeds, Pettisville *Also called Pettisville Grain Co (G-16182)*

PGT Healthcare LLP (HQ) 513 983-1100
  1 Procter And Gamble Plz Cincinnati (45202) *(G-4234)*

Pgw, Crestline *Also called Pittsburgh Glass Works LLC (G-7934)*

Pgw Auto Glass LLC 419 993-2421
  2599 Ft Shawnee Ind Dr Lima (45804) *(G-12070)*

Phantasm Designs 419 538-6737
  112 W Main St Ottawa (45875) *(G-15804)*

Phantom Fireworks 740 927-6943
  10442 Outville Rd Millersport (43046) *(G-14296)*

Phantom Fireworks 740 927-6943
  10442 Outville Rd Millersport (43046) *(G-14297)*

Phantom Fireworks Inc 419 237-2185
  25840 Us Highway 20 Fayette (43521) *(G-9777)*

Phantom Sound 513 759-4477
  104 Reading Rd Mason (45040) *(G-13072)*

Pharmacia Hepar LLC 937 746-3603
  160 Industrial Dr Franklin (45005) *(G-10045)*

Pharmaforce Inc (HQ) 614 436-2222
  960 Crupper Ave Columbus (43229) *(G-7481)*

Pharmaforce Inc 614 436-2222
  4150 Lyman Ct Hilliard (43026) *(G-10969)*

Phase Array Company LLC 513 785-0801
  9365 Allen Rd West Chester (45069) *(G-19914)*

Phase II Enterprises Inc 330 484-2113
  2154 Bolivar Rd Sw Canton (44706) *(G-2812)*

Phase One, Dayton *Also called Poi Holdings Inc (G-8115)*

PHC Divison Bic Manufacturing, Euclid *Also called Precision Hydraulic Connectors (G-9601)*

PHD Manufacturing Inc 330 482-9256
  44018 Clmbana Wterford Rd Columbiana (44408) *(G-6628)*

Phg Retail Services, Cincinnati *Also called Jhg Retail Services LLC (G-3945)*

PHI Werkes LLC 419 586-9222
  1201 Havemann Rd Celina (45822) *(G-3014)*

Phil D De Mint 740 474-7777
  6345 State Route 56 E Circleville (43113) *(G-4636)*

Phil Matic Screw Products Inc 440 942-7290
  1457 E 357th St Willoughby (44095) *(G-20568)*

Phil Vedda & Sons Inc 216 671-2222
  12000 Berea Rd Cleveland (44111) *(G-6000)*

Phil's Custom Cabinets, Circleville *Also called Phil D De Mint (G-4636)*

Philadelphia Instantwhip Inc (HQ) 614 488-2536
  2200 Cardigan Ave Columbus (43215) *(G-7482)*

Philip Armbrust 740 335-7285
  4939 Branen Dr Wshngtn CT Hs (43160) *(G-20919)*

Philips Medical Systems Clevel (HQ) 440 247-2652
  595 Miner Rd Cleveland (44143) *(G-6001)*

Philips Medical Systems Clevel 440 473-3001
  8020 Tyler Blvd Mentor (44060) *(G-13686)*

Philips Medical Systems Mr 440 483-2499
  603 Alpha Dr Highland Heights (44143) *(G-10919)*

Phillips & Sons Welding & Fabg 440 428-1625
  6720 N Ridge Rd W Geneva (44041) *(G-10355)*

Phillips Awning Co 740 653-2433
  2052 W Fair Ave Lancaster (43130) *(G-11738)*

Phillips Companies (PA) 937 426-5461
  620 Phillips Dr Beavercreek Township (45434) *(G-1386)*

Phillips Companies 937 431-7987
  555 Old Springfield Rd Vandalia (45377) *(G-19308)*

Phillips Companies 937 426-5461
  620 Phillips Dr Beavercreek Township (45434) *(G-1387)*

Phillips Contractors Sup LLC 216 861-5730
  1800 E 30th St Cleveland (44114) *(G-6002)*

Phillips Electric Co 216 361-0014
  4126 Saint Clair Ave Cleveland (44103) *(G-6003)*

Phillips Manufacturing Co 330 652-4335
  504 Walnut St Niles (44446) *(G-15173)*

Phillips Mch & Stamping Corp 330 882-6714
  5290 S Main St New Franklin (44319) *(G-14829)*

Phillips Mfg & Mch Corp 330 823-9178
  118 1/2 E Ely St Alliance (44601) *(G-533)*

Phillips Mfg and Tower Co (PA) 419 347-1720
  5578 State Route 61 N Shelby (44875) *(G-17140)*

Phillips Packaging Inc 937 484-4702
  1050 Phoenix Dr Unit B Urbana (43078) *(G-19173)*

Phillips Ready Mix Co 937 426-5151
  620 Phillips Dr Beavercreek Township (45434) *(G-1388)*

Phillips Sand & Gravel Co, Beavercreek Township *Also called Phillips Companies (G-1387)*

Phillips Shtmtl Fabrications 937 223-2722
  1215 Ray St Dayton (45404) *(G-8572)*

Phillipsburg Quarry, Brookville *Also called Marietta Martin Materials Inc (G-2189)*

Philpott Indus Plas Entps Ltd 330 225-3344
  1010 Industrial Pkwy N Brunswick (44212) *(G-2242)*

Philpott Intl Entps Ltd, Brunswick *Also called Philpott Indus Plas Entps Ltd (G-2242)*

Philpott Rubber Company, Brunswick *Also called Philpott Rubber LLC (G-2243)*

Philpott Rubber LLC (PA) 330 225-3344
  1010 Industrial Pkwy N Brunswick (44212) *(G-2243)*

Philway Products Inc 419 281-7777
  521 E 7th St Ashland (44805) *(G-765)*

Phoenix Asphalt Company Inc 330 339-4935
  18025 Imperial Rd Magnolia (44643) *(G-12518)*

Phoenix Associates 440 543-9701
  16760 W Park Circle Dr Chagrin Falls (44023) *(G-3112)*

Phoenix Bat Company 614 873-7776
  7801 Corp Blvd Unit E Plain City (43064) *(G-16354)*

Phoenix Forge Group LLC 800 848-6125
  1501 W Main St West Jefferson (43162) *(G-20082)*

Phoenix Graphix Pubg Svcs LLC 740 587-3659
  444 N Pearl St Granville (43023) *(G-10465)*

Phoenix Hydraulic Presses Inc 614 850-8940
  4299 Reynolds Dr Hilliard (43026) *(G-10970)*

Phoenix Hydraulics and Contrls, South Point *Also called Michael N Wheeler (G-17442)*

Phoenix Industries & Apparatus 513 722-1085
  6466 Snider Rd Apt C Loveland (45140) *(G-12377)*

Phoenix Metal Fabricators, Dayton *Also called Phoenix Metal Works Inc (G-8573)*

Phoenix Metal Works Inc 937 274-5555
  2528 Ashcraft Rd Dayton (45414) *(G-8573)*

Phoenix Mold & Die, Elyria *Also called Kastler & Reichlin Inc (G-9445)*

Phoenix Partners LLC 734 654-2201
  3464 Brookside Rd Ottawa Hills (43606) *(G-15817)*

Phoenix Safety Outfitters Inc 614 361-0544
  1619 Commerce Rd Springfield (45504) *(G-17627)*

Phoenix Technologies Inc 330 630-5888
  825 E Tallmadge Ave Akron (44310) *(G-338)*

Phoenix Technologies Intl LLC 419 353-7738
  1098 Fairview Ave Bowling Green (43402) *(G-2007)*

Phoenix Tool & Thread Grindng 216 433-7008
  4760 Briar Rd Cleveland (44135) *(G-6004)*

Phoenix Tool Co Inc 330 372-4627
  1351 Phoenix Rd Ne Warren (44483) *(G-19586)*

Phoenix Trinity Mfg Inc 937 619-0172
  1883 Sthtown Blvd Ste 102 Dayton (45439) *(G-8574)*

Phoenix/Electrotek LLC 740 681-1412
  890 Mill Park Dr Lancaster (43130) *(G-11739)*

Phonak LLC 513 420-4568
  2951 Cincinnati Dayton Rd Middletown (45044) *(G-14074)*

Photo Journals, Sandusky *Also called Douthit Communications Inc (G-16958)*

Photo Star 419 495-2696
  307 State St Willshire (45898) *(G-20651)*

Photo-Type Engraving Company 614 308-1900
  2500 Harrison Rd Columbus (43204) *(G-7483)*

Photo-Type Engraving Company 614 308-7914
  2500 Harrison Rd Columbus (43204) *(G-7484)*

Phpk Technologies, Columbus *Also called Kendall Holdings Ltd (G-7255)*

Phymet Inc (PA) 937 743-8061
  75 N Pioneer Blvd Springboro (45066) *(G-17496)*

Piada Sawmill LLC 614 389-2069
  6495 Sawmill Rd Unit Ts Dublin (43017) *(G-9125)*

Pickens Window Service Inc 513 931-4432
  7824 Hamilton Ave Cincinnati (45231) *(G-4235)*

Picker Health Care Products, Mentor *Also called Philips Medical Systems Clevel (G-13686)*

Pickett Concrete, Chesapeake *Also called G Big Inc (G-3187)*

Pickett Concrete, Ironton *Also called G Big Inc (G-11293)*

Piece of Cake 614 421-0399
  772 N High St Ste 104 Columbus (43215) *(G-7485)*

Pieco Inc (PA) 419 422-5335
  2151 Industrial Dr Findlay (45840) *(G-9878)*

Pieco Inc 937 399-5100
  5225 Prosperity Dr Springfield (45502) *(G-17628)*

Piedmont Chemical Co Inc 937 428-6640
  1516 Silver Lake Dr Dayton (45458) *(G-8575)*

Pier Tool & Die Inc 440 236-3188
  27369 Royalton Rd Columbia Station (44028) *(G-6594)*

(PA)=Parent Co (HQ)=Headquarters (DH)=Div Headquarters

Pierce Ohio, Willoughby *Also called Plastic Fabrication Svcs Inc* *(G-20570)*

Pierce-Spafford Metals Co Inc................................800 421-3778
1000 Warren Ave Niles (44446) *(G-15174)*

Pierce-Wright Precision Inc..................................216 362-2870
13606 Enterprise Ave Cleveland (44135) *(G-6005)*

Pierre Holding Corp (HQ)......................................513 874-8741
9990 Prnceton Glendale Rd West Chester (45246) *(G-20037)*

Pierre's Ice Cream Company, Cleveland *Also called Royal Ice Cream Co* *(G-6139)*

Pierre's Quickprint, Sandusky *Also called Flemish Investments* *(G-16967)*

Pierres French Ice Cream Inc..............................216 431-2555
6519 Carnegie Ave Cleveland (44103) *(G-6006)*

Piersante and Associates....................................330 533-9904
230 Russo Dr Canfield (44406) *(G-2569)*

Pietra Naturale Inc..937 438-8882
9308 Dayton Lebanon Pike Dayton (45458) *(G-8576)*

Pike County Paper Inc..740 947-5522
14572 Us Highway 23 Ste C Waverly (45690) *(G-19717)*

Pike Machine Products Co....................................216 731-1880
23460 Lakeland Blvd Euclid (44132) *(G-9597)*

Pike Tool & Manufacturing Co..............................740 947-7462
754 W 2nd St Waverly (45690) *(G-19718)*

Piketon Sand & Gravel..740 289-2316
3293 Us Highway 23 Piketon (45661) *(G-16227)*

Piland Parts..330 686-3083
3215 Darrow Rd Stow (44224) *(G-17787)*

Pile Dynamics Inc..216 831-6131
30725 Aurora Rd Cleveland (44139) *(G-6007)*

Pilgrim-Harp Co..440 249-4185
35050 Avon Commerce Pkwy Avon (44011) *(G-1003)*

Pilington Libbey-Owens-Ford Co, Rossford *Also called Pilkington North America Inc* *(G-16745)*

Pilkington Holdings Inc (HQ)................................419 247-3731
811 Madison Ave Fl 1 Toledo (43604) *(G-18643)*

Pilkington North America Inc................................800 547-9280
2401 E Broadway St Northwood (43619) *(G-15488)*

Pilkington North America Inc................................419 247-3211
140 Dixie Hwy Rossford (43460) *(G-16745)*

Pilkington North America Inc................................419 247-3731
3440 Centerpoint Dr Ste C Urbancrest (43123) *(G-19190)*

Pilkington North America Inc (HQ)........................419 247-4955
811 Madison Ave Fl 1 Toledo (43604) *(G-18644)*

Pillsbury Company LLC..740 286-2170
2403 S Pennsylvania Ave Wellston (45692) *(G-19767)*

Pillsbury Company LLC..419 845-3751
4136 Martel Rd Caledonia (43314) *(G-2441)*

Pilorusso Construction Div, Lowellville *Also called Lyco Corporation* *(G-12410)*

Pilot Chemical, Newark *Also called CP Industries Inc* *(G-14997)*

Pilot Chemical Company Ohio (PA)........................513 326-0600
2744 E Kemper Rd Cincinnati (45241) *(G-4236)*

Pilot Chemical Company Ohio..............................513 733-4880
606 Shepherd Dr Cincinnati (45215) *(G-4237)*

Pilot Chemical Corp (HQ)....................................513 326-0600
2744 E Kemper Rd Cincinnati (45241) *(G-4238)*

Pilot Chemical Corp..513 424-9700
3439 Yankee Rd Middletown (45044) *(G-14075)*

Pilot Plastics Inc..330 920-1718
200 Cyhoga Fls Indus Pkwy Peninsula (44264) *(G-16041)*

Pilot Production Solutions LLC............................513 602-1467
6253 Crooked Creek Dr Mason (45040) *(G-13073)*

Pilot-Run Stamping Company................................440 255-8821
8209 Tyler Blvd Mentor (44060) *(G-13687)*

Pin Oak Development LLC....................................440 933-9862
32329 Orchard Park Dr Avon Lake (44012) *(G-1043)*

Pin Oak Estates Ltd..330 657-2727
581 Lake Of The Wods Blvd Akron (44333) *(G-339)*

Pin Point Marketing LLC......................................330 336-5863
302 Eric Ln Wadsworth (44281) *(G-19428)*

Pine Acres Woodcraft..330 852-0190
123 Pleasant Valley Rd Nw Sugarcreek (44681) *(G-18031)*

Pine Ridge Meat Processing, Fleming *Also called Pine Ridge Processing* *(G-9913)*

Pine Ridge Processing..740 749-3166
4559 Anderson Rd Fleming (45729) *(G-9913)*

Pine Top Inc..330 929-2492
1932 Akron Peninsula Rd Akron (44313) *(G-340)*

Pines Engineering, Wickliffe *Also called Ajax Tocco Magnethermic Corp* *(G-20352)*

Pines Manufacturing Inc (PA)..............................440 835-5553
29100 Lakeland Blvd Westlake (44145) *(G-20293)*

Pines Manufacturing Inc......................................440 835-5553
30505 Clemens Rd Westlake (44145) *(G-20294)*

Pines Technology, Westlake *Also called Pines Manufacturing Inc* *(G-20293)*

Pink Corner Office Inc..614 547-9350
8595 Columbus Pike Lewis Center (43035) *(G-11910)*

Pinky & Thumb LLC..614 939-5216
5216 Sugar Run Dr New Albany (43054) *(G-14769)*

Pinnacle Data Systems Inc (HQ)..........................614 748-1150
6600 Port Rd Ste 100 Groveport (43125) *(G-10641)*

Pinnacle Drilling LLC..330 276-1096
10420 County Road 620 Killbuck (44637) *(G-11597)*

Pinnacle Graphics & Imaging..............................216 781-1800
1138 W 9th St Ste LI Cleveland (44113) *(G-6008)*

Pinnacle Industrial Entps Inc..............................419 352-8688
513 Napoleon Rd Bowling Green (43402) *(G-2008)*

Pinnacle Metal Products, Columbus *Also called McNeil Group Inc* *(G-7338)*

Pinnacle Plastic Products, Bowling Green *Also called Pinnacle Industrial Entps Inc* *(G-2008)*

Pinnacle Precision Pdts LLC................................440 786-0248
624 Golden Oak Pkwy Bedford (44146) *(G-1453)*

Pinnacle Press Inc..330 453-7060
2960 Harrisburg Rd Ne Canton (44705) *(G-2813)*

Pinnacle Roller Co..513 369-4830
2147 Spring Grove Ave Cincinnati (45214) *(G-4239)*

Pinnacle Sales Inc..440 777-2544
159 Crocker Park Blvd # 400 Westlake (44145) *(G-20295)*

Pinney Dock & Transport LLC..............................440 964-7186
1149 E 5th St Ashtabula (44004) *(G-832)*

Pioneer Automotive Tech, Springboro *Also called Pioneer North America Inc* *(G-17498)*

Pioneer Automotive Tech Inc (HQ)........................937 746-2293
100 S Pioneer Blvd Springboro (45066) *(G-17497)*

Pioneer City Casting Company..............................740 423-7533
904 Campus Dr Belpre (45714) *(G-1593)*

Pioneer Custom Coating LLC................................419 737-3152
255 Industrial Ave Bldg D Pioneer (43554) *(G-16236)*

Pioneer Custom Molding Inc................................419 737-3252
3 Kexon Dr Pioneer (43554) *(G-16237)*

Pioneer Equipment Company................................330 857-6340
16875 Jericho Rd Dalton (44618) *(G-8078)*

Pioneer Fabrication..419 737-9464
17455 County Road P Alvordton (43501) *(G-558)*

Pioneer Forge Div, Pioneer *Also called Powers and Sons LLC* *(G-16240)*

Pioneer Hi-Bred Intl Inc......................................419 748-8051
15180 Henry Wood Rd Grand Rapids (43522) *(G-10443)*

Pioneer Homes Inc..419 737-2371
1018 Lakeshore Dr Pioneer (43554) *(G-16238)*

Pioneer Industrial Systems LLC (PA)....................419 737-9506
16442 Us Highway 20 Alvordton (43501) *(G-559)*

Pioneer Machine Inc..330 948-6500
104 S Prospect St Lodi (44254) *(G-12168)*

Pioneer National Latex Inc (HQ)..........................419 289-3300
246 E 4th St Ashland (44805) *(G-766)*

Pioneer North America Inc..................................937 746-6600
355 S Pioneer Blvd Springboro (45066) *(G-17498)*

Pioneer Pipe Inc..740 376-2400
2021 Hanna Rd Marietta (45750) *(G-12816)*

Pioneer Pipe Fabricating, Marietta *Also called Pioneer Pipe Inc* *(G-12816)*

Pioneer Plastics Corporation................................330 896-2356
3330 Massillon Rd Akron (44312) *(G-341)*

Pioneer Precision Tool Inc..................................513 932-8805
5100 Bunnell Hill Rd Lebanon (45036) *(G-11827)*

Pioneer Table Pad, Cleveland *Also called A & W Table Pad Co* *(G-4667)*

Pioneer Transformer Company..............................419 737-2304
500 Cedar St Pioneer (43554) *(G-16239)*

PIP and Huds LLC..740 208-5519
334 2nd Ave Gallipolis (45631) *(G-10307)*

PIP Printing, Columbus *Also called Preisser Inc* *(G-7514)*

PIP Printing, Mentor *Also called Ultra Impressions Inc* *(G-13758)*

PIP Printing..440 951-2606
35401 Euclid Ave Ste 109 Willoughby (44094) *(G-20569)*

Pipe Coil Technology Inc......................................330 256-6070
111 Cardington Ln Burbank (44214) *(G-2367)*

Pipe Line Development Company............................440 871-5700
870 Canterbury Rd Westlake (44145) *(G-20296)*

Pipe Products Inc (HQ)..513 587-7532
5122 Rialto Rd West Chester (45069) *(G-19915)*

Pipeline Automation Syste Inc..............................419 462-8833
215 Harding Way W Galion (44833) *(G-10282)*

Pipeline Dept, Oregon *Also called Standard Oil Company* *(G-15718)*

Pipelines Inc..330 448-0000
7800 Addison Rd Masury (44438) *(G-13215)*

Piqua Champion Foundry Inc................................937 773-3375
918 S Main St Piqua (45356) *(G-16300)*

Piqua Chocolate Company Inc (PA)........................937 773-1981
310 Spring St Piqua (45356) *(G-16301)*

Piqua Concrete Corp..937 855-0410
9151 Township Park Dr Germantown (45327) *(G-10372)*

Piqua Concrete Corp (PA)....................................937 773-0841
8395 Piqua Lockington Rd Piqua (45356) *(G-16302)*

Piqua Concrete Corp..937 698-7229
555 Old Springfield Rd Vandalia (45377) *(G-19309)*

Piqua Emery Cutter & Fndry Co............................937 773-4134
821 S Downing St Piqua (45356) *(G-16303)*

Piqua Emery Foundry, Piqua *Also called Piqua Emery Cutter & Fndry Co* *(G-16303)*

Piqua Granite & Marble Co Inc (PA)......................937 773-2000
123 N Main St Piqua (45356) *(G-16304)*

Piqua Materials Inc..937 773-4824
1750 W Statler Rd Piqua (45356) *(G-16305)*

Piqua Materials Inc (PA)......................................513 771-0820
11641 Mosteller Rd Ste 1 Cincinnati (45241) *(G-4240)*

Piqua Mineral Division, Piqua *Also called Piqua Materials Inc* *(G-16305)*

Piqua Paper Box Company..................................937 773-0313
616 Covington Ave Piqua (45356) *(G-16306)*

Piqua Sign, Piqua Also called Jerry Pulfer *(G-16283)*

Pique Stripping Division, Moraine Also called Rack Processing Company Inc *(G-14522)*

Pirtek Reading Road, Cincinnati Also called Encore Distributing Inc *(G-3702)*

Piston Automotive LLC..................................419 464-0250
1212 E Alexis Rd Toledo (43612) *(G-18645)*

Piston Group, Toledo Also called Piston Automotive LLC *(G-18645)*

Pita Wrap LLC..................................330 886-8091
4721 Market St Boardman (44512) *(G-1922)*

Pitco Products Inc..................................513 228-7245
120 N Terry St Dayton (45403) *(G-8577)*

Pitney Bowes Inc..................................203 426-7025
6910 Treeline Dr Ste C Brecksville (44141) *(G-2069)*

Pitney Bowes Inc..................................740 374-5535
111 Marshall Rd Marietta (45750) *(G-12817)*

Pitt Plastics Inc (HQ)..................................614 868-8660
3980 Groves Rd Ste A Columbus (43232) *(G-7486)*

Pittsburgh Glass Works LLC..................................419 683-2400
5066 Lincoln Hwy Crestline (44827) *(G-7933)*

Pittsburgh Glass Works LLC..................................419 569-7521
5064 Lincoln Hwy Crestline (44827) *(G-7934)*

Pittsburgh Glass Works LLC..................................740 774-7600
848 Southern Ave Chillicothe (45601) *(G-3263)*

Pixslap Inc..................................937 559-2671
1634 Central Ave Middletown (45044) *(G-14076)*

Pixuru, Akron Also called Canvas 123 Inc *(G-108)*

Pizzazz, Wooster Also called Just Basic Sports Inc *(G-20793)*

PJ Bush Associates Inc..................................216 362-6700
15901 Industrial Pkwy Cleveland (44135) *(G-6009)*

Pj Woodwork LLC..................................419 886-0008
16 E Ogle St Bellville (44813) *(G-1574)*

Pj's, Canton Also called PJs Fabricating Inc *(G-2814)*

Pjl Enterprise Inc (HQ)..................................937 293-1415
3055 Kettering Blvd # 100 Moraine (45439) *(G-14513)*

Pjl Enterprise Inc..................................937 293-1415
2019 Springboro W Moraine (45439) *(G-14514)*

Pjs Corrugated Inc..................................419 644-3383
2330 Us Highway 20 Swanton (43558) *(G-18087)*

PJs Fabricating Inc..................................330 478-1120
1511 Linwood Ave Sw Canton (44710) *(G-2814)*

Pjs Towing Inc..................................330 478-1120
1511 Linwood Ave Sw Canton (44710) *(G-2815)*

Pjs Wholesale Inc..................................614 402-9363
2551 Westbelt Dr Columbus (43228) *(G-7487)*

Pkg Technologies Inc..................................513 967-2783
212 N Broadway St Ste 7 Lebanon (45036) *(G-11828)*

Pki Inc..................................859 291-8680
4500 Reading Rd Cincinnati (45229) *(G-4241)*

Plabell Rubber Products Corp (PA)..................................419 691-5878
300 S Saint Clair St # 324 Toledo (43604) *(G-18646)*

Placecrete Inc..................................937 298-2121
2475 Arbor Blvd Moraine (45439) *(G-14515)*

Plain City Molding, Plain City Also called GK Packaging Inc *(G-16342)*

Plain Dealer Publishing Co (HQ)..................................216 999-5000
4800 Tiedeman Rd Cleveland (44144) *(G-6010)*

Plain Dealer Publishing Co..................................614 228-8200
155 E Broad St Fl 23 Columbus (43215) *(G-7488)*

Plain Dealer Publishing Co..................................216 999-5000
4800 Tiedeman Rd Cleveland (44144) *(G-6011)*

Plain Dealer, The, Cleveland Also called Plain Dealer Publishing Co *(G-6010)*

Plains Precut Ltd..................................330 893-3300
4917 County Road 207 Millersburg (44654) *(G-14255)*

Plan B Toys Ltd..................................614 751-6605
4036 London Lancaster Rd Groveport (43125) *(G-10642)*

Planet Friendly Polymers, Lima Also called Pf Polymers LLC *(G-12069)*

Plank and Hide Co..................................513 378-3194
721a E Sharon Rd Cincinnati (45241) *(G-4242)*

Plant 101, Stow Also called Dupont Prfmce Elastomers LLC *(G-17744)*

Plant 105, Akron Also called Dupont Prfmce Elastomers LLC *(G-158)*

Plant 2, Ashtabula Also called Iten Industries Inc *(G-813)*

Plant 2, Wooster Also called Wooster Products Inc *(G-20851)*

Plant 2, Columbus Also called Fred D Pfening Company *(G-7100)*

Plant 25, Lima Also called Metokote Corporation *(G-12055)*

Plant 5, Dayton Also called Oerlikon Friction Systems *(G-8541)*

Plant 8, Sugarcreek Also called Belden Brick Company LLC *(G-18017)*

Plant Maintenance Engineering, Cincinnati Also called New Pme Inc *(G-4148)*

Plant Two, Cleveland Also called Falls Stamping & Welding Co *(G-5323)*

Plas-Mac Corp..................................440 349-3222
30250 Carter St Solon (44139) *(G-17361)*

Plas-Tanks Industries Inc (PA)..................................513 942-3800
39 Standen Dr Hamilton (45015) *(G-10730)*

Plas-TEC Corp..................................419 272-2731
601 W Indiana St Edon (43518) *(G-9343)*

Plaskolite Inc..................................740 450-1109
1175 5 Bs Dr Zanesville (43701) *(G-21341)*

Plaskolite Continental, Columbus Also called Plaskolite LLC *(G-7489)*

Plaskolite LLC (PA)..................................614 294-3281
1770 Joyce Ave Columbus (43219) *(G-7489)*

Plaskolite LLC..................................614 294-7294
1770 Joyce Ave Columbus (43219) *(G-7490)*

Plasmacare Inc..................................614 231-5322
3840 E Main St Columbus (43213) *(G-7491)*

Plaster Process Castings Co..................................216 663-1814
19800 Miles Rd Cleveland (44128) *(G-6012)*

Plastex Industries Inc..................................419 531-0189
4050 South Ave Toledo (43615) *(G-18647)*

Plasti-Kemm Inc..................................330 239-1555
2805 Stony Hill Rd Medina (44256) *(G-13458)*

Plasti-Kote Co Inc (HQ)..................................330 725-4511
1000 Lake Rd Medina (44256) *(G-13459)*

Plastic Card Inc (PA)..................................330 896-5555
3711 Boettler Oaks Dr Uniontown (44685) *(G-19093)*

Plastic Color Division, Minerva Also called General Color Investments Inc *(G-14322)*

Plastic Compounders Inc..................................740 432-7371
1125 Utica Dr Cambridge (43725) *(G-2472)*

Plastic Enterprises Inc (PA)..................................440 324-3240
41520 Schadden Rd Elyria (44035) *(G-9478)*

Plastic Extrusion Technologies..................................440 632-5611
15229 S State Ave Middlefield (44062) *(G-13982)*

Plastic Fabrication Svcs Inc..................................440 953-9990
38167 Airport Pkwy Unit 1 Willoughby (44094) *(G-20570)*

Plastic Forming Company Inc..................................330 830-5167
201 Vista Ave Se Massillon (44646) *(G-13194)*

Plastic Materials Inc (PA)..................................330 468-5706
775 Highland Rd E Macedonia (44056) *(G-12472)*

Plastic Materials Inc..................................330 468-0184
775 Highland Rd E Macedonia (44056) *(G-12473)*

Plastic Mold Technology Inc..................................330 848-4921
40 Stuver Pl Barberton (44203) *(G-1139)*

Plastic Moldings Company Llc (PA)..................................513 921-5040
9825 Kenwood Rd Ste 302 Blue Ash (45242) *(G-1851)*

Plastic Partners LLC..................................425 765-2416
1801 Newgarden Rd Salem (44460) *(G-16919)*

Plastic Platers LLC..................................216 961-1200
9921 Clinton Rd Cleveland (44144) *(G-6013)*

Plastic Process Equipment Inc (PA)..................................216 367-7000
8303 Corporate Park Dr Macedonia (44056) *(G-12474)*

Plastic Products and Supply..................................330 744-5076
1305 Lilac St Youngstown (44502) *(G-21171)*

Plastic Regrinders Inc..................................740 659-2346
3161 Cooperriders Rd Nw Glenford (43739) *(G-10399)*

Plastic Selection Group Inc (PA)..................................614 464-2008
692 N High St Ste 310 Columbus (43215) *(G-7492)*

Plastic Suppliers Inc (PA)..................................614 471-9100
2450 Marilyn Ln Columbus (43219) *(G-7493)*

Plastic Suppliers Inc..................................614 475-8010
2400 Marilyn Ln Columbus (43219) *(G-7494)*

Plastic Suppliers Inc..................................614 475-8010
2450 Marilyn Ln Columbus (43219) *(G-7495)*

Plastic Works Inc (PA)..................................419 433-6576
10502 Mudbrook Rd Huron (44839) *(G-11237)*

Plastic Works Inc..................................440 331-5575
19851 Ingersoll Dr Cleveland (44116) *(G-6014)*

Plastic-Kemm, Medina Also called Plasti-Kemm Inc *(G-13458)*

Plasticards Inc (PA)..................................330 896-5555
3711 Boettler Oaks Dr Uniontown (44685) *(G-19094)*

Plastics Converting Solutions..................................330 722-2537
5341 River Styx Rd Medina (44256) *(G-13460)*

Plastics Division, Stow Also called Esterle Mold & Machine Co Inc *(G-17748)*

Plastics Group Inc..................................630 325-1210
2101 Cedar St Fremont (43420) *(G-10175)*

Plastics Machinery Magazine, Peninsula Also called Peninsula Publishing LLC *(G-16040)*

Plastics Mentor LLC..................................440 352-1357
6160 Brownstone Ct Mentor (44060) *(G-13688)*

Plastiform Tool & Die, Port Clinton Also called Rexles Inc *(G-16411)*

Plastigraphics Inc..................................513 771-8848
722 Redna Ter Cincinnati (45215) *(G-4243)*

Plastikos Corporation..................................513 732-0961
700 Kent Rd Batavia (45103) *(G-1216)*

Plastipak Packaging Inc..................................330 725-0205
850 W Smith Rd Medina (44256) *(G-13461)*

Plastipak Packaging Inc..................................937 596-6142
18015 State Route 65 Jackson Center (45334) *(G-11344)*

Plastipak Packaging Inc..................................740 928-4435
610 O Neill Dr Bldg 22 Hebron (43025) *(G-10880)*

Plastipak Packaging Inc..................................937 596-5166
300 Washington St Jackson Center (45334) *(G-11345)*

Plasto-Tech Corporation..................................440 323-6300
708 Lowell St Elyria (44035) *(G-9479)*

Plastran Inc..................................440 237-8404
9841 York Alpha Dr Ste N Cleveland (44133) *(G-6015)*

Plate Engraving Corporation..................................330 239-2155
2324 Sharon Copley Rd Medina (44256) *(G-13462)*

Plate-All Metal Company Inc..................................330 633-6166
1210 Devalera St Akron (44310) *(G-342)*

Platform Beers LLC 440 539-3245
4125 Lorain Ave Cleveland (44113) *(G-6016)*
Plating Perceptions Inc 330 425-4180
8815 Herrick Rd Twinsburg (44087) *(G-19002)*
Plating Process Systems Inc 440 951-9667
7561 Tyler Blvd Ste 5 Mentor (44060) *(G-13689)*
Plating Resources Supply 330 908-3949
573 Highland Rd E Ste 7 Macedonia (44056) *(G-12475)*
Plating Solutions 513 771-1941
871 Redna Ter Cincinnati (45215) *(G-4244)*
Plating Technology Inc (PA) 937 268-6882
1525 W River Rd Dayton (45417) *(G-8578)*
Plating Technology Inc 937 268-6788
1525 W River Rd Dayton (45417) *(G-8579)*
Plating Test Cell Supply Co 216 486-8400
948 Wayside Rd B Cleveland (44110) *(G-6017)*
Platinum Productions Inc 614 888-7771
8100 N High St Columbus (43235) *(G-7496)*
Play All LLC 440 992-7529
4542 Main Ave Ashtabula (44004) *(G-833)*
Play Mor, Millersburg *Also called Hershberger Lawn Structures (G-14221)*
Playall Trophies & Awards, Ashtabula *Also called Play All LLC (G-833)*
Playground Equipment Service 513 481-3776
2980 Diehl Rd Cincinnati (45211) *(G-4245)*
Playtex Manufacturing Inc 937 498-4710
1905 Progress Way Sidney (45365) *(G-17209)*
Plaza At Sawmill Pl 614 889-6121
6472 Sawmill Rd Columbus (43235) *(G-7497)*
PLC Connections, Columbus *Also called Plcc2 LLC (G-7499)*
PLC Connections LLC 614 279-1796
673 N Wilson Rd Columbus (43204) *(G-7498)*
Plcc2 LLC 614 279-1796
673 N Wilson Rd Columbus (43204) *(G-7499)*
Pleasant Valley Ready Mix Inc 330 852-2613
559 Pleasant Valley Rd Nw Sugarcreek (44681) *(G-18032)*
Pleasant Valley Wdwkg LLC 440 636-5860
13424 Clay St Middlefield (44062) *(G-13983)*
Pleasant Vly Tardrop Trlrs LLC 330 752-4425
754 Edelweiss Dr Ne Sugarcreek (44681) *(G-18033)*
Plextrusions Inc 330 668-2587
38870 Taylor Pkwy North Ridgeville (44035) *(G-15394)*
Plibrico Company LLC 740 682-7755
454 County Road 33 Oak Hill (45656) *(G-15604)*
Plidco Ppline Repr Ppline Mint, Westlake *Also called Pipe Line Development Company (G-20296)*
Plott Graphic Directions Inc 614 475-0217
859 Harmony Dr Columbus (43230) *(G-7500)*
Pluggers Inc 330 383-7692
1617 Warren Ave Niles (44446) *(G-15175)*
Plus Mark LLC 216 252-6770
1 American Rd Cleveland (44144) *(G-6018)*
Plus Publications Inc 740 345-5542
57 S 3rd St Newark (43055) *(G-15046)*
Plx Industries Inc 330 896-7373
1505 Corporate Woods Pkwy # 500 Uniontown (44685) *(G-19095)*
Ply Gem Industries Inc 937 492-1111
2600 Campbell Rd Sidney (45365) *(G-17210)*
Plymouth Foam Incorporated 740 254-1188
1 Souther Gateway St Gnadenhutten (44629) *(G-10410)*
Plymouth Healthcare Pdts LLC 440 542-0762
6521 Davis Indus Pkwy Solon (44139) *(G-17362)*
Plymouth Locomotive Svc LLC 419 896-2854
48 E Main St Shiloh (44878) *(G-17152)*
Plymouth Locomotive Svc LLC 419 896-2854
8118 Shiloh Norwalk Rd Shiloh (44878) *(G-17153)*
PM Coal Company LLC 440 256-7624
9717 Chillicothe Rd Willoughby (44094) *(G-20571)*
PM Company, West Chester *Also called Pmco LLC (G-19916)*
PM Graphics Inc 330 650-0861
10170 Philipp Pkwy Streetsboro (44241) *(G-17868)*
PM Motor Fan Blade Company, North Ridgeville *Also called Beckett Air Incorporated (G-15359)*
PMC Acquisitions Inc (PA) 419 429-0042
2040 Industrial Dr Findlay (45840) *(G-9879)*
PMC Gage Inc (PA) 440 953-1672
38383 Willoughby Pkwy Willoughby (44094) *(G-20572)*
PMC Industries Corp 440 943-3300
29100 Lakeland Blvd Wickliffe (44092) *(G-20383)*
PMC Lonestar, Willoughby *Also called PMC Gage Inc (G-20572)*
PMC Mercury (PA) 440 953-3300
38383 Willoughby Pkwy Willoughby (44094) *(G-20573)*
PMC Smart Solutions LLC 513 921-5040
9825 Kenwood Rd Ste 300 Blue Ash (45242) *(G-1852)*
PMC Specialties Group Inc (HQ) 513 242-3300
501 Murray Rd Cincinnati (45217) *(G-4246)*
PMC Specialties Group Inc 513 242-3300
5220 Vine St Cincinnati (45217) *(G-4247)*
PMC Systems Limited 330 538-2268
12155 Commissioner Dr North Jackson (44451) *(G-15297)*
Pmco LLC 513 825-7626
9220 Glades Dr West Chester (45011) *(G-19916)*
Pmd Enterprises Inc 440 546-0901
6100 W Snowville Rd Brecksville (44141) *(G-2070)*
PME of Ohio Inc (PA) 513 671-1717
518 W Crescentville Rd Cincinnati (45246) *(G-4248)*
PME- Babbit Bearings, Cincinnati *Also called PME of Ohio Inc (G-4248)*
PMI, Macedonia *Also called Plastic Materials Inc (G-12473)*
PMI Operating Company Inc (HQ) 440 951-6600
7201 Industrial Park Blvd Mentor (44060) *(G-13690)*
Pmj Partners LLC 201 360-1914
281 Lenappe Dr Columbus (43214) *(G-7501)*
PMS, Norton *Also called Packaging Materials Svcs LLC (G-15520)*
Pneumatic Parts Co 330 923-6063
888 Hampshire Rd Stow (44224) *(G-17788)*
Pneumatic Scale Angelus, Cuyahoga Falls *Also called Pneumatic Scale Corporation (G-8033)*
Pneumatic Scale Corporation (HQ) 330 923-0491
10 Ascot Pkwy Cuyahoga Falls (44223) *(G-8033)*
Podnar Plastics Inc 330 673-2255
343 Portage Blvd Unit 3 Kent (44240) *(G-11501)*
Podnar Plastics Inc (PA) 330 673-2255
1510 Mogadore Rd Kent (44240) *(G-11502)*
Poet Biorefining-Leipsic, Leipsic *Also called Summit Ethanol LLC (G-11877)*
Poet Borefining- Marion 22200, Marion *Also called Marion Ethanol LLC (G-12882)*
Poet Brfining- Fostoria 23200, Fostoria *Also called Fostoria Ethanol LLC (G-9975)*
Pohl Machining Inc 513 353-2929
4901 Hamilton Cleves Rd Cleves (45002) *(G-6522)*
Poi Holdings Inc (HQ) 937 253-7377
3203 Plainfield Rd Dayton (45432) *(G-8115)*
Point Five Golf Co, Loveland *Also called Bay Island Company Inc (G-12341)*
Point Source Inc 937 855-6020
7996 Butter St Germantown (45327) *(G-10373)*
Poland Concrete Products Inc (PA) 330 757-1241
70 Poland Mnr Poland (44514) *(G-16384)*
Poland Print Shop, North Lima *Also called Print Factory Pll (G-15321)*
Polar Inc 937 297-0911
2297 N Moraine Dr Moraine (45439) *(G-14516)*
Polar Air, Englewood *Also called Eaton Comprsr Fabrication Inc (G-9518)*
Polar Products Inc 330 253-9973
3380 Cavalier Trl Stow (44224) *(G-17789)*
Polaris Industries Inc 937 283-1200
3435 Airborne Rd Ste A Wilmington (45177) *(G-20673)*
Polaris Technologies, Youngstown *Also called Modern Builders Supply Inc (G-21147)*
Polarx Ornaments LLC 866 298-0433
35490 Lorain Rd North Ridgeville (44039) *(G-15395)*
Pole/Zero Acquisition Inc 513 870-9060
5558 Union Centre Dr West Chester (45069) *(G-19917)*
Polgenix Inc 440 537-9691
11000 Cedar Ave Ste 100 Cleveland (44106) *(G-6019)*
Polhe Tool Inc 419 476-2433
312 W Laskey Rd Toledo (43612) *(G-18648)*
Polimeros Usa LLC 216 591-0162
26210 Emery Rd Ste 202 Warrensville Heights (44128) *(G-19634)*
Poling Group, Akron *Also called Akron Steel Fabricators Co (G-57)*
Poling Group, The, Akron *Also called Akron Special Machinery Inc (G-55)*
Polka DOT Pin Cushion Inc 330 659-0233
3807 Brecksville Rd Ste 8 Richfield (44286) *(G-16632)*
Polkadot Cupcakery Limited 614 304-1368
2926 Hayden Run Plz Columbus (43235) *(G-7502)*
Pollock Research & Design Inc 330 332-3300
1134 Salem Pkwy Salem (44460) *(G-16920)*
Poly Concepts LLC 419 678-3300
712 Ash St Saint Henry (45883) *(G-16821)*
Poly Flex, Baltic *Also called Flex Technologies Inc (G-1071)*
Poly Green Technologies LLC 419 529-9909
1237 W 4th St Ontario (44906) *(G-15694)*
Poly Products Inc 216 391-7659
837 E 79th St Cleveland (44103) *(G-6020)*
Poly TEC East Inc 330 799-7876
550 N Meridian Rd Youngstown (44509) *(G-21172)*
Poly Works 419 678-3758
4830 State Route 219 Coldwater (45828) *(G-6569)*
Poly-Carb Inc 440 248-1223
8440 Tower Dr Twinsburg (44087) *(G-19003)*
Poly-Met Inc 330 630-9006
1997 Nolt Dr Akron (44312) *(G-343)*
Polycase Division, Avon *Also called Ecp Corporation (G-994)*
Polycel Incorporated 614 252-2400
1633 Woodland Ave Columbus (43219) *(G-7503)*
Polychem Corporation (PA) 440 357-1500
6277 Heisley Rd Mentor (44060) *(G-13691)*
Polychem Corporation 440 357-1500
7214 Justin Way Mentor (44060) *(G-13692)*
Polychem Corporation 419 547-1400
202 Watertower Dr Clyde (43410) *(G-6543)*
Polychem Dispersions Inc 800 545-3530
16066 Industrial Pkwy Middlefield (44062) *(G-13984)*

Polycraft Products Inc 513 353-3334
5511 Hamilton Cleves Rd Cleves (45002) ***(G-6523)***
Polyfill LLC 937 493-0041
960 N Vandemark Rd Sidney (45365) ***(G-17211)***
Polyflex LLC 440 946-0758
4803 E 345th St Willoughby (44094) ***(G-20574)***
Polygon Spaceship 440 506-0403
5536 Linn Dr Amherst (44001) ***(G-606)***
Polygon Spaceship Games, Amherst *Also called Polygon Spaceship* ***(G-606)***
Polygroup Inc 877 476-5972
2808 Millbank Row Maineville (45039) ***(G-12531)***
Polymer & Steel Tech Inc 440 510-0108
34899 Curtis Blvd Eastlake (44095) ***(G-9285)***
Polymer Additives Inc (HQ) 216 875-7200
7500 E Pleasant Valley Rd Independence (44131) ***(G-11269)***
Polymer Additives Inc 216 262-7016
7050 Krick Rd Walton Hills (44146) ***(G-19475)***
Polymer Additives Holdings Inc (PA) 216 875-7200
7500 E Pleasant Valley Rd Independence (44131) ***(G-11270)***
Polymer Concepts Inc 440 953-9605
7555 Tyler Blvd Ste 1 Mentor (44060) ***(G-13693)***
Polymer Packaging Inc (PA) 330 832-2000
8333 Navarre Rd Se Massillon (44646) ***(G-13195)***
Polymer Protective Packaging, Massillon *Also called Polymer Packaging Inc* ***(G-13195)***
Polymer Steel Corp 330 562-6906
1818 Miller Pkwy Streetsboro (44241) ***(G-17869)***
Polymer Tech & Svcs Inc 740 929-5500
1835 James Pkwy Heath (43056) ***(G-10851)***
Polymerics Inc (PA) 330 434-6665
2828 2nd St Cuyahoga Falls (44221) ***(G-8034)***
Polymerics Inc 330 677-1131
1540 Saint Clair Ave Kent (44240) ***(G-11503)***
Polymers By Design LLC 937 361-7398
2150 Monroe Concord Rd Troy (45373) ***(G-18863)***
Polymet Corporation 513 874-3586
10073 Commerce Park Dr West Chester (45246) ***(G-20038)***
Polynew Inc 330 897-3202
3557 State Route 93 Baltic (43804) ***(G-1076)***
Polynt Composites USA Inc 816 391-6000
1321 1st St Sandusky (44870) ***(G-16997)***
Polyone Corporation 419 668-4844
80 Northwest St Norwalk (44857) ***(G-15559)***
Polyone Corporation 937 548-1395
1050 Landsdowne Ave Greenville (45331) ***(G-10513)***
Polyone Corporation 740 423-7571
2419 State Route 618 Belpre (45714) ***(G-1594)***
Polyone Corporation 573 468-6513
733 E Water St North Baltimore (45872) ***(G-15196)***
Polyone Corporation 440 930-1000
552 Moore Rd Avon Lake (44012) ***(G-1044)***
Polyone Corporation 440 930-3754
554 Moore Rd Bldg 482 Avon Lake (44012) ***(G-1045)***
Polyone Corporation 216 622-0100
680 N Rocky River Dr Berea (44017) ***(G-1632)***
Polyone Corporation 440 933-2000
33587 Walker Rd Avon Lake (44012) ***(G-1046)***
Polyone Corporation 440 930-1000
733 E Water St North Baltimore (45872) ***(G-15197)***
Polyone Corporation 800 727-4338
1050 Landsdowne Ave Greenville (45331) ***(G-10514)***
Polyone Corporation 937 548-2133
1050 Landsdowne Ave Greenville (45331) ***(G-10515)***
Polyone Corporation 330 834-3812
1675 Navarre Rd Se Massillon (44646) ***(G-13196)***
Polyone Corporation (PA) 440 930-1000
33587 Walker Rd Avon Lake (44012) ***(G-1047)***
Polyone Corporation 419 399-4050
925 W Gasser Rd Paulding (45879) ***(G-16013)***
Polyshield Corporation 614 755-7674
8643 Chateau Dr Pickerington (43147) ***(G-16200)***
Polystar Inc 234 678-9020
1676 Commerce Dr Stow (44224) ***(G-17790)***
Polystar Inc 330 963-5100
2030 Midway Dr Twinsburg (44087) ***(G-19004)***
Polytech Component Corp 330 726-3235
8469 Southern Blvd Youngstown (44512) ***(G-21173)***
Poma GL Specialty Windows Inc 330 965-1000
365 Mcclurg Rd Ste E Boardman (44512) ***(G-1923)***
Pomacon Inc 330 273-1576
2996 Interstate Pkwy Brunswick (44212) ***(G-2244)***
Pompili Precast Concrete, Cleveland *Also called E Pompili & Sons Inc* ***(G-5233)***
Ponderosa Consulting Services (PA) 330 264-2298
4060 Millbrook Rd Wooster (44691) ***(G-20821)***
Pooles Printing & Office Svcs 419 475-9000
4036 Monroe St Toledo (43606) ***(G-18649)***
Pop A Top Cruise Thru 419 947-5855
157 S Main St Mount Gilead (43338) ***(G-14565)***
Pop/Pos Advantage 440 543-9452
17911 Snyder Rd Ste A Chagrin Falls (44023) ***(G-3113)***
Popped 330 678-1893
175 E Erie St Ste 201 Kent (44240) ***(G-11504)***
Poppos Advantage Group, Chagrin Falls *Also called Pop/Pos Advantage* ***(G-3113)***
Pops Printed Apparel LLC 614 372-5651
1758 N High St Unit 2 Columbus (43201) ***(G-7504)***
Porath Business Services Inc 216 626-0060
21000 Miles Pkwy Cleveland (44128) ***(G-6021)***
Porath Printing, Cleveland *Also called Porath Business Services Inc* ***(G-6021)***
Porcelain Enamels, Cleveland *Also called Ferro Corporation* ***(G-5336)***
Porkbelly Bbq, Bowling Green *Also called Roare-Q LLC* ***(G-2014)***
Porocel Industries LLC (PA) 513 733-8519
1 Landy Ln Cincinnati (45215) ***(G-4249)***
Port Clinton Manufacturing LLC 419 734-2141
328 W Perry St Port Clinton (43452) ***(G-16409)***
Porta-Kleen, Lancaster *Also called Pro-Kleen Industrial Svcs Inc* ***(G-11741)***
Portage Electric Products Inc 330 499-2727
7700 Freedom Ave Nw North Canton (44720) ***(G-15259)***
Portage Knife Company, Akron *Also called Portage Machine Concepts Inc* ***(G-344)***
Portage Machine Concepts Inc 330 628-2343
75 Skelton Rd Akron (44312) ***(G-344)***
Portage Resources Inc 330 872-3827
8650 Kimblewick Ln Ne Warren (44484) ***(G-19587)***
Portage Septic Tank, Warren *Also called Richmond Concrete Products* ***(G-19595)***
Porter Precision Products Co (PA) 513 385-1569
2734 Banning Rd Cincinnati (45239) ***(G-4250)***
Porter-Guertin Co Inc 513 241-7663
2150 Colerain Ave Cincinnati (45214) ***(G-4251)***
Porters Welding Inc (PA) 740 452-4181
601 Linden Ave Zanesville (43701) ***(G-21342)***
Portico, Cincinnati *Also called Catalog Merchandiser Inc* ***(G-3505)***
Portion Pac Inc (HQ) 513 398-0400
7325 Snider Rd Mason (45040) ***(G-13074)***
Porto Pump Inc 740 454-2576
8th And South St Zanesville (43702) ***(G-21343)***
Portsmouth Block & Brick, Portsmouth *Also called Portsmouth Block Inc* ***(G-16448)***
Portsmouth Block Inc 740 353-4113
2700 Gallia St Portsmouth (45662) ***(G-16448)***
Portsmouth Division, Portsmouth *Also called Osco Industries Inc* ***(G-16446)***
Positech Corp 513 942-7411
11310 Williamson Rd Blue Ash (45241) ***(G-1853)***
Positive Images, Newton Falls *Also called Kens His & Hers Shop Inc* ***(G-15134)***
Positive Safety Mfr Co 440 951-2130
34099 Melinz Pkwy Unit A Willoughby (44095) ***(G-20575)***
Positool Technologies Inc 330 220-4002
2985 Nationwide Pkwy Brunswick (44212) ***(G-2245)***
Positrol Inc 513 272-0500
3890 Virginia Ave Cincinnati (45227) ***(G-4252)***
Positrol Workholding, Cincinnati *Also called Positrol Inc* ***(G-4252)***
Posm Software LLC 859 274-0041
4925 Sharon Hill Dr Columbus (43235) ***(G-7505)***
Possible Plastics Inc 614 277-2100
1620 Feddern Ave Bldg B Grove City (43123) ***(G-10583)***
Post Printing Co (PA) 859 254-7714
205 W 4th St Minster (45865) ***(G-14359)***
Post Products Inc 330 678-0048
1600 Franklin Ave Kent (44240) ***(G-11505)***
Post, The, Athens *Also called Ohio University* ***(G-880)***
Postal Uniform Xpress 513 621-4787
1202 York St Cincinnati (45214) ***(G-4253)***
Posterservice Incorporated (PA) 513 577-7100
225 Northland Blvd Cincinnati (45246) ***(G-4254)***
Postle Industries Inc 216 265-9000
5500 W 164th St Cleveland (44142) ***(G-6022)***
Potemkin Industries Inc (PA) 740 397-4888
8043 Columbus Rd Mount Vernon (43050) ***(G-14638)***
Potter House 419 584-1705
108 S Main St Celina (45822) ***(G-3015)***
Potters Industries LLC 216 621-0840
2380 W 3rd St Cleveland (44113) ***(G-6023)***
Pottery Making Illustrate, Westerville *Also called American Ceramic Society* ***(G-20137)***
Pouchr LLC 216 990-0535
11470 Euclid Ave Ste 119 Cleveland (44106) ***(G-6024)***
Powder Alloy Corporation 513 984-4016
101 Northeast Dr Loveland (45140) ***(G-12378)***
Powder Coatings, Strongsville *Also called PPG Industries Inc* ***(G-17951)***
Powdermet Inc (PA) 216 404-0053
24112 Rockwell Dr Euclid (44117) ***(G-9598)***
Powdermet Powder Production 216 404-0053
24112 Rockwell Dr Ste D Euclid (44117) ***(G-9599)***
Powell Electrical Systems Inc 330 966-1750
8967 Pleasantwood Ave Nw Canton (44720) ***(G-2816)***
Powell Logging 740 372-6131
7593 State Route 348 Otway (45657) ***(G-15831)***
Powell Prints LLC 614 771-4830
3991 Main St Hilliard (43026) ***(G-10971)***
Powell Valve, Cincinnati *Also called William Powell Company* ***(G-4596)***
Power Acquisition LLC (HQ) 614 228-5000
835 Goodale Blvd Columbus (43212) ***(G-7506)***

ALPHABETIC

Power Corp Sign Products Inc 740 344-0468
632 Swansea Rd Newark (43055) *(G-15047)*
Power Engineering LLC 513 793-5800
507 N Wayne Ave Cincinnati (45215) *(G-4255)*
Power Engineering Technology, Wyoming *Also called John McHael Priester Assoc Inc (G-20932)*
Power Grounding Solutions LLC 440 926-3219
1001 Commerce Dr Grafton (44044) *(G-10435)*
Power House Electric Sup LLC 419 523-6614
823 N Locust St Ottawa (45875) *(G-15805)*
Power Management Inc (PA) 937 222-2909
420 Davis Ave Dayton (45403) *(G-8580)*
Power Media Inc 330 475-0500
546 Grant St Akron (44311) *(G-345)*
Power Shelf LLC 419 775-6125
500 Industrial Park Dr Plymouth (44865) *(G-16378)*
Power Source Fuel LLC 419 690-6495
3738 Fairwood Dr Sylvania (43560) *(G-18123)*
Power-Pack Conveyor Company 440 975-9955
38363 Airport Pkwy Willoughby (44094) *(G-20576)*
Powerbuff Inc 419 241-2156
1001 Brown Ave Toledo (43607) *(G-18650)*
Powerclean Equipment Company 513 202-0001
5945 Dry Fork Rd Cleves (45002) *(G-6524)*
Powerex-Iwata Air Tech Inc 888 769-7979
150 Production Dr Harrison (45030) *(G-10795)*
Powerhouse Factories Inc 513 719-6417
1111 Saint Gregory St Cincinnati (45202) *(G-4256)*
Powerlasers, Pioneer *Also called Arcelormittal Tailored Blanks (G-16233)*
Powermount Systems Inc 740 499-4330
1602 Larue Marseilles Rd La Rue (43332) *(G-11622)*
Powers and Sons LLC 419 737-2373
101 Industrial Ave Pioneer (43554) *(G-16240)*
Powers and Sons LLC (HQ) 419 485-3151
1613 Magda Dr Montpelier (43543) *(G-14450)*
Powersonic Industries LLC 513 429-2339
2523 Crescentville Rd Cincinnati (45241) *(G-4257)*
Powerwash of Ohio 614 260-2756
8029 Cranes Crossing Dr Lewis Center (43035) *(G-11911)*
Powrkleen, Medina *Also called Woodbine Products Company (G-13497)*
Ppafco Inc 614 488-7259
1096 Ridge St Columbus (43215) *(G-7507)*
Ppe, Macedonia *Also called Plastic Process Equipment Inc (G-12474)*
PPG 4331, Cincinnati *Also called PPG Industries Inc (G-4259)*
PPG 4332, Cincinnati *Also called PPG Industries Inc (G-4262)*
PPG 4333, Cincinnati *Also called PPG Industries Inc (G-4260)*
PPG 4335, Middletown *Also called PPG Industries Inc (G-14077)*
PPG 4338, Fairfield *Also called PPG Industries Inc (G-9703)*
PPG 4339, Cincinnati *Also called PPG Industries Inc (G-4261)*
PPG 4341, West Chester *Also called PPG Industries Inc (G-20039)*
PPG 5404, Columbus *Also called PPG Industries Inc (G-7510)*
PPG 5412, Circleville *Also called PPG Industries Inc (G-4638)*
PPG 5414, Wooster *Also called PPG Industries Inc (G-20822)*
PPG 5537, Columbus *Also called PPG Industries Inc (G-7509)*
PPG 5538, Reynoldsburg *Also called PPG Industries Inc (G-16597)*
PPG 5539, Grove City *Also called PPG Industries Inc (G-10584)*
PPG 9282, Hilliard *Also called PPG Industries Inc (G-10972)*
PPG Architectural Finishes Inc 330 788-2421
4440 Market St Unit 127 Youngstown (44512) *(G-21174)*
PPG Architectural Finishes Inc 440 942-7708
7444 Mentor Ave Mentor (44060) *(G-13694)*
PPG Architectural Finishes Inc 614 846-0097
2840 N High St Columbus (43202) *(G-7508)*
PPG Architectural Finishes Inc 419 433-5664
300 Sprowl Rd Huron (44839) *(G-11238)*
PPG Architectural Finishes Inc 216 328-1581
5480 Cloverleaf Pkwy # 5 Cleveland (44125) *(G-6025)*
PPG Architectural Finishes Inc 330 477-8165
4575 Tuscarawas St W Canton (44708) *(G-2817)*
PPG Architectural Finishes Inc 513 563-0220
2960 Exon Ave Cincinnati (45241) *(G-4258)*
PPG Chillicothe, Chillicothe *Also called PPG Industries Inc (G-3264)*
PPG Industries, Lima *Also called Pgw Auto Glass LLC (G-12070)*
PPG Industries 419 433-0567
400 Sprowl Rd Huron (44839) *(G-11239)*
PPG Industries Inc 330 825-0831
4829 Fairland Rd Barberton (44203) *(G-1140)*
PPG Industries Inc 440 572-2800
19699 Progress Dr Strongsville (44149) *(G-17951)*
PPG Industries Inc 740 774-8734
848 Southern Ave Chillicothe (45601) *(G-3264)*
PPG Industries Inc 216 671-7793
14800 Emery Ave Cleveland (44135) *(G-6026)*
PPG Industries Inc 513 576-0360
500 Techne Center Dr Milford (45150) *(G-14167)*
PPG Industries Inc 330 825-6328
900 Columbia Ct 16th Barberton (44203) *(G-1141)*

PPG Industries Inc 740 474-3161
559 Pittsburgh Rd Circleville (43113) *(G-4637)*
PPG Industries Inc 740 774-7600
848 Southern Ave Chillicothe (45601) *(G-3265)*
PPG Industries Inc 740 774-7600
848 Southern Ave Chillicothe (45601) *(G-3266)*
PPG Industries Inc 419 683-2400
5066 Lincoln Hwy Crestline (44827) *(G-7935)*
PPG Industries Inc 513 231-3200
7198 Beechmont Ave Cincinnati (45230) *(G-4259)*
PPG Industries Inc 740 474-3945
221 E Main St Circleville (43113) *(G-4638)*
PPG Industries Inc 513 829-6006
726 Nilles Rd Fairfield (45014) *(G-9703)*
PPG Industries Inc 513 661-5220
6462 Glenway Ave Cincinnati (45211) *(G-4260)*
PPG Industries Inc 614 277-0620
2362 Stringtown Rd Grove City (43123) *(G-10584)*
PPG Industries Inc 614 921-9228
5054 Cemetery Rd Hilliard (43026) *(G-10972)*
PPG Industries Inc 513 424-1241
4480 Marie Dr Middletown (45044) *(G-14077)*
PPG Industries Inc 513 984-6761
9865 Montgomery Rd Cincinnati (45242) *(G-4261)*
PPG Industries Inc 614 939-2365
5548 N Hamilton Rd Columbus (43230) *(G-7509)*
PPG Industries Inc 614 268-2609
2840 N High St Columbus (43202) *(G-7510)*
PPG Industries Inc 513 779-2727
9304 Cincinnati Columbus West Chester (45241) *(G-20039)*
PPG Industries Inc 513 242-3050
4600 Reading Rd Cincinnati (45229) *(G-4262)*
PPG Industries Inc 614 501-7360
6585 E Main St Reynoldsburg (43068) *(G-16597)*
PPG Industries Inc 330 262-9741
239 W Liberty St Wooster (44691) *(G-20822)*
PPG Industries Inc 513 576-3100
500 Techne Center Dr Milford (45150) *(G-14168)*
PPG Industries Inc 330 824-2537
2823 Ellsworth Bailey Rd Warren (44481) *(G-19588)*
PPG Industries Ohio Inc 740 363-9610
760 Pittsburgh Dr Delaware (43015) *(G-8878)*
PPG Industries Ohio Inc 216 486-5300
23000 Saint Clair Ave Euclid (44117) *(G-9600)*
PPG Industries Ohio Inc (HQ) 216 671-0050
3800 W 143rd St Cleveland (44111) *(G-6027)*
PPG Kansai Automotive Finishes, Cleveland *Also called PPG Industries Ohio Inc (G-6027)*
PPG Regional Support Center, Chillicothe *Also called PPG Industries Inc (G-3265)*
Ppg-Metokote, Lima *Also called Metokote Corporation (G-12054)*
Ppl Holding Company 216 514-1840
25201 Chagrin Blvd # 360 Cleveland (44122) *(G-6028)*
Pps, Mason *Also called Pilot Production Solutions LLC (G-13073)*
PQ Corporation 216 341-2578
5200 Harvard Ave Newburgh Heights (44105) *(G-15078)*
PR Signs & Service 614 252-7090
3049 E 14th Ave Columbus (43219) *(G-7511)*
Prairie Lane Corporation 330 262-3322
4489 Prairie Ln Wooster (44691) *(G-20823)*
Prairie Lane Gravel Co, Wooster *Also called Prairie Lane Corporation (G-20823)*
Pratt (jet Corr) Inc 937 390-7100
1515 Baker Rd Springfield (45504) *(G-17629)*
Pratt Displays, Mason *Also called Pratt Industries USA Inc (G-13075)*
Pratt Industries USA, Springfield *Also called Pratt (jet Corr) Inc (G-17629)*
Pratt Industries USA Inc 513 770-0851
4700 Duke Dr Ste 140 Mason (45040) *(G-13075)*
Praxair Inc 440 994-1000
3102 Lake Rd E Ashtabula (44004) *(G-834)*
Praxair Inc 216 778-5555
2500 Metrohealth Dr Cleveland (44109) *(G-6029)*
Praxair Inc 440 237-8690
14788 York Rd Cleveland (44133) *(G-6030)*
Praxair Inc 419 698-8005
3742 Cedar Point Rd Oregon (43616) *(G-15713)*
Praxair Inc 740 453-0346
130 N 3rd St Zanesville (43701) *(G-21344)*
Praxair Inc 419 729-7732
6055 Brent Dr Toledo (43611) *(G-18651)*
Praxair Inc 937 323-6408
403 W Columbia St Springfield (45504) *(G-17630)*
Praxair Inc 330 264-6633
4265 E Lincoln Way Unit A Wooster (44691) *(G-20824)*
Praxair Inc 419 652-3562
5480 Cloverleaf Pkwy # 6 Cleveland (44125) *(G-6031)*
Praxair Inc 419 422-1353
961 Industry Ave Lima (45804) *(G-12071)*
Praxair Inc 440 944-8844
5324 Grant Ave Cleveland (44125) *(G-6032)*
Praxair Inc 740 374-5525
2034 Blue Knob Rd Marietta (45750) *(G-12818)*

Praxair Inc 330 453-9904
2225 Bolivar Rd Sw Canton (44706) *(G-2818)*

Praxair Inc 419 666-5206
Dixie Hwy Rossford (43460) *(G-16746)*

Praxair Inc 330 825-4449
4805 Fairland Rd Barberton (44203) *(G-1142)*

Praxair Distribution Inc 614 443-7687
450 Greenlawn Ave Columbus (43223) *(G-7512)*

Praxair Distribution Inc 419 422-1353
961 Industry Ave Lima (45804) *(G-12072)*

Praxair Distribution Inc 513 821-2192
8376 Reading Rd Cincinnati (45237) *(G-4263)*

Praxair Distribution Inc 937 283-3400
105 Praxair Way Wilmington (45177) *(G-20674)*

Praxair Distribution Inc 419 221-0517
961 Industry Ave Lima (45804) *(G-12073)*

Praxair Distribution Inc 419 476-0738
5254 Jackman Rd Ste A Toledo (43613) *(G-18652)*

PRC - Desoto International Inc 800 772-9378
848 Southern Ave Chillicothe (45601) *(G-3267)*

PRC Desoto International, Chillicothe Also called PRC - Desoto International Inc *(G-3267)*

PRC Printing, Canton Also called Professional Reports Corp *(G-2826)*

Prcc Holdings Inc 330 798-4790
175 Mntrose Ave W Ste 200 Akron (44321) *(G-346)*

Pre-Melt Systems Inc 330 818-8088
8984 Meridian Cir Nw Canton (44720) *(G-2819)*

Precast Services Inc 614 428-4541
6494 Taylor Rd Sw Reynoldsburg (43068) *(G-16598)*

Precious Metal Plating Co 440 585-7117
30335 Palisades Pkwy Wickliffe (44092) *(G-20384)*

Precise Metal Form Inc 419 636-5221
810 Commerce Dr Bryan (43506) *(G-2319)*

Precise Models Inc 440 365-5701
195 Canterbury Rd Elyria (44035) *(G-9480)*

Precise Pallets LLC 513 560-8236
4211 Curliss Ln Batavia (45103) *(G-1217)*

Precise Tool & Die Company 440 951-9173
38128 Willoughby Pkwy Willoughby (44094) *(G-20577)*

Precise Tool & Mfg Corp 216 524-1500
5755 Canal Rd Cleveland (44125) *(G-6033)*

Precise Tool Inc 937 778-3441
9676 Looney Rd Piqua (45356) *(G-16307)*

Precise Tube Forming Inc 440 237-3956
9591 York Alpha Dr Ste 7 North Royalton (44133) *(G-15445)*

Precision Aggregates, Portage Also called Palmer Bros Transit Mix Con *(G-16427)*

Precision Aircraft Components 937 278-0264
2787 Armstrong Ln Dayton (45414) *(G-8581)*

Precision Aluminum Inc 330 335-2351
733 Weber Dr Wadsworth (44281) *(G-19429)*

Precision Anlytical Instrs Inc 513 984-1600
10857 Millington Ct Blue Ash (45242) *(G-1854)*

Precision Applied Coatings 614 252-8711
3021 E 4th Ave Ste B Columbus (43219) *(G-7513)*

Precision Automotive Plastics, Bellevue Also called Windsor Mold Inc *(G-1565)*

Precision Brush Co 440 542-9600
6700 Parkland Blvd Solon (44139) *(G-17363)*

Precision Castparts Corp 330 868-7376
3860 Union Ave Se Minerva (44657) *(G-14338)*

Precision Cnc LLC 740 689-9009
1858 Cedar Hill Rd Lancaster (43130) *(G-11740)*

Precision Coatings Inc 216 441-0805
3289 E 80th St Cleveland (44104) *(G-6034)*

Precision Coatings Systems 937 642-4727
948 Columbus Ave Marysville (43040) *(G-12963)*

Precision Component & Mch Inc 740 867-6366
17 Rosslyn Rd Chesapeake (45619) *(G-3189)*

Precision Component Inds LLC 330 477-1052
5325 Southway St Sw Canton (44706) *(G-2820)*

Precision Conveyor Technology 440 352-3601
3785 Lane Rd Ext Perry (44081) *(G-16056)*

Precision Custom Products Inc 937 585-4011
4590 County Road 35 De Graff (43318) *(G-8583)*

Precision Cutoff LLC 419 866-8000
7400 Airport Hwy Holland (43528) *(G-11078)*

Precision Design Inc 419 289-1553
2395 Rock Rd Ashland (44805) *(G-767)*

Precision Details Inc 937 596-0068
104 Washington St Jackson Center (45334) *(G-11346)*

Precision Die & Stamping Inc 513 942-8220
9800 Harwood Ct West Chester (45014) *(G-19918)*

Precision Die Masters 440 255-1204
8724 East Ave Mentor (44060) *(G-13695)*

Precision Dynamics Inc 330 697-0611
1270 Linden Ave Akron (44310) *(G-347)*

Precision Energy & Tech LLC 937 558-2708
2000 Composite Dr Dayton (45420) *(G-8582)*

Precision Engineered Tech LLC (PA) 330 335-3300
1785 Wall Rd Wadsworth (44281) *(G-19430)*

Precision Environments Inc (PA) 513 847-1510
9830 Windisch Rd West Chester (45069) *(G-19919)*

Precision Equipment Llc 330 220-7600
1460 W 130th St Ste C Brunswick (44212) *(G-2246)*

Precision Fab Products Inc 937 526-5681
10061 Old State Route 121 Versailles (45380) *(G-19356)*

Precision Fabg & Stamping 740 453-7310
1755 Kemper Ct Zanesville (43701) *(G-21345)*

Precision Fabrications Inc 937 297-8606
272 High St Sunbury (43074) *(G-18074)*

Precision Finishing Systems 937 415-5794
6101 Webster St Dayton (45414) *(G-8583)*

Precision Fittings LLC 440 647-4143
709 N Main St Wellington (44090) *(G-19752)*

Precision Foam Fabrication Inc 330 270-2440
2716 Intertech Dr Youngstown (44509) *(G-21175)*

Precision Forged Products, Gallipolis Also called GKN Sinter Metals LLC *(G-10298)*

Precision Gage & Tool Company 937 866-9666
375 Gargrave Rd Dayton (45449) *(G-8584)*

Precision Geophysical Inc (PA) 330 674-2198
2695 State Route 83 Millersburg (44654) *(G-14256)*

Precision Geophysical Inc 740 849-3044
4700 Rucker Rd Mount Perry (43760) *(G-14593)*

Precision Graphic Services 419 241-5189
436 Wade St Toledo (43604) *(G-18653)*

Precision Honing Inc 440 942-7339
33000 Lakeland Blvd Willoughby (44095) *(G-20578)*

Precision Hydraulic Connectors 440 953-3778
26420 Cntury Corners Pkwy Euclid (44132) *(G-9601)*

Precision Imprint 740 592-5916
26 E State St Athens (45701) *(G-882)*

Precision Inc 330 897-8860
33725 County Road 10 Fresno (43824) *(G-10198)*

Precision International LLC 330 793-0900
843 N Cleveland Akron (44322) *(G-348)*

Precision Laser & Forming 419 943-4350
6500 Road 5 Leipsic (45856) *(G-11873)*

Precision Machine & Tool Co 419 334-8405
1016 N 5th St Fremont (43420) *(G-10176)*

Precision Machining Corp 419 433-3520
9307 Wikel Rd Huron (44839) *(G-11240)*

Precision Made Products, Brunswick Also called Alpha Sintered Metals LLC *(G-2204)*

Precision Manufacturing Co Inc 937 236-2170
2149 Valley Pike Dayton (45404) *(G-8585)*

Precision McHning Srfacing Inc 440 439-9850
5435 Perkins Rd Cleveland (44146) *(G-6035)*

Precision Metal Products Inc 216 447-1900
7641 Commerce Park Oval Cleveland (44131) *(G-6036)*

Precision Metalforming Assn (PA) 216 241-1482
6363 Oak Tree Blvd Independence (44131) *(G-11271)*

Precision Mfg & Assembly LLC 937 252-3507
2240 Richard St Dayton (45403) *(G-8586)*

Precision Mtal Fabrication Inc (PA) 937 235-9261
191 Heid Ave Dayton (45404) *(G-8587)*

Precision of Ohio Inc 330 793-0900
3850 Hendricks Rd Youngstown (44515) *(G-21176)*

Precision Pallet Inc 419 381-8191
3919 W Bancroft St Ottawa Hills (43606) *(G-15818)*

Precision Polymer Casting LLC 440 343-0461
140 Greentree Rd Moreland Hills (44022) *(G-14538)*

Precision Polymers Inc 614 322-9951
6919 Americana Pkwy Reynoldsburg (43068) *(G-16599)*

Precision Pressed Powdered Met 937 433-6802
1522 Manchester Rd Dayton (45449) *(G-8588)*

Precision Production Inc 216 252-0372
8250 Dow Cir Strongsville (44136) *(G-17952)*

Precision Products Group Inc 330 698-4711
339 Mill St Apple Creek (44606) *(G-647)*

Precision Q Systems LLC 614 286-5142
285 Old County Line Rd B Westerville (43081) *(G-20229)*

Precision Quincy Shelters Inc 888 312-5442
4600 N Masn Rd Montgomery Mason (45040) *(G-13076)*

Precision Reflex Inc 419 629-2603
710 Streine Dr New Bremen (45869) *(G-14792)*

Precision Replacement LLC 330 908-0410
9009 Freeway Dr Unit 7 Macedonia (44056) *(G-12476)*

Precision Runners LLC 330 240-5988
7186 State Route 609 Burghill (44404) *(G-2369)*

Precision Specialty Metals Inc 323 475-3200
200 W Old Wlson Bridge Rd Worthington (43085) *(G-20883)*

Precision Steel Services Inc (PA) 419 476-5702
31 E Sylvania Ave Toledo (43612) *(G-18654)*

Precision Strip Inc 937 667-6255
315 Park Ave Tipp City (45371) *(G-18293)*

Precision Strip Inc 419 674-4186
190 Bales Rd Kenton (43326) *(G-11564)*

Precision Swiss LLC 513 716-7000
9580 Wayne Ave Cincinnati (45215) *(G-4264)*

Precision Switching Inc 800 800-8143
2090 Harrington Mem Rd Mansfield (44903) *(G-12667)*

Precision Tek Manufacturing, Mason Also called Ashley F Ward Inc *(G-12984)*

Precision Temp, Cincinnati Also called RAD Technologies Incorporated *(G-4328)*

Precision Thrmplstc Componts 419 227-4500
  3765 Saint Johns Rd Lima (45806) *(G-12115)*

Precision Tower Products LLC 740 362-7876
  435 Park Ave Delaware (43015) *(G-8879)*

Precision Welding & Mfg 937 444-6925
  101 Day Rd Mount Orab (45154) *(G-14585)*

Precision Welding Corporation 216 524-6110
  7900 Exchange St Cleveland (44125) *(G-6037)*

Precision Wire Products Inc (PA) 216 265-7580
  4791 W 139th St Cleveland (44135) *(G-6038)*

Precision Wood & Metal Co 419 221-1512
  3960 E Bluelick Rd Lima (45801) *(G-12074)*

Precision Wood Products Inc (PA) 937 787-3523
  2456 Aukerman Creek Rd Camden (45311) *(G-2488)*

Precision Woodwork Ltd 440 257-3002
  6385 Mentor Park Blvd Mentor (44060) *(G-13696)*

Precisions Paint Systems LLC 740 894-6224
  5852 County Road 1 South Point (45680) *(G-17444)*

Precison Clean Rooms, West Chester *Also called Precision Environments Inc (G-19919)*

Precison Coating Technology, Cleveland *Also called Precision Coatings Inc (G-6034)*

Predict Inc 216 642-3223
  9555 Rockside Rd Ste 350 Cleveland (44125) *(G-6039)*

Predict Technologies Div, Cleveland *Also called Reid Asset Management Company (G-6098)*

Preemptive Solutions LLC 216 732-5895
  767 Beta Dr Cleveland (44143) *(G-6040)*

Preferred Compounding Corp (PA) 330 798-4790
  175 Montrose West Ave # 200 Copley (44321) *(G-7852)*

Preferred Global Equipment LLC 513 530-5800
  7800 Redsky Dr Cincinnati (45249) *(G-4265)*

Preferred Printing (PA) 937 492-6961
  3700 Michigan St Sidney (45365) *(G-17212)*

Preferred Solutions Inc 216 642-1200
  7819 Broadview Rd Ste 6 Seven Hills (44131) *(G-17062)*

Preform Sealants, Twinsburg *Also called Kes Industries LLC (G-18963)*

Preform Technologies LLC 419 720-0355
  11362 S Airfield Rd Swanton (43558) *(G-18088)*

Preformed Line Products Co (PA) 440 461-5200
  660 Beta Dr Mayfield Village (44143) *(G-13324)*

Prehistoric Antiquities 937 747-2225
  7045 State Route 245 North Lewisburg (43060) *(G-15308)*

Preisser Inc 614 345-0199
  3560 Millikin Ct Ste A Columbus (43228) *(G-7514)*

Premar Manufacturing Ltd 440 250-0373
  803 Sharon Dr Westlake (44145) *(G-20297)*

Premere Precast Products 740 533-3333
  317 Hecla St Ironton (45638) *(G-11298)*

Premier Building Solutions Inc (PA) 330 244-2907
  480 Nova Dr Se Massillon (44646) *(G-13197)*

Premier Coatings Ltd 513 942-1070
  9390 Le Saint Dr West Chester (45014) *(G-19920)*

Premier Construction Company 513 874-2611
  9361 Seward Rd Fairfield (45014) *(G-9704)*

Premier Farnell Holding Inc (HQ) 330 523-4273
  4180 Highlander Pkwy Richfield (44286) *(G-16633)*

Premier Feeds LLC (HQ) 937 584-2411
  292 N Howard St Sabina (45169) *(G-16776)*

Premier Industries Inc 513 271-2550
  5721 Dragon Way Ste 113 Cincinnati (45227) *(G-4266)*

Premier Ink Systems Inc (PA) 513 367-4700
  10420 N State St Harrison (45030) *(G-10796)*

Premier Kites & Designs Inc 888 416-0174
  1004 Findlay St Portsmouth (45662) *(G-16449)*

Premier Manufacturing Corp (HQ) 216 941-9700
  2500 Brookpark Rd Ste 200 Cleveland (44134) *(G-6041)*

Premier Material Concepts, Findlay *Also called Rowmark LLC (G-9885)*

Premier Material Concepts LLC 419 429-0042
  2040 Industrial Dr Findlay (45840) *(G-9880)*

Premier Meats, Fairfield *Also called Reuss Meats Inc (G-9710)*

Premier Metal Trading LLC 440 247-9494
  7 1/2 N Franklin St Chagrin Falls (44022) *(G-3068)*

Premier OEM, Cuyahoga Falls *Also called Kolpin Outdoors Corporation (G-8018)*

Premier Office 419 329-9692
  225 Ashland Rd Mansfield (44905) *(G-12668)*

Premier Pallet & Recycling 330 767-2221
  11361 Lawndell Rd Sw Navarre (44662) *(G-14724)*

Premier Printing and Packg Inc 937 436-5290
  90 Compark Rd Ste A Dayton (45459) *(G-8589)*

Premier Printing Corporation 216 478-9720
  18780 Cranwood Pkwy Cleveland (44128) *(G-6042)*

Premier Printing Solutions 740 374-2836
  115 Pineview Cir Marietta (45750) *(G-12819)*

Premier Prod Svc Inds Inc 330 527-0333
  10384 Industrial Dr C Garrettsville (44231) *(G-10332)*

Premier Seals Mfg 330 861-1060
  909 W Waterloo Rd Akron (44314) *(G-349)*

Premier Shot Company Inc 330 405-0583
  1666 Enterprise Pkwy Twinsburg (44087) *(G-19005)*

Premier Silica LLC 740 659-2241
  2446 State Route 204 Glenford (43739) *(G-10400)*

Premier Silica LLC 740 599-7773
  26900 Coshocton Rd Howard (43028) *(G-11124)*

Premier Southern Ticket, Cincinnati *Also called Gtlp Holdings LLC (G-3857)*

Premier Southern Ticket Co Inc 513 489-6700
  7911 School Rd Cincinnati (45249) *(G-4267)*

Premier Stamping and Assembly 440 293-8961
  7924 Mill St Williamsfield (44093) *(G-20416)*

Premier Tanning & Nutrition 419 342-6259
  35 Mansfield Ave Shelby (44875) *(G-17141)*

Premier Tool Inc 937 332-0996
  1333 E Main St Troy (45373) *(G-18864)*

Premier Uv Products LLC 330 715-2452
  1738 Front St Cuyahoga Falls (44221) *(G-8035)*

Premiere Con Solutions LLC 419 737-9808
  508 Cedar St Pioneer (43554) *(G-16241)*

Premiere Medical Resources Inc 330 923-5899
  2750 Front St Cuyahoga Falls (44221) *(G-8036)*

Premiere Mold and Machine Co 330 874-3000
  10882 Fort Laurens Rd Nw Bolivar (44612) *(G-1942)*

Premiere Printing & Signs Inc 330 688-6244
  778 Mccauley Rd Unit 120 Stow (44224) *(G-17791)*

Premiere Stamping, Williamsfield *Also called Premier Stamping and Assembly (G-20416)*

Premium Meats Inc 330 394-8651
  241 Logan Ave Ne Warren (44483) *(G-19589)*

Premium Panel & Tread 330 695-9979
  4910 Harrison Rd Fredericksburg (44627) *(G-10090)*

Premium Wood & Garden Products, Jackson *Also called Summers Organization LLC (G-11326)*

Premix Inc (HQ) 440 224-2181
  3365 E Center St North Kingsville (44068) *(G-15304)*

Prentke Romich Company (PA) 330 202-5800
  1022 Heyl Rd Wooster (44691) *(G-20825)*

Preserving Your Memories 614 861-4283
  1862 Drugan Ct Sw Reynoldsburg (43068) *(G-16600)*

Presrite Corporation (PA) 216 441-5990
  3665 E 78th St Cleveland (44105) *(G-6043)*

Presrite Corporation 440 576-0015
  322 S Cucumber St Jefferson (44047) *(G-11369)*

Press Chemical & Phrm Lab 614 863-2802
  2700 E Main St Ste 102 Columbus (43209) *(G-7515)*

Press For Less Printing Firm I 931 912-4606
  1836 Stubbs Mill Rd Lebanon (45036) *(G-11829)*

Press of Ohio Inc 330 678-5868
  3765 Sunnybrook Rd Kent (44240) *(G-11506)*

Press Resource LLC 614 794-9000
  237 E Broadway Ave Westerville (43081) *(G-20230)*

Press Technology & Mfg Inc 937 327-0755
  1401 Fotler St Springfield (45504) *(G-17631)*

Pressco Technology Inc (PA) 440 498-2600
  29200 Aurora Rd Cleveland (44139) *(G-6044)*

Pressed Coffee Bar & Eatery 330 746-8030
  215 Lincoln Ave Youngstown (44503) *(G-21177)*

Presslers Meats Inc 330 644-5636
  2553 Pressler Rd Akron (44312) *(G-350)*

Pressmark Inc 740 373-6005
  641 State Route 821 Ste A Marietta (45750) *(G-12820)*

Pressure Technology Ohio Inc 215 628-1975
  7996 Auburn Rd Painesville (44077) *(G-15912)*

Pressure Washer Mfrs Assn 216 241-7333
  1300 Sumner Ave Cleveland (44115) *(G-6045)*

Prestige Display and Packg LLC (HQ) 513 285-1040
  420 Distribution Cir Fairfield (45014) *(G-9705)*

Prestige Enterprise Intl Inc 513 469-6044
  11343 Grooms Rd Blue Ash (45242) *(G-1855)*

Prestige Fireworks LLC 513 492-7726
  222 Van Buren Dr Mason (45040) *(G-13077)*

Prestige Printing 937 236-8468
  5888 Executive Blvd Dayton (45424) *(G-8590)*

Prestige Store Interiors Inc 419 476-2106
  4500 N Detroit Ave Toledo (43612) *(G-18655)*

Preston 740 788-8208
  42 Sandalwood Dr Newark (43055) *(G-15048)*

Prestons Repair & Welding 937 947-1883
  11611 State Route 571 Laura (45337) *(G-11768)*

Prestress Services Inds LLC (PA) 859 299-0461
  2250 N Hartford Ave Columbus (43222) *(G-7516)*

Prestress Services Inds LLC 614 871-2900
  3350 Jackson Pike Grove City (43123) *(G-10585)*

Pretium Packaging LLC 419 943-3733
  150 S Werner St Leipsic (45856) *(G-11874)*

Pretreatment & Specialty Pdts, Euclid *Also called PPG Industries Ohio Inc (G-9600)*

Pretzel Fest, Brookville *Also called Mar Chele Inc (G-2188)*

Preuss Mold & Die 419 729-9100
  1010 Matzinger Rd Toledo (43612) *(G-18656)*

PRI Marine, Columbus *Also called Performance Research Inc (G-7479)*

Priamus System Technology 330 273-3393
  3061 Nationwide Pkwy Brunswick (44212) *(G-2247)*

Price Farms Organics Ltd 740 369-1000
  4838 Warrensburg Rd Delaware (43015) *(G-8880)*

Pride and True Garage, Cincinnati *Also called Outback Cycle Shack LLC* **(G-4203)**
Pride Cast Metals Inc 513 541-1295
2737 Colerain Ave Cincinnati (45225) **(G-4268)**
Pride Gage Associates LLC 419 318-3793
7862 W Central Ave Ste D Toledo (43617) **(G-18657)**
Pride Investments LLC 937 461-1121
1346 Morris Ave Dayton (45417) **(G-8591)**
Pride of Geneva 440 466-5695
72 W Main St Geneva (44041) **(G-10356)**
Pride of Hills Mfg Inc (PA) 330 567-3108
8275 State Route 514 Big Prairie (44611) **(G-1683)**
Pride of Hills Mfg Inc 800 345-1744
110 Straits Ln Killbuck (44637) **(G-11598)**
Pride Tool Co Inc 513 563-0070
10200 Wayne Ave Cincinnati (45215) **(G-4269)**
Pridecraft Enterprises, Cincinnati *Also called Standard Textile Co Inc* **(G-4455)**
Priesman Printery 419 898-2526
218 W Water St Oak Harbor (43449) **(G-15593)**
Priest Millwright Service 937 780-3405
101 Miller St Leesburg (45135) **(G-11856)**
Priest Services Inc (PA) 440 333-1123
1127 Linda St 5885 Mayfield Heights (44124) **(G-13321)**
Priest Services Inc 440 333-1123
1127 Linda St Rocky River (44116) **(G-16705)**
Primal Screen Inc 330 677-1766
1021 Mason Ave Kent (44240) **(G-11507)**
Primary Colors Design Corp 419 903-0403
1899 Cottage St Ashland (44805) **(G-768)**
Primary Packaging Incorporated 330 874-3131
10810 Industrial Pkwy Nw Bolivar (44612) **(G-1943)**
Prime Conduit Inc (PA) 216 464-3400
23240 Chagrin Blvd # 405 Cleveland (44122) **(G-6046)**
Prime Controls Inc 937 435-8659
4528 Gateway Cir Dayton (45440) **(G-8592)**
Prime Engineered Plastics Corp 330 452-5110
1505 Howington Cir Se Canton (44707) **(G-2821)**
Prime Equipment Group Inc 614 253-8590
2000 E Fulton St Columbus (43205) **(G-7517)**
Prime Industries Inc 440 288-3626
1817 Iowa Ave Lorain (44052) **(G-12268)**
Prime Instruments Inc 216 651-0400
9805 Walford Ave Cleveland (44102) **(G-6047)**
Prime Manufacturing Corp (HQ) 937 496-3900
1619 Kuntz Rd Dayton (45404) **(G-8593)**
Prime Printing Inc (PA) 937 438-3707
8929 Kingsridge Dr Dayton (45458) **(G-8594)**
Prime Time Machine Inc 440 942-7410
38302 Arprt Pkwy Unit 10 Willoughby (44094) **(G-20579)**
Prime Wood Craft Inc (HQ) 216 738-2222
1120 W 130th St Brunswick (44212) **(G-2248)**
Primeline Industries, Akron *Also called Sml Inc* **(G-406)**
Prince Plating Inc 216 881-7523
1530 E 40th St Cleveland (44103) **(G-6048)**
Principle Business Entps Inc (PA) 419 352-1551
20189 Pine Lake Rd Bowling Green (43402) **(G-2009)**
Principled Dynamics Inc 419 351-6303
6920 Hall St Holland (43528) **(G-11079)**
Print A Copy 440 845-9039
4710 Maplecrest Ave Cleveland (44134) **(G-6049)**
Print All Inc 419 534-2880
2375 Dorr St Ste 2 Toledo (43607) **(G-18658)**
Print Craft Inc 513 931-6828
8045 Colerain Ave Cincinnati (45239) **(G-4270)**
Print Digital, Stow *Also called Print-Digital Incorporated* **(G-17792)**
Print Direct For Less 2 Inc 440 236-8870
27500 Royalton Rd Columbia Station (44028) **(G-6595)**
Print Factory Pll 330 549-9640
11471 South Ave North Lima (44452) **(G-15321)**
Print Marketing Inc 330 625-1500
11820 Black River Schl Rd Homerville (44235) **(G-11114)**
Print Masters Ltd 740 450-2885
941 W Main St Zanesville (43701) **(G-21346)**
Print Shop 740 335-8030
1020 Leesburg Ave Wshngtn CT Hs (43160) **(G-20920)**
Print Shop Design and Print 440 232-2391
366 Broadway Ave Bedford (44146) **(G-1454)**
Print Shop of Canton Inc 330 497-3212
6536 Promler St Nw Canton (44720) **(G-2822)**
Print Shop, The, Newark *Also called Spencer-Walker Press Inc* **(G-15056)**
Print Shop, The, Wshngtn CT Hs *Also called Jim Davis* **(G-20914)**
Print Solutions Today LLC 614 848-4500
100 Dorchester Sq N # 101 Westerville (43081) **(G-20231)**
Print Squad LLC 440 315-5652
16972 Stag Thicket Ln Strongsville (44136) **(G-17953)**
Print Syndicate LLC 614 519-0341
901 W 3rd Ave Ste A Columbus (43212) **(G-7518)**
Print Zone 513 733-0067
9588 Cncnnati Columbus Rd West Chester (45241) **(G-20040)**
Print-Digital Incorporated 330 686-5945
4688 Darrow Rd Stow (44224) **(G-17792)**

Print-N-Copy, Saint Clairsville *Also called Office Print N Copy* **(G-16799)**
Printcraft Inc 440 599-8903
866 W Jackson St Conneaut (44030) **(G-7817)**
Printed Image 614 221-1412
41 S Grant Ave Columbus (43215) **(G-7519)**
Printed Image, The, Columbus *Also called V & C Enterprises Co* **(G-7729)**
Printers Bindery, Cincinnati *Also called Printers Bindery Services Inc* **(G-4271)**
Printers Bindery Services Inc 513 821-8039
925 Freeman Ave Cincinnati (45203) **(G-4271)**
Printers Devil Inc 330 650-1218
77 Maple Dr Hudson (44236) **(G-11194)**
Printers Emergency Service LLC 513 421-7799
2016 Elm St Side A Cincinnati (45202) **(G-4272)**
Printex Incorporated (PA) 740 773-0088
185 E Main St Chillicothe (45601) **(G-3268)**
Printex Incorporated 740 947-8800
101 Victory Dr Waverly (45690) **(G-19719)**
Printex-Same Day Printing, Chillicothe *Also called Printex Incorporated* **(G-3268)**
Printing & Reproduction Div, Cleveland *Also called City of Cleveland* **(G-5035)**
Printing 3d Parts Inc 330 759-9099
16 Belgrade St Youngstown (44505) **(G-21178)**
Printing Arts Press 740 397-6106
8028 Newark Rd Mount Vernon (43050) **(G-14639)**
Printing Center of Xenia 937 372-1687
402 W Church St Xenia (45385) **(G-20967)**
Printing Center, The, Xenia *Also called Sandy Smittcamp* **(G-20971)**
Printing Company, The, Columbus *Also called Newmast Mktg & Communications* **(G-7389)**
Printing Concepts, Stow *Also called Traxium LLC* **(G-17811)**
Printing Connection Inc 216 898-4878
5221 W 161st St Brookpark (44142) **(G-2168)**
Printing Depot Inc 330 783-5341
3828 Southern Blvd Youngstown (44507) **(G-21179)**
Printing Express 937 276-7794
3350 Kettering Blvd Moraine (45439) **(G-14517)**
Printing Express Inc 740 532-7003
1229 S 3rd St Ironton (45638) **(G-11299)**
Printing For Less 937 743-8268
45 Tahlequah Trl Springboro (45066) **(G-17499)**
Printing Partner, Cleveland *Also called John Kolesar and Sons Inc* **(G-5618)**
Printing Partners, Brunswick *Also called Wirick Press Inc* **(G-2269)**
Printing Partners, Solon *Also called Allen Graphics Inc* **(G-17253)**
Printing Plant, Cincinnati *Also called Tech/III Inc* **(G-4497)**
Printing Press, Toledo *Also called M & D Brink Inc* **(G-18566)**
Printing Service Company 937 425-6100
3233 S Tech Blvd Miamisburg (45342) **(G-13848)**
Printing Services 440 708-1999
16750 Park Circle Dr Chagrin Falls (44023) **(G-3114)**
Printing System Inc 330 375-9128
2249 14th St Sw Akron (44314) **(G-351)**
Printmanagement Llc 513 272-7000
3950 Virginia Ave Cincinnati (45227) **(G-4273)**
Printpoint Printing Inc 937 223-9041
150 S Patterson Blvd Dayton (45402) **(G-8595)**
Printprod Inc 937 228-2181
419 Bainbridge St Dayton (45410) **(G-8596)**
Prints & Paints Flr Cvg Co Inc 419 462-5663
888 Bucyrus Rd Galion (44833) **(G-10283)**
Printxcel, Toledo *Also called Crabar/Gbf Inc* **(G-18415)**
Printzone 513 733-0067
11974 Lebanon Rd Cincinnati (45241) **(G-4274)**
Priority Custom Molding Inc 937 431-8770
840 Distribution Dr Beavercreek Township (45434) **(G-1389)**
Priority Vending Inc 216 361-4100
3425 Prospect Ave E Cleveland (44115) **(G-6050)**
Prism Powder Coatings Ltd 330 225-5626
2890 Carquest Dr Brunswick (44212) **(G-2249)**
Prism Prints Inc 614 294-4981
5765 Westbourne Ave Columbus (43213) **(G-7520)**
Prism Prints T-Shirts, Columbus *Also called Prism Prints Inc* **(G-7520)**
Pristine Exteriors 330 957-5664
5925 Renninger Rd New Franklin (44319) **(G-14830)**
Pritt Enterprises Inc 330 453-2142
1800 Wallace Ave Ne Canton (44705) **(G-2823)**
Privacyware, New Albany *Also called Pwi Inc* **(G-14770)**
Pro Audio 513 752-7500
671 Cncnnati Batavia Pike Cincinnati (45245) **(G-3314)**
Pro Audio Innovations 330 705-5069
4428 Whipple Ave Nw Canton (44718) **(G-2824)**
Pro Companies Inc 614 738-1222
1162 Hill Rd N Pickerington (43147) **(G-16201)**
Pro Fab, Cleveland *Also called Professional Fabricators Inc* **(G-6054)**
Pro Fab Industries Inc 317 297-0461
9368 Massillon Rd Dundee (44624) **(G-9179)**
Pro Fab Welding Service LLC (PA) 937 272-2142
2765 Lance Dr Moraine (45409) **(G-14518)**
Pro Forma All Print Source, Mount Vernon *Also called State-Mate Company* **(G-14652)**
Pro Forma Supply International, Steubenville *Also called Supply International Inc* **(G-17718)**

ALPHABETIC

(PA)=Parent Co (HQ)=Headquarters (DH)=Div Headquarters

Pro Gram Engineering Corp............................330 745-1004
475 5th St Ne Barberton (44203) *(G-1143)*

Pro Hardware 13074, Sugarcreek *Also called Stony Point Hardwoods (G-18040)*

Pro Lighting LLC............................614 561-0089
5864 Hunting Haven Dr Hilliard (43026) *(G-10973)*

Pro Mold Design Inc............................440 352-1212
9853 Johnnycake Ridge Rd # 308 Mentor (44060) *(G-13697)*

Pro Oncall Technologies LLC............................614 761-1400
4374 Tuller Rd Ste B Dublin (43017) *(G-9126)*

Pro Printing Inc............................614 276-8366
4191 W Broad St Columbus (43228) *(G-7521)*

Pro Quip Inc............................330 468-1850
850 Highland Rd E Macedonia (44056) *(G-12477)*

Pro Roof Washers............................440 521-2622
1403 Ford Rd Cleveland (44124) *(G-6051)*

Pro Street Chassis Shop, Norton *Also called Allen Morgan Trucking & Repair (G-15506)*

Pro-Decal Inc............................330 484-0089
3638 Cleveland Ave S Canton (44707) *(G-2825)*

Pro-Fab Inc............................330 644-0044
2570 Pressler Rd Akron (44312) *(G-352)*

Pro-Hoe Utility LLC............................740 892-4765
2945 Johnstown Utica Rd Johnstown (43031) *(G-11403)*

Pro-Kleen Industrial Svcs Inc............................740 689-1886
1030 Mill Park Dr Lancaster (43130) *(G-11741)*

Pro-Pak Industries Inc (PA)............................419 729-0751
1125 Ford St Maumee (43537) *(G-13288)*

Pro-Pet LLC............................419 394-3374
1400 Mckinley Rd Saint Marys (45885) *(G-16849)*

Pro-Pet LLC (PA)............................419 394-3374
1601 Mckinley Rd Saint Marys (45885) *(G-16850)*

Pro-Print Business Center, Dover *Also called G A Spring Advertising (G-8986)*

Pro-Soy, Upper Sandusky *Also called Midwest Spray Drying Company (G-19133)*

Pro-TEC Coating Company Inc............................419 943-1211
5500 Pro-Tec Pkwy Leipsic (45856) *(G-11875)*

Pro-Tech Manufacturing Inc............................937 444-6484
14944 Hillcrest Rd Mount Orab (45154) *(G-14586)*

Proampac, Cincinnati *Also called Ampac Holdings LLC (G-3397)*

Proampac LLC (PA)............................513 671-1777
12025 Tricon Rd Cincinnati (45246) *(G-4275)*

Process Automation Specialists............................330 247-1384
7405 Diamondback Ave Nw Canal Fulton (44614) *(G-2510)*

Process Development Corp............................937 890-3388
6060 Milo Rd Dayton (45414) *(G-8597)*

Process Equipment Co Tipp City (HQ)............................937 667-7105
4754 Us Route 40 Tipp City (45371) *(G-18294)*

Process Equipment Company, Tipp City *Also called Process Equipment Co Tipp City (G-18294)*

Process Innovations Inc............................330 856-5192
4219 King Graves Rd Vienna (44473) *(G-19373)*

Process Machinery Inc............................614 278-1055
860 Kaderly Dr Columbus (43228) *(G-7522)*

Process Pigging Systems LLC............................513 731-6005
1776 Mentor Ave Ste 406 Cincinnati (45212) *(G-4276)*

Process Sltions For Indust Inc............................330 702-1685
480 S Broad St Ste A Canfield (44406) *(G-2570)*

Process Technology, Mentor *Also called Tom Richards Inc (G-13748)*

Procoat Painting Inc............................513 735-2500
601 W Main St Unit B Batavia (45103) *(G-1218)*

Procomsol Ltd............................216 221-1550
13001 Athens Ave Ste 220 Lakewood (44107) *(G-11677)*

Procter & Gamble Company (PA)............................513 983-1100
1 Procter And Gamble Plz Cincinnati (45202) *(G-4277)*

Procter & Gamble Company............................513 983-1100
6210 Center Hill Ave Cincinnati (45224) *(G-4278)*

Procter & Gamble Company............................513 266-4375
5280 Vine St Cincinnati (45217) *(G-4279)*

Procter & Gamble Company............................513 871-7557
654 Wilmer Ave Hngr 4 Cincinnati (45226) *(G-4280)*

Procter & Gamble Company............................513 983-1100
5299 Spring Grove Ave Cincinnati (45217) *(G-4281)*

Procter & Gamble Company............................513 626-2500
11520 Reed Hartman Hwy Blue Ash (45241) *(G-1856)*

Procter & Gamble Company............................513 482-6789
4460 Kings Run Dr Cincinnati (45232) *(G-4282)*

Procter & Gamble Company............................513 672-4044
8868 Beckett Rd West Chester (45069) *(G-19921)*

Procter & Gamble Company............................513 634-5069
6300 Center Hill Ave Fl 2 Cincinnati (45224) *(G-4283)*

Procter & Gamble Company............................513 627-7115
5348 Vine St Cincinnati (45217) *(G-4284)*

Procter & Gamble Company............................513 634-9600
8256 Union Centre Blvd West Chester (45069) *(G-19922)*

Procter & Gamble Company............................513 634-9110
8611 Beckett Rd West Chester (45069) *(G-19923)*

Procter & Gamble Company............................513 948-2462
2150 Sunnybrook Dr Cincinnati (45237) *(G-4285)*

Procter & Gamble Company............................513 983-1100
2 Procter And Gamble Plz Cincinnati (45202) *(G-4286)*

Procter & Gamble Company............................513 934-3406
600 S Waynesville Rd Oregonia (45054) *(G-15722)*

Procter & Gamble Company............................513 627-7779
5201 Spring Grove Ave Cincinnati (45217) *(G-4287)*

Procter & Gamble Company............................513 945-0340
6280 Center Hill Ave Cincinnati (45224) *(G-4288)*

Procter & Gamble Company............................513 626-2500
11530 Reed Hartman Hwy Blue Ash (45241) *(G-1857)*

Procter & Gamble Company............................513 622-1000
8700 Mason Montgomery Rd Mason (45040) *(G-13078)*

Procter & Gamble Company............................410 527-5735
2200 Southwest Blvd Grove City (43123) *(G-10586)*

Procter & Gamble Distrg LLC............................937 387-5189
1800 Union Park Blvd Union (45377) *(G-19067)*

Procter & Gamble Far East Inc (HQ)............................513 983-1100
1 Procter And Gamble Plz Cincinnati (45202) *(G-4289)*

Procter & Gamble Mfg Co (HQ)............................513 983-1100
1 Procter And Gamble Plz Cincinnati (45202) *(G-4290)*

Procter & Gamble Mfg Co............................419 226-5500
3875 Reservoir Rd Lima (45801) *(G-12075)*

Procter & Gamble Mfg Co............................513 626-6882
11530 Reed Hartman Hwy Blue Ash (45241) *(G-1858)*

Procter & Gamble Paper Pdts Co (HQ)............................513 983-1100
1 Procter And Gamble Plz Cincinnati (45202) *(G-4291)*

Procter & Gamble Paper Pdts Co............................513 983-2222
301 E 6th St Cincinnati (45202) *(G-4292)*

Procter Gamble Olay Co - Cayey, Blue Ash *Also called Olay LLC (G-1845)*

Proctoer & Gamble............................513 983-1100
11520 Reed Hartman Hwy Blue Ash (45241) *(G-1859)*

Prodeva Inc............................937 596-6713
100 Jerry Dr Jackson Center (45334) *(G-11347)*

Produce Packaging Inc............................216 391-6129
7501 Carnegie Ave Cleveland (44103) *(G-6052)*

Product Machine Company, North Royalton *Also called Paul Popov (G-15444)*

Product Tooling Inc............................740 524-2061
4290 N 3 Bs And K Rd Sunbury (43074) *(G-18075)*

Production, Cuyahoga Falls *Also called Gojo Industries Inc (G-8004)*

Production Control Units Inc............................937 299-5594
2280 W Dorothy Ln Moraine (45439) *(G-14519)*

Production Design Services Inc (PA)............................937 866-3377
401 Fame Rd Dayton (45449) *(G-8598)*

Production Div, Youngstown *Also called Gasser Chair Co Inc (G-21093)*

Production Manufacturing Inc............................513 892-2331
870 Hanover St Bldg A Hamilton (45011) *(G-10731)*

Production Packaging Inc............................330 392-4155
5232 Tod Ave Sw Ste 12 Warren (44481) *(G-19590)*

Production Paint Finishers Inc............................937 448-2627
140 Center St Bradford (45308) *(G-2026)*

Production Plus Corp............................614 492-8811
2490 Mcgaw Rd Obetz (43207) *(G-15658)*

Production Products Inc............................419 659-2978
200 Sugar Grove Ln Columbus Grove (45830) *(G-7797)*

Production Screw Machine, Dayton *Also called Gmd Industries LLC (G-8373)*

Production Support Inc............................937 526-3897
105 Francis St Russia (45363) *(G-16768)*

Production Turning LLC............................937 424-0034
2490 Arbor Blvd Unit A Moraine (45439) *(G-14520)*

Productive Carbides Inc............................513 771-7092
10265 Spartan Dr Ste K Cincinnati (45215) *(G-4293)*

Producto Dieco Corporation (HQ)............................440 542-0000
30600 Aurora Rd Ste 160 Solon (44139) *(G-17364)*

Products Chemical, Cleveland *Also called Strib Industries Inc (G-6252)*

Products Innovators............................216 932-5269
2567 Lafayette Dr Cleveland (44118) *(G-6053)*

Proepo Software Ltd............................937 243-3825
609 E Paint St Wshngtn CT Hs (43160) *(G-20921)*

Profac Inc............................440 942-0205
7198 Industrial Park Blvd Mentor (44060) *(G-13698)*

Professional Award Service............................513 389-3600
3901 N Bend Rd Cincinnati (45211) *(G-4294)*

Professional Case Inc............................513 682-2520
9790 Inter Ocean Dr West Chester (45246) *(G-20041)*

Professional Detailing Pdts, Canton *Also called Ohio Auto Supply Company (G-2798)*

Professional Fabricators Inc............................216 362-1208
15708 Brookpark Rd Cleveland (44135) *(G-6054)*

Professional Grinding Inc............................330 628-3001
3001 Mogadore Rd Akron (44312) *(G-353)*

Professional Image Apparel Inc............................513 984-1111
11444 Rockfield Ct Cincinnati (45241) *(G-4295)*

Professional Image Inc............................513 984-1111
11444 Rockfield Ct Cincinnati (45241) *(G-4296)*

Professional Oilfield Services............................740 685-5168
221 1/2 S 6th St Byesville (43723) *(G-2409)*

Professional Packaging Company (PA)............................440 238-8850
22360 Royalton Rd Strongsville (44149) *(G-17954)*

Professional Plastics Corp............................614 336-2498
4863 Rays Cir Dublin (43016) *(G-9127)*

Professional Reports Corp............................330 492-6063
3976b Fulton Dr Nw Canton (44718) *(G-2826)*

Professional Screen Printing 740 687-0760
731 N Pierce Ave Lancaster (43130) *(G-11742)*

Professional Supply Inc 419 332-7373
504 Liberty St Fremont (43420) *(G-10177)*

Profetion Transport, Canal Winchester *Also called William Minnier (G-2541)*

Proficient Machining Co 440 942-4942
7522 Tyler Blvd Unit B-G Mentor (44060) *(G-13699)*

Proficient Plastics Inc 440 205-9700
7777 Saint Clair Ave Mentor (44060) *(G-13700)*

Profile Digital Printing LLC 937 866-4241
5449 Marina Dr Dayton (45449) *(G-8599)*

Profile Discovery, Columbus *Also called Profile Imaging Columbus LLC (G-7523)*

Profile Grinding Inc 216 351-0600
4593 Spring Rd Cleveland (44131) *(G-6055)*

Profile Imaging Columbus LLC 614 222-2888
46 N High St Ste 200 Columbus (43215) *(G-7523)*

Profile Plastics Inc 330 452-7000
1226 Prospect Ave Sw Canton (44706) *(G-2827)*

Profile Products LLC 330 452-2630
1525 Waynesburg Dr Se Canton (44707) *(G-2828)*

Profile Rubber Corporation 330 239-1703
6784 Ridge Rd Wadsworth (44281) *(G-19431)*

Profiles In Design Inc 513 751-2212
860 Dellway St Cincinnati (45229) *(G-4297)*

Profiles In Diversity Journal, Westlake *Also called Rector Inc (G-20301)*

Profit Energy Company Inc 740 472-1018
36829 Township Road 2067 Jerusalem (43747) *(G-11385)*

Proflo Industries LLC 419 436-6008
2679 S Us Highway 23 Alvada (44802) *(G-556)*

Proform Group Inc 614 332-9654
1715 Georgesville Rd Columbus (43228) *(G-7524)*

Proforma Advantage 440 781-5255
640 Som Center Rd Mayfield Village (44143) *(G-13325)*

Proforma Buckeye, Westerville *Also called Buckeye Business Forms Inc (G-20141)*

Proforma Cnr Marketing, Dayton *Also called Cnr Marketing Ltd (G-8233)*

Proforma Joe Thomas Group, Cleveland *Also called In-Touch Corp (G-5559)*

Proforma Print & Imaging 216 520-8400
655 Metro Pl S Ste 600 Dublin (43017) *(G-9128)*

Proforma Signature Solutions, Brooklyn Heights *Also called R&D Marketing Group Inc (G-2145)*

Proforma Solution Ventures, Avon Lake *Also called Solution Ventures Inc (G-1051)*

Proforma Steinbacher & Assoc 330 241-5370
3745 Medina Rd Ste A Medina (44256) *(G-13463)*

Proforma Systems Advantage 419 224-8747
1207 Findlay Rd Lima (45801) *(G-12076)*

Profound Logic Software Inc 937 439-7925
396 Congress Park Dr Dayton (45459) *(G-8600)*

Proft & Gamble 513 945-0340
6280 Center Hill Ave Cincinnati (45224) *(G-4298)*

Profusion Industries LLC (PA) 800 938-2858
822 Kumho Dr Ste 202 Fairlawn (44333) *(G-9758)*

Profusion Industries LLC 740 374-6400
700 Bf Goodrich Rd Marietta (45750) *(G-12821)*

Progage, Mentor *Also called Event Inc (G-13575)*

Programmable Control Service 740 927-0744
6900 Blacks Rd Sw Pataskala (43062) *(G-15978)*

Prographics, Cincinnati *Also called Franchise Services Inc (G-3777)*

Prographics Printing Center, Cincinnati *Also called Brent Carter Enterprises Inc (G-3468)*

Progress Tool & Stamping Inc 419 628-2384
207 Southgate Dr Minster (45865) *(G-14360)*

Progress Tool Co, Minster *Also called Progress Tool & Stamping Inc (G-14360)*

Progressive Automotive Inc 740 862-4696
125 W Rome St Baltimore (43105) *(G-1085)*

Progressive Book Binding Co, Northfield *Also called Progressive Folding Binding Co (G-15470)*

Progressive Communications 740 397-5333
18 E Vine St Mount Vernon (43050) *(G-14640)*

Progressive Foam Tech Inc 330 756-3200
6753 Chestnut Ridge Rd Nw Beach City (44608) *(G-1250)*

Progressive Folding Binding Co 216 621-1893
8082 Augusta Ln Northfield (44067) *(G-15470)*

Progressive Furniture Inc (HQ) 419 446-4500
502 Middle St Archbold (43502) *(G-690)*

Progressive International, Archbold *Also called Progressive Furniture Inc (G-690)*

Progressive Labels LLC 570 688-9636
38601 Kennedy Pkwy Willoughby (44094) *(G-20580)*

Progressive Machine Die Inc 330 405-6600
8406 Bavaria Dr E Macedonia (44056) *(G-12478)*

Progressive Manufacturing Co 330 784-4717
300 Massillon Rd Akron (44312) *(G-354)*

Progressive Molding Tech 330 220-7030
5234 Portside Dr Medina (44256) *(G-13464)*

Progressive Pain Relief, Cleveland *Also called Casselberry Clinic Inc (G-4990)*

Progressive Plastics, Cleveland *Also called Alpha Packaging Holdings Inc (G-4768)*

Progressive Powder Coating Inc 440 974-3478
7742 Tyler Blvd Mentor (44060) *(G-13701)*

Progressive Printers Inc 937 222-1267
884 Valley St Dayton (45404) *(G-8601)*

Progressive Printing Services 330 534-8501
264 W Liberty St Frnt Hubbard (44425) *(G-11138)*

Progressive Ribbon Inc (PA) 513 705-9319
1533 Central Ave Middletown (45044) *(G-14078)*

Progressive Stamping Inc 419 453-1111
200 Progressive Dr Ottoville (45876) *(G-15825)*

Progressive Tool Division, Delphos *Also called Van Wert Machine Inc (G-8926)*

Progressor Times 419 396-7567
1198 E Findlay St Carey (43316) *(G-2924)*

Progrssive Molding Bolivar Inc 330 874-3000
10882 Fort Laurens Rd Nw Bolivar (44612) *(G-1944)*

Progrssive Mtllizing Machining, Akron *Also called Progressive Manufacturing Co (G-354)*

Prohos Inc 419 877-0153
10755 Logan St Whitehouse (43571) *(G-20343)*

Prohos Manufacturing Co Inc 419 877-0153
10755 Logan St Whitehouse (43571) *(G-20344)*

Proimage Printing & Design LLC 937 312-9544
1803 Roxbury Dr Xenia (45385) *(G-20968)*

Project Aloha, New Albany *Also called Pinky & Thumb LLC (G-14769)*

Project Engineering Company 937 743-9114
3010 S Tech Blvd Miamisburg (45342) *(G-13849)*

Projects Designed & Built 419 726-7400
5949 American Rd E Toledo (43612) *(G-18659)*

Proline Screenwear 440 205-3700
8586 East Ave Mentor (44060) *(G-13702)*

Proline Truss 419 895-9980
29 Free Rd Shiloh (44878) *(G-17154)*

Promac Inc 937 864-1961
350 Conley Dr Enon (45323) *(G-9548)*

Promac International Inc 440 967-2040
1121 Sunnyside Rd Vermilion (44089) *(G-19336)*

Promatch Solutions LLC 937 299-0185
20 Heatherwoode Cir Springboro (45066) *(G-17500)*

Promo Costumes Inc 740 383-5176
381 W Center St Marion (43302) *(G-12893)*

Promold Inc 330 633-3532
487 Commerce St Tallmadge (44278) *(G-18165)*

Promold Gauer, Tallmadge *Also called Promold Inc (G-18165)*

Promotional Fixtures, Rittman *Also called Pfi Displays Inc (G-16681)*

Promotional Spring, Miamisburg *Also called Mound Printing Company Inc (G-13838)*

Promotions Plus Inc 440 582-2855
3402 Magnolia Way Broadview Heights (44147) *(G-2116)*

Proof Research Acd, Moraine *Also called Performnce Plymr Solutions Inc (G-14512)*

Property Assist Inc 419 480-1700
1755 W Sylvania Ave Toledo (43613) *(G-18660)*

Propipe Technologies Inc 513 424-5311
1800 Clayton Ave Middletown (45042) *(G-14079)*

Propress Inc 216 631-8200
3135 Berea Rd Ste 1 Cleveland (44111) *(G-6056)*

Prospect Mold & Die Company 330 929-3311
1100 Main St Cuyahoga Falls (44221) *(G-8037)*

Prospeed SEC Doorjamb Systems, Dayton *Also called Evil Corporation Corporation (G-8335)*

Prosperity On Payne Inc 216 431-7677
1814 E 40th St Ste 5e Cleveland (44103) *(G-6057)*

Prostar Machine & Tool Co 937 223-1997
2039 Webster St Dayton (45404) *(G-8602)*

Prostate Theranostics Inc 216 595-1968
2532 Fairwood Ct Beachwood (44122) *(G-1291)*

Prosthetic Design Inc 937 836-1464
700 Harco Dr Englewood (45315) *(G-9537)*

Protec Industries Incorporated 440 937-4142
1384 Lear Industrial Pkwy Avon (44011) *(G-1004)*

Protech Electric LLC 937 427-0813
1632 Beaverbrook Dr Beavercreek (45432) *(G-1357)*

Protech Industries, Avon *Also called Protec Industries Incorporated (G-1004)*

Protective Industrial Polymers 440 327-0015
7875 Bliss Pkwy North Ridgeville (44039) *(G-15396)*

Protective Packg Solutions LLC 513 769-5777
10345 S Medallion Dr Cincinnati (45241) *(G-4299)*

Protein Express Inc 513 769-9654
9940 Reading Rd Ste 1 Cincinnati (45241) *(G-4300)*

Protein Express Laboratories 513 769-9654
10931 R Hartman Hwy B Blue Ash (45242) *(G-1860)*

Protel Systems and Svcs LLC 419 893-2440
1298 Conant St Ste 504 Maumee (43537) *(G-13289)*

Protel Systems and Svcs LLC (PA) 419 913-0825
3453 Chapel Dr Toledo (43615) *(G-18661)*

Proteus Electronics Inc 419 886-2296
161 Spayde Rd Bellville (44813) *(G-1575)*

Protista Tool, Canton *Also called Gilbert Geiser (G-2714)*

Proto Machine & Mfg Inc 330 677-1700
2190 State Route 59 Kent (44240) *(G-11508)*

Proto Plastics Inc 937 667-8416
316 Park Ave Tipp City (45371) *(G-18295)*

Proto Precision Fabricators, Hilliard *Also called Vicart Prcsion Fabricators Inc (G-10992)*

A
L
P
H
A
B
E
T
I
C

Proto-Mold Products Co Inc 937 778-1959
1750 Commerce Dr Piqua (45356) *(G-16308)*

Protofab Manufacturing Inc 937 849-4983
8 University Rd Medway (45341) *(G-13501)*

Prototype Fabricators Co 216 252-0080
10911 Briggs Rd Cleveland (44111) *(G-6058)*

Prout Boiler Htg & Wldg Inc 330 744-0293
3124 Temple St Youngstown (44510) *(G-21180)*

PROVIA - HERITAGE STONE, Sugarcreek Also called Provia Door Inc *(G-18034)*

Provia Door Inc (PA) 330 852-4711
2150 State Route 39 Sugarcreek (44681) *(G-18034)*

Provia Stone LLC 740 450-4236
1550 County Road 140 Sugarcreek (44681) *(G-18035)*

Providence Group Inc 440 350-4615
5950 Pinecone Dr Mentor (44060) *(G-13703)*

Providence Rees Inc 614 833-6231
2111 Builders Pl Columbus (43204) *(G-7525)*

Provimi North America Inc 937 770-2400
6531 State Route 503 N Lewisburg (45338) *(G-11940)*

Provimi North America Inc (HQ) 937 770-2400
10 Collective Way Brookville (45309) *(G-2197)*

Province of St John The Baptis 513 241-5615
28 W Liberty St Cincinnati (45202) *(G-4301)*

Prowrite Inc 614 864-2004
7508 Slate Ridge Blvd Reynoldsburg (43068) *(G-16601)*

PS Copy, Westlake Also called Penguin Enterprises Inc *(G-20292)*

PS Graphics Inc 440 356-9656
20284 Orchard Grove Ave Rocky River (44116) *(G-16706)*

Psa Consulting Inc 513 382-4315
19 Garfield Pl Ste 211 Cincinnati (45202) *(G-4302)*

PSC Holdings Inc (PA) 740 454-6253
109 Graham St Zanesville (43701) *(G-21347)*

Psd Partners LLC (PA) 419 294-3838
5968 State Highway 199 Carey (43316) *(G-2925)*

PSI, Springboro Also called Paper Systems Incorporated *(G-17494)*

PSI Products, Canfield Also called Process Sltions For Indust Inc *(G-2570)*

PSK Steel Corp 330 759-1251
2960 Gale Dr Hubbard (44425) *(G-11139)*

Pt Tech, Sharon Center Also called Ebo Group Inc *(G-17105)*

Pt Tech Inc 330 239-4933
1441 Wolf Creek Trl Sharon Center (44274) *(G-17108)*

Ptc Enterprises Inc 419 272-2524
3047 County Road K Edon (43518) *(G-9344)*

Ptc Inc 513 791-0330
625 Eden Park Dr Ste 860 Cincinnati (45202) *(G-4303)*

Ptc Industries, Cleveland Also called Parking & Traffic Control SEC *(G-5977)*

Pti, Bowling Green Also called Phoenix Technologies Intl LLC *(G-2007)*

Ptmj Enterprises 440 543-8000
32000 Aurora Rd Solon (44139) *(G-17365)*

Ptr Daily LLC 330 673-1990
4501 Eastwicke Blvd Stow (44224) *(G-17793)*

Pts, Heath Also called Polymer Tech & Svcs Inc *(G-10851)*

Pubco Corporation (PA) 216 881-5300
3830 Kelley Ave Cleveland (44114) *(G-6059)*

Public Safety Ohio Department 216 283-4000
16945 Chagrin Blvd Cleveland (44120) *(G-6060)*

Public Safety Concepts LLC 614 733-0200
8495 Estates Ct Plain City (43064) *(G-16355)*

Public Safety Ohio Department 440 943-5545
31517 Vine St Willowick (44095) *(G-20650)*

Public Works Dept Street Div 740 283-6013
238 S Lake Erie St Steubenville (43952) *(G-17710)*

Publishing Company, Bellefontaine Also called Cathie D Hubbard *(G-1524)*

Publishing Group Ltd 614 572-1240
781 Northwest Blvd # 202 Columbus (43212) *(G-7526)*

Pucel Enterprises Inc 216 881-4604
1440 E 36th St Cleveland (44114) *(G-6061)*

Puddle Shark Studios Inc 440 286-2811
13035 Vista Pointe Dr Chardon (44024) *(G-3173)*

Puehler Tool Co 216 447-0101
7670 Hub Pkwy Cleveland (44125) *(G-6062)*

Pughs Designer Jewelers Inc 740 344-9259
44 S 2nd St Newark (43055) *(G-15049)*

Puhd 216 244-3336
20806 Aurora Rd Bedford (44146) *(G-1455)*

Pukka Inc (PA) 419 429-7808
337 S Main St Fl 4 Findlay (45840) *(G-9881)*

Pukka Headwear, Findlay Also called Pukka Inc *(G-9881)*

Pullman Company 419 592-2055
11800 County Road 424 Napoleon (43545) *(G-14693)*

Pullman Company 419 499-2541
33 Lockwood Rd Milan (44846) *(G-14115)*

Pulse Journal 513 829-7900
7320 Yankee Rd Liberty Township (45044) *(G-11965)*

Pumphrey Machine Corp 440 417-0481
7240 N Ridge Rd Madison (44057) *(G-12511)*

Pumps Group, The, Canton Also called ASC Holdco Inc *(G-2607)*

Pun-U, Cincinnati Also called Lifestyle Nutraceuticals Ltd *(G-4022)*

Punch Components Inc 419 224-1242
505 N Cable Rd Lima (45805) *(G-12077)*

Puppy Paws Inc 440 461-9667
6763 Stafford Dr Cleveland (44124) *(G-6063)*

Pure Light Technology LLC 513 779-7474
9624 Cincinnati Columbus West Chester (45241) *(G-20042)*

Pure Water Global Inc 419 737-2352
50 Industrial Ave Pioneer (43554) *(G-16242)*

Purebred Publishing Inc 614 339-5393
1224 Alton Darby Creek Rd C Columbus (43228) *(G-7527)*

Puremonics, Cleveland Also called CPI Group Limited *(G-5138)*

Purina Mills LLC 330 682-1951
635 Collins Blvd Orrville (44667) *(G-15755)*

Puritan Systems Inc 330 686-0527
2713 York Dr Stow (44224) *(G-17794)*

Puritas Metal Products Inc 440 353-1917
7720 Race Rd North Ridgeville (44039) *(G-15397)*

Purushealth LLC 800 601-0580
3558 Lee Rd Shaker Heights (44120) *(G-17093)*

Purvi Oil Inc 419 207-8234
654 Us Highway 250 E Ashland (44805) *(G-769)*

Purvis Milling Co, West Union Also called Dinsmore Inc *(G-20120)*

Putnam County Sentinel, Ottawa Also called Hirt Publishing Co Inc *(G-15794)*

Putnam County Sentinel, Ottawa Also called Hirt Publishing Co Inc *(G-15795)*

Putnam Plastics Inc 937 866-6261
255 S Alex Rd Dayton (45449) *(G-8603)*

Puttco Inc 937 299-1527
2613 Oakley Ave Dayton (45419) *(G-8604)*

Puttmann Industries Inc 513 202-9444
320 N State St Harrison (45030) *(G-10797)*

Pvh Corp 330 562-4440
549 S Chilcothe Rd Ste 340 Aurora (44202) *(G-941)*

Pvm Incorporated 614 871-0302
3515 Grove City Rd Grove City (43123) *(G-10587)*

PVS Chemical Solutions Inc 330 666-0888
3149 Copley Rd Copley (44321) *(G-7853)*

PVS Plastics Technology Corp 937 233-4376
6290 Executive Blvd Huber Heights (45424) *(G-11151)*

Pwi Inc 732 212-8110
5195 Hampsted Vlg Ctr Way New Albany (43054) *(G-14770)*

Pwp Inc 216 251-2181
3535 W 140th St Cleveland (44111) *(G-6064)*

PWS Welding & Mtg 330 385-6922
14533 E Liverpool Rd East Liverpool (43920) *(G-9226)*

Pyramid Mold & Machine Company, Kent Also called Pyramid Mold Inc *(G-11509)*

Pyramid Mold Inc 330 673-5200
222 Martinel Dr Kent (44240) *(G-11509)*

Pyramid Plastics Inc 216 641-5904
9202 Reno Ave Cleveland (44105) *(G-6065)*

Pyramid Rebuild and Mch LLC 330 633-4452
123 S Thomas Rd Tallmadge (44278) *(G-18166)*

Pyramid Treating Inc 330 325-2811
3031 Sanford Rd Atwater (44201) *(G-902)*

Pyro-Chem Corporation 740 377-2244
2491 County Road 1 South Point (45680) *(G-17445)*

Pyrograf Products Inc 937 766-2020
154 W Xenia Ave Cedarville (45314) *(G-2983)*

Pyromatics Corp (PA) 440 352-3500
9321 Pineneedle Dr Mentor (44060) *(G-13704)*

Pyrotechnics By Presutti Inc (PA) 740 699-1224
54911 High Ridge Rd Bellaire (43906) *(G-1501)*

Pyrotek Incorporated 440 349-8800
355 Campus Dr Aurora (44202) *(G-942)*

Q C A Inc 513 681-8400
2832 Spring Grove Ave Cincinnati (45225) *(G-4304)*

Q C Printing 419 475-4266
3650 Upton Ave Toledo (43613) *(G-18662)*

Q Holding Company (HQ) 330 425-8472
1700 Highland Rd Twinsburg (44087) *(G-19006)*

Q M C Pleasants Inc 937 278-7302
5648 Wadsworth Rd Dayton (45414) *(G-8605)*

Q M P, Cleves Also called Stock Mfg & Design Co Inc *(G-6528)*

Q Model Inc 330 673-0473
711 Wooster Rd W Barberton (44203) *(G-1144)*

Q Music USA LLC 239 995-5888
5730 Great Northern Blvd E1 North Olmsted (44070) *(G-15343)*

Q S I Fabrication 419 832-1680
10333 Us Route 24 Grand Rapids (43522) *(G-10444)*

Q T Columbus LLC 800 758-2410
1330 Stimmel Rd Columbus (43223) *(G-7528)*

Q-Lab Corporation (PA) 440 835-8700
800 Canterbury Rd Westlake (44145) *(G-20298)*

Q2power Technologies Inc (PA) 740 415-2073
1858 Cedar Hill Rd Lancaster (43130) *(G-11743)*

Qc Industrial Inc 740 642-5004
526 Red Bud Rd Chillicothe (45601) *(G-3269)*

Qc Plastics, Dayton Also called Queen City Polymers Inc *(G-8607)*

Qc Prntng By Quality Craft, Toledo Also called Q C Printing *(G-18662)*

Qc Software, Cincinnati Also called Queen City Software Inc *(G-4321)*

Qcforge.com, Cincinnati *Also called Queen City Forging Company (G-4316)*
Qcsm LLC 216 531-5960
  23582 Saint Clair Ave Euclid (44117) *(G-9602)*
Qibco Buffing Pads Inc (PA) 937 743-0805
  301 Industry Dr Ste B Carlisle (45005) *(G-2935)*
Qkardz.com, Columbus *Also called Johnson Brothers Holdings LLC (G-7240)*
Qleanair Scandinavia Inc 614 323-1272
  7670 Whitewood Ct Columbus (43235) *(G-7529)*
Qlog Corp 513 874-1211
  33 Standen Dr Hamilton (45015) *(G-10732)*
Qm Scientific LLP 513 250-2397
  3344 Lakeview St Cincinnati (45211) *(G-4305)*
Qol Meds, Canton *Also called Specialized Pharmaceuticals (G-2853)*
Qp Manufacturing Co Inc 440 946-2120
  215 5th Ave Chardon (44024) *(G-3174)*
Qpi Cincinnati LLC 513 755-2670
  6455 Gano Rd West Chester (45069) *(G-19924)*
Qpi Multipress Inc 614 228-0185
  2222 S 3rd St Columbus (43207) *(G-7530)*
Qpmr Inc 330 723-1739
  7599 Hidden Acres Dr Medina (44256) *(G-13465)*
Qsi, Fairport Harbor *Also called Quartz Scientific Inc (G-9770)*
Qsr, Twinsburg *Also called Lexington Rubber Group Inc (G-18973)*
QT Equipment Company (PA) 330 724-3055
  151 W Dartmore Ave Akron (44301) *(G-355)*
Quad Fluid Dynamics Inc 330 220-3005
  2826 Westway Dr Brunswick (44212) *(G-2250)*
Quad/Graphics Inc 614 276-4800
  4051 Fondorf Dr Columbus (43228) *(G-7531)*
Quad/Graphics Inc 513 932-1064
  760 Fujitec Dr Lebanon (45036) *(G-11830)*
Quadcast 330 854-4511
  6845 Erie Ave Nw Canal Fulton (44614) *(G-2511)*
Quadco Rehabilitation Center (PA) 419 682-1011
  427 N Defiance St Stryker (43557) *(G-18006)*
Quadco Rehabilitation Center 419 445-1950
  600 Oak St Archbold (43502) *(G-691)*
Quadra - Tech Inc 614 445-0690
  864 E Jenkins Ave Columbus (43207) *(G-7532)*
Quadrel Inc 440 602-4700
  7670 Jenther Dr Mentor (44060) *(G-13705)*
Quadrel Labeling Systems, Mentor *Also called Quadrel Inc (G-13705)*
Quadriga Americas LLC (HQ) 614 890-6090
  480 Olde Worthington Rd # 350 Westerville (43082) *(G-20180)*
Quaker Chemical Corporation 216 265-5079
  5400 Chevrolet Blvd Cleveland (44130) *(G-6066)*
Quaker Chemical Corporation (HQ) 513 422-9600
  3431 Yankee Rd Middletown (45044) *(G-14080)*
Quaker City Casting, Salem *Also called Korff Holdings LLC (G-16905)*
Quaker City Septic Tanks LLC 330 427-2239
  290 E High St Leetonia (44431) *(G-11864)*
Quaker Express Stamping Inc 330 332-9266
  1134 Salem Pkwy Salem (44460) *(G-16921)*
Quaker Mfg Corp 330 332-4631
  187 Georgetown Rd Salem (44460) *(G-16922)*
Qual-Fab Inc 440 327-5000
  34250 Mills Rd Avon (44011) *(G-1005)*
Qualco LLC 614 257-7408
  2211 S James Rd Columbus (43232) *(G-7533)*
Quali-Tee Design Sports 937 382-7997
  59 W Sugartree St Wilmington (45177) *(G-20675)*
Quali-Tee Design Sportswear, Wilmington *Also called Quali-Tee Design Sports (G-20675)*
Qualico Inc 216 271-2550
  3201 E 66th St Cleveland (44127) *(G-6067)*
Qualiform Inc 330 336-6777
  689 Weber Dr Wadsworth (44281) *(G-19432)*
Qualitech Associates Inc 216 265-8702
  11324 Brookpark Rd Cleveland (44130) *(G-6068)*
Qualitee Design Sportswear Co (PA) 740 333-8337
  1270 Us Highway 22 Nw # 9 Wshngtn CT Hs (43160) *(G-20922)*
Qualitor Inc (PA) 248 204-8600
  1840 Mccullough St Lima (45801) *(G-12078)*
Qualiturn Inc 513 868-3333
  9081 Le Saint Dr West Chester (45014) *(G-19925)*
Quality Architectural and Fabr 937 743-2923
  8 Shotwell Dr Franklin (45005) *(G-10046)*
Quality Assurance, Fremont *Also called Kraft Heinz Foods Company (G-10162)*
Quality Bakery Company Inc (HQ) 614 846-2232
  380 Polaris Pkwy Ste 400 Westerville (43082) *(G-20181)*
Quality Bakery Company Inc 614 224-1424
  50 N Glenwood Ave Columbus (43222) *(G-7534)*
Quality Bar Inc 330 755-0000
  17 Union St Ste 7 Struthers (44471) *(G-17996)*
Quality Black Oxide, Dayton *Also called Hayes Metalfinishing Inc (G-8386)*
Quality Block & Supply Inc (HQ) 330 364-4411
  Rr 250 Mount Eaton (44659) *(G-14556)*
Quality Blow Molding Inc 440 458-6550
  635 Oberlin Elyria Rd Elyria (44035) *(G-9481)*

Quality Borate Co LLC 216 896-1949
  3690 Orange Pl Ste 495 Cleveland (44122) *(G-6069)*
Quality Castings Company (PA) 330 682-6871
  1200 N Main St Orrville (44667) *(G-15756)*
Quality Channel Letters 859 866-6500
  1115 N 11th St Miamisburg (45342) *(G-13850)*
Quality CNC Machining Inc 440 942-0542
  38195 Airport Pkwy Willoughby (44094) *(G-20581)*
Quality Components Inc 440 255-0606
  8825 East Ave Mentor (44060) *(G-13706)*
Quality Compound Mfg 440 353-0150
  5212 Mills Indus Pkwy North Ridgeville (44039) *(G-15398)*
Quality Concepts Telecom 740 385-2003
  19485 Harble Rd Logan (43138) *(G-12191)*
Quality Controls Inc 513 272-3900
  3411 Church St Cincinnati (45244) *(G-4306)*
Quality Craft Machine Inc 330 928-4064
  137 Ascot Pkwy Cuyahoga Falls (44223) *(G-8038)*
Quality Craftsman Inc 740 474-9685
  28155 River Dr Circleville (43113) *(G-4639)*
Quality Cutter Grinding Co 216 362-6444
  15501 Commerce Park Dr Cleveland (44142) *(G-6070)*
Quality Design Machining Inc 440 352-7290
  9349 Hamilton Dr Mentor (44060) *(G-13707)*
Quality Drble Indus Floors Inc 937 696-2833
  5005 Frmrsvll Germntwn Pa Farmersville (45325) *(G-9773)*
Quality Electrodynamics LLC 440 638-5106
  6655 Beta Dr Ste 100 Mayfield Village (44143) *(G-13326)*
Quality Envelope Inc 513 942-7578
  9792 Inter Ocean Dr West Chester (45246) *(G-20043)*
Quality Fabricated Metals Inc 330 332-7008
  14000 W Middletown Rd Salem (44460) *(G-16923)*
Quality Fabrications LLC 330 695-2478
  7108 Township Road 569 Fredericksburg (44627) *(G-10091)*
Quality Forms, Piqua *Also called Little Printing Company (G-16286)*
Quality Frp Fabrications 440 942-9067
  1450 E 363rd St Willoughby (44095) *(G-20582)*
Quality Gold Inc (PA) 513 942-7659
  500 Quality Blvd Fairfield (45014) *(G-9706)*
Quality Image Embroidery & AP 440 230-1109
  2643 Royalwood Rd Broadview Heights (44147) *(G-2117)*
Quality Industries Inc 216 961-5566
  3716 Clark Ave Cleveland (44109) *(G-6071)*
Quality Innovative Pdts LLC 330 990-9888
  787 Wye Rd Akron (44333) *(G-356)*
Quality Machine, Dayton *Also called Q M C Pleasants Inc (G-8605)*
Quality Machine 330 877-6163
  6788 Center St Ne Hartville (44632) *(G-10831)*
Quality Machine Systems LLC 440 223-2217
  7875 Enterprise Dr Mentor (44060) *(G-13708)*
Quality Machining and Mfg Inc 419 899-2543
  14168 State Route 18 Sherwood (43556) *(G-17147)*
Quality Match Plate Co 330 889-2462
  4211 State Route 534 Southington (44470) *(G-17454)*
Quality Mechanicals Inc 513 559-0998
  1225 Streng St Cincinnati (45223) *(G-4307)*
Quality Metal Products Inc 440 355-6165
  210 Commerce Dr Lagrange (44050) *(G-11636)*
Quality Metal Works, Cleveland *Also called Rezmann Karoly (G-6110)*
Quality Mfg Company Inc 513 921-4500
  4323 Spring Grove Ave Cincinnati (45223) *(G-4308)*
Quality Mold Inc 419 752-4511
  49 N Kniffin St Greenwich (44837) *(G-10534)*
Quality Mold Inc (PA) 330 645-6653
  2200 Massillon Rd Akron (44312) *(G-357)*
Quality Molded 330 645-6653
  2200 Massillon Rd Akron (44312) *(G-358)*
Quality Mtrlogy Stym Solutions 937 431-1800
  425 Mill Stone Dr Beavercreek (45434) *(G-1358)*
Quality Oil & Gas Corp 330 821-6375
  1654 S Union Ave Alliance (44601) *(G-534)*
Quality Parts, Jackson Center *Also called A G Parts Inc (G-11336)*
Quality Plastic Machine Repair, Medina *Also called Qpmr Inc (G-13465)*
Quality Plating Co 216 361-0151
  1443 E 40th St Cleveland (44103) *(G-6072)*
Quality Pllets Recyclables LLC 419 396-3244
  410 E Findlay St Carey (43316) *(G-2926)*
Quality Poly Corp 330 453-9559
  3000 Atlantic Blvd Ne Rear Canton (44705) *(G-2829)*
Quality Print Shop Inc 740 992-3345
  255 Mill St Middleport (45760) *(G-14011)*
Quality Printing & Publishing, Hamilton *Also called Quality Publishing Co (G-10733)*
Quality Printing Co, Bucyrus *Also called Bucyrus Graphics Inc (G-2333)*
Quality Products Inc (PA) 614 228-0185
  2222 S 3rd St Columbus (43207) *(G-7535)*
Quality Publishing Co 513 863-8210
  3200 Symmes Rd Hamilton (45015) *(G-10733)*
Quality Quartz Engineering Inc 937 236-3250
  131 Janney Rd Dayton (45404) *(G-8606)*

A
L
P
H
A
B
E
T
I
C

Quality Quartz of America Inc 440 352-2851
9362 Hamilton Dr Mentor (44060) *(G-13709)*

Quality Quick Print, Troy *Also called Western Ohio Graphics (G-18885)*

Quality Ready Mix Inc 419 738-2817
Quarry Dr Bluffton (45817) *(G-1914)*

Quality Ready Mix Inc 419 394-9097
16672 County Road 66a Saint Marys (45885) *(G-16851)*

Quality Ready Mix Inc (PA) 419 394-8870
16672 County Road 66a Saint Marys (45885) *(G-16852)*

Quality Replacement Parts Inc 216 674-0200
9099 Bank St Ste 2 Cleveland (44125) *(G-6073)*

Quality Reproductions Inc 330 335-5000
127 Hartman Rd Wadsworth (44281) *(G-19433)*

Quality Rubber Stamp Inc 614 235-2700
3314 Refugee Rd Columbus (43232) *(G-7536)*

Quality Screw Products Inc 440 975-1828
38302 Arprt Pkwy Unit 15 Willoughby (44094) *(G-20583)*

Quality Seating Company Inc 330 747-0181
4136 Logan Way Youngstown (44505) *(G-21181)*

Quality Security Door & Mfg Co (PA) 440 246-0770
1925 Broadway Lorain (44052) *(G-12269)*

Quality Sewing Inc 216 475-0411
5656 Dunham Rd Cleveland (44137) *(G-6074)*

Quality Specialists Inc 440 946-9129
1428 E 363rd St Willoughby (44095) *(G-20584)*

Quality Spt & Silk Screen Sp 513 769-8300
9217 Reading Rd Cincinnati (45215) *(G-4309)*

Quality Spt Silk Screen & EMB, Cincinnati *Also called Quality Spt & Silk Screen Sp (G-4309)*

Quality Stamp Co, East Liverpool *Also called Innovative Ceramic Corp (G-9219)*

Quality Stamping, Toledo *Also called Quality Tool Company (G-18663)*

Quality Stamping Products Co (PA) 216 441-2700
5322 Bragg Rd Cleveland (44127) *(G-6075)*

Quality Steel Fabrication 937 492-9503
2339 Industrial Dr Sidney (45365) *(G-17213)*

Quality Stitch Embroidery Inc 614 237-0480
3892 E Broad St Columbus (43213) *(G-7537)*

Quality Switch Inc 330 872-5707
715 Arlington Blvd Newton Falls (44444) *(G-15138)*

Quality Synthetic Rubber, Twinsburg *Also called Q Holding Company (G-19006)*

Quality Tool Company 419 476-8228
577 Mel Simon Dr Toledo (43612) *(G-18663)*

Quality Tooling Systems Inc 330 722-5025
650 W Smith Rd Ste 4 Medina (44256) *(G-13466)*

Quality Tube Service Inc 419 237-3014
701 E Industrial Pkwy Fayette (43521) *(G-9778)*

Quality Welding Inc 419 483-6067
104 Ronald Ln Bellevue (44811) *(G-1554)*

Quality-Service Products Inc 614 447-9522
528 E Hudson St Columbus (43202) *(G-7538)*

Qualtech NP, Batavia *Also called Curtiss-Wright Flow Control (G-1175)*

Qualtech NP, Cincinnati *Also called Curtiss-Wright Flow Ctrl Corp (G-3298)*

Qualtech NP, Cincinnati *Also called Curtiss-Wright Flow Control (G-3297)*

Qualtech Technologies Inc 440 946-8081
1685b Joseph Lloyd Pkwy Willoughby (44094) *(G-20585)*

Qualtek Electronics Corp 440 951-3300
7610 Jenther Dr Mentor (44060) *(G-13710)*

Quanex Building Products, Solon *Also called Quanex Ig Systems Inc (G-17366)*

Quanex Ig Systems Inc 740 439-2338
800 Cochran Ave Cambridge (43725) *(G-2473)*

Quanex Ig Systems Inc (HQ) 216 910-1519
6680 Parkland Blvd Solon (44139) *(G-17366)*

Quanex Screens LLC 419 662-5001
7597 Broadmoor Rd Perrysburg (43551) *(G-16145)*

Quantem Fbo Services 603 647-6763
1077 Celestial St Cincinnati (45202) *(G-4310)*

Quantum 740 328-2548
400 Case Ave Newark (43055) *(G-15050)*

Quantum Athletics LLC 513 248-2966
724 Stanton Ave Terrace Park (45174) *(G-18182)*

Quantum Commerce LLC 513 777-0737
6748 Dimmick Rd West Chester (45069) *(G-19926)*

Quantum Energy LLC (PA) 440 285-7381
10405 Locust Grove Dr Chardon (44024) *(G-3175)*

Quantum Integration Llc 330 609-0355
1980 Niles Cortland Rd Ne Cortland (44410) *(G-7874)*

Quantum Jewelry Dist 330 678-2222
4631 Mogadore Rd Kent (44240) *(G-11510)*

Quantum Sails 567 283-5335
207 W Water St Sandusky (44870) *(G-16998)*

Quantum Technologies Inc 330 645-2762
2634 S Arlington Rd # 101 Akron (44319) *(G-359)*

Quantum Techonology & Services 937 642-2929
648 Clymer Rd Marysville (43040) *(G-12964)*

Quantum World Technologies 937 747-3018
6973 Township Road 177 Zanesfield (43360) *(G-21262)*

Quarrymasters Inc 330 612-0474
7761 Hill Church St Se Canton (44730) *(G-2830)*

Quarter Bistro 513 271-5400
6904 Wooster Pike Cincinnati (45227) *(G-4311)*

Quarter Mile Fabrication LLC 440 298-1272
7289 Leroy Thompson Rd Thompson (44086) *(G-18190)*

Quartz, Mentor *Also called Aco Polymer Products Inc (G-13508)*

Quartz Scientific Inc (PA) 360 574-6254
819 East St Fairport Harbor (44077) *(G-9770)*

Quasonix Inc (PA) 513 942-1287
6025 Schumacher Park Dr West Chester (45069) *(G-19927)*

Quass Sheet Metal Inc 330 477-4841
5018 Yukon St Nw Canton (44708) *(G-2831)*

Quayle Consulting Inc 614 868-1363
8572 N Spring Ct Pickerington (43147) *(G-16202)*

Qube Corporation 440 543-2393
16744 W Park Circle Dr Chagrin Falls (44023) *(G-3115)*

Quebecor World Johnson Hardin 614 326-0299
3600 Red Bank Rd Cincinnati (45227) *(G-4312)*

Queen City Awning & Tent Co 513 530-9660
7225 E Kemper Rd Cincinnati (45249) *(G-4313)*

Queen City Bearers, Amelia *Also called Queen City Tool Company Inc (G-582)*

Queen City Carpets LLC 513 823-8238
6539 Harrison Ave 304 Cincinnati (45247) *(G-4314)*

Queen City Foam Inc 513 741-7722
3244 Mcgill Rd Cincinnati (45251) *(G-4315)*

Queen City Forging Company 513 321-2003
235b Tennyson St Cincinnati (45226) *(G-4316)*

Queen City Office Machine 513 251-7200
492 Pedretti Ave Cincinnati (45238) *(G-4317)*

Queen City Pallets 513 200-6426
7744 Reinhold Dr Cincinnati (45237) *(G-4318)*

Queen City Paper, Cincinnati *Also called Vemuri International LLC (G-4559)*

Queen City Polymers, West Chester *Also called Riotech International Ltd (G-19933)*

Queen City Polymers Inc (PA) 513 779-0990
6101 Schumacher Park Dr West Chester (45069) *(G-19928)*

Queen City Polymers Inc 937 236-2710
365 Leo St Dayton (45404) *(G-8607)*

Queen City Reprographics 513 326-2300
2863 E Sharon Rd Cincinnati (45241) *(G-4319)*

Queen City Sausage & Provision 513 541-5581
1136 Straight St Cincinnati (45214) *(G-4320)*

Queen City Software Inc 513 469-1424
11800 Conrey Rd Ste 150 Cincinnati (45249) *(G-4321)*

Queen City Steel Treating Co, Cincinnati *Also called Fbf Limited (G-3746)*

Queen City Technologies 513 253-1312
34 W Crescentville Rd West Chester (45246) *(G-20044)*

Queen City Tool Company Inc 513 752-4200
3939 Bach Buxton Rd Amelia (45102) *(G-582)*

Queen City Tool Works Inc 513 874-0111
125 Constitution Dr Ste 2 Fairfield (45014) *(G-9707)*

Ques Industries Inc 216 267-8989
5420 W 140th St Cleveland (44142) *(G-6076)*

Quest Lasercut, Franklin *Also called Quest Technologies Inc (G-10047)*

Quest Service Labs, Twinsburg *Also called A E Wilson Holdings Inc (G-18888)*

Quest Solutions Group LLC 513 703-4520
8046 Green Lake Dr Liberty Township (45044) *(G-11966)*

Quest Technologies Inc 937 743-1200
600 Commerce Center Dr Franklin (45005) *(G-10047)*

Quest Tool & Machine Ltd 937 969-8782
1675 W County Line Rd Urbana (43078) *(G-19174)*

Questline Inc 614 255-3166
5500 Frantz Rd Ste 156 Dublin (43017) *(G-9129)*

Questmark, Cincinnati *Also called Diversipak Inc (G-3658)*

Quez Media Marketing Inc 216 910-0202
1138 Prospect Ave E Cleveland (44115) *(G-6077)*

Quick As A Wink Printing Co 419 224-9786
321 W High St Lima (45801) *(G-12079)*

Quick Loadz Delivery Sys LLC 888 304-3946
185 W Canal St Nelsonville (45764) *(G-14735)*

Quick Print, Lorain *Also called Slutzkers Quickprint Center (G-12278)*

Quick Print, Canton *Also called USA Quickprint Inc (G-2892)*

Quick Print Center, New Philadelphia *Also called Robert H Shackelford (G-14926)*

Quick Service Welding & Mch Co 330 673-3818
117 E Summit St Kent (44240) *(G-11511)*

Quick Sign Works, Cincinnati *Also called Brent Bleh Company (G-3467)*

Quick Tab II Inc (PA) 419 448-6622
241 Heritage Dr Tiffin (44883) *(G-18238)*

Quick Tech Business Forms Inc 937 743-5952
408 Sharts Dr Springboro (45066) *(G-17501)*

Quick Tech Graphics Inc 937 743-5952
408 Sharts Dr Frnt Springboro (45066) *(G-17502)*

Quickdraft Inc 330 477-4574
1525 Perry Dr Sw Canton (44710) *(G-2832)*

Quickstitch Plus LLC 614 476-3186
124 Granville St Columbus (43230) *(G-7539)*

Quik-Pro, Ashland *Also called Paullin Driveway Sealing (G-763)*

Quikey Manufacturing Co Inc (PA) 330 633-8106
1500 Industrial Pkwy Akron (44310) *(G-360)*

Quikrete Cincinnati, Harrison *Also called Quikrete Companies Inc (G-10798)*

Quikrete Companies Inc 614 885-4406
6225 Huntley Rd Columbus (43229) *(G-7540)*

Quikrete Companies Inc 513 367-6135
  5425 Kilby Rd Harrison (45030) *(G-10798)*
Quikrete Companies Inc 419 241-1148
  873 Western Ave Toledo (43609) *(G-18664)*
Quikrete Companies Inc 330 296-6080
  2693 Lake Rockwell Rd Ravenna (44266) *(G-16551)*
Quikrete of Cleveland, Ravenna Also called Quikrete Companies Inc *(G-16551)*
Quikspray, Port Clinton Also called Quikstir Inc *(G-16410)*
Quikstir Inc 419 732-2601
  2105 W Lakeshore Dr Port Clinton (43452) *(G-16410)*
Quilting Inc (PA) 614 504-5971
  7600 Industrial Pkwy Plain City (43064) *(G-16356)*
Quilting Creations Intl 330 874-4741
  8778 Towpath Rd Ne Bolivar (44612) *(G-1945)*
Quintus Technologies LLC 614 891-2732
  8270 Green Meadows Dr N Lewis Center (43035) *(G-11912)*
Qumont Chemical Co 419 241-1057
  359 Hamilton St Ste 3 Toledo (43604) *(G-18665)*
Qure Medical, Twinsburg Also called Medical Elastomer Dev Inc *(G-18983)*
R & A Sports Inc 216 289-2254
  23780 Lakeland Blvd Euclid (44132) *(G-9603)*
R & B Enterprises USA Inc 330 674-2227
  1868 County Road 150 Millersburg (44654) *(G-14257)*
R & B Machining Inc (PA) 937 698-3528
  2695 Progress Way Wilmington (45177) *(G-20676)*
R & B Machining Inc 937 382-6710
  2695 Progress Way Wilmington (45177) *(G-20677)*
R & C Lortcher LLC 419 663-1531
  1384 Ridge Rd Norwalk (44857) *(G-15560)*
R & D Custom Machine & Tool 419 727-1700
  5961 American Rd E Toledo (43612) *(G-18666)*
R & D Equipment Inc 419 668-8439
  206 Republic St Norwalk (44857) *(G-15561)*
R & D Group, Columbus Also called Research and Development Group *(G-7556)*
R & D Hilltop Lumber Inc 740 342-3051
  2126 State Route 93 Se New Lexington (43764) *(G-14852)*
R & H Signs Unlimited Inc 937 293-3834
  3048 Wilmington Pike Dayton (45429) *(G-8608)*
R & J AG Manufacturing Inc 419 962-4707
  821 State Route 511 Ashland (44805) *(G-770)*
R & J Bardon Inc 614 457-5500
  4676 Larwell Dr Columbus (43220) *(G-7541)*
R & J Contracting, Caledonia Also called Jeffery A Burns *(G-2439)*
R & J Cylinder & Machine Inc 330 364-8263
  2155 Progress St Dover (44622) *(G-9007)*
R & J Drilling Company Inc 740 763-3991
  18586 Pinewood Trl Frazeysburg (43822) *(G-10076)*
R & J Printing Enterprises Inc 330 343-1242
  111 N Walnut St Dover (44622) *(G-9008)*
R & J Tool Inc 937 833-3200
  10550 Upper Lewisburg Brookville (45309) *(G-2198)*
R & K Industrial Supply, Coshocton Also called T JS Oil & Gas Inc *(G-7912)*
R & L Hydraulics Inc 937 399-3407
  109 Tremont City Rd Springfield (45502) *(G-17632)*
R & L Software LLC (PA) 513 847-4942
  421 Breaden Dr Ste 3 Monroe (45050) *(G-14412)*
R & L Truss Inc 419 587-3440
  17985 Road 60 Grover Hill (45849) *(G-10653)*
R & L Wood Products 937 444-2496
  16137 Eastwood Rd Williamsburg (45176) *(G-20411)*
R & M Fluid Power Inc 330 758-2766
  7953 Southern Blvd Youngstown (44512) *(G-21182)*
R & M Grinding Inc 513 732-3330
  5080 State Rd 132 Owensville (45160) *(G-15833)*
R & M Imports 513 897-5015
  3313 Harlan Carroll Rd Waynesville (45068) *(G-19734)*
R & M Welding Co 330 264-4788
  5663 Shreve Rd Wooster (44691) *(G-20826)*
R & R Comfort Experts LLC 216 475-3995
  13370 Hathaway Rd Cleveland (44125) *(G-6078)*
R & R Engine & Machine, Akron Also called Chemequip Sales Inc *(G-120)*
R & R Machine & Tool Co 216 281-7609
  3148 W 32nd St Ste 3 Cleveland (44109) *(G-6079)*
R & R Tool Inc 937 783-8665
  1449a Middleboro Rd Blanchester (45107) *(G-1715)*
R & S Label, Oberlin Also called RR Donnelley & Sons Company *(G-15647)*
R & S Monitions Inc 614 846-0597
  181 Rosslyn Ave Columbus (43214) *(G-7542)*
R & T Microcenters of Ohio, Toledo Also called T E Hubler Inc *(G-18714)*
R & W Printing Company 513 575-0131
  1394 Stella Dr Loveland (45140) *(G-12379)*
R A Hamed International Inc 330 247-0190
  8400 Darrow Rd Twinsburg (44087) *(G-19007)*
R A Heller Company 513 771-6100
  10530 Chester Rd Cincinnati (45215) *(G-4322)*
R A K Machine Inc 216 631-7750
  5900 Walworth Ave Cleveland (44102) *(G-6080)*
R A M Plastics Co Inc 330 549-3107
  11401 South Ave North Lima (44452) *(G-15322)*

R A M Precision Tool, Dayton Also called Ram Precision Industries Inc *(G-8614)*
R and D Incorporated 216 581-6328
  16645 Granite Rd Maple Heights (44137) *(G-12738)*
R and D Industries Unlimited 937 502-1374
  1030 Mcpherson Rd Xenia (45385) *(G-20969)*
R and J Corporation 440 871-6009
  24142 Detroit Rd Westlake (44145) *(G-20299)*
R and S Technologies 419 483-3691
  2474 State Route 4 Bellevue (44811) *(G-1555)*
R Anthony Enterprises LLC 419 341-0961
  2626 Whetstone River Rd S Marion (43302) *(G-12894)*
R B Mfg Co 419 626-9464
  4101 Venice Rd Sandusky (44870) *(G-16999)*
R B Robinson Inc 440 543-5547
  17800 Chillicothe Rd # 112 Chagrin Falls (44023) *(G-3116)*
R C A Rubber Company 330 784-1291
  1833 E Market St Akron (44305) *(G-361)*
R C Family Wood Products 937 295-2393
  5590 State Route 47 Fort Loramie (45845) *(G-9935)*
R C L Enterprises Inc 972 390-6500
  8805 Governors Hill Dr # 400 Cincinnati (45249) *(G-4323)*
R C M, Akron Also called Rubber City Machinery Corp *(G-380)*
R C Moore Lumber Co 740 732-4950
  820 Miller St Caldwell (43724) *(G-2431)*
R C Musson Rubber Co 330 773-7651
  1320 E Archwood Ave Akron (44306) *(G-362)*
R C Packaging Systems 248 684-6363
  6277 Heisley Rd Mentor (44060) *(G-13711)*
R C Poling Company Inc 740 939-0023
  2105 Clay Rd Junction City (43748) *(G-11411)*
R Carney Thomas 740 342-3388
  1600 Commerce Dr New Lexington (43764) *(G-14853)*
R D Baker Enterprises Inc 937 461-5225
  765 Liberty Ln Dayton (45449) *(G-8609)*
R D Cook Company LLC 614 262-0550
  883 E Hudson St Columbus (43211) *(G-7543)*
R D Holder Oil Co Inc 740 522-3136
  1000 Keller Dr Heath (43056) *(G-10852)*
R D Thompson Paper Pdts Co Inc 419 994-3614
  1 Madison St Loudonville (44842) *(G-12303)*
R Design & Printing Co 614 299-1420
  30 E 4th Ave Columbus (43201) *(G-7544)*
R Dunn Mold Inc 937 773-3388
  9055 State Route 66 Piqua (45356) *(G-16309)*
R E H Company Inc 513 242-0011
  5609 Center Hill Ave Cincinnati (45216) *(G-4324)*
R E May Inc 216 771-6332
  1401 E 24th St Cleveland (44114) *(G-6081)*
R E Smith Inc 513 771-0645
  10330 Chester Rd Cincinnati (45215) *(G-4325)*
R F Cook Manufacturing Co, Stow Also called Levan Enterprises Inc *(G-17769)*
R F W Holdings Inc 440 331-8300
  1200 Smith Ct Cleveland (44116) *(G-6082)*
R G C Inc 513 683-3110
  507 Loveland Madeira Rd Loveland (45140) *(G-12380)*
R Gordon Jones Inc 740 986-8381
  20849 Five Points Pike Williamsport (43164) *(G-20418)*
R H Industries Inc 216 281-5210
  3155 W 33rd St Cleveland (44109) *(G-6083)*
R H Little Co 330 477-3455
  4434 Southway St Sw Canton (44706) *(G-2833)*
R Houston Son Sndblst Spclists (PA) 513 367-5252
  115 May Dr Harrison (45030) *(G-10799)*
R J Cox Co 937 548-4699
  8903 State Route 571 Arcanum (45304) *(G-658)*
R J Displays, Toledo Also called Hill John *(G-18508)*
R J Dobay Enterprises Inc 440 834-4580
  14704 Main Market Rd Burton (44021) *(G-2382)*
R J Engineering Company Inc 419 843-8651
  2860 Heysler Rd Toledo (43617) *(G-18667)*
R J K Enterprises Inc 440 257-6018
  5565 Wilson Dr Mentor (44060) *(G-13712)*
R J Silvia 740 400-4066
  1235 E Walnut St Lancaster (43130) *(G-11744)*
R K Industries Inc 419 523-5001
  725 N Locust St Ottawa (45875) *(G-15806)*
R K Metals Ltd 513 874-6055
  3235 Homeward Way Fairfield (45014) *(G-9708)*
R K S Tool & Die Inc 513 870-0225
  200 Security Dr Fairfield (45014) *(G-9709)*
R L Corbett Co, The, Cleveland Also called Modern Design Stamping Div *(G-5826)*
R L Craig Inc 330 424-1525
  6496 State Route 45 Lisbon (44432) *(G-12133)*
R L Drake Company 937 746-4556
  230 Industrial Dr Franklin (45005) *(G-10048)*
R L Drake Holdings LLC (HQ) 937 746-4556
  710 Pleasant Valley Dr Springboro (45066) *(G-17503)*
R L Industries Inc 513 874-2800
  9355 Le Saint Dr West Chester (45014) *(G-19929)*

R L Parsons & Son Equipment Co 614 879-7601
7155 State Route 142 Se West Jefferson (43162) *(G-20083)*

R L Rush Tool & Pattern Inc 419 562-9849
1620 Whetstone St Bucyrus (44820) *(G-2356)*

R L S Corporation 740 773-1440
990 Eastern Ave Chillicothe (45601) *(G-3270)*

R L S Recycling, Chillicothe *Also called R L S Corporation (G-3270)*

R L Technologies Inc (PA) 937 321-5544
1711 Mccall St Dayton (45402) *(G-8610)*

R L Torbeck Industries Inc 513 367-0080
355 Industrial Dr Harrison (45030) *(G-10800)*

R L Y Inc 513 385-1950
5874 Cheviot Rd Cincinnati (45247) *(G-4326)*

R M Davis Inc 419 756-6719
517 Walfield Dr Mansfield (44904) *(G-12669)*

R M Industries Inc 419 529-8970
95 Ohio Brass Rd Mansfield (44902) *(G-12670)*

R M Tool & Die Inc 440 238-6459
19768 Progress Dr Strongsville (44149) *(G-17955)*

R M Welding Products 937 260-4510
1944 Stanley Ave Dayton (45404) *(G-8611)*

R M Wood Co 419 845-2661
5795 County Road 30 Mount Gilead (43338) *(G-14566)*

R M Yates Co Inc 216 441-0900
4452 Warner Rd Cleveland (44105) *(G-6084)*

R Molds, Euclid *Also called California Ceramic Supply Co (G-9569)*

R P A, Dayton *Also called Rpa Electronic Distrs Inc (G-8639)*

R R Donnelley, Hebron *Also called RR Donnelley & Sons Company (G-10882)*

R R Donnelley, Streetsboro *Also called RR Donnelley & Sons Company (G-17872)*

R R R Development Co (PA) 330 966-8855
8817 Pleasantwood Ave Nw North Canton (44720) *(G-15260)*

R S C, Columbus *Also called Safecor Health LLC (G-7583)*

R S C Sales Company 423 581-4916
1347 E 4th St Dayton (45402) *(G-8612)*

R S Manufacturing Inc 440 946-8002
8878 East Ave Mentor (44060) *(G-13713)*

R S V Wldg Fbrcation Machining 419 592-0993
M063 County Road 12 Napoleon (43545) *(G-14694)*

R Sportswear LLC 937 748-3507
8068 Forest Glen Dr Springboro (45066) *(G-17504)*

R T & T Machining Co Inc 440 974-8479
8195 Tyler Blvd Ste 56 Mentor (44060) *(G-13714)*

R T Communications Inc 330 726-7892
6031 Applecrest Dr Youngstown (44512) *(G-21183)*

R T H Processing Inc 419 692-3000
1430 N Main St Delphos (45833) *(G-8916)*

R T Industries Inc (PA) 937 335-5784
110 Foss Way Troy (45373) *(G-18865)*

R T R Slotting & Machine Inc 330 929-2608
2742 2nd St Cuyahoga Falls (44221) *(G-8039)*

R V Spa LLC 440 284-4800
42345 Oberlin Elyria Rd Elyria (44035) *(G-9482)*

R Vandewalle Inc 513 921-2657
4030 Delhi Ave Cincinnati (45204) *(G-4327)*

R W Machine & Tool Inc 330 296-5211
7944 State Route 44 Ravenna (44266) *(G-16552)*

R W Michael Printing Co 330 923-9277
665 E Cuyahoga Falls Ave Akron (44310) *(G-363)*

R W Screw Products Inc 330 837-9211
999 Oberlin Ave Sw Massillon (44647) *(G-13198)*

R W Sidley Inc 440 224-2664
3062 E Center St Kingsville (44068) *(G-11607)*

R W Sidley Incorporated (PA) 440 352-9343
436 Casement Ave Painesville (44077) *(G-15913)*

R W Sidley Incorporated 440 564-2221
10688 Kinsman Rd Newbury (44065) *(G-15102)*

R W Sidley Incorporated 330 499-5616
7545 Pittsburg Ave Nw Canton (44720) *(G-2834)*

R W Sidley Incorporated 330 750-1661
395 Lowellville Rd Struthers (44471) *(G-17997)*

R W Sidley Incorporated 440 352-9343
436 Casement Ave Painesville (44077) *(G-15914)*

R W Sidley Incorporated 330 793-7374
3424 Oregon Ave Youngstown (44509) *(G-21184)*

R Weir Inc 937 438-5730
978 Mmsburg Cnterville Rd Dayton (45459) *(G-8613)*

R&D Machine Inc 937 339-2545
1204 S Crawford St Troy (45373) *(G-18866)*

R&D Marketing Group Inc 216 398-9100
4597 Van Epps Rd Brooklyn Heights (44131) *(G-2145)*

R&D Software Services Inc 513 755-8851
4648 Mesa Pl Liberty Twp (45011) *(G-11978)*

R&S Carbon Trading LLC 614 264-3083
146 N Hamilton Rd Ste 127 Gahanna (43230) *(G-10227)*

R-K Electronics Inc 513 204-6060
7405 Industrial Row Dr Mason (45040) *(G-13079)*

R-Med Inc 419 693-7481
3465 Navarre Ave Oregon (43616) *(G-15714)*

R.W., Willoughby *Also called Spence Technologies Inc (G-20603)*

Ra Consultants LLC 513 469-6600
10856 Kenwood Rd Blue Ash (45242) *(G-1861)*

Raber Lumber Co 330 893-2797
4112 State Rte 557 Charm (44617) *(G-3184)*

Racedirector LLC 440 940-6675
38613 Andrews Ridge Way Willoughby (44094) *(G-20586)*

Racelite South Coast Inc 216 581-4600
16518 Broadway Ave Maple Heights (44137) *(G-12739)*

Raceway Beverage LLC 513 932-2214
11 S Broadway St Lebanon (45036) *(G-11831)*

Raceway Petroleum Inc 440 989-2660
3040 Oberlin Ave Lorain (44052) *(G-12270)*

Rack Coating Service Inc 330 854-2869
5760 Erie Ave Nw Canal Fulton (44614) *(G-2512)*

Rack Draft Service Inc 513 353-5520
11109 Guard Ln North Bend (45052) *(G-15207)*

Rack Processing Company Inc (PA) 937 294-1911
2350 Arbor Blvd Moraine (45439) *(G-14521)*

Rack Processing Company Inc 937 294-1911
2350 Arbor Blvd Moraine (45439) *(G-14522)*

Raco Cutting Inc (PA) 937 293-1228
2230 E River Rd Moraine (45439) *(G-14523)*

RAD Technologies Incorporated 513 641-0523
11 Sunnybrook Dr Cincinnati (45237) *(G-4328)*

RAD-Con Inc (PA) 440 871-5720
13001 Athens Ave Ste 300 Lakewood (44107) *(G-11678)*

Radcliffe Steel, Berea *Also called Rads LLC (G-1633)*

Radco Fire Protection Inc 419 476-0102
444 W Laskey Rd Ste S Toledo (43612) *(G-18668)*

Radco Industries Inc 419 531-4731
3226 Frenchmens Rd Toledo (43607) *(G-18669)*

Raddells Sausage 216 486-1944
478 E 152nd St Cleveland (44110) *(G-6085)*

Radiant Arts Inc 330 879-0013
8215 Mona St Sw Navarre (44662) *(G-14725)*

Radici Plastics Usa Inc 330 336-7611
960 Seville Rd Wadsworth (44281) *(G-19434)*

Radio Hospital 419 679-1103
30 N Main St Kenton (43326) *(G-11565)*

Radioshack, Cuyahoga Falls *Also called 4r Enterprises Incorporated (G-7960)*

Radix Wire, Cleveland *Also called Wire Holdings LLC (G-6467)*

Radix Wire Co (PA) 216 731-9191
26000 Lakeland Blvd Cleveland (44132) *(G-6086)*

Radix Wire Co 216 731-9191
26260 Lakeland Blvd Cleveland (44132) *(G-6087)*

Radix Wire Company 330 995-3677
350 Harris Dr Aurora (44202) *(G-943)*

Radix Wire Company, The, Cleveland *Also called Radix Wire Co (G-6086)*

Radocy Inc 419 666-4400
30652 E River Rd Rossford (43460) *(G-16747)*

Radon Be Gone Inc 614 268-4440
4319 Indianola Ave Columbus (43214) *(G-7545)*

Rads LLC 330 671-0464
135 Blaze Industrial Pkwy Berea (44017) *(G-1633)*

Raf Acquisition Co 440 572-5999
5478 Grafton Rd Valley City (44280) *(G-19227)*

Rafter Equipment Corporation 440 572-3700
12430 Alameda Dr Strongsville (44149) *(G-17956)*

Rage Corporation (PA) 614 771-4771
3949 Lyman Dr Hilliard (43026) *(G-10974)*

Rageon Inc 617 633-0544
1163 E 40th St Ste 2 Cleveland (44114) *(G-6088)*

Ragman Inc 419 255-8068
1201 N Summit St Toledo (43604) *(G-18670)*

Rail Road Corporation 614 771-2102
4881 Trabue Rd Columbus (43228) *(G-7546)*

Railing Crafters Ltd 440 506-9336
632 Argonne Dr Painesville (44077) *(G-15915)*

Railroad Brewing Company 440 723-8234
1010 Center Rd Avon (44011) *(G-1006)*

Railtech Boutet Inc 419 592-5050
25 Interstate Dr Napoleon (43545) *(G-14695)*

Railtech Matweld Inc 419 592-5050
15 Interstate Dr Napoleon (43545) *(G-14696)*

Railtech Matweld Inc (HQ) 419 591-3770
25 Interstate Dr Napoleon (43545) *(G-14697)*

Rain Drop Products Llc 419 207-1229
2121 Cottage St Ashland (44805) *(G-771)*

Rainbow Bedding 330 852-3127
3421 Township Road 166 Sugarcreek (44681) *(G-18036)*

Rainbow Cultured Marble 330 225-3400
1442 W 130th St Brunswick (44212) *(G-2251)*

Rainbow Hills Vineyards Inc 740 545-9305
26349 Township Road 251 Newcomerstown (43832) *(G-15122)*

Rainbow Industries Inc 937 323-6493
5975 E National Rd Springfield (45505) *(G-17633)*

Rainbow Plastics, Mentor *Also called Rlr Industries Inc (G-13716)*

Rainbow Printing, Uniontown *Also called Plastic Card Inc (G-19093)*

Rainbow Printing, Uniontown *Also called Plasticards Inc (G-19094)*

Rainbow Tarp, Springfield *Also called Rainbow Industries Inc (G-17633)*
Raindow Hills Vineyards, Newcomerstown *Also called Rainbow Hills Vineyards Inc (G-15122)*
Raka Corporation 419 476-6572
  203 Matzinger Rd Toledo (43612) *(G-18671)*
Ral Robotics Investment Group, Stone Creek *Also called Richard A Limbacher (G-17726)*
Ralph A Felice Inc 330 468-0482
  1532 Newport Dr Macedonia (44056) *(G-12479)*
Ralph Robinson Inc 740 385-2747
  700 Ohio Ave Logan (43138) *(G-12192)*
Ralston Food, Lancaster *Also called Treehouse Private Brands Inc (G-11758)*
Ralston Instruments LLC 440 564-1430
  15035 Cross Creek Pkwy Newbury (44065) *(G-15103)*
Ram Machining Inc 740 333-5522
  806 Delaware St Wshngtn CT Hs (43160) *(G-20923)*
Ram Precision Industries Inc 937 885-7700
  11125 Yankee St Ste A Dayton (45458) *(G-8614)*
Ram Products Inc 614 443-4634
  1091 Stimmel Rd Columbus (43223) *(G-7547)*
Ram Racewares, Warren *Also called Behlke Dalene (G-19528)*
Ram Sensors Inc (PA) 440 835-3540
  875 Canterbury Rd Cleveland (44145) *(G-6089)*
Ram Sensors Inc 440 835-3540
  875 Canterbury Rd Ste 875 Westlake (44145) *(G-20300)*
Ram Tool Inc 937 277-0717
  1944 Neva Dr Dayton (45414) *(G-8615)*
Ram Z Neon 330 788-5121
  1227 E Indianola Ave Youngstown (44502) *(G-21185)*
Rambasek Realty Inc 937 228-1189
  827 S Patterson Blvd Dayton (45402) *(G-8616)*
Ramco Electric Motors Inc 937 548-2525
  5763 Jysville St Johns Rd Greenville (45331) *(G-10516)*
Ramco Specialties Inc 330 653-5135
  5445 Hudson Indus Pkwy Hudson (44236) *(G-11195)*
Ramon Robinson 330 883-3244
  475 Niles Vienna Rd Vienna (44473) *(G-19374)*
Ramona Southworth 740 226-8202
  2882 Adams Rd Beaver (45613) *(G-1311)*
Ramp Creek III Ltd 740 522-0660
  1100 Thornwood Dr Lot 1 Heath (43056) *(G-10853)*
Rampe Manufacturing Company 440 352-8995
  1246 High St Fairport Harbor (44077) *(G-9771)*
Rampp Company (PA) 740 373-7886
  20445 State Route 550 Ofc Marietta (45750) *(G-12822)*
Ramzi, Cleveland *Also called Safe Systems Inc (G-6154)*
Rance Industries Inc 330 482-1745
  1361 Heck Rd Columbiana (44408) *(G-6629)*
Rancho Alegre Upper Arlin 614 273-1305
  3140 Kingsdale Ctr Upper Arlington (43221) *(G-19113)*
Randall Richard & Moore LLC 330 455-8873
  3710 Progress St Ne Canton (44705) *(G-2835)*
Randall Bearings Inc (PA) 419 223-1075
  1046 S Greenlawn Ave Lima (45804) *(G-12080)*
Randall Bearings Inc 419 678-2486
  821 Weis St Coldwater (45828) *(G-6570)*
Randall Foods Inc (PA) 513 793-6525
  312 Walnut St Ste 1600 Cincinnati (45202) *(G-4329)*
Randd Assoc Prtg & Promotions 937 294-1874
  330 Progress Rd Dayton (45449) *(G-8617)*
Randolph Research Co 330 666-1667
  2449 Kensington Rd Akron (44333) *(G-364)*
Randolph Tool Company Inc 330 877-4923
  750 Wales Dr Hartville (44632) *(G-10832)*
Randy Carter Logging Inc 740 634-2604
  1100 Schmidt Rd Bainbridge (45612) *(G-1062)*
Randy Gray 513 533-3200
  4142 Airport Rd Fl 1 Cincinnati (45226) *(G-4330)*
Randy Lewis Inc 330 784-0456
  1053 Bank St Akron (44305) *(G-365)*
Randy R Wilson 740 454-4440
  5100 Manchester Dr Zanesville (43701) *(G-21348)*
Randys, Toledo *Also called Slap N Tickle LLC (G-18698)*
Randys Countertops Inc 740 881-5831
  3208 Home Rd Powell (43065) *(G-16482)*
Randys Pickles LLC 440 864-6611
  2203 Superior Ave E Cleveland (44114) *(G-6090)*
Range Hood Store, The, Marysville *Also called Z Line Kitchen and Bath LLC (G-12977)*
Range Kleen Mfg Inc 419 331-8000
  4240 East Rd Elida (45807) *(G-9356)*
Range One Products & Fabg 330 533-1151
  580 W Main St Canfield (44406) *(G-2571)*
Range Rsurces - Appalachia LLC 330 866-3301
  1748 Saltwell Rd Nw Dover (44622) *(G-9009)*
Ranpak Corp (PA) 440 354-4445
  7990 Auburn Rd Concord Township (44077) *(G-7799)*
Rantek Products LLC 419 485-2421
  1826 Magda Dr Ste A Montpelier (43543) *(G-14451)*
Rapid Blanket Restorer Corp 330 821-6326
  188 N State St Painesville (44077) *(G-15916)*

Rapid Copy Printing, Cincinnati *Also called Dorothy Crooker (G-3665)*
Rapid Machine Inc 419 737-2377
  610 N State St Pioneer (43554) *(G-16243)*
Rapid Mold Repair & Machine 330 253-1000
  813 Home Ave Akron (44310) *(G-366)*
Rapid Mr International LLC 614 486-6300
  1500 Lake Shore Dr # 310 Columbus (43204) *(G-7548)*
Rapid Quality Manufacturing, West Chester *Also called GE Aviation Systems LLC (G-19872)*
Rapid Signs & More Inc 513 553-4040
  1044 Old Us Highway 52 New Richmond (45157) *(G-14944)*
Rapid Signs & Sportswear, New Richmond *Also called Rapid Signs & More Inc (G-14944)*
Rapiscan Systems High Energy I 937 879-4200
  514 E Dytn Yllow Sprng Rd Fairborn (45324) *(G-9629)*
Rapistan Systems, Brecksville *Also called Siemens Industry Inc (G-2073)*
Raptis Coffee Inc 330 399-7011
  341 Main Ave Sw Warren (44481) *(G-19591)*
Rasche Cabinetmakers, Westerville *Also called Mark Rasche (G-20170)*
Raschke Engraving Inc 330 677-5544
  4485 Crystal Pkwy Ste 200 Kent (44240) *(G-11512)*
Rassini Chassis Systems LLC 419 485-1524
  1812 Magda Dr Montpelier (43543) *(G-14452)*
Ratech 513 742-2111
  11110 Adwood Dr Cincinnati (45240) *(G-4331)*
Ratliff Metal Spinning Co Inc 937 836-3900
  40 Harrisburg Dr Englewood (45322) *(G-9538)*
Rauh Polymers Inc 330 376-1120
  420 Kenmore Blvd Akron (44301) *(G-367)*
Ravago Americas LLC 419 924-9090
  600 Oak St West Unity (43570) *(G-20134)*
Ravana Industries Inc 330 536-4015
  6170 Center Rd Lowellville (44436) *(G-12411)*
Raven Concealment Systems LLC 440 508-9000
  7889 Root Rd North Ridgeville (44039) *(G-15399)*
Raven Industries Inc 937 323-4625
  2130 Progress Rd Springfield (45505) *(G-17634)*
Ravens Sales & Service, Dover *Also called Kruz Inc (G-8996)*
Ravenworks Deer Skin 937 354-5151
  34477 Shertzer Rd Mount Victory (43340) *(G-14658)*
Raw Real and Wonderful LLC 614 529-8606
  4118 Anson Dr Hilliard (43026) *(G-10975)*
Rawac Plating Company 937 322-7491
  125 N Bell Ave Springfield (45504) *(G-17635)*
Rawhide Press, Bowling Green *Also called Rawhide Software Inc (G-2010)*
Rawhide Software Inc (PA) 419 878-0857
  17552 W River Rd Bowling Green (43402) *(G-2010)*
Rawlins Pallet & Lumber, Wheelersburg *Also called Forrest Rawlins (G-20330)*
Ray Barnes Newspaper Inc (PA) 419 674-4066
  201 E Columbus St 207 Kenton (43326) *(G-11566)*
Ray Communications Inc 330 686-0226
  1337 Commerce Dr Ste 11 Stow (44224) *(G-17795)*
Ray Fogg Construction Inc 216 351-7976
  981 Keynote Cir Ste 15 Cleveland (44131) *(G-6091)*
Ray H Miller Trucking and Log 330 378-2131
  6054 County Road 51 Big Prairie (44611) *(G-1684)*
Ray L Lute LL 740 372-7703
  494 Coldicott Hill Rd Lucasville (45648) *(G-12424)*
Ray Lewis & Son Incorporated 937 644-4015
  916 Delaware Ave Marysville (43040) *(G-12965)*
Ray Rieser Trophy Co 614 279-1128
  3852 Sullivant Ave Columbus (43228) *(G-7549)*
Ray Townsend 440 968-3617
  9168 Clay St Montville (44064) *(G-14461)*
Raydar Inc of Ohio 330 334-6111
  1734 Wall Rd Ste B Wadsworth (44281) *(G-19435)*
Rayhaven Group Inc 330 659-3183
  3842 Congress Pkwy Ste A Richfield (44286) *(G-16634)*
Rayle Coal Co (PA) 740 695-2197
  67705 Friends Church Rd Saint Clairsville (43950) *(G-16805)*
Raymath Company 937 335-1860
  2323 W State Route 55 Troy (45373) *(G-18867)*
Raymond W Reisiger 740 400-4090
  11885 Paddock View Ct Nw Baltimore (43105) *(G-1086)*
Raymonds Tool & Gauge LLC 419 485-8340
  6726 County Road N30 Montpelier (43543) *(G-14453)*
Rays Sausage Inc 216 921-8782
  3146 E 123rd St Cleveland (44120) *(G-6092)*
Rays Whistle Stop 740 965-2085
  5264 Settlement Dr New Albany (43054) *(G-14771)*
Raytec Systems, Stow *Also called Ray Communications Inc (G-17795)*
Raytheon Company 937 429-5429
  2970 Presidential Dr # 300 Beavercreek (45324) *(G-1359)*
RB Fabricators Inc 330 779-0263
  4021 Mahoning Ave Youngstown (44515) *(G-21186)*
RB Tool and Manufacturing, Cincinnati *Also called Kaws Inc (G-3973)*
RB&w Manufacturing LLC 740 363-1971
  700 London Rd Delaware (43015) *(G-8881)*
RB&w Manufacturing LLC (HQ) 234 380-8540
  10080 Wellman Rd Streetsboro (44241) *(G-17870)*

A
L
P
H
A
B
E
T
I
C

Rba Inc 330 336-6700
487 College St Wadsworth (44281) *(G-19436)*

Rbb Systems Inc (PA) 330 263-4502
4265 E Lincoln Way Unit C Wooster (44691) *(G-20827)*

Rbb Systems Inc 330 263-4502
4265 E Lincoln Way Unit C Wooster (44691) *(G-20828)*

Rbi Solar Inc (HQ) 513 242-2051
5513 Vine St Cincinnati (45217) *(G-4332)*

Rbm Environmental and Cnstr 419 693-5840
4526 Bayshore Rd Oregon (43616) *(G-15715)*

Rboog Industries LLC 330 350-0396
3132 Ipswich Ct Brunswick (44212) *(G-2252)*

Rbs Citizens NA 330 468-1600
500 W Aurora Rd Sagamore Hills (44067) *(G-16778)*

Rbs Mfg Inc 330 426-9486
145 E Martin St East Palestine (44413) *(G-9243)*

Rbs Technologies LLC 937 320-8189
1488 Champions Way Xenia (45385) *(G-20970)*

RC Industries Inc 330 879-5486
12 Oakbrook St Sw Navarre (44662) *(G-14726)*

RC Outsourcing LLC 330 536-8500
102 E Water St Lowellville (44436) *(G-12412)*

RCE Heat Exchangers LLC 330 627-0300
3165 Folsam Rd Nw Carrollton (44615) *(G-2963)*

Rci, Sidney Also called Ross Casting & Innovation LLC *(G-17219)*

Rcl Benziger, Cincinnati Also called Kendall/Hunt Publishing Co *(G-3982)*

Rcl Publishing Group LLC 972 390-6400
8805 Governors Hill Dr # 400 Cincinnati (45249) *(G-4333)*

RCM Engineering Company 330 666-0575
2089 N Clvland Mssllon Rd Akron (44333) *(G-368)*

Rcr Partnership 419 340-1202
424 N Martin Williston Rd Genoa (43430) *(G-10362)*

Rcs Brewhouse 440 984-3103
223 Church St Amherst (44001) *(G-607)*

Rct Industries Inc 937 602-1100
7494 Deep Woods Ct Springboro (45066) *(G-17505)*

Rda Group LLC 440 724-4347
2131 Clifton Way Avon (44011) *(G-1007)*

RE Connors Construction Ltd 740 644-0261
13352 Forrest Rd Ne Thornville (43076) *(G-18194)*

REA Elektronik Inc 440 232-0555
7307 Young Dr Ste B Bedford (44146) *(G-1456)*

REA Incorporated 330 666-7414
4808 Pin Oak Rd Akron (44333) *(G-369)*

REA Polishing Inc 419 470-0216
1606 W Laskey Rd Toledo (43612) *(G-18672)*

Reactive Resin Products Co 419 666-6119
327 5th St Perrysburg (43551) *(G-16146)*

Reading Rock Inc (PA) 513 874-2345
4600 Devitt Dr West Chester (45246) *(G-20045)*

Ready Made Rc LLC 740 936-4500
7719 Graphics Way Ste F Lewis Center (43035) *(G-11913)*

Ready Technology Inc 937 228-8181
630 Kiser St Dayton (45404) *(G-8618)*

Ready Technology Inc (HQ) 937 866-7200
333 Progress Rd Unit A Dayton (45449) *(G-8619)*

Ready To Haul Columbus LLC 614 329-5161
1240 Ethan Ave Streetsboro (44241) *(G-17871)*

Real Alloy Holding Inc (HQ) 216 755-8800
3700 Park East Dr Ste 300 Beachwood (44122) *(G-1292)*

Real Alloy Recycling Inc (HQ) 216 755-8900
3700 Park East Dr Ste 300 Beachwood (44122) *(G-1293)*

Real Alloy Recycling Inc 740 922-8301
7319 Newport Rd Se Uhrichsville (44683) *(G-19056)*

Real Alloy Specialty Products 440 563-3487
2639 E Water St Rock Creek (44084) *(G-16685)*

Real Alloy Specialty Products (HQ) 216 755-8836
3700 Park East Dr Ste 300 Beachwood (44122) *(G-1294)*

Real Alloy Specialty Products 440 322-0072
320 Huron St Elyria (44035) *(G-9483)*

Real Alloy Specification Inc (HQ) 260 563-7461
3700 Park East Dr Ste 300 Beachwood (44122) *(G-1295)*

Real Products Manufacturing, Ney Also called Janet Sullivan *(G-15142)*

Real Solution Communication, Akron Also called Robert F Sams *(G-376)*

Real Tactical Gear, Maineville Also called Contingncy Prcrments Group LLC *(G-12521)*

Ream and Haager Laboratory 330 343-3711
179 W Broadway St Dover (44622) *(G-9010)*

Reberland Equipment Inc 330 698-5883
5963 Fountain Nook Rd Apple Creek (44606) *(G-648)*

Rebiltco Inc 513 424-2024
8775 Thomas Rd Middletown (45042) *(G-14081)*

Rebsco Inc 937 548-2246
4362 Us Route 36 Greenville (45331) *(G-10517)*

Rebuilding & Fabricating Inc 440 322-0844
41821 Oberlin Rd Elyria (44035) *(G-9484)*

Rec Enterprises, Elyria Also called Denne Industries Inc *(G-9401)*

Reclamation Technologies Inc (HQ) 419 867-8990
1100 Haskins Rd Bowling Green (43402) *(G-2011)*

Reclamation Technologies Inc 419 867-8990
1100 Haskins Rd Bowling Green (43402) *(G-2012)*

Recob Great Lakes Express Inc 216 265-7940
20600 Sheldon Rd Cleveland (44142) *(G-6093)*

Recognition Robotics Inc (PA) 440 590-0499
151 Innovation Dr Elyria (44035) *(G-9485)*

Recon Systems LLC (PA) 330 484-8444
330 Wood St S East Canton (44730) *(G-9196)*

Record Publishing Co (HQ) 330 541-9400
1050 W Main St Kent (44240) *(G-11513)*

Recto Molded Products Inc 513 871-5544
4425 Appleton St Cincinnati (45209) *(G-4334)*

Rector Inc 440 892-0444
1991 Crocker Rd Ste 320 Westlake (44145) *(G-20301)*

Recycled Systems Furniture Inc 614 880-9110
401 E Wilson Bridge Rd Worthington (43085) *(G-20884)*

Recycling Div, Cleveland Also called Resolute FP US Inc *(G-6107)*

Recycling Div, Columbus Also called Resolute FP US Inc *(G-7557)*

Recycling Div, Cincinnati Also called Resolute FP US Inc *(G-4338)*

Recycling Eqp Solutions Corp 330 920-1500
276 Remington Rd Ste C Cuyahoga Falls (44224) *(G-8040)*

Red Barakuda LLC 614 596-5432
4439 Shoupmill Dr Columbus (43230) *(G-7550)*

Red Barn Cabinet Co 937 884-9800
8046 State Route 722 Arcanum (45304) *(G-659)*

Red Barn Screen Printing & EMB 740 474-6657
1144 Northridge Rd Circleville (43113) *(G-4640)*

Red Barn, The, Circleville Also called Red Barn Screen Printing & EMB *(G-4640)*

Red Book, Chagrin Falls Also called National Directory Morticians *(G-3065)*

Red Diamond Plant, Mc Arthur Also called Austin Powder Company *(G-13329)*

Red DOT Corporation 216 447-4294
15501 Chatfield Ave Cleveland (44111) *(G-6094)*

Red Head Brass, Shreve Also called Rhba Acquisitions LLC *(G-17162)*

Red Hill Development Company, Dover Also called Doris Kimble *(G-8977)*

Red Hot Studios 330 609-7446
728 Shadowood Ln Se Warren (44484) *(G-19592)*

Red Lion Nursery Inc 937 704-9840
3505 N State Route 741 Lebanon (45036) *(G-11832)*

Red Sea Truck Line, Columbus Also called Yemaneh Musie *(G-7783)*

Red Seal Electric Co 216 941-3900
3835 W 150th St Cleveland (44111) *(G-6095)*

Red Vette Printing Company 740 364-1766
75 Fern Hill Dr Granville (43023) *(G-10466)*

Red Wing Shoe Company Inc 419 531-1948
2122 N Reynolds Rd Toledo (43615) *(G-18673)*

Redbuilt LLC 740 363-0870
200 Colomet Dr Delaware (43015) *(G-8882)*

Redco Instrument 440 232-2132
659 Broadway Ave Cleveland (44146) *(G-6096)*

Redex Industries Inc (PA) 330 332-9800
1176 Salem Pkwy Salem (44460) *(G-16924)*

Redhawk Energy Systems LLC 740 927-8244
10340 Palmer Rd Sw Pataskala (43062) *(G-15979)*

Redi Rock Structures Oki LLC 513 965-9221
1050 Round Bottom Rd Milford (45150) *(G-14169)*

Redi-Quik Signs Inc 614 228-6641
123 E Spring St Columbus (43215) *(G-7551)*

Redmond Waltz Electric, Cleveland Also called Phillips Electric Co *(G-6003)*

Reds Auto Glass Shop, Warren Also called J W Goss Co Inc *(G-19562)*

Reduction Engineering Inc (PA) 330 677-2225
235 Progress Blvd Kent (44240) *(G-11514)*

Reebar Die Casting Inc 419 878-7591
1177 Farnsworth Rd Waterville (43566) *(G-19665)*

Reeces Las Vegas Supplies (PA) 937 274-5000
5425 Fishburg Rd Dayton (45424) *(G-8620)*

Reed Elvin Burl II 937 399-3242
1236 Villa Rd Springfield (45503) *(G-17636)*

Reed Machinery Inc 330 220-6668
629 Marsh Way Brunswick (44212) *(G-2253)*

Reef Runner Tackle Co Inc 419 798-9125
102 Cherry St Marblehead (43440) *(G-12746)*

Reel Image 937 296-9036
2520 Blackhawk Rd Dayton (45420) *(G-8621)*

Reelflyrodcom 937 434-8472
7635 Wilmington Pike D Dayton (45458) *(G-8622)*

Rees Wheelchair Mobility Svc 330 923-2345
1615 Akron Peninsula Rd # 101 Akron (44313) *(G-370)*

Reese Machine Company Inc 440 992-3942
2501 State Rd Ashtabula (44004) *(G-835)*

Reesers Machine Inc 937 548-5847
2624 Fox Rd Greenville (45331) *(G-10518)*

Refcotec, Orrville Also called Refractory Coating Tech Inc *(G-15757)*

Refractory Coating Tech Inc 330 683-2200
542 Collins Blvd Orrville (44667) *(G-15757)*

Refractory Specialties Inc 330 938-2101
230 W California Ave Sebring (44672) *(G-17050)*

Refrigeration Industries Corp 740 377-9166
719 County Road 1 South Point (45680) *(G-17446)*

Regal Beloit America Inc 419 352-8441
13300 Van Camp Rd Bowling Green (43402) *(G-2013)*

Regal Beloit America Inc...............................937 667-2431
531 N 4th St Tipp City (45371) *(G-18296)*

Regal Cabinet Inc...419 865-3932
315 N Holland Sylvania Rd Toledo (43615) *(G-18674)*

Regal Diamond Products Corp.......................440 944-7700
1405 E 286th St Wickliffe (44092) *(G-20385)*

Regal Industries Inc......................................440 352-9600
857 Richmond Rd Painesville (44077) *(G-15917)*

Regal Metal Products Co (PA).......................330 868-6343
3615 Union Ave Se Minerva (44657) *(G-14339)*

Regal Metal Products Co...............................330 868-6343
162 Arbor Rd Minerva (44657) *(G-14340)*

Regal Spring Co...614 278-7761
2140 Eakin Rd Ste J Columbus (43223) *(G-7552)*

Regal Technology Corporation......................614 272-7644
3860 Bramford Rd Columbus (43220) *(G-7553)*

Regal Tool & Die Inc.....................................330 746-6644
712 Andrews Ave Youngstown (44505) *(G-21187)*

Regal Trophy & Awards Company..................877 492-7531
1269 Wapakoneta Ave Sidney (45365) *(G-17214)*

Register Herald Office...................................937 456-5553
200 Eaton Lewisburg Rd # 105 Eaton (45320) *(G-9321)*

Registered Images Inc...................................859 781-9200
6545 Wiehe Rd Cincinnati (45237) *(G-4335)*

Rego Manufacturing Co Inc...........................419 562-0466
1870 E Mansfield St Bucyrus (44820) *(G-2357)*

Regol-G Industries, Cleveland Also called DCW Acquisition Inc *(G-5179)*

Rehn Co, Toledo Also called Whiteford Industries Inc *(G-18774)*

Reichard Controls, Dublin Also called Reichard Software Corp *(G-9130)*

Reichard Industries LLC (PA).........................330 482-5511
338 S Main St Columbiana (44408) *(G-6630)*

Reichard Software Corp.................................614 537-8598
655 Metro Pl S Ste 600 Dublin (43017) *(G-9130)*

Reid Asset Management Company (PA)..........216 642-3223
9555 Rockside Rd Ste 350 Cleveland (44125) *(G-6097)*

Reid Asset Management Company..................216 642-3223
9555 Rockside Rd Ste 350 Cleveland (44125) *(G-6098)*

Reid Asset Management Company..................440 942-8488
4500 Beidler Rd Willoughby (44094) *(G-20587)*

Reifel Industries Inc......................................419 737-2138
201 Ohio St Pioneer (43554) *(G-16244)*

Reighart Steel Products, Willoughby Also called Sticker Corporation *(G-20606)*

Reinecker Party Center & Catrg, Macedonia Also called Reineckers Bakery Ltd *(G-12480)*

Reineckers Bakery Ltd...................................330 467-2221
8575 Freeway Dr Macedonia (44056) *(G-12480)*

Reineke Company LLC....................................419 281-5800
1025 Faultless Dr Ashland (44805) *(G-772)*

Reinforcement Systems Ohio LLC..................330 469-6958
3121 W Market St Warren (44485) *(G-19593)*

Reisbeck Fd Mkts St Clirsville, Saint Clairsville Also called Riesbeck Food Markets Inc *(G-16806)*

Reiser Manufacturing.....................................330 846-8003
4571 Millrock Rd New Waterford (44445) *(G-14973)*

Reiter Dairy of Akron Inc (HQ)......................937 323-5777
1961 Commerce Cir Springfield (45504) *(G-17637)*

Reiter Dairy of Akron Inc..............................419 424-5060
10456 State Route 224 W Findlay (45840) *(G-9882)*

Reladyne Inc (PA)..513 489-6000
9395 Kenwood Rd Ste 104 Blue Ash (45242) *(G-1862)*

Related Metals Inc...330 799-4866
6011 Deer Spring Run Canfield (44406) *(G-2572)*

Relativity Digital Systems, Columbus Also called Thames Company Ltd *(G-7687)*

Relay Rail Div., Mineral Ridge Also called L B Foster Company *(G-14307)*

Relevium Labs Inc (PA)..................................614 568-7000
4663 Katie Ln Ste O Oxford (45056) *(G-15842)*

Reliable Buffing & Polishing, Spencerville Also called Reliable Buffing Co Inc *(G-17464)*

Reliable Buffing Co Inc..................................419 647-4432
222 N College St Spencerville (45887) *(G-17464)*

Reliable Castings Corporation.......................937 497-5217
1521 W Michigan Ave Sidney (45365) *(G-17215)*

Reliable Fur Co..513 288-5093
2541 State Route 222 New Richmond (45157) *(G-14945)*

Reliable Mfg Co LLC......................................740 756-9373
4411 Carroll Southern Rd Carroll (43112) *(G-2945)*

Reliable Pattern Works Inc............................440 232-8820
590 Golden Oak Pkwy Cleveland (44146) *(G-6099)*

Reliable Products Co Inc................................419 394-5854
315 S Park Dr Saint Marys (45885) *(G-16853)*

Reliable Wheelchair Trans.............................216 390-3999
28899 Harvard Rd Beachwood (44122) *(G-1296)*

Reliacheck Manufacturing Inc.......................440 933-6162
33554 Pin Oak Pkwy Avon Lake (44012) *(G-1048)*

Reliance Design Inc..216 267-5450
3463 Archwood Dr Rocky River (44116) *(G-16707)*

Reliance Medical Products Inc (HQ)...............513 398-3937
3535 Kings Mills Rd Mason (45040) *(G-13080)*

Reloading Supplies Corp................................440 228-0367
1040 Devon Dr Ashtabula (44004) *(G-836)*

Relx Inc...937 865-6800
9443 Springboro Pike Miamisburg (45342) *(G-13851)*

Relx Inc...937 865-6800
4700 Lyons Rd Miamisburg (45342) *(G-13852)*

Relx Inc...937 865-6800
9333 Springboro Pike Miamisburg (45342) *(G-13853)*

Rely-On Manufacturing Inc............................937 254-0118
955 Springfield St Dayton (45403) *(G-8623)*

Remel Products, Oakwood Village Also called Thermo Fisher Scientific Inc *(G-15630)*

Remington Engrg Machining Inc.....................513 965-8999
5105 River Valley Rd Milford (45150) *(G-14170)*

Remington Products Co..................................330 335-1571
961 Seville Rd Wadsworth (44281) *(G-19437)*

Remington Steel, Springfield Also called Westfield Steel Inc *(G-17677)*

Remlinger Manufacturing Co Inc....................419 532-3647
16394 Us 224 Kalida (45853) *(G-11416)*

Remnant Room..937 938-7350
1915 S Alex Rd Dayton (45449) *(G-8624)*

Remram Recovery LLC...................................740 667-0092
49705 E Park Dr Tuppers Plains (45783) *(G-18886)*

Remtec Corp..513 860-4299
6049 Hi Tek Ct Mason (45040) *(G-13081)*

Remtec Engineering.......................................513 860-4299
6049 Hi Tek Ct Mason (45040) *(G-13082)*

Remtec International, Bowling Green Also called Reclamation Technologies Inc *(G-2011)*

Remtec International, Bowling Green Also called Reclamation Technologies Inc *(G-2012)*

Remtron, Warren Also called Laird Controls North Amer Inc *(G-19568)*

Renco Mold Inc..937 233-3233
2801 Ome Ave Dayton (45414) *(G-8625)*

Renco Printing Inc...216 267-5585
5261 W 161st St Cleveland (44142) *(G-6100)*

Renee Barrett Winery.....................................513 471-1340
8129 Austin Ridge Dr Cincinnati (45247) *(G-4336)*

Renegade Brands LLC....................................216 342-4347
3201 Enterprise Pkwy Cleveland (44122) *(G-6101)*

Renegade Candle Company, New Albany Also called Faith Guiding Cafe LLC *(G-14758)*

Renegade Materials Corporation....................508 579-7888
3363 S Tech Blvd Miamisburg (45342) *(G-13854)*

Renegade Well Services LLC...........................330 488-6055
215 Trump Ave Ne Canton (44730) *(G-2836)*

Renewable Energy, Parma Also called North Amrcn Sstnable Enrgy Ltd *(G-15963)*

Renewal By Andersen LLC..............................614 781-9600
400 Lazelle Rd Ste 1 Columbus (43240) *(G-6658)*

Renewal Parts Maintenance, Euclid Also called Mechanical Dynamics Analis Ltd *(G-9592)*

Renite Company...614 253-5509
2500 E 5th Ave Columbus (43219) *(G-7554)*

Renite Lubrication Engineers, Columbus Also called Renite Company *(G-7554)*

Rennco Automation Systems Inc....................419 861-2340
971 Hamilton Dr Holland (43528) *(G-11080)*

Renoir Visions LLC...419 586-5679
1 Visions Pkwy Celina (45822) *(G-3016)*

Renosol Seating, Hebron Also called Lear Corporation *(G-10872)*

Rent A Mom Inc...216 901-9599
4531 Hillside Rd Seven Hills (44131) *(G-17063)*

Rent-A-Center Inc..740 373-1342
243 Captain D Seeley Mia Marietta (45750) *(G-12823)*

Rent-A-John, Columbus Also called BJ Equipment Ltd *(G-6834)*

Repko Machine Inc...216 267-1144
5081 W 164th St Cleveland (44142) *(G-6102)*

Replacment Prts Spcialists Inc (PA)...............440 248-0731
30400 Solon Indus Pkwy Solon (44139) *(G-17367)*

Replex Mirror Company..................................740 397-5535
11 Mount Vernon Ave Mount Vernon (43050) *(G-14641)*

Replex Plastics, Mount Vernon Also called Replex Mirror Company *(G-14641)*

Replica Engineering Inc..................................216 252-2204
3483 W 140th St Cleveland (44111) *(G-6103)*

Reporter Newspaper Inc.................................330 535-7061
1088 S Main St Akron (44301) *(G-371)*

Repository, Canton Also called Copley Ohio Newspapers Inc *(G-2668)*

Repp, Blue Ash Also called Check Yourself LLC *(G-1764)*

Repro Acquisition Company LLC.....................216 738-3800
25001 Rockwell Dr Cleveland (44117) *(G-6104)*

Repro Depot, Medina Also called Montview Corporation *(G-13449)*

Reprocenter, The, Cleveland Also called Repro Acquisition Company LLC *(G-6104)*

Republic Anode Fabricators, Valley City Also called Raf Acquisition Co *(G-19227)*

Republic EDM Services Inc.............................937 278-7070
5660 Wadsworth Rd Dayton (45414) *(G-8626)*

Republic Engineered Products........................440 277-2000
1807 E 28th St Lorain (44055) *(G-12271)*

Republic Metals, Cleveland Also called Vwm-Republic Inc *(G-6433)*

Republic Mills Inc..419 758-3511
888 School St Okolona (43545) *(G-15669)*

Republic Powdered Metals Inc (HQ)...............330 225-3192
2628 Pearl Rd Medina (44256) *(G-13467)*

Republic Rings Inc...440 238-2622
17295 Foltz Pkwy Ste A Strongsville (44149) *(G-17957)*

Republic Steel, Lorain Also called Republic Engineered Products *(G-12271)*

Republic Steel Inc 330 438-5533
2633 8th St Ne Canton (44704) *(G-2837)*

Republic Steel Inc (HQ) 330 438-5435
2633 8th St Ne Canton (44704) *(G-2838)*

Republic Steel Inc 440 277-2000
1807 E 28th St Lorain (44055) *(G-12272)*

Republic Steel Inc 330 837-7024
401 Rose Ave Se Massillon (44646) *(G-13199)*

Republic Steel Wire Proc LLC 440 996-0740
31000 Solon Rd Solon (44139) *(G-17368)*

Republic Storage Systems LLC (HQ) 330 438-5800
1038 Belden Ave Ne Canton (44705) *(G-2839)*

Republic Wire Inc 513 860-1800
5525 Union Centre Dr West Chester (45069) *(G-19930)*

RES Q Cleaning Solutions Inc 740 964-9494
638 Klema Dr E Reynoldsburg (43068) *(G-16602)*

Resaurus Company Inc 614 751-9352
240 Outerbelt St Ste A Columbus (43213) *(G-7555)*

Rescar Industries Inc 630 963-1114
700 Murray Ave Minerva (44657) *(G-14341)*

Resco Products Inc 330 372-3716
1929 Larchmont Ave Ne Warren (44483) *(G-19594)*

Resco Products Inc 740 682-7794
3542 State Route 93 Oak Hill (45656) *(G-15605)*

Resco Products Inc 330 488-1226
6878 Osnaburg St Se East Canton (44730) *(G-9197)*

Research & Development, Maumee *Also called Bprex Closures LLC (G-13232)*

Research & Development II, Mentor *Also called Steris Corporation (G-13732)*

Research Abrasive Products Inc 440 944-3200
1400 E 286th St Wickliffe (44092) *(G-20386)*

Research and Development Group 614 261-0454
1208 E Hudson St Columbus (43211) *(G-7556)*

Research Metrics LLC 419 464-3333
4832 Plank Rd Norwalk (44857) *(G-15562)*

Research Organics LLC 216 883-8025
4353 E 49th St Cleveland (44125) *(G-6105)*

Reserve Energy Exploration Co 440 543-0770
10155 Gottschalk Pkwy # 1 Chagrin Falls (44023) *(G-3117)*

Reserve Industries Inc 440 871-2796
386 Lake Park Dr Bay Village (44140) *(G-1243)*

Reserve Millwork Inc 216 531-6982
26881 Cannon Rd Bedford (44146) *(G-1457)*

Residential Electronic Svcs 740 681-9150
3155 Lancstr Kirkrsvll Nw Lancaster (43130) *(G-11745)*

Residents of Sawmill Park 614 659-6678
2765 Sawmill Park Dr Dublin (43017) *(G-9131)*

Residue National LLC 614 309-8963
3100 Wakeshire Dr Dublin (43017) *(G-9132)*

Resilience Fund III LP (PA) 216 292-0200
25101 Chagrin Blvd Cleveland (44122) *(G-6106)*

Resinoid Engineering Corp (PA) 847 673-1050
251 O Neill Dr Hebron (43025) *(G-10881)*

Resinoid Engineering Corp 740 928-2220
2040 James Pkwy Heath (43056) *(G-10854)*

Resistflame Acquisition Corp (PA) 513 561-5223
7115 Miami Ave Cincinnati (45243) *(G-4337)*

Resolute FP US Inc 216 961-3900
3400 Vega Ave Cleveland (44113) *(G-6107)*

Resolute FP US Inc 614 443-6300
995 Marion Rd Columbus (43207) *(G-7557)*

Resolute FP US Inc 513 242-3671
5535 Vine St Cincinnati (45217) *(G-4338)*

Resonance Group Ltd 419 509-2245
2300 Chriswood Rd Toledo (43617) *(G-18675)*

Resonetics LLC 937 865-4070
2941 College Dr Kettering (45420) *(G-11585)*

Resource America Inc 330 896-8510
3500 Massillon Rd Ste 100 Uniontown (44685) *(G-19096)*

Resource Development Co LLC 440 617-9087
30205 Clemens Rd Ste B Westlake (44145) *(G-20302)*

Resource Energy Inc 330 896-8510
3500 Massillon Rd Ste 100 Uniontown (44685) *(G-19097)*

Resource Exchange Company Inc 440 773-8915
383 Abbyshire Rd Akron (44319) *(G-372)*

Resource Fuels LLC (PA) 614 221-0101
41 S High St Ste 3750s Columbus (43215) *(G-7558)*

Resource Graphics 513 205-2686
2230 Gilbert Ave Cincinnati (45206) *(G-4339)*

Resource Mechanical Insul LLC 248 577-0200
6842 Commodore Dr Walbridge (43465) *(G-19462)*

Resource Mtl Hdlg & Recycl Inc (PA) 440 834-0727
14970 Brkshire Indus Pkwy Middlefield (44062) *(G-13985)*

Resource Recycling Inc 419 222-2702
1596 Neubrecht Rd Lima (45801) *(G-12081)*

Restless Noggins Mfg LLC 330 526-6908
334 Orchard Ave Ne North Canton (44720) *(G-15261)*

Retail Display Group, Columbus *Also called Plaskolite LLC (G-7490)*

Retail Management Products 740 548-1725
8851 Whitney Dr Lewis Center (43035) *(G-11914)*

Retalix Inc 937 384-2277
2490 Technical Dr Miamisburg (45342) *(G-13855)*

Retays Welding Company 440 327-4100
7650 Race Rd North Ridgeville (44039) *(G-15400)*

Retco Mold & Machine 330 633-5725
41 Industry St Tallmadge (44278) *(G-18167)*

Retek Inc 440 937-6282
34550 Chester Rd Avon (44011) *(G-1008)*

Retention Knob Supply & Mfg Co 937 686-6405
4905 State Route 274 W Huntsville (43324) *(G-11215)*

Retinagenix LLC 440 808-9334
11000 Cedar Ave Ste 280 Cleveland (44106) *(G-6108)*

Retriev Technologies Inc 740 653-6290
265 Quarry Rd Se Lancaster (43130) *(G-11746)*

Retterbush Fiberglass Corp 937 778-1936
719 Long St Piqua (45356) *(G-16310)*

Retterbush Graphic and Packg 513 779-4466
6187 Schumacher Park Dr West Chester (45069) *(G-19931)*

Retterer Manufacturing Company, Caledonia *Also called Claridon Tool & Die Inc (G-2435)*

Rettig Family Pallets Inc 419 264-1540
G510 County Road 14 Holgate (43527) *(G-11040)*

Reuland Electric Co 513 825-7314
9620 Colerain Ave Ste 22 Cincinnati (45251) *(G-4340)*

Reuss Meats Inc 513 874-3200
3765 Port Union Rd Fairfield (45014) *(G-9710)*

Reuter-Stokes Inc 330 425-3755
8499 Darrow Rd Ste 1 Twinsburg (44087) *(G-19008)*

Reuther Mold & Manufacturing, Cuyahoga Falls *Also called Reuther Mold & Mfg Co
Inc (G-8041)*

Reuther Mold & Mfg Co Inc (PA) 330 923-5266
1225 Munroe Falls Ave Cuyahoga Falls (44221) *(G-8041)*

Rev38 LLC 937 572-4000
8888 Beckett Rd West Chester (45069) *(G-19932)*

Revelation Fmly Child Care Ctr, Columbus *Also called Juana Williams (G-7247)*

Revenue Management Group LLC 419 993-2200
2348 Baton Rouge Lima (45805) *(G-12082)*

Revere Building Products, Cuyahoga Falls *Also called Gentek Building Products
Inc (G-8003)*

Revere Plas Systems Group LLC (HQ) 419 547-6918
401 Elm St Clyde (43410) *(G-6544)*

Revere Plastics Systems LLC (HQ) 419 547-6918
401 Elm St Clyde (43410) *(G-6545)*

Review Times, The, Fostoria *Also called Daily Fostoria Review Co (G-9969)*

Review, The, Alliance *Also called Alliance Publishing Co Inc (G-495)*

Revlis Corporation 330 535-2108
2845 Newpark Dr Barberton (44203) *(G-1145)*

Revlon, Barberton *Also called Revlis Corporation (G-1145)*

Revolution Group Inc 614 212-1111
600 N Cleveland Ave # 110 Westerville (43082) *(G-20182)*

Revolution Mobility, Cleveland *Also called Majors Wholesale Med Sup LLC (G-5733)*

Revonoc Inc 440 548-3491
18125 Madison Rd Parkman (44080) *(G-15953)*

Rex American Resources Corp (PA) 937 276-3931
7720 Paragon Rd Dayton (45459) *(G-8627)*

Rex Auto Seat Covers, Lima *Also called Rex Manufacturing Co (G-12083)*

Rex Automation Inc 614 766-4672
2211 Aspenwood Ln Columbus (43235) *(G-7559)*

Rex Burnett 740 927-4669
26 1st Ave Sw Etna (43062) *(G-9560)*

Rex International USA Inc 800 321-7950
3744 Jefferson Rd Ashtabula (44004) *(G-837)*

Rex M & Kim P Bellville 937 256-2526
4121 Cleveland Ave Dayton (45410) *(G-8628)*

Rex Manufacturing Co 419 224-5751
805 S Cable Rd Lima (45805) *(G-12083)*

Rexam Beverage Can Company 419 877-0401
10444 Waterville St Whitehouse (43571) *(G-20345)*

Rexam Beverage Can Company 419 334-4461
2145 Cedar St Fremont (43420) *(G-10178)*

Rexam Closure Systems, Perrysburg *Also called Bprex Hlthcare Brookville Inc (G-16069)*

Rexam PLC 330 893-2451
5091 County Road 120 Millersburg (44654) *(G-14258)*

Rexam Prescription Pdts Inc, Perrysburg *Also called Centor Inc (G-16076)*

Rexarc International Inc 937 839-4604
35 E 3rd St West Alexandria (45381) *(G-19781)*

Rexles Inc 419 732-8188
1850 W Lakeshore Dr Port Clinton (43452) *(G-16411)*

Rexnord Industries LLC 614 675-1800
3655 Brookham Dr Grove City (43123) *(G-10588)*

Rexon Components Inc 440 585-7086
24500 Highpoint Rd Cleveland (44122) *(G-6109)*

Reymond Products Intl Inc 330 339-3583
2066 Brightwood Rd Se New Philadelphia (44663) *(G-14923)*

Reynolds & Co Inc 937 592-8300
1515 S Main St Bellefontaine (43311) *(G-1538)*

Reynolds and Reynolds Company 419 584-7000
824 Murlin Ave Celina (45822) *(G-3017)*

(G-0000) Company's Geographic Section entry number

Reynolds and Reynolds Company 937 485-4771
354 Mound St Dayton (45402) *(G-8629)*

Reynolds and Reynolds Company 937 449-4039
115 S Ludlow St Dayton (45402) *(G-8630)*

Reynolds and Reynolds Company 937 485-2805
2405 County Line Rd Beavercreek (45430) *(G-1379)*

Reynolds Industries Group LLC 614 864-6199
7463 Old River Dr Blacklick (43004) *(G-1704)*

Reynolds Industries Inc 330 889-9466
380 W Main St West Farmington (44491) *(G-20075)*

Reynolds Metals Company LLC 614 228-7390
868 Goodale Blvd Columbus (43212) *(G-7560)*

Reynolds Residential Service, Columbus Also called Reynolds Metals Company
LLC *(G-7560)*

Rez Stone, Toledo Also called Hoover & Wells Inc *(G-18511)*

Rez-Tech Corporation 330 673-4009
1510 Mogadore Rd Kent (44240) *(G-11515)*

Rezkem Chemicals LLC 330 653-9104
77 Milford Dr Ste 258 Hudson (44236) *(G-11196)*

Rezmann Karoly 216 441-4357
7216 Bessemer Ave Cleveland (44127) *(G-6110)*

Rf Linx Inc 513 777-2774
2142 Greentree Rd Lebanon (45036) *(G-11833)*

RFS Fabrication 419 547-0650
2515 County Road 213 Clyde (43410) *(G-6546)*

RG Barry Corporation (HQ) 614 864-6400
13405 Yarmouth Rd Nw Pickerington (43147) *(G-16203)*

RG Mold 419 868-9390
8385 Water Park Dr Holland (43528) *(G-11081)*

Rhba Acquisitions LLC 330 567-2903
643 Legion Dr Shreve (44676) *(G-17162)*

Rhe-Tech Colors, Sandusky Also called Thermocolor LLC *(G-17012)*

Rhenium Alloys Inc (PA) 440 365-7388
38683 Taylor Pkwy North Ridgeville (44035) *(G-15401)*

Rhetech Color, Sandusky Also called Thermocolor LLC *(G-17013)*

Rhinestahl AMG, Mason Also called Rhinestahl Corporation *(G-13083)*

Rhinestahl Corporation (PA) 513 229-5300
7687 Innovation Way Mason (45040) *(G-13083)*

Rhinestahl Corporation 513 229-5300
7687 Innovation Way Mason (45040) *(G-13084)*

Rhino Gear Manufacturing Inc 440 639-1125
428 N Saint Clair St Painesville (44077) *(G-15918)*

Rhino Robotics Ltd 513 353-9772
5928 State Rte 128 Miamitown (45041) *(G-13891)*

Rhino Rubber LLC (PA) 877 744-6603
7054 Meadowlands Ave Nw North Canton (44720) *(G-15262)*

Rhino Tech Software LLC 614 456-9321
13938 Nantucket Ave Pickerington (43147) *(G-16204)*

Rhinosystems Inc 216 351-6262
800 Resource Dr Ste 12 Independence (44131) *(G-11272)*

Rhoads Printing Center Inc (PA) 330 678-2042
302 N Water St Kent (44240) *(G-11516)*

Rhodes Manufacturing Co Inc 740 743-2614
7045 Buckeye Valley Rd Ne Somerset (43783) *(G-17418)*

RI Alto Mfg Inc 740 914-4230
1632 Cascade Dr Marion (43302) *(G-12895)*

Ribbon Technology Corporation 614 864-5444
825 Taylor Station Rd Gahanna (43230) *(G-10228)*

Ribbon Technology Corporation (HQ) 614 864-5444
825 Taylor Station Rd Gahanna (43230) *(G-10229)*

Riblet Packaging Co 937 652-3087
955 Lippincott Rd Urbana (43078) *(G-19175)*

Ribs King Inc 513 791-1942
9406 Main St Cincinnati (45242) *(G-4341)*

Ribtec, Gahanna Also called Ribbon Technology Corporation *(G-10228)*

Ricci Anthony 330 758-5761
755 Boardman Canfield Rd Youngstown (44512) *(G-21188)*

Riceland Cabinet Inc 330 601-1071
326 N Hillcrest Dr Ste A Wooster (44691) *(G-20829)*

Riceland Dry Kiln 330 683-9151
1287 S Kansas Rd Orrville (44667) *(G-15758)*

Rich Industries Inc 330 339-4113
2384 Brightwood Rd Se New Philadelphia (44663) *(G-14924)*

Rich Print, Youngstown Also called Ricci Anthony *(G-21188)*

Rich Products Corporation 614 771-1117
4600 Northwest Pkwy Hilliard (43026) *(G-10976)*

Richard A Limbacher 330 897-4515
7148 Rocky Ridge Rd Sw Stone Creek (43840) *(G-17726)*

Richard A Scott 937 898-1592
8000 Allison Ave Dayton (45415) *(G-8631)*

Richard B Linneman 513 922-5537
5642 Victory Dr Cincinnati (45233) *(G-4342)*

Richard Benhase & Associates 513 772-1896
11741 Chesterdale Ave Cincinnati (45246) *(G-4343)*

Richard Farm Shop, Clyde Also called RFS Fabrication *(G-6546)*

Richard L Gibson 937 964-1521
2520 Leon Ln Springfield (45502) *(G-17638)*

Richard Paskiet Machinists 330 854-4160
468 Etheridge Blvd S Canal Fulton (44614) *(G-2513)*

Richard Pauley 740 965-6897
3308 N State Route 61 Sunbury (43074) *(G-18076)*

Richard Steel Company Inc 216 520-6390
11110 Avon Ave Cleveland (44105) *(G-6111)*

RICHARD'S FENCE COMPANY, Akron Also called Richards Whl Fence Co Inc *(G-373)*

Richards and Simmons Inc 614 268-3909
33 W Schreyer Pl Columbus (43214) *(G-7561)*

Richards Grinding Co Inc 216 631-7675
4914 Walworth Ave Cleveland (44102) *(G-6112)*

Richards Industries Inc 513 533-7340
3170 Wasson Rd Cincinnati (45209) *(G-4344)*

Richards Intrors Bldg Cmpnents, Youngstown Also called Shade Youngstown & Aluminum
Co *(G-21200)*

Richards Maple Products Inc 440 286-4160
545 Water St Chardon (44024) *(G-3176)*

Richards Whl Fence Co Inc 330 773-0423
1600 Firestone Pkwy Akron (44301) *(G-373)*

Richardson Printing Corp (PA) 740 373-5362
201 Acme St Marietta (45750) *(G-12824)*

Richardson Publishing Company 330 753-1068
70 4th St Nw Ste 1 Barberton (44203) *(G-1146)*

Richardson Supply LLC 614 539-3033
2080 Hardy Parkway St Grove City (43123) *(G-10589)*

Richardson Woodworking 614 893-8850
3834 Mann Rd Blacklick (43004) *(G-1705)*

Richelieu Foods Inc 740 335-4813
1104 Clinton Ave Wshngtn CT Hs (43160) *(G-20924)*

Richland Laminated Columns LLC 419 895-0036
8252 State Route 13 Greenwich (44837) *(G-10535)*

Richland Newhope Industries (PA) 419 774-4400
150 E 4th St Mansfield (44902) *(G-12671)*

Richland Screw Mch Pdts Inc 419 524-1272
531 Grant St Mansfield (44903) *(G-12672)*

Richland Twp Garage 419 358-4897
8435 Dixie Hwy Bluffton (45817) *(G-1915)*

Richlen Tool Co., Cincinnati Also called Madsco Inc *(G-4049)*

Richmond Builders Supply, Saint Henry Also called St Henry Tile Co Inc *(G-16822)*

Richmond Concrete Products 330 673-7892
3640 Kibler Toot Rd Sw Warren (44481) *(G-19595)*

Richmond Machine Co 419 485-5740
1528 Travis Dr Montpelier (43543) *(G-14454)*

Richmonds Woodworks Inc 330 343-8184
1115 Oak Shadows Dr Ne New Philadelphia (44663) *(G-14925)*

Richtech Industries Inc 440 937-4401
34000 Lear Indus Pkwy Avon (44011) *(G-1009)*

Richwood Gazette, Richwood Also called Marysville Newspaper Inc *(G-16660)*

Richwood Gazette, Marysville Also called Marysville Newspaper Inc *(G-12957)*

Ricking Paper and Specialty Co 513 825-3551
525 Northland Blvd Cincinnati (45240) *(G-4345)*

Rickly Hydrological Co 614 297-9877
1700 Joyce Ave Columbus (43219) *(G-7562)*

Rickly Hydrological Company 614 297-9877
1700 Joyce Ave Columbus (43219) *(G-7563)*

Ricks Graphic Accents Inc 330 644-4455
3554 S Arlington Rd Akron (44312) *(G-374)*

Ridge Corporation 614 421-7434
1201 Etna Pkwy Etna (43062) *(G-9561)*

Ridge Engineering Inc 513 681-5500
1700 Blue Rock St Cincinnati (45223) *(G-4346)*

Ridge Enterprises Inc 740 867-3456
1940 County Road 2 Chesapeake (45619) *(G-3190)*

Ridge Machine & Welding Co 740 537-2821
1015 Railroad St Toronto (43964) *(G-18784)*

Ridge Tool Company (HQ) 440 323-5581
400 Clark St Elyria (44035) *(G-9486)*

Ridge Tool Company 440 329-4737
321 Sumner St Elyria (44035) *(G-9487)*

Ridge Tool Company 740 432-8782
9877 Brick Church Rd Cambridge (43725) *(G-2474)*

Ridge Tool Manufacturing Co. 440 323-5581
400 Clark St Elyria (44035) *(G-9488)*

Ridge Township Stone Quarry 419 968-2222
16905 Middle Point Rd Van Wert (45891) *(G-19269)*

Ridgeview Sheet Metal 330 674-3768
4772 Township Road 352 Millersburg (44654) *(G-14259)*

Ridgeway Lumber, West Union Also called Kenneth Schrock *(G-20123)*

Ridgewood Brake Co, Cleveland Also called Beckworth Industries Inc *(G-4902)*

Ridgid, Elyria Also called Ridge Tool Company *(G-9486)*

Ridley USA Inc 800 837-8222
104 Oak St Botkins (45306) *(G-1953)*

Ridley USA Inc 937 693-6393
104 Oak St Botkins (45306) *(G-1954)*

Riegle Colors 937 548-8444
3566 N Creek Dr Greenville (45331) *(G-10519)*

Riesbeck Food Markets Inc 740 695-3401
104 Plaza Dr Saint Clairsville (43950) *(G-16806)*

Rieter Automotive-Oregon Plant, Oregon Also called Autoneum North America
Inc *(G-15703)*

Riffle & Sons, Chillicothe *Also called Riffle Machine Works Inc* *(G-3271)*
Riffle Machine Works Inc (PA)................................740 775-2838
  5746 State Route 159 Chillicothe (45601) *(G-3271)*
Rift Lake Aquatics...216 221-1437
  16385 Heather Ln Apt 104 Cleveland (44130) *(G-6113)*
Riggenbach Kitchens..330 669-2113
  790 E Main St Smithville (44677) *(G-17242)*
Right Away Division, Blue Ash *Also called Wornick Company* *(G-1900)*
Right Fit Ergonomics LLC..330 674-0977
  4613 Township Road 305 Millersburg (44654) *(G-14260)*
Right Srce Cmmunications Group, Cincinnati *Also called Jjkb Enterprises LLC* *(G-3946)*
Right Track Corp..937 663-0366
  11124 Helltown Rd Saint Paris (43072) *(G-16863)*
Righter Plumbing...614 604-7197
  1451 Galway Bnd N Pataskala (43062) *(G-15980)*
Rightway Fab & Machine Inc....................................937 295-2200
  4101 Rangeline Rd Russia (45363) *(G-16769)*
Rightway Food Service..419 223-4075
  3255 Saint Johns Rd Lima (45804) *(G-12084)*
Rikenkaki America Corporation................................614 336-2744
  5985 Wilcox Pl Ste D Dublin (43016) *(G-9133)*
Riker Products Inc..419 729-1626
  4901 Stickney Ave Toledo (43612) *(G-18676)*
Rimeco Products Inc...440 918-1220
  38198 Willoughby Pkwy Willoughby (44094) *(G-20588)*
Rimer Enterprises Inc...419 878-8156
  916 Rimer Dr Waterville (43566) *(G-19666)*
Rimm Kleen Systems, West Unity *Also called Hardline International Inc* *(G-20129)*
Rimrock Holdings Corporation (HQ)..........................614 471-5926
  1700 Jetway Blvd Columbus (43219) *(G-7564)*
Rinaldi and Packard Industries...............................330 395-4942
  775 And A Half Nles Rd Se Warren (44483) *(G-19596)*
Ring Container Tech LLC...937 492-0961
  603 Oak Ave Sidney (45365) *(G-17216)*
Ring Masters, Brunswick *Also called Alternative Surface Grinding* *(G-2205)*
Ringneck Brewing Company, Strongsville *Also called Brew Kettle Inc* *(G-17898)*
Rinker Materials..330 654-2511
  4200 Universal Dr Diamond (44412) *(G-8959)*
Rinos Woodworking Shop Inc..................................440 946-1718
  36475 Biltmore Pl Willoughby (44094) *(G-20589)*
Rinz-N-Reuz, Bowling Green *Also called Diamondback Filters* *(G-1985)*
Riotech International Ltd (PA)..................................513 779-0990
  6101 Schumacher Park Dr West Chester (45069) *(G-19933)*
Ripley Bee..937 392-4321
  134 N Front St Ripley (45167) *(G-16669)*
Ripley Metalworks Ltd..937 392-4992
  111 Waterworks Rd Ripley (45167) *(G-16670)*
Ripple Swimwear, Dublin *Also called Afi Brands LLC* *(G-9038)*
Rise N Shine Yard Signs...330 745-5868
  606 Grandview Ave Barberton (44203) *(G-1147)*
Risher & Co...216 732-8351
  27011 Tungsten Rd Euclid (44132) *(G-9604)*
Rising Moon Custom Apparel..................................614 882-1336
  19 E College Ave Westerville (43081) *(G-20232)*
Rita Caz Jwly Studio & Gallery.................................937 767-7713
  220 Xenia Ave Ste 2 Yellow Springs (45387) *(G-20998)*
Rita Fishel Inc...740 775-1957
  192 S Paint St Chillicothe (45601) *(G-3272)*
Ritchie Foods LLC..440 354-7474
  212 High St Fairport Harbor (44077) *(G-9772)*
Rite Machine Inc..216 267-6911
  13704 Enterprise Ave Cleveland (44135) *(G-6114)*
Rite Way Black & Deburr Inc...................................937 224-7762
  1138 E 2nd St Dayton (45403) *(G-8632)*
Riten Industries Incorporated.................................740 335-5353
  1100 Lakeview Ave Wshngtn CT Hs (43160) *(G-20925)*
Ritime Incorporated...330 273-3443
  6363 York Rd Ste 104 Cleveland (44130) *(G-6115)*
Ritrama Inc...216 851-7208
  341 Eddy Rd Cleveland (44108) *(G-6116)*
Rittal Corp..440 572-4999
  19541 Winding Trl Strongsville (44149) *(G-17958)*
Rittal Corp..937 399-0500
  1 Rittal Pl Urbana (43078) *(G-19176)*
Rittal Corp..937 399-0500
  3100 Upper Valley Pike Springfield (45504) *(G-17639)*
Rittman Inc...330 927-6855
  10 Mull Dr Rittman (44270) *(G-16682)*
River Bend Chair Co, Lebanon *Also called Colonial Woodcraft Inc* *(G-11789)*
River Cities Vault Inc..740 237-0010
  2901 S 11th St Ironton (45638) *(G-11300)*
River City Body Company..513 772-9317
  2660 Commerce Blvd Cincinnati (45241) *(G-4347)*
River City Pharma..513 870-1680
  8695 Seward Rd Fairfield (45011) *(G-9711)*
River Corp..513 641-3355
  32 W Mitchell Ave Cincinnati (45217) *(G-4348)*
River East Custom Cabinets....................................419 244-3226
  221 S Saint Clair St Toledo (43604) *(G-18677)*

River Foundry Supply, Cleveland *Also called River Smelting & Ref Mfg Co* *(G-6117)*
River Smelting & Ref Mfg Co....................................216 459-2100
  4195 Bradley Rd Cleveland (44109) *(G-6117)*
River Technology, Gahanna *Also called Ribbon Technology Corporation* *(G-10229)*
Riverbend Sand Rock and Gravel, Miamisburg *Also called Hilltop Basic Resources Inc* *(G-13817)*
Rivercity Woodworking Inc......................................513 860-1900
  9837 Harwood Ct West Chester (45014) *(G-19934)*
Rivercor LLC..330 784-1113
  2850 Gilchrist Rd Akron (44305) *(G-375)*
Riverrock Recycl Crushing LLC................................937 325-2052
  2484 Lindair Dr Springfield (45502) *(G-17640)*
Riverside Cnstr Svcs Inc...513 723-0900
  218 W Mcmicken Ave Cincinnati (45214) *(G-4349)*
Riverside Drives Inc..216 362-1211
  4509 W 160th St Cleveland (44135) *(G-6118)*
Riverside Drives Disc, Cleveland *Also called Riverside Drives Inc* *(G-6118)*
Riverside Engines Inc...419 927-6838
  7381 S State Route 231 Tiffin (44883) *(G-18239)*
Riverside Homemade Ice Cream, Marion *Also called Country Caterers Inc* *(G-12863)*
Riverside Mch & Automtn Inc (PA)............................419 855-8308
  1240 N Genoa Clay Ctr Rd Genoa (43430) *(G-10363)*
Riverside Mch & Automtn Inc....................................419 855-8308
  28701 E Broadway St Walbridge (43465) *(G-19463)*
Riverside Sand & Gravel Co.....................................330 673-2021
  69 Middlebury Rd Kent (44240) *(G-11517)*
Riverside Steel Inc..330 856-5299
  3102 Warren Sharon Rd Vienna (44473) *(G-19375)*
Riverside Wine and Imports, Kent *Also called Lamont Enterprises Inc* *(G-11484)*
Rivertown Brewing Company LLC.............................513 827-9280
  607 Shepherd Dr Unit 6 Cincinnati (45215) *(G-4350)*
Riverview Indus WD Pdts Inc...................................330 669-8509
  646 Industrial Blvd Wooster (44691) *(G-20830)*
Riverview Indus WD Pdts Inc...................................330 669-8509
  179 S Gilbert Dr Smithville (44677) *(G-17243)*
Riverview Packaging Inc...937 743-9530
  101 Shotwell Dr Franklin (45005) *(G-10049)*
Riverview Productions Inc.......................................740 441-1150
  652 Jackson Pike Gallipolis (45631) *(G-10308)*
Riverview Raquetball Club, Willoughby *Also called Melinz Industries Inc* *(G-20545)*
Riwco Corp...937 322-6521
  2330 Columbus Rd Springfield (45503) *(G-17641)*
Rixan Associates Inc..937 438-3005
  7560 Paragon Rd Dayton (45459) *(G-8633)*
Rj Drilling Company Inc..740 763-3991
  5755 Licking Valley Rd Se Nashport (43830) *(G-14707)*
Rj S Machine Shop Service......................................937 927-0137
  720 Pondlick Rd Seaman (45679) *(G-17042)*
Rjm Stamping Co..614 443-1191
  1641 Universal Rd Columbus (43207) *(G-7565)*
Rjm Tool...419 355-0900
  1718 Sycamore St Fremont (43420) *(G-10179)*
RJR & Associates Inc...419 237-2220
  21550 County Road L Fayette (43521) *(G-9779)*
RJR Surgical Inc..216 241-2804
  2530 Superior Ave E # 703 Cleveland (44114) *(G-6119)*
Rjw Trucking Company Ltd......................................740 363-5343
  124 Henderson Ct Delaware (43015) *(G-8883)*
Rke Trucking Co...614 891-1786
  6305 Frost Rd Westerville (43082) *(G-20183)*
Rki Inc (PA)...888 953-9400
  8901 Tyler Blvd Mentor (44060) *(G-13715)*
RL Best Company..330 758-8601
  723 Bev Rd Boardman (44512) *(G-1924)*
Rl Smith Printing Co...330 747-9590
  4030 Simon Rd Youngstown (44512) *(G-21189)*
Rlfshop LLC..937 898-6070
  6530 Poe Ave Dayton (45414) *(G-8634)*
Rlr Industries Inc..440 951-9501
  8677 Tyler Blvd Unit B Mentor (44060) *(G-13716)*
Rls Parts & Equipment LLC.....................................440 498-1843
  33595 Bnbridge Rd Ste 204 Solon (44139) *(G-17369)*
Rme Machining Co..513 541-3328
  2900 Spring Grove Ave Cincinnati (45225) *(G-4351)*
Rmi Titanium Company LLC (HQ)..............................330 652-9952
  1000 Warren Ave Niles (44446) *(G-15176)*
Rml Tool Inc..216 941-1615
  15115 Chatfield Ave B Cleveland (44111) *(G-6120)*
RMS Equipment LLC...330 564-1360
  1 Vision Ln Cuyahoga Falls (44223) *(G-8042)*
RMS Equipment Company, Cuyahoga Falls *Also called RMS Equipment LLC* *(G-8042)*
Rmt Corporation..513 942-8308
  2552 Titus Ave Dayton (45414) *(G-8635)*
Rmt Holdings Inc...419 221-1168
  1025 Findlay Rd Lima (45801) *(G-12085)*
Rmw Industries Inc..440 439-1971
  24869 Aurora Rd Bedford Heights (44146) *(G-1493)*
Rnm Holdings Inc..419 867-8712
  1810 Eber Rd Ste C Holland (43528) *(G-11082)*

Rnm Holdings Inc (PA) 937 704-9900
550 Conover Dr Franklin (45005) *(G-10050)*

Rnm Holdings Inc 614 444-5556
2350 Refugee Park Columbus (43207) *(G-7566)*

Rnr Enterprises LLC 330 852-3022
1361 County Road 108 Sugarcreek (44681) *(G-18037)*

Rnw Holdings Inc 330 792-0600
200 Division Street Ext Youngstown (44510) *(G-21190)*

Ro-MAI Industries Inc 330 425-9090
1605 Enterprise Pkwy Twinsburg (44087) *(G-19009)*

Roach Wood Products & Plas Inc 740 532-4855
25 Township Road 328 Ironton (45638) *(G-11301)*

Roadsafe Traffic Systems Inc 614 274-9782
1350 Stimmel Rd Columbus (43223) *(G-7567)*

Roare-Q LLC 419 801-4040
10232 Middleton Pike Bowling Green (43402) *(G-2014)*

Rob's Specialties, Wintersville *Also called Robs Creative Screen Printing (G-20713)*

Roban Inc 330 794-1059
1319 Main St Lakemore (44250) *(G-11645)*

Robbins Inc (PA) 513 871-8988
4777 Eastern Ave Cincinnati (45226) *(G-4352)*

Robbins & Myers Inc 937 327-3111
1895 W Jefferson St Springfield (45506) *(G-17642)*

Robbins & Myers Inc 937 327-3023
1895 W Jefferson St Springfield (45506) *(G-17643)*

Robbins & Myers Inc 937 454-3200
5870 Poe Ave Ste A Dayton (45414) *(G-8636)*

Robbins Company (HQ) 440 248-3303
29100 Hall St Ste 100 Solon (44139) *(G-17370)*

Robbins Furnace Works Inc 440 949-2292
3739 Colorado Ave Sheffield Village (44054) *(G-17129)*

Robbins Sports Surfaces, Cincinnati *Also called Robbins Inc (G-4352)*

Robby Yoder 740 679-2776
61388 Underwood Rd Quaker City (43773) *(G-16501)*

Robeck Fluid Power Co 330 562-1140
350 Lena Dr Aurora (44202) *(G-944)*

Roberds Converting Co Inc 513 683-6667
113 Northeast Dr Loveland (45140) *(G-12381)*

Robert A Reich Company 440 808-0033
24930 Detroit Rd D Westlake (44145) *(G-20303)*

Robert Alten Inc 740 653-2640
449 S Ewing St Lancaster (43130) *(G-11747)*

Robert Ashcraft 740 667-3690
4350 Bethany Ridge Rd Guysville (45735) *(G-10654)*

Robert Barr 740 826-7325
1245 Friendship Dr New Concord (43762) *(G-14821)*

Robert Becker Impressions Inc 419 385-5303
4646 Angola Rd Toledo (43615) *(G-18678)*

Robert C Bost Associates Inc (HQ) 301 206-9466
1783 Kenny Rd Columbus (43212) *(G-7568)*

Robert Coleman 740 393-4336
15850 Carson Rd Mount Vernon (43050) *(G-14642)*

Robert E McGrath Inc 440 572-7747
11606 Pearl Rd Strongsville (44136) *(G-17959)*

Robert E Moore 513 367-0006
10430 New Biddinger Rd Harrison (45030) *(G-10801)*

Robert Esterman 513 541-3311
2929 Spring Grove Ave # 100 Cincinnati (45225) *(G-4353)*

Robert F Sams 330 990-0477
1148 Monteray Dr Akron (44305) *(G-376)*

Robert Gorey 330 725-7272
6811 Stone Rd Medina (44256) *(G-13468)*

Robert H Shackelford (PA) 330 364-2221
147 Ashwood Ln Ne New Philadelphia (44663) *(G-14926)*

Robert J & Cindy K Hartz 513 521-6215
8734 Woodview Dr Cincinnati (45231) *(G-4354)*

Robert James Sales Inc 330 425-9116
1532 Enterprise Pkwy Twinsburg (44087) *(G-19010)*

Robert Long Manufacturing Inc 330 678-0911
4192 Karg Industrial Pkwy Kent (44240) *(G-11518)*

Robert Mayo Industries 330 426-2587
157 E Martin St East Palestine (44413) *(G-9244)*

Robert Midkiff 614 848-6677
6969 Wrthington Galena Rd Worthington (43085) *(G-20885)*

Robert Nickel 419 448-8256
125 Minerva St Tiffin (44883) *(G-18240)*

Robert Perez Carpentry 330 497-0043
430 Browning Ave Nw Canton (44720) *(G-2840)*

Robert Raack 216 932-6127
2943 Berkshire Rd Cleveland Heights (44118) *(G-6501)*

Robert Rothschild Farm LLC 937 653-7397
3143 E Us Highway 36 Urbana (43078) *(G-19177)*

Robert Rothschild Market Cafe, Urbana *Also called Robert Rothschild Farm LLC (G-19177)*

Robert Smart Inc 330 454-8881
1100 High Ave Sw Canton (44707) *(G-2841)*

Robert Tuneberg 440 899-9277
27016 Knickerbocker Rd # 1 Bay Village (44140) *(G-1244)*

Robert W Johnson Inc (PA) 614 336-4545
6280 Sawmill Rd Dublin (43017) *(G-9134)*

Robert Winner Sons Inc (PA) 419 582-4321
8544 State Route 705 Yorkshire (45388) *(G-21006)*

Robert Winner Sons Inc 937 548-7513
2259 State Route 502 Greenville (45331) *(G-10520)*

Roberts Brothers, Steubenville *Also called Fort Stben Burial Estates Assn (G-17695)*

Roberts Cabinetry LLC 330 421-4374
1718 Melody Ln Medina (44256) *(G-13469)*

Roberts Demand No 3 Corp 216 641-0660
4008 E 89th St Cleveland (44105) *(G-6121)*

Roberts Graphic Center 330 788-4642
5375 Market St Youngstown (44512) *(G-21191)*

Roberts Group Inc (PA) 614 486-0497
2646 Alliston Ct Columbus (43220) *(G-7569)*

Roberts Manufacturing Co Inc 419 594-2712
24338 Road 148 Oakwood (45873) *(G-15618)*

Roberts Screw Products, Rushsylvania *Also called Dayton Superior Corporation (G-16751)*

Roberts-Demand Corp 216 581-1300
17401 S Miles Rd Cleveland (44128) *(G-6122)*

Robertson Cabinets Inc 937 698-3755
1090 S Main St West Milton (45383) *(G-20110)*

Robertson EDM LLC 419 658-2219
9294 State Route 249 Edgerton (43517) *(G-9334)*

Robertson Incorporated (PA) 937 323-3747
14 N Lowry Ave Ste 200 Springfield (45504) *(G-17644)*

Robertson Manufacturing Co 216 531-8222
17917 Roseland Rd Cleveland (44112) *(G-6123)*

Robey Tool & Machine 614 251-0412
1593 E 5th Ave Columbus (43219) *(G-7570)*

Robin Enterprises Company 614 891-0250
111 N Otterbein Ave Westerville (43081) *(G-20233)*

Robin Industries Inc 330 359-5418
7227 State Route 515 Winesburg (44690) *(G-20707)*

Robin Industries Inc 330 695-9300
300 W Clay St Fredericksburg (44627) *(G-10092)*

Robin Industries Inc 216 267-3554
4780 W 139th St Cleveland (44135) *(G-6124)*

Robin Industries Inc 330 893-3501
5200 County Rd 120 Berlin (44610) *(G-1652)*

Robinson Fin Machines Inc 419 674-4152
13670 Us Highway 68 Kenton (43326) *(G-11567)*

Robinson Ordnance, Maineville *Also called Jmr Enterprises LLC (G-12525)*

Robinson Wood Products, Vienna *Also called Ramon Robinson (G-19374)*

Robotworx, Marion *Also called Scott Systems International (G-12898)*

Robotworx, Marion *Also called Ka Wanner Inc (G-12878)*

Roboworld Molded Products LLC 513 720-6900
8216 Princeton Glendale West Chester (45069) *(G-19935)*

Robs Creative Screen Printing (PA) 740 264-6383
350 Cadiz Rd Wintersville (43953) *(G-20713)*

Robs Welding Technologies Ltd 937 890-4963
2920 Production Ct Dayton (45414) *(G-8637)*

Rocal Inc (PA) 740 998-2122
3186 County Road 550 Frankfort (45628) *(G-10002)*

Rochester Manufacturing Inc 440 647-2463
24765 Quarry Rd Wellington (44090) *(G-19753)*

Rochling Automotive USA LLP 330 400-5785
2275 Picton Pkwy Akron (44312) *(G-377)*

Rochling Glastic Composites LP (HQ) 216 486-0100
4321 Glenridge Rd Cleveland (44121) *(G-6125)*

Rock Decor Company 330 857-7625
2877 Kidron Rd Orrville (44667) *(G-15759)*

Rock Lite, Maple Heights *Also called Charles Svec Inc (G-12730)*

Rock Mill Division, Lancaster *Also called Mid-West Fabricating Co (G-11729)*

Rock Tenn, Ravenna *Also called Westrock Rkt Company (G-16572)*

Rockbottom Oil & Gas 740 374-2478
1 Court House Ln Ste 3 Marietta (45750) *(G-12825)*

Rockbridge Outfitters 740 654-1956
2805 Clmbus Lncster Rd Nw Lancaster (43130) *(G-11748)*

Rockdale Systems LLC 513 379-3577
6 Rowley Ct Cincinnati (45246) *(G-4355)*

Rockhold Stone Quarry Inc 937 358-2224
20620 Spangler Rd West Mansfield (43358) *(G-20103)*

Rockport Cnstr & Mtls Inc 216 432-9465
3092 Rockefeller Ave Cleveland (44115) *(G-6126)*

Rockport Ready Mix, Cleveland *Also called Rockport Cnstr & Mtls Inc (G-6126)*

Rocks General Maintenance LLC 740 323-4711
10019 Jacksontown Rd Thornville (43076) *(G-18195)*

Rockside Winery & Vineyards LL 740 687-4414
2363 Lncster Newark Rd Ne Lancaster (43130) *(G-11749)*

Rockstedt Tool & Die Inc 330 273-9000
2974 Interstate Pkwy Brunswick (44212) *(G-2254)*

Rocktenn Merchandising Display, West Chester *Also called Westrock Company (G-19972)*

Rockware Corp 419 483-5649
1606 W Main St Bellevue (44811) *(G-1556)*

Rockwell Automation Inc 513 942-9828
9355 Allen Rd West Chester (45069) *(G-19936)*

Rockwell Automation Inc 440 604-8410
760 Beta Dr Ste A Cleveland (44143) *(G-6127)*

Rockwell Automation Inc 330 425-3211
8440 Darrow Rd Twinsburg (44087) *(G-19011)*

A
L
P
H
A
B
E
T

Rockwell Automation Inc 513 943-1145
1195 Clough Pike Batavia (45103) *(G-1219)*
Rockwell Automation Inc 440 646-5000
1 Allen Bradley Dr Cleveland (44124) *(G-6128)*
Rockwell Automation Inc 614 776-3021
350 Worthington Rd Ste A Westerville (43082) *(G-20184)*
Rockwell Automation Inc 440 646-7900
6680 Beta Dr Cleveland (44143) *(G-6129)*
Rockwell Metals Company LLC 440 242-2420
3709 W Erie Ave Lorain (44053) *(G-12273)*
Rocky Brands Inc (PA) 740 753-1951
39 E Canal St Nelsonville (45764) *(G-14736)*
Rocky Brands Inc 740 753-1951
39 E Canal St Nelsonville (45764) *(G-14737)*
Rocky Brands Inc 740 753-9100
45 E Canal St Nelsonville (45764) *(G-14738)*
Rocky Mountain Chocolate, Jeffersonville *Also called E R B Enterprises Inc* *(G-11379)*
Rocky River Brewing Co 440 895-2739
21290 Center Ridge Rd Rocky River (44116) *(G-16708)*
Rockys Gym 330 965-0464
1285 Boardman Canfield Rd Youngstown (44512) *(G-21192)*
Rockys Hinge Co 330 539-6296
1660 Harding Ave Girard (44420) *(G-10393)*
Roco Industries, Painesville *Also called Ropama Inc* *(G-15919)*
Roconex Corporation 937 339-2616
20 Marybill Dr S Troy (45373) *(G-18868)*
Rod McLellan Company 513 644-0011
14111 Scottslawn Rd Marysville (43040) *(G-12966)*
Rodco Petroleum Inc 330 477-9823
4600 Castlebar St Nw Canton (44708) *(G-2842)*
Roderer Enterprises Inc 513 942-3000
6560 Dixie Hwy Ste E Fairfield (45014) *(G-9712)*
Roe Transportation Entps Inc 937 497-7161
3680 W Michigan St Sidney (45365) *(G-17217)*
Roehlers Machine Products 937 354-4401
117 Taylor St E Mount Victory (43340) *(G-14659)*
Roemer Industries Inc 330 448-2000
1555 Masury Rd Masury (44438) *(G-13216)*
Roerig Machine 440 647-4718
27348 State Route 511 New London (44851) *(G-14864)*
Roessner Holdings Inc 419 356-2123
482 State Route 119 Fort Recovery (45846) *(G-9958)*
Roettger Hardwood Inc 937 693-6811
17066 Kettlersville Rd Kettlersville (45336) *(G-11589)*
Rogar International Inc 419 476-5500
4015 Dewey St Toledo (43612) *(G-18679)*
Roger Hall 740 778-2861
429 Railroad Hollow Rd South Webster (45682) *(G-17451)*
Roger Hoover 330 857-1815
571 Kidron Rd Orrville (44667) *(G-15760)*
Roger L Best 740 590-9133
3080 Blind Rd Stockport (43787) *(G-17723)*
Roger's Quick Print, Newark *Also called Doug Smith* *(G-15000)*
Rogers Industrial Products Inc 330 535-3331
532 S Main St Akron (44311) *(G-378)*
Rogers Mill Inc (PA) 330 227-3214
7431 Depot St Rogers (44455) *(G-16715)*
Rogue Fitness, Columbus *Also called Coulter Ventures Llc* *(G-6990)*
Rogue Manufacturing Inc 937 839-4026
304 Stotler Rd West Alexandria (45381) *(G-19782)*
Rohm and Haas Chemicals LLC 513 733-2100
2000 West St Cincinnati (45215) *(G-4356)*
Rohm and Haas Company 513 733-2100
2000 West St Cincinnati (45215) *(G-4357)*
Rohm and Haas Company 937 839-4612
10 Electric St West Alexandria (45381) *(G-19783)*
Rohrer Corporation (PA) 330 335-1541
717 Seville Rd Wadsworth (44281) *(G-19438)*
Rohrer Corporation 440 542-3100
29601 Solon Rd Solon (44139) *(G-17371)*
Roki America Co Ltd 419 424-9713
2001 Production Dr Findlay (45840) *(G-9883)*
Rol - Tech Inc 214 905-8050
4814 Calvert Dr Fort Loramie (45845) *(G-9936)*
Rol- Fab Inc 216 662-2500
4949 Johnston Pkwy Cleveland (44128) *(G-6130)*
Rolcon Inc 513 821-7259
510 Station Ave Cincinnati (45215) *(G-4358)*
Roll Formed Products Co Div, Youngstown *Also called Hynes Industries Inc* *(G-21111)*
Roll-In Saw Inc 216 459-9001
15851 Commerce Park Dr Brookpark (44142) *(G-2169)*
Roll-Kraft, Mentor *Also called Rki Inc* *(G-13715)*
Roller Plant, Canton *Also called Timken Company* *(G-2874)*
Roller Source Inc 440 748-4033
34100 E Royalton Rd Columbia Station (44028) *(G-6596)*
Rolo Sand & Gravel 740 886-7407
7165 County Road 107 Proctorville (45669) *(G-16491)*
Roman Cthlic Docese Youngstown 330 744-8451
144 W Wood St Fl 1 Youngstown (44503) *(G-21193)*
Romanoff Elc Residential LLC 614 755-4500
1288 Research Rd Gahanna (43230) *(G-10230)*
Romar Metal Fabricating Inc 740 682-7731
201 Zane Oak Rd Oak Hill (45656) *(G-15606)*
Romarc Enterprises Inc 419 287-4837
18784 Luckey Rd Pemberville (43450) *(G-16030)*
Romark Industries Inc 440 333-5480
24500 Center Ridge Rd # 250 Westlake (44145) *(G-20304)*
Rome Marble Inc 216 431-0334
3007 Clinton Ave Cleveland (44113) *(G-6131)*
Ron Roth Advertising, Columbus *Also called Platinum Productions Inc* *(G-7496)*
Ron-Al Mold & Machine Inc 330 673-7919
1057 Mason Ave Kent (44240) *(G-11519)*
Rona Enterprises Inc 740 927-9971
30 W Broad St Pataskala (43062) *(G-15981)*
Ronald J Dobay Enterprises, Burton *Also called R J Dobay Enterprises Inc* *(G-2382)*
Ronald T Dodge Co 937 439-4497
55 Westpark Rd Dayton (45459) *(G-8638)*
Rondy & Co., Barberton *Also called Tahoma Rubber & Plastics Inc* *(G-1152)*
Ronfeldt Associates Inc 419 382-5641
2345 S Byrne Rd Toledo (43614) *(G-18680)*
Ronfeldt Manufacturing LLC (HQ) 419 382-5641
2345 S Byrne Rd Toledo (43614) *(G-18681)*
Ronlen Industries Inc 330 273-6468
2809 Nationwide Pkwy Brunswick (44212) *(G-2255)*
Rons Texstyles LLC 513 936-9975
457 Thorburn Pl Columbus (43230) *(G-7571)*
Ronson Manufacturing Inc 440 256-1463
9933 Chillicothe Rd Willoughby (44094) *(G-20590)*
Ronyak Brothers Paving, Burton *Also called Shalersville Asphalt Co* *(G-2384)*
Roof Die Tool & Machine Inc 614 444-6253
2000 S High St Columbus (43207) *(G-7572)*
Roof To Road LLC 740 986-6923
27910 Chillicothe Pike Williamsport (43164) *(G-20419)*
Rooney Optical Inc (PA) 216 267-5600
9221 Ravenna Rd Ste 3 Twinsburg (44087) *(G-19012)*
Root Candles, Medina *Also called Al Root Company* *(G-13365)*
Roots Poultry Inc 419 332-0041
3721 W State St Fremont (43420) *(G-10180)*
Ropama Inc 440 358-1304
380 W Prospect St Painesville (44077) *(G-15919)*
Roper Lockbox LLC 330 656-5148
7600 Olde Eight Rd Hudson (44236) *(G-11197)*
Roppe Corporation 419 435-8546
1602 N Union St Fostoria (44830) *(G-9991)*
Roppe Holding Company 419 435-6601
106 N Main St Fostoria (44830) *(G-9992)*
Rose City Manufacturing Inc 937 325-5561
900 W Leffel Ln Springfield (45506) *(G-17645)*
Rose Grinding & Mfg Co, Miamisburg *Also called Gerald Rose* *(G-13813)*
Rose Metal Industries LLC (PA) 216 881-3355
1536 E 43rd St Cleveland (44103) *(G-6132)*
Rose Metal Industries LLC 216 426-8615
1155 Marquette St Cleveland (44114) *(G-6133)*
Rose of Sharon Enterprises 937 862-4543
9243 Old Stage Rd Waynesville (45068) *(G-19735)*
Rose Products and Services Inc 614 443-7647
545 Stimmel Rd Columbus (43223) *(G-7573)*
Rosebud Mining Company 740 658-4217
28490 Birmingham Rd Freeport (43973) *(G-10119)*
Rosebud Mining Company 740 768-2097
9076 County Road 53 Bergholz (43908) *(G-1642)*
Rosebud Mining Company 740 922-9122
5600 Pleasant Vly Rd Se Uhrichsville (44683) *(G-19057)*
Rosebud Mining Company 330 222-2334
95 N Lisbon St Carrollton (44615) *(G-2964)*
Rosemount Analytical Inc 440 914-1261
6565 Davis Industrial Solon (44139) *(G-17372)*
Rosenboom Machine & Tool Inc 419 352-9484
1032 S Maple St Bowling Green (43402) *(G-2015)*
Rosenfeld Jewelry Inc 440 446-0099
5668 Mayfield Rd Cleveland (44124) *(G-6134)*
Roseville Hardwood 740 221-8712
103 Church St Roseville (43777) *(G-16732)*
Rosie S Welding 614 506-2475
153 S Belmar Dr Reynoldsburg (43068) *(G-16603)*
Ross Aluminum Castings LLC 937 492-4134
815 Oak Ave Sidney (45365) *(G-17218)*
Ross Casting & Innovation LLC 937 497-4500
402 S Kuther Rd Sidney (45365) *(G-17219)*
Ross Co Redi Mix Co Inc 740 333-6833
1865 Old Us 35 Se Wshngtn CT Hs (43160) *(G-20926)*
Ross County License Bureau, Willowick *Also called Public Safety Ohio Department* *(G-20650)*
Ross Printing Co., Cleveland *Also called Yuckon International Corp* *(G-6488)*
Ross Products Division, Columbus *Also called Abbott Laboratories* *(G-6673)*
Ross Products Division, Columbus *Also called Abbott Laboratories* *(G-6676)*
Ross Special Products Inc 937 335-8406
2500 W State Route 55 Troy (45373) *(G-18869)*

Ross Tmber Harvstg For MGT Inc 513 383-6933
5300 Rapp Ln Batavia (45103) ***(G-1220)***
Ross-Co Redi-Mix Co Inc (PA) 740 775-4466
689 Marietta Rd Chillicothe (45601) ***(G-3273)***
Rossborough, Independence *Also called Magnesium Technologies Corp* ***(G-11266)***
Rossi Concept Arts 330 453-6366
1019 Mckinley Ave Nw Canton (44703) ***(G-2843)***
Rossi Machinery Services Inc (PA) 419 281-4488
1529 Cottage St Ashland (44805) ***(G-773)***
Rossi Pasta Factory Inc 740 376-2065
106 Front St Marietta (45750) ***(G-12826)***
Rost Boundry, Mansfield *Also called CSM Horvath Ledgebrook* ***(G-12590)***
Roswell Inc 419 433-4709
9808 Barrows Rd Huron (44839) ***(G-11241)***
Rotadyne, Franklin *Also called Rotation Dynamics Corporation* ***(G-10051)***
Rotary Compression Tech Inc 937 498-2555
211 E Russell Rd Sidney (45365) ***(G-17220)***
Rotary Forms Press Inc (PA) 937 393-3426
835 S High St Hillsboro (45133) ***(G-11013)***
Rotary Printing Company (PA) 419 668-4821
15 Schauss Ave Norwalk (44857) ***(G-15563)***
Rotary Products Inc (PA) 740 747-2623
117 E High St Ashley (43003) ***(G-790)***
Rotary Products Inc 740 747-2623
202 W High St Ashley (43003) ***(G-791)***
Rotary Tech Inc 440 862-8568
12710 Kinsman Rd Burton (44021) ***(G-2383)***
Rotation Dynamics Corporation 937 746-4069
315 Industrial Dr Franklin (45005) ***(G-10051)***
Rotech Products Incorporated 216 476-3722
16901 Albers Ave Cleveland (44111) ***(G-6135)***
Rotek Incorporated (HQ) 330 562-4000
1400 S Chillicothe Rd Aurora (44202) ***(G-945)***
Rotex Global Lcc 513 541-1236
1230 Knowlton St Cincinnati (45223) ***(G-4359)***
Rotex Silver Recovery Co, Lebanon *Also called Hess Technologies Inc* ***(G-11808)***
Roth Ready Mix Concrete Co, Cincinnati *Also called S J Roth Enterprises Inc* ***(G-4373)***
Roth Transit Inc 937 773-5051
8590 Industry Park Dr Piqua (45356) ***(G-16311)***
Roto Mold, Mentor *Also called Interpak Inc* ***(G-13611)***
Roto Solutions Inc 330 279-2424
8300 County Rd 189 Holmesville (44633) ***(G-11110)***
Rotocast Technologies Inc 330 798-9091
1900 Englewood Ave Akron (44312) ***(G-379)***
Rotoline USA LLC 330 677-3223
4429 Crystal Pkwy Ste B Kent (44240) ***(G-11520)***
Rotosolutions Inc 419 903-0800
1401 Jacobson Ave Ashland (44805) ***(G-774)***
Rough Brothers Mfg Inc 513 242-0310
5513 Vine St Ste 1 Cincinnati (45217) ***(G-4360)***
Roulet Company 419 241-2988
4221 Lewis Ave Toledo (43612) ***(G-18682)***
Rouse Marketing, Blue Ash *Also called Alifet USA Inc* ***(G-1740)***
Route 14 Storage EMB & More, Ravenna *Also called Route 14 Storage Inc* ***(G-16553)***
Route 14 Storage Inc 330 296-0084
7830 State Route 14 Ravenna (44266) ***(G-16553)***
Rowe Premix Inc 937 678-9015
10107 Us Rr 127 Box N West Manchester (45382) ***(G-20098)***
Rowend Industries Inc 419 333-8300
1035 Napoleon St Ste 101 Fremont (43420) ***(G-10181)***
Rowley J F Prosth & Orth Lab (PA) 513 861-3705
2729 Vine St Cincinnati (45219) ***(G-4361)***
Rowmark LLC (PA) 419 425-8974
5409 Hamlet Dr Findlay (45840) ***(G-9884)***
Rowmark LLC 419 429-0042
2040 Industrial Dr Findlay (45840) ***(G-9885)***
Rowtac Inc 419 994-4777
16125 Township Road 458 Loudonville (44842) ***(G-12304)***
Roxane Laboratories Inc 614 276-4000
1809 Wilson Rd Columbus (43228) ***(G-7574)***
Roy Holtzapple John Johns 419 657-2460
18526 Williams Rd Wapakoneta (45895) ***(G-19504)***
Roy I Kaufman Inc 740 382-0643
1672 Marion Uppr Sndsk Rd Marion (43302) ***(G-12896)***
Roy L Bayes 614 274-6729
1593 Harrisburg Pike Columbus (43223) ***(G-7575)***
Royal Acme, Cleveland *Also called Ace Rubber Stamp & Off Sup Co* ***(G-4690)***
Royal Acme Corporation (PA) 216 241-1477
3110 Payne Ave Cleveland (44114) ***(G-6136)***
Royal Adhesives & Sealants LLC 440 708-1212
17340 Munn Rd Chagrin Falls (44023) ***(G-3118)***
Royal Appliance Manufacturing, Solon *Also called TTI Floor Care North Amer Inc* ***(G-17409)***
Royal Cabinet Design Co Inc 216 267-5330
15800 Commerce Park Dr Cleveland (44142) ***(G-6137)***
Royal Canin USA Inc 937 962-7352
6574 State Route 503 N Lewisburg (45338) ***(G-11941)***
Royal Chemical Company Ltd 330 467-1300
1755 Entp Pkwy Ste 100 Twinsburg (44087) ***(G-19013)***
Royal Gateau 216 351-3553
4276 Pearl Rd Cleveland (44109) ***(G-6138)***
Royal Ice Cream Co 216 432-1144
6200 Euclid Ave Cleveland (44103) ***(G-6139)***
Royal Mfg 419 902-8222
2447 Tiffin Ave Findlay (45840) ***(G-9886)***
Royal Pad Products, Blue Ash *Also called Loroco Industries Inc* ***(G-1828)***
Royal Plastics Inc 440 352-1357
9410 Pineneedle Dr Mentor (44060) ***(G-13717)***
Royal Powder Corporation 216 898-0074
4800 Briar Rd Cleveland (44135) ***(G-6140)***
Royal Spa Columbus 614 529-8569
9022 Cotter St Lewis Center (43035) ***(G-11915)***
Royal Specialty Products Inc 513 841-1267
4114 Montgomery Rd Cincinnati (45212) ***(G-4362)***
Royal Tool and Machine LLC 419 836-7781
5740 Woodville Rd Northwood (43619) ***(G-15489)***
Royal Welding Inc 513 829-9353
5000 Factory Dr Fairfield (45014) ***(G-9713)***
Royal Wire Products Inc (PA) 440 237-8787
13450 York Delta Dr North Royalton (44133) ***(G-15446)***
Royalton Archtctral Fbrication 440 582-0400
13155 York Delta Dr North Royalton (44133) ***(G-15447)***
Royalton Food Service Eqp Co 440 237-0806
9981 York Theta Dr North Royalton (44133) ***(G-15448)***
Royalton Industries Inc 440 748-9900
12450 Eaton Commerce Pkwy Columbia Station (44028) ***(G-6597)***
Royalton Manufacturing Inc 440 237-2233
12777 Abbey Rd Ste E North Royalton (44133) ***(G-15449)***
Royalton Recorder 440 237-2235
13737 State Rd North Royalton (44133) ***(G-15450)***
Royce Co 513 933-0344
2340 Lebanon Rd Lebanon (45036) ***(G-11834)***
Royer Technologies Inc 937 743-6114
275 Hiawatha Trl Springboro (45066) ***(G-17506)***
Rozevink Engines LLC 419 789-1159
14316 State Route 281 Holgate (43527) ***(G-11041)***
Rozzi Company Inc (PA) 513 683-0620
118 Karl Brown Way Loveland (45140) ***(G-12382)***
RP Gatta Inc 330 562-2288
435 Gentry Dr Aurora (44202) ***(G-946)***
Rpa Electronic Distrs Inc 937 223-7001
122 S Terry St Dayton (45403) ***(G-8639)***
Rpg Industries Inc 937 698-9801
3571 Ginghmsbg Frdrck Rd Tipp City (45371) ***(G-18297)***
RPI Color Service Inc 513 471-4040
1950 Radcliff Dr Cincinnati (45204) ***(G-4363)***
RPI Graphic Data Solutions, Cincinnati *Also called RPI Color Service Inc* ***(G-4363)***
RPI of Indiana Inc 330 279-2421
8339 County Road 245 Holmesville (44633) ***(G-11111)***
RPM Carbide Die Inc 419 894-6426
202 E South St Arcadia (44804) ***(G-655)***
RPM Consumer Holding Company (HQ) 330 273-5090
2628 Pearl Rd Medina (44256) ***(G-13470)***
RPM Industries 440 268-8077
1444 Lowell St Elyria (44035) ***(G-9489)***
RPM International Inc (PA) 330 273-5090
2628 Pearl Rd Medina (44256) ***(G-13471)***
Rpmi Packaging Inc 513 398-4040
3899 S Us Route 42 Lebanon (45036) ***(G-11835)***
Rpp Containers, Cincinnati *Also called Dadco Inc* ***(G-3635)***
Rpp Containers, Cincinnati *Also called Dadco Inc* ***(G-3636)***
RPS, Solon *Also called Replacment Prts Spcialists Inc* ***(G-17367)***
RPS America Inc (PA) 937 231-9339
8808 Beckett Center Dr West Chester (45069) ***(G-19937)***
RR Donnelley, West Chester *Also called RR Donnelley & Sons Company* ***(G-19939)***
RR Donnelley & Sons Company 419 935-0111
1145 S Conwell Ave Willard (44890) ***(G-20400)***
RR Donnelley & Sons Company 513 870-4040
8740 Global Way West Chester (45069) ***(G-19938)***
RR Donnelley & Sons Company 513 552-1512
8720 Global Way West Chester (45069) ***(G-19939)***
RR Donnelley & Sons Company 740 928-6110
190 Milliken Dr Hebron (43025) ***(G-10882)***
RR Donnelley & Sons Company 330 562-5250
10400 Danner Dr Streetsboro (44241) ***(G-17872)***
RR Donnelley & Sons Company 614 221-8385
41 S High St Ste 3750 Columbus (43215) ***(G-7576)***
RR Donnelley & Sons Company 440 774-2101
450 Sterns Rd Oberlin (44074) ***(G-15647)***
Rrysburg Sunoco, Waterville *Also called Franklin* ***(G-19657)***
RS Industries Inc 216 524-2998
1455 E Schaaf Rd Brooklyn Heights (44131) ***(G-2146)***
Rs Pro Sales LLC 513 699-5329
1512 Eastern Ave Cincinnati (45202) ***(G-4364)***
Rsa Controls Inc 513 476-6277
6422 Fountains Blvd West Chester (45069) ***(G-19940)***
Rsb Spine LLC 216 241-2804
2530 Superior Ave E # 703 Cleveland (44114) ***(G-6141)***

Rsfi Office Furniture, Worthington *Also called Recycled Systems Furniture Inc* ***(G-20884)***
RSI Company (PA)......216 360-9800
24050 Commerce Park # 200 Beachwood (44122) ***(G-1297)***
Rsw Distributors LLC......502 587-8877
4700 Ashwood Dr Ste 200 Blue Ash (45241) ***(G-1863)***
Rsw Technologies LLC......419 662-8100
135 Dixie Hwy Rossford (43460) ***(G-16748)***
RTD Electronics Inc......330 487-0716
1632 Entp Pkwy Ste D Twinsburg (44087) ***(G-19014)***
Rti Alloys......330 652-9952
1000 Warren Ave Niles (44446) ***(G-15177)***
Rti Alloys Tpd, Canton *Also called Rti International Metals Inc* ***(G-2844)***
Rti Finance Corp......330 652-9952
1000 Warren Ave Niles (44446) ***(G-15178)***
Rti International Metals Inc......330 455-4010
1935 Warner Rd Se Canton (44707) ***(G-2844)***
Rti International Metals Inc......330 544-9470
2000 Warren Ave Niles (44446) ***(G-15179)***
Rti International Metals Inc......330 471-1844
208 15th St Sw Canton (44707) ***(G-2845)***
Rti International Metals Inc......330 544-7633
1000 Warren Ave Niles (44446) ***(G-15180)***
Rti International Metals Inc......330 652-9955
1000 Warren Ave Niles (44446) ***(G-15181)***
Rti Niles, Niles *Also called Rmi Titanium Company LLC* ***(G-15176)***
Rti Niles, Niles *Also called Rti International Metals Inc* ***(G-15180)***
Rti Niles, Niles *Also called Rti Finance Corp* ***(G-15178)***
Rti Niles......330 455-4010
1000 Warren Ave Niles (44446) ***(G-15182)***
Rtprocess LLC......937 366-6215
311 Davids Dr Wilmington (45177) ***(G-20678)***
RTS Companies (us) Inc......440 275-3077
2900 Industrial Park Dr Austinburg (44010) ***(G-965)***
Rtsi LLC......440 542-3066
6161 Cochran Rd Ste G Solon (44139) ***(G-17373)***
RTZ Manufacturing Co......614 848-8366
6530 Huntley Rd Columbus (43229) ***(G-7577)***
Rub-R-Road Inc......330 678-7050
431 W Elm St Kent (44240) ***(G-11521)***
Rubber & Plastics News, Akron *Also called Crain Communications Inc* ***(G-133)***
Rubber Associates Inc......330 745-2186
1522 Turkeyfoot Lake Rd New Franklin (44203) ***(G-14831)***
Rubber City Machinery Corp......330 434-3500
1 Thousand Sweitzer Ave Akron (44311) ***(G-380)***
Rubber Seal Products, Dayton *Also called Teknol Inc* ***(G-8708)***
Rubber World Magazine, Akron *Also called Lippincott & Peto Inc* ***(G-271)***
Rubber World Magazine Inc......330 864-2122
1741 Akron Peninsula Rd Akron (44313) ***(G-381)***
Rubber-Tech Inc......937 274-1114
5208 Wadsworth Rd Dayton (45414) ***(G-8640)***
Rubberduck 4x4......513 889-1735
1622 Smith Rd Hamilton (45013) ***(G-10734)***
Rubbermaid Incorporated......330 733-7771
3200 Gilchrist Rd Mogadore (44260) ***(G-14383)***
Rubberset Company......800 345-4939
101 W Prospect Ave Cleveland (44115) ***(G-6142)***
Rubbertec Industrial Pdts Co......740 657-3345
7580 Commerce Ct Lewis Center (43035) ***(G-11916)***
Ruber Polymer, Akron *Also called P C R Inc* ***(G-329)***
Rubex Inc......614 875-6343
3709 Grove City Rd Grove City (43123) ***(G-10590)***
Ruda Print & Graphics......419 331-7832
4129 Elida Rd Lima (45807) ***(G-12086)***
Rudd Equipment Company Inc......513 321-7833
11807 Enterprise Dr Cincinnati (45241) ***(G-4365)***
Rudolph Foods Company Inc (PA)......909 383-7463
6575 Bellefontaine Rd Lima (45804) ***(G-12087)***
Rudy's Strudel & Bakery, Cleveland *Also called Rudys Strudel Shop* ***(G-6143)***
Rudys Strudel Shop......440 886-4430
5580 Ridge Rd Cleveland (44129) ***(G-6143)***
Ruede Cabinet Company......614 875-8717
7171 State Route 104 Lockbourne (43137) ***(G-12151)***
Ruegg Mfg LLC......330 418-5617
13955 Elton St Sw Navarre (44662) ***(G-14727)***
Ruff Neon & Lighting Maint Inc......440 350-6267
295 W Prospect St Painesville (44077) ***(G-15920)***
Ruhe Sales Inc (PA)......419 943-3357
5450 State Route 109 Leipsic (45856) ***(G-11876)***
Rultract Inc......216 524-2990
5663 Brecksville Rd Cleveland (44131) ***(G-6144)***
Rumford Paper Company......937 242-9230
8540 Gander Creek Dr Miamisburg (45342) ***(G-13856)***
Rumpke Container Service, Cincinnati *Also called Rumpke Transportation Co LLC* ***(G-4367)***
Rumpke Transportation Co LLC (HQ)......513 851-0122
10795 Hughes Rd Cincinnati (45251) ***(G-4366)***
Rumpke Transportation Co LLC......513 242-4600
553 Vine St Cincinnati (45202) ***(G-4367)***
Runkles Sawmill LLC......937 663-0115
2534 Dialton Rd Saint Paris (43072) ***(G-16864)***
Runner Tool & Die Inc......330 794-8843
1678 Massillon Rd Akron (44312) ***(G-382)***
Rupcol Inc......419 924-5215
509 Parkway St West Unity (43570) ***(G-20135)***
Ruple Trucking, Willoughby *Also called Chagrin Vly Stl Erectors Inc* ***(G-20455)***
Rupp Construction Inc......330 855-2781
18228 Fulton Rd Marshallville (44645) ***(G-12920)***
Rural Farm Distributors Co......419 747-6807
2690 Bowman Street Rd Mansfield (44903) ***(G-12673)***
Rural Machine & Iron Works, Spencerville *Also called John A & William J Wiechart* ***(G-17461)***
Rural Products Inc......419 298-2677
6266 Us Highway 6 Edgerton (43517) ***(G-9335)***
Rural Urban Record Inc......440 236-8982
24487 Squire Rd Columbia Station (44028) ***(G-6598)***
Ruscilli Real Estate Services......614 923-6400
5100 Prkcnter Ave Ste 100 Dublin (43017) ***(G-9135)***
Ruscoe Company (PA)......330 253-8148
485 Kenmore Blvd Akron (44301) ***(G-383)***
Ruscoe Company......330 253-8148
219 E Miller Ave Akron (44301) ***(G-384)***
Rush Graphix Ltd......419 448-7874
30 Riverside Dr Tiffin (44883) ***(G-18241)***
Rush Welding & Machine Inc......740 354-7874
1657 12th St Portsmouth (45662) ***(G-16450)***
Rush, R L Tool & Pattern, Bucyrus *Also called R L Rush Tool & Pattern Inc* ***(G-2356)***
Russel Hunt Total Land Care, Steubenville *Also called Russell Hunt* ***(G-17711)***
Russell E Coy......419 658-2366
2543 Flickinger Rd Ney (43549) ***(G-15143)***
Russell Hunt......740 264-1196
175 Detmar Rd Steubenville (43953) ***(G-17711)***
Russell L Garber (PA)......937 548-6224
4891 Clark Station Rd Greenville (45331) ***(G-10521)***
Russell Products Co Inc......330 633-5252
275 N Forge St Ste 1 Akron (44304) ***(G-385)***
Russell Products Co Inc......330 535-3391
1066 Home Ave Akron (44310) ***(G-386)***
Russell Products Co Inc......330 434-9163
1066 Home Ave Akron (44310) ***(G-387)***
Russell Products Co Inc......216 267-0880
275 N Forge St Ste 2 Akron (44304) ***(G-388)***
Russell Standard Corporation......330 733-9400
990 Hazel St Akron (44305) ***(G-389)***
Russell T Bundy Associates Inc......419 526-4454
1711 N Main St Mansfield (44903) ***(G-12674)***
Russments Inc......513 602-5035
3714 Church St Cincinnati (45244) ***(G-4368)***
Rust Belt Brewing LLC......330 423-3818
1744 Overlook Ave Youngstown (44509) ***(G-21194)***
Ruth Leinasars......937 484-8542
460 E Dallas Rd Urbana (43078) ***(G-19178)***
Ruthie Ann Inc......800 231-3567
313 New Paris Ave New Paris (45347) ***(G-14881)***
Ruthman Pump and Engineering (PA)......513 559-1901
1212 Streng St Cincinnati (45223) ***(G-4369)***
Ruthman Pump and Engineering......937 783-2411
459 E Fancy St Blanchester (45107) ***(G-1716)***
Rutland Plastic Tech Inc......614 846-3055
777 Dearborn Park Ln N Columbus (43085) ***(G-7578)***
Rutland Township......740 742-2805
33325 Jessie Creek Rd Bidwell (45614) ***(G-1678)***
Rutobo Inc......614 236-2948
4279 E Main St Columbus (43213) ***(G-7579)***
Rv Xpress Inc......937 418-0127
501 East St Piqua (45356) ***(G-16312)***
RW Beckett Corporation (PA)......440 327-1060
38251 Center Ridge Rd North Ridgeville (44039) ***(G-15402)***
Rw Sidley Inc......330 545-1964
200 Mill St Girard (44420) ***(G-10394)***
Rx Frames N Lenses Ltd......513 557-2970
4270 Boomer Rd Cincinnati (45247) ***(G-4370)***
Rx Institutional Services LLC......330 505-1979
3379 Main St Ste A Mineral Ridge (44440) ***(G-14310)***
Rxpert Consultants LLC......614 579-9384
4719 Reed Rd Ste 250 Columbus (43220) ***(G-7580)***
Rxscan, Lewis Center *Also called Retail Management Products* ***(G-11914)***
Ryan Development Corp......937 587-2266
1 Ryan Rd Peebles (45660) ***(G-16024)***
Ryans Newark Leader Ex Prtg......740 522-2149
56 Westgate Dr Newark (43055) ***(G-15051)***
Ryanworks Inc......937 438-1282
175 E Alex Bell Rd # 264 Dayton (45459) ***(G-8641)***
Ryder Engraving Inc......740 927-7193
1029 Hazelton Etna Rd Sw Pataskala (43062) ***(G-15982)***
Ryder-Heil Bronze Inc......419 562-2841
126 E Irving St Bucyrus (44820) ***(G-2358)***
Rykon Plating Inc......440 933-3273
555 Miller Rd Avon Lake (44012) ***(G-1049)***
Rykrisp Llc......843 338-0750
4342 Centennial Dr Apt 33 Cincinnati (45227) ***(G-4371)***

Ryman Grinders Inc 330 652-5080
  704 Warren Ave Niles (44446) *(G-15183)*
S & A Industries Corporation (HQ) 330 733-6040
  571 Kennedy Rd Ste R Akron (44305) *(G-390)*
S & A Precision Bearing Inc (PA) 440 930-7600
  1050 Jaycox Rd Avon (44011) *(G-1010)*
S & B Metal Products Inc (PA) 330 487-5790
  2060 Case Pkwy Twinsburg (44087) *(G-19015)*
S & C Newman Enterprises Inc 740 772-7433
  66 E Water St Chillicothe (45601) *(G-3274)*
S & D Architectural Metals 440 582-2560
  12955 York Delta Dr North Royalton (44133) *(G-15451)*
S & G Manufacturing Group LLC (PA) 614 529-0100
  4830 Northwest Pkwy Hilliard (43026) *(G-10977)*
S & H Automation & Eqp Co 419 636-0020
  815 Commerce Dr Bryan (43506) *(G-2320)*
S & H Industries Inc 216 831-0550
  5200 Richmond Rd Cleveland (44146) *(G-6145)*
S & H Industries Inc 216 831-0550
  14577 Lorain Ave Cleveland (44111) *(G-6146)*
S & J Lumber Co 740 245-5804
  3667 Garners Ford Rd Thurman (45685) *(G-18200)*
S & J Precision Inc 937 296-0068
  2015 Dryden Rd Moraine (45439) *(G-14524)*
S & K Metal Polsg & Buffing 513 732-6662
  4194 Taylor Rd Batavia (45103) *(G-1221)*
S & M Products 419 272-2054
  County Rd 5 I Blakeslee (43505) *(G-1708)*
S & N Engineering and Supply, Cleveland Also called S & N Engineering Svcs Corp *(G-6147)*
S & N Engineering Svcs Corp 216 433-1700
  2901 Henninger Rd Cleveland (44109) *(G-6147)*
S & R Egg, Rossburg Also called Fort Recovery Equity Exchange *(G-16736)*
S & R Sheet Metal 937 865-9236
  320 Gargrave Rd Dayton (45449) *(G-8642)*
S & R Tool & Die Services Inc 937 584-4691
  246 Rose Ave Sabina (45169) *(G-16777)*
S & S Aggregates Inc (HQ) 740 453-0721
  3570 S River Rd Zanesville (43701) *(G-21349)*
S & S Aggregates Inc 419 938-5604
  4540 State Route 39 Perrysville (44864) *(G-16175)*
S & S Machining Ltd 419 524-9525
  76 Atenway St Mansfield (44902) *(G-12675)*
S & S Pallets 513 967-7432
  1536 Pointe Dr Milford (45150) *(G-14171)*
S & S Pallett 740 372-0238
  1974 Henley Deemer Rd Mc Dermott (45652) *(G-13343)*
S & S Panel 330 412-6735
  3314 S Kohler Rd Orrville (44667) *(G-15761)*
S & S Printing Service Inc 937 228-9411
  505 Hunter Ave Dayton (45404) *(G-8643)*
S & S Sign Co 614 837-1511
  10601 Lithopolis Rd Nw Canal Winchester (43110) *(G-2536)*
S & S Spring Shop 800 619-4652
  1755 Mount Perry Rd Mount Perry (43760) *(G-14594)*
S & S Wldg Fabg Machining Inc 330 392-7878
  2587 Miller Graber Rd Newton Falls (44444) *(G-15139)*
S & V Automatics 216 429-2228
  6511 Selma Ave Cleveland (44127) *(G-6148)*
S & W Custom Tops Inc 330 788-2525
  4300 Simon Rd Youngstown (44512) *(G-21195)*
S A E Manufacturing 440 322-9026
  7880 W River Rd S Elyria (44035) *(G-9490)*
S A Langmack Company 216 541-0500
  13400 Glenside Rd Cleveland (44110) *(G-6149)*
S A S Rubber, Painesville Also called Yokohama Tire Corporation *(G-15945)*
S and K Painting 330 505-1910
  1346 Clark St Niles (44446) *(G-15184)*
S and S Tool Inc 440 593-4000
  576 Blair St Conneaut (44030) *(G-7818)*
S Beckman Print & G 614 864-2232
  376 Morrison Rd Ste D Columbus (43213) *(G-7581)*
S C Fastening Systems, Macedonia Also called SC Fire Protection Ltd *(G-12481)*
S C Industries Inc 216 732-9000
  24460 Lakeland Blvd Euclid (44132) *(G-9605)*
S C Johnson & Son Inc 513 665-3600
  36 E 7th St Ste 2450 Cincinnati (45202) *(G-4372)*
S C Machine 419 752-6961
  116 Us Highway 224 W Greenwich (44837) *(G-10536)*
S E Johnson Companies Inc (HQ) 419 893-8731
  1360 Ford St Maumee (43537) *(G-13290)*
S F Mock & Associates LLC 937 438-0196
  105 Westpark Rd Dayton (45459) *(G-8644)*
S I Distributing Inc 419 647-4909
  13540 Spencerville Rd Spencerville (45887) *(G-17465)*
S I T Strings Co Inc 330 434-8010
  2493 Romig Rd Akron (44320) *(G-391)*
S J Cox Tool Inc 740 756-1100
  3800 Old Columbus Rd Nw Carroll (43112) *(G-2946)*
S J K Metalworking Inc 440 564-7877
  14940 Cross Creek Pkwy Newbury (44065) *(G-15104)*

S J Roth Enterprises Inc 513 242-8400
  900 Kieley Pl Cincinnati (45217) *(G-4373)*
S J T Enterprises Inc 440 617-1100
  28045 Ranney Pkwy Ste B Westlake (44145) *(G-20305)*
S K Industries, Newbury Also called S J K Metalworking Inc *(G-15104)*
S K M L Inc 330 220-7565
  580 Liverpool Dr Valley City (44280) *(G-19228)*
S K S Manufacturing Inc 330 669-9133
  212 E Eberly St Smithville (44677) *(G-17244)*
S L C Software Services 513 922-4303
  1958 Anderson Ferry Rd Cincinnati (45238) *(G-4374)*
S L M Inc 216 651-0666
  3148 W 32nd St Ste 3 Cleveland (44109) *(G-6150)*
S M C, Upper Sandusky Also called Schmidt Machine Company *(G-19139)*
S M C Aluminum Foundry Inc 419 257-2175
  100 Peters St North Baltimore (45872) *(G-15198)*
S O I T A, Dayton Also called Southwestern Ohio Instruction *(G-8664)*
S O S Graphics & Printing Inc 614 846-8229
  445 E Wilson Bridge Rd Worthington (43085) *(G-20886)*
S P I, Xenia Also called Spi Inc *(G-20973)*
S P Z Machine Co 330 848-3286
  2871 Newpark Dr Barberton (44203) *(G-1148)*
S R Door Inc (PA) 740 927-3558
  1120 O Neill Dr Hebron (43025) *(G-10883)*
S R P M Inc 440 248-8440
  30300 Bruce Industrial Pk Cleveland (44139) *(G-6151)*
S R T Prosthetics & Orthotics 419 272-3102
  6868 State Route 49 Edon (43518) *(G-9345)*
S R Technologies LLC (PA) 330 523-7184
  2200 N Clvland Msslln Rd Akron (44333) *(G-392)*
S S T Enterprises Inc 330 343-2656
  5165 Main St Ne New Philadelphia (44663) *(G-14927)*
S T A, Oak Harbor Also called Esperia Holdings LLC *(G-15589)*
S T C, Canton Also called Stark Truss Company Inc *(G-2858)*
S T Custom Signs 513 733-4227
  9493 Reading Rd Cincinnati (45215) *(G-4375)*
S T Tool & Design Inc 440 357-1250
  9452 Mercantile Dr Mentor (44060) *(G-13718)*
S Wj Llcred 330 938-6173
  1100 N Johnson Rd Sebring (44672) *(G-17051)*
S&G Distribution, Hilliard Also called S & G Manufacturing Group LLC *(G-10977)*
S&P Global Inc 216 749-9779
  5276 W 49th St Cleveland (44134) *(G-6152)*
S&S Manufactruing, Lancaster Also called Vic Mar Manufacturing Inc *(G-11761)*
S&S Sign Service 614 279-9722
  485 Ternstedt Ln Columbus (43228) *(G-7582)*
S&T Automotive America LLC 248 649-1020
  3900 Gantz Rd Grove City (43123) *(G-10591)*
S&V Industries Inc (PA) 330 666-1986
  5054 Paramount Dr Medina (44256) *(G-13472)*
S-K Mold & Tool Company (PA) 937 339-0299
  955 N 3rd St Tipp City (45371) *(G-18298)*
S-K Mold & Tool Company 937 339-0299
  2120 Corporate Dr Troy (45373) *(G-18870)*
S-L Distribution Company Inc 440 786-9990
  26400 Broadway Ave Ste C Bedford (44146) *(G-1458)*
S-L Snacks Real Estate Inc 440 786-9990
  26400 Broadway Ave Bedford (44146) *(G-1459)*
S-P Company Inc (PA) 330 482-0200
  400 W Railroad St Ste 1 Columbiana (44408) *(G-6631)*
S. C. Manufacturing, Akron Also called Hawk Manufacturing LLC *(G-217)*
S. C. Manufacturing, Akron Also called Hawk Manufacturing LLC *(G-218)*
S. C. Manufacturing, Akron Also called Hawk Manufacturing LLC *(G-219)*
S.E.S., Alliance Also called Steel Eqp Specialists Inc *(G-540)*
Sa-Mor Signs 937 441-4950
  185 Kindle St Wapakoneta (45895) *(G-19505)*
Sabatino Cabinet, Salem Also called Joseph Sabatino *(G-16904)*
Sabbagh Tool and Equipment Co, Akron Also called PC Systems *(G-333)*
Sabco Industries Inc 419 531-5347
  4511 South Ave Toledo (43615) *(G-18683)*
Sabre Energy Corporation 740 685-8266
  175 Main St Nw Lore City (43755) *(G-12294)*
Sabre Enterprises Inc 216 941-9700
  12119 Bennington Ave Cleveland (44135) *(G-6153)*
Sabre Publishing 440 243-4300
  398 W Bagley Rd Ste 210 Berea (44017) *(G-1634)*
Sabrecat Bat Company Inc 330 327-1532
  1616 W Main St Louisville (44641) *(G-12325)*
Sacks Bruce & Associates 419 537-0623
  4959 Damascus Dr Ottawa Hills (43615) *(G-15819)*
Saco Aei Polymers Inc 330 995-1600
  1395 Danner Dr Aurora (44202) *(G-947)*
Saco Lowell Parts LLC 330 794-1535
  1395 Triplett Blvd Akron (44306) *(G-393)*
Sadler Corporation 330 688-7400
  4600 Hudson Dr Stow (44224) *(G-17796)*
Saf-Holland Inc 513 874-7888
  246 Circle Freeway Dr West Chester (45246) *(G-20046)*

Safar Machine Company 330 644-0155
905 Brown St Akron (44311) *(G-394)*
Safc Cleveland, Cleveland *Also called Research Organics LLC* *(G-6105)*
Safe 4 People Inc 419 797-4087
4661 E Woodland Dr Port Clinton (43452) *(G-16412)*
Safe Air Valve Co., Mentor *Also called Aj Fluid Power Sales & Sup Inc* *(G-13514)*
Safe Grain Max Tronix, Wapakoneta *Also called Safe-Grain Inc* *(G-19506)*
Safe Rx Pharmacies Inc 740 377-4162
503 4th St E South Point (45680) *(G-17447)*
Safe Systems Inc 216 661-1166
5401 Brookpark Rd Cleveland (44129) *(G-6154)*
Safe-Grain Inc (PA) 513 398-2500
417 Wards Corner Rd Ste B Loveland (45140) *(G-12383)*
Safe-Grain Inc 513 398-2500
902 N Dixie Hwy Wapakoneta (45895) *(G-19506)*
Safecor Health LLC (PA) 781 933-8780
4060 Business Park Dr B Columbus (43204) *(G-7583)*
Safeguard Technology Inc 330 995-5200
1460 Miller Pkwy Streetsboro (44241) *(G-17873)*
Safelite Autoglass, Columbus *Also called Safelite Group Inc* *(G-7585)*
Safelite Autoglass, Columbus *Also called Safelite Glass Corp* *(G-7584)*
Safelite Glass Corp (HQ) 614 210-9000
7400 Safelite Way Columbus (43235) *(G-7584)*
Safelite Group Inc (HQ) 614 210-9000
7400 Safelite Way Columbus (43235) *(G-7585)*
Safesmart USA 404 703-1008
959 Lake Rd Medina (44256) *(G-13473)*
Safety Sign Company 440 238-7722
19511 Progress Dr Ste 4 Strongsville (44149) *(G-17960)*
Safeway Contact Lens Inc 330 536-6469
1212 Bedford Rd Lowellville (44436) *(G-12413)*
Safeway Packaging Inc (PA) 419 629-3200
300 White Mountain Dr New Bremen (45869) *(G-14793)*
Safeway Safety Step Llc 513 942-7837
5242 Rialto Rd West Chester (45069) *(G-19941)*
Safewhite Inc 614 340-1450
1275 Kinnear Rd Ste 237 Columbus (43212) *(G-7586)*
Sagequest LLC 216 896-7243
31500 Bainbridge Rd Ste 1 Solon (44139) *(G-17374)*
Saginomiya America Inc 614 766-7390
655 Metro Pl S Ste 700 Dublin (43017) *(G-9136)*
Saia-Burgess Lcc 937 898-3621
801 Scholz Dr Vandalia (45377) *(G-19310)*
Sail Medical Inc 513 961-3144
9873 Montgomery Rd Cincinnati (45242) *(G-4376)*
Sailors Tailor Inc 937 862-7781
1480 Spg Vly Paintrs Rd Spring Valley (45370) *(G-17469)*
Saint Croix Ltd 330 666-1544
3371 W Bath Rd Akron (44333) *(G-395)*
Saint Ctherines Metalworks Inc (PA) 216 409-0576
1985 W 68th St Cleveland (44102) *(G-6155)*
Saint Paris Tool and Grinding 937 526-9800
2270 Russia Versailles Rd Russia (45363) *(G-16770)*
Saint-Gobain Ceramics Plas Inc 330 673-5860
3840 Fishcreek Rd Stow (44224) *(G-17797)*
Saint-Gobain Ceramics Plas Inc 440 834-0061
17900 Great Lakes Pkwy Hiram (44234) *(G-11037)*
Saint-Gobain Norpro, Stow *Also called Saint-Gobain Ceramics Plas Inc* *(G-17797)*
Saint-Gobain Norpro Corp (HQ) 330 673-5860
3840 Fishcreek Rd Stow (44224) *(G-17798)*
Saint-Gobain Prfmce Plas Corp 330 296-9948
335 N Diamond St Ravenna (44266) *(G-16554)*
Saint-Gobain Prfmce Plas Corp (HQ) 440 836-6900
31500 Solon Rd Solon (44139) *(G-17375)*
Saint-Gobain Prfmce Plas Corp 330 798-6981
2664 Gilchrist Rd Akron (44305) *(G-396)*
Saint-Gobain Prfmce Plas Corp 614 889-2220
6250 Shier Rings Rd Dublin (43016) *(G-9137)*
Saircorp Ltd 330 669-9099
6020 N Honeytown Rd Smithville (44677) *(G-17245)*
Sajar Plastics Inc 440 632-5203
15285 S State Ave Middlefield (44062) *(G-13986)*
Sakamura USA Inc 740 223-7777
970 Kellogg Pkwy Marion (43302) *(G-12897)*
Sakas Incorporated 740 862-4114
312 Bltmore Smerset Rd Ne Baltimore (43105) *(G-1087)*
Sakrete Inc (PA) 513 242-3644
5155 Fischer Ave Cincinnati (45217) *(G-4377)*
Salco Machine Inc 330 456-8281
3822 Victory Ave Louisville (44641) *(G-12326)*
Salem Welding & Supply Company 330 332-4517
475 Prospect St Salem (44460) *(G-16925)*
Salem-Republic Rubber Company 330 938-2016
475 W California Ave Sebring (44672) *(G-17052)*
Sales Engineering Dept, Liberty Township *Also called Titan Metal Fabricators* *(G-11969)*
Sales Office Rob Jordan Vp Sls, Hilliard *Also called Textiles Inc* *(G-10986)*
Salient Systems Inc 614 792-5800
4393 Tuller Rd Ste K Dublin (43017) *(G-9138)*
Salindia LLC 614 501-4799
2756 Eastland Mall Columbus (43232) *(G-7587)*
Salley Tool & Die Co 937 258-3333
3180 Plainfield Rd Ste 1 Dayton (45432) *(G-8116)*
Sally Beauty Supply LLC 330 823-7476
2636 W State St Alliance (44601) *(G-535)*
Salon Styling Concepts Ltd 216 539-0437
20900 Libby Rd Maple Heights (44137) *(G-12740)*
Salsbury Industries Inc 614 409-1600
2300 Rickenbacker Pkwy Columbus (43217) *(G-7588)*
Salt Creek Lumber Company Inc 330 695-3500
11657 Salt Creek Rd Fredericksburg (44627) *(G-10093)*
Saltillo Corporation (PA) 330 674-6722
2143 Township Road 112 Millersburg (44654) *(G-14261)*
Sam Abdallah 330 532-3900
777 Hamnondsville Rd Hammondsville (43930) *(G-10760)*
Sam Americas Inc 330 628-1118
3555 Gilchrist Rd Mogadore (44260) *(G-14384)*
Sam Dong Ohio Inc 740 363-1985
801 Pittsburgh Dr Delaware (43015) *(G-8884)*
Samco Technologies Inc 216 641-5288
1600 Harvard Ave Newburgh Heights (44105) *(G-15079)*
Samhain Publishing Ltd (llc) 513 453-4688
11821 Mason Montgomery Rd # 2 Cincinnati (45249) *(G-4378)*
Sammartino Welding & Auto Sls 330 782-6086
155 W Indianola Ave Youngstown (44507) *(G-21196)*
Sammy S Auto Detail 614 263-2728
3514 Cleveland Ave Columbus (43224) *(G-7589)*
Sample Machining Inc 937 258-3338
220 N Jersey St Dayton (45403) *(G-8645)*
Sams Graphic Industries 330 821-4710
611 Homeworth Rd Alliance (44601) *(G-536)*
Samsel Rope & Marine Supply Co (PA) 216 241-0333
1285 Old River Rd Uppr Cleveland (44113) *(G-6156)*
Samsel Supply Company, Cleveland *Also called Samsel Rope & Marine Supply Co* *(G-6156)*
Samuel Clark (PA) 614 855-2263
5037 Babbitt Rd New Albany (43054) *(G-14772)*
Samuel Steel Pickling Company (PA) 330 963-3777
1400 Enterprise Pkwy Twinsburg (44087) *(G-19016)*
Samuel Strapping Systems Inc 740 522-2500
1455 James Pkwy Heath (43056) *(G-10855)*
Samuels Products Inc 513 891-4456
9851 Redhill Dr Blue Ash (45242) *(G-1864)*
San Marco Indiana, Toledo *Also called San Marco Super Marketo* *(G-18684)*
San Marco Super Marketo 419 469-8963
235 Broadway St Toledo (43604) *(G-18684)*
San Pallet LLC 937 271-5308
1860 State Route 718 Troy (45373) *(G-18871)*
San-Fab Conveyor and Automtn, Sandusky *Also called Sandusky Fabricating & Sls Inc* *(G-17001)*
Sanborn Plastics Corp 440 286-4122
415 Center St Chardon (44024) *(G-3177)*
Sancap Abrasives, Alliance *Also called Lexington Abrasives Inc* *(G-522)*
Sancast Inc 740 622-8660
535 Clow Ln Coshocton (43812) *(G-7908)*
Sanctuary Software Studio Inc 330 666-9690
3560 W Market St Ste 100 Fairlawn (44333) *(G-9759)*
Sand Hollow Winery 740 323-3959
12558 Sand Hollow Rd Heath (43056) *(G-10856)*
Sanders Fredrick Excvtg Co Inc 330 297-7980
5858 State Route 14 Ravenna (44266) *(G-16555)*
Sandra Weddington 740 417-4286
1400 Stratford Rd Delaware (43015) *(G-8885)*
Sandridge Food Corporation (PA) 330 725-2348
133 Commerce Dr Medina (44256) *(G-13474)*
Sandridge Food Corporation 330 725-8883
133 Commerce Dr Medina (44256) *(G-13475)*
Sandridge Gourmet Salads, Medina *Also called Sandridge Food Corporation* *(G-13474)*
Sandridge Gourmet Salads, Medina *Also called Sandridge Food Corporation* *(G-13475)*
Sands Co Jewelers 216 261-8270
26000 Chardon Rd Cleveland (44143) *(G-6157)*
Sands Hill Coal Hauling Co Inc (PA) 740 384-4211
38701 State Route 160 Hamden (45634) *(G-10657)*
Sands Hill Mining LLC 740 384-4211
38701 State Route 160 Hamden (45634) *(G-10658)*
Sandusky Dock Corporation 419 626-1214
2705 W Monroe St Sandusky (44870) *(G-17000)*
Sandusky Fabricating & Sls Inc (PA) 419 626-4465
2000 Superior St Sandusky (44870) *(G-17001)*
Sandusky International Inc 419 626-5340
615 W Market St Sandusky (44870) *(G-17002)*
Sandusky Machine & Tool Inc 419 626-8359
2223 Tiffin Ave Sandusky (44870) *(G-17003)*
Sandusky Newspapers Inc (PA) 419 625-5500
314 W Market St Sandusky (44870) *(G-17004)*
Sandusky Packaging Corporation 419 626-8520
2016 George St Sandusky (44870) *(G-17005)*
Sandy Creek Mining Co Inc 419 435-5891
522 S Poplar St Fostoria (44830) *(G-9993)*

Sandy Smittcamp..937 372-1687
402 W Church St Xenia (45385) **(G-20971)**

Sanese Services Inc.......................................330 494-5900
2590 Elm Rd Ne Warren (44483) **(G-19597)**

Sanese Vending Company, Warren Also called Sanese Services Inc **(G-19597)**

Sangraf International Inc.................................216 543-3288
6140 W Creek Rd Ste 206 Independence (44131) **(G-11273)**

Sanoh America Inc (HQ)..................................419 425-2600
1849 Industrial Dr Findlay (45840) **(G-9887)**

Sanoh America Inc..740 392-9200
7905 Industrial Park Dr Mount Vernon (43050) **(G-14643)**

Sanscan Inc...330 332-9365
157 N Ellsworth Ave Salem (44460) **(G-16926)**

Sansei Showa Co Ltd.....................................440 248-4440
31000 Bainbridge Rd Cleveland (44139) **(G-6158)**

Sant Sand & Gravel Co..................................740 397-0000
14220 Parrott Ext Mount Vernon (43050) **(G-14644)**

Santmyer Oil Co of Ashland (HQ)......................330 262-6501
1055 W Old Lincoln Way Wooster (44691) **(G-20831)**

Santmyer Oil Co of Ashland.............................419 289-8815
1011 Jacobson Ave Ashland (44805) **(G-775)**

Santos Industrial Ltd (PA)..............................937 299-7333
3034 Dryden Rd Moraine (45439) **(G-14525)**

Santos Industrial Ltd....................................937 299-7333
2960 Springboro W Moraine (45439) **(G-14526)**

Santrol, Chardon Also called Technisand Inc **(G-3181)**

Sapa Extrusions North Amer LLC.......................888 935-5759
401 N Stolle Ave Sidney (45365) **(G-17221)**

Sara Wood Pharmaceuticals LLC........................513 833-5502
4518 Margaret Ct Mason (45040) **(G-13085)**

Saras Little Cupcakes...................................419 305-7914
321 Sturgeon St Saint Marys (45885) **(G-16854)**

Sarcokinetics LLC..414 477-9585
11000 Cedar Ave Ste 265 Cleveland (44106) **(G-6159)**

Sardinia Concrete Company (PA)........................513 248-0090
911 Us Route 50 Milford (45150) **(G-14172)**

Sardinia Concrete Company.............................513 248-0090
1622 Mason Morrow Rd Lebanon (45036) **(G-11836)**

Sardinia Ready Mix Inc (PA)............................937 446-2523
9 Oakdale Ave Sardinia (45171) **(G-17031)**

Sardinia Ready Mix Inc..................................937 446-2523
9 Oakdale Ave Sardinia (45171) **(G-17032)**

Sare Plastics, Alliance Also called Stuchell Products LLC **(G-541)**

Sarica Manufacturing Company.........................937 484-4030
240 W Twain Ave Urbana (43078) **(G-19179)**

Saringer Sheet Metal Inc................................216 447-9755
4654 Crestwood Dr Independence (44131) **(G-11274)**

Sark Technologies LLC...................................216 932-3171
2270 Tudor Dr Cleveland (44106) **(G-6160)**

Sarka Bros Machining Inc................................419 532-2393
607 Ottawa St Kalida (45853) **(G-11417)**

Sarka Conveyor, Tiffin Also called Sarka Shtmtl & Fabrication Inc **(G-18242)**

Sarka Shtmtl & Fabrication Inc.........................419 447-4377
70 Clinton Ave Tiffin (44883) **(G-18242)**

Sas Automation LLC......................................937 372-5255
1200 S Patton St Xenia (45385) **(G-20972)**

Sas Institute Inc...216 643-6719
6100 Oak Tree Blvd # 400 Cleveland (44131) **(G-6161)**

Sash Foam Works Inc.....................................419 522-4074
555 Park Ave E Mansfield (44905) **(G-12676)**

Sasha Electronics Inc....................................419 662-8100
135 Dixie Hwy Rossford (43460) **(G-16749)**

Satco Inc...330 630-8866
59 Industry St Tallmadge (44278) **(G-18168)**

Satellite, Crestline Also called PPG Industries Inc **(G-7935)**

Satellite Gear Inc..216 514-8668
5135 Richmond Rd Cleveland (44146) **(G-6162)**

Sattler Companies Inc....................................330 239-2552
1455 Wolf Creek Trl Wadsworth (44281) **(G-19439)**

Saturday Knight Ltd (HQ)...............................513 641-1400
4330 Winton Rd Cincinnati (45232) **(G-4379)**

Saturn Press Inc..440 232-3344
177 Northfield Rd Bedford (44146) **(G-1460)**

Sauder Machine Ltd.......................................419 896-3722
3071 State Route 603 Plymouth (44865) **(G-16379)**

Sauder Manufacturing Co (HQ).........................419 445-7670
930 W Barre Rd Archbold (43502) **(G-692)**

Sauder Manufacturing Co................................419 682-3061
201 Horton St Stryker (43557) **(G-18007)**

Sauder Wdwkg Co Welfare Tr...........................419 446-2711
502 Middle St Archbold (43502) **(G-693)**

Sauder Woodworking Co (PA)...........................419 446-3828
502 Middle St Archbold (43502) **(G-694)**

Sauder Woodworking Co..................................419 446-2711
330 N Clydes Way Archbold (43502) **(G-695)**

Sauerwein Welding.......................................513 563-2979
605 Wayne Park Dr Cincinnati (45215) **(G-4380)**

Saunders Trucking Lcc...................................419 210-0551
4747 State Route 229 Marengo (43334) **(G-12753)**

Sausage Shoppe..216 351-5213
4501 Memphis Ave Cleveland (44144) **(G-6163)**

Sausser Steel Company Inc...............................419 422-9632
230 Crystal Ave Findlay (45840) **(G-9888)**

Sautter Bros Machine & Fabg, Galion Also called Sautter Brothers **(G-10284)**

Sautter Brothers...419 468-7443
6443 Brandt Rd Galion (44833) **(G-10284)**

Savanna Tool and Manufacturing.......................440 327-8330
34395 Mills Rd North Ridgeville (44039) **(G-15403)**

Savare Corporation (PA).................................614 255-2878
230 West St Ste 700 Columbus (43215) **(G-7590)**

Savare Specialty Adhesives LLC.........................614 255-2648
1201 S Houk Rd Delaware (43015) **(G-8886)**

Save Edge USA, Xenia Also called File Sharpening Company Inc **(G-20951)**

Savko Plastic Pipe & Fittings...........................614 885-8420
683 E Lincoln Ave Columbus (43229) **(G-7591)**

Savor Seasonings LLC....................................513 732-2333
4292 Armstrong Blvd Batavia (45103) **(G-1222)**

Savory Foods Inc...740 354-6655
2240 6th St Portsmouth (45662) **(G-16451)**

Saw Siefker Mill..419 339-1956
4700 Good Rd Delphos (45833) **(G-8917)**

Sawbrook Steel Castings Co (PA)........................513 554-1700
425 Shepherd Ave Cincinnati (45215) **(G-4381)**

Sawdust..740 862-0612
4799 Refugee Rd Nw Baltimore (43105) **(G-1088)**

Sawmill Crossing...614 766-1685
6700 Allister Way Columbus (43235) **(G-7592)**

Sawmill Eye Associates Inc..............................440 724-0396
8666 Scenicview Dr Broadview Heights (44147) **(G-2118)**

Sawmill Eye Associates Inc..............................614 734-2685
6500 Sawmill Rd Columbus (43235) **(G-7593)**

Sawmill Marathon, Columbus Also called Marathon At Sawmill **(G-7317)**

Sawmill Road Management Co LLC (PA).................937 342-9071
1990 Kingsgate Rd Ste A Springfield (45502) **(G-17646)**

Sawmill Station..614 434-6147
3062 Sawdust Ln Dublin (43017) **(G-9139)**

Sawyer Crystal Systems, Willoughby Also called Sawyer Technical Materials LLC **(G-20591)**

Sawyer Research Product................................440 951-8770
35400 Lakeland Blvd Eastlake (44095) **(G-9286)**

Sawyer Technical Materials LLC (HQ)..................440 951-8770
35400 Lakeland Blvd Willoughby (44095) **(G-20591)**

Saxon Jewelers, Cleveland Also called M B Saxon Co Inc **(G-5717)**

Saxon Products Inc.......................................419 241-6771
2283 Fulton St Toledo (43620) **(G-18685)**

Saylor Products Corporation............................419 832-2125
17484 Saylor Ln Grand Rapids (43522) **(G-10445)**

SBC, Columbus Also called Ameritech Publishing Inc **(G-6744)**

SBC, Uniontown Also called Ameritech Publishing Inc **(G-19075)**

SC Elearning LLC...513 852-6841
311 Elm St Ste 200 Cincinnati (45202) **(G-4382)**

SC Fire Protection Ltd...................................330 468-3300
8531 Freeway Dr Macedonia (44056) **(G-12481)**

SC Solutions Inc..614 317-7119
4119 Ashgrove Dr Grove City (43123) **(G-10592)**

Scadatech LLC..614 552-7726
7384 E Main St Ste B Reynoldsburg (43068) **(G-16604)**

Scale Tech Ltd..419 729-5240
5601 Enterprise Blvd Toledo (43612) **(G-18686)**

Scallywag Tag..513 922-4999
5055 Glencrossing Way Cincinnati (45238) **(G-4383)**

Scanacon Incorporated..................................330 877-7600
950 Wales Dr Hartville (44632) **(G-10833)**

Scarefactory Inc..614 252-8000
2905 E 4th Ave Columbus (43219) **(G-7594)**

Scarlett Kitty LLC..678 438-3796
2786 Wilmington Pike Dayton (45419) **(G-8646)**

Scarlett Ktty Bath Made Pretty, Dayton Also called Scarlett Kitty LLC **(G-8646)**

Scarred Hands Wood Creations.........................740 975-2835
8484 Hazelton Etna Rd Sw Etna (43062) **(G-9562)**

Scassa Asphalt Inc.......................................330 830-2039
4167 Beaumont Ave Nw Massillon (44647) **(G-13200)**

SCC Instruments...513 856-8444
4436 Hamilton Scipio Rd Hamilton (45013) **(G-10735)**

Scene Magazine, Cleveland Also called Northeast Scene Inc **(G-5907)**

Scenic Screen..419 468-3110
4463 State Route 309 Galion (44833) **(G-10285)**

Scenic Wood Products, Sugarcreek Also called Pallet Distributors Inc **(G-18030)**

Schaaf Co Inc..513 241-7044
2440 Spring Grove Ave Cincinnati (45214) **(G-4384)**

Schad Meats Inc..513 520-4888
2615 Cummins St Cincinnati (45225) **(G-4385)**

Schaefer Box & Pallet Co................................513 738-2500
11875 Paddys Run Rd Hamilton (45013) **(G-10736)**

Schaefer Equipment Inc..................................330 372-4006
1590 Phoenix Rd Ne Warren (44483) **(G-19598)**

Schaefer Group Inc......................................419 897-2883
29102 Glenwood Rd Ste A Perrysburg (43551) **(G-16147)**

Schaeffler Group USA Inc 330 273-4383
  5370 Wegman Dr Valley City (44280) *(G-19229)*
Schaerer Medical Usa Inc 513 561-2241
  675 Wilmer Ave Cincinnati (45226) *(G-4386)*
Schafer Driveline LLC 614 864-1116
  6635 Taylor Rd Blacklick (43004) *(G-1706)*
Schafer Driveline LLC (HQ) 740 694-0462
  123 Phoenix Pl Fredericktown (43019) *(G-10109)*
Schaffer Grinding Co Inc 323 724-4476
  8470 Chamberlin Rd Twinsburg (44087) *(G-19017)*
Schaffner Publication Inc 419 732-2154
  3956 E Hbr Lght Lnding Dr Port Clinton (43452) *(G-16413)*
Schantz Organ Company (PA) 330 682-6065
  626 S Walnut St Orrville (44667) *(G-15762)*
Scharenberg Sheet Metal 740 664-2431
  2261 Scott Rd New Marshfield (45766) *(G-14872)*
Schauer Battery Chargers, Cincinnati *Also called Brookwood Group Inc (G-3481)*
Schell Scenic Studio Inc 614 444-9550
  841 S Front St 843 Columbus (43206) *(G-7595)*
Schena Company Ltd 419 868-5207
  7710 Hill Ave Ste B Holland (43528) *(G-11083)*
Schenck Process LLC 513 576-9200
  1000 Ford Cir Ste B Milford (45150) *(G-14173)*
Schenz Theatrical Supply Inc 513 542-6100
  2959 Colerain Ave Cincinnati (45225) *(G-4387)*
Scherba Industries Inc 330 273-3200
  2880 Interstate Pkwy Brunswick (44212) *(G-2256)*
Scherer Industrial Group, Springfield *Also called Horner Industrial Services Inc (G-17576)*
Schien Equipment Company, Akron *Also called Heritage Manufacturing Inc (G-223)*
Schiffer Group Inc 937 694-8185
  1602 Marby Dr Troy (45373) *(G-18872)*
Schilling Enamels Company, Cleveland *Also called Schilling Enterprises Inc (G-6165)*
Schilling Enamels Company 216 252-6242
  12632 Triskett Rd Cleveland (44111) *(G-6164)*
Schilling Enterprises Inc (PA) 216 252-6242
  12632 Triskett Rd Cleveland (44111) *(G-6165)*
Schilling Graphics Inc (PA) 419 468-1037
  275 Gelsanliter Rd Galion (44833) *(G-10286)*
Schilling Truss Inc 740 984-2396
  230 Stony Run Rd Beverly (45715) *(G-1671)*
Schindler Elevator Corporation 513 341-2600
  5426 Duff Dr West Chester (45246) *(G-20047)*
Schindler Elevator Corporation 419 861-5900
  1530 Timber Wolf Dr Holland (43528) *(G-11084)*
Schindlers Broad Run Chese Hse 330 343-4108
  6011 Old Route 39 Nw Dover (44622) *(G-9011)*
Schlabach Printers, Sugarcreek *Also called Schlabach Printing Ltd (G-18038)*
Schlabach Printing Ltd 330 852-4687
  798 State Route 93 Nw Sugarcreek (44681) *(G-18038)*
Schlabach Woodworks Ltd 330 674-7488
  6678 State Route 241 Millersburg (44654) *(G-14262)*
Schlessman Seed Co (PA) 419 499-2572
  11513 Us Highway 250 N Milan (44846) *(G-14116)*
Schlezinger Metals, Columbus *Also called I H Schlezinger Inc (G-7178)*
Schloemer, Don Masonry, Willard *Also called Donald Schloemer (G-20394)*
Schloss Media, Cadiz *Also called Harrison News Herald Inc (G-2418)*
Schlumberger Completions, Strasburg *Also called Smith International (G-17829)*
Schlumberger Limited 330 878-0794
  211 Zeltman Ave Ne Strasburg (44680) *(G-17828)*
Schmelzer Industries Inc 740 743-2866
  7970 Wesley Chapel Rd Ne Somerset (43783) *(G-17419)*
Schmidt Machine Company 419 294-3814
  7013 State Highway 199 Upper Sandusky (43351) *(G-19139)*
Schmidt Progressive LLC 513 934-2600
  360 Harmon Ave Lebanon (45036) *(G-11837)*
Schmitmeyer Inc 937 295-2091
  195 Ben St Fort Loramie (45845) *(G-9937)*
Schneder Elc Bldngs Amrcas Inc 513 398-9800
  1770 Masn Mrrw Millgrv Rd Lebanon (45036) *(G-11838)*
Schneider Electric Usa Inc 513 755-5503
  5425 Longhunter Chase Dr Liberty Township (45044) *(G-11967)*
Schneider Electric Usa Inc 513 755-4231
  9870 Crescent Park Dr West Chester (45069) *(G-19942)*
Schneider Electric Usa Inc 513 755-5000
  9870 Crescent Park Dr West Chester (45069) *(G-19943)*
Schneider Electric Usa Inc 513 523-4171
  5735 College Corner Pike Oxford (45056) *(G-15843)*
Schneider Instrument Co 513 561-6803
  8115 Camargo Rd Cincinnati (45243) *(G-4388)*
Schneller LLC (HQ) 330 676-7183
  6019 Powdermill Rd Kent (44240) *(G-11522)*
Schneller LLC 330 673-1299
  6019 Powdermill Rd Kent (44240) *(G-11523)*
Schnider Pallet LLC 440 632-5346
  9782 Bundysburg Rd Middlefield (44062) *(G-13987)*
Schober Usa Inc 513 489-7393
  4690 Industry Dr Fairfield (45014) *(G-9714)*
Schodorf Truck Body & Eqp Co 614 228-6793
  885 Harmon Ave Columbus (43223) *(G-7596)*

Schoen Industries Inc 330 533-6659
  290 Southview Rd Canfield (44406) *(G-2573)*
Scholz & Ey Engravers Inc 614 444-8052
  1558 Parsons Ave Columbus (43207) *(G-7597)*
Schomaker Natural Resource 513 741-1370
  2741 Blue Rock Rd Cincinnati (45239) *(G-4389)*
School House Winery LLC 330 602-9463
  455 Schneiders Crssng Rd Dover (44622) *(G-9012)*
School Maintenance Supply Inc (PA) 513 376-8670
  10616 Millington Ct Blue Ash (45242) *(G-1865)*
School Pride Limited 614 568-0697
  3511 Johnny Appleseed Ct Columbus (43231) *(G-7598)*
Schoolbelles, Cleveland *Also called Kip-Craft Incorporated (G-5656)*
Schoonover Industries Inc 419 289-8332
  1440 Simonton Rd Ashland (44805) *(G-776)*
Schott Metal Products Company 330 773-7873
  2225 Lee Dr Akron (44306) *(G-397)*
Schreiner Cstm Stairs & Mllwk 419 435-8935
  1415 Sandusky St Fostoria (44830) *(G-9994)*
Schreiner Manufacturing 419 937-0300
  1997 Township Road 66 New Riegel (44853) *(G-14948)*
Schrock John 937 544-8457
  61 Poole Rd West Union (45693) *(G-20125)*
Schrock Woodworking 740 489-5229
  71444 Grapevine Rd Freeport (43973) *(G-10120)*
Schuerholz Printing Inc 937 294-5218
  3540 Marshall Rd Dayton (45429) *(G-8647)*
Schuetz Container 419 872-2295
  2105 S Wilkinson Way Perrysburg (43551) *(G-16148)*
Schulers Bakery Inc (PA) 937 323-4154
  1911 S Limestone St Springfield (45505) *(G-17647)*
Schumann Enterprises Inc 216 267-6850
  4775 Manufacturing Ave Cleveland (44135) *(G-6166)*
Schupp Advanced Materials LLC 440 488-6416
  10770 Chillicothe Rd Willoughby (44094) *(G-20592)*
Schuster Beverage Marketing 614 764-1420
  3231 Cranston Dr Dublin (43017) *(G-9140)*
Schuster Manufacturing Inc 419 476-5800
  1508 W Laskey Rd Ste 2 Toledo (43612) *(G-18687)*
Schwab Industries, Berea *Also called Medina Supply Company (G-1626)*
Schwab Industries Inc (HQ) 330 364-4411
  2301 Progress St Dover (44622) *(G-9013)*
Schwab Machine Co Inc 419 626-0245
  3120 Venice Rd Sandusky (44870) *(G-17006)*
Schwab Welding Inc 513 353-4262
  7046 Harrison Ave Cincinnati (45247) *(G-4390)*
Schwans Home Service Inc 419 222-9977
  2545 Saint Johns Rd Lima (45804) *(G-12088)*
Schwans Home Service Inc 937 335-4111
  2991 S County Road 25a Troy (45373) *(G-18873)*
Schwarz Partners Packaging LLC 317 290-1140
  2450 Campbell Rd Sidney (45365) *(G-17222)*
Schwebel Baking Co-Solon Bky, Solon *Also called Schwebel Baking Company (G-17376)*
Schwebel Baking Company (PA) 330 783-2860
  965 E Midlothian Blvd Youngstown (44502) *(G-21197)*
Schwebel Baking Company 440 846-1921
  22626 Royalton Rd Strongsville (44149) *(G-17961)*
Schwebel Baking Company 440 248-1500
  6250 Camp Industrial Rd Solon (44139) *(G-17376)*
Schwebel Baking Company 740 435-9857
  8277 Georgetown Rd Cambridge (43725) *(G-2475)*
Schwebel Baking Company 330 783-2860
  121 O Neill Dr Hebron (43025) *(G-10884)*
Schweizer Dipple Inc 440 786-8090
  7227 Division St Cleveland (44146) *(G-6167)*
Schwieterman Cy Inc 937 548-3965
  4240 State Route 49 Arcanum (45304) *(G-660)*
SCI Engineered Materials Inc 614 486-0261
  2839 Charter St Columbus (43228) *(G-7599)*
Scicompro - LLC 513 680-8686
  4861 Hampton Pond Ln Mason (45040) *(G-13086)*
Science/Electronics Inc 937 224-4444
  521 Kiser St Dayton (45404) *(G-8648)*
Scio Laminated Products Inc 740 945-1321
  117 Fowler Ave Scio (43988) *(G-17038)*
Scioto Ceramic Products Inc 614 436-0405
  854 Curleys Ct Columbus (43235) *(G-7600)*
Scioto Coca Cola 740 474-2180
  387 Walnut St Circleville (43113) *(G-4641)*
Scioto Ready Mix LLC 740 924-9273
  6214 Taylor Rd Sw Pataskala (43062) *(G-15983)*
Scioto Readymix Co 614 491-0773
  1500 Williams Rd Columbus (43207) *(G-7601)*
Scioto Sand & Gravel, Prospect *Also called Fleming Construction Co (G-16496)*
Scioto Sign Co Inc 419 673-1261
  6047 Us Highway 68 Kenton (43326) *(G-11568)*
Scis Aerospace LLC 216 533-8533
  1179 Alexandria Ln Medina (44256) *(G-13476)*
Scorecards Unlimited LLC 614 885-0796
  6334 Huntley Rd Columbus (43229) *(G-7602)*

Scorpion Case Mfg LLC...614 274-7246
329 Clover Ln Dublin (43017) **(G-9141)**
Scot Industries Inc...330 262-7585
6578 Ashland Rd Wooster (44691) **(G-20832)**
Scott A Zurbrugg...330 821-9814
6016 Union Ave Ne Alliance (44601) **(G-537)**
Scott Bader Inc...330 920-4410
4280 Hudson Dr Stow (44224) **(G-17799)**
Scott Emerson...330 372-1040
2541 Larchmont Ave Ne Warren (44483) **(G-19599)**
Scott Enterprises, North Olmsted *Also called Thrifty Print* **(G-15349)**
Scott Fetzer Company...216 267-9000
4801 W 150th St Cleveland (44135) **(G-6168)**
Scott Fetzer Company...216 228-2403
1920 W 114th St Cleveland (44102) **(G-6169)**
Scott Fetzer Company...216 252-1190
3881 W 150th St Cleveland (44111) **(G-6170)**
Scott Fetzer Company...440 871-2160
875 Bassett Rd Cleveland (44145) **(G-6171)**
Scott Fetzer Company...216 228-2400
16841 Park Circle Dr Chagrin Falls (44023) **(G-3119)**
Scott Fetzer Company...440 439-1616
23901 Aurora Rd Cleveland (44146) **(G-6172)**
Scott Fetzer Company...216 281-1100
10920 Madison Ave Cleveland (44102) **(G-6173)**
Scott Fetzer Company...216 433-7797
4750 W 160th St Cleveland (44135) **(G-6174)**
Scott Fetzer Company...440 871-2160
33672 Pin Oak Pkwy Avon Lake (44012) **(G-1050)**
Scott Fetzer Company (HQ)...440 892-3000
28800 Clemens Rd Westlake (44145) **(G-20306)**
Scott Models Inc...513 771-8005
607 Redna Ter Ste 400 Cincinnati (45215) **(G-4391)**
Scott Molders Incorporated...330 673-5777
7180 State Route 43 Kent (44240) **(G-11524)**
Scott Port-A-Fold, Napoleon *Also called Toy & Sport Trends Inc* **(G-14700)**
Scott Port-A-Fold Inc...419 748-8880
5963 State Route 110 Napoleon (43545) **(G-14698)**
Scott Process Systems Inc...330 877-2350
1160 Sunnyside St Sw Hartville (44632) **(G-10834)**
Scott Systems International...740 383-8383
370 W Fairground St Marion (43302) **(G-12898)**
Scott Thomas Furniture, Twinsburg *Also called R A Hamed International Inc* **(G-19007)**
Scott-Randall Systems Inc...937 446-2293
5815 Tracy Rd Sardinia (45171) **(G-17033)**
Scottcare Corporation (HQ)...216 362-0550
4791 W 150th St Cleveland (44135) **(G-6175)**
Scottdel Cushion LLC...419 825-0432
400 Church St Swanton (43558) **(G-18089)**
Scottissue LLC...937 293-2139
3275 Dryden Rd Moraine (45439) **(G-14527)**
Scottrods LLC...419 499-2705
2512 Higbee Rd Monroeville (44847) **(G-14428)**
Scotts Company LLC...614 863-3920
710 Cross Pointe Rd Gahanna (43230) **(G-10231)**
Scotts Company LLC...937 454-2782
20 Innovation Ct Dayton (45414) **(G-8649)**
Scotts Company LLC...614 733-0462
7400 Industrial Pkwy Plain City (43064) **(G-16357)**
Scotts Company LLC (HQ)...937 644-3729
14111 Scottslawn Rd Marysville (43040) **(G-12967)**
Scotts Company LLC...440 899-9339
28315 W Oviatt Rd Bay Village (44140) **(G-1245)**
Scotts Miracle-Gro Company...330 684-0421
1220 Schrock Rd Orrville (44667) **(G-15763)**
Scotts Miracle-Gro Company (PA)...937 644-0011
14111 Scottslawn Rd Marysville (43040) **(G-12968)**
Scotts Miracle-Gro Company...937 578-5065
14101 Industrial Pkwy Marysville (43040) **(G-12969)**
Scotts Miracle-Gro Products, Marysville *Also called Scotts Company LLC* **(G-12967)**
Scotts Miracle-Gro Products...937 644-0011
14111 Scottslawn Rd Marysville (43040) **(G-12970)**
Scotts, The, Marysville *Also called Scotts Miracle-Gro Company* **(G-12968)**
Scotts- Hyponex, Marysville *Also called Hyponex Corporation* **(G-12953)**
Scotts- Hyponex, Shreve *Also called Hyponex Corporation* **(G-17157)**
Scrambl-Gram Inc...419 635-2321
5225 W Lkshore Dr Ste 340 Port Clinton (43452) **(G-16414)**
Scrapbook Gallery...419 523-4419
7919 Road 13g Ottawa (45875) **(G-15807)**
Scratch Off Works...440 333-4302
19537 Lake Rd Rocky River (44116) **(G-16709)**
Scratch-Off Systems Inc...216 649-7800
6600 W Snowville Rd Brecksville (44141) **(G-2071)**
Screen Craft Plastics...440 286-4060
695 South St Ste 7 Chardon (44024) **(G-3178)**
Screen Images Inc...440 779-7356
6122 Croton Dr North Olmsted (44070) **(G-15344)**
Screen Machine, Pataskala *Also called SMI Holdings Inc* **(G-15985)**
Screen Machine, Pataskala *Also called SMI Holdings Inc* **(G-15986)**
Screen Machine Industries LLC...740 927-3464
10685 Columbus Pkwy Pataskala (43062) **(G-15984)**
Screen Printing Show House...614 252-2202
853 N Nelson Rd Columbus (43219) **(G-7603)**
Screen Printing Unlimited...419 621-2335
3410 Tiffin Ave Sandusky (44870) **(G-17007)**
Screen Tech Graphics...740 695-7950
152 Saint Patricks Aly B Saint Clairsville (43950) **(G-16807)**
Screen Works Inc (PA)...937 264-9111
3970 Image Dr Dayton (45414) **(G-8650)**
Screenmobile Inc...614 868-8663
6737 Thomas Rd Radnor (43066) **(G-16507)**
Screenplay Printing, Xenia *Also called Liming Printing Inc* **(G-20961)**
Scrip-Safe International, Loveland *Also called Scrip-Safe Security Products* **(G-12384)**
Scrip-Safe Security Products...513 697-7789
136 Commerce Dr Loveland (45140) **(G-12384)**
Scripps Media Inc...513 977-3000
312 Walnut St Fl 28 Cincinnati (45202) **(G-4392)**
Scriptel Corporation...614 276-8402
2174 Dividend Dr Columbus (43228) **(G-7604)**
Scriptype Publishing Inc...330 659-0303
4300 W Streetsboro Rd Richfield (44286) **(G-16635)**
Scs Construction Services Inc...513 929-0260
2130 Western Ave Cincinnati (45214) **(G-4393)**
Scs Gearbox Inc...419 483-7278
739 W Main St Bellevue (44811) **(G-1557)**
Scsrm Concrete Company Ltd...937 533-1001
4723 Hardin Wapakoneta Rd Sidney (45365) **(G-17223)**
SD Ip Holdings Company...513 483-3300
4747 Lake Forest Dr Blue Ash (45242) **(G-1866)**
Sdg News Group Inc...419 929-3411
43 E Main St New London (44851) **(G-14865)**
Sdi Industries...513 561-4032
8561 New England Ct Cincinnati (45236) **(G-4394)**
SDS Logistics Services, Youngstown *Also called SDS National LLC* **(G-21198)**
SDS National LLC...330 759-8066
19 Colonial Dr Ste 27 Youngstown (44505) **(G-21198)**
Sea Air Spc McG and Mld LLC...440 248-3025
30555 Solon Indus Pkwy Solon (44139) **(G-17377)**
Sea Bird Publications Inc...513 869-2200
311 Nilles Rd Ste B Fairfield (45014) **(G-9715)**
Seacor Painting Corporation...330 755-6361
98 Creed Cir Campbell (44405) **(G-2491)**
Seaforth Mineral & Ore Co Inc (PA)...216 292-5820
3690 Orange Pl Ste 495 Cleveland (44122) **(G-6176)**
Seagate Plastics Company (PA)...419 878-5010
1110 Disher Dr Waterville (43566) **(G-19667)**
Seal Master Corporation...330 673-8410
340 Martinel Dr Kent (44240) **(G-11525)**
Seal Tite LLC...937 393-4268
120 Moore Rd Hillsboro (45133) **(G-11014)**
Seal-Rite Door, Hebron *Also called S R Door Inc* **(G-10883)**
Sealant Solutions...614 599-8000
947 E Johnstown Rd Columbus (43230) **(G-7605)**
Sealco Inc...740 922-4122
6566 Superior Rd Se Uhrichsville (44683) **(G-19058)**
Sealmaster, Sandusky *Also called Thorworks Industries Inc* **(G-17015)**
Sealmaster, Kent *Also called Seal Master Corporation* **(G-11525)**
Sealtite Building Fasteners, West Chester *Also called Hargis Industries LP* **(G-20013)**
Sealwall Products, Cleveland *Also called Metalcrete Industries Inc* **(G-5790)**
Sealy Mattress Company...330 725-4146
1070 Lake Rd Medina (44256) **(G-13477)**
Sealy Mattress Mfg Co Inc...800 697-3259
1070 Lake Rd Medina (44256) **(G-13478)**
Seaman Corporation (PA)...330 262-1111
1000 Venture Blvd Wooster (44691) **(G-20833)**
Seapine Software Inc (HQ)...513 754-1655
6960 Cintas Blvd Mason (45040) **(G-13087)**
Seaport Mold & Casting Company...419 243-1422
1215 W Bancroft St Toledo (43606) **(G-18688)**
Seat Division Bridgestone, Upper Sandusky *Also called Bridgestone APM Company* **(G-19115)**
Seavival LLC...330 252-1151
526 S Main St Ste 518 Akron (44311) **(G-398)**
Seaway Enterprises, Toledo *Also called Initial Designs Inc* **(G-18523)**
Seaway Pattern Mfg Inc...419 865-5724
5749 Angola Rd Toledo (43615) **(G-18689)**
Seawin Inc...419 355-9111
728 Graham Dr Fremont (43420) **(G-10182)**
Sebring Fluid Power Corp...330 938-9984
513 N Johnson Rd Sebring (44672) **(G-17053)**
Sebring Industrial Plating...330 938-6666
546 W Tennessee Ave Sebring (44672) **(G-17054)**
Sebring Plating, Sebring *Also called Sebring Industrial Plating* **(G-17054)**
Seco Machine Inc...330 499-2150
7376 Whipple Ave Nw North Canton (44720) **(G-15263)**
Secondary Machining Services...440 593-1272
539 Center Rd Conneaut (44030) **(G-7819)**

ALPHABETIC

Secqure Surgical Corp....513 769-1916
4480 Lake Forest Dr # 414 Blue Ash (45242) ***(G-1867)***
Secret Image Promotion, Englewood *Also called Image Industries Inc* ***(G-9524)***
Sectional Stamping Inc....440 647-2100
350 Maple St Wellington (44090) ***(G-19754)***
Securcom Inc....419 628-1049
307 W 1st St Minster (45865) ***(G-14361)***
Secure Medical Mail LLC....216 269-1971
3257 Mayfield Rd Apt 21 Cleveland (44118) ***(G-6177)***
Secure Pak, Perrysburg *Also called Glassline Corporation* ***(G-16102)***
Security Fence Group Inc (PA)....513 681-3700
4260 Dane Ave Cincinnati (45223) ***(G-4395)***
Security Systems Eqp Corp....513 758-1070
3040 Forrer St Cincinnati (45209) ***(G-4396)***
Securus Medical Group Inc....216 445-4683
10000 Cedar Ave Cleveland (44106) ***(G-6178)***
Sedlak....330 908-2200
4020 Kinross Lakes Pkwy Richfield (44286) ***(G-16636)***
Sedona Office, Chagrin Falls *Also called Perennial Software Inc* ***(G-3067)***
See Ya There Inc....614 856-9037
12710 W Bank Dr Ne Millersport (43046) ***(G-14298)***
See Ya There Vacation and Trvl, Millersport *Also called See Ya There Inc* ***(G-14298)***
Seeb Industrial Inc....216 896-9016
5182 Richmond Rd Bedford (44146) ***(G-1461)***
Seebach Inc....937 275-3565
2622 Keenan Ave Dayton (45414) ***(G-8651)***
Seebach Tools & Molds Mfg, Dayton *Also called Seebach Inc* ***(G-8651)***
Seeburger Greenhouse....419 832-1834
11480 Us Route 24 Grand Rapids (43522) ***(G-10446)***
Seekirk Inc....614 278-9200
2420 Scioto Harper Dr Columbus (43204) ***(G-7606)***
Seelaus Instrument Co....513 733-8222
422 Alexandersville Rd Miamisburg (45342) ***(G-13857)***
Seemless Design & Printing LLC....513 871-2366
717 Linn St Cincinnati (45203) ***(G-4397)***
Seepex Inc....937 864-7150
511 Speedway Dr Enon (45323) ***(G-9549)***
Segna Inc....937 335-6700
1316 Barnhart Rd Troy (45373) ***(G-18874)***
Sei Inc....513 942-6170
10004 International Blvd West Chester (45246) ***(G-20048)***
Seifert Printing Company....330 759-7414
3200 Belmont Ave Ste 11 Youngstown (44505) ***(G-21199)***
Seilkop Industries Inc (PA)....513 761-1035
425 W North Bend Rd Cincinnati (45216) ***(G-4398)***
Seilkop Industries Inc....513 353-3090
5927 State Route 128 Miamitown (45041) ***(G-13892)***
Seilkop Industries Inc....513 679-5680
7211 Market Pl Cincinnati (45216) ***(G-4399)***
Seislove Brial Vlts Sptic Tnks, Tiffin *Also called Seislove Vault & Septic Tanks* ***(G-18243)***
Seislove Vault & Septic Tanks....419 447-5473
2168 S State Route 100 Tiffin (44883) ***(G-18243)***
Sekely Industries Inc (PA)....248 844-9201
240 Pennsylvania Ave Salem (44460) ***(G-16927)***
Selah Paperie....330 755-2759
130 S Bridge St Struthers (44471) ***(G-17998)***
Selas Heat Technology Co LLC....216 662-8800
11012 Aurora Hudson Rd Streetsboro (44241) ***(G-17874)***
Selas Heat Technology Co LLC (HQ)....800 523-6500
11012 Aurora Hudson Rd Streetsboro (44241) ***(G-17875)***
Selbro Inc....419 483-9918
555 Goodrich Rd Bellevue (44811) ***(G-1558)***
Selby Service/Roxy Press Inc....513 241-3445
2020 Elm St Cincinnati (45202) ***(G-4400)***
Selbys Upper Deck Company....513 451-5981
1028 Glenna Dr Cincinnati (45238) ***(G-4401)***
Selco Industries Inc....419 861-0336
1590 Albon Rd Ste 1 Holland (43528) ***(G-11085)***
Select Enterprises Inc....724 588-4141
6345 State Route 7 Kinsman (44428) ***(G-11611)***
Select Industries Corporation....937 233-9191
60 Heid Ave Dayton (45404) ***(G-8652)***
Select International Corp (PA)....937 233-9191
60 Heid Ave Dayton (45404) ***(G-8653)***
Select International Corp., Dayton *Also called Select Industries Corporation* ***(G-8652)***
Select Logging....419 564-0361
5739 Township Road 21 Marengo (43334) ***(G-12754)***
Select Machine Co Inc....330 678-7676
4125 Karg Industrial Pkwy Kent (44240) ***(G-11526)***
Select Mattress, Toledo *Also called Smp Manufacturing LLC* ***(G-18699)***
Select Mattress Co Inc....419 244-3645
1216 W Bancroft St Toledo (43606) ***(G-18690)***
Select Optical, Columbus *Also called Bsa Industries Inc* ***(G-6869)***
Select Seating, Columbus *Also called N Wasserstrom & Sons Inc* ***(G-7378)***
Select Security Screen Co Ltd....216 362-1850
1801 E 9th St Ste 1710 Cleveland (44114) ***(G-6179)***
Select Tool & Production, Toledo *Also called Hedges Selective Tool & Prod* ***(G-18504)***
Select Woodworking Inc....513 948-9901
427c W Seymour Ave Cincinnati (45216) ***(G-4402)***

Select-Arc Inc....937 295-5215
600 Enterprise Dr Fort Loramie (45845) ***(G-9938)***
Selecteon Corporation....614 228-8008
777 W Swan St Columbus (43212) ***(G-7607)***
Selective Med Components Inc....740 397-7838
504 Harcourt Rd Ste 3 Mount Vernon (43050) ***(G-14645)***
Selectronics Incorporated....440 546-5595
9771 Forge Dr Brecksville (44141) ***(G-2072)***
Selinick Co....440 632-1788
15879 Madison Rd Middlefield (44062) ***(G-13988)***
Sellyourmaccom....513 965-1144
11101 Kenwood Rd Blue Ash (45242) ***(G-1868)***
Selmco Metal Fabricators Inc....937 498-1331
1615 Ferguson Ct Sidney (45365) ***(G-17224)***
Selzer Tool & Die Inc....440 365-4124
163 Kenwood St Elyria (44035) ***(G-9491)***
Sem-Com Company Inc (PA)....419 537-8813
1040 N Westwood Ave Toledo (43607) ***(G-18691)***
Sematic Usa Inc....330 405-3004
7852 Bavaria Rd Twinsburg (44087) ***(G-19018)***
Semco....800 848-5764
1025 Pole Lane Rd Marion (43302) ***(G-12899)***
Semco Carbon, Lorain *Also called Sentinel Management Inc* ***(G-12274)***
Semco Ceramics, Uhrichsville *Also called Stebbins Engineering & Mfg Co* ***(G-19060)***
Seme & Son Automotive Inc....216 261-0066
1320 E 260th St Euclid (44132) ***(G-9606)***
Semper Quality Industry Inc....440 352-8111
9411 Mercantile Dr Mentor (44060) ***(G-13719)***
Semtorq Inc....330 487-0600
1953 Case Pkwy S Twinsburg (44087) ***(G-19019)***
Senator International Inc (PA)....419 887-5806
4111 N Jerome Rd Maumee (43537) ***(G-13291)***
Senco Brands Inc....513 388-2833
8450 Broadwell Rd Cincinnati (45244) ***(G-4403)***
Senco Brands Inc (HQ)....513 388-2000
4270 Ivy Pointe Blvd Cincinnati (45245) ***(G-3315)***
Senco Holdings Inc....800 543-4596
4270 Ivy Pointe Blvd # 125 Cincinnati (45245) ***(G-3316)***
Seneca Label Inc....440 237-1600
13821 Progress Pkwy Cleveland (44133) ***(G-6180)***
Seneca Millwork Inc....419 435-6671
300 Court Pl Fostoria (44830) ***(G-9995)***
Seneca Petroleum Co Inc....419 691-3581
1441 Woodville Rd Toledo (43605) ***(G-18692)***
Seneca Railroad & Mining Co....419 483-7764
1075 W Main St Bellevue (44811) ***(G-1559)***
Seneca Sheet Metal Company....419 447-8434
277 Water St Tiffin (44883) ***(G-18244)***
Seneca Tiles Inc....419 426-3561
7100 S County Road 23 Attica (44807) ***(G-895)***
Seneca Wire Group Inc (PA)....419 435-9261
319 S Vine St Fostoria (44830) ***(G-9996)***
Senior Impact Publication....513 791-8800
5980 Kugler Mill Rd Cincinnati (45236) ***(G-4404)***
Senneco Glass Inc (PA)....330 825-7717
1730 Newberry St Cuyahoga Falls (44221) ***(G-8043)***
Sense Diagnostics LLC....513 515-3853
1776 Mentor Ave Ste 411 Cincinnati (45212) ***(G-4405)***
Sense Labs LLC....740 590-0009
101 S May Ave Athens (45701) ***(G-883)***
Sensetronics LLC....614 292-2833
8407 Gleneagles Ct Dublin (43017) ***(G-9142)***
Sensible Products Inc....330 659-4212
3857 Brecksville Rd Richfield (44286) ***(G-16637)***
Sensical Inc....216 641-1141
31115 Aurora Rd Solon (44139) ***(G-17378)***
Sensopart USA Inc....419 931-7696
28400 Cedar Park Blvd Perrysburg (43551) ***(G-16149)***
Sensor Technology Systems, Miamisburg *Also called Steiner Eoptics Inc* ***(G-13865)***
Sensorwerks, Hilliard *Also called Sensotec LLC* ***(G-10978)***
Sensory Effects, Defiance *Also called Sensoryeffects Flavor Company* ***(G-8809)***
Sensoryeffects Flavor Company....419 782-5010
136 Fox Run Dr Defiance (43512) ***(G-8809)***
Sensoryffcts Powdr Systems Inc....419 783-5518
136 Fox Run Dr Defiance (43512) ***(G-8810)***
Sensotec LLC....614 481-8616
3964 Brown Park Dr Ste B Hilliard (43026) ***(G-10978)***
Sensource Global Sourcing LLC....513 659-8283
4270 Ivy Pointe Blvd Cincinnati (45245) ***(G-3317)***
Sensus, Hamilton *Also called Synergy Flavors (oh) LLC* ***(G-10743)***
Sensus LLC....513 892-7100
2991 Hamilton Mason Rd Hamilton (45011) ***(G-10737)***
Sentek Corporation....614 586-1123
1160b Alum Creek Dr Columbus (43209) ***(G-7608)***
Sentinel Consumer Products Inc (PA)....801 825-5671
7750 Tyler Blvd Mentor (44060) ***(G-13720)***
Sentinel Daily....740 992-2155
109 W 2nd St Pomeroy (45769) ***(G-16390)***
Sentinel Management Inc....440 821-7372
3000 Leavitt Rd Ste 1 Lorain (44052) ***(G-12274)***

Sentinel USA Inc 740 345-6412
1285 Granville Rd Newark (43055) *(G-15052)*
Sentinel Utility Services, Newark *Also called Sentinel USA Inc (G-15052)*
Sentrilock LLC 513 618-5800
7701 Service Center Dr West Chester (45069) *(G-19944)*
Sentronic, Hinckley *Also called Controlled Access Inc (G-11023)*
Sentry Graphics Inc 440 735-0850
114 Hiram College Dr Northfield (44067) *(G-15471)*
Sentry Products, Canton *Also called Canton Sterilized Wiping Cloth (G-2648)*
Sentry Protection LLC 216 228-3200
16927 Detroit Ave Ste 3 Lakewood (44107) *(G-11679)*
Sentry Protection Products, Lakewood *Also called Sentry Protection LLC (G-11679)*
Septic Products Inc 419 282-5933
1378 Township Road 743 Ashland (44805) *(G-777)*
Serappers Gallery, Newark *Also called M & R Phillips Enterprises (G-15032)*
Serena Safety 440 572-4481
8334 N Marks Rd Columbia Station (44028) *(G-6599)*
Sermonix Pharmaceuticals 614 864-4919
142 S Remington Rd Columbus (43209) *(G-7609)*
Sertek LLC 614 504-5828
6399 Shier Rings Rd Dublin (43016) *(G-9143)*
Servatii Inc 513 231-4455
7161 Beechmont Ave Cincinnati (45230) *(G-4406)*
Servatii Inc 513 271-5040
3774 Paxton Ave Cincinnati (45209) *(G-4407)*
Servepro of Parma, Valley City *Also called Matthew Koster (G-19216)*
Service Iron & Steel Company 330 253-9147
1372 Kenmore Blvd Akron (44314) *(G-399)*
Service Pdts Group of Bucyrus 419 562-4456
118 River St Bucyrus (44820) *(G-2359)*
Service Spring Corp (PA) 419 838-6081
1703 Toll Gate Dr Maumee (43537) *(G-13292)*
Service Stampings Inc 440 946-2330
4700 Hamann Pkwy Willoughby (44094) *(G-20593)*
Service Station Equipment Co (PA) 216 431-6100
1294 E 55th St Cleveland (44103) *(G-6181)*
Service Storage Intl Inc 440 951-7579
38316 Airport Pkwy Willoughby (44094) *(G-20594)*
Services Acquisition Co LLC 330 479-9267
4412 Pleasant Vly Rd Se Dennison (44621) *(G-8946)*
Serving Veterans Mobility Inc 937 746-4788
303 Conover Dr Franklin (45005) *(G-10052)*
Servo Systems Inc 440 779-2780
31375 Lorain Rd North Olmsted (44070) *(G-15345)*
Sesh Communications 513 851-1693
3440 Burnet Ave Ste 130 Cincinnati (45229) *(G-4408)*
Sest Inc 440 777-9777
24509 Annie Ln Westlake (44145) *(G-20307)*
Setco Sales Company (HQ) 513 941-5110
5880 Hillside Ave Cincinnati (45233) *(G-4409)*
Setex Inc 419 394-7800
1111 Mckinley Rd Saint Marys (45885) *(G-16855)*
Seth Enterprises, Zanesville *Also called Buckeye Energy Resources Inc (G-21283)*
Sevan At-Ndustrial Pnt Abr Ltd 614 258-4747
1555 Alum Creek Dr Columbus (43209) *(G-7610)*
Sevell + Sevell Inc 614 341-9700
939 N High St Columbus (43201) *(G-7611)*
Seven Hills Foods Ltd 513 518-3704
6425 Shadyglen Rd Cincinnati (45243) *(G-4410)*
Seven Hills Reporter 216 524-9515
6817 Parkgate Oval Seven Hills (44131) *(G-17064)*
Seven Mile Creek Corporation 937 456-3320
315 S Beech St Eaton (45320) *(G-9322)*
Seven Ranges Mfg Corp 330 627-7155
330 Industrial Dr Sw Carrollton (44615) *(G-2965)*
Seven-Ogun International LLC 614 888-8939
670 Lkview Plz Blvd Ste K Worthington (43085) *(G-20887)*
Seventh Son Brewing Co 614 783-4217
1101 N 4th St Columbus (43201) *(G-7612)*
Seves Glass Block Inc 440 627-6257
10576 Broadview Rd Broadview Heights (44147) *(G-2119)*
Seville Bronze, Seville *Also called Jj Seville LLC (G-17076)*
Seville Sand & Gravel Inc 330 948-0168
12663 Bristol Ln Strongsville (44149) *(G-17962)*
Sew It Seams, Woodsfield *Also called J C L S Enterprises LLC (G-20718)*
Sew-Eurodrive Inc 937 335-0036
2001 W Main St Troy (45373) *(G-18875)*
Sewah Studios Inc 740 373-2087
190 Mill Creek Rd Marietta (45750) *(G-12827)*
Sewer Rodding Equipment Co 419 991-2065
3434 S Dixie Hwy Lima (45804) *(G-12089)*
Sewline Products Inc 419 929-1114
30 S Railroad St New London (44851) *(G-14866)*
Sextant Group Inc 614 429-3606
4041 N High St Ste 204 Columbus (43214) *(G-7613)*
Sexton Industrial Inc 513 530-5555
366 Circle Freeway Dr West Chester (45246) *(G-20049)*
Seyekcub Inc 330 324-1394
615 W 4th St Uhrichsville (44683) *(G-19059)*
Seymour, Lloyd, Columbus *Also called Buckeye Cstm Screen Print EMB (G-6872)*
Seymours Logging 740 288-1825
1085 Loop Rd Wellston (45692) *(G-19768)*
Sfc Graphic Arts Div, Toledo *Also called Sfc Graphics Cleveland Ltd (G-18693)*
Sfc Graphics Cleveland Ltd 419 255-1283
110 E Woodruff Ave Toledo (43604) *(G-18693)*
Sfl Enterprises Inc 513 239-6822
10017 Somerset Dr Loveland (45140) *(G-12385)*
Sfs Truck Sales & Parts, Gallipolis *Also called King Kutter II Inc (G-10302)*
SGB Usa Inc 720 897-7090
1776 Constitution Ave Louisville (44641) *(G-12327)*
Sgi Matrix LLC (PA) 937 438-9033
1041 Byers Rd Miamisburg (45342) *(G-13858)*
Sgl, Millbury *Also called Spectra Group Limited Inc (G-14186)*
Sgl Technic Inc 440 572-3600
21945 Drake Rd Strongsville (44149) *(G-17963)*
Sgm Co Inc 440 255-1190
9000 Tyler Blvd Mentor (44060) *(G-13721)*
Sgo Designer Glass, Dayton *Also called Cadenza Enterprises LLC (G-8207)*
Sgt S Drive Thru 937 378-3813
3468 State Route 125 Georgetown (45121) *(G-10365)*
SH Bell Company 412 963-9910
2217 Michigan Ave East Liverpool (43920) *(G-9227)*
Shade Text Book Service Inc 740 696-1323
401 Gilkey Ridge Rd Shade (45776) *(G-17079)*
Shade Winery, Shade *Also called Shade Text Book Service Inc (G-17079)*
Shade Youngstown & Aluminum Co 330 782-2373
3335 South Ave Youngstown (44502) *(G-21200)*
Shades of Sugar Ltd 614 776-5998
5939 Lakewood Dr Galena (43021) *(G-10249)*
Shadetree Machine 513 727-8771
5994 Kalbfleisch Rd Middletown (45042) *(G-14082)*
Shadetree Systems LLC 614 844-5990
6317 Busch Blvd Columbus (43229) *(G-7614)*
Shafer, Ontario *Also called Emerson Process Management (G-15687)*
Shaffer Manufacturing Corp 937 652-2151
720 S Edgewood Ave Urbana (43078) *(G-19180)*
Shaffer Metal Fab Inc 937 492-1384
2031 Commerce Dr Sidney (45365) *(G-17225)*
Shaffer Mixers & Proc Eqp, Urbana *Also called Shaffer Manufacturing Corp (G-19180)*
Shafts Mfg 440 942-6012
1585 E 361st St Unit G1 Willoughby (44095) *(G-20595)*
Shagbark Seed & Mill, Athens *Also called Indie-Peasant Enterprises (G-872)*
Shaheen Oriental Rug Co Inc (PA) 330 493-9000
4120 Whipple Ave Nw Canton (44718) *(G-2846)*
Shaker Numeric Mfg, Euclid *Also called Tech-Med Inc (G-9608)*
Shaker Valley Foods Inc 216 961-8600
3304 W 67th Pl Cleveland (44102) *(G-6182)*
Shalelogix LLC 234 600-5839
1800 N River Rd Ne Warren (44483) *(G-19600)*
Shalersville Asphalt Co (PA) 440 834-4294
14376 N Cheshire St Burton (44021) *(G-2384)*
Shalix Inc 216 941-3546
10910 Briggs Rd Cleveland (44111) *(G-6183)*
Shallow Lake Corp 614 883-6350
8958 Cotter St Lewis Center (43035) *(G-11917)*
Shalmet Corporation 440 236-8840
164 Freedom Ct Elyria (44035) *(G-9492)*
Shamrock Companies Inc (PA) 440 899-9510
24090 Detroit Rd Westlake (44145) *(G-20308)*
Shamrock Materials Inc 513 988-0647
11641 Mosteller Rd Cincinnati (45241) *(G-4411)*
Shamrock Molded Products, Holland *Also called Doyle Manufacturing Inc (G-11055)*
Shamrock Plastics Inc 740 392-5555
633 Howard St Mount Vernon (43050) *(G-14646)*
Shan-Rod Inc 419 588-2066
7308 Driver Rd Berlin Heights (44814) *(G-1663)*
Shanafelt Manufacturing Co (PA) 330 455-0315
2600 Wnfeld Way Ne 2700 Canton (44705) *(G-2847)*
Shaneway Inc (PA) 330 868-2220
1032 Brush Rd Ne Minerva (44657) *(G-14342)*
Shannon Tool Inc 513 563-2300
3355 Hill St Cincinnati (45241) *(G-4412)*
Shape Supply Inc 513 863-6695
700 S Erie Hwy Hamilton (45011) *(G-10738)*
Sharc Industries 216 272-0668
10600 Bridle Path Columbia Station (44028) *(G-6600)*
Shark Solar LLC 216 630-7395
4386 Belmont Ct Medina (44256) *(G-13479)*
Sharon Manufacturing Inc 330 239-1561
6867 Ridge Rd Sharon Center (44274) *(G-17109)*
Sharon Printing Co Inc 330 239-1684
4983 Ridge Rd Sharon Center (44274) *(G-17110)*
Sharon Stone Co 740 374-3236
County Road 10 Dexter City (45727) *(G-8957)*
Sharon Stone Inc 740 732-7100
44895 Sharon Stone Rd Caldwell (43724) *(G-2432)*
Sharonco Inc 419 882-3443
5651 Main St Sylvania (43560) *(G-18124)*

ALPHABETIC

Sharp Enterprises Inc 937 295-2965
400 Enterprise Dr Fort Loramie (45845) *(G-9939)*

Sharp Industrial Tools Inc 513 741-9562
3348 Nandale Dr Cincinnati (45239) *(G-4413)*

Sharp Tool Service Inc 330 273-4144
4735 W 150th St Unit H Cleveland (44135) *(G-6184)*

Sharper Tooling 330 667-2960
9473 Smith Rd Litchfield (44253) *(G-12140)*

Sharpys Food Systems LLC 440 232-9601
26245 Broadway Ave Oakwood Village (44146) *(G-15627)*

Shasta Beverages Inc 614 491-5415
4685 Groveport Rd Obetz (43207) *(G-15659)*

Shasta Beverges, Obetz *Also called National Beverage Corp (G-15657)*

Shatzels Backhoe Service LLC 937 289-9630
4044 Pansy Rd Clarksville (45113) *(G-4653)*

Shaw Industries Inc 513 942-3692
4436 Muhlhauser Rd # 100 West Chester (45011) *(G-19945)*

Shaw Pallets & Specialties 740 498-7892
12269 Lick Brown Rd Newcomerstown (43832) *(G-15123)*

Shaw Wilbert Vaults LLC 740 498-7438
12269 Lick Run Rd Newcomerstown (43832) *(G-15124)*

Shawcor Inc 513 683-7800
173 Commerce Dr Loveland (45140) *(G-12386)*

Shawne Springs Winery 740 623-0744
20093 County Road 6 Coshocton (43812) *(G-7909)*

Shawnee Molds, Eaton *Also called Camden Concrete Products (G-9302)*

Shawnee Systems Inc 513 561-9932
3616 Church St Cincinnati (45244) *(G-4414)*

Shawnee Wood Products Inc 440 632-1771
8918 Bundysburg Rd Middlefield (44062) *(G-13989)*

She Said Yes Bridal & Formal, Chillicothe *Also called S & C Newman Enterprises Inc (G-3274)*

Shear Service Inc 216 341-2700
3175 E 81st St Cleveland (44104) *(G-6185)*

Shear Service, The, Cleveland *Also called Shear Service Inc (G-6185)*

Shear Tech Steel LLC 419 726-6174
5610 Enterprise Blvd Toledo (43612) *(G-18694)*

Shearer Farm Inc (PA) 330 345-9023
7762 Cleveland Rd Wooster (44691) *(G-20834)*

Shearers Foods LLC (PA) 330 834-4030
100 Lincoln Way E Massillon (44646) *(G-13201)*

Sheep & Farm Life Inc 419 492-2364
5696 Johnston Rd New Washington (44854) *(G-14964)*

Sheet Angle Bar Met Fbrication 513 829-8600
4875 Factory Dr Fairfield (45014) *(G-9716)*

Sheet Metal Products Co Inc 440 392-9000
5950 Pinecone Dr Mentor (44060) *(G-13722)*

Sheet Metal Products Company, Mentor *Also called Providence Group Inc (G-13703)*

Sheffield Bronze Paint Corp 216 481-8330
17814 S Waterloo Rd Cleveland (44119) *(G-6186)*

Sheffield Metals Cleveland LLC (PA) 800 283-5262
5467 Evergreen Pkwy Sheffield Village (44054) *(G-17130)*

Sheffield Metals International, Sheffield Village *Also called Sheffield Metals Cleveland LLC (G-17130)*

Sheffield Oldcastle, Sheffield Village *Also called Oldcastle Apg Midwest Inc (G-17128)*

Sheiban Jewelry Inc 440 238-0616
16938 Pearl Rd Strongsville (44136) *(G-17964)*

Shelburne Corp (PA) 216 321-9177
20001 Shelburne Rd Shaker Heights (44118) *(G-17094)*

Shelby County Review, Wapakoneta *Also called Horizon Ohio Publications Inc (G-19489)*

Shelby Daily Globe Inc 419 342-4276
37 W Main St Shelby (44875) *(G-17142)*

Shelby Printing Inc 419 342-3171
325 S Martin Dr Shelby (44875) *(G-17143)*

Shelby Welded Tube Div, Shelby *Also called Phillips Mfg and Tower Co (G-17140)*

Sheldon On Site Inc 419 339-1381
4848 Gomer Rd Elida (45807) *(G-9357)*

Shellenbarger Excavating & Log 740 397-9949
9260 Fairview Rd Mount Vernon (43050) *(G-14647)*

Shelley Company, Maumee *Also called Stoneco Inc (G-13298)*

Shells Inc (PA) 330 808-5558
350 State St Ste 8b Wadsworth (44281) *(G-19440)*

Shelly & Sands Zanesville OH, Perrysville *Also called S & S Aggregates Inc (G-16175)*

Shelly and Sands Inc 330 743-8850
2800 Center Rd Youngstown (44514) *(G-21201)*

Shelly and Sands Inc (PA) 740 453-0721
3570 S River Rd Zanesville (43701) *(G-21350)*

Shelly and Sands Inc 740 373-6495
Hc 7 Box S Marietta (45750) *(G-12828)*

Shelly and Sands Inc 740 859-2104
1731 Old State Route 7 Rayland (43943) *(G-16575)*

Shelly and Sands Inc 740 453-0721
3570 S River Rd Zanesville (43701) *(G-21351)*

Shelly and Shells, Zanesville *Also called Mansfield Asphalt Paving Inc (G-21327)*

Shelly and Zans, Bethesda *Also called Mar-Zane Inc (G-1666)*

Shelly Company 330 666-1125
3350 Sawmill Rd Copley (44321) *(G-7854)*

Shelly Company 740 687-4420
3232 Lgan Lancaster Rd Se Lancaster (43130) *(G-11750)*

Shelly Company 740 474-6255
24537 Canal Rd Circleville (43113) *(G-4642)*

Shelly Company 740 246-6315
80 Park Dr Thornville (43076) *(G-18196)*

Shelly Company, The, Thornville *Also called Shelly Materials Inc (G-18198)*

Shelly Fisher 419 522-6696
449 Newman St Mansfield (44902) *(G-12677)*

Shelly Liquid Division, Toledo *Also called Shelly Materials Inc (G-18695)*

Shelly Liquid Division 216 781-9264
101 Mahoning Ave Cleveland (44113) *(G-6187)*

Shelly Materials, East Fultonham *Also called Chesterhill Stone Co (G-9198)*

Shelly Materials, Lancaster *Also called Shelly Company (G-11750)*

Shelly Materials Inc 419 229-2741
600 N Sugar St Lima (45801) *(G-12090)*

Shelly Materials Inc 740 775-4567
1177 Hopetown Rd Chillicothe (45601) *(G-3275)*

Shelly Materials Inc 740 246-6315
352 George Hardy Dr Toledo (43605) *(G-18695)*

Shelly Materials Inc 740 246-5009
8775 Blackbird Ln Thornville (43076) *(G-18197)*

Shelly Materials Inc 330 274-0802
3943 Beck Rd Mantua (44255) *(G-12721)*

Shelly Materials Inc 330 722-2190
300 N State Rd Medina (44256) *(G-13480)*

Shelly Materials Inc 614 801-9105
3300 Jackson Pike Grove City (43123) *(G-10593)*

Shelly Materials Inc 330 364-4411
2301 Progress St Dover (44622) *(G-9014)*

Shelly Materials Inc 330 823-4646
8920 Canyon Falls Blvd # 120 Twinsburg (44087) *(G-19020)*

Shelly Materials Inc 740 446-7789
1248 State Route 7 N Gallipolis (45631) *(G-10309)*

Shelly Materials Inc 330 673-3646
1181 Cherry St Kent (44240) *(G-11527)*

Shelly Materials Inc 740 666-5841
8328 Watkins Rd Ostrander (43061) *(G-15789)*

Shelly Materials Inc 740 745-5965
6824 Mount Vernon Rd Newark (43055) *(G-15053)*

Shelly Materials Inc (HQ) 740 246-6315
80 Park Dr Thornville (43076) *(G-18198)*

Shelly Materials Inc 419 273-2510
3798 State Route 53 Forest (45843) *(G-9922)*

Shelter Studios, Blue Ash *Also called Organized Lightning LLC (G-1850)*

Shenango Valley Sand and Grav (PA) 330 758-9100
7240 Glenwood Ave Youngstown (44512) *(G-21202)*

Shenet LLC 614 563-9600
50 W Broad St Ste 12000 Columbus (43215) *(G-7615)*

Sheoga Hardwood Flrg Paneling, Middlefield *Also called Hardwood Flrg & Paneling Inc (G-13940)*

Shepherd Chemical Company 513 200-6987
2825 Highland Ave Cincinnati (45212) *(G-4415)*

Shepherd Chemical Company 513 731-1110
2803 Highland Ave Norwood (45212) *(G-15574)*

Shepherd Chemical Company 513 424-7276
3444 Yankee Rd Middletown (45044) *(G-14083)*

Shepherd Middletown Co, Middletown *Also called Shepherd Chemical Company (G-14083)*

Shepherd, The, New Washington *Also called Sheep & Farm Life Inc (G-14964)*

Sherbrooke Metals 440 942-3520
36490 Reading Ave Willoughby (44094) *(G-20596)*

Sheridan Mfg, Wauseon *Also called Lear Corporation (G-19688)*

Sheridan Mfg of Ohio LLC 419 825-2950
401 Broadway Ave Rear Swanton (43558) *(G-18090)*

Sheridan One Stop Carryout 740 687-1300
1510 Sheridan Dr Lancaster (43130) *(G-11751)*

Sheridan Woodworks Inc 216 663-9333
17801 S Miles Rd Cleveland (44128) *(G-6188)*

Shermco Industries Inc 614 836-8556
4383 Professional Pkwy Groveport (43125) *(G-10643)*

Sherwin Software Solutions 440 498-8010
5380 Naiman Pkwy Ste B Solon (44139) *(G-17379)*

Sherwin-Williams Company (PA) 216 566-2000
101 W Prospect Ave # 1020 Cleveland (44115) *(G-6189)*

Sherwin-Williams Company 440 282-2310
2280 Coper Foster Pk Rd W Lorain (44053) *(G-12275)*

Sherwin-Williams Company 330 253-6625
6483 Dressler Rd Nw North Canton (44720) *(G-15264)*

Sherwin-Williams Company 614 539-8456
3875 Brookham Dr Grove City (43123) *(G-10594)*

Sherwin-Williams Company 440 846-4328
11410 Alameda Dr Strongsville (44149) *(G-17965)*

Sherwin-Williams Company 216 662-3300
5020 Turney Rd Cleveland (44125) *(G-6190)*

Sherwin-Williams Company 330 528-0124
5860 Darrow Rd Hudson (44236) *(G-11198)*

Sherwn-Wllams Auto Fnshes Corp 216 332-8330
4440 Warrensville Ctr Rd Cleveland (44128) *(G-6191)*

Sherwn-Wllams Intl Hldings Inc (HQ) 216 566-2000
101 W Prospect Ave Cleveland (44115) *(G-6192)*

Sherwood Refractores, Cleveland Also called PCC Airfoils LLC *(G-5983)*

Sherwood Rtm Corp 330 875-7151
4043 Beck Ave Louisville (44641) *(G-12328)*

Sherwood Valve LLC 216 264-5023
7900 Hub Pkwy Cleveland (44125) *(G-6193)*

Sherwood Valve LLC 216 264-5028
7900 Hub Pkwy Cleveland (44125) *(G-6194)*

Shield Laminating, Columbus Also called The Guardtower Inc *(G-7689)*

Shiffler Equipment Sales Inc 440 285-9175
745 South St Chardon (44024) *(G-3179)*

Shilling Transport 330 948-1105
9718 Avon Lake Rd Lodi (44254) *(G-12169)*

Shiloh Automotive Inc 330 558-2600
880 Steel Dr Valley City (44280) *(G-19230)*

Shiloh Carriage Shop LLC 419 896-3869
8465 Shiloh Norwalk Rd Shiloh (44878) *(G-17155)*

Shiloh Corporation (HQ) 330 558-2600
880 Steel Dr Valley City (44280) *(G-19231)*

Shiloh Hotglass 937 274-7222
274 Briarcliff Rd Dayton (45415) *(G-8654)*

Shiloh Industries Inc 937 236-5100
5988 Executive Blvd Ste B Dayton (45424) *(G-8655)*

Shiloh Industries Inc 330 558-2300
5580 Wegman Dr Valley City (44280) *(G-19232)*

Shiloh Industries Inc 440 647-2100
350 Maple St Wellington (44090) *(G-19755)*

Shiloh Industries Inc 330 558-2000
5569 Innovation Dr Valley City (44280) *(G-19233)*

Shiloh Industries Inc (PA) 330 558-2600
880 Steel Dr Valley City (44280) *(G-19234)*

Shiloh Industries Inc 330 558-2600
880 Steel Dr Valley City (44280) *(G-19235)*

Shinagawa Advanced Materials A 330 628-1118
3555 Gilchrist Rd Mogadore (44260) *(G-14385)*

Shincor Silicones Inc (HQ) 330 630-9460
1030 Evans Ave Akron (44305) *(G-400)*

Ship Print E Sell 614 459-1205
3145 Kingsdale Ctr Columbus (43221) *(G-7616)*

Shipping Room Products Inc 216 531-4422
19400 Saint Clair Ave Cleveland (44117) *(G-6195)*

Shirer Brothers Meats 740 796-3214
7805 Adamsville Otsego Rd Adamsville (43802) *(G-9)*

Shirer Brothers Slaughter Hse, Adamsville Also called Shirer Brothers Meats *(G-9)*

Shirley KS Storage Trays LLC 740 868-8140
1150 Newark Rd Zanesville (43701) *(G-21352)*

Shirt Stop LLC 740 574-4774
11769 Gallia Pike Rd Wheelersburg (45694) *(G-20334)*

Shirtwork 937 322-7507
2133 Kittyhawk Ave Springfield (45503) *(G-17648)*

Shock Precast 419 426-0535
2467 S Township Road 197 Attica (44807) *(G-896)*

Shockakhan Express LLC 614 432-3133
4953 Bixby Ridge Dr W Groveport (43125) *(G-10644)*

Shoemaker Electric Company 614 294-5626
831 Bonham Ave Columbus (43211) *(G-7617)*

Shoemaker Industrial Solutions, Columbus Also called Shoemaker Electric Company *(G-7617)*

Shook Manufactured Pdts Inc (PA) 330 848-9780
1017 Kenmore Blvd Akron (44314) *(G-401)*

Shook Manufactured Pdts Inc 440 247-9130
3801 Wiltshire Rd Chagrin Falls (44022) *(G-3069)*

Shook Tool Inc 937 337-6471
405 W High St Ansonia (45303) *(G-626)*

Shoot A Way Inc 419 294-4654
3305 Township Highway 47 Upper Sandusky (43351) *(G-19140)*

Shoot-A-Way Inc 419 294-4654
8706 State Highway 67 Upper Sandusky (43351) *(G-19141)*

Shooters Choice LLC 440 834-8888
15050 Berkshire Ind Pkwy Middlefield (44062) *(G-13990)*

Shooting Range Supply LLC 440 576-7711
735 Fairway St Jefferson (44047) *(G-11370)*

Shoppers Compass 419 947-9234
114 Iberia St Mount Gilead (43338) *(G-14567)*

Shops By Todd Inc (PA) 937 458-3192
2727 Fairfld Comns W273 Beavercreek (45431) *(G-1360)*

Shopsmith, Dayton Also called Rlfshop LLC *(G-8634)*

Shore To Shore Inc (HQ) 937 866-1908
8170 Washington Vlg Dr Dayton (45458) *(G-8656)*

Shoreline Machine Products Co (PA) 216 481-8033
19301 Saint Clair Ave Cleveland (44117) *(G-6196)*

Shoreway Sports, Lorain Also called Swocat Design Inc *(G-12284)*

Shorr Packaging, Cincinnati Also called Hanchett Paper Company *(G-3865)*

Short Run Machine Products Inc 440 969-1313
4744 Kister Ct Ashtabula (44004) *(G-838)*

Shot Selector, Twinsburg Also called Golf Marketing Group Inc *(G-18950)*

Shot-Force Pro LLC 740 753-3927
13580 Kimberley Rd Nelsonville (45764) *(G-14739)*

Show What You Know, Dayton Also called Lorenz Corporation *(G-8460)*

Showa Aluminum Corp America 740 869-3333
10500 Oday Harrison Rd Mount Sterling (43143) *(G-14602)*

Showa Aluminum Corp America (HQ) 740 869-3333
10500 Oday Harrison Rd Mount Sterling (43143) *(G-14603)*

Showcase Cab Mar Rstoration LL 419 626-6715
5404 Sandy Acres Dr Sandusky (44870) *(G-17008)*

Showplace Inc 419 468-7368
201 S Market St Galion (44833) *(G-10287)*

Showplace Rental, Galion Also called Showplace Inc *(G-10287)*

Showroom Tracker LLC 888 407-0094
6543 Forestwood St Nw Canton (44718) *(G-2848)*

Shred Away 740 363-6327
227 Rockmill St Delaware (43015) *(G-8887)*

Shred Devil LLC 740 776-1400
6806 6th St Ste 200 Portsmouth (45662) *(G-16452)*

Shred-It Columbus, Columbus Also called Shred-It USA LLC *(G-7618)*

Shred-It USA LLC 614 231-7470
1784 Dividend Dr Columbus (43228) *(G-7618)*

Shred-It USA LLC (HQ) 513 699-0845
11311 Cornell Park Dr # 125 Blue Ash (45242) *(G-1869)*

Shree Krupa Inc 216 781-6054
230 W Huron Rd Ste 8503 Cleveland (44113) *(G-6197)*

Shreiner Sole Co Inc 330 276-6135
1 Taylor Dr Killbuck (44637) *(G-11599)*

Shreve Printing LLC 330 567-2341
390 E Wood St Shreve (44676) *(G-17163)*

Shriner Sheet Metal Inc 330 435-6735
196 S Main St Creston (44217) *(G-7943)*

Shrock Prefab LLC 740 599-9401
23403 College Hill Rd Danville (43014) *(G-8091)*

Shu Shop, The, Richfield Also called Gail J Shumaker Originals *(G-16625)*

Shuler International, Chagrin Falls Also called E L Ostendorf Inc *(G-3056)*

Shumaker Racing Components 419 238-0801
11037 Van Wert Decatur Rd Van Wert (45891) *(G-19270)*

Shur Clean Usa LLC 513 341-5486
7568 Wyandot Ln Unit 3 Liberty Township (45044) *(G-11968)*

Shur Fit Distributors Inc 937 746-0567
221 N Main St Franklin (45005) *(G-10053)*

Shur-Co LLC 330 297-0888
1100 N Freedom St Ravenna (44266) *(G-16556)*

Shur-Form Laminates Division, Franklin Also called Shur Fit Distributors Inc *(G-10053)*

Shurtape Technologies LLC 440 937-7000
32150 Just Imagine Dr Avon (44011) *(G-1011)*

Shurtech Brands LLC (HQ) 440 937-7000
32150 Just Imagine Dr Avon (44011) *(G-1012)*

Siata Ds Inc (PA) 216 503-7200
24665 Greenwich Ln Beachwood (44122) *(G-1298)*

Sibg, Cleveland Also called Snyder Intl Brewing Group LLC *(G-6215)*

Sickels Septic Tanks Inc 740 593-8302
10637 Oxley Rd Athens (45701) *(G-884)*

Sidari's Italian Foods, Cleveland Also called Gsi of Ohio LLC *(G-5462)*

Sideline Tech Inc 440 331-0560
19680 Center Ridge Rd Rocky River (44116) *(G-16710)*

Sidney Can & Tool LLC 937 492-0977
5670 Cecil Rd Sidney (45365) *(G-17226)*

Sidney Manufacturing Company 937 492-4154
405 N Main Ave Sidney (45365) *(G-17227)*

Sidney Plant, Sidney Also called Advanced Composites Inc *(G-17165)*

Sidney Printing Works Inc 513 542-4000
2611 Colerain Ave Cincinnati (45214) *(G-4416)*

Sidney Stiers 740 454-7368
620 Moxahala Ave Zanesville (43701) *(G-21353)*

Sidwell Materials Inc 740 849-2394
4200 Maysville Pike Zanesville (43701) *(G-21354)*

Sieb & Meyer America Inc 513 563-0860
3975 Port Union Rd Fairfield (45014) *(G-9717)*

Siefker Sawmill 419 339-1956
8705 W State Rd Elida (45807) *(G-9358)*

Siegfried, Akron Also called Ivan Extruders Co Inc *(G-237)*

Siemens Energy Inc 740 393-8897
105 N Sandusky St Mount Vernon (43050) *(G-14648)*

Siemens Energy Inc 740 393-8464
607 W Chestnut St Mount Vernon (43050) *(G-14649)*

Siemens Industry Inc 513 841-3100
4620 Forest Ave Cincinnati (45212) *(G-4417)*

Siemens Industry Inc 614 846-9540
530 Lkview Plz Blvd Ste D Worthington (43085) *(G-20888)*

Siemens Industry Inc 937 748-1726
10 Southfield Ct Springboro (45066) *(G-17507)*

Siemens Industry Inc 440 526-2770
6930 Treeline Dr Ste A Brecksville (44141) *(G-2073)*

Siemens Industry Inc 937 593-6010
811 N Main St Bellefontaine (43311) *(G-1539)*

Siemens Industry Inc 513 336-2267
4170 Columbia Rd Lebanon (45036) *(G-11839)*

Siemens Industry Inc 614 573-8212
977 Gahanna Pkwy Columbus (43230) *(G-7619)*

Siemer Distributing, New Lexington Also called Lori Holding Co *(G-14848)*

Sierra Precision Components 440 230-9570
11941 Abbey Rd Ste E Cleveland (44133) *(G-6198)*

Sietins Plastics Incorporated 440 232-8515
380 Solon Rd Ste 4 Cleveland (44146) *(G-6199)*

Sifco Applied Srfc Cncepts LLC (PA) 216 524-0099
5708 E Schaaf Rd Cleveland (44131) *(G-6200)*

Sifco ASC, Cleveland *Also called Sifco Applied Srfc Cncepts LLC (G-6200)*

Sifco Industries Inc (PA) 216 881-8600
970 E 64th St Cleveland (44103) *(G-6201)*

Sifted Sweet Shop LLC 216 901-7100
4496 Mahoning Ave Ste 905 Youngstown (44515) *(G-21203)*

Siglent Technologies Amer Inc 440 398-5800
6557 Cochran Rd Solon (44139) *(G-17380)*

Sigma Div, Newburgh Heights *Also called Howmet Aluminum Casting Inc (G-15072)*

Sigma T E K, Cincinnati *Also called Sigmatek Systems LLC (G-4418)*

Sigma-Aldrich, Miamisburg *Also called Aldrich Chemical (G-13781)*

Sigmatek Systems LLC (PA) 513 674-0005
1445 Kemper Meadow Dr Cincinnati (45240) *(G-4418)*

Sign A Rama 330 499-4653
435 Applegrove St Nw North Canton (44720) *(G-15265)*

Sign A Rama 614 337-6000
64 Granville St Gahanna (43230) *(G-10232)*

Sign A Rama Inc 440 442-5002
731 Beta Dr Ste D Cleveland (44143) *(G-6202)*

Sign A Rama Inc 513 671-2213
2519 Crescentville Rd Cincinnati (45241) *(G-4419)*

Sign America Incorporated 740 765-5555
3887 State Route 43 Richmond (43944) *(G-16649)*

Sign City Inc 614 486-6700
5357 State Route 95 Mount Gilead (43338) *(G-14568)*

Sign Connection Inc 937 435-4070
90 Compark Rd Ste B Dayton (45459) *(G-8657)*

Sign Design Wooster Inc 330 262-8838
1537 W Old Lincoln Way Wooster (44691) *(G-20835)*

Sign Dynamics, Dayton *Also called Jeffrey L Becht Inc (G-8426)*

Sign Graphics & Design 513 576-1639
420 Main St Unit A Milford (45150) *(G-14174)*

Sign Lady Inc 419 476-9191
5981 Telegraph Rd Toledo (43612) *(G-18696)*

Sign Pro of Lima 419 222-7767
404 Brower Rd Lima (45801) *(G-12091)*

Sign Shop 740 474-1499
3269 State Route 361 Circleville (43113) *(G-4643)*

Sign Smith LLC 614 519-9144
2760 County Road 26 Marengo (43334) *(G-12755)*

Sign Source USA Inc 419 224-1130
1700 S Dixie Hwy Lima (45804) *(G-12092)*

Sign Technologies LLC 937 439-3970
2001 Kuntz Rd Dayton (45404) *(G-8658)*

Sign Write 937 559-4388
3348 Dayton Xenia Rd Beavercreek (45432) *(G-1361)*

Sign-A-Rama, North Canton *Also called Sign A Rama (G-15265)*

Sign-A-Rama, Gahanna *Also called Sign A Rama (G-10232)*

Sign-A-Rama, Cleveland *Also called Sign A Rama Inc (G-6202)*

Sign-A-Rama, Columbus *Also called Business Idntification Systems (G-6879)*

Sign-A-Rama, Cincinnati *Also called Sign A Rama Inc (G-4419)*

Sign-Lite Corporation 216 851-1000
12655 Coit Rd Cleveland (44108) *(G-6203)*

Signa Stortech Systems Inc 214 357-0411
8990 Pleasantwood Ave Nw Canton (44720) *(G-2849)*

Signaffects Limited LLC 614 504-5324
8147 Industrial Pkwy Plain City (43064) *(G-16358)*

Signage Consultants Inc 614 297-7446
870 E 5th Ave Columbus (43201) *(G-7620)*

Signal Graphics Printing, Copley *Also called Vision Graphics (G-7857)*

Signal Group, Ashland *Also called Advanced Cylinder Repair Inc (G-701)*

Signalysis Inc 513 528-6164
539 Glenrose Ln Cincinnati (45244) *(G-4420)*

Signature 4 Image, Coldwater *Also called Signature Partners Inc (G-6571)*

Signature Beef LLC 740 468-3579
5500 Canal Rd Ne Pleasantville (43148) *(G-16375)*

Signature Partners Inc 419 678-1400
149 Harvest Dr Coldwater (45828) *(G-6571)*

Signature Salants Coatings LLC 513 922-8723
724 Rosewynne Ct Cleves (45002) *(G-6525)*

Signature Sign Co Inc 216 426-1234
1776 E 43rd St Cleveland (44103) *(G-6204)*

Signature Store Fixtures, Columbus *Also called A-Display Service Corp (G-6669)*

Signature Technologies Inc (HQ) 937 859-6323
3728 Benner Rd Miamisburg (45342) *(G-13859)*

Signcom Incorporated 614 228-9999
527 W Rich St Columbus (43215) *(G-7621)*

Signed By Josette LLC 419 796-9632
303 E Sandusky St Findlay (45840) *(G-9889)*

Signery 513 932-1938
1002 W Main St Apt D Lebanon (45036) *(G-11840)*

Signery2 LLC 513 738-3048
2571 Millville Shandon Rd Hamilton (45013) *(G-10739)*

Signetics, Dayton *Also called Sign Technologies LLC (G-8658)*

Significant Impressions Inc 513 874-5223
4050 Thunderbird Ln Fairfield (45014) *(G-9718)*

Signline Graphics & Lettering 740 397-5806
114 Clinton Rd Mount Vernon (43050) *(G-14650)*

Signmaker Shop, The, Coshocton *Also called Steven Mercer Inc (G-7911)*

Signmaster Inc 614 777-0670
758 Radio Dr Lewis Center (43035) *(G-11918)*

Signode Industrial Group LLC 513 248-2990
396 Wards Corner Rd # 100 Loveland (45140) *(G-12387)*

Signs 2 Graphics 740 493-2049
746 State Route 220 Piketon (45661) *(G-16228)*

Signs By George 216 394-2095
5815 Warren Sharon Rd Brookfield (44403) *(G-2126)*

Signs By Tomorrow, West Chester *Also called Meka Signs Enterprises Inc (G-20027)*

Signs By Tomorrow, Dublin *Also called Bambeck Inc (G-9052)*

Signs By Tomorrow, Columbus *Also called Krigbaum Inc (G-7267)*

Signs Limited LLC 740 282-7715
356 Technology Way Steubenville (43952) *(G-17712)*

Signs N Stuff Inc 440 974-3151
9354 Mentor Ave Ste 4 Mentor (44060) *(G-13723)*

Signs Now, Newark *Also called Gary Krinn (G-15012)*

Signs Now, Lima *Also called Tamblingson Inc (G-12101)*

Signs of The Times, Cleveland *Also called A Sign For The Times Inc (G-4678)*

Signs PDQ Inc 440 951-6651
35160 Topps Industrial Pk Willoughby (44094) *(G-20597)*

Signs To Go, Dover *Also called Kim Phillips Sign Co LLC (G-8995)*

Signs Unlimited (PA) 614 836-7446
21313 State Route 93 S Logan (43138) *(G-12193)*

Sika Corporation 740 375-3020
1550 Cascade Dr Marion (43302) *(G-12900)*

Sika Corporation 740 387-9224
1682 Mrn Williamsprt Rd E Marion (43302) *(G-12901)*

Silfex, Eaton *Also called Lam Research Corporation (G-9314)*

Silfex Inc 937 472-3311
950 S Franklin St Eaton (45320) *(G-9323)*

Silgan Can Company 419 592-1010
12773 State Route 110 Napoleon (43545) *(G-14699)*

Silgan Plastics LLC 419 523-3737
690 Woodland Dr Ottawa (45875) *(G-15808)*

Silica Press Inc 419 843-8500
3545 Silica Rd Unit A2 Sylvania (43560) *(G-18125)*

Silicon Processors Inc 740 373-2252
1988 Masonic Park Rd Marietta (45750) *(G-12829)*

Silicon USA Inc 330 928-6217
1220 Orlen Ave Cuyahoga Falls (44221) *(G-8044)*

Silicone Solutions Inc 330 920-3125
338 Remington Rd Cuyahoga Falls (44224) *(G-8045)*

Silicone Solutions Inc 419 720-8709
3441 South Ave Toledo (43609) *(G-18697)*

Silk Screen Special TS Inc 740 246-4843
9075 Boundaries Rd Thornville (43076) *(G-18199)*

Silmix Division, Canton *Also called Wacker Chemical Corporation (G-2899)*

Silver Creek Log Homes 419 335-3220
5350 County Road 16 Wauseon (43567) *(G-19694)*

Silver Expressions 740 687-0144
1635 River Valley Cir S # 5078 Lancaster (43130) *(G-11752)*

Silver Machine Co, Elyria *Also called Ultra Machine Inc (G-9504)*

Silver Maple Publications 937 767-1259
1308 Corry St Yellow Springs (45387) *(G-20999)*

Silver Threads Inc 614 733-0099
7710 Corporate Blvd Plain City (43064) *(G-16359)*

Silver Tool Inc 937 865-0012
2440 Cross Pointe Dr Miamisburg (45342) *(G-13860)*

Silver, Burdett & Ginn, Columbus *Also called Simon & Schuster Inc (G-7623)*

Silverado Trucks & Accessories 937 492-8862
720 Linden Ave Sidney (45365) *(G-17228)*

Silvercote LLC 330 748-8500
9600b Valley View Rd Macedonia (44056) *(G-12482)*

Silvesco Inc 740 373-6661
2985 State Route 26 Marietta (45750) *(G-12830)*

Simcote Inc 740 382-5000
250 N Greenwood St Marion (43302) *(G-12902)*

Simcote of Ohio Division, Marion *Also called Simcote Inc (G-12902)*

Simet, Hudson *Also called Sintered Metal Industries Inc (G-11199)*

Simex Inc 304 665-1104
181 Pleasants Indus Park Columbus (43224) *(G-7622)*

Simmons Company 614 871-8088
3960 Brookham Dr Grove City (43123) *(G-10595)*

Simon & Schuster Inc 614 876-0371
4350 Equity Dr Columbus (43228) *(G-7623)*

Simon & Simon Blue Pond Inc 330 928-2298
2211 Harding Rd Cuyahoga Falls (44223) *(G-8046)*

Simon De Young Corporation 440 834-3000
15010 Brkshire Indus Pkwy Middlefield (44062) *(G-13991)*

Simon Ellis Superabrasives 937 226-0683
501 Progress Rd Dayton (45449) *(G-8659)*

Simon Roofing and Shtmtl Corp (PA) 330 629-7392
   70 Karago Ave Youngstown (44512) *(G-21204)*
Simonds International LLC 978 424-0100
   76000 Old Twenty One Rd Kimbolton (43749) *(G-11603)*
Simple Products LLC 330 674-2448
   10336 Township Road 262 Millersburg (44654) *(G-14263)*
Simple Vms LLC 888 255-8918
   7373 Beechmont Ave # 130 Cincinnati (45230) *(G-4421)*
Simplex Time Recorder 584, Maumee Also called Simplex Time Recorder LLC *(G-13293)*
Simplex Time Recorder LLC 937 291-0355
   8899 Gander Creek Dr Miamisburg (45342) *(G-13861)*
Simplex Time Recorder LLC 419 861-0661
   3661 Brrfeld Blvd Ste 101 Maumee (43537) *(G-13293)*
Simplex-It LLC 234 380-1277
   4301 Darrow Rd Ste 1200 Stow (44224) *(G-17800)*
Simplexgrinnell LP 419 861-0662
   3661 Brrfeld Blvd Ste 101 Maumee (43537) *(G-13294)*
Simply Canvas Inc 330 436-6500
   1479 Exeter Rd Akron (44306) *(G-402)*
Simply Elegant Formals Inc 419 738-7722
   708 N Dixie Hwy Wapakoneta (45895) *(G-19507)*
Simply Unique Snacks LLC 513 223-7736
   4420 Haight Ave Cincinnati (45223) *(G-4422)*
Simpson & Sons Inc 513 367-0152
   10220 Harrison Ave Harrison (45030) *(G-10802)*
Simpson Brothers Machine Works 740 353-6870
   2204 Gallia St Portsmouth (45662) *(G-16453)*
Simpson Strong-Tie Company Inc 614 876-8060
   2600 International St Columbus (43228) *(G-7624)*
Sims-Lohman Inc (PA) 513 651-3510
   6325 Este Ave Cincinnati (45232) *(G-4423)*
Sims-Lohman Fine Kitchens Gran, Cincinnati Also called Sims-Lohman Inc *(G-4423)*
Simxperience, North Canton Also called Villers Enterprises Limited *(G-15282)*
Sinbon Usa LLC 937 667-8999
   4265 Gibson Dr Tipp City (45371) *(G-18299)*
Sine Wall LLC 919 453-2011
   7162 Liberty Ste 105 West Chester (45069) *(G-19946)*
Sinful Sweets LLC 330 721-0916
   3862 Turnberry Dr Medina (44256) *(G-13481)*
Singer Press 216 595-9400
   23500 Mercantile Rd Ste A Beachwood (44122) *(G-1299)*
Singleton Corporation 216 651-7800
   3280 W 67th Pl Cleveland (44102) *(G-6205)*
Singleton Reels Inc 330 274-2961
   11783 Timber Point Trl Mantua (44255) *(G-12722)*
Sinners N Saints LLC 614 231-7467
   1515 Alum Creek Dr Columbus (43209) *(G-7625)*
Sintered Metal Industries Inc 330 650-4000
   1890 Georgetown Rd Hudson (44236) *(G-11199)*
Sir Speedy, Fairlawn Also called Tcp Inc *(G-9764)*
Sir Speedy, Cleveland Also called Frank J Prucha & Associates *(G-5378)*
Sir Speedy, Pataskala Also called Grayson Graphics Inc *(G-15971)*
Sir Steak Machinery Inc 419 526-9181
   40 Baird Pkwy Mansfield (44903) *(G-12678)*
Sironrx Therapeutics Inc 216 445-5588
   10000 Cedar Ave Cleveland (44106) *(G-6206)*
Sirrus Inc 513 448-0308
   422 Wards Corner Rd Loveland (45140) *(G-12388)*
Sissel Logging LLC 740 858-4613
   69 Pond Lick Rd Portsmouth (45663) *(G-16454)*
Sister Sweet Shoppe The, Dublin Also called Grandmas Fruit Cakes *(G-9080)*
Site Tech (PA) 740 522-0019
   75 Central Pkwy Heath (43056) *(G-10857)*
Siteone Landscape Supply LLC 330 220-8691
   2925 Interstate Pkwy Brunswick (44212) *(G-2257)*
Sitler Printer Inc 330 482-4463
   707 E Park Ave Columbiana (44408) *(G-6632)*
Sivon Manufacturing Company, Perry Also called Sivon Mfr Co *(G-16057)*
Sivon Mfr Co 440 259-5505
   3131 Perry Park Rd Perry (44081) *(G-16057)*
Sizetec Inc 330 492-9682
   4825 Higbee Ave Nw # 103 Canton (44718) *(G-2850)*
Sjbs, Akron Also called Standard Jig Boring Svc LLC *(G-412)*
Sjpm Inc 614 475-4571
   264 Agler Rd Gahanna (43230) *(G-10233)*
Sk Machinery Corporation 330 733-7325
   487 Wellington Ave Akron (44305) *(G-403)*
Sk Tech Inc 937 836-3535
   200 Metro Dr Englewood (45315) *(G-9539)*
Sk Textile Inc 323 581-8986
   1 Knollcrest Dr Cincinnati (45237) *(G-4424)*
Skeeles Manufacturing Corp 614 274-4700
   4040 Fondorf Dr Columbus (43228) *(G-7626)*
SKF Machine Tools Service, Cleveland Also called American Precision Spindles *(G-4792)*
SKF Usa Inc (HQ) 440 720-1500
   670 Alpha Dr Highland Heights (44143) *(G-10920)*
Skid Guard, Cleveland Also called Sure-Foot Industries Corp *(G-6275)*
Skidmore Engineering Div, Chagrin Falls Also called Buckeye Gear Co *(G-3078)*

Skidmore-Wilhelm Mfg Company 216 481-4774
   30340 Solon Industrial B Solon (44139) *(G-17381)*
Skillsoft Corporation 216 524-5200
   6645 Acres Dr Independence (44131) *(G-11275)*
Skin 937 222-0222
   333 Wayne Ave Dayton (45410) *(G-8660)*
Skinner Machining Co 216 486-6636
   23574 Saint Clair Ave Cleveland (44117) *(G-6207)*
Skinner Metal Products, Strongsville Also called Skinner Sales Group Inc *(G-17966)*
Skinner Sales Group Inc 440 572-8455
   19706 Progress Dr Strongsville (44149) *(G-17966)*
Skinny Piggy Kombucha LLC 513 646-5753
   5510 Glengate Ln Cincinnati (45212) *(G-4425)*
Skinnytees, Cleveland Also called Skinnywear LLC *(G-6208)*
Skinnywear LLC 216 310-5599
   27825 Gates Ville Blvd Cleveland (44124) *(G-6208)*
Skirdle, Blue Ash Also called Protein Express Laboratories *(G-1860)*
Skladany Enterprises Inc 614 823-6883
   695 Mccorkle Blvd Westerville (43082) *(G-20185)*
SKLADANY PRINTING CENTER, Westerville Also called Skladany Enterprises Inc *(G-20185)*
Skr Enterprises LLC 419 891-1112
   127 W Wayne St Maumee (43537) *(G-13295)*
Skribs Tool and Die Inc 440 951-7774
   7555 Tyler Blvd Ste 11 Mentor (44060) *(G-13724)*
Skrl Die Casting Inc 440 946-7200
   34580 Lakeland Blvd Willoughby (44095) *(G-20598)*
Skuttle Indoor Air Qulty Pdts, Marietta Also called Skuttle Mfg Co *(G-12831)*
Skuttle Mfg Co 740 373-9169
   101 Margaret St Marietta (45750) *(G-12831)*
Sky Climber LLC (PA) 740 203-3900
   1800 Pittsburgh Dr Delaware (43015) *(G-8888)*
Sky Climber Fasteners LLC 740 816-9830
   1800 Pittsburgh Dr Delaware (43015) *(G-8889)*
Sky Climber Wind Solutions, Delaware Also called Sky Climber LLC *(G-8888)*
Sky Climber Wind Solutions LLC 740 203-3900
   1800 Pittsburgh Dr Delaware (43015) *(G-8890)*
Sky Riders Inc 440 310-6819
   3736 Dallas Ave Lorain (44055) *(G-12276)*
Sky Vault Ltd 740 549-0623
   1398 Royal Oak Dr Lewis Center (43035) *(G-11919)*
Sky-Tek, East Palestine Also called Carlson Aircraft Inc *(G-9230)*
Skybox Investments Inc 419 525-6013
   1275 Pollock Pkwy Mansfield (44905) *(G-12679)*
Skybox Packaging LLC 419 525-7209
   1275 Pollock Pkwy Mansfield (44905) *(G-12680)*
Skybryte Company Inc 216 771-1590
   3125 Perkins Ave Cleveland (44114) *(G-6209)*
Skylift Inc 440 960-2100
   3000 Leavitt Rd Ste 6 Lorain (44052) *(G-12277)*
Skyline Chili Inc (PA) 513 874-1188
   4180 Thunderbird Ln Fairfield (45014) *(G-9719)*
Skyline Corporation 330 852-2483
   580 Mill St Nw Sugarcreek (44681) *(G-18039)*
Skyline Exhibits Grtr Cncnt 513 671-4460
   9850 Prncton Glndle Rd Ste Cincinnati (45246) *(G-4426)*
Skyline Trisource Exhibits, Cleveland Also called Ternion Inc *(G-6307)*
Slabe Machine Products Co 440 946-6555
   4659 Hamann Pkwy Willoughby (44094) *(G-20599)*
Slabe Tool Company 740 439-1647
   1300 Oxford Ave Cambridge (43725) *(G-2476)*
Slade Gardner 440 355-8015
   233 Commerce Dr Unit B Lagrange (44050) *(G-11637)*
Slap N Tickle LLC 419 349-3226
   5645 Angola Rd Ste A Toledo (43615) *(G-18698)*
Slater Builders Supply, The Plains Also called Tyjen Inc *(G-18187)*
Slater's Builders Supplies, Logan Also called Tyjen Inc *(G-12196)*
Slats and Nails Inc 330 866-1008
   10465 Sandyville Ave Se East Sparta (44626) *(G-9255)*
Slice Mfg LLC 330 733-7600
   1800 Triplett Blvd Akron (44306) *(G-404)*
Slice of Heaven Bakery 419 656-6606
   463 N County Road 268 Clyde (43410) *(G-6547)*
Slicksaw.com, Brunswick Also called Rboog Industries LLC *(G-2252)*
Slimans Printery Inc 330 454-9141
   624 5th St Nw Canton (44703) *(G-2851)*
Slimline Surgical Devices LLC 937 335-0496
   1102 S Market St Troy (45373) *(G-18876)*
Sloat Inc 440 951-9554
   34099 Melinz Pkwy Unit A Willoughby (44095) *(G-20600)*
Slush Puppie 513 771-0940
   44 Carnegie Way West Chester (45246) *(G-20050)*
Sluterbeck Tool & Die Inc 937 836-5736
   7540 Jacks Ln Clayton (45315) *(G-4662)*
Sluterbeck Tool Co, Clayton Also called Sluterbeck Tool & Die Inc *(G-4662)*
Slutzkers Quickprint Center 440 244-0330
   721 Broadway Lorain (44052) *(G-12278)*
Sly Inc (PA) 440 891-3200
   8300 Dow Cir Ste 600 Strongsville (44136) *(G-17967)*

SMA Plastics LLC 330 627-1377
  755 N Lisbon St Carrollton (44615) *(G-2966)*

Small Business Products 800 553-6485
  8603 Winton Rd Cincinnati (45231) *(G-4427)*

Small Dog Printing 614 777-7620
  3972 Brown Park Dr Ste E Hilliard (43026) *(G-10979)*

Small Sand & Gravel Inc 740 427-3130
  10229 Killduff Rd Gambier (43022) *(G-10317)*

Smalls Asphalt Paving Inc 740 427-4096
  10229 Killduff Rd Gambier (43022) *(G-10318)*

Smart 3d Solutions LLC 330 972-7840
  411 Wolf Ledges Pkwy # 100 Akron (44311) *(G-405)*

Smart Business Magazine, Cleveland *Also called Smart Business Network Inc (G-6210)*

Smart Business Network Inc (PA) 440 250-7000
  835 Sharon Dr Ste 200 Cleveland (44145) *(G-6210)*

Smart Microsystems Ltd 440 366-4257
  141 Innovation Dr Elyria (44035) *(G-9493)*

Smart Snic Stencil Clg Systems, Cleveland *Also called Smart Sonic Corporation (G-6211)*

Smart Solutions, Beachwood *Also called Ohio Cllbrtive Lrng Sltons Inc (G-1286)*

Smart Sonic Corporation 818 610-7900
  837 E 79th St Cleveland (44103) *(G-6211)*

Smart Tooling, Xenia *Also called Spintech LLC (G-20974)*

Smartbill Ltd 740 928-6909
  1050 O Neill Dr Hebron (43025) *(G-10885)*

Smartcopy Inc (PA) 740 392-6162
  50 Parrott St Ste A Mount Vernon (43050) *(G-14651)*

Smartronix Inc 216 378-3300
  416 Apple Hill Dr Northfield (44067) *(G-15472)*

Smartshopper Electronics Inc 440 349-5119
  6659 Brandamore Ct Solon (44139) *(G-17382)*

Smartv Company LLC 614 890-6090
  480 Olde Worthington Rd Westerville (43082) *(G-20186)*

Smashing Events and Baking 513 415-9693
  693 Winding Way Cincinnati (45245) *(G-3318)*

SMC Corporation of America 330 659-2006
  4160 Highlander Pkwy # 200 Richfield (44286) *(G-16638)*

Smead Manufacturing Company 740 385-5601
  851 Smead Rd Logan (43138) *(G-12194)*

Smedleys Bar and Grill 216 941-0124
  17004 Lorain Ave Cleveland (44111) *(G-6212)*

Smg Growing Media Inc (HQ) 937 644-0011
  14111 Scottslawn Rd Marysville (43040) *(G-12971)*

SMH Manufacturing Inc 419 884-0071
  300 S Mill St Lexington (44904) *(G-11952)*

SMI Holdings Inc (PA) 740 927-3464
  10685 Columbus Pkwy Pataskala (43062) *(G-15985)*

SMI Holdings Inc 740 927-3464
  10685 Columbus Exp Park E Pataskala (43062) *(G-15986)*

Smile Brands Inc 440 471-6133
  25102 Brookpark Rd North Olmsted (44070) *(G-15346)*

Smith & Mills Shapers Inc 513 541-4031
  3640 Llewellyn Ave Cincinnati (45223) *(G-4428)*

Smith & Nephew Inc 513 821-5888
  5005 Barrow Ave Ste 100 Cincinnati (45209) *(G-4429)*

Smith Brothers Erection Inc 740 373-3575
  101 Industry Rd Marietta (45750) *(G-12832)*

Smith Carl E Cnslting Engnrs, Bath *Also called Warmus and Associates Inc (G-1240)*

Smith Concrete Co (PA) 740 373-7441
  2301 Progress St Dover (44622) *(G-9015)*

Smith Dairy Products Company 740 927-2688
  40 Cypress St Sw Reynoldsburg (43068) *(G-16605)*

Smith Electro Chemical Co 513 351-7227
  5936 Carthage Ct Cincinnati (45212) *(G-4430)*

Smith Facing and Supply Co, Cleveland *Also called Fleig Enterprises Inc (G-5355)*

Smith International Inc 570 368-2130
  211 Zeltman Ave Ne Strasburg (44680) *(G-17829)*

Smith International Inc 330 497-2999
  2616 Country Squire St Nw Uniontown (44685) *(G-19098)*

Smith Machine Inc 330 821-9898
  20651 Lake Park Blvd Alliance (44601) *(G-538)*

Smith Marathon Distributing, West Mansfield *Also called M J S Oil Inc (G-20101)*

Smith P K Woodcarving LLC 513 271-7077
  2021 A Riverside Drv Stea Louisville (44641) *(G-12329)*

Smith Pallets 937 564-6492
  9855 State Route 121 Versailles (45380) *(G-19357)*

Smith Rn Sheet Metal Shop Inc 740 653-5011
  1312 Campground Rd Lancaster (43130) *(G-11753)*

Smith Smith & Deyarman 330 866-5521
  9260 Bachelor Rd Nw Magnolia (44643) *(G-12519)*

Smith Springs Inc 800 619-4652
  1755 Mount Perry Rd Mount Perry (43760) *(G-14595)*

Smith Truck Cranes & Eqp Co 330 929-3303
  307 Munroe Falls Ave Cuyahoga Falls (44221) *(G-8047)*

Smith, Todd Products, Lakewood *Also called Todd Smith Products (G-11680)*

Smith-Feeman Inc 330 434-8882
  2034 Carlile Dr Uniontown (44685) *(G-19099)*

Smith-Lustig Paper Box Mfg Co 216 621-0453
  22475 Aurora Rd Bedford (44146) *(G-1462)*

Smithers-Oasis Company (PA) 330 945-5100
  295 S Water St Ste 201 Kent (44240) *(G-11528)*

Smithers-Oasis Company 330 673-5831
  919 Marvin St Kent (44240) *(G-11529)*

Smithers-Oasis North America, Kent *Also called Smithers-Oasis Company (G-11529)*

Smithfoods Inc (PA) 330 683-8710
  1381 Dairy Ln Orrville (44667) *(G-15764)*

Smithfoods Orrville Inc 330 684-6502
  230 N Vine St Orrville (44667) *(G-15765)*

Smiths Medical Asd Inc 800 796-8701
  5200 Upper Metro Pl # 200 Dublin (43017) *(G-9144)*

Smiths Medical Asd Inc 614 889-2220
  6250 Shier Rings Rd Dublin (43016) *(G-9145)*

Smiths Medical North America 614 210-7300
  5200 Upper Metro Pl Dublin (43017) *(G-9146)*

Smiths Medical Pm Inc (PA) 614 210-7300
  5200 Upper Metro Pl # 200 Dublin (43017) *(G-9147)*

Smiths Sawdust Studio 740 484-4656
  206 Maple Ave Bethesda (43719) *(G-1667)*

Smithville Manufacturing Co 330 345-5818
  6563 Cleveland Rd Wooster (44691) *(G-20836)*

Sml Inc (PA) 330 668-6555
  4083 Embassy Pkwy Akron (44333) *(G-406)*

Smoke Rings Inc 419 420-9966
  1928 Tiffin Ave Findlay (45840) *(G-9890)*

Smokeheal Inc 216 255-5119
  5135 Spencer Rd Cleveland (44124) *(G-6213)*

Smokey Bones Bbq, Columbus *Also called Barbeque Integrated Inc (G-6640)*

Smokin Guns LLC 440 324-4003
  41458 Griswold Rd Elyria (44035) *(G-9494)*

Smokin TS Smokehouse 440 577-1117
  1550 Stnhpe Kllggsvlle Jefferson (44047) *(G-11371)*

Smolic Machine Co 440 946-1747
  37127 Ben Hur Ave Willoughby (44094) *(G-20601)*

Smoothie Creations Inc 817 313-8212
  17137 Misty Lake Dr Strongsville (44136) *(G-17968)*

Smoothie-Licious 513 742-2260
  1325 Quail Ridge Rd Batavia (45103) *(G-1223)*

Smp Manufacturing LLC 419 244-3645
  1216 W Bancroft St Toledo (43606) *(G-18699)*

Smp Welding LLC 440 205-9353
  8171 Tyler Blvd Mentor (44060) *(G-13725)*

SMS Communications Inc 216 374-6686
  20116 Chagrin Blvd Shaker Heights (44122) *(G-17095)*

SMS Technologies Inc 419 465-4175
  3531 Everingin Rd Monroeville (44847) *(G-14429)*

Smucker International Inc (HQ) 330 682-3000
  1 Strawberry Ln Orrville (44667) *(G-15766)*

Smucker Latin America Inc, Orrville *Also called Smucker International Inc (G-15766)*

Smucker Natural Foods Inc 330 682-3000
  Strawberry Ln Orrville (44667) *(G-15767)*

Smurfit Stone, Cincinnati *Also called Westrock Cp LLC (G-4589)*

Smurfit-Stone, Blue Ash *Also called Westrock Cp LLC (G-1893)*

Smurfit-Stone Container, Coshocton *Also called Westrock Cp LLC (G-7915)*

Smw Manufacturing 937 781-4945
  2555 Woodman Dr Kettering (45420) *(G-11586)*

Smw Supplier Village, Kettering *Also called Smw Manufacturing (G-11586)*

Snack Alliance Inc (HQ) 330 767-3426
  100 Lincoln Way E Massillon (44646) *(G-13202)*

Snair Co 614 873-7020
  8163 Business Way Plain City (43064) *(G-16360)*

Snap Rite Manufacturing Inc 910 897-4080
  14300 Darley Ave Cleveland (44110) *(G-6214)*

Snap-On Business Solutions (HQ) 330 659-1600
  4025 Kinross Lakes Pkwy Richfield (44286) *(G-16639)*

Snappskin Inc 440 318-4879
  534 Manor Brook Dr Chagrin Falls (44022) *(G-3070)*

Snaps Inc 419 477-5100
  2557 Township Road 35 Mount Cory (45868) *(G-14554)*

Sneaky Pete Band 419 933-6251
  4418 N Greenfield Rd Willard (44890) *(G-20401)*

Sneller Machine Tool Division, Cleveland *Also called Grand Harbor Yacht Sales & Svc (G-5445)*

Sni Inc 937 427-9447
  75 Harbert Dr Ste A Beavercreek (45440) *(G-1380)*

Snook Advertising Al Publisher 614 866-3333
  1567 Alar Ave Reynoldsburg (43068) *(G-16606)*

Snook Al Advertising/Publisher, Reynoldsburg *Also called Snook Advertising Al Publisher (G-16606)*

Snow Aviation Intl Inc 614 588-2452
  949 Creek Dr Gahanna (43230) *(G-10234)*

Snow Metal Products Co, Solon *Also called Swagelok (G-17389)*

Snow Printing Co Inc 419 229-7669
  1000 W Grand Ave Frnt Lima (45801) *(G-12093)*

Snows Wood Shop Inc (PA) 419 836-3805
  7220 Brown Rd Oregon (43616) *(G-15716)*

Snowville Creamery LLC 740 698-2301
  32623 State Route 143 Pomeroy (45769) *(G-16391)*

(G-0000) Company's Geographic Section entry number

Sns Nano Fiber Technology LLC 330 655-0030
  5633 Hudson Indus Pkwy Hudson (44236) *(G-11200)*
Snyder Brick and Block, Moraine *Also called Snyder Concrete Products Inc (G-14528)*
Snyder Brick and Block, Monroe *Also called Snyder Concrete Products Inc (G-14413)*
Snyder Brick and Block, Dayton *Also called Snyder Concrete Products Inc (G-8661)*
Snyder Concrete Products Inc (PA) 937 885-5176
  2301 W Dorothy Ln Moraine (45439) *(G-14528)*
Snyder Concrete Products Inc 513 539-7686
  233 Senate Dr Monroe (45050) *(G-14413)*
Snyder Concrete Products Inc 937 224-1433
  1433 S Euclid Ave Dayton (45417) *(G-8661)*
Snyder Electronics 513 738-7200
  5501 Lawrenceburg Rd # 100 Harrison (45030) *(G-10803)*
Snyder Fabrication LLC 419 946-6616
  6145 County Road 30 Mount Gilead (43338) *(G-14569)*
Snyder Hot Shot, Wooster *Also called H & H Equipment Inc (G-20781)*
Snyder Intl Brewing Group LLC (PA) 216 619-7424
  1940 E 6th St Ste 200 Cleveland (44114) *(G-6215)*
Snyder Machine Co Inc 419 526-1527
  256 N Diamond St Mansfield (44902) *(G-12681)*
Snyder Manufacturing Inc 330 343-4456
  3001 Progress St Dover (44622) *(G-9016)*
Snyder Manufacturing Co Ltd 330 343-4456
  3001 Progress St Dover (44622) *(G-9017)*
Snyder Printing LLC 740 353-3947
  1552 Gallia St Portsmouth (45662) *(G-16455)*
Snyder Printing & Signs, Portsmouth *Also called Snyder Printing LLC (G-16455)*
Snyders Tool & Die Inc 614 878-2205
  6481 W Broad St Galloway (43119) *(G-10315)*
Snyders-Lance Inc 614 856-4616
  4000 Gantz Rd Ste E Grove City (43123) *(G-10596)*
Snyders-Lance Inc 419 289-0787
  2041 Claremont Ave Ashland (44805) *(G-778)*
So-Low Environmental Eqp Co 513 772-9410
  10310 Spartan Dr Cincinnati (45215) *(G-4431)*
Soam Seal, Cleveland *Also called Novagard Solutions Inc (G-5917)*
Sobel Corrugated Cntrs Inc 216 475-2100
  1111 Superior Ave E # 1111 Cleveland (44114) *(G-6216)*
Sober Sand & Gravel Co 330 325-7088
  2898 Tallmadge Rd Ravenna (44266) *(G-16557)*
Socar of Ohio Inc (PA) 419 596-3100
  21739 Road E16 Continental (45831) *(G-7828)*
Soccer Centre Owners Ltd 419 893-5425
  1620 Market Place Dr Maumee (43537) *(G-13296)*
Soccer First Inc (PA) 614 889-1115
  6490 Dublin Park Dr Dublin (43016) *(G-9148)*
Soccer Village Inc 513 451-8500
  9890 Colerain Ave Cincinnati (45251) *(G-4432)*
Social Supper, Dresden *Also called Dresden Specialties Inc (G-9032)*
Socialpay LLC 513 721-3900
  312 Walnut St Ste 2275 Cincinnati (45202) *(G-4433)*
Society of The Precious Blood 419 925-4516
  2860 Us Route 127 Celina (45822) *(G-3018)*
Soda Pig LLC 646 241-7126
  790 Kerr St Columbus (43215) *(G-7627)*
Soderberg Inc 937 298-0223
  1851 Ebert Ave Moraine (45439) *(G-14529)*
Soffseal Inc 513 367-0028
  104 May Dr Harrison (45030) *(G-10804)*
Soft Touch Wood LLC 330 545-4204
  1560 S State St Girard (44420) *(G-10395)*
Soft Tuch Furn Repr Rfinishing, Girard *Also called Soft Touch Wood LLC (G-10395)*
Soft-Lite LLC (HQ) 330 528-3400
  10250 Philipp Pkwy Streetsboro (44241) *(G-17876)*
Soft-Lite Windows, Streetsboro *Also called Soft-Lite LLC (G-17876)*
Softchoice Corporation 614 224-4123
  300 Marconi Blvd Ste 303 Columbus (43215) *(G-7628)*
Softpoint Industries 330 668-2645
  988 Traci Ln Copley (44321) *(G-7855)*
Softura Legal Solutions LLC 614 220-5611
  1555 Lake Shore Dr Columbus (43204) *(G-7629)*
Software Authority Inc 216 236-0200
  6001 W Creek Rd Cleveland (44131) *(G-6217)*
Software Management Group 513 618-2165
  1128 Main St Fl 6 Cincinnati (45202) *(G-4434)*
Software Solutions Inc (PA) 513 932-6667
  420 E Main St Lebanon (45036) *(G-11841)*
Software To Systems Inc 513 893-4367
  640 Glenna Dr Fairfield (45014) *(G-9720)*
Sojourners Truth 419 243-0007
  1811 Adams St Toledo (43604) *(G-18700)*
Sol-Fly Technologies LLC 330 465-8883
  3098 Tamarack Ln Wooster (44691) *(G-20837)*
Solae Central Soya, Bellevue *Also called Solae LLC (G-1560)*
Solae LLC 419 483-0400
  300 Great Lakes Pkwy Bellevue (44811) *(G-1560)*
Solae LLC 419 483-5340
  605 Goodrich Rd Bellevue (44811) *(G-1561)*

Solar Arts Graphic Designs 330 744-0535
  824 Tod Ave Youngstown (44502) *(G-21205)*
Solar Con Inc 419 865-5877
  7134 Railroad St Holland (43528) *(G-11086)*
Solar Integrated Resources LLC 937 608-4498
  4501 Kettering Blvd Moraine (45439) *(G-14530)*
Soldier Tech & Armor RES LLC 330 896-5217
  3300 Massillon Rd Akron (44312) *(G-407)*
Sole Choice Inc 740 354-2813
  830 Murray St Portsmouth (45662) *(G-16456)*
Solexy Usa LLC 513 860-5465
  10168 International Blvd West Chester (45246) *(G-20051)*
Solid Dimensions Inc 419 663-1134
  720 Townline Road 151 Norwalk (44857) *(G-15564)*
Solid Dimensions Line, Norwalk *Also called Solid Dimensions Inc (G-15564)*
Solid Light Company Inc 740 548-1219
  7750 Green Meadows Dr A Lewis Center (43035) *(G-11920)*
Solmet Technologies Inc 330 915-4160
  2716 Shepler Ch Ave Sw Canton (44706) *(G-2852)*
Solo Products Inc 513 321-7884
  838 Reedy St Cincinnati (45202) *(G-4435)*
Solomon Industries LLC 937 558-5334
  3365 Peebles Rd Troy (45373) *(G-18877)*
Solomons Mines Inc 330 337-0123
  7219 Salem Unity Rd Salem (44460) *(G-16928)*
Solon 440 498-1798
  38235 Mcdowell Dr Solon (44139) *(G-17383)*
Solon Glass Center Inc 440 248-5018
  33001 Station St Cleveland (44139) *(G-6218)*
Solon Glass Ctr, Cleveland *Also called Solon Glass Center Inc (G-6218)*
Solon Granite Memorial Works 440 248-6606
  36050 Aurora Rd Solon (44139) *(G-17384)*
Solon Manufacturing Company 440 286-7149
  425 Center St Chardon (44024) *(G-3180)*
Solon Specialty 0537, Cleveland *Also called Solon Specialty Wire Co (G-6219)*
Solon Specialty Wire Co 440 248-7600
  30000 Solon Rd Cleveland (44139) *(G-6219)*
Solstice Sleep Products, Columbus *Also called SSP Tennessee LLC (G-7649)*
Solstreme, Cincinnati *Also called X-3-5 LLC (G-4613)*
Solsys Inc 419 886-4683
  96 Vanderbilt Rd Mansfield (44904) *(G-12682)*
Solus Indus Innovations LLC 440 356-1933
  20782 Beaconsfield Blvd Rocky River (44116) *(G-16711)*
Solut, Lewis Center *Also called Duracorp LLC (G-11896)*
Solution Industries LLC 440 816-9500
  17830 Englewood Dr Ste 11 Middleburg Heights (44130) *(G-13908)*
Solution Ventures Inc 440 242-1658
  31728 Commodore Ct Avon Lake (44012) *(G-1051)*
Solutions Plus Inc 513 943-9600
  3907 Bach Buxton Rd Amelia (45102) *(G-583)*
Solvaira Specialties Inc 937 652-2101
  1228 Muzzy Rd Urbana (43078) *(G-19181)*
Solvay Spclty Polymers USA LLC 740 373-9242
  17005 State Route 7 Marietta (45750) *(G-12833)*
Solvay USA Inc 513 482-5700
  4775 Paddock Rd Cincinnati (45229) *(G-4436)*
Solvent Recovery Division, Columbus *Also called Babcock & Wilcox Megtec (G-6800)*
Somerset Commercial Prtg Co 740 536-7187
  9050 Pleasantville Rd Ne Rushville (43150) *(G-16753)*
Somerset Galleries Inc 614 443-0003
  1144 S 4th St Columbus (43206) *(G-7630)*
Somerville Manufacturing Inc 740 336-7847
  15 Townhall Rd Marietta (45750) *(G-12834)*
Sommers Foods Inc 888 906-7452
  6399 State Route 83 Holmesville (44633) *(G-11112)*
Sommers Noodles, Holmesville *Also called Sommers Foods Inc (G-11112)*
Sommers Wood N Door Company 614 873-3506
  7802 Amish Pike Plain City (43064) *(G-16361)*
Sonalysts Inc 937 429-9711
  2940 Presidential Dr # 160 Beavercreek (45324) *(G-1362)*
Sonic Drilling 330 359-0079
  9406 Massillon Rd Dundee (44624) *(G-9180)*
Sonoco Products Company 330 688-8247
  59 N Main St Munroe Falls (44262) *(G-14665)*
Sonoco Products Company 740 927-2525
  8865 Smiths Mill Rd N Johnstown (43031) *(G-11404)*
Sonoco Products Company 937 429-0040
  761 Space Dr Beavercreek Township (45434) *(G-1390)*
Sonoco Products Company 513 870-3985
  4633 Dues Dr West Chester (45246) *(G-20052)*
Sonoco Products Company 419 448-4428
  60 Heritage Dr Tiffin (44883) *(G-18245)*
Sonoco Products Company 614 759-8470
  444 Mccormick Blvd Columbus (43213) *(G-7631)*
Sonoco Products Company 513 455-6003
  4747 Lake Forest Dr # 100 Blue Ash (45242) *(G-1870)*
Sonoco Prtective Solutions Inc 419 420-0029
  1900 Industrial Dr Findlay (45840) *(G-9891)*

Sonoco Prtective Solutions Inc................................419 420-0029
   1900 Industrial Dr Findlay (45840) *(G-9892)*

Sonoco Trident, Blue Ash *Also called Sonoco Products Company (G-1870)*

Sonogage Inc...216 464-1119
   26650 Rnohance Pkwy Ste 3 Cleveland (44128) *(G-6220)*

Sonoma Grinding..440 918-7990
   37195 Ben Hur Ave Ste E Willoughby (44094) *(G-20602)*

Sonus-Usa Inc..419 474-9324
   3829 Woodley Rd Bldg B Toledo (43606) *(G-18701)*

Sonus-Usa Inc..513 475-8400
   222 Piedmont Ave Ste 5200 Cincinnati (45219) *(G-4437)*

SOO Nyeo Won Inc...562 569-8390
   1146 E St Lorain (44052) *(G-12279)*

Soprema USA Inc..330 334-0066
   310 Quadral Dr Wadsworth (44281) *(G-19441)*

Sorbothane Inc (PA)..330 678-9444
   2144 State Route 59 Kent (44240) *(G-11530)*

Sorta 4 U LLC..440 365-0091
   267 Bon Air Ave Elyria (44035) *(G-9495)*

Soulsby, John, Mentor *Also called Mentor Signs & Graphics Inc (G-13652)*

Sound and Vibration, Bay Village *Also called Acoustical Publications Inc (G-1241)*

Sound Communications Inc.......................................614 875-8500
   3474 Park St Grove City (43123) *(G-10597)*

Sound Publishing Holding Inc..................................330 996-3000
   44 E Exchange St Akron (44308) *(G-408)*

Sound Solutions Cnstr Svcs, Bedford *Also called Baswa Acoustics North Amer LLC (G-1404)*

Soundproof..440 864-8864
   15400 Highland Dr Grafton (44044) *(G-10436)*

Soundwich Inc (PA)...216 486-2666
   881 Wayside Rd Cleveland (44110) *(G-6221)*

Source3media Inc...330 467-9003
   9085 Freeway Dr Macedonia (44056) *(G-12483)*

Sourcelink Ohio LLC...937 885-8000
   3303 W Tech Blvd Miamisburg (45342) *(G-13862)*

Sourcepac Inc...614 899-0744
   275 Old County Line Rd L Westerville (43081) *(G-20234)*

Sourcepoint Logistics LLC..937 604-8209
   5575 Ross Rd Tipp City (45371) *(G-18300)*

South Akron Awning Co (PA).....................................330 848-7611
   763 Kenmore Blvd Akron (44314) *(G-409)*

South End Printing Co...216 341-0669
   3558 E 80th St Cleveland (44105) *(G-6222)*

South Shore Controls Inc...440 259-2500
   4485 N Ridge Rd Perry (44081) *(G-16058)*

South Shore Gas & Oil, Portsmouth *Also called Delmar E Hicks (G-16434)*

South Side Audio LLC...614 453-0757
   2501 S High St Frnt Frnt Columbus (43207) *(G-7632)*

South Side Drive Thru...937 295-2927
   9204 Hilgefort Rd Fort Loramie (45845) *(G-9940)*

Southast Diesl Acquisition Sub, Greenville *Also called Stateline Power Corp (G-10524)*

Southeast Ohio Timber Pdts Co................................740 344-2570
   67 Beech Rock Dr Zanesville (43701) *(G-21355)*

Southeast Publications Inc.......................................740 732-2341
   309 Main St Caldwell (43724) *(G-2433)*

Southeastern Container Inc......................................419 352-6300
   307 Industrial Pkwy Bowling Green (43402) *(G-2016)*

Southeastern Natural Gas Co....................................740 385-8583
   35200 Hocking Dr Logan (43138) *(G-12195)*

Southeastern Shafting Mfg.......................................740 342-4629
   402 W Broadway St New Lexington (43764) *(G-14854)*

Southern Adhsives Coatings Inc...............................513 561-8440
   8121 Camargo Rd Cincinnati (45243) *(G-4438)*

Southern Bag, Wilmington *Also called Hood Packaging Corporation (G-20669)*

Southern Cabinetry Inc...740 245-5992
   41 International Blvd Bidwell (45614) *(G-1679)*

Southern Division, Perrysburg *Also called Ohio Table Pad Company (G-16131)*

Southern Express Lubes Inc......................................937 278-5807
   3781 Salem Ave Dayton (45406) *(G-8662)*

Southern Glazers Wine & Sprt...................................513 755-7082
   4305 Muhlhauser Rd Ste 4 Fairfield (45014) *(G-9721)*

Southern Ohio Kitchens, Dayton *Also called C-Link Enterprises LLC (G-8205)*

Southern Ohio Lumber LLC..614 436-4472
   11855 State Route 73 Peebles (45660) *(G-16025)*

Southern Ohio Machine Repr Sp, Chesapeake *Also called Ridge Enterprises Inc (G-3190)*

Southern Ohio Materials..937 386-3200
   800 Nathan Denton Rd Seaman (45679) *(G-17043)*

Southern Ohio Mfg Inc..513 943-2555
   1147 Clough Pike Batavia (45103) *(G-1224)*

Southern Ohio Wood...740 288-1825
   1085 Loop Rd Wellston (45692) *(G-19769)*

Southern Ornamental Iron Co (PA)............................937 278-4319
   4267 Salem Ave Dayton (45416) *(G-8663)*

Southern Wholesale, Millersburg *Also called Affordable Barn Co Ltd (G-14190)*

Southpaw Enterprises Inc...937 252-7676
   2350 Dryden Rd Moraine (45439) *(G-14531)*

Southside Wolfies..419 422-5450
   546 6th St Findlay (45840) *(G-9893)*

Southstern Machining Field Svc (PA).........................740 689-1147
   500 Lincoln Ave Lancaster (43130) *(G-11754)*

Southwest Electric Co...330 875-7000
   609 Enterprise Cir Louisville (44641) *(G-12330)*

Southwest Greens Ohio LLC......................................614 389-6042
   1781 Westbelt Dr Columbus (43228) *(G-7633)*

Southwest Ohio Computer Assn, Hamilton *Also called Butler Tech Career Dev Schools (G-10679)*

Southwest Tire Molds, Akron *Also called Northeast Tire Molds Inc (G-319)*

Southwestern Ohio Instruction.................................937 746-6333
   1205 E 5th St Dayton (45402) *(G-8664)*

Southworth Wood Products, Beaver *Also called Ramona Southworth (G-1311)*

Sovereign Circuits Inc..330 538-3900
   12080 Debartolo Dr North Jackson (44451) *(G-15298)*

Sovereign Stitch..440 829-0678
   701 Jockeys Cir Avon Lake (44012) *(G-1052)*

Sp Acquisitions LLC..440 205-0143
   6989 Lindsay Dr Mentor (44060) *(G-13726)*

Sp Medical, Cleveland *Also called Superior Products Llc (G-6269)*

SP Mount Printing Company.......................................216 881-3316
   1306 E 55th St Cleveland (44103) *(G-6223)*

Sp3 Cutting Tools (PA)..937 667-4476
   835 N Hyatt St Tipp City (45371) *(G-18301)*

Spa Pool Covers Inc...440 235-9981
   7806 Royalton Rd North Royalton (44133) *(G-15452)*

Space Age Coatings LLC..937 275-5117
   4825 Wolf Creek Pike Dayton (45417) *(G-8665)*

Space Age Concepts, Dayton *Also called Space Age Coatings LLC (G-8665)*

Space Dynamics Corp...513 792-9800
   10080 Alliance Rd Blue Ash (45242) *(G-1871)*

Space-Links Inc..330 788-2401
   1110 Thalia Ave Youngstown (44512) *(G-21206)*

Spacelinks Enterprises Inc.......................................330 788-2401
   1110 Thalia Ave Youngstown (44512) *(G-21207)*

Spall Autoc Syste / US Millwr, Lima *Also called Spallinger Millwright Svc Co (G-12094)*

Spallinger Millwright Svc Co......................................419 225-5830
   1155 E Hanthorn Rd Lima (45804) *(G-12094)*

Spang & Company...440 350-6108
   9305 Progress Pkwy Mentor (44060) *(G-13727)*

Spanish Lngage Productions Inc...............................614 737-3424
   3017 Mounts Rd Alexandria (43001) *(G-481)*

Spanish Portugese Translation, Westlake *Also called Advanced Translation/Cnsltng (G-20246)*

SPAOS Inc (PA)...937 890-0783
   6012 N Dixie Dr Dayton (45414) *(G-8666)*

Spare Parts Warehouse, Dayton *Also called Ucr LLC (G-8120)*

Sparkpeople Inc...513 651-2062
   310 Culvert St Fl 3 Cincinnati (45202) *(G-4439)*

Spartan Chemical Company Inc (PA).........................419 897-5551
   1110 Spartan Dr Maumee (43537) *(G-13297)*

Spartan Fabrication...330 758-3512
   230 Mcclurg Rd Youngstown (44512) *(G-21208)*

Spartech Plastics, Greenville *Also called Polyone Corporation (G-10515)*

Spartech Plastics, Paulding *Also called Polyone Corporation (G-16013)*

Sparton Enterprises Inc...330 745-6088
   3717 Clark Mill Rd Norton (44203) *(G-15521)*

Sparton Medical Systems Inc...................................440 878-4630
   22740 Lunn Rd Strongsville (44149) *(G-17969)*

Spb Global LLC...419 931-6559
   26611 Nawash Dr Perrysburg (43551) *(G-16150)*

Spear USA Inc (PA)...513 459-1100
   5510 Courseview Dr Mason (45040) *(G-13088)*

Spearfysh Inc...330 487-0300
   8987 Darrow Rd Twinsburg (44087) *(G-19021)*

Spec Mask Ohio LLC...440 522-3055
   7899 Euclid Chardon Rd Kirtland (44094) *(G-11616)*

Specgrade Led, Columbus *Also called Lighting Solutions Group LLC (G-7295)*

Special Design Products Inc......................................614 272-6700
   500 Industrial Mile Rd Columbus (43228) *(G-7634)*

Special Machined Components..................................513 459-1113
   7626 Easy St Mason (45040) *(G-13089)*

Special Metals Corporation (HQ)...............................216 755-3030
   4832 Richmond Rd Ste 100 Warrensville Heights (44128) *(G-19635)*

Special Mtls RES & Tech Inc......................................440 777-4024
   27390 Lusandra Cir North Olmsted (44070) *(G-15347)*

Special t Foods LLC..330 793-8697
   6834 Pinebrook Ct Youngstown (44515) *(G-21209)*

Special t Foods LLC..330 533-9493
   5529 W Middletown Rd Canfield (44406) *(G-2574)*

Special Touch Midnight Press....................................740 596-5380
   57306 N Branch Rd South Bloomingville (43152) *(G-17423)*

Special Way 2..740 282-8281
   1592 State Route 213 Steubenville (43952) *(G-17713)*

Specialized Business Sftwr Inc..................................440 542-9145
   6325 Cochran Rd Ste 1 Solon (44139) *(G-17385)*

Specialized Castings Ltd...937 669-5620
   1569 Martindale Rd Greenville (45331) *(G-10522)*

Specialized Pharmaceuticals....................................330 453-3067
   400 Tuscarawas St W Canton (44702) *(G-2853)*

Specialized Pharmaceuticals 419 371-2081
799 S Main St Lima (45804) *(G-12095)*
Specialtee Sportswear & Design 614 877-0976
9819 Us Highway 62 Orient (43146) *(G-15724)*
Specialties Mds Induction Ltd 330 394-3338
762 E Market St Warren (44481) *(G-19601)*
Specialties Unlimited, Mentor *Also called J & P Products Inc (G-13616)*
Specialty Adhesive Film Co 513 353-1885
5838 Hamilton Cleves Rd Cleves (45002) *(G-6526)*
Specialty Ceramics Inc 330 482-0800
41995 State Route 344 Columbiana (44408) *(G-6633)*
Specialty Drapery Workroom 330 864-4190
50 S Frank Blvd Akron (44313) *(G-410)*
Specialty Fab, North Lima *Also called Bird Equipment LLC (G-15311)*
Specialty Films Inc 614 471-9100
2887 Johnstown Rd Columbus (43219) *(G-7635)*
Specialty Gas Publishing Inc 216 226-3796
12550 Lake Ave Apt 1312 Cleveland (44107) *(G-6224)*
Specialty Gas Report, Cleveland *Also called Specialty Gas Publishing Inc (G-6224)*
Specialty Hose Aerospace Corp 330 497-9650
7802 Freedom Ave Nw Canton (44720) *(G-2854)*
Specialty Hose Corporation (PA) 330 497-9650
7800 Freedom Ave Nw North Canton (44720) *(G-15266)*
Specialty Lithographing Co 513 621-0222
1035 W 7th St Cincinnati (45203) *(G-4440)*
Specialty Magnetics LLC 330 468-8834
440 Highland Rd E Macedonia (44056) *(G-12484)*
Specialty Metals Processing 330 656-2767
837 Seasons Rd Hudson (44224) *(G-11201)*
Specialty Nameplate Corp 614 444-6876
4670 Groves Rd Columbus (43232) *(G-7636)*
Specialty Pallet & Design Ltd 330 857-0257
2600 Kidron Rd Orrville (44667) *(G-15768)*
Specialty Pallet Entps LLC 419 673-0247
18031 State Route 309 Kenton (43326) *(G-11569)*
Specialty Pipe & Tube Inc (HQ) 330 505-8262
3600 Union St Mineral Ridge (44440) *(G-14311)*
Specialty Plas Fabrications 513 856-9475
1600 Irma Ave Hamilton (45011) *(G-10740)*
Specialty Printing and Proc 614 322-9035
4670 Groves Rd Columbus (43232) *(G-7637)*
Specialty Services Inc 614 421-1599
1382 Ohlen Ave Columbus (43211) *(G-7638)*
Specialty Steel Solutions 567 674-0011
14574 State Route 292 Kenton (43326) *(G-11570)*
Specialty Switch Co 330 427-3000
525 Mcclurg Rd Youngstown (44512) *(G-21210)*
Specialty Systems Electric LLC 304 529-3861
1853 County Road 411 Proctorville (45669) *(G-16492)*
Specialty Technologies Inc 330 638-0744
3470 Warren Meadville Rd Cortland (44410) *(G-7875)*
Specialty Technology & Res 614 870-0744
1150 Milepost Dr Columbus (43228) *(G-7639)*
Specialty Wood, Carey *Also called Anderson Co (G-2914)*
Specialty Wood Products, Cincinnati *Also called Wjf Enterprises LLC (G-4601)*
Specified Structures Inc 330 753-0693
643 Holmes Ave Barberton (44203) *(G-1149)*
Specilty Fbrics Converting Inc (HQ) 706 637-3000
703 S Clvland Mssillon Rd Fairlawn (44333) *(G-9760)*
Specmat, North Olmsted *Also called Special Mtls RES & Tech Inc (G-15347)*
Spectra Group Limited Inc 419 837-9783
27800 Lemoyne Rd Ste J Millbury (43447) *(G-14186)*
Spectra-Tech Manufacturing Inc 513 735-9300
4013 Borman Dr Batavia (45103) *(G-1225)*
Spectracam Ltd 937 223-3805
1112 E Race Dr Dayton (45404) *(G-8667)*
Spectral Uv Systems, Amherst *Also called Nordson Uv Inc (G-604)*
Spectramed Inc 740 263-3059
275 W Johnstown Rd Gahanna (43230) *(G-10235)*
Spectre EDM 513 469-7700
6082 Interstate Cir Blue Ash (45242) *(G-1872)*
Spectre Sensors Inc (PA) 440 250-0372
2392 Georgia Dr Westlake (44145) *(G-20309)*
Spectre Sensors Inc 440 250-0616
2392 Georgia Dr Westlake (44145) *(G-20310)*
Spectroglass Corp 614 297-0412
1380 Holly Ave Columbus (43212) *(G-7640)*
Spectron Inc 937 461-5590
132 S Terry St Dayton (45403) *(G-8668)*
Spectrum Adhesives Inc 740 763-2886
11047 Lambs Ln Newark (43055) *(G-15054)*
Spectrum Brands Inc 440 357-2600
447 Lexington Ave Painesville (44077) *(G-15921)*
Spectrum Brands Inc 513 231-0952
7794 5 Mile Rd Ste 190 Anderson Township (45230) *(G-610)*
Spectrum Dispersions Inc 330 296-0600
225 W Lake St Ravenna (44266) *(G-16558)*
Spectrum Dynamics Inc 614 486-3223
1951 Hampshire Rd Columbus (43221) *(G-7641)*
Spectrum Embroidery Inc 937 847-9905
332 Gargrave Rd Dayton (45449) *(G-8669)*
Spectrum Inc 440 951-6061
800 Resource Dr Ste 8 Brooklyn Heights (44131) *(G-2147)*
Spectrum Infared, Brooklyn Heights *Also called Spectrum Inc (G-2147)*
Spectrum Machine Inc 330 626-3666
1668 Frost Rd Streetsboro (44241) *(G-17877)*
Spectrum Metal Finishing Inc 330 758-8358
535 Bev Rd Youngstown (44512) *(G-21211)*
Spectrum Mfg & Sls Inc (PA) 614 486-3223
1951 Hampshire Rd Columbus (43221) *(G-7642)*
Spectrum Plastics Corporation 330 926-9766
99 E Ascot Ln Cuyahoga Falls (44223) *(G-8048)*
Spectrum Printing & Design, Dayton *Also called Eugene Stewart (G-8333)*
Spectrum Surgical Instruments, Stow *Also called Integrted Med Systems Intl Inc (G-17765)*
Speed North America Inc 330 202-7775
1700a Old Mansfield Rd Wooster (44691) *(G-20838)*
Speed Selector Inc 440 543-8233
17050 Munn Rd Chagrin Falls (44023) *(G-3120)*
Speed-O-Print, Crooksville *Also called Temple Oil & Gas Company (G-7954)*
Speedline Corporation (PA) 440 914-1122
6810 Cochran Rd Solon (44139) *(G-17386)*
Speedway LLC 330 874-4616
11099 State Route 212 Ne Bolivar (44612) *(G-1946)*
Speedway LLC 440 943-0044
29201 Euclid Ave Wickliffe (44092) *(G-20387)*
Speedway LLC (HQ) 937 864-3000
500 Speedway Dr Enon (45323) *(G-9550)*
Speedway LLC 330 644-2730
5211 Manchester Rd New Franklin (44319) *(G-14832)*
Speedway LLC 937 653-6840
725 N Main St Urbana (43078) *(G-19182)*
Speedway LLC 614 418-9325
2875 Stelzer Rd Columbus (43219) *(G-7643)*
Speedway LLC 513 829-3223
5010 Dixie Hwy Fairfield (45014) *(G-9722)*
Speedway LLC 937 390-6651
2040 N Bechtle Ave Springfield (45504) *(G-17649)*
Speedway LLC 614 861-6397
7881 E Main St Reynoldsburg (43068) *(G-16607)*
Speedway LLC 330 339-7770
1260 W High Ave New Philadelphia (44663) *(G-14928)*
Speedway LLC 937 372-7129
1455 Brush Row Rd Wilberforce (45384) *(G-20392)*
Speedway LLC 513 683-2034
12184 Mason Rd Cincinnati (45249) *(G-4441)*
Speedway LLC 330 468-3320
757 E Aurora Rd Macedonia (44056) *(G-12485)*
Speedway LLC 330 343-9469
225 S Wooster Ave Dover (44622) *(G-9018)*
Speedway LLC 419 468-9773
746 Harding Way W Galion (44833) *(G-10288)*
Speedway LLC 440 988-8014
712 N Leavitt Rd Amherst (44001) *(G-608)*
Speedway Superamerica, Urbana *Also called Speedway LLC (G-19182)*
Speedway Superamerica 1848, Macedonia *Also called Speedway LLC (G-12485)*
Speedway Superamerica 2034, Columbus *Also called Speedway LLC (G-7643)*
Speedway Superamerica 3027, Wickliffe *Also called Speedway LLC (G-20387)*
Speedway Superamerica 3187, Galion *Also called Speedway LLC (G-10288)*
Speedway Superamerica 3389, Fairfield *Also called Speedway LLC (G-9722)*
Speedway Superamerica 3672, New Franklin *Also called Speedway LLC (G-14832)*
Speedway Superamerica 4131, Springfield *Also called Speedway LLC (G-17649)*
Speedway Superamerica 4487, Reynoldsburg *Also called Speedway LLC (G-16607)*
Speedway Superamerica 5110, Cincinnati *Also called Speedway LLC (G-4441)*
Speedway Superamerica 5839, Wilberforce *Also called Speedway LLC (G-20392)*
Speedway Superamerica 6241, Bolivar *Also called Speedway LLC (G-1946)*
Speedway Superamerica 6243, Dover *Also called Speedway LLC (G-9018)*
Speedway Superamerica 6246, New Philadelphia *Also called Speedway LLC (G-14928)*
Speedway Superamerica 9975, Amherst *Also called Speedway LLC (G-608)*
Speelman Electric Inc 330 633-1410
358 Commerce St Tallmadge (44278) *(G-18169)*
Spence Technologies Inc 440 946-3035
4752 Topps Indus Pkwy Willoughby (44094) *(G-20603)*
Spencer Forge & Manufacturing, Spencer *Also called Spencer Manufacturing Company (G-17457)*
Spencer Forge & Manufacturing, Spencer *Also called Alta Mira Corporation (G-17455)*
Spencer Manufacturing Company 330 648-2461
225 N Main St Spencer (44275) *(G-17457)*
Spencer-Walker Press Inc (PA) 740 344-6110
1433 Amesbury Ln Newark (43055) *(G-15055)*
Spencer-Walker Press Inc 740 345-4494
44 S 4th St Newark (43055) *(G-15056)*
Sperco, Cleveland *Also called Sperzel Inc (G-6225)*
Sperling Railway Services Inc 330 479-2004
4313 Southway St Sw Canton (44706) *(G-2855)*

(PA)=Parent Co (HQ)=Headquarters (DH)=Div Headquarters

Sperry Rice Manufacturing LLC.................330 276-2801
1088 N Main St Killbuck (44637) **(G-11600)**

Sperzel Inc.................216 281-6868
15728 Industrial Pkwy Cleveland (44135) **(G-6225)**

Sphon Associates Inc.................614 741-4002
962 Bryn Mawr Dr Gahanna (43230) **(G-10236)**

Spi Inc.................937 374-2700
1170 S Patton St Xenia (45385) **(G-20973)**

SPI Mailing, Canton *Also called Slimans Printery Inc* **(G-2851)**

Spicy Olive LLC (PA).................513 847-4397
7671 Cox Ln West Chester (45069) **(G-19947)**

Spicy Olive LLC.................513 376-9061
2736 Erie Ave Cincinnati (45208) **(G-4442)**

Spiegelberg Manufacturing Inc (PA).................440 324-3042
12200 Alameda Dr Strongsville (44149) **(G-17970)**

Spiegler Brake Systems USA LLC.................937 291-1735
1699 Thomas Paine Pkwy Dayton (45459) **(G-8670)**

Spillman Company.................614 444-2184
1701 Moler Rd Columbus (43207) **(G-7644)**

Spinks Machine Products Co.................440 951-5814
37939 Stevens Blvd Willoughby (44094) **(G-20604)**

Spinnaker Coating LLC.................937 332-6300
518 E Water St Troy (45373) **(G-18878)**

Spinnaker Coating LLC (PA).................937 332-6500
518 E Water St Troy (45373) **(G-18879)**

Spintech LLC.................937 912-3250
1150 S Patton St Xenia (45385) **(G-20974)**

Spiral Brushes Inc.................330 686-2861
1355 Commerce Dr Stow (44224) **(G-17801)**

Spiralcool Company.................419 483-2510
186 Sheffield St Ste 188 Bellevue (44811) **(G-1562)**

Spirax Sarco Inc.................803 714-2023
500 W Wilson Bridge Rd # 145 Worthington (43085) **(G-20889)**

Spirit Aeronautics, Columbus *Also called Spirit Avionics Ltd* **(G-7645)**

Spirit Avionics Ltd.................614 358-0333
4808 E 5th Ave Columbus (43219) **(G-7645)**

Spirit of Clay.................440 684-0001
828 Som Center Rd Cleveland (44143) **(G-6226)**

Spirit Solutions Inc.................937 431-8041
2400 E River Rd Moraine (45439) **(G-14532)**

Spirol International Corp.................330 920-3655
321 Remington Rd Stow (44224) **(G-17802)**

Spitfire Technologies LLC.................937 463-7729
110 N Main St Dayton (45402) **(G-8671)**

Splicenet Inc.................513 563-3533
9624 Cincinnati Columbus West Chester (45241) **(G-20053)**

Spoerr Precast Concrete Inc.................419 625-9132
2020 Caldwell St Sandusky (44870) **(G-17009)**

Sponseller Group Inc (PA).................419 861-3000
1600 Timber Wolf Dr Holland (43528) **(G-11087)**

Sponseller Group Inc.................937 492-9949
808 W Russell Rd Ste A Sidney (45365) **(G-17229)**

Sports & Sports, Ashtabula *Also called Peska Inc* **(G-831)**

Sports Art, Nashport *Also called B D P Services Inc* **(G-14703)**

Sports Care Products Inc.................216 663-8110
4310 Cranwood Pkwy Cleveland (44128) **(G-6227)**

Sports Express.................330 297-1112
956 E Main St Ravenna (44266) **(G-16559)**

Sports Loft, Delphos *Also called Lion Clothing Inc* **(G-8914)**

Sportsales, Columbus *Also called Great Oppurtunities Inc* **(G-7130)**

Sportsartcom.................330 903-0895
939 Traci Ln Copley (44321) **(G-7856)**

Sportsco Imprinting.................513 641-5111
8277 Wicklow Ave Cincinnati (45236) **(G-4443)**

Sportsguard Laboratories Inc.................330 673-3932
821 W Main St Kent (44240) **(G-11531)**

Sportsmaster.................440 257-3900
9140 Lake Shore Blvd Mentor (44060) **(G-13728)**

Sportwing, Cleveland *Also called Dawn Enterprises Inc* **(G-5172)**

Spotted Horse Studio Inc.................330 533-2391
6385 State Rte 165 Greenford (44422) **(G-10483)**

SPR Machine Inc.................513 737-8040
2130 Tuley Rd Indian Spgs (45015) **(G-11286)**

Spradlin Bros Welding Co.................800 219-2182
2131 Quality Ln Springfield (45505) **(G-17650)**

Sprague Products, Brecksville *Also called Curtiss-Wright Flow Ctrl Corp* **(G-2042)**

Spring Grove Manufacturing.................513 542-0185
2838 Spring Grove Ave Cincinnati (45225) **(G-4444)**

Spring Grove Manufacturing.................513 542-6900
2838 Spring Grove Ave Cincinnati (45225) **(G-4445)**

Spring Team Inc.................440 275-5981
2851 Industrial Park Dr Austinburg (44010) **(G-966)**

Spring Works Inc.................614 351-9345
801 Distribution Dr Columbus (43228) **(G-7646)**

Springco Metal Coatings Inc (PA).................216 251-7023
12500 Elmwood Ave Cleveland (44111) **(G-6228)**

Springdale Bindery LLC.................513 772-8500
11411 Landan Ln Cincinnati (45246) **(G-4446)**

Springdale Ice Cream Beverage.................513 699-4984
11801 Chesterdale Rd Cincinnati (45246) **(G-4447)**

Springdot Inc.................513 542-4000
2611 Colerain Ave Cincinnati (45214) **(G-4448)**

Springfield Engraving Company.................937 390-0011
317 Canterbury Dr Springfield (45503) **(G-17651)**

Springfield Metal Finishing.................937 324-2353
640 S Belmont Ave Springfield (45505) **(G-17652)**

Springfield News Sun, Springfield *Also called Springfield Newspapers Inc* **(G-17653)**

Springfield Newspapers Inc (HQ).................937 323-5533
1 S Limestone St Ste 1010 Springfield (45502) **(G-17653)**

Springfield Plastics Inc.................937 322-6071
15 N Bechtle Ave Springfield (45504) **(G-17654)**

Springseal Inc.................330 626-0673
800 Enterprise Pkwy Ravenna (44266) **(G-16560)**

Springtime Manufacturing.................419 697-3720
1121 Hazelwood St Toledo (43605) **(G-18702)**

Sprint Print Inc.................740 622-4429
520 Main St Coshocton (43812) **(G-7910)**

Sprint Signs & Graphics, Youngstown *Also called R T Communications Inc* **(G-21183)**

Sprinter Marking Inc.................740 453-1000
1805 Chandlersville Rd Zanesville (43701) **(G-21356)**

SPS International Inc.................216 671-9911
11880 Bellaire Rd Cleveland (44135) **(G-6229)**

Spsi, Hartville *Also called Scott Process Systems Inc* **(G-10834)**

Spunfab, Cuyahoga Falls *Also called Keuchel & Associates Inc* **(G-8017)**

Spunfab Ltd (PA).................330 945-9455
175 Muffin Ln Cuyahoga Falls (44223) **(G-8049)**

Spurlino Materials LLC (PA).................513 705-0111
4000 Oxford State Rd Middletown (45044) **(G-14084)**

Spurlino Materials LLC.................513 202-1111
6600 Dry Fork Rd Cleves (45002) **(G-6527)**

Square D Field Services, West Chester *Also called Schneider Electric Usa Inc* **(G-19942)**

Square One Solutions LLC.................419 425-5445
105 Jefferson St Findlay (45840) **(G-9894)**

Squire Shoppe Bakery.................440 964-3303
511 Lake Ave Ashtabula (44004) **(G-839)**

Sr Products.................330 998-6500
1380 Highland Rd E Macedonia (44056) **(G-12486)**

SRC Liquidation LLC (PA).................937 221-1000
600 Albany St Dayton (45417) **(G-8672)**

SRC Worldwide Inc (HQ).................216 941-6115
3425 Service Rd Cleveland (44111) **(G-6230)**

Sreco Flexible, Lima *Also called Sewer Rodding Equipment Co* **(G-12089)**

SRI Ohio Inc.................740 653-5800
1061 Mill Park Dr Lancaster (43130) **(G-11755)**

Srico Inc.................614 799-0664
2724 Sawbury Blvd Columbus (43235) **(G-7647)**

Srm Graphics Inc.................614 263-4433
950 Oakland Park Ave Columbus (43224) **(G-7648)**

Sroka Inc.................440 572-2811
21265 Westwood Dr Strongsville (44149) **(G-17971)**

Sroka Industries Inc.................440 572-2811
21265 Westwood Dr Strongsville (44149) **(G-17972)**

Sroufe Healthcare Products LLC.................260 894-4171
961 Seville Rd Wadsworth (44281) **(G-19442)**

SRS Die Casting Holdings LLC (HQ).................330 467-0750
635 Highland Rd E Macedonia (44056) **(G-12487)**

SRS Light Metals Inc (PA).................330 467-0750
635 Highland Rd E Macedonia (44056) **(G-12488)**

SRS Manufacturing Corp.................937 746-3086
395 Industrial Dr Franklin (45005) **(G-10054)**

Ss Automotive Service.................419 859-2885
110 Market St Benton Ridge (45816) **(G-1598)**

Ss Industries, Dayton *Also called Stanco Precision Manufacturing* **(G-8675)**

Ss Metal Fabricators Inc.................937 226-9957
423 Rita St Dayton (45404) **(G-8673)**

SSC Controls Company, Mentor *Also called Peloton Manufacturing Corp* **(G-13684)**

Sseco, Cleveland *Also called Service Station Equipment Co* **(G-6181)**

Ssi, Willoughby *Also called Service Storage Intl Inc* **(G-20594)**

Ssi Manufacturing Inc.................513 761-7757
9615 Inter Ocean Dr West Chester (45246) **(G-20054)**

Ssi Tiles, Minerva *Also called Kepcor Inc* **(G-14327)**

Ssk Industries, Wintersville *Also called Johndavid D Jones* **(G-20711)**

Sso Inc.................440 235-3500
27064 Dogwood Ln Olmsted Twp (44138) **(G-15683)**

SSP Fittings Corp (PA).................330 425-4250
8250 Boyle Pkwy Twinsburg (44087) **(G-19022)**

SSP Industrial Group Inc.................330 665-2900
3560 W Market St Ste 300 Fairlawn (44333) **(G-9761)**

SSP Tennessee LLC.................614 279-8850
2652 Fisher Rd Ste A Columbus (43204) **(G-7649)**

Sst Conveyor Components Inc.................513 583-5500
185 Commerce Dr Loveland (45140) **(G-12389)**

Sst Precision Manufacturing.................513 583-5500
154 Commerce Dr Loveland (45140) **(G-12390)**

St Anthony Messenger Press, Cincinnati *Also called Province of St John The Baptis* **(G-4301)**

St Bernard Insulation LLC 513 266-2158
 8703 Pippin Rd Cincinnati (45251) *(G-4449)*
St Bernard Soap Company 513 242-2227
 5177 Spring Grove Ave Cincinnati (45217) *(G-4450)*
St Clair Plant, Eaton Also called Timkensteel Corporation *(G-9324)*
St Clairsville Dairy Queen 740 635-1800
 178 E Main St Saint Clairsville (43950) *(G-16808)*
St Henry Tile Co Inc (PA) 419 678-4841
 281 W Washington St Saint Henry (45883) *(G-16822)*
St Henry Tile Co Inc 937 548-1101
 5410 S State Route 49 Greenville (45331) *(G-10523)*
St Lawrence Steel Corporation 330 562-9000
 2500 Crane Centre Dr Streetsboro (44241) *(G-17878)*
St Mary's Ready Mix, Saint Marys Also called Quality Ready Mix Inc *(G-16851)*
St Marys Cement Inc (us) 937 642-4573
 14531 Industrial Pkwy Marysville (43040) *(G-12972)*
St Marys Foundry Inc (PA) 419 394-3346
 405 E South St Saint Marys (45885) *(G-16856)*
St Marys Iron Works Inc 419 300-6300
 1880 Celina Rd Saint Marys (45885) *(G-16857)*
St Media Group Intl Inc 513 421-2050
 11262 Cornell Park Dr Blue Ash (45242) *(G-1873)*
STA-Warm Electric Company 330 296-6461
 553 N Chestnut St Ravenna (44266) *(G-16561)*
Staber Industries Inc 614 836-5995
 4800 Homer Ohio Ln Groveport (43125) *(G-10645)*
Stable Step LLC 513 825-1888
 8930 Global Way West Chester (45069) *(G-19948)*
Staceys Kitchen Limited 614 921-1290
 4350 Kerr Dr Ste B Hilliard (43026) *(G-10980)*
Staci Corp (HQ) 440 355-5102
 110 Commerce Dr Lagrange (44050) *(G-11638)*
Staci Lagrange, Lagrange Also called Inservco Inc *(G-11627)*
Stack Constructyion Technology, Mason Also called To Scale Software LLC *(G-13099)*
Staco Energy Products Co (HQ) 937 253-1191
 1229 Byers Rd Miamisburg (45342) *(G-13863)*
Stadco Inc 937 878-0911
 632 Yllow Sprng Frfeld Rd Fairborn (45324) *(G-9630)*
STADCO AUTOMATICS, Fairborn Also called Stadco Inc *(G-9630)*
Stadvec Inc 330 644-7724
 579 W Tuscarawas Ave Barberton (44203) *(G-1150)*
Staely Custom Crating, Conover Also called Conover Lumber Company Inc *(G-7823)*
Stafast Products Inc (PA) 440 357-5546
 505 Lakeshore Blvd Painesville (44077) *(G-15922)*
Stafast West, Painesville Also called Stafast Products Inc *(G-15922)*
Stafford Gage & Tool Inc 937 277-9944
 4606 Webster St Dayton (45414) *(G-8674)*
Stafford Gravel Inc 419 298-2440
 4225 Co Rd 79 Edgerton (43517) *(G-9336)*
Stagecraft Costuming Inc 513 541-7150
 3950 Spring Grove Ave Cincinnati (45223) *(G-4451)*
Stagecraft Theatrical, Cincinnati Also called Stagecraft Costuming Inc *(G-4451)*
Stahl Cranesystems Inc 843 767-1951
 4401 Gateway Blvd Springfield (45502) *(G-17655)*
Stahl Farm Market 330 325-0640
 4560 State Route 14 Ravenna (44266) *(G-16562)*
Stahl Gear & Machine Co 216 431-2820
 3901 Hamilton Ave Cleveland (44114) *(G-6231)*
Stahl/Scott Fetzer Company (HQ) 800 277-8245
 3201 W Old Lincoln Way Wooster (44691) *(G-20839)*
Stainless Automation 216 961-4550
 1978 W 74th St Cleveland (44102) *(G-6232)*
Stainless Machine Engineering 330 501-1992
 5275 Woodville Rd Leetonia (44431) *(G-11865)*
Stainless Specialties Inc 440 942-4242
 33240 Lakeland Blvd Eastlake (44095) *(G-9287)*
Stainless Works, Chagrin Falls Also called Ohio Classic Street Rods Inc *(G-3108)*
Stainwood Products 440 244-1352
 2803 Toledo Ave Lorain (44055) *(G-12280)*
Stalder Spring Works Inc 937 322-6120
 2345 Springfield Xenia Rd Springfield (45506) *(G-17656)*
Staley & Sons Powerwashing LLC 937 843-2713
 6732 Wisharte Russells Point (43348) *(G-16757)*
Stam Inc 440 974-2500
 7350 Production Dr Mentor (44060) *(G-13729)*
Stambaugh Engineering Inc 330 666-0088
 1001 Heritage Ln Akron (44333) *(G-411)*
Stamco Industries Inc 216 731-9333
 26650 Lakeland Blvd Cleveland (44132) *(G-6233)*
Stamm Contracting Co Inc 330 274-8230
 4566 Orchard St Mantua (44255) *(G-12723)*
Stamped Steel Products Inc 330 538-3951
 151 S Bailey Rd North Jackson (44451) *(G-15299)*
Stamtex, Niles Also called Metal Products Company *(G-15169)*
Stamtex Metal Stampings, Niles Also called Metal Products Company *(G-15168)*
Stan Rileys Custom Draperies 513 821-3732
 7041 Vine St Cincinnati (45216) *(G-4452)*
Stanco Precision Manufacturing 937 274-1785
 1 Walbrook Ave Dayton (45405) *(G-8675)*

Stancorp Inc 330 545-6615
 712 Trumbull Ave Girard (44420) *(G-10396)*
Standard Advertising Co, Coshocton Also called Beach Company *(G-7882)*
Standard Car Truck Company 740 775-6450
 387 Wetzel Dr Chillicothe (45601) *(G-3276)*
Standard Die Supply, Dayton Also called Ready Technology Inc *(G-8618)*
Standard Energy Company 614 885-1901
 1105 Schrock Rd Ste 602 Columbus (43229) *(G-7650)*
Standard Engineering Group Inc 330 494-4300
 3516 Highland Park Nw North Canton (44720) *(G-15267)*
Standard Jig Boring Svc LLC (HQ) 330 896-9530
 3360 Miller Park Rd Akron (44312) *(G-412)*
Standard Jig Boring Svc LLC 330 644-5405
 3194 Massillon Rd Akron (44312) *(G-413)*
Standard Machine Inc 216 631-4440
 1952 W 93rd St Cleveland (44102) *(G-6234)*
Standard Oil Company 419 698-6200
 4001 Cedar Point Rd Oregon (43616) *(G-15717)*
Standard Oil Company 419 691-2460
 4151 Cedar Point Rd Oregon (43616) *(G-15718)*
Standard Pattern Works Inc 330 745-2295
 1409 Kenmore Blvd Akron (44314) *(G-414)*
Standard Printing Co Inc 419 586-2371
 123 E Market St Celina (45822) *(G-3019)*
Standard Prototyping Ideals 614 837-9180
 70 Cross St 100 Pickerington (43147) *(G-16205)*
Standard Publishing LLC 513 931-4050
 8805 Governors Hill Dr # 400 Cincinnati (45249) *(G-4453)*
Standard Register Inc 513 772-8860
 9100 Centre Pnte Dr 160 Cincinnati (45201) *(G-4454)*
Standard Register Inc 419 678-6000
 515 W Sycamore St Coldwater (45828) *(G-6572)*
Standard Register Inc 513 563-9700
 4500 Lake Forest Dr 518 Blue Ash (45242) *(G-1874)*
Standard Register Inc 440 974-1611
 7200 Justin Way Mentor (44060) *(G-13730)*
Standard Register Inc 216 265-9612
 4125 Highlander Pkwy # 230 Richfield (44286) *(G-16640)*
Standard Register Inc 860 870-2063
 600 Albany St Dayton (45417) *(G-8676)*
Standard Register Inc 614 277-7500
 3125 Lewis Centre Way Grove City (43123) *(G-10598)*
Standard Register Inc 732 356-0081
 7755 Paragon Rd Ste 101 Dayton (45459) *(G-8677)*
Standard Register Inc 480 763-1900
 600 Albany St Dayton (45417) *(G-8678)*
Standard Register Inc 937 221-3347
 3545 Urbancrest Indus Grove City (43123) *(G-10599)*
Standard Register Inc 937 228-5800
 220 E Monument Ave Dayton (45402) *(G-8679)*
Standard Register Inc 866 541-0937
 2222 Philadelphia Dr Dayton (45406) *(G-8680)*
Standard Signs Incorporated (PA) 330 467-2030
 9115 Freeway Dr Macedonia (44056) *(G-12489)*
Standard Technologies LLC 419 332-6434
 2641 Hayes Ave Fremont (43420) *(G-10183)*
Standard Textile Co Inc (PA) 513 761-9255
 1 Knollcrest Dr Cincinnati (45237) *(G-4455)*
Standard Welding & Lift Truck, Lorain Also called Perkins Motor Service Ltd *(G-12267)*
Standard Welding & Steel Pdts 330 273-2777
 260 S State Rd Medina (44256) *(G-13482)*
Standards Testing Labs Inc (PA) 330 833-8548
 1845 Harsh Ave Se Massillon (44646) *(G-13203)*
Standby Screw Machine Pdts Co 440 243-8200
 1122 W Bagley Rd Berea (44017) *(G-1635)*
Standex Electronics, Cincinnati Also called Standex International Corp *(G-4457)*
Standex Electronics Inc (HQ) 513 871-3777
 4538 Camberwell Rd Cincinnati (45209) *(G-4456)*
Standex International Corp 513 871-3777
 4538 Camberwell Rd Cincinnati (45209) *(G-4457)*
Standing Rock Designery 330 650-9089
 5194 Darrow Rd Hudson (44236) *(G-11202)*
Standing Rock Gallery, Hudson Also called Standing Rock Designery *(G-11202)*
Standout Stickers Inc 877 449-7703
 4930 Chippewa Rd Unit A Medina (44256) *(G-13483)*
Stanek E F and Assoc Inc 216 341-7700
 700 Highland Rd E Macedonia (44056) *(G-12490)*
Stanek Windows, Macedonia Also called Stanek E F and Assoc Inc *(G-12490)*
Stanley Access Tech LLC 440 461-5500
 5335 Avion Park Dr Cleveland (44143) *(G-6235)*
Stanley Bittinger 740 942-4302
 81331 Hines Rd Cadiz (43907) *(G-2422)*
Stanley Electric US Co Inc (HQ) 740 852-5200
 420 E High St London (43140) *(G-12219)*
Stanley Industrial & Auto LLC 614 755-7089
 505 N Cleveland Ave # 200 Westerville (43082) *(G-20187)*
Stanley Industrial & Auto LLC (HQ) 614 755-7000
 505 N Cleveland Ave Westerville (43082) *(G-20188)*
Stanley Industries Inc 216 475-4000
 19120 Cranwood Pkwy Cleveland (44128) *(G-6236)*

A
L
P
H
A
B
E
T
I
C

(PA)=Parent Co (HQ)=Headquarters (DH)=Div Headquarters

Stanley Proctor & Company Inc 330 425-7814
   2016 Midway Dr Twinsburg (44087) *(G-19023)*

Stanley Steemer Carpet Cleaner, Dublin Also called Stanley Steemer Intl Inc *(G-9149)*

Stanley Steemer Intl Inc (PA) 614 764-2007
   5800 Innovation Dr Dublin (43016) *(G-9149)*

Stansley Mineral Resources Inc (PA) 419 843-2813
   3793 Silica Rd B Sylvania (43560) *(G-18126)*

Stapins Qick Cpy/Print Ctr LLC 330 296-0123
   253 W Main St Ravenna (44266) *(G-16563)*

Star, Columbus Also called Specialty Technology & Res *(G-7639)*

Star, Marion Also called Steam Turb Alte Reso *(G-12903)*

Star Brite Express Car WA 330 674-0062
   887 S Washington St Millersburg (44654) *(G-14264)*

Star Calendar & Printing Co 216 741-3223
   4354 Pearl Rd Cleveland (44109) *(G-6237)*

Star City Art Co 937 865-9792
   421 S 9th St Miamisburg (45342) *(G-13864)*

Star Combustion Systems LLC 513 282-0810
   6506 Castle Dr Mason (45040) *(G-13090)*

Star Door & Sash Co Inc 419 841-3396
   4815 Kilburn Rd Berkey (43504) *(G-1643)*

Star Dynamics Corporation (PA) 614 334-4510
   4455 Reynolds Dr Hilliard (43026) *(G-10981)*

Star Engineering Inc 740 342-3514
   701 Madison St New Lexington (43764) *(G-14855)*

Star Extruded Shapes Inc 330 533-9863
   7055 Herbert Rd Canfield (44406) *(G-2575)*

Star Fab Inc (PA) 330 533-9863
   7055 Herbert Rd Canfield (44406) *(G-2576)*

Star Fab Inc 330 482-1601
   400 W Railroad St Ste 8 Columbiana (44408) *(G-6634)*

Star Fire Distributing, Akron Also called Thermo-Rite Mfg Company *(G-439)*

Star Jet LLC 614 338-4379
   4130 E 5th Ave Columbus (43219) *(G-7651)*

Star Metal Products Co Inc (PA) 440 899-7000
   30405 Clemens Rd Westlake (44145) *(G-20311)*

Star Newspaper 614 622-5930
   1472 Dobson Sq N Columbus (43229) *(G-7652)*

Star of West Milling Company 330 673-2941
   162 N Water St Kent (44240) *(G-11532)*

Star Pizza Box 740 967-1105
   495 E Coshocton St Johnstown (43031) *(G-11405)*

Star Precision Products, Mentor Also called Sp Acquisitions LLC *(G-13726)*

Star Printing, Steubenville Also called Ogden Newspapers Inc *(G-17708)*

Star Printing Company Inc 330 376-0514
   125 N Union St Akron (44304) *(G-415)*

Star Screw Machine Products 216 361-0307
   1531 E 41st St Cleveland (44103) *(G-6238)*

Star Seal of Ohio Inc 614 870-1590
   1400 Walcutt Rd Columbus (43228) *(G-7653)*

Star Spangled Spectacular Inc 419 879-3502
   4230 Elida Rd Lima (45807) *(G-12096)*

Starbringer Media Group Ltd 440 871-5448
   871 Canterbury Rd Ste B Westlake (44145) *(G-20312)*

Starbucks Corporation 513 754-5700
   6300 Kings Island Dr Mason (45040) *(G-13091)*

Starchem Inc (PA) 513 458-8262
   3000 Disney St Cincinnati (45209) *(G-4458)*

Starecasing Systems Inc 312 203-5632
   2822 Fisher Rd Columbus (43204) *(G-7654)*

Stark Airways 330 526-6416
   5430 Lauby Rd Bldg 27 North Canton (44720) *(G-15268)*

Stark Forest Products, Canton Also called Stark Truss Company Inc *(G-2859)*

Stark Industrial LLC 330 493-9773
   5103 Stoneham Rd North Canton (44720) *(G-15269)*

Stark Materials Inc 330 497-1648
   7345 Sunset Strip Ave Nw Canton (44720) *(G-2856)*

Stark Ready Mix & Supply Co 330 580-4307
   2905 Columbus Rd Ne Canton (44705) *(G-2857)*

Stark Truss Beach City Lumber, Beach City Also called Stark Truss Company Inc *(G-1251)*

Stark Truss Company Inc (PA) 330 478-2100
   109 Miles Ave Sw Canton (44710) *(G-2858)*

Stark Truss Company Inc 330 478-2100
   4933 Southway St Sw Canton (44706) *(G-2859)*

Stark Truss Company Inc 740 335-4156
   2000 Landmark Blvd Washington Court Hou (43160) *(G-19640)*

Stark Truss Company Inc 419 298-3777
   400 Component Dr Edgerton (43517) *(G-9337)*

Stark Truss Company Inc 330 756-3050
   6855 Chestnut Ridge Rd Nw Beach City (44608) *(G-1251)*

Starkey Machinery Inc 419 468-2560
   254 S Washington St Galion (44833) *(G-10289)*

Starks Plastics LLC 513 541-4591
   11236 Sebring Dr Cincinnati (45240) *(G-4459)*

Starpoint Extrusions LLC 330 825-2373
   3985 Eastern Rd C Norton (44203) *(G-15522)*

Starr Fabricating Inc 330 394-9891
   4175 Warren Sharon Rd Vienna (44473) *(G-19376)*

Starr Machine Inc 740 753-0009
   226 Sylvania Ave Nelsonville (45764) *(G-14740)*

Starr Printing Services Inc 513 241-7708
   3625 Spring Grove Ave Cincinnati (45223) *(G-4460)*

Starr Trophy & Awards, London Also called John C Starr *(G-12213)*

Start Printing 513 424-2121
   3140 Cincinnati Dayton Rd Middletown (45044) *(G-14085)*

Starwin Industries Inc 937 293-8568
   3387 Woodman Dr Dayton (45429) *(G-8681)*

Starwood, Middlefield Also called Norstar Aluminum Molds Inc *(G-13977)*

Stat Index Tab, Chillicothe Also called Stat Industries Inc *(G-3277)*

Stat Index Tab Company, Chillicothe Also called Stat Industries Inc *(G-3278)*

Stat Industries Inc 513 860-4482
   3269 Profit Dr Hamilton (45014) *(G-10741)*

Stat Industries Inc (PA) 740 779-6561
   137 Stone Rd Chillicothe (45601) *(G-3277)*

Stat Industries Inc 740 779-6561
   137 Stone Rd Chillicothe (45601) *(G-3278)*

State 8 Motorcycle & Atv, Peninsula Also called Wholecycle Inc *(G-16045)*

State Chemical Manufacturing, Cleveland Also called State Industrial Products Corp *(G-6239)*

State Chemical Manufacturing, Hebron Also called State Industrial Products Corp *(G-10886)*

State Electric Supply Company 330 308-0659
   201 Stonecreek Rd Nw New Philadelphia (44663) *(G-14929)*

State Farm Insurance, West Chester Also called Johnny Chin Insurance Agency *(G-20019)*

State Industrial Products Corp (PA) 877 747-6986
   5915 Landerbrook Dr # 300 Cleveland (44124) *(G-6239)*

State Industrial Products Corp. 740 929-5800
   383 N High St Hebron (43025) *(G-10886)*

State Line Resources Inc 330 426-9611
   51545 State Route 154 Negley (44441) *(G-14732)*

State Machine Co Inc 440 248-1050
   30400 Solon Indus Pkwy Cleveland (44139) *(G-6240)*

State Metal Hose Inc 614 527-4700
   4171 Lyman Dr Hilliard (43026) *(G-10982)*

State Molded Plastics Division, Cleveland Also called State Tool and Die Inc *(G-6241)*

State of Ohio Dayton Raceway 937 237-7802
   4701 Wagner Ford Rd Dayton (45414) *(G-8682)*

State Tool and Die Inc 216 267-6030
   4780 Briar Rd Cleveland (44135) *(G-6241)*

State-Mate Company 740 392-9487
   1558 Coshocton Ave Mount Vernon (43050) *(G-14652)*

Stateline Power Corp 937 547-1006
   650 Pine St Greenville (45331) *(G-10524)*

Stationery Shop Inc 330 376-2033
   30 N Summit St Akron (44308) *(G-416)*

Status Mens Accessories 440 232-6700
   7781 First Pl Cleveland (44146) *(G-6242)*

STC International Co Ltd (PA) 561 308-6002
   1499 Shaker Run Blvd Lebanon (45036) *(G-11842)*

Std Specialty Filters Inc 216 881-3727
   837 E 79th St Cleveland (44103) *(G-6243)*

Steam Engine Works LLC 513 813-3690
   2364 Heather Hill Blvd N Cincinnati (45244) *(G-4461)*

Steam Turb Alte Reso 740 387-5535
   116 Latourette St Marion (43302) *(G-12903)*

Stebbins Engineering & Mfg Co 740 922-3012
   4778 Belden Dr Se Uhrichsville (44683) *(G-19060)*

Steck Manufacturing Co Inc 937 222-0062
   1115 S Broadway St Ste 1 Dayton (45417) *(G-8683)*

Steel & Alloy Utility Pdts Inc 330 530-2220
   110 Ohio Ave Mc Donald (44437) *(G-13348)*

Steel Aviation Aircraft Sales 937 332-7587
   4433 E State Route 55 Casstown (45312) *(G-2971)*

Steel Ceilings Inc 740 967-1063
   451 E Coshocton St Ste A Johnstown (43031) *(G-11406)*

Steel City Corporation (PA) 330 792-7663
   1000 Hedstrom Dr Ashland (44805) *(G-779)*

Steel Eqp Specialists Inc 330 829-2626
   22623 Lake Park Blvd Alliance (44601) *(G-539)*

Steel Eqp Specialists Inc (PA) 330 823-8260
   1507 Beeson St Ne Alliance (44601) *(G-540)*

Steel Forming Inc (HQ) 714 532-6321
   1775 Logan Ave Youngstown (44505) *(G-21212)*

Steel Products Corp Akron 330 688-6633
   2288 Samira Rd Stow (44224) *(G-17803)*

Steel Quest Inc 513 772-5030
   8180 Corp Pk Dr Ste 250 Cincinnati (45242) *(G-4462)*

Steel Service Plus Ltd 216 391-9000
   6515 Juniata Ave Cleveland (44103) *(G-6244)*

Steel Services Inc 513 353-4173
   3150 State Line Rd North Bend (45052) *(G-15208)*

Steel Structures of Ohio LLC 330 374-9900
   1324 Firestone Pkwy A Akron (44301) *(G-417)*

Steel Technologies LLC 440 946-8666
   220 Joseph Lloyd Pkwy Willoughby (44094) *(G-20605)*

Steel Technologies LLC 419 523-5199
   740 E Williamstown Rd Ottawa (45875) *(G-15809)*

Steel Valley Sign 330 755-7446
  616 Youngstown Poland Rd Struthers (44471) *(G-17999)*

Steel Valley Tank & Welding 740 598-4994
  24 County Road 7e Brilliant (43913) *(G-2095)*

Steel Warehouse Company LLC 216 206-2800
  4700 Heidtman Pkwy Cleveland (44105) *(G-6245)*

Steel Warehouse Division, Columbus Also called Columbus Pipe and Equipment
Co *(G-6962)*

Steel Warehouse of Ohio LLC 888 225-3760
  3193 Independence Rd Cleveland (44105) *(G-6246)*

Steel Warehouse Ohio, Cleveland Also called Steel Warehouse Company LLC *(G-6245)*

Steelastic Company LLC 330 633-0505
  1 Vision Ln Cuyahoga Falls (44223) *(G-8050)*

Steelcon Inc 330 457-2419
  47287 State Route 558 New Waterford (44445) *(G-14974)*

Steelcon LLC 330 457-4003
  47287 State Route 558 New Waterford (44445) *(G-14975)*

Steeles 5 Acre Mill Inc 419 542-9363
  10860 State Route 2 Hicksville (43526) *(G-10906)*

Steeles Display Cases 740 965-6426
  5665 State Route 605 S Westerville (43082) *(G-20189)*

Steelial Cnstr Met Fabrication, Vinton Also called Steelial Wldg Met Fbrction Inc *(G-19383)*

Steelial Wldg Met Fbrction Inc 740 669-5300
  70764 State Route 124 Vinton (45686) *(G-19383)*

Steeltec Products LLC 216 681-1114
  13000 Saint Clair Ave Cleveland (44108) *(G-6247)*

Steer & Gear Inc 614 231-4064
  1000 Barnett Rd Columbus (43227) *(G-7655)*

Steer & Geer, Columbus Also called Steer & Gear Inc *(G-7655)*

Steer America, Uniontown Also called Steeramerica Inc *(G-19100)*

Steeramerica Inc 330 563-4407
  1525 Corporate Woods Pkwy Uniontown (44685) *(G-19100)*

Stefan Restoration, Cleveland Also called Keban Industries Inc *(G-5639)*

Stefra Inc 440 846-8240
  18021 Cliffside Dr Strongsville (44136) *(G-17973)*

Stegemeyer Machine 513 321-5651
  212 Mccullough St Cincinnati (45226) *(G-4463)*

Stehlin, John & Sons Meats, Cincinnati Also called John Stehlin & Sons Co Inc *(G-3955)*

Stein Inc 440 277-6148
  1807 E 28th St Lorain (44055) *(G-12281)*

Stein Inc (PA) 440 526-9301
  1929 E Royalton Rd Ste C Cleveland (44147) *(G-6248)*

Stein Inc 216 883-7444
  2032 Campbell Rd Cleveland (44105) *(G-6249)*

Stein Inc 419 747-2611
  1490 Old Bowman St Mansfield (44903) *(G-12683)*

Stein Steel Mill Services Inc 440 526-9301
  1929 E Royalton Rd Broadview Heights (44147) *(G-2120)*

Stein-Palmer Printing Co 740 633-3894
  1 Westwood Dr Unit 202 Saint Clairsville (43950) *(G-16809)*

Stein-Way Equipment 330 857-8700
  12335 Emerson Rd Apple Creek (44606) *(G-649)*

Steinbarger Precision Cnc Inc 937 252-0322
  3100 Plainfield Rd Ste A Dayton (45432) *(G-8117)*

Steinbarger Precision Cnc Inc 937 376-0322
  634 Cincinnati Ave Xenia (45385) *(G-20975)*

Steiner Eoptics Inc (PA) 937 426-2341
  3475 Newmark Dr Miamisburg (45342) *(G-13865)*

Steinert Industries Inc 330 678-0028
  1507 Franklin Ave Kent (44240) *(G-11533)*

Stelfast Inc (PA) 440 879-0077
  22979 Stelfast Pkwy Strongsville (44149) *(G-17974)*

Stella Lou LLC 937 935-9536
  3939 Hickory Rock Dr Powell (43065) *(G-16483)*

Stellar I T Co, Lancaster Also called Stellar Industrial Tech Co *(G-11756)*

Stellar Industrial Tech Co 740 654-7052
  1918 York Town Ct Lancaster (43130) *(G-11756)*

Stellar Systems Inc 513 921-8748
  1944 Harrison Ave Cincinnati (45214) *(G-4464)*

Stelter and Brinck Inc 513 367-9300
  201 Sales Ave Harrison (45030) *(G-10805)*

Stencilsmith LLC 614 876-4350
  3001 Stouenburgh Dr Hilliard (43026) *(G-10983)*

Step 2, Streetsboro Also called Step2 Company LLC *(G-17879)*

Step It Up LLC 720 289-1520
  580 N 4th St Columbus (43215) *(G-7656)*

Step2 Company LLC (HQ) 866 429-5200
  10010 Aurora Hudson Rd Streetsboro (44241) *(G-17879)*

Step2 Company LLC 419 938-6343
  2 Step 2 Dr Perrysville (44864) *(G-16176)*

Step2 Holdings LLC 330 656-0440
  10010 Aurora Hudson Rd Streetsboro (44241) *(G-17880)*

Stephen Andrews Inc 330 725-2672
  7634 Lafayette Rd Lodi (44254) *(G-12170)*

Stephen J Page 865 951-3316
  143 Winding Trails Dr Williamsburg (45176) *(G-20412)*

Stephen M Trudick 440 834-1891
  13813 Station Rd Burton (44021) *(G-2385)*

Stephen R Lilley 513 899-4400
  2900 S Waynesville Rd Morrow (45152) *(G-14551)*

Stephen R White 740 522-1512
  800 Hebron Rd Newark (43056) *(G-15057)*

Stephens & Associates Publr, Sandusky Also called Stephens Publishing Co Inc *(G-17010)*

Stephens Pipe & Steel LLC 740 869-2257
  10732 Schadel Ln Mount Sterling (43143) *(G-14604)*

Stephens Publishing Co Inc 419 626-5592
  311 W Perkins Ave Sandusky (44870) *(G-17010)*

Stepp Sewing Service 513 248-0822
  927 State Route 28 Unit B Milford (45150) *(G-14175)*

Stepping Stone Enterprises Inc 419 472-0505
  5847 Secor Rd Toledo (43623) *(G-18703)*

Sterlite Corporation 330 830-2204
  4495 Sterilite St Se Massillon (44646) *(G-13204)*

Steris Corporation 440 352-8724
  9260 Progress Pkwy Mentor (44060) *(G-13731)*

Steris Corporation 440 354-2600
  5900 Heisley Rd Mentor (44060) *(G-13732)*

Steris Corporation 330 686-4550
  1469 Commerce Dr Stow (44224) *(G-17804)*

Steris Corporation (HQ) 440 354-2600
  5960 Heisley Rd Mentor (44060) *(G-13733)*

Steris Corporation 440 354-2600
  6100 Heisley Rd Mentor (44060) *(G-13734)*

Steris Corporation 440 354-2600
  5914 Heisley Rd Mentor (44060) *(G-13735)*

Steris Corporation 440 354-2600
  6515 Hopkins Rd Mentor (44060) *(G-13736)*

Steris Corporation 440 354-2600
  9325 Pinecone Dr Mentor (44060) *(G-13737)*

Steris University, Mentor Also called Steris Corporation *(G-13735)*

Sterling Associates Inc 330 630-3500
  1783 Brittain Rd Akron (44310) *(G-418)*

Sterling Coating 513 942-4900
  9048 Port Union Rialto Rd West Chester (45069) *(G-19949)*

Sterling Collectables Inc 419 892-5708
  862 Pugh Rd Mansfield (44903) *(G-12684)*

Sterling Grinding Company Inc 614 836-3412
  62 High St Carroll (43112) *(G-2947)*

Sterling Industries, Cincinnati Also called Richard B Linneman *(G-4342)*

Sterling Industries Inc 419 523-3788
  740 E Main St Ottawa (45875) *(G-15810)*

Sterling Media, Willoughby Also called A & D Printing Co *(G-20421)*

Sterling Mining Corporation (HQ) 330 549-2165
  10900 South Ave North Lima (44452) *(G-15323)*

Sterling Paper Company Inc 513 242-3678
  960 Deneen Ave Monroe (45050) *(G-14414)*

Sterling Pipe & Tube Inc (PA) 419 729-9756
  5335 Enterprise Blvd Toledo (43612) *(G-18704)*

Steuben Coal-Anthony Min Ltd 740 266-8100
  72 Airport Rd Wintersville (43953) *(G-20714)*

Steubenville Bakery 740 282-6851
  525 South St Steubenville (43952) *(G-17714)*

Steubenville Truck Center Inc 740 282-2711
  620 South St Steubenville (43952) *(G-17715)*

Stevco, Wellsville Also called Stevenson Mfg Co *(G-19775)*

Steve Henderson 419 738-6999
  1311 Lincoln Hwy Wapakoneta (45895) *(G-19508)*

Steve Schaefer 513 792-9911
  9200 Montgomery Rd 23a Cincinnati (45242) *(G-4465)*

Steve Vore Welding and Steel 419 375-4087
  3234 State Route 49 Fort Recovery (45846) *(G-9959)*

Steven Douglas Corp 440 564-5200
  10420 Kinsman Rd Newbury (44065) *(G-15105)*

Steven L Lones 740 452-8851
  3275 Carnation Rd Zanesville (43701) *(G-21357)*

Steven Mercer Inc 740 623-0033
  801 Walnut St Coshocton (43812) *(G-7911)*

Steven Nickel 419 732-3377
  3117 E Shore Dr Port Clinton (43452) *(G-16415)*

Steven Yant 937 596-0497
  103 Jerry Dr Jackson Center (45334) *(G-11348)*

Stevens Auto Glaze and SEC LL 440 953-2900
  36250 Lkeland Blvd Unit 3 Eastlake (44095) *(G-9288)*

Stevens Auto Parts & Towng 740 988-2260
  2848 Big Rock Rd Jackson (45640) *(G-11325)*

Stevens Oil & Gas LLC 740 374-4542
  110 Lynch Church Rd Marietta (45750) *(G-12835)*

Stevens, Mel U-Cart & Rental, Toledo Also called Mel Stevens U-Cart Concrete *(G-18582)*

Stevenson Color Inc 513 321-7500
  535 Wilmer Ave Cincinnati (45226) *(G-4466)*

Stevenson Machine Inc 513 761-4121
  7666 Production Dr Cincinnati (45237) *(G-4467)*

Stevenson Mfg Co 330 532-1581
  1 1st St Wellsville (43968) *(G-19775)*

Steves Sports Inc 440 735-0044
  6442 Metro Ct Ste B Bedford Heights (44146) *(G-1494)*

Steves Vans & Accessories LLC 740 374-3154
  221 Pike St Marietta (45750) *(G-12836)*

Stewart Acquisition LLC 800 376-4466
7955 Euclid Chardon Rd Kirtland (44094) ***(G-11617)***
Stewart Acquisition LLC (PA) 330 963-0322
2146 Enterprise Pkwy Twinsburg (44087) ***(G-19024)***
Stewart Filmscreen Corp 513 753-0800
3919 Bach Buxton Rd Amelia (45102) ***(G-584)***
Stewart Manufacturing Corp 937 390-3333
5230 Prosperity Dr Springfield (45502) ***(G-17657)***
Stewart McDnalds Guitar Sp Sup, Athens *Also called Stewart-Macdonald Mfg Co* ***(G-885)***
Stewart-Macdonald Mfg Co (PA) 740 592-3021
21 N Shafer St Athens (45701) ***(G-885)***
Stewarts Machining Inc 513 422-5000
960 Holman Dr Monroe (45050) ***(G-14415)***
Stick-It Graphics LLC 330 407-0142
3161 Egypt Rd Ne New Philadelphia (44663) ***(G-14930)***
Sticker Corporation (PA) 440 946-2100
37877 Elm St Willoughby (44094) ***(G-20606)***
Sticky Petes Maple Syrup 740 662-2726
18216 S Canaan Rd Athens (45701) ***(G-886)***
Stiers Countertop Sales, Zanesville *Also called Sidney Stiers* ***(G-21353)***
Stiger Pre Cast Inc 740 482-2313
17793 State Highway 231 Nevada (44849) ***(G-14743)***
Stiglers Woodworks 513 733-3009
6 Kovach Dr Ste 600 Cincinnati (45215) ***(G-4468)***
Stillwell D L Equipment Rental, Peninsula *Also called Stillwell Equipment Co Inc* ***(G-16042)***
Stillwell Equipment Co Inc 330 650-1029
5398 Akron Cleveland Rd Peninsula (44264) ***(G-16042)***
Stine Consulting Inc 513 723-4800
120 W 7th St Cincinnati (45202) ***(G-4469)***
Stingray Energy Services (PA) 405 648-4177
42739 National Rd Belmont (43718) ***(G-1580)***
Stingray Pressure Pumping, Belmont *Also called Stingray Energy Services* ***(G-1580)***
Stirling Ultracold, Athens *Also called Global Cooling Inc* ***(G-869)***
Stock Equipment Company, Chagrin Falls *Also called Stock Fairfield Corporation* ***(G-3122)***
Stock Equipment Company Inc (HQ) 440 543-6000
16490 Chillicothe Rd Chagrin Falls (44023) ***(G-3121)***
Stock Fairfield Corporation 440 543-6000
16490 Chillicothe Rd Chagrin Falls (44023) ***(G-3122)***
Stock Mfg & Design Co Inc (PA) 513 353-3600
10040 Cilley Rd Cleves (45002) ***(G-6528)***
Stocker & Sitler Inc 614 888-9588
4770 Indianola Ave Columbus (43214) ***(G-7657)***
Stocker & Sitler Oil Company (HQ) 614 888-9588
4770 Indianola Ave Columbus (43214) ***(G-7658)***
Stocker Concrete Company 740 254-4626
7574 Us Hwy 36 Se Gnadenhutten (44629) ***(G-10411)***
Stocker Sand & Gravel Co (PA) 740 254-4635
Rr 36 Gnadenhutten (44629) ***(G-10412)***
Stoepfel Drilling Co 419 532-3307
12245 State Route 115 Ottawa (45875) ***(G-15811)***
Stoett Industries Inc 419 542-0247
600 Defiance Ave Hicksville (43526) ***(G-10907)***
Stofiel Aerospace LLC 216 389-0084
11115 Lake Ave Apt 309 Cleveland (44102) ***(G-6250)***
Stolle Machinery Company LLC 937 859-4644
7425 Webster St Dayton (45414) ***(G-8684)***
Stolle Machinery Company LLC 937 497-5400
2900 Campbell Rd Sidney (45365) ***(G-17230)***
Stolle Machinery-Sidney, Sidney *Also called Stolle Machinery Company LLC* ***(G-17230)***
Stolle Milk Biologics Inc 513 489-7997
4735 Devitt Dr West Chester (45246) ***(G-20055)***
Stolle Properties Inc 513 932-8664
6954 Cornell Rd Ste 100 Blue Ash (45242) ***(G-1875)***
Stoller Custom Cabinetry 330 939-6555
12573 Frick Rd Sterling (44276) ***(G-17685)***
Stone & Sullivan Industries 513 896-1976
1299 Roundhill Dr Hamilton (45013) ***(G-10742)***
Stone Center of Dayton, Moraine *Also called 3jd Inc* ***(G-14462)***
Stone Statements Incorporated 513 489-7866
7451 Fields Ertel Rd Cincinnati (45241) ***(G-4470)***
Stonebridge Oilfield Svcs LLC 740 373-6134
406 Colegate Dr Marietta (45750) ***(G-12837)***
Stonebridge Operating Co LLC 740 373-6134
1635 Warren Chapel Rd Fleming (45729) ***(G-9914)***
Stonebrook Machine 440 951-5013
1572 E 365th St Eastlake (44095) ***(G-9289)***
Stoneco Inc (HQ) 419 422-8854
1700 Fostoria Ave Ste 200 Findlay (45840) ***(G-9895)***
Stoneco Inc 419 393-2555
13762 Road 179 Oakwood (45873) ***(G-15619)***
Stoneco Inc 419 893-7645
1360 Ford St Maumee (43537) ***(G-13298)***
Stoneco Inc 419 693-3933
352 George Hardy Dr Toledo (43605) ***(G-18705)***
Stoneco Inc 419 686-3311
11580 S Dixie Hwy Portage (43451) ***(G-16428)***
Stonecote, Norton *Also called E L Stone Company* ***(G-15510)***
Stonefruit Coffee Co 330 509-2787
410 W Main St Canfield (44406) ***(G-2577)***
Stoneman Welding, Eastlake *Also called C Stoneman Corporation* ***(G-9261)***
Stoneridge Inc 419 884-1219
345 S Mill St Lexington (44904) ***(G-11953)***
Stoneware Palace Ltd 614 529-6974
3560 Mountshannon Rd Columbus (43221) ***(G-7659)***
Stoneworkd 740 920-4099
1050 Harris Ave Newark (43055) ***(G-15058)***
Stoney Acres Woodworking Llc 440 834-0717
14575 Patch Rd Burton (44021) ***(G-2386)***
Stoney Ridge Farm & Winery, Bryan *Also called Stoney Ridge Winery Ltd* ***(G-2321)***
Stoney Ridge Winery Ltd 419 636-3500
7144 County Road 16 Bryan (43506) ***(G-2321)***
Stony Point Hardwoods 330 852-4512
7842 Stony Point Rd Nw Sugarcreek (44681) ***(G-18040)***
Stony Point Metals LLC 330 852-7100
7820 Stony Point Rd Nw Sugarcreek (44681) ***(G-18041)***
Stop Stick Ltd 513 202-5500
365 Industrial Dr Harrison (45030) ***(G-10806)***
Stopol Equipment Sales LLC 440 499-0030
1321 Industrial Pkwy N # 600 Brunswick (44212) ***(G-2258)***
Storad Label Co 740 382-6440
126 Blaine Ave Marion (43302) ***(G-12904)***
Storage Buildings Unlimited 216 731-0010
12321 Hollow Ridge Rd Doylestown (44230) ***(G-9030)***
Storecom Equipment LLC 800 356-0368
1150 E Dixie Dr Dayton (45449) ***(G-8685)***
Storetek Engineering Inc 330 294-0678
399 Commerce St Tallmadge (44278) ***(G-18170)***
Storopack Inc (HQ) 513 874-0314
4758 Devitt Dr West Chester (45246) ***(G-20056)***
Stouffer Corporation (HQ) 440 349-5757
30003 Bainbridge Rd Solon (44139) ***(G-17387)***
Stoutheart Corporation (PA) 401 434-7640
7205 Chagrin Rd Ste 4 Chagrin Falls (44023) ***(G-3123)***
Stow Sentry, Kent *Also called Record Publishing Co* ***(G-11513)***
STP Products Manufacturing Co 440 352-6176
477 Lexington Ave Painesville (44077) ***(G-15923)***
Straight 72 Inc 740 943-5730
20078 State Route 4 Marysville (43040) ***(G-12973)***
Straight Creek Bushman LLC 513 732-1698
202 E Main St Batavia (45103) ***(G-1226)***
Straight Razor Designes 330 598-1414
23 Public Sq Ste L1 Medina (44256) ***(G-13484)***
Straightaway Fabrications Ltd 419 281-9440
481 Us Highway 250 E Ashland (44805) ***(G-780)***
Strait & Lamp Lumber Co Inc 614 833-6655
5200 Winchester Pike Canal Winchester (43110) ***(G-2537)***
Strasburg Provision Inc 330 878-1059
172 Rosanna Ave Strasburg (44680) ***(G-17830)***
Strassells Machine Inc 419 747-1088
1015 Springmill St Mansfield (44906) ***(G-12685)***
Strata Mine Services Inc 740 695-6880
68000 Bayberry Dr Bldg 2 Saint Clairsville (43950) ***(G-16810)***
Strata Mine Services LLC 740 695-0488
67925 Bayberry Dr Saint Clairsville (43950) ***(G-16811)***
Stratagraph Ne Inc 740 373-3091
116 Ellsworth Ave Marietta (45750) ***(G-12838)***
Strategic Materials Inc 740 349-9523
101 S Arch St Newark (43055) ***(G-15059)***
Strategic Technology Entp 440 354-2600
5960 Heisley Rd Mentor (44060) ***(G-13738)***
Stratton Creek Wood Works LLC 330 876-0005
5915 Burnett East Rd Kinsman (44428) ***(G-11612)***
Strawn Oil Field Service, Salem *Also called Everflow Eastern Partners LP* ***(G-16889)***
Strawser Hydrant Maintenance 614 875-1514
4391 Club Trail Ln Grove City (43123) ***(G-10600)***
Streamline Printing 740 549-0330
650 Radio Dr Lewis Center (43035) ***(G-11921)***
Streamsavvy LLC 614 256-7955
629 N High St Fl 4 Columbus (43215) ***(G-7660)***
Streamside Materials Llc 419 423-1290
7440 Township Road 95 Findlay (45840) ***(G-9896)***
Streetsboro Operations, Twinsburg *Also called Facil North America Inc* ***(G-18934)***
Streicher's Quickprint, Findlay *Also called Streichers Enterprises Inc* ***(G-9897)***
Streichers Enterprises Inc 419 423-8606
109 S Main St Findlay (45840) ***(G-9897)***
Stress-Crete Company 440 576-9073
1153 State Route 46 N Jefferson (44047) ***(G-11372)***
Stresscrete, Jefferson *Also called King Luminaire Company Inc* ***(G-11365)***
Stretcher Pad Company, The, Valley City *Also called S K M L Inc* ***(G-19228)***
Stretchtape Inc 216 486-9400
3100 Hamilton Ave Cleveland (44114) ***(G-6251)***
Strib Industries Inc 216 281-1155
6400 Herman Ave Cleveland (44102) ***(G-6252)***
Stricker Refinishing Inc 216 696-2906
2060 Hamilton Ave Cleveland (44114) ***(G-6253)***
Stricodynarad Corp 330 239-0005
605 Ledge Rd Hinckley (44233) ***(G-11029)***

Strictly Stitchery Inc...440 543-7128
13801 Shaker Blvd Apt 4a Cleveland (44120) *(G-6254)*
Stride Tool LLC..440 247-4600
30333 Emerald Valley Pkwy Solon (44139) *(G-17388)*
Striker Hydraulic Breakers, Willoughby *Also called Toku America Inc (G-20618)*
Stripmatic Products Inc..216 241-7143
5301 Grant Ave Ste 200 Cleveland (44125) *(G-6255)*
Strohecker Incorporated..330 426-9496
213 N Pleasant Dr East Palestine (44413) *(G-9245)*
Strong Bindery...216 231-0001
13015 Larchmere Blvd Cleveland (44120) *(G-6256)*
Strong M Llc...614 329-8025
2046 Leonard Ave Columbus (43219) *(G-7661)*
Strongbasics LLC..716 903-6151
35 E Gay St Ste 322 Columbus (43215) *(G-7662)*
Strongberg Hydramite, Carey *Also called Carl Hucke (G-2916)*
Strouse Industries Inc...440 257-2520
8090 Danbury Ct Mentor (44060) *(G-13739)*
Structural Steel Fabrication, Pataskala *Also called Ohio Steel Industries Inc (G-15975)*
Struers Inc (HQ)...440 871-0071
24766 Detroit Rd Westlake (44145) *(G-20313)*
Struktol Company America LLC (PA).........................330 928-5188
201 E Steels Corners Rd Stow (44224) *(G-17805)*
Strutt Products LLC..330 889-2727
6340 State Route 45 Cd Bristolville (44402) *(G-2100)*
Stryker Energy LLC...440 446-9214
6690 Beta Dr Ste 214 Cleveland (44143) *(G-6257)*
Stryker Plant, Stryker *Also called Sauder Manufacturing Co (G-18007)*
Stryker Steel Tube LLC...419 682-4527
100 Railroad Ave Stryker (43557) *(G-18008)*
Stryker Welding..419 682-2301
104 W Mulberry St Stryker (43557) *(G-18009)*
Stryver Mfg Inc...937 854-3048
15 N Broadway St Trotwood (45426) *(G-18799)*
Stuart Burial Vault Company...................................740 569-4158
527 Ford St Bremen (43107) *(G-2080)*
Stuart Company..513 621-9462
2160 Patterson St Cincinnati (45214) *(G-4471)*
Stuchell Products LLC..330 821-4299
14600 Commerce St Ne Alliance (44601) *(G-541)*
Stud Welding Associates, Strongsville *Also called Spiegelberg Manufacturing Inc (G-17970)*
Studio Arts & Glass Inc...330 494-9779
7495 Strauss Ave Nw Canton (44720) *(G-2860)*
Studio Eleven Inc (PA)..937 295-2225
301 S Main St Fort Loramie (45845) *(G-9941)*
Studio Foundry, Cleveland *Also called Foundry Artist Inc (G-5375)*
Studio Vertu Inc..513 241-9038
1208 Central Pkwy 1 Cincinnati (45202) *(G-4472)*
Studs N Hip Hop...614 477-0786
2032 E Hudson St Columbus (43211) *(G-7663)*
Stuebing Automatic Machine Co...............................513 771-8028
2518 Leslie Ave Cincinnati (45212) *(G-4473)*
Stull Woodworks..937 698-8181
7925 Fenner Rd Ludlow Falls (45339) *(G-12428)*
Stumbo Publishing Co...419 529-2847
347 Allen Dr Ontario (44906) *(G-15695)*
Stumps Converting Inc..419 492-2542
742 W Mansfield St New Washington (44854) *(G-14965)*
Stumptown Lbr Pallet Mills Ltd.................................740 757-2275
55613 Washington St Somerton (43713) *(G-17421)*
Stutzman Brothers Sawmill.....................................440 272-5179
15991 Nauvoo Rd Middlefield (44062) *(G-13992)*
Stutzman Manufacturing Ltd...................................330 674-4359
7727 Township Road 604 Millersburg (44654) *(G-14265)*
Style Crest Inc (HQ)...419 332-7369
2450 Enterprise St Fremont (43420) *(G-10184)*
Style Crest Enterprises Inc (PA)..............................419 355-8586
2450 Enterprise St Fremont (43420) *(G-10185)*
Style-Line Incorporated (PA)...................................614 291-0600
901 W 3rd Ave Ste A Columbus (43212) *(G-7664)*
Styner+bienz US Inc...216 362-1850
12200 Brookpark Rd Cleveland (44130) *(G-6258)*
Suarez Corporation Industries.................................330 494-4282
7800 Whipple Ave Nw Canton (44767) *(G-2861)*
Suarez Corporation Industries.................................330 494-5504
7800 Whipple Ave Nw Canton (44767) *(G-2862)*
Sub of Manitowoc Company, Cleveland *Also called Cleveland Range LLC (G-5074)*
Suburban Communications Inc................................440 632-0130
14905 N State Ave Middlefield (44062) *(G-13993)*
Suburban Electronics Assembly...............................330 483-4077
7877 Grafton Rd Valley City (44280) *(G-19236)*
Suburban Manufacturing Co....................................440 953-2024
1924 E 337th St Eastlake (44095) *(G-9290)*
Suburban Marble and Granite Co.............................216 281-5557
7818 Lake Ave Cleveland (44102) *(G-6259)*
Suburban Metal Products Inc...................................740 474-4237
1050 Tarlton Rd Circleville (43113) *(G-4644)*
Suburban Newpapers of Dayton...............................937 236-4990
7089 Taylorsville Rd A Dayton (45424) *(G-8686)*

Suburban Newpapers of Dayton...............................937 878-3993
1836 W Park Sq Xenia (45385) *(G-20976)*
Suburban Newpapers of Dayton...............................937 294-7000
694 W National Rd Vandalia (45377) *(G-19311)*
Suburban Press Inc...216 961-0766
3818 Lorain Ave Cleveland (44113) *(G-6260)*
Suburban Steel of Indiana, Columbus *Also called Suburban Stl Sup Co Ltd Partnr (G-7665)*
Suburban Stl Sup Co Ltd Partnr...............................317 783-6555
1900 Deffenbaugh Ct Columbus (43230) *(G-7665)*
Subway, Circleville *Also called Circleville Oil Co (G-4625)*
Success Pro Publications.......................................614 497-5674
3137 Houston Dr Columbus (43207) *(G-7666)*
Success Technologies Inc......................................614 761-0008
324 W Case St Powell (43065) *(G-16484)*
Suds..937 273-6007
160 Main Cross Eldorado (45321) *(G-9348)*
Suever Stone Company (PA)....................................419 331-1945
706 E Main St Lima (45807) *(G-12097)*
Sugar Creek Packing Co (PA)..................................740 335-7440
2101 Kenskill Ave Wshngtn CT Hs (43160) *(G-20927)*
Sugar Creek Packing Co...937 268-6601
1241 N Gettysburg Ave Dayton (45417) *(G-8687)*
Sugar Creek Packing Co...513 874-4422
4235 Thunderbird Ln West Chester (45014) *(G-19950)*
Sugar Creek Packing Co...513 874-4422
4585 Muhlhauser Rd West Chester (45011) *(G-19951)*
Sugar Shack...419 961-4016
4703 Flowers Rd Mansfield (44903) *(G-12686)*
Sugar Showcase...330 792-9154
1725 S Raccoon Rd Youngstown (44515) *(G-21213)*
Sugarbush Creek Farm...440 636-5371
13034 Madison Rd Middlefield (44062) *(G-13994)*
Sugarcreek Budget Publishers................................330 852-4634
134 Factory St Ne Sugarcreek (44681) *(G-18042)*
Sugarcreek Lime Service..330 364-4460
2068 Gordon Rd Nw Dover (44622) *(G-9019)*
Sugarcreek Pallett..330 852-9812
681 Belden Pkwy Ne Sugarcreek (44681) *(G-18043)*
Sugarcreek Ready Mix, Bellbrook *Also called Ernst Enterprises Inc (G-1507)*
Sugarcreek Shavings LLC.......................................330 763-4239
3121 Winklepleck Rd Nw Sugarcreek (44681) *(G-18044)*
Sugars Sweets Ltd..513 936-0104
10752 Jeff Ln Cincinnati (45241) *(G-4474)*
Sugartree Square Mercantile...................................740 345-3882
5541 Grumms Ln Ne Newark (43055) *(G-15060)*
Suite Solutions Technologies, Toledo *Also called Marrik Dish Company LLC (G-18574)*
Sulecki Precision Products......................................440 255-5454
8785 East Ave Mentor (44060) *(G-13740)*
Sullivan Company, The, Westerville *Also called Bluelogos Inc (G-20203)*
Sulmona Enegry LLC..234 736-3749
46 N Phelps St Youngstown (44503) *(G-21214)*
Sulo Enterprises Inc..440 926-3322
1017 Commerce Dr Grafton (44044) *(G-10437)*
Sulzer Transmission Tech.......................................937 449-4000
260 Detrick St Dayton (45404) *(G-8688)*
Sumiriko Ohio Inc (HQ)..419 358-2121
320 Snider Rd Bluffton (45817) *(G-1916)*
Sumitomo Elc Carbide Mfg Inc (HQ).........................440 354-0600
210 River St Grand River (44045) *(G-10453)*
Sumitomo Elc Wirg Systems Inc...............................937 642-7579
14800 Industrial Pkwy Marysville (43040) *(G-12974)*
Sumitomo Rubber Usa LLC....................................419 347-1067
31 Curtis Dr Shelby (44875) *(G-17144)*
Summa Holdings Inc (PA)......................................440 838-4700
8223 Brecksville Rd # 100 Cleveland (44141) *(G-6261)*
Summco Inc..330 965-7446
6981 Southern Blvd Ste D Youngstown (44512) *(G-21215)*
Summer Garden Food Mfg, Boardman *Also called Zidian Manufacturing Inc (G-1926)*
Summer Global Systems LLC...................................330 397-1653
115 Creed Cir Campbell (44405) *(G-2492)*
Summers Acquisition Corp (HQ)..............................216 941-7700
12555 Berea Rd Cleveland (44111) *(G-6262)*
Summers Acquisition Corp......................................419 526-5800
10 W Piper Rd Mansfield (44903) *(G-12687)*
Summers Acquisition Corp......................................419 423-5800
16406 E Us Route 224 Findlay (45840) *(G-9898)*
Summers Acquisition Corp......................................740 373-0303
100 Tennis Center Dr Marietta (45750) *(G-12839)*
Summers Acquisition Corp......................................440 946-5611
1857 E 337th St Unit B Eastlake (44095) *(G-9291)*
Summers Organization LLC....................................740 286-1322
345 E Main St Ste H Jackson (45640) *(G-11326)*
Summers Rubber Co Branch 06, Marietta *Also called Summers Acquisition Corp (G-12839)*
Summers Rubber Company, Cleveland *Also called Summers Acquisition Corp (G-6262)*
Summit Aerospace Products....................................330 612-7341
159 Ballantrae Dr Northfield (44067) *(G-15473)*
Summit Avionics Inc..330 425-1440
2225 E Entp Pkwy 1a 1 A Twinsburg (44087) *(G-19025)*

A
L
P
H
A
B
E
T
I
C

Summit Custom Cabinets 740 345-1734
10430 Hoover Rd Ne Newark (43055) ***(G-15061)***
Summit Diagnostic Imaging LLC 513 233-3320
7755 5 Mile Rd Cincinnati (45230) ***(G-4475)***
Summit Drilling Company Inc 800 775-5537
152 W Dartmore Ave Akron (44301) ***(G-419)***
Summit Engineered Products 330 854-5388
516 Elm Ridge Ave Canal Fulton (44614) ***(G-2514)***
Summit Ethanol LLC 419 943-7447
3875 State Rd 65 Leipsic (45856) ***(G-11877)***
Summit Finishing Technologies 937 424-5512
2490 Arbor Blvd Unit B Moraine (45439) ***(G-14533)***
Summit Machine Ltd 330 628-2663
3991 Mogadore Rd Mogadore (44260) ***(G-14386)***
Summit Millwork LLC 330 920-4000
1619 Main St Cuyahoga Falls (44221) ***(G-8051)***
Summit Online Products LLC 800 326-1972
3982 Powell Rd Ste 137 Powell (43065) ***(G-16485)***
Summit Packaging Center, Toledo *Also called Hearthside Food Solutions LLC* ***(G-18500)***
Summit Petroleum Inc 330 487-5494
8815 Herrick Rd Twinsburg (44087) ***(G-19026)***
Summit Plastic Company (PA) 330 633-3668
1169 Brittain Rd Akron (44305) ***(G-420)***
Summit Printing & Graphics 330 645-7644
1265 W Waterloo Rd Akron (44314) ***(G-421)***
Summit Printing and Graphics, Akron *Also called Summit Printing & Graphics* ***(G-421)***
Summit Research Group 330 689-1778
4466 Darrow Rd Ste 15 Stow (44224) ***(G-17806)***
Summit Resources Group Inc 330 653-3992
7476 Whitemarsh Way Hudson (44236) ***(G-11203)***
Summit Street News Inc 330 609-5600
645 Summit St Nw Warren (44485) ***(G-19602)***
Summit Tool Company (HQ) 330 535-7177
768 E North St Akron (44305) ***(G-422)***
Summit Trailer Sales & Svcs, Akron *Also called Friess Welding Inc* ***(G-195)***
Summit Well Services Inc 330 223-1074
28050 Speidel Rd East Rochester (44625) ***(G-9251)***
Summitville Lab, Minerva *Also called Summitville Tiles Inc* ***(G-14344)***
Summitville Tiles Inc 330 868-6771
1310 Alliance Rd Nw Minerva (44657) ***(G-14343)***
Summitville Tiles Inc 330 868-6463
81 Arbor Rd Ne Minerva (44657) ***(G-14344)***
Sun & Soil LLC 513 575-5900
1357 State Route 28 Loveland (45140) ***(G-12391)***
Sun Art Decals Inc 440 234-9045
83 Dorland Ave Berea (44017) ***(G-1636)***
Sun Chemical Corporation 513 671-0407
12049 Centron Pl Cincinnati (45246) ***(G-4476)***
Sun Chemical Corporation 513 681-5950
4526 Chickering Ave Cincinnati (45232) ***(G-4477)***
Sun Chemical Corporation 419 891-3514
1380 Ford St Maumee (43537) ***(G-13299)***
Sun Chemical Corporation 513 753-9550
3922 Bach Buxton Rd Amelia (45102) ***(G-585)***
Sun Chemical Corporation 513 681-5950
5020 Spring Grove Ave Cincinnati (45232) ***(G-4478)***
Sun Chemical Corporation 937 743-8055
125 Jaygee Dr Franklin (45005) ***(G-10055)***
Sun Chemical Corporation 513 771-4030
600 Redna Ter Cincinnati (45215) ***(G-4479)***
Sun Chemical Corporation 513 681-5950
5020 Spring Grove Ave Cincinnati (45232) ***(G-4480)***
Sun Chemical Corporation 513 830-8667
5000 Spring Grove Ave Cincinnati (45232) ***(G-4481)***
Sun Cleaners & Laundry Inc 740 756-4749
3739 Old Columbus Rd Nw Carroll (43112) ***(G-2948)***
Sun Communities Inc 740 548-1942
5277 Columbus Pike Lewis Center (43035) ***(G-11922)***
Sun Drenched Art Studios 513 375-9612
4277 Alex Ave Cincinnati (45211) ***(G-4482)***
Sun Microsystems, Blue Ash *Also called Oracle America Inc* ***(G-1848)***
Sun Newspaper Div, Cleveland *Also called Comcorp Inc* ***(G-5102)***
Sun Polishing Corp 440 237-5525
13800 Progress Pkwy Ste E Cleveland (44133) ***(G-6263)***
Sun Rush Water, Piketon *Also called Your Bottled Water LLC* ***(G-16230)***
Sun Shine Awards 740 425-2504
36099 Bethesda Street Ext Barnesville (43713) ***(G-1161)***
Sun State Plastics Inc 330 494-5220
4045 Kevin St Nw Canton (44720) ***(G-2863)***
Sunamericaconverting LLC 330 821-6300
46 N Rockhill Ave Alliance (44601) ***(G-542)***
Sunbeam Products Co LLC 419 691-1551
623 Main St Toledo (43605) ***(G-18706)***
Sunbright Usa Inc 440 205-0600
8909 East Ave Mentor (44060) ***(G-13741)***
Sunburst Light Corp America 419 886-3786
848 State Route 97 E Bellville (44813) ***(G-1576)***
Suncoke Energy Nc 513 727-5571
3353 Yankee Rd Middletown (45044) ***(G-14086)***
Suncolor Corporation 330 499-7010
1325 Irondale Cir Ne North Canton (44720) ***(G-15270)***
Sunday School Software 614 527-8776
4369 Brickwood Dr Hilliard (43026) ***(G-10984)***
Sunfield Inc 740 928-0404
116 Enterprise Dr Hebron (43025) ***(G-10887)***
Sunforest Vision Center Inc 419 475-4646
3915 Sunforest Ct Ste A Toledo (43623) ***(G-18707)***
Sunjoy Industries Group Inc (PA) 740 283-2815
619 Slack St Steubenville (43952) ***(G-17716)***
Sunless Inc (HQ) 440 836-0199
8909 Freeway Dr Ste A Macedonia (44056) ***(G-12491)***
Sunline Supply, Powell *Also called Success Technologies Inc* ***(G-16484)***
Sunnest Service LLC 740 283-2815
619 Slack St Steubenville (43952) ***(G-17717)***
Sunny Brook Pressed Con Co 330 673-7667
3586 Sunnybrook Rd Kent (44240) ***(G-11534)***
Sunny Delight Beverage Co (HQ) 513 483-3300
10300 Alliance Rd Ste 500 Blue Ash (45242) ***(G-1876)***
Sunny Side Feeds LLC 330 635-1455
6371 W Pleasant Home Rd West Salem (44287) ***(G-20117)***
Sunny Side Meats 419 387-7812
505 S Buffalo St Vanlue (45890) ***(G-19320)***
Sunoco Inc 216 912-2579
1375 Home Ave Akron (44310) ***(G-423)***
Sunpower Inc 740 594-2221
2005 E State St Ste 104 Athens (45701) ***(G-887)***
Sunprene Company 330 666-3751
3550 W Market St Fairlawn (44333) ***(G-9762)***
Sunrise Cooperative Inc 419 629-2338
435 S Herman St New Bremen (45869) ***(G-14794)***
Sunrise Cooperative Inc 419 929-1568
1981 Fitchville River Rd Wakeman (44889) ***(G-19453)***
Sunrise Cooperative Inc 419 628-4705
292 W 4th St Minster (45865) ***(G-14362)***
Sunrise Cooperative Inc 419 683-4600
3000 W Bucyrus St Crestline (44827) ***(G-7936)***
Sunrise Foods Inc 614 276-2880
1157 Baumock Burn Dr Columbus (43235) ***(G-7667)***
Sunset Golf LLC 419 994-5563
71 West Ave Ste 6 Tallmadge (44278) ***(G-18171)***
Sunset Industries Inc 216 731-8131
1272 E 286th St Euclid (44132) ***(G-9607)***
Sunset Metal Roofing, Pierpont *Also called Neal Miller* ***(G-16214)***
Sunshine Farms Dairy, Elyria *Also called Consun Food Industries Inc* ***(G-9397)***
Sunshine Performance Glass Inc 330 562-8600
1455 Danner Dr Aurora (44202) ***(G-948)***
Sunshine Products 303 478-4913
760 Warehouse Rd Ste O Toledo (43615) ***(G-18708)***
Sunstar Engrg Americas Inc 937 743-9049
700 Watkins Glen Dr Franklin (45005) ***(G-10056)***
Sunstar Engrg Americas Inc (HQ) 937 746-8575
85 S Pioneer Blvd Springboro (45066) ***(G-17508)***
Sunstar Sprockets, Franklin *Also called Sunstar Engrg Americas Inc* ***(G-10056)***
Suntan Supply, Avon *Also called JLW - TW Corp* ***(G-998)***
Suntwist Corp 800 935-3534
5461 Dunham Rd Maple Heights (44137) ***(G-12741)***
Sup-R-Die Inc 330 688-7600
1337 Commerce Dr Ste 3 Stow (44224) ***(G-17807)***
Super Fine Shine Inc 740 774-1700
2806 Patton Hill Rd Lot 6 Chillicothe (45601) ***(G-3279)***
Super Inn.com, Cleveland *Also called Sark Technologies LLC* ***(G-6160)***
Super Sheet Metal 330 482-9045
40811 Bonesville Schl Rd Leetonia (44431) ***(G-11866)***
Super Sign Guys LLC 330 477-3887
5060 Navarre Rd Sw Ste C Canton (44706) ***(G-2864)***
Super Signs Inc 480 968-2200
9890 Mount Nebo Rd North Bend (45052) ***(G-15209)***
Super Systems Inc (PA) 513 772-0060
7205 Edington Dr Cincinnati (45249) ***(G-4483)***
Superb Industries Inc 330 852-0500
330 3rd St Nw Sugarcreek (44681) ***(G-18045)***
Supercharger Systems Inc 216 676-5800
5300 W 140th St Brookpark (44142) ***(G-2170)***
Superfine Manufacturing Inc 330 897-9024
33715 County Road 10 Fresno (43824) ***(G-10199)***
Superfinishers Inc 330 467-2125
380 Highland Rd E Macedonia (44056) ***(G-12492)***
Superion Inc 937 374-0033
1285 S Patton St Xenia (45385) ***(G-20977)***
Superior Ag-Patoka Vlly Feed 419 294-3838
7148 State Highway 199 Upper Sandusky (43351) ***(G-19142)***
Superior Bar Products Inc 419 784-2590
1710 Spruce St Defiance (43512) ***(G-8811)***
Superior Clay Corp 740 922-4122
6566 Superior Rd Se Uhrichsville (44683) ***(G-19061)***
Superior Cup Inc 330 393-6187
448 E Market St Warren (44481) ***(G-19603)***
Superior Energy Systems LLC 440 236-6009
13660 Station Rd Columbia Station (44028) ***(G-6601)***

Superior Fibers Inc 740 394-2491
9702 Iron Point Rd Se Shawnee (43782) *(G-17117)*

Superior Flux & Mfg Co 440 349-3000
6615 Parkland Blvd Cleveland (44139) *(G-6264)*

Superior Forge & Steel Corp (PA) 419 222-4412
1820 Mcclain Rd Lima (45804) *(G-12098)*

Superior Hardwoods Cambridge, Cambridge *Also called Superior Hardwoods Ohio Inc (G-2477)*

Superior Hardwoods of Ohio 740 596-2561
62581 Us Highway 50 Mc Arthur (45651) *(G-13333)*

Superior Hardwoods of Ohio 740 384-6862
78 Jackson Hill Rd Jackson (45640) *(G-11327)*

Superior Hardwoods Ohio Inc (PA) 740 384-5677
134 Wellston Indus Pk Rd Wellston (45692) *(G-19770)*

Superior Hardwoods Ohio Inc 740 439-2727
9911 Ohio Ave Cambridge (43725) *(G-2477)*

Superior Holding LLC (HQ) 216 651-9400
3786 Ridge Rd Cleveland (44144) *(G-6265)*

Superior Image Llc 513 771-4565
11875 Kemper Springs Dr Cincinnati (45240) *(G-4484)*

Superior Impressions Inc 419 244-8676
327 12th St Toledo (43604) *(G-18709)*

Superior Label Systems Inc (HQ) 513 336-0825
7500 Industrial Row Dr Mason (45040) *(G-13092)*

Superior Machine and Tool 937 308-5771
7726 Crowl Rd De Graff (43318) *(G-8770)*

Superior Machine Co, Canton *Also called Robert Smart Inc (G-2841)*

Superior Machine Systems, Mason *Also called Superior Label Systems Inc (G-13092)*

Superior Machine Tool Inc 419 675-2363
13606 Us Highway 68 Kenton (43326) *(G-11571)*

Superior Machining Inc 937 236-9619
2946 Lindale Ave Dayton (45414) *(G-8689)*

Superior Marine Ways Inc (PA) 740 894-6224
5852 County Road 1 South Point (45680) *(G-17448)*

Superior Marine Ways Inc 740 894-6224
5852 County Rd 1 Suoth Pt Proctorville (45669) *(G-16493)*

Superior Metal Products, Lima *Also called American Trim LLC (G-11989)*

Superior Metal Products Inc (PA) 419 228-1145
1005 W Grand Ave Lima (45801) *(G-12099)*

Superior Mold & Die Co 330 688-8251
449 N Main St Munroe Falls (44262) *(G-14666)*

Superior Packaging 419 380-3335
2930 Airport Hwy Toledo (43609) *(G-18710)*

Superior Paving, Canton *Also called Canton Asphalt Co (G-2636)*

Superior Pneumatic & Mfg Inc 440 871-8780
855 Canterbury Rd Cleveland (44145) *(G-6266)*

Superior Precision Products 216 881-3696
968 E 69th Pl Cleveland (44103) *(G-6267)*

Superior Printing and Off Sup, Dayton *Also called SPAOS Inc (G-8666)*

Superior Printing Ink Co Inc 513 221-4707
10861 Millington Ct Ste B Blue Ash (45242) *(G-1877)*

Superior Printing Ink Co Inc 216 328-1720
7655 Hub Pkwy Ste 205 Cleveland (44125) *(G-6268)*

Superior Products Llc 216 651-9400
3786 Ridge Rd Cleveland (44144) *(G-6269)*

Superior Products LLC 216 651-9400
3786 Ridge Rd Cleveland (44144) *(G-6270)*

Superior Quality Machine Co 330 527-7146
10500 Industrial Dr Garrettsville (44231) *(G-10333)*

Superior Soda Service LLC 937 657-9700
3626 Napanee Dr Beavercreek (45430) *(G-1381)*

Superior Steel Service LLC 513 724-0437
2760 Old State Route 32 Batavia (45103) *(G-1227)*

Superior Steel Stamp Co 216 431-6460
3200 Lakeside Ave E Cleveland (44114) *(G-6271)*

Superior Structures Inc 513 942-5954
320 N State St Harrison (45030) *(G-10807)*

Superior Tasting Products Inc 614 442-0622
2555 Bethel Rd Columbus (43220) *(G-7668)*

Superior Trim, Findlay *Also called Pieco Inc (G-9878)*

Superior Trim, Bloomdale *Also called Bloomdale Plastics Co (G-1719)*

Superior Trims Springfield Div, Springfield *Also called Pieco Inc (G-17628)*

Superior Water Conditioning Co, Moraine *Also called Enting Water Conditioning Inc (G-14484)*

Superior Weld and Fabg Co Inc 216 249-5122
15002 Woodworth Rd Cleveland (44110) *(G-6272)*

Superior Welding Co 614 252-8539
906 S Nelson Rd Columbus (43205) *(G-7669)*

Superior's Brand Meats, Massillon *Also called Fresh Mark Inc (G-13135)*

Supermedia LLC 614 216-6566
470 Olde Worthington Rd Westerville (43082) *(G-20190)*

Superprinter Inc 440 277-0787
1925 N Ridge Rd E Lorain (44055) *(G-12282)*

Superprinter Ltd 440 277-0787
1901 N Ridge Rd E Lorain (44055) *(G-12283)*

Supertrapp Industries Inc 216 265-8400
4540 W 160th St Cleveland (44135) *(G-6273)*

Supplier Inspection Svcs Inc (PA) 937 263-7097
2941 S Gettysburg Ave Dayton (45439) *(G-8690)*

Supplier Park Industries LLC 440 476-1244
2890 Boston Mills Rd Brecksville (44141) *(G-2074)*

Supply Dynamics LLC 513 965-2000
6279 Tr Rdge Blvd Ste 310 Loveland (45140) *(G-12392)*

Supply International Inc 740 282-8604
602 Kingsdale Rd Ste 1 Steubenville (43952) *(G-17718)*

Supply Technologies LLC 614 759-9939
590 Claycraft Rd Columbus (43230) *(G-7670)*

Supply Technologies LLC (HQ) 440 947-2100
6065 Parkland Blvd Ste 1 Cleveland (44124) *(G-6274)*

Supply Technologies LLC 740 363-1971
700 London Rd Delaware (43015) *(G-8891)*

Support Service, Lexington *Also called Support Svc LLC (G-11954)*

Support Svc LLC 419 617-0660
25 Walnut St Rear Lexington (44904) *(G-11954)*

Supreme Fan/Industrial Air, Dayton *Also called Lau Industries Inc (G-8110)*

Supro Spring & Wire Forms Inc 330 722-5628
6440 Norwalk Rd Ste N Medina (44256) *(G-13485)*

Sur-Seal Corporation (PA) 513 574-8500
6156 Wesselman Rd Cincinnati (45248) *(G-4485)*

Sur-Seal Corporation 513 574-8500
10053 Simonson Rd Harrison (45030) *(G-10808)*

Sur-Seal Gasket & Packing, Cincinnati *Also called Sur-Seal Corporation (G-4485)*

Sure To Grow, Beachwood *Also called 6062 Holdings LLC (G-1252)*

Sure Tool & Manufacturing Co 937 253-9111
429 Winston Ave Dayton (45403) *(G-8691)*

Sure-Foot Industries Corp 440 234-4446
20260 1st Ave Cleveland (44130) *(G-6275)*

Surenergy LLC 419 626-8000
319 Howard Dr Sandusky (44870) *(G-17011)*

Surface Combustion Inc (PA) 419 891-7150
1700 Indian Wood Cir Maumee (43537) *(G-13300)*

Surface Dynamics Inc 513 772-6635
231 Northland Blvd Cincinnati (45246) *(G-4486)*

Surface Enhancement Tech LLC 513 561-1520
3929 Virginia Ave Cincinnati (45227) *(G-4487)*

Surface Enterprises Inc 419 476-5670
1465 W Alexis Rd Toledo (43612) *(G-18711)*

Surface Recovery Tech LLC 937 879-5864
833 Zapata Dr Fairborn (45324) *(G-9631)*

Surface Systems, Akron *Also called Cto Inc (G-134)*

Surface-All Inc 440 428-2233
745 N Hidden Harbor Dr Port Clinton (43452) *(G-16416)*

Surftech, Austinburg *Also called Euclid Refinishing Compnay Inc (G-960)*

Surftech Inc 440 275-3356
2937 Industrial Park Dr Austinburg (44010) *(G-967)*

Surgical Appliance Inds Inc (PA) 513 271-4594
3960 Rosslyn Dr Cincinnati (45209) *(G-4488)*

Surgical Appliance Inds Inc 937 392-4301
1311 S 2nd St Ripley (45167) *(G-16671)*

Surgical Theater LLC (PA) 216 452-2177
781 Beta Dr Ste A Mayfield Village (44143) *(G-13327)*

Surgical Theater LLC 216 496-7884
4541 Greenwold Rd Cleveland (44121) *(G-6276)*

Surgrx Inc 650 482-2400
4545 Creek Rd Blue Ash (45242) *(G-1878)*

Surplus Freight Inc (PA) 614 235-7660
501 Morrison Rd Ste 100 Gahanna (43230) *(G-10237)*

Surtec Inc 440 239-9710
3097 Interstate Pkwy Brunswick (44212) *(G-2259)*

Surveying Cannon Land 740 342-2835
7945 Township Road 114 Ne New Lexington (43764) *(G-14856)*

Survitec Group (usa) Inc (HQ) 330 239-4331
1420 Wolfcreek Trl Sharon Center (44274) *(G-17111)*

Susan Products, Cleveland *Also called Mystic Chemical Products Co (G-5846)*

Sushi On The Roll, Medina *Also called Jroll LLC (G-13430)*

Suspension Feeder, Fort Recovery *Also called Roessner Holdings Inc (G-9958)*

Suspension Feeder Corporation 419 763-1377
482 State Route 119 Fort Recovery (45846) *(G-9960)*

Suspension Technology Inc 330 458-3058
1424 Scales St Sw Canton (44706) *(G-2865)*

Sutphen Corporation (PA) 800 726-7030
6450 Eiterman Rd Dublin (43016) *(G-9150)*

Sutphen Corporation 937 969-8851
1701 W County Line Rd Springfield (45502) *(G-17658)*

Sutterlin Machine & Tool Co 440 357-0817
9445 Pineneedle Dr Mentor (44060) *(G-13742)*

Suzin L Chocolatiers 440 323-3372
230 Broad St Elyria (44035) *(G-9496)*

Suzuki of Toleda, Toledo *Also called Customers Car Care Center (G-18419)*

Svm America Ltd 937 218-7591
1004 River Forest Dr Maineville (45039) *(G-12532)*

Swagelok (HQ) 440 349-5657
29500 Solon Rd Solon (44139) *(G-17389)*

Swagelok Biopharm Services Co, Willoughby Hills *Also called Swagelok Company (G-20645)*

Swagelok Company (PA) 440 248-4600
29500 Solon Rd Solon (44139) *(G-17390)*

Swagelok Company 440 349-5652
6100 Cochran Rd Solon (44139) *(G-17391)*

Swagelok Company 440 248-4600
26653 Curtiss Wright Pkwy Willoughby Hills (44092) *(G-20644)*

Swagelok Company 440 944-8988
26651 Curtiss Wright Pkwy Willoughby Hills (44092) *(G-20645)*

Swagelok Company 440 442-6611
328 Bishop Rd Cleveland (44143) *(G-6277)*

Swagelok Company 440 473-1050
318 Bishop Rd Cleveland (44143) *(G-6278)*

Swagelok Company 440 461-7714
358 Bishop Rd Cleveland (44143) *(G-6279)*

Swagelok Company 440 349-5934
31400 Aurora Rd Solon (44139) *(G-17392)*

Swagelok Company 440 349-5836
6262 Cochran Rd Solon (44139) *(G-17393)*

Swagelok Company 440 542-1250
32550 Old South Miles Rd Solon (44139) *(G-17394)*

Swagelok Hy-Level Company (PA) 440 238-1260
15400 Foltz Pkwy Strongsville (44149) *(G-17975)*

Swagelok Manufacturing Co LLC 440 248-4600
29500 Solon Rd Solon (44139) *(G-17395)*

Swagg Productions2015llc 614 815-1173
2003 Chalfield Ct Reynoldsburg (43068) *(G-16608)*

Swanson Industries Inc 304 284-5199
464 Robinson Dr Se New Philadelphia (44663) *(G-14931)*

Swanson Orthotic & Prosthetic 419 690-0026
3048 Navarre Ave Oregon (43616) *(G-15719)*

Swanton Wldg Machining Co Inc (PA) 419 826-4816
407 Broadway Ave Swanton (43558) *(G-18091)*

Swarovski US Holding Limited 330 867-2201
3265 W Market St Ste 544 Fairlawn (44333) *(G-9763)*

Swartz Audie 740 820-2341
527 Flower Ison Rd Minford (45653) *(G-14346)*

Swartz Manufacturing Inc 440 284-0297
820 Walnut St Elyria (44035) *(G-9497)*

Swartz Race Cars, Minford *Also called Swartz Audie* *(G-14346)*

Swartz Woodworking 330 359-6359
7136 Township Road 654 Millersburg (44654) *(G-14266)*

Sweaty Bands LLC 513 871-1222
3802 Ford Cir Cincinnati (45227) *(G-4489)*

Sweet GS Cupcakery Ltd 419 610-8507
3820 Turnock Gln Columbus (43230) *(G-7671)*

Sweet Manufacturing Company 937 325-1511
2000 E Leffel Ln Springfield (45505) *(G-17659)*

Sweet Melissas 440 333-6357
19337 Detroit Rd Rocky River (44116) *(G-16712)*

Sweet Mobile Cupcakery 440 465-7333
428 Walmar Rd Bay Village (44140) *(G-1246)*

Sweet Persuasions LLC 614 216-9052
9636 Circle Dr Pickerington (43147) *(G-16206)*

Swift Filters Inc (PA) 440 735-0995
24040 Forbes Rd Oakwood Village (44146) *(G-15628)*

Swift Manufacturing Co Inc 740 237-4405
700 Lorain St Ironton (45638) *(G-11302)*

Swift Print, Cleveland *Also called D M J F Inc* *(G-5162)*

Swift Tool Inc 330 945-6973
1420 Ritchie St Cuyahoga Falls (44221) *(G-8052)*

Swigart Electric, Englewood *Also called Kent Swigart* *(G-9528)*

Swigart Refinishing Company 937 254-1141
2021 E 3rd St Dayton (45403) *(G-8692)*

Swiger Coil Systems Ltd 216 362-7500
4677 Manufacturing Ave Cleveland (44135) *(G-6280)*

Swimmer Printing Inc 216 623-1005
1701 E 12th St Cleveland (44114) *(G-6281)*

Swingle Drilling, Crooksville *Also called Petro Ware Inc* *(G-7953)*

Swisher Hygiene Inc 513 870-4830
5579 Spellmire Dr West Chester (45246) *(G-20057)*

Swiss Woodcraft Inc 330 925-1807
15 Industrial St Rittman (44270) *(G-16683)*

Switchback Group Inc 330 523-5200
3778 Timberlake Dr Richfield (44286) *(G-16641)*

Switzer Performance Engrg 440 774-4219
235 Artino St Oberlin (44074) *(G-15648)*

Switzer Performance Innovation, Oberlin *Also called Switzer Performance Engrg* *(G-15648)*

Swivel-Tek Industries LLC 419 636-7770
417 N Lynn St Bryan (43506) *(G-2322)*

Swocat Design Inc 440 282-4700
4325 Oberlin Ave Uppr Lorain (44053) *(G-12284)*

Sword Furs 440 249-5001
25112 Center Ridge Rd Westlake (44145) *(G-20314)*

Sylvan Forge Inc 440 237-3626
7420 James Dr North Royalton (44133) *(G-15453)*

Sylvan Studio, Sylvania *Also called Sharonco Inc* *(G-18124)*

Sylvan Studio Inc 419 882-3423
5651 Main St Sylvania (43560) *(G-18127)*

Symantec Corporation 614 793-3060
545 Metro Pl S Ste 100 Dublin (43017) *(G-9151)*

Symantec Corporation 216 643-6700
6100 Oak Tree Blvd Independence (44131) *(G-11276)*

Symatic Inc 330 225-1510
2831 Center Rd Brunswick (44212) *(G-2260)*

Symbol Tool & Die Inc 440 582-5989
11000 Industrial First Av North Royalton (44133) *(G-15454)*

Syme Inc (PA) 330 723-6000
300 Lake Rd Medina (44256) *(G-13486)*

Symrise Inc 440 324-6060
110 Liberty Ct Elyria (44035) *(G-9498)*

Synagro Midwest Inc 937 384-0669
4515 Infirmary Rd Miamisburg (45342) *(G-13866)*

Syndicate Printers Inc 513 779-3625
7291 Saint Ives Pl West Chester (45069) *(G-19952)*

Synergy Alliance 330 253-9475
738 W Market St Akron (44303) *(G-424)*

Synergy Flavors (oh) LLC 513 892-7100
2991 Hamilton Mason Rd Hamilton (45011) *(G-10743)*

Synergy Grinding Inc 216 447-4000
9005 Bank St Cleveland (44125) *(G-6282)*

Synergy Health North Amer Inc 513 398-6406
7086 Industrial Row Dr Mason (45040) *(G-13093)*

Synsei Medical 609 759-1101
6474 Weston Cir W Dublin (43016) *(G-9152)*

Synthetic Body Parts Inc 440 838-0985
6099 Warblers Roost Brecksville (44141) *(G-2075)*

Synthetic Rubber Technology 330 494-2221
11021 Wright Rd Nw Uniontown (44685) *(G-19101)*

Syracuse China Company (HQ) 419 727-2100
300 Madison Ave Toledo (43604) *(G-18712)*

Syrgis Holdings Inc 859 356-8000
4555 Lake Forest Dr # 650 Blue Ash (45242) *(G-1879)*

Sysco Guest Supply LLC 440 960-2515
7395 Lorain Indus Pkwy Lorain (44052) *(G-12285)*

Syscom Advanced Materials Inc 614 487-3626
1275 Kinnear Rd Columbus (43212) *(G-7672)*

Systech Environmental Corp (HQ) 800 888-8011
3085 Woodman Dr Ste 300 Dayton (45420) *(G-8693)*

Systech Handling Inc 419 445-8226
120 Taylor Pkwy Archbold (43502) *(G-696)*

Systecon Inc 513 777-7722
6121 Schumacher Park Dr West Chester (45069) *(G-19953)*

System Controls Inc 216 351-9121
4549 State Rd Cleveland (44109) *(G-6283)*

System EDM of Ohio, Mason *Also called Hi-Tek Manufacturing Inc* *(G-13037)*

System Packaging of Glassline 419 666-9712
28905 Glenwood Rd Perrysburg (43551) *(G-16151)*

System Seals Inc (HQ) 440 735-0200
9505 Midwest Ave Cleveland (44125) *(G-6284)*

Systematic Machine Corp 440 877-9884
12955 York Delta Dr Ste F North Royalton (44133) *(G-15455)*

Systemax Manufacturing Inc 937 368-2300
6450 Poe Ave Ste 200 Dayton (45414) *(G-8694)*

Systems Jay LLC Nanogate (PA) 419 524-3778
150 Longview Ave E Mansfield (44903) *(G-12688)*

Systems Jay LLC Nanogate 419 747-1096
1555 W Longview Ave Mansfield (44906) *(G-12689)*

Systems Jay LLC Nanogate 419 522-7745
515 Newman St Mansfield (44902) *(G-12690)*

Systems Jay LLC Nanogate 419 747-4161
1595 W Longview Ave Mansfield (44906) *(G-12691)*

Systems Jay LLC Nanogate 419 747-4161
1595 W Longview Ave Mansfield (44906) *(G-12692)*

Systems Pack Inc 330 467-5729
649 Highland Rd E Macedonia (44056) *(G-12493)*

Systems Specialty Ctrl Co Inc 419 478-4156
1550 Coining Dr Toledo (43612) *(G-18713)*

Szpak Manufacturing Co Inc 440 236-5233
27500 Royalton Rd Unit 5 Columbia Station (44028) *(G-6602)*

T & B Foundry Company 216 391-4200
2469 E 71st St Cleveland (44104) *(G-6285)*

T & D Fabricating Inc 440 951-5646
1489 E 363rd St Eastlake (44095) *(G-9292)*

T & D Thompson Inc 740 332-8515
15952 State Route 56 E Laurelville (43135) *(G-11772)*

T & J Nickum Inc 216 881-2565
5466 Lake Ct Cleveland (44114) *(G-6286)*

T & K Heins Corporation 740 452-6006
1326 Brandywine Blvd Zanesville (43701) *(G-21358)*

T & K Welding Co Inc 216 432-0221
1405 E 39th St Cleveland (44114) *(G-6287)*

T & L Custom Screening Inc 937 237-3121
3464 Successful Way Dayton (45414) *(G-8695)*

T & L Welding LLC 937 498-9170
211 E Russell Rd Sidney (45365) *(G-17231)*

T & M Machine Products Inc 740 753-2960
14265 State Route 691 Nelsonville (45764) *(G-14741)*

T & R Noodles LLC 614 537-4710
11400 State Route 37 E New Lexington (43764) *(G-14857)*

T & R Welding Systems Inc 937 228-7517
1 Janney Rd Dayton (45404) *(G-8696)*

T & S Discount Tires Inc 440 951-9084
  36525 Reading Ave Willoughby (44094) *(G-20607)*

T & S Enterprises 419 424-1122
  1616 Bliss Ave Findlay (45840) *(G-9899)*

T & S Machine Inc 419 453-2101
  712 Maple St Wapakoneta (45895) *(G-19509)*

T & T Machine Inc 440 354-0605
  892 Callendar Blvd Painesville (44077) *(G-15924)*

T & W Forge LLC 216 881-8600
  562 W Ely St Alliance (44601) *(G-543)*

T & W Stamping Inc 330 270-0891
  207 N Four Mile Run Rd Youngstown (44515) *(G-21216)*

T & W Tool & Machine Inc 937 667-2039
  467 N 5th St Tipp City (45371) *(G-18302)*

T A Bacon Co 216 851-1404
  11655 Chillicothe Rd Chesterland (44026) *(G-3220)*

T A C, Hilliard *Also called Thermoplastic Accessories Corp (G-10987)*

T C F C, Cleveland *Also called Those Charc From Cleve Inc (G-6323)*

T C I, Greenville *Also called Treaty City Industries Inc (G-10525)*

T C Redi Mix Youngstown Inc (PA) 330 755-2143
  2400 Poland Ave Youngstown (44502) *(G-21217)*

T C Woodworking, New Lexington *Also called R Carney Thomas (G-14853)*

T D Dynamics Inc 216 881-0800
  4101 Commerce Ave Cleveland (44103) *(G-6288)*

T D Group Holdings LLC 216 706-2939
  1301 E 9th St Ste 3710 Cleveland (44114) *(G-6289)*

T E Hubler Inc 419 476-2552
  236 New Towne Square Dr 1b Toledo (43612) *(G-18714)*

T E Martindale Enterprises 614 253-6826
  2840 E 5th Ave Columbus (43219) *(G-7673)*

T E S, Milford *Also called Tactical Envmtl Systems Inc (G-14176)*

T F O, Jeffersonville *Also called Tfo Tech Co Ltd (G-11382)*

T H E B Inc 216 391-4800
  3700 Kelley Ave Cleveland (44114) *(G-6290)*

T J Automation Inc 419 267-5687
  U075 State Route 66 Archbold (43502) *(G-697)*

T J Davies Company Inc 440 248-5510
  30745 Solon Rd Ste 1 Solon (44139) *(G-17396)*

T J Ellis Enterprises Inc 419 224-1969
  1505 Neubrecht Rd Lima (45801) *(G-12100)*

T J F Inc 419 878-4400
  1070 Disher Dr Waterville (43566) *(G-19668)*

T J Karg Company Inc 330 836-0921
  1055 Evans Ave Akron (44305) *(G-425)*

T J Target 330 658-3057
  235 Bailey Ct Doylestown (44230) *(G-9031)*

T J Tool Works Inc 440 439-1388
  7010 Krick Rd Ste 4 Bedford (44146) *(G-1463)*

T JS Oil & Gas Inc 740 623-0192
  23191 County Road 621 Coshocton (43812) *(G-7912)*

T K Holdings, Piqua *Also called Tk Holdings Inc (G-16315)*

T K L Lettering 937 832-2091
  300 W National Rd Ste C Englewood (45322) *(G-9540)*

T L H Windshield Repair ....
  405 W South St Botkins (45306) *(G-1955)*

T M D, Toledo *Also called Toledo Molding & Die Inc (G-18736)*

T M Industries Inc 330 627-4410
  4082 Thrasher Rd Sw Carrollton (44615) *(G-2967)*

T N T Technologies Inc 330 448-4744
  7848 Locust St Masury (44438) *(G-13217)*

T P F Inc 513 761-9968
  313 S Wayne Ave Cincinnati (45215) *(G-4490)*

T R C, Frankfort *Also called Jay Tackett (G-9999)*

T S I, Clayton *Also called Tom Smith Industries Inc (G-4663)*

T Shirts & Soccer Wearhouse, Twinsburg *Also called Custom Screen Printing (G-18920)*

T T Machine Tool, Willoughby *Also called McTt Machine Tool Inc (G-20542)*

T V Specialties Inc 330 364-6678
  320 W 3rd St Dover (44622) *(G-9020)*

T&A Pallets Inc 330 968-4743
  2849 Denny Rd Ravenna (44266) *(G-16564)*

T&K Laser Works Inc 937 693-3783
  401 N Main St Botkins (45306) *(G-1956)*

T&M Plastics Co Inc 216 651-7700
  1249 W 78th St Cleveland (44102) *(G-6291)*

T&R Logging LLC 740 288-1825
  1085 Loop Rd Wellston (45692) *(G-19771)*

T&R Wood Products, Middle Point *Also called Traveling & Recycle Wood Pdts (G-13899)*

T&T Welding 513 615-1156
  1469 State Route 28 Loveland (45140) *(G-12393)*

T-Fab, Willoughby *Also called Tkr Metal Fabricating LLC (G-20617)*

T-Top Shoppe 330 343-3481
  138 E High Ave New Philadelphia (44663) *(G-14932)*

Ta Die For Gourmet Cupcakes 740 751-4586
  2094 Harding Hwy E Marion (43302) *(G-12905)*

Taasi, Delaware *Also called Attia Applied Sciences Inc (G-8823)*

Tabco, Chesterland *Also called T A Bacon Co (G-3220)*

Tablox Inc 440 953-1951
  4821 E 345th St Willoughby (44094) *(G-20608)*

Tabtronics Inc 937 222-9969
  2153 Winners Cir Dayton (45404) *(G-8697)*

Tachometer Press, Cincinnati *Also called Micropress America LLC (G-4102)*

Tack-Anew Inc 419 734-4212
  451 W Lakeshore Dr Port Clinton (43452) *(G-16417)*

Tactical Envmtl Systems Inc 513 831-2663
  1156 Us Route 50 Milford (45150) *(G-14176)*

Tactical Revolution LLC 419 348-9526
  10436 Country Acres Dr # 7 Ottawa (45875) *(G-15812)*

Tadd Spring Co Inc 440 572-1313
  15060 Foltz Pkwy Strongsville (44149) *(G-17976)*

Tadlock Trailer Sales, West Union *Also called Jerry Tadlock (G-20122)*

Taflan Steel & Welding Inc 740 635-0841
  54364 National Rd Bridgeport (43912) *(G-2093)*

Taft Tool & Production Co 419 385-2576
  756 S Byrne Rd Ste 1 Toledo (43609) *(G-18715)*

Tag 614 921-1732
  2226 Wilson Rd Columbus (43228) *(G-7674)*

Tag Sportswear LLC 330 456-8867
  1300 Market Ave N Canton (44714) *(G-2866)*

Tahoe Interactive Systems Inc 614 891-2323
  60 Nadine Pl N Westerville (43081) *(G-20235)*

Tahoma Enterprises Inc (PA) 330 745-9016
  255 Wooster Rd N Barberton (44203) *(G-1151)*

Tahoma Rubber & Plastics Inc (HQ) 330 745-9016
  255 Wooster Rd N Barberton (44203) *(G-1152)*

Taiho Corporation of America 419 443-1645
  194 Heritage Dr Tiffin (44883) *(G-18246)*

Tailored Systems Inc 937 299-3900
  2853 Springboro W Moraine (45439) *(G-14534)*

Tailwind Technologies Inc (PA) 937 778-4200
  1 Propeller Pl Piqua (45356) *(G-16313)*

Taiyo America Inc (HQ) 419 300-8811
  1702 E Spring St Saint Marys (45885) *(G-16858)*

Take It For Granite LLC 513 735-0555
  3898 Mcmann Rd Cincinnati (45245) *(G-3319)*

Takeda Pharmaceuticals USA Inc 440 238-0872
  19495 Trotwood Park Strongsville (44149) *(G-17977)*

Takk Industries Inc 513 353-4306
  8665 E Miami River Rd Cincinnati (45247) *(G-4491)*

Talan Products Inc 216 458-0170
  18800 Cochran Ave Cleveland (44110) *(G-6292)*

Talbot Drake & Co, Cleveland *Also called Talbot Drake Incorporated (G-6293)*

Talbot Drake Incorporated 216 441-5600
  5808 Grant Ave Cleveland (44105) *(G-6293)*

Talecris Plasma Resources 937 275-5996
  3909 Salem Ave Dayton (45406) *(G-8698)*

Talent Tool & Die Inc 440 239-8777
  777 Berea Industrial Pkwy Berea (44017) *(G-1637)*

Talisman Racing, Cincinnati *Also called All Craft Manufacturing Co (G-3377)*

Talk of Town Silkscreen & EMB, Akron *Also called B Richardson Inc (G-80)*

Tallmadge Finishing Co Inc 330 633-7466
  879 Moe Dr Ste C20 Akron (44310) *(G-426)*

Tallmadge Spinning & Metal Co 330 794-2277
  2783 Gilchrist Rd Unit A Akron (44305) *(G-427)*

Tamarkin Company 330 634-0688
  205 West Ave Tallmadge (44278) *(G-18172)*

Tamarkin Company 614 878-8942
  4780 W Broad St Columbus (43228) *(G-7675)*

Tamblingson Inc 419 221-3437
  1942 Elida Rd Lima (45805) *(G-12101)*

Tambrands Sales Corp (HQ) 513 983-1100
  1 Procter And Gamble Plz Cincinnati (45202) *(G-4492)*

Tameran Inc 440 349-7100
  30300 Solon Industrial Pk Solon (44139) *(G-17397)*

Tampax, Cincinnati *Also called Tambrands Sales Corp (G-4492)*

Tangent Air Inc 740 474-1114
  127 Edison Ave Circleville (43113) *(G-4645)*

Tango Echo Bravo Mfg Inc 440 937-3800
  4915 Mills Indus Pkwy North Ridgeville (44039) *(G-15404)*

Tank Services, Dennison *Also called Services Acquisition Co LLC (G-8946)*

Tanner Industries Inc 419 221-1576
  8070 Harding Hwy Lima (45801) *(G-12102)*

Tanning 937 233-4554
  7109 Taylorsville Rd Dayton (45424) *(G-8699)*

Tap Packaging Solutions, Cleveland *Also called Chilcote Company (G-5028)*

Tapco Holdings Inc 800 771-4486
  200 Shotwell Dr Franklin (45005) *(G-10057)*

Taper Tool & Broach Inc 216 486-4435
  1066 E 222nd St Cleveland (44117) *(G-6294)*

Tara Acquisition Group 614 754-4777
  9042 Cotter St Lewis Center (43035) *(G-11923)*

Taradon Rubber Co Inc 330 896-3143
  1441 E Turkeyfoot Lake Rd Akron (44312) *(G-428)*

Tarahill Inc 706 864-0808
  3985 Groves Rd Columbus (43232) *(G-7676)*

Tarantula Performance Racg LLC 330 273-3456
  1669 W 130th St Ste 301 Hinckley (44233) *(G-11030)*

Targa Enterprises, Cleveland *Also called Darryl Smith (G-5169)*

A
L
P
H
A
B
E
T
I
C

Target Business Services 614 866-4065
 12920 Stonecreek Dr Ste B Pickerington (43147) *(G-16207)*
Target Holdings Inc 513 474-4409
 2300 E Kemper Rd Unit 5 Cincinnati (45241) *(G-4493)*
Target Printing & Graphics 937 228-0170
 233 Leo St Dayton (45404) *(G-8700)*
Target Thompson Technology 330 699-8000
 3651 Apache St Nw Uniontown (44685) *(G-19102)*
Target Typesetting, Pickerington *Also called Target Business Services (G-16207)*
Target World, Cincinnati *Also called Target Holdings Inc (G-4493)*
Targeted Cmpund Monitoring LLC 513 461-3535
 531 E 3rd St Dayton (45402) *(G-8701)*
Targeting Customer Safety Inc 330 865-9593
 1021 Galsworthy Dr Akron (44313) *(G-429)*
Tarigma Corporation 614 436-3734
 6161 Busch Blvd Ste 110 Columbus (43229) *(G-7677)*
Tark Inc (PA) 937 434-6766
 420 Congress Park Dr Dayton (45459) *(G-8702)*
Tarkett Inc 440 708-9366
 16910 Munn Rd Chagrin Falls (44023) *(G-3124)*
Tarkett Inc (HQ) 800 899-8916
 30000 Aurora Rd Solon (44139) *(G-17398)*
Tarkett Delaware, Solon *Also called Tarkett Inc (G-17398)*
Tarkett USA Inc (HQ) 440 543-8916
 30000 Aurora Rd Solon (44139) *(G-17399)*
Tarpco, Kent *Also called Hapco Inc (G-11469)*
Tarpco Inc 330 677-8277
 390 Portage Blvd Kent (44240) *(G-11535)*
Tarped Out Inc 330 325-7722
 4442 State Route 14 Ravenna (44266) *(G-16565)*
Tarpstop LLC (PA) 419 873-7867
 12000 Williams Rd Perrysburg (43551) *(G-16152)*
Tarrier Foods Corp 614 876-8594
 2700 International St # 100 Columbus (43226) *(G-7678)*
Tarrier Steel Company Inc 614 444-4000
 1379 S 22nd St Columbus (43206) *(G-7679)*
Tasi Group, Harrison *Also called Tasi Holdings Inc (G-10809)*
Tasi Holdings Inc (PA) 513 202-5182
 10100 Progress Way Harrison (45030) *(G-10809)*
Taste of Belgium LLC 513 381-3280
 1801 Race St Ste 9 Cincinnati (45202) *(G-4494)*
Taste of Heaven Original Gourm, Akron *Also called Waymakers Inc (G-469)*
Tastemorr Snacks, Coldwater *Also called Basic Grain Products Inc (G-6553)*
Tat Engineering, Nelsonville *Also called Tat Pumps Inc (G-14742)*
Tat Machine and Tool Ltd 419 836-7706
 1313 S Cousino Rd Curtice (43412) *(G-7959)*
Tat Pumps Inc 740 385-0008
 398 Poplar St Nelsonville (45764) *(G-14742)*
Tata America Intl Corp 513 677-6500
 1000 Summit Dr Unit 1 Milford (45150) *(G-14177)*
Tata Consultancy Services, Milford *Also called Tata America Intl Corp (G-14177)*
Tata Steel Plating, Warren *Also called Thomas Steel Strip Corporation (G-19608)*
Tate Lyle Ingrdnts Amricas LLC 937 236-5906
 5600 Brentlinger Dr Dayton (45414) *(G-8703)*
Tate Lyle Ingrdnts Amricas LLC 937 235-4074
 5584 Webster St Dayton (45414) *(G-8704)*
Tater Tool & Die Inc 330 648-1148
 11145 Old Mill Rd Spencer (44275) *(G-17458)*
Tatham Schulz Incorporated 216 861-4431
 836 Broadway Ave Cleveland (44115) *(G-6295)*
Tatum Landscaping & Lawncare, Gahanna *Also called Frankie Tatum (G-10207)*
Tatum Petroleum Corporation 740 819-6810
 667 Lkview Plz Blvd Ste E Worthington (43085) *(G-20890)*
Taupe Holdings Co 614 330-4600
 7758 Deercrest Ct Dublin (43016) *(G-9153)*
Tavens Container Inc 216 883-3333
 22475 Aurora Rd Bedford (44146) *(G-1464)*
Tavens Packg Display Solutions, Bedford *Also called Tavens Container Inc (G-1464)*
Tayjus Personalized Woodworks 440 427-9145
 25366 Tyndall Falls Dr Olmsted Falls (44138) *(G-15676)*
Tayjus Woodworks, Olmsted Falls *Also called Tayjus Personalized Woodworks (G-15676)*
Taylor & Moore Co 513 733-5530
 807 Wachendorf St Cincinnati (45215) *(G-4495)*
Taylor - Winfield Corporation (PA) 330 259-8500
 3200 Innovation Pl Hubbard (44425) *(G-11140)*
Taylor Company (PA) 513 271-2550
 5721 Dragon Way Ste 117 Cincinnati (45227) *(G-4496)*
Taylor Lumber Worldwide Inc 740 259-6222
 18253 State Route 73 Mc Dermott (45652) *(G-13344)*
Taylor Made Glass Systems, Payne *Also called Taylor Products Inc (G-16018)*
Taylor Manufacturing Company 937 322-8622
 1101 W Main St Springfield (45504) *(G-17660)*
Taylor Metal Products Co 419 522-3471
 700 Springmill St Mansfield (44903) *(G-12693)*
Taylor Mtl Hdlg & Conveyor, Toledo *Also called Bobco Enterprises Inc (G-18374)*
Taylor Products Inc 419 263-2313
 230 Laura St Payne (45880) *(G-16017)*

Taylor Products Inc 419 263-2313
 407 N Maple St Payne (45880) *(G-16018)*
Taylor Quick Print 740 439-2208
 1008 Woodlawn Ave A Cambridge (43725) *(G-2478)*
Taylor Tool & Die Inc 937 845-1491
 306 N Main St New Carlisle (45344) *(G-14813)*
Taylor Winfield Indus Wldg Eqp, Youngstown *Also called Taylor-Winfield Tech Inc (G-21218)*
Taylor-Winfield Tech Inc (HQ) 330 259-8500
 3200 Innovation Pl Youngstown (44509) *(G-21218)*
Tbec, Painesville *Also called Thirion Brothers Eqp Co LLC (G-15930)*
Tbh International 440 323-4651
 150 Ridge Circle Ln Apt A Elyria (44035) *(G-9499)*
Tbone Sales LLC 330 897-6131
 410 N Ray St Baltic (43804) *(G-1077)*
Tc Bros Choppers LLC 419 265-9399
 12052 Us Highway 20a Wauseon (43567) *(G-19695)*
Tc Precision Machine Inc 937 278-3334
 2540 Ashcraft Rd Dayton (45414) *(G-8705)*
TC Service Co 440 954-7500
 38285 Pelton Rd Willoughby (44094) *(G-20609)*
Tca Graphics, Fairborn *Also called Tee Creations (G-9632)*
Tce International Ltd 800 962-2376
 4843 N Ridge Rd Perry (44081) *(G-16059)*
Tcp Inc 330 836-4239
 2747 Crawfis Blvd Ste 108 Fairlawn (44333) *(G-9764)*
TCS, Akron *Also called Targeting Customer Safety Inc (G-429)*
TD Landscape Inc 740 694-0244
 16780 Pinkley Rd Fredericktown (43019) *(G-10110)*
Td Power Systems (usa) Inc 330 247-5264
 3380 Brecksville Rd # 300 Richfield (44286) *(G-16642)*
Tdc Systems Inc 440 953-5918
 38296 Western Pkwy Willoughby (44094) *(G-20610)*
Tdi, Dayton *Also called GE Aviation Systems LLC (G-8358)*
Tdl Tool Inc 937 374-0055
 1296 S Patton St Xenia (45385) *(G-20978)*
Tdm LLC 440 969-1442
 1303 W 38th St Ashtabula (44004) *(G-840)*
Tdm Fuelcell LLC Tdm LLC 440 969-1442
 12144 W Shiloh Dr Chesterland (44026) *(G-3221)*
TDS Custom Cabinets LLC 614 517-2220
 1819 Walcutt Rd Ste A Columbus (43228) *(G-7680)*
TE Brown LLC (PA) 937 223-2241
 1205 Lamar St Dayton (45404) *(G-8706)*
Te Connectivity Corporation 419 521-9500
 175 N Diamond St Mansfield (44902) *(G-12694)*
Te-Co Manufacturing LLC 937 836-0961
 109 Quinter Farm Rd Union (45322) *(G-19068)*
Tea Hills Gourmet Chicken Pdts 419 685-1689
 269 Township Road 2450 Loudonville (44842) *(G-12305)*
Teachers Publishing Group 614 486-0631
 4200 Parkway Ct Hilliard (43026) *(G-10985)*
Team, Warren *Also called Trumbull Engrg Assembly & Mch (G-19613)*
Team Inc 614 263-1808
 3005 Silver Dr Columbus (43224) *(G-7681)*
Team Amity Molds & Plastic 937 667-7856
 1435 Commerce Park Dr Tipp City (45371) *(G-18303)*
Team Cooperheat Mqs 614 501-7304
 5764 Westbourne Ave Columbus (43213) *(G-7682)*
Team Plastics Inc 216 251-8270
 3901 W 150th St Cleveland (44111) *(G-6296)*
Team Systems, Toledo *Also called Decoma Systems Integration Gro (G-18431)*
Team Wendy LLC 216 738-2518
 17000 Saint Clair Ave # 5 Cleveland (44110) *(G-6297)*
Tebben Rubber Stamp Company, Elida *Also called Ulrich Rubber Stamp Company (G-9359)*
TEC Design & Manufacturing Inc 937 435-2147
 4549 Gateway Cir Dayton (45440) *(G-8707)*
TEC Line Inc 740 881-5948
 8020 Strawberry Hill Rd Lewis Center (43035) *(G-11924)*
Teca, Vandalia *Also called Troy Engineered Components and (G-19312)*
Tech Art Productions, Columbus *Also called Technical Artistry Inc (G-7684)*
Tech Dynamics Inc 419 666-1666
 361 D St Ste B Perrysburg (43551) *(G-16153)*
Tech Group, Norton *Also called Buckeye Field Machining Inc (G-15507)*
Tech II Inc 937 969-7000
 1765 W County Line Rd Urbana (43078) *(G-19183)*
Tech Industries Inc 216 861-7337
 1313 Washington Ave Cleveland (44113) *(G-6298)*
Tech International, Johnstown *Also called Technical Rubber Company Inc (G-11407)*
Tech Mold & Tool Co Inc 937 667-8851
 4333 Lisa Dr Tipp City (45371) *(G-18304)*
Tech Pro Inc 330 923-3546
 3030 Gilchrist Rd Akron (44305) *(G-430)*
Tech Products Corporation (HQ) 937 438-1100
 2215 Lyons Rd Miamisburg (45342) *(G-13867)*
Tech Ready Mix Inc 216 361-5000
 5000 Crayton Ave Cleveland (44104) *(G-6299)*
Tech Solutions LLC 419 852-7190
 658 N Main St Celina (45822) *(G-3020)*

2017 Harris Ohio
Industrial Directory

(G-0000) Company's Geographic Section entry number

Tech Systems Inc 419 878-2100
 1070 Disher Dr Waterville (43566) *(G-19669)*

Tech Tool Inc 330 674-1176
 2901 County Road 150 Millersburg (44654) *(G-14267)*

Tech Wear Embroidery Company 740 344-1276
 738 W Main St Newark (43055) *(G-15062)*

Tech-Bond Solutions 614 327-8884
 3775 Columbus Lancaster Carroll (43112) *(G-2949)*

Tech-E-Z LLC 419 692-1700
 446 E Cleveland St Delphos (45833) *(G-8918)*

Tech-Med Inc 216 486-0900
 1080 E 222nd St Euclid (44117) *(G-9608)*

Tech-Sonic Inc 614 792-3117
 2710 Sawbury Blvd Columbus (43235) *(G-7683)*

Tech-Way Industries Inc 937 746-1004
 301 Industrial Dr Franklin (45005) *(G-10058)*

Tech/III Inc (PA) 513 482-7500
 1330 Tennessee Ave Ste 2 Cincinnati (45229) *(G-4497)*

Techalloy Inc 410 633-9300
 22801 Saint Clair Ave Euclid (44117) *(G-9609)*

Techbrite LLC 800 246-9977
 1000 Kieley Pl Cincinnati (45217) *(G-4498)*

Techcraft Seating Systems, Sheffield Village *Also called Magna Seating America Inc (G-17126)*

Techneglas Inc (HQ) 419 873-2000
 2100 N Wilkinson Way Perrysburg (43551) *(G-16154)*

Techneglas Inc 419 873-2000
 25875 Dixie Hwy Bldg 52 Perrysburg (43551) *(G-16155)*

Technibus Inc 330 479-4202
 1501 Raff Rd Sw Ste 6 Canton (44710) *(G-2867)*

Technical Artistry Inc 614 299-7777
 1945 Corvair Ave Columbus (43207) *(G-7684)*

Technical Engineered Products, Geneva *Also called American Guard Co Inc (G-10342)*

Technical Glass Products Inc 425 396-8420
 7460 Ponderosa Rd Perrysburg (43551) *(G-16156)*

Technical Glass Products Inc (PA) 440 639-6399
 881 Callendar Blvd Painesville (44077) *(G-15925)*

Technical Machine Products Inc 216 281-9500
 5500 Walworth Ave Cleveland (44102) *(G-6300)*

Technical Rubber Company Inc (PA) 740 967-9015
 200 E Coshocton St Johnstown (43031) *(G-11407)*

Technical Sales & Solution 614 793-9612
 4361 Wyandotte Woods Blvd Dublin (43016) *(G-9154)*

Technical Tool & Gauge Inc 330 273-1778
 2914 Westway Dr Brunswick (44212) *(G-2261)*

Technical Translation Services (PA) 440 942-3130
 37841 Euclid Ave Ste 7 Willoughby (44094) *(G-20611)*

Technicolor Usa Inc 614 474-8821
 24200 Us Highway 23 S Circleville (43113) *(G-4646)*

Technicote Inc (PA) 800 358-4448
 222 Mound Ave Miamisburg (45342) *(G-13868)*

Technicote Inc 330 928-1476
 70 Marc Dr Cuyahoga Falls (44223) *(G-8053)*

Technicote Westfield Inc 937 859-4448
 222 Mound Ave Miamisburg (45342) *(G-13869)*

Technidrill Systems Inc 330 678-9980
 429 Portage Blvd Kent (44240) *(G-11536)*

Technifab Inc 440 934-8324
 38600 Chester Rd Avon (44011) *(G-1013)*

Technifab Inc 440 934-8324
 1300 Chester Indus Pkwy Avon (44011) *(G-1014)*

Technifab Inc (PA) 440 934-8324
 1355 Chester Indus Pkwy Avon (44011) *(G-1015)*

Techniform Industries Inc 419 332-8484
 2107 Hayes Ave Fremont (43420) *(G-10186)*

Technimold Plus Inc 937 492-4077
 102 Wall St Port Jefferson (45360) *(G-16421)*

Techniplate Inc 216 486-8825
 700 E 163rd St Cleveland (44110) *(G-6301)*

Techniques Surfaces Usa Inc 937 323-2556
 2015 Progress Rd Springfield (45505) *(G-17661)*

Technisand Inc (HQ) 440 285-3132
 11833 Ravenna Rd Chardon (44024) *(G-3181)*

Technlogy Install Partners LLC 888 586-7040
 13701 Enterprise Ave Cleveland (44135) *(G-6302)*

Technofab, Wellington *Also called Forest City Technologies Inc (G-19747)*

Technoform GL Insul N Amer Inc 330 487-6600
 1755 Entp Pkwy Ste 300 Twinsburg (44087) *(G-19027)*

Technologies Inc Arlington VA, Beavercreek *Also called Drs Advanced Isr LLC (G-1330)*

Technology and Services Inc 740 626-2020
 1336 Baum Hill Rd Chillicothe (45601) *(G-3280)*

Technology Explortation Pdts, Mentor *Also called Gdj Inc (G-13590)*

Technology House The Ltd 440 248-3025
 30555 Solon Indus Pkwy Solon (44139) *(G-17400)*

Technology Products Inc 937 652-3412
 2423 Barger Rd Urbana (43078) *(G-19184)*

Technology Resources Inc 419 241-9248
 916 N Summit St Toledo (43604) *(G-18716)*

Technoprint Inc 614 899-1403
 515 S State St Westerville (43081) *(G-20236)*

Technosoft Inc 513 985-9877
 11180 Reed Hartman Hwy # 200 Blue Ash (45242) *(G-1880)*

Techtron Systems Inc 440 505-2990
 29500 Fountain Pkwy Solon (44139) *(G-17401)*

Tecmar Industries, Eaton *Also called Mark Cottle (G-9317)*

Tecmark Corporation (PA) 440 205-7600
 7745 Metric Dr Mentor (44060) *(G-13743)*

Tecmark Corporation 440 205-9188
 7335 Production Dr Mentor (44060) *(G-13744)*

Tecnocap LLC 330 392-7222
 2100 Griswold St Ne Warren (44483) *(G-19604)*

Teco, Toledo *Also called Toledo Engineering Co Inc (G-18731)*

Tecsis LP 614 430-0683
 771 Dearborn Park Ln F Worthington (43085) *(G-20891)*

Tecsis Corp Delta Metrics, Worthington *Also called Jual Corporation (G-20874)*

Tectum Inc 740 345-9691
 105 S 6th St Newark (43055) *(G-15063)*

Tecumseh Packg Solutions Inc 419 238-1122
 1275 Industrial Dr Van Wert (45891) *(G-19271)*

Tecumseh Redevelopment Inc 330 659-9100
 4020 Kinross Lakes Pkwy Richfield (44286) *(G-16643)*

Ted Tipple 740 432-3263
 6176 Simmons Rd Cambridge (43725) *(G-2479)*

Tedia Company Inc 513 874-5340
 1000 Tedia Way Fairfield (45014) *(G-9723)*

Tee Creations 937 878-2822
 701 N Broad St Ste C Fairborn (45324) *(G-9632)*

Tegam Inc (PA) 440 466-6100
 10 Tegam Way Geneva (44041) *(G-10357)*

Tegratek 513 742-5100
 500 Northland Blvd Cincinnati (45240) *(G-4499)*

Tegron Holding LLC 330 836-2004
 1208 Massillon Rd Akron (44306) *(G-431)*

Teikuro Corporation 937 327-3955
 4500 Gateway Blvd Springfield (45502) *(G-17662)*

Tek Gear & Machine Inc 330 455-3331
 1220 Camden Ave Sw Canton (44706) *(G-2868)*

Tek Group International Inc 330 706-0000
 567 Elm Ridge Ave Canal Fulton (44614) *(G-2515)*

Tek Manufacturing, Canal Fulton *Also called Tek Group International Inc (G-2515)*

Tekdog Inc 614 737-3743
 132 Northwoods Blvd Ste A Columbus (43235) *(G-7685)*

Tekfor Inc 330 202-7420
 3690 Long Rd Wooster (44691) *(G-20840)*

Tekfor USA, Wooster *Also called Tekfor Inc (G-20840)*

Tekmar-Dohrmann, Mason *Also called Teledyne Tekmar Company (G-13095)*

Tekni-Plex Inc 419 491-2407
 1445 Timber Wolf Dr Holland (43528) *(G-11088)*

Teknol Inc (PA) 937 264-0190
 5751 Webster St Dayton (45414) *(G-8708)*

Tekraft Industries Inc 440 352-8321
 244 Latimore St Painesville (44077) *(G-15926)*

Tektronix Inc 513 870-4729
 9639 Inter Ocean Dr Dr2 West Chester (45246) *(G-20058)*

Tektronix Inc 440 248-0400
 28775 Aurora Rd Solon (44139) *(G-17402)*

Tekus, L Sweater Design, Cleveland *Also called Fine Points Inc (G-5346)*

Tekworx LLC 513 533-4777
 4538 Cornell Rd Blue Ash (45241) *(G-1881)*

Telcon LLC 330 562-5566
 1677 Miller Pkwy Streetsboro (44241) *(G-17881)*

Teledyne Instruments Inc 513 229-7000
 4736 Scialville Foster Rd Mason (45040) *(G-13094)*

Teledyne Technologies Inc 419 470-3000
 1330 W Laskey Rd Toledo (43612) *(G-18717)*

Teledyne Tekmar, Mason *Also called Teledyne Instruments Inc (G-13094)*

Teledyne Tekmar Company (HQ) 513 229-7000
 4736 Scialville Foster Rd Mason (45040) *(G-13095)*

Telefast Industries Inc 440 826-0011
 777 W Bagley Rd Berea (44017) *(G-1638)*

Telegram 740 286-3604
 920 Veterans Dr Unit C Jackson (45640) *(G-11328)*

Telempu N Hayashi Amer Corp 513 932-9319
 1500 Kingsview Dr Lebanon (45036) *(G-11843)*

Telesis Marking Systems, Circleville *Also called Telesis Technologies Inc (G-4647)*

Telesis Technologies Inc (HQ) 740 477-5000
 28181 River Dr Circleville (43113) *(G-4647)*

Telex Communications Inc 419 865-0972
 5660 Southwyck Blvd # 105 Toledo (43614) *(G-18718)*

Telling Industries LLC (PA) 440 974-3370
 4420 Sherwin Rd Willoughby (44094) *(G-20612)*

Telling Industries Inc 928 681-2010
 4420 Sherwin Rd Ste 3 Willoughby (44094) *(G-20613)*

Telling Industries LLC 740 435-8900
 2105 Larrick Rd Cambridge (43725) *(G-2480)*

Telos Alliance, The, Cleveland *Also called Tls Corp (G-6327)*

Telos Systems, Cleveland *Also called Cutting Edge Technologies Inc (G-5154)*

Tema Isenmann Inc (HQ) 859 252-0613
 7806 Redsky Dr Cincinnati (45249) *(G-4500)*

A
L
P
H
A
B
E
T
I
C

Tema Systems Inc 513 489-7811
7806 Redsky Dr Cincinnati (45249) *(G-4501)*

Tembec Btlsr Inc 419 244-5856
2112 Sylvan Ave Toledo (43606) *(G-18719)*

Temo Candy Co, Akron *Also called Temos Inc (G-432)*

Temos Inc 330 376-7229
495 W Exchange St Akron (44302) *(G-432)*

Tempac LLC 513 505-9700
7370 Avenel Ct West Chester (45069) *(G-19954)*

Tempcraft Corporation 216 391-3885
3960 S Marginal Rd Cleveland (44114) *(G-6303)*

Temperature Controls Company 330 773-6633
661 Anderson Ave Akron (44306) *(G-433)*

Tempest Inc 216 883-6500
12750 Berea Rd Cleveland (44111) *(G-6304)*

Temple Architectural Products, Spencer *Also called John Baird (G-17456)*

Temple Inland 513 425-0830
912 Nelbar St Middletown (45042) *(G-14087)*

Temple Israel 330 762-8617
91 Springside Dr Akron (44333) *(G-434)*

Temple Oil & Gas Company 740 452-7878
6626 Ceramic Rd Ne Crooksville (43731) *(G-7954)*

Tempo Manufacturing Company 937 773-6613
727 E Ash St Piqua (45356) *(G-16314)*

Tempo Trophy Mfg, Piqua *Also called Tempo Manufacturing Company (G-16314)*

Tenacity Manufacturing Company 513 821-0201
4455 Muhlhauser Rd West Chester (45011) *(G-19955)*

Tenan Machine & Fabricating 440 997-5100
6002 State Rd Bldg A Ashtabula (44004) *(G-841)*

Tencate Advanced Armor USA Inc 740 928-0326
1051 O Neill Dr Hebron (43025) *(G-10888)*

Tenda Horse Products LLC 740 694-8836
18400 N Liberty Rd Fredericktown (43019) *(G-10111)*

Tendon Manufacturing Inc 216 663-3200
20805 Aurora Rd Cleveland (44146) *(G-6305)*

Tenex Tool Co 440 354-5979
546 Hoyt St Ste 2 Painesville (44077) *(G-15927)*

Tenkotte Tops Inc 513 738-7300
11029 State Route 128 Harrison (45030) *(G-10810)*

Tenneco, Napoleon *Also called Pullman Company (G-14693)*

Tenneco, Milan *Also called Pullman Company (G-14115)*

Tenneco Automotive Oper Co Inc 937 781-4940
2555 Woodman Dr Kettering (45420) *(G-11587)*

Tennessee Coatings Inc (HQ) 513 770-4900
8093 Columbia Rd Ste 201 Mason (45040) *(G-13096)*

Tenney Tool & Supply Co 330 666-2807
973 Wooster Rd N Barberton (44203) *(G-1153)*

Tenpoint Crossbow Technologies, Mogadore *Also called Hunters Manufacturing Co Inc (G-14377)*

Tep Bedding Grp Inc 440 437-7700
161 Grand Valley Ave Orwell (44076) *(G-15779)*

Teradata Corporation (PA) 866 548-8348
10000 Innovation Dr Miamisburg (45342) *(G-13870)*

Teradata Operations 937 866-0032
2461 Rosina Dr Miamisburg (45342) *(G-13871)*

Teradata Operations Inc (HQ) 937 242-4030
10000 Innovation Dr Miamisburg (45342) *(G-13872)*

Terewell Inc 216 334-6897
2683 W 14th St Cleveland (44113) *(G-6306)*

Terex Mhps Corp 440 349-8235
29201 Aurora Rd Solon (44139) *(G-17403)*

Terex Utilities Inc 513 539-9770
920 Deneen Ave Monroe (45050) *(G-14416)*

Terex Utilities Inc 440 262-3200
6400 W Snowville Rd Ste 1 Brecksville (44141) *(G-2076)*

Terminal Equipment Industries 330 468-0322
64 Privet Ln Northfield (44067) *(G-15474)*

Terminal Optical Lab 216 289-7722
26215 Tungsten Rd Euclid (44132) *(G-9610)*

Terminal Ready-Mix Inc 440 288-0181
524 Colorado Ave Lorain (44052) *(G-12286)*

Ternion Inc (PA) 216 642-6180
7635 Hub Pkwy Ste A Cleveland (44125) *(G-6307)*

Teron Lighting Inc 513 858-6004
33 Donald Dr Uppr Fairfield (45014) *(G-9724)*

Terra Coat LLC 216 254-8157
500 W Aurora Rd Ste 140 Northfield (44067) *(G-15475)*

Terra Comp Technology 330 745-8912
449 4th St Nw Barberton (44203) *(G-1154)*

Terra Sonic International LLC 740 374-6608
27825 State Route 7 Marietta (45750) *(G-12840)*

Terra Star Inc 405 200-1336
111 N Main St Waynesburg (44688) *(G-19728)*

Terrasource Global Corporation 330 923-5254
601-607 Munroe Falls Ave Cuyahoga Falls (44221) *(G-8054)*

Terrene Labs 404 408-2241
5939 Deerfield Blvd Mason (45040) *(G-13097)*

Terry & Jack Neon Sign Co 419 229-0674
225 S Collins Ave Lima (45804) *(G-12103)*

Terry A Johnson 614 561-0706
15094 Palmer Rd Sw Etna (43068) *(G-9552)*

Terry Asphalt Materials Inc (HQ) 513 874-6192
8600 Bilstein Blvd Hamilton (45015) *(G-10744)*

Terry G Sickles 740 286-8880
2207 Boy Scout Rd Ray (45672) *(G-16574)*

Terry Lumber and Supply Co 330 659-6800
1710 Mill St W Peninsula (44264) *(G-16043)*

Tersus Pharmaceuticals 440 951-2451
5966 Heisley Rd Mentor (44060) *(G-13745)*

Terydon Inc 330 879-2448
7260 Erie Ave Sw Navarre (44662) *(G-14728)*

Tesa Inc 614 847-8200
544 Enterprise Dr Ste A Lewis Center (43035) *(G-11925)*

Tessa Precision Product Inc 440 392-3470
850 Callendar Blvd Painesville (44077) *(G-15928)*

Tessec LLC 937 985-3552
5679 Webster St Dayton (45414) *(G-8709)*

Tessec Manufacturing Svcs LLC 937 985-3552
5679 Webster St Dayton (45414) *(G-8710)*

Test Mark Industries Inc 330 426-2200
995 N Market St East Palestine (44413) *(G-9246)*

Testlink USA 513 272-1081
11445 Century Cir W Cincinnati (45246) *(G-4502)*

Tetra Mold & Tool Inc 937 845-1651
51 Quick Rd New Carlisle (45344) *(G-14814)*

Tetra Tech Inc 330 286-3683
6715 Tippecanoe Rd C201 Canfield (44406) *(G-2578)*

Tetrad Electronics Inc (PA) 440 946-6443
2048 Joseph Lloyd Pkwy Willoughby (44094) *(G-20614)*

Teva Womens Health Inc (HQ) 513 731-9900
5040 Duramed Rd Cincinnati (45213) *(G-4503)*

Tewell & Associates 440 543-5190
10260 Washington St Chagrin Falls (44023) *(G-3125)*

Tex-Tyler Corporation 419 729-4951
5148 Stickney Ave Toledo (43612) *(G-18720)*

Tex-Vent Co 614 299-1902
6100 Huntley Rd Columbus (43229) *(G-7686)*

Texas Tile Manufacturing LLC 713 869-5811
30000 Aurora Rd Solon (44139) *(G-17404)*

Texmaster Tools Inc 740 965-8778
143 Tuttle Ave Fredericktown (43019) *(G-10112)*

Texstone Industries 419 722-4664
433 Oak Ave Findlay (45840) *(G-9900)*

Textileather Corporation (HQ) 419 729-3731
3729 Twining St Toledo (43608) *(G-18721)*

Textiles (PA) 740 852-0782
23 Old Springfield Rd London (43140) *(G-12220)*

Textiles Inc 614 529-8642
5892 Heritage Lakes Dr Hilliard (43026) *(G-10986)*

Textron Inc 330 626-7800
555 Mondial Pkwy Streetsboro (44241) *(G-17882)*

Tez Tool & Fabrication Inc 440 323-2300
115 Buckeye St Elyria (44035) *(G-9500)*

Tfo Tech Co Ltd 740 426-6381
221 State St Jeffersonville (43128) *(G-11382)*

Tfr Printing, Marion *Also called Tree Free Resources LLC (G-12908)*

Tg Can Technology USA Inc 614 410-6672
470 Olde Worthington Rd Westerville (43082) *(G-20191)*

Tgs Industries Inc (HQ) 330 339-2211
406 Mill Ave Sw New Philadelphia (44663) *(G-14933)*

Tgs International Inc 330 893-2428
4464 State Route 39 Millersburg (44654) *(G-14268)*

Th Magnesium Inc 513 285-7568
9435 Waterstone Blvd Cincinnati (45249) *(G-4504)*

Th Manufacturing Inc 330 893-3572
4674 County Road 120 Millersburg (44654) *(G-14269)*

Th Plastics Inc 419 352-2770
843 Miller Dr Bowling Green (43402) *(G-2017)*

Th Plastics Inc 419 425-5825
1640 Westfield Dr Findlay (45840) *(G-9901)*

Th Plastics Inc 419 425-5825
101 Bentley Ct Findlay (45840) *(G-9902)*

Thaler Machine Company 937 550-2400
216 Tahlequah Trl Springboro (45066) *(G-17509)*

Thames Company Ltd 614 228-4869
50 W Broad St Ste 1133 Columbus (43215) *(G-7687)*

Thanks Mom Designs, Cincinnati *Also called Apparel Impressions Inc (G-3407)*

Thapa Industries 419 234-3498
1324 W Elm St Lima (45805) *(G-12104)*

Thatcher Enterprises Co Ltd 614 228-2013
205 E Broad St Columbus (43215) *(G-7688)*

The Beacon Journal Pubg Co 330 996-3140
44 E Exchange St Akron (44308) *(G-435)*

The Blind Factory, Hilliard *Also called Blind Factory Showroom (G-10935)*

The Bookseller Inc 330 865-5831
39 Westgate Cir Akron (44313) *(G-436)*

The Cleveland Jewish Publ Co 216 454-8300
23880 Commerce Park Ste 1 Beachwood (44122) *(G-1300)*

The Cleveland-Cliffs Iron Co 216 694-5700
1100 Superior Ave E # 1500 Cleveland (44114) ***(G-6308)***
The County Classified's, Bellefontaine *Also called County Classifieds* ***(G-1525)***
The Dannon Company Inc 513 229-0092
7577 Central Parke Blvd Mason (45040) ***(G-13098)***
The Dannon Company Inc 419 628-3861
216 Southgate Dr Minster (45865) ***(G-14363)***
The Euclid Chemical Company (HQ) 800 321-7628
19218 Redwood Rd Cleveland (44110) ***(G-6309)***
The Euclid Chemical Company 216 292-5000
3735 Green Rd Beachwood (44122) ***(G-1301)***
The Euclid Chemical Company 216 531-9222
19218 Redwood Rd Cleveland (44110) ***(G-6310)***
The Euclid Chemical Company 216 531-9222
18900 Cochran Ave Cleveland (44110) ***(G-6311)***
The Ewart-Ohlson Machine Co 330 928-2171
1435 Main St Cuyahoga Falls (44221) ***(G-8055)***
The Fischer & Jirouch Company 216 361-3840
4821 Superior Ave Cleveland (44103) ***(G-6312)***
The Florand Company 330 747-8986
1776 Cherry St Ste A Youngstown (44506) ***(G-21219)***
The Fremont Kraut Company 419 332-6481
724 N Front St Fremont (43420) ***(G-10187)***
The Gazette Printing Co Inc (PA) 440 576-9125
46 W Jefferson St Jefferson (44047) ***(G-11373)***
The Gazette Printing Co Inc 440 593-6030
218 Washington St Conneaut (44030) ***(G-7820)***
The General's Books, Columbus *Also called Generals Books* ***(G-7109)***
The Great Lakes Brewing Co 216 771-4404
2516 Market Ave Cleveland (44113) ***(G-6313)***
The Guardtower Inc 614 488-4311
3600 Trabue Rd Columbus (43204) ***(G-7689)***
The Hartman Corp 614 475-5035
3216 Morse Rd Columbus (43231) ***(G-7690)***
The Holtkamp Organ Co 216 741-5180
2909 Meyer Ave Cleveland (44109) ***(G-6314)***
The Jeffersonian 740 498-7117
140 W Main St Newcomerstown (43832) ***(G-15125)***
The Label Team Inc 330 332-1067
1251 Quaker Cir Salem (44460) ***(G-16929)***
The Magic Seal Paper Pdts Co 614 299-1185
850 Williams Ave Columbus (43212) ***(G-7691)***
The Mahoning Valley Sani Dst 330 799-6315
1181 Ohltown Mcdonald Rd Mineral Ridge (44440) ***(G-14312)***
The Mansfield Strl & Erct Co (PA) 419 522-5911
429 Park Ave E Mansfield (44905) ***(G-12695)***
The Mansfield Strl & Erct Co 419 747-6571
817 Belmont Ave Mansfield (44906) ***(G-12696)***
The Max 440 357-0036
759 Lakeshore Blvd Painesville (44077) ***(G-15929)***
The Metal Marker Mfg Co 440 327-2300
6225 Lear Nagle Rd North Ridgeville (44039) ***(G-15405)***
The Mobility Store, Westerville *Also called Columbus Prescr Rehabilitation* ***(G-20204)***
The National Lime and Stone Co 330 455-5722
5377 Lauby Rd Ste 201 North Canton (44720) ***(G-15271)***
The Printed Image, Columbus *Also called Printed Image* ***(G-7519)***
THE QUIKRETE COMPANIES INC, Columbus *Also called Quikrete Companies Inc* ***(G-7540)***
THE QUIKRETE COMPANIES INC, Toledo *Also called Quikrete Companies Inc* ***(G-18664)***
The Reliable Spring Wire Frms 440 365-7400
300 Abbe Rd S Elyria (44035) ***(G-9501)***
The Rubber Stamp Shop 419 478-4444
4418 Lewis Ave Toledo (43612) ***(G-18722)***
The Salem Golf Club 330 332-0346
1967 S Lincoln Ave Salem (44460) ***(G-16930)***
The Shelby Co 440 871-9901
865 Canterbury Rd Westlake (44145) ***(G-20315)***
The W L Jenkins Company 330 477-3407
1445 Whipple Ave Sw Canton (44710) ***(G-2869)***
The Wood Shed 937 429-3355
2665 Trebein Rd Xenia (45385) ***(G-20979)***
The-Fischer-Group 513 285-1281
20282052 Bohlke Blvd Fairfield (45014) ***(G-9725)***
Thedkahn LLC 239 961-8757
15 Eagle Ct Amelia (45102) ***(G-586)***
Thees Machine & Tool Co 419 586-4766
2007 State Route 703 Celina (45822) ***(G-3021)***
Theiss Uav Solutions LLC 330 584-2070
10881 Johnson Rd North Benton (44449) ***(G-15214)***
Theken Companies LLC 330 733-7600
1800 Triplett Blvd Akron (44306) ***(G-437)***
Therapedic Mattress, Orwell *Also called Tep Bedding Grp Inc* ***(G-15779)***
Therm-All Inc (PA) 440 779-9494
31387 Industrial Pkwy North Olmsted (44070) ***(G-15348)***
Therm-O-Disc Incorporated (HQ) 419 525-8500
1320 S Main St Mansfield (44907) ***(G-12697)***
Therm-O-Link Inc (PA) 330 527-2124
10513 Freedom St Garrettsville (44231) ***(G-10334)***
Therm-O-Link Inc 330 393-7600
621 Dana St Ne Ste 5 Warren (44483) ***(G-19605)***
Therm-O-Link of Texas Inc 330 393-4300
621 Dana St Ne Ste V Warren (44483) ***(G-19606)***
Therm-O-Packaging Suppliers 440 543-5188
16815 Park Circle Dr Chagrin Falls (44023) ***(G-3126)***
Therm-O-Vent, Medina *Also called Thermo Vent Manufacturing Inc* ***(G-13487)***
Therma-Tru Corp (HQ) 419 891-7400
1750 Indian Wood Cir # 100 Maumee (43537) ***(G-13301)***
Thermacal Inc 440 498-1005
30325 Binbridge Rd Ste 2a Solon (44139) ***(G-17405)***
Thermafab Alloy Inc 216 861-0540
25367 Water St Olmsted Falls (44138) ***(G-15677)***
Thermagon Inc 216 939-2300
4707 Detroit Ave Cleveland (44102) ***(G-6315)***
Thermal Images, Bowling Green *Also called Novavision Inc* ***(G-2003)***
Thermal Industries Inc 216 464-0674
4920 Commerce Pkwy Ste 4 Cleveland (44128) ***(G-6316)***
Thermal Solutions Inc 614 263-1808
3005 Silver Dr Columbus (43224) ***(G-7692)***
Thermal Treatment Center Inc (HQ) 216 881-8100
1101 E 55th St Cleveland (44103) ***(G-6317)***
Thermal Treatment Center Inc 216 883-4820
11116 Avon Ave Cleveland (44105) ***(G-6318)***
Thermal Treatment Center Inc 440 943-4555
28910 Lakeland Blvd Wickliffe (44092) ***(G-20388)***
Thermal Treatment Center Inc 216 941-0440
10601 Briggs Rd Cleveland (44111) ***(G-6319)***
Thermal Visions Inc (PA) 740 587-4025
83 Stone Henge Dr Granville (43023) ***(G-10467)***
Thermalgraphics, Cincinnati *Also called Agnone-Kelly Enterprises Inc* ***(G-3367)***
Thermelectricity LLC 330 972-8054
411 Wolf Ledges Pkwy # 1 Akron (44311) ***(G-438)***
Thermeq Co, Waterville *Also called T J F Inc* ***(G-19668)***
Thermo Eberline LLC 440 703-1400
1 Thermo Fisher Way Oakwood Village (44146) ***(G-15629)***
Thermo Fisher Scientific, Oakwood Village *Also called Thermo Eberline LLC* ***(G-15629)***
Thermo Fisher Scientific 740 373-4763
401 Mill Creek Rd Marietta (45750) ***(G-12841)***
Thermo Fisher Scientific Inc 800 871-8909
1 Thermo Fisher Way Oakwood Village (44146) ***(G-15630)***
Thermo Fisher Scientific Inc 440 703-1400
1 Thermo Fisher Way Bedford (44146) ***(G-1465)***
Thermo King Corporation 478 625-7241
13 Orchard Cir Chagrin Falls (44022) ***(G-3071)***
Thermo King Corporation 478 625-7241
13 Orchard Cir Chagrin Falls (44022) ***(G-3072)***
Thermo Systems Technology 216 292-8250
2000 Auburn Dr Ste 200 Cleveland (44122) ***(G-6320)***
Thermo Vent Manufacturing Inc 330 239-0239
1213 Medina Rd Medina (44256) ***(G-13487)***
Thermo-Rite Mfg Company 330 633-8680
1355 Evans Ave Akron (44305) ***(G-439)***
Thermocolor LLC (HQ) 419 626-5677
2901 W Monroe St Sandusky (44870) ***(G-17012)***
Thermocolor LLC 419 626-5677
2108 Superior St Sandusky (44870) ***(G-17013)***
Thermodyn Corporation 419 874-5100
12265 Williams Rd Ste B Perrysburg (43551) ***(G-16157)***
Thermoform Products LLC 330 686-2050
1777 Commerce Dr Stow (44224) ***(G-17808)***
Thermogenics Corp 513 247-7963
300 E Bus Way Ste 200 Cincinnati (45241) ***(G-4505)***
Thermolock Mfg LLC 513 771-6555
2921 Mcbride Ct Hamilton (45011) ***(G-10745)***
Thermoplastic Accessories Corp 614 771-4777
3949 Lyman Dr Hilliard (43026) ***(G-10987)***
Thermotion Corp 440 639-8325
6520 Hopkins Rd Mentor (44060) ***(G-13746)***
Thermotion-Madison, Mentor *Also called Thermotion Corp* ***(G-13746)***
Thermtrol Corporation (PA) 330 497-4148
8914 Pleasantwood Ave Nw North Canton (44720) ***(G-15272)***
Thickemz Entertainment LLC 404 399-4255
1268 Wellingshire Cir Cuyahoga Falls (44221) ***(G-8056)***
Thiels Replacement Systems Inc 419 289-6139
419 E 8th St Ashland (44805) ***(G-781)***
Thieman Machine 419 628-2474
5395 State Route 119 Minster (45865) ***(G-14364)***
Thieman Quality Metal Fab Inc 419 629-2612
05140 Dicke Rd New Bremen (45869) ***(G-14795)***
Thieman Tailgates Inc 419 586-7727
600 E Wayne St Celina (45822) ***(G-3022)***
Thinkware Incorporated 513 598-3300
7611 Cheviot Rd Ste 2 Cincinnati (45247) ***(G-4506)***
Third Party Service Ltd 419 872-2312
1205 Louisiana Ave Perrysburg (43552) ***(G-16158)***
Thirion Brothers Eqp Co LLC 440 357-8004
340 W Prospect St Painesville (44077) ***(G-15930)***
Thirsty Dog Brewing Co 330 252-8740
529 Grant St Ste 103 Akron (44311) ***(G-440)***
This Week, Lewis Center *Also called Consumers News Services Inc* ***(G-11893)***

ALPHABETIC

Thk Manufacturing America Inc 740 928-1415
471 N High St Hebron (43025) *(G-10889)*

Thogus Products Company 440 933-8850
33490 Pin Oak Pkwy Avon Lake (44012) *(G-1053)*

Thomas Allen Co 330 823-8487
1062 Parkside Dr Alliance (44601) *(G-544)*

Thomas Cabinet Shop Inc 937 847-8239
321 Gargrave Rd Dayton (45449) *(G-8711)*

Thomas Creative Apparel Inc 419 929-1506
1 Harmony Pl New London (44851) *(G-14867)*

Thomas D Epperson 937 855-3300
7440 Weaver Rd Germantown (45327) *(G-10374)*

Thomas David Design 614 595-0379
30799 Pinetree Rd 263 Cleveland (44124) *(G-6321)*

Thomas Do-It Center Inc (PA) 740 446-2002
176 Mccormick Rd Gallipolis (45631) *(G-10310)*

Thomas Enterprises 330 394-4483
263 Lowell Ave Ne Warren (44483) *(G-19607)*

Thomas Entps of Georgetown 937 378-6300
933 S Main St Georgetown (45121) *(G-10366)*

Thomas Hora 740 622-1386
32441 County Rd Ste 12 Fresno (43824) *(G-10200)*

Thomas J Raffa DDS Inc 440 997-5208
355 W Prospect Rd Ste 120 Ashtabula (44004) *(G-842)*

Thomas J Weaver Inc (PA) 740 622-2040
1501 Kenilworth Ave Coshocton (43812) *(G-7913)*

Thomas Mfg 330 758-2384
696 Mcclurg Rd Ste 8 Youngstown (44512) *(G-21220)*

Thomas Panels Inc 330 758-2384
696 Mcclurg Rd Youngstown (44512) *(G-21221)*

Thomas Products Co Inc (PA) 513 756-9009
3625 Spring Grove Ave Cincinnati (45223) *(G-4507)*

Thomas Rental, Gallipolis *Also called Thomas Do-It Center Inc (G-10310)*

Thomas Ross Associates Inc 330 723-1110
303 N Broadway St Medina (44256) *(G-13488)*

Thomas Steel Inc 419 483-7540
305 Elm St Bellevue (44811) *(G-1563)*

Thomas Steel Strip Corporation 330 841-6429
2518 W Market St Warren (44485) *(G-19608)*

Thomas Tape and Supply Company 937 325-6414
1713 Sheridan Ave Springfield (45505) *(G-17663)*

Thomas Tool & Mold Company 614 890-4978
271 Broad St Westerville (43081) *(G-20237)*

Thomas Welding & Repair, Georgetown *Also called Thomas Entps of Georgetown (G-10366)*

Thomas-Wilbert Vault Co Inc 740 695-5671
49132 Randall Dr Saint Clairsville (43950) *(G-16812)*

Thompson Aluminum Casting Co 216 206-2781
5161 Canal Rd Cleveland (44125) *(G-6322)*

Thompson Assoc Hudson Ohio 330 655-2142
5771 Sunset Dr Hudson (44236) *(G-11204)*

Thompson Brothers Mining Co 330 549-3979
3379 E Garfield Rd New Springfield (44443) *(G-14952)*

Thompson Castings, Cleveland *Also called Thompson Aluminum Casting Co (G-6322)*

Thompson Culvert Company LLC (HQ) 513 645-7000
9025 Centre Pointe Dr # 400 West Chester (45069) *(G-19956)*

Thompson Distributing Co Inc 513 422-9011
3227 Seneca St Middletown (45044) *(G-14088)*

Thompson Metals and Tubing, Hamilton *Also called Butler Processing Inc (G-10678)*

Thompson Partners Inc 866 475-2500
82 Mill St Ste A Gahanna (43230) *(G-10238)*

Thompson Steel Company Inc 419 399-4803
815 W Gasser Rd Paulding (45879) *(G-16014)*

Thor Industries Inc 937 596-6111
419 W Pike St Jackson Center (45334) *(G-11349)*

Thorfood LLC (HQ) 419 626-4375
2520 Campbell St Sandusky (44870) *(G-17014)*

Thorncreek Winery & Garden 330 562-9245
155 Treat Rd Aurora (44202) *(G-949)*

Thornton Powder Coatings Inc 419 522-7183
2300 N Main St Mansfield (44903) *(G-12698)*

Thoroughbred Gt Mfg LLC 330 533-0048
6145 State Route 446 Canfield (44406) *(G-2579)*

Thorworks Industries Inc (PA) 419 626-4375
2520 Campbell St Sandusky (44870) *(G-17015)*

Those Charc From Cleve Inc 216 252-7300
1 American Rd Cleveland (44144) *(G-6323)*

Thoughts That Count, Millersburg *Also called Broty Enterprises Inc (G-14203)*

Thread-Rite Tool & Mfg Inc 937 222-2836
1200 E 1st St Dayton (45403) *(G-8712)*

Threaded Image 513 683-9069
10035 Dallasburg Rd Loveland (45140) *(G-12394)*

Three Bond International Inc 937 610-3000
101 Daruma Pkwy Dayton (45439) *(G-8713)*

Three Bond International Inc (HQ) 513 779-7300
6184 Schumacher Park Dr West Chester (45069) *(G-19957)*

Three Cord LLC 419 445-2673
203 E Lugbill Rd Archbold (43502) *(G-698)*

Three H Lumber 740 473-2515
176 Dana Rd Newport (45768) *(G-15127)*

Three Leaf Inc 888 308-1007
3189 Princeton Rd Ste 123 Hamilton (45011) *(G-10746)*

Threshhold, Granville *Also called Thermal Visions Inc (G-10467)*

Thrift Tool Inc 937 275-3600
5916 Milo Rd Dayton (45414) *(G-8714)*

Thrifty Print 440 360-7826
5168 Hampton Dr North Olmsted (44070) *(G-15349)*

Thriverx, Cincinnati *Also called Biorx LLC (G-3450)*

Throck Supply Co LLC 937 393-9276
439 N West St Hillsboro (45133) *(G-11015)*

Tht Presses, Dayton *Also called THT Presses Inc (G-8715)*

THT Presses Inc 937 898-2012
7475 Webster St Dayton (45414) *(G-8715)*

Thundawear LLC 419 787-2675
1709 Spielbusch Ave # 100 Toledo (43604) *(G-18723)*

Thundawear Skull Caps, Toledo *Also called Thundawear LLC (G-18723)*

Thunder Dreamer Publishing 419 424-2004
2500 Crystal Ave Findlay (45840) *(G-9903)*

Thurns Bakery & Deli 614 221-9246
541 S 3rd St Columbus (43215) *(G-7693)*

Thycurb, Akron *Also called Burt Manufacturing Company Inc (G-105)*

Thyssenkrupp Bilstein Amer Inc (HQ) 513 881-7600
8685 Bilstein Blvd Hamilton (45015) *(G-10747)*

Thyssenkrupp Bilstein Amer Inc 513 881-7600
4440 Muhlhauser Rd West Chester (45011) *(G-19958)*

Thyssenkrupp Elevator Corp 513 241-0222
934 Dalton Ave Cincinnati (45203) *(G-4508)*

Thyssenkrupp Materials NA Inc 216 883-8100
6050 Oak Tree Blvd # 110 Independence (44131) *(G-11277)*

TI Group Auto Systems Inc 740 929-2049
3600 Hebron Rd Hebron (43025) *(G-10890)*

Tia Marie & Company 513 521-8694
8694 Long Ln Cincinnati (45231) *(G-4509)*

Tidewater Products Inc 419 873-0223
12305 Williams Rd Perrysburg (43551) *(G-16159)*

Tidewater Products Inc 419 534-9870
4520 Brookside Rd Ottawa Hills (43615) *(G-15820)*

Tier Environmental 440 232-9400
7013 Krick Rd Bedford (44146) *(G-1466)*

Tierra-Derco International LLC 419 929-2240
40 S Main St New London (44851) *(G-14868)*

Tiffin Foundry & Machine Inc 419 447-3991
423 W Adams St Tiffin (44883) *(G-18247)*

Tiffin Metal Products Co (PA) 419 447-8414
450 Wall St Tiffin (44883) *(G-18248)*

Tiffin Scenic Studios Inc (PA) 800 445-1546
146 Riverside Dr Tiffin (44883) *(G-18249)*

Tig Welding Specialties Inc 216 621-1763
13616 Enterprise Ave Cleveland (44135) *(G-6324)*

Tig Wood & Die Inc 937 849-6741
1760 Dalton Dr New Carlisle (45344) *(G-14815)*

Tiger Cat Furniture 330 220-7232
294 Marks Rd Brunswick (44212) *(G-2262)*

Tiger Construction, Canal Winchester *Also called Tiger Oil Inc (G-2538)*

Tiger General LLC 330 239-4949
6867 Wooster Pike Medina (44256) *(G-13489)*

Tiger Mirror Corporation 419 855-3146
465 Main St Clay Center (43408) *(G-4654)*

Tiger Oil Inc (PA) 614 837-5552
650 Winchester Pike Canal Winchester (43110) *(G-2538)*

Tiger Sand & Gravel LLC 330 833-6325
411 Oberlin Ave Sw Massillon (44647) *(G-13205)*

Tigerpoly Manufacturing Inc 614 871-0045
6231 Enterprise Pkwy Grove City (43123) *(G-10601)*

Tii Treeman Industries, Boardman *Also called Treemen Industries Inc (G-1925)*

Tilden Mining Company LC (PA) 216 694-5278
1100 Superior Ave E Cleveland (44114) *(G-6325)*

Tiller Foods, Dayton *Also called Instantwhip-Dayton Inc (G-8410)*

Tiller Foods, Dayton *Also called Instantwhip-Dayton Inc (G-8411)*

Tillmans Entp -Signs Ship LLC 440 281-9340
810 Taylor St Elyria (44035) *(G-9502)*

Tilt 15 Inc 330 239-4192
1440 Wolf Creek Trl Sharon Center (44274) *(G-17112)*

Tilt-Or-Lift Inc (PA) 419 893-6944
124 E Dudley St Maumee (43537) *(G-13302)*

Tim Boutwell 419 358-4653
902 N Main St Bluffton (45817) *(G-1917)*

Tim Calvin Access Controls 740 494-4200
7585 Taway Rd Radnor (43066) *(G-16508)*

Tim Calvin Enterprises, Radnor *Also called Tim Calvin Access Controls (G-16508)*

Tim Crabtree 740 286-4535
117 Athens St Jackson (45640) *(G-11329)*

Tim L Humbert 330 497-4944
6535 Promler St Nw Canton (44720) *(G-2870)*

Tim's Woodshop, Jackson *Also called Tim Crabtree (G-11329)*

Timac Manufacturing Company 937 372-3305
825 Bellbrook Ave Xenia (45385) *(G-20980)*

Timar Enterprises Inc 440 942-4001
35665 Curtis Blvd Unit 5 Willoughby (44095) *(G-20615)*

Timber Products Inc......440 693-4098
8652 Parkman Mespo Rd Middlefield (44062) ***(G-13995)***
Timberlane Woodworking......419 895-9945
8425 Olvsburg Ftchvlle Rd Greenwich (44837) ***(G-10537)***
Timbermill Ltd......740 862-3426
11015 Stoudertown Rd Nw Baltimore (43105) ***(G-1089)***
Timbertech Limited......614 443-4891
2141 Fairwood Ave Columbus (43207) ***(G-7694)***
Timbertech Limited (HQ)......937 655-8766
894 Prairie Rd Wilmington (45177) ***(G-20679)***
Timcal America Inc......440 871-7504
29299 Clemens Rd Ste 1l Westlake (44145) ***(G-20316)***
Timco Inc......740 685-2594
57051 Marietta Rd Byesville (43723) ***(G-2410)***
Timco Machine Co, Willoughby *Also called Timar Enterprises Inc* ***(G-20615)***
Time Is Money......419 701-6098
1280 North Dr Fostoria (44830) ***(G-9997)***
Timekap Inc......330 747-2122
2315 Belmont Ave Youngstown (44505) ***(G-21222)***
Timekap Indus Sls Svc & Mch, Youngstown *Also called Timekap Inc* ***(G-21222)***
Timekeeping Systems Inc......216 595-0890
30700 Bainbridge Rd Ste H Solon (44139) ***(G-17406)***
Timely Tours Inc......419 734-3751
141 Maple St Ste A Port Clinton (43452) ***(G-16418)***
Times Bulletin Media......419 238-2285
700 Fox Rd Van Wert (45891) ***(G-19272)***
Times Journal......740 286-2187
1 Acy Ave Ste D Jackson (45640) ***(G-11330)***
Times Recorder, The, Zanesville *Also called Gannett Co Inc* ***(G-21314)***
Times Reporter, New Philadelphia *Also called Mansfield Journal Co* ***(G-14910)***
Times Reporter/Midwest Offset, New Philadelphia *Also called Copley Ohio Newspapers Inc* ***(G-14892)***
Timet Toronto, Toronto *Also called Titanium Metals Corporation* ***(G-18785)***
Timken Aircraft Operation, Canton *Also called Timken Company* ***(G-2871)***
Timken Company (PA)......234 262-3000
4500 Mount Pleasant St Nw North Canton (44720) ***(G-15273)***
Timken Company......419 563-2200
2325 E Mansfield St Bucyrus (44820) ***(G-2360)***
Timken Company......330 339-1151
1957 E High Ave New Philadelphia (44663) ***(G-14934)***
Timken Company......330 471-4300
5430 Lauby Rd Bldg 7 Canton (44720) ***(G-2871)***
Timken Company......614 476-3934
1027 Greythorne Pl Gahanna (43230) ***(G-10239)***
Timken Company......614 836-3337
3782 Potomac St Groveport (43125) ***(G-10646)***
Timken Company......330 471-5028
20th & Dueber Ave Sw Canton (44706) ***(G-2872)***
Timken Company......234 262-3000
4500 Mount Pleasant St Nw North Canton (44720) ***(G-15274)***
Timken Company......330 471-2121
4500 Mount Pleasant St Nw Canton (44720) ***(G-2873)***
Timken Company......234 262-3000
1819 N Main St Niles (44446) ***(G-15185)***
Timken Company......330 471-4791
22261 Margaret Ln Alliance (44601) ***(G-545)***
Timken Company......330 471-5043
786 Whipple Ave Sw Canton (44710) ***(G-2874)***
Timken Foundation......330 452-1144
200 Market Ave N Ste 210 Canton (44702) ***(G-2875)***
Timken Receivables Corporation......234 262-3000
4500 Mount Pleasant St Nw North Canton (44720) ***(G-15275)***
Timkensteel Corporation (PA)......330 471-7000
1835 Dueber Ave Sw Canton (44706) ***(G-2876)***
Timkensteel Corporation......330 471-7000
4511 Faircrest St Sw Canton (44706) ***(G-2877)***
Timkensteel Corporation......330 517-7300
1019 E Turkeyfoot Lake Rd Akron (44312) ***(G-441)***
Timkensteel Corporation......330 438-3000
1927 Harrison Ave Sw Canton (44706) ***(G-2878)***
Timkensteel Corporation......937 456-8002
401 Industrial Dr Eaton (45320) ***(G-9324)***
Timkensteel Corporation......330 438-3000
4511 Faircrest St Sw Canton (44706) ***(G-2879)***
Timkensteel Green Sales Office, Akron *Also called Timkensteel Corporation* ***(G-441)***
Timmys Sandwich Shop......419 350-8267
5426 Cresthaven Ln Toledo (43614) ***(G-18724)***
Timon J Reinhart......419 476-1990
1560 W Laskey Rd Ste B Toledo (43612) ***(G-18725)***
Timon Tool & Die, Toledo *Also called Timon J Reinhart* ***(G-18725)***
Timothy A. Lyons, New Marshfield *Also called Diesel Fltrtion Spcialists LLC* ***(G-14871)***
Timothy Allen Jewelers Inc......440 974-8885
8925 Mentor Ave Ste D Mentor (44060) ***(G-13747)***
Timothy Sasser......740 260-9499
59538 Lost Rd Byesville (43723) ***(G-2411)***
Timothy Sinfield......740 685-3684
54962 Marietta Rd Pleasant City (43772) ***(G-16368)***
Tin Indian Performance......216 214-5485
2656 Watervale Dr Uniontown (44685) ***(G-19103)***
Tin Shed LLC......330 636-2524
6 S Myrtle Ave Willard (44890) ***(G-20402)***
Tin Wizard Heating and Cooling......330 468-7884
8853 Robinwood Ter Macedonia (44056) ***(G-12494)***
Tin-Sau LLC......419 586-8886
1406 Canterbury Dr Celina (45822) ***(G-3023)***
Tinker Omega Manufacturing LLC......937 322-2272
2424 Columbus Rd Springfield (45503) ***(G-17664)***
Tinnerman Palnut Engineered PR......330 220-5100
1060 W 130th St Brunswick (44212) ***(G-2263)***
Tiny Lion Music Groups......419 874-7353
144 E 5th St Perrysburg (43551) ***(G-16160)***
Tiny Printing Co......614 920-0800
11764 Village Way Dr Pickerington (43147) ***(G-16208)***
Tip Products Inc......216 252-2535
15411 Chatfield Ave Ste 5 Cleveland (44111) ***(G-6326)***
Tip Top Canning Co (PA)......937 667-3713
505 S 2nd St Tipp City (45371) ***(G-18305)***
Tipco Punch Inc......513 874-9140
6 Rowe Ct Hamilton (45015) ***(G-10748)***
Tipp Machine & Tool Inc (HQ)......937 890-8428
4201 Little York Rd Dayton (45414) ***(G-8716)***
Tipp Stone Inc......937 890-4051
8172 Meeker Rd Dayton (45414) ***(G-8717)***
Tipton Environmental Intl Inc......513 735-2777
4446 State Route 132 Batavia (45103) ***(G-1228)***
TIS Incorporated......614 291-3950
2114 N High St Columbus (43201) ***(G-7695)***
Tisch Environmental Inc......513 467-9000
145 S Miami Ave Cleves (45002) ***(G-6529)***
Titan Chemical, Milford *Also called Jeff Pendergrass* ***(G-14156)***
Titan Fire Protection Inc......740 451-0838
146 Township Road 1523 Chesapeake (45619) ***(G-3191)***
Titan Manufacturing LLC......440 942-2258
4730 Beidler Rd Willoughby (44094) ***(G-20616)***
Titan Metal Fabricators......513 755-3394
7835 Kyles Station Rd Liberty Township (45044) ***(G-11969)***
Titan Tire Corporation......419 633-4221
927 S Union St Bryan (43506) ***(G-2323)***
Titan Tire Corporation Bryan, Bryan *Also called Titan Tire Corporation* ***(G-2323)***
Titanium Contractors Ltd......513 256-2152
9400 Reading Rd Cincinnati (45215) ***(G-4510)***
Titanium Industries Inc......216 661-4610
200 Ventura Cir Independence (44131) ***(G-11278)***
Titanium Lacrosse LLC......614 562-8082
2671 Coltsbridge Dr Lewis Center (43035) ***(G-11926)***
Titanium Metals Corporation......740 537-1571
100 Titanium Way Toronto (43964) ***(G-18785)***
Titanium Trout LLC......440 543-3187
18060 Birch Hill Dr Chagrin Falls (44023) ***(G-3127)***
Tite Seal Case Company Inc......440 647-2371
299 Clay St Wellington (44090) ***(G-19756)***
Tj Bell Inc......330 633-3644
1340 Home Ave Ste E Akron (44310) ***(G-442)***
Tj Metzgers Inc......419 861-8611
207 Arco Dr Toledo (43607) ***(G-18726)***
Tjar Innovations LLC......937 347-1999
1004 Cincinnati Ave Xenia (45385) ***(G-20981)***
Tk America, Cincinnati *Also called Toyobo Kureha America Co Ltd* ***(G-4515)***
Tk Gas Services Inc......740 826-0303
2303 John Glenn Hwy New Concord (43762) ***(G-14822)***
Tk Holdings Inc......937 778-9713
1401 Innovation Pkwy Piqua (45356) ***(G-16315)***
Tkg Operating, East Canton *Also called Foltz & Foltz Ltd Partnership* ***(G-9192)***
Tko Mfg Services Inc......937 299-1637
2360 W Dorothy Ln Ste 111 Moraine (45439) ***(G-14535)***
Tkr Metal Fabricating LLC......440 221-2770
37552 N Industrial Pkwy Willoughby (44094) ***(G-20617)***
Tks Industrial Company......614 444-5602
1939 Refugee Rd Columbus (43207) ***(G-7696)***
TL Industries Inc (PA)......419 666-8144
2541 Tracy Rd Northwood (43619) ***(G-15490)***
TL Krieg Offset Inc......513 542-1522
10600 Chester Rd Cincinnati (45215) ***(G-4511)***
Tla Designs, New Lexington *Also called C S A Enterprises* ***(G-14845)***
Tls Corp (PA)......216 574-4759
1241 Superior Ave E Cleveland (44114) ***(G-6327)***
Tlt-Turbo Inc......330 776-5115
2693 Wingate Ave Akron (44314) ***(G-443)***
Tm Machine & Tool Inc......419 478-0310
521 Mel Simon Dr Toledo (43612) ***(G-18727)***
Tmac Machine Inc......330 673-0621
924 Overholt Rd Kent (44240) ***(G-11537)***
Tmarzetti Company......614 268-3722
380 Polaris Pkwy Ste 400 Westerville (43082) ***(G-20192)***
Tmarzetti Company (HQ)......614 846-2232
380 Polaris Pkwy Ste 400 Westerville (43082) ***(G-20193)***
Tmarzetti Company......614 277-3577
5800 N Meadows Dr Grove City (43123) ***(G-10602)***

(PA)=Parent Co (HQ)=Headquarters (DH)=Div Headquarters

ALPHABETIC

Tmarzetti Company 330 674-2993
7445 County Road 68 Millersburg (44654) *(G-14270)*

Tmarzetti Company 614 279-8673
1709 Frank Rd Columbus (43223) *(G-7697)*

Tmarzetti Company 216 292-5655
25900 Fargo Ave Bedford (44146) *(G-1467)*

Tmb Enterprises LLC 419 243-2189
6509 Angola Rd Holland (43528) *(G-11089)*

Tmd Wek North LLC 440 576-6940
1085 Jffrsn Eagleville Rd Jefferson (44047) *(G-11374)*

TMI Inc 330 270-9780
6475 Victoria East Rd Youngstown (44515) *(G-21223)*

Tmk Farm Service, Sugarcreek *Also called Mullet Enterprises Inc (G-18029)*

Tms International LLC 330 847-0844
4000 Mahoning Ave Nw Warren (44483) *(G-19609)*

Tms International Corporation 740 223-0091
912 Cheney Ave Marion (43302) *(G-12906)*

Tmsi LLC 888 867-4872
9073 Pleasantwood Ave Nw North Canton (44720) *(G-15276)*

Tmt Inc 419 592-1041
655 D St Perrysburg (43551) *(G-16161)*

Tmt Logistics, Perrysville *Also called Tmt Inc (G-16161)*

Tmw Systems Inc 615 986-1900
6085 Parkland Blvd Cleveland (44124) *(G-6328)*

Tmw Systems Inc (HQ) 216 831-6606
6085 Parkland Blvd Mayfield Heights (44124) *(G-13322)*

To A T 216 621-3322
2101 Superior Ave E Cleveland (44114) *(G-6329)*

To Scale Software LLC 513 253-0053
6398 Thornberry Ct Mason (45040) *(G-13099)*

Toagosei America Inc 614 718-3855
1450 W Main St West Jefferson (43162) *(G-20084)*

Toastmasters International 937 429-2680
1854 Redleaf Ct Dayton (45432) *(G-8118)*

Tobacco Company, Cleveland *Also called Memphis Smokehouse Inc (G-5782)*

Tod Thin Brushes Inc 440 576-6859
1152 State Route 46 N Jefferson (44047) *(G-11375)*

Today's Bride Magazine, Akron *Also called Jadlyn Inc (G-238)*

Todco, Upper Sandusky *Also called Overhead Door Corporation (G-19138)*

Todd Industries Inc 440 439-2900
7300 Northfield Rd Ste 1 Cleveland (44146) *(G-6330)*

Todd Smith Products 216 529-0525
13001 Athens Ave Ste 203 Lakewood (44107) *(G-11680)*

Todd W Goings 740 389-5842
360 Summit St Marion (43302) *(G-12907)*

Toft Dairy Inc 419 625-4376
3717 Venice Rd Sandusky (44870) *(G-17016)*

Toibox Structructures, Carrollton *Also called All Steel Structures Inc (G-2951)*

Tokin America Corporation 513 644-9743
9844 Windisch Rd West Chester (45069) *(G-19959)*

Toku America Inc 440 954-9923
3900 Ben Hur Ave Ste 3 Willoughby (44094) *(G-20618)*

Tolco Corporation 419 241-1113
1920 Linwood Ave Toledo (43604) *(G-18728)*

Toledo Alfalfa Mills Inc 419 836-3705
861 S Stadium Rd Oregon (43616) *(G-15720)*

Toledo Automatic Screw Co 419 726-3441
2114 Champlain St Toledo (43611) *(G-18729)*

Toledo Blade Company 419 724-6000
541 N Superior St Toledo (43660) *(G-18730)*

Toledo Business Journals, Toledo *Also called Telex Communications Inc (G-18718)*

Toledo City Paper, Toledo *Also called Adams Street Publishing Co (G-18321)*

Toledo Cutting Tools, Perrysburg *Also called Imco Carbide Tool Inc (G-16110)*

Toledo Deburring Co, Northwood *Also called Toledo Metal Finishing Inc (G-15491)*

Toledo Driveline, Toledo *Also called Dana Light Axle Mfg LLC (G-18427)*

Toledo Electromotive Inc 419 874-7751
28765 White Rd Perrysburg (43551) *(G-16162)*

Toledo Engineering Co Inc (PA) 419 537-9711
3400 Executive Pkwy Ste 4 Toledo (43606) *(G-18731)*

Toledo Express, Swanton *Also called Toledo Jet Center LLC (G-18092)*

Toledo Grmtor Blffton Mtr Wrks, Sylvania *Also called Bluffton Motor Works LLC (G-18100)*

Toledo Integrated Systems, Holland *Also called Toledo Transducers Inc (G-11090)*

Toledo Jet Center LLC (PA) 419 866-9050
11591 W Airport Svc Rd Swanton (43558) *(G-18092)*

Toledo Journal 419 472-4521
3021 Douglas Rd Toledo (43606) *(G-18732)*

Toledo Metal Finishing Inc 419 661-1422
7880 Caple Blvd Northwood (43619) *(G-15491)*

Toledo Metal Spinning Company 419 535-5931
1819 Clinton St Toledo (43607) *(G-18733)*

Toledo Mobile Media LLC (PA) 419 389-0687
757 Warehouse Rd Ste D Toledo (43615) *(G-18734)*

Toledo Molding & Die Inc 419 443-9031
1441 Maule Rd Tiffin (44883) *(G-18250)*

Toledo Molding & Die Inc 419 720-3500
300 Phillips Ave Ste 2002 Toledo (43612) *(G-18735)*

Toledo Molding & Die Inc (PA) 419 470-3950
1429 Coining Dr Toledo (43612) *(G-18736)*

Toledo Molding & Die Inc 419 692-6022
900 Gressel Dr Delphos (45833) *(G-8919)*

Toledo Molding & Die Inc 419 692-6022
24086 State Route 697 Delphos (45833) *(G-8920)*

Toledo Molding & Die Inc 419 476-0581
4 E Laskey Rd Toledo (43612) *(G-18737)*

Toledo Optical Laboratory Inc 419 248-3384
1201 Jefferson Ave Toledo (43604) *(G-18738)*

Toledo Paint & Chemical Co 419 244-3726
33 Blucher St Toledo (43607) *(G-18739)*

Toledo Pro Fiberglass Inc 419 241-9390
210 Wade St Toledo (43604) *(G-18740)*

Toledo Scales & Systems, Worthington *Also called Mettler-Toledo LLC (G-20878)*

Toledo Screw Products, Toledo *Also called D L Salkil LLC (G-18424)*

Toledo Screw Products Inc 419 841-3341
8261 W Bancroft St Toledo (43617) *(G-18741)*

Toledo Signs & Designs Ltd 419 843-1073
6636 W Bancroft St Ste 2 Toledo (43615) *(G-18742)*

Toledo Streets Newspaper 419 214-3460
316 N Michigan St Ste 330 Toledo (43604) *(G-18743)*

Toledo Sword Newspaper 419 932-0767
3332 Stanhope Dr Toledo (43606) *(G-18744)*

Toledo Tape and Label Company 419 536-8316
4731 South Ave Ste 3 Toledo (43615) *(G-18745)*

Toledo Ticket Company 419 476-5424
3963 Catawba St Toledo (43612) *(G-18746)*

Toledo Tool and Die Co Inc 419 476-4422
105 W Alexis Rd Toledo (43612) *(G-18747)*

Toledo Transducers Inc 419 724-4170
6834 Spring Valley Dr # 3 Holland (43528) *(G-11090)*

Toledo Window & Awning Inc 419 474-3396
3035 W Sylvania Ave Toledo (43613) *(G-18748)*

Toledos Runway Rivalry Brough 419 724-6307
541 N Superior St Toledo (43604) *(G-18749)*

Tolento's Family Restaurant, Cleveland *Also called Adkins Marlena (G-4704)*

Tolloti Pipe LLC 330 364-6627
102 Barnhill Rd Se New Philadelphia (44663) *(G-14935)*

Tolloti Plastic Pipe Inc (PA) 330 364-6627
102 Barnhill Rd Se New Philadelphia (44663) *(G-14936)*

Tolloti Plastic Pipe Inc 740 922-6911
1830 Barbour Dr Se Uhrichsville (44683) *(G-19062)*

Tolson Pallet Mfg Inc 937 787-3511
10240 State Rte 122 Gratis (45330) *(G-10468)*

Tom Bad Brewing LLC 513 871-4677
4720 Eastern Ave Cincinnati (45226) *(G-4512)*

Tom Barbour Auto Parts Inc (PA) 740 354-4654
915 11th St Portsmouth (45662) *(G-16457)*

Tom Fucito Inc 513 273-2092
21 Lynn Ave Oxford (45056) *(G-15844)*

Tom Hudson 937 393-1285
6655 Us Highway 50 Hillsboro (45133) *(G-11016)*

Tom James Company 614 488-8400
1156 Dublin Rd Ste 101 Columbus (43215) *(G-7698)*

Tom Pallas Industries Inc 216 622-0230
1828 Fulton Rd Cleveland (44113) *(G-6331)*

Tom Richards Inc 440 974-1300
7010 Lindsay Dr Mentor (44060) *(G-13748)*

Tom Smith Industries Inc 937 832-1555
500 Smith Dr Clayton (45315) *(G-4663)*

Tom Thumb Clip Co Inc 440 953-9606
36300 Lkeland Blvd Unit 2 Willoughby (44095) *(G-20619)*

Tom's Print Shop, Zanesville *Also called Dresden Specialties Inc (G-21302)*

Tomahawk Printing (PA) 419 335-3161
229 N Fulton St Wauseon (43567) *(G-19696)*

Tomahawk Printing Inc 419 335-3161
229 N Fulton St Wauseon (43567) *(G-19697)*

Tomahawk Tool Supply 419 485-8737
1604 Magda Dr Montpelier (43543) *(G-14455)*

Tomak Precision, Lebanon *Also called Aws Industries Inc (G-11782)*

Tomco Industries 330 652-7531
1660 E County Line Rd Mineral Ridge (44440) *(G-14313)*

Tomco Machining Inc 937 264-1943
4962 Riverton Dr Dayton (45414) *(G-8718)*

Tomco Tool Inc 937 322-5768
203 S Wittenberg Ave Springfield (45506) *(G-17665)*

Tomlinson Industries, Cleveland *Also called Meyer Company (G-5793)*

Tomlinson Industries Co 216 332-1595
13700 Brdwy Ave Cleveland (44125) *(G-6332)*

Tommy B Manufacturing Inc 330 745-4539
374 5th St Nw Barberton (44203) *(G-1155)*

Toms Country Place Inc 440 934-4553
3442 Stoney Ridge Rd Avon (44011) *(G-1016)*

Tomson Steel Company 513 420-8600
1400 Made Industrial Dr Middletown (45044) *(G-14089)*

Tonns Fabrication 614 989-5097
7767 Harrisburg London Rd Orient (43146) *(G-15725)*

Tool & Die Systems Inc 440 327-5800
38900 Taylor Indus Pkwy North Ridgeville (44039) *(G-15406)*

Tool Service Co Inc 937 254-4000
4620 Tall Oaks Dr Dayton (45432) *(G-8119)*

Tool Systems Inc 440 461-6363
  71 Alpha Park Cleveland (44143) *(G-6333)*

Tool Technologies Van Dyke 937 349-4900
  639 Clymer Rd Marysville (43040) *(G-12975)*

Toolbold Corporation (PA) 216 676-9840
  5330 Commerce Pkwy W Cleveland (44130) *(G-6334)*

Toolbold Corporation 440 543-1660
  5330 Commerce Pkwy W Cleveland (44130) *(G-6335)*

Toolco Inc 419 667-3462
  16913 Wren Landeck Rd Van Wert (45891) *(G-19273)*

Toolcomp, Toledo Also called Tooling & Components Corp *(G-18750)*

Toolcraft Products Inc 937 223-8271
  1265 Mccook Ave Dayton (45404) *(G-8719)*

Tooling & Components Corp 419 478-9122
  5261 Tractor Rd Toledo (43612) *(G-18750)*

Tooling Components Division, Cleveland Also called Jergens Inc *(G-5610)*

Tooling Connection Inc 419 594-3339
  N Ste 12603 Hc 66 Oakwood (45873) *(G-15620)*

Tooling Tech Group, Fort Loramie Also called Tooling Technology LLC *(G-9943)*

Tooling Tech Holdings LLC (HQ) 937 295-3672
  100 Enterprise Dr Fort Loramie (45845) *(G-9942)*

Tooling Technology LLC (PA) 937 295-3672
  100 Enterprise Dr Fort Loramie (45845) *(G-9943)*

Tooling Zone Inc 937 550-4180
  285 S Pioneer Blvd Springboro (45066) *(G-17510)*

Toolovation LLC 216 514-3022
  23980 Mercantile Rd Uppr Cleveland (44122) *(G-6336)*

Toolrite Manufacturing Inc 937 278-1962
  5370 Wadsworth Rd Dayton (45414) *(G-8720)*

Tools Plus, Troy Also called Gary Compton *(G-18830)*

Tools Sales & Service, Cincinnati Also called TSS Technologies Inc *(G-4533)*

Tooltex Inc 614 539-3222
  6160 Seeds Rd Grove City (43123) *(G-10603)*

Toomey Inc 513 831-4771
  914 Lila Ave Milford (45150) *(G-14178)*

Toomey Natural Foods, Milford Also called Toomey Inc *(G-14178)*

Top Cat Air Tools, Willoughby Also called TC Service Co *(G-20609)*

Top Drilling Corporation (PA) 304 477-3333
  107 Lancaster St 301 Marietta (45750) *(G-12842)*

Top Fuel Coatings 330 758-1166
  20 Philrose Ln Poland (44514) *(G-16385)*

Top Hat Designs 614 898-1962
  776 Autumn Branch Rd Westerville (43081) *(G-20238)*

Top Network, Columbus Also called Essilor Laboratories Amer Inc *(G-7066)*

Top Notch Fleet Services LLC 419 260-4057
  801 Wall St Maumee (43537) *(G-13303)*

Top Notch Logging 330 466-1780
  8242 Secrest Rd Apple Creek (44606) *(G-650)*

Top Tier Storage Prodcuts LLC 937 242-6133
  6501 Centerville Business Centerville (45459) *(G-3045)*

Top Tool & Die Inc 216 267-5878
  15500 Brookpark Rd Cleveland (44135) *(G-6337)*

Tope Printing Inc 330 674-4993
  1056 S Washington St Millersburg (44654) *(G-14271)*

Topkote Inc 440 428-0525
  404 N Lake St Madison (44057) *(G-12512)*

Topps Products Inc 216 271-2550
  3201 E 66th St Cleveland (44127) *(G-6338)*

Tops Auto Interiors, Mentor Also called Tops Inc *(G-13749)*

Tops Inc 440 954-9451
  7564 Tyler Blvd Ste A Mentor (44060) *(G-13749)*

Torah Tech Inc 614 570-6298
  2671 E Main St Columbus (43209) *(G-7699)*

Torbot Group Inc 419 724-1475
  5030 Advantage Dr Ste 101 Toledo (43612) *(G-18751)*

Tormaxx Co 513 721-6299
  1150 W 8th St Ste 111 Cincinnati (45203) *(G-4513)*

Torok Supply Company 330 799-6677
  52 S Meridian Rd Youngstown (44509) *(G-21224)*

Torq Corporation 440 232-4100
  32 W Monroe Ave Bedford (44146) *(G-1468)*

Torque Transmission, Fairport Harbor Also called Rampe Manufacturing Company *(G-9771)*

Torr Metal Products Inc 216 671-1616
  12125 Bennington Ave Cleveland (44135) *(G-6339)*

Torsion Control Product 248 597-9997
  840 W Spring Valley Pike Dayton (45458) *(G-8721)*

Torso 614 421-7663
  772 N High St Ste 100 Columbus (43215) *(G-7700)*

Tortilla 614 557-3367
  8134 E Broad St Reynoldsburg (43068) *(G-16609)*

Tortilla Factory, Toledo Also called La Perla Inc *(G-18552)*

Tortilleria El Maizal LLP 330 209-9344
  1895 Greentree Pl Se Massillon (44646) *(G-13206)*

Tortilleria La Bamba 216 515-1600
  1849 W 24th St Cleveland (44113) *(G-6340)*

Tortilleria La Bamba LLC 216 469-0410
  1849 W 24th St Cleveland (44113) *(G-6341)*

Tosoh America Inc (HQ) 614 539-8622
  3600 Gantz Rd Grove City (43123) *(G-10604)*

Tosoh SMD Inc 614 875-7912
  2050 Southpark Pl Grove City (43123) *(G-10605)*

Tosoh SMD Inc (HQ) 614 875-7912
  3600 Gantz Rd Grove City (43123) *(G-10606)*

Total Cable Solutions Inc 513 457-7013
  475 Victory Ln Springboro (45066) *(G-17511)*

Total Lubrication MGT Co (HQ) 888 478-6996
  3713 Progress St Ne Canton (44705) *(G-2880)*

Total Maintenance Management 513 228-2345
  320 Harmon Ave Lebanon (45036) *(G-11844)*

Total Manufacturing Co Inc 440 205-9700
  7777 Saint Clair Ave Mentor (44060) *(G-13750)*

Total Plastics Inc 440 205-9700
  7895 Division Dr Mentor (44060) *(G-13751)*

Total Plastics Inc 440 891-1140
  17851 Englewood Dr Ste A Cleveland (44130) *(G-6342)*

Total Quality Machining Inc 937 746-7765
  10 Shotwell Dr Franklin (45005) *(G-10059)*

Total Repair Express Mich LLC 248 690-9410
  4575 Hudson Dr Stow (44224) *(G-17809)*

Total Supply Solutions LLC 614 989-6665
  4177 Wyandotte Woods Blvd Dublin (43016) *(G-9155)*

Total Tennis Inc 614 488-5004
  1733 Cardiff Rd Columbus (43221) *(G-7701)*

Total Voice Technologies, Broadview Heights Also called Cleveland Business Supply LLC *(G-2108)*

Totally Promotional, Coldwater Also called Casad Company Inc *(G-6555)*

Totes Isotoner Corporation (PA) 513 682-8200
  9655 International Blvd West Chester (45246) *(G-20059)*

Totes Isotoner Holdings Corp (PA) 513 682-8200
  9655 International Blvd West Chester (45246) *(G-20060)*

Toth Industries Inc 419 729-4669
  5102 Enterprise Blvd Toledo (43612) *(G-18752)*

Toth Mold & Die Inc 440 232-8530
  380 Solon Rd Ste 7 Cleveland (44146) *(G-6343)*

Touba Satellite R US 513 853-0700
  4144 Hamilton Ave Cincinnati (45223) *(G-4514)*

Touch Life Centers LLC 614 388-8075
  3455 Mill Run Dr Ste 310 Hilliard (43026) *(G-10988)*

Touch of Glass 419 861-2888
  908 Jean Rd Toledo (43615) *(G-18753)*

Touch Print Solution, Cincinnati Also called Onetouchpoint East Corp *(G-4189)*

Touchmark, Dublin Also called Advanced Prgrm Resources Inc *(G-9037)*

Touchpint Cmplete Slutions LLC 419 919-3222
  1978 Havemann Rd Celina (45822) *(G-3024)*

Touchstone Woodworks 330 297-1313
  7820 Cooley Rd Ravenna (44266) *(G-16566)*

Tow Path Materials, Lucasville Also called Tow Path Ready Mix *(G-12425)*

Tow Path Ready Mix 740 286-2131
  1668 Kessinger School Rd Jackson (45640) *(G-11331)*

Tow Path Ready Mix (PA) 740 259-3222
  12360 State Route 104 Lucasville (45648) *(G-12425)*

Tower Automotive Operations I 419 358-8966
  18717 County Road 15 Bluffton (45817) *(G-1918)*

Tower Automotive Operations I 419 483-1500
  630 Southwest St Bellevue (44811) *(G-1564)*

Tower Industries Ltd 330 837-2216
  2101 9th St Sw Massillon (44647) *(G-13207)*

Tower Manufacturing Company, Springfield Also called Robertson Incorporated *(G-17644)*

Tower Tool & Manufacturing Co 330 425-1623
  2057 E Aurora Rd Ste No Twinsburg (44087) *(G-19028)*

Towing Electrical Systems 330 793-3887
  150 Victoria Rd Youngstown (44515) *(G-21225)*

Town Planner, The, Richfield Also called Pauler Communications Inc *(G-16631)*

Townsend Machinery, Montville Also called Ray Townsend *(G-14461)*

Toxco Inc 740 653-6290
  265 Quarry Rd Se Lancaster (43130) *(G-11757)*

Toy & Sport Trends Inc 419 748-8880
  5963 State Route 110 Napoleon (43545) *(G-14700)*

Toyo Seiki Usa Inc 513 546-9657
  11130 Luschek Dr Blue Ash (45241) *(G-1882)*

Toyo System Usa Inc 614 414-0515
  2216 Citygate Dr Columbus (43219) *(G-7702)*

Toyobo Kureha America Co Ltd 513 771-6788
  11630 Mosteller Rd Cincinnati (45241) *(G-4515)*

Tpi Medical, Gahanna Also called Thompson Partners Inc *(G-10238)*

Tpr, Hinckley Also called Tarantula Performance Racg LLC *(G-11030)*

Tpr Plasma Center 419 244-3910
  625 Dorr St Toledo (43604) *(G-18754)*

Tpsc Inc 440 439-9320
  25801 Solon Rd Bedford Heights (44146) *(G-1495)*

Tq Manufacturing Company Inc 440 255-9000
  7345 Production Dr Mentor (44060) *(G-13752)*

Tracer Specialties Inc 216 696-2363
  1842 Columbus Rd Cleveland (44113) *(G-6344)*

Tracewell Power Inc 614 846-6175
  567 Enterprise Dr Westerville (43081) *(G-20239)*

Tracewell Systems Inc (PA) 614 846-6175
  567 Enterprise Dr Lewis Center (43035) *(G-11927)*

A
L
P
H
A
B
E
T
I
C

Track-It Systems 513 522-0083
1776 Mentor Ave Ste 560 Cincinnati (45212) *(G-4516)*

Tracker Machine Inc 330 482-4086
1370 Kauffman Ave Columbiana (44408) *(G-6635)*

Trademark Designs Inc 419 628-3897
17 Jackson St Minster (45865) *(G-14365)*

Trademark Solutions 740 374-9779
2167 State Route 821 B Marietta (45750) *(G-12843)*

Tradewinds Prin Twear 740 214-5005
35 E Athens Rd Roseville (43777) *(G-16733)*

Tradex International Inc 216 651-4788
5300 Tradex Pkwy Cleveland (44102) *(G-6345)*

Trading Corp of America, Columbus *Also called Marfo Company (G-7318)*

Trading Post 740 922-1199
202 N Water St Uhrichsville (44683) *(G-19063)*

Traditional Marble & Gran Ltd 419 625-3966
10105 Us Highway 250 N Milan (44846) *(G-14117)*

Traditions Sauces LLC 419 704-4506
606 Durango Dr Toledo (43609) *(G-18755)*

Tradye Machine & Tool Inc 740 625-7550
3116a Wilson Rd Centerburg (43011) *(G-3031)*

Traffic Cntrl Sgnls Signs & MA 740 670-7763
1195 E Main St Newark (43055) *(G-15064)*

Traffic Detectors & Signs Inc 330 707-9060
7521 Forest Hill Ave Youngstown (44514) *(G-21226)*

Traffic Engineering Department, Canton *Also called City of Canton (G-2656)*

Traichal Construction, Niles *Also called Warren Door (G-15188)*

Traichal Construction Company (PA) 800 255-3667
332 Plant St Niles (44446) *(G-15186)*

Trail Cabinet 330 893-3791
2270 Township Road 415 Dundee (44624) *(G-9181)*

Trailer Component Mfg Inc 440 255-2888
8120 Tyler Blvd Mentor (44060) *(G-13753)*

Trailer One Inc 330 723-7474
6378 Norwalk Rd Medina (44256) *(G-13490)*

Trailex Inc 330 533-6814
1 Industrial Park Dr Canfield (44406) *(G-2580)*

Trailway Wood 330 893-9966
3173 Township Road 414 Dundee (44624) *(G-9182)*

Trane Company 419 491-2278
1001 Hamilton Dr Holland (43528) *(G-11091)*

Trane National Account Service, Columbus *Also called Trane US Inc (G-7704)*

Trane US Inc 513 771-8884
10300 Springfield Pike Cincinnati (45215) *(G-4517)*

Trane US Inc 614 473-3131
2300 Citygate Dr Ste 100 Columbus (43219) *(G-7703)*

Trane US Inc 614 497-6300
6600 Port Rd Ste 200 Groveport (43125) *(G-10647)*

Trane US Inc 614 473-8701
2300 Citygate Dr Ste 250 Columbus (43219) *(G-7704)*

Tranquility, Bowling Green *Also called Principle Business Entps Inc (G-2009)*

Trans Ash Inc 859 341-1528
320 S Wayne Ave Cincinnati (45215) *(G-4518)*

Trans Foam Inc 330 630-9444
281 Southwest Ave Tallmadge (44278) *(G-18173)*

Trans-Acc Inc (PA) 513 793-6410
11167 Deerfield Rd Blue Ash (45242) *(G-1883)*

Transcendia Inc 740 929-5100
3700 Hebron Rd Hebron (43025) *(G-10891)*

Transcendia Inc 440 638-2000
22889 Lunn Rd Strongsville (44149) *(G-17978)*

Transco Railway Products Inc 330 872-0934
2310 S Center St Newton Falls (44444) *(G-15140)*

Transco Railway Products Inc 419 726-3383
4800 Schwartz Rd Toledo (43611) *(G-18756)*

Transcon Inc 440 255-7600
8824 Twinbrook Rd Mentor (44060) *(G-13754)*

Transcontinental Electric LLC 614 496-4379
3155 Wareham Rd Columbus (43221) *(G-7705)*

Transcontinental Oil & Gas 330 995-0777
1509 Page Rd Aurora (44202) *(G-950)*

Transdermal Inc 440 241-1846
938 Chestnut Run Gates Mills (44040) *(G-10338)*

Transdigm Inc 216 291-6025
4223 Monticello Blvd Cleveland (44121) *(G-6346)*

Transdigm Inc 440 352-6182
313 Gillett St Painesville (44077) *(G-15931)*

Transdigm Inc (HQ) 216 706-2939
4223 Monticello Blvd Cleveland (44121) *(G-6347)*

Transdigm Inc 440 352-6182
313 Gillett St Painesville (44077) *(G-15932)*

Transdigm Group Incorporated (PA) 216 706-2960
1301 E 9th St Ste 3000 Cleveland (44114) *(G-6348)*

Transducers Direct Llc 513 583-7597
112 Lakeview Ct Loveland (45140) *(G-12395)*

Transducers Direct Llc 513 247-0601
12115 Ellington Ct Cincinnati (45249) *(G-4519)*

Transel Corporation 513 897-3442
123 E South St Harveysburg (45032) *(G-10835)*

Transel Technologies, Harveysburg *Also called Transel Corporation (G-10835)*

Transfer Express Inc 440 918-1900
7650 Tyler Blvd Mentor (44060) *(G-13755)*

Transformer Associates Limited 330 430-0750
831 Market Ave N Canton (44702) *(G-2881)*

Transglobal Inc (PA) 419 396-9079
225 N Patterson St Carey (43316) *(G-2927)*

Transimage Inc 937 293-0261
314 Spirea Dr Oakwood (45419) *(G-15611)*

Transit Sittings of NA 330 797-2516
295 S Meridian Rd Youngstown (44509) *(G-21227)*

Transmet Corporation 614 276-5522
4290 Perimeter Dr Columbus (43228) *(G-7706)*

Transmit Identity LLC 330 576-4732
3916 Clk Pnte Trl Ste 101 Stow (44224) *(G-17810)*

Transport Container Corp 614 459-8140
950 Augusta Glen Dr Columbus (43235) *(G-7707)*

Transportation Group, Mantua *Also called Mantaline Corporation (G-12715)*

Transportation Ohio Department 740 927-2285
318 S Township Rd Pataskala (43062) *(G-15987)*

Transtar Holding Company (PA) 800 359-3339
5900 Landerbrook Dr Bsmt Cleveland (44124) *(G-6349)*

Transue & Williams Stampg Corp 330 821-5777
930 W Ely St Alliance (44601) *(G-546)*

Transue Williams Stamping Inc 330 270-0891
207 N Four Mile Run Rd Austintown (44515) *(G-976)*

Transue Williams Stamping Inc (HQ) 330 829-5007
930 W Ely St Alliance (44601) *(G-547)*

Tranzonic Companies (PA) 216 535-4300
26301 Curtiss Wright Pkwy # 200 Richmond Heights (44143) *(G-16656)*

Tranzonic Companies 216 535-4300
26301 Curtiss Wright Pkwy # 200 Richmond Heights (44143) *(G-16657)*

Tranzonic Companies 440 446-0643
26301 Curtiss Wright Pkwy # 200 Cleveland (44143) *(G-6350)*

Trapeze Software Group Inc 905 629-8727
23215 Commerce Park # 200 Beachwood (44122) *(G-1302)*

Travelers Custom Case Inc 216 621-8447
2261 E 14th St Cleveland (44115) *(G-6351)*

Travelers Vacation Guide 440 582-4949
10143 Royalton Rd North Royalton (44133) *(G-15456)*

Traveling & Recycle Wood Pdts 419 968-2649
19590 Bellis Rd Middle Point (45863) *(G-13899)*

Traxium LLC 330 572-8200
4246 Hudson Dr Stow (44224) *(G-17811)*

Trd Leathers 216 631-6233
6321 Detroit Ave Cleveland (44102) *(G-6352)*

Treadway Manufacturing LLC 937 264-8447
5667 Webster St Dayton (45414) *(G-8722)*

Treasured Times Enterprises, West Alexandria *Also called John M Hand (G-19780)*

Treaty City Industries Inc 937 548-9000
945 Sater St Greenville (45331) *(G-10525)*

Trebnick Systems Inc 937 743-1550
215 S Pioneer Blvd Springboro (45066) *(G-17512)*

Trebnick Tags and Labels, Springboro *Also called Trebnick Systems Inc (G-17512)*

Trec Industries Inc 216 741-4114
4713 Spring Rd Cleveland (44131) *(G-6353)*

Tree City Mold & Machine Co 330 673-9807
6752 State Route 43 Kent (44240) *(G-11538)*

Tree Free Resources LLC 740 751-4844
175 Park Blvd Marion (43302) *(G-12908)*

Treehouse Private Brands Inc 740 654-8880
3775 Lanc New Lex Rd Se Lancaster (43130) *(G-11758)*

Treehouse Private Brands Inc 740 654-8880
276 Bremen Rd Lancaster (43130) *(G-11759)*

Treemen Industries Inc 330 965-3777
691 Mcclurg Rd Boardman (44512) *(G-1925)*

Trellborg Sling Prfiles US Inc (HQ) 330 995-9725
500 Lena Dr Aurora (44202) *(G-951)*

Trelleborg Wheel Systems Ameri (HQ) 866 633-8473
1501 Exeter Rd Akron (44306) *(G-444)*

Tremac Corporation 937 372-8662
550 Bellbrook Ave Xenia (45385) *(G-20982)*

Tremcar USA Inc 330 878-7708
436 12th St Ne Strasburg (44680) *(G-17831)*

Tremco Glazing Solutions Group, Ashland *Also called Tremco Incorporated (G-782)*

Tremco Incorporated 216 752-4401
4475 E 175th St Cleveland (44128) *(G-6354)*

Tremco Incorporated (HQ) 216 292-5000
3735 Green Rd Beachwood (44122) *(G-1303)*

Tremco Incorporated 419 289-2050
1451 Jacobson Ave Ashland (44805) *(G-782)*

Tremelo 330 823-6359
884 Roseland Rd Alliance (44601) *(G-548)*

Tremont Electric Incorporated 888 214-3137
2112 W 7th St Cleveland (44113) *(G-6355)*

Trend Consulting Services, Solon *Also called Netsmart Technologies Inc (G-17349)*

Trend Curve, The, Cleveland *Also called Marketing Directions Inc (G-5747)*

Trent Manufacturing Company 216 391-1551
6212 Carnegie Ave Cleveland (44103) *(G-6356)*

Tresco International Ltd Co 330 757-8131
1637 Bluebell Trl Youngstown (44514) *(G-21228)*

Tresslers Plumbing LLC 419 784-2142
9170 State Route 15 Defiance (43512) ***(G-8812)***
Treved Exteriors 513 771-3888
10235 Spartan Dr Ste T Cincinnati (45215) ***(G-4520)***
Trevi Technology Inc 614 754-7175
1029 Dublin Rd Columbus (43215) ***(G-7708)***
Trexler Rubber Co Inc (PA) 330 296-9677
503 N Diamond St Ravenna (44266) ***(G-16567)***
Trey Corrugated Inc 513 942-4800
9048 Port Union Rialto Rd West Chester (45069) ***(G-19960)***
Tri - Flex of Ohio Inc (PA) 330 705-7084
2701 Applegrove St Nw North Canton (44720) ***(G-15277)***
Tri Cast Limited Partnership 330 733-8718
2128 Killian Rd Akron (44312) ***(G-445)***
Tri Chem Inc 330 677-1213
7285 State Route 43 Ste C Kent (44240) ***(G-11539)***
Tri Con Distribution LLC 937 399-3312
776 Deerfield Trl Springfield (45503) ***(G-17666)***
Tri County Asphalt Materials 330 549-2852
405 Andrews Ave Youngstown (44505) ***(G-21229)***
Tri County Concrete Inc (PA) 330 425-4464
9423 Darrow Rd Twinsburg (44087) ***(G-19029)***
Tri County Concrete Inc 330 425-4464
10155 Royalton Rd Cleveland (44133) ***(G-6357)***
Tri County Door Service Inc 216 531-2245
21701 Tungsten Rd Euclid (44117) ***(G-9611)***
Tri County Eggs, Versailles *Also called Weaver Bros Inc* ***(G-19360)***
Tri County Locksmith, Cincinnati *Also called AB Bonded Locksmiths Inc* ***(G-3342)***
Tri County Marble & Granite, Fostoria *Also called Fostoria Monument Co* ***(G-9978)***
Tri County Quality Wtr Systems 740 751-4764
659 N Main St Marion (43302) ***(G-12909)***
Tri County Ready Mixed Con Co, Cleveland *Also called Tri County Concrete Inc* ***(G-6357)***
Tri County Tarp Inc 419 288-3350
13100 State Route 23 Bradner (43406) ***(G-2030)***
Tri County Viking Warriors, Warren *Also called Tri County Vking Warriors* ***(G-19610)***
Tri County Vking Warriors 330 646-4632
1745 Ogden Ave Nw Warren (44483) ***(G-19610)***
Tri County Wheel and Rim Ltd 419 666-1760
6943 Wales Rd Ste A Northwood (43619) ***(G-15492)***
Tri R Tooling Inc 419 522-8665
220 Piper Rd Mansfield (44905) ***(G-12699)***
Tri State Countertop Service 740 354-3663
3350 Indian Dr Portsmouth (45662) ***(G-16458)***
Tri State Dairy 419 542-8788
210 Wendell Ave Hicksville (43526) ***(G-10908)***
Tri State Dairy LLC 330 897-5555
115 S Mill St Baltic (43804) ***(G-1078)***
Tri State Equipment Company 513 738-7227
5009 Cncnnt Brookville Rd Shandon (45063) ***(G-17098)***
Tri State Garden Supply, Archbold *Also called Gardenscape* ***(G-676)***
Tri State Media LLC 513 933-0101
325 Davids Dr Wilmington (45177) ***(G-20680)***
Tri State Pallet Inc 937 323-5210
854 Sherman Ave Springfield (45503) ***(G-17667)***
Tri State Pallet Inc (PA) 937 746-8702
8401 Claude Thomas Rd # 57 Franklin (45005) ***(G-10060)***
Tri Technologies Inc 513 422-1300
1300 Lafayette Ave Middletown (45044) ***(G-14090)***
Tri-America Contractors Inc (PA) 740 574-0148
1664 State Route 522 Wheelersburg (45694) ***(G-20335)***
Tri-America Contractors Inc 740 574-0148
1664 State Route 522 Wheelersburg (45694) ***(G-20336)***
Tri-Cast Inc (PA) 330 733-8718
2128 Killian Rd Akron (44312) ***(G-446)***
Tri-Co Industries 740 927-1928
13804 Refugee Rd Sw Pataskala (43062) ***(G-15988)***
Tri-County Block and Brick Inc 419 826-7060
1628 Us 20 Alternate Swanton (43558) ***(G-18093)***
Tri-Craft Inc 440 826-1050
17941 Englewood Dr Cleveland (44130) ***(G-6358)***
Tri-Fab Inc 330 337-3425
10372 W South Range Rd Salem (44460) ***(G-16931)***
Tri-K Enterprises Inc 330 832-7380
935 Mckinley Ave Sw Canton (44707) ***(G-2882)***
Tri-Mac Mfg & Serv, Hamilton *Also called Tri-Mac Mfg & Svcs Co* ***(G-10749)***
Tri-Mac Mfg & Svcs Co 513 896-4445
860 Belle Ave Hamilton (45015) ***(G-10749)***
Tri-R Dies Inc 330 758-8050
556 Bev Rd Youngstown (44512) ***(G-21230)***
Tri-Seal LLC 330 821-1166
16125 Armour St Ne Alliance (44601) ***(G-549)***
Tri-State Asphalt Co, Rayland *Also called Shelly and Sands Inc* ***(G-16575)***
Tri-State Beef Co Inc 513 579-1722
2124 Baymiller St Cincinnati (45214) ***(G-4521)***
Tri-State Belting Ltd 800 330-2358
5525 Vine St Cincinnati (45217) ***(G-4522)***
Tri-State Fabricators Inc 513 752-5005
1146 Ferris Rd Amelia (45102) ***(G-587)***
Tri-State Fasteners LLC 937 442-1904
2875 Gath North Rd Sardinia (45171) ***(G-17034)***
Tri-State Jet Mfg LLC 513 896-4538
1480 Beissinger Rd Hamilton (45013) ***(G-10750)***
Tri-State Machining LLC 513 257-9442
6088 Hamilton Cleves Rd # 2 Cleves (45002) ***(G-6530)***
Tri-State Model Flyers Inc 740 886-8429
358 Township Road 1161 Proctorville (45669) ***(G-16494)***
Tri-State Printing, Steubenville *Also called Tri-State Publishing Company* ***(G-17719)***
Tri-State Publishing Company (PA) 740 283-3686
157 N 3rd St Steubenville (43952) ***(G-17719)***
Tri-State Special Events Inc 513 221-2962
614 Tafel St Cincinnati (45225) ***(G-4523)***
Tri-State Supply Co Inc 614 272-6767
3840 Fisher Rd Columbus (43228) ***(G-7709)***
Tri-State Tool & Die Inc 330 655-2536
1396 Norton Rd Stow (44224) ***(G-17812)***
Tri-State Tool Grinding Inc 513 347-0100
5311 Robert Ave Ste A Cincinnati (45248) ***(G-4524)***
Tri-State Wilbert Vault Co, Ironton *Also called Allen Enterprises Inc* ***(G-11288)***
Tri-Tech Laboratories Inc 740 927-2817
8825 Smiths Mill Rd N Johnstown (43031) ***(G-11408)***
Tri-Tech Led Systems 614 593-2868
600 W Market St Baltimore (43105) ***(G-1090)***
Tri-Tech Machining LLC 513 575-3959
1885 Seven Lands Dr Milford (45150) ***(G-14179)***
Tri-Tech Medical Inc 800 253-8692
35401 Avon Commerce Pkwy Avon (44011) ***(G-1017)***
Tri-Tech Mfg LLC 419 238-0140
7404 State Route 66 Delphos (45833) ***(G-8921)***
Tri-Tech Research LLC 440 946-6122
34099 Melinz Pkwy Unit K Eastlake (44095) ***(G-9293)***
Tri-Way Rebar Inc (PA) 330 296-9662
625 S Walnut St Ravenna (44266) ***(G-16568)***
Tri-Way Rebar Inc 330 882-8043
625 S Walnut St Akron (44319) ***(G-447)***
Tri-Weld Inc 216 281-6009
4411 Detroit Ave Cleveland (44113) ***(G-6359)***
Triad Capital Aat LLC 440 236-4163
13676 Station Rd Columbia Station (44028) ***(G-6603)***
Triad Energy Corporation 740 374-2940
125 Putnam St Marietta (45750) ***(G-12844)***
Triad Governmental Systems 937 376-5446
358 S Monroe St Xenia (45385) ***(G-20983)***
Triad Hunter LLC (HQ) 740 374-2940
125 Putnam St Marietta (45750) ***(G-12845)***
Triad Hunter LLC 740 374-2940
125 Putnam St Marietta (45750) ***(G-12846)***
Triad Metal Products Company 216 676-6505
12990 Snow Rd Chagrin Falls (44023) ***(G-3128)***
Triage Ortho Group 937 653-6431
132 Lafayette Ave Urbana (43078) ***(G-19185)***
Triangle Biomedical Sciences, Cincinnati *Also called General Data Company Inc* ***(G-3306)***
Triangle Fastener Corporation 734 458-1700
4661 Hinckley Indus Pkwy Cleveland (44109) ***(G-6360)***
Triangle Label Inc 513 242-2822
6392 Gano Rd West Chester (45069) ***(G-19961)***
Triangle Machine Products Co 216 524-5872
6055 Hillcrest Dr Cleveland (44125) ***(G-6361)***
Triangle Precision Industries 937 299-6776
1650 Delco Park Dr Dayton (45420) ***(G-8723)***
Triangle Sign Co 513 863-2578
221 N B St Hamilton (45013) ***(G-10751)***
Triatrix LLC 440 263-8936
20006 Detroit Rd Ste 100 Cleveland (44116) ***(G-6362)***
Triaxis Machine & Tool LLC 440 230-0303
11941 Abbey Rd Ste H North Royalton (44133) ***(G-15457)***
Tribco Incorporated 216 486-2000
18901 Cranwood Pkwy Cleveland (44128) ***(G-6363)***
Tribune , The, Jefferson *Also called The Gazette Printing Co Inc* ***(G-11373)***
Tribune Chronicle, Warren *Also called Ogden Newspapers Inc* ***(G-19582)***
Tribune Courier, Ontario *Also called Stumbo Publishing Co* ***(G-15695)***
Tribune Printing Inc 419 542-7764
147 E High St Hicksville (43526) ***(G-10909)***
Tribune Shopping News, The, New Lexington *Also called Perry County Tribune* ***(G-14851)***
Trico Belting & Supply Company (HQ) 513 860-8400
9965 Farr Ct West Chester (45246) ***(G-20061)***
Trico Corporation 216 642-3223
9700 Rockside Rd Ste 430 Cleveland (44125) ***(G-6364)***
Trico Enterprises LLC 330 674-1157
6430 Township Road 348 Millersburg (44654) ***(G-14272)***
Trico Enterprises LLC 330 674-1157
6430 Tr 348 Millersburg (44654) ***(G-14273)***
Trico Machine Products Corp 216 662-4194
5081 Corbin Dr Cleveland (44128) ***(G-6365)***
Tricor Industrial Inc (PA) 330 264-3299
3225 W Old Lincoln Way Wooster (44691) ***(G-20841)***
Trident Polymer Solutions, Akron *Also called Next Design & Build LLC* ***(G-314)***

ALPHABETIC

Tridico Silk Screen & Sign Co 419 526-1695
  162 N Diamond St Mansfield (44902) *(G-12700)*

Trifecta Tool & Engrg LLC 937 291-0933
  4648 Gateway Cir Dayton (45440) *(G-8724)*

Trigon Industries Inc 937 299-1350
  1616 Delaine Ave Oakwood (45419) *(G-15612)*

Trillium Health Care Products 513 242-2227
  5177 Spring Grove Ave Cincinnati (45217) *(G-4525)*

Trilo Inc 937 276-4288
  2947 Boulder Ave Dayton (45414) *(G-8725)*

Trilogy Plastics Inc (PA) 330 821-4700
  2290 W Main St Alliance (44601) *(G-550)*

Trilogy Plastics Inc 440 893-5522
  7160 Chagrin Rd Chagrin Falls (44023) *(G-3129)*

Trilogy Plastics Inc 330 875-1789
  900 N Chapel St Louisville (44641) *(G-12331)*

Trim Parts Inc 513 934-0815
  2175 Deerfield Rd Lebanon (45036) *(G-11845)*

Trim Systems Operating Corp (HQ) 614 289-5360
  7800 Walton Pkwy New Albany (43054) *(G-14773)*

Trim Systems Operating Corp 614 289-5360
  7800 Walton Pkwy New Albany (43054) *(G-14774)*

Trim Systems Operating Corp 740 772-5998
  75 Chamber Dr Chillicothe (45601) *(G-3281)*

Trim Tool & Machine Inc 216 889-1916
  3431 Service Rd Cleveland (44111) *(G-6366)*

Trimble Inc 937 233-8921
  5475 Kellenburger Rd Dayton (45424) *(G-8726)*

Trimble Inc 937 245-5951
  5475 Kellenburger Rd Dayton (45424) *(G-8727)*

Trimline Die Corporation 440 355-6900
  421 Commerce Dr E Lagrange (44050) *(G-11639)*

Trimold LLC 740 474-7591
  200 Pittsburgh Rd Circleville (43113) *(G-4648)*

Trimtec Systems Ltd 614 820-0340
  2455 Harrisburg Pike Grove City (43123) *(G-10607)*

Trinel Inc 216 265-9190
  5251 W 137th St Cleveland (44142) *(G-6367)*

Trinity Door Systems 877 603-2018
  13886 Woodworth Rd New Springfield (44443) *(G-14953)*

Trinity Highway Products Llc 419 227-1296
  425 E O Connor Ave Lima (45801) *(G-12105)*

Trinity Printing Co 513 469-1000
  2300 E Kemper Rd Ste A19 Cincinnati (45241) *(G-4526)*

Trio Insulated Glass Inc 614 276-1647
  1094 Mckinley Ave Columbus (43222) *(G-7710)*

Trionetics Inc 216 812-3570
  4915 Van Epps Rd Ste B Brooklyn Heights (44131) *(G-2148)*

Trionix Research Laboratory 330 425-9055
  8037 Bavaria Rd Twinsburg (44087) *(G-19030)*

Triple Arrow Industries Inc 614 437-5588
  13311 Industrial Pkwy Marysville (43040) *(G-12976)*

Triple Diamond Plastics LLC 419 533-0085
  405 N Pleasantview Dr Liberty Center (43532) *(G-11956)*

Triple J Oilfield Services LLC 740 483-9030
  42722 State Route 7 Hannibal (43931) *(G-10764)*

Triple T Fabricating, Byesville *Also called Timothy Sasser (G-2411)*

Triplett Bluffton Corporation 419 358-8750
  1 Triplett Dr Bluffton (45817) *(G-1919)*

Tripoint Instruments Inc 513 702-9217
  7513 Hamilton Ave Cincinnati (45231) *(G-4527)*

Trison Tool Inc 440 352-1055
  69 Burton St Painesville (44077) *(G-15933)*

Tristan Rubber Molding Inc (PA) 330 499-4055
  7255 Whipple Ave Nw North Canton (44720) *(G-15278)*

Tristate Tubular Inc 330 339-5240
  2713 Stonecreek Rd Sw New Philadelphia (44663) *(G-14937)*

Triton Products LLC 440 248-5480
  30700 Carter St Ste D Solon (44139) *(G-17407)*

Triumph Signs & Consulting Inc 513 576-8090
  480 Milford Pkwy Milford (45150) *(G-14180)*

Triumph Thermal Systems LLC (HQ) 419 273-2511
  200 Railroad St Forest (45843) *(G-9923)*

Triumph Tool LLC 937 222-6885
  229 Leo St Dayton (45404) *(G-8728)*

Triumphant Enterprises Inc 513 617-1668
  7096 Hill Station Rd Goshen (45122) *(G-10417)*

Trivantis, Cincinnati *Also called SC Elearning (G-4382)*

Trivantis Corporation (PA) 513 929-0188
  311 Elm St Ste 200 Cincinnati (45202) *(G-4528)*

TRM Manufacturing Inc 330 769-2600
  601 Munroe Falls Ave Cuyahoga Falls (44221) *(G-8057)*

Trogdon Publishing Inc 330 721-7678
  5164 Normandy Park Dr # 100 Medina (44256) *(G-13491)*

Trogdon Publishing Inc 330 620-2407
  1635 Strathshire Hall Pl Powell (43065) *(G-16486)*

Trojon Gear Inc 937 254-1737
  418 San Jose St Dayton (45403) *(G-8729)*

Tronair Inc (HQ) 419 866-6301
  1740 Eber Rd Ste E Holland (43528) *(G-11092)*

Tronair Parent Inc (HQ) 419 866-6301
  1740 Eber Rd Ste E Holland (43528) *(G-11093)*

Trophy Nut Co (PA) 937 667-8478
  320 N 2nd St Tipp City (45371) *(G-18306)*

Trophy Nut Co 937 669-5513
  1567 Harmony Dr Tipp City (45371) *(G-18307)*

Tropical Ohio Smoothie Inc 937 673-6218
  2019 E State Route 73 Waynesville (45068) *(G-19736)*

Trotwood Corporation 937 854-3047
  11 N Broadway St Trotwood (45426) *(G-18800)*

Troy Chemical Industries Inc (PA) 440 834-4408
  17040 Rapids Rd Burton (44021) *(G-2387)*

Troy Daily News Inc (HQ) 937 339-2729
  224 S Market St Troy (45373) *(G-18880)*

Troy Engineered Components and 937 335-8070
  800 Scholz Dr Vandalia (45377) *(G-19312)*

Troy Innovative Instrs Inc 440 834-9567
  15111 White Rd Middlefield (44062) *(G-13996)*

Troy Laminating & Coating Inc 937 335-5611
  421 Union St Troy (45373) *(G-18881)*

Troy Manufacturing Co 440 834-8262
  17090 Rapids Rd Burton (44021) *(G-2388)*

Troy Precision Carbide Die 440 834-4477
  17720 Claridon Troy Rd Burton (44021) *(G-2389)*

Troy Sand and Gravel, Troy *Also called Marietta Martin Materials Inc (G-18856)*

Troy Valley Petroleum 937 604-0012
  201 Valley St Dayton (45404) *(G-8730)*

Troy Water Treatment Plant, Troy *Also called City of Troy (G-18809)*

Troy West LLC 937 339-2192
  650 Olympic Dr Troy (45373) *(G-18882)*

Troyer Cheese Inc 330 893-2479
  6597 County Road 625 Millersburg (44654) *(G-14274)*

Troyers Pallet Shop 330 897-1038
  31052 Township Road 227 Fresno (43824) *(G-10201)*

Troyers Trail Bologna Inc 330 893-2414
  6552 State Route 515 Dundee (44624) *(G-9183)*

Troyke Manufacturing Company 513 769-4242
  11294 Orchard St Cincinnati (45241) *(G-4529)*

Troymill Manufacturing Inc (PA) 440 632-5580
  17055 Kinsman Rd Middlefield (44062) *(G-13997)*

Troymill Wood Products, Middlefield *Also called Troymill Manufacturing Inc (G-13997)*

Trs Engineering LLC 419 714-7034
  26640 Lemoyne Rd Perrysburg (43551) *(G-16163)*

Tru Comfort Mattress 614 595-8600
  8994 Mediterra Pl Dublin (43016) *(G-9156)*

Tru Form Metal Products Inc 216 252-3700
  12305 Grimsby Ave Cleveland (44135) *(G-6368)*

Tru-Chem Company Inc 614 888-2436
  6645 Singletree Dr Columbus (43229) *(G-7711)*

Tru-Fab Inc 937 435-1733
  4751 Gateway Cir Dayton (45440) *(G-8731)*

Tru-Fab Technology Inc 440 954-9760
  34820 Lakeland Blvd Willoughby (44095) *(G-20620)*

Tru-Form Steel & Wire Inc 765 348-5001
  5509 Telegraph Rd Toledo (43612) *(G-18757)*

Tru-Har Products 330 338-6826
  7946 Darrow Rd Unit 334 Hudson (44236) *(G-11205)*

Tru-Tex International Corp 513 825-8844
  11050 Southland Rd Cincinnati (45240) *(G-4530)*

Truax Printing Inc 419 994-4166
  425 E Haskell St Loudonville (44842) *(G-12306)*

Trucast Inc 440 942-4923
  4382 Hamann Pkwy Willoughby (44094) *(G-20621)*

Truck Fax Inc 216 921-8866
  17700 S Woodland Rd Cleveland (44120) *(G-6369)*

Truck Stop Embroidery (PA) 419 257-2860
  12906 Deshler Rd North Baltimore (45872) *(G-15199)*

Truck Stop Embroidery 419 257-2860
  12906 Deshler Rd North Baltimore (45872) *(G-15200)*

Truco Inc 216 631-1000
  3033 W 44th St Cleveland (44113) *(G-6370)*

Trucut Incorporated (PA) 330 938-9806
  1145 Allied Dr Sebring (44672) *(G-17055)*

True Grinding 440 786-7608
  20502 Krick Rd Bedford (44146) *(G-1469)*

True Industries Inc 330 296-4342
  666 Pratt St Ravenna (44266) *(G-16569)*

True Kote Inc 419 334-8813
  2132 E Cole Rd Fremont (43420) *(G-10188)*

True North Energy LLC 440 442-0060
  6411 Mayfield Rd Mayfield Heights (44124) *(G-13323)*

True Torq, Blanchester *Also called Fulflo Specialties Company (G-1713)*

True Turn Industries 440 355-6256
  233 Commerce Dr Unit D Lagrange (44050) *(G-11640)*

True Value, Woodville *Also called Trumbull Inc (G-20727)*

True Value, North Baltimore *Also called Mid-Wood Inc (G-15195)*

Truechoicepack Corp 937 630-3832
  1285 Lyons Rd Ste H Dayton (45458) *(G-8732)*

Truenorth Energy, Mayfield Heights *Also called True North Energy LLC (G-13323)*

Truex Tool & Die Div, Youngstown *Also called Jamen Tool & Die Co* (G-21123)

Trufast, Bryan *Also called Altenloh Brinck & Co US Inc* (G-2277)

Truflex Rubber Products Co 740 967-9015
200 E Coshocton St Johnstown (43031) *(G-11409)*

Trugreen Cleaners LLC 740 703-1063
1733 Anderson Station Rd Chillicothe (45601) *(G-3282)*

Truline Industries Inc 440 729-0140
11685 Chillicothe Rd Chesterland (44026) *(G-3222)*

Trulite GL Alum Solutions LLC 740 929-2443
160 N High St Hebron (43025) *(G-10892)*

Trulite GL Alum Solutions LLC 614 876-1057
2395 Setterlin Dr Columbus (43228) *(G-7712)*

Trumbull Cement Products Co 330 372-4342
2185 Larchmont Ave Ne Warren (44483) *(G-19611)*

Trumbull County Dry Kilns Inc 330 562-3367
475 Wheatfield Dr Aurora (44202) *(G-952)*

Trumbull County Hardwoods 440 632-0555
9446 Bundysburg Rd Middlefield (44062) *(G-13998)*

Trumbull County Legal News 330 392-7112
108 Main Ave Sw Ste 700 Warren (44481) *(G-19612)*

Trumbull Engrg Assembly & Mch 330 394-6628
172 Forest St Nw Warren (44483) *(G-19613)*

Trumbull Inc 419 849-3561
850 1/2 Water St Woodville (43469) *(G-20727)*

Trumbull Industries Inc 330 434-6174
209 Perkins St Akron (44304) *(G-448)*

Trumbull Locker Plant Inc 440 474-4631
3393 State Route 534 Rock Creek (44084) *(G-16686)*

Trumbull Manufacturing Inc 330 393-6624
400 Dietz Rd Ne Warren (44483) *(G-19614)*

Trumbull Mobile Meals Inc 330 394-2538
323 E Market St Warren (44481) *(G-19615)*

Trupoint Products 330 204-3302
Uknown Sugarcreek (44681) *(G-18046)*

Truseal Technologies Inc (HQ) 216 910-1500
6680 Parkland Blvd Solon (44139) *(G-17408)*

Truss Worx LLC 419 363-2100
12412 Frysinger Rd Rockford (45882) *(G-16693)*

Trust Manufacturing LLC 216 531-8787
20080 Saint Clair Ave Euclid (44117) *(G-9612)*

Trust Technologies, Eastlake *Also called Kilroy Company* (G-9278)

Trustone Distributors Co 513 469-0335
3273 E Sharon Rd Cincinnati (45241) *(G-4531)*

Trutech Cabinetry 614 338-0680
2121 S James Rd Columbus (43232) *(G-7713)*

Trv Incorporated 440 951-7722
4860 E 345th St Willoughby (44094) *(G-20622)*

TRW Automotive Fayette Plant, Fayette *Also called TRW Automotive Inc* (G-9780)

TRW Automotive Inc 419 237-2511
705 N Fayette St Fayette (43521) *(G-9780)*

TRW Automotive Inc 216 750-2400
8333 Rockside Rd Cleveland (44125) *(G-6371)*

TRW Automotive US LLC 216 750-2400
8333 Rockside Rd Cleveland (44125) *(G-6372)*

TRW Automotive US LLC 419 726-5599
5915 Jason St Toledo (43611) *(G-18758)*

TRW Automotive US LLC 216 332-7100
19501 Emery Rd Cleveland (44128) *(G-6373)*

TRW Shared Services, Cleveland *Also called TRW Automotive Inc* (G-6371)

TS Engineering, Washingtonville *Also called Turvey Engineering* (G-19643)

TS Tech USA Corporation (HQ) 614 577-1088
8400 E Broad St Reynoldsburg (43068) *(G-16610)*

TS Trim Industries Inc 614 837-4114
6380 Canal St Canal Winchester (43110) *(G-2539)*

TS Trim Industries Inc 740 593-5958
10 Kenny Dr Athens (45701) *(G-888)*

TS Trim Trimold Inc 614 920-1927
6380 Canal St Canal Winchester (43110) *(G-2540)*

Tsjmedia, Blue Ash *Also called Gate West Coast Ventures LLC* (G-1802)

Tsk America Co Ltd 513 942-4002
9668 Inter Ocean Dr West Chester (45246) *(G-20062)*

Tsp Inc 513 732-8900
2009 Glenn Pkwy Batavia (45103) *(G-1229)*

TSR Machinery Services Inc 513 874-9697
100 Security Dr Fairfield (45014) *(G-9726)*

TSS Medical, West Chester *Also called TSS Technologies Inc* (G-19962)

TSS Technologies Inc (PA) 513 772-7000
8800 Global Way West Chester (45069) *(G-19962)*

TSS Technologies Inc 513 772-7000
10200 Chester Rd Cincinnati (45215) *(G-4532)*

TSS Technologies Inc 513 772-7000
8800 Global Way West Chester (45069) *(G-19963)*

TSS Technologies Inc 513 772-7000
1201 Hill Smith Dr Cincinnati (45215) *(G-4533)*

TSS Technologies Inc 513 772-7000
8800 Global Way West Chester (45069) *(G-19964)*

Tsw Industries Inc 440 572-7200
14960 Foltz Pkwy Strongsville (44149) *(G-17979)*

TTI Floor Care North Amer Inc (HQ) 440 996-2000
7005 Cochran Rd Solon (44139) *(G-17409)*

TTI Sports Equipment, Columbus *Also called Total Tennis Inc* (G-7701)

Ttr Manufacturing 440 366-5005
740 Sugar Ln Elyria (44035) *(G-9503)*

Tubar Eureka Industrial Group, Sugarcreek *Also called Belden Brick Company* (G-18016)

Tube Fitting, Lewisburg *Also called Parker-Hannifin Corporation* (G-11938)

Tube Fittings Division, Lewisburg *Also called Parker-Hannifin Corporation* (G-11939)

Tubetech (PA) 330 426-9476
900 E Taggart St East Palestine (44413) *(G-9247)*

Tubetech North America, East Palestine *Also called Tubetech Inc* (G-9247)

Tubular Techniques Inc 614 529-4130
3025 Scioto Darby Exec Ct Hilliard (43026) *(G-10989)*

Tuckers Mold Polishing 937 339-3063
3225 E Peterson Rd Troy (45373) *(G-18883)*

Tuf-N-Lite, Springboro *Also called Feather Lite Innovations Inc* (G-17480)

Tuf-Tex, Norwalk *Also called Maple City Rubber Company* (G-15551)

Tuf-Tug Products Div, Moraine *Also called Deuer Developments Inc* (G-14478)

Tuff Stuff Performance, Cleveland *Also called Hurst Auto-Truck Electric* (G-5538)

Tuffy Manufacturing 330 940-2356
140 Ascot Pkwy Cuyahoga Falls (44223) *(G-8058)*

Tuffy Pad Company Inc 330 688-0043
454 Seasons Rd Stow (44224) *(G-17813)*

Tune Town Car Audio 419 627-1100
2018 E Perkins Ave Sandusky (44870) *(G-17017)*

Tungsten and Capital, Solon *Also called Bowes Manufacturing Inc* (G-17271)

Tungsten Sltons Group Intl Inc 440 708-3096
17523 Merry Oaks Trl Chagrin Falls (44023) *(G-3130)*

Tunnell Hill Reclamation, New Lexington *Also called Oxford Mining Company Inc* (G-14850)

Tuppas Software Corporation 419 897-7902
1690 Woodlands Dr Maumee (43537) *(G-13304)*

Turbine Eng Cmpnents Tech Corp 216 692-6173
23555 Euclid Ave Cleveland (44117) *(G-6374)*

Turbine Standard Ltd (PA) 419 865-0355
10550 Industrial St Holland (43528) *(G-11094)*

Turbo Machine & Tool Inc 216 651-1940
2151 W 117th St Cleveland (44111) *(G-6375)*

Turbo-Mold Inc 440 352-2530
440 Blackbrook Rd Painesville (44077) *(G-15934)*

Turbonics Inc 216 741-8300
4001 Pearl Rd Lowr Cleveland (44109) *(G-6376)*

Turf Care Supply Corp (HQ) 877 220-1014
50 Pearl Rd Ste 200 Brunswick (44212) *(G-2264)*

Turk+hillinger Usa Inc 440 781-1900
6650 W Snowville Rd Ste W Brecksville (44141) *(G-2077)*

Turkeyfoot Creek Creamery 419 335-0224
11313 County Road D Wauseon (43567) *(G-19698)*

Turkeyfoot Hill Sand & Gravel 330 899-1997
465 E Turkeyfoot Lake Rd Akron (44319) *(G-449)*

Turkeyfoot Printing, Napoleon *Also called Mustang Printing* (G-14690)

Turn-All Machine & Gear Co 937 342-8710
5499 Tremont Ln Springfield (45502) *(G-17668)*

Turn-Key Industrial Svcs LLC 614 274-1128
820 Distribution Dr Columbus (43228) *(G-7714)*

Turn-Key Tunneling Inc 614 275-4832
1247 Stimmel Rd Columbus (43223) *(G-7715)*

Turner Lightning Protection Co 614 738-6225
5193 Dry Creek Dr Dublin (43016) *(G-9157)*

Turner Machine Co 330 332-5821
1433 Salem Pkwy Salem (44460) *(G-16932)*

Turner Pressure 614 871-7775
3997 Thistlewood Dr Grove City (43123) *(G-10608)*

Turner Vault 419 223-6861
1488 Elida Rd Lima (45805) *(G-12106)*

Turner Vault Co 419 537-1133
2121 Tracy Rd Northwood (43619) *(G-15493)*

Turning Technologies LLC (PA) 330 746-3015
255 W Federal St Youngstown (44503) *(G-21231)*

Turning Technologies LLC 330 746-3015
265 W Federal St Youngstown (44503) *(G-21232)*

Turnkey Technology Sales, Cincinnati *Also called Ela Holding Corporation* (G-3691)

Turnwood Industries Inc 330 278-2421
365 State Rd Hinckley (44233) *(G-11031)*

Turtle Plastics, Lorain *Also called Cleveland Reclaim Inds Inc* (G-12238)

Turtlecreek Township 513 932-4080
670 N Rte 123 Lebanon (45036) *(G-11846)*

Turvey Engineering 330 427-0125
240 High St Washingtonville (44490) *(G-19643)*

Tusco Hardwoods LLC 330 852-4281
10887 Gerber Valley Rd Nw Sugarcreek (44681) *(G-18047)*

Tutto Vino, Dublin *Also called Muirfield Wine Company LLC* (G-9107)

TV Facts, East Liverpool *Also called Larry C White* (G-9224)

Tvh Parts Co 877 755-7311
8950 Global Way West Chester (45069) *(G-19965)*

TW Corporation 440 461-3234
99 S Seiberling St Akron (44305) *(G-450)*

TW Tank LLC 419 334-2664
721 Graham Dr Fremont (43420) *(G-10189)*

TW Tank LLC 419 334-2664
  721 Graham Dr Fremont (43420) *(G-10190)*

Tween Brands Inc 937 435-6928
  2700 Mmsburg Cntrville Rd Dayton (45459) *(G-8733)*

Twenty Second Cntury Foods LLC 419 866-6343
  6546 Weatherfield Ct C Maumee (43537) *(G-13305)*

Twin Cities Concrete Co (HQ) 330 343-4491
  141 S Tuscarawas Ave Dover (44622) *(G-9021)*

Twin Cities Concrete Co 330 627-2158
  1031 Kensington Rd Ne Carrollton (44615) *(G-2968)*

Twin Design AP Promotions Ltd 937 732-6798
  5785 Far Hills Ave Dayton (45429) *(G-8734)*

Twin Fin, Austinburg Also called Multi-Design Inc *(G-963)*

Twin Oaks Barn 330 893-3126
  3337 Us Route 62 Dundee (44624) *(G-9184)*

Twin Point Inc (PA) 419 923-7525
  11955 County Road 10 2 Delta (43515) *(G-8940)*

Twin Rivers Technologies Mfg, Painesville Also called Twin Rvers Tech - Pnsville LLC *(G-15935)*

Twin Rvers Tech - Pnsville LLC 440 350-6300
  679 Hardy Rd Painesville (44077) *(G-15935)*

Twin Tool LLC 937 435-8946
  4648 Gateway Cir Dayton (45440) *(G-8735)*

Twin Valley Metalcraft Asm LLC 937 787-4634
  4739 Enterprise Rd West Alexandria (45381) *(G-19784)*

Twin Ventures Inc 330 405-3838
  2457 Edison Blvd Twinsburg (44087) *(G-19031)*

Twinsburg Development Corp (PA) 440 357-5562
  1 Williams St Grand River (44045) *(G-10454)*

Twinsource LLC 440 248-6800
  32333 Aurora Rd Ste 50 Solon (44139) *(G-17410)*

Twist Inc (PA) 937 675-9581
  47 S Limestone St Jamestown (45335) *(G-11353)*

Twist Inc 937 675-9581
  5100 Waynesville Jamestown (45335) *(G-11354)*

Twister Displays, East Liverpool Also called Delta Manufacturing Inc *(G-9213)*

Two Bandits Brewing Co LLC 419 636-4045
  206 Scott Dr Bryan (43506) *(G-2324)*

Two Grandmothers Gourmet Kit 614 746-0888
  9127 Firstgate Dr Reynoldsburg (43068) *(G-16611)*

Two M Precision Co Inc 440 946-2120
  1747 Joseph Lloyd Pkwy # 3 Willoughby (44094) *(G-20623)*

Tyjen Inc (PA) 740 380-3215
  35255 Hocking Dr Logan (43138) *(G-12196)*

Tyjen Inc 740 797-4064
  8 Slater Dr The Plains (45780) *(G-18187)*

Tykma Inc 877 318-9562
  370 Gateway Dr Chillicothe (45601) *(G-3283)*

Tykma Electrox, Chillicothe Also called Tykma Inc *(G-3283)*

Tyler Electric Motor Repair 330 836-5537
  1888 Copley Rd Akron (44320) *(G-451)*

Tyler Elevator Products, Twinsburg Also called Sematic Usa Inc *(G-19018)*

Tyler Grain & Fertilizer Co 330 669-2341
  3388 Eby Rd Smithville (44677) *(G-17246)*

Tyler Haver Inc (HQ) 440 974-1047
  8570 Tyler Blvd Mentor (44060) *(G-13756)*

Tyler Haver Inc 800 255-1259
  8570 Tyler Blvd Mentor (44060) *(G-13757)*

Tyler Mold & Machine Inc 330 645-6653
  2200 Massillon Rd Akron (44312) *(G-452)*

Tylok International Inc 216 261-7310
  1061 E 260th St Cleveland (44132) *(G-6377)*

Tymex Plastics Inc 216 429-8950
  5300 Harvard Ave Cleveland (44105) *(G-6378)*

Tymoca Partners LLC 440 946-4327
  33220 Lakeland Blvd Eastlake (44095) *(G-9294)*

Tyseka 419 860-9585
  1021 Brower Rd Lima (45801) *(G-12107)*

Tytek Industries Inc (PA) 513 874-7326
  4700 Ashwood Dr Ste 445 Blue Ash (45241) *(G-1884)*

Tytek Medical Inc 513 247-2002
  4700 Ashwood Dr Ste 445 Blue Ash (45241) *(G-1885)*

Tz Acquisition Corp 216 535-4300
  26301 Curtiss Wright Pkwy Richmond Heights (44143) *(G-16658)*

U C G, Independence Also called United Computer Group Inc *(G-11280)*

U C Printing Service, Cincinnati Also called University of Cincinnati *(G-4543)*

U C Signs, Unionville Center Also called Unionville Center Sign Co *(G-19105)*

U C X, Cleveland Also called Undercar Express LLC *(G-6381)*

U D F, Cincinnati Also called United Dairy Farmers Inc *(G-4538)*

U Haul Neighborhood Dealer 740 445-4125
  6900 State Route 339 Vincent (45784) *(G-19381)*

U M D Automated Systems Inc 740 694-8614
  9855 Salem Rd Fredericktown (43019) *(G-10113)*

U S Alloy Die Corp 216 749-9700
  4007 Brookpark Rd Cleveland (44134) *(G-6379)*

U S Army Corps of Engineers 740 537-2571
  29501 State Rte 7 Toronto (43964) *(G-18786)*

U S Chemical & Plastics 740 254-4311
  600 Nova Dr Se Massillon (44646) *(G-13208)*

U S Chrome Corporation Ohio 937 224-0548
  107 Westboro St Dayton (45417) *(G-8736)*

U S Development Corp 570 966-5990
  900 W Main St Kent (44240) *(G-11540)*

U S Development Corp (PA) 330 673-6900
  900 W Main St Kent (44240) *(G-11541)*

U S Electrical Tool Inc 513 353-3660
  5928 Hamilton Cleves Rd Miamitown (45041) *(G-13893)*

U S Filter/Envirex, Milford Also called Evoqua Water Technologies LLC *(G-14140)*

U S Fuel Development Co (PA) 614 486-0614
  1445 Goodale Blvd Columbus (43212) *(G-7716)*

U S Graphics, Urbana Also called David Brandeberry *(G-19156)*

U S Hair Inc 614 235-5190
  3727 E Broad St Columbus (43213) *(G-7717)*

U S M, Willoughby Also called Usm Precision Products Inc *(G-20628)*

U S Terminals Inc 513 561-8145
  7504 Camargo Rd Cincinnati (45243) *(G-4534)*

U S Thermal Inc 513 777-7763
  9846 Crescent Park Dr West Chester (45069) *(G-19966)*

U S Weatherford L P 330 746-2502
  1100 Performance Pl Youngstown (44502) *(G-21233)*

U-Sonico 423 348-7117
  543 Cookston Ave Springfield (45503) *(G-17669)*

U.S. Bridge, Cambridge Also called Ohio Bridge Corporation *(G-2470)*

UAS, Blue Ash Also called United Air Specialists Inc *(G-1886)*

Uc Trailer Co., Sunbury Also called Universal Composite LLC *(G-18077)*

UCAR Carbon, Independence Also called Graftech Intl Holdings Inc *(G-11258)*

Ucr LLC 937 253-8898
  1332 Woodman Dr Ste 2 Dayton (45432) *(G-8120)*

Udderly Smooth, Salem Also called Redex Industries Inc *(G-16924)*

Udecx LLC 937 830-0374
  320 N 4th St Tipp City (45371) *(G-18308)*

Ufo's, Amelia Also called Thedkahn LLC *(G-586)*

Ufp Blanchester LLC 937 783-2443
  940 Cherry St Blanchester (45107) *(G-1717)*

Ufp Hamilton LLC 513 285-7190
  115 Distribution Dr Hamilton (45014) *(G-10752)*

Ugn Inc 513 360-3500
  201 Exploration Dr Lebanon (45036) *(G-11847)*

Uhcmc Cellular Therapy Lab, Cleveland Also called Cwru Irland Cncer Ctr Cellular *(G-5160)*

Uhrichsville Carbide Inc 740 922-9197
  410 N Water St Uhrichsville (44683) *(G-19064)*

UIC Energy LLC 614 839-0250
  3000 Corp Exchange Dr # 600 Columbus (43231) *(G-7718)*

Ulrich Rubber Stamp Company 419 339-9939
  2130 Larkspur Dr Elida (45807) *(G-9359)*

Ulterior Products LLC 614 519-3210
  2459 Scioto Harper Dr Hilliard (43026) *(G-10990)*

Ultimate Chem Solutions Inc 440 998-6751
  1800 E 21st St Ashtabula (44004) *(G-843)*

Ultimate Cloth, Plain City Also called Advanced Cleaning Tech LLC *(G-16318)*

Ultimate Pallet & Trucking LLC 440 693-4090
  4774 Parks West Rd Middlefield (44062) *(G-13999)*

Ultimate Printing Co Inc 330 847-2941
  6090 Mahoning Ave Nw C Warren (44481) *(G-19616)*

Ultimate Rb Inc (HQ) 419 692-3000
  1430 N Main St Delphos (45833) *(G-8922)*

Ultimate Signs and Graphics 740 633-8928
  904 Indiana St Martins Ferry (43935) *(G-12926)*

Ultra Graphics, Cleveland Also called Gail Zeilmann *(G-5391)*

Ultra Impressions Inc 440 951-4777
  7533 Tyler Blvd Ste D Mentor (44060) *(G-13758)*

Ultra Machine Inc 440 323-7632
  530 Lowell St Elyria (44035) *(G-9504)*

Ultra Printing & Design Inc 440 887-0393
  707 Brookpark Rd Ste 3 Cleveland (44109) *(G-6380)*

Ultra Punch, Dayton Also called Stolle Machinery Company LLC *(G-8684)*

Ultra Tech Machinery Inc 330 929-5544
  297 Ascot Pkwy Cuyahoga Falls (44223) *(G-8059)*

Ultra-Met Company 937 653-7133
  720 N Main St Urbana (43078) *(G-19186)*

Ultrabuilt Play Systems Inc 419 652-2294
  1114 Us Highway 224 Nova (44859) *(G-15580)*

Ultratech Polymers Inc 330 945-9410
  280 Ascot Pkwy Cuyahoga Falls (44223) *(G-8060)*

Umat LLC 937 224-3303
  272 Leo St Dayton (45404) *(G-8737)*

Umd Contractors Inc 740 694-8614
  9855 Salem Rd Fredericktown (43019) *(G-10114)*

Umecc, West Chester Also called Mecc-Usa LLC *(G-19899)*

Umicore Spclty Mtls Recycl LLC 440 833-3000
  28960 Lakeland Blvd Wickliffe (44092) *(G-20389)*

Unarco Material Handling Inc 419 384-3211
  407 E Washington St Pandora (45877) *(G-15948)*

Unbridled Brewing Company LLC 937 361-2573
  3387 Cincinnati Dayton Rd Middletown (45044) *(G-14091)*

Uncle Jesters Fine Foods LLC 937 550-1025
  2564 Kohnle Dr Miamisburg (45342) *(G-13873)*

Under Armour Inc 330 995-9557
549 S Chillicothe Rd Aurora (44202) *(G-953)*

Under Hill Water Well 740 852-0858
1789 Itawamba Trl London (43140) *(G-12221)*

Under Pressure Systems Inc 330 602-4466
322 North Ave Ne New Philadelphia (44663) *(G-14938)*

Undercar Express LLC 216 531-7004
18451 Euclid Ave Cleveland (44112) *(G-6381)*

Underground Professionals 419 282-6400
506 Us Highway 250 E Ashland (44805) *(G-783)*

Underground Sport Shop Inc 513 751-1662
1233 Findlay St Ste Frnt Cincinnati (45214) *(G-4535)*

Undiscovered Radio Network 740 533-1032
621 S 6th St Ironton (45638) *(G-11303)*

Unger Kosher Bakery Inc 216 321-7176
1831 S Taylor Rd Cleveland Heights (44118) *(G-6502)*

Ungers Bakery, Cleveland Heights *Also called Unger Kosher Bakery Inc (G-6502)*

UNI Corp 330 489-6500
1300 Market Ave N Canton (44714) *(G-2883)*

UNI-Facs, Columbus *Also called Universal Fabg Cnstr Svcs Inc (G-7723)*

UNI-Ref United Refractories Co 513 563-9955
11301 Jefferson St Cincinnati (45241) *(G-4536)*

Unibat, Cleveland *Also called Cleanlife Energy LLC (G-5044)*

Unibilt Industries Inc 937 890-7570
8005 Johnson Station Rd Vandalia (45377) *(G-19313)*

Unican Ohio LLC 419 636-5461
4600 Oak Harbor Rd Fremont (43420) *(G-10191)*

Unicontrol Inc (PA) 216 398-0330
1111 Brookpark Rd Cleveland (44109) *(G-6382)*

Unified Scrn & Crush-Oh Inc 937 836-3201
200 Cass Dr Englewood (45315) *(G-9541)*

Unifin Chesapeake, Salem *Also called Cardinal Pumps Exchangers Inc (G-16878)*

Unifirst Corporation 216 658-6900
1450 E Granger Rd Independence (44131) *(G-11279)*

Uniloy Milacron Inc 513 487-5000
4165 Half Acre Rd Batavia (45103) *(G-1230)*

Uninterrupted LLC 216 771-2323
3800 Embassy Pkwy Ste 360 Akron (44333) *(G-453)*

Union Camp Corp 330 343-7701
875 Harger St Dover (44622) *(G-9022)*

Union Enterprises Division, Plain City *Also called Gold Metal Machining Inc (G-16343)*

Union Fabricating & Machine Co 419 626-5963
3427 Venice Rd Sandusky (44870) *(G-17018)*

Union Flonetics, Salem *Also called Hunt Valve Company Inc (G-16902)*

Union Gospel Press Division, Cleveland *Also called Incorporated Trst Gspl Wk Scty (G-5560)*

Union Metal Corporation (PA) 330 456-7653
1432 Maple Ave Ne Canton (44705) *(G-2884)*

Union Process Inc 330 929-3333
1925 Akron Peninsula Rd Akron (44313) *(G-454)*

Union Sewing Company, Akron *Also called Jordan E Armour (G-242)*

Uniontown Septic Tanks Inc 330 699-3386
2781 Raber Rd Uniontown (44685) *(G-19104)*

Unionville Center Sign Co 614 873-5834
110 W Main St Unionville Center (43077) *(G-19105)*

Unipac Inc 740 929-2000
2109 National Rd Sw Hebron (43025) *(G-10893)*

Unique Awards & Signs, Saint Marys *Also called Behrco Inc (G-16832)*

Unique Covers 419 925-9600
8758 State Route 119 Maria Stein (45860) *(G-12761)*

Unique Expressions, Gallipolis *Also called Riverview Productions Inc (G-10308)*

Unique Fabrications Inc 419 355-1700
2520 Hayes Ave Fremont (43420) *(G-10192)*

Unique Packaging & Printing 440 785-6730
9086 Goldfinch Ct Mentor (44060) *(G-13759)*

Unique Paving Materials Corp 216 341-7711
3993 E 93rd St Cleveland (44105) *(G-6383)*

Unique Plastics LLC 419 352-0066
13350 Bishop Rd Bowling Green (43402) *(G-2018)*

Unique Solutions, Newark *Also called Holophane Corporation (G-15018)*

Unique Straight Line & Sfety S 740 452-2724
2776 Coopermill Rd Zanesville (43701) *(G-21359)*

Unique Woodmasters LLC 419 268-9663
6750 Guadalupe Rd Celina (45822) *(G-3025)*

Unique-Chardan Inc 419 636-6900
705 S Union St Bryan (43506) *(G-2325)*

Unisand Incorporated 330 722-0222
1097 Industrial Pkwy Medina (44256) *(G-13492)*

Unison Industries LLC 937 426-0621
2455 Dayton Xenia Rd Dayton (45434) *(G-8121)*

Unison Industries LLC 937 426-4676
530 Orchard Ln Alpha (45301) *(G-555)*

Unison Industries LLC 937 426-0621
2455 Dayton Xenia Rd Dayton (45434) *(G-8122)*

Unison Industries LLC 937 427-0550
2070 Heller Dr Beavercreek (45434) *(G-1363)*

Unison Industries LLC 937 426-0621
2156 Heller Dr Beavercreek (45434) *(G-1364)*

Unisport Inc 419 529-4727
2254 Stumbo Rd Ontario (44906) *(G-15696)*

Unit Dle, Eastlake *Also called Lange Equipment (G-9281)*

Unit Sets Inc 937 840-6123
835 S High St Hillsboro (45133) *(G-11017)*

Unitec, Canton *Also called UNI Corp (G-2883)*

United Advg Publications Inc 513 469-8818
11177 Reading Rd Ste 1 Cincinnati (45241) *(G-4537)*

United Air Specialists Inc (HQ) 513 891-0400
4440 Creek Rd Blue Ash (45242) *(G-1886)*

United Auto Worker AFL CIO 419 592-0434
410 Fillmore St Napoleon (43545) *(G-14701)*

United Buff & Supply Co Inc 419 738-2417
2 E Harrison St Wapakoneta (45895) *(G-19510)*

United Chart Processors Inc 740 373-5801
1461 Masonic Park Rd Marietta (45750) *(G-12847)*

United Circuits Inc 440 926-1000
1000 Commerce Dr Grafton (44044) *(G-10438)*

United Computer Group Inc 216 520-1333
7100 E Pleasant Valley Rd # 250 Independence (44131) *(G-11280)*

United Controls Group Inc (PA) 740 936-0005
400 Lazelle Rd Ste 13 Columbus (43240) *(G-6659)*

United Controls Group Inc 740 936-0005
400 Lazelle Rd Ste 14 Columbus (43240) *(G-6660)*

United Converting Inc 614 863-9972
3960 Groves Rd Unit B Columbus (43232) *(G-7719)*

United Dairy Inc (PA) 740 633-1451
300 N 5th St Martins Ferry (43935) *(G-12927)*

United Dairy Farmers Inc (PA) 513 396-8700
3955 Montgomery Rd Cincinnati (45212) *(G-4538)*

United Dental Laboratories (PA) 330 253-1810
261 South Ave Akron (44302) *(G-455)*

United Die & Mfg Co 330 938-6141
100 S 17th St Sebring (44672) *(G-17056)*

United Engineering & Fndry Co 330 456-2761
1400 Grace Ave Ne Canton (44705) *(G-2885)*

United Engraving, Cincinnati *Also called Wood Graphics Inc (G-4603)*

United Envelope LLC 513 542-4700
4890 Spring Grove Ave Cincinnati (45232) *(G-4539)*

United Extrusion Dies Inc 330 533-2915
5171 W Western Reserve Rd Canfield (44406) *(G-2581)*

United Feed Screws Ltd 330 798-5532
487 Wellington Ave Akron (44305) *(G-456)*

United Fiberglass America Inc 937 325-7305
2145 Airpark Dr Springfield (45502) *(G-17670)*

United Finshg & Die Cutng Inc 216 881-0239
3875 King Ave Cleveland (44114) *(G-6384)*

United Fire Apparatus Corp 419 645-4083
204 S Gay St Cridersville (45806) *(G-7947)*

United Graphics, Cincinnati *Also called Cns Inc (G-3593)*

United Grinding and Machine Co 330 453-7402
2315 Ellis Ave Ne Canton (44705) *(G-2886)*

United Group Services Inc (PA) 800 633-9690
9740 Near Dr West Chester (45246) *(G-20063)*

United Hard Chrome Corporation 330 453-2786
2202 Gilbert Ave Ne Canton (44705) *(G-2887)*

United Hardwoods Ltd 330 878-9510
5508 Hilltop Dr Nw Strasburg (44680) *(G-17832)*

United Hydraulics, Willoughby *Also called Two M Precision Co Inc (G-20623)*

United Hydraulics 440 585-0906
29627 Lakeland Blvd Wickliffe (44092) *(G-20390)*

United Ignition Wire Corp 216 898-1112
15620 Industrial Pkwy Cleveland (44135) *(G-6385)*

United Initiators Inc (HQ) 440 326-2416
555 Garden St Elyria (44035) *(G-9505)*

United Landmark Llc 740 852-2062
131 S Walnut St London (43140) *(G-12222)*

United Lubricants Corporation 513 422-9600
3431 Yankee Rd Middletown (45044) *(G-14092)*

United Machine and Tool Inc 440 946-7677
1956 E 337th St Eastlake (44095) *(G-9295)*

United McGill 614 829-1226
1777 Refugee Rd Columbus (43207) *(G-7720)*

United McGill Corporation (HQ) 614 829-1200
1 Mission Park Groveport (43125) *(G-10648)*

United Metal Fabricators Inc 216 662-2000
14301 Industrial Ave S Maple Heights (44137) *(G-12742)*

United Packaging Supply Co Div, Bedford *Also called Overseas Packing LLC (G-1451)*

United Process Controls Inc (HQ) 414 462-8200
8904 Beckett Rd West Chester (45069) *(G-19967)*

United Prtrs & Lithographers 216 771-2759
1045 French St Cleveland (44113) *(G-6386)*

United Quality Chekd Dairy, Martins Ferry *Also called United Dairy Inc (G-12927)*

United Ready Mix Inc 216 696-1600
7820 Carnegie Ave Cleveland (44103) *(G-6387)*

United Rolls Inc (HQ) 330 456-2761
1400 Grace Ave Ne Canton (44705) *(G-2888)*

United Rotary Brush Inc 937 644-3515
8150 Business Way Plain City (43064) *(G-16362)*

United Safety Authority, Warren *Also called D M V Supply Corporation (G-19540)*

United Seal Company, Columbus *Also called United Security Seals Inc (G-7721)*

United Security Seals Inc (PA) 614 443-7633
2000 Fairwood Ave Columbus (43207) *(G-7721)*

United Sport Apparel 330 722-0818
229 Harding St Ste B Medina (44256) *(G-13493)*

United State Pltg Bumper Svc 614 403-4666
1937 W Dblin Granville Rd Worthington (43085) *(G-20892)*

United States Controls Inc 330 758-1147
8511 Foxwood Ct Poland (44514) *(G-16386)*

United States Dept of Army 419 221-9500
1155 Buckeye Rd Lima (45804) *(G-12108)*

United States Drill Head Co 513 941-0300
5298 River Rd Cincinnati (45233) *(G-4540)*

United States Endoscopy 440 639-4494
6091 Heisley Rd Mentor (44060) *(G-13760)*

United States Endoscopy (HQ) 440 639-4494
5976 Heisley Rd Mentor (44060) *(G-13761)*

United States Gypsum Company 419 734-3161
121 S Lake St Gypsum (43433) *(G-10655)*

United States Steel Corp 440 240-2500
2199 E 28th St Lorain (44055) *(G-12287)*

United Surface Finishing Inc 330 453-2786
2202 Gilbert Ave Ne Canton (44705) *(G-2889)*

United Taconite LLC (HQ) 218 744-7800
1100 Superior Ave E # 1500 Cleveland (44114) *(G-6388)*

United Technologies, Toledo *Also called Otis Elevator Company (G-18623)*

United Technologies Corp 330 784-5477
6051 W Airport Dr North Canton (44720) *(G-15279)*

United Titanium Inc (PA) 330 264-2111
3450 Old Airport Rd Wooster (44691) *(G-20842)*

United Tool & Gage Co 216 676-1000
15740 Industrial Pkwy Cleveland (44135) *(G-6389)*

United Tool and Machine Inc 937 843-5603
490 S Main St Lakeview (43331) *(G-11650)*

United Tool Supply Inc 513 752-6000
851 Ohio Pike Ste 101 Cincinnati (45245) *(G-3320)*

United Trade Printers LLC 614 326-4829
94 N High St Ste 290 Dublin (43017) *(G-9158)*

United Tube Corporation 330 725-4196
960 Lake Rd Medina (44256) *(G-13494)*

United Ultra Violet Inc 614 875-8088
3280 Hrrsbrg Gvl Rd Grove City (43123) *(G-10609)*

United Wire Edm Inc 440 239-8777
777 Berea Industrial Pkwy Berea (44017) *(G-1639)*

United-Maier Signs Inc 513 681-6600
1030 Straight St Cincinnati (45214) *(G-4541)*

Unitherm Inc 937 278-1900
2601 Timber Ln Dayton (45414) *(G-8738)*

Unitus, Solon *Also called Sensical Inc (G-17378)*

Unity Cable Technologies Inc 419 322-4118
1811 Adams St Toledo (43604) *(G-18759)*

Unity Defense Systems, Inc., Toledo *Also called Unity Cable Technologies Inc (G-18759)*

Unity Tube Inc 330 426-4282
1862 State Route 165 East Palestine (44413) *(G-9248)*

Univar USA Inc 513 714-5264
4600 Dues Dr West Chester (45246) *(G-20064)*

Universal Bindery, Toledo *Also called Fergusons Finishing Inc (G-18469)*

Universal Black Oxiding, Cleveland *Also called Universal Heat Treating Inc (G-6390)*

Universal Cargo, Cleveland *Also called Acme Lifting Products Inc (G-4693)*

Universal Coatings Division, Twinsburg *Also called Universal Rack & Equipment Co (G-19033)*

Universal Composite LLC 614 507-1646
200 Kintner Pkwy Sunbury (43074) *(G-18077)*

Universal Drect Flfllment Corp 330 650-5000
5581 Hudson Indus Pkwy Hudson (44236) *(G-11206)*

Universal Electronics Inc 330 487-1110
1864 Entp Pkwy Ste B Twinsburg (44087) *(G-19032)*

Universal Equipment Mfg 614 586-1780
2140 Advance Ave Columbus (43207) *(G-7722)*

Universal Fabg Cnstr Svcs Inc 614 274-1128
1241 Mckinley Ave Columbus (43222) *(G-7723)*

Universal Fabrication Assembly, Cleveland *Also called Wire Products Company Inc (G-6468)*

Universal Forest Products, Blanchester *Also called Ufp Blanchester LLC (G-1717)*

Universal Ground Cullet Inc 419 637-2630
400 Cedar St Gibsonburg (43431) *(G-10378)*

Universal Heat Treating Inc 216 641-2000
3878 E 93rd St Cleveland (44105) *(G-6390)*

Universal Hydraulik USA Corp 419 873-6340
25651 Fort Meigs Rd Ste A Perrysburg (43551) *(G-16164)*

Universal Industrial Pdts Inc 419 737-9584
1 Coreway Dr Pioneer (43554) *(G-16245)*

Universal J&Z Machine LLC 216 486-2220
4781 E 355th St Willoughby (44094) *(G-20624)*

Universal Lettering Inc 419 238-9320
1197 Grill Rd B Van Wert (45891) *(G-19274)*

Universal Machine, Willoughby *Also called Usm Acquisition Corporation (G-20627)*

Universal Machine Division, New Philadelphia *Also called Coshocton Industries Inc (G-14893)*

Universal Machine Products 513 860-4530
9060 Goldpark Dr West Chester (45011) *(G-19968)*

Universal Metal Products Inc (PA) 440 943-3040
29980 Lakeland Blvd Wickliffe (44092) *(G-20391)*

Universal Metal Products Inc 419 287-3223
850 W Front St Pemberville (43450) *(G-16031)*

Universal Metals Cutting Inc 330 580-5192
2656 Harrison Ave Sw Canton (44706) *(G-2890)*

Universal Oil Inc 216 771-4300
265 Jefferson Ave Cleveland (44113) *(G-6391)*

Universal Packg Systems Inc 513 674-9400
470 Northland Blvd Cincinnati (45240) *(G-4542)*

Universal Packg Systems Inc 513 732-2000
5055 State Route 276 Batavia (45103) *(G-1231)*

Universal Packg Systems Inc 513 735-4777
5069 State Route 276 Batavia (45103) *(G-1232)*

Universal Pallets Inc (PA) 614 444-1095
659 Marion Rd Columbus (43207) *(G-7724)*

Universal Pallets Inc 614 444-1095
611 Marion Rd Columbus (43207) *(G-7725)*

Universal Percussion Inc 330 482-5750
1431 Heck Rd Columbiana (44408) *(G-6636)*

Universal Plastics, North Canton *Also called Upl International Inc (G-15280)*

Universal Plastics Inc 440 942-7510
9081 Agard Ct Mentor (44060) *(G-13762)*

Universal Polymer & Rubber Ltd (PA) 440 632-1691
15730 Madison Rd Middlefield (44062) *(G-14000)*

Universal Precision Products 330 633-6128
1480 Industrial Pkwy Akron (44310) *(G-457)*

Universal Production Corp 740 522-1147
1776 Tamarack Rd Newark (43055) *(G-15065)*

Universal Prototype Product Co 440 953-3550
36781 Lake Shore Blvd Eastlake (44095) *(G-9296)*

Universal Rack & Equipment Co 330 963-6776
8511 Tower Dr Twinsburg (44087) *(G-19033)*

Universal Scientific Inc 440 428-1777
6210 Campbell Dr Madison (44057) *(G-12513)*

Universal Stainless, North Jackson *Also called North Jckson Specialty Stl LLC (G-15295)*

Universal Steel Company 216 883-4972
6600 Grant Ave Cleveland (44105) *(G-6392)*

Universal Tire Molds Inc 330 253-5101
5127 Boyer Pkwy Akron (44312) *(G-458)*

Universal Tool Technology, Dayton *Also called Mdf Enterprises LLC (G-8481)*

Universal Tool Technology LLC 937 222-4608
3488 Stop 8 Rd Dayton (45414) *(G-8739)*

Universal Urethane Pdts Inc 419 693-7400
410 1st St Toledo (43605) *(G-18760)*

Universal Veneer Sales, Newark *Also called Krajewski Corp (G-15028)*

Universal Well Services Inc 330 264-1109
11 S Washington St Millersburg (44654) *(G-14275)*

Universitees, Columbus *Also called TIS Incorporated (G-7695)*

University Accessories Inc 440 327-4151
5152 Mills Indus Pkwy North Ridgeville (44039) *(G-15407)*

University Crdc & Thrc Grp 216 844-3053
11100 Euclid Ave Cleveland (44106) *(G-6393)*

University Hring Aid Assctions, Cincinnati *Also called Communications Aid Inc (G-3599)*

University of Cincinnati 513 556-5042
2900 Rerading Rd B101 Cincinnati (45221) *(G-4543)*

University Plastic Surgery 216 778-4450
2866 W Park Blvd Cleveland (44120) *(G-6394)*

University Sports Publications 614 291-6416
1265 Indianola Ave Columbus (43201) *(G-7726)*

Uniwall Manufacturing Co (HQ) 330 875-1444
3750 Beck Ave Louisville (44641) *(G-12332)*

Unlimited Machine and Tool LLC 419 269-1730
5139 Tractor Rd Ste C Toledo (43612) *(G-18761)*

Unlimited Promotions Inc 513 844-2211
1120 Hicks Blvd Ste 1 Fairfield (45014) *(G-9727)*

Unlimted Rcovery Solutions LLC 419 868-4888
2701 S Eberd Rd Ste B Wauseon (43567) *(G-19699)*

Unmanned Science Inc 614 581-9893
565 Metro Pl S Ste 300 Dublin (43017) *(G-9159)*

Unmanned Solutions Tech LLC 937 771-7023
3908 Eagle Point Dr Beavercreek (45430) *(G-1382)*

Unocal, Danville *Also called Carol Mickley (G-8086)*

Unverferth Mfg Co Inc (PA) 419 532-3121
601 S Broad St Kalida (45853) *(G-11418)*

Unverferth Mfg Co Inc 419 695-2060
24325 State Route 697 Delphos (45833) *(G-8923)*

UPA Technology Inc 513 755-1380
8963 Cncnnati Columbus Rd West Chester (45069) *(G-19969)*

Updegraff Inc 216 621-7600
1335 Main Ave Cleveland (44113) *(G-6395)*

Updike Supply Company (PA) 937 482-4000
8241 Expansion Way Huber Heights (45424) *(G-11152)*

Upl International Inc 330 433-2860
7661 Freedom Ave Nw North Canton (44720) *(G-15280)*

Upm Inc 419 595-2600
  4777 S Us Highway 23 Alvada (44802) *(G-557)*
Upper Cut 740 397-0330
  444 Columbus Rd Ste F Mount Vernon (43050) *(G-14653)*
Upper Echelon Bar LLC 513 531-2814
  1747 Avonlea Ave Cincinnati (45237) *(G-4544)*
Upper Monument 419 310-2387
  436 N Sandusky Ave Upper Sandusky (43351) *(G-19143)*
Upper Paw 419 277-9000
  5746 Staghorn Dr Toledo (43614) *(G-18762)*
Upper Sandusky Senior Housing 419 731-4104
  102 Westbrook Blvd Upper Sandusky (43351) *(G-19144)*
Upper Sarahsville LLC 740 732-2071
  48726 Sarahsville Rd Caldwell (43724) *(G-2434)*
Upperroom Action Ministries 330 848-9246
  1142 Morse St Akron (44320) *(G-459)*
Upright Steel LLC 216 923-0852
  1335 E 171st St Cleveland (44110) *(G-6396)*
UPS, New Philadelphia *Also called Allen Green Enterprises LLC (G-14883)*
Upside Innovations LLC 513 889-2492
  5470 Spellmire Dr West Chester (45246) *(G-20065)*
Uptivity, Columbus *Also called Callcopy Inc (G-6890)*
Uptown Dog The Inc 740 592-4600
  9 W Union St Athens (45701) *(G-889)*
Uptown Graphics, Norwood *Also called Blt Inc (G-15571)*
Urbana Machine & Tool Company, Urbana *Also called Ruth Leinasars (G-19178)*
Urc, Chagrin Falls *Also called Utility Relay Co Ltd (G-3131)*
Us Inc 513 791-1162
  10937 Reed Hartman Hwy Blue Ash (45242) *(G-1887)*
US 261 Corp 216 531-7143
  341 E 131st St Cleveland (44108) *(G-6397)*
US Aeroteam Inc 937 458-0344
  2601 W Stroop Rd Unit 60 Dayton (45439) *(G-8740)*
US Brands Inc 216 595-9700
  23600 Mercantile Rd Ste H Cleveland (44122) *(G-6398)*
US Coexcell Inc 419 897-9110
  400 W Dussel Dr Ste C Maumee (43537) *(G-13306)*
US Corrugated Inc 740 681-1600
  1290 Campground Rd Lancaster (43130) *(G-11760)*
US Corrugated of Massillon 216 663-3344
  16645 Granite Rd Maple Heights (44137) *(G-12743)*
US Cotton LLC 216 676-6400
  15501 Industrial Pkwy Cleveland (44135) *(G-6399)*
US Die & Mold, Canal Winchester *Also called Manifold & Phalor Inc (G-2531)*
US Endoscopy, Mentor *Also called United States Endoscopy (G-13761)*
US Filter, Pickerington *Also called Evoqua Water Technologies LLC (G-16192)*
US Fittings Inc 234 212-9420
  2182 E Aurora Rd Twinsburg (44087) *(G-19034)*
US Foam Corporation (PA) 513 528-9800
  7412 Jager Ct Cincinnati (45230) *(G-4545)*
US Foils, Willoughby *Also called USA Foils Inc (G-20626)*
US Government Publishing Off 614 469-5657
  200 N High St Rm 207 Columbus (43215) *(G-7727)*
US Greenfiber LLC 419 692-7015
  1601 Gressel Dr Delphos (45833) *(G-8924)*
US Greentech 513 371-5520
  3607 Church St Cincinnati (45244) *(G-4546)*
US Group, East Palestine *Also called E R Advanced Ceramics Inc (G-9237)*
US Industrial Lubricants Inc 513 541-2225
  3330 Beekman St Cincinnati (45223) *(G-4547)*
US Machine Prcsion Grnding LLC 440 284-0711
  880 Taylor St Elyria (44035) *(G-9506)*
US Metalcraft Inc 419 692-4962
  101 S Franklin St Delphos (45833) *(G-8925)*
US Mold Machine Tool Company, Painesville *Also called J & H Corporation (G-15893)*
US Molding Machinery Co Inc 440 918-1701
  38294 Pelton Rd Willoughby (44094) *(G-20625)*
US Powder Coating Inc 440 255-3090
  8665 Tyler Blvd Mentor (44060) *(G-13763)*
US Pro Painters (PA) 937 298-2142
  4504 S Yellow Springs St Springfield (45506) *(G-17671)*
US Refractory Products LLC 440 386-4580
  7660 Race Rd North Ridgeville (44039) *(G-15408)*
US Screen Co 419 736-2400
  462 County Road 40 Sullivan (44880) *(G-18055)*
US Technology Corporation 330 455-1181
  4200 Munson St Nw Canton (44718) *(G-2891)*
US Technology Media Inc 330 874-3094
  509 Water St Sw Bolivar (44612) *(G-1947)*
US Tsubaki Power Transm LLC 419 626-4560
  1010 Edgewater Ave Sandusky (44870) *(G-17019)*
US Tubular Products Inc 330 832-1734
  14852 Lincoln Way W North Lawrence (44666) *(G-15307)*
US Video 440 734-6463
  23551 Westchester Dr North Olmsted (44070) *(G-15350)*
US Water Company LLC 740 453-0604
  1115 Newark Rd Zanesville (43701) *(G-21360)*
US Yachiyo Inc 740 223-3134
  1177 Kellogg Pkwy Marion (43302) *(G-12910)*

USA Foils Inc 440 975-1145
  38264 Willoughby Pkwy Willoughby (44094) *(G-20626)*
USA Heat Treating Inc 216 587-4700
  4500 Lee Rd Ste B Cleveland (44128) *(G-6400)*
USA Label Express Inc 330 874-1001
  11206 Industrial Pkwy Nw Bolivar (44612) *(G-1948)*
USA Precast Concrete Limited 330 854-9600
  801 Elm Ridge Ave Canal Fulton (44614) *(G-2516)*
USA Quickprint Inc (PA) 330 455-5119
  409 3rd St Sw Canton (44702) *(G-2892)*
USA Rolls, Canfield *Also called Alstart Enterprises LLC (G-2547)*
Usalco LLC 440 993-2721
  3050 Lake Rd E Ashtabula (44004) *(G-844)*
USB Corporation 216 765-5000
  26111 Miles Rd Cleveland (44128) *(G-6401)*
Usc Metal Fabricators, Grand Rapids *Also called Seeburger Greenhouse (G-10446)*
User Friendly Phone Book LLC 216 674-6500
  2 Summit Park Dr Ste 105 Independence (44131) *(G-11281)*
Usm Acquisition Corporation (PA) 440 975-8600
  2002 Joseph Lloyd Pkwy Willoughby (44094) *(G-20627)*
Usm Precision Products Inc 440 975-8600
  2002 Joseph Lloyd Pkwy Willoughby (44094) *(G-20628)*
Ustek Incorporated 614 538-8000
  4663 Executive Dr Ste 3 Columbus (43220) *(G-7728)*
Usui International Corporation 513 448-0410
  88 Partnership Way Sharonville (45241) *(G-17115)*
Usui International Corporation 513 448-0410
  88 Partnership Way Cincinnati (45241) *(G-4548)*
Usv Optical Inc 614 717-0238
  5083 Tuttle Crossing Blvd Dublin (43016) *(G-9160)*
UTAC, Cleveland *Also called United Taconite LLC (G-6388)*
UTC Aerospace Systems, Troy *Also called Goodrich Corporation (G-18833)*
UTC Aerospace Systems 216 341-1700
  8000 Marble Ave Cleveland (44105) *(G-6402)*
UTC Fire SEC Americas Corp Inc 513 821-7945
  14 Knollcrest Dr Cincinnati (45237) *(G-4549)*
Utica Herald 740 892-2771
  60 N Main St Utica (43080) *(G-19197)*
Utility Relay Co Ltd 440 708-1000
  10100 Queens Way Chagrin Falls (44023) *(G-3131)*
Utility Solutions Inc 740 369-4300
  327 Curtis St Delaware (43015) *(G-8892)*
Utility Wire Products Inc 216 441-2180
  3302 E 87th St Cleveland (44127) *(G-6403)*
Utopia Products Inc 330 666-2602
  3867 Medina Rd 202 Akron (44333) *(G-460)*
Utv Hitchworks LLC 513 615-8568
  1295 W Us Highway 22 & 3 Maineville (45039) *(G-12533)*
Uv Doctor Systems LLC 513 553-9000
  1184 Ferris Rd Amelia (45102) *(G-588)*
Uvisir Inc 216 374-9376
  23600 Merc Rd Ste 102 Beachwood (44122) *(G-1304)*
V & A Process Inc 440 288-8137
  2345 E 28th St Lorain (44055) *(G-12288)*
V & C Enterprises Co 614 221-1412
  41 S Grant Ave Columbus (43215) *(G-7729)*
V & M Star LP 330 742-6300
  2669 Mrtn Luthr Kg Jr Bld Youngstown (44510) *(G-21234)*
V & P Hydraulic Products LLC 740 203-3600
  1700 Pittsburgh Dr Delaware (43015) *(G-8893)*
V & R Molded Products Inc 419 752-4171
  181 Us Highway 224 W Willard (44890) *(G-20403)*
V & S Columbus Galanizing LLC 614 449-8281
  987 Buckeye Park Rd Columbus (43207) *(G-7730)*
V & S Schuler Engineering Inc 330 452-5200
  2240 Allen Ave Se Canton (44707) *(G-2893)*
V & W Woodcraft 330 674-0073
  5071 Township Road 353 Millersburg (44654) *(G-14276)*
V Collection 419 517-0508
  5630 Main St Sylvania (43560) *(G-18128)*
V H Cooper & Co Inc 419 678-4853
  1 Cooper Farm Dr Saint Henry (45883) *(G-16823)*
V H Cooper & Co Inc 419 678-4853
  1 Cooper Farm Dr Saint Henry (45883) *(G-16824)*
V H Cooper & Co Inc (HQ) 419 375-4116
  2321 State Route 49 Fort Recovery (45846) *(G-9961)*
V I E W I N G, Cleveland *Also called Visualy Imp Exp Wm Isues Fr Gr (G-6422)*
V I I Craft, Xenia *Also called Visual Information Institute (G-20985)*
V I P Printing & Design 513 777-7468
  4836 Duff Dr Ste A West Chester (45246) *(G-20066)*
V K C Inc 440 951-9634
  7667 Jenther Dr Mentor (44060) *(G-13764)*
V M Machine Co Inc 216 281-4569
  9607 Clinton Rd Cleveland (44144) *(G-6404)*
V M Systems Inc 419 535-1044
  3125 Hill Ave Toledo (43607) *(G-18763)*
V Mast Manufacturing Inc 330 409-8116
  1712 Kimball Rd Se Canton (44707) *(G-2894)*
V Metro, Fairborn *Also called Vmetro Inc (G-9633)*

A
L
P
H
A
B
E
T
I
C

V P, Newton Falls *Also called Venture Plastics Inc* ***(G-15141)***
V R I, Franklin *Also called Valued Relationships Inc* ***(G-10061)***
V S I, Massillon *Also called Vehicle Systems Inc* ***(G-13210)***
V T S, Aurora *Also called Vibration Test Systems Inc* ***(G-954)***
V&P Group International LLC....703 349-6432
1931 Lawn Ave Cincinnati (45237) ***(G-4550)***
V-Ash Machine Company....216 267-3400
1220 Orlen Ave Cuyahoga Falls (44221) ***(G-8061)***
V-Seal Concrete Sealer, Lewis Center *Also called Tara Acquisition Group* ***(G-11923)***
VA Technology, Brunswick *Also called Versatile Automation Tech Ltd* ***(G-2265)***
Vacalon Company Inc....614 577-1945
12960 Stonecreek Dr Ste D Pickerington (43147) ***(G-16209)***
Vacca Inc (PA)....513 697-0270
9501 Union Cemetery Rd # 100 Loveland (45140) ***(G-12396)***
Vacono America LLC....216 938-7428
1163 E 40th St Ste 301 Cleveland (44114) ***(G-6405)***
Vacuflo Factory....330 875-2450
512 W Gorgas St Louisville (44641) ***(G-12333)***
Vacuform Inc....330 938-9674
500 Courtney Rd Sebring (44672) ***(G-17057)***
Vacupanel, Dayton *Also called Energy Storage Technologies* ***(G-8326)***
Vacuum Electric Switch Co Inc (PA)....330 374-5156
526 S Main St Ste 122 Akron (44311) ***(G-461)***
Vacuum Finishing Company....440 286-4386
10275 Old State Rd Chardon (44024) ***(G-3182)***
Vadose Syn Fuels Inc....330 564-0545
323 S Main St Munroe Falls (44262) ***(G-14667)***
Vagabond Creations Inc....937 298-1124
2560 Lance Dr Moraine (45409) ***(G-14536)***
Vail Rubber Works Inc....513 705-2060
605 Clark St Middletown (45042) ***(G-14093)***
Val Casting Inc....419 562-2499
108 E Rensselaer St Bucyrus (44820) ***(G-2361)***
Val Products, Coldwater *Also called Val-Co Pax Inc* ***(G-6573)***
Val-Co Pax Inc (HQ)....717 354-4586
210 E Main St Coldwater (45828) ***(G-6573)***
Val-Con Inc....440 357-1898
7201 Hermitage Rd Painesville (44077) ***(G-15936)***
Valco Cincinnati Inc (PA)....513 874-6550
497 Circle Freeway Dr # 490 West Chester (45246) ***(G-20067)***
Valco Cincinnati Inc....513 874-6550
411 Circle Freeway Dr West Chester (45246) ***(G-20068)***
Valco Division, North Royalton *Also called Valley Tool & Die Inc* ***(G-15458)***
Valco Industries Inc....937 399-7400
625 Burt St Springfield (45505) ***(G-17672)***
Valco Melton, West Chester *Also called Valco Cincinnati Inc* ***(G-20067)***
Valco Melton Inc....513 874-6550
411 Circle Freeway Dr West Chester (45246) ***(G-20069)***
Valentine Research Inc....513 984-8900
10280 Alliance Rd Blue Ash (45242) ***(G-1888)***
Valentino Industries LLC....330 523-7216
3615 Southern Rd Richfield (44286) ***(G-16644)***
Valero Renewable Fuels Co LLC....740 437-6211
3979 State Route 238 Ne Bloomingburg (43106) ***(G-1721)***
Valfilm LLC....419 423-6500
3441 N Main St Findlay (45840) ***(G-9904)***
Valley Asphalt, Morrow *Also called Morrow Gravel Company Inc* ***(G-14549)***
Valley Asphalt Corporation....513 381-0652
4850 Stubbs Mills Rd Morrow (45152) ***(G-14552)***
Valley Asphalt Corporation....937 426-7682
782 N Valley Rd Xenia (45385) ***(G-20984)***
Valley Asphalt Corporation....937 335-3664
250 Dye Mill Rd Troy (45373) ***(G-18884)***
Valley Asphalt Corporation....513 353-2171
5073 Kilby Rd Cleves (45002) ***(G-6531)***
Valley Asphalt Corporation....513 561-1551
7940 Main St Cincinnati (45244) ***(G-4551)***
Valley Asphalt Corporation....513 784-1476
612 W Mehring Way Cincinnati (45202) ***(G-4552)***
Valley Clay Mining Co....740 697-0620
451 Gordon St Roseville (43777) ***(G-16734)***
Valley Concrete, Carrollton *Also called Ernst Enterprises Inc* ***(G-2955)***
Valley Concrete Division, Fairborn *Also called Ernst Enterprises Inc* ***(G-9620)***
Valley Containers Inc....330 544-2244
3515 Union St Mineral Ridge (44440) ***(G-14314)***
Valley Converting Co Inc (PA)....740 537-2152
405 Daniels St Toronto (43964) ***(G-18787)***
Valley Converting Co Inc....740 537-2152
310 Loretta Ave Toronto (43964) ***(G-18788)***
Valley Graphics....330 652-0484
1494 Salt Springs Rd Niles (44446) ***(G-15187)***
Valley Machine Tool Co Inc....513 899-2737
9773 Morrow Cozaddale Rd Morrow (45152) ***(G-14553)***
Valley Metal Works Inc....513 554-1022
698 W Columbia Ave Cincinnati (45215) ***(G-4553)***
Valley Petroleum Inc....740 668-4901
25010 Divan Rd Utica (43080) ***(G-19198)***
Valley Plastics Co Inc....419 666-2349
399 Phillips Ave Toledo (43612) ***(G-18764)***
Valley Printing & Graphics....330 364-5010
226 W 2nd St Dover (44622) ***(G-9023)***
Valley Rubber Mixing Inc....330 434-4442
115 W Bartges St Akron (44311) ***(G-462)***
Valley Tool & Die Inc....440 237-0160
10020 York Theta Dr North Royalton (44133) ***(G-15458)***
Valley Trailers, Leesburg *Also called Creative Fab & Welding LLC* ***(G-11851)***
Valley Veneer & Lumber Co....440 293-6025
4261 Us Route 322 Williamsfield (44093) ***(G-20417)***
Valley View Pallets Partners....740 393-9282
22414 Hostetler Rd Danville (43014) ***(G-8092)***
Valley View Woodcraft....330 852-3000
1190 Shutt Valley Rd Nw Sugarcreek (44681) ***(G-18048)***
Valley View Woodcraft & Finshg, Sugarcreek *Also called Valley View Woodcraft* ***(G-18048)***
Valley Vitamins II Inc....330 533-0051
4449 Easton Way Fl 2 Columbus (43219) ***(G-7731)***
Valley Welding Service, Harrison *Also called Robert E Moore* ***(G-10801)***
Valleyview Wood Turning Co....330 763-0407
8260 Township Road 652 Millersburg (44654) ***(G-14277)***
Vallourec Star LP (HQ)....330 742-6300
2669 M L K J Blvd Youngstown (44510) ***(G-21235)***
Valspar, Medina *Also called Plasti-Kote Co Inc* ***(G-13459)***
Valspar Corporation....330 830-6000
600 Nova Dr Se Massillon (44646) ***(G-13209)***
Valtris Specialty Chemicals, Independence *Also called Polymer Additives Inc* ***(G-11269)***
Valtronic Technology Inc....440 349-1239
29200 Fountain Pkwy Solon (44139) ***(G-17411)***
Value Added Business Svcs Co (PA)....614 854-9755
120 Twin Oaks Dr Jackson (45640) ***(G-11332)***
Value Added Packaging Inc....937 832-9595
44 Lau Pkwy Englewood (45315) ***(G-9542)***
Valued Relationships Inc....800 860-4230
1400 Commerce Center Dr B Franklin (45005) ***(G-10061)***
Valv-Trol Company....330 686-2800
1340 Commerce Dr Stow (44224) ***(G-17814)***
Valve Related Controls Inc....513 677-8724
143 Commerce Dr Loveland (45140) ***(G-12397)***
Valveco Inc....330 337-9535
1913 E State St Salem (44460) ***(G-16933)***
Valvole America LLC....330 464-8872
2550 Medina Rd Medina (44256) ***(G-13495)***
Valvoline, West Chester *Also called Ashland LLC* ***(G-19810)***
Valvsys LLC....513 539-1234
421 Breaden Dr Ste 15 Monroe (45050) ***(G-14417)***
Vampire Optical Coatings Inc....740 919-4596
63 E Mill St Unit B Pataskala (43062) ***(G-15989)***
Van Burens Welding & Machine....740 787-2636
11496 Cherry Hill Rd Glenford (43739) ***(G-10401)***
Van Deleigh Industries LLC....419 467-2244
5611 Bent Oak Rd Sylvania (43560) ***(G-18129)***
Van Dyke Custom Iron Inc....614 860-9300
311 Outerbelt St Columbus (43213) ***(G-7732)***
Van Engineering Co, Cincinnati *Also called R Vandewalle Inc* ***(G-4327)***
Van Heusen, Aurora *Also called Pvh Corp* ***(G-941)***
Van Lock Co Inc....513 561-9692
6834 Center St Cincinnati (45244) ***(G-4554)***
Van Orders Pallet Company Inc....419 875-6932
2452 County Road 2 Swanton (43558) ***(G-18094)***
Van Rob Waverly, Waverly *Also called Vr Waverly Inc* ***(G-19720)***
Van Wert Division, Van Wert *Also called Tecumseh Packg Solutions Inc* ***(G-19271)***
Van Wert Machine Inc....419 692-6836
210 E Cleveland St Delphos (45833) ***(G-8926)***
Van Wert Pallets LLC....419 203-1823
9042 John Brown Rd Van Wert (45891) ***(G-19275)***
Van-Griner LLC....419 733-7951
1009 Delta Ave Cincinnati (45208) ***(G-4555)***
Vanamatic Company....419 692-6085
701 Ambrose Dr Delphos (45833) ***(G-8927)***
Vance Adams....330 424-9670
123 E Lincoln Way Lisbon (44432) ***(G-12134)***
Vance's Wonder Store, Manchester *Also called Vances Department Store* ***(G-12552)***
Vances Department Store (PA)....937 549-2188
37 E 2nd St Manchester (45144) ***(G-12552)***
Vances Department Store....937 549-3033
600 Washington St Manchester (45144) ***(G-12553)***
Vandalia Drummer, The, Vandalia *Also called Suburban Newpapers of Dayton* ***(G-19311)***
Vandalia Machining Inc....937 264-9155
884 Center Dr Vandalia (45377) ***(G-19314)***
Vandalia Massage Therapy....937 890-8660
147 W National Rd Vandalia (45377) ***(G-19315)***
Vanderpool Motor Sports....513 424-2166
6315 Howe Rd Middletown (45042) ***(G-14094)***
Vandiley Industries Ltd....419 618-1970
3384 N State Route 53 Tiffin (44883) ***(G-18251)***
Vanguard Die & Machine Inc....330 394-4170
2070 Mcmyler St Nw Warren (44485) ***(G-19617)***

Vanguard Fabrication Division, Mantua *Also called Aetna Plastics Corp* **(G-12706)**
Vanguard Oil & Gas 330 223-1074
28050 Speidel Rd East Rochester (44625) **(G-9252)**
Vanity Classics, Cincinnati *Also called Custom Cast Marbleworks Inc* **(G-3625)**
Vanner Holdings Inc 614 771-2718
4282 Reynolds Dr Hilliard (43026) **(G-10991)**
Vanni Wang Couture, Rocky River *Also called Lucio Vanni LLC* **(G-16701)**
Vans Inc 419 471-1541
5001 Monroe St Ste 1560 Toledo (43623) **(G-18765)**
Vantage Specialty Ingredients 937 264-1222
707 Harco Dr Englewood (45315) **(G-9543)**
Vantech21, Cincinnati *Also called Van Lock Co Inc* **(G-4554)**
Varbros LLC 216 267-5200
16025 Brookpark Rd Cleveland (44142) **(G-6406)**
Varbros Tool and Die Company 216 267-5200
16025 Brookpark Rd Cleveland (44142) **(G-6407)**
Varco LP 440 277-8696
1807 E 28th St Lorain (44055) **(G-12289)**
Vari-Wall Tube Specialists Inc 330 482-0000
1350 Wardingsley Ave Columbiana (44408) **(G-6637)**
Variety Glass Inc 740 432-3643
201 Foster Ave Cambridge (43725) **(G-2481)**
Variety Printing 216 676-9815
5707 Van Wert Ave Brookpark (44142) **(G-2171)**
Variflow Equipment Inc 513 245-0420
3834 Ridgedale Dr Cincinnati (45247) **(G-4556)**
Varmland Inc 216 741-1510
1200 Brookpark Rd Cleveland (44109) **(G-6408)**
Varo Energy Services LLC 914 437-6906
2751 Tuller Pkwy Dublin (43017) **(G-9161)**
Varsity Sporting Goods, Grove City *Also called Joe Sestito* **(G-10566)**
Vasil Co Inc 419 562-2901
119 E Mary St Bucyrus (44820) **(G-2362)**
Vasil Fashions, Bucyrus *Also called Vasil Co Inc* **(G-2362)**
Vast Mold & Tool Co Inc 440 942-7585
7154 Industrial Park Blvd Mentor (44060) **(G-13765)**
Vdm Biochemicals LLC 440 786-9400
5386 Majestic Pkwy Ste 9 Bedford (44146) **(G-1470)**
Ve Global Vending Inc 216 785-2611
8700 Brookpark Rd Cleveland (44129) **(G-6409)**
Vector Electromagnetics LLC 937 478-5904
1400 Grange Hall Rd # 500 Beavercreek (45430) **(G-1383)**
Vector International Corp 440 942-2002
7404 Tyler Blvd Mentor (44060) **(G-13766)**
Vector Laboratories, Youngstown *Also called Howard Grant Corporation* **(G-21109)**
Vector Screenprinting & EMB, Mentor *Also called Vector International Corp* **(G-13766)**
Vectra Inc (HQ) 614 351-6868
3950 Business Park Dr Columbus (43204) **(G-7733)**
Vectron Inc 440 323-3369
201 Perry Ct Elyria (44035) **(G-9507)**
Vedda Printing, Cleveland *Also called Phil Vedda & Sons Inc* **(G-6000)**
Vee Gee Enterprise Corporation 330 493-9780
4897 Fulton Dr Nw Canton (44718) **(G-2895)**
Veeam Software Corporation (PA) 678 353-2140
8800 Lyra Dr Ste 350 Columbus (43240) **(G-6661)**
Veeders Mailbox Inc 513 984-8749
10050 Montgomery Rd # 324 Cincinnati (45242) **(G-4557)**
Vega Americas Inc (HQ) 513 272-0131
4170 Rosslyn Dr Ste A Cincinnati (45209) **(G-4558)**
Vega Technology Group LLC 216 772-1434
412 Sheraton Dr Nw North Canton (44720) **(G-15281)**
Veggie Valley Farm LLC 330 866-2712
3444 Dueber Rd Ne Sandyville (44671) **(G-17023)**
Vegv, Cleveland *Also called Ve Global Vending Inc* **(G-6409)**
Vehicle Systems Inc 330 854-0535
7130 Lutz Ave Nw Massillon (44646) **(G-13210)**
Vehtek Systems Inc 419 373-8741
2125 Wood Bridge Blvd Bowling Green (43402) **(G-2019)**
Vein Center and Medspa 330 629-9400
965 Windham Ct Ste 2 Youngstown (44512) **(G-21236)**
Vein Center, The, Youngstown *Also called Vein Center and Medspa* **(G-21236)**
Vela 614 500-0150
58560 Kennonsburg Rd Salesville (43778) **(G-16938)**
Velocity Concept Dev Group LLC (PA) 513 204-2100
4393 Digital Way Mason (45040) **(G-13100)**
Velocity Concept Dev Group LLC 740 685-2637
8824 Clay Pike Byesville (43723) **(G-2412)**
Velocys Inc 614 733-3300
7950 Corporate Blvd Plain City (43064) **(G-16363)**
Velvet Ice Cream Company 419 562-2009
1233 Whetstone St Bucyrus (44820) **(G-2363)**
Vemuri International LLC (PA) 513 483-6300
10600 Evendale Dr Cincinnati (45241) **(G-4559)**
Venco Manufacturing Inc (HQ) 513 772-8448
12110 Best Pl Cincinnati (45241) **(G-4560)**
Venco Venturo Industries LLC (PA) 513 772-8448
12110 Best Pl Cincinnati (45241) **(G-4561)**
Venco/Venturo Div, Cincinnati *Also called Venco Venturo Industries LLC* **(G-4561)**
Vendfriend, Dublin *Also called Neil Barton* **(G-9111)**
Venice Cornerstone Newspaper 513 738-7151
2640 Cncnnati Brkville Rd Hamilton (45014) **(G-10753)**
Venom Exterminating LLC 330 637-3366
40 Monte Ln Cortland (44410) **(G-7876)**
Venom Towing LLC 937 344-6530
5620 Red Lion 5 Points Rd Springboro (45066) **(G-17513)**
Ventari Corporation 937 278-4269
8641 Washington Church Rd Miamisburg (45342) **(G-13874)**
Ventco Inc 440 834-8888
15050 Brkshire Indus Pkwy Middlefield (44062) **(G-14001)**
Ventilation Systems Jsc 513 348-3853
11013 Kenwood Rd Blue Ash (45242) **(G-1889)**
Ventra Sandusky LLC 419 627-3600
3020 Tiffin Ave Sandusky (44870) **(G-17020)**
Vents - US, Blue Ash *Also called Ventilation Systems Jsc* **(G-1889)**
Venture Lighting Intl Inc (HQ) 800 451-2606
2451 E Enterprise Pkwy Twinsburg (44087) **(G-19035)**
Venture Lighting Intl Inc 440 248-3510
2451 E Enterprise Pkwy Twinsburg (44087) **(G-19036)**
Venture Medical, Plain City *Also called Bahler Medical Inc* **(G-16323)**
Venture Packaging Inc 419 465-2534
311 Monroe St Monroeville (44847) **(G-14430)**
Venture Packaging Midwest Inc 419 465-2534
311 Monroe St Monroeville (44847) **(G-14431)**
Venture Plas Middlefield LLC 440 834-0704
15005 Enterprise Way Middlefield (44062) **(G-14002)**
Venture Plastics Inc (PA) 330 872-5774
4000 Warren Rd Newton Falls (44444) **(G-15141)**
Venture Therapeutics Inc 614 430-3300
10739 Johnstown Rd New Albany (43054) **(G-14775)**
Venturemedgroup Ltd 567 661-0768
2865 N Reynolds Rd 220a Toledo (43615) **(G-18766)**
Venturo Manufacturing Inc 513 772-8448
12110 Best Pl Cincinnati (45241) **(G-4562)**
Venue Lifestyle & Event Guide 513 405-6822
11959 Tramway Dr Cincinnati (45241) **(G-4563)**
Venus Trading LLC 513 374-0066
10965 Rednor Ct Loveland (45140) **(G-12398)**
Veolia Water Technologies Inc 937 890-4075
945 S Brown School Rd Vandalia (45377) **(G-19316)**
Ver Mich Ltd 330 493-7330
4210 Cleveland Ave Nw Canton (44709) **(G-2896)**
Ver-Mac Industries Inc 740 397-6511
100 Progress Dr Mount Vernon (43050) **(G-14654)**
Verantis Corporation (HQ) 440 243-0700
7251 Engle Rd Ste 300 Middleburg Heights (44130) **(G-13909)**
Verco Seal, Troy *Also called Freudenberg-Nok General Partnr* **(G-18828)**
Verdin Company, Cincinnati *Also called I T Verdin Co* **(G-3906)**
Vergeline LLC 419 730-0300
1301 N Summit St Toledo (43604) **(G-18767)**
Verhoff Alfalfa Mills Inc (PA) 419 523-4767
1188 Sugar Mill Dr Ottawa (45875) **(G-15813)**
Verhoff Alfalfa Mills Inc 419 653-4161
1577 Henry Y New Bavaria (43548) **(G-14776)**
Verhoff Machine & Welding Inc 419 596-3202
7300 Road 18 Continental (45831) **(G-7829)**
Veritas, Kent *Also called Schneller LLC* **(G-11522)**
Veritiv Operating Company 513 242-0800
375 Distribution Cir Fairfield (45014) **(G-9728)**
Vermilion Dock Masters 440 244-5370
858 Vermilion Rd Vermilion (44089) **(G-19337)**
Vernay Manufacturing Inc (HQ) 937 767-7261
120 E South College St Yellow Springs (45387) **(G-21000)**
Vero Security Group Ltd 513 731-8376
5296 Montgomery Rd Cincinnati (45212) **(G-4564)**
Verona Agriculture Center, Verona *Also called Harvest Land Co-Op Inc* **(G-19338)**
Versa Conveyors, London *Also called Conveyors Ltd* **(G-12206)**
Versa-Pak Ltd 419 586-5466
500 Staeger Rd Celina (45822) **(G-3026)**
Versailles Building Supply 937 526-3238
741 N Center St Versailles (45380) **(G-19358)**
Versalift East Inc 610 866-1400
4884 Corporate St Sw Canton (44706) **(G-2897)**
Versatile Automation Tech Ltd 330 220-2600
2853 Westway Dr Brunswick (44212) **(G-2265)**
Versatile Machine 330 618-9895
402 Commerce St Tallmadge (44278) **(G-18174)**
Versitech Mold, Greenwich *Also called Quality Mold Inc* **(G-10534)**
Versitech Mold Div, Akron *Also called Quality Mold Inc* **(G-357)**
Verso Corporation 901 369-4105
8540 Gander Creek Dr Miamisburg (45342) **(G-13875)**
Verso Paper, Miamisburg *Also called Verso Corporation* **(G-13875)**
Verso Paper Holding LLC (HQ) 877 855-7243
8540 Gander Creek Dr Miamisburg (45342) **(G-13876)**
Vertebration Inc 614 395-3346
3982 Powell Rd 220 Powell (43065) **(G-16487)**
Vertex Inc 330 628-6230
3956 Mogadore Indus Pkwy Mogadore (44260) **(G-14387)**

ALPHABETIC

Vertex Computer Systems Inc 513 662-6888
11260 Chester Rd Ste 300 Cincinnati (45246) *(G-4565)*

Vertex Refining OH LLC 419 668-8373
4376 State Route 601 Norwalk (44857) *(G-15565)*

Vertical Data LLC 330 289-0313
2169 Chuckery Ln Akron (44333) *(G-463)*

Vertical Runner 330 262-3000
207 S Market St Wooster (44691) *(G-20843)*

Vertiflo Pump Company 513 530-0888
7807 Redsky Dr Cincinnati (45249) *(G-4566)*

Vertiv, Columbus *Also called Liebert Corporation (G-7292)*

Vertiv, Ironton *Also called Liebert Corporation (G-11296)*

Vertiv, Columbus *Also called Liebert North America Inc (G-7293)*

Vertiv Co (HQ) 614 888-0246
1050 Dearborn Dr Columbus (43085) *(G-7734)*

Vertiv Co 440 288-1122
1510 Kansas Ave Lorain (44052) *(G-12290)*

Vertiv Co 440 460-3600
5900 Landerbrook Dr # 300 Cleveland (44124) *(G-6410)*

Vertiv Group Corporation (HQ) 614 888-0246
1050 Dearborn Dr Columbus (43085) *(G-7735)*

Vesco Medical LLC 614 914-5991
692 N High St Ste 205 Columbus (43215) *(G-7736)*

Vesi Incorporated 513 563-6002
16 Techview Dr Cincinnati (45215) *(G-4567)*

Vesuvius U S A Corporation 419 986-5126
495 Emma St Bettsville (44815) *(G-1670)*

Vesuvius U S A Corporation 440 593-1161
1100 Maple Ave Conneaut (44030) *(G-7821)*

Vesuvius U S A Corporation 440 816-3051
20200 Sheldon Rd Cleveland (44142) *(G-6411)*

Veteran Industries LLC 937 751-2133
147 Lake Bluff Dr Columbus (43235) *(G-7737)*

Veterans Representative Co LLC 330 779-0768
1584 Tamarisk Trl Youngstown (44514) *(G-21237)*

Veterans Steel Inc 216 938-7476
900 E 69th St Cleveland (44103) *(G-6412)*

Vetz USA Inc 937 237-8764
7174 Montague Rd Dayton (45424) *(G-8741)*

Vexos, Lagrange *Also called Staci Corp (G-11638)*

Vf Outdoor LLC 614 337-1147
4025 Gramercy St Columbus (43219) *(G-7738)*

Vgs Inc 216 431-7800
2239 E 55th St Cleveland (44103) *(G-6413)*

Vgu Industries Inc 216 676-9093
4747 Manufacturing Ave Cleveland (44135) *(G-6414)*

Via Vecchia Winery 614 469-4940
485 S Front St Columbus (43215) *(G-7739)*

Viasat Inc 216 706-7800
5990 W Creek Rd Ste 1 Independence (44131) *(G-11282)*

Viasystems Tech Corp LLC 330 538-3900
12080 Debartolo Dr North Jackson (44451) *(G-15300)*

Vibra Finish Co 513 870-6300
8411 Seward Rd Fairfield (45011) *(G-9729)*

Vibration Test Systems Inc 330 562-5729
10246 Clipper Cv Aurora (44202) *(G-954)*

Vibrodyne Division, Moraine *Also called Tailored Systems Inc (G-14534)*

Vibronic 937 274-1114
5208 Wadsworth Rd Dayton (45414) *(G-8742)*

Vic Mar Manufacturing Inc 740 687-5434
730 Lawrence St Lancaster (43130) *(G-11761)*

Vic Maroscher 330 332-4958
36135 Salem Grange Rd Salem (44460) *(G-16934)*

Vicart Prcsion Fabricators Inc 614 771-0080
4101 Leap Rd Hilliard (43026) *(G-10992)*

Vicas Manufacturing Co Inc 513 791-7741
8407 Monroe Ave Cincinnati (45236) *(G-4568)*

Vickers International Inc 419 867-2200
3000 Strayer Rd Maumee (43537) *(G-13307)*

Vicon Fabricating Company Ltd 440 205-6700
7200 Justin Way Mentor (44060) *(G-13767)*

Vicrobiz, Westerville *Also called World Development & Conslt LLC (G-20242)*

Vics Turning Co Inc 216 531-5016
16911 Saint Clair Ave Cleveland (44110) *(G-6415)*

Victor, Cincinnati *Also called Vy Inc (G-4572)*

Victor McKenzie Drilling Co 740 453-0834
3596 Maple Ave Ste A Zanesville (43701) *(G-21361)*

Victor Organ Company 330 792-1321
5340 Mahoning Ave Youngstown (44515) *(G-21238)*

Victoria Ventures Inc (PA) 330 793-9321
425 Victoria Rd Ste 427 Youngstown (44515) *(G-21239)*

Victorian Farms 330 628-9188
1375 Aberagg Rd Atwater (44201) *(G-903)*

Victory Athletics Inc 330 274-2854
10702 Second St Mantua (44255) *(G-12724)*

Victory Direct LLC 614 626-0000
750 Cross Pointe Rd Ste M Gahanna (43230) *(G-10240)*

Victory Postcards & Souvenirs, Columbus *Also called Victory Postcards Inc (G-7740)*

Victory Postcards Inc 614 764-8975
1005 Old Henderson Rd Columbus (43220) *(G-7740)*

Victory Store Fixtures Inc 740 499-3494
3153 Winnemac Pike S La Rue (43332) *(G-11623)*

Victory White Metal Company 216 641-2575
7930 Jones Rd Cleveland (44105) *(G-6416)*

Victory White Metal Company (PA) 216 271-1400
6100 Roland Ave Cleveland (44127) *(G-6417)*

Victory White Metal Company 216 271-7200
3027 E 55th St Cleveland (44127) *(G-6418)*

Vida Ve Corp 614 203-2607
8210 Timber Mist Ct Dublin (43017) *(G-9162)*

Video Products Inc 330 562-2622
1275 Danner Dr Aurora (44202) *(G-955)*

Vidonish Stained Glass Studio, Mansfield *Also called Vidonish Studios (G-12701)*

Vidonish Studios 419 884-1119
20 E Main St Mansfield (44904) *(G-12701)*

Viewpoint Graphic Design 419 447-6073
132 S Washington St Tiffin (44883) *(G-18252)*

Viewray Incorporated 440 703-3210
2 Thermo Fisher Way Oakwood Village (44146) *(G-15631)*

Vigilant Defense 513 214-1635
9378 S Masn Montgomery Rd Mason (45040) *(G-13101)*

Vigilant Technology Solutions, Mason *Also called Vigilant Defense (G-13101)*

Viking Explosives LLC 218 263-8845
25800 Science Park Dr Cleveland (44122) *(G-6419)*

Viking Fabricators 740 374-5246
2021 Hanna Rd Marietta (45750) *(G-12848)*

Viking Group Inc 937 443-0433
2806 Wayne Ave Dayton (45420) *(G-8743)*

Viking Intl Resources Co Inc 304 628-3878
125 Putnam St Marietta (45750) *(G-12849)*

Viking Paper, Toledo *Also called Tex-Tyler Corporation (G-18720)*

Viking Paper Company (PA) 419 729-4951
5148 Stickney Ave Toledo (43612) *(G-18768)*

Village of Somerset 740 743-1986
1672 Big Inch Rd Nw Somerset (43783) *(G-17420)*

Village of West Alexandria (PA) 937 839-4168
16 N Main St Unit 2 West Alexandria (45381) *(G-19785)*

Village Outdoors 440 256-1172
7875 Euclid Chardon Rd Kirtland (44094) *(G-11618)*

Village Plastics Co 330 753-0100
100 16th St Sw Barberton (44203) *(G-1156)*

Village Reporter 419 485-4851
115 Broad St Montpelier (43543) *(G-14456)*

Village Square Antique Mall, Sunbury *Also called Indian River Industries (G-18064)*

Village Voice of Ottawa Hills, Toledo *Also called Village Voice Publishing Ltd (G-18769)*

Village Voice Publishing Ltd 419 537-0286
4041 W Central Ave Ste 6 Toledo (43606) *(G-18769)*

Village Woodworking 740 326-4461
8033 Ridge Rd Fredericktown (43019) *(G-10115)*

Villager Newspaper, The, Bay Village *Also called Robert Tuneberg (G-1244)*

Villager Publishing Co Inc 330 527-5761
8088 Main St Garrettsville (44231) *(G-10335)*

Villager Weekly, Garrettsville *Also called Villager Publishing Co Inc (G-10335)*

Villers Enterprises Limited (PA) 330 818-9838
3146 Brumbaugh St Nw North Canton (44720) *(G-15282)*

Vinco Machine Products Inc 216 475-6708
17601 Pennsylvania Ave Cleveland (44137) *(G-6420)*

Vindicator 330 755-0135
3770 Wilson Ave Campbell (44405) *(G-2493)*

Vindicator Boardman Office 330 259-1732
8075 Southern Blvd Youngstown (44512) *(G-21240)*

Vindicator Printing Company 330 392-0176
135 Pine Ave Se Ste 208 Warren (44481) *(G-19618)*

Vinnies Drive Thru 419 225-5272
864 W North St Lima (45801) *(G-12109)*

Vintage Electric Ltd Inc 419 472-9349
3335 Mcgregor Ln Toledo (43623) *(G-18770)*

Vintage Heating and Air, Toledo *Also called Vintage Electric Ltd Inc (G-18770)*

Vinyl Building Products LLC 513 539-4444
351 N Garver Rd Monroe (45050) *(G-14418)*

Vinyl Design Corporation 419 283-4009
7856 Hill Ave Holland (43528) *(G-11095)*

Vinyl Graphics, Cleveland *Also called Vgu Industries Inc (G-6414)*

Vinyl Profiles Acquisition LLC 330 538-0660
11675 Mahoning Ave North Jackson (44451) *(G-15301)*

Vinyl Tech Storage Barn 330 674-5670
5930 State Route 39 Millersburg (44654) *(G-14278)*

Vinyl Tool & Die Company Inc 330 782-0254
1144 Meadowbrook Ave Youngstown (44512) *(G-21241)*

Vinylmax Corporation 800 847-3736
2921 Mcbride Ct Hamilton (45011) *(G-10754)*

Vinyltech Inc 330 538-0369
11635 Mahoning Ave North Jackson (44451) *(G-15302)*

Vinylume Products Inc 330 799-2000
3745 Hendricks Rd Youngstown (44515) *(G-21242)*

Viotec LLC 614 596-2054
5970 Pirthshire St Dublin (43016) *(G-9163)*

VIP-Scs, West Chester Also called VIP-Supply Chain Solutions LLC (G-19970)
VIP-Supply Chain Solutions LLC (PA) 513 454-2020
  9166 Sutton Pl West Chester (45011) (G-19970)
Viral Antigens, Cincinnati Also called Meridian Life Science Inc (G-4086)
Virant Family Winery Inc 440 466-6279
  541 Atkins Rd Geneva (44041) (G-10358)
Virco, Marietta Also called Viking Intl Resources Co Inc (G-12849)
Virgail Industries Inc 740 928-6001
  145 S High St Hebron (43025) (G-10894)
Virgils Kitchens Inc 440 355-5058
  100 Public Sq Lagrange (44050) (G-11641)
Virginia Air Distributors Inc 614 262-1129
  2821 Silver Dr Columbus (43211) (G-7741)
Virtual Boss Inc 419 872-7686
  517 Prairie Rose Dr Perrysburg (43551) (G-16165)
Virtual Hold Technology LLC (PA) 330 666-1181
  3875 Embassy Pkwy Ste 350 Akron (44333) (G-464)
Virtus Stunts LLC 440 543-0472
  16320 Snyder Rd Chagrin Falls (44023) (G-3132)
Visi-Trak Worldwide LLC (PA) 216 524-2363
  8400 Sweet Valley Dr # 406 Cleveland (44125) (G-6421)
Visible Solutions Inc (PA) 440 925-2810
  1991 Crocker Rd Ste 222 Westlake (44145) (G-20317)
Visimax Technologies Inc 330 405-8330
  9177 Dutton Dr Twinsburg (44087) (G-19037)
Vision Color LLC 419 924-9450
  214 S Defiance St West Unity (43570) (G-20136)
Vision Graphics 330 665-4451
  3545 Copley Rd Copley (44321) (G-7857)
Vision Graphix Inc 440 835-6540
  29260 Clemens Rd Ste A Westlake (44145) (G-20318)
Vision Press Inc 440 357-6362
  1634 W Jackson St Painesville (44077) (G-15937)
Vision Projects Inc 937 667-8648
  1350 Commerce Park Dr Tipp City (45371) (G-18309)
Vision Quest, Elmore Also called Alvin L Roepke (G-9360)
Visionary Signs LLC 614 504-5899
  6155 Huntley Rd Ste C Columbus (43229) (G-7742)
Visionmark Nameplate Co LLC 419 977-3131
  100 White Mountain Dr New Bremen (45869) (G-14796)
Visiontech Automation LLC 614 554-2013
  6682 Weston Cir W Dublin (43016) (G-9164)
Vista Industrial Packaging LLC 800 454-6117
  4700 Fisher Rd Columbus (43228) (G-7743)
Vista Packaging & Logistics, Columbus Also called Vista Industrial Packaging LLC (G-7743)
Vista Research Group LLC 419 281-3927
  1554 Township Road 805 Ashland (44805) (G-784)
Vistanet, Ashland Also called Vista Research Group LLC (G-784)
Vistech Mfg Solutions LLC 513 933-9300
  265 S West St Lebanon (45036) (G-11848)
Visual Advantage LLC 714 671-0988
  13010 Five Point Rd Perrysburg (43551) (G-16166)
Visual Art Graphic Services 330 274-2775
  5244 Goodell Rd Mantua (44255) (G-12725)
Visual Education Association 937 325-5503
  581 W Leffel Ln Springfield (45506) (G-17673)
Visual Expressions Sign Co 440 245-6660
  901 Broadway Lorain (44052) (G-12291)
Visual Information Institute 937 376-4361
  1065 Lower Bellbrook Rd Xenia (45385) (G-20985)
Visualy Imp Exp Wm Isues Fr Gr 216 561-6864
  3041 E 121st St Cleveland (44120) (G-6422)
Vitakraft Sun Seed Inc 419 832-1641
  20584 Long Judson Rd Weston (43569) (G-20327)
Vital Connections Incorporated 937 667-3880
  955 N 3rd St Tipp City (45371) (G-18310)
Vital Signs & Advertising LLC 937 292-7967
  224 S Madriver St Bellefontaine (43311) (G-1540)
Vitalrock LLC 888 596-8892
  19885 Detroit Rd Ste 108 Rocky River (44116) (G-16713)
Vitamin Lac 440 548-5294
  17642 Tavern Rd Middlefield (44062) (G-14003)
Vitamin Shoppe Inc 440 238-5987
  17893 Southpark Ctr Strongsville (44136) (G-17980)
Vitec Inc 216 464-4670
  26901 Cannon Rd Bedford (44146) (G-1471)
Vitex Corporation 216 883-0920
  2960 Broadway Ave Cleveland (44115) (G-6423)
Vius Services Corp., Blue Ash Also called Leadec Corp (G-1826)
Vivid Graphix, Bellaire Also called Charles Wisvari (G-1497)
Vivid Wraps LLC 513 515-8386
  12130 Royal Point Dr Cincinnati (45249) (G-4569)
Vivo Brothers LLC 330 629-8686
  8420 South Ave Poland (44514) (G-16387)
Vlchek Plastics 440 632-1631
  15981 Valplast St Middlefield (44062) (G-14004)
Vmaxx Inc 419 738-4044
  323 Commerce Rd Wapakoneta (45895) (G-19511)

Vmetro Inc (HQ) 281 584-0728
  2600 Paramount Pl Ste 200 Fairborn (45324) (G-9633)
Vmi Americas Inc (HQ) 330 929-6800
  4670 Allen Rd Stow (44224) (G-17815)
Vmi Liquidating Inc 937 492-3100
  2309 Industrial Dr Sidney (45365) (G-17232)
Vocational Services Inc 216 431-8085
  2239 E 55th St Cleveland (44103) (G-6424)
Voci, Pataskala Also called Vampire Optical Coatings Inc (G-15989)
Vogelsang Brazil Comercio E, Ravenna Also called Hugo Vglsang Maschinenbau GMBH (G-16532)
Voice Media Group Inc 216 241-7550
  1468 W 9th St Ste 805 Cleveland (44113) (G-6425)
Voice Products Inc 216 360-0433
  23715 Merc Rd Ste A200 Cleveland (44122) (G-6426)
Voigt & Schweitzer LLC (HQ) 614 449-8281
  987 Buckeye Park Rd Columbus (43207) (G-7744)
Voisard Tool Service 937 526-5451
  2700 Russia Versailles Rd Russia (45363) (G-16771)
Volk Corporation 513 621-1052
  635 Main St Ste 1 Cincinnati (45202) (G-4570)
Volk Optical Inc 440 942-6161
  7893 Enterprise Dr Mentor (44060) (G-13768)
Voll Hockey Inc 216 521-4625
  11820 Edgewater Dr # 418 Lakewood (44107) (G-11681)
Volpe Millwork Inc 216 581-0200
  4500 Lee Rd Cleveland (44128) (G-6427)
Voltage Regulator Sales & Svcs 937 878-0673
  590 E Dayton Dr Fairborn (45324) (G-9634)
Von Roll Isola, Cleveland Also called Von Roll Usa Inc (G-6428)
Von Roll Usa Inc 216 433-7474
  4853 W 130th St Cleveland (44135) (G-6428)
Voodoo Industries 440 653-5333
  33640 Pin Oak Pkwy Ste 4 Avon Lake (44012) (G-1054)
Vores Steve Welding & Steel, Fort Recovery Also called Steve Vore Welding and Steel (G-9959)
Vorhees Logging LLC 740 385-0216
  15275 Mount Olive Rd Rockbridge (43149) (G-16690)
Vorlage Special Tool 419 697-1201
  205 Utah St Oregon (43605) (G-15721)
Vortec and Paxton Products 513 891-7474
  10125 Carver Rd Blue Ash (45242) (G-1890)
Vortec Corporation 513 686-8210
  10125 Carver Rd Blue Ash (45242) (G-1891)
Vortec-An Illinois TI Works Co, Blue Ash Also called Vortec Corporation (G-1891)
Vortex Metals Ltd 216 365-2300
  19200 Cranwood Pkwy Warrensville Heights (44128) (G-19636)
Vorti-Siv, Salem Also called M M Industries Inc (G-16912)
Voss Clamp Technology Division, Cleveland Also called Voss Industries Inc (G-6430)
Voss Industries Inc (PA) 216 771-0870
  2168 W 25th St Cleveland (44113) (G-6429)
Voss Industries Inc 216 771-7655
  2168 W 25th St Cleveland (44113) (G-6430)
Voyale Minority Enterprise LLC 216 271-3661
  5855 Grant Ave Cleveland (44105) (G-6431)
VPI, Aurora Also called Video Products Inc (G-955)
Vpp Industries Inc 937 526-3775
  960 E Main St Versailles (45380) (G-19359)
Vr Waverly Inc (HQ) 740 947-7763
  611 W 2nd St Waverly (45690) (G-19720)
Vrc, Loveland Also called Valve Related Controls Inc (G-12397)
Vrc Inc 440 243-6666
  696 W Bagley Rd Berea (44017) (G-1640)
Vrc Manufacturers, Berea Also called Vrc Inc (G-1640)
Vsl Signs 740 441-7578
  1049 Blazer Rd Gallipolis (45631) (G-10311)
Vsp Lab Columbus 614 409-8900
  2605 Rohr Rd Lockbourne (43137) (G-12152)
Vtd Systems Inc 440 323-4122
  7600 W River Rd S Elyria (44035) (G-9508)
Vti Instruments Corporation 216 447-8950
  7525 Granger Rd Ste 7 Cleveland (44125) (G-6432)
Vts Co Ltd 419 273-4010
  607 E Lima St Forest (45843) (G-9924)
Vulcan International Corp 513 621-2850
  30 Garfield Pl Ste 1000 Cincinnati (45202) (G-4571)
Vulcan Machinery Corporation 330 376-6025
  20 N Case Ave Akron (44305) (G-465)
Vulcan Oil Company, Cincinnati Also called New Vulco Mfg & Sales Co LLC (G-4149)
Vulcan Products Co Inc 419 468-1039
  208 S Washington St Galion (44833) (G-10290)
Vulcan Tool Company 937 253-6194
  730 Lorain Ave Dayton (45410) (G-8744)
Vulkor, Warren Also called Therm-O-Link Inc (G-19605)
Vulkor Incorporated (PA) 330 393-7600
  621 Dana St Ne Ste V Warren (44483) (G-19619)
Vwm Republic Metals, Cleveland Also called Victory White Metal Company (G-6416)

Vwm-Republic Inc.....................216 271-1400
6100 Roland Ave Cleveland (44127) *(G-6433)*

Vy Inc.....................513 421-8100
37 W 7th St Fl 6 Cincinnati (45202) *(G-4572)*

Vya Inc.....................513 772-5400
1325 Glendale Milford Rd Cincinnati (45215) *(G-4573)*

W & W Automotive, Beavercreek Township *Also called W&W Automotive & Towing Inc (G-1391)*

W & W Custom Fabrication Inc.....................513 353-4617
4801 Hamilton Cleves Rd Cleves (45002) *(G-6532)*

W & W Custom Fabrication Inc (PA).....................513 353-4617
143 E Fairway Dr Hamilton (45013) *(G-10755)*

W A S P Inc.....................740 439-2398
59100 Claysville Rd Cambridge (43725) *(G-2482)*

W B, Marion *Also called Wilson Bohannan Company (G-12915)*

W B Coal Company Inc.....................614 221-0101
17 S High St Ste 1220 Columbus (43215) *(G-7745)*

W C Heller & Co Inc.....................419 485-3176
201 W Wabash St Montpelier (43543) *(G-14457)*

W C J Corp.....................216 523-1135
1740 Columbus Rd Cleveland (44113) *(G-6434)*

W C R, Fairborn *Also called Wcr Inc (G-9635)*

W C Sims Co Inc (PA).....................937 325-7035
3845 W National Rd Springfield (45504) *(G-17674)*

W G Lockhart Construction Co.....................330 745-6520
800 W Waterloo Rd Akron (44314) *(G-466)*

W G Machine Tool Service Co.....................330 723-3428
7735 Spieth Rd Medina (44256) *(G-13496)*

W H Heimkreiter Manufacturing.....................513 681-9192
3106 Spring Grove Ave Cincinnati (45225) *(G-4574)*

W H K Company.....................937 372-3368
1720 State Route 380 Xenia (45385) *(G-20986)*

W H Patten Drilling Co Inc.....................330 674-3046
6336 County Road 207 Millersburg (44654) *(G-14279)*

W J Egli Company Inc (PA).....................330 823-3666
205 E Columbia St Alliance (44601) *(G-551)*

W L Arehart Computing Systems.....................937 383-4710
555 Fife Rd Wilmington (45177) *(G-20681)*

W L Beck Printing & Design.....................330 762-3020
1326 S Main St Akron (44301) *(G-467)*

W M Inc.....................330 427-6115
275 High St Washingtonville (44490) *(G-19644)*

W M Dauch Concrete Inc.....................419 562-6917
900 Nevada Rd Bucyrus (44820) *(G-2364)*

W N Albums and Frames Inc.....................800 325-5179
2160 Superior Ave E Cleveland (44114) *(G-6435)*

W O Hardwoods Inc.....................740 425-1588
58098 Wright Rd Barnesville (43713) *(G-1162)*

W P Brown Enterprises Inc.....................740 685-2594
57051 Marietta Rd Byesville (43723) *(G-2413)*

W Pole Contracting Inc.....................330 325-7177
4188 State Route 14 Ravenna (44266) *(G-16570)*

W Productions, Urbana *Also called Wright John (G-19188)*

W R G Inc.....................216 351-8494
3961 Pearl Rd Cleveland (44109) *(G-6436)*

W S Tyler, Mentor *Also called Tyler Haver Inc (G-13756)*

W T Inc.....................419 224-6942
606 N Jackson St Lima (45801) *(G-12110)*

W W Cross Industries Inc.....................330 588-8400
2510 Allen Ave Se Canton (44707) *(G-2898)*

W W F, Fayetteville *Also called Wiederhold Wldg & Fabrication (G-9785)*

W W Williams Company LLC.....................330 659-3084
2920 Brecksville Rd B1 Richfield (44286) *(G-16645)*

W W Williams Company LLC (HQ).....................614 228-5000
835 Goodale Blvd Columbus (43212) *(G-7746)*

W&W Automotive & Towing Inc.....................937 429-1699
680 Orchard Ln Beavercreek Township (45434) *(G-1391)*

W&W Rock Sand and Gravel.....................513 266-3708
1451 Maple Grove Rd Williamsburg (45176) *(G-20413)*

W-J Inc.....................440 248-8282
34180 Solon Rd Solon (44139) *(G-17412)*

W.T.nickell Co., Batavia *Also called D&D Design Concepts Inc (G-1176)*

W/S Packaging Group Inc.....................513 459-2400
7500 Industrial Row Dr Mason (45040) *(G-13102)*

W3 Ultrasonics LLC.....................330 284-3667
5288 Huckleberry St Nw North Canton (44720) *(G-15283)*

WA Hammond Drierite Co Ltd.....................937 376-2927
138 Dayton Ave Xenia (45385) *(G-20987)*

Wabash National Corporation.....................419 434-9409
2000 Fostoria Ave Findlay (45840) *(G-9905)*

Wabash River Conservancy.....................419 375-2577
14574 State Route 49 Fort Recovery (45846) *(G-9962)*

Wabash River Conservancy Dst, Fort Recovery *Also called Wabash River Conservancy (G-9962)*

Wabtec Corporation.....................216 362-7500
4677 Manufacturing Ave Cleveland (44135) *(G-6437)*

Wabush Mines Cliffs Mining Co.....................216 694-5700
200 Public Sq Ste 3300 Cleveland (44114) *(G-6438)*

Wacker Chemical Corporation.....................330 899-0847
2215 International Pkwy Canton (44720) *(G-2899)*

Waddell A Div GMI Companies, Greenfield *Also called GMI Companies Inc (G-10477)*

Waddell Manufacturing Company, Stow *Also called Baker McMillen Co (G-17734)*

Wade Dynamics Inc.....................216 431-8484
1411 E 39th St Cleveland (44114) *(G-6439)*

Wades Woodworking Inc.....................937 374-6470
1427 Bellbrook Ave Xenia (45385) *(G-20988)*

Waeco Valve Division, Salem *Also called Hunt Valve Company Inc (G-16901)*

Waffle House Inc.....................937 746-6830
6840 Franklin Lebanon Rd Franklin (45005) *(G-10062)*

Waffle House Inc.....................513 539-8372
1225 Hamilton Lebanon Rd Monroe (45050) *(G-14419)*

Wagers Inc.....................513 825-6300
2464 California Rd Okeana (45053) *(G-15666)*

Wagner Farms & Sawmill LLC.....................419 653-4126
13201 Road X Leipsic (45856) *(G-11878)*

Wagner Machine Inc.....................330 706-0700
5151 Wooster Rd W Norton (44203) *(G-15523)*

Wagner Quarries Company.....................419 625-8141
4203 Milan Rd Sandusky (44870) *(G-17021)*

Wagner Rustproofing Co Inc.....................216 361-4930
7708 Quincy Ave Cleveland (44104) *(G-6440)*

Wagoner Stores Inc (PA).....................937 836-3636
324 Union Blvd Englewood (45322) *(G-9544)*

Wagoners Red Wing Shs Fabrics, Englewood *Also called Wagoner Stores Inc (G-9544)*

Wagram, Etna *Also called Alice Beougher (G-9551)*

Wahconah Group Inc.....................216 923-0570
2295 E 55th St Cleveland (44103) *(G-6441)*

Wahl Refractory Solutions LLC.....................419 334-2658
767 S State Route 19 Fremont (43420) *(G-10193)*

Wahlies Cstm Cft Drapery Uphl.....................419 229-1731
605 W Kibby St Lima (45804) *(G-12111)*

Waibel Electric Co Inc.....................740 964-2956
133 Humphries Dr Etna (43068) *(G-9553)*

Waino Sheet Metal Inc.....................330 945-4226
4198 Ellsworth Rd Stow (44224) *(G-17816)*

Waits Instruments LLC.....................513 600-5996
1337 Karahill Dr Cincinnati (45240) *(G-4575)*

Wake Nation.....................513 887-9253
201 Joe Nuxhall Way Fairfield (45014) *(G-9730)*

Wake Robin Fermented Foods LLC.....................216 961-9944
1303 W 103rd St Cleveland (44102) *(G-6442)*

Wakeman Auto and Tractor Parts.....................440 839-2835
31 W Main St Wakeman (44889) *(G-19454)*

Wakeman Power, Wakeman *Also called Wakeman Auto and Tractor Parts (G-19454)*

Wal Plax, Bedford *Also called Walton Plastics Inc (G-1472)*

Wal-Bon of Ohio Inc (PA).....................740 423-6351
210 Main St Belpre (45714) *(G-1595)*

Wal-Bon of Ohio Inc.....................740 423-8178
708 Main St Belpre (45714) *(G-1596)*

Walbridge Coatings, Walbridge *Also called MSC Walbridge Coatings Inc (G-19461)*

Walden Industries Inc.....................740 633-5971
101 Walden Ave Tiltonsville (43963) *(G-18255)*

Waldock Eqp Sls & Svc Inc (PA).....................419 426-7771
12178 E County Road 6 Attica (44807) *(G-897)*

Waldorf Marking Devices, New London *Also called Monode Marking Products Inc (G-14861)*

Waldorf Marking Devices Div, Mentor *Also called Monode Marking Products Inc (G-13660)*

Walest Incorporated.....................216 362-8110
15500 Commerce Park Dr Cleveland (44142) *(G-6443)*

Walker Magnetics Group Inc.....................614 492-1614
2195 Wright Brothers Ave Columbus (43217) *(G-7747)*

Walker National, Columbus *Also called Walker Magnetics Group Inc (G-7747)*

Walker National Inc.....................614 492-1614
2195 Wright Brothers Ave Columbus (43217) *(G-7748)*

Walker Printing Co, Mentor *Also called Jack G Walker (G-13617)*

Walker Tool & Machine Co.....................419 661-8000
7700 Ponderosa Dr Perrysburg (43551) *(G-16167)*

Wall Colmonoy Corporation.....................937 278-9111
940 Redna Ter Cincinnati (45215) *(G-4576)*

Wall Colmonoy Corporation.....................513 842-4200
940 Redna Ter Cincinnati (45215) *(G-4577)*

Wall Polishing LLC.....................937 698-1330
1953 S State Route 48 Ludlow Falls (45339) *(G-12429)*

Wallace Forge Company.....................330 488-1203
3700 Georgetown Rd Ne Canton (44704) *(G-2900)*

Wallen Commercial Hardware.....................937 426-5711
832 Space Dr Beavercreek Township (45434) *(G-1392)*

Waller Brothers Stone Company.....................740 858-1948
744 Mcdermott Rushtown Rd Mc Dermott (45652) *(G-13345)*

Wallingford Coffee Mills Inc (PA).....................513 771-3131
11401 Rockfield Ct Cincinnati (45241) *(G-4578)*

Wallover Enterprises Inc (HQ).....................440 238-9250
21845 Drake Rd Strongsville (44149) *(G-17981)*

Wallover Enterprises Inc.....................440 238-9250
1032 Pennsylvania Ave East Liverpool (43920) *(G-9228)*

Wallover Oil Company Inc (HQ).....................440 238-9250
21845 Drake Rd Strongsville (44149) *(G-17982)*

Wallover Oil Hamilton Inc 513 896-6692
1000 Forest Ave Hamilton (45015) *(G-10756)*

Walls Asphalt Manufacturing, Greenville *Also called Walls Bros Asphalt Co Inc (G-10526)*

Walls Bros Asphalt Co Inc (PA) 937 548-7158
3690 Hllnsburg Sampson Rd Greenville (45331) *(G-10526)*

Wallseye Concrete Corp (PA) 440 235-1800
26000 Sprague Rd Cleveland (44138) *(G-6444)*

Wallseye Concrete Corp 419 483-2738
8802 Portland Rd Castalia (44824) *(G-2978)*

Walman Optical, Moraine *Also called Soderberg Inc (G-14529)*

Walnut Creek Cart Shop 330 893-1097
3309 State Route 39 Millersburg (44654) *(G-14280)*

Walnut Creek Chocolate Company 330 893-2995
4917 State Rte 515 Walnut Creek (44687) *(G-19471)*

Walnut Creek Lumber Co Ltd 330 852-4559
10433 Pleasant Hill Rd Nw Dundee (44624) *(G-9185)*

Walnut Creek Planing Ltd 330 893-3244
5778 State Route 515 Millersburg (44654) *(G-14281)*

Walnut Creek Wood Design 330 852-9663
1689 State Route 39 Sugarcreek (44681) *(G-18049)*

Walnut Creek Woodworking LLC 513 504-3520
1878 Jones Florer Rd Bethel (45106) *(G-1665)*

Walnut Hill Shop 740 828-3346
17388a Frampton Rd Frazeysburg (43822) *(G-10077)*

Walsh Manufacturing, Cleveland *Also called Herman Manufacturing LLC (G-5504)*

Walt Myers 937 325-0313
303 N Greenmount Ave Springfield (45503) *(G-17675)*

Waltco Lift Corp (HQ) 330 633-9191
285 Northeast Ave Tallmadge (44278) *(G-18175)*

Waltek & Company, Cincinnati *Also called Wt Acquisition Company Ltd (G-4610)*

Walter F Stephens Jr Inc 937 746-0521
415 South Ave Franklin (45005) *(G-10063)*

Walter Graphics Inc 419 522-5261
850 Oak St Mansfield (44907) *(G-12702)*

Walter Grinders Inc 937 859-1975
510 Earl Blvd Miamisburg (45342) *(G-13877)*

Walter H Drane Co Inc 216 514-1022
23811 Chagrin Blvd # 344 Beachwood (44122) *(G-1305)*

Walters Buildings, Urbana *Also called Jack Walters & Sons Corp (G-19164)*

Walther EMC, Franklin *Also called Walther Engrg & Mfg Co Inc (G-10064)*

Walther Engrg & Mfg Co Inc 937 743-8125
3501 Shotwell Dr Franklin (45005) *(G-10064)*

Walton Hills, Walton Hills *Also called Controllix Corporation (G-19472)*

Walton Plastics Inc 440 786-7711
20493 Hannan Pkwy Bedford (44146) *(G-1472)*

Walton, Rego and Roy, West Chester *Also called Wrr Creative Concepts LLC (G-19974)*

Wanashab Inc 330 606-6675
1768 E 25th St Ste 308 Cleveland (44114) *(G-6445)*

Wannemacher Enterprises Inc 419 771-1101
422 W Guthrie Dr Upper Sandusky (43351) *(G-19145)*

Wannemacher Packaging, Upper Sandusky *Also called Wannemacher Enterprises Inc (G-19145)*

Wanner Metal Worx Inc 740 369-4034
525 London Rd Delaware (43015) *(G-8894)*

Wapak Tool & Die Inc 419 738-6215
732 Keller Dr Wapakoneta (45895) *(G-19512)*

Wapakoneta Daily News, Wapakoneta *Also called Horizon Publications Inc (G-19490)*

Wapakoneta Plant, Wapakoneta *Also called General Aluminum Mfg Company (G-19487)*

Wappoo Wood Products Inc 937 492-1166
12877 Kirkwood Rd Sidney (45365) *(G-17233)*

Ward Construction Co (PA) 419 943-2450
385 Oak St Leipsic (45856) *(G-11879)*

Ward Mold & Machine 740 472-5303
317 Fairground Rd Woodsfield (43793) *(G-20722)*

Ward/Kraft Forms of Ohio Inc 740 694-0015
700 Salem Ave Ext Fredericktown (43019) *(G-10116)*

Warehouse, Mansfield *Also called Gorman-Rupp Company (G-12616)*

Warehousingconverting, Mansfield *Also called Graphic Paper (G-12619)*

Warlock Inc 614 471-4055
2179 Citygate Dr Columbus (43219) *(G-7749)*

Warmus and Associates Inc 330 659-4440
2324 N Clvland Mssllon Rd Bath (44210) *(G-1240)*

Warner Chlcott Phrmcticals Inc (PA) 513 983-1100
1 Procter And Gamble Plz Cincinnati (45202) *(G-4579)*

Warner Fabricating Inc 330 848-3191
7812 Hartman Rd Wadsworth (44281) *(G-19443)*

Warner Hildebrant 740 286-1903
714 Bear Run Rd South Webster (45682) *(G-17452)*

Warner Vess Inc 740 585-2481
12 Warner Second St Lower Salem (45745) *(G-12416)*

Warren Castings Inc 216 883-2520
2934 E 55th St Cleveland (44127) *(G-6446)*

Warren Concrete and Supply Co 330 393-1581
1113 Parkman Rd Nw Warren (44485) *(G-19620)*

Warren Door, Niles *Also called Traichal Construction Company (G-15186)*

Warren Door 330 652-6346
332 Plant St Niles (44446) *(G-15188)*

Warren Drilling Co Inc 740 783-2775
305 Smithson St Dexter City (45727) *(G-8958)*

Warren Enterprises 330 836-6119
1067 Winhurst Dr Akron (44313) *(G-468)*

Warren Fabricating Corporation (PA) 330 847-0596
3240 Mahoning Ave Nw Warren (44483) *(G-19621)*

Warren Fire Equipment Inc (PA) 330 824-3523
6880 Tod Ave Sw Warren (44481) *(G-19622)*

Warren Fire Equipment Inc 937 866-8918
2240 E Central Ave Miamisburg (45342) *(G-13878)*

Warren Metal Lithography, Warren *Also called Tecnocap LLC (G-19604)*

Warren Printing & Off Pdts Inc 419 523-3635
250 E Main St Ottawa (45875) *(G-15814)*

Warren Rupp Inc 419 524-8388
800 N Main St Mansfield (44902) *(G-12703)*

Warren Screw Machine Inc 330 609-6020
3869 Niles Rd Se Warren (44484) *(G-19623)*

Warren Steel Specialties Corp 330 399-8360
1309 Niles Rd Se Warren (44484) *(G-19624)*

Warren Trucking, Dexter City *Also called Warren Drilling Co Inc (G-8958)*

Warren Welding and Fabrication, Lebanon *Also called Kirbys Auto & Truck Repair (G-11812)*

Warren Zachman Contracting 740 389-4503
5005 Marion Edison Rd Marion (43302) *(G-12911)*

Warrenton Copper LLC 636 456-3488
1240 Marquette St Cleveland (44114) *(G-6447)*

Warrior Imports Inc 954 935-5536
112 S Meridian Rd Youngstown (44509) *(G-21243)*

Warrior Technologies Inc 937 438-0279
7320 Kings Run Rd Dayton (45459) *(G-8745)*

Warrior Trikes Inc 419 264-6008
E366 County Road 13 Holgate (43527) *(G-11042)*

Warther Woodworking, Dover *Also called Warthers Music Box Bells (G-9024)*

Warthers Music Box Bells 330 343-4706
115 W Front St Dover (44622) *(G-9024)*

Warthman Drilling Inc 740 746-9950
7525 Lancaster Logan Rd Sugar Grove (43155) *(G-18013)*

Warwick Products Company 216 334-1200
5350 Tradex Pkwy Cleveland (44102) *(G-6448)*

Washing Systems LLC 800 272-1974
167 Commerce Dr Loveland (45140) *(G-12399)*

Washington Crt Hse Converting, Wshngtn CT Hs *Also called Weyerhaeuser Company (G-20931)*

Washington Group, Oregon *Also called Aecom Energy & Cnstr Inc (G-15701)*

Washington Laboratories Inc 330 452-4928
1922 26th St Ne Canton (44705) *(G-2901)*

Washington Products Inc 330 837-5101
1875 Harsh Ave Se Ste 1 Massillon (44646) *(G-13211)*

Washita Valley Enterprises Inc 330 510-1568
3707 Tulane Ave Bldg 9 Louisville (44641) *(G-12334)*

Wasserstrom Company (PA) 614 737-8472
477 S Front St Columbus (43215) *(G-7750)*

Wasserstrom Company 614 228-2233
2777 Silver Dr Columbus (43211) *(G-7751)*

Wasserstrom Marketing Division, Columbus *Also called N Wasserstrom & Sons Inc (G-7377)*

Waste King, North Olmsted *Also called Anaheim Manufacturing Company (G-15326)*

Waste Parchment Inc 330 674-6868
4510 Township Road 307 Millersburg (44654) *(G-14282)*

Waste Water Plant, The, Ravenna *Also called City of Ravenna (G-16522)*

Waste Water Pollution Control 330 263-5290
1123 Columbus Rd Wooster (44691) *(G-20844)*

Waste Water Treatment Plant, Madison *Also called County of Lake (G-12502)*

Wastequip Manufacturing Co LLC 330 674-1119
930 Massillon Rd Millersburg (44654) *(G-14283)*

Watch-Us Inc 513 829-8870
4450 Dixie Hwy Fairfield (45014) *(G-9731)*

Water & Sewer, Chardon *Also called City of Chardon (G-3147)*

Water & Waste Water Dept., Mount Vernon *Also called City of Mount Vernon (G-14615)*

Water & Waste Water Eqp Co 440 542-0972
32100 Solon Rd Ste 101a Solon (44139) *(G-17413)*

Water Drop Media Inc 234 600-5817
289 Youngstown Kingsvl Se Vienna (44473) *(G-19377)*

Water Ink Technologies, Blue Ash *Also called Actega North America Inc (G-1733)*

Water Poll Control 740 383-4446
1810 Marion Agosta Rd Marion (43302) *(G-12912)*

Water Star Inc 440 564-1001
12369 Kinsman Rd Bldg K Newbury (44065) *(G-15106)*

Water Systems Services 513 523-6766
4164 Miami Western Dr Oxford (45056) *(G-15845)*

Water Treatment, Middletown *Also called City of Middletown (G-14030)*

Water Treatment Dept 937 498-8180
880 E Court St Sidney (45365) *(G-17234)*

Water Treatment Plant, Marietta *Also called City of Marietta (G-12774)*

Waterford Signs Inc 740 362-7446
288 S Sandusky St Ste C Delaware (43015) *(G-8895)*

Waterford Tank Fabrication Ltd 740 984-4100
203 State Route 83 Beverly (45715) *(G-1672)*

A L P H A B E T I C

Waterloo Industries Inc 800 833-8851
  12487 Plaza Dr Cleveland (44130) *(G-6449)*

Waterloo Manufacturing Co Inc 330 947-2917
  6298 Waterloo Rd Atwater (44201) *(G-904)*

Waterlox Coatings Corporation 216 641-4877
  9808 Meech Ave Cleveland (44105) *(G-6450)*

Waterpro 330 372-3565
  2926 Commonwealth Ave Ne Warren (44483) *(G-19625)*

Waterville Sheet Metal Company 419 878-5050
  1210 Wtrville Monclova Rd Waterville (43566) *(G-19670)*

Watkins Auto Body Shop, Holland *Also called Custom Color Match and Spc (G-11050)*

Watkins Grinding Inc 937 461-4487
  1245 Leonhard St Dayton (45404) *(G-8746)*

Watkins Printing Company 614 297-8270
  1401 E 17th Ave Columbus (43211) *(G-7752)*

Watson Electric Motor Svc Inc 614 836-9904
  536 Stockbridge Rd Columbus (43207) *(G-7753)*

Watson Gravel Inc 513 422-3781
  2100 S Main St Middletown (45044) *(G-14095)*

Watson Gravel Inc (PA) 513 863-0070
  2728 Hamilton Cleves Rd Hamilton (45013) *(G-10757)*

Watson Haran & Company Inc 937 436-1414
  1500 Yankee Park Pl Dayton (45458) *(G-8747)*

Watson Logging 740 985-4465
  39511 Sumner Rd Pomeroy (45769) *(G-16392)*

Watson Meeks and Company 937 378-2355
  10402 W Fork Rd Georgetown (45121) *(G-10367)*

Watson's, Cincinnati *Also called Entertrainment Junction (G-3710)*

Watt Printers, Cleveland *Also called Gergel-Kellem Company Inc (G-5425)*

Watteredge LLC (HQ) 440 933-6110
  567 Miller Rd Avon Lake (44012) *(G-1055)*

Watters Manufacturing Co Inc 216 281-8600
  1931 W 47th St Cleveland (44102) *(G-6451)*

Watts Acquisition Company II, Eastlake *Also called Tri-Tech Research LLC (G-9293)*

Wausau Mosinee Paper, Middletown *Also called Wausau Paper Corp (G-14096)*

Wausau Paper Corp 513 217-3623
  700 Columbia Ave Middletown (45042) *(G-14096)*

Wausau Ppr Towel & Tissue LLC 513 424-2999
  700 Columbia Ave Middletown (45042) *(G-14097)*

Wauseon Machine & Mfg Inc (PA) 419 337-0940
  995 Enterprise Ave Wauseon (43567) *(G-19700)*

Wauseon Precast, Wauseon *Also called Wauseon Silo & Coal Company (G-19701)*

Wauseon Silo & Coal Company 419 335-6041
  535 Wood St Wauseon (43567) *(G-19701)*

Waverly Tool Co Ltd 740 988-4831
  2596 Glade Rd Beaver (45613) *(G-1312)*

Waxco International Inc 937 746-4845
  727 Dayton Oxford Rd Miamisburg (45342) *(G-13879)*

Waxler Machine Tool Company 419 422-1240
  535 6th St Findlay (45840) *(G-9906)*

Waxman Industries Inc (PA) 440 439-1830
  24460 Aurora Rd Cleveland (44146) *(G-6452)*

Waymakers Inc 330 352-1096
  628 Roscoe Ave Akron (44306) *(G-469)*

Wayne - Dalton Plastics, Conneaut *Also called Hrh Door Corp (G-7809)*

Wayne - Dalton Rolling Doors, Dalton *Also called Hrh Door Corp (G-8070)*

Wayne Builders Supply, Greenville *Also called St Henry Tile Co Inc (G-10523)*

Wayne Concrete Company 937 545-9919
  223 Western Dr Medway (45341) *(G-13502)*

Wayne County Rubber Inc 330 264-5553
  1205 E Bowman St Wooster (44691) *(G-20845)*

Wayne Dalton, Mount Hope *Also called Hrh Door Corp (G-14572)*

Wayne Frame Products Inc 419 726-7715
  5832 Lakeside Ave Toledo (43611) *(G-18771)*

Wayne Manufacturing, Zanesville *Also called New Wayne Inc (G-21333)*

Wayne Pak Ltd 440 323-8744
  214 Brace Ave Elyria (44035) *(G-9509)*

Wayne Signer Enterprises Inc 513 841-1351
  6545 Wiehe Rd Cincinnati (45237) *(G-4580)*

Wayne Sporting Goods 937 236-6665
  7101 Taylorsville Rd Dayton (45424) *(G-8748)*

Wayne Trail Technologies Inc 937 295-2120
  203 E Park St Fort Loramie (45845) *(G-9944)*

Wayne Water Systems, Harrison *Also called Wayne/Scott Fetzer Company (G-10811)*

Wayne's Precision Mach Shop, East Palestine *Also called Waynes Precision Machine Inc (G-9249)*

Wayne-Dalton, Millersburg *Also called Hrh Door Corp (G-14233)*

Wayne/Scott Fetzer Company 800 237-0987
  101 Production Dr Harrison (45030) *(G-10811)*

Waynedale Truss & Panel Co 330 683-4471
  93 Lake Dr Dalton (44618) *(G-8079)*

Waynedale Truss and Panel Co 330 698-7373
  8971 Dover Rd Apple Creek (44606) *(G-651)*

Waynes Precision Machine Inc 330 426-4626
  354 N Liberty St East Palestine (44413) *(G-9249)*

Waytek Corporation 937 743-6142
  400 Shotwell Dr Franklin (45005) *(G-10065)*

Wb Industries Inc 440 708-0309
  16461 Messenger Rd Burton (44021) *(G-2390)*

Wbc Group LLC (PA) 866 528-2144
  6333 Hudson Crossing Pkwy Hudson (44236) *(G-11207)*

Wc Sales Inc 419 836-2300
  5732 Woodville Rd Ste C Northwood (43619) *(G-15494)*

Wccv Floor Coverings Inc 330 688-0114
  4535 State Rd Peninsula (44264) *(G-16044)*

Wch Molding LLC 740 335-6320
  1850 Lowes Blvd Wshngtn CT Hs (43160) *(G-20928)*

Wcho AM, Wshngtn CT Hs *Also called Iheartcommunications Inc (G-20911)*

Wcm Holdings Inc (PA) 513 705-2100
  11500 Canal Rd Cincinnati (45241) *(G-4581)*

Wcr Inc (PA) 937 223-0703
  2377 Commerce Center Blvd B Fairborn (45324) *(G-9635)*

Wcr Incorporated 740 333-3448
  809 Delaware St Wshngtn CT Hs (43160) *(G-20929)*

Wear Magic, Cincinnati *Also called Cincinnati Advg Pdts LLC (G-3537)*

Wear Technology, Batavia *Also called Milacron Marketing Company LLC (G-1207)*

Weastec Incorporated 614 734-9645
  6195 Enterprise Ct Dublin (43016) *(G-9165)*

Weastec Incorporated (HQ) 937 393-6800
  1600 N High St Hillsboro (45133) *(G-11018)*

Weaver Barns Ltd 330 852-2103
  1696 State Route 39 Sugarcreek (44681) *(G-18050)*

Weaver Boos Consultants Inc 419 933-5216
  1145 S Conwell Ave Willard (44890) *(G-20404)*

Weaver Bros Inc (PA) 937 526-3907
  895 E Main St Versailles (45380) *(G-19360)*

Weaver Craft of Sugarcreek, Sugarcreek *Also called Weavers Furniture Ltd (G-18051)*

Weaver Fab & Finishing, Akron *Also called Bogie Industries Inc Ltd (G-95)*

Weaver Lumber Co 330 359-5091
  1925 Us Route 62 Wilmot (44689) *(G-20687)*

Weaver Meats Inc 440 639-1954
  380 Fountain Ave Painesville (44077) *(G-15938)*

Weaver Pallet Ltd 330 682-4022
  9380 Ely Rd Apple Creek (44606) *(G-652)*

Weaver Woodcraft L L C 330 695-2150
  9652 Harrison Rd Apple Creek (44606) *(G-653)*

Weavers Furniture Ltd 330 852-2701
  7011 Old Route 39 Nw Sugarcreek (44681) *(G-18051)*

Web3box Software LLC 330 794-7397
  34 Merz Blvd Ste D Tallmadge (44278) *(G-18176)*

Webb Machine & Fab Inc 330 717-5745
  15262 Hoyle Rd Berlin Center (44401) *(G-1659)*

Webb-Stiles Company (PA) 330 225-7761
  675 Liverpool Dr Valley City (44280) *(G-19237)*

WEBB-STILES OF ALABAMA, Valley City *Also called Webb-Stiles Company (G-19237)*

Weber Jewelers Incorporated 937 643-9200
  3155 Far Hills Ave Dayton (45429) *(G-8749)*

Weber Orthopedic Inc 440 934-1812
  1324 Chester Indus Pkwy Avon (44011) *(G-1018)*

Weber Sand & Gravel Inc 419 298-2388
  2702 County Road 3b Edgerton (43517) *(G-9338)*

Weber Sand & Gravel Inc 419 636-7920
  14586 Us Highway 127 Ew Bryan (43506) *(G-2326)*

Weber Technologies Inc 440 946-8833
  34000 Melinz Pkwy Eastlake (44095) *(G-9297)*

Weber Tool & Mfg Inc 440 786-0221
  7761 First Pl Oakwood Village (44146) *(G-15632)*

Webers Body & Frame 937 839-5946
  2017 State Route 503 N West Alexandria (45381) *(G-19786)*

Webster Industries Inc (PA) 419 447-8232
  325 Hall St Tiffin (44883) *(G-18253)*

Webster Manufacturing Company, Tiffin *Also called Webster Industries Inc (G-18253)*

Wecall Inc 440 437-8202
  64 Penniman Rd Orwell (44076) *(G-15780)*

Wecan Fabricators LLC 740 667-0731
  49425 E Park Dr Tuppers Plains (45783) *(G-18887)*

Wedco LLC 513 309-0781
  716 N High St Mount Orab (45154) *(G-14587)*

Wedding Pages, Canton *Also called Brahler Inc (G-2627)*

Wedding Plantation, Columbus *Also called Beverly Snider (G-6824)*

Wedge Hardwood Products 330 525-7775
  2137 Knox School Rd Alliance (44601) *(G-552)*

Wedge Products Inc 330 405-4477
  2181 Enterprise Pkwy Twinsburg (44087) *(G-19038)*

Wedgeworks Mch Tl & Boring Co 216 441-1200
  3169 E 80th St Cleveland (44104) *(G-6453)*

Weed Instrument Company Inc 216 676-5005
  6133 Rockside Rd Ste 300 Independence (44131) *(G-11283)*

Weekly Brothers Cnty Line Far 330 674-4195
  1533 Township Road 110 Millersburg (44654) *(G-14284)*

Weekly Chatter 740 336-4704
  1564 Calder Ridge Rd Belpre (45714) *(G-1597)*

Weekly Juicery 513 321-0680
  2727 Erie Ave Cincinnati (45208) *(G-4582)*

Weenk Labs LLC 614 448-0160
  221 N 4th St Columbus (43215) *(G-7754)*

Weidingr, Wm A Gldsmth-Jwlry, Columbus *Also called William A Weidinger Jewelry* **(G-7763)**

Weidmann Electrical Tech Inc 937 652-1220
700 W Court St Urbana (43078) *(G-19187)*

Weighing Division, Columbus *Also called Interface Logic Systems Inc* **(G-7202)**

Weirton Daily Times 740 283-4711
401 Herald Sq Steubenville (43952) *(G-17720)*

Weiskopf Industries Corp 440 442-4400
731 Beta Dr Ste B Cleveland (44143) *(G-6454)*

Weiss Construction & Sewer, Mentor *Also called L B Weiss Construction Inc* **(G-13625)**

Weiss Industries Inc 419 526-2480
2480 N Main St Mansfield (44903) *(G-12704)*

Weiss Metallurgical Services, Mansfield *Also called Weiss Industries Inc* **(G-12704)**

Weiss Motors 330 678-5585
101 E Crain Ave Kent (44240) *(G-11542)*

Weiss North America Inc 440 269-8031
3860 Ben Hur Ave Unit 2 Willoughby (44094) *(G-20629)*

Wek Industries, Jefferson *Also called Tmd Wek North LLC* **(G-11374)**

Welage Corporation 513 681-2300
1925 Powers St Cincinnati (45223) *(G-4583)*

Welch Holdings Inc 513 353-3220
8953 E Miami River Rd Cincinnati (45247) *(G-4584)*

Welch Packaging Columbus, Columbus *Also called Welch Packaging Group Inc* **(G-7755)**

Welch Packaging Group Inc 614 870-2000
4700 Alkire Rd Columbus (43228) *(G-7755)*

Welch Publishing Co (PA) 419 874-2528
117 E 2nd St Perrysburg (43551) *(G-16168)*

Welch Publishing Co 419 666-5344
215 Osborne St Rossford (43460) *(G-16750)*

Weld-Action Company Inc 330 372-1063
2100 N River Rd Ne Warren (44483) *(G-19626)*

Weldcraft Products Co 937 233-6141
1933 Kuntz Rd Dayton (45404) *(G-8750)*

Welded Ring Products Co (PA) 216 961-3800
2180 W 114th St Cleveland (44102) *(G-6455)*

Welded Tube Pros LLC 330 854-2966
215 Market St W Canal Fulton (44614) *(G-2517)*

Welded Tubes Inc (PA) 216 378-2092
135 Penniman Rd Orwell (44076) *(G-15781)*

Welded Tubes Inc 440 437-5144
135 Penniman Rd Orwell (44076) *(G-15782)*

WELDED TUBES, INC., Orwell *Also called Welded Tubes Inc* **(G-15782)**

Welders Supply Inc (HQ) 216 241-1696
2020 Train Ave Cleveland (44113) *(G-6456)*

Weldfab Inc 440 563-3310
2642 E Water St Rock Creek (44084) *(G-16687)*

Welding Consultants Inc 614 258-7018
889 N 22nd St Columbus (43219) *(G-7756)*

Welding Equipment Repair Co 330 536-2125
142 E Water St Lowellville (44436) *(G-12414)*

Welding Improvement Company 330 424-9666
10070 Stookesberry Rd Lisbon (44432) *(G-12135)*

Weldments Inc 937 235-9261
167 Heid Ave Dayton (45404) *(G-8751)*

Weldon 330 263-9533
3834 Zane Trace Dr Columbus (43228) *(G-7757)*

Weldon Ice Cream Company 740 467-2400
2887 Canal Dr Millersport (43046) *(G-14299)*

Weldon Plastics Corporation 330 425-9660
1962 Case Pkwy Twinsburg (44087) *(G-19039)*

Weldon Pump, Cleveland *Also called Bergstrom Company Ltd Partnr* **(G-4905)**

Weldon Pump Acquition LLC 440 232-2282
640 Golden Oak Pkwy Oakwood Village (44146) *(G-15633)*

Weldon Technologies, Columbus *Also called Akron Brass Company* **(G-6708)**

Weldon West, Akron *Also called West Motorsports Inc* **(G-470)**

Weldparts Inc 513 530-0064
6500 Corporate Dr Blue Ash (45242) *(G-1892)*

Weldtec Inc 419 394-9440
8319 Us Route 127 Celina (45822) *(G-3027)*

Weldtec Ltd 419 394-9440
8319 Us Route 127 Celina (45822) *(G-3028)*

Welker Machine & Grinding Co 216 481-1360
718 E 163rd St Cleveland (44110) *(G-6457)*

Well Service Group Inc 330 308-0880
1490 Truss Rd Sw New Philadelphia (44663) *(G-14939)*

Wellington Industries 734 942-1060
920 Illinois Ave Maumee (43537) *(G-13308)*

Wellington Manufacturing 440 647-1162
200 Erie St Wellington (44090) *(G-19757)*

Wellington Maumee, Maumee *Also called Wellington Industries* **(G-13308)**

Wellington Stamping, Wellington *Also called Sectional Stamping Inc* **(G-19754)**

Wellnitz, Columbus *Also called Hazelbaker Industries Ltd* **(G-7146)**

Wells Group LLC 740 532-9240
487 Gallia Pike Ironton (45638) *(G-11304)*

Wells Inc 419 457-2611
8176 Us Highway 23 Risingsun (43457) *(G-16673)*

Wells Manufacturing Co Llc 937 987-2481
280 W Main St New Vienna (45159) *(G-14957)*

Wellston Aerosol Mfg Co Inc 740 384-2320
105 W A St Wellston (45692) *(G-19772)*

Wellsville Foundry Inc 330 532-2995
18150 Fife Coal Rd Wellsville (43968) *(G-19776)*

Welly's Horseradish Co, Fremont *Also called Wellys Horseradish* **(G-10194)**

Wellys Horseradish 419 334-3134
141 N Monroe St Fremont (43420) *(G-10194)*

Welsh Farms LLC 513 723-4487
221 E 4th St Ste 2000 Cincinnati (45202) *(G-4585)*

Wendell August Gift Sp & Forge 330 893-3713
7007 Dutch Country Ln Berlin (44610) *(G-1653)*

Wendell Machine Shop 330 627-3480
2076 Mobile Rd Ne Carrollton (44615) *(G-2969)*

Wendling Patterns Inc 937 233-7770
2121 Jergens Rd Dayton (45404) *(G-8752)*

Wenger Pipeline Construction 330 828-8803
14945 Lincoln Way E Dalton (44618) *(G-8080)*

Wengerd Cabinets 330 231-0879
6605 Township Road 362 Millersburg (44654) *(G-14285)*

Wengerd Wood Inc 330 359-4300
2000 Us Route 62 Wilmot (44689) *(G-20688)*

Wengerd's Machine, Dalton *Also called Pioneer Equipment Company* **(G-8078)**

Wenrick Machine and Tool Corp 937 667-7307
4685 Us Route 40 Tipp City (45371) *(G-18311)*

Wentworth Mold Inc Electra 937 898-8460
852 Scholz Dr Vandalia (45377) *(G-19317)*

Wentworth Solutions 440 212-7696
2868 Westway Dr Ste B Brunswick (44212) *(G-2266)*

Wentworth Technologies LLC 440 212-7696
2868 Westway Dr Brunswick (44212) *(G-2267)*

Weprintquick.com, Cleveland *Also called Eveready Printing Inc* **(G-5307)**

Wepuko Pahnke Engineering LP 937 390-2100
4949 Urbana Rd Rear Springfield (45502) *(G-17676)*

Were Rolling Pretzle Company 419 784-0762
1500 N Clinton St Ste 144 Defiance (43512) *(G-8813)*

Wereb Metal Fabricating, Willoughby *Also called James L Wereb* **(G-20515)**

Werk-Brau Company 419 422-2912
2800 Fostoria Ave Findlay (45840) *(G-9907)*

Werling and Sons Inc 937 338-3281
100 S Plum St Burkettsville (45310) *(G-2370)*

Werling Meats Inc 419 375-0037
100 Plum St Burkettsville (45310) *(G-2371)*

Werlor Inc 419 784-4285
1420 Ralston Ave Defiance (43512) *(G-8814)*

Werlor Waste Control, Defiance *Also called Werlor Inc* **(G-8814)**

Wernke Wldg & Stl Erection Co 513 353-4173
3150 State Line Rd North Bend (45052) *(G-15210)*

Wernli Realty Inc 937 258-7878
1300 Grange Hall Rd Beavercreek (45430) *(G-1384)*

Wes-Garde Components Group Inc 614 885-0319
300 Enterprise Dr Westerville (43081) *(G-20240)*

Weschler Instruments, Strongsville *Also called Hughes Corporation* **(G-17928)**

Wesco Distribution Inc 419 666-1670
6519 Fairfield Dr Northwood (43619) *(G-15495)*

Wesco Machine Inc 330 688-6973
99 Rustic Ter Munroe Falls (44262) *(G-14668)*

West & Barker Inc 330 652-9923
950 Summit Ave Niles (44446) *(G-15189)*

West Bend Printing & Pubg Inc 419 258-2000
101 N Main St Antwerp (45813) *(G-632)*

West Carrollton Converting Inc 937 859-3621
400 E Dixie Dr Dayton (45449) *(G-8753)*

West Carrollton Parchment 513 594-3341
400 E Dixie Dr West Carrollton (45449) *(G-19794)*

West Chester Lock Co LLC 513 777-6486
6847 Lakota Plaza Dr West Chester (45069) *(G-19971)*

West Chester Protective Gear, Sharonville *Also called Chester West Holdings Inc* **(G-17113)**

West Equipment Company Inc (PA) 419 698-1601
1545 E Broadway St Toledo (43605) *(G-18772)*

West Erie Fuel 440 282-3493
4935 W Erie Ave Lorain (44053) *(G-12292)*

West Extrusion LLC 330 744-0625
75 Mccartney Rd Campbell (44405) *(G-2494)*

West Liberty Commons, Medina *Also called Al Root Company* **(G-13364)**

West Motorsports Inc 330 350-0375
1018 Ironwood Rd Ste A Akron (44306) *(G-470)*

West Ohio Tool & Mfg LLC 419 678-4745
3965 Lange Rd Saint Henry (45883) *(G-16825)*

West Ohio Tool Company 937 842-6688
7311 World Class Dr Russells Point (43348) *(G-16758)*

West Pharmaceutical Svcs Inc 513 741-3004
3309 Wheatcroft Dr Cincinnati (45239) *(G-4586)*

West Ridge Resources Inc (PA) 740 338-3100
46220 National Rd W Saint Clairsville (43950) *(G-16813)*

West Side Leader, Fairlawn *Also called Leader Publications Inc* **(G-9756)**

West Troy, Troy *Also called Troy West LLC* **(G-18882)**

West-Camp Press Inc 614 818-6279
39 Collegeview Rd Westerville (43081) *(G-20241)*

West-Ward Pharmaceuticals Corp 614 276-4000
  1809 Wilson Rd Columbus (43228) *(G-7758)*

Westar Plastics Llc 419 636-1333
  4271 County Road 15d Bryan (43506) *(G-2327)*

Westend Brewing LLC 513 922-0289
  5091 Orangelawn Dr Cincinnati (45238) *(G-4587)*

Westerman Inc (HQ) 740 569-4143
  245 N Broad St Bremen (43107) *(G-2081)*

Westerman Inc 330 262-6946
  899 Venture Blvd Wooster (44691) *(G-20846)*

Westerman Acquisition Co LLC 330 264-2447
  776 Kemrow Ave Wooster (44691) *(G-20847)*

Western & Southern Lf Insur Co (HQ) 513 629-1800
  400 Broadway St Cincinnati (45202) *(G-4588)*

Western Branch Diesel Inc 330 454-8800
  1616 Metric Ave Sw Canton (44706) *(G-2902)*

Western Digital Corporation 440 684-1331
  2635 Butternut Ln Cleveland (44124) *(G-6458)*

Western Enterprises, Westlake *Also called Western/Scott Fetzer Company (G-20319)*

Western Entps A Scott Fetzer, Avon Lake *Also called Scott Fetzer Company (G-1050)*

Western Ohio Cut Stone Ltd 937 492-4722
  1130 Dingman Slagle Rd Sidney (45365) *(G-17235)*

Western Ohio Graphics, Troy *Also called Painted Hill Inv Group Inc (G-18861)*

Western Ohio Graphics 937 335-8769
  402 E Main St Troy (45373) *(G-18885)*

Western Ohio Hall Service, Dayton *Also called Morton International LLC (G-8510)*

Western Reserve Distillers LLC 330 671-0347
  6549 Thornbrook Cir Hudson (44236) *(G-11208)*

Western Reserve Foods LLC 330 770-0885
  325 Bell St Chagrin Falls (44022) *(G-3073)*

Western Reserve Furniture Co 440 235-6216
  29701 Wellington Rd North Olmsted (44070) *(G-15351)*

Western Reserve Graphics 440 729-9527
  13404 Caves Rd Chesterland (44026) *(G-3223)*

Western Reserve Lubricants 440 951-5700
  13981 Leroy Center Rd Painesville (44077) *(G-15939)*

Western Reserve Metals Inc 330 448-4092
  7775 Addison Rd Masury (44438) *(G-13218)*

Western Reserve Mfg Co 216 641-0500
  9200 Inman Ave Cleveland (44105) *(G-6459)*

Western Reserve Orthodontics & 330 792-6826
  6431 Mahoning Ave Austintown (44515) *(G-977)*

Western Reserve Printing 330 650-9800
  218 N Main St Hudson (44236) *(G-11209)*

Western Reserve Sleeve Inc 440 238-8850
  22360 Royalton Rd Strongsville (44149) *(G-17983)*

Western Reserve Wire Products, Twinsburg *Also called Wrwp LLC (G-19041)*

Western Roto Engravers Inc 330 336-7636
  668 Seville Rd Wadsworth (44281) *(G-19444)*

Western Rserve Wtr Systems Inc 216 341-9797
  4133 E 49th St Newburgh Heights (44105) *(G-15080)*

Western Star Newspaper, Liberty Township *Also called Cox Newspapers LLC (G-11959)*

Western Star Rail Services, Newark *Also called Dennis Lavender (G-14999)*

Western States Envelope Co 419 666-7480
  6859 Commodore Dr Walbridge (43465) *(G-19464)*

Western States Envelope Label, Walbridge *Also called Western States Envelope Co (G-19464)*

Western Stress, Northwood *Also called Analytic Stress Relieving Inc (G-15476)*

Western-Southern Life, Cincinnati *Also called Western & Southern Lf Insur Co (G-4588)*

Western/Scott Fetzer Company 440 871-2160
  875 Bassett Rd Westlake (44145) *(G-20319)*

Western/Scott Fetzer Company (HQ) 440 892-3000
  28800 Clemens Rd Westlake (44145) *(G-20320)*

Westerville Endoscopy Ctr LLC 614 568-1666
  300 Polaris Pkwy Ste 1500 Westerville (43082) *(G-20194)*

Westerville Lawn & Garden 740 936-8452
  5064 S Old 3c Hwy Westerville (43082) *(G-20195)*

Westfield Steel Inc 937 322-2414
  1120 S Burnett Rd Springfield (45505) *(G-17677)*

Westgate Machine Co Inc 216 889-9745
  10665 Knights Way North Royalton (44133) *(G-15459)*

Westgerdes Cabinets 419 375-2113
  2664 Sawmill Rd Fort Recovery (45846) *(G-9963)*

Westinghouse A Brake Tech Corp 419 526-5323
  472 Rembrandt St Mansfield (44902) *(G-12705)*

Westlake Tool & Die Mfg Co 440 934-5305
  1280 Moore Rd Avon (44011) *(G-1019)*

Westmont Inc 330 862-3080
  3035 Union Ave Ne Minerva (44657) *(G-14345)*

Westmoreland Resources Gp LLC 740 622-6302
  544 Chestnut St Coshocton (43812) *(G-7914)*

Westmount Technology Inc 216 328-2011
  6100 Oak Tree Blvd Independence (44131) *(G-11284)*

Westrock Commercial LLC 419 476-9101
  1635 Coining Dr Toledo (43612) *(G-18773)*

Westrock Company 513 860-5546
  9245 Meridian Way West Chester (45069) *(G-19972)*

Westrock Converting Company 513 860-0225
  9266 Meridian Way West Chester (45069) *(G-19973)*

Westrock Cp LLC 513 745-2400
  9960 Alliance Rd Blue Ash (45242) *(G-1893)*

Westrock Cp LLC 740 622-0581
  500 N 4th St Coshocton (43812) *(G-7915)*

Westrock Cp LLC 330 297-0841
  975 N Freedom St Ravenna (44266) *(G-16571)*

Westrock Cp LLC 614 445-6850
  1015 Marion Rd Columbus (43207) *(G-7759)*

Westrock Cp LLC 513 745-2586
  414 S Cooper Ave Cincinnati (45215) *(G-4589)*

Westrock CP LLC 770 448-2193
  1010 Mead St Wshngtn CT Hs (43160) *(G-20930)*

Westrock CP LLC 937 898-2115
  7032 N Dixie Dr Dayton (45414) *(G-8754)*

Westrock Mwv LLC 937 495-6323
  10 W 2nd St Dayton (45402) *(G-8755)*

Westrock Mwv LLC 937 495-6323
  4751 Hempstead Station Dr Kettering (45429) *(G-11588)*

Westrock Rkt Company 330 296-5155
  975 N Freedom St Ravenna (44266) *(G-16572)*

Westside Supply Co Inc 216 267-9353
  5010 W 140th St Brookpark (44142) *(G-2172)*

Westview Concrete Corp 440 458-5800
  40105 Butternut Ridge Rd Elyria (44035) *(G-9510)*

Westwood Fbrction Shtmetal Inc 937 837-0494
  1752 Stanley Ave Dayton (45404) *(G-8756)*

Wetsu Group Inc 937 324-9353
  125 W North St Springfield (45504) *(G-17678)*

Wettle Corporation 419 865-6923
  952 Holland Park Blvd Holland (43528) *(G-11096)*

Weyerhaeuser Co Containeerboar 740 397-5215
  8800 Granville Rd Mount Vernon (43050) *(G-14655)*

Weyerhaeuser Company 740 335-4480
  1803 Lowes Blvd Wshngtn CT Hs (43160) *(G-20931)*

Wfs Filter Co, Cleveland *Also called Micropure Filtration Inc (G-5800)*

Wfsr Holdings LLC 877 735-4966
  220 E Monument Ave Dayton (45402) *(G-8757)*

Wg Mobile Welding LLC 440 720-1940
  6151 Wilson Mills Rd # 210 Highland Heights (44143) *(G-10921)*

WH Fetzer & Sons Mfg Inc 419 687-8237
  500 Donnenwirth Dr Plymouth (44865) *(G-16380)*

Wheat Ridge Pallet & Lumber, West Union *Also called Schrock John (G-20125)*

Wheatland Tube Company, Cambridge *Also called Zekelman Industries Inc (G-2483)*

Wheatland Tube Company, Warren *Also called Zekelman Industries Inc (G-19628)*

Wheatland Tube Company, Niles *Also called John Maneely Company (G-15165)*

Wheatley Electric Service Co 513 531-4951
  2046 Ross Ave Cincinnati (45212) *(G-4590)*

Wheel Group Holdings LLC 614 253-6247
  2901 E 4th Ave Ste 3 Columbus (43219) *(G-7760)*

Wheel One, Columbus *Also called Wheel Group Holdings LLC (G-7760)*

Wheeler Embroidery 740 550-9751
  1007 N 2nd St Ironton (45638) *(G-11305)*

Wheeler Manufacturing, Ashtabula *Also called Rex International USA Inc (G-837)*

Wheeler Sheet Metal Inc 419 668-0481
  4640 Plank Rd Norwalk (44857) *(G-15566)*

Whelco Industrial Ltd (PA) 419 385-4627
  28210 Cedar Park Blvd Perrysburg (43551) *(G-16169)*

Whemco, Canton *Also called United Rolls Inc (G-2888)*

Whemco-Ohio Foundry Inc 419 222-2111
  1600 Mcclain Rd Lima (45804) *(G-12112)*

Whempys Corp 614 888-6670
  6969 Worth Galena Rd P Worthington (43085) *(G-20893)*

Whip Guide Co 440 543-5151
  16829 Park Circle Dr Chagrin Falls (44023) *(G-3133)*

Whirlaway Corporation (HQ) 440 647-4711
  720 Shiloh Ave Wellington (44090) *(G-19758)*

Whirlaway Corporation 440 647-4711
  125 Bennett St Wellington (44090) *(G-19759)*

Whirlaway Corporation 440 647-4711
  720 Shiloh Ave Wellington (44090) *(G-19760)*

Whirlpool Corporation 937 548-4126
  1701 Kitchen Aid Way Greenville (45331) *(G-10527)*

Whirlpool Corporation 740 383-7122
  1300 Marion Agosta Rd Marion (43302) *(G-12913)*

Whirlpool Corporation 419 547-7711
  119 Birdseye St Clyde (43410) *(G-6548)*

Whirlpool Corporation 419 423-8123
  4901 N Main St Findlay (45840) *(G-9908)*

Whirlpool Corporation 937 547-0773
  1301 Sater St Greenville (45331) *(G-10528)*

Whirlpool Corporation 614 409-4340
  6241 Shook Rd Lockbourne (43137) *(G-12153)*

Whirlpool Corporation 419 523-5100
  677 Woodland Dr Ottawa (45875) *(G-15815)*

Whiskey Fox Corporation 440 779-6767
  26814 Lorain Rd North Olmsted (44070) *(G-15352)*

Whit S Frozen Custard 740 927-0025
  564 E Broad St Pataskala (43062) *(G-15990)*

Whitacre Enterprises Inc 740 934-2331
35651 State Route 537 Graysville (45734) **(G-10470)**
Whitacre Greer Company (PA) 330 823-1610
1400 S Mahoning Ave Alliance (44601) **(G-553)**
Whitaker Finishing LLC 419 666-7746
2707 Tracy Rd Northwood (43619) **(G-15496)**
Whitaker Surface Systems 419 874-1211
2707 Tracy Rd Northwood (43619) **(G-15497)**
White Castle System Inc (PA) 614 228-5781
555 W Goodale St Columbus (43215) **(G-7761)**
White Castle System Inc 513 563-2290
3126 Exon Ave Cincinnati (45241) **(G-4591)**
White Co David 440 247-2920
10161 Music St Novelty (44072) **(G-15584)**
White Dove Mattress, Newburgh Heights *Also called H Goodman Inc* **(G-15070)**
White Dove Mattress Ltd 216 341-0200
3201 Harvard Ave Newburgh Heights (44105) **(G-15081)**
White Feather Foods Inc 419 738-8975
13845 Cemetery Rd Wapakoneta (45895) **(G-19513)**
White House Chocolate 440 834-3133
14607 Kinsman Rd Middlefield (44062) **(G-14005)**
White Industrial Tool Inc 330 773-6889
102 W Wilbeth Rd Akron (44301) **(G-471)**
White Jewelers 330 264-3324
211 E Liberty St Wooster (44691) **(G-20848)**
White Machine & Mfg Co (PA) 740 453-3444
120 Graham St Zanesville (43701) **(G-21362)**
White Machine Inc 440 237-3282
9621 York Alpha Dr Side North Royalton (44133) **(G-15460)**
White Mule Company 740 382-9008
2420 W 4th St Ontario (44906) **(G-15697)**
White Rock Quarry L P 419 855-8388
3800 N Bolander Rd Clay Center (43408) **(G-4655)**
White Tiger Inc 740 852-4873
131 S Oak St London (43140) **(G-12223)**
White Tiger Graphics, London *Also called White Tiger Inc* **(G-12223)**
White Tool, Akron *Also called White Industrial Tool Inc* **(G-471)**
Whitefeather Foods, Wapakoneta *Also called White Feather Foods Inc* **(G-19513)**
Whitefeather Meats LLC 330 435-6300
14079 Cleveland Rd Creston (44217) **(G-7944)**
Whiteford Industries Inc 419 381-1155
3323 South Ave Toledo (43609) **(G-18774)**
Whitehouse, Tiffin *Also called Bradleys Beacons Ltd* **(G-18211)**
Whitehouse Bros Inc 513 621-2259
4393 Creek Rd Blue Ash (45241) **(G-1894)**
Whiterock Pigments Inc 216 391-7765
1768 E 25th St Cleveland (44114) **(G-6460)**
Whiteside Manufacturing Co 740 363-1179
309 Hayes St Delaware (43015) **(G-8896)**
Whitewater Processing Co 513 367-4133
10964 Campbell Rd Harrison (45030) **(G-10812)**
Whiteys Food Systems Inc 330 659-4070
3600 Brecksville Rd Ofc Richfield (44286) **(G-16646)**
Whitman Corporation 513 541-3223
2530 Joyce Ln Okeana (45053) **(G-15667)**
Whitmore Productions Inc 216 752-3960
20209 Harvard Ave Warrensville Heights (44122) **(G-19637)**
Whitmore's Bbq, Warrensville Heights *Also called Whitmore Productions Inc* **(G-19637)**
Whitney Company, Northwood *Also called Wc Sales Inc* **(G-15494)**
Whitney House 614 396-7846
666 High St Ste 102 Worthington (43085) **(G-20894)**
Whitney Stained Glass Studio 216 348-1616
5939 Broadway Ave Cleveland (44127) **(G-6461)**
Whits Frozen Custard 740 965-1427
101 W Cherry St Unit A Sunbury (43074) **(G-18078)**
Whits Frozen Custard of Upper 614 230-2213
2124 Arlington Ave Columbus (43221) **(G-7762)**
Whitt Machine Inc 513 423-7624
806 Central Ave Middletown (45044) **(G-14098)**
Whitten Studios 419 368-8366
1180 County Road 30a Ashland (44805) **(G-785)**
Whitworth Knife Company 513 321-9177
508 Missouri Ave Cincinnati (45226) **(G-4592)**
Whole Shop Inc 330 630-5305
181 S Thomas Rd Tallmadge (44278) **(G-18177)**
Whole Solutions 330 652-1725
1217 Salt Springs Rd Mineral Ridge (44440) **(G-14315)**
Wholecycle Inc 330 929-8123
100 Cyhoga Fls Indus Pkwy Peninsula (44264) **(G-16045)**
Wholesale Bait Co Inc (PA) 513 863-2380
2619 Bobmeyer Rd Fairfield (45014) **(G-9732)**
Wholesale Carpet Outlet Inc 937 447-4265
301 E Main St Gettysburg (45328) **(G-10376)**
Wholesale Channel Letters 440 256-3200
8603 Euclid Chardon Rd Kirtland (44094) **(G-11619)**
Wholesale Electronics, Solon *Also called Smartshopper Electronics Inc* **(G-17382)**
Wholesale Printers Ltd 440 354-5788
195 N Doan Ave Painesville (44077) **(G-15940)**
Wholesale Supplies Plus Inc 440 526-6556
7820 E Pleasant Valley Rd Independence (44131) **(G-11285)**
Wicktek Inc 724 329-8310
8097 Sacred Heart Ln Cincinnati (45255) **(G-4593)**
Wico Products Inc 937 783-0000
311 E Fancy St Blanchester (45107) **(G-1718)**
Wide Area Media LLC 440 356-3133
24500 Center Ridge Rd # 205 Westlake (44145) **(G-20321)**
Wiederhold Wldg & Fabrication 513 875-3755
1843 Us Highway 50 Fayetteville (45118) **(G-9785)**
Wieland, Archbold *Also called Sauder Manufacturing Co* **(G-692)**
Wifi-Plus Inc 877 838-4195
2950 Westway Dr Ste 101 Brunswick (44212) **(G-2268)**
Wififace LLC 419 754-4816
5424 Westcastle Dr Apt D Toledo (43615) **(G-18775)**
Wikoff Color Corporation 513 423-0727
1330 Hook Dr Middletown (45042) **(G-14099)**
Wil-Mark Froyo LLC 330 421-6043
1090 Williams Reserve Blv Wadsworth (44281) **(G-19445)**
Wilbert Shaw Valts, Newcomerstown *Also called Shaw Wilbert Vaults LLC* **(G-15124)**
Wilcoxon, James H Jr, Columbus *Also called Johnsons Real Ice Cream Co* **(G-7241)**
Wild Berry Incense Inc 513 523-8583
5475 College Corner Pike Oxford (45056) **(G-15846)**
Wild Berry Incense Factory, Oxford *Also called Wild Berry Incense Inc* **(G-15846)**
Wild Fire Systems 440 442-8999
535 Ransome Rd Cleveland (44143) **(G-6462)**
Wild Joe's Beef Jerky, Cincinnati *Also called Wild Joes Inc* **(G-4594)**
Wild Joes Inc 513 681-9200
2905 Jessamine St Cincinnati (45225) **(G-4594)**
Wild Penguin Llc 513 533-4356
4 Elmhurst Pl Cincinnati (45208) **(G-4595)**
Wildcat Creek Farms Inc 419 263-2549
4633 Road 94 Payne (45880) **(G-16019)**
Wildcat Creek Popcorn, Payne *Also called Wildcat Creek Farms Inc* **(G-16019)**
Wiley Farms 937 537-0676
29984 State Route 739 Richwood (43344) **(G-16661)**
Wileys Finest LLC 740 622-1072
545 Walnut St Ste B Coshocton (43812) **(G-7916)**
Wilguss Automotive Machine 937 465-0043
216 Runkle St West Liberty (43357) **(G-20095)**
Wilkes Energy Inc 330 252-4560
17 S Main St Ste 101a Akron (44308) **(G-472)**
Wilkett Enterprises LLC 740 384-2890
109 Mitchell Dr 4 Wellston (45692) **(G-19773)**
Wilkinson Printing Co 419 238-3615
710 W Ervin Rd Van Wert (45891) **(G-19276)**
Wilkshire Dry Cleaners LLC 330 674-7696
5660 County Road 203 Millersburg (44654) **(G-14286)**
Will-Burt Advnced Cmpsites Inc 330 684-5286
356 Collins Blvd Orrville (44667) **(G-15769)**
Will-Burt Company (PA) 330 682-7015
169 S Main St Orrville (44667) **(G-15770)**
Will-Burt Company 330 683-9991
150 Allen Ave Orrville (44667) **(G-15771)**
Will-Burt Company 330 682-7015
401 Collins Blvd Orrville (44667) **(G-15772)**
Willard Kelsey Solar Group LLC 419 931-2001
1775 Progress Dr Perrysburg (43551) **(G-16170)**
Willard Machine & Welding Inc 330 467-0642
556 Highland Rd E Ste 3 Macedonia (44056) **(G-12495)**
Willard Times Junction 419 935-0184
211 S Myrtle Ave Willard (44890) **(G-20405)**
Willet Enterprises 937 298-8622
1945 Southtown Blvd Ste A Dayton (45439) **(G-8758)**
William A Selz, Dayton *Also called S & S Printing Service Inc* **(G-8643)**
William A Weidinger Jewelry 614 481-8866
1458 W 5th Ave Columbus (43212) **(G-7763)**
William Darling Company Inc 614 878-0085
615 Hilliard Rome Rd A Columbus (43228) **(G-7764)**
William Dauch Concrete Company (PA) 419 668-4458
84 Cleveland Rd Norwalk (44857) **(G-15567)**
William Evanko Dgs, Wadsworth *Also called Evanko Wm/Barringer Richd DDS* **(G-19405)**
William Exline Inc 216 941-0800
12301 Bennington Ave Cleveland (44135) **(G-6463)**
William F Kelly, North Olmsted *Also called Western Reserve Furniture Co* **(G-15351)**
William J Bergen & Co 440 248-6132
32520 Arthur Rd Solon (44139) **(G-17414)**
William J Dupps 419 734-2126
126 Madison St Port Clinton (43452) **(G-16419)**
William Minnier 614 562-8080
3936 Cleggan St Canal Winchester (43110) **(G-2541)**
William Oeder Ready Mix Inc 513 899-3901
8807 State Route 134 Martinsville (45146) **(G-12930)**
William Powell Company (PA) 513 852-2000
2503 Spring Grove Ave Cincinnati (45214) **(G-4596)**
William R Hague Inc 614 836-2115
4343 S Hamilton Rd Groveport (43125) **(G-10649)**
William S Miller Inc 330 223-1794
11250 Montgomery Rd Kensington (44427) **(G-11421)**

(PA)=Parent Co (HQ)=Headquarters (DH)=Div Headquarters

William Thompson 440 232-4363
11304 Chamberlain Rd Aurora (44202) *(G-956)*

William Weber 440 350-9397
411 N State St Painesville (44077) *(G-15941)*

Williams Carrier Transicold, Richfield *Also called W W Williams Company LLC (G-16645)*

Williams Concrete Inc 419 893-3251
1350 Ford St Maumee (43537) *(G-13309)*

Williams County Publishing, Montpelier *Also called Advance Reporter (G-14438)*

Williams Design & Printing Ser 937 320-9449
2858 Tara Trl Beavercreek (45434) *(G-1365)*

Williams Executive Entps Inc 440 887-1000
6886 Pearl Rd Ste A Middleburg Heights (44130) *(G-13910)*

Williams Grgory Martin Fnrl HM, Steubenville *Also called Martin M Hardin (G-17705)*

Williams Industrial Svc Inc 419 353-2120
2120 Wood Bridge Blvd Bowling Green (43402) *(G-2020)*

Williams John F Oil Field Svcs 740 622-7692
20669 Coshocton Co Rd 6 Jackson (45640) *(G-11333)*

Williams Leather Products Inc 740 223-1604
1476 Likens Rd Ste 104 Marion (43302) *(G-12914)*

Williams Machine Co Inc 330 534-3058
461 N Main St Hubbard (44425) *(G-11141)*

Williams Partners LP 330 966-3674
7235 Whipple Ave Nw North Canton (44720) *(G-15284)*

Williams Pork Co Op 419 682-9022
18487 County Road F Stryker (43557) *(G-18010)*

Williams Precision Tool Inc 937 384-0608
6855 Gillen Ln Miamisburg (45342) *(G-13880)*

Williams Steel Rule Die Co 216 431-3232
1633 E 40th St Cleveland (44103) *(G-6464)*

Williamson Safe Inc 937 393-9919
5631 State Route 73 Hillsboro (45133) *(G-11019)*

Willis Music Company 513 671-3288
11700 Princeton Pike E209 Cincinnati (45246) *(G-4597)*

Willmac Enterprises Inc 740 967-1979
12200 Johnstown Utica Rd Johnstown (43031) *(G-11410)*

Willoughby Brewing Company 440 975-0202
4057 Erie St Willoughby (44094) *(G-20630)*

Willoughby Manufacturing Inc 330 402-8217
47415 Heck Rd New Waterford (44445) *(G-14976)*

Willow Frog LLC 513 861-4834
9 Briarwood Ln Cincinnati (45218) *(G-4598)*

Willow Hill Industries LLC 440 942-3003
37611 Euclid Ave Willoughby (44094) *(G-20631)*

Willow Tool & Machining Ltd 440 572-2288
15110 Foltz Pkwy Ste 1 Strongsville (44149) *(G-17984)*

Willow Water Treatment Inc 440 254-6313
7855 Jennings Dr Painesville (44077) *(G-15942)*

Willowwood, Mount Sterling *Also called Ohio Willow Wood Company (G-14601)*

Willy's Fresh Salsa, Swanton *Also called Willys Inc (G-18095)*

Willys Inc 419 823-3200
11305 W Airport Svc Rd Swanton (43558) *(G-18095)*

Wilmar, Coldwater *Also called Standard Register Inc (G-6572)*

Wilmer 419 678-6000
515 W Sycamore St Coldwater (45828) *(G-6574)*

Wilmington Forest Products 937 382-5013
5562 S Us Highway 68 Wilmington (45177) *(G-20682)*

Wilmington Precision Machining, Wilmington *Also called Cliffco Stands Inc (G-20659)*

Wilson Blacktop Corporation 740 635-3566
915 Carlisle St Rear Martins Ferry (43935) *(G-12928)*

Wilson Bohannan Company 740 382-3639
621 Buckeye St Marion (43302) *(G-12915)*

Wilson Cabinet Co 330 276-8711
Straits Industrial Park Killbuck (44637) *(G-11601)*

Wilson Concrete Products Inc (PA) 937 885-7965
10075 Sheehan Rd Dayton (45458) *(G-8759)*

Wilson Mobility LLC 216 921-9457
17602 Deforest Ave Cleveland (44128) *(G-6465)*

Wilson Optical Laboratory Inc 440 357-7000
9450 Pineneedle Dr Mentor (44060) *(G-13769)*

Wilson Prtg Graphics of London (PA) 740 852-5934
158 S Main St London (43140) *(G-12224)*

Wilson Seat Company Inc 513 732-2460
199 Foundry Ave Batavia (45103) *(G-1233)*

Wilson Sign Co Inc 937 253-2246
300 Hamilton Ave Dayton (45403) *(G-8760)*

Wilson Specialties, North Jackson *Also called Canfield Manufacturing Co Inc (G-15289)*

Wilson Sporting Goods Co 419 634-9901
217 Liberty St Ada (45810) *(G-7)*

Wilson Well Service, Malta *Also called Wolfe Creek Farms (G-12538)*

Wilsonart LLC 614 876-1515
2500 International St Columbus (43228) *(G-7765)*

Wilsons Country Creations 330 377-4190
13248 County Road 6 Killbuck (44637) *(G-11602)*

Win Cd Inc 330 929-1999
3333 Win St Cuyahoga Falls (44223) *(G-8062)*

Win Plex, Cuyahoga Falls *Also called Win Cd Inc (G-8062)*

Winans Chocolate and Coffee, Piqua *Also called Piqua Chocolate Company Inc (G-16301)*

Winans Manufacturing Co Inc 440 338-8599
7861 Kinsman Rd Novelty (44072) *(G-15585)*

Winco Stamping Inc 937 859-5522
650 Precision Ct Miamisburg (45342) *(G-13881)*

Windsor Airmotive, West Chester *Also called Barnes Group Inc (G-19815)*

Windsor Mold Inc 419 484-2400
122 Hirt Dr Bellevue (44811) *(G-1565)*

Windsor Mold USA Inc 419 483-0653
560 Goodrich Rd Bellevue (44811) *(G-1566)*

Windsor Tool Inc 216 671-1900
10714 Bellaire Rd Cleveland (44111) *(G-6466)*

Wine Cellar Innovations LLC 513 321-3733
4575 Eastern Ave Cincinnati (45226) *(G-4599)*

Wine Vault Enterprises LLC 614 850-0047
4907 Hawkstone Rd Hilliard (43026) *(G-10993)*

Winery At Spring Hill Inc 440 466-0626
6062 S Ridge Rd W Geneva (44041) *(G-10359)*

Wines For You 440 946-1420
7344 Mentor Ave Mentor (44060) *(G-13770)*

Winesburg Hardwood Lumber Co 330 893-2705
2871 Us Route 62 Dundee (44624) *(G-9186)*

Winesburg Meats Inc 330 359-5092
2181 Us Rte 62 Winesburg (44690) *(G-20708)*

Wingate Packaging South 513 745-8600
4347 Indeco Ct Blue Ash (45241) *(G-1895)*

Wings Way Drive Thru Inc 330 533-2788
9194 Salem Warren Rd Salem (44460) *(G-16935)*

Wings Way Ice, Salem *Also called Wings Way Drive Thru Inc (G-16935)*

Winkle Industries Inc 330 823-9730
2080 W Main St Alliance (44601) *(G-554)*

Winkler Co Inc 937 294-2662
435 Patterson Rd Dayton (45419) *(G-8761)*

Winner Welding Fabricating, New Weston *Also called Fred Winner (G-14977)*

Winner's Meat Service, Yorkshire *Also called Robert Winner Sons Inc (G-21006)*

Winners Meat Farm, Greenville *Also called Robert Winner Sons Inc (G-10520)*

Winsell Incorporated 330 836-7421
1720 Merriman Rd Unit J Akron (44313) *(G-473)*

Winspec Inc 440 834-9068
15470 Chipmunk Ln Middlefield (44062) *(G-14006)*

Winston Campbell LLC 614 274-7015
1777 Mckinley Ave Columbus (43222) *(G-7766)*

Winston Heat Treating Inc 937 226-0110
711 E 2nd St Dayton (45402) *(G-8762)*

Winston Oil Co Inc 740 373-9664
1 Court House Ln Ste 3 Marietta (45750) *(G-12850)*

Winsupply Inc 937 346-0600
2187 W 1st St Springfield (45504) *(G-17679)*

Winters Concrete, Jackson *Also called Winters Products Inc (G-11334)*

Winters Products Inc 740 286-4149
109 Athens St Jackson (45640) *(G-11334)*

Winzeler Stamping Co 419 485-3147
129 W Wabash St Montpelier (43543) *(G-14458)*

Wipe Out Enterprises 937 497-9473
6523 Dawson Rd Sidney (45365) *(G-17236)*

Wire Holdings LLC 216 731-9191
26000 Lakeland Blvd Cleveland (44132) *(G-6467)*

Wire Lab Company, Cleveland *Also called Omni Technical Products Inc (G-5942)*

Wire Products Company Inc (PA) 216 267-0777
14601 Industrial Pkwy Cleveland (44135) *(G-6468)*

Wire Products Company Inc 216 267-0777
14700 Industrial Pkwy Cleveland (44135) *(G-6469)*

Wire Shop Inc 440 354-6842
5959 Pinecone Dr Mentor (44060) *(G-13771)*

Wired Inc 440 567-8379
38849 Courtland Dr Willoughby (44094) *(G-20632)*

Wireless Toyz of Eastlake, Willowick *Also called Jhs Toyz LLC (G-20648)*

Wiremax Ltd 419 531-9500
705 Wamba Ave Toledo (43607) *(G-18776)*

Wirenet Inc 513 774-7759
250 E Kemper Rd Loveland (45140) *(G-12400)*

Wirick Press Inc 330 273-3488
839 Pearl Rd Brunswick (44212) *(G-2269)*

Wisco Products Incorporated 937 228-2101
109 Commercial St Dayton (45402) *(G-8763)*

Wise Consumer Products Company 513 484-6530
7972 Shelldale Way Montgomery (45242) *(G-14436)*

Wise Contracts, Cleveland *Also called Wise Window Treatment Inc (G-6470)*

Wise Enterprises Inc 330 568-7095
1911 Wick Campbell Rd Hubbard (44425) *(G-11142)*

Wise Window Treatment Inc 216 676-4080
5293 W 137th St Cleveland (44142) *(G-6470)*

Wiseman Bros Fabg & Stl Ltd 740 988-5121
2598 Glade Rd Beaver (45613) *(G-1313)*

Wissman & Wood Incorporated 513 793-6222
7849 Palace Dr Cincinnati (45249) *(G-4600)*

Witt Enterprises Inc 440 992-8333
2024 Aetna Rd Ashtabula (44004) *(G-845)*

Witt Industries Inc (HQ) 513 871-5700
4600 N Masn Montgomery Rd Mason (45040) *(G-13103)*

Witt Products, Mason *Also called Witt Industries Inc (G-13103)*

Witt-Gor Inc 419 659-2151
   108 S High St 110 Columbus Grove (45830) *(G-7798)*

Wittich's Candy Shop, Circleville *Also called Wittichs Candies Inc* *(G-4649)*

Wittichs Candies Inc 740 474-3313
   117 W High St Circleville (43113) *(G-4649)*

Wittrock Wdwkg & Mfg Co Inc 513 891-5800
   4201 Malsbary Rd Blue Ash (45242) *(G-1896)*

Wiwa LLC 419 757-0141
   107 N Main St Alger (45812) *(G-482)*

Wiwa LP 419 757-0141
   107 N Main St Alger (45812) *(G-483)*

Wizard Graphics Inc 419 354-3098
   112 S Main St Bowling Green (43402) *(G-2021)*

Wizard Publications Inc 808 821-1214
   1979 Wilshire Ln Nw Lancaster (43130) *(G-11762)*

Wjf Enterprises Inc 513 871-7320
   1347 Custer Ave Cincinnati (45208) *(G-4601)*

Wk Brick Company 614 416-6700
   970 Claycraft Rd Columbus (43230) *(G-7767)*

WLS Fabricating Co 440 449-0543
   5405 Avion Park Dr Cleveland (44143) *(G-6471)*

WLS Stamping Co (PA) 216 271-5100
   3292 E 80th St Cleveland (44104) *(G-6472)*

Wm Caxton Printing, Westerville *Also called Mc Vay Ventures Inc* *(G-20223)*

Wm Lang & Sons Company 513 541-3304
   3280 Beekman St Cincinnati (45223) *(G-4602)*

Wm Plotz Machine and Forge Co 216 861-0441
   2514 Center St Cleveland (44113) *(G-6473)*

Wm Software Inc 330 558-0501
   3660 Center Rd Ste 371 Brunswick (44212) *(G-2270)*

WMI Group LLC 330 535-8848
   219 Annadale Ave Akron (44304) *(G-474)*

Wmre of Ohio-American LLC 713 328-7345
   7916 Chapel St Se Waynesburg (44688) *(G-19729)*

Wmt, Independence *Also called Westmount Technology Inc* *(G-11284)*

Woco, East Liverpool *Also called Wallover Enterprises Inc* *(G-9228)*

Woco, Strongsville *Also called Wallover Oil Company Inc* *(G-17982)*

Wodin Inc 440 439-4222
   5441 Perkins Rd Cleveland (44146) *(G-6474)*

Woeber Mustard Mfg Co 937 323-6281
   1966 Commerce Cir Springfield (45504) *(G-17680)*

Wolf Composite Solutions, Columbus *Also called Wolfden Products Inc* *(G-7769)*

Wolf G T Awning & Tent Co 937 548-4161
   3352 State Route 571 Greenville (45331) *(G-10529)*

Wolf Machine Company (PA) 513 791-5194
   5570 Creek Rd Blue Ash (45242) *(G-1897)*

Wolf Metals Inc 614 461-6361
   1625 W Mound St Columbus (43223) *(G-7768)*

Wolfden Products Inc 614 219-6990
   3991 Fondorf Dr Columbus (43228) *(G-7769)*

Wolfden Products LLC 614 219-6990
   3991 Fondorf Dr Columbus (43228) *(G-7770)*

Wolfe Associates Inc 614 461-5000
   34 S 3rd St Columbus (43215) *(G-7771)*

Wolfe Creek Farms 740 962-4563
   433 Wilson Dr Malta (43758) *(G-12538)*

Wolfe Grinding Inc 330 929-6677
   4582 Allen Rd Stow (44224) *(G-17817)*

Wolfe Oil Company LLC 513 732-6220
   2944 Quitter Rd Williamsburg (45176) *(G-20414)*

Wolfe Paper Co., Avon Lake *Also called JMJ Paper Inc* *(G-1034)*

Wolff House Art Papers Inc 740 501-3766
   133 S Main St Mount Vernon (43050) *(G-14656)*

Wolff Tool & Manufacturing Co 440 933-7797
   139 Lear Rd Avon Lake (44012) *(G-1056)*

Wollam AG Center Inc 419 596-3896
   202 N Main St Continental (45831) *(G-7830)*

Wolters Kluwer Clinical Drug 330 650-6506
   1100 Terex Rd Hudson (44236) *(G-11210)*

Womens Imaging Center LLC 614 457-7660
   921 Jasonway Ave Columbus (43214) *(G-7772)*

Wonder Machine Services Inc 440 937-7500
   35340 Avon Commerce Pkwy Avon (44011) *(G-1020)*

Wonder Weld Inc 614 875-1447
   6127 Harrisburg Pike Orient (43146) *(G-15726)*

Wonder-Shirts Inc 917 679-2336
   7695 Crawley Dr Dublin (43017) *(G-9166)*

Wonderful Failure LLC 440 666-0919
   2140 Bunts Rd Lakewood (44107) *(G-11682)*

Wood County Ohio 419 353-1227
   1090 Fairview Ave Bowling Green (43402) *(G-2022)*

Wood Duck Enterprises Ltd 937 426-0506
   2225 La Grange Rd Beavercreek (45431) *(G-1366)*

Wood Graphics Inc (HQ) 513 771-6300
   1270 Hill Smith Dr Cincinnati (45215) *(G-4603)*

Wood Kraft 440 487-4634
   8928 Ely Rd Garrettsville (44231) *(G-10336)*

Wood Recovery, Newark *Also called Hope Timber & Marketing Group* *(G-15019)*

Wood Specialists 440 639-9797
   9485 Pinecone Dr Mentor (44060) *(G-13772)*

Wood Stove Shed 419 562-1545
   4602 Stetzer Rd Bucyrus (44820) *(G-2365)*

Wood Trader Inc 216 397-7671
   13429 Cedar Rd Cleveland Heights (44118) *(G-6503)*

Wood Works 330 674-0333
   9210 Township Road 304 Millersburg (44654) *(G-14287)*

Wood-Sebring Corporation 216 267-3191
   13800 Enterprise Ave Cleveland (44135) *(G-6475)*

Woodbine Products Company 330 725-0165
   915 W Smith Rd Medina (44256) *(G-13497)*

Woodbridge Group 419 334-3666
   827 Graham Dr Fremont (43420) *(G-10195)*

Woodburn Press LLC 937 293-9245
   405 Littell Ave Dayton (45419) *(G-8764)*

Woodbury Vineyards Inc (PA) 440 835-2828
   2001 Crocker Rd Ste 440 Westlake (44145) *(G-20322)*

Woodbury Welding Inc 937 968-3573
   10393 Oh In State Line Rd Union City (45390) *(G-19073)*

Woodcor America Inc (PA) 614 277-2930
   2965 Columbus St Ste C Grove City (43123) *(G-10610)*

Woodcraft, Dayton *Also called Ryanworks Inc* *(G-8641)*

Woodcraft Floor & Roof Trusses 740 927-9015
   1076 Mink St Sw Pataskala (43062) *(G-15991)*

Woodcraft Industries Inc 440 437-7811
   131 Grand Valley Ave Orwell (44076) *(G-15783)*

Woodcraft Industries Inc 440 632-9655
   15351 S State Ave Middlefield (44062) *(G-14007)*

Woodcraft Manufacturing Co 740 927-6609
   1076 Mink St Sw Pataskala (43062) *(G-15992)*

Woodcraft Pattern Works Inc 330 630-2158
   210 Southwest Ave Tallmadge (44278) *(G-18178)*

Wooden Creations 419 874-6367
   26730 Sheringham Rd Perrysburg (43551) *(G-16171)*

Wooden Horse 740 503-5243
   204 N Main St Baltimore (43105) *(G-1091)*

Wooden Horse Corporation 419 663-1472
   819 Dublin Rd Norwalk (44857) *(G-15568)*

Woodford Logistics 513 417-8453
   15 Sprague Rd South Charleston (45368) *(G-17427)*

Woodhill Plating Works Company 216 883-1344
   9114 Reno Ave Cleveland (44105) *(G-6476)*

Woodland Woodworking 330 897-7282
   2586 Township Road 183 Baltic (43804) *(G-1079)*

Woodlawn Rubber Co 513 489-1718
   11268 Williamson Rd Blue Ash (45241) *(G-1898)*

Woodman Agitator Inc 440 937-9865
   1404 Lear Industrial Pkwy Avon (44011) *(G-1021)*

Woodpeckers Inc 440 238-1824
   13700 Prospect Rd Strongsville (44149) *(G-17985)*

Woodrow Corp 937 322-7696
   105 N Thompson Ave Springfield (45504) *(G-17681)*

Woodrow Manufacturing Co 937 399-9333
   4300 River Rd Springfield (45502) *(G-17682)*

Woodsage Corporation 419 476-3553
   7400 Airport Hwy Holland (43528) *(G-11097)*

Woodsage LLC 419 866-8000
   7400 Airport Hwy Holland (43528) *(G-11098)*

Woodsfeld True Vlue HM Ctr Inc 740 472-1651
   218 State Rte 78 Woodsfield (43793) *(G-20723)*

Woodsmiths Design & Mfg, Bowerston *Also called L J Smith Inc* *(G-1958)*

Woodson Distribution LLC 937 864-9013
   1470 Deer Creek Dr Ste 7 Xenia (45385) *(G-20989)*

Woodspirits Limited Inc (PA) 937 663-5025
   1920 Apple Rd Saint Paris (43072) *(G-16865)*

Woodstock Products Inc 216 641-3811
   2914 Broadway Ave Cleveland (44115) *(G-6477)*

Woodworks Design 440 693-4414
   9005 N Girdle Rd Middlefield (44062) *(G-14008)*

Woodworks For You 440 277-8147
   465 W River Rd Wakeman (44889) *(G-19455)*

Woodworks Unlimited 740 574-4523
   330 Lambro Ln Franklin Furnace (45629) *(G-10070)*

Wooldridge Lumber Co 740 289-4912
   3264 Laurel Ridge Rd Piketon (45661) *(G-16229)*

Woosco, Wooster *Also called Westerman Acquisition Co LLC* *(G-20847)*

Wooster, Wooster *Also called Waste Water Pollution Control* *(G-20844)*

Wooster Book Company, The, Wooster *Also called Ketman Corporation* *(G-20795)*

Wooster Brush Company 440 322-8081
   870 Infirmary Rd Elyria (44035) *(G-9511)*

Wooster Daily Record Inc (HQ) 330 264-1125
   212 E Liberty St Wooster (44691) *(G-20849)*

Wooster Products Inc (PA) 330 264-2844
   1000 Spruce St Wooster (44691) *(G-20850)*

Wooster Products Inc 330 264-2854
   1000 Spruce St Wooster (44691) *(G-20851)*

Wooster Tool and Supply Co, Wooster *Also called Westerman Inc* *(G-20846)*

Wordcross Enterprises Inc 614 410-4140
   735 Taylor Rd Ste 230 Columbus (43230) *(G-7773)*

Workflex Solutions LLC (PA) 513 257-0215
7872 Cooper Rd Cincinnati (45242) *(G-4604)*

Workhorse Group Inc (PA) 513 297-3640
100 Commerce Dr Loveland (45140) *(G-12401)*

Workman Electronics, Delta Also called Twin Point Inc *(G-8940)*

Workpros 740 512-8512
401 Labelle St Lot 4 Brilliant (43913) *(G-2096)*

Workshop Wire Cut and Mch Inc 330 995-6404
100 Francis D Kenneth Dr Aurora (44202) *(G-957)*

Workspeed Management LLC 917 369-9025
28925 Fountain Pkwy Solon (44139) *(G-17415)*

Workstream Inc (HQ) 513 870-4400
3158 Production Dr Fairfield (45014) *(G-9733)*

World Automtn Measurement Tech 216 651-1883
5710 Detroit Ave Cleveland (44102) *(G-6478)*

World Class Plastics Inc 937 843-3003
7695 State Route 708 Russells Point (43348) *(G-16759)*

World Color (usa) Corp 847 230-1547
235 Artino St Oberlin (44074) *(G-15649)*

World Connections Corps 419 363-2681
10803 Erastus Durbin Rd Rockford (45882) *(G-16694)*

World Development & Conslt LLC 614 805-4450
855 S Sunbury Rd Westerville (43081) *(G-20242)*

World Express Packaging Corp 216 634-9000
3607 W 56th St Cleveland (44113) *(G-6479)*

World Harvest Church Inc (PA) 614 837-1990
4595 Gender Rd Canal Winchester (43110) *(G-2542)*

World Journal 216 458-0988
1735 E 36th St Cleveland (44114) *(G-6480)*

World Prep Inc 419 843-3869
8432 Central Ave Ste 10 Sylvania (43560) *(G-18130)*

World Resource Solutons Corp 614 733-3737
8485 Estates Ct Plain City (43064) *(G-16364)*

World Systems, Cleveland Also called World Automtn Measurement Tech *(G-6478)*

World Wide Medical Physics Inc 419 266-7530
26302 Thompson Rd Perrysburg (43551) *(G-16172)*

World Wide Recyclers Inc 614 554-3296
3131 S Hamilton Rd Columbus (43232) *(G-7774)*

Worldclass Processing Corp 724 251-9000
1400 Enterprise Pkwy Twinsburg (44087) *(G-19040)*

Worldmark, Strongsville Also called Donprint Inc *(G-17911)*

Worldwide Graphics and Sign, Blue Ash Also called Beebe Worldwide Graphics Sign *(G-1748)*

Worldwide Machine Tool LLC 614 496-9414
9000 Cotter St Lewis Center (43035) *(G-11928)*

Worleys Machine & Fab Inc 740 532-3337
1003 State Rr 650 Hanging Rock (45638) *(G-10762)*

Wornick Company (HQ) 800 860-4555
4700 Creek Rd Blue Ash (45242) *(G-1899)*

Wornick Company 513 552-7463
4700 Creek Rd Blue Ash (45242) *(G-1900)*

Wornick Foods, Blue Ash Also called Wornick Company *(G-1899)*

Wornick Holding Company Inc 513 794-9800
4700 Creek Rd Blue Ash (45242) *(G-1901)*

Worthignton Products Inc 330 452-7400
3405 Kuemerle Ct Ne Canton (44705) *(G-2903)*

Worthington, Beachwood Also called RSI Company *(G-1297)*

Worthington Cnstr Group Inc 216 472-1511
3100 E 45th St Ste 400 Cleveland (44127) *(G-6481)*

Worthington Cylinder Corp 740 569-4143
245 N Broad St Bremen (43107) *(G-2082)*

Worthington Cylinder Corp 330 262-1762
899 Venture Blvd Wooster (44691) *(G-20852)*

Worthington Cylinder Corp (HQ) 614 840-3210
200 W Old Wlson Bridge Rd Worthington (43085) *(G-20895)*

Worthington Cylinder Corp 440 576-5847
863 State Route 307 E Jefferson (44047) *(G-11376)*

Worthington Cylinder Corp 614 438-7900
1085 Dearborn Dr Columbus (43085) *(G-7775)*

Worthington Cylinder Corp 614 840-3800
333 Maxtown Rd Westerville (43082) *(G-20196)*

Worthington Energy Innovations, Fremont Also called Professional Supply Inc *(G-10177)*

Worthington Foods Inc 740 453-5501
1675 Fairview Rd Zanesville (43701) *(G-21363)*

Worthington Industries, Cleveland Also called Worthington Mid-Rise Cnstr Inc *(G-6482)*

Worthington Industries Inc (PA) 614 438-3210
200 W Old Wlson Bridge Rd Worthington (43085) *(G-20896)*

Worthington Industries Inc 937 556-6111
351 Apple St Mount Orab (45154) *(G-14588)*

Worthington Industries Inc 513 539-9291
350 Lawton Ave Monroe (45050) *(G-14420)*

Worthington Industries Inc 614 438-3113
2170 West Case Rd Columbus (43235) *(G-7776)*

Worthington Industries Inc 614 438-3190
1127 Dearborn Dr Columbus (43085) *(G-7777)*

Worthington Industries Inc 419 822-2500
6303 County Road 10 Delta (43515) *(G-8941)*

Worthington Industries Inc (HQ) 614 438-3077
200 W Old Wlson Bridge Rd Worthington (43085) *(G-20897)*

Worthington Industries Lsg LLC 614 438-3210
200 W Old Wlson Bridge Rd Worthington (43085) *(G-20898)*

Worthington Jewelers, Worthington Also called M S Abbott Jewelers *(G-20877)*

Worthington Mid-Rise Cnstr Inc (HQ) 216 472-1511
3100 E 45th St Ste 400 Cleveland (44127) *(G-6482)*

Worthington Pallet 614 888-1573
160 Tucker Dr Worthington (43085) *(G-20899)*

Worthington Steel, Worthington Also called Precision Specialty Metals Inc *(G-20883)*

Worthington Steel Company (HQ) 614 438-3210
200 W Old Wlson Bridge Rd Worthington (43085) *(G-20900)*

Worthington Steel Company 216 441-8300
4310 E 49th St Cleveland (44125) *(G-6483)*

Worthington Steel Company 513 702-0130
1501 Made Dr Middletown (45044) *(G-14100)*

Worthington Steel Div, Columbus Also called Worthington Industries Inc *(G-7777)*

Worthmore Food Products Co 513 559-1473
1021 Ludlow Ave Cincinnati (45223) *(G-4605)*

Worthngton Stelpac Systems LLC 937 747-2370
5256 Burton Rd North Lewisburg (43060) *(G-15309)*

Worthngton Stelpac Systems LLC (HQ) 614 438-3205
1205 Dearborn Dr Columbus (43085) *(G-7778)*

Worthngton Stl Cmpny-Baltimore (HQ) 410 574-5835
200 W Old Wlson Bridge Rd Worthington (43085) *(G-20901)*

Wray Precision Products Inc 513 228-5000
3650 Turtlecreek Rd Lebanon (45036) *(G-11849)*

Wre Color Tech, Wadsworth Also called Western Roto Engravers Inc *(G-19444)*

Wrena LLC 937 667-4403
265 Lightner Rd Tipp City (45371) *(G-18312)*

Wright Brothers Inc (PA) 513 731-2222
7825 Cooper Rd Cincinnati (45242) *(G-4606)*

Wright Brothers Global Gas LLC 513 731-2222
1930 Losantiville Ave Cincinnati (45237) *(G-4607)*

Wright Buffing Wheel Company 330 424-7887
300 S Market St Lisbon (44432) *(G-12136)*

Wright Designs Inc (PA) 216 524-6662
5099 Valley Woods Dr Cleveland (44131) *(G-6484)*

Wright John 937 653-4570
935 N Main St Urbana (43078) *(G-19188)*

Wright Tool Company 330 848-0600
1 Wright Pl Barberton (44203) *(G-1157)*

Wright Way Patterns 513 574-5776
6109 W Fork Rd Cincinnati (45247) *(G-4608)*

Wrights Saw Mill 937 773-2546
9018 Piqua Lockington Rd Piqua (45356) *(G-16316)*

Wrights Well Service 740 380-9602
37940 Scout Rd Logan (43138) *(G-12197)*

Writely Sew LLC 513 728-2682
3862 Race Rd Cincinnati (45211) *(G-4609)*

Wrl of Indiana Inc 419 289-8700
1407 George Rd Ashland (44805) *(G-786)*

Wrp Energy Inc 330 533-1921
12 W Main St Canfield (44406) *(G-2582)*

Wrr Creative Concepts LLC 513 659-2284
6082 Ash Hill Ct West Chester (45069) *(G-19974)*

Wrwp LLC 330 425-3421
1920 Case Pkwy S Twinsburg (44087) *(G-19041)*

Ws Thermal Process Tech Inc 440 385-6829
8301 W Erie Ave Lorain (44053) *(G-12293)*

Wsny FM, Columbus Also called Franklin Communications Inc *(G-7097)*

Wt Acquisition Company Ltd 513 577-7980
2130 Waycross Rd Cincinnati (45240) *(G-4610)*

Wt Tool & Die Inc 330 332-2254
1300 Pennsylvania Ave Salem (44460) *(G-16936)*

Wtp Engineering, Canal Fulton Also called Welded Tube Pros LLC *(G-2517)*

Wulco Inc 513 679-2600
6900 Steger Dr Cincinnati (45237) *(G-4611)*

Wulco Inc (PA) 513 679-2600
6899 Steger Dr Ste A Cincinnati (45237) *(G-4612)*

Wurms Woodworking Company 419 492-2184
725 W Mansfield St New Washington (44854) *(G-14966)*

Wurtec Manufacturing Service 419 726-1066
6200 Brent Dr Toledo (43611) *(G-18777)*

Wurth Elecktronik, Dayton Also called Wurth Electronics Ics Inc *(G-8765)*

Wurth Electronics Ics Inc 937 415-7700
7496 Webster St Dayton (45414) *(G-8765)*

Www Boat Services Inc 419 626-0883
2218 River Ave Sandusky (44870) *(G-17022)*

Www.slidepartsexpress.com, Willoughby Also called Quality Specialists Inc *(G-20584)*

Wyandot Inc 740 383-4031
135 Wyandot Ave Marion (43302) *(G-12916)*

Wyandot Seating, Bucyrus Also called Service Pdts Group of Bucyrus *(G-2359)*

Wyatt Industries LLC 330 954-1790
1790 Miller Pkwy Streetsboro (44241) *(G-17883)*

Wyatt Printing, Mentor Also called Bill Wyatt Inc *(G-13535)*

Wyatt Specialties Inc 614 989-5362
4761 State Route 361 Circleville (43113) *(G-4650)*

Wyeth-Scott Company 740 345-4528
85 Dayton Rd Ne Newark (43055) *(G-15066)*

Wyman Gordon, Cleveland Also called Wyman-Gordon Company *(G-6485)*

Wyman Woodworking 614 338-0615
389 Robinwood Ave Columbus (43213) *(G-7779)*
Wyman-Gordon Company 216 341-0085
3097 E 61st St Cleveland (44127) *(G-6485)*
Wyoming Casing Service Inc 330 479-8785
1414 Raff Rd Sw Canton (44710) *(G-2904)*
Wyse Electric Motor Repair 419 445-5921
2101 S Defiance St Archbold (43502) *(G-699)*
Wyse Industrial Carts Inc 419 923-7353
10510 County Road 12 Wauseon (43567) *(G-19702)*
Wysong Concrete Products LLC 513 874-3109
2138 Resor Rd Fairfield (45014) *(G-9734)*
Wysong Gravel Co Inc (PA) 937 456-4539
2332 State Route 503 N West Alexandria (45381) *(G-19787)*
Wysong Gravel Co Inc 937 452-1523
120 Cmden Cllege Cornr Rd Camden (45311) *(G-2489)*
Wysong Gravel Co Inc 937 839-5497
2032 State Route 503 N West Alexandria (45381) *(G-19788)*
Wysong Stone Co 937 962-2559
5897 State Route 503 N Lewisburg (45338) *(G-11942)*
X L Sand and Gravel Co Inc 330 426-9876
9289 Jackman Rd Negley (44441) *(G-14733)*
X M C, Sylvania *Also called Don-Ell Corporation (G-18104)*
X M C Division, Sylvania *Also called Don-Ell Corporation (G-18103)*
X Press Printing Services Inc 440 951-8848
4405 Glenbrook Rd Willoughby (44094) *(G-20633)*
X-3-5 LLC 513 489-5477
7621 E Kemper Rd Cincinnati (45249) *(G-4613)*
X-Mil Inc 937 444-1323
220 Homan Way Mount Orab (45154) *(G-14589)*
X-Press Tool Inc 330 225-8748
2845 Interstate Pkwy Brunswick (44212) *(G-2271)*
X-Spine Systems Inc 937 847-8400
452 Alexandersville Rd Miamisburg (45342) *(G-13882)*
X-Treme Finishes Inc 330 474-0614
387 Medina Rd Ste 1000 Medina (44256) *(G-13498)*
X-Treme Shooting Products LLC 513 313-3464
2008 Glenn Pkwy Batavia (45103) *(G-1234)*
Xact Spec Industires LLC 440 543-8157
16959 Munn Rd Chagrin Falls (44023) *(G-3134)*
Xact Spec Industries LLC (PA) 440 543-8157
16959 Munn Rd Chagrin Falls (44023) *(G-3135)*
Xapc Co (PA) 216 362-4100
15583 Brookpark Rd Cleveland (44142) *(G-6486)*
XCEL Mold and Machine Inc 330 499-8450
7661 Freedom Ave Nw Canton (44720) *(G-2905)*
Xcite Systems Corporation 513 965-0300
675 Cncnnati Batavia Pike Cincinnati (45245) *(G-3321)*
Xellia Pharmaceuticals USA LLC 847 986-7984
200 Northfield Rd Bedford (44146) *(G-1473)*
Xenia City Water Treatment Div, Xenia *Also called City of Xenia (G-20943)*
Xenotronix/Tli Inc 407 331-4793
2541 Tracy Rd Northwood (43619) *(G-15498)*
Xerox Corporation 740 592-5609
35 Elliott St Athens (45701) *(G-890)*
Xerox Corporation 513 539-4858
6500 Hamilton Lebanon Rd Monroe (45044) *(G-14421)*
Xerox Corporation 513 539-4808
6490 Hamilton Lebanon Rd Monroe (45044) *(G-14422)*
Xerox Corporation 513 860-8600
4622 Interstate Dr West Chester (45246) *(G-20070)*
Xerox Corporation 513 554-3200
10560 Ashview Pl Blue Ash (45242) *(G-1902)*
Xerox Corporation 614 409-6527
6500 Port Rd Groveport (43125) *(G-10650)*
Xerox Corporation C/O Genco 503 582-6059
6290 Opus Dr Groveport (43125) *(G-10651)*
Xgs.it, West Chester *Also called It XCEL Consulting LLC (G-19886)*
Xigent Automation Systems Inc 740 548-3700
8303 Green Meadows Dr N Lewis Center (43035) *(G-11929)*
Xim Products Inc 440 871-4737
1169 Bassett Rd Westlake (44145) *(G-20323)*
Xl Pattern Shop Inc 330 682-2981
242 N Kansas Rd Orrville (44667) *(G-15773)*
Xomox Corporation 513 947-1200
4576 Helmsdale Ct Batavia (45103) *(G-1235)*
Xomox Corporation 936 271-6500
4444 Cooper Rd Cincinnati (45242) *(G-4614)*
Xomox Corporation 513 745-6000
4477 Malsbary Rd Blue Ash (45242) *(G-1903)*
Xorb Corporation 419 354-6021
2121 S Woodland Cir Bowling Green (43402) *(G-2023)*
Xperion E&E USA LLC 740 788-9560
1475 James Pkwy Heath (43056) *(G-10858)*
Xponet Inc 440 354-6617
20 Elberta Rd Painesville (44077) *(G-15943)*
Xpress Print & Bus Systems, Louisville *Also called Xpress Print Inc (G-12335)*
Xpress Print Inc 330 494-7246
6424 Easton St Louisville (44641) *(G-12335)*

Xpressions LLC 330 898-8591
707 Meadowbrook Ave Se Warren (44484) *(G-19627)*
Xray Media Ltd 513 751-9641
445 Mcgregor Ave Cincinnati (45206) *(G-4615)*
Xt Innovations Ltd 419 562-1989
4799 Stetzer Rd Bucyrus (44820) *(G-2366)*
Xtek Inc (PA) 513 733-7800
11451 Reading Rd Cincinnati (45241) *(G-4616)*
Xto Energy Inc 740 671-9901
2358 W 23rd St Bellaire (43906) *(G-1502)*
Xxx Intrntional Amusements Inc (PA) 216 671-6900
3313 W 140th St D Cleveland (44111) *(G-6487)*
Y City Recycling LLC 740 452-2500
4005 All American Way Zanesville (43701) *(G-21364)*
Y Z Enterprises Inc 419 893-8777
1930 Indian Wood Cir # 100 Maumee (43537) *(G-13310)*
Y&B Logging 440 437-1053
3647 Montgomery Rd Orwell (44076) *(G-15784)*
Yabos Tacos 614 824-2485
3051 Northwest Blvd Columbus (43221) *(G-7780)*
Yachiyo of America Inc (HQ) 614 876-3220
2285 Walcutt Rd Columbus (43228) *(G-7781)*
Yagoot 513 791-6600
7875 Montgomery Rd # 1241 Cincinnati (45236) *(G-4617)*
Yale Industries, Dayton *Also called Otter Group LLC (G-8554)*
Yamada North America Inc 937 462-7111
9000 Clmbus Cincinnati Rd South Charleston (45368) *(G-17428)*
Yanfeng US Automotive 419 662-4905
7560 Arbor Dr Northwood (43619) *(G-15499)*
Yanfeng US Automotive 419 636-4211
918 S Union St Bryan (43506) *(G-2328)*
Yanke Bionics Inc (PA) 330 762-6411
303 W Exchange St Akron (44302) *(G-475)*
Yanke Bionics Inc 330 833-0955
2400 Wales Ave Nw Massillon (44646) *(G-13212)*
Yanke Bionics Inc 330 668-4070
3975 Embassy Pkwy Ste 1 Akron (44333) *(G-476)*
Yankee Candle Company Inc 419 223-0073
2400 Elida Rd Lima (45805) *(G-12113)*
Yankee Wire Cloth Products Inc 740 545-9129
221 W Main St West Lafayette (43845) *(G-20090)*
Yant Beef Jerky, Jackson Center *Also called Steven Yant (G-11348)*
YAR Corporation 330 652-1222
406 S Main St Niles (44446) *(G-15190)*
Yarder Manufacturing Company (PA) 419 476-3933
722 Phillips Ave Toledo (43612) *(G-18778)*
Yarder Manufacturing Company 419 269-3474
730 Phillips Ave Toledo (43612) *(G-18779)*
Yarn Shop Inc 614 457-7836
1125 Kenny Centre Mall Columbus (43220) *(G-7782)*
Yarnell Bros Inc 419 278-2831
103 E North St Deshler (43516) *(G-8952)*
Yaskawa America Inc 614 733-3200
8628 Industrial Pkwy A Plain City (43064) *(G-16365)*
Yaskawa America Inc 937 847-6200
100 Automation Way Miamisburg (45342) *(G-13883)*
Yeager Sports, Cincinnati *Also called R L Y Inc (G-4326)*
Yellow Creek Casting Company 330 532-4608
18141 Fife Coal Rd Wellsville (43968) *(G-19777)*
Yellow Springs International, Yellow Springs *Also called Ysi Incorporated (G-21005)*
Yellow Springs News Inc 937 767-7373
253 And A Half Xenia Ave Yellow Springs (45387) *(G-21001)*
Yellow Springs Pottery 937 767-1666
222 Xenia Ave Ste 1 Yellow Springs (45387) *(G-21002)*
Yellow Tang Interiors LLC 330 629-9279
1255 Barbie Dr Youngstown (44512) *(G-21244)*
Yemaneh Musie 614 506-3687
2734 Rosedale Ave Columbus (43204) *(G-7783)*
Yes Management Inc (PA) 330 747-8593
44612 State Route 14 Columbiana (44408) *(G-6638)*
Yes Press Printing Co 330 535-8398
720 E Glenwood Ave Front Akron (44310) *(G-477)*
Yi Xing Inc 614 785-9631
850 Busch Ct Columbus (43229) *(G-7784)*
YKK AP America Inc 513 942-7200
5406 Spellmire Dr West Chester (45246) *(G-20071)*
YKK USA, West Chester *Also called YKK AP America Inc (G-20071)*
Yngstn Plastic Fabrication 330 743-6404
6820 E Garfield Rd Petersburg (44454) *(G-16179)*
Yockey Group Inc 513 860-9053
9053 Le Saint Dr West Chester (45014) *(G-19975)*
Yocom Brothers 937 653-8767
773 Perry Rd Cable (43009) *(G-2414)*
Yoder & Frey Inc 419 445-2070
3649 County Road 24 Archbold (43502) *(G-700)*
Yoder Cabinets Ltd 614 873-5186
9996 Amish Pike Plain City (43064) *(G-16366)*
Yoder Industries Inc (PA) 937 278-5769
2520 Needmore Rd Dayton (45414) *(G-8766)*

A
L
P
H
A
B
E
T
I
C

Yoder Industries Inc 937 890-4322
   3009 Production Ct Dayton (45414) *(G-8767)*

Yoder Logging 740 679-2635
   22144 Oxford Rd Quaker City (43773) *(G-16502)*

Yoder Lumber Co Inc (PA) 330 893-3121
   4515 Township Road 367 Millersburg (44654) *(G-14288)*

Yoder Lumber Co Inc 330 674-1435
   7100 County Road 407 Millersburg (44654) *(G-14289)*

Yoder Lumber Co Inc 330 893-3131
   3799 County Road 70 Sugarcreek (44681) *(G-18052)*

Yoder Manufacturing 740 504-5028
   7679 Flack Rd Howard (43028) *(G-11125)*

Yoder Window & Siding Ltd 330 857-4530
   7165 Fredericksburg Rd Fredericksburg (44627) *(G-10094)*

Yoder Window & Siding Ltd (PA) 330 695-6960
   7846 Harrison Rd Fredericksburg (44627) *(G-10095)*

Yoder Window and Siding, Fredericksburg *Also called Yoder Window & Siding Ltd (G-10095)*

Yoder Woodworking 740 399-9400
   21198 Swendal Rd Butler (44822) *(G-2394)*

Yoder's Cider Barn, Gambier *Also called Yoders Cider Barn (G-10319)*

Yoders Cider Barn 740 668-4961
   3361 Martinsburg Rd Gambier (43022) *(G-10319)*

Yoders Harness Shop 440 632-1505
   14698 Bundysburg Rd Middlefield (44062) *(G-14009)*

Yoders Nylon Halter Shop 330 893-3479
   7682 Township Road 652 Millersburg (44654) *(G-14290)*

Yoders Woodworking 888 818-0568
   2249 Township Road 112 Millersburg (44654) *(G-14291)*

Yokohama Inds Amricas Ohio Inc 440 352-3321
   474 Newell St Painesville (44077) *(G-15944)*

Yokohama Tire Corporation 440 352-3321
   474 Newell St Painesville (44077) *(G-15945)*

Yonezawa USA Inc 614 799-2210
   7920 Corporate Blvd A Plain City (43064) *(G-16367)*

York Fabrication & Machine 419 483-6275
   6964 County Road 191 Bellevue (44811) *(G-1567)*

York Paving Co (PA) 740 594-3600
   758 W Union St Athens (45701) *(G-891)*

Yost & Son Inc 440 779-8025
   5502 Barton Rd North Olmsted (44070) *(G-15353)*

Yost Candy Co 330 828-2777
   51 N Cochran St Dalton (44618) *(G-8081)*

Yost Labs Inc 740 876-4936
   630 2nd St Portsmouth (45662) *(G-16459)*

Yost Superior Co 937 323-7591
   300 S Center St Ste 1 Springfield (45506) *(G-17683)*

Yotec, South Charleston *Also called Yamada North America Inc (G-17428)*

You Dough Girl LLC 330 207-5031
   12725 Kent Rd Salem (44460) *(G-16937)*

You52 .... 440 477-7704
   921 Bunker Hill Rd Ashtabula (44004) *(G-846)*

Young & Bertke Air Systems, Cincinnati *Also called Pcy Enterprises Inc (G-4219)*

Young Regulator Company Inc 440 232-9452
   7100 Krick Rd Ste A Bedford (44146) *(G-1474)*

Young Sand & Gravel Co Inc 419 994-3040
   689 State Route 39 Loudonville (44842) *(G-12307)*

Youngs Jersey Dairy Inc 937 325-0629
   6880 Springfield Xenia Rd Yellow Springs (45387) *(G-21003)*

Youngs Locker Serv & Meat Proc, Danville *Also called Youngs Locker Service Inc (G-8093)*

Youngs Locker Service Inc 740 599-6833
   16201 Nashville Rd Danville (43014) *(G-8093)*

Youngs Publishing Inc 937 259-6575
   2171 N Fairfield Rd Beavercreek (45431) *(G-1367)*

Youngs Screenprinting & Embro 330 922-5777
   1245 Munroe Falls Ave Cuyahoga Falls (44221) *(G-8063)*

Youngstown ARC Engraving Co 330 793-2471
   380 Victoria Rd Youngstown (44515) *(G-21245)*

Youngstown Bending Rolling 330 799-2227
   3710 Hendricks Rd Bldg 2b Youngstown (44515) *(G-21246)*

Youngstown Bolt & Supply Co 330 799-3201
   340 N Meridian Rd Youngstown (44509) *(G-21247)*

Youngstown Burial Vault Co 330 782-0015
   546 E Indianola Ave Youngstown (44502) *(G-21248)*

Youngstown Casket Co Inc 330 758-2008
   450 Melbourne Ave Youngstown (44512) *(G-21249)*

Youngstown Curve Form Inc 330 744-3028
   1102 Rigby St Youngstown (44506) *(G-21250)*

Youngstown Die Development 330 755-0722
   137 Walton Ave Struthers (44471) *(G-18000)*

Youngstown Electric Supply, Columbiana *Also called Yes Management Inc (G-6638)*

Youngstown Fence Inc 330 788-8110
   235 E Indianola Ave Youngstown (44507) *(G-21251)*

Youngstown Hard Chrome Plating 330 758-9721
   8451 Southern Blvd Youngstown (44512) *(G-21252)*

Youngstown Letter Shop Inc 330 793-4935
   615 N Meridian Rd Youngstown (44509) *(G-21253)*

Youngstown Lithographing Co, Youngstown *Also called Youngstown ARC Engraving Co (G-21245)*

Youngstown Metal Fabricating, Youngstown *Also called M F Y Inc (G-21137)*

Youngstown Plant, Struthers *Also called Munroe Incorporated (G-17995)*

Youngstown Plas Fabrication, Petersburg *Also called Ypf Corporation (G-16180)*

Youngstown Plastic Tooling (PA) 330 782-7222
   1209 Velma Ct Youngstown (44512) *(G-21254)*

Youngstown Pre-Press Inc 330 793-3690
   3691 Leharps Dr Youngstown (44515) *(G-21255)*

Youngstown Rubber Products, Youngstown *Also called Mid-State Sales Inc (G-21145)*

Youngstown Specialty Mtls Inc 330 259-1110
   571 Andrews Ave Youngstown (44505) *(G-21256)*

Youngstown Tool & Die Company 330 747-4464
   1261 Poland Ave Youngstown (44502) *(G-21257)*

Youngstown Tube Co 330 743-7414
   401 Andrews Ave Youngstown (44505) *(G-21258)*

Youngstown-Kenworth Inc (PA) 330 534-9761
   7255 Hubbard Masury Rd Hubbard (44425) *(G-11143)*

Your Bottled Water LLC 740 443-6079
   705 E 2nd St Piketon (45661) *(G-16230)*

Your Cabinetry 440 638-4925
   16488 Pearl Rd Strongsville (44136) *(G-17986)*

Your Daily Bargains 330 715-8324
   2495 Valleydale Rd Stow (44224) *(G-17818)*

Your Daily Motivation Ydm Fitn 440 954-1038
   6631 Vrooman Rd Painesville (44077) *(G-15946)*

Your Personal Jeweler Inc 330 836-2446
   1262 Weathervane Ln Akron (44313) *(G-478)*

Youthtopia Beverages, Marietta *Also called Youthtopia LLC (G-12851)*

Youthtopia LLC 740 525-1734
   110 Windy Pt Marietta (45750) *(G-12851)*

Ypf Corporation 330 743-6404
   6820 E Garfield Rd Petersburg (44454) *(G-16180)*

Yrp Industries Inc 330 533-2524
   854 Mahoning Ave Youngstown (44502) *(G-21259)*

Ysd Industries Inc 330 792-6521
   3710 Henricks Rd Youngstown (44515) *(G-21260)*

Yse, Youngstown *Also called Homer G Waller Jr (G-21108)*

Ysi Environmental Inc 937 767-7241
   1725 Brannum Ln Yellow Springs (45387) *(G-21004)*

Ysi Incorporated (HQ) 937 767-7241
   1700 Brannum Ln 1725 Yellow Springs (45387) *(G-21005)*

Ysie, Yellow Springs *Also called Ysi Environmental Inc (G-21004)*

Ysk Corporation 740 774-7315
   1 Colomet Rd Chillicothe (45601) *(G-3284)*

Yuckon International Corp 216 361-2103
   1400 E 34th St Cleveland (44114) *(G-6488)*

Yugo Mold Inc 330 606-0710
   1733 Wadsworth Rd Akron (44320) *(G-479)*

Yusa Corporation 740 335-0335
   151 Jamison Rd Sw Washington Court Hou (43160) *(G-19641)*

Yutec LLC (PA) 440 725-5353
   3940 Ellendale Rd Chagrin Falls (44022) *(G-3074)*

Yutzy Woodworking Ltd 330 359-6166
   6995 Township Road 654 Millersburg (44654) *(G-14292)*

Yxlon 234 284-7862
   5675 Hudson Indus Pkwy Hudson (44236) *(G-11211)*

Yxlon International, Hudson *Also called Comet Technologies USA Inc (G-11165)*

Z & Z Manufacturing Inc 440 953-2800
   4765 E 355th St Willoughby (44094) *(G-20634)*

Z and M Screw Machine Products 330 467-5822
   10232 Hopkins Rd Garrettsville (44231) *(G-10337)*

Z Line Kitchen and Bath LLC (PA) 614 777-5004
   916 Delaware Ave Marysville (43040) *(G-12977)*

Z M O Company Inc (PA) 614 875-0230
   4188 Alkire Rd Grove City (43123) *(G-10611)*

Z M O Oil, Grove City *Also called Z M O Company Inc (G-10611)*

Z P Enterprises Inc 513 863-3393
   223 Court St Hamilton (45011) *(G-10758)*

Z Track Magazine 614 764-1703
   6142 Northcliff Blvd Dublin (43016) *(G-9167)*

Zaclon LLC 216 271-1601
   2981 Independence Rd Cleveland (44115) *(G-6489)*

Zaenkert Surveying Essentials 513 738-2917
   7461a Cncnnati Brkvlle Rd Okeana (45053) *(G-15668)*

Zagar Inc 216 731-0500
   24000 Lakeland Blvd Cleveland (44132) *(G-6490)*

Zahler Enterprises LLC 614 870-7872
   129 Beacon Run W Columbus (43228) *(G-7785)*

Zak Box Co Inc 216 961-5636
   7100 Clark Ave Cleveland (44102) *(G-6491)*

Zal Air Products Inc 440 237-7155
   1687 W Royalton Rd Cleveland (44147) *(G-6492)*

Zane Casket Company Inc 740 452-4680
   1201 Hall Ave Zanesville (43701) *(G-21365)*

Zane Petroleum Inc 740 454-8779
   1615 W Main St Zanesville (43701) *(G-21366)*

Zaner-Bloser Inc (HQ) 614 486-0221
   1400 Goodale Blvd Ste 200 Columbus (43212) *(G-7786)*

Zanesville Bearing Div, Zanesville *Also called H & R Tool & Machine Co Inc (G-21316)*

Zanesville Newspaper 740 452-4561
  34 S 4th St Zanesville (43701) *(G-21367)*
Zanesville Terminal Warehouse, Zanesville *Also called Porto Pump Inc* *(G-21343)*
Zanesville Tool Grinding 740 453-9356
  624 Main St Zanesville (43701) *(G-21368)*
Zanesvlle Cnfectionary Hse LLC 740 452-7501
  2200 Linden Ave Zanesville (43701) *(G-21369)*
Zap, Cleveland *Also called Zal Air Products Inc* *(G-6492)*
Zarbana Alum Extrusions LLC 330 482-5092
  41738 Esterly Dr Columbiana (44408) *(G-6639)*
Zaromet Inc 513 891-0773
  10851 Millington Ct Blue Ash (45242) *(G-1904)*
Zartic LLC (HQ) 513 874-8741
  9990 Prnceton Glendale Rd West Chester (45246) *(G-20072)*
Zaytran Corporation 440 324-2814
  41535 Schadden Rd Elyria (44035) *(G-9512)*
Zebco Industries Inc 740 654-4510
  211 N Columbus St Lancaster (43130) *(G-11763)*
Zebec of North America Inc 513 829-5533
  210 Donald Dr Fairfield (45014) *(G-9735)*
Zebu Compliance Solutions Inc 740 355-9029
  609 2nd St Unit 2 Portsmouth (45662) *(G-16460)*
Zech Printing Industries Inc 937 748-2776
  6310 Este Ave Cincinnati (45232) *(G-4618)*
Zed Digital, Columbus *Also called IPA Ltd* *(G-7210)*
Zed Industries Inc 937 667-8407
  3580 Lightner Rd Vandalia (45377) *(G-19318)*
Zeeco Equipment Commodity 440 838-1102
  6581 Glen Coe Dr Brecksville (44141) *(G-2078)*
Zehrco-Giancola Composites Inc (PA) 440 994-6317
  1501 W 47th St Ashtabula (44004) *(G-847)*
Zehrco-Giancola Composites Inc 440 576-9941
  382 E Erie St Jefferson (44047) *(G-11377)*
Zeiger Industries 330 484-4413
  4704 Wiseland Ave Se Canton (44707) *(G-2906)*
Zekelman Industries Inc 740 432-2146
  9208 Jeffrey Dr Cambridge (43725) *(G-2483)*
Zekelman Industries Inc 330 373-4410
  901 Dietz Rd Ne Warren (44483) *(G-19628)*
Zelcor Group LLC 419 592-0803
  L902 State Route 108 Napoleon (43545) *(G-14702)*
Zen Industries Inc 216 432-3240
  6200 Harvard Ave Cleveland (44105) *(G-6493)*
Zenex International 440 232-4155
  7777 First Pl Bedford (44146) *(G-1475)*
Zenith Energy Group LLC 216 587-9510
  5069 Corbin Dr Cleveland (44128) *(G-6494)*
Zenos Activewear Inc 614 443-0070
  1354 Parsons Ave Columbus (43206) *(G-7787)*
Zephyr Industries Inc 419 281-4485
  600 Township Road 1500 Ashland (44805) *(G-787)*
Zero-D Products Inc (PA) 440 417-1843
  7183 Lake Rd Madison (44057) *(G-12514)*
Zerust Consumer Products LLC 330 405-1965
  9345 Ravenna Rd Unit E Twinsburg (44087) *(G-19042)*
Zeus Electronics LLC 330 220-1571
  5083 Creekside Blvd Brunswick (44212) *(G-2272)*
Zhai Hui Filters & Home Pdts, Chagrin Falls *Also called Zhao Hui Filters (us) Inc* *(G-3136)*
Zhao Hui Filters (us) Inc (PA) 440 519-9300
  7160 Chagrin Rd Ste 220 Chagrin Falls (44023) *(G-3136)*
Zide Screen Printing, Marietta *Also called Zide Sport Shop of Ohio Inc* *(G-12852)*
Zide Sport Shop of Ohio Inc 740 373-8199
  118 Industry Rd Marietta (45750) *(G-12852)*
Zidian Manufacturing Inc (PA) 330 965-8455
  500 Mcclurg Rd Boardman (44512) *(G-1926)*
Zie Bart Rhino Linings Toledo, Toledo *Also called Zie Bart Rhino Linings Toledo* *(G-18780)*
Zie Bart Rhino Linings Toledo 419 841-2886
  3343 N Hlland Sylvania Rd Toledo (43615) *(G-18780)*

Ziegler Bros Tool & Mch Inc 419 738-6048
  13790 Infirmary Rd Wapakoneta (45895) *(G-19514)*
Ziegler Brothers Tool & Mch, Wapakoneta *Also called Ziegler Bros Tool & Mch Inc* *(G-19514)*
Ziegler Engineering Inc 440 582-8515
  9840 York Alpha Dr Ste F North Royalton (44133) *(G-15461)*
Zimcom Internet Solutions, Cincinnati *Also called One Cloud Services LLC* *(G-4187)*
Zimme Ortho Surgi Produ Inc (HQ) 800 321-5533
  200 W Ohio Ave Dover (44622) *(G-9025)*
Zimmer Inc 614 508-6000
  6816 Lauffer Rd Columbus (43231) *(G-7788)*
Zimmer Enterprises Inc (PA) 937 428-1057
  911 Senate Dr Dayton (45459) *(G-8768)*
Zimmerman Shtmtl Stl & Wldg 419 335-3806
  1179 N Ottokee St Wauseon (43567) *(G-19703)*
Zimmerman Steel & Sup Co LLC 330 828-1010
  18543 Davis Rd Dalton (44618) *(G-8082)*
Zing Pac Inc 440 248-7997
  30300 Solon Indus Pkwy Cleveland (44139) *(G-6495)*
Zinkan Enterprises Inc (PA) 330 487-1500
  1919 Case Pkwy Twinsburg (44087) *(G-19043)*
Zion Industries Inc (PA) 330 225-3246
  6229 Grafton Rd Valley City (44280) *(G-19238)*
Zip Center, The-Division, Marietta *Also called Richardson Printing Corp* *(G-12824)*
Zip Graphics, Cincinnati *Also called Margaret Trentman* *(G-4059)*
Zip Laser Systems Inc 740 286-6613
  345 E Main St Ste H Jackson (45640) *(G-11335)*
Zip Systems of Jackson, Jackson *Also called Zip Laser Systems Inc* *(G-11335)*
Zip Tool & Die Inc 216 267-1117
  12200 Sprecher Ave Cleveland (44135) *(G-6496)*
Zipper Manufacturing LLC 937 444-0904
  16698 Edgington Rd Williamsburg (45176) *(G-20415)*
Zippity Print 216 438-0001
  1600 E 23rd St Cleveland (44114) *(G-6497)*
Zipscene LLC 513 201-5174
  602 Main St Ste 900 Cincinnati (45202) *(G-4619)*
Zircoa Inc (PA) 440 248-0500
  31501 Solon Rd Cleveland (44139) *(G-6498)*
Zircon Industries Inc 216 595-0200
  4920 Commerce Pkwy Ste 9 Cleveland (44128) *(G-6499)*
Zitnik Enterprises Inc 440 951-0089
  35530 Lakeland Blvd Willoughby (44095) *(G-20635)*
Znode Inc 614 468-7900
  8415 Pulsar Pl Ste 200 Columbus (43240) *(G-6662)*
Zoia, Cleveland *Also called Artistic Metal Spinning Inc* *(G-4839)*
Zoo Publishing Inc 513 824-8297
  11258 Cornell Park Dr # 608 Blue Ash (45242) *(G-1905)*
Zook Enterprises LLC 440 543-1010
  16809 Park Circle Dr Chagrin Falls (44023) *(G-3137)*
Zorbx Inc 440 238-1847
  17647 Foltz Pkwy Strongsville (44149) *(G-17987)*
ZS Cream & Bean 440 652-6369
  2706 Boston Rd Hinckley (44233) *(G-11032)*
Zshot Inc 800 385-8581
  746 Carle Ave Lewis Center (43035) *(G-11930)*
Zts Inc 513 271-2557
  5628 Wooster Pike Cincinnati (45227) *(G-4620)*
Zukowski Rack Co 440 942-5889
  1647 E 361st St Willoughby (44095) *(G-20636)*
Zurbrugg Machine, Alliance *Also called Scott A Zurbrugg* *(G-537)*
Zurn Industries LLC 814 455-0921
  4501 Sutphen Ct Hilliard (43026) *(G-10994)*
Zwf Golf LLC 937 767-5621
  920 N Broad St Fairborn (45324) *(G-9636)*
Zygo Inc 513 281-0888
  2832 Jefferson Ave Cincinnati (45219) *(G-4621)*
Zyvex Performance Mtls Inc (HQ) 614 481-2222
  1255 Kinnear Rd Ste 100 Columbus (43212) *(G-7789)*
Zyvex Technologies, Columbus *Also called Zyvex Performance Mtls Inc* *(G-7789)*

A L P H A B E T I C

PRODUCT INDEX

• Product categories are listed in alphabetical order.

A

ABRASIVE STONES, EXC GRINDING STONES: Ground Or Whole
ABRASIVES
ABRASIVES: Coated
ABRASIVES: Grains
ABRASIVES: Synthetic
ACCELERATION INDICATORS & SYSTEM COMPONENTS: Aerospace
ACCELERATORS, RUBBER PROCESSING: Cyclic or Acyclic
ACCELERATORS: Electron Linear
ACCELERATORS: Linear
ACCOUNTING MACHINES & CASH REGISTERS
ACCOUNTING SVCS, NEC
ACCOUNTING SVCS: Certified Public
ACIDS: Hydrochloric
ACIDS: Inorganic
ACIDS: Sulfuric, Oleum
ACOUSTICAL BOARD & TILE
ACRYLIC RESINS
ACTUATORS: Indl, NEC
ADAPTERS: Well
ADDITIVE BASED PLASTIC MATERIALS: Plasticizers
ADDRESSING SVCS
ADDRESSOGRAPHING SVCS
ADHESIVES
ADHESIVES & SEALANTS
ADHESIVES & SEALANTS WHOLESALERS
ADHESIVES: Adhesives, plastic
ADHESIVES: Epoxy
ADVERTISING AGENCIES
ADVERTISING AGENCIES: Consultants
ADVERTISING DISPLAY PRDTS
ADVERTISING REPRESENTATIVES: Electronic Media
ADVERTISING REPRESENTATIVES: Media
ADVERTISING REPRESENTATIVES: Newspaper
ADVERTISING SPECIALTIES, WHOLESALE
ADVERTISING SVCS, NEC
ADVERTISING SVCS: Billboards
ADVERTISING SVCS: Direct Mail
ADVERTISING SVCS: Display
ADVERTISING SVCS: Outdoor
ADVERTISING SVCS: Poster, Exc Outdoor
ADVERTISING SVCS: Poster, Outdoor
AERIAL WORK PLATFORMS
AEROSOLS
AGENTS, BROKERS & BUREAUS: Personal Service
AGRICULTURAL EQPT: BARN, SILO, POULTRY, DAIRY/LIVESTOCK MACH
AGRICULTURAL EQPT: Combine, Digger, Packer/Thresher, Peanut
AGRICULTURAL EQPT: Elevators, Farm
AGRICULTURAL EQPT: Fertilizing Machinery
AGRICULTURAL EQPT: Fillers & Unloaders, Silo
AGRICULTURAL EQPT: Grounds Mowing Eqpt
AGRICULTURAL EQPT: Loaders, Manure & General Utility
AGRICULTURAL EQPT: Shakers, Tree, Nuts, Fruits, Etc
AGRICULTURAL EQPT: Stackers, Grain
AGRICULTURAL EQPT: Tractors, Farm
AGRICULTURAL EQPT: Turf & Grounds Eqpt
AGRICULTURAL LIMESTONE: Ground
AGRICULTURAL MACHINERY & EQPT REPAIR
AGRICULTURAL MACHINERY & EQPT: Wholesalers
AIR CLEANING SYSTEMS
AIR CONDITIONERS: Motor Vehicle
AIR CONDITIONING & VENTILATION EQPT & SPLYS: Wholesales
AIR CONDITIONING EQPT
AIR CONDITIONING REPAIR SVCS
AIR CONDITIONING UNITS: Complete, Domestic Or Indl
AIR MATTRESSES: Plastic
AIR POLLUTION CONTROL EQPT & SPLYS WHOLE-SALERS
AIR PURIFICATION EQPT
AIR TRAFFIC CONTROL SVCS
AIR, WATER & SOLID WASTE PROGRAMS ADMINISTRA-TION SVCS
AIR-CONDITIONING SPLY SVCS

AIRCRAFT & AEROSPACE FLIGHT INSTRUMENTS & GUID-ANCE SYSTEMS
AIRCRAFT & HEAVY EQPT REPAIR SVCS
AIRCRAFT ASSEMBLY PLANTS
AIRCRAFT CLEANING & JANITORIAL SVCS
AIRCRAFT CONTROL SYSTEMS:
AIRCRAFT CONTROL SYSTEMS: Electronic Totalizing Coun-ters
AIRCRAFT ELECTRICAL EQPT REPAIR SVCS
AIRCRAFT ENGINES & ENGINE PARTS: Airfoils
AIRCRAFT ENGINES & ENGINE PARTS: Pumps
AIRCRAFT ENGINES & ENGINE PARTS: Research & Devel-opment, Mfr
AIRCRAFT ENGINES & ENGINE PARTS: Rocket Motors
AIRCRAFT ENGINES & PARTS
AIRCRAFT EQPT & SPLYS WHOLESALERS
AIRCRAFT FLIGHT INSTRUMENTS
AIRCRAFT HANGAR OPERATION SVCS
AIRCRAFT MAINTENANCE & REPAIR SVCS
AIRCRAFT PARTS & AUX EQPT: Governors, Propeller Feath-ering
AIRCRAFT PARTS & AUXILIARY EQPT: Assys, Subassem-blies/Parts
AIRCRAFT PARTS & AUXILIARY EQPT: Blades, Prop, Metal Or Wood
AIRCRAFT PARTS & AUXILIARY EQPT: Body & Wing Assys & Parts
AIRCRAFT PARTS & AUXILIARY EQPT: Body Assemblies & Parts
AIRCRAFT PARTS & AUXILIARY EQPT: Brakes
AIRCRAFT PARTS & AUXILIARY EQPT: Landing Assemblies & Brakes
AIRCRAFT PARTS & AUXILIARY EQPT: Lighting/Landing Gear Assy
AIRCRAFT PARTS & AUXILIARY EQPT: Military Eqpt & Arma-ment
AIRCRAFT PARTS & AUXILIARY EQPT: Oxygen Systems
AIRCRAFT PARTS & AUXILIARY EQPT: Refueling Eqpt, In Flight
AIRCRAFT PARTS & AUXILIARY EQPT: Research & Devel-opment, Mfr
AIRCRAFT PARTS & EQPT, NEC
AIRCRAFT PARTS WHOLESALERS
AIRCRAFT PROPELLERS & PARTS
AIRCRAFT SERVICING & REPAIRING
AIRCRAFT WHEELS
AIRCRAFT: Airplanes, Fixed Or Rotary Wing
AIRCRAFT: Motorized
AIRCRAFT: Research & Development, Manufacturer
AIRPORTS, FLYING FIELDS & SVCS
ALARMS: Burglar
ALARMS: Fire
ALCOHOL: Ethyl & Ethanol
ALCOHOL: Methyl & Methanol, Synthetic
ALKALIES & CHLORINE
ALLOYS: Additive, Exc Copper Or Made In Blast Furnaces
ALTERNATORS: Automotive
ALUMINUM
ALUMINUM & BERYLLIUM ORES MINING
ALUMINUM PRDTS
ALUMINUM: Coil & Sheet
ALUMINUM: Ingots & Slabs
ALUMINUM: Pigs
ALUMINUM: Rolling & Drawing
ALUMINUM: Slabs, Primary
AMMUNITION
AMMUNITION: Arming & Fusing Devices
AMMUNITION: Cartridges Case, 30 mm & Below
AMMUNITION: Jet Propulsion Projectiles
AMMUNITION: Pellets & BB's, Pistol & Air Rifle
AMMUNITION: Shot, Steel
AMMUNITION: Small Arms
AMPLIFIERS
AMPLIFIERS: RF & IF Power
AMUSEMENT & REC SVCS: Baseball Club, Exc Pro & Semi-Pro
AMUSEMENT & REC SVCS: Cake/Pastry Decorating Instruc-tion

AMUSEMENT & RECREATION SVCS: Arts & Crafts Instruc-tion
AMUSEMENT & RECREATION SVCS: Exhibition Operation
AMUSEMENT & RECREATION SVCS: Exposition Operation
AMUSEMENT & RECREATION SVCS: Game Machines
AMUSEMENT & RECREATION SVCS: Golf Svcs & Profes-sionals
AMUSEMENT & RECREATION SVCS: Gun & Hunting Clubs
AMUSEMENT & RECREATION SVCS: Gun Club, Member-ship
AMUSEMENT & RECREATION SVCS: Ice Skating Rink
AMUSEMENT & RECREATION SVCS: Indoor Court Clubs
AMUSEMENT & RECREATION SVCS: Juke Box
AMUSEMENT & RECREATION SVCS: Outfitters, Recreation
AMUSEMENT & RECREATION SVCS: Racquetball Club, Non-Member
AMUSEMENT & RECREATION SVCS: Shooting Range
AMUSEMENT & RECREATION SVCS: Zoological Garden, Commercial
AMUSEMENT MACHINES: Coin Operated
AMUSEMENT PARK DEVICES & RIDES
AMUSEMENT PARK DEVICES & RIDES Carousels Or Merry-Go-Rounds
AMUSEMENT PARK DEVICES & RIDES: Carnival Mach & Eqpt, NEC
ANALYZERS: Blood & Body Fluid
ANALYZERS: Moisture
ANALYZERS: Network
ANALYZERS: Respiratory
ANESTHESIA EQPT
ANIMAL BASED MEDICINAL CHEMICAL PRDTS
ANIMAL FEED & SUPPLEMENTS: Livestock & Poultry
ANIMAL FEED: Wholesalers
ANIMAL FOOD & SUPPLEMENTS: Alfalfa Or Alfalfa Meal
ANIMAL FOOD & SUPPLEMENTS: Bird Food, Prepared
ANIMAL FOOD & SUPPLEMENTS: Bone Meal
ANIMAL FOOD & SUPPLEMENTS: Cat
ANIMAL FOOD & SUPPLEMENTS: Chicken Feeds, Prepared
ANIMAL FOOD & SUPPLEMENTS: Dog
ANIMAL FOOD & SUPPLEMENTS: Dog & Cat
ANIMAL FOOD & SUPPLEMENTS: Feed Concentrates
ANIMAL FOOD & SUPPLEMENTS: Feed Premixes
ANIMAL FOOD & SUPPLEMENTS: Feed Supplements
ANIMAL FOOD & SUPPLEMENTS: Livestock
ANIMAL FOOD & SUPPLEMENTS: Mineral feed supplements
ANIMAL FOOD & SUPPLEMENTS: Pet, Exc Dog & Cat, Dry
ANIMAL FOOD & SUPPLEMENTS: Poultry
ANIMAL FOOD & SUPPLEMENTS: Specialty, Mice & Other Pets
ANIMAL FOOD & SUPPLEMENTS: Stock Feeds, Dry
ANIMAL FOOD/SUPPLEMENTS: Feeds Fm Meat/Meat/Veg Combnd Meals
ANNEALING: Metal
ANNUNCIATORS
ANODIZING EQPT
ANODIZING SVC
ANTENNA REPAIR & INSTALLATION SVCS
ANTENNAS: Radar Or Communications
ANTENNAS: Receiving
ANTIBIOTICS
ANTIFREEZE
ANTIQUE & CLASSIC AUTOMOBILE RESTORATION
ANTIQUE FURNITURE RESTORATION & REPAIR
ANTIQUE REPAIR & RESTORATION SVCS, EXC FURNI-TURE & AUTOS
ANTIQUE SHOPS
ANTIQUES, WHOLESALE
APPAREL DESIGNERS: Commercial
APPAREL PRESSING SVCS
APPAREL: Hand Woven
APPLIANCE CORDS: Household Electrical Eqpt
APPLIANCE PARTS: Porcelain Enameled
APPLIANCES, HOUSEHOLD OR COIN OPERATED: Laundry Dryers
APPLIANCES, HOUSEHOLD: Kitchen, Major, Exc Refrigs & Stoves
APPLIANCES, HOUSEHOLD: Laundry Machines, Incl Coin-Operated

APPLIANCES, HOUSEHOLD: Refrigs, Mechanical & Absorption
APPLIANCES, HOUSEHOLD: Sweepers, Electric
APPLIANCES: Household, NEC
APPLIANCES: Household, Refrigerators & Freezers
APPLIANCES: Major, Cooking
APPLIANCES: Small, Electric
APPLICATIONS SOFTWARE PROGRAMMING
APPRAISAL SVCS, EXC REAL ESTATE
APRONS: Rubber, Vulcanized Or Rubberized Fabric
AQUARIUM ACCESS, METAL
AQUARIUMS & ACCESS: Glass
AQUARIUMS & ACCESS: Plastic
ARCHERY & SHOOTING RANGES
ARCHITECTURAL PANELS OR PARTS: Porcelain Enameled
ARCHITECTURAL SVCS
ARCHITECTURAL SVCS: House Designer
ARMATURE REPAIRING & REWINDING SVC
ARMORED CAR SVCS
AROMATIC CHEMICAL PRDTS
ART & ORNAMENTAL WARE: Pottery
ART DEALERS & GALLERIES
ART DESIGN SVCS
ART MARBLE: Concrete
ART RELATED SVCS
ART RESTORATION SVC
ART SPLY STORES
ARTIFICIAL FLOWER SHOPS
ARTISTS' AGENTS & BROKERS
ARTISTS' MATERIALS: Brushes, Air
ARTISTS' MATERIALS: Canvas, Prepared On Frames
ARTISTS' MATERIALS: Ink, Drawing, Black & Colored
ARTISTS' MATERIALS: Palettes
ARTISTS' MATERIALS: Pencil Holders
ARTS & CRAFTS SCHOOL
ARTWORK: Framed
ASBESTOS PRDTS: Textiles, Exc Insulating Material
ASPHALT & ASPHALT PRDTS
ASPHALT COATINGS & SEALERS
ASPHALT MINING & BITUMINOUS STONE QUARRYING SVCS
ASPHALT MINING SVCS
ASPHALT MIXTURES WHOLESALERS
ASPHALT PLANTS INCLUDING GRAVEL MIX TYPE
ASSEMBLING SVC: Plumbing Fixture Fittings, Plastic
ASSOCIATION FOR THE HANDICAPPED
ASSOCIATIONS: Business
ASSOCIATIONS: Fraternal
ASSOCIATIONS: Manufacturers'
ASSOCIATIONS: Real Estate Management
ASSOCIATIONS: Trade
ATOMIZERS
AUCTION SVCS: Motor Vehicle
AUDIO & VIDEO EQPT, EXC COMMERCIAL
AUDIO COMPONENTS
AUDIO ELECTRONIC SYSTEMS
AUDIO-VISUAL PROGRAM PRODUCTION SVCS
AUDIOLOGICAL EQPT: Electronic
AUDIOLOGISTS' OFFICES
AUTO & HOME SUPPLY STORES: Auto & Truck Eqpt & Parts
AUTO & HOME SUPPLY STORES: Automotive Access
AUTO & HOME SUPPLY STORES: Automotive parts
AUTO & HOME SUPPLY STORES: Batteries, Automotive & Truck
AUTO & HOME SUPPLY STORES: Speed Shops, Incl Race Car Splys
AUTO & HOME SUPPLY STORES: Trailer Hitches, Automotive
AUTO & HOME SUPPLY STORES: Truck Eqpt & Parts
AUTOMATED TELLER MACHINE OR ATM REPAIR SVCS
AUTOMATIC REGULATING CNTRLS: Liq Lvl, Residential/Comm Heat
AUTOMATIC REGULATING CNTRLS: Steam Press, Residential/ Comm
AUTOMATIC REGULATING CONTROL: Building Svcs Monitoring, Auto
AUTOMATIC REGULATING CONTROLS: AC & Refrigeration
AUTOMATIC REGULATING CONTROLS: Appliance Regulators
AUTOMATIC REGULATING CONTROLS: Appliance, Exc Air-Cond/Refr
AUTOMATIC REGULATING CONTROLS: Energy Cutoff, Residtl/Comm
AUTOMATIC REGULATING CONTROLS: Hardware, Environmental Reg

AUTOMATIC REGULATING CONTROLS: Pressure, Air-Cond Sys
AUTOMATIC REGULATING CONTROLS: Refrigeration, Pressure
AUTOMATIC REGULATING CONTROLS: Surface Burner, Temperature
AUTOMATIC REGULATING CTRLS: Damper, Pneumatic Or Electric
AUTOMATIC REGULATING CTRLS: Elec Heat Proportion, Modultg
AUTOMATIC TELLER MACHINES
AUTOMOBILE RECOVERY SVCS
AUTOMOBILES & OTHER MOTOR VEHICLES WHOLESALERS
AUTOMOBILES: Off-Road, Exc Recreational Vehicles
AUTOMOTIVE & TRUCK GENERAL REPAIR SVC
AUTOMOTIVE BATTERIES WHOLESALERS
AUTOMOTIVE BODY SHOP
AUTOMOTIVE BODY, PAINT & INTERIOR REPAIR & MAINTENANCE SVC
AUTOMOTIVE BRAKE REPAIR SHOPS
AUTOMOTIVE CUSTOMIZING SVCS, NONFACTORY BASIS
AUTOMOTIVE GLASS REPLACEMENT SHOPS
AUTOMOTIVE PAINT SHOP
AUTOMOTIVE PARTS, ACCESS & SPLYS
AUTOMOTIVE PARTS: Plastic
AUTOMOTIVE PRDTS: Rubber
AUTOMOTIVE RADIATOR REPAIR SHOPS
AUTOMOTIVE REPAIR SHOPS: Alternators/Generator, Rebuild/Rpr
AUTOMOTIVE REPAIR SHOPS: Brake Repair
AUTOMOTIVE REPAIR SHOPS: Diesel Engine Repair
AUTOMOTIVE REPAIR SHOPS: Electrical Svcs
AUTOMOTIVE REPAIR SHOPS: Engine Rebuilding
AUTOMOTIVE REPAIR SHOPS: Engine Repair
AUTOMOTIVE REPAIR SHOPS: Machine Shop
AUTOMOTIVE REPAIR SHOPS: Tire Repair Shop
AUTOMOTIVE REPAIR SHOPS: Trailer Repair
AUTOMOTIVE REPAIR SHOPS: Truck Engine Repair, Exc Indl
AUTOMOTIVE REPAIR SHOPS: Wheel Alignment
AUTOMOTIVE REPAIR SVC
AUTOMOTIVE REPAIR SVCS, MISCELLANEOUS
AUTOMOTIVE RUSTPROOFING & UNDERCOATING SHOPS
AUTOMOTIVE SPLYS & PARTS, NEW, WHOL: Auto Servicing Eqpt
AUTOMOTIVE SPLYS & PARTS, NEW, WHOL: Testing Eqpt, Electric
AUTOMOTIVE SPLYS & PARTS, NEW, WHOLESALE: Bumpers
AUTOMOTIVE SPLYS & PARTS, NEW, WHOLESALE: Clutches
AUTOMOTIVE SPLYS & PARTS, NEW, WHOLESALE: Engines/Eng Parts
AUTOMOTIVE SPLYS & PARTS, NEW, WHOLESALE: Filters, Air & Oil
AUTOMOTIVE SPLYS & PARTS, NEW, WHOLESALE: Pumps, Oil & Gas
AUTOMOTIVE SPLYS & PARTS, NEW, WHOLESALE: Seat Covers
AUTOMOTIVE SPLYS & PARTS, NEW, WHOLESALE: Splys
AUTOMOTIVE SPLYS & PARTS, NEW, WHOLESALE: Stampings
AUTOMOTIVE SPLYS & PARTS, NEW, WHOLESALE: Tools & Eqpt
AUTOMOTIVE SPLYS & PARTS, NEW, WHOLESALE: Trailer Parts
AUTOMOTIVE SPLYS & PARTS, NEW, WHOLESALE: Wheels
AUTOMOTIVE SPLYS & PARTS, USED, RETAIL ONLY: Tires, Used
AUTOMOTIVE SPLYS & PARTS, USED, WHOLESALE
AUTOMOTIVE SPLYS & PARTS, WHOLESALE, NEC
AUTOMOTIVE SPLYS/PART, NEW, WHOL: Spring, Shock Absorb/Strut
AUTOMOTIVE SPLYS/PARTS, NEW, WHOL: Body Rpr/Paint Shop Splys
AUTOMOTIVE SVCS, EXC REPAIR & CARWASHES: Customizing
AUTOMOTIVE SVCS, EXC REPAIR & CARWASHES: Maintenance
AUTOMOTIVE SVCS, EXC REPAIR & CARWASHES: Road Svc

AUTOMOTIVE SVCS, EXC REPAIR & CARWASHES: Trailer Maintenance
AUTOMOTIVE SVCS, EXC REPAIR: Truck Wash
AUTOMOTIVE TOPS INSTALLATION OR REPAIR: Canvas Or Plastic
AUTOMOTIVE TOWING & WRECKING SVC
AUTOMOTIVE TOWING SVCS
AUTOMOTIVE TRANSMISSION REPAIR SVC
AUTOMOTIVE WELDING SVCS
AUTOMOTIVE: Bodies
AUTOMOTIVE: Seat Frames, Metal
AUTOMOTIVE: Seating
AUTOTRANSFORMERS: Electric
AWNING REPAIR SHOP
AWNINGS & CANOPIES
AWNINGS & CANOPIES: Awnings, Fabric, From Purchased Matls
AWNINGS & CANOPIES: Fabric
AWNINGS: Fiberglass
AWNINGS: Metal
AXLES
Ammunition Loading & Assembling Plant

B

BACKHOES
BADGES: Identification & Insignia
BAFFLES
BAGS: Canvas
BAGS: Cellophane
BAGS: Food Storage & Trash, Plastic
BAGS: Garment Storage Exc Paper Or Plastic Film
BAGS: Paper
BAGS: Paper, Made From Purchased Materials
BAGS: Plastic
BAGS: Plastic & Pliofilm
BAGS: Plastic, Made From Purchased Materials
BAGS: Pliofilm, Made From Purchased Materials
BAGS: Rubber Or Rubberized Fabric
BAGS: Shipping
BAGS: Shopping, Made From Purchased Materials
BAGS: Textile
BAGS: Trash, Plastic Film, Made From Purchased Materials
BAGS: Vacuum cleaner, Made From Purchased Materials
BAIT, FISHING, WHOLESALE
BAKERIES, COMMERCIAL: On Premises Baking Only
BAKERIES: On Premises Baking & Consumption
BAKERY FOR HOME SVC DELIVERY
BAKERY MACHINERY
BAKERY PRDTS, FROZEN: Wholesalers
BAKERY PRDTS: Bakery Prdts, Partially Cooked, Exc frozen
BAKERY PRDTS: Biscuits, Baked, Baking Powder & Raised
BAKERY PRDTS: Biscuits, Dry
BAKERY PRDTS: Bread, All Types, Fresh Or Frozen
BAKERY PRDTS: Buns, Bread Type, Fresh Or Frozen
BAKERY PRDTS: Cakes, Bakery, Exc Frozen
BAKERY PRDTS: Cakes, Bakery, Frozen
BAKERY PRDTS: Cones, Ice Cream
BAKERY PRDTS: Cookies
BAKERY PRDTS: Cookies & crackers
BAKERY PRDTS: Doughnuts, Exc Frozen
BAKERY PRDTS: Dry
BAKERY PRDTS: Frozen
BAKERY PRDTS: Pastries, Exc Frozen
BAKERY PRDTS: Pies, Exc Frozen
BAKERY PRDTS: Pretzels
BAKERY PRDTS: Rice Cakes
BAKERY PRDTS: Wholesalers
BAKERY: Wholesale Or Wholesale & Retail Combined
BALLOONS: Toy & Advertising, Rubber
BANDS: Plastic
BANNERS: Fabric
BANQUET HALL FACILITIES
BAR
BAR JOISTS & CONCRETE REINFORCING BARS: Fabricated
BARBECUE EQPT
BARBER SHOP SELLING WIGS
BARGES BUILDING & REPAIR
BARRELS: Shipping, Metal
BARRICADES: Metal
BARS & BAR SHAPES: Copper & Copper Alloy
BARS & BAR SHAPES: Steel, Cold-Finished, Own Hot-Rolled
BARS & BAR SHAPES: Steel, Hot-Rolled
BARS, COLD FINISHED: Steel, From Purchased Hot-Rolled

BARS, PIPES, PLATES & SHAPES: Lead/Lead Alloy Bars, Pipe
BARS: Concrete Reinforcing, Fabricated Steel
BARS: Iron, Made In Steel Mills
BARS: Rolled, Aluminum
BASALT: Crushed & Broken
BASEMENT WINDOW AREAWAYS: Concrete
BASES, BEVERAGE
BASKETS, WHOLESALE
BASKETS: Steel Wire
BATH SALTS
BATH SHOPS
BATHMATS: Rubber
BATHROOM ACCESS & FITTINGS: Vitreous China & Earthenware
BATTERIES, EXC AUTOMOTIVE: Wholesalers
BATTERIES: Alkaline, Cell Storage
BATTERIES: Dry
BATTERIES: Lead Acid, Storage
BATTERIES: Rechargeable
BATTERIES: Storage
BATTERIES: Wet
BATTERY CASES: Plastic Or Plastics Combination
BATTERY CHARGERS
BATTERY CHARGERS: Storage, Motor & Engine Generator Type
BATTERY CHARGING GENERATORS
BATTERY REPAIR & SVCS
BAUXITE MINING
BEADS: Unassembled
BEARINGS
BEARINGS & PARTS Ball
BEARINGS: Ball & Roller
BEARINGS: Plastic
BEARINGS: Roller & Parts
BEAUTY & BARBER SHOP EQPT
BEAUTY & BARBER SHOP EQPT & SPLYS WHOLESALERS
BEAUTY SALONS
BED & BREAKFAST INNS
BEDDING & BEDSPRINGS STORES
BEDDING, BEDSPREADS, BLANKETS & SHEETS
BEDDING, BEDSPREADS, BLANKETS & SHEETS: Comforters & Quilts
BEDS: Hospital
BEDS: Institutional
BEDSPREADS & BED SETS, FROM PURCHASED MATERIALS
BEDSPREADS, COTTON
BEER & ALE WHOLESALERS
BEER, WINE & LIQUOR STORES: Beer, Packaged
BEER, WINE & LIQUOR STORES: Wine
BELLOWS
BELLOWS ASSEMBLIES: Missiles, Metal
BELLS: Electric
BELTING: Plastic
BELTING: Rubber
BELTS: Conveyor, Made From Purchased Wire
BELTS: Seat, Automotive & Aircraft
BENTONITE MINING
BERYLLIUM
BEVERAGE BASES & SYRUPS
BEVERAGE PRDTS: Brewers' Grain
BEVERAGE, NONALCOHOLIC: Iced Tea/Fruit Drink, Bottled/Canned
BEVERAGES, ALCOHOLIC: Ale
BEVERAGES, ALCOHOLIC: Beer
BEVERAGES, ALCOHOLIC: Beer & Ale
BEVERAGES, ALCOHOLIC: Bourbon Whiskey
BEVERAGES, ALCOHOLIC: Cocktails
BEVERAGES, ALCOHOLIC: Distilled Liquors
BEVERAGES, ALCOHOLIC: Liquors, Malt
BEVERAGES, ALCOHOLIC: Near Beer
BEVERAGES, ALCOHOLIC: Rye Whiskey
BEVERAGES, ALCOHOLIC: Vodka
BEVERAGES, ALCOHOLIC: Wines
BEVERAGES, NONALCOHOLIC: Bottled & canned soft drinks
BEVERAGES, NONALCOHOLIC: Carbonated
BEVERAGES, NONALCOHOLIC: Carbonated, Canned & Bottled, Etc
BEVERAGES, NONALCOHOLIC: Cider
BEVERAGES, NONALCOHOLIC: Flavoring extracts & syrups, nec
BEVERAGES, NONALCOHOLIC: Fruit Drnks, Under 100% Juice, Can

BEVERAGES, NONALCOHOLIC: Lemonade, Bottled & Canned, Etc
BEVERAGES, NONALCOHOLIC: Soft Drinks, Canned & Bottled, Etc
BEVERAGES, WINE & DISTILLED ALCOHOLIC, WHOLESALE: Wine
BIBS: Rubber, Vulcanized Or Rubberized Fabric
BICYCLES, PARTS & ACCESS
BILLFOLD INSERTS: Plastic
BILLIARD & POOL TABLES & SPLYS
BILLING & BOOKKEEPING SVCS
BINDING SVC: Books & Manuals
BINDING SVC: Pamphlets
BINDING SVC: Trade
BINDINGS: Bias, Made From Purchased Materials
BINDINGS: Cap & Hat, Made From Purchased Materials
BINGO HALL
BINOCULARS
BINS: Prefabricated, Sheet Metal
BIOLOGICAL PRDTS: Bacteriological Media
BIOLOGICAL PRDTS: Exc Diagnostic
BIOLOGICAL PRDTS: Serums
BIOLOGICAL PRDTS: Vaccines
BIOLOGICAL PRDTS: Vaccines & Immunizing
BIOLOGICAL PRDTS: Venoms
BIOLOGICAL PRDTS: Veterinary
BLACKBOARDS & CHALKBOARDS
BLACKBOARDS: Slate
BLADES: Knife
BLADES: Saw, Hand Or Power
BLANKBOOKS
BLANKBOOKS & LOOSELEAF BINDERS
BLANKBOOKS: Account
BLANKBOOKS: Albums
BLANKBOOKS: Checkbooks & Passbooks, Bank
BLANKBOOKS: Passbooks, Bank, Etc
BLANKBOOKS: Scrapbooks
BLANKETS & BLANKETING, COTTON
BLAST FURNACE & RELATED PRDTS
BLASTING SVC: Sand, Metal Parts
BLINDS & SHADES: Mini
BLINDS & SHADES: Vertical
BLINDS : Window
BLOCK & BRICK: Sand Lime
BLOCKS & BRICKS: Concrete
BLOCKS: Insulating, Concrete
BLOCKS: Landscape Or Retaining Wall, Concrete
BLOCKS: Paving
BLOCKS: Paving, Asphalt, Not From Refineries
BLOCKS: Paving, Concrete
BLOCKS: Standard, Concrete Or Cinder
BLOOD BANK
BLOWERS & FANS
BLOWERS & FANS
BLUEPRINTING SVCS
BOAT BUILDING & REPAIR
BOAT BUILDING & REPAIRING: Dories
BOAT BUILDING & REPAIRING: Kits, Not Models
BOAT BUILDING & REPAIRING: Lifeboats
BOAT BUILDING & REPAIRING: Motorized
BOAT BUILDING & REPAIRING: Tenders, Small Motor Craft
BOAT DEALERS
BOAT DEALERS: Marine Splys & Eqpt
BOAT LIFTS
BOAT REPAIR SVCS
BOAT YARD: Boat yards, storage & incidental repair
BOATS & OTHER MARINE EQPT: Plastic
BODIES: Truck & Bus
BODY PARTS: Automobile, Stamped Metal
BOILER & HEATING REPAIR SVCS
BOILER GAGE COCKS
BOILER REPAIR SHOP
BOILERS: Low-Pressure Heating, Steam Or Hot Water
BOLTS: Metal
BONDERIZING: Bonderizing, Metal Or Metal Prdts
BONDS, RAIL: Electric, Propulsion & Signal Circuit Uses
BOOK STORES
BOOK STORES: Religious
BOOKS, WHOLESALE
BOOTHS: Spray, Sheet Metal, Prefabricated
BORING MILL
BOTTLE CAPS & RESEALERS: Plastic
BOTTLED GAS DEALERS: Liquefied Petro, Dlvrd To Customers
BOTTLED GAS DEALERS: Propane

BOTTLED WATER DELIVERY
BOTTLES: Plastic
BOWL COVERS: Plastic
BOWLING CENTERS
BOWLING EQPT & SPLY STORES
BOWLING EQPT & SPLYS
BOXES & CRATES: Rectangular, Wood
BOXES & SHOOK: Nailed Wood
BOXES: Corrugated
BOXES: Filing, Paperboard Made From Purchased Materials
BOXES: Fuse, Electric
BOXES: Mail Or Post Office, Collection/Storage, Sheet Metal
BOXES: Packing & Shipping, Metal
BOXES: Paperboard, Folding
BOXES: Paperboard, Set-Up
BOXES: Plastic
BOXES: Stamped Metal
BOXES: Wooden
BRAKES & BRAKE PARTS
BRAKES: Bicycle, Friction Clutch & Other
BRAKES: Electromagnetic
BRAKES: Metal Forming
BRASS & BRONZE PRDTS: Die-casted
BRASS FOUNDRY, NEC
BRASS ROLLING & DRAWING
BRAZING SVCS
BRAZING: Metal
BRIC-A-BRAC
BRICK, STONE & RELATED PRDTS WHOLESALERS
BRICKS & BLOCKS: Structural
BRICKS : Ceramic Glazed, Clay
BRICKS : Flooring, Clay
BRICKS : Paving, Clay
BRICKS: Clay
BRICKS: Concrete
BRIDAL SHOPS
BROACHING MACHINES
BROADCASTING & COMMS EQPT: Antennas, Transmitting/Comms
BROADCASTING & COMMS EQPT: Rcvr-Transmitter Unt, Transceiver
BROADCASTING & COMMUNICATIONS EQPT: Cellular Radio Telephone
BROADCASTING & COMMUNICATIONS EQPT: Light Comms Eqpt
BROKERS' SVCS
BROKERS, MARINE TRANSPORTATION
BROKERS: Contract Basis
BROKERS: Food
BROKERS: Log & Lumber
BROKERS: Printing
BRONZE FOUNDRY, NEC
BRONZE ROLLING & DRAWING
BRONZING SVCS: Baby Shoes
BROOMS & BRUSHES
BROOMS & BRUSHES: Household Or Indl
BROOMS & BRUSHES: Paint & Varnish
BROOMS & BRUSHES: Street Sweeping, Hand Or Machine
BROOMS & BRUSHES: Vacuum Cleaners & Carpet Sweepers
BRUSH BLOCKS: Carbon Or Molded Graphite
BRUSHES & BRUSH STOCK CONTACTS: Electric
BUCKETS: Plastic
BUFFING FOR THE TRADE
BUILDING & OFFICE CLEANING SVCS
BUILDING & STRUCTURAL WOOD MBRS: Timbers, Struct, Lam Lumber
BUILDING & STRUCTURAL WOOD MEMBERS
BUILDING & STRUCTURAL WOOD MEMBERS: Arches, Laminated Lumber
BUILDING CLEANING & MAINTENANCE SVCS
BUILDING CLEANING SVCS
BUILDING COMPONENT CLEANING SVCS
BUILDING COMPONENTS: Structural Steel
BUILDING ITEM REPAIR SVCS, MISCELLANEOUS
BUILDING MAINTENANCE SVCS, EXC REPAIRS
BUILDING PRDTS & MATERIALS DEALERS
BUILDING PRDTS: Concrete
BUILDING PRDTS: Stone
BUILDING SCALES MODELS
BUILDING STONE, ARTIFICIAL: Concrete
BUILDINGS & COMPONENTS: Prefabricated Metal
BUILDINGS, PREFABRICATED: Wholesalers
BUILDINGS: Chicken Coops, Prefabricated, Wood
BUILDINGS: Farm & Utility

INDEX

BUILDINGS: Farm, Prefabricated Or Portable, Wood
BUILDINGS: Portable
BUILDINGS: Prefabricated, Metal
BUILDINGS: Prefabricated, Plastic
BUILDINGS: Prefabricated, Wood
BUILDINGS: Prefabricated, Wood
BULLETIN BOARDS: Cork
BULLETIN BOARDS: Wood
BULLETPROOF VESTS
BUOYS: Metal
BUOYS: Plastic
BURGLAR ALARM MAINTENANCE & MONITORING SVCS
BURIAL VAULTS: Concrete Or Precast Terrazzo
BURIAL VAULTS: Stone
BURLAP & BURLAP PRDTS
BURNERS: Gas, Domestic
BURNERS: Gas, Indl
BURNERS: Oil, Domestic Or Indl
BUS BARS: Electrical
BUSHINGS & BEARINGS
BUSHINGS & BEARINGS: Brass, Exc Machined
BUSHINGS & BEARINGS: Bronze, Exc Machined
BUSINESS ACTIVITIES: Non-Commercial Site
BUSINESS FORMS WHOLESALERS
BUSINESS FORMS: Printed, Continuous
BUSINESS FORMS: Printed, Manifold
BUSINESS FORMS: Unit Sets, Manifold
BUSINESS MACHINE REPAIR, ELECTRIC
BUSINESS SUPPORT SVCS
BUSINESS TRAINING SVCS
BUTTER WHOLESALERS

C

CABINETS & CASES: Radio, Wood
CABINETS & CASES: Show, Display & Storage, Exc Wood
CABINETS: Bathroom Vanities, Wood
CABINETS: Entertainment
CABINETS: Entertainment Units, Household, Wood
CABINETS: Factory
CABINETS: Filing, Wood
CABINETS: Kitchen, Metal
CABINETS: Kitchen, Wood
CABINETS: Office, Metal
CABINETS: Office, Wood
CABINETS: Show, Display, Etc, Wood, Exc Refrigerated
CABLE & OTHER PAY TELEVISION DISTRIBUTION
CABLE TELEVISION
CABLE WIRING SETS: Battery, Internal Combustion Engines
CABLE: Fiber
CABLE: Fiber Optic
CABLE: Noninsulated
CABLE: Ropes & Fiber
CABLE: Steel, Insulated Or Armored
CABS: Indl Trucks & Tractors
CAFFEINE & DERIVATIVES
CAGES: Wire
CALENDARS, WHOLESALE
CALIBRATING SVCS, NEC
CAMERAS & RELATED EQPT: Photographic
CAMPGROUNDS
CAMSHAFTS
CANDLE SHOPS
CANDLES
CANDY & CONFECTIONS: Cake Ornaments
CANDY & CONFECTIONS: Candy Bars, Including Chocolate Covered
CANDY & CONFECTIONS: Chocolate Candy, Exc Solid Chocolate
CANDY & CONFECTIONS: Chocolate Covered Dates
CANDY & CONFECTIONS: Cough Drops, Exc Pharmaceutical Preps
CANDY & CONFECTIONS: Fruit, Chocolate Covered, Exc Dates
CANDY & CONFECTIONS: Fudge
CANDY & CONFECTIONS: Nuts, Glace
CANDY & CONFECTIONS: Popcorn Balls/Other Trtd Popcorn Prdts
CANDY, NUT & CONFECTIONERY STORE: Popcorn, Incl Caramel Corn
CANDY, NUT & CONFECTIONERY STORES: Candy
CANDY, NUT & CONFECTIONERY STORES: Confectionery
CANDY, NUT & CONFECTIONERY STORES: Nuts
CANDY: Chocolate From Cacao Beans
CANDY: Hard
CANNED SPECIALTIES

CANOPIES: Sheet Metal
CANS & TUBES: Ammunition, Board Laminated With Metal Foil
CANS: Aluminum
CANS: Beer, Metal
CANS: Composite Foil-Fiber, Made From Purchased Materials
CANS: Fiber
CANS: Garbage, Stamped Or Pressed Metal
CANS: Metal
CANS: Tin
CANVAS PRDTS
CANVAS PRDTS: Air Cushions & Mattresses
CANVAS PRDTS: Convertible Tops, Car/Boat, Fm Purchased Mtrl
CANVAS PRDTS: Shades, Made From Purchased Materials
CAPACITORS: NEC
CAPS: Plastic
CAR LOADING SVCS
CAR WASH EQPT
CAR WASH EQPT & SPLYS WHOLESALERS
CAR WASHES
CARBIDES
CARBON & GRAPHITE PRDTS, NEC
CARBON BLACK
CARBON DISULFIDE
CARBON PAPER & INKED RIBBONS
CARDS: Beveled
CARDS: Color
CARDS: Greeting
CARDS: Identification
CARDS: Playing
CARNIVAL & AMUSEMENT PARK EQPT WHOLESALERS
CARNIVAL SPLYS, WHOLESALE
CARPET & UPHOLSTERY CLEANING SVCS
CARPET & UPHOLSTERY CLEANING SVCS: Carpet/Furniture, On Loc
CARPETS & RUGS: Tufted
CARPETS, RUGS & FLOOR COVERING
CARPORTS: Prefabricated Metal
CARRIAGES: Horse Drawn
CARRIER EQPT: Telephone Or Telegraph
CARRIERS: Infant, Textile
CARS: Electric
CARTONS: Egg, Molded Pulp, Made From Purchased Materials
CARVING SETS, STAINLESS STEEL
CASEMENTS: Aluminum
CASES, WOOD
CASES: Carrying
CASES: Carrying, Clothing & Apparel
CASES: Plastic
CASES: Shipping, Nailed Or Lock Corner, Wood
CASH REGISTERS & PARTS
CASING-HEAD BUTANE & PROPANE PRODUCTION
CASINGS: Rocket Transportation
CASINGS: Sheet Metal
CASINGS: Storage, Missile & Missile Components
CASKETS & ACCESS
CASKETS WHOLESALERS
CAST STONE: Concrete
CASTERS
CASTINGS GRINDING: For The Trade
CASTINGS: Aerospace Investment, Ferrous
CASTINGS: Aerospace, Aluminum
CASTINGS: Aerospace, Nonferrous, Exc Aluminum
CASTINGS: Aluminum
CASTINGS: Brass, NEC, Exc Die
CASTINGS: Bronze, NEC, Exc Die
CASTINGS: Commercial Investment, Ferrous
CASTINGS: Copper & Copper-Base Alloy, NEC, Exc Die
CASTINGS: Die, Aluminum
CASTINGS: Die, Copper & Copper Alloy
CASTINGS: Die, Magnesium & Magnesium-Base Alloy
CASTINGS: Die, Nonferrous
CASTINGS: Die, Zinc
CASTINGS: Ductile
CASTINGS: Gray Iron
CASTINGS: Machinery, Aluminum
CASTINGS: Magnesium
CASTINGS: Precision
CASTINGS: Steel
CASTINGS: Zinc
CATALOG & MAIL-ORDER HOUSES
CATALOG SALES
CATALYSTS: Chemical

CATAPULTS
CATCH BASIN COVERS: Concrete
CATERERS
CATTLE WHOLESALERS
CAULKING COMPOUNDS
CEILING SYSTEMS: Luminous, Commercial
CELLULOSE ACETATE
CELLULOSE DERIVATIVE MATERIALS
CEMENT & CONCRETE RELATED PRDTS & EQPT: Bituminous
CEMENT ROCK: Crushed & Broken
CEMENT, EXC LINOLEUM & TILE
CEMENT: Heat Resistant
CEMENT: Hydraulic
CEMENT: Masonry
CEMENT: Natural
CEMENT: Portland
CEMENT: Rubber
CEMETERIES: Real Estate Operation
CEMETERY & FUNERAL DIRECTOR'S EQPT & SPLYS WHOLESALERS
CEMETERY MEMORIAL DEALERS
CERAMIC FIBER
CERAMIC FLOOR & WALL TILE WHOLESALERS
CHAIN: Wire
CHAINS: Power Transmission
CHALK MINING: Crushed & Broken
CHANDELIERS: Residential
CHARCOAL, WHOLESALE
CHARCOAL: Activated
CHASSIS: Automobile Trailer
CHASSIS: Motor Vehicle
CHEESE WHOLESALERS
CHEMICAL CLEANING SVCS
CHEMICAL ELEMENTS
CHEMICAL PROCESSING MACHINERY & EQPT
CHEMICAL SPLYS FOR FOUNDRIES
CHEMICALS & ALLIED PRDTS WHOLESALERS, NEC
CHEMICALS & ALLIED PRDTS, WHOLESALE: Anti-Corrosion Prdts
CHEMICALS & ALLIED PRDTS, WHOLESALE: Aromatic
CHEMICALS & ALLIED PRDTS, WHOLESALE: Caustic Soda
CHEMICALS & ALLIED PRDTS, WHOLESALE: Chemical Additives
CHEMICALS & ALLIED PRDTS, WHOLESALE: Chemicals, Indl
CHEMICALS & ALLIED PRDTS, WHOLESALE: Chemicals, Indl & Heavy
CHEMICALS & ALLIED PRDTS, WHOLESALE: Concrete Additives
CHEMICALS & ALLIED PRDTS, WHOLESALE: Detergent/Soap
CHEMICALS & ALLIED PRDTS, WHOLESALE: Detergents
CHEMICALS & ALLIED PRDTS, WHOLESALE: Dry Ice
CHEMICALS & ALLIED PRDTS, WHOLESALE: Glue
CHEMICALS & ALLIED PRDTS, WHOLESALE: Indl Gases
CHEMICALS & ALLIED PRDTS, WHOLESALE: Oxygen
CHEMICALS & ALLIED PRDTS, WHOLESALE: Plastics Materials, NEC
CHEMICALS & ALLIED PRDTS, WHOLESALE: Plastics Prdts, NEC
CHEMICALS & ALLIED PRDTS, WHOLESALE: Plastics Sheets & Rods
CHEMICALS & ALLIED PRDTS, WHOLESALE: Plastics, Basic Shapes
CHEMICALS & ALLIED PRDTS, WHOLESALE: Resins
CHEMICALS & ALLIED PRDTS, WHOLESALE: Rubber, Synthetic
CHEMICALS & ALLIED PRDTS, WHOLESALE: Sealants
CHEMICALS & ALLIED PRDTS, WHOLESALE: Syn Resin, Rub/Plastic
CHEMICALS & ALLIED PRDTS, WHOLESALE: Waxes, Exc Petroleum
CHEMICALS & OTHER PRDTS DERIVED FROM COKING
CHEMICALS, AGRICULTURE: Wholesalers
CHEMICALS: Agricultural
CHEMICALS: Alcohols
CHEMICALS: Alkalies
CHEMICALS: Aluminum Compounds
CHEMICALS: Aluminum Oxide
CHEMICALS: Aluminum Sulfate
CHEMICALS: Anhydrous Ammonia
CHEMICALS: Bauxite, Refined
CHEMICALS: Bleaching Powder, Lime Bleaching Compounds
CHEMICALS: Calcium & Calcium Compounds

CHEMICALS: Caustic Potash & Potassium Hydroxide
CHEMICALS: Caustic Soda
CHEMICALS: Copper Compounds Or Salts, Inorganic
CHEMICALS: Fire Retardant
CHEMICALS: High Purity Grade, Organic
CHEMICALS: High Purity, Refined From Technical Grade
CHEMICALS: Inorganic, NEC
CHEMICALS: Isotopes, Radioactive
CHEMICALS: Lead Compounds/Salts, Inorganic, Not Pigments
CHEMICALS: Lithium Compounds, Inorganic
CHEMICALS: Medicinal
CHEMICALS: Medicinal, Organic, Uncompounded, Bulk
CHEMICALS: Metal Salts/Compounds, Exc Sodium, Potassium/Alum
CHEMICALS: NEC
CHEMICALS: Nonmetallic Compounds
CHEMICALS: Organic, NEC
CHEMICALS: Phenol
CHEMICALS: Phosphates, Defluorinated/Ammoniated, Exc Fertlr
CHEMICALS: Reagent Grade, Refined From Technical Grade
CHEMICALS: Sodium Bicarbonate
CHEMICALS: Sulfur Chloride
CHEMICALS: Tin, Stannic/Stannous, Compounds/Salts, Inorganic
CHEMICALS: Water Treatment
CHEMICALS: Zinc Chloride
CHICKEN SLAUGHTERING & PROCESSING
CHILD DAY CARE SVCS
CHILDREN'S WEAR STORES
CHIMNEY CAPS: Concrete
CHIMNEY CLEANING SVCS
CHINA: Fired & Decorated
CHINAWARE WHOLESALERS
CHIROPRACTORS' OFFICES
CHLORINE
CHOCOLATE, EXC CANDY FROM BEANS: Chips, Powder, Block, Syrup
CHOCOLATE, EXC CANDY FROM PURCH CHOC: Chips, Powder, Block
CHRISTMAS NOVELTIES, WHOLESALE
CHRISTMAS TREE LIGHTING SETS: Electric
CHUCKS
CHUTES & TROUGHS
CIGAR & CIGARETTE HOLDERS
CIGARETTE & CIGAR PRDTS & ACCESS
CIRCUIT BOARD REPAIR SVCS
CIRCUIT BOARDS, PRINTED: Television & Radio
CIRCUIT BOARDS: Wiring
CIRCUIT BREAKERS
CIRCUITS: Electronic
CLAMPS & COUPLINGS: Hose
CLAMPS: Metal
CLAY MINING, COMMON
CLAY: Ground Or Treated
CLAYS, EXC KAOLIN & BALL
CLEANING & DESCALING SVC: Metal Prdts
CLEANING COMPOUNDS: Rifle Bore
CLEANING EQPT: Blast, Dustless
CLEANING EQPT: Commercial
CLEANING EQPT: Floor Washing & Polishing, Commercial
CLEANING EQPT: High Pressure
CLEANING EQPT: Janitors' Carts
CLEANING OR POLISHING PREPARATIONS, NEC
CLEANING PRDTS: Automobile Polish
CLEANING PRDTS: Bleaches, Household, Dry Or Liquid
CLEANING PRDTS: Degreasing Solvent
CLEANING PRDTS: Deodorants, Nonpersonal
CLEANING PRDTS: Drain Pipe Solvents Or Cleaners
CLEANING PRDTS: Drycleaning Preparations
CLEANING PRDTS: Dusting Cloths, Chemically Treated
CLEANING PRDTS: Floor Waxes
CLEANING PRDTS: Indl Plant Disinfectants Or Deodorants
CLEANING PRDTS: Laundry Preparations
CLEANING PRDTS: Metal Polish
CLEANING PRDTS: Paint & Wallpaper
CLEANING PRDTS: Polishing Preparations & Related Prdts
CLEANING PRDTS: Rug, Upholstery/Dry Clng Detergents/Spotters
CLEANING PRDTS: Sanitation Preparations
CLEANING PRDTS: Sanitation Preps, Disinfectants/Deodorants
CLEANING PRDTS: Specialty
CLEANING PRDTS: Stain Removers

CLEANING SVCS
CLEANING SVCS: Industrial Or Commercial
CLIPS & FASTENERS, MADE FROM PURCHASED WIRE
CLOCKS
CLOSURES: Closures, Stamped Metal
CLOSURES: Plastic
CLOTHING & ACCESS STORES
CLOTHING & ACCESS, WOMEN, CHILD & INFANT, WHOLESALE: Rack
CLOTHING & ACCESS, WOMEN, CHILD & INFANT, WHSLE: Sportswear
CLOTHING & ACCESS, WOMEN, CHILDREN & INFANT, WHOL: Sweaters
CLOTHING & ACCESS, WOMEN, CHILDREN & INFANT, WHOL: Uniforms
CLOTHING & ACCESS, WOMEN, CHILDREN/INFANT, WHOL: Outerwear
CLOTHING & ACCESS: Costumes, Lodge
CLOTHING & ACCESS: Costumes, Theatrical
CLOTHING & ACCESS: Garter Belts
CLOTHING & ACCESS: Hospital Gowns
CLOTHING & ACCESS: Men's Miscellaneous Access
CLOTHING & APPAREL STORES: Custom
CLOTHING & FURNISHINGS, MEN'S & BOYS', WHOLESALE: Shirts
CLOTHING & FURNISHINGS, MEN'S & BOYS', WHOLESALE: Uniforms
CLOTHING ACCESS STORES: Belts, Custom
CLOTHING ACCESS STORES: Umbrellas
CLOTHING STORES, NEC
CLOTHING STORES: Formal Wear
CLOTHING STORES: Leather
CLOTHING STORES: T-Shirts, Printed, Custom
CLOTHING STORES: Uniforms & Work
CLOTHING STORES: Unisex
CLOTHING/ACCESS, WOMEN, CHILDREN/INFANT, WHOL: Hosp Gowns
CLOTHING: Access
CLOTHING: Access, Women's & Misses'
CLOTHING: Aprons, Exc Rubber/Plastic, Women, Misses, Junior
CLOTHING: Aprons, Harness
CLOTHING: Athletic & Sportswear, Men's & Boys'
CLOTHING: Baker, Barber, Lab/Svc Ind Apparel, Washable, Men
CLOTHING: Bibs, Waterproof, From Purchased Materials
CLOTHING: Blouses, Women's & Girls'
CLOTHING: Blouses, Womens & Juniors, From Purchased Mtrls
CLOTHING: Bras & Corsets, Maternity
CLOTHING: Bridal Gowns
CLOTHING: Caps, Baseball
CLOTHING: Chemises, Camisoles/Teddies, Women, Misses/Junior
CLOTHING: Children & Infants'
CLOTHING: Children's, Girls'
CLOTHING: Coats & Suits, Men's & Boys'
CLOTHING: Costumes
CLOTHING: Disposable
CLOTHING: Dresses
CLOTHING: Foundation Garments, Women's
CLOTHING: Gowns & Dresses, Wedding
CLOTHING: Hats & Caps, NEC
CLOTHING: Hosiery, Men's & Boys'
CLOTHING: Hospital, Men's
CLOTHING: Leather
CLOTHING: Lounge, Bed & Leisurewear
CLOTHING: Men's & boy's clothing, nec
CLOTHING: Men's & boy's underwear & nightwear
CLOTHING: Outerwear, Knit
CLOTHING: Outerwear, Lthr, Wool/Down-Filled, Men, Youth/Boy
CLOTHING: Outerwear, Women's & Misses' NEC
CLOTHING: Robes & Dressing Gowns
CLOTHING: Shirts, Dress, Men's & Boys'
CLOTHING: Shirts, Knit
CLOTHING: Shirts, Sports & Polo, Men & Boy, Purchased Mtrl
CLOTHING: Shirts, Sports & Polo, Men's & Boys'
CLOTHING: Socks
CLOTHING: Sportswear, Women's
CLOTHING: Suits, Men's & Boys', From Purchased Materials
CLOTHING: Sweaters & Sweater Coats, Knit
CLOTHING: Sweatshirts & T-Shirts, Men's & Boys'
CLOTHING: T-Shirts & Tops, Knit
CLOTHING: Tuxedos, From Purchased Materials

CLOTHING: Underwear, Women's & Children's
CLOTHING: Uniforms & Vestments
CLOTHING: Uniforms, Ex Athletic, Women's, Misses' & Juniors'
CLOTHING: Uniforms, Firemen's, From Purchased Materials
CLOTHING: Uniforms, Men's & Boys'
CLOTHING: Uniforms, Military, Men/Youth, Purchased Materials
CLOTHING: Uniforms, Work
CLOTHING: Vests, Sport, Suede, Leatherette, Etc, Mens & Boys
CLOTHING: Work Apparel, Exc Uniforms
CLOTHING: Work, Men's
CLOTHING: Work, Waterproof, Exc Raincoats
CLOTHS: Polishing, Plain
CLUTCHES OR BRAKES: Electromagnetic
CLUTCHES, EXC VEHICULAR
COAL & OTHER MINERALS & ORES WHOLESALERS
COAL MINING SERVICES
COAL MINING SVCS: Bituminous, Contract Basis
COAL MINING: Anthracite
COAL MINING: Bituminous & Lignite Surface
COAL MINING: Bituminous Coal & Lignite-Surface Mining
COAL MINING: Bituminous Underground
COAL MINING: Bituminous, Auger
COAL MINING: Bituminous, Strip
COAL MINING: Bituminous, Surface, NEC
COAL MINING: Lignite, Surface, NEC
COAL PREPARATION PLANT: Bituminous or Lignite
COAL PYROLYSIS
COAL, MINERALS & ORES, WHOLESALE: Iron Ore
COATED OR PLATED PRDTS
COATING COMPOUNDS: Tar
COATING OR WRAPPING SVC: Steel Pipe
COATING SVC
COATING SVC: Aluminum, Metal Prdts
COATING SVC: Electrodes
COATING SVC: Hot Dip, Metals Or Formed Prdts
COATING SVC: Metals & Formed Prdts
COATING SVC: Metals, With Plastic Or Resins
COATING SVC: Rust Preventative
COATING SVC: Silicon
COATINGS: Epoxy
COATINGS: Polyurethane
COILS & TRANSFORMERS
COILS, WIRE: Aluminum, Made In Rolling Mills
COILS: Electric Motors Or Generators
COIN COUNTERS
COIN-OPERATED LAUNDRY
COINS & TOKENS: Non-Currency
COLLECTION AGENCY, EXC REAL ESTATE
COLLETS
COLOR LAKES OR TONERS
COLOR PIGMENTS
COLOR SEPARATION: Photographic & Movie Film
COLORS IN OIL, EXC ARTISTS'
COLORS: Pigments, Inorganic
COLORS: Pigments, Organic
COMBINED ELEMENTARY & SECONDARY SCHOOLS, PUBLIC
COMBS, EXC HARD RUBBER
COMMERCIAL & OFFICE BUILDINGS RENOVATION & REPAIR
COMMERCIAL ART & GRAPHIC DESIGN SVCS
COMMERCIAL ART & ILLUSTRATION SVCS
COMMERCIAL CONTAINERS WHOLESALERS
COMMERCIAL EQPT & SPLYS, WHOLESALE: Price Marking
COMMERCIAL EQPT WHOLESALERS, NEC
COMMERCIAL EQPT, WHOLESALE: Bakery Eqpt & Splys
COMMERCIAL EQPT, WHOLESALE: Comm Cooking & Food Svc Eqpt
COMMERCIAL EQPT, WHOLESALE: Display Eqpt, Exc Refrigerated
COMMERCIAL EQPT, WHOLESALE: Food Warming
COMMERCIAL EQPT, WHOLESALE: Neon Signs
COMMERCIAL EQPT, WHOLESALE: Restaurant, NEC
COMMERCIAL EQPT, WHOLESALE: Scales, Exc Laboratory
COMMERCIAL EQPT, WHOLESALE: Store Eqpt
COMMERCIAL EQPT, WHOLESALE: Store Fixtures & Display Eqpt
COMMERCIAL PRINTING & NEWSPAPER PUBLISHING COMBINED
COMMODITY CONTRACT TRADING COMPANIES
COMMON SAND MINING
COMMUNICATION HEADGEAR: Telephone

INDEX

COMMUNICATIONS CARRIER: Wired
COMMUNICATIONS EQPT & SYSTEMS, NEC
COMMUNICATIONS EQPT REPAIR & MAINTENANCE
COMMUNICATIONS EQPT WHOLESALERS
COMMUNICATIONS SVCS
COMMUNICATIONS SVCS: Cellular
COMMUNICATIONS SVCS: Data
COMMUNICATIONS SVCS: Internet Connectivity Svcs
COMMUNICATIONS SVCS: Online Svc Providers
COMMUNICATIONS SVCS: Radio Pager Or Beeper
COMMUNICATIONS SVCS: Signal Enhancement Network Svcs
COMMUNICATIONS SVCS: Telephone, Local & Long Distance
COMMUNICATIONS SVCS: Telephone, Long Distance
COMMUNITY ACTION AGENCY
COMMUNITY DEVELOPMENT GROUPS
COMMUTATORS: Electric Motors
COMMUTATORS: Electronic
COMPACT DISCS OR CD'S, WHOLESALE
COMPACT LASER DISCS: Prerecorded
COMPARATORS: Machinists
COMPOST
COMPRESSORS, AIR CONDITIONING: Wholesalers
COMPRESSORS: Air & Gas
COMPRESSORS: Air & Gas, Including Vacuum Pumps
COMPRESSORS: Refrigeration & Air Conditioning Eqpt
COMPRESSORS: Repairing
COMPRESSORS: Wholesalers
COMPUTER & COMPUTER SOFTWARE STORES
COMPUTER & COMPUTER SOFTWARE STORES: Computer Tapes
COMPUTER & COMPUTER SOFTWARE STORES: Peripheral Eqpt
COMPUTER & COMPUTER SOFTWARE STORES: Printers & Plotters
COMPUTER & COMPUTER SOFTWARE STORES: Software & Access
COMPUTER & COMPUTER SOFTWARE STORES: Software, Bus/Non-Game
COMPUTER & COMPUTER SOFTWARE STORES: Software, Computer Game
COMPUTER & DATA PROCESSING EQPT REPAIR & MAINTENANCE
COMPUTER & OFFICE MACHINE MAINTENANCE & REPAIR
COMPUTER FORMS
COMPUTER GRAPHICS SVCS
COMPUTER INTERFACE EQPT: Indl Process
COMPUTER PERIPHERAL EQPT REPAIR & MAINTENANCE
COMPUTER PERIPHERAL EQPT, NEC
COMPUTER PERIPHERAL EQPT, WHOLESALE
COMPUTER PERIPHERAL EQPT: Decoders
COMPUTER PERIPHERAL EQPT: Graphic Displays, Exc Terminals
COMPUTER PERIPHERAL EQPT: Input Or Output
COMPUTER PROGRAMMING SVCS
COMPUTER PROGRAMMING SVCS: Custom
COMPUTER RELATED MAINTENANCE SVCS
COMPUTER RELATED SVCS, NEC
COMPUTER SERVICE BUREAU
COMPUTER SOFTWARE DEVELOPMENT
COMPUTER SOFTWARE DEVELOPMENT & APPLICATIONS
COMPUTER SOFTWARE SYSTEMS ANALYSIS & DESIGN: Custom
COMPUTER SOFTWARE WRITERS
COMPUTER STORAGE DEVICES, NEC
COMPUTER STORAGE UNITS: Auxiliary
COMPUTER SYSTEM SELLING SVCS
COMPUTER SYSTEMS ANALYSIS & DESIGN
COMPUTER TERMINALS
COMPUTER TERMINALS: CRT
COMPUTER TIME-SHARING
COMPUTER-AIDED DESIGN SYSTEMS SVCS
COMPUTER-AIDED ENGINEERING SYSTEMS SVCS
COMPUTER-AIDED SYSTEM SVCS
COMPUTERS, NEC
COMPUTERS, NEC, WHOLESALE
COMPUTERS, PERIPH & SOFTWARE, WHLSE: Personal & Home Entrtn
COMPUTERS, PERIPHERALS & SOFTWARE, WHOLESALE: Software
COMPUTERS: Mini

COMPUTERS: Personal
CONCENTRATES, DRINK
CONCENTRATES, FLAVORING, EXC DRINK
CONCRETE BUILDING PRDTS WHOLESALERS
CONCRETE CURING & HARDENING COMPOUNDS
CONCRETE PLANTS
CONCRETE PRDTS
CONCRETE PRDTS, PRECAST, NEC
CONCRETE: Asphaltic, Not From Refineries
CONCRETE: Bituminous
CONCRETE: Dry Mixture
CONCRETE: Ready-Mixed
CONDENSERS & CONDENSING UNITS: Air Conditioner
CONDENSERS: Heat Transfer Eqpt, Evaporative
CONDENSERS: Refrigeration
CONDUITS & FITTINGS: Electric
CONES, PYROMETRIC: Earthenware
CONFECTIONS & CANDY
CONNECTORS & TERMINALS: Electrical Device Uses
CONNECTORS: Cord, Electric
CONNECTORS: Electrical
CONNECTORS: Electronic
CONNECTORS: Power, Electric
CONSTRUCTION & MINING MACHINERY WHOLESALERS
CONSTRUCTION EQPT REPAIR SVCS
CONSTRUCTION EQPT: Airport
CONSTRUCTION EQPT: Attachments
CONSTRUCTION EQPT: Attachments, Snow Plow
CONSTRUCTION EQPT: Backhoes, Tractors, Cranes & Similar Eqpt
CONSTRUCTION EQPT: Blade, Grader, Scraper, Dozer/Snow Plow
CONSTRUCTION EQPT: Buckets, Excavating, Clamshell, Etc
CONSTRUCTION EQPT: Crane Carriers
CONSTRUCTION EQPT: Cranes
CONSTRUCTION EQPT: Crushers, Portable
CONSTRUCTION EQPT: Entrenching Machines
CONSTRUCTION EQPT: Grinders, Stone, Portable
CONSTRUCTION EQPT: Roofing Eqpt
CONSTRUCTION EQPT: Tunneling
CONSTRUCTION MATERIALS, WHOL: Concrete/Cinder Bldg Prdts
CONSTRUCTION MATERIALS, WHOLESALE: Architectural Metalwork
CONSTRUCTION MATERIALS, WHOLESALE: Block, Concrete & Cinder
CONSTRUCTION MATERIALS, WHOLESALE: Brick, Exc Refractory
CONSTRUCTION MATERIALS, WHOLESALE: Building Stone
CONSTRUCTION MATERIALS, WHOLESALE: Building Stone, Granite
CONSTRUCTION MATERIALS, WHOLESALE: Building Stone, Marble
CONSTRUCTION MATERIALS, WHOLESALE: Building, Exterior
CONSTRUCTION MATERIALS, WHOLESALE: Building, Interior
CONSTRUCTION MATERIALS, WHOLESALE: Ceiling Systems & Prdts
CONSTRUCTION MATERIALS, WHOLESALE: Cement
CONSTRUCTION MATERIALS, WHOLESALE: Door Frames
CONSTRUCTION MATERIALS, WHOLESALE: Doors, Garage
CONSTRUCTION MATERIALS, WHOLESALE: Doors, Sliding
CONSTRUCTION MATERIALS, WHOLESALE: Drywall Materials
CONSTRUCTION MATERIALS, WHOLESALE: Glass
CONSTRUCTION MATERIALS, WHOLESALE: Gravel
CONSTRUCTION MATERIALS, WHOLESALE: Joists
CONSTRUCTION MATERIALS, WHOLESALE: Limestone
CONSTRUCTION MATERIALS, WHOLESALE: Masons' Materials
CONSTRUCTION MATERIALS, WHOLESALE: Millwork
CONSTRUCTION MATERIALS, WHOLESALE: Molding, All Materials
CONSTRUCTION MATERIALS, WHOLESALE: Pallets, Wood
CONSTRUCTION MATERIALS, WHOLESALE: Particleboard
CONSTRUCTION MATERIALS, WHOLESALE: Paving Materials
CONSTRUCTION MATERIALS, WHOLESALE: Prefabricated Structures
CONSTRUCTION MATERIALS, WHOLESALE: Roof, Asphalt/Sheet Metal

CONSTRUCTION MATERIALS, WHOLESALE: Roofing & Siding Material
CONSTRUCTION MATERIALS, WHOLESALE: Sand
CONSTRUCTION MATERIALS, WHOLESALE: Septic Tanks
CONSTRUCTION MATERIALS, WHOLESALE: Sewer Pipe, Clay
CONSTRUCTION MATERIALS, WHOLESALE: Siding, Exc Wood
CONSTRUCTION MATERIALS, WHOLESALE: Stone, Crushed Or Broken
CONSTRUCTION MATERIALS, WHOLESALE: Tile & Clay Prdts
CONSTRUCTION MATERIALS, WHOLESALE: Tile, Clay/Other Ceramic
CONSTRUCTION MATERIALS, WHOLESALE: Trim, Sheet Metal
CONSTRUCTION MATERIALS, WHOLESALE: Windows
CONSTRUCTION MATL, WHOLESALE: Structural Assy, Prefab, Wood
CONSTRUCTION MATLS, WHOL: Composite Board Prdts, Woodboard
CONSTRUCTION MATLS, WHOL: Doors, Combination, Screen-Storm
CONSTRUCTION MATLS, WHOL: Lumber, Rough, Dressed/Finished
CONSTRUCTION MATLS, WHOLESALE: Soil Erosion Cntrl Fabrics
CONSTRUCTION MTRLS, WHOL: Exterior Flat Glass, Plate/Window
CONSTRUCTION SAND MINING
CONSTRUCTION SITE PREPARATION SVCS
CONSTRUCTION: Agricultural Building
CONSTRUCTION: Aqueduct
CONSTRUCTION: Athletic & Recreation Facilities
CONSTRUCTION: Bridge
CONSTRUCTION: Commercial & Institutional Building
CONSTRUCTION: Commercial & Office Building, New
CONSTRUCTION: Factory
CONSTRUCTION: Food Prdts Manufacturing or Packing Plant
CONSTRUCTION: Foundation & Retaining Wall
CONSTRUCTION: Garage
CONSTRUCTION: Golf Course
CONSTRUCTION: Grain Elevator
CONSTRUCTION: Greenhouse
CONSTRUCTION: Guardrails, Highway
CONSTRUCTION: Heavy Highway & Street
CONSTRUCTION: Hospital
CONSTRUCTION: Indl Building & Warehouse
CONSTRUCTION: Indl Building, Prefabricated
CONSTRUCTION: Indl Buildings, New, NEC
CONSTRUCTION: Indl Plant
CONSTRUCTION: Institutional Building
CONSTRUCTION: Oil & Gas Line & Compressor Station
CONSTRUCTION: Oil & Gas Pipeline Construction
CONSTRUCTION: Pipeline, NEC
CONSTRUCTION: Power Plant
CONSTRUCTION: Residential, Nec
CONSTRUCTION: Sewer Line
CONSTRUCTION: Single-Family Housing
CONSTRUCTION: Single-family Housing, New
CONSTRUCTION: Street Sign Installation & Mntnce
CONSTRUCTION: Street Surfacing & Paving
CONSTRUCTION: Swimming Pools
CONSTRUCTION: Telephone & Communication Line
CONSTRUCTION: Tennis Court
CONSTRUCTION: Transmitting Tower, Telecommunication
CONSTRUCTION: Utility Line
CONSTRUCTION: Water Main
CONSULTING SVC: Business, NEC
CONSULTING SVC: Computer
CONSULTING SVC: Data Processing
CONSULTING SVC: Educational
CONSULTING SVC: Engineering
CONSULTING SVC: Human Resource
CONSULTING SVC: Management
CONSULTING SVC: Marketing Management
CONSULTING SVC: Online Technology
CONSULTING SVC: Sales Management
CONSULTING SVC: Telecommunications
CONSULTING SVCS, BUSINESS: Agricultural
CONSULTING SVCS, BUSINESS: Energy Conservation
CONSULTING SVCS, BUSINESS: Environmental
CONSULTING SVCS, BUSINESS: Safety Training Svcs
CONSULTING SVCS, BUSINESS: Sys Engnrg, Exc Computer/Prof

CONSULTING SVCS, BUSINESS: Systems Analysis & Engineering
CONSULTING SVCS, BUSINESS: Systems Analysis Or Design
CONSULTING SVCS, BUSINESS: Testing, Educational Or Personnel
CONSULTING SVCS, BUSINESS: Traffic
CONSULTING SVCS: Geological
CONSULTING SVCS: Oil
CONTACT LENSES
CONTACTS: Electrical
CONTAINERS: Air Cargo, Metal
CONTAINERS: Cargo, Wood
CONTAINERS: Cargo, Wood & Metal Combination
CONTAINERS: Cargo, Wood & Wood With Metal
CONTAINERS: Corrugated
CONTAINERS: Foil, Bakery Goods & Frozen Foods
CONTAINERS: Food & Beverage
CONTAINERS: Food, Folding, Made From Purchased Materials
CONTAINERS: Food, Liquid Tight, Including Milk
CONTAINERS: Food, Metal
CONTAINERS: Food, Wood Wirebound
CONTAINERS: Glass
CONTAINERS: Ice Cream, Made From Purchased Materials
CONTAINERS: Laminated Phenolic & Vulcanized Fiber
CONTAINERS: Metal
CONTAINERS: Plastic
CONTAINERS: Plywood & Veneer, Wood
CONTAINERS: Sanitary, Food
CONTAINERS: Shipping & Mailing, Fiber
CONTAINERS: Shipping, Bombs, Metal Plate
CONTAINERS: Shipping, Metal, Milk, Fluid
CONTAINERS: Shipping, Wood
CONTAINERS: Wood
CONTAINMENT VESSELS: Reactor, Metal Plate
CONTRACTOR: Dredging
CONTRACTOR: Rigging & Scaffolding
CONTRACTORS: Access Control System Eqpt
CONTRACTORS: Access Flooring System Installation
CONTRACTORS: Acoustical & Insulation Work
CONTRACTORS: Asphalt
CONTRACTORS: Awning Installation
CONTRACTORS: Bathtub Refinishing
CONTRACTORS: Blasting, Exc Building Demolition
CONTRACTORS: Boiler & Furnace
CONTRACTORS: Boiler Maintenance Contractor
CONTRACTORS: Boiler Setting
CONTRACTORS: Building Eqpt & Machinery Installation
CONTRACTORS: Building Sign Installation & Mntnce
CONTRACTORS: Cable Laying
CONTRACTORS: Cable TV Installation
CONTRACTORS: Carpentry Work
CONTRACTORS: Carpentry, Cabinet & Finish Work
CONTRACTORS: Carpentry, Cabinet Building & Installation
CONTRACTORS: Central Vacuum Cleaning System Installation
CONTRACTORS: Chimney Construction & Maintenance
CONTRACTORS: Closet Organizers, Installation & Design
CONTRACTORS: Coating, Caulking & Weather, Water & Fire
CONTRACTORS: Commercial & Office Building
CONTRACTORS: Communications Svcs
CONTRACTORS: Computer Installation
CONTRACTORS: Concrete
CONTRACTORS: Concrete Block Masonry Laying
CONTRACTORS: Concrete Pumping
CONTRACTORS: Concrete Structure Coating, Plastic
CONTRACTORS: Construction Caulking
CONTRACTORS: Construction Site Metal Structure Coating
CONTRACTORS: Core Drilling & Cutting
CONTRACTORS: Corrosion Control Installation
CONTRACTORS: Countertop Installation
CONTRACTORS: Demolition, Building & Other Structures
CONTRACTORS: Diamond Drilling & Sawing
CONTRACTORS: Directional Oil & Gas Well Drilling Svc
CONTRACTORS: Drapery Track Installation
CONTRACTORS: Driveway
CONTRACTORS: Earthmoving
CONTRACTORS: Electric Power Systems
CONTRACTORS: Electrical
CONTRACTORS: Electronic Controls Installation
CONTRACTORS: Elevator Front Installation, Metal
CONTRACTORS: Energy Management Control
CONTRACTORS: Epoxy Application
CONTRACTORS: Excavating

CONTRACTORS: Exterior Painting
CONTRACTORS: Fence Construction
CONTRACTORS: Fiber Optic Cable Installation
CONTRACTORS: Fire Detection & Burglar Alarm Systems
CONTRACTORS: Floor Laying & Other Floor Work
CONTRACTORS: Flooring
CONTRACTORS: Foundation Building
CONTRACTORS: Garage Doors
CONTRACTORS: Gas Field Svcs, NEC
CONTRACTORS: General Electric
CONTRACTORS: Glass Tinting, Architectural & Automotive
CONTRACTORS: Glass, Glazing & Tinting
CONTRACTORS: Gutters & Downspouts
CONTRACTORS: Heating & Air Conditioning
CONTRACTORS: Heating Systems Repair & Maintenance Svc
CONTRACTORS: Highway & Street Construction, General
CONTRACTORS: Highway & Street Paving
CONTRACTORS: Highway Sign & Guardrail Construction & Install
CONTRACTORS: Home & Office Intrs Finish, Furnish/Remodel
CONTRACTORS: Hotel, Motel/Multi-Famly Home Renovtn/Remodel
CONTRACTORS: Hydraulic Eqpt Installation & Svcs
CONTRACTORS: Hydraulic Well Fracturing Svcs
CONTRACTORS: Indl Building Renovation, Remodeling & Repair
CONTRACTORS: Insulation Installation, Building
CONTRACTORS: Kitchen & Bathroom Remodeling
CONTRACTORS: Kitchen Cabinet Installation
CONTRACTORS: Lightweight Steel Framing Installation
CONTRACTORS: Machine Rigging & Moving
CONTRACTORS: Machinery Installation
CONTRACTORS: Maintenance, Parking Facility Eqpt
CONTRACTORS: Marble Installation, Interior
CONTRACTORS: Masonry & Stonework
CONTRACTORS: Mechanical
CONTRACTORS: Metal Ceiling Construction & Repair Work
CONTRACTORS: Millwrights
CONTRACTORS: Nonresidential Building Design & Construction
CONTRACTORS: Oil & Gas Building, Repairing & Dismantling Svc
CONTRACTORS: Oil & Gas Field Geological Exploration Svcs
CONTRACTORS: Oil & Gas Field Geophysical Exploration Svcs
CONTRACTORS: Oil & Gas Field Salt Water Impound/Storing Svc
CONTRACTORS: Oil & Gas Field Tools Fishing Svcs
CONTRACTORS: Oil & Gas Well Casing Cement Svcs
CONTRACTORS: Oil & Gas Well Drilling Svc
CONTRACTORS: Oil & Gas Well Flow Rate Measurement Svcs
CONTRACTORS: Oil & Gas Well Foundation Grading Svcs
CONTRACTORS: Oil & Gas Well On-Site Foundation Building Svcs
CONTRACTORS: Oil & Gas Well Plugging & Abandoning Svcs
CONTRACTORS: Oil & Gas Well Redrilling
CONTRACTORS: Oil & Gas Wells Pumping Svcs
CONTRACTORS: Oil & Gas Wells Svcs
CONTRACTORS: Oil Field Haulage Svcs
CONTRACTORS: Oil Field Mud Drilling Svcs
CONTRACTORS: Oil Field Pipe Testing Svcs
CONTRACTORS: Oil Sampling Svcs
CONTRACTORS: Oil/Gas Field Casing,Tube/Rod Running,Cut/Pull
CONTRACTORS: Oil/Gas Well Construction, Rpr/Dismantling Svcs
CONTRACTORS: On-Site Welding
CONTRACTORS: Ornamental Metal Work
CONTRACTORS: Painting & Wall Covering
CONTRACTORS: Painting, Commercial, Interior
CONTRACTORS: Painting, Indl
CONTRACTORS: Painting, Residential
CONTRACTORS: Parking Lot Maintenance
CONTRACTORS: Patio & Deck Construction & Repair
CONTRACTORS: Pipe & Boiler Insulating
CONTRACTORS: Pipe Laying
CONTRACTORS: Plumbing
CONTRACTORS: Pollution Control Eqpt Installation
CONTRACTORS: Post Disaster Renovations
CONTRACTORS: Power Generating Eqpt Installation

CONTRACTORS: Prefabricated Window & Door Installation
CONTRACTORS: Process Piping
CONTRACTORS: Refrigeration
CONTRACTORS: Rigging, Theatrical
CONTRACTORS: Roof Repair
CONTRACTORS: Roofing
CONTRACTORS: Roustabout Svcs
CONTRACTORS: Sandblasting Svc, Building Exteriors
CONTRACTORS: Screening, Window & Door
CONTRACTORS: Septic System
CONTRACTORS: Sheet Metal Work, NEC
CONTRACTORS: Sheet metal Work, Architectural
CONTRACTORS: Siding
CONTRACTORS: Single-family Home General Remodeling
CONTRACTORS: Skylight Installation
CONTRACTORS: Solar Energy Eqpt

CONTRACTORS: Sound Eqpt Installation
CONTRACTORS: Specialized Public Building
CONTRACTORS: Storage Tank Erection, Metal
CONTRACTORS: Store Fixture Installation
CONTRACTORS: Structural Iron Work, Structural
CONTRACTORS: Structural Steel Erection
CONTRACTORS: Svc Station Eqpt Installation, Maint & Repair
CONTRACTORS: Svc Well Drilling Svcs
CONTRACTORS: Tile Installation, Ceramic
CONTRACTORS: Trenching
CONTRACTORS: Tuck Pointing & Restoration
CONTRACTORS: Underground Utilities
CONTRACTORS: Ventilation & Duct Work
CONTRACTORS: Warm Air Heating & Air Conditioning
CONTRACTORS: Water Intake Well Drilling Svc
CONTRACTORS: Water Well Drilling
CONTRACTORS: Waterproofing
CONTRACTORS: Well Bailing, Cleaning, Swabbing & Treating Svc
CONTRACTORS: Well Casings Perforating Svcs
CONTRACTORS: Well Logging Svcs
CONTRACTORS: Well Swabbing Svcs
CONTRACTORS: Windows & Doors
CONTRACTORS: Wood Floor Installation & Refinishing
CONTRACTORS: Wrecking & Demolition
CONTROL EQPT: Electric
CONTROL EQPT: Electric Buses & Locomotives
CONTROL EQPT: Noise
CONTROL PANELS: Electrical
CONTROLS & ACCESS: Indl, Electric
CONTROLS & ACCESS: Motor
CONTROLS: Access, Motor
CONTROLS: Adjustable Speed Drive
CONTROLS: Air Flow, Refrigeration
CONTROLS: Automatic Temperature
CONTROLS: Crane & Hoist, Including Metal Mill
CONTROLS: Electric Motor
CONTROLS: Environmental
CONTROLS: Hydronic
CONTROLS: Numerical
CONTROLS: Relay & Ind
CONTROLS: Resistance Welder
CONTROLS: Thermostats
CONTROLS: Thermostats, Built-in
CONTROLS: Voice
CONVENIENCE STORES
CONVENTION & TRADE SHOW SVCS
CONVERTERS: Data
CONVERTERS: Frequency
CONVERTERS: Phase Or Rotary, Electrical
CONVERTERS: Power, AC to DC
CONVEYOR SYSTEMS
CONVEYOR SYSTEMS: Belt, General Indl Use
CONVEYOR SYSTEMS: Bucket Type
CONVEYOR SYSTEMS: Bulk Handling
CONVEYOR SYSTEMS: Pneumatic Tube
CONVEYOR SYSTEMS: Robotic
CONVEYORS & CONVEYING EQPT
CONVEYORS: Overhead
COOKING & FOOD WARMING EQPT: Commercial
COOKING & FOODWARMING EQPT: Coffee Brewing
COOKING & FOODWARMING EQPT: Commercial
COOKWARE, STONEWARE: Coarse Earthenware & Pottery
COOLING TOWERS: Metal
COOPERAGE STOCK PRODUCTS
COPINGS: Concrete
COPPER ORE MINING

INDEX

COPPER: Blocks
COPPER: Rolling & Drawing
CORRECTION FLUID
CORRESPONDENCE SCHOOLS
CORRUGATED PRDTS: Boxes, Partition, Display Items, Sheet/Pad
COSMETIC PREPARATIONS
COSMETICS & TOILETRIES
COSMETICS WHOLESALERS
COSTUME JEWELRY & NOVELTIES: Apparel, Exc Precious Metals
COSTUME JEWELRY & NOVELTIES: Exc Semi & Precious
COSTUME JEWELRY & NOVELTIES: Ornament, Exc Precious Mtl/Gem
COSTUME JEWELRY STORES
COUNTER & SINK TOPS
COUNTERS & COUNTER DISPLAY CASES: Refrigerated
COUNTERS & COUNTING DEVICES
COUNTERS OR COUNTER DISPLAY CASES, EXC WOOD
COUNTERS OR COUNTER DISPLAY CASES, WOOD
COUNTING DEVICES: Controls, Revolution & Timing
COUNTING DEVICES: Predetermining
COUNTING DEVICES: Speedometers
COUNTING DEVICES: Tachometer, Centrifugal
COUNTRY CLUBS
COUPLINGS, EXC PRESSURE & SOIL PIPE
COUPLINGS: Hose & Tube, Hydraulic Or Pneumatic
COUPLINGS: Pipe
COUPLINGS: Shaft
COURIER SVCS: Air
COURIER SVCS: Ground
COURTS OF LAW: County Government
COVERS & PADS Chair, Made From Purchased Materials
COVERS: Automobile Seat
COVERS: Metal Plate
COVERS: Slip Made Of Fabric, Plastic, Etc.
CRADLES: Aircraft Engine
CRANE & AERIAL LIFT SVCS
CRANES & MONORAIL SYSTEMS
CRANES: Indl Plant
CRANES: Indl Truck
CRANES: Locomotive
CRANES: Overhead
CRANKSHAFTS & CAMSHAFTS: Machining
CRANKSHAFTS: Motor Vehicle
CRATING SVCS: Shipping
CREATIVE SVCS: Advertisers, Exc Writers
CREMATORIES
CROWNS & CLOSURES
CRUCIBLES
CRUDE PETROLEUM & NATURAL GAS PRODUCTION
CRUDE PETROLEUM & NATURAL GAS PRODUCTION
CRUDE PETROLEUM PRODUCTION
CRYOGENIC COOLING DEVICES: Infrared Detectors, Masers
CRYSTALS
CULTURE MEDIA
CULVERTS: Metal Plate
CULVERTS: Sheet Metal
CUPS: Paper, Made From Purchased Materials
CUPS: Plastic Exc Polystyrene Foam
CURBING: Granite Or Stone
CURTAIN & DRAPERY FIXTURES: Poles, Rods & Rollers
CURTAIN WALLS: Building, Steel
CURTAINS: Shower
CURTAINS: Window, From Purchased Materials
CUSHIONS & PILLOWS
CUSHIONS & PILLOWS: Bed, From Purchased Materials
CUSHIONS: Carpet & Rug, Foamed Plastics
CUSHIONS: Textile, Exc Spring & Carpet
CUSTOM COMPOUNDING OF RUBBER MATERIALS
CUSTOMIZING SVCS
CUT STONE & STONE PRODUCTS
CUTLERY
CUTLERY: Table, Exc Metal Handled
CUTOUTS: Cardboard, Die-Cut, Made From Purchased Materials
CUTOUTS: Distribution
CUTTING EQPT: Glass Cutters
CUTTING SVC: Paper, Exc Die-Cut
CUTTING SVC: Paperboard
CYCLIC CRUDES & INTERMEDIATES
CYLINDER & ACTUATORS: Fluid Power
CYLINDERS: Pressure
CYLINDERS: Pump

D

DAIRY EQPT
DAIRY PRDTS STORE: Cheese
DAIRY PRDTS STORE: Ice Cream, Packaged
DAIRY PRDTS STORES
DAIRY PRDTS WHOLESALERS: Fresh
DAIRY PRDTS: Butter
DAIRY PRDTS: Canned Cream
DAIRY PRDTS: Canned Milk, Whole
DAIRY PRDTS: Cheese
DAIRY PRDTS: Cheese, Cottage
DAIRY PRDTS: Concentrated Milk
DAIRY PRDTS: Condensed Milk
DAIRY PRDTS: Cream Substitutes
DAIRY PRDTS: Cream, Whipped
DAIRY PRDTS: Dietary Supplements, Dairy & Non-Dairy Based
DAIRY PRDTS: Dips & Spreads, Cheese Based
DAIRY PRDTS: Dips & Spreads, Sour Cream Based
DAIRY PRDTS: Evaporated Milk
DAIRY PRDTS: Frozen Desserts & Novelties
DAIRY PRDTS: Half & Half
DAIRY PRDTS: Ice Cream & Ice Milk
DAIRY PRDTS: Ice Cream, Bulk
DAIRY PRDTS: Ice Cream, Packaged, Molded, On Sticks, Etc.
DAIRY PRDTS: Ice milk, Bulk
DAIRY PRDTS: Milk, Condensed & Evaporated
DAIRY PRDTS: Milk, Fluid
DAIRY PRDTS: Milk, Processed, Pasteurized, Homogenized/Btld
DAIRY PRDTS: Natural Cheese
DAIRY PRDTS: Powdered Milk
DAIRY PRDTS: Processed Cheese
DAIRY PRDTS: Sour Cream
DAIRY PRDTS: Whipped Topping, Exc Frozen Or Dry Mix
DAIRY PRDTS: Yogurt, Exc Frozen
DAIRY PRDTS: Yogurt, Frozen
DATA PROCESSING & PREPARATION SVCS
DATA PROCESSING SVCS
DATABASE INFORMATION RETRIEVAL SVCS
DECALS, WHOLESALE
DECORATIVE WOOD & WOODWORK
DEFENSE SYSTEMS & EQPT
DEFOLIANTS
DEGREASING MACHINES
DEHUMIDIFIERS: Electric
DEHYDRATION EQPT
DEICING OR DEFROSTING FLUID
DENTAL EQPT & SPLYS
DENTAL EQPT & SPLYS WHOLESALERS
DENTAL EQPT & SPLYS: Denture Materials
DENTAL EQPT & SPLYS: Enamels
DENTAL EQPT & SPLYS: Orthodontic Appliances
DENTAL EQPT & SPLYS: Teeth, Artificial, Exc In Dental Labs
DENTAL EQPT & SPLYS: Tools, NEC
DENTISTS' OFFICES & CLINICS
DEODORANTS: Personal
DEPARTMENT STORES
DEPARTMENT STORES: Army-Navy Goods
DEPARTMENT STORES: Country General
DEPILATORIES, COSMETIC
DERMATOLOGICALS
DESALTER KITS: Sea Water
DESIGN SVCS, NEC
DESIGN SVCS: Commercial & Indl
DESIGN SVCS: Computer Integrated Systems
DESIGN SVCS: Hand Tools
DETECTION APPARATUS: Electronic/Magnetic Field, Light/Heat
DETECTION EQPT: Magnetic Field
DETECTIVE & ARMORED CAR SERVICES
DETECTORS: Water Leak
DIAGNOSTIC SUBSTANCES
DIAGNOSTIC SUBSTANCES OR AGENTS: In Vitro
DIAGNOSTIC SUBSTANCES OR AGENTS: Radioactive
DIAMOND SETTER SVCS
DIAPERS: Disposable
DIE CUTTING SVC: Paper
DIE SETS: Presses, Metal Stamping
DIE SPRINGS
DIES & TOOLS: Special
DIES: Cutting, Exc Metal
DIES: Extrusion

DIES: Paper Cutting
DIES: Plastic Forming
DIES: Steel Rule
DIES: Wire Drawing & Straightening
DIFFERENTIAL ASSEMBLIES & PARTS
DIMENSION STONE: Buildings
DIODES: Light Emitting
DIODES: Solid State, Germanium, Silicon, Etc
DIRECT SELLING ESTABLISHMENTS: Beverage Svcs
DIRECT SELLING ESTABLISHMENTS: Food Svcs
DIRECT SELLING ESTABLISHMENTS: Snacks
DISCOUNT DEPARTMENT STORES
DISCS & TAPE: Optical, Blank
DISHWASHING EQPT: Commercial
DISHWASHING EQPT: Household
DISK DRIVES: Computer
DISPENSING EQPT & PARTS, BEVERAGE: Beer
DISPENSING EQPT & PARTS, BEVERAGE: Coolers, Milk/Water, Elec
DISPENSING EQPT & PARTS, BEVERAGE: Fountain/Other Beverage
DISPLAY FIXTURES: Showcases, Wood, Exc Refrigerated
DISPLAY FIXTURES: Wood
DISPLAY ITEMS: Corrugated, Made From Purchased Materials
DISPLAY ITEMS: Solid Fiber, Made From Purchased Materials
DISPLAY LETTERING SVCS
DISPLAY STANDS: Merchandise, Exc Wood
DISTILLATION PRDTS: Wood
DISTILLERS DRIED GRAIN & SOLUBLES
DISTRIBUTORS: Motor Vehicle Engine
DOCK EQPT & SPLYS, INDL
DOCKS: Prefabricated Metal
DOCUMENT DESTRUCTION SVC
DOGS, WHOLESALE
DOLLIES: Mechanics'
DOLOMITE: Crushed & Broken
DOOR & WINDOW REPAIR SVCS
DOOR FRAMES: Wood
DOOR OPERATING SYSTEMS: Electric
DOORS & WINDOWS WHOLESALERS: All Materials
DOORS & WINDOWS: Screen & Storm
DOORS & WINDOWS: Storm, Metal
DOORS: Combination Screen & Storm, Wood
DOORS: Fiberglass
DOORS: Folding, Plastic Or Plastic Coated Fabric
DOORS: Garage, Overhead, Metal
DOORS: Garage, Overhead, Wood
DOORS: Glass
DOORS: Hangar, Metal
DOORS: Louver, Wood
DOORS: Rolling, Indl Building Or Warehouse, Metal
DOORS: Screen, Metal
DOORS: Wooden
DOWELS & DOWEL RODS
DRAFTING SPLYS WHOLESALERS
DRAFTING SVCS
DRAINAGE PRDTS: Concrete
DRAPERIES & CURTAINS
DRAPERIES & DRAPERY FABRICS, COTTON
DRAPERIES: Plastic & Textile, From Purchased Materials
DRAPERY & UPHOLSTERY STORES: Draperies
DRAPES & DRAPERY FABRICS, FROM MANMADE FIBER
DRIED FRUITS WHOLESALERS
DRILL BITS
DRILLING MACHINERY & EQPT: Oil & Gas
DRILLS & DRILLING EQPT: Mining
DRILLS: Core
DRILLS: Rock, Portable
DRINK MIXES, NONALCOHOLIC: Cocktail
DRINKING FOUNTAINS: Metal, Nonrefrigerated
DRINKING PLACES: Alcoholic Beverages
DRINKING PLACES: Bars & Lounges
DRINKING PLACES: Tavern
DRIVE SHAFTS
DRIVES: High Speed Indl, Exc Hydrostatic
DRUG STORES
DRUG TESTING KITS: Blood & Urine
DRUGS & DRUG PROPRIETARIES, WHOL: Biologicals/Allied Prdts
DRUGS & DRUG PROPRIETARIES, WHOLESALE
DRUGS & DRUG PROPRIETARIES, WHOLESALE: Antiseptics

DRUGS & DRUG PROPRIETARIES, WHOLESALE: Druggists' Sundries
DRUGS & DRUG PROPRIETARIES, WHOLESALE: Medicinals/Botanicals
DRUGS & DRUG PROPRIETARIES, WHOLESALE: Patent Medicines
DRUGS & DRUG PROPRIETARIES, WHOLESALE: Pharmaceuticals
DRUGS & DRUG PROPRIETARIES, WHOLESALE: Vitamins & Minerals
DRUMS: Fiber
DRUMS: Shipping, Metal
DRYCLEANING EQPT & SPLYS: Commercial
DRYCLEANING PLANTS
DRYCLEANING SVC: Drapery & Curtain
DRYERS & REDRYERS: Indl
DUCTING: Plastic
DUCTS: Sheet Metal
DUMPSTERS: Garbage
DURABLE GOODS WHOLESALERS, NEC
DUST OR FUME COLLECTING EQPT: Indl
DYES & PIGMENTS: Organic
DYES OR COLORS: Food, Synthetic
DYES: Synthetic Organic

E

EARTH SCIENCE SVCS
EATING PLACES
EDITORIAL SVCS
EDUCATIONAL SVCS
EDUCATIONAL SVCS, NONDEGREE GRANTING: Continuing Education
EGG WHOLESALERS
ELASTOMERS
ELECTRIC & OTHER SERVICES COMBINED
ELECTRIC FENCE CHARGERS
ELECTRIC MOTOR & GENERATOR AUXILIARY PARTS
ELECTRIC MOTOR REPAIR SVCS
ELECTRIC SERVICES
ELECTRIC SVCS, NEC Power Transmission
ELECTRIC TOOL REPAIR SVCS
ELECTRICAL APPARATUS & EQPT WHOLESALERS
ELECTRICAL APPLIANCES, TELEVISIONS & RADIOS WHOLESALERS
ELECTRICAL CURRENT CARRYING WIRING DEVICES
ELECTRICAL DEVICE PARTS: Porcelain, Molded
ELECTRICAL DISCHARGE MACHINING, EDM
ELECTRICAL EQPT & SPLYS
ELECTRICAL EQPT FOR ENGINES
ELECTRICAL EQPT REPAIR & MAINTENANCE
ELECTRICAL EQPT REPAIR SVCS
ELECTRICAL EQPT REPAIR SVCS: High Voltage
ELECTRICAL EQPT: Automotive, NEC
ELECTRICAL EQPT: Household
ELECTRICAL GOODS, WHOL: Antennas, Receiving/Satellite Dishes
ELECTRICAL GOODS, WHOLESALE: Alarms & Signaling Eqpt
ELECTRICAL GOODS, WHOLESALE: Boxes & Fittings
ELECTRICAL GOODS, WHOLESALE: Cable Conduit
ELECTRICAL GOODS, WHOLESALE: Connectors
ELECTRICAL GOODS, WHOLESALE: Electronic Parts
ELECTRICAL GOODS, WHOLESALE: Generators
ELECTRICAL GOODS, WHOLESALE: Ground Fault Interrupters
ELECTRICAL GOODS, WHOLESALE: Hanging & Fastening Devices
ELECTRICAL GOODS, WHOLESALE: Household Appliances, NEC
ELECTRICAL GOODS, WHOLESALE: Insulators
ELECTRICAL GOODS, WHOLESALE: Motor Ctrls, Starters & Relays
ELECTRICAL GOODS, WHOLESALE: Motors
ELECTRICAL GOODS, WHOLESALE: Radio Parts & Access, NEC
ELECTRICAL GOODS, WHOLESALE: Security Control Eqpt & Systems
ELECTRICAL GOODS, WHOLESALE: Sound Eqpt
ELECTRICAL GOODS, WHOLESALE: Suntanning Eqpt & Splys
ELECTRICAL GOODS, WHOLESALE: Switchboards
ELECTRICAL GOODS, WHOLESALE: Switches, Exc Electronic, NEC
ELECTRICAL GOODS, WHOLESALE: Telephone Eqpt
ELECTRICAL GOODS, WHOLESALE: Transformers

ELECTRICAL GOODS, WHOLESALE: Washing Machines
ELECTRICAL GOODS, WHOLESALE: Wire & Cable
ELECTRICAL GOODS, WHOLESALE: Wire & Cable, Ctrl & Sig
ELECTRICAL GOODS, WHOLESALE: Wire/Cable, Telephone/Telegraph
ELECTRICAL INDL APPARATUS, NEC
ELECTRICAL MEASURING INSTRUMENT REPAIR & CALIBRATION SVCS
ELECTRICAL SPLYS
ELECTRICAL SUPPLIES: Porcelain
ELECTRODES: Indl Process
ELECTRODES: Thermal & Electrolytic
ELECTROMEDICAL EQPT
ELECTROMEDICAL EQPT WHOLESALERS
ELECTROMETALLURGICAL PRDTS
ELECTRONIC COMPONENTS
ELECTRONIC DEVICES: Solid State, NEC
ELECTRONIC EQPT REPAIR SVCS
ELECTRONIC LOADS & POWER SPLYS
ELECTRONIC PARTS & EQPT WHOLESALERS
ELECTRONIC SHOPPING
ELECTRONIC TRAINING DEVICES
ELECTROPLATING & PLATING SVC
ELEMENTARY & SECONDARY SCHOOLS, PRIVATE NEC
ELEMENTARY & SECONDARY SCHOOLS, SPECIAL EDUCATION
ELEVATOR: Grain, Storage Only
ELEVATORS & EQPT
ELEVATORS: Installation & Conversion
EMBALMING FLUID
EMBLEMS: Embroidered
EMBOSSING SVC: Paper
EMBROIDERING & ART NEEDLEWORK FOR THE TRADE
EMBROIDERING SVC
EMBROIDERING: Swiss Loom
EMBROIDERY ADVERTISING SVCS
EMERGENCY ALARMS
EMERGENCY SHELTERS
EMPLOYMENT AGENCY SVCS
EMPLOYMENT SVCS: Labor Contractors
ENAMELING SVC: Metal Prdts, Including Porcelain
ENAMELS
ENCLOSURES: Electronic
ENCLOSURES: Screen
ENCODERS: Digital
ENERGY MEASUREMENT EQPT
ENGINE PARTS & ACCESS: Internal Combustion
ENGINE REBUILDING: Diesel
ENGINE REBUILDING: Gas
ENGINEERING SVCS
ENGINEERING SVCS: Acoustical
ENGINEERING SVCS: Aviation Or Aeronautical
ENGINEERING SVCS: Civil
ENGINEERING SVCS: Construction & Civil
ENGINEERING SVCS: Electrical Or Electronic
ENGINEERING SVCS: Energy conservation
ENGINEERING SVCS: Heating & Ventilation
ENGINEERING SVCS: Industrial
ENGINEERING SVCS: Machine Tool Design
ENGINEERING SVCS: Mechanical
ENGINEERING SVCS: Pollution Control
ENGINEERING SVCS: Professional
ENGINES: Diesel & Semi-Diesel Or Duel Fuel
ENGINES: Gasoline, NEC
ENGINES: Internal Combustion, NEC
ENGINES: Jet Propulsion
ENGINES: Marine
ENGINES: Steam
ENGRAVING SVC, NEC
ENGRAVING SVC: Jewelry & Personal Goods
ENGRAVING SVCS
ENGRAVING: Steel line, For The Printing Trade
ENGRAVINGS: Plastic
ENTERTAINERS
ENTERTAINERS & ENTERTAINMENT GROUPS
ENTERTAINMENT GROUP
ENTERTAINMENT SVCS
ENVELOPES
ENVELOPES WHOLESALERS
ENZYMES
EPOXY RESINS
EQUIPMENT: Pedestrian Traffic Control
EQUIPMENT: Rental & Leasing, NEC
ETCHING & ENGRAVING SVC

ETCHING SVC: Metal
ETHYLENE GLYCOL TEREPHTHALIC ACID: Mylar
ETHYLENE-PROPYLENE RUBBERS: EPDM Polymers
EXCAVATING EQPT
EXECUTIVE OFFICES: Federal, State & Local
EXERCISE EQPT STORES
EXHAUST SYSTEMS: Eqpt & Parts
EXPLOSIVES
EXPLOSIVES, EXC AMMO & FIREWORKS WHOLESALERS
EXPLOSIVES, FUSES & DETONATORS: Primary explosives
EXTENSION CORDS
EXTERMINATING PRDTS: Household Or Indl Use
EXTRACTS, FLAVORING
EXTRACTS: Dying Or Tanning, Natural
EYEGLASSES
EYES: Artificial
Ethylene Glycols

F

FABRIC SOFTENERS
FABRIC STORES
FABRICATED METAL PRODUCTS, NEC
FABRICS & CLOTHING: Rubber Coated
FABRICS: Apparel & Outerwear, Cotton
FABRICS: Bags & Bagging, Cotton
FABRICS: Broadwoven, Cotton
FABRICS: Broadwoven, Synthetic Manmade Fiber & Silk
FABRICS: Broadwoven, Wool
FABRICS: Canvas
FABRICS: Chemically Coated & Treated
FABRICS: Coated Or Treated
FABRICS: Cotton, Narrow
FABRICS: Decorative Trim & Specialty, Including Twist Weave
FABRICS: Denims
FABRICS: Diaper, NEC
FABRICS: Duck, Cotton
FABRICS: Fiberglass, Broadwoven
FABRICS: Flannels, Cotton
FABRICS: Glass & Fiberglass, Broadwoven
FABRICS: Laminated
FABRICS: Manmade Fiber, Narrow
FABRICS: Metallized
FABRICS: Moleskins
FABRICS: Nonwoven
FABRICS: Nylon, Broadwoven
FABRICS: Osnaburgs
FABRICS: Papermakers Felt, Woven, Wool, Mohair/Similar Fiber
FABRICS: Polyester, Broadwoven
FABRICS: Polyethylene, Broadwoven
FABRICS: Print, Cotton
FABRICS: Resin Or Plastic Coated
FABRICS: Rubberized
FABRICS: Scrub Cloths
FABRICS: Shoe Laces, Exc Leather
FABRICS: Sleeving, Textile, Saturated
FABRICS: Tracing Cloth, Cotton
FABRICS: Trimmings
FABRICS: Umbrella Cloth, Cotton
FABRICS: Upholstery, Wool
FABRICS: Varnished Glass & Coated Fiberglass
FABRICS: Wall Covering, From Manmade Fiber Or Silk
FABRICS: Waterproofed, Exc Rubberized
FABRICS: Woven, Narrow Cotton, Wool, Silk
FACILITIES SUPPORT SVCS
FACILITY RENTAL & PARTY PLANNING SVCS
FAMILY CLOTHING STORES
FAMILY PLANNING CENTERS
FANS, BLOWING: Indl Or Commercial
FANS, EXHAUST: Indl Or Commercial
FANS, VENTILATING: Indl Or Commercial
FANS: Ceiling
FARM & GARDEN MACHINERY WHOLESALERS
FARM MACHINERY REPAIR SVCS
FARM PRDTS, RAW MATERIALS, WHOLESALE: Hides
FARM PRDTS, RAW MATERIALS, WHOLESALE: Nuts & Nut By-Prdts
FARM SPLY STORES
FARM SPLYS WHOLESALERS
FARM SPLYS, WHOLESALE: Feed
FARM SPLYS, WHOLESALE: Fertilizers & Agricultural Chemicals
FARM SPLYS, WHOLESALE: Harness Eqpt
FARM SPLYS, WHOLESALE: Limestone, Agricultural
FASTENERS: Metal

FASTENERS: Metal
FASTENERS: Notions, NEC
FASTENERS: Notions, Zippers
FASTENERS: Wire, Made From Purchased Wire
FAUCETS & SPIGOTS: Metal & Plastic
FEATHERS & FEATHER PRODUCTS
FELT PARTS
FELT: Automotive
FENCES OR POSTS: Ornamental Iron Or Steel
FENCING DEALERS
FENCING MADE IN WIREDRAWING PLANTS
FENCING MATERIALS: Docks & Other Outdoor Prdts, Wood
FENCING MATERIALS: Plastic
FENCING MATERIALS: Wood
FENCING: Chain Link
FENDERS: Automobile, Stamped Or Pressed Metal
FERRALLOY ORES, EXC VANADIUM
FERROALLOYS
FERROALLOYS: Produced In Blast Furnaces
FERROMANGANESE, NOT MADE IN BLAST FURNACES
FERROSILICON, EXC MADE IN BLAST FURNACES
FERTILIZER MINERAL MINING
FERTILIZER, AGRICULTURAL: Wholesalers
FERTILIZERS: NEC
FERTILIZERS: Nitrogen Solutions
FERTILIZERS: Nitrogenous
FERTILIZERS: Phosphatic
FIBER & FIBER PRDTS: Acrylic
FIBER & FIBER PRDTS: Acrylonitrile
FIBER & FIBER PRDTS: Cuprammonium
FIBER & FIBER PRDTS: Elastomeric
FIBER & FIBER PRDTS: Organic, Noncellulose
FIBER & FIBER PRDTS: Synthetic Cellulosic
FIBER & FIBER PRDTS: Vinyl
FIBER OPTICS
FIBERS: Carbon & Graphite
FIELD WAREHOUSING SVCS
FILE FOLDERS
FILM & SHEET: Unsuppported Plastic
FILM BASE: Cellulose Acetate Or Nitrocellulose Plastics
FILM DEVELOPING & PRINTING SVCS
FILM: Rubber
FILTER ELEMENTS: Fluid & Hydraulic Line
FILTERS
FILTERS & SOFTENERS: Water, Household
FILTERS & STRAINERS: Pipeline
FILTERS: Air
FILTERS: Air Intake, Internal Combustion Engine, Exc Auto
FILTERS: General Line, Indl
FILTERS: Motor Vehicle
FILTERS: Oil, Internal Combustion Engine, Exc Auto
FILTRATION DEVICES: Electronic
FILTRATION SAND MINING
FINANCIAL SVCS
FINDINGS & TRIMMINGS: Fabric
FINGERNAILS, ARTIFICIAL
FINGERPRINT EQPT
FINISHING AGENTS
FIRE ARMS, SMALL: Guns Or Gun Parts, 30 mm & Below
FIRE ARMS, SMALL: Machine Guns & Grenade Launchers
FIRE ARMS, SMALL: Rifles Or Rifle Parts, 30 mm & below
FIRE ARMS, SMALL: Shotguns Or Shotgun Parts, 30 mm & Below
FIRE CLAY MINING
FIRE CONTROL EQPT REPAIR SVCS, MILITARY
FIRE CONTROL OR BOMBING EQPT: Electronic
FIRE DETECTION SYSTEMS
FIRE EXTINGUISHER CHARGES
FIRE EXTINGUISHER SVC
FIRE EXTINGUISHERS, WHOLESALE
FIRE EXTINGUISHERS: Portable
FIRE OR BURGLARY RESISTIVE PRDTS
FIRE PROTECTION EQPT
FIREARMS & AMMUNITION, EXC SPORTING, WHOLESALE
FIREARMS: Large, Greater Than 30mm
FIREARMS: Small, 30mm or Less
FIREFIGHTING APPARATUS
FIREPLACE & CHIMNEY MATERIAL: Concrete
FIREPLACE EQPT & ACCESS
FIREWORKS
FIREWORKS SHOPS
FIREWORKS: Wholesalers
FISH & SEAFOOD PROCESSORS: Canned Or Cured
FISH & SEAFOOD WHOLESALERS
FISH FOOD

FISH, PACKAGED FROZEN: Wholesalers
FISHING EQPT: Lures
FITTINGS & ASSEMBLIES: Hose & Tube, Hydraulic Or Pneumatic
FITTINGS & SPECIALTIES: Steam
FITTINGS: Pipe
FITTINGS: Pipe, Fabricated
FIXTURES & EQPT: Kitchen, Metal, Exc Cast Aluminum
FIXTURES & EQPT: Kitchen, Porcelain Enameled
FIXTURES: Cut Stone
FLAGS: Fabric
FLAGSTONES
FLAKES: Metal
FLARES
FLAT GLASS: Building
FLAT GLASS: Construction
FLAT GLASS: Float
FLAT GLASS: Picture
FLAT GLASS: Plate, Polished & Rough
FLAT GLASS: Tempered
FLAT GLASS: Window, Clear & Colored
FLAVORS OR FLAVORING MATERIALS: Synthetic
FLIGHT RECORDERS
FLOATING DRY DOCKS
FLOCKING SVC: Fabric
FLOOR COVERING STORES
FLOOR COVERING STORES: Carpets
FLOOR COVERING STORES: Rugs
FLOOR COVERING: Plastic
FLOOR COVERINGS WHOLESALERS
FLOOR COVERINGS: Asphalted-Felt Base, Linoleum Or Carpet
FLOOR COVERINGS: Rubber
FLOOR COVERINGS: Twisted Paper, Grass, Reed, Coir, Etc
FLOORING & SIDING: Metal
FLOORING: Hard Surface
FLOORING: Hardwood
FLOORING: Rubber
FLOORING: Tile
FLORIST: Flowers, Fresh
FLORISTS
FLOWER POTS Plastic
FLOWERS, ARTIFICIAL, WHOLESALE
FLOWERS, FRESH, WHOLESALE
FLUID METERS & COUNTING DEVICES
FLUID POWER PUMPS & MOTORS
FLUID POWER VALVES & HOSE FITTINGS
FLUSH TANKS: Vitreous China
FLUXES
FOAM RUBBER
FOAMS & RUBBER, WHOLESALE
FOIL & LEAF: Metal
FOIL: Copper
FOIL: Laminated To Paper Or Other Materials
FOLDERS: Manila
FOLIAGE: Artificial & Preserved
FOOD CONTAMINATION TESTING OR SCREENING KITS
FOOD PRDTS, BREAKFAST: Cereal, Granola & Muesli
FOOD PRDTS, BREAKFAST: Cereal, Oatmeal
FOOD PRDTS, BREAKFAST: Cereal, Rice: Cereal Breakfast Food
FOOD PRDTS, BREAKFAST: Cereal, Wheat Flakes
FOOD PRDTS, CANNED OR FRESH PACK: Vegetable Juices
FOOD PRDTS, CANNED, NEC
FOOD PRDTS, CANNED: Baby Food
FOOD PRDTS, CANNED: Barbecue Sauce
FOOD PRDTS, CANNED: Beans, Without Meat
FOOD PRDTS, CANNED: Catsup
FOOD PRDTS, CANNED: Chili
FOOD PRDTS, CANNED: Chili Sauce, Tomato
FOOD PRDTS, CANNED: Ethnic
FOOD PRDTS, CANNED: Fruit Juices, Fresh
FOOD PRDTS, CANNED: Fruit Pie Mixes & Fillings
FOOD PRDTS, CANNED: Fruits
FOOD PRDTS, CANNED: Fruits
FOOD PRDTS, CANNED: Italian
FOOD PRDTS, CANNED: Jams, Including Imitation
FOOD PRDTS, CANNED: Jams, Jellies & Preserves
FOOD PRDTS, CANNED: Jellies, Edible, Including Imitation
FOOD PRDTS, CANNED: Mexican, NEC
FOOD PRDTS, CANNED: Puddings, Exc Meat
FOOD PRDTS, CANNED: Ravioli
FOOD PRDTS, CANNED: Soups
FOOD PRDTS, CANNED: Soups, Exc Seafood

FOOD PRDTS, CANNED: Spaghetti & Other Pasta Sauce
FOOD PRDTS, CANNED: Tomato Sauce.
FOOD PRDTS, CANNED: Tomatoes
FOOD PRDTS, CANNED: Vegetables
FOOD PRDTS, CANNED: Vegetables
FOOD PRDTS, CONFECTIONERY, WHOLESALE: Candy
FOOD PRDTS, CONFECTIONERY, WHOLESALE: Nuts, Salted/Roasted
FOOD PRDTS, CONFECTIONERY, WHOLESALE: Potato Chips
FOOD PRDTS, CONFECTIONERY, WHOLESALE: Snack Foods
FOOD PRDTS, CONFECTIONERY, WHOLESALE: Syrups, Fountain
FOOD PRDTS, FISH & SEAFOOD, WHOLESALE: Seafood
FOOD PRDTS, FROZEN: Breakfasts, Packaged
FOOD PRDTS, FROZEN: Dinners, Packaged
FOOD PRDTS, FROZEN: Ethnic Foods, NEC
FOOD PRDTS, FROZEN: Fruit Juice, Concentrates
FOOD PRDTS, FROZEN: Fruit Juices
FOOD PRDTS, FROZEN: Fruits
FOOD PRDTS, FROZEN: Fruits & Vegetables
FOOD PRDTS, FROZEN: Fruits, Juices & Vegetables
FOOD PRDTS, FROZEN: NEC
FOOD PRDTS, FROZEN: Pizza
FOOD PRDTS, FROZEN: Potato Prdts
FOOD PRDTS, FROZEN: Snack Items
FOOD PRDTS, FROZEN: Vegetables, Exc Potato Prdts
FOOD PRDTS, FRUITS & VEGETABLES, FRESH, WHOLESALE
FOOD PRDTS, FRUITS & VEGETABLES, FRESH, WHOLESALE: Vegetable
FOOD PRDTS, FRUITS & VEGETABLES, FRESH, WHOLESALE: Vegetable
FOOD PRDTS, MEAT & MEAT PRDTS, WHOLESALE: Cured Or Smoked
FOOD PRDTS, MEAT & MEAT PRDTS, WHOLESALE: Fresh
FOOD PRDTS, WHOL: Canned Goods, Fruit, Veg, Seafood/Meats
FOOD PRDTS, WHOLESALE: Baking Splys
FOOD PRDTS, WHOLESALE: Beverages, Exc Coffee & Tea
FOOD PRDTS, WHOLESALE: Chocolate
FOOD PRDTS, WHOLESALE: Coffee & Tea
FOOD PRDTS, WHOLESALE: Coffee, Green Or Roasted
FOOD PRDTS, WHOLESALE: Corn
FOOD PRDTS, WHOLESALE: Dried or Canned Foods
FOOD PRDTS, WHOLESALE: Flour
FOOD PRDTS, WHOLESALE: Grain Elevators
FOOD PRDTS, WHOLESALE: Grains
FOOD PRDTS, WHOLESALE: Health
FOOD PRDTS, WHOLESALE: Salt, Edible
FOOD PRDTS, WHOLESALE: Specialty
FOOD PRDTS, WHOLESALE: Starch
FOOD PRDTS, WHOLESALE: Syrups, Exc Fountain Use
FOOD PRDTS, WHOLESALE: Water, Distilled
FOOD PRDTS, WHOLESALE: Water, Mineral Or Spring, Bottled
FOOD PRDTS: Animal & marine fats & oils
FOOD PRDTS: Baking Powder, Soda, Yeast & Leavenings
FOOD PRDTS: Cake Fillings, Exc Fruit
FOOD PRDTS: Cereals
FOOD PRDTS: Chicken, Processed, Cooked
FOOD PRDTS: Chicken, Processed, Fresh
FOOD PRDTS: Chicken, Processed, NEC
FOOD PRDTS: Chocolate Bars, Solid
FOOD PRDTS: Cocoa, Powdered
FOOD PRDTS: Coffee
FOOD PRDTS: Coffee Roasting, Exc Wholesale Grocers
FOOD PRDTS: Corn Chips & Other Corn-Based Snacks
FOOD PRDTS: Dips, Exc Cheese & Sour Cream Based
FOOD PRDTS: Dough, Pizza, Prepared
FOOD PRDTS: Doughs, Frozen Or Refrig From Purchased Flour
FOOD PRDTS: Dressings, Salad, Raw & Cooked Exc Dry Mixes
FOOD PRDTS: Dried & Dehydrated Fruits, Vegetables & Soup Mix
FOOD PRDTS: Edible fats & oils
FOOD PRDTS: Eggs, Processed
FOOD PRDTS: Eggs, Processed, Frozen
FOOD PRDTS: Emulsifiers
FOOD PRDTS: Flour
FOOD PRDTS: Flour & Other Grain Mill Products
FOOD PRDTS: Flour Mixes & Doughs
FOOD PRDTS: Flour, Blended From Purchased Flour

FOOD PRDTS: Fruit Juices
FOOD PRDTS: Fruits, Dehydrated Or Dried
FOOD PRDTS: Fruits, Dried Or Dehydrated, Exc Freeze-Dried
FOOD PRDTS: Gelatin Dessert Preparations
FOOD PRDTS: Granola & Energy Bars, Nonchocolate
FOOD PRDTS: Honey
FOOD PRDTS: Horseradish, Exc Sauce
FOOD PRDTS: Ice, Blocks
FOOD PRDTS: Ice, Cubes
FOOD PRDTS: Macaroni, Noodles, Spaghetti, Pasta, Etc
FOOD PRDTS: Mayonnaise & Dressings, Exc Tomato Based
FOOD PRDTS: Mixes, Bread & Bread-Type Roll
FOOD PRDTS: Mixes, Bread & Roll From Purchased Flour
FOOD PRDTS: Mixes, Cake, From Purchased Flour
FOOD PRDTS: Mixes, Flour
FOOD PRDTS: Mixes, Sauces, Dry
FOOD PRDTS: Mixes, Seasonings, Dry
FOOD PRDTS: Mustard, Prepared
FOOD PRDTS: Noodles, Uncooked, Packaged W/Other Ingredients
FOOD PRDTS: Nuts & Seeds
FOOD PRDTS: Oils & Fats, Animal
FOOD PRDTS: Olive Oil
FOOD PRDTS: Oriental Noodles
FOOD PRDTS: Pasta, Rice/Potatoes, Uncooked, Pkgd
FOOD PRDTS: Pasta, Uncooked, Packaged With Other Ingredients
FOOD PRDTS: Peanut Butter
FOOD PRDTS: Pickles, Vinegar
FOOD PRDTS: Pizza Doughs From Purchased Flour
FOOD PRDTS: Popcorn, Unpopped
FOOD PRDTS: Pork Rinds
FOOD PRDTS: Potato & Corn Chips & Similar Prdts
FOOD PRDTS: Potato Chips & Other Potato-Based Snacks
FOOD PRDTS: Potatoes, Dried
FOOD PRDTS: Poultry, Processed, Frozen
FOOD PRDTS: Preparations
FOOD PRDTS: Prepared Sauces, Exc Tomato Based
FOOD PRDTS: Rice, Milled
FOOD PRDTS: Salad Oils, Refined Vegetable, Exc Corn
FOOD PRDTS: Salads
FOOD PRDTS: Sandwiches
FOOD PRDTS: Sausage, Poultry
FOOD PRDTS: Seasonings & Spices
FOOD PRDTS: Shortening & Solid Edible Fats
FOOD PRDTS: Soy Sauce
FOOD PRDTS: Soybean Protein Concentrates & Isolates
FOOD PRDTS: Spices, Including Ground
FOOD PRDTS: Starch, Corn
FOOD PRDTS: Sugar
FOOD PRDTS: Sugar, Beet
FOOD PRDTS: Syrup, Maple
FOOD PRDTS: Syrups
FOOD PRDTS: Tea
FOOD PRDTS: Tortillas
FOOD PRDTS: Turkey, Processed, Canned
FOOD PRDTS: Turkey, Processed, NEC
FOOD PRDTS: Turkey, Slaughtered & Dressed
FOOD PRDTS: Variety Meats, Poultry
FOOD PRODUCTS MACHINERY
FOOD STORES: Convenience, Chain
FOOD STORES: Convenience, Independent
FOOD STORES: Delicatessen
FOOD STORES: Grocery, Independent
FOOD STORES: Supermarkets
FOOD STORES: Supermarkets, Chain
FOOTWEAR, WHOLESALE: Athletic
FOOTWEAR, WHOLESALE: Boots
FOOTWEAR, WHOLESALE: Shoes
FOOTWEAR: Custom Made
FOOTWEAR: Cut Stock
FORGINGS
FORGINGS: Aircraft, Ferrous
FORGINGS: Aluminum
FORGINGS: Armor Plate, Iron Or Steel
FORGINGS: Automotive & Internal Combustion Engine
FORGINGS: Construction Or Mining Eqpt, Ferrous
FORGINGS: Gear & Chain
FORGINGS: Iron & Steel
FORGINGS: Machinery, Ferrous
FORGINGS: Metal , Ornamental, Ferrous
FORGINGS: Nonferrous
FORGINGS: Plumbing Fixture, Nonferrous
FORMS: Concrete, Sheet Metal

FOUNDRIES: Aluminum
FOUNDRIES: Brass, Bronze & Copper
FOUNDRIES: Gray & Ductile Iron
FOUNDRIES: Iron
FOUNDRIES: Nonferrous
FOUNDRIES: Steel
FOUNDRIES: Steel Investment
FOUNDRY MACHINERY & EQPT
FOUNDRY MATERIALS: Insulsleeves
FOUNDRY SAND MINING
FOUNTAINS, METAL, EXC DRINKING
FOUNTAINS: Concrete
FOUNTAINS: Plaster Of Paris
FRACTIONATION PRDTS OF CRUDE PETROLEUM, HYDROCARBONS, NEC
FRANCHISES, SELLING OR LICENSING
FREEZERS: Household
FREIGHT FORWARDING ARRANGEMENTS
FREIGHT TRANSPORTATION ARRANGEMENTS
FREON
FRICTION MATERIAL, MADE FROM POWDERED METAL
FRITS
FRUIT & VEGETABLE MARKETS
FRUIT STANDS OR MARKETS
FRUITS & VEGETABLES WHOLESALERS: Fresh
FUEL ADDITIVES
FUEL CELLS: Solid State
FUEL DEALERS: Coal
FUEL OIL DEALERS
FUEL TREATING
FUELS: Diesel
FUELS: Ethanol
FUELS: Gas, Liquefied
FUELS: Jet
FUELS: Oil
FUNDRAISING SVCS
FUNERAL HOMES & SVCS
FUNGICIDES OR HERBICIDES
FUR FINISHING & LINING: For The Fur Goods Trade
FURNACES & OVENS: Fuel-Fired
FURNACES & OVENS: Indl
FURNACES: Indl, Electric
FURNACES: Warm Air, Electric
FURNITURE & CABINET STORES: Cabinets, Custom Work
FURNITURE & CABINET STORES: Custom
FURNITURE & FIXTURES Factory
FURNITURE PARTS: Metal
FURNITURE REFINISHING SVCS
FURNITURE REPAIR & MAINTENANCE SVCS
FURNITURE STOCK & PARTS: Carvings, Wood
FURNITURE STOCK & PARTS: Chair Seats, Hardwood
FURNITURE STOCK/PARTS: Chair Stk, Hardwd, Turnd, Shapd/Carvd
FURNITURE STORES
FURNITURE STORES: Custom Made, Exc Cabinets
FURNITURE STORES: Office
FURNITURE STORES: Outdoor & Garden
FURNITURE WHOLESALERS
FURNITURE, BARBER & BEAUTY SHOP
FURNITURE, CHURCH: Concrete
FURNITURE, GARDEN: Concrete
FURNITURE, MATTRESSES: Wholesalers
FURNITURE, OFFICE: Wholesalers
FURNITURE, WHOLESALE: Chairs
FURNITURE, WHOLESALE: Filing Units
FURNITURE, WHOLESALE: Racks
FURNITURE, WHOLESALE: Tables, Occasional
FURNITURE: Bar furniture
FURNITURE: Bed Frames & Headboards, Wood
FURNITURE: Bedroom, Wood
FURNITURE: Beds, Household, Incl Folding & Cabinet, Metal
FURNITURE: Bookcases & Partitions, Office, Exc Wood
FURNITURE: Bookcases, Wood
FURNITURE: Box Springs, Assembled
FURNITURE: Cabinets & Filing Drawers, Office, Exc Wood
FURNITURE: Cabinets & Vanities, Medicine, Metal
FURNITURE: Chairs, Bentwood
FURNITURE: Chairs, Folding
FURNITURE: Chairs, Household Upholstered
FURNITURE: Chairs, Household Wood
FURNITURE: Chairs, Office Exc Wood
FURNITURE: Chairs, Office Wood
FURNITURE: Church
FURNITURE: Club Room, Wood
FURNITURE: Console Tables, Wood

FURNITURE: Desks & Tables, Office, Exc Wood
FURNITURE: Dining Room, Wood
FURNITURE: Fiberglass & Plastic
FURNITURE: Foundations & Platforms
FURNITURE: Frames, Box Springs Or Bedsprings, Metal
FURNITURE: Hospital
FURNITURE: Hotel
FURNITURE: Household, Metal
FURNITURE: Household, NEC
FURNITURE: Household, Upholstered, Exc Wood Or Metal
FURNITURE: Household, Wood
FURNITURE: Hydraulic Barber & Beauty Shop Chairs
FURNITURE: Institutional, Exc Wood
FURNITURE: Juvenile, Metal
FURNITURE: Juvenile, Wood
FURNITURE: Kitchen & Dining Room
FURNITURE: Lawn & Garden, Except Wood & Metal
FURNITURE: Lawn & Garden, Metal
FURNITURE: Lawn, Exc Wood, Metal, Stone Or Concrete
FURNITURE: Living Room, Upholstered On Wood Frames
FURNITURE: Mattresses & Foundations
FURNITURE: Mattresses, Box & Bedsprings
FURNITURE: Mattresses, Innerspring Or Box Spring
FURNITURE: NEC
FURNITURE: Novelty, Wood
FURNITURE: Office Panel Systems, Exc Wood
FURNITURE: Office Panel Systems, Wood
FURNITURE: Office, Exc Wood
FURNITURE: Office, Wood
FURNITURE: Outdoor, Wood
FURNITURE: Picnic Tables Or Benches, Park
FURNITURE: Play Pens, Children's, Wood
FURNITURE: Restaurant
FURNITURE: School
FURNITURE: Silverware Chests, Wood
FURNITURE: Stools, Household, Wood
FURNITURE: Tables & Table Tops, Wood
FURNITURE: Unfinished, Wood
FURNITURE: Upholstered
FURNITURE: Vehicle
FUSE MOUNTINGS: Electric Power
Furs

G

GAMES & TOYS: Banks
GAMES & TOYS: Baskets
GAMES & TOYS: Bingo Boards
GAMES & TOYS: Board Games, Children's & Adults'
GAMES & TOYS: Cars, Play, Children's Vehicles
GAMES & TOYS: Child Restraint Seats, Automotive
GAMES & TOYS: Craft & Hobby Kits & Sets
GAMES & TOYS: Dolls, Exc Stuffed Toy Animals
GAMES & TOYS: Electronic
GAMES & TOYS: Game Machines, Exc Coin-Operated
GAMES & TOYS: Kits, Science, Incl Microscopes/Chemistry Sets
GAMES & TOYS: Miniature Dolls, Collectors'
GAMES & TOYS: Models, Airplane, Toy & Hobby
GAMES & TOYS: Models, Automobile & Truck, Toy & Hobby
GAMES & TOYS: Models, Railroad, Toy & Hobby
GAMES & TOYS: Strollers, Baby, Vehicle
GAMES & TOYS: Structural Toy Sets
GAMES & TOYS: Wagons, Coaster, Express & Play, Children's
GARAGE DOOR REPAIR SVCS
GARBAGE CONTAINERS: Plastic
GARBAGE DISPOSALS: Household
GARBAGE DISPOSERS & COMPACTORS: Commercial
GAS & OIL FIELD EXPLORATION SVCS
GAS & OIL FIELD SVCS, NEC
GAS & OTHER COMBINED SVCS
GAS FIELD MACHINERY & EQPT
GAS STATIONS
GAS SYSTEM CONVERSION SVCS
GASES: Acetylene
GASES: Argon
GASES: Carbon Dioxide
GASES: Hydrogen
GASES: Indl
GASES: Neon
GASES: Nitrogen
GASES: Oxygen
GASKET MATERIALS
GASKETS
GASKETS & SEALING DEVICES

INDEX

GASOLINE BLENDING PLANT
GASOLINE FILLING STATIONS
GASOLINE WHOLESALERS
GATES: Ornamental Metal
GAUGE BLOCKS
GAUGES
GEARS
GEARS & GEAR UNITS: Reduction, Exc Auto
GEARS: Power Transmission, Exc Auto
GEMSTONE & INDL DIAMOND MINING SVCS
GENERAL MERCHANDISE, NONDURABLE, WHOLESALE
GENERATING APPARATUS & PARTS: Electrical
GENERATION EQPT: Electronic
GENERATORS: Automotive & Aircraft
GENERATORS: Electric
GENERATORS: Gas
GENERATORS: Ultrasonic
GIFT SHOP
GIFT WRAP: Paper, Made From Purchased Materials
GIFT, NOVELTY & SOUVENIR STORES: Artcraft & carvings
GIFT, NOVELTY & SOUVENIR STORES: Gift Baskets
GIFT, NOVELTY & SOUVENIR STORES: Gifts & Novelties
GIFT, NOVELTY & SOUVENIR STORES: Party Favors
GIFT, NOVELTY & SOUVENIR STORES: Trading Cards, Sports
GIFTS & NOVELTIES: Wholesalers
GLACE, FOR GLAZING FOOD
GLASS & GLASS CERAMIC PRDTS, PRESSED OR BLOWN: Tableware
GLASS FABRICATORS
GLASS PRDTS, FROM PURCHASED GLASS: Art
GLASS PRDTS, FROM PURCHASED GLASS: Glass Beads, Reflecting
GLASS PRDTS, FROM PURCHASED GLASS: Glassware
GLASS PRDTS, FROM PURCHASED GLASS: Insulating
GLASS PRDTS, FROM PURCHASED GLASS: Mirrored
GLASS PRDTS, FROM PURCHASED GLASS: Novelties, Fruit, Etc
GLASS PRDTS, FROM PURCHASED GLASS: Reflecting
GLASS PRDTS, FROM PURCHASED GLASS: Sheet, Bent
GLASS PRDTS, FROM PURCHASED GLASS: Windshields
GLASS PRDTS, FROM PURCHD GLASS: Strengthened Or Reinforced
GLASS PRDTS, PRESSED OR BLOWN: Blocks & Bricks
GLASS PRDTS, PRESSED OR BLOWN: Bulbs, Electric Lights
GLASS PRDTS, PRESSED OR BLOWN: Furnishings & Access
GLASS PRDTS, PRESSED OR BLOWN: Glass Fibers, Textile
GLASS PRDTS, PRESSED OR BLOWN: Glassware, Art Or Decorative
GLASS PRDTS, PRESSED OR BLOWN: Glassware, Novelty
GLASS PRDTS, PRESSED OR BLOWN: Lantern Globes
GLASS PRDTS, PRESSED OR BLOWN: Scientific Glassware
GLASS PRDTS, PRESSED OR BLOWN: Tubing
GLASS PRDTS, PRESSED OR BLOWN: Yarn, Fiberglass
GLASS PRDTS, PRESSED/BLOWN: Glassware, Art, Decor/Novelty
GLASS PRDTS, PURCHSD GLASS: Ornamental, Cut, Engraved/Dtor
GLASS STORE: Leaded Or Stained
GLASS STORES
GLASS, AUTOMOTIVE: Wholesalers
GLASS: Fiber
GLASS: Flat
GLASS: Indl Prdts
GLASS: Insulating
GLASS: Laminated
GLASS: Leaded
GLASS: Pressed & Blown, NEC
GLASS: Safety
GLASS: Stained
GLASS: Structural
GLASS: Tempered
GLASSWARE, NOVELTY, WHOLESALE
GLASSWARE: Cut & Engraved
GLOBAL POSITIONING SYSTEMS & EQPT
GLOVES: Fabric
GLOVES: Leather
GLOVES: Linings, Exc Fur
GLOVES: Plastic
GLOVES: Safety
GLOVES: Work
GLOVES: Woven Or Knit, From Purchased Materials
GLUE

GLYCERIN
GLYCOL ETHERS
GOLF CARTS: Powered
GOLF COURSES: Public
GOLF DRIVING RANGES
GOLF EQPT
GOLF GOODS & EQPT
GOURMET FOOD STORES
GOVERNMENT, EXECUTIVE OFFICES: City & Town Managers' Offices
GOVERNMENT, EXECUTIVE OFFICES: County Supervisor/Exec Office
GOVERNMENT, EXECUTIVE OFFICES: Mayors'
GOVERNMENT, GENERAL: Administration
GOVERNMENT, GENERAL: Administration, Federal
GOVERNORS: Diesel Engine
GRADING SVCS
GRAIN & FIELD BEANS WHOLESALERS
GRANITE: Crushed & Broken
GRANITE: Cut & Shaped
GRANITE: Dimension
GRANITE: Dimension
GRAPHIC ARTS & RELATED DESIGN SVCS
GRAPHIC LAYOUT SVCS: Printed Circuitry
GRAPHITE MINING SVCS
GRATINGS: Open Steel Flooring
GRATINGS: Tread, Fabricated Metal
GRAVE MARKERS: Concrete
GRAVE VAULTS, METAL
GRAVEL & PEBBLE MINING
GRAVEL MINING
GREASES & INEDIBLE FATS, RENDERED
GREASES: Lubricating
GREENHOUSES: Prefabricated Metal
GREETING CARD SHOPS
GRILLES & REGISTERS: Ornamental Metal Work
GRINDING MEDIA: Pottery
GRINDING SVC: Precision, Commercial Or Indl
GRINDING SVCS: Ophthalmic Lens, Exc Prescription
GRIPS OR HANDLES: Rubber
GRITS: Crushed & Broken
GROCERIES WHOLESALERS, NEC
GROCERIES, GENERAL LINE WHOLESALERS
GROUTING EQPT: Concrete
GUARD SVCS
GUARDRAILS
GUARDS: Machine, Sheet Metal
GUIDED MISSILES & SPACE VEHICLES
GUIDED MISSILES/SPACE VEHICLE PARTS/AUX EQPT: Research/Devel
GUN SIGHTS: Optical
GUN SVCS
GUTTERS: Sheet Metal
GYPSUM PRDTS
GYROSCOPES

H

HAIR & HAIR BASED PRDTS
HAIR CARE PRDTS
HAIR CARE PRDTS: Hair Coloring Preparations
HAIR CURLERS: Beauty Shop
HAIR NETS
HAMPERS: Solid Fiber, Made From Purchased Materials
HAND TOOLS, NEC: Wholesalers
HANDBAGS
HANDBAGS: Women's
HANDLES: Wood
HANGERS: Garment, Wire
HARD RUBBER PRDTS, NEC
HARDWARE
HARDWARE & BUILDING PRDTS: Plastic
HARDWARE & EQPT: Stage, Exc Lighting
HARDWARE CLOTH: Woven Wire, Made From Purchased Wire
HARDWARE STORES
HARDWARE STORES: Builders'
HARDWARE STORES: Chainsaws
HARDWARE STORES: Pumps & Pumping Eqpt
HARDWARE STORES: Snowblowers
HARDWARE STORES: Tools
HARDWARE WHOLESALERS
HARDWARE, WHOLESALE: Bolts
HARDWARE, WHOLESALE: Builders', NEC
HARDWARE, WHOLESALE: Nuts
HARDWARE, WHOLESALE: Power Tools & Access

HARDWARE, WHOLESALE: Saw Blades
HARDWARE, WHOLESALE: Staples
HARDWARE: Aircraft
HARDWARE: Aircraft & Marine, Incl Pulleys & Similar Items
HARDWARE: Builders'
HARDWARE: Cabinet
HARDWARE: Casket
HARDWARE: Furniture, Builders' & Other Household
HARDWARE: Hangers, Wall
HARDWARE: Padlocks
HARDWARE: Plastic
HARDWARE: Rubber
HARDWARE: Saddlery
HARNESS ASSEMBLIES: Cable & Wire
HARNESS REPAIR SHOP
HARNESS WIRING SETS: Internal Combustion Engines
HARNESSES, HALTERS, SADDLERY & STRAPS
HATS: Paper, Novelty, Made From Purchased Paper
HEALTH & ALLIED SERVICES, NEC
HEALTH AIDS: Exercise Eqpt
HEALTH AIDS: Vaporizers
HEALTH FOOD & SUPPLEMENT STORES
HEALTH SYSTEMS AGENCY
HEARING AIDS
HEAT EMISSION OPERATING APPARATUS
HEAT EXCHANGERS
HEAT EXCHANGERS: After Or Inter Coolers Or Condensers, Etc
HEAT TREATING: Metal
HEATERS: Room & Wall, Including Radiators
HEATING & AIR CONDITIONING EQPT & SPLYS WHOLESALERS
HEATING & AIR CONDITIONING UNITS, COMBINATION
HEATING APPARATUS: Steam
HEATING EQPT & SPLYS
HEATING EQPT: Complete
HEATING EQPT: Dielectric
HEATING EQPT: Induction
HEATING PADS: Nonelectric
HEATING UNITS & DEVICES: Indl, Electric
HEATING UNITS: Gas, Infrared
HEAVY DISTILLATES
HELP SUPPLY SERVICES
HITCHES: Trailer
HOBBY, TOY & GAME STORES: Ceramics Splys
HOBBY, TOY & GAME STORES: Children's Toys & Games, Exc Dolls
HOBBY, TOY & GAME STORES: Dolls & Access
HOBBY, TOY & GAME STORES: Toys & Games
HOGS WHOLESALERS
HOISTING SLINGS
HOISTS
HOISTS: Mine
HOLDING COMPANIES: Banks
HOLDING COMPANIES: Investment, Exc Banks
HOLDING COMPANIES: Personal, Exc Banks
HOME ENTERTAINMENT EQPT: Electronic, NEC
HOME ENTERTAINMENT REPAIR SVCS
HOME FOR THE MENTALLY HANDICAPPED
HOME FURNISHINGS WHOLESALERS
HOME HEALTH CARE SVCS
HOMEBUILDERS & OTHER OPERATIVE BUILDERS
HOMEFURNISHING STORE: Bedding, Sheet, Blanket,Spread/Pillow
HOMEFURNISHING STORES: Brushes
HOMEFURNISHING STORES: Cutlery
HOMEFURNISHING STORES: Metalware
HOMEFURNISHING STORES: Mirrors
HOMEFURNISHING STORES: Pictures, Wall
HOMEFURNISHING STORES: Pottery
HOMEFURNISHING STORES: Venetian Blinds
HOMEFURNISHING STORES: Vertical Blinds
HOMEFURNISHING STORES: Window Furnishings
HOMEFURNISHING STORES: Window Shades, NEC
HOMEFURNISHINGS & SPLYS, WHOLESALE: Decorative
HOMEFURNISHINGS, WHOLESALE: Blinds, Venetian
HOMEFURNISHINGS, WHOLESALE: Blinds, Vertical
HOMEFURNISHINGS, WHOLESALE: Draperies
HOMEFURNISHINGS, WHOLESALE: Grills, Barbecue
HOMEFURNISHINGS, WHOLESALE: Kitchenware
HOMEFURNISHINGS, WHOLESALE: Linens, Table
HOMEFURNISHINGS, WHOLESALE: Mirrors/Pictures, Framed/Unframd
HOMEFURNISHINGS, WHOLESALE: Pottery

HOMEFURNISHINGS, WHOLESALE: Window Covering Parts & Access
HOMES, MODULAR: Wooden
HOMES: Log Cabins
HONING & LAPPING MACHINES
HOODS: Range, Sheet Metal
HOOKS: Crane, Laminated Plate
HOPPERS: Sheet Metal
HORSE & PET ACCESSORIES: Textile
HOSE: Automobile, Rubber
HOSE: Flexible Metal
HOSE: Plastic
HOSE: Rubber
HOSES & BELTING: Rubber & Plastic
HOSPITALS: Medical & Surgical
HOTELS & MOTELS
HOUSEHOLD APPLIANCE STORES
HOUSEHOLD APPLIANCE STORES: Air Cond Rm Units, Self-Contnd
HOUSEHOLD APPLIANCE STORES: Ranges, Gas
HOUSEHOLD APPLIANCE STORES: Suntanning Eqpt & Splys
HOUSEHOLD ARTICLES, EXC KITCHEN: Pottery
HOUSEHOLD ARTICLES: Metal
HOUSEHOLD FURNISHINGS, NEC
HOUSEWARES, ELECTRIC, EXC COOKING APPLIANCES & UTENSILS
HOUSEWARES, ELECTRIC: Air Purifiers, Portable
HOUSEWARES, ELECTRIC: Cooking Appliances
HOUSEWARES, ELECTRIC: Cooking Utensils
HOUSEWARES, ELECTRIC: Curlers, Hair
HOUSEWARES, ELECTRIC: Fans, Exhaust & Ventilating
HOUSEWARES, ELECTRIC: Heating, Bsbrd/Wall, Radiant Heat
HOUSEWARES, ELECTRIC: Humidifiers, Household
HOUSEWARES: Dishes, China
HOUSEWARES: Dishes, Earthenware
HOUSEWARES: Dishes, Plastic
HOUSEWARES: Household & Commercial, Vitreous China
HOUSING COMPONENTS: Prefabricated, Concrete
HOUSINGS: Business Machine, Sheet Metal
HOUSINGS: Pressure
HUB CAPS: Automobile, Stamped Metal
HUMIDIFIERS & DEHUMIDIFIERS
HYDRAULIC EQPT REPAIR SVC
HYDRAULIC FLUIDS: Synthetic Based
HYDROPONIC EQPT
Hard Rubber & Molded Rubber Prdts

I

ICE
ICE CREAM & ICES WHOLESALERS
ICE WHOLESALERS
ICE: Dry
IDENTIFICATION PLATES
IGNEOUS ROCK: Crushed & Broken
IGNITERS: Jet Fuel
IGNITION APPARATUS & DISTRIBUTORS
IGNITION SYSTEMS: High Frequency
IGNITION SYSTEMS: Internal Combustion Engine
INCENSE
INCUBATORS & BROODERS: Farm
INDL & PERSONAL SVC PAPER WHOLESALERS
INDL & PERSONAL SVC PAPER, WHOL: Bags, Paper/Disp Plastic
INDL & PERSONAL SVC PAPER, WHOL: Boxes, Corrugtd/Solid Fiber
INDL & PERSONAL SVC PAPER, WHOL: Paper, Wrap/Coarse/Prdts
INDL & PERSONAL SVC PAPER, WHOLESALE: Boxes & Containers
INDL & PERSONAL SVC PAPER, WHOLESALE: Boxes, Fldng Pprboard
INDL & PERSONAL SVC PAPER, WHOLESALE: Disposable
INDL & PERSONAL SVC PAPER, WHOLESALE: Paper Tubes & Cores
INDL & PERSONAL SVC PAPER, WHOLESALE: Shipping Splys
INDL & PERSONAL SVC PAPER, WHOLESALE: Towels, Paper
INDL CONTRACTORS: Exhibit Construction
INDL DIAMONDS WHOLESALERS
INDL EQPT CLEANING SVCS
INDL EQPT SVCS
INDL GASES WHOLESALERS

INDL HELP SVCS
INDL MACHINERY & EQPT WHOLESALERS
INDL MACHINERY REPAIR & MAINTENANCE
INDL PATTERNS: Foundry Cores
INDL PATTERNS: Foundry Patternmaking
INDL PROCESS INSTRUMENTS: Absorp Analyzers, Infrared, X-Ray
INDL PROCESS INSTRUMENTS: Chromatographs
INDL PROCESS INSTRUMENTS: Control
INDL PROCESS INSTRUMENTS: Controllers, Process Variables
INDL PROCESS INSTRUMENTS: Data Loggers
INDL PROCESS INSTRUMENTS: Digital Display, Process Variables
INDL PROCESS INSTRUMENTS: Draft Gauges
INDL PROCESS INSTRUMENTS: Fluidic Devices, Circuit & Systems
INDL PROCESS INSTRUMENTS: Indl Flow & Measuring
INDL PROCESS INSTRUMENTS: Moisture Meters
INDL PROCESS INSTRUMENTS: Temperature
INDL PROCESS INSTRUMENTS: Water Quality Monitoring/Cntrl Sys
INDL SPLYS WHOLESALERS
INDL SPLYS, WHOL: Fasteners, Incl Nuts, Bolts, Screws, Etc
INDL SPLYS, WHOLESALE: Abrasives
INDL SPLYS, WHOLESALE: Adhesives, Tape & Plasters
INDL SPLYS, WHOLESALE: Barrels, New Or Reconditioned
INDL SPLYS, WHOLESALE: Bearings
INDL SPLYS, WHOLESALE: Bins & Containers, Storage
INDL SPLYS, WHOLESALE: Bottler Splys
INDL SPLYS, WHOLESALE: Brushes, Indl
INDL SPLYS, WHOLESALE: Clean Room Splys
INDL SPLYS, WHOLESALE: Drums, New Or Reconditioned
INDL SPLYS, WHOLESALE: Fasteners & Fastening Eqpt
INDL SPLYS, WHOLESALE: Fittings
INDL SPLYS, WHOLESALE: Gaskets
INDL SPLYS, WHOLESALE: Gaskets & Seals
INDL SPLYS, WHOLESALE: Gears
INDL SPLYS, WHOLESALE: Hydraulic & Pneumatic Pistons/Valves
INDL SPLYS, WHOLESALE: Knives, Indl
INDL SPLYS, WHOLESALE: Power Transmission, Eqpt & Apparatus
INDL SPLYS, WHOLESALE: Rubber Goods, Mechanical
INDL SPLYS, WHOLESALE: Seals
INDL SPLYS, WHOLESALE: Signmaker Eqpt & Splys
INDL SPLYS, WHOLESALE: Tools
INDL SPLYS, WHOLESALE: Tools, NEC
INDL SPLYS, WHOLESALE: Valves & Fittings
INDL TOOL GRINDING SVCS
INDUSTRIAL & COMMERCIAL EQPT INSPECTION SVCS
INFORMATION RETRIEVAL SERVICES
INGOT, EXTRUSION: Extrusion ingot, aluminum: rolling mills
INGOT: Aluminum
INK OR WRITING FLUIDS
INK: Letterpress Or Offset
INK: Lithographic
INK: Printing
INSECTICIDES & PESTICIDES
INSPECTION & TESTING SVCS
INSTRUMENT DIALS: Painted
INSTRUMENTS & METERS: Measuring, Electric
INSTRUMENTS, LAB: Refractometers, Exc Indl Process Types
INSTRUMENTS, LAB: Spectroscopic/Optical Properties Measuring
INSTRUMENTS, LABORATORY: Analyzers, Automatic Chemical
INSTRUMENTS, LABORATORY: Blood Testing
INSTRUMENTS, LABORATORY: Infrared Analytical
INSTRUMENTS, LABORATORY: Ultraviolet Analytical
INSTRUMENTS, MEASURING & CNTRL: Gauges, Auto, Computer
INSTRUMENTS, MEASURING & CNTRL: Geophysical & Meteorological
INSTRUMENTS, MEASURING & CNTRL: Radiation & Testing, Nuclear
INSTRUMENTS, MEASURING & CNTRL: Testing, Abrasion, Etc
INSTRUMENTS, MEASURING & CNTRL: Whole Body Counters, Nuclear
INSTRUMENTS, MEASURING & CNTRLG: Aircraft & Motor Vehicle
INSTRUMENTS, MEASURING & CNTRLG: Electrogamma Ray Loggers

INSTRUMENTS, MEASURING & CNTRLG: Stress, Strain & Measure
INSTRUMENTS, MEASURING & CNTRLG: Thermometers/Temp Sensors
INSTRUMENTS, MEASURING & CNTRLNG: Nuclear Instrument Modules
INSTRUMENTS, MEASURING & CONTROLLING: Anamometers
INSTRUMENTS, MEASURING & CONTROLLING: Breathalyzers
INSTRUMENTS, MEASURING & CONTROLLING: Cable Testing
INSTRUMENTS, MEASURING & CONTROLLING: Gas Detectors
INSTRUMENTS, MEASURING & CONTROLLING: Magnetometers
INSTRUMENTS, MEASURING & CONTROLLING: Surveying & Drafting
INSTRUMENTS, MEASURING & CONTROLLING: Torsion Testing
INSTRUMENTS, MEASURING & CONTROLLING: Transits, Surveyors'
INSTRUMENTS, MEASURING & CONTROLLING: Ultrasonic Testing
INSTRUMENTS, MEASURING/CNTRL: Gauging, Ultrasonic Thickness
INSTRUMENTS, MEASURING/CNTRLG: Fare Registers, St Cars/Buses
INSTRUMENTS, MEASURING/CNTRLG: Fire Detect Sys, Non-Electric
INSTRUMENTS, MEASURING/CNTRLNG: Med Diagnostic Sys, Nuclear
INSTRUMENTS, OPTICAL: Lenses, All Types Exc Ophthalmic
INSTRUMENTS, OPTICAL: Test & Inspection
INSTRUMENTS, SURGICAL & MEDICAL: Blood & Bone Work
INSTRUMENTS, SURGICAL & MEDICAL: Forceps
INSTRUMENTS, SURGICAL & MEDICAL: IV Transfusion
INSTRUMENTS, SURGICAL & MEDICAL: Inhalation Therapy
INSTRUMENTS, SURGICAL & MEDICAL: Inhalators
INSTRUMENTS, SURGICAL & MEDICAL: Lasers, Surgical
INSTRUMENTS, SURGICAL & MEDICAL: Operating Tables
INSTRUMENTS, SURGICAL & MEDICAL: Optometers
INSTRUMENTS, SURGICAL & MEDICAL: Physiotherapy, Electrical
INSTRUMENTS, SURGICAL & MEDICAL: Probes, Surgical
INSTRUMENTS, SURGICAL/MED: Microsurgical, Exc Electromedical
INSTRUMENTS: Airspeed
INSTRUMENTS: Analytical
INSTRUMENTS: Combustion Control, Indl
INSTRUMENTS: Differential Pressure, Indl
INSTRUMENTS: Electrocardiographs
INSTRUMENTS: Endoscopic Eqpt, Electromedical
INSTRUMENTS: Eye Examination
INSTRUMENTS: Flow, Indl Process
INSTRUMENTS: Gastroscopes, Electromedical
INSTRUMENTS: Indicating, Electric
INSTRUMENTS: Indl Process Control
INSTRUMENTS: Infrared, Indl Process
INSTRUMENTS: Laser, Scientific & Engineering
INSTRUMENTS: Measurement, Indl Process
INSTRUMENTS: Measuring & Controlling
INSTRUMENTS: Measuring Electricity
INSTRUMENTS: Measuring, Current, NEC
INSTRUMENTS: Measuring, Electrical Energy
INSTRUMENTS: Measuring, Electrical Power
INSTRUMENTS: Measuring, Electrical Quantities
INSTRUMENTS: Medical & Surgical
INSTRUMENTS: Particle Size Analyzers
INSTRUMENTS: Power Measuring, Electrical
INSTRUMENTS: Pressure Measurement, Indl
INSTRUMENTS: Radio Frequency Measuring
INSTRUMENTS: Recorders, Oscillographic
INSTRUMENTS: Refractometers, Indl Process
INSTRUMENTS: Signal Generators & Averagers

INSTRUMENTS: Surface Area Analyzers
INSTRUMENTS: Temperature Measurement, Indl
INSTRUMENTS: Test, Electrical, Engine
INSTRUMENTS: Test, Electronic & Electric Measurement
INSTRUMENTS: Test, Electronic & Electrical Circuits
INSTRUMENTS: Thermal Conductive, Indl
INSTRUMENTS: Transducers, Volts, Amperes, Watts, VARs & Freq

INSTRUMENTS: Vibration
INSULATING BOARD, CELLULAR FIBER
INSULATING COMPOUNDS
INSULATION & CUSHIONING FOAM: Polystyrene
INSULATION & ROOFING MATERIALS: Wood, Reconstituted
INSULATION MATERIALS WHOLESALERS
INSULATION: Fiberglass
INSULATORS & INSULATION MATERIALS: Electrical
INSURANCE AGENCIES & BROKERS
INSURANCE BROKERS, NEC
INSURANCE CARRIERS: Hospital & Medical
INSURANCE CARRIERS: Life
INSURANCE CLAIM PROCESSING, EXC MEDICAL
INSURANCE PATROL SVCS
INSURANCE RESEARCH SVCS
INTEGRATED CIRCUITS, SEMICONDUCTOR NETWORKS, ETC
INTERCOMMUNICATION EQPT REPAIR SVCS
INTERCOMMUNICATIONS SYSTEMS: Electric
INTERIOR DECORATING SVCS
INTERIOR DESIGN SVCS, NEC
INTERIOR DESIGNING SVCS
INTERIOR REPAIR SVCS
INTERMEDIATE CARE FACILITY
INTRAVENOUS SOLUTIONS
INVERTERS: Nonrotating Electrical
INVESTMENT ADVISORY SVCS
INVESTMENT FIRM: General Brokerage
INVESTMENT FUNDS, NEC
INVESTMENT FUNDS: Open-Ended
INVESTORS, NEC
INVESTORS: Real Estate, Exc Property Operators
IRON & STEEL PRDTS: Hot-Rolled
IRON ORE MINING
IRON ORE PELLETIZING
IRON ORES
IRON OXIDES
IRRADIATION EQPT: Nuclear

J

JACKETS: Indl, Metal Plate
JACKS: Hydraulic
JANITORIAL & CUSTODIAL SVCS
JANITORIAL EQPT & SPLYS WHOLESALERS
JEWELERS' FINDINGS & MATERIALS
JEWELERS' FINDINGS & MATERIALS: Castings
JEWELERS' FINDINGS & MATERIALS: Pin Stems
JEWELERS' FINDINGS & MTLS: Jewel Prep, Instr, Tools, Watches
JEWELRY & PRECIOUS STONES WHOLESALERS
JEWELRY APPAREL
JEWELRY FINDINGS & LAPIDARY WORK
JEWELRY REPAIR SVCS
JEWELRY STORES
JEWELRY STORES: Precious Stones & Precious Metals
JEWELRY STORES: Silverware
JEWELRY, PRECIOUS METAL: Bracelets
JEWELRY, PRECIOUS METAL: Buttons, Precious Or Semi Or Stone
JEWELRY, PRECIOUS METAL: Cigar & Cigarette Access
JEWELRY, PRECIOUS METAL: Medals, Precious Or Semi-precious
JEWELRY, PRECIOUS METAL: Mountings & Trimmings
JEWELRY, PRECIOUS METAL: Pearl, Natural Or Cultured
JEWELRY, PRECIOUS METAL: Pins
JEWELRY, PRECIOUS METAL: Rings, Finger
JEWELRY, WHOLESALE
JEWELRY: Decorative, Fashion & Costume
JEWELRY: Precious Metal
JIGS & FIXTURES
JIGS: Welding Positioners
JOB PRINTING & NEWSPAPER PUBLISHING COMBINED
JOB TRAINING & VOCATIONAL REHABILITATION SVCS
JOB TRAINING SVCS
JOINTS & COUPLINGS
JOINTS OR FASTENINGS: Rail
JOINTS: Expansion
JOINTS: Expansion, Pipe
JOISTS: Long-Span Series, Open Web Steel

K

KAOLIN & BALL CLAY MINING
KEYS, KEY BLANKS
KILNS & FURNACES: Ceramic
KITCHEN & COOKING ARTICLES: Pottery

KITCHEN CABINET STORES, EXC CUSTOM
KITCHEN CABINETS WHOLESALERS
KITCHEN TOOLS & UTENSILS WHOLESALERS
KITCHEN UTENSILS: Food Handling & Processing Prdts, Wood
KITCHEN UTENSILS: Wooden
KITCHENWARE STORES
KITCHENWARE: Plastic
KITS: Plastic
KNIVES: Agricultural Or indl

L

LABELS: Cotton, Printed
LABELS: Paper, Made From Purchased Materials
LABELS: Woven
LABORATORIES, TESTING: Food
LABORATORIES, TESTING: Hazardous Waste
LABORATORIES, TESTING: Hydrostatic
LABORATORIES, TESTING: Metallurgical
LABORATORIES, TESTING: Pollution
LABORATORIES, TESTING: Product Testing
LABORATORIES, TESTING: Product Testing, Safety/Performance
LABORATORIES, TESTING: Water
LABORATORIES, TESTING: Welded Joint Radiographing
LABORATORIES: Biological Research
LABORATORIES: Biotechnology
LABORATORIES: Commercial Nonphysical Research
LABORATORIES: Dental
LABORATORIES: Dental, Denture Production
LABORATORIES: Electronic Research
LABORATORIES: Medical
LABORATORIES: Physical Research, Commercial
LABORATORIES: Testing
LABORATORIES: Testing
LABORATORIES: Ultrasound
LABORATORY APPARATUS & FURNITURE
LABORATORY APPARATUS, EXC HEATING & MEASURING
LABORATORY APPARATUS: Calibration Tapes, Phy Testing Mach
LABORATORY APPARATUS: Crushing & Grinding
LABORATORY APPARATUS: Freezers
LABORATORY APPARATUS: Furnaces
LABORATORY APPARATUS: Particle Size Reduction
LABORATORY APPARATUS: Pipettes, Hemocytometer
LABORATORY CHEMICALS: Organic
LABORATORY EQPT, EXC MEDICAL: Wholesalers
LABORATORY EQPT: Chemical
LABORATORY EQPT: Clinical Instruments Exc Medical
LABORATORY EQPT: Measuring
LABORATORY INSTRUMENT REPAIR SVCS
LADDER & WORKSTAND COMBINATION ASSEMBLIES: Metal
LADDERS: Metal
LADLE BRICK: Clay
LADLES: Metal Plate
LAMINATED PLASTICS: Plate, Sheet, Rod & Tubes
LAMINATING MATERIALS
LAMINATING SVCS
LAMP & LIGHT BULBS & TUBES
LAMP BULBS & TUBES, ELECTRIC: Electrotherapeutic
LAMP BULBS & TUBES, ELECTRIC: Filaments
LAMP BULBS & TUBES, ELECTRIC: For Specialized Applications
LAMP BULBS & TUBES, ELECTRIC: Health, Infrared/Ultraviolet
LAMP BULBS & TUBES, ELECTRIC: Sealed Beam
LAMP BULBS & TUBES, ELECTRIC: Sealed Low-Pressure Gas
LAMP BULBS & TUBES/PARTS, ELECTRIC: Generalized Applications
LAMP FIXTURES: Ultraviolet
LAMP REPAIR & MOUNTING SVCS
LAMP STORES
LAMPS: Desk, Residential
LAMPS: Fluorescent
LAMPS: Incandescent, Filament
LAMPS: Table, Residential
LAND SUBDIVISION & DEVELOPMENT
LANTERNS
LAPIDARY WORK: Contract Or Other
LAPIDARY WORK: Jewel Cut, Drill, Polish, Recut/Setting
LASER SYSTEMS & EQPT
LASERS: Welding, Drilling & Cutting Eqpt
LATEX: Foamed

LATH: Expanded Metal
LATH: Snow Fence
LATHES
LAUNDRY & GARMENT SVCS, NEC: Garment Alteration & Repair
LAUNDRY EQPT: Commercial
LAUNDRY EQPT: Household
LAUNDRY SVCS: Indl
LAWN & GARDEN EQPT
LAWN & GARDEN EQPT STORES
LAWN & GARDEN EQPT: Grass Catchers, Lawn Mower
LAWN & GARDEN EQPT: Lawnmowers, Residential, Hand Or Power
LAWN & GARDEN EQPT: Rototillers
LAWN & GARDEN EQPT: Tractors & Eqpt
LAWN & GARDEN EQPT: Trimmers
LAWN MOWER REPAIR SHOP
LEAD & ZINC
LEAD PENCILS & ART GOODS
LEAD-IN WIRES: Electric Lamp
LEASING & RENTAL SVCS: Oil Field Eqpt
LEASING & RENTAL SVCS: Oil Well Drilling
LEASING & RENTAL: Computers & Eqpt
LEASING & RENTAL: Construction & Mining Eqpt
LEASING & RENTAL: Medical Machinery & Eqpt
LEASING & RENTAL: Mobile Home Sites
LEASING & RENTAL: Office Machines & Eqpt
LEASING & RENTAL: Other Real Estate Property
LEASING & RENTAL: Trucks, Indl
LEASING & RENTAL: Trucks, Without Drivers
LEASING: Residential Buildings
LEATHER & CANVAS GOODS: Leggings Or Chaps, NEC
LEATHER GOODS, EXC FOOTWEAR, GLOVES, LUGGAGE/BELTING, WHOL
LEATHER GOODS: Billfolds
LEATHER GOODS: Coin Purses
LEATHER GOODS: Corners, Luggage
LEATHER GOODS: Feed Bags, Horse
LEATHER GOODS: Garments
LEATHER GOODS: Harnesses Or Harness Parts
LEATHER GOODS: Holsters
LEATHER GOODS: NEC
LEATHER GOODS: Personal
LEATHER GOODS: Razor Strops
LEATHER GOODS: Saddles Or Parts
LEATHER GOODS: Safety Belts
LEATHER GOODS: Stirrups, Wood Or Metal
LEATHER TANNING & FINISHING
LEATHER, CHAMOIS, WHOLESALE
LEGAL OFFICES & SVCS
LEGAL SVCS: General Practice Attorney or Lawyer
LENS COATING: Ophthalmic
LENSES: Plastic, Exc Optical
LESSORS: Farm Land
LICENSE TAGS: Automobile, Stamped Metal
LIFE INSURANCE AGENTS
LIFE INSURANCE CARRIERS
LIGHTING EQPT: Flashlights
LIGHTING EQPT: Miners' Lamps
LIGHTING EQPT: Motor Vehicle
LIGHTING EQPT: Motor Vehicle, Headlights
LIGHTING EQPT: Motor Vehicle, NEC
LIGHTING EQPT: Outdoor
LIGHTING EQPT: Searchlights
LIGHTING EQPT: Spotlights
LIGHTING FIXTURES WHOLESALERS
LIGHTING FIXTURES, NEC
LIGHTING FIXTURES: Airport
LIGHTING FIXTURES: Fluorescent, Commercial
LIGHTING FIXTURES: Indl & Commercial
LIGHTING FIXTURES: Motor Vehicle
LIGHTING FIXTURES: Ornamental, Commercial
LIGHTING FIXTURES: Public
LIGHTING FIXTURES: Residential
LIGHTING FIXTURES: Residential, Electric
LIGHTING FIXTURES: Street
LIGHTING FIXTURES: Underwater
LIGHTS: Trouble lights
LIME
LIME ROCK: Ground
LIME: Agricultural
LIMESTONE & MARBLE: Dimension
LIMESTONE: Crushed & Broken
LIMESTONE: Cut & Shaped
LIMESTONE: Dimension

LIMESTONE: Ground
LINEN SPLY SVC
LINEN SPLY SVC: Table Cover
LINERS & COVERS: Fabric
LINERS & LINING
LINIMENTS
LININGS: Vulcanizable Rubber
LINTELS: Steel, Light Gauge
LIP BALMS
LIQUEFIED PETROLEUM GAS DEALERS
LIQUEFIED PETROLEUM GAS WHOLESALERS
LIQUID CRYSTAL DISPLAYS
LITHOGRAPHIC PLATES
LIVESTOCK WHOLESALERS, NEC
LOADS: Electronic
LOCKERS
LOCKS
LOCKS & LOCK SETS, WHOLESALE
LOCKS: Safe & Vault, Metal
LOCKSMITHS
LOCOMOTIVES & PARTS
LOG SPLITTERS
LOGGING
LOGGING CAMPS & CONTRACTORS
LOGGING: Saw Logs
LOGGING: Stump Harvesting
LOGGING: Timber, Cut At Logging Camp
LOGGING: Veneer Logs
LOGGING: Wood Chips, Produced In The Field
LOGS: Gas, Fireplace
LOOSELEAF BINDERS
LOTIONS OR CREAMS: Face
LUBRICANTS: Corrosion Preventive
LUBRICATING EQPT: Indl
LUBRICATING OIL & GREASE WHOLESALERS
LUBRICATING SYSTEMS: Centralized
LUBRICATION SYSTEMS & EQPT
LUGGAGE & BRIEFCASES
LUGGAGE & LEATHER GOODS STORES
LUGGAGE & LEATHER GOODS STORES: Leather, Exc Luggage & Shoes
LUMBER & BLDG MATLS DEALER, RET: Garage Doors, Sell/Install
LUMBER & BLDG MATRLS DEALERS, RET: Bath Fixtures, Eqpt/Sply
LUMBER & BLDG MATRLS DEALERS, RETAIL: Doors, Wood/Metal
LUMBER & BLDG MTRLS DEALERS, RET: Closets, Interiors/Access
LUMBER & BLDG MTRLS DEALERS, RET: Doors, Storm, Wood/Metal
LUMBER & BLDG MTRLS DEALERS, RET: Planing Mill Prdts/Lumber
LUMBER & BLDG MTRLS DEALERS, RET: Windows, Storm, Wood/Metal
LUMBER & BUILDING MATERIAL DEALERS, RETAIL: Roofing Material
LUMBER & BUILDING MATERIALS DEALER, RET: Door & Window Prdts
LUMBER & BUILDING MATERIALS DEALER, RET: Masonry Matls/Splys
LUMBER & BUILDING MATERIALS DEALERS, RET: Solar Heating Eqpt
LUMBER & BUILDING MATERIALS DEALERS, RETAIL: Brick
LUMBER & BUILDING MATERIALS DEALERS, RETAIL: Cement
LUMBER & BUILDING MATERIALS DEALERS, RETAIL: Countertops
LUMBER & BUILDING MATERIALS DEALERS, RETAIL: Jalousies
LUMBER & BUILDING MATERIALS DEALERS, RETAIL: Modular Homes
LUMBER & BUILDING MATERIALS DEALERS, RETAIL: Sand & Gravel
LUMBER & BUILDING MATERIALS DEALERS, RETAIL: Siding
LUMBER & BUILDING MATERIALS DEALERS, RETAIL: Tile, Ceramic
LUMBER & BUILDING MATERIALS RET DEALERS: Millwork & Lumber
LUMBER & BUILDING MATLS DEALERS, RET: Concrete/Cinder Block
LUMBER & BUILDING MTRLS DEALERS, RET: Insulation Mtrl, Bldg
LUMBER: Box

LUMBER: Dimension, Hardwood
LUMBER: Fiberboard
LUMBER: Flooring, Dressed, Softwood
LUMBER: Furniture Dimension Stock, Softwood
LUMBER: Hardwood Dimension
LUMBER: Hardwood Dimension & Flooring Mills
LUMBER: Kiln Dried
LUMBER: Plywood, Hardwood
LUMBER: Plywood, Hardwood or Hardwood Faced
LUMBER: Plywood, Prefinished, Hardwood
LUMBER: Plywood, Softwood
LUMBER: Plywood, Softwood
LUMBER: Rails, Fence, Round Or Split
LUMBER: Treated
LUMBER: Veneer, Hardwood
LUMBER: Veneer, Softwood

M

MACHINE PARTS: Stamped Or Pressed Metal
MACHINE SHOPS
MACHINE TOOL ACCESS: Broaches
MACHINE TOOL ACCESS: Cams
MACHINE TOOL ACCESS: Collars
MACHINE TOOL ACCESS: Cutting
MACHINE TOOL ACCESS: Diamond Cutting, For Turning, Etc
MACHINE TOOL ACCESS: Dies, Thread Cutting
MACHINE TOOL ACCESS: Dressing/Wheel Crushing Attach, Diamond
MACHINE TOOL ACCESS: Drill Bushings, Drilling Jig
MACHINE TOOL ACCESS: Drills
MACHINE TOOL ACCESS: End Mills
MACHINE TOOL ACCESS: Hopper Feed Devices
MACHINE TOOL ACCESS: Knives, Metalworking
MACHINE TOOL ACCESS: Knives, Shear
MACHINE TOOL ACCESS: Machine Attachments & Access, Drilling
MACHINE TOOL ACCESS: Milling Machine Attachments
MACHINE TOOL ACCESS: Rotary Tables
MACHINE TOOL ACCESS: Shaping Tools
MACHINE TOOL ACCESS: Sockets
MACHINE TOOL ACCESS: Threading Tools
MACHINE TOOL ACCESS: Tool Holders
MACHINE TOOL ACCESS: Tools & Access
MACHINE TOOL ACCESS: Wheel Turning Eqpt, Diamond Point, Etc
MACHINE TOOL ATTACHMENTS & ACCESS
MACHINE TOOLS & ACCESS
MACHINE TOOLS, METAL CUTTING: Chucking, Automatic
MACHINE TOOLS, METAL CUTTING: Die Sinking
MACHINE TOOLS, METAL CUTTING: Drilling
MACHINE TOOLS, METAL CUTTING: Drilling & Boring
MACHINE TOOLS, METAL CUTTING: Electron-Discharge
MACHINE TOOLS, METAL CUTTING: Exotic, Including Explosive
MACHINE TOOLS, METAL CUTTING: Grind, Polish, Buff, Lapp
MACHINE TOOLS, METAL CUTTING: Home Workshop
MACHINE TOOLS, METAL CUTTING: Lathes
MACHINE TOOLS, METAL CUTTING: Numerically Controlled
MACHINE TOOLS, METAL CUTTING: Pipe Cutting & Threading
MACHINE TOOLS, METAL CUTTING: Plasma Process
MACHINE TOOLS, METAL CUTTING: Regrinding, Crankshaft
MACHINE TOOLS, METAL CUTTING: Sawing & Cutoff
MACHINE TOOLS, METAL CUTTING: Tool Replacement & Rpr Parts
MACHINE TOOLS, METAL CUTTING: Ultrasonic
MACHINE TOOLS, METAL FORMING: Bending
MACHINE TOOLS, METAL FORMING: Crimping, Metal
MACHINE TOOLS, METAL FORMING: Die Casting & Extruding
MACHINE TOOLS, METAL FORMING: Electroforming
MACHINE TOOLS, METAL FORMING: Forging Machinery & Hammers
MACHINE TOOLS, METAL FORMING: Gear Rolling
MACHINE TOOLS, METAL FORMING: Headers
MACHINE TOOLS, METAL FORMING: Magnetic Forming
MACHINE TOOLS, METAL FORMING: Marking
MACHINE TOOLS, METAL FORMING: Mechanical, Pneumatic Or Hyd
MACHINE TOOLS, METAL FORMING: Nail Heading
MACHINE TOOLS, METAL FORMING: Presses, Hyd & Pneumatic
MACHINE TOOLS, METAL FORMING: Pressing
MACHINE TOOLS, METAL FORMING: Rebuilt

MACHINE TOOLS, METAL FORMING: Spinning, Metal
MACHINE TOOLS, METAL FORMING: Spinning, Spline Rollg/Windg
MACHINE TOOLS: Metal Cutting
MACHINE TOOLS: Metal Forming
MACHINERY & EQPT, AGRICULTURAL, WHOLESALE: Farm Implements
MACHINERY & EQPT, AGRICULTURAL, WHOLESALE: Lawn & Garden
MACHINERY & EQPT, AGRICULTURAL, WHOLESALE: Livestock Eqpt
MACHINERY & EQPT, AGRICULTURAL, WHOLESALE: Tractors
MACHINERY & EQPT, INDL, WHOL: Controlling Instruments/Access
MACHINERY & EQPT, INDL, WHOL: Environ Pollution Cntrl, Air
MACHINERY & EQPT, INDL, WHOL: Environ Pollution Cntrl, Water
MACHINERY & EQPT, INDL, WHOL: Meters, Consumption Registerng
MACHINERY & EQPT, INDL, WHOLESALE: Cement Making
MACHINERY & EQPT, INDL, WHOLESALE: Chemical Process
MACHINERY & EQPT, INDL, WHOLESALE: Conveyor Systems
MACHINERY & EQPT, INDL, WHOLESALE: Cranes
MACHINERY & EQPT, INDL, WHOLESALE: Engines & Parts, Diesel
MACHINERY & EQPT, INDL, WHOLESALE: Engines, Gasoline
MACHINERY & EQPT, INDL, WHOLESALE: Fans
MACHINERY & EQPT, INDL, WHOLESALE: Food Manufacturing
MACHINERY & EQPT, INDL, WHOLESALE: Heat Exchange
MACHINERY & EQPT, INDL, WHOLESALE: Hydraulic Systems
MACHINERY & EQPT, INDL, WHOLESALE: Indl Machine Parts
MACHINERY & EQPT, INDL, WHOLESALE: Instruments & Cntrl Eqpt
MACHINERY & EQPT, INDL, WHOLESALE: Lift Trucks & Parts
MACHINERY & EQPT, INDL, WHOLESALE: Machine Tools & Access
MACHINERY & EQPT, INDL, WHOLESALE: Machine Tools & Metalwork
MACHINERY & EQPT, INDL, WHOLESALE: Measure/Test, Electric
MACHINERY & EQPT, INDL, WHOLESALE: Metal Refining
MACHINERY & EQPT, INDL, WHOLESALE: Noise Control
MACHINERY & EQPT, INDL, WHOLESALE: Packaging
MACHINERY & EQPT, INDL, WHOLESALE: Paint Spray
MACHINERY & EQPT, INDL, WHOLESALE: Paper Manufacturing
MACHINERY & EQPT, INDL, WHOLESALE: Petroleum Industry
MACHINERY & EQPT, INDL, WHOLESALE: Plastic Prdts Machinery
MACHINERY & EQPT, INDL, WHOLESALE: Pneumatic Tools
MACHINERY & EQPT, INDL, WHOLESALE: Processing & Packaging
MACHINERY & EQPT, INDL, WHOLESALE: Robots
MACHINERY & EQPT, INDL, WHOLESALE: Safety Eqpt
MACHINERY & EQPT, INDL, WHOLESALE: Tool & Die Makers
MACHINERY & EQPT, INDL, WHOLESALE: Woodworking
MACHINERY & EQPT, TEXTILE: Fabric Forming
MACHINERY & EQPT, WHOLESALE: Concrete Processing
MACHINERY & EQPT, WHOLESALE: Construction & Mining, Ladders
MACHINERY & EQPT, WHOLESALE: Construction, General
MACHINERY & EQPT, WHOLESALE: Contractors Materials
MACHINERY & EQPT, WHOLESALE: Logging & Forestry
MACHINERY & EQPT, WHOLESALE: Masonry
MACHINERY & EQPT, WHOLESALE: Oil Field Eqpt
MACHINERY & EQPT, WHOLESALE: Road Construction & Maintenance
MACHINERY & EQPT: Electroplating
MACHINERY & EQPT: Farm
MACHINERY & EQPT: Gas Producers, Generators/Other Rltd Eqpt
MACHINERY & EQPT: Liquid Automation
MACHINERY & EQPT: Metal Finishing, Plating Etc
MACHINERY & EQPT: Petroleum Refinery

INDEX

MACHINERY & EQPT: Silver Recovery
MACHINERY & EQPT: Smelting & Refining
MACHINERY & EQPT: Vibratory Parts Handling Eqpt
MACHINERY BASES
MACHINERY, CALCULATING: Calculators & Adding
MACHINERY, COMMERCIAL LAUNDRY & Drycleaning: Ironers
MACHINERY, COMMERCIAL LAUNDRY: Dryers, Incl Coin-Operated
MACHINERY, EQPT & SUPPLIES: Parking Facility
MACHINERY, FOOD PRDTS: Beverage
MACHINERY, FOOD PRDTS: Choppers, Commercial
MACHINERY, FOOD PRDTS: Cutting, Chopping, Grinding, Mixing
MACHINERY, FOOD PRDTS: Food Processing, Smokers
MACHINERY, FOOD PRDTS: Mixers, Commercial
MACHINERY, FOOD PRDTS: Ovens, Bakery
MACHINERY, FOOD PRDTS: Presses, Cheese, Beet, Cider & Sugar
MACHINERY, FOOD PRDTS: Processing, Poultry
MACHINERY, FOOD PRDTS: Slicers, Commercial
MACHINERY, LUBRICATION: Automatic
MACHINERY, MAILING: Postage Meters
MACHINERY, METALWORKING: Assembly, Including Robotic
MACHINERY, METALWORKING: Coil Winding, For Springs
MACHINERY, METALWORKING: Coiling
MACHINERY, METALWORKING: Cutting & Slitting
MACHINERY, METALWORKING: Cutting-Up Lines
MACHINERY, METALWORKING: Drawing
MACHINERY, METALWORKING: Rotary Slitters, Metalworking
MACHINERY, OFFICE: Paper Handling
MACHINERY, OFFICE: Perforators
MACHINERY, OFFICE: Sorters, Filing
MACHINERY, OFFICE: Time Clocks &Time Recording Devices
MACHINERY, PACKAGING: Aerating, Beverages
MACHINERY, PACKAGING: Canning, Food
MACHINERY, PACKAGING: Packing & Wrapping
MACHINERY, PACKAGING: Vacuum
MACHINERY, PACKAGING: Wrapping
MACHINERY, PAPER INDUSTRY: Converting, Die Cutting & Stampng
MACHINERY, PAPER INDUSTRY: Paper Mill, Plating, Etc
MACHINERY, PAPER INDUSTRY: Pulp Mill
MACHINERY, PAPER INDUSTRY: Sandpaper
MACHINERY, PRINTING TRADES: Linotype, Monotype, Intertype
MACHINERY, PRINTING TRADES: Mats, Advertising & Newspaper
MACHINERY, PRINTING TRADES: Plates
MACHINERY, PRINTING TRADES: Plates, Engravers' Metal
MACHINERY, PRINTING TRADES: Plates, Offset
MACHINERY, PRINTING TRADES: Type Casting, Founding/Melting
MACHINERY, SEWING: Bag Seaming & Closing
MACHINERY, SEWING: Sewing & Hat & Zipper Making
MACHINERY, TEXTILE: Braiding
MACHINERY, TEXTILE: Embroidery
MACHINERY, TEXTILE: Finishing
MACHINERY, TEXTILE: Printing
MACHINERY, TEXTILE: Silk Screens
MACHINERY, WOODWORKING: Cabinet Makers'
MACHINERY, WOODWORKING: Furniture Makers
MACHINERY, WOODWORKING: Lathes, Wood Turning Includes Access
MACHINERY, WOODWORKING: Pattern Makers'
MACHINERY/EQPT, INDL, WHOL: Machinist Precision Measrng Tool
MACHINERY: Ammunition & Explosives Loading
MACHINERY: Assembly, Exc Metalworking
MACHINERY: Automobile Garage, Frame Straighteners
MACHINERY: Automotive Maintenance
MACHINERY: Automotive Related
MACHINERY: Binding
MACHINERY: Blasting, Electrical
MACHINERY: Bottle Washing & Sterilzing
MACHINERY: Bottling & Canning
MACHINERY: Brewery & Malting
MACHINERY: Bridge Or Gate, Hydraulic
MACHINERY: Centrifugal
MACHINERY: Clay Working & Tempering
MACHINERY: Concrete Prdts
MACHINERY: Construction
MACHINERY: Cryogenic, Industrial

MACHINERY: Custom
MACHINERY: Deburring
MACHINERY: Die Casting
MACHINERY: Electrical Discharge Erosion
MACHINERY: Electronic Component Making
MACHINERY: Engraving
MACHINERY: Extruding
MACHINERY: Fiber Optics Strand Coating
MACHINERY: Folding
MACHINERY: Gas Separators
MACHINERY: Gear Cutting & Finishing
MACHINERY: General, Industrial, NEC
MACHINERY: Glassmaking
MACHINERY: Grinding
MACHINERY: Ice Cream
MACHINERY: Industrial, NEC
MACHINERY: Jewelers
MACHINERY: Kilns
MACHINERY: Knitting
MACHINERY: Labeling
MACHINERY: Logging Eqpt
MACHINERY: Marking, Metalworking
MACHINERY: Metalworking
MACHINERY: Milling
MACHINERY: Mining
MACHINERY: Pack-Up Assemblies, Wheel Overhaul
MACHINERY: Packaging
MACHINERY: Paint Making
MACHINERY: Paper Industry Miscellaneous
MACHINERY: Pharmaciutical
MACHINERY: Photographic Reproduction
MACHINERY: Plastic Working
MACHINERY: Polishing & Buffing
MACHINERY: Printing Presses
MACHINERY: Recycling
MACHINERY: Riveting
MACHINERY: Road Construction & Maintenance
MACHINERY: Robots, Molding & Forming Plastics
MACHINERY: Rubber Working
MACHINERY: Saw & Sawing
MACHINERY: Screening Eqpt, Electric
MACHINERY: Semiconductor Manufacturing
MACHINERY: Separation Eqpt, Magnetic
MACHINERY: Service Industry, NEC
MACHINERY: Sheet Metal Working
MACHINERY: Sifting & Screening
MACHINERY: Specialty
MACHINERY: Stone Working
MACHINERY: Tapping
MACHINERY: Textile
MACHINERY: Tire Retreading
MACHINERY: Tire Shredding
MACHINERY: Wire Drawing
MACHINERY: Woodworking
MACHINES: Forming, Sheet Metal
MACHINISTS' TOOLS & MACHINES: Measuring, Metalworking Type
MACHINISTS' TOOLS: Measuring, Precision
MACHINISTS' TOOLS: Precision
MAGAZINE STAND
MAGNESIUM
MAGNESIUM
MAGNETIC INK & OPTICAL SCANNING EQPT
MAGNETIC RESONANCE IMAGING DEVICES: Nonmedical
MAGNETIC TAPE, AUDIO: Prerecorded
MAGNETS: Ceramic
MAGNETS: Permanent
MAIL PRESORTING SVCS
MAIL-ORDER HOUSE, NEC
MAIL-ORDER HOUSES: Books, Exc Book Clubs
MAIL-ORDER HOUSES: Cards
MAIL-ORDER HOUSES: Cheese
MAIL-ORDER HOUSES: Computers & Peripheral Eqpt
MAIL-ORDER HOUSES: Educational Splys & Eqpt
MAIL-ORDER HOUSES: Food
MAIL-ORDER HOUSES: Gift Items
MAIL-ORDER HOUSES: Novelty Merchandise
MAIL-ORDER HOUSES: Record & Tape, Music Or Video Club
MAIL-ORDER HOUSES: Tools & Hardware
MAILING & MESSENGER SVCS
MAILING LIST: Compilers
MAILING MACHINES WHOLESALERS
MAILING SVCS, NEC
MANAGEMENT CONSULTING SVCS: Automation & Robotics
MANAGEMENT CONSULTING SVCS: Business

MANAGEMENT CONSULTING SVCS: Construction Project
MANAGEMENT CONSULTING SVCS: Corporation Organizing
MANAGEMENT CONSULTING SVCS: General
MANAGEMENT CONSULTING SVCS: Industrial
MANAGEMENT CONSULTING SVCS: Industry Specialist
MANAGEMENT CONSULTING SVCS: New Products & Svcs
MANAGEMENT CONSULTING SVCS: Public Utilities
MANAGEMENT CONSULTING SVCS: Real Estate
MANAGEMENT CONSULTING SVCS: Training & Development
MANAGEMENT CONSULTING SVCS: Transportation
MANAGEMENT SERVICES
MANAGEMENT SVCS, FACILITIES SUPPORT: Environ Remediation
MANAGEMENT SVCS: Administrative
MANAGEMENT SVCS: Business
MANAGEMENT SVCS: Construction
MANAGEMENT SVCS: Financial, Business
MANHOLES & COVERS: Metal
MANICURE PREPARATIONS
MANIFOLDS: Pipe, Fabricated From Purchased Pipe
MANNEQUINS
MANUFACTURED & MOBILE HOME DEALERS
MANUFACTURING INDUSTRIES, NEC
MAPS
MAPS & CHARTS, WHOLESALE
MARBLE, BUILDING: Cut & Shaped
MARINAS
MARINE CARGO HANDLING SVCS
MARINE HARDWARE
MARINE PROPELLER REPAIR SVCS
MARINE RELATED EQPT
MARINE SPLY DEALERS
MARINE SPLYS WHOLESALERS
MARKETS: Meat & fish
MARKING DEVICES
MARKING DEVICES: Canceling Stamps, Hand, Rubber Or Metal
MARKING DEVICES: Date Stamps, Hand, Rubber Or Metal
MARKING DEVICES: Embossing Seals & Hand Stamps
MARKING DEVICES: Embossing Seals, Corporate & Official
MARKING DEVICES: Figures, Metal
MARKING DEVICES: Letters, Metal
MARKING DEVICES: Numbering Stamps, Hand, Rubber Or Metal
MARKING DEVICES: Pads, Inking & Stamping
MARKING DEVICES: Screens, Textile Printing
MARKING DEVICES: Stationary Embossers, Personal
MARKING DEVICES: Textile Making Stamps, Hand, Rubber/Metal
MASQUERADE OR THEATRICAL COSTUMES STORES
MASSAGE MACHINES, ELECTRIC: Barber & Beauty Shops
MASSAGE PARLORS
MASTIC ROOFING COMPOSITION
MASTS: Cast Aluminum
MATERIAL GRINDING & PULVERIZING SVCS NEC
MATERIALS HANDLING EQPT WHOLESALERS
MATS & MATTING, MADE FROM PURCHASED WIRE
MATS OR MATTING, NEC: Rubber
MATS, MATTING & PADS: Auto, Floor, Exc Rubber Or Plastic
MATS, MATTING & PADS: Nonwoven
MATS: Table, Plastic & Textile
MATTRESS STORES
MEAT & FISH MARKETS: Food & Freezer Plans, Meat
MEAT & FISH MARKETS: Freezer Provisioners, Meat
MEAT & MEAT PRDTS WHOLESALERS
MEAT CUTTING & PACKING
MEAT MARKETS
MEAT PRDTS: Bacon, Side & Sliced, From Purchased Meat
MEAT PRDTS: Cooked Meats, From Purchased Meat
MEAT PRDTS: Corned Beef, From Slaughtered Meat
MEAT PRDTS: Cured, From Slaughtered Meat
MEAT PRDTS: Dried Beef, From Purchased Meat
MEAT PRDTS: Frozen
MEAT PRDTS: Hams & Picnics, From Slaughtered Meat
MEAT PRDTS: Luncheon Meat, From Purchased Meat
MEAT PRDTS: Pork, Cured, From Purchased Meat
MEAT PRDTS: Pork, From Slaughtered Meat
MEAT PRDTS: Prepared Beef Prdts From Purchased Beef
MEAT PRDTS: Prepared Pork Prdts, From Purchased Meat
MEAT PRDTS: Sausages, From Purchased Meat
MEAT PRDTS: Sausages, From Slaughtered Meat
MEAT PRDTS: Snack Sticks, Incl Jerky, From Purchased Meat

MEAT PRDTS: Veal, From Slaughtered Meat
MEAT PROCESSED FROM PURCHASED CARCASSES
MEATS, PACKAGED FROZEN: Wholesalers
MECHANICAL INSTRUMENT REPAIR SVCS
MEDIA BUYING AGENCIES
MEDIA: Magnetic & Optical Recording
MEDICAL & HOSPITAL EQPT WHOLESALERS
MEDICAL & HOSPITAL SPLYS: Radiation Shielding Garments
MEDICAL & SURGICAL SPLYS: Atomizers, Medical
MEDICAL & SURGICAL SPLYS: Bandages & Dressings
MEDICAL & SURGICAL SPLYS: Belts, Surg, Sanitary & Corrective
MEDICAL & SURGICAL SPLYS: Braces, Elastic
MEDICAL & SURGICAL SPLYS: Braces, Orthopedic
MEDICAL & SURGICAL SPLYS: Clothing, Fire Resistant & Protect
MEDICAL & SURGICAL SPLYS: Cosmetic Restorations
MEDICAL & SURGICAL SPLYS: Foot Appliances, Orthopedic
MEDICAL & SURGICAL SPLYS: Grafts, Artificial
MEDICAL & SURGICAL SPLYS: Hosiery, Support
MEDICAL & SURGICAL SPLYS: Limbs, Artificial
MEDICAL & SURGICAL SPLYS: Live Preservers, Exc Cork & Inflat
MEDICAL & SURGICAL SPLYS: Orthopedic Appliances
MEDICAL & SURGICAL SPLYS: Personal Safety Eqpt
MEDICAL & SURGICAL SPLYS: Prosthetic Appliances
MEDICAL & SURGICAL SPLYS: Respiratory Protect Eqpt, Personal
MEDICAL & SURGICAL SPLYS: Splints, Pneumatic & Wood
MEDICAL & SURGICAL SPLYS: Stretchers
MEDICAL & SURGICAL SPLYS: Technical Aids, Handicapped
MEDICAL & SURGICAL SPLYS: Trusses, Orthopedic & Surgical
MEDICAL & SURGICAL SPLYS: Welders' Hoods
MEDICAL CENTERS
MEDICAL EQPT REPAIR SVCS, NON-ELECTRIC
MEDICAL EQPT: CAT Scanner Or Computerized Axial Tomography
MEDICAL EQPT: Defibrillators
MEDICAL EQPT: Diagnostic
MEDICAL EQPT: Electromedical Apparatus
MEDICAL EQPT: Electrotherapeutic Apparatus
MEDICAL EQPT: Laser Systems
MEDICAL EQPT: MRI/Magnetic Resonance Imaging Devs, Nuclear
MEDICAL EQPT: Pacemakers
MEDICAL EQPT: Patient Monitoring
MEDICAL EQPT: Sterilizers
MEDICAL EQPT: Ultrasonic Scanning Devices
MEDICAL EQPT: X-Ray Apparatus & Tubes, Radiographic
MEDICAL INSURANCE CLAIM PROCESSING: Contract Or Fee Basis
MEDICAL SUNDRIES: Rubber
MEDICAL TRAINING SERVICES
MEDICAL, DENTAL & HOSP EQPT, WHOLESALE: X-ray Film & Splys
MEDICAL, DENTAL & HOSPITAL EQPT, WHOL: Dentists' Prof Splys
MEDICAL, DENTAL & HOSPITAL EQPT, WHOL: Hospital Eqpt & Splys
MEDICAL, DENTAL & HOSPITAL EQPT, WHOL: Hosptl Eqpt/Furniture
MEDICAL, DENTAL & HOSPITAL EQPT, WHOL: Surgical Eqpt & Splys
MEDICAL, DENTAL & HOSPITAL EQPT, WHOLESALE: Diagnostic, Med
MEDICAL, DENTAL & HOSPITAL EQPT, WHOLESALE: Med Eqpt & Splys
MEDICAL, DENTAL & HOSPITAL EQPT, WHOLESALE: Safety
MEDICAL, DENTAL & HOSPITAL EQPT, WHOLESALE: Therapy
MEDICAL, DENTAL/HOSPITAL EQPT, WHOL: Veterinarian Eqpt/Sply
MELAMINE RESINS: Melamine-Formaldehyde
MEMBERSHIP HOTELS
MEMBERSHIP ORGANIZATIONS, CIVIC, SOCIAL/FRAT: Social Assoc
MEMBERSHIP ORGANIZATIONS, NEC: Bowling club
MEMBERSHIP ORGANIZATIONS, NEC: Flying Club
MEMBERSHIP ORGANIZATIONS, NEC: Personal Interest
MEMBERSHIP ORGANIZATIONS, REL: Christian & Reformed Church

MEMBERSHIP ORGANIZATIONS, RELIGIOUS: Brethren Church
MEMBERSHIP ORGANIZATIONS, RELIGIOUS: Nonchurch
MEMORIALS, MONUMENTS & MARKERS
MEN'S & BOYS' CLOTHING STORES
MEN'S & BOYS' CLOTHING WHOLESALERS, NEC
MEN'S & BOYS' SPORTSWEAR CLOTHING STORES
MEN'S & BOYS' SPORTSWEAR WHOLESALERS
MEN'S & BOYS' WORK CLOTHING WHOLESALERS
METAL & STEEL PRDTS: Abrasive
METAL COMPONENTS: Prefabricated
METAL CUTTING SVCS
METAL DETECTORS
METAL FABRICATORS: Architechtural
METAL FABRICATORS: Plate
METAL FABRICATORS: Sheet
METAL FABRICATORS: Structural, Ship
METAL FINISHING SVCS
METAL MINING SVCS
METAL RESHAPING & REPLATING SVCS
METAL SERVICE CENTERS & OFFICES
METAL SLITTING & SHEARING
METAL SPINNING FOR THE TRADE
METAL STAMPING, FOR THE TRADE
METAL STAMPINGS: Ornamental
METAL STAMPINGS: Patterned
METAL TREATING COMPOUNDS
METAL TREATING: Cryogenic
METAL, TITANIUM: Sponge & Granules
METAL: Battery
METALS SVC CENTERS & WHOL: Structural Shapes, Iron Or Steel
METALS SVC CENTERS & WHOLESALERS: Bars, Metal
METALS SVC CENTERS & WHOLESALERS: Cable, Wire
METALS SVC CENTERS & WHOLESALERS: Casting, Rough, Iron/Steel
METALS SVC CENTERS & WHOLESALERS: Copper
METALS SVC CENTERS & WHOLESALERS: Ferroalloys
METALS SVC CENTERS & WHOLESALERS: Ferrous Metals
METALS SVC CENTERS & WHOLESALERS: Flat Prdts, Iron Or Steel
METALS SVC CENTERS & WHOLESALERS: Foundry Prdts
METALS SVC CENTERS & WHOLESALERS: Iron & Steel Prdt, Ferrous
METALS SVC CENTERS & WHOLESALERS: Lead
METALS SVC CENTERS & WHOLESALERS: Misc Nonferrous Prdts
METALS SVC CENTERS & WHOLESALERS: Pipe & Tubing, Steel
METALS SVC CENTERS & WHOLESALERS: Plates, Metal
METALS SVC CENTERS & WHOLESALERS: Rails & Access
METALS SVC CENTERS & WHOLESALERS: Rope, Wire, Exc Insulated
METALS SVC CENTERS & WHOLESALERS: Sheets, Metal
METALS SVC CENTERS & WHOLESALERS: Stampings, Metal
METALS SVC CENTERS & WHOLESALERS: Steel
METALS SVC CENTERS & WHOLESALERS: Tubing, Metal
METALS SVC CTRS & WHOLESALERS: Aluminum Bars, Rods, Etc
METALS: Precious NEC
METALS: Precious, Secondary
METALS: Primary Nonferrous, NEC
METALWORK: Miscellaneous
METALWORK: Ornamental
METALWORKING MACHINERY WHOLESALERS
METEOROLOGICAL INSTRUMENT REPAIR SVCS
METER READERS: Remote
METERING DEVICES: Flow Meters, Impeller & Counter Driven
METERING DEVICES: Gas Meters, Domestic & Large Cap, Indl
METERING DEVICES: Gasoline Dispensing
METERING DEVICES: Water Quality Monitoring & Control Systems
METERS: Pyrometers, Indl Process
METERS: Resistance
MGMT CONSULTING SVCS: Matls, Incl Purch, Handle & Invntry
MICA PRDTS
MICROCIRCUITS, INTEGRATED: Semiconductor
MICROPHONES
MICROPROCESSORS
MICROPUBLISHER
MICROSCOPES

MICROWAVE COMPONENTS
MILITARY INSIGNIA
MILL PRDTS: Structural & Rail
MILLINERY SUPPLIES: Sweat Bands, Hat/Cap, From Purchsd Mtrls
MILLINERY SUPPLIES: Veils & Veiling, Bridal, Funeral, Etc
MILLING: Cereal Flour, Exc Rice
MILLING: Chemical
MILLING: Grains, Exc Rice
MILLS: Ferrous & Nonferrous
MILLWORK
MINE & QUARRY SVCS: Nonmetallic Minerals
MINE DEVELOPMENT SVCS: Nonmetallic Minerals
MINE EXPLORATION SVCS: Nonmetallic Minerals
MINE PREPARATION SVCS
MINE PUMPING OR DRAINING SVCS: Nonmetallic Minerals
MINERAL WOOL
MINERAL WOOL INSULATION PRDTS
MINERALS: Ground Or Otherwise Treated
MINERALS: Ground or Treated
MINIATURES
MINING EXPLORATION & DEVELOPMENT SVCS
MINING MACHINERY & EQPT WHOLESALERS
MINING MACHINES & EQPT: Augers
MINING MACHINES & EQPT: Bits, Rock, Exc Oil/Gas Field Tools
MINING MACHINES & EQPT: Cages, Mine Shaft
MINING MACHINES & EQPT: Crushers, Stationary
MINING MACHINES & EQPT: Rock Crushing, Stationary
MINING MACHINES & EQPT: Shuttle Cars, Underground
MINING SVCS, NEC: Bituminous
MIRRORS: Motor Vehicle
MISSILES: Ballistic, Complete
MIXING EQPT
MIXTURES & BLOCKS: Asphalt Paving
MOBILE COMMUNICATIONS EQPT
MOBILE HOME & TRAILER REPAIR
MOBILE HOMES
MOBILE HOMES, EXC RECREATIONAL
MODELS
MODELS: Airplane, Exc Toy
MODELS: General, Exc Toy
MODULES: Computer Logic
MOLDED RUBBER PRDTS
MOLDING COMPOUNDS
MOLDING SAND MINING
MOLDINGS & TRIM: Metal, Exc Automobile
MOLDINGS & TRIM: Wood
MOLDINGS OR TRIM: Automobile, Stamped Metal
MOLDINGS, ARCHITECTURAL: Plaster Of Paris
MOLDINGS: Picture Frame
MOLDS: Gray, Ingot, Cast Iron
MOLDS: Indl
MOLDS: Plastic Working & Foundry
MOLYBDENUM SILICON, EXC MADE IN BLAST FURNACES
MONORAIL SYSTEMS
MONUMENTS: Concrete
MONUMENTS: Cut Stone, Exc Finishing Or Lettering Only
MOPS: Floor & Dust
MOTION PICTURE & VIDEO PRODUCTION SVCS
MOTION PICTURE EQPT
MOTION PICTURE PRODUCTION & DISTRIBUTION: Television
MOTOR & GENERATOR PARTS: Electric
MOTOR HOMES
MOTOR REBUILDING SVCS, EXC AUTOMOTIVE
MOTOR REPAIR SVCS
MOTOR SCOOTERS & PARTS
MOTOR VEHICLE ASSEMBLY, COMPLETE: Ambulances
MOTOR VEHICLE ASSEMBLY, COMPLETE: Autos, Incl Specialty
MOTOR VEHICLE ASSEMBLY, COMPLETE: Bus/Large Spclty Vehicles
MOTOR VEHICLE ASSEMBLY, COMPLETE: Buses, All Types
MOTOR VEHICLE ASSEMBLY, COMPLETE: Cars, Armored
MOTOR VEHICLE ASSEMBLY, COMPLETE: Fire Department Vehicles
MOTOR VEHICLE ASSEMBLY, COMPLETE: Hearses
MOTOR VEHICLE ASSEMBLY, COMPLETE: Military Motor Vehicle
MOTOR VEHICLE ASSEMBLY, COMPLETE: Mobile Lounges
MOTOR VEHICLE ASSEMBLY, COMPLETE: Snow Plows
MOTOR VEHICLE ASSEMBLY, COMPLETE: Truck & Tractor Trucks

INDEX

MOTOR VEHICLE ASSEMBLY, COMPLETE: Truck Tractors, Highway
MOTOR VEHICLE ASSEMBLY, COMPLETE: Wreckers, Tow Truck
MOTOR VEHICLE DEALERS: Automobiles, New & Used
MOTOR VEHICLE DEALERS: Cars, Used Only
MOTOR VEHICLE DEALERS: Pickups & Vans, Used
MOTOR VEHICLE DEALERS: Pickups, New & Used
MOTOR VEHICLE DEALERS: Trucks, Tractors/Trailers, New & Used
MOTOR VEHICLE DEALERS: Vans, New & Used
MOTOR VEHICLE PARTS & ACCESS: Acceleration Eqpt
MOTOR VEHICLE PARTS & ACCESS: Air Conditioner Parts
MOTOR VEHICLE PARTS & ACCESS: Axel Housings & Shafts
MOTOR VEHICLE PARTS & ACCESS: Bearings
MOTOR VEHICLE PARTS & ACCESS: Body Components & Frames
MOTOR VEHICLE PARTS & ACCESS: Booster Cables, Jump-Start
MOTOR VEHICLE PARTS & ACCESS: Brakes, Air
MOTOR VEHICLE PARTS & ACCESS: Clutches
MOTOR VEHICLE PARTS & ACCESS: Connecting Rods
MOTOR VEHICLE PARTS & ACCESS: Cylinder Heads
MOTOR VEHICLE PARTS & ACCESS: Electrical Eqpt
MOTOR VEHICLE PARTS & ACCESS: Engines & Parts
MOTOR VEHICLE PARTS & ACCESS: Engs & Trans,Factory, Rebuilt
MOTOR VEHICLE PARTS & ACCESS: Frames
MOTOR VEHICLE PARTS & ACCESS: Fuel Pumps
MOTOR VEHICLE PARTS & ACCESS: Fuel Systems & Parts
MOTOR VEHICLE PARTS & ACCESS: Gas Tanks
MOTOR VEHICLE PARTS & ACCESS: Gears
MOTOR VEHICLE PARTS & ACCESS: Heaters
MOTOR VEHICLE PARTS & ACCESS: Ice Scrapers & Window Brushes
MOTOR VEHICLE PARTS & ACCESS: Instrument Board Assemblies
MOTOR VEHICLE PARTS & ACCESS: Manifolds
MOTOR VEHICLE PARTS & ACCESS: Mufflers, Exhaust
MOTOR VEHICLE PARTS & ACCESS: Power Steering Eqpt
MOTOR VEHICLE PARTS & ACCESS: Propane Conversion Eqpt
MOTOR VEHICLE PARTS & ACCESS: Pumps, Hydraulic Fluid Power
MOTOR VEHICLE PARTS & ACCESS: Sanders, Safety
MOTOR VEHICLE PARTS & ACCESS: Tie Rods
MOTOR VEHICLE PARTS & ACCESS: Tire Valve Cores
MOTOR VEHICLE PARTS & ACCESS: Trailer Hitches
MOTOR VEHICLE PARTS & ACCESS: Transmission Housings Or Parts
MOTOR VEHICLE PARTS & ACCESS: Transmissions
MOTOR VEHICLE PARTS & ACCESS: Water Pumps
MOTOR VEHICLE PARTS & ACCESS: Wheel rims
MOTOR VEHICLE PARTS & ACCESS: Windshield Frames
MOTOR VEHICLE PARTS & ACCESS: Winter Fronts
MOTOR VEHICLE PARTS & ACCESS: Wiring Harness Sets
MOTOR VEHICLE SPLYS & PARTS WHOLESALERS: New
MOTOR VEHICLE SPLYS & PARTS WHOLESALERS: Used
MOTOR VEHICLE: Hardware
MOTOR VEHICLE: Radiators
MOTOR VEHICLE: Shock Absorbers
MOTOR VEHICLE: Wheels
MOTOR VEHICLES & CAR BODIES
MOTOR VEHICLES, WHOLESALE: Ambulances
MOTOR VEHICLES, WHOLESALE: Commercial
MOTOR VEHICLES, WHOLESALE: Fire Trucks
MOTOR VEHICLES, WHOLESALE: Trailers for passenger vehicles
MOTOR VEHICLES, WHOLESALE: Trailers, Truck, New & Used
MOTOR VEHICLES, WHOLESALE: Truck bodies
MOTOR VEHICLES, WHOLESALE: Trucks, Noncommercial
MOTOR VEHICLES, WHOLESALE: Trucks, commercial
MOTORCYCLE & BICYCLE PARTS: Frames
MOTORCYCLE ACCESS
MOTORCYCLE DEALERS
MOTORCYCLE DEALERS
MOTORCYCLE PARTS & ACCESS DEALERS
MOTORCYCLE PARTS: Wholesalers
MOTORCYCLE REPAIR SHOPS
MOTORCYCLES & RELATED PARTS
MOTORCYCLES: Wholesalers
MOTORS: Electric
MOTORS: Generators

MOTORS: Pneumatic
MOTORS: Starting, Automotive & Aircraft
MOTORS: Torque
MOUNTING RINGS, MOTOR Rubber Covered Or Bonded
MOUTHWASHES
MOVING SVC: Local
MOWERS & ACCESSORIES
MUSEUMS
MUSIC BROADCASTING SVCS
MUSIC DISTRIBUTION APPARATUS
MUSIC RECORDING PRODUCER
MUSICAL INSTRUMENT REPAIR
MUSICAL INSTRUMENTS & ACCESS: Carrying Cases
MUSICAL INSTRUMENTS & ACCESS: NEC
MUSICAL INSTRUMENTS & ACCESS: Pipe Organs
MUSICAL INSTRUMENTS & PARTS: Brass
MUSICAL INSTRUMENTS & PARTS: Percussion
MUSICAL INSTRUMENTS & PARTS: String
MUSICAL INSTRUMENTS & SPLYS STORES
MUSICAL INSTRUMENTS & SPLYS STORES: String instruments
MUSICAL INSTRUMENTS WHOLESALERS
MUSICAL INSTRUMENTS: Banjos & Parts
MUSICAL INSTRUMENTS: Bells
MUSICAL INSTRUMENTS: Carillon Bells
MUSICAL INSTRUMENTS: Guitars & Parts, Electric & Acoustic
MUSICAL INSTRUMENTS: Keyboards
MUSICAL INSTRUMENTS: Keyboards & Parts|
MUSICAL INSTRUMENTS: Organ Parts & Materials
MUSICAL INSTRUMENTS: Organs
MUSICAL INSTRUMENTS: Recorders, Musical
MUSICAL INSTRUMENTS: Violins & Parts

N

NAIL SALONS
NAME PLATES: Engraved Or Etched
NAMEPLATES
NATIONAL SECURITY FORCES
NATIONAL SECURITY, GOVERNMENT: Air Force
NATIONAL SECURITY, GOVERNMENT: Army
NATURAL GAS DISTRIBUTION TO CONSUMERS
NATURAL GAS LIQUIDS PRODUCTION
NATURAL GAS POWER BROKER
NATURAL GAS PRODUCTION
NATURAL GAS TRANSMISSION
NATURAL GAS TRANSMISSION & DISTRIBUTION
NATURAL GASOLINE PRODUCTION
NATURAL PROPANE PRODUCTION
NAUTICAL REPAIR SVCS
NAVIGATIONAL SYSTEMS & INSTRUMENTS
NET & NETTING PRDTS
NETTING: Cargo
NEW & USED CAR DEALERS
NEWS DEALERS & NEWSSTANDS
NEWS SYNDICATES
NEWSSTAND
NICKEL ALLOY
NIPPLES: Rubber
NITRILE RUBBERS: Butadiene-Acrylonitrile
NONCURRENT CARRYING WIRING DEVICES
NONDURABLE GOODS WHOLESALERS, NEC
NONFERROUS: Rolling & Drawing, NEC
NONMETALLIC MINERALS & CONCENTRATE WHOLESALERS
NONMETALLIC MINERALS DEVELOPMENT & TEST BORING SVC
NONMETALLIC MINERALS: Support Activities, Exc Fuels
NOTEBOOKS, MADE FROM PURCHASED MATERIALS
NOTIONS: Pins, Straight, Steel Or Brass
NOVELTIES
NOVELTIES & SPECIALTIES: Metal
NOVELTIES, DURABLE, WHOLESALE
NOVELTIES: Leather
NOVELTIES: Plastic
NOVELTY SHOPS
NOZZLES: Fire Fighting
NOZZLES: Spray, Aerosol, Paint Or Insecticide
NUCLEAR DETECTORS: Solid State
NUCLEAR FUELS SCRAP REPROCESSING
NUCLEAR REACTORS: Military Or Indl
NUCLEAR SHIELDING: Metal Plate
NURSERIES & LAWN & GARDEN SPLY STORE, RET: Fountain, Outdoor

NURSERIES & LAWN & GARDEN SPLY STORE, RET: Lawn/Garden Splys
NURSERIES & LAWN & GARDEN SPLY STORES, RETAIL
NURSERIES & LAWN & GARDEN SPLY STORES, RETAIL: Fertilizer
NURSERIES & LAWN & GARDEN SPLY STORES, RETAIL: Lawn Ornament
NURSERIES & LAWN & GARDEN SPLY STORES, RETAIL: Top Soil
NURSERIES & LAWN/GARDEN SPLY STORE, RET: Lawnmowers/Tractors
NURSERY & GARDEN CENTERS
NURSING CARE FACILITIES: Skilled
NUTRITION SVCS
NUTS: Metal
NYLON FIBERS

O

OFCS & CLINICS,MEDICAL DRS: Specl, Physician Or Surgn, ENT
OFFICE EQPT WHOLESALERS
OFFICE EQPT, WHOL: Check Writing, Signing/Endorsing Mach
OFFICE EQPT, WHOLESALE: Blueprinting
OFFICE EQPT, WHOLESALE: Duplicating Machines
OFFICE EQPT, WHOLESALE: Typewriter & Dictation
OFFICE EQPT, WHOLESALE: Typewriters
OFFICE FIXTURES: Exc Wood
OFFICE FIXTURES: Wood
OFFICE FURNITURE REPAIR & MAINTENANCE SVCS
OFFICE MACHINES, NEC
OFFICE SPLY & STATIONERY STORES
OFFICE SPLY & STATIONERY STORES: Office Forms & Splys
OFFICE SPLY & STATIONERY STORES: School Splys
OFFICE SPLYS, NEC, WHOLESALE
OFFICES & CLINICS OF DOCTORS OF MEDICINE: Dermatologist
OFFICES & CLINICS OF DOCTORS OF MEDICINE: Surgeon
OFFICES & CLINICS OF DRS OF MED: Cardiologist & Vascular
OFFICES & CLINICS OF DRS OF MED: Physician/Surgeon, Int Med
OIL & GAS FIELD EQPT: Drill Rigs
OIL & GAS FIELD MACHINERY
OIL ABSORPTION Eqpt
OIL FIELD MACHINERY & EQPT
OIL FIELD SVCS, NEC
OIL ROYALTY TRADERS
OIL TREATING COMPOUNDS
OILS & ESSENTIAL OILS
OILS & GREASES: Blended & Compounded
OILS & GREASES: Lubricating
OILS: Cutting
OILS: Lubricating
OILS: Lubricating
OINTMENTS
OLEFINS
ON-LINE DATABASE INFORMATION RETRIEVAL SVCS
OPENERS, BOTTLE Stamped Metal
OPERATOR TRAINING, COMPUTER
OPERATOR: Apartment Buildings
OPERATOR: Nonresidential Buildings
OPHTHALMIC GOODS
OPHTHALMIC GOODS, NEC, WHOLESALE: Contact Lenses
OPHTHALMIC GOODS, NEC, WHOLESALE: Lenses
OPHTHALMIC GOODS: Lenses, Ophthalmic
OPTICAL GOODS STORES
OPTICAL GOODS STORES: Eyeglasses, Prescription
OPTICAL INSTRUMENTS & APPARATUS
OPTICAL INSTRUMENTS & LENSES
OPTICAL SCANNING SVCS
OPTOMETRIC EQPT & SPLYS WHOLESALERS
OPTOMETRISTS' OFFICES
ORAL PREPARATIONS
ORDNANCE
ORGAN TUNING & REPAIR SVCS
ORGANIZATIONS: Civic & Social
ORGANIZATIONS: Medical Research
ORGANIZATIONS: Physical Research, Noncommercial
ORGANIZATIONS: Professional
ORGANIZATIONS: Religious
ORGANIZATIONS: Scientific Research Agency
ORNAMENTS: Christmas Tree, Exc Electrical & Glass
ORNAMENTS: Lawn

ORTHOPEDIC SUNDRIES: Molded Rubber
OUTBOARD MOTORS & PARTS
OUTLETS: Electric, Convenience
OVENS: Core Baking & Mold Drying
OVENS: Laboratory

P

PACKAGE DESIGN SVCS
PACKAGED FROZEN FOODS WHOLESALERS, NEC
PACKAGING & LABELING SVCS
PACKAGING MATERIALS, WHOLESALE
PACKAGING MATERIALS: Paper
PACKAGING MATERIALS: Paper, Coated Or Laminated
PACKAGING MATERIALS: Paperboard Backs For Blister/Skin Pkgs
PACKAGING MATERIALS: Plastic Film, Coated Or Laminated
PACKAGING MATERIALS: Polystyrene Foam
PACKAGING: Blister Or Bubble Formed, Plastic
PACKING & CRATING SVC
PACKING MATERIALS: Mechanical
PACKING SVCS: Shipping
PADDING: Foamed Plastics
PADS: Athletic, Protective
PAILS: Shipping, Metal
PAINT & PAINTING SPLYS STORE
PAINT DRIERS
PAINT STORE
PAINTING SVC: Metal Prdts
PAINTS & ADDITIVES
PAINTS & ALLIED PRODUCTS
PAINTS, VARNISHES & SPLYS WHOLESALERS
PAINTS, VARNISHES & SPLYS, WHOLESALE: Paints
PAINTS, VARNISHES & SPLYS, WHOLESALE: Stain
PAINTS: Asphalt Or Bituminous
PAINTS: Marine
PAINTS: Oil Or Alkyd Vehicle Or Water Thinned
PALLET REPAIR SVCS
PALLETIZERS & DEPALLETIZERS
PALLETS
PALLETS & SKIDS: Wood
PALLETS: Corrugated
PALLETS: Plastic
PALLETS: Wooden
PAN GLAZING SVC
PANEL & DISTRIBUTION BOARDS & OTHER RELATED APPARATUS
PANEL & DISTRIBUTION BOARDS: Electric
PANELS & SECTIONS: Prefabricated, Concrete
PANELS: Building, Metal
PANELS: Building, Plastic, NEC

PANELS: Building, Wood
PANELS: Wood
PAPER & BOARD: Die-cut
PAPER CONVERTING
PAPER MANUFACTURERS: Exc Newsprint
PAPER NAPKINS WHOLESALERS
PAPER PRDTS: Book Covers
PAPER PRDTS: Feminine Hygiene Prdts
PAPER PRDTS: Infant & Baby Prdts
PAPER PRDTS: Napkins, Made From Purchased Materials
PAPER PRDTS: Napkins, Sanitary, Made From Purchased Material
PAPER PRDTS: Sanitary
PAPER PRDTS: Tampons, Sanitary, Made From Purchased Material
PAPER PRDTS: Towels, Napkins/Tissue Paper, From Purchd Mtrls
PAPER PRDTS: Wrappers, Blank, Made From Purchased Materials
PAPER, WHOLESALE: Printing
PAPER: Adding Machine Rolls, Made From Purchased Materials
PAPER: Adhesive
PAPER: Book
PAPER: Building, Insulating & Packaging
PAPER: Building, Insulation
PAPER: Cardboard
PAPER: Chemically Treated, Made From Purchased Materials
PAPER: Cigarette
PAPER: Cloth, Lined, Made From Purchased Materials
PAPER: Coated & Laminated, NEC
PAPER: Coated, Exc Photographic, Carbon Or Abrasive
PAPER: Corrugated
PAPER: Enameled, Made From Purchased Materials

PAPER: Envelope
PAPER: Fine
PAPER: Gummed, Made From Purchased Materials
PAPER: Milk Filter
PAPER: Newsprint
PAPER: Packaging
PAPER: Parchment
PAPER: Printer
PAPER: Specialty
PAPER: Specialty Or Chemically Treated
PAPER: Tissue
PAPER: Waxed, Made From Purchased Materials
PAPER: Wrapping
PAPER: Wrapping & Packaging
PAPERBOARD
PAPERBOARD CONVERTING
PAPERBOARD PRDTS: Container Board
PAPERBOARD PRDTS: Folding Boxboard
PAPERBOARD PRDTS: Packaging Board
PAPERBOARD PRDTS: Specialty Board
PAPERBOARD PRDTS: Stencil Board
PAPERBOARD: Corrugated
PAPETERIES & WRITING PAPER SETS
PARKING GARAGE
PARKING METERS
PARTICLEBOARD: Laminated, Plastic
PARTITIONS & FIXTURES: Except Wood
PARTITIONS WHOLESALERS
PARTITIONS: Nonwood, Floor Attached
PARTITIONS: Solid Fiber, Made From Purchased Materials
PARTITIONS: Wood & Fixtures
PARTS: Metal
PARTY & SPECIAL EVENT PLANNING SVCS
PASTES, FLAVORING
PASTES: Metal
PATIENT MONITORING EQPT WHOLESALERS
PATTERNS: Indl
PAVERS
PAVING MATERIALS: Coal Tar, Not From Refineries
PAVING MATERIALS: Prefabricated, Concrete
PAVING MIXTURES
PAYROLL SVCS
PENCILS & PENS WHOLESALERS
PENS & PARTS: Ball Point
PENS & PENCILS: Mechanical, NEC
PERFUME: Perfumes, Natural Or Synthetic
PERIODICALS, WHOLESALE
PERSONAL APPEARANCE SVCS
PERSONAL CREDIT INSTITUTIONS: Financing, Autos, Furniture
PERSONAL DEVELOPMENT SCHOOL
PERSONAL SVCS, NEC
PEST CONTROL SVCS
PESTICIDES
PESTICIDES WHOLESALERS
PET & PET SPLYS STORES
PET ACCESS: Collars, Leashes, Etc, Exc Leather
PET COLLARS, LEASHES, MUZZLES & HARNESSES: Leather
PET SPLYS
PET SPLYS WHOLESALERS
PETROLEUM & PETROLEUM PRDTS, WHOLESALE Crude Oil
PETROLEUM & PETROLEUM PRDTS, WHOLESALE Diesel Fuel
PETROLEUM & PETROLEUM PRDTS, WHOLESALE Engine Fuels & Oils
PETROLEUM & PETROLEUM PRDTS, WHOLESALE Fuel Oil
PETROLEUM & PETROLEUM PRDTS, WHOLESALE: Bulk Stations
PETROLEUM PRDTS WHOLESALERS
PETS & PET SPLYS, WHOLESALE
PEWTER WARE
PHARMACEUTICAL PREPARATIONS: Druggists' Preparations
PHARMACEUTICAL PREPARATIONS: Emulsions
PHARMACEUTICAL PREPARATIONS: Medicines, Capsule Or Ampule
PHARMACEUTICAL PREPARATIONS: Pills
PHARMACEUTICAL PREPARATIONS: Proprietary Drug PRDTS
PHARMACEUTICAL PREPARATIONS: Solutions
PHARMACEUTICALS
PHARMACEUTICALS: Medicinal & Botanical Prdts

PHARMACIES & DRUG STORES
PHOSPHATES
PHOTOCOPY MACHINES
PHOTOCOPYING & DUPLICATING SVCS
PHOTOELECTRIC DEVICES: Magnetic
PHOTOENGRAVING SVC
PHOTOFINISHING LABORATORIES
PHOTOGRAPHIC EQPT & SPLYS
PHOTOGRAPHIC EQPT & SPLYS WHOLESALERS
PHOTOGRAPHIC EQPT & SPLYS, WHOLESALE: Project, Motion/Slide
PHOTOGRAPHIC EQPT & SPLYS: Blueprint Reproduction Mach/Eqpt
PHOTOGRAPHIC EQPT & SPLYS: Film, Cloth & Paper, Sensitized
PHOTOGRAPHIC EQPT & SPLYS: Graphic Arts Plates, Sensitized
PHOTOGRAPHIC EQPT & SPLYS: Lens Shades, Camera
PHOTOGRAPHIC EQPT & SPLYS: Paper & Cloth, All Types, NEC
PHOTOGRAPHIC EQPT & SPLYS: Plates, Sensitized
PHOTOGRAPHIC EQPT & SPLYS: Printing Eqpt
PHOTOGRAPHIC EQPT & SPLYS: Processing Eqpt
PHOTOGRAPHIC EQPT & SPLYS: Toners, Prprd, Not Chem Plnts
PHOTOGRAPHIC EQPT REPAIR SVCS
PHOTOGRAPHY SVCS: Commercial
PHOTOGRAPHY SVCS: Portrait Studios
PHOTOGRAPHY SVCS: Still Or Video
PHOTOTYPESETTING SVC
PHOTOVOLTAIC Solid State
PHYSICAL EXAMINATION & TESTING SVCS
PHYSICAL FITNESS CENTERS
PHYSICIANS' OFFICES & CLINICS: Medical
PHYSICIANS' OFFICES & CLINICS: Medical doctors
PICTURE FRAMES: Metal
PICTURE FRAMES: Wood
PICTURE FRAMING SVCS, CUSTOM
PIECE GOODS & NOTIONS WHOLESALERS
PIECE GOODS, NOTIONS & DRY GOODS, WHOL: Fabrics Broadwoven
PIECE GOODS, NOTIONS & DRY GOODS, WHOL: Textile Converters
PIECE GOODS, NOTIONS & DRY GOODS, WHOLESALE: Fabrics, Lace
PIECE GOODS, NOTIONS & DRY GOODS, WHOLESALE: Sewing Access
PIECE GOODS, NOTIONS & DRY GOODS, WHOLESALE: Tape, Textile
PIECE GOODS, NOTIONS & OTHER DRY GOODS, WHOL: Flags/Banners
PIECE GOODS, NOTIONS/DRY GOODS, WHOL: Drapery Mtrl, Woven
PIGMENTS, INORGANIC: Metallic & Mineral, NEC
PILOT SVCS: Aviation
PINS
PINS: Dowel
PINS: Spring
PIPE & FITTING: Fabrication
PIPE & FITTINGS: Cast Iron
PIPE & TUBES: Seamless
PIPE CLEANERS
PIPE FITTINGS: Plastic
PIPE JOINT COMPOUNDS
PIPE SECTIONS, FABRICATED FROM PURCHASED PIPE
PIPE, CULVERT: Concrete
PIPE, CYLINDER: Concrete, Prestressed Or Pretensioned
PIPE, SEWER: Concrete
PIPE: Concrete
PIPE: Plastic
PIPE: Seamless Steel
PIPE: Sheet Metal
PIPE: Water, Cast Iron
PIPELINES: Crude Petroleum
PIPELINES: Natural Gas
PIPES & TUBES
PIPES & TUBES: Steel
PIPES & TUBES: Welded
PIPES OR FITTINGS: Sewer, Clay
PIPES: Steel & Iron
PISTONS & PISTON RINGS
PLACER GOLD MINING
PLANING MILL, NEC
PLANING MILLS: Millwork
PLANTERS: Plastic

INDEX

PLANTS, POTTED, WHOLESALE
PLANTS: Artificial & Preserved
PLAQUES: Clay, Plaster/Papier-Mache, Factory Production
PLAQUES: Picture, Laminated
PLASMAS
PLASTER WORK: Ornamental & Architectural
PLASTER, ACOUSTICAL: Gypsum
PLASTIC COLORING & FINISHING
PLASTIC PRDTS
PLASTIC PRDTS REPAIR SVCS
PLASTICIZERS, ORGANIC: Cyclic & Acyclic
PLASTICS FILM & SHEET
PLASTICS FILM & SHEET: Polyethylene
PLASTICS FILM & SHEET: Polypropylene
PLASTICS FILM & SHEET: Polyvinyl
PLASTICS FILM & SHEET: Vinyl
PLASTICS FINISHED PRDTS: Laminated
PLASTICS MATERIAL & RESINS
PLASTICS MATERIALS, BASIC FORMS & SHAPES
  WHOLESALERS
PLASTICS PROCESSING
PLASTICS SHEET: Packing Materials
PLASTICS: Blow Molded
PLASTICS: Cast
PLASTICS: Extruded
PLASTICS: Finished Injection Molded
PLASTICS: Injection Molded
PLASTICS: Molded
PLASTICS: Polystyrene Foam
PLASTICS: Protein
PLASTICS: Thermoformed
PLATE WORK: For Nuclear Industry
PLATE WORK: Metalworking Trade
PLATEMAKING SVC: Color Separations, For The Printing
  Trade
PLATEMAKING SVC: Embossing, For The Printing Trade
PLATENS, EXC PRINTERS': Rubber, Solid Or Covered
PLATES
PLATES: Paper, Made From Purchased Materials
PLATES: Plastic Exc Polystyrene Foam
PLATES: Sheet & Strip, Exc Coated Prdts
PLATES: Steel
PLATING & FINISHING SVC: Decorative, Formed Prdts
PLATING & POLISHING SVC
PLATING COMPOUNDS
PLATING SVC: Chromium, Metals Or Formed Prdts
PLATING SVC: Electro
PLATING SVC: NEC
PLAYGROUND EQPT
PLEATING & STITCHING FOR THE TRADE: Decorative &
  Novelty
PLEATING & STITCHING SVC
PLUMBERS' GOODS: Rubber
PLUMBING & HEATING EQPT & SPLY, WHOL: Htg
  Eqpt/Panels, Solar
PLUMBING & HEATING EQPT & SPLY, WHOLESALE: Hy-
  dronic Htg Eqpt
PLUMBING & HEATING EQPT & SPLYS WHOLESALERS
PLUMBING & HEATING EQPT & SPLYS, WHOL: Fireplaces,
  Prefab
PLUMBING & HEATING EQPT & SPLYS, WHOL: Pipe/Fitting,
  Plastic
PLUMBING & HEATING EQPT & SPLYS, WHOL: Plumbing
  Fitting/Sply
PLUMBING & HEATING EQPT & SPLYS, WHOL:
  Plumbng/Heatng Valves
PLUMBING & HEATING EQPT & SPLYS, WHOL: Water Purif
  Eqpt
PLUMBING & HEATING EQPT, WHOLESALE: Water
  Heaters/Purif
PLUMBING FIXTURES
PLUMBING FIXTURES: Brass, Incl Drain Cocks,
  Faucets/Spigots
PLUMBING FIXTURES: Plastic
PLUMBING FIXTURES: Vitreous
PLUMBING FIXTURES: Vitreous China
POINT OF SALE DEVICES
POLE LINE HARDWARE
POLICE PROTECTION
POLISHING SVC: Metals Or Formed Prdts
POLYESTERS
POLYETHYLENE CHLOROSULFONATED RUBBER
POLYETHYLENE RESINS
POLYMETHYL METHACRYLATE RESINS: Plexiglas
POLYPROPYLENE RESINS

POLYSTYRENE RESINS
POLYTETRAFLUOROETHYLENE RESINS
POLYURETHANE RESINS
POLYVINYL CHLORIDE RESINS
POLYVINYLIDENE CHLORIDE RESINS
PONTOONS: Rubber
POSTERS, WHOLESALE
POSTS: Floor, Adjustable, Metal
POTPOURRI
POTTERY
POTTING SOILS
POULTRY & POULTRY PRDTS WHOLESALERS
POULTRY & SMALL GAME SLAUGHTERING & PROCESS-
  ING
POULTRY SLAUGHTERING & PROCESSING
POWDER: Iron
POWDER: Metal
POWDER: Silver
POWER GENERATORS
POWER SPLY CONVERTERS: Static, Electronic Applications
POWER SUPPLIES: All Types, Static
POWER SUPPLIES: Transformer, Electronic Type
POWER SWITCHING EQPT
POWER TOOLS, HAND: Drills, Port, Elec/Pneumatic, Exc
  Rock
POWER TOOLS, HAND: Hammers, Portable, Elec/Pneu-
  matic, Chip
POWER TRANSMISSION EQPT WHOLESALERS
POWER TRANSMISSION EQPT: Mechanical
POWER TRANSMISSION EQPT: Vehicle
POWERED GOLF CART DEALERS
PRECAST TERRAZZO OR CONCRETE PRDTS
PRECIOUS STONES & METALS, WHOLESALE
PRECIPITATORS: Electrostatic
PRECISION INSTRUMENT REPAIR SVCS
PRESSED FIBER & MOLDED PULP PRDTS, EXC FOOD
  PRDTS
PRESSES
PRESSURIZERS OR AUXILIARY EQPT: Nuclear, Metal Plate
PRESTRESSED CONCRETE PRDTS
PRIMARY FINISHED OR SEMIFINISHED SHAPES
PRIMARY METAL PRODUCTS
PRINT CARTRIDGES: Laser & Other Computer Printers
PRINTED CIRCUIT BOARDS
PRINTERS & PLOTTERS
PRINTERS' SVCS: Folding, Collating, Etc
PRINTERS: Computer
PRINTERS: Magnetic Ink, Bar Code
PRINTING & BINDING: Books
PRINTING & BINDING: Pamphlets
PRINTING & BINDING: Textbooks
PRINTING & EMBOSSING: Plastic Fabric Articles
PRINTING & ENGRAVING: Financial Notes & Certificates
PRINTING & ENGRAVING: Invitation & Stationery
PRINTING & STAMPING: Fabric Articles
PRINTING & WRITING PAPER WHOLESALERS
PRINTING INKS WHOLESALERS
PRINTING MACHINERY
PRINTING MACHINERY, EQPT & SPLYS: Wholesalers
PRINTING TRADES MACHINERY & EQPT REPAIR SVCS
PRINTING, COMMERCIAL: Newspapers, NEC
PRINTING, COMMERCIAL: Business Forms, NEC
PRINTING, COMMERCIAL: Calendars, NEC
PRINTING, COMMERCIAL: Cards, Visiting, Incl Business,
  NEC
PRINTING, COMMERCIAL: Decals, NEC
PRINTING, COMMERCIAL: Directories, Telephone, NEC
PRINTING, COMMERCIAL: Envelopes, NEC
PRINTING, COMMERCIAL: Imprinting
PRINTING, COMMERCIAL: Invitations, NEC
PRINTING, COMMERCIAL: Labels & Seals, NEC
PRINTING, COMMERCIAL: Letterpress & Screen
PRINTING, COMMERCIAL: Literature, Advertising, NEC
PRINTING, COMMERCIAL: Magazines, NEC
PRINTING, COMMERCIAL: Menus, NEC
PRINTING, COMMERCIAL: Post Cards, Picture, NEC
PRINTING, COMMERCIAL: Promotional
PRINTING, COMMERCIAL: Publications
PRINTING, COMMERCIAL: Screen
PRINTING, COMMERCIAL: Stationery, NEC
PRINTING, COMMERCIAL: Tickets, NEC
PRINTING, COMMERCIAL: Wrappers, NEC
PRINTING, LITHOGRAPHIC: Advertising Posters
PRINTING, LITHOGRAPHIC: Calendars
PRINTING, LITHOGRAPHIC: Calendars & Cards

PRINTING, LITHOGRAPHIC: Color
PRINTING, LITHOGRAPHIC: Decals
PRINTING, LITHOGRAPHIC: Forms & Cards, Business
PRINTING, LITHOGRAPHIC: Forms, Business
PRINTING, LITHOGRAPHIC: Letters, Circular Or Form
PRINTING, LITHOGRAPHIC: Offset & photolithographic print-
  ing
PRINTING, LITHOGRAPHIC: On Metal
PRINTING, LITHOGRAPHIC: Posters
PRINTING, LITHOGRAPHIC: Publications
PRINTING, LITHOGRAPHIC: Tags
PRINTING, LITHOGRAPHIC: Tickets
PRINTING, LITHOGRAPHIC: Transfers, Decalcomania Or Dry
PRINTING: Book Music
PRINTING: Books
PRINTING: Books
PRINTING: Broadwoven Fabrics. Cotton
PRINTING: Commercial, NEC
PRINTING: Engraving & Plate
PRINTING: Flexographic
PRINTING: Gravure, Business Form & Card
PRINTING: Gravure, Color
PRINTING: Gravure, Coupons
PRINTING: Gravure, Directories, Phone, No Publishing On-
  Site
PRINTING: Gravure, Envelopes
PRINTING: Gravure, Forms, Business
PRINTING: Gravure, Invitations
PRINTING: Gravure, Job
PRINTING: Gravure, Labels
PRINTING: Gravure, Rotogravure
PRINTING: Laser
PRINTING: Letterpress
PRINTING: Lithographic
PRINTING: Offset
PRINTING: Pamphlets
PRINTING: Photo-Offset
PRINTING: Photolithographic
PRINTING: Rotary Photogravure
PRINTING: Rotogravure
PRINTING: Screen, Broadwoven Fabrics, Cotton
PRINTING: Screen, Fabric
PRINTING: Screen, Manmade Fiber & Silk, Broadwoven Fab-
  ric
PRINTING: Thermography
PRODUCTS: Petroleum & coal, NEC
PROFESSIONAL EQPT & SPLYS, WHOLESALE: Analytical
  Instruments
PROFESSIONAL EQPT & SPLYS, WHOLESALE: Bank
PROFESSIONAL EQPT & SPLYS, WHOLESALE: Engineers',
  NEC
PROFESSIONAL EQPT & SPLYS, WHOLESALE: Optical
  Goods
PROFESSIONAL EQPT & SPLYS, WHOLESALE: Precision
  Tools
PROFESSIONAL EQPT & SPLYS, WHOLESALE: Scientific &
  Engineerg
PROFESSIONAL INSTRUMENT REPAIR SVCS
PROFILE SHAPES: Unsupported Plastics
PROPELLERS: Boat & Ship, Cast
PROPERTY & CASUALTY INSURANCE AGENTS
PROPRIETARY STORES, NON-PRESCRIPTION MEDICINE
PROTECTION EQPT: Lightning
PROTECTIVE FOOTWEAR: Rubber Or Plastic
PUBLIC RELATIONS & PUBLICITY SVCS
PUBLIC RELATIONS SVCS
PUBLISHERS: Atlases
PUBLISHERS: Book
PUBLISHERS: Books, No Printing
PUBLISHERS: Catalogs
PUBLISHERS: Directories, NEC
PUBLISHERS: Directories, Telephone
PUBLISHERS: Guides
PUBLISHERS: Magazines, No Printing
PUBLISHERS: Maps
PUBLISHERS: Miscellaneous
PUBLISHERS: Music Book
PUBLISHERS: Music Book & Sheet Music
PUBLISHERS: Music, Sheet
PUBLISHERS: Newsletter
PUBLISHERS: Newspaper
PUBLISHERS: Newspapers, No Printing
PUBLISHERS: Pamphlets, No Printing
PUBLISHERS: Periodical, With Printing
PUBLISHERS: Periodicals, Magazines

PUBLISHERS: Periodicals, No Printing
PUBLISHERS: Sheet Music
PUBLISHERS: Technical Manuals
PUBLISHERS: Technical Manuals & Papers
PUBLISHERS: Telephone & Other Directory
PUBLISHERS: Television Schedules, No Printing
PUBLISHERS: Textbooks, No Printing
PUBLISHERS: Trade journals, No Printing
PUBLISHING & BROADCASTING: Internet Only
PUBLISHING & PRINTING: Art Copy
PUBLISHING & PRINTING: Book Music
PUBLISHING & PRINTING: Books
PUBLISHING & PRINTING: Catalogs
PUBLISHING & PRINTING: Directories, NEC
PUBLISHING & PRINTING: Directories, Telephone
PUBLISHING & PRINTING: Guides
PUBLISHING & PRINTING: Magazines: publishing & printing
PUBLISHING & PRINTING: Newsletters, Business Svc
PUBLISHING & PRINTING: Newspapers
PUBLISHING & PRINTING: Pamphlets
PUBLISHING & PRINTING: Periodical Statistical Reports
PUBLISHING & PRINTING: Posters
PUBLISHING & PRINTING: Shopping News
PUBLISHING & PRINTING: Technical Papers
PUBLISHING & PRINTING: Textbooks
PUBLISHING & PRINTING: Trade Journals
PULLEYS: Metal
PULLEYS: Power Transmission
PULP MILLS
PULP MILLS: Mechanical & Recycling Processing
PUMP SLEEVES: Rubber
PUMPS
PUMPS & PARTS: Indl
PUMPS & PUMPING EQPT REPAIR SVCS
PUMPS & PUMPING EQPT WHOLESALERS
PUMPS: Domestic, Water Or Sump
PUMPS: Fluid Power
PUMPS: Gasoline, Measuring Or Dispensing
PUMPS: Hydraulic Power Transfer
PUMPS: Measuring & Dispensing
PUMPS: Oil Well & Field
PUMPS: Oil, Measuring Or Dispensing
PUNCHES: Forming & Stamping
PURCHASING SVCS
PURIFICATION & DUST COLLECTION EQPT
PURLINS: Steel, Light Gauge

Q

QUARTZ CRYSTALS: Electronic
QUICKLIME
QUILTING SVC & SPLYS, FOR THE TRADE

R

RABBIT SLAUGHTERING & PROCESSING
RACEWAYS
RACKS & SHELVING: Household, Wood
RACKS: Book & Magazine, Wood
RACKS: Display
RACKS: Railroad Car, Vehicle Transportation, Steel
RADAR SYSTEMS & EQPT
RADIO & TELEVISION COMMUNICATIONS EQUIPMENT
RADIO BROADCASTING & COMMUNICATIONS EQPT
RADIO BROADCASTING STATIONS
RADIO COMMUNICATIONS: Airborne Eqpt
RADIO COMMUNICATIONS: Carrier Eqpt
RADIO RECEIVER NETWORKS
RADIO REPAIR & INSTALLATION SVCS
RADIO, TELEVISION & CONSUMER ELECTRONICS
   STORES: Eqpt, NEC
RADIO, TV & CONSUMER ELEC STORES: Automotive
   Sound Eqpt
RADIO, TV & CONSUMER ELEC STORES: High Fidelity
   Stereo Eqpt
RADIO, TV/CONSUMER ELEC STORES: Antennas, Satellite
   Dish
RADIOS WHOLESALERS
RAILINGS: Prefabricated, Metal
RAILINGS: Wood
RAILROAD CAR CUSTOMIZING SVCS
RAILROAD CAR RENTING & LEASING SVCS
RAILROAD CAR REPAIR SVCS
RAILROAD CARGO LOADING & UNLOADING SVCS
RAILROAD CROSSINGS: Steel Or Iron
RAILROAD EQPT
RAILROAD EQPT & SPLYS WHOLESALERS

RAILROAD EQPT: Brakes, Air & Vacuum
RAILROAD EQPT: Cars & Eqpt, Dining
RAILROAD EQPT: Cars & Eqpt, Interurban
RAILROAD EQPT: Cars & Eqpt, Train, Freight Or Passenger
RAILROAD EQPT: Cars, Rebuilt
RAILROAD EQPT: Cars, Tank Freight & Eqpt
RAILROAD EQPT: Locomotives & Parts, Indl
RAILROAD MAINTENANCE & REPAIR SVCS
RAILROAD RELATED EQPT
RAILROAD RELATED EQPT: Railway Track
RAILROAD TIES: Concrete
RAILROAD TIES: Wood
RAMPS: Prefabricated Metal
RAZORS, RAZOR BLADES
REACTORS: Current Limiting
REACTORS: Saturable
REAL ESTATE AGENCIES & BROKERS
REAL ESTATE AGENCIES: Buying
REAL ESTATE AGENCIES: Commercial
REAL ESTATE AGENCIES: Leasing & Rentals
REAL ESTATE AGENTS & MANAGERS
REAL ESTATE INVESTMENT TRUSTS
REAL ESTATE OPERATORS, EXC DEVELOPERS: Commer-
   cial/Indl Bldg
REAL ESTATE OPERATORS, EXC DEVELOPERS: Property,
   Retail
REALTY INVESTMENT TRUSTS
RECEIVERS: Radio Communications
RECHROMING SVC: Automobile Bumpers
RECLAIMED RUBBER: Reworked By Manufacturing Process
RECORDING TAPE: Video, Blank
RECORDS & TAPES: Prerecorded
RECORDS OR TAPES: Masters
RECOVERY SVC: Iron Ore, From Open Hearth Slag
RECOVERY SVC: Silver, From Used Photographic Film
RECOVERY SVCS: Metal
RECREATIONAL & SPORTING CAMPS
RECREATIONAL DEALERS: Camper & Travel Trailers
RECREATIONAL SPORTING EQPT REPAIR SVCS
RECREATIONAL VEHICLE PARTS & ACCESS STORES
RECREATIONAL VEHICLE REPAIR SVCS
RECTIFIERS: Electronic, Exc Semiconductor
RECYCLABLE SCRAP & WASTE MATERIALS WHOLE-
   SALERS
RECYCLING: Paper
REELS: Cable, Metal
REELS: Fiber, Textile, Made From Purchased Materials
REELS: Wood
REFINERS & SMELTERS: Aluminum
REFINERS & SMELTERS: Brass, Secondary
REFINERS & SMELTERS: Copper
REFINERS & SMELTERS: Copper, Secondary
REFINERS & SMELTERS: Gold
REFINERS & SMELTERS: Gold, Secondary
REFINERS & SMELTERS: Lead, Secondary
REFINERS & SMELTERS: Nonferrous Metal
REFINERS & SMELTERS: Rhenium, Primary
REFINERS & SMELTERS: Silicon, Primary, Over 99% Pure
REFINERS & SMELTERS: Zirconium
REFINING LUBRICATING OILS & GREASES, NEC
REFINING: Petroleum
REFLECTIVE ROAD MARKERS, WHOLESALE
REFRACTORIES: Brick
REFRACTORIES: Cement
REFRACTORIES: Clay
REFRACTORIES: Graphite, Carbon Or Ceramic Bond
REFRACTORIES: Nonclay
REFRIGERATION & HEATING EQUIPMENT
REFRIGERATION EQPT & SPLYS WHOLESALERS
REFRIGERATION EQPT & SPLYS, WHOLESALE: Beverage
   Dispensers
REFRIGERATION EQPT & SPLYS, WHOLESALE: Commer-
   cial Eqpt
REFRIGERATION EQPT: Complete
REFRIGERATION REPAIR SVCS
REFRIGERATORS & FREEZERS WHOLESALERS
REFUGEE SVCS
REFUSE SYSTEMS
REGISTERS: Air, Metal
REGULATION & ADMIN, GOVT: Facility Licensing & Inspec-
   tion
REGULATORS: Generator Voltage
REGULATORS: Power
REHABILITATION SVCS
RELAYS & SWITCHES: Indl, Electric

RELAYS: Control Circuit, Ind
RELAYS: Electronic Usage
RELIGIOUS SPLYS WHOLESALERS
REMOVERS & CLEANERS
REMOVERS: Paint
RENDERING PLANT
RENT-A-CAR SVCS
RENTAL SVCS: Business Machine & Electronic Eqpt
RENTAL SVCS: Clothing
RENTAL SVCS: Costume
RENTAL SVCS: Eqpt, Theatrical
RENTAL SVCS: Home Cleaning & Maintenance Eqpt
RENTAL SVCS: Motor Home
RENTAL SVCS: Musical Instrument
RENTAL SVCS: Pallet
RENTAL SVCS: Saddle Horse
RENTAL SVCS: Sign
RENTAL SVCS: Sound & Lighting Eqpt
RENTAL SVCS: Sporting Goods, NEC
RENTAL SVCS: Stores & Yards Eqpt
RENTAL SVCS: Tent & Tarpaulin
RENTAL SVCS: Trailer
RENTAL SVCS: Vending Machine
RENTAL SVCS: Work Zone Traffic Eqpt, Flags, Cones, Etc
RENTAL: Portable Toilet
RENTAL: Trucks, With Drivers
RENTAL: Video Tape & Disc
REPAIR SERVICES, NEC
REPAIR TRAINING, COMPUTER
REPOSSESSION SVCS
REPRODUCTION SVCS: Video Tape Or Disk
RESEARCH & DEVELOPMENT SVCS, COMMERCIAL: Engi-
   neering Lab
RESEARCH, DEV & TESTING SVCS, COMM: Chem Lab,
   Exc Testing
RESEARCH, DEVEL & TEST SVCS, COMM: Sociological &
   Education
RESEARCH, DEVELOPMENT & TEST SVCS, COMM: Cmptr
   Hardware Dev
RESEARCH, DEVELOPMENT & TEST SVCS, COMM: Re-
   search, Exc Lab
RESEARCH, DEVELOPMENT & TESTING SVCS, COMM:
   Agricultural
RESEARCH, DEVELOPMENT & TESTING SVCS, COMM:
   Research Lab
RESEARCH, DEVELOPMENT & TESTING SVCS, COMMER-
   CIAL: Business
RESEARCH, DEVELOPMENT & TESTING SVCS, COMMER-
   CIAL: Education
RESEARCH, DEVELOPMENT & TESTING SVCS, COMMER-
   CIAL: Energy
RESEARCH, DEVELOPMENT & TESTING SVCS, COMMER-
   CIAL: Food
RESEARCH, DEVELOPMENT & TESTING SVCS, COMMER-
   CIAL: Medical
RESEARCH, DEVELOPMENT & TESTING SVCS, COMMER-
   CIAL: Physical
RESEARCH, DVLPT & TEST SVCS, COMM: Mkt Analysis or
   Research
RESEARCH, DVLPT & TESTING SVCS, COMM: Mkt, Bus &
   Economic
RESIDENTIAL MENTAL HEALTH & SUBSTANCE ABUSE FA-
   CILITIES
RESIDENTIAL REMODELERS
RESIDUES
RESINS: Custom Compound Purchased
RESISTORS
RESISTORS & RESISTOR UNITS
RESOLVERS
RESPIRATORS
RESTAURANT EQPT REPAIR SVCS
RESTAURANT EQPT: Carts
RESTAURANT EQPT: Food Wagons
RESTAURANT EQPT: Sheet Metal
RESTAURANTS:Full Svc, American
RESTAURANTS:Full Svc, Barbecue
RESTAURANTS:Full Svc, Chinese
RESTAURANTS:Full Svc, Family, Chain
RESTAURANTS:Full Svc, Family, Independent
RESTAURANTS:Full Svc, Italian
RESTAURANTS:Limited Svc, Chicken
RESTAURANTS:Limited Svc, Chili Stand
RESTAURANTS:Limited Svc, Fast-Food, Chain
RESTAURANTS:Limited Svc, Ice Cream Stands Or Dairy
   Bars

INDEX

RESTAURANTS:Limited Svc, Lunch Counter
RESTAURANTS:Limited Svc, Pizzeria, Chain
RESTAURANTS:Limited Svc, Pizzeria, Independent
RESTAURANTS:Limited Svc, Sandwiches & Submarines Shop
RESTAURANTS:Limited Svc, Snack Shop
RESTAURANTS:Ltd Svc, Ice Cream, Soft Drink/Fountain Stands
RETAIL BAKERY: Bread
RETAIL BAKERY: Cakes
RETAIL BAKERY: Cookies
RETAIL BAKERY: Doughnuts
RETAIL BAKERY: Pastries
RETAIL BAKERY: Pies
RETAIL BAKERY: Pretzels
RETAIL FIREPLACE STORES
RETAIL LUMBER YARDS
RETAIL STORES, NEC
RETAIL STORES: Alarm Signal Systems
RETAIL STORES: Alcoholic Beverage Making Eqpt & Splys
RETAIL STORES: Art & Architectural Splys
RETAIL STORES: Artificial Limbs
RETAIL STORES: Audio-Visual Eqpt & Splys
RETAIL STORES: Awnings
RETAIL STORES: Banners
RETAIL STORES: Batteries, Non-Automotive
RETAIL STORES: Business Machines & Eqpt
RETAIL STORES: Cake Decorating Splys
RETAIL STORES: Children's Furniture, NEC
RETAIL STORES: Christmas Lights & Decorations
RETAIL STORES: Cleaning Eqpt & Splys
RETAIL STORES: Communication Eqpt
RETAIL STORES: Concrete Prdts, Precast
RETAIL STORES: Cosmetics
RETAIL STORES: Decals
RETAIL STORES: Educational Aids & Electronic Training Mat
RETAIL STORES: Electronic Parts & Eqpt
RETAIL STORES: Engine & Motor Eqpt & Splys
RETAIL STORES: Farm Eqpt & Splys
RETAIL STORES: Farm Tractors
RETAIL STORES: Fiberglass Materials, Exc Insulation
RETAIL STORES: Fire Extinguishers
RETAIL STORES: Flags
RETAIL STORES: Gravestones, Finished
RETAIL STORES: Hair Care Prdts
RETAIL STORES: Hearing Aids
RETAIL STORES: Hospital Eqpt & Splys
RETAIL STORES: Ice
RETAIL STORES: Medical Apparatus & Splys
RETAIL STORES: Monuments, Finished To Custom Order
RETAIL STORES: Motors, Electric
RETAIL STORES: Orthopedic & Prosthesis Applications
RETAIL STORES: Pet Splys
RETAIL STORES: Photocopy Machines
RETAIL STORES: Picture Frames, Ready Made
RETAIL STORES: Plumbing & Heating Splys
RETAIL STORES: Police Splys
RETAIL STORES: Religious Goods
RETAIL STORES: Rock & Stone Specimens
RETAIL STORES: Rubber Stamps
RETAIL STORES: Safety Splys & Eqpt
RETAIL STORES: Sunglasses
RETAIL STORES: Swimming Pools, Above Ground
RETAIL STORES: Technical Aids For The Handicapped
RETAIL STORES: Telephone & Communication Eqpt
RETAIL STORES: Telephone Eqpt & Systems
RETAIL STORES: Tents
RETAIL STORES: Theatrical Eqpt & Splys
RETAIL STORES: Typewriters & Business Machines
RETAIL STORES: Vaults & Safes
RETAIL STORES: Water Purification Eqpt
RETAIL STORES: Welding Splys
RETREADING MATERIALS: Tire
REUPHOLSTERY & FURNITURE REPAIR
REUPHOLSTERY SVCS
RHEOSTATS: Electronic
RIBBONS & BOWS
RIBBONS: Machine, Inked Or Carbon
RIVETS: Metal
ROAD CONSTRUCTION EQUIPMENT WHOLESALERS
ROAD MATERIALS: Bituminous, Not From Refineries
ROBOTS: Assembly Line
ROBOTS: Indl Spraying, Painting, Etc
ROD & BAR Aluminum
RODS: Plastic

RODS: Rolled, Aluminum
RODS: Steel & Iron, Made In Steel Mills
RODS: Welding
ROLL COVERINGS: Rubber
ROLL FORMED SHAPES: Custom
ROLLING MILL EQPT: Finishing
ROLLING MILL EQPT: Galvanizing Lines
ROLLING MILL MACHINERY
ROLLING MILL ROLLS: Cast Steel
ROLLS & ROLL COVERINGS: Rubber
ROOF DECKS
ROOFING MATERIALS: Asphalt
ROOFING MATERIALS: Sheet Metal
ROOFING MEMBRANE: Rubber
ROOM COOLERS: Portable
ROTORS: Motor
RUBBER
RUBBER BANDS
RUBBER PRDTS
RUBBER PRDTS REPAIR SVCS
RUBBER PRDTS: Appliance, Mechanical
RUBBER PRDTS: Automotive, Mechanical
RUBBER PRDTS: Mechanical
RUBBER PRDTS: Medical & Surgical Tubing, Extrudd & Lathe-Cut
RUBBER PRDTS: Oil & Gas Field Machinery, Mechanical
RUBBER PRDTS: Reclaimed
RUBBER PRDTS: Sheeting
RUBBER PRDTS: Silicone
RUBBER PRDTS: Sponge
RUBBER STAMP, WHOLESALE
RUBBER STRUCTURES: Air-Supported
RUST ARRESTING COMPOUNDS: Animal Or Vegetable Oil Based
RUST PROOFING SVC: Hot Dipping, Metals & Formed Prdts
RUST REMOVERS
RUST RESISTING

S

SADDLERY STORES
SAFE DEPOSIT BOXES
SAFES & VAULTS: Metal
SAFETY EQPT & SPLYS WHOLESALERS
SAILBOAT BUILDING & REPAIR
SAILS
SALT
SALT & SULFUR MINING
SALT MINING: Common
SALT: Packers'
SAND & GRAVEL
SAND LIME PRDTS
SAND MINING
SAND: Hygrade
SANDBLASTING EQPT
SANDBLASTING SVC: Building Exterior
SANDSTONE: Dimension
SANITARY SVC, NEC
SANITARY SVCS: Environmental Cleanup
SANITARY SVCS: Hazardous Waste, Collection & Disposal
SANITARY SVCS: Liquid Waste Collection & Disposal
SANITARY SVCS: Refuse Collection & Disposal Svcs
SANITARY SVCS: Rubbish Collection & Disposal
SANITARY SVCS: Waste Materials, Recycling
SANITARY WARE: Metal
SANITATION CHEMICALS & CLEANING AGENTS
SASHES: Door Or Window, Metal
SATELLITES: Communications
SAW BLADES
SAWDUST & SHAVINGS
SAWING & PLANING MILLS
SAWING & PLANING MILLS: Custom
SAWMILL MACHINES
SAWS & SAWING EQPT
SAWS: Hand, Metalworking Or Woodworking
SCAFFOLDS: Mobile Or Stationary, Metal
SCALE REPAIR SVCS
SCALES & BALANCES, EXC LABORATORY
SCALES: Indl
SCALES: Truck
SCHOOL SPLYS, EXC BOOKS: Wholesalers
SCHOOLS & EDUCATIONAL SVCS, NEC
SCHOOLS: Vocational, NEC
SCIENTIFIC EQPT REPAIR SVCS
SCIENTIFIC INSTRUMENTS WHOLESALERS
SCRAP & WASTE MATERIALS, WHOLESALE: Ferrous Metal

SCRAP & WASTE MATERIALS, WHOLESALE: Junk & Scrap
SCRAP & WASTE MATERIALS, WHOLESALE: Lumber Scrap
SCRAP & WASTE MATERIALS, WHOLESALE: Metal
SCRAP & WASTE MATERIALS, WHOLESALE: Nonferrous Metals Scrap
SCRAP & WASTE MATERIALS, WHOLESALE: Rubber Scrap
SCRAP STEEL CUTTING
SCREENS: Door, Metal Covered Wood
SCREENS: Door, Wood Frame
SCREENS: Projection
SCREENS: Window, Metal
SCREENS: Window, Wood Framed
SCREENS: Woven Wire
SCREW MACHINE PRDTS
SCREW MACHINES
SCREWS: Metal
SCREWS: Wood
SEALANTS
SEALING COMPOUNDS: Sealing, synthetic rubber or plastic
SEALS: Hermetic
SEALS: Oil, Rubber
SEARCH & NAVIGATION SYSTEMS
SEAT BELTS: Automobile & Aircraft
SEATING: Chairs, Table & Arm
SEATING: Stadium
SEATING: Transportation
SECRETARIAL & COURT REPORTING
SECRETARIAL SVCS
SECURITY CONTROL EQPT & SYSTEMS
SECURITY DEVICES
SECURITY EQPT STORES
SECURITY PROTECTIVE DEVICES MAINTENANCE & MONITORING SVCS
SECURITY SYSTEMS SERVICES
SEMICONDUCTOR CIRCUIT NETWORKS
SEMICONDUCTORS & RELATED DEVICES
SENSORS: Infrared, Solid State
SENSORS: Radiation
SENSORS: Temperature, Exc Indl Process
SENSORS: Ultraviolet, Solid State
SEPARATORS: Metal Plate
SEPTIC TANK CLEANING SVCS
SEPTIC TANKS: Concrete
SEPTIC TANKS: Plastic
SEWAGE & WATER TREATMENT EQPT
SEWAGE FACILITIES
SEWAGE TREATMENT SYSTEMS & EQPT
SEWER CLEANING & RODDING SVC
SEWER CLEANING EQPT: Power
SEWING CONTRACTORS
SEWING MACHINES & PARTS: Indl
SEWING, NEEDLEWORK & PIECE GOODS STORE: Needlework Gds/Sply
SEWING, NEEDLEWORK & PIECE GOODS STORE: Quilting Matls/Splys
SEWING, NEEDLEWORK & PIECE GOODS STORES: Knitting Splys
SEWING, NEEDLEWORK & PIECE GOODS STORES: Notions, Incl Trim
SEWING, NEEDLEWORK & PIECE GOODS STORES: Sewing & Needlework
SEXTANTS
SHADES: Window
SHAFTS: Shaft Collars
SHALE MINING, COMMON
SHAPES & PILINGS, STRUCTURAL: Steel
SHAPES: Extruded, Aluminum, NEC
SHAVING PREPARATIONS
SHEARS
SHEET METAL SPECIALTIES, EXC STAMPED
SHEETING: Laminated Plastic
SHEETS & STRIPS: Aluminum
SHEETS: Hard Rubber
SHELLAC
SHELTERED WORKSHOPS
SHELVES & SHELVING: Wood
SHELVING, MADE FROM PURCHASED WIRE
SHELVING: Office & Store, Exc Wood
SHIMS: Metal
SHIP BUILDING & REPAIRING: Cargo Vessels
SHIP BUILDING & REPAIRING: Lighthouse Tenders
SHIP BUILDING & REPAIRING: Tankers
SHIP BUILDING & REPAIRING: Tugboats
SHIP COMPONENTS: Metal, Prefabricated
SHIPBUILDING & REPAIR

SHOE MATERIALS: Counters
SHOE MATERIALS: Inner Soles
SHOE MATERIALS: Quarters
SHOE MATERIALS: Rands
SHOE MATERIALS: Rubber
SHOE MATERIALS: Uppers
SHOE REPAIR SHOP
SHOE STORES
SHOE STORES: Boots, Men's
SHOE STORES: Men's
SHOE STORES: Women's
SHOES & BOOTS WHOLESALERS
SHOES: Athletic, Exc Rubber Or Plastic
SHOES: Canvas, Rubber Soled
SHOES: Men's
SHOES: Plastic Or Rubber
SHOES: Plastic Soles Molded To Fabric Uppers
SHOES: Rubber Or Rubber Soled Fabric Uppers
SHOES: Women's
SHOT PEENING SVC
SHOWCASES & DISPLAY FIXTURES: Office & Store
SHOWER STALLS: Plastic & Fiberglass
SHREDDERS: Indl & Commercial
SHUTTERS, DOOR & WINDOW: Metal
SHUTTERS, DOOR & WINDOW: Plastic
SIDING & STRUCTURAL MATERIALS: Wood
SIDING MATERIALS
SIDING: Plastic
SIDING: Precast Stone
SIDING: Sheet Metal
SIGN LETTERING & PAINTING SVCS
SIGN PAINTING & LETTERING SHOP
SIGNALS: Traffic Control, Electric
SIGNALS: Transportation
SIGNS & ADVERTISING SPECIALTIES
SIGNS & ADVERTISING SPECIALTIES: Artwork, Advertising
SIGNS & ADVERTISING SPECIALTIES: Displays, Paint Process
SIGNS & ADVERTISING SPECIALTIES: Letters For Signs, Metal
SIGNS & ADVERTISING SPECIALTIES: Novelties
SIGNS & ADVERTISING SPECIALTIES: Scoreboards, Electric
SIGNS & ADVERTISING SPECIALTIES: Signs
SIGNS & ADVERTSG SPECIALTIES: Displays/Cutouts Window/Lobby
SIGNS, ELECTRICAL: Wholesalers
SIGNS, EXC ELECTRIC, WHOLESALE
SIGNS: Electrical
SIGNS: Neon
SILICON: Pure
SILICONES
SILK SCREEN DESIGN SVCS
SILVERWARE & PLATED WARE
SIMULATORS: Electronic Countermeasure
SIMULATORS: Flight
SINK TOPS, PLASTIC LAMINATED
SINTER: Iron
SIZES: Indl
SKIDS
SKIDS: Wood
SKYLIGHTS
SLAB & TILE: Precast Concrete, Floor
SLAG PRDTS
SLAG: Crushed Or Ground
SLAUGHTERING & MEAT PACKING
SLINGS: Lifting, Made From Purchased Wire
SLIPPER SOCKS, MADE FROM PURCHASED SOCKS
SLIPPERS: House
SLOT MACHINES
SMOKE DETECTORS
SNOW PLOWING SVCS
SNOW REMOVAL EQPT: Residential
SOAP DISHES: Vitreous China
SOAPS & DETERGENTS
SOCIAL SVCS: Individual & Family
SOCKETS: Electric
SOFT DRINKS WHOLESALERS
SOFTWARE PUBLISHERS: Application
SOFTWARE PUBLISHERS: Business & Professional
SOFTWARE PUBLISHERS: Computer Utilities
SOFTWARE PUBLISHERS: Education
SOFTWARE PUBLISHERS: Home Entertainment
SOFTWARE PUBLISHERS: NEC
SOFTWARE PUBLISHERS: Operating Systems

SOFTWARE PUBLISHERS: Publisher's
SOFTWARE TRAINING, COMPUTER
SOLAR CELLS
SOLAR HEATING EQPT
SOLDERING EQPT: Electrical, Exc Handheld
SOLDERING EQPT: Electrical, Handheld
SOLDERS
SOLENOIDS
SOLES, BOOT OR SHOE: Rubber, Composition Or Fiber
SOLVENTS
SOLVENTS: Organic
SONAR SYSTEMS & EQPT
SOUND EFFECTS & MUSIC PRODUCTION: Motion Picture
SOUND EQPT: Electric
SOUND REPRODUCING EQPT
SOUVENIR SHOPS
SOUVENIRS, WHOLESALE
SOYBEAN PRDTS
SPACE PROPULSION UNITS & PARTS
SPACE RESEARCH & TECHNOLOGY PROGRAMS ADMINISTRATION
SPACE VEHICLE EQPT
SPARK PLUGS: Internal Combustion Engines
SPARK PLUGS: Porcelain
SPEAKER MONITORS
SPEAKER SYSTEMS
SPECIALIZED LIBRARIES
SPECIALTY FOOD STORES: Coffee
SPECIALTY FOOD STORES: Dried Fruit
SPECIALTY FOOD STORES: Eggs & Poultry
SPECIALTY FOOD STORES: Health & Dietetic Food
SPEED CHANGERS
SPINDLES: Textile
SPONGES, ANIMAL, WHOLESALE
SPONGES: Bleached & Dyed
SPONGES: Plastic
SPOOLS: Indl
SPORTING & ATHLETIC GOODS: Balls, Baseball, Football, Etc
SPORTING & ATHLETIC GOODS: Bases, Baseball
SPORTING & ATHLETIC GOODS: Basketball Eqpt & Splys, NEC
SPORTING & ATHLETIC GOODS: Bows, Archery
SPORTING & ATHLETIC GOODS: Boxing Eqpt & Splys, NEC
SPORTING & ATHLETIC GOODS: Camping Eqpt & Splys
SPORTING & ATHLETIC GOODS: Cases, Gun & Rod
SPORTING & ATHLETIC GOODS: Crossbows
SPORTING & ATHLETIC GOODS: Decoys, Duck & Other Game Birds
SPORTING & ATHLETIC GOODS: Driving Ranges, Golf, Electronic
SPORTING & ATHLETIC GOODS: Dumbbells & Other Weight Eqpt
SPORTING & ATHLETIC GOODS: Fishing Eqpt
SPORTING & ATHLETIC GOODS: Fishing Tackle, General
SPORTING & ATHLETIC GOODS: Flies, Fishing, Artificial
SPORTING & ATHLETIC GOODS: Guards, Football, Soccer, Etc
SPORTING & ATHLETIC GOODS: Gymnasium Eqpt
SPORTING & ATHLETIC GOODS: Hooks, Fishing
SPORTING & ATHLETIC GOODS: Hunting Eqpt
SPORTING & ATHLETIC GOODS: Masks, Hockey, Baseball, Etc
SPORTING & ATHLETIC GOODS: Pigeons, Clay Targets
SPORTING & ATHLETIC GOODS: Pools, Swimming, Exc Plastic
SPORTING & ATHLETIC GOODS: Pools, Swimming, Plastic
SPORTING & ATHLETIC GOODS: Reels, Fishing
SPORTING & ATHLETIC GOODS: Shafts, Golf Club
SPORTING & ATHLETIC GOODS: Shooting Eqpt & Splys, General
SPORTING & ATHLETIC GOODS: Skateboards
SPORTING & ATHLETIC GOODS: Soccer Eqpt & Splys
SPORTING & ATHLETIC GOODS: Target Shooting Eqpt
SPORTING & ATHLETIC GOODS: Targets, Archery & Rifle Shooting
SPORTING & ATHLETIC GOODS: Team Sports Eqpt
SPORTING & ATHLETIC GOODS: Tennis Eqpt & Splys
SPORTING & ATHLETIC GOODS: Track & Field Athletic Eqpt
SPORTING & ATHLETIC GOODS: Water Sports Eqpt
SPORTING & RECREATIONAL GOODS & SPLYS WHOLESALERS
SPORTING & RECREATIONAL GOODS, WHOLESALE: Athletic Goods

SPORTING & RECREATIONAL GOODS, WHOLESALE: Bowling
SPORTING & RECREATIONAL GOODS, WHOLESALE: Fitness
SPORTING & RECREATIONAL GOODS, WHOLESALE: Golf
SPORTING & RECREATIONAL GOODS, WHOLESALE: Golf & Skiing
SPORTING & RECREATIONAL GOODS, WHOLESALE: Gymnasium
SPORTING & RECREATIONAL GOODS, WHOLESALE: Hot Tubs
SPORTING & RECREATIONAL GOODS, WHOLESALE: Hunting
SPORTING & RECREATIONAL GOODS, WHOLESALE: Spa
SPORTING GOODS
SPORTING GOODS STORES, NEC
SPORTING GOODS STORES: Ammunition
SPORTING GOODS STORES: Baseball Eqpt
SPORTING GOODS STORES: Camping Eqpt
SPORTING GOODS STORES: Firearms
SPORTING GOODS STORES: Hunting Eqpt
SPORTING GOODS STORES: Playground Eqpt
SPORTING GOODS STORES: Skateboarding Eqpt
SPORTING GOODS STORES: Soccer Splys
SPORTING GOODS STORES: Team sports Eqpt
SPORTING GOODS: Archery
SPORTS APPAREL STORES
SPOUTING: Plastic & Fiberglass Reinforced
SPRAYING & DUSTING EQPT
SPRAYING EQPT: Agricultural
SPRAYS: Self-Defense
SPRINGS: Coiled Flat
SPRINGS: Cold Formed
SPRINGS: Leaf, Automobile, Locomotive, Etc
SPRINGS: Mechanical, Precision
SPRINGS: Precision
SPRINGS: Steel
SPRINGS: Torsion Bar
SPRINGS: Wire
SPRINKLER SYSTEMS: Field
SPRINKLING SYSTEMS: Fire Control
SPROCKETS: Power Transmission
STACKING MACHINES: Automatic
STAGE LIGHTING SYSTEMS
STAINED GLASS ART SVCS
STAINLESS STEEL
STAINLESS STEEL WARE
STAIR TREADS: Rubber
STAIRCASES & STAIRS, WOOD
STAMPED ART GOODS FOR EMBROIDERING
STAMPING: Fabric Articles
STAMPINGS: Automotive
STAMPINGS: Metal
STANDS & RACKS: Engine, Metal
STARTERS & CONTROLLERS: Motor, Electric
STARTERS: Electric Motor
STARTERS: Motor
STATIC ELIMINATORS: Ind
STATIONARY & OFFICE SPLYS, WHOL: Albums, Scrapbooks/Binders
STATIONARY & OFFICE SPLYS, WHOL: Writing Instruments & Splys
STATIONARY & OFFICE SPLYS, WHOLESALE: Inked Ribbons
STATIONARY & OFFICE SPLYS, WHOLESALE: Marking Devices
STATIONARY & OFFICE SPLYS, WHOLESALE: Office Filing Splys
STATIONER'S SUNDRIES: Rubber
STATIONERY & OFFICE SPLYS WHOLESALERS
STATIONERY ARTICLES: Pottery
STATIONERY PRDTS
STATIONERY: Made From Purchased Materials
STATUARY & OTHER DECORATIVE PRDTS: Nonmetallic
STATUARY GOODS, EXC RELIGIOUS: Wholesalers
STATUES: Nonmetal
STEAM SPLY SYSTEMS SVCS INCLUDING GEOTHERMAL
STEEL & ALLOYS: Tool & Die
STEEL Electrometallurgical
STEEL FABRICATORS
STEEL MILLS
STEEL SHEET: Cold-Rolled
STEEL, COLD-ROLLED: Flat Bright, From Purchased Hot-Rolled

STEEL, COLD-ROLLED: Sheet Or Strip, From Own Hot-Rolled
STEEL, COLD-ROLLED: Strip NEC, From Purchased Hot-Rolled
STEEL, COLD-ROLLED: Strip Or Wire
STEEL, HOT-ROLLED: Sheet Or Strip
STEEL: Cold-Rolled
STEEL: Galvanized
STEERING SYSTEMS & COMPONENTS
STENCILS
STEREOGRAPHS: Photographic Message Svcs
STITCHING SVCS
STITCHING SVCS: Custom
STONE: Cast Concrete
STONE: Crushed & Broken, NEC
STONE: Dimension, NEC
STONE: Quarrying & Processing, Own Stone Prdts
STONES, SYNTHETIC: Gem Stone & Indl Use
STONEWARE PRDTS: Pottery
STORE FIXTURES, EXC REFRIGERATED: Wholesalers
STORE FIXTURES: Exc Wood
STORE FIXTURES: Wood
STORE FRONTS: Prefabricated, Metal
STORES: Auto & Home Supply
STORES: Drapery & Upholstery
STRAINERS: Line, Piping Systems
STRAPPING
STRAPS: Bindings, Textile
STRAPS: Braids, Textile
STRAPS: Spindle Banding
STRAPS: Webbing, Woven
STRIPS: Copper & Copper Alloy
STRUCTURAL SUPPORT & BUILDING MATERIAL: Concrete
STUCCO
STUDIOS: Artist
STUDIOS: Artists & Artists' Studios
STUDS & JOISTS: Sheet Metal
STYRENE
SUBDIVIDERS & DEVELOPERS: Real Property, Cemetery Lots Only
SUBPRESSES, METALWORKING
SUNDRIES & RELATED PRDTS: Medical & Laboratory, Rubber
SUNROOFS: Motor Vehicle
SUNROOMS: Prefabricated Metal
SUPERMARKETS & OTHER GROCERY STORES
SURFACE ACTIVE AGENTS
SURFACE ACTIVE AGENTS: Emulsifiers, Exc Food & Pharmaceuticl
SURFACE ACTIVE AGENTS: Oils & Greases
SURGICAL & MEDICAL INSTRUMENTS WHOLESALERS
SURGICAL APPLIANCES & SPLYS
SURGICAL APPLIANCES & SPLYS
SURGICAL EQPT: See Also Instruments
SURGICAL IMPLANTS
SURVEYING & MAPPING: Land Parcels
SURVEYING INSTRUMENTS WHOLESALERS
SUSPENSION SYSTEMS: Acoustical, Metal
SVC ESTABLISH EQPT, WHOLESALE: Carpet/Rug Clean Eqpt & Sply
SVC ESTABLISHMENT EQPT & SPLYS WHOLESALERS
SVC ESTABLISHMENT EQPT, WHOL: Cleaning & Maint Eqpt & Splys
SVC ESTABLISHMENT EQPT, WHOL: Concrete Burial Vaults & Boxes
SVC ESTABLISHMENT EQPT, WHOLESALE: Beauty Parlor Eqpt & Sply
SVC ESTABLISHMENT EQPT, WHOLESALE: Firefighting Eqpt
SVC ESTABLISHMENT EQPT, WHOLESALE: Restaurant Splys
SVC ESTABLISHMENT EQPT, WHOLESALE: Shredders, Indl & Comm
SWEEPING COMPOUNDS
SWIMMING POOL ACCESS: Leaf Skimmers Or Pool Rakes
SWIMMING POOL EQPT: Filters & Water Conditioning Systems
SWIMMING POOLS, EQPT & SPLYS: Wholesalers
SWITCHBOARDS & PARTS: Power
SWITCHES
SWITCHES: Electric Power
SWITCHES: Electric Power, Exc Snap, Push Button, Etc
SWITCHES: Electronic
SWITCHES: Electronic Applications
SWITCHES: Flow Actuated, Electrical

SWITCHES: Knife, Electric
SWITCHES: Thermostatic
SWITCHES: Time, Electrical Switchgear Apparatus
SWITCHGEAR & SWITCHBOARD APPARATUS
SWITCHGEAR & SWITCHGEAR ACCESS, NEC
SWITCHING EQPT: Radio & Television Communications
SYNAGOGUES
SYNTHETIC RESIN FINISHED PRDTS, NEC
SYRUPS, DRINK
SYRUPS, FLAVORING, EXC DRINK
SYSTEMS ENGINEERING: Computer Related
SYSTEMS INTEGRATION SVCS
SYSTEMS INTEGRATION SVCS: Local Area Network
SYSTEMS INTEGRATION SVCS: Office Computer Automation
SYSTEMS SOFTWARE DEVELOPMENT SVCS

T

TABLE OR COUNTERTOPS, PLASTIC LAMINATED
TABLES: Lift, Hydraulic
TABLETS & PADS: Newsprint, Made From Purchased Materials
TABLETS: Bronze Or Other Metal
TABLEWARE OR KITCHEN ARTICLES: Commercial, Fine Earthenware
TABLEWARE: Plastic
TABLEWARE: Vitreous China
TACKS: Steel, Wire Or Cut
TAGS & LABELS: Paper
TAGS: Paper, Blank, Made From Purchased Paper
TANK & BOILER CLEANING SVCS
TANK REPAIR & CLEANING SVCS
TANK REPAIR SVCS
TANKS & OTHER TRACKED VEHICLE CMPNTS
TANKS: Cryogenic, Metal
TANKS: For Tank Trucks, Metal Plate
TANKS: Fuel, Including Oil & Gas, Metal Plate
TANKS: Lined, Metal
TANKS: Military, Including Factory Rebuilding
TANKS: Plastic & Fiberglass
TANKS: Standard Or Custom Fabricated, Metal Plate
TANKS: Storage, Farm, Metal Plate
TANNING SALON EQPT & SPLYS, WHOLESALE
TANNING SALONS
TAPE DRIVES
TAPES, ADHESIVE: Medical
TAPES: Fabric
TAPES: Insulating
TAPES: Magnetic
TAPES: Plastic Coated
TAPES: Pressure Sensitive
TARPAULINS
TARPAULINS, WHOLESALE
TATTOO PARLORS
TAX RETURN PREPARATION SVCS
TECHNICAL INSTITUTE
TECHNICAL MANUAL PREPARATION SVCS
TELECOMMUNICATION EQPT REPAIR SVCS, EXC TELEPHONES
TELECOMMUNICATION SYSTEMS & EQPT
TELECOMMUNICATIONS CARRIERS & SVCS: Wired
TELEMETERING EQPT
TELEPHONE BOOTHS, EXC WOOD
TELEPHONE CENTRAL OFFICE EQPT: Dial Or Manual
TELEPHONE EQPT INSTALLATION
TELEPHONE EQPT: Modems
TELEPHONE EQPT: NEC
TELEPHONE SET REPAIR SVCS
TELEPHONE STATION EQPT & PARTS: Wire
TELEPHONE SWITCHING EQPT: Toll Switching
TELEPHONE: Fiber Optic Systems
TELEPHONE: Sets, Exc Cellular Radio
TELEVISION BROADCASTING & COMMUNICATIONS EQPT
TELEVISION BROADCASTING STATIONS
TELEVISION REPAIR SHOP
TELEVISION: Closed Circuit Eqpt
TEMPORARY HELP SVCS
TENT REPAIR SHOP
TENTS: All Materials
TERMINAL BOARDS
TEST BORING SVCS: Nonmetallic Minerals
TEST BORING, METAL MINING
TESTERS: Battery
TESTERS: Environmental
TESTERS: Gas, Exc Indl Process

TESTERS: Physical Property
TESTERS: Water, Exc Indl Process
TESTING SVCS
TEXTILE & APPAREL SVCS
TEXTILE FABRICATORS
TEXTILE FINISHING: Chem Coat/Treat, Man, Broadwoven, Cotton
TEXTILE FINISHING: Chemical Coating Or Treating, Narrow
TEXTILE FINISHING: Decorative, Man Fiber & Silk, Broadwoven
TEXTILE FINISHING: Napping, Manmade Fiber & Silk, Broadwoven
TEXTILE: Finishing, Cotton Broadwoven
TEXTILE: Finishing, Raw Stock NEC
TEXTILES
TEXTILES: Jute & Flax Prdts
TEXTILES: Tops & Top Processing, Manmade Or Other Fiber
TEXTILES: Tops, Combing & Converting
THEATRICAL LIGHTING SVCS
THEATRICAL PRODUCTION SVCS
THEATRICAL SCENERY
THEATRICAL TALENT & BOOKING AGENCIES
THERMISTORS, EXC TEMPERATURE SENSORS
THERMOCOUPLES
THERMOCOUPLES: Indl Process
THERMOELECTRIC DEVICES: Solid State
THERMOMETERS: Indl
THERMOMETERS: Medical, Digital
THERMOPLASTIC MATERIALS
THERMOPLASTICS
THERMOSETTING MATERIALS
THREAD: Embroidery
THREAD: Rubber
TIES, FORM: Metal
TILE: Brick & Structural, Clay
TILE: Clay, Drain & Structural
TILE: Clay, Roof
TILE: Drain, Clay
TILE: Sand Lime
TILE: Vinyl, Asbestos
TILE: Wall & Floor, Ceramic
TILE: Wall, Ceramic
TIN
TIN-BASE ALLOYS, PRIMARY
TIRE & INNER TUBE MATERIALS & RELATED PRDTS
TIRE & TUBE REPAIR MATERIALS, WHOLESALE
TIRE CORD & FABRIC
TIRE CORD & FABRIC: Indl, Reinforcing
TIRE DEALERS
TIRE RECAPPING & RETREADING
TIRE SUNDRIES OR REPAIR MATERIALS: Rubber
TIRES & INNER TUBES
TIRES & TUBES WHOLESALERS
TIRES: Auto
TIRES: Indl Vehicles
TIRES: Plastic
TITANIUM MILL PRDTS
TOBACCO & TOBACCO PRDTS WHOLESALERS
TOBACCO STORES & STANDS
TOBACCO: Chewing & Snuff
TOBACCO: Cigarettes
TOBACCO: Cigars
TOBACCO: Smoking
TOILET FIXTURES: Plastic
TOILET PREPARATIONS
TOILETRIES, COSMETICS & PERFUME STORES
TOILETRIES, WHOLESALE: Toiletries
TOMBSTONES: Terrazzo Or Concrete, Precast
TOOL & DIE STEEL
TOOL REPAIR SVCS
TOOLS & EQPT: Used With Sporting Arms
TOOLS: Carpenters', Including Levels & Chisels, Exc Saws
TOOLS: Hand
TOOLS: Hand, Engravers'
TOOLS: Hand, Hammers
TOOLS: Hand, Jewelers'
TOOLS: Hand, Masons'
TOOLS: Hand, Mechanics
TOOLS: Hand, Plumbers'
TOOLS: Hand, Power
TOOLS: Hand, Stonecutters'
TOOLS: Soldering
TOWELS: Fabric & Nonwoven, Made From Purchased Materials
TOWERS, SECTIONS: Transmission, Radio & Television

TOWERS: Cooling, Sheet Metal
TOWING & TUGBOAT SVC
TOWING SVCS: Marine
TOYS
TOYS & HOBBY GOODS & SPLYS, WHOLESALE: Amusement Goods
TOYS & HOBBY GOODS & SPLYS, WHOLESALE: Arts/Crafts Eqpt/Sply
TOYS & HOBBY GOODS & SPLYS, WHOLESALE: Balloons, Novelty
TOYS & HOBBY GOODS & SPLYS, WHOLESALE: Dolls
TOYS & HOBBY GOODS & SPLYS, WHOLESALE: Educational Toys
TOYS & HOBBY GOODS & SPLYS, WHOLESALE: Playing Cards
TOYS & HOBBY GOODS & SPLYS, WHOLESALE: Toys & Games
TOYS & HOBBY GOODS & SPLYS, WHOLESALE: Toys, NEC
TOYS & HOBBY GOODS & SPLYS, WHOLESALE: Video Games
TOYS, HOBBY GOODS & SPLYS WHOLESALERS
TOYS: Dolls, Stuffed Animals & Parts
TOYS: Kites
TOYS: Rubber
TRADE SHOW ARRANGEMENT SVCS
TRAILERS & PARTS: Boat
TRAILERS & PARTS: Horse
TRAILERS & PARTS: Truck & Semi's
TRAILERS & TRAILER EQPT
TRAILERS OR VANS: Horse Transportation, Fifth-Wheel Type
TRAILERS: Bodies
TRAILERS: Camping, Tent-Type
TRAILERS: Semitrailers, Missile Transportation
TRAILERS: Semitrailers, Truck Tractors
TRANSDUCERS: Electrical Properties
TRANSDUCERS: Pressure
TRANSFORMERS: Distribution
TRANSFORMERS: Distribution, Electric
TRANSFORMERS: Electric
TRANSFORMERS: Florescent Lighting
TRANSFORMERS: Furnace, Electric
TRANSFORMERS: Ignition, Domestic Fuel Burners
TRANSFORMERS: Machine Tool
TRANSFORMERS: Meters, Electronic
TRANSFORMERS: Power Related
TRANSFORMERS: Specialty
TRANSFORMERS: Voltage Regulating
TRANSLATION & INTERPRETATION SVCS
TRANSMISSION FLUID, MADE FROM PURCHASED MATERIALS
TRANSMISSIONS: Motor Vehicle
TRANSPORTATION EPQT & SPLYS, WHOLESALE: Combat Vehicles
TRANSPORTATION EPQT & SPLYS, WHOLESALE: Nav Eqpt & Splys
TRANSPORTATION EPQT & SPLYS, WHOLESALE: Tanks & Tank Compnts
TRANSPORTATION EQPT & SPLYS WHOLESALERS, NEC
TRANSPORTATION EQUIPMENT, NEC
TRANSPORTATION PROG REG & ADMIN, GOVT: Licensing Agencies
TRANSPORTATION PROGRAM REGULATION & ADMIN, GOVT: State
TRANSPORTATION PROGRAMS REGULATION & ADMINISTRATION SVCS
TRANSPORTATION SVCS, AIR, NONSCHEDULED: Air Cargo Carriers
TRANSPORTATION SVCS, NEC
TRANSPORTATION: Air, Scheduled Passenger
TRANSPORTATION: Horse-Drawn
TRAPS: Animal, Iron Or Steel
TRAVEL TRAILERS & CAMPERS
TRAVELER ACCOMMODATIONS, NEC
TRAYS: Plastic
TROPHIES, NEC
TROPHIES, PLATED, ALL METALS
TROPHIES, STAINLESS STEEL
TROPHIES, WHOLESALE
TROPHIES: Metal, Exc Silver
TROPHY & PLAQUE STORES
TRUCK & BUS BODIES: Ambulance
TRUCK & BUS BODIES: Automobile Wrecker Truck
TRUCK & BUS BODIES: Bus Bodies
TRUCK & BUS BODIES: Car Carrier

TRUCK & BUS BODIES: Cement Mixer
TRUCK & BUS BODIES: Dump Truck
TRUCK & BUS BODIES: Garbage Or Refuse Truck
TRUCK & BUS BODIES: Motor Vehicle, Specialty
TRUCK & BUS BODIES: Tank Truck
TRUCK & BUS BODIES: Truck Beds
TRUCK & BUS BODIES: Truck Cabs, Motor Vehicles
TRUCK & BUS BODIES: Truck, Motor Vehicle
TRUCK & BUS BODIES: Utility Truck
TRUCK & BUS BODIES: Van Bodies
TRUCK BODIES: Body Parts
TRUCK BODY SHOP
TRUCK DRIVER SVCS
TRUCK GENERAL REPAIR SVC
TRUCK PAINTING & LETTERING SVCS
TRUCK PARTS & ACCESSORIES: Wholesalers
TRUCKING & HAULING SVCS: Animal & Farm Prdt
TRUCKING & HAULING SVCS: Contract Basis
TRUCKING & HAULING SVCS: Garbage, Collect/Transport Only
TRUCKING & HAULING SVCS: Heavy Machinery, Local
TRUCKING & HAULING SVCS: Liquid, Local
TRUCKING & HAULING SVCS: Machinery, Heavy
TRUCKING & HAULING SVCS: Mail Carriers, Contract
TRUCKING, ANIMAL
TRUCKING, AUTOMOBILE CARRIER
TRUCKING, DUMP
TRUCKING: Except Local
TRUCKING: Local, With Storage
TRUCKING: Local, Without Storage
TRUCKS & TRACTORS: Industrial
TRUCKS, INDL: Wholesalers
TRUCKS: Forklift
TRUCKS: Indl
TRUSSES & FRAMING: Prefabricated Metal
TRUSSES: Wood, Floor
TRUSSES: Wood, Roof
TRUST MANAGEMENT SVC, EXC EDUCATIONAL, RELIGIOUS & CHARITY
TUB CONTAINERS: Plastic
TUBE & PIPE MILL EQPT
TUBE & TUBING FABRICATORS
TUBES: Finned, For Heat Transfer
TUBES: Generator, Electron Beam, Beta Ray
TUBES: Hard Rubber
TUBES: Paper
TUBES: Paper Or Fiber, Chemical Or Electrical Uses
TUBES: Steel & Iron
TUBES: Wrought, Welded Or Lock Joint
TUBING: Copper
TUBING: Electrical Use, Quartz
TUBING: Flexible, Metallic
TUBING: Glass
TUBING: Plastic
TUBING: Rubber
TUBING: Seamless
TUGBOAT SVCS
TUNGSTEN CARBIDE POWDER
TUNGSTEN MILL PRDTS
TURBINE GENERATOR SET UNITS: Hydraulic, Complete
TURBINES & TURBINE GENERATOR SET UNITS, COMPLETE
TURBINES & TURBINE GENERATOR SETS
TURBINES & TURBINE GENERATOR SETS & PARTS
TURBINES: Gas, Mechanical Drive
TURBINES: Hydraulic, Complete
TURBINES: Steam
TURNSTILES
TWINE PRDTS
TYPE: Rubber
TYPESETTING SVC
TYPESETTING SVC: Computer

U

ULTRASONIC EQPT: Cleaning, Exc Med & Dental
UMBRELLAS & CANES
UNDERCOATINGS: Paint
UNIFORM SPLY SVCS: Indl
UNIFORM STORES
UNISEX HAIR SALONS
UNIVERSITY
UNSUPPORTED PLASTICS: Floor Or Wall Covering
UPHOLSTERY WORK SVCS
URANIUM ORE MINING, NEC
USED BOOK STORES

USED CAR DEALERS
USED MERCHANDISE STORES: Musical Instruments
USED MERCHANDISE STORES: Rare Books
UTENSILS: Cast Aluminum
UTENSILS: Cast Aluminum, Cooking Or Kitchen
UTILITY TRAILER DEALERS

V

VACUUM CLEANER STORES
VACUUM CLEANERS: Household
VACUUM CLEANERS: Indl Type
VALUE-ADDED RESELLERS: Computer Systems
VALVE REPAIR SVCS, INDL
VALVES
VALVES & PARTS: Gas, Indl
VALVES & PIPE FITTINGS
VALVES & REGULATORS: Pressure, Indl
VALVES: Aerosol, Metal
VALVES: Aircraft
VALVES: Aircraft, Fluid Power
VALVES: Aircraft, Hydraulic
VALVES: Control, Automatic
VALVES: Engine
VALVES: Fluid Power, Control, Hydraulic & pneumatic
VALVES: Hard Rubber
VALVES: Indl
VALVES: Nuclear Power Plant, Ferrous
VALVES: Plumbing & Heating
VALVES: Regulating & Control, Automatic
VALVES: Regulating, Process Control
VALVES: Water Works
VAN CONVERSIONS
VANADIUM ORE MINING, NEC
VARIETY STORES
VARNISHES, NEC
VASES: Pottery
VAULTS & SAFES WHOLESALERS
VEHICLES: All Terrain
VEHICLES: Recreational
VENDING MACHINE OPERATORS: Cigarette
VENDING MACHINE OPERATORS: Sandwich & Hot Food
VENDING MACHINES & PARTS
VENETIAN BLIND REPAIR SHOP
VENETIAN BLINDS & SHADES
VENTILATING EQPT: Metal
VENTILATING EQPT: Sheet Metal
VENTURE CAPITAL COMPANIES
VESSELS: Process, Indl, Metal Plate
VETERINARY PHARMACEUTICAL PREPARATIONS
VETERINARY PRDTS: Instruments & Apparatus
VIBRATORS, ELECTRIC: Beauty & Barber Shop
VIBRATORS: Concrete Construction
VIBRATORS: Interrupter
VIDEO & AUDIO EQPT, WHOLESALE
VIDEO CAMERA-AUDIO RECORDERS: Household Use
VIDEO TAPE PRODUCTION SVCS
VIDEO TRIGGERS EXC REMOTE CONTROL TV DEVICES
VIDEO TRIGGERS: Remote Control TV Devices
VINYL RESINS, NEC
VISES: Machine
VISUAL COMMUNICATIONS SYSTEMS
VITAMINS: Pharmaceutical Preparations
VOCATIONAL REHABILITATION AGENCY
VOCATIONAL TRAINING AGENCY

W

WALL COVERINGS: Rubber
WALLPAPER & WALL COVERINGS
WALLS: Curtain, Metal
WAREHOUSING & STORAGE FACILITIES, NEC
WAREHOUSING & STORAGE, REFRIGERATED: Cold Storage Or Refrig
WAREHOUSING & STORAGE, REFRIGERATED: Frozen Or Refrig Goods
WAREHOUSING & STORAGE: Farm Prdts
WAREHOUSING & STORAGE: General
WAREHOUSING & STORAGE: General
WAREHOUSING & STORAGE: Self Storage
WARM AIR HEATING & AC EQPT & SPLYS, WHOLESALE Air Filters
WARM AIR HEATING & AC EQPT & SPLYS, WHOLESALE Furnaces, Elec
WARM AIR HEATING/AC EQPT/SPLYS, WHOL Warm Air Htg Eqpt/Splys
WASHERS

INDEX

WASHERS: Metal
WASHERS: Rubber
WASHERS: Spring, Metal
WATCH & CLOCK STORES
WATCH REPAIR SVCS
WATER BOTTLES: Rubber
WATER HEATERS
WATER PURIFICATION EQPT: Household
WATER PURIFICATION PRDTS: Chlorination Tablets & Kits
WATER SOFTENER SVCS
WATER SOFTENING WHOLESALERS
WATER SPLY: Irrigation
WATER SUPPLY
WATER TREATMENT EQPT: Indl
WATER: Distilled
WATER: Mineral, Carbonated, Canned & Bottled, Etc
WATER: Pasteurized & Mineral, Bottled & Canned
WATERPROOFING COMPOUNDS
WEATHER STRIP: Sponge Rubber
WEATHER STRIPS: Metal
WEIGHING MACHINERY & APPARATUS
WELDING & CUTTING APPARATUS & ACCESS, NEC
WELDING EQPT
WELDING EQPT & SPLYS WHOLESALERS
WELDING EQPT & SPLYS: Gas
WELDING EQPT & SPLYS: Generators, Arc Welding, AC & DC
WELDING EQPT & SPLYS: Resistance, Electric
WELDING EQPT & SPLYS: Spot, Electric
WELDING EQPT & SPLYS: Wire, Bare & Coated
WELDING EQPT REPAIR SVCS
WELDING EQPT: Electric
WELDING EQPT: Electrical
WELDING MACHINES & EQPT: Ultrasonic
WELDING REPAIR SVC
WELDING SPLYS, EXC GASES: Wholesalers
WELDING TIPS: Heat Resistant, Metal
WELDMENTS
WELL CURBING: Concrete
WET CORN MILLING
WHEELBARROWS
WHEELCHAIR LIFTS
WHEELCHAIRS
WHEELS
WHEELS & BRAKE SHOES: Railroad, Cast Iron
WHEELS & GRINDSTONES, EXC ARTIFICIAL: Abrasive
WHEELS & PARTS
WHEELS, GRINDING: Artificial
WHEELS: Abrasive
WHEELS: Buffing & Polishing

WHEELS: Disc, Wheelbarrow, Stroller, Etc, Stamped Metal
WHEELS: Iron & Steel, Locomotive & Car
WHEELS: Railroad Car, Cast Steel
WHEELS: Water
WHIRLPOOL BATHS: Hydrotherapy
WHISTLES
WICKING
WINCHES
WINDINGS: Coil, Electronic
WINDMILLS: Electric Power Generation
WINDMILLS: Farm Type
WINDOW & DOOR FRAMES
WINDOW FRAMES & SASHES: Plastic
WINDOW FRAMES, MOLDING & TRIM: Vinyl
WINDOW FURNISHINGS WHOLESALERS
WINDOW SCREENING: Plastic
WINDOWS: Frames, Wood
WINDOWS: Wood
WINDSHIELD WIPER SYSTEMS
WINDSHIELDS: Plastic
WINE & DISTILLED ALCOHOLIC BEVERAGES WHOLE-SALERS
WINE CELLARS, BONDED: Wine, Blended
WIRE
WIRE & CABLE: Aluminum
WIRE & CABLE: Nonferrous, Automotive, Exc Ignition Sets
WIRE & CABLE: Nonferrous, Building
WIRE & WIRE PRDTS
WIRE CLOTH & WOVEN WIRE PRDTS, MADE FROM PUR-CHASED WIRE
WIRE FABRIC: Welded Steel
WIRE FENCING & ACCESS WHOLESALERS
WIRE MATERIALS: Aluminum
WIRE MATERIALS: Copper
WIRE MATERIALS: Steel
WIRE PRDTS: Ferrous Or Iron, Made In Wiredrawing Plants
WIRE PRDTS: Steel & Iron
WIRE WINDING OF PURCHASED WIRE
WIRE, FLAT: Strip, Cold-Rolled, Exc From Hot-Rolled Mills
WIRE: Communication
WIRE: Magnet
WIRE: Mesh
WIRE: Nonferrous
WIRE: Nonferrous, Appliance Fixture
WIRE: Steel, Insulated Or Armored
WIRE: Wire, Ferrous Or Iron
WIRING DEVICES WHOLESALERS
WOMEN'S & CHILDREN'S CLOTHING WHOLESALERS, NEC
WOMEN'S & GIRLS' SPORTSWEAR WHOLESALERS

WOMEN'S CLOTHING STORES
WOMEN'S CLOTHING STORES: Ready-To-Wear
WOMEN'S SPORTSWEAR STORES
WOOD & WOOD BY-PRDTS, WHOLESALE
WOOD CHIPS, PRODUCED AT THE MILL
WOOD PRDTS
WOOD PRDTS: Applicators
WOOD PRDTS: Baskets, Fruit & Veg, Round Stave, Till, Etc
WOOD PRDTS: Door Trim
WOOD PRDTS: Engraved
WOOD PRDTS: Furniture Inlays, Veneers
WOOD PRDTS: Ladders & Stepladders
WOOD PRDTS: Laundry
WOOD PRDTS: Mantels
WOOD PRDTS: Moldings, Unfinished & Prefinished
WOOD PRDTS: Mulch Or Sawdust
WOOD PRDTS: Mulch, Wood & Bark
WOOD PRDTS: Novelties, Fiber
WOOD PRDTS: Plugs
WOOD PRDTS: Reed, Rattan, Wicker & Willow ware, Exc Furnitr
WOOD PRDTS: Saddle Trees
WOOD PRDTS: Signboards
WOOD PRDTS: Survey Stakes
WOOD PRDTS: Trophy Bases
WOOD PRDTS: Veneer Work, Inlaid
WOOD PRDTS: Washboards, Wood & Part Wood
WOOD PRDTS: Weather Strip, Wood
WOOD PRODUCTS: Reconstituted
WOOD TREATING: Millwork
WOOD TREATING: Structural Lumber & Timber
WOOD TREATING: Wood Prdts, Creosoted
WOODWORK & TRIM: Exterior & Ornamental
WOODWORK & TRIM: Interior & Ornamental
WOODWORK: Carved & Turned
WOODWORK: Interior & Ornamental, NEC
WOODWORK: Ornamental, Cornices, Mantels, Etc.
WOOL: Felted
WORD PROCESSING EQPT
WOVEN WIRE PRDTS, NEC
WRENCHES

X

X-RAY EQPT & TUBES
X-RAY EQPT REPAIR SVCS

Y

YARN & YARN SPINNING
YARN: Manmade & Synthetic Fiber, Twisting Or Winding

PRODUCT SECTION

ABRASIVE STONES, EXC GRINDING STONES: *Ground Or Whole*

Abrasive Technology Inc ....C....... 740 548-4100
　Lewis Center (G-11880)

ABRASIVES

Abrasive Source Inc ....F....... 937 526-9753
　Russia (G-16761)
Ali Industries Inc ....C....... 937 878-3946
　Fairborn (G-9613)
Alliance Abrasives LLC ....F....... 330 823-7957
　Alliance (G-490)
ARC Abrasives Inc ....D....... 800 888-4885
　Troy (G-18805)
Baaron Abrasives Inc ....G....... 330 263-7737
　Wooster (G-20745)
Braun Machine Technologies LLC ....F....... 330 777-5433
　Vienna (G-19363)
Coastal Diamond Incorporated ....G....... 440 946-7171
　Mentor (G-13548)
Diamond Innovations Inc ....B....... 614 438-2000
　Columbus (G-7025)
Even-Cut Abrasive Company ....D....... 216 881-9595
　Cleveland (G-5306)
Hec Investments Inc ....C....... 937 278-9123
　Dayton (G-8388)
Inner City Abrasives LLC ....G....... 216 391-4402
　Cleveland (G-5570)
Jason Incorporated ....F....... 513 860-3400
　Hamilton (G-10711)
Lawrence Industries Inc ....E....... 216 518-7000
　Cleveland (G-5687)
Mill-Rose Company ....C....... 440 255-9171
　Mentor (G-13657)
Nanolap Technologies LLC ....E....... 877 658-4949
　Englewood (G-9534)
National Lime and Stone Co ....C....... 419 396-7671
　Carey (G-2921)
Ohio Slitting & Storage ....E....... 937 452-1108
　Camden (G-2486)
Performance Abrasives Inc ....G....... 513 733-9283
　Cincinnati (G-4224)
Sure-Foot Industries Corp ....E....... 440 234-4446
　Cleveland (G-6275)
Universal Ground Cullet Inc ....G....... 419 637-2630
　Gibsonburg (G-10378)
US Technology Corporation ....E....... 330 455-1181
　Canton (G-2891)
US Technology Media Inc ....F....... 330 874-3094
　Bolivar (G-1947)
Vibra Finish Co ....E....... 513 870-6300
　Fairfield (G-9729)

ABRASIVES: *Coated*

Lexington Abrasives Inc ....D....... 330 821-1166
　Alliance (G-522)
Premier Coatings Ltd ....F....... 513 942-1070
　West Chester (G-19920)

ABRASIVES: *Grains*

Golden Dynamic Inc ....G....... 614 575-1222
　Columbus (G-7122)

ABRASIVES: *Synthetic*

Noritake Co Inc ....E....... 513 234-0770
　Mason (G-13067)

ACCELERATION INDICATORS & SYSTEM COMPONENTS: *Aerospace*

Eaton Aerospace LLC ....F....... 216 523-5000
　Cleveland (G-5243)
Eaton Aerospace LLC ....E....... 216 523-5000
　Cleveland (G-5244)
Nhvs International Inc ....B....... 440 527-8610
　Mentor (G-13665)

ACCELERATORS, RUBBER PROCESSING: *Cyclic or Acyclic*

Image Armor LLC ....G....... 877 673-4377
　New Philadelphia (G-14903)
Valero Renewable Fuels Co LLC ....D....... 740 437-6211
　Bloomingburg (G-1721)

ACCELERATORS: *Electron Linear*

Spang & Company ....E....... 440 350-6108
　Mentor (G-13727)

ACCELERATORS: *Linear*

Ci Disposition Co ....E....... 216 587-5200
　Brooklyn Heights (G-2135)

ACCOUNTING MACHINES & CASH REGISTERS

Cambridge Ohio Production & As ....F....... 740 432-6383
　Cambridge (G-2448)

ACCOUNTING SVCS, NEC

Patterson Colburne ....G....... 419 866-5544
　Holland (G-11077)

ACCOUNTING SVCS: *Certified Public*

Patrick J Burke & Co ....E....... 513 455-8200
　Cincinnati (G-4215)
Watson Haran & Company Inc ....G....... 937 436-1414
　Dayton (G-8747)

ACIDS: *Hydrochloric*

Jones-Hamilton Co ....D....... 419 666-9838
　Walbridge (G-19460)

ACIDS: *Inorganic*

Capital Resin Corporation ....D....... 614 445-7177
　Columbus (G-6901)

ACIDS: *Sulfuric, Oleum*

Chemours Company Fc LLC ....F....... 513 941-4121
　North Bend (G-15203)

ACOUSTICAL BOARD & TILE

Mpc Inc ....F....... 440 835-1405
　Westlake (G-20284)

ACRYLIC RESINS

Plaskolite Inc ....D....... 740 450-1109
　Zanesville (G-21341)
Plaskolite LLC ....B....... 614 294-7294
　Columbus (G-7490)

ACTUATORS: *Indl, NEC*

Automation Technology Inc ....E....... 937 233-6084
　Dayton (G-8174)
Kz Solutions Inc ....G....... 513 942-9378
　West Chester (G-19889)
Moog Inc ....D....... 330 682-0010
　Orrville (G-15748)
Norgren Inc ....C....... 937 833-4033
　Brookville (G-2194)
SMC Corporation of America ....E....... 330 659-2006
　Richfield (G-16638)
Thermotion Corp ....F....... 440 639-8325
　Mentor (G-13746)

ADAPTERS: *Well*

Grip Force LLC ....G....... 440 497-7014
　Eastlake (G-9272)
Wells Inc ....F....... 419 457-2611
　Risingsun (G-16673)

ADDITIVE BASED PLASTIC MATERIALS: *Plasticizers*

Mum Industries Inc ....E....... 440 269-4966
　Mentor (G-13663)

ADDRESSING SVCS

Cleveland Letter Service Inc ....E....... 216 781-8300
　Chagrin Falls (G-3052)
Franklins Printing Company ....F....... 740 452-6375
　Zanesville (G-21311)
Gerald L Hermann Co Inc ....F....... 513 661-1818
　Cincinnati (G-3822)
Hecks Direct Mail & Prtg Svc ....E....... 419 697-3505
　Toledo (G-18502)

ADDRESSOGRAPHING SVCS

Selby Service/Roxy Press Inc ....G....... 513 241-3445
　Cincinnati (G-4400)

ADHESIVES

Akzo Nobel Paints LLC ....G....... 513 242-0530
　Cincinnati (G-3374)
Certon Technologies Inc ....F....... 440 786-7185
　Bedford (G-1414)
Choice Brands Adhesives Ltd ....G....... 513 772-1234
　Cincinnati (G-3530)
Conversion Tech Intl Inc ....E....... 419 924-5566
　West Unity (G-20127)
Entrochem Inc ....F....... 614 946-7602
　Columbus (G-7061)
Evans Adhesive Corporation Ltd ....E....... 614 451-2665
　Columbus (G-7070)
Evans Adhesive Corporation Ltd ....G....... 614 451-2665
　Columbus (G-7071)
Fairchild Labs LLC ....F....... 614 235-7040
　Columbus (G-7076)
Fairmount Santrol Inc ....G....... 440 214-3200
　Chesterland (G-3206)
Har Equipment Sales Inc ....G....... 440 786-7189
　Bedford (G-1428)
Henkel Corporation ....C....... 216 475-3600
　Cleveland (G-5498)
Imperial Adhesives ....G....... 513 351-1300
　Cincinnati (G-3914)
Invisible Repair Products Inc ....G....... 330 798-0441
　Akron (G-236)
Lord Corporation ....C....... 440 333-5750
　Rocky River (G-16700)

Employee Codes: A=Over 500 employees, B=251-500
C=101-250, D=51-100, E=20-50, F=10-19, G=3-9

2017 Harris Ohio
Industrial Directory

1389

PRODUCT

ADHESIVES (continued)

Millennium Adhesive Products ....G...... 440 708-1212
  Chagrin Falls *(G-3104)*
Mitsubishi Chls Perf Plyrs Inc ....D...... 419 483-2931
  Bellevue *(G-1553)*
Morgan Adhesives Company LLC ....B....... 330 688-1111
  Stow *(G-17775)*
Nova Films and Foils Inc ....F...... 440 201-1300
  Bedford *(G-1448)*
Paramelt Argueso Kindt Inc ....G...... 216 252-4122
  Cleveland *(G-5963)*
PPG Architectural Finishes Inc ....G...... 330 788-2421
  Youngstown *(G-21174)*
PPG Architectural Finishes Inc ....G...... 440 942-7708
  Mentor *(G-13694)*
PPG Architectural Finishes Inc ....G...... 614 846-0097
  Columbus *(G-7508)*
PPG Architectural Finishes Inc ....C...... 419 433-5664
  Huron *(G-11238)*
Premier Building Solutions Inc ....D...... 330 244-2907
  Massillon *(G-13197)*
RPM Consumer Holding Company ....G...... 330 273-5090
  Medina *(G-13470)*
Savare Corporation ....G...... 614 255-2878
  Columbus *(G-7590)*
Savare Specialty Adhesives LLC ....E...... 614 255-2648
  Delaware *(G-8886)*
Southern Adhsives Coatings Inc ....G...... 513 561-8440
  Cincinnati *(G-4438)*
Sunstar Engrg Americas Inc ....E...... 937 746-8575
  Springboro *(G-17508)*
Technicote Inc ....E...... 330 928-1476
  Cuyahoga Falls *(G-8053)*
Three Bond International Inc ....E...... 937 610-3000
  Dayton *(G-8713)*
Toagosei America Inc ....D...... 614 718-3855
  West Jefferson *(G-20084)*

ADHESIVES & SEALANTS

Adchem Adhesives Inc ....F...... 440 526-1976
  Cleveland *(G-4701)*
Akron Paint & Varnish Inc ....D...... 330 773-8911
  Akron *(G-50)*
Alpha Coatings Inc ....C...... 419 435-5111
  Fostoria *(G-9964)*
Arclin ....G...... 877 689-9145
  Holland *(G-11045)*
Arclin USA LLC ....E...... 419 726-5013
  Toledo *(G-18354)*
Avery Dennison Corporation ....B...... 440 358-3700
  Painesville *(G-15857)*
Boltaron Inc ....D...... 740 498-5900
  Newcomerstown *(G-15109)*
Borden Chemical Inc ....E...... 614 225-4000
  Columbus *(G-6848)*
Brewer Company ....G...... 513 576-6300
  Cincinnati *(G-3470)*
Brewer Company ....E...... 614 279-8688
  Columbus *(G-6855)*
Cardinal Rubber Company Inc ....E...... 330 745-2191
  Barberton *(G-1113)*
Chemspec Ltd ....F...... 330 896-0355
  Uniontown *(G-19079)*
Cincinnati Assn For The Blind ....C...... 513 221-8558
  Cincinnati *(G-3539)*
Consolidated Coatings Corp ....E...... 216 514-7596
  Cleveland *(G-5118)*
Continental Products Company ....E...... 216 531-0710
  Cleveland *(G-5126)*
Cornerstone Indus Holdings ....G...... 440 893-9144
  Chagrin Falls *(G-3054)*
CP Industries Inc ....F...... 740 763-2886
  Newark *(G-14997)*
Dyna Tech Molding & Beta ....G...... 330 296-2315
  Ravenna *(G-16527)*
Econo Products Inc ....F...... 330 923-4101
  Cuyahoga Falls *(G-7989)*
Elaston Company ....F...... 330 863-2865
  Malvern *(G-12543)*
Engineered Mtls Systems Inc ....E...... 740 362-4444
  Delaware *(G-8843)*
Gdc Inc ....F...... 574 533-3128
  Wooster *(G-20775)*
Gold Key Processing Inc ....C...... 440 632-0901
  Middlefield *(G-13937)*
HB Fuller Company ....E...... 513 719-3600
  Blue Ash *(G-1806)*
HB Fuller Company ....E...... 513 719-3600
  Blue Ash *(G-1807)*
Henkel Corporation ....D...... 513 830-0260
  Cincinnati *(G-3878)*

Hexpol Compounding LLC ....C...... 440 834-4644
  Burton *(G-2376)*
Hoover & Wells Inc ....F...... 419 691-9220
  Toledo *(G-18511)*
ICP Adhesives and Sealants Inc ....G...... 330 753-4585
  Norton *(G-15513)*
Illinois Tool Works Inc ....C...... 513 489-7600
  Blue Ash *(G-1812)*
Kcg Inc ....G...... 614 238-9450
  Columbus *(G-7252)*
Laminate Technologies Inc ....D...... 419 448-0812
  Tiffin *(G-18226)*
Lord Corporation ....C...... 440 992-0193
  Ashtabula *(G-818)*
Lubrizol Advanced Mtls Inc ....F...... 216 447-5000
  Brecksville *(G-2061)*
Mactac Americas LLC ....G...... 330 688-1111
  Stow *(G-17771)*
Mameco International Inc ....F...... 216 752-4400
  Cleveland *(G-5738)*
Marlen Manufacturing & Dev Co ....E...... 216 292-7546
  Bedford *(G-1442)*
Millennium Adhesive Pdts Inc ....F...... 440 708-1212
  Chagrin Falls *(G-3064)*
National Adhesives Inc ....F...... 513 683-8650
  Cincinnati *(G-4138)*
National Starch Chemical ....G...... 513 830-0260
  Cincinnati *(G-4141)*
Polymerics Inc ....D...... 330 434-6665
  Cuyahoga Falls *(G-8034)*
PPG Architectural Finishes Inc ....F...... 513 563-0220
  Cincinnati *(G-4258)*
PRC - Desoto International Inc ....F...... 800 772-9378
  Chillicothe *(G-3267)*
Priest Services Inc ....G...... 440 333-1123
  Mayfield Heights *(G-13321)*
Quest Solutions Group LLC ....G...... 513 703-4520
  Liberty Township *(G-11966)*
Republic Powdered Metals Inc ....D...... 330 225-3192
  Medina *(G-13467)*
RPM International Inc ....D...... 330 273-5090
  Medina *(G-13471)*
Rubex Inc ....F...... 614 875-6343
  Grove City *(G-10590)*
Ruscoe Company ....E...... 330 253-8148
  Akron *(G-383)*
Sem-Com Company Inc ....F...... 419 537-8813
  Toledo *(G-18691)*
Shincor Silicones Inc ....G...... 330 630-9460
  Akron *(G-400)*
Silicone Solutions Inc ....F...... 330 920-3125
  Cuyahoga Falls *(G-8045)*
Sirrus Inc ....E...... 513 448-0308
  Loveland *(G-12388)*
Sonoco Products Company ....D...... 937 429-0040
  Beavercreek Township *(G-1390)*
Spinnaker Coating LLC ....C...... 937 332-6300
  Troy *(G-18878)*
Sportsmaster ....F...... 440 257-3900
  Mentor *(G-13728)*
The Euclid Chemical Company ....F...... 216 292-5000
  Beachwood *(G-1301)*
Thermagon Inc ....D...... 216 939-2300
  Cleveland *(G-6315)*
Thorworks Industries Inc ....E...... 419 626-4375
  Sandusky *(G-17015)*
Three Bond International Inc ....D...... 513 779-7300
  West Chester *(G-19957)*
Tremco Incorporated ....D...... 419 289-2050
  Ashland *(G-782)*
United McGill Corporation ....E...... 614 829-1200
  Groveport *(G-10648)*
Valspar Corporation ....C...... 330 830-6000
  Massillon *(G-13209)*
Waytek Corporation ....E...... 937 743-6142
  Franklin *(G-10065)*

ADHESIVES & SEALANTS WHOLESALERS

Brewpro Inc ....G...... 513 577-7200
  Cincinnati *(G-3472)*
Consolidated Coatings Corp ....E...... 216 514-7596
  Cleveland *(G-5118)*
National Polymer Inc ....F...... 440 708-1245
  Chagrin Falls *(G-3106)*
Silicone Solutions Inc ....G...... 419 720-8709
  Toledo *(G-18697)*

ADHESIVES: Adhesives, plastic

Durez Corporation ....C...... 567 295-6400
  Kenton *(G-11546)*

National Polymer Inc ....F...... 440 708-1245
  Chagrin Falls *(G-3106)*

ADHESIVES: Epoxy

Nanosperse LLC ....G...... 937 296-5030
  Kettering *(G-11583)*
Renegade Materials Corporation ....E...... 508 579-7888
  Miamisburg *(G-13854)*
Summitville Tiles Inc ....E...... 330 868-6463
  Minerva *(G-14344)*

ADVERTISING AGENCIES

Aardvark Screen Prtg & EMB LLC ....F...... 419 354-6686
  Bowling Green *(G-1964)*
Beer Communications Inc ....G...... 419 756-6882
  Mansfield *(G-12566)*
Buckeye Business Forms Inc ....F...... 614 882-1890
  Westerville *(G-20141)*
D & S Crtive Cmmunications Inc ....D...... 419 524-6699
  Mansfield *(G-12591)*
David Esrati ....G...... 937 228-4433
  Dayton *(G-8266)*
Dee Printing Inc ....F...... 614 777-8700
  Columbus *(G-7017)*
International Advg Concepts ....G...... 440 331-4733
  Cleveland *(G-5579)*
Job News ....G...... 513 984-5724
  Blue Ash *(G-1818)*
L M Berry and Company ....A...... 937 296-2121
  Moraine *(G-14500)*
Mark Advertising Agency Inc ....F...... 419 626-9000
  Sandusky *(G-16985)*
McQueen Advertising Inc ....G...... 440 967-1137
  Vermilion *(G-19334)*
Paul/Jay Associates ....G...... 740 676-8776
  Bellaire *(G-1500)*
Penca Design Group Ltd ....G...... 440 210-4422
  Painesville *(G-15910)*
Pixslap Inc ....G...... 937 559-2671
  Middletown *(G-14076)*
Propress Inc ....F...... 216 631-8200
  Cleveland *(G-6056)*
Quad/Graphics Inc ....C...... 614 276-4800
  Columbus *(G-7531)*

ADVERTISING AGENCIES: Consultants

Airmate Company ....D...... 419 636-3184
  Bryan *(G-2274)*
George D Kanaan & Associates ....G...... 440 243-6410
  Berea *(G-1617)*
Just Business Inc ....F...... 866 577-3303
  Dayton *(G-8431)*

ADVERTISING DISPLAY PRDTS

Aster Industries Inc ....F...... 330 762-7965
  Akron *(G-75)*
Markethatch Co Inc ....F...... 330 376-6363
  Akron *(G-285)*
On Display LLC ....E...... 513 841-1600
  Batavia *(G-1214)*
Power Media Inc ....G...... 330 475-0500
  Akron *(G-345)*
Procter & Gamble Distrg LLC ....C...... 937 387-5189
  Union *(G-19067)*
Skr Enterprises LLC ....G...... 419 891-1112
  Maumee *(G-13295)*
Toledo Mobile Media LLC ....G...... 419 389-0687
  Toledo *(G-18734)*

ADVERTISING REPRESENTATIVES: Electronic Media

Moments To Remember USA LLC ....G...... 330 830-0839
  Massillon *(G-13181)*

ADVERTISING REPRESENTATIVES: Media

Agri Communicators Inc ....E...... 614 273-0465
  Columbus *(G-6702)*

ADVERTISING REPRESENTATIVES: Newspaper

American City Bus Journals Inc ....E...... 937 528-4400
  Dayton *(G-8152)*
B G News ....E...... 419 372-2601
  Bowling Green *(G-1969)*

Copley Ohio Newspapers Inc ....C ... 330 364-5577
New Philadelphia *(G-14892)*

Gazette Publishing Company ....F ... 419 335-2010
Wauseon *(G-19679)*

News Watchman & Paper ....F ... 740 947-2149
Waverly *(G-19713)*

Ohio Newspaper Services Inc ....F ... 614 486-6677
Columbus *(G-7424)*

Progressor Times ....G ... 419 396-7567
Carey *(G-2924)*

The Jeffersonian ....G ... 740 498-7117
Newcomerstown *(G-15125)*

Trumbull County Legal News ....G ... 330 392-7112
Warren *(G-19612)*

ADVERTISING SPECIALTIES, WHOLESALE

Ace Plastics Co ....G ... 330 928-7720
Stow *(G-17728)*

Akos Promotions Inc ....G ... 513 398-6324
Mason *(G-12980)*

Auto Dealer Designs Inc ....E ... 330 374-7666
Akron *(G-78)*

Baker Plastics Inc ....G ... 330 743-3142
Youngstown *(G-21031)*

Benchmark Prints ....F ... 419 332-7640
Fremont *(G-10129)*

Cal Sales Embroidery ....G ... 440 236-3820
Columbia Station *(G-6582)*

Capehart Enterprises LLC ....F ... 614 769-7746
Columbus *(G-6895)*

Charizma Corp ....G ... 216 621-2220
Cleveland *(G-5014)*

Cnr Marketing Ltd ....G ... 937 293-1030
Dayton *(G-8233)*

Custom Sportswear Imprints LLC ....G ... 330 335-8326
Wadsworth *(G-19400)*

Echographics Inc ....G ... 440 846-2330
North Ridgeville *(G-15371)*

Evolution Crtive Solutions LLC ....E ... 513 681-4450
Cincinnati *(G-3725)*

F & K Concepts Inc ....G ... 937 426-6843
Beavercreek *(G-1337)*

Flashions Sportswear Ltd ....G ... 937 323-5885
Springfield *(G-17560)*

G Q Business Products ....G ... 513 792-4750
Blue Ash *(G-1801)*

Gail Berner ....G ... 937 322-0314
Springfield *(G-17563)*

Galaxy Balloons Incorporated ....C ... 216 476-3360
Cleveland *(G-5392)*

Gauntlet Awards & Engraving ....G ... 937 890-5811
Dayton *(G-8357)*

Harris Hawk ....G ... 800 459-4295
Mason *(G-13036)*

In-Touch Corp ....G ... 440 268-0881
Cleveland *(G-5559)*

Madison Group Inc ....G ... 216 362-9000
Cleveland *(G-5727)*

Marathon Mfg & Sup Co ....D ... 330 343-2656
New Philadelphia *(G-14911)*

Mr Emblem Inc ....G ... 419 697-1888
Oregon *(G-15710)*

Novelty Advertising Co Inc ....E ... 740 622-3113
Coshocton *(G-7903)*

Ohio State Institute of Fin ....G ... 614 861-8811
Reynoldsburg *(G-16596)*

P S Superior Inc ....F ... 216 587-1000
Cleveland *(G-5958)*

Peter Graham Dunn Inc ....E ... 330 816-0035
Dalton *(G-8077)*

Professional Image Inc ....F ... 513 984-1111
Cincinnati *(G-4296)*

Publishing Group Ltd ....F ... 614 572-1240
Columbus *(G-7526)*

Randd Assoc Prtg & Promotions ....G ... 937 294-1874
Dayton *(G-8617)*

Route 14 Storage Inc ....G ... 330 296-0084
Ravenna *(G-16553)*

Screen Works Inc ....E ... 937 264-9111
Dayton *(G-8650)*

Shamrock Companies Inc ....D ... 440 899-9510
Westlake *(G-20308)*

Silk Screen Special TS Inc ....G ... 740 246-4843
Thornville *(G-18199)*

Smartv Company LLC ....E ... 614 890-6090
Westerville *(G-20186)*

Solar Arts Graphic Designs ....G ... 330 744-0535
Youngstown *(G-21205)*

Specialtee Sportswear & Design ....G ... 614 877-0976
Orient *(G-15724)*

Star Calendar & Printing Co ....G ... 216 741-3223
Cleveland *(G-6237)*

Supply International Inc ....G ... 740 282-8604
Steubenville *(G-17718)*

T & L Custom Screening Inc ....G ... 937 237-3121
Dayton *(G-8695)*

Traichal Construction Company ....E ... 800 255-3667
Niles *(G-15186)*

Underground Sport Shop Inc ....F ... 513 751-1662
Cincinnati *(G-4535)*

W C Sims Co Inc ....G ... 937 325-7035
Springfield *(G-17674)*

White Tiger Inc ....G ... 740 852-4873
London *(G-12223)*

ADVERTISING SVCS, NEC

Gibbs E & Associates LLC ....G ... 614 939-1672
New Albany *(G-14760)*

ADVERTISING SVCS: Billboards

Hart Advertising Inc ....F ... 419 668-1194
Norwalk *(G-15543)*

ADVERTISING SVCS: Direct Mail

Advanced Fitness Inc ....G ... 513 563-1000
Cincinnati *(G-3358)*

Angstrom Graphics Inc Midwest ....B ... 216 271-5300
Cleveland *(G-4815)*

Cap City Direct LLC ....F ... 614 252-6245
Columbus *(G-6894)*

Consolidated Graphics Group Inc ....C ... 216 881-9191
Cleveland *(G-5116)*

Digital Color Intl LLC ....E ... 330 762-6959
Akron *(G-152)*

Directconnectgroup Ltd ....A ... 216 281-2866
Cleveland *(G-5196)*

E L Frueh Inc ....G ... 419 222-9741
Lima *(G-12007)*

Hecks Direct Mail & Prtg Svc ....G ... 419 661-6028
Toledo *(G-18503)*

Hkm Drect Mkt Cmmnications Inc ....C ... 216 651-9500
Cleveland *(G-5516)*

Jscs Group Inc ....G ... 513 563-4900
Cincinnati *(G-3961)*

Laipplys Prtg Mktg Sltions Inc ....G ... 740 387-9282
Marion *(G-12879)*

List Media Inc ....G ... 330 995-0864
Aurora *(G-934)*

Lsc Communications Us LLC ....C ... 419 935-0111
Willard *(G-20396)*

Moments To Remember USA LLC ....G ... 330 830-0839
Massillon *(G-13181)*

Network Printing & Graphics ....F ... 614 230-2084
Columbus *(G-7387)*

Quez Media Marketing Inc ....F ... 216 910-0202
Cleveland *(G-6077)*

Sevell + Sevell Inc ....G ... 614 341-9700
Columbus *(G-7611)*

Sourcelink Ohio LLC ....C ... 937 885-8000
Miamisburg *(G-13862)*

Target Business Services ....F ... 614 866-4065
Pickerington *(G-16207)*

Traxium LLC ....E ... 330 572-8200
Stow *(G-17811)*

Victory Direct LLC ....G ... 614 626-0000
Gahanna *(G-10240)*

Youngstown Letter Shop Inc ....G ... 330 793-4935
Youngstown *(G-21253)*

ADVERTISING SVCS: Display

A Sign Above Inc ....F ... 330 723-3650
Twinsburg *(G-18889)*

Design Masters Inc ....G ... 513 772-7175
Cincinnati *(G-3649)*

Digital Color Intl LLC ....E ... 330 762-6959
Akron *(G-152)*

Display Dynamics Inc ....F ... 937 832-2830
Englewood *(G-9516)*

Schiffer Group Inc ....G ... 937 694-8185
Troy *(G-18872)*

ADVERTISING SVCS: Outdoor

Barnes Advertising Corp ....F ... 740 453-6836
Zanesville *(G-21275)*

Bench Billboard Company Inc ....G ... 513 271-2222
Cincinnati *(G-3444)*

Kessler Sign Company ....E ... 740 453-0668
Zanesville *(G-21326)*

Kessler Sign Company ....G ... 937 898-0633
Dayton *(G-8440)*

Ohio Shelterall Inc ....F ... 614 882-1110
Westerville *(G-20227)*

Orange Barrel Media LLC ....E ... 614 294-4898
Columbus *(G-7445)*

ADVERTISING SVCS: Poster, Exc Outdoor

Hollywood Imprints LLC ....F ... 614 501-6040
Gahanna *(G-10211)*

Sprint Print Inc ....G ... 740 622-4429
Coshocton *(G-7910)*

ADVERTISING SVCS: Poster, Outdoor

Norton Outdoor Advertising ....E ... 513 631-4864
Cincinnati *(G-4164)*

AERIAL WORK PLATFORMS

G & T Manufacturing Co ....F ... 440 639-7777
Mentor *(G-13588)*

Haulotte US Inc ....E ... 419 445-8915
Archbold *(G-680)*

AEROSOLS

C A P Industries Inc ....F ... 937 773-1824
Piqua *(G-16254)*

Eveready Products Corporation ....F ... 216 661-2755
Cleveland *(G-5308)*

Wellston Aerosol Mfg Co Inc ....E ... 740 384-2320
Wellston *(G-19772)*

Zenex International ....E ... 440 232-4155
Bedford *(G-1475)*

AGENTS, BROKERS & BUREAUS: Personal Service

D+h USA Corporation ....E ... 937 435-2335
Miamisburg *(G-13796)*

Loroco Industries Inc ....G ... 513 554-0356
Cincinnati *(G-4033)*

Matly Digital Solutions LLC ....G ... 513 860-3435
Fairfield *(G-9681)*

Tema Isenmann Inc ....G ... 859 252-0613
Cincinnati *(G-4500)*

AGRICULTURAL EQPT: BARN, SILO, POULTRY, DAIRY/LIVESTOCK MACH

Fort Recovery Equipment Inc ....E ... 419 375-1006
Fort Recovery *(G-9949)*

Stein-Way Equipment ....F ... 330 857-8700
Apple Creek *(G-649)*

AGRICULTURAL EQPT: Combine, Digger, Packer/Thresher, Peanut

Birds Eye Foods Inc ....E ... 330 854-0818
Canal Fulton *(G-2499)*

AGRICULTURAL EQPT: Elevators, Farm

Afs Technology LLC ....F ... 937 669-3548
Tipp City *(G-18262)*

Gerald Grain Center Inc ....F ... 419 445-2451
Archbold *(G-678)*

Hord Elevator LLC ....F ... 419 562-5934
Bucyrus *(G-2349)*

Keynes Brothers Inc ....G ... 740 426-6332
Jeffersonville *(G-11381)*

Sweet Manufacturing Company ....E ... 937 325-1511
Springfield *(G-17659)*

AGRICULTURAL EQPT: Fertilizing Machinery

Shearer Farm Inc ....E ... 330 345-9023
Wooster *(G-20834)*

AGRICULTURAL EQPT: Fillers & Unloaders, Silo

Flying Dutchman Inc ....G ... 740 694-1734
Smithville *(G-17239)*

AGRICULTURAL EQPT: Grounds Mowing Eqpt

Landscape Group LLC ....G ... 614 302-4537
Mount Sterling *(G-14600)*

PRODUCT

AGRICULTURAL EQPT: Grounds Mowing Eqpt

R L Parsons & Son Equipment Co ....G...... 614 879-7601
West Jefferson *(G-20083)*

TD Landscape Inc ....F...... 740 694-0244
Fredericktown *(G-10110)*

AGRICULTURAL EQPT: Loaders, Manure & General Utility

END Separation LLC................................G...... 419 438-0879
Oakwood *(G-15616)*

AGRICULTURAL EQPT: Shakers, Tree, Nuts, Fruits, Etc

Kriss Kreations ....G...... 330 405-6102
Twinsburg *(G-18968)*

AGRICULTURAL EQPT: Stackers, Grain

Hawthorne Systems Inc ....F...... 419 643-5861
Beaverdam *(G-1393)*

AGRICULTURAL EQPT: Tractors, Farm

Hershberger & Sons LLC........................G...... 937 588-2195
Hillsboro *(G-11000)*

AGRICULTURAL EQPT: Turf & Grounds Eqpt

Randall Richard & Moore LLC ....F...... 330 455-8873
Canton *(G-2835)*

Rhinestahl Corporation............................D...... 513 229-5300
Mason *(G-13083)*

AGRICULTURAL LIMESTONE: Ground

Carmeuse Lime Inc ....G...... 419 986-2000
Tiffin *(G-18214)*

AGRICULTURAL MACHINERY & EQPT REPAIR

Friesen Fab and Equipment.....................G...... 614 873-4354
Plain City *(G-16340)*

Jayron Fabrication LLC............................G...... 740 335-3184
Leesburg *(G-11852)*

MCS Midwest LLC ....F...... 513 217-0805
Franklin *(G-10035)*

AGRICULTURAL MACHINERY & EQPT: Wholesalers

Buckeye Companies.................................E...... 740 452-3641
Zanesville *(G-21282)*

R J Cox Co..G...... 937 548-4699
Arcanum *(G-658)*

Reberland Equipment Inc ....F...... 330 698-5883
Apple Creek *(G-648)*

S I Distributing Inc ....F...... 419 647-4909
Spencerville *(G-17465)*

Yoder & Frey Inc.....................................G...... 419 445-2070
Archbold *(G-700)*

AIR CLEANING SYSTEMS

Radon Be Gone Inc.................................G...... 614 268-4440
Columbus *(G-7545)*

United Air Specialists Inc ....C...... 513 891-0400
Blue Ash *(G-1886)*

AIR CONDITIONERS: Motor Vehicle

Jbar A/C Inc ....F...... 216 447-4294
Cleveland *(G-5609)*

U Haul Neighborhood Dealer...................G...... 740 445-4125
Vincent *(G-19381)*

AIR CONDITIONING & VENTILATION EQPT & SPLYS: Wholesales

Tactical Envmtl Systems Inc...................G...... 513 831-2663
Milford *(G-14176)*

AIR CONDITIONING EQPT

Duro Dyne Midwest Corp ....B...... 513 870-6000
Hamilton *(G-10685)*

Emerson Electric Co................................C...... 513 731-2020
Cincinnati *(G-3698)*

J D Indoor Comfort Inc............................F...... 440 949-8758
Sheffield Village *(G-17123)*

Liebert Corporation ....A...... 614 888-0246
Columbus *(G-7292)*

Rs Pro Sales LLC....................................G...... 513 699-5329
Cincinnati *(G-4364)*

Snap Rite Manufacturing Inc ....G...... 910 897-4080
Cleveland *(G-6214)*

Tactical Envmtl Systems Inc...................G...... 513 831-2663
Milford *(G-14176)*

AIR CONDITIONING REPAIR SVCS

Air-Rite Inc...E...... 216 228-8200
Cleveland *(G-4735)*

AIR CONDITIONING UNITS: Complete, Domestic Or Indl

Airtex Manufacturing Lllp ....G...... 614 436-9693
Columbus *(G-6705)*

BMC Holdings Inc ....G...... 419 636-1194
Bryan *(G-2283)*

Ecu Corporation......................................E...... 513 898-9294
Cincinnati *(G-3690)*

Electrolux Professional Inc....................E...... 216 898-1800
Cleveland *(G-5269)*

Ellis & Watts Intl LLC.............................G...... 513 752-9000
Batavia *(G-1183)*

Fred D Pfening Company ....E...... 614 294-5361
Columbus *(G-7099)*

Hdt Ep Inc ....C...... 216 438-6111
Solon *(G-17307)*

Hdt Expeditionary Systems Inc...............F...... 440 466-6640
Geneva *(G-10350)*

Lintern Corporation.................................E...... 440 255-9333
Mentor *(G-13635)*

Taylor & Moore Co ....F...... 513 733-5530
Cincinnati *(G-4495)*

Vertiv Group Corporation ....A...... 614 888-0246
Columbus *(G-7735)*

Whirlpool Corporation.............................C...... 614 409-4340
Lockbourne *(G-12153)*

AIR MATTRESSES: Plastic

Oe Plastics LLC......................................G...... 513 847-8101
Liberty Twp *(G-11977)*

Plastic Materials Inc..............................E...... 330 468-5706
Macedonia *(G-12472)*

Plastic Materials Inc..............................E...... 330 468-0184
Macedonia *(G-12473)*

Polimeros Usa LLC ....F...... 216 591-0162
Warrensville Heights *(G-19634)*

AIR POLLUTION CONTROL EQPT & SPLYS WHOLESALERS

Verantis Corporation ....E...... 440 243-0700
Middleburg Heights *(G-13909)*

AIR PURIFICATION EQPT

Adwest Technologies Inc ....G...... 513 458-2600
Cincinnati *(G-3362)*

Air Plastics Inc ....F...... 513 469-1074
Blue Ash *(G-1737)*

Airecon Manufacturing Corp ....E...... 513 561-5522
Cincinnati *(G-3370)*

Clearflite Inc ....G...... 440 281-7368
Sheffield Lake *(G-17118)*

Guardian Technologies LLC ....E...... 216 706-2250
Euclid *(G-9582)*

JD Enterprises.......................................G...... 937 764-1611
Hillsboro *(G-11005)*

Verantis Corporation ....E...... 440 243-0700
Middleburg Heights *(G-13909)*

AIR TRAFFIC CONTROL SVCS

Arges...G...... 440 574-1305
Oberlin *(G-15634)*

AIR, WATER & SOLID WASTE PROGRAMS ADMINISTRATION SVCS

City of Columbus ....E...... 614 645-3152
Lockbourne *(G-12146)*

X-3-5 LLC ....G...... 513 489-5477
Cincinnati *(G-4613)*

AIR-CONDITIONING SPLY SVCS

Marketing Comm Resource Inc ....D...... 440 484-3010
Willoughby *(G-20538)*

AIRCRAFT & AEROSPACE FLIGHT INSTRUMENTS & GUIDANCE SYSTEMS

HI Tech Aero Spares ....G...... 513 942-4150
West Chester *(G-19882)*

Tri-State Jet Mfg LLC ....G...... 513 896-4538
Hamilton *(G-10750)*

AIRCRAFT & HEAVY EQPT REPAIR SVCS

Carlson Aircraft Inc................................G...... 330 426-3934
East Palestine *(G-9230)*

Grimes Aerospace Company ....B...... 937 484-2001
Urbana *(G-19158)*

K & J Machine Inc ....F...... 740 425-3282
Barnesville *(G-1160)*

McNational Inc..E...... 740 377-4391
South Point *(G-17441)*

Pas Technologies Inc ....D...... 937 840-1000
Hillsboro *(G-11012)*

Tri State Equipment Company ....G...... 513 738-7227
Shandon *(G-17098)*

AIRCRAFT ASSEMBLY PLANTS

Aero Composites Inc ....G...... 937 849-0244
Medway *(G-13499)*

Air One Jet Center ....G...... 513 867-9500
Hamilton *(G-10663)*

American Aero Components LLC ....G...... 937 367-5068
Dayton *(G-8150)*

Capital City Aviation Inc ....F...... 614 459-2541
Columbus *(G-6896)*

Carlson Aircraft Inc................................G...... 330 426-3934
East Palestine *(G-9230)*

Clm Marketing Inc ....G...... 440 526-8613
Brecksville *(G-2041)*

Edward S Eveland ....G...... 937 233-6568
Dayton *(G-8320)*

Executive Wings Inc ....G...... 440 254-1812
Painesville *(G-15878)*

Flightlogix LLC ....G...... 513 321-1200
Cincinnati *(G-3760)*

Goodrich Corporation..............................A...... 937 339-3811
Troy *(G-18833)*

Lockheed Martin Corporation ....B...... 330 796-2800
Akron *(G-273)*

Mercury Air Services LLC ....E...... 216 898-4800
Cleveland *(G-5783)*

Nextant Aerospace Holdings LLC ....D...... 216 261-9000
Cleveland *(G-5881)*

Ruhe Sales Inc ....F...... 419 943-3357
Leipsic *(G-11876)*

Sea Air Spc McG and Mld LLC ....F...... 440 248-3025
Solon *(G-17377)*

Sky Riders Inc ....G...... 440 310-6819
Lorain *(G-12276)*

Snow Aviation Intl Inc ....C...... 614 588-2452
Gahanna *(G-10234)*

Star Jet LLC ....F...... 614 338-4379
Columbus *(G-7651)*

Stark Airways ....G...... 330 526-6416
North Canton *(G-15268)*

Summit Aerospace Products ....G...... 330 612-7341
Northfield *(G-15473)*

Tessec Manufacturing Svcs LLC ....E...... 937 985-3552
Dayton *(G-8710)*

Textron Inc ....F...... 330 626-7800
Streetsboro *(G-17882)*

Theiss Uav Solutions LLC ....G...... 330 584-2070
North Benton *(G-15214)*

Toledo Jet Center LLC ....F...... 419 866-9050
Swanton *(G-18092)*

Tri-State Model Flyers Inc ....D...... 740 886-8429
Proctorville *(G-16494)*

AIRCRAFT CLEANING & JANITORIAL SVCS

Aero Jet Wash Llc ....F...... 866 381-7955
West Carrollton *(G-19789)*

AIRCRAFT CONTROL SYSTEMS:

Saircorp Ltd...G...... 330 669-9099
Smithville *(G-17245)*

AIRCRAFT CONTROL SYSTEMS: Electronic Totalizing Counters

3gc LLC..G...... 740 703-0580
Cardington *(G-2907)*

GE Aviation Systems LLC ....G...... 513 470-2889
Cincinnati (G-3804)
GE Aviation Systems LLC ....C...... 513 977-1500
Cincinnati (G-3806)
GE Aviation Systems LLC ....G...... 513 243-2000
Cincinnati (G-3808)
GE Aviation Systems LLC ....C...... 937 898-9600
Dayton (G-8359)
Honeywell International Inc ....A...... 937 484-2000
Urbana (G-19162)

AIRCRAFT ELECTRICAL EQPT REPAIR SVCS

General Electric Company ....B...... 513 977-1500
Cincinnati (G-3813)
Spirit Avionics Ltd ....F...... 614 358-0333
Columbus (G-7645)

AIRCRAFT ENGINES & ENGINE PARTS: Airfoils

Certech Inc ....G...... 330 405-1033
Twinsburg (G-18910)
PCC Airfoils LLC ....C...... 440 255-9770
Mentor (G-13683)
Turbine Eng Cmpnents Tech Corp ......E...... 216 692-6173
Cleveland (G-6374)

AIRCRAFT ENGINES & ENGINE PARTS: Pumps

At Holdings Corporation ....G...... 216 692-6000
Cleveland (G-4850)
Eaton Industrial Corporation ....B...... 216 692-5456
Cleveland (G-5252)

AIRCRAFT ENGINES & ENGINE PARTS: Research & Development, Mfr

Aerospace Co Inc ....D...... 413 998-1637
Cleveland (G-4724)
Parker Aircraft Sales........................G...... 937 833-4820
Brookville (G-2195)
Scis Aerospace LLC ....G...... 216 533-8533
Medina (G-13476)

AIRCRAFT ENGINES & ENGINE PARTS: Rocket Motors

Stofiel Aerospace LLC ....G...... 216 389-0084
Cleveland (G-6250)

AIRCRAFT ENGINES & PARTS

Advanced Ground Systems ....F...... 513 402-7226
Monroe (G-14390)
Aero Jet Wash Llc ....F...... 866 381-7955
West Carrollton (G-19789)
American Aero Components LLC ....G...... 937 367-5068
Dayton (G-8150)
Avion Tool Corporation ....F...... 937 278-0779
Dayton (G-8175)
Barnes Group Inc ....A...... 513 759-3528
West Chester (G-19814)
Barnes Group Inc ....A...... 513 779-6888
West Chester (G-19815)
CFM International Inc ....E...... 513 552-2787
West Chester (G-19825)
CFM International Inc ....E...... 513 563-4180
Cincinnati (G-3519)
Challenger Aviation Products ....G...... 937 387-6500
Vandalia (G-19285)
Enginetics Corporation ....C...... 937 878-3800
Huber Heights (G-11146)
Ferrotherm Corporation ....C...... 216 883-9350
Cleveland (G-5339)
GE Aircraft Engines ....E...... 513 243-2000
Cincinnati (G-3803)
GE Aviation Systems LLC ....C...... 937 898-9600
Dayton (G-8358)
GE Military Systems ....A...... 513 243-2000
Cincinnati (G-3810)
General Electric Company ....G...... 513 948-4170
Cincinnati (G-3814)
General Electric Company ....G...... 513 552-5364
West Chester (G-19875)
General Electric Company ....A...... 513 552-2000
Cincinnati (G-3815)
Henry Tools Inc ....G...... 216 291-1011
Cleveland (G-5501)

Hi-Tek Manufacturing Inc ....C...... 513 459-1094
Mason (G-13037)
Honeywell ....G...... 614 850-8228
Columbus (G-7162)
Honeywell International Inc ....A...... 216 459-6048
Independence (G-11259)
Honeywell International Inc ....A...... 440 349-7330
Solon (G-17310)
Honeywell International Inc ....G...... 216 682-1600
Cleveland (G-5523)
Lsp Technologies Inc ....E...... 614 718-3000
Dublin (G-9100)
Magellan Arospc Middletown Inc ....D...... 513 422-2751
Middletown (G-14058)
Metro Mech Inc ....G...... 216 641-6262
Cleveland (G-5792)
Meyer Tool Inc ....A...... 513 681-7362
Cincinnati (G-4097)
Otto Konigslow Mfg Co ....F...... 216 851-7900
Cleveland (G-5952)
Parker-Hannifin Corporation ....C...... 440 284-6277
Elyria (G-9476)
Pas Technologies Inc ....D...... 937 840-1000
Hillsboro (G-11012)
Pierce-Spafford Metals Co Inc ....G...... 800 421-3778
Niles (G-15174)
Polycraft Products Inc ....G...... 513 353-3334
Cleves (G-6523)
Sifco Industries Inc ....B...... 216 881-8600
Cleveland (G-6201)
Snow Aviation Intl Inc ....C...... 614 588-2452
Gahanna (G-10234)
Spirit Avionics Ltd ....F...... 614 358-0333
Columbus (G-7645)
Trojon Gear Inc ....F...... 937 254-1737
Dayton (G-8729)
Turbine Standard Ltd ....F...... 419 865-0355
Holland (G-11094)
US Aeroteam Inc ....E...... 937 458-0344
Dayton (G-8740)
Welded Ring Products Co ....D...... 216 961-3800
Cleveland (G-6455)

AIRCRAFT EQPT & SPLYS WHOLESALERS

Aerovent Inc ....G...... 937 473-3789
Covington (G-7917)
Cleveland Wheels ....D...... 440 937-6211
Avon (G-989)
Clm Marketing Inc ....G...... 440 526-8613
Brecksville (G-2041)
Integrated Aircraft Systems ....G...... 330 686-2982
Stow (G-17764)
Transdigm Inc ....G...... 216 706-2939
Cleveland (G-6347)
Transdigm Group Incorporated ....D...... 216 706-2960
Cleveland (G-6348)

AIRCRAFT FLIGHT INSTRUMENTS

L3 Aviation Products Inc ....D...... 614 825-2001
Columbus (G-7278)

AIRCRAFT HANGAR OPERATION SVCS

General Electric Company ....A...... 513 552-2000
Cincinnati (G-3815)
Swagelok Company ....F...... 440 442-6611
Cleveland (G-6277)

AIRCRAFT MAINTENANCE & REPAIR SVCS

Toledo Jet Center LLC ....F...... 419 866-9050
Swanton (G-18092)

AIRCRAFT PARTS & AUX EQPT: Governors, Propeller Feathering

Hartzell Propeller Inc ....F...... 937 778-4200
Piqua (G-16274)

AIRCRAFT PARTS & AUXILIARY EQPT: Assys, Subassemblies/Parts

Electronic Concepts Engrg Inc............F...... 419 861-9000
Holland (G-11059)
Master Swaging Inc ....G...... 937 596-6171
Jackson Center (G-11343)
Parker-Hannifin Corporation ....C...... 440 284-6277
Elyria (G-9476)
Pitco Products Inc ....F...... 513 228-7245
Dayton (G-8577)

Precision Aircraft Components ....E...... 937 278-0264
Dayton (G-8581)
Snow Aviation Intl Inc ....C...... 614 588-2452
Gahanna (G-10234)
Summa Holdings Inc ....G...... 440 838-4700
Cleveland (G-6261)

AIRCRAFT PARTS & AUXILIARY EQPT: Blades, Prop, Metal Or Wood

Triaxis Machine & Tool LLC ....G...... 440 230-0303
North Royalton (G-15457)

AIRCRAFT PARTS & AUXILIARY EQPT: Body & Wing Assys & Parts

Achilles Aerospace Pdts Inc...............E...... 330 425-8444
Twinsburg (G-18892)
Industrial Mfg Co LLC ....F...... 440 838-4700
Brecksville (G-2055)

AIRCRAFT PARTS & AUXILIARY EQPT: Body Assemblies & Parts

Jeff Cales Customer AVI LLC ....G...... 330 298-9479
Ravenna (G-16534)
Magellan Arospc Middletown Inc ....D...... 513 422-2751
Middletown (G-14058)
Milan Tool Corp ....E...... 216 661-1078
Cleveland (G-5813)

AIRCRAFT PARTS & AUXILIARY EQPT: Brakes

Meggitt Aircraft Braking ....A...... 330 796-4400
Akron (G-294)

AIRCRAFT PARTS & AUXILIARY EQPT: Landing Assemblies & Brakes

Friction Products Co ....B...... 330 725-4941
Medina (G-13413)

AIRCRAFT PARTS & AUXILIARY EQPT: Lighting/Landing Gear Assy

Goodrich Corporation ....B...... 216 429-4018
Independence (G-11255)
Hdi Landing Gear Usa Inc ....C...... 513 619-1203
Springfield (G-17569)
Hdi Landing Gear Usa Inc ....E...... 440 783-5255
Strongsville (G-17924)

AIRCRAFT PARTS & AUXILIARY EQPT: Military Eqpt & Armament

Dircksen and Associates Inc ....G...... 614 238-0413
Columbus (G-7027)
Salley Tool & Die Co ....F...... 937 258-3333
Dayton (G-8116)
Scis Aerospace LLC ....G...... 216 533-8533
Medina (G-13476)

AIRCRAFT PARTS & AUXILIARY EQPT: Oxygen Systems

Fluid Power Inc ....F...... 330 653-5107
Hudson (G-11171)

AIRCRAFT PARTS & AUXILIARY EQPT: Refueling Eqpt, In Flight

Garsite/Progress LLC ....F...... 419 424-1100
Findlay (G-9830)
Proflo Industries LLC ....E...... 419 436-6008
Alvada (G-556)

AIRCRAFT PARTS & AUXILIARY EQPT: Research & Development, Mfr

Airwolf Aerospace LLC ....G...... 440 632-1687
Middlefield (G-13913)
Drt Power Systems LLC - Sidney ....C...... 937 492-6121
Sidney (G-17180)
Weldon Pump Acquition LLC................E...... 440 232-2282
Oakwood Village (G-15633)

PRODUCT

AIRCRAFT PARTS & EQPT, NEC

8888 Butler Investments Inc ....G....... 440 748-0810
North Ridgeville (G-15354)

Ace Products Co of Toledo Inc ....G....... 419 472-1247
Toledo (G-18320)

Advanced Fuel Systems Inc ....G....... 614 252-8422
Columbus (G-6697)

Aero Tube & Connector Company ......G....... 614 885-2514
Worthington (G-20853)

Aeroquip-Vickers Inc ....G....... 216 523-5000
Cleveland (G-4722)

Airtug LLC ....G....... 440 829-2167
Avon (G-983)

Allen Aircraft Products Inc ....E....... 330 296-9621
Ravenna (G-16514)

American Aero Components LLC ....G....... 937 367-5068
Dayton (G-8150)

At Holdings Corporation ....G....... 216 692-6000
Cleveland (G-4850)

Auto-Valve Inc ....E....... 937 854-3037
Dayton (G-8172)

Aviation Cmpnent Solutions Inc ....F....... 440 295-6590
Richmond Heights (G-16652)

Aviation Technologies Inc ....G....... 216 706-2960
Cleveland (G-4872)

Avtron Aerospace Inc ....C....... 216 750-5152
Cleveland (G-4875)

Aws Industries Inc ....E....... 513 932-7941
Lebanon (G-11782)

Cleveland Instrument Corp ....G....... 440 826-1800
Brookpark (G-2153)

Columbus Jack Corporation ....D....... 614 228-0185
Columbus (G-6958)

Ctl-Aerospace Inc ....C....... 513 874-1118
West Chester (G-19994)

Ctl-Aerospace Inc ....D....... 513 874-7900
West Chester (G-19995)

Cuda Composites LLC ....G....... 937 499-0360
Dayton (G-8256)

Eaton Hydraulics LLC ....E....... 419 232-7777
Van Wert (G-19254)

Eaton Industrial Corporation ....B....... 216 692-5456
Cleveland (G-5252)

Eaton-Aeroquip Llc ....C....... 216 523-5000
Cleveland (G-5254)

Enginetics Corporation ....C....... 937 878-3800
Huber Heights (G-11146)

Eti Tech Inc ....F....... 937 832-4200
Englewood (G-9519)

Exito Manufacturing ....G....... 937 291-9871
Dayton (G-8337)

Federal Equipment Company ....D....... 513 621-5260
Cincinnati (G-3747)

Ferco Tech LLC ....C....... 937 746-6696
Franklin (G-10022)

Fgc Plasma Solutions LLC ....G....... 954 591-1429
Cleveland (G-5342)

Field Aviation Inc ....G....... 513 792-2282
Cincinnati (G-3753)

General Electric Company ....B....... 513 977-1500
Cincinnati (G-3813)

Goodrich Corporation ....A....... 937 339-3811
Troy (G-18833)

Grimes Aerospace Company ....C....... 937 484-2000
Urbana (G-19159)

Heico Aerospace Parts Corp ....B....... 954 987-6101
Highland Heights (G-10915)

Heller Machine Products Inc ....G....... 216 281-2951
Cleveland (G-5496)

JCB Arrowhead Products Inc ....G....... 440 546-4288
Brecksville (G-2057)

Jo-Bar Manufacturing Corp ....F....... 440 232-5555
Chagrin Falls (G-3097)

Jonathan Bishop ....G....... 330 836-6947
Akron (G-241)

Lawrence Technologies Inc ....G....... 937 274-7771
Dayton (G-8454)

Lockheed Martin Integ ....D....... 330 796-2800
Akron (G-274)

Logan Machine Company ....D....... 330 633-6163
Akron (G-275)

M & L Machine ....G....... 937 386-2604
Seaman (G-17041)

Maverick Molding Co ....F....... 513 469-9919
Blue Ash (G-1836)

Microweld Engineering Inc ....F....... 614 847-9410
Worthington (G-20880)

Midwest Aircraft Products Co ....F....... 419 884-2164
Mansfield (G-12648)

Nona Composites LLC ....G....... 937 490-4814
Beavercreek (G-1376)

Orbital Atk Inc ....C....... 937 429-9261
Beavercreek (G-1377)

Pako Inc ....C....... 440 946-8030
Mentor (G-13678)

Parker-Hannifin Corporation ....C....... 440 205-8230
Mentor (G-13682)

PCC Airfoils LLC ....B....... 740 982-6025
Crooksville (G-7952)

Schneller LLC ....D....... 330 673-1299
Kent (G-11523)

Skidmore-Wilhelm Mfg Company ....E....... 216 481-4774
Solon (G-17381)

Summit Avionics Inc ....F....... 330 425-1440
Twinsburg (G-19025)

Taylor Manufacturing Company ....E....... 937 322-8622
Springfield (G-17660)

Tracewell Systems Inc ....D....... 614 846-6175
Lewis Center (G-11927)

Transdigm Inc ....D....... 440 352-6182
Painesville (G-15932)

Transdigm Group Incorporated ....D....... 216 706-2960
Cleveland (G-6348)

Triumph Thermal Systems LLC ....C....... 419 273-2511
Forest (G-9923)

Tronair Inc ....D....... 419 866-6301
Holland (G-11092)

Tronair Parent Inc ....D....... 419 866-6301
Holland (G-11093)

Truline Industries Inc ....D....... 440 729-0140
Chesterland (G-3222)

Turbine Eng Cmpnents Tech Corp ....E....... 216 692-6173
Cleveland (G-6374)

Unison Industries LLC ....B....... 937 426-0621
Dayton (G-8121)

Unison Industries LLC ....B....... 937 427-0550
Beavercreek (G-1363)

Unison Industries LLC ....D....... 937 426-4676
Alpha (G-555)

US Aeroteam Inc ....G....... 937 458-0344
Dayton (G-8740)

US Technology Corporation ....E....... 330 455-1181
Canton (G-2891)

UTC Aerospace Systems ....F....... 216 341-1700
Cleveland (G-6402)

Wayne Trail Technologies Inc ....G....... 937 295-2120
Fort Loramie (G-9944)

White Machine Inc ....G....... 440 237-3282
North Royalton (G-15460)

AIRCRAFT PARTS WHOLESALERS

Grimes Aerospace Company ....B....... 937 484-2001
Urbana (G-19158)

AIRCRAFT PROPELLERS & PARTS

Hartzell Propeller Inc ....C....... 937 778-4200
Piqua (G-16275)

AIRCRAFT SERVICING & REPAIRING

Spirit Avionics Ltd ....F....... 614 358-0333
Columbus (G-7645)

Unison Industries LLC ....B....... 937 426-0621
Dayton (G-8121)

Unison Industries LLC ....B....... 937 427-0550
Beavercreek (G-1363)

AIRCRAFT WHEELS

Jay-Em Aerospace Corporation ....E....... 330 923-0333
Cuyahoga Falls (G-8013)

Parker-Hannifin Corporation ....C....... 440 937-6211
Avon (G-1002)

AIRCRAFT: Airplanes, Fixed Or Rotary Wing

Steel Aviation Aircraft Sales ....G....... 937 332-7587
Casstown (G-2971)

AIRCRAFT: Motorized

Tessec LLC ....E....... 937 985-3552
Dayton (G-8709)

AIRCRAFT: Research & Development, Manufacturer

Aerovation Tech Holdings LLC ....G....... 567 208-5525
Forest (G-9917)

E Star Aerospace Corporation ....G....... 614 396-6868
Westerville (G-20147)

Jetoptera Inc ....G....... 516 456-7609
Mason (G-13050)

Tdc Systems Inc ....G....... 440 953-5918
Willoughby (G-20610)

Unmanned Solutions Tech LLC ....G....... 937 771-7023
Beavercreek (G-1382)

Wanashab Inc ....G....... 330 606-6675
Cleveland (G-6445)

AIRPORTS, FLYING FIELDS & SVCS

Boeing Company ....A....... 740 788-4000
Newark (G-14985)

Grand Aire Inc ....E....... 419 861-6700
Swanton (G-18084)

Ruhe Sales Inc ....F....... 419 943-3357
Leipsic (G-11876)

ALARMS: Burglar

Alert Safety Products Inc ....G....... 513 791-4790
Blue Ash (G-1739)

David Boswell ....E....... 614 441-2497
Columbus (G-7014)

Safe Systems Inc ....G....... 216 661-1166
Cleveland (G-6154)

ALARMS: Fire

Honeywell International Inc ....D....... 937 754-4134
Fairborn (G-9625)

Honeywell International Inc ....A....... 937 484-2000
Urbana (G-19162)

Viking Group Inc ....G....... 937 443-0433
Dayton (G-8743)

ALCOHOL: Ethyl & Ethanol

Andersons Marathon Ethanol LLC ....E....... 937 316-3700
Greenville (G-10488)

Coshocton Ethanol LLC ....E....... 740 623-3046
Coshocton (G-7885)

Fostoria Ethanol LLC ....E....... 419 436-0954
Fostoria (G-9975)

Greater Ohio Ethanol LLC ....G....... 567 940-9500
Lima (G-12019)

Guardian Lima LLC ....E....... 567 940-9500
Lima (G-12021)

Harrison 20 Mtd Borefinery LLC ....G....... 740 796-4797
Adamsville (G-8)

Marion Ethanol LLC ....E....... 740 383-4400
Marion (G-12882)

Summit Ethanol LLC ....E....... 419 943-7447
Leipsic (G-11877)

ALCOHOL: Methyl & Methanol, Synthetic

Es Manufacturing Inc ....G....... 888 331-3443
Newark (G-15005)

ALKALIES & CHLORINE

GFS Chemicals Inc ....E....... 740 881-5501
Powell (G-16472)

National Colloid Company ....E....... 740 282-1171
Steubenville (G-17706)

National Lime and Stone Co ....C....... 419 396-7671
Carey (G-2921)

Occidental Chemical Corp ....E....... 513 242-2900
Cincinnati (G-4172)

Occidental Chemical Corp ....E....... 330 764-3441
Medina (G-13451)

PPG Industries Inc ....E....... 419 683-2400
Crestline (G-7935)

ALLOYS: Additive, Exc Copper Or Made In Blast Furnaces

GE Aviation Systems LLC ....F....... 513 552-5663
Cincinnati (G-3805)

GE Aviation Systems LLC ....C....... 513 733-1611
Cincinnati (G-3807)

GE Aviation Systems LLC ....F....... 513 889-5150
West Chester (G-19872)

Morris Technologies Inc ....C....... 513 733-1611
Cincinnati (G-4123)

Slice Mfg LLC ....G....... 330 733-7600
Akron (G-404)

ALTERNATORS: Automotive

Cuyahoga Rebuilders Inc ....G 440 846-0532
Cleveland (G-5159)
M W Solutions LLC ....F 419 782-1611
Defiance (G-8800)
Ohio Generator Remanufacturing ....G 330 875-6677
Louisville (G-12321)
Td Power Systems (usa) Inc ....G 330 247-5264
Richfield (G-16642)

ALUMINUM

Alcan Primary Products Corp ....A 440 460-3300
Independence (G-11247)
Alcoa Inc ....F 216 391-3885
Cleveland (G-4743)
Alcoa Inc ....E 608 363-5214
Newburgh Heights (G-15068)
Benjamin Steel Company Inc ....E 937 233-1212
Springfield (G-17522)
Boggs Recycling Inc ....G 800 837-8101
Newbury (G-15082)
D-Flite Mfg LLC ....G 419 485-3081
Montpelier (G-14442)
Fabrication Group LLC ....E 216 251-1125
Cleveland (G-5318)
Kaiser Aluminum Fab Pdts LLC ....C 740 522-1151
Heath (G-10848)
Ormet Corporation ....A 740 483-1381
Hannibal (G-10763)
Specialized Castings Ltd ....F 937 669-5620
Greenville (G-10522)
Wagner Rustproofing Co Inc ....F 216 361-4930
Cleveland (G-6440)

ALUMINUM & BERYLLIUM ORES MINING

Al Chem Specialties LLC ....G 440 255-2826
Mentor (G-13515)

ALUMINUM PRDTS

Accu-Tek Tool & Die Inc ....G 330 726-1946
Salem (G-16867)
Alanod Westlake Metal Ind Inc ....E 440 327-8184
North Ridgeville (G-15356)
Aleris Corporation ....G 216 910-3400
Cleveland (G-4746)
Aleris International Inc ....E 216 910-3400
Beachwood (G-1253)
Aluminum Extruded Shapes Inc ....C 513 563-2205
Cincinnati (G-3383)
American Aluminum Extrusions ....C 330 458-0300
Canton (G-2602)
Arem Co ....F 440 974-6740
Mentor (G-13526)
Astro Shapes LLC ....C 330 755-1414
Struthers (G-17989)
BRT Extrusions Inc ....C 330 544-0177
Niles (G-15145)
Bug-Barrier Screen Corp ....G 330 723-2551
Medina (G-13384)
Central Aluminum Company LLC ....E 614 491-5700
Obetz (G-15652)
Compliant Access Products LLC ....G 513 518-4525
Cleves (G-6510)
Datco Mfg Company Inc ....E 330 781-6100
Youngstown (G-21065)
Exal Corporation ....E 330 744-9505
Youngstown (G-21080)
Extrudex Aluminum Inc ....C 330 538-4444
North Jackson (G-15290)
Hydro Aluminum Fayetteville ....G 937 492-9194
Sidney (G-17193)
Industrial Mold Inc ....E 330 425-7374
Twinsburg (G-18959)
Isaiah Industries Inc ....E 937 773-9840
Piqua (G-16280)
James C Denier Co Inc ....G 513 385-6272
Cincinnati (G-3939)
Klb Industries Inc ....E 937 592-9010
Bellefontaine (G-1535)
Knoble Glass & Metal Inc ....G 513 753-1246
Cincinnati (G-3998)
L & L Ornamental Iron Co ....F 513 353-1930
Cleves (G-6520)
Langstons Ultmate Clg Svcs Inc ....F 330 298-9150
Ravenna (G-16537)
Loxcreen Company Inc ....F 513 539-2255
Middletown (G-14056)

Magnode Corporation ....C 513 988-6351
Trenton (G-18795)
National Metal Shapes Inc ....E 740 363-9559
Delaware (G-8873)
Navarre Industries Inc ....E 330 767-3003
Navarre (G-14721)
Northern States Metals Company ....D 860 521-6001
Youngstown (G-21151)
Orrvilon Inc ....C 330 684-9400
Orrville (G-15754)
Owens Corning Sales Inc ....G 740 983-1300
Ashville (G-853)
Precision of Ohio Inc ....F 330 793-0900
Youngstown (G-21176)
Rexam Beverage Can Company ....C 419 877-0401
Whitehouse (G-20345)
Rexam Beverage Can Company ....C 419 334-4461
Fremont (G-10178)
Sheet Angle Bar Met Fbrication ....G 513 829-8600
Fairfield (G-9716)
Star Extruded Shapes Inc ....B 330 533-9863
Canfield (G-2575)
Star Fab Inc ....C 330 533-9863
Canfield (G-2576)
Star Fab Inc ....E 330 482-1601
Columbiana (G-6634)
T & D Fabricating Inc ....E 440 951-5646
Eastlake (G-9292)
Tecnocap LLC ....D 330 392-7222
Warren (G-19604)
Tri County Tarp Inc ....E 419 288-3350
Bradner (G-2030)
Youngstown Tool & Die Company ....D 330 747-4464
Youngstown (G-21257)
Zarbana Alum Extrusions LLC ....E 330 482-5092
Columbiana (G-6639)

ALUMINUM: Coil & Sheet

Monarch Steel Company Inc ....E 216 587-8000
Cleveland (G-5830)

ALUMINUM: Ingots & Slabs

Homan Metals LLC ....G 513 721-5010
Cincinnati (G-3891)

ALUMINUM: Pigs

Real Alloy Holding Inc ....D 216 755-8800
Beachwood (G-1292)
Real Alloy Specification Inc ....D 260 563-7461
Beachwood (G-1295)

ALUMINUM: Rolling & Drawing

Aleris Rm Inc ....G 216 910-3400
Beachwood (G-1255)
Aleris Rolled Products LLC ....E 216 910-3400
Cleveland (G-4749)
Eastman Kodak Company ....E 937 259-3000
Kettering (G-11579)
Eastman Kodak Company ....E 937 259-3000
Dayton (G-8317)
Novelis Corporation ....D 330 841-3456
Warren (G-19580)
Nuvox ....G 614 232-9115
Columbus (G-7407)
Real Alloy Specialty Products ....C 216 755-8836
Beachwood (G-1294)

ALUMINUM: Slabs, Primary

Imperial Alum - Minerva LLC ....D 330 868-7765
Minerva (G-14326)

AMMUNITION

Ithaca Gun Company ....E 419 294-4113
Upper Sandusky (G-19126)
Vergeline LLC ....G 419 730-0300
Toledo (G-18767)

AMMUNITION: Arming & Fusing Devices

L-3 Fuzing and Ord Systems Inc ....A 513 943-2000
Cincinnati (G-3310)

AMMUNITION: Cartridges Case, 30 mm & Below

Mons Meg Cartridges Inc ....G 937 849-9646
Medway (G-13500)

AMMUNITION: Jet Propulsion Projectiles

Marine Jet Power Inc ....G 614 759-9000
Blacklick (G-1701)

AMMUNITION: Pellets & BB's, Pistol & Air Rifle

Johndavid D Jones ....G 740 264-0176
Wintersville (G-20711)

AMMUNITION: Shot, Steel

Premier Shot Company Inc ....G 330 405-0583
Twinsburg (G-19005)

AMMUNITION: Small Arms

Ares Inc ....D 419 635-2175
Port Clinton (G-16393)
Big Iron Guns Inc ....G 740 464-0852
Portsmouth (G-16432)
Center Mass Ammo LLC ....G 440 796-6207
Madison (G-12498)
Galion LLC ....C 419 468-5214
Galion (G-10268)
Grindel Sales Corp ....G 740 382-1528
Marion (G-12870)
Jmr Enterprises LLC ....G 937 618-1736
Maineville (G-12525)
National Bullet Co ....G 800 317-9506
Eastlake (G-9284)
R & S Monitions Inc ....G 614 846-0597
Columbus (G-7542)

AMPLIFIERS

Dare Electronics Inc ....E 937 335-0031
Troy (G-18814)
Dr Z Amps Inc ....F 216 475-1444
Maple Heights (G-12733)

AMPLIFIERS: RF & IF Power

Rf Linx Inc ....G 513 777-2774
Lebanon (G-11833)

AMUSEMENT & REC SVCS: Baseball Club, Exc Pro & Semi-Pro

Lake Township Trustees ....G 419 836-1143
Millbury (G-14184)

AMUSEMENT & REC SVCS: Cake/Pastry Decorating Instruction

Sugar Showcase ....G 330 792-9154
Youngstown (G-21213)

AMUSEMENT & RECREATION SVCS: Arts & Crafts Instruction

Frame Depot Inc ....G 330 652-7865
Niles (G-15153)

AMUSEMENT & RECREATION SVCS: Exhibition Operation

Asm International ....D 440 338-5151
Novelty (G-15582)

AMUSEMENT & RECREATION SVCS: Exposition Operation

Park Corporation ....B 216 267-4870
Cleveland (G-5965)
Relx Inc ....E 937 865-6800
Miamisburg (G-13851)

AMUSEMENT & RECREATION SVCS: Game Machines

Alligator Cmpt Systems Corp ....F 513 542-1000
Cincinnati (G-3380)

AMUSEMENT & RECREATION SVCS: Golf Svcs & Professionals

X-Press Tool Inc ....E 330 225-8748
Brunswick (G-2271)

PRODUCT

AMUSEMENT & RECREATION SVCS: Gun & Hunting Clubs

Target Holdings Inc ....E 513 474-4409
  Cincinnati **(G-4493)**

AMUSEMENT & RECREATION SVCS: Gun Club, Membership

Smokin Guns LLC ....G 440 324-4003
  Elyria **(G-9494)**

AMUSEMENT & RECREATION SVCS: Ice Skating Rink

Jmac Inc ....F 614 436-2418
  Columbus **(G-7235)**

AMUSEMENT & RECREATION SVCS: Indoor Court Clubs

Soccer Centre Owners Ltd ....E 419 893-5425
  Maumee **(G-13296)**

AMUSEMENT & RECREATION SVCS: Juke Box

Glenn Michael Brick ....F 740 391-5735
  Flushing **(G-9916)**

AMUSEMENT & RECREATION SVCS: Outfitters, Recreation

Reelflyrodcom ....G 937 434-8472
  Dayton **(G-8622)**

AMUSEMENT & RECREATION SVCS: Racquetball Club, Non-Member

Melinz Industries Inc ....F 440 946-3512
  Willoughby **(G-20545)**

AMUSEMENT & RECREATION SVCS: Shooting Range

Kelblys Rifle Range Inc ....G 330 683-0070
  North Lawrence **(G-15306)**

AMUSEMENT & RECREATION SVCS: Zoological Garden, Commercial

Kabler Farms ....G 513 732-0501
  Batavia **(G-1195)**

AMUSEMENT MACHINES: Coin Operated

Alligator Cmpt Systems Corp ....F 513 542-1000
  Cincinnati **(G-3380)**

AMUSEMENT PARK DEVICES & RIDES

Advanced Indus Machining Inc ....F 614 596-4183
  Powell **(G-16461)**
Alpha Machining LLC ....G 330 889-2207
  West Farmington **(G-20074)**
ARM (usa) Inc ....F 740 264-6599
  Steubenville **(G-17688)**
Delta Manufacturing Inc ....E 330 386-1270
  East Liverpool **(G-9213)**
Owen S Precision Grinding ....G 513 745-9335
  Cincinnati **(G-4204)**
Quality Design Machining Inc ....G 440 352-7290
  Mentor **(G-13707)**
Reeces Las Vegas Supplies ....G 937 274-5000
  Dayton **(G-8620)**

AMUSEMENT PARK DEVICES & RIDES Carousels Or Merry-Go-Rounds

Carousel Magic LLC ....G 419 522-6456
  Mansfield **(G-12575)**
Carousel Works Inc ....E 419 522-7558
  Mansfield **(G-12576)**

AMUSEMENT PARK DEVICES & RIDES: Carnival Mach & Eqpt, NEC

Majestic Manufacturing Inc ....E 330 457-2447
  New Waterford **(G-14972)**

Murray Brothers Shows Inc ....F 513 941-6500
  Cincinnati **(G-4133)**

ANALYZERS: Blood & Body Fluid

Keyghobad Ventures LLC ....G 440 366-3278
  Elyria **(G-9447)**

ANALYZERS: Moisture

Koster Crop Tester Inc ....G 330 220-2116
  Brunswick **(G-2236)**

ANALYZERS: Network

Community Care Network Inc ....E 216 671-0977
  Cleveland **(G-5108)**
Complete Network Solutions Inc ....G 330 328-2596
  Stow **(G-17742)**
Simplex-It LLC ....G 234 380-1277
  Stow **(G-17800)**

ANALYZERS: Respiratory

Health Care Solutions Inc ....G 419 636-4189
  Bryan **(G-2300)**
Medical Equipment Provider ....G 937 778-2190
  Piqua **(G-16291)**
Medinvent LLC ....G 330 247-0921
  Medina **(G-13446)**

ANESTHESIA EQPT

Lababidi Enterprises Inc ....E 330 733-2907
  Akron **(G-266)**

ANIMAL BASED MEDICINAL CHEMICAL PRDTS

Badizo LLC ....G 844 344-3833
  Stow **(G-17732)**

ANIMAL FEED & SUPPLEMENTS: Livestock & Poultry

Archer-Daniels-Midland Company ....G 330 852-3025
  Sugarcreek **(G-18015)**
Archer-Daniels-Midland Company ....G 419 705-3292
  Toledo **(G-18353)**
Cooper Hatchery Inc ....C 419 594-3325
  Oakwood **(G-15615)**
Granville Milling Co ....G 740 345-1305
  Newark **(G-15015)**
Hamlet Protein Inc ....E 567 525-5627
  Findlay **(G-9835)**
Hartz Mountain Corporation ....D 513 877-2131
  Pleasant Plain **(G-16372)**
IAMS Company ....B 800 675-3849
  Mason **(G-13038)**
J & B Feed Co Inc ....G 419 335-5821
  Wauseon **(G-19685)**
Legacy Farmers Cooperative ....F 419 423-2611
  Findlay **(G-9851)**
Magnus International Group Inc ....G 216 592-8355
  Chagrin Falls **(G-3100)**
Mid-Wood Inc ....F 419 257-3331
  North Baltimore **(G-15195)**
Occidental Chemical Corp ....E 513 242-2900
  Cincinnati **(G-4172)**
Ohio Blenders Inc ....F 419 726-2655
  Toledo **(G-18615)**
Pettisville Grain Co ....E 419 446-2547
  Pettisville **(G-16182)**
Premier Feeds LLC ....G 937 584-2411
  Sabina **(G-16776)**
Pro-Pet LLC ....E 419 394-3374
  Saint Marys **(G-16849)**
Pro-Pet LLC ....G 419 394-3374
  Saint Marys **(G-16850)**
Provimi North America Inc ....D 937 770-2400
  Lewisburg **(G-11940)**
Provimi North America Inc ....B 937 770-2400
  Brookville **(G-2197)**
Psd Partners LLC ....G 419 294-3838
  Carey **(G-2925)**
Ridley USA Inc ....F 800 837-8222
  Botkins **(G-1953)**
Ridley USA Inc ....E 937 693-6393
  Botkins **(G-1954)**
Rogers Mill Inc ....G 330 227-3214
  Rogers **(G-16715)**

Sunrise Cooperative Inc ....G 419 629-2338
  New Bremen **(G-14794)**
Terry A Johnson ....G 614 561-0706
  Etna **(G-9552)**

ANIMAL FEED: Wholesalers

Gerald Grain Center Inc ....F 419 445-2451
  Archbold **(G-678)**
Granville Milling Co ....G 740 345-1305
  Newark **(G-15015)**
J & B Feed Co Inc ....G 419 335-5821
  Wauseon **(G-19685)**
Land OLakes Inc ....E 330 879-2158
  Massillon **(G-13166)**
Provimi North America Inc ....B 937 770-2400
  Brookville **(G-2197)**
Ridley USA Inc ....F 800 837-8222
  Botkins **(G-1953)**

ANIMAL FOOD & SUPPLEMENTS: Alfalfa Or Alfalfa Meal

Toledo Alfalfa Mills Inc ....G 419 836-3705
  Oregon **(G-15720)**
Verhoff Alfalfa Mills Inc ....G 419 653-4161
  New Bavaria **(G-14776)**
Verhoff Alfalfa Mills Inc ....G 419 523-4767
  Ottawa **(G-15813)**
Yarnell Bros Inc ....G 419 278-2831
  Deshler **(G-8952)**

ANIMAL FOOD & SUPPLEMENTS: Bird Food, Prepared

Centerra Co-Op ....E 330 769-3469
  Seville **(G-17072)**
Centerra Co-Op ....E 800 362-9598
  Jefferson **(G-11358)**
Centerra Co-Op ....E 419 281-2153
  Ashland **(G-717)**
Four Natures Keepers Inc ....F 740 363-8007
  Delaware **(G-8845)**
Lakeshore Feed & Seed Inc ....G 216 961-5729
  Cleveland **(G-5677)**
Lizzie Maes Birdseed & Dg Co ....G 330 927-1795
  Rittman **(G-16678)**
Sunny Side Feeds LLC ....G 330 635-1455
  West Salem **(G-20117)**
Vitakraft Sun Seed Inc ....D 419 832-1641
  Weston **(G-20327)**

ANIMAL FOOD & SUPPLEMENTS: Bone Meal

Holmes By Products Co ....E 330 893-2322
  Millersburg **(G-14228)**
Manco Inc ....G 937 962-2661
  Lewisburg **(G-11937)**

ANIMAL FOOD & SUPPLEMENTS: Cat

Hartz Mountain Corporation ....D 513 877-2131
  Pleasant Plain **(G-16372)**
Pro-Pet LLC ....G 419 394-3374
  Saint Marys **(G-16850)**

ANIMAL FOOD & SUPPLEMENTS: Chicken Feeds, Prepared

Buckeye Feed & Grain ....G 937 526-3914
  Versailles **(G-19342)**

ANIMAL FOOD & SUPPLEMENTS: Dog

Bil-Jac Foods Inc ....E 330 722-7888
  Medina **(G-13377)**
G & C Raw LLC ....G 937 827-0010
  Versailles **(G-19348)**
IAMS Company ....B 800 675-3849
  Mason **(G-13038)**
IAMS Company ....C 419 943-4267
  Leipsic **(G-11870)**
IAMS Company ....D 937 962-2624
  Lewisburg **(G-11935)**
Lakeshore Feed & Seed Inc ....G 216 961-5729
  Cleveland **(G-5677)**
Lucky Paws LLC ....G 859 620-2525
  Cincinnati **(G-4037)**
Nom Nom Nom ....G 614 302-4815
  Columbus **(G-7396)**
Ohio Pet Foods Inc ....E 330 424-1431
  Lisbon **(G-12130)**

Royal Canin USA Inc ....G....... 937 962-7352
Lewisburg *(G-11941)*

ANIMAL FOOD & SUPPLEMENTS: Dog & Cat

About and Dogs LLC ....G....... 440 263-8989
Hudson *(G-11153)*
Big Heart Pet Brands ....C....... 412 222-2200
Orrville *(G-15731)*
In Good Hlth & Animal Wellness ....G....... 330 908-1234
Northfield *(G-15467)*
Kelly Foods Corporation ....E....... 330 722-8855
Medina *(G-13433)*
Land OLakes Inc ....E....... 330 879-2158
Massillon *(G-13166)*
Mars Petcare Us Inc ....E....... 614 878-7242
Columbus *(G-7319)*
Nestle Purina Petcare Company.............D....... 740 454-8575
Zanesville *(G-21332)*
Ohio Blenders Inc ....F....... 419 726-2655
Toledo *(G-18615)*
Pro-Pet LLC ....E....... 419 394-3374
Saint Marys *(G-16849)*
Rex M & Kim P Bellville ....F....... 937 256-2526
Dayton *(G-8628)*
Vitakraft Sun Seed Inc ....D....... 419 832-1641
Weston *(G-20327)*

ANIMAL FOOD & SUPPLEMENTS: Feed Concentrates

Woodstock Products Inc........................G....... 216 641-3811
Cleveland *(G-6477)*

ANIMAL FOOD & SUPPLEMENTS: Feed Premixes

Juana Williams ....G....... 614 351-9844
Columbus *(G-7247)*
Purina Mills LLC ....G....... 330 682-1951
Orrville *(G-15755)*
Rowe Premix Inc ....F....... 937 678-9015
West Manchester *(G-20098)*

ANIMAL FOOD & SUPPLEMENTS: Feed Supplements

Agri-Products Inc..................................G....... 216 831-5890
Cleveland *(G-4732)*
Direct Action Co Inc ....F....... 330 364-3219
Dover *(G-8976)*

ANIMAL FOOD & SUPPLEMENTS: Livestock

Commodity Blenders Inc.......................G....... 419 846-3155
West Salem *(G-20112)*
Edward Keiter & Sons ....G....... 937 382-3249
Wilmington *(G-20664)*
Geauga Feed and Grain Supply............G....... 440 564-5000
Newbury *(G-15092)*
Gerber & Sons Inc ....E....... 330 897-6201
Baltic *(G-1072)*
Hanby Farms Inc ....E....... 740 763-3554
Nashport *(G-14705)*
International Multifoods Corp ....G....... 330 682-3000
Orrville *(G-15741)*
Kalmbach Feeds Inc ....C....... 419 294-3838
Upper Sandusky *(G-19127)*
Land OLakes Inc ....E....... 330 879-2158
Massillon *(G-13166)*
Le Summer Kidron Inc..........................E....... 330 857-2031
Apple Creek *(G-642)*
Republic Mills Inc.................................F....... 419 758-3511
Okolona *(G-15669)*
Superior Ag-Patoka Vlly Feed..............F....... 419 294-3838
Upper Sandusky *(G-19142)*

ANIMAL FOOD & SUPPLEMENTS: Mineral feed supplements

Tenda Horse Products LLC...................G....... 740 694-8836
Fredericktown *(G-10111)*

ANIMAL FOOD & SUPPLEMENTS: Pet, Exc Dog & Cat, Dry

Kelly Foods Corporation ....E....... 330 722-8855
Medina *(G-13433)*

ANIMAL FOOD & SUPPLEMENTS: Poultry

2nd Roe LLC ....G....... 419 499-3031
Monroeville *(G-14423)*
Cooper Farms Inc ....D....... 419 375-4116
Fort Recovery *(G-9946)*
Cooper Farms Inc ....D....... 419 375-4119
Fort Recovery *(G-9947)*
Cooper Farms Inc ....F....... 419 375-4619
Fort Recovery *(G-9948)*
Nature Pure LLC ....G....... 937 358-2364
Raymond *(G-16576)*

ANIMAL FOOD & SUPPLEMENTS: Specialty, Mice & Other Pets

Ohio Pet Foods Inc ....E....... 330 424-1431
Lisbon *(G-12130)*

ANIMAL FOOD & SUPPLEMENTS: Stock Feeds, Dry

Stahl Farm Market................................F....... 330 325-0640
Ravenna *(G-16562)*

ANIMAL FOOD/SUPPLEMENTS: Feeds Fm Meat/Meat/Veg Combnd Meals

G A Wintzer and Son Company ....D....... 419 739-4913
Wapakoneta *(G-19485)*

ANNEALING: Metal

Atmosphere Annealing LLC..................D....... 330 478-0314
Kenton *(G-11544)*
Northlake Steel Corporation ....D....... 330 220-7717
Valley City *(G-19225)*
Ohio Coatings Company ....D....... 740 859-5500
Yorkville *(G-21007)*

ANNUNCIATORS

Seekirk Inc ....F....... 614 278-9200
Columbus *(G-7606)*

ANODIZING EQPT

Singleton Corporation...........................F....... 216 651-7800
Cleveland *(G-6205)*

ANODIZING SVC

Amac Enterprises Inc ....D....... 216 362-1880
Cleveland *(G-4775)*
Anomatic Corporation ....B....... 740 522-2203
New Albany *(G-14745)*
Bedford Anodizing Co ....D....... 330 650-6052
Hudson *(G-11160)*
Commercial Anodizing Co ....E....... 440 942-8384
Willoughby *(G-20460)*
Electrolizing Corporation Ohio..............E....... 216 451-3153
Cleveland *(G-5267)*
Electrolizing Corporation Ohio ....F....... 216 451-8653
Cleveland *(G-5268)*
K-B Plating Inc ....F....... 216 341-1115
Cleveland *(G-5630)*
Luke Engineering & Mfg Corp ....E....... 330 335-1501
Wadsworth *(G-19418)*
Noble Anodizing Inc ....G....... 216 268-1263
Cleveland *(G-5884)*
Russell Products Co Inc ....E....... 330 633-5252
Akron *(G-385)*
Sifco Industries Inc ....B....... 216 881-8600
Cleveland *(G-6201)*

ANTENNA REPAIR & INSTALLATION SVCS

Central USA Wireless LLC ....E....... 513 469-1500
Cincinnati *(G-3518)*

ANTENNAS: Radar Or Communications

Circle Prime Manufacturing ....E....... 330 923-0019
Cuyahoga Falls *(G-7980)*
Quasonix Inc ....E....... 513 942-1287
West Chester *(G-19927)*

ANTENNAS: Receiving

Sinbon Usa LLC ....G....... 937 667-8999
Tipp City *(G-18299)*
Solar Con Inc ....E....... 419 865-5877
Holland *(G-11086)*

Wifi-Plus Inc ....G....... 877 838-4195
Brunswick *(G-2268)*

ANTIBIOTICS

Pfizer Inc ....C....... 937 746-3603
Franklin *(G-10044)*

ANTIFREEZE

BASF Corporation.................................G....... 614 662-5682
Columbus *(G-6812)*

ANTIQUE & CLASSIC AUTOMOBILE RESTORATION

Cincinnati Woodworks Inc ....G....... 513 241-6412
Cincinnati *(G-3570)*

ANTIQUE FURNITURE RESTORATION & REPAIR

Mark Rasche ....G....... 614 882-1810
Westerville *(G-20170)*
Swigart Refinishing Company ....G....... 937 254-1141
Dayton *(G-8692)*
Todd W Goings......................................G....... 740 389-5842
Marion *(G-12907)*

ANTIQUE REPAIR & RESTORATION SVCS, EXC FURNITURE & AUTOS

Carousel Magic LLC ....G....... 419 522-6456
Mansfield *(G-12575)*

ANTIQUE SHOPS

Indian River Industries ....G....... 740 965-4377
Sunbury *(G-18064)*
John Purdum ....G....... 513 897-9686
Waynesville *(G-19731)*

ANTIQUES, WHOLESALE

Indian River Industries ....G....... 740 965-4377
Sunbury *(G-18064)*

APPAREL DESIGNERS: Commercial

Heather B Moore Inc ....G....... 216 932-5430
Cleveland *(G-5492)*

APPAREL PRESSING SVCS

Graphix Junction ....G....... 234 284-8392
Hudson *(G-11176)*

APPAREL: Hand Woven

Specilty Fbrics Converting Inc ....E....... 706 637-3000
Fairlawn *(G-9760)*

APPLIANCE CORDS: Household Electrical Eqpt

Rent-A-Center Inc ....G....... 740 373-1342
Marietta *(G-12823)*

APPLIANCE PARTS: Porcelain Enameled

Destiny Manufacturing Inc.....................E....... 330 273-9000
Brunswick *(G-2220)*
Ice Industries Columbus Inc..................G....... 419 842-3600
Sylvania *(G-18111)*
Whirlaway Corporation...........................C....... 440 647-4711
Wellington *(G-19758)*

APPLIANCES, HOUSEHOLD OR COIN OPERATED: Laundry Dryers

Carly Co LLC ....G....... 937 477-6411
Centerville *(G-3038)*
Junebugs Wash N Dry...........................G....... 513 988-5863
Trenton *(G-18794)*
Whirlpool Corporation............................C....... 740 383-7122
Marion *(G-12913)*

APPLIANCES, HOUSEHOLD: Kitchen, Major, Exc Refrigs & Stoves

ABC Appliance Inc................................E....... 419 693-4414
Oregon *(G-15699)*

PRODUCT

New Path International LLC ....E 614 410-3974
 Powell (G-16481)

APPLIANCES, HOUSEHOLD: Laundry Machines, Incl Coin-Operated

Whirlpool Corporation ....C 937 547-0773
 Greenville (G-10528)
Whirlpool Corporation ....C 419 523-5100
 Ottawa (G-15815)

APPLIANCES, HOUSEHOLD: Refrigs, Mechanical & Absorption

Norcold Inc ....B 937 497-3080
 Sidney (G-17206)
Whirlpool Corporation ....C 419 523-5100
 Ottawa (G-15815)
Whirlpool Corporation ....C 614 409-4340
 Lockbourne (G-12153)

APPLIANCES, HOUSEHOLD: Sweepers, Electric

Hoover Inc ....F 330 499-9200
 Canton (G-2730)

APPLIANCES: Household, NEC

JC and Associates Sylvania LLC ....G 419 824-0011
 Sylvania (G-18114)

APPLIANCES: Household, Refrigerators & Freezers

Norcold Inc ....C 937 447-2241
 Gettysburg (G-10375)
Whirlpool Corporation ....D 419 423-8123
 Findlay (G-9908)
Whirlpool Corporation ....C 740 383-7122
 Marion (G-12913)

APPLIANCES: Major, Cooking

Nacco Industries Inc ....E 440 229-5151
 Cleveland (G-5848)
Royalton Food Service Eqp Co ....E 440 237-0806
 North Royalton (G-15448)

APPLIANCES: Small, Electric

Budzar Industries Inc ....D 440 530-1000
 Willoughby (G-20448)
Ces Nationwide ....G 937 322-0771
 Springfield (G-17530)
Cleveland Range LLC ....C 216 481-4900
 Cleveland (G-5075)
Driven Innovations LLC ....G 330 818-7681
 Englewood (G-9517)
Glo-Quartz Electric Heater Co ....E 440 255-9701
 Mentor (G-13593)
Johnson Bros Rubber Co Inc ....E 419 752-4814
 Greenwich (G-10531)
Qualtek Electronics Corp ....C 440 951-3300
 Mentor (G-13710)

APPLICATIONS SOFTWARE PROGRAMMING

B-Tek Scales LLC ....E 330 471-8900
 Canton (G-2613)
Foundation Software Inc ....D 330 220-8383
 Strongsville (G-17920)
Pwi Inc ....F 732 212-8110
 New Albany (G-14770)
Teradata Corporation ....B 866 548-8348
 Miamisburg (G-13870)

APPRAISAL SVCS, EXC REAL ESTATE

Amos Press Inc ....C 937 498-2111
 Sidney (G-17168)
Jaffe & Gross Jewelry Company ....G 937 461-9450
 Dayton (G-8419)
Pughs Designer Jewelers Inc ....G 740 344-9259
 Newark (G-15049)

APRONS: Rubber, Vulcanized Or Rubberized Fabric

Ansell Healthcare Products LLC ....C 740 295-5414
 Coshocton (G-7880)

AQUARIUM ACCESS, METAL

Rift Lake Aquatics ....G 216 221-1437
 Cleveland (G-6113)

AQUARIUMS & ACCESS: Glass

Frigid Units Inc ....G 419 478-4000
 Toledo (G-18473)

AQUARIUMS & ACCESS: Plastic

Acrylic Arts ....G 440 537-0300
 West Farmington (G-20073)
Th Plastics Inc ....C 419 425-5825
 Findlay (G-9902)

ARCHERY & SHOOTING RANGES

Black Wing Shooting Center LLC ....G 740 363-7555
 Delaware (G-8825)

ARCHITECTURAL PANELS OR PARTS: Porcelain Enameled

Eurocase Architectural Cabinet ....F 330 674-0681
 Millersburg (G-14214)

ARCHITECTURAL SVCS

Barr Engineering Incorporated ....F 614 892-0162
 Columbus (G-6807)
Ceso Inc ....D 937 435-8584
 Dayton (G-8224)
Dlz Ohio Inc ....C 614 888-0040
 Columbus (G-7033)
Garland Industries Inc ....G 216 641-7500
 Cleveland (G-5399)
Garland/Dbs Inc ....C 216 641-7500
 Cleveland (G-5400)

ARCHITECTURAL SVCS: House Designer

Dishtronix Inc ....G 937 292-7981
 Bellefontaine (G-1528)

ARMATURE REPAIRING & REWINDING SVC

City Machine Technologies Inc ....F 330 747-2639
 Youngstown (G-21047)
City Machine Technologies Inc ....E 330 740-8186
 Youngstown (G-21048)
Diversified Air Systems Inc ....E 216 741-1700
 Brooklyn Heights (G-2139)
Dolin Supply Co ....E 304 529-4171
 South Point (G-17436)
Econ-O-Machine Products Inc ....G 937 882-6307
 Donnelsville (G-8961)
Electric Motor Svc of Athens ....F 740 592-1682
 The Plains (G-18186)
Gunter Electric LLC ....G 304 253-4671
 Athens (G-871)
Hennings Quality Service Inc ....F 216 941-9120
 Cleveland (G-5499)
Horner Industrial Services Inc ....F 513 874-8722
 West Chester (G-20014)
Integrated Power Services LLC ....E 216 433-7808
 Cleveland (G-5575)
K C N Technologies LLC ....G 440 439-4219
 Bedford (G-1434)
Setco Sales Company ....D 513 941-5110
 Cincinnati (G-4409)

ARMORED CAR SVCS

Garda CL Technical Svcs Inc ....E 937 294-4099
 Moraine (G-14490)

AROMATIC CHEMICAL PRDTS

Dark Continent ....G 330 454-7804
 Canton (G-2679)

ART & ORNAMENTAL WARE: Pottery

Benzle Porcelain Company Inc ....G 614 876-2159
 Hilliard (G-10931)
Carruth Studio Inc ....F 419 878-3060
 Waterville (G-19653)
J-Vac Industries Inc ....D 740 384-2155
 Wellston (G-19765)
Klopfenstein Art Equipment ....G 419 884-2900
 Mansfield (G-12633)

ART DEALERS & GALLERIES

Marchione Studio Inc ....G 330 454-7408
 Canton (G-2768)
Strictly Stitchery Inc ....F 440 543-7128
 Cleveland (G-6254)

ART DEALERS & GALLERIES

Fenwick Gallery of Fine Arts ....G 419 475-1651
 Toledo (G-18468)
Lazars Art Gllery Crtive Frmng ....G 330 477-8351
 Canton (G-2759)

ART DESIGN SVCS

Eugene Stewart ....G 937 898-1117
 Dayton (G-8333)
Graphic Image ....G 937 320-0302
 Beavercreek (G-1341)
Graphicsource Inc ....G 440 248-9200
 Solon (G-17302)
Meridian Arts and Graphics ....F 330 759-9099
 Youngstown (G-21143)
Rapid Signs & More Inc ....G 513 553-4040
 New Richmond (G-14944)
Shamrock Companies Inc ....D 440 899-9510
 Westlake (G-20308)
Youngstown Pre-Press Inc ....F 330 793-3690
 Youngstown (G-21255)

ART MARBLE: Concrete

Agean Marble Manufacturing ....F 513 874-1475
 West Chester (G-19978)
Marblelife of Central Ohio ....G 614 837-6146
 Pickerington (G-16197)

ART RELATED SVCS

Smartcopy Inc ....G 740 392-6162
 Mount Vernon (G-14651)
Those Charc From Cleve Inc ....F 216 252-7300
 Cleveland (G-6323)

ART RESTORATION SVC

Bonfoey Co ....F 216 621-0178
 Cleveland (G-4924)

ART SPLY STORES

Print Craft Inc ....G 513 931-6828
 Cincinnati (G-4270)

ARTIFICIAL FLOWER SHOPS

Hall Creations ....G 330 357-2428
 Kent (G-11468)

ARTISTS' AGENTS & BROKERS

Thickemz Entertainment LLC ....G 404 399-4255
 Cuyahoga Falls (G-8056)

ARTISTS' MATERIALS: Brushes, Air

RPM Consumer Holding Company ....G 330 273-5090
 Medina (G-13470)

ARTISTS' MATERIALS: Canvas, Prepared On Frames

Whitten Studios ....G 419 368-8366
 Ashland (G-785)

ARTISTS' MATERIALS: Ink, Drawing, Black & Colored

Modern Ink Technology LLC ....F 419 738-9664
 Lima (G-12059)

ARTISTS' MATERIALS: Palettes

Clay Logan Products Company ....D 740 385-2184
 Logan (G-12172)

ARTISTS' MATERIALS: Pencil Holders

Pen Pal LLC ....G 614 348-2517
 New Albany (G-14768)

ARTS & CRAFTS SCHOOL

Studio Arts & Glass Inc ....F 330 494-9779
 Canton (G-2860)

Wooden Horse..................................G...... 740 503-5243
Baltimore *(G-1091)*

ARTWORK: Framed

Sun Drenched Art Studios ....G...... 513 375-9612
Cincinnati *(G-4482)*

ASBESTOS PRDTS: Textiles, Exc Insulating Material

Pop/Pos Advantage ....G...... 440 543-9452
Chagrin Falls *(G-3113)*

ASPHALT & ASPHALT PRDTS

Canton Asphalt Co ....G...... 330 499-6888
Canton *(G-2636)*
Central Oil Asphalt Corp ....G...... 614 224-8111
Columbus *(G-6919)*
D & R Supply Inc ....G...... 330 855-3781
Marshallville *(G-12917)*
Full Circle Technologies LLC ....G...... 216 650-0007
Pepper Pike *(G-16046)*
Grand River Asphalt ....G...... 440 352-2254
Grand River *(G-10449)*
Heritage Group Inc ....E...... 330 875-5566
Louisville *(G-12314)*
Kokosing Materials Inc ....F...... 419 522-2715
Mansfield *(G-12634)*
Kokosing Materials Inc ....G...... 614 891-5090
Westerville *(G-20220)*
Kokosing Materials Inc ....E...... 614 491-1199
Columbus *(G-7265)*
Koski Construction Co ....G...... 440 997-5337
Ashtabula *(G-815)*
Lucas County Asphalt Inc ....E...... 419 476-0705
Toledo *(G-18564)*
Lynn James Contracting LLC ....G...... 419 467-4505
Delta *(G-8938)*
Morris Paving ....F...... 740 373-2457
Marietta *(G-12809)*
Morrow Gravel Company Inc ....E...... 513 771-0820
Cincinnati *(G-4124)*
Mt Pleasant Blacktopping Inc ....G...... 513 874-3777
Fairfield *(G-9688)*
S E Johnson Companies Inc ....F...... 419 893-8731
Maumee *(G-13290)*
Seneca Petroleum Co Inc ....F...... 419 691-3581
Toledo *(G-18692)*
Shalersville Asphalt Co ....E...... 440 834-4294
Burton *(G-2384)*
Shelly and Sands Inc ....F...... 740 373-6495
Marietta *(G-12828)*
Shelly and Sands Inc ....E...... 740 453-0721
Zanesville *(G-21351)*
Shelly and Sands Inc ....F...... 740 453-0721
Zanesville *(G-21350)*
Shelly Materials Inc...........................G...... 740 446-7789
Gallipolis *(G-10309)*
Shelly Materials Inc...........................G...... 740 666-5841
Ostrander *(G-15789)*
Stoneco ....C...... 419 422-8854
Findlay *(G-9895)*
Unique Paving Materials Corp ....E...... 216 341-7711
Cleveland *(G-6383)*
Valley Asphalt Corporation ....G...... 937 426-7682
Xenia *(G-20984)*
Valley Asphalt Corporation ....G...... 513 353-2171
Cleves *(G-6531)*
Valley Asphalt Corporation ....G...... 513 784-1476
Cincinnati *(G-4552)*
Valley Asphalt Corporation ....G...... 513 561-1551
Cincinnati *(G-4551)*
Walls Bros Asphalt Co Inc ....G...... 937 548-7158
Greenville *(G-10526)*
Wilson Blacktop Corporation ....E...... 740 635-3566
Martins Ferry *(G-12928)*

ASPHALT COATINGS & SEALERS

Aluminum Coating Manufacturers ....E...... 216 341-2000
Cleveland *(G-4774)*
Atlas Roofing Corporation ....C...... 937 746-9941
Franklin *(G-10008)*
Brewer Company ....E...... 614 279-8688
Columbus *(G-6855)*
Certainteed Corporation.....................C...... 419 499-2581
Milan *(G-14110)*
Consolidated Coatings Corp ....E...... 216 514-7596
Cleveland *(G-5118)*

Hy-Grade Corporation ....E...... 216 341-7711
Cleveland *(G-5541)*
Hyload Inc ....F...... 330 336-6604
Seville *(G-17075)*
Isaiah Industries Inc ....E...... 937 773-9840
Piqua *(G-16280)*
Johns Manville Corporation................D...... 419 499-1400
Milan *(G-14114)*
Kettering Roofing & Shtmtl.................F...... 513 281-6413
Cincinnati *(G-3986)*
Metal Sales Manufacturing Corp ....E...... 440 576-9070
Jefferson *(G-11367)*
Midwest Industrial Products ....G...... 216 771-8555
Cleveland *(G-5810)*
Midwest Trmnals Tledo Intl Inc............G...... 419 897-6868
Maumee *(G-13283)*
National Tool & Equipment Inc ....F...... 330 629-8665
Youngstown *(G-21148)*
Owens Corning ....A...... 419 248-8000
Toledo *(G-18625)*
Owens Corning Sales LLC ....C...... 330 764-7800
Medina *(G-13456)*
Owens Corning Sales LLC ....G...... 419 248-8000
Toledo *(G-18626)*
Qualico Inc.......................................G...... 216 271-2550
Cleveland *(G-6067)*
Riverside Sand & Gravel Co ....G...... 330 673-2021
Kent *(G-11517)*
Simon Roofing and Shtmtl Corp ....C...... 330 629-7392
Youngstown *(G-21204)*
Sr Products ....G...... 330 998-6500
Macedonia *(G-12486)*
State Industrial Products Corp ....B...... 877 747-6986
Cleveland *(G-6239)*
Surface-All Inc ....G...... 440 428-2233
Port Clinton *(G-16416)*
Terry Asphalt Materials Inc ....E...... 513 874-6192
Hamilton *(G-10744)*
Thorworks Industries Inc ....E...... 419 626-4375
Sandusky *(G-17015)*
Transtar Holding Company ....G...... 800 359-3339
Cleveland *(G-6349)*

ASPHALT MINING & BITUMINOUS STONE QUARRYING SVCS

Kellstone ....G...... 419 621-8140
Sandusky *(G-16976)*
Shelly Liquid Division ....G...... 216 781-9264
Cleveland *(G-6187)*

ASPHALT MINING SVCS

Asphalt Materials Inc ....F...... 419 693-0626
Oregon *(G-15702)*
Mar-Zane Inc ....G...... 419 529-2086
Ontario *(G-15689)*
National Lime and Stone Co ....G...... 330 339-2144
New Philadelphia *(G-14918)*
National Lime and Stone Co ....G...... 216 883-9840
Cleveland *(G-5857)*

ASPHALT MIXTURES WHOLESALERS

Barrett Paving Materials Inc................C...... 513 271-6200
Middletown *(G-14101)*
Hy-Grade Corporation ....E...... 216 341-7711
Cleveland *(G-5541)*
Russell Standard Corporation..............G...... 330 733-9400
Akron *(G-389)*

ASPHALT PLANTS INCLUDING GRAVEL MIX TYPE

G & J Asphalt & Material Inc ....F...... 740 773-6358
Chillicothe *(G-3238)*
Rls Parts & Equipment LLC ....G...... 440 498-1843
Solon *(G-17369)*
Tri County Asphalt Materials ....G...... 330 549-2852
Youngstown *(G-21229)*

ASSEMBLING SVC: Plumbing Fixture Fittings, Plastic

Langenau Manufacturing Company .....F...... 216 651-3400
Cleveland *(G-5680)*

ASSOCIATION FOR THE HANDICAPPED

Cincinnati Assn For The Blind..............C...... 513 221-8558
Cincinnati *(G-3539)*

ASSOCIATIONS: Business

Diversifd OH Vlly Eqpt & Srvcs ....F...... 740 458-9881
Clarington *(G-4651)*
Hirzel Canning Company ....E...... 419 693-0531
Northwood *(G-15482)*
Interstate Contractors LLC ....E...... 513 372-5393
Mason *(G-13048)*
OFA Services Inc ....F...... 614 884-1203
Columbus *(G-7413)*
Superior Clay Corp ....D...... 740 922-4122
Uhrichsville *(G-19061)*

ASSOCIATIONS: Fraternal

Collegiate Connection ....G...... 419 352-8333
Bowling Green *(G-1982)*

ASSOCIATIONS: Manufacturers'

Albin Sales Inc ....G...... 740 927-7210
Pataskala *(G-15966)*
James J Fairbanks Company Inc ....G...... 330 534-1374
Hubbard *(G-11132)*

ASSOCIATIONS: Real Estate Management

Ajami Holdings Group LLC ....G...... 216 396-6089
Richmond Heights *(G-16651)*
Elite Property Group LLC ....F...... 216 316-8222
Cleveland *(G-5272)*
Nesco Inc ....E...... 440 461-6000
Cleveland *(G-5871)*

ASSOCIATIONS: Trade

Heat Exchange Institute Inc ....G...... 216 241-7333
Cleveland *(G-5490)*
Ohio Association Realtors Inc ....E...... 614 228-6675
Columbus *(G-7415)*
Precision Metalforming Assn ....E...... 216 241-1482
Independence *(G-11271)*

ATOMIZERS

Altec Industries ....G...... 419 289-6066
Ashland *(G-702)*
American Inks and Coatings Co ....F...... 513 552-7200
Fairfield *(G-9641)*
AT&f Nuclear Inc ....G...... 216 252-1500
Cleveland *(G-4852)*
Bay Industries Incorporated ....G...... 740 549-2305
Lewis Center *(G-11889)*
Bison USA Corp ....G...... 513 713-0513
West Chester *(G-19818)*
Centaur Inc ....G...... 419 469-8000
Toledo *(G-18392)*
CK Technologies LLC ....C...... 419 485-1110
Montpelier *(G-14441)*
Cr Brands Inc ....D...... 513 860-5039
West Chester *(G-19846)*
Datco Mfg Company Inc ....E...... 330 787-1127
Youngstown *(G-21064)*
Ferguson Fire Fabrication Inc ....F...... 614 299-2070
Columbus *(G-7081)*
Goodwill Idstrs Grtr Clvlnd L ....E...... 330 456-8020
Canton *(G-2716)*
H Rosen Usa LLC ....C...... 614 354-6707
Columbus *(G-7135)*
Henry-Griffitts Limited ....G...... 419 482-9095
Maumee *(G-13266)*
Marcy Industries Company LLC ....E...... 740 387-1213
Marion *(G-12881)*
MD Solutions Inc ....G...... 866 637-6588
Plain City *(G-16348)*
PPG Industries ....G...... 419 433-0567
Huron *(G-11239)*
Shermco Industries Inc ....G...... 614 836-8556
Groveport *(G-10643)*
Tanner Industries Inc ....F...... 419 221-1576
Lima *(G-12102)*
Velocity Concept Dev Group LLC.........G...... 513 204-2100
Mason *(G-13100)*

AUCTION SVCS: Motor Vehicle

Rikenkaki America Corporation ....G...... 614 336-2744
Dublin *(G-9133)*

AUDIO & VIDEO EQPT, EXC COMMERCIAL

Dayton Audio LLC..............................G...... 937 743-3000
Springboro *(G-17478)*

P R O D U C T

Dlng Products ....G... 440 442-7777
  Cleveland (G-5195)
Dream Space ....G... 440 945-6596
  Bedford (G-1421)
E3 Diagnostics Inc ....G... 937 435-2250
  Dayton (G-8316)
Eprad Inc ....G... 419 666-3266
  Perrysburg (G-16093)
Eq Technologies LLC ....G... 216 548-3684
  Cleveland (G-5290)
Gadgets Manufacturing Co ....G... 937 686-5371
  Huntsville (G-11214)
Greyfield Industries Inc ....F... 513 860-1785
  Trenton (G-18793)
Hudson Access Group II ....G... 330 283-6214
  Hudson (G-11179)
Knukonceptzcom Ltd ....G... 216 310-6555
  Windham (G-20698)
Markeys Audio/Visual Inc ....G... 419 244-8844
  Toledo (G-18573)
Mitsubishi Elc Auto Amer Inc ....B... 513 573-6614
  Mason (G-13065)
Pioneer Automotive Tech Inc ....C... 937 746-2293
  Springboro (G-17497)
R L Drake Company ....D... 937 746-4556
  Franklin (G-10048)
Rs Pro Sales LLC ....G... 513 699-5329
  Cincinnati (G-4364)
Soundproof ....G... 440 864-8864
  Grafton (G-10436)
Tech Products Corporation ....E... 937 438-1100
  Miamisburg (G-13867)
Technicolor Usa Inc ....A... 614 474-8821
  Circleville (G-4646)
Thomas David Design ....G... 614 595-0379
  Cleveland (G-6321)
Tls Corp ....E... 216 574-4759
  Cleveland (G-6327)
Tune Town Car Audio ....G... 419 627-1100
  Sandusky (G-17017)

AUDIO COMPONENTS

Avtek International Inc ....G... 330 633-7500
  Tallmadge (G-18134)
Bose Corporation ....G... 614 475-8565
  Columbus (G-6850)
Bose Corporation ....G... 513 891-4384
  Cincinnati (G-3462)
China Enterprises Inc ....G... 419 885-1485
  Toledo (G-18396)

AUDIO ELECTRONIC SYSTEMS

Advanced Custom Sound ....G... 330 372-9900
  Warren (G-19516)
Andersound PA Service ....G... 216 561-2636
  Cleveland (G-4811)
Digital Media Integration LLC ....G... 937 305-5582
  Dayton (G-8303)
House of Hindenach ....G... 419 422-0392
  Findlay (G-9843)
Lightyearmusiccom ....G... 216 929-1022
  Cleveland (G-5695)
Pro Audio ....G... 513 752-7500
  Cincinnati (G-3314)
Pro Audio Innovations ....G... 330 705-5069
  Canton (G-2824)
Snyder Electronics ....G... 513 738-7200
  Harrison (G-10803)
South Side Audio LLC ....G... 614 453-0757
  Columbus (G-7632)
Undiscovered Radio Network ....G... 740 533-1032
  Ironton (G-11303)

AUDIO-VISUAL PROGRAM PRODUCTION SVCS

Technical Translation Services ....G... 440 942-3130
  Willoughby (G-20611)

AUDIOLOGICAL EQPT: Electronic

E3 Diagnostics Inc ....G... 330 926-0594
  Cuyahoga Falls (G-7988)
E3 Diagnostics Inc ....G... 937 435-2250
  Dayton (G-8316)

AUDIOLOGISTS' OFFICES

Akron Ent Hearing Services Inc ....G... 330 762-8959
  Akron (G-41)

AUTO & HOME SUPPLY STORES: Auto & Truck Eqpt & Parts

Tbone Sales LLC ....E... 330 897-6131
  Baltic (G-1077)

AUTO & HOME SUPPLY STORES: Automotive Access

Bucyrus Precision Tech Inc ....C... 419 563-9950
  Bucyrus (G-2334)
Epix Tube Co Inc ....D... 937 529-4858
  Dayton (G-8328)
Horizon Global Americas Inc ....D... 440 498-0001
  Solon (G-17311)
Kemper Automotive ....G... 800 783-8004
  Franklin (G-10030)
Rex Manufacturing Co ....G... 419 224-5751
  Lima (G-12083)
Stevens Auto Glaze and SEC LL ....G... 440 953-2900
  Eastlake (G-9288)
Steves Vans & Accessories LLC ....G... 740 374-3154
  Marietta (G-12836)

AUTO & HOME SUPPLY STORES: Automotive parts

Center Automotive Parts Co ....G... 330 434-2174
  Akron (G-117)
Crown Dielectric Inds Inc ....C... 614 224-5161
  Columbus (G-7001)
Gellner Engineering Inc ....G... 216 398-8500
  Cleveland (G-5407)
General Parts Inc ....G... 614 891-6014
  Westerville (G-20215)
Ill Williams LLC ....G... 440 721-8191
  Chardon (G-3158)
Jenkins Motor Parts ....G... 330 525-4011
  Beloit (G-1583)
K-M-S Industries Inc ....E... 440 243-6680
  Brookpark (G-2165)
Ken Veney Industries LLC ....G... 330 336-5825
  Wadsworth (G-19413)
Liber Limited LLC ....G... 440 427-0647
  Olmsted Twp (G-15680)
M Technologies ....F... 330 477-9009
  Canton (G-2764)
Mader Automotive Center Inc ....F... 937 339-2681
  Troy (G-18855)
Ohio Auto Supply Company ....E... 330 454-5105
  Canton (G-2798)
Performance Motorsports ....G... 513 931-9999
  Cincinnati (G-4226)
Stevens Auto Parts & Towng ....G... 740 988-2260
  Jackson (G-11325)
Supercharger Systems Inc ....G... 216 676-5800
  Brookpark (G-2170)
Tom Barbour Auto Parts Inc ....F... 740 354-4654
  Portsmouth (G-16457)
Wakeman Auto and Tractor Parts ......G... 440 839-2835
  Wakeman (G-19454)

AUTO & HOME SUPPLY STORES: Batteries, Automotive & Truck

B W T Inc ....G... 330 928-9107
  Akron (G-81)
Battery Unlimited ....G... 740 452-5030
  Zanesville (G-21276)
Interstate Batteries Inc ....G... 740 968-2211
  Saint Clairsville (G-16792)
N S T Battery ....G... 937 433-9222
  Bellbrook (G-1510)

AUTO & HOME SUPPLY STORES: Speed Shops, Incl Race Car Splys

Algie Composites Inc ....G... 614 529-0477
  Columbus (G-6715)

AUTO & HOME SUPPLY STORES: Trailer Hitches, Automotive

Custom Hitch and Trailer/ Over ....G... 740 289-3925
  Piketon (G-16218)

AUTO & HOME SUPPLY STORES: Truck Eqpt & Parts

Ace Truck Equipment Co ....E... 740 453-0551
  Zanesville (G-21264)
Galion-Godwin Truck Bdy Co LLC ......D... 330 359-5495
  Millersburg (G-14217)
H & H Truck Parts LLC ....G... 216 642-4540
  Cleveland (G-5467)
Jerry Tadlock ....G... 937 544-2851
  West Union (G-20122)
Kaffenbarger Truck Eqp Co ....E... 513 772-6800
  Cincinnati (G-3967)
Marlow-2000 Inc ....F... 216 362-8500
  Cleveland (G-5751)
Martin Diesel Inc ....G... 419 782-9911
  Defiance (G-8802)
Perkins Motor Service Ltd ....F... 440 277-1256
  Lorain (G-12267)
Shur-Co LLC ....G... 330 297-0888
  Ravenna (G-16556)
Western Branch Diesel Inc ....G... 330 454-8800
  Canton (G-2902)

AUTOMATED TELLER MACHINE OR ATM REPAIR SVCS

American Merchant Servic ....G... 216 598-3100
  Westlake (G-20251)
Glenn Michael Brick ....F... 740 391-5735
  Flushing (G-9916)

AUTOMATIC REGULATING CNTRLS: Liq Lvl, Residential/Comm Heat

Cfrc Wtr & Enrgy Solutions Inc ....G... 216 479-0290
  Cleveland (G-5011)
Conery Manufacturing Inc ....F... 419 289-1444
  Ashland (G-724)

AUTOMATIC REGULATING CNTRLS: Steam Press, Residential/ Comm

Turner Pressure ....G... 614 871-7775
  Grove City (G-10608)

AUTOMATIC REGULATING CONTROL: Building Svcs Monitoring, Auto

A & P Tool Inc ....E... 419 542-6681
  Hicksville (G-10897)
Qleanair Scandinavia Inc ....G... 614 323-1272
  Columbus (G-7529)
Siemens Industry Inc ....D... 614 846-9540
  Worthington (G-20888)

AUTOMATIC REGULATING CONTROLS: AC & Refrigeration

Fes-Ohio Inc ....G... 513 772-8566
  Cincinnati (G-3750)
Providence Group Inc ....E... 440 350-4615
  Mentor (G-13703)
Siemens Industry Inc ....G... 937 748-1726
  Springboro (G-17507)
Siemens Industry Inc ....D... 513 336-2267
  Lebanon (G-11839)
Siemens Industry Inc ....D... 614 573-8212
  Columbus (G-7619)
Young Regulator Company Inc ....E... 440 232-9452
  Bedford (G-1474)

AUTOMATIC REGULATING CONTROLS: Appliance Regulators

Tecmark Corporation ....E... 440 205-9188
  Mentor (G-13744)

AUTOMATIC REGULATING CONTROLS: Appliance, Exc Air-Cond/Refr

Melink Corporation ....F... 513 685-0958
  Milford (G-14161)
Portage Electric Products Inc ....C... 330 499-2727
  North Canton (G-15259)

AUTOMATIC REGULATING CONTROLS: Energy Cutoff, Residtl/Comm

Estabrook Assembly Svcs Inc ....F 440 243-3350
  Berea **(G-1614)**

Sasha Electronics Inc ....F 419 662-8100
  Rossford **(G-16749)**

AUTOMATIC REGULATING CONTROLS: Hardware, Environmental Reg

Mestek Inc ....D 419 288-2703
  Bradner **(G-2029)**

AUTOMATIC REGULATING CONTROLS: Pressure, Air-Cond Sys

Blue Wolfe Air Systems Inc ....G 937 295-3632
  Houston **(G-11120)**

AUTOMATIC REGULATING CONTROLS: Refrigeration, Pressure

Etc Enterprises LLC ....G 417 262-6382
  Delphos **(G-8908)**

Norcold Inc ....C 937 447-2241
  Gettysburg **(G-10375)**

AUTOMATIC REGULATING CONTROLS: Surface Burner, Temperature

Ohio Coatings Company ....D 740 859-5500
  Yorkville **(G-21007)**

AUTOMATIC REGULATING CTRLS: Damper, Pneumatic Or Electric

Howden North America Inc ....D 330 867-8540
  Akron **(G-224)**

Mader Machine Co Inc ....E 440 355-4505
  Lagrange **(G-11632)**

AUTOMATIC REGULATING CTRLS: Elec Heat Proportion, Modultg

Furnace Control Corp ....E 513 772-1000
  West Chester **(G-19870)**

AUTOMATIC TELLER MACHINES

American Merchant Servic ....G 216 598-3100
  Westlake **(G-20251)**

Cme Federal Credit Union ....F 614 876-1382
  Hilliard **(G-10940)**

Diebold Incorporated ....D 330 899-0097
  Uniontown **(G-19082)**

Diebold Incorporated ....D 330 490-4000
  North Canton **(G-15227)**

Diebold Incorporated ....B 330 490-4000
  Canton **(G-2688)**

Diebold Nixdorf Incorporated ....A 330 490-4000
  North Canton **(G-15228)**

Diebold Self Service Systems ....A 330 490-5099
  Canton **(G-2689)**

Ginko Voting Systems LLC ....G 937 291-4060
  Dayton **(G-8364)**

Glenn Michael Brick ....F 740 391-5735
  Flushing **(G-9916)**

Jpmorgan Chase Bank Nat Assn ....G 937 443-6260
  Vandalia **(G-19299)**

Jpmorgan Chase Bank Nat Assn ....G 330 287-5102
  Wooster **(G-20792)**

Peoples Bancorp Inc ....E 740 685-1500
  Byesville **(G-2408)**

Testlink USA ....F 513 272-1081
  Cincinnati **(G-4502)**

AUTOMOBILE RECOVERY SVCS

D & D Classic Auto Restoration ....E 937 473-2229
  Covington **(G-7921)**

AUTOMOBILES & OTHER MOTOR VEHICLES WHOLESALERS

Btw LLC ....G 419 382-4443
  Toledo **(G-18383)**

Diversifd OH Vlly Eqpt & Srvcs ....F 740 458-9881
  Clarington **(G-4651)**

Doug Marine Motors Inc ....E 740 335-3700
  Wshngtn CT Hs **(G-20907)**

Interstate Truckway Inc ....E 614 771-1220
  Columbus **(G-7209)**

Sevan At-Ndustrial Pnt Abr Ltd ....G 614 258-4747
  Columbus **(G-7610)**

Warren Fire Equipment Inc ....G 937 866-8918
  Miamisburg **(G-13878)**

AUTOMOBILES: Off-Road, Exc Recreational Vehicles

Mx Spring Inc ....G 330 426-4600
  East Palestine **(G-9242)**

Swartz Audie ....G 740 820-2341
  Minford **(G-14346)**

AUTOMOTIVE & TRUCK GENERAL REPAIR SVC

Contitech North America Inc ....E 440 225-5363
  Akron **(G-129)**

Dalin Auto Service ....G 440 997-3301
  Ashtabula **(G-801)**

Diesel Recon Service Inc ....G 513 625-1887
  Pleasant Plain **(G-16370)**

Doug Marine Motors Inc ....E 740 335-3700
  Wshngtn CT Hs **(G-20907)**

Goodyear Tire & Rubber Company ....A 330 796-2121
  Akron **(G-207)**

Gregory Auto Service ....G 513 248-0423
  Loveland **(G-12355)**

Hutter Racing Engines Ltd ....F 440 285-2175
  Chardon **(G-3157)**

Jeff Wyler Chevrolet Inc ....B 513 752-3447
  Batavia **(G-1194)**

Johnson Engine & Machine ....G 614 876-0724
  Hilliard **(G-10957)**

Kelley Brothers Roofing Inc ....F 330 273-3700
  Medina **(G-13432)**

Kennedy Mint Inc ....D 440 572-3222
  Cleveland **(G-5645)**

Kirbys Auto & Truck Repair ....G 513 934-3999
  Lebanon **(G-11812)**

Knippen Chrysler Dodge Jeep ....E 419 695-4976
  Delphos **(G-8909)**

Ohio Trailer Inc ....F 330 392-4444
  Warren **(G-19584)**

Pattons Truck & Heavy Eqp Svc ....F 740 385-4067
  Logan **(G-12189)**

Prestons Repair & Welding ....G 937 947-1883
  Laura **(G-11768)**

Sammartino Welding & Auto Sls ....G 330 782-6086
  Youngstown **(G-21196)**

Sammy S Auto Detail ....F 614 263-2728
  Columbus **(G-7589)**

Wilguss Automotive Machine ....G 937 465-0043
  West Liberty **(G-20095)**

Youngstown-Kenworth Inc ....E 330 534-9761
  Hubbard **(G-11143)**

AUTOMOTIVE BATTERIES WHOLESALERS

All Power Battery Inc ....G 330 453-5236
  Canton **(G-2597)**

AUTOMOTIVE BODY SHOP

Johns Body Shop ....G 419 358-1200
  Bluffton **(G-1913)**

Obs Inc ....F 330 453-3725
  Canton **(G-2796)**

W&W Automotive & Towing Inc ....F 937 429-1699
  Beavercreek Township **(G-1391)**

Webers Body & Frame ....G 937 839-5946
  West Alexandria **(G-19786)**

AUTOMOTIVE BODY, PAINT & INTERIOR REPAIR & MAINTENANCE SVC

Bobbart Industries Inc ....E 419 350-5477
  Sylvania **(G-18101)**

Jeff Wyler Chevrolet Inc ....B 513 752-3447
  Batavia **(G-1194)**

Weiss Motors ....G 330 678-5585
  Kent **(G-11542)**

Willard Machine & Welding Inc ....F 330 467-0642
  Macedonia **(G-12495)**

AUTOMOTIVE BRAKE REPAIR SHOPS

Circleville Oil Co ....G 740 477-3341
  Circleville **(G-4625)**

AUTOMOTIVE CUSTOMIZING SVCS, NONFACTORY BASIS

Aerotech Styling Inc ....G 419 923-6970
  Lyons **(G-12430)**

Silverado Trucks & Accessories ....G 937 492-8862
  Sidney **(G-17228)**

AUTOMOTIVE GLASS REPLACEMENT SHOPS

A Service Glass Inc ....F 937 426-4920
  Beavercreek **(G-1315)**

J W Goss Co Inc ....F 330 395-0739
  Warren **(G-19562)**

Mentor Glass Supplies and Repr ....G 440 255-9444
  Mentor **(G-13651)**

Pgw Auto Glass LLC ....E 419 993-2421
  Lima **(G-12070)**

Safelite Group Inc ....A 614 210-9000
  Columbus **(G-7585)**

Support Svc LLC ....G 419 617-0660
  Lexington **(G-11954)**

Webers Body & Frame ....G 937 839-5946
  West Alexandria **(G-19786)**

AUTOMOTIVE PAINT SHOP

L & N Olde Car Co ....G 440 564-7204
  Newbury **(G-15099)**

Newtons Paint & Body ....G 740 352-9334
  Lucasville **(G-12423)**

Precision Coatings Systems ....E 937 642-4727
  Marysville **(G-12963)**

AUTOMOTIVE PARTS, ACCESS & SPLYS

1 A Lifesafer Hawaii Inc ....F 513 651-9560
  Blue Ash **(G-1730)**

A G Parts Inc ....F 937 596-6448
  Jackson Center **(G-11336)**

Accel Performance Group LLC ....C 216 658-6413
  Independence **(G-11245)**

Access 2 Communications Inc ....G 800 561-1110
  Steubenville **(G-17686)**

Ach LLC ....G 419 621-5748
  Sandusky **(G-16943)**

Actuation Kongsberg Systems II ....F 440 639-8778
  Grand River **(G-10447)**

Aerotech Styling Inc ....G 419 923-6970
  Lyons **(G-12430)**

Airstream Inc ....B 937 596-6111
  Jackson Center **(G-11337)**

Alex Products Inc ....C 419 399-4500
  Paulding **(G-15999)**

Alpha Coatins Inc ....G 419 436-6144
  Fostoria **(G-9965)**

AM General LLC ....G 937 704-0160
  Franklin **(G-10006)**

American Manufacturing & Eqp ....G 513 829-2248
  Fairfield **(G-9642)**

AMP Electric Vehicles Inc ....F 513 360-4704
  Loveland **(G-12339)**

Amsoil Inc ....G 614 274-9851
  Columbus **(G-6746)**

Amsted Industries Incorporated ....C 614 836-2323
  Groveport **(G-10612)**

Arlington Rack & Packaging Co ....G 419 476-7700
  Toledo **(G-18355)**

Atc Lighting & Plastics Inc ....C 440 466-7670
  Andover **(G-613)**

Atlas Industries Inc ....B 419 637-2117
  Tiffin **(G-18207)**

Atwood Mobile Products LLC ....E 419 258-5531
  Antwerp **(G-629)**

Auto-Seat Tec LLC ....E 419 267-5240
  Ridgeville Corners **(G-16664)**

Automtive Cmpnnts Holdings LLC ....A 419 627-3600
  Sandusky **(G-16947)**

Automtive Cmpnnts Holdings LLC ....F 419 483-5622
  Bellevue **(G-1544)**

Autoneum North America Inc ....B 419 693-0511
  Oregon **(G-15703)**

B A Malcuit Racing Inc ....G 330 878-7111
  Strasburg **(G-17820)**

B&C Machine Co LLC ....B 330 745-4013
  Barberton **(G-1103)**

Bandon Corp ....G 614 766-7243
  Dublin **(G-9053)**

Beach Manufacturing Co ....C 937 882-6372
  Donnelsville **(G-8960)**

Bloomdale Plastics Co ....E...... 419 454-5135
  Bloomdale *(G-1719)*

Bobbart Industries Inc ....E...... 419 350-5477
  Sylvania *(G-18101)*

Bores Manufacturing Co Inc ....F...... 419 465-2606
  Monroeville *(G-14425)*

Bucyrus Precision Tech Inc ....C...... 419 563-9950
  Bucyrus *(G-2334)*

Buyers Products Company ....C...... 440 974-8888
  Mentor *(G-13540)*

Buyers Products Company ....G...... 440 974-8888
  Mentor *(G-13542)*

Bwi North America Inc ....C...... 937 455-5190
  Kettering *(G-11576)*

Bwi North America Inc ....E...... 937 253-1130
  Kettering *(G-11577)*

Cadillac Products Inc ....E...... 248 813-8255
  Lebanon *(G-11786)*

Cardington Yutaka Tech Inc ....A...... 419 864-8777
  Cardington *(G-2909)*

Classic Reproductions ....G...... 937 548-9839
  Greenville *(G-10493)*

Commercial Vehicle Group Inc ....A...... 614 289-5360
  New Albany *(G-14753)*

Comprehensive Logistics Co Inc ....E...... 330 793-0504
  Youngstown *(G-21055)*

Continental Strl Plas Inc ....B...... 419 396-1980
  Carey *(G-2917)*

Continental Strl Plas Inc ....B...... 419 238-4628
  Van Wert *(G-19248)*

Continental Strl Plas Inc ....C...... 419 257-2231
  North Baltimore *(G-15192)*

Coupled Products LLC ....C...... 419 294-3827
  Wharton *(G-20328)*

Custer Products Limited ....F...... 330 490-3158
  North Canton *(G-15225)*

Dana Auto Systems Group LLC ....D...... 419 887-3000
  Maumee *(G-13237)*

Dana Brazil Holdings I LLC ....G...... 419 887-3000
  Maumee *(G-13238)*

Dana Commercial Vhcl Mfg LLC ....D...... 419 887-3000
  Maumee *(G-13239)*

Dana Commercial Vhcl Pdts LLC ....C...... 419 887-3000
  Maumee *(G-13240)*

Dana Corporation ....E...... 419 887-3000
  Toledo *(G-18426)*

Dana Driveshaft Mfg LLC ....E...... 419 222-9708
  Lima *(G-12004)*

Dana Driveshaft Mfg LLC ....E...... 419 887-3000
  Maumee *(G-13241)*

Dana Driveshaft Products LLC ....E...... 419 887-3000
  Maumee *(G-13242)*

Dana Global Products Inc ....H...... 419 887-3000
  Maumee *(G-13243)*

Dana Global Products Inc ....G...... 419 887-3000
  Maumee *(G-13244)*

Dana Heavy Vehicle Systems ....E...... 419 887-3000
  Maumee *(G-13245)*

Dana Incorporated ....B...... 419 887-3000
  Maumee *(G-13246)*

Dana Light Axle Mfg LLC ....B...... 419 887-3000
  Toledo *(G-18427)*

Dana Light Axle Mfg LLC ....F...... 419 887-3000
  Maumee *(G-13247)*

Dana Limited ....D...... 419 482-2000
  Maumee *(G-13248)*

Dana Limited ....B...... 630 697-3783
  Maumee *(G-13249)*

Dana Off Highway Products LLC ....E...... 614 864-1116
  Blacklick *(G-1695)*

Dana Off Highway Products LLC ....C...... 740 694-2055
  Fredericktown *(G-10098)*

Dana Off Highway Products LLC ....E...... 419 887-3000
  Maumee *(G-13250)*

Dana Sealing Manufacturing LLC ......D...... 419 887-3000
  Maumee *(G-13251)*

Dana Sealing Products LLC ....E...... 419 887-3000
  Maumee *(G-13252)*

Dana Structural Products LLC ....G...... 419 887-3000
  Maumee *(G-13253)*

Dana Thermal Products LLC ....F...... 419 887-3000
  Maumee *(G-13254)*

Dana World Trade Corp ....G...... 419 887-3000
  Maumee *(G-13255)*

Dayton Air Control Pdts LLC ....G...... 937 254-4441
  Moraine *(G-14476)*

Dayton Clutch & Joint Inc ....F...... 937 236-9770
  Dayton *(G-8271)*

Dcm Manufacturing Inc ....E...... 216 265-8006
  Cleveland *(G-5178)*

Delphi Automotive Systems LLC ......C...... 330 367-6000
  Vienna *(G-19364)*

Doug Marine Motors Inc ....E...... 740 335-3700
  Wshngtn CT Hs *(G-20907)*

Dove Machine Inc ....F...... 440 864-2645
  Columbia Station *(G-6589)*

Dti Molded Products Inc ....F...... 937 492-5008
  Sidney *(G-17181)*

Ebo Group Inc ....D...... 330 239-4933
  Sharon Center *(G-17105)*

Edgerton Forge Inc ....D...... 419 298-2333
  Edgerton *(G-9327)*

Egr Products Company Inc ....F...... 330 833-6554
  Dalton *(G-8068)*

Exito Manufacturing ....G...... 937 291-9871
  Dayton *(G-8337)*

F&P America Mfg Inc ....C...... 937 339-0212
  Troy *(G-18825)*

Falls Stamping & Welding Co ....C...... 330 928-1191
  Cuyahoga Falls *(G-7996)*

Faurecia Exhaust Systems Inc ....E...... 419 727-5000
  Toledo *(G-18462)*

Federal-Mogul Corporation ....C...... 740 432-2393
  Cambridge *(G-2457)*

First Place Auto Products ....G...... 330 493-1420
  Canton *(G-2704)*

Flex Technologies Inc ....D...... 330 359-5415
  Mount Eaton *(G-14555)*

Florida Production Engrg Inc ....D...... 937 996-4361
  New Madison *(G-14869)*

Force Control Industries Inc ....D...... 513 868-0900
  Fairfield *(G-9659)*

Ford Motor Company ....A...... 216 676-3989
  Brookpark *(G-2160)*

Ford Motor Company ....F...... 216 587-7700
  Cleveland *(G-5368)*

Fram Group Operations LLC ....A...... 419 436-5827
  Fostoria *(G-9979)*

Fremont Plastic Products Inc ....C...... 419 332-6407
  Fremont *(G-10150)*

FT Precision Inc ....A...... 740 694-1500
  Fredericktown *(G-10103)*

Ftech R&D North America Inc..............D...... 937 339-2777
  Troy *(G-18829)*

Gellner Engineering Inc ....E...... 216 398-8500
  Cleveland *(G-5407)*

General Aluminum Mfg Company ....C...... 419 739-9300
  Wapakoneta *(G-19487)*

General Metals Powder Co ....D...... 330 633-1226
  Akron *(G-203)*

General Motors LLC ....B...... 330 824-5840
  Warren *(G-19554)*

General Motors LLC ....A...... 216 265-5000
  Cleveland *(G-5419)*

Grand-Rock Company Inc ....E...... 440 639-2000
  Painesville *(G-15884)*

Green Rdced Emssons Netwrk LLC ....G...... 330 340-0941
  Strasburg *(G-17823)*

Green Tokai Co Ltd ....G...... 937 237-1630
  Dayton *(G-8379)*

H O Fibertrends ....G...... 740 983-3864
  Ashville *(G-851)*

Hall-Toledo Inc ....F...... 419 893-4334
  Maumee *(G-13263)*

Haltec Corporation ....D...... 330 222-1501
  Salem *(G-16898)*

Harco Industries Inc ....F...... 937 832-9697
  Moraine *(G-14493)*

Hendrickson International Corp ....D...... 740 929-5600
  Hebron *(G-10870)*

Hfi LLC ....B...... 614 491-0700
  Canal Winchester *(G-2525)*

Hfi Manufacturing Holdings LLC ....G...... 614 491-0700
  Canal Winchester *(G-2528)*

Hi-Tek Manufacturing Inc ....C...... 513 459-1094
  Mason *(G-13037)*

Hirschvogel Incorporated ....C...... 614 340-5657
  Columbus *(G-7159)*

Honda of America Mfg Inc ....C...... 937 644-0724
  Marysville *(G-12951)*

Honda Transm Mfg Amer Inc ....A...... 937 843-5555
  Russells Point *(G-16754)*

Horizon Global Americas Inc ....D...... 440 498-0001
  Solon *(G-17311)*

Hot Shot Motor Works M LLC ....G...... 419 294-1997
  Upper Sandusky *(G-19125)*

Hp2g LLC ....E...... 419 906-1525
  Napoleon *(G-14683)*

Hurst Auto-Truck Electric ....G...... 216 961-1800
  Cleveland *(G-5538)*

Illinois Tool Works Inc ....C...... 513 489-7600
  Blue Ash *(G-1812)*

Illinois Tool Works Inc ....C...... 262 248-8277
  Bryan *(G-2303)*

Imasen Bucyrus Technology Inc ....C...... 419 563-9590
  Bucyrus *(G-2350)*

Industry Products Co ....B...... 937 778-0585
  Piqua *(G-16279)*

International Automotive ....A...... 419 335-1000
  Wauseon *(G-19684)*

International Automotive ....C...... 937 492-1225
  Sidney *(G-17195)*

International Automotive ....A...... 419 433-5653
  Huron *(G-11228)*

Inteva Products LLC ....F...... 937 280-8500
  Vandalia *(G-19297)*

Ishikawa Gasket America Inc ....C...... 419 353-7300
  Bowling Green *(G-1991)*

Jeff Wyler Chevrolet Inc ....B...... 513 752-3447
  Batavia *(G-1194)*

Joseph Industries Inc ....D...... 330 528-0091
  Streetsboro *(G-17860)*

Jr Engineering Inc ....C...... 330 848-0960
  Barberton *(G-1123)*

Julie Maynard Inc ....D...... 937 443-0408
  Dayton *(G-8429)*

K Wm Beach Mfg Co Inc ....C...... 937 399-3838
  Springfield *(G-17584)*

Kalida Manufacturing Inc ....C...... 419 532-2026
  Kalida *(G-11414)*

Kasai North America Inc ....F...... 614 356-1494
  Dublin *(G-9094)*

Kenley Enterprises LLC ....E...... 419 630-0921
  Bryan *(G-2308)*

Kilar Manufacturing Inc ....E...... 330 534-8961
  Hubbard *(G-11133)*

Knippen Chrysler Dodge Jeep ....E...... 419 695-4976
  Delphos *(G-8909)*

Kth Parts Industries Inc ....A...... 937 663-5941
  Saint Paris *(G-16862)*

Kurts Auto Parts LLC ....D...... 330 723-0166
  Medina *(G-13435)*

Lacal Equipment Inc ....E...... 800 543-6161
  Jackson Center *(G-11342)*

Lawrence Technologies Inc ....G...... 937 274-7771
  Dayton *(G-8454)*

Leadec Corp ....E...... 513 731-3590
  Blue Ash *(G-1826)*

Lear Corporation ....E...... 740 928-4358
  Hebron *(G-10872)*

Leggett & Platt Incorporated ....G...... 330 262-6010
  Apple Creek *(G-643)*

Linde Hydraulics Corporation ....E...... 330 533-6801
  Canfield *(G-2562)*

Luk Clutch Systems LLC ....E...... 330 264-4383
  Wooster *(G-20798)*

Luk Transmission Systems LLC ....A...... 330 264-4383
  Wooster *(G-20799)*

Luk USA LLC ....B...... 330 264-4383
  Wooster *(G-20800)*

Lynn Truck Parts & Service ....G...... 330 966-1470
  North Canton *(G-15248)*

M-Tek Inc ....A...... 419 209-0399
  Upper Sandusky *(G-19130)*

Maags Automotive & Machine ....G...... 419 626-1539
  Sandusky *(G-16982)*

Maca Plastics Inc ....F...... 937 544-8618
  Winchester *(G-20695)*

Magna Seating America Inc ....C...... 330 824-3101
  Warren *(G-19576)*

Magnaco Industries Inc ....E...... 216 961-3636
  Lodi *(G-12166)*

Mahle Behr Dayton LLC ....B...... 937 356-2001
  Vandalia *(G-19301)*

Mahle Behr Dayton LLC ....D...... 937 369-2900
  Dayton *(G-8471)*

Mahle Industries Incorporated ....C...... 937 890-2739
  Dayton *(G-8473)*

Marmon Highway Tech LLC ....E...... 330 878-5595
  Dover *(G-9000)*

Maxion Wheels Akron LLC ....E...... 330 794-2310
  Akron *(G-289)*

Millat Industries Corp ....E...... 937 535-1500
  Dayton *(G-8502)*

Millat Industries Corp ....G...... 937 434-6666
  Dayton *(G-8501)*

Mitec Powertrain Inc ....E...... 567 525-5606
  Findlay *(G-9864)*

Mitsubishi Elc Auto Amer Inc ....B...... 513 573-6614
  Mason *(G-13065)*

Monarch Plastic Inc .... F 330 683-0822
   Orrville (G-15747)
Multi-Design Inc .... G 440 275-2255
   Austinburg (G-963)
Navistar Inc .... D 937 390-5653
   Springfield (G-17614)
Navistar Inc .... E 937 390-5704
   Springfield (G-17616)
Neaton Auto Products Mfg Inc .... B 937 456-7103
   Eaton (G-9319)
Nebraska Industries Corp .... E 419 335-6010
   Wauseon (G-19691)
Newman Technology Inc .... C 419 525-1856
   Mansfield (G-12656)
Norlake Manufacturing Company ...... D 440 353-3200
   North Ridgeville (G-15391)
North Coast Exotics Inc .... G 216 651-5512
   Cleveland (G-5895)
Northern Stamping Co .... C 216 642-8081
   Cleveland (G-5913)
Ohio Auto Supply Company .... E 330 454-5105
   Canton (G-2798)
Ohta Press US Inc .... F 937 374-3382
   Xenia (G-20966)
Pacific Manufacturing Ohio Inc .... B 513 860-3900
   Fairfield (G-9696)
Pako Inc .... C 440 946-8030
   Mentor (G-13678)
Parker-Hannifin Corporation .... B 440 943-5700
   Wickliffe (G-20379)
Parker-Hannifin Corporation .... A 216 531-3000
   Cleveland (G-5975)
Pioneer Automotive Tech Inc .... C 937 746-2293
   Springboro (G-17497)
Piston Automotive LLC .... G 419 464-0250
   Toledo (G-18645)
PMI Operating Company Inc .... B 440 951-6600
   Mentor (G-13690)
Powers and Sons LLC .... G 419 485-3151
   Montpelier (G-14450)
Powers and Sons LLC .... D 419 737-2373
   Pioneer (G-16240)
Pullman Company .... C 419 592-2055
   Napoleon (G-14693)
Quality Reproductions Inc .... G 330 335-5000
   Wadsworth (G-19433)
Ramco Specialties Inc .... D 330 653-5135
   Hudson (G-11195)
Reactive Resin Products Co .... E 419 666-6119
   Perrysburg (G-16146)
Reineke Company LLC .... F 419 281-5800
   Ashland (G-772)
Resinoid Engineering Corp .... E 740 928-2220
   Heath (G-10854)
Riverside Engines Inc .... G 419 927-6838
   Tiffin (G-18239)
Rochling Automotive USA LLP .... D 330 400-5785
   Akron (G-377)
Rubberduck 4x4 .... G 513 889-1735
   Hamilton (G-10734)
Saf-Holland Inc .... G 513 874-7888
   West Chester (G-20046)
Saia-Burgess Lcc .... D 937 898-3621
   Vandalia (G-19310)
Sanoh America Inc .... C 740 392-9200
   Mount Vernon (G-14643)
Schott Metal Products Company ...... D 330 773-7873
   Akron (G-397)
Senneco Glass Inc .... G 330 825-7717
   Cuyahoga Falls (G-8043)
Sew-Eurodrive Inc .... D 937 335-0036
   Troy (G-18875)
Sheet Angle Bar Met Fbrication ...... G 513 829-8600
   Fairfield (G-9716)
Showa Aluminum Corp America ...... B 740 869-3333
   Mount Sterling (G-14602)
Spectrum Brands Inc .... F 440 357-2600
   Painesville (G-15921)
SPS International Inc .... G 216 671-9911
   Cleveland (G-6229)
Std Specialty Filters Inc .... F 216 881-3727
   Cleveland (G-6243)
Steck Manufacturing Co Inc .... F 937 222-0062
   Dayton (G-8683)
Sumiriko Ohio Inc .... C 419 358-2121
   Bluffton (G-1916)
Sutphen Corporation .... D 937 969-8851
   Springfield (G-17658)
Systems Jay LLC Nanogate .... C 419 522-7745
   Mansfield (G-12690)

Tetra Mold & Tool Inc .... E 937 845-1651
   New Carlisle (G-14814)
Tfo Tech Co Ltd .... C 740 426-6381
   Jeffersonville (G-11382)
Thyssenkrupp Bilstein Amer Inc ...... E 513 881-7600
   West Chester (G-19958)
TI Group Auto Systems LLC .... C 740 929-2049
   Hebron (G-10890)
Tigerpoly Manufacturing Inc .... B 614 871-0045
   Grove City (G-10601)
Tko Mfg Services Inc .... E 937 299-1637
   Moraine (G-14535)
Toledo Molding & Die Inc .... C 419 692-6022
   Delphos (G-8919)
Toledo Molding & Die Inc .... D 419 692-6022
   Delphos (G-8920)
Toledo Pro Fiberglass Inc .... G 419 241-9390
   Toledo (G-18740)
Tom Smith Industries Inc .... C 937 832-1555
   Clayton (G-4663)
Trailer Component Mfg Inc .... E 440 255-2888
   Mentor (G-13753)
Tri-Mac Mfg & Svcs Co .... F 513 896-4445
   Hamilton (G-10749)
Trim Parts Inc .... E 513 934-0815
   Lebanon (G-11845)
Trim Systems Operating Corp .... D 614 289-5360
   New Albany (G-14773)
TRW Automotive Inc .... C 419 237-2511
   Fayette (G-9780)
TS Trim Industries Inc .... B 740 593-5958
   Athens (G-888)
Ugn Inc .... C 513 360-3500
   Lebanon (G-11847)
Unique-Chardan Inc .... E 419 636-6900
   Bryan (G-2325)
Unison Industries LLC .... G 937 426-0621
   Dayton (G-8121)
US Tsubaki Power Transm LLC .... C 419 626-4560
   Sandusky (G-17019)
Varbros LLC .... C 216 267-5200
   Cleveland (G-6406)
Vari-Wall Tube Specialists Inc .... D 330 482-0000
   Columbiana (G-6637)
Venco Manufacturing Inc .... F 513 772-8448
   Cincinnati (G-4560)
Venco Venturo Industries LLC .... E 513 772-8448
   Cincinnati (G-4561)
Ventra Sandusky LLC .... D 419 627-3600
   Sandusky (G-17020)
Walther Engrg & Mfg Co Inc .... E 937 743-8125
   Franklin (G-10064)
West & Barker Inc .... E 330 652-9923
   Niles (G-15189)
Western Branch Diesel Inc .... E 330 454-8800
   Canton (G-2902)
Whirlaway Corporation .... C 440 647-4711
   Wellington (G-19759)
Whirlaway Corporation .... E 440 647-4711
   Wellington (G-19760)
Woodbridge Group .... C 419 334-3666
   Fremont (G-10195)
Workhorse Group Inc .... F 513 297-3640
   Loveland (G-12401)

AUTOMOTIVE PARTS: Plastic

A & A Discount Tire .... G 330 863-1936
   Carrollton (G-2950)
Bta Enterprises Inc .... G 937 277-0881
   Dayton (G-8201)
Daddy Katz LLC .... G 937 296-0347
   Moraine (G-14474)
Detroit Technologies Inc .... G 248 647-0400
   Toledo (G-18435)
Greenville Techniology Inc .... G 937 642-6744
   Marysville (G-12946)
Hfi Inc .... G 614 491-0700
   Canal Winchester (G-2527)
IAC Holmesville LLC .... F 330 279-4505
   Holmesville (G-11107)
IAC Sidney LLC .... G 937 492-1225
   Sidney (G-17194)
International Automotive .... B 419 332-1587
   Fremont (G-10159)
Ken Veney Industries LLC .... G 330 336-5825
   Wadsworth (G-19413)
M W Solutions .... F 419 782-1611
   Defiance (G-8800)
Molten North America Corp .... C 419 425-2700
   Findlay (G-9865)

Mos International Inc .... F 330 329-0905
   Stow (G-17776)
National Fleet Svcs Ohio LLC .... F 440 930-5177
   Avon Lake (G-1041)
Nifco America Corporation .... B 614 920-6800
   Canal Winchester (G-2532)
Nifco America Corporation .... C 614 836-3808
   Canal Winchester (G-2533)
Nifco America Corporation .... C 614 836-8691
   Groveport (G-10637)
Polyfill LLC .... E 937 493-0041
   Sidney (G-17211)
Precision Mfg & Assembly LLC .... D 937 252-3507
   Dayton (G-8586)
RG Mold .... G 419 868-9390
   Holland (G-11081)
S&T Automotive America LLC .... G 248 649-1020
   Grove City (G-10591)
Th Plastics Inc .... F 419 425-5825
   Findlay (G-9901)
Toledo Molding & Die Inc .... B 419 443-9031
   Tiffin (G-18250)
Trifecta Tool & Engrg LLC .... G 937 291-0933
   Dayton (G-8724)

AUTOMOTIVE PRDTS: Rubber

Ds Technologies Group Ltd .... G 419 841-5388
   Toledo (G-18445)
Enterprise / Ameriseal Inc .... G 937 284-3003
   South Charleston (G-17425)
Green Tokai Co Ltd .... A 937 833-5444
   Brookville (G-2185)
Kn Rubber LLC .... C 419 739-4200
   Wapakoneta (G-19494)
Myers Industries Inc .... C 330 336-6621
   Wadsworth (G-19420)
Myers Industries Inc .... E 330 253-5592
   Akron (G-309)
Performance Additives .... G 330 365-9256
   New Philadelphia (G-14922)
Soffseal Inc .... E 513 367-0028
   Harrison (G-10804)

AUTOMOTIVE RADIATOR REPAIR SHOPS

Albright Radiator Inc .... G 330 264-8886
   Wooster (G-20738)
Brock RAD & Wldg Fabrication .... G 740 773-2540
   Chillicothe (G-3230)
D & M Welding & Radiator .... G 740 947-9032
   Waverly (G-19707)
Friess Welding Inc .... F 330 644-8160
   Akron (G-195)
Perkins Motor Service Ltd .... F 440 277-1256
   Lorain (G-12267)

AUTOMOTIVE REPAIR SHOPS: Alternators/Generator, Rebuild/Rpr

Support Svc LLC .... G 419 617-0660
   Lexington (G-11954)

AUTOMOTIVE REPAIR SHOPS: Brake Repair

Jbf Repair Service LLC .... G 740 550-0089
   Proctorville (G-16490)

AUTOMOTIVE REPAIR SHOPS: Diesel Engine Repair

Cummins Bridgeway LLC .... E 614 771-1000
   Hilliard (G-10946)
Jbf Repair Service LLC .... G 740 550-0089
   Proctorville (G-16490)
Power Acquisition LLC .... G 614 228-5000
   Columbus (G-7506)
W W Williams Company LLC .... F 330 659-3084
   Richfield (G-16645)
W W Williams Company LLC .... D 614 228-5000
   Columbus (G-7746)

AUTOMOTIVE REPAIR SHOPS: Electrical Svcs

C RC Automotive .... G 513 422-4775
   Middletown (G-14025)
Entratech Systems LLC .... G 419 433-7683
   Sandusky (G-16963)
Vintage Electric Ltd Inc .... F 419 472-9349
   Toledo (G-18770)

P
R
O
D
U
C
T

AUTOMOTIVE REPAIR SHOPS: Engine Rebuilding

H & R Tool & Machine Co Inc .... G 740 452-0784
Zanesville *(G-21316)*

Jenkins Motor Parts .... G 330 525-4011
Beloit *(G-1583)*

Maags Automotive & Machine .... G 419 626-1539
Sandusky *(G-16982)*

Seme & Son Automotive Inc .... G 216 261-0066
Euclid *(G-9606)*

AUTOMOTIVE REPAIR SHOPS: Engine Repair

Done Right Engine & Machine .... G 440 582-1366
Cleveland *(G-5206)*

Joe Baker Equipment Sales .... G 513 451-1327
Cincinnati *(G-3948)*

AUTOMOTIVE REPAIR SHOPS: Machine Shop

B K Fabrication & Machine Shop .... G 740 695-4164
Saint Clairsville *(G-16781)*

Debolt Machine Inc .... G 740 454-8082
Zanesville *(G-21298)*

Deuer Developments Inc .... F 937 299-1213
Moraine *(G-14478)*

Engine Machine Service Inc .... G 330 505-1804
Niles *(G-15151)*

Frecon Technologies Inc .... F 513 874-8981
West Chester *(G-19868)*

Gellner Engineering Inc .... G 216 398-8500
Cleveland *(G-5407)*

Ohio Harness LLC .... E 937 292-7355
Bellefontaine *(G-1537)*

RL Best Company .... E 330 758-8601
Boardman *(G-1924)*

AUTOMOTIVE REPAIR SHOPS: Tire Repair Shop

Tyler Mold & Machine Inc .... E 330 645-6653
Akron *(G-452)*

AUTOMOTIVE REPAIR SHOPS: Trailer Repair

Capitol City Trailers Inc .... D 614 491-2616
Obetz *(G-15651)*

Greggs Specialty Services .... F 419 478-0803
Toledo *(G-18488)*

M & W Trailers Inc .... F 419 453-3331
Ottoville *(G-15824)*

Mac Trailer Manufacturing Inc .... C 330 823-9900
Alliance *(G-525)*

Marmon Highway Tech LLC .... E 330 878-5595
Dover *(G-9000)*

Nelson Manufacturing Company .... D 419 523-5321
Ottawa *(G-15802)*

AUTOMOTIVE REPAIR SHOPS: Truck Engine Repair, Exc Indl

Carl E Oeder Sons Sand & Grav .... E 513 494-1555
Lebanon *(G-11787)*

Kaffenbarger Truck Eqp Co .... E 513 772-6800
Cincinnati *(G-3967)*

Steubenville Truck Center Inc .... E 740 282-2711
Steubenville *(G-17715)*

AUTOMOTIVE REPAIR SHOPS: Wheel Alignment

U Haul Neighborhood Dealer .... G 740 445-4125
Vincent *(G-19381)*

AUTOMOTIVE REPAIR SVC

East Manufacturing Corporation .... B 330 325-9921
Randolph *(G-16509)*

Goodyear Tire & Rubber Company .... A 330 796-2121
Akron *(G-207)*

Hurst Auto-Truck Electric .... G 216 961-1800
Cleveland *(G-5538)*

Jeff Wyler Chevrolet Inc .... B 513 752-3447
Batavia *(G-1194)*

Jordon Auto Service & Tire Inc .... G 216 214-6528
Cleveland *(G-5622)*

Maags Automotive & Machine .... G 419 626-1539
Sandusky *(G-16982)*

Mikes Automotive LLC .... G 937 233-1433
Dayton *(G-8500)*

Sanoh America Inc .... C 740 392-9200
Mount Vernon *(G-14643)*

Smith Springs Inc .... G 800 619-4652
Mount Perry *(G-14595)*

AUTOMOTIVE REPAIR SVCS, MISCELLANEOUS

North Coast Exotics Inc .... G 216 651-5512
Cleveland *(G-5895)*

AUTOMOTIVE RUSTPROOFING & UNDERCOATING SHOPS

X-Treme Finishes Inc .... F 330 474-0614
Medina *(G-13498)*

AUTOMOTIVE SPLYS & PARTS, NEW, WHOL: Auto Servicing Eqpt

C RC Automotive .... G 513 422-4775
Middletown *(G-14025)*

D & J Electric Motor Repair Co .... F 330 336-4343
Wadsworth *(G-19401)*

Tuffy Manufacturing .... G 330 940-2356
Cuyahoga Falls *(G-8058)*

AUTOMOTIVE SPLYS & PARTS, NEW, WHOL: Testing Eqpt, Electric

Nu-Di Products Co Inc .... D 216 251-9070
Cleveland *(G-5922)*

Tmsi LLC .... F 888 867-4872
North Canton *(G-15276)*

AUTOMOTIVE SPLYS & PARTS, NEW, WHOLESALE: Bumpers

Durable Corporation .... D 419 668-8138
Norwalk *(G-15535)*

AUTOMOTIVE SPLYS & PARTS, NEW, WHOLESALE: Clutches

All Wright Enterprises LLC .... G 440 259-5656
Perry *(G-16047)*

AUTOMOTIVE SPLYS & PARTS, NEW, WHOLESALE: Engines/Eng Parts

Ds Technologies Group Ltd .... G 419 841-5388
Toledo *(G-18445)*

Interstate Diesel Service Inc .... C 216 881-0015
Cleveland *(G-5582)*

Keihin Thermal Tech Amer Inc .... B 740 869-3000
Mount Sterling *(G-14599)*

Mantapart .... G 330 549-2389
New Springfield *(G-14951)*

AUTOMOTIVE SPLYS & PARTS, NEW, WHOLESALE: Filters, Air & Oil

Oil Skimmers Inc .... E 440 237-4600
North Royalton *(G-15440)*

AUTOMOTIVE SPLYS & PARTS, NEW, WHOLESALE: Pumps, Oil & Gas

Motionsource International LLC .... F 440 287-7037
Solon *(G-17339)*

AUTOMOTIVE SPLYS & PARTS, NEW, WHOLESALE: Seat Covers

School Maintenance Supply Inc .... G 513 376-8670
Blue Ash *(G-1865)*

AUTOMOTIVE SPLYS & PARTS, NEW, WHOLESALE: Splys

Enterprise / Ameriseal Inc .... G 937 284-3003
South Charleston *(G-17425)*

Finishmaster Inc .... D 614 228-4328
Columbus *(G-7086)*

AUTOMOTIVE SPLYS & PARTS, NEW, WHOLESALE: Stampings

T A Bacon Co .... F 216 851-1404
Chesterland *(G-3220)*

AUTOMOTIVE SPLYS & PARTS, NEW, WHOLESALE: Tools & Eqpt

Matco Tools Corporation 1 .... B 330 929-4949
Stow *(G-17773)*

Myers Industries Inc .... E 330 253-5592
Akron *(G-309)*

AUTOMOTIVE SPLYS & PARTS, NEW, WHOLESALE: Trailer Parts

Frontier Tank Center Inc .... E 330 659-3888
Richfield *(G-16624)*

Ohio Trailer Supply Inc .... G 614 471-9121
Columbus *(G-7435)*

AUTOMOTIVE SPLYS & PARTS, NEW, WHOLESALE: Wheels

Chestnut Holdings Inc .... G 330 849-6503
Akron *(G-122)*

Herbert E Orr Company .... C 419 399-4866
Paulding *(G-16005)*

AUTOMOTIVE SPLYS & PARTS, USED, RETAIL ONLY: Tires, Used

A & A Discount Tire .... G 330 863-1936
Carrollton *(G-2950)*

AUTOMOTIVE SPLYS & PARTS, USED, WHOLESALE

Stevens Auto Parts & Towng .... G 740 988-2260
Jackson *(G-11325)*

AUTOMOTIVE SPLYS & PARTS, WHOLESALE, NEC

A & H Automotive Industries .... G 614 235-1759
Columbus *(G-6666)*

Accel Performance Group LLC .... C 216 658-6413
Independence *(G-11245)*

Air Enterprises LLC .... E 330 794-9770
Akron *(G-34)*

Alegre Inc .... F 937 885-6786
Miamisburg *(G-13782)*

Alex Products Inc .... C 419 399-4500
Paulding *(G-15999)*

Atlas Industries Inc .... B 419 637-2117
Tiffin *(G-18207)*

Brookville Roadster Inc .... E 937 833-4605
Brookville *(G-2176)*

Crown Dielectric Inds Inc .... C 614 224-5161
Columbus *(G-7001)*

Florence Alloys Inc .... G 330 745-9141
Barberton *(G-1115)*

General Parts Inc .... G 614 891-6014
Westerville *(G-20215)*

Gmelectric Inc .... G 330 477-3392
Canton *(G-2715)*

H & R Tool & Machine Co Inc .... G 740 452-0784
Zanesville *(G-21316)*

H O Fibertrends .... G 740 983-3864
Ashville *(G-851)*

Hebco Products Inc .... A 419 562-7987
Bucyrus *(G-2347)*

Hite Parts Exchange Inc .... E 614 272-5115
Columbus *(G-7160)*

Interstate Batteries Inc .... G 740 968-2211
Saint Clairsville *(G-16792)*

Jenkins Motor Parts .... G 330 525-4011
Beloit *(G-1583)*

Mader Automotive Center Inc .... F 937 339-2681
Troy *(G-18855)*

Martin Diesel Inc .... E 419 782-9911
Defiance *(G-8802)*

Ohashi Technica USA Inc .... E 740 965-5115
Sunbury *(G-18070)*

Ohio Auto Supply Company .... E 330 454-5105
Canton *(G-2798)*

Ohio Classic Street Rods Inc .... G 440 543-6593
Chagrin Falls *(G-3108)*

R S C Sales Company ....E 423 581-4916
   Dayton *(G-8612)*

Rex Manufacturing Co ....G 419 224-5751
   Lima *(G-12083)*

Satco Inc ....G 330 630-8866
   Tallmadge *(G-18168)*

Stevens Auto Glaze and SEC LL ....G 440 953-2900
   Eastlake *(G-9288)*

Vintage Electric Ltd Inc ....F 419 472-9349
   Toledo *(G-18770)*

AUTOMOTIVE SPLYS/PART, NEW, WHOL: Spring, Shock Absorb/Strut

Thyssenkrupp Bilstein Amer Inc ....C 513 881-7600
   Hamilton *(G-10747)*

AUTOMOTIVE SPLYS/PARTS, NEW, WHOL: Body Rpr/Paint Shop Splys

Midwest Spray Booths ....G 937 439-6600
   Dayton *(G-8497)*

AUTOMOTIVE SVCS, EXC REPAIR & CARWASHES: Customizing

AGC Automotive Americas ....D 937 599-3131
   Bellefontaine *(G-1515)*

AUTOMOTIVE SVCS, EXC REPAIR & CARWASHES: Maintenance

Tbone Sales LLC ....E 330 897-6131
   Baltic *(G-1077)*

AUTOMOTIVE SVCS, EXC REPAIR & CARWASHES: Road Svc

Top Notch Fleet Services LLC ....G 419 260-4057
   Maumee *(G-13303)*

AUTOMOTIVE SVCS, EXC REPAIR & CARWASHES: Trailer Maintenance

Jbf Repair Service LLC ....G 740 550-0089
   Proctorville *(G-16490)*

AUTOMOTIVE SVCS, EXC REPAIR: Truck Wash

Brovig Engineering Inc ....G 419 426-1333
   Attica *(G-893)*

AUTOMOTIVE TOPS INSTALLATION OR REPAIR: Canvas Or Plastic

D & D Classic Auto Restoration ....E 937 473-2229
   Covington *(G-7921)*

AUTOMOTIVE TOWING & WRECKING SVC

Johns Welding & Towing Inc ....F 419 447-8937
   Tiffin *(G-18225)*

Precision Coatings Systems ....E 937 642-4727
   Marysville *(G-12963)*

AUTOMOTIVE TOWING SVCS

Stevens Auto Parts & Towng ....G 740 988-2260
   Jackson *(G-11325)*

AUTOMOTIVE TRANSMISSION REPAIR SVC

Jbf Repair Service LLC ....G 740 550-0089
   Proctorville *(G-16490)*

Power Acquisition LLC ....G 614 228-5000
   Columbus *(G-7506)*

Rumpke Transportation Co LLC ....F 513 851-0122
   Cincinnati *(G-4366)*

Selinick Co ....G 440 632-1788
   Middlefield *(G-13988)*

W W Williams Company LLC ....F 330 659-3084
   Richfield *(G-16645)*

W W Williams Company LLC ....D 614 228-5000
   Columbus *(G-7746)*

AUTOMOTIVE WELDING SVCS

Artiflex Manufacturing LLC ....F 419 547-9211
   Clyde *(G-6537)*

Bridgetown Welders LLC ....G 513 574-4851
   Cincinnati *(G-3473)*

Brock RAD & Wldg Fabrication ....G 740 773-2540
   Chillicothe *(G-3230)*

Brown Industrial Inc ....E 937 693-3838
   Botkins *(G-1951)*

Central Ohio Fabrication LLC ....G 740 969-2976
   Amanda *(G-561)*

Industry Products Co ....B 937 778-0585
   Piqua *(G-16279)*

Jatdco LLC ....G 440 238-6570
   Strongsville *(G-17933)*

Perkins Motor Service Ltd ....F 440 277-1256
   Lorain *(G-12267)*

Prestons Repair & Welding ....G 937 947-1883
   Laura *(G-11768)*

R K Industries Inc ....D 419 523-5001
   Ottawa *(G-15806)*

Rose City Manufacturing Inc ....D 937 325-5561
   Springfield *(G-17645)*

Sammartino Welding & Auto Sls ....G 330 782-6086
   Youngstown *(G-21196)*

Top Notch Fleet Services LLC ....G 419 260-4057
   Maumee *(G-13303)*

Turn-Key Industrial Svcs LLC ....D 614 274-1128
   Columbus *(G-7714)*

AUTOMOTIVE: Bodies

Biggys Auto Buffet ....G 740 455-4663
   Zanesville *(G-21278)*

Dave Foreign Cars ....G 419 727-0685
   Toledo *(G-18428)*

Johns Body Shop ....G 419 358-1200
   Bluffton *(G-1913)*

Kps NAPA ....F 740 522-9445
   Heath *(G-10849)*

Monarch Plastic Inc ....F 330 683-0822
   Orrville *(G-15747)*

Scottrods LLC ....G 419 499-2705
   Monroeville *(G-14428)*

AUTOMOTIVE: Seat Frames, Metal

Alex Products Inc ....C 419 399-4500
   Paulding *(G-15999)*

Camaco LLC ....A 440 288-4444
   Lorain *(G-12236)*

Cctm Inc ....G 513 934-3533
   Lebanon *(G-11788)*

Systems Jay LLC Nanogate ....B 419 747-4161
   Mansfield *(G-12691)*

Systems Jay LLC Nanogate ....B 419 747-4161
   Mansfield *(G-12692)*

AUTOMOTIVE: Seating

Adient US LLC ....C 937 383-5200
   Greenfield *(G-10472)*

Gra-Mag Truck Intr Systems LLC ....E 740 490-1000
   London *(G-12211)*

Gramag LLC ....E 614 875-8435
   Grove City *(G-10559)*

International Automotive ....B 937 492-1225
   Sidney *(G-17195)*

Johnson Controls Inc ....D 419 636-4211
   Bryan *(G-2307)*

Johnson Controls Inc ....D 216 587-0100
   Cleveland *(G-5621)*

Johnson Controls Inc ....F 513 671-6338
   Cincinnati *(G-3956)*

Lear Corporation ....C 419 335-6010
   Wauseon *(G-19688)*

Lear Corporation ....F 614 850-8630
   Columbus *(G-7289)*

Magna International Amer Inc ....E 905 853-3604
   Ridgeville Corners *(G-16665)*

Magna Seating America Inc ....D 440 846-5680
   Sheffield Village *(G-17126)*

Magna Seating America Inc ....C 330 824-3101
   Warren *(G-19576)*

Setex Inc ....B 419 394-7800
   Saint Marys *(G-16855)*

Systems Jay LLC Nanogate ....C 419 524-3778
   Mansfield *(G-12688)*

AUTOTRANSFORMERS: Electric

SGB Usa Inc ....G 720 897-7090
   Louisville *(G-12327)*

AWNING REPAIR SHOP

Willet Enterprises ....G 937 298-8622
   Dayton *(G-8758)*

AWNINGS & CANOPIES

Patio Room Factory Inc ....G 614 449-7900
   Columbus *(G-7464)*

Rex Burnett ....G 740 927-4669
   Etna *(G-9560)*

AWNINGS & CANOPIES: Awnings, Fabric, From Purchased Matls

A B C Sign Inc ....F 513 241-8884
   Cincinnati *(G-3332)*

Awning Fabri Caters Inc ....G 216 476-4888
   Cleveland *(G-4878)*

Canvas Specialty Mfg Co ....G 216 881-0647
   Cleveland *(G-4968)*

Capital City Awning Company ....E 614 221-5404
   Columbus *(G-6897)*

Independent Awning & Canvas Co........G 937 223-9661
   Dayton *(G-8401)*

Main Awning & Tent Inc ....G 513 621-6947
   Cincinnati *(G-4054)*

Phillips Awning Co ....G 740 653-2433
   Lancaster *(G-11738)*

Queen City Awning & Tent Co ....E 513 530-9660
   Cincinnati *(G-4313)*

South Akron Awning Co ....G 330 848-7611
   Akron *(G-409)*

Tarped Out Inc ....F 330 325-7722
   Ravenna *(G-16565)*

AWNINGS & CANOPIES: Fabric

Ohio Awning & Manufacturing Co........E 216 861-2400
   Cleveland *(G-5928)*

P C R Restorations Inc ....F 419 747-7957
   Mansfield *(G-12666)*

AWNINGS: Fiberglass

Mor-Lite Co Inc ....G 513 661-8587
   Cincinnati *(G-4122)*

P C R Restorations Inc ....F 419 747-7957
   Mansfield *(G-12666)*

Superior Fibers Inc ....B 740 394-2491
   Shawnee *(G-17117)*

AWNINGS: Metal

Alumetal Manufacturing Company........E 419 268-2311
   Coldwater *(G-6550)*

Color Brite Company Inc ....G 216 441-4117
   Cleveland *(G-5100)*

Crest Awning & Home Imprv Co............G 440 942-3092
   Willoughby *(G-20465)*

Crest Products Inc ....F 440 942-5770
   Mentor *(G-13556)*

General Awning Company Inc ....F 216 749-0110
   Cleveland *(G-5411)*

Joyce Manufacturing Co ....D 440 239-9100
   Berea *(G-1624)*

Mor-Lite Co Inc ....G 513 661-8587
   Cincinnati *(G-4122)*

Shade Youngstown & Aluminum Co ....G 330 782-2373
   Youngstown *(G-21200)*

Toledo Window & Awning Inc ....G 419 474-3396
   Toledo *(G-18748)*

AXLES

Alta Mira Corporation ....D 330 648-2461
   Spencer *(G-17455)*

Axle Surgeons of NW Ohio ....G 419 822-5775
   Delta *(G-8928)*

Meritor Inc ....C 740 348-3498
   Granville *(G-10461)*

Schafer Driveline LLC ....G 614 864-1116
   Blacklick *(G-1706)*

Schafer Driveline LLC ....E 740 694-0462
   Fredericktown *(G-10109)*

Spencer Manufacturing Company........D 330 648-2461
   Spencer *(G-17457)*

Ammunition Loading & Assembling Plant

Center Mass Ammo LLC ....G 440 796-6207
   Madison *(G-12498)*

BACKHOES

Donald E Dornon ....G 740 926-9144
   Beallsville *(G-1308)*

PRODUCT

Shatzels Backhoe Service LLC.............G...... 937 289-9630
  Clarksville *(G-4653)*

BADGES: Identification & Insignia

ID Card Systems Inc..........................G...... 330 963-7446
  Twinsburg *(G-18958)*

BAFFLES

Dynamic Control North Amer Inc ....F...... 513 860-5094
  Hamilton *(G-10686)*

BAGS: Canvas

Capital City Awning Company ....E...... 614 221-5404
  Columbus *(G-6897)*
Hdt Expeditionary Systems Inc ....C...... 216 438-6111
  Solon *(G-17309)*

BAGS: Cellophane

Vee Gee Enterprise Corporation...........G...... 330 493-9780
  Canton *(G-2895)*

BAGS: Food Storage & Trash, Plastic

Accutech Films Inc ....F...... 419 678-8700
  Coldwater *(G-6549)*

BAGS: Garment Storage Exc Paper Or Plastic Film

Db Rediheat Inc ....E...... 216 361-0530
  Cleveland *(G-5175)*
Henty USA ....F...... 513 984-5590
  Cincinnati *(G-3879)*

BAGS: Paper

Cleveland Canvas Goods Mfg Co.........D...... 216 361-4567
  Cleveland *(G-5050)*
Mid-America Packaging LLC ....C...... 330 963-4199
  New Philadelphia *(G-14914)*

BAGS: Paper, Made From Purchased Materials

Gibson Greetings Inc ....E...... 216 252-7300
  Cleveland *(G-5428)*
Greif Inc ....E...... 740 657-6500
  Delaware *(G-8848)*
Greif Inc ....E...... 740 549-6000
  Delaware *(G-8847)*

BAGS: Plastic

Atlapac Corp......................................D...... 614 252-2121
  Columbus *(G-6782)*
Automated Packg Systems Inc ....D...... 330 342-2000
  Bedford *(G-1401)*
Automated Packg Systems Inc ....C...... 216 663-2000
  Cleveland *(G-4866)*
Buckeye Boxes Inc ....D...... 614 274-8484
  Columbus *(G-6870)*
Command Plastic Corporation ....F...... 800 321-8001
  Tallmadge *(G-18139)*
Dayton Industrial Drum Inc ....E...... 937 253-8933
  Dayton *(G-8103)*
Factory Direct International ....E...... 419 425-9636
  Findlay *(G-9821)*
Flavorseal LLC ....D...... 440 937-3900
  Avon *(G-995)*
Hcf of Bowling Green Inc ....E...... 419 999-2010
  Lima *(G-12022)*
Hood Packaging Corporation ....C...... 937 382-6681
  Wilmington *(G-20669)*
Kennedy Group Incorporated ....D...... 440 951-7660
  Willoughby *(G-20520)*
Multiplast Systems Inc ....F...... 440 349-0800
  Solon *(G-17341)*
Packaging Materials Inc ....E...... 740 432-6337
  Cambridge *(G-2471)*
Pitt Plastics Inc ....D...... 614 868-8660
  Columbus *(G-7486)*
Safeway Packaging Inc ....D...... 419 629-3200
  New Bremen *(G-14793)*

BAGS: Plastic & Pliofilm

Advanced Poly-Packaging Inc............E...... 330 785-4000
  Akron *(G-33)*
Charter Nex Films - Delaware ....E...... 740 369-2770
  Delaware *(G-8832)*

Charter Nex Holding Company ....E...... 740 369-2770
  Delaware *(G-8833)*
Engineered Films Division ....G...... 419 884-8150
  Lexington *(G-11950)*
General Films Inc ....D...... 888 436-3456
  Covington *(G-7923)*
Mid-West Poly Pak Inc ....E...... 330 658-2921
  Doylestown *(G-9029)*
Next Generation Bag Inc ....B...... 419 884-1327
  Mansfield *(G-12658)*
Next Generation Films Inc.................C...... 419 884-8150
  Lexington *(G-11951)*
North American Plas Chem Inc ....E...... 216 531-3400
  Euclid *(G-9595)*

BAGS: Plastic, Made From Purchased Materials

Ampac Holdings LLC ....A...... 513 671-1777
  Cincinnati *(G-3397)*
B K Plastics Inc ....G...... 937 473-2087
  Covington *(G-7920)*
Bag-Pack Inc ....E...... 513 346-3900
  West Chester *(G-19813)*
Cpg - Ohio LLC ....D...... 513 825-4800
  Cincinnati *(G-3616)*
Inpaco Corporation ....F...... 614 888-9288
  Worthington *(G-20872)*
L & C Plastic Bags Inc ....E...... 937 473-2968
  Covington *(G-7925)*
Liqui-Box Corporation ....D...... 614 888-9280
  Columbus *(G-7300)*
Liqui-Box Corporation ....C...... 419 289-9696
  Ashland *(G-750)*
Pexco Packaging Corp ....E...... 419 470-5935
  Toledo *(G-18642)*
Poly Works ....G...... 419 678-3758
  Coldwater *(G-6569)*
Primary Packaging Incorporated..........D...... 330 874-3131
  Bolivar *(G-1943)*

BAGS: Pliofilm, Made From Purchased Materials

Ampac Packaging LLC ....D...... 513 671-1777
  Cincinnati *(G-3398)*

BAGS: Rubber Or Rubberized Fabric

Midwestern Bag Co Inc ....E...... 419 241-3112
  Toledo *(G-18586)*

BAGS: Shipping

Hood Packaging Corporation ....C...... 937 382-6681
  Wilmington *(G-20669)*

BAGS: Shopping, Made From Purchased Materials

Ampac Holdings LLC..........................A...... 513 671-1777
  Cincinnati *(G-3397)*

BAGS: Textile

Cleveland Canvas Goods Mfg Co.........D...... 216 361-4567
  Cleveland *(G-5050)*
DCW Acquisition Inc ....F...... 216 451-0666
  Cleveland *(G-5179)*
Jordan E Armour ....E...... 330 252-0290
  Akron *(G-242)*
King Bag and Manufacturing Co ....E...... 513 541-5440
  Cincinnati *(G-3990)*
Lamports Filter Media Inc ....F...... 216 881-2050
  Cleveland *(G-5679)*
Loctote LLC ....G...... 614 407-0882
  Blacklick *(G-1700)*
Rich Industries Inc ....E...... 330 339-4113
  New Philadelphia *(G-14924)*
Sailors Tailor Inc ....G...... 937 862-7781
  Spring Valley *(G-17469)*
Seven Mile Creek Corporation.............F...... 937 456-3320
  Eaton *(G-9322)*

BAGS: Trash, Plastic Film, Made From Purchased Materials

Heritage Bag Company ....D...... 513 874-3311
  West Chester *(G-19881)*

BAGS: Vacuum cleaner, Made From Purchased Materials

Home Care Products LLC ....G...... 919 693-1002
  Chagrin Falls *(G-3092)*

BAIT, FISHING, WHOLESALE

Wholesale Bait Co Inc ....F...... 513 863-2380
  Fairfield *(G-9732)*

BAKERIES, COMMERCIAL: On Premises Baking Only

614 Cupcakes LLC ....G...... 614 245-8800
  New Albany *(G-14744)*
7 Little Cupcakes ....G...... 419 252-0858
  Perrysburg *(G-16060)*
A Cupcake A Day LLC........................G...... 330 389-1247
  Stow *(G-17727)*
Alfred Nickles Bakery Inc ....E...... 740 453-6522
  Zanesville *(G-21269)*
Amish Door Inc ....C...... 330 359-5464
  Wilmot *(G-20683)*
An Baiceir Bakery ....G...... 740 739-0501
  Etna *(G-9554)*
Angry Cupcakes Productions LLC........G...... 216 229-2394
  Cleveland *(G-4813)*
Auntie Annes ....G...... 330 652-1939
  Niles *(G-15144)*
B L F Enterprises Inc ....F...... 937 642-6425
  Westerville *(G-20201)*
Bakers Choice Distributing ....G...... 330 273-5745
  Brunswick *(G-2210)*
Berlin Natural Bakery Inc ....E...... 330 893-2734
  Berlin *(G-1645)*
Bimbo Bakeries Usa Inc ....G...... 419 726-6183
  Toledo *(G-18367)*
Bites Baking Company LLC ....G...... 614 457-6092
  Dublin *(G-9055)*
Blue Cottage Bakery LLC ....G...... 216 221-9733
  Lakewood *(G-11658)*
Bread Kneads Inc...............................G...... 419 422-3863
  Findlay *(G-9801)*
Breaking Bread Pizza Company ....E...... 614 754-4777
  Lewis Center *(G-11891)*
Buns of Delaware Inc.........................E...... 740 363-2867
  Delaware *(G-8826)*
Busken Bakery Inc ....E...... 513 671-8454
  Cincinnati *(G-3488)*
Busken Bakery Inc ....E...... 513 791-6736
  Cincinnati *(G-3489)*
Cincy Cupcakes LLC ....G...... 513 985-4440
  Cincinnati *(G-3572)*
Colossal Cupcakes ....G...... 216 322-7656
  Lakewood *(G-11660)*
Cora Cupcakes ....G...... 440 227-7145
  Painesville *(G-15870)*
Country Crust Bakery ....G...... 888 860-2940
  Bainbridge *(G-1057)*
Cupcake Divaz ....G...... 216 509-3850
  North Ridgeville *(G-15365)*
Cupcake Wishes ....G...... 440 315-3856
  North Ridgeville *(G-15366)*
Cupcake Wishes Ltd............................G...... 440 934-5550
  Avon *(G-992)*
Cupcakes For A Cure ....G...... 419 764-1719
  Perrysburg *(G-16080)*
Danis Sweet Cupcakes ....G...... 614 581-8978
  Centerburg *(G-3030)*
Dulcelicious Cupcakes and More.........G...... 440 385-7706
  Cleveland *(G-5221)*
Eat Moore Cupcakes............................G...... 513 713-8139
  Batavia *(G-1178)*
Fields Associates Inc..........................G...... 513 426-8652
  Cincinnati *(G-3755)*
Flowers Bakeries LLC ....E...... 330 724-1604
  Akron *(G-191)*
Fragapane Bakeries Inc........................G...... 440 779-6050
  North Olmsted *(G-15335)*
Garys Chesecakes Fine Desserts ....G...... 513 574-1700
  Cincinnati *(G-3800)*
Geyers Markets Inc.............................D...... 419 468-9477
  Galion *(G-10271)*
Gigis Cupcakes of Kenwood ....G...... 513 985-4440
  Cincinnati *(G-3823)*
Glorious Cupcakes ....G...... 216 544-2325
  Medina *(G-13418)*
Go Cupcake ....G...... 937 299-4985
  Dayton *(G-8374)*

Graeters Manufacturing Co..................D 513 721-3323
　Cincinnati (G-3843)
Grandmas Fruit Cakes.........................G 614 761-1118
　Dublin (G-9080)
Heinens Inc.......................................D 330 562-5297
　Aurora (G-924)
Hot Mama Foods Inc...........................F 419 474-3402
　Toledo (G-18513)
I Heart Cupcakes................................G 614 787-3896
　Columbus (G-7179)
J M Smucker Company.........................E 440 323-5100
　Elyria (G-9442)
K Cupcakes.......................................G 440 576-3464
　Jefferson (G-11362)
Kellogg Company................................B 513 271-3500
　Cincinnati (G-3978)
Kennedys Bakery Inc...........................E 740 432-2301
　Cambridge (G-2461)
Klosterman Baking Co..........................E 513 242-5667
　Cincinnati (G-3995)
Klosterman Baking Co..........................F 513 398-2707
　Mason (G-13053)
Klosterman Baking Co..........................D 513 242-1004
　Cincinnati (G-3996)
Klosterman Baking Co Inc.....................G 937 743-9021
　Springboro (G-17487)
Kmart Supercenter..............................G 440 974-7300
　Cleveland (G-5660)
Kroger Co...C 513 742-9500
　Cincinnati (G-4004)
Kroger Co...C 937 743-5900
　Springboro (G-17488)
Kroger Co...C 740 335-4030
　Wshngtn CT Hs (G-20915)
Kroger Co...C 740 264-5057
　Steubenville (G-17702)
Kroger Co...D 419 423-2065
　Findlay (G-9848)
Kroger Co...C 614 263-1766
　Columbus (G-7271)
Kroger Co...C 614 575-3742
　Columbus (G-7272)
Kroger Co...C 740 671-5164
　Bellaire (G-1499)
Kroger Co...D 513 683-4001
　Maineville (G-12526)
Kroger Co...C 937 277-0950
　Dayton (G-8447)
Kroger Co...D 740 374-2523
　Marietta (G-12798)
M Mazzone & Sons Bakery Inc...............G 216 631-6511
　Cleveland (G-5718)
Main Street Gourmet LLC......................C 330 929-0000
　Cuyahoga Falls (G-8022)
Martans Foods...................................G 330 483-9009
　Valley City (G-19215)
Meeks Pastry Shop..............................G 419 782-4871
　Defiance (G-8803)
Morselicious Cupcakes.........................G 216 408-7508
　Brookpark (G-2167)
Mustard Seed Health Fd Mkt Inc.............E 440 519-3663
　Solon (G-17342)
My Lady Muffins LLC............................G 937 854-5317
　Dayton (G-8516)
Nanak Bakery.....................................G 614 882-0882
　Westerville (G-20226)
New Bakery of Zanesville LLC.................B 614 764-3100
　Dublin (G-9112)
New Horizon Baking Company.................G 567 315-8703
　Toledo (G-18602)
Olde Home Market LLC........................G 614 738-3975
　Grove City (G-10580)
Osmans Pies Inc.................................E 330 607-9083
　Stow (G-17786)
Perkins & Marie Callenders LLC..............C 513 881-7900
　Fairfield (G-9702)
Pesce Baking Company Ltd....................E 330 746-6537
　Youngstown (G-21170)
Pf Management Inc...............................G 513 874-8741
　West Chester (G-20036)
Pierre Holding Corp..............................G 513 874-8741
　West Chester (G-20037)
Polkadot Cupcakery Limited...................G 614 304-1368
　Columbus (G-7502)
Quality Bakery Company Inc...................G 614 846-2232
　Westerville (G-20181)
Quality Bakery Company Inc...................E 614 224-1424
　Columbus (G-7534)
Rich Products Corporation.....................C 614 771-1117
　Hilliard (G-10976)

Riesbeck Food Markets Inc....................C 740 695-3401
　Saint Clairsville (G-16806)
Rudys Strudel Shop.............................G 440 886-4430
　Cincinnati (G-6143)
Saras Little Cupcakes..........................G 419 305-7914
　Saint Marys (G-16854)
Schulers Bakery Inc.............................E 937 323-4154
　Springfield (G-17647)
Schwebel Baking Company.....................B 330 783-2860
　Youngstown (G-21197)
Schwebel Baking Company.....................C 440 846-1921
　Strongsville (G-17961)
Schwebel Baking Company.....................G 740 435-9857
　Cambridge (G-2475)
Schwebel Baking Company.....................D 330 783-2860
　Hebron (G-10884)
Schwebel Baking Company.....................C 440 248-1500
　Solon (G-17376)
Servatii Inc.......................................F 513 271-5040
　Cincinnati (G-4407)
Smashing Events and Baking..................G 513 415-9693
　Cincinnati (G-3318)
Squire Shoppe Bakery..........................G 440 964-3303
　Ashtabula (G-839)
Sweet GS Cupcakery Ltd.......................G 419 610-8507
　Columbus (G-7671)
Sweet Mobile Cupcakery.......................G 440 465-7333
　Bay Village (G-1246)
Taste of Belgium LLC...........................G 513 381-3280
　Cincinnati (G-4494)
Thurns Bakery & Deli............................E 614 221-9246
　Columbus (G-7693)
Unger Kosher Bakery Inc.......................E 216 321-7176
　Cleveland Heights (G-6502)
White Castle System Inc.......................B 614 228-5781
　Columbus (G-7761)

BAKERIES: On Premises Baking & Consumption

Alfred Nickles Bakery Inc......................E 740 453-6522
　Zanesville (G-21269)
Buns of Delaware Inc............................E 740 363-2867
　Delaware (G-8826)
Campbell Soup Company........................D 419 592-1010
　Napoleon (G-14674)
Crumbs Inc.......................................F 740 592-3803
　Athens (G-859)
Evans Bakery Inc................................G 937 228-4151
　Dayton (G-8334)
Fields Associates Inc...........................G 513 426-8652
　Cincinnati (G-3755)
Fragapane Bakeries Inc.........................G 440 779-6050
　North Olmsted (G-15335)
Giminetti Baking Company......................G 513 751-7655
　Cincinnati (G-3826)
I Dream of Cakes................................G 937 533-6024
　Eaton (G-9310)
Jims Donut Shop................................G 937 898-4222
　Vandalia (G-19298)
Kennedys Bakery Inc............................E 740 432-2301
　Cambridge (G-2461)
Osmans Pies Inc.................................E 330 607-9083
　Stow (G-17786)
Pepperidge Farm Incorporated................G 419 933-2611
　Willard (G-20399)
Schulers Bakery Inc.............................E 937 323-4154
　Springfield (G-17647)
Schwebel Baking Company.....................C 440 248-1500
　Solon (G-17376)
Schwebel Baking Company.....................D 330 783-2860
　Hebron (G-10884)
Thurns Bakery & Deli............................E 614 221-9246
　Columbus (G-7693)
Unger Kosher Bakery Inc.......................E 216 321-7176
　Cleveland Heights (G-6502)
Wal-Bon of Ohio Inc............................D 740 423-8178
　Belpre (G-1596)

BAKERY FOR HOME SVC DELIVERY

Alfred Nickles Bakery Inc......................F 937 256-3762
　Dayton (G-8143)
Trumbull Mobile Meals Inc.....................F 330 394-2538
　Warren (G-19615)

BAKERY MACHINERY

Fred D Pfening Company........................G 614 294-5361
　Columbus (G-7100)
Magna Machine Co...............................C 513 851-6900
　Cincinnati (G-4052)

Peerless Foods Inc..............................C 937 492-4158
　Sidney (G-17207)
Security Systems Eqp Corp.....................G 513 758-1070
　Cincinnati (G-4396)
Shaffer Manufacturing Corp....................E 937 652-2151
　Urbana (G-19180)
Tpsc Inc...F 440 439-9320
　Bedford Heights (G-1495)

BAKERY PRDTS, FROZEN: Wholesalers

Bake ME Happy LLC.............................G 614 477-3642
　Columbus (G-6802)

BAKERY PRDTS: Bakery Prdts, Partially Cooked, Exc frozen

Champa Ventures LLC...........................G 614 726-1801
　Dublin (G-9062)

BAKERY PRDTS: Biscuits, Baked, Baking Powder & Raised

Perfection Bakeries Inc.........................D 937 492-2220
　Sidney (G-17208)

BAKERY PRDTS: Biscuits, Dry

Consolidated Biscuit Company..................F 419 293-2911
　Mc Comb (G-13336)
Kellogg Company................................B 513 271-3500
　Cincinnati (G-3978)

BAKERY PRDTS: Bread, All Types, Fresh Or Frozen

Alfred Nickles Bakery Inc......................B 330 879-5635
　Navarre (G-14708)
New York Frozen Foods Inc.....................B 216 292-5655
　Bedford (G-1447)
Orlando Baking Company........................C 216 361-1872
　Cleveland (G-5948)
Perfection Bakeries Inc.........................E 513 942-1442
　West Chester (G-20035)

BAKERY PRDTS: Buns, Bread Type, Fresh Or Frozen

B & J Baking Company Inc......................F 513 541-2386
　Cincinnati (G-3432)
East Balt Ohio LLC..............................F 740 454-6876
　Zanesville (G-21303)
East Balt Ohio LLC..............................G 740 454-6876
　Zanesville (G-21304)
East Balt Us LLC.................................G 740 454-6876
　Zanesville (G-21305)
Jtm Provisions Company Inc....................B 513 367-4900
　Harrison (G-10787)
New Horizons Baking Company..................C 419 668-8226
　Norwalk (G-15553)

BAKERY PRDTS: Cakes, Bakery, Exc Frozen

Abby Girl Sweets Cupcakery....................G 513 335-0898
　Cincinnati (G-3343)
Baked & More LLC...............................G 330 324-4981
　Louisville (G-12309)
Bakehouse Bread Co Inc........................E 937 339-8100
　Troy (G-18807)
Beckers Bakeshop Inc...........................F 216 752-4161
　Cleveland (G-4901)
Cake Arts Supplies..............................G 419 472-4959
　Toledo (G-18387)
Carlas Cake Pops Cnfctions LLC...............G 614 321-9280
　Columbus (G-6909)
Caryns Cuisine...................................G 614 237-4143
　Columbus (G-6915)
Destination Donuts LLC..........................G 614 370-0754
　Columbus (G-7022)
George Weston Co...............................G 614 868-7565
　Columbus (G-7110)
Gluten-Free Expressions........................G 740 928-0338
　Hebron (G-10868)
Sifted Sweet Shop LLC..........................G 216 901-7100
　Youngstown (G-21203)
Sinful Sweets LLC...............................G 330 721-0916
　Medina (G-13481)

BAKERY PRDTS: Cakes, Bakery, Frozen

Atk2 Inc...G 513 661-5869
　Cincinnati (G-3424)

PRODUCT

Bartells Cupcakery ....G....... 330 957-1793
Austintown (G-969)
Beautiful Bites ....G....... 937 397-4225
Xenia (G-20938)
Cleveland Bagel Company LLC ....G....... 216 385-7723
Cleveland (G-5048)
Junebugs Cupcaked ....G....... 937 723-9040
Dayton (G-8430)
Kissicakes - N-Sweets LLC ....G....... 614 940-2779
Columbus (G-7263)
Mammas Mandel ....G....... 513 827-2457
Mason (G-13059)

BAKERY PRDTS: Cones, Ice Cream

Frischco Inc ....G....... 740 363-7537
Delaware (G-8846)
Jagger Cone Company Inc ....G....... 419 682-1816
Stryker (G-18004)
Norse Dairy Systems LP ....B....... 614 421-5297
Columbus (G-7398)

BAKERY PRDTS: Cookies

Adrians Place ....G....... 513 651-2154
Cincinnati (G-3357)
Beckers Bakeshop Inc ....F....... 216 752-4161
Cleveland (G-4901)
Cheryl & Co ....C....... 614 776-1500
Westerville (G-20144)
Cleveland Bean Sprout Inc ....F....... 216 881-2112
Cleveland (G-5049)
CTB Consulting LLC ....F....... 216 712-7764
Rocky River (G-16697)
Great American Cookie Company ....F....... 419 474-9417
Toledo (G-18486)
Hearthside Food Solutions LLC ....E....... 419 727-1298
Toledo (G-18500)
Hearthside Food Solutions LLC ....A....... 419 293-2911
Mc Comb (G-13338)
Keebler Company ....E....... 513 271-3500
Cincinnati (G-3976)
Keebler Company ....E....... 614 836-3094
Columbus (G-7253)
Keebler Company ....E....... 513 671-0880
Cincinnati (G-3977)
Nonnies Goodies LLC ....G....... 419 435-4685
Fostoria (G-9989)
Snyders-Lance Inc ....G....... 614 856-4616
Grove City (G-10596)
Snyders-Lance Inc ....C....... 419 289-0787
Ashland (G-778)
Y Z Enterprises Inc ....E....... 419 893-8777
Maumee (G-13310)

BAKERY PRDTS: Cookies & crackers

B L F Enterprises Inc ....F....... 937 642-6425
Westerville (G-20201)
Cheryl & Co ....D....... 614 776-1500
Obetz (G-15653)
Cookie Bouquets Inc ....G....... 614 888-2171
Columbus (G-6980)
Hen of Woods LLC ....G....... 513 833-7357
Cincinnati (G-3877)
Kennedys Bakery Inc ....E....... 740 432-2301
Cambridge (G-2461)
Kroger Co ....C....... 740 671-5164
Bellaire (G-1499)
Kroger Co ....D....... 614 462-2000
Columbus (G-7270)
Kroger Co ....D....... 513 683-4001
Maineville (G-12526)
Kroger Co ....C....... 937 277-0950
Dayton (G-8447)
Kroger Co ....D....... 740 374-2523
Marietta (G-12798)
Lenas Amish Granola ....G....... 330 600-1599
Shreve (G-17160)
Main Street Gourmet LLC ....C....... 330 929-0000
Cuyahoga Falls (G-8022)
Norcia Bakery ....E....... 330 454-1077
Canton (G-2790)
Osmans Pies Inc ....E....... 330 607-9083
Stow (G-17786)
Patjim Holdings Company ....F....... 419 727-1298
Toledo (G-18635)
Pepperidge Farm Incorporated ....G....... 419 933-2611
Willard (G-20399)
Rudys Strudel Shop ....G....... 440 886-4430
Cleveland (G-6143)

Rykrisp Llc ....G....... 843 338-0750
Cincinnati (G-4371)
S-L Snacks Real Estate Inc ....B....... 440 786-9990
Bedford (G-1459)
Schulers Bakery Inc ....E....... 937 323-4154
Springfield (G-17647)
Shades of Sugar Ltd ....G....... 614 776-5998
Galena (G-10249)

BAKERY PRDTS: Doughnuts, Exc Frozen

Crispie Creme of Chillicothe ....E....... 740 774-3770
Chillicothe (G-3235)
Dandi Enterprises Inc ....F....... 419 516-9070
Solon (G-17282)
Georges Donuts Inc ....G....... 330 963-9902
Twinsburg (G-18945)
Jims Donut Shop ....G....... 937 898-4222
Vandalia (G-19298)
McHappys Donuts of Parkersburg ....G....... 740 593-8744
Athens (G-875)
Servatii Inc ....F....... 513 231-4455
Cincinnati (G-4406)
Wal-Bon of Ohio Inc ....D....... 740 423-8178
Belpre (G-1596)

BAKERY PRDTS: Dry

Four Generations Inc ....G....... 330 784-2243
Lakemore (G-11644)
Good Fortunes Inc ....F....... 440 942-2888
Willoughby (G-20500)
LLC Brand Castle ....F....... 216 292-7700
Bedford Heights (G-1487)

BAKERY PRDTS: Frozen

Chefs Pantry Inc ....G....... 440 288-0146
Amherst (G-594)
Main Street Gourmet LLC ....C....... 330 929-0000
Cuyahoga Falls (G-8022)

BAKERY PRDTS: Pastries, Exc Frozen

Krispy Kreme Doughnut Corp ....F....... 614 798-0812
Columbus (G-7268)
Royal Gateau ....G....... 216 351-3553
Cleveland (G-6138)

BAKERY PRDTS: Pies, Exc Frozen

Bake ME Happy LLC ....G....... 614 477-3642
Columbus (G-6802)
K & B Acquisitions Inc ....F....... 937 253-1163
Dayton (G-8432)

BAKERY PRDTS: Pretzels

Annes Auntie Pretzels ....E....... 614 418-7021
Columbus (G-6758)
J & J Snack Foods Corp ....G....... 440 248-2084
Solon (G-17319)
K & R Pretzel Co ....G....... 937 299-2231
Dayton (G-8433)
Mar Chele Inc ....G....... 937 833-3400
Brookville (G-2188)
S-L Distribution Company Inc ....G....... 440 786-9990
Bedford (G-1458)

BAKERY PRDTS: Rice Cakes

Basic Grain Products Inc ....D....... 419 678-2304
Coldwater (G-6553)

BAKERY PRDTS: Wholesalers

Brownie Points Inc ....G....... 614 860-8470
Columbus (G-6868)
Osmans Pies Inc ....E....... 330 607-9083
Stow (G-17786)
Thurns Bakery & Deli ....E....... 614 221-9246
Columbus (G-7693)
Unger Kosher Bakery Inc ....E....... 216 321-7176
Cleveland Heights (G-6502)

BAKERY: Wholesale Or Wholesale & Retail Combined

A Bun In Oven ....G....... 419 559-3056
Fremont (G-10121)
Atlas Produce LLC ....G....... 937 223-1446
Dayton (G-8168)
Bimbo Bakeries Usa Inc ....E....... 740 797-4449
The Plains (G-18183)

Bimbo Bakeries Usa Inc ....E....... 740 797-4449
The Plains (G-18184)
Bonbonneri Inc ....F....... 513 321-3399
Cincinnati (G-3458)
Borden Bakers Inc ....G....... 614 457-9800
Columbus (G-6847)
Calvary Christian Ch of Ohio ....E....... 740 828-9000
Frazeysburg (G-10071)
Crumbs Inc ....F....... 740 592-3803
Athens (G-859)
DUrso Bakery Inc ....F....... 330 652-4741
Niles (G-15150)
Empire Bakery Commissary LLC ....C....... 513 793-6241
Blue Ash (G-1784)
Evans Bakery Inc ....F....... 937 228-4151
Dayton (G-8334)
Gibson Bros Inc ....E....... 440 774-2401
Oberlin (G-15641)
Giminetti Baking Company ....E....... 513 751-7655
Cincinnati (G-3826)
Hoffmans Country Market ....G....... 740 216-0115
Logan (G-12179)
Home Bakery ....F....... 419 678-3018
Coldwater (G-6564)
International Multifoods Corp ....G....... 440 323-5100
Elyria (G-9432)
Jeffs Bakery ....G....... 937 890-9703
Dayton (G-8427)
Klosterman ....G....... 419 242-3400
Toledo (G-18546)
Klosterman Baking Co Inc ....E....... 937 322-9588
Springfield (G-17587)
Kustom Cases LLC ....G....... 240 380-6275
Dayton (G-8448)
McL Inc...D....... 614 861-6259
Columbus (G-7336)
Nikkicakes ....G....... 330 606-5745
Cuyahoga Falls (G-8029)
Norcia Bakery ....G....... 330 454-1077
Canton (G-2790)
Perfection Bakeries Inc ....D....... 614 866-8171
Blacklick (G-1703)
Perfection Bakeries Inc ....D....... 419 221-2359
Lima (G-12068)
Reineckers Bakery Ltd ....G....... 330 467-2221
Macedonia (G-12480)
Slice of Heaven Bakery ....G....... 419 656-6606
Clyde (G-6547)
Steubenville Bakery ....G....... 740 282-6851
Steubenville (G-17714)
Sweet Persuasions LLC ....G....... 614 216-9052
Pickerington (G-16206)
Ta Die For Gourmet Cupcakes ....G....... 740 751-4586
Marion (G-12905)
Wal-Bon of Ohio Inc ....F....... 740 423-6351
Belpre (G-1595)
You Dough Girl LLC ....G....... 330 207-5031
Salem (G-16937)

BALLOONS: Toy & Advertising, Rubber

Maple City Rubber Company ....E....... 419 668-8261
Norwalk (G-15551)
North Sails Toledo LLC ....F....... 419 726-2933
Toledo (G-18608)
Perfect Products Company ....E....... 330 863-1466
Malvern (G-12548)
Scherba Industries Inc ....D....... 330 273-3200
Brunswick (G-2256)

BANDS: Plastic

Chica Bands LLC ....G....... 513 871-4300
Cincinnati (G-3528)

BANNERS: Fabric

Party Animal Inc ....G....... 440 471-1030
Westlake (G-20291)

BANQUET HALL FACILITIES

Buns of Delaware Inc..........................E....... 740 363-2867
Delaware (G-8826)
Mustard Seed Health Fd Mkt Inc..........E....... 440 519-3663
Solon (G-17342)
Todd W Goings ....E....... 740 389-5842
Marion (G-12907)
Vulcan Machinery Corporation ....E....... 330 376-6025
Akron (G-465)

BAR

The Great Lakes Brewing Co ....D 216 771-4404
  Cleveland (G-6313)

BAR JOISTS & CONCRETE REINFORCING BARS: Fabricated

Foundation Systems Anchors Inc ....E ... 330 454-1700
  Canton (G-2707)

Worthington Industries Inc ....C ... 614 438-3210
  Worthington (G-20896)

BARBECUE EQPT

Lapa Lowe Enterprises LLC ....G ... 440 944-9410
  Willoughby (G-20527)

BARBER SHOP SELLING WIGS

Mels Life Like Hair ....G ... 937 278-9486
  Dayton (G-8483)

BARGES BUILDING & REPAIR

McGinnis Inc ....C ... 740 377-4391
  South Point (G-17440)

McNational Inc ....E ... 740 377-4391
  South Point (G-17441)

Superior Marine Ways Inc ....C ... 740 894-6224
  Proctorville (G-16493)

BARRELS: Shipping, Metal

Cleveland Steel Container Corp ....E ... 330 544-2271
  Niles (G-15147)

Mauser Usa LLC ....E ... 614 856-5982
  Gahanna (G-10217)

BARRICADES: Metal

Midwest Metals & Supply LLC ....G ... 513 489-1666
  Maineville (G-12529)

BARS & BAR SHAPES: Copper & Copper Alloy

Avtron Aerospace Inc ....C ... 216 750-5152
  Cleveland (G-4875)

BARS & BAR SHAPES: Steel, Cold-Finished, Own Hot-Rolled

Bertin Steel Processing Inc ....E ... 440 943-0094
  Wickliffe (G-20357)

Republic Steel Inc ....C ... 330 438-5533
  Canton (G-2837)

BARS & BAR SHAPES: Steel, Hot-Rolled

J & L Steel Bar LLC ....G ... 440 526-0050
  Broadview Heights (G-2111)

McDonald Steel Corporation ....C ... 330 530-9118
  Mc Donald (G-13347)

BARS, COLD FINISHED: Steel, From Purchased Hot-Rolled

Akron Rebar Co ....F ... 216 433-0000
  Cleveland (G-4740)

Columbia Steel and Wire Inc ....G ... 330 468-2709
  Northfield (G-15463)

New Dimension Metals Corp ....E ... 937 299-2233
  Moraine (G-14510)

Nucor Bright Bar Orville LLC ....F ... 330 682-5555
  Orrville (G-15751)

Telling Industries LLC ....F ... 440 974-3370
  Willoughby (G-20612)

Telling Industries LLC ....F ... 928 681-2010
  Willoughby (G-20613)

Telling Industries LLC ....D ... 740 435-8900
  Cambridge (G-2480)

BARS, PIPES, PLATES & SHAPES: Lead/Lead Alloy Bars, Pipe

G A Avril Company ....F ... 513 731-5133
  Cincinnati (G-3791)

BARS: Concrete Reinforcing, Fabricated Steel

Action Group Inc ....D ... 614 868-8868
  Blacklick (G-1686)

Akron Rebar Co ....E ... 330 745-7100
  Akron (G-54)

Alpha Control LLC ....E ... 740 377-3400
  South Point (G-17431)

Arcelormittal USA LLC ....F ... 740 375-2299
  Marion (G-12856)

Austintown Metal Works Inc ....F ... 330 259-4673
  Youngstown (G-21028)

Bridge Components Incorporated ....G ... 614 873-0777
  Columbus (G-6858)

Falcon Fab and Finishes LLC ....G ... 740 820-4458
  Lucasville (G-12420)

Gateway Concrete Forming Svcs ....D ... 513 353-2000
  Miamitown (G-13887)

Hartford Steel Sales ....G ... 513 275-1744
  Hamilton (G-10703)

J & L Welding Fabricating Inc ....F ... 330 393-9353
  Warren (G-19561)

L B Steel Plate ....G ... 440 893-0680
  Chagrin Falls (G-3062)

Melinz-Rebar Inc ....E ... 216 531-8988
  Cleveland (G-5781)

Mound Steel Corp ....E ... 937 748-2937
  Springboro (G-17490)

Mound Technologies Inc ....E ... 937 748-2937
  Springboro (G-17491)

Ohio Bridge Corporation ....C ... 740 432-6334
  Cambridge (G-2470)

Sarka Shtmtl & Fabrication Inc ....E ... 419 447-4377
  Tiffin (G-18242)

Smith Brothers Erection Inc ....E ... 740 373-3575
  Marietta (G-12832)

Steel Structures of Ohio LLC ....E ... 330 374-9900
  Akron (G-417)

Steel Warehouse Company LLC ....E ... 216 206-2800
  Cleveland (G-6245)

Steelcon Inc ....F ... 330 457-2419
  New Waterford (G-14974)

Superior Steel Service LLC ....F ... 513 724-0437
  Batavia (G-1227)

Veterans Steel Inc ....F ... 216 938-7476
  Cleveland (G-6412)

Zelcor Group LLC ....G ... 419 592-0803
  Napoleon (G-14702)

BARS: Iron, Made In Steel Mills

D Johnson Services ....G ... 330 386-4588
  East Liverpool (G-9210)

Republic Engineered Products ....E ... 440 277-2000
  Lorain (G-12271)

Republic Steel Inc ....D ... 330 438-5435
  Canton (G-2838)

BARS: Rolled, Aluminum

Aleris Corporation ....G ... 216 910-3400
  Cleveland (G-4746)

Aleris International Inc ....E ... 216 910-3400
  Beachwood (G-1253)

Real Alloy Recycling Inc ....G ... 740 922-8301
  Uhrichsville (G-19056)

BASALT: Crushed & Broken

Riverrock Recycl Crushing LLC ....G ... 937 325-2052
  Springfield (G-17640)

BASEMENT WINDOW AREAWAYS: Concrete

Bilco Company ....E ... 740 455-9020
  Zanesville (G-21279)

BASES, BEVERAGE

Bayswater Beverages LLC ....G ... 312 224-8012
  Cincinnati (G-3441)

BASKETS, WHOLESALE

Buhi Imports ....G ... 440 224-0013
  North Kingsville (G-15303)

BASKETS: Steel Wire

Sunrise Cooperative Inc ....E ... 419 683-4600
  Crestline (G-7936)

BATH SALTS

Ashland Specialty Ingredients ....D ... 614 529-3311
  Columbus (G-6776)

BATH SHOPS

Savko Plastic Pipe & Fittings ....F ... 614 885-8420
  Columbus (G-7591)

BATHMATS: Rubber

Innocor Foam Tech - Acp Inc ....F ... 419 647-4172
  Spencerville (G-17460)

BATHROOM ACCESS & FITTINGS: Vitreous China & Earthenware

A C Products Co ....D ... 330 698-1105
  Apple Creek (G-633)

Crane Plumbing LLC ....F ... 419 522-4211
  Mansfield (G-12588)

Crane Plumbing LLC ....C ... 419 522-0321
  Mansfield (G-12589)

F K Holding Inc ....F ... 513 641-1400
  Cincinnati (G-3735)

BATTERIES, EXC AUTOMOTIVE: Wholesalers

Ametek Inc ....F ... 937 440-0800
  Troy (G-18804)

B W T Inc ....G ... 330 928-9107
  Akron (G-81)

Battery Unlimited ....G ... 740 452-5030
  Zanesville (G-21276)

D C Systems Inc ....F ... 330 273-3030
  Brunswick (G-2219)

Forklifts of Americas LLC ....G ... 440 821-5143
  Highland Heights (G-10912)

Interstate Batteries Inc ....G ... 740 968-2211
  Saint Clairsville (G-16792)

N S T Battery ....G ... 937 433-9222
  Bellbrook (G-1510)

One Wish LLC ....F ... 800 505-6883
  Beachwood (G-1289)

BATTERIES: Alkaline, Cell Storage

Transdigm Inc ....F ... 216 291-6025
  Cleveland (G-6346)

Transdigm Inc ....G ... 216 706-2939
  Cleveland (G-6347)

BATTERIES: Dry

D C Systems Inc ....F ... 330 273-3030
  Brunswick (G-2219)

BATTERIES: Lead Acid, Storage

All Power Battery Inc ....G ... 330 453-5236
  Canton (G-2597)

Enersys ....D ... 513 737-2268
  West Chester (G-19858)

Enersys Delaware Inc ....G ... 216 252-4242
  Cleveland (G-5282)

Megajoule Storage Inc ....G ... 216 496-8302
  Cleveland (G-5778)

BATTERIES: Rechargeable

Graywacke Engineering Inc ....F ... 419 884-7014
  Mansfield (G-12621)

Johnson Contrls Btry Group Inc ....A ... 419 865-0542
  Holland (G-11068)

Retriev Technologies Inc ....D ... 740 653-6290
  Lancaster (G-11746)

Toxco Inc ....D ... 740 653-6290
  Lancaster (G-11757)

BATTERIES: Storage

B W T Inc ....G ... 330 928-9107
  Akron (G-81)

Crown Battery Manufacturing Co ....B ... 419 332-0563
  Fremont (G-10139)

Dynalite Corp ....G ... 419 873-1706
  Perrysburg (G-16086)

Energizer Manufacturing Inc ....D ... 440 835-7866
  Westlake (G-20267)

Gould Electronics Inc ....C ... 440 953-5000
  Eastlake (G-9271)

PRODUCT

Innovative Weld Solutions Ltd.............G..... 937 545-7695
Dayton (G-8408)
Interstate Batteries Inc.............G..... 740 968-2211
Saint Clairsville (G-16792)
Lithchem Intl Toxco Inc.............G..... 740 653-6290
Lancaster (G-11726)
Ovonic Energy Products Inc.............C..... 937 743-1001
Springboro (G-17493)

BATTERIES: Wet

N S T Battery ....G..... 937 433-9222
Bellbrook (G-1510)
Spectrum Brands Inc ....D..... 513 231-0952
Anderson Township (G-610)
Toyo System Usa Inc ....G..... 614 414-0515
Columbus (G-7702)

BATTERY CASES: Plastic Or Plastics Combination

Koroseal Interior Products LLC.............C..... 330 668-7600
Fairlawn (G-9755)

BATTERY CHARGERS

Brookwood Group Inc ....F..... 513 791-3030
Cincinnati (G-3481)
D C Systems Inc ....G..... 330 273-3030
Brunswick (G-2219)
Ecotec Ltd LLC ....G..... 937 606-2793
Troy (G-18821)
Japlar Group Inc ....F..... 513 791-7192
Cincinnati (G-3942)
TL Industries Inc ....C..... 419 666-8144
Northwood (G-15490)
Xenotronix/Tli Inc ....G..... 407 331-4793
Northwood (G-15498)

BATTERY CHARGERS: Storage, Motor & Engine Generator Type

Brinkley Technology Group LLC ....F..... 330 830-2498
Massillon (G-13115)
Charger Connection ....G..... 888 427-5829
Cincinnati (G-3522)
Design Flux Technologies LLC.............G..... 216 543-6066
Akron (G-147)
Lesch Btry & Pwr Solution LLC.............G..... 419 884-0219
Mansfield (G-12636)

BATTERY CHARGING GENERATORS

Design Flux Technologies LLC.............G..... 216 543-6066
Akron (G-147)

BATTERY REPAIR & SVCS

All Power Battery Inc ....G..... 330 453-5236
Canton (G-2597)
Battery Unlimited ....G..... 740 452-5030
Zanesville (G-21276)
D C Systems Inc ....F..... 330 273-3030
Brunswick (G-2219)

BAUXITE MINING

Alcoa Inc.............F..... 216 391-3885
Cleveland (G-4743)
Alcoa Inc.............E..... 608 363-5214
Newburgh Heights (G-15068)

BEADS: Unassembled

Bead Shoppe At Home ....G..... 330 479-9598
Canton (G-2618)

BEARINGS

Art Metals Group Inc.............D..... 513 942-8800
Hamilton (G-10671)
Erie Shore Industrial Svc Co.............G..... 440 933-4301
Avon Lake (G-1028)

BEARINGS & PARTS Ball

Federal-Mogul Corporation.............C..... 740 432-2393
Cambridge (G-2457)
Jay Dee Service Corporation.............G..... 330 425-1546
Macedonia (G-12463)
Miller Bearing Company Inc.............E..... 330 678-8844
Kent (G-11493)
Nn Inc.............G..... 440 647-4711
Wellington (G-19751)

Rotek Incorporated ....C..... 330 562-4000
Aurora (G-945)

BEARINGS: Ball & Roller

Bearings Manufacturing Company ......E..... 440 846-5517
Strongsville (G-17895)
FAg Bearings Corporation ....C..... 513 398-1139
Mason (G-13019)
Gt Technologies Inc.............C..... 419 782-8955
Defiance (G-8792)
Jtekt North America Corp ....C..... 440 835-1000
Westlake (G-20279)
Randolph Research Co ....G..... 330 666-1667
Akron (G-364)
Timken Company ....A..... 234 262-3000
North Canton (G-15273)
Timken Company ....A..... 419 563-2200
Bucyrus (G-2360)
Timken Company ....C..... 330 339-1151
New Philadelphia (G-14934)
Timken Company ....G..... 330 471-4300
Canton (G-2871)
Timken Company ....G..... 614 476-3934
Gahanna (G-10239)
Timken Company ....F..... 614 836-3337
Groveport (G-10646)
Timken Company ....G..... 330 471-5028
Canton (G-2872)
Timken Company ....G..... 234 262-3000
North Canton (G-15274)
Timken Company ....C..... 330 471-2121
Canton (G-2873)
Timken Company ....D..... 234 262-3000
Niles (G-15185)
Timken Company ....G..... 330 471-4791
Alliance (G-545)
Timken Company ....A..... 330 471-5043
Canton (G-2874)
Tsk America Co Ltd.............F..... 513 942-4002
West Chester (G-20062)

BEARINGS: Plastic

Ptc Enterprises Inc ....E..... 419 272-2524
Edon (G-9344)

BEARINGS: Roller & Parts

Ashland Precision Tooling LLC.............D..... 419 289-1736
Ashland (G-707)
HMS Industries LLC ....G..... 440 899-0001
Westlake (G-20277)
Schaeffler Group USA Inc ....B..... 330 273-4383
Valley City (G-19229)

BEAUTY & BARBER SHOP EQPT

Aluminum Line Products Company ......D..... 440 835-8880
Westlake (G-20249)
Beauty Systems Group LLC ....G..... 740 456-5434
New Boston (G-14779)
Carroll Hills Industries Inc ....D..... 330 627-5524
Carrollton (G-2953)
Columbus Industries Inc ....F..... 937 544-6896
West Union (G-20119)
Country Clippins ....G..... 740 472-5228
Woodsfield (G-20716)
Dem Technology LLC ....G..... 937 223-1317
Dayton (G-8298)
Dmi Products Inc ....G..... 440 951-1828
Mentor (G-13561)
Duraflow Industries Inc ....G..... 440 965-5047
Wakeman (G-19448)
Exikon Industries LLC.............F..... 216 485-2947
Cleveland (G-5313)
Firelands Manufacturing LLC ....F..... 419 687-8237
Plymouth (G-16376)
Gibraltar Industries Inc.............G..... 440 617-9230
Westlake (G-20272)
GKN Driveline Bowl Green Inc.............G..... 419 354-3955
Bowling Green (G-1989)
Goodwill Inds NW Ohio Inc.............E..... 419 255-0070
Toledo (G-18483)
James J Fairbanks Company Inc ....G..... 330 534-1374
Hubbard (G-11132)
Mab Fabrication Inc ....G..... 855 622-3221
Harrison (G-10788)
Medline Industries Inc ....G..... 330 484-1450
Canton (G-2778)
New Can Company Inc ....G..... 937 547-9050
Greenville (G-10512)

Phoenix Trinity Mfg Inc.............G..... 937 619-0172
Dayton (G-8574)
Pinnacle Sales Inc.............G..... 440 777-2544
Westlake (G-20295)
PPG Industries Inc.............G..... 330 825-6328
Barberton (G-1141)
Quick Tech Business Forms Inc.............E..... 937 743-5952
Springboro (G-17501)
Rowend Industries Inc.............G..... 419 333-8300
Fremont (G-10181)
Schreiner Manufacturing.............G..... 419 937-0300
New Riegel (G-14948)
Shaw Industries Inc.............G..... 513 942-3692
West Chester (G-19945)
Tango Echo Bravo Mfg Inc.............G..... 440 937-3800
North Ridgeville (G-15404)
Utopia Products Inc.............G..... 330 666-2602
Akron (G-460)
Vulcan International Corp.............G..... 513 621-2850
Cincinnati (G-4571)

BEAUTY & BARBER SHOP EQPT & SPLYS WHOLESALERS

Beauty Systems Group LLC ....G..... 740 456-5434
New Boston (G-14779)

BEAUTY SALONS

James C Robinson.............G..... 513 969-7482
Cincinnati (G-3941)

BED & BREAKFAST INNS

Breitenbach Wine Cellar Inc ....G..... 330 343-3603
Dover (G-8970)

BEDDING & BEDSPRINGS STORES

Ahmf Inc.............E..... 614 921-1223
Columbus (G-6704)
Original Mattress Factory Inc ....G..... 216 661-8388
Cleveland (G-5947)
Original Mattress Factory Inc ....G..... 513 752-6600
Cincinnati (G-3313)

BEDDING, BEDSPREADS, BLANKETS & SHEETS

Sewline Products Inc.............F..... 419 929-1114
New London (G-14866)

BEDDING, BEDSPREADS, BLANKETS & SHEETS: Comforters & Quilts

Aunties Attic.............E..... 740 548-5059
Lewis Center (G-11886)

BEDS: Hospital

Belmont Community Hospital.............B..... 740 671-1216
Bellaire (G-1496)

BEDS: Institutional

Success Technologies Inc ....G..... 614 761-0008
Powell (G-16484)

BEDSPREADS & BED SETS, FROM PURCHASED MATERIALS

Wise Window Treatment Inc ....F..... 216 676-4080
Cleveland (G-6470)

BEDSPREADS, COTTON

Sk Textile Inc.............C..... 323 581-8986
Cincinnati (G-4424)

BEER & ALE WHOLESALERS

Victoria Ventures Inc ....G..... 330 793-9321
Youngstown (G-21239)

BEER, WINE & LIQUOR STORES: Beer, Packaged

Csv Inc.............F..... 937 438-1142
Dayton (G-8254)
Currier Richard & James.............G..... 440 988-4132
Amherst (G-596)
Millersburg Ice Co.............E..... 330 674-3016
Millersburg (G-14249)

Wings Way Drive Thru Inc......................G...... 330 533-2788
Salem (G-16935)

BEER, WINE & LIQUOR STORES: Wine

CWC Partners LLC..............................G...... 567 208-1573
Findlay (G-9815)
Kelleys Island Wine Co........................G...... 419 746-2678
Kelleys Island (G-11419)
Lamont Enterprises Inc.........................G...... 330 677-4400
Kent (G-11484)
Sandra Weddington...............................G...... 740 417-4286
Delaware (G-8885)

BELLOWS

Alloy Bllows Prcision Wldg Inc ....D...... 440 684-3000
Cleveland (G-4767)
International Bellows.............................F...... 937 832-4501
Englewood (G-9526)
Xorb Corporation..................................G...... 419 354-6021
Bowling Green (G-2023)

BELLOWS ASSEMBLIES: Missiles, Metal

Shelburne Corp.....................................G...... 216 321-9177
Shaker Heights (G-17094)

BELLS: Electric

I T Verdin Co...E...... 513 241-4010
Cincinnati (G-3906)
I T Verdin Co...E...... 513 559-3947
Cincinnati (G-3908)
S R Technologies LLC............................G...... 330 523-7184
Akron (G-392)

BELTING: Plastic

Engineered Plastics Corp ....E...... 330 376-7700
Akron (G-167)
Polychem Corporation...........................G...... 419 547-1400
Clyde (G-6543)

BELTING: Rubber

Fenner Dunlop (toledo) LLC ....E...... 419 531-5300
Toledo (G-18467)
Novex Inc..F...... 330 335-2371
Wadsworth (G-19422)

BELTS: Conveyor, Made From Purchased Wire

American Pennekamp Mfg Inc...............G...... 740 687-0096
Lancaster (G-11685)
Apache Hose & Belting Co Inc ....D...... 513 587-8313
West Chester (G-19981)
Con-Belt Inc..F...... 330 273-2003
Valley City (G-19201)
Contitech Usa Inc.................................E...... 937 644-8900
Marysville (G-12937)
May Conveyor Inc ....F...... 440 237-8012
North Royalton (G-15435)
Seven-Ogun International LLC ....G...... 614 888-8939
Worthington (G-20887)
Tri-State Belting Ltd.............................G...... 800 330-2358
Cincinnati (G-4522)

BELTS: Seat, Automotive & Aircraft

Tk Holdings Inc.....................................E...... 937 778-9713
Piqua (G-16315)

BENTONITE MINING

American Colloid Company ....G...... 419 445-9085
Archbold (G-662)

BERYLLIUM

Materion Brush Inc ....A...... 419 862-2745
Elmore (G-9365)
Materion Brush Inc ....D...... 216 486-4200
Mayfield Heights (G-13317)
Materion Corporation ....C...... 216 486-4200
Mayfield Heights (G-13318)

BEVERAGE BASES & SYRUPS

J M Smucker Company ....A...... 330 682-3000
Orrville (G-15742)
Mapledale Farm Inc..............................F...... 440 286-3389
Chardon (G-3166)

BEVERAGE PRDTS: Brewers' Grain

Rivertown Brewing Company LLC ......E...... 513 827-9280
Cincinnati (G-4350)
Wedco LLC ....G...... 513 309-0781
Mount Orab (G-14587)

BEVERAGE, NONALCOHOLIC: Iced Tea/Fruit Drink, Bottled/Canned

Arizona Beverage Company LLC ....D...... 516 837-1999
Cincinnati (G-3413)

BEVERAGES, ALCOHOLIC: Ale

Seventh Son Brewing Co ....G...... 614 783-4217
Columbus (G-7612)

BEVERAGES, ALCOHOLIC: Beer

American Craft Brewery LLC ....C...... 513 412-3200
Cincinnati (G-3387)
Birdfish Brewing Company LLC ....G...... 330 397-4010
Columbiana (G-6606)
Black Cloister Brewing Co LLC ....G...... 419 481-3891
Toledo (G-18371)
Brewery Real Estate Partnr ....G...... 614 224-9023
Columbus (G-6856)
Brufist LLC ....G...... 330 221-4472
Bowling Green (G-1974)
Carry Grandview Out ....G...... 614 487-0305
Columbus (G-6913)
Choice Brands.......................................G...... 740 598-4121
Mingo Junction (G-14347)
Cineen Inc...G...... 440 236-3658
Columbia Station (G-6583)
Dayton Heidelberg Distrg Co ....C...... 440 989-1027
Lorain (G-12243)
Dinos Drive Thru LLC...........................G...... 330 263-1111
Wooster (G-20765)
District Brewing Co Inc ....G...... 614 224-3626
Columbus (G-7032)
Eagles Club ....G...... 740 962-6490
McConnelsville (G-13349)
Elevator Brewing Company LLC ....G...... 614 679-2337
Columbus (G-7052)
Hill James R & Hill Earley W ....G...... 740 591-4203
Albany (G-480)
Jackie Os Pub Brewery LLC ....D...... 740 274-0777
Athens (G-873)
Larrys Drive Thru & Mini Mart............G...... 330 953-0512
Youngstown (G-21133)
Marios Drive Thru ....G...... 330 452-8793
Canton (G-2769)
Marks Brew Thru ....G...... 330 699-1755
Akron (G-287)
Maumee Bay Brewing Company ....E...... 419 243-1253
Toledo (G-18577)
Minnicks Drive-Thru ....G...... 513 868-6126
Hamilton (G-10725)
Pop A Top Cruise Thru ....G...... 419 947-5855
Mount Gilead (G-14565)
Sgt S Drive Thru...................................G...... 937 378-3813
Georgetown (G-10365)
Snyder Intl Brewing Group LLC ....E...... 216 619-7424
Cleveland (G-6215)
South Side Drive Thru ....G...... 937 295-2927
Fort Loramie (G-9940)
Southern Glazers Wine & Sprt..............D...... 513 755-7082
Fairfield (G-9721)
The Great Lakes Brewing Co ....G...... 216 771-4404
Cleveland (G-6313)
Unbridled Brewing Company LLC.......F 937 361-2573
Middletown (G-14091)

BEVERAGES, ALCOHOLIC: Beer & Ale

Actual Brewing......................................F...... 614 636-3825
Columbus (G-6692)
Anheuser-Busch LLC ....B...... 614 847-6213
Columbus (G-6757)
Barbeque Integrated Inc ....D...... 614 430-0572
Columbus (G-6640)
Barnstorm Brewing Company LLC ....G...... 419 852-9366
Coldwater (G-6551)
Brew Kettle Inc.....................................F...... 440 234-8788
Strongsville (G-17898)
Brewery X LLC ....G...... 513 240-3600
Cincinnati (G-3471)
Brewpub Restaurant Corp ....G...... 614 228-2537
Columbus (G-6857)

Burgie Brauerei Inc ....G...... 740 344-1620
Newark (G-14990)
Columbus Kombucha Company LLC ..G...... 614 262-0000
Columbus (G-6959)
Commissary Brewing ....G...... 614 636-3164
Columbus (G-6972)
Euclid Brewing Company LLC ....G...... 216 289-5100
Euclid (G-9578)
Guys Brewing Gear................................G...... 330 554-9362
Kent (G-11464)
McKinleys Meadery LLC ....G...... 740 928-0229
Hebron (G-10873)
Millercoors LLC ....D...... 513 896-9200
Trenton (G-18796)
Nine Giant Brewing LLC ....G...... 510 220-5104
Cincinnati (G-4157)
Rocky River Brewing Co ....E...... 440 895-2739
Rocky River (G-16708)
Rust Belt Brewing LLC ....G...... 330 423-3818
Youngstown (G-21194)
Schuster Beverage Marketing ....G...... 614 764-1420
Dublin (G-9140)
Thirsty Dog Brewing Co ....G...... 330 252-8740
Akron (G-440)
Tom Bad Brewing LLC ....G...... 513 871-4677
Cincinnati (G-4512)
Two Bandits Brewing Co LLC ....G...... 419 636-4045
Bryan (G-2324)
Victoria Ventures Inc ....G...... 330 793-9321
Youngstown (G-21239)
Westend Brewing LLC ....G...... 513 922-0289
Cincinnati (G-4587)
Willoughby Brewing Company ....D...... 440 975-0202
Willoughby (G-20630)
Wright Designs Inc ....G...... 216 524-6662
Cleveland (G-6484)

BEVERAGES, ALCOHOLIC: Bourbon Whiskey

Luxco Inc ....E...... 216 671-6300
Cleveland (G-5713)

BEVERAGES, ALCOHOLIC: Cocktails

Catawba Island Brewing Co ....G...... 419 960-7764
Port Clinton (G-16396)

BEVERAGES, ALCOHOLIC: Distilled Liquors

Cleveland Whiskey LLC ....G...... 216 881-8481
Cleveland (G-5086)
Crooked Handle Brewing Co LLC ....G...... 937 241-5965
Springboro (G-17477)
Smedleys Bar and Grill ....G...... 216 941-0124
Cleveland (G-6212)
Western Reserve Distillers LLC ....G...... 330 671-0347
Hudson (G-11208)

BEVERAGES, ALCOHOLIC: Liquors, Malt

AEC Brews LLC DBA Old Frhuse B .....G...... 513 536-9071
Williamsburg (G-20406)

BEVERAGES, ALCOHOLIC: Near Beer

Green Room Brewing LLC ....G...... 614 596-3655
Columbus (G-7131)
North High Brewing LLC ....F...... 614 407-5278
Columbus (G-7400)
Platform Beers LLC ....F...... 440 539-3245
Cleveland (G-6016)

BEVERAGES, ALCOHOLIC: Rye Whiskey

Five Points Distillery LLC.......................G...... 937 776-4634
Dayton (G-8344)

BEVERAGES, ALCOHOLIC: Vodka

Crystal Spirits LLC................................G...... 937 228-0201
Dayton (G-8253)

BEVERAGES, ALCOHOLIC: Wines

Breitenbach Wine Cellar Inc ....G...... 330 343-3603
Dover (G-8970)
Chalet Debonne Vineyards Inc ....F...... 440 466-3485
Madison (G-12499)
CWC Partners LLC ....G...... 567 208-1573
Findlay (G-9815)
Deluca Vineyards ....G...... 440 685-4242
North Bloomfield (G-15216)

PRODUCT

Drake Brothers Ltd .... G 415 819-4941
Columbus (G-7039)

Europia Gourmet Foods LLC .... G 614 460-3000
Columbus (G-7068)

Ferrante Wine Farm Inc .... E 440 466-8466
Geneva (G-10347)

Gar-Nays Winery .... G 419 668-6802
Collins (G-6575)

Gillig Custom Winery Inc .... G 419 202-6057
Findlay (G-9831)

Glenn Ravens Winery .... E 740 545-1000
West Lafayette (G-20086)

Hundley Cellars LLC .... G 843 368-5016
Geneva (G-10351)

John Christ Winery Inc .... G 440 933-9672
Avon Lake (G-1035)

Kelleys Island Wine Co .... G 419 746-2678
Kelleys Island (G-11419)

King Vineyards .... G 440 967-4191
Vermilion (G-19331)

Klingshirn Winery Inc .... G 440 933-6666
Avon Lake (G-1036)

Lamont Enterprises Inc .... G 330 677-4400
Kent (G-11484)

Larrys Drive Thru & Mini Mart .... G 330 953-0512
Youngstown (G-21133)

Markko Vineyard .... G 440 593-3197
Conneaut (G-7815)

Mastropietro Winery Inc .... G 330 547-2151
Berlin Center (G-1656)

Meiers Wine Cellars Inc .... E 513 891-2900
Cincinnati (G-4082)

Mt Carmel Brewing Company .... G 513 519-7161
Cincinnati (G-4129)

Odyssey Cellars Inc .... G 330 782-0177
Youngstown (G-21152)

Old Mason Winery Inc .... G 937 698-1122
West Milton (G-20109)

Old Mill Winery Inc .... F 440 466-5560
Geneva (G-10354)

Olde Schlhuse Vnyrd Winery LLC ...... G 937 273-6023
Eldorado (G-9347)

Rainbow Hills Vineyards Inc .... G 740 545-9305
Newcomerstown (G-15122)

Renee Barrett Winery .... G 513 471-1340
Cincinnati (G-4336)

Sand Hollow Winery .... G 740 323-3959
Heath (G-10856)

Sandra Weddington .... G 740 417-4286
Delaware (G-8885)

Shade Text Book Service Inc .... G 740 696-1323
Shade (G-17079)

Shawne Springs Winery .... G 740 623-0744
Coshocton (G-7909)

Stoney Ridge Winery Ltd .... G 419 636-3500
Bryan (G-2321)

Thorncreek Winery & Garden .... G 330 562-9245
Aurora (G-949)

Virant Family Winery Inc .... G 440 466-6279
Geneva (G-10358)

Wines For You .... G 440 946-1420
Mentor (G-13770)

Woodbury Vineyards Inc .... G 440 835-2828
Westlake (G-20322)

BEVERAGES, NONALCOHOLIC: Bottled & canned soft drinks

7 Up of Marietta Inc .... E 740 423-9230
Little Hocking (G-12141)

Abbott Laboratories .... A 614 624-3191
Columbus (G-6671)

Alaskan Falls Bottling Company ...... G 614 888-9280
Worthington (G-20854)

American Bottling Company .... D 614 237-4201
Columbus (G-6730)

American Bottling Company .... D 937 236-0333
Dayton (G-8151)

American Bottling Company .... E 740 922-5253
Midvale (G-14104)

American Bottling Company .... D 740 423-9230
Little Hocking (G-12142)

American Bottling Company .... D 614 237-4201
Columbus (G-6731)

American Bottling Company .... E 419 229-7777
Lima (G-11988)

American Bottling Company .... D 419 535-0777
Toledo (G-18336)

American Bottling Company .... C 513 242-5151
Cincinnati (G-3385)

Belton Foods .... E 937 890-7768
Dayton (G-8184)

Borden Dairy Co Cincinnati LLC ...... C 513 948-8811
Cincinnati (G-3461)

Cadbury Schweppes Bottling .... G 614 238-0469
Columbus (G-6887)

Cleveland Coca-Cola Btlg Inc .... C 216 690-2653
Bedford Heights (G-1480)

Coca-Cola .... G 937 446-4644
Sardinia (G-17027)

Coca-Cola Bottling Co Cnsld .... G 419 422-3743
Lima (G-12000)

Coca-Cola Bottling Co Cnsld .... E 740 353-3133
Portsmouth (G-16433)

Coca-Cola Bottling Co Cnsld .... E 419 229-2000
Lima (G-12001)

Coca-Cola Bottling Co Cnsld .... B 513 527-6600
Cincinnati (G-3595)

Coca-Cola Company .... C 614 491-6305
Columbus (G-6942)

Coca-Cola Company .... D 614 863-7200
Columbus (G-6943)

Coca-Cola Company .... D 330 783-1982
Youngstown (G-21053)

Coca-Cola Company .... E 419 522-2653
Mansfield (G-12582)

Coca-Cola Company .... F 937 446-4644
Sardinia (G-17028)

Coca-Cola Company .... D 440 324-3335
Elyria (G-9396)

Coca-Cola Company .... E 740 452-3608
Zanesville (G-21291)

Coca-Cola Company .... C 513 898-7800
Blue Ash (G-1767)

Coca-Cola Company .... D 440 269-1433
Willoughby (G-20457)

Coca-Cola Refreshments USA Inc ...... D 330 425-4401
Twinsburg (G-18917)

Creekside Springs LLC .... E 330 679-1010
Salineville (G-16941)

Csv Inc .... F 937 438-1142
Dayton (G-8254)

Currier Richard & James .... G 440 988-4132
Amherst (G-596)

Delite Fruit Juices .... G 614 470-4333
Columbus (G-7019)

Dr Pepper Snapple Group Inc .... D 614 237-4201
Columbus (G-7036)

Dr Pepper/Seven Up Inc .... D 419 229-7777
Lima (G-12005)

Dragon Beverage Inc .... E 614 506-5592
Columbus (G-7038)

Fbg Bottling Group LLC .... F 614 554-4646
Columbus (G-7077)

G & J Pepsi-Cola Bottlers Inc .... E 740 774-2148
Chillicothe (G-3239)

Gordon Brothers Btlg Group Inc ...... G 330 337-8754
Salem (G-16894)

Haus Mathias .... G 330 533-5305
Canfield (G-2557)

Hornell Brewing Co Inc .... G 516 812-0384
Cincinnati (G-3899)

Kroger Co .... C 513 671-2790
Cincinnati (G-4003)

L & F Lauch LLC .... G 513 732-5805
Batavia (G-1200)

Medi Home Health Agency Inc .... G 740 472-3220
Woodsfield (G-20719)

Meiers Wine Cellars Inc .... E 513 891-2900
Cincinnati (G-4082)

Niagara Bottling LLC .... F 614 751-7420
Gahanna (G-10224)

Nurture Brands LLC .... G 513 307-2338
Cincinnati (G-4168)

P-Americas LLC .... C 330 746-7652
Youngstown (G-21161)

P-Americas LLC .... E 419 227-3541
Lima (G-12065)

Pepsi-Cola Metro Btlg Co Inc .... B 330 963-0426
Twinsburg (G-18998)

Scioto Coca Cola .... G 740 474-2180
Circleville (G-4641)

Smucker International Inc .... G 330 682-3000
Orrville (G-15766)

Smucker Natural Foods Inc .... E 330 682-3000
Orrville (G-15767)

Vinnies Drive Thru .... G 419 225-5272
Lima (G-12109)

BEVERAGES, NONALCOHOLIC: Carbonated

Burton Bottling Company Inc .... E 216 681-0025
Cleveland (G-4950)

G & J Pepsi-Cola Bottlers Inc .... B 740 354-9191
Franklin Furnace (G-10069)

G & J Pepsi-Cola Bottlers Inc .... D 937 392-4937
Ripley (G-16666)

G & J Pepsi-Cola Bottlers Inc .... C 513 896-3700
Hamilton (G-10694)

G & J Pepsi-Cola Bottlers Inc .... A 614 253-8771
Columbus (G-7104)

G & J Pepsi-Cola Bottlers Inc .... D 740 452-2721
Zanesville (G-21313)

P-Americas LLC .... E 740 266-6121
Wintersville (G-20712)

P-Americas LLC .... B 513 948-5100
Cincinnati (G-4207)

P-Americas LLC .... C 614 253-8771
Columbus (G-7452)

P-Americas LLC .... C 440 323-5524
Elyria (G-9474)

P-Americas LLC .... C 330 336-3553
Wadsworth (G-19424)

P-Americas LLC .... C 330 837-4224
Massillon (G-13191)

P-Americas LLC .... C 937 328-6750
Springfield (G-17621)

P-Americas LLC .... E 330 963-0090
Twinsburg (G-18994)

Pepsi-Cola Metro Btlg Co Inc .... C 614 261-8193
Columbus (G-7477)

Pepsi-Cola Metro Btlg Co Inc .... E 330 963-5300
Twinsburg (G-18999)

Pepsi-Cola Metro Btlg Co Inc .... E 419 534-2186
Toledo (G-18638)

SD Ip Holdings Company .... G 513 483-3300
Blue Ash (G-1866)

BEVERAGES, NONALCOHOLIC: Carbonated, Canned & Bottled, Etc

Bawls Acquisition LLC .... G 888 731-9708
Twinsburg (G-18904)

Coca-Cola Bottling Co Cnsld .... D 937 878-5000
Dayton (G-8235)

Coca-Cola Refreshments USA Inc ...... C 419 476-6622
Toledo (G-18404)

Copper Mountain Beverages LLC .... G 513 484-9550
Cincinnati (G-3610)

Dominion Liquid Tech LLC .... G 513 272-2824
Cincinnati (G-3663)

G & J Pepsi-Cola Bottlers Inc .... D 740 593-3366
Athens (G-867)

Gehm & Sons Limited .... G 330 724-8423
Akron (G-202)

Jmike LLC .... G 740 525-1734
Marietta (G-12795)

L & J Drive Thru .... G 330 767-2185
Brewster (G-2085)

Lynn Lyons .... G 740 599-7811
Danville (G-8089)

Youthtopia LLC .... G 740 525-1734
Marietta (G-12851)

BEVERAGES, NONALCOHOLIC: Cider

Beckwith Orchards Inc .... F 330 673-6433
Kent (G-11433)

Fuhrmann Orchards LLC .... G 740 776-6406
Wheelersburg (G-20331)

Haus Mathias .... G 330 533-5305
Canfield (G-2557)

Hays Orchard & Cider Mill LLC .... F 330 482-2924
Columbiana (G-6619)

BEVERAGES, NONALCOHOLIC: Flavoring extracts & syrups, nec

Abbott Laboratories .... A 614 624-3191
Columbus (G-6671)

Agrana Fruit Us Inc .... C 937 693-3821
Anna (G-620)

Bickford Laboratories Inc .... G 440 354-7747
Wickliffe (G-20359)

Cargill Incorporated .... E 937 236-1971
Dayton (G-8210)

Flavor Systems Intl Inc .... E 513 870-4900
West Chester (G-20003)

Givaudan Flavors Corporation .... F 513 948-8000
Cincinnati (G-3829)

Givaudan Flvors Fragrances Inc ....G..... 513 948-8000
Cincinnati *(G-3830)*
Givaudan Fragrances Corp ....B..... 513 948-3428
Cincinnati *(G-3832)*
Givaudan Roure US Inc ....G..... 513 948-8000
Cincinnati *(G-3833)*
Joseph Adams Corp ....F..... 330 225-9125
Valley City *(G-19208)*
Mane Inc ....D..... 513 248-9876
Lebanon *(G-11815)*
Mane Inc ....D..... 513 248-9876
Lebanon *(G-11816)*
Tate Lyle Ingrdnts Amricas LLC ....D..... 937 236-5906
Dayton *(G-8703)*

BEVERAGES, NONALCOHOLIC: Fruit Drnks, Under 100% Juice, Can

Beverages Holdings LLC ....E..... 513 483-3300
Blue Ash *(G-1750)*
Country Pure Foods Inc ....C..... 330 848-6875
Akron *(G-131)*
Life Support Development Ltd ....G..... 614 221-1765
Columbus *(G-7294)*
Ohio Beverage Systems Inc ....F..... 216 475-3900
Cleveland *(G-5929)*
Ohio Pure Foods Inc ....D..... 330 753-2293
Akron *(G-326)*
Our Heart Health Care Svcs LLC ....G..... 614 943-5216
Columbus *(G-7448)*
Sunny Delight Beverage Co ....D..... 513 483-3300
Blue Ash *(G-1876)*

BEVERAGES, NONALCOHOLIC: Lemonade, Bottled & Canned, Etc

Paradise Lemonade ....F..... 740 816-0771
Westerville *(G-20178)*

BEVERAGES, NONALCOHOLIC: Soft Drinks, Canned & Bottled, Etc

American Bottling Company ....E..... 740 377-4371
South Point *(G-17432)*
American Bottling Company ....D..... 513 381-4891
Cincinnati *(G-3384)*
American Bottling Company ....E..... 419 529-6773
Mansfield *(G-12560)*
Cincinnati Marlins Inc ....G..... 513 761-3320
Cincinnati *(G-3558)*
Dr Pepper Bottlers Associates ....G..... 330 746-7651
Youngstown *(G-21072)*
Dr Pepper Bottling Company ....G..... 740 452-2721
Zanesville *(G-21301)*
Dr Pepper Snapple Group ....G..... 419 529-6773
Mansfield *(G-12596)*
Dr Pepper Snapple Group Inc ....D..... 614 237-4201
Columbus *(G-7037)*
G & J Pepsi-Cola Bottlers Inc ....F..... 513 785-6060
Cincinnati *(G-3789)*
Gem Beverages Inc ....F..... 740 384-2411
Wellston *(G-19763)*
National Beverage Corp ....E..... 614 491-5415
Obetz *(G-15657)*
Pepsi-Cola Metro Btlg Co Inc ....B..... 937 461-4664
Dayton *(G-8570)*
Shasta Beverages Inc ....E..... 614 491-5415
Obetz *(G-15659)*
Skinny Piggy Kombucha LLC ....G..... 513 646-5753
Cincinnati *(G-4425)*

BEVERAGES, WINE & DISTILLED ALCOHOLIC, WHOLESALE: Wine

CWC Partners LLC ....G..... 567 208-1573
Findlay *(G-9815)*
Sandra Weddington ....G..... 740 417-4286
Delaware *(G-8885)*
Wedco LLC ....G..... 513 309-0781
Mount Orab *(G-14587)*

BIBS: Rubber, Vulcanized Or Rubberized Fabric

Okamoto Sandusky Mfg LLC ....D..... 419 626-1633
Sandusky *(G-16991)*

BICYCLES, PARTS & ACCESS

Old Mill Power Equipment ....G..... 740 982-3246
Crooksville *(G-7951)*

BILLFOLD INSERTS: Plastic

Armeton US Co ....G..... 419 554-1866
Norwalk *(G-15526)*

BILLIARD & POOL TABLES & SPLYS

American Heritage Blld LLC ....D..... 330 626-3710
Streetsboro *(G-17838)*
Bullseye Dart Shoppe Inc ....G..... 440 951-9277
Willoughby *(G-20449)*
Clark & Son Pool Table Company ....G..... 330 454-9153
Canton *(G-2657)*

BILLING & BOOKKEEPING SVCS

C S A Enterprises ....G..... 740 342-9367
New Lexington *(G-14845)*

BINDING SVC: Books & Manuals

21st Century Printers Inc ....G..... 513 771-4150
Cincinnati *(G-3322)*
A-1 Printing Inc ....F..... 419 562-3111
Bucyrus *(G-2330)*
A-A Blueprint Co Inc ....E..... 330 794-8803
Akron *(G-22)*
AAA Laminating & Bindery ....G..... 513 860-2680
Fairfield *(G-9637)*
Activities Press Inc ....E..... 440 953-1200
Mentor *(G-13509)*
AGS Custom Graphics Inc ....D..... 330 963-7770
Macedonia *(G-12433)*
Allen Graphics Inc ....G..... 440 349-4100
Solon *(G-17253)*
Anderson Graphics Inc ....E..... 330 745-2165
Barberton *(G-1098)*
Aran Inc ....G..... 216 464-1508
Cleveland *(G-4821)*
Baise Enterprises Inc ....G..... 614 444-3171
Columbus *(G-6801)*
Barnhart Printing Corp ....F..... 330 456-2279
Canton *(G-2616)*
Bill Wyatt Inc ....G..... 330 535-1113
Mentor *(G-13535)*
Bindery & Spc Presswrks Inc ....D..... 614 873-4623
Plain City *(G-16326)*
Bindery Tech Inc ....F..... 440 934-3247
Avon *(G-985)*
Bindusa ....F..... 513 247-3000
Blue Ash *(G-1751)*
Bock & Pierce Enterprises ....G..... 513 474-9500
Cincinnati *(G-3455)*
Boldman Printing LLC ....G..... 937 653-3431
Urbana *(G-19148)*
Bookbinders Incorporated ....G..... 330 848-4980
Barberton *(G-1111)*
Bookfactory LLC ....G..... 937 226-7100
Dayton *(G-8191)*
Century Graphics Inc ....E..... 614 895-7698
Westerville *(G-20142)*
Cleveland Letter Service Inc ....E..... 216 781-8300
Chagrin Falls *(G-3052)*
Clints Printing Inc ....G..... 937 426-2771
Beavercreek *(G-1373)*
Commercial Bindery Inc ....G..... 419 517-9914
Toledo *(G-18408)*
Consolidated Graphics Group Inc ....C..... 216 881-9191
Cleveland *(G-5116)*
Copley Ohio Newspapers Inc ....C..... 330 364-5577
New Philadelphia *(G-14892)*
COS Blueprint Inc ....F..... 330 376-0022
Akron *(G-130)*
Cox Printing Co ....G..... 937 382-2312
Wilmington *(G-20661)*
D & S Crtive Cmmunications Inc ....D..... 419 524-6699
Mansfield *(G-12591)*
D B Hess Company ....E..... 330 678-5868
Kent *(G-11444)*
D B Hess Company ....G..... 330 676-2006
Kent *(G-11445)*
Dayton Bindery Service Inc ....E..... 937 235-3111
Dayton *(G-8269)*
Debandale Printing Inc ....G..... 330 725-5122
Medina *(G-13401)*
Delphos Herald Inc ....D..... 419 695-0015
Delphos *(G-8905)*
Douglas Michalske ....G..... 216 631-0567
Cleveland *(G-5210)*
E Z Binderys ....G..... 513 733-0005
Cincinnati *(G-3680)*

Earl D Arnold Printing Company ....E..... 513 533-6900
Cincinnati *(G-3685)*
Easterdays Printing Center ....G..... 330 726-1182
Youngstown *(G-21073)*
Eugene Stewart ....G..... 937 898-1117
Dayton *(G-8333)*
Fedex Office & Print Svcs Inc ....E..... 937 436-0677
Dayton *(G-8339)*
Fedex Office & Print Svcs Inc ....E..... 614 575-0800
Reynoldsburg *(G-16590)*
Fedex Office & Print Svcs Inc ....E..... 216 573-1511
Cleveland *(G-5333)*
Folks Creative Printers Inc ....E..... 740 383-6326
Marion *(G-12865)*
Frank J Prucha & Associates ....G..... 216 642-3838
Cleveland *(G-5378)*
Franklins Printing Company ....F..... 740 452-6375
Zanesville *(G-21311)*
G W Steffen Bookbinders Inc ....E..... 330 963-0300
Macedonia *(G-12454)*
Ganger Enterprises Inc ....E..... 614 776-3985
Westerville *(G-20154)*
Golden Graphics Ltd ....F..... 419 673-6260
Kenton *(G-11548)*
Grant John ....G..... 937 298-0633
Dayton *(G-8376)*
Great Lakes Integrated Inc ....D..... 216 651-1500
Cleveland *(G-5452)*
Greg Blume ....G..... 740 574-2308
Wheelersburg *(G-20332)*
Harris & Company Inc ....G..... 330 332-4127
Salem *(G-16899)*
Harris Paper Crafts Inc ....F..... 614 299-2141
Columbus *(G-7145)*
Hecks Direct Mail & Prtg Svc ....E..... 419 697-3505
Toledo *(G-18502)*
Henry Bussman ....G..... 614 224-0417
Columbus *(G-7150)*
Homewood Press Inc ....E..... 419 478-0695
Toledo *(G-18510)*
Hopewell Industries Inc ....D..... 740 622-3563
Coshocton *(G-7895)*
ICI Binding Corp ....E..... 440 729-2445
Chesterland *(G-3213)*
Innomark Communications LLC ....G..... 937 454-5555
Dayton *(G-8404)*
Jack G Walker ....F..... 440 352-4222
Mentor *(G-13617)*
Kad Holdings Inc ....G..... 614 792-3399
Dublin *(G-9093)*
Kehl-Kolor Inc ....E..... 419 281-3107
Ashland *(G-746)*
Kenwel Printers Inc ....E..... 614 261-1011
Columbus *(G-7257)*
Kevin K Tidd ....G..... 419 885-5603
Sylvania *(G-18115)*
Keystone Press Inc ....G..... 419 243-7326
Toledo *(G-18544)*
Keystone Printing & Copy Cat ....G..... 740 354-6542
Portsmouth *(G-16439)*
Laipplys Prtg Mktg Sltions Inc ....G..... 740 387-9282
Marion *(G-12879)*
Lam Pro Inc ....F..... 216 426-0661
Cleveland *(G-5678)*
Lee Corporation ....F..... 513 771-3602
Cincinnati *(G-4019)*
Legal News Publishing Co ....E..... 216 696-3322
Cleveland *(G-5692)*
Lilienthal Southeastern Inc ....F..... 740 439-1640
Cambridge *(G-2464)*
Lund Printing Co ....G..... 330 628-4047
Akron *(G-277)*
Mmp Printing Inc ....E..... 513 381-0990
Cincinnati *(G-4112)*
Monco Enterprises Inc ....A..... 937 461-0034
Dayton *(G-8507)*
Montview Corporation ....G..... 330 723-3409
Medina *(G-13449)*
Nari Inc ....G..... 440 960-2280
Monroeville *(G-14427)*
Network Printing & Graphics ....F..... 614 230-2084
Columbus *(G-7387)*
Newfax Corporation ....F..... 419 241-5157
Toledo *(G-18603)*
North End Press Incorporated ....E..... 740 653-6514
Lancaster *(G-11734)*
Ohio Laminating & Binding Inc ....G..... 614 771-4868
Hilliard *(G-10966)*
Old Trail Printing Company ....C..... 614 443-4852
Columbus *(G-7440)*

PRODUCT

Onetouchpoint East Corp ....D...... 513 421-1600
Cincinnati *(G-4189)*
Orange Blossom Press Inc ....G...... 216 781-8655
Willoughby *(G-20562)*
Orrville Printing Co Inc ....G...... 330 682-5066
Orrville *(G-15752)*
Painesville Publishing Co ....G...... 440 354-4142
Austinburg *(G-964)*
Patricia Lee Burd ....G...... 513 302-4860
Cincinnati *(G-4214)*
Penguin Enterprises Inc ....E...... 440 899-5110
Westlake *(G-20292)*
Pooles Printing & Office Svcs ....G...... 419 475-9000
Toledo *(G-18649)*
Prime Printing Inc ....E...... 937 438-3707
Dayton *(G-8594)*
Print-Digital Incorporated..................G...... 330 686-5945
Stow *(G-17792)*
Printed Image ....F...... 614 221-1412
Columbus *(G-7519)*
Promatch Solutions LLC ....F...... 937 299-0185
Springfield *(G-17500)*
Quick Tab II Inc ....D...... 419 448-6622
Tiffin *(G-18238)*
R T Industries Inc ....G...... 937 335-5784
Troy *(G-18865)*
R W Michael Printing Co ....G...... 330 923-9277
Akron *(G-363)*
Repro Acquisition Company LLC........E...... 216 738-3800
Cleveland *(G-6104)*
Ricci Anthony ....G...... 330 758-5761
Youngstown *(G-21188)*
Robert Esterman ....G...... 513 541-3311
Cincinnati *(G-4353)*
Robert H Shackelford ....G...... 330 364-2221
New Philadelphia *(G-14926)*
Robin Enterprises Company................C...... 614 891-0250
Westerville *(G-20233)*
Ryans Newark Leader Ex Prtg ....F...... 740 522-2149
Newark *(G-15051)*
Sandy Smittcamp...............................G...... 937 372-1687
Xenia *(G-20971)*
Slutzkers Quickprint Center................G...... 440 244-0330
Lorain *(G-12278)*
Spencer-Walker Press Inc ....F...... 740 344-6110
Newark *(G-15055)*
Spring Grove Manufacturing ....F...... 513 542-6900
Cincinnati *(G-4445)*
Springdale Bindery LLC ....G...... 513 772-8500
Cincinnati *(G-4446)*
Springfield Engraving Company ....G...... 937 390-0011
Springfield *(G-17651)*
Standard Register Inc ....G...... 937 228-5800
Dayton *(G-8679)*
Star Printing Company Inc ....G...... 330 376-0514
Akron *(G-415)*
Strong Bindery ....G...... 216 231-0001
Cleveland *(G-6256)*
Suburban Press Inc ....E...... 216 961-0766
Cleveland *(G-6260)*
Target Printing & Graphics ....G...... 937 228-0170
Dayton *(G-8700)*
Tj Metzgers Inc ....D...... 419 861-8611
Toledo *(G-18726)*
TL Krieg Offset Inc ....E...... 513 542-1522
Cincinnati *(G-4511)*
Traxium LLC ....E...... 330 572-8200
Stow *(G-17811)*
Watkins Printing Company ....E...... 614 297-8270
Columbus *(G-7752)*
West-Camp Press Inc ....D...... 614 818-6279
Westerville *(G-20241)*
Wfsr Holdings LLC.............................A...... 877 735-4966
Dayton *(G-8757)*
William J Dupps ....G...... 419 734-2126
Port Clinton *(G-16419)*
Youngstown ARC Engraving Co...........E...... 330 793-2471
Youngstown *(G-21245)*

BINDING SVC: Pamphlets

Fergusons Finishing Inc ....E...... 419 241-9123
Toledo *(G-18469)*
Macke Brothers Inc............................D...... 513 771-7500
Cincinnati *(G-4048)*

BINDING SVC: Trade

Bip Printing Solutions LLC ....F...... 216 832-5673
Beachwood *(G-1259)*

BINDINGS: Bias, Made From Purchased Materials

National Bias Fabric Co......................E...... 216 361-0530
Cleveland *(G-5853)*

BINDINGS: Cap & Hat, Made From Purchased Materials

Elken Co...G...... 513 459-7207
Maineville *(G-12523)*

BINGO HALL

Access To Independence Inc ....G...... 330 296-8111
Ravenna *(G-16512)*

BINOCULARS

Vance Adams.....................................G...... 330 424-9670
Lisbon *(G-12134)*

BINS: Prefabricated, Sheet Metal

Beacon Metal Fabricators Inc ....F...... 216 391-7444
Cleveland *(G-4900)*
Metal Fabricating Corporation.............D...... 216 631-8121
Cleveland *(G-5787)*

BIOLOGICAL PRDTS: Bacteriological Media

General Envmtl Science Corp...............G...... 216 464-0680
Cleveland *(G-5418)*

BIOLOGICAL PRDTS: Exc Diagnostic

Automatic Bacterial Injection ....F...... 216 378-1336
Bedford *(G-1402)*
Bio-Blood Components Inc ....E...... 614 294-3183
Columbus *(G-6829)*
Carbogene USA LLC...........................G...... 215 378-4306
Columbus *(G-6904)*
Copernicus Therapeutics Inc ....F...... 216 707-1776
Cleveland *(G-5131)*
EMD Millipore Corporation..................C...... 513 631-0445
Norwood *(G-15572)*
Ferro Corporation ....D...... 216 577-7144
Bedford *(G-1423)*
Microbiological Labs Inc ....G...... 330 626-2264
Streetsboro *(G-17862)*
Perkinelmer Hlth Sciences Inc.............E...... 330 825-4525
Akron *(G-336)*
Protein Express Laboratories................G...... 513 769-9654
Blue Ash *(G-1860)*
Safewhite Inc ....G...... 614 340-1450
Columbus *(G-7586)*
Supply Dynamics LLC ....F...... 513 965-2000
Loveland *(G-12392)*
Wmre of Ohio-American LLC................G...... 713 328-7345
Waynesburg *(G-19729)*

BIOLOGICAL PRDTS: Serums

Columbus Serum Co ....G...... 614 793-0615
Columbus *(G-6965)*

BIOLOGICAL PRDTS: Vaccines

Global Health Services Inc...................G...... 513 777-8111
West Chester *(G-19876)*

BIOLOGICAL PRDTS: Vaccines & Immunizing

Decaria Brothers Inc..........................G...... 330 385-0825
East Liverpool *(G-9212)*
Tamarkin Company ....G...... 330 634-0688
Tallmadge *(G-18172)*
Tamarkin Company ....G...... 614 878-8942
Columbus *(G-7675)*

BIOLOGICAL PRDTS: Venoms

Venom Exterminating LLC ....G...... 330 637-3366
Cortland *(G-7876)*
Venom Towing LLC ....G...... 937 344-6530
Springboro *(G-17513)*

BIOLOGICAL PRDTS: Veterinary

No Rinse Laboratories LLC ....G...... 937 746-7357
Springboro *(G-17492)*

BLACKBOARDS & CHALKBOARDS

GMI Companies Inc............................C...... 513 932-3445
Lebanon *(G-11804)*
GMI Companies Inc............................G...... 937 981-0244
Greenfield *(G-10476)*

BLACKBOARDS: Slate

Michael Kaufman Companies Inc..........F...... 330 673-4881
Kent *(G-11490)*
Michael Kaufman Companies Inc..........F...... 330 673-4881
Kent *(G-11491)*

BLADES: Knife

A & P Tech Services Inc ....G...... 330 535-1700
Akron *(G-16)*
Advetech Inc ....E...... 330 533-2227
Canfield *(G-2543)*
American Quicksilver Co ....G...... 513 871-4517
Cincinnati *(G-3393)*
Evolution Resources LLC ....G...... 937 438-2390
Centerville *(G-3041)*

BLADES: Saw, Hand Or Power

M K Morse Company ....B...... 330 453-8187
Canton *(G-2762)*
Peerless Saw Company.........................E...... 614 836-5790
Groveport *(G-10640)*

BLANKBOOKS

Lilienthal Southeastern Inc ....F...... 740 439-1640
Cambridge *(G-2464)*

BLANKBOOKS & LOOSELEAF BINDERS

Deluxe Corporation.............................C...... 330 342-1500
Hudson *(G-11168)*
Dupli-Systems Inc ....G...... 440 234-9415
Strongsville *(G-17913)*
Ed Thomas ....G...... 937 325-4300
Springfield *(G-17551)*
Elken Co...G...... 513 459-7207
Maineville *(G-12523)*
Quick Tech Graphics Inc ....E...... 937 743-5952
Springboro *(G-17502)*

BLANKBOOKS: Account

Gotta Groove Records Inc ....E...... 216 431-7373
Cleveland *(G-5440)*

BLANKBOOKS: Albums

Chilcote Company ....C...... 216 781-6000
Cleveland *(G-5028)*
W N Albums and Frames Inc ....G...... 800 325-5179
Cleveland *(G-6435)*

BLANKBOOKS: Checkbooks & Passbooks, Bank

Farmers National Banc Corp ....F...... 330 726-8896
Youngstown *(G-21083)*

BLANKBOOKS: Passbooks, Bank, Etc

William Exline Inc................................E...... 216 941-0800
Cleveland *(G-6463)*

BLANKBOOKS: Scrapbooks

My Scrapbook Paradise LLC ....G...... 419 584-1393
Celina *(G-3011)*
Scrapbook Gallery ....G...... 419 523-4419
Ottawa *(G-15807)*

BLANKETS & BLANKETING, COTTON

Grow With Me- Creations ....G...... 800 850-1889
Hartville *(G-10821)*
Keepsakes Etc....................................G...... 330 559-6716
Canfield *(G-2560)*

BLAST FURNACE & RELATED PRDTS

Custom Blast & Coat Inc ....G...... 419 225-6024
Lima *(G-12003)*
Rti International Metals Inc ....D...... 330 471-1844
Canton *(G-2845)*

BLASTING SVC: Sand, Metal Parts

American Indus Maintenance ....G...... 937 254-3400
Dayton *(G-8154)*

Badboy Blasters Incorporated ....F...... 330 454-2699
Canton *(G-2614)*

Boville Indus Coatings Inc ....E...... 330 669-8558
Smithville *(G-17238)*

Derrick Company Inc ....E...... 513 321-8122
Cincinnati *(G-3648)*

Industrial Mill Maintenance ....E...... 330 746-1155
Youngstown *(G-21115)*

L & N Olde Car Co ....G...... 440 564-7204
Newbury *(G-15099)*

Lima Sandblasting & Pntg Co ....G...... 419 331-2939
Lima *(G-12044)*

Newsome & Work Metalizing Co ....F...... 330 376-7144
Akron *(G-313)*

Pki Inc ....G...... 859 291-8680
Cincinnati *(G-4241)*

Witt Enterprises Inc ....E...... 440 992-8333
Ashtabula *(G-845)*

BLINDS & SHADES: Mini

Hob Enterprises LLC ....G...... 440 290-8861
Mentor *(G-13603)*

BLINDS & SHADES: Vertical

11 92 Holdings LLC ....E...... 216 920-7790
Chagrin Falls *(G-3047)*

Blind Factory Showroom ....E...... 614 771-6549
Hilliard *(G-10935)*

Blind Outlet ....G...... 614 895-2002
Westerville *(G-20202)*

Optimun Blinds Inc ....G...... 740 598-5808
Brilliant *(G-2094)*

Vertical Runner ....G...... 330 262-3000
Wooster *(G-20843)*

BLINDS : Window

ARC Blinds Inc ....E...... 513 889-4864
Liberty Twp *(G-11971)*

E W Perry Service Co Inc ....G...... 419 473-1231
Toledo *(G-18448)*

M C L Window Coverings Inc ....G...... 513 868-6000
Hamilton *(G-10719)*

BLOCK & BRICK: Sand Lime

Kent Paverbrick LLC ....G...... 330 995-7000
Aurora *(G-930)*

R W Sidley Incorporated ....E...... 440 352-9343
Painesville *(G-15913)*

BLOCKS & BRICKS: Concrete

All Ohio Ready Mix Concrete ....G...... 419 841-3838
Perrysburg *(G-16062)*

Charles Svec Inc ....E...... 216 662-5200
Maple Heights *(G-12730)*

Hanson Aggregates East LLC ....F...... 937 382-2557
Wilmington *(G-20668)*

Hazelbaker Industries Ltd ....E...... 614 276-2631
Columbus *(G-7146)*

K & L Ready Mix Inc ....F...... 419 532-3585
Kalida *(G-11413)*

Mapes Concrete Construction ....G...... 513 245-2631
Cincinnati *(G-4057)*

Midwest Specialties Inc ....F...... 419 738-8147
Wapakoneta *(G-19501)*

Oberfields LLC ....F...... 614 252-0955
Columbus *(G-7410)*

R W Sidley Incorporated ....E...... 440 564-2221
Newbury *(G-15102)*

RE Connors Construction Ltd ....G...... 740 644-0261
Thornville *(G-18194)*

S & S Aggregates Inc ....G...... 740 453-0721
Zanesville *(G-21349)*

St Henry Tile Co Inc ....E...... 419 678-4841
Saint Henry *(G-16822)*

St Henry Tile Co Inc ....F...... 937 548-1101
Greenville *(G-10523)*

Stocker Concrete Company ....F...... 740 254-4626
Gnadenhutten *(G-10411)*

Walden Industries Inc ....E...... 740 633-5971
Tiltonsville *(G-18255)*

William Dauch Concrete Company ......F...... 419 668-4458
Norwalk *(G-15567)*

BLOCKS: Insulating, Concrete

ICC Safety Service Inc ....G...... 614 261-4557
Columbus *(G-7181)*

North Central Concrete Design ....F...... 419 606-1908
Wooster *(G-20816)*

BLOCKS: Landscape Or Retaining Wall, Concrete

Bryce Hill Inc ....E...... 937 663-4152
Saint Paris *(G-16859)*

Bryce Hill Inc ....G...... 937 325-0651
Springfield *(G-17525)*

Frankie Tatum ....G...... 614 216-1556
Gahanna *(G-10207)*

Green Vision Materials Inc ....F...... 440 564-5500
Newbury *(G-15093)*

Kathy Edie ....G...... 740 763-4887
Newark *(G-15026)*

Simon & Simon Blue Pond Inc ....G...... 330 928-2298
Cuyahoga Falls *(G-8046)*

BLOCKS: Paving

B & S Blacktop Co ....G...... 513 797-5759
New Richmond *(G-14940)*

Husac Paving ....G...... 513 200-2818
Harrison *(G-10784)*

La Rose Paving Co Inc ....G...... 440 632-0330
Middlefield *(G-13950)*

BLOCKS: Paving, Asphalt, Not From Refineries

Concord Paving Co ....G...... 440 354-8580
Painesville *(G-15866)*

BLOCKS: Paving, Concrete

B & S Blacktop Co ....G...... 513 797-5759
New Richmond *(G-14940)*

Gennaro Pavers ....G...... 330 536-6825
Lowellville *(G-12409)*

BLOCKS: Standard, Concrete Or Cinder

American Concrete Products ....F...... 937 224-1433
Dayton *(G-8153)*

Cantelli Block and Brick Inc ....E...... 419 433-0102
Huron *(G-11218)*

Cement Products Inc ....E...... 419 524-4342
Mansfield *(G-12578)*

Dearth Resources Inc ....G...... 937 325-0651
Springfield *(G-17539)*

Dearth Resources Inc ....G...... 937 663-4171
Springfield *(G-17540)*

Hanson Aggregates East LLC ....E...... 740 773-2172
Chillicothe *(G-3242)*

J P Sand & Gravel Company ....E...... 614 497-0083
Lockbourne *(G-12147)*

Koltcz Concrete Block Co ....E...... 440 232-3630
Bedford *(G-1437)*

Martin Block Company ....G...... 740 286-7507
Jackson *(G-11319)*

Medina Supply Company ....G...... 440 234-1321
Berea *(G-1626)*

National Lime and Stone Co ....E...... 614 497-0083
Lockbourne *(G-12150)*

Oberfields LLC ....F...... 614 491-7643
Columbus *(G-7409)*

Osborne Inc ....F...... 440 942-7000
Mentor *(G-13677)*

Portsmouth Block Inc ....F...... 740 353-4113
Portsmouth *(G-16448)*

Quality Block & Supply Inc ....E...... 330 364-4411
Mount Eaton *(G-14556)*

Reading Rock Inc ....E...... 513 874-2345
West Chester *(G-20045)*

Snyder Concrete Products Inc ....F...... 937 885-5176
Moraine *(G-14528)*

Snyder Concrete Products Inc ....G...... 937 224-1433
Dayton *(G-8661)*

Stiger Pre Cast Inc ....G...... 740 482-2313
Nevada *(G-14743)*

Stocker Sand & Gravel Co ....F...... 740 254-4635
Gnadenhutten *(G-10412)*

Tri-County Block and Brick Inc ....F...... 419 826-7060
Swanton *(G-18093)*

Trumbull Cement Products Co ....G...... 330 372-4342
Warren *(G-19611)*

BLOWERS & FANS

Tyjen Inc ....G...... 740 380-3215
Logan *(G-12196)*

Tyjen Inc ....G...... 740 797-4064
The Plains *(G-18187)*

BLOOD BANK

Bio-Blood Components Inc ....E...... 614 294-3183
Columbus *(G-6829)*

BLOWERS & FANS

A A S Amels Sheet Meta L Inc ....E...... 330 793-9326
Youngstown *(G-21010)*

Air-Rite Inc ....E...... 216 228-8200
Cleveland *(G-4735)*

American Manufacturing & Eqp ....G...... 513 829-2248
Fairfield *(G-9642)*

Automtve Cmpnnts Holdings LLC ......A...... 419 627-3600
Sandusky *(G-16947)*

Babcock & Wilcox Megtec ....C...... 614 258-9501
Columbus *(G-6799)*

Beckett Air Incorporated ....D...... 440 327-9999
North Ridgeville *(G-15359)*

Bry-Air Inc ....E...... 740 965-2974
Sunbury *(G-18056)*

Burt Manufacturing Company Inc ....C...... 330 762-0061
Akron *(G-105)*

Diamond Power Intl Inc ....B...... 740 687-6500
Lancaster *(G-11708)*

Ellis & Watts Intl LLC ....E...... 513 752-9000
Batavia *(G-1183)*

Famous Industries Inc ....D...... 740 685-2592
Byesville *(G-2401)*

Flex Technologies Inc ....D...... 330 359-5415
Mount Eaton *(G-14555)*

Illinois Tool Works Inc ....C...... 262 248-8277
Bryan *(G-2303)*

Kirk Williams Company Inc ....D...... 614 875-9023
Grove City *(G-10568)*

Langdon Inc ....E...... 513 733-5955
Cincinnati *(G-4011)*

Mestek Inc ....D...... 419 288-2703
Bradner *(G-2029)*

Midwestern Industries Inc ....C...... 330 837-4203
Massillon *(G-13180)*

Nupro Company ....C...... 440 951-9729
Willoughby *(G-20559)*

Ohio Blow Pipe Company ....E...... 216 681-7379
Cleveland *(G-5930)*

Oil Skimmers Inc ....E...... 440 237-4600
North Royalton *(G-15440)*

Orica Ground Support Inc ....D...... 740 377-9146
South Point *(G-17443)*

Pcy Enterprises Inc ....E...... 513 241-5566
Cincinnati *(G-4219)*

Plas-Tanks Industries Inc ....E...... 513 942-3800
Hamilton *(G-10730)*

Qualtek Electronics Corp ....C...... 440 951-3300
Mentor *(G-13710)*

Quickdraft Inc ....E...... 330 477-4574
Canton *(G-2832)*

Selas Heat Technology Co LLC ....E...... 800 523-6500
Streetsboro *(G-17875)*

Starr Fabricating Inc ....D...... 330 394-9891
Vienna *(G-19376)*

Stelter and Brinck Inc ....E...... 513 367-9300
Harrison *(G-10805)*

Thermo Vent Manufacturing Inc ....F...... 330 239-0239
Medina *(G-13487)*

Thompson Culvert Company LLC ....F...... 513 645-7000
West Chester *(G-19956)*

Tisch Environmental Inc ....F...... 513 467-9000
Cleves *(G-6529)*

Tosoh America Inc ....B...... 614 539-8622
Grove City *(G-10604)*

BLOWERS & FANS

Americraft Mfg Co Inc ....F...... 513 489-1047
Cincinnati *(G-3395)*

Buckeye BOP LLC ....G...... 740 498-9898
Newcomerstown *(G-15110)*

Hartzell Fan Inc ....C...... 937 773-7411
Piqua *(G-16271)*

Howden North America Inc ....D...... 330 867-8540
Akron *(G-224)*

OEM Corporation ....F...... 937 859-7492
Miamisburg *(G-13845)*

Vortec and Paxton Products ....F...... 513 891-7474
Blue Ash *(G-1890)*

Employee Codes: A=Over 500 employees, B=251-500
C=101-250, D=51-100, E=20-50, F=10-19, G=3-9

2017 Harris Ohio
Industrial Directory

PRODUCT

1415

BLUEPRINTING SVCS

Fedex Office & Print Svcs Inc ....F 937 335-3816
Troy *(G-18827)*
Northeast Blueprint & Sup Co 216 261-7500
Cleveland *(G-5903)*
Queen City Reprographics ....C 513 326-2300
Cincinnati *(G-4319)*
Robert Becker Impressions ....F 419 385-5303
Toledo *(G-18678)*

BOAT BUILDING & REPAIR

Checkmate Marine Inc ....F 419 562-3881
Bucyrus *(G-2335)*
Don Wartko Construction Co ....D 330 673-5252
Kent *(G-11450)*
Jacks Marine Inc ....G 440 997-5060
Ashtabula *(G-814)*
Marinemax Inc ....C 918 782-3277
Port Clinton *(G-16405)*
Mariners Landing Inc ....F 513 941-3625
Cincinnati *(G-4060)*
O-Kan Marine Repair Inc ....E 740 446-4686
Gallipolis *(G-10306)*
Racelite South Coast Inc ....F 216 581-4600
Maple Heights *(G-12739)*
William Thompson ....G 440 232-4363
Aurora *(G-956)*
Www Boat Services Inc ....G 419 626-0883
Sandusky *(G-17022)*

BOAT BUILDING & REPAIRING: Dories

Mentor Inc ....G 440 255-1250
Mentor On The Lake *(G-13774)*

BOAT BUILDING & REPAIRING: Kits, Not Models

Brewster Sugarcreek Twp Histo ....F 330 767-0045
Brewster *(G-2084)*

BOAT BUILDING & REPAIRING: Lifeboats

Healthcare Benefits Inc ....G 419 433-4499
Huron *(G-11223)*

BOAT BUILDING & REPAIRING: Motorized

Nauticus Inc ....G 440 746-1290
Brecksville *(G-2066)*

BOAT BUILDING & REPAIRING: Tenders, Small Motor Craft

Gallagher Wood & Crafts ....G 513 523-2748
Oxford *(G-15836)*

BOAT DEALERS

Dynamic Plastics Inc ....G 937 437-7261
New Paris *(G-14879)*
Marinemax Inc ....C 918 782-3277
Port Clinton *(G-16405)*
Mariners Landing Inc ....F 513 941-3625
Cincinnati *(G-4060)*
Www Boat Services Inc ....G 419 626-0883
Sandusky *(G-17022)*

BOAT DEALERS: Marine Splys & Eqpt

Hydromotive Engineering Co ....G 330 425-4266
Twinsburg *(G-18956)*
Minderman Marine Products Inc ....G 419 732-2626
Port Clinton *(G-16406)*
Sailors Tailor Inc ....G 937 862-7781
Spring Valley *(G-17469)*

BOAT LIFTS

American Power Hoist Inc ....G 740 964-2035
Pataskala *(G-15967)*
Cincinnati Recreation Comm ....G 513 921-5657
Cincinnati *(G-3564)*
Indian Lake Boat Lift ....G 937 539-2868
Russells Point *(G-16755)*
Westerman Inc ....D 330 262-6946
Wooster *(G-20846)*

BOAT REPAIR SVCS

Superior Marine Ways Inc ....C 740 894-6224
Proctorville *(G-16493)*

BOAT YARD: Boat yards, storage & incidental repair

Jacks Marine Inc ....G 440 997-5060
Ashtabula *(G-814)*

BOATS & OTHER MARINE EQPT: Plastic

Mustang Aerial Services Inc ....G 740 373-9262
Reno *(G-16578)*

BODIES: Truck & Bus

Ace Truck Equipment Co ....E 740 453-0551
Zanesville *(G-21264)*
Airstream Inc ....B 937 596-6111
Jackson Center *(G-11337)*
ARE Inc ....C 330 830-7800
Massillon *(G-13112)*
Atc Lighting & Plastics Inc ....C 440 466-7670
Andover *(G-613)*
Bloomdale Plastics Co ....E 419 454-5135
Bloomdale *(G-1719)*
Bores Manufacturing Co Inc ....F 419 465-2606
Monroeville *(G-14425)*
Cascade Corporation ....G 937 327-0300
Springfield *(G-17527)*
Cleveland Hdwr & Forging Co ....E 216 641-5200
Cleveland *(G-5064)*
Columbus McKinnon Corporation ....D 330 424-7248
Lisbon *(G-12118)*
Field Gymmy Inc ....G 419 538-6511
Glandorf *(G-10397)*
Galion-Godwin Truck Bdy Co LLC ....D 330 359-5495
Millersburg *(G-14217)*
Hendrickson International Corp ....D 740 929-5600
Hebron *(G-10870)*
Johns Body Shop ....G 419 358-1200
Bluffton *(G-1913)*
Joseph Industries Inc ....D 330 528-0091
Streetsboro *(G-17860)*
King Kutter II Inc ....E 740 446-0351
Gallipolis *(G-10302)*
Kuka Toledo Production ....C 419 727-5500
Toledo *(G-18550)*
Leyman Manufacturing Corp ....D 513 891-6210
Cincinnati *(G-4021)*
Martin Sheet Metal Inc ....D 216 377-8200
Cleveland *(G-5753)*
Meritor Inc ....C 740 348-3498
Granville *(G-10461)*
Navistar Inc ....D 937 390-2800
Springfield *(G-17613)*
Paccar Inc ....A 740 774-5111
Chillicothe *(G-3257)*
Tarpstop LLC ....E 419 873-7867
Perrysburg *(G-16152)*
Trim Systems Operating Corp ....C 614 289-5360
New Albany *(G-14774)*
Wallace Forge Company ....D 330 488-1203
Canton *(G-2900)*
Youngstown-Kenworth Inc ....E 330 534-9761
Hubbard *(G-11143)*

BODY PARTS: Automobile, Stamped Metal

Artiflex Manufacturing LLC ....B 330 262-2015
Wooster *(G-20741)*
Buyers Products Company ....G 440 974-8888
Mentor *(G-13541)*
Custom Floaters LLC ....G 216 337-9118
Brookpark *(G-2155)*
Decoma Systems Integration Gro ....D 419 324-3387
Toledo *(G-18431)*
General Motors LLC ....A 216 265-5000
Cleveland *(G-5419)*
Ksi Distribution Inc ....G 440 256-2500
Mentor *(G-13624)*
Liber Limited LLC ....G 440 427-0647
Olmsted Twp *(G-15680)*
Lwb/ISE LP ....F 937 778-3828
Piqua *(G-16288)*
Mahle Behr USA Inc ....C 937 356-2001
Vandalia *(G-19302)*
Matsu Ohio Inc ....C 419 298-2394
Edgerton *(G-9332)*
Murotech Ohio Corporation ....D 419 394-6529
Saint Marys *(G-16844)*
Parts Channel Inc ....F 614 497-9199
Groveport *(G-10638)*
Synergy Alliance ....G 330 253-9475
Akron *(G-424)*

Trellborg Sling Prfiles US Inc ....E 330 995-9725
Aurora *(G-951)*
Valco Industries Inc ....E 937 399-7400
Springfield *(G-17672)*
Vehtek Systems Inc ....A 419 373-8741
Bowling Green *(G-2019)*

BOILER & HEATING REPAIR SVCS

Air-Rite Inc ....E 216 228-8200
Cleveland *(G-4735)*
Babcock & Wilcox Company ....A 330 753-4511
Barberton *(G-1104)*
Lim Services LLC ....F 513 217-0801
Middletown *(G-14054)*
Nbw Inc ....E 216 377-1700
Cleveland *(G-5864)*

BOILER GAGE COCKS

Cfrc Wtr & Enrgy Solutions Inc ....E 216 479-0290
Cleveland *(G-5011)*
Xomox Corporation ....E 936 271-6500
Cincinnati *(G-4614)*

BOILER REPAIR SHOP

Acme Boiler Co Inc ....G 216 961-2471
Cleveland *(G-4691)*
Gurina Company ....G 614 279-3891
Columbus *(G-7132)*
Manitowoc Company Inc ....G 920 746-3332
Cleveland *(G-5739)*

BOILERS: Low-Pressure Heating, Steam Or Hot Water

Nbbi ....G 614 888-8320
Columbus *(G-7385)*

BOLTS: Metal

Airfasco Inc ....E 330 430-6190
Canton *(G-2591)*
Bowes Manufacturing Inc ....F 216 378-2110
Solon *(G-17271)*
Consolidated Metal Pdts Inc ....C 513 251-2624
Cincinnati *(G-3604)*
Curtiss-Wright Flow Ctrl Corp ....D 216 267-3200
Cleveland *(G-5148)*
Elgin Fastener Group LLC ....G 440 717-7650
Brecksville *(G-2045)*
Elgin Fastener Group LLC ....F 812 717-2544
Brecksville *(G-2046)*
Iwata Bolt USA Inc ....F 513 942-5050
Fairfield *(G-9669)*
Jacodar Inc ....F 330 832-9557
Massillon *(G-13159)*
Matdan Corporation ....E 513 794-0500
Blue Ash *(G-1834)*
Mid-West Fabricating Co ....G 740 681-4411
Lancaster *(G-11729)*
Mid-West Fabricating Co ....G 740 969-4411
Amanda *(G-563)*
Nova Machine Products Inc ....C 216 267-3200
Middleburg Heights *(G-13907)*
R S Manufacturing Inc ....F 440 946-8002
Mentor *(G-13713)*
Ronson Manufacturing Inc ....G 440 256-1463
Willoughby *(G-20590)*
Stelfast Inc ....E 440 879-0077
Strongsville *(G-17974)*

BONDERIZING: Bonderizing, Metal Or Metal Prdts

Cardinal Rubber Company Inc ....E 330 745-2191
Barberton *(G-1113)*
High Tech Elastomers Inc ....E 937 236-6575
Vandalia *(G-19296)*
Kecamm LLC ....G 330 527-2918
Garrettsville *(G-10326)*

BONDS, RAIL: Electric, Propulsion & Signal Circuit Uses

Omnithruster Inc ....F 330 963-6310
Twinsburg *(G-18992)*

BOOK STORES

Bookfactory LLC ....E 937 226-7100
Dayton (G-8191)

Ketman Corporation ....G 330 262-1688
Wooster (G-20795)

Province of St John The Baptis ....D 513 241-5615
Cincinnati (G-4301)

US Government Publishing Off ....G 614 469-5657
Columbus (G-7727)

BOOK STORES: Religious

Incorporated Trst Gspl Wk Scty ....D 216 749-2100
Cleveland (G-5560)

BOOKS, WHOLESALE

CSS Publishing Co Inc ....E 419 227-1818
Lima (G-12002)

Hubbard Company ....E 419 784-4455
Defiance (G-8794)

Zaner-Bloser Inc ....D 614 486-0221
Columbus (G-7786)

BOOTHS: Spray, Sheet Metal, Prefabricated

Midwest Spray Booths ....G 937 439-6600
Dayton (G-8497)

BORING MILL

Tri-State Tool Grinding Inc ....E 513 347-0100
Cincinnati (G-4524)

BOTTLE CAPS & RESEALERS: Plastic

6s Products LLC ....G 937 394-7440
Anna (G-619)

Berry Plas Technical Svcs Inc ....F 330 995-3459
Kent (G-11435)

Berry Plastics Corporation ....F 330 896-6700
Streetsboro (G-17843)

Bprex Closures LLC ....D 812 424-2904
Maumee (G-13232)

Venture Packaging Midwest Inc ....G 419 465-2534
Monroeville (G-14431)

BOTTLED GAS DEALERS: Liquefied Petro, Dlvrd To Customers

Jefferson Landmark Inc ....F 740 944-1971
Bloomingdale (G-1724)

BOTTLED GAS DEALERS: Propane

Brightstar Propane & Fuels ....G 614 891-8395
Westerville (G-20140)

Jomac Ltd ....G 330 627-7727
Carrollton (G-2958)

Ngo Development Corporation ....F 740 622-9560
Coshocton (G-7901)

BOTTLED WATER DELIVERY

Bayswater Beverages LLC ....G 312 224-8012
Cincinnati (G-3441)

Pro-Kleen Industrial Svcs Inc ....E 740 689-1886
Lancaster (G-11741)

Rambasek Realty Inc ....F 937 228-1189
Dayton (G-8616)

BOTTLES: Plastic

Al Root Company ....C 330 723-4359
Medina (G-13364)

Al Root Company ....C 330 725-6677
Medina (G-13365)

Alpha Packaging Holdings Inc ....B 216 252-5595
Cleveland (G-4768)

Alpla Inc ....F 419 991-9484
Lima (G-12114)

Amcor Rigid Plastics Usa LLC ....D 419 483-4343
Bellevue (G-1541)

Eco-Groupe Inc ....E 937 898-2603
Dayton (G-8318)

Encon Inc ....C 937 898-2603
Dayton (G-8325)

GK Packaging Inc ....D 614 873-3900
Plain City (G-16342)

Graham Packaging Company LP ....E 740 439-4242
Cambridge (G-2459)

Graham Packaging Company LP ....E 419 334-4197
Fremont (G-10155)

Graham Packaging Company LP ....E 513 874-1770
West Chester (G-20011)

Graham Packaging Pet Tech Inc ....C 419 334-4197
Fremont (G-10156)

Graham Packg Plastic Pdts Inc ....C 419 421-8037
Findlay (G-9833)

Kirtland Cpitl Partners III LP ....G 440 585-9010
Willoughby Hills (G-20640)

Novatex North America Inc ....D 419 282-4264
Ashland (G-757)

Phoenix Technologies Intl LLC ....E 419 353-7738
Bowling Green (G-2007)

Plastipak Packaging Inc ....C 330 725-0205
Medina (G-13461)

Plastipak Packaging Inc ....B 937 596-6142
Jackson Center (G-11344)

Plastipak Packaging Inc ....C 740 928-4435
Hebron (G-10880)

Pure Water Global Inc ....G 419 737-2352
Pioneer (G-16242)

Quality-Service Products Inc ....F 614 447-9522
Columbus (G-7538)

Rexam PLC ....F 330 893-2451
Millersburg (G-14258)

Ring Container Tech LLC ....E 937 492-0961
Sidney (G-17216)

Silgan Plastics LLC ....C 419 523-3737
Ottawa (G-15808)

Southeastern Container Inc ....D 419 352-6300
Bowling Green (G-2016)

BOWL COVERS: Plastic

Mon-Say Corp ....G 419 720-0163
Toledo (G-18590)

BOWLING CENTERS

Greater Cincinnati Bowl Assn ....E 513 761-7387
Cincinnati (G-3847)

BOWLING EQPT & SPLY STORES

The Hartman Corp ....G 614 475-5035
Columbus (G-7690)

BOWLING EQPT & SPLYS

Done-Rite Bowling Service Co ....E 440 232-3280
Bedford (G-1420)

Forrest Enterprises Inc ....G 937 773-1714
Piqua (G-16265)

BOXES & CRATES: Rectangular, Wood

Cassis Packaging Co ....F 937 223-8563
Dayton (G-8214)

Custom Built Crates Inc ....E 513 248-4422
Milford (G-14135)

Dp Products LLC ....G 440 834-9663
Burton (G-2373)

J & L Wood Products Inc ....E 937 667-4064
Tipp City (G-18286)

Lefco Worthington LLC ....E 216 432-4422
Cleveland (G-5691)

Schaefer Box & Pallet Co ....E 513 738-2500
Hamilton (G-10736)

Silvesco Inc ....F 740 373-6661
Marietta (G-12830)

Terry Lumber and Supply Co ....F 330 659-6800
Peninsula (G-16043)

VIP-Supply Chain Solutions LLC ....G 513 454-2020
West Chester (G-19970)

BOXES & SHOOK: Nailed Wood

Caravan Packaging Inc ....F 440 243-4100
Cleveland (G-4974)

Cassady Woodworks Inc ....E 937 256-7948
Dayton (G-8099)

Clark Rm Inc ....E 419 425-9889
Findlay (G-9808)

Dp Products LLC ....G 440 834-9663
Burton (G-2373)

H Gerstner & Sons Inc ....F 937 228-1662
Dayton (G-8382)

Hann Manufacturing Inc ....E 740 962-3752
McConnelsville (G-13352)

Hines Builders Inc ....F 937 335-4586
Troy (G-18834)

J & L Wood Products Inc ....E 937 667-4064
Tipp City (G-18286)

Kennedy Group Incorporated ....D 440 951-7660
Willoughby (G-20520)

Lima Pallet Company Inc ....E 419 229-5736
Lima (G-12041)

Packaging Plus Inc ....G 304 429-5900
Dayton (G-8562)

Quadco Rehabilitation Center ....B 419 682-1011
Stryker (G-18006)

Schaefer Box & Pallet Co ....E 513 738-2500
Hamilton (G-10736)

Van Orders Pallet Company Inc ....F 419 875-6932
Swanton (G-18094)

BOXES: Corrugated

Adapt-A-Pak Inc ....E 937 845-0386
Tipp City (G-18260)

American Made Corrugated Packg ....F 937 981-2111
Greenfield (G-10473)

Archbold Container Corp ....C 800 446-2520
Archbold (G-664)

Argrov Box Co ....F 937 898-1700
Dayton (G-8163)

B & B Box Company Inc ....F 419 872-5600
Perrysburg (G-16067)

BDS Packaging Inc ....D 937 643-0530
Moraine (G-14468)

Bryan Packaging Inc ....F 419 636-2600
Bryan (G-2287)

Buckeye Boxes Inc ....D 614 274-8484
Columbus (G-6870)

Buckeye Corrugated Inc ....G 330 576-0590
Fairlawn (G-9744)

Cambridge Packaging Inc ....E 740 432-3351
Cambridge (G-2449)

Clecorr Inc ....E 216 961-5500
Cleveland (G-5047)

Family Packaging Inc ....G 937 325-4106
Springfield (G-17557)

General Packaging Products ....E 330 725-7731
Medina (G-13416)

Graphic Paper Products Corp ....D 937 325-5503
Springfield (G-17564)

Green Bay Packaging Inc ....C 419 332-5593
Fremont (G-10157)

Green Bay Packaging Inc ....C 513 228-5560
Lebanon (G-11806)

Greif Inc ....E 740 657-6500
Delaware (G-8848)

International Paper Company ....C 330 264-1322
Wooster (G-20788)

International Paper Company ....C 937 456-4131
Eaton (G-9311)

International Paper Company ....C 740 397-5215
Mount Vernon (G-14623)

International Paper Company ....C 740 363-9882
Delaware (G-8862)

International Paper Company ....C 740 369-7691
Delaware (G-8863)

International Paper Company ....D 740 522-3123
Newark (G-15023)

Jet Container Company ....E 614 444-2133
Columbus (G-7230)

Lewisburg Container Company ....C 937 962-2681
Lewisburg (G-11936)

Mid Ohio Packaging LLC ....E 740 383-9200
Marion (G-12884)

Midwest Box Company ....E 216 281-9021
Cleveland (G-5807)

Midwest Container Corporation ....E 513 870-3000
Fairfield (G-9684)

Mount Vernon Packaging Inc ....F 740 397-3221
Mount Vernon (G-14632)

N-Stock Box Inc ....E 513 423-0319
Middletown (G-14067)

Northeast Box Company ....D 440 992-5500
Ashtabula (G-827)

Novolex Holdings Inc ....B 937 746-1933
Franklin (G-10041)

Omer J Smith Inc ....E 513 921-4717
West Chester (G-19909)

Orora North America ....G 513 539-8274
Monroe (G-14411)

Pallet & Cont Corp of Amer ....G 419 255-1256
Toledo (G-18634)

Phillips Packaging Inc ....G 937 484-4702
Urbana (G-19173)

Pjs Corrugated Inc ....F 419 644-3383
Swanton (G-18087)

Pro-Pak Industries Inc ....C 419 729-0751
Maumee (G-13288)

R and D Incorporated ....E 216 581-6328
   Maple Heights *(G-12738)*

Riblet Packaging Co ....F 937 652-3087
   Urbana *(G-19175)*

Riverview Packaging Inc ....E 937 743-9530
   Franklin *(G-10049)*

Skybox Investments Inc ....E 419 525-6013
   Mansfield *(G-12679)*

Smith-Lustig Paper Box Mfg Co ....E 216 621-0453
   Bedford *(G-1462)*

Sobel Corrugated Cntrs Inc ....C 216 475-2100
   Cleveland *(G-6216)*

Square One Solutions LLC ....F 419 425-5445
   Findlay *(G-9894)*

Tavens Container Inc ....D 216 883-3333
   Bedford *(G-1464)*

Tecumseh Packg Solutions Inc ....E 419 238-1122
   Van Wert *(G-19271)*

Unipac Inc ....E 740 929-2000
   Hebron *(G-10893)*

Value Added Packaging Inc ....F 937 832-9595
   Englewood *(G-9542)*

Verso Corporation ....D 901 369-4105
   Miamisburg *(G-13875)*

Westrock CP LLC ....D 770 448-2193
   Wshngtn CT Hs *(G-20930)*

BOXES: Filing, Paperboard Made From Purchased Materials

A To Z Paper Box Co ....G 330 325-8722
   Rootstown *(G-16718)*

BOXES: Fuse, Electric

Tri-Fab Inc ....E 330 337-3425
   Salem *(G-16931)*

BOXES: Mail Or Post Office, Collection/Storage, Sheet Metal

Gdm Mailbox Company LLC ....G 419 433-3022
   Huron *(G-11221)*

Salsbury Industries Inc ....G 614 409-1600
   Columbus *(G-7588)*

BOXES: Packing & Shipping, Metal

Industrial Fabricators Inc ....E 614 882-7423
   Westerville *(G-20218)*

Karyall-Telday Inc ....E 216 281-4063
   Cleveland *(G-5633)*

Yarder Manufacturing Company ....D 419 476-3933
   Toledo *(G-18778)*

Yarder Manufacturing Company ....G 419 269-3474
   Toledo *(G-18779)*

BOXES: Paperboard, Folding

American Corrugated Pdts Inc ....C 614 870-2000
   Columbus *(G-6735)*

B & L Labels and Packg Co Inc ....G 937 773-9080
   Piqua *(G-16252)*

Bell Ohio Inc ....F 605 332-6721
   Groveport *(G-10616)*

Boxit Corporation ....G 216 416-9475
   Cleveland *(G-4928)*

Boxit Corporation ....D 216 631-6900
   Cleveland *(G-4927)*

Carton Service Incorporated ....C 419 342-5010
   Shelby *(G-17134)*

Chilcote Company ....C 216 781-6000
   Cleveland *(G-5028)*

Graphic Packaging Intl Inc ....C 740 387-6543
   Marion *(G-12869)*

Graphic Packaging Intl Inc ....C 513 424-4200
   Middletown *(G-14044)*

Graphic Packaging Intl Inc ....C 440 248-4370
   Solon *(G-17301)*

Jefferson Smurfit Corporation ....F 440 248-4370
   Solon *(G-17321)*

Oak Hills Carton Co ....E 513 948-4200
   Cincinnati *(G-4171)*

Rohrer Corporation ....C 440 542-3100
   Solon *(G-17371)*

RR Donnelley & Sons Company ....G 513 870-4040
   West Chester *(G-19938)*

Sandusky Packaging Corporation ....E 419 626-8520
   Sandusky *(G-17005)*

Star Pizza Box ....E 740 967-1105
   Johnstown *(G-11405)*

The Shelby Co ....E 440 871-9901
   Westlake *(G-20315)*

Therm-O-Packaging Suppliers ....F 440 543-5188
   Chagrin Falls *(G-3126)*

Unipac Inc ....E 740 929-2000
   Hebron *(G-10893)*

Yuckon International Corp ....G 216 361-2103
   Cleveland *(G-6488)*

BOXES: Paperboard, Set-Up

Boxit Corporation ....D 216 631-6900
   Cleveland *(G-4927)*

Boxit Corporation ....G 216 416-9475
   Cleveland *(G-4928)*

Graphic Paper Products Corp ....D 937 325-5503
   Springfield *(G-14541)*

Piqua Paper Box Company ....E 937 773-0313
   Piqua *(G-16306)*

R and D Incorporated ....E 216 581-6328
   Maple Heights *(G-12738)*

Sandusky Packaging Corporation ....E 419 626-8520
   Sandusky *(G-17005)*

BOXES: Plastic

Chatelain Plastics Inc ....G 419 422-4323
   Findlay *(G-9807)*

Metro Recycling Company ....G 513 251-1800
   Cincinnati *(G-4094)*

Oldcastle Precast Inc ....E 419 592-2309
   Napoleon *(G-14692)*

Triple Diamond Plastics LLC ....D 419 533-0085
   Liberty Center *(G-11956)*

BOXES: Stamped Metal

Roper Lockbox LLC ....G 330 656-5148
   Hudson *(G-11197)*

BOXES: Wooden

Aslan Worldwide ....F 513 671-0671
   West Chester *(G-19811)*

Boxes & Such ....G 440 237-7122
   Wooster *(G-20752)*

Buckeye Diamond Logistics Inc ....C 937 462-8361
   South Charleston *(G-17424)*

Built-Rite Box & Crate Inc ....E 330 263-0936
   Wooster *(G-20756)*

Cedar Craft Products Inc ....E 614 759-1600
   Blacklick *(G-1692)*

Damar Products Inc ....G 937 492-9023
   Sidney *(G-17174)*

Damar Products Inc ....F 937 492-9023
   Sidney *(G-17175)*

Forest City Companies Inc ....E 216 586-5279
   Cleveland *(G-5369)*

Ohio Box & Crate Inc ....F 440 526-3133
   Burton *(G-2381)*

Packaging Materials Svcs LLC ....F 330 745-9722
   Norton *(G-15520)*

Sterling Industries Inc ....F 419 523-3788
   Ottawa *(G-15810)*

Thomas J Weaver Inc ....F 740 622-2040
   Coshocton *(G-7913)*

Traveling & Recycle Wood Pdts ....F 419 968-2649
   Middle Point *(G-13899)*

World Express Packaging Corp ....G 216 634-9000
   Cleveland *(G-6479)*

Zak Box Co Inc ....G 216 961-5636
   Cleveland *(G-6491)*

BRAKES & BRAKE PARTS

Advics Manufacturing Ohio Inc ....A 513 934-0023
   Lebanon *(G-11776)*

Autoliv Nissin Brake ....B 419 425-6725
   Findlay *(G-9791)*

Buckeye Brake Manufacturing ....F 740 782-1379
   Morristown *(G-14541)*

Carlisle Brake & Friction Inc ....F 440 528-4000
   Solon *(G-17276)*

Cooper-Standard Automotive Inc ....B 740 342-3523
   New Lexington *(G-14846)*

Friction Products Co ....B 330 725-4941
   Medina *(G-13413)*

Harco Manufacturing Group LLC ....C 937 528-5000
   Moraine *(G-14494)*

Harco Manufacturing Group LLC ....C 937 528-5000
   Moraine *(G-14495)*

Hebco Products Inc ....A 419 562-7987
   Bucyrus *(G-2347)*

Kerr Friction Products Inc ....E 330 455-3983
   Canton *(G-2751)*

Nissin Brake Ohio Inc ....A 419 420-3800
   Findlay *(G-9868)*

Nissin Brake Ohio Inc ....E 937 642-7556
   East Liberty *(G-9202)*

Undercar Express LLC ....E 216 531-7004
   Cleveland *(G-6381)*

Vehicle Systems Inc ....G 330 854-0535
   Massillon *(G-13210)*

Whirlaway Corporation ....C 440 647-4711
   Wellington *(G-19758)*

BRAKES: Bicycle, Friction Clutch & Other

Carlisle Brake & Friction Inc ....E 330 725-4941
   Medina *(G-13385)*

Carlisle Brake & Friction Inc ....C 440 528-4000
   Solon *(G-17277)*

Farin Industries Inc ....F 440 275-2755
   Austinburg *(G-961)*

Multi-Design Inc ....C 440 275-2255
   Austinburg *(G-963)*

BRAKES: Electromagnetic

Beckworth Industries Inc ....E 216 268-5557
   Cleveland *(G-4902)*

BRAKES: Metal Forming

Ata Tools Inc ....D 330 928-7744
   Cuyahoga Falls *(G-7973)*

Eaton Corporation ....C 216 281-2211
   Cleveland *(G-5247)*

Ebo Group Inc ....D 330 239-4933
   Sharon Center *(G-17105)*

BRASS & BRONZE PRDTS: Die-casted

Akron Brass Company ....E 309 444-4440
   Wooster *(G-20733)*

American Bronze Corporation ....E 216 341-7800
   Cleveland *(G-4779)*

Hamilton Brass & Alum Castings ....E 513 867-0400
   Hamilton *(G-10701)*

Model Pattern & Foundry Co ....E 513 542-2322
   Cincinnati *(G-4113)*

Ryder-Heil Bronze Inc ....E 419 562-2841
   Bucyrus *(G-2358)*

BRASS FOUNDRY, NEC

Bunting Bearings LLC ....D 419 866-7000
   Holland *(G-11047)*

Maass Midwest Mfg Inc ....G 419 894-6424
   Arcadia *(G-654)*

National Brass Company Inc ....G 216 651-8530
   Cleveland *(G-5854)*

Non-Ferrous Casting Co ....G 937 228-1162
   Dayton *(G-8525)*

BRASS ROLLING & DRAWING

Chase Brass and Copper Co LLC ....B 419 485-3193
   Montpelier *(G-14440)*

BRAZING SVCS

Paulo Products Company ....E 440 942-0153
   Willoughby *(G-20567)*

BRAZING: Metal

Advanced Flame Hardening Inc ....G 216 431-0370
   Cleveland *(G-4712)*

American Metal Treating Co ....E 216 431-4492
   Cleveland *(G-4790)*

Brazing Service Inc ....G 440 871-1120
   Westlake *(G-20259)*

HI Tecmetal Group Inc ....E 216 881-8100
   Cleveland *(G-5508)*

J W Harris Co Inc ....E 216 481-8100
   Euclid *(G-9587)*

Kando of Cincinnati Inc ....E 513 459-7782
   Lebanon *(G-11811)*

Ohio Flame Hardening Company ....E 513 336-6160
   Lebanon *(G-11821)*

Ohio Flame Hardening Company ....E 513 733-5162
   Cincinnati *(G-4177)*

Surface Enhancement Tech LLC ....F 513 561-1520
   Cincinnati *(G-4487)*

Wall Colmonoy Corporation ....F 937 278-9111
   Cincinnati *(G-4576)*

BRIC-A-BRAC

CM Paula Company ....E 513 759-7473
Mason (G-13002)

BRICK, STONE & RELATED PRDTS WHOLESALERS

Grafton Ready Mix Concret Inc ....E 440 926-2911
Grafton (G-10427)

Kuhlman Corporation ....E 419 897-6000
Maumee (G-13273)

Lancaster West Side Coal Co ....F 740 862-4713
Lancaster (G-11725)

Modern Builders Supply Inc ....C 330 729-2690
Youngstown (G-21147)

Modern Builders Supply Inc ....F 419 526-0002
Mansfield (G-12651)

Myko Industries ....G 216 431-0900
Cleveland (G-5845)

Ohio Beauty Inc ....G 330 644-2241
Akron (G-322)

R W Sidley Incorporated ....E 330 793-7374
Youngstown (G-21184)

Sidwell Materials Inc ....C 740 849-2394
Zanesville (G-21354)

Stamm Contracting Co Inc ....G 330 274-8230
Mantua (G-12723)

Trumbull Cement Products Co ....G 330 372-4342
Warren (G-19611)

Wallseye Concrete Corp ....F 419 483-2738
Castalia (G-2978)

Warren Concrete and Supply Co ....F 330 393-1581
Warren (G-19620)

William Dauch Concrete Company .....F 419 668-4458
Norwalk (G-15567)

BRICKS & BLOCKS: Structural

Belden Brick Company LLC ....C 330 456-0031
Sugarcreek (G-18017)

Boral Bricks Inc ....G 937 294-1548
Franklin (G-10010)

Glen-Gery Corporation ....E 419 468-5002
Iberia (G-11243)

BRICKS : Ceramic Glazed, Clay

Afc Company ....F 330 533-5581
Canfield (G-2545)

Nutro Inc ....E 440 572-3800
Strongsville (G-17947)

Wk Brick Company ....G 614 416-6700
Columbus (G-7767)

BRICKS : Flooring, Clay

Kona Blackbird Inc ....F 440 285-3189
Chardon (G-3160)

BRICKS : Paving, Clay

Whitacre Greer Company ....E 330 823-1610
Alliance (G-553)

BRICKS: Clay

Bowerston Shale Company ....E 740 763-3921
Newark (G-14988)

Bowerston Shale Company ....E 740 269-2921
Bowerston (G-1957)

Glen-Gery Corporation ....D 419 845-3321
Caledonia (G-2437)

Glen-Gery Corporation ....D 419 468-4890
Galion (G-10274)

BRICKS: Concrete

Belden Brick Company LLC ....C 330 456-0031
Sugarcreek (G-18017)

Turner Vault ....G 419 223-6861
Lima (G-12106)

BRIDAL SHOPS

Beverly Snider ....G 614 837-5817
Columbus (G-6824)

Brahler Inc ....G 330 966-7730
Canton (G-2627)

BROACHING MACHINES

Accurate Machining & Welding ....G 937 584-4518
Sabina (G-16772)

Ohio Broach & Machine Company ....E 440 946-1040
Willoughby (G-20560)

Taper Tool & Broach Inc ....G 216 486-4435
Cleveland (G-6294)

BROADCASTING & COMMS EQPT: Antennas, Transmitting/Comms

AG Antenna Group LLC ....F 513 289-6521
Cincinnati (G-3366)

Always Better Communications ....F 330 445-2220
Canton (G-2600)

Central USA Wireless LLC ....E 513 469-1500
Cincinnati (G-3518)

Electro-Magwave Inc ....G 216 453-1160
Cleveland (G-5266)

BROADCASTING & COMMS EQPT: Rcvr-Transmitter Unt, Transceiver

Control Industries Inc ....G 937 653-7694
Findlay (G-9810)

BROADCASTING & COMMUNICATIONS EQPT: Cellular Radio Telephone

Radio Hospital ....G 419 679-1103
Kenton (G-11565)

BROADCASTING & COMMUNICATIONS EQPT: Light Comms Eqpt

Armada Power LLC ....G 614 204-9341
Columbus (G-6772)

LSI Industries Inc ....B 513 793-3200
Blue Ash (G-1830)

BROKERS' SVCS

Shamrock Companies Inc ....D 440 899-9510
Westlake (G-20308)

BROKERS, MARINE TRANSPORTATION

Ogc Industries Inc ....F 330 456-1500
Canton (G-2797)

BROKERS: Contract Basis

Tewell & Associates ....G 440 543-5190
Chagrin Falls (G-3125)

BROKERS: Food

General Mills Inc ....D 513 770-0558
Mason (G-13026)

Homestat Farm Ltd ....G 614 718-3060
Dublin (G-9085)

Shaker Valley Foods Inc ....E 216 961-8600
Cleveland (G-6182)

BROKERS: Log & Lumber

Hochstetler Milling LLC ....E 419 368-0004
Loudonville (G-12298)

Kenneth Schrock ....G 937 544-7566
West Union (G-20123)

Ned A Shreve ....G 740 732-6465
Sarahsville (G-17025)

BROKERS: Printing

C Massouh Printing Co Inc ....G 330 832-6334
Massillon (G-13116)

Scrip-Safe Security Products ....E 513 697-7789
Loveland (G-12384)

BRONZE FOUNDRY, NEC

Foundry Artist Inc ....G 216 391-9030
Cleveland (G-5375)

Meierjohan-Wengler Inc ....F 513 771-6074
Cincinnati (G-4081)

BRONZE ROLLING & DRAWING

Jj Seville LLC ....F 330 769-2071
Seville (G-17076)

BRONZING SVCS: Baby Shoes

Bron-Shoe Company ....E 614 252-0967
Columbus (G-6867)

BROOMS & BRUSHES

Deco Tools Inc ....E 419 476-9321
Toledo (G-18430)

Demel Enterprises Inc ....G 740 592-5800
Athens (G-860)

Designetics Inc ....D 419 866-0700
Holland (G-11054)

Enercon Systems Inc ....G 305 213-3997
Elyria (G-9419)

Fimm USA Inc ....F 253 243-1522
Columbus (G-7084)

Hoge Lumber Company ....F 419 753-2351
New Knoxville (G-14837)

Mill Rose Laboratories Inc ....E 440 974-6730
Mentor (G-13656)

Stephen M Trudick ....E 440 834-1891
Burton (G-2385)

Unique Packaging & Printing ....F 440 785-6730
Mentor (G-13759)

BROOMS & BRUSHES: Household Or Indl

Brushes Inc ....E 216 267-8084
Cleveland (G-4941)

Malish Corporation ....C 440 951-5356
Mentor (G-13644)

Mill-Rose Company ....C 440 255-9171
Mentor (G-13657)

Ohio Brush Company ....F 216 791-3265
Cleveland (G-5931)

Ohio Carbon Company ....G 216 251-7274
Ashland (G-758)

Precision Brush Co ....F 440 542-9600
Solon (G-17363)

Spiral Brushes Inc ....E 330 686-2861
Stow (G-17801)

Tod Thin Brushes Inc ....F 440 576-6859
Jefferson (G-11375)

Trent Manufacturing Company ....F 216 391-1551
Cleveland (G-6356)

United Rotary Brush Inc ....D 937 644-3515
Plain City (G-16362)

BROOMS & BRUSHES: Paint & Varnish

D A L E S Corporation ....F 419 255-5335
Toledo (G-18423)

Wooster Brush Company ....G 440 322-8081
Elyria (G-9511)

BROOMS & BRUSHES: Street Sweeping, Hand Or Machine

Public Works Dept Street Div ....E 740 283-6013
Steubenville (G-17710)

Taupe Holdings Co ....G 614 330-4600
Dublin (G-9153)

BROOMS & BRUSHES: Vacuum Cleaners & Carpet Sweepers

Venture Plas Middlefield LLC ....E 440 834-0704
Middlefield (G-14002)

BRUSH BLOCKS: Carbon Or Molded Graphite

Buckeye Molded Products Ltd ....F 440 323-2244
Elyria (G-9383)

BRUSHES & BRUSH STOCK CONTACTS: Electric

Ohio Power Tool Brush Co ....G 419 736-3010
Ashland (G-760)

BUCKETS: Plastic

Graham Packaging Co Europe LLC ......C 513 398-5000
Mason (G-13032)

Impact Products LLC ....C 419 841-2891
Toledo (G-18518)

BUFFING FOR THE TRADE

Anchor Fabricators Inc ....E 937 836-5117
Clayton (G-4656)

Buffex Metal Finishing Inc ....F 216 631-2202
Cleveland (G-4946)

Reliable Buffing Co Inc ....G 419 647-4432
Spencerville (G-17464)

S & K Metal Polsg & Buffing ....G 513 732-6662
  Batavia (G-1221)

BUILDING & OFFICE CLEANING SVCS

Cbr Industrial Llc ....G 419 645-6447
  Wapakoneta (G-19483)
High-TEC Industrial Services ....C 937 667-1772
  Tipp City (G-18281)
Taupe Holdings Co ....G 614 330-4600
  Dublin (G-9153)

BUILDING & STRUCTURAL WOOD MBRS: Timbers, Struct, Lam Lumber

Amish Timber Framers ....F 330 658-5699
  Doylestown (G-9026)

BUILDING & STRUCTURAL WOOD MEMBERS

Baker McMillen Co ....E 330 923-3303
  Stow (G-17734)
Byler Truss ....G 330 465-5412
  Ashland (G-715)
C & M Truss LLC ....F 937 446-3400
  Sardinia (G-17026)
Carter-Jones Lumber Company ....C 330 674-9060
  Millersburg (G-14211)
Contract Building Components ....E 937 644-0739
  Marysville (G-12938)
Dutchcraft Truss Component Inc ....F 330 862-2220
  Minerva (G-14320)
Holmes Lumber & Bldg Ctr Inc ....C 330 674-9060
  Millersburg (G-14231)
Laminate Technologies Inc ....D 419 448-0812
  Tiffin (G-18226)
Orica Ground Support Inc ....D 740 377-9146
  South Point (G-17443)
Socar of Ohio Inc ....D 419 596-3100
  Continental (G-7828)
Stark Truss Company Inc ....D 330 478-2100
  Canton (G-2859)
Stark Truss Company Inc ....E 330 756-3050
  Beach City (G-1251)
Truss Worx LLC ....G 419 363-2100
  Rockford (G-16693)
Waynedale Truss & Panel Co ....G 330 683-4471
  Dalton (G-8079)
Woodcraft Manufacturing Co ....E 740 927-6609
  Pataskala (G-15992)

BUILDING & STRUCTURAL WOOD MEMBERS: Arches, Laminated Lumber

Richland Laminated Columns LLC ....F 419 895-0036
  Greenwich (G-10535)

BUILDING CLEANING & MAINTENANCE SVCS

All Pack Services LLC ....F 614 935-0964
  Grove City (G-10541)
Ccw Group Pacesetter Inc ....C 740 474-0122
  Circleville (G-4624)
City of Kent ....F 330 673-8897
  Kent (G-11438)
Hopewell Industries Inc ....D 740 622-3563
  Coshocton (G-7895)
Obersons Nurs & Landscapes Inc ....F 513 894-0669
  Fairfield (G-9692)
Phase II Enterprises Inc ....G 330 484-2113
  Canton (G-2812)
Richland Newhope Industries ....C 419 774-4400
  Mansfield (G-12671)
Rossi Machinery Services Inc ....G 419 281-4488
  Ashland (G-773)

BUILDING CLEANING SVCS

Leadec Corp ....E 513 731-3590
  Blue Ash (G-1826)

BUILDING COMPONENT CLEANING SVCS

Cincinnati A Fltr Sls Svc Inc ....E 513 242-3400
  Cincinnati (G-3536)

BUILDING COMPONENTS: Structural Steel

American Qulty Fabrication Inc ....G 937 667-2861
  Vandalia (G-19281)

Dietrich Industries Inc ....C 330 372-4014
  Warren (G-19543)
Dietrich Industries Inc ....F 614 438-3210
  Worthington (G-20863)
Dietrich Industries Inc ....D 216 472-1511
  Cleveland (G-5194)
Dietrich Industries Inc ....E 614 438-3210
  Worthington (G-20864)
Frederick Steel Company LLC ....G 513 821-6400
  Cincinnati (G-3782)
Fwt LLC ....F 419 542-1420
  Hicksville (G-10902)
J&J Precision Machine Ltd ....E 330 923-5783
  Cuyahoga Falls (G-8012)
Mad River Steel Ltd ....G 937 845-4046
  New Carlisle (G-14806)
McNichols Company ....G 877 884-4653
  Cincinnati (G-4071)
Orica Ground Support Inc ....B 740 269-8100
  Bowerston (G-1960)
Precision Tower Products LLC ....G 740 362-7876
  Delaware (G-8879)
Turn-Key Industrial Svcs LLC ....D 614 274-1128
  Columbus (G-7714)
Universal Fabg Cnstr Svcs Inc ....D 614 274-1128
  Columbus (G-7723)
Waterford Tank Fabrication Ltd ....D 740 984-4100
  Beverly (G-1672)
Wernli Realty Inc ....D 937 258-7878
  Beavercreek (G-1384)

BUILDING ITEM REPAIR SVCS, MISCELLANEOUS

IV J Telecommunications LLC ....G 606 694-1762
  South Point (G-17438)

BUILDING MAINTENANCE SVCS, EXC REPAIRS

Lima Sheet Metal Machine & Mfg ....E 419 229-1161
  Lima (G-12045)

BUILDING PRDTS & MATERIALS DEALERS

Adams Brothers Inc ....F 740 819-0323
  Zanesville (G-21265)
Avon Concrete Corporation ....G 440 937-6264
  Avon (G-984)
Building Concepts Inc ....F 419 298-2371
  Edgerton (G-9326)
Carter-Jones Lumber Company ....C 330 674-9060
  Millersburg (G-14211)
Chappell-Zimmerman Inc ....E 330 337-8711
  Salem (G-16880)
Consumeracq Inc ....F 440 277-9305
  Lorain (G-12239)
Consumers Builders Supply Co ....E 440 277-9306
  Lorain (G-12240)
Crosco Wood Products ....G 330 857-0228
  Dalton (G-8065)
Dearth Resources Inc ....G 937 325-0651
  Springfield (G-17539)
Dnl Oil Corp ....G 740 342-4970
  New Lexington (G-14847)
Fort Loramie Cast Stone Pdts ....G 937 420-2257
  Fort Loramie (G-9931)
Friends Ornamental Iron Co ....G 216 431-6710
  Cleveland (G-5382)
Great Lakes Window Inc ....A 419 666-5555
  Walbridge (G-19458)
Holmes Lumber & Bldg Ctr Inc ....C 330 674-9060
  Millersburg (G-14231)
Holmes Panel ....G 330 897-5040
  Baltic (G-1074)
Hull Builders Supply Inc ....E 440 967-3159
  Vermilion (G-19328)
Hyde Park Lumber Company ....E 513 271-1500
  Cincinnati (G-3903)
Judy Mills Company Inc ....E 513 271-4241
  Cincinnati (G-3962)
K M B Inc ....E 330 889-3451
  Bristolville (G-2098)
Khempco Bldg Sup Co Ltd Partnr ....D 740 549-0465
  Delaware (G-8865)
Lancaster West Side Coal Co ....F 740 862-4713
  Lancaster (G-11725)
Lang Stone Company Inc ....D 614 235-4099
  Columbus (G-7284)
Martin Block Company ....G 740 286-7507
  Jackson (G-11319)

Ohio Beauty Inc ....G 330 644-2241
  Akron (G-322)
Osborne Inc ....E 440 942-7000
  Mentor (G-13677)
Portsmouth Block Inc ....F 740 353-4113
  Portsmouth (G-16448)
Stamm Contracting Co Inc ....E 330 274-8230
  Mantua (G-12723)
T C Redi Mix Youngstown Inc ....E 330 755-2143
  Youngstown (G-21217)
Terry Lumber and Supply Co ....F 330 659-6800
  Peninsula (G-16043)
Thomas Do-It Center Inc ....E 740 446-2002
  Gallipolis (G-10310)
Tri-County Block and Brick Inc ....E 419 826-7060
  Swanton (G-18093)
Trumbull Cement Products Co ....G 330 372-4342
  Warren (G-19611)
Tyjen Inc ....G 740 380-3215
  Logan (G-12196)
Vances Department Store ....E 937 549-2188
  Manchester (G-12552)
Vances Department Store ....E 937 549-3033
  Manchester (G-12553)
Warren Concrete and Supply Co ....F 330 393-1581
  Warren (G-19620)
Wilson Concrete Products Inc ....E 937 885-7965
  Dayton (G-8759)
Zaenkert Surveying Essentials ....G 513 738-2917
  Okeana (G-15668)

BUILDING PRDTS: Concrete

Baird Concrete Products Inc ....F 740 623-8600
  Coshocton (G-7881)
Baswa Acoustics North Amer LLC ....F 216 475-7197
  Bedford (G-1404)
Evan Ragouzis Co ....G 513 242-5900
  Hamilton (G-10689)
Kcg Inc ....G 614 238-9450
  Columbus (G-7252)
Motz Mobile Containers Inc ....G 513 772-6689
  Cincinnati (G-4127)
Olde Wood Ltd ....E 330 866-1441
  Magnolia (G-12517)
One Wish LLC ....F 800 505-6883
  Beachwood (G-1289)
Patriot Holdings Unlimited LLC ....G 740 574-2112
  Wheelersburg (G-20333)
Shelly Materials Inc ....G 614 801-9105
  Grove City (G-10593)

BUILDING PRDTS: Stone

Jalco Industries Inc ....F 740 286-3808
  Jackson (G-11317)
Rome Marble Inc ....G 216 431-0334
  Cleveland (G-6131)

BUILDING SCALES MODELS

3-D Technical Services Inc ....E 937 746-2901
  Franklin (G-10004)

BUILDING STONE, ARTIFICIAL: Concrete

Provia Stone LLC ....E 740 450-4236
  Sugarcreek (G-18035)

BUILDINGS & COMPONENTS: Prefabricated Metal

Benchmark Archtectural Systems ....E 614 444-0110
  Columbus (G-6821)
Benko Products Inc ....E 440 934-2180
  Sheffield Village (G-17121)
Better Built Barns ....G 606 348-6146
  Winchester (G-20690)
Consolidatd Analytical Sys Inc ....F 513 542-1200
  Cleves (G-6511)
Cover Up Building Systems ....G 740 668-8985
  Martinsburg (G-12929)
Haz-Safe LLC ....F 330 793-0900
  Austintown (G-974)
Hoge Lumber Company ....E 419 753-2263
  New Knoxville (G-14836)
Lab-Pro Inc ....G 937 434-9600
  Dayton (G-8450)
Mobile Mini Inc ....F 614 449-8655
  Columbus (G-7360)
Morton Buildings Inc ....F 330 345-6188
  Wooster (G-20812)

ONeals Tarpaulin & Awning Co ....F 330 788-6504
Youngstown *(G-21157)*
R L Torbeck Industries Inc ....D 513 367-0080
Harrison *(G-10800)*
Rebsco Inc ....F 937 548-2246
Greenville *(G-10517)*
Skyline Corporation ....C 330 852-2483
Sugarcreek *(G-18039)*
Sorta 4 U LLC ....G 440 365-0091
Elyria *(G-9495)*
Storage Buildings Unlimited ....G 216 731-0010
Doylestown *(G-9030)*
Will-Burt Advnced Cmpsites Inc ....F 330 684-5286
Orrville *(G-15769)*

BUILDINGS, PREFABRICATED: Wholesalers

Lab-Pro Inc ....G 937 434-9600
Dayton *(G-8450)*

BUILDINGS: Chicken Coops, Prefabricated, Wood

Cconly Inc ....F 614 607-2288
Delaware *(G-8830)*

BUILDINGS: Farm & Utility

Barncraft Storage Buildings ....G 513 738-5654
Hamilton *(G-10672)*
Morton Buildings Inc ....F 740 783-2331
Caldwell *(G-2430)*
Morton Buildings Inc ....E 419 673-0741
Kenton *(G-11560)*
Morton Buildings Inc ....D 419 675-2311
Kenton *(G-11561)*
Vinyl Tech Storage Barn ....G 330 674-5670
Millersburg *(G-14278)*

BUILDINGS: Farm, Prefabricated Or Portable, Wood

Millers Storage Barns LLC ....E 330 893-3293
Millersburg *(G-14248)*

BUILDINGS: Portable

Affordable Barn Co Ltd ....F 330 674-3001
Millersburg *(G-14190)*
Golden Giant Inc ....E 419 674-4038
Kenton *(G-11547)*
Mobile Mini Inc ....E 303 305-9515
Canton *(G-2783)*
Mobile Mini Inc ....E 513 353-9800
Fairfield *(G-9686)*

BUILDINGS: Prefabricated, Metal

Enclosure Suppliers LLC ....E 513 782-3900
Cincinnati *(G-3701)*
Great Day Improvements LLC ....G 330 468-0700
Macedonia *(G-12456)*
Jack Walters & Sons Corp ....F 937 653-8986
Urbana *(G-19164)*
Joyce Manufacturing Co ....D 440 239-9100
Berea *(G-1624)*
Nci Building Systems Inc ....C 937 584-3300
Middletown *(G-14069)*
Pei Liquidation Company ....E 615 781-5020
Macedonia *(G-12471)*
Pei Liquidation Company ....C 330 467-4267
Macedonia *(G-12470)*
Rayhaven Group Inc ....F 330 659-3183
Richfield *(G-16634)*
Rupcol Inc ....G 419 924-5215
West Unity *(G-20135)*

BUILDINGS: Prefabricated, Plastic

ALC Holdings Inc ....C 740 452-2500
Zanesville *(G-21268)*
J & M Construction LLP ....G 740 454-8986
Hopewell *(G-11119)*

BUILDINGS: Prefabricated, Wood

Americraft Stor Buildings Ltd ....G 330 877-6900
Hartville *(G-10816)*
Fifth Avenue Lumber Co ....D 614 833-6655
Canal Winchester *(G-2524)*
Millers Mini Barns ....G 937 544-6317
West Union *(G-20124)*

Morton Buildings Inc ....D 419 675-2311
Kenton *(G-11561)*
Patio Enclosures ....F 513 733-4646
Cincinnati *(G-4213)*
Rona Enterprises Inc ....G 740 927-9971
Pataskala *(G-15981)*
Skyline Corporation ....C 330 852-2483
Sugarcreek *(G-18039)*
Vinyl Design Corporation ....E 419 283-4009
Holland *(G-11095)*
Weaver Barns Ltd ....F 330 852-2103
Sugarcreek *(G-18050)*

BUILDINGS: Prefabricated, Wood

Carter-Jones Lumber Company ....F 440 834-8164
Middlefield *(G-13920)*
Consolidatd Analytical Sys Inc ....F 513 542-1200
Cleves *(G-6511)*
Hershbergers Dutch Market LLP ....E 740 489-5322
Old Washington *(G-15671)*
Smiths Sawdust Studio ....G 740 484-4656
Bethesda *(G-1667)*
Twin Oaks Barn ....F 330 893-3126
Dundee *(G-9184)*

BULLETIN BOARDS: Cork

GMI Companies Inc ....G 937 981-0244
Greenfield *(G-10476)*
Michael Kaufman Companies Inc ....F 330 673-4881
Kent *(G-11490)*
Michael Kaufman Companies Inc ....F 330 673-4881
Kent *(G-11491)*
Mpc Inc ....F 440 835-1405
Westlake *(G-20284)*

BULLETIN BOARDS: Wood

GMI Companies Inc ....C 513 932-3445
Lebanon *(G-11804)*
Tri-State Supply Co Inc ....F 614 272-6767
Columbus *(G-7709)*

BULLETPROOF VESTS

Forceone LLC ....E 513 939-1018
Hebron *(G-10865)*

BUOYS: Metal

Worthignton Products Inc ....G 330 452-7400
Canton *(G-2903)*

BUOYS: Plastic

Worthignton Products Inc ....G 330 452-7400
Canton *(G-2903)*

BURGLAR ALARM MAINTENANCE & MONITORING SVCS

Area Wide Protective Inc ....E 513 321-9889
Fairfield *(G-9643)*

BURIAL VAULTS: Concrete Or Precast Terrazzo

Akron Vault Company Inc ....F 330 784-5475
Akron *(G-60)*
Alexander Wilbert Vault Co ....G 419 468-3477
Galion *(G-10252)*
Andras Corp ....G 440 323-2528
Elyria *(G-9373)*
Bell Burial Vault Co ....G 513 896-9044
Hamilton *(G-10674)*
Bell Vault & Monument Works ....E 937 866-2444
Miamisburg *(G-13785)*
Brock Burial Vault Inc ....G 740 894-5246
South Point *(G-17433)*
Buckeye Vault Service Inc ....G 419 747-1976
Mansfield *(G-12571)*
Click Burial Vault and Mfg Co ....G 330 343-1143
New Philadelphia *(G-14891)*
Coate Concrete Products Inc ....G 937 698-4181
West Milton *(G-20106)*
Crummitt & Son Vault Corp ....G 304 281-2420
Martins Ferry *(G-12923)*
Fithian-Wilbert Burial Vlt Co ....F 330 758-2327
Youngstown *(G-21087)*
Fort Stben Burial Estates Assn ....G 740 266-6101
Steubenville *(G-17695)*

Galena Vault Ltd ....G 740 965-2200
Galena *(G-10242)*
Harn Vault Service Inc ....F 330 832-1995
Minerva *(G-14324)*
Hilles Burial Vaults Inc ....G 330 823-2251
Alliance *(G-514)*
Landon Vault Company ....F 614 443-5505
Columbus *(G-7283)*
Mack Industries ....C 419 353-7081
Bowling Green *(G-1999)*
Mack Industries Inc ....G 330 460-7005
Brunswick *(G-2237)*
Money Jewelry Vaults ....G 937 366-6391
Wilmington *(G-20671)*
Neher Burial Vault Company ....F 937 399-4494
Springfield *(G-17617)*
Paper Vault ....G 614 859-5538
Columbus *(G-7459)*
River Cities Vault Inc ....F 740 237-0010
Ironton *(G-11300)*
Seislove Vault & Septic Tanks ....G 419 447-5473
Tiffin *(G-18243)*
Shaw Wilbert Vaults LLC ....G 740 498-7438
Newcomerstown *(G-15124)*
Sky Vault Ltd ....G 740 549-0623
Lewis Center *(G-11919)*
Stuart Burial Vault Company ....G 740 569-4158
Bremen *(G-2080)*
Thomas-Wilbert Vault Co Inc ....G 740 695-5671
Saint Clairsville *(G-16812)*
Turner Vault ....G 419 223-6861
Lima *(G-12106)*
Turner Vault Co ....E 419 537-1133
Northwood *(G-15493)*
Youngstown Burial Vault Co ....G 330 782-0015
Youngstown *(G-21248)*

BURIAL VAULTS: Stone

Bell Burial Vault Co ....G 513 896-9044
Hamilton *(G-10674)*
Gallipolis Vault Co Inc ....G 740 446-3357
Gallipolis *(G-10297)*

BURLAP & BURLAP PRDTS

Dayton Bag & Burlap Co ....F 937 253-1722
Dayton *(G-8268)*

BURNERS: Gas, Domestic

BMC Holdings Inc ....G 419 636-1194
Bryan *(G-2283)*

BURNERS: Gas, Indl

Burner Technology Unlimited ....G 440 232-6181
Cleveland *(G-4949)*
Selas Heat Technology Co LLC ....G 216 662-8800
Streetsboro *(G-17874)*
Ws Thermal Process Tech Inc ....G 440 385-6829
Lorain *(G-12293)*

BURNERS: Oil, Domestic Or Indl

Es Thermal Inc ....E 440 323-3291
Elyria *(G-9422)*
RW Beckett Corporation ....C 440 327-1060
North Ridgeville *(G-15402)*

BUS BARS: Electrical

Crown Electric Engrg & Mfg LLC ....E 513 539-7394
Middletown *(G-14035)*
Schneider Electric Usa Inc ....B 513 523-4171
Oxford *(G-15843)*
Schneider Electric Usa Inc ....C 513 755-4231
West Chester *(G-19942)*
Schneider Electric Usa Inc ....C 513 755-5000
West Chester *(G-19943)*

BUSHINGS & BEARINGS

Advance Bronze Inc ....D 330 948-1231
Lodi *(G-12155)*
Climax Metal Products Company ....D 440 943-8898
Mentor *(G-13547)*
Connell Limited Partnership ....D 877 534-8986
Northfield *(G-15464)*
Daido Metal Bellefontaine LLC ....C 937 592-5010
Bellefontaine *(G-1526)*
E I Du Pont De Nemours & Co ....C 216 901-3600
Cleveland *(G-5232)*

PRODUCT

McNeil Industries Inc ....E 440 951-7756
Painesville *(G-15901)*

S C Industries Inc ....E 216 732-9000
Euclid *(G-9605)*

BUSHINGS & BEARINGS: Brass, Exc Machined

A & H Automotive Industries ....G 614 235-1759
Columbus *(G-6666)*

BUSHINGS & BEARINGS: Bronze, Exc Machined

Bunting Bearings LLC ....E 419 522-3323
Mansfield *(G-12572)*

BUSINESS ACTIVITIES: Non-Commercial Site

Advanced Med Interfaces LLC ....G 937 361-8385
Lebanon *(G-11775)*

AG Designs LLC ....G 614 506-2849
Delaware *(G-8819)*

Aja Industries LLC ....G 614 216-9566
Gahanna *(G-10203)*

Apostrophe Apps LLC ....G 513 608-4399
Liberty Twp *(G-11970)*

Aqua Lily Products LLC ....F 951 246-9610
Willoughby *(G-20439)*

Aquapro Systems LLC ....F 877 278-2797
West Chester *(G-19808)*

Big Bills Trucking LLC ....G 614 850-0626
Hilliard *(G-10934)*

Bjond Inc ....G 614 537-7246
Columbus *(G-6835)*

Bridgits Bath LLC ....G 937 259-1960
Dayton *(G-8194)*

Calvin Lanier ....E 937 952-4221
Dayton *(G-8208)*

Canvas 123 LLC ....G 312 805-0563
Akron *(G-108)*

Casentric LLC ....G 216 233-6300
Shaker Heights *(G-17087)*

Cbr Industrial LLC ....G 419 645-6447
Wapakoneta *(G-19483)*

CFC Startec LLC ....G 330 688-8316
Stow *(G-17737)*

Collaborative For Adaptive Lif ....G 216 513-0572
Fairlawn *(G-9746)*

Corcadence Inc ....G 216 702-6371
Beachwood *(G-1265)*

Creative Fabrication Ltd ....G 740 262-5789
Richwood *(G-16659)*

Cult Couture LLC ....G 330 801-9475
Akron *(G-135)*

Custom Built Crates Inc ....E 513 248-4422
Milford *(G-14135)*

Custom Machining Solutions LLC ....G 330 221-1523
Rootstown *(G-16720)*

D&M Fencing LLC ....G 419 604-0698
Spencerville *(G-17459)*

Digionyx LLC ....G 614 594-9897
London *(G-12209)*

Dip It Good Foods Inc ....G 330 219-3137
Newton Falls *(G-15132)*

Dwllr Inc ....G 513 400-5544
West Chester *(G-19854)*

Eae Logistics Company LLC ....G 440 417-4788
Madison *(G-12505)*

Echo Mobile Solutions LLC ....G 614 282-3756
Pickerington *(G-16191)*

Ecoponics Group LLC ....G 330 819-1233
Kent *(G-11453)*

Elite Biomedical Solutions LLC ....F 513 207-0602
Cincinnati *(G-3301)*

Enerchem Incorporated ....G 513 745-0580
Cincinnati *(G-3703)*

Eq Technologies LLC ....G 216 548-3684
Cleveland *(G-5290)*

Ergo Desktop LLC ....E 567 890-3746
Celina *(G-2995)*

Erik V Lamb ....G 330 962-1540
Copley *(G-7846)*

Essential Pathways Ohio LLC ....G 330 518-3091
Youngstown *(G-21079)*

Everykey Inc ....G 866 798-5577
Cleveland *(G-5309)*

Everything In America ....G 347 871-6872
Cleveland *(G-5310)*

Fabstar Tanks Inc ....F 419 587-3639
Grover Hill *(G-10652)*

Fgm Media Inc ....G 440 376-0487
North Royalton *(G-15419)*

Garden of Delight LLC ....G 513 300-7205
Cincinnati *(G-3797)*

Garys Classic Guitars ....G 513 891-0555
Loveland *(G-12351)*

Gdw Woodworking LLC ....G 513 494-3041
South Lebanon *(G-17429)*

Gro2 Bags & Accessories LLC ....G 740 622-0928
Coshocton *(G-7894)*

Groundhogs 2000 LLC ....G 440 653-1647
Oakwood Village *(G-15625)*

Hands On International LLC ....G 513 502-9000
Mason *(G-13034)*

Health Nuts Media LLC ....G 818 802-5222
Cleveland *(G-5489)*

Hundley Cellars LLC ....G 843 368-5016
Geneva *(G-10351)*

Immersus Health Company LLC ....G 855 994-4325
Cincinnati *(G-3912)*

Innovative Integrations Inc ....G 216 533-5353
Mesopotamia *(G-13775)*

Instruction & Design Concepts ....G 937 439-2698
Dayton *(G-8412)*

Jeff Pendergrass ....G 513 575-1226
Milford *(G-14156)*

Jls Funeral Home ....F 614 625-1220
Columbus *(G-7234)*

Jnp Group LLC ....G 800 735-9645
Wooster *(G-20791)*

Joan B Mailloux ....G 361 992-5311
Mansfield *(G-12627)*

JPb Lures Manufacturing LLC ....G 419 734-9488
Marblehead *(G-12745)*

Ksn Clearing LLC ....F 304 269-3306
Gallipolis *(G-10303)*

Kustom Cases LLC ....G 240 380-6275
Dayton *(G-8448)*

Kw River Hydroelectric I LLC ....G 513 673-2251
Cincinnati *(G-4007)*

Leap Publishing Services Inc ....F 234 738-0082
Stow *(G-17768)*

Lifo Enterprises Inc ....G 513 225-8801
Loveland *(G-12371)*

Liquid Shock Games LLC ....G 386 627-0840
Elyria *(G-9453)*

M&M Great Adventures LLC ....G 937 344-1415
Westerville *(G-20169)*

Matrix Measuring System ....G 330 718-2804
Newton Falls *(G-15136)*

Mbenztech ....G 937 291-1527
Centerville *(G-3044)*

Micropress America LLC ....G 513 746-0689
Cincinnati *(G-4102)*

Midwest Exposure Magazine ....G 937 626-6738
Dayton *(G-8495)*

Monitored Therapeutics Inc ....G 614 761-3555
Dublin *(G-9106)*

Nanbrands LLC ....G 513 313-9581
Cincinnati *(G-4136)*

Olde Man Granola LLC ....F 419 819-9576
Findlay *(G-9872)*

Paradise Lemonade ....F 740 816-0771
Westerville *(G-20178)*

Park Press Direct ....G 419 626-4426
Sandusky *(G-16993)*

Parrot University LLC ....G 740 965-1965
Sunbury *(G-18073)*

Pentagear Products LLC ....F 937 660-8182
Dayton *(G-8569)*

Pilot Production Solutions LLC ....G 513 602-1467
Mason *(G-13073)*

Pmj Partners LLC ....G 201 360-1914
Columbus *(G-7501)*

Popped ....F 330 678-1893
Kent *(G-11504)*

Qleanair Scandinavia Inc ....G 614 323-1272
Columbus *(G-7529)*

Quality Drble Indus Floors Inc ....E 937 696-2833
Farmersville *(G-9773)*

Quayle Consulting Inc ....G 614 868-1363
Pickerington *(G-16202)*

Rageon Inc ....F 617 633-0544
Cleveland *(G-6088)*

RE Connors Construction Ltd ....G 740 644-0261
Thornville *(G-18194)*

Red Barakuda LLC ....G 614 596-5432
Columbus *(G-7550)*

Resource Exchange Company Inc ....G 440 773-8915
Akron *(G-372)*

Riverrock Recycl Crushing LLC ....G 937 325-2052
Springfield *(G-17640)*

Rj S Machine Shop Service ....G 937 927-0137
Seaman *(G-17042)*

Robby Yoder ....G 740 679-2776
Quaker City *(G-16501)*

Roboworld Molded Products LLC ....G 513 720-6900
West Chester *(G-19935)*

San Pallet LLC ....G 937 271-5308
Troy *(G-18871)*

Scottrods LLC ....G 419 499-2705
Monroeville *(G-14428)*

Shade Text Book Service Inc ....G 740 696-1323
Shade *(G-17079)*

Shot-Force Pro LLC ....G 740 753-3927
Nelsonville *(G-14739)*

Signalysis Inc ....F 513 528-6164
Cincinnati *(G-4420)*

Simply Unique Snacks LLC ....G 513 223-7736
Cincinnati *(G-4422)*

Sourcepoint Logistics LLC ....E 937 604-8209
Tipp City *(G-18300)*

Star Newspaper ....G 614 622-5930
Columbus *(G-7652)*

Stephen J Page ....G 865 951-3316
Williamsburg *(G-20412)*

Steven L Lones ....G 740 452-8851
Zanesville *(G-21357)*

Stutzman Manufacturing Ltd ....G 330 674-4359
Millersburg *(G-14265)*

Swagg Productions2015llc ....F 614 815-1173
Reynoldsburg *(G-16608)*

Thedkahn LLC ....G 239 961-8757
Amelia *(G-586)*

Three H Lumber ....G 740 473-2515
Newport *(G-15127)*

Tillmans Entp -Signs Ship LLC ....G 440 281-9340
Elyria *(G-9502)*

Time Is Money ....G 419 701-6098
Fostoria *(G-9997)*

Timmys Sandwich Shop ....G 419 350-8267
Toledo *(G-18724)*

Tri County Vking Warriors ....E 330 646-4632
Warren *(G-19610)*

Ulrich Rubber Stamp Company ....G 419 339-9939
Elida *(G-9359)*

Vela ....G 614 500-0150
Salesville *(G-16938)*

Wonderful Failure LLC ....G 440 666-0919
Lakewood *(G-11682)*

BUSINESS FORMS WHOLESALERS

Anthony Business Forms Inc ....F 937 253-0072
Dayton *(G-8096)*

Bay Business Forms Inc ....F 937 322-3000
Springfield *(G-17521)*

Bloch Printing Company ....G 330 576-6760
Copley *(G-7840)*

Custom Products Corporation ....D 440 528-7100
Solon *(G-17280)*

Delores E OBeirn ....G 440 582-3610
Cleveland *(G-5182)*

G Q Business Products ....G 513 792-4750
Blue Ash *(G-1801)*

GBS Corp ....C 330 494-5330
North Canton *(G-15233)*

Marles Business Systems Inc ....G 440 268-8380
Brooklyn Heights *(G-2142)*

Optimum System Products Inc ....E 614 885-4464
Westerville *(G-20228)*

Rotary Printing Company ....G 419 668-4821
Norwalk *(G-15563)*

Sentry Graphics Inc ....G 440 735-0850
Northfield *(G-15471)*

Shamrock Companies Inc ....D 440 899-9510
Westlake *(G-20308)*

William J Bergen & Co ....G 440 248-6132
Solon *(G-17414)*

BUSINESS FORMS: Printed, Continuous

Highland Computer Forms Inc ....D 937 393-4215
Hillsboro *(G-11001)*

Rotary Forms Press Inc ....E 937 393-3426
Hillsboro *(G-11013)*

BUSINESS FORMS: Printed, Manifold

Anderson Graphics Inc ....E 330 745-2165
Barberton *(G-1098)*

Anthony Business Forms Inc ....F 937 253-0072
Dayton *(G-8096)*

Crabar/Gbf Inc ....G 419 943-2141
Leipsic *(G-11868)*

Custom Products Corporation ....D 440 528-7100
Solon *(G-17280)*

Delores E OBeirn ....G 440 582-3610
Cleveland *(G-5182)*

Dupli-Systems Inc ....C 440 234-9415
Strongsville *(G-17913)*

Eleet Cryogenics Inc ....E 330 874-4009
Bolivar *(G-1933)*

GBS Corp ....C 330 863-1828
Malvern *(G-12545)*

GBS Corp ....C 330 494-5330
North Canton *(G-15233)*

Geygan Enterprises Inc ....F 513 932-4222
Lebanon *(G-11803)*

Hubert Enterprises Inc ....G 513 367-8600
Harrison *(G-10783)*

Kroy LLC ....C 216 426-5600
Cleveland *(G-5666)*

Lakeshore Graphic Industries ....F 419 626-8631
Sandusky *(G-16978)*

Little Printing Company ....E 937 773-4595
Piqua *(G-16286)*

Misato Computer Products Inc ....G 937 890-8410
Vandalia *(G-19305)*

Print-Digital Incorporated ....G 330 686-5945
Stow *(G-17792)*

Quick Tech Graphics Inc ....E 937 743-5952
Springboro *(G-17502)*

Reynolds and Reynolds Company ....F 419 584-7000
Celina *(G-3017)*

Reynolds and Reynolds Company ....E 937 449-4039
Dayton *(G-8630)*

Reynolds and Reynolds Company ....F 937 485-2805
Beavercreek *(G-1379)*

RR Donnelley & Sons Company ....E 440 774-2101
Oberlin *(G-15647)*

S F Mock & Associates LLC ....F 937 438-0196
Dayton *(G-8644)*

Shawnee Systems Inc ....D 513 561-9932
Cincinnati *(G-4414)*

SRC Liquidation LLC ....A 937 221-1000
Dayton *(G-8672)*

Standard Register Inc ....F 513 772-8860
Cincinnati *(G-4454)*

Standard Register Inc ....F 513 563-9700
Blue Ash *(G-1874)*

Standard Register Inc ....G 440 974-1611
Mentor *(G-13730)*

Standard Register Inc ....D 216 265-9612
Richfield *(G-16640)*

Standard Register Inc ....E 860 870-2063
Dayton *(G-8676)*

Standard Register Inc ....F 732 356-0081
Dayton *(G-8677)*

Standard Register Inc ....G 480 763-1900
Dayton *(G-8678)*

Standard Register Inc ....D 937 221-3347
Grove City *(G-10599)*

Standard Register Inc ....G 937 228-5800
Dayton *(G-8679)*

Tcp Inc ....G 330 836-4239
Fairlawn *(G-9764)*

Thomas Products Co Inc ....E 513 756-9009
Cincinnati *(G-4507)*

Wfsr Holdings LLC ....A 877 735-4966
Dayton *(G-8757)*

BUSINESS FORMS: Unit Sets, Manifold

Unit Sets Inc ....E 937 840-6123
Hillsboro *(G-11017)*

BUSINESS MACHINE REPAIR, ELECTRIC

JJ Delong & Associates Inc ....G 216 861-4727
Cleveland *(G-5616)*

Matrix Measuring System ....G 330 718-2804
Newton Falls *(G-15136)*

Queen City Office Machine ....F 513 251-7200
Cincinnati *(G-4317)*

BUSINESS SUPPORT SVCS

Advanced Propeller Systems ....G 937 409-1038
Dayton *(G-8094)*

Gardella Jewelry LLC ....G 440 877-9261
North Royalton *(G-15420)*

Industrial Application Svs ....G 419 875-5093
Grand Rapids *(G-10440)*

Jrg Performance Technologies ....G 216 408-5974
Cleveland *(G-5625)*

Lesch Btry & Pwr Solution LLC ....G 419 884-0219
Mansfield *(G-12636)*

BUSINESS TRAINING SVCS

Pakra LLC ....F 614 477-6965
Columbus *(G-7455)*

BUTTER WHOLESALERS

Frank L Harter & Son Inc ....G 513 574-1330
Cincinnati *(G-3778)*

CABINETS & CASES: Radio, Wood

Masco Cabinetry LLC ....A 440 632-2547
Middlefield *(G-13954)*

CABINETS & CASES: Show, Display & Storage, Exc Wood

Bedford Cabinet Inc ....G 440 439-4830
Cleveland *(G-4903)*

D Lewis Inc ....G 740 695-2615
Saint Clairsville *(G-16788)*

Metal Fabricating Corporation ....D 216 631-8121
Cleveland *(G-5787)*

Paul Yoder ....G 740 439-5811
Senecaville *(G-17059)*

CABINETS: Bathroom Vanities, Wood

Bison Builders LLC ....F 614 636-0365
Columbus *(G-6832)*

Profiles In Design Inc ....F 513 751-2212
Cincinnati *(G-4297)*

S & G Manufacturing Group LLC ....C 614 529-0100
Hilliard *(G-10977)*

Tenkotte Tops Inc ....G 513 738-7300
Harrison *(G-10810)*

CABINETS: Entertainment

Innerwood & Company ....F 513 677-2229
Loveland *(G-12360)*

Kraftmaid Trucking Inc ....D 440 632-2531
Middlefield *(G-13949)*

Xxx Intrntional Amusements Inc ....E 216 671-6900
Cleveland *(G-6487)*

CABINETS: Entertainment Units, Household, Wood

Progressive Furniture Inc ....E 419 446-4500
Archbold *(G-690)*

CABINETS: Factory

Bolons Custom Kitchens Inc ....F 330 499-0092
Canton *(G-2625)*

Columbia Cabinets Inc ....G 440 748-1010
Columbia Station *(G-6584)*

Custom Surroundings Inc ....F 330 483-9020
Valley City *(G-19202)*

Don Walter Kitchen Distrs Inc ....G 330 793-9338
Youngstown *(G-21071)*

Home Idea Center Inc ....F 419 375-4951
Fort Recovery *(G-9954)*

Kinnemyers Cornerstone Cab Inc ....E 513 353-3030
Cleves *(G-6518)*

Mro Built Inc ....D 330 526-0555
North Canton *(G-15252)*

The Wood Shed ....G 937 429-3355
Xenia *(G-20979)*

Tri-Co Industries ....G 740 927-1928
Pataskala *(G-15988)*

Vivo Brothers LLC ....F 330 629-8686
Poland *(G-16387)*

Wades Woodworking Inc ....F 937 374-6470
Xenia *(G-20988)*

CABINETS: Filing, Wood

Innerwood & Company ....F 513 677-2229
Loveland *(G-12360)*

Innovative Woodworking Inc ....G 513 531-1940
Cincinnati *(G-3923)*

CABINETS: Kitchen, Metal

C-Link Enterprises LLC ....F 937 222-2829
Dayton *(G-8205)*

Cabintpak Kitchens of Columbus ....G 614 294-4646
Columbus *(G-6886)*

CABINETS: Kitchen, Wood

4-B Wood Specialties Inc ....G 330 769-2188
Seville *(G-17067)*

A & J Woodworking Inc ....G 419 695-5655
Delphos *(G-8898)*

Affordable Cabinet Doors ....G 513 734-9663
Bethel *(G-1664)*

Agean Marble Manufacturing ....F 513 874-1475
West Chester *(G-19978)*

Ailes Millwork Inc ....F 330 678-4300
Kent *(G-11424)*

Al-Co Products Inc ....F 419 399-3867
Latty *(G-11767)*

Alpine Cabinets Inc ....G 330 273-2131
Hinckley *(G-11021)*

Approved Plumbing Co ....G 216 663-5063
Cleveland *(G-4820)*

Baird Cabinet Shop Inc ....G 330 837-9075
Massillon *(G-13113)*

Benchmark Cabinets ....E 740 397-4615
Mount Vernon *(G-14609)*

Benchmark Cabinets ....E 740 694-1144
Fredericktown *(G-10096)*

Bestway Cabinets LLC ....G 614 306-3518
Hilliard *(G-10932)*

Bowes Mill and Cabinet LLC ....G 440 236-3255
Columbia Station *(G-6581)*

Bricolage Inc ....G 614 853-6789
Grove City *(G-10547)*

Brower Products Inc ....D 937 563-1111
Cincinnati *(G-3482)*

Bruewer Woodwork Mfg Co ....D 513 353-3505
Cleves *(G-6507)*

Cabinet Concepts Inc ....G 440 232-4644
Cleveland *(G-4960)*

Cabinet Source ....G 330 336-5600
Wadsworth *(G-19397)*

Cabinet Specialties Inc ....E 330 695-3463
Fredericksburg *(G-10079)*

Cabinet Systems Inc ....G 440 237-1924
Cleveland *(G-4961)*

Cabinetry By Ebbing ....G 419 678-2191
Celina *(G-2988)*

Cabinets Inc ....G 740 377-4629
South Point *(G-17435)*

Canton Cabinet Co ....G 330 455-2585
Canton *(G-2637)*

Cardinal Custom Cabinets Ltd ....G 216 281-1570
Cleveland *(G-4975)*

Care Cabinetry Inc ....G 216 481-7445
Euclid *(G-9570)*

Carnegie Plas Cabinetry Inc ....G 216 451-3300
Cleveland *(G-4981)*

Carter-Jones Lumber Company ....C 330 674-9060
Millersburg *(G-14211)*

Cedee Cedar Inc ....F 740 363-3148
Delaware *(G-8831)*

Chesterland Cabinet Company ....G 440 564-1157
Newbury *(G-15083)*

Cirjak Furniture and Design ....G 330 296-8035
Ravenna *(G-16521)*

Clancys Cabinet Shop ....E 419 445-4455
Archbold *(G-668)*

Clark Son Actn Liquidation Inc ....G 330 866-9330
East Sparta *(G-9254)*

Cleveland Custom Cabinets LLC ....G 213 663-0606
Cleveland *(G-5056)*

Colonial Cabinets Inc ....F 440 355-9663
Lagrange *(G-11624)*

Commercial Bar & Cabinetry ....G 330 743-1420
Youngstown *(G-21054)*

Contemporary Cabinets Inc ....G 937 833-1135
Brookville *(G-2178)*

Crane Plumbing LLC ....E 419 522-4211
Mansfield *(G-12587)*

Custom Woodworking Inc ....G 419 456-3330
Ottawa *(G-15791)*

PRODUCT

D Lewis Inc ... G ... 740 695-2615
Saint Clairsville (G-16788)
Dgl Woodworking Inc ... F ... 937 837-7091
Dayton (G-8302)
Distinctive Surfaces LLC ... F ... 614 431-0898
Columbus (G-7031)
Dover Cabinet Inc ... F ... 330 343-9074
Dover (G-8978)
Dutch Valley Woodworking Inc ... F ... 330 852-4319
Sugarcreek (G-18022)
E J Skok Industries ... E ... 216 292-7533
Bedford (G-1422)
East Oberlin Cabinets ... G ... 440 775-1166
Oberlin (G-15637)
Ernst Custom Cabinets LLC ... G ... 513 376-9554
Cincinnati (G-3717)
Fairfield Woodworks Ltd ... G ... 740 689-1953
Lancaster (G-11715)
Fdi Cabinetry LLC ... G ... 513 353-4500
Cleves (G-6514)
Fine Wood Design Inc ... G ... 440 327-0751
North Ridgeville (G-15374)
Fleetwood Custom Countertops ... F ... 740 965-9833
Johnstown (G-11398)
Flottemesch Anthony & Son ... F ... 513 561-1212
Cincinnati (G-3762)
Formware Inc ... G ... 614 231-9387
Columbus (G-7093)
Forum III Inc ... F ... 513 961-5123
Cincinnati (G-3773)
Franklin Cabinet Company Inc ... E ... 937 743-9606
Franklin (G-10023)
Gillard Construction Inc ... F ... 740 376-9744
Marietta (G-12786)
Hampshire Co ... E ... 937 773-3493
Piqua (G-16268)
Harold Flory ... G ... 937 473-3030
Covington (G-7924)
Hattenbach Company ... E ... 330 744-2732
Youngstown (G-21107)
Hattenbach Company ... D ... 216 881-5200
Cleveland (G-5485)
Heartland Home Cabinetry Ltd ... G ... 740 936-5100
Sunbury (G-18062)
Holmes Lumber & Bldg Ctr Inc ... C ... 330 674-9060
Millersburg (G-14231)
Idx Corporation ... C ... 937 401-3225
Dayton (G-8400)
Inter Cab Corporation ... G ... 216 351-0770
Cleveland (G-5576)
J & K Cabinetry Incorporated ... G ... 513 860-3461
West Chester (G-20017)
J & L Door ... G ... 330 684-1496
Dalton (G-8071)
James F Seme ... G ... 440 759-6455
Berea (G-1623)
Kellogg Cabinets Inc ... E ... 614 833-9596
Canal Winchester (G-2529)
Kelly Cabinet Company LLC ... G ... 614 563-2971
Powell (G-16474)
Kinnemyers Cornerstone Cab Inc ... G ... 513 353-3030
Cleves (G-6518)
Kinsella Manufacturing Co Inc ... F ... 513 561-5285
Cincinnati (G-3991)
Kitchen Designs Plus Inc ... E ... 419 536-6605
Toledo (G-18545)
Kitchen Works Inc ... G ... 440 353-0939
North Ridgeville (G-15385)
Kitchens By Rutenschroer Inc ... F ... 513 251-8333
Cincinnati (G-3994)
Lima Millwork Inc ... E ... 419 331-3303
Elida (G-9351)
M A Miller ... G ... 440 636-5697
Middlefield (G-13951)
Malco Laminated Inc ... G ... 513 541-8300
Cincinnati (G-4055)
Marsh Industries Inc ... E ... 330 308-8667
New Philadelphia (G-14912)
Masco Cabinetry LLC ... B ... 740 286-5033
Jackson (G-11320)
Masco Cbinetry Middlefield LLC ... A ... 440 632-5333
Middlefield (G-13955)
Masco Cbinetry Middlefield LLC ... D ... 440 632-5058
Middlefield (G-13956)
Masco Cbinetry Middlefield LLC ... B ... 440 437-8537
Orwell (G-15778)
Midwest Woodworking Co Inc ... E ... 513 631-6684
Cincinnati (G-4106)
Miller Cabinet Company LLC ... E ... 614 873-4221
Plain City (G-16351)
Mock Woodworking Company LLC ... E ... 740 452-2701
Zanesville (G-21329)
Mro Built Inc ... D ... 330 526-0555
North Canton (G-15252)
Nagele Manufacturing Co Inc ... E ... 216 433-1100
Cleveland (G-5849)
Navigator Construction LLC ... G ... 330 244-0221
North Canton (G-15254)
Northeast Cabinet Co LLC ... G ... 614 759-0800
Columbus (G-7402)
Northpointe Cabinetry LLC ... G ... 740 455-4045
Zanesville (G-21334)
Oakwood Furniture Inc ... G ... 740 896-3162
Lowell (G-12403)
Oen Custom Cabinets Inc ... G ... 419 738-8115
Wapakoneta (G-19503)
Ohio River Valley Cabinet ... G ... 740 975-8846
Newark (G-15042)
Old Mill Custom Cabinetry Co ... G ... 419 423-8897
Findlay (G-9871)
Online Mega Sellers Corp ... G ... 888 384-6468
Toledo (G-18619)
Peters Cabinetry ... G ... 937 884-7514
Brookville (G-2196)
Phil D De Mint ... G ... 740 474-7777
Circleville (G-4636)
Pleasant Valley Wdwkg LLC ... G ... 440 636-5860
Middlefield (G-13983)
Precision Woodwork Ltd ... G ... 440 257-3002
Mentor (G-13696)
R Carney Thomas ... G ... 740 342-3388
New Lexington (G-14853)
Red Barn Cabinet Co ... G ... 937 884-9800
Arcanum (G-659)
Regal Cabinet Inc ... G ... 419 865-3932
Toledo (G-18674)
Reserve Millwork Inc ... E ... 216 531-6982
Bedford (G-1457)
Riceland Cabinet Inc ... D ... 330 601-1071
Wooster (G-20829)
Richard Benhase & Associates ... F ... 513 772-1896
Cincinnati (G-4343)
Riggenbach Kitchens ... G ... 330 669-2113
Smithville (G-17242)
River East Custom Cabinets ... E ... 419 244-3226
Toledo (G-18677)
Riverside Cnstr Svcs Inc ... E ... 513 723-0900
Cincinnati (G-4349)
Roberts Cabinetry LLC ... G ... 330 421-4374
Medina (G-13469)
Roettger Hardwood Inc ... F ... 937 693-6811
Kettlersville (G-11589)
Royal Cabinet Design Co Inc ... F ... 216 267-5330
Cleveland (G-6137)
Ruede Cabinet Company ... G ... 614 875-8717
Lockbourne (G-12151)
S & W Custom Tops Inc ... G ... 330 788-2525
Youngstown (G-21195)
Schrock Woodworking ... G ... 740 489-5229
Freeport (G-10120)
Shawnee Wood Products Inc ... G ... 440 632-1771
Middlefield (G-13989)
Showcase Cab Mar Rstoration LL ... G ... 419 626-6715
Sandusky (G-17008)
Sidney Stiers ... G ... 740 454-7368
Zanesville (G-21353)
Snows Wood Shop Inc ... E ... 419 836-3805
Oregon (G-15716)
Specified Structures Inc ... G ... 330 753-0693
Barberton (G-1149)
Summit Custom Cabinets ... G ... 740 345-1734
Newark (G-15061)
Surface Enterprises Inc ... E ... 419 476-5670
Toledo (G-18711)
TDS Custom Cabinets LLC ... G ... 614 517-2220
Columbus (G-7680)
Thomas Cabinet Shop Inc ... F ... 937 847-8239
Dayton (G-8711)
Tiffin Metal Products Co ... D ... 419 447-8414
Tiffin (G-18248)
Trail Cabinet ... G ... 330 893-3791
Dundee (G-9181)
Trutech Cabinetry ... G ... 614 338-0680
Columbus (G-7713)
Turnwood Industries Inc ... E ... 330 278-2421
Hinckley (G-11031)
Unique Woodmasters LLC ... G ... 419 268-9663
Celina (G-3025)
Virgils Kitchens Inc ... G ... 440 355-5058
Lagrange (G-11641)
Wengerd Cabinets ... G ... 330 231-0879
Millersburg (G-14285)
Westgerdes Cabinets ... G ... 419 375-2113
Fort Recovery (G-9963)
Wilson Cabinet Co ... E ... 330 276-8711
Killbuck (G-11601)
Woodcraft Industries Inc ... D ... 440 437-7811
Orwell (G-15783)
Woodcraft Industries Inc ... C ... 440 632-9655
Middlefield (G-14007)
Wurms Woodworking Company ... E ... 419 492-2184
New Washington (G-14966)
Xxx Intrntional Amusements Inc ... E ... 216 671-6900
Cleveland (G-6487)
Yoder Cabinets Ltd ... G ... 614 873-5186
Plain City (G-16366)
Your Cabinetry ... G ... 440 638-4925
Strongsville (G-17986)

CABINETS: Office, Metal

Dgl Woodworking Inc ... F ... 937 837-7091
Dayton (G-8302)
Edsal Sandusky Corporation ... C ... 419 626-5465
Sandusky (G-16960)

CABINETS: Office, Wood

Cabinet Systems Inc ... G ... 440 237-1924
Cleveland (G-4961)
Custom Millcraft Corp ... E ... 513 874-7080
West Chester (G-19851)
East Woodworking Company ... G ... 216 791-5950
Cleveland (G-5240)
Geograph Industries Inc ... E ... 513 202-9200
Harrison (G-10780)
Hoge Lumber Company ... E ... 419 753-2263
New Knoxville (G-14836)
Interior Products Co Inc ... F ... 216 641-1919
Cleveland (G-5578)
Macwood Inc ... G ... 614 279-7676
Columbus (G-7312)
R Carney Thomas ... G ... 740 342-3388
New Lexington (G-14853)
Richard Benhase & Associates ... F ... 513 772-1896
Cincinnati (G-4343)
Specialty Services Inc ... G ... 614 421-1599
Columbus (G-7638)

CABINETS: Show, Display, Etc, Wood, Exc Refrigerated

A J Construction Co ... G ... 330 539-9544
Girard (G-10380)
Amtekco Industries Inc ... D ... 614 228-6590
Columbus (G-6749)
Bauman Custom Woodworking LLC ... G ... 330 482-4330
Salem (G-16875)
Custom Design Cabinets & Tops ... G ... 440 639-9900
Painesville (G-15872)
Designer Cntemporary Laminates ... G ... 440 946-8207
Willoughby (G-20473)
Gary L Gast ... G ... 419 626-5915
Sandusky (G-16968)
Hattenbach Company ... D ... 216 881-5200
Cleveland (G-5485)
Hattenbach Company ... E ... 330 744-2732
Youngstown (G-21107)
Kellogg Cabinets Inc ... E ... 614 833-9596
Canal Winchester (G-2529)
Macwood Inc ... G ... 614 279-7676
Columbus (G-7312)
Mespo Woodworking ... G ... 440 693-4041
Middlefield (G-13958)
Miller Cabinet Company LLC ... E ... 614 873-4221
Plain City (G-16351)
R D Cook Company LLC ... G ... 614 262-0550
Columbus (G-7543)
Rinos Woodworking Shop Inc ... F ... 440 946-1718
Willoughby (G-20589)
Robertson Cabinets Inc ... E ... 937 698-3755
West Milton (G-20110)
Vances Department Store ... G ... 937 549-2188
Manchester (G-12552)
Vances Department Store ... F ... 937 549-3033
Manchester (G-12553)
Woodworks For You ... G ... 440 277-8147
Wakeman (G-19455)

CABLE & OTHER PAY TELEVISION DISTRIBUTION

EW Scripps Company ....E 513 977-3000
Cincinnati *(G-3728)*
Ohio News Network ....D 614 460-3700
Columbus *(G-7423)*

CABLE TELEVISION

Block Communications Inc ....F 419 724-6212
Toledo *(G-18372)*

CABLE WIRING SETS: Battery, Internal Combustion Engines

Empire Power Systems Co ....G 440 796-4401
Madison *(G-12506)*
Noco Company ....B 216 464-8131
Solon *(G-17350)*

CABLE: Fiber

Capital Connection Cabling ....G 330 620-6311
Akron *(G-109)*
Connect Television ....G 614 876-4402
Hilliard *(G-10943)*

CABLE: Fiber Optic

Integrated Systems Professiona ....G 614 875-0104
Grove City *(G-10565)*

CABLE: Noninsulated

Assembly Specialty Pdts Inc ....E 216 676-5600
Cleveland *(G-4848)*
Cable and Ctrl Solutions LLC ....G 937 254-2227
Dayton *(G-8097)*
Cable Mfg & Assembly Inc ....C 330 874-2900
Bolivar *(G-1929)*
Microplex Inc ....E 330 498-0600
North Canton *(G-15249)*

CABLE: Ropes & Fiber

Phoenix/Electrotek LLC ....E 740 681-1412
Lancaster *(G-11739)*
Wire Holdings LLC ....G 216 731-9191
Cleveland *(G-6467)*

CABLE: Steel, Insulated Or Armored

Electroduct LLC ....E 330 220-9300
Brunswick *(G-2223)*
Murphy Industries Inc ....E 740 387-7890
Marion *(G-12887)*

CABS: Indl Trucks & Tractors

Martin Sheet Metal Inc ....D 216 377-8200
Cleveland *(G-5753)*

CAFFEINE & DERIVATIVES

Avitae USA LLC ....G 216 416-3461
Cleveland *(G-4874)*
Goosefoot Acres Inc ....G 330 225-7184
Valley City *(G-19205)*

CAGES: Wire

Darryl Smith ....G 216 991-5468
Cleveland *(G-5169)*
Mason Company LLC ....E 937 780-2321
Leesburg *(G-11855)*
Precision Wire Products Inc ....G 216 265-7580
Cleveland *(G-6038)*

CALENDARS, WHOLESALE

Gordon Bernard Co Inc ....E 513 248-7600
Milford *(G-14146)*

CALIBRATING SVCS, NEC

Continental Testing Inc ....F 937 832-3322
Union *(G-19065)*
Measurement Specialties Inc ....F 937 885-0800
Dayton *(G-8482)*

CAMERAS & RELATED EQPT: Photographic

Sensopart USA Inc ....G 419 931-7696
Perrysburg *(G-16149)*

CAMPGROUNDS

Caskeys Inc ....G 330 683-0249
Orrville *(G-15733)*

CAMSHAFTS

Mahle Industries Incorporated ....C 740 962-2040
McConnelsville *(G-13353)*
North Coast Camshaft Inc ....G 216 671-3700
Cleveland *(G-5892)*
Park-Ohio Industries Inc ....C 216 341-2300
Newburgh Heights *(G-15077)*

CANDLE SHOPS

Candle Cottage ....G 937 526-4041
Versailles *(G-19343)*

CANDLES

Al Root Company ....C 330 723-4359
Medina *(G-13364)*
Al Root Company ....C 330 725-6677
Medina *(G-13365)*
Ambrosia Inc ....G 419 825-1151
Swanton *(G-18079)*
Amish Lights Candles ....G 330 546-3900
North Canton *(G-15219)*
Candle Cottage ....G 937 526-4041
Versailles *(G-19343)*
Candle-Lite Company LLC ....E 937 780-2711
Leesburg *(G-11850)*
Candle-Lite Company LLC ....D 513 563-1113
Blue Ash *(G-1762)*
Candles By Joyce ....G 740 886-6355
Proctorville *(G-16489)*
Cleveland Plant and Flower Co ....E 614 478-9900
Columbus *(G-6937)*
Connies Candles ....G 740 574-1224
Wheelersburg *(G-20329)*
Dano Jr LLC ....G 440 781-5774
Cleveland *(G-5165)*
Faith Guiding Cafe LLC ....F 614 245-8451
New Albany *(G-14758)*
Gibson Greetings Inc ....G 216 252-7300
Cleveland *(G-5428)*
Glasslight Candles LLC ....G 443 509-5505
Mason *(G-13028)*
Gorant Chocolatier LLC ....C 330 726-8821
Boardman *(G-1921)*
Heart Warming Candles ....G 937 456-2720
Eaton *(G-9308)*
Kendee Candles LLC ....G 330 899-9898
Uniontown *(G-19088)*
Lincoln Candle Company Inc ....G 419 749-4224
Convoy *(G-7832)*
Lumi-Lite Candle Company ....D 740 872-3248
Norwich *(G-15569)*
Ohio Candle Co Inc ....G 740 289-8000
Waverly *(G-19715)*
Wholesale Supplies Plus Inc ....E 440 526-6556
Independence *(G-11285)*
Yankee Candle Company Inc ....G 419 223-0073
Lima *(G-12113)*

CANDY & CONFECTIONS: Cake Ornaments

Decko Products Inc ....D 419 626-5757
Sandusky *(G-16957)*

CANDY & CONFECTIONS: Candy Bars, Including Chocolate Covered

69 Taps ....G 330 253-4554
Akron *(G-14)*
Gwen Rosenberg Enterprises LLC ....G 330 678-1893
Kent *(G-11465)*
Malleys Candies ....D 216 362-8700
Lakewood *(G-11674)*
Marrie S Candies LLC ....E 937 465-3061
West Liberty *(G-20094)*
Rcs Brewhouse ....G 440 984-3103
Amherst *(G-607)*
Snyders-Lance Inc ....G 614 856-4616
Grove City *(G-10596)*

CANDY & CONFECTIONS: Chocolate Candy, Exc Solid Chocolate

Al Meda Chocolates Inc ....G 419 446-2676
Archbold *(G-661)*

Daffins Candies ....G 330 545-0325
Girard *(G-10385)*
Suzin L Chocolatiers ....F 440 323-3372
Elyria *(G-9496)*
Zanesvlle Cnfectionary Hse LLC ....E 740 452-7501
Zanesville *(G-21369)*

CANDY & CONFECTIONS: Chocolate Covered Dates

Walnut Creek Chocolate Company ....E 330 893-2995
Walnut Creek *(G-19471)*

CANDY & CONFECTIONS: Cough Drops, Exc Pharmaceutical Preps

American Health Packaging ....D 614 492-8177
Columbus *(G-6738)*

CANDY & CONFECTIONS: Fruit, Chocolate Covered, Exc Dates

PA & Jjs Fruity Smiles Inc ....G 937 449-0999
Dayton *(G-8560)*

CANDY & CONFECTIONS: Fudge

Gift Cove Inc ....G 419 285-2920
Put In Bay *(G-16498)*
White House Chocolate ....G 440 834-3133
Middlefield *(G-14005)*

CANDY & CONFECTIONS: Nuts, Glace

Great Lakes Popcorn Company ....G 419 732-3080
Port Clinton *(G-16401)*

CANDY & CONFECTIONS: Popcorn Balls/Other Trtd Popcorn Prdts

Crawford Acquisition Corp ....F 216 486-0702
Cleveland *(G-5141)*
Humphrey Company ....F 216 662-6629
Cleveland *(G-5537)*

CANDY, NUT & CONFECTIONERY STORE: Popcorn, Incl Caramel Corn

Gwen Rosenberg Enterprises LLC ....G 330 678-1893
Kent *(G-11465)*

CANDY, NUT & CONFECTIONERY STORES: Candy

Campbells Candies ....G 330 493-1805
Canton *(G-2635)*
Coffelt Candy Inc ....G 937 399-8772
Springfield *(G-17533)*
Coons Homemade Candies ....G 740 496-4141
Harpster *(G-10765)*
E R B Enterprises Inc ....E 740 948-9174
Jeffersonville *(G-11379)*
Fannie May Cnfctons Brands Inc ....A 330 494-0833
North Canton *(G-15230)*
Fawn Confectionery ....F 513 574-9612
Cincinnati *(G-3742)*
Harry London Candies Inc ....C 330 494-0833
North Canton *(G-15239)*
Hartville Chocolates Inc ....F 330 877-1999
Hartville *(G-10822)*
Haute Chocolate Inc ....G 513 793-9999
Montgomery *(G-14432)*
Malleys Candies ....D 216 362-8700
Lakewood *(G-11674)*
Marrie S Candies LLC ....E 937 465-3061
West Liberty *(G-20094)*
Neumeisters Candy Shoppe LLC ....G 419 294-3647
Upper Sandusky *(G-19135)*
Normant Candy Co ....F 419 886-4214
Mansfield *(G-12659)*
Piqua Chocolate Company Inc ....G 937 773-1981
Piqua *(G-16301)*
Robert E McGrath Inc ....E 440 572-7747
Strongsville *(G-17959)*
Suzin L Chocolatiers ....F 440 323-3372
Elyria *(G-9496)*
Walnut Creek Chocolate Company ....E 330 893-2995
Walnut Creek *(G-19471)*
Wittichs Candies Inc ....G 740 474-3313
Circleville *(G-4649)*

PRODUCT

CANDY, NUT & CONFECTIONERY STORES: Confectionery

Dietsch Brothers Incorporated ....E 419 422-4474
Findlay (G-9816)

CANDY, NUT & CONFECTIONERY STORES: Nuts

Krema Products Inc ....G 614 889-4824
Dublin (G-9097)
Trophy Nut Co ....E 937 667-8478
Tipp City (G-18306)

CANDY: Chocolate From Cacao Beans

American Confections Co LLC ....G 614 888-8838
Columbus (G-6734)
Campbells Candies ....G 330 493-1805
Canton (G-2635)
Giannios Candy Co Inc ....E 330 755-7000
Struthers (G-17991)
L C F Inc ....F 330 877-3322
Hartville (G-10828)
Sugars Sweets Ltd ....G 513 936-0104
Cincinnati (G-4474)
Walnut Creek Chocolate Company .....E 330 893-2995
Walnut Creek (G-19471)

CANDY: Hard

Yost Candy Co ....E 330 828-2777
Dalton (G-8081)

CANNED SPECIALTIES

Abbott Laboratories......................A 614 624-3191
Columbus (G-6671)
Bittersweet Inc ....E 419 875-6986
Whitehouse (G-20338)
Hayden Valley Foods Inc ....E 614 539-7233
Urbancrest (G-19189)
JES Foods/Celina Inc ....E 419 586-7446
Celina (G-3004)
Milnot Company ....G 888 656-3245
Gahanna (G-10220)
Oasis Mediterranean Cuisine............E 419 269-1516
Toledo (G-18612)
P3 Secure LLC ....E 937 610-5500
Dayton (G-8559)
Robert Rothschild Farm LLC ....E 937 653-7397
Urbana (G-19177)
Silgan Can Company ....F 419 592-1010
Napoleon (G-14699)
Skyline Chili Inc ....C 513 874-1188
Fairfield (G-9719)
Werling Meats Inc ....E 419 375-0037
Burkettsville (G-2371)
Wornick Company ....A 513 552-7463
Blue Ash (G-1900)
Wornick Holding Company Inc ....A 513 794-9800
Blue Ash (G-1901)

CANOPIES: Sheet Metal

Geist Co Inc ....F 216 771-2200
Cleveland (G-5406)
Shadetree Systems LLC..................F 614 844-5990
Columbus (G-7614)
Upside Innovations LLC................G 513 889-2492
West Chester (G-20065)

CANS & TUBES: Ammunition, Board Laminated With Metal Foil

Greif Bros Corp Ohio Inc ....F 740 549-6000
Delaware (G-8853)

CANS: Aluminum

Busch Properties Inc ....G 614 888-0946
Columbus (G-6877)
Crown Cork & Seal Usa Inc ....B 330 833-1011
Massillon (G-13123)
Exal Corporation ....E 330 744-9505
Youngstown (G-21080)
Sidney Can & Tool LLC ....G 937 492-0977
Sidney (G-17226)

CANS: Beer, Metal

Ball Metal Beverage Cont Corp ....C 419 423-3071
Findlay (G-9793)

Container Manufacturing Ltd..............G 937 264-2370
Dayton (G-8242)

CANS: Composite Foil-Fiber, Made From Purchased Materials

Artistic Composite & Mold Co ....G 330 352-6632
Litchfield (G-12137)
Burch Plastics Corp ....G 440 835-2059
Cleveland (G-4948)
Companies of North Coast LLC..........G 216 398-8550
Cleveland (G-5109)
Hpc Holdings LLC ....F 330 666-3751
Fairlawn (G-9753)
North Coast Composites Inc ....G 216 398-8550
Cleveland (G-5893)
Sonoco Products Company ....E 513 870-3985
West Chester (G-20052)

CANS: Fiber

Sonoco Products Company ....D 937 429-0040
Beavercreek Township (G-1390)

CANS: Garbage, Stamped Or Pressed Metal

Counts Container Corporation ....E 216 433-4336
Cleveland (G-5135)
Witt Industries Inc ....D 513 871-5700
Mason (G-13103)

CANS: Metal

Anchor Hocking LLC ....A 740 681-6478
Lancaster (G-11687)
Ball Corporation ....D 614 771-9112
Columbus (G-6804)
Ball Corporation ....F 330 534-7418
Hubbard (G-11129)
Buckeye Stamping Company ....D 614 445-0059
Columbus (G-6875)
BWAY Corporation ....E 513 388-2200
Cincinnati (G-3491)
Cardinal Welding Inc ....G 330 426-2404
East Palestine (G-9229)
Cleveland Steel Container Corp ....E 330 656-5600
Streetsboro (G-17845)
Crown Cork & Seal Usa Inc ....E 419 727-8201
Toledo (G-18416)
Crown Cork & Seal Usa Inc ....E 740 681-6593
Lancaster (G-11703)
Crown Cork & Seal Usa Inc ....D 740 681-3000
Lancaster (G-11702)
Encore Plastics Corporation..............F 419 626-8000
Sandusky (G-16962)
Ghp II LLC ....C 740 687-2500
Lancaster (G-11719)
Industrial Container Svcs LLC ....E 513 921-8811
Cincinnati (G-3917)
Industrial Container Svcs LLC ....D 614 864-1900
Blacklick (G-1699)
Organized Living Inc ....E 513 489-9300
Cincinnati (G-4194)
Packaging Specialties Inc ....E 330 723-6000
Medina (G-13457)
Rexam Beverage Can Company ....C 419 877-0401
Whitehouse (G-20345)
Rexam Beverage Can Company ....C 419 334-4461
Fremont (G-10178)
Tg Can Technology USA Inc ....G 614 410-6672
Westerville (G-20191)
Witt Industries Inc ....D 513 871-5700
Mason (G-13103)

CANS: Tin

Independent Can Company ....E 440 593-5300
Conneaut (G-7810)

CANVAS PRDTS

Advantage Tent Fittings Inc ....F 740 773-3015
Chillicothe (G-3226)
Canvas Exchange Inc ....G 216 749-2233
Cleveland (G-4967)
Canvas Products Co ....F 440 232-8716
Bedford (G-1411)
Catawba Canvas Company LLC ....G 419 797-2050
Port Clinton (G-16395)
Chalfant Sew Fabricators Inc............E 216 521-7922
Cleveland (G-5012)
Cleveland Canvas Goods Mfg Co ....D 216 361-4567
Cleveland (G-5050)

DCW Acquisition Inc....................F 216 451-0666
Cleveland (G-5179)
Forest City Companies Inc ....E 216 586-5279
Cleveland (G-5369)
Galion Canvas Products Co ....G 419 468-5333
Galion (G-10269)
Glawe Manufacturing Co Inc ....E 937 754-0064
Fairborn (G-9623)
Hdt Expeditionary Systems Inc ....C 216 438-6111
Solon (G-17309)
J & W Canvas Company ....G 330 652-7678
Mineral Ridge (G-14306)
National Bias Fabric Co ....E 216 361-0530
Cleveland (G-5853)
Odyssey Canvas Works Inc ....G 937 392-4422
Ripley (G-16668)
ONeals Tarpaulin & Awning Co ....F 330 788-6504
Youngstown (G-21157)
Rainbow Industries Inc ....G 937 323-6493
Springfield (G-17633)
Raven Industries Inc ....G 937 323-4625
Springfield (G-17634)
Samsel Rope & Marine Supply Co ......E 216 241-0333
Cleveland (G-6156)
Schaaf Co Inc ....G 513 241-7044
Cincinnati (G-4384)
Scherba Industries Inc ....G 330 273-3200
Brunswick (G-2256)
Shade Youngstown & Aluminum Co ......G 330 782-2373
Youngstown (G-21200)
Shur-Co LLC ....G 330 297-0888
Ravenna (G-16556)
Stan Rileys Custom Draperies ....G 513 821-3732
Cincinnati (G-4452)
Tri County Tarp Inc ....E 419 288-3350
Bradner (G-2030)
Wolf G T Awning & Tent Co ....F 937 548-4161
Greenville (G-10529)

CANVAS PRDTS: Air Cushions & Mattresses

Rainbow Bedding ....G 330 852-3127
Sugarcreek (G-18036)

CANVAS PRDTS: Convertible Tops, Car/Boat, Fm Purchased Mtrl

Allen Zahradnik Inc ....G 419 729-1201
Toledo (G-18328)
American Canvas Products Inc ....F 419 382-8450
Toledo (G-18337)
Crown Dielectric Inds Inc ....C 614 224-5161
Columbus (G-7001)
Griffin Fisher Co Inc ....G 513 961-2110
Cincinnati (G-3853)
Hogan Awning Inc ....G 440 352-4033
Grand River (G-10450)
Rex Manufacturing Co ....G 419 224-5751
Lima (G-12083)
William Thompson ....G 440 232-4363
Aurora (G-956)

CANVAS PRDTS: Shades, Made From Purchased Materials

Lumenomics Inc..........................E 614 798-3500
Lewis Center (G-11906)

CAPACITORS: NEC

CPI Group Limited ....G 216 525-0046
Cleveland (G-5138)
Elliott Oren Products Inc ....E 419 298-2306
Edgerton (G-9329)

CAPS: Plastic

Bprex Halthcare Brookville Inc..........C 847 541-9700
Perrysburg (G-16069)
Electro-Cap International Inc ....F 937 456-6099
Eaton (G-9305)
Wisco Products Incorporated ....E 937 228-2101
Dayton (G-8763)

CAR LOADING SVCS

Yemaneh Musie ....G 614 506-3687
Columbus (G-7783)

CAR WASH EQPT

Car-Nation Inc ....G........ 330 862-9001
Paris *(G-15949)*

Chiefs Manufacturing & Eqp Co ....G........ 216 291-3200
Cleveland *(G-5027)*

Eastern Ohio Investments Inc ....G........ 740 266-2228
Steubenville *(G-17693)*

Giant Industries Inc ....E........ 419 531-4600
Toledo *(G-18480)*

Hilo Tech Inc ....G........ 440 979-1155
North Olmsted *(G-15339)*

L A Express ....G........ 513 752-6999
Batavia *(G-1201)*

Majic Touch ....G........ 330 923-8259
Cuyahoga Falls *(G-8023)*

National Pride Equipment Inc ....G........ 419 289-2886
Ashland *(G-756)*

Powerwash of Ohio ....G........ 614 260-2756
Lewis Center *(G-11911)*

Sammy S Auto Detail ....F........ 614 263-2728
Columbus *(G-7589)*

Wb Industries Inc ....G........ 440 708-0309
Burton *(G-2390)*

CAR WASH EQPT & SPLYS WHOLESALERS

National Pride Equipment Inc ....G........ 419 289-2886
Ashland *(G-756)*

Service Station Equipment Co ....F........ 216 431-6100
Cleveland *(G-6181)*

CAR WASHES

Lawnview Industries Inc ....C........ 937 653-5217
Urbana *(G-19168)*

Tops Inc ....G........ 440 954-9451
Mentor *(G-13749)*

CARBIDES

Nap Asset Holdings Ltd ....F........ 330 633-0599
Tallmadge *(G-18158)*

Ohio Metal Working Products ....E........ 330 455-2009
Canton *(G-2801)*

CARBON & GRAPHITE PRDTS, NEC

Advanced Energy Tech LLC ....E........ 216 676-2259
Lakewood *(G-11654)*

Albemarle Corporation ....G........ 330 425-2354
Twinsburg *(G-18897)*

American Spring Wire Corp ....C........ 216 292-4620
Bedford Heights *(G-1478)*

Americarb Inc ....D........ 419 281-5800
Ashland *(G-703)*

Americarb International Corp ....G........ 419 281-5800
Ashland *(G-704)*

Angstron Materials Inc ....G........ 937 331-9884
Dayton *(G-8159)*

Applied Sciences Inc ....E........ 937 766-2020
Cedarville *(G-2980)*

Babcock & Wilcox Megtec ....C........ 614 258-9501
Columbus *(G-6799)*

Cammann Inc ....F........ 440 965-4051
Birmingham *(G-1685)*

GE Aviation Systems LLC ....B........ 937 898-5881
Vandalia *(G-19293)*

Graftech Advanced Graphite ....E........ 216 676-2259
Parma *(G-15960)*

Graftech Holdings Inc ....A........ 216 676-2000
Independence *(G-11256)*

Graftech International Ltd ....E........ 216 676-2000
Independence *(G-11257)*

Graftech Intl Holdings Inc ....C........ 216 529-3777
Cleveland *(G-5443)*

Graftech Intl Holdings Inc ....C........ 330 239-3023
Parma *(G-15961)*

Graftech Intl Holdings Inc ....C........ 216 676-2000
Independence *(G-11258)*

Graphite Sales Inc ....F........ 440 543-8221
Chagrin Falls *(G-3090)*

Graphite Sales Inc ....E........ 419 652-3388
Nova *(G-15578)*

Mill-Rose Company ....C........ 440 255-9171
Mentor *(G-13657)*

National Elec Carbn Pdts Inc ....D........ 419 435-8182
Fostoria *(G-9986)*

Ohio Carbon Blank Inc ....G........ 440 953-9302
Willoughby *(G-20561)*

Ohio Carbon Industries Inc ....E........ 419 496-2530
Ashland *(G-759)*

Pyrograf Products Inc ....F........ 937 766-2020
Cedarville *(G-2983)*

Pyrotek Incorporated ....C........ 440 349-8800
Aurora *(G-942)*

R&S Carbon Trading LLC ....G........ 614 264-3083
Gahanna *(G-10227)*

Randall Bearings Inc ....D........ 419 223-1075
Lima *(G-12080)*

Randall Bearings Inc ....F........ 419 678-2486
Coldwater *(G-6570)*

Sentinel Management Inc ....E........ 440 821-7372
Lorain *(G-12274)*

Timcal America Inc ....G........ 440 871-7504
Westlake *(G-20316)*

Zyvex Performance Mtls Inc ....E........ 614 481-2222
Columbus *(G-7789)*

CARBON BLACK

Jacobi Carbons Inc ....E........ 215 546-3900
Columbus *(G-7221)*

North Central Processing Inc ....G........ 216 623-1090
Cleveland *(G-5891)*

CARBON DISULFIDE

New Mulch In A Bottle Limited ....G........ 724 290-2341
Marietta *(G-12810)*

CARBON PAPER & INKED RIBBONS

Adaptive Data Inc ....F........ 937 436-2343
Centerville *(G-3032)*

Kroy LLC ....C........ 216 426-5600
Cleveland *(G-5666)*

Nanotechlabs Inc ....F........ 937 297-9518
Kettering *(G-11584)*

Pubco Corporation ....D........ 216 881-5300
Cleveland *(G-6059)*

CARDS: Beveled

Cott Systems Inc ....D........ 614 847-4405
Columbus *(G-6989)*

CARDS: Color

Coloramic Process Inc ....F........ 440 275-1199
Austinburg *(G-959)*

Golf Marketing Group Inc ....G........ 330 963-5155
Twinsburg *(G-18950)*

CARDS: Greeting

American Greetings Corporation ....A........ 216 252-7300
Cleveland *(G-4782)*

American Greetings Corporation ....G........ 216 685-9167
Cleveland *(G-4783)*

Century Intermediate Holdg Co ....F........ 216 252-7300
Cleveland *(G-5006)*

Frogs In Bloom ....G........ 330 678-9508
Kent *(G-11460)*

Gibson Greetings Inc ....G........ 216 252-7300
Cleveland *(G-5428)*

Naptime Productions LLC ....F........ 419 662-9521
Rossford *(G-16743)*

Plus Mark LLC ....E........ 216 252-6770
Cleveland *(G-6018)*

Those Charc From Cleve Inc ....F........ 216 252-7300
Cleveland *(G-6323)*

Vagabond Creations Inc ....G........ 937 298-1124
Moraine *(G-14536)*

CARDS: Identification

Octsys Security Corp ....G........ 614 470-4510
Columbus *(G-7412)*

Plasticards Inc ....E........ 330 896-5555
Uniontown *(G-19094)*

CARDS: Playing

Harbro LLC ....G........ 810 229-4755
Lakewood *(G-11666)*

CARNIVAL & AMUSEMENT PARK EQPT WHOLESALERS

Majestic Manufacturing Inc ....E........ 330 457-2447
New Waterford *(G-14972)*

CARNIVAL SPLYS, WHOLESALE

Jackpot Festival & Gaming ....G........ 216 531-3500
Cleveland *(G-5604)*

CARPET & UPHOLSTERY CLEANING SVCS

Downey Enterprises Inc ....G........ 740 587-4258
Granville *(G-10457)*

CARPET & UPHOLSTERY CLEANING SVCS: Carpet/Furniture, On Loc

Shaheen Oriental Rug Co Inc ....F........ 330 493-9000
Canton *(G-2846)*

Stanley Steemer Intl Inc ....C........ 614 764-2007
Dublin *(G-9149)*

CARPETS & RUGS: Tufted

Mohawk Industries Inc ....C........ 800 837-3812
Grove City *(G-10574)*

CARPETS, RUGS & FLOOR COVERING

Alliance Carpet Cushion Co ....D........ 740 966-5001
Johnstown *(G-11388)*

Boardman Molded Products Inc ....D........ 330 788-2401
Youngstown *(G-21032)*

Buckeye Volleyball Center LLC ....E........ 614 764-1075
Powell *(G-16463)*

Davies Since 1900 ....G........ 419 756-4212
Mansfield *(G-12593)*

International Automotive ....B........ 937 492-1225
Sidney *(G-17195)*

Johns Manville Corporation ....B........ 419 878-8111
Waterville *(G-19660)*

Kadee Industries Newco Inc ....F........ 440 439-8650
Bedford *(G-1435)*

Remnant Room ....G........ 937 938-7350
Dayton *(G-8624)*

Wholesale Carpet Outlet Inc ....G........ 937 447-4265
Gettysburg *(G-10376)*

Xt Innovations Ltd ....G........ 419 562-1989
Bucyrus *(G-2366)*

CARPORTS: Prefabricated Metal

American Steel Carports Inc ....F........ 419 737-1331
Pioneer *(G-16232)*

CARRIAGES: Horse Drawn

Burkholder Buggy Shop ....G........ 330 674-5891
Millersburg *(G-14208)*

Farmerstown Axle Co ....G........ 330 897-2711
Baltic *(G-1070)*

London Coach Shop ....G........ 419 347-4803
Shelby *(G-17137)*

Shiloh Carriage Shop LLC ....G........ 419 896-3869
Shiloh *(G-17155)*

Victorian Farms ....G........ 330 628-9188
Atwater *(G-903)*

Walnut Creek Cart Shop ....G........ 330 893-1097
Millersburg *(G-14280)*

CARRIER EQPT: Telephone Or Telegraph

Interline Brands Inc ....G........ 614 527-9475
Columbus *(G-7204)*

CARRIERS: Infant, Textile

Sewline Products Inc ....F........ 419 929-1114
New London *(G-14866)*

CARS: Electric

Mobile Solutions LLC ....F........ 614 286-3944
Columbus *(G-7361)*

Myers Motors LLC ....G........ 330 630-7000
Tallmadge *(G-18157)*

CARTONS: Egg, Molded Pulp, Made From Purchased Materials

Tekni-Plex Inc ....E........ 419 491-2407
Holland *(G-11088)*

CARVING SETS, STAINLESS STEEL

Ahner Fabricating & Shtmtl Inc ....E........ 419 626-6641
Sandusky *(G-16945)*

PRODUCT

CASEMENTS: Aluminum

American Window Pdts of Ohio ....F 330 830-0274
Massillon (G-13107)

CASES, WOOD

Aerocase Incorporated ....F 440 617-9294
Westlake (G-20247)

Custom Displays LLC ....G 330 454-8850
Bolivar (G-1931)

Fca LLC ....F 309 644-2424
Clayton (G-4658)

Global Packaging & Exports Inc ....G 513 454-2020
West Chester (G-19877)

CASES: Carrying

Clipper Products Inc ....G 513 688-7300
Cincinnati (G-3295)

Professional Case Inc ....F 513 682-2520
West Chester (G-20041)

Travelers Custom Case Inc ....F 216 621-8447
Cleveland (G-6351)

UNI Corp ....E 330 489-6500
Canton (G-2883)

Whitman Corporation ....G 513 541-3223
Okeana (G-15667)

CASES: Carrying, Clothing & Apparel

Professional Image Apparel Inc ....F 513 984-1111
Cincinnati (G-4295)

CASES: Plastic

Aerocase Incorporated ....F 440 617-9294
Westlake (G-20247)

Checkpoint Systems Inc ....C 330 456-7776
Canton (G-2652)

M T M Molded Products Company ....E 937 890-7461
Dayton (G-8464)

Warwick Products Company ....E 216 334-1200
Cleveland (G-6448)

CASES: Shipping, Nailed Or Lock Corner, Wood

Hawthorne Caravan & Assoc LLC ....F 440 366-9065
Elyria (G-9428)

Scorpion Case Mfg LLC ....F 614 274-7246
Dublin (G-9141)

CASH REGISTERS & PARTS

Allied Retail Solutions ....G 330 332-8141
Salem (G-16870)

Bartek Systems ....G 614 759-6014
Columbus (G-6810)

CASING-HEAD BUTANE & PROPANE PRODUCTION

United Landmark Llc ....G 740 852-2062
London (G-12222)

CASINGS: Rocket Transportation

Ds Express Carriers Inc ....G 419 433-6200
Norwalk (G-15534)

CASINGS: Sheet Metal

Art Fremont Iron Co ....G 419 332-5554
Fremont (G-10125)

CASINGS: Storage, Missile & Missile Components

Tdm Fuelcell LLC Tdm LLC ....G 440 969-1442
Chesterland (G-3221)

CASKETS & ACCESS

Case Ohio Burial Co ....F 440 779-1992
Cleveland (G-4986)

McCord Products Inc ....F 419 352-3691
Bowling Green (G-2001)

Milso Midwest ....G 513 745-0760
West Chester (G-20031)

Youngstown Casket Co Inc ....G 330 758-2008
Youngstown (G-21249)

Zane Casket Company Inc ....E 740 452-4680
Zanesville (G-21365)

CASKETS WHOLESALERS

Case Ohio Burial Co ....F 440 779-1992
Cleveland (G-4986)

CAST STONE: Concrete

Fibreboard Corporation ....C 419 248-8000
Toledo (G-18470)

CASTERS

Extreme Caster Services Inc ....G 330 637-9030
Cortland (G-7868)

Gemini Advertising Associates ....D 513 896-3541
Hamilton (G-10698)

Western Reserve Mfg Co ....G 216 641-0500
Cleveland (G-6459)

CASTINGS GRINDING: For The Trade

Able Grinding Co Inc ....G 216 961-6555
Cleveland (G-4686)

Arlington Prcsion Grinding LLC ....G 937 833-1553
Brookville (G-2175)

Axis Tool & Grinding LLC ....G 330 535-4713
Akron (G-79)

Brockman Jig Grinding Service ....G 937 220-9780
Dayton (G-8198)

Centerless Grinding Solutions ....G 216 520-4612
Cleveland (G-5004)

Combine Grinding Co Inc ....G 440 439-6148
Bedford (G-1417)

F & J Grinding Inc ....G 440 942-4430
Willoughby (G-20483)

Grandview Grind ....G 614 485-9005
Columbus (G-7129)

Hr Parts N Stuff ....G 330 947-2433
Atwater (G-898)

Jamar Precision Grinding Co ....E 330 220-0099
Hinckley (G-11026)

M L Grinding Co ....G 440 975-9111
Willoughby (G-20531)

Micro Lapping & Grinding Co ....E 216 267-6500
Cleveland (G-5798)

Ohio Engineering and Mfg Sls ....G 937 855-6971
Germantown (G-10371)

P & L Heat Trting Grinding Inc ....E 330 746-1339
Youngstown (G-21159)

Performance Point Grinding ....G 330 220-0871
Hinckley (G-11028)

Trinel Inc ....F 216 265-9190
Cleveland (G-6367)

True Grinding ....G 440 786-7608
Bedford (G-1469)

V M Machine Co Inc ....G 216 281-4569
Cleveland (G-6404)

Youngstown Hard Chrome Plating ....E 330 758-9721
Youngstown (G-21252)

CASTINGS: Aerospace Investment, Ferrous

Bescast Inc ....C 440 946-5300
Willoughby (G-20444)

Caspa Home Page Inc ....G 216 781-0748
Cleveland (G-4989)

General Aluminum Mfg Company ....C 419 739-9300
Wapakoneta (G-19487)

Interntnal Precision Cast Sups ....G 330 342-0407
Hudson (G-11182)

CASTINGS: Aerospace, Aluminum

Htci Co ....F 937 845-1204
New Carlisle (G-14802)

Lockheed Martin Investments ....F 937 429-0100
Beavercreek (G-1349)

Mpe Aeroengines Inc ....G 937 878-3800
Huber Heights (G-11150)

Reliable Pattern Works Inc ....G 440 232-8820
Cleveland (G-6099)

TW Corporation ....E 440 461-3234
Akron (G-450)

CASTINGS: Aerospace, Nonferrous, Exc Aluminum

Computational Engineering Svcs ....G 513 745-0313
Blue Ash (G-1768)

Microweld Engineering Inc ....F 614 847-9410
Worthington (G-20880)

Voss Industries Inc ....C 216 771-0870
Cleveland (G-6429)

CASTINGS: Aluminum

Alumalloy Metalcasting Company ....C 440 930-2222
Avon Lake (G-1023)

Anchor Foundry & Machine Inc ....G 330 453-3441
Canton (G-2603)

Boscott Metals Inc ....F 937 448-2018
Bradford (G-2024)

Brost Foundry Company ....E 216 641-1131
Cleveland (G-4936)

Cushman Foundry LLC ....F 513 984-5570
Blue Ash (G-1773)

General Aluminum Mfg Company ....B 440 947-2000
Cleveland (G-5410)

General Aluminum Mfg Company ....E 330 297-1020
Ravenna (G-16531)

General Aluminum Mfg Company ....B 440 593-6225
Conneaut (G-7805)

General Motors LLC ....A 419 782-2244
Defiance (G-8790)

Howmet Aluminum Casting Inc ....E 216 641-4340
Newburgh Heights (G-15072)

I A B F Inc ....G 614 279-4498
Columbus (G-7177)

Merit Foundry Co Inc ....G 216 741-4282
Cleveland (G-5785)

Morris Bean & Company ....C 937 767-7301
Yellow Springs (G-20996)

New London Foundry Inc ....F 419 929-2073
New London (G-14863)

Ohio Aluminum Industries Inc ....C 216 641-8865
Cleveland (G-5927)

OKeefe Casting Co ....G 440 277-5427
Lorain (G-12265)

P C M Co ....E 330 336-8040
Wadsworth (G-19423)

Piqua Emery Cutter & Fndry Co ....D 937 773-4134
Piqua (G-16303)

Pride Cast Metals Inc ....D 513 541-1295
Cincinnati (G-4268)

Sawbrook Steel Castings Co ....D 513 554-1700
Cincinnati (G-4381)

US Metalcraft Inc ....E 419 692-4962
Delphos (G-8925)

CASTINGS: Brass, NEC, Exc Die

Accurate Products Company ....G 740 498-7202
Newcomerstown (G-15108)

CASTINGS: Bronze, NEC, Exc Die

Brost Foundry Company ....E 216 641-1131
Cleveland (G-4936)

Cincinnati Valve Company ....F 513 471-8258
Cincinnati (G-3567)

Oakes Foundry Inc ....E 330 372-4010
Warren (G-19581)

OKeefe Casting Co ....E 440 277-5427
Lorain (G-12265)

Piqua Emery Cutter & Fndry Co ....D 937 773-4134
Piqua (G-16303)

Pride Cast Metals Inc ....D 513 541-1295
Cincinnati (G-4268)

R E H Company Inc ....D 513 242-0011
Cincinnati (G-4324)

CASTINGS: Commercial Investment, Ferrous

B W Grinding Co ....E 419 923-1376
Lyons (G-12431)

Dd Foundry Inc ....C 216 362-4100
Brookpark (G-2156)

Howmet Castings & Services Inc ....B 216 641-4400
Newburgh Heights (G-15073)

Howmet Corporation ....E 800 242-9898
Newburgh Heights (G-15074)

Kovatch Castings Inc ....C 330 896-9944
Uniontown (G-19089)

Rimer Enterprises Inc ....E 419 878-8156
Waterville (G-19666)

CASTINGS: Copper & Copper-Base Alloy, NEC, Exc Die

Falcon Foundry Company ....D 330 536-6221
Lowellville (G-12407)

M A Harrison Mfg Co Inc ....E 440 965-4306
Wakeman (G-19451)

CASTINGS: Die, Aluminum

Ahresty Wilmington Corporation ....B....... 937 382-6112
Wilmington (G-20653)

Akron Foundry Co ....C....... 330 745-3101
Akron (G-44)

Alumacast LLC ....G....... 419 584-1473
Celina (G-2985)

American Light Metals LLC ....C....... 330 467-0750
Macedonia (G-12435)

Apex Aluminum Die Cast Co Inc ....E....... 937 773-0432
Piqua (G-16248)

Buckeye Aluminum Foundry Inc ....G....... 440 428-7180
Madison (G-12496)

Cast Specialties Inc ....E....... 216 292-7393
Cleveland (G-4991)

CSM Horvath Ledgebrook ....G....... 419 522-1133
Mansfield (G-12590)

Custom Industries Inc ....G....... 216 251-2804
Cleveland (G-5150)

Destin Die Casting LLC ....E....... 937 347-1111
Xenia (G-20947)

Enterprise Machine Inc...........................F....... 513 541-4031
Cincinnati (G-3709)

Fort Recovery Industries Inc ....C....... 419 375-4121
Fort Recovery (G-9951)

General Aluminum Mfg Company ....C....... 419 739-9300
Wapakoneta (G-19487)

General Die Casters Inc..........................D....... 330 467-6700
Northfield (G-15466)

General Die Casters Inc..........................E....... 330 678-2528
Twinsburg (G-18942)

J & M Precision Die Cast Inc..................F....... 440 365-7388
Elyria (G-9441)

Matalco (us) Inc ....G....... 234 806-0600
Warren (G-19578)

Matalco (us) Inc ....F....... 330 452-4760
Canton (G-2772)

Model Pattern & Foundry Co ....E....... 513 542-2322
Cincinnati (G-4113)

Ohio Decorative Products LLC................C....... 419 647-9033
Spencerville (G-17463)

Omni Die Casting Inc ....E....... 330 830-5500
Massillon (G-13188)

Park-Ohio Holdings Corp ....F....... 440 947-2000
Cleveland (G-5966)

Park-Ohio Industries Inc ....C....... 440 947-2000
Cleveland (G-5967)

Plaster Process Castings Co ....E....... 216 663-1814
Cleveland (G-6012)

Ramco Electric Motors Inc ....D....... 937 548-2525
Greenville (G-10516)

Ravana Industries Inc.............................G....... 330 536-4015
Lowellville (G-12411)

Reliable Castings Corporation ....D....... 937 497-5217
Sidney (G-17215)

Ross Casting & Innovation LLC ....B....... 937 497-4500
Sidney (G-17219)

Seilkop Industries Inc ....E....... 513 761-1035
Cincinnati (G-4398)

Seilkop Industries Inc ....E....... 513 679-5680
Cincinnati (G-4399)

Seyekcub Inc ....G....... 330 324-1394
Uhrichsville (G-19059)

SRS Die Casting Holdings LLC ....G....... 330 467-0750
Macedonia (G-12487)

SRS Light Metals Inc ....G....... 330 467-0750
Macedonia (G-12488)

Thompson Aluminum Casting Co ....D....... 216 206-2781
Cleveland (G-6322)

Tooling Technology LLC ....D....... 937 295-3672
Fort Loramie (G-9943)

United States Drill Head Co ....E....... 513 941-0300
Cincinnati (G-4540)

Yoder Industries Inc ....C....... 937 278-5769
Dayton (G-8766)

CASTINGS: Die, Copper & Copper Alloy

D Picking & Co ....G....... 419 562-5016
Bucyrus (G-2337)

Federal Metal Company...........................D....... 440 232-8700
Cleveland (G-5331)

CASTINGS: Die, Magnesium & Magnesium-Base Alloy

Elektron N Magnesium Amer Inc ....E....... 419 424-8878
Findlay (G-9819)

Thompson Aluminum Casting Co ....D....... 216 206-2781
Cleveland (G-6322)

CASTINGS: Die, Nonferrous

Certech Inc ....G....... 330 405-1033
Twinsburg (G-18910)

Clinton Foundry Ltd................................F....... 419 243-6885
Toledo (G-18401)

Custom Industries Inc ....G....... 216 251-2804
Cleveland (G-5150)

Dd Foundry Inc ....C....... 216 362-4100
Brookpark (G-2156)

Empire Brass Co ....E....... 216 431-6565
Cleveland (G-5276)

M & M Dies Inc......................................G....... 216 883-6628
Cleveland (G-5715)

Martina Metal LLC ....E....... 614 291-9700
Columbus (G-7321)

Oakwood Industries Inc ....D....... 440 232-8700
Bedford (G-1450)

Support Svc LLC ....G....... 419 617-0660
Lexington (G-11954)

Tessec LLC ....E....... 937 985-3552
Dayton (G-8709)

Yoder Industries Inc ....G....... 937 890-4322
Dayton (G-8767)

Yoder Industries Inc ....C....... 937 278-5769
Dayton (G-8766)

CASTINGS: Die, Zinc

American Light Metals LLC ....C....... 330 467-0750
Macedonia (G-12435)

Cast Specialties Inc ....E....... 216 292-7393
Cleveland (G-4991)

General Die Casters Inc..........................E....... 330 678-2528
Twinsburg (G-18942)

General Die Casters Inc..........................D....... 330 467-6700
Northfield (G-15466)

Omni USA Inc ....D....... 330 830-5500
Massillon (G-13189)

Plaster Process Castings Co ....E....... 216 663-1814
Cleveland (G-6012)

Ray Lewis & Son Incorporated ....E....... 937 644-4015
Marysville (G-12965)

Reebar Die Casting Inc...........................F....... 419 878-7591
Waterville (G-19665)

SRS Die Casting Holdings LLC ....G....... 330 467-0750
Macedonia (G-12487)

SRS Light Metals Inc ....G....... 330 467-0750
Macedonia (G-12488)

CASTINGS: Ductile

Sancast Inc ....E....... 740 622-8660
Coshocton (G-7908)

CASTINGS: Gray Iron

A C Williams Co Inc ....E....... 330 296-6110
Ravenna (G-16511)

Blanchester Foundry Co Inc ....F....... 937 783-2091
Blanchester (G-1711)

Cast Metals Incorporated ....E....... 419 278-2010
Deshler (G-8948)

Casting Solutions LLC ....C....... 740 452-9371
Zanesville (G-21288)

Chris Erhart Foundry & Mch Co ....E....... 513 421-6550
Cincinnati (G-3531)

Col-Pump Company Inc ....D....... 330 482-1029
Columbiana (G-6611)

Domestic Casting Company LLC ....C....... 717 532-6615
Delaware (G-8839)

Ej Usa Inc ....E....... 216 692-3001
Cleveland (G-5261)

General Motors LLC ....A....... 419 782-2244
Defiance (G-8790)

Knapp Foundry Co Inc ....F....... 330 434-0916
Akron (G-261)

Liberty Casting Company LLC ....D....... 740 363-1941
Delaware (G-8868)

Miami-Cast Inc ....E....... 937 866-2951
Miamisburg (G-13833)

Osco Industries Inc................................C....... 740 286-5004
Jackson (G-11323)

Pioneer City Casting Company ....E....... 740 423-7533
Belpre (G-1593)

Quality Castings Company ....B....... 330 682-6871
Orrville (G-15756)

T & B Foundry Company..........................D....... 216 391-4200
Cleveland (G-6285)

Tri Cast Limited Partnership ....E....... 330 733-8718
Akron (G-445)

Tri-Cast Inc ....E....... 330 733-8718
Akron (G-446)

Yellow Creek Casting Company ....E....... 330 532-4608
Wellsville (G-19777)

CASTINGS: Machinery, Aluminum

Clinton Machine Co Inc ....G....... 330 882-6743
New Franklin (G-14823)

Enprotech Industrial Tech LLC ....C....... 216 883-3220
Cleveland (G-5283)

General Precision Corporation ....G....... 440 951-9380
Willoughby (G-20498)

Nelson Aluminum Foundry Inc ....D....... 440 543-1941
Chagrin Falls (G-3107)

S M C Aluminum Foundry Inc ....F....... 419 257-2175
North Baltimore (G-15198)

Tri - Flex of Ohio Inc ....F....... 330 705-7084
North Canton (G-15277)

Zephyr Industries Inc.............................G....... 419 281-4485
Ashland (G-787)

CASTINGS: Magnesium

A C Williams Co Inc ....E....... 330 296-6110
Ravenna (G-16511)

Garfield Alloys Inc ....F....... 216 587-4843
Cleveland (G-5397)

Thompson Aluminum Casting Co ....D....... 216 206-2781
Cleveland (G-6322)

CASTINGS: Precision

Akron Foundry Co ....C....... 330 745-3101
Akron (G-44)

Consoldted Precision Pdts Corp.............E....... 440 953-0053
Eastlake (G-9263)

McM Precision Castings Inc ....E....... 419 669-3226
Weston (G-20326)

PCC Airfoils LLC ....B....... 740 982-6025
Crooksville (G-7952)

PCC Airfoils LLC ....E....... 216 692-7900
Cleveland (G-5983)

PCC Airfoils LLC ....E....... 440 255-9770
Mentor (G-13683)

Sam Americas Inc ....E....... 330 628-1118
Mogadore (G-14384)

Sandusky International Inc ....E....... 419 626-5340
Sandusky (G-17002)

Warren Castings Inc ....F....... 216 883-2520
Cleveland (G-6446)

CASTINGS: Steel

Alcon Industries Inc...............................D....... 216 961-1100
Cleveland (G-4745)

Aza Enterprises LLC ....G....... 740 678-8482
Fleming (G-9910)

Fisher Cast Steel Products Inc ....E....... 614 879-8325
West Jefferson (G-20078)

Harbor Castings Inc...............................E....... 231 733-1053
Cuyahoga Falls (G-8006)

Precision Polymer Casting LLC ....G....... 440 343-0461
Moreland Hills (G-14538)

Rampp Company ....E....... 740 373-7886
Marietta (G-12822)

Sandusky International Inc ....E....... 419 626-5340
Sandusky (G-17002)

Santos Industrial Ltd ....E....... 937 299-7333
Moraine (G-14525)

Sawbrook Steel Castings Co ....D....... 513 554-1700
Cincinnati (G-4381)

Sns Nano Fiber Technology LLC..............G....... 330 655-0030
Hudson (G-11200)

Worthington Industries Inc ....C....... 614 438-3210
Worthington (G-20896)

CASTINGS: Zinc

Castmor Products Inc.............................G....... 440 953-1103
Willoughby (G-20453)

Custom Industries Inc ....G....... 216 251-2804
Cleveland (G-5150)

Liberty Die Casting Company ....G....... 419 636-3971
Bryan (G-2312)

Ohio Decorative Products LLC................C....... 419 647-9033
Spencerville (G-17463)

CATALOG & MAIL-ORDER HOUSES

Sailors Tailor Inc ....G....... 937 862-7781
Spring Valley (G-17469)

PRODUCT

Universal Drect Flfilment Corp ....C 330 650-5000
Hudson (G-11206)

CATALOG SALES

Jmr Enterprises LLC ....G 937 618-1736
Maineville (G-12525)

CATALYSTS: Chemical

BASF Catalysts LLC ....E 216 867-1047
Independence (G-11250)

BLaster Corporation ....E 216 901-5800
Cleveland (G-4916)

Johnson Mtthey Prcess Tech Inc ....E 330 298-7005
Ravenna (G-16535)

Nease Co LLC ....F 513 587-2800
West Chester (G-19904)

Solvay USA Inc ....E 513 482-5700
Cincinnati (G-4436)

United Initiators Inc ....D 440 326-2416
Elyria (G-9505)

CATAPULTS

Leader Engnrng-Fabrication Inc ....G 419 636-1731
Bryan (G-2311)

Universal Fabg Cnstr Svcs Inc ....D 614 274-1128
Columbus (G-7723)

CATCH BASIN COVERS: Concrete

Wauseon Silo & Coal Company ....F 419 335-6041
Wauseon (G-19701)

CATERERS

American Showa Inc ....A 937 783-4961
Blanchester (G-1709)

Country Caterers Inc ....G 740 389-1013
Marion (G-12863)

Disalvos Deli & Italian Store ....G 937 298-5053
Dayton (G-8306)

Mustard Seed Health Fd Mkt Inc ....E 440 519-3663
Solon (G-17342)

Reineckers Bakery Ltd ....G 330 467-2221
Macedonia (G-12480)

Todd W Goings ....G 740 389-5842
Marion (G-12907)

CATTLE WHOLESALERS

Gardner Lumber Co Inc ....F 740 254-4664
Tippecanoe (G-18313)

CAULKING COMPOUNDS

Dap Products Inc ....C 937 667-4461
Tipp City (G-18274)

CEILING SYSTEMS: Luminous, Commercial

M-Boss Inc ....E 216 441-6080
Cleveland (G-5719)

Nordic Light America Inc ....F 614 981-9497
Columbus (G-7397)

Norton Industries Inc ....F 888 357-2345
Lakewood (G-11676)

CELLULOSE ACETATE

Aviles Construction Company ....E 216 939-1084
Cleveland (G-4873)

CELLULOSE DERIVATIVE MATERIALS

Advanced Fiber Technology Inc ....E 513 860-4446
Bucyrus (G-2331)

CEMENT & CONCRETE RELATED PRDTS & EQPT: Bituminous

Koski Construction Co ....G 440 964-8171
Ashtabula (G-816)

Mesa Industries Inc ....E 513 321-2950
Cincinnati (G-4087)

CEMENT ROCK: Crushed & Broken

R W Sidley Incorporated ....E 440 352-9343
Painesville (G-15914)

CEMENT, EXC LINOLEUM & TILE

Hartline Products Coinc ....G 216 291-2303
Cleveland (G-5482)

Hartline Products Coinc ....G 216 851-7189
Cleveland (G-5483)

Metalcrete Industries Inc ....G 440 526-5600
Cleveland (G-5790)

CEMENT: Heat Resistant

Refractory Coating Tech Inc ....E 330 683-2200
Orrville (G-15757)

CEMENT: Hydraulic

Asphalt Services Ohio Inc ....G 614 864-4600
Columbus (G-6778)

Cincinnati Blacktop Company ....F 513 681-0952
Cincinnati (G-3544)

Essroc Cement Corp ....F 330 499-9100
Middlebranch (G-13900)

Essroc Cement Corp ....G 614 497-2001
Columbus (G-7067)

Hartline Products Coinc ....G 216 851-7189
Cleveland (G-5483)

Huron Cement Products Company ....E 419 433-4161
Huron (G-11224)

Lafarge North America Inc ....C 419 399-4861
Paulding (G-16009)

Lafarge North America Inc ....G 216 781-9330
Cleveland (G-5676)

Lafarge North America Inc ....G 419 241-5256
Toledo (G-18553)

Lafarge North America Inc ....F 419 897-7656
Maumee (G-13274)

Lafarge North America Inc ....G 740 423-5900
Belpre (G-1590)

Myko Industries ....G 216 431-0900
Cleveland (G-5845)

Quikrete Companies Inc ....E 614 885-4406
Columbus (G-7540)

Quikrete Companies Inc ....G 419 241-1148
Toledo (G-18664)

Quikrete Companies Inc ....G 330 296-6080
Ravenna (G-16551)

St Marys Cement Inc (us) ....G 937 642-4573
Marysville (G-12972)

CEMENT: Masonry

Appc Plumbing Co ....G 330 722-7754
Medina (G-13372)

Cemex Cnstr Mtls ATL LLC ....D 937 878-8651
Xenia (G-20941)

Kona Blackbird Inc ....F 440 285-3189
Chardon (G-3160)

Lozinak & Sons Inc ....G 440 877-1819
North Royalton (G-15433)

Murphy James Construction LLC ....E 740 667-3626
Coolville (G-7836)

Riverside Sand & Gravel Co ....G 330 673-2021
Kent (G-11517)

CEMENT: Natural

Fairborn Cement Company LLC ....C 937 879-8393
Xenia (G-20950)

Hudecek Cement Inc ....G 216 676-0362
Cleveland (G-5534)

CEMENT: Portland

Wallseye Concrete Corp ....F 440 235-1800
Cleveland (G-6444)

Wallseye Concrete Corp ....F 419 483-2738
Castalia (G-2978)

CEMENT: Rubber

LMI Custom Mixing LLC ....D 740 435-0444
Cambridge (G-2465)

CEMETERIES: Real Estate Operation

Fort Stben Burial Estates Assn ....G 740 266-6101
Steubenville (G-17695)

CEMETERY & FUNERAL DIRECTOR'S EQPT & SPLYS WHOLESALERS

Jls Funeral Home ....F 614 625-1220
Columbus (G-7234)

CEMETERY MEMORIAL DEALERS

3-G Incorporated ....G 513 921-4515
Cincinnati (G-3323)

Artistic Memorials Ltd ....G 419 873-0433
Perrysburg (G-16066)

Ellinger Monument Inc ....G 740 385-3687
Rockbridge (G-16688)

Hirons Memorial Works Inc ....G 937 444-2917
Mount Orab (G-14581)

Linden Monuments ....E 419 468-4130
Galion (G-10279)

Maumee Valley Memorials Inc ....F 419 878-9030
Waterville (G-19663)

Solon Granite Memorial Works ....G 440 248-6606
Solon (G-17384)

CERAMIC FIBER

Astro Met Inc ....E 513 772-1242
Cincinnati (G-3421)

Maverick Corporation ....F 513 469-9919
Blue Ash (G-1835)

Scioto Ceramic Products Inc ....E 614 436-0405
Columbus (G-7600)

CERAMIC FLOOR & WALL TILE WHOLESALERS

Artfinders ....G 330 264-7706
Wooster (G-20740)

Clay Burley Products Co ....E 740 452-3633
Roseville (G-16728)

CHAIN: Wire

Manufacturers Equipment Co ....F 513 424-3573
Middletown (G-14059)

CHAINS: Power Transmission

Rexnord Industries LLC ....D 614 675-1800
Grove City (G-10588)

US Tsubaki Power Transm LLC ....C 419 626-4560
Sandusky (G-17019)

CHALK MINING: Crushed & Broken

Chalk Outline Pictures ....G 216 291-3944
Cleveland (G-5013)

CHANDELIERS: Residential

Country Tin ....G 937 746-7229
Franklin (G-10015)

Degaetano Sales ....G 440 729-8877
Chesterland (G-3202)

CHARCOAL, WHOLESALE

Nucon International Inc ....F 614 846-5710
Columbus (G-7405)

CHARCOAL: Activated

Calgon Carbon Corporation ....C 614 258-9501
Columbus (G-6888)

CHASSIS: Automobile Trailer

Miba Bearings US LLC ....B 740 962-4242
McConnelsville (G-13354)

CHASSIS: Motor Vehicle

Allen Morgan Trucking & Repair ....G 330 336-5192
Norton (G-15506)

American Race Cars ....G 419 836-5070
Millbury (G-14182)

Custom Chassis Inc ....G 440 839-5574
Wakeman (G-19447)

Falls Stamping & Welding Co ....C 330 928-1191
Cuyahoga Falls (G-7996)

Jefferson Industries Corp ....C 614 879-5300
West Jefferson (G-20079)

Mobis North America LLC ....E 419 729-6700
Toledo (G-18589)

Progressive Automotive Inc ....G 740 862-4696
Baltimore (G-1085)

Sutphen Corporation ....D 937 969-8851
Springfield (G-17658)

W&W Automotive & Towing Inc ....F 937 429-1699
Beavercreek Township (G-1391)

CHEESE WHOLESALERS

Great Lakes Cheese Co Inc ....B 440 834-2500
Hiram (G-11036)

International Multifoods Corp ....G 330 682-3000
Orrville (G-15741)

Lori Holding Co ....E 740 342-3230
New Lexington (G-14848)

Troyer Cheese Inc ....E 330 893-2479
Millersburg (G-14274)

CHEMICAL CLEANING SVCS

Bleachtech LLC ....E 216 921-1980
Seville (G-17071)

Chemical Solvents Inc ....E 216 741-9310
Cleveland (G-5025)

Ozone Systems Svcs Group Inc ....G 513 899-4131
Morrow (G-14550)

CHEMICAL ELEMENTS

Compliance Elements LLC ....G 419 217-1793
Bellevue (G-1549)

Creative Elements Studio ....G 330 606-2068
Mogadore (G-14372)

Extreme Elements ....G 330 325-2807
Akron (G-175)

M & G Polymers Usa LLC ....E 330 239-7400
Sharon Center (G-17107)

Perstorp Polyols Inc ....C 419 729-5448
Toledo (G-18641)

CHEMICAL PROCESSING MACHINERY & EQPT

Aquila Pharmatech LLC ....G 419 386-2527
Waterville (G-19652)

Cammann Inc ....F 440 965-4051
Birmingham (G-1685)

Cold Jet LLC ....D 513 831-3211
Loveland (G-12346)

Design Fabricators of Mantua ....G 330 274-5353
Mantua (G-12709)

Guild Associates Inc ....E 614 798-8215
Dublin (G-9081)

Guild Associates Inc ....G 843 573-0095
Dublin (G-9082)

Heil Engneered Process Eqp Inc ....F 440 327-6051
North Ridgeville (G-15378)

Jbw Systems Inc ....F 614 882-5008
Westerville (G-20162)

Nalco Company LLC ....F 432 528-5214
Louisville (G-12320)

Regal Industries Inc ....G 440 352-9600
Painesville (G-15917)

Yost & Son Inc ....G 440 779-8025
North Olmsted (G-15353)

Zeeco Equipment Commodity ....G 440 838-1102
Brecksville (G-2078)

CHEMICAL SPLYS FOR FOUNDRIES

Atotech USA Inc ....D 216 398-0550
Cleveland (G-4857)

Global Chemical Inc ....G 419 242-1004
Toledo (G-18481)

Lynx Chemical ....G 513 856-9161
Franklin (G-10033)

Merry X-Ray Chemical Corp ....G 614 219-2011
Hilliard (G-10960)

CHEMICALS & ALLIED PRDTS WHOLESALERS, NEC

AIN Industries Inc ....G 440 781-0950
Cleveland (G-4733)

Akzo Nobel Coatings Inc ....G 614 294-3361
Columbus (G-6710)

American Metal Cleaning Inc ....G 419 255-1828
Toledo (G-18341)

Aquablue Inc ....G 330 343-0220
New Philadelphia (G-14884)

Ashland LLC ....C 614 790-3333
Dublin (G-9047)

Ashland LLC ....G 513 557-3100
Cincinnati (G-3418)

Bleachtech LLC ....E 216 921-1980
Seville (G-17071)

Calvary Industries Inc ....E 513 874-1113
Fairfield (G-9649)

Chem-Sales Inc ....F 419 531-4292
Toledo (G-18394)

Chemmasters Inc ....E 440 428-2105
Madison (G-12501)

Corrugated Chemicals Inc ....G 513 561-7773
Cincinnati (G-3614)

Cs Products ....G 330 452-8566
Canton (G-2672)

Inceptor Inc ....G 419 726-8804
Toledo (G-18519)

Koch Knight LLC ....D 330 488-1651
East Canton (G-9194)

Netherland Rubber Company ....F 513 733-0883
Cincinnati (G-4146)

Polar Inc ....G 937 297-0911
Moraine (G-14516)

Polymer Additives Inc ....E 216 875-7200
Independence (G-11269)

Polymer Additives Inc ....G 216 262-7016
Walton Hills (G-19475)

Polymer Additives Holdings Inc ....G 216 875-7200
Independence (G-11270)

PVS Chemical Solutions Inc ....F 330 666-0888
Copley (G-7853)

Quality Borate Co LLC ....F 216 896-1949
Cleveland (G-6069)

Qumont Chemical Co ....G 419 241-1057
Toledo (G-18665)

Sika Corporation ....G 740 375-3020
Marion (G-12900)

Singleton Corporation ....F 216 651-7800
Cleveland (G-6205)

Stevens Auto Glaze and SEC LL ....G 440 953-2900
Eastlake (G-9288)

Tricor Industrial Inc ....D 330 264-3299
Wooster (G-20841)

CHEMICALS & ALLIED PRDTS, WHOLESALE: Anti-Corrosion Prdts

Electro Prime Group LLC ....D 419 476-0100
Toledo (G-18453)

Mesocoat Inc ....F 216 453-0866
Euclid (G-9593)

CHEMICALS & ALLIED PRDTS, WHOLESALE: Aromatic

Dark Continent ....G 330 454-7804
Canton (G-2679)

CHEMICALS & ALLIED PRDTS, WHOLESALE: Caustic Soda

National Colloid Company ....E 740 282-1171
Steubenville (G-17706)

CHEMICALS & ALLIED PRDTS, WHOLESALE: Chemical Additives

Chemcore Inc ....F 937 228-6118
Dayton (G-8228)

CHEMICALS & ALLIED PRDTS, WHOLESALE: Chemicals, Indl

Jamtek Enterprises Inc ....G 513 738-4700
Harrison (G-10786)

Lanxess Corporation ....C 440 279-2367
Chardon (G-3164)

Nexeo Solutions LLC ....F 800 531-7106
Dublin (G-9113)

Rotech Products Incorporated ....G 216 476-3722
Cleveland (G-6135)

Tembec Btlsr Inc ....E 419 244-5856
Toledo (G-18719)

Tosoh America Inc ....B 614 539-8622
Grove City (G-10604)

Univar USA Inc ....C 513 714-5264
West Chester (G-20064)

CHEMICALS & ALLIED PRDTS, WHOLESALE: Chemicals, Indl & Heavy

J & K Wade Ltd ....G 419 352-6163
Bowling Green (G-1992)

CHEMICALS & ALLIED PRDTS, WHOLESALE: Concrete Additives

Sika Corporation ....D 740 387-9224
Marion (G-12901)

CHEMICALS & ALLIED PRDTS, WHOLESALE: Detergent/Soap

Chemical Solvents Inc ....E 216 741-9310
Cleveland (G-5025)

Cr Brands Inc ....D 513 860-5039
West Chester (G-19846)

Jeff Pendergrass ....G 513 575-1226
Milford (G-14156)

CHEMICALS & ALLIED PRDTS, WHOLESALE: Detergents

Cleaning Lady Inc ....F 419 589-5566
Mansfield (G-12581)

Jabco & Associates Inc ....G 513 752-0600
Amelia (G-578)

Washing Systems LLC ....C 800 272-1974
Loveland (G-12399)

CHEMICALS & ALLIED PRDTS, WHOLESALE: Dry Ice

Gehm & Sons Limited ....G 330 724-8423
Akron (G-202)

CHEMICALS & ALLIED PRDTS, WHOLESALE: Glue

Tech-Bond Solutions ....G 614 327-8884
Carroll (G-2949)

CHEMICALS & ALLIED PRDTS, WHOLESALE: Indl Gases

Airgas USA LLC ....E 937 228-8594
Dayton (G-8142)

CHEMICALS & ALLIED PRDTS, WHOLESALE: Oxygen

Jerrys Welding Supply Inc ....G 937 364-1500
Hillsboro (G-11006)

CHEMICALS & ALLIED PRDTS, WHOLESALE: Plastics Materials, NEC

Alro Steel Corporation ....E 419 720-5300
Toledo (G-18331)

Chatelain Plastics Inc ....G 419 422-4323
Findlay (G-9807)

Hillman Group Inc ....G 800 800-4900
Parma (G-15962)

Laird Plastics Inc ....F 614 272-0777
Columbus (G-7280)

CHEMICALS & ALLIED PRDTS, WHOLESALE: Plastics Prdts, NEC

Carney Plastics Inc ....G 330 746-8273
Youngstown (G-21044)

Inno-Pak Holding Inc ....G 740 363-0090
Delaware (G-8861)

Polymer Packaging Inc ....D 330 832-2000
Massillon (G-13195)

Queen City Polymers Inc ....E 513 779-0990
West Chester (G-19928)

Tahoma Enterprises Inc ....D 330 745-9016
Barberton (G-1151)

Tahoma Rubber & Plastics Inc ....D 330 745-9016
Barberton (G-1152)

Upl International Inc ....E 330 433-2860
North Canton (G-15280)

CHEMICALS & ALLIED PRDTS, WHOLESALE: Plastics Sheets & Rods

HP Manufacturing Company Inc ....D 216 361-6500
Cleveland (G-5530)

Ilpea Industries Inc ....C 330 562-2916
Aurora (G-926)

CHEMICALS & ALLIED PRDTS, WHOLESALE: Plastics, Basic Shapes

Meridian Machine Inc...........................G....... 330 308-0296
New Philadelphia (G-14913)

CHEMICALS & ALLIED PRDTS, WHOLESALE: Resins

Hexpol Compounding LLC....................C....... 440 834-4644
Burton (G-2376)
Polyone Corporation ....D....... 440 930-1000
Avon Lake (G-1047)

CHEMICALS & ALLIED PRDTS, WHOLESALE: Rubber, Synthetic

E I Du Pont De Nemours & Co ....E....... 330 929-2961
Stow (G-17745)
Goldsmith & Eggleton LLC ....F....... 203 855-6000
Wadsworth (G-19408)
Mantaline Corporation ....D....... 330 274-2264
Mantua (G-12715)

CHEMICALS & ALLIED PRDTS, WHOLESALE: Sealants

McGill Corporation.............................F....... 614 829-1200
Groveport (G-10635)
United McGill Corporation ....E....... 614 829-1200
Groveport (G-10648)

CHEMICALS & ALLIED PRDTS, WHOLESALE: Syn Resin, Rub/Plastic

Flex Technologies Inc.........................E....... 330 897-6311
Baltic (G-1071)
Kraton Polymers US LLC ....B....... 740 423-7571
Belpre (G-1589)
Phoenix Technologies Intl LLC.............E....... 419 353-7738
Bowling Green (G-2007)
Polyone Corporation ....D....... 440 930-1000
North Baltimore (G-15197)

CHEMICALS & ALLIED PRDTS, WHOLESALE: Waxes, Exc Petroleum

K2 Petroleum & Supply LLC ....G....... 937 503-2614
Cincinnati (G-3966)

CHEMICALS & OTHER PRDTS DERIVED FROM COKING

FBC Chemical Corporation...................F....... 216 341-2000
Cleveland (G-5328)

CHEMICALS, AGRICULTURE: Wholesalers

Tyler Grain & Fertilizer Co ....F....... 330 669-2341
Smithville (G-17246)

CHEMICALS: Agricultural

BASF Corporation...............................G....... 614 662-5682
Columbus (G-6812)
E I Du Pont De Nemours & Co ....C....... 330 364-6002
Dover (G-8983)
Harvest Land Co-Op Inc ....G....... 937 884-5526
Verona (G-19338)
Mercer Landmark Inc..........................G....... 419 363-3391
Rockford (G-16692)
Modern AG Supply Inc ....G....... 419 753-3484
New Knoxville (G-14838)
Quality Borate Co LLC ....F....... 216 896-1949
Cleveland (G-6069)

CHEMICALS: Alcohols

Catholic Charity Hispanic Off ....F....... 216 696-2197
Cleveland (G-4994)

CHEMICALS: Alkalies

Valvsys LLC.......................................V....... 513 539-1234
Monroe (G-14417)

CHEMICALS: Aluminum Compounds

Drs Industries Inc..............................D....... 419 861-0334
Holland (G-11057)
Pennex Aluminum................................D....... 330 427-6704
Leetonia (G-11863)

CHEMICALS: Aluminum Oxide

Custom Metal Shearing Inc ....F....... 937 233-6950
Dayton (G-8260)

CHEMICALS: Aluminum Sulfate

Chemtrade Chemicals US LLC ....G....... 513 422-6319
Middletown (G-14029)
Dpa Investments Inc ....F....... 440 992-7039
Ashtabula (G-804)

CHEMICALS: Anhydrous Ammonia

Airgas Inc...G....... 419 695-7085
Delphos (G-8900)

CHEMICALS: Bauxite, Refined

Porocel Industries LLC.......................G....... 513 733-8519
Cincinnati (G-4249)

CHEMICALS: Bleaching Powder, Lime Bleaching Compounds

Bleachtech LLC ....E....... 216 921-1980
Seville (G-17071)

CHEMICALS: Calcium & Calcium Compounds

New Eezy-Gro Inc ....F....... 419 927-6110
Upper Sandusky (G-19136)
Omya Distribution LLC ....G....... 513 387-4600
Blue Ash (G-1846)

CHEMICALS: Caustic Potash & Potassium Hydroxide

Ashta Chemicals Inc...........................D....... 440 997-5221
Ashtabula (G-793)

CHEMICALS: Caustic Soda

Gbc Metals LLC ....E....... 330 823-1700
Alliance (G-510)

CHEMICALS: Copper Compounds Or Salts, Inorganic

Three Leaf Inc....................................G....... 888 308-1007
Hamilton (G-10746)

CHEMICALS: Fire Retardant

Flame Safe of Northern Ohio ....G....... 419 626-6204
Sandusky (G-16966)
No Burn Inc..G....... 330 336-1500
Wadsworth (G-19421)
No Burn North America Inc ....F....... 419 841-6055
Toledo (G-18607)
Pyro-Chem Corporation ....F....... 740 377-2244
South Point (G-17445)
Viking Group Inc ....G....... 937 443-0433
Dayton (G-8743)

CHEMICALS: High Purity Grade, Organic

Enzyme Catalyzed Polymers LLC ....G....... 330 310-1072
Akron (G-170)
Ronald T Dodge Co.............................F....... 937 439-4497
Dayton (G-8638)

CHEMICALS: High Purity, Refined From Technical Grade

Arboris LLC ....E....... 740 522-9350
Newark (G-14983)
Gabriel Performance Pdts LLC.............G....... 440 992-3200
Akron (G-197)
Gabriel Performance Pdts LLC.............G....... 440 992-3200
Ashtabula (G-809)
Helena Chemical Company ....G....... 419 596-3806
Continental (G-7826)
Helena Chemical Company ....G....... 614 275-4200
Columbus (G-7148)
Heraeus Precious Metals North............E....... 937 264-1000
Vandalia (G-19295)

CHEMICALS: Inorganic, NEC

Airgas Usa LLC ....G....... 440 232-6397
Oakwood Village (G-15622)

Airgas USA LLC ....G....... 419 726-2719
Toledo (G-18325)
Akron Dispersions Inc ....E....... 330 666-0045
Copley (G-7838)
Alchem Corporation ....G....... 330 725-2436
Medina (G-13366)
Allyn Corp...G....... 614 442-3900
Columbus (G-6727)
Alpha Zeta Holdings Inc ....E....... 216 271-1601
Cleveland (G-4770)
Americhem Inc ....D....... 330 929-4213
Cuyahoga Falls (G-7965)
Amresco LLC......................................C....... 440 349-2805
Cleveland (G-4798)
Arizona Chemical Company LLC ....C....... 330 343-7701
Dover (G-8964)
BASF Catalysts LLC ....B....... 440 322-3741
Elyria (G-9379)
BASF Catalysts LLC ....E....... 216 360-5005
Cleveland (G-4894)
BASF Corporation...............................A....... 513 482-3000
Cincinnati (G-3438)
BASF Corporation...............................G....... 614 662-5682
Columbus (G-6812)
Bond Chemicals Inc............................G....... 330 725-5935
Medina (G-13379)
Borchers Americas Inc ....D....... 440 899-2950
Westlake (G-20258)
C T Chemicals Inc ....G....... 513 336-6160
Lebanon (G-11785)
Calvary Industries Inc.........................E....... 513 874-1113
Fairfield (G-9649)
Chem Masters ....G....... 440 428-2105
Madison (G-12500)
Chem Technologies Ltd ....E....... 440 632-9311
Middlefield (G-13921)
Cil Isotope Separations LLC ....F....... 937 376-5413
Xenia (G-20942)
Cincinnati Specialties LLC ....C....... 513 242-3300
Cincinnati (G-3566)
Coolant Control Inc ....E....... 513 471-8770
Cincinnati (G-3609)
Coulton Chemical ....G....... 419 698-8181
Oregon (G-15706)
Crop Production Services Inc...............E....... 513 941-4100
North Bend (G-15204)
Curtis Chemical Inc ....G....... 330 656-2514
Hudson (G-11167)
Db Parent Inc.....................................C....... 513 475-3265
Cincinnati (G-3644)
Df Consumer Products ....F....... 440 239-4795
Berea (G-1611)
Diversified Brands ....G....... 216 595-8777
Bedford (G-1419)
Dover Chemical Corporation ....C....... 330 343-7711
Dover (G-8979)
Dubois Chemicals Inc.........................F....... 513 868-9662
Hamilton (G-10684)
E I Du Pont De Nemours & Co ....E....... 330 929-2961
Stow (G-17745)
Elco Corporation ....E....... 440 997-6131
Ashtabula (G-805)
Elf Atochem NA OH.............................G....... 740 363-1351
Delaware (G-8841)
Enerchem Incorporated ....G....... 513 745-0580
Cincinnati (G-3703)
Engelhard Corp ....G....... 440 322-3741
Elyria (G-9420)
Eomg Harko Holdings LLC ....E....... 216 781-0083
Cleveland (G-5287)
Ferro Corporation ....D....... 216 577-7144
Bedford (G-1423)
General Electric Company ....D....... 216 268-3846
Cleveland (G-5417)
Globe Metallurgical Inc.......................C....... 740 984-2361
Waterford (G-19647)
Gnrl Chemical L ....G....... 419 255-0193
Toledo (G-18482)
Graphite Sales Inc ....E....... 419 652-3388
Nova (G-15578)
Hilltop Energy Inc...............................E....... 330 859-2108
Mineral City (G-14301)
Ineos Americas LLC ....B....... 419 226-1200
Lima (G-12028)
Kerry Flavor Systems Us LLC ....E....... 513 539-7373
Monroe (G-14407)
Littlern Corporation ....G....... 330 848-8847
Barberton (G-1124)
McGean-Rohco Inc ....D....... 216 441-4900
Newburgh Heights (G-15076)

Molecular Research Center...........F.......513 841-0900
Cincinnati (G-4117)

Nachurs Alpine Solutions Corp.......E.......740 382-5701
Marion (G-12888)

National Colloid Company.............E.......740 282-1171
Steubenville (G-17706)

Occidental Chemical Corp.............E.......513 242-2900
Cincinnati (G-4172)

Occidental Chemical Durez.............G.......419 675-5300
Kenton (G-11563)

Ohio Oxide Corporation Del...........F.......740 654-6555
Pleasantville (G-16374)

Omnova Solutions Inc.................D.......330 734-1237
Akron (G-328)

Omnova Solutions Inc.................C.......216 682-7000
Beachwood (G-1287)

Omnova Wallcovering USA Inc..........G.......216 682-7000
Beachwood (G-1288)

PMC Specialties Group Inc............E.......513 242-3300
Cincinnati (G-4246)

PMC Specialties Group Inc............E.......513 242-3300
Cincinnati (G-4247)

Polymerics Inc.......................E.......330 434-6665
Cuyahoga Falls (G-8034)

PQ Corporation.......................G.......216 341-2578
Newburgh Heights (G-15078)

Press Chemical & Phrm Lab............G.......614 863-2802
Columbus (G-7515)

Process Sltions For Indust Inc.......G.......330 702-1685
Canfield (G-2570)

Rtprocess LLC........................G.......937 366-6215
Wilmington (G-20678)

Saint-Gobain Ceramics Plas Inc.......A.......330 673-5860
Stow (G-17797)

Saint-Gobain Ceramics Plas Inc.......C.......440 834-0061
Hiram (G-11037)

Shepherd Chemical Company............F.......513 200-6987
Cincinnati (G-4415)

Tate Lyle Ingrdnts Amricas LLC.......D.......937 236-5906
Dayton (G-8703)

TEC Line Inc.........................G.......740 881-5948
Lewis Center (G-11924)

Total Plastics Inc...................G.......440 205-9700
Mentor (G-13751)

Tru-Chem Company Inc.................F.......614 888-2436
Columbus (G-7711)

Union Camp Corp......................G.......330 343-7701
Dover (G-9022)

Univar USA Inc.......................C.......513 714-5264
West Chester (G-20064)

Zaclon LLC...........................E.......216 271-1601
Cleveland (G-6489)

CHEMICALS: Isotopes, Radioactive

Aldrich Chemical.....................D.......937 859-1808
Miamisburg (G-13781)

CHEMICALS: Lead Compounds/Salts, Inorganic, Not Pigments

Metals and Additives Corp Inc........F.......740 654-6555
Pleasantville (G-16373)

CHEMICALS: Lithium Compounds, Inorganic

Lithium Innovations Co LLC...........G.......419 725-3525
Toledo (G-18562)

CHEMICALS: Medicinal

Amresco LLC..........................D.......440 349-2805
Solon (G-17259)

Pharmacia Hepar LLC..................D.......937 746-3603
Franklin (G-10045)

Polar Products Inc...................G.......330 253-9973
Stow (G-17789)

Proctoer & Gamble....................G.......513 983-1100
Blue Ash (G-1859)

CHEMICALS: Medicinal, Organic, Uncompounded, Bulk

Press Chemical & Phrm Lab............G.......614 863-2802
Columbus (G-7515)

CHEMICALS: Metal Salts/Compounds, Exc Sodium, Potassium/Alum

Shepherd Chemical Company............F.......513 731-1110
Norwood (G-15574)

Shepherd Chemical Company............F.......513 424-7276
Middletown (G-14083)

CHEMICALS: NEC

Advanced Chem Solutions Inc..........G.......216 692-3005
Orrville (G-15728)

Advanced Chem Solutions Inc..........G.......330 283-5157
Medina (G-13363)

Akron Dispersions Inc................E.......330 666-0045
Copley (G-7838)

Akzo Nobel Chemicals LLC.............G.......419 229-0088
Lima (G-11985)

Akzo Nobel Coatings Inc..............G.......614 294-3361
Columbus (G-6710)

Aldrich Chemical.....................D.......937 859-1808
Miamisburg (G-13781)

Allyn Corp...........................G.......614 442-3900
Columbus (G-6727)

American Fireworks Company Inc.......F.......330 650-1776
Hudson (G-11156)

Amresco LLC..........................C.......440 349-2805
Cleveland (G-4798)

Andersons Lawn Fert Div Inc..........F.......419 893-5050
Maumee (G-13226)

Aps-Materials Inc....................D.......937 278-6547
Dayton (G-8161)

Ashland LLC..........................C.......614 790-3333
Dublin (G-9047)

Ashland LLC..........................G.......513 682-2405
West Chester (G-19810)

Ashland LLC..........................E.......419 998-8728
Lima (G-11995)

Ask Chemicals LP.....................C.......614 763-0384
Dublin (G-9049)

Attia Applied Sciences Inc...........F.......740 369-1891
Delaware (G-8823)

Babcock & Wilcox Megtec..............C.......614 258-9501
Columbus (G-6799)

Bernard Laboratories Inc.............E.......513 681-7373
Cincinnati (G-3447)

Biofocus Inc.........................G.......937 890-3068
Dayton (G-8188)

Bird Control International............E.......330 425-2377
Twinsburg (G-18905)

BLaster Corporation..................E.......216 901-5800
Cleveland (G-4916)

Bond Distributing LLC................G.......440 461-7920
Cleveland (G-4923)

Borchers Americas Inc................D.......440 899-2950
Westlake (G-20258)

Braden-Sutphin Ink Company...........C.......216 271-2300
Cleveland (G-4929)

Brewer Industries LLC................E.......216 469-0808
Chagrin Falls (G-3050)

Bulk Molding Compounds Inc...........D.......419 874-7941
Perrysburg (G-16071)

Capital Chemical Co..................E.......330 494-9535
Canton (G-2649)

Cargill Incorporated.................F.......513 941-7400
Cincinnati (G-3500)

Cargill Incorporated.................C.......216 651-7200
Cleveland (G-4977)

Celsus Laboratories Inc..............E.......513 772-8130
Cincinnati (G-3512)

Chem Technologies Ltd................E.......440 632-9311
Middlefield (G-13921)

Chemical Methods Inc.................E.......216 476-8400
Strongsville (G-17901)

Cinchempro Inc.......................C.......513 724-6111
Batavia (G-1171)

Cincinnati - Vulcan Company..........D.......513 242-5300
Cincinnati (G-3535)

Coolant Control Inc..................E.......513 471-8770
Cincinnati (G-3609)

Coventya Inc.........................E.......216 351-1500
Brooklyn Heights (G-2136)

CP Chemicals Group LP................E.......440 833-3000
Wickliffe (G-20363)

Creative Commercial Finishing........G.......513 722-9393
Loveland (G-12347)

Cresset Chemical Co Inc..............F.......419 669-2041
Weston (G-20324)

Cytec Industries Inc.................G.......740 374-7171
Marietta (G-12777)

Dayton Superior Corporation..........C.......937 866-0711
Miamisburg (G-13798)

Dover Chemical Corporation...........D.......330 343-7711
Dover (G-8979)

E I Du Pont De Nemours & Co..........E.......330 929-2961
Stow (G-17745)

E3 Materials LLC.....................G.......330 972-6457
Akron (G-159)

Earth Safe Chemical LLC..............G.......419 648-7801
Harrod (G-10813)

Elco Corporation.....................E.......440 997-6131
Ashtabula (G-805)

EMD Millipore Corporation............D.......513 631-0445
Norwood (G-15572)

Emerald Performance Mtls LLC.........D.......513 841-4000
Cincinnati (G-3695)

Emerald Performance Mtls LLC.........D.......330 374-2418
Akron (G-164)

Emery Oleochemicals LLC..............C.......513 762-2500
Cincinnati (G-3699)

Ensign Product Company Inc...........E.......216 341-5911
Cleveland (G-5284)

Envirnmntal Prtctive Ctngs LLC.......E.......740 363-6180
Ostrander (G-15786)

Environment Chemical Corp............G.......330 453-5200
Uniontown (G-19083)

Etna Products Incorporated...........E.......440 543-9845
Chagrin Falls (G-3087)

Ferro Corporation....................D.......216 875-5600
Cleveland (G-5336)

Flexsys America LP...................D.......330 666-4111
Akron (G-190)

Fort Amanda Specialties LLC..........E.......419 229-0088
Lima (G-12015)

Fuchs Lubricants Co..................E.......330 963-0400
Twinsburg (G-18938)

Fusion Automation Inc................G.......440 602-5595
Willoughby (G-20493)

GE Betz Inc..........................E.......330 339-2292
New Philadelphia (G-14900)

General Electric Company.............D.......216 268-3846
Cleveland (G-5417)

GFS Chemicals Inc....................E.......740 881-5501
Powell (G-16472)

GFS Chemicals Inc....................D.......614 224-5345
Columbus (G-7112)

Harsco Corporation...................D.......330 372-1781
Warren (G-19557)

Hexion LLC...........................D.......614 225-4000
Columbus (G-7153)

Hexpol Compounding LLC...............C.......440 834-4644
Burton (G-2376)

Hill & Griffith Company..............G.......513 921-1075
Cincinnati (G-3882)

Hunt Imaging LLC.....................E.......440 826-0433
Berea (G-1620)

I P Specrete Inc.....................G.......216 721-2050
Cleveland (G-5547)

Ink Factory Inc......................G.......330 799-0888
Youngstown (G-21116)

Jay Tackett..........................G.......740 779-1715
Frankfort (G-9999)

Jeff Pendergrass.....................G.......513 575-1226
Milford (G-14156)

Joules Angstrom UV Printing..........E.......740 964-9113
Etna (G-9558)

Key Resin Company....................F.......513 943-4225
Batavia (G-1198)

Leonhardt Plating Company............E.......513 242-1410
Cincinnati (G-4020)

Liquid Development Company...........G.......216 641-9366
Independence (G-11265)

Lubrizol Advanced Mtls Inc...........F.......216 447-5000
Brecksville (G-2061)

Lubrizol Advanced Mtls Inc...........E.......440 933-0400
Avon Lake (G-1037)

Lubrizol Corporation.................E.......440 357-7064
Painesville (G-15898)

McGean-Rohco Inc.....................D.......216 441-4900
Newburgh Heights (G-15076)

Midwest Industrial Supply Inc........D.......330 456-3121
Canton (G-2780)

Momentive Performance................G.......281 325-3536
Columbus (G-7364)

Monarch Engraving Inc................E.......440 638-1500
Strongsville (G-17942)

Morton Salt Inc......................C.......330 925-3015
Rittman (G-16680)

National Colloid Company.............E.......740 282-1171
Steubenville (G-17706)

New Vulco Mfg & Sales Co LLC.........D.......513 242-2672
Cincinnati (G-4149)

Noco Company.........................B.......216 464-8131
Solon (G-17350)

Nof Metal Coatings N Amer Inc........E.......440 285-2231
Chardon (G-3168)

Noveon Fcc Inc ....G...... 440 943-4200
Wickliffe (G-20374)

Ohio Aluminum Chemicals LLC ....G...... 513 860-3842
West Chester (G-19908)

Oliver Chemical Co Inc ....G...... 513 541-4540
Cincinnati (G-4185)

Parker Trutec Incorporated ....D...... 937 653-8500
Urbana (G-19172)

Phantom Fireworks Inc ....E...... 740 927-6943
Millersport (G-14297)

Polymer Additives Inc ....E...... 216 875-7200
Independence (G-11269)

Polymer Additives Inc ....G...... 216 262-7016
Walton Hills (G-19475)

Polymer Additives Holdings Inc ....G...... 216 875-7200
Independence (G-11270)

Polymerics Inc ....E...... 330 677-1131
Kent (G-11503)

Premier Ink Systems Inc ....F...... 513 367-4700
Harrison (G-10796)

Quaker Chemical Corporation ....D...... 513 422-9600
Middletown (G-14080)

Quikrete Companies Inc ....E...... 614 885-4406
Columbus (G-7540)

Railtech Boutet Inc ....D...... 419 592-5050
Napoleon (G-14695)

Railtech Matweld Inc ....G...... 419 592-5050
Napoleon (G-14696)

Railtech Matweld Inc ....F...... 419 591-3770
Napoleon (G-14697)

Research Organics LLC ....D...... 216 883-8025
Cleveland (G-6105)

Rhenium Alloys Inc ....D...... 440 365-7388
North Ridgeville (G-15401)

Rozzi Company Inc ....E...... 513 683-0620
Loveland (G-12382)

Sika Corporation ....G...... 740 375-3020
Marion (G-12900)

Solvay USA Inc ....E...... 513 482-5700
Cincinnati (G-4436)

Spectra Group Limited Inc ....G...... 419 837-9783
Millbury (G-14186)

State Industrial Products Corp ....B...... 877 747-6986
Cleveland (G-6239)

Summitville Tiles Inc ....E...... 330 868-6463
Minerva (G-14344)

Sun & Soil LLC ....G...... 513 575-5900
Loveland (G-12391)

Tate Lyle Ingrdnts Amricas LLC ....D...... 937 236-5906
Dayton (G-8703)

Teknol Inc ....D...... 937 264-0190
Dayton (G-8708)

The Euclid Chemical Company ....E...... 800 321-7628
Cleveland (G-6309)

The Euclid Chemical Company ....F...... 216 531-9222
Cleveland (G-6311)

U S Chemical & Plastics ....G...... 740 254-4311
Massillon (G-13208)

United Lubricants Corporation ....D...... 513 422-9600
Middletown (G-14092)

Univar USA Inc ....C...... 513 714-5264
West Chester (G-20064)

Vesuvius U S A Corporation ....E...... 440 593-1161
Conneaut (G-7821)

Vesuvius U S A Corporation ....E...... 440 816-3051
Cleveland (G-6411)

Wrl of Indiana Inc ....A...... 419 289-8700
Ashland (G-786)

Zinkan Enterprises Inc ....F...... 330 487-1500
Twinsburg (G-19043)

CHEMICALS: Nonmetallic Compounds

Baerlocher Production Usa LLC ....E...... 513 482-6300
Cincinnati (G-3434)

Baerlocher USA LLC ....F...... 330 364-6000
Dover (G-8965)

CHEMICALS: Organic, NEC

Abitec Corporation ....E...... 614 429-6464
Columbus (G-6678)

ABS Materials Inc ....D...... 330 234-7999
Wooster (G-20730)

Akzo Nobel Chemicals LLC ....G...... 419 229-0088
Lima (G-11985)

Alco-Chem Inc ....E...... 330 253-3535
Akron (G-61)

Aldrich Chemical ....D...... 937 859-1808
Miamisburg (G-13781)

Alpha Zeta Holdings Inc ....G...... 216 271-1601
Cleveland (G-4770)

Ampacet Corporation ....C...... 740 929-5521
Newark (G-14982)

B-F Processing LLC ....G...... 614 225-4000
Columbus (G-6798)

BASF Corporation ....C...... 937 547-6700
Greenville (G-10489)

BASF Corporation ....C...... 419 877-0876
Whitehouse (G-20337)

BASF Corporation ....C...... 614 662-5682
Columbus (G-6812)

BASF Corporation ....C...... 513 482-3000
Cincinnati (G-3439)

Borchers Americas Inc ....D...... 440 899-2950
Westlake (G-20258)

Borden Chemical Foundry LLC ....E...... 614 225-4000
Columbus (G-6849)

Cargill Incorporated ....F...... 513 941-7400
Cincinnati (G-3500)

Chem-Sales Inc ....F...... 419 531-4292
Toledo (G-18394)

Chemcore Inc ....F...... 937 228-6118
Dayton (G-8228)

Clariant Corporation ....G...... 513 791-2964
Blue Ash (G-1766)

Corrugated Chemicals Inc ....G...... 513 561-7773
Cincinnati (G-3614)

Creative Fuels LLC ....F...... 330 923-2222
Cuyahoga Falls (G-7983)

Dnd Emulsions Inc ....G...... 419 525-4988
Mansfield (G-12595)

Dover Chemical Corporation ....C...... 330 343-7711
Dover (G-8979)

Dubois Chemicals Inc ....B...... 513 731-6350
Cincinnati (G-3673)

Elco Corporation ....E...... 440 997-6131
Ashtabula (G-805)

Elco Corporation ....D...... 800 321-0467
Ashtabula (G-5262)

Emerald Polymer Additives LLC ....D...... 330 374-2424
Akron (G-165)

Eqm Technologies & Energy Inc ....F...... 513 825-7500
Cincinnati (G-3715)

Equistar Chemicals LP ....E...... 513 530-4000
Cincinnati (G-3716)

Evonik Corporation ....D...... 513 554-8969
Cincinnati (G-3726)

Ferro Corporation ....D...... 216 577-7144
Bedford (G-1423)

Flow Polymers LLC ....C...... 216 249-4900
Cleveland (G-5360)

Geo Specialty Chemical ....G...... 330 650-0237
Hudson (G-11172)

GFS Chemicals Inc ....E...... 740 881-5501
Powell (G-16472)

GFS Chemicals Inc ....D...... 614 224-5345
Columbus (G-7112)

Green Harvest Energy LLC ....F...... 330 716-3068
Columbiana (G-6618)

Ha-International LLC ....E...... 419 537-0096
Toledo (G-18492)

Heraeus Precious Metals North ....E...... 937 264-1000
Vandalia (G-19295)

Hill & Griffith Company ....G...... 513 921-1075
Cincinnati (G-3882)

Homeland AG Fuels LLC ....G...... 216 763-1004
Cleveland (G-5522)

Hunt Imaging LLC ....E...... 440 826-0433
Berea (G-1620)

Ineos Americas LLC ....B...... 419 226-1200
Lima (G-12028)

Insightfuel LLC ....F...... 330 998-7380
Macedonia (G-12460)

J R M Chemical Inc ....F...... 216 475-8488
Cleveland (G-5600)

Jatrodiesel Inc ....F...... 937 847-8050
Miamisburg (G-13821)

K & E Chemical Co Inc ....F...... 216 341-0500
Cleveland (G-5627)

Karl Industries Inc ....G...... 330 562-4100
Aurora (G-929)

Littlern Corporation ....G...... 330 848-8847
Barberton (G-1124)

Lubrizol Corporation ....A...... 440 943-4200
Wickliffe (G-20370)

Lyondell Chemical Company ....E...... 440 352-9393
Fairport Harbor (G-9767)

Michelman Inc ....E...... 513 793-7766
Cincinnati (G-4099)

Mid America Chemical Corp ....G...... 216 749-0100
Cleveland (G-5803)

Momentive Specialty Chem Inc ....F...... 740 452-5451
Zanesville (G-21330)

Nachurs Alpine Solutions Corp ....E...... 740 382-5701
Marion (G-12888)

Nanofilm Ltd ....E...... 216 674-1430
Cleveland (G-5851)

National Colloid Company ....E...... 740 282-1171
Steubenville (G-17706)

Noveon Fcc Inc ....G...... 440 943-4200
Wickliffe (G-20374)

Occidental Chemical Corp ....E...... 513 242-2900
Cincinnati (G-4172)

Ohio Biosystems Coop Inc ....G...... 419 980-7663
Loudonville (G-12302)

Orion Engineered Carbons LLC ....D...... 740 423-9571
Belpre (G-1592)

Patriot Energy LLC ....D...... 330 923-4442
Cuyahoga Falls (G-8032)

Polychem Dispersions Inc ....E...... 800 545-3530
Middlefield (G-13984)

Research Organics LLC ....D...... 216 883-8025
Cleveland (G-6105)

Shepherd Chemical Company ....F...... 513 200-6987
Cincinnati (G-4415)

Shincor Silicones Inc ....D...... 330 630-9460
Akron (G-400)

Struktol Company America LLC ....C...... 330 928-5188
Stow (G-17805)

Syrgis Holdings Inc ....G...... 859 356-8000
Blue Ash (G-1879)

Trugreen Cleaners LLC ....G...... 740 703-1063
Chillicothe (G-3282)

Twin Rvers Tech - Pnsville LLC ......D...... 440 350-6300
Painesville (G-15935)

Ultimate Chem Solutions Inc ....E...... 440 998-6751
Ashtabula (G-843)

United Initiators Inc ....D...... 440 326-2416
Elyria (G-9505)

Univar USA Inc ....C...... 513 714-5264
West Chester (G-20064)

Vantage Specialty Ingredients ....G...... 937 264-1222
Englewood (G-9543)

Vetz USA Inc ....G...... 937 237-8764
Dayton (G-8741)

Zaclon LLC ....E...... 216 271-1601
Cleveland (G-6489)

CHEMICALS: Phenol

Altivia Petrochemicals LLC ....E...... 740 532-3420
Haverhill (G-10836)

CHEMICALS: Phosphates, Defluorinated/Ammoniated, Exc Fertlr

Pcs Phosphate Company Inc ....E...... 513 738-1261
Harrison (G-10794)

CHEMICALS: Reagent Grade, Refined From Technical Grade

Adna Inc ....G...... 614 397-4974
Dublin (G-9036)

GFS Chemicals Inc ....E...... 740 881-5501
Powell (G-16472)

GFS Chemicals Inc ....D...... 614 224-5345
Columbus (G-7112)

GFS Chemicals Inc ....D...... 740 881-5501
Columbus (G-7113)

GFS Chemicals Inc ....D...... 614 351-5347
Columbus (G-7114)

Rapid Blanket Restorer Corp ....G...... 330 821-6326
Painesville (G-15916)

CHEMICALS: Sodium Bicarbonate

Church & Dwight Co Inc ....D...... 740 852-3621
London (G-12204)

Church & Dwight Co Inc ....F...... 419 992-4244
Old Fort (G-15670)

CHEMICALS: Sulfur Chloride

PVS Chemical Solutions Inc ....F...... 330 666-0888
Copley (G-7853)

CHEMICALS: Tin, Stannic/Stannous, Compounds/Salts, Inorganic

Ohio Coatings Company ....D...... 740 859-5500
Yorkville (G-21007)

CHEMICALS: Water Treatment

Anchor Corporation ....G...... 614 836-9590
Columbus (G-6753)
Aqua Science Inc ....E...... 614 252-5000
Columbus (G-6766)
Aquablue Inc ....G...... 330 343-0220
New Philadelphia (G-14884)
Bond Chemicals Inc ....F...... 330 725-5935
Medina (G-13379)
Chemtech Inc ....F...... 330 454-2127
Canton (G-2653)
City of Mount Vernon ....G...... 740 393-9508
Mount Vernon (G-14615)
Dpa Investments Inc ....G...... 440 992-3377
Ashtabula (G-803)
Enviro Polymers & Chemicals ....G...... 937 427-1315
Beavercreek (G-1336)
Ques Industries Inc ....F...... 216 267-8989
Cleveland (G-6076)
Qumont Chemical Co ....G...... 419 241-1057
Toledo (G-18665)
Tidewater Products Inc ....G...... 419 873-0223
Perrysburg (G-16159)
Tidewater Products Inc ....G...... 419 534-9870
Ottawa Hills (G-15820)
US Water Company LLC ....G...... 740 453-0604
Zanesville (G-21360)

CHEMICALS: Zinc Chloride

Columbia Chemical Corporation .....E...... 330 225-3200
Brunswick (G-2217)

CHICKEN SLAUGHTERING & PROCESSING

Pf Management Inc ....G...... 513 874-8741
West Chester (G-20036)
Pierre Holding Corp ....G...... 513 874-8741
West Chester (G-20037)
V H Cooper & Co Inc ....C...... 419 375-4116
Fort Recovery (G-9961)

CHILD DAY CARE SVCS

L & H Printing ....G...... 937 855-4512
Germantown (G-10370)

CHILDREN'S WEAR STORES

L Brands Inc ....C...... 614 479-2000
Columbus (G-7275)
Locker Room Lettering Ltd ....G...... 419 359-1761
Castalia (G-2977)
Rita Fishel Inc ....E...... 740 775-1957
Chillicothe (G-3272)

CHIMNEY CAPS: Concrete

Day Pre-Cast Products Co ....G...... 419 536-2909
Toledo (G-18429)
Whempys Corp ....G...... 614 888-6670
Worthington (G-20893)

CHIMNEY CLEANING SVCS

Whempys Corp ....G...... 614 888-6670
Worthington (G-20893)

CHINA: Fired & Decorated

Kiln of Hyde Park Inc ....F...... 513 321-3307
Cincinnati (G-3988)
Potter House ....G...... 419 584-1705
Celina (G-3015)

CHINAWARE WHOLESALERS

Ghp II LLC ....B...... 740 681-6825
Lancaster (G-11720)

CHIROPRACTORS' OFFICES

Polar Products Inc ....G...... 330 253-9973
Stow (G-17789)

CHLORINE

Clorox Company ....F...... 513 445-1840
Mason (G-13001)
Clorox Sales Company ....E...... 440 892-1700
Westlake (G-20261)
Jci Jones Chemicals Inc ....F...... 330 825-2531
New Franklin (G-14826)

CHOCOLATE, EXC CANDY FROM BEANS: Chips, Powder, Block, Syrup

Anthony-Thomas Candy Company ....C...... 614 274-8405
Columbus (G-6759)
Becky Knapp ....G...... 330 854-4400
Canal Fulton (G-2498)
Brandts Candies ....G...... 440 942-1016
Willoughby (G-20445)
Brownie Points Inc ....G...... 614 860-8470
Columbus (G-6868)
Cheryl & Co ....D...... 614 776-1500
Obetz (G-15653)
Chocolate Pig Inc ....G...... 440 461-4511
Cleveland (G-5029)
Dietsch Brothers Incorporated ....E...... 419 422-4474
Findlay (G-9816)
E R B Enterprises Inc ....G...... 740 948-9174
Jeffersonville (G-11379)
Fawn Confectionery ....F...... 513 574-9612
Cincinnati (G-3742)
Godiva Chocolatier Inc ....E...... 216 831-9414
Beachwood (G-1273)
Gorant Chocolatier LLC ....C...... 330 726-8821
Boardman (G-1921)
Graeters Manufacturing Co ....D...... 513 721-3323
Cincinnati (G-3843)
Harry London Candies Inc ....C...... 330 494-0833
North Canton (G-15239)
Haute Chocolate Inc ....G...... 513 793-9999
Montgomery (G-14432)
Mageros Candies ....G...... 330 534-1146
Hubbard (G-11134)
Malleys Candies ....D...... 216 362-8700
Lakewood (G-11674)
Malleys Candies ....E...... 216 529-6262
Cleveland (G-5736)
Maverick Chocolate Company ....G...... 513 381-0561
Cincinnati (G-4068)
Milk & Honey ....F...... 330 492-5884
Canton (G-2782)
Neumeisters Candy Shoppe LLC .....G...... 419 294-3647
Upper Sandusky (G-19135)
Robert E McGrath Inc ....E...... 440 572-7747
Strongsville (G-17959)

CHOCOLATE, EXC CANDY FROM PURCH CHOC: Chips, Powder, Block

Golden Turtle Chocolate Fctry ....G...... 513 932-1990
Lebanon (G-11805)
Hartville Chocolates Inc ....F...... 330 877-1999
Hartville (G-10822)
Hershey Creamery Co ....G...... 937 374-0688
Xenia (G-20955)

CHRISTMAS NOVELTIES, WHOLESALE

Sterling Collectables Inc ....G...... 419 892-5708
Mansfield (G-12684)

CHRISTMAS TREE LIGHTING SETS: Electric

Christmas Ranch LLC ....E...... 513 505-3865
Morrow (G-14545)

CHUCKS

Ajax Industries Inc ....E...... 614 272-6944
Columbus (G-6707)
Dillon Manufacturing Inc ....F...... 937 325-8482
Springfield (G-17544)
Flex-E-On Inc ....F...... 330 928-4496
Cuyahoga Falls (G-7997)
Hammill Manufacturing Co ....D...... 419 476-0789
Maumee (G-13264)
Jerry Tools Inc ....F...... 513 242-3211
Cincinnati (G-3944)
Shook Manufactured Pdts Inc ....G...... 330 848-9780
Akron (G-401)
Shook Manufactured Pdts Inc ....G...... 440 247-9130
Chagrin Falls (G-3069)

CHUTES & TROUGHS

Cbr Industrial Llc ....G...... 419 645-6447
Wapakoneta (G-19483)
Chute Source LLC ....F...... 330 475-0377
Akron (G-123)

CIGAR & CIGARETTE HOLDERS

Smokeheal Inc ....G...... 216 255-5119
Cleveland (G-6213)

CIGARETTE & CIGAR PRDTS & ACCESS

Gumbys LLC ....D...... 740 671-0818
Bellaire (G-1498)
Priority Vending Inc ....G...... 216 361-4100
Cleveland (G-6050)

CIRCUIT BOARD REPAIR SVCS

Mid-Ohio Electric Co ....E...... 614 274-8000
Columbus (G-7349)

CIRCUIT BOARDS, PRINTED: Television & Radio

Staci Corp ....F...... 440 355-5102
Lagrange (G-11638)

CIRCUIT BOARDS: Wiring

R-K Electronics Inc ....F...... 513 204-6060
Mason (G-13079)

CIRCUIT BREAKERS

Gould Electronics Inc ....C...... 440 953-5000
Eastlake (G-9271)

CIRCUITS: Electronic

Accurate Electronics Inc ....C...... 330 682-7015
Orrville (G-15727)
Adco Products Inc ....D...... 937 339-6267
Tipp City (G-18261)
Advantage Circuits Ltd ....G...... 330 256-7768
Rootstown (G-16719)
Astro Industries Inc ....E...... 937 429-5900
Beavercreek (G-1319)
B5 Systems Inc ....G...... 937 372-4768
Xenia (G-20937)
C E Electronics Inc ....D...... 419 636-6705
Bryan (G-2289)
CEC Electronics Corp ....G...... 330 916-8100
Akron (G-115)
Channel Products Inc ....D...... 440 423-0113
Chesterland (G-3199)
Circuits Alive LLC ....G...... 937 427-4141
Beavercreek (G-1324)
Cleveland Circuits Corp ....E...... 216 267-9020
Cleveland (G-5051)
Cutting Edge Technologies Inc ....E...... 216 574-4759
Cleveland (G-5154)
Dynalab Ems Inc ....C...... 614 866-9999
Reynoldsburg (G-16587)
Educational Electronics Inc ....G...... 234 301-9077
Millersburg (G-14213)
Electro-Line Inc ....F...... 937 461-5683
Dayton (G-8323)
Epic Technologies LLC ....D...... 513 683-5455
Mason (G-13018)
Eti Tech Inc ....F...... 937 832-4200
Englewood (G-9519)
Ingram Products Inc ....F...... 904 778-1010
Ashland (G-743)
Inservco Inc ....D...... 847 855-9600
Lagrange (G-11627)
J & C Group Inc of Ohio ....E...... 440 205-9658
Mentor (G-13613)
John B Allen ....G...... 614 488-7122
Columbus (G-7238)
Kirby Electronics Inc ....G...... 614 395-8926
Pickerington (G-16196)
Lintech Electronics LLC ....F...... 513 528-6190
Cincinnati (G-3312)
Mc Gregor & Associates Inc ....G...... 937 833-6768
Brookville (G-2192)
Mitchell Electronics Inc ....G...... 740 594-8532
Athens (G-879)
Ms Squared Inc ....G...... 330 666-0255
Akron (G-306)
Niktec LLC ....G...... 513 282-3747
Franklin (G-10040)
Parker-Hannifin Corporation ....C...... 937 644-3915
Marysville (G-12962)
Performance Electronics Ltd ....G...... 513 777-5233
Cincinnati (G-4225)
Qlog Corp ....G...... 513 874-1211
Hamilton (G-10732)

PRODUCT

Rct Industries Inc.............................F....... 937 602-1100
  Springboro (G-17505)
Rpa Electronic Distrs Inc ....F....... 937 223-7001
  Dayton (G-8639)
Shiloh Industries Inc.........................F....... 937 236-5100
  Dayton (G-8655)
Showplace Inc ....G....... 419 468-7368
  Galion (G-10287)
Sovereign Circuits Inc ....F....... 330 538-3900
  North Jackson (G-15298)
Spectron Inc ....G....... 937 461-5590
  Dayton (G-8668)
The W L Jenkins Company ....F....... 330 477-3407
  Canton (G-2869)
Tls Corp ....E....... 216 574-4759
  Cleveland (G-6327)
Twin Point Inc ....F....... 419 923-7525
  Delta (G-8940)
U S Terminals Inc ....G....... 513 561-8145
  Cincinnati (G-4534)
Zeus Electronics LLC ....G....... 330 220-1571
  Brunswick (G-2272)

CLAMPS & COUPLINGS: Hose

Aeroquip-Vickers Inc ....G....... 216 523-5000
  Cleveland (G-4722)
Bowes Manufacturing Inc ....F....... 216 378-2110
  Solon (G-17271)
Eaton Corporation ....A....... 419 238-1190
  Van Wert (G-19253)
Eaton-Aeroquip Llc ....G....... 216 523-5000
  Cleveland (G-5254)
Eaton-Aeroquip Llc ....D....... 419 238-1190
  Van Wert (G-19255)
Voss Industries Inc ....C....... 216 771-0870
  Cleveland (G-6429)
Voss Industries Inc ....D....... 216 771-7655
  Cleveland (G-6430)
Winzeler Stamping Co ....D....... 419 485-3147
  Montpelier (G-14458)

CLAMPS: Metal

Case-Maul Clamps Inc ....F....... 419 668-6563
  Norwalk (G-15529)
Clampco Products Inc ....D....... 330 336-8857
  Wadsworth (G-19398)
Herman Machine Inc ....F....... 330 633-3261
  Tallmadge (G-18145)
Ottawa Products Co ....E....... 419 836-5115
  Curtice (G-7958)

CLAY MINING, COMMON

L & M Mineral Co ....G....... 330 852-3696
  Sugarcreek (G-18025)

CLAY: Ground Or Treated

J R Goslee Co ....F....... 330 723-4904
  Medina (G-13428)

CLAYS, EXC KAOLIN & BALL

Valley Clay Mining Co ....F....... 740 697-0620
  Roseville (G-16734)

CLEANING & DESCALING SVC: Metal Prdts

American Metal Cleaning Inc ....G....... 419 255-1828
  Toledo (G-18341)
American Mtal Clg Cncnnati Inc ....G....... 513 825-1171
  Cincinnati (G-3392)
Auto Core Systems ....G....... 740 362-5599
  Delaware (G-8824)
Chemical Solvents Inc ....E....... 216 741-9310
  Cleveland (G-5025)
Colonial Surface Solutions Inc ....E....... 419 358-0129
  Bluffton (G-1910)
Colonial Surface Solutions Inc ....D....... 419 659-5639
  Columbus Grove (G-7793)
Roberts Demand No 3 Corp ....F....... 216 641-0660
  Cleveland (G-6121)

CLEANING COMPOUNDS: Rifle Bore

Sports Care Products Inc ....G....... 216 663-8110
  Cleveland (G-6227)

CLEANING EQPT: Blast, Dustless

Cleaning Tech Group LLC ....E....... 513 870-0100
  West Chester (G-19991)

Nmgg Ctg LLC ....G....... 419 447-5211
  Tiffin (G-18234)

CLEANING EQPT: Commercial

Aurand Manufacturing & Eqp Co ....G....... 513 541-7200
  Cincinnati (G-3429)
Environmental Closure Systems...........F....... 614 759-9186
  Reynoldsburg (G-16588)
Evers Enterprises Inc ....G....... 513 541-7200
  Cincinnati (G-3722)
EZ Wall LLC ....G....... 800 424-8251
  Winchester (G-20692)
Friess Equipment Inc..........................G....... 330 945-9440
  Akron (G-194)
Holdren Brothers Inc ....F....... 937 465-7050
  West Liberty (G-20092)
Kaivac Inc ....E....... 513 887-4600
  Hamilton (G-10714)
MPW Industrial Svcs Group Inc............C....... 740 927-8790
  Hebron (G-10875)
Oh-LI Commercial Cleaning LLC ....G....... 614 390-3628
  Grove City (G-10579)
Reid Asset Management Company ....G....... 216 642-3223
  Cleveland (G-6097)
Staley & Sons Powerwashing LLC........G....... 937 843-2713
  Russells Point (G-16757)
W3 Ultrasonics LLC ....G....... 330 284-3667
  North Canton (G-15283)

CLEANING EQPT: Floor Washing & Polishing, Commercial

Nss Enterprises Inc ....C....... 419 531-2121
  Toledo (G-18610)
Powerbuff Inc ....F....... 419 241-2156
  Toledo (G-18650)

CLEANING EQPT: High Pressure

Complete Dry Flood............................G....... 513 200-9274
  Cincinnati (G-3601)
Homer G Waller Jr ....G....... 330 788-4023
  Youngstown (G-21108)
Mork Process Inc ....E....... 330 928-3700
  Worthington (G-20881)

CLEANING EQPT: Janitors' Carts

Flexcart LLC ....G....... 614 348-2517
  New Albany (G-14759)

CLEANING OR POLISHING PREPARATIONS, NEC

American Chemical Products ....F....... 216 267-7722
  Cleveland (G-4780)
Chem 1 Inc ....G....... 216 475-7443
  Warrensville Heights (G-19631)
Chemical Methods Inc ....E....... 216 476-8400
  Strongsville (G-17901)
Chempace Corporation ....F....... 419 535-0101
  Toledo (G-18395)
Clayton Manufacturing Company..........F....... 513 563-1300
  Cincinnati (G-3585)
Diversey Inc ....G....... 513 326-8300
  Cincinnati (G-3657)
EZ Brite Brands Inc............................F....... 440 871-7817
  Cleveland (G-5316)
Inceptor Inc ....G....... 419 726-8804
  Toledo (G-18519)
Jeyes US Holdings Inc ....B....... 614 984-2896
  New Albany (G-14764)
Kleen Test Products Corp ....F....... 330 878-5586
  Strasburg (G-17824)
Kona Blackbird Inc ....F....... 440 285-3189
  Chardon (G-3160)
Ohio Auto Supply Company ....E....... 330 454-5105
  Canton (G-2798)
Paro Services Co ....F....... 330 467-1300
  Twinsburg (G-18995)
Strib Industries Inc ....E....... 216 281-1155
  Cleveland (G-6252)
Ventco Inc ....F....... 440 834-8888
  Middlefield (G-14001)
Vitex Corporation ....F....... 216 883-0920
  Cleveland (G-6423)
Wise Consumer Products Company .....G....... 513 484-6530
  Montgomery (G-14436)
Woodbine Products Company ....F....... 330 725-0165
  Medina (G-13497)

CLEANING PRDTS: Automobile Polish

BLaster Corporation ....E....... 216 901-5800
  Cleveland (G-4916)
Custom Chemical Packaging LLC........E....... 330 331-7416
  Wadsworth (G-19399)
James C Robinson ....G....... 513 969-7482
  Cincinnati (G-3941)
Sevan At-Ndustrial Pnt Abr Ltd ....G....... 614 258-4747
  Columbus (G-7610)

CLEANING PRDTS: Bleaches, Household, Dry Or Liquid

K-O-K Products Inc ....F....... 740 548-0526
  Galena (G-10245)

CLEANING PRDTS: Degreasing Solvent

Leesburg Modern Sales Inc ....G....... 937 780-2613
  Leesburg (G-11854)

CLEANING PRDTS: Deodorants, Nonpersonal

Fresh Products LLC ....D....... 419 531-9741
  Perrysburg (G-16099)
Nilodor Inc ....E....... 800 443-4321
  Bolivar (G-1939)

CLEANING PRDTS: Drain Pipe Solvents Or Cleaners

Allen Drain Service Inc ....G....... 330 253-4206
  Kent (G-11426)

CLEANING PRDTS: Drycleaning Preparations

All Prem Cleaners Inc ....G....... 440 349-3649
  Solon (G-17251)
Pats Nu-Style Cleaners Inc ....G....... 216 676-4855
  Cleveland (G-5980)
Wilkshire Dry Cleaners LLC ....G....... 330 674-7696
  Millersburg (G-14286)

CLEANING PRDTS: Dusting Cloths, Chemically Treated

Ohio Mills Corporation ....G....... 216 431-3979
  Cleveland (G-5934)

CLEANING PRDTS: Floor Waxes

Betco Corporation Ltd ....E....... 419 241-2156
  Toledo (G-18366)
S C Johnson & Son Inc ....E....... 513 665-3600
  Cincinnati (G-4372)

CLEANING PRDTS: Indl Plant Disinfectants Or Deodorants

Solutions Plus Inc ....E....... 513 943-9600
  Amelia (G-583)
Trigon Industries Inc...........................G....... 937 299-1350
  Oakwood (G-15612)

CLEANING PRDTS: Laundry Preparations

Cedar Point Laundry...........................G....... 419 627-2274
  Sandusky (G-16953)
Clorox Company ....F....... 513 445-1840
  Mason (G-13001)
Procter & Gamble Far East Inc ....C....... 513 983-1100
  Cincinnati (G-4289)

CLEANING PRDTS: Metal Polish

Aman & Co Inc ....G....... 330 854-1122
  Canal Fulton (G-2495)
Easy Care Products Inc ....G....... 330 405-1380
  Twinsburg (G-18928)
Saint Ctherines Metalworks Inc ....G....... 216 409-0576
  Cleveland (G-6155)

CLEANING PRDTS: Paint & Wallpaper

Advanced Cleaning Tech LLC ....G....... 614 504-5433
  Plain City (G-16318)

CLEANING PRDTS: Polishing Preparations & Related Prdts

Mix-Masters Inc ....F 513 228-2800
Lebanon *(G-11817)*

CLEANING PRDTS: Rug, Upholstery/Dry Clng Detergents/Spotters

Carolyn Chemical Company ....F 614 252-5000
Columbus *(G-6911)*

Jackson Deluxe Cleaners Ltd ....G 419 592-2826
Napoleon *(G-14686)*

CLEANING PRDTS: Sanitation Preparations

L-Mor Inc ....F 216 541-2224
Cleveland *(G-5672)*

New Waste Concepts Inc ....G 419 872-2190
Perrysburg *(G-16126)*

Oliver Chemical Co Inc ....G 513 541-4540
Cincinnati *(G-4185)*

CLEANING PRDTS: Sanitation Preps, Disinfectants/Deodorants

D & J Distributing & Mfg ....E 419 865-2552
Holland *(G-11052)*

Ecolab Inc ....G 513 932-0830
Lebanon *(G-11796)*

Scottissue LLC ....E 937 293-2139
Moraine *(G-14527)*

Tranzonic Companies ....C 216 535-4300
Richmond Heights *(G-16656)*

Tranzonic Companies ....C 440 446-0643
Cleveland *(G-6350)*

Tz Acquisition Corp ....A 216 535-4300
Richmond Heights *(G-16658)*

CLEANING PRDTS: Specialty

Alumin Nu Corp ....G 216 421-2116
Cleveland *(G-4772)*

Bevclean Products Inc ....G 937 233-5000
Dayton *(G-8187)*

Cleaning By Sndra Msters Touch ....F 216 524-6827
Seven Hills *(G-17061)*

Kinzua Environmental Inc ....E 216 881-4040
Cleveland *(G-5655)*

Orchem Corporation ....E 513 874-9700
Cincinnati *(G-4193)*

Procter & Gamble Company ....B 513 983-1100
Cincinnati *(G-4277)*

Procter & Gamble Company ....B 513 983-1100
Cincinnati *(G-4286)*

Republic Powdered Metals Inc ....D 330 225-3192
Medina *(G-13467)*

Rose Products and Services Inc ....E 614 443-7647
Columbus *(G-7573)*

RPM International Inc ....D 330 273-5090
Medina *(G-13471)*

Shur Clean Usa LLC ....G 513 341-5486
Liberty Township *(G-11968)*

Troy Chemical Industries Inc ....F 440 834-4408
Burton *(G-2387)*

US Industrial Lubricants Inc ....E 513 541-2225
Cincinnati *(G-4547)*

CLEANING PRDTS: Stain Removers

Valspar Corporation..........................C 330 830-6000
Massillon *(G-13209)*

CLEANING SVCS

Cleaning By Sndra Msters Touch ....F 216 524-6827
Seven Hills *(G-17061)*

Evoqua Water Technologies LLC ....E 614 491-4000
Groveport *(G-10620)*

Langstons Ultmate Clg Svcs Inc ....F 330 298-9150
Ravenna *(G-16537)*

Liberty Casting Company LLC ....D 740 363-1941
Delaware *(G-8869)*

CLEANING SVCS: Industrial Or Commercial

MPW Industrial Svcs Group Inc ....C 740 927-8790
Hebron *(G-10875)*

Omega Cementing Co ....G 330 695-7147
Apple Creek *(G-646)*

Paro Services Co ....F 330 467-1300
Twinsburg *(G-18995)*

Phoenix Technologies Inc ....F 330 630-5888
Akron *(G-338)*

CLIPS & FASTENERS, MADE FROM PURCHASED WIRE

Tom Thumb Clip Co Inc ....F 440 953-9606
Willoughby *(G-20619)*

CLOCKS

I T Verdin Co ....E 513 241-4010
Cincinnati *(G-3906)*

I T Verdin Co ....E 513 559-3947
Cincinnati *(G-3908)*

CLOSURES: Closures, Stamped Metal

Crown Cork & Seal Usa Inc ....D 740 681-3000
Lancaster *(G-11702)*

CLOSURES: Plastic

Crown Cork & Seal Usa Inc ....D 740 681-3000
Lancaster *(G-11702)*

Modern Store Fixtures Inc ....F 330 427-6906
Garrettsville *(G-10331)*

CLOTHING & ACCESS STORES

Joe Sestito ....G 614 871-7778
Grove City *(G-10566)*

CLOTHING & ACCESS, WOMEN, CHILD & INFANT, WHOLESALE: Rack

One Universal Brands LLC ....G 513 362-4326
Cincinnati *(G-4188)*

CLOTHING & ACCESS, WOMEN, CHILD & INFANT, WHSLE: Sportswear

K Ventures Inc ....F 419 678-2308
Coldwater *(G-6566)*

CLOTHING & ACCESS, WOMEN, CHILDREN & INFANT, WHOL: Sweaters

Majestic Sportswear Company ....G 937 773-1144
Piqua *(G-16290)*

CLOTHING & ACCESS, WOMEN, CHILDREN & INFANT, WHOL: Uniforms

Cintas Sales Corporation ....B 513 459-1200
Cincinnati *(G-3579)*

Digitek Corp....................................F 513 794-3190
Blue Ash *(G-1775)*

Impact Sports Wear Inc ....G 513 922-7406
North Bend *(G-15205)*

CLOTHING & ACCESS, WOMEN, CHILDREN/INFANT, WHOL: Outerwear

Swocat Design Inc ....G 440 282-4700
Lorain *(G-12284)*

CLOTHING & ACCESS: Costumes, Lodge

Thomas Creative Apparel Inc ....E 419 929-1506
New London *(G-14867)*

CLOTHING & ACCESS: Costumes, Theatrical

Costume Specialists Inc ....E 614 464-2115
Columbus *(G-6987)*

Costume Specialists Inc ....E 614 464-2115
Columbus *(G-6988)*

Schenz Theatrical Supply Inc ....F 513 542-6100
Cincinnati *(G-4387)*

Snaps Inc ....G 419 477-5100
Mount Cory *(G-14554)*

Stagecraft Costuming Inc ....F 513 541-7150
Cincinnati *(G-4451)*

Top Hat Designs ....G 614 898-1962
Westerville *(G-20238)*

CLOTHING & ACCESS: Garter Belts

Kern Manufacturing Inc ....G 216 464-5490
Cleveland *(G-5650)*

CLOTHING & ACCESS: Hospital Gowns

Standard Textile Co Inc ....B 513 761-9255
Cincinnati *(G-4455)*

CLOTHING & ACCESS: Men's Miscellaneous Access

Donegal Bay Ltd...............................F 216 360-9966
Cleveland *(G-5207)*

Inner Fire Sports LLC ....G 719 244-6622
Cincinnati *(G-3922)*

L Brands Inc ....C 614 479-2000
Columbus *(G-7275)*

M M A Authentics LLC ....G 614 274-1141
Columbus *(G-7309)*

Rocky Brands Inc ....B 740 753-1951
Nelsonville *(G-14736)*

Salindia LLC ....G 614 501-4799
Columbus *(G-7587)*

Status Mens Accessories ....G 440 232-6700
Cleveland *(G-6242)*

CLOTHING & APPAREL STORES: Custom

Carols Ultra Stitch & Variety ....G 419 935-8991
Willard *(G-20393)*

Charles Wisvari ....F 740 671-9960
Bellaire *(G-1497)*

Dpi Inc ....G 419 273-1400
Forest *(G-9919)*

Eagle Rock Brand Cons LLC ....G 614 403-4802
Plain City *(G-16338)*

Embroidme Co ....G 614 933-9194
Columbus *(G-7056)*

Pelz Lettering Inc ....G 419 625-3567
Sandusky *(G-16996)*

CLOTHING & FURNISHINGS, MEN'S & BOYS', WHOLESALE: Shirts

Swocat Design Inc ....G 440 282-4700
Lorain *(G-12284)*

CLOTHING & FURNISHINGS, MEN'S & BOYS', WHOLESALE: Uniforms

Cintas Sales Corporation ....B 513 459-1200
Cincinnati *(G-3579)*

Digitek Corp....................................F 513 794-3190
Blue Ash *(G-1775)*

Impact Sports Wear Inc ....G 513 922-7406
North Bend *(G-15205)*

Standard Textile Co Inc ....B 513 761-9255
Cincinnati *(G-4455)*

Walter F Stephens Jr Inc ....E 937 746-0521
Franklin *(G-10063)*

CLOTHING ACCESS STORES: Belts, Custom

Aresgear ....G 518 966-2737
Columbus *(G-6771)*

CLOTHING ACCESS STORES: Umbrellas

Totes Isotoner Corporation ....F 513 682-8200
West Chester *(G-20059)*

Totes Isotoner Holdings Corp ....C 513 682-8200
West Chester *(G-20060)*

CLOTHING STORES, NEC

Owl Be Sweatin ....G 513 260-2026
Cincinnati *(G-4205)*

CLOTHING STORES: Formal Wear

Dresden Specialties Inc.......................G 740 754-2451
Dresden *(G-9032)*

CLOTHING STORES: Leather

LLC Bowman Leather ....G 330 893-1954
Millersburg *(G-14242)*

CLOTHING STORES: T-Shirts, Printed, Custom

Cotton Pickin Tees & Caps ....G 419 636-3595
Bryan *(G-2291)*

Jones & Assoc Advg & Design ....G 330 799-6876
Youngstown *(G-21127)*

P
R
O
D
U
C
T

CLOTHING STORES: T-Shirts, Printed, Custom

Odyssey Spirits Inc ....F 330 562-1523
Aurora (G-938)
Robs Creative Screen Printing ....G 740 264-6383
Wintersville (G-20713)

CLOTHING STORES: Uniforms & Work

Appleheart ....G 937 384-0430
Miamisburg (G-13784)

CLOTHING STORES: Unisex

Ohio Mills Corporation ....G 216 431-3979
Cleveland (G-5934)
Stepp Sewing Service ....G 513 248-0822
Milford (G-14175)

CLOTHING/ACCESS, WOMEN, CHILDREN/INFANT, WHOL: Hosp Gowns

Philips Medical Systems Clevel ....B 440 247-2652
Cleveland (G-6001)

CLOTHING: Access

Jki Sales ....G 614 581-5498
Columbus (G-7233)
Rageon Inc ....E 617 633-0544
Cleveland (G-6088)
Tactical Revolution LLC ....G 419 348-9526
Ottawa (G-15812)
V Collection ....G 419 517-0508
Sylvania (G-18128)

CLOTHING: Access, Women's & Misses'

Lena Fiore Inc ....F 330 468-3226
Akron (G-270)
Rocky Brands Inc ....B 740 753-1951
Nelsonville (G-14736)

CLOTHING: Aprons, Exc Rubber/Plastic, Women, Misses, Junior

Carrera Holdings Inc ....G 216 687-1311
Cleveland (G-4984)

CLOTHING: Aprons, Harness

Seven Mile Creek Corporation ....F 937 456-3320
Eaton (G-9322)

CLOTHING: Athletic & Sportswear, Men's & Boys'

Afi Brands LLC ....G 614 999-6426
Dublin (G-9038)
Dunhams Sports ....F 330 334-3257
Wadsworth (G-19403)
Fanz Stop ....G 937 310-1436
Bellbrook (G-1508)
Hilliard Cat Shack LLC ....G 614 527-9711
Hilliard (G-10952)
Inner Fire Sports LLC ....G 719 244-6622
Cincinnati (G-3922)
J America LLC ....G 614 914-2091
Columbus (G-7216)
Kam Manufacturing Inc ....C 419 238-6037
Van Wert (G-19261)
Rocky Brands Inc ....B 740 753-1951
Nelsonville (G-14736)
Torso ....G 614 421-7663
Columbus (G-7700)
Under Armour Inc ....G 330 995-9557
Aurora (G-953)
Vesi Incorporated ....E 513 563-6002
Cincinnati (G-4567)

CLOTHING: Baker, Barber, Lab/Svc Ind Apparel, Washable, Men

All-Bilt Uniform Corp ....E 513 793-5400
Blue Ash (G-1742)

CLOTHING: Bibs, Waterproof, From Purchased Materials

Grow With Me- Creations ....G 800 850-1889
Hartville (G-10821)

CLOTHING: Blouses, Women's & Girls'

Afi Brands LLC ....G 614 999-6426
Dublin (G-9038)
Kam Manufacturing Inc ....C 419 238-6037
Van Wert (G-19261)
Quality Sewing Inc ....G 216 475-0411
Cleveland (G-6074)
Rocky Brands Inc ....B 740 753-1951
Nelsonville (G-14736)

CLOTHING: Blouses, Womens & Juniors, From Purchased Mtrls

J C L S Enterprises LLC ....G 740 472-0314
Woodsfield (G-20718)

CLOTHING: Bras & Corsets, Maternity

Kern Manufacturing Inc ....G 216 464-5490
Cleveland (G-5650)

CLOTHING: Bridal Gowns

Jillians Ltd ....G 740 450-7766
Zanesville (G-21323)
Lavander Bridal Salon ....F 330 602-0333
Dover (G-8997)
S & C Newman Enterprises Inc ....G 740 772-7433
Chillicothe (G-3274)

CLOTHING: Caps, Baseball

Barbs Graffiti Inc ....E 216 881-5550
Cleveland (G-4889)

CLOTHING: Chemises, Camisoles/Teddies, Women, Misses/Junior

Skinnywear LLC ....G 216 310-5599
Cleveland (G-6208)

CLOTHING: Children & Infants'

Tween Brands Inc ....F 937 435-6928
Dayton (G-8733)

CLOTHING: Children's, Girls'

Rita Fishel Inc ....E 740 775-1957
Chillicothe (G-3272)

CLOTHING: Coats & Suits, Men's & Boys'

Bea-Ecc Apparels Inc ....G 216 650-6336
Cleveland (G-4899)
Wahconah Group Inc ....F 216 923-0570
Cleveland (G-6441)

CLOTHING: Costumes

Akron Design & Costume Co ....G 330 644-4849
Akron (G-40)
Promo Costumes Inc ....F 740 383-5176
Marion (G-12893)

CLOTHING: Disposable

Direct Disposables LLC ....G 440 717-3335
Brecksville (G-2043)
Rich Industries Inc ....E 330 339-4113
New Philadelphia (G-14924)

CLOTHING: Dresses

Quality Sewing Inc ....G 216 475-0411
Cleveland (G-6074)

CLOTHING: Foundation Garments, Women's

Laura Dawson ....G 513 777-2513
West Chester (G-19891)

CLOTHING: Gowns & Dresses, Wedding

Finishing Touch ....F 440 263-9264
Cleveland (G-5348)

CLOTHING: Hats & Caps, NEC

Genesco Inc ....G 330 633-8179
Akron (G-204)
Genesco Inc ....G 513 947-1200
Cincinnati (G-3307)

CLOTHING: Hats & Caps, NEC (continued)

Lids Corporation ....F 419 621-8742
Sandusky (G-16980)
Lids Corporation ....G 440 974-9127
Mentor (G-13633)
Wagoner Stores Inc ....G 937 836-3636
Englewood (G-9544)

CLOTHING: Hosiery, Men's & Boys'

Forepleasure ....G 330 821-1293
Alliance (G-509)

CLOTHING: Hospital, Men's

Affordable Med Scrubs LLC ....E 419 222-1088
Lima (G-11982)
Standard Textile Co Inc ....B 513 761-9255
Cincinnati (G-4455)

CLOTHING: Leather

Fionas Fineries ....G 440 796-7426
Willoughby (G-20487)

CLOTHING: Lounge, Bed & Leisurewear

Heritage Inc ....G 614 860-1185
Reynoldsburg (G-16594)

CLOTHING: Men's & boy's clothing, nec

Promotions Plus Inc ....G 440 582-2855
Broadview Heights (G-2116)
Sacks Bruce & Associates ....G 419 537-0623
Ottawa Hills (G-15819)

CLOTHING: Men's & boy's underwear & nightwear

Tranzonic Companies ....B 216 535-4300
Richmond Heights (G-16657)

CLOTHING: Outerwear, Knit

Okm LLC ....G 216 272-6375
Cleveland (G-5935)

CLOTHING: Outerwear, Lthr, Wool/Down-Filled, Men, Youth/Boy

Universal Lettering Inc ....E 419 238-9320
Van Wert (G-19274)

CLOTHING: Outerwear, Women's & Misses' NEC

Barton-Carey Medical Products ....E 419 887-1285
Maumee (G-13230)
Fechheimer Brothers Company ....C 513 793-7819
Blue Ash (G-1792)
Inner Fire Sports LLC ....G 719 244-6622
Cincinnati (G-3922)
Kip-Craft Incorporated ....D 216 898-5500
Cleveland (G-5656)
Rita Fishel Inc ....E 740 775-1957
Chillicothe (G-3272)

CLOTHING: Robes & Dressing Gowns

Thomas Creative Apparel Inc ....E 419 929-1506
New London (G-14867)

CLOTHING: Shirts, Dress, Men's & Boys'

Pvh Corp ....G 330 562-4440
Aurora (G-941)

CLOTHING: Shirts, Knit

Factory Direct International ....E 419 425-9636
Findlay (G-9821)

CLOTHING: Shirts, Sports & Polo, Men & Boy, Purchased Mtrl

Professional Image Apparel Inc ....F 513 984-1111
Cincinnati (G-4295)

CLOTHING: Shirts, Sports & Polo, Men's & Boys'

One Universal Brands LLC ....G 513 362-4326
Cincinnati (G-4188)

CLOTHING: Socks

Broken Spinning Wheel......................G...... 419 825-1609
  Swanton (G-18081)
Disante Socks.....................................G...... 614 481-3243
  Columbus (G-7028)
Hype Socks..G...... 614 506-5248
  Columbus (G-7172)

CLOTHING: Sportswear, Women's

Fanz Stop..G...... 937 310-1436
  Bellbrook (G-1508)
Vesi Incorporated.............................E...... 513 563-6002
  Cincinnati (G-4567)

CLOTHING: Suits, Men's & Boys', From Purchased Materials

Hugo Boss Usa Inc...........................B...... 216 671-8100
  Cleveland (G-5536)
Tom James Company.........................F...... 614 488-8400
  Columbus (G-7698)

CLOTHING: Sweaters & Sweater Coats, Knit

Fine Points Inc.................................F...... 216 229-6644
  Cleveland (G-5346)

CLOTHING: Sweatshirts & T-Shirts, Men's & Boys'

J C L S Enterprises LLC....................G...... 740 472-0314
  Woodsfield (G-20718)

CLOTHING: T-Shirts & Tops, Knit

Digitek Corp......................................F...... 513 794-3190
  Blue Ash (G-1775)
E Retailing Associates LLC................D...... 614 300-5785
  Columbus (G-7043)
Embroidme..G...... 330 484-8484
  Canton (G-2697)
Gibbs E & Associates LLC.................G...... 614 939-1672
  New Albany (G-14760)
Pjs Wholesale Inc.............................G...... 614 402-9363
  Columbus (G-7487)
TIS Incorporated..............................G...... 614 291-3950
  Columbus (G-7695)
Wonder-Shirts Inc............................G...... 917 679-2336
  Dublin (G-9166)

CLOTHING: Tuxedos, From Purchased Materials

American Commodore Tuxedos..........G...... 440 324-2889
  Elyria (G-9370)
Cinderella...G...... 937 312-9969
  Dayton (G-8229)
Simply Elegant Formals Inc..............G...... 419 738-7722
  Wapakoneta (G-19507)

CLOTHING: Underwear, Women's & Children's

Tranzonic Companies........................B...... 216 535-4300
  Richmond Heights (G-16657)

CLOTHING: Uniforms & Vestments

Fire-Dex LLC.....................................D...... 330 723-0000
  Medina (G-13410)
Novak Supply LLC.............................G...... 216 741-5112
  Cleveland (G-5919)
Walter F Stephens Jr Inc...................E...... 937 746-0521
  Franklin (G-10063)

CLOTHING: Uniforms, Ex Athletic, Women's, Misses' & Juniors'

Cintas Corporation...........................A...... 513 459-1200
  Cincinnati (G-3577)
Cintas Corporation...........................D...... 513 631-5750
  Cincinnati (G-3578)
Cintas Corporation No 2....................D...... 330 966-7800
  Canton (G-2655)
Standard Textile Co Inc.....................B...... 513 761-9255
  Cincinnati (G-4455)

CLOTHING: Uniforms, Firemen's, From Purchased Materials

Lion Apparel Inc...............................C...... 937 898-1949
  Dayton (G-8458)

CLOTHING: Uniforms, Men's & Boys'

Fechheimer Brothers Company...........C...... 513 793-7819
  Blue Ash (G-1792)

CLOTHING: Uniforms, Military, Men/Youth, Purchased Materials

Contingncy Prcrments Group LLC.......G...... 513 204-9590
  Maineville (G-12521)
Global Gear LLC................................G...... 941 830-0531
  Chagrin Falls (G-3088)
Government Specialty Pdts LLC.........G...... 937 672-9473
  Dayton (G-8375)
Vgs Inc...C...... 216 431-7800
  Cleveland (G-6413)

CLOTHING: Uniforms, Work

Cintas Corporation...........................F...... 513 336-6300
  Mason (G-12997)
Cintas Corporation...........................D...... 513 631-5750
  Cincinnati (G-3578)
Cintas Corporation...........................A...... 513 459-1200
  Cincinnati (G-3577)
Cintas Corporation No 2....................D...... 330 966-7800
  Canton (G-2655)
Cintas Sales Corporation...................B...... 513 459-1200
  Cincinnati (G-3579)
Lawft...G...... 419 422-5293
  Findlay (G-9850)
Postal Uniform Xpress......................D...... 513 621-4787
  Cincinnati (G-4253)
Professional Image Apparel Inc.........F...... 513 984-1111
  Cincinnati (G-4295)
Rons Texstyles LLC...........................G...... 513 936-9975
  Columbus (G-7571)
Vgs Inc...C...... 216 431-7800
  Cleveland (G-6413)

CLOTHING: Vests, Sport, Suede, Leatherette, Etc, Mens & Boys

Noxgear LLC......................................G...... 937 248-1860
  Columbus (G-7404)

CLOTHING: Work Apparel, Exc Uniforms

Eagle Rock Brand Cons LLC...............G...... 614 403-4802
  Plain City (G-16338)
Hall Safety Apparel Inc......................F...... 740 922-3671
  Uhrichsville (G-19051)
Hands On International LLC................G...... 513 502-9000
  Mason (G-13034)
Mypro Apparel LLC...........................G...... 419 462-9464
  Ontario (G-15690)
RG Barry Corporation........................C...... 614 864-6400
  Pickerington (G-16203)

CLOTHING: Work, Men's

3n1 Mens Fashion.............................G...... 513 851-3610
  Cincinnati (G-3325)
Ansell Healthcare Products LLC..........C...... 740 295-5414
  Coshocton (G-7880)
Barton-Carey Medical Products..........E...... 419 887-1285
  Maumee (G-13230)
Carhartt Inc......................................G...... 513 657-7130
  Cincinnati (G-3501)
Cleveland Canvas Goods Mfg Co.........D...... 216 361-4567
  Cleveland (G-5050)
DCW Acquisition Inc..........................F...... 216 451-0666
  Cleveland (G-5179)
Euclid Vidaro Manufacturing Co.........D...... 330 673-7413
  Kent (G-11457)
High Lvel Fshion Athletes Foot..........G...... 614 577-8800
  Columbus (G-7155)
Kip-Craft Incorporated......................D...... 216 898-5500
  Cleveland (G-5656)
Morning Pride Mfg LLC.......................A...... 937 264-2662
  Dayton (G-8508)
Rich Industries Inc...........................E...... 330 339-4113
  New Philadelphia (G-14924)
Seven Mile Creek Corporation............F...... 937 456-3320
  Eaton (G-9322)

Unifirst Corporation.........................D...... 216 658-6900
  Independence (G-11279)
Wagoner Stores Inc...........................G...... 937 836-3636
  Englewood (G-9544)

CLOTHING: Work, Waterproof, Exc Raincoats

Aresgear...G...... 518 966-2737
  Columbus (G-6771)
Linsalata Capital Partners Fun...........G...... 440 684-1400
  Cleveland (G-5703)
Tranzonic Companies........................C...... 216 535-4300
  Richmond Heights (G-16656)
Tranzonic Companies........................C...... 440 446-0643
  Cleveland (G-6350)
Tz Acquisition Corp...........................A...... 216 535-4300
  Richmond Heights (G-16658)

CLOTHS: Polishing, Plain

Cotton Fabrics Company Inc...............G...... 419 389-9904
  Toledo (G-18414)

CLUTCHES OR BRAKES: Electromagnetic

Eaton Corporation.............................C...... 216 281-2211
  Cleveland (G-5247)

CLUTCHES, EXC VEHICULAR

Eaton Corporation.............................C...... 216 281-2211
  Cleveland (G-5247)
Ebo Group Inc....................................D...... 330 239-4933
  Sharon Center (G-17105)
Logan Clutch Corporation...................E...... 440 808-4258
  Cleveland (G-5707)

COAL & OTHER MINERALS & ORES WHOLESALERS

B & S Transport Inc...........................G...... 330 767-4319
  Navarre (G-14709)
Graphel Corporation..........................C...... 513 779-6166
  West Chester (G-19879)
Johnson Energy Company...................G...... 937 435-5401
  Miamisburg (G-13822)
Tosoh America Inc.............................B...... 614 539-8622
  Grove City (G-10604)

COAL MINING SERVICES

American Energy Corporation.............B...... 740 926-2430
  Beallsville (G-1307)
Anthony Mining Co Inc.......................G...... 740 266-8100
  Wintersville (G-20710)
Appalachian Fuels LLC.......................G...... 606 928-0460
  Dublin (G-9045)
Boich Companies LLC.........................G...... 614 221-0101
  Columbus (G-6845)
Buckingham Coal Company LLC..........D...... 740 767-2907
  Zanesville (G-21284)
Coal Resources Inc............................F...... 740 338-3100
  Saint Clairsville (G-16786)
Coal Services Inc...............................D...... 740 795-5220
  Powhatan Point (G-16488)
Consol Coal Company.........................D...... 740 942-4353
  Cadiz (G-2415)
Don Gamertsfelder............................G...... 740 797-4495
  The Plains (G-18185)
Global Coal Sales Group LLC..............G...... 614 221-0101
  Columbus (G-7119)
Global Mining Holding Co LLC............G...... 614 221-0101
  Columbus (G-7120)
Harrison County Coal Company..........E...... 740 338-3100
  Saint Clairsville (G-16791)
Kurtz Bros Inc...................................E...... 614 491-0868
  Groveport (G-10632)
North American Auger Mining.............G...... 740 622-8782
  Coshocton (G-7902)
Ohio Valley Resources Inc..................E...... 740 795-5220
  Saint Clairsville (G-16802)
Oxford Mining Company Inc................G...... 330 878-5120
  Strasburg (G-17827)
Oxford Mining Company LLC...............G...... 740 622-6302
  Coshocton (G-7907)
Oxford Mining Inc..............................G...... 330 339-4546
  Stone Creek (G-17725)
Peabody Coal Company.......................B...... 740 450-2420
  Zanesville (G-21340)
Resource Fuels LLC...........................G...... 614 221-0101
  Columbus (G-7558)

Employee Codes: A=Over 500 employees, B=251-500
C=101-250, D=51-100, E=20-50, F=10-19, G=3-9

2017 Harris Ohio
Industrial Directory

P R O D U C T

1439

Rosebud Mining Company...................E...... 330 222-2334
Carrollton (G-2964)
Sandusky Dock Corporation...............F...... 419 626-1214
Sandusky (G-17000)
State Line Resources Inc.................G...... 330 426-9611
Negley (G-14732)
Steuben Coal-Anthony Min Ltd...........G...... 740 266-8100
Wintersville (G-20714)
Strata Mine Services Inc.................G...... 740 695-6880
Saint Clairsville (G-16810)
Suncoke Energy Nc........................E...... 513 727-5571
Middletown (G-14086)

COAL MINING SVCS: Bituminous, Contract Basis

Ohio Valley Coal Company................B...... 740 926-1351
Saint Clairsville (G-16801)
Ohio Valley Transloading Co.............A...... 740 795-4967
Saint Clairsville (G-16803)

COAL MINING: Anthracite

Coal Services Inc.........................D...... 740 795-5220
Powhatan Point (G-16488)

COAL MINING: Bituminous & Lignite Surface

Commercial Minerals Inc..................G...... 330 549-2165
North Lima (G-15313)
Daron Coal Company LLC.................C...... 614 643-0337
Cadiz (G-2417)
Ivi Mining Group Ltd......................G...... 740 418-7745
Vinton (G-19382)
J & D Mining Inc..........................E...... 330 339-4935
New Philadelphia (G-14904)
Kenneth Mc Beth..........................G...... 740 922-9494
Dennison (G-8945)
Murray American Energy Inc..............A...... 740 338-3100
Saint Clairsville (G-16796)
PM Coal Company LLC....................G...... 440 256-7624
Willoughby (G-20571)

COAL MINING: Bituminous Coal & Lignite-Surface Mining

American Coal Co..........................G...... 740 926-1372
Alledonia (G-484)
Coal Services Inc.........................D...... 740 795-5220
Powhatan Point (G-16488)
East Fairfield Coal Co....................E...... 330 542-1010
Petersburg (G-16177)
King Quarries Inc.........................G...... 740 732-2923
Caldwell (G-2429)
L & M Mineral Co..........................G...... 330 852-3696
Sugarcreek (G-18025)
Morning Sun Technologies Inc...........G...... 513 461-1417
Oxford (G-15841)
Oxford Mining Company Inc..............F...... 740 588-0190
Zanesville (G-21339)
Rosebud Mining Company...................E...... 740 768-2097
Bergholz (G-1642)
Straight Creek Bushman LLC.............G...... 513 732-1698
Batavia (G-1226)
Ted Tipple.................................G...... 740 432-3263
Cambridge (G-2479)
Westmoreland Resources Gp LLC.......F...... 740 622-6302
Coshocton (G-7914)

COAL MINING: Bituminous Underground

American Energy Corporation.............B...... 740 926-2430
Beallsville (G-1307)
Coal Services Inc.........................D...... 740 795-5220
Powhatan Point (G-16488)
Ivi Mining Group Ltd......................G...... 740 418-7745
Vinton (G-19382)
Kenamerican Resources Inc..............G...... 740 338-3100
Saint Clairsville (G-16793)
Maple Creek Mining Inc...................G...... 740 926-9205
Alledonia (G-485)
Murray Energy Corporation...............G...... 740 338-3100
Saint Clairsville (G-16797)
Rosebud Mining Company...................E...... 740 658-4217
Freeport (G-10119)
Rosebud Mining Company...................E...... 740 768-2097
Bergholz (G-1642)
Rosebud Mining Company...................E...... 740 922-9122
Uhrichsville (G-19057)
Rosebud Mining Company...................E...... 330 222-2334
Carrollton (G-2964)

Sterling Mining Corporation..............F...... 330 549-2165
North Lima (G-15323)
West Ridge Resources Inc.................G...... 740 338-3100
Saint Clairsville (G-16813)

COAL MINING: Bituminous, Auger

CAM Co Inc................................G...... 740 922-4533
Dennison (G-8943)
Edwards Auger Mining Inc................G...... 330 339-7318
New Philadelphia (G-14896)

COAL MINING: Bituminous, Strip

B&N Coal Inc..............................D...... 740 783-3575
Dexter City (G-8954)
D & D Mining Co Inc......................F...... 330 549-3127
New Springfield (G-14950)
F & M Coal Company......................G...... 740 544-5203
Toronto (G-18782)
Holmes Limestone Co.....................G...... 330 893-2721
Berlin (G-1649)
Oxford Min Cmpany-Kentucky LLC......C...... 740 622-6302
Coshocton (G-7905)
Oxford Mining Company Inc..............D...... 740 342-7666
New Lexington (G-14850)
Oxford Mining Company Inc..............E...... 740 622-6302
Coshocton (G-7906)
Rosebud Mining Company...................E...... 740 922-9122
Uhrichsville (G-19057)
Sands Hill Coal Hauling Co Inc...........E...... 740 384-4211
Hamden (G-10657)
Thompson Brothers Mining Co...........F...... 330 549-3979
New Springfield (G-14952)
W B Coal Company Inc....................F...... 614 221-0101
Columbus (G-7745)

COAL MINING: Bituminous, Surface, NEC

Marietta Coal Co..........................G...... 740 695-2197
Saint Clairsville (G-16795)
Rayle Coal Co.............................G...... 740 695-2197
Saint Clairsville (G-16805)

COAL MINING: Lignite, Surface, NEC

Nacco Industries Inc......................E...... 440 229-5151
Cleveland (G-5848)

COAL PREPARATION PLANT: Bituminous or Lignite

Bramhi Inc................................G...... 740 367-0467
Bidwell (G-1674)
Cliffs Logan County Coal LLC............G...... 216 694-5700
Cleveland (G-5089)

COAL PYROLYSIS

Enrevo Pyro LLC..........................G...... 203 517-5002
Brookfield (G-2124)

COAL, MINERALS & ORES, WHOLESALE: Iron Ore

Masters Group Inc.........................G...... 440 893-1900
Chagrin Falls (G-3103)

COATED OR PLATED PRDTS

Ohio Coatings Company...................D...... 740 859-5500
Yorkville (G-21007)

COATING COMPOUNDS: Tar

Brewer Company...........................G...... 800 394-0017
Milford (G-14127)
Brewer Company...........................E...... 440 944-3800
Wickliffe (G-20361)
Brewer Company...........................G...... 513 576-6300
Cincinnati (G-3470)
Dnd Emulsions Inc.........................G...... 419 525-4988
Mansfield (G-12595)

COATING OR WRAPPING SVC: Steel Pipe

Imperial Metal Solutions LLC.............F...... 216 781-4094
Cleveland (G-5556)

COATING SVC

Coat All...................................G...... 419 659-2757
Columbus Grove (G-7792)

Syscom Advanced Materials Inc..........F...... 614 487-3626
Columbus (G-7672)
Terra Coat LLC............................G...... 216 254-8157
Northfield (G-15475)

COATING SVC: Aluminum, Metal Prdts

American Utility Proc LLC.................E...... 330 535-3000
Akron (G-69)
E L Stone Company........................E...... 330 825-4565
Norton (G-15510)
Epco Extrusion Painting Co...............E...... 330 781-6100
Youngstown (G-21078)
Hardline International Inc.................F...... 419 924-9556
West Unity (G-20129)
Materials Science Intl Inc.................E...... 614 870-0400
Columbus (G-7323)
SH Bell Company..........................E...... 412 963-9910
East Liverpool (G-9227)
Treemen Industries Inc...................E...... 330 965-3777
Boardman (G-1925)
Vacono America LLC.......................E...... 216 938-7428
Cleveland (G-6405)
Vacuum Finishing Company...............F...... 440 286-4386
Chardon (G-3182)
W C J Corp................................G...... 216 523-1135
Cleveland (G-6434)

COATING SVC: Electrodes

Advanced Coatings Intl....................G...... 330 794-6361
Akron (G-31)
De Nora North America Inc...............F...... 440 357-4000
Painesville (G-15874)
Visimax Technologies Inc.................F...... 330 405-8330
Twinsburg (G-19037)

COATING SVC: Hot Dip, Metals Or Formed Prdts

AAA Galvanizing - Joliet Inc.............E...... 513 871-5700
Cincinnati (G-3341)
Azz Incorporated..........................E...... 330 445-2170
Canton (G-2612)
Carlisle Plastics Company Inc.............G...... 937 845-9411
New Carlisle (G-14798)
Poly-Met Inc...............................F...... 330 630-9006
Akron (G-343)
Rack Coating Service Inc.................E...... 330 854-2869
Canal Fulton (G-2512)

COATING SVC: Metals & Formed Prdts

A Class Coatings Inc......................F...... 440 960-6869
Lorain (G-12229)
A Plus Powder Coaters Inc...............F...... 330 482-4389
Columbiana (G-6604)
Aesthetic Finishers Inc...................E...... 937 778-8777
Piqua (G-16246)
Alpha Coatings Inc........................C...... 419 435-5111
Fostoria (G-9964)
American Tchnical Coatings Inc..........G...... 440 401-2270
Westlake (G-20253)
Architectural and Industrial..............F...... 440 963-0410
Vermilion (G-19323)
Armoloy of Ohio Inc.......................F...... 937 323-8702
Springfield (G-17519)
Bekaert Corporation.......................C...... 330 683-5060
Orrville (G-15729)
Boville Indus Coatings Inc................E...... 330 669-8558
Smithville (G-17238)
Cast Plus Inc.............................E...... 937 743-7278
Franklin (G-10011)
Cincinnati Thermal Spray Inc.............C...... 513 793-1037
Blue Ash (G-1765)
Ferro Corporation.........................D...... 216 875-5600
Mayfield Heights (G-13313)
Greber Machine Tool Inc..................G...... 440 322-3685
Elyria (G-9427)
Greenkote Usa Inc........................G...... 440 243-2865
Brookpark (G-2162)
Hartzell Manufacturing Co Inc............E...... 937 859-5955
Miamisburg (G-13815)
Howmet Corporation......................E...... 800 242-9898
Newburgh Heights (G-15074)
Ionbond LLC...............................F...... 216 831-0880
Cleveland (G-5586)
Ivac Technologies Corp...................F...... 216 662-4987
Cleveland (G-5592)
Logan Coatings LLC.......................G...... 740 380-0047
Logan (G-12184)

Mesocoat Inc ....F 216 453-0866
  Euclid (G-9593)
Metokote Corporation ....D 440 934-4686
  Sheffield Village (G-17127)
Miamisburg Coating ....F 937 866-1323
  Miamisburg (G-13834)
Niles Manufacturing & Finshg ....C 330 544-0402
  Niles (G-15171)
Oerlikon Blzers Cating USA Inc ....E 330 220-7716
  Brunswick (G-2240)
Omni Manufacturing Inc ....D 419 394-7424
  Saint Marys (G-16846)
Omni Manufacturing Inc ....F 419 394-7424
  Saint Marys (G-16847)
Pioneer Custom Coating LLC ....G 419 737-3152
  Pioneer (G-16236)
Progressive Powder Coating Inc ....E 440 974-3478
  Mentor (G-13701)
Raf Acquisition Co ....F 440 572-5999
  Valley City (G-19227)
Reifel Industries Inc ....D 419 737-2138
  Pioneer (G-16244)
Semper Quality Industry Inc ....G 440 352-8111
  Mentor (G-13719)
Tennessee Coatings Inc ....F 513 770-4900
  Mason (G-13096)
Thornton Powder Coatings Inc ....F 419 522-7183
  Mansfield (G-12698)
Trans-Acc Inc ....E 513 793-6410
  Blue Ash (G-1883)
Venus Trading LLC ....G 513 374-0066
  Loveland (G-12398)

COATING SVC: Metals, With Plastic Or Resins

Corrotec Inc ....E 937 325-3585
  Springfield (G-17536)
Gem Coatings Ltd ....E 740 589-2998
  Athens (G-868)
Godfrey & Wing Inc ....E 330 562-1440
  Aurora (G-922)
Harwood Rubber Products Inc ....E 330 923-3256
  Cuyahoga Falls (G-8008)
Industrial Thermoset Plas Inc ....F 440 975-0411
  Mentor (G-13608)
Master Vac Incorporated ....G 419 335-7796
  Wauseon (G-19689)
Metokote Corporation ....D 319 232-6994
  Lima (G-12056)
Metokote Corporation ....C 419 221-2754
  Lima (G-12057)
Metokote Corporation ....C 937 235-2811
  Dayton (G-8487)
Perfection Finishers Inc ....E 419 337-8015
  Wauseon (G-19693)
Pki Inc ....G 859 291-8680
  Cincinnati (G-4241)
Rack Processing Company Inc ....E 937 294-1911
  Moraine (G-14522)
Surftech Inc ....G 440 275-3356
  Austinburg (G-967)
Techneglas Inc ....G 419 873-2000
  Perrysburg (G-16154)
Universal Rack & Equipment Co ....E 330 963-6776
  Twinsburg (G-19033)

COATING SVC: Rust Preventative

Anotex Industries Inc ....G 513 860-1165
  West Chester (G-19805)

COATING SVC: Silicon

Momentive Performance Mtls Inc ....C 740 928-7010
  Hebron (G-10874)
Momentive Performance Mtls Inc ....A 440 878-5705
  Richmond Heights (G-16655)
Momentive Prfmce Mtls Qrtz Inc ....C 440 878-5700
  Strongsville (G-17941)

COATINGS: Epoxy

BASF Construction Chem LLC ....E 216 831-5500
  Cleveland (G-4895)
CPI Industrial Co ....E 614 445-0800
  Columbus (G-6995)
Dynafloor Systems Inc ....F 330 467-6005
  Solon (G-17283)
Epoxy Systems Blstg Cating Inc ....G 513 924-1800
  Cleves (G-6513)

Nanosperse LLC ....G 937 296-5030
  Kettering (G-11583)
Postle Industries Inc ....E 216 265-9000
  Cleveland (G-6022)
X-Treme Finishes Inc ....F 330 474-0614
  Medina (G-13498)

COATINGS: Polyurethane

Baker Built Products Inc ....G 419 965-2646
  Ohio City (G-15660)
Trexler Rubber Co Inc ....E 330 296-9677
  Ravenna (G-16567)

COILS & TRANSFORMERS

Barnes International Inc ....D 419 352-7501
  Bowling Green (G-1970)
Canfield Industries Inc ....G 800 554-5071
  Youngstown (G-21042)
Custom Coil & Transformer Co ....E 740 452-5211
  Zanesville (G-21297)
Electromotive Inc ....G 330 688-6494
  Stow (G-17746)
GE Healthcare Fincl Svcs Inc ....C 312 697-3999
  Aurora (G-921)
General Electric Company ....E 740 498-5151
  Newcomerstown (G-15113)
Industrial Quartz Corp ....F 440 942-0909
  Mentor (G-13606)
Kurz-Kasch Inc ....C 740 498-8343
  Newcomerstown (G-15118)
PCC Airfoils LLC ....C 216 692-7900
  Cleveland (G-5983)
Precision Switching Inc ....G 800 800-8143
  Mansfield (G-12667)
Rapid Mr International LLC ....G 614 486-6300
  Columbus (G-7548)
Schneider Electric Usa Inc ....B 513 523-4171
  Oxford (G-15843)
Staco Energy Products Co ....G 937 253-1191
  Miamisburg (G-13863)
Standard Car Truck Company ....D 740 775-6450
  Chillicothe (G-3276)
Standex Electronics Inc ....E 513 871-3777
  Cincinnati (G-4456)
Swiger Coil Systems Ltd ....C 216 362-7500
  Cleveland (G-6280)
Wabtec Corporation ....G 216 362-7500
  Cleveland (G-6437)
Wonder Weld Inc ....G 614 875-1447
  Orient (G-15726)

COILS, WIRE: Aluminum, Made In Rolling Mills

Amh Holdings LLC ....A 330 929-1811
  Cuyahoga Falls (G-7966)
Amh Holdings II Inc ....A 330 929-1811
  Cuyahoga Falls (G-7967)

COILS: Electric Motors Or Generators

Custom Coil & Transformer Co ....E 740 452-5211
  Zanesville (G-21297)
General Electric Company ....E 740 498-5151
  Newcomerstown (G-15113)
High Performance Servo LLC ....G 440 541-3529
  Westlake (G-20276)

COIN COUNTERS

Garda CL Technical Svcs Inc ....E 937 294-4099
  Moraine (G-14490)

COIN-OPERATED LAUNDRY

Premier Office ....B 419 329-9692
  Mansfield (G-12668)

COINS & TOKENS: Non-Currency

Osborne Coinage Company ....D 513 681-5424
  Cincinnati (G-4197)

COLLECTION AGENCY, EXC REAL ESTATE

C & S Associates Inc ....E 440 461-9661
  Highland Heights (G-10910)

COLLETS

Advanced Holding Designs Inc ....F 330 928-4456
  Cuyahoga Falls (G-7962)

COLOR LAKES OR TONERS

Ferro Corporation ....C 216 875-6178
  Cleveland (G-5337)
Office Link Inc ....G 440 498-1364
  Solon (G-17353)

COLOR PIGMENTS

Ferro Corporation ....C 216 875-5600
  Mayfield Heights (G-13313)
Ferro International Svcs Inc ....C 216 875-5600
  Mayfield Heights (G-13314)
General Color Investments Inc ....D 330 868-4161
  Minerva (G-14322)
Spectrum Dispersions Inc ....F 330 296-0600
  Ravenna (G-16558)

COLOR SEPARATION: Photographic & Movie Film

Tj Metzgers Inc ....D 419 861-8611
  Toledo (G-18726)

COLORS IN OIL, EXC ARTISTS'

Robert Raack ....G 216 932-6127
  Cleveland Heights (G-6501)

COLORS: Pigments, Inorganic

Americhem Inc ....E 330 926-3185
  Cuyahoga Falls (G-7964)
Americhem Inc ....D 330 929-4213
  Cuyahoga Falls (G-7965)
Ampacet Corporation ....C 740 929-5521
  Newark (G-14982)
Chromaflo Technologies Corp ....C 440 997-0081
  Ashtabula (G-795)
Chromaflo Technologies Corp ....C 513 733-5111
  Cincinnati (G-3532)
Chromaflo Technologies Corp ....C 440 997-5137
  Ashtabula (G-796)
Colormatrix Group Inc ....C 216 622-0100
  Berea (G-1608)
Colormatrix Holdings Inc ....C 440 930-3162
  Berea (G-1609)
Colortrend USA LLC ....C 513 733-5111
  Cincinnati (G-3597)
Day-Glo Color Corp ....C 216 391-7070
  Cleveland (G-5173)
Day-Glo Color Corp ....C 216 391-7070
  Cleveland (G-5174)
Day-Glo Color Corp ....F 216 391-7070
  Twinsburg (G-18922)
Degussa Incorporated ....G 513 733-5111
  Cincinnati (G-3646)
Eckart America Corporation ....D 440 954-7600
  Painesville (G-15876)
Leonhardt Plating Company ....E 513 242-1410
  Cincinnati (G-4020)
Lightstab Ltd Co ....G 216 751-5800
  Shaker Heights (G-17091)
PMC Specialties Group Inc ....E 513 242-3300
  Cincinnati (G-4246)
PMC Specialties Group Inc ....G 513 242-3300
  Cincinnati (G-4247)
Polyone Corporation ....C 419 668-4844
  Norwalk (G-15559)
Revlis Corporation ....E 330 535-2108
  Barberton (G-1145)
Rti Niles ....G 330 455-4010
  Niles (G-15182)
Sun Chemical Corporation ....C 513 681-5950
  Cincinnati (G-4477)
Sun Chemical Corporation ....B 513 681-5950
  Cincinnati (G-4480)
Thorworks Industries Inc ....E 419 626-4375
  Sandusky (G-17015)

COLORS: Pigments, Organic

Americhem Inc ....E 330 926-3185
  Cuyahoga Falls (G-7964)
Americhem Inc ....D 330 929-4213
  Cuyahoga Falls (G-7965)
Chromaflo Technologies Corp ....C 513 733-5111
  Cincinnati (G-3532)
Chromaflo Technologies Corp ....C 440 997-0081
  Ashtabula (G-795)
Flint Group US LLC ....D 513 771-1900
  Cincinnati (G-3761)

PRODUCT

Ruscoe Company ....E 330 253-8148
  Akron (G-384)
Spectrum Dispersions Inc ....F 330 296-0600
  Ravenna (G-16558)
Tri Chem Inc ....G 330 677-1213
  Kent (G-11539)

COMBINED ELEMENTARY & SECONDARY SCHOOLS, PUBLIC

Butler Tech Career Dev Schools ....F 513 867-1028
  Hamilton (G-10679)

COMBS, EXC HARD RUBBER

Sunbright Usa Inc ....G 440 205-0600
  Mentor (G-13741)

COMMERCIAL & OFFICE BUILDINGS RENOVATION & REPAIR

Shade Youngstown & Aluminum Co ....G 330 782-2373
  Youngstown (G-21200)
Thomas Cabinet Shop Inc ....F 937 847-8239
  Dayton (G-8711)

COMMERCIAL ART & GRAPHIC DESIGN SVCS

AG Designs LLC ....G 614 506-2849
  Delaware (G-8819)
Am Graphics ....G 330 799-7319
  Youngstown (G-21022)
Converters/Prepress Inc ....G 937 743-0935
  Carlisle (G-2929)
Creatia Inc ....G 937 368-3100
  Fletcher (G-9915)
Eastgate Custom Graphics Ltd ....G 513 528-7922
  Cincinnati (G-3686)
Echographics Inc ....G 440 846-2330
  North Ridgeville (G-15371)
Enlarging Arts Inc ....G 330 434-3433
  Akron (G-168)
Envoi Design Inc ....G 513 651-4229
  Cincinnati (G-3711)
Evolution Crtive Solutions LLC ....E 513 681-4450
  Cincinnati (G-3725)
Fire Ball Press ....G 614 280-0100
  Columbus (G-7087)
General Theming Contrs LLC ....C 614 252-6342
  Columbus (G-7108)
Graphic Touch Inc ....G 330 337-3341
  Salem (G-16896)
Hardmagic ....F 415 390-6232
  Marietta (G-12789)
Hotcardscom Inc ....E 216 241-4040
  Cleveland (G-5528)
Innovtive Crtive Solutions LLC ....E 614 491-9638
  Groveport (G-10626)
Instruction & Design Concepts ....G 937 439-2698
  Dayton (G-8412)
Jeffrey A Clark ....G 419 866-8775
  Holland (G-11067)
Johnson Brothers Holdings LLC ....G 614 868-5273
  Columbus (G-7240)
Jscs Group Inc ....G 513 563-4900
  Cincinnati (G-3961)
La Dua Inc ....G 440 243-9600
  Olmsted Twp (G-15679)
Maximum Graphix Inc ....G 440 353-3301
  North Ridgeville (G-15390)
Mc Sign Company ....C 440 209-6200
  Mentor (G-13649)
Middlefield Sign Co ....G 440 632-0708
  Middlefield (G-13963)
Morse Enterprises Inc ....G 513 229-3600
  Mason (G-13066)
Penca Design Group Ltd ....G 440 210-4422
  Painesville (G-15910)
Quez Media Marketing Inc ....F 216 910-0202
  Cleveland (G-6077)
Sign City Inc ....G 614 486-6700
  Mount Gilead (G-14568)
Stick-It Graphics LLC ....G 330 407-0142
  New Philadelphia (G-14930)
Sylvan Studio Inc ....G 419 882-3423
  Sylvania (G-18127)
Visual Art Graphic Services ....E 330 274-2775
  Mantua (G-12725)
Vivid Wraps LLC ....G 513 515-8386
  Cincinnati (G-4569)

COMMERCIAL ART & ILLUSTRATION SVCS

ONeil & Associates Inc ....C 937 865-0800
  Miamisburg (G-13847)

COMMERCIAL CONTAINERS WHOLESALERS

Askia Inc ....G 513 828-7443
  Cincinnati (G-3419)

COMMERCIAL EQPT & SPLYS, WHOLESALE: Price Marking

Century Marketing Corporation ....C 419 354-2591
  Bowling Green (G-1978)

COMMERCIAL EQPT WHOLESALERS, NEC

Bar Codes Unlimited Inc ....G 937 434-2633
  Dayton (G-8181)
CMC Daymark Corporation ....C 419 354-2591
  Bowling Green (G-1980)
Cummins - Allison Corp ....G 614 529-1940
  Hilliard (G-10945)
Cummins - Allison Corp ....G 440 824-5050
  Cleveland (G-5146)
Cummins - Allison Corp ....G 513 469-2924
  Blue Ash (G-1772)
General Data Company Inc ....G 513 752-7978
  Cincinnati (G-3304)
National Pride Equipment Inc ....G 419 289-2886
  Ashland (G-756)
Precision Equipment Llc ....G 330 220-7600
  Brunswick (G-2246)
Rayhaven Group Inc ....F 330 659-3183
  Richfield (G-16634)

COMMERCIAL EQPT, WHOLESALE: Bakery Eqpt & Splys

Ervan Guttman Co ....G 513 791-0767
  Cincinnati (G-3718)

COMMERCIAL EQPT, WHOLESALE: Comm Cooking & Food Svc Eqpt

Dmi Products Inc ....G 440 951-1828
  Mentor (G-13561)
Harry C Lobalzo & Sons Inc ....E 330 666-6758
  Akron (G-216)
RS Industries Inc ....G 216 524-2998
  Brooklyn Heights (G-2146)
Wasserstrom Company ....B 614 737-8472
  Columbus (G-7750)

COMMERCIAL EQPT, WHOLESALE: Display Eqpt, Exc Refrigerated

Abstract Displays Inc ....G 513 985-9700
  Blue Ash (G-1732)
Ternion Inc ....E 216 642-6180
  Cleveland (G-6307)

COMMERCIAL EQPT, WHOLESALE: Food Warming

Joneszylon Company LLC ....G 740 545-6341
  West Lafayette (G-20089)

COMMERCIAL EQPT, WHOLESALE: Neon Signs

Behrco Inc ....G 419 394-1612
  Saint Marys (G-16832)

COMMERCIAL EQPT, WHOLESALE: Restaurant, NEC

International Beverage Works ....G 614 798-5398
  Columbus (G-7205)
ITW Food Equipment Group LLC ....A 937 332-2396
  Troy (G-18848)
Joseph Knapp ....F 330 832-3515
  Massillon (G-13160)
N Wasserstrom & Sons Inc ....C 614 228-5550
  Columbus (G-7377)
Rightway Food Service ....G 419 223-4075
  Lima (G-12084)

COMMERCIAL EQPT, WHOLESALE: Scales, Exc Laboratory

Kanawha Scales & Systems Inc ....F 513 576-0700
  Milford (G-14158)
Perfect Measuring Tape Company ......G 419 243-6811
  Toledo (G-18639)

COMMERCIAL EQPT, WHOLESALE: Store Eqpt

Hubert Enterprises Inc ....G 513 367-8600
  Harrison (G-10783)

COMMERCIAL EQPT, WHOLESALE: Store Fixtures & Display Eqpt

Baker Plastics Inc ....G 330 743-3142
  Youngstown (G-21031)
Ffr-DSI Company ....E 330 998-7800
  Twinsburg (G-18936)
Possible Plastics Inc ....G 614 277-2100
  Grove City (G-10583)

COMMERCIAL PRINTING & NEWSPAPER PUBLISHING COMBINED

Bakers Print Shop ....G 740 423-1717
  Little Hocking (G-12143)
Cincinnati Crt Index Press Inc ....F 513 241-1450
  Cincinnati (G-3546)
Copley Ohio Newspapers Inc ....D 585 598-0030
  Canton (G-2668)
Digicom Inc ....G 216 642-3838
  Independence (G-11252)
Dispatch Printing Company ....C 740 548-5331
  Lewis Center (G-11895)
Dispatch Printing Company ....E 614 885-6020
  Columbus (G-7030)
Gannett Publishing Svcs LLC ....D 419 522-3311
  Mansfield (G-12611)
Horizon Ohio Publications Inc ....F 419 394-7414
  Saint Marys (G-16840)
Hubbard Publishing Co ....E 937 592-3060
  Bellefontaine (G-1533)
King Media Enterprises Inc ....E 216 588-6700
  Cleveland (G-5654)
Knowles Press Inc ....G 330 877-9345
  Hartville (G-10827)
Knox County Printing Co ....G 740 848-4032
  Galion (G-10278)
Kroner Publications Inc ....E 330 544-5500
  Niles (G-15167)
M & D Brink Inc ....G 419 531-6699
  Toledo (G-18566)
New Urban Distributors LLC ....G 216 373-2349
  Cleveland (G-5879)
Progressive Communications ....D 740 397-5333
  Mount Vernon (G-14640)
Southeast Publications Inc ....F 740 732-2341
  Caldwell (G-2433)
Suburban Newpapers of Dayton ....G 937 236-4990
  Dayton (G-8686)
Suburban Newpapers of Dayton ....G 937 294-7000
  Vandalia (G-19311)
Troy Daily News Inc ....E 937 339-2729
  Troy (G-18880)
Truax Printing Inc ....E 419 994-4166
  Loudonville (G-12306)
Vpp Industries Inc ....F 937 526-3775
  Versailles (G-19359)

COMMODITY CONTRACT TRADING COMPANIES

Cac Energy Ltd ....G 937 867-5593
  Dayton (G-8206)

COMMON SAND MINING

De Milta Sand and Gravel ....F 440 942-2015
  Willoughby (G-20471)
Demmy Sand and Gravel LLC ....E 937 325-8840
  Springfield (G-17543)
Feikert Sand & Gravel Co Inc ....E 330 674-0038
  Millersburg (G-14215)
FML Sand LLC ....G 440 214-3200
  Chesterland (G-3208)
Kirby and Sons Inc ....F 419 927-2260
  Upper Sandusky (G-19128)

Nelson Sand & Gravel Inc ....F 440 224-0198
  Kingsville (G-11606)
Shenango Valley Sand and Grav ....G... 330 758-9100
  Youngstown (G-21202)
Stocker Sand & Gravel Co ....F 740 254-4635
  Gnadenhutten (G-10412)
Weber Sand & Gravel Inc ....F 419 298-2388
  Edgerton (G-9338)
Welch Holdings Inc ....E 513 353-3220
  Cincinnati (G-4584)
X L Sand and Gravel Co Inc ....F 330 426-9876
  Negley (G-14733)

COMMUNICATION HEADGEAR: Telephone

Commtech Solutions Inc ....G...... 440 458-4870
  Grafton (G-10421)

COMMUNICATIONS CARRIER: Wired

Iq Solutions Group LLC ....F 855 367-4774
  Westerville (G-20161)
Protech Electric LLC......................F 937 427-0813
  Beavercreek (G-1357)

COMMUNICATIONS EQPT & SYSTEMS, NEC

Jhs Toyz LLC ....F 440 946-6600
  Willowick (G-20648)
Robert F Sams ....G...... 330 990-0477
  Akron (G-376)
Special Way 2 ....G...... 740 282-8281
  Steubenville (G-17713)

COMMUNICATIONS EQPT REPAIR & MAINTENANCE

House of Hindenach ....G...... 419 422-0392
  Findlay (G-9843)
Laird Controls Holdings Inc ....E 234 806-0018
  Warren (G-19567)

COMMUNICATIONS EQPT WHOLESALERS

Cota International Inc ....F 937 526-5520
  Versailles (G-19344)
Laird Controls Holdings Inc ....E 234 806-0018
  Warren (G-19567)
Quasonix Inc ....E 513 942-1287
  West Chester (G-19927)
Ray Communications Inc ....G...... 330 686-0226
  Stow (G-17795)
Securcom Inc ....E 419 628-1049
  Minster (G-14361)

COMMUNICATIONS SVCS

Harris Hawk ....G...... 800 459-4295
  Mason (G-13036)
S T Custom Signs ....G...... 513 733-4227
  Cincinnati (G-4375)

COMMUNICATIONS SVCS: Cellular

Alltel Communications Corp ....G...... 419 784-3808
  Defiance (G-8777)

COMMUNICATIONS SVCS: Data

Springdot Inc ....D...... 513 542-4000
  Cincinnati (G-4448)
Water Drop Media Inc ....G...... 234 600-5817
  Vienna (G-19377)

COMMUNICATIONS SVCS: Internet Connectivity Svcs

Great Lakes Telcom Ltd ....E 330 629-8848
  Youngstown (G-21103)
Revolution Group Inc ....D...... 614 212-1111
  Westerville (G-20182)

COMMUNICATIONS SVCS: Online Svc Providers

Vista Research Group LLC ....G...... 419 281-3927
  Ashland (G-784)

COMMUNICATIONS SVCS: Radio Pager Or Beeper

Airwave Communications Cons ....G...... 419 331-1526
  Lima (G-11984)

COMMUNICATIONS SVCS: Signal Enhancement Network Svcs

Alanax Technologies Inc ....G....... 216 469-1545
  Belmont (G-1577)

COMMUNICATIONS SVCS: Telephone, Local & Long Distance

Airwave Communications Cons ....G....... 419 331-1526
  Lima (G-11984)
Alltel Communications Corp ....G....... 419 784-3808
  Defiance (G-8777)
Johnson Brothers Holdings LLC ....G....... 614 868-5273
  Columbus (G-7240)

COMMUNICATIONS SVCS: Telephone, Long Distance

Mitel (delaware) Inc ....E 513 733-8000
  West Chester (G-19902)

COMMUNITY ACTION AGENCY

Community Action Program Corp ....F 740 374-8501
  Marietta (G-12776)

COMMUNITY DEVELOPMENT GROUPS

Access To Independence Inc ....G 330 296-8111
  Ravenna (G-16512)
News Reel Inc ....G...... 614 469-0700
  Columbus (G-7390)

COMMUTATORS: Electric Motors

Kirkwood Holding Inc ....G...... 216 267-6200
  Cleveland (G-5659)

COMMUTATORS: Electronic

Ra Consultants LLC......................E 513 469-6600
  Blue Ash (G-1861)

COMPACT DISCS OR CD'S, WHOLESALE

CD Solutions Inc ....G...... 937 676-2376
  Pleasant Hill (G-16369)

COMPACT LASER DISCS: Prerecorded

Jk Digital Publishing LLC ....E 937 299-0185
  Springboro (G-17484)

COMPARATORS: Machinists

Certified Comparator Products ....G...... 937 426-9677
  Beavercreek (G-1372)

COMPOST

Charles Daniel Young ....G...... 937 968-3423
  Union City (G-19070)
City of Columbus ....E 614 645-3152
  Lockbourne (G-12146)
Compost Cincy ....G...... 513 278-8178
  Cincinnati (G-3602)
Hyponex Corporation ....E 330 262-1300
  Shreve (G-17157)
Kurtz Bros Compost Services ....E 330 864-2621
  Akron (G-263)
Midwest Compost Inc ....E 419 547-7979
  Clyde (G-6542)
Opal Diamond LLC ....G...... 330 653-5876
  Rocky River (G-16703)
Price Farms Organics Ltd ....F 740 369-1000
  Delaware (G-8880)
Werlor Inc ....G...... 419 784-4285
  Defiance (G-8814)

COMPRESSORS, AIR CONDITIONING: Wholesalers

Diversified Air Systems Inc ....E 216 741-1700
  Brooklyn Heights (G-2139)

COMPRESSORS: Air & Gas

Airtx International Ltd......................F 513 631-0660
  Cincinnati (G-3372)
Anest Iwata Air Engrg Inc ....F 513 755-3100
  Hamilton (G-10669)
Arete Innovative Solutions LLC ....G...... 513 503-2712
  Morrow (G-14543)

Ariel Corporation ....F 740 397-0311
  Mount Vernon (G-14607)
Atlas Machine and Supply Inc ....G...... 614 351-1603
  Hilliard (G-10928)
Coulson Cmprssion Msrement Ltd ......F 740 697-0220
  Roseville (G-16730)
Eaton Comprsr Fabrication Inc ....E 877 283-7614
  Englewood (G-9518)
Ecowise LLC ....G...... 216 692-3700
  Cleveland (G-5257)
Ernest Industries Inc ....F 937 325-9851
  Springfield (G-17553)
Field Gymmy Inc ....G...... 419 538-6511
  Glandorf (G-10397)
General Fabrications Corp ....E 419 625-6055
  Sandusky (G-16970)
Giti Tech Group Ltd ....G...... 866 381-7955
  West Carrollton (G-19793)
Kingsly Compression Inc ....G...... 740 439-0772
  Cambridge (G-2462)
Lsq Manufacturing Inc ....F 330 725-4905
  Medina (G-13437)
Mack Industrial LLC.....................G...... 800 918-9986
  Perrysburg (G-16119)
Optimair Ltd.............................G...... 419 661-9568
  Perrysburg (G-16137)
Optime Air MSP Ltd ....G...... 419 661-9568
  Perrysburg (G-16138)
Powerex-Iwata Air Tech Inc ....D...... 888 769-7979
  Harrison (G-10795)
Rotary Compression Tech Inc ....E 937 498-2555
  Sidney (G-17220)
T D Group Holdings LLC ....G...... 216 706-2939
  Cleveland (G-6289)
Transdigm Inc...........................G...... 216 706-2939
  Cleveland (G-6347)
Transdigm Inc...........................F 216 291-6025
  Cleveland (G-6346)

COMPRESSORS: Air & Gas, Including Vacuum Pumps

Aci Services Inc ....E 740 435-0240
  Cambridge (G-2442)
Ariel Corporation ....F 740 397-0311
  Mount Vernon (G-14606)
Campbell Hausfeld LLC...................C 513 367-4811
  Harrison (G-10770)
Finishmaster Inc ....D...... 614 228-4328
  Columbus (G-7086)
National Compressor Svcs LLC ....E 419 865-3126
  Holland (G-11073)
Potemkin Industries Inc ....E 740 397-4888
  Mount Vernon (G-14638)

COMPRESSORS: Refrigeration & Air Conditioning Eqpt

Certified Service Inc ....G...... 937 643-0393
  Dayton (G-8223)
Emerson Climate Tech Inc ....A 937 498-3011
  Sidney (G-17186)
Hanon Systems Usa LLC ....C 313 920-0583
  Carey (G-2919)
IV J Telecommunications LLC ....G...... 606 694-1762
  South Point (G-17438)
Midwest Compressor Co Inc...............G...... 216 941-9200
  Cleveland (G-5808)

COMPRESSORS: Repairing

Fmh Electric Inc ....F 419 782-0671
  Lima (G-12013)

COMPRESSORS: Wholesalers

A P O Holdings Inc ....E 330 455-8925
  Canton (G-2585)
Diversified Air Systems Inc ....E 216 741-1700
  Brooklyn Heights (G-2139)
General Electric Intl Inc ....E 330 963-2066
  Twinsburg (G-18944)
Harbor Freight Tools Usa Inc ....E 937 415-0770
  Dayton (G-8385)

COMPUTER & COMPUTER SOFTWARE STORES

Copier Resources Inc ....G...... 614 268-1100
  Columbus (G-6981)

PRODUCT

Golubitsky Corporation............................G...... 800 552-4204
   Cleveland *(G-5436)*
Gordons Graphics Inc...............................G...... 330 863-2322
   Malvern *(G-12546)*
J3 Systems Ltd..G...... 419 562-5522
   Bucyrus *(G-2351)*
Journey Systems LLC..............................F...... 513 831-6200
   Milford *(G-14157)*
Merkur Group Inc......................................G...... 937 429-4288
   Beavercreek *(G-1351)*
T E Hubler Inc...G...... 419 476-2552
   Toledo *(G-18714)*
Tech-E-Z LLC...G...... 419 692-1700
   Delphos *(G-8918)*

COMPUTER & COMPUTER SOFTWARE STORES: Computer Tapes

Ohio Graphic Supply Inc..........................G...... 937 433-7537
   Dayton *(G-8543)*

COMPUTER & COMPUTER SOFTWARE STORES: Peripheral Eqpt

B W T Inc...G...... 330 928-9107
   Akron *(G-81)*
Computer Zoo Inc.....................................G...... 937 310-1474
   Bellbrook *(G-1504)*
Lazer Action Inc..G...... 330 630-9200
   Akron *(G-268)*
PC Systems...G...... 330 825-7966
   Akron *(G-333)*

COMPUTER & COMPUTER SOFTWARE STORES: Printers & Plotters

Kehler Enterprises Inc.............................G...... 614 889-8488
   Dublin *(G-9095)*
Nickum Enterprises Inc............................G...... 513 561-2292
   Cincinnati *(G-4154)*

COMPUTER & COMPUTER SOFTWARE STORES: Software & Access

Ezshred LLC..G...... 440 256-7640
   Kirtland *(G-11614)*

COMPUTER & COMPUTER SOFTWARE STORES: Software, Bus/Non-Game

A Graphic Solution....................................F...... 216 228-7223
   Cleveland *(G-4672)*
Delores E OBeirn......................................G...... 440 582-3610
   Cleveland *(G-5182)*
Retalix Inc..C...... 937 384-2277
   Miamisburg *(G-13855)*

COMPUTER & COMPUTER SOFTWARE STORES: Software, Computer Game

Lasermark LLC...G...... 513 312-9889
   Dayton *(G-8452)*
Moonstruck Games Inc.............................G...... 513 721-3900
   Cincinnati *(G-4121)*

COMPUTER & DATA PROCESSING EQPT REPAIR & MAINTENANCE

Thomas Ross Associates Inc...................G...... 330 723-1110
   Medina *(G-13488)*

COMPUTER & OFFICE MACHINE MAINTENANCE & REPAIR

Click It Connect Corp...............................G...... 440 247-4998
   Chagrin Falls *(G-3053)*
Davis Laser Products................................G...... 614 252-7711
   Columbus *(G-7015)*
Eaj Services LLC.......................................F...... 513 792-3400
   Blue Ash *(G-1780)*
Freedom Usa Inc.......................................F...... 216 503-6374
   Twinsburg *(G-18937)*
Government Acquisitions Inc....................E...... 513 721-8700
   Cincinnati *(G-3842)*
Magnum Computers Inc............................F...... 216 781-1757
   Cleveland *(G-5730)*
P C Power Inc..G...... 440 779-4080
   North Olmsted *(G-15342)*
Pinnacle Data Systems Inc......................C...... 614 748-1150
   Groveport *(G-10641)*

Programmable Control Service.................F...... 740 927-0744
   Pataskala *(G-15978)*
T E Hubler Inc...G...... 419 476-2552
   Toledo *(G-18714)*
Tech-E-Z LLC...G...... 419 692-1700
   Delphos *(G-8918)*
Terra Comp Technology............................G...... 330 745-8912
   Barberton *(G-1154)*
Ucr LLC..F...... 937 253-8898
   Dayton *(G-8120)*

COMPUTER FORMS

Crabar/Gbf Inc..E...... 419 269-1720
   Toledo *(G-18415)*
Feld Printing Co..G...... 513 271-6806
   Cincinnati *(G-3749)*

COMPUTER GRAPHICS SVCS

Bob King Sign Company Inc......................G...... 330 753-2679
   Akron *(G-94)*
Columbus Advanced Mfg Sftwr.................G...... 614 433-0415
   Powell *(G-16467)*
Datatex Media Dolls..................................G...... 216 598-1000
   Cleveland *(G-5170)*
Great Lakes Publishing Company.............D...... 216 771-2833
   Cleveland *(G-5455)*
IPA Ltd...F...... 614 523-3974
   Columbus *(G-7210)*
Jjkb Enterprises LLC.................................G...... 513 731-4332
   Cincinnati *(G-3946)*
M Grafix LLC..F...... 419 528-8665
   Mansfield *(G-12638)*
Quez Media Marketing Inc........................F...... 216 910-0202
   Cleveland *(G-6077)*
R T Communications Inc............................G...... 330 726-7892
   Youngstown *(G-21183)*
Sevell + Sevell Inc....................................G...... 614 341-9700
   Columbus *(G-7611)*

COMPUTER INTERFACE EQPT: Indl Process

Comtec Incorporated.................................F...... 330 425-8102
   Twinsburg *(G-18918)*
Keithley Instruments LLC..........................C...... 440 248-0400
   Solon *(G-17328)*
Measurement Computing Corp...................E...... 440 439-4091
   Cleveland *(G-5774)*
Technology Resources Inc........................G...... 419 241-9248
   Toledo *(G-18716)*
Vertiv Co..G...... 614 888-0246
   Columbus *(G-7734)*
Wild Fire Systems.....................................G...... 440 442-8999
   Cleveland *(G-6462)*

COMPUTER PERIPHERAL EQPT REPAIR & MAINTENANCE

Ascendtech Inc..E...... 216 458-1101
   Willoughby *(G-20441)*
Lazer Action Inc..G...... 330 630-9200
   Akron *(G-268)*
PC Systems...G...... 330 825-7966
   Akron *(G-333)*
Smartronix Inc...F...... 216 378-3300
   Northfield *(G-15472)*

COMPUTER PERIPHERAL EQPT, NEC

Adaptive Data Inc......................................F...... 937 436-2343
   Centerville *(G-3032)*
Advanced Microbeam Inc..........................G...... 330 394-1255
   Vienna *(G-19362)*
Airwave Communications Cons.................G...... 419 331-1526
   Lima *(G-11984)*
AT&T Corp..G...... 513 792-9300
   Cincinnati *(G-3423)*
Black Box Corporation..............................F...... 937 438-8660
   Brecksville *(G-2037)*
Black Box Corporation..............................E...... 614 825-7400
   Lewis Center *(G-11890)*
Cisco Systems Inc.....................................A...... 419 977-2404
   New Bremen *(G-14781)*
Data Processing Sciences Corp................D...... 513 791-7100
   Cincinnati *(G-3640)*
Dataq Instruments.....................................F...... 330 668-1444
   Akron *(G-141)*
Eastman Kodak Company...........................E...... 937 259-3000
   Dayton *(G-8317)*
Electronic Vision Inc.................................F...... 740 592-2433
   Athens *(G-864)*

Embedded Planet Inc................................F...... 216 245-4180
   Warrensville Heights *(G-19632)*
Enterasys Networks Inc............................B...... 330 245-0240
   Akron *(G-169)*
Epic Technologies LLC..............................D...... 513 683-5455
   Mason *(G-13018)*
Esterline Georgia US LLC..........................E...... 937 372-7579
   Xenia *(G-20949)*
Fitne Inc..F...... 740 592-2433
   Athens *(G-865)*
Gleason Metrology Systems Corp.............E...... 937 384-8901
   Dayton *(G-8365)*
Government Acquisitions Inc....................E...... 513 721-8700
   Cincinnati *(G-3842)*
Intermec Inc..F...... 513 874-5882
   West Chester *(G-19883)*
Intermec Technologies Corp.....................F...... 513 874-5882
   West Chester *(G-19884)*
Kern Inc...E...... 614 317-2600
   Grove City *(G-10567)*
Kern Inc...G...... 440 930-7315
   Cleveland *(G-5649)*
Lazer Action Inc..G...... 330 630-9200
   Akron *(G-268)*
Parker-Hannifin Corporation.....................D...... 513 831-2340
   Milford *(G-14166)*
Prentke Romich Company...........................C...... 330 202-5800
   Wooster *(G-20825)*
Qualtek Electronics Corp..........................C...... 440 951-3300
   Mentor *(G-13710)*
Scriptel Corporation.................................F...... 614 276-8402
   Columbus *(G-7604)*
Signature Technologies Inc......................E...... 937 859-6323
   Miamisburg *(G-13859)*
Stellar Systems Inc...................................G...... 513 921-8748
   Cincinnati *(G-4464)*
Superior Label Systems Inc......................B...... 513 336-0825
   Mason *(G-13092)*
Systemax Manufacturing Inc.....................C...... 937 368-2300
   Dayton *(G-8694)*
T E Hubler Inc...G...... 419 476-2552
   Toledo *(G-18714)*
Tech Pro Inc..E...... 330 923-3546
   Akron *(G-430)*
Timekeeping Systems Inc.........................F...... 216 595-0890
   Solon *(G-17406)*
Ucr LLC..F...... 937 253-8898
   Dayton *(G-8120)*
University Accessories Inc.......................G...... 440 327-4151
   North Ridgeville *(G-15407)*
Video Products Inc....................................D...... 330 562-2622
   Aurora *(G-955)*
Vmetro Inc...G...... 281 584-0728
   Fairborn *(G-9633)*
Xerox Corporation.....................................D...... 740 592-5609
   Athens *(G-890)*
Xerox Corporation.....................................D...... 513 539-4858
   Monroe *(G-14421)*
Xerox Corporation.....................................D...... 513 539-4808
   Monroe *(G-14422)*
Xerox Corporation.....................................D...... 614 409-6527
   Groveport *(G-10650)*
Xponet Inc...E...... 440 354-6617
   Painesville *(G-15943)*
Yonezawa USA Inc.....................................G...... 614 799-2210
   Plain City *(G-16367)*

COMPUTER PERIPHERAL EQPT, WHOLESALE

Eagle Wright Innovations Inc....................G...... 937 640-8093
   Moraine *(G-14482)*
Legrand North America LLC........................B...... 937 224-0639
   Moraine *(G-14503)*
Microplex Inc...E...... 330 498-0600
   North Canton *(G-15249)*
PC Systems...G...... 330 825-7966
   Akron *(G-333)*

COMPUTER PERIPHERAL EQPT: Decoders

Harris Mackessy & Brennan......................C...... 614 221-6831
   Westerville *(G-20157)*

COMPUTER PERIPHERAL EQPT: Graphic Displays, Exc Terminals

Abstract Displays Inc...............................G...... 513 985-9700
   Blue Ash *(G-1732)*
AGE Graphics LLC......................................F...... 740 989-0006
   Long Bottom *(G-12228)*

Penca Design Group Ltd ....G...... 440 210-4422
Painesville (G-15910)
Star City Art Co ....F...... 937 865-9792
Miamisburg (G-13864)
United Ultra Violet Inc ....F...... 614 875-8088
Grove City (G-10609)

COMPUTER PERIPHERAL EQPT: Input Or Output

Computer Zoo Inc ....G...... 937 310-1474
Bellbrook (G-1504)

COMPUTER PROGRAMMING SVCS

Aclara Technologies LLC ....C...... 440 528-7200
Solon (G-17248)
Advanced Prgrm Resources Inc.....E...... 614 761-9994
Dublin (G-9037)
Ajeh & Company Unlimited ....G...... 440 729-2367
Chesterland (G-3196)
Application Link Inc ....F...... 614 934-1735
Columbus (G-6764)
Applied Imagination Inc ....G...... 419 352-8373
Bowling Green (G-1968)
Brown Dave Products Inc ....F...... 513 738-1576
Hamilton (G-10677)
Cimx LLC ....G...... 513 248-7700
Cincinnati (G-3534)
Clinical Computing Inc ....F...... 513 651-3803
Cincinnati (G-3587)
Command Alkon Incorporated ....D...... 614 799-0600
Dublin (G-9064)
Computer Workshop Inc ....E...... 614 798-9505
Dublin (G-9065)
Computer Workshop Inc ....G...... 216 901-0106
Cleveland (G-5114)
Drb Systems LLC ....D...... 330 645-3299
Akron (G-157)
Drs Signal Technologies Inc...........E...... 937 429-7470
Beavercreek (G-1333)
Eclipse Blind Systems Inc ....C...... 330 296-0112
Ravenna (G-16528)
Embedded Planet Inc....................F...... 216 245-4180
Warrensville Heights (G-19632)
Gordon Bernard Company LLC........G...... 513 248-7600
Milford (G-14147)
Gracie Plum Investments Inc ....E...... 740 355-9029
Portsmouth (G-16436)
Immigration Law Systems Inc ....G...... 614 252-3078
Columbus (G-7184)
Intelligrated Inc ....E...... 513 874-0788
West Chester (G-20016)
IPA Ltd ....G...... 614 523-3974
Columbus (G-7210)
List Media Inc ....G...... 330 995-0864
Aurora (G-934)
Mainstream Software Inc ....F...... 330 963-0103
Twinsburg (G-18977)
Mapsys Inc.................................E...... 614 255-7258
Columbus (G-7316)
North Coast Security Group LLC ......G...... 614 887-7255
Columbus (G-7399)
Pathfinder Computer Systems ....G...... 330 928-1961
Barberton (G-1138)
Patient Focus Systems ....G...... 330 655-7222
Hudson (G-11193)
Pdmb Inc ....G...... 513 522-7362
Cincinnati (G-4220)
Pixslap Inc ....G...... 937 559-2671
Middletown (G-14076)
Quayle Consulting Inc ....G...... 614 868-1363
Pickerington (G-16202)
Reichard Software Corp ....G...... 614 537-8598
Dublin (G-9130)
Reynolds and Reynolds Company.......F...... 937 485-2805
Beavercreek (G-1379)
Seapine Software Inc ....E...... 513 754-1655
Mason (G-13087)
Tahoe Interactive Systems Inc........F...... 614 891-2323
Westerville (G-20235)
Tata America Intl Corp ....B...... 513 677-6500
Milford (G-14177)
Technology and Services Inc ....G...... 740 626-2020
Chillicothe (G-3280)
Technosoft Inc............................F...... 513 985-9877
Blue Ash (G-1880)
Trivantis Corporation ....D...... 513 929-0188
Cincinnati (G-4528)
Westmount Technology Inc ....G...... 216 328-2011
Independence (G-11284)

Zebu Compliance Solutions Inc ....E...... 740 355-9029
Portsmouth (G-16460)

COMPUTER PROGRAMMING SVCS: Custom

Avasax Ltd ....G...... 937 694-0807
Beavercreek (G-1369)
Corporate Elevator LLC ....F...... 614 288-1847
Columbus (G-6985)
Fgm Media Inc ....G...... 440 376-0487
North Royalton (G-15419)
Jasstek Inc.................................F...... 614 808-3600
Dublin (G-9091)
Rockware Corp ....G...... 419 483-5649
Bellevue (G-1556)
Sentinel USA Inc ....F...... 740 345-6412
Newark (G-15052)
Teachers Publishing Group ....G...... 614 486-0631
Hilliard (G-10985)
Timekeeping Systems Inc ....F...... 216 595-0890
Solon (G-17406)

COMPUTER RELATED MAINTENANCE SVCS

Ascendtech Inc ....E...... 216 458-1101
Willoughby (G-20441)
Digital Controls Corporation...........D...... 513 746-8118
Miamisburg (G-13801)
Lync Corp ....E...... 513 655-7286
Cincinnati (G-4041)
Wolters Kluwer Clinical Drug ....D...... 330 650-6506
Hudson (G-11210)

COMPUTER RELATED SVCS, NEC

Brakers Publishing & Prtg Svc.............G...... 440 576-0136
Jefferson (G-11357)

COMPUTER SERVICE BUREAU

CD Solutions Inc ....G...... 937 676-2376
Pleasant Hill (G-16369)

COMPUTER SOFTWARE DEVELOPMENT

Alanax Technologies Inc ....G...... 216 469-1545
Belmont (G-1577)
Brainmaster Technologies Inc..........G...... 440 232-6000
Bedford (G-1409)
Compuware Corporation ....D...... 614 847-8212
Columbus (G-6975)
Coso Media LLC ....G...... 330 904-5889
Hudson (G-11166)
Einstruction Corporation ....D...... 330 746-3015
Youngstown (G-21075)
Electronic Concepts Engrg Inc.........F...... 419 861-9000
Holland (G-11059)
Elynx Holdings LLC ....G...... 513 612-5969
Cincinnati (G-3693)
Exact Software North Amer LLC ....C...... 978 539-6186
Dublin (G-9075)
Ganymede Technologies Corp ....G...... 419 562-5522
Bucyrus (G-2344)
Intelligrated Systems Inc ....A...... 866 936-7300
Mason (G-13045)
Intelligrated Systems LLC ....A...... 513 701-7300
Mason (G-13046)
John B Allen ....G...... 614 488-7122
Columbus (G-7238)
Keithley Instruments LLC ....C...... 440 248-0400
Solon (G-17328)
Leidos Inc ....D...... 937 431-2400
Beavercreek (G-1348)
Liquid Shock Games LLC ....G...... 386 627-0840
Elyria (G-9453)
Parker-Hannifin Corporation............D...... 513 831-2340
Milford (G-14166)
Queen City Software Inc ....G...... 513 469-1424
Cincinnati (G-4321)
Queen City Technologies ....F...... 513 253-1312
West Chester (G-20044)
Rawhide Software Inc ....G...... 419 878-0857
Bowling Green (G-2010)
Sanctuary Software Studio Inc ....E...... 330 666-9690
Fairlawn (G-9759)
Stellar Systems Inc ....G...... 513 921-8748
Cincinnati (G-4464)
Strongbasics LLC ....G...... 716 903-6151
Columbus (G-7662)
Thinkware Incorporated ....G...... 513 598-3300
Cincinnati (G-4506)
Triad Governmental Systems ....E...... 937 376-5446
Xenia (G-20983)

Truck Fax Inc..............................G...... 216 921-8866
Cleveland (G-6369)

COMPUTER SOFTWARE DEVELOPMENT & APPLICATIONS

Agent Technologies Inc ....G...... 513 942-9444
West Chester (G-19800)
Applied Systems Inc.....................E...... 513 943-0000
Milford (G-14121)
Auto Des Sys Inc ....E...... 614 488-7984
Upper Arlington (G-19110)
Callcopy Inc ....G...... 614 340-3346
Columbus (G-6890)
Computer Allied Technology Co ....G...... 614 457-2292
Columbus (G-6973)
Cott Systems Inc ....D...... 614 847-4405
Columbus (G-6989)
Deemsys Inc ....D...... 614 322-9928
Gahanna (G-10206)
Electronic Vision Inc ....E...... 740 592-2433
Athens (G-864)
Ezshred LLC ....G...... 440 256-7640
Kirtland (G-11614)
Fitne Inc ....F...... 740 592-2433
Athens (G-865)
Forcam Inc ....F...... 513 878-2780
Cincinnati (G-3768)
Gatesair Inc ....E...... 513 459-3400
Mason (G-13025)
Generic Systems Inc.....................F...... 419 841-8460
Holland (G-11062)
Lync Corp ....E...... 513 655-7286
Cincinnati (G-4041)
Mamsys Consulting Services ....G...... 440 287-6824
Solon (G-17332)
Pearl Tech Corporation ....G...... 614 284-8357
Dublin (G-9119)
Sest Inc ....F...... 440 777-9777
Westlake (G-20307)
Signalysis Inc ....F...... 513 528-6164
Cincinnati (G-4420)
Simple Vms LLC ....G...... 888 255-8918
Cincinnati (G-4421)
Tech Solutions LLC ....G...... 419 852-7190
Celina (G-3020)
Virtual Hold Technology LLC ....D...... 330 666-1181
Akron (G-464)

COMPUTER SOFTWARE SYSTEMS ANALYSIS & DESIGN: Custom

Airwave Communications Cons ....G...... 419 331-1526
Lima (G-11984)
Armada Power LLC ....G...... 614 204-9341
Columbus (G-6772)
Associated Software Cons Inc ....E...... 440 826-1010
Middleburg Heights (G-13902)
Eighty Six Inc ....G...... 800 760-0722
Huber Heights (G-11145)
Empyracom Inc ....E...... 330 744-5570
Canfield (G-2553)
Facts Inc ....E...... 330 928-2332
Cuyahoga Falls (G-7995)
Lockheed Martin Corporation ....G...... 614 418-1930
Columbus (G-7302)
Microstrategy Incorporated ....G...... 513 792-2253
Cincinnati (G-4104)
Nvision Technology Inc ....F...... 412 254-4668
Norton (G-15519)
Online Mega Sellers Corp ....G...... 888 384-6468
Toledo (G-18619)
Quez Media Marketing Inc..............F...... 216 910-0202
Cleveland (G-6077)
Technology Resources Inc ....G...... 419 241-9248
Toledo (G-18716)

COMPUTER SOFTWARE WRITERS

Dwllr Inc...................................G...... 513 400-5544
West Chester (G-19854)
Health Nuts Media LLC ....G...... 818 802-5222
Cleveland (G-5489)
Wentworth Solutions ....F...... 440 212-7696
Brunswick (G-2266)

COMPUTER STORAGE DEVICES, NEC

Capsa Solutions LLC ....D...... 614 864-9966
Canal Winchester (G-2521)

PRODUCT

EMC Corporation ....D...... 614 865-4200
Westerville *(G-20149)*

EMC Corporation ....D...... 513 794-9624
Blue Ash *(G-1783)*

EMC Corporation ....E...... 216 606-2000
Independence *(G-11254)*

Enviroscape EMC ....G...... 419 278-2000
Deshler *(G-8950)*

Expansion Programs Intl ....G...... 216 631-8544
Cleveland *(G-5314)*

Magnext Ltd ....G...... 614 406-4136
Columbus *(G-7314)*

Quantem Fbo Services ....G...... 603 647-6763
Cincinnati *(G-4310)*

Quantum ....G...... 740 328-2548
Newark *(G-15050)*

Quantum Athletics LLC ....G...... 513 248-2966
Terrace Park *(G-18182)*

Quantum Commerce LLC ....G...... 513 777-0737
West Chester *(G-19926)*

Quantum Integration Llc ....G...... 330 609-0355
Cortland *(G-7874)*

Quantum Sails ....G...... 567 283-5335
Sandusky *(G-16998)*

Quantum Technologies Inc ....G...... 330 645-2762
Akron *(G-359)*

Quantum Techonology & Services........G...... 937 642-2929
Marysville *(G-12964)*

Quantum World Technologies ....G...... 937 747-3018
Zanesfield *(G-21262)*

Solsys Inc ....G...... 419 886-4683
Mansfield *(G-12682)*

Teradata Corporation ....B...... 866 548-8348
Miamisburg *(G-13870)*

Tracewell Systems Inc ....D...... 614 846-6175
Lewis Center *(G-11927)*

COMPUTER STORAGE UNITS: Auxiliary

Pinnacle Data Systems Inc ....C...... 614 748-1150
Groveport *(G-10641)*

Service Storage Intl Inc ....G...... 440 951-7579
Willoughby *(G-20594)*

COMPUTER SYSTEM SELLING SVCS

R & L Software LLC ....G...... 513 847-4942
Monroe *(G-14412)*

COMPUTER SYSTEMS ANALYSIS & DESIGN

Honeywell International Inc ....D...... 513 745-7200
Cincinnati *(G-3897)*

COMPUTER TERMINALS

Fivepoint LLC ....F...... 937 374-3193
Xenia *(G-20952)*

Parker-Hannifin Corporation ....D...... 513 831-2340
Milford *(G-14166)*

Pinnacle Data Systems Inc ....C...... 614 748-1150
Groveport *(G-10641)*

Thames Company Ltd ....G...... 614 228-4869
Columbus *(G-7687)*

COMPUTER TERMINALS: CRT

Copier Resources Inc ....G...... 614 268-1100
Columbus *(G-6981)*

COMPUTER TIME-SHARING

Miami Valley Eductl Cmpt Assn ....F...... 937 767-1468
Yellow Springs *(G-20995)*

COMPUTER-AIDED DESIGN SYSTEMS SVCS

Industrial Screen Process ....F...... 419 255-4900
Toledo *(G-18522)*

COMPUTER-AIDED ENGINEERING SYSTEMS SVCS

Sest Inc ....F...... 440 777-9777
Westlake *(G-20307)*

COMPUTER-AIDED SYSTEM SVCS

Engineering Methods Inc ....E...... 513 563-0400
Cincinnati *(G-3706)*

COMPUTERS, NEC

3d Systems Inc ....C...... 215 757-9611
Columbus *(G-6664)*

Analog Bridge Inc ....G...... 937 901-4832
Beavercreek *(G-1317)*

Apple Inc ....G...... 614 478-5592
Columbus *(G-6763)*

Applied Imagination Inc ....G...... 419 352-8373
Bowling Green *(G-1968)*

Ascendtech Inc ....E...... 216 458-1101
Willoughby *(G-20441)*

AT&T Corp ....G...... 513 792-9300
Cincinnati *(G-3423)*

Cardinal Health Tech LLC ....G...... 614 757-5000
Dublin *(G-9059)*

Chaos Matrix Ltd ....G...... 614 638-4748
Oberlin *(G-15636)*

Codonics Inc ....C...... 216 226-1066
Cleveland *(G-5096)*

Computer Zoo Inc ....G...... 937 310-1474
Bellbrook *(G-1504)*

Dapsco ....F...... 937 294-5331
Moraine *(G-14475)*

Davis Laser Products ....G...... 614 252-7711
Columbus *(G-7015)*

Delohio Tech ....F...... 740 816-5628
Delaware *(G-8837)*

Dupont Electronic Polymers LP ....D...... 937 268-3411
Dayton *(G-8314)*

Eaj Services LLC ....F...... 513 792-3400
Blue Ash *(G-1780)*

Falcon Ridge Technologies LLC ....G...... 216 674-1649
Cleveland *(G-5322)*

Freedom Usa Inc ....F...... 216 503-6374
Twinsburg *(G-18937)*

Golubitsky Corporation ....G...... 800 552-4204
Cleveland *(G-5436)*

Hardware Exchange Inc ....G...... 440 449-8006
Solon *(G-17306)*

International Products ....G...... 614 334-1500
Columbus *(G-7206)*

International Products ....F...... 614 850-3000
Hilliard *(G-10954)*

Journey Systems LLC ....F...... 513 831-6200
Milford *(G-14157)*

Kenneth Hickman Co ....F...... 513 348-0016
Batavia *(G-1197)*

Lab Electronics Inc ....G...... 330 674-9818
Millersburg *(G-14238)*

Magnum Computers Inc ....F...... 216 781-1757
Cleveland *(G-5730)*

Mbenztech ....G...... 937 291-1527
Centerville *(G-3044)*

Micro Center Corporation ....G...... 614 326-8500
Columbus *(G-7346)*

Parker-Hannifin Corporation ....D...... 513 831-2340
Milford *(G-14166)*

Sense Labs LLC ....G...... 740 590-0009
Athens *(G-883)*

Site Tech ....G...... 740 522-0019
Heath *(G-10857)*

Smartronix Inc ....F...... 216 378-3300
Northfield *(G-15472)*

Systemax Manufacturing Inc ....G...... 937 368-2300
Dayton *(G-8694)*

Teradata Corporation ....B...... 866 548-8348
Miamisburg *(G-13870)*

Teradata Operations Inc ....G...... 937 866-0032
Miamisburg *(G-13871)*

Teradata Operations Inc ....D...... 937 242-4030
Miamisburg *(G-13872)*

Terra Comp Technology ....G...... 330 745-8912
Barberton *(G-1154)*

Thomas Ross Associates Inc ....G...... 330 723-1110
Medina *(G-13488)*

Tracewell Systems Inc ....D...... 614 846-6175
Lewis Center *(G-11927)*

You52 ....F...... 440 477-7704
Ashtabula *(G-846)*

COMPUTERS, NEC, WHOLESALE

Tech-E-Z LLC ....G...... 419 692-1700
Delphos *(G-8918)*

Thomas Ross Associates Inc ....G...... 330 723-1110
Medina *(G-13488)*

COMPUTERS, PERIPH & SOFTWARE, WHLSE: Personal & Home Entrtn

Clark Associates Inc ....G...... 419 334-3838
Fremont *(G-10138)*

Reynolds and Reynolds Company ....G...... 937 485-4771
Dayton *(G-8629)*

COMPUTERS, PERIPHERALS & SOFTWARE, WHOLESALE: Software

A Graphic Solution ....F...... 216 228-7223
Cleveland *(G-4672)*

Callcopy Inc ....G...... 614 340-3346
Columbus *(G-6890)*

Columbus Advanced Mfg Sftwr ....G...... 614 433-0415
Powell *(G-16467)*

Exact Software North Amer LLC ....C...... 978 539-6186
Dublin *(G-9075)*

Federal Barcode Label Systems ....G...... 440 748-8060
North Ridgeville *(G-15373)*

Investment Systems Company ....G...... 440 247-2865
Chagrin Falls *(G-3061)*

Mitel (delaware) Inc ....E...... 513 733-8000
West Chester *(G-19902)*

T E Hubler Inc ....G...... 419 476-2552
Toledo *(G-18714)*

COMPUTERS: Mini

Oracle America Inc ....F...... 513 381-0125
Blue Ash *(G-1848)*

COMPUTERS: Personal

Eaton Corporation ....B...... 216 523-5000
Cleveland *(G-5245)*

Eaton Corporation ....C...... 216 416-2500
Cleveland *(G-5246)*

HP Inc ....E...... 513 956-4253
Blue Ash *(G-1810)*

CONCENTRATES, DRINK

Belton Foods ....E...... 937 890-7768
Dayton *(G-8184)*

Inter American Products Inc ....E...... 800 645-2233
Cincinnati *(G-3927)*

CONCENTRATES, FLAVORING, EXC DRINK

Givaudan Flavors Corporation ....B...... 513 948-8000
Cincinnati *(G-3828)*

CONCRETE BUILDING PRDTS WHOLESALERS

CMA Supply Company Inc ....F...... 513 942-6663
West Chester *(G-19992)*

Jalco Industries Inc ....F...... 740 286-3808
Jackson *(G-11317)*

Michaels Pre-Cast Con Pdts ....F...... 513 683-1292
Loveland *(G-12374)*

Moritz Materials Inc ....E...... 419 281-0575
Ashland *(G-755)*

Stocker Concrete Company ....F...... 740 254-4626
Gnadenhutten *(G-10411)*

CONCRETE CURING & HARDENING COMPOUNDS

BASF Construction Chem LLC ....E...... 216 831-5500
Cleveland *(G-4895)*

Blackthorn LLC ....F...... 937 836-9296
Clayton *(G-4657)*

Chemmasters Inc ....F...... 440 428-2105
Madison *(G-12501)*

Sika Corporation ....D...... 740 387-9224
Marion *(G-12901)*

Wicktek Inc ....E...... 724 329-8310
Cincinnati *(G-4593)*

CONCRETE PLANTS

McNeilus Truck and Mfg Inc ....E...... 513 874-2022
Fairfield *(G-9683)*

McTech Corp ....F...... 216 391-7700
Cleveland *(G-5773)*

CONCRETE PRDTS

A K Ready Mix LLC ....F 740 286-8900
Jackson (G-11307)

American Spring Wire Corp ....C 216 292-4620
Bedford Heights (G-1478)

B & B Cast Stone Co Inc ....G 740 697-0008
Roseville (G-16726)

Baxter Burial Vault Service ....E 513 641-1010
Cincinnati (G-3440)

Bluffton Precast Concrete Co ....F 419 358-6946
Bluffton (G-1908)

Carruth Studio Inc ....F 419 878-3060
Waterville (G-19653)

Cashen Inc ....G 440 428-1148
Madison (G-12497)

Cement Products Inc ....E 419 524-4342
Mansfield (G-12578)

Cemex Materials LLC ....D 937 268-6706
Dayton (G-8219)

Cemex Materials LLC ....E 937 268-6706
Dayton (G-8220)

Charles Svec Inc ....E 216 662-5200
Maple Heights (G-12730)

Concrete Material Supply LLC ....G 419 261-6404
Woodville (G-20725)

Contech Bridge Solutions LLC ....F 937 878-2170
Dayton (G-8243)

Dalaco Materials LLC ....F 513 893-5483
Liberty Twp (G-11974)

Douglas Industries LLC ....E 740 775-2400
Chillicothe (G-3237)

Everly Concrete Products ....G 740 635-1415
Bridgeport (G-2089)

Fort Loramie Cast Stone Pdts ....G 937 420-2257
Fort Loramie (G-9931)

Forterra Pipe & Precast LLC ....E 937 268-6707
Dayton (G-8348)

Forterra Pipe & Precast LLC ....G 937 268-6707
Dayton (G-8349)

Gallipolis Vault Co Inc ....G 740 446-3357
Gallipolis (G-10297)

Hanson Aggregates East LLC ....E 740 773-2172
Chillicothe (G-3242)

Hanson Concrete Products Ohio ....E 614 443-4846
Columbus (G-7143)

Hazelbaker Industries Ltd ....E 614 276-2631
Columbus (G-7146)

Highland Stone ....G 937 364-2311
Hillsboro (G-11003)

Hilltop Basic Resources Inc ....E 513 621-1500
Cincinnati (G-3885)

Hilltop Stone Llc ....G 513 651-5000
Cincinnati (G-3886)

Huron Cement Products Company ....E 419 433-4161
Huron (G-11224)

Janell Inc ....G 740 532-9111
Ironton (G-11295)

K M B Inc ....E 330 889-3451
Bristolville (G-2098)

Koppers Industries Inc ....E 740 776-3238
Portsmouth (G-16441)

Lang Stone Company Inc ....D 614 235-4099
Columbus (G-7284)

Latorre Concrete Cnstr Inc ....E 614 257-1401
Columbus (G-7288)

Mack Industries PA Inc ....F 330 638-7680
Vienna (G-19369)

Metro Mech Inc ....G 216 641-6262
Cleveland (G-5792)

Michaels Pre-Cast Con Pdts ....F 513 683-1292
Loveland (G-12374)

Millinium 3 Inc ....G 513 770-3122
Mason (G-13064)

North American Cast Stone Inc ....G 440 286-1999
Chardon (G-3169)

O K Brugmann Jr & Sons Inc ....F 330 274-2106
Mantua (G-12718)

Oberfields LLC ....F 614 252-0955
Columbus (G-7410)

Oberfields LLC ....E 614 491-7643
Columbus (G-7409)

Ohio Cast Stone Co LLC ....G 614 524-0666
Ashville (G-852)

Ohio Cast Stone Co LLC ....G 614 444-2278
Columbus (G-7416)

Oldcastle Apg Midwest Inc ....D 440 949-1815
Sheffield Village (G-17128)

Orrville Trucking & Grading Co ....E 330 682-4010
Orrville (G-15753)

Pawnee Maintenance Inc ....D 740 373-6861
Marietta (G-12814)

Premiere Con Solutions LLC ....F 419 737-9808
Pioneer (G-16241)

Prestress Services Inds LLC ....C 859 299-0461
Columbus (G-7516)

R W Sidley Inc ....F 440 224-2664
Kingsville (G-11607)

R W Sidley Incorporated ....E 440 564-2221
Newbury (G-15102)

S & S Aggregates Inc ....G 740 453-0721
Zanesville (G-21349)

Snyder Concrete Products Inc ....E 937 885-5176
Moraine (G-14528)

Spoerr Precast Concrete Inc ....F 419 625-9132
Sandusky (G-17009)

Tri County Concrete Inc ....E 330 425-4464
Twinsburg (G-19029)

Tri-Way Rebar Inc ....G 330 882-8043
Akron (G-447)

William Dauch Concrete Company ....F 419 668-4458
Norwalk (G-15567)

Wilson Concrete Products Inc ....E 937 885-7965
Dayton (G-8759)

Wilsons Country Creations ....F 330 377-4190
Killbuck (G-11602)

Wine Vault Enterprises LLC ....G 614 850-0047
Hilliard (G-10993)

Wysong Concrete Products LLC ....G 513 874-3109
Fairfield (G-9734)

CONCRETE PRDTS, PRECAST, NEC

Aco Polymer Products Inc ....E 440 285-7000
Mentor (G-13508)

Carey Precast Concrete Company ....G 419 396-7142
Carey (G-2915)

Contech Bridge Solutions LLC ....F 513 645-7000
West Chester (G-19838)

Cox Inc ....F 740 858-4400
Lucasville (G-12418)

Donald Schloemer ....G 419 933-2002
Willard (G-20394)

E Pompili & Sons Inc ....E 216 581-8080
Cleveland (G-5233)

Fin Pan Inc ....E 513 870-9200
Hamilton (G-10692)

Jim Bumen Construction Company ....G 740 663-2659
Chillicothe (G-3247)

Mack Industries PA Inc ....D 330 483-3111
Valley City (G-19213)

Mansfield Brick & Supply Co ....G 419 526-1191
Mansfield (G-12641)

McGill Septic Tank Co ....E 330 876-2171
Kinsman (G-11610)

Norwalk Concrete Inds Inc ....E 419 668-8167
Norwalk (G-15554)

Norwalk Concrete Inds Inc ....E 419 668-8167
Norwalk (G-15555)

Oberfields LLC ....D 740 369-7644
Delaware (G-8876)

Oberfields LLC ....E 740 369-7644
Sunbury (G-18069)

Oberfields LLC ....G 937 885-3711
Dayton (G-8538)

Poland Concrete Products Inc ....G 330 757-1241
Poland (G-16384)

Precast Services Inc ....G 614 428-4541
Reynoldsburg (G-16598)

Resco Products Inc ....E 330 372-3716
Warren (G-19594)

Snyder Concrete Products Inc ....F 513 539-7686
Monroe (G-14413)

St Henry Tile Co Inc ....F 937 548-1101
Greenville (G-10523)

USA Precast Concrete Limited ....G 330 854-9600
Canal Fulton (G-2516)

Walden Industries Inc ....E 740 633-5971
Tiltonsville (G-18255)

CONCRETE: Asphaltic, Not From Refineries

H P Streicher Inc ....G 419 841-4715
Toledo (G-18490)

Robert Gorey ....G 330 725-7272
Medina (G-13468)

Shelly Materials Inc ....G 330 673-3646
Kent (G-11527)

Shelly Materials Inc ....D 740 246-6315
Thornville (G-18198)

CONCRETE: Bituminous

Russell Standard Corporation ....G 330 733-9400
Akron (G-389)

Shelly Company ....G 740 474-6255
Circleville (G-4642)

CONCRETE: Dry Mixture

Quikrete Companies Inc ....E 614 885-4406
Columbus (G-7540)

Quikrete Companies Inc ....E 513 367-6135
Harrison (G-10798)

Quikrete Companies Inc ....E 419 241-1148
Toledo (G-18664)

Quikrete Companies Inc ....E 330 296-6080
Ravenna (G-16551)

Smith Concrete Co ....E 740 373-7441
Dover (G-9015)

CONCRETE: Ready-Mixed

ACE Ready Mix Company Inc ....G 330 745-8125
Norton (G-15501)

Ace Ready Mix Concrete Co Inc ....F 330 745-8125
Norton (G-15502)

Adams Brothers Inc ....F 740 819-0323
Zanesville (G-21265)

Alexis Concrete Enterprise Inc ....F 440 366-0031
Elyria (G-9368)

Allega Concrete Corp ....E 216 447-0814
Cleveland (G-4762)

Anderson Concrete Corp ....C 614 443-0123
Columbus (G-6755)

Arrow Coal Grove Inc ....F 740 532-6143
Ironton (G-11289)

ASAP Ready Mix Inc ....G 513 797-1774
Amelia (G-568)

Associated Associates Inc ....E 330 626-3300
Mantua (G-12707)

Avon Concrete Corporation ....G 440 937-6264
Avon (G-984)

Baker-Shindler Contracting Co ....F 419 399-4841
Cecil (G-2979)

Baker-Shindler Contracting Co ....F 419 782-5080
Defiance (G-8780)

Buckeye Ready-Mix ....G 419 294-2389
Upper Sandusky (G-19116)

Buckeye Ready-Mix LLC ....G 740 967-4801
Johnstown (G-11393)

Buckeye Ready-Mix LLC ....G 614 879-6316
West Jefferson (G-20076)

Buckeye Ready-Mix LLC ....F 740 387-8846
Marion (G-12858)

Buckeye Ready-Mix LLC ....E 614 575-2132
Reynoldsburg (G-16583)

Buckeye Ready-Mix LLC ....E 937 642-2951
Marysville (G-12935)

Buckeye Ready-Mix LLC ....F 740 654-4423
Lancaster (G-11693)

C F Poeppelman Inc ....E 937 448-2191
Bradford (G-2025)

Caldwell Lumber & Supply Co ....E 740 732-2306
Caldwell (G-2425)

Caldwell Redi Mix Company ....G 740 732-2906
Caldwell (G-2426)

Caldwell Redi Mix Company ....G 740 685-6554
Byesville (G-2395)

Camden Ready Mix Co ....F 937 456-4539
Camden (G-2484)

Carbros ....F 330 375-5000
Akron (G-110)

Carr Bros Inc ....G 440 232-3700
Bedford (G-1412)

Carr Bros Bldrs Sup & Coal Co ....E 440 232-3700
Cleveland (G-4983)

Castalia Trenching & Ready Mix ....F 419 684-5502
Castalia (G-2973)

Cement Products Inc ....E 419 524-4342
Mansfield (G-12578)

Cemex USA Inc ....F 937 879-8350
Fairborn (G-9617)

Central Ready Mix LLC ....E 513 402-5001
Cincinnati (G-3515)

Central Ready Mix LLC ....E 513 367-1939
Cleves (G-6508)

Central Ready-Mix of Ohio LLC ....E 614 252-3452
Cincinnati (G-3516)

Central Ready-Mix Ohio LLC ....E 614 252-3452
Cincinnati (G-3517)

Chappell-Zimmerman Inc ....E 330 337-8711
Salem (G-16880)

P
R
O
D
U
C
T

Christman Supply Co Inc	G	740 472-0046
Woodsfield (G-20715)		
Citywide Materials Inc	E	513 533-1111
Cincinnati (G-3581)		
Consumeracq Inc	F	440 277-9305
Lorain (G-12239)		
Consumers Builders Supply Co	E	440 277-9306
Lorain (G-12240)		
Cremeans Concrete and Sup Co	G	740 446-1142
Gallipolis (G-10293)		
D W Dickey and Son Inc	E	330 424-1441
Lisbon (G-12119)		
Dan K Williams Inc	E	419 893-3251
Maumee (G-13236)		
Dan Shrock Cement	G	440 548-2498
Parkman (G-15951)		
Dearth Resources Inc	G	937 325-0651
Springfield (G-17539)		
Dearth Resources Inc	G	937 663-4171
Springfield (G-17540)		
Diano Construction and Sup Co	E	330 456-7229
Canton (G-2687)		
Diversified Ready Mix Ltd	G	330 628-3355
Tallmadge (G-18142)		
Eci	G	419 483-2738
Castalia (G-2974)		
Ernst Enterprises Inc	F	937 878-9378
Fairborn (G-9620)		
Ernst Enterprises Inc	E	937 233-5555
Dayton (G-8331)		
Ernst Enterprises Inc	E	513 874-8300
Lebanon (G-11798)		
Ernst Enterprises Inc	E	937 848-6811
Bellbrook (G-1507)		
Ernst Enterprises Inc	E	937 866-9441
Carrollton (G-2955)		
Ernst Enterprises Inc	E	937 339-6249
Troy (G-18822)		
Ernst Enterprises Inc	E	614 443-9456
Columbus (G-7065)		
Feikert Sand & Gravel Co Inc	E	330 674-0038
Millersburg (G-14215)		
G Big Inc	E	740 867-5758
Chesapeake (G-3187)		
G Big Inc	G	740 532-9123
Ironton (G-11293)		
Geauga Concrete Inc	F	440 338-4915
Newbury (G-15091)		
Grafton Ready Mix Concret Inc	E	440 926-2911
Grafton (G-10427)		
Hanson Aggregates East LLC	E	740 773-2172
Chillicothe (G-3242)		
Hanson Aggregates East LLC	E	937 364-2311
Hillsboro (G-10999)		
Hanson Aggregates East LLC	F	937 382-2557
Wilmington (G-20668)		
Hanson Aggregates East LLC	E	937 587-2671
Peebles (G-16021)		
Hensel Ready Mix	G	419 253-9200
Marengo (G-12751)		
Hensel Ready Mix Inc	F	419 675-1808
Kenton (G-11550)		
Hilltop Basic Resources Inc	E	937 878-8631
Fairborn (G-9624)		
Hilltop Basic Resources Inc	E	513 621-1500
Cincinnati (G-3885)		
Hilltop Basic Resources Inc	F	513 651-5000
Cincinnati (G-3884)		
Hocking Valley Concrete Inc	F	740 385-2165
Logan (G-12177)		
Hocking Valley Concrete Inc	F	740 385-2165
Logan (G-12178)		
Hull Builders Supply Inc	E	440 967-3159
Vermilion (G-19328)		
Hull Ready Mix Concrete Inc	F	419 625-8070
Sandusky (G-16972)		
Huron Cement Products Company	E	419 433-4161
Huron (G-11224)		
Huth Ready Mix & Supply Co	F	330 833-4191
Massillon (G-13152)		
IMI-Irving Materials Inc	E	513 844-8444
Hamilton (G-10704)		
In The Mix Dj Service	G	330 704-2833
North Canton (G-15242)		
Ioppolo Concrete Corporation	E	440 439-6606
Bedford (G-1433)		
Irving Materials Inc	E	513 844-8444
Hamilton (G-10708)		
Irving Materials Inc	F	513 523-7127
Oxford (G-15838)		

Joe McClelland Inc	E	740 452-3036
Zanesville (G-21324)		
K & L Ready Mix Inc	F	419 523-4376
Ottawa (G-15798)		
K & L Ready Mix Inc	F	419 532-3585
Kalida (G-11413)		
K & L Ready Mix Inc	F	419 293-2937
Mc Comb (G-13339)		
K M B Inc	E	330 889-3451
Bristolville (G-2098)		
Kuhlman Corporation	E	419 321-1670
Toledo (G-18548)		
Kuhlman Corporation	F	419 897-6000
Maumee (G-13273)		
Lancaster West Side Coal Co	F	740 862-4713
Lancaster (G-11725)		
M & R Redi Mix Inc	E	419 445-7771
Pettisville (G-16181)		
M & R Redi Mix Inc	G	419 748-8442
Mc Clure (G-13335)		
Mack Concrete Industries Inc	F	330 483-3111
Valley City (G-19212)		
Mack Concrete Industries Inc	E	330 784-7008
Akron (G-279)		
Market Ready	E	513 289-9231
Maineville (G-12528)		
Marvin Mix	G	614 774-9337
Columbus (G-7322)		
Maysville Ready Mix Concr	G	937 795-2020
Aberdeen (G-2)		
McGovney Ready Mix Inc	E	740 353-4111
Portsmouth (G-16443)		
Mecco Inc	E	513 422-3651
Middletown (G-14061)		
Medina Supply Company	E	330 425-0752
Twinsburg (G-18984)		
Medina Supply Company	E	330 723-3681
Medina (G-13445)		
Mel Stevens U-Cart Concrete	G	419 478-2600
Toledo (G-18582)		
Miami Valley Ready Mix Inc	E	513 738-2616
Harrison (G-10791)		
Mini-Mix Inc	E	740 345-3186
Newark (G-15034)		
Moritz Concrete Inc	E	419 529-3232
Mansfield (G-12652)		
Moritz Materials Inc	E	419 281-0575
Ashland (G-755)		
Nalcon Ready Mix Inc	G	419 422-4341
Kenton (G-11562)		
National Lime and Stone Co	E	419 423-3400
Findlay (G-9866)		
National Lime and Stone Co	G	330 339-2144
New Philadelphia (G-14918)		
National Lime and Stone Co	G	216 883-9840
Cleveland (G-5857)		
Nissen Lumber & Coal Co Inc	E	419 836-8035
Oregon (G-15711)		
O K Brugmann Jr & Sons Inc	F	330 274-2106
Mantua (G-12718)		
Olen Corporation	F	419 294-2611
Upper Sandusky (G-19137)		
Orrville Trucking & Grading Co	E	330 682-4010
Orrville (G-15753)		
Osborne Inc	E	440 942-7000
Mentor (G-13677)		
Osborne Inc	E	216 771-0010
Cleveland (G-5949)		
Pahl Ready Mix Concrete Inc	E	419 636-4238
Bryan (G-2317)		
Pahl Ready Mix Concrete Inc	F	419 636-4238
Waterville (G-19664)		
Palmer Bros Transit Mix Con	F	419 332-6363
Fremont (G-10174)		
Palmer Bros Transit Mix Con	F	419 352-4681
Bowling Green (G-2006)		
Palmer Bros Transit Mix Con	G	419 447-2018
Tiffin (G-18237)		
Palmer Bros Transit Mix Con	F	419 686-2366
Portage (G-16427)		
Paul R Lipp & Son Inc	F	330 227-9614
Rogers (G-16714)		
Petros Concrete Inc	G	330 868-6130
Waynesburg (G-19727)		
Philip Armbrust	G	740 335-7285
Wshngtn CT Hs (G-20919)		
Phillips Companies	E	937 426-5461
Beavercreek Township (G-1387)		
Phillips Ready Mix Co	D	937 426-5151
Beavercreek Township (G-1388)		

Piqua Concrete Corp	E	937 773-0841
Piqua (G-16302)		
Piqua Concrete Corp	F	937 698-7229
Vandalia (G-19309)		
Piqua Concrete Corp	G	937 855-0410
Germantown (G-10372)		
Placecrete Inc	F	937 298-2121
Moraine (G-14515)		
Pleasant Valley Ready Mix Inc	F	330 852-2613
Sugarcreek (G-18032)		
Quadcast	G	330 854-4511
Canal Fulton (G-2511)		
Quality Block & Supply Inc	E	330 364-4411
Mount Eaton (G-14556)		
Quality Ready Mix Inc	E	419 738-2817
Bluffton (G-1914)		
Quality Ready Mix Inc	G	419 394-9097
Saint Marys (G-16851)		
Quality Ready Mix Inc	F	419 394-8870
Saint Marys (G-16852)		
Quikrete Companies Inc	E	513 367-6135
Harrison (G-10798)		
Quikrete Companies Inc	E	330 296-6080
Ravenna (G-16551)		
R W Sidley Incorporated	E	440 564-2221
Newbury (G-15102)		
R W Sidley Incorporated	F	330 499-5616
Canton (G-2834)		
R W Sidley Incorporated	E	330 793-7374
Youngstown (G-21184)		
Rinker Materials	G	330 654-2511
Diamond (G-8959)		
Rockport Cnstr & Mtls Inc	E	216 432-9465
Cleveland (G-6126)		
Ross Co Redi Mix Co Inc	G	740 333-6833
Wshngtn CT Hs (G-20926)		
Ross-Co Redi-Mix Co Inc	F	740 775-4466
Chillicothe (G-3273)		
Rw Sidley Inc	G	330 545-1964
Girard (G-10394)		
S J Roth Enterprises Inc	E	513 242-8400
Cincinnati (G-4373)		
Sakrete Inc	E	513 242-3644
Cincinnati (G-4377)		
Sardinia Concrete Company	E	513 248-0090
Milford (G-14172)		
Sardinia Concrete Company	F	513 248-0090
Lebanon (G-11836)		
Sardinia Ready Mix Inc	G	937 446-2523
Sardinia (G-17031)		
Sardinia Ready Mix Inc	F	937 446-2523
Sardinia (G-17032)		
Schwab Industries Inc	F	330 364-4411
Dover (G-9013)		
Scioto Ready Mix LLC	D	740 924-9273
Pataskala (G-15983)		
Scioto Readymix Co	G	614 491-0773
Columbus (G-7601)		
Scsrm Concrete Company Ltd	E	937 533-1001
Sidney (G-17223)		
Shelly Company	G	740 246-6315
Thornville (G-18196)		
Smith Concrete Inc	E	740 373-7441
Dover (G-9015)		
Spurlino Materials LLC	E	513 705-0111
Middletown (G-14084)		
Spurlino Materials LLC	G	513 202-1111
Cleves (G-6527)		
St Henry Tile Co Inc	E	419 678-4841
Saint Henry (G-16822)		
Stamm Contracting Co Inc	E	330 274-8230
Mantua (G-12723)		
Stark Ready Mix & Supply Co	E	330 580-4307
Canton (G-2857)		
Stocker Concrete Company	F	740 254-4626
Gnadenhutten (G-10411)		
T C Redi Mix Youngstown Inc	E	330 755-2143
Youngstown (G-21217)		
Tech Ready Mix Inc	E	216 361-5000
Cleveland (G-6299)		
Terminal Ready-Mix Inc	E	440 288-0181
Lorain (G-12286)		
Tow Path Ready Mix	F	740 286-2131
Jackson (G-11331)		
Tow Path Ready Mix	G	740 259-3222
Lucasville (G-12425)		
Tri County Concrete Inc	E	330 425-4464
Twinsburg (G-19029)		
Tri County Concrete Inc	F	330 425-4464
Cleveland (G-6357)		

(G-0000) Company's Geographic Section entry number

Twin Cities Concrete Co ....F 330 343-4491
Dover *(G-9021)*

Twin Cities Concrete Co ....G 330 627-2158
Carrollton *(G-2968)*

United Ready Mix Inc ....E 216 696-1600
Cleveland *(G-6387)*

W G Lockhart Construction Co ....D 330 745-6520
Akron *(G-466)*

W M Dauch Concrete Inc ....G 419 562-6917
Bucyrus *(G-2364)*

Warren Concrete and Supply Co ....F 330 393-1581
Warren *(G-19620)*

Wells Group LLC ....F 740 532-9240
Ironton *(G-11304)*

Westview Concrete Corp ....E 440 458-5800
Elyria *(G-9510)*

William Dauch Concrete Company ....F 419 668-4458
Norwalk *(G-15567)*

William Oeder Ready Mix Inc ....E 513 899-3901
Martinsville *(G-12930)*

Williams Concrete Inc ....F 419 893-3251
Maumee *(G-13309)*

Winters Products Inc ....F 740 286-4149
Jackson *(G-11334)*

CONDENSERS & CONDENSING UNITS: Air Conditioner

Cleveland Smacna ....G 440 877-3500
Cleveland *(G-5078)*

CONDENSERS: Heat Transfer Eqpt, Evaporative

Hydro-Dyne Inc ....E 330 832-5076
Massillon *(G-13153)*

Lfg Specialties LLC ....E 419 424-4999
Findlay *(G-9852)*

CONDENSERS: Refrigeration

Emerson Climate Tech Inc ....C 937 498-3011
Sidney *(G-17187)*

Emerson Climate Tech Inc ....E 937 498-3587
Sidney *(G-17188)*

CONDUITS & FITTINGS: Electric

Allied Tube & Conduit Corp ....F 740 928-1018
Hebron *(G-10860)*

Emco Electric International ....G 440 878-1199
Strongsville *(G-17917)*

M & W Electric Mfg Co LLC ....G 330 332-9553
Salem *(G-16911)*

Madison Electric Products Inc ....E 216 391-7776
Bedford Heights *(G-1488)*

Saylor Products Corporation ....F 419 832-2125
Grand Rapids *(G-10445)*

United Fiberglass America Inc ....F 937 325-7305
Springfield *(G-17670)*

CONES, PYROMETRIC: Earthenware

Edward Orton Jr Crmic Fndation ....E 614 895-2663
Westerville *(G-20148)*

Orton Edward Jr Crmic Fndation ....E 614 895-2663
Westerville *(G-20176)*

CONFECTIONS & CANDY

Anthony-Thomas Candy Company ....C 614 274-8405
Columbus *(G-6759)*

Anthony-Thomas Candy Company ....G 614 870-8899
Columbus *(G-6760)*

Arnolds Candies Inc ....G 330 733-4022
Akron *(G-73)*

Becky Knapp ....G 330 854-4400
Canal Fulton *(G-2498)*

Buckeye Chocolate Co ....F 440 564-8086
Middlefield *(G-13919)*

Celebrations ....G 419 381-8088
Toledo *(G-18391)*

Chocolate Pig Inc ....G 440 461-4511
Cleveland *(G-5029)*

Christies Candies & Mints ....G 419 382-7313
Toledo *(G-18397)*

Cincinnatti Premier Candy LLC ....E 513 253-0079
Cincinnati *(G-3571)*

Coffelt Candy Inc ....G 937 399-8772
Springfield *(G-17533)*

Coons Homemade Candies ....G 740 496-4141
Harpster *(G-10765)*

Doschers Candies Inc ....F 513 381-8656
Cincinnati *(G-3666)*

E R B Enterprises Inc ....G 740 948-9174
Jeffersonville *(G-11379)*

Ervan Guttman Co ....G 513 791-0767
Cincinnati *(G-3718)*

Fawn Confectionery ....F 513 574-9612
Cincinnati *(G-3742)*

Giannios Candy Co Inc ....E 330 755-7000
Struthers *(G-17991)*

Gibson Bros Inc ....E 440 774-2401
Oberlin *(G-15641)*

Graeters Manufacturing Co ....E 513 721-3323
Cincinnati *(G-3843)*

Hake Head LLC ....E 614 291-2244
Columbus *(G-7138)*

Kevin G Ryba Inc ....G 419 627-2010
Huron *(G-11230)*

Light Vision ....E 513 351-9444
Cincinnati *(G-4023)*

Malleys Candies Inc ....E 216 529-6262
Cleveland *(G-5736)*

Marshas Buckeyes LLC ....E 419 872-7666
Perrysburg *(G-16120)*

McJak Candy Company LLC ....E 330 722-3531
Medina *(G-13441)*

Milk & Honey ....F 330 492-5884
Canton *(G-2782)*

Nestle R&D Center Inc ....E 440 349-5757
Solon *(G-17346)*

Neumeisters Candy Shoppe LLC ....E 419 294-3647
Upper Sandusky *(G-19135)*

Normant Candy Co ....E 419 886-4214
Mansfield *(G-12659)*

Piqua Chocolate Company Inc ....G 937 773-1981
Piqua *(G-16301)*

Popped ....F 330 678-1893
Kent *(G-11504)*

Richards Maple Products Inc ....G 440 286-4160
Chardon *(G-3176)*

Sweet Melissas ....G 440 333-6357
Rocky River *(G-16712)*

Temos Inc ....G 330 376-7229
Akron *(G-432)*

Wittichs Candies Inc ....G 740 474-3313
Circleville *(G-4649)*

CONNECTORS & TERMINALS: Electrical Device Uses

Alcon Inc ....E 513 722-1037
Loveland *(G-12337)*

Brumall Mfg Coroporation ....E 440 974-2622
Mentor *(G-13538)*

Connectronics Corp ....D 419 537-0020
Toledo *(G-18410)*

Hermetic Seal Technology Inc ....F 513 851-4899
Cincinnati *(G-3880)*

T & S Enterprises ....E 419 424-1122
Findlay *(G-9899)*

CONNECTORS: Cord, Electric

Tip Products Inc ....E 216 252-2535
Cleveland *(G-6326)*

CONNECTORS: Electrical

Bardes Corporation ....B 513 533-6200
Cincinnati *(G-3436)*

Connector Manufacturing Co ....C 513 860-4455
Hamilton *(G-10681)*

Cooper Interconnect Inc ....G 800 386-1911
Cleveland *(G-5130)*

Ericson Manufacturing Co ....D 440 951-8000
Willoughby *(G-20480)*

Newact Inc ....F 513 321-5177
Batavia *(G-1213)*

Ohio Associated Entps LLC ....C 440 354-3148
Painesville *(G-15907)*

P C Power Inc ....G 440 779-4080
North Olmsted *(G-15342)*

CONNECTORS: Electronic

Ankim Enterprises Incorporated ....E 937 599-1121
Bellefontaine *(G-1518)*

Astro Industries Inc ....E 937 429-5900
Beavercreek *(G-1319)*

Aviation Technologies Inc ....G 216 706-2960
Cleveland *(G-4872)*

Canadus Power Systems LLC ....F 216 831-6600
Twinsburg *(G-18907)*

Canfield Industries Inc ....G 800 554-5071
Youngstown *(G-21042)*

Connective Design Incorporated ....F 937 746-8252
Miamisburg *(G-13793)*

Connectors Unlimited Inc ....E 440 357-1161
Painesville *(G-15868)*

Connectronics Corp ....D 419 537-0020
Toledo *(G-18410)*

Cooper Interconnect Inc ....G 800 386-1911
Cleveland *(G-5130)*

D C M Industries Inc ....G 937 254-8500
Dayton *(G-8264)*

HCC/Sealtron ....E 513 733-8400
Cincinnati *(G-3873)*

Lastar Inc ....G 937 224-0639
Moraine *(G-14502)*

Mueller Electric Company Inc ....E 614 888-8855
New Albany *(G-14765)*

Ohio Associated Entps LLC ....E 440 354-2106
Painesville *(G-15906)*

Ohio Associated Entps LLC ....E 440 354-3148
Painesville *(G-15908)*

Plcc2 LLC ....G 614 279-1796
Columbus *(G-7499)*

Powell Electrical Systems Inc ....D 330 966-1750
Canton *(G-2816)*

Servo Systems Inc ....G 440 779-2780
North Olmsted *(G-15345)*

Spi Inc ....G 937 374-2700
Xenia *(G-20973)*

Superb Industries Inc ....D 330 852-0500
Sugarcreek *(G-18045)*

U S Terminals Inc ....G 513 561-8145
Cincinnati *(G-4534)*

Xponet Inc ....G 440 354-6617
Painesville *(G-15943)*

CONNECTORS: Power, Electric

Nolan Manufacturing LLC ....G 614 859-2302
Westerville *(G-20173)*

CONSTRUCTION & MINING MACHINERY WHOLESALERS

Advanced Specialty Products ....D 419 882-6528
Bowling Green *(G-1966)*

Columbus Pipe and Equipment Co ....F 614 444-7871
Columbus *(G-6962)*

Dayton Tractor & Crane ....G 937 317-5014
Xenia *(G-20946)*

Great Lakes Power Service Co ....F 440 259-0025
Perry *(G-16050)*

JD Power Systems LLC ....F 614 317-9394
Hilliard *(G-10955)*

Koenig Equipment Inc ....F 937 653-5281
Urbana *(G-19167)*

La Mfg Inc ....E 513 577-7200
Cincinnati *(G-4009)*

Mesa Industries Inc ....E 513 321-2950
Cincinnati *(G-4087)*

Murphy Tractor & Eqp Co Inc ....G 614 876-1141
Columbus *(G-7374)*

Murphy Tractor & Eqp Co Inc ....G 937 898-4198
Vandalia *(G-19306)*

Murphy Tractor & Eqp Co Inc ....G 419 221-3666
Lima *(G-12061)*

Murphy Tractor & Eqp Co Inc ....G 330 477-9304
Canton *(G-2785)*

Murphy Tractor & Eqp Co Inc ....G 330 220-4999
Brunswick *(G-2238)*

Npk Construction Equipment Inc ....D 440 232-7900
Bedford *(G-1449)*

Shearer Farm Inc ....E 330 345-9023
Wooster *(G-20834)*

Simpson Strong-Tie Company Inc ....C 614 876-8060
Columbus *(G-7624)*

West Equipment Company Inc ....F 419 698-1601
Toledo *(G-18772)*

CONSTRUCTION EQPT REPAIR SVCS

Mine Equipment Services LLC ....E 740 936-5427
Sunbury *(G-18067)*

Morris Material Handling Inc ....G 937 525-5520
Springfield *(G-17608)*

West Equipment Company Inc ....F 419 698-1601
Toledo *(G-18772)*

Employee Codes: A=Over 500 employees, B=251-500
C=101-250, D=51-100, E=20-50, F=10-19, G=3-9

2017 Harris Ohio
Industrial Directory

1449

PRODUCT

CONSTRUCTION EQPT: Airport

Brewpro Inc ....G..... 513 577-7200
Cincinnati (G-3472)

CONSTRUCTION EQPT: Attachments

Aim Attachments ....E..... 614 539-3030
Grove City (G-10540)

Jrb Attachments LLC.....................G..... 330 734-3000
Akron (G-243)

New River Equipment Corp.............G..... 330 669-0040
North Canton (G-15255)

CONSTRUCTION EQPT: Attachments, Snow Plow

H Y O Inc.......................................F..... 614 488-2861
Columbus (G-7136)

CONSTRUCTION EQPT: Backhoes, Tractors, Cranes & Similar Eqpt

Mazzella Lifting Tech Inc ....D..... 440 239-5700
Cleveland (G-5766)

CONSTRUCTION EQPT: Blade, Grader, Scraper, Dozer/Snow Plow

ARM Opco Inc ....E..... 330 868-7724
Canton (G-2605)

Bucyrus Blades Inc........................D..... 419 562-6015
Bucyrus (G-2332)

Jennmar McSweeney LLC...............C..... 740 377-3354
South Point (G-17439)

CONSTRUCTION EQPT: Buckets, Excavating, Clamshell, Etc

D & L Excavating Ltd ....G..... 419 271-0635
Port Clinton (G-16398)

Werk-Brau Company ....D..... 419 422-2912
Findlay (G-9907)

CONSTRUCTION EQPT: Crane Carriers

Rnm Holdings Inc ....E..... 937 704-9900
Franklin (G-10050)

CONSTRUCTION EQPT: Cranes

Terex Utilities Inc ....D..... 513 539-9770
Monroe (G-14416)

CONSTRUCTION EQPT: Crushers, Portable

Toku America Inc ....F..... 440 954-9923
Willoughby (G-20618)

CONSTRUCTION EQPT: Entrenching Machines

M S K Partnership..........................G..... 419 394-4444
Celina (G-3005)

CONSTRUCTION EQPT: Grinders, Stone, Portable

Ryman Grinders Inc.......................F..... 330 652-5080
Niles (G-15183)

CONSTRUCTION EQPT: Roofing Eqpt

Dimensional Metals Inc ....D..... 740 927-3633
Reynoldsburg (G-16586)

JC Roofing Supply..........................G..... 937 258-9999
Dayton (G-8424)

Stony Point Metals LLC..................G..... 330 852-7100
Sugarcreek (G-18041)

CONSTRUCTION EQPT: Tunneling

Barbco Inc ....E..... 330 488-9400
East Canton (G-9190)

Robbins Company ....C..... 440 248-3303
Solon (G-17370)

Turn-Key Tunneling Inc ....E..... 614 275-4832
Columbus (G-7715)

CONSTRUCTION MATERIALS, WHOL: Concrete/Cinder Bldg Prdts

Encore Precast LLC........................F..... 513 726-5678
Seven Mile (G-17065)

O K Brugmann Jr & Sons Inc............F..... 330 274-2106
Mantua (G-12718)

Piqua Concrete Corp ....G..... 937 855-0410
Germantown (G-10372)

CONSTRUCTION MATERIALS, WHOLESALE: Architectural Metalwork

Charles Mfg Co...............................F..... 330 395-3490
Warren (G-19534)

CONSTRUCTION MATERIALS, WHOLESALE: Block, Concrete & Cinder

Basetek LLC ....G..... 877 712-2273
Dayton (G-8182)

Basetek LLC ....F..... 877 712-2273
Middlefield (G-13916)

Quality Block & Supply Inc ....E..... 330 364-4411
Mount Eaton (G-14556)

Schwab Industries Inc....................F..... 330 364-4411
Dover (G-9013)

CONSTRUCTION MATERIALS, WHOLESALE: Brick, Exc Refractory

Mansfield Brick & Supply Co ....G..... 419 526-1191
Mansfield (G-12641)

Snyder Concrete Products Inc ....E..... 937 885-5176
Moraine (G-14528)

Snyder Concrete Products Inc ....G..... 937 224-1433
Dayton (G-8661)

CONSTRUCTION MATERIALS, WHOLESALE: Building Stone

Lang Stone Company Inc.................D..... 614 235-4099
Columbus (G-7284)

CONSTRUCTION MATERIALS, WHOLESALE: Building Stone, Granite

Mayfair Granite Co Inc ....G..... 216 382-8150
Cleveland (G-5763)

Piqua Granite & Marble Co Inc ....G..... 937 773-2000
Piqua (G-16304)

CONSTRUCTION MATERIALS, WHOLESALE: Building Stone, Marble

Castelli Marble Inc ....G..... 216 361-2410
Cleveland (G-4993)

Helmart Company Inc ....G..... 513 941-3095
Cincinnati (G-3876)

CONSTRUCTION MATERIALS, WHOLESALE: Building, Exterior

Christman Supply Co Inc ....G..... 740 472-0046
Woodsfield (G-20715)

Francis-Schulze Co.........................E..... 937 295-3941
Russia (G-16764)

Orrville Trucking & Grading Co ....E..... 330 682-4010
Orrville (G-15753)

Style Crest Inc ....B..... 419 332-7369
Fremont (G-10184)

CONSTRUCTION MATERIALS, WHOLESALE: Building, Interior

Youngstown Curve Form Inc ....F..... 330 744-3028
Youngstown (G-21250)

CONSTRUCTION MATERIALS, WHOLESALE: Ceiling Systems & Prdts

Eger Products Inc ....D..... 513 753-4200
Amelia (G-575)

CONSTRUCTION MATERIALS, WHOLESALE: Cement

Essroc Cement Corp ....G..... 614 497-2001
Columbus (G-7067)

Huron Cement Products Company ....E..... 419 433-4161
Huron (G-11224)

CONSTRUCTION MATERIALS, WHOLESALE: Door Frames

Provia Door Inc ....C..... 330 852-4711
Sugarcreek (G-18034)

CONSTRUCTION MATERIALS, WHOLESALE: Doors, Garage

Alumo Extrusions & Mfr Company.......E..... 330 779-3333
Youngstown (G-21021)

CONSTRUCTION MATERIALS, WHOLESALE: Doors, Sliding

Alumo Extrusions & Mfr Company.......E..... 330 779-3333
Youngstown (G-21021)

CONSTRUCTION MATERIALS, WHOLESALE: Drywall Materials

Kcg Inc ....G..... 614 238-9450
Columbus (G-7252)

CONSTRUCTION MATERIALS, WHOLESALE: Glass

A Service Glass Inc.........................F..... 937 426-4920
Beavercreek (G-1315)

Dale Kestler ....G..... 513 871-9000
Cincinnati (G-3637)

Global Glass Block Inc ....G..... 216 731-2333
Euclid (G-9581)

Machined Glass Specialist Inc ....F..... 937 743-6166
Springboro (G-17489)

CONSTRUCTION MATERIALS, WHOLESALE: Gravel

Hilltop Basic Resources Inc.............F..... 937 859-3616
Miamisburg (G-13817)

CONSTRUCTION MATERIALS, WHOLESALE: Joists

Marysville Steel Inc........................E..... 937 642-5971
Marysville (G-12959)

CONSTRUCTION MATERIALS, WHOLESALE: Limestone

Hanson Aggregates Midwest Inc...........G..... 419 399-4846
Paulding (G-16004)

Hull Builders Supply Inc..................E..... 440 967-3159
Vermilion (G-19328)

Pinney Dock & Transport LLC ....E..... 440 964-7186
Ashtabula (G-832)

CONSTRUCTION MATERIALS, WHOLESALE: Masons' Materials

Koltcz Concrete Block Co.................E..... 440 232-3630
Bedford (G-1437)

CONSTRUCTION MATERIALS, WHOLESALE: Millwork

Bwd Woodwork LLC........................G..... 740 335-9766
Wshngtn CT Hs (G-20903)

CONSTRUCTION MATERIALS, WHOLESALE: Molding, All Materials

A & B Wood Design Assoc Inc ....G..... 330 721-2789
Wadsworth (G-19385)

Toledo Molding & Die Inc ....D..... 419 692-6022
Delphos (G-8920)

CONSTRUCTION MATERIALS, WHOLESALE: Pallets, Wood

Mulch World ....G..... 419 873-6852
Perrysburg (G-16123)

Universal Pallets Inc ....E..... 614 444-1095
Columbus (G-7725)

CONSTRUCTION MATERIALS, WHOLESALE: Particleboard

Litco International Inc ....E 330 539-5433
Vienna (G-19368)

CONSTRUCTION MATERIALS, WHOLESALE: Paving Materials

Erie Materials Inc ....G 419 483-4648
Castalia (G-2975)

CONSTRUCTION MATERIALS, WHOLESALE: Prefabricated Structures

Morton Buildings Inc ....F 330 345-6188
Wooster (G-20812)
Morton Buildings Inc ....D 419 675-2311
Kenton (G-11561)
Patio Enclosures ....F 513 733-4646
Cincinnati (G-4213)
Will-Burt Company ....B 330 682-7015
Orrville (G-15770)
Will-Burt Company ....E 330 682-7015
Orrville (G-15772)

CONSTRUCTION MATERIALS, WHOLESALE: Roof, Asphalt/Sheet Metal

Modern Builders Supply Inc ....F 419 526-0002
Mansfield (G-12651)

CONSTRUCTION MATERIALS, WHOLESALE: Roofing & Siding Material

Associated Materials LLC ....B 330 929-1811
Cuyahoga Falls (G-7971)
Associated Mtls Holdings LLC ....A 330 929-1811
Cuyahoga Falls (G-7972)
Homeguard Products Inc ....G 616 846-0804
Baltimore (G-1083)
Midwest Industrial Products ....G 216 771-8555
Cleveland (G-5810)

CONSTRUCTION MATERIALS, WHOLESALE: Sand

Acme Company ....D 330 758-2313
Poland (G-16381)
Allied Corporation Inc ....G 330 425-7861
Twinsburg (G-18898)
Phoenix Asphalt Company Inc ....G 330 339-4935
Magnolia (G-12518)

CONSTRUCTION MATERIALS, WHOLESALE: Septic Tanks

Allen Enterprises Inc ....G 740 532-5913
Ironton (G-11288)
Green Forward Technologies LLC ....G 513 607-9639
Cincinnati (G-3848)

CONSTRUCTION MATERIALS, WHOLESALE: Sewer Pipe, Clay

Sewer Rodding Equipment Co ....E 419 991-2065
Lima (G-12089)

CONSTRUCTION MATERIALS, WHOLESALE: Siding, Exc Wood

O A R Vinyl Windows & Siding ....G 440 636-5573
Middlefield (G-13978)
Stony Point Metals LLC ....G 330 852-7100
Sugarcreek (G-18041)
Vinyl Design Corporation ....E 419 283-4009
Holland (G-11095)

CONSTRUCTION MATERIALS, WHOLESALE: Stone, Crushed Or Broken

Canton Cut Stone Co ....G 330 456-8408
North Canton (G-15223)
Olen Corporation ....F 419 294-2611
Upper Sandusky (G-19137)
Palmer Bros Transit Mix Con ....F 419 686-2366
Portage (G-16427)
Ridge Township Stone Quarry ....G 419 968-2222
Van Wert (G-19269)

Sharon Stone Co ....G 740 374-3236
Dexter City (G-8957)
Stoneco Inc ....F 419 893-7645
Maumee (G-13298)

CONSTRUCTION MATERIALS, WHOLESALE: Tile & Clay Prdts

Hess & Gault Lumber Co ....G 419 281-3105
Ashland (G-739)

CONSTRUCTION MATERIALS, WHOLESALE: Tile, Clay/Other Ceramic

Ohio Tile & Marble Co ....E 513 541-4211
Cincinnati (G-4180)

CONSTRUCTION MATERIALS, WHOLESALE: Trim, Sheet Metal

Dublin Millwork Co Inc ....E 614 889-7776
Dublin (G-9069)

CONSTRUCTION MATERIALS, WHOLESALE: Windows

Associated Materials LLC ....B 330 929-1811
Cuyahoga Falls (G-7971)
Associated Mtls Holdings LLC ....A 330 929-1811
Cuyahoga Falls (G-7972)

CONSTRUCTION MATL, WHOLESALE: Structural Assy, Prefab, Wood

Custom Sink Top Mfg ....F 440 245-6220
Lorain (G-12242)

CONSTRUCTION MATLS, WHOL: Composite Board Prdts, Woodboard

BAC Technologies Ltd ....G 937 465-2228
West Liberty (G-20091)

CONSTRUCTION MATLS, WHOL: Doors, Combination, Screen-Storm

Otter Group LLC ....F 937 315-1199
Dayton (G-8554)

CONSTRUCTION MATLS, WHOL: Lumber, Rough, Dressed/Finished

Appalachia Wood Inc ....F 740 596-2551
Mc Arthur (G-13328)
Baillie Lumber Co LP ....E 419 462-2000
Galion (G-10254)
Berea Hardwood Co Inc ....G 216 898-8956
Cleveland (G-4904)
Cabot Lumber Inc ....G 740 545-7109
West Lafayette (G-20085)
Clarksville Stave & Lumber Co ....G 937 376-4618
Xenia (G-20944)
Gross Lumber Inc ....E 330 683-2055
Apple Creek (G-638)
Hartzell Hardwoods Inc ....D 937 773-7054
Piqua (G-16272)
Khempco Bldg Sup Co Ltd Partnr ....D 740 549-0465
Delaware (G-8865)
Premier Construction Company ....E 513 874-2611
Fairfield (G-9704)
Salt Creek Lumber Company Inc ....G 330 695-3500
Fredericksburg (G-10093)
Stephen M Trudick ....E 440 834-1891
Burton (G-2385)
Three H Lumber ....G 740 473-2515
Newport (G-15127)
Walnut Creek Lumber Co Ltd ....E 330 852-4559
Dundee (G-9185)
Wappoo Wood Products Inc ....E 937 492-1166
Sidney (G-17233)

CONSTRUCTION MATLS, WHOLESALE: Soil Erosion Cntrl Fabrics

Johnston-Morehouse-Dickey Co ....G 330 405-6050
Macedonia (G-12464)

CONSTRUCTION MTRLS, WHOL: Exterior Flat Glass, Plate/Window

Anderson Glass Co Inc ....E 614 476-4877
Columbus (G-6756)
Trulite GL Alum Solutions LLC ....D 740 929-2443
Hebron (G-10892)

CONSTRUCTION SAND MINING

Arden J Neer Sr ....F 937 585-6733
Bellefontaine (G-1519)
Central Allied Enterprises Inc ....G 330 879-2132
Navarre (G-14711)
Columbus Equipment Company ....G 740 455-4036
Zanesville (G-21293)
Hilltop Basic Resources Inc ....F 513 651-5000
Cincinnati (G-3884)
Hilltop Basic Resources Inc ....E 937 878-8631
Fairborn (G-9624)
Hocking Valley Concrete Inc ....F 740 385-2165
Logan (G-12177)
Hugo Sand Company ....G 216 570-1212
Kent (G-11471)
J P Sand & Gravel Company ....E 614 497-0083
Lockbourne (G-12147)
Lakeside Sand & Gravel Inc ....E 330 274-2569
Mantua (G-12714)
Masons Sand and Gravel Co ....G 614 491-3611
Obetz (G-15655)
Mecco Inc ....E 513 422-3651
Middletown (G-14061)
Mechanicsburg Sand & Gravel ....F 937 834-2606
Mechanicsburg (G-13358)
Morrow Gravel Company Inc ....E 513 771-0820
Cincinnati (G-4124)
National Lime and Stone Co ....E 614 497-0083
Lockbourne (G-12150)
Olen Corporation ....G 740 745-5865
Saint Louisville (G-16829)
Oscar Brugmann Sand & Gravel ....F 330 274-8224
Mantua (G-12719)
S & S Aggregates Inc ....F 419 938-5604
Perrysville (G-16175)
Seville Sand & Gravel Inc ....E 330 948-0168
Strongsville (G-17962)
Shelly and Sands Inc ....F 740 453-0721
Zanesville (G-21350)
Shelly Company ....F 740 687-4420
Lancaster (G-11750)
Sober Sand & Gravel Co ....G 330 325-7088
Ravenna (G-16557)

CONSTRUCTION SITE PREPARATION SVCS

C & L Erectors & Riggers Inc ....E 740 332-7185
Laurelville (G-11769)
Great Lakes Crushing Ltd ....E 440 944-5500
Wickliffe (G-20366)
L&L Excavating & Land Clearing ....G 740 682-7823
Oak Hill (G-15600)
Miller Logging Inc ....E 330 279-4721
Holmesville (G-11109)

CONSTRUCTION: Agricultural Building

Barncraft Storage Buildings ....G 513 738-5654
Hamilton (G-10672)

CONSTRUCTION: Aqueduct

Neptune Equipment Company ....F 513 851-8008
Cincinnati (G-4145)

CONSTRUCTION: Athletic & Recreation Facilities

MGM Construction Inc ....F 440 234-7660
Berea (G-1627)

CONSTRUCTION: Bridge

Ashland LLC ....G 513 557-3100
Cincinnati (G-3418)
Ohio Bridge Corporation ....C 740 432-6334
Cambridge (G-2470)
S E Johnson Companies Inc ....F 419 893-8731
Maumee (G-13290)

PRODUCT

CONSTRUCTION: Commercial & Institutional Building

A Metalcraft Associates Inc ....G...... 937 693-4008
Botkins *(G-1949)*

Aecom Energy & Cnstr Inc ....C...... 419 698-6277
Oregon *(G-15701)*

Brenmar Construction Inc ....D...... 740 286-2151
Jackson *(G-11312)*

Bud Corp ....G...... 740 967-9992
Johnstown *(G-11394)*

Falls Metal Fabricators Ind...............F...... 330 253-7181
Akron *(G-178)*

Jim Nier Construction Inc ....F...... 740 289-3925
Piketon *(G-16222)*

Jjs3 Foundation ....G...... 513 751-3292
Cincinnati *(G-3947)*

Kellys Welding & Fabricating ....G...... 440 593-6040
Conneaut *(G-7811)*

Shelly and Sands Inc ....D...... 740 859-2104
Rayland *(G-16575)*

CONSTRUCTION: Commercial & Office Building, New

A W S Incorporated...........................G...... 419 352-5397
Bowling Green *(G-1962)*

Fleming Construction Co ....E...... 740 494-2177
Prospect *(G-16496)*

Jim Bumen Construction Company ...G...... 740 663-2659
Chillicothe *(G-3247)*

Thomas J Weaver Inc ....F...... 740 622-2040
Coshocton *(G-7913)*

CONSTRUCTION: Factory

Falls Metal Fabricators Ind...............F...... 330 253-7181
Akron *(G-178)*

CONSTRUCTION: Food Prdts Manufacturing or Packing Plant

Milos Whole World Gourmet LLC ....G...... 740 589-6456
Athens *(G-877)*

CONSTRUCTION: Foundation & Retaining Wall

Motz Mobile Containers Inc ....G...... 513 772-6689
Cincinnati *(G-4127)*

CONSTRUCTION: Garage

Overhead Door of Salem Inc ....G...... 330 332-9530
Salem *(G-16918)*

CONSTRUCTION: Golf Course

Bay Island Company Inc ....G...... 513 248-0356
Loveland *(G-12341)*

CONSTRUCTION: Grain Elevator

Agridry LLC ....E...... 419 459-4399
Edon *(G-9339)*

CONSTRUCTION: Greenhouse

Ecoponics Group LLC ....G...... 330 819-1233
Kent *(G-11453)*

Ludy Greenhouse Mfg Corp ....D...... 800 255-5839
New Madison *(G-14870)*

Rough Brothers Mfg Inc ....D...... 513 242-0310
Cincinnati *(G-4360)*

CONSTRUCTION: Guardrails, Highway

Paul Peterson Company.......................E...... 614 486-4375
Columbus *(G-7467)*

Security Fence Group Inc ....E...... 513 681-3700
Cincinnati *(G-4395)*

CONSTRUCTION: Heavy Highway & Street

Able Industries Inc..............................G...... 614 252-1050
Columbus *(G-6680)*

Ashland LLC ....G...... 513 557-3100
Cincinnati *(G-3418)*

Hull Ready Mix Concrete Inc...............F...... 419 625-8070
Sandusky *(G-16972)*

Smalls Asphalt Paving Inc ....E...... 740 427-4096
Gambier *(G-10318)*

W G Lockhart Construction Co ....D...... 330 745-6520
Akron *(G-466)*

CONSTRUCTION: Hospital

Healthcare Benefits Inc ....G...... 419 433-4499
Huron *(G-11223)*

CONSTRUCTION: Indl Building & Warehouse

Diversifd OH Vlly Eqpt & Srvcs ....F...... 740 458-9881
Clarington *(G-4651)*

Enerfab Inc ....B...... 513 641-0500
Cincinnati *(G-3704)*

Hadsell Chemical Proc LLC ....E...... 740 941-1792
Waverly *(G-19710)*

Jim Nier Construction Inc ....F...... 740 289-3925
Piketon *(G-16222)*

Pawnee Maintenance Inc ....D...... 740 373-6861
Marietta *(G-12814)*

Stamm Contracting Co Inc ....E...... 330 274-8230
Mantua *(G-12723)*

CONSTRUCTION: Indl Building, Prefabricated

Rupcol Inc...G...... 419 924-5215
West Unity *(G-20135)*

CONSTRUCTION: Indl Buildings, New, NEC

Baker-Shindler Contracting Co ....E...... 419 782-5080
Defiance *(G-8780)*

Fleming Construction Co ....E...... 740 494-2177
Prospect *(G-16496)*

Hines Builders Inc ....F...... 937 335-4586
Troy *(G-18834)*

Jim Bumen Construction Company ......G...... 740 663-2659
Chillicothe *(G-3247)*

Thomas J Weaver Inc ....F...... 740 622-2040
Coshocton *(G-7913)*

CONSTRUCTION: Indl Plant

Advanced Indus Machining Inc ....F...... 614 596-4183
Powell *(G-16461)*

Babcock & Wilcox Company ....A...... 330 753-4511
Barberton *(G-1104)*

Htec Systems Inc ....F...... 937 438-3010
Dayton *(G-8394)*

Tri-America Contractors Inc.................E...... 740 574-0148
Wheelersburg *(G-20335)*

CONSTRUCTION: Institutional Building

Consoldted Grnhse Slutions LLC ....G...... 330 844-8598
Strongsville *(G-17907)*

CONSTRUCTION: Oil & Gas Line & Compressor Station

Don Wartko Construction Co................D...... 330 673-5252
Kent *(G-11450)*

Global Oilfield Services LLC ....G...... 419 756-8027
Mansfield *(G-12613)*

CONSTRUCTION: Oil & Gas Pipeline Construction

Bluefoot Industrial LLC ....E...... 740 314-5299
Steubenville *(G-17689)*

IV J Telecommunications LLC ....G...... 606 694-1762
South Point *(G-17438)*

Terra Sonic International LLC ....E...... 740 374-6608
Marietta *(G-12840)*

CONSTRUCTION: Pipeline, NEC

Eastern Automated Piping ....G...... 740 535-8184
Mingo Junction *(G-14348)*

CONSTRUCTION: Power Plant

Enerfab Inc ....B...... 513 641-0500
Cincinnati *(G-3704)*

Siemens Energy Inc ....B...... 740 393-8897
Mount Vernon *(G-14648)*

CONSTRUCTION: Residential, Nec

Bearcat Construction Inc ....G...... 513 314-0867
Mason *(G-12987)*

Byrd Prcurement Specialist Inc............G...... 419 936-0019
Swanton *(G-18082)*

Kim Phillips Sign Co LLC.....................G...... 330 364-4280
Dover *(G-8995)*

M J Coates Construction Co ....G...... 937 886-9546
Dayton *(G-8463)*

Mohican Log Homes Inc ....G...... 419 994-4088
Loudonville *(G-12299)*

CONSTRUCTION: Sewer Line

Connolly Construction Co Inc ....G...... 937 644-8831
Marysville *(G-12936)*

Fleming Construction Co ....E...... 740 494-2177
Prospect *(G-16496)*

Mack Ready Mix Concrete Inc ....G...... 330 483-3111
Valley City *(G-19214)*

Mt Pleasant Blacktopping Inc ....G...... 513 874-3777
Fairfield *(G-9688)*

Robert Gorey ....G...... 330 725-7272
Medina *(G-13468)*

CONSTRUCTION: Single-Family Housing

A W S Incorporated.............................G...... 419 352-5397
Bowling Green *(G-1962)*

Building Concepts Inc ....F...... 419 298-2371
Edgerton *(G-9326)*

Community RE Group-Comvet ....G...... 440 319-6714
Ashtabula *(G-798)*

Elite Mill Service & Cnstr....................G...... 513 422-4234
Trenton *(G-18790)*

Gillard Construction Inc ....F...... 740 376-9744
Marietta *(G-12786)*

Gutter Topper Ltd ....G...... 513 797-5800
Batavia *(G-1189)*

Humble Construction Inc ....E...... 614 888-8960
Columbus *(G-7169)*

Manufactured Housing Entps Inc.........C...... 419 636-4511
Bryan *(G-2313)*

RE Connors Construction Ltd ....G...... 740 644-0261
Thornville *(G-18194)*

Silver Creek Log Homes.......................G...... 419 335-3220
Wauseon *(G-19694)*

Volpe Millwork Inc ....G...... 216 581-0200
Cleveland *(G-6427)*

Walden Industries Inc ....E...... 740 633-5971
Tiltonsville *(G-18255)*

CONSTRUCTION: Single-family Housing, New

Al Yoder Construction Company ....G...... 330 359-5726
Millersburg *(G-14191)*

Cabinet Systems Inc ....G...... 440 237-1924
Cleveland *(G-4961)*

Connolly Construction Co Inc ....G...... 937 644-8831
Marysville *(G-12936)*

Hoge Lumber Company ....E...... 419 753-2263
New Knoxville *(G-14836)*

M J Coates Construction Co ....F...... 937 886-9546
Dayton *(G-8462)*

Mohican Log Homes Inc ....G...... 419 994-4088
Loudonville *(G-12299)*

Thomas J Weaver Inc ....F...... 740 622-2040
Coshocton *(G-7913)*

Wright Designs Inc ....G...... 216 524-6662
Cleveland *(G-6484)*

CONSTRUCTION: Street Sign Installation & Mntnce

A & A Safety Inc..................................E...... 513 943-6100
Amelia *(G-564)*

CONSTRUCTION: Street Surfacing & Paving

Action Blacktop Sealcoating & ....G...... 937 667-4769
Tipp City *(G-18259)*

Baileys Asphalt Sealing ....F...... 740 453-9409
South Zanesville *(G-17453)*

Barrett Paving Materials Inc.................C...... 513 271-6200
Middletown *(G-14101)*

Image Pavement Maintenance ....E...... 937 833-9200
Brookville *(G-2187)*

John R Jurgensen Co ....G...... 937 293-3112
Springfield *(G-17582)*

Koski Construction Co ....G...... 440 997-5337
Ashtabula *(G-815)*

Mar-Zane Inc ....G...... 330 626-2079
Mantua *(G-12716)*

(G-0000) Company's Geographic Section entry number

Shelly Materials Inc............E......740 666-5841
  Ostrander (G-15789)
Suever Stone Company............F......419 331-1945
  Lima (G-12097)

CONSTRUCTION: Swimming Pools

Imperial On-Pece Fibrgls Pools............F......740 747-2971
  Ashley (G-788)
Spa Pool Covers Inc............G......440 235-9981
  North Royalton (G-15452)

CONSTRUCTION: Telephone & Communication Line

Fishel Company............D......614 850-4400
  Columbus (G-7089)
Palmer Properties LLC............G......419 938-3114
  Perrysville (G-16174)
Parallel Technologies Inc............D......614 798-9700
  Dublin (G-9117)

CONSTRUCTION: Tennis Court

Image Pavement Maintenance............E......937 833-9200
  Brookville (G-2187)

CONSTRUCTION: Transmitting Tower, Telecommunication

Wirenet Inc............F......513 774-7759
  Loveland (G-12400)

CONSTRUCTION: Utility Line

Groundhogs 2000 LLC............G......440 653-1647
  Oakwood Village (G-15625)

CONSTRUCTION: Water Main

Coleman Machine Inc............G......740 695-3006
  Saint Clairsville (G-16787)

CONSULTING SVC: Business, NEC

Biorx LLC............C......866 442-4679
  Cincinnati (G-3450)
D M L Steel Tech............F......513 737-9911
  Liberty Twp (G-11973)
Deemsys Inc............D......614 322-9928
  Gahanna (G-10206)
E Retailing Associates LLC............D......614 300-5785
  Columbus (G-7043)
Enviro Crest Services Inc............G......330 932-0345
  East Liverpool (G-9214)
Harco Industries Inc............F......937 832-9697
  Moraine (G-14493)
Ktsdi LLC............G......330 783-2000
  North Lima (G-15318)
Lake Publishing Inc............G......440 299-8500
  Mentor (G-13628)
Magnum Computers Inc............F......216 781-1757
  Cleveland (G-5730)
Mamsys Consulting Services............G......440 287-6824
  Solon (G-17332)
Metal-Mation Inc............C......216 651-1083
  Cleveland (G-5789)
Neola Inc............G......330 926-0514
  Stow (G-17783)
Petro Evaluation Services Inc............G......330 264-4454
  Wooster (G-20820)
Ponderosa Consulting Services............G......330 264-2298
  Wooster (G-20821)
Rapid Blanket Restorer Corp............G......330 821-6326
  Painesville (G-15916)
Ream and Haager Laboratory............F......330 343-3711
  Dover (G-9010)
Rxpert Consultants LLC............G......614 579-9384
  Columbus (G-7580)
Simple Vms LLC............G......888 255-8918
  Cincinnati (G-4421)
Telex Communications Inc............F......419 865-0972
  Toledo (G-18718)
Truechoicepack Corp............E......937 630-3832
  Dayton (G-8732)
Vista Research Group LLC............G......419 281-3927
  Ashland (G-784)

CONSULTING SVC: Computer

Advanced Prgrm Resources Inc............E......614 761-9994
  Dublin (G-9037)

Akron Council of Engineering............G......330 535-8835
  Akron (G-39)
Albert Bickel............G......513 530-5700
  Cincinnati (G-3375)
Casentric LLC............G......216 233-6300
  Shaker Heights (G-17087)
Click It Connect Corp............G......440 247-4998
  Chagrin Falls (G-3053)
Complete Network Solutions Inc............G......330 328-2596
  Stow (G-17742)
Concept Xxi Inc............F......216 831-2121
  Beachwood (G-1264)
Einstruction Corporation............D......330 746-3015
  Youngstown (G-21075)
Empyracom Inc............E......330 744-5570
  Canfield (G-2553)
It XCEL Consulting LLC............F......513 847-8261
  West Chester (G-19886)
Netsmart Technologies Inc............E......440 942-4040
  Solon (G-17349)
Onx Holdings LLC............G......800 559-2497
  Mayfield Heights (G-13320)
Onx USA LLC............D......440 569-2300
  Cleveland (G-5943)
Quayle Consulting Inc............G......614 868-1363
  Pickerington (G-16202)
Rawhide Software Inc............G......419 878-0857
  Bowling Green (G-2010)
Revolution Group Inc............D......614 212-1111
  Westerville (G-20182)
S L C Software Services............G......513 922-4303
  Cincinnati (G-4374)
Strongbasics LLC............G......716 903-6151
  Columbus (G-7662)
Wild Fire Systems............G......440 442-8999
  Cleveland (G-6462)

CONSULTING SVC: Data Processing

Image Integrations Systems............F......419 872-0003
  Perrysburg (G-16109)
Mamsys Consulting Services............G......440 287-6824
  Solon (G-17332)
W L Arehart Computing Systems............G......937 383-4710
  Wilmington (G-20681)

CONSULTING SVC: Educational

Align Assess Achieve LLC............G......614 505-6820
  Columbus (G-6716)
Instruction & Design Concepts............G......937 439-2698
  Dayton (G-8412)

CONSULTING SVC: Engineering

4r Enterprises Incorporated............G......330 923-9799
  Cuyahoga Falls (G-7960)
ACC Automation Co Inc............E......330 928-3821
  Akron (G-25)
Aero Composites Inc............G......937 849-0244
  Medway (G-13499)
Amcan Productions Ltd............G......330 332-9129
  Salem (G-16871)
BSK Industries Inc............G......440 230-9299
  North Royalton (G-15412)
Dlz Ohio Inc............C......614 888-0040
  Columbus (G-7033)
Fischer Engineering Company............G......937 754-1750
  Dayton (G-8343)
Fluid Equipment Corp............G......419 636-0777
  Bryan (G-2296)
Forte Indus Eqp Systems Inc............E......513 398-2800
  Mason (G-13022)
Halliday Technologies Inc............G......614 504-4150
  Plain City (G-16345)
Independent Digital Consulting............G......330 753-0777
  Norton (G-15514)
James Engineering Inc............G......740 373-9521
  Marietta (G-12794)
Keuchel & Associates Inc............E......330 945-9455
  Cuyahoga Falls (G-8017)
Maval Industries LLC............G......330 405-1600
  Twinsburg (G-18981)
On-Power Inc............E......513 228-2100
  Lebanon (G-11823)
Ozone Systems Svcs Group Inc............G......513 899-4131
  Morrow (G-14550)
P G M Diversified Industries............G......440 885-3500
  Cleveland (G-5955)
Reliance Design Inc............F......216 267-5450
  Rocky River (G-16707)

Signalysis Inc............F......513 528-6164
  Cincinnati (G-4420)
Sponseller Group Inc............E......419 861-3000
  Holland (G-11087)
Sponseller Group Inc............G......937 492-9949
  Sidney (G-17229)
Visiontech Automation LLC............G......614 554-2013
  Dublin (G-9164)
Warmus and Associates Inc............F......330 659-4440
  Bath (G-1240)
Watson Meeks and Company............G......937 378-2355
  Georgetown (G-10367)
Welded Tube Pros LLC............G......330 854-2966
  Canal Fulton (G-2517)

CONSULTING SVC: Human Resource

360water Inc............G......614 294-3600
  Columbus (G-6663)
Delphia Consulting LLC............G......614 421-2000
  Columbus (G-7021)
Simple Vms LLC............G......888 255-8918
  Cincinnati (G-4421)

CONSULTING SVC: Management

A C Knox Inc............G......513 921-5028
  Cincinnati (G-3333)
Advanced Prgrm Resources Inc............E......614 761-9994
  Dublin (G-9037)
AT&T Government Solutions Inc............D......937 306-3030
  Beavercreek (G-1320)
Cac Energy Ltd............G......937 867-5593
  Dayton (G-8206)
Comprehensive Logistics Co Inc............E......330 793-0504
  Youngstown (G-21055)
D & L Gas Energy Ltd............C......330 792-9524
  Youngstown (G-21062)
Digital Controls Corporation............D......513 746-8118
  Miamisburg (G-13801)
Enerchem Incorporated............G......513 745-0580
  Cincinnati (G-3703)
EP Ferris & Associates Inc............G......614 299-2999
  Columbus (G-7063)
Frisbie Engine & Machine Co............F......513 542-1770
  Cincinnati (G-3784)
Harris Mackessy & Brennan............G......614 221-6831
  Westerville (G-20157)
Instruction & Design Concepts............G......937 439-2698
  Dayton (G-8412)
International Trade Group Inc............G......614 486-4634
  Columbus (G-7207)
Pakra LLC............F......614 477-6965
  Columbus (G-7455)
Power Management Inc............E......937 222-2909
  Dayton (G-8580)
SSP Industrial Group Inc............G......330 665-2900
  Fairlawn (G-9761)
Transel Corporation............G......513 897-3442
  Harveysburg (G-10835)
US Brands Inc............G......216 595-9700
  Cleveland (G-6398)
Value Added Business Svcs Co............G......614 854-9755
  Jackson (G-11332)
Vehicle Systems Inc............G......330 854-0535
  Massillon (G-13210)
Welding Consultants Inc............G......614 258-7018
  Columbus (G-7756)
Wide Area Media LLC............G......440 356-3133
  Westlake (G-20321)
Wirenet Inc............F......513 774-7759
  Loveland (G-12400)

CONSULTING SVC: Marketing Management

Applied Marketing Services............E......440 716-9962
  Westlake (G-20255)
Capehart Enterprises LLC............F......614 769-7746
  Columbus (G-6895)
David Esrati............G......937 228-4433
  Dayton (G-8266)
Dsk Imaging LLC............F......513 554-1797
  Blue Ash (G-1777)
Eagle Rock Brand Cons LLC............G......614 403-4802
  Plain City (G-16338)
Eltool Corporation............G......513 723-1772
  Mansfield (G-12599)
Frankes Wood Products LLC............G......937 642-0706
  Marysville (G-12944)
International Advg Concepts............G......440 331-4733
  Cleveland (G-5579)

PRODUCT

Just Business Inc ....F 866 577-3303
Dayton *(G-8431)*
Minor Corporation ....G 216 291-8723
Cleveland *(G-5822)*
Nsa Technologies LLC ....C 330 576-4600
Akron *(G-321)*
One Wish LLC ....F 800 505-6883
Beachwood *(G-1289)*
Page One Group ....G 740 397-4240
Mount Vernon *(G-14636)*
Peloton Manufacturing Corp ...F 440 205-1600
Mentor *(G-13684)*
Quez Media Marketing Inc ....F 216 910-0202
Cleveland *(G-6077)*

CONSULTING SVC: Online Technology

Cisco Systems Inc ....A 937 427-4264
Beavercreek *(G-1325)*
Estreamz Inc ....E 513 278-7836
Cincinnati *(G-3719)*
Jasstek Inc ....F 614 808-3600
Dublin *(G-9091)*
Penton Business Media Inc ...A 216 696-7000
Cleveland *(G-5990)*
Sns Nano Fiber Technology LLC ....G 330 655-0030
Hudson *(G-11200)*
Wentworth Technologies LLC ....F 440 212-7696
Brunswick *(G-2267)*
Westmount Technology Inc ....G 216 328-2011
Independence *(G-11284)*

CONSULTING SVC: Sales Management

Chemigon LLC ....G 330 592-1875
Akron *(G-121)*
Pure Light Technology LLC ...G 513 779-7474
West Chester *(G-20042)*

CONSULTING SVC: Telecommunications

Digital Automation Associates ....G 419 352-6977
Bowling Green *(G-1986)*

CONSULTING SVCS, BUSINESS: Agricultural

Advancing Eco-Agriculture LLC ....G 800 495-6603
Middlefield *(G-13912)*
Tyler Grain & Fertilizer Co ....F 330 669-2341
Smithville *(G-17246)*

CONSULTING SVCS, BUSINESS: Energy Conservation

Melink Corporation ....F 513 685-0958
Milford *(G-14161)*

CONSULTING SVCS, BUSINESS: Environmental

Alpha Omega Bioremediation LLC ...F 614 287-2600
Columbus *(G-6728)*
Summit Drilling Company Inc ....F 800 775-5537
Akron *(G-419)*

CONSULTING SVCS, BUSINESS: Safety Training Svcs

American Apex Corporation ....F 614 652-2000
Plain City *(G-16319)*

CONSULTING SVCS, BUSINESS: Sys Engnrg, Exc Computer/Prof

A Graphic Solution ....F 216 228-7223
Cleveland *(G-4672)*
Carey Color Llc/Cincinnati ....F 513 241-5210
Cincinnati *(G-3499)*
Fluid Equipment Corp ....G 419 636-0777
Bryan *(G-2296)*
Jasstek Inc ....F 614 808-3600
Dublin *(G-9091)*
Mv Designlabs LLC ....G 724 355-7986
Cleveland *(G-5842)*
North Coast Security Group LLC ...G 614 887-7255
Columbus *(G-7399)*

CONSULTING SVCS, BUSINESS: Systems Analysis & Engineering

Interactive Engineering Corp ...E 330 239-6888
Medina *(G-13427)*

Nvision Technology Inc ....G 412 254-4668
Norton *(G-15519)*
Sentek Corporation ....G 614 586-1123
Columbus *(G-7608)*
Tekworx LLC ....F 513 533-4777
Blue Ash *(G-1881)*

CONSULTING SVCS, BUSINESS: Systems Analysis Or Design

Akers Identity LLC ....G 330 493-0055
Canton *(G-2596)*
Architctral Identification Inc ...E 614 868-8400
Gahanna *(G-10204)*
Qlog Corp ....G 513 874-1211
Hamilton *(G-10732)*

CONSULTING SVCS, BUSINESS: Testing, Educational Or Personnel

Community RE Group-Comvet ....G 440 319-6714
Ashtabula *(G-798)*
Terewell Inc ....G 216 334-6897
Cleveland *(G-6306)*

CONSULTING SVCS, BUSINESS: Traffic

Athens Technical Specialists ...F 740 592-2874
Athens *(G-857)*
Barr Engineering Incorporated ...F 614 892-0162
Columbus *(G-6807)*

CONSULTING SVCS: Geological

David A Waldron & Associates ...G 330 264-7275
Wooster *(G-20764)*

CONSULTING SVCS: Oil

Diamond Oilfield Tech LLC ....F 234 806-4185
Vienna *(G-19365)*
Washita Valley Enterprises Inc ...E 330 510-1568
Louisville *(G-12334)*

CONTACT LENSES

Albright Albright & Schn ......G 614 825-4829
Worthington *(G-20855)*
Brunswick Eye & Contact Lens C ...G 419 439-3381
Defiance *(G-8782)*
Safeway Contact Lens Inc ....G 330 536-6469
Lowellville *(G-12413)*

CONTACTS: Electrical

Aviation Technologies Inc ....G 216 706-2960
Cleveland *(G-4872)*

CONTAINERS: Air Cargo, Metal

G P Manufacturing Inc ....G 937 544-3190
Peebles *(G-16020)*
Shanafelt Manufacturing Co ...E 330 455-0315
Canton *(G-2847)*

CONTAINERS: Cargo, Wood

Frankes Wood Products LLC ...E 937 642-0706
Marysville *(G-12944)*
Riverview Indus WD Pdts Inc ...D 330 669-8509
Wooster *(G-20830)*
Riverview Indus WD Pdts Inc ...F 330 669-8509
Smithville *(G-17243)*
Universal Pallets Inc ....E 614 444-1095
Columbus *(G-7725)*

CONTAINERS: Cargo, Wood & Metal Combination

Schuetz Container ....E 419 872-2295
Perrysburg *(G-16148)*

CONTAINERS: Cargo, Wood & Wood With Metal

Findlay Pallet Inc ....G 419 423-0511
Findlay *(G-9824)*
Kmak Group LLC ....F 937 308-1023
London *(G-12214)*
Ohio Specialty Mfg Co ....G 419 531-5402
Toledo *(G-18617)*

CONTAINERS: Corrugated

1923 W 25th St Inc ....G 216 696-7529
Cleveland *(G-4664)*
Akers Packaging Solutions Inc ...E 513 422-6312
Middletown *(G-14017)*
Alpha Container Co Inc ....F 937 644-5511
Marysville *(G-12931)*
American Corrugated Pdts Inc ...C 614 870-2000
Columbus *(G-6735)*
Basic Packaging Ltd ....F 330 634-9665
Tallmadge *(G-18135)*
Bruce Box Co Inc ....G 740 533-0670
Franklin Furnace *(G-10066)*
Buckeye Boxes Inc ....G 937 599-2551
Bellefontaine *(G-1523)*
Buckeye Boxes Inc ....E 614 274-8484
Columbus *(G-6871)*
Buckeye Corrugated Inc ....D 330 264-6336
Wooster *(G-20753)*
Cameron Packaging Inc ....G 419 222-9404
Lima *(G-11999)*
Charles Messina ....G 216 663-3344
Cleveland *(G-5016)*
Container King Inc ....G 937 652-3087
Urbana *(G-19154)*
Containercraft Inc ....F 419 884-2414
Mansfield *(G-12584)*
Contract Pckg Dist Specialists ...F 513 942-0300
West Chester *(G-19993)*
Creative Packaging LLC ....E 740 452-8497
Zanesville *(G-21295)*
Georgia-Pacific LLC ....C 740 477-3347
Circleville *(G-4631)*
Greif Inc ....E 740 549-6000
Delaware *(G-8847)*
Greif Inc ....D 740 549-6000
Delaware *(G-8851)*
Greif U S Holdings Inc ....G 740 549-6000
Delaware *(G-8856)*
Honeymoon Paper Products Inc ...D 513 755-7200
Fairfield *(G-9666)*
Innovative Packaging LLC ......F 419 222-6071
Lima *(G-12030)*
JIT Packaging Inc ....E 330 562-8080
Aurora *(G-927)*
Joseph T Snyder Industries ...G 216 883-6900
Cleveland *(G-5623)*
Marshalltown Packaging Inc ...G 641 753-5272
Columbus *(G-7320)*
Miami Vly Packg Solutions Inc ...F 937 224-1800
Dayton *(G-8492)*
Midwest Filtration LLC ....E 513 874-6510
West Chester *(G-20030)*
Nicofibers Inc ....G 740 394-2491
Shawnee *(G-17116)*
Packaging Corporation America ...D 513 424-3542
Middletown *(G-14073)*
Packaging Corporation America ...C 419 282-5809
Ashland *(G-762)*
Packaging Corporation America ...E 513 860-1145
Fairfield *(G-9697)*
Packaging Corporation America ...E 513 582-0690
Cincinnati *(G-4208)*
Packaging Corporation America ...D 740 344-1126
Newark *(G-15044)*
Packaging Corporation America ...E 330 644-9542
Akron *(G-330)*
Pactiv LLC ....E 330 644-9542
Akron *(G-331)*
Pax Corrugated Products Inc ...D 513 932-9855
Lebanon *(G-11826)*
Pratt (jet Corr) Inc ....E 937 390-7100
Springfield *(G-17629)*
Schwarz Partners Packaging LLC ...F 317 290-1140
Sidney *(G-17222)*
Sonoco Products Company .....E 614 759-8470
Columbus *(G-7631)*
Systems Pack Inc ....E 330 467-5729
Macedonia *(G-12493)*
Temple Inland ....G 513 425-0830
Middletown *(G-14087)*
US Corrugated Inc ....C 740 681-1600
Lancaster *(G-11760)*
US Corrugated of Massillon ....F 216 663-3344
Maple Heights *(G-12743)*
Westrock Cp LLC ....B 513 745-2400
Blue Ash *(G-1893)*
Westrock Cp LLC ....C 330 297-0841
Ravenna *(G-16571)*

Westrock Rkt Company..........................G......330 296-5155
  Ravenna (G-16572)
Weyerhaeuser Co Containeerboar........F......740 397-5215
  Mount Vernon (G-14655)

CONTAINERS: Foil, Bakery Goods & Frozen Foods

CC Investors Management Co LLC.......G......740 374-8129
  Marietta (G-12772)
Nestle R&D Center Inc.......................G......440 349-5757
  Solon (G-17346)

CONTAINERS: Food & Beverage

Amcor Rigid Plastics Usa LLC...........G......419 483-4343
  Bellevue (G-1542)
Ball Arosol Specialty Cont Inc............C......330 534-9273
  Hubbard (G-11128)
Ball Corporation................................C......419 423-3071
  Findlay (G-9792)
Ball Corporation................................G......330 244-2313
  North Canton (G-15222)
Broodle Brands LLC.........................F......855 276-6353
  Cincinnati (G-3480)
G&M Media Packaging Inc.................G......419 636-5461
  Bryan (G-2297)
Seven-Ogun International LLC............G......614 888-8939
  Worthington (G-20887)
SSP Industrial Group Inc..................G......330 665-2900
  Fairlawn (G-9761)

CONTAINERS: Food, Folding, Made From Purchased Materials

Americraft Carton Inc.......................E......419 668-1006
  Norwalk (G-15525)

CONTAINERS: Food, Liquid Tight, Including Milk

Island Aseptics LLC...........................C......740 685-2548
  Byesville (G-2405)
Ohio State Plastics.............................F......614 299-5618
  Columbus (G-7430)
Verso Corporation..............................D......901 369-4105
  Miamisburg (G-13875)

CONTAINERS: Food, Metal

G W Cobb Co.....................................F......216 341-0100
  Cleveland (G-5389)
Reynolds Metals Company LLC..........F......614 228-7390
  Columbus (G-7560)

CONTAINERS: Food, Wood Wirebound

Patriotic Buildings LLC......................G......740 853-3970
  Patriot (G-15997)

CONTAINERS: Glass

Anchor Glass Container Corp.............C......740 452-2743
  Zanesville (G-21272)
Anchor Hocking LLC...........................A......740 681-6478
  Lancaster (G-11687)
Bprex Plastic Packaging Inc...............F......419 247-5000
  Toledo (G-18379)
Chantilly Development Corp................F......419 243-8109
  Toledo (G-18393)
Dura Temp Corporation.......................F......419 866-4348
  Holland (G-11058)
Ghp II LLC..C......740 687-2500
  Lancaster (G-11719)
Owens-Brockway Glass Cont Inc........C......567 336-8449
  Perrysburg (G-16139)
Owens-Brockway Glass Cont Inc........D......740 455-4500
  Zanesville (G-21338)
Owens-Brockway Packaging Inc.........G......567 336-5000
  Perrysburg (G-16140)
Owens-Illinois Inc..............................B......567 336-5000
  Perrysburg (G-16141)
Owens-Illinois De Puerto Rico............D......419 874-9708
  Toledo (G-18628)
Owens-Illinois General Inc.................B......567 336-5000
  Perrysburg (G-16142)
Owens-Illinois Group Inc...................A......567 336-5000
  Perrysburg (G-16143)
Pyromatics Corp.................................F......440 352-3500
  Mentor (G-13704)

CONTAINERS: Ice Cream, Made From Purchased Materials

Norse Dairy Systems LP....................B......614 421-5297
  Columbus (G-7398)

CONTAINERS: Laminated Phenolic & Vulcanized Fiber

Polystar Inc..F......330 963-5100
  Twinsburg (G-19004)

CONTAINERS: Metal

Bentley World-Packaging Ltd.............F......440 232-1100
  Bedford (G-1407)
Champion Company.............................D......937 324-5681
  Springfield (G-17532)
Champion Company.............................D......937 324-5681
  Springfield (G-17531)
Georgia-Pacific LLC...........................C......740 477-3347
  Circleville (G-4631)
Green Bay Packaging Inc....................C......419 332-5593
  Fremont (G-10157)
Green Bay Packaging Inc....................D......513 228-5560
  Lebanon (G-11806)
Hawthorne Caravan & Assoc LLC......F......440 366-9065
  Elyria (G-9428)
Horwitz & Pintis Co............................F......419 666-2220
  Toledo (G-18512)
Industrial Container Svcs LLC............E......513 921-8811
  Cincinnati (G-3917)
Industrial Container Svcs LLC............D......614 864-1900
  Blacklick (G-1699)
Mauser USA LLC...............................E......614 856-5982
  Columbus (G-7328)
Mobile Mini Inc..................................F......614 449-8655
  Columbus (G-7360)
Overseas Packing LLC........................F......440 232-2917
  Bedford (G-1451)
Packaging Specialties Inc...................E......330 723-6000
  Medina (G-13457)
Rexam Beverage Can Company...........C......419 334-4461
  Fremont (G-10178)
Sabco Industries Inc..........................E......419 531-5347
  Toledo (G-18683)
Schwarz Partners Packaging LLC.......F......317 290-1140
  Sidney (G-17222)
SSP Industrial Group Inc..................G......330 665-2900
  Fairlawn (G-9761)
Syme Inc..E......330 723-6000
  Medina (G-13486)
Tavens Container Inc.........................D......216 883-3333
  Bedford (G-1464)
Unican Ohio LLC...............................G......419 636-5461
  Fremont (G-10191)
Werk-Brau Company...........................D......419 422-2912
  Findlay (G-9907)
Westrock Cp LLC...............................C......330 297-0841
  Ravenna (G-16571)
Westrock Cp LLC...............................B......513 745-2400
  Blue Ash (G-1893)
Westrock CP LLC...............................D......770 448-2193
  Wshngtn CT Hs (G-20930)
Witt Industries Inc.............................D......513 871-5700
  Mason (G-13103)

CONTAINERS: Plastic

Amcor Rigid Plastics Usa LLC...........E......419 592-1998
  Napoleon (G-14670)
Aspen Machine and Plastics...............G......937 526-4644
  Versailles (G-19339)
Astro Qcb Inc....................................B......513 921-8811
  Cincinnati (G-3422)
Bakelite N Sumitomo Amer Inc...........G......419 675-1282
  Kenton (G-11545)
Bkhn Inc..D......513 831-4402
  Milford (G-14126)
Black Diamnd Eco Solutions LLC.......G......877 892-3370
  Eastlake (G-9259)
Bprex Plastic Packaging Inc...............F......419 247-5000
  Toledo (G-18379)
Buckhorn Inc......................................E......513 831-4402
  Milford (G-14128)
Buckhorn Material Hdlg Group...........D......513 831-4402
  Milford (G-14129)
Century Container LLC........................E......330 457-2367
  New Waterford (G-14969)
Century Container LLC........................G......330 457-2367
  Columbiana (G-6609)

CK Technologies LLC..........................C......419 485-1110
  Montpelier (G-14441)
Composite Technologies Co LLC.........D......937 228-2880
  Dayton (G-8241)
Dadco Inc..F......513 489-2244
  Cincinnati (G-3636)
Dadco Inc..C......513 489-2244
  Cincinnati (G-3635)
Dometic Sanitation Corporation.........D......330 439-5550
  Big Prairie (G-1680)
Dynamic Polymers LLC......................G......614 575-1222
  Columbus (G-7041)
Eaton Corporation..............................C......330 274-0743
  Aurora (G-916)
Encon Inc...C......937 898-2603
  Dayton (G-8325)
Enpac LLC..E......440 975-0070
  Eastlake (G-9268)
Fabohio Inc..E......740 922-4233
  Uhrichsville (G-19050)
Flambeau Inc......................................E......440 632-3752
  Middlefield (G-13935)
Graham Packaging Company LP.........E......513 874-1770
  West Chester (G-20011)
Graham Packaging Company LP.........E......419 334-4197
  Fremont (G-10155)
Graham Packg Plastic Pdts Inc...........E......717 849-8500
  Toledo (G-18485)
Greif Inc..E......740 549-6000
  Delaware (G-8847)
Greif Inc..E......740 657-6500
  Delaware (G-8848)
Hamilton Custom Molding Inc............G......513 844-6643
  Hamilton (G-10702)
Hendrickson International Corp..........D......740 929-5600
  Hebron (G-10870)
Hub Plastics Inc.................................D......614 861-1791
  Blacklick (G-1698)
Huhtamaki Inc...................................B......937 987-3078
  New Vienna (G-14955)
Hydrant Hat LLC................................C......440 224-1007
  Kingsville (G-11604)
Ilpea Industries Inc...........................C......330 562-2916
  Aurora (G-926)
Inhance Technologies LLC..................F......614 846-6400
  Columbus (G-7187)
Kennedy Group Incorporated.............D......440 951-7660
  Willoughby (G-20520)
Klw Plastics Inc.................................G......678 674-2990
  Monroe (G-14408)
Landmark Plastic Corporation............C......330 785-2200
  Akron (G-267)
Liqui-Box Corporation.........................D......614 888-9280
  Columbus (G-7300)
Mastic Home Exteriors Inc.................C......937 497-7008
  Sidney (G-17199)
Med Center Systems LLC....................G......513 942-6066
  West Chester (G-20026)
Midwest Plastic Systems Inc..............G......513 553-4380
  New Richmond (G-14943)
Olan Plastics Inc................................E......614 834-6526
  Canal Winchester (G-2535)
Philpott Indus Plas Entps Ltd.............G......330 225-3344
  Brunswick (G-2242)
Plastipak Packaging Inc......................C......740 928-4435
  Hebron (G-10880)
Polymer & Steel Tech Inc....................E......440 510-0108
  Eastlake (G-9285)
Polyone Corporation...........................D......937 548-1395
  Greenville (G-10513)
Polystar Inc..E......234 678-9020
  Stow (G-17790)
Pouchr LLC..G......216 990-0535
  Cleveland (G-6024)
Pretium Packaging LLC.......................C......419 943-3733
  Leipsic (G-11874)
Resource Mtl Hdlg & Recycl Inc.........E......440 834-0727
  Middlefield (G-13985)
Roswell Inc...G......419 433-4709
  Huron (G-11241)
Shirley KS Storage Trays LLC.............G......740 868-8140
  Zanesville (G-21352)
Southeastern Container Inc.................D......419 352-6300
  Bowling Green (G-2016)
Specialty Plas Fabrications.................G......513 856-9475
  Hamilton (G-10740)
Step2 Holdings LLC............................A......330 656-0440
  Streetsboro (G-17880)
US Coexcell Inc..................................E......419 897-9110
  Maumee (G-13306)

PRODUCT

Wayne Pak Ltd .... F 440 323-8744
Elyria *(G-9509)*

CONTAINERS: Plywood & Veneer, Wood

Pallet & Cont Corp of Amer .... G 419 255-1256
Toledo *(G-18634)*

CONTAINERS: Sanitary, Food

Ecologic Fdsrvice Slutions LLC .... G 419 467-8758
Toledo *(G-18449)*
Huhtamaki Inc .... B 513 201-1525
Batavia *(G-1192)*
Huhtamaki Inc .... B 937 746-9700
Franklin *(G-10028)*
Novolex Holdings Inc .... B 937 746-1933
Franklin *(G-10041)*
Sonoco Products Company .... E 513 870-3985
West Chester *(G-20052)*
Superior Cup Inc .... E 330 393-6187
Warren *(G-19603)*
Washington Products Inc .... F 330 837-5101
Massillon *(G-13211)*

CONTAINERS: Shipping & Mailing, Fiber

Operational Support Svcs LLC .... F 419 425-0889
Findlay *(G-9873)*
Shockakhan Express LLC .... G 614 432-3133
Groveport *(G-10644)*

CONTAINERS: Shipping, Bombs, Metal Plate

Buckeye Stamping Company .... D 614 445-0059
Columbus *(G-6875)*
Industrial Repair & Mfg Inc .... E 419 822-4232
Delta *(G-8936)*

CONTAINERS: Shipping, Metal, Milk, Fluid

Fluid-Bag LLC .... G 513 310-9550
Blue Ash *(G-1798)*

CONTAINERS: Shipping, Wood

Frankes Wood Products LLC .... E 937 642-0706
Marysville *(G-12944)*
Greif Inc .... E 740 657-6500
Delaware *(G-8848)*
Greif Inc .... F 740 549-6000
Delaware *(G-8850)*
Greif Inc .... E 740 549-6000
Delaware *(G-8847)*

CONTAINERS: Wood

A-Z Packaging Company .... F 614 444-8441
Columbus *(G-6670)*
Brown-Forman Corporation .... E 740 384-3027
Wellston *(G-19761)*
Clark Rm Inc .... E 419 425-9889
Findlay *(G-9808)*
Denoon Lumber Company LLC .... D 740 768-2220
Bergholz *(G-1641)*
Haessly Lumber Sales Co .... D 740 373-6681
Marietta *(G-12788)*
Hann Box Works .... E 740 962-3752
McConnelsville *(G-13351)*
Joe Gonda Company Inc .... F 440 458-6000
Elyria *(G-9443)*
Overseas Packing LLC .... E 440 232-2917
Bedford *(G-1451)*
T & D Thompson Inc .... E 740 332-8515
Laurelville *(G-11772)*
Traveling & Recycle Wood Pdts .... F 419 968-2649
Middle Point *(G-13899)*

CONTAINMENT VESSELS: Reactor, Metal Plate

FSRc Tanks Inc .... E 234 221-2015
Bolivar *(G-1934)*

CONTRACTOR: Dredging

Metropolitan Envmtl Svcs Inc .... D 614 771-1881
Hilliard *(G-10961)*

CONTRACTOR: Rigging & Scaffolding

AM Industrial Group LLC .... G 216 433-7171
Brookpark *(G-2149)*

Janson Industries .... D 330 455-7029
Canton *(G-2745)*

CONTRACTORS: Access Control System Eqpt

Safe Systems Inc .... G 216 661-1166
Cleveland *(G-6154)*

CONTRACTORS: Access Flooring System Installation

X-Treme Finishes Inc .... F 330 474-0614
Medina *(G-13498)*

CONTRACTORS: Acoustical & Insulation Work

Holland Assocts LLC DBA Archou .... F 513 891-0006
Cincinnati *(G-3888)*
One Wish LLC .... F 800 505-6883
Beachwood *(G-1289)*

CONTRACTORS: Asphalt

Asphalt Services Ohio Inc .... G 614 864-4600
Columbus *(G-6778)*
H P Streicher Inc .... G 419 841-4715
Toledo *(G-18490)*
Lucas County Asphalt Inc .... E 419 476-0705
Toledo *(G-18564)*
Massillon Asphalt Co .... G 330 833-6330
Massillon *(G-13173)*
Morris Paving .... F 740 373-2457
Marietta *(G-12809)*
Morrow Gravel Company Inc .... E 513 771-0820
Cincinnati *(G-4124)*
Mt Pleasant Blacktopping Inc .... E 513 874-3777
Fairfield *(G-9688)*
Smalls Asphalt Paving Inc .... F 740 427-4096
Gambier *(G-10318)*
Wilson Blacktop Corporation .... E 740 635-3566
Martins Ferry *(G-12928)*

CONTRACTORS: Awning Installation

Color Brite Company Inc .... G 216 441-4117
Cleveland *(G-5100)*
South Akron Awning Co .... F 330 848-7611
Akron *(G-409)*

CONTRACTORS: Bathtub Refinishing

Thiels Replacement Systems Inc .... D 419 289-6139
Ashland *(G-781)*

CONTRACTORS: Blasting, Exc Building Demolition

Kars Ohio LLC .... G 614 655-1099
Pataskala *(G-15973)*

CONTRACTORS: Boiler & Furnace

E & M Liberty Welding Inc .... G 330 866-2338
Waynesburg *(G-19724)*

CONTRACTORS: Boiler Maintenance Contractor

Holgate Metal Fab Inc .... F 419 599-2000
Napoleon *(G-14682)*
Park Corporation .... B 216 267-4870
Cleveland *(G-5965)*
Prout Boiler Htg & Wldg Inc .... E 330 744-0293
Youngstown *(G-21180)*

CONTRACTORS: Boiler Setting

Gurina Company .... G 614 279-3891
Columbus *(G-7132)*
Nbw Inc .... E 216 377-1700
Cleveland *(G-5864)*

CONTRACTORS: Building Eqpt & Machinery Installation

Cincinnati Crane & Hoist LLC .... F 513 202-1408
Harrison *(G-10772)*
Edmonds Elevator Company .... F 216 781-9135
Thompson *(G-18188)*

Fmt Repair Service Co .... G 330 347-7374
Mentor *(G-13579)*
Nbw Inc .... E 216 377-1700
Cleveland *(G-5864)*
Terex Utilities Inc .... F 440 262-3200
Brecksville *(G-2076)*
Trinity Door Systems .... G 877 603-2018
New Springfield *(G-14953)*

CONTRACTORS: Building Sign Installation & Mntnce

A B C Sign Inc .... F 513 241-8884
Cincinnati *(G-3332)*
All Signs of Chillicothe Inc .... G 740 773-5016
Chillicothe *(G-3227)*
Archer Corporation .... E 330 455-9995
Canton *(G-2604)*
Bird Corporation .... G 419 424-3095
Findlay *(G-9795)*
Bob King Sign Company Inc .... G 330 753-2679
Akron *(G-94)*
Boyer Signs & Graphics Inc .... E 216 383-7242
Euclid *(G-9568)*
Brilliant Electric Sign Co Ltd .... D 216 741-3800
Brooklyn Heights *(G-2132)*
Custom Neon & Commercial Signs ...... G 440 327-0225
North Ridgeville *(G-15367)*
Danite Holdings Ltd .... E 614 444-3333
Columbus *(G-7011)*
Exchange Signs .... G 330 644-4552
Akron *(G-174)*
Gus Holthaus Signs Inc .... E 513 861-0060
Cincinnati *(G-3858)*
Identitek Systems Inc .... D 330 832-9844
Massillon *(G-13155)*
Kessler Sign Company .... G 937 898-0633
Dayton *(G-8440)*
Macray Co LLC .... G 937 325-1726
Springfield *(G-17596)*
Mel Wacker Sign Inc .... G 330 832-1726
Massillon *(G-13178)*
R M Davis Inc .... G 419 756-6719
Mansfield *(G-12669)*
Signature Sign Co Inc .... F 216 426-1234
Cleveland *(G-6204)*
United-Maier Signs Inc .... D 513 681-6600
Cincinnati *(G-4541)*

CONTRACTORS: Cable Laying

Cambridge Cable Service Co .... G 740 685-5775
Byesville *(G-2396)*

CONTRACTORS: Cable TV Installation

Xxx Intrntional Amusements Inc .... E 216 671-6900
Cleveland *(G-6487)*

CONTRACTORS: Carpentry Work

AK Fabrication Inc .... F 330 458-1037
Canton *(G-2595)*
Custom Hitch and Trailer/ Over .... G 740 289-3925
Piketon *(G-16218)*
Finelli Ornamental Iron Co .... F 440 248-0050
Cleveland *(G-5347)*
Joseph Sabatino .... G 330 332-5879
Salem *(G-16904)*
Millwood Wholesale Inc .... F 330 359-6109
Dundee *(G-9177)*
Premier Construction Company .... E 513 874-2611
Fairfield *(G-9704)*
Riverside Cnstr Svcs Inc .... E 513 723-0900
Cincinnati *(G-4349)*
Tri County Door Service Inc .... F 216 531-2245
Euclid *(G-9611)*
Woodpeckers Inc .... E 440 238-1824
Strongsville *(G-17985)*

CONTRACTORS: Carpentry, Cabinet & Finish Work

Battershell Cabinets .... G 419 542-6448
Hicksville *(G-10901)*
Bobs Custom Str Interiors LLC .... G 567 316-7490
Toledo *(G-18375)*
Cabintpak Kitchens of Columbus .... G 614 294-4646
Columbus *(G-6886)*
Case Crafters Inc .... G 937 667-9473
Tipp City *(G-18271)*

Chesterland Cabinet Company..............G..... 440 564-1157
Newbury (G-15083)

Cirjak Furniture and Design..................G..... 330 296-8035
Ravenna (G-16521)

Contemporary Cabinets Inc..................G..... 937 833-1135
Brookville (G-2178)

Dgl Woodworking Inc............................F..... 937 837-7091
Dayton (G-8302)

Display Dynamics Inc............................F..... 937 832-2830
Englewood (G-9516)

Kbi Group Inc..G..... 614 873-5825
Plain City (G-16346)

Modern Designs Inc..............................G..... 330 644-1771
Akron (G-299)

Oakwood Furniture Inc..........................G..... 740 896-3162
Lowell (G-12403)

Snows Wood Shop Inc...........................E..... 419 836-3805
Oregon (G-15716)

Summit Custom Cabinets.......................G..... 740 345-1734
Newark (G-15061)

Wades Woodworking Inc........................F..... 937 374-6470
Xenia (G-20988)

CONTRACTORS: Carpentry, Cabinet Building & Installation

A & J Woodworking Inc..........................G..... 419 695-5655
Delphos (G-8898)

Accent Manufacturing Inc......................F..... 330 724-7704
Norton (G-15500)

Colby Woodworking Inc..........................G..... 937 224-7676
Dayton (G-8236)

East Woodworking Company....................G..... 216 791-5950
Cleveland (G-5240)

Kitchen Works Inc..................................G..... 440 353-0939
North Ridgeville (G-15385)

Nagele Manufacturing Co Inc..................E..... 216 433-1100
Cleveland (G-5849)

R Carney Thomas...................................G..... 740 342-3388
New Lexington (G-14853)

S & W Custom Tops Inc..........................G..... 330 788-2525
Youngstown (G-21195)

Sheridan Woodworks Inc........................F..... 216 663-9333
Cleveland (G-6188)

Ssi Manufacturing Inc.............................F..... 513 761-7757
West Chester (G-20054)

Thomas Cabinet Shop Inc.......................F..... 937 847-8239
Dayton (G-8711)

CONTRACTORS: Central Vacuum Cleaning System Installation

Metropolitan Envmtl Svcs Inc..................D..... 614 771-1881
Hilliard (G-10961)

CONTRACTORS: Chimney Construction & Maintenance

Donald Schloemer..................................G..... 419 933-2002
Willard (G-20394)

Whempys Corp.......................................G..... 614 888-6670
Worthington (G-20893)

CONTRACTORS: Closet Organizers, Installation & Design

Ptmj Enterprises.....................................C..... 440 543-8000
Solon (G-17365)

CONTRACTORS: Coating, Caulking & Weather, Water & Fire

Asb Industries Inc...................................E..... 330 753-8458
Barberton (G-1099)

CONTRACTORS: Commercial & Office Building

Arrow Coal Grove Inc..............................F..... 740 532-6143
Ironton (G-11289)

Bent Wood Solutions LLC........................G..... 330 674-1454
Millersburg (G-14199)

MGM Construction Inc............................F..... 440 234-7660
Berea (G-1627)

Rebsco Inc...F..... 937 548-2246
Greenville (G-10517)

Scs Construction Services Inc.................E..... 513 929-0260
Cincinnati (G-4393)

Stamm Contracting Co Inc.......................E..... 330 274-8230
Mantua (G-12723)

CONTRACTORS: Communications Svcs

Gatesair Inc..E..... 513 459-3400
Mason (G-13025)

Legrand North America LLC.....................B..... 937 224-0639
Moraine (G-14503)

Vertiv Co...G..... 440 460-3600
Cleveland (G-6410)

CONTRACTORS: Computer Installation

Data Power Solutions..............................G..... 614 471-1911
Columbus (G-7013)

Thomas Ross Associates Inc...................G..... 330 723-1110
Medina (G-13488)

CONTRACTORS: Concrete

Concrete Material Supply LLC...................G..... 419 261-6404
Woodville (G-20725)

Dan Shrock Cement.................................G..... 440 548-2498
Parkman (G-15951)

Forterra Pipe & Precast LLC.....................G..... 937 268-6707
Dayton (G-8349)

G Big Inc..E..... 740 867-5758
Chesapeake (G-3187)

Gateway Concrete Forming Svcs...............D..... 513 353-2000
Miamitown (G-13887)

Gennaro Pavers......................................G..... 330 536-6825
Lowellville (G-12409)

Hanson Concrete Products Ohio................E..... 614 443-4846
Columbus (G-7143)

Hilltop Basic Resources Inc.....................F..... 937 882-6357
Springfield (G-17573)

Koski Construction Co.............................G..... 440 997-5337
Ashtabula (G-815)

Lynn James Contracting LLC....................G..... 419 467-4505
Delta (G-8938)

Mack Industries Inc.................................G..... 330 460-7005
Brunswick (G-2237)

Precast Services Inc...............................G..... 614 428-4541
Reynoldsburg (G-16598)

R W Sidley Incorporated..........................E..... 440 352-9343
Painesville (G-15913)

RE Connors Construction Ltd....................G..... 740 644-0261
Thornville (G-18194)

Shelly and Sands Inc...............................G..... 740 453-0721
Zanesville (G-21351)

Spillman Company...................................E..... 614 444-2184
Columbus (G-7644)

Stamm Contracting Co Inc.......................E..... 330 274-8230
Mantua (G-12723)

W M Dauch Concrete Inc..........................G..... 419 562-6917
Bucyrus (G-2364)

Ward Construction Co..............................F..... 419 943-2450
Leipsic (G-11879)

CONTRACTORS: Concrete Block Masonry Laying

North Central Concrete Design..................F..... 419 606-1908
Wooster (G-20816)

CONTRACTORS: Concrete Pumping

Phillips Companies..................................E..... 937 426-5461
Beavercreek Township (G-1387)

Phillips Ready Mix Co..............................D..... 937 426-5151
Beavercreek Township (G-1388)

CONTRACTORS: Concrete Structure Coating, Plastic

Paulo Products Company..........................E..... 440 942-0153
Willoughby (G-20567)

CONTRACTORS: Construction Caulking

BASF Construction Chem LLC...................E..... 216 831-5500
Cleveland (G-4895)

CONTRACTORS: Construction Site Metal Structure Coating

Bogie Industries Inc Ltd...........................E..... 330 745-3105
Akron (G-95)

Colonial Surface Solutions Inc..................D..... 419 659-5639
Columbus Grove (G-7793)

Colonial Surface Solutions Inc..................E..... 419 358-0129
Bluffton (G-1910)

L B Foster Company................................E..... 330 652-1461
Mineral Ridge (G-14307)

CONTRACTORS: Core Drilling & Cutting

Barr Engineering Incorporated..................F..... 614 892-0162
Columbus (G-6807)

Barr Engineering Incorporated..................E..... 614 714-0299
Columbus (G-6808)

CONTRACTORS: Corrosion Control Installation

Mesocoat Inc..F..... 216 453-0866
Euclid (G-9593)

CONTRACTORS: Countertop Installation

Brad Snoderly..F..... 419 476-0184
Toledo (G-18380)

Classic Countertops LLC..........................G..... 330 882-4220
Akron (G-125)

Columbia Cabinets Inc.............................G..... 440 748-1010
Columbia Station (G-6584)

Dell Fixtures Inc.....................................E..... 614 449-1750
Columbus (G-7020)

Imperial Countertops..............................F..... 216 851-0888
Cleveland (G-5555)

Laminate Shop..F..... 740 749-3536
Waterford (G-19649)

Pietra Naturale Inc..................................F..... 937 438-8882
Dayton (G-8576)

Stone Statements Incorporated.................G..... 513 489-7866
Cincinnati (G-4470)

CONTRACTORS: Demolition, Building & Other Structures

Js Fabrications Inc..................................G..... 419 333-0323
Fremont (G-10161)

Sidwell Materials Inc...............................G..... 740 849-2394
Zanesville (G-21354)

CONTRACTORS: Diamond Drilling & Sawing

Curtiss-Wright Flow Control......................D..... 513 735-2538
Batavia (G-1175)

Curtiss-Wright Flow Control......................D..... 513 528-7900
Cincinnati (G-3296)

CONTRACTORS: Directional Oil & Gas Well Drilling Svc

Brendel Producing Company.....................G..... 330 854-4151
Canton (G-2628)

Camphire Drilling Inc...............................G..... 740 599-6928
Danville (G-8085)

Clearpath Utility Solutions LLC.................F..... 740 661-4240
Zanesville (G-21289)

D Anderson Corp....................................G..... 330 433-0606
Canton (G-2676)

Directional One Svcs Inc USA...................G..... 740 371-5031
Marietta (G-12779)

J Valtier Gas and Oil Co Inc.....................G..... 740 342-2839
Malta (G-12537)

JAC Construction Ohio Llc.......................G..... 440 564-5005
Newbury (G-15097)

Kirk Excavating & Construction..................E..... 614 444-4008
Columbus (G-7262)

Ngo Development Corporation...................F..... 740 344-3790
Newark (G-15039)

Oak Dale Drilling Inc...............................G..... 740 385-5888
Logan (G-12187)

Palmer Properties LLC.............................G..... 419 938-3114
Perrysville (G-16174)

R & J Drilling Company Inc.......................G..... 740 763-3991
Frazeysburg (G-10076)

Temple Oil & Gas Company.......................G..... 740 452-7878
Crooksville (G-7954)

Top Drilling Corporation...........................F..... 304 477-3333
Marietta (G-12842)

Warren Drilling Co Inc.............................G..... 740 783-2775
Dexter City (G-8958)

CONTRACTORS: Drapery Track Installation

Carmens Installation Co...........................F..... 216 371-5633
Cleveland (G-4979)

E W Perry Service Co Inc.........................G..... 419 473-1231
Toledo (G-18448)

M C L Window Coverings Inc.....................G..... 513 868-6000
Hamilton (G-10719)

Nancys Draperies....................................F..... 330 855-7751
Marshallville (G-12919)

PRODUCT

Style-Line Incorporated ....E 614 291-0600
Columbus (G-7664)

CONTRACTORS: Driveway

Action Blacktop Sealcoating & ....G 937 667-4769
Tipp City (G-18259)
Baileys Asphalt Sealing ....F 740 453-9409
South Zanesville (G-17453)
Image Pavement Maintenance ....E 937 833-9200
Brookville (G-2187)
Parkins Asphalt Sealing ....G 419 422-2399
Findlay (G-9876)

CONTRACTORS: Earthmoving

Biedenbach Logging ....G 740 732-6477
Sarahsville (G-17024)

CONTRACTORS: Electric Power Systems

Columbia Energy Group ....G 614 460-4683
Columbus (G-6945)

CONTRACTORS: Electrical

Akron Foundry Co ....E 330 745-3101
Barberton (G-1095)
ARC Elec ....F 440 774-2800
Wellington (G-19737)
Atlas Industrial Contrs LLC ....B 614 841-4500
Columbus (G-6784)
Connor Electric Inc ....G 513 932-5798
Lebanon (G-11790)
D & E Electric Inc ....F 513 738-1172
Okeana (G-15665)
Electric Ctrl & Mtr Repr Svc ....G 216 881-3143
Cleveland (G-5264)
Fishel Company ....D 614 850-4400
Columbus (G-7089)
Gould Group LLC ....G 740 807-4294
Hilliard (G-10949)
Hess Advanced Solutions Llc ....G 937 829-4794
Dayton (G-8389)
Instrmntation Ctrl Systems Inc ....E 513 662-2600
Cincinnati (G-3925)
JC Electric ....E 330 760-2915
Garrettsville (G-10325)
Jeff Bonham Electric Inc ....E 937 233-7662
Dayton (G-8425)
Jobap Assembly Inc ....F 440 632-5393
Middlefield (G-13947)
Mirus Adapted Tech LLC ....E 614 402-4585
Dublin (G-9103)
Mr Electric ....G 419 289-7474
Mansfield (G-12654)
Schneder Elc Bldngs Amrcas Inc ....D 513 398-9800
Lebanon (G-11838)

CONTRACTORS: Electronic Controls Installation

Control Associates Inc ....G 440 708-1770
Chagrin Falls (G-3082)
Controls Inc ....E 330 239-4345
Medina (G-13392)
Safe-Grain Inc ....G 513 398-2500
Loveland (G-12383)

CONTRACTORS: Elevator Front Installation, Metal

Architectural Products Dev ....G 216 631-6260
Cleveland (G-4826)

CONTRACTORS: Energy Management Control

Siemens Energy Inc ....B 740 393-8897
Mount Vernon (G-14648)
Tekworx LLC ....F 513 533-4777
Blue Ash (G-1881)

CONTRACTORS: Epoxy Application

Flow-Liner Systems Ltd ....E 800 348-0020
Zanesville (G-21309)
Hy-Blast Inc ....F 513 424-0704
Middletown (G-14045)

CONTRACTORS: Excavating

Alden Sand & Gravel Co Inc ....F 330 928-3249
Cuyahoga Falls (G-7963)
Arrow Coal Grove Inc ....F 740 532-6143
Ironton (G-11289)
Castalia Trenching & Ready Mix ....F 419 684-5502
Castalia (G-2973)
David Cox ....G 740 254-4858
Gnadenhutten (G-10405)
Dennis Constuction Sanitation ....G 419 332-8301
Fremont (G-10142)
Don Wartko Construction Co ....D 330 673-5252
Kent (G-11450)
H & S Drilling Co Inc ....G 740 828-2411
Frazeysburg (G-10074)
Ingles Logging ....G 740 379-2760
Patriot (G-15996)
Kelchner Inc ....C 937 704-9890
Springboro (G-17486)
Kipps Gravel Company Inc ....F 513 732-1024
Batavia (G-1199)
Kirk Excavating & Construction ....E 614 444-4008
Columbus (G-7262)
Koski Construction Co ....G 440 997-5337
Ashtabula (G-815)
Liebrecht Manufacturing ....G 419 596-3501
Continental (G-7827)
Metropolitan Envmtl Svcs Inc ....D 614 771-1881
Hilliard (G-10961)
Paul R Lipp & Son Inc ....F 330 227-9614
Rogers (G-16714)
Phillips Companies ....E 937 426-5461
Beavercreek Township (G-1386)
Phillips Ready Mix Co ....D 937 426-5151
Beavercreek Township (G-1388)
Pipelines Inc ....G 330 448-0000
Masury (G-13215)
R & B Enterprises USA Inc ....G 330 674-2227
Millersburg (G-14257)
R J Dobay Enterprises Inc ....G 440 834-4580
Burton (G-2382)
Rbm Environmental and Cnstr ....E 419 693-5840
Oregon (G-15715)
Sanders Fredrick Excvtg Co Inc ....G 330 297-7980
Ravenna (G-16555)

CONTRACTORS: Exterior Painting

All Ohio Companies Inc ....E 216 420-9274
Cleveland (G-4756)

CONTRACTORS: Fence Construction

Connaughton Wldg & Fence LLC ....G 513 867-0230
Hamilton (G-10680)
Fence One Inc ....F 216 441-2600
Cleveland (G-5334)
Security Fence Group Inc ....E 513 681-3700
Cincinnati (G-4395)
Youngstown Fence Inc ....G 330 788-8110
Youngstown (G-21251)

CONTRACTORS: Fiber Optic Cable Installation

JAC Construction Ohio Llc ....G 440 564-5005
Newbury (G-15097)

CONTRACTORS: Fire Detection & Burglar Alarm Systems

Independent Protection Systems ....G 330 832-7992
Massillon (G-13156)

CONTRACTORS: Floor Laying & Other Floor Work

Done-Rite Bowling Service Co ....E 440 232-3280
Bedford (G-1420)
Dynafloor Systems Inc ....F 330 467-6005
Solon (G-17283)
Hoover & Wells Inc ....C 419 691-9220
Toledo (G-18511)
Myko Industries ....G 216 431-0900
Cleveland (G-5845)
Tremco Incorporated ....B 216 292-5000
Beachwood (G-1303)
True Kote Inc ....G 419 334-8813
Fremont (G-10188)
Western Reserve Furniture Co ....G 440 235-6216
North Olmsted (G-15351)

CONTRACTORS: Flooring

Mount Hope Planing ....F 330 359-0538
Millersburg (G-14250)
Protective Industrial Polymers ....F 440 327-0015
North Ridgeville (G-15396)

CONTRACTORS: Foundation Building

North Central Insulation Inc ....F 419 886-2030
Bellville (G-1573)

CONTRACTORS: Garage Doors

Division Overhead Door Inc ....F 513 872-0888
Cincinnati (G-3659)
Nofziger Door Sales Inc ....C 419 337-9900
Wauseon (G-19692)

CONTRACTORS: Gas Field Svcs, NEC

Catress LLC ....G 740 695-0918
Saint Clairsville (G-16784)
Clearfield Ohio Holdings Inc ....D 740 947-5121
Waverly (G-19705)
Exelon Energy Company ....F 614 797-4377
Westerville (G-20152)
Gas Analytical Services Inc ....G 330 539-4267
Girard (G-10389)
James L Williams ....G 740 865-3382
Wingett Run (G-20709)
Natural Gas Construction Inc ....G 330 364-9240
Dover (G-9005)
OS Power Tong Inc ....G 330 866-3815
Waynesburg (G-19726)
Standard Oil Company ....G 419 691-2460
Oregon (G-15718)
Stingray Energy Services ....E 405 648-4177
Belmont (G-1580)
Sulmona Enegry LLC ....G 234 736-3749
Youngstown (G-21214)
United Chart Processors Inc ....G 740 373-5801
Marietta (G-12847)

CONTRACTORS: General Electric

Burkett Industries Inc ....G 419 332-4391
Fremont (G-10132)
Commercial Electric Pdts Corp ....E 216 241-2886
Cleveland (G-5104)
D & J Electric Motor Repair Co ....F 330 336-4343
Wadsworth (G-19401)
Franks Electric Inc ....G 513 542-0342
Cincinnati (G-3781)
Magnum Computers Inc ....F 216 781-1757
Cleveland (G-5730)
P S C Inc ....G 216 531-3375
Cleveland (G-5957)
Security Fence Group Inc ....E 513 681-3700
Cincinnati (G-4395)
Speelman Electric Inc ....D 330 633-1410
Tallmadge (G-18169)
Waibel Electric Co Inc ....F 740 964-2956
Etna (G-9553)

CONTRACTORS: Glass Tinting, Architectural & Automotive

AGC Automotive Americas ....D 937 599-3131
Bellefontaine (G-1515)

CONTRACTORS: Glass, Glazing & Tinting

A Service Glass Inc ....F 937 426-4920
Beavercreek (G-1315)
AGC Automotive Americas ....D 937 599-3131
Bellefontaine (G-1515)
All State GL Block Fctry Inc ....G 440 205-8410
Mentor (G-13519)
Kimmatt Corp ....G 937 228-3811
Dayton (G-8441)
M/W International Inc ....F 440 526-6900
Brecksville (G-2063)
Mentor Glass Supplies and Repr ....G 440 255-9444
Mentor (G-13651)
Pentagon Protection Usa LLC ....F 614 734-7240
Dublin (G-9123)
Solon Glass Center Inc ....F 440 248-5018
Cleveland (G-6218)
Trinity Door Systems ....G 877 603-2018
New Springfield (G-14953)

(G-0000) Company's Geographic Section entry number

CONTRACTORS: Gutters & Downspouts

Barnett Spouting Inc..................................G...... 330 644-0853
Akron (G-85)

Thiels Replacement Systems Inc ....D...... 419 289-6139
Ashland (G-781)

Yoder Window & Siding Ltd ....F...... 330 695-6960
Fredericksburg (G-10095)

CONTRACTORS: Heating & Air Conditioning

A A A Professional Htg & Coolg ....G...... 513 933-0564
Lebanon (G-11773)

Carrier Corporation...................................E...... 937 275-0645
Dayton (G-8212)

Cartwright Construction Inc ....G...... 330 929-3020
Cuyahoga Falls (G-7976)

Cincinnati Air Conditioning Co..............D...... 513 721-5622
Cincinnati (G-3538)

Hess Advanced Solutions Llc ....G...... 937 829-4794
Dayton (G-8389)

IV J Telecommunications LLC ....G...... 606 694-1762
South Point (G-17438)

J Feldkamp Design Build Ltd ....G...... 513 870-0601
Fairfield (G-9670)

Northeastern Rfrgn Corp..........................E...... 440 942-7676
Willoughby (G-20557)

Us Inc ....G...... 513 791-1162
Blue Ash (G-1887)

CONTRACTORS: Heating Systems Repair & Maintenance Svc

Whempys Corp...G...... 614 888-6670
Worthington (G-20893)

Wood Stove Shed ....G...... 419 562-1545
Bucyrus (G-2365)

CONTRACTORS: Highway & Street Construction, General

J A Donadee Corporation.........................E...... 330 533-3305
Canfield (G-2559)

Kenmore Construction Co Inc ....E...... 330 832-8888
Massillon (G-13162)

S E Johnson Companies Inc.....................F...... 419 893-8731
Maumee (G-13290)

Valley Asphalt Corporation ....G...... 513 561-1551
Cincinnati (G-4551)

Walls Bros Asphalt Co Inc ....G...... 937 548-7158
Greenville (G-10526)

Ward Construction Co ....F...... 419 943-2450
Leipsic (G-11879)

CONTRACTORS: Highway & Street Paving

Shelly and Sands Inc ....F...... 740 453-0721
Zanesville (G-21350)

Shelly and Sands Inc ....E...... 740 453-0721
Zanesville (G-21351)

Shelly Company ....G...... 740 474-6255
Circleville (G-4642)

Terminal Ready-Mix Inc ....E...... 440 288-0181
Lorain (G-12286)

Wilson Blacktop Corporation ....E...... 740 635-3566
Martins Ferry (G-12928)

CONTRACTORS: Highway Sign & Guardrail Construction & Install

Traffic Detectors & Signs Inc ....G...... 330 707-9060
Youngstown (G-21226)

CONTRACTORS: Home & Office Intrs Finish, Furnish/Remodel

Boyce Ltd..G...... 614 236-8901
Columbus (G-6851)

Fdi Cabinetry LLC ....G...... 513 353-4500
Cleves (G-6514)

CONTRACTORS: Hotel, Motel/Multi-Family Home Renovtn/Remodel

Bison Builders LLC....................................F...... 614 636-0365
Columbus (G-6832)

Cardinal Builders Inc ....E...... 614 237-1000
Columbus (G-6905)

Northpointe Cabinetry LLC ....G...... 740 455-4045
Zanesville (G-21334)

CONTRACTORS: Hydraulic Eqpt Installation & Svcs

K C N Technologies LLC ....G...... 440 439-4219
Bedford (G-1434)

Pakk Systems LLC....................................G...... 440 839-9999
Wakeman (G-19452)

CONTRACTORS: Hydraulic Well Fracturing Svcs

PSC Holdings Inc ....G...... 740 454-6253
Zanesville (G-21347)

Universal Well Services Inc ....E...... 330 264-1109
Millersburg (G-14275)

CONTRACTORS: Indl Building Renovation, Remodeling & Repair

Halman Inc...F...... 440 992-4239
Ashtabula (G-811)

Herbert Wood Products Inc ....G...... 440 834-1410
Middlefield (G-13942)

Universal Fabg Cnstr Svcs Inc ....D...... 614 274-1128
Columbus (G-7723)

CONTRACTORS: Insulation Installation, Building

North Central Insulation Inc....................F...... 419 886-2030
Bellville (G-1573)

CONTRACTORS: Kitchen & Bathroom Remodeling

Cardinal Builders Inc ....E...... 614 237-1000
Columbus (G-6905)

James F Seme ....G...... 440 759-6455
Berea (G-1623)

Kitchen Works Inc....................................G...... 440 353-0939
North Ridgeville (G-15385)

CONTRACTORS: Kitchen Cabinet Installation

Old Mill Custom Cabinetry Co ....G...... 419 423-8897
Findlay (G-9871)

CONTRACTORS: Lightweight Steel Framing Installation

J N Linrose Mfg LLC ....G...... 513 867-5500
Hamilton (G-10709)

CONTRACTORS: Machine Rigging & Moving

Atlas Industrial Contrs LLC ....B...... 614 841-4500
Columbus (G-6784)

Chagrin Vly Stl Erectors Inc....................F...... 440 975-1556
Willoughby (G-20455)

CONTRACTORS: Machinery Installation

Camton Mechanical Inc ....G...... 614 864-7620
Columbus (G-6892)

De-Ko Inc ....G...... 440 951-2585
Willoughby (G-20472)

Hilo Tech Inc ....G...... 440 979-1155
North Olmsted (G-15339)

Intertec Corporation ....B...... 419 537-9711
Toledo (G-18527)

Molding Machine Services Inc.................G...... 330 461-2270
Medina (G-13448)

Northwest Installations Inc ....E...... 419 423-5738
Findlay (G-9869)

Spallinger Millwright Svc Co ....G...... 419 225-5830
Lima (G-12094)

CONTRACTORS: Maintenance, Parking Facility Eqpt

Parking & Traffic Control SEC ....F...... 440 243-7565
Cleveland (G-5977)

CONTRACTORS: Marble Installation, Interior

Cutting Edge Countertops Inc ....E...... 419 873-9500
Perrysburg (G-16081)

Davies Since 1900...................................G...... 419 756-4212
Mansfield (G-12593)

Distinctive Marble & Gran Inc ....F...... 614 760-0003
Plain City (G-16335)

CONTRACTORS: Masonry & Stonework

Albert Freytag Inc ....E...... 419 628-2018
Minster (G-14349)

North Hill Marble & Granite Co ....F...... 330 253-2179
Akron (G-318)

Rmi Titanium Company LLC ....E...... 330 652-9952
Niles (G-15176)

CONTRACTORS: Mechanical

Debra-Kuempel Inc ....D...... 513 271-6500
Cincinnati (G-3645)

Edwards Electrical & Mech ....E...... 614 485-2003
Columbus (G-7047)

Enerfab Inc ....B...... 513 641-0500
Cincinnati (G-3704)

Greer & Whitehead Cnstr Inc ....E...... 513 202-1757
Harrison (G-10781)

Jan Squires Inc ....G...... 440 988-7859
Amherst (G-599)

K-Js Mechanical Service ....F...... 419 729-1103
Toledo (G-18536)

Kirk Williams Company Inc ....D...... 614 875-9023
Grove City (G-10568)

Schweizer Dipple Inc ....D...... 440 786-8090
Cleveland (G-6167)

Sexton Industrial Inc................................C...... 513 530-5555
West Chester (G-20049)

Temperature Controls Company ....F...... 330 773-6633
Akron (G-433)

CONTRACTORS: Metal Ceiling Construction & Repair Work

Andy Russo Jr Inc ....F...... 440 585-1456
Wickliffe (G-20354)

CONTRACTORS: Millwrights

D & G Welding Inc ....G...... 419 445-5751
Archbold (G-670)

K F T Inc ....D...... 513 241-5910
Cincinnati (G-3965)

CONTRACTORS: Nonresidential Building Design & Construction

McDannald Welding & Machining ....G...... 937 644-0300
Marysville (G-12960)

CONTRACTORS: Oil & Gas Building, Repairing & Dismantling Svc

Binder Oil Field Construction ....G...... 330 484-3680
Magnolia (G-12515)

Dow Cameron Oil & Gas LLC ....G...... 740 452-1568
Zanesville (G-21300)

Dp2 Energy LLC ....G...... 330 376-5068
Akron (G-156)

Elsaan Energy LLC ....G...... 740 294-9399
Walhonding (G-19469)

Formation Cementing Inc.........................G...... 740 453-6926
Zanesville (G-21310)

Hill & Associates Inc................................G...... 740 685-5168
Byesville (G-2403)

Interden Industries Inc ....G...... 419 368-9011
Lakeville (G-11651)

Ralph Robinson Inc ....G...... 740 385-2747
Logan (G-12192)

CONTRACTORS: Oil & Gas Field Geological Exploration Svcs

Clarence Tussel Jr ....G...... 440 576-3415
Jefferson (G-11360)

David R Hill Inc ....G...... 740 685-5168
Byesville (G-2397)

New World Energy Resources ....F...... 740 344-4087
Newark (G-15038)

CONTRACTORS: Oil & Gas Field Geophysical Exploration Svcs

Dlz Ohio Inc ....C...... 614 888-0040
Columbus (G-7033)

Hocking Hills Energy & Well SE ....G...... 740 385-6690
Logan (G-12176)

CONTRACTORS: Oil & Gas Field Salt Water Impound/Storing Svc

Shalelogix LLC ....G........ 234 600-5839
Warren (G-19600)

CONTRACTORS: Oil & Gas Field Tools Fishing Svcs

Lakeside Sport Shop Inc ....G........ 330 637-2862
Cortland (G-7870)

CONTRACTORS: Oil & Gas Well Casing Cement Svcs

Franks Casing ....G........ 330 236-4264
Massillon (G-13133)
Terra Star Inc ....F........ 405 200-1336
Waynesburg (G-19728)
Wyoming Casing Service Inc ....E........ 330 479-8785
Canton (G-2904)

CONTRACTORS: Oil & Gas Well Drilling Svc

Advent Drilling Inc ....E........ 330 497-2533
Canton (G-2589)
Anderson Energy Inc ....G........ 740 678-8608
Fleming (G-9909)
Artex Oil Company ....E........ 740 373-3313
Marietta (G-12763)
Bancequity Petroleum Corp ....G........ 330 468-5935
Macedonia (G-12436)
Buckeye Oil Producing Co ....F........ 330 264-8847
Wooster (G-20754)
Clarence Tussel Jr ....G........ 440 576-3415
Jefferson (G-11360)
Columbus Oilfield Exploration ....G........ 614 895-9520
Powell (G-16468)
Dnl Oil Corp ....G........ 740 342-4970
New Lexington (G-14847)
Domestic Oil & Gas Co Inc ....G........ 440 232-3150
Cleveland (G-5203)
Doris Kimble ....E........ 330 343-1226
Dover (G-8977)
Drillex Inc ....G........ 440 255-7500
Mentor (G-13564)
Dugan Drilling Incorporated ....G........ 740 668-3811
Walhonding (G-19468)
Echo Drilling Inc ....G........ 740 254-4127
Gnadenhutten (G-10406)
Eclipse Resources - Ohio LLC ....E........ 740 452-4503
Zanesville (G-21306)
Energy Resources of America In ....G........ 330 953-1813
Youngstown (G-21077)
Frank Csapo ....G........ 330 435-4458
Creston (G-7939)
Fredebaugh Well Drilling Co ....F........ 440 357-6924
Grand River (G-10448)
Future Productions Inc ....G........ 330 478-0477
Canton (G-2709)
G & H Drilling Inc ....E........ 330 674-4868
Millersburg (G-14216)
Groundhogs 2000 LLC ....G........ 440 653-1647
Oakwood Village (G-15625)
H & A Drilling ....G........ 740 763-2575
Newark (G-15016)
H & D Drilling Co Inc ....G........ 740 745-2236
Frazeysburg (G-10073)
Hocking Hills Energy & Well SE ....G........ 740 385-6690
Logan (G-12176)
Hopewell Oil & Gas Dev Co ....G........ 740 452-9326
Zanesville (G-21319)
Interden Industries Inc ....G........ 419 368-9011
Lakeville (G-11651)
J D Drilling Co ....E........ 740 949-2512
Racine (G-16504)
James R Smail Inc ....G........ 330 264-7500
Wooster (G-20790)
Keito Gas Inc ....G........ 740 374-5463
Marietta (G-12796)
Kilbarger Construction Inc ....C........ 740 385-5531
Logan (G-12182)
King Energy Inc ....G........ 330 297-5508
Ravenna (G-16536)
Kleese Development Associates ....G........ 330 392-7899
Warren (G-19566)
Lee Oil & Gas Inc ....G........ 937 223-8891
Oakwood (G-15608)
Maric Drilling Company Inc ....F........ 330 830-8178
Winesburg (G-20705)

Moore Well Services Inc ....E........ 330 650-4443
Mogadore (G-14381)
Nomac Drilling LLC ....G........ 330 476-7040
Carrollton (G-2962)
Nomac Drilling LLC ....F........ 724 324-2205
Saint Clairsville (G-16798)
Ohio L & M Company Inc ....E........ 330 493-0440
Canton (G-2800)
Ohio Valley Energy Systems ....G........ 330 799-2268
Youngstown (G-21156)
Oogeep ....G........ 740 587-0410
Granville (G-10463)
Osair Inc ....G........ 440 974-6500
Mentor (G-13675)
P & S Energy Inc ....G........ 330 652-2525
Mineral Ridge (G-14309)
PAC Drilling O & G LLC ....G........ 330 874-3781
Bolivar (G-1941)
Parrot Energy Company ....G........ 330 637-0151
Cortland (G-7873)
Paul A Grim Inc ....G........ 740 385-9637
Logan (G-12190)
Petro Quest Inc ....G........ 740 593-3800
Athens (G-881)
Pine Top Inc ....G........ 330 929-2492
Akron (G-340)
Pinnacle Drilling LLC ....F........ 330 276-1096
Killbuck (G-11597)
Ponderosa Consulting Services ....G........ 330 264-2298
Wooster (G-20821)
Portage Resources Inc ....G........ 330 872-3827
Warren (G-19587)
Professional Oilfield Services ....G........ 740 685-5168
Byesville (G-2409)
Quality Oil & Gas Corp ....G........ 330 821-6375
Alliance (G-534)
Rj Drilling Company Inc ....G........ 740 763-3991
Nashport (G-14707)
Rockbottom Oil & Gas ....G........ 740 374-2478
Marietta (G-12825)
Sabre Energy Corporation ....G........ 740 685-8266
Lore City (G-12294)
Smith Smith & Deyarman ....G........ 330 866-5521
Magnolia (G-12519)
Stratagraph Ne Inc ....E........ 740 373-3091
Marietta (G-12838)
Summit Drilling Company Inc ....F........ 800 775-5537
Akron (G-419)
Tiger Oil Inc ....G........ 614 837-5552
Canal Winchester (G-2538)
Timco Inc ....F........ 740 685-2594
Byesville (G-2410)
Transcontinental Oil & Gas ....G........ 330 995-0777
Aurora (G-950)
U S Fuel Development Co ....G........ 614 486-0614
Columbus (G-7716)
Victor McKenzie Drilling Co ....E........ 740 453-0834
Zanesville (G-21361)
Warthman Drilling Inc ....G........ 740 746-9950
Sugar Grove (G-18013)

CONTRACTORS: Oil & Gas Well Flow Rate Measurement Svcs

Fts International Inc ....B........ 330 754-2375
East Canton (G-9193)

CONTRACTORS: Oil & Gas Well Foundation Grading Svcs

Ksn Clearing LLC ....F........ 304 269-3306
Gallipolis (G-10303)

CONTRACTORS: Oil & Gas Well On-Site Foundation Building Svcs

Bearcat Construction Inc ....G........ 513 314-0867
Mason (G-12987)
Greer & Whitehead Cnstr Inc ....E........ 513 202-1757
Harrison (G-10781)

CONTRACTORS: Oil & Gas Well Plugging & Abandoning Svcs

Omega Cementing Co ....G........ 330 695-7147
Apple Creek (G-646)
Pluggers Inc ....G........ 330 383-7692
Niles (G-15175)

CONTRACTORS: Oil & Gas Well Redrilling

Decker Drilling Inc ....E........ 740 749-3939
Vincent (G-19379)

CONTRACTORS: Oil & Gas Wells Pumping Svcs

Ottawa Oil Co Inc ....F........ 419 425-3301
Findlay (G-9874)
Performance Technologies LLC ....G........ 330 875-1216
Louisville (G-12324)
Pettigrew Pumping Inc ....G........ 330 297-7900
Ravenna (G-16550)
Stocker & Sitler Oil Company ....G........ 614 888-9588
Columbus (G-7658)

CONTRACTORS: Oil & Gas Wells Svcs

A W Tipka Oil & Gas Inc ....G........ 330 364-4333
Dover (G-8962)
Bakerwell Inc ....E........ 330 276-2161
Killbuck (G-11592)
Canton Oil Well Service Inc ....F........ 330 494-1221
Canton (G-2643)
Dp Operating Company Inc ....G........ 330 938-2172
Beloit (G-1582)
Hackworth Oil Field Electric ....G........ 330 345-6504
Wooster (G-20783)
Harmon John ....G........ 740 934-2032
Graysville (G-10469)
J Valtier Gas and Oil Co Inc ....G........ 740 342-2839
Malta (G-12537)
Karlco Oilfield Services Inc ....F........ 440 576-3415
Jefferson (G-11363)
Ohio L & M Company Inc ....E........ 330 493-0440
Canton (G-2800)
Pyramid Treating Inc ....G........ 330 325-2811
Atwater (G-902)
Renegade Well Services LLC ....G........ 330 488-6055
Canton (G-2836)
Wrights Well Service ....G........ 740 380-9602
Logan (G-12197)

CONTRACTORS: Oil Field Haulage Svcs

Fishburn Tank Truck Service ....D........ 419 253-6031
Marengo (G-12750)

CONTRACTORS: Oil Field Mud Drilling Svcs

Kelchner Inc ....C........ 937 704-9890
Springboro (G-17486)

CONTRACTORS: Oil Field Pipe Testing Svcs

Express Energy Svcs Oper LP ....E........ 740 337-4530
Toronto (G-18781)
Ream and Haager Laboratory ....F........ 330 343-3711
Dover (G-9010)

CONTRACTORS: Oil Sampling Svcs

Bdi Inc ....C........ 216 642-9100
Cleveland (G-4898)
Predict Inc ....F........ 216 642-3223
Cleveland (G-6039)

CONTRACTORS: Oil/Gas Field Casing,Tube/Rod Running,Cut/Pull

Varco LP ....E........ 440 277-8696
Lorain (G-12289)

CONTRACTORS: Oil/Gas Well Construction, Rpr/Dismantling Svcs

Acer Contracting LLC ....G........ 702 236-5917
Columbus (G-6688)
Ajami Holdings Group LLC ....G........ 216 396-6089
Richmond Heights (G-16651)
Barnes Services LLC ....G........ 440 319-2088
Maple Heights (G-12727)
Boyce Ltd ....G........ 614 236-8901
Columbus (G-6851)
Brightstar Propane & Fuels ....G........ 614 891-8395
Westerville (G-20140)
Byrd Prcurement Specialist Inc ....G........ 419 936-0019
Swanton (G-18082)
Carper Well Service Inc ....F........ 740 374-2567
Marietta (G-12771)
Circleville Oil Co ....G........ 740 477-3341
Circleville (G-4625)

Collier Well Eqp & Sup Inc ....F 330 345-3968
Wooster *(G-20760)*
Elite Property Group LLC ....F 216 316-8222
Cleveland *(G-5272)*
Kbc Services ....F 513 693-3743
Loveland *(G-12365)*
MGM Construction Inc ....F 440 234-7660
Berea *(G-1627)*
R Anthony Enterprises LLC ....F 419 341-0961
Marion *(G-12894)*
Scassa Asphalt Inc ....F 330 830-2039
Massillon *(G-13200)*

CONTRACTORS: On-Site Welding

Accurate Machining & Welding ....G 937 584-4518
Sabina *(G-16772)*
Bob Lanes Welding Inc ....F 740 373-3567
Marietta *(G-12767)*
Burdens Machine & Welding ....E 740 345-9246
Newark *(G-14989)*
C Stoneman Corporation ....G 440 942-3325
Eastlake *(G-9261)*
D & M Welding & Radiator ....G 740 947-9032
Waverly *(G-19707)*
Dennis Corso Co Inc ....G 330 673-2411
Kent *(G-11448)*
DMC Welding Incorporated ....G 330 877-1935
Hartville *(G-10820)*
Dover Fabrication and Burn Inc ....G 330 339-1057
New Philadelphia *(G-14895)*
G & R Welding & Machining ....G 937 323-9353
Springfield *(G-17562)*
Geyer Transport & Mfg ....F 740 382-9008
Marion *(G-12868)*
Halls Welding & Supplies Inc ....G 330 385-9353
East Liverpool *(G-9217)*
Holdsworth Industrial Fabg ....G 330 874-3945
Bolivar *(G-1936)*
Jackson Machine & Fabrication ....G 740 682-3994
Oak Hill *(G-15598)*
Kellys Welding & Fabricating ....G 440 593-6040
Conneaut *(G-7811)*
Kent Swigart ....G 937 836-5292
Englewood *(G-9528)*
Knowlton Machine Inc ....G 419 281-6802
Ashland *(G-748)*
Lefeld Welding & Stl Sups Inc ....E 419 678-2397
Coldwater *(G-6567)*
Leon Newswanger ....F 419 896-3336
Shiloh *(G-17151)*
Lim Services LLC ....F 513 217-0801
Middletown *(G-14054)*
M & M Certified Welding Inc ....F 330 467-1729
Macedonia *(G-12467)*
M M I Services Inc ....F 440 259-2939
Perry *(G-16053)*
Mansfield Welding Services LLC ....G 419 594-2738
Oakwood *(G-15617)*
Marsam Metalfab Inc ....E 330 405-1520
Twinsburg *(G-18978)*
McDannald Welding & Machining ....G 937 644-0300
Marysville *(G-12960)*
Mh & Son Machining & Wldg Co ....G 419 621-0690
Sandusky *(G-16988)*
P & S Welding Co ....G 330 274-2850
Mantua *(G-12720)*
Quality Fabricated Metals Inc ....E 330 332-7008
Salem *(G-16923)*
Robs Welding Technologies Ltd ....G 937 890-4963
Dayton *(G-8637)*
Select International Corp ....G 937 233-9191
Dayton *(G-8653)*
Steve Vore Welding and Steel ....F 419 375-4087
Fort Recovery *(G-9959)*
Warrior Technologies Inc ....G 937 438-0279
Dayton *(G-8745)*
Weldments Inc ....F 937 235-9261
Dayton *(G-8751)*

CONTRACTORS: Ornamental Metal Work

Custom Way Welding Inc ....F 937 845-9469
New Carlisle *(G-14800)*
Fabrication Group LLC ....E 216 251-1125
Cleveland *(G-5318)*
Friends Ornamental Iron Co ....G 216 431-6710
Cleveland *(G-5382)*
Spradlin Bros Welding Co ....F 800 219-2182
Springfield *(G-17650)*

CONTRACTORS: Painting & Wall Covering

A & A Safety Inc ....E 513 943-6100
Amelia *(G-564)*
National Electro-Coatings Inc ....D 216 898-0080
Cleveland *(G-5855)*
Premier Coatings Ltd ....F 513 942-1070
West Chester *(G-19920)*
Procoat Painting Inc ....G 513 735-2500
Batavia *(G-1218)*

CONTRACTORS: Painting, Commercial, Interior

Davies Since 1900 ....G 419 756-4212
Mansfield *(G-12593)*

CONTRACTORS: Painting, Indl

Banks Manufacturing Company ....F 440 458-8661
Grafton *(G-10420)*
Industrial Mill Maintenance ....E 330 746-1155
Youngstown *(G-21115)*
Js Fabrications Inc ....G 419 333-0323
Fremont *(G-10161)*
Kars Ohio LLC ....G 614 655-1099
Pataskala *(G-15973)*
Phoenix Technologies Inc ....F 330 630-5888
Akron *(G-338)*
Semper Quality Industry Inc ....G 440 352-8111
Mentor *(G-13719)*

CONTRACTORS: Painting, Residential

Lim Services LLC ....F 513 217-0801
Middletown *(G-14054)*

CONTRACTORS: Parking Lot Maintenance

Action Blacktop Sealcoating & ....G 937 667-4769
Tipp City *(G-18259)*
Baileys Asphalt Sealing ....F 740 453-9409
South Zanesville *(G-17453)*
Image Pavement Maintenance ....E 937 833-9200
Brookville *(G-2187)*

CONTRACTORS: Patio & Deck Construction & Repair

Americraft Stor Buildings Ltd ....G 330 877-6900
Hartville *(G-10816)*
Better Living Sunrooms NW Ohio ....G 419 692-4526
Delphos *(G-8902)*
Byrd Prcurement Specialist Inc ....G 419 936-0019
Swanton *(G-18082)*
Patio Enclosures ....F 513 733-4646
Cincinnati *(G-4213)*
Pei Liquidation Company ....E 615 781-5020
Macedonia *(G-12471)*

CONTRACTORS: Pipe & Boiler Insulating

BT Investments II Inc ....G 937 434-4321
Dayton *(G-8200)*

CONTRACTORS: Pipe Laying

Bob Lanes Welding Inc ....F 740 373-3567
Marietta *(G-12767)*
Steelial Wldg Met Fbrction Inc ....E 740 669-5300
Vinton *(G-19383)*

CONTRACTORS: Plumbing

Approved Plumbing Co ....F 216 663-5063
Cleveland *(G-4820)*
Dennis Constuction Sanitation ....G 419 332-8301
Fremont *(G-10142)*
Mansfield Plumbing Pdts LLC ....E 330 496-2301
Big Prairie *(G-1682)*
Pioneer Pipe Inc ....B 740 376-2400
Marietta *(G-12816)*

CONTRACTORS: Pollution Control Eqpt Installation

Corro-Tech Equipment Corp ....G 216 941-1552
Cleveland *(G-5133)*
L Haberny Co Inc ....F 440 543-5999
Chagrin Falls *(G-3098)*
McGill Airclean LLC ....D 614 829-1200
Columbus *(G-7330)*

CONTRACTORS: Post Disaster Renovations

Complete Dry Flood ....G 513 200-9274
Cincinnati *(G-3601)*

CONTRACTORS: Power Generating Eqpt Installation

Clopay Corporation ....C 800 282-2260
Mason *(G-12999)*
John McHael Priester Assoc Inc ....G 513 761-8605
Wyoming *(G-20932)*

CONTRACTORS: Prefabricated Window & Door Installation

General Awning Company Inc ....F 216 749-0110
Cleveland *(G-5411)*
M/W International Inc ....F 440 526-6900
Brecksville *(G-2063)*
Midwest Curtainwalls Inc ....D 216 641-7900
Cleveland *(G-5809)*
Mor-Lite Co Inc ....G 513 661-8587
Cincinnati *(G-4122)*
Thiels Replacement Systems Inc ....D 419 289-6139
Ashland *(G-781)*
Yoder Window & Siding Ltd ....G 330 695-6960
Fredericksburg *(G-10095)*

CONTRACTORS: Process Piping

United Group Services Inc ....C 800 633-9690
West Chester *(G-20063)*

CONTRACTORS: Refrigeration

Hattenbach Company ....D 216 881-5200
Cleveland *(G-5485)*
Hattenbach Company ....E 330 744-2732
Youngstown *(G-21107)*
Integrated Development & Mfg ....F 440 247-5100
Chagrin Falls *(G-3060)*

CONTRACTORS: Rigging, Theatrical

Beck Studios Inc ....E 513 831-6650
Milford *(G-14125)*

CONTRACTORS: Roof Repair

Boyce Ltd ....G 614 236-8901
Columbus *(G-6851)*

CONTRACTORS: Roofing

Celcore Inc ....F 440 234-7888
Cleveland *(G-5001)*
Four Js Bldg Components LLC ....F 740 886-6112
Scottown *(G-17039)*
Home Sheet Metal & Roofing Co ....G 419 562-7806
Bucyrus *(G-2348)*
Maines Brothers Tin Shop ....G 937 393-1633
Hillsboro *(G-11008)*
MGM Construction Inc ....F 440 234-7660
Berea *(G-1627)*
Nr Lee Restoration Ltd ....G 419 692-2233
Delphos *(G-8915)*
Related Metals Inc ....G 330 799-4866
Canfield *(G-2572)*
Simon Roofing and Shtmtl Corp ....C 330 629-7392
Youngstown *(G-21204)*
Tremco Incorporated ....B 216 292-5000
Beachwood *(G-1303)*

CONTRACTORS: Roustabout Svcs

R & B Enterprises USA Inc ....G 330 674-2227
Millersburg *(G-14257)*
Ruscilli Real Estate Services ....F 614 923-6400
Dublin *(G-9135)*

CONTRACTORS: Sandblasting Svc, Building Exteriors

Banks Manufacturing Company ....F 440 458-8661
Grafton *(G-10420)*
Universal Fabg Cnstr Svcs Inc ....D 614 274-1128
Columbus *(G-7723)*

CONTRACTORS: Screening, Window & Door

Screenmobile Inc ....G 614 868-8663
Radnor *(G-16507)*

PRODUCT

CONTRACTORS: Septic System

Accurate Mechanical Inc ....E 740 654-5898
  Lancaster (G-11683)
Mack Industries ....C 419 353-7081
  Bowling Green (G-1999)

CONTRACTORS: Sheet Metal Work, NEC

All-Type Welding & Fabrication ....E 440 439-3990
  Cleveland (G-4761)
Anchor Metal Processing Inc ....F 216 362-6463
  Cleveland (G-4804)
Anchor Metal Processing Inc ....E 216 362-1850
  Cleveland (G-4805)
Avon Lake Sheet Metal Co ....E 440 933-3505
  Avon Lake (G-1025)
Budde Sheet Metal Works Inc ....E 937 224-0868
  Dayton (G-8202)
Ceco Group Inc ....G 513 458-2600
  Cincinnati (G-3510)
Cmt Machining & Fabg LLC ....F 937 652-3740
  Urbana (G-19151)
Ducts Inc ....E 216 391-2400
  Cleveland (G-5220)
Franck and Fric Incorporated ....D 216 524-4451
  Cleveland (G-5377)
Holgate Metal Fab Inc ....F 419 599-2000
  Napoleon (G-14682)
Jim Nier Construction Inc ....F 740 289-3925
  Piketon (G-16222)
Kettering Roofing & Shtmtl ....E 513 281-6413
  Cincinnati (G-3986)
Kirk & Blum Manufacturing Co ....C 513 458-2600
  Cincinnati (G-3992)
Kirk & Blum Manufacturing Co ....E 419 782-9885
  Defiance (G-8798)
Martina Metal LLC ....E 614 291-9700
  Columbus (G-7321)
Metrodeck Inc ....F 513 541-4370
  Cincinnati (G-4095)
Ontario Mechanical LLC ....E 419 529-2578
  Ontario (G-15691)
Pcy Enterprises Inc ....E 513 241-5566
  Cincinnati (G-4219)
Saringer Sheet Metal Inc ....E 216 447-9755
  Independence (G-11274)
Seneca Sheet Metal Company ....F 419 447-8434
  Tiffin (G-18244)
Sheet Angle Bar Met Fbrication ....G 513 829-8600
  Fairfield (G-9716)
Tendon Manufacturing Inc ....E 216 663-3200
  Cleveland (G-6305)

CONTRACTORS: Sheet metal Work, Architectural

Ameridian Specialty Services ....E 513 769-0150
  Cincinnati (G-3396)
Federal Iron Works Company ....E 330 482-5910
  Columbiana (G-6616)
M/W International Inc ....F 440 526-6900
  Brecksville (G-2063)

CONTRACTORS: Siding

Cardinal Builders Inc ....E 614 237-1000
  Columbus (G-6905)
Champion Opco LLC ....B 513 924-4858
  Cincinnati (G-3521)
Color Brite Company Inc ....G 216 441-4117
  Cleveland (G-5100)
General Awning Company Inc ....F 216 749-0110
  Cleveland (G-5411)
Mor-Lite Co Inc ....G 513 661-8587
  Cincinnati (G-4122)
O A R Vinyl Windows & Siding ....G 440 636-5573
  Middlefield (G-13978)
Waxco International Inc ....F 937 746-4845
  Miamisburg (G-13879)

CONTRACTORS: Single-family Home General Remodeling

C-Link Enterprises LLC ....F 937 222-2829
  Dayton (G-8205)
Cardinal Builders Inc ....E 614 237-1000
  Columbus (G-6905)
Fence One Inc ....F 216 441-2600
  Cleveland (G-5334)
Henderson Builders Inc ....G 419 665-2684
  Gibsonburg (G-10377)

Kitchen Works Inc ....G 440 353-0939
  North Ridgeville (G-15385)
Mikes Mill Shop Inc ....G 419 538-6091
  Ottawa (G-15801)
Van Dyke Custom Iron Inc ....G 614 860-9300
  Columbus (G-7732)
Waxco International Inc ....F 937 746-4845
  Miamisburg (G-13879)

CONTRACTORS: Skylight Installation

Scs Construction Services Inc ....E 513 929-0260
  Cincinnati (G-4393)

CONTRACTORS: Solar Energy Eqpt

Edison Solar Inc ....F 419 499-0000
  Milan (G-14111)
Hunters Hightech Energy Systm ....G 614 275-4777
  Columbus (G-7171)
Shark Solar LLC ....G 216 630-7395
  Medina (G-13479)

CONTRACTORS: Sound Eqpt Installation

Background Music & Sound Inc ....G 937 898-9871
  Dayton (G-8180)
House of Hindenach ....G 419 422-0392
  Findlay (G-9843)
Importers Direct LLC ....E 330 436-3260
  Akron (G-230)
Tri-Tech Machining LLC ....G 513 575-3959
  Milford (G-14179)

CONTRACTORS: Specialized Public Building

Baker-Shindler Contracting Co ....E 419 782-5080
  Defiance (G-8780)

CONTRACTORS: Storage Tank Erection, Metal

Columbiana Boiler Company LLC ....E 330 482-3373
  Columbiana (G-6612)

CONTRACTORS: Store Fixture Installation

Couch Business Development Inc ....F 937 253-1099
  Dayton (G-8244)

CONTRACTORS: Structural Iron Work, Structural

Wernke Wldg & Stl Erection Co ....F 513 353-4173
  North Bend (G-15210)
White Mule Company ....E 740 382-9008
  Ontario (G-15697)

CONTRACTORS: Structural Steel Erection

Buckeye Steel Incorporated ....F 740 425-2306
  Barnesville (G-1159)
Chagrin Vly Stl Erectors Inc ....F 440 975-1556
  Willoughby (G-20455)
Concord Fabricators Inc ....E 614 875-2500
  Grove City (G-10550)
Evers Welding Co Inc ....E 513 385-7352
  Cincinnati (G-3723)
Frederick Steel Company LLC ....D 513 821-6400
  Cincinnati (G-3782)
FSRc Tanks Inc ....E 234 221-2015
  Bolivar (G-1934)
GL Nause Co Inc ....G 513 722-9500
  Loveland (G-12353)
Henderson Fabricating Co Inc ....F 216 432-0404
  Cleveland (G-5497)
Marysville Steel Inc ....E 937 642-5971
  Marysville (G-12959)
Ontario Mechanical LLC ....E 419 529-2578
  Ontario (G-15691)
Pro-Fab Inc ....E 330 644-0044
  Akron (G-352)
Rittman Inc ....D 330 927-6855
  Rittman (G-16682)
Smith Brothers Erection Inc ....E 740 373-3575
  Marietta (G-12832)
Tri-Way Rebar Inc ....G 330 296-9662
  Ravenna (G-16568)
Upright Steel LLC ....E 216 923-0852
  Cleveland (G-6396)

CONTRACTORS: Svc Station Eqpt Installation, Maint & Repair

Industrial Fiberglass Spc Inc ....E 937 222-9000
  Dayton (G-8402)

CONTRACTORS: Svc Well Drilling Svcs

Bakerwell Service Rigs Inc ....F 330 276-2161
  Killbuck (G-11593)
Geocore Drilling Inc ....G 419 864-4011
  Cardington (G-2910)
Jackson Wells Services ....G 419 886-2017
  Bellville (G-1571)
Well Service Group Inc ....F 330 308-0880
  New Philadelphia (G-14939)

CONTRACTORS: Tile Installation, Ceramic

Prints & Paints Flr Cvg Co Inc ....E 419 462-5663
  Galion (G-10283)

CONTRACTORS: Trenching

Breaker Technology Inc ....E 440 248-7168
  Solon (G-17274)

CONTRACTORS: Tuck Pointing & Restoration

Nr Lee Restoration Ltd ....G 419 692-2233
  Delphos (G-8915)

CONTRACTORS: Underground Utilities

Great Lakes Crushing Ltd ....E 440 944-5500
  Wickliffe (G-20366)

CONTRACTORS: Ventilation & Duct Work

A A S Amels Sheet Meta L Inc ....E 330 793-9326
  Youngstown (G-21010)
Franck and Fric Incorporated ....D 216 524-4451
  Cleveland (G-5377)
Jacobs Mechanical Co ....C 513 681-6800
  Cincinnati (G-3937)
Scharenberg Sheet Metal ....G 740 664-2431
  New Marshfield (G-14872)

CONTRACTORS: Warm Air Heating & Air Conditioning

Columbus Heating & Vent Co ....C 614 274-1177
  Columbus (G-6954)
Gundlach Sheet Metal Works Inc ....E 419 626-4525
  Sandusky (G-16971)
Hvac Inc ....F 330 343-5511
  Dover (G-8991)
Langdon Inc ....E 513 733-5955
  Cincinnati (G-4011)
Lowry Furnace Company Inc ....G 330 745-4822
  Akron (G-276)
Northeast Ohio Contractors LLC ....G 216 269-7881
  Cleveland (G-5906)
S L M Inc ....E 216 651-0666
  Cleveland (G-6150)
Shriner Sheet Metal Inc ....F 330 435-6735
  Creston (G-7943)
V M Systems Inc ....D 419 535-1044
  Toledo (G-18763)
Wheeler Sheet Metal Inc ....G 419 668-0481
  Norwalk (G-15566)

CONTRACTORS: Water Intake Well Drilling Svc

Jersey West Drilling Inc ....G 513 398-0774
  Mason (G-13049)

CONTRACTORS: Water Well Drilling

Layne Heavy Civil Inc ....E 513 424-7287
  Middletown (G-14053)
Stoepfel Drilling Co ....G 419 532-3307
  Ottawa (G-15811)
Warthman Drilling Inc ....G 740 746-9950
  Sugar Grove (G-18013)

CONTRACTORS: Waterproofing

Paul Peterson Company ....E 614 486-4375
  Columbus (G-7467)

Richtech Industries Inc ....G.... 440 937-4401
  Avon *(G-1009)*

CONTRACTORS: Well Bailing, Cleaning, Swabbing & Treating Svc

Diesel Fltrtion Spcialists LLC ....G.... 740 698-0255
  New Marshfield *(G-14871)*

CONTRACTORS: Well Casings Perforating Svcs

Appalachian Well Surveys Inc ....G.... 740 255-7652
  Cambridge *(G-2446)*

CONTRACTORS: Well Logging Svcs

Oaktree Wireline LLC ....G.... 330 352-7250
  New Philadelphia *(G-14919)*
Schlumberger Limited ....G.... 330 878-0794
  Strasburg *(G-17828)*

CONTRACTORS: Well Swabbing Svcs

Bill Hall Well Service ....G.... 330 695-4671
  Fredericksburg *(G-10078)*
Martz Well Service ....G.... 330 323-7417
  Canton *(G-2770)*

CONTRACTORS: Windows & Doors

3-G Incorporated ....G.... 513 921-4515
  Cincinnati *(G-3323)*
Bert Radebaugh ....G.... 740 382-8134
  Marion *(G-12857)*
Traichal Construction Company...........E.... 800 255-3667
  Niles *(G-15186)*

CONTRACTORS: Wood Floor Installation & Refinishing

Attractive Kitchens & Flrg LLC............G.... 440 406-9299
  Elyria *(G-9376)*

CONTRACTORS: Wrecking & Demolition

Allgeier & Son Inc ....F.... 513 574-3735
  Cincinnati *(G-3378)*
Rnw Holdings Inc ....E.... 330 792-0600
  Youngstown *(G-21190)*

CONTROL EQPT: Electric

Asco Valve Inc..................................F.... 216 360-0366
  Cleveland *(G-4843)*
Central Systems & Control ....G.... 440 835-0015
  Cleveland *(G-5005)*
Cincinnati Ctrl Dynamics Inc ....G.... 513 242-7300
  Cincinnati *(G-3547)*
Controls Inc ....E.... 330 239-4345
  Medina *(G-13392)*
Davis Technologies Inc ....F.... 330 823-2544
  Alliance *(G-505)*
ITT Corporation ....D.... 937 256-1705
  Dayton *(G-8109)*
Jay Instruments ....G.... 513 733-5200
  Cincinnati *(G-3943)*
Lake Shore Electric Corp ....E.... 440 232-0200
  Bedford *(G-1438)*
Positive Safety Mfr Co ....F.... 440 951-2130
  Willoughby *(G-20575)*
Spang & Company ....E.... 440 350-6108
  Mentor *(G-13727)*

CONTROL EQPT: Electric Buses & Locomotives

Precision Design Inc...........................G.... 419 289-1553
  Ashland *(G-767)*

CONTROL EQPT: Noise

Acon Inc..G.... 513 276-2111
  Tipp City *(G-18258)*
Hueston Industries Inc ....G.... 937 264-8163
  Dayton *(G-8396)*
McGill Airsilence LLC ....F.... 614 443-0192
  Columbus *(G-7333)*
Noise Suppression Technologies........F.... 614 275-1818
  Columbus *(G-7395)*
Robert C Bost Associates Inc ....F.... 301 206-9466
  Columbus *(G-7568)*

Tech Products Corporation..................E.... 937 438-1100
  Miamisburg *(G-13867)*

CONTROL PANELS: Electrical

Adgo Incorporated ....E.... 513 752-6880
  Cincinnati *(G-3292)*
Advanced Controls Inc ....E.... 440 354-5413
  Eastlake *(G-9257)*
Agent Technologies Inc ....E.... 513 942-9444
  West Chester *(G-19800)*
Altronic LLC ....C.... 330 545-9768
  Girard *(G-10381)*
American Controls Inc ....E.... 440 944-9735
  Wickliffe *(G-20353)*
Apex Circuits Inc................................E.... 513 942-4400
  West Chester *(G-19806)*
Auto-Tronic Control Co ....F.... 419 666-5100
  Northwood *(G-15477)*
Bentronix Corp ....G.... 440 632-0606
  Middlefield *(G-13917)*
City Machine Technologies Inc.............E.... 330 747-2639
  Youngstown *(G-21049)*
City Machine Technologies Inc.............G.... 330 747-2639
  Youngstown *(G-21050)*
Control Craft LLC ....F.... 513 674-0056
  Cincinnati *(G-3606)*
Control Interface Inc ....E.... 513 874-2062
  West Chester *(G-19843)*
Control Works Inc ....E.... 513 831-9959
  Milford *(G-14133)*
Custom Craft Controls Inc ....F.... 330 630-9599
  Akron *(G-136)*
Cutler Richard DBA Ohio Contro...........G.... 440 892-1858
  Cleveland *(G-5153)*
DRDC Realty Inc ....G.... 419 478-7091
  Toledo *(G-18444)*
Dynamics Research & Dev ....G.... 419 478-7091
  Toledo *(G-18446)*
Electrical Control Systems ....G.... 937 859-7136
  Dayton *(G-8321)*
Electro Controls Inc ....E.... 866 497-1717
  Sidney *(G-17184)*
Emt Inc ....G.... 330 399-6939
  Warren *(G-19547)*
Etched Metal Company ....E.... 440 248-0240
  Solon *(G-17290)*
Industrial and Mar Eng Svc Co ....F.... 740 694-0791
  Fredericktown *(G-10104)*
Industrial Ctrl Dsign Mint Inc ....F.... 330 785-9840
  Tallmadge *(G-18148)*
Industrial Thermal Systems Inc............F.... 513 561-2100
  Cincinnati *(G-3918)*
Innovative Control Systems..................E.... 513 894-3712
  Hamilton *(G-10705)*
Innovative Controls Corp ....D.... 419 691-6684
  Toledo *(G-18524)*
Instrmntation Ctrl Systems Inc ....E.... 513 662-2600
  Cincinnati *(G-3925)*
Koester Corporation ....D.... 419 599-0291
  Napoleon *(G-14687)*
Matrix Cable and Mould.......................G.... 513 832-2577
  Cincinnati *(G-4067)*
Otr Controls LLC ....G.... 513 621-2197
  Cincinnati *(G-4200)*
Panel Control Inc ....G.... 937 394-2201
  Anna *(G-624)*
Panel Master LLC ....E.... 440 355-4442
  Lagrange *(G-11635)*
Panel-Fab Inc ....D.... 513 771-1462
  Cincinnati *(G-4210)*
Panelmatic Inc ....G.... 513 829-3666
  Fairfield *(G-9698)*
Panelmatic Inc ....E.... 330 782-8007
  Youngstown *(G-21162)*
Panelmatic Cincinnati Inc ....E.... 513 829-1960
  Fairfield *(G-9699)*
Panelmatic Youngstown Inc ....E.... 330 782-8007
  Youngstown *(G-21163)*
Scott Fetzer Company ....C.... 216 267-9000
  Cleveland *(G-6168)*
System Controls Inc ....G.... 216 351-9121
  Cleveland *(G-6283)*
Systems Specialty Ctrl Co Inc ....E.... 419 478-4156
  Toledo *(G-18713)*
Trucut Incorporated ....D.... 330 938-9806
  Sebring *(G-17055)*
United Rolls Inc ....C.... 330 456-2761
  Canton *(G-2888)*

CONTROLS & ACCESS: Indl, Electric

Avtron Holdings LLC ....B.... 216 642-1230
  Cleveland *(G-4876)*
Barry Brothers Electric ....G.... 614 299-8187
  Columbus *(G-6809)*
Corrotec Inc ....E.... 937 325-3585
  Springfield *(G-17536)*
Electrical Control Design Inc ....G.... 419 443-9290
  Perrysburg *(G-16088)*
Filnor Inc ....F.... 330 821-8731
  Alliance *(G-506)*
Filnor Inc ....G.... 330 829-3180
  Alliance *(G-507)*
Filnor Inc ....F.... 330 821-7667
  Alliance *(G-508)*
Fuse Chicken Llc ....G.... 330 338-7108
  Cuyahoga Falls *(G-8001)*
Hyde Park Electronics LLC ....G.... 937 252-2121
  Dayton *(G-8398)*
Inductive Components Mfg ....E.... 513 752-4731
  Amelia *(G-577)*
PMC Systems Limited ....E.... 330 538-2268
  North Jackson *(G-15297)*
Tekworx LLC ....F.... 513 533-4777
  Blue Ash *(G-1881)*
Tri-Tech Research LLC ....F.... 440 946-6122
  Eastlake *(G-9293)*

CONTROLS & ACCESS: Motor

Eaton Corporation ....B.... 216 523-5000
  Cleveland *(G-5245)*
Eaton Corporation ....C.... 216 416-2500
  Cleveland *(G-5246)*
Eaton Corporation ....C.... 888 328-6677
  Cleveland *(G-5248)*
Eaton Corporation ....C.... 440 748-2236
  Grafton *(G-10424)*
Grill ....G.... 937 673-6768
  Eaton *(G-9307)*
James R Eaton ....G.... 937 435-7767
  Dayton *(G-8421)*
Parkside & Eaton Estate ....G.... 330 467-2995
  Northfield *(G-15469)*

CONTROLS: Access, Motor

Quality Controls Inc ....F.... 513 272-3900
  Cincinnati *(G-4306)*

CONTROLS: Adjustable Speed Drive

Axel Austin LLC ....G.... 440 237-1610
  North Royalton *(G-15410)*
Lincoln Electric Company ....C.... 216 524-8800
  Cleveland *(G-5696)*
United States Controls Inc ....G.... 330 758-1147
  Poland *(G-16386)*

CONTROLS: Air Flow, Refrigeration

Cool Times ....G.... 513 608-5201
  Cincinnati *(G-3608)*
Mestek Inc...D.... 419 288-2703
  Holland *(G-11072)*

CONTROLS: Automatic Temperature

Acutemp Thermal Systems ....F.... 937 312-0114
  Moraine *(G-14464)*
Building Ctrl Integrators LLC................E.... 614 334-3300
  Powell *(G-16464)*
Building Ctrl Integrators LLC................G.... 513 247-6154
  Cincinnati *(G-3486)*
Building Ctrl Integrators LLC................G.... 440 526-6660
  Broadview Heights *(G-2106)*
Building Ctrl Integrators LLC................G.... 513 860-9600
  West Chester *(G-19985)*
Honeywell International Inc ....D.... 937 754-4134
  Fairborn *(G-9625)*
Ignio Systems LLC ....F.... 419 708-0503
  Toledo *(G-18516)*

CONTROLS: Crane & Hoist, Including Metal Mill

Konecranes Inc ....G.... 937 328-5123
  Springfield *(G-17588)*
Midwest Minicranes Inc ....G.... 330 332-3700
  Salem *(G-16915)*
Morris Material Handling Inc.................G.... 937 525-5520
  Springfield *(G-17608)*

Employee Codes: A=Over 500 employees, B=251-500
C=101-250, D=51-100, E=20-50, F=10-19, G=3-9

2017 Harris Ohio
Industrial Directory

1463

PRODUCT

CONTROLS: Electric Motor

Ignio Systems LLC .... F 419 708-0503
  Toledo (G-18516)

Toledo Electromotive Inc .... G 419 874-7751
  Perrysburg (G-16162)

CONTROLS: Environmental

Action Air & Hydraulics Inc .... G 937 372-8614
  Xenia (G-20933)

Alan Manufacturing Inc .... E 330 262-1555
  Wooster (G-20737)

Babcock & Wilcox Company .... A 330 753-4511
  Barberton (G-1104)

Balta Technology Inc .... G 513 724-0247
  Batavia (G-1167)

Bry-Air Inc .... E 740 965-2974
  Sunbury (G-18056)

Budzar Industries Inc .... D 440 530-1000
  Willoughby (G-20448)

Channel Products Inc .... D 440 423-0113
  Chesterland (G-3199)

Cincinnati Air Conditioning Co ...... D 513 721-5622
  Cincinnati (G-3538)

Data Analysis Technologies .... G 614 873-0710
  Plain City (G-16333)

Follow River Designs LLC .... G 614 325-9954
  McConnelsville (G-13350)

Future Controls Corporation .... E 440 275-3191
  Austinburg (G-962)

Helm Instrument Company Inc ...... E 419 893-4356
  Maumee (G-13265)

Honeywell International Inc .... A 937 484-2000
  Urbana (G-19162)

Hunter Defense Tech Inc .... C 513 943-7880
  Cincinnati (G-3309)

Hunter Defense Tech Inc .... E 216 438-6111
  Solon (G-17312)

Integrated Development & Mfg ..... F 440 247-5100
  Chagrin Falls (G-3060)

Integrated Development & Mfg ..... E 440 543-2423
  Chagrin Falls (G-3095)

Kanawha Scales & Systems Inc .... F 513 576-0700
  Milford (G-14158)

Karman Rubber Company .... E 330 864-2161
  Akron (G-251)

Midwest Energy Emissions Corp ... F 614 505-6115
  Lewis Center (G-11908)

Peco II Inc .... D 614 431-0694
  Columbus (G-7473)

Pepperl + Fuchs Inc .... C 330 425-3555
  Twinsburg (G-18997)

Prentke Romich Company .... C 330 202-5800
  Wooster (G-20825)

Schneder Elc Bldngs Amrcas Inc ... 513 398-9800
  Lebanon (G-11838)

Skuttle Mfg Co .... F 740 373-9169
  Marietta (G-12831)

Tetra Tech Inc .... F 330 286-3683
  Canfield (G-2578)

Thermo King Corporation .... B 478 625-7241
  Chagrin Falls (G-3071)

Thomas Enterprises .... G 330 394-4483
  Warren (G-19607)

Tier Environmental .... F 440 232-9400
  Bedford (G-1466)

Ventra Sandusky LLC .... D 419 627-3600
  Sandusky (G-17020)

Vortec Corporation .... E 513 686-8210
  Blue Ash (G-1891)

Zenith Energy Group LLC .... F 216 587-9510
  Cleveland (G-6494)

CONTROLS: Hydronic

ABB Automation Inc .... B 440 347-9668
  Wickliffe (G-20346)

Certified Labs & Service Inc .... G 419 289-7462
  Ashland (G-718)

CONTROLS: Numerical

GE Intelligent Platforms Inc .... G 937 459-5404
  Greenville (G-10502)

CONTROLS: Relay & Ind

Altronic LLC .... C 330 545-9768
  Girard (G-10381)

Amano Cincinnati Incorporated ..... D 513 697-9000
  Loveland (G-12338)

Automatic Timing & Contrls Inc .... D 614 888-8855
  New Albany (G-14747)

Autoneum North America Inc .... B 419 693-0511
  Oregon (G-15703)

C-Tech Industries LLC .... F 877 755-7311
  West Chester (G-19822)

Chandler Systems Incorporated .... D 419 281-5767
  Ashland (G-721)

Channel Products Inc .... D 440 423-0113
  Chesterland (G-3199)

Clark Substations LLC .... E 330 452-5200
  Canton (G-2659)

Cleveland Hdwr & Forging Co ...... E 216 641-5200
  Cleveland (G-5064)

Command Alkon Incorporated .... D 614 799-0600
  Dublin (G-9064)

Comtec Incorporated .... F 330 425-8102
  Twinsburg (G-18918)

Control Associates Inc .... D 440 708-1770
  Chagrin Falls (G-3082)

Control Works Inc .... E 513 831-9959
  Milford (G-14133)

Cook Bonding & Mfg Co Inc .... G 216 661-1698
  Cleveland (G-5129)

Creative Electronic Design .... G 937 256-5106
  Beavercreek (G-1327)

Curtiss-Wright Controls .... E 937 252-5601
  Fairborn (G-9618)

Delta Systems Inc .... C 330 626-2811
  Streetsboro (G-17850)

Dimcogray Corporation .... D 937 433-7600
  Centerville (G-3039)

Divelbiss Corporation .... E 800 245-2327
  Fredericktown (G-10100)

Eaton Corporation .... C 440 826-1115
  Cleveland (G-5250)

Electrocraft Ohio Inc .... C 740 441-6200
  Gallipolis (G-10295)

Electrodynamics Inc .... G 847 259-0740
  Cincinnati (G-3300)

Ellis & Watts Intl LLC .... G 513 752-9000
  Batavia (G-1183)

Energy Technologies Inc .... D 419 522-4444
  Mansfield (G-12600)

Fabriweld Corporation .... G 419 668-3358
  Norwalk (G-15539)

Future Controls Corporation .... E 440 275-3191
  Austinburg (G-962)

GE Aviation Systems LLC .... B 937 898-5881
  Vandalia (G-19293)

Harris Instrument Corporation ...... G 740 369-3580
  Delaware (G-8857)

Helm Instrument Company Inc ...... E 419 893-4356
  Maumee (G-13265)

Hite Parts Exchange Inc .... E 614 272-5115
  Columbus (G-7160)

Hurst Auto-Truck Electric .... G 216 961-1800
  Cleveland (G-5538)

Hyundai Ideal Electric Co .... C 419 520-3314
  Mansfield (G-12626)

Independent Digital Consulting ..... G 330 753-0777
  Norton (G-15514)

Innovative Controls Corp .... D 419 691-6684
  Toledo (G-18524)

Job One Control Services .... G 216 347-0133
  Cleveland (G-5617)

Kahle Technologies Inc .... G 419 523-3951
  Ottawa (G-15799)

Laird Controls Holdings Inc .... E 234 806-0018
  Warren (G-19567)

Laird Controls North Amer Inc ...... F 234 806-0018
  Warren (G-19568)

Maags Automotive & Machine ...... G 419 626-1539
  Sandusky (G-16982)

Miami Control Systems Inc .... G 937 698-5725
  West Milton (G-20107)

Mission Control Systems Inc .... G 419 472-3791
  Toledo (G-18587)

Ohio Magnetics Inc .... E 216 662-8484
  Maple Heights (G-12736)

Ohio Semitronics Inc .... D 614 777-1005
  Hilliard (G-10967)

Opw Engineered Systems Inc .... D 888 771-9438
  Lebanon (G-11824)

Panel Master LLC .... E 440 355-4442
  Lagrange (G-11635)

Peco II Inc .... D 614 431-0694
  Columbus (G-7473)

Peloton Manufacturing Corp .... F 440 205-1600
  Mentor (G-13684)

Pepperl + Fuchs Inc .... C 330 425-3555
  Twinsburg (G-18997)

Precision Switching Inc .... G 800 800-8143
  Mansfield (G-12667)

Prime Controls Inc .... G 937 435-8659
  Dayton (G-8592)

R-K Electronics Inc .... F 513 204-6060
  Mason (G-13079)

Ramco Electric Motors Inc .... D 937 548-2525
  Greenville (G-10516)

Rbb Systems Inc .... D 330 263-4502
  Wooster (G-20827)

Rbb Systems Inc .... D 330 263-4502
  Wooster (G-20828)

Resinoid Engineering Corp .... E 740 928-2220
  Heath (G-10854)

Rex Automation Inc .... G 614 766-4672
  Columbus (G-7559)

Rockwell Automation Inc .... D 513 942-9828
  West Chester (G-19936)

Rockwell Automation Inc .... E 440 604-8410
  Cleveland (G-6127)

Rockwell Automation Inc .... B 330 425-3211
  Twinsburg (G-19011)

Rockwell Automation Inc .... E 513 943-1145
  Batavia (G-1219)

Rockwell Automation Inc .... D 440 646-5000
  Cleveland (G-6128)

Rockwell Automation Inc .... D 614 776-3021
  Westerville (G-20184)

Rockwell Automation Inc .... F 440 646-7900
  Cleveland (G-6129)

Satco Inc .... G 330 630-8866
  Tallmadge (G-18168)

Schneider Electric Usa Inc .... C 513 755-4231
  West Chester (G-19942)

Schneider Electric Usa Inc .... D 513 755-5000
  West Chester (G-19943)

Sieb & Meyer America Inc .... E 513 563-0860
  Fairfield (G-9717)

Stock Fairfield Corporation .... C 440 543-6000
  Chagrin Falls (G-3122)

T D Group Holdings LLC .... G 216 706-2939
  Cleveland (G-6289)

Tabtronics Inc .... F 937 222-9969
  Dayton (G-8697)

Technology Products Inc .... G 937 652-3412
  Urbana (G-19184)

Toledo Transducers Inc .... E 419 724-4170
  Holland (G-11090)

Transdigm Inc .... G 216 706-2939
  Cleveland (G-6347)

Transdigm Inc .... F 216 291-6025
  Cleveland (G-6346)

Tvh Parts Co .... F 877 755-7311
  West Chester (G-19965)

Valve Related Controls Inc .... F 513 677-8724
  Loveland (G-12397)

Vintage Electric Ltd Inc .... F 419 472-9349
  Toledo (G-18770)

CONTROLS: Resistance Welder

Retek Inc .... G 440 937-6282
  Avon (G-1008)

CONTROLS: Thermostats

Grid Sentry LLC .... F 937 490-2101
  Beavercreek (G-1342)

Thermtrol Corporation .... E 330 497-4148
  North Canton (G-15272)

CONTROLS: Thermostats, Built-in

Therm-O-Disc Incorporated .... A 419 525-8500
  Mansfield (G-12697)

CONTROLS: Voice

Innocomp .... G 440 248-5104
  Solon (G-17316)

CONVENIENCE STORES

Delmar E Hicks .... G 740 354-4333
  Portsmouth (G-16434)

Larrys Drive Thru & Mini Mart ...... G 330 953-0512
  Youngstown (G-21133)

Tbone Sales LLC .... E 330 897-6131
  Baltic (G-1077)

CONVENTION & TRADE SHOW SVCS

Columbus Bride ....D 614 888-4567
Columbus (G-6948)

CONVERTERS: Data

Cisco Systems Inc ....A 937 427-4264
Beavercreek (G-1325)
Electrodynamics Inc ....C 847 259-0740
Cincinnati (G-3300)

CONVERTERS: Frequency

R E Smith Inc ....F 513 771-0645
Cincinnati (G-4325)

CONVERTERS: Phase Or Rotary, Electrical

Electric Service Co Inc ....E 513 271-6387
Cincinnati (G-3692)
Pace Converting Eqp Co Inc ....F 216 631-4555
Cleveland (G-5959)

CONVERTERS: Power, AC to DC

10155 Broadview Business ....G 440 546-1901
Broadview Heights (G-2101)
Core Technology Inc ....F 440 934-9935
Avon (G-991)

CONVEYOR SYSTEMS

Hostar International Inc ....F 440 564-5362
Newbury (G-15095)
Ulterior Products LLC ....G 614 519-3210
Hilliard (G-10990)

CONVEYOR SYSTEMS: Belt, General Indl Use

Alloy Welding & Fabricating ....F 440 914-0650
Solon (G-17254)
Almo Process Technology Inc ....G 513 402-2566
West Chester (G-19804)
Blair Rubber Company ....D 330 769-5583
Seville (G-17070)
Conveyor Solutions LLC ....G 513 367-4845
Cleves (G-6512)
Manufacturers Equipment Co ....F 513 424-3573
Middletown (G-14059)
Martin Rubber Company ....F 330 336-6604
Seville (G-17078)
Mayfran International Inc ....C 440 461-4100
Cleveland (G-5764)
Mfh Partners Inc ....C 440 461-4100
Cleveland (G-5795)
Midwest Conveyor Products Inc ....E 419 281-1235
Ashland (G-754)
Mine Equipment Services LLC ....E 740 936-5427
Sunbury (G-18067)
Nkc of America Inc ....G 937 642-4033
Marysville (G-12961)
T J Davies Company Inc ....G 440 248-5510
Solon (G-17396)

CONVEYOR SYSTEMS: Bucket Type

Fenner Dunlop Port Clinton Inc ....C 419 635-2191
Port Clinton (G-16399)
Joy Global Underground Min LLC ......F 440 248-7970
Cleveland (G-5624)

CONVEYOR SYSTEMS: Bulk Handling

Air Technical Industries Inc ....E 440 951-5191
Mentor (G-13512)
Bulk Handling Equipment Co ....G 330 468-5703
Northfield (G-15462)
Lewco Inc ....C 419 625-4014
Sandusky (G-16979)
Webster Industries Inc ....B 419 447-8232
Tiffin (G-18253)

CONVEYOR SYSTEMS: Pneumatic Tube

American Solving Inc ....G 440 234-7373
Brookpark (G-2150)
Fred D Pfening Company ....E 614 294-5361
Columbus (G-7099)
Hamilton Air Products Inc ....G 513 874-4030
Fairfield (G-9664)
Schenck Process LLC ....F 513 576-9200
Milford (G-14173)

CONVEYOR SYSTEMS: Robotic

Automation Systems Designs Inc ......E 937 387-0351
Dayton (G-8173)
Grob Systems Inc ....C 419 358-9015
Bluffton (G-1912)
Ins Robotics Inc ....G 888 293-5325
Hilliard (G-10953)
Ka Wanner Inc ....E 740 251-4636
Marion (G-12878)
Rhino Robotics Ltd ....G 513 353-9772
Miamitown (G-13891)
Scott-Randall Systems Inc ....F 937 446-2293
Sardinia (G-17033)

CONVEYORS & CONVEYING EQPT

Advanced Equipment Systems LLC ...G 216 289-6505
Euclid (G-9564)
Alba Manufacturing Inc ....D 513 874-0551
Fairfield (G-9640)
Allied Consolidated Industries ....C 330 744-0808
Youngstown (G-21020)
Allied Fabricating & Wldg Co ....E 614 751-6664
Columbus (G-6725)
Ambaflex Inc ....E 330 478-1858
Canton (G-2601)
Ashtech Corporation ....G 440 646-9911
Cleveland (G-4847)
Barth Industries Co LP ....D 216 267-0531
Cleveland (G-4893)
Belden Brick Company ....E 330 852-2411
Sugarcreek (G-18016)
Bobco Enterprises Inc ....F 419 867-3560
Toledo (G-18374)
Bry-Air Inc ....E 740 965-2974
Sunbury (G-18056)
Building & Conveyer Maint LLC ....G 303 882-0912
Ravenna (G-16520)
C S Bell Co ....F 419 448-0791
Tiffin (G-18213)
CA Litzler Co Inc ....E 216 267-8020
Cleveland (G-4958)
Ccw Group Pacesetter Inc ....C 740 474-0122
Circleville (G-4624)
Cincinnati Mine Machinery Co ....D 513 522-7777
Cincinnati (G-3560)
Conveyor Metal Works Inc ....E 740 477-8700
Frankfort (G-9998)
Conveyor Technologies Ltd ....G 513 248-0663
Milford (G-14134)
Conveyors Ltd ....C 740 490-0300
London (G-12206)
Decision Systems Inc ....E 330 456-7600
Canton (G-2682)
Dillin Engineered Systems Corp ....E 419 666-6789
Perrysburg (G-16085)
Dover Conveyor Inc ....E 740 922-9390
Midvale (G-14106)
Duplex Mill & Manufacturing Co ....E 937 325-5555
Springfield (G-17548)
E S Industries Inc ....G 419 643-2625
Lima (G-12008)
Eagle Crusher Co Inc ....D 419 468-2265
Galion (G-10266)
Ethos Corp ....G 513 242-6336
Cincinnati (G-3720)
Fabacraft Inc ....E 513 677-0500
Maineville (G-12524)
Fabco Inc ....E 419 421-4740
Findlay (G-9820)
Falcon Industries Inc ....E 330 723-0099
Medina (G-13409)
Federal Equipment Company ....E 513 621-5260
Cincinnati (G-3747)
Feedall Inc ....F 440 942-8100
Willoughby (G-20486)
Formtek Inc ....D 216 292-6300
Cleveland (G-5371)
Formtek Inc ....D 216 292-4460
Cleveland (G-5372)
Glassline Corporation ....E 419 666-9712
Perrysburg (G-16102)
Grasan Equipment Company Inc ....D 419 526-4440
Mansfield (G-12620)
Gray-Eering Ltd ....G 740 498-8816
Tippecanoe (G-18314)
Harsco Corporation ....E 740 387-1150
Marion (G-12873)
Hawthorne-Seving Inc ....E 419 643-5531
Cridersville (G-7945)

Hostar International Inc ....F 440 564-5362
Newbury (G-15096)
Ibiza Holdings Inc ....E 513 701-7300
Mason (G-13039)
Innovative Controls Corp ....D 419 691-6684
Toledo (G-18524)
Innovative Hdlg & Metalfab LLC ....E 419 882-7480
Sylvania (G-18112)
Intelligrated Inc ....E 866 936-7300
Mason (G-13042)
Intelligrated Inc ....E 513 874-0788
West Chester (G-20016)
Intelligrated Headquarters LLC ....G 866 936-7300
Mason (G-13043)
Intelligrated Products LLC ....E 740 490-0300
London (G-12212)
Intelligrated Sub Holdings Inc ....E 513 701-7300
Mason (G-13044)
Intelligrated Systems Inc ....A 866 936-7300
Mason (G-13045)
Intelligrated Systems LLC ....A 513 701-7300
Mason (G-13046)
Intelligrated Systems Ohio LLC ....A 513 701-7300
Mason (G-13047)
K F T Inc ....D 513 241-5910
Cincinnati (G-3965)
King Conveyor LLC ....F 740 332-6200
Laurelville (G-11770)
Kolinahr Systems Inc ....E 513 745-9401
Blue Ash (G-1823)
Laser Automation Inc ....F 440 543-9291
Chagrin Falls (G-3099)
Ledow Company Inc ....G 330 657-2837
Peninsula (G-16038)
Logitech Inc ....E 614 871-2822
Grove City (G-10569)
Martin Sprocket & Gear Inc ....D 419 485-5515
Montpelier (G-14448)
Met Fab Fabrication and Mch ....G 513 724-3715
Batavia (G-1203)
Midwest Industrial Rubber Inc ....F 614 876-3110
Hilliard (G-10963)
Miller Products Inc ....E 330 308-5934
New Philadelphia (G-14915)
Mountaineer Mining Corp ....G 740 418-1817
Jackson (G-11322)
Mulhern Belting Inc ....E 201 337-5700
Fairfield (G-9689)
Nesco Inc ....E 440 461-6000
Cleveland (G-5871)
Ocs Intellitrak Inc ....F 513 742-5600
Fairfield (G-9693)
Ohio Magnetics Inc ....E 216 662-8484
Maple Heights (G-12736)
Opw Engineered Systems Inc ....D 888 771-9438
Lebanon (G-11824)
P B Fabrication Mech Contr ....F 419 478-4869
Toledo (G-18631)
Parker-Hannifin Corporation ....F 330 336-3511
Wadsworth (G-19427)
Pfpc Enterprises Inc ....B 513 941-6200
Cincinnati (G-4233)
Pneumatic Scale Corporation ....C 330 923-0491
Cuyahoga Falls (G-8033)
Pomacon Inc ....F 330 273-1576
Brunswick (G-2244)
Power-Pack Conveyor Company ....E 440 975-9955
Willoughby (G-20576)
Precision Conveyor Technology ....F 440 352-3601
Perry (G-16056)
Quickdraft Inc ....E 330 477-4574
Canton (G-2832)
Richmond Machine Co ....E 419 485-5740
Montpelier (G-14454)
Robbins Company ....C 440 248-3303
Solon (G-17370)
Rolcon Inc ....F 513 821-7259
Cincinnati (G-4358)
Sandusky Fabricating & Sls Inc ....E 419 626-4465
Sandusky (G-17001)
Siemens Industry Inc ....E 440 526-2770
Brecksville (G-2073)
Sst Conveyor Components Inc ....E 513 583-5500
Loveland (G-12389)
Stock Equipment Company Inc ....C 440 543-6000
Chagrin Falls (G-3121)
Stock Fairfield Corporation ....C 440 543-6000
Chagrin Falls (G-3122)
Sweet Manufacturing Company ....E 937 325-1511
Springfield (G-17659)

PRODUCT

Transcon Inc ....E 440 255-7600
Mentor **(G-13754)**

Trico Belting & Supply Company ....E 513 860-8400
West Chester **(G-20061)**

Webb-Stiles Company ....D 330 225-7761
Valley City **(G-19237)**

CONVEYORS: Overhead

Hoist Equipment Co Inc ....E 440 232-0300
Bedford Heights **(G-1486)**

COOKING & FOOD WARMING EQPT: Commercial

Cleveland Range LLC ....C 216 481-4900
Cleveland **(G-5075)**

High-TEC Industrial Services ....C 937 667-1772
Tipp City **(G-18281)**

Lima Sheet Metal Machine & Mfg ....E 419 229-1161
Lima **(G-12045)**

Tema Systems Inc ....E 513 489-7811
Cincinnati **(G-4501)**

COOKING & FOODWARMING EQPT: Coffee Brewing

Nestle R&D Center Inc ....G 440 349-5757
Solon **(G-17346)**

COOKING & FOODWARMING EQPT: Commercial

Frontline International Inc ....F 330 861-1100
Cuyahoga Falls **(G-8000)**

Henny Penny Corporation ....A 937 456-8400
Eaton **(G-9309)**

JE Grote Company Inc ....D 614 868-8414
Columbus **(G-7229)**

Peerless Stove & Mfg Co Inc ....F 419 625-4514
Sandusky **(G-16994)**

COOKWARE, STONEWARE: Coarse Earthenware & Pottery

Gosun Inc ....F 513 709-2519
Cincinnati **(G-3841)**

COOLING TOWERS: Metal

Airtech Mechanical Inc ....F 419 292-0074
Toledo **(G-18326)**

COOPERAGE STOCK PRODUCTS

Brown-Forman Corporation ....E 740 384-3027
Wellston **(G-19761)**

COPINGS: Concrete

Douglas S Kutz ....G 440 238-8426
Strongsville **(G-17912)**

COPPER ORE MINING

Warrenton Copper LLC ....E 636 456-3488
Cleveland **(G-6447)**

COPPER: Blocks

Hildreth Mfg LLC ....E 740 375-5832
Marion **(G-12875)**

COPPER: Rolling & Drawing

T & D Fabricating Inc ....E 440 951-5646
Eastlake **(G-9292)**

CORRECTION FLUID

Milacron LLC ....E 513 487-5000
Blue Ash **(G-1842)**

CORRESPONDENCE SCHOOLS

Zaner-Bloser Inc ....D 614 486-0221
Columbus **(G-7786)**

CORRUGATED PRDTS: Boxes, Partition, Display Items, Sheet/Pad

A-Kobak Container Company ....F 330 225-7791
Hinckley **(G-11020)**

Akers Packaging Service Inc ....C 513 422-6312
Middletown **(G-14016)**

Greif Inc ....D 740 657-6500
Delaware **(G-8849)**

Hinkle Manufacturing Inc ....D 419 666-5550
Perrysburg **(G-16107)**

Innomark Perm Disply Grp LLC ....F 513 285-1040
Fairfield **(G-9668)**

International Paper Company ....C 330 626-7300
Streetsboro **(G-17858)**

Jamestown Cont Cleveland Inc ....B 216 831-3700
Cleveland **(G-5606)**

Kennedy Mint Inc ....D 440 572-3222
Cleveland **(G-5645)**

Martin Paper Products Inc ....E 740 756-9271
Carroll **(G-2944)**

Prestige Display and Packg LLC ....F 513 285-1040
Fairfield **(G-9705)**

Safeway Packaging Inc ....D 419 629-3200
New Bremen **(G-14793)**

Valley Containers Inc ....F 330 544-2244
Mineral Ridge **(G-14314)**

Weyerhaeuser Company ....D 740 335-4480
Wshngtn CT Hs **(G-20931)**

Wood Specialists Inc ....G 440 639-9797
Mentor **(G-13772)**

COSMETIC PREPARATIONS

Art of Beauty Company Inc ....F 216 438-6363
Bedford **(G-1399)**

B & P Company Inc ....G 937 298-0265
Dayton **(G-8177)**

Bonne Bell LLC ....G 440 835-2440
Westlake **(G-20257)**

Dayton Environmental ....F 937 478-1536
Dayton **(G-8102)**

Galleria Co ....G 513 983-1490
Cincinnati **(G-3794)**

Honey Gold Company ....G 330 688-5502
Kent **(G-11470)**

House of Delara Fragrances ....G 216 651-5803
Cleveland **(G-5529)**

KAO USA Inc ....B 513 421-1400
Cincinnati **(G-3972)**

Oils By Nature Incorporated ....G 330 468-8897
Hudson **(G-11190)**

OKeeffes Working Hands Creme ....F 800 275-2718
Cincinnati **(G-4182)**

Universal Packg Systems Inc ....B 513 674-9400
Cincinnati **(G-4542)**

Universal Packg Systems Inc ....B 513 732-2000
Batavia **(G-1231)**

Universal Packg Systems Inc ....E 513 735-4777
Batavia **(G-1232)**

Vein Center and Medspa ....G 330 629-9400
Youngstown **(G-21236)**

COSMETICS & TOILETRIES

Abbott Laboratories ....A 614 624-3078
Columbus **(G-6674)**

Abitec Corporation ....E 614 429-6464
Columbus **(G-6678)**

Bath & Body Works LLC ....B 614 856-6000
Reynoldsburg **(G-16582)**

Cameo Inc ....E 419 661-9611
Perrysburg **(G-16074)**

Donegal Bay Ltd ....F 216 360-9966
Cleveland **(G-5207)**

Erik V Lamb ....G 330 962-1540
Copley **(G-7846)**

Expressive Scents By A ....G 513 254-5399
Cincinnati **(G-3732)**

Facial Sensation Products ....G 937 293-2280
Oakwood **(G-15607)**

Garden Art Innovations LLC ....G 330 697-0007
Barberton **(G-1116)**

Gojo Industries Inc ....C 330 255-6000
Akron **(G-206)**

Gojo Industries Inc ....C 330 255-6525
Stow **(G-17760)**

Gojo Industries Inc ....C 330 922-4522
Cuyahoga Falls **(G-8005)**

Jackson David Do ....F 419 872-3201
Perrysburg **(G-16113)**

LS Bombshelles ....G 513 254-6898
Cincinnati **(G-4036)**

Luminex Home Decor ....A 513 563-1113
Blue Ash **(G-1831)**

Meridian Industries Inc ....E 330 359-5809
Beach City **(G-1248)**

Natural Essentials Inc ....E 330 562-8022
Aurora **(G-937)**

Nehemiah Manufacturing Co LLC ......E 513 351-5700
Cincinnati **(G-4143)**

Oil Bar LLC ....F 614 880-3950
Columbus **(G-6657)**

Olay LLC ....G 787 535-2191
Blue Ash **(G-1845)**

Olfactorium Corp Inc ....G 216 663-8831
Cleveland **(G-5938)**

Procter & Gamble Company ....B 513 983-1100
Cincinnati **(G-4277)**

Procter & Gamble Company ....E 513 266-4375
Cincinnati **(G-4279)**

Procter & Gamble Company ....E 513 871-7557
Cincinnati **(G-4280)**

Procter & Gamble Company ....B 513 482-6789
Cincinnati **(G-4282)**

Procter & Gamble Company ....B 513 672-4044
West Chester **(G-19921)**

Procter & Gamble Company ....B 513 634-5069
Cincinnati **(G-4283)**

Procter & Gamble Company ....B 513 627-7115
Cincinnati **(G-4284)**

Procter & Gamble Company ....C 513 948-2462
Cincinnati **(G-4285)**

Procter & Gamble Company ....B 513 945-0340
Cincinnati **(G-4288)**

Procter & Gamble Company ....C 513 622-1000
Mason **(G-13078)**

Procter & Gamble Company ....G 513 626-2500
Blue Ash **(G-1857)**

Sally Beauty Supply LLC ....G 330 823-7476
Alliance **(G-535)**

Sentinel Consumer Products Inc ......D 801 825-5671
Mentor **(G-13720)**

Sysco Guest Supply LLC ....F 440 960-2515
Lorain **(G-12285)**

US Cotton LLC ....B 216 676-6400
Cleveland **(G-6399)**

Woodbine Products Company ....F 330 725-0165
Medina **(G-13497)**

COSMETICS WHOLESALERS

Safe 4 People Inc ....G 419 797-4087
Port Clinton **(G-16412)**

COSTUME JEWELRY & NOVELTIES: Apparel, Exc Precious Metals

Gardella Jewelry LLC ....G 440 877-9261
North Royalton **(G-15420)**

Prosperity On Payne Inc ....G 216 431-7677
Cleveland **(G-6057)**

COSTUME JEWELRY & NOVELTIES: Exc Semi & Precious

Benzle Porcelain Company Inc ....G 614 876-2159
Hilliard **(G-10931)**

COSTUME JEWELRY & NOVELTIES: Ornament, Exc Precious Mtl/Gem

Polarx Ornaments LLC ....F 866 298-0433
North Ridgeville **(G-15395)**

COSTUME JEWELRY STORES

Elizabeths Closet ....G 513 646-5025
Maineville **(G-12522)**

COUNTER & SINK TOPS

3jd Inc ....F 513 324-9655
Moraine **(G-14462)**

Benchmark Cabinets ....E 740 694-1144
Fredericktown **(G-10096)**

Brad Snoderly ....F 419 476-0184
Toledo **(G-18380)**

C & D Counters ....G 740 259-5529
Lucasville **(G-12417)**

Cameo Countertops Inc ....G 419 865-6371
Holland **(G-11048)**

Counter- Advice Inc ....F 937 291-1600
Franklin **(G-10014)**

Countertop Sales ....F 614 626-4476
Columbus **(G-6991)**

Countertop Xpress ....G 440 358-0500
Painesville **(G-15871)**

Formica Corporation ....E 513 786-3400
Cincinnati (G-3772)
Imperial Countertops ....F 216 851-0888
Cleveland (G-5555)
Kbi Group Inc ....G 614 873-5825
Plain City (G-16346)
Kitchen & Bath Factory Inc ....G 440 510-8111
Mentor (G-13623)
Miami Valley Counters & Spc ....G 937 865-0562
Miamisburg (G-13831)
Sidney Stiers ....G 740 454-7368
Zanesville (G-21353)
Skeeles Manufacturing Corp ....F 614 274-4700
Columbus (G-7626)

COUNTERS & COUNTER DISPLAY CASES: Refrigerated

Florline Display Products Corp ....G 440 975-9449
Willoughby (G-20490)

COUNTERS & COUNTING DEVICES

Aclara Technologies LLC ....C 440 528-7200
Solon (G-17248)
Commercial Electric Pdts Corp ....E 216 241-2886
Cleveland (G-5104)
Eaton Corporation ....B 440 523-5000
Beachwood (G-1267)
Westmont Inc ....G 330 862-3080
Minerva (G-14345)

COUNTERS OR COUNTER DISPLAY CASES, EXC WOOD

Formatech Inc ....E 330 273-2800
Brunswick (G-2225)

COUNTERS OR COUNTER DISPLAY CASES, WOOD

Counter Concepts Inc ....F 330 848-4848
Doylestown (G-9028)
Custom Counter Tops & Spc Co ....G 330 637-4856
Cortland (G-7867)
Formatech Inc ....E 330 273-2800
Brunswick (G-2225)
Kinsella Manufacturing Co Inc ....F 513 561-5285
Cincinnati (G-3991)
Randys Countertops Inc ....F 740 881-5831
Powell (G-16482)

COUNTING DEVICES: Controls, Revolution & Timing

Electrodynamics Inc ....C 847 259-0740
Cincinnati (G-3300)

COUNTING DEVICES: Predetermining

Graco Ohio Inc ....D 330 494-1313
North Canton (G-15235)

COUNTING DEVICES: Speedometers

Hanger Prsthetcs & Ortho Inc ....G 440 892-6665
Westlake (G-20274)

COUNTING DEVICES: Tachometer, Centrifugal

Lake Shore Cryotronics Inc ....C 614 891-2243
Westerville (G-20165)

COUNTRY CLUBS

Cincinnati Marlins Inc ....G 513 761-3320
Cincinnati (G-3558)

COUPLINGS, EXC PRESSURE & SOIL PIPE

Eaton Corporation ....C 440 826-1115
Berea (G-1613)
Fulflo Specialties Company ....E 937 783-2411
Blanchester (G-1713)

COUPLINGS: Hose & Tube, Hydraulic Or Pneumatic

Custom Cltch Jint Hydrlics Inc ....F 216 431-1630
Cleveland (G-5149)

Dyna-Flex Inc ....F 440 946-9424
Mentor (G-13567)

COUPLINGS: Pipe

B S F Inc ....F 937 890-6121
Dayton (G-8179)
B S F Inc ....F 937 890-6121
Tipp City (G-18264)

COUPLINGS: Shaft

B S F Inc ....F 937 890-6121
Dayton (G-8179)
B S F Inc ....F 937 890-6121
Tipp City (G-18264)
Bowes Manufacturing Inc ....F 216 378-2110
Solon (G-17271)
Climax Metal Products Company .....D 440 943-8898
Mentor (G-13547)
Eicom Corporation ....E 937 294-5692
Moraine (G-14483)

COURIER SVCS: Air

Garda CL Technical Svcs Inc ....E 937 294-4099
Moraine (G-14490)

COURIER SVCS: Ground

Asb Industries Inc ....E 330 753-8458
Barberton (G-1099)
Grand Aire Inc ....E 419 861-6700
Swanton (G-18084)

COURTS OF LAW: County Government

Belmont County of Ohio ....G 740 699-2140
Saint Clairsville (G-16783)

COVERS & PADS Chair, Made From Purchased Materials

National Seating Company ....D 219 872-7295
New Albany (G-14766)

COVERS: Automobile Seat

Besi Manufacturing Inc ....E 513 874-0232
West Chester (G-19817)
Buckeye Seating LLC ....G 330 473-2379
Millersburg (G-14205)
Crown Dielectric Inds Inc ....C 614 224-5161
Columbus (G-7001)
Griffin Fisher Co Inc ....G 513 961-2110
Cincinnati (G-3853)
Rex Manufacturing Co ....G 419 224-5751
Lima (G-12083)
School Maintenance Supply Inc ......G 513 376-8670
Blue Ash (G-1865)
TS Trim Industries Inc ....B 740 593-5958
Athens (G-888)

COVERS: Metal Plate

Ayling and Reichert Co Consent .....E 419 898-2471
Oak Harbor (G-15586)

COVERS: Slip Made Of Fabric, Plastic, Etc.

Eastern Slipcover Company Inc ....G 440 951-2310
Mentor (G-13569)

CRADLES: Aircraft Engine

Gvs Inc ....G 330 310-8275
Fairlawn (G-9751)

CRANE & AERIAL LIFT SVCS

Ibi Brake Products Inc ....G 440 543-7962
Chagrin Falls (G-3094)
J & A Machine ....G 330 424-5235
Lisbon (G-12123)
Konecranes Inc ....F 440 461-8400
Highland Heights (G-10916)
Pollock Research & Design Inc ....G 330 332-3300
Salem (G-16920)

CRANES & MONORAIL SYSTEMS

Emh Inc ....E 330 220-8600
Valley City (G-19203)

CRANES: Indl Plant

Delta Crane Systems Inc ....F 937 324-7425
Springfield (G-17542)
Hiab USA Inc ....D 419 482-6000
Perrysburg (G-16106)
Kci Holding USA Inc ....C 937 525-5533
Springfield (G-17585)
Konecranes Inc ....E 937 328-5100
Springfield (G-17589)
Konecranes Inc ....B 937 525-5533
Springfield (G-17590)
Radocy Inc ....F 419 666-4400
Rossford (G-16747)
Terex Mhps Corp ....G 440 349-8235
Solon (G-17403)

CRANES: Indl Truck

Hoist Equipment Co Inc ....E 440 232-0300
Bedford Heights (G-1486)
Skylift Inc ....G 440 960-2100
Lorain (G-12277)
Venturo Manufacturing Inc ....E 513 772-8448
Cincinnati (G-4562)

CRANES: Locomotive

Ers Industries Inc ....E 419 562-6010
Bucyrus (G-2342)

CRANES: Overhead

ACC Automation Co Inc ....E 330 928-3821
Akron (G-25)
Morgan Engineering Systems Inc .....E 330 821-4721
Alliance (G-528)
Ohio Mechanical Handling Co ....F 330 773-5165
Akron (G-325)
Rnm Holdings Inc ....F 614 444-5556
Columbus (G-7566)

CRANKSHAFTS & CAMSHAFTS: Machining

Atlas Industries Inc ....C 419 355-1000
Fremont (G-10126)
Atlas Industries Inc ....D 419 447-4730
Tiffin (G-18206)
Atlas Industries Inc ....B 419 637-2117
Tiffin (G-18207)
Custom Crankshaft Inc ....E 330 382-1200
East Liverpool (G-9209)
Ellwood Group Inc ....E 216 862-6341
Cleveland (G-5274)
Galactic Precision Mfg LLC ....G 937 540-1800
Englewood (G-9521)
Nippon Stl Smkin Crnkshaft LLC ......F 419 435-0411
Fostoria (G-9988)
Sst Precision Manufacturing ....F 513 583-5500
Loveland (G-12390)

CRANKSHAFTS: Motor Vehicle

Nippon Stl Smkin Crnkshaft LLC ......F 419 435-0411
Fostoria (G-9988)

CRATING SVCS: Shipping

Cassis Packaging Co ....F 937 223-8563
Dayton (G-8214)

CREATIVE SVCS: Advertisers, Exc Writers

Digital Color Intl LLC ....E 330 762-6959
Akron (G-152)

CREMATORIES

Martin M Hardin ....G 740 282-1234
Steubenville (G-17705)

CROWNS & CLOSURES

American Flange & Mfg Co Inc ....G 740 549-6073
Delaware (G-8820)
Boardman Molded Products Inc ....D 330 788-2401
Youngstown (G-21032)

CRUCIBLES

General Electric Company ....G 740 928-7010
Hebron (G-10867)

CRUDE PETROLEUM & NATURAL GAS PRODUCTION

AB Resources LLC ....E...... 440 922-1098
Brecksville (G-2031)
Broad Street Energy Company ....G...... 614 228-0326
Columbus (G-6865)
Broad Street Financial Company ....G...... 614 228-0326
Columbus (G-6866)
Buckeye Oil Producing Co ....F...... 330 264-8847
Wooster (G-20754)
D & L Energy Inc ....E...... 330 270-1201
Canton (G-2675)
Franklin Gas & Oil Company LLC ....G...... 330 264-8739
Wooster (G-20773)
Gulfport Energy Corporation ....E...... 740 251-0407
Saint Clairsville (G-16790)
John D Oil and Gas Company ....G...... 440 255-6325
Mentor (G-13620)
Kenoil Inc ....E...... 330 262-1144
Wooster (G-20794)
Lee A Williams Jr ....G...... 419 225-6751
Lima (G-12038)
Stocker & Sitler Oil Company ....G...... 614 888-9588
Columbus (G-7658)
Viking Intl Resources Co Inc ....G...... 304 628-3878
Marietta (G-12849)
Xto Energy Inc ....D...... 740 671-9901
Bellaire (G-1502)

CRUDE PETROLEUM & NATURAL GAS PRODUCTION

A S Nf Producing Inc ....G...... 330 933-0622
Hartville (G-10815)
American Rodpump Ltd ....G...... 440 987-9457
Dublin (G-9044)
Bakerwell Inc ....E...... 330 276-2161
Killbuck (G-11592)
Blaze Oil & Gas Inc ....G...... 330 345-6700
Wooster (G-20749)
Bpi Energy Holdings Inc ....G...... 281 556-6200
Solon (G-17272)
Brendel Producing Company ....G...... 330 854-4151
Canton (G-2628)
Buckeye Energy Resources Inc ....G...... 740 452-9506
Zanesville (G-21283)
Cac Energy Ltd ....G...... 937 867-5593
Dayton (G-8206)
City of Lancaster ....E...... 740 687-6670
Lancaster (G-11697)
Columbia Gas Meter Shop ....F...... 614 460-5519
Columbus (G-6946)
David A Waldron & Associates ....G...... 330 264-7275
Wooster (G-20764)
Drillex Inc ....G...... 440 255-7500
Mentor (G-13564)
East Ohio Gas Company ....G...... 740 439-2721
Byesville (G-2400)
Equity Oil & Gas Funds Inc ....G...... 234 231-1004
Stow (G-17747)
Everflow Eastern Partners LP ....E...... 330 533-2692
Canfield (G-2555)
Foltz & Foltz Ltd Partnership ....G...... 330 488-1898
East Canton (G-9192)
General Electric Company ....F...... 330 425-3755
Twinsburg (G-18943)
Green Energy Inc ....G...... 330 262-5112
Wooster (G-20779)
Hanini Seven Oil ....G...... 216 857-0172
Cleveland (G-5478)
Hunter Eureka Pipeline LLC ....F...... 740 374-2940
Marietta (G-12791)
Icon Energy Systems Inc ....G...... 937 423-4786
Greenville (G-10505)
James R Bernhardt Producing ....G...... 330 345-5306
Wooster (G-20789)
Killbuck Creek Oil Co ....G...... 330 601-0921
Wooster (G-20796)
Lagc Ltd ....G...... 419 886-2141
Fredericktown (G-10105)
Mason Producing Inc ....G...... 740 913-0686
Galena (G-10247)
MFC Drilling Inc ....F...... 740 622-5600
Coshocton (G-7898)
MRC Global (us) Inc ....F...... 614 475-4033
Gahanna (G-10221)
MRC Global (us) Inc ....E...... 330 686-4988
Stow (G-17777)
P & S Energy Inc ....G...... 330 652-2525
Mineral Ridge (G-14309)

Petro Evaluation Services Inc ....G...... 330 264-4454
Wooster (G-20820)
Purvi Oil Inc ....G...... 419 207-8234
Ashland (G-769)
R D Holder Oil Co Inc ....G...... 740 522-3136
Heath (G-10852)
Resource America Inc ....E...... 330 896-8510
Uniontown (G-19096)
Sheridan One Stop Carryout ....G...... 740 687-1300
Lancaster (G-11751)
Stonebridge Operating Co LLC ....G...... 740 373-6134
Fleming (G-9914)
Triad Hunter LLC ....F...... 740 374-2940
Marietta (G-12845)
Triad Hunter LLC ....G...... 740 374-2940
Marietta (G-12846)
U S Fuel Development Co ....G...... 614 486-0614
Columbus (G-7716)
Valley Petroleum Inc ....G...... 740 668-4901
Utica (G-19198)
W H Patten Drilling Co Inc ....G...... 330 674-3046
Millersburg (G-14279)

CRUDE PETROLEUM PRODUCTION

A P Production & Service ....G...... 740 745-5317
Utica (G-19191)
Alliance Petroleum Corporation ....E...... 330 493-0440
Canton (G-2599)
Barclay Petroleum Inc ....G...... 740 569-4327
Bremen (G-2079)
Belden & Blake Corporation ....E...... 330 602-5551
Dover (G-8968)
Beucler Brothers Inc ....G...... 330 735-2267
Dellroy (G-8897)
BT Energy Corporation ....G...... 740 373-6134
Fleming (G-9911)
Cameron Drilling Co Inc ....F...... 740 453-3300
Zanesville (G-21285)
Carlton Oil Corp ....G...... 740 473-2629
Newport (G-15126)
Carol Mickley ....G...... 740 599-7870
Danville (G-8086)
Cgas Exploration Inc ....G...... 614 436-4631
Worthington (G-20859)
Cgas Inc ....G...... 614 975-4697
Worthington (G-20860)
Chesapeake Energy Corporation ....E...... 740 695-1623
Saint Clairsville (G-16785)
Chevron Ae Resources LLC ....E...... 330 654-4343
Deerfield (G-8771)
Columbia Energy Group ....G...... 614 460-4683
Columbus (G-6945)
Crude Oil Company ....G...... 740 452-3335
Zanesville (G-21296)
Derrick Petroleum Inc ....G...... 740 668-5711
Bladensburg (G-1707)
Dome Drilling Co ....G...... 440 892-9434
Westlake (G-20264)
Dome Drilling Co ....G...... 330 262-5113
Wooster (G-20766)
Elkhead Gas & Oil Co ....G...... 740 763-3966
Newark (G-15002)
Excalibur Exploration Inc ....G...... 330 966-7003
Greentown (G-10486)
Geopetro LLC ....G...... 614 885-9350
Worthington (G-20866)
H & S Drilling Co Inc ....G...... 740 828-2411
Frazeysburg (G-10074)
H I Smith Oil & Gas Inc ....G...... 330 279-2361
Holmesville (G-11101)
Hess Corporation ....G...... 740 346-0581
Steubenville (G-17698)
Hopco Resources Inc ....G...... 614 882-8533
Columbus (G-7167)
Hopewell Oil & Gas Dev Co ....G...... 740 452-9326
Zanesville (G-21319)
Jerry Moore Inc ....G...... 330 877-1155
Hartville (G-10825)
Kilbarger Investments Inc ....G...... 740 385-6019
Logan (G-12183)
King Drilling Co ....G...... 330 769-3434
Seville (G-17077)
Koch Knight LLC ....D...... 330 488-1651
East Canton (G-9194)
Konoil Inc ....G...... 330 499-9811
Canton (G-2757)
Kramer Exploration Company ....G...... 740 362-1805
Delaware (G-8866)
Lake Region Oil Inc ....F...... 330 837-4767
Dalton (G-8073)

Marietta Resources Corporation ....F...... 740 373-6305
Marietta (G-12803)
Midland Oil Co ....G...... 740 787-2557
Brownsville (G-2199)
Northwood Energy Corporation ....E...... 614 457-1024
Columbus (G-7403)
Orion Petro Corporation ....G...... 330 364-8155
Atwater (G-901)
Penick Gas & Oil ....G...... 740 323-3040
Newark (G-15045)
Profit Energy Company Inc ....G...... 740 472-1018
Jerusalem (G-11385)
R C Poling Company Inc ....G...... 740 939-0023
Junction City (G-11411)
Resource Energy Inc ....D...... 330 896-8510
Uniontown (G-19097)
Robert Barr ....F...... 740 826-7325
New Concord (G-14821)
Rodco Petroleum Inc ....G...... 330 477-9823
Canton (G-2842)
Saint Croix Ltd ....G...... 330 666-1544
Akron (G-395)
Speedway LLC ....F...... 330 874-4616
Bolivar (G-1946)
Speedway LLC ....F...... 440 943-0044
Wickliffe (G-20387)
Speedway LLC ....G...... 330 644-2730
New Franklin (G-14832)
Speedway LLC ....G...... 937 653-6840
Urbana (G-19182)
Speedway LLC ....F...... 614 418-9325
Columbus (G-7643)
Speedway LLC ....F...... 513 829-3223
Fairfield (G-9722)
Speedway LLC ....F...... 937 390-6651
Springfield (G-17649)
Speedway LLC ....G...... 614 861-6397
Reynoldsburg (G-16607)
Speedway LLC ....G...... 330 339-7770
New Philadelphia (G-14928)
Speedway LLC ....F...... 937 372-7129
Wilberforce (G-20392)
Speedway LLC ....F...... 513 683-2034
Cincinnati (G-4441)
Speedway LLC ....F...... 330 468-3320
Macedonia (G-12485)
Speedway LLC ....G...... 330 343-9469
Dover (G-9018)
Speedway LLC ....F...... 419 468-9773
Galion (G-10288)
Speedway LLC ....F...... 440 988-8014
Amherst (G-608)
Standard Energy Company ....G...... 614 885-1901
Columbus (G-7650)
Stocker & Sitler Inc ....G...... 614 888-9588
Columbus (G-7657)
Summit Petroleum Inc ....G...... 330 487-5494
Twinsburg (G-19026)
T JS Oil & Gas Inc ....G...... 740 623-0192
Coshocton (G-7912)
Tatum Petroleum Corporation ....G...... 740 819-6810
Worthington (G-20890)
W P Brown Enterprises Inc ....G...... 740 685-2594
Byesville (G-2413)
William S Miller Inc ....G...... 330 223-1794
Kensington (G-11421)

CRYOGENIC COOLING DEVICES: Infrared Detectors, Masers

Advanced Cryogenic Entps LLC ....F...... 330 922-0750
Akron (G-32)
Drivetrain USA Inc ....F...... 614 733-0940
Plain City (G-16337)
Lake Shore Cryotronics Inc ....C...... 614 891-2243
Westerville (G-20165)
Philips Medical Systems Mr ....C...... 440 483-2499
Highland Heights (G-10919)

CRYSTALS

Saint-Gobain Ceramics Plas Inc ....A...... 330 673-5860
Stow (G-17797)

CULTURE MEDIA

Edzplace ....G...... 216 289-4834
Euclid (G-9577)
Sellyourmaccom ....G...... 513 965-1144
Blue Ash (G-1868)
Sneaky Pete Band ....G...... 419 933-6251
Willard (G-20401)

Star Spangled Spectacular Inc ....G..... 419 879-3502
Lima *(G-12096)*

CULVERTS: Metal Plate

Contech Engnered Solutions LLC........F 513 425-5337
Middletown *(G-14033)*

CULVERTS: Sheet Metal

Edwards Sheet Metal Works Inc...........F 740 694-0010
Fredericktown *(G-10101)*
G & C Drainage Supplies Inc ....G..... 513 563-8616
Cincinnati *(G-3788)*

CUPS: Paper, Made From Purchased Materials

American Greetings Corporation ....A 216 252-7300
Cleveland *(G-4782)*
Century Intermediate Holdg Co ....F 216 252-7300
Cleveland *(G-5006)*
Gibson Greetings Inc ....G..... 216 252-7300
Cleveland *(G-5428)*
International Paper Company ....B 419 673-0711
Kenton *(G-11553)*
Ricking Paper and Specialty Co ....E 513 825-3551
Cincinnati *(G-4345)*

CUPS: Plastic Exc Polystyrene Foam

Anchor Hocking LLC ....A 740 681-6478
Lancaster *(G-11687)*
Ghp II LLC ....C 740 687-2500
Lancaster *(G-11719)*

CURBING: Granite Or Stone

Distinctive Marble & Gran Inc ....F 614 760-0003
Plain City *(G-16335)*
Granex Industries Inc ....F 440 248-4915
Solon *(G-17300)*
Keystone Granite and Tile Inc ....G..... 614 541-9749
Columbus *(G-7261)*

CURTAIN & DRAPERY FIXTURES: Poles, Rods & Rollers

Custom Blind Corporation ....F 937 643-2907
Dayton *(G-8257)*
Gannons Discount Blinds ....G..... 216 398-2761
Cleveland *(G-5394)*
Hang-UPS Instllation Group Inc ....G..... 614 239-7004
Columbus *(G-7141)*
Lumenomics Inc.....................................E 614 798-3500
Lewis Center *(G-11906)*
Mag Resources LLC ....G..... 330 294-0494
Barberton *(G-1126)*

CURTAIN WALLS: Building, Steel

Scs Construction Services Inc ....E 513 929-0260
Cincinnati *(G-4393)*

CURTAINS: Shower

Seven Mile Creek Corporation ....F 937 456-3320
Eaton *(G-9322)*

CURTAINS: Window, From Purchased Materials

Anthony Decorative Fabrics and ....G..... 937 299-4637
Moraine *(G-14466)*
Style-Line Incorporated..........................E 614 291-0600
Columbus *(G-7664)*

CUSHIONS & PILLOWS

Easy Way Leisure Corporation ....C 513 731-5640
Cincinnati *(G-3687)*
Innocor Foam Tech - Acp Inc ....F 419 647-4172
Spencerville *(G-17460)*

CUSHIONS & PILLOWS: Bed, From Purchased Materials

Brentwood Originals Inc ....B 330 793-2255
Youngstown *(G-21034)*
Down-Lite International Inc.....................C 513 229-3696
Mason *(G-13011)*
Downhome Inc ....E 513 921-3373
Cincinnati *(G-3670)*

CUSHIONS: Carpet & Rug, Foamed Plastics

Johnsonite Inc......................................B 440 632-3441
Middlefield *(G-13948)*
Scottdel Cushion LLC ....E 419 825-0432
Swanton *(G-18089)*

CUSHIONS: Textile, Exc Spring & Carpet

Luxaire Cushion Co ....F 330 872-0995
Newton Falls *(G-15135)*
Polka DOT Pin Cushion Inc....................G..... 330 659-0233
Richfield *(G-16632)*
Queen City Carpets LLC ....F 513 823-8238
Cincinnati *(G-4314)*

CUSTOM COMPOUNDING OF RUBBER MATERIALS

Killian Latex Inc....................................F 330 644-6746
Akron *(G-256)*
Kiltex Corporation ....E 330 644-6746
Akron *(G-257)*
Maine Rubber Preforms LLC ....G..... 216 210-2094
Middlefield *(G-13952)*
Polymerics Inc.......................................E 330 434-6665
Cuyahoga Falls *(G-8034)*
Prcc Holdings Inc..................................C 330 798-4790
Akron *(G-346)*
Preferred Compounding Corp ....C 330 798-4790
Copley *(G-7852)*
Wayne County Rubber Inc ....E 330 264-5553
Wooster *(G-20845)*

CUSTOMIZING SVCS

Architectural Art Glass Studio...............G..... 513 731-7336
Milford *(G-14122)*
Handcrafted Jewelry Inc ....G..... 330 650-9011
Hudson *(G-11178)*

CUT STONE & STONE PRODUCTS

Accent Manufacturing Inc......................F 330 724-7704
Norton *(G-15500)*
Agean Marble Manufacturing..................E 513 874-1475
West Chester *(G-19978)*
Akron Cultured Marble Pdts LLC ....G..... 330 628-6757
Mogadore *(G-14366)*
Bell Vault & Monument Works ....E 937 866-2444
Miamisburg *(G-13785)*
Brower Products Inc..............................D 937 563-1111
Cincinnati *(G-3482)*
Cascade Cut Stone ....G..... 419 422-4341
Findlay *(G-9804)*
Castelli Marble Inc ....G..... 216 361-2410
Cleveland *(G-4993)*
Classic Stone Company Inc ....F 614 833-3946
Columbus *(G-6934)*
Crane Plumbing LLC ....E 419 522-4211
Mansfield *(G-12587)*
Creative Design Marble Inc ....G..... 937 434-8892
Dayton *(G-8248)*
Drake Monument Company ....G..... 937 399-7941
Springfield *(G-17547)*
Jack Huffman ....G..... 740 384-5178
Wellston *(G-19766)*
Korkan Granite Co Inc ....F 330 677-1883
Kent *(G-11483)*
Lang Stone Company Inc........................D 614 235-4099
Columbus *(G-7284)*
Lima Millwork Inc..................................E 419 331-3303
Elida *(G-9351)*
Lind Stoneworks Ltd ....F 614 866-9733
Columbus *(G-7296)*
Marble Works ....G..... 216 496-7745
Cleveland *(G-5741)*
Marsh Industries Inc.............................E 330 308-8667
New Philadelphia *(G-14912)*
Maumee Valley Memorials Inc ....F 419 878-9030
Waterville *(G-19663)*
Medina Supply Company ....E 330 723-3681
Medina *(G-13445)*
Melvin Stone Co LLC ....G..... 513 771-0820
Cincinnati *(G-4083)*
Milano Monuments LLC ....G..... 216 362-1199
Cleveland *(G-5814)*
National Lime and Stone Co ....D 419 562-0771
Bucyrus *(G-2354)*
National Lime and Stone Co ....F 419 396-7671
Carey *(G-2921)*

NORTH HILL MARBLE & GRANITE CO

North Hill Marble & Granite Co ....F 330 253-2179
Akron *(G-318)*
OBrien Cut Stone Company.....................E 216 663-7800
Cleveland *(G-5925)*
Ohio Beauty Inc ....G..... 330 644-2241
Akron *(G-322)*
Ohio Centech...G..... 513 477-8779
Cincinnati *(G-4175)*
Pavestone LLC ....D 513 474-3783
Cincinnati *(G-4218)*
Pietra Naturale Inc ....F 937 438-8882
Dayton *(G-8576)*
Riceland Cabinet Inc.............................D 330 601-1071
Wooster *(G-20829)*
Studio Vertu Inc....................................E 513 241-9038
Cincinnati *(G-4472)*
Take It For Granite LLC ....F 513 735-0555
Cincinnati *(G-3319)*
Traditional Marble & Gran Ltd................F 419 625-3966
Milan *(G-14117)*
Transtar Holding Company ....G..... 800 359-3339
Cleveland *(G-6349)*
Western Ohio Cut Stone Ltd ....E 937 492-4722
Sidney *(G-17235)*

CUTLERY

Air Technical Industries Inc ....E 440 951-5191
Mentor *(G-13512)*
Alliance Knife Inc ....E 513 367-9000
Harrison *(G-10768)*
American Punch Co Inc..........................E 216 731-4501
Euclid *(G-9566)*
Busse Knife Co ....E 419 923-6471
Wauseon *(G-19673)*
Cut Off Blades Inc.................................G..... 440 543-2947
Chagrin Falls *(G-3084)*
Dan Wilzynski ....E 800 531-3343
Columbus *(G-7010)*
Fred Marvin and Associates Inc ....G..... 330 784-9211
Stow *(G-17756)*
General Cutlery Inc ....F 419 332-2316
Fremont *(G-10154)*
Libbey Glass Inc ....A 419 729-7272
Toledo *(G-18559)*
Npk Construction Equipment Inc ....D 440 232-7900
Bedford *(G-1449)*

CUTLERY: Table, Exc Metal Handled

Ernest Warther and Sons Inc ....F 330 343-7513
Dover *(G-8984)*

CUTOUTS: Cardboard, Die-Cut, Made From Purchased Materials

Alliance Indus Masking Inc.....................G..... 937 681-5569
Dayton *(G-8146)*

CUTOUTS: Distribution

International Bus Mchs Corp ....B 513 826-1001
Blue Ash *(G-1816)*

CUTTING EQPT: Glass Cutters

Crystal Carvers Inc ....G..... 800 365-9782
Powell *(G-16470)*
Glass Medic Inc.....................................G..... 800 356-4009
Westerville *(G-20155)*

CUTTING SVC: Paper, Exc Die-Cut

Customformed Products Inc....................F 937 388-0480
Miamisburg *(G-13795)*
Rmt Holdings Inc...................................F 419 221-1168
Lima *(G-12085)*

CUTTING SVC: Paperboard

Loroco Industries Inc ....E 513 891-9544
Blue Ash *(G-1828)*

CYCLIC CRUDES & INTERMEDIATES

Cleveland FP Inc ....D 216 249-4900
Cleveland *(G-5061)*
Emerald Hilton Davis LLC ....D 513 841-0057
Cincinnati *(G-3694)*
Ferro Corporation ....F 330 682-8015
Orrville *(G-15736)*
Marathon Petroleum Company LP ....F 419 422-2121
Findlay *(G-9855)*

P R O D U C T

Polymerics Inc ....E 330 434-6665
Cuyahoga Falls (G-8034)
Sun Chemical Corporation ....C 513 681-5950
Cincinnati (G-4477)
Sun Chemical Corporation ....D 513 753-9950
Amelia (G-585)
Thermocolor LLC ....E 419 626-5677
Sandusky (G-17012)
Thermocolor LLC ....F 419 626-5677
Sandusky (G-17013)

CYLINDER & ACTUATORS: Fluid Power

Cascade Corporation ....C 937 327-0300
Springfield (G-17527)
Control Line Equipment Inc ....F 216 433-7766
Cleveland (G-5127)
Custom Hoists Inc ....C 419 368-4721
Ashland (G-727)
Cylinders & Valves Inc ....G 440 238-7343
Strongsville (G-17910)
Eaton Leasing Corporation ....G 216 382-2292
Beachwood (G-1270)
Eaton-Aeroquip Inc ....D 419 891-7775
Maumee (G-13258)
Hydraulic Parts Store Inc ....E 330 364-6667
New Philadelphia (G-14902)
Hydraulic Specialists Inc ....E 740 922-3343
Midvale (G-14108)
Malcolm Hydraulics ....G 330 819-2033
Atwater (G-900)
Mrf Machine and Hydraulics Inc ......F 330 673-0135
Kent (G-11495)
Nook Industries Inc ....C 216 271-7900
Cleveland (G-5887)
North Coast Instruments Inc ....E 216 251-2353
Cleveland (G-5896)
Parker-Hannifin Corporation ....B 216 896-3000
Cleveland (G-5973)
Parker-Hannifin Corporation ....C 419 394-9600
Saint Marys (G-16848)
Parker-Hannifin Corporation ....C 330 336-3511
Wadsworth (G-19425)
Qcsm LLC ....G 216 531-5960
Euclid (G-9602)
R & M Fluid Power Inc ....E 330 758-2766
Youngstown (G-21182)
Robeck Fluid Power Co ....D 330 562-1140
Aurora (G-944)
Sebring Fluid Power Corp ....G 330 938-9984
Sebring (G-17053)
Skidmore-Wilhelm Mfg Company ....E 216 481-4774
Solon (G-17381)
Steel Eqp Specialists Inc ....E 330 829-2626
Alliance (G-539)
Steel Eqp Specialists Inc ....D 330 823-8260
Alliance (G-540)
Suburban Manufacturing Co ....D 440 953-2024
Eastlake (G-9290)
Swagelok Company ....D 440 349-5934
Solon (G-17392)

CYLINDERS: Pressure

Enk Tenofour LLC ....G 419 661-1465
Northwood (G-15480)
Hutnik Company ....G 330 336-9700
Wadsworth (G-19411)
Toledo Metal Spinning Company ....E 419 535-5931
Toledo (G-18733)
Worthington Cylinder Corp ....C 740 569-4143
Bremen (G-2082)
Worthington Cylinder Corp ....C 330 262-1762
Wooster (G-20852)
Worthington Cylinder Corp ....C 614 840-3210
Worthington (G-20895)
Worthington Cylinder Corp ....C 440 576-5847
Jefferson (G-11376)
Worthington Cylinder Corp ....C 614 438-7900
Columbus (G-7775)
Worthington Cylinder Corp ....C 614 840-3800
Westerville (G-20196)
Worthington Industries Inc ....C 614 438-3210
Worthington (G-20896)

CYLINDERS: Pump

Custom Cltch Jjint Hydrlics Inc ....F 216 431-1630
Cleveland (G-5149)
Eric Allshouse LLC ....G 330 533-4258
Canfield (G-2554)

Hr Parts N Stuff ....G 330 947-2433
Atwater (G-898)
Rolcon Inc ....F 513 821-7259
Cincinnati (G-4358)

DAIRY EQPT

Hollmann Inc ....G 513 522-1800
Cincinnati (G-3889)

DAIRY PRDTS STORE: Cheese

Bunker Hill Cheese Co Inc ....D 330 893-2131
Millersburg (G-14207)
Guggisberg Cheese Inc ....E 330 893-2550
Millersburg (G-14219)
Schindlers Broad Run Chese Hse .....F 330 343-4108
Dover (G-9011)

DAIRY PRDTS STORE: Ice Cream, Packaged

Malleys Candies ....D 216 362-8700
Lakewood (G-11674)
Milk & Honey ....F 330 492-5884
Canton (G-2782)
Superior Tasting Products Inc ....E 614 442-0622
Columbus (G-7668)

DAIRY PRDTS STORES

Broughton Foods Company ....C 740 373-4121
Marietta (G-12768)
Hans Rothenbuhler & Son Inc ....E 440 632-6000
Middlefield (G-13939)
United Dairy Farmers Inc ....C 513 396-8700
Cincinnati (G-4538)
Youngs Jersey Dairy Inc ....B 937 325-0629
Yellow Springs (G-21003)

DAIRY PRDTS WHOLESALERS: Fresh

Acme Steak & Seafood Inc ....F 330 270-8000
Youngstown (G-21016)
Auburn Dairy Products Inc ....E 614 488-2536
Columbus (G-6785)
Barkett Fruit Co Inc ....E 330 364-6645
Dover (G-8967)
Borden Dairy Co Cincinnati LLC ....C 513 948-8811
Cincinnati (G-3461)
Country Parlour Ice Cream Co ....F 440 237-4040
Cleveland (G-5134)
Dallas Instantwhip Inc ....E 614 488-2536
Columbus (G-7009)
Hans Rothenbuhler & Son Inc ....E 440 632-6000
Middlefield (G-13939)
Hershey Creamery Co ....G 937 374-0688
Xenia (G-20955)
Instantwhip Connecticut Inc ....F 614 488-2536
Columbus (G-7192)
Instantwhip Detroit Inc ....F 800 544-9447
Columbus (G-7194)
Instantwhip Foods Inc ....F 614 488-2536
Columbus (G-7195)
Instantwhip of Buffalo Inc ....F 614 488-2536
Columbus (G-7196)
Instantwhip Products Co PA ....F 614 488-2536
Columbus (G-7197)
Instantwhip-Columbus Inc ....E 614 871-9447
Grove City (G-10564)
Instantwhip-Dayton Inc ....F 937 235-5930
Dayton (G-8410)
Johnsons Real Ice Cream Co ....E 614 231-0014
Columbus (G-7241)
Louis Instantwhip-St Inc ....F 614 488-2536
Columbus (G-7305)
Louis Trauth Dairy LLC ....B 859 431-7553
West Chester (G-20021)
Ohio Processors Inc ....G 740 852-9243
Columbus (G-7428)
Philadelphia Instantwhip Inc ....G 614 488-2536
Columbus (G-7482)
Weaver Bros Inc ....D 937 526-3907
Versailles (G-19360)

DAIRY PRDTS: Butter

Black Radish Creamery Ltd ....G 614 323-6016
New Albany (G-14749)
Butt Kickn Creamery Inc ....G 419 482-6610
Perrysburg (G-16072)
Dairy Farmers America Inc ....E 330 670-7800
Medina (G-13400)

Fairmont Creamery LLC ....G 216 357-2560
Cleveland (G-5320)
Land OLakes Inc ....C 330 678-1578
Kent (G-11485)
Minerva Dairy Inc ....D 330 868-4196
Minerva (G-14334)
Turkeyfoot Creek Creamery ....G 419 335-0224
Wauseon (G-19698)

DAIRY PRDTS: Canned Cream

Tmarzetti Company ....C 614 279-8673
Columbus (G-7697)

DAIRY PRDTS: Canned Milk, Whole

J M Smucker Company ....A 330 682-3000
Orrville (G-15742)

DAIRY PRDTS: Cheese

9444 Ohio Holding Co ....E 330 359-6291
Winesburg (G-20701)
Amish Wedding Foods Inc ....E 330 674-9199
Millersburg (G-14193)
Biery Cheese Co ....C 330 875-3381
Louisville (G-12310)
Brewster Cheese Company ....C 330 767-3492
Brewster (G-2083)
Dairy Farmers America Inc ....E 330 670-7800
Medina (G-13400)
Es Steiner Dairy LLC ....F 330 897-5555
Baltic (G-1069)
Lake Erie Frozen Foods Mfg Co ....E 419 289-9204
Ashland (G-749)
Lakeview Farms LLC ....C 419 695-9925
Delphos (G-8913)
Oakvale Farm Cheese Inc ....C 740 857-1230
London (G-12217)
Tri State Dairy ....G 419 542-8788
Hicksville (G-10908)
Tri State Dairy LLC ....F 330 897-5555
Baltic (G-1078)

DAIRY PRDTS: Cheese, Cottage

Broughton Foods Company ....C 740 373-4121
Marietta (G-12768)
Broughton Foods Company ....F 800 598-7545
South Point (G-17434)

DAIRY PRDTS: Concentrated Milk

L & F Lauch LLC ....G 513 732-5805
Batavia (G-1200)

DAIRY PRDTS: Condensed Milk

Eagle Family Foods Group LLC ....E 330 382-3725
Richfield (G-16621)

DAIRY PRDTS: Cream Substitutes

Instantwhip-Dayton Inc ....F 937 235-5930
Dayton (G-8410)
Instantwhip-Dayton Inc ....G 937 435-4371
Dayton (G-8411)

DAIRY PRDTS: Cream, Whipped

Instantwhip Detroit Inc ....F 800 544-9447
Columbus (G-7194)

DAIRY PRDTS: Dietary Supplements, Dairy & Non-Dairy Based

Aggregate Tersornance LLC ....G 330 418-4751
Canton (G-2590)
Alifet USA Inc ....G 513 793-8033
Blue Ash (G-1740)
Freedom Health LLC ....E 330 562-0888
Aurora (G-920)
Healthy Living ....G 937 962-4705
Lewisburg (G-11934)
Infinit Nutrition LLC ....F 513 791-3500
Blue Ash (G-1815)
Innovated Health LLC ....G 330 858-0651
Cuyahoga Falls (G-8010)
Instantwhip-Columbus Inc ....E 614 871-9447
Grove City (G-10564)
Lifestyle Nutraceuticals Ltd ....F 513 376-7218
Cincinnati (G-4022)
Muscle Feast LLC ....F 740 877-8808
Hebron (G-10878)

Toomey Inc ....G 513 831-4771
  Milford *(G-14178)*
Wileys Finest LLC ....G 740 622-1072
  Coshocton *(G-7916)*

DAIRY PRDTS: Dips & Spreads, Cheese Based

Lakeview Farms LLC ....E 419 695-9925
  Delphos *(G-8912)*

DAIRY PRDTS: Dips & Spreads, Sour Cream Based

Dip It Good Foods Inc ....G 330 219-3137
  Newton Falls *(G-15132)*

DAIRY PRDTS: Evaporated Milk

Nestle Usa Inc ....C 216 524-7738
  Cleveland *(G-5872)*
Nestle Usa Inc ....C 216 524-3397
  Cleveland *(G-5873)*
Nestle Usa Inc ....C 440 349-5757
  Solon *(G-17347)*

DAIRY PRDTS: Frozen Desserts & Novelties

ABC Refreshments LLC ....F 866 382-5575
  Euclid *(G-9563)*
Archies Too ....D 419 427-2663
  Findlay *(G-9790)*
B M DS Fish N More LLC ....F 419 238-2722
  Van Wert *(G-19244)*
Better Than Sex Ice Cream LLC ....G 614 444-5505
  Columbus *(G-6823)*
Cone of West Chester ....E 513 779-7040
  West Chester *(G-19837)*
Country Maid Ice Cream Inc ....G 330 659-6830
  Richfield *(G-16619)*
Country Parlour Ice Cream Co ....F 440 237-4040
  Cleveland *(G-5134)*
CTB Consulting LLC ....F 216 712-7764
  Rocky River *(G-16697)*
Dari Freeze ....G 937 678-6171
  West Manchester *(G-20097)*
Dietsch Brothers Incorporated ....E 419 422-4474
  Findlay *(G-9816)*
Frosty Twins ....G 330 359-0708
  Winesburg *(G-20703)*
Home City Ice Company ....F 419 562-4953
  Delaware *(G-8860)*
Honeybaked Ham Company ....E 513 583-9700
  Cincinnati *(G-3895)*
ICEE USA ....G 513 771-0630
  West Chester *(G-20015)*
Jim H Niemeyer ....F 419 422-2465
  Findlay *(G-9845)*
Johnsons Real Ice Cream Co ....G 614 231-0014
  Columbus *(G-7241)*
Joshua Leigh Enterprises Inc ....G 330 244-9200
  Canton *(G-2749)*
Louis Trauth Dairy LLC ....B 859 431-7553
  West Chester *(G-20021)*
Mitchell Bros Ice Cream Inc ....F 216 861-2799
  Cleveland *(G-5824)*
Robert E McGrath Inc ....E 440 572-7747
  Strongsville *(G-17959)*
Springdale Ice Cream Beverage ....E 513 699-4984
  Cincinnati *(G-4447)*
St Clairsville Dairy Queen ....G 740 635-1800
  Saint Clairsville *(G-16808)*
Stella Lou LLC ....F 937 935-9536
  Powell *(G-16483)*
Weldon Ice Cream Company ....G 740 467-2400
  Millersport *(G-14299)*
Welsh Farms LLC ....G 513 723-4487
  Cincinnati *(G-4585)*
Wild Penguin Llc ....G 513 533-4356
  Cincinnati *(G-4595)*
Youngs Jersey Dairy Inc ....B 937 325-0629
  Yellow Springs *(G-21003)*

DAIRY PRDTS: Half & Half

Instantwhip-Dayton Inc ....F 937 235-5930
  Dayton *(G-8410)*
Instantwhip-Dayton Inc ....G 937 435-4371
  Dayton *(G-8411)*

DAIRY PRDTS: Ice Cream & Ice Milk

Double Dippin Inc ....G 937 847-2572
  Miamisburg *(G-13802)*
Gibson Bros Inc ....E 440 774-2401
  Oberlin *(G-15641)*
International Brand Services ....F 513 376-8209
  Cincinnati *(G-3930)*
Malleys Candies ....D 216 362-8700
  Lakewood *(G-11674)*
Pierres French Ice Cream Inc ....E 216 431-2555
  Cleveland *(G-6006)*
Royal Ice Cream Co ....D 216 432-1144
  Cleveland *(G-6139)*
Toft Dairy Inc ....D 419 625-4376
  Sandusky *(G-17016)*
United Dairy Farmers Inc ....E 513 396-8700
  Cincinnati *(G-4538)*

DAIRY PRDTS: Ice Cream, Bulk

3 Dips ....G 937 247-5914
  Miamisburg *(G-13777)*
Bacconis Lickety Split ....G 330 924-0418
  Cortland *(G-7861)*
Bojos Cream ....G 330 270-3332
  Austintown *(G-970)*
Country Caterers Inc ....G 740 389-1013
  Marion *(G-12863)*
Dairy Shed ....G 937 848-3504
  Bellbrook *(G-1506)*
Fritzie Freeze Inc ....G 419 727-0818
  Toledo *(G-18474)*
Froyo Twist ....G 440 974-1001
  Mentor *(G-13586)*
Orange Leaf ....G 614 898-5323
  Westerville *(G-20175)*
Reiter Dairy of Akron Inc ....E 419 424-5060
  Findlay *(G-9882)*
Smithfoods Inc ....G 330 683-8710
  Orrville *(G-15764)*
United Dairy Inc ....C 740 633-1451
  Martins Ferry *(G-12927)*
Whit S Frozen Custard ....E 740 927-0025
  Pataskala *(G-15990)*
Whits Frozen Custard ....G 740 965-1427
  Sunbury *(G-18078)*
Yagoot ....G 513 791-6600
  Cincinnati *(G-4617)*
ZS Cream & Bean ....G 440 652-6369
  Hinckley *(G-11032)*

DAIRY PRDTS: Ice Cream, Packaged, Molded, On Sticks, Etc.

Broughton Foods Company ....C 740 373-4121
  Marietta *(G-12768)*
Graeters Manufacturing Co ....D 513 721-3323
  Cincinnati *(G-3843)*
Home City Ice ....G 859 441-1700
  Aberdeen *(G-1)*
Schwans Home Service Inc ....E 419 222-9977
  Lima *(G-12088)*
Schwans Home Service Inc ....E 937 335-4111
  Troy *(G-18873)*

DAIRY PRDTS: Ice milk, Bulk

Superior Tasting Products Inc ....E 614 442-0622
  Columbus *(G-7668)*

DAIRY PRDTS: Milk, Condensed & Evaporated

Hans Rothenbuhler & Son Inc ....E 440 632-6000
  Middlefield *(G-13939)*
Ingredia Inc ....E 419 738-4060
  Wapakoneta *(G-19491)*
Kerry Flavor Systems Us LLC ....D 513 771-4682
  Cincinnati *(G-3985)*
Milnot Company ....G 888 656-3245
  Gahanna *(G-10220)*
Minerva Dairy Inc ....D 330 868-4196
  Minerva *(G-14334)*
Moo Technologies Inc ....G 513 732-5805
  Batavia *(G-1209)*
Muscle Feast LLC ....G 888 734-3634
  Hebron *(G-10877)*
Nestle Usa Inc ....D 216 861-8350
  Cleveland *(G-5874)*
Rich Products Corporation ....C 614 771-1117
  Hilliard *(G-10976)*

Smithfoods Orrville Inc ....C 330 684-6502
  Orrville *(G-15765)*

DAIRY PRDTS: Milk, Fluid

Borden Dairy Company Ohio LLC ....C 216 671-2300
  Cleveland *(G-4925)*
Consun Food Industries Inc ....D 440 322-6301
  Elyria *(G-9397)*
Dairy Farmers America Inc ....E 330 670-7800
  Medina *(G-13400)*
Instantwhip Foods Inc ....F 614 488-2536
  Columbus *(G-7195)*
Instantwhip-Chicago Inc ....E 614 488-2536
  Columbus *(G-7198)*
Louis Trauth Dairy LLC ....B 859 431-7553
  West Chester *(G-20021)*

DAIRY PRDTS: Milk, Processed, Pasteurized, Homogenized/Btld

Arps Dairy Inc. ....F 419 782-9116
  Defiance *(G-8779)*
Borden Dairy Co Cincinnati LLC ....C 513 948-8811
  Cincinnati *(G-3461)*
Daisy Brand LLC ....F 330 202-4376
  Wooster *(G-20762)*
Reiter Dairy of Akron Inc ....E 937 323-5777
  Springfield *(G-17637)*
Reiter Dairy of Akron Inc ....E 419 424-5060
  Findlay *(G-9882)*
Smith Dairy Products Company ....E 740 927-2688
  Reynoldsburg *(G-16605)*
Smithfoods Inc ....G 330 683-8710
  Orrville *(G-15764)*
Snowville Creamery LLC ....E 740 698-2301
  Pomeroy *(G-16391)*
Toft Dairy Inc ....D 419 625-4376
  Sandusky *(G-17016)*
United Dairy Inc. ....C 740 633-1451
  Martins Ferry *(G-12927)*
United Dairy Farmers Inc ....E 513 396-8700
  Cincinnati *(G-4538)*

DAIRY PRDTS: Natural Cheese

Bunker Hill Cheese Co Inc ....D 330 893-2131
  Millersburg *(G-14207)*
Great Lakes Cheese Co Inc ....B 440 834-2500
  Hiram *(G-11036)*
Guggisberg Cheese Inc ....E 330 893-2550
  Millersburg *(G-14219)*
Hans Rothenbuhler & Son Inc ....E 440 632-6000
  Middlefield *(G-13939)*
Holmes Cheese Co ....E 330 674-6451
  Millersburg *(G-14229)*
Miceli Dairy Products Co ....D 216 791-6222
  Cleveland *(G-5797)*
Middlefield Mix Inc ....F 440 632-0157
  Middlefield *(G-13960)*
Middlfeld Original Cheese Coop ....E 440 632-5567
  Middlefield *(G-13964)*
Pearl Valley Cheese Inc ....E 740 545-6002
  Fresno *(G-10197)*
Schindlers Broad Run Chese Hse ....F 330 343-4108
  Dover *(G-9011)*

DAIRY PRDTS: Powdered Milk

Stolle Milk Biologics Inc ....C 513 489-7997
  West Chester *(G-20055)*

DAIRY PRDTS: Processed Cheese

A & M Cheese Co ....D 419 476-8369
  Toledo *(G-18317)*
Inter American Products Inc ....E 800 645-2233
  Cincinnati *(G-3927)*
Kathys Krafts and Kollectibles ....G 423 787-3709
  Medina *(G-13431)*
Kraft House No 5 ....G 614 396-9091
  Powell *(G-16475)*
Kraft of Writing ....G 614 620-2476
  Columbus *(G-7266)*
Minerva Dairy Inc ....D 330 868-4196
  Minerva *(G-14334)*
Wood Kraft ....G 440 487-4634
  Garrettsville *(G-10336)*

DAIRY PRDTS: Sour Cream

Lakeview Farms Inc ....D 419 695-9925
  Delphos *(G-8911)*

PRODUCT

Lakeview Farms LLC ....E 419 695-9925
Delphos (G-8912)
Lakeview Farms LLC ....C 419 695-9925
Delphos (G-8913)

DAIRY PRDTS: Whipped Topping, Exc Frozen Or Dry Mix

Auburn Dairy Products Inc ....E 614 488-2536
Columbus (G-6785)
Dallas Instantwhip Inc ....F 614 488-2536
Columbus (G-7009)
Instantwhip Connecticut Inc ......E 614 488-2536
Columbus (G-7192)
Instantwhip Detroit Inc ....F 614 488-2536
Columbus (G-7193)
Instantwhip of Buffalo Inc ....F 614 488-2536
Columbus (G-7196)
Instantwhip Products Co PA ....E 614 488-2536
Columbus (G-7197)
Instantwhip-Columbus Inc ....E 614 871-9447
Grove City (G-10564)
Instantwhip-Syracuse Inc ....E 614 488-2536
Columbus (G-7199)
Louis Instantwhip-St Inc ....F 614 488-2536
Columbus (G-7305)
Ohio Processors Inc ....G 740 852-9243
Columbus (G-7428)
Peak Foods Llc ....D 937 440-0707
Troy (G-18862)
Philadelphia Instantwhip Inc ....G 614 488-2536
Columbus (G-7482)

DAIRY PRDTS: Yogurt, Exc Frozen

American Confections Co LLC ......G 614 888-8838
Columbus (G-6734)

DAIRY PRDTS: Yogurt, Frozen

Awesome Yogurt LLC ....G 937 643-0879
Dayton (G-8176)
The Dannon Company Inc ....B 513 229-0092
Mason (G-13098)
The Dannon Company Inc ....B 419 628-3861
Minster (G-14363)
Tmarzetti Company ....C 614 279-8673
Columbus (G-7697)
Wil-Mark Froyo LLC ....G 330 421-6043
Wadsworth (G-19445)

DATA PROCESSING & PREPARATION SVCS

3dlt LLC ....F 513 452-3358
Cincinnati (G-3324)
Datatrak International Inc ....E 440 443-0082
Mayfield Heights (G-13312)
Gracie Plum Investments Inc ......E 740 355-9029
Portsmouth (G-16436)
List Media Inc ....G 330 995-0864
Aurora (G-934)
Northrop Grmmn Spce & Mssn Sys ..D 937 259-4956
Dayton (G-8529)
Thinkware Incorporated ....E 513 598-3300
Cincinnati (G-4506)
Zebu Compliance Solutions Inc .....E 740 355-9029
Portsmouth (G-16460)

DATA PROCESSING SVCS

Aero Fulfillment Services Corp .....D 800 225-7145
Mason (G-12979)
Alltel Communications Corp ....G 419 784-3808
Defiance (G-8777)
Capitol Citicom Inc ....E 614 472-2679
Columbus (G-6903)
Cpmm Services Group Inc ....F 614 447-0165
Columbus (G-6996)
Image Integrations Systems ....F 419 872-0003
Perrysburg (G-16109)
Sourcelink Ohio LLC ....C 937 885-8000
Miamisburg (G-13862)

DATABASE INFORMATION RETRIEVAL SVCS

Lexisnexis Group ....C 937 865-6800
Miamisburg (G-13825)

DECALS, WHOLESALE

Blang Acquisition LLC ....F 937 223-2155
Dayton (G-8190)

DECORATIVE WOOD & WOODWORK

77 Coach Supply Ltd ....E 330 674-1454
Millersburg (G-14187)
Adroit Thinking Inc ....F 419 542-9363
Hicksville (G-10898)
Barkman Products LLC ....G 330 893-2520
Millersburg (G-14197)
Brown Wood Products Company .....G 330 339-8000
New Philadelphia (G-14886)
Cado Door & Design Inc ....G 330 343-4288
New Philadelphia (G-14889)
Cedar Chest ....G 937 878-9097
Fairborn (G-9616)
CM Paula Company ....E 513 759-7473
Mason (G-13002)
Colby Woodworking Inc ....G 937 224-7676
Dayton (G-8236)
Crosco Wood Products ....G 330 857-0228
Dalton (G-8065)
Family Woodworks LLC ....G 740 289-4071
Piketon (G-16220)
G R K Manufacturing Co Inc ....E 513 863-3131
Hamilton (G-10697)
Handicraft LLC ....G 216 295-1950
Cleveland (G-5475)
Hardwood Solutions ....G 330 359-5755
Wilmot (G-20686)
Hardwood Store Inc ....G 937 864-2899
Enon (G-9547)
Herbert Wood Products Inc ....G 440 834-1410
Middlefield (G-13942)
Homestead Collections ....G 419 422-8286
Findlay (G-9841)
Insta Plak Inc ....F 419 537-1555
Toledo (G-18525)
J & R Woodworking ....G 330 893-0713
Millersburg (G-14234)
J R Custom Unlimited ....F 513 894-9800
Hamilton (G-10710)
Judith C Zell ....G 740 385-0386
Logan (G-12180)
Marcum Crew Cut Inc ....G 740 862-3400
Baltimore (G-1084)
Mikes Mill Shop Inc ....G 419 538-6091
Ottawa (G-15801)
Miller Manufacturing Inc ....E 330 852-0689
Sugarcreek (G-18028)
Millwork Designs Inc ....G 740 335-5203
Wshngtn CT Hs (G-20917)
Newbury Woodworks ....G 440 564-5273
Newbury (G-15100)
P & T Millwork Inc ....E 440 543-2151
Chagrin Falls (G-3109)
Peters Family Enterprises Inc ....G 419 339-0555
Elida (G-9355)
Revonoc Inc ....G 440 548-3491
Parkman (G-15953)
Ryanworks Inc ....F 937 438-1282
Dayton (G-8641)
Steeles 5 Acre Mill Inc ....F 419 542-9363
Hicksville (G-10906)
Tayjus Personalized Woodworks .....G 440 427-9145
Olmsted Falls (G-15676)
W H K Company ....G 937 372-3368
Xenia (G-20986)
Walnut Creek Planing Ltd ....D 330 893-3244
Millersburg (G-14281)
Walnut Creek Wood Design ....G 330 852-9663
Sugarcreek (G-18049)
Warthers Music Box Bells ....G 330 343-4706
Dover (G-9024)
Wengerd Wood Inc ....G 330 359-4300
Wilmot (G-20688)
Woodcraft Pattern Works Inc ....G 330 630-2158
Tallmadge (G-18178)
Woodpeckers Inc ....E 440 238-1824
Strongsville (G-17985)
Woodworks Design ....G 440 693-4414
Middlefield (G-14008)

DEFENSE SYSTEMS & EQPT

IMT Defense Corp ....G 614 891-8812
Westerville (G-20159)
MCO Solutions Inc ....G 937 205-9512
Dayton (G-8480)
Unmanned Science Inc ....G 614 581-9893
Dublin (G-9159)
Vector Electromagnetics LLC ....G 937 478-5904
Beavercreek (G-1383)

DEFOLIANTS

WA Hammond Drierite Co Ltd ....E 937 376-2927
Xenia (G-20987)

DEGREASING MACHINES

Auto-Tap Inc ....E 216 671-1043
Cleveland (G-4864)
Crowne Group LLC ....D 216 589-0198
Cleveland (G-5143)
Findlay Machine & Tool Inc ....E 419 434-3100
Findlay (G-9823)

DEHUMIDIFIERS: Electric

Bry-Air Inc ....E 740 965-2974
Sunbury (G-18056)

DEHYDRATION EQPT

Cleveland Range LLC ....G 216 481-4900
Cleveland (G-5074)

DEICING OR DEFROSTING FLUID

Visible Solutions Inc ....G 440 925-2810
Westlake (G-20317)
Zircon Industries Inc ....G 216 595-0200
Cleveland (G-6499)

DENTAL EQPT & SPLYS

Asch-Klaassen Sonics LLC ....G 513 671-3226
Cincinnati (G-3417)
Chicago Dental Supply Inc ....G 800 571-5211
Harrison (G-10771)
Coltene/Whaledent Inc ....C 330 916-8800
Cuyahoga Falls (G-7981)
Dental Ceramics Inc ....E 330 523-5240
Richfield (G-16620)
Dentsply International Inc ....D 419 865-9497
Maumee (G-13256)
Dresch Tolson Dental Labs ....D 419 842-6730
Sylvania (G-18105)
Duncan Dental Lab LLC ....G 614 793-0330
Dublin (G-9070)
Midmark Corporation ....A 937 526-3662
Versailles (G-19352)
Obsidian Biodent ....G 937 938-9244
Oakwood (G-15610)
Precision Swiss LLC ....G 513 716-7000
Cincinnati (G-4264)
Smile Brands Inc ....G 440 471-6133
North Olmsted (G-15346)
Sportsguard Laboratories Inc ....G 330 673-3932
Kent (G-11531)
United Dental Laboratories ....E 330 253-1810
Akron (G-455)
Vacalon Company Inc ....G 614 577-1945
Pickerington (G-16209)
Wbc Group LLC ....C 866 528-2144
Hudson (G-11207)

DENTAL EQPT & SPLYS WHOLESALERS

Dentronix Inc ....E 330 916-7300
Cuyahoga Falls (G-7987)

DENTAL EQPT & SPLYS: Denture Materials

Chewrite Co ....D 937 746-5509
Springboro (G-17476)

DENTAL EQPT & SPLYS: Enamels

Absolute Smile LLC ....G 937 293-9866
Dayton (G-8128)

DENTAL EQPT & SPLYS: Orthodontic Appliances

Dentronix Inc ....E 330 916-7300
Cuyahoga Falls (G-7987)
Mark Dental Laboratory ....G 216 464-6424
Cleveland (G-5744)
Thomas J Raffa DDS Inc ....G 440 997-5208
Ashtabula (G-842)

DENTAL EQPT & SPLYS: Teeth, Artificial, Exc In Dental Labs

Dentsply Sirona Inc ....E 419 893-5672
Maumee (G-13257)

DENTAL EQPT & SPLYS: Tools, NEC

Endodent Inc ....E 626 359-5715
  Cuyahoga Falls *(G-7991)*

DENTISTS' OFFICES & CLINICS

Thomas J Raffa DDS Inc ....G 440 997-5208
  Ashtabula *(G-842)*

DEODORANTS: Personal

Bertsherm Products Inc ....G 440 268-8389
  Cleveland *(G-4908)*
Dover Wipes Company ....F 513 983-1100
  Cincinnati *(G-3669)*
Natures Simple Solution Inc ....G 440 567-6913
  Cleveland *(G-5862)*
Procter & Gamble Company ....B 513 983-1100
  Cincinnati *(G-4286)*
Procter & Gamble Company ....C 513 634-9110
  West Chester *(G-19923)*
Procter & Gamble Company ....C 410 527-5735
  Grove City *(G-10586)*

DEPARTMENT STORES

Kmart Supercenter ....G 440 974-7300
  Cleveland *(G-5660)*
Wagoner Stores Inc ....G 937 836-3636
  Englewood *(G-9544)*

DEPARTMENT STORES: Army-Navy Goods

Raven Concealment Systems LLC ....G 440 508-9000
  North Ridgeville *(G-15399)*

DEPARTMENT STORES: Country General

Andersons Lawn Fert Div Inc ....F 419 893-5050
  Maumee *(G-13226)*
John Purdum ....G 513 897-9686
  Waynesville *(G-19731)*

DEPILATORIES, COSMETIC

Scarlett Kitty LLC ....F 678 438-3796
  Dayton *(G-8646)*

DERMATOLOGICALS

Essence Maker ....G 440 729-3894
  Chesterland *(G-3203)*
Family Medical Clinic & Laser ....G 740 345-2767
  Newark *(G-15006)*

DESALTER KITS: Sea Water

Luxfer Magtech Inc ....E 513 772-3066
  Cincinnati *(G-4040)*
Natures Own Source LLC ....G 440 838-5135
  Brecksville *(G-2065)*

DESIGN SVCS, NEC

A & B Wood Design Assoc Inc ....G 330 721-2789
  Wadsworth *(G-19385)*
B C Wilson Inc ....G 937 439-1866
  Dayton *(G-8178)*
Bollin & Sons Inc ....E 419 693-6573
  Toledo *(G-18376)*
Controls Inc ....E 330 239-4345
  Medina *(G-13392)*
Equipment Concepts ....G 937 291-9734
  Dayton *(G-8329)*
Htec Systems Inc ....F 937 438-3010
  Dayton *(G-8394)*
IEC Infrared Systems LLC ....E 440 234-8000
  Middleburg Heights *(G-13906)*
Laura Dawson ....G 513 777-2513
  West Chester *(G-19891)*
Manchik Engineering & Co ....G 740 927-4454
  Dublin *(G-9101)*
Twin Design AP Promotions Ltd ....G 937 732-6798
  Dayton *(G-8734)*

DESIGN SVCS: Commercial & Indl

Acreo Inc ....G 513 734-3327
  Amelia *(G-565)*
David Wolfe Design Inc ....F 330 633-6124
  Akron *(G-142)*
Electrovations Inc ....E 330 274-3558
  Aurora *(G-918)*

Elite Enclosure Company LLC ....E 937 492-3548
  Sidney *(G-17185)*
Hutnik Company ....G 330 336-9700
  Wadsworth *(G-19411)*
Ies Systems Inc ....G 330 533-6683
  Canfield *(G-2558)*
Joseph B Stinson Co ....G 419 334-4151
  Fremont *(G-10160)*
K C Creations ....G 937 748-8181
  Troy *(G-18850)*
Military Resources LLC ....G 330 263-1040
  Wooster *(G-20809)*
Military Resources LLC ....G 330 309-9970
  Wooster *(G-20810)*
New Path International LLC ....E 614 410-3974
  Powell *(G-16481)*
Precision Inc ....G 330 897-8860
  Fresno *(G-10198)*
R and J Corporation ....E 440 871-6009
  Westlake *(G-20299)*
R J K Enterprises Inc ....F 440 257-6018
  Mentor *(G-13712)*
Ultra Tech Machinery Inc ....E 330 929-5544
  Cuyahoga Falls *(G-8059)*

DESIGN SVCS: Computer Integrated Systems

Aclara Technologies LLC ....C 440 528-7200
  Solon *(G-17248)*
Applied Experience LLC ....G 614 943-2970
  Columbus *(G-6765)*
Applied Imagination Inc ....G 419 352-8373
  Bowling Green *(G-1968)*
Cott Systems Inc ....D 614 847-4405
  Columbus *(G-6989)*
Eaj Services LLC ....F 513 792-3400
  Blue Ash *(G-1780)*
Electronic Concepts Engrg Inc ....F 419 861-9000
  Holland *(G-11059)*
IPA Ltd ....F 614 523-3974
  Columbus *(G-7210)*
M T Systems Inc ....G 330 453-4646
  Canton *(G-2763)*
Matrix Management Solutions ....C 330 470-3700
  Canton *(G-2773)*
New ERA Controls Inc ....G 216 641-8683
  Cleveland *(G-5877)*
Rockware Corp ....G 419 483-5649
  Bellevue *(G-1556)*
Sgi Matrix LLC ....D 937 438-9033
  Miamisburg *(G-13858)*
Software Solutions Inc ....E 513 932-6667
  Lebanon *(G-11841)*
Tata America Intl Corp ....B 513 677-6500
  Milford *(G-14177)*

DESIGN SVCS: Hand Tools

Harbor Freight Tools Usa Inc ....E 937 415-0770
  Dayton *(G-8385)*

DETECTION APPARATUS: Electronic/Magnetic Field, Light/Heat

L-3 Communications Cincinnati ....A 513 573-6100
  Mason *(G-13055)*

DETECTION EQPT: Magnetic Field

Ceia Usa Ltd ....E 330 405-3190
  Twinsburg *(G-18909)*
Peerless-Winsmith Inc ....G 614 526-7000
  Dublin *(G-9122)*

DETECTIVE & ARMORED CAR SERVICES

Contingncy Prcrments Group LLC ....G 513 204-9590
  Maineville *(G-12521)*

DETECTORS: Water Leak

Fluid Conservation Systems ....F 513 831-9335
  Milford *(G-14141)*
Robert J & Cindy K Hartz ....G 513 521-6215
  Cincinnati *(G-4354)*
Tegratek ....G 513 742-5100
  Cincinnati *(G-4499)*

DIAGNOSTIC SUBSTANCES

Core Quantum Technologies Inc ....G 614 214-7210
  Columbus *(G-6984)*
Diagnostic Hybrids Inc ....C 740 593-1784
  Athens *(G-861)*
Diramed LLC ....F 614 487-3660
  Columbus *(G-7026)*
Enlyton Ltd ....G 614 888-9220
  Columbus *(G-7059)*
GE Health ....F 513 241-5955
  Cincinnati *(G-3809)*
John P Ellis Clinic Podiatry ....G 440 460-0444
  Cleveland *(G-5620)*
Meridian Bioscience Inc ....B 513 271-3700
  Cincinnati *(G-4085)*
Meridian Life Science Inc ....D 513 271-3700
  Cincinnati *(G-4086)*
Nanofiber Solutions Inc ....G 614 559-9065
  Columbus *(G-7380)*
Navidea Biopharmaceuticals Inc ....D 614 793-7500
  Dublin *(G-9110)*
Perkinelmer Hlth Sciences Inc ....E 330 825-4525
  Akron *(G-336)*
Sarcokinetics LLC ....G 414 477-9585
  Cleveland *(G-6159)*
Thermo Fisher Scientific Inc ....C 800 871-8909
  Oakwood Village *(G-15630)*
USB Corporation ....D 216 765-5000
  Cleveland *(G-6401)*

DIAGNOSTIC SUBSTANCES OR AGENTS: In Vitro

Apollo Medical Devices LLC ....G 440 935-5027
  Cleveland *(G-4819)*
Filament LLC ....G 614 732-0754
  Columbus *(G-7083)*
Prostate Theranostics LLC ....G 216 595-1968
  Beachwood *(G-1291)*

DIAGNOSTIC SUBSTANCES OR AGENTS: Radioactive

Cardinal Health 414 LLC ....G 614 473-0786
  Columbus *(G-6906)*
Cardinal Health 414 LLC ....C 614 757-5000
  Dublin *(G-9058)*
Cardinal Health 414 LLC ....G 513 759-1900
  West Chester *(G-19823)*
Petnet Solutions Inc ....G 865 218-2000
  Cincinnati *(G-4232)*
Petnet Solutions Inc ....G 865 218-2000
  Cleveland *(G-5996)*
Petnet Solutions Cleveland LLC ....G 865 218-2000
  Cleveland *(G-5997)*

DIAMOND SETTER SVCS

Jewels By Img Inc ....F 440 461-4464
  Cleveland *(G-5614)*

DIAPERS: Disposable

Absorbent Products Company Inc ....E 419 352-5353
  Bowling Green *(G-1965)*
Principle Business Entps Inc ....C 419 352-1551
  Bowling Green *(G-2009)*

DIE CUTTING SVC: Paper

Forest Converting Company Inc ....G 513 631-4190
  Cincinnati *(G-3769)*
P & R Specialty Inc ....E 937 773-0263
  Piqua *(G-16297)*
Williams Steel Rule Die Co ....F 216 431-3232
  Cleveland *(G-6464)*

DIE SETS: Presses, Metal Stamping

Centaur Tool & Die Inc ....F 419 352-7704
  Bowling Green *(G-1976)*
Columbia Stamping Inc ....F 440 236-6677
  Columbia Station *(G-6585)*
Connell Limited Partnership ....D 877 534-8986
  Northfield *(G-15464)*
Kurtz Tool & Die Co Inc ....G 330 755-7723
  Struthers *(G-17993)*
McAfee Tool & Die Inc ....E 330 896-9555
  Uniontown *(G-19092)*
Misumi Investment USA Corp ....G 937 859-5111
  Dayton *(G-8504)*

PRODUCT

Producto Dieco Corporation ....F 440 542-0000
Solon (G-17364)
Superb Industries Inc ....D 330 852-0500
Sugarcreek (G-18045)
Toolcraft Products Inc ....D 937 223-8271
Dayton (G-8719)
W H Heimkreiter Manufacturing ....G 513 681-9192
Cincinnati (G-4574)

DIE SPRINGS

Fremont Cutting Dies Inc ....G 419 334-5153
Fremont (G-10148)

DIES & TOOLS: Special

Absolute Grinding Co Inc ....F 440 974-4030
Mentor (G-13504)
Accu Tool Inc ....G 937 667-5878
Tipp City (G-18257)
Accu-Tek Tool & Die Inc ....G 330 726-1946
Salem (G-16867)
Accurate Machining & Welding ....G 937 584-4518
Sabina (G-16772)
Accurate Tool Co Inc ....G 330 332-9448
Salem (G-16868)
Acro Tool & Die Company ....D 330 773-5173
Akron (G-29)
Allen Tool Co Inc ....G 937 987-2037
New Vienna (G-14954)
Allied Tool & Die Inc ....F 216 941-6196
Cleveland (G-4766)
Aluminum Fence & Mfg Co ....G 330 755-3323
Burton (G-2372)
Amcraft Inc ....G 419 729-7900
Toledo (G-18335)
Argo Tool Corporation ....F 330 425-2407
Twinsburg (G-18901)
Artisan Tool & Die Corp ....E 216 883-2769
Cleveland (G-4838)
Atlantic Tool & Die Company ....C 330 769-4500
Seville (G-17068)
Automation Tool & Die Inc ....D 330 225-8336
Valley City (G-19199)
Banner Metals Group Inc ....D 614 291-3105
Columbus (G-6805)
Blitz Tool & Die Inc ....G 440 237-1177
Cleveland (G-4917)
Brainin-Advance Industries LLC ....E 513 874-9760
West Chester (G-19821)
Brinkman Tool & Die Inc ....E 937 222-1161
Dayton (G-8196)
Browder Tool Co Inc ....G 937 233-6731
Dayton (G-8199)
Brw Tool Inc ....F 419 394-3371
Saint Marys (G-16835)
C-H Tool & Die ....G 740 397-7214
Mount Vernon (G-14610)
Capital Tool Company ....E 216 661-5750
Cleveland (G-4971)
Chippewa Tool & Mfg Co ....F 419 849-2790
Woodville (G-20724)
Claridon Tool & Die Inc ....G 740 389-1944
Caledonia (G-2435)
Cleveland Die & Mfg Co ....G 216 941-7268
Cleveland (G-5058)
Cleveland Metal Processing Inc ....C 440 243-3404
Cleveland (G-5070)
Cliffco Stands Inc ....E 937 382-3700
Wilmington (G-20659)
Clyde Tool & Die Inc ....G 419 547-9574
Clyde (G-6538)
Cole Tool & Die Company ....E 419 522-1272
Ontario (G-15686)
Colonial Machine Company Inc ....D 330 673-5859
Kent (G-11439)
Companies of North Coast LLC ....G 216 398-8550
Cleveland (G-5109)
Concord Design Inc ....G 330 722-5133
Medina (G-13391)
Conti Tool & Die Inc ....G 330 633-1414
Akron (G-128)
Contour Tool Inc ....E 440 365-7333
North Ridgeville (G-15364)
Cornerstone Manufacturing Inc ....G 937 456-5930
Eaton (G-9303)
Custom Machine Inc ....G 419 986-5122
Tiffin (G-18217)
Custom Tooling Company Inc ....F 513 733-5790
Cincinnati (G-3627)
D A Fitzgerald Co Inc ....G 937 548-0511
Greenville (G-10497)

D J Metro Mold & Die Inc ....G 440 237-1130
North Royalton (G-15416)
Dayton Tool Co Inc ....E 937 222-5501
Dayton (G-8288)
Deepwood Roll Tooling ....G 440 946-5640
Mentor (G-13560)
Defiance Metal Products Co ....B 419 784-5332
Defiance (G-8785)
Die Cast Division ....G 330 769-2013
Seville (G-17074)
Die-Mension Corporation ....F 330 273-5872
Brunswick (G-2221)
Die-Namic Tool & Die Inc ....G 330 296-6923
Ravenna (G-16525)
Dove Die and Stamping Company ....E 216 267-3720
Cleveland (G-5211)
Dreier Tool & Die Corp ....G 513 521-8200
Cincinnati (G-3671)
Drt Mfg Co ....G 937 297-6670
Dayton (G-8313)
Duco Tool & Die Inc ....F 419 628-2031
Minster (G-14351)
Duncan Tool Inc ....F 937 667-9364
Tipp City (G-18276)
Dyco Manufacturing Inc ....F 419 485-5525
Montpelier (G-14444)
Dynamic Tool Die ....G 440 834-0007
Middlefield (G-13932)
Eagle Precision Products LLC ....G 440 582-9393
North Royalton (G-15418)
Eagle Tool & Die Inc ....G 216 671-5055
Cleveland (G-5237)
Equipment Concepts ....G 937 291-9734
Dayton (G-8329)
Fabrication Shop Inc ....F 419 435-7934
Fostoria (G-9970)
Falls Tool & Die Incorporated ....G 330 633-4884
Akron (G-179)
Fargo Toolite Incorporated ....F 440 997-2442
Ashtabula (G-806)
Faull & Son LLC ....F 330 652-4341
Niles (G-15152)
Feller Tool Co Inc ....F 440 324-6277
Elyria (G-9423)
Fostoria Machine Products ....F 419 435-4262
Fostoria (G-9977)
G & S Custom Tooling LLC ....G 419 286-2888
Fort Jennings (G-9926)
Garvin Tool & Die Inc ....G 419 334-2392
Fremont (G-10153)
Gasdorf Tool and Mch Co Inc ....E 419 227-0103
Lima (G-12017)
Gem City Engineering Co ....C 937 223-5544
Dayton (G-8361)
General Die Casters ....G 330 678-2528
Cuyahoga Falls (G-8002)
General Tool Company ....C 513 733-5500
Cincinnati (G-3820)
Gentzler Tool & Die Corp ....E 330 896-1941
Akron (G-205)
Gokoh Corporation ....F 937 339-4977
Troy (G-18832)
Gottschall Tool & Die Inc ....E 330 332-1544
Salem (G-16895)
H Machining Inc ....F 419 636-6890
Bryan (G-2298)
Hardin Creek Machine & Tool ....F 419 678-4913
Coldwater (G-6561)
Herd Manufacturing Inc ....E 216 651-4221
Cleveland (G-5503)
Hofacker Prcsion Machining LLC ....F 937 832-7712
Clayton (G-4659)
Honda Engineering N Amer Inc ....B 937 642-5000
Marysville (G-12948)
Honda Engineering NA Inc ....G 937 707-5357
Marysville (G-12949)
Horizon Industries Corp ....G 937 323-0801
Springfield (G-17575)
I-Dee-X Inc ....G 330 788-2186
Youngstown (G-21112)
Ibycorp ....G 330 425-8226
Twinsburg (G-18957)
Impact Industries Inc ....E 440 327-2360
North Ridgeville (G-15380)
Imperial Die & Mfg Co ....F 440 268-9080
Strongsville (G-17929)
Independent Stamping Inc ....E 216 251-3500
Cleveland (G-5563)
Innovative Tool & Die Inc ....G 419 599-0492
Napoleon (G-14684)

Ishmael Precision Tool Corp ....E 937 335-8070
Troy (G-18846)
J & J Tool & Die Inc ....G 330 343-4721
Dover (G-8994)
J W Harwood Co ....F 216 531-6230
Cleveland (G-5602)
JB Products Co ....G 330 342-0223
Streetsboro (G-17859)
Johnston Manufacturing Inc ....G 440 269-1420
Mentor (G-13621)
K & L Die & Manufacturing ....G 419 895-1301
Greenwich (G-10532)
K & L Tool Inc ....F 419 258-2086
Antwerp (G-630)
K B Machine & Tool Inc ....G 937 773-1624
Piqua (G-16285)
K P Precision Tool and Mch Co ....G 419 237-2596
Fayette (G-9775)
Ken Forging Inc ....C 440 993-8091
Jefferson (G-11364)
Knoble Tool Corp ....E 937 461-4040
Dayton (G-8443)
Knous Tool & Machine Inc ....G 419 394-3541
Saint Marys (G-16841)
Knowlton Manufacturing Co Inc ....F 513 631-7353
Cincinnati (G-3999)
La Ganke & Sons Stamping Co ....F 216 451-0278
Columbia Station (G-6590)
Lako Tool & Mfg ....F 419 662-5256
Perrysburg (G-16118)
Larosa Die Engineering Inc ....G 513 284-9195
Cincinnati (G-4012)
Laspina Tool & Die Inc ....F 330 923-9996
Stow (G-17767)
Lowry Tool & Die Inc ....G 330 332-1722
Salem (G-16908)
Lukens Inc ....D 937 440-2500
Troy (G-18854)
Lunar Tool & Mold Inc ....F 440 237-2141
North Royalton (G-15434)
M & M Dies Inc ....G 216 883-6628
Cleveland (G-5715)
Madsco Inc ....F 513 242-4200
Cincinnati (G-4049)
Magnum Tool Corp ....G 937 228-0900
Dayton (G-8469)
Mar-Vel Tool Co Inc ....E 937 223-2137
Dayton (G-8476)
Martin Machine & Tool Inc ....F 419 373-1711
Bowling Green (G-2000)
Mdf Tool Corporation ....F 440 237-2277
North Royalton (G-15436)
Metro Tool & Die Co Inc ....G 937 836-8242
Englewood (G-9531)
Meyer Machine Tool Company ....G 614 235-0039
Columbus (G-7344)
Midwest Tool & Engineering Co ....E 937 224-0756
Dayton (G-8498)
Mikan Die and Tool LLC ....G 216 265-2811
Cleveland (G-5812)
Mold Shop Inc ....F 419 829-2041
Sylvania (G-18118)
Moldmakers Inc ....F 419 673-0902
Kenton (G-11559)
Monarch Products Co ....E 330 868-7717
Minerva (G-14336)
Moran Tool Inc ....G 937 526-5210
Versailles (G-19354)
Mtd Holdings Inc ....B 330 225-2600
Valley City (G-19220)
National Roller Die Inc ....F 440 951-3850
Willoughby (G-20552)
New Bremen Machine & Tool Co ....E 419 629-3295
New Bremen (G-14790)
Omni Manufacturing Inc ....D 419 394-7424
Saint Marys (G-16846)
Omni Manufacturing Inc ....G 419 394-7424
Saint Marys (G-16847)
PA MA Inc ....G 440 846-3799
Strongsville (G-17950)
Paramount Stamping & Wldg Co ....E 216 631-1755
Cleveland (G-5964)
Phillips Mch & Stamping Corp ....G 330 882-6714
New Franklin (G-14829)
Pier Tool & Die Inc ....F 440 236-3188
Columbia Station (G-6594)
Pioneer Precision Tool Inc ....G 513 932-8805
Lebanon (G-11827)
Pitco Products Inc ....F 513 228-7245
Dayton (G-8577)

Precision Component Inds LLC ....E 330 477-1052
Canton (G-2820)

Precision Die Masters.................F 440 255-1204
Mentor (G-13695)

Prime Time Machine Inc ....G 440 942-7410
Willoughby (G-20579)

Progress Tool & Stamping Inc ....E 419 628-2384
Minster (G-14360)

PSK Steel Corp.....................E 330 759-1251
Hubbard (G-11139)

Puehler Tool Co.....................G 216 447-0101
Cleveland (G-6062)

Quaker Mfg Corp....................C 330 332-4631
Salem (G-16922)

Quality Specialists Inc...............G 440 946-9129
Willoughby (G-20584)

R & R Machine & Tool Co ....G 216 281-7609
Cleveland (G-6079)

R K S Tool & Die Inc.................G 513 870-0225
Fairfield (G-9709)

R M Tool & Die Inc..................F 440 238-6459
Strongsville (G-17955)

Rapid Mold Repair & Machine ....G 330 253-1000
Akron (G-366)

Raymath Company...................C 937 335-1860
Troy (G-18867)

Regal Metal Products Co ....F 330 868-6343
Minerva (G-14340)

Regal Tool & Die Inc ....G 330 746-6644
Youngstown (G-21187)

Renco Mold Inc.....................G 937 233-3233
Dayton (G-8625)

Reserve Industries Inc ....E 440 871-2796
Bay Village (G-1243)

Rme Machining Co...................G 513 541-3328
Cincinnati (G-4351)

Rockstedt Tool & Die Inc ....F 330 273-9000
Brunswick (G-2254)

Ronlen Industries Inc ....G 330 273-6468
Brunswick (G-2255)

RPM Carbide Die Inc ....E 419 894-6426
Arcadia (G-655)

Rural Products Inc ....G 419 298-2677
Edgerton (G-9335)

S-K Mold & Tool Company ....E 937 339-0299
Tipp City (G-18298)

S-K Mold & Tool Company ....E 937 339-0299
Troy (G-18870)

Saint-Gobain Ceramics Plas Inc ....A 330 673-5860
Stow (G-17797)

Schmitmeyer Inc ....G 937 295-2091
Fort Loramie (G-9937)

Seilkop Industries Inc ....E 513 761-1035
Cincinnati (G-4398)

Sekely Industries Inc ....C 248 844-9201
Salem (G-16927)

Shiloh Corporation..................B 330 558-2600
Valley City (G-19231)

Shiloh Industries Inc ....G 330 558-2600
Valley City (G-19234)

Shiloh Industries Inc ....A 330 558-2600
Valley City (G-19235)

Smithville Manufacturing Co ....E 330 345-5818
Wooster (G-20836)

Sni Inc ....G 937 427-9447
Beavercreek (G-1380)

Snyders Tool & Die Inc ....G 614 878-2205
Galloway (G-10315)

Sroka Industries Inc ....E 440 572-2811
Strongsville (G-17972)

Stanco Precision Manufacturing ....G 937 274-1785
Dayton (G-8675)

Sup-R-Die Inc ....G 330 688-7600
Stow (G-17807)

Sure Tool & Manufacturing Co ....E 937 253-9111
Dayton (G-8691)

Sutterlin Machine & Tool Co ....F 440 357-0817
Mentor (G-13742)

T & W Tool & Machine Inc ....G 937 667-2039
Tipp City (G-18302)

Taft Tool & Production Co ....F 419 385-2576
Toledo (G-18715)

Tater Tool & Die Inc ....G 330 648-1148
Spencer (G-17458)

Taylor Tool & Die Inc.................G 937 845-1491
New Carlisle (G-14813)

Tech Industries Inc ....E 216 861-7337
Cleveland (G-6298)

Tipp Machine & Tool Inc ....C 937 890-8428
Dayton (G-8716)

Tomahawk Tool Supply ....G 419 485-8737
Montpelier (G-14455)

Tooling Connection Inc ....G 419 594-3339
Oakwood (G-15620)

Tooling Zone Inc ....E 937 550-4180
Springboro (G-17510)

Top Tool & Die Inc..................F 216 267-5878
Cleveland (G-6337)

Trimline Die Corporation ....F 440 355-6900
Lagrange (G-11639)

U S Alloy Die Corp ....F 216 749-9700
Cleveland (G-6379)

United Extrusion Dies Inc ....F 330 533-2915
Canfield (G-2581)

United Finshg & Die Cutng Inc ....F 216 881-0239
Cleveland (G-6384)

Universal Tool Technology LLC ....E 937 222-4608
Dayton (G-8739)

Unlimited Machine and Tool LLC ....F 419 269-1730
Toledo (G-18761)

Valley Tool & Die Inc ....D 440 237-0160
North Royalton (G-15458)

Van Wert Machine Inc ....F 419 692-6836
Delphos (G-8926)

Varbros Tool and Die Company ....G 216 267-5200
Cleveland (G-6407)

Voisard Tool Service ....E 937 526-5451
Russia (G-16771)

Vulcan Tool Company ....G 937 253-6194
Dayton (G-8744)

Walest Incorporated ....G 216 362-8110
Cleveland (G-6443)

Walker Tool & Machine Co ....F 419 661-8000
Perrysburg (G-16167)

Waverly Tool Co Ltd ....G 740 988-4831
Beaver (G-1312)

Weiss Industries Inc ....E 419 526-2480
Mansfield (G-12704)

Windsor Tool Inc ....F 216 671-1900
Cleveland (G-6466)

Wire Shop Inc ....G 440 354-6842
Mentor (G-13771)

WLS Stamping Co ....G 216 271-5100
Cleveland (G-6472)

Wrena LLC ....E 937 667-4403
Tipp City (G-18312)

Youngstown Tool & Die Company ....D 330 747-4464
Youngstown (G-21257)

DIES: Cutting, Exc Metal

Ashco Manufacturing Inc ....G 419 838-7157
Toledo (G-18357)

D & M Saw & Tool Inc ....G 513 871-5433
Cincinnati (G-3630)

Jbc Technologies Inc.................D 440 327-4522
North Ridgeville (G-15383)

National Steel Rule Die LLC ....G 937 667-0967
Vandalia (G-19307)

DIES: Extrusion

American Extrusion Svcs Inc ....G 937 743-1210
Springboro (G-17473)

Amex Dies Inc ....F 330 545-9766
Girard (G-10382)

B V Mfg Inc ....F 330 549-5331
New Springfield (G-14949)

Fine Line Tool and Die Inc ....F 330 782-8139
Warren (G-19550)

International Dies Co Inc...............G 330 744-7951
Youngstown (G-21119)

Jamen Tool & Die Co ....F 330 788-6521
Youngstown (G-21123)

Tomco Industries ....G 330 652-7531
Mineral Ridge (G-14313)

Tri-R Dies Inc ....E 330 758-8050
Youngstown (G-21230)

Village Plastics Co ....G 330 753-0100
Barberton (G-1156)

Vinyl Tool & Die Company Inc ....F 330 782-0254
Youngstown (G-21241)

DIES: Paper Cutting

Tig Wood & Die Inc ....F 937 849-6741
New Carlisle (G-14815)

Williams Steel Rule Die Co ....F 216 431-3232
Cleveland (G-6464)

DIES: Plastic Forming

Die Cast Tool LLC ....F 419 874-1211
Perrysburg (G-16084)

Fremar Industries Inc ....E 330 220-3700
Brunswick (G-2227)

Kelch Manufacturing Corp ....G 440 366-5060
Elyria (G-9446)

Liberty Mold & Machine Company ....G 330 278-7825
Hinckley (G-11027)

National Pattern Mfg Co ....G 330 682-6871
Orrville (G-15750)

Progrssive Molding Bolivar Inc ....C 330 874-3000
Bolivar (G-1944)

Trico Machine Products Corp ....F 216 662-4194
Cleveland (G-6365)

DIES: Steel Rule

Aukerman J F Steel Rule Die ....G 937 456-4498
Eaton (G-9299)

Container Graphics Corp ....E 937 746-5666
Franklin (G-10013)

Csw of Ny Inc ....F 413 589-1311
Sylvania (G-18102)

Customformed Products Inc ....F 937 388-0480
Miamisburg (G-13795)

D A Stirling Inc ....G 330 923-3195
Cuyahoga Falls (G-7985)

Die Guys Inc ....E 330 948-1984
Medina (G-13402)

Hedalloy Die Corp ....F 216 341-3768
Cleveland (G-5493)

Lorain Ruled Die Products Inc ....G 440 281-8607
North Ridgeville (G-15389)

Loroco Industries Inc ....E 513 891-9544
Blue Ash (G-1828)

True Kote Inc ....G 419 334-8813
Fremont (G-10188)

DIES: Wire Drawing & Straightening

Carbide Specialist Inc.................F 440 951-4027
Willoughby (G-20452)

Lanko Industries Inc ....G 440 269-1641
Mentor (G-13629)

Runner Tool & Die Inc................G 330 794-8843
Akron (G-382)

DIFFERENTIAL ASSEMBLIES & PARTS

Adelmans Truck Parts Corp ....F 216 362-0500
Canton (G-2588)

DIMENSION STONE: Buildings

Cleveland Granite & Marble LLC ....E 216 291-7637
Cleveland (G-5063)

DIODES: Light Emitting

Bright Focus Sales Inc ....F 216 751-8384
Cleveland (G-4931)

Ceso Inc ....D 937 435-8584
Dayton (G-8224)

Energy Focus Inc ....C 440 715-1300
Solon (G-17286)

Tri-Tech Led Systems ....G 614 593-2868
Baltimore (G-1090)

DIODES: Solid State, Germanium, Silicon, Etc

Measurement Specialties Inc............F 937 427-1231
Beavercreek (G-1374)

DIRECT SELLING ESTABLISHMENTS: Beverage Svcs

Superior Soda Service LLC ....G 937 657-9700
Beavercreek (G-1381)

DIRECT SELLING ESTABLISHMENTS: Food Svcs

Schwans Home Service Inc ....E 419 222-9977
Lima (G-12088)

P
R
O
D
U
C
T

DIRECT SELLING ESTABLISHMENTS: Snacks

Conns Potato Chip Co Inc..................E....... 740 452-4615
Zanesville **(G-21294)**

DISCOUNT DEPARTMENT STORES

Gold Toe Moretz Holdings Corp............G....... 740 948-0004
Jeffersonville **(G-11380)**

DISCS & TAPE: Optical, Blank

Folio Photonics LLC..........................G....... 440 420-4500
Solon **(G-17294)**

DISHWASHING EQPT: Commercial

Hobart Corporation...........................E....... 937 332-3000
Troy **(G-18840)**
Hobart Corporation...........................E....... 937 335-7171
Troy **(G-18841)**
Hobart Corporation...........................C....... 937 332-2797
Piqua **(G-16277)**

DISHWASHING EQPT: Household

Whirlpool Corporation.......................D....... 419 423-8123
Findlay **(G-9908)**
Whirlpool Corporation.......................B....... 419 547-7711
Clyde **(G-6548)**
Whirlpool Corporation.......................C....... 419 523-5100
Ottawa **(G-15815)**

DISK DRIVES: Computer

Western Digital Corporation...............G....... 440 684-1331
Cleveland **(G-6458)**

DISPENSING EQPT & PARTS, BEVERAGE: Beer

Beverage Engineering Inc..................G....... 216 641-6678
Brooklyn Heights **(G-2131)**
Boston Beer Company.......................F....... 267 240-4429
Cincinnati **(G-3463)**
Rack Draft Service Inc......................F....... 513 353-5520
North Bend **(G-15207)**

DISPENSING EQPT & PARTS, BEVERAGE: Coolers, Milk/Water, Elec

Brookpark Laboratories Inc................G....... 216 267-7140
Cleveland **(G-4935)**
DTE Cool Co...................................G....... 513 579-0160
Cincinnati **(G-3672)**
Lvd Acquisition LLC..........................E....... 614 861-1350
Columbus **(G-7306)**

DISPENSING EQPT & PARTS, BEVERAGE: Fountain/Other Beverage

Dj Beverage Innovations Inc..............G....... 614 769-1569
Plain City **(G-16336)**
International Beverage Works.............G....... 614 798-5398
Columbus **(G-7205)**
Liqui-Box Corporation.......................D....... 614 888-9280
Columbus **(G-7300)**

DISPLAY FIXTURES: Showcases, Wood, Exc Refrigerated

GMI Companies Inc..........................E....... 937 981-7724
Greenfield **(G-10477)**
GMI Companies Inc..........................C....... 513 932-3445
Lebanon **(G-11804)**
GMI Companies Inc..........................G....... 937 981-0244
Greenfield **(G-10476)**
Indian River Industries......................G....... 740 965-4377
Sunbury **(G-18064)**
Roy L Bayes...................................G....... 614 274-6729
Columbus **(G-7575)**

DISPLAY FIXTURES: Wood

A-Display Service Corp......................F....... 614 469-1230
Columbus **(G-6669)**
Accel Group Inc...............................D....... 330 336-0317
Wadsworth **(G-19387)**
AG Industries Inc.............................E....... 216 252-7300
Cleveland **(G-4730)**

Couch Business Development Inc........F....... 937 253-1099
Dayton **(G-8244)**
Gabriel Logan LLC............................D....... 740 380-6809
Logan **(G-12174)**
Kdm Signs Inc.................................E....... 513 769-3900
Cincinnati **(G-3974)**
Midwest Woodworking Co Inc.............E....... 513 631-6684
Cincinnati **(G-4106)**
Ohio Woodworking Co Inc..................G....... 513 631-0870
Cincinnati **(G-4181)**
Ptmj Enterprises..............................C....... 440 543-8000
Solon **(G-17365)**
Tim Crabtree...................................G....... 740 286-4535
Jackson **(G-11329)**
Ultrabuilt Play Systems Inc.................F....... 419 652-2294
Nova **(G-15580)**
W J Egli Company Inc.......................F....... 330 823-3666
Alliance **(G-551)**
Witt-Gor Inc....................................G....... 419 659-2151
Columbus Grove **(G-7798)**

DISPLAY ITEMS: Corrugated, Made From Purchased Materials

Pratt Industries USA Inc....................D....... 513 770-0851
Mason **(G-13075)**
The Shelby Co.................................E....... 440 871-9901
Westlake **(G-20315)**

DISPLAY ITEMS: Solid Fiber, Made From Purchased Materials

Acrylicon Inc...................................G....... 614 263-2086
Columbus **(G-6691)**
Digital Color Intl LLC.........................E....... 330 762-6959
Akron **(G-152)**

DISPLAY LETTERING SVCS

P S Superior Inc..............................G....... 216 587-1000
Cleveland **(G-5958)**

DISPLAY STANDS: Merchandise, Exc Wood

Warren Steel Specialties Corp............F....... 330 399-8360
Warren **(G-19624)**

DISTILLATION PRDTS: Wood

Arizona Chemical Company LLC..........C....... 330 343-7701
Dover **(G-8964)**

DISTILLERS DRIED GRAIN & SOLUBLES

Buckeye Distillery............................G....... 937 877-1901
Tipp City **(G-18267)**
Indian Creek Distillery.......................G....... 937 846-1443
New Carlisle **(G-14803)**

DISTRIBUTORS: Motor Vehicle Engine

Brinkley Technology Group LLC...........F....... 330 830-2498
Massillon **(G-13115)**
Industrial Systems & Solutions...........G....... 440 205-1658
Mentor **(G-13607)**
Legacy Supplies Inc.........................F....... 330 405-4565
Twinsburg **(G-18971)**
Power Acquisition LLC.......................G....... 614 228-5000
Columbus **(G-7506)**
Stellar Industrial Tech Co..................G....... 740 654-7052
Lancaster **(G-11756)**
Thirion Brothers Eqp Co LLC..............G....... 440 357-8004
Painesville **(G-15930)**
W W Williams Company LLC...............D....... 614 228-5000
Columbus **(G-7746)**
Weldon Pump Acquition LLC...............E....... 440 232-2282
Oakwood Village **(G-15633)**

DOCK EQPT & SPLYS, INDL

Tmt Inc..C....... 419 592-1041
Perrysburg **(G-16161)**

DOCKS: Prefabricated Metal

Amto Acquisition Corp......................F....... 419 347-1185
Shelby **(G-17131)**
Commercial Dock & Door Inc..............G....... 440 951-1210
Mentor **(G-13550)**
Jet Dock Systems Inc.......................G....... 216 750-2264
Cleveland **(G-5613)**
Metal Craft Docks Inc.......................G....... 440 286-7135
Mentor **(G-13653)**

DOCUMENT DESTRUCTION SVC

P C Workshop Inc............................D....... 419 399-4805
Paulding **(G-16012)**

DOGS, WHOLESALE

Dog Depot.......................................G....... 513 771-9274
Cincinnati **(G-3661)**

DOLLIES: Mechanics'

Pegasus Products Company Inc..........G....... 330 677-1123
Kent **(G-11500)**

DOLOMITE: Crushed & Broken

Drummond Dolomite Inc.....................F....... 440 942-7000
Mentor **(G-13565)**

DOOR & WINDOW REPAIR SVCS

Bert Radebaugh...............................G....... 740 382-8134
Marion **(G-12857)**
Pickens Window Service Inc...............F....... 513 931-4432
Cincinnati **(G-4235)**
Screenmobile Inc..............................G....... 614 868-8663
Radnor **(G-16507)**

DOOR FRAMES: Wood

All Pro Ovrhd Door Systems LLC.........G....... 614 444-3667
Columbus **(G-6721)**
Architectural Door Systems LLC..........G....... 513 808-9900
Lebanon **(G-11780)**
Evil Corporation Corporation...............G....... 937 902-5921
Dayton **(G-8335)**

DOOR OPERATING SYSTEMS: Electric

A L Callahan Door Sales....................G....... 419 884-3667
Mansfield **(G-12554)**
Action Industries Ltd........................F....... 216 252-7800
Cleveland **(G-4698)**
Bert Radebaugh...............................G....... 740 382-8134
Marion **(G-12857)**
Bonham Enterprsises........................G....... 740 333-0501
Wshngtn CT Hs **(G-20902)**
GMI Holdings Inc..............................B....... 330 821-5360
Mount Hope **(G-14571)**
GMI Holdings Inc..............................C....... 330 897-4424
Baltic **(G-1073)**
JC Electric.......................................E....... 330 760-2915
Garrettsville **(G-10325)**
Oakes Door Serv..............................G....... 937 323-6188
Springfield **(G-17618)**
Overhead Door of Salem Inc..............G....... 330 332-9530
Salem **(G-16918)**
Trinity Door Systems.........................G....... 877 603-2018
New Springfield **(G-14953)**

DOORS & WINDOWS WHOLESALERS: All Materials

Bert Radebaugh...............................G....... 740 382-8134
Marion **(G-12857)**
Gorell Enterprises Inc.......................B....... 724 465-1800
Streetsboro **(G-17855)**
Great Lakes Stair & Mllwk Co.............G....... 330 225-2005
Hinckley **(G-11024)**
Mason Structural Steel Inc.................D....... 440 439-1040
Walton Hills **(G-19474)**
Toledo Window & Awning Inc..............G....... 419 474-3396
Toledo **(G-18748)**
Traichal Construction Company...........E....... 800 255-3667
Niles **(G-15186)**

DOORS & WINDOWS: Screen & Storm

Duo-Corp...E....... 330 549-2149
North Lima **(G-15315)**
Euclid Jalousies Inc..........................G....... 440 953-1112
Cleveland **(G-5300)**
Quanex Screens LLC.........................G....... 419 662-5001
Perrysburg **(G-16145)**
Select Security Screen Co Ltd............F....... 216 362-1850
Cleveland **(G-6179)**
Stoett Industries Inc.........................E....... 419 542-0247
Hicksville **(G-10907)**

DOORS & WINDOWS: Storm, Metal

Allied Window Inc.............................E....... 513 559-1212
Cincinnati **(G-3379)**

Angel Window Mfg Corp ....G...... 440 891-1006
  Berea *(G-1601)*
Champion Opco LLC ....B 513 924-4858
  Cincinnati *(G-3521)*
Champion Win Co Cleveland LLC ....E 440 899-2562
  Macedonia *(G-12440)*
Larson Manufacturing Co Inc ....F 419 435-9400
  Fostoria *(G-9981)*
Otter Group LLC ....F 937 315-1199
  Dayton *(G-8554)*

DOORS: Combination Screen & Storm, Wood

R C Moore Lumber Co ....F 740 732-4950
  Caldwell *(G-2431)*

DOORS: Fiberglass

Schmidt Progressive LLC ....E 513 934-2600
  Lebanon *(G-11837)*
Toledo Pro Fiberglass Inc ....G 419 241-9390
  Toledo *(G-18740)*

DOORS: Folding, Plastic Or Plastic Coated Fabric

Alumo Extrusions & Mfr Company........E 330 779-3333
  Youngstown *(G-21021)*
Clear Fold Door Inc ....G 440 735-1351
  Cleveland *(G-5045)*
Eckel Industries Inc ....E 978 772-0480
  West Chester *(G-19999)*
Modern Builders Supply Inc ....F 419 526-0002
  Mansfield *(G-12651)*
National Access Design LLC ....F 513 351-3400
  Cincinnati *(G-4137)*
Pease Industies Inc ....B 513 870-3600
  Fairfield *(G-9700)*

DOORS: Garage, Overhead, Metal

All Around Garage Door Inc ....G 440 759-5079
  North Ridgeville *(G-15357)*
Amarr Company ....G 216 573-7100
  Independence *(G-11248)*
Anderson Door Co ....E 216 475-5700
  Cleveland *(G-4809)*
Clopay Building Pdts Co Inc ....E 513 770-4800
  Mason *(G-12998)*
Clopay Building Pdts Co Inc ....G 937 526-4301
  Russia *(G-16762)*
Clopay Building Pdts Co Inc ....G 937 440-6403
  Troy *(G-18810)*
Clopay Corporation ....C 800 282-2260
  Mason *(G-12999)*
Custom Hitch and Trailer/ Over ....G 740 289-3925
  Piketon *(G-16218)*
Division Overhead Door Inc ....F 513 872-0888
  Cincinnati *(G-3659)*
Haas Door Company ....C 419 337-9900
  Wauseon *(G-19681)*
Hrh Door Corp ....A 850 208-3400
  Mount Hope *(G-14572)*
Hrh Door Corp ....E 513 674-9300
  Cincinnati *(G-3900)*
Overhead Door Corporation ....D 740 383-6376
  Marion *(G-12892)*
Overhead Door Corporation ....F 419 294-3874
  Upper Sandusky *(G-19138)*
Overhead Door Corporation ....D 330 674-7015
  Mount Hope *(G-14573)*
Overhead Door Corporation ....D 330 674-7015
  Mount Hope *(G-14574)*
Tri County Door Service Inc ....F 216 531-2245
  Euclid *(G-9611)*

DOORS: Garage, Overhead, Wood

All Around Garage Door Inc ....G 440 759-5079
  North Ridgeville *(G-15357)*
Amarr Company ....G 216 573-7100
  Independence *(G-11248)*
Anderson Door Co ....E 216 475-5700
  Cleveland *(G-4809)*
Arrow Tru-Line Inc ....C 419 446-2785
  Archbold *(G-666)*
Clark Township Garage ....G 330 897-4844
  Baltic *(G-1066)*
Clopay Building Pdts Co Inc ....E 513 770-4800
  Mason *(G-12998)*
Clopay Building Pdts Co Inc ....G 937 526-4301
  Russia *(G-16762)*

Clopay Building Pdts Co Inc................G 937 440-6403
  Troy *(G-18810)*
Clopay Corporation ....C 800 282-2260
  Mason *(G-12999)*
D & L Overhead Door Co Ltd ....G 440 255-9720
  Mentor *(G-13557)*
Division Overhead Door Inc ....F 513 872-0888
  Cincinnati *(G-3659)*
Door Guys Inc ....F 419 562-3376
  Bucyrus *(G-2339)*
Hrh Door Corp ....A 850 208-3400
  Mount Hope *(G-14572)*
Hrh Door Corp ....E 513 674-9300
  Cincinnati *(G-3900)*

DOORS: Glass

A Service Glass Inc ....F 937 426-4920
  Beavercreek *(G-1315)*
Basco Manufacturing Company ....C 513 573-1900
  Mason *(G-12986)*
Scs Construction Services Inc ....E 513 929-0260
  Cincinnati *(G-4393)*

DOORS: Hangar, Metal

Machine Tool & Fab Corp ....F 419 435-7676
  Fostoria *(G-9983)*

DOORS: Louver, Wood

C Square Lumber Products ....F 740 557-3129
  Stockport *(G-17722)*

DOORS: Rolling, Indl Building Or Warehouse, Metal

Dynaco Usa Inc ....G 419 227-3000
  Lima *(G-12006)*

DOORS: Screen, Metal

Central Ohio Rtrctable Screens............G 614 868-5080
  Radnor *(G-16506)*

DOORS: Wooden

Courthouse Manufacturing LLC ....E 740 335-2727
  Washington Court Hou *(G-19638)*
Khempco Bldg Sup Co Ltd Partnr ....D 740 549-0465
  Delaware *(G-8865)*
Masco Cbinetry Middlefield LLC ....B 440 437-8537
  Orwell *(G-15778)*
Masonite Corporation ....D 937 454-9207
  Vandalia *(G-19303)*
Overhead Door Corporation ....D 740 383-6376
  Marion *(G-12892)*
Overhead Door Corporation ....F 419 294-3874
  Upper Sandusky *(G-19138)*
Pease Industies Inc ....B 513 870-3600
  Fairfield *(G-9700)*
Precision Wood Products Inc ....E 937 787-3523
  Camden *(G-2488)*
S R Door Inc ....D 740 927-3558
  Hebron *(G-10883)*
Sommers Wood N Door Company ....G 614 873-3506
  Plain City *(G-16361)*
Star Door & Sash Co Inc ....F 419 841-3396
  Berkey *(G-1643)*
Swiss Woodcraft Inc ....E 330 925-1807
  Rittman *(G-16683)*

DOWELS & DOWEL RODS

Berlin Wood Products Inc ....E 330 893-3281
  Berlin *(G-1646)*
Cincinnati Dowel & WD Pdts Co ....E 937 444-2502
  Mount Orab *(G-14576)*
Puttmann Industries Inc ....F 513 202-9444
  Harrison *(G-10797)*

DRAFTING SPLYS WHOLESALERS

Queen City Reprographics....................C 513 326-2300
  Cincinnati *(G-4319)*

DRAFTING SVCS

Applied Experience LLC......................G 614 943-2970
  Columbus *(G-6765)*

DRAINAGE PRDTS: Concrete

Hanson Aggregates East LLC ....E 330 467-7890
  Macedonia *(G-12457)*
Mack Ready Mix Concrete Inc ....G 330 483-3111
  Valley City *(G-19214)*

DRAPERIES & CURTAINS

A Designers Workroom ....G 513 251-7396
  Cincinnati *(G-3334)*
Accent Drapery Co Inc ....E 614 488-0741
  Columbus *(G-6683)*
Biaginis Draperies ....G 614 876-1706
  Hilliard *(G-10933)*
Carter Drapery Service Inc ....F 419 289-2530
  Ashland *(G-716)*
Drapery Stitch of Delphos ....E 419 692-3921
  Delphos *(G-8906)*
Janson Industries ....D 330 455-7029
  Canton *(G-2745)*
Silver Threads Inc ....G 614 733-0099
  Plain City *(G-16359)*
Sk Textile Inc ....C 323 581-8986
  Cincinnati *(G-4424)*
Specialty Drapery Workroom ....G 330 864-4190
  Akron *(G-410)*
Vocational Services Inc ....C 216 431-8085
  Cleveland *(G-6424)*
Wise Window Treatment Inc ....F 216 676-4080
  Cleveland *(G-6470)*

DRAPERIES & DRAPERY FABRICS, COTTON

Carmens Installation Co......................F 216 371-5633
  Cleveland *(G-4979)*
Cleveland Drapery Stitch Inc ....E 216 252-3857
  Cleveland *(G-5060)*
Custom Craft Drap Inc........................G 330 929-5728
  Cuyahoga Falls *(G-7984)*
Lumenomics Inc.................................E 614 798-3500
  Lewis Center *(G-11906)*
Nancys Draperies...............................F 330 855-7751
  Marshallville *(G-12919)*
Silver Threads Inc ....E 614 733-0099
  Plain City *(G-16359)*
Winspec Inc......................................G 440 834-9068
  Middlefield *(G-14006)*

DRAPERIES: Plastic & Textile, From Purchased Materials

A & B Interiors Shine A Blind ....G 937 371-4731
  Tipp City *(G-18256)*
E W Perry Service Co Inc ....E 419 473-1231
  Toledo *(G-18448)*
Elden Draperies of Toledo Inc ....F 419 535-1909
  Toledo *(G-18452)*
Stan Rileys Custom Draperies ....G 513 821-3732
  Cincinnati *(G-4452)*
Standard Textile Co Inc ....B 513 761-9255
  Cincinnati *(G-4455)*
Tiffin Scenic Studios Inc ....E 800 445-1546
  Tiffin *(G-18249)*
Wahlies Cstm Cft Drapery Uphl ....G 419 229-1731
  Lima *(G-12111)*
Willet Enterprises..............................G 937 298-8622
  Dayton *(G-8758)*

DRAPERY & UPHOLSTERY STORES: Draperies

Accent Drapery Co Inc ....E 614 488-0741
  Columbus *(G-6683)*
Custom Craft Drap Inc........................G 330 929-5728
  Cuyahoga Falls *(G-7984)*
Elden Draperies of Toledo Inc ....F 419 535-1909
  Toledo *(G-18452)*
Nancys Draperies...............................F 330 855-7751
  Marshallville *(G-12919)*

DRAPES & DRAPERY FABRICS, FROM MANMADE FIBER

Cleveland Drapery Stitch Inc ....F 216 252-3857
  Cleveland *(G-5060)*
Lumenomics Inc.................................E 614 798-3500
  Lewis Center *(G-11906)*

PRODUCT

DRIED FRUITS WHOLESALERS

Ohio Hickory Harvest Brand Pro ....E 330 644-6266
Akron (G-324)

DRILL BITS

Custom Carbide Cutter Inc ....F 513 851-6363
West Chester (G-19996)

DRILLING MACHINERY & EQPT: Oil & Gas

Arete Innovative Solutions LLC ....G 513 503-2712
Morrow (G-14543)
D & L Gas Energy Ltd ....C 330 792-9524
Youngstown (G-21062)
Dynamic Leasing Ltd ....G 330 892-0164
New Waterford (G-14970)
Monroe Drilling Operations ....G 740 472-0866
Woodsfield (G-20721)
Rmi Titanium Company LLC ....E 330 652-9952
Niles (G-15176)
Tiger General LLC ....D 330 239-4949
Medina (G-13489)

DRILLS & DRILLING EQPT: Mining

Davey Kent Inc ....E 330 673-5400
Kent (G-11446)

DRILLS: Core

Underground Professionals ....G 419 282-6400
Ashland (G-783)

DRILLS: Rock, Portable

Furukawa Rock Drill ....G 330 673-5821
Kent (G-11461)

DRINK MIXES, NONALCOHOLIC: Cocktail

Great Western Juice Company ....F 216 475-5770
Cleveland (G-5457)

DRINKING FOUNTAINS: Metal, Nonrefrigerated

Murdock Inc ....F 513 471-7700
Cincinnati (G-4132)

DRINKING PLACES: Alcoholic Beverages

Barbeque Integrated Inc ....D 614 430-0572
Columbus (G-6640)
Rocky River Brewing Co ....E 440 895-2739
Rocky River (G-16708)

DRINKING PLACES: Bars & Lounges

Green Room Brewing LLC ....G 614 596-3655
Columbus (G-7131)
Tom Bad Brewing LLC ....G 513 871-4677
Cincinnati (G-4512)

DRINKING PLACES: Tavern

Railroad Brewing Company ....G 440 723-8234
Avon (G-1006)

DRIVE SHAFTS

Cincinnati Drveline Hydraulics ....G 513 651-2406
Cincinnati (G-3548)

DRIVES: High Speed Indl, Exc Hydrostatic

Jamtek Enterprises Inc ....E 513 738-4700
Harrison (G-10786)
Nidec Indus Automtn USA LLC ....E 216 901-2400
Cleveland (G-5882)
Speed Selector Inc ....F 440 543-8233
Chagrin Falls (G-3120)

DRUG STORES

Kmart Supercenter ....G 440 974-7300
Cleveland (G-5660)
Omnicare Phrm of Midwest LLC ....D 513 719-2600
Cincinnati (G-4186)

DRUG TESTING KITS: Blood & Urine

Aufbackgroundscreeningcom ....G 216 831-4113
Beachwood (G-1258)

DRUGS & DRUG PROPRIETARIES, WHOL: Biologicals/Allied Prdts

Wmre of Ohio-American LLC ....G 713 328-7345
Waynesburg (G-19729)

DRUGS & DRUG PROPRIETARIES, WHOLESALE

Buderer Drug Co ....G 419 626-3429
Sandusky (G-16950)
Buderer Drug Company Inc ....F 419 627-2800
Sandusky (G-16951)
Buderer Drug Company Inc ....F 419 873-2800
Perrysburg (G-16070)
Buderer Drug Company Inc ....G 440 934-3100
Avon (G-987)
Omnicare Phrm of Midwest LLC ....D 513 719-2600
Cincinnati (G-4186)

DRUGS & DRUG PROPRIETARIES, WHOLESALE: Antiseptics

Beiersdorf Inc ....C 513 682-7300
West Chester (G-19984)

DRUGS & DRUG PROPRIETARIES, WHOLESALE: Druggists' Sundries

Samuels Products Inc ....E 513 891-4456
Blue Ash (G-1864)

DRUGS & DRUG PROPRIETARIES, WHOLESALE: Medicinals/Botanicals

Goosefoot Acres Inc ....G 330 225-7184
Valley City (G-19205)

DRUGS & DRUG PROPRIETARIES, WHOLESALE: Patent Medicines

Teva Womens Health Inc ....C 513 731-9900
Cincinnati (G-4503)

DRUGS & DRUG PROPRIETARIES, WHOLESALE: Pharmaceuticals

Amerisourcebergen Corporation ....D 614 497-3665
Lockbourne (G-12145)
Biorx LLC ....C 866 442-4679
Cincinnati (G-3450)
Pharmaforce Inc ....F 614 436-2222
Hilliard (G-10969)
River City Pharma ....D 513 870-1680
Fairfield (G-9711)

DRUGS & DRUG PROPRIETARIES, WHOLESALE: Vitamins & Minerals

Direct Action Co Inc ....F 330 364-3219
Dover (G-8976)
Suarez Corporation Industries ....E 330 494-4282
Canton (G-2861)
Vitamin Shoppe Inc ....E 440 238-5987
Strongsville (G-17980)
Wbc Group LLC ....C 866 528-2144
Hudson (G-11207)

DRUMS: Fiber

Greif Inc ....E 419 238-0565
Van Wert (G-19259)
Greif Inc ....E 740 657-6500
Delaware (G-8848)

DRUMS: Shipping, Metal

Astro Qcb Inc ....B 513 921-8811
Cincinnati (G-3422)
Cqcb Inc ....B 614 864-1900
Blacklick (G-1694)
Greif Inc ....E 740 657-6500
Delaware (G-8848)
Greif Inc ....E 740 549-6000
Delaware (G-8847)
Mauser Usa LLC ....D 513 398-1300
Mason (G-13061)
North Coast Container Corp ....D 216 441-6214
Cleveland (G-5894)

DRYCLEANING EQPT & SPLYS: Commercial

Thompson Distributing Co Inc ....G 513 422-9011
Middletown (G-14088)

DRYCLEANING PLANTS

Jackson Deluxe Cleaners Ltd ....G 419 592-2826
Napoleon (G-14686)

DRYCLEANING SVC: Drapery & Curtain

Willet Enterprises ....G 937 298-8622
Dayton (G-8758)

DRYERS & REDRYERS: Indl

Agridry LLC ....E 419 459-4399
Edon (G-9339)

DUCTING: Plastic

Aetna Plastics Corp ....G 330 274-2855
Mantua (G-12706)

DUCTS: Sheet Metal

A A A Professional Htg & Coolg ....G 513 933-0564
Lebanon (G-11773)
Controls and Sheet Metal Inc ....E 513 721-3610
Cincinnati (G-3607)
Custom Duct & Supply Co Inc ....G 937 228-2058
Dayton (G-8258)
D & D Metal Supply Inc ....E 513 272-1246
Cincinnati (G-3629)
Eastern Sheet Metal Inc ....D 513 793-3440
Blue Ash (G-1781)
Langdon Inc ....E 513 733-5955
Cincinnati (G-4011)
Lukjan Metal Products Inc ....C 440 599-8127
Conneaut (G-7814)
McGill Airflow LLC ....E 614 829-1200
Groveport (G-10634)
McGill Corporation ....F 614 829-1200
Groveport (G-10635)
Saringer Sheet Metal Inc ....E 216 447-9755
Independence (G-11274)
Scharenberg Sheet Metal ....G 740 664-2431
New Marshfield (G-14872)
United McGill Corporation ....E 614 829-1200
Groveport (G-10648)

DUMPSTERS: Garbage

E-Pak Manufacturing LLC ....D 800 235-1632
Wooster (G-20769)
Gerald H Smith ....G 740 446-3455
Bidwell (G-1676)
RPI of Indiana Inc ....E 330 279-2421
Holmesville (G-11111)
Wastequip Manufacturing Co LLC ....E 330 674-1119
Millersburg (G-14283)

DURABLE GOODS WHOLESALERS, NEC

Aerovent Inc ....G 937 473-3789
Covington (G-7917)
Assoc Talents Inc ....G 440 716-1265
Westlake (G-20256)
Atrium Corp ....G 740 966-8200
Johnstown (G-11390)

DUST OR FUME COLLECTING EQPT: Indl

Camfil USA Inc ....G 937 773-0866
Piqua (G-16255)
Envirofab Inc ....F 216 651-1767
Cleveland (G-5286)
Herman Manufacturing LLC ....F 216 251-6400
Cleveland (G-5504)
Jacp Inc ....G 513 353-3660
Miamitown (G-13888)
Process Automation Specialists ....G 330 247-1384
Canal Fulton (G-2510)
Schenck Process LLC ....F 513 576-9200
Milford (G-14173)
Sly Inc ....F 440 891-3200
Strongsville (G-17967)

DYES & PIGMENTS: Organic

Accel Corporation ....F 440 327-7418
Avon (G-980)

Colormatrix Group Inc ....G....... 216 622-0100
Berea (G-1608)
Colormatrix Holdings Inc ....C....... 440 930-3162
Berea (G-1609)
Dorum Color Co Inc ....G....... 330 773-1900
Akron (G-154)
Exciton Inc ....F....... 937 252-2989
Dayton (G-8336)
Hexpol Compounding LLC ....C....... 440 834-4644
Burton (G-2376)
Norlab Inc ....G....... 440 282-5265
Lorain (G-12262)
Polyone Corporation ....C....... 419 668-4844
Norwalk (G-15559)
Polyone Corporation ....G....... 216 622-0100
Berea (G-1632)
Republic Powdered Metals Inc ....D....... 330 225-3192
Medina (G-13467)
RPM International Inc ....D....... 330 273-5090
Medina (G-13471)
Sun Chemical Corporation ....E....... 513 830-8667
Cincinnati (G-4481)

DYES OR COLORS: Food, Synthetic

Berghausen Corporation ....E....... 513 541-5631
Cincinnati (G-3445)

DYES: Synthetic Organic

Inceptor Inc ....G....... 419 726-8804
Toledo (G-18519)
Kingscote Chemicals Inc ....G....... 937 886-9100
Miamisburg (G-13824)

EARTH SCIENCE SVCS

Ecoponics Group LLC ....G....... 330 819-1233
Kent (G-11453)
Nucon International Inc ....F....... 614 846-5710
Columbus (G-7405)

EATING PLACES

Auntie Annes ....G....... 330 652-1939
Niles (G-15144)
Best Bite Grill LLC ....G....... 419 344-7462
Versailles (G-19341)
Breitenbach Wine Cellar Inc ....G....... 330 343-3603
Dover (G-8970)
Buns of Delaware Inc ....E....... 740 363-2867
Delaware (G-8826)
Ferrante Wine Farm Inc ....E....... 440 466-8466
Geneva (G-10347)
Guggisberg Cheese Inc ....E....... 330 893-2550
Millersburg (G-14219)
John Purdum ....G....... 513 897-9686
Waynesville (G-19731)
Kmart Supercenter ....G....... 440 974-7300
Cleveland (G-5660)
Kroger Co ....C....... 740 671-5164
Bellaire (G-1499)
Kroger Co ....D....... 740 374-2523
Marietta (G-12798)
Old World Foods Inc ....G....... 216 341-5665
Cleveland (G-5937)
Rocky River Brewing Co ....E....... 440 895-2739
Rocky River (G-16708)
Sausage Shoppe ....G....... 216 351-5213
Cleveland (G-6163)
Skinny Piggy Kombucha LLC ....G....... 513 646-5753
Cincinnati (G-4425)
Willoughby Brewing Company ....D....... 440 975-0202
Willoughby (G-20630)

EDITORIAL SVCS

Outdoor News Service ....G....... 419 734-5172
Port Clinton (G-16408)

EDUCATIONAL SVCS

Dietrich Von Hildebrand Legacy ....G....... 703 496-7821
Steubenville (G-17691)
International Cntr Artfcial or ....G....... 440 358-1102
Painesville (G-15891)
Visual Education Association ....G....... 937 325-5503
Springfield (G-17673)

EDUCATIONAL SVCS, NONDEGREE GRANTING: Continuing Education

360water Inc ....G....... 614 294-3600
Columbus (G-6663)
Deemsys Inc ....D....... 614 322-9928
Gahanna (G-10206)
Toastmasters International ....F....... 937 429-2680
Dayton (G-8118)

EGG WHOLESALERS

Ballas Egg Products Corp ....D....... 614 453-0386
Zanesville (G-21274)
Barkett Fruit Co Inc ....E....... 330 364-6645
Dover (G-8967)
Frank L Harter & Son Inc ....G....... 513 574-1330
Cincinnati (G-3778)
Ohio Fresh Eggs LLC ....G....... 740 893-7200
Croton (G-7955)
Ohio Fresh Eggs LLC ....G....... 937 354-2233
Mount Victory (G-14657)

ELASTOMERS

Advanced Elastomer Systems LP ....D....... 330 336-7641
Wadsworth (G-19389)
Altera Polymers LLC ....G....... 864 973-7000
Jefferson (G-11356)
Asi Investment Holding Co ....D....... 330 666-3751
Fairlawn (G-9738)
Sunprene Company ....C....... 330 666-3751
Fairlawn (G-9762)

ELECTRIC & OTHER SERVICES COMBINED

Cliffs Minnesota Minerals Co ....A....... 216 694-5700
Cleveland (G-5092)
Northshore Mining Company ....G....... 216 694-5700
Cleveland (G-5914)

ELECTRIC FENCE CHARGERS

Agratronix LLC ....E....... 330 562-2222
Streetsboro (G-17834)
D&M Fencing LLC ....G....... 419 604-0698
Spencerville (G-17459)

ELECTRIC MOTOR & GENERATOR AUXILIARY PARTS

Mv Designlabs LLC ....G....... 724 355-7986
Cleveland (G-5842)

ELECTRIC MOTOR REPAIR SVCS

3-D Service Ltd ....C....... 330 830-3500
Massillon (G-13104)
A E Ruston Electric LLC ....G....... 740 286-3022
Jackson (G-11306)
Akron Industrial Motor Service ....G....... 330 753-7624
Norton (G-15504)
Al Bradshaw Jr ....G....... 513 422-8870
Middletown (G-14018)
Allan A Irish ....G....... 419 394-3284
Saint Marys (G-16831)
Als High Tech Inc ....F....... 440 232-7090
Bedford (G-1395)
American Electric Motor Svc ....G....... 614 297-1600
Columbus (G-6737)
B W Electrical & Maint Svc ....G....... 330 534-7870
Hubbard (G-11126)
Barry Brothers Electric ....G....... 614 299-8187
Columbus (G-6809)
Bay Electric Co ....G....... 419 625-1046
Sandusky (G-16948)
Bennett Electric Inc ....F....... 800 874-5405
Norwalk (G-15527)
Big River Electric Inc ....G....... 740 446-4360
Gallipolis (G-10292)
Bornhorst Motor Service Inc ....G....... 937 773-0426
Piqua (G-16253)
Brian Franks Electric Inc ....G....... 330 821-5457
Alliance (G-499)
C and O Electric Motor Service ....G....... 614 491-6387
Columbus (G-6882)
C P Electric Motor Repair Inc ....G....... 330 425-9593
Twinsburg (G-18906)
Campton Electric Sales & Svc ....G....... 740 826-4429
New Concord (G-14816)
Carnation Elc Mtr Repr Sls Inc ....G....... 330 823-7116
Alliance (G-501)

Clark-Fowler Enterprises Inc ....E....... 330 262-0906
Wooster (G-20757)
Columbus Electrical Works Co ....F....... 614 294-4651
Columbus (G-6950)
D & J Electric Motor Repair Co ....F....... 330 336-4343
Wadsworth (G-19401)
E-Z Electric Motor Svc Corp ....F....... 216 581-8820
Cleveland (G-5235)
Electric Ctrl & Mtr Repr Svc ....G....... 216 881-3143
Cleveland (G-5264)
Fenton Bros Electric Co ....E....... 330 343-0093
New Philadelphia (G-14898)
Fmh Electric Inc ....F....... 419 782-0671
Lima (G-12013)
Franks Electric Inc ....G....... 513 542-0342
Cincinnati (G-3781)
Hackworth Electric Motors Inc ....G....... 330 345-6049
Wooster (G-20782)
Hannon Company ....E....... 740 453-0527
Zanesville (G-21318)
Hannon Company ....F....... 330 343-7758
Dover (G-8990)
Horner Industrial Services Inc ....E....... 937 390-6667
Springfield (G-17576)
Hunnell Electric Co Inc ....G....... 330 773-8278
Akron (G-225)
James W Cunningham ....F....... 419 639-2111
Green Springs (G-10471)
K B Electric Motor Service ....G....... 740 537-1346
Toronto (G-18783)
Kaman Automation Inc ....G....... 216 663-0072
Cleveland (G-5632)
Kent Swigart ....G....... 937 836-5292
Englewood (G-9528)
Kiemle-Hankins Company ....E....... 419 661-2430
Perrysburg (G-16117)
Kw Services LLC ....G....... 419 636-3438
Bryan (G-2309)
Kw Services LLC ....G....... 419 228-1325
Lima (G-12036)
Lebanon Electric Motor Svc LLC ....G....... 513 932-2889
Lebanon (G-11813)
Lemsco Inc ....G....... 419 242-4005
Toledo (G-18557)
Lima Armature Works Inc ....G....... 419 222-4010
Lima (G-12039)
Lorain Armature & Mtr Repr Inc ....G....... 440 967-2620
Vermilion (G-19332)
M & R Electric Motor Svc Inc ....E....... 937 222-6282
Dayton (G-8461)
Mac Electric Inc ....G....... 419 782-0671
Lima (G-12050)
Machine Doctors Inc ....G....... 513 422-3060
Cincinnati (G-4045)
Mader Electr Motor & Power Tra ....G....... 937 325-5576
Springfield (G-17599)
Magnetech Industrial Svcs Inc ....C....... 330 830-3500
Massillon (G-13170)
Matlock Electric Co Inc ....E....... 513 731-9600
Cincinnati (G-4066)
Mid-Ohio Electric Co ....E....... 614 274-8000
Columbus (G-7349)
Moto-Electric Inc ....G....... 419 668-7894
Norwalk (G-15552)
National Electric Coil Inc ....B....... 614 488-1151
Columbus (G-7382)
Ohio Electric Motor Svc LLC ....G....... 419 525-2225
Mansfield (G-12661)
Oliver Pool and Spa Inc ....G....... 740 264-5368
Steubenville (G-17709)
Phillips Electric Co ....F....... 216 361-0014
Cleveland (G-6003)
Sheldon On Site Inc ....G....... 419 339-1381
Elida (G-9357)
Shoemaker Electric Company ....E....... 614 294-5626
Columbus (G-7617)
T & J Nickum Inc ....G....... 216 881-2565
Cleveland (G-6286)
Total Maintenance Management ....G....... 513 228-2345
Lebanon (G-11844)
Tyler Electric Motor Repair ....G....... 330 836-5537
Akron (G-451)
Watson Electric Motor Svc Inc ....F....... 614 836-9904
Columbus (G-7753)
Wheatley Electric Service Co ....G....... 513 531-4951
Cincinnati (G-4590)
Whelco Industrial Ltd ....F....... 419 385-4627
Perrysburg (G-16169)
Wyse Electric Motor Repair ....G....... 419 445-5921
Archbold (G-699)

Employee Codes: A=Over 500 employees, B=251-500
C=101-250, D=51-100, E=20-50, F=10-19, G=3-9

2017 Harris Ohio
Industrial Directory

1479

PRODUCT

ELECTRIC SERVICES

National Gas & Oil Corporation...........E....... 740 344-2102
Newark (G-15037)

ELECTRIC SVCS, NEC Power Transmission

Gould Group LLC..............................G....... 740 807-4294
Hilliard (G-10949)

ELECTRIC TOOL REPAIR SVCS

T & J Nickum Inc...............................G....... 216 881-2565
Cleveland (G-6286)

ELECTRICAL APPARATUS & EQPT WHOLESALERS

Acorn Technology Corporation...........E....... 216 663-1244
Cleveland (G-4697)

Allen Fields Assoc Inc.......................G....... 513 228-1010
Lebanon (G-11778)

Als High Tech Inc..............................F....... 440 232-7090
Bedford (G-1395)

Best Lighting Products Inc...............D....... 740 964-0063
Etna (G-9555)

Case Industries Inc..........................G....... 330 963-7717
Twinsburg (G-18908)

Chaffin Electronics Inc.....................G....... 740 354-9896
Franklin Furnace (G-10068)

Controllix Corporation.......................F....... 440 232-8757
Walton Hills (G-19472)

Enersys Delaware Inc.......................G....... 216 252-4242
Cleveland (G-5282)

Filnor Inc..F....... 330 821-8731
Alliance (G-506)

Hughes Corporation...........................E....... 440 238-2550
Strongsville (G-17928)

Kirk Key Interlock Company LLC.......E....... 330 833-8223
North Canton (G-15245)

Powell Electrical Systems Inc...........D....... 330 966-1750
Canton (G-2816)

S L C Software Services....................G....... 513 922-4303
Cincinnati (G-4374)

Schneider Electric Usa Inc...............C....... 513 755-4231
West Chester (G-19942)

Schneider Electric Usa Inc...............D....... 513 755-5000
West Chester (G-19943)

Sieb & Meyer America Inc.................F....... 513 563-0860
Fairfield (G-9717)

Spb Global LLC................................G....... 419 931-6559
Perrysburg (G-16150)

Specialty Switch Co..........................F....... 330 427-3000
Youngstown (G-21210)

Spi Inc..G....... 937 374-2700
Xenia (G-20973)

Tesa Inc...G....... 614 847-8200
Lewis Center (G-11925)

Towing Electrical Systems................C....... 330 793-3887
Youngstown (G-21225)

Warmus and Associates Inc.............F....... 330 659-4440
Bath (G-1240)

ELECTRICAL APPLIANCES, TELEVISIONS & RADIOS WHOLESALERS

Pdi Communication Systems Inc.......D....... 937 743-6010
Springboro (G-17495)

Spb Global LLC................................G....... 419 931-6559
Perrysburg (G-16150)

ELECTRICAL CURRENT CARRYING WIRING DEVICES

Accurate Electronics Inc...................C....... 330 682-7015
Orrville (G-15727)

Bud Industries Inc............................G....... 440 946-3200
Willoughby (G-20447)

Cambridge Ohio Production & As.......F....... 740 432-6383
Cambridge (G-2448)

Chalfant Manufacturing Company......G....... 330 273-3510
Brunswick (G-2216)

Chalfant Manufacturing Company......F....... 440 323-9870
Elyria (G-9392)

Channel Products Inc........................D....... 440 423-0113
Chesterland (G-3199)

D & E Electric Inc.............................F....... 513 738-1172
Okeana (G-15665)

Da-Lite Screen Company LLC............E....... 574 267-8101
Blue Ash (G-1774)

Desco Corporation............................G....... 614 888-8855
New Albany (G-14757)

Dreison International Inc....................C....... 216 362-0755
Cleveland (G-5215)

Electric Cord Sets Inc.......................G....... 216 261-1000
Cleveland (G-5263)

Erie Copper Works Inc......................G....... 330 725-5590
Medina (G-13406)

Filnor Inc..F....... 330 821-7667
Alliance (G-508)

Formed Metal Products Inc................F....... 440 775-0819
Oberlin (G-15639)

GE Aviation Systems LLC..................B....... 937 898-5881
Vandalia (G-19292)

GE Aviation Systems LLC..................B....... 937 898-5881
Vandalia (G-19293)

General Plug and Mfg Co...................C....... 440 926-2411
Grafton (G-10426)

Hubbell Incorporated.........................E....... 330 335-2361
Wadsworth (G-19410)

I Sq R Power Cable Co......................F....... 330 588-3000
Canton (G-2736)

International Hydraulics Inc................E....... 440 951-1781
Mentor (G-13610)

Kathom Manufacturing Co Inc............E....... 513 868-8890
Hamilton (G-10715)

Lake Shore Electric Corp...................E....... 440 232-0200
Bedford (G-1438)

Legrand North America LLC...............B....... 937 224-0639
Moraine (G-14503)

MJM Industries Inc...........................D....... 440 350-1230
Fairport Harbor (G-9768)

Mueller Electric Company Inc............E....... 216 771-5225
Akron (G-307)

Parker-Hannifin Corporation..............C....... 330 336-3511
Wadsworth (G-19425)

Pave Technology Co..........................E....... 937 890-1592
Dayton (G-8566)

Power Grounding Solutions LLC.........G....... 440 926-3219
Grafton (G-10435)

Qualtek Electronics Corp...................C....... 440 951-3300
Mentor (G-13710)

Rogers Industrial Products Inc...........E....... 330 535-3331
Akron (G-378)

Royal Plastics Inc.............................G....... 440 352-1357
Mentor (G-13717)

Siemens Industry Inc........................G....... 937 593-6010
Bellefontaine (G-1539)

Simpson Strong-Tie Company Inc......C....... 614 876-8060
Columbus (G-7624)

SMH Manufacturing Inc.....................F....... 419 884-0071
Lexington (G-11952)

Solon Manufacturing Company...........E....... 440 286-7149
Chardon (G-3180)

Tecmark Corporation.........................D....... 440 205-7600
Mentor (G-13743)

Torq Corporation...............................E....... 440 232-4100
Bedford (G-1468)

Turner Lightning Protection Co...........G....... 614 738-6225
Dublin (G-9157)

Vital Connections Incorporated..........E....... 937 667-3880
Tipp City (G-18310)

Vulcan Tool Company.........................G....... 937 253-6194
Dayton (G-8744)

Watteredge LLC.................................D....... 440 933-6110
Avon Lake (G-1055)

Wedge Products Inc...........................B....... 330 405-4477
Twinsburg (G-19038)

Wiremax Ltd.......................................G....... 419 531-9500
Toledo (G-18776)

Xponet Inc...E....... 440 354-6617
Painesville (G-15943)

ELECTRICAL DEVICE PARTS: Porcelain, Molded

Materion Brush Inc............................D....... 216 486-4200
Mayfield Heights (G-13317)

ELECTRICAL DISCHARGE MACHINING, EDM

Detroit Diesl Specialty TI Inc.............E....... 740 435-4452
Byesville (G-2399)

E D M Services Inc............................G....... 216 486-2068
Euclid (G-9575)

Evolutions North America...................F....... 330 688-2630
Stow (G-17750)

GKN Aerospace Cincinnati Inc...........C....... 513 489-9800
Blue Ash (G-1804)

Max Daetwyler Corp...........................F....... 937 428-1781
Miamisburg (G-13828)

Morris Technologies Inc.....................C....... 513 733-1611
Cincinnati (G-4123)

Precision Inc......................................G....... 330 897-8860
Fresno (G-10198)

Runner Tool & Die Inc........................G....... 330 794-8843
Akron (G-382)

Skinner Machining Co........................G....... 216 486-6636
Cleveland (G-6207)

U S Alloy Die Corp.............................F....... 216 749-9700
Cleveland (G-6379)

ELECTRICAL EQPT & SPLYS

AEG Photoconductor Corporation.......D....... 513 874-4939
West Chester (G-19799)

Akron Brass Company........................E....... 614 529-7230
Columbus (G-6708)

Akron Brass Company........................B....... 330 264-5678
Wooster (G-20735)

Akron Brass Holding Corp..................G....... 330 264-5678
Wooster (G-20736)

Akron Foundry Co..............................E....... 330 745-3101
Barberton (G-1095)

Allen Fields Assoc Inc.......................G....... 513 228-1010
Lebanon (G-11778)

Allied Moulded Products Inc...............B....... 419 636-4217
Bryan (G-2275)

Ametek Inc..F....... 937 440-0800
Troy (G-18804)

ARC Elec...F....... 440 774-2800
Wellington (G-19737)

Asco Power Technologies LP.............C....... 937 748-8884
Springboro (G-17474)

Azz Inc..E....... 330 456-3241
Canton (G-2611)

Barth Industries Co LP.......................D....... 216 267-0531
Cleveland (G-4893)

Beta Industries Inc.............................E....... 937 299-7385
Dayton (G-8186)

Buckeye Electrical Products...............E....... 937 693-7519
Botkins (G-1952)

Ces Nationwide.................................G....... 937 322-0771
Springfield (G-17530)

Chandler Systems Incorporated.........G....... 419 281-6829
Ashland (G-720)

Circle Prime Manufacturing................E....... 330 923-0019
Cuyahoga Falls (G-7980)

Clark Substations LLC.......................E....... 330 452-5200
Canton (G-2659)

Commercial Electric Pdts Corp...........E....... 216 241-2886
Cleveland (G-5104)

Control System Manufacturing............B....... 330 542-0000
New Middletown (G-14876)

Control Works Inc..............................E....... 513 831-9959
Milford (G-14133)

Corrpro Companies Inc......................E....... 330 723-5082
Medina (G-13394)

Corrpro Companies Inc......................F....... 330 725-6681
Medina (G-13395)

Corrpro Companies Intl Inc.................G....... 330 723-5082
Medina (G-13396)

Cv Electric...G....... 419 630-0800
Bryan (G-2292)

Debra Harbour...................................G....... 937 440-9618
Troy (G-18816)

E-One Electric....................................G....... 937 296-4420
Moraine (G-14481)

Elcor Inc..E....... 440 365-5941
Elyria (G-9411)

Emega Technologies LLC...................G....... 740 407-3712
Zanesville (G-21307)

Engineered Mfg & Eqp Co..................G....... 937 642-7776
Marysville (G-12942)

Federal Equipment Company..............D....... 513 621-5260
Cincinnati (G-3747)

General Electric Company...................C....... 216 266-2357
Cleveland (G-5416)

Halex/Scott Fetzer Company...............D....... 440 439-1616
Bedford Heights (G-1485)

Halls Welding & Supplies Inc..............G....... 330 385-9353
East Liverpool (G-9217)

Hannon Company................................D....... 330 456-4728
Canton (G-2723)

Heat Exchange Institute Inc................G....... 216 241-7333
Cleveland (G-5490)

Hess Advanced Solutions Llc.............G....... 937 829-4794
Dayton (G-8389)

I T Verdin Co.....................................E....... 513 241-4010
Cincinnati (G-3907)

Insource Technologies Inc..................C....... 419 399-3600
Paulding (G-16008)

J Beischel Electric.............................G....... 513 860-3290
West Chester (G-20018)

(G-0000) Company's Geographic Section entry number

Jech Technologies Inc .... G 740 927-3495
 Pickerington (G-16194)
Jobap Assembly Inc .... F 440 632-5393
 Middlefield (G-13947)
Kiemle-Hankins Company .... E 419 661-2430
 Perrysburg (G-16117)
Kraft Electrical Contg Inc .... E 614 836-9300
 Groveport (G-10630)
Levans Electric & Hvac .... G 937 468-2269
 Rushsylvania (G-16752)
Libra Industries Inc .... C 440 974-7770
 Mentor (G-13631)
Liebert North America Inc .... A 614 888-0246
 Columbus (G-7293)
Linear Dynamics .... E 419 806-6689
 Risingsun (G-16672)
Linear Technology Corporation .... G 440 239-0817
 Cleveland (G-5701)
Lockheed Martin Integ .... D 330 796-2800
 Akron (G-274)
Matlock Electric Co Inc .... E 513 731-9600
 Cincinnati (G-4066)
Mr Electric .... G 419 289-7474
 Mansfield (G-12654)
Mueller Electric Company Inc ...... E 216 771-5225
 Akron (G-307)
Mv Innovative Technologies LLC ... G 937 221-7639
 Dayton (G-8515)
Niftech Inc .... F 440 257-6018
 Mentor (G-13667)
Nook Industries Inc .... C 216 271-7900
 Cleveland (G-5887)
Ohio Electric Motor Svc LLC .... G 419 525-2225
 Mansfield (G-12661)
Overly Hautz Motor Base Co .... E 513 932-0025
 Lebanon (G-11825)
P & B Electric .... G 937 754-4695
 Fairborn (G-9628)
Philips Medical Systems Clevel .... B 440 247-2652
 Cleveland (G-6001)
Powell Electrical Systems Inc ...... D 330 966-1750
 Canton (G-2816)
Qualtech Technologies Inc .... E 440 946-8081
 Willoughby (G-20585)
Resonance Group Ltd .... G 419 509-2245
 Toledo (G-18675)
Riverside Drives Inc .... E 216 362-1211
 Cleveland (G-6118)
RPS America Inc .... G 937 231-9339
 West Chester (G-19937)
Schneider Electric Usa Inc .... B 513 523-4171
 Oxford (G-15843)
Sew-Eurodrive Inc .... D 937 335-0036
 Troy (G-18875)
State Electric Supply Company .... F 330 308-0659
 New Philadelphia (G-14929)
Technibus Inc .... D 330 479-4202
 Canton (G-2867)
The W L Jenkins Company .... F 330 477-3407
 Canton (G-2869)
Tip Products Inc .... E 216 252-2535
 Cleveland (G-6326)
TSS Technologies Inc .... E 513 772-7000
 West Chester (G-19964)
Vanner Holdings Inc .... D 614 771-2718
 Hilliard (G-10991)
Vortec Corporation .... E 513 686-8210
 Blue Ash (G-1891)
Vti Instruments Corporation .... G 216 447-8950
 Cleveland (G-6432)
Wesco Distribution Inc .... E 419 666-1670
 Northwood (G-15495)
Yaskawa America Inc .... F 614 733-3200
 Plain City (G-16365)

ELECTRICAL EQPT FOR ENGINES

Ewh Spectrum LLC .... D 937 593-8010
 Bellefontaine (G-1530)
Exact-Tool & Die Inc .... E 216 676-9140
 Cleveland (G-5311)
Ferrotherm Corporation .... C 216 883-9350
 Cleveland (G-5339)
Flex Technologies Inc .... D 330 359-5415
 Mount Eaton (G-14555)
Gmelectric Inc .... G 330 477-3392
 Canton (G-2715)
GSW Manufacturing Inc .... B 419 423-7111
 Findlay (G-9834)
Hurst Auto-Truck Electric .... G 216 961-1800
 Cleveland (G-5538)

Machine Products Company .... E 937 890-6600
 Dayton (G-8466)
Per-Tech Inc .... E 330 833-8824
 Massillon (G-13193)
Satco Inc .... E 330 630-8866
 Tallmadge (G-18168)
Sk Tech Inc .... E 937 836-3535
 Englewood (G-9539)
Sumitomo Elc Wirg Systems Inc ... E 937 642-7579
 Marysville (G-12974)
Towing Electrical Systems .... E 330 793-3887
 Youngstown (G-21225)
United Controls Group Inc .... E 740 936-0005
 Columbus (G-6659)
United Controls Group Inc .... G 740 936-0005
 Columbus (G-6660)
Unity Cable Technologies Inc .... E 419 322-4118
 Toledo (G-18759)
Vintage Electric Ltd Inc .... F 419 472-9349
 Toledo (G-18770)

ELECTRICAL EQPT REPAIR & MAINTENANCE

Allied Machine Works Inc .... G 740 454-2534
 Zanesville (G-21270)
Amko Service Company .... E 330 364-8857
 Midvale (G-14105)
Ascendtech Inc .... E 216 458-1101
 Willoughby (G-20441)
Boeing Company .... E 740 788-4000
 Newark (G-14986)
Brocks Welding & Repair Svc .... G 740 453-3943
 Zanesville (G-21281)
Carlton Natco .... G 216 451-5588
 Cleveland (G-4978)
Copier Resources Inc .... G 614 268-1100
 Columbus (G-6981)
Enprotech Industrial Tech LLC ...... E 216 883-3220
 Cleveland (G-5283)
Exchange Signs .... G 330 644-4552
 Akron (G-174)
Fosbel Inc .... C 216 362-3900
 Brookpark (G-2161)
General Electric Company .... D 216 883-1000
 Cleveland (G-5412)
Greggs Specialty Services .... F 419 478-0803
 Toledo (G-18488)
Hannon Company .... F 330 343-7758
 Dover (G-8990)
J-C-R Tech Inc .... F 937 783-2296
 Blanchester (G-1714)
K C N Technologies LLC .... G 440 439-4219
 Bedford (G-1434)
Michael Bradley Apparatus LLC .... F 740 374-6255
 Marietta (G-12807)
Narrow Way Custom Technology .... E 937 743-1611
 Carlisle (G-2933)
Niktec LLC .... E 513 282-3747
 Franklin (G-10040)
Oaks Welding Inc .... G 330 482-4216
 Columbiana (G-6627)
Rubber City Machinery Corp .... E 330 434-3500
 Akron (G-380)
Steel Eqp Specialists Inc .... D 330 823-8260
 Alliance (G-540)
Terex Utilities Inc .... D 513 539-9770
 Monroe (G-14416)
Voltage Regulator Sales & Svcs .... G 937 878-0673
 Fairborn (G-9634)
Wauseon Machine & Mfg Inc .... D 419 337-0940
 Wauseon (G-19700)

ELECTRICAL EQPT REPAIR SVCS

D & J Electric Motor Repair Co ..... F 330 336-4343
 Wadsworth (G-19401)
General Electric Intl Inc .... E 410 737-7228
 Cincinnati (G-3816)
Kiemle-Hankins Company .... E 419 661-2430
 Perrysburg (G-16117)
Palesh & Associates Inc .... G 440 942-9168
 Willoughby (G-20566)

ELECTRICAL EQPT REPAIR SVCS: High Voltage

Delta Transformer Inc .... G 513 242-9400
 Cincinnati (G-3647)
Wilson Sign Co Inc .... F 937 253-2246
 Dayton (G-8760)

ELECTRICAL EQPT: Automotive, NEC

Electra Sound Inc .... D 216 433-9600
 Parma (G-15957)
Stanley Electric US Co Inc .... B 740 852-5200
 London (G-12219)

ELECTRICAL EQPT: Household

Romanoff Elc Residential LLC .... E 614 755-4500
 Gahanna (G-10230)

ELECTRICAL GOODS, WHOL: Antennas, Receiving/Satellite Dishes

Wifi-Plus Inc .... G 877 838-4195
 Brunswick (G-2268)

ELECTRICAL GOODS, WHOLESALE: Alarms & Signaling Eqpt

Laird Controls Holdings Inc .... E 234 806-0018
 Warren (G-19567)

ELECTRICAL GOODS, WHOLESALE: Boxes & Fittings

Akron Foundry Co .... C 330 745-3101
 Akron (G-44)
Ignio Systems LLC .... F 419 708-0503
 Toledo (G-18516)
Osburn Associates Inc .... F 740 385-5732
 Logan (G-12188)

ELECTRICAL GOODS, WHOLESALE: Cable Conduit

Legrand North America LLC .... B 937 224-0639
 Moraine (G-14503)

ELECTRICAL GOODS, WHOLESALE: Connectors

Spi Inc .... G 937 374-2700
 Xenia (G-20973)

ELECTRICAL GOODS, WHOLESALE: Electronic Parts

C P Electric Motor Repair Inc .... G 330 425-9593
 Twinsburg (G-18906)
Case Industries Inc .... G 330 963-7717
 Twinsburg (G-18908)
Rixan Associates Inc .... E 937 438-3005
 Dayton (G-8633)
Rpa Electronic Distrs Inc .... F 937 223-7001
 Dayton (G-8639)
Simplex Time Recorder LLC .... D 419 861-0661
 Maumee (G-13293)

ELECTRICAL GOODS, WHOLESALE: Generators

Lima Equipment Co .... G 419 222-4181
 Lima (G-12040)
Mr Electric .... G 419 289-7474
 Mansfield (G-12654)
Western Branch Diesel Inc .... E 330 454-8800
 Canton (G-2902)

ELECTRICAL GOODS, WHOLESALE: Ground Fault Interrupters

Askia Inc .... G 513 828-7443
 Cincinnati (G-3419)

ELECTRICAL GOODS, WHOLESALE: Hanging & Fastening Devices

Pure Light Technology LLC .... G 513 779-7474
 West Chester (G-20042)

ELECTRICAL GOODS, WHOLESALE: Household Appliances, NEC

World Wide Recyclers Inc .... F 614 554-3296
 Columbus (G-7774)

P
R
O
D
U
C
T

ELECTRICAL GOODS, WHOLESALE: Insulators

Unity Cable Technologies Inc ....G 419 322-4118
Toledo *(G-18759)*

ELECTRICAL GOODS, WHOLESALE: Motor Ctrls, Starters & Relays

Servo Systems Inc ....G 440 779-2780
North Olmsted *(G-15345)*

ELECTRICAL GOODS, WHOLESALE: Motors

Akron Industrial Motor Service ....G 330 753-7624
Norton *(G-15504)*
Allan A Irish ....G 419 394-3284
Saint Marys *(G-16831)*
American Electric Motor Svc ....G 614 297-1600
Columbus *(G-6737)*
Ametek Technical & Indus Pdts ....D 330 677-3754
Kent *(G-11429)*
Bay Electric Co ....G 419 625-1046
Sandusky *(G-16948)*
Bennett Electric Inc ....F 800 874-5405
Norwalk *(G-15527)*
Big River Electric Inc ....G 740 446-4360
Gallipolis *(G-10292)*
Bornhorst Motor Service Inc ....G 937 773-0426
Piqua *(G-16253)*
C P Electric Motor Repair Inc ....G 330 425-9593
Twinsburg *(G-18906)*
Campton Electric Sales & Svc ....G 740 826-4429
New Concord *(G-14816)*
Clark-Fowler Enterprises Inc ....E 330 262-0906
Wooster *(G-20757)*
Columbus Electrical Works Co ....F 614 294-4651
Columbus *(G-6950)*
Fmh Electric Inc ....F 419 782-0671
Lima *(G-12013)*
Hackworth Electric Motors Inc ....G 330 345-6049
Wooster *(G-20782)*
Hannon Company ....F 330 343-7758
Dover *(G-8990)*
Hannon Company ....E 740 453-0527
Zanesville *(G-21318)*
Horner Industrial Services Inc ....E 937 390-6667
Springfield *(G-17576)*
Hunnell Electric Co Inc ....G 330 773-8278
Akron *(G-225)*
Kaman Automation Inc ....G 216 663-0072
Cleveland *(G-5632)*
Lebanon Electric Motor Svc LLC ....G 513 932-2889
Lebanon *(G-11813)*
Lima Armature Works Inc ....G 419 222-4010
Lima *(G-12039)*
M & R Electric Motor Svc Inc ....G 937 222-6282
Dayton *(G-8461)*
Mader Electr Motor & Power Tra ....G 937 325-5576
Springfield *(G-17599)*
Matlock Electric Co Inc ....E 513 731-9600
Cincinnati *(G-4066)*
Mid-Ohio Electric Co ....E 614 274-8000
Columbus *(G-7349)*
Moto-Electric Inc ....E 419 668-7894
Norwalk *(G-15552)*
Palesh & Associates Inc ....G 440 942-9168
Willoughby *(G-20566)*
Phillips Electric Co ....F 216 361-0014
Cleveland *(G-6003)*
Shoemaker Electric Company ....E 614 294-5626
Columbus *(G-7617)*
Tyler Electric Motor Repair ....G 330 836-5537
Akron *(G-451)*
Watson Electric Motor Svc Inc ....F 614 836-9904
Columbus *(G-7753)*
Wheatley Electric Service Co ....G 513 531-4951
Cincinnati *(G-4590)*

ELECTRICAL GOODS, WHOLESALE: Radio Parts & Access, NEC

T V Specialties Inc ....F 330 364-6678
Dover *(G-9020)*

ELECTRICAL GOODS, WHOLESALE: Security Control Eqpt & Systems

Mace Personal Def & SEC Inc ....E 440 424-5321
Cleveland *(G-5722)*

MAI Media Group Llc ....G 513 779-0604
West Chester *(G-20023)*
Modular Security Systems Inc ....G 740 532-7822
Ironton *(G-11297)*

ELECTRICAL GOODS, WHOLESALE: Sound Eqpt

Background Music & Sound Inc ....G 937 898-9871
Dayton *(G-8180)*
Electra Sound Inc ....D 216 433-9600
Parma *(G-15957)*
Holland Assocts LLC DBA Archou ....F 513 891-0006
Cincinnati *(G-3888)*

ELECTRICAL GOODS, WHOLESALE: Suntanning Eqpt & Splys

Uv Doctor Systems LLC ....G 513 553-9000
Amelia *(G-588)*

ELECTRICAL GOODS, WHOLESALE: Switchboards

Industrial Ctrl Dsign Mint Inc ....F 330 785-9840
Tallmadge *(G-18148)*

ELECTRICAL GOODS, WHOLESALE: Switches, Exc Electronic, NEC

Etc Enterprises LLC ....G 417 262-6382
Delphos *(G-8908)*
Wes-Garde Components Group Inc ......G 614 885-0319
Westerville *(G-20240)*

ELECTRICAL GOODS, WHOLESALE: Telephone Eqpt

ABC Appliance Inc ....E 419 693-4414
Oregon *(G-15699)*
Alltel Communications Corp ....E 419 784-3808
Defiance *(G-8777)*
Famous Industries Inc ....E 330 535-1811
Akron *(G-181)*
Mitel (delaware) Inc ....E 513 733-8000
West Chester *(G-19902)*
Pro Oncall Technologies LLC ....F 614 761-1400
Dublin *(G-9126)*

ELECTRICAL GOODS, WHOLESALE: Transformers

Etc Enterprises LLC ....G 417 262-6382
Delphos *(G-8908)*

ELECTRICAL GOODS, WHOLESALE: Washing Machines

Whirlpool Corporation ....C 740 383-7122
Marion *(G-12913)*

ELECTRICAL GOODS, WHOLESALE: Wire & Cable

Associated Mtls Holdings LLC ....A 330 929-1811
Cuyahoga Falls *(G-7972)*
Max Mighty Inc ....F 937 862-9530
Spring Valley *(G-17468)*
Multilink Inc ....C 440 366-6966
Elyria *(G-9465)*
Noco Company ....B 216 464-8131
Solon *(G-17350)*
Scott Fetzer Company ....C 216 267-9000
Cleveland *(G-6168)*
Sumitomo Elc Wirg Systems Inc ....E 937 642-7579
Marysville *(G-12974)*

ELECTRICAL GOODS, WHOLESALE: Wire & Cable, Ctrl & Sig

Winkle Industries Inc ....D 330 823-9730
Alliance *(G-554)*

ELECTRICAL GOODS, WHOLESALE: Wire/Cable, Telephone/Telegraph

Alltel Communications Corp ....G 419 784-3808
Defiance *(G-8777)*

ELECTRICAL INDL APPARATUS, NEC

Amplified Solar Inc ....G 216 236-4225
Lakewood *(G-11656)*
Avtron Inc ....E 216 642-1230
Independence *(G-11249)*
Industrial Application Svs ....G 419 875-5093
Grand Rapids *(G-10440)*
Wired Inc ....G 440 567-8379
Willoughby *(G-20632)*

ELECTRICAL MEASURING INSTRUMENT REPAIR & CALIBRATION SVCS

Instrmntation Ctrl Systems Inc ....E 513 662-2600
Cincinnati *(G-3925)*
Interface Logic Systems Inc ....G 614 236-8388
Columbus *(G-7202)*
Tegam Inc ....E 440 466-6100
Geneva *(G-10357)*

ELECTRICAL SPLYS

Accurate Mechanical Inc ....E 740 654-5898
Lancaster *(G-11683)*
Ces Nationwide ....G 937 322-0771
Springfield *(G-17530)*
Creative Electronic Design ....G 937 256-5106
Beavercreek *(G-1327)*
Fenton Bros Electric Co ....E 330 343-0093
New Philadelphia *(G-14898)*
Ohio Electric Motor Svc LLC ....G 419 525-2225
Mansfield *(G-12661)*
Yes Management Inc ....G 330 747-8593
Columbiana *(G-6638)*

ELECTRICAL SUPPLIES: Porcelain

Akron Porcelain & Plastics Co ....C 330 745-2159
Akron *(G-53)*
CAM-Lem Inc ....G 216 391-7750
Cleveland *(G-4963)*
Channel Products Inc ....D 440 423-0113
Chesterland *(G-3199)*
Crane Plumbing LLC ....C 419 522-0321
Mansfield *(G-12589)*
Ferro Corporation ....C 216 875-6178
Cleveland *(G-5337)*
Fram Group Operations LLC ....A 419 436-5827
Fostoria *(G-9979)*
Petro Ware Inc ....D 740 982-1302
Crooksville *(G-7953)*

ELECTRODES: Indl Process

Mettler-Toledo Intl Fin Inc ....G 614 438-4511
Columbus *(G-6653)*
Selective Med Components Inc ....E 740 397-7838
Mount Vernon *(G-14645)*

ELECTRODES: Thermal & Electrolytic

De Nora Tech Inc ....D 440 710-5300
Painesville *(G-15875)*
Graphel Corporation ....C 513 779-6166
West Chester *(G-19879)*
Sangraf International Inc ....F 216 543-3288
Independence *(G-11273)*
Sherbrooke Metals ....E 440 942-3520
Willoughby *(G-20596)*
Spectramed Inc ....F 740 263-3059
Gahanna *(G-10235)*

ELECTROMEDICAL EQPT

Acela Biomedical ....F 937 544-8618
Winchester *(G-20689)*
Brainmaster Technologies Inc ....G 440 232-6000
Bedford *(G-1409)*
Cardiac Analytics LLC ....F 614 314-1332
Powell *(G-16466)*
Checkpoint Surgical Inc ....G 216 378-9107
Cleveland *(G-5023)*
Cri Inc ....G 513 266-0882
Blue Ash *(G-1771)*
Critical Patient Care Inc ....G 937 434-5455
Dayton *(G-8252)*
Ctl Analyzers LLC ....G 216 791-5084
Shaker Heights *(G-17089)*
Eoi Inc ....F 740 201-3300
Lewis Center *(G-11897)*
Furniss Corporation Ltd ....F 614 871-1470
Mount Sterling *(G-14598)*

Gvi Neuro Inc..................................G....... 330 963-4083
Twinsburg (G-18952)

Gyrus Acmi LP..............................C....... 419 668-8201
Norwalk (G-15542)

Lumitex Inc...................................D....... 440 243-8401
Strongsville (G-17939)

Medforall LLC...............................G....... 614 947-0791
Columbus (G-7340)

Medtronic Inc................................F....... 216 642-1977
Cleveland (G-5777)

Mercury Biomed LLC.....................G....... 216 777-1492
Cleveland (G-5784)

Monitored Therapeutics Inc...........G....... 614 761-3555
Dublin (G-9106)

N K H Safety Inc............................G....... 513 771-3839
Cincinnati (G-4134)

Nano Mark LLC..............................G....... 216 409-3104
Cleveland (G-5850)

Ndi Medical LLC.............................G....... 216 378-9106
Cleveland (G-5866)

Neuros Medical Inc........................G....... 440 951-2565
Willoughby Hills (G-20642)

Nxstage Medical Inc.......................G....... 513 712-1300
Cincinnati (G-4170)

Osteodynamics..............................G....... 405 921-9271
Cincinnati (G-4198)

Pemco Inc.....................................E....... 216 524-2990
Cleveland (G-5989)

Philips Medical Systems Mr...........C....... 440 483-2499
Highland Heights (G-10919)

Rapiscan Systems High Energy I...G....... 937 879-4200
Fairborn (G-9629)

Relevium Labs Inc.........................G....... 614 568-7000
Oxford (G-15842)

Sail Medical Inc.............................G....... 513 961-3144
Cincinnati (G-4376)

Sensetronics LLC..........................G....... 614 292-2833
Dublin (G-9142)

Viewray Incorporated.....................D....... 440 703-3210
Oakwood Village (G-15631)

ELECTROMEDICAL EQPT WHOLESALERS

Acela Biomedical...........................F....... 937 544-8618
Winchester (G-20689)

Relevium Labs Inc.........................G....... 614 568-7000
Oxford (G-15842)

Smiths Medical Pm Inc..................F....... 614 210-7300
Dublin (G-9147)

ELECTROMETALLURGICAL PRDTS

Rhenium Alloys Inc........................D....... 440 365-7388
North Ridgeville (G-15401)

ELECTRONIC COMPONENTS

Artificial Neural Systems Inc..........G....... 740 593-7675
Athens (G-856)

Autosyte.......................................G....... 440 858-3226
Painesville (G-15854)

CMC Electronics Cincinn................G....... 513 573-6316
Mason (G-13003)

Sawyer Research Product................G....... 440 951-8770
Eastlake (G-9286)

Sol-Fly Technologies LLC...............G....... 330 465-8883
Wooster (G-20837)

Suburban Electronics Assembly......G....... 330 483-4077
Valley City (G-19236)

Weldon...G....... 330 263-9533
Columbus (G-7757)

ELECTRONIC DEVICES: Solid State, NEC

Burke Products Inc........................E....... 937 372-3516
Xenia (G-20940)

D F Electronics Inc........................D....... 513 772-7792
Cincinnati (G-3631)

Dan-Mar Company Inc...................E....... 419 660-8830
Norwalk (G-15532)

ELECTRONIC EQPT REPAIR SVCS

Bentronix Corp..............................G....... 440 632-0606
Middlefield (G-13917)

Electric Service Co Inc...................E....... 513 271-6387
Cincinnati (G-3692)

Kirby Electronics Inc......................G....... 614 395-8926
Pickerington (G-16196)

Liebert Corporation........................A....... 614 888-0246
Columbus (G-7292)

Sasha Electronics Inc....................F....... 419 662-8100
Rossford (G-16749)

Vacuum Electric Switch Co Inc........G....... 330 374-5156
Akron (G-461)

ELECTRONIC LOADS & POWER SPLYS

Evension.......................................G....... 330 634-1430
Akron (G-172)

ELECTRONIC PARTS & EQPT WHOLESALERS

Cartessa Corporation.....................F....... 513 738-4477
Shandon (G-17096)

Certified Comparator Products........G....... 937 426-9677
Beavercreek (G-1372)

Creative Electronic Design.............G....... 937 256-5106
Beavercreek (G-1327)

Electro-Line Inc.............................F....... 937 461-5683
Dayton (G-8323)

Element14 US Holdings Inc............G....... 330 523-4280
Richfield (G-16622)

Foxtronix Inc.................................G....... 937 866-2112
Miamisburg (G-13810)

John F Kilfoil Co............................G....... 513 791-6150
Cincinnati (G-3951)

Keithley Instruments Intl Corp........B....... 440 248-0400
Cleveland (G-5642)

Northcoast Process Contrls Inc......G....... 440 498-0542
Cleveland (G-5901)

Pepperl + Fuchs Inc......................C....... 330 425-3555
Twinsburg (G-18997)

Premier Farnell Holding Inc............E....... 330 523-4273
Richfield (G-16633)

Spirit Avionics Ltd.........................F....... 614 358-0333
Columbus (G-7645)

University Accessories Inc..............G....... 440 327-4151
North Ridgeville (G-15407)

Vmetro Inc....................................G....... 281 584-0728
Fairborn (G-9633)

Wes-Garde Components Group Inc.....G....... 614 885-0319
Westerville (G-20240)

ELECTRONIC SHOPPING

E Retailing Associates LLC.............G....... 614 300-5785
Columbus (G-7043)

ELECTRONIC TRAINING DEVICES

E-Beam Services Inc......................E....... 513 933-0031
Lebanon (G-11795)

ELECTROPLATING & PLATING SVC

Abel Metal Processing Inc..............F....... 216 881-4156
Cleveland (G-4683)

Acme Industrial Group Inc..............F....... 330 821-3900
Alliance (G-488)

Automated Wheel LLC....................D....... 216 651-9022
Cleveland (G-4867)

Automation Finishing Inc................E....... 216 251-8805
Cleveland (G-4870)

City Plating and Polishing LLC.........G....... 216 267-8158
Cleveland (G-5038)

Custom Nickel LLC........................G....... 937 222-1995
Dayton (G-8261)

Diamond Hard Chrome Co Inc.........F....... 216 391-3618
Cleveland (G-5188)

Duray Plating Company Inc.............E....... 216 941-5540
Cleveland (G-5224)

Guaranteed Fnshg Unlimited Inc.....E....... 216 252-8200
Cleveland (G-5463)

Krendl Rack Co Inc........................G....... 419 667-4800
Venedocia (G-19321)

Lake City Plating LLC.....................F....... 440 964-3555
Ashtabula (G-817)

National Plating Corporation...........E....... 216 341-6707
Cleveland (G-5858)

Sifco Applied Srfc Cncepts LLC.......E....... 216 524-0099
Cleveland (G-6200)

Swagelok.......................................G....... 440 349-5657
Solon (G-17389)

Twist Inc.......................................C....... 937 675-9581
Jamestown (G-11353)

Woodhill Plating Works Company.....E....... 216 883-1344
Cleveland (G-6476)

ELEMENTARY & SECONDARY SCHOOLS, PRIVATE NEC

Society of The Precious Blood.........E....... 419 925-4516
Celina (G-3018)

ELEMENTARY & SECONDARY SCHOOLS, SPECIAL EDUCATION

Community RE Group-Comvet.........G....... 440 319-6714
Ashtabula (G-798)

ELEVATOR: Grain, Storage Only

E S Industries Inc..........................G....... 419 643-2625
Lima (G-12008)

ELEVATORS & EQPT

Aimco Mfg Inc...............................G....... 419 476-6572
Toledo (G-18324)

Elevator Cncepts By Wurtec LLC.....F....... 734 246-4700
Toledo (G-18455)

Fujitec America Inc........................C....... 513 755-6100
Mason (G-13024)

Gray-Eering Ltd.............................G....... 740 498-8816
Tippecanoe (G-18314)

Otis Elevator Company...................F....... 419 867-7758
Toledo (G-18623)

Otis Elevator Company...................D....... 216 573-2333
Cleveland (G-5951)

Schindler Elevator Corporation.......E....... 513 341-2600
West Chester (G-20047)

Schindler Elevator Corporation.......E....... 419 861-5900
Holland (G-11084)

Sematic Usa Inc............................E....... 330 405-3004
Twinsburg (G-19018)

Sweet Manufacturing Company.......E....... 937 325-1511
Springfield (G-17659)

Thyssenkrupp Elevator Corp..........D....... 513 241-0222
Cincinnati (G-4508)

ELEVATORS: Installation & Conversion

Otis Elevator Company...................D....... 216 573-2333
Cleveland (G-5951)

EMBALMING FLUID

Champion Company.......................D....... 937 324-5681
Springfield (G-17531)

Martin M Hardin............................G....... 740 282-1234
Steubenville (G-17705)

EMBLEMS: Embroidered

Atlantis Sportswear Inc..................E....... 937 773-0680
Piqua (G-16250)

Craco Embroidery Inc.....................G....... 513 563-6999
Cincinnati (G-3617)

Glorias...G....... 330 264-8963
Wooster (G-20778)

Lion Clothing Inc...........................G....... 419 692-9981
Delphos (G-8914)

Novak J F Manufacturing Co LLC....G....... 216 741-5112
Cleveland (G-5918)

Pelz Lettering Inc..........................G....... 419 625-3567
Sandusky (G-16996)

Randy Gray...................................G....... 513 533-3200
Cincinnati (G-4330)

Sportsco Imprinting.......................G....... 513 641-5111
Cincinnati (G-4443)

EMBOSSING SVC: Paper

Precision Graphic Services..............F....... 419 241-5189
Toledo (G-18653)

EMBROIDERING & ART NEEDLEWORK FOR THE TRADE

A To Z Wear Ltd............................G....... 513 923-4662
Cincinnati (G-3337)

Aida Embroidery & Printing.............G....... 440 498-8981
Solon (G-17250)

All For Show Inc............................G....... 440 729-7186
Chesterland (G-3197)

All Sport Printwear Inc...................F....... 330 887-6505
Westfield Center (G-20243)

Alphabet Soup Inc.........................G....... 330 467-4418
Macedonia (G-12434)

Assoc Talents Inc..........................G....... 440 716-1265
Westlake (G-20256)

Avina Specialties Inc......................G....... 419 592-5646
Napoleon (G-14672)

Barbs Custom Embroidery.............G....... 419 393-2216
Defiance (G-8781)

Barbs Embroidery..........................G....... 614 875-9933
Grove City (G-10545)

P R O D U C T

Cal Sales Embroidery ....G...... 440 236-3820
 Columbia Station *(G-6582)*

Campbell Signs & Apparel LLC ....F...... 330 386-4768
 East Liverpool *(G-9205)*

Carter Evans Enterprises Inc ....G...... 614 920-2276
 Granville *(G-10455)*

Cheryl A Lucas ....G...... 614 755-2100
 Columbus *(G-6925)*

CNG Business Group ....G...... 614 771-0877
 Hilliard *(G-10941)*

Color 3 Embroidery Inc ....G...... 330 652-9495
 Warren *(G-19536)*

Eastgate Custom Graphics Ltd ....G...... 513 528-7922
 Cincinnati *(G-3686)*

Elegant Embroidery Llc ....G...... 440 878-0904
 Strongsville *(G-17916)*

Embroid ME ....G...... 216 459-9250
 Cleveland *(G-5275)*

Embroidery Design Group LLC ....F...... 614 798-8152
 Columbus *(G-7055)*

Expert TS ....G...... 330 263-4588
 Wooster *(G-20770)*

Fastpatch Ltd ....F...... 513 367-1838
 Harrison *(G-10777)*

Fcs Graphics Inc ....G...... 216 771-5177
 Cleveland *(G-5330)*

Fine Line Embroidery Company ....G...... 440 331-7030
 Rocky River *(G-16699)*

Garment Specialties Inc ....G...... 330 425-2928
 Twinsburg *(G-18940)*

Graphic Stitch Inc ....G...... 937 642-6707
 Marysville *(G-12945)*

H & H Screen Process Inc ....G...... 937 253-7520
 Dayton *(G-8381)*

Hang Time Group Inc ....G...... 216 771-5885
 Cleveland *(G-5476)*

Heller Acquisitions Inc ....G...... 937 833-2676
 Brookville *(G-2186)*

Initial Designs Inc ....G...... 419 475-3900
 Toledo *(G-18523)*

Jetts Embroideries ....G...... 937 981-3716
 Greenfield *(G-10481)*

Joan B Mailloux ....G...... 361 992-5311
 Mansfield *(G-12627)*

K Ventures Inc ....F...... 419 678-2308
 Coldwater *(G-6566)*

Kathy Simecek ....G...... 440 886-2468
 Cleveland *(G-5635)*

Kens His & Hers Shop Inc ....G...... 330 872-3190
 Newton Falls *(G-15134)*

Kts Cstm Lgs/Xclsvely You Inc ....G...... 440 285-9803
 Chardon *(G-3161)*

Kts Custom Logos ....G...... 440 285-9803
 Chardon *(G-3162)*

Kuhls Hot Sportspot ....F...... 513 474-2282
 Cincinnati *(G-4006)*

McCc Sportswear Inc ....E...... 513 583-9210
 West Chester *(G-20025)*

Mr Emblem Inc ....G...... 419 697-1888
 Oregon *(G-15710)*

National Ntwrk EMB Prfssionals ....G...... 502 212-7500
 Stow *(G-17782)*

Oasis Embroidery ....G...... 614 785-7266
 Columbus *(G-7408)*

Permanent Impressions ....G...... 740 892-3045
 Utica *(G-19196)*

Personal Stitch Monogramming ....G...... 440 282-7707
 Amherst *(G-605)*

Phantasm Designs ....G...... 419 538-6737
 Ottawa *(G-15804)*

Qualitee Design Sportswear Co ....F...... 740 333-8337
 Wshngtn CT Hs *(G-20922)*

Quality Rubber Stamp Inc ....G...... 614 235-2700
 Columbus *(G-7536)*

Quickstitch Plus LLC ....G...... 614 476-3186
 Columbus *(G-7539)*

R Sportswear LLC ....G...... 937 748-3507
 Springboro *(G-17504)*

Red Barn Screen Printing & EMB ....F...... 740 474-6657
 Circleville *(G-4640)*

Sovereign Stitch ....G...... 440 829-0678
 Avon Lake *(G-1052)*

Stepp Sewing Service ....G...... 513 248-0822
 Milford *(G-14175)*

Sun Shine Awards ....F...... 740 425-2504
 Barnesville *(G-1161)*

Superior Image Llc ....F...... 513 771-4565
 Cincinnati *(G-4484)*

Tech Wear Embroidery Company ....G...... 740 344-1276
 Newark *(G-15062)*

Thompson Assoc Hudson Ohio ....G...... 330 655-2142
 Hudson *(G-11204)*

Threaded Image ....G...... 513 683-9069
 Loveland *(G-12394)*

Twin Design AP Promotions Ltd ....G...... 937 732-6798
 Dayton *(G-8734)*

Vector International Corp ....G...... 440 942-2002
 Mentor *(G-13766)*

Walnut Hill Shop ....G...... 740 828-3346
 Frazeysburg *(G-10077)*

EMBROIDERING SVC

5 BS Inc ....C...... 740 454-8453
 Zanesville *(G-21263)*

Aardvark Sportswear Inc ....G...... 330 793-9428
 Youngstown *(G-21012)*

Absolute Impressions Inc ....G...... 614 840-0599
 Lewis Center *(G-11882)*

Alley Cat Designs Inc ....G...... 937 885-7950
 Dayton *(G-8145)*

Alphabet Embroidery Studios ....F...... 937 372-6557
 Xenia *(G-20935)*

Apparel Impressions Inc ....G...... 513 247-0555
 Cincinnati *(G-3407)*

Appleheart ....G...... 937 384-0430
 Miamisburg *(G-13784)*

B D P Services Inc ....D...... 740 828-9685
 Nashport *(G-14703)*

Carols Ultra Stitch & Variety ....G...... 419 935-8991
 Willard *(G-20393)*

Charles Wisvari ....F...... 740 671-9960
 Bellaire *(G-1497)*

Collegiate Connection ....G...... 419 352-8333
 Bowling Green *(G-1982)*

Embroidered ID Inc ....G...... 440 974-8113
 Mentor *(G-13572)*

Ems/Hooptech ....G...... 513 829-7768
 West Chester *(G-19857)*

Ernst Sporting Gds Minster LLC ....G...... 937 526-9822
 Versailles *(G-19346)*

Gail Berner ....G...... 937 322-0314
 Springfield *(G-17563)*

Good JP ....G...... 419 207-8484
 Ashland *(G-735)*

Great Oppurtunities Inc ....G...... 614 868-1899
 Columbus *(G-7130)*

J America LLC ....G...... 614 914-2091
 Columbus *(G-7216)*

Jane Valentine ....G...... 330 452-3154
 North Canton *(G-15244)*

Jaquas Monogramming & Design ....G...... 419 422-2244
 Findlay *(G-9844)*

Judy Dubois ....G...... 419 738-6979
 Wapakoneta *(G-19493)*

Kiwi Promotional AP & Prtg Co ....E...... 330 487-5115
 Twinsburg *(G-18966)*

Locker Room Lettering Ltd ....G...... 419 359-1761
 Castalia *(G-2977)*

Logo This ....G...... 419 445-1355
 Archbold *(G-685)*

Lynns Logos Inc ....G...... 440 786-1156
 Cleveland *(G-5714)*

M & Y Marketing ....G...... 937 322-3423
 Springfield *(G-17595)*

Precision Imprint ....G...... 740 592-5916
 Athens *(G-882)*

Quality Image Embroidery & AP ....G...... 440 230-1109
 Broadview Heights *(G-2117)*

Quality Stitch Embroidery Inc ....G...... 614 237-0480
 Columbus *(G-7537)*

Route 14 Storage Inc ....G...... 330 296-0084
 Ravenna *(G-16553)*

Spectrum Embroidery Inc ....G...... 937 847-9905
 Dayton *(G-8669)*

T & L Custom Screening Inc ....G...... 937 237-3121
 Dayton *(G-8695)*

Tag Sportswear LLC ....G...... 330 456-8867
 Canton *(G-2866)*

Trademark Solutions ....G...... 740 374-9779
 Marietta *(G-12843)*

Truck Stop Embroidery ....G...... 419 257-2860
 North Baltimore *(G-15200)*

Unisport Inc ....F...... 419 529-4727
 Ontario *(G-15696)*

United Sport Apparel ....F...... 330 722-0818
 Medina *(G-3493)*

Zimmer Enterprises Inc ....E...... 937 428-1057
 Dayton *(G-8768)*

EMBROIDERING: Swiss Loom

Quali-Tee Design Sports ....F...... 937 382-7997
 Wilmington *(G-20675)*

EMBROIDERY ADVERTISING SVCS

Custom Sportswear Imprints LLC ....G...... 330 335-8326
 Wadsworth *(G-19400)*

Evolution Crtive Solutions LLC ....E...... 513 681-4450
 Cincinnati *(G-3725)*

Heller Acquisitions Inc ....G...... 937 833-2676
 Brookville *(G-2186)*

Madison Group Inc ....G...... 216 362-9000
 Cleveland *(G-5727)*

Rossi Concept Arts ....G...... 330 453-6366
 Canton *(G-2843)*

Screen Works Inc ....E...... 937 264-9111
 Dayton *(G-8650)*

Underground Sport Shop Inc ....F...... 513 751-1662
 Cincinnati *(G-4535)*

EMERGENCY ALARMS

Cincinnati Bell Any Dstnce Inc ....A...... 513 397-9900
 Cincinnati *(G-3540)*

Simplexgrinnell LP ....E...... 419 861-0662
 Maumee *(G-13294)*

Storecom Equipment LLC ....G...... 800 356-0368
 Dayton *(G-8685)*

UTC Fire SEC Americas Corp Inc ....G...... 513 821-7945
 Cincinnati *(G-4549)*

EMERGENCY SHELTERS

Lighthouse Youth Services Inc ....F...... 513 961-4080
 Cincinnati *(G-4024)*

EMPLOYMENT AGENCY SVCS

JJ Delong & Associates Inc ....G...... 216 861-4727
 Cleveland *(G-5616)*

EMPLOYMENT SVCS: Labor Contractors

Shaneway Inc ....G...... 330 868-2220
 Minerva *(G-14342)*

ENAMELING SVC: Metal Prdts, Including Porcelain

Cto Inc ....G...... 330 785-1130
 Akron *(G-134)*

Erie Ceramic Arts Company LLC ....G...... 419 228-1145
 Lima *(G-12010)*

ENAMELS

Ferro Corporation ....D...... 216 875-5600
 Mayfield Heights *(G-13313)*

North Shore Strapping Inc ....E...... 216 661-5200
 Brooklyn Heights *(G-2144)*

ENCLOSURES: Electronic

American Rugged Enclosures ....F...... 513 942-3004
 Hamilton *(G-10666)*

Brooks Utility Products Group ....E...... 330 455-0301
 Canton *(G-2629)*

Buckeye Stamping Company ....D...... 614 445-0059
 Columbus *(G-6875)*

Bud Industries Inc ....G...... 440 946-3200
 Willoughby *(G-20447)*

Ecp Corporation ....E...... 440 934-0444
 Avon *(G-994)*

Electrical Control Systems ....G...... 937 859-7136
 Dayton *(G-8321)*

N N Metal Stampings Inc ....E...... 419 737-2311
 Pioneer *(G-16235)*

Rittal Corp ....C...... 440 572-4999
 Strongsville *(G-17958)*

ENCLOSURES: Screen

Patton Aluminum Products Inc ....F...... 937 845-9404
 New Carlisle *(G-14811)*

ENCODERS: Digital

Liquid Image Corp of America ....G...... 216 458-9800
 Cleveland *(G-5705)*

ENERGY MEASUREMENT EQPT

Val-Con Inc ....G 440 357-1898
Painesville *(G-15936)*

ENGINE PARTS & ACCESS: Internal Combustion

American Fine Sinter Co Ltd ....C 419 443-8880
Tiffin *(G-18202)*

DW Hercules LLC ....E 330 830-2498
Massillon *(G-13127)*

Industrial Parts Depot LLC ....G 440 237-9164
North Royalton *(G-15427)*

Mantapart ....G 330 549-2389
New Springfield *(G-14951)*

Metaldyne Pwrtrain Cmpnnts Inc ....C 330 486-3200
Twinsburg *(G-18986)*

ENGINE REBUILDING: Diesel

Chemequip Sales Inc ....E 330 724-8300
Akron *(G-120)*

Detroit Desl Rmnfacturing Corp ....F 740 439-7701
Cambridge *(G-2454)*

Detroit Desl Rmnfctrng-Ast Inc ....B 740 439-7701
Byesville *(G-2398)*

General Engine Products LLC ....D 937 704-0160
Franklin *(G-10024)*

Jatrodiesel Inc ....F 937 847-8050
Miamisburg *(G-13821)*

Maags Automotive & Machine ....G 419 626-1539
Sandusky *(G-16982)*

Navistar Inc ....E 937 390-5704
Springfield *(G-17616)*

Performace Diesel Inc ....F 740 392-3693
Mount Vernon *(G-14637)*

ENGINE REBUILDING: Gas

Rozevink Engines LLC ....G 419 789-1159
Holgate *(G-11041)*

ENGINEERING SVCS

A C Knox Inc ....G 513 921-5028
Cincinnati *(G-3333)*

A+ Engineering Fabrication Inc ....F 419 832-0748
Grand Rapids *(G-10439)*

Advanced Engrg Solutions Inc ....D 937 743-6900
Springboro *(G-17470)*

Alfons Haar Inc ....E 937 560-2031
Springboro *(G-17472)*

Applied Experience LLC ....G 614 943-2970
Columbus *(G-6765)*

B&N Coal Inc ....D 740 783-3575
Dexter City *(G-8954)*

Bender Engineering Company ....G 330 938-2355
Beloit *(G-1581)*

Beringer Plating Inc ....G 330 633-8409
Akron *(G-88)*

Bison USA Corp ....G 513 713-0513
West Chester *(G-19818)*

Ceco Group Inc ....G 513 458-2600
Cincinnati *(G-3510)*

Circle Prime Manufacturing ....E 330 923-0019
Cuyahoga Falls *(G-7980)*

Clarkwestern Dietrich Building ....G 330 372-5564
Warren *(G-19535)*

Clarkwestern Dietrich Building ....G 513 870-1100
West Chester *(G-19835)*

Coal Services Inc ....D 740 795-5220
Powhatan Point *(G-16488)*

Comtec Incorporated ....F 330 425-8102
Twinsburg *(G-18918)*

Consolidatd Analytical Sys Inc ....F 513 542-1200
Cleves *(G-6511)*

Control Electric Co ....E 216 671-8010
Columbia Station *(G-6586)*

Corrpro Companies Inc ....E 330 723-5082
Medina *(G-13394)*

Corrpro Companies Inc ....F 330 725-6681
Medina *(G-13395)*

Curtiss-Wright Controls ....E 937 252-5601
Fairborn *(G-9618)*

Custom Craft Controls Inc ....F 330 630-9599
Akron *(G-136)*

Dante Solutions Inc ....G 440 234-8477
Cleveland *(G-5166)*

Davis Technologies Inc ....F 330 823-2544
Alliance *(G-505)*

Decision Systems Inc ....E 330 456-7600
Canton *(G-2682)*

Delta Control Inc ....G 937 277-3444
Dayton *(G-8297)*

DIhbowles Inc ....B 330 478-2503
Canton *(G-2691)*

Donald E Didion II ....E 419 483-2226
Bellevue *(G-1550)*

Electrovations Inc ....E 330 274-3558
Aurora *(G-918)*

Emh Inc ....E 330 220-8600
Valley City *(G-19203)*

Enprotech Industrial Tech LLC ....C 216 883-3220
Cleveland *(G-5283)*

Eti Tech Inc ....F 937 832-4200
Englewood *(G-9519)*

Fishel Company ....D 614 850-4400
Columbus *(G-7089)*

Frost Engineering Inc ....E 513 541-6330
Cincinnati *(G-3785)*

General Electric Intl Inc ....G 410 737-7228
Cincinnati *(G-3816)*

General Precision Corporation ....G 440 951-9380
Willoughby *(G-20498)*

Htec Systems Inc ....F 937 438-3010
Dayton *(G-8394)*

Hunter Defense Tech Inc ....E 216 438-6111
Solon *(G-17312)*

Hydro-Dyne Inc ....E 330 832-5076
Massillon *(G-13153)*

Imax Industries Inc ....F 440 639-0242
Painesville *(G-15889)*

Innovative Controls Corp ....D 419 691-6684
Toledo *(G-18524)*

JBI Corporation ....F 419 855-3389
Genoa *(G-10361)*

Jotco Inc ....G 513 721-4943
Mansfield *(G-12630)*

Kendall Holdings Ltd ....E 614 486-4750
Columbus *(G-7255)*

L3 Aviation Products Inc ....D 614 825-2001
Columbus *(G-7278)*

Majestic Engineering & TI LLC ....G 937 845-1079
New Carlisle *(G-14807)*

Matrix Research Inc ....E 937 427-8433
Beavercreek *(G-1350)*

Micro Industries Corporation ....D 740 548-7878
Westerville *(G-20224)*

Midwest Telemetry Inc ....G 440 725-5718
Chesterland *(G-3215)*

Mitchell Electronics Inc ....G 740 594-8532
Athens *(G-879)*

Nesco Inc ....E 440 461-6000
Cleveland *(G-5871)*

New Path International LLC ....E 614 410-3974
Powell *(G-16481)*

Nona Composites LLC ....G 937 490-4814
Beavercreek *(G-1376)*

Ohio Blow Pipe Company ....E 216 681-7379
Cleveland *(G-5930)*

Ohio Structures Inc ....E 330 533-0084
Canfield *(G-2568)*

Owens Corning Sales LLC ....G 330 633-6735
Tallmadge *(G-18163)*

Peco II Inc ....D 614 431-0694
Columbus *(G-7473)*

Plate-All Metal Company Inc ....G 330 633-6166
Akron *(G-342)*

Plcc2 LLC ....G 614 279-1796
Columbus *(G-7499)*

Process Innovations Inc ....G 330 856-5192
Vienna *(G-19373)*

Providence Rees Inc ....E 614 833-6231
Columbus *(G-7525)*

Quality Plating Co ....G 216 361-0151
Cleveland *(G-6072)*

Quayle Consulting Inc ....G 614 868-1363
Pickerington *(G-16202)*

Ra Consultants LLC ....E 513 469-6600
Blue Ash *(G-1861)*

RAD-Con Inc ....E 440 871-5720
Lakewood *(G-11678)*

Sest Inc ....F 440 777-9777
Westlake *(G-20307)*

Sgi Matrix LLC ....D 937 438-9033
Miamisburg *(G-13858)*

Sizetec Inc ....G 330 492-9682
Canton *(G-2850)*

Stambaugh Engineering Inc ....G 330 666-0088
Akron *(G-411)*

Storetek Engineering Inc ....E 330 294-0678
Tallmadge *(G-18170)*

Sunpower Inc ....D 740 594-2221
Athens *(G-887)*

Support Svc LLC ....G 419 617-0660
Lexington *(G-11954)*

Systech Handling Inc ....F 419 445-8226
Archbold *(G-696)*

Tetra Tech Inc ....F 330 286-3683
Canfield *(G-2578)*

Thermal Treatment Center Inc ....E 216 881-8100
Cleveland *(G-6317)*

Timekeeping Systems Inc ....F 216 595-0890
Solon *(G-17406)*

TL Industries Inc ....C 419 666-8144
Northwood *(G-15490)*

Tri-Tech Research LLC ....G 440 946-6122
Eastlake *(G-9293)*

Trumbull Industries Inc ....E 330 434-6174
Akron *(G-448)*

U S Army Corps of Engineers ....F 740 537-2571
Toronto *(G-18786)*

Updegraff Inc ....G 216 621-7600
Cleveland *(G-6395)*

V&P Group International LLC ....F 703 349-6432
Cincinnati *(G-4550)*

Welding Consultants Inc ....G 614 258-7018
Columbus *(G-7756)*

Xcite Systems Corporation ....E 513 965-0300
Cincinnati *(G-3321)*

ENGINEERING SVCS: Acoustical

Straight 72 Inc ....D 740 943-5730
Marysville *(G-12973)*

ENGINEERING SVCS: Aviation Or Aeronautical

Aerovation Tech Holdings LLC ....G 567 208-5525
Forest *(G-9917)*

GE Aviation Systems LLC ....B 937 898-5881
Vandalia *(G-19293)*

ENGINEERING SVCS: Civil

Ceso Inc ....D 937 435-8584
Dayton *(G-8224)*

Pollock Research & Design Inc ....E 330 332-3300
Salem *(G-16920)*

ENGINEERING SVCS: Construction & Civil

Barr Engineering Incorporated ....F 614 892-0162
Columbus *(G-6807)*

Barr Engineering Incorporated ....E 614 714-0299
Columbus *(G-6808)*

EP Ferris & Associates Inc ....G 614 299-2999
Columbus *(G-7063)*

ENGINEERING SVCS: Electrical Or Electronic

American Controls Inc ....E 440 944-9735
Wickliffe *(G-20353)*

CPI Group Limited ....G 216 525-0046
Cleveland *(G-5138)*

Crown Elec Svcs & Automtn Inc ....G 330 270-9890
Youngstown *(G-21058)*

Digital Automation Associates ....G 419 352-6977
Bowling Green *(G-1986)*

Field Apparatus Service & Tstg ....G 513 353-9399
Cincinnati *(G-3752)*

L-3 Cmmncations Nova Engrg Inc ....C 877 282-1168
Mason *(G-13054)*

Lintech Electronics LLC ....F 513 528-6190
Cincinnati *(G-3312)*

Mid-Ohio Electric Co ....E 614 274-8000
Columbus *(G-7349)*

PMC Systems Limited ....E 330 538-2268
North Jackson *(G-15297)*

Stock Fairfield Corporation ....C 440 543-6000
Chagrin Falls *(G-3122)*

Vector Electromagnetics LLC ....G 937 478-5904
Beavercreek *(G-1383)*

ENGINEERING SVCS: Energy conservation

Albemarle Corporation ....G 330 425-2354
Twinsburg *(G-18897)*

Tekworx LLC ....F 513 533-4777
Blue Ash *(G-1881)*

ENGINEERING SVCS: Heating & Ventilation

Hess Advanced Solutions Llc ....G....... 937 829-4794
Dayton (G-8389)
Melink Corporation ....F 513 685-0958
Milford (G-14161)

ENGINEERING SVCS: Industrial

Control Associates Inc ....G....... 440 708-1770
Chagrin Falls (G-3082)
Crowne Group LLC ....D...... 216 589-0198
Cleveland (G-5143)
Farnsworth Engineering ....F 330 385-1745
East Liverpool (G-9215)
Imds Corporation ....F 330 747-4637
Youngstown (G-21113)
JB Industries Ltd ....F 330 856-4587
Warren (G-19563)
Mercury Iron & Steel ....F 440 349-1500
Solon (G-17334)
Production Design Services Inc ....D...... 937 866-3377
Dayton (G-8598)
Technology House The Ltd ....D...... 440 248-3025
Solon (G-17400)

ENGINEERING SVCS: Machine Tool Design

Guardian Engineering & Mfg Co..........G....... 419 335-1784
Wauseon (G-19680)
Invotec Engineering Inc ....D...... 937 886-3232
Miamisburg (G-13820)
Magna Group LLC ....G....... 513 388-9463
Cincinnati (G-4051)
Mound Manufacturing Center Inc..........F 937 236-8387
Dayton (G-8512)
Terydon Inc ....F 330 879-2448
Navarre (G-14728)
Youngstown Plastic Tooling ....E 330 782-7222
Youngstown (G-21254)

ENGINEERING SVCS: Mechanical

Chipmatic Tool & Machine Inc ....D...... 419 862-2737
Elmore (G-9362)
Dillin Engineered Systems Corp ....E 419 666-6789
Perrysburg (G-16085)
Johnson Machining Services LLC ....G....... 937 866-4744
Miamisburg (G-13823)
Markley Enterprises LLC ....E 513 771-1290
Cincinnati (G-4061)
Morris Technologies Inc ....C...... 513 733-1611
Cincinnati (G-4123)
Performnce Plymr Solutions Inc ....F 937 298-3713
Moraine (G-14512)
Qcsm LLC ....G....... 216 531-5960
Euclid (G-9602)
TSS Technologies Inc ....C...... 513 772-7000
West Chester (G-19962)

ENGINEERING SVCS: Pollution Control

Neundorfer Inc ....E 440 942-8990
Willoughby (G-20553)
Nucon International Inc ....F 614 846-5710
Columbus (G-7405)

ENGINEERING SVCS: Professional

Eaton-Aeroquip Inc..........................D...... 419 891-7775
Maumee (G-13258)
Inovent Engineering Inc ....G....... 330 468-0005
Macedonia (G-12459)
Lawrence Technologies Inc ....G....... 937 274-7771
Dayton (G-8454)

ENGINES: Diesel & Semi-Diesel Or Duel Fuel

Dmax Ltd.....................................D...... 937 425-9700
Moraine (G-14479)
Hy-Production Inc ....C...... 330 273-2400
Valley City (G-19206)

ENGINES: Gasoline, NEC

Graham Ford Power Products ....G....... 614 801-0049
Columbus (G-7127)

ENGINES: Internal Combustion, NEC

B A Malcuit Racing Inc ....G....... 330 878-7111
Strasburg (G-17820)
Cameron International Corp ....G....... 740 397-4888
Mount Vernon (G-14611)

Cummins - Allison Corp ....G....... 614 529-1940
Hilliard (G-10945)
Cummins - Allison Corp ....G....... 513 469-2924
Blue Ash (G-1772)
Cummins - Allison Corp ....G....... 440 824-5050
Cleveland (G-5146)
Cummins Bridgeway LLC ....E 513 563-6670
West Chester (G-19850)
Cummins Bridgeway LLC ....E 614 604-6000
Grove City (G-10552)
Cummins Bridgeway LLC ....G....... 614 771-1000
Hilliard (G-10946)
Cummins Bridgeway Columbus LLC....D...... 614 771-1000
Hilliard (G-10947)
Cummins Bridgeway Toledo LLC ....F 419 893-8711
Maumee (G-13235)
Debolt Machine Inc ....G....... 740 454-8082
Zanesville (G-21298)
Draime Enterprises Inc ....G....... 330 837-2254
Massillon (G-13126)
Ford Motor Company........................A....... 419 226-7000
Lima (G-12014)
GE Honda Aero Engines LLC ....F 513 552-4322
West Chester (G-19873)
Gellner Engineering Inc ....G....... 216 398-8500
Cleveland (G-5407)
Jjb Engineer ....G....... 330 807-0671
Cuyahoga Falls (G-8014)
Kenworth of Dayton ....F 937 235-2589
Dayton (G-8438)
Western Branch Diesel Inc ....E 330 454-8800
Canton (G-2902)

ENGINES: Jet Propulsion

Enginetics Corporation ....C...... 937 878-3800
Huber Heights (G-11146)
GE Rolls Royce Fighter ....G....... 513 243-2787
Cincinnati (G-3811)

ENGINES: Marine

Performance Research Inc ....G....... 614 475-8300
Columbus (G-7479)

ENGINES: Steam

Steam Engine Works LLC ....E 513 813-3690
Cincinnati (G-4461)

ENGRAVING SVC, NEC

Gordons Graphics Inc ....G....... 330 863-2322
Malvern (G-12546)
Handcrafted Jewelry Inc ....G....... 330 650-9011
Hudson (G-11178)
Irwin Engraving & Printing Co ....G....... 216 391-7300
Cleveland (G-5589)
Sams Graphic Industries....................F 330 821-4710
Alliance (G-536)

ENGRAVING SVC: Jewelry & Personal Goods

F & K Concepts Inc ....G....... 937 426-6843
Beavercreek (G-1337)
Scholz & Ey Engravers Inc.................F 614 444-8052
Columbus (G-7597)

ENGRAVING SVCS

Canton Graphic Arts Service ....G....... 330 456-9868
Canton (G-2641)
Designer Awards Inc........................G....... 937 339-4444
Troy (G-18819)
Engravers Gallery & Sign Co ....G....... 330 830-1271
Massillon (G-13130)
Gauntlet Awards & Engraving ....G....... 937 890-5811
Dayton (G-8357)
Hafner Hardwood Connection LLC ....G....... 419 726-4828
Toledo (G-18493)
John C Starr ....G....... 740 852-5592
London (G-12213)
Plastic Products and Supply ....G....... 330 744-5076
Youngstown (G-21171)
Professional Award Service ....G....... 513 389-3600
Cincinnati (G-4294)
Raschke Engraving Inc ....G....... 330 677-5544
Kent (G-11512)
Ryder Engraving Inc ....G....... 740 927-7193
Pataskala (G-15982)

ENGRAVING: Steel line, For The Printing Trade

Bomen Marking Products Inc ....G....... 440 582-0053
Cleveland (G-4922)

ENGRAVINGS: Plastic

Foundation Industries Inc ....D...... 330 564-1250
Akron (G-193)
Hathaway Stamp Co ....F 513 621-1052
Cincinnati (G-3871)
Minotas Trophies & Awards ....G....... 440 720-1288
Cleveland (G-5823)
Plate Engraving Corporation ....F 330 239-2155
Medina (G-13462)

ENTERTAINERS

Amcan Productions Ltd ....G....... 330 332-9129
Salem (G-16871)

ENTERTAINERS & ENTERTAINMENT GROUPS

American Guild of English Hand ....G....... 937 438-0085
Cincinnati (G-3389)
Swagg Productions2015llc ....F 614 815-1173
Reynoldsburg (G-16608)

ENTERTAINMENT GROUP

Club 513 LLC ....G....... 800 530-2574
Cincinnati (G-3591)

ENTERTAINMENT SVCS

Smartv Company LLC ....E 614 890-6090
Westerville (G-20186)
Technical Artistry Inc ....G....... 614 299-7777
Columbus (G-7684)

ENVELOPES

Ampac Holdings LLC ....A....... 513 671-1777
Cincinnati (G-3397)
Bayley Envelope Inc ....G....... 330 821-2150
Alliance (G-498)
Church Budget Monthly Inc ....D...... 330 337-1122
Salem (G-16881)
Church-Budget Envelope Company .....E 800 446-9780
Salem (G-16882)
Envelope 1 Inc ....D...... 330 482-3900
Columbiana (G-6615)
Envelope Mart of Ohio Inc ....E 440 365-8177
Elyria (G-9421)
Ohio Envelope Manufacturing Co ....E 216 267-2920
Cleveland (G-5933)
Pac Worldwide Corporation ....E 513 217-3200
Middletown (G-14071)
Pac Worldwide Corporation ....D...... 800 610-9367
Middletown (G-14072)
Quality Envelope Inc........................G....... 513 942-7578
West Chester (G-20043)
SRC Liquidation LLC ....A....... 937 221-1000
Dayton (G-8672)
Tcp Inc ....G....... 330 836-4239
Fairlawn (G-9764)
United Envelope LLC ....D...... 513 542-4700
Cincinnati (G-4539)
Western States Envelope Co ....D...... 419 666-7480
Walbridge (G-19464)

ENVELOPES WHOLESALERS

Envelope Mart of Ohio Inc.................E 440 365-8177
Elyria (G-9421)
Pac Worldwide Corporation ....D...... 800 610-9367
Middletown (G-14072)
Western States Envelope Co ....D...... 419 666-7480
Walbridge (G-19464)

ENZYMES

Biowish Technologies Inc ....G....... 312 572-6700
Cincinnati (G-3451)
Enzyme Industries of The U S A ....G....... 740 929-4975
Newark (G-15003)
Mp Biomedicals LLC ....C...... 440 337-1200
Solon (G-17340)
Oxyrase Inc ....F 419 589-8800
Ontario (G-15692)

EPOXY RESINS

Nona Composites LLC ....G...... 937 490-4814
  Beavercreek *(G-1376)*
Renegade Materials Corporation ....E...... 508 579-7888
  Miamisburg *(G-13854)*

EQUIPMENT: Pedestrian Traffic Control

Area Wide Protective Inc ....E...... 330 644-0655
  Kent *(G-11431)*
Area Wide Protective Inc ....G...... 419 221-2997
  Lima *(G-11993)*
Lightle Enterprises Ohio LLC ....G...... 740 998-5363
  Frankfort *(G-10000)*
Lightle Enterprises Ohio LLC ....G...... 740 998-5363
  Frankfort *(G-10001)*

EQUIPMENT: Rental & Leasing, NEC

Aircraft Dynamics Corporation ....F...... 419 331-0371
  Elida *(G-9350)*
Askia Inc ....E...... 513 828-7443
  Cincinnati *(G-3419)*
BJ Equipment Ltd ....F...... 614 497-1776
  Columbus *(G-6834)*
Brinkman LLC ....F...... 419 204-5934
  Lima *(G-11997)*
De Nora Tech Inc ....D...... 440 710-5300
  Painesville *(G-15875)*
Diversifd OH Vlly Eqpt & Srvcs ....F...... 740 458-9881
  Clarington *(G-4651)*
DRDC Realty Inc ....G...... 419 478-7091
  Toledo *(G-18444)*
Eaton Leasing Corporation ....G...... 216 382-2292
  Beachwood *(G-1270)*
Elliott Tool Technologies Ltd ....D...... 937 253-6133
  Dayton *(G-8324)*
Glawe Manufacturing Co Inc ....E...... 937 754-0064
  Fairborn *(G-9623)*
Great Lakes Crushing Ltd ....E...... 440 944-5500
  Wickliffe *(G-20366)*
Hansen Scaffolding LLC ....F...... 513 574-9000
  West Chester *(G-20012)*
Laird Controls Holdings Inc ....E...... 234 806-0018
  Warren *(G-19567)*
M C L Window Coverings Inc ....G...... 513 868-6000
  Hamilton *(G-10719)*
Mitel (delaware) Inc ....E...... 513 733-8000
  West Chester *(G-19902)*
Mobile Mini Inc ....F...... 614 449-8655
  Columbus *(G-7360)*
Powerclean Equipment Company ....G...... 513 202-0001
  Cleves *(G-6524)*
Rambasek Realty Inc ....F...... 937 228-1189
  Dayton *(G-8616)*
Snyder Manufacturing Co Ltd ....G...... 330 343-4456
  Dover *(G-9017)*
Summa Holdings Inc ....G...... 440 838-4700
  Cleveland *(G-6261)*
Thomas Do-It Center Inc ....E...... 740 446-2002
  Gallipolis *(G-10310)*
Trailer One Inc ....G...... 330 723-7474
  Medina *(G-13490)*
Tri State Equipment Company ....G...... 513 738-7227
  Shandon *(G-17098)*
West Equipment Company Inc ....F...... 419 698-1601
  Toledo *(G-18772)*

ETCHING & ENGRAVING SVC

Allied Coating Co ....G...... 937 615-0391
  Piqua *(G-16247)*
Carved Stone LLC ....G...... 614 778-9855
  Radnor *(G-16505)*
Cubbison Company ....D...... 330 793-2481
  Youngstown *(G-21059)*
Dayton Coating Tech LLC ....G...... 937 278-2060
  Dayton *(G-8272)*
Doak Laser ....G...... 740 374-0090
  Marietta *(G-12781)*
Georgia Metal Coatings Company ....F...... 770 446-3930
  Chardon *(G-3155)*
Hadronics Inc ....D...... 513 321-9350
  Cincinnati *(G-3861)*
M & M Engraving ....G...... 216 749-7166
  Cleveland *(G-5716)*
Mark True Engraving Company ....G...... 216 252-7422
  Cleveland *(G-5746)*
Play All LLC ....G...... 440 992-7529
  Ashtabula *(G-833)*

Rite Way Black & Deburr Inc ....G...... 937 224-7762
  Dayton *(G-8632)*
Sterling Coating ....G...... 513 942-4900
  West Chester *(G-19949)*
T&K Laser Works Inc ....G...... 937 693-3783
  Botkins *(G-1956)*
Tce International Ltd ....F...... 800 962-2376
  Perry *(G-16059)*
Worldclass Processing Corp ....E...... 724 251-9000
  Twinsburg *(G-19040)*
X-Treme Finishes Inc ....F...... 330 474-0614
  Medina *(G-13498)*

ETCHING SVC: Metal

Akron Metal Etching Co ....G...... 330 762-7687
  Akron *(G-48)*
Five Handicap Inc ....F...... 419 525-2511
  Mansfield *(G-12603)*
Great Lakes Etching Finshg Co ....F...... 440 439-3624
  Cleveland *(G-5449)*
Master Marking Company Inc ....F...... 330 688-6797
  Stow *(G-17772)*
Roban Inc ....G...... 330 794-1059
  Lakemore *(G-11645)*
Woodrow Manufacturing Co ....E...... 937 399-9333
  Springfield *(G-17682)*

ETHYLENE GLYCOL TEREPHTHALIC ACID: Mylar

Global Biochem ....G...... 513 792-2218
  Cincinnati *(G-3835)*

ETHYLENE-PROPYLENE RUBBERS: EPDM Polymers

Canton OH Rubber Speclty Prods ....G...... 330 454-3847
  Canton *(G-2642)*
Matterworks ....G...... 740 200-0071
  Heath *(G-10850)*
Mexichem Specialty Resins Inc ....E...... 440 930-1435
  Avon Lake *(G-1040)*
Polyshield Corporation ....F...... 614 755-7674
  Pickerington *(G-16200)*
Protective Industrial Polymers ....F...... 440 327-0015
  North Ridgeville *(G-15396)*
San Pallet LLC ....G...... 937 271-5308
  Troy *(G-18871)*
Toyo Seiki Usa Inc ....G...... 513 546-9657
  Blue Ash *(G-1882)*

EXCAVATING EQPT

Liebrecht Manufacturing ....G...... 419 596-3501
  Continental *(G-7827)*
Tgs Industries Inc ....E...... 330 339-2211
  New Philadelphia *(G-14933)*

EXECUTIVE OFFICES: Federal, State & Local

ARC Elec ....F...... 440 774-2800
  Wellington *(G-19737)*

EXERCISE EQPT STORES

R T H Processing Inc ....D...... 419 692-3000
  Delphos *(G-8916)*

EXHAUST SYSTEMS: Eqpt & Parts

Classic Exhaust ....G...... 440 466-5460
  Geneva *(G-10344)*
Faurecia Exhaust Systems Inc ....B...... 937 339-0551
  Troy *(G-18826)*
Faurecia Exhaust Systems Inc ....B...... 937 743-0551
  Franklin *(G-10021)*
Hmf Engineering Inc ....E...... 216 631-6980
  Cleveland *(G-5518)*
Ohio Classic Street Rods Inc ....G...... 440 543-6593
  Chagrin Falls *(G-3108)*

EXPLOSIVES

Additive Technology Inc ....G...... 419 968-2777
  Middle Point *(G-13896)*
Austin Powder Company ....D...... 216 464-2000
  Cleveland *(G-4860)*
Austin Powder Company ....C...... 740 596-5286
  Mc Arthur *(G-13329)*
Austin Powder Company ....E...... 740 968-1555
  Saint Clairsville *(G-16780)*

Austin Powder Holdings Company ....D...... 216 464-2400
  Cleveland *(G-4861)*
Hilltop Energy Inc ....E...... 330 859-2108
  Mineral City *(G-14301)*
Regal Technology Corporation ....G...... 614 272-7644
  Columbus *(G-7553)*
Viking Explosives LLC ....E...... 218 263-8845
  Cleveland *(G-6419)*

EXPLOSIVES, EXC AMMO & FIREWORKS WHOLESALERS

D W Dickey and Son Inc ....E...... 330 424-1441
  Lisbon *(G-12119)*
Viking Explosives LLC ....E...... 218 263-8845
  Cleveland *(G-6419)*

EXPLOSIVES, FUSES & DETONATORS: Primary explosives

Sloat Inc ....G...... 440 951-9554
  Willoughby *(G-20600)*

EXTENSION CORDS

Alert Stamping & Mfg Co Inc ....E...... 440 232-5020
  Bedford Heights *(G-1476)*
Electra - Cord Inc ....D...... 330 832-8124
  Massillon *(G-13129)*

EXTERMINATING PRDTS: Household Or Indl Use

J T Eaton & Co Inc ....E...... 330 425-7801
  Twinsburg *(G-18960)*

EXTRACTS, FLAVORING

Beck Flavors Inc ....G...... 513 889-1268
  Loveland *(G-12342)*
Berghausen Corporation ....E...... 513 541-5631
  Cincinnati *(G-3445)*
Flavor Systems International ....G...... 513 870-0420
  West Chester *(G-20002)*
Frutarom USA Inc ....C...... 513 870-4900
  West Chester *(G-20005)*
Sensoryeffects Flavor Company ....E...... 419 782-5010
  Defiance *(G-8809)*
Synergy Flavors (oh) LLC ....G...... 513 892-7100
  Hamilton *(G-10743)*

EXTRACTS: Dying Or Tanning, Natural

Tanning ....G...... 937 233-4554
  Dayton *(G-8699)*

EYEGLASSES

Central Optical Inc ....E...... 330 783-9660
  Youngstown *(G-21046)*
Essilor Laboratories Amer Inc ....G...... 330 425-3003
  Twinsburg *(G-18931)*
Essilor Laboratories Amer Inc ....E...... 614 274-0840
  Columbus *(G-7066)*
Fresh Look Laser Eye Ctrs LLC ....G...... 614 885-2745
  Cuyahoga Falls *(G-7999)*
Hollywood Family Eye Care ....G...... 740 264-1220
  Steubenville *(G-17699)*
Libbey Inc ....F...... 419 244-5697
  Toledo *(G-18560)*
Nexus Vision Group LLC ....E...... 866 492-6499
  Grove City *(G-10578)*
Optical Distribution Corp ....F...... 937 405-7280
  Columbus *(G-7444)*
Rooney Optical Inc ....E...... 216 267-5600
  Twinsburg *(G-19012)*
Soderberg Inc ....F...... 937 298-0223
  Moraine *(G-14529)*
Toledo Optical Laboratory Inc ....D...... 419 248-3384
  Toledo *(G-18738)*

EYES: Artificial

Sunforest Vision Center Inc ....G...... 419 475-4646
  Toledo *(G-18707)*

Ethylene Glycols

Global Biochem ....G...... 513 792-2218
  Cincinnati *(G-3835)*

Employee Codes: A=Over 500 employees, B=251-500
C=101-250, D=51-100, E=20-50, F=10-19, G=3-9

2017 Harris Ohio
Industrial Directory

1487

P R O D U C T

FABRIC SOFTENERS

Edmar Chemical Company ....G...... 440 247-9560
Chagrin Falls *(G-3058)*
Procter & Gamble Mfg Co ....C...... 419 226-5500
Lima *(G-12075)*

FABRIC STORES

Decor At 124 ....G...... 260 319-4213
Convoy *(G-7831)*
Fabric Square Shop ....G...... 330 752-3044
Stow *(G-17751)*
Rita Fishel Inc ....E...... 740 775-1957
Chillicothe *(G-3272)*

FABRICATED METAL PRODUCTS, NEC

A&E Machine & Fabrication Inc ....F...... 740 820-4701
Beaver *(G-1309)*
Buckeye Metals ....G...... 740 446-9590
Bidwell *(G-1675)*
CDI ....G...... 440 249-4178
Avon *(G-988)*
Cpmg ....G...... 440 263-2780
North Royalton *(G-15415)*
Eastern Automated Piping ....G...... 740 535-8184
Mingo Junction *(G-14348)*
Fisher Metal Fabricating....................F...... 419 838-7200
Walbridge *(G-19457)*
Mad Metal Wldg Fabrication LLC ....G...... 614 256-4163
Columbus *(G-7313)*
Mills Aluminum Fab ....G...... 330 821-4108
Alliance *(G-527)*
Olwin Metal Fabrication LLC................G...... 937 277-4501
Dayton *(G-8547)*

FABRICS & CLOTHING: Rubber Coated

Ansell Healthcare Products LLC ....D...... 740 622-4311
Coshocton *(G-7879)*
Paullin Driveway Sealing....................G...... 419 289-2228
Ashland *(G-763)*
Textileather Corporation ....B...... 419 729-3731
Toledo *(G-18721)*

FABRICS: Apparel & Outerwear, Cotton

Fabric Square Shop ....G...... 330 752-3044
Stow *(G-17751)*
Mary James Inc ....E...... 419 599-2941
Napoleon *(G-14689)*
Twin Design AP Promotions Ltd............G...... 937 732-6798
Dayton *(G-8734)*

FABRICS: Bags & Bagging, Cotton

Anita Plastics Inc ....G...... 216 831-5773
Solon *(G-17260)*

FABRICS: Broadwoven, Cotton

Compass Energy LLC.........................D...... 866 665-2225
Cleveland *(G-5110)*

FABRICS: Broadwoven, Synthetic Manmade Fiber & Silk

Detroit Technologies Inc ....E...... 937 492-2708
Sidney *(G-17179)*
Ets Schaefer LLC ....E...... 330 468-6600
Macedonia *(G-12448)*
Owens Corning Sales LLC ....B...... 740 587-3562
Granville *(G-10464)*
Snyder Manufacturing Co Ltd ....G...... 330 343-4456
Dover *(G-9017)*

FABRICS: Broadwoven, Wool

Resistflame Acquisition Corp..............G...... 513 561-5223
Cincinnati *(G-4337)*

FABRICS: Canvas

Canvas Salon and Skin Bar ....G...... 614 336-3942
Powell *(G-16465)*
Custom Marine Canvas Training ....G...... 419 732-8362
Port Clinton *(G-16397)*

FABRICS: Chemically Coated & Treated

Omnova Overseas Inc ....C...... 330 869-4200
Fairlawn *(G-9757)*

FABRICS: Coated Or Treated

Biothane Coated Webbing Corp ....E...... 440 327-0485
North Ridgeville *(G-15361)*

FABRICS: Cotton, Narrow

US Cotton LLC ....B...... 216 676-6400
Cleveland *(G-6399)*

FABRICS: Decorative Trim & Specialty, Including Twist Weave

Omnova Solutions Inc ....C...... 216 682-7000
Beachwood *(G-1287)*

FABRICS: Denims

Noble Denim Workshop ....G...... 513 560-5640
Cincinnati *(G-4161)*

FABRICS: Diaper, NEC

Associated Hygienic Pdts LLC ....B...... 770 497-9800
Delaware *(G-8822)*

FABRICS: Duck, Cotton

Mmi Textiles Inc ....F...... 440 899-8050
Westlake *(G-20283)*

FABRICS: Fiberglass, Broadwoven

Chautauqua Fiberglass & Plasti ....G...... 513 423-8840
Middletown *(G-14028)*
Schmelzer Industries Inc ....E...... 740 743-2866
Somerset *(G-17419)*

FABRICS: Flannels, Cotton

Franjinhas Inc.................................G...... 440 463-1523
Strongsville *(G-17921)*

FABRICS: Glass & Fiberglass, Broadwoven

Architectural Fiberglass Inc ....E...... 216 641-8300
Cleveland *(G-4825)*
Sunshine Performance Glass Inc...........E...... 330 562-8600
Aurora *(G-948)*

FABRICS: Laminated

Prints & Paints Flr Cvg Co Inc ....E...... 419 462-5663
Galion *(G-10283)*
Trim Systems Operating Corp ....C...... 614 289-5360
New Albany *(G-14774)*

FABRICS: Manmade Fiber, Narrow

Spunfab Ltd ....G...... 330 945-9455
Cuyahoga Falls *(G-8049)*

FABRICS: Metallized

Alron...G...... 330 477-3405
Strasburg *(G-17819)*
Laserflex Corporation ....D...... 614 850-9600
Hilliard *(G-10958)*
Ohio Metalizing LLC ....G...... 330 830-1092
Massillon *(G-13185)*

FABRICS: Moleskins

Moleman ....G...... 513 662-3017
Cincinnati *(G-4118)*

FABRICS: Nonwoven

Autoneum North America Inc ....B...... 419 693-0511
Oregon *(G-15703)*
Polyflex LLC ....F...... 440 946-0758
Willoughby *(G-20574)*
Toyobo Kureha America Co Ltd ....E...... 513 771-6788
Cincinnati *(G-4515)*

FABRICS: Nylon, Broadwoven

Seaman Corporation..........................C...... 330 262-1111
Wooster *(G-20833)*
Yoders Nylon Halter Shop...................G...... 330 893-3479
Millersburg *(G-14290)*

FABRICS: Osnaburgs

Osnaburg Quilt Fibr Art Guild..............G...... 330 488-2591
East Canton *(G-9195)*

FABRICS: Papermakers Felt, Woven, Wool, Mohair/Similar Fiber

Orr Felt Company..............................D...... 937 773-0551
Piqua *(G-16296)*

FABRICS: Polyester, Broadwoven

Anita Plastics Inc ....G...... 216 831-5773
Solon *(G-17260)*

FABRICS: Polyethylene, Broadwoven

King Bag and Manufacturing Co ....E...... 513 541-5440
Cincinnati *(G-3990)*

FABRICS: Print, Cotton

The Max...G...... 440 357-0036
Painesville *(G-15929)*

FABRICS: Resin Or Plastic Coated

Automated Packaging Systems ....G...... 330 342-0205
Streetsboro *(G-17841)*
Duracote Corporation ....E...... 330 296-9600
Ravenna *(G-16526)*
Durez Corporation ....C...... 567 295-6400
Kenton *(G-11546)*
Gvc Plastics & Metals LLC ....G...... 440 232-9360
Bedford *(G-1427)*
Schneller LLC ....C...... 330 676-7183
Kent *(G-11522)*

FABRICS: Rubberized

Salem-Republic Rubber Company ....E...... 330 938-2016
Sebring *(G-17052)*

FABRICS: Scrub Cloths

Akron Cotton Products Inc ....G...... 330 434-7171
Akron *(G-38)*
Canton Sterilized Wiping Cloth ....G...... 330 455-5179
Canton *(G-2648)*
Linsalata Capital Partners Fun ....G...... 440 684-1400
Cleveland *(G-5703)*
Tranzonic Companies ....C...... 216 535-4300
Richmond Heights *(G-16656)*
Tranzonic Companies ....C...... 440 446-0643
Cleveland *(G-6350)*
Tz Acquisition Corp ....A...... 216 535-4300
Richmond Heights *(G-16658)*

FABRICS: Shoe Laces, Exc Leather

Joe Busby.......................................G...... 513 821-1716
Cincinnati *(G-3949)*
Mitchellace Inc ....E...... 740 354-2813
Portsmouth *(G-16444)*
Sole Choice Inc ....E...... 740 354-2813
Portsmouth *(G-16456)*

FABRICS: Sleeving, Textile, Saturated

Bexley Fabrics Inc ....G...... 614 231-7272
Columbus *(G-6825)*

FABRICS: Tracing Cloth, Cotton

Weiskopf Industries Corp ....E...... 440 442-4400
Cleveland *(G-6454)*

FABRICS: Trimmings

A C Hadley - Printing Inc ....G...... 937 426-0952
Beavercreek *(G-1314)*
Adcraft Decals Inc............................E...... 216 524-2934
Cleveland *(G-4702)*
Air Waves Inc ....C...... 740 548-1200
Lewis Center *(G-11883)*
Am Graphics....................................G...... 330 799-7319
Youngstown *(G-21022)*
Angell-Demmel North Amer Corp ....D...... 937 461-5800
Dayton *(G-8158)*
Anomatic Corporation ....B...... 740 522-2203
New Albany *(G-14745)*
Art Tees Inc ....G...... 614 338-8337
Columbus *(G-6774)*
Atlantis Sportswear Inc ....E...... 937 773-0680
Piqua *(G-16250)*
Bates Metal Products Inc ....D...... 740 498-8371
Port Washington *(G-16422)*

Brown Cnty Bd Mntal Rtardation ....E 937 378-4891
Georgetown *(G-10364)*
Crabar/Gbf Inc ....G 419 943-2141
Leipsic *(G-11868)*
Design Original Inc ....F 937 596-5121
Jackson Center *(G-11339)*
Dresden Specialties Inc ....G 740 754-2451
Dresden *(G-9032)*
Dupli-Systems Inc ....C 440 234-9415
Strongsville *(G-17913)*
E L Frueh Inc ....F 419 222-9741
Lima *(G-12007)*
Eastgate Custom Graphics Ltd ....E 513 528-7922
Cincinnati *(G-3686)*
Ed Thomas ....G 937 325-4300
Springfield *(G-17551)*
Fair Publishing House Inc ....E 419 668-3746
Norwalk *(G-15540)*
Fedex Office & Print Svcs Inc ....E 614 898-0000
Westerville *(G-20214)*
Fried Daddy ....G 937 854-4542
Dayton *(G-8351)*
Gail Berner ....G 937 322-0314
Springfield *(G-17563)*
Gail Zeilmann ....G 440 888-4858
Cleveland *(G-5391)*
General Theming Contrs LLC ....C 614 252-6342
Columbus *(G-7108)*
Greenfield Research Inc ....C 937 981-7763
Greenfield *(G-10478)*
Hall Company ....E 937 652-1376
Urbana *(G-19160)*
Hayes Reconditioning Group ....G 937 299-8013
Dayton *(G-8387)*
Hunt Products Inc ....E 440 667-2457
Newburgh Heights *(G-15075)*
J America LLC ....G 614 914-2091
Columbus *(G-7216)*
Jerry Pulfer ....G 937 778-1861
Piqua *(G-16283)*
Jim Davis ....G 740 335-8030
Wshngtn CT Hs *(G-20914)*
Kemper Automotive ....G 800 783-8004
Franklin *(G-10030)*
Kent Stow Screen Printing Inc ....F 330 923-5118
Akron *(G-255)*
Logan Screen Printing ....G 740 385-3303
Logan *(G-12185)*
Lund Printing Co ....G 330 628-4047
Akron *(G-277)*
Northeastern Plastics Inc ....G 330 453-5925
Canton *(G-2795)*
Outsourcing Services Inc ....F 330 963-2710
Solon *(G-17357)*
Plus Mark LLC ....E 216 252-6770
Cleveland *(G-6018)*
Randy Gray ....G 513 533-3200
Cincinnati *(G-4330)*
Schilling Graphics Inc ....E 419 468-1037
Galion *(G-10286)*
Screen Works Inc ....E 937 264-9111
Dayton *(G-8650)*
Standard Prototyping Ideals ....G 614 837-9180
Pickerington *(G-16205)*
T & L Custom Screening Inc ....G 937 237-3121
Dayton *(G-8695)*
Tendon Manufacturing Inc ....E 216 663-3200
Cleveland *(G-6305)*
Trim Systems Operating Corp ....C 740 772-5998
Chillicothe *(G-3281)*
Universal Drect Flfilment Corp ....C 330 650-5000
Hudson *(G-11206)*
Vgu Industries Inc ....E 216 676-9093
Cleveland *(G-6414)*
W J Egli Company Inc ....E 330 823-3666
Alliance *(G-551)*
West & Barker Inc ....E 330 652-9923
Niles *(G-15189)*
Woodrow Manufacturing Co ....E 937 399-9333
Springfield *(G-17682)*
Yi Xing Inc ....G 614 785-9631
Columbus *(G-7784)*
Zenos Activewear Inc ....G 614 443-0070
Columbus *(G-7787)*

FABRICS: Umbrella Cloth, Cotton

Totes Isotoner Corporation ....F 513 682-8200
West Chester *(G-20059)*
Totes Isotoner Holdings Corp ....C 513 682-8200
West Chester *(G-20060)*

FABRICS: Upholstery, Wool

Midwest Composites LLC ....E 419 738-2431
Wapakoneta *(G-19497)*

FABRICS: Varnished Glass & Coated Fiberglass

Spectroglass Corp ....G 614 297-0412
Columbus *(G-7640)*

FABRICS: Wall Covering, From Manmade Fiber Or Silk

C S A Enterprises ....G 740 342-9367
New Lexington *(G-14845)*

FABRICS: Waterproofed, Exc Rubberized

Excello Fabric Finishers Inc ....F 740 622-7444
Coshocton *(G-7889)*

FABRICS: Woven, Narrow Cotton, Wool, Silk

A & P Technology Inc ....D 513 688-3200
Cincinnati *(G-3288)*
A & P Technology Inc ....D 513 688-3200
Cincinnati *(G-3289)*
A & P Technology Inc ....E 513 688-3200
Cincinnati *(G-3290)*
Armotec Materials Corporation ....G 216 476-2766
Cleveland *(G-4832)*
Keuchel & Associates Inc ....G 330 945-9455
Cuyahoga Falls *(G-8017)*
Paxar Corporation ....G 937 681-4541
Dayton *(G-8567)*
Samsel Rope & Marine Supply Co ....E 216 241-0333
Cleveland *(G-6156)*
Shurtape Technologies LLC ....B 440 937-7000
Avon *(G-1011)*

FACILITIES SUPPORT SVCS

MPW Industrial Svcs Group Inc ....C 740 927-8790
Hebron *(G-10875)*

FACILITY RENTAL & PARTY PLANNING SVCS

Loris Printing Inc ....G 419 626-6648
Sandusky *(G-16981)*

FAMILY CLOTHING STORES

Cotton Pickin Tees & Caps ....G 419 636-3595
Bryan *(G-2291)*
Odyssey Spirits Inc ....F 330 562-1523
Aurora *(G-938)*
Vances Department Store ....G 937 549-2188
Manchester *(G-12552)*
Vances Department Store ....F 937 549-3033
Manchester *(G-12553)*

FAMILY PLANNING CENTERS

Community Action Program Corp ....F 740 374-8501
Marietta *(G-12776)*

FANS, BLOWING: Indl Or Commercial

Howden North America Inc ....E 330 723-0492
Medina *(G-13423)*

FANS, EXHAUST: Indl Or Commercial

ARI Phoenix Inc ....E 513 229-3750
Lebanon *(G-11781)*
Criticalaire LLC ....F 513 475-3800
Columbus *(G-7000)*
Criticalaire LLC ....G 614 499-7744
Cincinnati *(G-3620)*
Howden American Fan Company ....C 513 773-0103
Fairfield *(G-9667)*
Multi-Wing America Inc ....E 440 834-9400
Middlefield *(G-13969)*

FANS, VENTILATING: Indl Or Commercial

Duro Dyne Midwest Corp ....B 513 870-6000
Hamilton *(G-10685)*
Lau Industries Inc ....C 937 476-6500
Dayton *(G-8110)*
Tlt-Turbo Inc ....G 330 776-5115
Akron *(G-443)*

Usui International Corporation ....E 513 448-0410
Cincinnati *(G-4548)*

FANS: Ceiling

Acorn Technology Corporation ....E 216 663-1244
Cleveland *(G-4697)*

FARM & GARDEN MACHINERY WHOLESALERS

All Power Equipment LLC ....F 740 593-3279
Athens *(G-855)*
J L Wannemacher Sales & Svc ....F 419 453-3445
Ottoville *(G-15823)*
Schmidt Machine Company ....E 419 294-3814
Upper Sandusky *(G-19139)*
Smg Growing Media Inc ....G 937 644-0011
Marysville *(G-12971)*

FARM MACHINERY REPAIR SVCS

Dalin Auto Service ....G 440 997-3301
Ashtabula *(G-801)*
J L Wannemacher Sales & Svc ....F 419 453-3445
Ottoville *(G-15823)*
Reberland Equipment Inc ....F 330 698-5883
Apple Creek *(G-648)*

FARM PRDTS, RAW MATERIALS, WHOLESALE: Hides

Inland Products Inc ....E 614 443-3425
Columbus *(G-7188)*

FARM PRDTS, RAW MATERIALS, WHOLESALE: Nuts & Nut By-Prdts

Krema Products Inc ....G 614 889-4824
Dublin *(G-9097)*

FARM SPLY STORES

Centerra Co-Op ....E 419 281-2153
Ashland *(G-717)*
Dinsmore Inc ....G 937 544-3332
West Union *(G-20120)*
Farmers Commission Company ....E 419 294-2371
Upper Sandusky *(G-19122)*
J & B Feed Co Inc ....G 419 335-5821
Wauseon *(G-19685)*
Jefferson Landmark Inc ....F 740 944-1971
Bloomingdale *(G-1724)*
Pettisville Grain Co ....F 419 446-2547
Pettisville *(G-16182)*
RJR & Associates Inc ....G 419 237-2220
Fayette *(G-9779)*
Sunrise Cooperative Inc ....F 419 929-1568
Wakeman *(G-19453)*

FARM SPLYS WHOLESALERS

Andersons Inc ....C 419 893-5050
Maumee *(G-13224)*
Andersons Inc ....C 419 536-0460
Toledo *(G-18349)*
Centerra Co-Op ....E 800 362-9598
Jefferson *(G-11358)*
Countyline Co-Op Inc ....F 419 287-3241
Pemberville *(G-16026)*
Darling International Inc ....F 216 651-9300
Cleveland *(G-5167)*
Harvest Land Co-Op Inc ....G 937 884-5526
Verona *(G-19338)*
Legacy Farmers Cooperative ....F 419 423-2611
Findlay *(G-9851)*
Luckey Farmers Inc ....G 419 287-3275
Bradner *(G-2027)*
Phillips Ready Mix Co ....D 937 426-5151
Beavercreek Township *(G-1388)*
Rogers Mill Inc ....G 330 227-3214
Rogers *(G-16715)*
Rural Farm Distributors Co ....G 419 747-6807
Mansfield *(G-12673)*
Sunrise Cooperative Inc ....F 419 628-4705
Minster *(G-14362)*

FARM SPLYS, WHOLESALE: Feed

Cooper Farms Inc ....D 419 375-4116
Fort Recovery *(G-9946)*

PRODUCT

Cooper Farms Inc ....F...... 419 375-4619
  Fort Recovery (G-9948)
K M B Inc ....E...... 330 889-3451
  Bristolville (G-2098)
Keynes Bros Inc ....E...... 740 385-6824
  Logan (G-12181)
Republic Mills Inc ....F...... 419 758-3511
  Okolona (G-15669)

FARM SPLYS, WHOLESALE: Fertilizers & Agricultural Chemicals

Andersons Lawn Fert Div Inc ....F...... 419 893-5050
  Maumee (G-13226)
Crop Production Services Inc ....G...... 614 873-4253
  Milford Center (G-14181)
Helena Chemical Company ....G...... 614 275-4200
  Columbus (G-7148)
Helena Chemical Company ....G...... 419 596-3806
  Continental (G-7826)
Hoopes Fertilizer Works Inc ....G...... 330 894-2121
  East Rochester (G-9250)

FARM SPLYS, WHOLESALE: Harness Eqpt

Yoders Harness Shop ....G...... 440 632-1505
  Middlefield (G-14009)

FARM SPLYS, WHOLESALE: Limestone, Agricultural

Lesco Inc ....F...... 740 633-6366
  Martins Ferry (G-12925)

FASTENERS: Metal

Aerotech Industries Inc ....G...... 216 881-6660
  Cleveland (G-4725)
Bricolage Inc ....G...... 614 853-6789
  Grove City (G-10547)
C & P Metals Inc ....G...... 724 510-4293
  Warren (G-19533)
Elgin Fastener Group LLC ....F...... 812 717-2544
  Brecksville (G-2046)
Hilti Inc ....F...... 614 258-8384
  Columbus (G-7158)
Midwest Motor Supply Co ....C...... 800 233-1294
  Columbus (G-7351)
National Fasteners Inc ....G...... 216 771-6473
  Brooklyn Heights (G-2143)
Robert A Reich Company ....G...... 440 808-0033
  Westlake (G-20303)
Stonebrook Machine ....G...... 440 951-5013
  Eastlake (G-9289)
Tru-Har Products ....G...... 330 338-6826
  Hudson (G-11205)

FASTENERS: Metal

Hudson Fasteners Inc ....G...... 330 270-9500
  Youngstown (G-21110)
Sky Climber Fasteners LLC ....G...... 740 816-9830
  Delaware (G-8889)
Supply International Inc ....G...... 740 282-8604
  Steubenville (G-17718)
Wecall Inc ....G...... 440 437-8202
  Orwell (G-15780)

FASTENERS: Notions, NEC

A Raymond Tinnerman Mfg Inc ....E...... 330 220-5179
  Brunswick (G-2202)
Cardinal Fstener Specialty Inc ....E...... 216 831-3800
  Bedford Heights (G-1479)
Dimcogray Corporation ....D...... 937 433-7600
  Centerville (G-3039)
Dubose Energy Fasteners & Mach ....F...... 216 362-1700
  Middleburg Heights (G-13905)
Eaglehead Manufacturing Co ....E...... 216 692-1240
  Euclid (G-9576)
Erico International Corp ....B...... 440 248-0100
  Solon (G-17289)
Heads & Threads Intl LLC ....F...... 216 433-1660
  North Olmsted (G-15338)
Hillman Fastener ....F...... 513 851-6200
  Cincinnati (G-3883)
Interfast Inc ....G...... 216 581-3000
  Cleveland (G-5577)
Midwest Motor Supply Co ....C...... 800 233-1294
  Columbus (G-7351)
Ohashi Technica USA Mfg Inc ....E...... 740 965-9002
  Sunbury (G-18071)

Optimas Oe Solutions LLC ....G...... 740 774-4553
  Chillicothe (G-3254)
Phillips Contractors Sup LLC ....F...... 216 861-5730
  Cleveland (G-6002)
R L Technologies Inc ....F...... 937 321-5544
  Dayton (G-8610)
Ramco Specialties Inc ....D...... 330 653-5135
  Hudson (G-11195)
Silicon USA Inc ....G...... 330 928-6217
  Cuyahoga Falls (G-8044)
Tri-State Fasteners LLC ....G...... 937 442-1904
  Sardinia (G-17034)
W W Cross Industries Inc ....F...... 330 588-8400
  Canton (G-2898)
Wodin Inc ....E...... 440 439-4222
  Cleveland (G-6474)
Youngstown Bolt & Supply Co ....G...... 330 799-3201
  Youngstown (G-21247)

FASTENERS: Notions, Zippers

Zipper Manufacturing LLC ....G...... 937 444-0904
  Williamsburg (G-20415)

FASTENERS: Wire, Made From Purchased Wire

Fastener Industries Inc ....F...... 216 267-2240
  Cleveland (G-5326)

FAUCETS & SPIGOTS: Metal & Plastic

Toolbold Corporation ....E...... 440 543-1660
  Cleveland (G-6335)

FEATHERS & FEATHER PRODUCTS

Ohio Feather Company Inc ....G...... 513 921-3373
  Cincinnati (G-4176)

FELT PARTS

Ohio Table Pad Company ....F...... 419 872-6400
  Perrysburg (G-16130)

FELT: Automotive

NC Works Inc ....E...... 937 514-7781
  Franklin (G-10039)

FENCES OR POSTS: Ornamental Iron Or Steel

Akron Products Company ....F...... 330 576-1750
  Wadsworth (G-19391)
City Iron LLC ....G...... 513 721-5678
  Cincinnati (G-3580)
Randy Lewis Inc ....F...... 330 784-0456
  Akron (G-365)

FENCING DEALERS

Bugh Vinyl Products Inc ....G...... 330 305-0978
  Canton (G-2631)
Randy Lewis Inc ....F...... 330 784-0456
  Akron (G-365)
Youngstown Fence Inc ....G...... 330 788-8110
  Youngstown (G-21251)

FENCING MADE IN WIREDRAWING PLANTS

Hsm Wire International Inc ....G...... 330 244-8501
  North Canton (G-15241)

FENCING MATERIALS: Docks & Other Outdoor Prdts, Wood

Cornerstone Spclty WD Pdts LLC ....D...... 513 772-5560
  Cincinnati (G-3611)

FENCING MATERIALS: Plastic

All Around Garage Door Inc ....G...... 440 759-5079
  North Ridgeville (G-15357)
American Way Manufacturing Inc ....E...... 330 824-2353
  Warren (G-19522)
Bugh Vinyl Products Inc ....G...... 330 305-0978
  Canton (G-2631)
Customized Vinyl Sales ....G...... 330 518-3238
  East Palestine (G-9232)
Doglok Inc ....G...... 440 223-1836
  Perry (G-16049)

Perimeter Technologies Inc ....F...... 513 322-5453
  Cincinnati (G-4229)
Randy Lewis Inc ....F...... 330 784-0456
  Akron (G-365)

FENCING MATERIALS: Wood

Greenes Fence Co Inc ....G...... 216 464-3160
  Solon (G-17305)
Kalinich Fence Company Inc ....F...... 440 238-6127
  Strongsville (G-17935)
Mi-Lar Fence Co Inc ....G...... 216 464-3160
  Solon (G-17337)
Randy Lewis Inc ....F...... 330 784-0456
  Akron (G-365)
Youngstown Fence Inc ....G...... 330 788-8110
  Youngstown (G-21251)

FENCING: Chain Link

Aluminum Fence & Mfg Co ....G...... 330 755-3323
  Burton (G-2372)
D&M Fencing LLC ....F...... 419 604-0698
  Spencerville (G-17459)
Randy Lewis Inc ....F...... 330 784-0456
  Akron (G-365)
Richards Whl Fence Co Inc ....E...... 330 773-0423
  Akron (G-373)
Stephens Pipe & Steel LLC ....C...... 740 869-2257
  Mount Sterling (G-14604)

FENDERS: Automobile, Stamped Or Pressed Metal

Fiberglass Link Inc ....G...... 216 531-5515
  Cleveland (G-5343)
Ltf Acquisition LLC ....F...... 330 533-0111
  Canfield (G-2563)

FERRALLOY ORES, EXC VANADIUM

General Electric Company ....D...... 330 343-8841
  Dover (G-8987)
Rhenium Alloys Inc ....D...... 440 365-7388
  North Ridgeville (G-15401)

FERROALLOYS

Marietta Eramet Inc ....C...... 740 374-1000
  Marietta (G-12802)

FERROALLOYS: Produced In Blast Furnaces

Pelletier Brothers Mfg ....F...... 740 774-4704
  Chillicothe (G-3260)

FERROMANGANESE, NOT MADE IN BLAST FURNACES

Real Alloy Holding Inc ....D...... 216 755-8800
  Beachwood (G-1292)

FERROSILICON, EXC MADE IN BLAST FURNACES

Globe Metallurgical Inc ....C...... 740 984-2361
  Waterford (G-19647)

FERTILIZER MINERAL MINING

Everris NA Inc ....E...... 614 726-7100
  Dublin (G-9074)

FERTILIZER, AGRICULTURAL: Wholesalers

Farmers Commission Company ....E...... 419 294-2371
  Upper Sandusky (G-19122)
Hanby Farms Inc ....E...... 740 763-3554
  Nashport (G-14705)
Ohigro Inc ....E...... 740 726-2429
  Waldo (G-19467)

FERTILIZERS: NEC

All Ways Green Lawn & Turf LLC ....G...... 937 763-4766
  Seaman (G-17040)
Countyline Co-Op Inc ....F...... 419 287-3241
  Pemberville (G-16026)
Crop Production Services Inc ....G...... 419 274-2701
  Hamler (G-10759)
Crop Production Services Inc ....F...... 740 869-3369
  Mount Sterling (G-14597)

Crop Production Services Inc..............E 513 941-4100
North Bend (G-15204)
Crop Production Services Inc..............G 614 873-4253
Milford Center (G-14181)
Gardenscape ....E 419 445-6561
Archbold (G-676)
Growmark Fs LLC ....F 330 386-7626
East Liverpool (G-9216)
Hoopes Fertilizer Works Inc..............G 330 894-2121
East Rochester (G-9250)
Hoopes Fertilizer Works Inc..............G 330 821-3550
Alliance (G-516)
Hyponex Corporation ....D 937 644-0011
Marysville (G-12953)
Insta-Gro Manufacturing Inc ....G 419 845-3046
Caledonia (G-2438)
Jefferson Landmark Inc ....F 740 944-1971
Bloomingdale (G-1724)
Legacy Farmers Cooperative............F 419 423-2611
Findlay (G-9851)
Lesco Inc ....G 740 549-2141
Lewis Center (G-11905)
Lesco Inc ....F 740 633-6366
Martins Ferry (G-12925)
Luckey Farmers Inc ....G 419 287-3275
Bradner (G-2027)
Nachurs Alpine Solutions Corp ....E 740 382-5701
Marion (G-12888)
Ohigro Inc ....E 740 726-2429
Waldo (G-19467)
Ottokee Group Inc ....G 419 636-1932
Bryan (G-2316)
Rod McLellan Company ....G 513 644-0011
Marysville (G-12966)
Rural Farm Distributors Co...............G 419 747-6807
Mansfield (G-12673)
Tyler Grain & Fertilizer Co ....F 330 669-2341
Smithville (G-17246)

FERTILIZERS: Nitrogen Solutions

Pcs Nitrogen Inc...........................B 419 226-1200
Lima (G-12066)

FERTILIZERS: Nitrogenous

Agrium Advanced Tech US Inc ....G 614 276-5103
Columbus (G-6703)
Agrium US Inc ....D 513 941-4100
North Bend (G-15201)
Crop Production Services Inc..............E 513 941-4100
North Bend (G-15204)
Everris NA Inc ....E 800 492-8255
Dublin (G-9073)
Harvest Land Co-Op Inc ....G 937 884-5526
Verona (G-19338)
Ineos Americas LLC ....B 419 226-1200
Lima (G-12028)
Pcs Nitrogen Ohio LP ....G 419 879-8989
Lima (G-12067)
R & J AG Manufacturing Inc ....F 419 962-4707
Ashland (G-770)
Scotts Miracle-Gro Company............D 330 684-0421
Orrville (G-15763)
Scotts Miracle-Gro Products ....E 937 644-0011
Marysville (G-12970)
Synagro Midwest Inc ....F 937 384-0669
Miamisburg (G-13866)
Turf Care Supply Corp ....B 877 220-1014
Brunswick (G-2264)

FERTILIZERS: Phosphatic

Andersons Inc ....C 419 893-5050
Maumee (G-13224)
Andersons Inc ....G 419 536-0460
Toledo (G-18349)
Occidental Chemical Corp ....E 513 242-2900
Cincinnati (G-4172)

FIBER & FIBER PRDTS: Acrylic

Success Technologies Inc ....G 614 761-0008
Powell (G-16484)

FIBER & FIBER PRDTS: Acrylonitrile

Buckeye Polymers Inc ....E 330 948-3007
Lodi (G-12158)

FIBER & FIBER PRDTS: Cuprammonium

Laser Horizons ....G 330 208-0575
Norton (G-15517)

FIBER & FIBER PRDTS: Elastomeric

Bridge Components Incorporated........G 614 873-0777
Columbus (G-6858)

FIBER & FIBER PRDTS: Organic, Noncellulose

Ecm Biofilms Inc ....G 440 350-1400
Painesville (G-15877)
Omnova Solutions Inc ....C 330 628-6550
Mogadore (G-14382)
Organic Roots Horticulture LLC ....G 330 620-1108
Ravenna (G-16546)

FIBER & FIBER PRDTS: Synthetic Cellulosic

3M Company ....C 440 323-6161
Elyria (G-9366)
Flexsys America LP ....D 330 666-4111
Akron (G-190)
Mfg Composite Systems Company ....B 440 997-5851
Ashtabula (G-820)
Morgan Adhesives Company LLC.......B 330 688-1111
Stow (G-17775)
Solvaira Specialties Inc ....D 937 652-2101
Urbana (G-19181)

FIBER & FIBER PRDTS: Vinyl

Mytee Products Inc ....F 440 591-4301
Aurora (G-936)

FIBER OPTICS

Nextgen Fiber Optics LLC ....G 513 549-4691
Cincinnati (G-4152)
PLC Connections LLC ....F 614 279-1796
Columbus (G-7498)
Sourcepoint Logistics LLC ....E 937 604-8209
Tipp City (G-18300)
Srico Inc ....G 614 799-0664
Columbus (G-7647)

FIBERS: Carbon & Graphite

Algie Composites Inc ....G 614 529-0477
Columbus (G-6715)
Wolfden Products Inc ....G 614 219-6990
Columbus (G-7769)
Wolfden Products LLC ....G 614 219-6990
Columbus (G-7770)
Xperion E&E USA LLC ....E 740 788-9560
Heath (G-10858)

FIELD WAREHOUSING SVCS

Truechoicepack Corp ....E 937 630-3832
Dayton (G-8732)

FILE FOLDERS

GBS Corp ....C 330 863-1828
Malvern (G-12545)
GBS Corp ....C 330 494-5330
North Canton (G-15233)
Keeler Enterprises Inc ....G 330 336-7601
Wadsworth (G-19412)
Smead Manufacturing Company ....C 740 385-5601
Logan (G-12194)

FILM & SHEET: Unsuppported Plastic

Advanced Polymer Coatings Ltd..........E 440 937-6218
Avon (G-982)
Ampac Holdings LLC ....A 513 671-1777
Cincinnati (G-3397)
Avery Dennison Corporation ....E 440 358-3466
Painesville (G-15855)
Avery Dennison Corporation ....D 440 358-3408
Painesville (G-15859)
Berry Plastics Filmco Inc ....D 330 562-6111
Aurora (G-911)
CCL Label Inc ....C 216 676-2703
Cleveland (G-4998)
CCL Label Inc ....E 440 878-7000
Brunswick (G-2215)
Charter Nex Films - Delaware ....E 740 369-2770
Delaware (G-8832)

Charter Nex Holding Company............E 740 369-2770
Delaware (G-8833)
Clopay Corporation ....G 440 542-9215
Solon (G-17278)
Command Plastic Corporation ....F 800 321-8001
Tallmadge (G-18139)
Dayton Molded Urethanes LLC ....D 937 279-9987
Dayton (G-8280)
DJM Plastics Ltd ....F 419 424-5250
Findlay (G-9817)
E I Du Pont De Nemours & Co ....E 740 474-0220
Circleville (G-4627)
General Data Company Inc ....C 513 752-7978
Cincinnati (G-3304)
Industry Products Co ....B 937 778-0585
Piqua (G-16279)
James McGuire ....G 614 483-9825
Columbus (G-7225)
Liqui-Box Corporation ....C 419 289-9696
Ashland (G-750)
Mar-Bal Inc ....D 440 543-7526
Chagrin Falls (G-3101)
Mar-Bal Inc ....D 440 543-7526
Chagrin Falls (G-3102)
North Shore Strapping Inc ....E 216 661-5200
Brooklyn Heights (G-2144)
North Shore Strapping Inc ....E 216 661-5200
Cleveland (G-5900)
Omnova Solutions Inc ....C 216 682-7000
Beachwood (G-1287)
Packaging Materials Inc ....E 740 432-6337
Cambridge (G-2471)
Pexco Packaging Corp ....F 419 470-5935
Toledo (G-18642)
Plastic Suppliers Inc ....E 614 471-9100
Columbus (G-7493)
Polyone Corporation ....D 937 548-1395
Greenville (G-10513)
Polyone Corporation ....C 419 399-4050
Paulding (G-16013)
Polyone Corporation ....D 440 930-1000
Avon Lake (G-1047)
Priority Custom Molding Inc ....F 937 431-8770
Beavercreek Township (G-1389)
Profusion Industries LLC ....G 800 938-2858
Fairlawn (G-9758)
Profusion Industries LLC ....D 740 374-6400
Marietta (G-12821)
Quality Poly Corp...........................F 330 453-9559
Canton (G-2829)
Ritrama Inc ....D 216 851-7208
Cleveland (G-6116)
Rotary Products Inc ....F 740 747-2623
Ashley (G-791)
Snyder Manufacturing Co Ltd ....G 330 343-4456
Dover (G-9017)
Summit Plastic Company ....D 330 633-3668
Akron (G-420)
Team Plastics Inc ....F 216 251-8270
Cleveland (G-6296)
Transcendia Inc ....C 740 929-5100
Hebron (G-10891)
Transcendia Inc ....D 440 638-2000
Strongsville (G-17978)
Vinyl Building Products LLC ....B 513 539-4444
Monroe (G-14418)

FILM BASE: Cellulose Acetate Or Nitrocellulose Plastics

American Insulation Tech LLC ....F 513 733-4248
Milford (G-14120)
Boltaron Inc ....D 740 498-5900
Newcomerstown (G-15109)

FILM DEVELOPING & PRINTING SVCS

SMS Communications Inc..................E 216 374-6686
Shaker Heights (G-17095)

FILM: Rubber

B D G Wrap-Tite Inc ....D 440 349-5400
Solon (G-17263)

FILTER ELEMENTS: Fluid & Hydraulic Line

Parker-Hannifin Corporation..............B 216 896-3000
Cleveland (G-5973)
Parker-Hannifin Corporation..............F 216 896-3000
Cleveland (G-5976)

PRODUCT

Two M Precision Co Inc............E....... 440 946-2120
Willoughby (G-20623)

FILTERS

Abanaki Corporation ....F....... 440 543-7400
Chagrin Falls (G-3075)
Aronit Machine LLC ....F....... 419 782-4740
Defiance (G-8778)
Barney Corporation Inc ....G....... 614 274-9069
Hilliard (G-10930)
Columbus Industries Inc ....D....... 740 983-2552
Ashville (G-849)
Diamondback Filters ....G....... 419 494-1156
Bowling Green (G-1985)
E R Advanced Ceramics Inc ....E....... 330 426-9433
East Palestine (G-9237)
Evoqua Water Technologies LLC ....E....... 614 861-5440
Pickerington (G-16192)
Filter Factory-Ttn Inc ....G....... 440 963-2034
Vermilion (G-19326)
Foseco Inc ....G....... 440 826-4548
Cleveland (G-5374)
Hdt Expeditionary Systems Inc ....G 216 438-6111
Solon (G-17308)
Hunter Defense Tech Inc ....E....... 216 438-6111
Solon (G-17312)
Lawrence Technologies Inc ....G....... 937 274-7771
Dayton (G-8454)
Oil Skimmers Inc ....E....... 440 237-4600
North Royalton (G-15440)
Process Machinery Inc ....F....... 614 278-1055
Columbus (G-7522)
Raymond W Reisiger ....G....... 740 400-4090
Baltimore (G-1086)
Russell E Coy ....G....... 419 658-2366
Ney (G-15143)
Swift Filters Inc ....E....... 440 735-0995
Oakwood Village (G-15628)
Zhao Hui Filters (us) Inc ....G....... 440 519-9300
Chagrin Falls (G-3136)

FILTERS & SOFTENERS: Water, Household

Amsoil Inc ....G....... 614 274-9851
Columbus (G-6746)
Enting Water Conditioning Inc ....E....... 937 294-5100
Moraine (G-14484)
Mountain Filtration Systems ....G....... 419 395-2526
Defiance (G-8806)
Tri County Quality Wtr Systems ....G....... 740 751-4764
Marion (G-12909)
United McGill ....G....... 614 829-1226
Columbus (G-7720)
Water Systems Services ....G....... 513 523-6766
Oxford (G-15845)

FILTERS & STRAINERS: Pipeline

City of Mansfield ....F....... 419 884-3310
Mansfield (G-12580)
Hellan Strainer Company ....G....... 216 206-4200
Cleveland (G-5495)

FILTERS: Air

Air Cleaning Solutions ....G....... 937 832-3600
Dayton (G-8141)
Ceco Group Inc ....G....... 513 458-2600
Cincinnati (G-3510)
Cincinnati A Flter Sls Svc Inc ....E....... 513 242-3400
Cincinnati (G-3536)
Complete Filter Media LLC ....E....... 740 438-0929
Lancaster (G-11698)
First Filter LLC ....G....... 419 666-5260
Perrysburg (G-16095)
Glasfloss Industries Inc ....C....... 740 687-1100
Lancaster (G-11721)
Hdt Ep Inc ....E....... 216 438-6111
Solon (G-17307)
Hdt Expeditionary Systems Inc ....F....... 440 466-6640
Geneva (G-10350)
Skuttle Mfg Co ....F....... 740 373-9169
Marietta (G-12831)
Std Specialty Filters Inc ....F....... 216 881-3727
Cleveland (G-6243)

FILTERS: Air Intake, Internal Combustion Engine, Exc Auto

Donaldson Company Inc ....D....... 330 928-4100
Stow (G-17743)

Engine Machine Service Inc ....G....... 330 505-1804
Niles (G-15151)
Lariat Machine Inc ....G....... 330 297-5765
Ravenna (G-16538)
Norwood Medical ....G....... 937 228-4101
Dayton (G-8530)
Plas-Mac Corp ....D....... 440 349-3222
Solon (G-17361)

FILTERS: General Line, Indl

D C Filter & Chemical Inc ....G....... 419 626-3967
Sandusky (G-16955)
Edjean Technical Services Inc ....G....... 440 647-3300
Sullivan (G-18054)
Falls Filtration Tech Inc ....E....... 330 928-4100
Stow (G-17752)
Kuss Filtration Inc ....B....... 419 423-9040
Findlay (G-9849)
Membrane Specialists LLC ....G....... 513 860-9490
Hamilton (G-10724)
Met-Chem Inc ....E....... 216 881-7900
Cleveland (G-5786)
Midwest Filtration LLC ....E....... 513 874-6510
West Chester (G-20030)
Nupro Company ....C....... 440 951-9729
Willoughby (G-20559)
Petro Ware Inc ....D....... 740 982-1302
Crooksville (G-7953)
Pyrotek Incorporated ....C....... 440 349-8800
Aurora (G-942)
S A Langmack Company ....F....... 216 541-0500
Cleveland (G-6149)

FILTERS: Motor Vehicle

Bellevue Manufacturing Company ....D....... 419 483-3190
Bellevue (G-1545)
Bellevue Manufacturing Company ....G....... 419 483-3190
Bellevue (G-1546)
Entratech Systems LLC ....G....... 419 433-7683
Sandusky (G-16963)
Fram Group Operations LLC ....G....... 937 316-3000
Greenville (G-10499)
Roki America Co Ltd ....B....... 419 424-9713
Findlay (G-9883)

FILTERS: Oil, Internal Combustion Engine, Exc Auto

Brinkley Technology Group LLC ....F....... 330 830-2498
Massillon (G-13115)

FILTRATION DEVICES: Electronic

Captor Corporation ....D....... 937 667-8484
Tipp City (G-18270)
Chicopee Engineering Assoc Inc ....E....... 413 592-2273
Twinsburg (G-18911)
Contech Strmwter Solutions LLC ....G....... 513 645-7000
West Chester (G-19842)
Crawford Resources Inc ....G....... 419 624-8400
Sandusky (G-16954)
Enviro Crest Services Inc ....G....... 330 932-0345
East Liverpool (G-9214)
Illinois Tool Works Inc ....C....... 262 248-8277
Bryan (G-2303)
Media Matrix LLC ....G....... 888 833-8681
Mount Vernon (G-14630)
Micropure Filtration Inc ....F....... 952 472-2323
Cleveland (G-5800)

FILTRATION SAND MINING

I P Contractors LLC ....G....... 330 452-1643
Canton (G-2735)

FINANCIAL SVCS

International Supply Corp ....G....... 513 793-0393
Cincinnati (G-3931)

FINDINGS & TRIMMINGS: Fabric

Detroit Technologies Inc ....E....... 937 492-2708
Sidney (G-17179)
Greenfield Research Inc ....G....... 937 876-9224
Greenfield (G-10479)
Griffin Fisher Co Inc ....G....... 513 961-2110
Cincinnati (G-3853)
Hfi LLC ....B....... 614 491-0700
Canal Winchester (G-2525)

Hfi LLC ....C....... 614 491-0700
Canal Winchester (G-2526)
Lesch Boat Cover Canvas Co LLC ....G....... 419 668-6374
Norwalk (G-15550)
Pieco Inc ....E....... 419 422-5335
Findlay (G-9878)
Pieco Inc ....D....... 937 399-5100
Springfield (G-17628)
Spirit Avionics Ltd ....F....... 614 358-0333
Columbus (G-7645)
Telempu N Hayashi Amer Corp ....G....... 513 932-9319
Lebanon (G-11843)

FINGERNAILS, ARTIFICIAL

Hung Pham ....G....... 614 850-9695
Columbus (G-7170)
Nail Art ....G....... 614 899-7155
Westerville (G-20225)
Nail Secret ....G....... 513 459-3373
Maineville (G-12530)

FINGERPRINT EQPT

Advanced Livescan Technologies ....G....... 440 759-7028
Cleveland (G-4715)

FINISHING AGENTS

Pilot Chemical Company Ohio ....E....... 513 326-0600
Cincinnati (G-4236)
Pilot Chemical Company Ohio ....G....... 513 733-4880
Cincinnati (G-4237)

FIRE ARMS, SMALL: Guns Or Gun Parts, 30 mm & Below

762mm Firearms LLC ....G....... 440 655-8572
Wadsworth (G-19384)
Highpoint Firearms ....E....... 419 747-9444
Mansfield (G-12625)
Iberia Firearms Inc ....G....... 419 468-3746
Galion (G-10276)
Jmr Enterprises LLC ....G....... 937 618-1736
Maineville (G-12525)
Ohio Ordnance Works Inc ....E....... 440 285-3481
Chardon (G-3170)
Smokin Guns LLC ....G....... 440 324-4003
Elyria (G-9494)

FIRE ARMS, SMALL: Machine Guns & Grenade Launchers

Reloading Supplies Corp ....G....... 440 228-0367
Ashtabula (G-836)

FIRE ARMS, SMALL: Rifles Or Rifle Parts, 30 mm & below

Inland Manufacturing LLC ....G....... 937 835-0220
Dayton (G-8403)
Kelblys Rifle Range Inc ....G....... 330 683-0070
North Lawrence (G-15306)

FIRE ARMS, SMALL: Shotguns Or Shotgun Parts, 30 mm & Below

Quality Replacement Parts Inc ....G....... 216 674-0200
Cleveland (G-6073)

FIRE CLAY MINING

E J Bognar Inc ....F....... 330 426-9292
East Palestine (G-9236)

FIRE CONTROL EQPT REPAIR SVCS, MILITARY

Fire Foe Corp ....E....... 330 759-9834
Girard (G-10387)

FIRE CONTROL OR BOMBING EQPT: Electronic

Fire-End & Croker Corp ....G....... 513 870-0517
West Chester (G-20001)

FIRE DETECTION SYSTEMS

Hyq Technologies LLC ....G....... 513 225-6911
Oxford (G-15837)

FIRE EXTINGUISHER CHARGES

SC Fire Protection Ltd ....G....... 330 468-3300
  Macedonia *(G-12481)*
Warren Fire Equipment Inc ....E....... 330 824-3523
  Warren *(G-19622)*

FIRE EXTINGUISHER SVC

Antram Fire Equipment ....G....... 330 525-7171
  North Georgetown *(G-15286)*
Fire Safety Services Inc ....F....... 937 686-2000
  Huntsville *(G-11213)*
L-Mor Inc ....E....... 216 541-2224
  Cleveland *(G-5672)*
Warren Fire Equipment Inc ....G....... 937 866-8918
  Miamisburg *(G-13878)*

FIRE EXTINGUISHERS, WHOLESALE

Fire Safety Services Inc ....F....... 937 686-2000
  Huntsville *(G-11213)*

FIRE EXTINGUISHERS: Portable

Fire Safety Services Inc ....F....... 937 686-2000
  Huntsville *(G-11213)*

FIRE OR BURGLARY RESISTIVE PRDTS

Alchemical Transmutation ....C....... 216 313-8674
  Cleveland *(G-4742)*
B K Fabrication & Machine Shop ....G....... 740 695-4164
  Saint Clairsville *(G-16781)*
Donald E Didion II ....E....... 419 483-2226
  Bellevue *(G-1550)*
Fabricating Solutions Inc ....F....... 330 486-0998
  Twinsburg *(G-18933)*
M A K Fabricating Inc ....F....... 330 747-0040
  Youngstown *(G-21136)*
Mast Farm Service Ltd ....E....... 330 893-2972
  Walnut Creek *(G-19470)*
MTS Enterprises LLC ....G....... 937 324-7510
  Springfield *(G-17609)*
Quest Technologies Inc ....F....... 937 743-1200
  Franklin *(G-10047)*
Zimmerman Steel & Sup Co LLC ....F....... 330 828-1010
  Dalton *(G-8082)*

FIRE PROTECTION EQPT

A-1 Sprinkler Company Inc ....D....... 937 859-6198
  Miamisburg *(G-13779)*
Action Coupling & Eqp Inc ....D....... 330 279-4242
  Holmesville *(G-11099)*
Akron Brass Company ....E....... 309 444-4440
  Wooster *(G-20733)*
Akron Brass Company ....B....... 330 264-5678
  Wooster *(G-20734)*
American Rescue Technology ....F....... 937 293-6240
  Dayton *(G-8155)*
E S H Inc ....G....... 330 345-1010
  Wooster *(G-20768)*
Elite Fire Services LLC ....F....... 614 586-4255
  Columbus *(G-7053)*
Fire & Marine Inc ....E....... 937 323-2770
  Springfield *(G-17559)*
Globe Pipe Hanger Products Inc ....E....... 216 362-6300
  Cleveland *(G-5434)*
Rhba Acquisitions LLC ....D....... 330 567-2903
  Shreve *(G-17162)*
Warren Fire Equipment Inc ....G....... 937 866-8918
  Miamisburg *(G-13878)*
Zephyr Industries Inc ....G....... 419 281-4485
  Ashland *(G-787)*

FIREARMS & AMMUNITION, EXC SPORTING, WHOLESALE

Fedex Office & Print Svcs Inc ....F....... 937 335-3816
  Troy *(G-18827)*
Hanger Prsthetcs & Ortho Inc ....G....... 330 374-9544
  Akron *(G-215)*

FIREARMS: Large, Greater Than 30mm

Expert Outfitters ....G....... 330 965-9620
  North Lima *(G-15316)*

FIREARMS: Small, 30mm or Less

American Apex Corporation ....F....... 614 652-2000
  Plain City *(G-16319)*

Ares Inc ....D....... 419 635-2175
  Port Clinton *(G-16393)*
Beech Armament LLC ....G....... 330 962-4694
  Cuyahoga Falls *(G-7974)*
Faxon Firearms LLC ....G....... 513 674-2580
  Cincinnati *(G-3744)*
Global Precision Parts Inc ....D....... 419 453-0010
  Ottoville *(G-15821)*
Nicana Consulting Inc ....G....... 419 615-9703
  Kalida *(G-11415)*
Parabellum Armament Co LLC ....G....... 614 557-5987
  Grove City *(G-10582)*
X-Treme Shooting Products LLC ....G....... 513 313-3464
  Batavia *(G-1234)*
Zshot Inc ....G....... 800 385-8581
  Lewis Center *(G-11930)*

FIREFIGHTING APPARATUS

United Fire Apparatus Corp ....G....... 419 645-4083
  Cridersville *(G-7947)*

FIREPLACE & CHIMNEY MATERIAL: Concrete

Ohio Flame ....G....... 330 953-0863
  Youngstown *(G-21154)*

FIREPLACE EQPT & ACCESS

Doan Machinery & Eqp Co Inc ....G....... 216 932-6243
  University Heights *(G-19108)*
Hearth & Home Technologies LLC ....G....... 513 874-4770
  Cincinnati *(G-3875)*
Strawser Hydrant Maintenance ....G....... 614 875-1514
  Grove City *(G-10600)*
Strutt Products LLC ....G....... 330 889-2727
  Bristolville *(G-2100)*
Thermo-Rite Mfg Company ....E....... 330 633-8680
  Akron *(G-439)*

FIREWORKS

Alan BJ Company ....G....... 330 372-1201
  Warren *(G-19518)*
Colonial Fireworks Company ....F....... 419 478-4945
  Toledo *(G-18406)*
Diamond Sparkler Mfg Co ....G....... 330 746-1064
  Youngstown *(G-21068)*
Eagle Fireworks Co ....G....... 740 373-3357
  Marietta *(G-12782)*
Eagle Fireworks Co ....G....... 740 758-5649
  Quaker City *(G-16499)*
James Sorgi ....G....... 330 653-5180
  Hudson *(G-11186)*
Midwest Fireworks Mfg Co II ....G....... 330 584-7000
  Deerfield *(G-8774)*
Phantom Fireworks ....E....... 740 927-6943
  Millersport *(G-14296)*
Phantom Fireworks Inc ....G....... 419 237-2185
  Fayette *(G-9777)*
Prestige Fireworks LLC ....F....... 513 492-7726
  Mason *(G-13077)*
Pyrotechnics By Presutti Inc ....F....... 740 699-1224
  Bellaire *(G-1501)*
Sam Abdallah ....E....... 330 532-3900
  Hammondsville *(G-10760)*

FIREWORKS SHOPS

Eagle Fireworks Co ....G....... 740 373-3357
  Marietta *(G-12782)*
Eagle Fireworks Co ....G....... 740 758-5649
  Quaker City *(G-16499)*
Phantom Fireworks Inc ....G....... 419 237-2185
  Fayette *(G-9777)*

FIREWORKS: Wholesalers

Eagle Fireworks Co ....G....... 740 758-5649
  Quaker City *(G-16499)*

FISH & SEAFOOD PROCESSORS: Canned Or Cured

Strasburg Provision Inc ....E....... 330 878-1059
  Strasburg *(G-17830)*

FISH & SEAFOOD WHOLESALERS

Jroll LLC ....F....... 330 661-0600
  Medina *(G-13430)*

FISH FOOD

Jroll LLC ....F....... 330 661-0600
  Medina *(G-13430)*
Ocean Providence Columbus LLC ....G....... 614 272-5973
  Columbus *(G-7411)*

FISH, PACKAGED FROZEN: Wholesalers

King Kold Inc ....E....... 937 836-2731
  Englewood *(G-9529)*

FISHING EQPT: Lures

AC Shiners Inc ....G....... 513 738-1573
  Okeana *(G-15662)*
Drowned Lure ....G....... 330 548-5873
  Tallmadge *(G-18144)*
JPb Lures Manufacturing LLC ....G....... 419 734-9488
  Marblehead *(G-12745)*
Lure Inc ....E....... 440 951-8862
  Willoughby *(G-20530)*
N Bass Bait Co ....G....... 419 647-4501
  Spencerville *(G-17462)*
Nemire Lures LLC ....G....... 419 729-1280
  Toledo *(G-18599)*
Ouchless Lures Inc ....G....... 330 653-3867
  Hudson *(G-11192)*
Reef Runner Tackle Co Inc ....G....... 419 798-9125
  Marblehead *(G-12746)*

FITTINGS & ASSEMBLIES: Hose & Tube, Hydraulic Or Pneumatic

Ace Manufacturing Company ....E....... 513 541-2490
  West Chester *(G-19976)*
Aeroquip-Vickers Inc ....G....... 216 523-5000
  Cleveland *(G-4722)*
Air-Way Manufacturing Company ....C....... 419 298-2366
  Edgerton *(G-9325)*
Eaton Hydraulics LLC ....E....... 419 232-7777
  Van Wert *(G-19254)*
Eaton-Aeroquip Llc ....C....... 216 523-5000
  Cleveland *(G-5254)*
Eaton-Aeroquip Llc ....D....... 419 238-1190
  Van Wert *(G-19255)*
Industrial Connections Inc ....G....... 330 274-2155
  Mantua *(G-12713)*
Integrated Aircraft Systems ....G....... 330 686-2982
  Stow *(G-17764)*
Kaman Fluid Power LLC ....G....... 330 315-3100
  Akron *(G-248)*
Malone Specialty Inc ....F....... 440 255-4200
  Mentor *(G-13645)*
Maverick Industries Inc ....F....... 440 838-5335
  Brecksville *(G-2064)*
Mid-State Sales Inc ....G....... 330 744-2158
  Youngstown *(G-21145)*
Netherland Rubber Company ....F....... 513 733-0883
  Cincinnati *(G-4146)*
Ohio Hydraulics Inc ....E....... 513 771-2590
  Cincinnati *(G-4178)*
Parker-Hannifin Corporation ....E....... 440 943-5700
  Wickliffe *(G-20381)*
Parker-Hannifin Corporation ....C....... 937 962-5566
  Lewisburg *(G-11939)*
Quality Machining and Mfg Inc ....E....... 419 899-2543
  Sherwood *(G-17147)*
Summers Acquisition Corp ....G....... 740 373-0303
  Marietta *(G-12839)*
Tylok International Inc ....D....... 216 261-7310
  Cleveland *(G-6377)*
United States Controls Inc ....G....... 330 758-1147
  Poland *(G-16386)*

FITTINGS & SPECIALTIES: Steam

Spirax Sarco Inc ....G....... 803 714-2023
  Worthington *(G-20889)*

FITTINGS: Pipe

Adaptall America Inc ....F....... 330 425-4114
  Twinsburg *(G-18894)*
Drainage Pipe & Fitting ....G....... 419 538-6337
  Ottawa *(G-15793)*
General Plug and Mfg Co ....C....... 440 926-2411
  Grafton *(G-10426)*
Greater Cleve Pipe Ftting Fund ....F....... 216 524-8334
  Cleveland *(G-5458)*
Parker-Hannifin Corporation ....B....... 937 456-5571
  Eaton *(G-9320)*

P
R
O
D
U
C
T

FITTINGS: Pipe

Parker-Hannifin Corporation..................C...... 614 279-7070
Columbus (G-7462)
Parker-Hannifin Corporation..................C...... 937 962-5301
Lewisburg (G-11938)
PHD Manufacturing Inc..........................C...... 330 482-9256
Columbiana (G-6628)
Richards Industries Inc.........................C...... 513 533-7340
Cincinnati (G-4344)
SSP Fittings Corp...................................D...... 330 425-4250
Twinsburg (G-19022)
Steven L Lones.......................................G...... 740 452-8851
Zanesville (G-21357)
Swagelok Company..................................A...... 440 248-4600
Solon (G-17390)
Swagelok Company..................................D...... 440 349-5652
Solon (G-17391)
Swagelok Company..................................E...... 440 349-5836
Solon (G-17393)
Swagelok Company..................................E...... 440 542-1250
Solon (G-17394)
US Fittings Inc.......................................F...... 234 212-9420
Twinsburg (G-19034)

FITTINGS: Pipe, Fabricated

Cleveland Coppersmithing Works.........G...... 330 607-3998
Richfield (G-16618)
Phoenix Forge Group LLC.......................C...... 800 848-6125
West Jefferson (G-20082)
Pipe Line Development Company.........D...... 440 871-5700
Westlake (G-20296)
Pipe Products Inc....................................D...... 513 587-7532
West Chester (G-19915)

FIXTURES & EQPT: Kitchen, Metal, Exc Cast Aluminum

American Pan Company............................C...... 937 652-3232
Urbana (G-19146)
Amtekco Industries Inc..........................D...... 614 228-6590
Columbus (G-6749)

FIXTURES & EQPT: Kitchen, Porcelain Enameled

Everyware Global Inc.............................D...... 740 687-2500
Lancaster (G-11711)
Schoen Industries Inc............................G...... 330 533-6659
Canfield (G-2573)

FIXTURES: Cut Stone

Rainbow Cultured Marble.......................F...... 330 225-3400
Brunswick (G-2251)

FLAGS: Fabric

Annin & Co...D...... 740 622-4447
Coshocton (G-7878)
Flag Lady Inc...G...... 614 263-1776
Columbus (G-7090)

FLAGSTONES

Brocks Chimney......................................G...... 740 819-2489
Nashport (G-14704)

FLAKES: Metal

Ohio Valley Manufacturing Inc............D...... 419 522-5818
Mansfield (G-12662)
Premar Manufacturing Ltd.....................G...... 440 250-0373
Westlake (G-20297)
Transmet Corporation............................G...... 614 276-5522
Columbus (G-7706)

FLARES

Lfg Specialties LLC................................E...... 419 424-4999
Findlay (G-9852)

FLAT GLASS: Building

Anchor Hocking Corporation..................D...... 740 681-6461
Lancaster (G-11689)
Therm-All Inc..E...... 440 779-9494
North Olmsted (G-15348)

FLAT GLASS: Construction

Imaging Sciences LLC............................G...... 440 975-9640
Willoughby (G-20509)
S R Door Inc...D...... 740 927-3558
Hebron (G-10883)

Wt Acquisition Company Ltd...............E...... 513 577-7980
Cincinnati (G-4610)

FLAT GLASS: Float

Pilkington North America Inc...............B...... 419 247-3211
Rossford (G-16745)

FLAT GLASS: Picture

Knight Industries Corp...........................E...... 419 478-8550
Toledo (G-18547)

FLAT GLASS: Plate, Polished & Rough

Custom GL Sltons Millbury Corp.........C...... 419 855-7706
Millbury (G-14183)

FLAT GLASS: Tempered

Glasstech Inc..C...... 419 661-9500
Perrysburg (G-16103)
Trulite GL Alum Solutions LLC............D...... 740 929-2443
Hebron (G-10892)

FLAT GLASS: Window, Clear & Colored

Sonalysts Inc..E...... 937 429-9711
Beavercreek (G-1362)

FLAVORS OR FLAVORING MATERIALS: Synthetic

Frutarom USA Holding Inc.....................G...... 201 861-9500
West Chester (G-20004)
Givaudan..F...... 513 482-2536
Cincinnati (G-3827)
Givaudan Flavors Corporation..............B...... 513 948-8000
Cincinnati (G-3828)
Givaudan Flvors Fragrances Inc..........G...... 513 948-8000
Cincinnati (G-3830)
Givaudan Fragrances Corp.....................B...... 513 948-3428
Cincinnati (G-3832)
Kerry Flavor Systems Us LLC..............E...... 513 539-7373
Monroe (G-14407)

FLIGHT RECORDERS

Electrodynamics Inc..............................C...... 847 259-0740
Cincinnati (G-3300)

FLOATING DRY DOCKS

Pinney Dock & Transport LLC...............E...... 440 964-7186
Ashtabula (G-832)

FLOCKING SVC: Fabric

Ohio Flock-Cote Company Inc...............G...... 440 498-3877
Solon (G-17354)

FLOOR COVERING STORES

Armstrong World Industries Inc...........D...... 614 771-9307
Hilliard (G-10927)
Bwd Woodwork LLC.................................G...... 740 335-9766
Wshngtn CT Hs (G-20903)
Davies Since 1900..................................G...... 419 756-4212
Mansfield (G-12593)
Quality Drble Indus Floors Inc.............E...... 937 696-2833
Farmersville (G-9773)
Witt-Gor Inc..G...... 419 659-2151
Columbus Grove (G-7798)

FLOOR COVERING STORES: Carpets

Dpi Inc...G...... 419 273-1400
Forest (G-9919)
Stanley Steemer Intl Inc........................C...... 614 764-2007
Dublin (G-9149)
Wccv Floor Coverings Inc......................E...... 330 688-0114
Peninsula (G-16044)

FLOOR COVERING STORES: Rugs

Shaheen Oriental Rug Co Inc................F...... 330 493-9000
Canton (G-2846)

FLOOR COVERING: Plastic

Armaly LLC..E...... 740 852-3621
London (G-12200)
Cleveland Reclaim Inds Inc...................F...... 440 282-4917
Lorain (G-12238)

Next Generation Films Inc.....................C...... 419 884-8150
Lexington (G-11951)
Udecx LLC..G...... 937 830-0374
Tipp City (G-18308)

FLOOR COVERINGS WHOLESALERS

Pfpc Enterprises Inc..............................B...... 513 941-6200
Cincinnati (G-4233)

FLOOR COVERINGS: Asphalted-Felt Base, Linoleum Or Carpet

Prints & Paints Flr Cvg Co Inc............E...... 419 462-5663
Galion (G-10283)

FLOOR COVERINGS: Rubber

Champion Manufacturing Inc.................G...... 419 253-7930
Marengo (G-12747)
Dandy Products Inc.................................F...... 513 625-3000
Goshen (G-10414)
Mameco International Inc.......................F...... 216 752-4400
Cleveland (G-5738)

FLOOR COVERINGS: Twisted Paper, Grass, Reed, Coir, Etc

B and L Sales Inc...................................G...... 330 279-2007
Millersburg (G-14195)

FLOORING & SIDING: Metal

Americas Best Siding Co.......................G...... 419 589-5900
Mansfield (G-12562)
Associated Materials LLC......................G...... 937 236-5679
Dayton (G-8166)

FLOORING: Hard Surface

Armstrong World Industries Inc...........D...... 614 771-9307
Hilliard (G-10927)
Quality Drble Indus Floors Inc.............E...... 937 696-2833
Farmersville (G-9773)
Schlabach Woodworks Ltd......................E...... 330 674-7488
Millersburg (G-14262)

FLOORING: Hardwood

Hardwood Flrg & Paneling Inc..............D...... 440 834-1710
Middlefield (G-13940)
Kelco Hardwood Floors Inc....................G...... 440 354-0974
Painesville (G-15895)
Marsh Valley Forest Pdts Ltd................G...... 440 632-1889
Middlefield (G-13953)
Prestige Enterprise Intl Inc...................D...... 513 469-6044
Blue Ash (G-1855)
Property Assist Inc................................G...... 419 480-1700
Toledo (G-18660)
Robbins Inc...E...... 513 871-8988
Cincinnati (G-4352)
Trumbull County Dry Kilns Inc..............F...... 330 562-3367
Aurora (G-952)

FLOORING: Rubber

Roppe Corporation..................................B...... 419 435-8546
Fostoria (G-9991)
Tarkett Inc..G...... 440 708-9366
Chagrin Falls (G-3124)
Tarkett Inc..D...... 800 899-8916
Solon (G-17398)

FLOORING: Tile

PCC Ceramic Group 1..............................G...... 440 516-3672
Wickliffe (G-20382)
Summitville Tiles Inc..............................C...... 330 868-6771
Minerva (G-14343)

FLORIST: Flowers, Fresh

Cleveland Plant and Flower Co.............E...... 614 478-9900
Columbus (G-6937)
Huston Gifts Dolls and Flowers.............G...... 740 775-9141
Chillicothe (G-3244)

FLORISTS

Kroger Co..D...... 513 683-4001
Maineville (G-12526)
Kroger Co..D...... 740 374-2523
Marietta (G-12798)

Kroger Co ....C 937 277-0950
Dayton (G-8447)

FLOWER POTS Plastic

Janorpot LLC ....E 330 564-0232
Mogadore (G-14378)

FLOWERS, ARTIFICIAL, WHOLESALE

Hall Creations ....G 330 357-2428
Kent (G-11468)

FLOWERS, FRESH, WHOLESALE

Cleveland Plant and Flower Co ....E 614 478-9900
Columbus (G-6937)
Huston Gifts Dolls and Flowers ....G 740 775-9141
Chillicothe (G-3244)

FLUID METERS & COUNTING DEVICES

Aqua Technology Group LLC ....G 513 298-1183
West Chester (G-19807)
Automatic Timing & Contrls Inc ....D 614 888-8855
New Albany (G-14747)
Exact Equipment Corporation ....F 215 295-2000
Columbus (G-6645)
Flow Line Options Corp ....G 330 331-7331
Wadsworth (G-19407)
Harris Instrument Corporation ....G 740 369-3580
Delaware (G-8857)
K-Hill Signal Co Inc ....G 740 922-0421
Uhrichsville (G-19054)
Triplett Bluffton Corporation ....E 419 358-8750
Bluffton (G-1919)
United Process Controls Inc ....E 414 462-8200
West Chester (G-19967)

FLUID POWER PUMPS & MOTORS

Aerocontrolex Group Inc ....D 440 352-6182
Cleveland (G-4719)
Ban-Fam Industries Inc ....G 216 265-9588
Cleveland (G-4888)
Bergstrom Company Ltd Partnr ....E 440 232-2282
Cleveland (G-4905)
Crown Elec Svcs & Automtn Inc ....G 330 270-9890
Youngstown (G-21058)
Eaton Leasing Corporation ....E 216 382-2292
Beachwood (G-1270)
Eaton-Aeroquip Inc ....D 419 891-7775
Maumee (G-13258)
Emerson Process Management ....E 419 529-4311
Ontario (G-15687)
Force Control Industries Inc ....D 513 868-0900
Fairfield (G-9659)
Furukawa Rock Drill USA Co Ltd ....E 330 673-5826
Kent (G-11462)
George A Mitchell Company ....E 330 758-5777
Youngstown (G-21099)
Giant Industries Inc ....E 419 531-4600
Toledo (G-18480)
Gorman-Rupp Company ....G 419 755-1011
Mansfield (G-12617)
Gorman-Rupp Company ....B 419 755-1011
Mansfield (G-12614)
H Y O Inc ....F 614 488-2861
Columbus (G-7136)
Hite Parts Exchange Inc ....E 614 272-5115
Columbus (G-7160)
Hy-Production Inc ....C 330 273-2400
Valley City (G-19206)
Hydraulic Parts Store Inc ....E 330 364-6667
New Philadelphia (G-14902)
Hydraulic Products Inc ....G 440 946-4575
Willoughby (G-20506)
Ingersoll-Rand Company ....E 419 633-6800
Bryan (G-2306)
Midwest Tool & Engineering Co ....E 937 224-0756
Dayton (G-8498)
Parker Royalty Partnership ....D 216 896-3000
Cleveland (G-5971)
Parker-Hannifin Corporation ....B 216 896-3000
Cleveland (G-5973)
Parker-Hannifin Corporation ....C 330 963-0601
Macedonia (G-12468)
Parker-Hannifin Corporation ....C 513 847-1758
West Chester (G-19912)
Parker-Hannifin Corporation ....F 216 896-3000
Macedonia (G-12469)
Parker-Hannifin Corporation ....C 419 394-9600
Saint Marys (G-16848)

Pfpc Enterprises Inc ....B 513 941-6200
Cincinnati (G-4233)
Quad Fluid Dynamics Inc ....F 330 220-3005
Brunswick (G-2250)
Radocy Inc ....F 419 666-4400
Rossford (G-16747)
Robeck Fluid Power Co ....D 330 562-1140
Aurora (G-944)
Semtorq Inc ....F 330 487-0600
Twinsburg (G-19019)
Starkey Machinery Inc ....E 419 468-2560
Galion (G-10289)
Sunset Industries Inc ....E 216 731-8131
Euclid (G-9607)
Swagelok Company ....E 440 349-5836
Solon (G-17393)
Swanson Industries Inc ....D 304 284-5199
New Philadelphia (G-14931)
Toth Industries Inc ....D 419 729-4669
Toledo (G-18752)

FLUID POWER VALVES & HOSE FITTINGS

Alkon Corporation ....D 419 355-9111
Fremont (G-10124)
Canfield Industries Inc ....G 800 554-5071
Youngstown (G-21042)
Commercial Honing Ohio Inc ....D 330 343-8896
Dover (G-8972)
Dixon Valve & Coupling Co Inc ....F 330 425-3000
Twinsburg (G-18926)
Eaton-Aeroquip Inc ....D 419 891-7775
Maumee (G-13258)
Encore Distributing Inc ....G 513 948-1242
Cincinnati (G-3702)
Fluid Line Products Inc ....C 440 946-9470
Willoughby (G-20491)
Freudenberg-Nok General Partnr ....C 419 427-5221
Findlay (G-9827)
Hydraulic Parts Store Inc ....E 330 364-6667
New Philadelphia (G-14902)
Kirtland Capital Partners LP ....E 216 593-0100
Beachwood (G-1276)
Parker-Hannifin Corporation ....B 440 943-5700
Wickliffe (G-20379)
Parker-Hannifin Corporation ....D 218 534-3148
Wickliffe (G-20380)
Parker-Hannifin Corporation ....B 937 456-5571
Eaton (G-9320)
SSP Fittings Corp ....D 330 425-4250
Twinsburg (G-19022)
State Metal Hose Inc ....G 614 527-4700
Hilliard (G-10982)
Superior Holding LLC ....G 216 651-9400
Cleveland (G-6265)
Superior Products LLC ....D 216 651-9400
Cleveland (G-6270)
Superior Products Llc ....D 216 651-9400
Cleveland (G-6269)
Swagelok ....G 440 349-5657
Solon (G-17389)
Swagelok Company ....E 440 349-5836
Solon (G-17393)
T D Group Holdings LLC ....G 216 706-2939
Cleveland (G-6289)
Thogus Products Company ....D 440 933-8850
Avon Lake (G-1053)
Transdigm Inc ....F 216 291-6025
Cleveland (G-6346)
Transdigm Inc ....G 216 706-2939
Cleveland (G-6347)
Winzeler Stamping Co ....D 419 485-3147
Montpelier (G-14458)
Zaytran Corporation ....E 440 324-2814
Elyria (G-9512)

FLUSH TANKS: Vitreous China

Dittmar Sales and Service ....G 740 653-7933
Lancaster (G-11709)

FLUXES

American Metal Chemical Corp ....E 330 725-4501
Medina (G-13369)
American Metal Chemical Corp ....G 440 244-1800
Lorain (G-12232)
Bluefoot Industrial LLC ....E 740 314-5299
Steubenville (G-17689)
Gasflux Company ....G 440 365-1941
Elyria (G-9424)

Kona Blackbird Inc ....F 440 285-3189
Chardon (G-3160)
Morgan Advanced Ceramics Inc ....C 440 232-8604
Bedford (G-1445)
SRC Worldwide Inc ....F 216 941-6115
Cleveland (G-6230)
Superior Flux & Mfg Co ....F 440 349-3000
Cleveland (G-6264)
Worthington Industries Inc ....F 937 556-6111
Mount Orab (G-14588)

FOAM RUBBER

Ohio Foam Corporation ....G 614 252-4877
Columbus (G-7421)
Ohio Foam Corporation ....G 419 563-0399
Bucyrus (G-2355)
Ohio Foam Corporation ....F 419 492-2151
New Washington (G-14963)
Precision Fab Products Inc ....G 937 526-5681
Versailles (G-19356)

FOAMS & RUBBER, WHOLESALE

Global Manufacturing Solutions ....F 937 236-8315
Dayton (G-8367)
Johnson Bros Rubber Co Inc ....D 419 853-4122
West Salem (G-20114)
Johnson Bros Rubber Co Inc ....E 419 752-4814
Greenwich (G-10531)
Tahoma Enterprises Inc ....D 330 745-9016
Barberton (G-1151)
Tahoma Rubber & Plastics Inc ....D 330 745-9016
Barberton (G-1152)

FOIL & LEAF: Metal

A J Oster Foils LLC ....D 330 823-1700
Alliance (G-486)
CCL Label Inc ....C 216 676-2703
Cleveland (G-4998)
CCL Label Inc ....E 440 878-7000
Brunswick (G-2215)
Quaker Mfg Corp ....C 330 332-4631
Salem (G-16922)
USA Foils Inc ....G 440 975-1145
Willoughby (G-20626)

FOIL: Copper

Gould Electronics Inc ....C 440 953-5000
Eastlake (G-9271)

FOIL: Laminated To Paper Or Other Materials

United Ultra Violet Inc ....F 614 875-8088
Grove City (G-10609)

FOLDERS: Manila

R D Thompson Paper Pdts Co Inc ....E 419 994-3614
Loudonville (G-12303)

FOLIAGE: Artificial & Preserved

Autograph Inc ....E 216 881-1911
Cleveland (G-4865)

FOOD CONTAMINATION TESTING OR SCREENING KITS

Nelson Professional Mktg Inc ....G 513 482-6150
Cincinnati (G-4144)

FOOD PRDTS, BREAKFAST: Cereal, Granola & Muesli

Olde Man Granola LLC ....F 419 819-9576
Findlay (G-9872)

FOOD PRDTS, BREAKFAST: Cereal, Oatmeal

Niese Farms ....G 419 347-1204
Crestline (G-7932)

FOOD PRDTS, BREAKFAST: Cereal, Rice: Cereal Breakfast Food

General Mills Inc ....E 513 563-8866
Cincinnati (G-3818)

PRODUCT

FOOD PRDTS, BREAKFAST: Cereal, Wheat Flakes

General Mills Inc ....F 419 269-3100
Toledo (G-18479)

FOOD PRDTS, CANNED OR FRESH PACK: Vegetable Juices

Garden of Flavor LLC ....G 216 702-7991
Cleveland (G-5396)

FOOD PRDTS, CANNED, NEC

Conagra Brands Inc ....B 419 445-8015
Archbold (G-669)

FOOD PRDTS, CANNED: Baby Food

Wornick Company ....B 800 860-4555
Blue Ash (G-1899)

FOOD PRDTS, CANNED: Barbecue Sauce

Buckeye Sauce Corporation ....F 216 751-0440
Cleveland (G-4944)
Dominion Liquid Tech LLC ....E 513 272-2824
Cincinnati (G-3663)
Guys Barbeque Inc ....G 330 872-7256
Newton Falls (G-15133)
Uncle Jesters Fine Foods LLC ....G 937 550-1025
Miamisburg (G-13873)

FOOD PRDTS, CANNED: Beans, Without Meat

Beckman & Gast Company ....F 419 678-4195
Saint Henry (G-16815)
Randall Foods Inc ....G 513 793-6525
Cincinnati (G-4329)

FOOD PRDTS, CANNED: Catsup

Portion Pac Inc ....B 513 398-0400
Mason (G-13074)

FOOD PRDTS, CANNED: Chili

D & A Rofael Enterprises Inc ....G 513 751-4929
Cincinnati (G-3628)
Whiteys Food Systems Inc ....G 330 659-4070
Richfield (G-16646)

FOOD PRDTS, CANNED: Chili Sauce, Tomato

Traditions Sauces LLC ....G 419 704-4506
Toledo (G-18755)

FOOD PRDTS, CANNED: Ethnic

Magic Wok Inc ....G 419 531-1818
Toledo (G-18569)
Troyer Cheese Inc ....E 330 893-2479
Millersburg (G-14274)

FOOD PRDTS, CANNED: Fruit Juices, Fresh

Bossa Nova Beverage Group Inc ......F 513 483-3300
Blue Ash (G-1753)
Country Pure Foods Inc ....C 330 848-6875
Akron (G-131)
Great Western Juice Company ....F 216 475-5770
Cleveland (G-5457)
Meiers Wine Cellars Inc ....E 513 891-2900
Cincinnati (G-4082)
Natural Country Farms Inc ....G 330 753-2293
Akron (G-311)
Ohio Pure Foods Inc ....D 330 753-2293
Akron (G-326)

FOOD PRDTS, CANNED: Fruit Pie Mixes & Fillings

Cincinnati Preserving Company ....F 513 771-2000
Cincinnati (G-3563)

FOOD PRDTS, CANNED: Fruits

Clovervale Farms Inc ....D 440 960-0146
Amherst (G-595)
Landec Corporation ....D 419 931-1095
Bowling Green (G-1995)

FOOD PRDTS, CANNED: Fruits

Campbell Soup Company ....D 419 592-1010
Napoleon (G-14674)
Fremont Company ....E 419 363-2924
Rockford (G-16691)
Fry Foods Inc ....E 419 448-0831
Tiffin (G-18221)
Gofast LLC ....G 419 562-8027
Bucyrus (G-2346)
Hermann Pickle Company ....E 330 527-2696
Garrettsville (G-10324)
J M Smucker Company ....G 330 497-0073
Canton (G-2743)
JES Foods/Celina Inc ....E 419 586-7446
Celina (G-3004)
Louis Trauth Dairy LLC ....B 859 431-7553
West Chester (G-20021)
Milos Whole World Gourmet LLC ......G 740 589-6456
Athens (G-877)
Pillsbury Company LLC ....F 740 286-2170
Wellston (G-19767)
Pillsbury Company LLC ....D 419 845-3751
Caledonia (G-2441)
Robert Rothschild Farm LLC ....E 937 653-7397
Urbana (G-19177)
Smucker International Inc ....G 330 682-3000
Orrville (G-15766)
The Fremont Kraut Company ....D 419 332-6481
Fremont (G-10187)
Two Grandmothers Gourmet Kit ....G 614 746-0888
Reynoldsburg (G-16611)

FOOD PRDTS, CANNED: Italian

Disalvos Deli & Italian Store ....G 937 298-5053
Dayton (G-8306)
Gia Russa ....F 330 743-6050
Youngstown (G-21100)

FOOD PRDTS, CANNED: Jams, Including Imitation

Yoders Cider Barn ....F 740 668-4961
Gambier (G-10319)

FOOD PRDTS, CANNED: Jams, Jellies & Preserves

Coopers Mill ....F 419 562-4215
Bucyrus (G-2336)
J M Smucker Company ....A 330 682-3000
Orrville (G-15742)

FOOD PRDTS, CANNED: Jellies, Edible, Including Imitation

Inter American Products Inc ....E 800 645-2233
Cincinnati (G-3927)

FOOD PRDTS, CANNED: Mexican, NEC

Elizabeths Closet ....G 513 646-5025
Maineville (G-12522)
Lifo Enterprises Inc ....G 513 225-8801
Loveland (G-12371)
San Marco Super Marketo ....G 419 469-8963
Toledo (G-18684)

FOOD PRDTS, CANNED: Puddings, Exc Meat

Clovervale Farms Inc ....D 440 960-0146
Amherst (G-595)

FOOD PRDTS, CANNED: Ravioli

Food Designs Inc ....F 216 651-9221
Cleveland (G-5366)

FOOD PRDTS, CANNED: Soups

More Than Gourmet Inc ....E 330 762-6652
Akron (G-302)

FOOD PRDTS, CANNED: Soups, Exc Seafood

Worthmore Food Products Co ....F 513 559-1473
Cincinnati (G-4605)

FOOD PRDTS, CANNED: Spaghetti & Other Pasta Sauce

Bellisio Foods Inc ....A 740 286-5505
Jackson (G-11311)
RC Industries Inc ....E 330 879-5486
Navarre (G-14726)

FOOD PRDTS, CANNED: Tomato Sauce.

Kraft Heinz Company ....A 330 837-8331
Massillon (G-13165)

FOOD PRDTS, CANNED: Tomatoes

Beckman & Gast Company ....F 419 678-4195
Saint Henry (G-16815)
Hirzel Canning Company ....E 419 287-3288
Pemberville (G-16028)
Hirzel Canning Company ....E 419 693-0531
Northwood (G-15482)
Hirzel Canning Company ....F 419 523-3225
Ottawa (G-15796)
Tip Top Canning Co ....E 937 667-3713
Tipp City (G-18305)

FOOD PRDTS, CANNED: Vegetables

Anderson Brothers Entps Inc ....E 440 269-3920
Willoughby (G-20432)
Fremont Company ....G 419 334-8995
Fremont (G-10146)
Fremont Company ....E 419 334-8995
Fremont (G-10147)

FOOD PRDTS, CANNED: Vegetables

Beckman & Gast Co Inc ....D 419 678-4195
Saint Henry (G-16814)
JES Foods Inc ....E 216 883-8987
Cleveland (G-5612)

FOOD PRDTS, CONFECTIONERY, WHOLESALE: Candy

Gorant Chocolatier LLC ....C 330 726-8821
Boardman (G-1921)
International Multifoods Corp ....G 330 682-3000
Orrville (G-15741)
Robert E McGrath Inc ....E 440 572-7747
Strongsville (G-17959)

FOOD PRDTS, CONFECTIONERY, WHOLESALE: Nuts, Salted/Roasted

Nuts Are Good Inc ....F 586 619-2400
Columbus (G-7406)
Ohio Hickory Harvest Brand Pro ....E 330 644-6266
Akron (G-324)
Tarrier Foods Corp ....E 614 876-8594
Columbus (G-7678)

FOOD PRDTS, CONFECTIONERY, WHOLESALE: Potato Chips

Jones Potato Chip Co ....E 419 529-9424
Mansfield (G-12629)

FOOD PRDTS, CONFECTIONERY, WHOLESALE: Snack Foods

J & J Snack Foods Corp ....G 440 248-2084
Solon (G-17319)
Mike-Sells Potato Chip Co ....E 937 228-9400
Dayton (G-8499)
Shearers Foods LLC ....A 330 834-4030
Massillon (G-13201)
Waffle House Inc ....E 937 746-6830
Franklin (G-10062)
Waffle House Inc ....F 513 539-8372
Monroe (G-14419)

FOOD PRDTS, CONFECTIONERY, WHOLESALE: Syrups, Fountain

Gehm & Sons Limited ....G 330 724-8423
Akron (G-202)

FOOD PRDTS, FISH & SEAFOOD, WHOLESALE: Seafood

Acme Steak & Seafood Inc.................F...... 330 270-8000
  Youngstown (G-21016)

FOOD PRDTS, FROZEN: Breakfasts, Packaged

Aunt Minnies Food Services Inc...........F...... 419 872-4396
  Toledo (G-18358)
Richelieu Foods Inc..........................F...... 740 335-4813
  Wshngtn CT Hs (G-20924)

FOOD PRDTS, FROZEN: Dinners, Packaged

Bellisio Foods Inc............................A...... 740 286-5505
  Jackson (G-11311)
Classic Recipe Chili Inc....................G...... 513 771-1441
  Cincinnati (G-3584)
Empress Chili..................................E...... 513 312-9589
  Blue Ash (G-1785)
Nestle Prepared Foods Company........A...... 440 248-3600
  Solon (G-17344)
Stouffer Corporation.........................G...... 440 349-5757
  Solon (G-17387)

FOOD PRDTS, FROZEN: Ethnic Foods, NEC

Sunrise Foods Inc............................E...... 614 276-2880
  Columbus (G-7667)

FOOD PRDTS, FROZEN: Fruit Juice, Concentrates

Beverages Holdings LLC....................E...... 513 483-3300
  Blue Ash (G-1750)
Country Pure Foods Inc.....................C...... 330 848-6875
  Akron (G-131)
Natural Country Farms Inc.................G...... 330 753-2293
  Akron (G-311)
Schwans Home Service Inc................E...... 419 222-9977
  Lima (G-12088)

FOOD PRDTS, FROZEN: Fruit Juices

Simply Unique Snacks LLC.................G...... 513 223-7736
  Cincinnati (G-4422)

FOOD PRDTS, FROZEN: Fruits

National Fruit Vegetable Tech..............E...... 740 400-4055
  Columbus (G-7383)

FOOD PRDTS, FROZEN: Fruits & Vegetables

Heinz Foreign Investment Co ....G...... 330 837-8331
  Massillon (G-13146)
HJ Heinz Company LP........................A...... 330 837-8331
  Massillon (G-13150)

FOOD PRDTS, FROZEN: Fruits, Juices & Vegetables

Creek Smoothies LLC.......................G...... 937 429-1519
  Beavercreek (G-1328)
Cwm Smoothie LLC..........................G...... 419 283-6387
  Toledo (G-18421)
Nestle Prepared Foods Company........D...... 440 349-5757
  Solon (G-17345)
NRG Smoothies LLC.........................G...... 972 800-1002
  Vienna (G-19372)
Smoothie Creations Inc......................G...... 817 313-8212
  Strongsville (G-17968)
Smoothie-Licious..............................G...... 513 742-2260
  Batavia (G-1223)
Tri-State Special Events Inc................G...... 513 221-2962
  Cincinnati (G-4523)
Tropical Ohio Smoothie Inc.................G...... 937 673-6218
  Waynesville (G-19736)

FOOD PRDTS, FROZEN: NEC

Athens Foods Inc.............................C...... 216 676-8500
  Cleveland (G-4853)
Chef 2 Chef Foods............................G...... 216 696-0080
  Cleveland (G-5024)
Clovervale Farms Inc.........................D...... 440 960-0146
  Amherst (G-595)
Frozen Specialties Inc........................C...... 419 445-9015
  Archbold (G-674)

FSI/Mfp Inc.....................................G...... 419 445-9015
  Archbold (G-675)
Kahiki Foods Inc...............................C...... 614 322-3180
  Gahanna (G-10215)
King Kold Inc...................................E...... 937 836-2731
  Englewood (G-9529)
Lancaster Colony Corporation.............E...... 614 224-7141
  Westerville (G-20166)
Nestle Prepared Foods Company........D...... 440 349-5757
  Solon (G-17345)
Rsw Distributors LLC.........................D...... 502 587-8877
  Blue Ash (G-1863)
Skyline Chili Inc...............................C...... 513 874-1188
  Fairfield (G-9719)
Worthington Foods Inc.......................D...... 740 453-5501
  Zanesville (G-21363)

FOOD PRDTS, FROZEN: Pizza

Frozen Specialties Inc........................E...... 419 445-9015
  Perrysburg (G-16100)
Hudson Village Pizza Inc....................G...... 330 968-4563
  Stow (G-17763)
Paleomd LLC...................................G...... 248 854-0031
  Bedford (G-1452)
Schwans Home Service Inc................E...... 937 335-4111
  Troy (G-18873)

FOOD PRDTS, FROZEN: Potato Prdts

Old World Foods Inc..........................G...... 216 341-5665
  Cleveland (G-5937)

FOOD PRDTS, FROZEN: Snack Items

Ascot Valley Foods LLC.....................G...... 330 376-9411
  Cuyahoga Falls (G-7970)
Brilista Foods Company Inc.................G...... 614 299-4132
  Columbus (G-6861)
Fry Foods Inc..................................E...... 419 448-0831
  Tiffin (G-18221)
Lake Erie Frozen Foods Mfg Co ....E...... 419 289-9204
  Ashland (G-749)

FOOD PRDTS, FROZEN: Vegetables, Exc Potato Prdts

Big Gus Onion Rings Inc....................E...... 216 883-9045
  Cleveland (G-4912)
Lake Erie Frozen Foods Mfg Co ....E...... 419 289-9204
  Ashland (G-749)
Nestle Prepared Foods Company........A...... 440 248-3600
  Solon (G-17344)

FOOD PRDTS, FRUITS & VEGETABLES, FRESH, WHOLESALE

Big Gus Onion Rings Inc....................E...... 216 883-9045
  Cleveland (G-4912)
C J Kraft Enterprises Inc....................E...... 740 653-9606
  Lancaster (G-11694)

FOOD PRDTS, FRUITS & VEGETABLES, FRESH, WHOLESALE: Vegetable

Barkett Fruit Co Inc..........................E...... 330 364-6645
  Dover (G-8967)

FOOD PRDTS, FRUITS & VEGETABLES, FRESH, WHOLESALE: Vegetable

Freshway Foods Inc ....C...... 937 498-4664
  Sidney (G-17190)

FOOD PRDTS, MEAT & MEAT PRDTS, WHOLESALE: Cured Or Smoked

Mama Mias Foods Inc.......................G...... 216 281-2188
  Cleveland (G-5737)
Troyer Cheese Inc............................E...... 330 893-2479
  Millersburg (G-14274)

FOOD PRDTS, MEAT & MEAT PRDTS, WHOLESALE: Fresh

A To Z Portion Ctrl Meats Inc...............E...... 419 358-2926
  Bluffton (G-1906)
Acme Steak & Seafood Inc.................F...... 330 270-8000
  Youngstown (G-21016)
Caven and Sons Meat Packing Co ....F...... 937 368-3841
  Conover (G-7822)

Empire Packing Company LP...............D...... 513 942-5400
  West Chester (G-20000)
Fink Meat Company Inc......................G...... 937 390-2750
  Springfield (G-17558)
John Krusinski...............................F...... 216 441-0100
  Cleveland (G-5619)
Links Country Meats.........................G...... 419 683-2195
  Crestline (G-7931)
Lori Holding Co...............................E...... 740 342-3230
  New Lexington (G-14848)
Marshallville Packing Co Inc................E...... 330 855-2871
  Marshallville (G-12918)

FOOD PRDTS, WHOL: Canned Goods, Fruit, Veg, Seafood/Meats

Acme Steak & Seafood Inc.................F...... 330 270-8000
  Youngstown (G-21016)

FOOD PRDTS, WHOLESALE: Baking Splys

Marble Works..................................G...... 216 496-7745
  Cleveland (G-5741)

FOOD PRDTS, WHOLESALE: Beverages, Exc Coffee & Tea

G & J Pepsi-Cola Bottlers Inc ....D...... 740 593-3366
  Athens (G-867)
Louis Trauth Dairy LLC......................B...... 859 431-7553
  West Chester (G-20021)

FOOD PRDTS, WHOLESALE: Chocolate

Walnut Creek Chocolate Company.......E...... 330 893-2995
  Walnut Creek (G-19471)

FOOD PRDTS, WHOLESALE: Coffee & Tea

Crooked River Coffee Co ....G...... 440 442-8330
  Cleveland (G-5142)

FOOD PRDTS, WHOLESALE: Coffee, Green Or Roasted

International Multifoods Corp...............G...... 330 682-3000
  Orrville (G-15741)

FOOD PRDTS, WHOLESALE: Corn

Hanby Farms Inc..............................E...... 740 763-3554
  Nashport (G-14705)
Pioneer Hi-Bred Intl Inc.....................E...... 419 748-8051
  Grand Rapids (G-10443)

FOOD PRDTS, WHOLESALE: Dried or Canned Foods

James C Robinson............................G...... 513 969-7482
  Cincinnati (G-3941)
Tarrier Foods Corp............................E...... 614 876-8594
  Columbus (G-7678)

FOOD PRDTS, WHOLESALE: Flour

Ardent Mills LLC...............................F...... 419 994-4181
  Loudonville (G-12296)
Cleveland Syrup Corp........................G...... 330 963-1900
  Twinsburg (G-18916)

FOOD PRDTS, WHOLESALE: Grain Elevators

Ardent Mills LLC...............................E...... 614 274-2545
  Columbus (G-6770)
Fort Recovery Equity Inc....................E...... 419 375-4119
  Fort Recovery (G-9950)
Harvest Land Co-Op Inc.....................G...... 937 884-5526
  Verona (G-19338)
Mullet Enterprises Inc........................G...... 330 852-4681
  Sugarcreek (G-18029)
Mullet Enterprises Inc........................G...... 330 897-3911
  Bakersville (G-1063)
Pettisville Grain Co...........................E...... 419 446-2547
  Pettisville (G-16182)
Sunrise Cooperative Inc.....................F...... 419 628-4705
  Minster (G-14362)

FOOD PRDTS, WHOLESALE: Grains

Archer-Daniels-Midland Company........G...... 419 705-3292
  Toledo (G-18353)
Cooper Farms Inc.............................F...... 419 375-4619
  Fort Recovery (G-9948)

PRODUCT

Cooper Hatchery Inc ....C 419 594-3325
Oakwood (G-15615)
Countyline Co-Op Inc ....F 419 287-3241
Pemberville (G-16026)
Geauga Feed and Grain Supply ....G 440 564-5000
Newbury (G-15092)
Hansen-Mueller Co ....E 419 729-5535
Toledo (G-18496)
Legacy Farmers Cooperative ....F 419 423-2611
Findlay (G-9851)
Mid-Wood Inc ....F 419 257-3331
North Baltimore (G-15195)
Premier Feeds LLC ....G 937 584-2411
Sabina (G-16776)

FOOD PRDTS, WHOLESALE: Health

Lifestyle Nutraceuticals Ltd ....F 513 376-7218
Cincinnati (G-4022)
Muscle Feast LLC ....F 740 877-8808
Hebron (G-10878)

FOOD PRDTS, WHOLESALE: Salt, Edible

Morton Salt Inc ....C 330 925-3015
Rittman (G-16680)

FOOD PRDTS, WHOLESALE: Specialty

Troyer Cheese Inc ....E 330 893-2479
Millersburg (G-14274)

FOOD PRDTS, WHOLESALE: Starch

G & J Pepsi-Cola Bottlers Inc ....E 740 774-2148
Chillicothe (G-3239)

FOOD PRDTS, WHOLESALE: Syrups, Exc Fountain Use

Richards Maple Products Inc ....G 440 286-4160
Chardon (G-3176)
Stumps Converting Inc ....F 419 492-2542
New Washington (G-14965)

FOOD PRDTS, WHOLESALE: Water, Distilled

Rambasek Realty Inc ....F 937 228-1189
Dayton (G-8616)

FOOD PRDTS, WHOLESALE: Water, Mineral Or Spring, Bottled

Distillata Company ....D 216 771-2900
Cleveland (G-5197)
Liqui-Box Corporation ....D 614 888-9280
Columbus (G-7300)

FOOD PRDTS: Animal & marine fats & oils

Archer-Daniels-Midland Company ....E 419 435-6633
Fostoria (G-9966)
Cargill Incorporated ....D 937 498-4555
Sidney (G-17170)
Darling International Inc ....F 216 651-9300
Cleveland (G-5167)
Fiske Brothers Refining Co ....D 419 691-2491
Toledo (G-18471)

FOOD PRDTS: Baking Powder, Soda, Yeast & Leavenings

Coalescence LLC ....E 614 861-3639
Columbus (G-6941)

FOOD PRDTS: Cake Fillings, Exc Fruit

Pfizer Inc ....C 937 746-3603
Franklin (G-10044)

FOOD PRDTS: Cereals

General Mills Inc ....D 513 771-8200
Cincinnati (G-3817)
Kellogg Company ....E 513 772-8980
Cincinnati (G-3979)
Kellogg Company ....B 614 879-9659
West Jefferson (G-20080)
Kellogg Company ....B 330 306-1500
Warren (G-19565)
Kellogg Company ....B 513 792-2700
Cincinnati (G-3980)

Kellogg Company ....A 614 855-3437
Delaware (G-8864)
Kellogg Company ....C 740 453-5501
Zanesville (G-21325)
Seven Hills Foods Ltd ....G 513 518-3704
Cincinnati (G-4410)
Treehouse Private Brands Inc ....B 740 654-8880
Lancaster (G-11758)
Treehouse Private Brands Inc ....G 740 654-8880
Lancaster (G-11759)

FOOD PRDTS: Chicken, Processed, Cooked

Roots Poultry Inc ....F 419 332-0041
Fremont (G-10180)

FOOD PRDTS: Chicken, Processed, Fresh

Gerber Farm Division Inc ....G 800 362-7381
Kidron (G-11590)
Nutrifresh Eggs ....G 567 224-7676
Willard (G-20398)

FOOD PRDTS: Chicken, Processed, NEC

Advancepierre Foods Inc ....B 513 874-8741
Blue Ash (G-1734)

FOOD PRDTS: Chocolate Bars, Solid

Fannie May Cnfctons Brands Inc .....A 330 494-0833
North Canton (G-15230)

FOOD PRDTS: Cocoa, Powdered

Benjamin P Forbes Company ....F 440 838-4400
Broadview Heights (G-2104)

FOOD PRDTS: Coffee

Altraserv LLC ....G 614 889-2500
Dublin (G-9041)
Essential Wonders Inc ....G 888 525-5282
Cuyahoga Falls (G-7992)
Folger Coffee Company ....F 800 937-9745
Orrville (G-15737)
Generations Coffee Company LLC ....E 440 546-0901
Brecksville (G-2051)
Good Beans Coffee Roasters LLC ....G 513 310-9516
Milford (G-14145)
Harbor Perk LLC ....G 440 964-9277
Ashtabula (G-812)
Inter American Products Inc ....E 800 645-2233
Cincinnati (G-3927)
Little Ghost Roasters ....G 614 325-2065
Columbus (G-7301)
Mc Concepts Llc ....G 330 933-6402
Canton (G-2774)
Raptis Coffee Inc ....G 330 399-7011
Warren (G-19591)
Stonefruit Coffee Co ....G 330 509-2787
Canfield (G-2577)

FOOD PRDTS: Coffee Roasting, Exc Wholesale Grocers

Boston Stoker Inc ....G 937 890-6401
Vandalia (G-19284)
Crooked River Coffee Co ....G 440 442-8330
Cleveland (G-5142)
Euclid Coffee Co Inc ....G 216 481-3330
Cleveland (G-5299)
Millstone Coffee Inc ....D 513 983-1100
Cincinnati (G-4108)
Pmd Enterprises Inc ....F 440 546-0901
Brecksville (G-2070)
Wallingford Coffee Mills Inc ....D 513 771-3131
Cincinnati (G-4578)

FOOD PRDTS: Corn Chips & Other Corn-Based Snacks

Basic Grain Products Inc ....E 614 408-3091
Coldwater (G-6552)
Wyandot Inc ....B 740 383-4031
Marion (G-12916)

FOOD PRDTS: Dips, Exc Cheese & Sour Cream Based

Lakeview Farms LLC ....C 419 695-9925
Delphos (G-8913)

Oasis Mediterranean Cuisine ....E 419 269-1516
Toledo (G-18612)

FOOD PRDTS: Dough, Pizza, Prepared

Crestar Crusts Inc ....B 740 335-4813
Wshngtn CT Hs (G-20905)
International Multifoods Corp ....G 330 682-3000
Orrville (G-15741)

FOOD PRDTS: Doughs, Frozen Or Refrig From Purchased Flour

Mid American Ventures Inc ....F 216 524-0974
Cleveland (G-5804)

FOOD PRDTS: Dressings, Salad, Raw & Cooked Exc Dry Mixes

Consumer Guild Foods Inc ....E 419 726-3406
Toledo (G-18411)
Lancaster Colony Corporation ....E 614 224-7141
Westerville (G-20166)
Lancaster Colony Corporation ....F 614 792-9774
Westerville (G-20167)
Lancaster Colony Corporation ....D 614 224-7141
Westerville (G-20168)
Tmarzetti Company ....C 614 268-3722
Westerville (G-20192)
Tmarzetti Company ....C 614 846-2232
Westerville (G-20193)

FOOD PRDTS: Dried & Dehydrated Fruits, Vegetables & Soup Mix

Dismat Corporation ....G 419 531-8963
Toledo (G-18439)
Hirzel Canning Company ....E 419 693-0531
Northwood (G-15482)

FOOD PRDTS: Edible fats & oils

Cincinnati Biorefining Corp ....G 513 482-8800
Cincinnati (G-3543)
Cincinnati Renewable Fuels LLC ......D 513 482-8800
Cincinnati (G-3565)
Garden of Delight LLC ....G 513 300-7205
Cincinnati (G-3797)
Kerry Flavor Systems Us LLC ....D 513 771-4682
Cincinnati (G-3985)
Wileys Finest LLC ....G 740 622-1072
Coshocton (G-7916)

FOOD PRDTS: Eggs, Processed

Ballas Egg Products Corp ....D 614 453-0386
Zanesville (G-21274)
BE Products Inc ....D 740 453-0386
Zanesville (G-21277)
Fort Recovery Equity Inc ....E 419 375-4119
Fort Recovery (G-9950)
Fort Recovery Equity Exchange ....E 937 338-8901
Rossburg (G-16736)
Hemmelgarn & Sons Inc ....D 419 678-2351
Coldwater (G-6563)
Nature Pure LLC ....F 937 358-2364
West Mansfield (G-20102)
Ohio Fresh Eggs LLC ....G 740 893-7200
Croton (G-7955)

FOOD PRDTS: Eggs, Processed, Frozen

Cal-Maine Foods Inc ....E 937 968-4874
Union City (G-19069)

FOOD PRDTS: Emulsifiers

Chemtura Corporation ....E 440 324-6060
Elyria (G-9393)
Dik Jaxon Products Co ....G 937 890-7350
Dayton (G-8305)
Feinkost Ingredient Co U S A ....G 330 948-3006
Lodi (G-12161)
Staceys Kitchen Limited ....G 614 921-1290
Hilliard (G-10980)

FOOD PRDTS: Flour

Ardent Mills LLC ....E 614 274-2545
Columbus (G-6770)
Star of West Milling Company ....E 330 673-2941
Kent (G-11532)

(G-0000) Company's Geographic Section entry number

FOOD PRDTS: Flour & Other Grain Mill Products

Bunge North America Foundation........G...... 419 483-5340
  Bellevue (G-1547)
Cargill Incorporated...........................E...... 937 236-1971
  Dayton (G-8210)
Countyline Co-Op Inc........................F...... 419 287-3241
  Pemberville (G-16026)
Farmers Commission Company...........E...... 419 294-2371
  Upper Sandusky (G-19122)
Hansen-Mueller Co............................E...... 419 729-5535
  Toledo (G-18496)
I Dream of Cakes...............................G...... 937 533-6024
  Eaton (G-9310)
Indie-Peasant Enterprises...................G...... 740 590-8240
  Athens (G-872)
Legacy Farmers Cooperative...............F...... 419 423-2611
  Findlay (G-9851)
Mennel Milling Company.....................G...... 419 436-5130
  Fostoria (G-9985)
Mondelez Global LLC.........................D...... 419 691-5200
  Toledo (G-18591)
Mullet Enterprises Inc.......................G...... 330 852-4681
  Sugarcreek (G-18029)
Mullet Enterprises Inc.......................G...... 330 897-3911
  Bakersville (G-1063)
Pettisville Grain Co...........................E...... 419 446-2547
  Pettisville (G-16182)
Pillsbury Company LLC.......................F...... 740 286-2170
  Wellston (G-19767)
Pillsbury Company LLC.......................D...... 419 845-3751
  Caledonia (G-2441)
Pioneer Hi-Bred Intl Inc......................E...... 419 748-8051
  Grand Rapids (G-10443)
Premier Feeds LLC.............................G...... 937 584-2411
  Sabina (G-16776)
Sunrise Cooperative Inc.....................F...... 419 628-4705
  Minster (G-14362)

FOOD PRDTS: Flour Mixes & Doughs

Abitec Corporation.............................E...... 614 429-6464
  Columbus (G-6678)
Alamarra Inc.....................................G...... 800 336-3007
  Mentor (G-13516)
Athens Foods Inc...............................C...... 216 676-8500
  Cleveland (G-4853)
J M Smucker Company.........................E...... 419 470-7914
  Toledo (G-18532)
Rich Products Corporation..................C...... 614 771-1117
  Hilliard (G-10976)

FOOD PRDTS: Flour, Blended From Purchased Flour

Fleetchem LLC..................................F...... 513 539-1111
  Monroe (G-14401)

FOOD PRDTS: Fruit Juices

Elations Company..............................F...... 513 483-3300
  Blue Ash (G-1782)
Griffin Cider Works LLC.......................G...... 440 785-7418
  Westlake (G-20273)

FOOD PRDTS: Fruits, Dehydrated Or Dried

Raw Real and Wonderful LLC...............F...... 614 529-8606
  Hilliard (G-10975)

FOOD PRDTS: Fruits, Dried Or Dehydrated, Exc Freeze-Dried

Kanan Enterprises Inc.......................C...... 440 248-8484
  Solon (G-17325)
Kanan Enterprises Inc.......................F...... 440 349-0719
  Solon (G-17326)

FOOD PRDTS: Gelatin Dessert Preparations

Clovervale Farms Inc.........................D...... 440 960-0146
  Amherst (G-595)

FOOD PRDTS: Granola & Energy Bars, Nonchocolate

Good Nutrition LLC............................F...... 216 534-6617
  Oakwood Village (G-15624)

FOOD PRDTS: Honey

Deer Creek Honey Farms Ltd...............G...... 740 852-0899
  London (G-12208)

FOOD PRDTS: Horseradish, Exc Sauce

Wellys Horseradish............................G...... 419 334-3134
  Fremont (G-10194)

FOOD PRDTS: Ice, Blocks

Donahues Hilltop Ice Company............F...... 740 432-3348
  Cambridge (G-2455)
Luc Ice Inc.......................................G...... 419 734-2201
  Port Clinton (G-16404)

FOOD PRDTS: Ice, Cubes

Home City Ice Company.......................C...... 513 574-1800
  Cincinnati (G-3892)
Home City Ice Company.......................E...... 513 851-4040
  Cincinnati (G-3893)
Home City Ice Company.......................E...... 216 429-0535
  Cleveland (G-5519)
Zygo Inc...G...... 513 281-0888
  Cincinnati (G-4621)

FOOD PRDTS: Macaroni, Noodles, Spaghetti, Pasta, Etc

Chieffos Frozen Foods Inc...................G...... 330 652-1222
  Niles (G-15146)
Lariccias Italian Foods......................F...... 330 729-0222
  Youngstown (G-21132)
YAR Corporation................................G...... 330 652-1222
  Niles (G-15190)

FOOD PRDTS: Mayonnaise & Dressings, Exc Tomato Based

Food Specialties Co...........................G...... 513 761-1242
  Cincinnati (G-3766)

FOOD PRDTS: Mixes, Bread & Bread-Type Roll

Jaz Foods Inc....................................G...... 800 456-7115
  Canton (G-2746)

FOOD PRDTS: Mixes, Bread & Roll From Purchased Flour

Aspen Mulling Company.......................G...... 970 925-5027
  Bedford (G-1400)
B O K Inc..C...... 937 322-9588
  Springfield (G-17520)

FOOD PRDTS: Mixes, Cake, From Purchased Flour

J M Smucker Company.........................E...... 440 323-5100
  Elyria (G-9442)
Procter & Gamble Mfg Co....................F...... 513 983-1100
  Cincinnati (G-4290)

FOOD PRDTS: Mixes, Flour

1-2-3 Gluten Free Inc.........................G...... 216 378-9233
  Chagrin Falls (G-3046)
Fowlers Milling Co Inc........................G...... 440 286-2024
  Chardon (G-3154)
General Mills Inc...............................G...... 513 770-0558
  Mason (G-13026)
General Mills Inc...............................E...... 513 563-8866
  Cincinnati (G-3818)

FOOD PRDTS: Mixes, Sauces, Dry

Whitmore Productions Inc....................F...... 216 752-3960
  Warrensville Heights (G-19637)

FOOD PRDTS: Mixes, Seasonings, Dry

Dismat Corporation.............................G...... 419 531-8963
  Toledo (G-18439)

FOOD PRDTS: Mustard, Prepared

Woeber Mustard Mfg Co......................C...... 937 323-6281
  Springfield (G-17680)

FOOD PRDTS: Noodles, Uncooked, Packaged W/Other Ingredients

Amish Wedding Foods Inc....................E...... 330 674-9199
  Millersburg (G-14193)
Ganeden Biotech Inc..........................E...... 440 229-5200
  Mayfield Heights (G-13315)

FOOD PRDTS: Nuts & Seeds

Anthony-Thomas Candy Company..........C...... 614 274-8405
  Columbus (G-6759)
Back Development LLC.........................G...... 937 671-7896
  Cleveland (G-4887)
Nuts Are Good Inc..............................F...... 586 619-2400
  Columbus (G-7406)
Simply Unique Snacks LLC...................G...... 513 223-7736
  Cincinnati (G-4422)
Southside Wolfies..............................G...... 419 422-5450
  Findlay (G-9893)
Thorfood LLC.....................................E...... 419 626-4375
  Sandusky (G-17014)

FOOD PRDTS: Oils & Fats, Animal

Wileys Finest LLC..............................G...... 740 622-1072
  Coshocton (G-7916)

FOOD PRDTS: Olive Oil

Lms LLC..G...... 513 981-1412
  Cincinnati (G-4031)
Olivamed Corporation.........................G...... 937 401-0821
  Franklin (G-10042)
Olive Serafino Oils Balsamics.............G...... 440 773-0200
  Cleveland (G-5939)
Olive Smuckers Oil.............................G...... 513 646-7103
  Cincinnati (G-4184)
Olive Tap..G...... 330 721-6500
  Medina (G-13453)
Spicy Olive LLC..................................F...... 513 847-4397
  West Chester (G-19947)
Spicy Olive LLC..................................G...... 513 376-9061
  Cincinnati (G-4442)

FOOD PRDTS: Oriental Noodles

Best Bite Grill LLC.............................G...... 419 344-7462
  Versailles (G-19341)

FOOD PRDTS: Pasta, Rice/Potatoes, Uncooked, Pkgd

Gsi of Ohio LLC.................................D...... 216 431-3344
  Cleveland (G-5462)

FOOD PRDTS: Pasta, Uncooked, Packaged With Other Ingredients

Food Designs Inc...............................F...... 216 651-9221
  Cleveland (G-5366)
Rossi Pasta Factory Inc......................F...... 740 376-2065
  Marietta (G-12826)

FOOD PRDTS: Peanut Butter

J M Smucker Company.........................D...... 513 482-8000
  Cincinnati (G-3936)
Krema Products Inc............................G...... 614 889-4824
  Dublin (G-9097)
Procter & Gamble Mfg Co....................F...... 513 983-1100
  Cincinnati (G-4290)

FOOD PRDTS: Pickles, Vinegar

Kaiser Foods Inc...............................E...... 513 621-2053
  Cincinnati (G-3969)
Kaiser Foods Inc...............................F...... 513 241-6833
  Cincinnati (G-3970)

FOOD PRDTS: Pizza Doughs From Purchased Flour

B & D Commissary LLC........................E...... 740 743-3890
  Mount Perry (G-14590)

FOOD PRDTS: Popcorn, Unpopped

Great Lakes Popcorn Company.............G...... 419 732-3080
  Port Clinton (G-16401)
Wildcat Creek Farms Inc.....................F...... 419 263-2549
  Payne (G-16019)

P
R
O
D
U
C
T

FOOD PRDTS: Pork Rinds

Rudolph Foods Company Inc ....C 909 383-7463
Lima (G-12087)

Savory Foods Inc ....D 740 354-6655
Portsmouth (G-16451)

White Feather Foods Inc ....F 419 738-8975
Wapakoneta (G-19513)

FOOD PRDTS: Potato & Corn Chips & Similar Prdts

ABC Refreshments LLC ....F 866 382-5575
Euclid (G-9563)

Basic Grain Products Inc ....D 419 678-2304
Coldwater (G-6553)

Birds Eye Foods Inc ....E 330 854-0818
Canal Fulton (G-2499)

Dure Foods Us LLC ....F 614 409-9030
Columbus (G-7040)

Frito-Lay North America Inc ....C 513 759-1000
West Chester (G-19869)

Frito-Lay North America Inc ....E 419 595-2338
New Riegel (G-14946)

Frito-Lay North America Inc ....C 513 229-3000
Mason (G-13023)

Frito-Lay North America Inc ....E 972 334-7000
Wooster (G-20774)

Kroger Co ....D 614 462-2000
Columbus (G-7270)

Pats Delicious LLC ....G 614 441-7047
Columbus (G-7466)

Robert E McGrath Inc ....E 440 572-7747
Strongsville (G-17959)

Shearers Foods LLC ....A 330 834-4030
Massillon (G-13201)

Snack Alliance Inc ....E 330 767-3426
Massillon (G-13202)

Waffle House Inc ....E 937 746-6830
Franklin (G-10062)

Waffle House Inc ....F 513 539-8372
Monroe (G-14419)

FOOD PRDTS: Potato Chips & Other Potato-Based Snacks

Ballreich Bros Inc ....E 419 447-1814
Tiffin (G-18209)

Conns Potato Chip Co Inc ....E 740 452-4615
Zanesville (G-21294)

Daniel Meenan ....G 330 756-2818
Beach City (G-1247)

Frito-Lay North America Inc ....D 330 477-7009
Canton (G-2708)

Gold N Krisp Chips & Pretzels ....G 330 832-8395
Massillon (G-13140)

Grippo Potato Chip Co Inc ....D 513 923-1900
Cincinnati (G-3854)

Herr Foods Incorporated ....E 740 773-8282
Chillicothe (G-3243)

Jones Potato Chip Co ....E 419 529-9424
Mansfield (G-12629)

Mike-Sells Potato Chip Co ....E 937 228-9400
Dayton (G-8499)

Mumfords Potato Chips & Deli ....G 937 653-3491
Urbana (G-19170)

FOOD PRDTS: Potatoes, Dried

Green Gourmet Foods LLC ....E 740 400-4212
Baltimore (G-1082)

FOOD PRDTS: Poultry, Processed, Frozen

Martin-Brower Company LLC ....B 513 773-2301
West Chester (G-19898)

Zartic LLC ....D 513 874-8741
West Chester (G-20072)

FOOD PRDTS: Preparations

Agrana Fruit Us Inc ....C 937 693-3821
Anna (G-620)

Alacwin Nutrition Corporation ....G 614 961-6479
Columbus (G-6713)

Allenbaugh Foods LLC ....G 216 952-3984
Lakewood (G-11655)

American Foods Dist Co LLC ....G 614 218-4049
Blacklick (G-1687)

American Sweet Bean Co LLC ....G 888 995-0007
Tiffin (G-18203)

Amir International Foods Inc ....G 614 332-1742
Grove City (G-10543)

Andys Mdterranean Fd Pdts LLC ....G 513 281-9791
Cincinnati (G-3404)

Artic Diamond ....G 513 742-4921
Cincinnati (G-3416)

Artistic Foods Incorporated ....G 330 401-1313
Lodi (G-12157)

Atlantic Investment ....G 440 567-5054
Lorain (G-12233)

Ballreich Bros Inc ....E 419 447-1814
Tiffin (G-18209)

Basic Grain Products Inc ....D 419 678-2304
Coldwater (G-6553)

Beatty Foods LLC ....G 330 327-2442
Cincinnati (G-2619)

Big Gus Onion Rings Inc ....E 216 883-9045
Cleveland (G-4912)

Bread Kneads Inc ....G 419 422-3863
Findlay (G-9801)

Chez Rama Restaurant ....G 614 237-9315
Columbus (G-6926)

Cincinnatti Premier Candy LLC ....E 513 253-0079
Cincinnati (G-3571)

Conagra Brands Inc ....C 513 229-0305
Mason (G-13006)

Conagra Brands Inc ....F 740 465-3912
Morral (G-14539)

Conagra Brands Inc ....A 937 440-2800
Troy (G-18811)

Conagra Brands Inc ....B 419 445-8015
Archbold (G-669)

Country Parlour Ice Cream Co ....F 440 237-4040
Cleveland (G-5134)

Cuyahoga Vending Co Inc ....E 440 353-9595
North Ridgeville (G-15368)

Daniel Meenan ....G 330 756-2818
Beach City (G-1247)

Dole Fresh Vegetables Inc ....F 937 525-4300
Springfield (G-17546)

Firehouse Foods ....G 614 592-8115
Columbus (G-7088)

Food 4 Your Soul ....F 330 402-4073
Youngstown (G-21088)

Fremont Company ....E 419 363-2924
Rockford (G-16691)

Fresh Table LLC ....G 513 381-3774
Cincinnati (G-3783)

Freshway Foods Inc ....G 937 498-4664
Sidney (G-17190)

Frito-Lay North America Inc ....C 972 334-7000
Wooster (G-20774)

Frito-Lay North America Inc ....D 330 477-7009
Canton (G-2708)

Frog Ranch Foods Ltd ....F 740 767-3705
Glouster (G-10404)

General Mills Inc ....D 513 771-8200
Cincinnati (G-3817)

Gold Star Chili Inc ....E 513 631-1990
Cincinnati (G-3839)

Graffiti Foods Limited ....F 614 759-1921
Columbus (G-7126)

Grippo Potato Chip Co Inc ....D 513 923-1900
Cincinnati (G-3854)

Heather Creek Foods LLC ....E 330 792-8654
North Jackson (G-15291)

Hiland Group Incorporated ....D 330 499-8404
Canton (G-2728)

Homestat Farm Ltd ....G 614 718-3060
Dublin (G-9085)

Honeybaked Ham Company ....E 513 583-9700
Cincinnati (G-3895)

Infant Food Project Inc ....G 614 239-5763
Columbus (G-7186)

Ingredient Innovations Intl Co ....G 330 262-4440
Wooster (G-20786)

Injoy Foods LLC ....G 614 798-2033
Dublin (G-9089)

J M Smucker Company ....E 419 470-7914
Toledo (G-18532)

J M Smucker Company ....E 440 323-5100
Elyria (G-9442)

John Krusinski ....F 216 441-0100
Cleveland (G-5619)

Kerry Flavor Systems Us LLC ....D 513 771-4682
Cincinnati (G-3985)

Koch Foods of Cincinnati LLC ....G 513 874-3500
Fairfield (G-9673)

Kraft Heinz Company ....A 330 837-8331
Massillon (G-13165)

Kroger Co ....D 614 462-2000
Columbus (G-7270)

Main Street Gourmet LLC ....C 330 929-0000
Cuyahoga Falls (G-8022)

Mane Inc ....D 513 248-9876
Lebanon (G-11815)

Miami Valley Pizza Hut Inc ....E 419 586-5900
Celina (G-3009)

Mid American Ventures Inc ....F 216 524-0974
Cleveland (G-5804)

Nestle Brands Company ....F 440 264-6600
Solon (G-17343)

Oceanside Foods ....G 440 554-7810
Avon Lake (G-1042)

Ohio Hickory Harvest Brand Pro ....E 330 644-6266
Akron (G-324)

Ohio Processors Inc ....E 740 852-9243
London (G-12218)

Peer Pantry LLC ....G 216 236-4087
Willowick (G-20649)

Pita Wrap LLC ....G 330 886-8091
Boardman (G-1922)

Purushealth LLC ....F 800 601-0580
Shaker Heights (G-17093)

Rich Products Corporation ....C 614 771-1117
Hilliard (G-10976)

Ritchie Foods LLC ....G 440 354-7474
Fairport Harbor (G-9772)

Roare-Q LLC ....G 419 801-4040
Bowling Green (G-2014)

Rudolph Foods Company Inc ....C 909 383-7463
Lima (G-12087)

Sanese Services Inc ....E 330 494-5900
Warren (G-19597)

Sensoryffcts Powdr Systems Inc ....D 419 783-5518
Defiance (G-8810)

Sharpys Food Systems LLC ....G 440 232-9601
Oakwood Village (G-15627)

Special t Foods LLC ....G 330 793-8697
Youngstown (G-21209)

Special t Foods LLC ....G 330 533-9493
Canfield (G-2574)

Sunrise Foods Inc ....E 614 276-2880
Columbus (G-7667)

Tarrier Foods Corp ....G 614 876-8594
Columbus (G-7678)

Tom Pallas Industries Inc ....G 216 622-0230
Cleveland (G-6331)

Toms Country Place Inc ....G 440 934-4553
Avon (G-1016)

Twenty Second Cntury Foods LLC ....G 419 866-6343
Maumee (G-13305)

Unger Kosher Bakery Inc ....E 216 321-7176
Cleveland Heights (G-6502)

Wake Robin Fermented Foods LLC ....G 216 961-9944
Cleveland (G-6442)

Wal-Bon of Ohio Inc ....D 740 423-8178
Belpre (G-1596)

Wannemacher Enterprises Inc ....F 419 771-1101
Upper Sandusky (G-19145)

Western Reserve Foods LLC ....G 330 770-0885
Chagrin Falls (G-3073)

White Feather Foods Inc ....F 419 738-8975
Wapakoneta (G-19513)

Woeber Mustard Mfg Co ....C 937 323-6281
Springfield (G-17680)

FOOD PRDTS: Prepared Sauces, Exc Tomato Based

Hinkle Fine Foods Inc ....G 937 836-3665
Englewood (G-9523)

Niidex Enterprise LLC ....G 614 653-8526
Columbus (G-7393)

Portion Pac Inc ....B 513 398-0400
Mason (G-13074)

Ribs King Inc ....G 513 791-1942
Cincinnati (G-4341)

FOOD PRDTS: Rice, Milled

Cargill Incorporated ....E 513 625-2863
Goshen (G-10413)

FOOD PRDTS: Salad Oils, Refined Vegetable, Exc Corn

Inter American Products Inc ....E 800 645-2233
Cincinnati (G-3927)

FOOD PRDTS: Salads

Barkett Fruit Co Inc ....E 330 364-6645
Dover (G-8967)
Bob Evans Farms Inc ....B 614 491-2225
New Albany (G-14750)
Dno Inc ....D 614 231-3601
Columbus (G-7034)
Frank L Harter & Son Inc ....G 513 574-1330
Cincinnati (G-3778)
Herold Salads Inc ....E 216 991-7500
Cleveland (G-5505)
Sandridge Food Corporation ......G 330 725-2348
Medina (G-13474)
Sandridge Food Corporation ......C 330 725-8883
Medina (G-13475)

FOOD PRDTS: Sandwiches

Advancperre Foods Holdings Inc ....G 800 969-2747
Blue Ash (G-1735)
White Castle System Inc ....E 513 563-2290
Cincinnati (G-4591)

FOOD PRDTS: Sausage, Poultry

Freak-N-Fries Inc ....G 440 453-1877
Lagrange (G-11625)

FOOD PRDTS: Seasonings & Spices

Aspen Mulling Company ....G 970 925-5027
Bedford (G-1400)
Midwest Spray Drying Company ...G 419 294-4221
Upper Sandusky (G-19133)
Savor Seasonings LLC ....G 513 732-2333
Batavia (G-1222)

FOOD PRDTS: Shortening & Solid Edible Fats

Procter & Gamble Company ....C 513 634-9110
West Chester (G-19923)
Procter & Gamble Company ....C 410 527-5735
Grove City (G-10586)
Procter & Gamble Company ....B 513 983-1100
Cincinnati (G-4286)
Procter & Gamble Mfg Co ....F 513 983-1100
Cincinnati (G-4290)

FOOD PRDTS: Soy Sauce

SOO Nyeo Won Inc ....G 562 569-8390
Lorain (G-12279)

FOOD PRDTS: Soybean Protein Concentrates & Isolates

Bunge North America Foundation ....G 740 426-6332
Jeffersonville (G-11378)

FOOD PRDTS: Spices, Including Ground

Frutarom USA Inc ....C 513 870-4900
West Chester (G-20005)
Frutarom USA Inc ....F 513 870-4900
West Chester (G-20006)
Frutarom USA Inc ....G 513 870-4900
West Chester (G-20007)
Inter American Products Inc ....E 800 645-2233
Cincinnati (G-3927)

FOOD PRDTS: Starch, Corn

Cargill Incorporated ....E 937 236-1971
Dayton (G-8210)

FOOD PRDTS: Sugar

Domino Foods Inc ....D 216 432-3222
Cleveland (G-5205)

FOOD PRDTS: Sugar, Beet

Michigan Sugar Company ....F 419 332-9931
Fremont (G-10170)
Michigan Sugar Company ....G 419 423-1666
Findlay (G-9860)

FOOD PRDTS: Syrup, Maple

Goodell Farms ....G 330 274-2161
Mantua (G-12711)

Sticky Petes Maple Syrup ....G 740 662-2726
Athens (G-886)
Sugarbush Creek Farm ....G 440 636-5371
Middlefield (G-13994)

FOOD PRDTS: Syrups

J M Smucker Company ....A 330 682-3000
Orrville (G-15742)
National Foods Packaging Inc ......F 216 415-7102
Cleveland (G-5856)
Simple Products LLC ....G 330 674-2448
Millersburg (G-14263)
Smucker International Inc ....G 330 682-3000
Orrville (G-15766)

FOOD PRDTS: Tea

H & K Products Inc ....G 419 659-5110
Columbus Grove (G-7795)
Wallingford Coffee Mills Inc ....D 513 771-3131
Cincinnati (G-4578)

FOOD PRDTS: Tortillas

Indie-Peasant Enterprises ....G 740 590-8240
Athens (G-872)
La Perla Inc ....F 419 534-2074
Toledo (G-18552)
Perez Foods LLC ....G 419 264-0303
Holgate (G-11039)
Tortilla ....G 614 557-3367
Reynoldsburg (G-16609)
Tortilleria El Maizal LLP ....G 330 209-9344
Massillon (G-13206)
Tortilleria La Bamba ....G 216 515-1600
Cleveland (G-6340)
Tortilleria La Bamba LLC ....G 216 469-0410
Cleveland (G-6341)

FOOD PRDTS: Turkey, Processed, Canned

Brinkman Turkey Farms Inc ....F 419 365-5127
Findlay (G-9802)

FOOD PRDTS: Turkey, Processed, NEC

Cooper Hatchery Inc ....C 419 594-3325
Oakwood (G-15615)
V H Cooper & Co Inc ....B 419 678-4853
Saint Henry (G-16823)

FOOD PRDTS: Turkey, Slaughtered & Dressed

Whitewater Processing Co ....D 513 367-4133
Harrison (G-10812)

FOOD PRDTS: Variety Meats, Poultry

Medina Foods Inc ....E 330 725-1390
Litchfield (G-12138)

FOOD PRODUCTS MACHINERY

Abj Equipfix ....E 419 684-5236
Castalia (G-2972)
Acreo Inc ....G 513 734-3327
Amelia (G-565)
Anderson International Corp ....D 216 641-1112
Stow (G-17730)
Ashco ....G 330 385-2400
East Liverpool (G-9203)
Avure Technologies Inc ....D 513 433-2500
Middletown (G-14022)
Biro Manufacturing Company ....D 419 798-4451
Lakeside Marblehead (G-11647)
Christy Machine Company ....F 419 332-6451
Fremont (G-10137)
Cleveland Gas Systems LLC ....G 216 391-7780
Streetsboro (G-17844)
Cleveland Range LLC ....C 216 481-4900
Cleveland (G-5075)
Crescent Metal Products Inc ....C 440 350-1100
Mentor (G-13555)
E S Industries Inc ....E 419 643-2625
Lima (G-12008)
G F Frank and Sons Inc ....F 513 870-9075
West Chester (G-19871)
Harry C Lobalzo & Sons Inc ....E 330 666-6758
Akron (G-216)
Hawthorne-Seving Inc ....G 419 643-5531
Cridersville (G-7945)

Hobart Corporation ....E 937 332-3000
Troy (G-18840)
Hobart Corporation ....G 937 332-2797
Piqua (G-16277)
Hobart International Holdings ....G 937 332-3000
Troy (G-18842)
Innovative Controls Corp ....D 419 691-6684
Toledo (G-18524)
ITW Food Equipment Group LLC ...G 937 332-3000
Troy (G-18847)
ITW Food Equipment Group LLC ...A 937 332-2396
Troy (G-18848)
JE Grote Company Inc ....D 614 868-8414
Columbus (G-7229)
John Bean Technologies Corp ....B 419 627-4349
Sandusky (G-16975)
Lima Sheet Metal Machine & Mfg ....E 419 229-1161
Lima (G-12045)
Maverick Corp Partners LLC ....G 330 669-2631
Smithville (G-17241)
Maverick Innvtive Slutions LLC .....G 419 281-7944
Ashland (G-751)
Meyer Company ....C 216 587-3400
Cleveland (G-5793)
N Wasserstrom & Sons Inc ....C 614 228-5550
Columbus (G-7377)
National Oilwell Varco LP ....E 937 454-3200
Dayton (G-8520)
Nemco Food Equipment Ltd ....D 419 542-7751
Hicksville (G-10904)
Omar Associates LLC ....G 419 426-0610
Attica (G-894)
Premier Industries Inc ....E 513 271-2550
Cincinnati (G-4266)
R and J Corporation ....E 440 871-6009
Westlake (G-20299)
Richard B Linneman ....E 513 922-5537
Cincinnati (G-4342)
Royalton Food Service Eqp Co ......E 440 237-0806
North Royalton (G-15448)
RS Industries Inc ....E 216 524-2998
Brooklyn Heights (G-2146)
Sarka Bros Machining Inc ....G 419 532-2393
Kalida (G-11417)
Sidney Manufacturing Company ....E 937 492-4154
Sidney (G-17227)
Tomlinson Industries Co ....E 216 332-1595
Cleveland (G-6332)
Wolf Machine Company ....E 513 791-5194
Blue Ash (G-1897)

FOOD STORES: Convenience, Chain

Speedway LLC ....A 937 864-3000
Enon (G-9550)
United Dairy Farmers Inc ....C 513 396-8700
Cincinnati (G-4538)

FOOD STORES: Convenience, Independent

Whitacre Enterprises Inc ....F 740 934-2331
Graysville (G-10470)

FOOD STORES: Delicatessen

Baltic Country Meats ....G 330 897-7025
Baltic (G-1065)
Bread Kneads Inc ....G 419 422-3863
Findlay (G-9801)
Fragapane Bakeries Inc ....G 440 779-6050
North Olmsted (G-15335)
Mumfords Potato Chips & Deli ....G 937 653-3491
Urbana (G-19170)
Zygo Inc ....G 513 281-0888
Cincinnati (G-4621)

FOOD STORES: Grocery, Independent

Brinkman Turkey Farms Inc ....F 419 365-5127
Findlay (G-9802)
Geyers Markets Inc ....D 419 468-9477
Galion (G-10271)
Gibson Bros Inc ....E 440 774-2401
Oberlin (G-15641)
Lariccias Italian Foods ....F 330 729-0222
Youngstown (G-21132)
Troyers Trail Bologna Inc ....E 330 893-2414
Dundee (G-9183)
Unger Kosher Bakery Inc ....E 216 321-7176
Cleveland Heights (G-6502)

P
R
O
D
U
C
T

FOOD STORES: Supermarkets

Riesbeck Food Markets Inc ....C 740 695-3401
Saint Clairsville *(G-16806)*

FOOD STORES: Supermarkets, Chain

Heinens Inc ....D 330 562-5297
Aurora *(G-924)*

Kroger Co ....C 740 671-5164
Bellaire *(G-1499)*

Kroger Co ....D 614 462-2000
Columbus *(G-7270)*

Kroger Co ....C 513 671-2790
Cincinnati *(G-4003)*

Kroger Co ....C 740 335-4030
Wshngtn CT Hs *(G-20915)*

Kroger Co ....C 740 264-5057
Steubenville *(G-17702)*

Kroger Co ....D 513 683-4001
Maineville *(G-12526)*

Kroger Co ....D 740 374-2523
Marietta *(G-12798)*

Kroger Co ....C 513 742-9500
Cincinnati *(G-4004)*

Kroger Co ....D 419 423-2065
Findlay *(G-9848)*

Kroger Co ....C 937 277-0950
Dayton *(G-8447)*

Kroger Co ....C 614 263-1766
Columbus *(G-7271)*

Kroger Co ....C 937 743-5900
Springboro *(G-17488)*

Kroger Co ....C 614 575-3742
Columbus *(G-7272)*

FOOTWEAR, WHOLESALE: Athletic

NTS Enterprises Ltd ....G 513 531-1166
Cincinnati *(G-4167)*

FOOTWEAR, WHOLESALE: Boots

Hudson Leather Ltd ....G 419 485-8531
Pioneer *(G-16234)*

FOOTWEAR, WHOLESALE: Shoes

Georgia Boot LLC ....D 740 753-1951
Nelsonville *(G-14734)*

FOOTWEAR: Custom Made

Cobblers Corner LLC ....F 330 482-4005
Columbiana *(G-6610)*

FOOTWEAR: Cut Stock

Hudson Leather Ltd ....G 419 485-8531
Pioneer *(G-16234)*

Remington Products Co ....C 330 335-1571
Wadsworth *(G-19437)*

FORGINGS

Akron Gear & Engineering Inc ....E 330 773-6608
Akron *(G-45)*

Alta Mira Corporation ....D 330 648-2461
Spencer *(G-17455)*

Brooker Bros Forging Co Inc ....F 419 668-2535
Norwalk *(G-15528)*

Buckeye Gear Co ....F 216 292-7998
Chagrin Falls *(G-3078)*

Bula Forge & Machine Inc ....E 216 252-7600
Cleveland *(G-4947)*

Cailin Dev Ltd Lblty Co ....F 216 408-6261
Cleveland *(G-4962)*

Canton Drop Forge Inc ....B 330 477-4511
Canton *(G-2638)*

Carbo Forge Inc ....E 419 334-9788
Fremont *(G-10134)*

Cleveland Hdwr & Forging Co ....E 216 641-5200
Cleveland *(G-5064)*

Cleveland Hollow Boring Inc ....G 216 883-1926
Cleveland *(G-5065)*

Colfor Manufacturing Inc ....B 330 863-0404
Malvern *(G-12541)*

Colfor Manufacturing Inc ....C 330 863-0404
Minerva *(G-14319)*

Cordier Group Holdings Inc ....G 330 477-4511
Canton *(G-2669)*

Dayton Forging Heat Treating ....D 937 253-4126
Dayton *(G-8273)*

Edgerton Forge Inc ....D 419 298-2333
Edgerton *(G-9327)*

Edward W Daniel LLC ....E 440 647-1960
Wellington *(G-19742)*

Engineered Metal Products ....G 740 446-9211
Gallipolis *(G-10296)*

For Call Inc ....B 330 863-0404
Malvern *(G-12544)*

Forge Products Corporation ....D 216 231-2600
Cleveland *(G-5370)*

Forging Eqp Solutions Inc ....G 330 239-2222
Medina *(G-13411)*

Gam ....G 330 427-6470
Leetonia *(G-11860)*

Geneva Gear & Machine Inc ....F 937 866-0318
Dayton *(G-8363)*

GKN Sinter Metals LLC ....C 740 441-3203
Gallipolis *(G-10298)*

Ken Forging Inc ....E 440 993-8091
Jefferson *(G-11364)*

King-Indiana Forge Inc ....F 330 425-4250
Twinsburg *(G-18965)*

Lange Precision Inc ....F 513 530-9500
Blue Ash *(G-1824)*

Lextech Industries Ltd ....G 216 883-7900
Cleveland *(G-5694)*

Martin Sprocket & Gear Inc ....D 419 485-5515
Montpelier *(G-14448)*

Metal Forming & Coining Corp ....D 419 897-9530
Maumee *(G-13281)*

Mid-West Forge Corporation ....C 216 481-3030
Cleveland *(G-5806)*

Omnisource Corporation ....E 419 784-5669
Defiance *(G-8808)*

Park-Ohio Holdings Corp ....F 440 947-2000
Cleveland *(G-5966)*

Park-Ohio Industries Inc ....C 440 947-2000
Cleveland *(G-5967)*

Penn Machine Company ....E 814 288-1547
Twinsburg *(G-18996)*

Powers and Sons LLC ....D 419 737-2373
Pioneer *(G-16240)*

Presrite Corporation ....B 216 441-5990
Cleveland *(G-6043)*

Presrite Corporation ....C 440 576-0015
Jefferson *(G-11369)*

Queen City Forging Company ....F 513 321-2003
Cincinnati *(G-4316)*

Rose Metal Industries LLC ....E 216 881-3355
Cleveland *(G-6132)*

Rotek Incorporated ....C 330 562-4000
Aurora *(G-945)*

Schaefer Equipment Inc ....D 330 372-4006
Warren *(G-19598)*

Solmet Technologies Inc ....E 330 915-4160
Canton *(G-2852)*

Stahl Gear & Machine Co ....E 216 431-2820
Cleveland *(G-6231)*

T & W Forge LLC ....E 216 881-8600
Alliance *(G-543)*

TRM Manufacturing Inc ....E 330 769-2600
Cuyahoga Falls *(G-8057)*

US Tsubaki Power Transm LLC ....C 419 626-4560
Sandusky *(G-17019)*

Wallace Forge Company ....D 330 488-1203
Canton *(G-2900)*

Wendell August Gift Sp & Forge .....F 330 893-3713
Berlin *(G-1653)*

Wright Tool Company ....C 330 848-0600
Barberton *(G-1157)*

Wyman-Gordon Company ....E 216 341-0085
Cleveland *(G-6485)*

FORGINGS: Aircraft, Ferrous

Sifco Industries Inc ....B 216 881-8600
Cleveland *(G-6201)*

FORGINGS: Aluminum

Alcoa Inc ....A 216 641-3600
Newburgh Heights *(G-15067)*

Arconic Inc ....A 216 641-3600
Newburgh Heights *(G-15069)*

Gateway Industries ....G 330 633-3700
Akron *(G-199)*

Showa Aluminum Corp America ......F 740 869-3333
Mount Sterling *(G-14603)*

FORGINGS: Armor Plate, Iron Or Steel

Shot-Force Pro LLC ....G 740 753-3927
Nelsonville *(G-14739)*

FORGINGS: Automotive & Internal Combustion Engine

Cliffs High Performance ....G 740 397-2921
Mount Vernon *(G-14616)*

Ohio Metal Technologies Inc ....D 740 928-8288
Hebron *(G-10879)*

Performance Motorsports ....G 513 931-9999
Cincinnati *(G-4226)*

FORGINGS: Construction Or Mining Eqpt, Ferrous

Dayton Superior Corporation ....C 937 866-0711
Miamisburg *(G-13798)*

Dependable Gear Corp ....G 440 942-4969
Eastlake *(G-9264)*

Rudd Equipment Company Inc ....E 513 321-7833
Cincinnati *(G-4365)*

FORGINGS: Gear & Chain

Hand Screw Machine Co ....G 216 475-0220
Stow *(G-17761)*

FORGINGS: Iron & Steel

Forge Products Corporation ....D 216 231-2600
Cleveland *(G-5370)*

Pilgrim-Harp Co ....G 440 249-4185
Avon *(G-1003)*

S&V Industries Inc ....G 330 666-1986
Medina *(G-13472)*

T J Tool Works Inc ....E 440 439-1388
Bedford *(G-1463)*

FORGINGS: Machinery, Ferrous

Wodin Inc ....E 440 439-4222
Cleveland *(G-6474)*

FORGINGS: Metal , Ornamental, Ferrous

Alliance Forging Group LLC ....F 330 680-4861
Alliance *(G-494)*

FORGINGS: Nonferrous

Canton Drop Forge Inc ....B 330 477-4511
Canton *(G-2638)*

Cleveland Hdwr & Forging Co ....E 216 641-5200
Cleveland *(G-5064)*

Colfor Manufacturing Inc ....B 330 863-0404
Malvern *(G-12541)*

Edward W Daniel LLC ....E 440 647-1960
Wellington *(G-19742)*

Forge Products Corporation ....D 216 231-2600
Cleveland *(G-5370)*

Powers and Sons LLC ....D 419 737-2373
Pioneer *(G-16240)*

Rotek Incorporated ....C 330 562-4000
Aurora *(G-945)*

Turbine Eng Cmpnents Tech Corp ...E 216 692-6173
Cleveland *(G-6374)*

Wallace Forge Company ....D 330 488-1203
Canton *(G-2900)*

Wendell August Gift Sp & Forge .....F 330 893-3713
Berlin *(G-1653)*

Wodin Inc ....E 440 439-4222
Cleveland *(G-6474)*

FORGINGS: Plumbing Fixture, Nonferrous

Guarantee Specialties Inc ....D 216 451-9744
Strongsville *(G-17923)*

Mansfield Plumbing Pdts LLC ....A 419 938-5211
Perrysville *(G-16173)*

FORMS: Concrete, Sheet Metal

Adjustable Kicker LLC ....G 740 362-9170
Delaware *(G-8817)*

C L W Inc ....G 740 374-8443
Marietta *(G-12769)*

C M L Concrete Construction ....G 330 758-8314
Youngstown *(G-21041)*

Carroll Distrg & Cnstr Sup Inc ....G 513 422-3327
Middletown *(G-14026)*

Carroll Distrg & Cnstr Sup Inc ....G...... 614 564-9799
Columbus (G-6912)
CMA Supply Company Inc ....F...... 513 942-6663
West Chester (G-19992)
Creative Concepts ....G...... 216 513-6463
Medina (G-13398)
Efco Corp..E...... 614 876-1226
Columbus (G-7048)
Feather Lite Innovations Inc ....E...... 937 743-9008
Springboro (G-17480)

FOUNDRIES: Aluminum

Acuity Brands Lighting Inc ....B...... 740 349-4343
Newark (G-14979)
Admiral Foundry Inc ....E...... 330 336-7651
Wadsworth (G-19388)
Advanced Metals Group LLC ....C...... 937 492-4134
Sidney (G-17166)
Air Craft Wheels LLC ....G...... 440 937-7903
Ravenna (G-16513)
Akron Foundry Co ....C...... 330 745-3101
Akron (G-44)
Akron Foundry Co ....E...... 330 745-3101
Barberton (G-1095)
Aluminum Line Products Company ....D...... 440 835-8880
Westlake (G-20249)
Aztec Manufacturing Inc ....E...... 330 783-9747
Youngstown (G-21030)
C M M S - Re LLC ....F...... 513 489-5111
Blue Ash (G-1760)
Cast Metals Technology Inc ....C...... 740 363-1690
Delaware (G-8829)
Castek Aluminum Inc ....E...... 440 365-2333
Elyria (G-9391)
Consoldted Precision Pdts Corp ....C...... 909 595-2252
Cleveland (G-5117)
Dd Foundry Inc ....C...... 216 362-4100
Brookpark (G-2156)
Durivage Pattern & Mfg Co ....E...... 419 836-8655
Williston (G-20420)
Euclid Products Co Inc ....C...... 440 942-7310
Willoughby (G-20482)
Francis Manufacturing Company ....C...... 937 526-4551
Russia (G-16763)
General Die Casters Inc ....E...... 330 678-2528
Twinsburg (G-18942)
Globe Motors Inc ....C...... 937 228-3171
Dayton (G-8369)
Kovatch Castings Inc ....C...... 330 896-9944
Uniontown (G-19089)
Lite Metals Company ....E...... 330 296-6110
Ravenna (G-16539)
Lodi Foundry Co Inc ....E...... 330 948-1516
Lodi (G-12164)
Mansfield Brass & Alum Corp ....D...... 419 492-2154
New Washington (G-14961)
Metal-Mation Inc ....F...... 216 651-1083
Cleveland (G-5789)
Miller Casting Inc ....F...... 330 482-2923
Columbiana (G-6624)
Model Pattern & Foundry Co ....E...... 513 542-2322
Cincinnati (G-4113)
Multi Cast LLC ....E...... 419 335-0010
Wauseon (G-19690)
Myron D Budd ....G...... 330 682-5866
Orrville (G-15749)
New Mansfield Brass & Alum Co ....E...... 419 492-2166
New Washington (G-14962)
Palmer Engineered Products Inc ....G...... 937 322-1481
Springfield (G-17622)
Reliable Castings Corporation ....D...... 937 497-5217
Sidney (G-17215)
Ross Aluminum Castings LLC ....C...... 937 492-4134
Sidney (G-17218)
Rotocast Technologies Inc ....E...... 330 798-9091
Akron (G-379)
Seilkop Industries Inc ....F...... 513 679-5680
Cincinnati (G-4399)
Stripmatic Products Inc ....E...... 216 241-7143
Cleveland (G-6255)
Thompson Aluminum Casting Co ....D...... 216 206-2781
Cleveland (G-6322)
Tooling Technology LLC ....D...... 937 295-3672
Fort Loramie (G-9943)
Yoder Industries Inc ....E...... 937 890-4322
Dayton (G-8767)
Yoder Industries Inc ....C...... 937 278-5769
Dayton (G-8766)

FOUNDRIES: Brass, Bronze & Copper

Anchor Bronze and Metals Inc ....E...... 440 549-5653
Cleveland (G-4802)
Brost Foundry Company ....F...... 419 522-1133
Mansfield (G-12570)
Calmego Specialized Pdts LLC ....F...... 937 669-5620
Greenville (G-10491)
D Picking & Co ....G...... 419 562-5016
Bucyrus (G-2337)
Hadronics Inc ....D...... 513 321-9350
Cincinnati (G-3861)
Kovatch Castings Inc ....C...... 330 896-9944
Uniontown (G-19089)
Model Pattern & Foundry Co ....E...... 513 542-2322
Cincinnati (G-4113)
National Bronze and Metals ....E...... 440 277-1226
Lorain (G-12261)
Randall Bearings Inc ....D...... 419 223-1075
Lima (G-12080)
Randall Bearings Inc ....F...... 419 678-2486
Coldwater (G-6570)
Semco ....D...... 800 848-5764
Marion (G-12899)
Snair Co ....F...... 614 873-7020
Plain City (G-16360)
Stripmatic Products Inc ....E...... 216 241-7143
Cleveland (G-6255)
Whip Guide Co ....F...... 440 543-5151
Chagrin Falls (G-3133)

FOUNDRIES: Gray & Ductile Iron

Akron Gear & Engineering Inc ....E...... 330 773-6608
Akron (G-45)
Arcelormittal Tubular ....A...... 419 347-2424
Shelby (G-17132)
Arconic Inc ....A...... 216 641-3600
Newburgh Heights (G-15069)
Castco Inc ....E...... 440 365-2333
Elyria (G-9390)
Castings Usa Inc ....G...... 330 339-3611
New Philadelphia (G-14890)
D Picking & Co ....G...... 419 562-5016
Bucyrus (G-2337)
Dd Foundry Inc ....C...... 216 362-4100
Brookpark (G-2156)
Foote Foundry LLC ....D...... 740 694-1595
Fredericktown (G-10102)
Ford Motor Company ....A...... 216 676-3989
Brookpark (G-2160)
Hamilton Brass & Alum Castings ....E...... 513 867-0400
Hamilton (G-10701)
Hobart Corporation ....E...... 937 332-3000
Troy (G-18840)
Hobart Corporation ....C...... 937 332-2797
Piqua (G-16277)
Korff Holdings LLC ....C...... 330 332-1566
Salem (G-16905)
Oak Hill Foundry & Mch Works ....E...... 740 682-7746
Oak Hill (G-15603)
OS Kelly Corporation ....E...... 937 322-4921
Springfield (G-17620)
Osco Industries Inc ....B...... 740 354-3183
Portsmouth (G-16446)
Piqua Champion Foundry Inc ....E...... 937 773-3375
Piqua (G-16300)
Rotek Incorporated ....C...... 330 562-4000
Aurora (G-945)
St Marys Foundry Inc ....E...... 419 394-3346
Saint Marys (G-16856)
Tiffin Foundry & Machine Inc ....E...... 419 447-3991
Tiffin (G-18247)
Wallace Forge Company ....D...... 330 488-1203
Canton (G-2900)
Wellsville Foundry Inc ....C...... 330 532-2995
Wellsville (G-19776)
Whemco-Ohio Foundry Inc ....C...... 419 222-2111
Lima (G-12112)

FOUNDRIES: Iron

Ej Usa Inc ....C...... 216 692-3001
Cleveland (G-5261)
Ellwood Engineered Castings Co ....C...... 330 568-3000
Hubbard (G-11130)
General Aluminum Mfg Company ....C...... 419 739-9300
Wapakoneta (G-19487)
General Motors LLC ....A...... 419 782-2244
Defiance (G-8790)
Kenton Iron Products Inc ....E...... 419 674-4178
Kenton (G-11554)

Osco Industries Inc...........................C...... 740 286-5004
Jackson (G-11323)
Pioneer City Casting Company ....E...... 740 423-7533
Belpre (G-1593)
Sancast Inc ....E...... 740 622-8660
Coshocton (G-7908)
St Marys Foundry Inc ....C...... 419 394-3346
Saint Marys (G-16856)
T & B Foundry Company ....D...... 216 391-4200
Cleveland (G-6285)
Tiffin Foundry & Machine Inc ....E...... 419 447-3991
Tiffin (G-18247)
Tooling Technology LLC ....D...... 937 295-3672
Fort Loramie (G-9943)
Whemco-Ohio Foundry Inc ....C...... 419 222-2111
Lima (G-12112)
Yellow Creek Casting Company ....C...... 330 532-4608
Wellsville (G-19777)

FOUNDRIES: Nonferrous

Air Craft Wheels LLC ....G...... 440 937-7903
Ravenna (G-16513)
Alcon Industries Inc............................D...... 216 961-1100
Cleveland (G-4745)
Apex Aluminum Die Cast Co Inc ....C...... 937 773-0432
Piqua (G-16248)
Brost Foundry Company ....E...... 216 641-1131
Cleveland (G-4936)
Bunting Bearings LLC ....E...... 419 522-3323
Mansfield (G-12572)
Catania Medallic Specialty ....E...... 440 933-9595
Avon Lake (G-1026)
Concorde Castings Inc ....C...... 440 953-0053
Willoughby (G-20461)
Curtiss-Wright Flow Ctrl Corp ....C...... 216 267-3200
Cleveland (G-5148)
Dd Foundry Inc ....C...... 216 362-4100
Brookpark (G-2156)
Dmk Industries Inc ....F...... 513 727-4549
Middletown (G-14038)
Durivage Pattern & Mfg Co ....E...... 419 836-8655
Williston (G-20420)
Ellwood Engineered Castings Co ....C...... 330 568-3000
Hubbard (G-11130)
Francis Manufacturing Company ....C...... 937 526-4551
Russia (G-16763)
General Aluminum Mfg Company ....B...... 440 947-2000
Cleveland (G-5410)
General Aluminum Mfg Company ....E...... 330 297-1020
Ravenna (G-16531)
General Aluminum Mfg Company ....B...... 440 593-6225
Conneaut (G-7805)
General Die Casters Inc ....E...... 330 678-2528
Twinsburg (G-18942)
General Motors LLC ....A...... 419 782-2244
Defiance (G-8790)
Globe Motors Inc ....C...... 937 228-3171
Dayton (G-8369)
Harbor Castings Inc ....E...... 330 499-7178
Cuyahoga Falls (G-8007)
I A B F Inc ....G...... 614 279-4498
Columbus (G-7177)
Kovatch Castings Inc ....C...... 330 896-9944
Uniontown (G-19089)
Lite Metals Company ....E...... 330 296-6110
Ravenna (G-16539)
Materion Brush Inc ....A...... 419 862-2745
Elmore (G-9365)
Morris Bean & Company ....C...... 937 767-7301
Yellow Springs (G-20996)
Nelson Aluminum Foundry Inc ....G...... 440 543-1941
Chagrin Falls (G-3107)
New London Foundry Inc ....F...... 419 929-2073
New London (G-14863)
Nova Machine Products Inc ....C...... 216 267-3200
Middleburg Heights (G-13907)
PCC Airfoils LLC ....C...... 330 868-6441
Minerva (G-14337)
PCC Airfoils LLC ....E...... 216 831-3590
Cleveland (G-5984)
Piqua Emery Cutter & Fndry Co ....D...... 937 773-4134
Piqua (G-16303)
Ray Lewis & Son Incorporated ....E...... 937 644-4015
Marysville (G-12965)
Reliable Castings Corporation ....D...... 937 497-5217
Sidney (G-17215)
Ross Aluminum Castings LLC ....C...... 937 492-4134
Sidney (G-17218)
Sawbrook Steel Castings Co ....D...... 513 554-1700
Cincinnati (G-4381)

PRODUCT

Seaport Mold & Casting Company ....F 419 243-1422
Toledo (G-18688)

Seilkop Industries Inc ....F 513 679-5680
Cincinnati (G-4399)

St Marys Foundry Inc ....C 419 394-3346
Saint Marys (G-16856)

T & B Foundry Company ....D 216 391-4200
Cleveland (G-6285)

Technology House The Ltd ....D 440 248-3025
Solon (G-17400)

Telcon LLC ....D 330 562-5566
Streetsboro (G-17881)

Yoder Industries Inc ....C 937 278-5769
Dayton (G-8766)

FOUNDRIES: Steel

Anointed Design & Technologies ....G 330 826-1493
Massillon (G-13108)

B-Tek Scales LLC ....E 330 471-8900
Canton (G-2613)

Brost Foundry Company ....E 216 641-1131
Cleveland (G-4936)

Castings Usa Inc ....G 330 339-3611
New Philadelphia (G-14890)

Columbus Steel Castings Co ....A 614 444-2121
Columbus (G-6967)

Dd Foundry Inc ....C 216 362-4100
Brookpark (G-2156)

Durivage Pattern & Mfg Co ....D 419 836-8655
Williston (G-20420)

Evertz Technology Service Usa ....E 513 422-8400
Middletown (G-14040)

Harbor Castings Inc ....E 330 499-7178
Cuyahoga Falls (G-8007)

Island Castings Inc ....D 231 733-1053
North Canton (G-15243)

Jmac Inc ....F 614 436-2418
Columbus (G-7235)

Korff Holdings LLC ....C 330 332-1566
Salem (G-16905)

Kovatch Castings Inc ....C 330 896-9944
Uniontown (G-19089)

Lakeway Mfg Inc ....E 419 433-3030
Huron (G-11232)

Medina Blanking Inc ....C 330 558-2300
Valley City (G-19217)

Munroe Incorporated ....G 330 755-7216
Struthers (G-17995)

PC Campana Inc ....E 440 246-6500
Lorain (G-12266)

Steel Service Plus Ltd ....F 216 391-9000
Cleveland (G-6244)

Tecumseh Redevelopment Inc ....G 330 659-9100
Richfield (G-16643)

Tiffin Foundry & Machine Inc ....E 419 447-3991
Tiffin (G-18247)

Whemco-Ohio Foundry Inc ....C 419 222-2111
Lima (G-12112)

Worthington Industries Inc ....C 513 539-9291
Monroe (G-14420)

Worthngton Stelpac Systems LLC ....C 614 438-3205
Columbus (G-7778)

FOUNDRIES: Steel Investment

Alcon Industries Inc ....D 216 961-1100
Cleveland (G-4745)

Brost Foundry Company ....E 216 641-1131
Cleveland (G-4936)

Castalloy Inc ....D 216 961-7990
Cleveland (G-4992)

Consoldted Precision Pdts Corp ....C 909 595-2252
Cleveland (G-5117)

Harbor Castings Inc ....E 231 733-1053
Cuyahoga Falls (G-8006)

Harbor Castings Inc ....E 330 499-7178
Cuyahoga Falls (G-8007)

Island Castings Inc ....D 231 733-1053
North Canton (G-15243)

Mercury Machine Co ....D 440 349-3222
Solon (G-17335)

Mold Masters Intl Inc ....C 440 953-0220
Mentor (G-13659)

PCC Airfoils LLC ....C 330 868-6441
Minerva (G-14337)

PCC Airfoils LLC ....C 440 255-9770
Mentor (G-13683)

Steel Ceilings Inc ....E 740 967-1063
Johnstown (G-11406)

Summit Resources Group Inc ....G 330 653-3992
Hudson (G-11203)

Xapc Co ....D 216 362-4100
Cleveland (G-6486)

FOUNDRY MACHINERY & EQPT

Equipment Manufacturers Intl ....E 216 651-6700
Cleveland (G-5291)

Fremont Flask Co ....F 419 332-2231
Fremont (G-10149)

Gokoh Corporation ....F 937 339-4977
Troy (G-18832)

Herschal Products Inc ....G 330 659-2165
Richfield (G-16627)

Mark Carpenter Industries Inc ....C 419 294-4568
Fremont (G-10169)

Mosbro Machine and Tool Inc ....G 330 467-0913
Northfield (G-15468)

Palmer Klein Inc ....G 937 323-6339
Springfield (G-17623)

Palmer Mfg and Supply Inc ....E 937 323-6339
Springfield (G-17624)

FOUNDRY MATERIALS: Insulsleeves

Exochem Corporation ....E 800 807-7464
Lorain (G-12247)

FOUNDRY SAND MINING

C E D Process Minerals Inc ....C 330 666-5500
Akron (G-106)

Fairmount Water Solutions LLC ....G 440 285-3132
Newbury (G-15090)

FOUNTAINS, METAL, EXC DRINKING

Fountain Specialists Inc ....G 513 831-5717
Milford (G-14142)

Manufacturing Futures Inc ....G 216 903-7993
Shaker Heights (G-17092)

FOUNTAINS: Concrete

Fountain Specialists Inc ....G 513 831-5717
Milford (G-14142)

FOUNTAINS: Plaster Of Paris

Custom Fountains Inc ....F 513 398-1447
Mason (G-13007)

FRACTIONATION PRDTS OF CRUDE PETROLEUM, HYDROCARBONS, NEC

Arizona Chemical Company LLC ....C 330 343-7701
Dover (G-8964)

Enrevo Pyro LLC ....G 203 517-5002
Brookfield (G-2124)

FRANCHISES, SELLING OR LICENSING

Instantwhip Foods Inc ....F 614 488-2536
Columbus (G-7195)

Pei Liquidation Company ....E 615 781-5020
Macedonia (G-12471)

R&D Marketing Group Inc ....G 216 398-9100
Brooklyn Heights (G-2145)

Skyline Chili Inc ....C 513 874-1188
Fairfield (G-9719)

Stanley Steemer Intl Inc ....C 614 764-2007
Dublin (G-9149)

FREEZERS: Household

Liebrecht Manufacturing ....G 419 596-3501
Continental (G-7827)

Whirlpool Corporation ....B 419 547-7711
Clyde (G-6548)

FREIGHT FORWARDING ARRANGEMENTS

Tgs International Inc ....E 330 893-2428
Millersburg (G-14268)

FREIGHT TRANSPORTATION ARRANGEMENTS

Ds Express Carriers Inc ....G 419 433-6200
Norwalk (G-15534)

Eae Logistics Company LLC ....G 440 417-4788
Madison (G-12505)

Kendall & Sons Company ....G 937 222-6996
Dayton (G-8436)

Millwood Inc ....E 330 393-4400
Vienna (G-19370)

Millwood Natural LLC ....D 330 393-4400
Vienna (G-19371)

SDS National LLC ....G 330 759-8066
Youngstown (G-21198)

Taupe Holdings Co ....G 614 330-4600
Dublin (G-9153)

VIP-Supply Chain Solutions LLC ....G 513 454-2020
West Chester (G-19970)

FREON

Reclamation Technologies Inc ....D 419 867-8990
Bowling Green (G-2011)

Reclamation Technologies Inc ....F 419 867-8990
Bowling Green (G-2012)

FRICTION MATERIAL, MADE FROM POWDERED METAL

General Metals Powder Co ....D 330 633-1226
Akron (G-203)

Lewark Metal Spinning Inc ....E 937 275-3303
Dayton (G-8457)

Miscellnous Mtals Fbrction Inc ....G 740 779-3071
Chillicothe (G-3252)

Ratliff Metal Spinning Co Inc ....E 937 836-3900
Englewood (G-9538)

Rti International Metals Inc ....D 330 455-4010
Canton (G-2844)

Tribco Incorporated ....E 216 486-2000
Cleveland (G-6363)

US Powder Coating Inc ....G 440 255-3090
Mentor (G-13763)

FRITS

Ferro Corporation ....C 216 875-6178
Cleveland (G-5337)

Fusion Ceramics Inc ....E 330 627-5821
Carrollton (G-2956)

FRUIT & VEGETABLE MARKETS

Country Maid Ice Cream Inc ....G 330 659-6830
Richfield (G-16619)

FRUIT STANDS OR MARKETS

Beckwith Orchards Inc ....F 330 673-6433
Kent (G-11433)

Coopers Mill ....F 419 562-4215
Bucyrus (G-2336)

FRUITS & VEGETABLES WHOLESALERS: Fresh

Dno Inc ....D 614 231-3601
Columbus (G-7034)

Dole Fresh Vegetables Inc ....C 937 525-4300
Springfield (G-17546)

Frank L Harter & Son Inc ....C 513 574-1330
Cincinnati (G-3778)

FUEL ADDITIVES

BLaster Corporation ....E 216 901-5800
Cleveland (G-4916)

FUEL CELLS: Solid State

Firstfuelcellscom LLC ....G 440 884-2503
Cleveland (G-5351)

Hydrogen 411 Technology LLC ....G 440 941-6760
Cleveland (G-5543)

Precision Energy & Tech LLC ....G 937 558-2708
Dayton (G-8582)

FUEL DEALERS: Coal

Cliffs Logan County Coal LLC ....G 216 694-5700
Cleveland (G-5089)

FUEL OIL DEALERS

Centerra Co-Op ....E 419 281-2153
Ashland (G-717)

Cincinnati - Vulcan Company ....D 513 242-5300
Cincinnati (G-3535)

New Vulco Mfg & Sales Co LLC ....D 513 242-2672
Cincinnati (G-4149)

Santmyer Oil Co of Ashland ....G 330 262-6501
Wooster (G-20831)

Santmyer Oil Co of Ashland ....G 419 289-8815
Ashland *(G-775)*

FUEL TREATING

Opw Fueling Components Inc ....E 800 422-2525
West Chester *(G-19911)*

FUELS: Diesel

Appal Energy ....G 740 448-4605
Amesville *(G-589)*
Bloom Center Biodiesel LLC ....G 937 585-6412
Lewistown *(G-11943)*
Diesel Recon Service Inc ....G 513 625-1887
Pleasant Plain *(G-16370)*
Santmyer Oil Co of Ashland ....G 419 289-8815
Ashland *(G-775)*

FUELS: Ethanol

Adr Fuel Inc ....G 419 872-2178
Perrysburg *(G-16061)*
AMA Fuel Services LLC ....G 513 836-3800
Lebanon *(G-11779)*
B P Oil Company ....G 513 671-4107
Cincinnati *(G-3433)*
Bam Fuel Inc ....G 740 397-6674
Howard *(G-11122)*
Beloit Fuel LLC ....G 330 584-1915
North Benton *(G-15212)*
Brightstar Propane & Fuels ....G 614 891-8395
Westerville *(G-20140)*
Canton Fuel ....G 330 455-3400
Canton *(G-2639)*
Daniels Brothers Fuel Co ....G 440 942-1800
Willoughby *(G-20470)*
East Side Fuel Plus Operations ....G 419 563-0777
Bucyrus *(G-2341)*
Eco Chem Alternative Fuels LLC ....G 614 764-3835
Dublin *(G-9072)*
Eco Fuel Solution LLC ....G 440 282-8592
Amherst *(G-598)*
Exp Fuels Inc ....G 419 382-7713
Toledo *(G-18460)*
Fly Race Fuels LLC ....G 419 744-9402
North Fairfield *(G-15285)*
Franklin ....G 419 699-5757
Waterville *(G-19657)*
Franklin Fueling Systems ....G 513 231-7840
Cincinnati *(G-3780)*
Fuel America ....G 419 586-5609
Celina *(G-2998)*
Fuel G USA LLC ....G 440 617-0950
Westlake *(G-20269)*
Green Fuel Today ....G 440 925-7820
Grafton *(G-10429)*
Greene Fuel Plaza Inc ....G 937 532-4826
Kettering *(G-11580)*
Hardy Industrial Tech LLC ....D 440 350-6300
Painesville *(G-15887)*
International Fuel Systems Inc ....G 419 475-5276
Toledo *(G-18526)*
Ishos Bros Fuel Ventures Inc ....G 586 634-0187
Maumee *(G-13268)*
Ishos Bros Fuel Ventures Inc ....G 419 913-5718
Toledo *(G-18530)*
L and S Express Fuel Center ....G 330 549-9566
North Lima *(G-15319)*
Leaf Lono Earth Alternty Fuels ....G 614 829-7159
Canal Winchester *(G-2530)*
Lost Nation Fuel ....G 440 951-9088
Willoughby *(G-20529)*
M J S Oil Inc ....G 937 982-3519
West Mansfield *(G-20101)*
Mart Plus Fuel ....G 216 261-0420
Euclid *(G-9591)*
North East Fuel Inc ....G 330 264-4454
Wooster *(G-20817)*
P S P Inc ....E 330 283-5635
Kent *(G-11498)*
Power Source Fuel LLC ....G 419 690-6495
Sylvania *(G-18123)*
Rex American Resources Corp ....C 937 276-3931
Dayton *(G-8627)*
Speedway LLC ....A 937 864-3000
Enon *(G-9550)*
Systech Environmental Corp ....E 800 888-8011
Dayton *(G-8693)*
Top Fuel Coatings ....G 330 758-1166
Poland *(G-16385)*

Vadose Syn Fuels Inc ....G 330 564-0545
Munroe Falls *(G-14667)*
West Erie Fuel ....G 440 282-3493
Lorain *(G-12292)*

FUELS: Gas, Liquefied

Sherwood Valve LLC ....F 216 264-5023
Cleveland *(G-6193)*

FUELS: Jet

Jet Fuel Tech Inc ....G 614 463-1986
Columbus *(G-7231)*

FUELS: Oil

Capital City Oil Inc ....G 740 397-4483
Mount Vernon *(G-14612)*
Knox Energy Inc ....F 740 927-6731
Pataskala *(G-15974)*
Knox Energy Inc ....G 740 787-1391
Mount Perry *(G-14591)*
STP Products Manufacturing Co ....D 440 352-6176
Painesville *(G-15923)*
Usalco LLC ....G 440 993-2721
Ashtabula *(G-844)*

FUNDRAISING SVCS

Clovernook Center For The Bli ....C 513 522-3860
Cincinnati *(G-3590)*

FUNERAL HOMES & SVCS

Bell Vault & Monument Works ....E 937 866-2444
Miamisburg *(G-13785)*

FUNGICIDES OR HERBICIDES

Dow Chemical Company ....F 937 254-1550
Dayton *(G-8309)*
Scotts Company LLC ....A 937 644-3729
Marysville *(G-12967)*
Scotts Miracle-Gro Company ....E 937 578-5065
Marysville *(G-12969)*

FUR FINISHING & LINING: For The Fur Goods Trade

Reliable Fur Co ....G 513 288-5093
New Richmond *(G-14945)*

FURNACES & OVENS: Fuel-Fired

Facultatieve Tech Americas Inc ....E 330 723-6339
Medina *(G-13408)*

FURNACES & OVENS: Indl

A Jacks Manufacturing Co ....E 216 531-1010
Cleveland *(G-4676)*
Abp Induction LLC ....F 330 830-6252
Massillon *(G-13106)*
Ajax Tocco Magnethermic Corp ....D 330 818-8080
Canton *(G-2594)*
Allstates Refr Contrs LLC ....F 419 878-4691
Waterville *(G-19651)*
Armature Coil Equipment Inc ....F 216 267-6366
Cleveland *(G-4831)*
Benko Products Inc ....E 440 934-2180
Sheffield Village *(G-17121)*
CA Litzler Co Inc ....E 216 267-8020
Cleveland *(G-4958)*
CA Litzler Holding Company ....D 216 267-8020
Cleveland *(G-4959)*
Crescent Metal Products Inc ....C 440 350-1100
Mentor *(G-13555)*
Delta H Technologies LLC ....G 614 561-8860
Pickerington *(G-16190)*
Ebner Furnaces Inc ....D 330 335-2311
Wadsworth *(G-19404)*
Fives N Amercn Combustn Inc ....E 216 271-6000
Cleveland *(G-5352)*
Furnace Technologies Inc ....D 419 878-2100
Waterville *(G-19658)*
Hannon Company ....D 330 456-4728
Canton *(G-2723)*
Haynn Construction Co Inc ....D 419 853-4747
West Salem *(G-20113)*
I Cerco Inc ....D 740 982-2050
Crooksville *(G-7950)*
Kaufman Engineered Systems Inc ....D 419 878-9727
Waterville *(G-19661)*

Komar Industries Inc ....E 614 836-2366
Groveport *(G-10629)*
L Haberny Co Inc ....F 440 543-5999
Chagrin Falls *(G-3098)*
Lakeway Mfg Inc ....E 419 433-3030
Huron *(G-11232)*
Lanly Company ....E 216 731-1115
Cleveland *(G-5582)*
Lewco Inc ....C 419 625-4014
Sandusky *(G-16979)*
McGill Airpressure LLC ....G 614 882-5455
Columbus *(G-7332)*
Micropyretics Heaters Intl Inc ....F 513 772-0404
Cincinnati *(G-4103)*
RAD-Con Inc ....E 440 871-5720
Lakewood *(G-11678)*
Resilience Fund III LP ....G 216 292-0200
Cleveland *(G-6106)*
Robbins Furnace Works Inc ....F 440 949-2292
Sheffield Village *(G-17129)*
Selas Heat Technology Co LLC ....E 800 523-6500
Streetsboro *(G-17875)*
Stelter and Brinck Inc ....E 513 367-9300
Harrison *(G-10805)*
Stricodynarad Corp ....F 330 239-0005
Hinckley *(G-11029)*
Strohecker Incorporated ....E 330 426-9496
East Palestine *(G-9245)*
Surface Combustion Inc ....C 419 891-7150
Maumee *(G-13300)*
United McGill Corporation ....E 614 829-1200
Groveport *(G-10648)*
Williams Industrial Svc Inc ....E 419 353-2120
Bowling Green *(G-2020)*

FURNACES: Indl, Electric

Ajax Tocco Magnethermic Corp ....C 330 372-8511
Warren *(G-19517)*
CMI Industry Americas Inc ....D 330 332-4661
Salem *(G-16883)*

FURNACES: Warm Air, Electric

Columbus Heating & Vent Co ....C 614 274-1177
Columbus *(G-6954)*

FURNITURE & CABINET STORES: Cabinets, Custom Work

Bobs Custom Str Interiors LLC ....G 567 316-7490
Toledo *(G-18375)*
River East Custom Cabinets ....E 419 244-3226
Toledo *(G-18677)*
Virgils Kitchens Inc ....G 440 355-5058
Lagrange *(G-11641)*

FURNITURE & CABINET STORES: Custom

Fine Wood Design Inc ....G 440 327-0751
North Ridgeville *(G-15374)*

FURNITURE & FIXTURES Factory

Custom Sink Top Mfg ....F 440 245-6220
Lorain *(G-12242)*
Epix Tube Co Inc ....D 937 529-4858
Dayton *(G-8328)*
Master Mfg Co Inc ....E 216 641-0500
Cleveland *(G-5758)*

FURNITURE PARTS: Metal

Pucel Enterprises Inc ....D 216 881-4604
Cleveland *(G-6061)*

FURNITURE REFINISHING SVCS

Dura Bilt Drapery & Upholstery ....F 440 269-8438
Willoughby *(G-20477)*
Feslers Refinishing ....G 740 622-4849
Coshocton *(G-7890)*
Mielke Furniture Repair Inc ....G 419 625-4572
Sandusky *(G-16989)*
Soft Touch Wood LLC ....E 330 545-4204
Girard *(G-10395)*

FURNITURE REPAIR & MAINTENANCE SVCS

Furniture Concepts Inc ....F 216 292-9100
Cleveland *(G-5385)*
Joseph G Betz & Sons ....G 513 481-0322
Cincinnati *(G-3958)*

PRODUCT

FURNITURE STOCK & PARTS: Carvings, Wood

Little Cottage Company.................G...... 330 893-4212
  Millersburg (G-14241)
Plank and Hide Co ....F...... 513 378-3194
  Cincinnati (G-4242)

FURNITURE STOCK & PARTS: Chair Seats, Hardwood

Hillcrest ....G...... 740 824-4849
  Brinkhaven (G-2097)
Hillside Wood Ltd ....E...... 330 359-5991
  Millersburg (G-14225)

FURNITURE STOCK/PARTS: Chair Stk, Hardwd, Turnd, Shapd/Carvd

Valleyview Wood Turning Co ....F...... 330 763-0407
  Millersburg (G-14277)

FURNITURE STORES

Archbold Furniture Co......................E...... 567 444-4666
  Archbold (G-665)
Banner Mattress Co Inc....................G...... 419 324-7181
  Toledo (G-18363)
Bruening Glass Works Inc ....G...... 440 333-4768
  Cleveland (G-4940)
Eoi Inc ....F...... 740 201-3300
  Lewis Center (G-11897)
Fortner Upholstering Inc ....F...... 614 475-8282
  Columbus (G-7095)
Furniture By Otmar Inc ....F...... 937 435-2039
  Dayton (G-8355)
Furniture By Otmar Inc ....G...... 513 891-5141
  Cincinnati (G-3787)
Green Acres Furniture Ltd ....F...... 330 359-6251
  Navarre (G-14713)
Hallmark Industries Inc ....E...... 937 864-7378
  Enon (G-9545)
Home Stor & Off Solutions Inc ....F...... 216 362-4660
  Cleveland (G-5521)
J-J Berlin Woodcraft Inc...................G...... 330 893-9171
  Berlin (G-1650)
Newbury Woodworks ....G...... 440 564-5273
  Newbury (G-15100)
Oakwood Furniture Inc ....G...... 740 896-3162
  Lowell (G-12403)
Ohio Table Pad Company ....F...... 419 872-6400
  Perrysburg (G-16130)
Precision Fab Products Inc...............G...... 937 526-5681
  Versailles (G-19356)
Sailors Tailor Inc ....G...... 937 862-7781
  Spring Valley (G-17469)
Stiglers Woodworks ....G...... 513 733-3009
  Cincinnati (G-4468)
Wahlies Cstm Cft Drapery Uphl ....G...... 419 229-1731
  Lima (G-12111)

FURNITURE STORES: Custom Made, Exc Cabinets

Kennewegs Wood Products ....G...... 330 832-1540
  Massillon (G-13163)

FURNITURE STORES: Office

COS Blueprint Inc ....F...... 330 376-0022
  Akron (G-130)
Recycled Systems Furniture Inc ....E...... 614 880-9110
  Worthington (G-20884)

FURNITURE STORES: Outdoor & Garden

Great Day Improvements LLC ....G...... 330 468-0700
  Macedonia (G-12456)
Pei Liquidation Company ....E...... 615 781-5020
  Macedonia (G-12471)
Pei Liquidation Company ....C...... 330 467-4267
  Macedonia (G-12470)
Queen City Awning & Tent Co ....E...... 513 530-9660
  Cincinnati (G-4313)

FURNITURE WHOLESALERS

Friends Service Co Inc.....................F...... 800 427-1704
  Dayton (G-8352)
Friends Service Co Inc.....................G...... 800 427-1704
  Kent (G-11459)

Friends Service Co Inc ....D...... 419 427-1704
  Findlay (G-9828)
J & F Furniture Shop ....G...... 330 852-2478
  Sugarcreek (G-18024)
Sauder Woodworking Co ....A...... 419 446-3828
  Archbold (G-694)
Sauder Woodworking Co ....G...... 419 446-2711
  Archbold (G-695)

FURNITURE, BARBER & BEAUTY SHOP

Natural Beauty Hc Express ....G...... 440 459-1776
  Mayfield Heights (G-13319)

FURNITURE, CHURCH: Concrete

Gdy Installations Inc ....E...... 419 467-0036
  Toledo (G-18478)

FURNITURE, GARDEN: Concrete

Sunjoy Industries Group Inc..............G...... 740 283-2815
  Steubenville (G-17716)

FURNITURE, MATTRESSES: Wholesalers

Ahmf Inc...E...... 614 921-1223
  Columbus (G-6704)

FURNITURE, OFFICE: Wholesalers

Furniture Concepts Inc.....................F...... 216 292-9100
  Cleveland (G-5385)
Wasserstrom Company ....B...... 614 737-8472
  Columbus (G-7750)
Wasserstrom Company ....F...... 614 228-2233
  Columbus (G-7751)
William J Dupps ....G...... 419 734-2126
  Port Clinton (G-16419)

FURNITURE, WHOLESALE: Chairs

Gasser Chair Co Inc.........................F...... 330 534-2234
  Youngstown (G-21092)
Millwood Wholesale Inc ....F...... 330 359-6109
  Dundee (G-9177)

FURNITURE, WHOLESALE: Filing Units

Jsc Employee Leasing Corp ....F...... 330 773-8971
  Akron (G-245)

FURNITURE, WHOLESALE: Racks

Partitions Plus LLC ....F...... 419 422-2600
  Findlay (G-9877)
Touchpint Cmplete Slutions LLC ....G...... 419 919-3222
  Celina (G-3024)

FURNITURE, WHOLESALE: Tables, Occasional

Progressive Furniture Inc ....E...... 419 446-4500
  Archbold (G-690)

FURNITURE: Bar furniture

Lasting Impression Llc ....G...... 614 806-1186
  Columbus (G-7287)
Wood Works ....G...... 330 674-0333
  Millersburg (G-14287)

FURNITURE: Bed Frames & Headboards, Wood

Progressive Furniture Inc ....E...... 419 446-4500
  Archbold (G-690)
Yoders Woodworking ....G...... 888 818-0568
  Millersburg (G-14291)

FURNITURE: Bedroom, Wood

Andal Woodworking ....F...... 330 897-8059
  Baltic (G-1064)
Simmons Company ....G...... 614 871-8088
  Grove City (G-10595)

FURNITURE: Beds, Household, Incl Folding & Cabinet, Metal

Invacare Corporation ....A...... 440 329-6000
  Elyria (G-9435)
Invacare Corporation ....D...... 800 333-6900
  Elyria (G-9436)

Invacare Holdings Corporation ....G...... 440 329-6000
  Elyria (G-9438)
Invacare International Corp ....G...... 440 329-6000
  Elyria (G-9439)

FURNITURE: Bookcases & Partitions, Office, Exc Wood

Hobart Cabinet Company ....G...... 937 335-4666
  Troy (G-18839)
Innovative Woodworking Inc ....G...... 513 531-1940
  Cincinnati (G-3923)

FURNITURE: Bookcases, Wood

Modern American Design Inc ....G...... 330 633-0227
  Tallmadge (G-18156)

FURNITURE: Box Springs, Assembled

National Bedding Company LLC ....C...... 513 421-4094
  Cincinnati (G-4139)

FURNITURE: Cabinets & Filing Drawers, Office, Exc Wood

East Woodworking Company ....G...... 216 791-5950
  Cleveland (G-5240)
Jsc Employee Leasing Corp ....F...... 330 773-8971
  Akron (G-245)

FURNITURE: Cabinets & Vanities, Medicine, Metal

Installed Building Pdts LLC ....E...... 614 308-9900
  Columbus (G-7190)

FURNITURE: Chairs, Bentwood

Hochstetler Wood ....F...... 330 893-2384
  Millersburg (G-14226)

FURNITURE: Chairs, Folding

Gasser Chair Co Inc.........................F...... 330 534-2234
  Youngstown (G-21092)
Sauder Manufacturing Co ....C...... 419 682-3061
  Stryker (G-18007)

FURNITURE: Chairs, Household Upholstered

Gasser Chair Co Inc.........................F...... 330 534-2234
  Youngstown (G-21092)

FURNITURE: Chairs, Household Wood

Colonial Woodcraft Inc ....F...... 513 779-8088
  Lebanon (G-11789)

FURNITURE: Chairs, Office Exc Wood

Gasser Chair Co Inc.........................F...... 330 534-2234
  Youngstown (G-21092)
Geograph Industries Inc ....E...... 513 202-9200
  Harrison (G-10780)
Service Pdts Group of Bucyrus ....G...... 419 562-4456
  Bucyrus (G-2359)
Veterans Representative Co LLC ....F...... 330 779-0768
  Youngstown (G-21237)

FURNITURE: Chairs, Office Wood

Buzz Seating Inc ....F...... 877 263-5737
  Cincinnati (G-3490)
Gasser Chair Co Inc.........................E...... 330 534-2234
  Youngstown (G-21091)

FURNITURE: Church

Sauder Manufacturing Co ....C...... 419 445-7670
  Archbold (G-692)

FURNITURE: Club Room, Wood

Paradise Inc...................................G...... 330 928-3789
  Cuyahoga Falls (G-8031)

FURNITURE: Console Tables, Wood

Dorel Home Furnishings Inc...............C...... 419 447-7448
  Tiffin (G-18218)

FURNITURE: Desks & Tables, Office, Exc Wood

Office Magic Inc ....F 510 782-6100
  Medina *(G-13452)*

FURNITURE: Dining Room, Wood

Canal Dover Furniture LLC ....D 330 359-5375
  Millersburg *(G-14210)*

FURNITURE: Fiberglass & Plastic

Evenflo Company Inc ....D 937 773-3971
  Troy *(G-18823)*
Evenflo Company Inc ....C 937 415-3300
  Miamisburg *(G-13806)*
Office Magic Inc ....F 510 782-6100
  Medina *(G-13452)*
Sauder Woodworking Co ....G 419 446-2711
  Archbold *(G-695)*

FURNITURE: Foundations & Platforms

Timken Foundation ....G 330 452-1144
  Canton *(G-2875)*

FURNITURE: Frames, Box Springs Or Bedsprings, Metal

Albion Industries Inc ....E 440 238-1955
  Strongsville *(G-17885)*
Mantua Manufacturing Co ....D 800 333-8333
  Bedford *(G-1440)*

FURNITURE: Hospital

Brodwill LLC ....G 513 258-2716
  Cincinnati *(G-3479)*

FURNITURE: Hotel

Textiles Inc ....G 614 529-8642
  Hilliard *(G-10986)*

FURNITURE: Household, Metal

Bailey & Jensen Inc ....F 937 272-1784
  Centerville *(G-3036)*
Medallion Lighting Corporation ....E 440 255-8383
  Mentor *(G-13650)*
Metal Fabricating Corporation ....D 216 631-8121
  Cleveland *(G-5787)*
Pine Acres Woodcraft ....G 330 852-0190
  Sugarcreek *(G-18031)*

FURNITURE: Household, NEC

Entertainment Junction ....D 513 326-1100
  Cincinnati *(G-3710)*

FURNITURE: Household, Upholstered, Exc Wood Or Metal

Bulk Carrier Trnsp Eqp Co ....E 330 339-3333
  New Philadelphia *(G-14887)*
John Purdum ....G 513 897-9686
  Waynesville *(G-19731)*
Kitchens By Rutenschroer Inc ....F 513 251-8333
  Cincinnati *(G-3994)*
Norwalk Custom Order Furn LLC ....C 419 744-3200
  Norwalk *(G-15556)*
Sailors Tailor Inc ....G 937 862-7781
  Spring Valley *(G-17469)*

FURNITURE: Household, Wood

Allied Plastic Co Inc ....G 419 389-1688
  Toledo *(G-18330)*
Archbold Furniture Co. ....E 567 444-4666
  Archbold *(G-665)*
Ariels Oak Inc ....E 330 343-7453
  Sherrodsville *(G-17145)*
Armada Fortress Inc ....G 330 953-2185
  Youngstown *(G-21027)*
Artistic Finishes Inc ....F 440 951-7850
  Willoughby *(G-20440)*
Basic Cases Inc ....G 216 662-3900
  Cleveland *(G-4896)*
Battershell Cabinets ....G 419 542-6448
  Hicksville *(G-10901)*
Benners Custom Woodworking ....G 513 932-9159
  Lebanon *(G-11783)*

Berlin Gardens Gazebos Ltd ....E 330 893-3411
  Berlin *(G-1644)*
Briar Hill Furniture ....G 330 223-2109
  Kensington *(G-11420)*
Cabinet Systems Inc ....G 440 237-1924
  Cleveland *(G-4961)*
Carlisle Oak ....G 330 852-8734
  Sugarcreek *(G-18019)*
Cirjak Furniture and Design ....G 330 296-8035
  Ravenna *(G-16521)*
Clearwater Wood Group LLC ....G 567 644-9951
  Hebron *(G-10862)*
Criswell Furniture ....G 330 695-2082
  Fredericksburg *(G-10082)*
Diversified Products & Svcs ....G 740 393-6202
  Mount Vernon *(G-14619)*
Dutch Heritage Woodcraft ....E 330 893-2211
  Berlin *(G-1648)*
Dutch Legacy LLC ....G 330 359-0270
  Dundee *(G-9172)*
Dutch Valley Woodcraft Ltd ....G 330 695-2364
  Fredericksburg *(G-10084)*
Fleetwood Custom Countertops ....F 740 965-9833
  Johnstown *(G-11398)*
Flottemesch Anthony & Son ....F 513 561-1212
  Cincinnati *(G-3762)*
Furniture By Otmar Inc ....F 937 435-2039
  Dayton *(G-8355)*
Furniture By Otmar Inc ....G 513 891-5141
  Cincinnati *(G-3787)*
G R K Manufacturing Co Inc ....E 513 863-3131
  Hamilton *(G-10697)*
Gasser Chair Co Inc ....D 330 759-2234
  Youngstown *(G-21093)*
Grabo Interiors Inc ....G 216 391-6677
  Cleveland *(G-5442)*
Green Acres Furniture Ltd ....F 330 359-6251
  Navarre *(G-14713)*
Greenway Home Products Inc ....F 419 874-6770
  Perrysburg *(G-16105)*
Hidden View Woodworking ....G 330 674-5196
  Millersburg *(G-14224)*
Hochstetler Wood Ltd ....F 330 893-1601
  Millersburg *(G-14227)*
Holmes Panel ....G 330 897-5040
  Baltic *(G-1074)*
Hopewood Inc ....G 330 359-5656
  Millersburg *(G-14232)*
Idx Corporation ....C 937 401-3225
  Dayton *(G-8400)*
Integral Design Inc ....F 216 524-0555
  Cleveland *(G-5574)*
J & F Furniture Shop ....G 330 852-2478
  Sugarcreek *(G-18024)*
J Treharn Co Inc ....F 330 743-8215
  Youngstown *(G-21122)*
J-J Berlin Woodcraft Inc ....G 330 893-9171
  Berlin *(G-1650)*
Jeffco Sheltered Workshop ....E 740 264-4608
  Steubenville *(G-17701)*
Joe P Fischer Woodcraft ....G 513 474-4316
  Cincinnati *(G-3950)*
Ken Harper ....C 740 439-4452
  Byesville *(G-2406)*
Kencraft Co Inc ....G 419 536-0333
  Toledo *(G-18542)*
Kenway Corp ....G 937 767-1660
  Yellow Springs *(G-20994)*
Kitchens By Rutenschroer Inc ....F 513 251-8333
  Cincinnati *(G-3994)*
Lauber Manufacturing Co ....G 419 446-2450
  Archbold *(G-682)*
Legacy Oak and Hardwoods LLC ....F 330 859-2656
  Zoarville *(G-21371)*
Lima Millwork Inc ....E 419 331-3303
  Elida *(G-9351)*
Mark Rasche ....G 614 882-1810
  Westerville *(G-20170)*
Masco Cbinetry Middlefield LLC ....D 440 632-5058
  Middlefield *(G-13956)*
Michaels Pre-Cast Con Pdts ....F 513 683-1292
  Loveland *(G-12374)*
Mielke Furniture Repair Inc ....G 419 625-4572
  Sandusky *(G-16989)*
Miller Cabinet Company LLC ....G 614 873-4221
  Plain City *(G-16351)*
N Wasserstrom & Sons Inc ....D 614 737-5410
  Columbus *(G-7378)*
Nagele Manufacturing Co Inc ....E 216 433-1100
  Cleveland *(G-5849)*

P Graham Dunn Inc ....D 330 828-2105
  Dalton *(G-8076)*
Patrician Furniture Builders ....G 330 746-6354
  Youngstown *(G-21167)*
R A Hamed International Inc ....F 330 247-0190
  Twinsburg *(G-19007)*
R D Cook Company LLC ....G 614 262-0550
  Columbus *(G-7543)*
Regal Cabinet Inc ....G 419 865-3932
  Toledo *(G-18674)*
Richard Benhase & Associates ....F 513 772-1896
  Cincinnati *(G-4343)*
Rnr Enterprises LLC ....F 330 852-3022
  Sugarcreek *(G-18037)*
Senator International Inc ....E 419 887-5806
  Maumee *(G-13291)*
Specialty Services Inc ....G 614 421-1599
  Columbus *(G-7638)*
Stark Truss Company Inc ....D 330 478-2100
  Canton *(G-2859)*
Stark Truss Company Inc ....G 419 298-3777
  Edgerton *(G-9337)*
Stephen J Page ....G 865 951-3316
  Williamsburg *(G-20412)*
Swigart Refinishing Company ....G 937 254-1141
  Dayton *(G-8692)*
Textiles Inc ....G 740 852-0782
  London *(G-12220)*
Textiles Inc ....G 614 529-8642
  Hilliard *(G-10986)*
Thomas Hora ....G 740 622-1386
  Fresno *(G-10200)*
Vocational Services Inc ....C 216 431-8085
  Cleveland *(G-6424)*
Waller Brothers Stone Company ....E 740 858-1948
  Mc Dermott *(G-13345)*
Weaver Woodcraft L L C ....G 330 695-2150
  Apple Creek *(G-653)*
Western Reserve Furniture Co ....G 440 235-6216
  North Olmsted *(G-15351)*
Wine Cellar Innovations LLC ....C 513 321-3733
  Cincinnati *(G-4599)*

FURNITURE: Hydraulic Barber & Beauty Shop Chairs

Global Manufacturing Inds ....G 513 271-2180
  Cincinnati *(G-3837)*

FURNITURE: Institutional, Exc Wood

Absolutely Paper Established ....G 216 932-4822
  Cleveland *(G-4688)*
Bell Vault & Monument Works ....E 937 866-2444
  Miamisburg *(G-13785)*
Columbiana Metro Hsing Auth ....E 330 385-6662
  East Liverpool *(G-9207)*
Franklin Cabinet Company Inc ....E 937 743-9606
  Franklin *(G-10023)*
General Motors LLC ....A 216 265-5000
  Cleveland *(G-5419)*
Global Furnishings Inc ....G 216 595-0901
  Beachwood *(G-1272)*
Grand-Rock Company Inc ....E 440 639-2000
  Painesville *(G-15884)*
Granite Industries Inc ....D 419 445-4733
  Archbold *(G-679)*
Hann Manufacturing Inc ....E 740 962-3752
  McConnelsville *(G-13352)*
Lorain County Metro Pk Dst ....G 440 327-3626
  North Ridgeville *(G-15388)*
McGill Septic Tank Co ....E 330 876-2171
  Kinsman *(G-11610)*
Michaels Pre-Cast Con Pdts ....F 513 683-1292
  Loveland *(G-12374)*
Mock Woodworking Company LLC ....E 740 452-2701
  Zanesville *(G-21329)*
Modern Manufacturing Inc ....F 513 251-3600
  Cincinnati *(G-4116)*
N Wasserstrom & Sons Inc ....D 614 737-5410
  Columbus *(G-7378)*
Oberfields LLC ....F 614 252-0955
  Columbus *(G-7410)*
Quality Seating Company Inc ....E 330 747-0181
  Youngstown *(G-21181)*
Soft Touch Wood LLC ....E 330 545-4204
  Girard *(G-10395)*
Tiffin Metal Products Co. ....D 419 447-8414
  Tiffin *(G-18248)*
Tri-State Supply Co Inc ....F 614 272-6767
  Columbus *(G-7709)*

PRODUCT

Trim Systems Operating Corp ....C 614 289-5360
New Albany *(G-14774)*

Yanfeng US Automotive ....D 419 662-4905
Northwood *(G-15499)*

FURNITURE: Juvenile, Metal

Angels Landing Inc ....G 513 687-3681
Moraine *(G-14465)*

FURNITURE: Juvenile, Wood

Foundations Worldwide Inc ....E 330 722-5033
Medina *(G-13412)*

FURNITURE: Kitchen & Dining Room

Millwood Wholesale Inc ....F 330 359-6109
Dundee *(G-9177)*

Tri State Countertop Service ....G 740 354-3663
Portsmouth *(G-16458)*

FURNITURE: Lawn & Garden, Except Wood & Metal

G Keener & Co...............G 937 846-1210
New Carlisle *(G-14801)*

Poly Concepts LLC ....G 419 678-3300
Saint Henry *(G-16821)*

Valley View Woodcraft ....G 330 852-3000
Sugarcreek *(G-18048)*

FURNITURE: Lawn & Garden, Metal

Sunnest Service LLC ....E 740 283-2815
Steubenville *(G-17717)*

FURNITURE: Lawn, Exc Wood, Metal, Stone Or Concrete

Hershy Way Ltd ....G 330 893-2809
Millersburg *(G-14223)*

FURNITURE: Living Room, Upholstered On Wood Frames

Hallmark Industries Inc ....E 937 864-7378
Enon *(G-9545)*

Hallmark Industries Inc ....F 937 864-7378
Enon *(G-9546)*

Quality Fabrications LLC...............G 330 695-2478
Fredericksburg *(G-10091)*

FURNITURE: Mattresses & Foundations

Ahmf Inc...............E 614 921-1223
Columbus *(G-6704)*

Central Ohio Mat Company ....G 740 627-7261
Mount Vernon *(G-14614)*

Homecare Mattress Inc...............F 937 746-2556
Franklin *(G-10027)*

Innocor Foam Tech - Acp Inc ....F 419 647-4172
Spencerville *(G-17460)*

Ohio Mattress...............G 740 739-8219
Lancaster *(G-11736)*

Original Mattress Factory Inc ....G 216 661-8388
Cleveland *(G-5947)*

Original Mattress Factory Inc ....G 513 752-6600
Cincinnati *(G-3313)*

Select Mattress Co Inc...............F 419 244-3645
Toledo *(G-18690)*

Smp Manufacturing LLC ....G 419 244-3645
Toledo *(G-18699)*

Tru Comfort Mattress...............G 614 595-8600
Dublin *(G-9156)*

Walter F Stephens Jr Inc ....E 937 746-0521
Franklin *(G-10063)*

FURNITURE: Mattresses, Box & Bedsprings

Banner Mattress Co Inc...............G 419 324-7181
Toledo *(G-18363)*

H Goodman Inc ....D 216 341-0200
Newburgh Heights *(G-15070)*

Heritage Sleep Products LLC ....E 440 437-4425
Orwell *(G-15776)*

Lcmf Inc ....E 513 860-9988
Fairfield *(G-9677)*

Leggett & Platt Incorporated...............E 440 322-4865
Elyria *(G-9452)*

Midwest Quality Bedding Inc ....G 614 504-5971
Columbus *(G-7352)*

Midwest Quality Bedding Inc ....F 504-5971
Plain City *(G-16350)*

SSP Tennessee LLC ....G 614 279-8850
Columbus *(G-7649)*

Tep Bedding Grp Inc ....F 440 437-7700
Orwell *(G-15779)*

White Dove Mattress Ltd ....E 216 341-0200
Newburgh Heights *(G-15081)*

FURNITURE: Mattresses, Innerspring Or Box Spring

Original Mattress Factory Inc ....G 614 291-8085
Columbus *(G-7446)*

Quilting Inc ....D 614 504-5971
Plain City *(G-16356)*

Sealy Mattress Mfg Co Inc ....D 800 697-3259
Medina *(G-13478)*

FURNITURE: NEC

Bio Fit Engineered Procucts ....D 419 823-1089
Bowling Green *(G-1973)*

FURNITURE: Novelty, Wood

Feslers Refinishing ....G 740 622-4849
Coshocton *(G-7890)*

FURNITURE: Office Panel Systems, Exc Wood

GMI Companies Inc ....C 513 932-3445
Lebanon *(G-11804)*

GMI Companies Inc ....G 937 981-0244
Greenfield *(G-10476)*

H S Morgan Limited Partnership ....G 513 870-4400
Fairfield *(G-9663)*

Workstream Inc ....D 513 870-4400
Fairfield *(G-9733)*

FURNITURE: Office Panel Systems, Wood

GMI Companies Inc ....C 513 932-3445
Lebanon *(G-11804)*

GMI Companies Inc ....G 937 981-0244
Greenfield *(G-10476)*

H S Morgan Limited Partnership ....G 513 870-4400
Fairfield *(G-9663)*

Workstream Inc ....D 513 870-4400
Fairfield *(G-9733)*

FURNITURE: Office, Exc Wood

American Interiors Inc ....E 419 324-0365
Toledo *(G-18338)*

Axess International LLC ....D 330 460-4840
Brunswick *(G-2208)*

Casco Mfg Solutions Inc ....D 513 681-0003
Cincinnati *(G-3504)*

Custom Millcraft Corp ....E 513 874-7080
West Chester *(G-19851)*

Design Trac Inc ....G 330 759-3131
Youngstown *(G-21067)*

Ergo Desktop LLC ....E 567 890-3746
Celina *(G-2995)*

Frontier Signs & Displays Inc ....G 513 367-0813
Harrison *(G-10779)*

Furniture Concepts Inc...............F 216 292-9100
Cleveland *(G-5385)*

Gasser Chair Co Inc ....D 330 759-2234
Youngstown *(G-21093)*

Infinium Wall Systems Inc ....E 440 572-5000
Strongsville *(G-17930)*

Kellogg Cabinets Inc ....E 614 833-9596
Canal Winchester *(G-2529)*

M/W International Inc...............F 440 526-6900
Brecksville *(G-2063)*

Mark Rasche ....G 614 882-1810
Westerville *(G-20170)*

Marsh Industries Inc ....E 330 308-8667
New Philadelphia *(G-14912)*

Metal Fabricating Corporation ....D 216 631-8121
Cleveland *(G-5787)*

National Electro-Coatings Inc...............D 216 898-0080
Cleveland *(G-5855)*

Patriot Seating Inc ....F 330 779-0768
Youngstown *(G-21168)*

Pucel Enterprises Inc ....D 216 881-4604
Cleveland *(G-6061)*

R B Mfg Co ....F 419 626-9464
Sandusky *(G-16999)*

Recycled Systems Furniture Inc ....E 614 880-9110
Worthington *(G-20884)*

Right Fit Ergonomics LLC ....G 330 674-0977
Millersburg *(G-14260)*

Starr Fabricating Inc ....D 330 394-9891
Vienna *(G-19376)*

Tiffin Metal Products Co...............D 419 447-8414
Tiffin *(G-18248)*

FURNITURE: Office, Wood

August Incorporated...............E 937 434-2520
Dayton *(G-8171)*

Basic Cases Inc ....G 216 662-3900
Cleveland *(G-4896)*

Creative Woodworks ....G 440 355-8155
Grafton *(G-10422)*

DIng Products ....G 440 442-7777
Cleveland *(G-5195)*

Dutch Design Products LLC ....E 330 674-1167
Fredericksburg *(G-10083)*

Dvuv LLC ....F 216 741-5511
Cleveland *(G-5226)*

Frontier Signs & Displays Inc ....G 513 367-0813
Harrison *(G-10779)*

Gasser Chair Co Inc ....D 330 759-2234
Youngstown *(G-21093)*

Global Design Factory LLC ....G 330 322-8775
Hudson *(G-11174)*

Idx Corporation ....C 937 401-3225
Dayton *(G-8400)*

LAtelier Custom Woodworking ....G 234 759-3359
North Lima *(G-15320)*

Lima Millwork Inc ....E 419 331-3303
Elida *(G-9351)*

Mark Rasche ....G 614 882-1810
Westerville *(G-20170)*

Miller Cabinet Company LLC ....E 614 873-4221
Plain City *(G-16351)*

National Electro-Coatings Inc...............D 216 898-0080
Cleveland *(G-5855)*

Sauder Manufacturing Co ....E 419 682-3061
Stryker *(G-18007)*

Stephen J Page ....G 865 951-3316
Williamsburg *(G-20412)*

Symatic Inc ....E 330 225-1510
Brunswick *(G-2260)*

Tiffin Metal Products Co...............D 419 447-8414
Tiffin *(G-18248)*

Yellow Tang Interiors LLC ....G 330 629-9279
Youngstown *(G-21244)*

FURNITURE: Outdoor, Wood

Cedar Outdoor Furniture Inc...............G 330 863-2580
Malvern *(G-12540)*

FURNITURE: Picnic Tables Or Benches, Park

City of Conneaut ....G 440 599-7071
Conneaut *(G-7802)*

City of Kent ....F 330 673-8897
Kent *(G-11438)*

County of Summit ....G 330 865-8065
Akron *(G-132)*

FURNITURE: Play Pens, Children's, Wood

Western & Southern Lf Insur Co ....A 513 629-1800
Cincinnati *(G-4588)*

FURNITURE: Restaurant

Joseph Knapp ....F 330 832-3515
Massillon *(G-13160)*

Quality Seating Company Inc ....E 330 747-0181
Youngstown *(G-21181)*

Rightway Food Service ....G 419 223-4075
Lima *(G-12084)*

FURNITURE: School

Shiffler Equipment Sales Inc ....E 440 285-9175
Chardon *(G-3179)*

W C Heller & Co Inc ....F 419 485-3176
Montpelier *(G-14457)*

FURNITURE: Silverware Chests, Wood

East Oberlin Cabinets...............G 440 775-1166
Oberlin *(G-15637)*

FURNITURE: Stools, Household, Wood

Hen House Inc ....E 419 663-3377
Norwalk (G-15544)

FURNITURE: Tables & Table Tops, Wood

Richmonds Woodworks Inc ....F 330 343-8184
New Philadelphia (G-14925)
Trailway Wood ....F 330 893-9966
Dundee (G-9182)

FURNITURE: Unfinished, Wood

Chris Haughey ....G 937 652-3338
Urbana (G-19150)

FURNITURE: Upholstered

Central Design Services ....G 513 829-7027
Fairfield (G-9652)
Decor At 124 ....G 260 319-4213
Convoy (G-7831)
Dura Bilt Drapery & Upholstery ....F 440 269-8438
Willoughby (G-20477)
Fortner Upholstering Inc ....F 614 475-8282
Columbus (G-7095)
Franklin Cabinet Company Inc ....E 937 743-9606
Franklin (G-10023)
G R K Manufacturing Co Inc ....E 513 863-3131
Hamilton (G-10697)
H Goodman Inc ....D 216 341-0200
Newburgh Heights (G-15070)
Hopewood Inc ....E 330 359-5656
Millersburg (G-14232)
Joseph G Betz & Sons ....G 513 481-0322
Cincinnati (G-3958)
Kenneth Shannon ....G 513 777-8888
Liberty Twp (G-11975)
Kroehler Furniture Mfg Co Inc ....B 828 459-9865
Columbus (G-7269)
LAtelier Custom Woodworking ......G 234 759-3359
North Lima (G-15320)
Mastercraft Mfg Inc ....E 330 893-3366
Berlin (G-1651)
Njm Furniture Outlet Inc ....F 330 893-3514
Millersburg (G-14254)
Robert Mayo Industries ....G 330 426-2587
East Palestine (G-9244)
Stiglers Woodworks ....G 513 733-3009
Cincinnati (G-4468)
Weavers Furniture Ltd ....F 330 852-2701
Sugarcreek (G-18051)

FURNITURE: Vehicle

Wurms Woodworking Company ......E 419 492-2184
New Washington (G-14966)

FUSE MOUNTINGS: Electric Power

Regal Beloit America Inc ....C 419 352-8441
Bowling Green (G-2013)

Furs

Fin Feather Fur ....G 330 493-8300
Canton (G-2701)
Reliable Fur Co ....G 513 288-5093
New Richmond (G-14945)
Sword Furs ....G 440 249-5001
Westlake (G-20314)

GAMES & TOYS: Banks

First Merit ....G 330 849-8750
Akron (G-188)
Mag-Nif Inc ....D 440 946-4308
Mentor (G-13643)
Rbs Citizens NA ....G 330 468-1600
Sagamore Hills (G-16778)

GAMES & TOYS: Baskets

American Traditions Basket Co ......E 330 854-0900
Canal Fulton (G-2496)

GAMES & TOYS: Bingo Boards

Cowells - Arrow Bingo Company ....G 216 961-3500
Cleveland (G-5137)

GAMES & TOYS: Board Games, Children's & Adults'

Late For Sky Production Co ....E 513 531-4400
Cincinnati (G-4013)

GAMES & TOYS: Cars, Play, Children's Vehicles

Brp Inc ....G 440 988-4398
Amherst (G-593)

GAMES & TOYS: Child Restraint Seats, Automotive

Rockys Hinge Co ....G 330 539-6296
Girard (G-10393)

GAMES & TOYS: Craft & Hobby Kits & Sets

Gingerbread N Bows ....G 740 945-1027
Scio (G-17037)
Larose Industries LLC ....E 419 237-1600
Fayette (G-9776)
Michaels Stores Inc ....E 330 505-1168
Niles (G-15170)
Ramon Robinson ....G 330 883-3244
Vienna (G-19374)

GAMES & TOYS: Dolls, Exc Stuffed Toy Animals

Gail J Shumaker Originals ....G 330 659-0680
Richfield (G-16625)
Huston Gifts Dolls and Flowers ....G 740 775-9141
Chillicothe (G-3244)
Middleton Llyd Dolls Inc ....G 740 989-2082
Coolville (G-7835)
Middleton Lee Original Dolls ....F .....
Columbus (G-7350)

GAMES & TOYS: Electronic

Moonstruck Games Inc ....G 513 721-3900
Cincinnati (G-4121)
Weenk Labs LLC ....G 614 448-0160
Columbus (G-7754)

GAMES & TOYS: Game Machines, Exc Coin-Operated

Applied Concepts Inc ....F 440 229-5033
Willoughby (G-20436)

GAMES & TOYS: Kits, Science, Incl Microscopes/Chemistry Sets

Dunecraft Inc ....E 800 306-4168
Cleveland (G-5222)
M G 3d ....F 614 262-0956
Columbus (G-7308)

GAMES & TOYS: Miniature Dolls, Collectors'

Alice Beougher ....G 740 927-2470
Etna (G-9551)

GAMES & TOYS: Models, Airplane, Toy & Hobby

Brown Dave Products Inc ....F 513 738-1576
Hamilton (G-10677)
Ready Made Rc LLC ....G 740 936-4500
Lewis Center (G-11913)

GAMES & TOYS: Models, Automobile & Truck, Toy & Hobby

Parma International Inc ....E 440 237-8650
North Royalton (G-15442)

GAMES & TOYS: Models, Railroad, Toy & Hobby

D L H Locomotive Works ....G 937 629-0321
Springfield (G-17538)

GAMES & TOYS: Strollers, Baby, Vehicle

Foundations Worldwide Inc ....E 330 722-5033
Medina (G-13412)

Mahoning Valley Manufacturing ....E 330 537-4492
Beloit (G-1584)

GAMES & TOYS: Structural Toy Sets

Hershberger Lawn Structures ....F 330 674-3900
Millersburg (G-14221)

GAMES & TOYS: Wagons, Coaster, Express & Play, Children's

Berlin Wood Products Inc ....E 330 893-3281
Berlin (G-1646)

GARAGE DOOR REPAIR SVCS

A L Callahan Door Sales ....G 419 884-3667
Mansfield (G-12554)
Division Overhead Door Inc ....F 513 872-0888
Cincinnati (G-3659)

GARBAGE CONTAINERS: Plastic

1 888 U Pitch It ....G 440 796-9028
Mentor (G-13503)
MCS Midwest LLC ....F 513 217-0805
Franklin (G-10035)
Mwe of Ohio ....G 419 777-7192
Galion (G-10280)

GARBAGE DISPOSALS: Household

Anaheim Manufacturing Company ....E 800 767-6293
North Olmsted (G-15326)

GARBAGE DISPOSERS & COMPACTORS: Commercial

City of Ashland ....G 419 289-8728
Ashland (G-722)
Knight Manufacturing Co Inc ....G 740 676-5516
Shadyside (G-17082)
Master Disposers Inc ....F 513 553-2289
New Richmond (G-14942)

GAS & OIL FIELD EXPLORATION SVCS

Alliance Petroleum Corporation ....E 330 493-0440
Canton (G-2599)
Alteirs Oil Inc ....G 740 347-4335
Corning (G-7858)
American Envmtl Group Ltd ....B 330 659-5930
Richfield (G-16613)
Antero Resources Corporation ....C 303 357-7310
Caldwell (G-2423)
Atlas America Inc ....E 330 339-3155
New Philadelphia (G-14885)
Bakerwell Inc ....D 614 898-7590
Westerville (G-20139)
Bands Company Inc ....G 330 674-0446
Millersburg (G-14196)
Barclay Petroleum Inc ....G 740 569-4327
Bremen (G-2079)
Beck Energy Corp ....F 330 297-6891
Ravenna (G-16517)
Belden & Blake Corporation ....E 330 602-5551
Dover (G-8968)
Bergstein Oil & Gas Partnr ....G 513 771-6220
Cincinnati (G-3446)
Bocor Holdings LLC ....G 330 494-1221
Canton (G-2624)
C & A Land and Energy LLC ....G 606 434-1420
New Philadelphia (G-14888)
Capital City Energy Group Inc ....G 614 485-3110
Columbus (G-6898)
Capital Oil & Gas Inc ....G 330 533-1828
Austintown (G-971)
Cardinal Energy Group Inc ....G 325 762-2112
Upper Arlington (G-19111)
Carrizo Oil & Gas Inc ....G 740 432-5463
Cambridge (G-2450)
Cgas Exploration Inc ....G 614 436-4631
Worthington (G-20859)
Chevron Ae Resources LLC ....E 330 654-4343
Deerfield (G-8771)
Columbus Oilfield Exploration ....G 614 895-9520
Powell (G-16468)
Deep Resources LLC ....F 419 869-7441
Polk (G-16388)
Delmar E Hicks ....G 740 354-4333
Portsmouth (G-16434)

Dome Drilling Co.............................G...... 440 892-9434
  Westlake (G-20264)
Dome Drilling Co.............................G...... 330 262-5113
  Wooster (G-20766)
Dome Energicorp.............................G...... 440 892-4900
  Westlake (G-20265)
Dunn S Tank Service Inc.................G...... 330 863-2200
  Malvern (G-12542)
Eastern Reserve Development...........G...... 614 319-3179
  Columbus (G-7045)
Elkhead Gas & Oil Co.......................G...... 740 763-3966
  Newark (G-15002)
Everflow Eastern Partners LP.........E...... 330 533-2692
  Canfield (G-2555)
Flint Ridge Energy...........................G...... 740 344-1351
  Newark (G-15007)
H & S Drilling Co Inc.......................G...... 740 828-2411
  Frazeysburg (G-10074)
Husky Marketing and Supply Co.......E...... 614 210-2300
  Dublin (G-9087)
John D Oil and Gas Company............G...... 440 255-6325
  Mentor (G-13620)
K Petroleum Inc...............................F...... 614 532-5420
  Gahanna (G-10214)
Mori Shuji.......................................G...... 614 459-1296
  Columbus (G-7369)
Ngo Development Corporation...........F...... 740 622-9560
  Coshocton (G-7901)
Ohio Valley Energy Systems.............G...... 330 799-2268
  Youngstown (G-21156)
Pine Top Inc....................................G...... 330 929-2492
  Akron (G-340)
Precision Geophysical Inc................E...... 330 674-2198
  Millersburg (G-14256)
Precision Geophysical Inc................F...... 740 849-3044
  Mount Perry (G-14593)
Quantum Energy LLC.......................F...... 440 285-7381
  Chardon (G-3175)
Range Rsurces - Appalachia LLC.......E...... 330 866-3301
  Dover (G-9009)
Reserve Energy Exploration Co.........G...... 440 543-0770
  Chagrin Falls (G-3117)
Resource America Inc......................E...... 330 896-8510
  Uniontown (G-19096)
Resource Energy Inc........................D...... 330 896-8510
  Uniontown (G-19097)
Santmyer Oil Co of Ashland..............G...... 330 262-6501
  Wooster (G-20831)
Standard Energy Company.................G...... 614 885-1901
  Columbus (G-7650)
Standard Oil Company......................G...... 419 691-2460
  Oregon (G-15718)
Stryker Energy LLC..........................G...... 440 446-9214
  Cleveland (G-6257)
Summit Well Services Inc..................G...... 330 223-1074
  East Rochester (G-9251)
Triad Energy Corporation..................E...... 740 374-2940
  Marietta (G-12844)
True North Energy LLC....................E...... 440 442-0060
  Mayfield Heights (G-13323)
Whitacre Enterprises Inc.................F...... 740 934-2331
  Graysville (G-10470)
Wilkes Energy Inc............................G...... 330 252-4560
  Akron (G-472)
Wrp Energy Inc................................G...... 330 533-1921
  Canfield (G-2582)
Zane Petroleum Inc..........................F...... 740 454-8779
  Zanesville (G-21366)

GAS & OIL FIELD SVCS, NEC

Altheirs Oil Inc................................G...... 740 347-4335
  Corning (G-7859)
Bradner Oil Company Inc...................G...... 419 288-2945
  Wayne (G-19721)
Complete Energy Services Inc...........F...... 440 577-1070
  Pierpont (G-16211)
Crescent Services LLC......................G...... 405 603-1200
  Cambridge (G-2453)
D & D Energy Co...............................F...... 330 495-1631
  Canton (G-2674)
Naw Petroleum Service......................G...... 740 464-7988
  Chillicothe (G-3253)
Stevens Oil & Gas LLC......................G...... 740 374-4542
  Marietta (G-12835)
Timothy Sinfield..............................E...... 740 685-3684
  Pleasant City (G-16368)
Vanguard Oil & Gas..........................G...... 330 223-1074
  East Rochester (G-9252)

GAS & OTHER COMBINED SVCS

National Gas & Oil Corporation...........E...... 740 344-2102
  Newark (G-15037)

GAS FIELD MACHINERY & EQPT

Jet Rubber Company..........................E...... 330 325-1821
  Rootstown (G-16723)
Westerman Inc..................................D...... 330 262-6946
  Wooster (G-20846)

GAS STATIONS

J & A Auto Service............................G...... 614 837-6820
  Pickerington (G-16193)
Northeast Tubular Service Inc...........G...... 330 262-1881
  Wooster (G-20818)
Standard Oil Company.......................E...... 419 698-6200
  Oregon (G-15717)
True North Energy LLC.....................E...... 440 442-0060
  Mayfield Heights (G-13323)

GAS SYSTEM CONVERSION SVCS

Compliant Healthcare Tech LLC..........E...... 216 255-9607
  Cleveland (G-5112)

GASES: Acetylene

Delille Oxygen Company.....................E...... 614 444-1177
  Columbus (G-7018)

GASES: Argon

Airgas Usa LLC................................G...... 419 228-2828
  Lima (G-11983)

GASES: Carbon Dioxide

Praxair Distribution Inc..................G...... 419 422-1353
  Lima (G-12072)
Praxair Distribution Inc..................G...... 513 821-2192
  Cincinnati (G-4263)

GASES: Hydrogen

Hydrogen Energy Systems LLC............G...... 330 236-0358
  Akron (G-227)
Ihod USA LLC....................................G...... 216 459-7179
  Cleveland (G-5549)

GASES: Indl

Air Products and Chemicals Inc...........D...... 513 420-3663
  Middletown (G-14013)
Air Products and Chemicals Inc...........F...... 216 781-2801
  Cleveland (G-4734)
Air Products and Chemicals Inc...........G...... 513 242-9215
  Cincinnati (G-3369)
Airgas Usa LLC................................G...... 440 232-6397
  Oakwood Village (G-15622)
Airgas USA LLC.................................F...... 513 563-9400
  Cincinnati (G-3371)
Airgas USA LLC.................................E...... 937 228-8594
  Dayton (G-8142)
Airgas USA LLC.................................G...... 419 726-2719
  Toledo (G-18325)
Delille Oxygen Company.....................G...... 937 325-9595
  Springfield (G-17541)
Endurance Manufacturing Inc.............G...... 330 628-2600
  Mogadore (G-14374)
Gsf Energy LLC................................G...... 513 825-0504
  Cincinnati (G-3855)
Ineos Americas LLC...........................B...... 419 226-1200
  Lima (G-12028)
Invacare Corporation.........................A...... 440 329-6000
  Elyria (G-9435)
Invacare Corporation.........................D...... 800 333-6900
  Elyria (G-9436)
Linde LLC...E...... 330 608-3008
  Uniontown (G-19090)
Linde LLC...E...... 419 435-8153
  Fostoria (G-9982)
Linde LLC...E...... 513 831-4742
  Miamiville (G-13895)
Linde LLC...E...... 216 533-7256
  Cleveland (G-5700)
Linde LLC...E...... 419 227-9585
  Lima (G-12047)
Linde LLC...G...... 330 394-4541
  Warren (G-19572)
Linde LLC...E...... 419 221-5043
  Lima (G-12048)

Linde LLC...G...... 419 822-3909
  Delta (G-8937)
Matheson Tri-Gas Inc........................E...... 513 727-9638
  Middletown (G-14060)
Matheson Tri-Gas Inc........................F...... 330 425-4407
  Twinsburg (G-18979)
Matheson Tri-Gas Inc........................F...... 419 865-8881
  Holland (G-11071)
National Gas & Oil Corporation...........E...... 740 344-2102
  Newark (G-15037)
Nyeco Gas Inc..................................G...... 419 447-2712
  Sandusky (G-16990)
Osair Inc...G...... 440 974-6500
  Mentor (G-13675)
Plasti-Kote Co Inc.............................C...... 330 725-4511
  Medina (G-13459)
Praxair Inc.......................................E...... 216 778-5555
  Cleveland (G-6029)
Praxair Inc.......................................G...... 440 237-8690
  Cleveland (G-6030)
Praxair Inc.......................................G...... 419 698-8005
  Oregon (G-15713)
Praxair Inc.......................................G...... 740 453-0346
  Zanesville (G-21344)
Praxair Inc.......................................G...... 419 729-7732
  Toledo (G-18651)
Praxair Inc.......................................G...... 937 323-6408
  Springfield (G-17630)
Praxair Inc.......................................F...... 330 264-6633
  Wooster (G-20824)
Praxair Inc.......................................E...... 419 652-3562
  Cleveland (G-6031)
Praxair Inc.......................................G...... 419 422-1353
  Lima (G-12071)
Praxair Inc.......................................G...... 440 944-8844
  Cleveland (G-6032)
Praxair Inc.......................................F...... 740 374-5525
  Marietta (G-12818)
Praxair Inc.......................................E...... 330 453-9904
  Canton (G-2818)
Praxair Inc.......................................D...... 419 666-5206
  Rossford (G-16746)
Praxair Inc.......................................G...... 330 825-4449
  Barberton (G-1142)
Praxair Distribution Inc....................F...... 614 443-7687
  Columbus (G-7512)
Praxair Distribution Inc..................G...... 937 283-3400
  Wilmington (G-20674)
Praxair Distribution Inc..................G...... 419 221-0517
  Lima (G-12073)
Praxair Distribution Inc..................E...... 419 476-0738
  Toledo (G-18652)
Reliable Mfg Co LLC..........................G...... 740 756-9373
  Carroll (G-2945)
Wright Brothers Inc.........................F...... 513 731-2222
  Cincinnati (G-4606)
Wright Brothers Global Gas LLC..........G...... 513 731-2222
  Cincinnati (G-4607)

GASES: Neon

Neo Tech..G...... 937 845-0999
  New Carlisle (G-14809)
Neon..G...... 216 761-4782
  Cleveland (G-5868)
Neon Health Services Inc...................E...... 216 231-7700
  Cleveland (G-5869)
Neon Hussy LLC................................G...... 513 374-7644
  Columbus (G-7386)
Neon Light Manufacturing Co..............G...... 216 851-1000
  Cleveland (G-5870)
Neon Paintbrush...............................G...... 419 436-1202
  Fostoria (G-9987)
Northeast OH Neighborhood Heal.......C...... 216 231-7700
  Cleveland (G-5905)

GASES: Nitrogen

Linde Gas North America LLC..............F...... 614 846-7048
  Columbus (G-7297)

GASES: Oxygen

Airgas Merchant Gases LLC...............E...... 330 454-1330
  Canton (G-2593)
Gayston Corporation.........................C...... 937 743-6050
  Miamisburg (G-13812)
Linde Gas North America LLC..............F...... 330 425-3989
  Twinsburg (G-18974)
Praxair Inc.......................................D...... 440 994-1000
  Ashtabula (G-834)

Welders Supply Inc................................F......216 241-1696
Cleveland *(G-6456)*

GASKET MATERIALS

Flow Dry Technology Inc....................C......937 833-2161
Brookville *(G-2183)*
Forest City Technologies Inc.............C......440 647-2115
Wellington *(G-19745)*
Forest City Technologies Inc.............C......440 647-2115
Wellington *(G-19746)*

GASKETS

Ace Gasket Manufacturing Co.............G......513 271-6321
Cincinnati *(G-3349)*
Akron Gasket & Packg Entps Inc.........F......330 633-3742
Tallmadge *(G-18132)*
Ashtabula Rubber Co..........................C......440 992-2195
Ashtabula *(G-794)*
Chestnut Holdings Inc.........................G......330 849-6503
Akron *(G-122)*
Cincinnati Gasket Pkg Mfg Inc.............E......513 761-3458
Cincinnati *(G-3550)*
Columbus Gasket and Sup Co LLC......G......614 878-6041
Columbus *(G-6952)*
Columbus Gasket Co Inc.....................G......614 878-6041
Columbus *(G-6953)*
Epg Inc...D......330 995-5125
Aurora *(G-919)*
Epg Inc...F......330 995-9725
Streetsboro *(G-17852)*
Fouty & Company Inc..........................G......419 693-0017
Oregon *(G-15709)*
Freudenberg-Nok General Partnr.........C......419 427-5221
Findlay *(G-9827)*
Industry Products Co..........................B......937 778-0585
Piqua *(G-16279)*
K Wm Beach Mfg Co Inc......................C......937 399-3838
Springfield *(G-17584)*
May Lin Silicone Products Inc.............G......330 825-9019
Barberton *(G-1129)*
Miami Valley Gasket Co Inc.................E......937 228-0781
Dayton *(G-8490)*
Netherland Rubber Company................F......513 733-0883
Cincinnati *(G-4146)*
Newman Sanitary Gasket Company......E......513 932-7379
Lebanon *(G-11818)*
Ohio Gasket and Shim Co Inc.............E......330 630-0626
Akron *(G-323)*
P & R Specialty Inc.............................E......937 773-0263
Piqua *(G-16297)*
Paul J Tatulinski Ltd...........................F......330 584-8251
North Benton *(G-15213)*
Phoenix Associates............................E......440 543-9701
Chagrin Falls *(G-3112)*
Sur-Seal Corporation..........................C......513 574-8500
Cincinnati *(G-4485)*
Sur-Seal Corporation..........................G......513 574-8500
Harrison *(G-10808)*

GASKETS & SEALING DEVICES

Cornerstone Indus Holdings................G......440 893-9144
Chagrin Falls *(G-3054)*
Dana Incorporated..............................B......419 887-3000
Maumee *(G-13246)*
Dana Limited......................................B......630 697-3783
Maumee *(G-13249)*
Durox Company...................................D......440 238-5350
Strongsville *(G-17914)*
Essential Sealing Products Inc............G......440 543-8108
Chagrin Falls *(G-3086)*
Federal-Mogul Corporation.................C......740 432-2393
Cambridge *(G-2457)*
Forest City Technologies Inc.............B......440 647-2115
Wellington *(G-19743)*
Forest City Technologies Inc.............B......440 647-2115
Wellington *(G-19744)*
Gasko Fabricated Products LLC...........E......330 239-1781
Medina *(G-13414)*
Ishikawa Gasket America Inc.............F......419 353-7300
Bowling Green *(G-1990)*
Ishikawa Gasket America Inc.............C......419 353-7300
Bowling Green *(G-1991)*
Jbm Technologies Inc.........................G......419 368-4362
Hayesville *(G-10844)*
Nitto Denko Auto Ohio Inc...................C......937 773-4820
Piqua *(G-16295)*
Parker-Hannifin Corporation................B......216 896-3000
Cleveland *(G-5973)*

Parker-Hannifin Corporation................F......216 896-3000
Cleveland *(G-5976)*
SKF Usa Inc.......................................F......440 720-1500
Highland Heights *(G-10920)*
Thermodyn Corporation......................G......419 874-5100
Perrysburg *(G-16157)*
Tri-Seal LLC.......................................G......330 821-1166
Alliance *(G-549)*

GASOLINE BLENDING PLANT

Certified Oil Company Inc...................C......614 421-7500
Columbus *(G-6920)*
Lavy Inc...G......937 692-8189
Arcanum *(G-657)*

GASOLINE FILLING STATIONS

Calvary Christian Ch of Ohio...............E......740 828-9000
Frazeysburg *(G-10071)*
N M R Inc...E......513 530-9075
Cincinnati *(G-4135)*
Speedway LLC....................................A......937 864-3000
Enon *(G-9550)*
Tbone Sales LLC.................................E......330 897-6131
Baltic *(G-1077)*
United Dairy Farmers Inc....................C......513 396-8700
Cincinnati *(G-4538)*

GASOLINE WHOLESALERS

Lavy Inc...G......937 692-8189
Arcanum *(G-657)*
Marathon Petroleum Company LP........F......419 422-2121
Findlay *(G-9855)*
Marathon Petroleum Corporation........B......419 422-2121
Findlay *(G-9856)*

GATES: Ornamental Metal

All Ohio Companies Inc.......................F......216 420-9274
Cleveland *(G-4756)*
Autogate Inc......................................E......419 588-2796
Berlin Heights *(G-1660)*
Quality Security Door & Mfg Co...........G......440 246-0770
Lorain *(G-12269)*

GAUGE BLOCKS

Blue Ash Tool & Die Co Inc.................F......513 793-4530
Blue Ash *(G-1752)*
LS Starrett Company...........................D......440 835-0005
Westlake *(G-20282)*

GAUGES

Angstrom Corp....................................G......330 405-0524
Twinsburg *(G-18899)*
Chart Tech Tool Inc............................E......937 667-3543
Tipp City *(G-18272)*
Jones Industrial Service LLC...............G......419 287-4553
Pemberville *(G-16029)*
Knoble Tool Corp................................E......937 461-4040
Dayton *(G-8443)*
PMC Mercury......................................G......440 953-3300
Willoughby *(G-20573)*
Precision Gage & Tool Company...........E......937 866-9666
Dayton *(G-8584)*
Silver Tool Inc....................................E......937 865-0012
Miamisburg *(G-13860)*
Taft Tool & Production Co....................F......419 385-2576
Toledo *(G-18715)*
World Automtn Measurement Tech.......F......216 651-1883
Cleveland *(G-6478)*

GEARS

Cincinnati Gearing Systems Inc...........C......513 527-8634
Cincinnati *(G-3553)*
Gear Company of America Inc.............D......216 671-5400
Cleveland *(G-5404)*
Landerwood Industries Inc..................E......440 233-4234
Willoughby *(G-20525)*
Satellite Gear Inc..............................E......216 514-8668
Cleveland *(G-6162)*
Summa Holdings Inc...........................G......440 838-4700
Cleveland *(G-6261)*
T & S Discount Tires Inc......................G......440 951-9084
Willoughby *(G-20607)*

GEARS & GEAR UNITS: Reduction, Exc Auto

Bluffton Motor Works LLC...................E......419 885-3769
Sylvania *(G-18100)*

Hefty Hoist Inc...................................E......740 467-2515
Millersport *(G-14294)*
Westerman Inc....................................C......740 569-4143
Bremen *(G-2081)*
Westerman Inc....................................D......330 262-6946
Wooster *(G-20846)*

GEARS: Power Transmission, Exc Auto

Akron Gear & Engineering Inc............E......330 773-6608
Akron *(G-45)*
B & B Gear & Machine Co Inc.............F......937 687-1771
New Lebanon *(G-14840)*
Buckeye Gear Co.................................F......216 292-7998
Chagrin Falls *(G-3078)*
Cage Gear & Machine LLC...................F......330 452-1532
Canton *(G-2633)*
Dayton Gear & Tool Co Inc.................E......937 866-4327
Dayton *(G-8275)*
Forge Industries Inc............................A......330 782-8301
Youngstown *(G-21089)*
Gear Company of America Inc.............D......216 671-5400
Cleveland *(G-5404)*
Geneva Gear & Machine Inc................F......937 866-0318
Dayton *(G-8363)*
Horsburgh & Scott Co.........................C......216 432-5858
Cleveland *(G-5526)*
Horsburgh & Scott Co.........................G......216 383-2909
Cleveland *(G-5527)*
Linde Hydraulics Corporation..............E......330 533-6801
Canfield *(G-2562)*
Martin Sprocket & Gear Inc................D......419 485-5515
Montpelier *(G-14448)*
Petro Gear Corporation.......................E......216 431-2820
Cleveland *(G-5998)*
Robertson Manufacturing Co...............F......216 531-8222
Cleveland *(G-6123)*
Stahl Gear & Machine Co....................E......216 431-2820
Cleveland *(G-6231)*

GEMSTONE & INDL DIAMOND MINING SVCS

Massillon Metaphysics........................G......330 837-1653
Massillon *(G-13174)*

GENERAL MERCHANDISE, NONDURABLE, WHOLESALE

M&M Great Adventures LLC................G......937 344-1415
Westerville *(G-20169)*

GENERATING APPARATUS & PARTS: Electrical

Turk+hillinger Usa Inc.........................G......440 781-1900
Brecksville *(G-2077)*
Turtlecreek Township..........................F......513 932-4080
Lebanon *(G-11846)*
Visiontech Automation LLC..................G......614 554-2013
Dublin *(G-9164)*

GENERATION EQPT: Electronic

Cable and Ctrl Solutions LLC..............G......937 254-2227
Dayton *(G-8097)*
Cvc Limited 1 LLC...............................G......740 605-3853
Lebanon *(G-11792)*
Dishtronix Inc.....................................G......937 292-7981
Bellefontaine *(G-1528)*
Energy Technologies Inc.....................D......419 522-4444
Mansfield *(G-12600)*
Eti Tech Inc..F......937 832-4200
Englewood *(G-9519)*
Lubrizol Advanced Mtls Inc.................F......216 447-5000
Brecksville *(G-2061)*
McGregor-Surmount Corporation.........C......937 833-6768
Brookville *(G-2193)*
Proteus Electronics Inc.......................G......419 886-2296
Bellville *(G-1575)*
Sarica Manufacturing Company...........E......937 484-4030
Urbana *(G-19179)*
Smartshopper Electronics Inc.............G......440 349-5119
Solon *(G-17382)*
Spirit Avionics Ltd..............................F......614 358-0333
Columbus *(G-7645)*
Superior Packaging.............................F......419 380-3335
Toledo *(G-18710)*
Tasi Holdings Inc................................E......513 202-5182
Harrison *(G-10809)*
Tecmark Corporation..........................D......440 205-7600
Mentor *(G-13743)*

PRODUCT

GENERATORS: Automotive & Aircraft

Charles Auto Electric Co Inc ....G...... 330 535-6269
Akron (G-118)
Cycle Electric Inc ....F...... 937 884-7300
Brookville (G-2179)
Egr Products Company Inc ....F...... 330 833-6554
Dalton (G-8068)

GENERATORS: Electric

Accurate Electronics Inc ....C...... 330 682-7015
Orrville (G-15727)
Hyundai Ideal Electric Co ....C...... 419 520-3314
Mansfield (G-12626)
Martin Diesel Inc ....E...... 419 782-9911
Defiance (G-8802)

GENERATORS: Gas

Rexarc International Inc ....E...... 937 839-4604
West Alexandria (G-19781)

GENERATORS: Ultrasonic

Tech-Sonic Inc ....F...... 614 792-3117
Columbus (G-7683)

GIFT SHOP

Amish Door Inc ....C...... 330 359-5464
Wilmot (G-20683)
Beckwith Orchards Inc ....F...... 330 673-6433
Kent (G-11433)
Broty Enterprises Inc ....G...... 330 674-6900
Millersburg (G-14203)
Crystal Art Imports Inc ....F...... 614 505-6001
Columbus (G-7002)
Custom Engraving & Screen Prtg ....G...... 440 933-2902
Avon Lake (G-1027)
Daffins Candies ....G...... 330 545-0325
Girard (G-10385)
Down Home ....G...... 740 393-1186
Mount Vernon (G-14620)
Dresden Specialties Inc ....G...... 740 754-2451
Dresden (G-9032)
Ernest Warther and Sons Inc ....F...... 330 343-7513
Dover (G-8984)
Friends of Bears Mill Inc ....G...... 937 548-5112
Greenville (G-10500)
Handcrafted Jewelry Inc ....G...... 330 650-9011
Hudson (G-11178)
Huston Gifts Dolls and Flowers ....G...... 740 775-9141
Chillicothe (G-3244)
John C Starr ....G...... 740 852-5592
London (G-12213)
Odyssey Spirits Inc ....F...... 330 562-1523
Aurora (G-938)
S-P Company Inc ....F...... 330 482-0200
Columbiana (G-6631)
Schindlers Broad Run Chese Hse ....F...... 330 343-4108
Dover (G-9011)
Scholz & Ey Engravers Inc ....F...... 614 444-8052
Columbus (G-7597)
Shops By Todd Inc ....G...... 937 458-3192
Beavercreek (G-1360)
Suzin L Chocolatiers ....F...... 440 323-3372
Elyria (G-9496)
Youngs Jersey Dairy Inc ....B...... 937 325-0629
Yellow Springs (G-21003)

GIFT WRAP: Paper, Made From Purchased Materials

American Greetings Corporation ....A...... 216 252-7300
Cleveland (G-4782)
Century Intermediate Holdg Co ....F...... 216 252-7300
Cleveland (G-5006)
Gibson Greetings Inc ....G...... 216 252-7300
Cleveland (G-5428)

GIFT, NOVELTY & SOUVENIR STORES: Artcraft & carvings

Ohio Designer Craftsmen Entps ....F...... 614 486-7119
Columbus (G-7419)

GIFT, NOVELTY & SOUVENIR STORES: Gift Baskets

American Traditions Basket Co ....E...... 330 854-0900
Canal Fulton (G-2496)

Cookie Bouquets Inc ....G...... 614 888-2171
Columbus (G-6980)
Fowlers Milling Co Inc ....G...... 440 286-2024
Chardon (G-3154)

GIFT, NOVELTY & SOUVENIR STORES: Gifts & Novelties

Global Manufacturing Solutions ....F...... 937 236-8315
Dayton (G-8367)
Golden Turtle Chocolate Fctry ....G...... 513 932-1990
Lebanon (G-11805)
Middleton Lee Original Dolls ....G...... 614 ___
Columbus (G-7350)

GIFT, NOVELTY & SOUVENIR STORES: Party Favors

Adyl Inc ....G...... 330 797-8700
Austintown (G-968)

GIFT, NOVELTY & SOUVENIR STORES: Trading Cards, Sports

Baseball Card Corner ....G...... 513 677-0464
Loveland (G-12340)
The Hartman Corp ....G...... 614 475-5035
Columbus (G-7690)

GIFTS & NOVELTIES: Wholesalers

Aunties Attic ....E...... 740 548-5059
Lewis Center (G-11886)
Polarx Ornaments LLC ....F...... 866 298-0433
North Ridgeville (G-15395)
Scholz & Ey Engravers Inc ....F...... 614 444-8052
Columbus (G-7597)

GLACE, FOR GLAZING FOOD

Roare-Q LLC ....G...... 419 801-4040
Bowling Green (G-2014)

GLASS & GLASS CERAMIC PRDTS, PRESSED OR BLOWN: Tableware

Anchor Hocking LLC ....A...... 740 681-6478
Lancaster (G-11687)
Custom Deco South Inc ....E...... 419 698-2900
Toledo (G-18418)
Ghp II LLC ....C...... 740 687-2500
Lancaster (G-11719)
Libbey Glass Inc ....C...... 419 325-2100
Toledo (G-18558)
Libbey Glass Inc ....A...... 419 729-7272
Toledo (G-18559)

GLASS FABRICATORS

A & B Iron & Metal Company ....F...... 937 228-1561
Dayton (G-8125)
Addis Glass Fabricating Inc ....F...... 513 860-3340
West Chester (G-19798)
AGC Automotive Americas ....D...... 937 599-3131
Bellefontaine (G-1515)
American Woodwork Specialty Co ....E...... 937 263-1053
Dayton (G-8156)
Anchi Inc ....A...... 740 653-2527
Lancaster (G-11686)
Anderson Glass Co Inc ....E...... 614 476-4877
Columbus (G-6756)
Atc Lighting & Plastics Inc ....C...... 440 466-7670
Andover (G-613)
Cadenza Enterprises LLC ....G...... 937 428-6058
Dayton (G-8207)
Cardinal CT Company ....G...... 740 892-2324
Utica (G-19192)
Catalina Tempering - Ohio Inc ....F...... 740 892-2324
Utica (G-19193)
Champion Window Co of Toledo ....E...... 419 841-0154
Perrysburg (G-16077)
Custom GL Sltons Millbury Corp ....C...... 419 855-7706
Millbury (G-14183)
Enclosure Suppliers LLC ....E...... 513 782-3900
Cincinnati (G-3701)
General Electric Company ....D...... 740 385-2114
Logan (G-12175)
General Glass & Screen Inc ....G...... 440 350-9033
Mentor (G-13591)
Ghp II LLC ....B...... 740 681-6825
Lancaster (G-11720)

Great Day Improvements LLC ....G...... 330 468-0700
Macedonia (G-12456)
Libbey Glass Inc ....C...... 419 325-2100
Toledo (G-18558)
North Central Insulation Inc ....F...... 419 886-2030
Bellville (G-1573)
Ohio Mirror Technologies Inc ....F...... 419 399-5903
Paulding (G-16010)
Ohio Mirror Technologies Inc ....F...... 419 399-5903
Paulding (G-16011)
Pei Liquidation Company ....C...... 330 467-4267
Macedonia (G-12470)
Perfection Glass ....G...... 614 920-0652
Pickerington (G-16199)
Pilkington North America Inc ....B...... 419 247-3211
Rossford (G-16745)
Pyromatics Corp ....F...... 440 352-3500
Mentor (G-13704)
R G C Inc ....F...... 513 683-3110
Loveland (G-12380)
R M Yates Co Inc ....G...... 216 441-0900
Cleveland (G-6084)
Rumpke Transportation Co LLC ....C...... 513 242-4600
Cincinnati (G-4367)
Sem-Com Company Inc ....F...... 419 537-8813
Toledo (G-18691)
Solon Glass Center Inc ....F...... 440 248-5018
Cleveland (G-6218)
Strategic Materials Inc ....G...... 740 349-9523
Newark (G-15059)
Taylor Products Inc ....E...... 419 263-2313
Payne (G-16017)
Taylor Products Inc ....E...... 419 263-2313
Payne (G-16018)
Technicolor Usa Inc ....A...... 614 474-8821
Circleville (G-4646)
Trulite GL Alum Solutions LLC ....D...... 740 929-2443
Hebron (G-10892)

GLASS PRDTS, FROM PURCHASED GLASS: Art

Fire Nation Ltd ....F...... 419 866-6288
Holland (G-11061)
Shiloh Hotglass ....G...... 937 274-7222
Dayton (G-8654)

GLASS PRDTS, FROM PURCHASED GLASS: Glass Beads, Reflecting

Potters Industries LLC ....E...... 216 621-0840
Cleveland (G-6023)

GLASS PRDTS, FROM PURCHASED GLASS: Glassware

Dresden Specialties Inc ....G...... 740 754-2451
Dresden (G-9032)
East Palestine Decorating LLC ....F...... 330 426-9600
East Palestine (G-9238)
Etching Concepts ....G...... 419 691-9086
Rossford (G-16740)
Jafe Decorating Co Inc ....E...... 937 547-1888
Greenville (G-10506)

GLASS PRDTS, FROM PURCHASED GLASS: Insulating

Intigral Inc ....C...... 440 439-0980
Bedford (G-1432)
Intigral Inc ....E...... 440 439-0980
Youngstown (G-21120)
Monarch Ig Inc ....F...... 330 897-2302
Baltic (G-1075)
Pittsburgh Glass Works LLC ....D...... 740 774-7600
Chillicothe (G-3263)
Trio Insulated Glass Inc ....G...... 614 276-1647
Columbus (G-7710)

GLASS PRDTS, FROM PURCHASED GLASS: Mirrored

Bruening Glass Works Inc ....G...... 440 333-4768
Cleveland (G-4940)
Chantilly Development Corp ....F...... 419 243-8109
Toledo (G-18393)
Installed Building Pdts LLC ....E...... 614 308-9900
Columbus (G-7190)

GLASS PRDTS, FROM PURCHASED GLASS: Novelties, Fruit, Etc

Colleen D Turner ....G....... 419 886-4810
Bellville (G-1568)
Hall Creations..G....... 330 357-2428
Kent (G-11468)

GLASS PRDTS, FROM PURCHASED GLASS: Reflecting

Macpherson Engineering Inc...............E....... 440 243-6565
Berea (G-1625)

GLASS PRDTS, FROM PURCHASED GLASS: Sheet, Bent

Glasstech Inc..C....... 419 661-9500
Perrysburg (G-16103)

GLASS PRDTS, FROM PURCHASED GLASS: Windshields

Safelite Glass Corp...............................A....... 614 210-9000
Columbus (G-7584)
Safelite Group Inc ....A....... 614 210-9000
Columbus (G-7585)

GLASS PRDTS, FROM PURCHD GLASS: Strengthened Or Reinforced

Glass Surface Systems Inc ....D....... 330 745-8500
Barberton (G-1119)
Kimmatt Corp ....G....... 937 228-3811
Dayton (G-8441)
PPG Industries Inc ....E....... 419 683-2400
Crestline (G-7935)

GLASS PRDTS, PRESSED OR BLOWN: Blocks & Bricks

All State GL Block Fctry Inc..................G....... 440 205-8410
Mentor (G-13519)
Global Glass Block Inc ....G....... 216 731-2333
Euclid (G-9581)

GLASS PRDTS, PRESSED OR BLOWN: Bulbs, Electric Lights

Axis Led Group LLC ....G....... 614 633-7955
Dublin (G-9051)
Katies Light House LLC ....E....... 419 645-5451
Cridersville (G-7946)
Leveck Lighting Products Inc...............E....... 937 667-4421
Tipp City (G-18287)
Peak Electric Inc ....G....... 419 726-4848
Toledo (G-18636)

GLASS PRDTS, PRESSED OR BLOWN: Furnishings & Access

Angel Glass Lost....................................G....... 419 353-2831
Bowling Green (G-1967)
Libbey Inc ....C....... 419 325-2100
Toledo (G-18561)

GLASS PRDTS, PRESSED OR BLOWN: Glass Fibers, Textile

Knoble Glass & Metal Inc ....G....... 513 753-1246
Cincinnati (G-3998)
Owens Corning ....A....... 419 248-8000
Toledo (G-18625)
Owens Corning Sales LLC ....A....... 419 248-8000
Toledo (G-18626)

GLASS PRDTS, PRESSED OR BLOWN: Glassware, Art Or Decorative

Anchor Hocking Consmr GL Corp ....G....... 740 653-2527
Lancaster (G-11688)
Modern China Inc ....E....... 330 938-6104
Sebring (G-17048)

GLASS PRDTS, PRESSED OR BLOWN: Glassware, Novelty

Mosser Glass Incorporated..................E....... 740 439-1827
Cambridge (G-2468)

GLASS PRDTS, PRESSED OR BLOWN: Lantern Globes

Brubaker Metalcrafts Inc ....G....... 937 456-5834
Eaton (G-9300)

GLASS PRDTS, PRESSED OR BLOWN: Scientific Glassware

Adria Scientific GL Works Co ....G....... 440 474-6691
Geneva (G-10339)
Technical Glass Products Inc ....G....... 425 396-8420
Perrysburg (G-16156)
Variety Glass Inc ....F....... 740 432-3643
Cambridge (G-2481)

GLASS PRDTS, PRESSED OR BLOWN: Tubing

Echo EMR Inc ....F....... 937 322-4972
Springfield (G-17550)

GLASS PRDTS, PRESSED OR BLOWN: Yarn, Fiberglass

Tencate Advanced Armor USA Inc ....D....... 740 928-0326
Hebron (G-10888)

GLASS PRDTS, PRESSED/BLOWN: Glassware, Art, Decor/Novelty

John Krizay Inc ....E....... 330 332-5607
Salem (G-16903)

GLASS PRDTS, PURCHSD GLASS: Ornamental, Cut, Engraved/DE cor

Crystal Art Imports Inc ....F....... 614 505-6001
Columbus (G-7002)
Marchione Studio Inc............................G....... 330 454-7408
Canton (G-2768)

GLASS STORE: Leaded Or Stained

Franklin Art Glass Studios ....E....... 614 221-2972
Columbus (G-7096)
Middlefield Glass Incorporated ....E....... 440 632-5699
Middlefield (G-13959)
Standing Rock Designery ....G....... 330 650-9089
Hudson (G-11202)

GLASS STORES

A Service Glass Inc ....F....... 937 426-4920
Beavercreek (G-1315)
All State GL Block Fctry Inc..................G....... 440 205-8410
Mentor (G-13519)
Dale Kestler ....G....... 513 871-9000
Cincinnati (G-3637)
General Glass & Screen Inc ....G....... 440 350-9033
Mentor (G-13591)
Glass Mirror Awards Inc ....G....... 419 638-2221
Helena (G-10896)
Oldcastle Buildingenvelope Inc............E....... 419 887-1228
Maumee (G-13287)
Oldcastle Buildingenvelope Inc............D....... 419 661-5079
Perrysburg (G-16133)

GLASS, AUTOMOTIVE: Wholesalers

Pgw Auto Glass LLC..............................E....... 419 993-2421
Lima (G-12070)

GLASS: Fiber

Celstar Group Inc ....G....... 937 224-1730
Dayton (G-8218)
Dal-Little Fabricating Inc ....G....... 216 883-3323
Cleveland (G-5163)
Industrial Fiberglass Spc Inc ....E....... 937 222-9000
Dayton (G-8402)
Mfg Composite Systems Company ......B....... 440 997-5851
Ashtabula (G-820)
Midwest Composites LLC ....E....... 419 738-2431
Wapakoneta (G-19497)
Molded Fiber Glass Research................E....... 440 994-5100
Ashtabula (G-825)
PPG Industries Inc ....E....... 419 683-2400
Crestline (G-7935)
Scottrods LLC ....G....... 419 499-2705
Monroeville (G-14428)

GLASS: Flat

Addis Glass Fabricating Inc...................F....... 513 860-3340
West Chester (G-19798)
AGC Flat Glass North Amer Inc.............G....... 937 292-7784
Bellefontaine (G-1516)
AGC Flat Glass North Amer Inc.............G....... 937 599-3131
Bellefontaine (G-1517)
Catalina Tempering - Ohio Inc ....F....... 740 892-2324
Utica (G-19193)
Glass Fabricators Inc ....G....... 216 529-1919
Lakewood (G-11665)
Guardian Industries Corp ....E....... 614 431-6309
Worthington (G-20868)
Machined Glass Specialist Inc ....F....... 937 743-6166
Springboro (G-17489)
Pilkington Holdings Inc ....B....... 419 247-3731
Toledo (G-18643)
Pilkington North America Inc ....C....... 800 547-9280
Northwood (G-15488)
Pilkington North America Inc ....C....... 419 247-3731
Urbancrest (G-19190)
Pilkington North America Inc ....B....... 419 247-4955
Toledo (G-18644)
PPG Industries Inc ....E....... 419 683-2400
Crestline (G-7935)
Schodorf Truck Body & Eqp Co ....E....... 614 228-6793
Columbus (G-7596)
Taylor Products Inc...............................E....... 419 263-2313
Payne (G-16018)
Vinylume Products Inc ....D....... 330 799-2000
Youngstown (G-21242)
Yoder Window & Siding Ltd ....G....... 330 857-4530
Fredericksburg (G-10094)

GLASS: Indl Prdts

201 E Liberty St ....G....... 234 249-0145
Wooster (G-20728)
Cincinnati Gasket Pkg Mfg Inc ....E....... 513 761-3458
Cincinnati (G-3550)

GLASS: Insulating

3-G Incorporated ....G....... 513 921-4515
Cincinnati (G-3323)
Dela-Glassware Ltd LLC ....G....... 740 369-6737
Delaware (G-8835)
Mentor Glass Supplies and Repr..........G....... 440 255-9444
Mentor (G-13651)
Poma GL Specialty Windows Inc ....G....... 330 965-1000
Boardman (G-1923)

GLASS: Laminated

Custom Glass Solutions Upr Snd ....B....... 419 294-4921
Upper Sandusky (G-19117)

GLASS: Leaded

Fergusons Cut Glass Works...................G....... 419 734-0808
Marblehead (G-12744)

GLASS: Pressed & Blown, NEC

Anderson Glass Co Inc ....E....... 614 476-4877
Columbus (G-6756)
Custom Glass Solutions Corp ....D....... 614 987-1390
Worthington (G-20862)
Eye Lighting Intl N Amer Inc ....C....... 440 350-7000
Mentor (G-13576)
General Electric Company ....D....... 740 385-2114
Logan (G-12175)
General Electric Company ....A....... 330 373-1400
Niles (G-15155)
Glass Axis ....G....... 614 291-4250
Columbus (G-7115)
International Automotive........................A....... 419 433-5653
Huron (G-11228)
Jjs3 Foundation ....G....... 513 751-3292
Cincinnati (G-3947)
Johns Manville Corporation...................B....... 419 878-8111
Waterville (G-19660)
Matthews Art Glass................................G....... 419 335-2448
Archbold (G-686)
Pgw Auto Glass LLC..............................E....... 419 993-2421
Lima (G-12070)
R G C Inc ....F....... 513 683-3110
Loveland (G-12380)
Robert Coleman ....G....... 740 393-4336
Mount Vernon (G-14642)
Sem-Com Company Inc ....F....... 419 537-8813
Toledo (G-18691)

PRODUCT

Touch of Glass ....G 419 861-2888
Toledo (G-18753)
Wilson Optical Laboratory Inc ....E 440 357-7000
Mentor (G-13769)

GLASS: Safety

AGC Flat Glass North Amer Inc ....G 937 599-3131
Bellefontaine (G-1517)

GLASS: Stained

Architectural Art Glass Studio ....G 513 731-7336
Milford (G-14122)
Franklin Art Glass Studios ....E 614 221-2972
Columbus (G-7096)
Glass Seale Ltd ....G 513 733-1464
Cincinnati (G-3834)
Kessler Studios Inc ....G 513 683-7500
Loveland (G-12366)
Middlefield Glass Incorporated ....E 440 632-5699
Middlefield (G-13959)
Radiant Arts Inc ....G 330 879-0013
Navarre (G-14725)
Standing Rock Designery ....G 330 650-9089
Hudson (G-11202)
Studio Arts & Glass Inc ....F 330 494-9779
Canton (G-2860)
Vidonish Studios ....G 419 884-1119
Mansfield (G-12701)
Whitney Stained Glass Studio ....G 216 348-1616
Cleveland (G-6461)

GLASS: Structural

Continental GL Sls & Inv Group ....B 614 679-1201
Powell (G-16469)

GLASS: Tempered

Auto Temp Inc ....C 513 732-6969
Batavia (G-1164)
Oldcastle Buildingenvelope Inc ....G 419 887-1228
Maumee (G-13287)
Oldcastle Buildingenvelope Inc ....D 419 661-5079
Perrysburg (G-16133)

GLASSWARE, NOVELTY, WHOLESALE

Etching Concepts ....G 419 691-9086
Rossford (G-16740)

GLASSWARE: Cut & Engraved

Tyseka ....G 419 860-9585
Lima (G-12107)

GLOBAL POSITIONING SYSTEMS & EQPT

Hyq Technologies LLC ....G 513 225-6911
Oxford (G-15837)
Total Supply Solutions LLC ....G 614 989-6665
Dublin (G-9155)
Trimble Inc ....D 937 245-5951
Dayton (G-8727)

GLOVES: Fabric

C & G Associates Inc ....G 419 756-6583
Mansfield (G-12573)

GLOVES: Leather

Totes Isotoner Corporation ....F 513 682-8200
West Chester (G-20059)
Totes Isotoner Holdings Corp ....C 513 682-8200
West Chester (G-20060)

GLOVES: Linings, Exc Fur

Independent Protection Systems ....G 330 832-7992
Massillon (G-13156)

GLOVES: Plastic

Tradex International Inc ....D 216 651-4788
Cleveland (G-6345)

GLOVES: Safety

Ansell Healthcare Products LLC ....D 740 622-4311
Coshocton (G-7879)
Ansell Healthcare Products LLC ....C 740 295-5414
Coshocton (G-7880)

GLOVES: Work

Chester West Holdings Inc ....C 800 647-1900
Sharonville (G-17113)
Hall Safety Apparel Inc ....F 740 922-3671
Uhrichsville (G-19051)
Wcm Holdings Inc ....G 513 705-2100
Cincinnati (G-4581)

GLOVES: Woven Or Knit, From Purchased Materials

Totes Isotoner Corporation ....F 513 682-8200
West Chester (G-20059)
Totes Isotoner Holdings Corp ....C 513 682-8200
West Chester (G-20060)

GLUE

Spectrum Adhesives Inc ....F 740 763-2886
Newark (G-15054)
Tech-Bond Solutions ....G 614 327-8884
Carroll (G-2949)

GLYCERIN

Coil Specialty Chemicals LLC ....G 740 236-2407
Marietta (G-12775)

GLYCOL ETHERS

Nease Co LLC ....D 513 738-1255
Harrison (G-10793)

GOLF CARTS: Powered

Kmj Leasing Ltd ....E 614 871-3883
Orient (G-15723)

GOLF COURSES: Public

Carol Mickley ....G 740 599-7870
Danville (G-8086)
Drillex Inc ....G 440 255-7500
Mentor (G-13564)
Joe McClelland Inc ....E 740 452-3036
Zanesville (G-21324)

GOLF DRIVING RANGES

Hole Hunter Golf Inc ....G 937 339-5833
Piqua (G-16278)
Youngs Jersey Dairy Inc ....B 937 325-0629
Yellow Springs (G-21003)

GOLF EQPT

Bay Island Company Inc ....G 513 248-0356
Loveland (G-12341)
Dayton Stencil Works Company ....E 937 223-3233
Dayton (G-8287)
Golf Galaxy Golfworks Inc ....C 740 328-4193
Newark (G-15014)
Hole Hunter Golf Inc ....G 937 339-5833
Piqua (G-16278)
Jason Stuller Pro Shop LLC ....G 419 882-3197
Sylvania (G-18113)
Sunset Golf LLC ....E 419 994-5563
Tallmadge (G-18171)

GOLF GOODS & EQPT

Hole Hunter Golf Inc ....G 937 339-5833
Piqua (G-16278)

GOURMET FOOD STORES

Disalvos Deli & Italian Store ....G 937 298-5053
Dayton (G-8306)
Mustard Seed Health Fd Mkt Inc ....E 440 519-3663
Solon (G-17342)
Rossi Pasta Factory Inc ....F 740 376-2065
Marietta (G-12826)

GOVERNMENT, EXECUTIVE OFFICES: City & Town Managers' Offices

Lake Township Trustees ....G 419 836-1143
Millbury (G-14184)

GOVERNMENT, EXECUTIVE OFFICES: County Supervisor/Exec Office

County of Summit ....G 330 865-8065
Akron (G-132)

GOVERNMENT, EXECUTIVE OFFICES: Mayors'

City of Canton ....E 330 489-3370
Canton (G-2656)
City of Marietta ....E 740 374-6864
Marietta (G-12774)
Liverpool Township ....G 330 483-4747
Valley City (G-19211)

GOVERNMENT, GENERAL: Administration

City of Cleveland ....F 216 664-3013
Cleveland (G-5035)
Turtlecreek Township ....F 513 932-4080
Lebanon (G-11846)

GOVERNMENT, GENERAL: Administration, Federal

US Government Publishing Off ....G 614 469-5657
Columbus (G-7727)

GOVERNORS: Diesel Engine

Brinkley Technology Group LLC ....F 330 830-2498
Massillon (G-13115)
HK Engine Components LLC ....G 330 830-3500
Massillon (G-13151)

GRADING SVCS

Great Lakes Crushing Ltd ....E 440 944-5500
Wickliffe (G-20366)

GRAIN & FIELD BEANS WHOLESALERS

Andersons Inc ....G 419 893-5050
Maumee (G-13224)
Andersons Inc ....G 419 536-0460
Toledo (G-18349)

GRANITE: Crushed & Broken

Bradley Stone Industries LLC ....F 440 519-3277
Solon (G-17273)
Martin Marietta Materials Inc ....F 513 701-1120
Mason (G-13060)
Martin Marietta Materials Inc ....E 513 701-1140
West Chester (G-19897)
Martin Marietta Materials Inc ....E 937 766-2351
Cedarville (G-2982)
Martin Marietta Materials Inc ....E 513 871-7152
Cincinnati (G-4063)
National Lime and Stone Co ....G 419 294-3049
Upper Sandusky (G-19134)
National Lime and Stone Co ....G 330 339-2144
New Philadelphia (G-14918)
National Lime and Stone Co ....G 216 883-9840
Cleveland (G-5857)

GRANITE: Cut & Shaped

Angelina Stone & Marble Ltd ....G 740 633-3360
Bridgeport (G-2088)
Barta Viorel ....G 440 735-1699
Bedford (G-1403)
Bartan Design Inc ....G 216 267-6474
Cleveland (G-4892)
Creative Countertops Ohio LLC ....F 937 540-9450
Englewood (G-9514)
Cutting Edge Countertops Inc ....E 419 873-9500
Perrysburg (G-16081)
HBK Stoneworks ....G 740 817-2244
Johnstown (G-11400)
Quarrymasters Inc ....G 330 612-0474
Canton (G-2830)
Schena Company Ltd ....G 419 868-5207
Holland (G-11083)

GRANITE: Dimension

Family Memorials ....G 330 477-4900
Canton (G-2700)

GRANITE: Dimension

C & C Marble & Granite LLC ....F 614 873-1919
Hilliard (G-10937)
Designer Stone Co ....G 740 492-1300
Port Washington (G-16423)
Helmart Company Inc ....G 513 941-3095
Cincinnati (G-3876)
Stone Statements Incorporated ....G 513 489-7866
Cincinnati (G-4470)

GRAPHIC ARTS & RELATED DESIGN SVCS

A Graphic Solution ....F 216 228-7223
Cleveland (G-4672)
Abstract Displays Inc ....G 513 985-9700
Blue Ash (G-1732)
Academy Graphic Comm Inc ....E 216 661-2550
Cleveland (G-4689)
Alfacomp Inc ....E 216 459-1790
Cleveland (G-4751)
Art-American Printing Plates ....E 216 241-4420
Cleveland (G-4836)
David Esrati ....G 937 228-4433
Dayton (G-8266)
Design Avenue Inc ....G 330 487-5280
Twinsburg (G-18924)
Golden Graphics Ltd ....F 419 673-6260
Kenton (G-11548)
Graphic Publications Inc ....E 330 674-2300
Millersburg (G-14218)
Great Lakes Graphics Inc ....E 216 391-0077
Cleveland (G-5450)
Gregg Macmillan ....G 513 248-2121
Milford (G-14148)
Insignia Signs Inc ....G 937 866-2341
Dayton (G-8409)
Key Marketing Group ....G 440 748-3479
Grafton (G-10432)
King Retail Solutions Inc ....F 513 729-5858
Hamilton (G-10716)
Laipplys Prtg Mktg Sltions Inc ....G 740 387-9282
Marion (G-12879)
Lsc Communications Us LLC ....C 419 935-0111
Willard (G-20396)
M L Advertising & Design LLC ....G 419 447-6523
Tiffin (G-18230)
Mueller Art Cover & Binding Co ....E 440 238-3303
Strongsville (G-17944)
Northeast Scene Inc ....E 216 241-7550
Cleveland (G-5907)
Nova Creative Group Inc ....F 937 291-8653
Dayton (G-8533)
Painted Hill Inv Group Inc ....F 937 339-1756
Troy (G-18861)
Perrons Printing Company ....E 440 236-8870
Columbia Station (G-6593)
Phantasm Designs ....G 419 538-6737
Ottawa (G-15804)
Rba Inc ....G 330 336-6700
Wadsworth (G-19436)
Roberts Graphic Center ....G 330 788-4642
Youngstown (G-21191)
Schiffer Group Inc ....G 937 694-8185
Troy (G-18872)
Schuerholz Printing Inc ....G 937 294-5218
Dayton (G-8647)
Sevell + Sevell Inc ....G 614 341-9700
Columbus (G-7611)
Signage Consultants Inc ....G 614 297-7446
Columbus (G-7620)
Sjpm Inc ....G 614 475-4571
Gahanna (G-10233)
Ultra Printing & Design Inc ....G 440 887-0393
Cleveland (G-6380)
White Tiger Inc ....F 740 852-4873
London (G-12223)
Wordcross Enterprises Inc ....F 614 410-4140
Columbus (G-7773)

GRAPHIC LAYOUT SVCS: Printed Circuitry

Atchley Signs & Graphics ....G 614 421-7446
Columbus (G-6781)

GRAPHITE MINING SVCS

Graftech Holdings Inc ....A 216 676-2000
Independence (G-11256)

GRATINGS: Open Steel Flooring

Brown-Campbell Company ....E 513 860-3564
Fairfield (G-9647)
Brown-Campbell Company ....F 216 332-0101
Maple Heights (G-12729)
Ohio Gratings Inc ....B 330 477-6707
Canton (G-2799)

GRATINGS: Tread, Fabricated Metal

Final Touch Metal Fabricating ....G 216 348-1750
Cleveland (G-5345)

GRAVE MARKERS: Concrete

Ashland Monument Company Inc ....G 419 281-2688
Ashland (G-706)

GRAVE VAULTS, METAL

American Steel Grave Vault Co ....F 419 468-6715
Galion (G-10253)
Clark Grave Vault Company ....C 614 294-3761
Columbus (G-6933)

GRAVEL & PEBBLE MINING

M J Coates Construction Co ....F 937 886-9546
Dayton (G-8462)

GRAVEL MINING

Fleming Construction Co ....E 740 494-2177
Prospect (G-16496)
Fouremans Sand & Gravel Inc ....G 937 547-1005
Greenville (G-10498)
Haueter Construction Co ....G 440 834-8220
Newbury (G-15094)
John L Garber Materials Corp ....F 419 884-1567
Mansfield (G-12628)
Kipps Gravel Company Inc ....F 513 732-1024
Batavia (G-1199)
M J Coates Construction Co ....G 937 886-9546
Dayton (G-8463)
Morrow Gravel Company Inc ....F 513 899-2000
Morrow (G-14549)
Shelly Materials Inc ....F 740 775-4567
Chillicothe (G-3275)
Stansley Mineral Resources Inc ....E 419 843-2813
Sylvania (G-18126)
Watson Gravel Inc ....E 513 422-3781
Middletown (G-14095)
Watson Gravel Inc ....E 513 863-0070
Hamilton (G-10757)
Wysong Gravel Co Inc ....F 937 456-4539
West Alexandria (G-19787)
Wysong Gravel Co Inc ....G 937 452-1523
Camden (G-2489)
Wysong Gravel Co Inc ....G 937 839-5497
West Alexandria (G-19788)

GREASES & INEDIBLE FATS, RENDERED

Inland Products Inc ....E 614 443-3425
Columbus (G-7188)

GREASES: Lubricating

Foam Seal Inc ....D 216 881-8111
Cleveland (G-5363)

GREENHOUSES: Prefabricated Metal

Consoldted Grnhse Slutions LLC ....G 330 844-8598
Strongsville (G-17907)
Cropking Incorporated ....F 330 302-4203
Lodi (G-12159)
Ludy Greenhouse Mfg Corp ....D 800 255-5839
New Madison (G-14870)
Rough Brothers Mfg Inc ....D 513 242-0310
Cincinnati (G-4360)
Superior Structures Inc ....D 513 942-5954
Harrison (G-10807)

GREETING CARD SHOPS

Gorant Chocolatier LLC ....C 330 726-8821
Boardman (G-1921)
Naptime Productions LLC ....F 419 662-9521
Rossford (G-16743)
Piqua Chocolate Company Inc ....G 937 773-1981
Piqua (G-16301)

GRILLES & REGISTERS: Ornamental Metal Work

E C S Corp ....F 440 323-1707
Elyria (G-9409)

GRINDING MEDIA: Pottery

E R Advanced Ceramics Inc ....E 330 426-9433
East Palestine (G-9237)

GRINDING SVC: Precision, Commercial Or Indl

Advanced Cryogenic Entps LLC ....F 330 922-0750
Akron (G-32)
Afc Company ....F 330 533-5581
Canfield (G-2545)
Blade Manufacturing Co Inc ....F 614 294-1649
Columbus (G-6840)
Brockman Jig Grinding Service ....G 937 220-9780
Dayton (G-8198)
G H Cutter Services Inc ....G 419 476-0476
Toledo (G-18476)
Herman Machine Inc ....F 330 633-3261
Tallmadge (G-18145)
Micro Products Co Inc ....D 440 943-0258
Willoughby Hills (G-20641)
P & J Manufacturing Inc ....F 419 241-7369
Toledo (G-18630)
P & L Heat Treating & Grinding ....G 330 746-8081
Youngstown (G-21158)
Professional Grinding Inc ....G 330 628-3001
Akron (G-353)
S C Industries Inc ....E 216 732-9000
Euclid (G-9605)
Tc Precision Machine Inc ....G 937 278-3334
Dayton (G-8705)
Thread-Rite Tool & Mfg Inc ....G 937 222-2836
Dayton (G-8712)
Tipp Machine & Tool Inc ....C 937 890-8428
Dayton (G-8716)
Triaxis Machine & Tool LLC ....G 440 230-0303
North Royalton (G-15457)
Wright Buffing Wheel Company ....G 330 424-7887
Lisbon (G-12136)

GRINDING SVCS: Ophthalmic Lens, Exc Prescription

Di Walt Optical Inc ....F 330 453-8427
Canton (G-2686)

GRIPS OR HANDLES: Rubber

US 261 Corp ....G 216 531-7143
Cleveland (G-6397)

GRITS: Crushed & Broken

Sands Hill Mining LLC ....F 740 384-4211
Hamden (G-10658)
Southern Ohio Materials ....G 937 386-3200
Seaman (G-17043)

GROCERIES WHOLESALERS, NEC

American Bottling Company ....D 614 237-4201
Columbus (G-6731)
Bread Kneads Inc ....G 419 422-3863
Findlay (G-9801)
Brew Kettle Inc ....F 440 234-8788
Strongsville (G-17898)
Coca-Cola Refreshments USA Inc ....C 419 476-6622
Toledo (G-18404)
Ervan Guttman Co ....G 513 791-0767
Cincinnati (G-3718)
G & J Pepsi-Cola Bottlers Inc ....B 740 354-9191
Franklin Furnace (G-10069)
G & J Pepsi-Cola Bottlers Inc ....D 740 452-2721
Zanesville (G-21313)
Generations Coffee Company LLC ....E 440 546-0901
Brecksville (G-2051)
Hiland Group Incorporated ....D 330 499-8404
Canton (G-2728)
Klosterman Baking Co ....D 513 242-1004
Cincinnati (G-3996)
Luxfer Magtech Inc ....E 513 772-3066
Cincinnati (G-4040)
Norcia Bakery ....E 330 454-1077
Canton (G-2790)

P-Americas LLC ....C 330 746-7652
  Youngstown (G-21161)
Pepsi-Cola Metro Btlg Co Inc ....B 937 461-4664
  Dayton (G-8570)
Pepsi-Cola Metro Btlg Co Inc ....B 330 963-0426
  Twinsburg (G-18998)
Schwebel Baking Company ....C 440 248-1500
  Solon (G-17376)
Skyline Chili Inc ....C 513 874-1188
  Fairfield (G-9719)

GROCERIES, GENERAL LINE WHOLESALERS

La Perla Inc ....F 419 534-2074
  Toledo (G-18552)
Ricking Paper and Specialty Co ....E 513 825-3551
  Cincinnati (G-4345)
Sandridge Food Corporation ....C 330 725-8883
  Medina (G-13475)
Uncle Jesters Fine Foods LLC ....G 937 550-1025
  Miamisburg (G-13873)

GROUTING EQPT: Concrete

Black Lab LLC ....G 815 313-0400
  Chardon (G-3142)

GUARD SVCS

Area Wide Protective Inc ....E 513 321-9889
  Fairfield (G-9643)

GUARDRAILS

Highway Safety Corp ....F 740 387-6991
  Marion (G-12874)

GUARDS: Machine, Sheet Metal

Custom Enclosures Corp ....G 330 786-9000
  Akron (G-137)
Hennig Inc ....G 513 247-0838
  Blue Ash (G-1808)
Tkr Metal Fabricating LLC ....G 440 221-2770
  Willoughby (G-20617)

GUIDED MISSILES & SPACE VEHICLES

Boeing Company ....A 740 788-4000
  Newark (G-14985)
Tessec Manufacturing Svcs LLC ....E 937 985-3552
  Dayton (G-8710)

GUIDED MISSILES/SPACE VEHICLE PARTS/AUX EQPT: Research/Devel

Defense Co Inc ....D 413 998-1637
  Cleveland (G-5181)

GUN SIGHTS: Optical

Mbm Industries Ltd ....G 937 522-0719
  Beavercreek Township (G-1385)

GUN SVCS

J & J Performance Inc ....F 330 567-2455
  Shreve (G-17159)

GUTTERS: Sheet Metal

Aba Gutters Inc ....G 440 729-2177
  Chesterland (G-3193)
Elg Inc ....F 216 518-0476
  Maple Heights (G-12734)
J O Y Aluminum Products Inc ......F 513 797-1100
  Batavia (G-1193)
Matteo Aluminum Inc ....E 440 585-5213
  Wickliffe (G-20372)
Mid-America Gutters Inc ....G 513 671-3505
  Cincinnati (G-4105)

GYPSUM PRDTS

California Ceramic Supply Co ....G 216 531-9185
  Euclid (G-9569)
Caraustar Industries Inc ....E 330 665-7700
  Copley (G-7841)
Ernst Enterprises Inc ....F 419 222-2015
  Lima (G-12011)
Mineral Processing Company ....G 419 396-3501
  Carey (G-2920)

Owens Corning Sales LLC ....C 330 634-0460
  Tallmadge (G-18162)
Priest Services Inc ....G 440 333-1123
  Mayfield Heights (G-13321)
Priest Services Inc ....F 440 333-1123
  Rocky River (G-16705)
United States Gypsum Company ....B 419 734-3161
  Gypsum (G-10655)

GYROSCOPES

Atlantic Inertial Systems Inc ....E 740 788-3800
  Heath (G-10845)

HAIR & HAIR BASED PRDTS

Mels Life Like Hair ....G 937 278-9486
  Dayton (G-8483)
My Major Family LLP ....G 567 218-1206
  Toledo (G-18595)
Safe 4 People Inc ....G 419 797-4087
  Port Clinton (G-16412)
U S Hair Inc ....G 614 235-5190
  Columbus (G-7717)

HAIR CARE PRDTS

John Frieda Prof Hair Care Inc ....E 800 521-3189
  Cincinnati (G-3952)
LOreal Usa Inc ....A 440 248-3700
  Cleveland (G-5709)
Mantra Haircare LLC ....F 440 526-3304
  Broadview Heights (G-2113)
Natural Beauty Products Inc ....F 513 420-9400
  Middletown (G-14068)
Pfizer Inc ....C 937 746-3603
  Franklin (G-10044)

HAIR CARE PRDTS: Hair Coloring Preparations

Fantastic Sams Hair Care Salon ....G 740 456-4296
  Portsmouth (G-16435)

HAIR CURLERS: Beauty Shop

Salon Styling Concepts Ltd ....E 216 539-0437
  Maple Heights (G-12740)

HAIR NETS

Tradex International Inc ....D 216 651-4788
  Cleveland (G-6345)

HAMPERS: Solid Fiber, Made From Purchased Materials

Westrock Company ....E 513 860-5546
  West Chester (G-19972)

HAND TOOLS, NEC: Wholesalers

Acorn Products Inc ....B 614 222-4400
  Columbus (G-6689)
CR Laurence Co Inc ....G 440 248-0003
  Cleveland (G-5139)
Elliott Tool Technologies Ltd ....D 937 253-6133
  Dayton (G-8324)
National Tool & Equipment Inc ....F 330 629-8665
  Youngstown (G-21148)
Norbar Torque Tools Inc ....F 440 953-1175
  Willoughby (G-20555)

HANDBAGS

Coach Inc ....F 513 539-8087
  Monroe (G-14398)
Gro2 Bags & Accessories LLC ....G 740 622-0928
  Coshocton (G-7894)
Judith Leiber LLC ....E 614 449-4217
  Columbus (G-7248)
Ravenworks Deer Skin ....G 937 354-5151
  Mount Victory (G-14658)

HANDBAGS: Women's

Coach Inc ....F 330 491-8658
  Canton (G-2661)
Coach Inc ....F 614 885-6184
  Columbus (G-6644)
Coach Inc ....F 419 471-9033
  Toledo (G-18403)
Coach Inc ....F 440 871-0103
  Westlake (G-20262)

Hugo Bosca Company Inc ....E 937 323-5523
  Springfield (G-17578)

HANDLES: Wood

Canfield Manufacturing Co Inc ....G 330 533-3333
  North Jackson (G-15289)

HANGERS: Garment, Wire

Wire Products Company Inc ....C 216 267-0777
  Cleveland (G-6469)

HARD RUBBER PRDTS, NEC

Dacon Industries Co ....E 330 298-9491
  Ravenna (G-16524)
International Automotive ....F 330 279-6557
  Holmesville (G-11108)

HARDWARE

AB Bonded Locksmiths Inc ....F 513 531-7334
  Cincinnati (G-3342)
Action Coupling & Eqp Inc ....D 330 279-4242
  Holmesville (G-11099)
Aluminum Bearing Co of America ....E 216 267-8560
  Cleveland (G-4773)
Ampex Metal Products Company ....E 216 267-9242
  Brookpark (G-2151)
Annin & Co ....D 740 622-4447
  Coshocton (G-7878)
Architectural Door Systems LLC ....G 513 808-9900
  Lebanon (G-11780)
Arnco Corporation ....C 800 847-7661
  Elyria (G-9375)
Baker McMillen Co ....E 330 923-3303
  Stow (G-17734)
Boardman Molded Products Inc ....D 330 788-2401
  Youngstown (G-21032)
Brass Accents Inc ....F 330 332-9500
  Salem (G-16876)
Chantilly Development Corp ....F 419 243-8109
  Toledo (G-18393)
Cleveland Hdwr & Forging Co ......E 216 641-5200
  Cleveland (G-5064)
CT Hydraulics Inc ....F 440 437-2101
  Orwell (G-15774)
Curtiss-Wright Flow Ctrl Corp ......D 216 267-3200
  Cleveland (G-5148)
Custom Metal Works Inc ....F 419 668-7831
  Norwalk (G-15531)
Dayton Metal Products Company ....G 937 849-0071
  Cincinnati (G-3643)
Dayton Superior Corporation ....E 937 682-4015
  Rushsylvania (G-16751)
Desco Corporation ....G 614 888-8855
  New Albany (G-14757)
Detroit Technologies Inc ....E 937 492-2708
  Sidney (G-17179)
Die Co Inc ....E 440 942-8856
  Eastlake (G-9265)
Eaton Corporation ....C 330 274-0743
  Aurora (G-916)
Edward W Daniel LLC ....E 440 647-1960
  Wellington (G-19742)
Elster Perfection Corporation ......D 440 428-1171
  Geneva (G-10346)
Exact Pipe Tools ....G 330 922-8150
  Cuyahoga Falls (G-7993)
Exline Manufacturing Co Inc ....G 937 866-1515
  Miamisburg (G-13808)
Fastenal Company ....G 419 629-3024
  New Bremen (G-14787)
Faull & Son LLC ....F 330 652-4341
  Niles (G-15152)
Federal Equipment Company ....D 513 621-5260
  Cincinnati (G-3747)
First Francis Company Inc ....E 440 352-8927
  Painesville (G-15881)
Flex-Strut Inc ....D 330 372-9999
  Warren (G-19551)
Florida Production Engrg Inc ....D 937 996-4361
  New Madison (G-14869)
Fort Recovery Industries Inc ....C 419 375-4121
  Fort Recovery (G-9951)
Gateway Concrete Forming Svcs ....D 513 353-2000
  Miamitown (G-13887)
Group Industries Inc ....E 216 271-0702
  Cleveland (G-5461)
Hawthorne Bolt Works Corp ....G 330 723-0555
  Medina (G-13419)

Hbd/Thermoid Inc ....C 937 593-5010
  Bellefontaine (G-1532)
Hebco Products Inc ....A 419 562-7987
  Bucyrus (G-2347)
Heller Machine Products Inc ....G 216 281-2951
  Cleveland (G-5496)
Hercules Industries Inc ....E 740 494-2620
  Prospect (G-16497)
Hfi LLC ....B 614 491-0700
  Canal Winchester (G-2525)
International Automotive ....A 419 433-5653
  Huron (G-11228)
J B Kepple Sheet Metal ....G 740 393-2971
  Mount Vernon (G-14624)
John Stieg & Associates ....G 614 889-7954
  Dublin (G-9092)
Kasai North America Inc ....F 614 356-1494
  Dublin (G-9094)
L & W Inc ....D 734 397-6300
  Avon (G-999)
Lake Park Tool & Machine LLC ....F 330 788-2437
  Youngstown (G-21131)
Marlboro Manufacturing Inc..........E 330 935-2221
  Alliance (G-526)
Matdan Corporation ....E 513 794-0500
  Blue Ash (G-1834)
Mecc-Usa LLC ....G 513 891-0301
  West Chester (G-19899)
Meese Inc ....D 440 998-1202
  Ashtabula (G-819)
Midlake Products & Mfg Co ....D 330 875-4202
  Louisville (G-12319)
Miller Studio Inc ....D 330 339-1100
  New Philadelphia (G-14916)
Morgal Machine Tool Co ....D 937 325-5561
  Springfield (G-17607)
Netherland Rubber Company ....F 513 733-0883
  Cincinnati (G-4146)
Nova Machine Products Inc ....C 216 267-3200
  Middleburg Heights (G-13907)
Ohio Hydraulics Inc ....E 513 771-2590
  Cincinnati (G-4178)
Progressive Machine Die Inc ....E 330 405-6600
  Macedonia (G-12478)
R & R Tool Inc ....E 937 783-8665
  Blanchester (G-1715)
Samsel Rope & Marine Supply Co ..E 216 241-0333
  Cleveland (G-6156)
Sheet Metal Products Co Inc ....E 440 392-9000
  Mentor (G-13722)
Summers Acquisition Corp ....E 216 941-7700
  Cleveland (G-6262)
Summers Acquisition Corp ....G 419 526-5800
  Mansfield (G-12687)
Summers Acquisition Corp ....G 440 946-5611
  Eastlake (G-9291)
Summers Acquisition Corp ....G 419 423-5800
  Findlay (G-9898)
Superior Metal Products Inc ....E 419 228-1145
  Lima (G-12099)
Te-Co Manufacturing LLC ....D 937 836-0961
  Union (G-19068)
Technoform GL Insul N Amer Inc ...E 330 487-6600
  Twinsburg (G-19027)
Texmaster Tools Inc....................F 740 965-8778
  Fredericktown (G-10112)
Trim Parts Inc ....E 513 934-0815
  Lebanon (G-11845)
Trim Systems Operating Corp ....C 614 289-5360
  New Albany (G-14774)
Trust Manufacturing LLC ....F 216 531-8787
  Euclid (G-9612)
United Die & Mfg Co ....E 330 938-6141
  Sebring (G-17056)
Verhoff Machine & Welding Inc .....C 419 596-3202
  Continental (G-7829)
Wallen Commercial Hardware ....G 937 426-5711
  Beavercreek Township (G-1392)
Washington Products Inc ....F 330 837-5101
  Massillon (G-13211)
Whiteside Manufacturing Co ....E 740 363-1179
  Delaware (G-8896)

HARDWARE & BUILDING PRDTS: Plastic

Advanced Drainage Systems Inc ....F 419 384-3140
  Pandora (G-15947)
Ames Lock Specialties Inc.............G 419 474-2995
  Toledo (G-18348)
Associated Materials LLC ....B 330 929-1811
  Cuyahoga Falls (G-7971)

Associated Mtls Holdings LLC ....A 330 929-1811
  Cuyahoga Falls (G-7972)
Blackthorn LLC ....F 937 836-9296
  Clayton (G-4657)
Buckeye Stamping Company ....D 614 445-0059
  Columbus (G-6875)
Dayton Superior Corporation ....C 937 866-0711
  Miamisburg (G-13798)
Deflecto LLC ....E 330 602-0840
  Dover (G-8975)
Fox Lite Inc ....F 937 864-1966
  Fairborn (G-9622)
Fypon Ltd ....C 800 446-3040
  Maumee (G-13260)
Gilkey Window Company Inc ....E 513 769-9663
  Cincinnati (G-3824)
Gilkey Window Company Inc ....D 513 769-4527
  Cincinnati (G-3825)
Gorell Enterprises Inc ....B 724 465-1800
  Streetsboro (G-17855)
Harbor Industrial Corp ....F 440 599-8366
  Conneaut (G-7807)
Interntnl Plstic Cmpnents Inc ....F 330 744-0625
  Campbell (G-2490)
Johnston-Morehouse-Dickey Co ....G 614 866-0452
  Columbus (G-7242)
Johnston-Morehouse-Dickey Co ....G 330 405-6050
  Macedonia (G-12464)
MTI Acquisition LLC ....E 740 929-2065
  Hebron (G-10876)
Protec Industries Incorporated.......G 440 937-4142
  Avon (G-1004)
Resinoid Engineering Corp ....E 740 928-2220
  Heath (G-10854)
Style Crest Enterprises Inc ....D 419 355-8586
  Fremont (G-10185)
Timbertech Limited ....F 614 443-4891
  Columbus (G-7694)
Timbertech Limited ....F 937 655-8766
  Wilmington (G-20679)
West & Barker Inc ....E 330 652-9923
  Niles (G-15189)

HARDWARE & EQPT: Stage, Exc Lighting

Beck Studios Inc ....E 513 831-6650
  Milford (G-14125)
Janson Industries ....D 330 455-7029
  Canton (G-2745)
Tiffin Scenic Studios Inc ....E 800 445-1546
  Tiffin (G-18249)

HARDWARE CLOTH: Woven Wire, Made From Purchased Wire

Cleveland Wire Cloth & Mfg Co .....E 216 341-1832
  Cleveland (G-5087)

HARDWARE STORES

Caldwell Lumber & Supply Co........E 740 732-2306
  Caldwell (G-2425)
Cambridge Cable Service Co ....G 740 685-5775
  Byesville (G-2396)
Hershbergers Dutch Market LLP ....E 740 489-5322
  Old Washington (G-15671)
Matco Tools Corporation 1 ....B 330 929-4949
  Stow (G-17773)
Mid-Wood Inc ....F 419 257-3331
  North Baltimore (G-15195)
Rockys Hinge Co ....G 330 539-6296
  Girard (G-10393)
Terry Lumber and Supply Co ....F 330 659-6800
  Peninsula (G-16043)
Thomas Do-It Center Inc ....E 740 446-2002
  Gallipolis (G-10310)
Woodsfeld True Vlue HM Ctr Inc .....F 740 472-1651
  Woodsfield (G-20723)

HARDWARE STORES: Builders'

Wauseon Silo & Coal Company.......F 419 335-6041
  Wauseon (G-19701)

HARDWARE STORES: Chainsaws

D & M Saw & Tool Inc ....G 513 871-5433
  Cincinnati (G-3630)
Dittmar Sales and Service ....G 740 653-7933
  Lancaster (G-11709)

HARDWARE STORES: Pumps & Pumping Eqpt

Fountain Specialists Inc.................G 513 831-5717
  Milford (G-14142)
Graco Ohio Inc ....D 330 494-1313
  North Canton (G-15235)
Layne Heavy Civil Inc ....E 513 424-7287
  Middletown (G-14053)

HARDWARE STORES: Snowblowers

Mapledale Farm Inc ....F 440 286-3389
  Chardon (G-3166)

HARDWARE STORES: Tools

Accu Jet Corp ....E 937 252-9931
  Dayton (G-8129)
Cammel Saw Company Inc ....F 330 477-3764
  Canton (G-2634)
Gary Compton ....G 937 339-6829
  Troy (G-18830)
Gordon Tool Inc ....F 419 263-3151
  Payne (G-16015)
Mataco.......................................G 440 546-8355
  Broadview Heights (G-2114)
National Tool & Equipment Inc ....F 330 629-8665
  Youngstown (G-21148)
Royer Technologies Inc ....G 937 743-6114
  Springboro (G-17506)
Simonds International LLC ....E 978 424-0100
  Kimbolton (G-11603)
Stanley Industrial & Auto LLC ....C 614 755-7089
  Westerville (G-20187)
Triaxis Machine & Tool LLC ....G 440 230-0303
  North Royalton (G-15457)

HARDWARE WHOLESALERS

Atlas Bolt & Screw Company LLC ...C 419 289-6171
  Ashland (G-709)
Barnes Group Inc ....E 419 891-9292
  Maumee (G-13229)
Chrisnik Inc ....G 513 738-2920
  Okeana (G-15663)
Custer Products Limited ....F 330 490-3158
  North Canton (G-15225)
Diy Holster LLC ....G 419 921-2168
  Elyria (G-9405)
Khempco Bldg Sup Co Ltd Partnr ...D 740 549-0465
  Delaware (G-8865)
Matco Tools Corporation 1 ....B 330 929-4949
  Stow (G-17773)
Ohashi Technica USA Inc ....E 740 965-5115
  Sunbury (G-18070)
Ohio Power Tool Brush Co ....G 419 736-3010
  Ashland (G-760)
Paulin Industries Inc ....E 216 433-7633
  Parma (G-15965)
Shook Manufactured Pdts Inc ....G 330 848-9780
  Akron (G-401)
Texmaster Tools Inc....................F 740 965-8778
  Fredericktown (G-10112)
Twin Ventures Inc ....F 330 405-3838
  Twinsburg (G-19031)
Waxman Industries Inc ....C 440 439-1830
  Cleveland (G-6452)

HARDWARE, WHOLESALE: Bolts

Akko Fastener Inc ....E 513 489-8300
  Blue Ash (G-1738)
Hudson Fasteners Inc ....G 330 270-9500
  Youngstown (G-21110)

HARDWARE, WHOLESALE: Builders', NEC

LE Smith Company ....D 419 636-4555
  Bryan (G-2310)
Twin Cities Concrete Co................F 330 343-4491
  Dover (G-9021)

HARDWARE, WHOLESALE: Nuts

Facil North America Inc ....C 330 487-2500
  Twinsburg (G-18934)

HARDWARE, WHOLESALE: Power Tools & Access

Form-A-Chip Inc..........................G 937 223-4135
  Dayton (G-8347)

PRODUCT

Noco Company..........................B...... 216 464-8131
Solon *(G-17350)*

TTI Floor Care North Amer Inc..........B...... 440 996-2000
Solon *(G-17409)*

HARDWARE, WHOLESALE: Saw Blades

Cammel Saw Company Inc..............F...... 330 477-3764
Canton *(G-2634)*

Uhrichsville Carbide Inc..............F...... 740 922-9197
Uhrichsville *(G-19064)*

HARDWARE, WHOLESALE: Staples

Heads & Threads Intl LLC..............F...... 216 433-1660
North Olmsted *(G-15338)*

HARDWARE: Aircraft

Twin Valley Metalcraft Asm LLC.........G...... 937 787-4634
West Alexandria *(G-19784)*

HARDWARE: Aircraft & Marine, Incl Pulleys & Similar Items

Acorn Technology Corporation..........E...... 216 663-1244
Cleveland *(G-4697)*

HARDWARE: Builders'

Allfasteners Usa LLC..................F...... 440 232-6060
Medina *(G-13367)*

Arrow Tru-Line Inc....................D...... 419 636-7013
Bryan *(G-2279)*

Cleveland Steel Specialty Co..........E...... 216 464-9400
Bedford Heights *(G-1481)*

Leetonia Tool Company.................F...... 330 427-6944
Leetonia *(G-11851)*

Napoleon Spring Works Inc.............C...... 419 445-1010
Archbold *(G-688)*

Stanley Industrial & Auto LLC.........D...... 614 755-7000
Westerville *(G-20188)*

HARDWARE: Cabinet

Hardware Unlimited LLC................G...... 419 472-8745
Toledo *(G-18497)*

HARDWARE: Casket

Langenau Manufacturing Company.......F...... 216 651-3400
Cleveland *(G-5680)*

HARDWARE: Furniture, Builders' & Other Household

Fortner Upholstering Inc..............F...... 614 475-8282
Columbus *(G-7095)*

Master Mfg Co Inc....................E...... 216 641-0500
Cleveland *(G-5758)*

PA Stratton & Co Inc..................G...... 419 660-9979
Collins *(G-6576)*

HARDWARE: Hangers, Wall

Design Magnetics Ltd..................G...... 234 380-5500
Hudson *(G-11169)*

J W Goss Co Inc.......................F...... 330 395-0739
Warren *(G-19562)*

Triton Products LLC...................F...... 440 248-5480
Solon *(G-17407)*

HARDWARE: Padlocks

Wilson Bohannan Company...............D...... 740 382-3639
Marion *(G-12915)*

HARDWARE: Plastic

Chuck Meadors Plastics Co.............F...... 440 813-4466
Jefferson *(G-11359)*

HARDWARE: Rubber

Reynolds Industries Inc...............E...... 330 889-9466
West Farmington *(G-20075)*

HARDWARE: Saddlery

Paddock Corporation...................G...... 440 543-0631
Chagrin Falls *(G-3110)*

HARNESS ASSEMBLIES: Cable & Wire

Alphabet Inc..........................D...... 330 856-3366
Warren *(G-19519)*

American Advnced Assmblies LLC........E...... 937 339-6267
Troy *(G-18802)*

Ankim Enterprises Incorporated........E...... 937 599-1121
Bellefontaine *(G-1518)*

Co- Ax Technology Inc.................C...... 440 914-9200
Solon *(G-17279)*

Connective Design Incorporated........F...... 937 746-8252
Miamisburg *(G-13793)*

Deca Manufacturing Co Inc.............D...... 419 884-0071
Mansfield *(G-12594)*

Empire Power Systems Co...............G...... 440 796-4401
Madison *(G-12506)*

Ewh Spectrum LLC......................D...... 937 593-8010
Bellefontaine *(G-1530)*

Fischer-Backus Corp...................F...... 740 362-2100
Lewis Center *(G-11898)*

Gmelectric Inc........................G...... 330 477-3392
Canton *(G-2715)*

L & J Cable Inc.......................E...... 937 526-9445
Russia *(G-16765)*

La Grange Elec Assemblies Co..........F...... 440 355-5388
Lagrange *(G-11630)*

Microplex Inc.........................E...... 330 498-0600
North Canton *(G-15249)*

Mk Enterprises Inc....................E...... 440 632-0121
Middlefield *(G-13967)*

Mssl Wiring System Inc................D...... 330 856-3344
Warren *(G-19579)*

Mueller Electric Company Inc..........E...... 614 888-8855
New Albany *(G-14765)*

Nexergy Inc...........................C...... 614 351-2191
Dublin *(G-9114)*

Ogc Industries Inc....................F...... 330 456-1500
Canton *(G-2797)*

Otr Controls LLC......................G...... 513 621-2197
Cincinnati *(G-4200)*

Per-Tech Inc..........................E...... 330 833-8824
Massillon *(G-13193)*

Precision Manufacturing Co Inc........D...... 937 236-2170
Dayton *(G-8585)*

RTD Electronics Inc...................F...... 330 487-0716
Twinsburg *(G-19014)*

SMH Manufacturing Inc.................F...... 419 884-0071
Lexington *(G-11952)*

Spi Inc...............................F...... 937 374-2700
Xenia *(G-20973)*

Thermtrol Corporation.................E...... 330 497-4148
North Canton *(G-15272)*

Total Cable Solutions Inc.............G...... 513 457-7013
Springboro *(G-17511)*

Valtronic Technology Inc..............D...... 440 349-1239
Solon *(G-17411)*

Wetsu Group Inc.......................F...... 937 324-9353
Springfield *(G-17678)*

HARNESS REPAIR SHOP

Charm Harness and Boot Ltd............F...... 330 893-0402
Charm *(G-3183)*

Maysville Harness Shop Ltd............G...... 330 695-9977
Apple Creek *(G-644)*

HARNESS WIRING SETS: Internal Combustion Engines

Elcor Inc.............................E...... 440 365-5941
Elyria *(G-9411)*

Electripack Inc.......................E...... 937 433-2602
Miamisburg *(G-13804)*

Mueller Electric Company Inc..........E...... 216 771-5225
Akron *(G-307)*

HARNESSES, HALTERS, SADDLERY & STRAPS

Featherweight Turf Inc................G...... 920 452-4861
Wshngtn CT Hs *(G-20908)*

HATS: Paper, Novelty, Made From Purchased Paper

Mid-States Packaging Inc..............E...... 937 843-3243
Lewistown *(G-11946)*

HEALTH & ALLIED SERVICES, NEC

Kapios LLC............................G...... 567 661-0772
Toledo *(G-18539)*

HEALTH AIDS: Exercise Eqpt

Balbo Industries Inc..................G...... 440 333-0630
Rocky River *(G-16695)*

Wooden Horse Corporation..............G...... 419 663-1472
Norwalk *(G-15568)*

HEALTH AIDS: Vaporizers

Ohio Valley Vapor Station.............G...... 740 449-2288
Saint Clairsville *(G-16804)*

HEALTH FOOD & SUPPLEMENT STORES

Nestle Usa Inc........................D...... 216 861-8350
Cleveland *(G-5874)*

Wileys Finest LLC.....................G...... 740 622-1072
Coshocton *(G-7916)*

HEALTH SYSTEMS AGENCY

American Heart Association Inc........F...... 419 740-6180
Maumee *(G-13223)*

HEARING AIDS

Akron Ent Hearing Services Inc........G...... 330 762-8959
Akron *(G-41)*

Bills Sports Center...................G...... 419 335-2405
Wauseon *(G-19672)*

Boston Scntfic Nrmdlation Corp........C...... 330 372-2652
Warren *(G-19530)*

Communications Aid Inc................F...... 513 475-8453
Cincinnati *(G-3599)*

Ear Medical Center Inc................F...... 812 537-0031
Cincinnati *(G-3684)*

Ent Physicians Inc....................F...... 419 698-4505
Oregon *(G-15708)*

Hearing Aid Center of NW Ohio.........G...... 419 636-8959
Bryan *(G-2301)*

Morris Maico Hearing Aid Svc..........G...... 419 232-6200
Van Wert *(G-19267)*

Phonak LLC............................G...... 513 420-4568
Middletown *(G-14074)*

Sonus-Usa Inc.........................E...... 419 474-9324
Toledo *(G-18701)*

Sonus-Usa Inc.........................E...... 513 475-8400
Cincinnati *(G-4437)*

HEAT EMISSION OPERATING APPARATUS

Electrowarmth Products LLC............G...... 740 599-7222
Danville *(G-8088)*

Hanon Systems Usa LLC.................C...... 313 920-0583
Carey *(G-2919)*

HEAT EXCHANGERS

Chart Asia Inc........................C...... 440 753-1490
Cleveland *(G-5018)*

Chart Industries Inc..................A...... 440 753-1490
Cleveland *(G-5019)*

Chart International Inc................D...... 440 753-1490
Cleveland *(G-5021)*

Wcr Incorporated......................E...... 740 333-3448
Wshngtn CT Hs *(G-20929)*

HEAT EXCHANGERS: After Or Inter Coolers Or Condensers, Etc

Ohio Heat Transfer Ltd................F...... 740 695-0635
Saint Clairsville *(G-16800)*

Sgl Technic Inc.......................E...... 440 572-3600
Strongsville *(G-17963)*

Universal Hydraulik USA Corp..........G...... 419 873-6340
Perrysburg *(G-16164)*

HEAT TREATING: Metal

A M Castle & Co.......................D...... 330 425-7000
Bedford *(G-1394)*

Accuphase Metal Treating LLC..........G...... 937 610-5934
Moraine *(G-14463)*

Akron Steel Treating Co...............E...... 330 773-8211
Akron *(G-58)*

Al Fe Heat Treating-Ohio Inc..........E...... 330 336-0211
Wadsworth *(G-19392)*

Al-Fe Heat Treating Inc...............E...... 419 782-7200
Defiance *(G-8776)*

Allegheny Ludlum LLC..................E...... 330 875-2244
Louisville *(G-12308)*

Alternative Flash Inc.................E...... 330 334-6111
Wadsworth *(G-19393)*

Amac Enterprises Inc ....C 216 362-1880
Parma (G-15954)

American Metal Proc Co LLC ....E 216 486-4600
Cleveland (G-4789)

American Quality Stripping ....E 419 625-6288
Sandusky (G-16946)

American Steel Treating Inc ....E 419 662-5500
Perrysburg (G-16063)

American Steel Treating Inc ....E 419 874-2044
Perrysburg (G-16064)

Analytic Stress Relieving Inc ....G 804 271-7198
Northwood (G-15476)

Arcelormittal Columbus LLC ....C 614 492-6800
Columbus (G-6768)

B&C Machine Co LLC ....B 330 745-4013
Barberton (G-1103)

Bekaert Corporation ....C 330 683-5060
Orrville (G-15729)

Bob Lanes Welding Inc ....F 740 373-3567
Marietta (G-12767)

Bodycote Imt Inc ....E 740 852-5000
London (G-12201)

Bodycote Thermal Proc Inc ....E 614 444-1181
Columbus (G-6843)

Bodycote Thermal Proc Inc ....F 440 473-2020
Cleveland (G-4921)

Bodycote Thermal Proc Inc ....E 513 921-2300
Cincinnati (G-3456)

Bodycote Thermal Proc Inc ....G 740 852-4955
London (G-12202)

Bowdil Company ....F 800 356-8663
Canton (G-2626)

Byron Products Inc ....D 513 870-9111
Fairfield (G-9648)

Certified Heat Treating Inc ....E 937 866-0245
Dayton (G-8222)

Cincinnati Gearing Systems Inc ......D 513 527-8600
Cincinnati (G-3552)

Cleveland Hollow Boring Inc ....G 216 883-1926
Cleveland (G-5065)

Clifton Steel Company ....D 216 662-6111
Maple Heights (G-12731)

Colonial Surface Solutions Inc ......E 419 358-0129
Bluffton (G-1910)

Colonial Surface Solutions Inc ......D 419 659-5639
Columbus Grove (G-7793)

Columbus Coatings Company ....D 614 492-6800
Columbus (G-6949)

Commercial Steel Treating Co ......F 216 431-8204
Cleveland (G-5105)

Dayton Forging Heat Treating ......D 937 253-4126
Dayton (G-8273)

Derrick Company Inc ....E 513 321-8122
Cincinnati (G-3648)

Detroit Flame Hardening Co ....G 216 531-4273
Euclid (G-9574)

Detroit Flame Hardening Co ....F 513 942-1400
Fairfield (G-9658)

Dewitt Inc ....G 216 662-0800
Maple Heights (G-12732)

Die Co Inc ....E 440 942-8856
Eastlake (G-9265)

Dowa Tht America Inc ....E 419 354-4144
Bowling Green (G-1988)

Ellison Srfc Tech - Mexico LLC ......B 513 770-4900
Mason (G-13014)

Erie Steel Ltd ....E 419 478-3743
Toledo (G-18458)

Euclid Heat Treating Co ....D 216 481-8444
Euclid (G-9579)

Fbf Limited ....E 513 541-6300
Cincinnati (G-3746)

Flynn Inc ....B 419 478-3743
Toledo (G-18472)

Franklin Field Service ....G 614 885-1779
Columbus (G-7098)

Fusion Automation Inc ....G 440 602-5595
Willoughby (G-20493)

General Steel Corporation ....F 216 883-4200
Cleveland (G-5421)

Gerdau Macsteel Atmosphere Ann ......D 330 478-0314
Canton (G-2713)

Gt Technologies Inc ....C 419 782-8955
Defiance (G-8792)

H & M Metal Processing Co ....E 330 745-3075
Akron (G-210)

H & S Steel Treating Inc ....F 330 678-5245
Kent (G-11466)

Harvard Metal Treating Inc ....G 216 271-4424
Newburgh Heights (G-15071)

Heat Treating Inc ....E 937 325-3121
Springfield (G-17570)

Heat Treating Inc ....F 937 325-3121
Springfield (G-17571)

Heat Treating Inc ....G 614 759-9963
Gahanna (G-10209)

Heat Treating Technologies ....E 419 224-8324
Lima (G-12023)

HI Tecmetal Group Inc ....E 440 373-5101
Wickliffe (G-20368)

HI Tecmetal Group Inc ....E 440 946-2280
Willoughby (G-20504)

HI Tecmetal Group Inc ....F 216 941-0440
Cleveland (G-5509)

Hmt Inc ....G 440 599-7005
Conneaut (G-7808)

Isostatic Pressing Svcs LLC ....G 614 370-2140
Columbus (G-7213)

Kowalski Heat Treating Co ....F 216 631-4411
Cleveland (G-5665)

Lapham-Hickey Steel Corp ....E 614 443-4881
Columbus (G-7286)

Metal Improvement Company LLC ......E 330 425-1490
Twinsburg (G-18985)

Metallurgical Service Inc ....E 937 294-2681
Moraine (G-14505)

Miller Consolidated Industries ......E 937 294-2681
Moraine (G-14507)

Moore Mc Millen Holdings ....D 330 745-3075
Cuyahoga Falls (G-8027)

Neturen America Corporation ......F 513 863-1900
Hamilton (G-10726)

Northwind Industries Inc ....E 216 433-0666
Cleveland (G-5916)

Ohio Metallurgical Service Inc ......D 440 365-4104
Elyria (G-9471)

P & L Heat Treating & Grinding ......G 330 746-8081
Youngstown (G-21158)

P & L Heat Trting Grinding Inc ......G 330 746-1339
Youngstown (G-21159)

Parker Trutec Incorporated ....D 937 323-8833
Springfield (G-17625)

Pike Machine Products Co ....E 216 731-1880
Euclid (G-9597)

Pressure Technology Ohio Inc ......E 215 628-1975
Painesville (G-15912)

Pride Investments LLC ....F 937 461-1121
Dayton (G-8591)

Ridge Machine & Welding Co ......G 740 537-2821
Toronto (G-18784)

Ropama Inc ....F 440 358-1304
Painesville (G-15919)

Samuel Steel Pickling Company ......E 330 963-3777
Twinsburg (G-19016)

Team Inc ....F 614 263-1808
Columbus (G-7681)

Team Cooperheat Mqs ....G 614 501-7304
Columbus (G-7682)

Techniques Surfaces Usa Inc ......G 937 323-2556
Springfield (G-17661)

Thermal Solutions Inc ....G 614 263-1808
Columbus (G-7692)

Thermal Treatment Center Inc ......E 216 881-8100
Cleveland (G-6317)

Thermal Treatment Center Inc ......E 216 883-4820
Cleveland (G-6318)

Thermal Treatment Center Inc ......E 440 943-4555
Wickliffe (G-20388)

Thermal Treatment Center Inc ......F 216 941-0440
Cleveland (G-6319)

Thompson Steel Company Inc ......D 419 399-4803
Paulding (G-16014)

Universal Heat Treating Inc ....E 216 641-2000
Cleveland (G-6390)

USA Heat Treating Inc ....E 216 587-4700
Cleveland (G-6400)

Vicon Fabricating Company Ltd ......E 440 205-6700
Mentor (G-13767)

Weiss Industries Inc ....E 419 526-2480
Mansfield (G-12704)

Winston Heat Treating Inc ....E 937 226-0110
Dayton (G-8762)

Xtek Inc ....B 513 733-7800
Cincinnati (G-4616)

Zion Industries Inc ....D 330 225-3246
Valley City (G-19238)

HEATERS: Room & Wall, Including Radiators

Hunter Defense Tech Inc ....E 216 438-6111
Solon (G-17312)

Suarez Corporation Industries ....F 330 494-5504
Canton (G-2862)

HEATING & AIR CONDITIONING EQPT & SPLYS WHOLESALERS

Controls and Sheet Metal Inc ....E 513 721-3610
Cincinnati (G-3607)

Custom Duct & Supply Co Inc ....G 937 228-2058
Dayton (G-8258)

Daikin Applied Americas Inc ....G 614 351-9862
Columbus (G-7007)

Reynolds & Co Inc ....G 937 592-8300
Bellefontaine (G-1538)

Style Crest Inc ....B 419 332-7369
Fremont (G-10184)

Style Crest Enterprises Inc ....D 419 355-8586
Fremont (G-10185)

Torok Supply Company ....G 330 799-6677
Youngstown (G-21224)

Yanfeng US Automotive ....D 419 662-4905
Northwood (G-15499)

HEATING & AIR CONDITIONING UNITS, COMBINATION

Albin Sales Inc ....G 740 927-7210
Pataskala (G-15966)

Aquapro Systems LLC ....F 877 278-2797
West Chester (G-19808)

Cartwright Construction Inc ....G 330 929-3020
Cuyahoga Falls (G-7976)

Famous Realty Cleveland Inc ....F 740 685-2533
Byesville (G-2402)

Goodman Distribution Inc ....G 440 324-4071
Elyria (G-9426)

Insource Tech Inc ....F 419 399-3600
Paulding (G-16007)

Keith Chrissinger ....G 740 549-0683
Lewis Center (G-11903)

R & R Comfort Experts LLC ....G 216 475-3995
Cleveland (G-6078)

Throck Supply Co LLC ....G 937 393-9276
Hillsboro (G-11015)

HEATING APPARATUS: Steam

Grid Industrial Heating Inc ....G 330 332-9931
Salem (G-16897)

HEATING EQPT & SPLYS

Accent Manufacturing Inc ....F 330 724-7704
Norton (G-15500)

Air Enterprises LLC ....E 330 794-9770
Akron (G-34)

Air Entrprises Acquisition LLC ......C 330 794-9770
Akron (G-35)

Airtech Mechanical Inc ....F 419 292-0074
Toledo (G-18326)

Beckett Air Incorporated ....D 440 327-9999
North Ridgeville (G-15359)

Dcm Manufacturing Inc ....E 216 265-8006
Cleveland (G-5178)

Duro Dyne Midwest Corp ....B 513 870-6000
Hamilton (G-10685)

Ebner Furnaces Inc ....D 330 335-2311
Wadsworth (G-19404)

Ets Schaefer LLC ....E 330 468-6600
Macedonia (G-12448)

Famous Industries Inc ....D 740 685-2592
Byesville (G-2401)

Firestone Sheet Metal Inc ....E 330 337-9551
Salem (G-16890)

First Solar Inc ....B 419 661-1478
Perrysburg (G-16096)

Glo-Quartz Electric Heater Co ......E 440 255-9701
Mentor (G-13593)

Hartzell Fan Inc ....C 937 773-7411
Piqua (G-16271)

Hdt Ep Inc ....C 216 438-6111
Solon (G-17307)

Hdt Expeditionary Systems Inc ......F 440 466-6640
Geneva (G-10350)

Lakeway Mfg Inc ....E 419 433-3030
Huron (G-11232)

North Amrcn Sstnable Enrgy Ltd ......C 440 539-7133
Parma (G-15963)

Onix Corporation ....G 800 844-0076
Perrysburg (G-16135)

Employee Codes: A=Over 500 employees, B=251-500
C=101-250, D=51-100, E=20-50, F=10-19, G=3-9

2017 Harris Ohio
Industrial Directory

1519

PRODUCT

HEATING EQPT & SPLYS (continued)

Qual-Fab Inc .... E 440 327-5000
   Avon (G-1005)

Selas Heat Technology Co LLC .... E 800 523-6500
   Streetsboro (G-17875)

Sgm Co Inc .... E 440 255-1190
   Mentor (G-13721)

Stelter and Brinck Inc .... E 513 367-9300
   Harrison (G-10805)

Sticker Corporation .... F 440 946-2100
   Willoughby (G-20606)

Swagelok Company .... E 440 349-5836
   Solon (G-17393)

T J F Inc .... F 419 878-4400
   Waterville (G-19668)

Thermo Systems Technology .... E 216 292-8250
   Cleveland (G-6320)

Trumbull Manufacturing Inc .... D 330 393-6624
   Warren (G-19614)

Turbonics Inc .... G 216 741-8300
   Cleveland (G-6376)

UNI-Ref United Refractories Co .... E 513 563-9955
   Cincinnati (G-4536)

HEATING EQPT: Complete

Adams Manufacturing Company .... E 216 662-1600
   Cleveland (G-4700)

Briskheat Corporation .... C 614 294-3376
   Columbus (G-6863)

Chilltex LLC .... F 937 710-3308
   Anna (G-621)

Edison Solar Inc .... F 419 499-0000
   Milan (G-14111)

Hatfield Industries LLC .... G 513 225-0456
   West Chester (G-19880)

Hbb Pro Sales .... G 216 901-7900
   Cleveland (G-5486)

Heat Exchange Applied Tech .... F 330 682-4328
   Orrville (G-15740)

Red DOT Corporation .... G 216 447-4294
   Cleveland (G-6094)

Sticker Corporation .... F 440 946-2100
   Willoughby (G-20606)

Trane Company .... F 419 491-2278
   Holland (G-11091)

HEATING EQPT: Dielectric

P S C Inc .... G 216 531-3375
   Cleveland (G-5957)

HEATING EQPT: Induction

Custom Coils .... G 330 426-3797
   Negley (G-14729)

Induction Services Inc .... G 330 652-4494
   Niles (G-15159)

Induction Tooling Inc .... E 440 237-0711
   North Royalton (G-15426)

Inter-Power Corporation .... G 330 652-4494
   Niles (G-15160)

Magneforce Inc .... F 330 856-9300
   Warren (G-19577)

Park-Ohio Holdings Corp .... F 440 947-2000
   Cleveland (G-5966)

Park-Ohio Industries Inc .... G 440 947-2000
   Cleveland (G-5967)

Specialties Mds Induction Ltd .... G 330 394-3338
   Warren (G-19601)

Taylor - Winfield Corporation .... G 330 259-8500
   Hubbard (G-11140)

HEATING PADS: Nonelectric

Vacca Inc .... G 513 697-0270
   Loveland (G-12396)

HEATING UNITS & DEVICES: Indl, Electric

Briskheat Corporation .... D 614 429-3232
   Columbus (G-6864)

Euclid Products Co Inc .... G 440 942-7310
   Willoughby (G-20482)

Glenro Inc .... E 937 392-0111
   Ripley (G-16667)

Glo-Quartz Electric Heater Co .... E 440 255-9701
   Mentor (G-13593)

Heat and Sensor Tech LLC .... D 513 228-0481
   Lebanon (G-11807)

James Thomas Shively .... G 330 468-2601
   Macedonia (G-12462)

Sivon Mfr Co .... G 440 259-5505
   Perry (G-16057)

STA-Warm Electric Company .... F 330 296-6461
   Ravenna (G-16561)

Tegratek .... G 513 742-5100
   Cincinnati (G-4499)

Thermo Systems Technology .... E 216 292-8250
   Cleveland (G-6320)

HEATING UNITS: Gas, Infrared

Aitken Products Inc .... G 440 466-5711
   Geneva (G-10341)

Enerco Group Inc .... C 216 916-3000
   Cleveland (G-5280)

Enerco Technical Products Inc .... C 216 916-3000
   Cleveland (G-5281)

Mr Heater Inc .... C 216 916-3000
   Cleveland (G-5838)

Panelbloc Inc .... G 440 974-8877
   Mentor (G-13679)

Spectrum Inc .... F 440 951-6061
   Brooklyn Heights (G-2147)

HEAVY DISTILLATES

Ashland LLC .... G 513 557-3100
   Cincinnati (G-3418)

HELP SUPPLY SERVICES

CPC Logistics Inc .... D 513 874-5787
   Fairfield (G-9657)

HITCHES: Trailer

Geyer Transport & Mfg .... F 740 382-9008
   Marion (G-12868)

HOBBY, TOY & GAME STORES: Ceramics Splys

California Ceramic Supply Co .... G 216 531-9185
   Euclid (G-9569)

HOBBY, TOY & GAME STORES: Children's Toys & Games, Exc Dolls

Ready Made Rc LLC .... G 740 936-4500
   Lewis Center (G-11913)

HOBBY, TOY & GAME STORES: Dolls & Access

Middleton Lee Original Dolls .... F
   Columbus (G-7350)

HOBBY, TOY & GAME STORES: Toys & Games

Ohio Art Company .... D 419 636-3141
   Bryan (G-2315)

HOGS WHOLESALERS

Robert Winner Sons Inc .... E 419 582-4321
   Yorkshire (G-21006)

HOISTING SLINGS

Acme Lifting Products Inc .... G 440 838-4430
   Cleveland (G-4693)

HOISTS

American Climber & Mch Corp .... G 330 420-0019
   Lisbon (G-12117)

ARI Phoenix Inc .... E 513 229-3750
   Lebanon (G-11781)

Columbus McKinnon Corporation .... D 330 332-5769
   Salem (G-16884)

David Round Company Inc .... E 330 656-1600
   Streetsboro (G-17847)

Hoist Equipment Co Inc .... E 440 232-0300
   Bedford Heights (G-1486)

HOISTS: Mine

Gray-Eering Ltd .... G 740 498-8816
   Tippecanoe (G-18314)

HOLDING COMPANIES: Banks

Fincom Corporation .... G 330 456-8341
   Canton (G-2703)

HOLDING COMPANIES: Investment, Exc Banks

Ajami Holdings Group LLC .... G 216 396-6089
   Richmond Heights (G-16651)

Akron Brass Holding Corp .... G 330 264-5678
   Wooster (G-20736)

Ampac Holdings LLC .... A 513 671-1777
   Cincinnati (G-3397)

Companies of North Coast LLC .... G 216 398-8550
   Cleveland (G-5109)

Dayton Lamina Corporation .... G 937 859-5111
   Dayton (G-8277)

Dcc Corp .... G 330 494-0494
   Canton (G-2680)

Elite Property Group LLC .... F 216 316-8222
   Cleveland (G-5272)

Esperia Holdings LLC .... G 714 249-7888
   Oak Harbor (G-15589)

Misumi Investment USA Corp .... G 937 859-5111
   Dayton (G-8504)

Mmh Americas Inc .... G 414 764-6200
   Springfield (G-17605)

PMC Acquisitions Inc .... G 419 429-0042
   Findlay (G-9879)

Sp3 Cutting Tools Inc .... G 937 667-4476
   Tipp City (G-18301)

Tronair Parent Inc .... G 419 866-6301
   Holland (G-11093)

HOLDING COMPANIES: Personal, Exc Banks

Hartzell Industries Inc .... F 937 773-6295
   Piqua (G-16273)

Select-Arc Inc .... C 937 295-5215
   Fort Loramie (G-9938)

HOME ENTERTAINMENT EQPT: Electronic, NEC

Beacon Audio Video Systems Inc .... G 937 723-9587
   Centerville (G-3037)

Custom Automation Technologies .... G 614 939-4228
   New Albany (G-14755)

Daca Vending Wholesale LLC .... G 513 753-1600
   Amelia (G-571)

Electrimotion Inc .... G 740 362-0251
   Delaware (G-8840)

HOME ENTERTAINMENT REPAIR SVCS

Markeys Audio/Visual Inc .... G 419 244-8844
   Toledo (G-18573)

HOME FOR THE MENTALLY HANDICAPPED

Bittersweet Inc .... E 419 875-6986
   Whitehouse (G-20338)

R T Industries Inc .... G 937 335-5784
   Troy (G-18865)

HOME FURNISHINGS WHOLESALERS

American Frame Corporation .... D 419 893-5595
   Maumee (G-13222)

Greenway Home Products Inc .... F 419 874-6770
   Perrysburg (G-16105)

V&P Group International LLC .... F 703 349-6432
   Cincinnati (G-4550)

Weavers Furniture Ltd .... F 330 852-2701
   Sugarcreek (G-18051)

HOME HEALTH CARE SVCS

Terewell Inc .... G 216 334-6897
   Cleveland (G-6306)

HOMEBUILDERS & OTHER OPERATIVE BUILDERS

Superior Structures Inc .... F 513 942-5954
   Harrison (G-10807)

HOMEFURNISHING STORE: Bedding, Sheet, Blanket, Spread/Pillow

Down-Lite International Inc .... C 513 229-3696
   Mason (G-13011)

HOMEFURNISHING STORES: Brushes

Buckeye BOP LLC ....G....... 740 498-9898
Newcomerstown (G-15110)

HOMEFURNISHING STORES: Cutlery

Handy Twine Knife Co ....G....... 419 294-3424
Upper Sandusky (G-19124)

HOMEFURNISHING STORES: Metalware

Scs Construction Services Inc ....E....... 513 929-0260
Cincinnati (G-4393)
Stainless Machine Engineering.............G....... 330 501-1992
Leetonia (G-11865)

HOMEFURNISHING STORES: Mirrors

Bruening Glass Works Inc ....G....... 440 333-4768
Cleveland (G-4940)
Dale Kestler ....G....... 513 871-9000
Cincinnati (G-3637)

HOMEFURNISHING STORES: Pictures, Wall

Bonfoey Co..F 216 621-0178
Cleveland (G-4924)
House of 10000 Picture Frames...........G....... 937 254-5541
Dayton (G-8393)

HOMEFURNISHING STORES: Pottery

All Fired Up Pnt Your Own Pot ....G....... 330 865-5858
Copley (G-7839)
Annies Mud Pie Shop LLC ....G....... 513 871-2529
Cincinnati (G-3405)
Kiln of Hyde Park Inc ....F 513 321-3307
Cincinnati (G-3988)

HOMEFURNISHING STORES: Venetian Blinds

Miles Pk Vntian Blind Shds Mfg ....G....... 216 239-0850
Beachwood (G-1279)

HOMEFURNISHING STORES: Vertical Blinds

Blind Factory Showroom ....E....... 614 771-6549
Hilliard (G-10935)
Blind Outlet...G....... 614 895-2002
Westerville (G-20202)
Optimun Blinds Inc ....G....... 740 598-5808
Brilliant (G-2094)

HOMEFURNISHING STORES: Window Furnishings

Great Day Improvements LLC ....G....... 330 468-0700
Macedonia (G-12456)
Hob Enterprises LLC ....G....... 440 290-8861
Mentor (G-13603)
Pei Liquidation Company.......................E....... 615 781-5020
Macedonia (G-12471)
Pei Liquidation Company.......................C....... 330 467-4267
Macedonia (G-12470)

HOMEFURNISHING STORES: Window Shades, NEC

Cincinnati Window Shade Inc ....G....... 513 398-8510
Mason (G-12995)
Cincinnati Window Shade Inc ....F 513 631-7200
Cincinnati (G-3568)
Gotcha Covered ....G....... 513 829-7555
Fairfield (G-9661)

HOMEFURNISHINGS & SPLYS, WHOLESALE: Decorative

Lena Fiore Inc..F 330 468-3226
Akron (G-270)
Luminex Home Decor............................A....... 513 563-1113
Blue Ash (G-1831)

HOMEFURNISHINGS, WHOLESALE: Blinds, Venetian

Style-Line Incorporated.........................E....... 614 291-0600
Columbus (G-7664)

HOMEFURNISHINGS, WHOLESALE: Blinds, Vertical

Blind Factory Showroom ....E....... 614 771-6549
Hilliard (G-10935)
Blind Outlet...G....... 614 895-2002
Westerville (G-20202)
Custom Blind Corporation ....F 937 643-2907
Dayton (G-8257)

HOMEFURNISHINGS, WHOLESALE: Draperies

Accent Drapery Co Inc ....E....... 614 488-0741
Columbus (G-6683)
Lumenomics Inc....................................E....... 614 798-3500
Lewis Center (G-11906)

HOMEFURNISHINGS, WHOLESALE: Grills, Barbecue

S I Distributing Inc ....F 419 647-4909
Spencerville (G-17465)

HOMEFURNISHINGS, WHOLESALE: Kitchenware

Brighteye Innovations LLC ....F 800 573-0052
Akron (G-100)
Us Inc ....G....... 513 791-1162
Blue Ash (G-1887)
Walter F Stephens Jr Inc ....E....... 937 746-0521
Franklin (G-10063)

HOMEFURNISHINGS, WHOLESALE: Linens, Table

Rons Texstyles LLC..............................G....... 513 936-9975
Columbus (G-7571)

HOMEFURNISHINGS, WHOLESALE: Mirrors/Pictures, Framed/Unframd

Dale Kestler ....G....... 513 871-9000
Cincinnati (G-3637)

HOMEFURNISHINGS, WHOLESALE: Pottery

Annies Mud Pie Shop LLC ....G....... 513 871-2529
Cincinnati (G-3405)
Yellow Springs Pottery..........................F 937 767-1666
Yellow Springs (G-21002)

HOMEFURNISHINGS, WHOLESALE: Window Covering Parts & Access

E W Perry Service Co Inc ....G....... 419 473-1231
Toledo (G-18448)

HOMES, MODULAR: Wooden

Everything In America ....G....... 347 871-6872
Cleveland (G-5310)
J L Wannemacher Sales & Svc ....F 419 453-3445
Ottoville (G-15823)
Unibilt Industries Inc ....E....... 937 890-7570
Vandalia (G-19313)

HOMES: Log Cabins

Al Yoder Construction Company...........G....... 330 359-5726
Millersburg (G-14191)
Gillard Construction Inc ....F 740 376-9744
Marietta (G-12786)
Hochstetler Milling LLC ....E....... 419 368-0004
Loudonville (G-12298)
Mohican Log Homes Inc.......................G....... 419 994-4088
Loudonville (G-12299)
Silver Creek Log Homes........................G....... 419 335-3220
Wauseon (G-19694)

HONING & LAPPING MACHINES

Diversified Honing Inc ....E....... 330 874-4663
Bolivar (G-1932)
Precision Honing Inc ....F 440 942-7339
Willoughby (G-20578)

HOODS: Range, Sheet Metal

Z Line Kitchen and Bath LLC................G....... 614 777-5004
Marysville (G-12977)

HOOKS: Crane, Laminated Plate

Morris Material Handling Inc.................G....... 937 525-5520
Springfield (G-17608)
Rampp Company ....E....... 740 373-7886
Marietta (G-12822)

HOPPERS: Sheet Metal

Apex Welding Incorporated ....F 440 232-6770
Bedford (G-1398)

HORSE & PET ACCESSORIES: Textile

Vitamin Lac ....F 440 548-5294
Middlefield (G-14003)

HOSE: Automobile, Rubber

Cooper-Standard Automotive Inc..........B....... 419 352-3533
Bowling Green (G-1983)
Myers Industries Inc ....C....... 330 336-6621
Wadsworth (G-19420)
Myers Industries Inc ....E....... 330 253-5592
Akron (G-309)
Sumiriko Ohio Inc ....C....... 419 358-2121
Bluffton (G-1916)

HOSE: Flexible Metal

Ace Manufacturing Company ....E....... 513 541-2490
West Chester (G-19976)
First Francis Company Inc....................E....... 440 352-8927
Painesville (G-15881)
Specialty Hose Aerospace Corp...........F 330 497-9650
Canton (G-2854)
Specialty Hose Corporation ....F 330 497-9650
North Canton (G-15266)
Swagelok Manufacturing Co LLC ....E....... 440 248-4600
Solon (G-17395)

HOSE: Plastic

Kentak Products Company ....D....... 330 386-3700
East Liverpool (G-9221)
Kentak Products Company ....C....... 330 382-2000
East Liverpool (G-9222)
Kentak Products Company ....G....... 330 532-6211
East Palestine (G-9240)
Universal Plastics Inc............................E....... 440 942-7510
Mentor (G-13762)

HOSE: Rubber

Aeroquip-Vickers Inc............................G....... 216 523-5000
Cleveland (G-4722)
Eaton Corporation ....A....... 419 238-1190
Van Wert (G-19253)
Eaton Hydraulics LLC............................E....... 419 232-7777
Van Wert (G-19254)
Eaton-Aeroquip Llc...............................C....... 216 523-5000
Cleveland (G-5254)
Eaton-Aeroquip Llc...............................D....... 419 238-1190
Van Wert (G-19255)
Milligan Workshops Inc.........................E....... 419 353-0099
Bowling Green (G-2002)
Salem-Republic Rubber Company........E....... 330 938-2016
Sebring (G-17052)
Summers Acquisition Corp....................G....... 740 373-0303
Marietta (G-12839)

HOSES & BELTING: Rubber & Plastic

Aeroquip Corp.......................................G....... 419 238-1190
Van Wert (G-19242)
Allied Fabricating & Wldg Co.................E....... 614 751-6664
Columbus (G-6725)
Cmt Machining & Fabg LLC ....F 937 652-3740
Urbana (G-19151)
Contitech North America Inc ....E....... 440 225-5363
Akron (G-129)
Eaton Corporation ....C....... 330 274-0743
Aurora (G-916)
Eaton-Aeroquip Inc...............................D....... 419 891-7775
Maumee (G-13258)
Goodyear Tire & Rubber Company ....A....... 330 796-2121
Akron (G-207)
Hbd/Thermoid Inc ....C....... 937 593-5010
Bellefontaine (G-1532)
Kent Elastomer Products Inc ....G....... 800 331-4762
Mogadore (G-14379)
Kent Elastomer Products Inc ....C....... 330 673-1011
Kent (G-11478)

PRODUCT

Mechanical Elastomerics Inc ....G...... 330 863-1014
Malvern (G-12547)
Parker-Hannifin Corporation..............E...... 330 296-2871
Ravenna (G-16549)
Roller Source Inc ....F...... 440 748-4033
Columbia Station (G-6596)
Sperry Rice Manufacturing LLC ....F...... 330 276-2801
Killbuck (G-11600)
Summers Acquisition Corp ....G...... 419 526-5800
Mansfield (G-12687)
Summers Acquisition Corp ....G...... 419 423-5800
Findlay (G-9898)
Watteredge LLC ....D...... 440 933-6110
Avon Lake (G-1055)

HOSPITALS: Medical & Surgical

Optoquest Inc ....G...... 216 445-3637
Cleveland (G-5944)

HOTELS & MOTELS

Continental GL Sls & Inv Group ....B...... 614 679-1201
Powell (G-16469)

HOUSEHOLD APPLIANCE STORES

Carr Supply Co....................................G...... 937 276-2555
Dayton (G-8211)

HOUSEHOLD APPLIANCE STORES: Air Cond Rm Units, Self-Contnd

Carr Supply Co....................................G...... 937 316-6300
Greenville (G-10492)
Winsupply Inc ....F...... 937 346-0600
Springfield (G-17679)

HOUSEHOLD APPLIANCE STORES: Ranges, Gas

Z Line Kitchen and Bath LLC ....G...... 614 777-5004
Marysville (G-12977)

HOUSEHOLD APPLIANCE STORES: Suntanning Eqpt & Splys

Success Technologies Inc ....G...... 614 761-0008
Powell (G-16484)

HOUSEHOLD ARTICLES, EXC KITCHEN: Pottery

Bodycote Imt Inc ....E...... 740 852-5000
London (G-12201)

HOUSEHOLD ARTICLES: Metal

Gregory Industries Inc.......................D...... 330 477-4800
Canton (G-2719)
Hoffman Machining & Repair LLC.......G...... 419 547-9204
Clyde (G-6540)
R L Torbeck Industries Inc ....D...... 513 367-0080
Harrison (G-10800)
Voyale Minority Enterprise LLC...........E...... 216 271-3661
Cleveland (G-6431)

HOUSEHOLD FURNISHINGS, NEC

Ace-Tex Enterprises Inc ....F...... 513 829-8899
Hamilton (G-10661)
Casco Mfg Solutions Inc ....D...... 513 681-0003
Cincinnati (G-3504)
DCW Acquisition Inc..........................F...... 216 451-0666
Cleveland (G-5179)
F K Holding Inc ....F...... 513 641-1400
Cincinnati (G-3735)
Master Mfg Co Inc ....E...... 216 641-0500
Cleveland (G-5758)
Nanofilm Ltd ....E...... 216 674-1430
Cleveland (G-5851)
Ohio Table Pad Company....................F...... 419 872-6400
Perrysburg (G-16130)
Silver Threads Inc ....E...... 614 733-0099
Plain City (G-16359)
Stan Rileys Custom Draperies............G...... 513 821-3732
Cincinnati (G-4452)

HOUSEWARES, ELECTRIC, EXC COOKING APPLIANCES & UTENSILS

Klawhorn Industries Inc ....G...... 330 335-8191
Wadsworth (G-19414)

HOUSEWARES, ELECTRIC: Air Purifiers, Portable

Hmi Industries Inc ....E...... 440 846-7800
Strongsville (G-17926)

HOUSEWARES, ELECTRIC: Cooking Appliances

Didonato Products Inc ....G...... 330 535-1119
Akron (G-151)
Nacco Industries Inc..........................E...... 440 229-5151
Cleveland (G-5848)
Whirlpool Corporation ....B...... 937 548-4126
Greenville (G-10527)

HOUSEWARES, ELECTRIC: Cooking Utensils

Peerless-Winsmith Inc ....G...... 614 526-7000
Dublin (G-9122)

HOUSEWARES, ELECTRIC: Curlers, Hair

Fhi Heat Inc ....G...... 216 456-0353
Solon (G-17291)

HOUSEWARES, ELECTRIC: Fans, Exhaust & Ventilating

Anson Co ....G...... 216 524-8838
Bedford (G-1397)
Broan-Nutone LLC ....G...... 888 336-3948
Blue Ash (G-1755)
Ventilation Systems Jsc ....G...... 513 348-3853
Blue Ash (G-1889)

HOUSEWARES, ELECTRIC: Heating, Bsbrd/Wall, Radiant Heat

Aitken Products Inc ....G...... 440 466-5711
Geneva (G-10341)

HOUSEWARES, ELECTRIC: Humidifiers, Household

Skuttle Mfg Co ....F...... 740 373-9169
Marietta (G-12831)

HOUSEWARES: Dishes, China

Libbey Glass Inc ....A...... 419 729-7272
Toledo (G-18559)
Warrior Imports Inc ....E...... 954 935-5536
Youngstown (G-21243)

HOUSEWARES: Dishes, Earthenware

Added Touch Decorating Gallery ....G...... 419 747-3146
Ontario (G-15684)
Modern China Inc ....E...... 330 938-6104
Sebring (G-17048)

HOUSEWARES: Dishes, Plastic

Everyware Global Inc ....D...... 740 687-2500
Lancaster (G-11711)
F K Holding Inc ....F...... 513 641-1400
Cincinnati (G-3735)
Fukuvi Usa Inc ....D...... 937 236-7288
Dayton (G-8354)
Joneszylon Company LLC ....G...... 740 545-6341
West Lafayette (G-20089)
Riotech International Ltd ....G...... 513 779-0990
West Chester (G-19933)
Sterilite Corporation ....B...... 330 830-2204
Massillon (G-13204)

HOUSEWARES: Household & Commercial, Vitreous China

Syracuse China Company ....C...... 419 727-2100
Toledo (G-18712)

HOUSING COMPONENTS: Prefabricated, Concrete

Ramp Creek III Ltd ....G...... 740 522-0660
Heath (G-10853)

HOUSINGS: Business Machine, Sheet Metal

Samuel Clark ....F...... 614 855-2263
New Albany (G-14772)

HOUSINGS: Pressure

Hyq Technologies LLC ....G...... 513 225-6911
Oxford (G-15837)

HUB CAPS: Automobile, Stamped Metal

Blackburn Hubcaps & Wheels LLC ....G...... 330 467-0236
Macedonia (G-12438)

HUMIDIFIERS & DEHUMIDIFIERS

Guardian Technologies LLC ....E...... 216 706-2250
Euclid (G-9582)

HYDRAULIC EQPT REPAIR SVC

Advanced Cylinder Repair Inc ....G...... 419 289-0538
Ashland (G-701)
Fluid System Service Inc ....G...... 216 651-2450
Cleveland (G-5361)
Hhi Company Inc ....G...... 330 455-3983
Canton (G-2727)
Hunger Hydraulics CC Ltd ....F...... 419 666-4510
Rossford (G-16741)
Hunter Hydraulics Inc ....G...... 330 455-3983
Canton (G-2732)
Hydraulic Products Inc ....G...... 440 946-4575
Willoughby (G-20506)
Hydraulic Specialists Inc ....E...... 740 922-3343
Midvale (G-14108)
Jrs Hydraulic & Welding ....G...... 614 497-1100
Columbus (G-7246)
Perkins Motor Service Ltd ....F...... 440 277-1256
Lorain (G-12267)
Quad Fluid Dynamics Inc ....F...... 330 220-3005
Brunswick (G-2250)
R & L Hydraulics Inc ....G...... 937 399-3407
Springfield (G-17632)
Swanson Industries Inc ....D...... 304 284-5199
New Philadelphia (G-14931)

HYDRAULIC FLUIDS: Synthetic Based

Advanced Engine Tech LLC ....G...... 937 439-0224
Bellbrook (G-1503)
Permco Inc...C...... 330 626-2801
Streetsboro (G-17866)

HYDROPONIC EQPT

Cropking Incorporated ....F...... 330 302-4203
Lodi (G-12159)

Hard Rubber & Molded Rubber Prdts

Ashtabula Rubber Co ....G...... 440 992-2195
Ashtabula (G-794)
Cep Holdings LLC ....G...... 330 665-2900
Fairlawn (G-9745)
Colonial Rubber Company ....E...... 330 296-2831
Ravenna (G-16523)
Eckel Industries Inc ....E...... 978 772-0480
West Chester (G-19999)
Foxtronix Inc ....G...... 937 866-2112
Miamisburg (G-13810)
G Grafton Machine & Rubber..............F...... 330 297-1062
Ravenna (G-16530)
Lexington Rubber Group Inc ....E...... 330 425-8472
Twinsburg (G-18973)
Martin Industries Inc..........................C...... 419 862-2694
Elmore (G-9364)
Master Mfg Co Inc ....E...... 216 641-0500
Cleveland (G-5758)
May Lin Silicone Products Inc ....G...... 330 825-9019
Barberton (G-1129)
Merrico Inc ....G...... 419 525-2711
Mansfield (G-12646)
Spiralcool Company ....F...... 419 483-2510
Bellevue (G-1562)
Starpoint Extrusions LLC ....E...... 330 825-2373
Norton (G-15522)

Tallmadge Finishing Co Inc ....E 330 633-7466
Akron (G-426)

Universal Urethane Pdts Inc ....D 419 693-7400
Toledo (G-18760)

Woodbridge Group ....C 419 334-3666
Fremont (G-10195)

ICE

Haller Enterprises Inc ....F 330 733-9693
Akron (G-211)

Home City Ice Company ....E 937 461-6028
Dayton (G-8392)

Home City Ice Company ....F 419 562-4953
Delaware (G-8860)

Home City Ice Company ....F 440 439-5001
Bedford (G-1429)

Home City Ice Company ....E 614 836-2877
Groveport (G-10625)

J Davis Sales and Assoc LLC ....G 330 947-2038
Atwater (G-899)

Lori Holding Co ....E 740 342-3230
New Lexington (G-14848)

Millersburg Ice Co ....E 330 674-3016
Millersburg (G-14249)

Olmsted Ice Inc ....E 440 235-8411
Olmsted Twp (G-15682)

Penguin Serv Ice ....G 614 848-6511
Worthington (G-20882)

Velvet Ice Cream Company ....F 419 562-2009
Bucyrus (G-2363)

Wings Way Drive Thru Inc ....G 330 533-2788
Salem (G-16935)

ICE CREAM & ICES WHOLESALERS

Country Maid Ice Cream Inc ....G 330 659-6830
Richfield (G-16619)

United Dairy Farmers Inc ....C 513 396-8700
Cincinnati (G-4538)

Velvet Ice Cream Company ....F 419 562-2009
Bucyrus (G-2363)

ICE WHOLESALERS

Home City Ice Company ....E 614 836-2877
Groveport (G-10625)

Lori Holding Co ....E 740 342-3230
New Lexington (G-14848)

ICE: Dry

Continental Carbonic Pdts Inc ....G 614 491-4327
Obetz (G-15654)

Continental Carbonic Pdts Inc ....G 937 316-6160
Greenville (G-10495)

IDENTIFICATION PLATES

API Machining Fabrication Inc ....G 740 369-0455
Delaware (G-8821)

Partners In Recognition Inc ....E 937 420-2150
Fort Loramie (G-9934)

Trademark Designs Inc ....E 419 628-3897
Minster (G-14365)

IGNEOUS ROCK: Crushed & Broken

Great Lakes Crushing Ltd ....E 440 944-5500
Wickliffe (G-20366)

Stoneco Inc ....G 419 686-3311
Portage (G-16428)

IGNITERS: Jet Fuel

K2 Petroleum & Supply LLC ....G 937 503-2614
Cincinnati (G-3966)

IGNITION APPARATUS & DISTRIBUTORS

Unison Industries LLC ....C 937 426-0621
Beavercreek (G-1364)

IGNITION SYSTEMS: High Frequency

Altronic LLC ....C 330 545-9768
Girard (G-10381)

IGNITION SYSTEMS: Internal Combustion Engine

United Ignition Wire Corp ....G 216 898-1112
Cleveland (G-6385)

INCENSE

Wild Berry Incense Inc ....F 513 523-8583
Oxford (G-15846)

INCUBATORS & BROODERS: Farm

Chick Master Incubator Company ....C 330 722-5591
Medina (G-13386)

INDL & PERSONAL SVC PAPER WHOLESALERS

Buckeye Boxes Inc ....E 614 274-8484
Columbus (G-6871)

Buckeye Paper Co Inc ....E 330 477-5925
Canton (G-2630)

Dayton Industrial Drum Inc ....E 937 253-8933
Dayton (G-8103)

Gvs Industries Inc ....G 513 887-8660
Hamilton (G-10699)

Millcraft Group LLC ....D 216 441-5500
Cleveland (G-5817)

Putnam Plastics Inc ....G 937 866-6261
Dayton (G-8603)

Ricking Paper and Specialty Co ....G 513 825-3551
Cincinnati (G-4345)

Zebco Industries Inc ....F 740 654-4510
Lancaster (G-11763)

INDL & PERSONAL SVC PAPER, WHOL: Bags, Paper/Disp Plastic

A To Z Paper Box Co ....G 330 325-8722
Rootstown (G-16718)

Atlapac Corp ....D 614 252-2121
Columbus (G-6782)

Qumont Chemical Co ....G 419 241-1057
Toledo (G-18665)

INDL & PERSONAL SVC PAPER, WHOL: Boxes, Corrugtd/Solid Fiber

American Corrugated Pdts Inc ....E 800 248-6840
Columbus (G-6736)

American Made Corrugated Packg ....F 937 981-2111
Greenfield (G-10473)

JIT Packaging Inc ....E 330 562-8080
Aurora (G-927)

Westrock CP LLC ....D 770 448-2193
Wshngtn CT Hs (G-20930)

INDL & PERSONAL SVC PAPER, WHOL: Paper, Wrap/Coarse/Prdts

Orora North America ....G 513 539-8274
Monroe (G-14411)

Polymer Packaging Inc ....D 330 832-2000
Massillon (G-13195)

INDL & PERSONAL SVC PAPER, WHOLESALE: Boxes & Containers

Argrov Box Co ....F 937 898-1700
Dayton (G-8163)

Bentley World-Packaging Ltd ....F 440 232-1100
Bedford (G-1407)

INDL & PERSONAL SVC PAPER, WHOLESALE: Boxes, Fldng Pprboard

O T Packaging ....G 330 482-2224
Columbiana (G-6626)

INDL & PERSONAL SVC PAPER, WHOLESALE: Disposable

Acme Steak & Seafood Inc ....F 330 270-8000
Youngstown (G-21016)

INDL & PERSONAL SVC PAPER, WHOLESALE: Paper Tubes & Cores

Sonoco Products Company ....D 937 429-0040
Beavercreek Township (G-1390)

INDL & PERSONAL SVC PAPER, WHOLESALE: Shipping Splys

Adapt-A-Pak Inc ....E 937 845-0386
Tipp City (G-18260)

Systems Pack Inc ....E 330 467-5729
Macedonia (G-12493)

INDL & PERSONAL SVC PAPER, WHOLESALE: Towels, Paper

Aci Industries Converting Ltd ....E 740 368-4160
Delaware (G-8816)

INDL CONTRACTORS: Exhibit Construction

Abstract Displays Inc ....G 513 985-9700
Blue Ash (G-1732)

Benchmark Craftsman Inc ....E 330 975-4214
Seville (G-17069)

Display Dynamics Inc ....F 937 832-2830
Englewood (G-9516)

INDL DIAMONDS WHOLESALERS

Chardon Tool & Supply Co Inc ....E 440 286-6440
Chardon (G-3146)

INDL EQPT CLEANING SVCS

Hy-Blast Inc ....F 513 424-0704
Middletown (G-14045)

INDL EQPT SVCS

3-D Service Ltd ....C 330 830-3500
Massillon (G-13104)

Commercial Electric Pdts Corp ....E 216 241-2886
Cleveland (G-5104)

Dayton Industrial Drum Inc ....E 937 253-8933
Dayton (G-8103)

E E Controls Inc ....E 440 585-5554
Willowick (G-20647)

Forge Industries Inc ....A 330 782-8301
Youngstown (G-21089)

GL Nause Co Inc ....E 513 722-9500
Loveland (G-12353)

Graphic Systems Services Inc ....E 937 746-0708
Springboro (G-17482)

Grob Systems Inc ....C 419 358-9015
Bluffton (G-1912)

Industrial Repair & Mfg Inc ....E 419 822-4232
Delta (G-8936)

Kc Robotics Inc ....E 513 860-4442
West Chester (G-19887)

L M Equipment & Design Inc ....E 330 332-9951
Salem (G-16907)

Magnetech Industrial Svcs Inc ....C 330 830-3500
Massillon (G-13170)

Mesocoat Inc ....F 216 453-0866
Euclid (G-9593)

Miami Valley Punch & Mfg ....E 937 237-0533
Dayton (G-8491)

Midwest Metrology LLC ....G 937 832-0965
Englewood (G-9533)

Northwood Industries Inc ....F 419 666-2100
Perrysburg (G-16128)

Obr Cooling Towers Inc ....E 419 243-3443
Rossford (G-16744)

Quintus Technologies LLC ....E 614 891-2732
Lewis Center (G-11912)

Sunbeam Products Co LLC ....G 419 691-1551
Toledo (G-18706)

TE Brown LLC ....G 937 223-2241
Dayton (G-8706)

US Molding Machinery Co Inc ....E 440 918-1701
Willoughby (G-20625)

Walker National Inc ....E 614 492-1614
Columbus (G-7748)

INDL GASES WHOLESALERS

Airgas Usa LLC ....G 440 232-6397
Oakwood Village (G-15622)

Airgas USA LLC ....G 419 726-2719
Toledo (G-18325)

Matheson Tri-Gas Inc ....E 440 365-1741
Twinsburg (G-18980)

INDL HELP SVCS

Aqua Technology Group LLC ....G 513 298-1183
West Chester (G-19807)

INDL MACHINERY & EQPT WHOLESALERS

Addisonmckee Inc ....C 513 228-7000
Lebanon (G-11774)

PRODUCT

Aerocontrolex Group Inc	D	440 352-6182
Cleveland *(G-4719)*			
Alkon Corporation	D	419 355-9111
Fremont *(G-10124)*			
Alkon Corporation	E	614 799-6650
Dublin *(G-9039)*			
AM Industrial Group LLC	G	216 433-7171
Brookpark *(G-2149)*			
American Rescue Technology	F	937 293-6240
Dayton *(G-8155)*			
Amtech Inc	G	440 238-2141
Strongsville *(G-17888)*			
Armour Spray Systems Inc	F	216 398-3838
Cleveland *(G-4833)*			
Ashtech Corporation	G	440 646-9911
Cleveland *(G-4847)*			
Atlas Machine and Supply Inc	E	502 584-7262
West Chester *(G-19982)*			
Atlas Machine and Supply Inc	G	614 351-1603
Hilliard *(G-10928)*			
Ats Systems Oregon Inc	B	541 738-0932
Lewis Center *(G-11885)*			
Automation Solutions Inc	G	614 235-4060
Columbus *(G-6790)*			
Avure Autoclave Systems Inc	E	614 891-2732
Columbus *(G-6794)*			
Brown Industrial Inc	E	937 693-3838
Botkins *(G-1951)*			
Carlton Natco	G	216 451-5588
Cleveland *(G-4978)*			
Cincinnati Electrical Tool	F	513 941-5000
Cleves *(G-6509)*			
Control Line Equipment Inc	F	216 433-7766
Cleveland *(G-5127)*			
Cortest Inc	F	440 942-1235
Willoughby *(G-20463)*			
Ctm Integration Incorporated	E	330 332-1800
Salem *(G-16887)*			
Dengensha America Corporation	F	440 439-8081
Bedford *(G-1418)*			
Dinkmar Inc	G	419 468-8516
Galion *(G-10263)*			
Dura Magnetics Inc	F	419 882-0591
Sylvania *(G-18106)*			
Dynamics Research & Dev	G	419 478-7091
Toledo *(G-18446)*			
Edjean Technical Services Inc	G	440 647-3300
Sullivan *(G-18054)*			
Eltool Corporation	G	513 723-1772
Mansfield *(G-12599)*			
EMI Corp	D	937 596-5511
Jackson Center *(G-11341)*			
Equipment Guys Inc	F	614 871-9220
Newark *(G-15004)*			
Equipment Manufacturers Intl	E	216 651-6700
Cleveland *(G-5291)*			
Freeman Manufacturing & Sup Co	E	440 934-1902
Avon *(G-996)*			
G W Cobb Co	F	216 341-0100
Cleveland *(G-5389)*			
Ged Holdings Inc	C	330 963-5401
Twinsburg *(G-18941)*			
Glavin Industries Inc	E	440 349-0049
Solon *(G-17297)*			
Gokoh Corporation	F	937 339-4977
Troy *(G-18832)*			
Grand Harbor Yacht Sales & Svc	G	440 442-2919
Cleveland *(G-5445)*			
Grenga Machine & Welding	F	330 743-1113
Youngstown *(G-21104)*			
Hannon Company	D	330 456-4728
Canton *(G-2723)*			
Hendrickson International Corp	D	740 929-5600
Hebron *(G-10870)*			
Hirons Memorial Works Inc	G	937 444-2917
Mount Orab *(G-14581)*			
Hug Manufacturing Corporation	F	419 668-5086
Norwalk *(G-15546)*			
I C Consultants Inc	F	216 731-9992
Cleveland *(G-5545)*			
Ibi Brake Products Inc	G	440 543-7962
Chagrin Falls *(G-3094)*			
Industrial Machine Tool Svc	G	216 651-1122
Cleveland *(G-5564)*			
Intelligrated Inc	E	513 874-0788
West Chester *(G-20016)*			
Intelligrated Systems Inc	A	866 936-7300
Mason *(G-13045)*			
Intelligrated Systems Ohio LLC	A	513 701-7300
Mason *(G-13047)*			
International Trade Group Inc	G	614 486-4634
Columbus *(G-7207)*			
Interntnal Plstic Cmpnents Inc	F	330 744-0625
Campbell *(G-2490)*			
Interstate Tool Corporation	E	216 671-1077
Cleveland *(G-5583)*			
J McCaman Enterprises Inc	F	330 825-2401
New Franklin *(G-14825)*			
Jay Dee Service Corporation	G	330 425-1546
Macedonia *(G-12463)*			
Jcl Equipment Co Inc	G	937 374-1010
Xenia *(G-20958)*			
Jed Industries Inc	G	440 639-9973
Grand River *(G-10451)*			
Jones Industrial Service LLC	G	419 287-4553
Pemberville *(G-16029)*			
JPS Technologies Inc	F	513 984-6400
Blue Ash *(G-1820)*			
JPS Technologies Inc	F	513 984-6400
Blue Ash *(G-1821)*			
Kolinahr Systems Inc	E	513 745-9401
Blue Ash *(G-1823)*			
Kyocera SGS Precision Tools	G	330 688-6667
Munroe Falls *(G-14661)*			
Linden Industries Inc	E	330 928-4064
Cuyahoga Falls *(G-8020)*			
Mataco	G	440 546-8355
Broadview Heights *(G-2114)*			
Mc Kinley Machinery Inc	G	440 937-6300
Avon *(G-1000)*			
Mfh Partners Inc	F	440 461-4100
Cleveland *(G-5795)*			
Midlands Millroom Supply Inc	G	330 453-9100
Canton *(G-2779)*			
Midwest Conveyor Products Inc	E	419 281-1235
Ashland *(G-754)*			
Mine Equipment Services LLC	E	740 936-5427
Sunbury *(G-18067)*			
Minerva Welding and Fabg Inc	E	330 868-7731
Minerva *(G-14335)*			
Monaghan & Associates Inc	E	937 253-7706
Dayton *(G-8506)*			
Multi Products Company	E	330 674-5981
Millersburg *(G-14252)*			
National Safety Tech LLC	E	419 727-0552
Toledo *(G-18598)*			
Neil R Scholl Inc	F	740 653-6593
Lancaster *(G-11733)*			
Off Contact Inc	F	419 255-5546
Toledo *(G-18614)*			
Orbytel Print and Packg Inc	G	216 267-8734
Cleveland *(G-5946)*			
Park Corporation	B	216 267-4870
Cleveland *(G-5965)*			
Pfpc Enterprises Inc	B	513 941-6200
Cincinnati *(G-4233)*			
Pines Manufacturing Inc	E	440 835-5553
Westlake *(G-20293)*			
Plastic Process Equipment Inc	E	216 367-7000
Macedonia *(G-12474)*			
Plastran Inc	G	440 237-8404
Cleveland *(G-6015)*			
Power-Pack Conveyor Company	E	440 975-9955
Willoughby *(G-20576)*			
Process Automation Specialists	G	330 247-1384
Canal Fulton *(G-2510)*			
Progressive Manufacturing Co	G	330 784-4717
Akron *(G-354)*			
Prospect Mold & Die Company	D	330 929-3311
Cuyahoga Falls *(G-8037)*			
Rayhaven Group Inc	F	330 659-3183
Richfield *(G-16634)*			
Reduction Engineering Inc	E	330 677-2225
Kent *(G-11514)*			
Reid Asset Management Company	E	216 642-3223
Cleveland *(G-6098)*			
Rhino Robotics Ltd	G	513 353-9772
Miamitown *(G-13891)*			
Rubber City Machinery Corp	G	330 434-3500
Akron *(G-380)*			
Samuel Strapping Systems Inc	D	740 522-2500
Heath *(G-10855)*			
Screen Machine Industries LLC	G	740 927-3464
Pataskala *(G-15984)*			
Siemens Industry Inc	E	440 526-2770
Brecksville *(G-2073)*			
Stanley Bittinger	G	740 942-4302
Cadiz *(G-2422)*			
Starkey Machinery Inc	E	419 468-2560
Galion *(G-10289)*			
Stein Inc	F	440 526-9301
Cleveland *(G-6248)*			
Super Systems Inc	E	513 772-0060
Cincinnati *(G-4483)*			
Taiyo America Inc	F	419 300-8811
Saint Marys *(G-16858)*			
Taper Tool & Broach Inc	G	216 486-4435
Cleveland *(G-6294)*			
Tilt-Or-Lift Inc	G	419 893-6944
Maumee *(G-13302)*			
Tj Bell Inc	G	330 633-3644
Akron *(G-442)*			
Tri State Equipment Company	E	513 738-7227
Shandon *(G-17098)*			
U S Electrical Tool Inc	F	513 353-3660
Miamitown *(G-13893)*			
Unarco Material Handling Inc	G	419 384-3211
Pandora *(G-15948)*			
United Hydraulics	F	440 585-0906
Wickliffe *(G-20390)*			
Valv-Trol Company	F	330 686-2800
Stow *(G-17814)*			
Valve Related Controls Inc	F	513 677-8724
Loveland *(G-12397)*			
Venturo Manufacturing Inc	E	513 772-8448
Cincinnati *(G-4562)*			
W W Williams Company LLC	F	330 659-3084
Richfield *(G-16645)*			
Waterloo Manufacturing Co Inc	G	330 947-2917
Atwater *(G-904)*			
Welded Tube Pros LLC	G	330 854-2966
Canal Fulton *(G-2517)*			
William Darling Company Inc	G	614 878-0085
Columbus *(G-7764)*			
Wolf Machine Company	E	513 791-5194
Blue Ash *(G-1897)*			
Zal Air Products Inc	G	440 237-7155
Cleveland *(G-6492)*			

INDL MACHINERY REPAIR & MAINTENANCE

Abj Equipfix	E	419 684-5236
Castalia *(G-2972)*			
Ajax Tocco Magnethermic Corp	C	330 372-8511
Warren *(G-19517)*			
Bradford Neal Machinery Inc	G	440 632-1393
Middlefield *(G-13918)*			
Chelsea Machine Service Inc	G	937 233-6330
Dayton *(G-8227)*			
Cleveland Electric Labs Co	E	800 447-2207
Twinsburg *(G-18915)*			
Custom Metal Works Inc	F	419 668-7831
Norwalk *(G-15531)*			
Cuyahoga Mch Co Ltd Lblty Co	G	216 267-3560
Cleveland *(G-5158)*			
DNC Hydraulics LLC	F	419 963-2800
Rawson *(G-16573)*			
Equipment Spcalists Dayton LLC	G	937 415-2151
Dayton *(G-8330)*			
Fawcett Co Inc	G	330 659-4187
Richfield *(G-16623)*			
General Plastex Inc	E	330 745-7775
Barberton *(G-1117)*			
Grodhaus & Young Inc	F	330 866-3321
Waynesburg *(G-19725)*			
Hydro Supply Co	F	740 454-3842
Zanesville *(G-21320)*			
Ivan Extruders Co Inc	G	330 644-7400
Akron *(G-237)*			
J&J Precision Machine Ltd	E	330 923-5783
Cuyahoga Falls *(G-8012)*			
Jack Gruber	G	740 408-2718
Cardington *(G-2912)*			
JF Martt and Associates Inc	F	330 938-4000
Sebring *(G-17046)*			
Jonmar Gear and Machine Inc	G	330 854-6500
Canal Fulton *(G-2503)*			
Justin P Straub LLC	G	513 761-0282
Cincinnati *(G-3963)*			
Laserflex Corporation	D	614 850-9600
Hilliard *(G-10958)*			
Lees Machinery	G	440 259-2222
Perry *(G-16052)*			
Machine Tool Rebuilders Inc	G	614 228-1070
Columbus *(G-7311)*			
McGuire Machine LLC	G	330 868-3072
Minerva *(G-14333)*			
Measurement Specialties Inc	F	937 885-0800
Dayton *(G-8482)*			
Mechanical Dynamics Analis Ltd	E	440 946-0082
Euclid *(G-9592)*			

2017 Harris Ohio
Industrial Directory

(G-0000) Company's Geographic Section entry number

Odyssey Machine Company Ltd............G..... 419 455-6621
  Perrysburg *(G-16129)*

OKL Can Line Inc.............................E..... 513 825-1655
  Cincinnati *(G-4183)*

Palesh & Associates Inc....................G..... 440 942-9168
  Willoughby *(G-20566)*

Qpmr Inc..F..... 330 723-1739
  Medina *(G-13465)*

Rossi Machinery Services Inc............G..... 419 281-4488
  Ashland *(G-773)*

Steel Eqp Specialists Inc..................D..... 330 823-8260
  Alliance *(G-540)*

T P F Inc...G..... 513 761-9968
  Cincinnati *(G-4490)*

Taft Tool & Production Co.................F..... 419 385-2576
  Toledo *(G-18715)*

Terex Utilities Inc.............................F..... 440 262-3200
  Brecksville *(G-2076)*

Winkle Industries Inc.......................D..... 330 823-9730
  Alliance *(G-554)*

Wood Graphics Inc...........................E..... 513 771-6300
  Cincinnati *(G-4603)*

INDL PATTERNS: Foundry Cores

Exochem Corporation........................D..... 440 277-6116
  Lorain *(G-12246)*

Founder Service & Mfg Co.................F..... 330 584-7759
  Deerfield *(G-8773)*

PCC Airfoils LLC...............................C..... 216 692-7900
  Cleveland *(G-5983)*

INDL PATTERNS: Foundry Patternmaking

Accuform Manufacturing Inc..............E..... 330 797-9291
  Youngstown *(G-21014)*

Case Pattern Co Inc...........................G..... 216 531-0744
  Cleveland *(G-4987)*

Cincinnati Pattern Company...............F..... 513 241-9872
  Cincinnati *(G-3562)*

Morcast Precision Inc.........................G..... 614 258-5071
  Columbus *(G-7368)*

National Pattern Mfg Co.....................F..... 330 682-6871
  Orrville *(G-15750)*

North Coast Pattern Inc......................G..... 440 322-5064
  Strongsville *(G-17946)*

Plas-Mac Corp...................................D..... 440 349-3222
  Solon *(G-17361)*

Seilkop Industries Inc.........................F..... 513 679-5680
  Cincinnati *(G-4399)*

Wright Way Patterns..........................G..... 513 574-5776
  Cincinnati *(G-4608)*

INDL PROCESS INSTRUMENTS: Absorp Analyzers, Infrared, X-Ray

Godfrey & Wing Inc............................F..... 419 980-4616
  Defiance *(G-8791)*

INDL PROCESS INSTRUMENTS: Chromatographs

Consolidatd Analytical Sys Inc..............F..... 513 542-1200
  Cleves *(G-6511)*

INDL PROCESS INSTRUMENTS: Control

Aqua Technology Group LLC..............G..... 513 298-1183
  West Chester *(G-19807)*

Avure Technologies Inc......................E..... 614 891-2732
  Lewis Center *(G-11888)*

Brighton Technologies LLC.................F..... 513 469-1800
  Saint Bernard *(G-16779)*

BSK Industries Inc.............................G..... 440 230-9299
  North Royalton *(G-15412)*

Clark-Reliance Corporation.................C..... 440 572-1500
  Strongsville *(G-17902)*

Control Associates Inc.......................G..... 440 708-1770
  Chagrin Falls *(G-3082)*

Corro-Tech Equipment Corp...............G..... 216 941-1552
  Cleveland *(G-5133)*

Dynetech LLC....................................E..... 419 690-4281
  Toledo *(G-18447)*

E E Controls Inc................................G..... 440 585-5554
  Willowick *(G-20647)*

Facts Inc...E..... 330 928-2332
  Cuyahoga Falls *(G-7995)*

John McHael Priester Assoc Inc.........G..... 513 761-8605
  Wyoming *(G-20932)*

Journey Electronics Corp...................G..... 513 539-9836
  Monroe *(G-14406)*

Monitortech Corp...............................G..... 614 231-0500
  Columbus *(G-7366)*

Nanostatics Corporation.....................F..... 740 477-5900
  Circleville *(G-4635)*

NDC Technologies Inc........................C..... 937 233-9935
  Dayton *(G-8522)*

Nidec Indus Automtn USA LLC...........E..... 216 901-2400
  Cleveland *(G-5882)*

Production Control Units Inc...............D..... 937 299-5594
  Moraine *(G-14519)*

INDL PROCESS INSTRUMENTS: Controllers, Process Variables

Hunkar Technologies Inc....................C..... 513 272-1010
  Cincinnati *(G-3902)*

Overhoff Technology Corp...................F..... 513 248-2400
  Milford *(G-14165)*

Quad/Graphics Inc..............................A..... 513 932-1064
  Lebanon *(G-11830)*

Schneider Electric Usa Inc..................C..... 513 755-4231
  West Chester *(G-19942)*

Schneider Electric Usa Inc..................D..... 513 755-5000
  West Chester *(G-19943)*

Tegron Holding LLC............................G..... 330 836-2004
  Akron *(G-431)*

INDL PROCESS INSTRUMENTS: Data Loggers

Computer Aided Solutions LLC............E..... 440 729-2570
  Chesterland *(G-3201)*

INDL PROCESS INSTRUMENTS: Digital Display, Process Variables

Gem Instrument Co.............................F..... 330 273-6117
  Brunswick *(G-2229)*

Snappskin Inc....................................G..... 440 318-4879
  Chagrin Falls *(G-3070)*

INDL PROCESS INSTRUMENTS: Draft Gauges

Pride Gage Associates LLC.................G..... 419 318-3793
  Toledo *(G-18657)*

INDL PROCESS INSTRUMENTS: Fluidic Devices, Circuit & Systems

Fluid Equipment Corp..........................G..... 419 636-0777
  Bryan *(G-2296)*

INDL PROCESS INSTRUMENTS: Indl Flow & Measuring

Intek Inc..E..... 614 895-0301
  Westerville *(G-20160)*

Tasi Holdings Inc................................E..... 513 202-5182
  Harrison *(G-10809)*

INDL PROCESS INSTRUMENTS: Moisture Meters

GE Infrastructure Sensing Inc.............B..... 740 928-7010
  Hebron *(G-10866)*

INDL PROCESS INSTRUMENTS: Temperature

Altronic LLC.......................................C..... 330 545-9768
  Girard *(G-10381)*

Automatic Timing & Contrls Inc...........D..... 614 888-8855
  New Albany *(G-14747)*

Budzar Industries Inc.........................D..... 440 530-1000
  Willoughby *(G-20448)*

Caron Products and Svcs Inc..............E..... 740 373-6809
  Marietta *(G-12770)*

Doubleday Acquisitions LLC................C..... 937 242-6768
  Moraine *(G-14480)*

Future Controls Corporation................E..... 440 275-3191
  Austinburg *(G-962)*

Logan Enterprises Inc.........................G..... 937 465-8170
  West Liberty *(G-20093)*

Ram Sensors Inc................................F..... 440 835-3540
  Cleveland *(G-6089)*

Tempest Inc.......................................F..... 216 883-6500
  Cleveland *(G-6304)*

INDL PROCESS INSTRUMENTS: Water Quality Monitoring/Cntrl Sys

American Water Services Inc...............G..... 440 243-9840
  Strongsville *(G-17887)*

C H Washington Water Plan..................G..... 740 636-2382
  Wshngtn CT Hs *(G-20904)*

Danaher Corporation...........................C..... 440 995-3003
  Cleveland *(G-5164)*

Danaher Corporation...........................C..... 440 995-3025
  Mentor *(G-13558)*

Fondriest Environmental Inc................F..... 937 426-2151
  Fairborn *(G-9621)*

Wabash River Conservancy.................G..... 419 375-2577
  Fort Recovery *(G-9962)*

Ysi Environmental Inc.........................C..... 937 767-7241
  Yellow Springs *(G-21004)*

INDL SPLYS WHOLESALERS

Alkon Corporation...............................G..... 614 799-6650
  Dublin *(G-9039)*

All Ohio Threaded Rod Co Inc.............G..... 216 426-1800
  Cleveland *(G-4757)*

Alro Steel Corporation........................E..... 419 720-5300
  Toledo *(G-18331)*

Aqua Technology Group LLC...............G..... 513 298-1183
  West Chester *(G-19807)*

B W Grinding Co.................................G..... 419 923-1376
  Lyons *(G-12431)*

Baaron Abrasives Inc..........................G..... 330 263-7737
  Wooster *(G-20745)*

Ci Disposition Co................................E..... 216 587-5200
  Brooklyn Heights *(G-2135)*

Cleveland Plastic Fabricat...................F..... 216 797-7300
  Euclid *(G-9572)*

Cmt Machining & Fabg LLC..................G..... 937 652-3740
  Urbana *(G-19151)*

Coastal Diamond Incorporated.............G..... 440 946-7171
  Mentor *(G-13548)*

Computer System Enhancement...........G..... 513 251-6791
  Cincinnati *(G-3603)*

Cornwell Quality Tools Company...........D..... 330 628-2627
  Mogadore *(G-14370)*

Cotton Fabrics Company Inc.................G..... 419 389-9904
  Toledo *(G-18414)*

Dan Wilzynski.....................................G..... 800 531-3343
  Columbus *(G-7010)*

Dayton Stencil Works Company............E..... 937 223-3233
  Dayton *(G-8287)*

Dexport Tool Manufacturing Co............G..... 513 625-1600
  Loveland *(G-12348)*

Dolin Supply Co..................................E..... 304 529-4171
  South Point *(G-17436)*

Dynatech Systems Inc.........................E..... 440 365-1774
  Elyria *(G-9408)*

Edward W Daniel LLC...........................E..... 440 647-1960
  Wellington *(G-19742)*

Fastener Industries Inc........................F..... 216 267-2240
  Cleveland *(G-5326)*

Fcx Performance Inc............................E..... 614 324-6050
  Columbus *(G-7078)*

First Francis Company Inc....................E..... 440 352-8927
  Painesville *(G-15881)*

General Machine & Supply Co...............G..... 740 453-4804
  Zanesville *(G-21315)*

Gokoh Corporation...............................F..... 937 339-4977
  Troy *(G-18832)*

Great Lakes Textiles Inc.......................E..... 440 439-1300
  Solon *(G-17304)*

H3d Tool Corporation...........................G..... 740 498-5181
  Newcomerstown *(G-15114)*

HMS Industries LLC............................G..... 440 899-0001
  Westlake *(G-20277)*

I-Dee-X Inc..G..... 330 788-2186
  Youngstown *(G-21112)*

Industrial Mold Inc..............................G..... 330 425-7374
  Twinsburg *(G-18959)*

Jamtek Enterprises Inc.........................G..... 513 738-4700
  Harrison *(G-10786)*

JIT Packaging Inc.................................E..... 330 562-8080
  Aurora *(G-927)*

Jtekt North America Corp......................C..... 440 835-1000
  Westlake *(G-20279)*

Kaufman Container Company.................C..... 216 898-2000
  Cleveland *(G-5636)*

Lancaster Commercial Pdts LLC...........E..... 740 286-5081
  Columbus *(G-7282)*

Lapcraft Inc...G..... 614 764-8993
  Powell *(G-16477)*

PRODUCT

Lawrence Industries Inc ....E..... 216 518-7000
Cleveland (G-5687)

Liberty Casting Company LLC ....D..... 740 363-1941
Delaware (G-8869)

Lima Equipment Co ....G..... 419 222-4181
Lima (G-12040)

Logan Clutch Corporation ....E..... 440 808-4258
Cleveland (G-5707)

Maintenance Repair Supply Inc ....E..... 740 922-3006
Midvale (G-14109)

Maumee Hose & Fitting Inc ....G..... 419 893-7252
Maumee (G-13279)

McWane Inc ....B..... 740 622-6651
Coshocton (G-7897)

Metzger Machine Co ....F..... 513 241-3360
Cincinnati (G-4096)

Mill-Rose Company ....C..... 440 255-9171
Mentor (G-13657)

Newact Inc ....F..... 513 321-5177
Batavia (G-1213)

Orbytel Print and Packg Inc ....G..... 216 267-8734
Cleveland (G-5946)

Pinnacle Sales Inc ....G..... 440 777-2544
Westlake (G-20295)

Plastic Process Equipment Inc ....E..... 216 367-7000
Macedonia (G-12474)

S & N Engineering Svcs Corp ....G..... 216 433-1700
Cleveland (G-6147)

Samsel Rope & Marine Supply Co ....E..... 216 241-0333
Cleveland (G-6156)

Samuel Strapping Systems Inc ....D..... 740 522-2500
Heath (G-10855)

SSP Fittings Corp ....D..... 330 425-4250
Twinsburg (G-19022)

Stark Industrial LLC ....E..... 330 493-9773
North Canton (G-15269)

Summers Acquisition Corp ....G..... 419 423-5800
Findlay (G-9898)

Superior Holding LLC ....G..... 216 651-9400
Cleveland (G-6265)

Tricor Industrial Inc ....D..... 330 264-3299
Wooster (G-20841)

United Tool Supply Inc ....G..... 513 752-6000
Cincinnati (G-3320)

Watteredge LLC ....D..... 440 933-6110
Avon Lake (G-1055)

Wesco Distribution Inc ....E..... 419 666-1670
Northwood (G-15495)

Wulco Inc ....D..... 513 679-2600
Cincinnati (G-4612)

Zal Air Products Inc ....G..... 440 237-7155
Cleveland (G-6492)

INDL SPLYS, WHOL: Fasteners, Incl Nuts, Bolts, Screws, Etc

Andre Corporation ....E..... 574 293-0207
Mason (G-12981)

Atlas Bolt & Screw Company LLC ....C..... 419 289-6171
Ashland (G-709)

Crawford Products Inc ....E..... 614 890-1822
Columbus (G-6999)

Facil North America Inc ....C..... 330 487-2500
Twinsburg (G-18934)

Fastenal Company ....G..... 330 745-2996
Akron (G-182)

Hargis Industries LP ....E..... 513 874-5905
West Chester (G-20013)

RB&w Manufacturing LLC ....G..... 740 363-1971
Delaware (G-8881)

RB&w Manufacturing LLC ....F..... 234 380-8540
Streetsboro (G-17870)

Stafast Products Inc ....E..... 440 357-5546
Painesville (G-15922)

Supply Technologies LLC ....C..... 440 947-2100
Cleveland (G-6274)

Youngstown Bolt & Supply Co ....G..... 330 799-3201
Youngstown (G-21247)

INDL SPLYS, WHOLESALE: Abrasives

ARC Abrasives Inc ....D..... 800 888-4885
Troy (G-18805)

Sevan At-Ndustrial Pnt Abr Ltd ....G..... 614 258-4747
Columbus (G-7610)

INDL SPLYS, WHOLESALE: Adhesives, Tape & Plasters

National Adhesives Inc ....F..... 513 683-8650
Cincinnati (G-4138)

INDL SPLYS, WHOLESALE: Barrels, New Or Reconditioned

Sabco Industries Inc ....E..... 419 531-5347
Toledo (G-18683)

INDL SPLYS, WHOLESALE: Bearings

Federal-Mogul Corporation ....C..... 740 432-2393
Cambridge (G-2457)

Forge Industries Inc ....A..... 330 782-8301
Youngstown (G-21089)

INDL SPLYS, WHOLESALE: Bins & Containers, Storage

Creative Plastic Concepts LLC ....G..... 419 927-9588
Sycamore (G-18096)

Dadco Inc ....G..... 513 489-2244
Cincinnati (G-3635)

Dadco Inc ....F..... 513 489-2244
Cincinnati (G-3636)

Modroto ....G..... 800 772-7659
Ashtabula (G-821)

INDL SPLYS, WHOLESALE: Bottler Splys

Pure Water Global Inc ....G..... 419 737-2352
Pioneer (G-16242)

Tolco Corporation ....D..... 419 241-1113
Toledo (G-18728)

INDL SPLYS, WHOLESALE: Brushes, Indl

Trent Manufacturing Company ....F..... 216 391-1551
Cleveland (G-6356)

INDL SPLYS, WHOLESALE: Clean Room Splys

Precision Environments Inc ....E..... 513 847-1510
West Chester (G-19919)

INDL SPLYS, WHOLESALE: Drums, New Or Reconditioned

Dayton Industrial Drum Inc ....E..... 937 253-8933
Dayton (G-8103)

Horwitz & Pintis Co ....F..... 419 666-2220
Toledo (G-18512)

INDL SPLYS, WHOLESALE: Fasteners & Fastening Eqpt

Fastenal Company ....G..... 419 629-3024
New Bremen (G-14787)

McFeelys Inc ....F..... 800 443-7937
Harrison (G-10790)

INDL SPLYS, WHOLESALE: Fittings

Superior Products LLC ....D..... 216 651-9400
Cleveland (G-6270)

Superior Products Llc ....D..... 216 651-9400
Cleveland (G-6269)

INDL SPLYS, WHOLESALE: Gaskets

Ishikawa Gasket America Inc ....C..... 419 353-7300
Bowling Green (G-1991)

INDL SPLYS, WHOLESALE: Gaskets & Seals

P & E Sales Ltd ....G..... 330 829-0100
Alliance (G-532)

Service Pdts Group of Bucyrus ....G..... 419 562-4456
Bucyrus (G-2359)

INDL SPLYS, WHOLESALE: Gears

Ig Watteeuw Usa LLC ....F..... 740 588-1722
Zanesville (G-21321)

INDL SPLYS, WHOLESALE: Hydraulic & Pneumatic Pistons/Valves

Alkon Corporation ....D..... 419 355-9111
Fremont (G-10124)

INDL SPLYS, WHOLESALE: Knives, Indl

Alliance Knife Inc ....E..... 513 367-9000
Harrison (G-10768)

CB Manufacturing & Sls Co Inc ....D..... 937 866-5986
Miamisburg (G-13790)

INDL SPLYS, WHOLESALE: Power Transmission, Eqpt & Apparatus

Commercial Electric Pdts Corp ....E..... 216 241-2886
Cleveland (G-5104)

Great Lakes Power Products Inc ....D..... 440 951-5111
Mentor (G-13596)

Siglent Technologies Amer Inc ....G..... 440 398-5800
Solon (G-17380)

Stevenson Machine Inc ....F..... 513 761-4121
Cincinnati (G-4467)

INDL SPLYS, WHOLESALE: Rubber Goods, Mechanical

Fouty & Company Inc ....G..... 419 693-0017
Oregon (G-15709)

Jet Rubber Company ....E..... 330 325-1821
Rootstown (G-16723)

Mid-State Sales Inc ....G..... 330 744-2158
Youngstown (G-21145)

Netherland Rubber Company ....F..... 513 733-0883
Cincinnati (G-4146)

R C Musson Rubber Co ....E..... 330 773-7651
Akron (G-362)

Solo Products Inc ....F..... 513 321-7884
Cincinnati (G-4435)

Summers Acquisition Corp ....E..... 216 941-7700
Cleveland (G-6262)

Summers Acquisition Corp ....G..... 419 526-5800
Mansfield (G-12687)

Summers Acquisition Corp ....G..... 440 946-5611
Eastlake (G-9291)

INDL SPLYS, WHOLESALE: Seals

Datwyler Sling Sltions USA Inc ....D..... 937 387-2800
Vandalia (G-19289)

McNeil Industries Inc ....E..... 440 951-7756
Painesville (G-15901)

INDL SPLYS, WHOLESALE: Signmaker Eqpt & Splys

Interstate Sign Products Inc ....G..... 419 683-1962
Crestline (G-7930)

Sign Source USA Inc ....D..... 419 224-1130
Lima (G-12092)

INDL SPLYS, WHOLESALE: Tools

Bluelevel Technologies Inc ....G..... 330 523-5215
Richfield (G-16616)

File Sharpening Company Inc ....E..... 937 376-8268
Xenia (G-20951)

H & D Steel Service Inc ....E..... 440 237-3390
North Royalton (G-15423)

High Quality Tools Inc ....F..... 440 975-9684
Eastlake (G-9273)

Ohio Drill & Tool Co ....E..... 330 525-7717
Homeworth (G-11117)

Tenney Tool & Supply Co ....F..... 330 666-2807
Barberton (G-1153)

INDL SPLYS, WHOLESALE: Tools, NEC

F & B Engraving Tls & Sup LLC ....G..... 937 332-7994
Troy (G-18824)

T & J Nickum Inc ....G..... 216 881-2565
Cleveland (G-6286)

T M Industries Inc ....G..... 330 627-4410
Carrollton (G-2967)

INDL SPLYS, WHOLESALE: Valves & Fittings

Crane Pumps & Systems Inc ....B..... 937 773-2442
Piqua (G-16256)

Pipe Products Inc ....D..... 513 587-7532
West Chester (G-19915)

Quad Fluid Dynamics Inc ....F..... 330 220-3005
Brunswick (G-2250)

Ruthman Pump and Engineering ....E..... 937 783-2411
Blanchester (G-1716)

Victory White Metal Company ....D..... 216 271-1400
Cleveland (G-6417)

INDL TOOL GRINDING SVCS

Seilkop Industries Inc ....E 513 761-1035
Cincinnati *(G-4398)*

Sst Precision Manufacturing ....F 513 583-5500
Loveland *(G-12390)*

Triumph Tool LLC ....G 937 222-6885
Dayton *(G-8728)*

INDUSTRIAL & COMMERCIAL EQPT INSPECTION SVCS

4r Enterprises Incorporated ....G 330 923-9799
Cuyahoga Falls *(G-7960)*

Quintus Technologies LLC ....E 614 891-2732
Lewis Center *(G-11912)*

Reid Asset Management Company ......E 216 642-3223
Cleveland *(G-6098)*

INFORMATION RETRIEVAL SERVICES

Advant-E Corporation ....F 937 429-4288
Beavercreek *(G-1316)*

AGS Custom Graphics Inc ....D 330 963-7770
Macedonia *(G-12433)*

Hkm Drect Mkt Cmmnications Inc ......C 216 651-9500
Cleveland *(G-5516)*

Promatch Solutions LLC ....F 937 299-0185
Springboro *(G-17500)*

Repro Acquisition Company LLC ......E 216 738-3800
Cleveland *(G-6104)*

Sevell + Sevell Inc ....G 614 341-9700
Columbus *(G-7611)*

Tahoe Interactive Systems Inc ....F 614 891-2323
Westerville *(G-20235)*

Welch Publishing Co ....E 419 874-2528
Perrysburg *(G-16168)*

INGOT, EXTRUSION: Extrusion ingot, aluminum: rolling mills

Aluminum Extrusion Tech LLC ....G 330 533-3994
Canfield *(G-2548)*

Powermount Systems Inc ....F 740 499-4330
La Rue *(G-11622)*

INGOT: Aluminum

Homan Metals LLC ....G 513 721-5010
Cincinnati *(G-3891)*

INK OR WRITING FLUIDS

International Paper Company ....C 740 363-9882
Delaware *(G-8862)*

Sun Chemical Corporation ....D 513 671-0407
Cincinnati *(G-4476)*

Superior Printing Ink Co Inc ....F 513 221-4707
Blue Ash *(G-1877)*

Wagers Inc ....G 513 825-6300
Okeana *(G-15666)*

INK: Letterpress Or Offset

Dischem Inc ....G 330 494-5210
Canton *(G-2690)*

INK: Lithographic

Sun Chemical Corporation ....E 513 771-4030
Cincinnati *(G-4479)*

INK: Printing

Actega North America Inc ....G 513 489-5691
Blue Ash *(G-1733)*

American Inks and Coatings Co ....F 513 552-7200
Fairfield *(G-9641)*

An Environmental Inks ....E 513 870-0288
West Chester *(G-19980)*

Braden-Sutphin Ink Company ....C 216 271-2300
Cleveland *(G-4929)*

Braden-Sutphin Ink Company ....G 614 443-9100
Columbus *(G-6853)*

Braden-Sutphin Ink Company ....E 937 704-9047
Carlisle *(G-2928)*

DOT-2-Dot Inc ....F 440 891-9388
Cleveland *(G-5209)*

Eckart America Corporation ....D 440 954-7600
Painesville *(G-15876)*

Erie Laser Ink LLC ....G 419 346-0600
Toledo *(G-18457)*

Ferro Corporation ....C 216 875-6178
Cleveland *(G-5337)*

Flint Group US LLC ....G 513 934-6500
Lebanon *(G-11800)*

Flint Group US LLC ....F 216 267-1927
Cleveland *(G-5357)*

Flint Group US LLC ....D 513 771-1900
Cincinnati *(G-3761)*

Glass Coatings & Concepts LLC ......E 513 539-5300
Monroe *(G-14403)*

Grand Rapids Printing Ink Co ....G 859 261-4530
Cincinnati *(G-3844)*

Ink Factory Inc ....G 330 799-0888
Youngstown *(G-21116)*

Ink Production Services Inc ....F 513 733-9338
Cincinnati *(G-3921)*

Ink Technology Corporation ....E 216 486-6720
Cleveland *(G-5569)*

INX International Ink Co ....F 513 282-2920
Lebanon *(G-11809)*

INX International Ink Co ....F 440 239-1766
Cleveland *(G-5585)*

Kennedy Ink Company Inc ....F 513 871-2515
Cincinnati *(G-3983)*

Kennedy Ink Company Inc ....G 937 461-5600
Dayton *(G-8437)*

Premier Ink Systems Inc ....F 513 367-4700
Harrison *(G-10796)*

Sun Chemical Corporation ....D 513 671-0407
Cincinnati *(G-4476)*

Sun Chemical Corporation ....D 419 891-3514
Maumee *(G-13299)*

Sun Chemical Corporation ....D 513 753-9550
Amelia *(G-585)*

Sun Chemical Corporation ....E 513 681-5950
Cincinnati *(G-4478)*

Sun Chemical Corporation ....E 937 743-8055
Franklin *(G-10055)*

Sun Chemical Corporation ....E 513 830-8667
Cincinnati *(G-4481)*

Superior Printing Ink Co Inc ....G 216 328-1720
Cleveland *(G-6268)*

Wikoff Color Corporation ....G 513 423-0727
Middletown *(G-14099)*

INSECTICIDES & PESTICIDES

A Best Trmt & Pest Ctrl Sups ....G 330 434-5555
Akron *(G-17)*

Advanced Biological Mktg Inc ....F 419 232-2461
Van Wert *(G-19241)*

INSPECTION & TESTING SVCS

Brown Company of Findlay Ltd ....E 419 425-3002
Findlay *(G-9803)*

Cleveland Specialty Insptn Svc ....F 440 578-1046
Mentor *(G-13546)*

Fluid Conservation Systems ....F 513 831-9335
Milford *(G-14141)*

National Welding & Tanker Repr ......G 614 875-3399
Grove City *(G-10576)*

Supplier Inspection Svcs Inc ....E 937 263-7097
Dayton *(G-8690)*

Vista Industrial Packaging LLC ....D 800 454-6117
Columbus *(G-7743)*

INSTRUMENT DIALS: Painted

Trumbull Inc ....G 419 849-3561
Woodville *(G-20727)*

INSTRUMENTS & METERS: Measuring, Electric

FT Group Inc ....E 937 746-6439
Cincinnati *(G-3786)*

Lake Shore Cryotronics Inc ....C 614 891-2243
Westerville *(G-20165)*

Lawhorn Machine & Tool Inc ....G 937 884-5674
Phillipsburg *(G-16184)*

P G M Diversified Industries ....G 440 885-3500
Cleveland *(G-5955)*

INSTRUMENTS, LAB: Refractometers, Exc Indl Process Types

Mettler-Toledo Intl Fin Inc ....G 614 438-4511
Columbus *(G-6653)*

INSTRUMENTS, LAB: Spectroscopic/Optical Properties Measuring

Akron Council of Engineering ....G 330 535-8835
Akron *(G-39)*

Innovative Lab Services LLC ....G 614 554-6446
Pataskala *(G-15972)*

INSTRUMENTS, LABORATORY: Analyzers, Automatic Chemical

Quaker Chemical Corporation ....G 216 265-5079
Cleveland *(G-6066)*

Targeted Cmpund Monitoring LLC ......G 513 461-3535
Dayton *(G-8701)*

INSTRUMENTS, LABORATORY: Blood Testing

C D C At Cityview ....E 216 426-2020
Cleveland *(G-4955)*

INSTRUMENTS, LABORATORY: Infrared Analytical

IEC Infrared Systems LLC ....E 440 234-8000
Middleburg Heights *(G-13906)*

Spirit Solutions Inc ....G 937 431-8041
Moraine *(G-14532)*

INSTRUMENTS, LABORATORY: Ultraviolet Analytical

Filament LLC ....G 614 732-0754
Columbus *(G-7083)*

Nordson Uv Inc ....F 440 985-4573
Amherst *(G-604)*

INSTRUMENTS, MEASURING & CNTRL: Gauges, Auto, Computer

Lawhorn Machine & Tool Inc ....G 937 884-5674
Phillipsburg *(G-16184)*

INSTRUMENTS, MEASURING & CNTRL: Geophysical & Meteorological

Electric Speed Indicator Co ....F 216 251-2540
Cleveland *(G-5265)*

INSTRUMENTS, MEASURING & CNTRL: Radiation & Testing, Nuclear

Fluke Biomedical LLC ....C 440 248-9300
Cleveland *(G-5362)*

Nucon International Inc ....F 614 846-5710
Columbus *(G-7405)*

Reuter-Stokes Inc ....B 330 425-3755
Twinsburg *(G-19008)*

INSTRUMENTS, MEASURING & CNTRL: Testing, Abrasion, Etc

American Cube Mold Inc ....G 330 558-0044
Hinckley *(G-11022)*

Gilson Screen Incorporated ....E 419 256-7711
Malinta *(G-12534)*

Magnetic Analysis Corporation ....F 330 758-1367
Youngstown *(G-21140)*

MB Dynamics Inc ....E 216 292-5850
Cleveland *(G-5768)*

Nanologix Inc ....G 330 534-0800
Hubbard *(G-11135)*

Saginomiya America Inc ....F 614 766-7390
Dublin *(G-9136)*

Standards Testing Labs Inc ....E 330 833-8548
Massillon *(G-13203)*

INSTRUMENTS, MEASURING & CNTRL: Whole Body Counters, Nuclear

Multi Lapping Service Inc ....F 440 944-7592
Wickliffe *(G-20373)*

INSTRUMENTS, MEASURING & CNTRLG: Aircraft & Motor Vehicle

Nidec Motor Corporation ....C 216 642-1230
Independence *(G-11268)*

PRODUCT

Parker-Hannifin Corporation...............B.......216 896-3000
Cleveland (G-5973)
Parker-Hannifin Corporation...............F.......216 896-3000
Cleveland (G-5976)

INSTRUMENTS, MEASURING & CNTRLG: Electrogamma Ray Loggers

P H Glatfelter Company..........................G.......740 289-5100
Piketon (G-16226)

INSTRUMENTS, MEASURING & CNTRLG: Stress, Strain & Measure

Fiomet LLC ....G.......513 519-7622
Cincinnati (G-3757)
Xcite Systems Corporation ....G.......513 965-0300
Cincinnati (G-3321)

INSTRUMENTS, MEASURING & CNTRLG: Thermometers/Temp Sensors

Excelitas Technologies Corp ....C.......937 865-4621
Miamisburg (G-13807)

INSTRUMENTS, MEASURING & CNTRLNG: Nuclear Instrument Modules

Overhoff Technology Corp......................F.......513 248-2400
Milford (G-14165)

INSTRUMENTS, MEASURING & CONTROLLING: Anamometers

Certified Pressure Testing LLC ....G.......740 374-2071
Marietta (G-12773)

INSTRUMENTS, MEASURING & CONTROLLING: Breathalyzers

1 A Lifesafer Hawaii Inc ....F.......513 651-9560
Blue Ash (G-1730)
National Patent Analytical Sys ....E.......419 526-6727
Mansfield (G-12655)

INSTRUMENTS, MEASURING & CONTROLLING: Cable Testing

Multilink Inc ....C.......440 366-6966
Elyria (G-9465)

INSTRUMENTS, MEASURING & CONTROLLING: Gas Detectors

Furnace Control Corp.............................E.......513 772-1000
West Chester (G-19870)

INSTRUMENTS, MEASURING & CONTROLLING: Magnetometers

Ceia Usa Ltd ....E.......330 405-3190
Twinsburg (G-18909)

INSTRUMENTS, MEASURING & CONTROLLING: Surveying & Drafting

J C Equipment Sales & Lsg ....G.......513 772-7612
Cincinnati (G-3934)

INSTRUMENTS, MEASURING & CONTROLLING: Torsion Testing

Skidmore-Wilhelm Mfg Company..........E.......216 481-4774
Solon (G-17381)

INSTRUMENTS, MEASURING & CONTROLLING: Transits, Surveyors'

Novitran LLC ....G.......513 792-2727
Cincinnati (G-4166)

INSTRUMENTS, MEASURING & CONTROLLING: Ultrasonic Testing

Advanced OEM Solutions LLC ....G.......513 846-5755
Liberty Township (G-11957)
Amron LLC ....G.......330 457-8570
New Waterford (G-14968)

INSTRUMENTS, MEASURING/CNTRL: Gauging, Ultrasonic Thickness

Global Gauge Corporation ....F.......937 222-0797
Moraine (G-14491)
Rickly Hydrological Company ....G.......614 297-9877
Columbus (G-7563)

INSTRUMENTS, MEASURING/CNTRL: Fare Registers, St Cars/Buses

Euclid Products Co Inc...........................G.......440 942-7310
Willoughby (G-20482)

INSTRUMENTS, MEASURING/CNTRL: Fire Detect Sys, Non-Electric

Tripoint Instruments Inc ....G.......513 702-9217
Cincinnati (G-4527)

INSTRUMENTS, MEASURING/CNTRLNG: Med Diagnostic Sys, Nuclear

GLC Biotechnology Inc ....G.......440 349-2193
Hudson (G-11173)
Nuclear Physicians Limited ....G.......330 920-3770
Stow (G-17785)
Tuppas Software Corporation ....C.......419 897-7902
Maumee (G-13304)

INSTRUMENTS, OPTICAL: Lenses, All Types Exc Ophthalmic

Bright Eyes Inc......................................G.......937 277-9991
Dayton (G-8195)
Bsa Industries Inc ....D.......614 846-5515
Columbus (G-6869)

INSTRUMENTS, OPTICAL: Test & Inspection

Lear Engineering Corp ....F.......937 429-0534
Beavercreek (G-1347)
Ncrx Optical Solutions Inc ....F.......330 239-5353
Hudson (G-11189)
Vampire Optical Coatings Inc ....G.......740 919-4596
Pataskala (G-15989)
Welded Tube Pros LLC.........................G.......330 854-2966
Canal Fulton (G-2517)

INSTRUMENTS, SURGICAL & MEDICAL: Blood & Bone Work

Advanced Medical Solutions Inc ....G.......937 291-0069
Centerville (G-3033)
Findlay American Prosthetic &.............G.......419 424-1622
Findlay (G-9822)
Innovative Medical Eqp LLC ....G.......440 646-1286
Cleveland (G-5572)
Lifes Products Inc..................................G.......740 965-9711
Sunbury (G-18066)
Resonetics LLC.....................................D.......937 865-4070
Kettering (G-11585)

INSTRUMENTS, SURGICAL & MEDICAL: Forceps

Dayton Hawker Corporation ....F.......937 293-8147
Dayton (G-8276)

INSTRUMENTS, SURGICAL & MEDICAL: IV Transfusion

Smiths Medical Asd Inc ....C.......614 889-2220
Dublin (G-9145)

INSTRUMENTS, SURGICAL & MEDICAL: Inhalation Therapy

Invacare Holdings Corporation ....G.......440 329-6000
Elyria (G-9438)
Invacare International Corp ....G.......440 329-6000
Elyria (G-9439)
Pediavascular Inc...................................F.......216 236-5533
Chagrin Falls (G-3111)
Rhinosystems Inc ....F.......216 351-6262
Independence (G-11272)

INSTRUMENTS, SURGICAL & MEDICAL: Inhalators

Acela Biomedical ....F.......937 544-8618
Winchester (G-20689)
Advanced Med Interfaces LLC...............G.......937 361-8385
Lebanon (G-11775)

INSTRUMENTS, SURGICAL & MEDICAL: Lasers, Surgical

Fountain of Youth ....G.......937 723-9743
Centerville (G-3042)
Olentangy Eye and Laser A ....G.......614 267-4122
Columbus (G-7441)

INSTRUMENTS, SURGICAL & MEDICAL: Operating Tables

Midmark Corporation.............................A.......937 526-3662
Versailles (G-19352)

INSTRUMENTS, SURGICAL & MEDICAL: Optometers

Ellen L Ellsworth ....G.......440 352-8031
Mentor (G-13571)

INSTRUMENTS, SURGICAL & MEDICAL: Physiotherapy, Electrical

Grimm Scientific Industries ....F.......740 374-3412
Marietta (G-12787)

INSTRUMENTS, SURGICAL & MEDICAL: Probes, Surgical

Mac Dhui Probe of America Inc ....G.......440 942-5597
Mentor (G-13640)

INSTRUMENTS, SURGICAL/MED: Microsurgical, Exc Electromedical

3d Systems Inc......................................D.......216 229-2040
Cleveland (G-4665)

INSTRUMENTS: Airspeed

John Wolf & Co Inc................................G.......440 942-0083
Willoughby (G-20516)

INSTRUMENTS: Analytical

Acense LLC ....G.......330 242-0046
Twinsburg (G-18891)
Affymetrix Inc ....C.......216 765-5000
Cleveland (G-4729)
Affymetrix Inc ....F.......419 887-1233
Maumee (G-13220)
Astro Instrumentation LLC ....D.......440 238-2005
Strongsville (G-17889)
Columbus Instruments Intl Corp ....E.......614 276-0593
Columbus (G-6956)
Consolidatd Analytical Sys Inc ....F.......513 542-1200
Cleves (G-6511)
Dentronix Inc ....E.......330 916-7300
Cuyahoga Falls (G-7987)
Diascopic LLC ....G.......312 282-1800
Cleveland (G-5191)
Fertility Solutions Inc ....G.......216 491-0030
Cleveland (G-5340)
Health Bridge Imaging LLC....................G.......740 423-3300
Belpre (G-1587)
Isotopx Inc ....G.......508 337-8467
Hudson (G-11183)
Laserlinc Inc ....E.......937 318-2440
Fairborn (G-9626)
Markes International Inc.........................D.......513 745-0241
Blue Ash (G-1832)
Measurenet Technology Ltd ....F.......513 396-6765
Cincinnati (G-4073)
Metron Instruments Inc ....G.......216 332-0592
Bedford Heights (G-1489)
Mettler-Toledo Intl Inc ....B.......614 438-4511
Columbus (G-6654)
Mettlr-Tledo Globl Hldings LLC ....G.......614 438-4511
Columbus (G-6655)
Nanotronics Imaging Inc ....E.......330 926-9809
Cuyahoga Falls (G-8028)
National Safety Tech LLC ....E.......419 727-0552
Toledo (G-18598)

Ohio Lumex Co Inc ....G....... 440 264-2500
  Solon (G-17355)
Omnitech Electronics Inc ....F....... 800 822-1344
  Columbus (G-7442)
Orton Edward Jr Crmic Fndation ....E....... 614 895-2663
  Westerville (G-20176)
PMC Gage Inc ....E....... 440 953-1672
  Willoughby (G-20572)
Precision Anlytical Instrs Inc ....G....... 513 984-1600
  Blue Ash (G-1854)
Q-Lab Corporation ....D....... 440 835-8700
  Westlake (G-20298)
Reid Asset Management Company ....E....... 216 642-3223
  Cleveland (G-6098)
Teledyne Instruments Inc ....G....... 513 229-7000
  Mason (G-13094)
Teledyne Tekmar Company ....E....... 513 229-7000
  Mason (G-13095)
Thermo Fisher Scientific Inc ....G....... 440 703-1400
  Bedford (G-1465)

INSTRUMENTS: Combustion Control, Indl

Burner Technology Unlimited ....G....... 440 232-6181
  Cleveland (G-4949)
Cleveland Controls Inc ....D....... 216 398-0330
  Cleveland (G-5053)
Maxon Corporation ....G....... 216 459-6056
  Independence (G-11267)
Star Combustion Systems LLC ....G....... 513 282-0810
  Mason (G-13090)
Unicontrol Inc ....D....... 216 398-0330
  Cleveland (G-6382)

INSTRUMENTS: Differential Pressure, Indl

Stewart Manufacturing Corp ....E....... 937 390-3333
  Springfield (G-17657)

INSTRUMENTS: Electrocardiographs

Cardioinsight Technologies Inc ....G....... 216 274-2221
  Cleveland (G-4976)
Daniel M Beyerbach ....G....... 513 206-1180
  Cincinnati (G-3639)
Kamala K Tamirisa MD ....G....... 419 842-3000
  Toledo (G-18538)
Synsei Medical ....G....... 609 759-1101
  Dublin (G-9152)

INSTRUMENTS: Endoscopic Eqpt, Electromedical

Clear Image Technology LLC ....G....... 440 366-4330
  Westlake (G-20260)
Steris Corporation ....A....... 440 354-2600
  Mentor (G-13733)

INSTRUMENTS: Eye Examination

Eye Center ....E....... 614 228-3937
  Columbus (G-7074)

INSTRUMENTS: Flow, Indl Process

Aquacalc LLC ....G....... 916 372-0534
  Columbus (G-6767)
Ernst Flow Industries LLC ....F....... 732 938-5641
  Strongsville (G-17918)
L J Star Incorporated ....E....... 330 405-3040
  Twinsburg (G-18969)
Manico Inc ....G....... 440 946-5333
  Willoughby (G-20534)
Poi Holdings Inc ....F....... 937 253-7377
  Dayton (G-8115)
Westerman Inc ....D....... 330 262-6946
  Wooster (G-20846)

INSTRUMENTS: Gastroscopes, Electromedical

Westerville Endoscopy Ctr LLC ....F....... 614 568-1666
  Westerville (G-20194)

INSTRUMENTS: Indicating, Electric

Aqua Technology Group LLC ....G....... 513 298-1183
  West Chester (G-19807)

INSTRUMENTS: Indl Process Control

ABB Inc ....C....... 440 585-8500
  Wickliffe (G-20348)

ABB Inc ....G....... 440 585-8500
  Wickliffe (G-20349)
Air Logic Power Systems LLC ....G....... 513 202-5130
  Harrison (G-10767)
Airmate Company ....D....... 419 636-3184
  Bryan (G-2274)
Alpha Technologies Svcs LLC ....D....... 330 745-1641
  Akron (G-65)
Appleton Grp LLC ....C....... 330 689-1904
  Cuyahoga Falls (G-7968)
Arzel Technology Inc ....E....... 216 831-6068
  Cleveland (G-4840)
Ascon Tecnologic N Amer LLC ....G....... 216 485-8350
  Cleveland (G-4844)
Automation and Ctrl Tech Inc ....E....... 614 495-1120
  Dublin (G-9050)
Automation Technology Inc ....E....... 937 233-6084
  Dayton (G-8174)
Bry-Air Inc ....E....... 740 965-2974
  Sunbury (G-18056)
Cammann Inc ....F....... 440 965-4051
  Birmingham (G-1685)
Chandler Systems Incorporated ....D....... 419 281-5767
  Ashland (G-721)
Cincinnati Test Systems Inc ....C....... 800 850-3189
  Harrison (G-10773)
Cleveland Instrument Corp ....G....... 440 826-1800
  Brookpark (G-2153)
Control Works Inc ....E....... 513 831-9959
  Milford (G-14133)
Crown Elec Svcs & Automtn Inc ....G....... 330 270-9890
  Youngstown (G-21058)
Deban Enterprises Inc ....G....... 937 426-4235
  Dayton (G-8295)
Diamond Power Intl Inc ....F....... 740 687-4001
  Lancaster (G-11707)
Dynamic Temperature Sups LLC ....G....... 216 767-5799
  Parma (G-15956)
Electrodynamics Inc ....C....... 847 259-0740
  Cincinnati (G-3300)
Elpro Services Inc ....G....... 740 568-9900
  Marietta (G-12783)
Emerson Electric Co ....E....... 513 631-6112
  Cincinnati (G-3697)
Emerson Electric Co ....E....... 440 288-1122
  Lorain (G-12244)
Emerson Electric Co ....E....... 440 248-9400
  Solon (G-17285)
Emerson Electric Co ....G....... 513 942-1118
  West Chester (G-19856)
Emerson Network Power System ....G....... 614 841-6309
  Westerville (G-20150)
Encompass Automation & ....F....... 419 873-0000
  Perrysburg (G-16092)
Ets Solution NA LLC ....G....... 330 666-8696
  Bath (G-1236)
Furnace Parts LLC ....E....... 216 916-9601
  Cleveland (G-5384)
Gilbarco Catlow LLC ....G....... 937 898-3236
  Tipp City (G-18279)
Gleason Metrology Systems Corp ....E....... 937 384-8901
  Dayton (G-8365)
Glo-Quartz Electric Heater Co ....E....... 440 255-9701
  Mentor (G-13593)
Gooch & Housego (ohio) LLC ....D....... 216 486-6100
  Highland Heights (G-10914)
H W Fairway International Inc ....E....... 330 678-2540
  Kent (G-11467)
Harris Corporation ....C....... 973 284-2866
  Beavercreek (G-1344)
Harris Instrument Corporation ....G....... 740 369-3580
  Delaware (G-8857)
Helm Instrument Company Inc ....E....... 419 893-4356
  Maumee (G-13265)
Henry & Wright Corporation ....F....... 216 851-3750
  Cleveland (G-5500)
Homeworth Fabrications & Mchs ....F....... 330 525-5459
  Homeworth (G-11116)
Honeywell International Inc ....A....... 937 484-2000
  Urbana (G-19162)
Huntington Instruments Inc ....G....... 937 767-7001
  Yellow Springs (G-20993)
Ingersoll-Rand Company ....E....... 419 633-6800
  Bryan (G-2306)
Innovative Controls Corp ....D....... 419 691-6684
  Toledo (G-18524)
Jual Corporation ....E....... 614 430-0683
  Worthington (G-20874)
Kuhlman Instrument Company ....G....... 419 668-9533
  Norwalk (G-15548)

Lake Shore Cryotronics Inc ....C....... 614 891-2243
  Westerville (G-20165)
Liebert Corporation ....B....... 740 547-5100
  Ironton (G-11296)
Lincoln Electric Company ....C....... 216 524-8800
  Cleveland (G-5696)
LS Starrett Company ....D....... 440 835-0005
  Westlake (G-20282)
M T Systems Inc ....G....... 330 453-4646
  Canton (G-2763)
Machine Applications Corp ....E....... 419 621-2322
  Sandusky (G-16983)
Mettler-Toledo Intl Inc ....B....... 614 438-4511
  Columbus (G-6654)
Newtech Materials & Analytical ....G....... 330 329-1080
  Copley (G-7851)
Nidec Motor Corporation ....C....... 216 642-1230
  Independence (G-11268)
Noramar Company Inc ....G....... 440 338-5740
  Novelty (G-15583)
Noshok Inc ....E....... 440 243-0888
  Berea (G-1630)
Onevision Corporation ....G....... 614 794-1144
  Westerville (G-20174)
Parker-Hannifin Corporation ....A....... 216 531-3000
  Cleveland (G-5975)
Process Pigging Systems LLC ....G....... 513 731-6005
  Cincinnati (G-4276)
Production Design Services Inc ....D....... 937 866-3377
  Dayton (G-8598)
Q-Lab Corporation ....D....... 440 835-8700
  Westlake (G-20298)
Quality Mtrlrogy Stym Solutions ....G....... 937 431-1800
  Beavercreek (G-1358)
Refractory Specialties Inc ....E....... 330 938-2101
  Sebring (G-17050)
Reuter-Stokes Inc ....B....... 330 425-3755
  Twinsburg (G-19008)
Richards Industries Inc ....C....... 513 533-7340
  Cincinnati (G-4344)
Ridge Tool Company ....E....... 440 329-4737
  Elyria (G-9487)
Rsw Technologies LLC ....F....... 419 662-8100
  Rossford (G-16748)
Sansei Showa Co Ltd ....E....... 440 248-4440
  Cleveland (G-6158)
Scadatech LLC ....G....... 614 552-7726
  Reynoldsburg (G-16604)
Selas Heat Technology Co LLC ....E....... 800 523-6500
  Streetsboro (G-17875)
Sherbrooke Metals ....E....... 440 942-3520
  Willoughby (G-20596)
Stancorp Inc ....G....... 330 545-6615
  Girard (G-10396)
Stock Fairfield Corporation ....C....... 440 543-6000
  Chagrin Falls (G-3122)
Tecmark Corporation ....D....... 440 205-7600
  Mentor (G-13743)
Tecsis LP ....E....... 614 430-0683
  Worthington (G-20891)
Therm-O-Disc Incorporated ....A....... 419 525-8500
  Mansfield (G-12697)
Thk Manufacturing America Inc ....C....... 740 928-1415
  Hebron (G-10889)
Tis Corp ....E....... 216 574-4759
  Cleveland (G-6327)
Toledo Transducers Inc ....E....... 419 724-4170
  Holland (G-11090)
United Tool Supply Inc ....G....... 513 752-6000
  Cincinnati (G-3320)
Vanner Holdings Inc ....D....... 614 771-2718
  Hilliard (G-10991)
Vega Americas Inc ....C....... 513 272-0131
  Cincinnati (G-4558)
Visi-Trak Worldwide LLC ....F....... 216 524-2363
  Cleveland (G-6421)
Vitec Inc ....F....... 216 464-4670
  Bedford (G-1471)
Weed Instrument Company Inc ....E....... 216 676-5005
  Independence (G-11283)
World Automtn Measurement Tech ....F....... 216 651-1883
  Cleveland (G-6478)
Ysi Incorporated ....D....... 937 767-7241
  Yellow Springs (G-21005)

INSTRUMENTS: Infrared, Indl Process

Infrared Imaging Systems Inc ....G....... 614 989-1148
  Marysville (G-12954)
L-3 Communications Cincinnati ....A....... 513 573-6100
  Mason (G-13055)

PRODUCT

INSTRUMENTS: Laser, Scientific & Engineering

Doncasters Group Ltd ....G...... 440 329-0400
Elyria *(G-9406)*

Nvision Technology Inc ....G...... 412 254-4668
Norton *(G-15519)*

INSTRUMENTS: Measurement, Indl Process

Automation Metrology Intl LLC ....G...... 440 354-6436
Mentor *(G-13529)*

Beaumont Machine LLC ....F...... 513 701-0421
Mason *(G-12988)*

Command Alkon Incorporated ....D...... 614 799-0600
Dublin *(G-9064)*

Hickok Incorporated ....D...... 216 541-8060
Cleveland *(G-5513)*

Meech Sttic Elminators USA Inc ....F...... 330 564-2000
Barberton *(G-1130)*

Northern Instruments Corp LLC ....E...... 216 450-5073
Cleveland *(G-5910)*

Rickly Hydrological Co ....E...... 614 297-9877
Columbus *(G-7562)*

Seelaus Instrument Co ....G...... 513 733-8222
Miamisburg *(G-13857)*

INSTRUMENTS: Measuring & Controlling

Aclara Technologies LLC ....C...... 440 528-7200
Solon *(G-17248)*

Acuren Inspection Inc ....G...... 419 698-5040
Oregon *(G-15700)*

Advanced Industrial Measuremnt ....E...... 937 320-4930
Miamisburg *(G-13780)*

Amano Cincinnati Incorporated ....D...... 513 697-9000
Loveland *(G-12338)*

American Ndt Incorporated ....F...... 740 687-1321
Lancaster *(G-11684)*

Arnco Corporation ....C...... 800 847-7661
Elyria *(G-9375)*

AT&T Government Solutions Inc ....D...... 937 306-3030
Beavercreek *(G-1320)*

Automation and Ctrl Tech Inc ....E...... 614 495-1120
Dublin *(G-9050)*

Automation Technology Inc ....E...... 937 233-6084
Dayton *(G-8174)*

Bionix Development Corporation ....E...... 419 727-8421
Toledo *(G-18368)*

Cincinnati Ctrl Dynamics Inc ....G...... 513 242-7300
Cincinnati *(G-3547)*

Continental Testing Inc ....F...... 937 832-3322
Union *(G-19065)*

Control Measurement Inc ....G...... 440 639-0020
Painesville *(G-15869)*

David Boswell ....E...... 614 441-2497
Columbus *(G-7014)*

Daytronic Corporation ....F...... 937 866-3300
Miamisburg *(G-13800)*

Denton Atd Inc ....E...... 567 265-5200
Huron *(G-11220)*

Ets Solutions Usa LLC ....G...... 330 666-8696
Bath *(G-1237)*

Ferry Industries Inc ....D...... 330 920-9200
Stow *(G-17753)*

Fischer Engineering Company ....G...... 937 754-1750
Dayton *(G-8343)*

Fowler Products Inc ....F...... 419 683-4057
Crestline *(G-7929)*

Gem Instrument Co ....F...... 330 273-6117
Brunswick *(G-2229)*

Glass Sensors LLC ....G...... 330 234-7999
Wooster *(G-20776)*

Gleason Metrology Systems Corp ....E...... 937 384-8901
Dayton *(G-8365)*

Grale Technologies Inc ....G...... 724 683-8141
Youngstown *(G-21102)*

Halliday Technologies Inc ....G...... 614 504-4150
Plain City *(G-16345)*

Harris Instrument Corporation ....G...... 740 369-3580
Delaware *(G-8857)*

Helm Instrument Company Inc ....E...... 419 893-4356
Maumee *(G-13265)*

Henry & Wright Corporation ....F...... 216 851-3750
Cleveland *(G-5500)*

Hickok Incorporated ....D...... 216 541-8060
Cleveland *(G-5513)*

Honeywell Lebow Products ....C...... 614 850-5000
Columbus *(G-7165)*

Indicator Shop ....G...... 513 897-0055
Waynesville *(G-19730)*

Industrial Masurement Ctrl Inc ....G...... 440 877-1140
Cleveland *(G-5565)*

Instrumentors Inc ....G...... 440 238-3430
Strongsville *(G-17931)*

Karman Rubber Company ....G...... 330 864-2161
Akron *(G-251)*

Low Stress Grind Inc ....F...... 513 771-7977
Cincinnati *(G-4034)*

LS Starrett Company ....D...... 440 835-0005
Westlake *(G-20282)*

Matrix Measuring System ....G...... 330 718-2804
Newton Falls *(G-15136)*

Matrix Research Inc ....F...... 937 427-8433
Beavercreek *(G-1350)*

Measurement Specialties Inc ....D...... 330 659-3312
Akron *(G-293)*

Micro Laboratories Inc ....E...... 440 918-0001
Mentor *(G-13655)*

Micro Systems Development Inc ....G...... 937 438-3567
Dayton *(G-8493)*

National Safety Tech LLC ....E...... 419 727-0552
Toledo *(G-18598)*

Nebulatronics Inc ....E...... 440 243-2370
Olmsted Twp *(G-15681)*

Newall Electronics Inc ....F...... 614 771-0213
Columbus *(G-7388)*

Perfect Measuring Tape Company ....G...... 419 243-6811
Toledo *(G-18639)*

PMC Gage Inc ....G...... 440 953-1672
Willoughby *(G-20572)*

Portage Electric Products Inc ....D...... 330 499-2727
North Canton *(G-15259)*

Precision Environments Inc ....E...... 513 847-1510
West Chester *(G-19919)*

Prentke Romich Company ....C...... 330 202-5800
Wooster *(G-20825)*

Production Control Units Inc ....D...... 937 299-5594
Moraine *(G-14519)*

Q-Lab Corporation ....D...... 440 835-8700
Westlake *(G-20298)*

Quality Controls Inc ....E...... 513 272-3900
Cincinnati *(G-4306)*

R J Engineering Company Inc ....G...... 419 843-8651
Toledo *(G-18667)*

Ralston Instruments LLC ....E...... 440 564-1430
Newbury *(G-15103)*

Rosemount Analytical Inc ....C...... 440 914-1261
Solon *(G-17372)*

Schneider Instrument Co ....F...... 513 561-6803
Cincinnati *(G-4388)*

Science/Electronics Inc ....F...... 937 224-4444
Dayton *(G-8648)*

Struers Inc ....D...... 440 871-0071
Westlake *(G-20313)*

Sumiriko Ohio Inc ....C...... 419 358-2121
Bluffton *(G-1916)*

Super Systems Inc ....E...... 513 772-0060
Cincinnati *(G-4483)*

Te-Co Manufacturing LLC ....D...... 937 836-0961
Union *(G-19068)*

Tech Pro Inc ....E...... 330 923-3546
Akron *(G-430)*

Tech Products Corporation ....E...... 937 438-1100
Miamisburg *(G-13867)*

Tegam Inc ....E...... 440 466-6100
Geneva *(G-10357)*

Teledyne Instruments Inc ....E...... 513 229-7000
Mason *(G-13094)*

Teledyne Tekmar Company ....E...... 513 229-7000
Mason *(G-13095)*

Thermo Eberline LLC ....C...... 440 703-1400
Oakwood Village *(G-15629)*

Tmw Systems Inc ....F...... 615 986-1900
Cleveland *(G-6328)*

Toledo Transducers Inc ....E...... 419 724-4170
Holland *(G-11090)*

Tool Technologies Van Dyke ....F...... 937 349-4900
Marysville *(G-12975)*

UPA Technology Inc ....F...... 513 755-1380
West Chester *(G-19969)*

Welding Consultants Inc ....G...... 614 258-7018
Columbus *(G-7756)*

Womens Imaging Center LLC ....E...... 614 457-7660
Columbus *(G-7772)*

INSTRUMENTS: Measuring Electricity

Aclara Technologies LLC ....C...... 440 528-7200
Solon *(G-17248)*

Ats Assembly and Test Inc ....B...... 937 222-3030
Dayton *(G-8169)*

Avtron Holdings LLC ....B...... 216 642-1230
Cleveland *(G-4876)*

CDI Industries Inc ....E...... 440 243-1100
Cleveland *(G-4999)*

Contact Industries Inc ....E...... 419 884-9788
Lexington *(G-11949)*

Data Power Solutions ....G...... 614 471-1911
Columbus *(G-7013)*

Desco Corporation ....G...... 614 888-8855
New Albany *(G-14757)*

Fisher Testers LLC ....G...... 937 416-6554
Huber Heights *(G-11147)*

Gould Electronics Inc ....C...... 440 953-5000
Eastlake *(G-9271)*

Hana Microdisplay Tech Inc ....D...... 330 405-4600
Twinsburg *(G-18954)*

Helm Instrument Company Inc ....E...... 419 893-4356
Maumee *(G-13265)*

Hughes Corporation ....E...... 440 238-2550
Strongsville *(G-17928)*

Japlar Group Inc ....F...... 513 791-7192
Cincinnati *(G-3942)*

Keithley Instruments LLC ....C...... 440 248-0400
Solon *(G-17328)*

Machine Products Company ....E...... 937 890-6600
Dayton *(G-8466)*

Midwest Telemetry Inc ....G...... 440 725-5718
Chesterland *(G-3215)*

O H Technologies Inc ....G...... 440 354-8780
Mentor *(G-13670)*

Omega Engineering Inc ....E...... 740 965-9340
Sunbury *(G-18072)*

Opw Engineered Systems Inc ....D...... 888 771-9438
Lebanon *(G-11824)*

Orton Edward Jr Crmic Fndation ....E...... 614 895-2663
Westerville *(G-20176)*

P P M Inc ....F...... 216 701-0419
Chagrin Falls *(G-3066)*

Pressco Technology Inc ....D...... 440 498-2600
Cleveland *(G-6044)*

Rosemount Analytical Inc ....C...... 440 914-1261
Solon *(G-17372)*

Skidmore-Wilhelm Mfg Company ....E...... 216 481-4774
Solon *(G-17381)*

Tech Pro Inc ....E...... 330 923-3546
Akron *(G-430)*

Tektronix Inc ....E...... 513 870-4729
West Chester *(G-20058)*

Tektronix Inc ....E...... 440 248-0400
Solon *(G-17402)*

Tmsi LLC ....F...... 888 867-4872
North Canton *(G-15276)*

Visual Information Institute ....F...... 937 376-4361
Xenia *(G-20985)*

INSTRUMENTS: Measuring, Current, NEC

Dynamp LLC ....E...... 614 871-6900
Grove City *(G-10555)*

INSTRUMENTS: Measuring, Electrical Energy

Drs Signal Technologies Inc ....E...... 937 429-7470
Beavercreek *(G-1333)*

INSTRUMENTS: Measuring, Electrical Power

F Squared Inc ....G...... 419 752-7273
Greenwich *(G-10530)*

INSTRUMENTS: Measuring, Electrical Quantities

Alpine Gage Inc ....G...... 937 669-8665
Tipp City *(G-18263)*

INSTRUMENTS: Medical & Surgical

Acouflow Therapeutics LLC ....G...... 513 558-0073
Cincinnati *(G-3350)*

Altitude Medical Inc ....G...... 440 799-7701
Chardon *(G-3139)*

Applied Medical Technology Inc ....E...... 440 717-4000
Brecksville *(G-2034)*

Apto Orthopaedics Corporation ....E...... 330 572-7544
Akron *(G-70)*

Atc Group Inc ....D...... 440 293-4064
Andover *(G-612)*

Avalign Technologies Inc ....F...... 419 542-7743
Hicksville *(G-10900)*

Aws Industries Inc ....E...... 513 932-7941
Lebanon *(G-11782)*

Axon Medical LLC ....E 216 276-0262
Medina (G-13374)

Beam Technologies Inc ....G 800 648-1179
Columbus (G-6815)

Bionix Development Corporation ....E 419 727-8421
Toledo (G-18368)

Blue Bell Bio-Medical Inc ....G 419 238-4442
Van Wert (G-19245)

Boston Scntfic Nrmdlation Corp ....G 419 720-9510
Toledo (G-18377)

Buckeye Medical Tech LLC ....G 330 719-9868
Warren (G-19531)

Bulk Molding Compounds Inc ....D 419 874-7941
Perrysburg (G-16071)

Casco Mfg Solutions Inc ....D 513 681-0003
Cincinnati (G-3504)

Clevex Inc ....G 614 675-3757
Columbus (G-6938)

Collaborative For Adaptive Lif ....G 216 513-0572
Fairlawn (G-9746)

Cqt Kennedy LLC ....E 419 238-2442
Van Wert (G-19252)

Daavlin Distributing Co ....E 419 636-6304
Bryan (G-2293)

Dentronix Inc ....E 330 916-7300
Cuyahoga Falls (G-7987)

Devicor Med Pdts Holdings Inc ....A 513 864-9000
Cincinnati (G-3652)

Devicor Medical Products Inc ....G 513 864-9000
Cincinnati (G-3653)

Drt Medical LLC ....G 937 298-7391
Dayton (G-8312)

Elite Biomedical Solutions LLC ....F 513 207-0602
Cincinnati (G-3301)

Em Innovations Inc ....G 614 853-1504
Galloway (G-10313)

Encore Plastics Corporation ....F 419 626-8000
Sandusky (G-16962)

Ennovea Medical LLC ....G 855 997-2273
Columbus (G-7060)

Estech Inc ....G 805 895-1263
West Chester (G-19860)

Falls Welding & Fabg Inc ....G 330 253-3437
Akron (G-180)

Frantz Medical Development Ltd ....G 212 308-4860
Mentor (G-13582)

Frantz Medical Development Ltd ....D 440 205-9026
Mentor (G-13583)

Fresenius Med Care Hldings Inc ....G 216 661-1627
Cleveland (G-5381)

General Data Company Inc ....E 919 384-0037
Cincinnati (G-3306)

General Data Company Inc ....C 513 752-7978
Cincinnati (G-3304)

Goal Medical LLC ....E 541 654-5951
Mentor (G-13595)

Gyrus Acmi LP ....C 419 668-8201
Norwalk (G-15542)

Haag-Streit Holding Us Inc ....E 513 336-7255
Mason (G-13033)

Hill-Rom Holdings Inc ....G 937 604-6019
Lima (G-12025)

I D X Medical Ltd ....G 513 583-9081
Loveland (G-12359)

Immersus Health Company LLC ....G 855 994-4325
Cincinnati (G-3912)

Immersus Health Company LLC ....G 855 994-4325
Blue Ash (G-1814)

Integrated Med Solutions Inc ....D 440 269-6984
Mentor (G-13609)

Integrted Med Systems Intl Inc ....E 800 783-9251
Stow (G-17765)

Intellirod Spine Inc ....G 234 678-8965
Akron (G-234)

Invacare Respiratory Corp ....E 440 329-6000
Elyria (G-9440)

Klarity Medical Products LLC ....F 740 788-8107
Newark (G-15027)

Liquid Logic LLC ....G 937 865-3068
Miamisburg (G-13826)

M & S Acquistion Co LLC ....E 440 951-8700
Mentor (G-13638)

Majors Wholesale Med Sup LLC ....G 800 376-7263
Cleveland (G-5733)

Medinvent LLC ....G 330 247-0921
Medina (G-13446)

Minimally Invasive Devices Inc ....E 614 484-5036
Columbus (G-7356)

Mobility Revolution LLC ....E 909 980-2259
Cleveland (G-5825)

Morris Technologies Inc ....C 513 733-1611
Cincinnati (G-4123)

Morrison Medical ....E 614 461-4400
Columbus (G-7370)

National Biological Corp ....E 216 831-0600
Beachwood (G-1283)

Neptune Aquatic Systems Inc ....G 513 575-2989
Loveland (G-12375)

Nervive Inc ....F 847 274-1790
Akron (G-312)

New Leaf Medical Inc ....G 216 391-7749
Cleveland (G-5878)

North Coast Medi-Tek Inc ....F 440 974-0750
Mentor (G-13668)

Office Bsed Ansthesia Svcs LLC ....G 513 582-5170
Montgomery (G-14435)

Optoquest Inc ....G 216 445-3637
Cleveland (G-5944)

Patriot Products Inc ....F 419 865-9712
Holland (G-11076)

Pemco Inc ....E 216 524-2990
Cleveland (G-5989)

Percuvision LLC ....F 614 891-4800
Columbus (G-7478)

Perfusion Solutions Inc ....G 216 848-1610
Cleveland (G-5993)

Philips Medical Systems Clevel ....E 440 473-3001
Mentor (G-13686)

Prentke Romich Company ....C 330 202-5800
Wooster (G-20825)

Quality Electrodynamics LLC ....C 440 638-5106
Mayfield Village (G-13326)

R-Med Inc ....G 419 693-7481
Oregon (G-15714)

REA Incorporated ....G 330 666-7414
Akron (G-369)

Reliance Medical Products Inc ....D 513 398-3937
Mason (G-13080)

RJR Surgical Inc ....G 216 241-2804
Cleveland (G-6119)

Rsb Spine LLC ....F 216 241-2804
Cleveland (G-6141)

Secqure Surgical Corp ....G 513 769-1916
Blue Ash (G-1867)

Securus Medical Group Inc ....G 216 445-4683
Cleveland (G-6178)

Smiths Medical North America ....G 614 210-7300
Dublin (G-9146)

Sparton Medical Systems Inc ....D 440 878-4630
Strongsville (G-17969)

Steris Corporation ....A 440 354-2600
Mentor (G-13733)

Summit Online Products LLC ....G 800 326-1972
Powell (G-16485)

Surgical Theater LLC ....G 216 452-2177
Mayfield Village (G-13327)

Surgical Theater LLC ....G 216 496-7884
Cleveland (G-6276)

Surgrx Inc ....F 650 482-2400
Blue Ash (G-1878)

Synergy Health North Amer Inc ....D 513 398-6406
Mason (G-13093)

Theken Companies LLC ....E 330 733-7600
Akron (G-437)

Thermo Fisher Scientific Inc ....C 800 871-8909
Oakwood Village (G-15630)

Thompson Partners Inc ....G 866 475-2500
Gahanna (G-10238)

Torbot Group Inc ....E 419 724-1475
Toledo (G-18751)

Tri-Tech Medical Inc ....F 800 253-8692
Avon (G-1017)

Triatrix LLC ....G 440 263-8936
Cleveland (G-6362)

Troy Innovative Instrs Inc ....E 440 834-9567
Middlefield (G-13996)

Venturemedgroup Ltd ....G 567 661-0768
Toledo (G-18766)

Vertebration Inc ....G 614 395-3346
Powell (G-16487)

Vesco Medical LLC ....F 614 914-5991
Columbus (G-7736)

INSTRUMENTS: Particle Size Analyzers

Rotex Global Lcc ....C 513 541-1236
Cincinnati (G-4359)

INSTRUMENTS: Power Measuring, Electrical

TTI Floor Care North Amer Inc ....B 440 996-2000
Solon (G-17409)

INSTRUMENTS: Pressure Measurement, Indl

Avure Autoclave Systems Inc ....E 614 891-2732
Columbus (G-6794)

Honeywell Inc ....C 513 272-1111
Cincinnati (G-3896)

Koester Corporation ....D 419 599-0291
Napoleon (G-14687)

Solon Manufacturing Company ....E 440 286-7149
Chardon (G-3180)

INSTRUMENTS: Radio Frequency Measuring

Strong M Llc ....F 614 329-8025
Columbus (G-7661)

INSTRUMENTS: Recorders, Oscillographic

County of Medina ....F 330 723-3641
Medina (G-13397)

INSTRUMENTS: Refractometers, Indl Process

Mercury Iron & Steel ....F 440 349-1500
Solon (G-17334)

INSTRUMENTS: Signal Generators & Averagers

Palstar Inc ....F 937 773-6255
Piqua (G-16298)

INSTRUMENTS: Surface Area Analyzers

4r Enterprises Incorporated ....G 330 923-9799
Cuyahoga Falls (G-7960)

HEF USA Corporation ....F 937 323-2556
Springfield (G-17572)

INSTRUMENTS: Temperature Measurement, Indl

Shelburne Corp ....G 216 321-9177
Shaker Heights (G-17094)

TE Brown LLC ....G 937 223-2241
Dayton (G-8706)

Thermacal Inc ....G 440 498-1005
Solon (G-17405)

INSTRUMENTS: Test, Electrical, Engine

Nu-Di Products Co Inc ....D 216 251-9070
Cleveland (G-5922)

INSTRUMENTS: Test, Electronic & Electric Measurement

Advanced Kiffer Systems Inc ....F 216 267-8181
Cleveland (G-4714)

Automtiq Msurement Systems LLC .....G 614 431-2667
Columbus (G-6791)

Bird Electronic Corporation ....C 440 248-1200
Solon (G-17268)

Bird Technologies Group Inc ....G 440 248-1200
Solon (G-17269)

Field Apparatus Service & Tstg ....G 513 353-9399
Cincinnati (G-3752)

Keithley Instruments Intl Corp ....B 440 248-0400
Cleveland (G-5642)

Midwest Metrology LLC ....G 937 832-0965
Englewood (G-9533)

Mueller Electric Company Inc ....E 614 888-8855
New Albany (G-14765)

National Safety Tech LLC ....E 419 727-0552
Toledo (G-18598)

Paneltech LLC ....F 440 516-1300
Wickliffe (G-20378)

Prime Instruments Inc ....D 216 651-0400
Cleveland (G-6047)

Speelman Electric Inc ....D 330 633-1410
Tallmadge (G-18169)

Vmetro Inc ....G 281 584-0728
Fairborn (G-9633)

INSTRUMENTS: Test, Electronic & Electrical Circuits

Andromeda Research ....G 513 831-9708
Cincinnati (G-3403)

Automation Technology Inc ....E 937 233-6084
Dayton (G-8174)

Hannon Company ....D...... 330 456-4728
 Canton (G-2723)
Infinity Plus ....G...... 937 828-1350
 Mechanicsburg (G-13357)
Key Principal Partners Corp ....F...... 888 539-3322
 Cleveland (G-5651)
Lomar Enterprises Inc ....F...... 614 409-9104
 Groveport (G-10633)
Pile Dynamics Inc ....E...... 216 831-6131
 Cleveland (G-6007)
Triplett Bluffton Corporation............G...... 419 358-8750
 Bluffton (G-1919)

INSTRUMENTS: Thermal Conductive, Indl

Rsa Controls Inc ....G...... 513 476-6277
 West Chester (G-19940)

INSTRUMENTS: Transducers, Volts, Amperes, Watts, VARs & Freq

Nebulatronics Inc ....E...... 440 243-2370
 Olmsted Twp (G-15681)

INSTRUMENTS: Vibration

Balmac Inc ....F...... 614 873-8222
 Plain City (G-16324)
Bilz Vibration Technology Inc ....F...... 330 468-2459
 Macedonia (G-12437)
Vibration Test Systems Inc ....G...... 330 562-5729
 Aurora (G-954)

INSULATING BOARD, CELLULAR FIBER

US Greenfiber LLC.............................F...... 419 692-7015
 Delphos (G-8924)

INSULATING COMPOUNDS

St Bernard Insulation LLC..................F...... 513 266-2158
 Cincinnati (G-4449)

INSULATION & CUSHIONING FOAM: Polystyrene

Astro Shapes LLC..............................C...... 330 755-1414
 Struthers (G-17989)
Atlas Roofing Corporation ....C...... 937 746-9941
 Franklin (G-10008)
Austin Foam Plastics Inc ....E...... 614 921-0824
 Columbus (G-6789)
Energy Storage Technologies ....E...... 937 312-0114
 Dayton (G-8326)
Jason Incorporated...........................D...... 419 668-4474
 Milan (G-14113)
Pacemaker Plastic Company Inc........E...... 740 498-4181
 Newcomerstown (G-15121)
Surface Dynamics Inc.......................G...... 513 772-6635
 Cincinnati (G-4486)
Technifab Inc ....D...... 440 934-8324
 Avon (G-1014)
Technifab Inc ....E...... 440 934-8324
 Avon (G-1015)

INSULATION & ROOFING MATERIALS: Wood, Reconstituted

Celcore Inc..F...... 440 234-7888
 Cleveland (G-5001)

INSULATION MATERIALS WHOLESALERS

Denizen Inc ....F...... 937 615-9561
 Piqua (G-16261)
Great Lakes Textiles Inc ....E...... 440 439-1300
 Solon (G-17304)

INSULATION: Fiberglass

American Insulation Tech LLC ....F...... 513 733-4248
 Milford (G-14120)
Blackthorn LLC ....F...... 937 836-9296
 Clayton (G-4657)
Cpic Automotive Inc ....G...... 740 587-3262
 Granville (G-10456)
Derby Fabg Solutions LLC.................E...... 937 498-4054
 Sidney (G-17176)
Johns Manville Corporation ....A...... 419 784-7000
 Defiance (G-8795)
Johns Manville Corporation ....C...... 419 467-8189
 Maumee (G-13271)

Owens Corning ....C...... 740 964-1727
 Pataskala (G-15976)
Owens Corning ....A...... 419 248-8000
 Toledo (G-18625)
Owens Corning Sales LLC ....A...... 419 248-8000
 Toledo (G-18626)
Owens-Corning Capital LLC...............A...... 419 248-8000
 Toledo (G-18627)

INSULATORS & INSULATION MATERIALS: Electrical

Bourbon Plastics Inc ....E...... 574 342-0893
 Cuyahoga Falls (G-7975)
Cornerstone Indus Holdings................G...... 440 893-9144
 Chagrin Falls (G-3054)
Eger Products Inc ....D...... 513 753-4200
 Amelia (G-575)
Glt Fabricators Inc ....G...... 440 914-1122
 Solon (G-17299)
Merrico Inc ....G...... 419 525-2711
 Mansfield (G-12646)
Monti Incorporated............................D...... 513 761-7775
 Cincinnati (G-4120)
Mueller Electric Company Inc ....E...... 216 771-5225
 Akron (G-307)
Resource Mechanical Insul LLC ....E...... 248 577-0200
 Walbridge (G-19462)
Von Roll Usa Inc ....E...... 216 433-7474
 Cleveland (G-6428)
Weidmann Electrical Tech Inc ....D...... 937 652-1220
 Urbana (G-19187)

INSURANCE AGENCIES & BROKERS

Johnny Chin Insurance Agency ....G...... 513 777-8695
 West Chester (G-20019)

INSURANCE BROKERS, NEC

Forge Industries Inc.........................A...... 330 782-8301
 Youngstown (G-21089)

INSURANCE CARRIERS: Hospital & Medical

Vitamin Shoppe Inc ....E...... 440 238-5987
 Strongsville (G-17980)

INSURANCE CARRIERS: Life

Western & Southern Lf Insur Co ....A...... 513 629-1800
 Cincinnati (G-4588)

INSURANCE CLAIM PROCESSING, EXC MEDICAL

Safelite Group Inc ....A...... 614 210-9000
 Columbus (G-7585)

INSURANCE PATROL SVCS

Henderson Partners LLC...................G...... 614 883-1310
 Columbus (G-7149)

INSURANCE RESEARCH SVCS

Frisbie Engine & Machine Co ....F...... 513 542-1770
 Cincinnati (G-3784)

INTEGRATED CIRCUITS, SEMICONDUCTOR NETWORKS, ETC

A M D ....G...... 440 918-8930
 Willoughby (G-20422)
Leidos Inc ....D...... 937 431-2400
 Beavercreek (G-1348)
Philips Medical Systems Mr...............C...... 440 483-2499
 Highland Heights (G-10919)
Sideline Tech Inc ....G...... 440 331-0560
 Rocky River (G-16710)

INTERCOMMUNICATION EQPT REPAIR SVCS

Industrial Electronic Service ....F...... 937 746-9750
 Carlisle (G-2931)

INTERCOMMUNICATIONS SYSTEMS: Electric

Bird Technologies Group Inc ....G...... 440 248-1200
 Solon (G-17269)

Data Processing Sciences Corp...........D...... 513 791-7100
 Cincinnati (G-3640)
Milicom LLC ....G...... 216 765-8875
 Beachwood (G-1280)
Musair Ohio ....G...... 330 455-2800
 Massillon (G-13183)
Public Safety Concepts LLC ....G...... 614 733-0200
 Plain City (G-16355)
Quasonix Inc ....E...... 513 942-1287
 West Chester (G-19927)
Saltillo Corporation...........................G...... 330 674-6722
 Millersburg (G-14261)
Sound Communications Inc ....F...... 614 875-8500
 Grove City (G-10597)

INTERIOR DECORATING SVCS

Hang-UPS Instllation Group Inc ....G...... 614 239-7004
 Columbus (G-7141)

INTERIOR DESIGN SVCS, NEC

Nordic Light America Inc ....F...... 614 981-9497
 Columbus (G-7397)

INTERIOR DESIGNING SVCS

Added Touch Decorating Gallery ....G...... 419 747-3146
 Ontario (G-15684)
CIP International Inc ....D...... 513 874-9925
 West Chester (G-19833)
Silver Threads Inc ....E...... 614 733-0099
 Plain City (G-16359)
Wright Designs Inc ....G...... 216 524-6662
 Cleveland (G-6484)

INTERIOR REPAIR SVCS

Boyce Ltd...G...... 614 236-8901
 Columbus (G-6851)

INTERMEDIATE CARE FACILITY

Bittersweet Inc ....E...... 419 875-6986
 Whitehouse (G-20338)

INTRAVENOUS SOLUTIONS

Clinical Specialties Inc ....D...... 888 873-7888
 Brecksville (G-2040)
Fresenius Usa Inc ....E...... 330 837-2575
 Massillon (G-13134)
Fresenius Usa Inc ....E...... 440 734-7474
 North Olmsted (G-15336)
Molorokalin Inc..................................F...... 330 629-1332
 Canfield (G-2566)

INVERTERS: Nonrotating Electrical

Myers Controlled Power LLC ....F...... 909 923-1800
 Canton (G-2786)
Vanner Holdings Inc ....D...... 614 771-2718
 Hilliard (G-10991)

INVESTMENT ADVISORY SVCS

Linsalata Capital Partners Fun ....G...... 440 684-1400
 Cleveland (G-5703)

INVESTMENT FIRM: General Brokerage

Western & Southern Lf Insur Co ....A...... 513 629-1800
 Cincinnati (G-4588)

INVESTMENT FUNDS, NEC

Key Principal Partners Corp ....F...... 888 539-3322
 Cleveland (G-5651)

INVESTMENT FUNDS: Open-Ended

Broad Street Financial Company ....G...... 614 228-0326
 Columbus (G-6866)

INVESTORS, NEC

Alpha Zeta Holdings Inc ....G...... 216 271-1601
 Cleveland (G-4770)
Key Principal Partners Corp ....F...... 888 539-3322
 Cleveland (G-5651)
NM Group Global LLC ....G...... 419 447-5211
 Tiffin (G-18233)
Resilience Fund III LP ....G...... 216 292-0200
 Cleveland (G-6106)

Taylor Company ....G....... 513 271-2550
Cincinnati *(G-4496)*

INVESTORS: Real Estate, Exc Property Operators

Ajami Holdings Group LLC ....G....... 216 396-6089
Richmond Heights *(G-16651)*
Broad Street Financial Company ....G....... 614 228-0326
Columbus *(G-6866)*

IRON & STEEL PRDTS: Hot-Rolled

Hmt Associates Inc ....E....... 216 369-0109
Broadview Heights *(G-2110)*
North Star Bluescope Steel LLC...........B....... 419 822-2399
Delta *(G-8939)*

IRON ORE MINING

Bloom Lake Iron Ore Mine Ltd ....A....... 216 694-5700
Cleveland *(G-4918)*
Cliffs Minnesota Minerals Co ....A....... 216 694-5700
Cleveland *(G-5092)*
Cliffs Natural Resources Inc ....D....... 216 694-5700
Cleveland *(G-5093)*
Empire Iron Mining Partnership ....G....... 216 694-5700
Cleveland *(G-5277)*
Hibbing Taconite A Joint Ventr ....G....... 216 694-5700
Cleveland *(G-5512)*
Northshore Mining Company ....G....... 216 694-5700
Cleveland *(G-5914)*
The Cleveland-Cliffs Iron Co ....C....... 216 694-5700
Cleveland *(G-6308)*
Tilden Mining Company LC ....A....... 216 694-5278
Cleveland *(G-6325)*
Wabush Mines Cliffs Mining Co ....G....... 216 694-5700
Cleveland *(G-6438)*

IRON ORE PELLETIZING

United Taconite LLC ....G....... 218 744-7800
Cleveland *(G-6388)*

IRON ORES

Cliffs & Associates Ltd ....G....... 216 694-5700
Cleveland *(G-5088)*
Cliffs Michigan Operation ....E....... 216 694-5303
Cleveland *(G-5090)*
Cliffs Mining Company ....F....... 216 694-5700
Cleveland *(G-5091)*
International Steel Group ....C....... 330 841-2800
Warren *(G-19560)*

IRON OXIDES

Ironics Inc ....G....... 330 652-0583
Niles *(G-15162)*

IRRADIATION EQPT: Nuclear

Trionix Research Laboratory ....G....... 330 425-9055
Twinsburg *(G-19030)*

JACKETS: Indl, Metal Plate

Austin Engineering Inc ....G....... 330 848-0815
Barberton *(G-1100)*

JACKS: Hydraulic

Joyce/Dayton Corp ....E....... 937 294-6261
Dayton *(G-8428)*
Marmac Co ....G....... 937 372-8093
Xenia *(G-20963)*
Quality Products Inc ....D....... 614 228-0185
Columbus *(G-7535)*

JANITORIAL & CUSTODIAL SVCS

Cleaning Lady Inc ....F....... 419 589-5566
Mansfield *(G-12581)*
R T Industries Inc ....G....... 937 335-5784
Troy *(G-18865)*

JANITORIAL EQPT & SPLYS WHOLESALERS

Alco-Chem Inc ....E....... 330 253-3535
Akron *(G-61)*
Chem-Sales Inc ....F....... 419 531-4292
Toledo *(G-18394)*
Cotton Fabrics Company Inc ....G....... 419 389-9904
Toledo *(G-18414)*

Friends Service Co Inc ....D....... 419 427-1704
Findlay *(G-9828)*
Impact Products LLC ....C....... 419 841-2891
Toledo *(G-18518)*
Rose Products and Services Inc ....E....... 614 443-7647
Columbus *(G-7573)*

JEWELERS' FINDINGS & MATERIALS

Zero-D Products Inc ....G....... 440 417-1843
Madison *(G-12514)*

JEWELERS' FINDINGS & MATERIALS: Castings

Dentsply International Inc ....D....... 419 865-9497
Maumee *(G-13256)*

JEWELERS' FINDINGS & MATERIALS: Pin Stems

Dayton Hawker Corporation ....F....... 937 293-8147
Dayton *(G-8276)*

JEWELERS' FINDINGS & MTLS: Jewel Prep, Instr, Tools, Watches

Lapcraft Inc ....G....... 614 764-8993
Powell *(G-16477)*

JEWELRY & PRECIOUS STONES WHOLESALERS

Goyal Enterprises Inc ....F....... 513 874-9303
West Chester *(G-20010)*
Jaffe & Gross Jewelry Company ....G....... 937 461-9450
Dayton *(G-8419)*
Renoir Visions LLC ....F....... 419 586-5679
Celina *(G-3016)*

JEWELRY APPAREL

Bensan Jewelers Inc ....G....... 216 221-1434
Lakewood *(G-11657)*
Cambridge Mfg Jewelers ....G....... 330 528-0207
Hudson *(G-11162)*
Marfo Company ....D....... 614 276-3352
Columbus *(G-7318)*
Stephen R White ....G....... 740 522-1512
Newark *(G-15057)*
Timothy Allen Jewelers Inc ....G....... 440 974-8885
Mentor *(G-13747)*
Vy Inc ....F....... 513 421-8100
Cincinnati *(G-4572)*

JEWELRY FINDINGS & LAPIDARY WORK

Sunshine Products ....G....... 303 478-4913
Toledo *(G-18708)*

JEWELRY REPAIR SVCS

Barany Jewelry Inc ....G....... 330 220-4367
Brunswick *(G-2211)*
Benchworks Jewelers Inc ....G....... 937 439-4243
Dayton *(G-8185)*
Bensan Jewelers Inc ....G....... 216 221-1434
Lakewood *(G-11657)*
C M Stephanoff Jewelers Inc ....G....... 440 526-5890
Brecksville *(G-2039)*
Davidson Jewelers Inc ....G....... 513 932-3936
Lebanon *(G-11794)*
Gustave Julian Jewelers Inc ....G....... 440 888-1100
Cleveland *(G-5465)*
H P Nielsen Inc ....G....... 440 244-4255
Lorain *(G-12248)*
Koop Diamond Cutters Inc ....F....... 513 621-2838
Cincinnati *(G-4002)*
Michael W Hyes Desgr Goldsmith ....G....... 440 519-0889
Solon *(G-17338)*
Mr 14k Inc ....G....... 440 234-6661
Berea *(G-1628)*
N J Thomas Fine Jewelry Inc ....G....... 440 892-0656
Cleveland *(G-5847)*
Pughs Designer Jewelers Inc ....G....... 740 344-9259
Newark *(G-15049)*
Roulet Company ....G....... 419 241-2988
Toledo *(G-18682)*
Your Personal Jeweler Inc ....G....... 330 836-2446
Akron *(G-478)*

JEWELRY STORES

Barany Jewelry Inc ....G....... 330 220-4367
Brunswick *(G-2211)*
Benchworks Jewelers Inc ....G....... 937 439-4243
Dayton *(G-8185)*
Bensan Jewelers Inc ....G....... 216 221-1434
Lakewood *(G-11657)*
Farah Jewelers Inc ....F....... 614 438-6140
Columbus *(G-6646)*
Marcus Jewelers ....G....... 513 474-4950
Cincinnati *(G-4058)*
Michael W Hyes Desgr Goldsmith ....G....... 440 519-0889
Solon *(G-17338)*
N J Thomas Fine Jewelry Inc ....G....... 440 892-0656
Cleveland *(G-5847)*
Ohio Silver Co ....G....... 937 767-8261
Yellow Springs *(G-20997)*
Panama Jewelers LLC ....G....... 440 376-6987
Painesville *(G-15909)*
Pughs Designer Jewelers Inc ....G....... 740 344-9259
Newark *(G-15049)*
Rita Caz Jwly Studio & Gallery ....G....... 937 767-7713
Yellow Springs *(G-20998)*
Rosenfeld Jewelry Inc ....G....... 440 446-0099
Cleveland *(G-6134)*
Timothy Allen Jewelers Inc ....G....... 440 974-8885
Mentor *(G-13747)*
Your Personal Jeweler Inc ....G....... 330 836-2446
Akron *(G-478)*

JEWELRY STORES: Precious Stones & Precious Metals

Cambridge Mfg Jewelers ....G....... 330 528-0207
Hudson *(G-11162)*
Davidson Jewelers Inc ....G....... 513 932-3936
Lebanon *(G-11794)*
Goyal Enterprises Inc ....F....... 513 874-9303
West Chester *(G-20010)*
H P Nielsen Inc ....G....... 440 244-4255
Lorain *(G-12248)*
Handcrafted Jewelry Inc ....G....... 330 650-9011
Hudson *(G-11178)*
Jaffe & Gross Jewelry Company ....G....... 937 461-9450
Dayton *(G-8419)*
James C Free Inc ....E....... 937 298-0171
Dayton *(G-8420)*
James C Free Inc ....G....... 513 793-0133
Cincinnati *(G-3940)*
La Gra Jewelers Inc ....G....... 440 439-5869
Cleveland *(G-5673)*
M B Saxon Co Inc ....F....... 440 229-5006
Cleveland *(G-5717)*
Ms Barkin Company ....G....... 216 761-9500
Cleveland *(G-5839)*
Old Village ....F....... 614 791-8467
Delaware *(G-8877)*
Robert W Johnson Inc ....D....... 614 336-4545
Dublin *(G-9134)*
Roulet Company ....G....... 419 241-2988
Toledo *(G-18682)*
Sheiban Jewelry Inc ....F....... 440 238-0616
Strongsville *(G-17964)*
Stephen R White ....G....... 740 522-1512
Newark *(G-15057)*
White Jewelers ....G....... 330 264-3324
Wooster *(G-20848)*

JEWELRY STORES: Silverware

Gustave Julian Jewelers Inc ....G....... 440 888-1100
Cleveland *(G-5465)*

JEWELRY, PRECIOUS METAL: Bracelets

C M Stephanoff Jewelers Inc ....G....... 440 526-5890
Brecksville *(G-2039)*
Goyal Enterprises Inc ....F....... 513 874-9303
West Chester *(G-20010)*

JEWELRY, PRECIOUS METAL: Buttons, Precious Or Semi Or Stone

Puppy Paws Inc ....G....... 440 461-9667
Cleveland *(G-6063)*

JEWELRY, PRECIOUS METAL: Cigar & Cigarette Access

Boos Make & Take ....G....... 440 647-0000
Wellington *(G-19738)*

P R O D U C T

Cigs N Such ....G..... 614 389-6115
  Columbus (G-6929)
M & M Tobacco ....G..... 330 573-8543
  Carrollton (G-2961)

JEWELRY, PRECIOUS METAL: Medals, Precious Or Semiprecious

Crest Craft Company ....F..... 513 271-4858
  Blue Ash (G-1770)

JEWELRY, PRECIOUS METAL: Mountings & Trimmings

Farah Jewelers Inc ....F..... 614 438-6140
  Columbus (G-6646)

JEWELRY, PRECIOUS METAL: Pearl, Natural Or Cultured

Auld Crafters Inc ....G..... 614 221-6825
  Columbus (G-6787)

JEWELRY, PRECIOUS METAL: Pins

O C Tanner Company ....G..... 513 583-1100
  Mason (G-13069)

JEWELRY, PRECIOUS METAL: Rings, Finger

Jostens Inc ....G..... 513 615-3281
  Cincinnati (G-3959)
Jostens Inc ....G..... 419 794-7343
  Maumee (G-13272)
Jostens Inc ....G..... 513 731-5900
  Cincinnati (G-3960)
Jostens Inc ....E..... 419 874-5835
  Perrysburg (G-16116)

JEWELRY, WHOLESALE

Cambridge Mfg Jewelers ....G..... 330 528-0207
  Hudson (G-11162)
M B Saxon Co Inc ....F..... 440 229-5006
  Cleveland (G-5717)
Marfo Company ....D..... 614 276-3352
  Columbus (G-7318)
Ohio Silver Co ....G..... 937 767-8261
  Yellow Springs (G-20997)
Scholz & Ey Engravers Inc ....F..... 614 444-8052
  Columbus (G-7597)
Sheiban Jewelry Inc ....F..... 440 238-0616
  Strongsville (G-17964)
Vy Inc ....F..... 513 421-8100
  Cincinnati (G-4572)

JEWELRY: Decorative, Fashion & Costume

Cult Couture LLC ....G..... 330 801-9475
  Akron (G-135)
Johnstons Banks Inc ....G..... 614 499-4374
  Westerville (G-20163)
Pughs Designer Jewelers Inc .....G..... 740 344-9259
  Newark (G-15049)
Swarovski US Holding Limited .....G..... 330 867-2201
  Fairlawn (G-9763)

JEWELRY: Precious Metal

A R Jester Co ....G..... 513 241-1465
  Cincinnati (G-3335)
Baldwin B AA Design ....G..... 740 374-5844
  Marietta (G-12766)
Barany Jewelry Inc ....G..... 330 220-4367
  Brunswick (G-2211)
Benchworks Jewelers Inc ....G..... 937 439-4243
  Dayton (G-8185)
C & J Jewelers Inc ....G..... 614 221-8588
  Columbus (G-6881)
Davidson Jewelers Inc ....G..... 513 932-3936
  Lebanon (G-11794)
Diamond Designs Inc ....G..... 330 434-6776
  Akron (G-150)
Dimensional Works of Art ....G..... 330 657-2681
  Peninsula (G-16036)
Don Basch Jewelers Inc ....F..... 330 467-2116
  Macedonia (G-12446)
Ginos Awards Inc ....E..... 216 831-5653
  Cleveland (G-5431)
Gold Mine Inc ....G..... 614 378-8308
  Dublin (G-9079)

Gold Pro Inc ....G..... 216 241-5143
  Cleveland (G-5435)
Gustave Julian Jewelers Inc ....G..... 440 888-1100
  Cleveland (G-5465)
H P Nielsen Inc ....G..... 440 244-4255
  Lorain (G-12248)
Heather B Moore Inc ....G..... 216 932-5430
  Cleveland (G-5492)
J and L Jewelry Manufacturing ....G..... 440 546-9988
  Cleveland (G-5594)
Jaffe & Gross Jewelry Company ...G..... 937 461-9450
  Dayton (G-8419)
James C Free Inc ....E..... 937 298-0171
  Dayton (G-8420)
James C Free Inc ....G..... 513 793-0133
  Cincinnati (G-3940)
Jensen & Sons Inc ....F..... 419 471-1000
  Toledo (G-18534)
Jewels By Img Inc ....G..... 440 461-4464
  Cleveland (G-5614)
Koop Diamond Cutters Inc ....F..... 513 621-2838
  Cincinnati (G-4002)
La Gra Jewelers Inc ....G..... 440 439-5869
  Cleveland (G-5673)
Levit Jewelers Inc ....G..... 440 985-1685
  Lorain (G-12255)
M B Saxon Co Inc ....F..... 440 229-5006
  Cleveland (G-5717)
M S Abbott Jewelers ....G..... 614 430-8800
  Worthington (G-20877)
Marcus Jewelers ....G..... 513 474-4950
  Cincinnati (G-4058)
Michael W Hyes Desgr Goldsmith ...G..... 440 519-0889
  Solon (G-17338)
Mr 14k Inc ....G..... 440 234-6661
  Berea (G-1628)
Ms Barkin Company ....G..... 216 761-9500
  Cleveland (G-5839)
N J Thomas Fine Jewelry Inc ....G..... 440 892-0656
  Cleveland (G-5847)
Ohio Silver Co ....G..... 937 767-8261
  Yellow Springs (G-20997)
Old Village ....F..... 614 791-8467
  Delaware (G-8877)
Rego Manufacturing Co Inc ....D..... 419 562-0466
  Bucyrus (G-2357)
Rita Caz Jwly Studio & Gallery .....G..... 937 767-7713
  Yellow Springs (G-20998)
Robert W Johnson Inc ....D..... 614 336-4545
  Dublin (G-9134)
Rosenfeld Jewelry Inc ....G..... 440 446-0099
  Cleveland (G-6134)
Roulet Company ....G..... 419 241-2988
  Toledo (G-18682)
Sands Co Jewelers ....G..... 216 261-8270
  Cleveland (G-6157)
Sheiban Jewelry Inc ....F..... 440 238-0616
  Strongsville (G-17964)
Val Casting Inc ....E..... 419 562-2499
  Bucyrus (G-2361)
Weber Jewelers Incorporated ......G..... 937 643-9200
  Dayton (G-8749)
White Jewelers ....G..... 330 264-3324
  Wooster (G-20848)
Whitehouse Bros Inc ....G..... 513 621-2259
  Blue Ash (G-1894)
William A Weidinger Jewelry ....G..... 614 481-8866
  Columbus (G-7763)
Your Personal Jeweler Inc ....G..... 330 836-2446
  Akron (G-478)

JIGS & FIXTURES

Cmt Machining & Fabg LLC ....F..... 937 652-3740
  Urbana (G-19151)
Coach Tool & Die Inc ....G..... 937 890-4716
  Dayton (G-8234)
Delta Tool & Die Stl Block Inc ......F..... 419 822-5939
  Delta (G-8930)
Event Inc ....F..... 440 951-4477
  Mentor (G-13575)
First Tool Corp ....E..... 937 254-6197
  Dayton (G-8342)
Glendale Machine Inc ....G..... 440 248-8646
  Solon (G-17298)
Homeworth Fabrications & Mchs ...F..... 330 525-5459
  Homeworth (G-11116)
Hudak Machine & Tool Inc ....G..... 440 366-8955
  Elyria (G-9429)
JBI Corporation ....F..... 419 855-3389
  Genoa (G-10361)

Kilroy Company ....D..... 440 951-8700
  Eastlake (G-9278)
Krisdale Industries Inc ....G..... 330 225-2392
  Valley City (G-19209)
P O McIntire Company ....E..... 440 269-1848
  Wickliffe (G-20376)
Schuster Manufacturing Inc ....G..... 419 476-5800
  Toledo (G-18687)

JIGS: Welding Positioners

Kinninger Prod Wldg Co Inc ....D..... 419 629-3491
  New Bremen (G-14788)

JOB PRINTING & NEWSPAPER PUBLISHING COMBINED

Bluffton News Pubg & Prtg Co .....F..... 419 358-8010
  Bluffton (G-1907)
County Classifieds ....G..... 937 592-8847
  Bellefontaine (G-1525)
Douthit Communications Inc ....D..... 419 625-5825
  Sandusky (G-16958)
First Catholc Slovak Union U S ....F..... 216 642-9406
  Cleveland (G-5349)
Hardin County Publishing Co ....E..... 419 674-4066
  Kenton (G-11549)
Job News 513 984-5724
  Blue Ash (G-1818)
Merrill Corporation ....C..... 614 801-4700
  Grove City (G-10571)
Ogden Newspapers Ohio Inc ......E..... 330 424-9541
  Lisbon (G-12129)
Ray Barnes Newspaper Inc ....G..... 419 674-4066
  Kenton (G-11566)
Springfield Newspapers Inc ....E..... 937 323-5533
  Springfield (G-17653)
Utica Herald ....G..... 740 892-2771
  Utica (G-19197)
Welch Publishing Co ....E..... 419 874-2528
  Perrysburg (G-16168)
Yellow Springs News Inc ....F..... 937 767-7373
  Yellow Springs (G-21001)

JOB TRAINING & VOCATIONAL REHABILITATION SVCS

County of Lake ....D..... 440 269-2193
  Willoughby (G-20464)
Findaway World LLC ....G..... 440 893-0808
  Solon (G-17292)
Pakra LLC ....F..... 614 477-6965
  Columbus (G-7455)
Richland Newhope Industries ....C..... 419 774-4400
  Mansfield (G-12671)
Vgs Inc ....C..... 216 431-7800
  Cleveland (G-6413)
Vocational Services Inc ....C..... 216 431-8085
  Cleveland (G-6424)

JOB TRAINING SVCS

Tekdog Inc ....G..... 614 737-3743
  Columbus (G-7685)

JOINTS & COUPLINGS

Holmbury Inc ....G..... 440 578-1070
  Eastlake (G-9274)

JOINTS OR FASTENINGS: Rail

Mc Cully Supply & Sales Inc ....G..... 330 497-2211
  Canton (G-2775)
Seneca Railroad & Mining Co ......F..... 419 483-7764
  Bellevue (G-1559)

JOINTS: Expansion

Steel Services Inc ....G..... 513 353-4173
  North Bend (G-15208)

JOINTS: Expansion, Pipe

Bosch Rexroth Corporation ....B..... 330 263-3300
  Wooster (G-20751)

JOISTS: Long-Span Series, Open Web Steel

Promac International Inc ....G..... 440 967-2040
  Vermilion (G-19336)
Socar of Ohio Inc ....D..... 419 596-3100
  Continental (G-7828)

KAOLIN & BALL CLAY MINING

State Line Resources Inc ....G....... 330 426-9611
Negley (G-14732)

KEYS, KEY BLANKS

Hillman Group Inc ....G....... 800 800-4900
Parma (G-15962)

KILNS & FURNACES: Ceramic

I Cerco Inc ....D....... 304 387-0178
East Liverpool (G-9218)
I Cerco Inc ....C....... 330 567-2145
Shreve (G-17158)
Star Engineering Inc ....E....... 740 342-3514
New Lexington (G-14855)

KITCHEN & COOKING ARTICLES: Pottery

Grandpas Pottery ....G....... 937 382-6442
Wilmington (G-20665)

KITCHEN CABINET STORES, EXC CUSTOM

Brower Products Inc ....D....... 937 563-1111
Cincinnati (G-3482)
Carl C Andre Inc ....G....... 614 864-0123
Brice (G-2087)
Contemporary Cabinets Inc ....G....... 937 833-1135
Brookville (G-2178)
Creative Products Inc ....E....... 419 866-5501
Holland (G-11049)
Custom Counter Tops & Spc Co ....G....... 330 637-4856
Cortland (G-7867)
Don Walter Kitchen Distrs Inc ....G....... 330 793-9338
Youngstown (G-21071)
Gillard Construction Inc ....F....... 740 376-9744
Marietta (G-12786)
Kinsella Manufacturing Co Inc ....F....... 513 561-5285
Cincinnati (G-3991)
Laminate Shop ....F....... 740 749-3536
Waterford (G-19649)
Oakwood Furniture Inc ....G....... 740 896-3162
Lowell (G-12403)
Thiels Replacement Systems Inc ....D....... 419 289-6139
Ashland (G-781)

KITCHEN CABINETS WHOLESALERS

Bison Builders LLC ....F....... 614 636-0365
Columbus (G-6832)
Brower Products Inc ....D....... 937 563-1111
Cincinnati (G-3482)
Clark Wood Specialties Inc ....G....... 330 499-8711
Clinton (G-6534)
Custom Design Cabinets & Tops ....G....... 440 639-9900
Painesville (G-15872)
Kitchen Designs Plus Inc ....E....... 419 536-6605
Toledo (G-18545)
Modern Builders Supply Inc ....F....... 419 526-0002
Mansfield (G-12651)
Sims-Lohman Inc ....E....... 513 651-3510
Cincinnati (G-4423)

KITCHEN TOOLS & UTENSILS WHOLESALERS

Creative Products Inc ....E....... 419 866-5501
Holland (G-11049)

KITCHEN UTENSILS: Food Handling & Processing Prdts, Wood

AP Tech Group Inc ....F....... 513 761-8111
Blue Ash (G-1743)
Mt Perry Foods Inc ....D....... 740 743-3890
Mount Perry (G-14592)
Rightway Food Service ....G....... 419 223-4075
Lima (G-12084)

KITCHEN UTENSILS: Wooden

Anderson Co ....G....... 419 396-7056
Carey (G-2914)
Attractive Kitchens & Flrg LLC ....G....... 440 406-9299
Elyria (G-9376)
Bushworks Incorporated ....G....... 937 767-1713
Yellow Springs (G-20990)
Henly Corporation ....G....... 419 476-0851
Toledo (G-18507)

KITCHENWARE STORES

Added Touch Decorating Gallery ....G....... 419 747-3146
Ontario (G-15684)
Crystal Art Imports Inc ....F....... 614 505-6001
Columbus (G-7002)
Nacco Industries Inc ....G....... 440 229-5151
Cleveland (G-5848)
Wasserstrom Company ....B....... 614 737-8472
Columbus (G-7750)

KITCHENWARE: Plastic

Brighteye Innovations LLC ....F....... 800 573-0052
Akron (G-100)
HI Lite Plastic Products ....G....... 614 235-9050
Columbus (G-7154)

KITS: Plastic

RPM Consumer Holding Company ....G....... 330 273-5090
Medina (G-13470)

KNIVES: Agricultural Or Indl

Advetech Inc ....E....... 330 533-2227
Canfield (G-2544)
Advetech Inc ....E....... 330 533-2227
Canfield (G-2543)
CB Manufacturing & Sls Co Inc ....D....... 937 866-5986
Miamisburg (G-13790)
Handy Twine Knife Co ....G....... 419 294-3424
Upper Sandusky (G-19124)
Randolph Tool Company Inc ....F....... 330 877-4923
Hartville (G-10832)
Superion Inc ....E....... 937 374-0033
Xenia (G-20977)

LABELS: Cotton, Printed

Grace Imaging LLC ....G....... 419 874-2127
Perrysburg (G-16104)
Trebnick Systems Inc ....E....... 937 743-1550
Springboro (G-17512)

LABELS: Paper, Made From Purchased Materials

Acme Label & Tag Inc ....G....... 440 729-1040
Chesterland (G-3194)
Adaptive Data Inc ....F....... 937 436-2343
Centerville (G-3032)
CCL Label Inc ....C....... 216 676-2703
Cleveland (G-4998)
CMC Daymark Corporation ....C....... 419 354-2591
Bowling Green (G-1980)
GBS Corp ....E....... 330 929-8050
Stow (G-17758)
General Data Company Inc ....C....... 513 752-7978
Cincinnati (G-3304)
General Data Company Inc ....E....... 513 752-7978
Cincinnati (G-3305)
Inline Label Company ....F....... 513 217-5662
Middletown (G-14048)
Joshua Enterprises Inc ....G....... 419 872-9699
Perrysburg (G-16115)
Keithley Enterprises Inc ....G....... 937 890-1878
Dayton (G-8434)
Maderite LLC ....G....... 937 570-1042
Tipp City (G-18288)
Model Graphics & Media Inc ....E....... 513 541-2355
West Chester (G-19903)
Multi-Color Corporation ....F....... 513 381-1480
Batavia (G-1211)
Scratch-Off Systems Inc ....E....... 216 649-7800
Brecksville (G-2071)
Shore To Shore Inc ....D....... 937 866-1908
Dayton (G-8656)
Tri State Media LLC ....F....... 513 933-0101
Wilmington (G-20680)
W/S Packaging Group Inc ....C....... 513 459-2400
Mason (G-13102)

LABELS: Woven

Crane Consumables LLC ....E....... 513 539-9980
Middletown (G-14034)
Shore To Shore Inc ....D....... 937 866-1908
Dayton (G-8656)

LABORATORIES, TESTING: Food

Agrana Fruit Us Inc ....C....... 937 693-3821
Anna (G-620)

LABORATORIES, TESTING: Hazardous Waste

Clean Harbors Envmtl Svcs Inc ....F....... 330 425-3825
Twinsburg (G-18914)

LABORATORIES, TESTING: Hydrostatic

US Tubular Products Inc ....D....... 330 832-1734
North Lawrence (G-15307)

LABORATORIES, TESTING: Metallurgical

Metcut Research Associates Inc ....D....... 513 271-5100
Cincinnati (G-4092)
Phymet Inc ....F....... 937 743-8061
Springboro (G-17496)

LABORATORIES, TESTING: Pollution

Data Analysis Technologies ....G....... 614 873-0710
Plain City (G-16333)
Nucon International Inc ....F....... 614 846-5710
Columbus (G-7405)

LABORATORIES, TESTING: Product Testing

Wallover Enterprises Inc ....E....... 440 238-9250
Strongsville (G-17981)

LABORATORIES, TESTING: Product Testing, Safety/Performance

Amron LLC ....G....... 330 457-8570
New Waterford (G-14968)
Chemsultants International Inc ....G....... 440 974-3080
Mentor (G-13543)
Global Manufacturing Solutions ....F....... 937 236-8315
Dayton (G-8367)
Standards Testing Labs Inc ....E....... 330 833-8548
Massillon (G-13203)

LABORATORIES, TESTING: Water

R D Baker Enterprises Inc ....G....... 937 461-5225
Dayton (G-8609)
Ream and Haager Laboratory ....F....... 330 343-3711
Dover (G-9010)

LABORATORIES, TESTING: Welded Joint Radiographing

PWS Welding & Mtg ....F....... 330 385-6922
East Liverpool (G-9226)

LABORATORIES: Biological Research

Aeiou Scientific LLC ....G....... 614 325-2103
Columbus (G-6699)
Mp Biomedicals LLC ....C....... 440 337-1200
Solon (G-17340)

LABORATORIES: Biotechnology

Elastance Imaging LLC ....G....... 614 579-9520
Columbus (G-7049)
Sensetronics LLC ....G....... 614 292-2833
Dublin (G-9142)

LABORATORIES: Commercial Nonphysical Research

Intek Inc ....E....... 614 895-0301
Westerville (G-20160)
Power Management Inc ....E....... 937 222-2909
Dayton (G-8580)

LABORATORIES: Dental

Delmar E Hicks ....G....... 740 354-4333
Portsmouth (G-16434)
Dental Ceramics Inc ....E....... 330 523-5240
Richfield (G-16620)
Doling & Associates Dental Lab ....E....... 937 254-0075
Dayton (G-8307)
Dresch Tolson Dental Labs ....D....... 419 842-6730
Sylvania (G-18105)
Duncan Dental Lab LLC ....G....... 614 793-0330
Dublin (G-9070)

PRODUCT

Mark Dental Laboratory ....G..... 216 464-6424
Cleveland (G-5744)

LABORATORIES: Dental, Denture Production

United Dental Laboratories ....E 330 253-1810
Akron (G-455)

LABORATORIES: Electronic Research

Advanced Microbeam Inc.........................G..... 330 394-1255
Vienna (G-19362)
Electronic Concepts Engrg Inc ....F 419 861-9000
Holland (G-11059)
Point Source Inc......................................F 937 855-6020
Germantown (G-10373)
Srico Inc..G..... 614 799-0664
Columbus (G-7647)
Steiner Eoptics Inc ....D..... 937 426-2341
Miamisburg (G-13865)

LABORATORIES: Medical

Cellular Technology Limited ....E 216 791-5084
Shaker Heights (G-17088)
Hanger Prsthetcs & Ortho Inc ....G..... 740 454-6215
Zanesville (G-21317)
Hanger Prsthetcs & Ortho Inc ....G..... 419 522-0055
Marion (G-12871)
Hanger Prsthetcs & Ortho Inc ....G..... 740 354-4775
Portsmouth (G-16437)
Mp Biomedicals LLC ....C..... 440 337-1200
Solon (G-17340)
Nuclear Physicians Limited ....G..... 330 920-3770
Stow (G-17785)
Standards Testing Labs Inc ....E 330 833-8548
Massillon (G-13203)

LABORATORIES: Physical Research, Commercial

Albemarle Corporation ....G..... 330 425-2354
Twinsburg (G-18897)
Arges..G..... 440 574-1305
Oberlin (G-15634)
BASF Catalysts LLC ....D..... 216 360-5005
Cleveland (G-4894)
Borchers Americas Inc ....D..... 440 899-2950
Westlake (G-20258)
Circle Prime Manufacturing ....E 330 923-0019
Cuyahoga Falls (G-7980)
Copernicus Therapeutics Inc....................F 216 707-1776
Cleveland (G-5131)
Curtiss-Wright Controls ....E 937 252-5601
Fairborn (G-9618)
EMD Millipore Corporation ....C..... 513 631-0445
Norwood (G-15572)
Farmed Materials LLC..............................G..... 513 680-4046
Cincinnati (G-3740)
Fertility Solutions Inc ....G..... 216 491-0030
Cleveland (G-5340)
Flexsys America LP ....D..... 330 666-4111
Akron (G-190)
Fram Group Operations LLC ....D..... 419 661-6700
Perrysburg (G-16097)
Lyondell Chemical Company ....D..... 513 530-4000
Cincinnati (G-4042)
Medpace Holdings Inc ....G..... 513 579-9911
Cincinnati (G-4079)
Microbiological Labs Inc ....G..... 330 626-2264
Streetsboro (G-17862)
Microweld Engineering Inc ....F 614 847-9410
Worthington (G-20880)
Morris Technologies ....G..... 330 384-3084
Akron (G-304)
Northcoast Environmental Labs.................G..... 330 342-3377
Streetsboro (G-17865)
Nsa Technologies LLC ....C..... 330 576-4600
Akron (G-321)
Ohio Elastomers ....G..... 440 354-9750
Perry (G-16055)
Owens Corning Sales LLC ....B..... 740 587-3562
Granville (G-10464)
Owens Corning Sales LLC ....F 330 633-6735
Tallmadge (G-18163)
Protein Express Inc ....G..... 513 769-9654
Cincinnati (G-4300)
Schneller LLC ....D..... 330 673-1299
Kent (G-11523)
Specialty Technology & Res ....G..... 614 870-0744
Columbus (G-7639)

Sunpower Inc ....D..... 740 594-2221
Athens (G-887)
Vehicle Systems Inc ....G..... 330 854-0535
Massillon (G-13210)

LABORATORIES: Testing

Personnel Selection Services...................F 440 835-3255
Cleveland (G-5994)

LABORATORIES: Testing

Akzo Nobel Coatings Inc..........................C..... 614 294-3361
Columbus (G-6711)
American Polymer Standards ....G..... 440 255-2211
Mentor (G-13520)
Balancing Company Inc ....E 937 898-9111
Vandalia (G-19282)
Barr Engineering Incorporated ....F 614 892-0162
Columbus (G-6807)
Barr Engineering Incorporated ....E 614 714-0299
Columbus (G-6808)
Ceco Group Inc ....G..... 513 458-2600
Cincinnati (G-3510)
Cleveland Instrument Corp ....G..... 440 826-1800
Brookpark (G-2153)
Curtiss-Wright Flow Control ....D..... 513 528-7900
Cincinnati (G-3297)
Curtiss-Wright Flow Ctrl Corp ....D..... 513 528-7900
Cincinnati (G-3298)
E I Du Pont De Nemours & Co ....E 330 929-2961
Stow (G-17745)
Fertility Solutions Inc ....G..... 216 491-0030
Cleveland (G-5340)
Fram Group Operations LLC ....D..... 419 661-6700
Perrysburg (G-16097)
Godfrey & Wing Inc..................................E 330 562-1440
Aurora (G-922)
Hoya Optical Labs ....G..... 440 239-1924
Berea (G-1619)
JBI Corporation ....F 419 855-3389
Genoa (G-10361)
Jci Jones Chemicals Inc ....F 330 825-2531
New Franklin (G-14826)
Micro Laboratories Inc ....G..... 440 918-0001
Mentor (G-13655)
Microbiological Labs Inc ....G..... 330 626-2264
Streetsboro (G-17862)
National Polymer Inc ....F 440 708-1245
Chagrin Falls (G-3106)
Ohio Lumex Co Inc ....G..... 440 264-2500
Solon (G-17355)
Reid Asset Management Company ....E 216 642-3223
Cleveland (G-6098)
Sample Machining Inc ....E 937 258-3338
Dayton (G-8645)
Welding Consultants Inc ....G..... 614 258-7018
Columbus (G-7756)
Yoder Industries Inc ....C..... 937 278-5769
Dayton (G-8766)

LABORATORIES: Ultrasound

John P Ellis Clinic Podiatry ....G..... 440 460-0444
Cleveland (G-5620)

LABORATORY APPARATUS & FURNITURE

Amteco Inc...G..... 513 217-4430
Middletown (G-14020)
Asbeka Custom Products LLC ....F 440 352-0839
Painesville (G-15852)
Cheminstruments Inc ....G..... 513 860-1598
West Chester (G-19827)
Chemsultants International Inc ....G..... 513 860-1598
West Chester (G-19829)
Chemsultants International Inc ....G..... 440 974-3080
Mentor (G-13543)
Cortest Inc ....F 440 942-1235
Willoughby (G-20463)
Dentronix Inc...E 330 916-7300
Cuyahoga Falls (G-7987)
Ies Systems Inc ....E 330 533-6683
Canfield (G-2558)
Philips Medical Systems Clevel ....B..... 440 247-2652
Cleveland (G-6001)
Poi Holdings Inc ....F 937 253-7377
Dayton (G-8115)
So-Low Environmental Eqp Co ....E 513 772-9410
Cincinnati (G-4431)
Tech Pro Inc ....E 330 923-3546
Akron (G-430)

Teledyne Instruments Inc ....E 513 229-7000
Mason (G-13094)
Teledyne Tekmar Company ....E 513 229-7000
Mason (G-13095)
Universal Scientific Inc.............................G..... 440 428-1777
Madison (G-12513)
Waller Brothers Stone Company ....E 740 858-1948
Mc Dermott (G-13345)

LABORATORY APPARATUS, EXC HEATING & MEASURING

Accuscan Instruments Inc ....F 614 878-6644
Columbus (G-6686)
Caron Products and Svcs Inc ....E 740 373-6809
Marietta (G-12770)

LABORATORY APPARATUS: Calibration Tapes, Phy Testing Mach

Denton Atd Inc ....E 567 265-5200
Huron (G-11220)
Qualitech Associates Inc ....G..... 216 265-8702
Cleveland (G-6068)

LABORATORY APPARATUS: Crushing & Grinding

Powdermet Powder Production..................F 216 404-0053
Euclid (G-9599)
Regal Industries Inc.................................G..... 440 352-9600
Painesville (G-15917)

LABORATORY APPARATUS: Freezers

Global Cooling Inc ....E 740 274-7900
Athens (G-869)
Thermo Fisher Scientific ....A..... 740 373-4763
Marietta (G-12841)

LABORATORY APPARATUS: Furnaces

American Isostatic Presses Inc ....F 614 445-9081
Columbus (G-6739)

LABORATORY APPARATUS: Particle Size Reduction

E R Advanced Ceramics Inc ....E 330 426-9433
East Palestine (G-9237)

LABORATORY APPARATUS: Pipettes, Hemocytometer

Mettler-Toledo Intl Fin Inc ....G..... 614 438-4511
Columbus (G-6653)

LABORATORY CHEMICALS: Organic

Bonded Chemicals Inc ....G..... 330 723-4570
Medina (G-13380)
Chempak International LLC ....G..... 440 543-8511
Chagrin Falls (G-3079)
Cwru Irland Cncer Ctr Cellular..................G..... 216 368-1007
Cleveland (G-5160)
Detrex Corporation ....G..... 440 997-6131
Ashtabula (G-802)
Nanotech West Lab ....F 614 688-3055
Columbus (G-7381)
Nationwide Chemical Products ....G..... 419 714-7075
Perrysburg (G-16124)
Ohio Chemical Two ....G..... 614 482-8073
Columbus (G-7417)
Ohio State University ....E 614 292-7656
Columbus (G-7431)
Rezkem Chemicals LLC ....F 330 653-9104
Hudson (G-11196)

LABORATORY EQPT, EXC MEDICAL: Wholesalers

Acela Biomedical ....F 937 544-8618
Winchester (G-20689)
Perkinelmer Hlth Sciences Inc ....E 330 825-4525
Akron (G-336)
Teledyne Instruments Inc ....E 513 229-7000
Mason (G-13094)
Teledyne Tekmar Company ....E 513 229-7000
Mason (G-13095)
Test Mark Industries Inc ....E 330 426-2200
East Palestine (G-9246)

LABORATORY EQPT: Chemical

Cheminstruments Inc ....G...... 513 860-1598
West Chester (G-19828)
Continental Hydrodyne Systems ....F 330 494-2740
Canton (G-2667)
H & N Instruments Inc ....G...... 740 344-4351
Newark (G-15017)

LABORATORY EQPT: Clinical Instruments Exc Medical

Ashton Pumpmatic Inc ....G...... 937 424-1380
Dayton (G-8165)
Cellular Technology Limited ....E 216 791-5084
Shaker Heights (G-17088)
Center For Excptonal Practices ....G...... 330 523-5240
Richfield (G-16617)
Strategic Technology Entp ....E 440 354-2600
Mentor (G-13738)

LABORATORY EQPT: Measuring

4r Enterprises Incorporated ....G...... 330 923-9799
Cuyahoga Falls (G-7960)
Mettler-Toledo Intl Inc ....B 614 438-4511
Columbus (G-6654)

LABORATORY INSTRUMENT REPAIR SVCS

Tech Pro Inc ....E 330 923-3546
Akron (G-430)

LADDER & WORKSTAND COMBINATION ASSEMBLIES: Metal

Heim Sheet Metal Inc ....G...... 330 424-7820
Lisbon (G-12121)

LADDERS: Metal

American Scaffolding Inc ....G...... 216 524-7733
Cleveland (G-4795)
Avenue Fabricating Inc ....E 513 752-1911
Batavia (G-1165)
B C Composites Corporation ....F 330 262-3070
Medina (G-13376)
Bauer Corporation ....E 800 321-4760
Wooster (G-20746)
Bc Investment Corporation ....G...... 330 262-3070
Wooster (G-20747)

LADLE BRICK: Clay

Resco Products Inc ....E 740 682-7794
Oak Hill (G-15605)
Resco Products Inc ....D 330 488-1226
East Canton (G-9197)

LADLES: Metal Plate

Rimrock Holdings Corporation ....E 614 471-5926
Columbus (G-7564)
Rose Metal Industries LLC ....F 216 881-3355
Cleveland (G-6132)

LAMINATED PLASTICS: Plate, Sheet, Rod & Tubes

Advanced Drainage Systems Inc ....D 330 264-4949
Wooster (G-20731)
Advanced Drainage Systems Inc ....E 419 599-9565
Napoleon (G-14669)
Advanced Drainage Systems Inc ....E 419 424-8324
Findlay (G-9788)
Advanced Elastomer Systems LP ....D 330 336-7641
Wadsworth (G-19389)
Aetna Plastics Corp ....G...... 330 274-2855
Mantua (G-12706)
Applied Medical Technology Inc ....E 440 717-4000
Brecksville (G-2034)
Arthur Corporation ....D 419 433-7202
Huron (G-11216)
Biothane Coated Webbing Corp ....E 440 327-0485
North Ridgeville (G-15361)
Cool Seal Usa LLC ....F 419 666-1111
Perrysburg (G-16079)
Duracote Corporation ....E 330 296-9600
Ravenna (G-16526)
Durivage Pattern & Mfg Co ....E 419 836-8655
Williston (G-20420)
Elster Perfection Corporation ....D 440 428-1171
Geneva (G-10346)

Fiber Tech Industries Inc ....D 740 636-3232
Wshngtn CT Hs (G-20909)
Fowler Products Inc ....F 419 683-4057
Crestline (G-7929)
Hancor Inc ....B 614 658-0050
Hilliard (G-10950)
Hrh Door Corp ....D 440 593-5226
Conneaut (G-7809)
Iko Production Inc ....E 937 746-4561
Franklin (G-10029)
Ilpea Industries Inc ....C 330 562-2916
Aurora (G-926)
International Laminating Corp ....E 937 254-8181
Dayton (G-8417)
Interntnal Cnvrter Cldwell Inc ....C 740 732-5665
Caldwell (G-2428)
Laminate Shop ....F 740 749-3536
Waterford (G-19649)
Meridian Industries Inc ....D 330 673-1011
Kent (G-11488)
Meridienne International Inc ....G...... 330 274-8317
Mantua (G-12717)
Monarch Engraving Inc ....E 440 638-1500
Strongsville (G-17942)
Organized Living Inc ....E 513 489-9300
Cincinnati (G-4194)
Plaskolite LLC ....B 614 294-7294
Columbus (G-7490)
Polyone Corporation ....C 419 399-4050
Paulding (G-16013)
Raven Industries Inc ....G...... 937 323-4625
Springfield (G-17634)
Recto Molded Products Inc ....D 513 871-5544
Cincinnati (G-4334)
Resinoid Engineering Corp ....D 847 673-1050
Hebron (G-10881)
Rowmark LLC ....D 419 425-8974
Findlay (G-9884)
Saint-Gobain Prfmce Plas Corp ....C 330 798-6981
Akron (G-396)
Shurtape Technologies LLC ....B 440 937-7000
Avon (G-1011)
Snyder Manufacturing Inc ....D 330 343-4456
Dover (G-9016)
Snyder Manufacturing Co Ltd ....G...... 330 343-4456
Dover (G-9017)
Somerset Galleries Inc ....G...... 614 443-0003
Columbus (G-7630)
Specialty Adhesive Film Co ....G...... 513 353-1885
Cleves (G-6526)
Trim Systems Operating Corp ....C 614 289-5360
New Albany (G-14774)
Ultratech Polymers Inc ....F 330 945-9410
Cuyahoga Falls (G-8060)
Wurms Woodworking Company ....E 419 492-2184
New Washington (G-14966)

LAMINATING MATERIALS

Specialty Adhesive Film Co ....G...... 513 353-1885
Cleves (G-6526)

LAMINATING SVCS

Conversion Tech Intl Inc ....E 419 924-5566
West Unity (G-20127)
Kent Adhesive Products Co ....D 330 678-1626
Kent (G-11475)
Ohio Laminating & Binding Inc ....E 614 771-4868
Hilliard (G-10966)

LAMP & LIGHT BULBS & TUBES

Acuity Brands Lighting Inc ....C 740 349-4409
Newark (G-14980)
Carlisle and Finch Company ....E 513 681-6080
Cincinnati (G-3502)
Emitted Energy Inc ....E 513 752-9999
Cincinnati (G-3302)
Eye Lightning International ....D 440 354-2938
Mentor (G-13577)
General Electric Company ....C 440 593-1156
Conneaut (G-7806)
General Electric Company ....A 330 297-0861
Niles (G-15154)
General Electric Company ....B 740 477-5200
Circleville (G-4630)
L D Kichler Co ....D 866 558-5706
Cleveland (G-5671)
Lumitex Inc ....G...... 949 250-8557
Strongsville (G-17940)

Lumitex Inc ....D 440 243-8401
Strongsville (G-17939)
Medallion Lighting Corporation ....E 440 255-8383
Mentor (G-13650)
Sunburst Light Corp America ....G...... 419 886-3786
Bellville (G-1576)
Venture Lighting Intl Inc ....D 800 451-2606
Twinsburg (G-19035)
Venture Lighting Intl Inc ....F 440 248-3510
Twinsburg (G-19036)

LAMP BULBS & TUBES, ELECTRIC: Electrotherapeutic

Drs Milburn-Medina Inc ....G...... 330 725-4680
Medina (G-13404)

LAMP BULBS & TUBES, ELECTRIC: Filaments

General Electric Company ....C 330 793-3911
Youngstown (G-21095)

LAMP BULBS & TUBES, ELECTRIC: For Specialized Applications

Magenta Incorporated ....E 216 571-4094
Cleveland (G-5728)
Resource Exchange Company Inc ......G...... 440 773-8915
Akron (G-372)

LAMP BULBS & TUBES, ELECTRIC: Health, Infrared/Ultraviolet

Pure Light Technology LLC ....G...... 513 779-7474
West Chester (G-20042)

LAMP BULBS & TUBES, ELECTRIC: Sealed Beam

General Electric Company ....A 330 373-1400
Niles (G-15155)

LAMP BULBS & TUBES, ELECTRIC: Sealed Low-Pressure Gas

GE Lighting LLC ....D 216 266-2000
Cleveland (G-5402)

LAMP BULBS & TUBES/PARTS, ELECTRIC: Generalized Applications

Advanced Lighting Tech Inc ....D 440 519-0500
Solon (G-17249)
Eye Lighting Intl N Amer Inc ....C 440 350-7000
Mentor (G-13576)

LAMP FIXTURES: Ultraviolet

National Biological Corp ....E 216 831-0600
Beachwood (G-1283)
Uv Doctor Systems LLC ....G...... 513 553-9000
Amelia (G-588)

LAMP REPAIR & MOUNTING SVCS

Johnsons Lamp Shop & Antq Co ....G...... 937 568-4551
South Vienna (G-17450)

LAMP STORES

Palette Studios Inc ....G...... 513 961-1316
Cincinnati (G-4209)

LAMPS: Desk, Residential

Microsun Lamps LLC ....G...... 888 328-8701
Dayton (G-8494)

LAMPS: Fluorescent

Alert Stamping & Mfg Co Inc ....E 440 232-5020
Bedford Heights (G-1476)
Energy Focus Inc ....C 440 715-1300
Solon (G-17286)
General Electric Company ....B 419 563-1200
Bucyrus (G-2345)
Johnsons Lamp Shop & Antq Co ....G...... 937 568-4551
South Vienna (G-17450)

Employee Codes: A=Over 500 employees, B=251-500
C=101-250, D=51-100, E=20-50, F=10-19, G=3-9

2017 Harris Ohio
Industrial Directory

PRODUCT

1537

LAMPS: Incandescent, Filament

General Electric Company ....B 216 391-8741
Cleveland *(G-5415)*

LAMPS: Table, Residential

J Schrader Co ....F 216 961-2890
Cleveland *(G-5601)*

Medallion Lighting Corporation ....E 440 255-8383
Mentor *(G-13650)*

LAND SUBDIVISION & DEVELOPMENT

Phillips Companies ....E 937 426-5461
Beavercreek Township *(G-1386)*

U S Fuel Development Co ....G 614 486-0614
Columbus *(G-7716)*

V&P Group International LLC ....F 703 349-6432
Cincinnati *(G-4550)*

LANTERNS

Lintern Corporation ....E 440 255-9333
Mentor *(G-13635)*

LAPIDARY WORK: Contract Or Other

The-Fischer-Group ....E 513 285-1281
Fairfield *(G-9725)*

LAPIDARY WORK: Jewel Cut, Drill, Polish, Recut/Setting

Koop Diamond Cutters Inc ....F 513 621-2838
Cincinnati *(G-4002)*

LASER SYSTEMS & EQPT

Automation Metrology Intl LLC ....G 440 354-6436
Mentor *(G-13529)*

Daskal Enterprise LLC ....G 614 848-5700
Columbus *(G-7012)*

Eagle Wldg & Fabrication Inc ....E 440 946-0692
Willoughby *(G-20478)*

FM Manufacturing Inc ....G 419 445-0700
Archbold *(G-673)*

Fortec Medical Lithotripsy LLC ....E 330 656-4301
Streetsboro *(G-17854)*

Global Laser Tek ....E 513 701-0452
Mason *(G-13029)*

H W Fairway International Inc ....E 330 678-2540
Kent *(G-11467)*

Northeast Laser Inc ....G 330 633-2897
Tallmadge *(G-18160)*

Resonetics LLC ....D 937 865-4070
Kettering *(G-11585)*

Transdermal Inc ....F 440 241-1846
Gates Mills *(G-10338)*

LASERS: Welding, Drilling & Cutting Eqpt

C L S Inc ....G 216 251-5011
Cleveland *(G-4956)*

Cincinnati Laser Cutting LLC ....E 513 772-6999
Cincinnati *(G-3556)*

Great Lakes Power Service Co ....F 440 259-0025
Perry *(G-16050)*

Innovar Systems Limited ....F 330 538-3942
North Jackson *(G-15292)*

Laser Automation Inc ....F 440 543-9291
Chagrin Falls *(G-3099)*

Lucky Thirteen Inc ....G 216 631-0013
Cleveland *(G-5712)*

Peerless Laser Processors Inc ....E 614 836-5790
Groveport *(G-10639)*

LATEX: Foamed

Firestone Polymers LLC ....D 330 379-7000
Akron *(G-187)*

Rub-R-Road Inc ....G 330 678-7050
Kent *(G-11521)*

Trexler Rubber Co Inc ....E 330 296-9677
Ravenna *(G-16567)*

LATH: Expanded Metal

Metrodeck Inc ....F 513 541-4370
Cincinnati *(G-4095)*

LATH: Snow Fence

D&M Fencing LLC ....G 419 604-0698
Spencerville *(G-17459)*

LATHES

Blairs Cnc Turning Inc ....G 937 461-1100
Dayton *(G-8189)*

LAUNDRY & GARMENT SVCS, NEC: Garment Alteration & Repair

Quality Sewing Inc ....G 216 475-0411
Cleveland *(G-6074)*

LAUNDRY EQPT: Commercial

Ha-International LLC ....E 419 537-0096
Toledo *(G-18492)*

Process Development Corp ....E 937 890-3388
Dayton *(G-8597)*

Swisher Hygiene Inc ....G 513 870-4830
West Chester *(G-20057)*

Whirlpool Corporation ....B 419 547-7711
Clyde *(G-6548)*

LAUNDRY EQPT: Household

Staber Industries Inc ....E 614 836-5995
Groveport *(G-10645)*

Whirlpool Corporation ....B 419 547-7711
Clyde *(G-6548)*

Whirlpool Corporation ....C 614 409-4340
Lockbourne *(G-12153)*

LAUNDRY SVCS: Indl

Linen Care Plus Inc ....F 614 224-1791
Columbus *(G-7299)*

LAWN & GARDEN EQPT

Albright Saw Company Inc ....G 740 887-2107
Londonderry *(G-12225)*

Cannon Salt & Supply Inc ....G 440 232-1700
Bedford *(G-1410)*

Commercial Turf Products Ltd ....C 330 995-7000
Streetsboro *(G-17846)*

Country Manufacturing Inc ....F 740 694-9926
Fredericktown *(G-10097)*

Dinsmore Inc ....G 937 544-3332
West Union *(G-20120)*

Elan Designs Inc ....G 614 985-5600
Westerville *(G-20212)*

Extrudex Limited Partnership ....E 440 352-7101
Painesville *(G-15879)*

Franklin Equipment LLC ....E 614 228-2014
Groveport *(G-10623)*

Gececo Inc ....E 614 861-4479
Columbus *(G-7106)*

Johnson Tool Distributors ....G 740 653-6959
Lancaster *(G-11724)*

Klawhorn Industries Inc ....G 330 335-8191
Wadsworth *(G-19414)*

Koenig Equipment Inc ....F 937 653-5281
Urbana *(G-19167)*

Mm Service ....G 330 474-3098
Streetsboro *(G-17863)*

Mtd Holdings Inc ....B 330 225-2600
Valley City *(G-19220)*

Mtd LLC ....G 800 269-6215
Valley City *(G-19221)*

Mtd Products Inc ....B 330 225-2600
Valley City *(G-19222)*

Mtd Products Inc ....A 419 935-6611
Willard *(G-20397)*

Mtd Products Inc ....C 419 342-6455
Shelby *(G-17139)*

Mtd Products Inc ....B 330 225-1940
Valley City *(G-19224)*

Outback Tree Works ....G 937 332-7300
Troy *(G-18860)*

Schomaker Natural Resource ....G 513 741-1370
Cincinnati *(G-4389)*

Scotts Company LLC ....A 937 644-3729
Marysville *(G-12967)*

Smg Growing Media Inc ....G 937 644-0011
Marysville *(G-12971)*

Tierra-Derco International LLC ....G 419 929-2240
New London *(G-14868)*

Village Outdoors ....G 440 256-1172
Kirtland *(G-11618)*

Westerville Lawn & Garden ....G 740 936-8452
Westerville *(G-20195)*

WH Fetzer & Sons Mfg Inc ....E 419 687-8237
Plymouth *(G-16380)*

LAWN & GARDEN EQPT STORES

All Power Equipment LLC ....F 740 593-3279
Athens *(G-855)*

Bortnick Tractor Sales Inc ....F 330 924-2555
Cortland *(G-7862)*

Ohio Drill & Tool Co ....E 330 525-7717
Homeworth *(G-11117)*

LAWN & GARDEN EQPT: Grass Catchers, Lawn Mower

Bortnick Tractor Sales Inc ....F 330 924-2555
Cortland *(G-7862)*

LAWN & GARDEN EQPT: Lawnmowers, Residential, Hand Or Power

Mtd Products Inc ....B 330 225-9127
Valley City *(G-19223)*

LAWN & GARDEN EQPT: Rototillers

Rotoline USA LLC ....G 330 677-3223
Kent *(G-11520)*

LAWN & GARDEN EQPT: Tractors & Eqpt

Mid-West Fabricating Co ....C 740 969-4411
Amanda *(G-563)*

Mo-Trim Inc ....E 740 432-2098
Cambridge *(G-2467)*

Mtd Consumer Group Inc ....F 330 225-2600
Valley City *(G-19219)*

Park-Ohio Holdings Corp ....F 440 947-2000
Cleveland *(G-5966)*

Park-Ohio Industries Inc ....C 440 947-2000
Cleveland *(G-5967)*

LAWN & GARDEN EQPT: Trimmers

Speed North America Inc ....E 330 202-7775
Wooster *(G-20838)*

LAWN MOWER REPAIR SHOP

Bens Welding Service Inc ....G 937 878-4052
Fairborn *(G-9615)*

Wilguss Automotive Machine ....G 937 465-0043
West Liberty *(G-20095)*

LEAD & ZINC

Victory White Metal Company ....F 216 641-2575
Cleveland *(G-6416)*

LEAD PENCILS & ART GOODS

North Shore Strapping Inc ....E 216 661-5200
Brooklyn Heights *(G-2144)*

Ramon Robinson ....G 330 883-3244
Vienna *(G-19374)*

LEAD-IN WIRES: Electric Lamp

Oldaker Manufacturing Corp ....G 419 759-3551
Dunkirk *(G-9189)*

LEASING & RENTAL SVCS: Oil Field Eqpt

Eleet Cryogenics Inc ....E 330 874-4009
Bolivar *(G-1933)*

Terra Sonic International LLC ....E 740 374-6608
Marietta *(G-12840)*

LEASING & RENTAL SVCS: Oil Well Drilling

Dover Fabrication and Burn Inc ....G 330 339-1057
New Philadelphia *(G-14895)*

LEASING & RENTAL: Computers & Eqpt

Data Processing Sciences Corp ....D 513 791-7100
Cincinnati *(G-3640)*

LEASING & RENTAL: Construction & Mining Eqpt

Bluefoot Industrial LLC ....E 740 314-5299
Steubenville *(G-17689)*

Brewpro Inc ....G 513 577-7200
Cincinnati *(G-3472)*

Dolin Supply Co ....E 304 529-4171
South Point *(G-17436)*

Efco Corp ....E 614 876-1226
Columbus *(G-7048)*

Ioppolo Concrete Corporation...........E 440 439-6606
Bedford *(G-1433)*

Lefeld Welding & Stl Sups Inc ....E 419 678-2397
Coldwater *(G-6567)*

Mel Stevens U-Cart Concrete............G 419 478-2600
Toledo *(G-18582)*

Phillips Ready Mix Co........................D 937 426-5151
Beavercreek Township *(G-1388)*

Pollock Research & Design Inc ....G 330 332-3300
Salem *(G-16920)*

Rnm Holdings Inc ....F 614 444-5556
Columbus *(G-7566)*

Stillwell Equipment Co Inc ....G 330 650-1029
Peninsula *(G-16042)*

LEASING & RENTAL: Medical Machinery & Eqpt

Columbus Prescr Rehabilitation ....G 614 294-1600
Westerville *(G-20204)*

Kempf Surgical Appliances Inc ....E 513 984-5758
Montgomery *(G-14433)*

LEASING & RENTAL: Mobile Home Sites

Kedar D Army ....G 419 238-6929
Van Wert *(G-19262)*

L C Liming & Sons Inc ....G 513 876-2555
Felicity *(G-9786)*

LEASING & RENTAL: Office Machines & Eqpt

Copier Resources Inc ....G 614 268-1100
Columbus *(G-6981)*

LEASING & RENTAL: Other Real Estate Property

Lloyd F Helber ....E 740 756-9607
Carroll *(G-2943)*

LEASING & RENTAL: Trucks, Indl

Bluefoot Industrial LLC ....E 740 314-5299
Steubenville *(G-17689)*

Hull Ready Mix Concrete Inc...............F 419 625-8070
Sandusky *(G-16972)*

LEASING & RENTAL: Trucks, Without Drivers

Knippen Chrysler Dodge Jeep............E 419 695-4976
Delphos *(G-8909)*

Marlow-2000 Inc ....F 216 362-8500
Cleveland *(G-5751)*

LEASING: Residential Buildings

Resinoid Engineering Corp.................D 847 673-1050
Hebron *(G-10881)*

LEATHER & CANVAS GOODS: Leggings Or Chaps, NEC

Trd Leathers ....G 216 631-6233
Cleveland *(G-6352)*

LEATHER GOODS, EXC FOOTWEAR, GLOVES, LUGGAGE/BELTING, WHOL

B D G Wrap-Tite Inc ....D 440 349-5400
Solon *(G-17263)*

LEATHER GOODS: Billfolds

Global Payments Inc ....G 440 356-0325
Cleveland *(G-5433)*

LEATHER GOODS: Coin Purses

Hamilton Manufacturing Corp ....E 419 867-4858
Holland *(G-11063)*

LEATHER GOODS: Corners, Luggage

Brighton Collectibles LLC...................E 614 418-7561
Columbus *(G-6860)*

LEATHER GOODS: Feed Bags, Horse

Lockbourne AG Center Inc ....G 614 491-0635
Lockbourne *(G-12148)*

LEATHER GOODS: Garments

AM Retail Group Inc ....G 513 539-7837
Monroe *(G-14391)*

LEATHER GOODS: Harnesses Or Harness Parts

Charm Harness and Boot Ltd ....F 330 893-0402
Charm *(G-3183)*

Ervin Yoder ....G 330 359-5862
Mount Hope *(G-14570)*

Hamilton Animal Products LLC ....E 937 293-9994
Moraine *(G-14492)*

Maysville Harness Shop Ltd ....G 330 695-9977
Apple Creek *(G-644)*

Rantek Products LLC ....G 419 485-2421
Montpelier *(G-14451)*

Yoders Harness Shop........................G 440 632-1505
Middlefield *(G-14009)*

LEATHER GOODS: Holsters

Diy Holster LLC ....G 419 921-2168
Elyria *(G-9405)*

LEATHER GOODS: NEC

Berlin Custom Leather Ltd ....G 330 674-3768
Millersburg *(G-14200)*

LLC Bowman Leather ....G 330 893-1954
Millersburg *(G-14242)*

LEATHER GOODS: Personal

Bison Leather Co ....G 419 517-1737
Toledo *(G-18369)*

Down Home ....G 740 393-1186
Mount Vernon *(G-14620)*

Ed Thomas ....G 937 325-4300
Springfield *(G-17551)*

Hugo Bosca Company Inc ....E 937 323-5523
Springfield *(G-17578)*

Ravenworks Deer Skin ....G 937 354-5151
Mount Victory *(G-14658)*

Williams Leather Products Inc ....G 740 223-1604
Marion *(G-12914)*

LEATHER GOODS: Razor Strops

Straight Razor Designes ....G 330 598-1414
Medina *(G-13484)*

LEATHER GOODS: Saddles Or Parts

Dwayne Hall.....................................G 740 685-5270
Senecaville *(G-17058)*

Whitman Corporation ....G 513 541-3223
Okeana *(G-15667)*

LEATHER GOODS: Safety Belts

Dnd Products Inc ....G 440 286-7275
Chardon *(G-3150)*

LEATHER GOODS: Stirrups, Wood Or Metal

Holmes Wheel Shop Inc ....E 330 279-2891
Holmesville *(G-11106)*

LEATHER TANNING & FINISHING

Old West Industries Inc ....G 513 889-0500
Hamilton *(G-10728)*

Premier Tanning & Nutrition ....G 419 342-6259
Shelby *(G-17141)*

LEATHER, CHAMOIS, WHOLESALE

Canton Sterilized Wiping Cloth ....G 330 455-5179
Canton *(G-2648)*

LEGAL OFFICES & SVCS

Akron Legal News Inc ....F 330 296-7578
Akron *(G-46)*

Bigmar Inc ....E 740 966-5800
Johnstown *(G-11391)*

General Bar Inc ....F 440 835-2000
Westlake *(G-20271)*

Gongwer News Service Inc ....F 614 221-1992
Columbus *(G-7123)*

Perfect Probate ....G 513 791-4100
Cincinnati *(G-4223)*

LEGAL SVCS: General Practice Attorney or Lawyer

Petro Quest Inc ....G 740 593-3800
Athens *(G-881)*

LENS COATING: Ophthalmic

Wilson Optical Laboratory Inc ....E 440 357-7000
Mentor *(G-13769)*

LENSES: Plastic, Exc Optical

Greenlight Optics LLC ....E 513 247-9777
Loveland *(G-12354)*

LESSORS: Farm Land

Prairie Lane Corporation.....................G 330 262-3322
Wooster *(G-20823)*

LICENSE TAGS: Automobile, Stamped Metal

Barbara A Lieurance ....G 937 382-2864
Wilmington *(G-20656)*

Clemens License Agency ....G 614 288-8007
Pickerington *(G-16188)*

D J Klingler Inc ....G 513 891-2284
Cincinnati *(G-3632)*

Fairfield License Center Inc ....G 513 829-6224
Hamilton *(G-10691)*

Heatherdowns License Bureau ....G 419 381-1109
Toledo *(G-18501)*

Huber Heights License Bureau ....F 937 233-7560
Dayton *(G-8395)*

Middletown License Agency Inc ....F 513 422-7225
Middletown *(G-14062)*

Parma Heights License Bureau ....G 440 888-0388
Cleveland *(G-5978)*

Public Safety Ohio Department ....G 216 283-4000
Cleveland *(G-6060)*

Public Safety Ohio Department ....G 440 943-5545
Willowick *(G-20650)*

Transportation Ohio Department ....G 740 927-2285
Pataskala *(G-15987)*

LIFE INSURANCE AGENTS

First Catholc Slovak Union U S ....F 216 642-9406
Cleveland *(G-5349)*

LIFE INSURANCE CARRIERS

First Merit.......................................G 330 849-8750
Akron *(G-188)*

LIGHTING EQPT: Flashlights

Fulton Industries Inc ....D 419 335-3015
Wauseon *(G-19678)*

LIGHTING EQPT: Miners' Lamps

Shelly Company ....G 330 666-1125
Copley *(G-7854)*

LIGHTING EQPT: Motor Vehicle

Atc Lighting & Plastics Inc ....C 440 466-7670
Andover *(G-613)*

Automtve Cmpnnts Holdings LLC ....F 419 483-5622
Bellevue *(G-1544)*

Federal-Mogul Corporation ....C 740 432-2393
Cambridge *(G-2457)*

Lighting Products Inc ....D 440 293-4064
Andover *(G-617)*

LIGHTING EQPT: Motor Vehicle, Headlights

K D Lamp Company...........................E 440 293-4064
Andover *(G-616)*

PRODUC

LIGHTING EQPT: Motor Vehicle, NEC

Stanley Electric US Co Inc ....B 740 852-5200
London (G-12219)
Washington Products Inc...............F 330 837-5101
Massillon (G-13211)

LIGHTING EQPT: Outdoor

ATI Irrigation LLC ....G 937 750-2976
Troy (G-18806)
Holophane Corporation ....C 866 759-1577
Granville (G-10459)
Moonlighting ....G 330 533-3324
Canfield (G-2567)

LIGHTING EQPT: Searchlights

Carlisle and Finch Company ....E 513 681-6080
Cincinnati (G-3502)
Sunburst Light Corp America ....G 419 886-3786
Bellville (G-1576)

LIGHTING EQPT: Spotlights

Broadview Heights Spotlights ....G 440 526-4404
Broadview Heights (G-2105)

LIGHTING FIXTURES WHOLESALERS

Architectural Busstrut Corp ....G 614 933-8695
New Albany (G-14746)
Contract Lighting Inc ....G 614 746-7022
Columbus (G-6978)
GE Lighting Solutions LLC ....E 216 266-4800
Cleveland (G-5403)
Gt Industrial Supply Inc ....G 513 771-7000
Cincinnati (G-3856)
Technical Artistry Inc ....G 614 299-7777
Columbus (G-7684)

LIGHTING FIXTURES, NEC

Acuity Brands Lighting Inc ....B 740 349-4343
Newark (G-14979)
Advanced Lighting Tech Inc ....D 440 519-0500
Solon (G-17249)
Akron Brass Company ....E 614 529-7230
Columbus (G-6708)
Atc Lighting & Plastics Inc ....C 440 466-7670
Andover (G-613)
Aviation Technologies Inc ....G 216 706-2960
Cleveland (G-4872)
Energy Focus Inc ....C 440 715-1300
Solon (G-17286)
Ericson Manufacturing Co ....D 440 951-8000
Willoughby (G-20480)
GE Lighting Solutions LLC ....E 216 266-4800
Cleveland (G-5403)
General Electric Company ....A 330 373-1400
Niles (G-15155)
Genesis Lamp Corp ....F 440 354-0095
Painesville (G-15883)
Global E-Lumenation Tech ....G 513 821-8687
Cincinnati (G-3836)
Global Lighting Tech Inc ....E 440 922-4584
Brecksville (G-2052)
Hughey & Phillips LLC ....E 937 652-3500
Urbana (G-19163)
L D Kichler Co ....B 866 558-5706
Cleveland (G-5671)
Lighting Solutions Group LLC ....F 614 868-5337
Columbus (G-7295)
LSI Industries Inc ....E 513 793-3200
Blue Ash (G-1829)
LSI Industries Inc ....B 513 793-3200
Blue Ash (G-1830)
Lumitex Inc ....D 440 243-8401
Strongsville (G-17939)
Medina Lighting Inc ....G 330 721-1441
Medina (G-13442)
Midmark Corporation ....A 937 526-3662
Versailles (G-19352)
Midmark Corporation ....A 937 526-8387
Versailles (G-19353)
Pro Lighting LLC ....G 614 561-0089
Hilliard (G-10973)
UIC Energy LLC ....G 614 839-0250
Columbus (G-7718)
Vanner Holdings Inc ....D 614 771-2718
Hilliard (G-10991)
Will-Burt Company ....B 330 682-7015
Orrville (G-15770)

LIGHTING FIXTURES: Airport

ADB Safegate Americas LLC ....B 614 861-1304
Columbus (G-6694)
Manairco Inc ....G 419 524-2121
Mansfield (G-12640)

LIGHTING FIXTURES: Fluorescent, Commercial

Techbrite LLC ....E 800 246-9977
Cincinnati (G-4498)
Teron Lighting Inc ....E 513 858-6004
Fairfield (G-9724)

LIGHTING FIXTURES: Indl & Commercial

Acuity Brands Lighting Inc ....B 740 349-4343
Newark (G-14979)
Acuity Brands Lighting Inc ....C 740 349-4409
Newark (G-14980)
Advanced Lighting Tech Inc ....D 440 519-0500
Solon (G-17249)
Besa Lighting Co Inc ....E 614 475-7046
Blacklick (G-1690)
Best Lighting Products Inc ....D 740 964-0063
Etna (G-9555)
Bock Company LLC ....G 216 912-7050
Solon (G-17270)
Eaton Electric Holdings LLC ....E 440 523-5000
Cleveland (G-5251)
Evp International LLC ....G 513 761-7614
Cincinnati (G-3727)
General Electric Company ....B 740 477-5200
Circleville (G-4630)
General Electric Company ....A 216 266-2121
Cleveland (G-5413)
General Electric Company ....E 330 458-3200
Canton (G-2712)
Genesis Lamp Corp ....F 440 354-0095
Painesville (G-15883)
Holophane Corporation ....F 740 349-4194
Newark (G-15018)
Holophane Corporation ....C 866 759-1577
Granville (G-10459)
Holophane Lighting ....G 330 823-5535
Alliance (G-515)
Importers Direct LLC ....E 330 436-3260
Akron (G-230)
J Schrader Co ....F 216 961-2890
Cleveland (G-5601)
JB Machining Concepts LLC ....G 419 523-0096
Ottawa (G-15797)
Less Cost Lighting Inc ....F 866 633-6883
Etna (G-9559)
Light Craft Manufacturing Inc ....F 419 332-0536
Fremont (G-10164)
LSI Industries Inc ....E 513 793-3200
Blue Ash (G-1829)
Lumitex Inc ....D 440 243-8401
Strongsville (G-17939)
Mega Bright LLC ....F 330 577-8859
Cuyahoga Falls (G-8026)
Mills Led LLC ....G 800 690-6403
Columbus (G-7353)
Mills Led LLC ....G 800 690-6403
Columbus (G-7354)
Patriot Consulting LLC ....G 614 554-6455
Columbus (G-7465)
SMS Technologies Inc ....F 419 465-4175
Monroeville (G-14429)
Stress-Crete Company ....F 440 576-9073
Jefferson (G-11372)
Sunburst Light Corp America ....G 419 886-3786
Bellville (G-1576)
Treemen Industries Inc ....E 330 965-3777
Boardman (G-1925)

LIGHTING FIXTURES: Motor Vehicle

Advanced Technology Corp ....C 440 293-4064
Andover (G-611)
Akron Brass Company ....E 614 529-7230
Columbus (G-6708)
Akron Brass Company ....B 330 264-5678
Wooster (G-20734)
Akron Brass Company ....B 330 264-5678
Wooster (G-20735)
Akron Brass Holding Corp ....B 330 264-5678
Wooster (G-20736)
Atc Group Inc ....D 440 293-4064
Andover (G-612)

LIGHTING FIXTURES: Airport

Automtive Cmpnnts Holdings LLC .....A 419 627-3600
Sandusky (G-16947)
Grimes Aerospace Company ....B 937 484-2001
Urbana (G-19158)
Treemen Industries Inc ....E 330 965-3777
Boardman (G-1925)

LIGHTING FIXTURES: Ornamental, Commercial

King Luminaire Company Inc ....E 440 576-9073
Jefferson (G-11365)

LIGHTING FIXTURES: Public

Union Metal Corporation ....C 330 456-7653
Canton (G-2884)

LIGHTING FIXTURES: Residential

Acuity Brands Lighting Inc ....C 740 349-4409
Newark (G-14980)
Acuity Brands Lighting Inc ....B 740 349-4343
Newark (G-14979)
Advanced Lighting Tech Inc ....D 440 519-0500
Solon (G-17249)
Aladdinslights Inc ....G 330 963-6997
Twinsburg (G-18896)
Alert Stamping & Mfg Co Inc ....E 440 232-5020
Bedford Heights (G-1476)
American Superior Lighting ....G 740 266-2959
Steubenville (G-17687)
Besa Lighting Co Inc ....E 614 475-7046
Blacklick (G-1690)
Contract Lighting Inc ....G 614 746-7022
Columbus (G-6978)
E L Ostendorf Inc ....G 440 247-7631
Chagrin Falls (G-3056)
Hinkley Lighting Inc ....E 216 671-3132
Avon Lake (G-1033)
JB Machining Concepts LLC ....G 419 523-0096
Ottawa (G-15797)
L D Kichler Co ....B 866 558-5706
Cleveland (G-5671)
Lighting Concepts & Controls ....G 513 761-6360
West Chester (G-19894)
LSI Industries Inc ....E 513 793-3200
Blue Ash (G-1829)
Manairco Inc ....G 419 524-2121
Mansfield (G-12640)
Mega Bright LLC ....F 330 577-8859
Cuyahoga Falls (G-8026)
Palette Studios Inc ....E 513 961-1316
Cincinnati (G-4209)
Pike Machine Products Co ....E 216 731-1880
Euclid (G-9597)
Tresco International Ltd Co ....G 330 757-8131
Youngstown (G-21228)

LIGHTING FIXTURES: Residential, Electric

Architectural Busstrut Corp ....G 614 933-8695
New Albany (G-14746)
Specialty Systems Electric LLC ....G 304 529-3861
Proctorville (G-16492)

LIGHTING FIXTURES: Street

Miami Valley Lighting LLC ....G 937 224-6000
Dayton (G-8112)

LIGHTING FIXTURES: Underwater

Jeff Katz ....G 614 834-0404
Pickerington (G-16195)

LIGHTS: Trouble lights

Alert Safety Lite Products Co ....F 440 232-5020
Cleveland (G-4750)

LIME

Bluffton Stone Co ....E 419 358-6941
Bluffton (G-1909)
Carmeuse Lime Inc ....E 419 986-5200
Bettsville (G-1668)
Graymont Dolime (oh) Inc ....D 419 855-8682
Genoa (G-10360)
Hanson Aggregates East LLC ....E 937 587-2671
Peebles (G-16021)
Hanson Aggregates East LLC ....D 419 483-4390
Castalia (G-2976)

Mineral Processing Company ....G...... 419 396-3501
  Carey (G-2920)
Naked Lime ....D...... 937 485-1932
  Beavercreek (G-1375)
National Lime and Stone Co ....C...... 419 396-7671
  Carey (G-2921)
Piqua Materials Inc ....E...... 937 773-4824
  Piqua (G-16305)
Shelly Materials Inc ....E...... 740 666-5841
  Ostrander (G-15789)
Sugarcreek Lime Service ....G...... 330 364-4460
  Dover (G-9019)

LIME ROCK: Ground

National Lime and Stone Co ....C...... 419 396-7671
  Carey (G-2921)

LIME: Agricultural

Wollam AG Center Inc ....F...... 419 596-3896
  Continental (G-7830)

LIMESTONE & MARBLE: Dimension

Marble Cliff Limestone Inc ....G...... 614 488-3030
  Hilliard (G-10959)
North Shore Stone Inc ....F...... 614 870-7531
  Columbus (G-7401)

LIMESTONE: Crushed & Broken

Acme Company ....D...... 330 758-2313
  Poland (G-16381)
Allgeier & Son Inc ....F...... 513 574-3735
  Cincinnati (G-3378)
Bluffton Stone Co ....E...... 419 358-6941
  Bluffton (G-1909)
Chesterhill Stone Co ....E...... 740 849-2338
  East Fultonham (G-9198)
Duff Quarry Inc ....F...... 937 686-2811
  Huntsville (G-11212)
Duff Quarry Inc ....F...... 419 273-2518
  Forest (G-9920)
Erie Sand & Gravel Co Inc ....G...... 216 961-1010
  Cleveland (G-5296)
Feikert Sand & Gravel Co Inc ....E...... 330 674-0038
  Millersburg (G-14215)
Gerald Christman ....G...... 740 838-2475
  Lewisville (G-11948)
Hanson Aggregates East LLC ....E...... 937 587-2671
  Peebles (G-16021)
Hanson Aggregates East LLC ....E...... 937 364-2311
  Hillsboro (G-10999)
Hanson Aggregates LLC ....E...... 419 841-3413
  Sylvania (G-18108)
Hanson Aggregates Midwest Inc ....G...... 419 399-4846
  Paulding (G-16004)
Hanson Aggregates Midwest LLC ....F...... 419 882-0123
  Sylvania (G-18109)
King Limestone Inc ....F...... 740 638-3942
  Cumberland (G-7956)
Lang Stone Company Inc ....D...... 614 235-4099
  Columbus (G-7284)
Mac Ritchie Materials Inc ....F...... 419 288-2790
  West Millgrove (G-20104)
Martin Marietta Materials Inc ....D...... 513 353-1400
  North Bend (G-15206)
Martin Marietta Materials Inc ....E...... 513 701-1140
  West Chester (G-19897)
Melvin Stone Company LLC ....G...... 740 998-5016
  Wshngtn CT Hs (G-20916)
Miami River Stone Co ....F...... 937 492-5412
  Sidney (G-17202)
Millersville Lime Inc 3 ....F...... 419 986-2019
  Bettsville (G-1669)
National Lime and Stone Co ....G...... 419 657-6745
  Wapakoneta (G-19502)
National Lime and Stone Co ....E...... 740 548-4206
  Delaware (G-8872)
National Lime and Stone Co ....E...... 419 228-3434
  Lima (G-12062)
National Lime and Stone Co ....E...... 740 387-3485
  Marion (G-12889)
National Lime and Stone Co ....G...... 419 642-6690
  Columbus Grove (G-7796)
National Lime and Stone Co ....G...... 216 883-9840
  Cleveland (G-5857)
National Lime and Stone Co ....E...... 419 423-3400
  Findlay (G-9866)
National Lime and Stone Co ....D...... 419 562-0771
  Bucyrus (G-2354)

Omya Industries Inc ....D...... 513 387-4600
  Blue Ash (G-1847)
Oster Sand and Gravel Inc ....G...... 330 833-2649
  Massillon (G-13190)
Ridge Township Stone Quarry ....G...... 419 968-2222
  Van Wert (G-19269)
Shelly Materials Inc ....G...... 740 246-6315
  Toledo (G-18695)
Shelly Materials Inc ....G...... 330 274-0802
  Mantua (G-12721)
Shelly Materials Inc ....G...... 330 722-2190
  Medina (G-13480)
Shelly Materials Inc ....G...... 330 364-4411
  Dover (G-9014)
Shelly Materials Inc ....G...... 330 823-4646
  Twinsburg (G-19020)
Shelly Materials Inc ....G...... 330 673-3646
  Kent (G-11527)
Shelly Materials Inc ....E...... 740 666-5841
  Ostrander (G-15789)
Shelly Materials Inc ....D...... 740 246-6315
  Thornville (G-18198)
Sidwell Materials Inc ....C...... 740 849-2394
  Zanesville (G-21354)
Stoneco Inc ....E...... 419 393-2555
  Oakwood (G-15619)
Stoneco Inc ....F...... 419 893-7645
  Maumee (G-13298)
Suever Stone Company ....F...... 419 331-1945
  Lima (G-12097)
The National Lime and Stone Co ....G...... 330 455-5722
  North Canton (G-15271)
Wagner Quarries Company ....E...... 419 625-8141
  Sandusky (G-17021)
White Rock Quarry L P ....A...... 419 855-8388
  Clay Center (G-4655)
Wysong Stone Co ....F...... 937 962-2559
  Lewisburg (G-11942)

LIMESTONE: Cut & Shaped

Carmeuse Lime Inc ....E...... 419 638-2511
  Millersville (G-14300)
Maple Grove Materials Inc ....G...... 419 992-4235
  Tiffin (G-18231)
National Lime and Stone Co ....G...... 419 657-6745
  Wapakoneta (G-19502)

LIMESTONE: Dimension

C F Poeppelman Inc ....E...... 937 448-2191
  Bradford (G-2025)
Gerald Christman ....G...... 740 838-2475
  Lewisville (G-11948)
Gregory Stone Co Inc ....G...... 937 275-7455
  Dayton (G-8380)
National Lime and Stone Co ....D...... 419 562-0771
  Bucyrus (G-2354)
S E Johnson Companies Inc ....F...... 419 893-8731
  Maumee (G-13290)
Stoneco Inc ....C...... 419 422-8854
  Findlay (G-9895)

LIMESTONE: Ground

Conag Inc ....E...... 419 394-8870
  Saint Marys (G-16837)
Hanson Aggregates East LLC ....D...... 419 483-4390
  Castalia (G-2976)
Hanson Aggregates Midwest LLC ....G...... 419 983-2211
  Bloomville (G-1728)
Latham Limestone LLC ....G...... 740 493-2677
  Latham (G-11765)
Marietta Martin Materials Inc ....F...... 937 884-5814
  Brookville (G-2190)
National Lime and Stone Co ....G...... 330 262-1317
  Wooster (G-20814)
Ohio Asphaltic Limestone Corp ....F...... 937 364-2191
  Hillsboro (G-11009)
Piqua Materials Inc ....E...... 937 773-4824
  Piqua (G-16305)
Piqua Materials Inc ....E...... 513 771-0820
  Cincinnati (G-4240)
Sharon Stone Inc ....E...... 740 732-7100
  Caldwell (G-2432)

LINEN SPLY SVC

Linen Care Plus Inc ....F...... 614 224-1791
  Columbus (G-7299)
Synergy Health North Amer Inc ....D...... 513 398-6406
  Mason (G-13093)

LINEN SPLY SVC: Table Cover

Joseph Knapp ....F...... 330 832-3515
  Massillon (G-13160)

LINERS & COVERS: Fabric

Berlin Boat Covers ....G...... 330 547-7600
  Berlin Center (G-1654)
Custom Canvas & Boat Repair ....F...... 419 732-3314
  Lakeside (G-11646)
Sailors Tailor Inc ....G...... 937 862-7781
  Spring Valley (G-17469)

LINERS & LINING

Ridge Corporation ....D...... 614 421-7434
  Etna (G-9561)

LINIMENTS

Millers Liniments LLC ....G...... 440 548-5800
  Middlefield (G-13966)
Nanofiber Solutions Inc ....E...... 614 559-9065
  Columbus (G-7380)
Z M O Company Inc ....G...... 614 875-0230
  Grove City (G-10611)

LININGS: Vulcanizable Rubber

Blair Rubber Company ....D...... 330 769-5583
  Seville (G-17070)
Martin Rubber Company ....F...... 330 336-6604
  Seville (G-17078)

LINTELS: Steel, Light Gauge

J N Linrose Mfg LLC ....G...... 513 867-5500
  Hamilton (G-10709)

LIP BALMS

Amish Country Essentials LLC ....G...... 330 674-3088
  Millersburg (G-14192)

LIQUEFIED PETROLEUM GAS DEALERS

Airgas USA LLC ....E...... 937 228-8594
  Dayton (G-8142)
Legacy Farmers Cooperative ....F...... 419 423-2611
  Findlay (G-9851)

LIQUEFIED PETROLEUM GAS WHOLESALERS

Centerra Co-Op ....E...... 800 362-9598
  Jefferson (G-11358)
Centerra Co-Op ....E...... 419 281-2153
  Ashland (G-717)
Matheson Tri-Gas Inc ....E...... 440 365-1741
  Twinsburg (G-18980)

LIQUID CRYSTAL DISPLAYS

Aviation Technologies Inc ....G...... 216 706-2960
  Cleveland (G-4872)
Cks Solution Incorporated ....E...... 513 947-1277
  Fairfield (G-9656)
Cleanlife Energy LLC ....F...... 216 661-7872
  Cleveland (G-5044)
Kent Displays Inc ....C...... 330 673-8784
  Kent (G-11477)
Liquid Crystal Tech LLC ....F...... 440 232-8590
  Cleveland (G-5704)

LITHOGRAPHIC PLATES

Great Lakes Integrated Inc ....D...... 216 651-1500
  Cleveland (G-5452)
Great Lakes Integrated Inc ....F...... 440 892-7760
  Avon Lake (G-1030)
Kehl-Kolor Inc ....E...... 419 281-3107
  Ashland (G-746)
Litho-Craft Lithography Inc ....G...... 513 542-6404
  Cincinnati (G-4028)
R E May Inc ....F...... 216 771-6332
  Cleveland (G-6081)
South End Printing Co ....G...... 216 341-0669
  Cleveland (G-6222)

LIVESTOCK WHOLESALERS, NEC

Werling and Sons Inc ....F...... 937 338-3281
  Burkettsville (G-2370)

PRODUCT

LOADS: Electronic

Electronic Solutions Inc .... F 419 666-4700
  Perrysburg (G-16089)
Omega Engineering Inc .... E 740 965-9340
  Sunbury (G-18072)
TL Industries Inc .... C 419 666-8144
  Northwood (G-15490)

LOCKERS

Industrial Mfg Co LLC .... F 440 838-4700
  Brecksville (G-2055)
Republic Storage Systems LLC .... C 330 438-5800
  Canton (G-2839)
Summa Holdings Inc .... G 440 838-4700
  Cleveland (G-6261)
Tiffin Metal Products Co .... D 419 447-8414
  Tiffin (G-18248)

LOCKS

Greyfield Industries Inc .... F 513 860-1785
  Trenton (G-18793)
Van Lock Co Inc .... F 513 561-9692
  Cincinnati (G-4554)

LOCKS & LOCK SETS, WHOLESALE

Roper Lockbox LLC .... G 330 656-5148
  Hudson (G-11197)

LOCKS: Safe & Vault, Metal

National Security Products .... G 216 566-9962
  Cleveland (G-5860)

LOCKSMITHS

AB Bonded Locksmiths Inc .... G 513 531-7334
  Cincinnati (G-3342)
Ames Lock Specialties Inc .... G 419 474-2995
  Toledo (G-18348)
Dayton Safe Company .... G 937 461-3900
  Dayton (G-8286)

LOCOMOTIVES & PARTS

B&C Machine Co LLC .... B 330 745-4013
  Barberton (G-1103)
Plymouth Locomotive Svc LLC .... G 419 896-2854
  Shiloh (G-17153)

LOG SPLITTERS

G & D Leasing Services Inc .... F 303 457-9189
  Columbus (G-7103)

LOGGING

A & M Logging .... G 740 543-3171
  Salineville (G-16939)
Appalachia Wood Inc .... F 740 596-2551
  Mc Arthur (G-13328)
Art Saylor Logging .... F 740 682-6188
  Oak Hill (G-15594)
Baker Logging .... G 740 686-2817
  Belmont (G-1578)
Beachs Trees Selective Harvest .... F 513 289-5976
  Cincinnati (G-3294)
Brett Purdum .... G 740 626-2890
  South Salem (G-17449)
Broty Enterprises Inc .... G 330 674-6900
  Millersburg (G-14203)
Brown Forest Products .... G 937 544-1515
  Otway (G-15828)
Busy Bee Lumber .... G 330 674-1305
  Millersburg (G-14209)
C & L Erectors & Riggers Inc .... E 740 332-7185
  Laurelville (G-11769)
Chili Logging Ltd .... G 740 545-9502
  Fresno (G-10196)
Chipmunk Logging & Lumber LLC .... Chipmunk 440 834-4660
  Middlefield (G-13923)
Coldwell Family Tree Farm .... G 330 506-9012
  Salineville (G-16940)
Crisenbery Logging LLC .... G 740 256-1439
  Patriot (G-15994)
Ervin Lee Logging .... G 330 771-0039
  Minerva (G-14321)
For Every Home .... G 740 710-1253
  Jackson (G-11314)
Gadd Logging .... G 513 312-3941
  Trenton (G-18792)

Gerald D Damron .... G 740 894-3680
  Chesapeake (G-3188)
GM Logging .... G 740 501-0819
  Johnstown (G-11399)
Haessly Lumber Sales Co .... G 740 373-6681
  Marietta (G-12788)
Huntington Hardwood Lbr Co Inc .... G 440 647-2283
  Wellington (G-19748)
Ingles Logging .... G 740 379-2909
  Patriot (G-15995)
J & J Logging .... G 740 896-2827
  Lowell (G-12402)
J D Knisley Logging .... G 740 634-3207
  Bainbridge (G-1058)
Jacobs & Sons Logging LLC .... G 419 678-3802
  Saint Henry (G-16820)
Jason C Gibson .... F 740 663-4520
  Chillicothe (G-3246)
Jeffrey Adams Logging Inc .... G 740 634-2286
  Bainbridge (G-1059)
Jim Logging LLC .... G 330 340-4863
  Millersburg (G-14235)
JM Logging Inc .... G 740 441-0941
  Gallipolis (G-10301)
John Byler .... G 330 627-7635
  Carrollton (G-2957)
John J Yoder Logging .... G 330 749-6324
  Apple Creek (G-641)
L&L Excavating & Land Clearing .... G 740 682-7823
  Oak Hill (G-15600)
Litzinger Logging .... G 740 743-2245
  Somerset (G-17416)
M H Logging & Lumber .... G 740 694-1988
  Fredericktown (G-10106)
McFadden Logging .... G 740 599-6902
  Danville (G-8090)
Michael D Strickland .... G 740 682-6902
  Oak Hill (G-15601)
Miller & Son Logging .... G 330 738-2031
  Mechanicstown (G-13360)
Miller Logging Inc .... E 330 279-4721
  Holmesville (G-11109)
Millwood Lumber Inc .... E 740 254-4681
  Gnadenhutten (G-10408)
Ned A Shreve .... G 740 732-6465
  Sarahsville (G-17025)
NY Logging & Lumber .... G 740 679-2085
  Quaker City (G-16500)
Omega Logging Inc .... G 330 534-0378
  Hubbard (G-11137)
Perkins Logging LLC .... G 740 288-7311
  Chillicothe (G-3261)
Perkins Wood Products .... G 740 884-4046
  Chillicothe (G-3262)
Powell Logging .... G 740 372-6131
  Otway (G-15831)
Ray L Lute LL .... G 740 372-7703
  Lucasville (G-12424)
Robby Yoder .... G 740 679-2776
  Quaker City (G-16501)
Robert Ashcraft .... G 740 667-3690
  Guysville (G-10654)
Roger L Best .... G 740 590-9133
  Stockport (G-17723)
Ross Tmber Harvstg For MGT Inc .... G 513 383-6933
  Batavia (G-1220)
Select Logging .... G 419 564-0361
  Marengo (G-12754)
Sissel Logging LLC .... G 740 858-4613
  Portsmouth (G-16454)
Stark Truss Company Inc .... D 419 298-3777
  Edgerton (G-9337)
Steve Henderson .... G 419 738-6999
  Wapakoneta (G-19508)
T J Ellis Enterprises Inc .... G 419 224-1969
  Lima (G-12100)
Terry G Sickles .... G 740 286-8880
  Ray (G-16574)
Top Notch Logging .... G 330 466-1780
  Apple Creek (G-650)
Valley Veneer & Lumber Co .... F 440 293-6025
  Williamsfield (G-20417)
Vorhees Logging .... G 740 385-0216
  Rockbridge (G-16690)
Warner Hildebrant .... G 740 286-1903
  South Webster (G-17452)
Y&B Logging .... G 440 437-1053
  Orwell (G-15784)
Yoder Logging .... G 740 679-2635
  Quaker City (G-16502)

LOGGING CAMPS & CONTRACTORS

A & P Wood Products Inc .... G 419 673-1196
  Kenton (G-11543)
Alfman Logging LLC .... G 740 982-6227
  Crooksville (G-7948)
Beekman Logging .... G 740 493-2763
  Piketon (G-16216)
Biedenbach Logging .... G 740 732-6477
  Sarahsville (G-17024)
Blair Logging .... G 740 934-2730
  Lower Salem (G-12415)
Blankenship Logging LLC .... G 740 372-3833
  Otway (G-15826)
Bolon Timber LLC .... G 740 567-4102
  Lewisville (G-11947)
C & B Logging Inc .... G 740 347-4844
  Glouster (G-10403)
Chester F Hale .... G 740 379-2437
  Patriot (G-15993)
Chub Gibsons Logging .... G 740 884-4079
  Chillicothe (G-3233)
Custom Material Hdlg Eqp LLC .... G 513 235-5336
  Cincinnati (G-3626)
D&D Logging .... G 740 679-2573
  Woodsfield (G-20717)
David Adkins Logging .... G 740 533-0297
  Kitts Hill (G-11620)
Denver Adkins .... F 740 682-3123
  Oak Hill (G-15595)
Dunagan Logging .... G 740 599-9368
  Danville (G-8087)
Ingles Logging .... G 740 379-2760
  Patriot (G-15996)
J K Logging & Chipwood Company ...... G 330 738-3571
  Salineville (G-16942)
Knauff Bros Logging & Lumber .... F 740 634-2432
  Bainbridge (G-1060)
Miller Logging .... G 440 693-4001
  Middlefield (G-13965)
Randy Carter Logging Inc .... G 740 634-2604
  Bainbridge (G-1062)
Ray H Miller Trucking and Log .... G 330 378-2131
  Big Prairie (G-1684)
Shellenbarger Excavating & Log .... G 740 397-9949
  Mount Vernon (G-14647)
T&R Logging LLC .... G 740 288-1825
  Wellston (G-19771)
Watson Logging .... G 740 985-4465
  Pomeroy (G-16392)

LOGGING: Saw Logs

B Hogenkamp & R Harlamert .... G 419 925-0526
  Celina (G-2986)

LOGGING: Stump Harvesting

Affordable Stump Removal LLC .... G 419 841-8331
  Toledo (G-18323)

LOGGING: Timber, Cut At Logging Camp

Boreman Hardwoods Inc .... G 330 262-0403
  Wooster (G-20750)
H & H Tree Service LLC .... G 440 632-0551
  Middlefield (G-13938)
Itl California LLC .... F 216 831-4734
  Cleveland (G-5590)
Oakbridge Timber Framing .... G 419 994-1052
  Loudonville (G-12301)
Superior Hardwoods of Ohio .... D 740 384-6862
  Jackson (G-11327)

LOGGING: Veneer Logs

Facemyer Lumber Co Inc .... F 740 992-5965
  Pomeroy (G-16389)
Krajewski Corp .... C 740 522-1147
  Newark (G-15028)
Milestone Ventures LLC .... G 317 908-2093
  Granville (G-10462)

LOGGING: Wood Chips, Produced In The Field

Erichar Inc .... G 216 402-2628
  Cleveland (G-5293)
Seymours Logging .... F 740 288-1825
  Wellston (G-19768)

(G-0000) Company's Geographic Section entry number

LOGS: Gas, Fireplace

Specialty Ceramics Inc....................D...... 330 482-0800
Columbiana **(G-6633)**

LOOSELEAF BINDERS

A H Pelz Co..G...... 216 861-1882
Cleveland **(G-4674)**

Acco Brands Corporation ....E...... 937 495-5723
Kettering **(G-11572)**

Art Guild Binders Inc.....................E...... 513 242-3000
Cincinnati **(G-3414)**

Beck & Orr Inc...............................G...... 614 276-8809
Columbus **(G-6816)**

Bell Binders LLC...........................F...... 419 242-3201
Toledo **(G-18365)**

Mueller Art Cover & Binding Co ....E...... 440 238-3303
Strongsville **(G-17944)**

Tenacity Manufacturing Company ....E...... 513 821-0201
West Chester **(G-19955)**

LOTIONS OR CREAMS: Face

Amish Country Essentials LLC ....G...... 330 674-3088
Millersburg **(G-14192)**

Beiersdorf Inc...............................C...... 513 682-7300
West Chester **(G-19984)**

Kahuna Bay Spray Tan LLC ....G...... 419 386-2387
Toledo **(G-18537)**

M D Complete Prof Skincare ....G...... 513 965-3760
Terrace Park **(G-18181)**

Redex Industries Inc.......................F...... 330 332-9800
Salem **(G-16924)**

Skin...G...... 937 222-0222
Dayton **(G-8660)**

LUBRICANTS: Corrosion Preventive

Interlube Corporation ....F...... 513 531-1777
Cincinnati **(G-3929)**

LUBRICATING EQPT: Indl

Koehler Rubber & Supply Co..............F...... 216 749-5100
Cleveland **(G-5662)**

Motionsource International LLC..........F...... 440 287-7037
Solon **(G-17339)**

Renite Company.............................F...... 614 253-5509
Columbus **(G-7554)**

LUBRICATING OIL & GREASE WHOLESALERS

American Ultra Specialties Inc ....F...... 330 656-5000
Hudson **(G-11157)**

Commercial Lubricants Inc.................G...... 614 475-5952
Columbus **(G-6971)**

Digilube Systems Inc.......................F...... 937 748-2209
Springboro **(G-17479)**

LUBRICATING SYSTEMS: Centralized

Parker-Hannifin Corporation..............E...... 330 335-6740
Wadsworth **(G-19426)**

Summa Holdings Inc.........................G...... 440 838-4700
Cleveland **(G-6261)**

LUBRICATION SYSTEMS & EQPT

A S Manufacturing Inc ....G...... 216 476-0656
Cleveland **(G-4677)**

Cleveland Gear Company Inc ....C...... 216 641-9000
Cleveland **(G-5062)**

Digilube Systems Inc.......................F...... 937 748-2209
Springboro **(G-17479)**

Groeneveld Atlantic South ....F...... 330 225-4949
Brunswick **(G-2231)**

Koester Corporation........................D...... 419 599-0291
Napoleon **(G-14687)**

Pax Products Inc.............................F...... 419 586-2337
Celina **(G-3013)**

LUGGAGE & BRIEFCASES

Buckeye Stamping Company ....D...... 614 445-0059
Columbus **(G-6875)**

Cleveland Canvas Goods Mfg Co ....D...... 216 361-4567
Cleveland **(G-5050)**

Eagle Creek Inc..............................D...... 513 385-4442
Cincinnati **(G-3682)**

Hawthorne Caravan & Assoc LLC ....F...... 440 366-9065
Elyria **(G-9428)**

Kam Manufacturing Inc ....C...... 419 238-6037
Van Wert **(G-19261)**

Plastic Forming Company Inc ....E...... 330 830-5167
Massillon **(G-13194)**

Tia Marie & Company ....G...... 513 521-8694
Cincinnati **(G-4509)**

LUGGAGE & LEATHER GOODS STORES

Tia Marie & Company ....G...... 513 521-8694
Cincinnati **(G-4509)**

LUGGAGE & LEATHER GOODS STORES: Leather, Exc Luggage & Shoes

Yoders Harness Shop.......................G...... 440 632-1505
Middlefield **(G-14009)**

LUMBER & BLDG MATLS DEALER, RET: Garage Doors, Sell/Install

Amarr Company ....G...... 216 573-7100
Independence **(G-11248)**

Bonham Enterprsises ....G...... 740 333-0501
Wshngtn CT Hs **(G-20902)**

Jerry Harolds Doors Unlimited ....G...... 740 635-4949
Bridgeport **(G-2090)**

Nofziger Door Sales Inc ....F...... 419 445-2961
Archbold **(G-689)**

Overhead Door of Salem Inc ....G...... 330 332-9530
Salem **(G-16918)**

Overhead Inc ....G...... 419 476-0300
Toledo **(G-18624)**

LUMBER & BLDG MATRLS DEALERS, RET: Bath Fixtures, Eqpt/Sply

Agean Marble Manufacturing..............F...... 513 874-1475
West Chester **(G-19978)**

LUMBER & BLDG MATRLS DEALERS, RETAIL: Doors, Wood/Metal

Nofziger Door Sales Inc....................C...... 419 337-9900
Wauseon **(G-19692)**

LUMBER & BLDG MTRLS DEALERS, RET: Closets, Interiors/Access

Home Stor & Off Solutions Inc ....F...... 216 362-4660
Cleveland **(G-5521)**

LUMBER & BLDG MTRLS DEALERS, RET: Doors, Storm, Wood/Metal

Champion Window Co of Toledo...........E...... 419 841-0154
Perrysburg **(G-16077)**

Toledo Window & Awning Inc ....G...... 419 474-3396
Toledo **(G-18748)**

LUMBER & BLDG MTRLS DEALERS, RET: Planing Mill Prdts/Lumber

Cox Wood Product Inc ....F...... 740 372-4735
Otway **(G-15829)**

Fivecoat Lumber Inc.........................F...... 740 254-4681
Gnadenhutten **(G-10407)**

Marsh Industries Inc........................E...... 330 308-8667
New Philadelphia **(G-14912)**

Yoder Lumber Co Inc........................D...... 330 893-3131
Sugarcreek **(G-18052)**

LUMBER & BLDG MTRLS DEALERS, RET: Windows, Storm, Wood/Metal

Euclid Jalousies Inc.........................G...... 440 953-1112
Cleveland **(G-5300)**

Pickens Window Service Inc................F...... 513 931-4432
Cincinnati **(G-4235)**

LUMBER & BUILDING MATERIAL DEALERS, RETAIL: Roofing Material

Stony Point Metals LLC.....................E...... 330 852-7100
Sugarcreek **(G-18041)**

LUMBER & BUILDING MATERIALS DEALER, RET: Door & Window Prdts

A L Callahan Door Sales....................G...... 419 884-3667
Mansfield **(G-12554)**

Associated Materials LLC ....G...... 937 236-5679
Dayton **(G-8166)**

Bert Radebaugh ....G...... 740 382-8134
Marion **(G-12857)**

Dale Kestler..................................G...... 513 871-9000
Cincinnati **(G-3637)**

Dela-Glassware Ltd LLC ....G...... 740 369-6737
Delaware **(G-8835)**

P & T Millwork Inc ....E...... 440 543-2151
Chagrin Falls **(G-3109)**

Waxco International Inc.....................F...... 937 746-4845
Miamisburg **(G-13879)**

LUMBER & BUILDING MATERIALS DEALER, RET: Masonry Matls/Splys

Associated Associates Inc ....E...... 330 626-3300
Mantua **(G-12707)**

Cashen Inc....................................G...... 440 428-1148
Madison **(G-12497)**

Cemex Materials LLC ....D...... 937 268-6706
Dayton **(G-8219)**

Feather Lite Innovations Inc ....E...... 937 743-9008
Springboro **(G-17480)**

Forterra Pipe & Precast LLC...............G...... 937 268-6707
Dayton **(G-8349)**

Grafton Ready Mix Concret Inc ....E...... 440 926-2911
Grafton **(G-10427)**

Gregory Stone Co Inc.......................G...... 937 275-7455
Dayton **(G-8380)**

Hazelbaker Industries Ltd ....E...... 614 276-2631
Columbus **(G-7146)**

Koltcz Concrete Block Co ....E...... 440 232-3630
Bedford **(G-1437)**

Lafarge North America Inc ....G...... 740 423-5900
Belpre **(G-1590)**

Mack Industries.............................C...... 419 353-7081
Bowling Green **(G-1999)**

Melvin Stone Company LLC ....G...... 740 998-5016
Wshngtn CT Hs **(G-20916)**

Oberfields LLC ....E...... 614 491-7643
Columbus **(G-7409)**

Pleasant Valley Ready Mix Inc ....F...... 330 852-2613
Sugarcreek **(G-18032)**

Quikrete Companies Inc.....................E...... 330 296-6080
Ravenna **(G-16551)**

St Henry Tile Co Inc.........................E...... 419 678-4841
Saint Henry **(G-16822)**

St Henry Tile Co Inc.........................F...... 937 548-1101
Greenville **(G-10523)**

Stocker Concrete Company ....F...... 740 254-4626
Gnadenhutten **(G-10411)**

Westview Concrete Corp.....................E...... 440 458-5800
Elyria **(G-9510)**

LUMBER & BUILDING MATERIALS DEALERS, RET: Solar Heating Eqpt

Greenfield Solar Inc.........................E...... 216 535-9200
Oberlin **(G-15642)**

LUMBER & BUILDING MATERIALS DEALERS, RETAIL: Brick

American Concrete Products ....F...... 937 224-1433
Dayton **(G-8153)**

Glen-Gery Corporation......................D...... 419 845-3321
Caledonia **(G-2437)**

Huth Ready Mix & Supply Co ....F...... 330 833-4191
Massillon **(G-13152)**

Mansfield Brick & Supply Co ....G...... 419 526-1191
Mansfield **(G-12641)**

Medina Supply Company ....E...... 330 723-3681
Medina **(G-13445)**

Snyder Concrete Products Inc ....F...... 513 539-7686
Monroe **(G-14413)**

LUMBER & BUILDING MATERIALS DEALERS, RETAIL: Cement

Dan Shrock Cement..........................G...... 440 548-2498
Parkman **(G-15951)**

Ernst Enterprises Inc ....E...... 614 443-9456
Columbus **(G-7065)**

Employee Codes: A=Over 500 employees, B=251-500
C=101-250, D=51-100, E=20-50, F=10-19, G=3-9

2017 Harris Ohio
Industrial Directory

P R O D U C T

1543

Huron Cement Products Company ....E 419 433-4161
Huron (G-11224)

Piqua Concrete Corp ....G 937 855-0410
Germantown (G-10372)

Rw Sidley Inc ....G 330 545-1964
Girard (G-10394)

Scioto Ready Mix LLC ....D 740 924-9273
Pataskala (G-15983)

LUMBER & BUILDING MATERIALS DEALERS, RETAIL: Countertops

Attractive Kitchens & Flrg LLC ....G 440 406-9299
Elyria (G-9376)

Imperial Countertops ....F 216 851-0888
Cleveland (G-5555)

LUMBER & BUILDING MATERIALS DEALERS, RETAIL: Jalousies

Phillips Awning Co ....G 740 653-2433
Lancaster (G-11738)

LUMBER & BUILDING MATERIALS DEALERS, RETAIL: Modular Homes

Everything In America ....G 347 871-6872
Cleveland (G-5310)

LUMBER & BUILDING MATERIALS DEALERS, RETAIL: Sand & Gravel

National Lime and Stone Co ....G 419 294-3049
Upper Sandusky (G-19134)

Nissen Lumber & Coal Co Inc ....G 419 836-8035
Oregon (G-15711)

LUMBER & BUILDING MATERIALS DEALERS, RETAIL: Siding

Dj & Woodies Vinyl Frontier ....G 740 623-2818
Coshocton (G-7888)

O A R Vinyl Windows & Siding ....G 440 636-5573
Middlefield (G-13978)

LUMBER & BUILDING MATERIALS DEALERS, RETAIL: Tile, Ceramic

Artfinders ....G 330 264-7706
Wooster (G-20740)

Ohio Tile & Marble Co ....E 513 541-4211
Cincinnati (G-4180)

Saint-Gobain Norpro Corp ....C 330 673-5860
Stow (G-17798)

LUMBER & BUILDING MATERIALS RET DEALERS: Millwork & Lumber

Kencraft Co Inc ....G 419 536-0333
Toledo (G-18542)

Laborie Enterprises LLC ....G 419 686-6245
Portage (G-16425)

Mohler Lumber Company ....E 330 499-5461
North Canton (G-15250)

Walnut Creek Planing Ltd ....D 330 893-3244
Millersburg (G-14281)

LUMBER & BUILDING MATLS DEALERS, RET: Concrete/Cinder Block

Encore Precast LLC ....F 513 726-5678
Seven Mile (G-17065)

Ernst Enterprises Inc ....F 419 222-2015
Lima (G-12011)

Hensel Ready Mix ....G 419 253-9200
Marengo (G-12751)

O K Brugmann Jr & Sons Inc ....F 330 274-2106
Mantua (G-12718)

Osborne Inc ....E 216 771-0010
Cleveland (G-5949)

LUMBER & BUILDING MTRLS DEALERS, RET: Insulation Mtrl, Bldg

St Bernard Insulation LLC ....F 513 266-2158
Cincinnati (G-4449)

LUMBER: Box

Clyde Ferenbaugh ....G 740 397-0287
Mount Vernon (G-14617)

LUMBER: Dimension, Hardwood

Creative Concepts ....G 216 513-6463
Medina (G-13398)

Halliday Holdings Inc ....E 740 335-1430
Wshngtn CT Hs (G-20910)

Hinchcliff Lumber Company ....G 440 238-5200
Strongsville (G-17925)

J McCoy Lumber Co Ltd ....F 937 587-3423
Peebles (G-16022)

J McCoy Lumber Co Ltd ....G 937 544-2968
West Union (G-20121)

Stephen M Trudick ....E 440 834-1891
Burton (G-2385)

Woodcraft Industries Inc ....D 440 437-7811
Orwell (G-15783)

Woodcraft Industries Inc ....C 440 632-9655
Middlefield (G-14007)

LUMBER: Fiberboard

Frankes Wood Products LLC ....E 937 642-0706
Marysville (G-12944)

Tectum Inc ....E 740 345-9691
Newark (G-15063)

LUMBER: Flooring, Dressed, Softwood

Conover Lumber Company Inc ....F 937 368-3010
Conover (G-7823)

LUMBER: Furniture Dimension Stock, Softwood

Leppert Companies Inc ....G 614 889-2818
Dublin (G-9099)

LUMBER: Hardwood Dimension

Canfield Manufacturing Co Inc ....G 330 533-3333
North Jackson (G-15289)

Itl LLC ....B 216 831-3140
Beachwood (G-1274)

Ohio Valley Veneer Inc ....E 740 493-2901
Piketon (G-16225)

Siefker Sawmill ....E 419 339-1956
Elida (G-9358)

LUMBER: Hardwood Dimension & Flooring Mills

Armstrong Custom Moulding Inc ....G 740 922-5931
Uhrichsville (G-19045)

Baillie Lumber Co LP ....E 419 462-2000
Galion (G-10254)

Beaver Wood Products ....E 740 226-6211
Beaver (G-1310)

Bwd Woodwork LLC ....G 740 335-9766
Wshngtn CT Hs (G-20903)

Carter-Jones Lumber Company ....C 330 674-9060
Millersburg (G-14211)

Cherokee Hardwoods Inc ....F 440 632-0322
Middlefield (G-13922)

Crownover Lumber Co Inc ....D 740 596-5229
Mc Arthur (G-13330)

Denoon Lumber Company LLC ....D 740 768-2220
Bergholz (G-1641)

Dutch Heritage Woodcraft ....E 330 893-2211
Berlin (G-1648)

Gross Lumber Inc ....E 330 683-2055
Apple Creek (G-638)

Haessly Lumber Sales Co ....D 740 373-6681
Marietta (G-12788)

Hartzell Hardwoods Inc ....D 937 773-7054
Piqua (G-16272)

Hochstetler Wood ....F 330 893-2384
Millersburg (G-14226)

Holmes Lumber & Bldg Ctr Inc ....C 330 674-9060
Millersburg (G-14231)

Itl Corp ....E 216 831-3140
Cleveland (G-5591)

Knisley Lumber ....F 740 634-2935
Bainbridge (G-1061)

Mid Ohio Wood Products Inc ....E 740 323-0427
Newark (G-15033)

Mohler Lumber Company ....E 330 499-5461
North Canton (G-15250)

Stony Point Hardwoods ....F 330 852-4512
Sugarcreek (G-18040)

Superior Hardwoods of Ohio ....E 740 596-2561
Mc Arthur (G-13333)

Superior Hardwoods Ohio Inc ....D 740 384-5677
Wellston (G-19770)

Superior Hardwoods Ohio Inc ....E 740 439-2727
Cambridge (G-2477)

T & D Thompson Inc ....E 740 332-8515
Laurelville (G-11772)

Trumbull County Hardwoods ....E 440 632-0555
Middlefield (G-13998)

Valley Veneer & Lumber Co ....F 440 293-6025
Williamsfield (G-20417)

Wagner Farms & Sawmill LLC ....F 419 653-4126
Leipsic (G-11878)

Walnut Creek Planing Ltd ....D 330 893-3244
Millersburg (G-14281)

Wappoo Wood Products Inc ....E 937 492-1166
Sidney (G-17233)

Woodcraft Manufacturing Co ....E 740 927-6609
Pataskala (G-15992)

Wooden Horse ....G 740 503-5243
Baltimore (G-1091)

Yoder Lumber Co Inc ....D 330 893-3131
Sugarcreek (G-18052)

Yoder Lumber Co Inc ....D 330 893-3121
Millersburg (G-14288)

LUMBER: Kiln Dried

Itl Corp ....E 216 831-3140
Cleveland (G-5591)

Miller Lumber Co Inc ....E 330 674-0273
Millersburg (G-14247)

Trumbull County Dry Kilns Inc ....F 330 562-3367
Aurora (G-952)

LUMBER: Plywood, Hardwood

Automated Bldg Components Inc ....E 419 257-2152
North Baltimore (G-15191)

Beaver Wood Products ....E 740 226-6211
Beaver (G-1310)

Bruewer Woodwork Mfg Co ....D 513 353-3505
Cleves (G-6507)

Carl C Andre Inc ....G 614 864-0123
Brice (G-2087)

Dimension Hardwood Veneers Inc ......E 419 272-2245
Edon (G-9340)

Fifth Avenue Lumber Co ....D 614 833-6655
Canal Winchester (G-2524)

Haessly Lumber Sales Co ....D 740 373-6681
Marietta (G-12788)

Knisley Lumber ....F 740 634-2935
Bainbridge (G-1061)

Lattasburg Lumberworks Co LLC ....G 330 202-7671
West Salem (G-20115)

Miller Manufacturing Inc ....E 330 852-0689
Sugarcreek (G-18028)

Mohler Lumber Company ....E 330 499-5461
North Canton (G-15250)

Ohio Valley Veneer Inc ....E 740 493-2901
Piketon (G-16225)

S & G Manufacturing Group LLC ....C 614 529-0100
Hilliard (G-10977)

Sims-Lohman Inc ....E 513 651-3510
Cincinnati (G-4423)

Stony Point Hardwoods ....F 330 852-4512
Sugarcreek (G-18040)

Valley Veneer & Lumber Co ....F 440 293-6025
Williamsfield (G-20417)

Wappoo Wood Products Inc ....E 937 492-1166
Sidney (G-17233)

Yoder Lumber Co Inc ....D 330 893-3131
Sugarcreek (G-18052)

LUMBER: Plywood, Hardwood or Hardwood Faced

A & M Kiln Dry Ltd ....F 330 852-0505
Dundee (G-9170)

LUMBER: Plywood, Prefinished, Hardwood

Decorative Panels Intl Inc ....D 419 535-5921
Toledo (G-18433)

Miller Crist ....F 330 359-7877
Fredericksburg (G-10088)

Starecasing Systems Inc ....G 312 203-5632
Columbus (G-7654)

LUMBER: Plywood, Softwood

Clopay Building Pdts Co Inc .... E 513 770-4800
  Mason **(G-12998)**
Clopay Building Pdts Co Inc .... G 937 526-4301
  Russia **(G-16762)**
Clopay Building Pdts Co Inc .... G 937 440-6403
  Troy **(G-18810)**

LUMBER: Plywood, Softwood

Beaver Wood Products .... E 740 226-6211
  Beaver **(G-1310)**
S & G Manufacturing Group LLC .... C 614 529-0100
  Hilliard **(G-10977)**
Wappoo Wood Products Inc .... E 937 492-1166
  Sidney **(G-17233)**

LUMBER: Rails, Fence, Round Or Split

D&M Fencing LLC .... G 419 604-0698
  Spencerville **(G-17459)**

LUMBER: Treated

Appalachia Wood Inc .... F 740 596-2551
  Mc Arthur **(G-13328)**
Appalachian Wood Floors Inc .... D 740 354-4572
  Portsmouth **(G-16430)**
ISK Americas Incorporated .... E 440 357-4600
  Painesville **(G-15892)**
Preserving Your Memories .... G 614 861-4283
  Reynoldsburg **(G-16600)**
Ufp Blanchester LLC .... E 937 783-2443
  Blanchester **(G-1717)**
Ufp Hamilton LLC .... F 513 285-7190
  Hamilton **(G-10752)**
US Pro Painters .... G 937 298-2142
  Springfield **(G-17671)**

LUMBER: Veneer, Hardwood

American Veneer Edgebanding .... G 740 928-0266
  Newark **(G-14981)**
Arkansas Face Veneer Co Inc .... E 937 773-6295
  Piqua **(G-16249)**
Erath Veneer Corp Virginia .... F 540 483-5223
  Granville **(G-10458)**
Hartzell Industries Inc .... F 937 773-6295
  Piqua **(G-16273)**
Southeast Ohio Timber Pdts Co .... G 740 344-2570
  Zanesville **(G-21355)**

LUMBER: Veneer, Softwood

American Veneer Edgebanding .... G 740 928-0266
  Newark **(G-14981)**

MACHINE PARTS: Stamped Or Pressed Metal

Abbott Tool Inc .... E 419 476-6742
  Toledo **(G-18318)**
Artisan Equipment Inc .... F 740 756-9135
  Carroll **(G-2936)**
Avion Manufacturing Company .... G 330 220-1989
  Brunswick **(G-2207)**
CA Picard Surface Engrg Inc .... F 440 366-5400
  Elyria **(G-9386)**
Cleveland Hollow Boring Inc .... G 216 883-1926
  Cleveland **(G-5065)**
Compressor Technologies Inc .... E 937 492-3711
  Sidney **(G-17172)**
Coreworth Holdings LLC .... G 419 468-7100
  Iberia **(G-11242)**
Five Star Machine & Tool .... G 937 420-2170
  Fort Loramie **(G-9930)**
Global Manufacturing Tech LLC .... G 440 205-1001
  Mentor **(G-13594)**
Hamlin Newco LLC .... D 330 753-7791
  Akron **(G-212)**
Hidaka Usa Inc .... E 614 889-8611
  Dublin **(G-9084)**
Howland Machine Corp .... E 330 544-4029
  Niles **(G-15158)**
Independent Power Consultants .... G 419 476-8383
  Toledo **(G-18520)**
J R Machining Inc .... G 330 528-3406
  Hudson **(G-11184)**
Jebco Machine Company Inc .... G 330 452-2909
  Canton **(G-2747)**
L C G Machine & Tool Inc .... G 614 261-1651
  Columbus **(G-7276)**

Lowery Industries .... G 740 745-5045
  Saint Louisville **(G-16828)**
M S C Industries Inc .... G 440 474-8788
  Rome **(G-16717)**
Modern Engineering .... G 440 593-5414
  Conneaut **(G-7816)**
Msd Products Inc .... G 440 946-0040
  Mentor **(G-13662)**
Northwood Industries Inc .... F 419 666-2100
  Perrysburg **(G-16128)**
P M Motor Company .... F 440 327-9999
  North Ridgeville **(G-15393)**
PDQ Technologies Inc .... F 937 274-4958
  Dayton **(G-8568)**
Perry Welding Service Inc .... E 330 425-2211
  Twinsburg **(G-19001)**
Plating Technology Inc .... D 937 268-6882
  Dayton **(G-8578)**
Precision Pressed Powdered Met .... F 937 433-6802
  Dayton **(G-8588)**
Project Engineering Company .... E 937 743-9114
  Miamisburg **(G-13849)**
Saco Lowell Parts LLC .... E 330 794-1535
  Akron **(G-393)**
Sakas Incorporated .... E 740 862-4114
  Baltimore **(G-1087)**
Spectrum Machine Inc .... E 330 626-3666
  Streetsboro **(G-17877)**
SPR Machine Inc .... G 513 737-8040
  Indian Spgs **(G-11286)**
TEC Design & Manufacturing Inc .... E 937 435-2147
  Dayton **(G-8707)**
Tech-Med Inc .... F 216 486-0900
  Euclid **(G-9608)**
Tenacity Manufacturing Company .... E 513 821-0201
  West Chester **(G-19955)**
Thk Manufacturing America Inc .... C 740 928-1415
  Hebron **(G-10889)**
True Turn Industries .... G 440 355-6256
  Lagrange **(G-11640)**
Voss Industries Inc .... C 216 771-0870
  Cleveland **(G-6429)**
Ysk Corporation .... B 740 774-7315
  Chillicothe **(G-3284)**

MACHINE SHOPS

Abco Bar & Tube Cutting Svc .... E 513 697-9487
  Maineville **(G-12520)**
Able Tool Corporation .... E 513 733-8989
  Cincinnati **(G-3346)**
Absolute Cnc Machining LLC .... G 937 855-0406
  Germantown **(G-10368)**
Accu-Tech Mfg & Support .... F 440 205-8882
  Mentor **(G-13505)**
Ace Precision Industries Inc .... E 330 633-8523
  Akron **(G-28)**
Adisco Inc .... F 937 296-5070
  Kettering **(G-11574)**
Advanced Welding Co .... E 937 746-6800
  Franklin **(G-10005)**
Aero-Med Industries Inc .... G 216 459-0004
  Cleveland **(G-4718)**
Aisco Metallizing Corp .... F 216 441-7244
  Cleveland **(G-4738)**
All-Type Welding & Fabrication .... E 440 439-3990
  Cleveland **(G-4761)**
Amcan Productions Ltd .... G 330 332-9129
  Salem **(G-16871)**
American Aero Components LLC .... G 937 367-5068
  Dayton **(G-8150)**
Apex Bolt & Machine Company .... E 419 729-3741
  Toledo **(G-18351)**
Applied Experience LLC .... G 614 943-2970
  Columbus **(G-6765)**
ARC Drilling Inc .... F 216 525-0920
  Cleveland **(G-4822)**
Austins Machine Shop .... E 614 855-2525
  Blacklick **(G-1689)**
B C Metals Inc .... G 513 732-9644
  Batavia **(G-1166)**
Balancing Company Inc .... G 937 898-9111
  Vandalia **(G-19282)**
Bardons & Oliver Inc .... C 440 498-5800
  Solon **(G-17264)**
Beacon Metal Fabricators Inc .... F 216 391-7444
  Cleveland **(G-4900)**
Berea Manufacturing Inc .... F 440 260-0590
  Berea **(G-1604)**
Bits & Chips Machining Company .... G 513 539-0800
  Monroe **(G-14394)**

Bmi Machine Inc .... G 614 785-7020
  Columbus **(G-6842)**
Boyds Machine and Met Finshg .... F 937 698-5623
  West Milton **(G-20105)**
Brown Machine Co .... G 216 631-1255
  Cleveland **(G-4939)**
C G Egli Inc .... G 937 254-8898
  Dayton **(G-8204)**
Capital Machine & Fabrication .... G 740 773-4976
  Chillicothe **(G-3231)**
Centerline Tool & Machine .... G 937 222-3600
  Dayton **(G-8221)**
Christopher Tool & Mfg Co .... C 440 248-8080
  Cleveland **(G-5030)**
Circle Machine Rolls Inc .... E 330 938-9010
  Sebring **(G-17044)**
Conison Tool and Die Inc .... G 330 758-1574
  Youngstown **(G-21056)**
Crowe Manufacturing Services .... D 800 831-1893
  Troy **(G-18813)**
Crum Manufacturing Inc .... E 419 878-9779
  Waterville **(G-19654)**
Cutting Dynamics Inc .... C 440 249-4662
  Avon **(G-993)**
Cutting Edge Manufacturing LLC .... G 419 547-9204
  Clyde **(G-6539)**
D & B Industries Inc .... G 937 253-8658
  Dayton **(G-8100)**
Dalton Stryker McHining Fcilty .... D 419 682-6328
  Stryker **(G-18002)**
Design Tech Inc .... G 937 254-7000
  Dayton **(G-8301)**
Devault Machine & Mould Co LLC .... G 740 654-5925
  Lancaster **(G-11705)**
Dimension Industries Inc .... F 440 236-3265
  Columbia Station **(G-6587)**
Diversified Fittings Inc .... F 440 259-0093
  Perry **(G-16048)**
Eagle Machine and Welding Inc .... G 740 345-5210
  Newark **(G-15001)**
EMC Precision Machining II LLC .... E 440 365-4171
  Elyria **(G-9418)**
Eos Technology Inc .... E 216 281-2999
  Cleveland **(G-5288)**
F A Tech Corp .... E 513 942-1920
  West Chester **(G-19861)**
F3 Defense Systems LLC .... G 419 982-2020
  Lima **(G-12012)**
Falmer Screw Pdts & Mfg Inc .... F 330 758-0593
  Youngstown **(G-21082)**
Fincom Corporation .... G 330 456-8341
  Canton **(G-2703)**
Fred W Hanks Company .... G 216 731-1774
  Cleveland **(G-5380)**
G L Heller Co Inc .... F 419 877-5122
  Whitehouse **(G-20339)**
Glendale Machine Inc .... G 440 248-8646
  Solon **(G-17298)**
Global Body & Equipment Co .... D 330 264-6640
  Wooster **(G-20777)**
Goodwin Farms .... G 513 877-2636
  Pleasant Plain **(G-16371)**
Haiss Fabripart LLC .... E 330 821-2028
  Alliance **(G-512)**
Hardin Creek Machine & Tool .... F 419 678-4913
  Coldwater **(G-6561)**
Hawk Engine & Machine .... G 440 582-0900
  North Royalton **(G-15424)**
Hawk Manufacturing LLC .... D 330 784-3151
  Akron **(G-218)**
Hephaestus Technologies LLC .... E 216 252-0430
  Cleveland **(G-5502)**
Highland Products Corp .... F 440 352-4777
  Mentor **(G-13602)**
Holdren Brothers Inc .... F 937 465-7050
  West Liberty **(G-20092)**
Innovative Tool & Die Inc .... G 419 599-0492
  Napoleon **(G-14684)**
Isco Inc .... F 614 792-2206
  Columbus **(G-7212)**
Izit Cain Sheet Metal Corp .... G 937 667-6521
  Tipp City **(G-18284)**
Jade Products Inc .... F 440 352-1700
  Mentor **(G-13618)**
Jed Industries Inc .... E 440 639-9973
  Grand River **(G-10451)**
Jit Company Inc .... F 614 529-8010
  Hilliard **(G-10956)**
Johnson Machining Services LLC .... G 937 866-4744
  Miamisburg **(G-13823)**

Jotco Inc .... G ... 513 721-4943
Mansfield *(G-12630)*

Kastler & Reichlin Inc .... E ... 440 322-0970
Elyria *(G-9445)*

Kent Automation Inc .... F ... 330 678-6343
Kent *(G-11476)*

Kerf Waterjet Ltd .... G ... 937 254-9711
Dayton *(G-8439)*

Knous Tool & Machine Inc .... G ... 419 394-3541
Saint Marys *(G-16841)*

Korff Machine LLC .... G ... 330 332-1566
Salem *(G-16906)*

Krdc Inc .... G ... 937 222-2332
Dayton *(G-8446)*

Krendl Machine Company .... D ... 419 692-3060
Delphos *(G-8910)*

Leader Engnrng-Fabrication Inc ..... G ... 419 592-0008
Napoleon *(G-14688)*

Lesage Machine Inc .... G ... 419 687-0131
Plymouth *(G-16377)*

M & J Machine Shop Inc .... F ... 330 645-0042
Akron *(G-278)*

Machine Parts International .... G ... 216 251-4334
Cleveland *(G-5725)*

Magic City Machine Inc .... F ... 330 825-0048
Barberton *(G-1127)*

Majestic Engineering & TI LLC ...... G ... 937 845-1079
New Carlisle *(G-14807)*

Mark Cottle .... G ... 937 787-4791
Eaton *(G-9317)*

Marsch Machine Products .... G ... 440 298-3932
Madison *(G-12510)*

McIntosh Machine .... G ... 937 687-3936
New Lebanon *(G-14844)*

Melinz Industries Inc .... F ... 440 946-3512
Willoughby *(G-20545)*

Meridian Machine Inc .... G ... 330 308-0296
New Philadelphia *(G-14913)*

Meridian Manufacturing Company ... G ... 330 793-9632
Youngstown *(G-21144)*

Met Fab Fabrication and Mch .... G ... 513 724-3715
Batavia *(G-1203)*

Meta Manufacturing Corporation .... E ... 513 793-6382
Blue Ash *(G-1837)*

Metcut Research Associates Inc ..... D ... 513 271-5100
Cincinnati *(G-4092)*

Miami Vly Mfg & Assembly Inc ...... F ... 937 254-6665
Dayton *(G-8113)*

Micro Machine Ltd .... G ... 330 438-7078
Brewster *(G-2086)*

Miracle Welding Inc .... G ... 513 746-9977
Franklin *(G-10037)*

Mirmat Cnc Machining Inc .... G ... 440 951-2410
Willoughby *(G-20551)*

Mission Industrial Group LLC .... F ... 740 387-2287
Marion *(G-12886)*

Mossing Machine and Tool .... G ... 419 476-5657
Toledo *(G-18592)*

Munson Machine Company Inc ...... G ... 740 967-6867
Johnstown *(G-11402)*

Mutual Tool LLC .... D ... 937 667-5818
Tipp City *(G-18290)*

Mysta Equipment Co .... G ... 330 879-5353
Navarre *(G-14720)*

National Aviation Products Inc .... D ... 330 688-6494
Stow *(G-17779)*

Nauvod Machine Co. .... G ... 440 632-1990
Middlefield *(G-13973)*

Neff Machinery and Supplies .... E ... 740 454-0128
Zanesville *(G-21331)*

Nevels Precision Machining LLC ..... G ... 937 387-6037
Dayton *(G-8523)*

Northeast Machine Tool Corp .... G ... 216 641-0141
Cleveland *(G-5904)*

Northern Machine Tool Co .... G ... 216 961-0444
Cleveland *(G-5911)*

Northern Precision Inc .... F ... 513 860-4701
Fairfield *(G-9691)*

Northshore Mold Inc .... G ... 440 838-8212
Cleveland *(G-5915)*

Nt Machine Inc .... G ... 440 968-3506
Montville *(G-14460)*

Oak Industrial Inc .... G ... 440 263-2780
North Royalton *(G-15439)*

Ohio Metalizing LLC .... G ... 330 830-1092
Massillon *(G-13185)*

Omnimold LLC .... D ... 419 332-4466
Fremont *(G-10172)*

Performance Services .... G ... 419 385-1236
Toledo *(G-18640)*

PME of Ohio Inc .... E ... 513 671-1717
Cincinnati *(G-4248)*

Pohl Machining Inc .... E ... 513 353-2929
Cleves *(G-6522)*

Precision Dynamics Inc .... G ... 330 697-0611
Akron *(G-347)*

Precision Hydraulic Connectors ..... F ... 440 953-3778
Euclid *(G-9601)*

Premier Prod Svc Inds Inc .... G ... 330 527-0333
Garrettsville *(G-10332)*

Process Development Corp .... G ... 937 890-3388
Dayton *(G-8597)*

Qcsm LLC .... G ... 216 531-5960
Euclid *(G-9602)*

Quaker Mfg Corp .... C ... 330 332-4631
Salem *(G-16922)*

Quality Craft Machine Inc .... F ... 330 928-4064
Cuyahoga Falls *(G-8038)*

Queen City Tool Company Inc .... G ... 513 752-4200
Amelia *(G-582)*

Queen City Tool Works Inc .... G ... 513 874-0111
Fairfield *(G-9707)*

Quest Technologies Inc .... F ... 937 743-1200
Franklin *(G-10047)*

R & J Cylinder & Machine Inc .... D ... 330 364-8263
Dover *(G-9007)*

R and S Technologies Inc .... G ... 419 483-3691
Bellevue *(G-1555)*

Reliance Design Inc .... F ... 216 267-5450
Rocky River *(G-16707)*

Remington Engrg Machining Inc ..... G ... 513 965-8999
Milford *(G-14170)*

Rjm Tool .... G ... 419 355-0900
Fremont *(G-10179)*

Robey Tool & Machine .... G ... 614 251-0412
Columbus *(G-7570)*

Rpg Industries Inc .... G ... 937 698-9801
Tipp City *(G-18297)*

S & N Engineering Svcs Corp .... G ... 216 433-1700
Cleveland *(G-6147)*

S A E Manufacturing .... G ... 440 322-9026
Elyria *(G-9490)*

Santos Industrial Ltd .... G ... 937 299-7333
Moraine *(G-14526)*

Short Run Machine Products Inc ..... F ... 440 969-1313
Ashtabula *(G-838)*

Slimline Surgical Devices LLC .... G ... 937 335-0496
Troy *(G-18876)*

Spartan Fabrication .... G ... 330 758-3512
Youngstown *(G-21208)*

Spectre EDM .... G ... 513 469-7700
Blue Ash *(G-1872)*

Spectrum Dynamics Inc .... G ... 614 486-3223
Columbus *(G-7641)*

SRS Manufacturing Corp .... G ... 937 746-3086
Franklin *(G-10054)*

Starr Machine Inc .... E ... 740 753-0009
Nelsonville *(G-14740)*

Summer Global Systems LLC .... G ... 330 397-1653
Campbell *(G-2492)*

Swanton Wldg Machining Co Inc .... D ... 419 826-4816
Swanton *(G-18091)*

T E Martindale Enterprises .... G ... 614 253-6826
Columbus *(G-7673)*

Tdl Tool Inc .... G ... 937 374-0055
Xenia *(G-20978)*

Trailer Component Mfg Inc .... E ... 440 255-2888
Mentor *(G-13753)*

Tri R Tooling Inc .... F ... 419 522-8665
Mansfield *(G-12699)*

Tri-State Machining LLC .... G ... 513 257-9442
Cleves *(G-6530)*

Trojon Gear Inc .... F ... 937 254-1737
Dayton *(G-8729)*

Trs Engineering LLC .... G ... 419 714-7034
Perrysburg *(G-16163)*

Trucast Inc .... D ... 440 942-4923
Willoughby *(G-20621)*

Universal Machine Products .... G ... 513 860-4530
West Chester *(G-19968)*

Vandalia Machining Inc .... G ... 937 264-9155
Vandalia *(G-19314)*

Wc Sales Inc .... G ... 419 836-2300
Northwood *(G-15494)*

Wendell Machine Shop .... G ... 330 627-3480
Carrollton *(G-2969)*

Westerman Acquisition Co LLC ...... E ... 330 264-2447
Wooster *(G-20847)*

White Machine & Mfg Co .... F ... 740 453-3444
Zanesville *(G-21362)*

William Weber .... G ... 440 350-9397
Painesville *(G-15941)*

Wire Shop Inc .... E ... 440 354-6842
Mentor *(G-13771)*

Wulco Inc .... D ... 513 679-2600
Cincinnati *(G-4611)*

Xact Spec Industires LLC .... G ... 440 543-8157
Chagrin Falls *(G-3134)*

Xact Spec Industries LLC .... E ... 440 543-8157
Chagrin Falls *(G-3135)*

MACHINE TOOL ACCESS: Broaches

Northeast Broach & Tool .... G ... 440 918-0048
Willoughby *(G-20556)*

MACHINE TOOL ACCESS: Cams

Connell Limited Partnership .... D ... 877 534-8986
Northfield *(G-15464)*

MACHINE TOOL ACCESS: Collars

Preston .... F ... 740 788-8208
Newark *(G-15048)*

MACHINE TOOL ACCESS: Cutting

Advantage Tool Supply Inc .... G ... 330 896-8869
Uniontown *(G-19074)*

BAP Manufacturing Inc .... G ... 419 332-5041
Fremont *(G-10127)*

Certified Tool & Grinding Inc .... G ... 937 865-5934
Miamisburg *(G-13791)*

Clapp & Haney Brazed Tool Co ..... E ... 740 922-3515
Dennison *(G-8944)*

Cleveland Carbide Tool Co .... G ... 440 974-1155
Mentor *(G-13545)*

Cr Supply LLC .... G ... 440 759-5408
Mentor *(G-13554)*

Edge-Rite Tools Inc .... F ... 216 642-0966
Cleveland *(G-5258)*

Electrofuel Industries Inc .... G ... 937 783-2846
Batavia *(G-1181)*

Expert Regrind Service Inc .... G ... 937 526-5662
Versailles *(G-19347)*

Fox Tool Co Inc .... E ... 330 928-3402
Cuyahoga Falls *(G-7998)*

H Duane Leis Acquisitions .... E ... 937 835-5621
New Lebanon *(G-14842)*

Herco Inc .... E ... 740 498-5181
Newcomerstown *(G-15115)*

HI Tech Tool Corporation .... G ... 513 346-4061
Monroe *(G-14404)*

Independent Die & Mfg Co .... G ... 216 362-6778
Cleveland *(G-5562)*

Interstate Tool Corporation .... E ... 216 671-1077
Cleveland *(G-5583)*

Jump N Sales LLC .... G ... 513 509-7661
Hamilton *(G-10713)*

Kennametal Inc .... C ... 419 877-5358
Whitehouse *(G-20341)*

Knb Tools of America Inc .... K ... 614 733-0400
Plain City *(G-16347)*

Knox Machinery Inc .... F ... 937 743-2641
Franklin *(G-10031)*

Kyocera SGS Precision Tools .... E ... 330 688-6667
Munroe Falls *(G-14661)*

Kyocera SGS Precision Tools .... E ... 330 688-6667
Cuyahoga Falls *(G-8019)*

North-West Tool Co .... G ... 937 278-7995
Dayton *(G-8527)*

P F S Incorporated .... G ... 440 582-1620
Cleveland *(G-5954)*

P O McIntire Company .... E ... 440 269-1848
Wickliffe *(G-20376)*

Precise Tool & Mfg Corp .... F ... 216 524-1500
Cleveland *(G-6033)*

Quality Cutter Grinding Co .... F ... 216 362-6444
Cleveland *(G-6070)*

R & J Tool Inc .... F ... 937 833-3200
Brookville *(G-2198)*

R A Heller Company .... F ... 513 771-6100
Cincinnati *(G-4322)*

Regal Diamond Products Corp .... E ... 440 944-7700
Wickliffe *(G-20385)*

T M Industries Inc .... G ... 330 627-4410
Carrollton *(G-2967)*

Tool Systems Inc .... F ... 440 461-6363
Cleveland *(G-6333)*

Trison Tool Inc .... G ... 440 352-1055
Painesville *(G-15933)*

Uhrichsville Carbide Inc ....F 740 922-9197
Uhrichsville (G-19064)
Ultra-Met Company ....D 937 653-7133
Urbana (G-19186)
William Darling Company Inc ....G 614 878-0085
Columbus (G-7764)

MACHINE TOOL ACCESS: Diamond Cutting, For Turning, Etc

Abrasive Technology Lapidary ....C 740 548-4855
Lewis Center (G-11881)
Chardon Tool & Supply Co Inc ....E 440 286-6440
Chardon (G-3146)
Dark Diamond Tools Inc ....G 440 701-6424
Chardon (G-3148)
Diamond Reserve Inc ....F 440 892-7877
Westlake (G-20263)
Diamonds Products LLC ....G 440 323-4616
Elyria (G-9403)
H3d Tool Corporation ....G 740 498-5181
Newcomerstown (G-15114)
Schumann Enterprises Inc ....E 216 267-6850
Cleveland (G-6166)
Sp3 Cutting Tools Inc ....G 937 667-4476
Tipp City (G-18301)

MACHINE TOOL ACCESS: Dies, Thread Cutting

Aeroll Engineering Corp ....G 216 481-2266
Cleveland (G-4720)
National Rolled Thread Die Co ....F 440 232-8101
Cleveland (G-5859)

MACHINE TOOL ACCESS: Dressing/Wheel Crushing Attach, Diamond

Glassline Corporation ....E 419 666-9712
Perrysburg (G-16102)

MACHINE TOOL ACCESS: Drill Bushings, Drilling Jig

Jergens Inc ....C 216 486-5540
Cleveland (G-5610)

MACHINE TOOL ACCESS: Drills

H Machining Inc ....F 419 636-6890
Bryan (G-2298)

MACHINE TOOL ACCESS: End Mills

Commercial Grinding Services ....E 330 273-5040
Medina (G-13390)

MACHINE TOOL ACCESS: Hopper Feed Devices

Feedall Inc ....F 440 942-8100
Willoughby (G-20486)

MACHINE TOOL ACCESS: Knives, Metalworking

Alliance Knife Inc ....E 513 367-9000
Harrison (G-10768)

MACHINE TOOL ACCESS: Knives, Shear

Precision Component Inds LLC ....E 330 477-1052
Canton (G-2820)
Whitworth Knife Company ....G 513 321-9177
Cincinnati (G-4592)

MACHINE TOOL ACCESS: Machine Attachments & Access, Drilling

McRill Service LLC ....G 419 408-3113
Kenton (G-11557)
Whip Guide Co ....F 440 543-5151
Chagrin Falls (G-3133)

MACHINE TOOL ACCESS: Milling Machine Attachments

JM Performance Products Inc ....F 440 357-1234
Fairport Harbor (G-9766)

MACHINE TOOL ACCESS: Rotary Tables

Troyke Manufacturing Company ....F 513 769-4242
Cincinnati (G-4529)

MACHINE TOOL ACCESS: Shaping Tools

H E Long Company ....F 513 899-2610
Morrow (G-14547)

MACHINE TOOL ACCESS: Sockets

National Machine Company ....E 330 688-2584
Stow (G-17781)

MACHINE TOOL ACCESS: Threading Tools

Cleveland Specialty Insptn Svc ....F 440 578-1046
Mentor (G-13546)
Reed Machinery Inc ....G 330 220-6668
Brunswick (G-2253)

MACHINE TOOL ACCESS: Tool Holders

Kennametal Inc ....C 440 349-5151
Solon (G-17329)

MACHINE TOOL ACCESS: Tools & Access

Bully Tools Inc ....E 740 282-5834
Steubenville (G-17690)
Cowles Industrial Tool Co LLC ....E 330 799-9100
Austintown (G-972)
Cyber Tech Tooling ....G 937 320-2298
Dayton (G-8262)
Furukawa Rock Drill USA Co Ltd ....G 330 673-5826
Kent (G-11462)
H & S Tool Inc ....F 330 335-1536
Wadsworth (G-19409)
HI Carb Corp ....F 216 486-5000
Cleveland (G-5507)
High Quality Tools Inc ....F 440 975-9684
Eastlake (G-9273)
Hilti Inc ....F 614 258-8384
Columbus (G-7158)
M S C Industries Inc ....G 440 474-8788
Rome (G-16717)
Numatx Inc ....G 937 435-8178
Dayton (G-8536)
Oakley Die & Mold Co ....E 513 754-8500
Mason (G-13070)
Polhe Tool Inc ....G 419 476-2433
Toledo (G-18648)
Tomco Tool Inc ....G 937 322-5768
Springfield (G-17665)

MACHINE TOOL ACCESS: Wheel Turning Eqpt, Diamond Point, Etc

Performance Superabrasives LLC ......G 440 946-7171
Mentor (G-13685)

MACHINE TOOL ATTACHMENTS & ACCESS

Allied Machine & Engrg Corp ....C 330 343-4283
Dover (G-8963)
Carbide Probes Inc ....E 937 490-2994
Beavercreek (G-1322)
Dayton Precision Punch ....G 937 275-8700
Dayton (G-8283)
Ellison Technologies Inc ....G 513 874-2736
Hamilton (G-10687)
Frecon Engineering ....G 513 874-8981
West Chester (G-19867)
Global Trade Network Inc ....G 513 701-0411
Mason (G-13031)
Hydra Air Equipment Inc ....G 330 274-2222
Mantua (G-12712)
Lear Manufacturing Inc ....G 440 327-4545
North Ridgeville (G-15387)
Ovase Manufacturing LLC ....E 937 275-0617
Dayton (G-8557)
Positrol Inc ....E 513 272-0500
Cincinnati (G-4252)
Retention Knob Supply & Mfg Co ......F 937 686-6405
Huntsville (G-11215)
Riten Industries Incorporated ....E 740 335-5353
Wshngtn CT Hs (G-20925)
Star Metal Products Co Inc ....D 440 899-7000
Westlake (G-20311)
Te-Co Manufacturing LLC ....D 937 836-0961
Union (G-19068)

MACHINE TOOLS & ACCESS

Able Tool Corporation ....E 513 733-8989
Cincinnati (G-3346)
Accu Jet Corp ....E 937 252-9931
Dayton (G-8129)
Akron Gear & Engineering Inc ....E 330 773-6608
Akron (G-45)
Anchor Lamina America Inc ....E 330 952-1595
Medina (G-13370)
Antwerp Tool & Die Inc ....F 419 258-5271
Antwerp (G-628)
Apollo Products Inc ....F 440 269-8551
Willoughby (G-20434)
Atlantic Tool & Die Company ....C 330 769-4500
Seville (G-17068)
B & R Machine Co Inc ....F 216 961-7370
Cleveland (G-4882)
Bendel Inc ....G 614 478-9013
Columbus (G-6822)
Bender Engineering Company ....G 330 938-2355
Beloit (G-1581)
Big Chief Manufacturing Ltd ....E 513 934-3888
Lebanon (G-11784)
Capital Tool Company ....E 216 661-5750
Cleveland (G-4971)
Carlton Natco ....G 216 451-5588
Cleveland (G-4978)
Cnc Indexing Feeding Tech LLC ....G 513 770-4200
Mason (G-13004)
Coleys Inc ....F 440 967-5630
Vermilion (G-19325)
Contour Tool Inc ....E 440 365-7333
North Ridgeville (G-15364)
Covert Manufacturing Inc ....C 419 468-1761
Galion (G-10261)
Dayton Progress Corporation ....A 937 859-5111
Dayton (G-8284)
Delta Machine & Tool Co ....F 216 524-2477
Cleveland (G-5183)
Diamond Products Limited ....F 440 323-4616
Elyria (G-9402)
Diversified Mch Components LLC ......E 440 942-5701
Eastlake (G-9266)
Drt Mfg Co ....C 937 297-6670
Dayton (G-8313)
E & J Demark Inc ....F 419 337-5866
Wauseon (G-19675)
E & J Demark Inc ....G 419 337-5866
Wauseon (G-19676)
Evandy Co Inc ....G 216 518-9713
Cleveland (G-5305)
Eversharpe Deburring Tool Co ....G 513 988-6240
Trenton (G-18791)
Ferguson Tools Inc ....E 419 298-2327
Edgerton (G-9330)
Firstar Precision Corporation ....E 216 362-7888
Cleveland (G-5350)
Fischer Special Tooling Corp ....F 440 951-8411
Mentor (G-13578)
Formed Metal Products Inc ....F 440 775-0819
Oberlin (G-15639)
Galaxy Products Inc ....G 419 843-7337
Sylvania (G-18107)
Gem Tool LLC ....G 216 771-8444
Cleveland (G-5409)
George Whalley Company ....E 216 453-0099
Fairport Harbor (G-9765)
Gleason Metrology Systems Corp ......E 937 384-8901
Dayton (G-8365)
Hapco Inc ....F 330 678-9353
Kent (G-11469)
Hudson Supply Company Inc ....G 216 518-3000
Cleveland (G-5535)
Hyper Tool Company ....F 440 543-5151
Chagrin Falls (G-3093)
Imco Carbide Tool Inc ....D 419 661-6313
Perrysburg (G-16110)
J and L Manufacturing Inc ....G 937 492-0008
Sidney (G-17197)
Johnson Bros Rubber Co Inc ....E 419 752-4814
Greenwich (G-10531)
Kaeper Machine Inc ....G 440 974-1010
Mentor (G-13622)
Kalt Manufacturing Company ....D 440 327-2102
North Ridgeville (G-15384)
Kennametal Inc ....C 440 437-5131
Orwell (G-15777)
Kennametal Inc ....C 216 898-6120
Cleveland (G-5644)

PRODUCT

Kilroy Company ....D 440 951-8700
Eastlake (G-9278)
Lange Precision Inc ....F 513 530-9500
Blue Ash (G-1824)
Lord Corporation ....C 937 278-9431
Dayton (G-8459)
Master Carbide Tools Company ......F 440 352-1112
Mentor (G-13647)
Matrix Tool & Machine Inc ....E 440 255-0300
Mentor (G-13648)
Matvest Inc ....E 614 487-8720
Columbus (G-7327)
Mdf Tool Corporation ....F 440 237-2277
North Royalton (G-15436)
Medina Blanking Inc ....C 330 558-2300
Valley City (G-19217)
Medway Tool Corp ....E 937 335-7717
Troy (G-18857)
Melin Tool Company Inc ....D 216 362-4200
Cleveland (G-5780)
Metalex Manufacturing Inc ....C 513 489-0507
Blue Ash (G-1839)
Midwest Tool & Engineering Co ......E 937 224-0756
Dayton (G-8498)
Mikan Die and Tool LLC ....G 216 265-2811
Cleveland (G-5812)
Monaghan & Associates Inc ....E 937 253-7706
Dayton (G-8506)
Nook Industries Inc ....C 216 271-7900
Cleveland (G-5887)
Obars Machine and Tool Company ....E 419 535-6307
Toledo (G-18613)
Ohio Broach & Machine Company ....E 440 946-1040
Willoughby (G-20560)
Ohio Drill & Tool Co ....E 330 525-7717
Homeworth (G-11117)
Omwp Company ....E 330 453-8438
Canton (G-2804)
OReilly Precision Pdts Inc ....G 937 526-4677
Russia (G-16766)
Osg-Sterling Die Inc ....D 216 267-1300
Parma (G-15964)
Pakk Systems LLC ....G 440 839-9999
Wakeman (G-19452)
Patriot Mfg Group Inc ....D 937 746-2117
Carlisle (G-2934)
Pemco Inc ....E 216 524-2990
Cleveland (G-5989)
Pike Tool & Manufacturing Co ....G 740 947-7462
Waverly (G-19718)
Production Design Services Inc ....D 937 866-3377
Dayton (G-8598)
Productive Carbides Inc ....G 513 771-7092
Cincinnati (G-4293)
R T & T Machining Co Inc ....F 440 974-8479
Mentor (G-13714)
Rex International USA Inc ....E 800 321-7950
Ashtabula (G-837)
Ridge Tool Manufacturing Co ....A 440 323-5581
Elyria (G-9488)
Roehlers Machine Products ....F 937 354-4401
Mount Victory (G-14659)
Rol - Tech Inc ....C 214 905-8050
Fort Loramie (G-9936)
Rossi Machinery Services Inc ....G 419 281-4488
Ashland (G-773)
Royer Technologies Inc ....G 937 743-6114
Springboro (G-17506)
Setco Sales Company ....D 513 941-5110
Cincinnati (G-4409)
Sharp Tool Service Inc ....E 330 273-4144
Cleveland (G-6184)
Sharper Tooling ....G 330 667-2960
Litchfield (G-12140)
Skidmore-Wilhelm Mfg Company ....E 216 481-4774
Solon (G-17381)
Sorbothane Inc ....E 330 678-9444
Kent (G-11530)
Spectrum Machine Inc ....E 330 626-3666
Streetsboro (G-17877)
Stanley Bittinger ....G 740 942-4302
Cadiz (G-2422)
Stark Industrial LLC ....G 330 493-9773
North Canton (G-15269)
STC International Co Ltd ....G 561 308-6002
Lebanon (G-11842)
Sumitomo Elc Carbide Mfg Inc ....F 440 354-0600
Grand River (G-10453)
Superion Inc ....E 937 374-0033
Xenia (G-20977)

Supplier Inspection Svcs Inc ....E 937 263-7097
Dayton (G-8690)
Technidrill Systems Inc ....E 330 678-9980
Kent (G-11536)
Tormaxx Co ....G 513 721-6299
Cincinnati (G-4513)
United States Drill Head Co ....E 513 941-0300
Cincinnati (G-4540)
Voisard Tool Service ....E 937 526-5451
Russia (G-16771)
Worldwide Machine Tool LLC ....G 614 496-9414
Lewis Center (G-11928)
Wright Buffing Wheel Company ....G 330 424-7887
Lisbon (G-12136)
X-Press Tool Inc ....E 330 225-8748
Brunswick (G-2271)

MACHINE TOOLS, METAL CUTTING: Chucking, Automatic

Applied Automation Enterprise ....F 419 929-2428
New London (G-14858)

MACHINE TOOLS, METAL CUTTING: Die Sinking

Masheen Specialties ....E 330 652-7535
Mineral Ridge (G-14308)

MACHINE TOOLS, METAL CUTTING: Drilling

Martin & Marianne Tools Inc ....G 440 255-5107
Mentor (G-13646)

MACHINE TOOLS, METAL CUTTING: Drilling & Boring

Alliance Drilling Inc ....F 330 584-2781
North Benton (G-15211)
Barbco Inc ....E 330 488-9400
East Canton (G-9190)
Bor-It Manufacturing Inc ....E 419 289-6639
Ashland (G-714)
Faxon Machining Inc ....C 513 851-4644
Cincinnati (G-3745)
Grt Utilicorp Inc ....E 330 264-8444
Wooster (G-20780)
Hdi Rock Drilling Group Ltd ....G 740 369-2968
Delaware (G-8858)
Leland-Gifford Inc ....G 330 785-9730
Akron (G-269)
Sonic Drilling ....G 330 359-0079
Dundee (G-9180)
Technidrill Systems Inc ....E 330 678-9980
Kent (G-11536)
Whole Solutions ....G 330 652-1725
Mineral Ridge (G-14315)

MACHINE TOOLS, METAL CUTTING: Electron-Discharge

Global Specialty Machines LLC ....F 513 701-0452
Mason (G-13030)
Republic EDM Services Inc ....G 937 278-7070
Dayton (G-8626)

MACHINE TOOLS, METAL CUTTING: Exotic, Including Explosive

C M M S - Re LLC ....F 513 489-5111
Blue Ash (G-1760)
Fischer Special Tooling Corp ....F 440 951-8411
Mentor (G-13578)
National Machine Tool Company ....G 513 541-6682
Cincinnati (G-4140)

MACHINE TOOLS, METAL CUTTING: Grind, Polish, Buff, Lapp

Bud May Inc ....F 216 676-8850
Cleveland (G-4945)
Rapid Machine Inc ....F 419 737-2377
Pioneer (G-16243)
Tool Service Co Inc ....G 937 254-4000
Dayton (G-8119)

MACHINE TOOLS, METAL CUTTING: Home Workshop

H & D Steel Service Inc ....E 440 237-3390
North Royalton (G-15423)

MACHINE TOOLS, METAL CUTTING: Lathes

Bardons & Oliver Inc ....C 440 498-5800
Solon (G-17264)
Boye & Emmes Machine Tool Co ......F 513 541-2520
Cincinnati (G-3464)
Monarch Lathes LP ....E 937 492-4111
Sidney (G-17205)

MACHINE TOOLS, METAL CUTTING: Numerically Controlled

Masters Prcision Machining Inc ....F 330 419-1933
Kent (G-11487)

MACHINE TOOLS, METAL CUTTING: Pipe Cutting & Threading

Rex International USA Inc ....E 800 321-7950
Ashtabula (G-837)

MACHINE TOOLS, METAL CUTTING: Plasma Process

Accurate Plasma Cutting Inc ....F 440 943-1655
Wickliffe (G-20350)
Cutting Systems Inc ....F 216 928-0500
Cleveland (G-5155)
Dbcr Inc ....E 330 920-1900
Cuyahoga Falls (G-7986)

MACHINE TOOLS, METAL CUTTING: Regrinding, Crankshaft

Walter Grinders Inc ....G 937 859-1975
Miamisburg (G-13877)

MACHINE TOOLS, METAL CUTTING: Sawing & Cutoff

AM Industrial Group LLC ....G 216 433-7171
Brookpark (G-2149)
Kmi Processing LLC ....G 330 862-2185
Minerva (G-14328)
Kmi Processing LLC ....F 330 862-2185
Minerva (G-14329)
Lawrence Industries Inc ....D 216 518-1400
Cleveland (G-5686)
Lawrence Industries Inc ....E 216 518-7000
Cleveland (G-5687)
Roll-In Saw Inc ....F 216 459-9001
Brookpark (G-2169)

MACHINE TOOLS, METAL CUTTING: Tool Replacement & Rpr Parts

Ald Group LLC ....G 440 942-9800
Willoughby (G-20427)
Automatic Parts ....E 419 524-5841
Mansfield (G-12564)
Bar Tech Service Inc ....G 440 943-5286
Wickliffe (G-20356)
Cardinal Builders Inc ....E 614 237-1000
Columbus (G-6905)
Center Line Machining LLC ....G 216 289-6828
Euclid (G-9571)
Cincinnati Electrical Tool ....F 513 941-5000
Cleves (G-6509)
Drake Manufacturing Svcs Co ....D 330 847-7291
Warren (G-19545)
Eagle Machinery & Supply Inc ....E 330 852-1300
Sugarcreek (G-18023)
J-C-R Inc ....E 937 783-2296
Blanchester (G-1714)
Jeb Modern Machines Ltd ....G 419 639-3937
Republic (G-16579)
Mataco ....G 440 546-8355
Broadview Heights (G-2114)
Mk Global Enterprises LLC ....G 440 823-0081
Beachwood (G-1282)
Molding Machine Services Inc ....G 330 461-2270
Medina (G-13448)
More Manufacturing LLC ....F 937 233-3898
Tipp City (G-18289)
Parkn Manufacturing LLC ....F 330 723-8172
Litchfield (G-12139)
Ravana Industries Inc ....G 330 536-4015
Lowellville (G-12411)
Warner Vess Inc ....G 740 585-2481
Lower Salem (G-12416)

MACHINE TOOLS, METAL CUTTING:
Ultrasonic

Nmgg Ctg LLC.................................G...... 419 447-5211
Tiffin (G-18234)
U-Sonico.......................................F...... 423 348-7117
Springfield (G-17669)

MACHINE TOOLS, METAL FORMING:
Bending

Addisonmckee Inc.........................C...... 513 228-7000
Lebanon (G-11774)
Bendco Machine & Tool Co Inc.......F...... 419 628-3802
Minster (G-14350)
K & L Tool Inc...............................F...... 419 258-2086
Antwerp (G-630)
Pines Manufacturing Inc................E...... 440 835-5553
Westlake (G-20293)
R & B Machining Inc.......................E...... 937 382-6710
Wilmington (G-20677)
S & H Automation & Eqp Co.............E...... 419 636-0020
Bryan (G-2320)

MACHINE TOOLS, METAL FORMING:
Crimping, Metal

Eaton Hydraulics LLC......................E...... 419 232-7777
Van Wert (G-19254)

MACHINE TOOLS, METAL FORMING: Die
Casting & Extruding

American Metal Tech LLC................D...... 937 347-1111
Xenia (G-20936)
Nu-Tool Industries Inc....................F...... 440 237-9240
North Royalton (G-15438)

MACHINE TOOLS, METAL FORMING:
Electroforming

Allied Mask and Tooling Inc............G...... 419 470-2555
Toledo (G-18329)

MACHINE TOOLS, METAL FORMING:
Forging Machinery & Hammers

Ajax Manufacturing Company............E...... 440 295-0244
Wickliffe (G-20351)
NM Group Global LLC.....................G...... 419 447-5211
Tiffin (G-18233)
Sakamura USA Inc..........................F...... 740 223-7777
Marion (G-12897)

MACHINE TOOLS, METAL FORMING: Gear
Rolling

Heimann Manufacturing Co..............G...... 937 652-1865
Urbana (G-19161)

MACHINE TOOLS, METAL FORMING:
Headers

National Machinery LLC...................B...... 419 447-5211
Tiffin (G-18232)

MACHINE TOOLS, METAL FORMING:
Magnetic Forming

Green Corp Magnetic Inc.................E...... 614 801-4000
Grove City (G-10560)

MACHINE TOOLS, METAL FORMING:
Marking

Monode Marking Products Inc..........E...... 440 975-8802
Mentor (G-13660)
Monode Marking Products Inc..........F...... 419 929-0346
New London (G-14861)
Monode Steel Stamp Inc..................G...... 419 929-3501
New London (G-14862)
Monode Steel Stamp Inc..................F...... 440 975-8802
Mentor (G-13661)

MACHINE TOOLS, METAL FORMING:
Mechanical, Pneumatic Or Hyd

Apeks LLC.....................................E...... 740 809-1160
Johnstown (G-11389)

Compass Systems & Sales LLC.........D...... 330 733-2111
Norton (G-15508)
Hawk Manufacturing LLC.................D...... 330 784-3151
Akron (G-218)
Omni Technical Products Inc............F...... 216 433-1970
Cleveland (G-5942)
Recycling Eqp Solutions Corp...........G...... 330 920-1500
Cuyahoga Falls (G-8040)

MACHINE TOOLS, METAL FORMING: Nail
Heading

Stutzman Manufacturing Ltd............G...... 330 674-4359
Millersburg (G-14265)

MACHINE TOOLS, METAL FORMING:
Presses, Hyd & Pneumatic

Accurate Manufacturing Company......E...... 614 878-6510
Columbus (G-6685)
Asb Industries Inc..........................E...... 330 753-8458
Barberton (G-1099)
Columbus Jack Corporation.............D...... 614 228-0185
Columbus (G-6958)
Connell Limited Partnership............D...... 877 534-8986
Northfield (G-15464)
DRG Hydraulics Inc........................E...... 216 663-9747
Cleveland (G-5216)
French Oil Mill Machinery Co............D...... 937 773-3420
Piqua (G-16266)
Gadjets Inc...................................G...... 937 274-2111
Dayton (G-8356)
Henry & Wright Corporation.............F...... 216 851-3750
Cleveland (G-5500)
High Production Technology LLC........F...... 419 591-7000
Napoleon (G-14680)
Hunter Hydraulics Inc.....................G...... 330 455-3983
Canton (G-2732)
Multipress Inc...............................G...... 614 228-0185
Columbus (G-7373)
Parker-Hannifin Corporation............C...... 419 644-4311
Metamora (G-13776)
Phoenix Hydraulic Presses Inc.........F...... 614 850-8940
Hilliard (G-10970)
Qpi Multipress Inc.........................G...... 614 228-0185
Columbus (G-7530)
Quality Products Inc......................D...... 614 228-0185
Columbus (G-7535)
Ram Products Inc..........................F...... 614 443-4634
Columbus (G-7547)
Rogers Industrial Products Inc.........E...... 330 535-3331
Akron (G-378)
Tri-K Enterprises Inc......................G...... 330 832-7380
Canton (G-2882)

MACHINE TOOLS, METAL FORMING:
Pressing

Meadors Machine Inc......................G...... 937 452-5571
Camden (G-2485)
Technical Machine Products Inc.........F...... 216 281-9500
Cleveland (G-6300)

MACHINE TOOLS, METAL FORMING: Rebuilt

Advanced Tech Utilization Co............F...... 440 238-3770
Strongsville (G-17884)
Edwards Machine Service Inc............F...... 937 295-2929
Fort Loramie (G-9929)
Industrial Machine Tool Svc.............G...... 216 651-1122
Cleveland (G-5564)
Machine Tool Rebuilders Inc.............G...... 614 228-1070
Columbus (G-7311)
Pyramid Rebuild and Mch LLC...........F...... 330 633-4452
Tallmadge (G-18166)
Rossi Machinery Services Inc............G...... 419 281-4488
Ashland (G-773)
W G Machine Tool Service Co............G...... 330 723-3428
Medina (G-13496)

MACHINE TOOLS, METAL FORMING:
Spinning, Metal

Ohio Metal Fabricating Inc...............G...... 937 233-2400
Dayton (G-8544)

MACHINE TOOLS, METAL FORMING:
Spinning, Spline Rollg/Windg

BAC Technologies Ltd.....................G...... 937 465-2228
West Liberty (G-20091)

MACHINE TOOLS: Metal Cutting

3 Brothers Torching Inc...................G...... 419 339-9985
Lima (G-11979)
A & P Tool Inc................................E...... 419 542-6681
Hicksville (G-10897)
Acro Tool & Die Company.................D...... 330 773-5173
Akron (G-29)
Advanced Innovative Mfg Inc............G...... 440 759-2034
Aurora (G-905)
Advetech Inc.................................E...... 330 533-2227
Canfield (G-2543)
Alcon Tool Company.......................G...... 330 773-9171
Akron (G-62)
Alien Products LLC.........................E...... 440 946-9100
Mentor (G-13517)
Alliance Knife Inc..........................E...... 513 367-9000
Harrison (G-10768)
Barth Industries Co LP....................E...... 216 267-0531
Cleveland (G-4893)
Cammann Inc................................F...... 440 965-4051
Birmingham (G-1685)
Carlton Natco..............................G...... 216 451-5588
Cleveland (G-4978)
Carter Manufacturing Co Inc............E...... 513 398-7303
Mason (G-12991)
Channel Products Inc.....................D...... 440 423-0113
Chesterland (G-3199)
Chart Tech Tool Inc........................F...... 937 667-3543
Tipp City (G-18272)
Cincinnati Gilbert Mch TI LLC............E...... 513 541-4815
Cincinnati (G-3555)
Cincinnati Mine Machinery Co...........D...... 513 522-7777
Cincinnati (G-3560)
Cleveland Tool and Machine Inc........F...... 216 267-6010
Cleveland (G-5081)
Coil Technology Inc........................G...... 330 601-1350
Wooster (G-20759)
Commercial Grinding Services..........G...... 330 273-5040
Medina (G-13390)
Competetive Carbide Inc.................E...... 440 350-9393
Mentor (G-13551)
Criterion Tool & Die Inc...................E...... 216 267-1733
Brookpark (G-2154)
Dan Wilzynski................................G...... 800 531-3343
Columbus (G-7010)
Dexport Tool Manufacturing Co.........G...... 513 625-1600
Loveland (G-12348)
Dixie Machinery Inc........................F...... 513 360-0091
Monroe (G-14400)
Elliott Tool Technologies Ltd.............D...... 937 253-6133
Dayton (G-8324)
Falcon Industries Inc......................E...... 330 723-0099
Medina (G-13409)
Falcon Tool & Machine Inc...............E...... 937 534-9999
Moraine (G-14487)
Frazier Machine and Prod Inc...........E...... 419 661-1656
Perrysburg (G-16098)
Gbi Cincinnati Inc..........................G...... 513 841-8684
Cincinnati (G-3801)
Genex Tool & Die Inc......................F...... 330 788-2466
Youngstown (G-21098)
George A Mitchell Company..............E...... 330 758-5777
Youngstown (G-21099)
Glassline Corporation.....................E...... 419 666-9712
Perrysburg (G-16102)
Glt Inc..F...... 937 237-0055
Dayton (G-8372)
Hawk Manufacturing LLC.................D...... 330 784-3151
Akron (G-218)
Hawk Manufacturing LLC.................E...... 330 784-4815
Akron (G-219)
Hesler Machine Tool.......................G...... 937 299-3833
Moraine (G-14496)
Houston Machine Products Inc..........E...... 937 322-8022
Springfield (G-17577)
Hyper Tool Company........................F...... 440 543-5151
Chagrin Falls (G-3093)
Interstate Tool Corporation..............E...... 216 671-1077
Cleveland (G-5583)
J and S Tool Incorporated.................E...... 216 676-8330
Cleveland (G-5595)
K L M Manufacturing Company...........G...... 740 666-5171
Ostrander (G-15787)
Kay Capital Company......................G...... 216 531-1010
Cleveland (G-5638)
Kilroy Company.............................D...... 440 951-8700
Eastlake (G-9278)
Klawhorn Industries Inc...................G...... 330 335-8191
Wadsworth (G-19414)

PRODUCT

Lahm-Trosper Inc ....F 937 252-8791
Dayton *(G-8451)*

Lees Machinery ....G 440 259-2222
Perry *(G-16052)*

Levan Enterprises Inc ....E 330 923-9797
Stow *(G-17769)*

Machine Component Mfg ....F 330 454-4566
Canton *(G-2765)*

Machine Tl Sltons Unlmted LLC ....F 513 761-0709
Cincinnati *(G-4046)*

Makino Inc ....B 513 573-7200
Mason *(G-13058)*

Mansfield Screw Mch Pdts Co ....D 419 884-1511
Mansfield *(G-12644)*

Martindale Electric Company ....E 216 521-8567
Cleveland *(G-5754)*

Max Pro Tools Inc ....F 440 885-9522
Cleveland *(G-5762)*

Melin Tool Company Inc ....D 216 362-4200
Cleveland *(G-5780)*

Metal Cutting Technology LLC ......G 419 733-1236
Celina *(G-3008)*

Micron Manufacturing Inc ....D 440 355-4200
Lagrange *(G-11633)*

Midwest Knife Grinding Inc ....F 330 854-1030
Canal Fulton *(G-2508)*

Milacron Marketing Company LLC ...E 513 536-2000
Batavia *(G-1207)*

Monaghan & Associates Inc ....E 937 253-7706
Dayton *(G-8506)*

Mrd Solutions LLC ....G 440 942-6969
Eastlake *(G-9283)*

Nesco Inc ....E 440 461-6000
Cleveland *(G-5871)*

New Holland Engineering Inc ....G 740 495-5200
New Holland *(G-14835)*

Northwood Industries Inc ....F 419 666-2100
Perrysburg *(G-16128)*

Obars Machine and Tool Company ...E 419 535-6307
Toledo *(G-18613)*

Oceco Inc ....F 419 447-0916
Tiffin *(G-18235)*

P M R Inc ....G 440 937-6241
Avon *(G-1001)*

P R Racing Engines ....G 419 472-2277
Toledo *(G-18632)*

Page Slotting Saw Co Inc ....F 419 476-7475
Toledo *(G-18633)*

Peerless Saw Company ....E 614 836-5790
Groveport *(G-10640)*

Phillips Manufacturing Co ....D 330 652-4335
Niles *(G-15173)*

Pilgrim-Harp Co ....G 440 249-4185
Avon *(G-1003)*

Pinnacle Precision Pdts LLC ....G 440 786-0248
Bedford *(G-1453)*

Power Engineering LLC ....G 513 793-5800
Cincinnati *(G-4255)*

Rafter Equipment Corporation ....E 440 572-3700
Strongsville *(G-17956)*

Raka Corporation ....D 419 476-6572
Toledo *(G-18671)*

Raymath Company ....C 937 335-1860
Troy *(G-18867)*

Reliable Products Co Inc ....G 419 394-5854
Saint Marys *(G-16853)*

Ridge Tool Company ....F 440 323-5581
Elyria *(G-9486)*

Ridge Tool Company ....D 740 432-8782
Cambridge *(G-2474)*

Ridge Tool Manufacturing Co ....A 440 323-5581
Elyria *(G-9488)*

Rimrock Holdings Corporation ....E 614 471-5926
Columbus *(G-7564)*

Robbins Company ....C 440 248-3303
Solon *(G-17370)*

Rossi Machinery Services Inc ....G 419 281-4488
Ashland *(G-773)*

Sharp Industrial Tools Inc ....G 513 741-9562
Cincinnati *(G-4413)*

Shumaker Racing Components ....G 419 238-0801
Van Wert *(G-19270)*

Specialty Metals Processing ....E 330 656-2767
Hudson *(G-11201)*

Stadco Inc ....E 937 878-0911
Fairborn *(G-9630)*

STC International Co Ltd ....G 561 308-6002
Lebanon *(G-11842)*

Strouse Industries Inc ....G 440 257-2520
Mentor *(G-13739)*

Sumitomo Elc Carbide Mfg Inc ....F 440 354-0600
Grand River *(G-10453)*

Superion Inc ....E 937 374-0033
Xenia *(G-20977)*

Supply Dynamics LLC ....F 513 965-2000
Loveland *(G-12392)*

Swagelok Hy-Level Company ....C 440 238-1260
Strongsville *(G-17975)*

Systematic Machine Corp ....G 440 877-9884
North Royalton *(G-15455)*

Tessec Manufacturing Svcs LLC .....G 937 985-3552
Dayton *(G-8710)*

Tooling Connection Inc ....G 419 594-3339
Oakwood *(G-15620)*

Twin Tool LLC ....E 937 435-8946
Dayton *(G-8735)*

Tykma Inc ....E 877 318-9562
Chillicothe *(G-3283)*

U S Alloy Die Corp ....F 216 749-9700
Cleveland *(G-6379)*

Union Process Inc ....G 330 929-3333
Akron *(G-454)*

Updike Supply Company ....G 937 482-4000
Huber Heights *(G-11152)*

Usm Acquisition Corporation ....G 440 975-8600
Willoughby *(G-20627)*

Vulcan Tool Company ....G 937 253-6194
Dayton *(G-8744)*

West Ohio Tool & Mfg LLC ....G 419 678-4745
Saint Henry *(G-16825)*

West Ohio Tool Company ....F 937 842-6688
Russells Point *(G-16758)*

Willow Tool & Machining Ltd ....G 440 572-2288
Strongsville *(G-17984)*

Wonder Machine Services Inc ....E 440 937-7500
Avon *(G-1020)*

Zagar Inc ....G 216 731-0500
Cleveland *(G-6490)*

MACHINE TOOLS: *Metal Forming*

Ajax Tocco Magnethermic Corp ......C 440 278-7200
Wickliffe *(G-20352)*

Akron Specialized Products ....G 330 762-9269
Akron *(G-56)*

Alco Manufacturing Corp LLC ....E 440 458-5165
Elyria *(G-9367)*

Alien Products LLC ....E 440 946-9100
Mentor *(G-13517)*

American Fluid Power Inc ....G 877 223-8742
Elyria *(G-9371)*

American Laser and Machine LLC ...G 419 214-0880
Toledo *(G-18339)*

Anderson & Vreeland Inc ....D 419 636-5002
Bryan *(G-2278)*

Barclay Machine Inc ....F 330 337-9541
Salem *(G-16874)*

Barth Industries Co LP ....D 216 267-0531
Cleveland *(G-4893)*

Bintzler Inc ....F 513 677-1164
Loveland *(G-12343)*

Brilex Industries Inc ....D 330 744-1114
Youngstown *(G-21036)*

Brilex Industries Inc ....C 330 744-1114
Youngstown *(G-21037)*

Dover Corporation ....G 513 696-1790
Mason *(G-13010)*

E Systems Design & Automtn Inc ....G 419 443-0220
Tiffin *(G-18219)*

Elliott Tool Technologies Ltd ....D 937 253-6133
Dayton *(G-8324)*

Exito Manufacturing ....G 937 291-9871
Dayton *(G-8337)*

F & G Tool and Die Co ....E 937 746-3658
Franklin *(G-10019)*

Fabriweld Corporation ....E 419 668-3358
Norwalk *(G-15539)*

First Tool Corp ....E 937 254-6197
Dayton *(G-8342)*

Gem City Metal Tech LLC ....E 937 252-8998
Dayton *(G-8362)*

High Production Technology LLC ......G 419 599-1511
Napoleon *(G-14681)*

Hill & Griffith Company ....G 513 921-1075
Cincinnati *(G-3882)*

Howmet Corporation ....C 800 242-9898
Newburgh Heights *(G-15074)*

J and S Tool Incorporated ....E 216 676-8330
Cleveland *(G-5595)*

Kay Capital Company ....G 216 531-1010
Cleveland *(G-5638)*

Kiraly Tool and Die Inc ....F 330 744-5773
Youngstown *(G-21129)*

Levan Enterprises Inc ....E 330 923-9797
Stow *(G-17769)*

Machine Concepts Inc ....E 419 628-3498
Minster *(G-14357)*

McNeil & Nrm Inc ....D 330 761-1855
Akron *(G-291)*

Metal & Wire Products Company ......E 330 332-9448
Salem *(G-16914)*

Meyer Machine Tool Company ....G 614 235-0039
Columbus *(G-7344)*

Parker-Hannifin Corporation ....C 419 394-9600
Saint Marys *(G-16848)*

Rafter Equipment Corporation ....E 440 572-3700
Strongsville *(G-17956)*

Ready Technology Inc ....F 937 228-8181
Dayton *(G-8618)*

Ready Technology Inc ....F 937 866-7200
Dayton *(G-8619)*

Ritime Incorporated ....F 330 273-3443
Cleveland *(G-6115)*

Scotts Miracle-Gro Company ....B 937 644-0011
Marysville *(G-12968)*

Semtorq Inc ....F 330 487-0600
Twinsburg *(G-19019)*

Slade Gardner ....G 440 355-8015
Lagrange *(G-11637)*

Spencer Manufacturing Company ....D 330 648-2461
Spencer *(G-17457)*

Standard Engineering Group Inc ......G 330 494-4300
North Canton *(G-15267)*

Starkey Machinery Inc ....E 419 468-2560
Galion *(G-10289)*

Stolle Machinery Company LLC ....C 937 497-5400
Sidney *(G-17230)*

Taylor - Winfield Corporation ....D 330 259-8500
Hubbard *(G-11140)*

TEC Design & Manufacturing Inc .....F 937 435-2147
Dayton *(G-8707)*

Terminal Equipment Industries ....G 330 468-0322
Northfield *(G-15474)*

Trucut Incorporated ....D 330 938-9806
Sebring *(G-17055)*

Turner Machine Co ....F 330 332-5821
Salem *(G-16932)*

Twist Inc ....C 937 675-9581
Jamestown *(G-11353)*

Twist Inc ....E 937 675-9581
Jamestown *(G-11354)*

Uhrichsville Carbide Inc ....F 740 922-9197
Uhrichsville *(G-19064)*

Valley Tool & Die Inc ....D 440 237-0160
North Royalton *(G-15458)*

Van Burens Welding & Machine ....G 740 787-2636
Glenford *(G-10401)*

Vulcan Tool Company ....G 937 253-6194
Dayton *(G-8744)*

MACHINERY & EQPT, AGRICULTURAL, WHOLESALE: *Farm Implements*

R L Parsons & Son Equipment Co .....G 614 879-7601
West Jefferson *(G-20083)*

MACHINERY & EQPT, AGRICULTURAL, WHOLESALE: *Lawn & Garden*

Johnson Tool Distributors ....G 740 653-6959
Lancaster *(G-11724)*

Siteone Landscape Supply LLC ....G 330 220-8691
Brunswick *(G-2257)*

MACHINERY & EQPT, AGRICULTURAL, WHOLESALE: *Livestock Eqpt*

Fort Recovery Equipment Inc ....E 419 375-1006
Fort Recovery *(G-9949)*

RJR & Associates Inc ....G 419 237-2220
Fayette *(G-9779)*

MACHINERY & EQPT, AGRICULTURAL, WHOLESALE: *Tractors*

Franklin Equipment LLC ....E 614 228-2014
Groveport *(G-10623)*

MACHINERY & EQPT, INDL, WHOL: Controlling Instruments/Access

Russments Inc ....G....... 513 602-5035
Cincinnati *(G-4368)*

MACHINERY & EQPT, INDL, WHOL: Environ Pollution Cntrl, Air

Air Plastics Inc ....F....... 513 469-1074
Blue Ash *(G-1737)*

MACHINERY & EQPT, INDL, WHOL: Environ Pollution Cntrl, Water

X-3-5 LLC ....G....... 513 489-5477
Cincinnati *(G-4613)*

MACHINERY & EQPT, INDL, WHOL: Meters, Consumption Registerng

Flow Line Options Corp ....G....... 330 331-7331
Wadsworth *(G-19407)*

MA Flynn Associates LLC ....G....... 513 893-7873
Hamilton *(G-10721)*

MACHINERY & EQPT, INDL, WHOLESALE: Cement Making

Spillman Company ....E....... 614 444-2184
Columbus *(G-7644)*

MACHINERY & EQPT, INDL, WHOLESALE: Chemical Process

Aldrich Chemical ....D....... 937 859-1808
Miamisburg *(G-13781)*

MACHINERY & EQPT, INDL, WHOLESALE: Conveyor Systems

Alba Manufacturing Inc ....D....... 513 874-0551
Fairfield *(G-9640)*

Digilube Systems Inc...........................F....... 937 748-2209
Springboro *(G-17479)*

Logitech Inc ....E....... 614 871-2822
Grove City *(G-10569)*

Tegron Holding LLC............................G....... 330 836-2004
Akron *(G-431)*

Trico Belting & Supply Company ....E....... 513 860-8400
West Chester *(G-20061)*

MACHINERY & EQPT, INDL, WHOLESALE: Cranes

De-Ko Inc ....G....... 440 951-2585
Willoughby *(G-20472)*

Hiab USA Inc ....D....... 419 482-6000
Perrysburg *(G-16106)*

Rnm Holdings Inc ....E....... 419 867-8712
Holland *(G-11082)*

Rnm Holdings Inc ....F....... 614 444-5556
Columbus *(G-7566)*

Terex Utilities Inc ....F....... 440 262-3200
Brecksville *(G-2076)*

Venco Venturo Industries LLC.............E....... 513 772-8448
Cincinnati *(G-4561)*

MACHINERY & EQPT, INDL, WHOLESALE: Engines & Parts, Diesel

Cummins Bridgeway LLC.....................E....... 614 604-6000
Grove City *(G-10552)*

Cummins Bridgeway LLC.....................E....... 614 771-1000
Hilliard *(G-10946)*

Cummins Bridgeway Columbus LLC...D....... 614 771-1000
Hilliard *(G-10947)*

Cummins Bridgeway Toledo LLC.........F....... 419 893-8711
Maumee *(G-13235)*

Industrial Parts Depot LLC.................G....... 440 237-9164
North Royalton *(G-15427)*

Interstate-Mcbee LLC ....G....... 800 321-4234
Cleveland *(G-5584)*

Martin Diesel Inc ....E 419 782-9911
Defiance *(G-8802)*

Western Branch Diesel Inc...................E....... 330 454-8800
Canton *(G-2902)*

MACHINERY & EQPT, INDL, WHOLESALE: Engines, Gasoline

Graham Ford Power Products ....G....... 614 801-0049
Columbus *(G-7127)*

MACHINERY & EQPT, INDL, WHOLESALE: Fans

National Tool & Equipment Inc ....F....... 330 629-8665
Youngstown *(G-21148)*

MACHINERY & EQPT, INDL, WHOLESALE: Food Manufacturing

R and J Corporation ....E....... 440 871-6009
Westlake *(G-20299)*

MACHINERY & EQPT, INDL, WHOLESALE: Heat Exchange

Gerow Equipment Company Inc............G....... 216 383-8800
Cleveland *(G-5426)*

MACHINERY & EQPT, INDL, WHOLESALE: Hydraulic Systems

Breaker Technology Inc ....E....... 440 248-7168
Solon *(G-17274)*

Cuyahoga Mch Co Ltd Lblty Co............G....... 216 267-3560
Cleveland *(G-5158)*

Eaton Corporation ....B....... 216 523-5000
Beachwood *(G-1268)*

Eaton Corporation ....B....... 216 920-2000
Cleveland *(G-5249)*

Hydra Air Equipment Inc ....G....... 330 274-2222
Mantua *(G-12712)*

Hydraulic Parts Store Inc ....E....... 330 364-6667
New Philadelphia *(G-14902)*

Hydro Supply Co..................................F....... 740 454-3842
Zanesville *(G-21320)*

Industrial Connections Inc...................G....... 330 274-2155
Mantua *(G-12713)*

Modern Design Stamping Div ....G....... 216 382-6318
Cleveland *(G-5826)*

Ohio Hydraulics Inc ....E....... 513 771-2590
Cincinnati *(G-4178)*

R & M Fluid Power Inc ....E....... 330 758-2766
Youngstown *(G-21182)*

Robeck Fluid Power Co........................D....... 330 562-1140
Aurora *(G-944)*

Rumpke Transportation Co LLC...........F....... 513 851-0122
Cincinnati *(G-4366)*

Swanson Industries Inc.......................D....... 304 284-5199
New Philadelphia *(G-14931)*

System Seals Inc.................................D....... 440 735-0200
Cleveland *(G-6284)*

MACHINERY & EQPT, INDL, WHOLESALE: Indl Machine Parts

F & W Auto Supply ....G....... 419 445-3350
Archbold *(G-671)*

Grt Utilicorp Inc...................................E....... 330 264-8444
Wooster *(G-20780)*

Retek Inc ....G....... 440 937-6282
Avon *(G-1008)*

Spectrum Mfg & Sls Inc ....G....... 614 486-3223
Columbus *(G-7642)*

Transducers Direct Llc ....F....... 513 247-0601
Cincinnati *(G-4519)*

MACHINERY & EQPT, INDL, WHOLESALE: Instruments & Cntrl Eqpt

ABB Inc ....C....... 440 585-8500
Wickliffe *(G-20348)*

Airgas ....G....... 330 345-1257
Wooster *(G-20732)*

Fcx Performance Inc............................E....... 614 324-6050
Columbus *(G-7078)*

Instrumentors Inc................................G....... 440 238-3430
Strongsville *(G-17931)*

Prime Controls Inc ....G....... 937 435-8659
Dayton *(G-8592)*

South Shore Controls Inc....................E....... 440 259-2500
Perry *(G-16058)*

MACHINERY & EQPT, INDL, WHOLESALE: Lift Trucks & Parts

Crown Equipment Corporation..............D 419 629-2311
New Bremen *(G-14785)*

Fastener Industries Inc........................E....... 440 891-2031
Berea *(G-1615)*

Joseph Industries Inc..........................D....... 330 528-0091
Streetsboro *(G-17860)*

Suspension Technology Inc ....F....... 330 458-3058
Canton *(G-2865)*

MACHINERY & EQPT, INDL, WHOLESALE: Machine Tools & Access

Boye & Emmes Machine Tool Co ....F....... 513 541-2520
Cincinnati *(G-3464)*

Clear Fold Door Inc ....G....... 440 735-1351
Cleveland *(G-5045)*

Evolution Resources LLC ....G....... 937 438-2390
Centerville *(G-3041)*

Frecon Technologies Inc ....F....... 513 874-8981
West Chester *(G-19868)*

Imco Carbide Tool Inc.........................D....... 419 661-6313
Perrysburg *(G-16110)*

J and S Tool Incorporated ....E....... 216 676-8330
Cleveland *(G-5595)*

Jergens Inc ....C....... 216 486-5540
Cleveland *(G-5610)*

Jett Industries Inc ....G....... 740 344-4140
Newark *(G-15024)*

Lees Machinery...................................E....... 440 259-2222
Perry *(G-16052)*

Neff Machinery and Supplies ....G....... 740 454-0128
Zanesville *(G-21331)*

New Tech ....G....... 330 494-8338
Canton *(G-2787)*

Smith & Mills Shapers Inc....................F....... 513 541-4031
Cincinnati *(G-4428)*

MACHINERY & EQPT, INDL, WHOLESALE: Machine Tools & Metalwork

Armeton US Co ....G....... 419 554-1866
Norwalk *(G-15526)*

Friess Equipment Inc...........................G....... 330 945-9440
Akron *(G-194)*

Gbi Cincinnati Inc ....G....... 513 841-8684
Cincinnati *(G-3801)*

Northern Machine Tool Co ....G....... 216 961-0444
Cleveland *(G-5911)*

Tool Service Co Inc.............................G....... 937 254-4000
Dayton *(G-8119)*

Tool Systems Inc.................................F....... 440 461-6363
Cleveland *(G-6333)*

MACHINERY & EQPT, INDL, WHOLESALE: Measure/Test, Electric

Automation Metrology Intl LLC ....G....... 440 354-6436
Mentor *(G-13529)*

MACHINERY & EQPT, INDL, WHOLESALE: Metal Refining

A & B Deburring Company ....F....... 513 723-0777
Cincinnati *(G-3328)*

Stanley Industries Inc..........................E....... 216 475-4000
Cleveland *(G-6236)*

MACHINERY & EQPT, INDL, WHOLESALE: Noise Control

Tech Products Corporation...................E....... 937 438-1100
Miamisburg *(G-13867)*

MACHINERY & EQPT, INDL, WHOLESALE: Packaging

Alfons Haar Inc....................................E....... 937 560-2031
Springboro *(G-17472)*

Bollin & Sons Inc ....E....... 419 693-6573
Toledo *(G-18376)*

Millwood Inc ....F....... 513 860-4567
West Chester *(G-19901)*

PRODUCT

MACHINERY & EQPT, INDL, WHOLESALE: Paint Spray

Kecamm LLC .... G 330 527-2918
Garrettsville (G-10326)

Tri Chem Inc .... G 330 677-1213
Kent (G-11539)

MACHINERY & EQPT, INDL, WHOLESALE: Paper Manufacturing

Advanced Fiber Technology Inc .... E 513 860-4446
Bucyrus (G-2331)

MACHINERY & EQPT, INDL, WHOLESALE: Petroleum Industry

T JS Oil & Gas Inc .... G 740 623-0192
Coshocton (G-7912)

MACHINERY & EQPT, INDL, WHOLESALE: Plastic Prdts Machinery

Grit Guard Inc .... G 937 592-9003
Bellefontaine (G-1531)

Maintenance Repair Supply Inc .... E 740 922-3006
Midvale (G-14109)

MACHINERY & EQPT, INDL, WHOLESALE: Pneumatic Tools

Belle Center Air Tool Co Inc .... G 937 464-7474
Belle Center (G-1511)

Schenck Process LLC .... F 513 576-9200
Milford (G-14173)

MACHINERY & EQPT, INDL, WHOLESALE: Processing & Packaging

Esperia Holdings LLC .... G 714 249-7888
Oak Harbor (G-15589)

Kingsly Compression Inc .... G 740 439-0772
Cambridge (G-2462)

MACHINERY & EQPT, INDL, WHOLESALE: Robots

Kc Robotics Inc .... E 513 860-4442
West Chester (G-19887)

Programmable Control Service .... F 740 927-0744
Pataskala (G-15978)

Remtec Engineering .... E 513 860-4299
Mason (G-13082)

Rixan Associates Inc .... E 937 438-3005
Dayton (G-8633)

Versatile Automation Tech Ltd .... G 330 220-2600
Brunswick (G-2265)

MACHINERY & EQPT, INDL, WHOLESALE: Safety Eqpt

A & A Safety Inc .... E 513 943-6100
Amelia (G-564)

Cintas Corporation .... A 513 459-1200
Cincinnati (G-3577)

Cintas Corporation .... D 513 631-5750
Cincinnati (G-3578)

D M V Supply Corporation .... G 330 847-0450
Warren (G-19540)

Impact Products LLC .... C 419 841-2891
Toledo (G-18518)

Paul Peterson Company .... E 614 486-4375
Columbus (G-7467)

MACHINERY & EQPT, INDL, WHOLESALE: Tool & Die Makers

Oerlikon Friction Systems .... E 937 233-7002
Dayton (G-8539)

Ready Technology Inc .... F 937 228-8181
Dayton (G-8618)

MACHINERY & EQPT, INDL, WHOLESALE: Woodworking

Ryanworks Inc .... F 937 438-1282
Dayton (G-8641)

MACHINERY & EQPT, TEXTILE: Fabric Forming

Leesburg Looms Incorporated .... G 419 238-2738
Van Wert (G-19263)

MACHINERY & EQPT, WHOLESALE: Concrete Processing

McNeilus Truck and Mfg Inc .... G 614 868-0760
Gahanna (G-10218)

MACHINERY & EQPT, WHOLESALE: Construction & Mining, Ladders

American Scaffolding Inc .... G 216 524-7733
Cleveland (G-4795)

Bauer Corporation .... E 800 321-4760
Wooster (G-20746)

MACHINERY & EQPT, WHOLESALE: Construction, General

Baswa Acoustics North Amer LLC .... F 216 475-7197
Bedford (G-1404)

Thirion Brothers Eqp Co LLC .... G 440 357-8004
Painesville (G-15930)

MACHINERY & EQPT, WHOLESALE: Contractors Materials

Carroll Distrg & Cnstr Sup Inc .... G 513 422-3327
Middletown (G-14026)

Carroll Distrg & Cnstr Sup Inc .... G 614 564-9799
Columbus (G-6912)

Cincinnati Gutter Supply Inc .... G 513 825-0500
West Chester (G-19831)

Hilti Inc .... F 614 258-8384
Columbus (G-7158)

Johnston-Morehouse-Dickey Co .... G 614 866-0452
Columbus (G-7242)

MACHINERY & EQPT, WHOLESALE: Logging & Forestry

L&L Excavating & Land Clearing .... G 740 682-7823
Oak Hill (G-15600)

MACHINERY & EQPT, WHOLESALE: Masonry

EZ Grout Corporation Inc .... E 740 962-2024
Malta (G-12536)

Fastenal Company .... G 330 745-2996
Akron (G-182)

MACHINERY & EQPT, WHOLESALE: Oil Field Eqpt

Belden & Blake Corporation .... E 330 602-5551
Dover (G-8968)

Global Oilfield Services LLC .... G 419 756-8027
Mansfield (G-12613)

Kelley Brothers Roofing Inc .... F 330 273-3700
Medina (G-13432)

Petrox Inc .... F 330 653-5526
Streetsboro (G-17867)

MACHINERY & EQPT, WHOLESALE: Road Construction & Maintenance

Terry Asphalt Materials Inc .... E 513 874-6192
Hamilton (G-10744)

MACHINERY & EQPT: Electroplating

Corrotec Inc .... G 937 325-3585
Springfield (G-17536)

Liquid Development Company .... G 216 641-9366
Independence (G-11265)

Universal Rack & Equipment Co .... E 330 963-6776
Twinsburg (G-19033)

MACHINERY & EQPT: Farm

American Baler Co .... D 419 483-5790
Bellevue (G-1543)

Baker Built Products Inc .... G 419 965-2646
Ohio City (G-15660)

Beth Otto Independent Case Exa .... G 513 868-0484
Fairfield (G-9645)

Buckeye Tractor Company Corp .... G 419 659-2162
Columbus Grove (G-7791)

Cailin Dev Ltd Lblty Co .... F 216 408-6261
Cleveland (G-4962)

Case Western Reserve Univ .... G 216 368-2574
Cleveland (G-4988)

Creamer Metal Products Inc .... E 740 852-1752
London (G-12207)

Empire Plow Company Inc .... E 216 641-2290
Cleveland (G-5278)

Field Gymmy Inc .... G 419 538-6511
Glandorf (G-10397)

Fremont Plastic Products Inc .... C 419 332-6407
Fremont (G-10150)

Gilbert Geiser .... G 330 237-7901
Canton (G-2714)

H & S Company Inc .... F 419 394-4444
Celina (G-2999)

Intertec Corporation .... B 419 537-9711
Toledo (G-18527)

J & M Manufacturing Co Inc .... C 419 375-2376
Fort Recovery (G-9955)

Komar Industries Inc .... E 614 836-2366
Groveport (G-10629)

Ley Equipment Co .... G 419 238-6742
Van Wert (G-19264)

Ley Industries Inc .... G 419 238-6742
Van Wert (G-19265)

Motrin Corporation .... G 740 439-2725
Cambridge (G-2469)

Ntech Industries Inc .... F 707 467-3747
Dayton (G-8534)

Pioneer Equipment Company .... F 330 857-6340
Dalton (G-8078)

Remlinger Manufacturing Co Inc .... E 419 532-3647
Kalida (G-11416)

Safe-Grain Inc .... G 513 398-2500
Wapakoneta (G-19506)

Stephens Pipe & Steel LLC .... C 740 869-2257
Mount Sterling (G-14604)

Universal Equipment Mfg .... G 614 586-1780
Columbus (G-7722)

Unverferth Mfg Co Inc .... C 419 532-3121
Kalida (G-11418)

Unverferth Mfg Co Inc .... D 419 695-2060
Delphos (G-8923)

Warren Zachman Contracting .... G 740 389-4503
Marion (G-12911)

Woodbury Welding Inc .... G 937 968-3573
Union City (G-19073)

Yoder & Frey Inc .... G 419 445-2070
Archbold (G-700)

MACHINERY & EQPT: Gas Producers, Generators/Other Rltd Eqpt

Applied Marketing Services .... E 440 716-9962
Westlake (G-20255)

Chart Industries Inc .... E 440 753-1490
Cleveland (G-5020)

Stateline Power Corp .... F 937 547-1006
Greenville (G-10524)

Winston Oil Co Inc .... G 740 373-9664
Marietta (G-12850)

MACHINERY & EQPT: Liquid Automation

Dosmatic USA Inc .... F 972 245-9765
Cincinnati (G-3667)

Fluid Automation Inc .... E 248 912-1970
North Canton (G-15232)

Laureate Machine & Automtn LLC .... E 419 615-4601
Leipsic (G-11871)

National Oilwell Varco LP .... E 978 687-0101
Dayton (G-8519)

Nutro Corporation .... D 440 572-3800
Cleveland (G-5923)

Weiss North America Inc .... F 440 269-8031
Willoughby (G-20629)

MACHINERY & EQPT: Metal Finishing, Plating Etc

Broco Products Inc .... G 216 531-0880
Cleveland (G-4933)

Burton Metal Finishing Inc .... E 614 252-9523
Columbus (G-6876)

Conforming Matrix Corporation .... E 419 729-3777
Toledo (G-18409)

Fanuc America Corporation .... E 513 754-2400
Mason (G-13020)

International Finishing LLC ....G.... 937 293-3340
Dayton (G-8416)
Lange Equipment ....G.... 440 953-1621
Eastlake (G-9281)
Luke Engineering & Mfg Corp ....E.... 330 335-1501
Wadsworth (G-19418)
Silver Tool Inc ....E.... 937 865-0012
Miamisburg (G-13860)
Tks Industrial Company ....D.... 614 444-5602
Columbus (G-7696)
Tom Richards Inc ....C.... 440 974-1300
Mentor (G-13748)

MACHINERY & EQPT: Petroleum Refinery

Cantrell Rfinery Sls Trnsp Inc ....F.... 937 695-0318
Winchester (G-20691)
Service Station Equipment Co.............F.... 216 431-6100
Cleveland (G-6181)
Wolfe Oil Company LLC ....G.... 513 732-6220
Williamsburg (G-20414)
Zook Enterprises LLC ....E.... 440 543-1010
Chagrin Falls (G-3137)

MACHINERY & EQPT: Silver Recovery

Hess Technologies Inc ....G.... 513 228-0909
Lebanon (G-11808)

MACHINERY & EQPT: Smelting & Refining

High Temperature Systems Inc ....G.... 440 543-8271
Chagrin Falls (G-3091)

MACHINERY & EQPT: Vibratory Parts Handling Eqpt

Stainless Automation ....G.... 216 961-4550
Cleveland (G-6232)

MACHINERY BASES

Blue Chip Machine & Tool Ltd ....G.... 419 626-9559
Sandusky (G-16949)
COW Industries Inc ....E.... 614 443-6537
Columbus (G-6992)
Elite Enclosure Company LLC............E.... 937 492-3548
Sidney (G-17185)
G & M Metal Products Inc...................G.... 513 863-3353
Hamilton (G-10695)
Jaguar Medical Supplies Inc...............G.... 440 263-2780
North Royalton (G-15428)
Johnson Machining Services LLC ....G.... 937 866-4744
Miamisburg (G-13823)
Kard Welding Inc ....E.... 419 628-2598
Minster (G-14356)
Labcraft Inc ....F.... 419 878-4400
Waterville (G-19662)
Mansfield Welding Services LLC..........G.... 419 594-2738
Oakwood (G-15617)
Riverside Steel Inc ....F.... 330 856-5299
Vienna (G-19375)
Thieman Quality Metal Fab Inc ....D.... 419 629-2612
New Bremen (G-14795)
Weldcraft Products Co ....F.... 937 233-6141
Dayton (G-8750)

MACHINERY, CALCULATING: Calculators & Adding

Ganymede Technologies Corp ....G.... 419 562-5522
Bucyrus (G-2344)

MACHINERY, COMMERCIAL LAUNDRY & Drycleaning: Ironers

Ellis Laundry & Linen Supply ....G.... 330 339-4941
New Philadelphia (G-14897)

MACHINERY, COMMERCIAL LAUNDRY: Dryers, Incl Coin-Operated

Husqvarna US Holding Inc..................D.... 216 898-1800
Cleveland (G-5539)
Linen Care Plus Inc..............................F.... 614 224-1791
Columbus (G-7299)

MACHINERY, EQPT & SUPPLIES: Parking Facility

Amano Cincinnati Incorporated ....D.... 513 697-9000
Loveland (G-12338)

City of Cleveland.................................G.... 216 664-2711
Cleveland (G-5036)

MACHINERY, FOOD PRDTS: Beverage

Mojonnier Usa LLC ....G.... 844 665-6664
Streetsboro (G-17864)

MACHINERY, FOOD PRDTS: Choppers, Commercial

Kraft Heinz Foods Company ....E.... 419 332-7357
Fremont (G-10162)

MACHINERY, FOOD PRDTS: Cutting, Chopping, Grinding, Mixing

5 Axis Grinding Inc ....G.... 937 312-9797
Dayton (G-8124)
Lem Products Holding LLC ....E.... 513 202-1188
West Chester (G-19892)

MACHINERY, FOOD PRDTS: Food Processing, Smokers

Frost Engineering Inc ....E.... 513 541-6330
Cincinnati (G-3785)

MACHINERY, FOOD PRDTS: Mixers, Commercial

Fred D Pfening Company ....E.... 614 294-5361
Columbus (G-7099)

MACHINERY, FOOD PRDTS: Ovens, Bakery

Lincoln Foodservice Pdts LLC ....E.... 260 459-8200
Cleveland (G-5699)
Piece of Cake ....G.... 614 421-0399
Columbus (G-7485)

MACHINERY, FOOD PRDTS: Presses, Cheese, Beet, Cider & Sugar

French Oil Mill Machinery Co.................D.... 937 773-3420
Piqua (G-16266)

MACHINERY, FOOD PRDTS: Processing, Poultry

Prime Equipment Group Inc.................D.... 614 253-8590
Columbus (G-7517)

MACHINERY, FOOD PRDTS: Slicers, Commercial

C M Slicechief Co ....G.... 419 241-7647
Toledo (G-18386)
Kasel Engineering LLC..........................G.... 937 854-8875
Trotwood (G-18798)

MACHINERY, LUBRICATION: Automatic

Total Lubrication MGT Co ....E.... 888 478-6996
Canton (G-2880)

MACHINERY, MAILING: Postage Meters

Pitney Bowes Inc ....D.... 203 426-7025
Brecksville (G-2069)
Pitney Bowes Inc ....D.... 740 374-5535
Marietta (G-12817)

MACHINERY, METALWORKING: Assembly, Including Robotic

Added Edge Assembly Inc ....F.... 216 464-4305
Cleveland (G-4703)
Automated Machinery Solutions ....F.... 419 727-1772
Toledo (G-18359)
Combined Tech Group Inc ....F.... 937 274-4866
Dayton (G-8237)
Dallas Design & Technology Inc...........F.... 419 884-9750
Mansfield (G-12592)
Design Technologies & Mfg Co ....F.... 937 335-0757
Troy (G-18818)
Flexomation LLC ....F.... 513 825-0555
Cincinnati (G-3759)
Generic Systems Inc ....F.... 419 841-8460
Holland (G-11062)
Hunter Defense Tech Inc ....E.... 216 438-6111
Solon (G-17312)

Omega Automation Inc.......................D.... 937 890-2350
Dayton (G-8548)
Omega International Inc ....E.... 937 890-2350
Dayton (G-8549)
Peco Holdings Corp ....F.... 937 667-4451
Tipp City (G-18292)
Precision Metal Products Inc ....F.... 216 447-1900
Cleveland (G-6036)
Process Equipment Co Tipp City ....D.... 937 667-7105
Tipp City (G-18294)
Richard A Limbacher ....G.... 330 897-4515
Stone Creek (G-17726)
Riverside Mch & Automtn Inc ....G.... 419 855-8308
Walbridge (G-19463)
Scott Systems International.................G.... 740 383-8383
Marion (G-12898)
Semtorq Inc ....G.... 330 487-0600
Twinsburg (G-19019)

MACHINERY, METALWORKING: Coil Winding, For Springs

Armature Coil Equipment Inc ....F.... 216 267-6366
Cleveland (G-4831)
Standard Car Truck Company ....D.... 740 775-6450
Chillicothe (G-3276)

MACHINERY, METALWORKING: Coiling

Formtek Inc..D.... 216 292-4460
Cleveland (G-5372)
Guild International Inc ....E.... 440 232-5887
Bedford (G-1426)
Kent Corporation ....E.... 440 582-3400
North Royalton (G-15430)
Motion Industries Inc ....F.... 419 224-1988
Lima (G-12060)
Nova Industrial Machine Co...................F.... 419 535-0800
Whitehouse (G-20342)
Perfecto Industries Inc ....E.... 937 778-1900
Piqua (G-16299)
Pipe Coil Technology Inc ....F.... 330 256-6070
Burbank (G-2367)

MACHINERY, METALWORKING: Cutting & Slitting

Ged Holdings Inc ....C.... 330 963-5401
Twinsburg (G-18941)

MACHINERY, METALWORKING: Cutting-Up Lines

Automatic Feed Co ....D.... 419 592-0050
Napoleon (G-14671)

MACHINERY, METALWORKING: Drawing

Steinbarger Precision Cnc Inc...............G.... 937 376-0322
Xenia (G-20975)

MACHINERY, METALWORKING: Rotary Slitters, Metalworking

Portage Machine Concepts Inc.............F.... 330 628-2343
Akron (G-344)

MACHINERY, OFFICE: Paper Handling

Symatic Inc..E.... 330 225-1510
Brunswick (G-2260)

MACHINERY, OFFICE: Perforators

Central Business Products Inc..............G.... 513 385-5899
Cincinnati (G-3513)

MACHINERY, OFFICE: Sorters, Filing

Signa Stortech Systems Inc.................E.... 214 357-0411
Canton (G-2849)

MACHINERY, OFFICE: Time Clocks &Time Recording Devices

Advanced Time Systems........................G.... 440 466-2689
Geneva (G-10340)
Industrial Electronic Service.................F.... 937 746-9750
Carlisle (G-2931)
Parallel Solutions ....G.... 440 498-9920
Cleveland (G-5962)

Employee Codes: A=Over 500 employees, B=251-500
C=101-250, D=51-100, E=20-50, F=10-19, G=3-9

2017 Harris Ohio
Industrial Directory

1553

PRODUCT

Simplex Time Recorder LLC ....D 937 291-0355
  Miamisburg (G-13861)

MACHINERY, PACKAGING: Aerating, Beverages

Beckermills Inc ....G 419 738-3450
  Wapakoneta (G-19481)

MACHINERY, PACKAGING: Canning, Food

Dayton Systems Group Inc ....D 937 885-5665
  Miamisburg (G-13799)
Scanacon Incorporated ....G 330 877-7600
  Hartville (G-10833)

MACHINERY, PACKAGING: Packing & Wrapping

Able Tool Corporation ....E 513 733-8989
  Cincinnati (G-3346)
Labeldata ....G 614 891-5858
  Westerville (G-20222)

MACHINERY, PACKAGING: Vacuum

Precision Replacement LLC ....G 330 908-0410
  Macedonia (G-12476)

MACHINERY, PACKAGING: Wrapping

Samuel Strapping Systems Inc ....D 740 522-2500
  Heath (G-10855)

MACHINERY, PAPER INDUSTRY: Converting, Die Cutting & Stampng

Grandon Mfg Co Inc ....G 614 294-2694
  Columbus (G-7128)
Mc Kinley Machinery Inc ....E 440 937-6300
  Avon (G-1000)
Nilpeter Usa Inc ....C 513 489-4400
  Cincinnati (G-4156)

MACHINERY, PAPER INDUSTRY: Paper Mill, Plating, Etc

Miami Machine Corporation ....F 513 863-6707
  Overpeck (G-15832)
Press Technology & Mfg Inc ....G 937 327-0755
  Springfield (G-17631)

MACHINERY, PAPER INDUSTRY: Pulp Mill

Fluid Quip Inc ....E 937 324-0352
  Springfield (G-17561)
French Oil Mill Machinery Co ....D 937 773-3420
  Piqua (G-16266)

MACHINERY, PAPER INDUSTRY: Sandpaper

Sso Inc ....F 440 235-3500
  Olmsted Twp (G-15683)

MACHINERY, PRINTING TRADES: Linotype, Monotype, Intertype

Springfield Engraving Company ....G 937 390-0011
  Springfield (G-17651)

MACHINERY, PRINTING TRADES: Mats, Advertising & Newspaper

Moments To Remember USA LLC ....G 330 830-0839
  Massillon (G-13181)

MACHINERY, PRINTING TRADES: Plates

E C Shaw Co ....E 513 721-6334
  Cincinnati (G-3677)
Flexodie ....G 513 489-0433
  Middletown (G-14042)
Flexoplate Inc ....E 513 489-0433
  Blue Ash (G-1796)
Klebaum Machinery Inc ....G 330 455-2046
  Canton (G-2753)

MACHINERY, PRINTING TRADES: Plates, Engravers' Metal

Hays Fabricating & Welding ....E 937 325-0031
  Springfield (G-17568)

MACHINERY, PRINTING TRADES: Plates, Offset

Great Lakes Graphics Inc ....E 216 391-0077
  Cleveland (G-5450)

MACHINERY, PRINTING TRADES: Type Casting, Founding/Melting

Tinker Omega Manufacturing LLC ....E 937 322-2272
  Springfield (G-17664)

MACHINERY, SEWING: Bag Seaming & Closing

Eaton Corporation ....C 216 416-2500
  Cleveland (G-5246)

MACHINERY, SEWING: Sewing & Hat & Zipper Making

US Machine Prcsion Grnding LLC ....G 440 284-0711
  Elyria (G-9506)

MACHINERY, TEXTILE: Braiding

Karg Corporation ....F 330 633-4916
  Tallmadge (G-18149)
Oma USA Inc ....G 330 487-0602
  Twinsburg (G-18991)
Simon De Young Corporation ....G 440 834-3000
  Middlefield (G-13991)

MACHINERY, TEXTILE: Embroidery

Barudan America Inc ....F 440 248-8770
  Solon (G-17265)
Protofab Manufacturing Inc ....G 937 849-4983
  Medway (G-13501)
Truck Stop Embroidery ....G 419 257-2860
  North Baltimore (G-15199)
Wayne Sporting Goods ....G 937 236-6665
  Dayton (G-8748)

MACHINERY, TEXTILE: Finishing

Professional Grinding Inc ....G 330 628-3001
  Akron (G-353)

MACHINERY, TEXTILE: Printing

Alley Cat Designs Inc ....G 937 885-7950
  Dayton (G-8145)

MACHINERY, TEXTILE: Silk Screens

Impact Sports Wear Inc ....G 513 922-7406
  North Bend (G-15205)
R Sportswear LLC ....G 937 748-3507
  Springboro (G-17504)
Schilling Graphics Inc ....E 419 468-1037
  Galion (G-10286)
Solid Light Company Inc ....E 740 548-1219
  Lewis Center (G-11920)

MACHINERY, WOODWORKING: Cabinet Makers'

Closettec of North East Ohio ....G 216 464-0042
  Bedford (G-1416)
Northcoast Woodcraft Inc ....G 330 677-1189
  Kent (G-11497)

MACHINERY, WOODWORKING: Furniture Makers

ITR Manufacturing LLC ....F 419 852-8574
  Saint Henry (G-16819)
Senco Holdings Inc ....G 800 543-4596
  Cincinnati (G-3316)

MACHINERY, WOODWORKING: Lathes, Wood Turning Includes Access

Dayton Hawker Corporation ....F 937 293-8147
  Dayton (G-8276)

MACHINERY, WOODWORKING: Pattern Makers'

Boko Patterns Models & Molds ....G 937 426-9667
  Beavercreek (G-1371)

Seilkop Industries Inc.....................E 513 761-1035
  Cincinnati (G-4398)

MACHINERY/EQPT, INDL, WHOL: Machinist Precision Measrng Tool

Bilz Vibration Technology Inc ....F 330 468-2459
  Macedonia (G-12437)

MACHINERY: Ammunition & Explosives Loading

Military Resources LLC ....E 330 263-1040
  Wooster (G-20809)
Military Resources LLC ....G 330 309-9970
  Wooster (G-20810)

MACHINERY: Assembly, Exc Metalworking

Ats Assembly and Test Inc ....B 937 222-3030
  Dayton (G-8169)
Automation Tooling Systems ....C 614 781-8063
  Lewis Center (G-11887)
Gem City Engineering Co ....C 937 223-5544
  Dayton (G-8361)
Innovative Assembly Svcs LLC ....F 419 399-3886
  Paulding (G-16006)
Joseph B Stinson Co ....G 419 334-4151
  Fremont (G-10160)
Kc Robotics Inc ....E 513 860-4442
  West Chester (G-19887)
Mac Ltt Inc ....C 330 474-3795
  Kent (G-11486)
Phoenix Safety Outfitters LLC ....G 614 361-0544
  Springfield (G-17627)
Remtec Corp ....G 513 860-4299
  Mason (G-13081)
Remtec Engineering ....E 513 860-4299
  Mason (G-13082)
Selecteon Corporation ....E 614 228-8008
  Columbus (G-7607)
Steel & Alloy Utility Pdts Inc ....E 330 530-2220
  Mc Donald (G-13348)
Steven Douglas Corp.....................E 440 564-5200
  Newbury (G-15105)

MACHINERY: Automobile Garage, Frame Straighteners

Halifax Industries Inc.....................G 216 990-8951
  Hudson (G-11177)

MACHINERY: Automotive Maintenance

Automated Mfg Solutions Inc ....F 440 878-3711
  Strongsville (G-17893)
Camton Mechanical Inc ....G 614 864-7620
  Columbus (G-6892)
Handle Light Inc ....G 330 772-8901
  Kinsman (G-11609)
I T W Automotive Finishing ....G 419 470-2000
  Toledo (G-18515)
Jbf Repair Service LLC ....G 740 550-0089
  Proctorville (G-16490)
Johndow Industries Inc ....E 330 753-6895
  Barberton (G-1122)
Lube Depot ....G 330 758-0570
  Youngstown (G-21135)
Micro-Pise Msrment Systems LLC ....C 330 541-9100
  Streetsboro (G-17861)
Ratech 513 742-2111
  Cincinnati (G-4331)
Segna Inc ....F 937 335-6700
  Troy (G-18874)
Stevens Auto Glaze and SEC LL ....G 440 953-2900
  Eastlake (G-9288)

MACHINERY: Automotive Related

Autotool Inc ....E 614 733-0222
  Plain City (G-16322)
Beam Machines Inc........................G 513 745-4510
  Blue Ash (G-1747)
Buddy Backyard Inc ....E 330 393-9353
  Warren (G-19532)
Customers Car Care Center..............G 419 841-6646
  Toledo (G-18419)
Dengensha America Corporation ....F 440 439-8081
  Bedford (G-1418)
Designetics Inc ....D 419 866-0700
  Holland (G-11054)

Freeman Schwabe Machinery LLC......E 513 947-2888
Batavia (G-1188)
Ganzcorp Investments Inc ....D...... 330 963-5400
Twinsburg (G-18939)
Gary Compton ....G...... 937 339-6829
Troy (G-18830)
M W Solutions LLC ....F...... 419 782-1611
Defiance (G-8800)
Manufctring Bus Dev Sltons LLC ....E 419 294-1313
Findlay (G-9853)
Modular Assembly Innovations ....F...... 614 389-4860
Dublin (G-9104)
Process Development Corp ....E...... 937 890-3388
Dayton (G-8597)
RP Gatta Inc ....E 330 562-2288
Aurora (G-946)
Steelastic Company LLC ....E...... 330 633-0505
Cuyahoga Falls (G-8050)
Wauseon Machine & Mfg Inc ....D...... 419 337-0940
Wauseon (G-19700)

MACHINERY: Binding

Baumer HHS Corp. ....E 937 886-3160
Dayton (G-8183)
Baumfolder Corporation ....D...... 937 492-1281
Sidney (G-17169)
Collated Products Corp...........................F...... 440 946-1950
Willoughby (G-20459)

MACHINERY: Blasting, Electrical

Dan-Mar Company Inc ....E...... 419 660-8830
Norwalk (G-15532)
Waterloo Manufacturing Co Inc ....G...... 330 947-2917
Atwater (G-904)

MACHINERY: Bottle Washing & Sterilzing

S A Langmack Company ....F 216 541-0500
Cleveland (G-6149)

MACHINERY: Bottling & Canning

OKL Can Line Inc ....E 513 825-1655
Cincinnati (G-4183)

MACHINERY: Brewery & Malting

Ford Piping and Brewry Svc LLC ....G...... 614 284-2409
Columbus (G-7092)
Listermann Mfg Co Inc ....G...... 513 731-1130
Cincinnati (G-4027)
Railroad Brewing Company ....G...... 440 723-8234
Avon (G-1006)

MACHINERY: Bridge Or Gate, Hydraulic

Ogden Hydraulics LLC ....G....... 419 686-1108
Portage (G-16426)

MACHINERY: Centrifugal

Pneumatic Scale Corporation.................C...... 330 923-0491
Cuyahoga Falls (G-8033)

MACHINERY: Clay Working & Tempering

Starkey Machinery Inc ....E...... 419 468-2560
Galion (G-10289)

MACHINERY: Concrete Prdts

Tegratek ....G...... 513 742-5100
Cincinnati (G-4499)

MACHINERY: Construction

Allied Consolidated Industries ....C...... 330 744-0808
Youngstown (G-21020)
Allied Construction Pdts LLC ....E...... 216 431-2600
Cleveland (G-4764)
Allied Construction Pdts LLC ....E...... 216 431-2600
Cleveland (G-4765)
Ballinger Industries Inc ....F....... 419 422-4533
Findlay (G-9794)
Basetek LLC ....F....... 877 712-2273
Middlefield (G-13916)
Basetek LLC ....G....... 877 712-2273
Dayton (G-8182)
Belden Brick Company.............................E...... 330 852-2411
Sugarcreek (G-18016)
Brovig Engineering Inc...........................G...... 419 426-1333
Attica (G-893)

Cityscapes International Inc ....E...... 614 850-2540
Hilliard (G-10938)
Coe Manufacturing Company ....D...... 440 352-9381
Painesville (G-15865)
Concrete Cnstr McHy Co LLC.................G...... 330 638-1515
Cortland (G-7863)
Concrete Leveling Systems Inc ....G...... 330 966-8120
Canton (G-2666)
Connor Electric Inc ....G...... 513 932-5798
Lebanon (G-11790)
Construction Polymers Co ....G...... 440 591-9018
Chagrin Falls (G-3081)
Custom Machining Solutions LLC ....G...... 330 221-1523
Rootstown (G-16720)
CW Machine Worx Ltd ....F....... 740 654-5304
Carroll (G-2939)
Dandy Products Inc ....G...... 800 591-2284
Mount Vernon (G-14618)
Desco Corporation ....G...... 614 888-8855
New Albany (G-14757)
Dover Corporation ....G...... 513 696-1790
Mason (G-13010)
Dynamic Plastics Inc ....G...... 937 437-7261
New Paris (G-14879)
E R Advanced Ceramics Inc ....E...... 330 426-9433
East Palestine (G-9237)
Eagle Crusher Co Inc ....D...... 419 468-2288
Galion (G-10266)
Fabco Inc ....E...... 419 421-4740
Findlay (G-9820)
Field Gymmy Inc ....G...... 419 538-6511
Glandorf (G-10397)
Gibson Machinery LLC ....G...... 440 439-4000
Cleveland (G-5429)
Gradall Industries Inc ....C...... 330 339-2211
New Philadelphia (G-14901)
Grand Harbor Yacht Sales & Svc ....G...... 440 442-2919
Cleveland (G-5445)
Grasan Equipment Company Inc ....D...... 419 526-4440
Mansfield (G-12620)
Great Lakes Machine and Tool ....G...... 419 836-2346
Curtice (G-7957)
Harsco Corporation ....E...... 740 387-1150
Marion (G-12873)
Howard & Blake Excavating LLC...........G...... 740 701-7938
Richmond Dale (G-16650)
Hudco Manufacturing Inc ....G...... 440 951-4040
Willoughby (G-20505)
Indy Eqp Indpndence Recycl Inc............C...... 216 524-0999
Independence (G-11260)
Jbw Systems Inc ....F....... 614 882-5008
Westerville (G-20162)
Jlg Industries Inc ....G...... 330 684-0132
Orrville (G-15743)
Jlg Industries Inc ....G...... 330 684-0200
Orrville (G-15744)
Kaffenbarger Truck Eqp Co ....E...... 513 772-6800
Cincinnati (G-3967)
Komar Industries Inc ....E...... 614 836-2366
Groveport (G-10629)
Kubota Tractor Corporation....................F...... 614 835-3800
Groveport (G-10631)
Magna Group LLC ....G...... 513 388-9463
Cincinnati (G-4051)
Metro Mech Inc ....G...... 216 641-6262
Cleveland (G-5792)
Meyer Products LLC ....D...... 216 486-1313
Cleveland (G-5794)
Msk Trencher Mfg Inc ....F....... 419 394-4444
Celina (G-3010)
Murphy Tractor & Eqp Co Inc ....G...... 614 876-1141
Columbus (G-7374)
Murphy Tractor & Eqp Co Inc ....G...... 937 898-4198
Vandalia (G-19306)
Murphy Tractor & Eqp Co Inc ....G...... 419 221-3666
Lima (G-12061)
Murphy Tractor & Eqp Co Inc ....G...... 330 477-9304
Canton (G-2785)
Murphy Tractor & Eqp Co Inc ....G...... 330 220-4999
Brunswick (G-2238)
National Oilwell Varco LP ....E...... 978 687-0101
Dayton (G-8519)
Npk Construction Equipment Inc ....D...... 440 232-7900
Bedford (G-1449)
Pace Consolidated Inc.............................D...... 440 942-1234
Willoughby (G-20564)
Pace Engineering Inc...............................C...... 440 942-1234
Willoughby (G-20565)
Precision Engineered Tech LLC ....G...... 330 335-3300
Wadsworth (G-19430)

Pubco Corporation ....D...... 216 881-5300
Cleveland (G-6059)
Roadsafe Traffic Systems Inc ....G...... 614 274-9782
Columbus (G-7567)
Rogue Manufacturing Inc ....G...... 937 839-4026
West Alexandria (G-19782)
Safesmart USA ....G...... 404 703-1008
Medina (G-13473)
Scott Port-A-Fold Inc ....E...... 419 748-8880
Napoleon (G-14698)
Screen Machine Industries LLC ....G...... 740 927-3464
Pataskala (G-15984)
Shaffer Manufacturing Corp ....E...... 937 652-2151
Urbana (G-19180)
Sk Machinery Corporation ....G...... 330 733-7325
Akron (G-403)
Stillwell Equipment Co Inc ....G...... 330 650-1029
Peninsula (G-16042)
Thorworks Industries Inc ....E...... 419 626-4375
Sandusky (G-17015)
Tri-Way Rebar Inc ....G...... 330 296-9662
Ravenna (G-16568)
Wilkett Enterprises LLC ....G...... 740 384-2890
Wellston (G-19773)
Workpros ....G...... 740 512-8512
Brilliant (G-2096)

MACHINERY: Cryogenic, Industrial

Chart Industries Inc ....E...... 440 753-1490
Cleveland (G-5020)
Chart International Inc ....E...... 440 753-1490
Cleveland (G-5021)
Eden Cryogenics LLC ....E...... 614 873-3949
Plain City (G-16339)
JC Carter LLC ....G...... 949 764-6465
Richmond Heights (G-16654)

MACHINERY: Custom

A & R Machine Co Inc ....G...... 330 832-4631
Massillon (G-13105)
Active Roads LLC ....G...... 937 242-6555
West Chester (G-19797)
Aja Industries LLC ....G...... 614 216-9566
Gahanna (G-10203)
Albright Machine ....G...... 419 483-1088
Monroeville (G-14424)
Alfons Haar Inc...E...... 937 560-2031
Springboro (G-17472)
Alliance Automation LLC ....F....... 419 238-2520
Van Wert (G-19243)
Alpha Omega Dev & Mch Co ....G...... 440 352-9915
Painesville (G-15848)
Amt Machine Systems Ltd ....F....... 614 635-8050
Columbus (G-6748)
Artisan Equipment Inc ....F....... 740 756-9135
Carroll (G-2936)
Astro Technical Services Inc ....E...... 330 394-7350
Warren (G-19525)
Autotec Engineering Company ....F....... 419 885-2529
Toledo (G-18360)
Berran Industrial Group Inc ....E...... 330 253-5800
Akron (G-89)
Bomen Marking Products Inc ....G...... 440 582-0053
Cleveland (G-4922)
Bonnot Company ....E...... 330 896-6544
Akron (G-96)
Bowdil Company ....F....... 800 356-8663
Canton (G-2626)
Brandts Custom Machining LLC ....G...... 419 566-3192
Mansfield (G-12568)
Bsm Columbus Llp ....G...... 740 755-2380
Johnstown (G-11392)
Cleaning Tech Group LLC ....E...... 513 870-0100
West Chester (G-19991)
Dollman Technical Services ....G...... 419 877-9404
Toledo (G-18442)
East End Welding Company ....C...... 330 677-6000
Kent (G-11452)
Enprotech Industrial Tech LLC...............C...... 216 883-3220
Cleveland (G-5283)
F & G Tool and Die Co ....E...... 937 294-1405
Moraine (G-14486)
Farnsworth Engineering...........................F....... 330 385-1745
East Liverpool (G-9215)
Farr Automation Inc ....F....... 419 289-1883
Ashland (G-732)
Ferry Industries Inc ....D...... 330 920-9200
Stow (G-17753)
Fredon Corporation ....D...... 440 951-5200
Mentor (G-13584)

PRODUCT

Friend Engrg & Mch Co Inc ....G...... 419 589-5066
  Mansfield **(G-12608)**
Friess Equipment Inc ....G...... 330 945-9440
  Akron **(G-194)**
Gasdorf Tool and Mch Co Inc ....E...... 419 227-0103
  Lima **(G-12017)**
Global Sourcing & Support Svcs ....G...... 513 321-0957
  Cincinnati **(G-3838)**
Global Trade Network Inc ....G...... 513 701-0411
  Mason **(G-13031)**
Globe Products Inc ....E...... 937 233-0233
  Dayton **(G-8371)**
Guardian Engineering & Mfg Co ....G...... 419 335-1784
  Wauseon **(G-19680)**
Heisler Tool Company ....F...... 440 951-2424
  Willoughby **(G-20503)**
Herd Manufacturing Inc ....E...... 216 651-4221
  Cleveland **(G-5503)**
Htec Systems Inc ....F...... 937 438-3010
  Dayton **(G-8394)**
Inovent Engineering Inc ....G...... 330 468-0005
  Macedonia **(G-12459)**
Integrity Crane Services Ltd ....G...... 330 479-2003
  Massillon **(G-13157)**
Interscope Manufacturing Inc ....E...... 513 423-8866
  Middletown **(G-14050)**
Invotec Engineering Inc ....D...... 937 886-3232
  Miamisburg **(G-13820)**
JF Martt and Associates Inc ....F...... 330 938-4000
  Sebring **(G-17046)**
Keban Industries Inc ....G...... 216 446-0159
  Cleveland **(G-5639)**
Kiley Machine Company Inc ....G...... 513 875-3223
  Fayetteville **(G-9783)**
Kimble Machines Inc ....F...... 419 485-8449
  Montpelier **(G-14447)**
Latanick Equipment Inc ....E...... 419 433-2200
  Huron **(G-11233)**
Lawson Precision Machining Inc ....G...... 419 562-1543
  Bucyrus **(G-2352)**
Lightning Mold & Machine Inc ....F...... 440 593-6460
  Conneaut **(G-7813)**
Logan Machine Company ....D...... 330 633-6163
  Akron **(G-275)**
M L C Technologies Inc ....G...... 513 874-7792
  Hamilton **(G-10720)**
Machine Development Corp ....G...... 513 825-5885
  Cincinnati **(G-4044)**
Machine Tool & Fab Corp ....F...... 419 435-7676
  Fostoria **(G-9983)**
Margo Tool Technology Inc ....F...... 740 653-8115
  Lancaster **(G-11727)**
Markwith Tool Company Inc ....F...... 937 548-6808
  Greenville **(G-10510)**
Matrix Tool & Machine Inc ....E...... 440 255-0300
  Mentor **(G-13648)**
McNeil & Nrm Inc ....D...... 330 761-1855
  Akron **(G-291)**
McNeil & Nrm Intl Inc ....D...... 330 253-2525
  Akron **(G-292)**
Messerman Corp ....G...... 419 782-1136
  Defiance **(G-8804)**
Metalex Manufacturing Inc ....C...... 513 489-0507
  Blue Ash **(G-1839)**
Metro Design Inc ....F...... 440 458-4200
  Elyria **(G-9462)**
Midwest Laser Systems Inc ....E...... 419 424-0062
  Findlay **(G-9861)**
Modern Design Stamping Div ....G...... 216 382-6318
  Cleveland **(G-5826)**
Narrow Way Custom Technology ....E...... 937 743-1611
  Carlisle **(G-2933)**
Neil R Scholl Inc ....F...... 740 653-6593
  Lancaster **(G-11733)**
NM Group Global LLC ....G...... 419 447-5211
  Tiffin **(G-18233)**
Odawara Automation Inc ....E...... 937 667-8433
  Tipp City **(G-18291)**
Odyssey Machine Company Ltd ....G...... 419 455-6621
  Perrysburg **(G-16129)**
Ohio Tool Works LLC ....D...... 419 281-3700
  Ashland **(G-761)**
Patriot Precision Products ....D...... 330 966-7177
  Canton **(G-2807)**
Perfecto Industries Inc ....E...... 937 778-1900
  Piqua **(G-16299)**
Perry Welding Service Inc ....F...... 330 425-2211
  Twinsburg **(G-19001)**
Phase Array Company LLC ....G...... 513 785-0801
  West Chester **(G-19914)**

Pioneer Industrial Systems LLC ....F...... 419 737-9506
  Alvordton **(G-559)**
Precision Machine & Tool Co ....F...... 419 334-8405
  Fremont **(G-10176)**
Quality Specialists Inc ....G...... 440 946-9129
  Willoughby **(G-20584)**
R J K Enterprises Inc ....F...... 440 257-6018
  Mentor **(G-13712)**
Radco Industries Inc ....F...... 419 531-4731
  Toledo **(G-18669)**
Rapid Mold Repair & Machine ....G...... 330 253-1000
  Akron **(G-366)**
Reichard Industries LLC ....G...... 330 482-5511
  Columbiana **(G-6630)**
Richmond Machine Co ....E...... 419 485-5740
  Montpelier **(G-14454)**
Royalton Industries Inc ....F...... 440 748-9900
  Columbia Station **(G-6597)**
RTZ Manufacturing Co ....G...... 614 848-8366
  Columbus **(G-7577)**
S & R Tool & Die Services Inc ....G...... 937 584-4691
  Sabina **(G-16777)**
S R P M Inc ....F...... 440 248-8440
  Cleveland **(G-6151)**
S-P Company Inc ....G...... 330 482-0200
  Columbiana **(G-6631)**
Sample Machining Inc ....E...... 937 258-3338
  Dayton **(G-8645)**
Southstern Machining Field Svc ....E...... 740 689-1147
  Lancaster **(G-11754)**
Steel Eqp Specialists Inc ....G...... 330 829-2626
  Alliance **(G-539)**
Steel Eqp Specialists Inc ....D...... 330 823-8260
  Alliance **(G-540)**
Swift Tool Inc ....G...... 330 945-6973
  Cuyahoga Falls **(G-8052)**
Systech Handling Inc ....F...... 419 445-8226
  Archbold **(G-696)**
T J Automation Inc ....F...... 419 267-5687
  Archbold **(G-697)**
Techniform Industries Inc ....F...... 419 332-8484
  Fremont **(G-10186)**
Tema Systems Inc ....E...... 513 489-7811
  Cincinnati **(G-4501)**
Terydon Inc ....F...... 330 879-2448
  Navarre **(G-14728)**
Tj Bell Inc ....G...... 330 633-3644
  Akron **(G-442)**
Tower Tool & Manufacturing Co ....F...... 330 425-1623
  Twinsburg **(G-19028)**
Tru-Fab Technology Inc ....F...... 440 954-9760
  Willoughby **(G-20620)**

MACHINERY: Deburring

Cleveland Deburring Machine Co ....G...... 216 472-0200
  Cleveland **(G-5057)**
Tailored Systems Inc ....G...... 937 299-3900
  Moraine **(G-14534)**

MACHINERY: Die Casting

Columbia Stamping Inc ....F...... 440 236-6677
  Columbia Station **(G-6585)**
Hendricks Vacuum Forming Inc ....G...... 330 833-8913
  Massillon **(G-13148)**
HPM North America Corp ....E...... 740 382-5600
  Marion **(G-12876)**
L B Machine & Mfg Co Inc ....G...... 513 471-6137
  Cincinnati **(G-4008)**
Snair Co ....F...... 614 873-7020
  Plain City **(G-16360)**
THT Presses Inc ....E...... 937 898-2012
  Dayton **(G-8715)**

MACHINERY: Electrical Discharge Erosion

E D M Electrofying Inc ....G...... 440 322-8900
  Elyria **(G-9410)**
United Wire Edm Inc ....G...... 440 239-8777
  Berea **(G-1639)**

MACHINERY: Electronic Component Making

Inpower LLC ....F...... 740 548-0965
  Lewis Center **(G-11901)**
Mactek Corporation ....F...... 330 487-5477
  Twinsburg **(G-18976)**
Storetek Engineering Inc ....E...... 330 294-0678
  Tallmadge **(G-18170)**

MACHINERY: Engraving

Tykma Inc ....E...... 877 318-9562
  Chillicothe **(G-3283)**

MACHINERY: Extruding

Diamond America Corporation ....G...... 330 535-3330
  Akron **(G-149)**
George A Mitchell Company ....E...... 330 758-5777
  Youngstown **(G-21099)**
Vmaxx Inc ....F...... 419 738-4044
  Wapakoneta **(G-19511)**

MACHINERY: Fiber Optics Strand Coating

Diptech Systems Inc ....G...... 330 673-4400
  Kent **(G-11449)**

MACHINERY: Folding

G Fordyce Co ....G...... 937 393-3241
  Hillsboro **(G-10998)**
L B Folding Co Inc ....G...... 216 961-0888
  Cleveland **(G-5670)**
Pearce Inc ....F...... 216 252-0550
  Cleveland **(G-5986)**

MACHINERY: Gas Separators

H P E Inc ....F...... 330 833-3161
  Massillon **(G-13145)**

MACHINERY: Gear Cutting & Finishing

North East Technologies Inc ....G...... 440 327-9278
  North Ridgeville **(G-15392)**

MACHINERY: General, Industrial, NEC

La Mfg Inc ....G...... 513 577-7200
  Cincinnati **(G-4009)**
Titan Fire Protection Inc ....G...... 740 451-0838
  Chesapeake **(G-3191)**

MACHINERY: Glassmaking

Dura Temp Corporation ....F...... 419 866-4348
  Holland **(G-11058)**
Emhart Glass Manufacturing Inc ....D...... 567 336-7733
  Perrysburg **(G-16090)**
Emhart Glass Manufacturing Inc ....D...... 567 336-8784
  Perrysburg **(G-16091)**
Ged Holdings Inc ....C...... 330 963-5401
  Twinsburg **(G-18941)**
Intertec Corporation ....B...... 419 537-9711
  Toledo **(G-18527)**
J & S Industrial Mch Pdts Inc ....D...... 419 691-1380
  Toledo **(G-18531)**
J M Hamilton Group Inc ....F...... 419 229-4010
  Lima **(G-12032)**
Manifold & Phalor Inc ....E...... 614 920-1200
  Canal Winchester **(G-2531)**
Steinert Industries Inc ....F...... 330 678-0028
  Kent **(G-11533)**
Technical Glass Products Inc ....F...... 440 639-6399
  Painesville **(G-15925)**
Toledo Engineering Co Inc ....D...... 419 537-9711
  Toledo **(G-18731)**

MACHINERY: Grinding

Accu-Grind & Mfg Co Inc ....E...... 937 224-3303
  Dayton **(G-8130)**
Applied Metals Technologies ....E...... 216 741-2440
  Brooklyn Heights **(G-2130)**
B V Grinding Machining Inc ....G...... 440 918-1884
  Willoughby **(G-20442)**
C S Bell Co ....F...... 419 448-0791
  Tiffin **(G-18213)**
Fives Landis Corp ....D...... 440 709-0700
  Painesville **(G-15882)**
Fredon Corporation ....D...... 440 951-5200
  Mentor **(G-13584)**
Grind-All Corporation ....E...... 330 220-1600
  Brunswick **(G-2230)**
Jacp Inc ....G...... 513 353-3660
  Miamitown **(G-13888)**
Master Grinding Company Inc ....G...... 440 944-3680
  Wickliffe **(G-20371)**
Milan Tool Corp ....E...... 216 661-1078
  Cleveland **(G-5813)**
Stevenson Mfg Co ....G...... 330 532-1581
  Wellsville **(G-19775)**

Synergy Grinding Inc ....F 216 447-4000
Cleveland *(G-6282)*

TSR Machinery Services Inc ....E 513 874-9697
Fairfield *(G-9726)*

U S Electrical Tool Inc ....F 513 353-3660
Miamitown *(G-13893)*

MACHINERY: Ice Cream

Big Drum Usa Ltd ....G 614 626-0843
Columbus *(G-6827)*

Country Freezer Units LLC ....G 740 623-8658
Baltic *(G-1067)*

Home City Ice ....G 859 441-1700
Aberdeen *(G-1)*

Norse Dairy Systems LP ....B 614 421-5297
Columbus *(G-7398)*

MACHINERY: Industrial, NEC

AMP-Tech Inc ....G 419 652-3444
Nova *(G-15575)*

Avs Oil Recovery LLC ....G 937 645-4600
Marysville *(G-12932)*

CC Ironworks LLC ....G 330 542-0500
New Middletown *(G-14874)*

Combined Industrial Solutions ....G 513 659-3091
Milford *(G-14131)*

McAttack Machine LLC ....G 440 946-3855
Willoughby *(G-20541)*

Mes Material Hdlg Systems LLC ......G 740 477-8920
Circleville *(G-4633)*

Michaels Tool Service Co Inc ....G 330 772-1119
Burghill *(G-2368)*

Monovision Machine ....G 330 833-2146
Massillon *(G-13182)*

Morning Glory Technologies ....F 440 796-5076
Chesterland *(G-3216)*

Munson Sales & Engineering ....G 216 496-5436
Chardon *(G-3167)*

Northcoast Prfmce & Mch Co ....G 330 753-7333
Barberton *(G-1134)*

MACHINERY: Jewelers

House Silva-Strongsville Inc ....G 330 464-6419
Strongsville *(G-17927)*

MACHINERY: Kilns

A & M Kiln Dry Ltd ....G 330 473-8634
Millersburg *(G-14188)*

A & M Kiln Dry Ltd ....F 330 852-0505
Dundee *(G-9170)*

Industrial Thermal Systems Inc ....F 513 561-2100
Cincinnati *(G-3918)*

Kiln ....G 440 717-1880
Brecksville *(G-2058)*

Mirion Technologies Ist Corp ....G 614 367-2050
Pickerington *(G-16198)*

Riceland Dry Kiln ....G 330 683-9151
Orrville *(G-15758)*

MACHINERY: Knitting

Knitting Machinery Corp ....G 216 851-9900
Cleveland *(G-5661)*

Knitting Machinery Corp ....F 937 548-2338
Greenville *(G-10509)*

MACHINERY: Labeling

D&D Design Concepts Inc ....F 513 752-2191
Batavia *(G-1176)*

Dynamic Bar Code Systems Inc ......G 330 220-5451
Brunswick *(G-2222)*

Huhtamaki Inc ....B 513 201-1525
Batavia *(G-1192)*

Huhtamaki Inc ....B 937 746-9700
Franklin *(G-10028)*

Hunkar Technologies Inc ....C 513 272-1010
Cincinnati *(G-3902)*

M PI Label Systems ....G 330 938-2134
Sebring *(G-17047)*

Morgan Adhesives Company LLC .....B 330 688-1111
Stow *(G-17775)*

Mpi Labels of Baltimore Inc ....F 330 938-2134
Sebring *(G-17049)*

Quadrel Inc ....E 440 602-4700
Mentor *(G-13705)*

Superior Label Systems Inc ....B 513 336-0825
Mason *(G-13092)*

MACHINERY: Logging Eqpt

Buck Equipment Inc ....E 614 539-3039
Grove City *(G-10548)*

MACHINERY: Marking, Metalworking

Cauffiel Corporation ....G 419 843-7262
Toledo *(G-18390)*

Tdm LLC ....G 440 969-1442
Ashtabula *(G-840)*

MACHINERY: Metalworking

Addisonmckee Inc ....C 513 228-7000
Lebanon *(G-11774)*

ADS Machinery Corp ....D 330 399-3601
Warren *(G-19515)*

Advance Manufacturing Corp ....E 216 333-1684
Cleveland *(G-4708)*

Bardons & Oliver Inc ....C 440 498-5800
Solon *(G-17264)*

Barth Industries Co LP ....D 216 267-0531
Cleveland *(G-4893)*

Berran Industrial Group Inc ....E 330 253-5800
Akron *(G-89)*

Binns Machinery Company ....G 513 242-3388
Cincinnati *(G-3449)*

Bison USA Corp ....G 513 713-0513
West Chester *(G-19818)*

Brilex Industries Inc ....D 330 744-1114
Youngstown *(G-21036)*

Brilex Industries Inc ....C 330 744-1114
Youngstown *(G-21037)*

CA Litzler Co Inc ....E 216 267-8020
Cleveland *(G-4958)*

Cammann Inc ....F 440 965-4051
Birmingham *(G-1685)*

Coating Control Inc ....G 330 453-9136
Canton *(G-2663)*

Ctm Integration Incorporated ....E 330 332-1800
Salem *(G-16887)*

Dango & Dienenthal Inc ....G 330 829-0277
Alliance *(G-504)*

Econ-O-Machine Products Inc ....G 937 882-6307
Donnelsville *(G-8961)*

Elite Mfg Solutions LLC ....G 330 612-7434
Macedonia *(G-12447)*

F L Enterprises ....E 216 898-5551
Cleveland *(G-5317)*

Fabriweld Corporation ....G 419 668-3358
Norwalk *(G-15539)*

Forrest Machine Pdts Co Ltd ....F 419 589-3774
Mansfield *(G-12607)*

Gem City Engineering Co ....C 937 223-5544
Dayton *(G-8361)*

Gilson Machine & Tool Co Inc ....E 419 592-2911
Napoleon *(G-14678)*

Glunt Industries Inc ....C 330 399-7585
Warren *(G-19555)*

Hahn Manufacturing Company ....E 216 391-9300
Cleveland *(G-5472)*

Heisler Tool Company ....F 440 951-2424
Willoughby *(G-20503)*

Holdren Brothers Inc ....F 937 465-7050
West Liberty *(G-20092)*

I C Consultants Inc ....F 216 731-9992
Cleveland *(G-5545)*

J Horst Manufacturing Co ....D 330 828-2216
Dalton *(G-8072)*

Kalt Manufacturing Company ....D 440 327-2102
North Ridgeville *(G-15384)*

Kay Capital Company ....G 216 531-1010
Cleveland *(G-5638)*

Kilroy Company ....G 440 951-8700
Eastlake *(G-9278)*

Louis Leasing LLC ....E 440 243-3810
Medina *(G-13436)*

Manufctring Sltons Brbrton Inc ....G 330 745-4539
Barberton *(G-1128)*

Master Marking Company Inc ....F 330 688-6797
Stow *(G-17772)*

Mathew Odonnell ....G 440 969-4054
Andover *(G-618)*

Midwest Laser Systems Inc ....E 419 424-0062
Findlay *(G-9861)*

Milacron LLC ....E 513 487-5000
Blue Ash *(G-1842)*

Pines Manufacturing Inc ....E 440 835-5553
Westlake *(G-20293)*

Pre-Melt Systems Inc ....F 330 818-8088
Canton *(G-2819)*

Precision Cnc LLC ....E 740 689-9009
Lancaster *(G-11740)*

Rafter Equipment Corporation ....E 440 572-3700
Strongsville *(G-17956)*

Riverside Mch & Automtn Inc ....D 419 855-8308
Genoa *(G-10363)*

Sir Steak Machinery Inc ....E 419 526-9181
Mansfield *(G-12678)*

South Shore Controls Inc ....E 440 259-2500
Perry *(G-16058)*

Stainless Automation ....G 216 961-4550
Cleveland *(G-6232)*

Stein Inc ....D 216 883-7444
Cleveland *(G-6249)*

Sticker Corporation ....F 440 946-2100
Willoughby *(G-20606)*

Todd Industries Inc ....E 440 439-2900
Cleveland *(G-6330)*

Tri-Mac Mfg & Svcs Co ....F 513 896-4445
Hamilton *(G-10749)*

Universal Precision Products ....G 330 633-6128
Akron *(G-457)*

MACHINERY: Milling

L M Equipment & Design Inc ....E 330 332-9951
Salem *(G-16907)*

My Catered Table LLC ....G 614 882-7323
Columbus *(G-7376)*

Superior Machining Inc ....E 937 236-9619
Dayton *(G-8689)*

MACHINERY: Mining

2828 Clinton Inc ....E 216 241-7157
Leetonia *(G-11857)*

80 Acres Urban Agriculture LLC ......G 513 218-4387
Cincinnati *(G-3327)*

Belden Brick Company ....B 330 852-2411
Sugarcreek *(G-18016)*

Bowdil Company ....F 800 356-8663
Canton *(G-2626)*

Breaker Technology Inc ....E 440 248-7168
Solon *(G-17274)*

Cailin Dev Ltd Lblty Co ....F 216 408-6261
Cleveland *(G-4962)*

Carr Tool Company ....E 513 825-2900
Fairfield *(G-9651)*

Cool Machines Inc ....F 419 232-4871
Van Wert *(G-19249)*

Deep Springs Technology LLC ....G 419 536-5741
Toledo *(G-18434)*

Enercon Systems Inc ....G 305 213-3997
Elyria *(G-9419)*

Engines Inc of Ohio ....D 740 377-9874
South Point *(G-17437)*

Esco Corporation ....E 419 562-6015
Bucyrus *(G-2343)*

Joy Global Inc ....G 216 503-5029
Independence *(G-11262)*

Joy Mining Machinery ....C 440 248-7970
Solon *(G-17323)*

Kaffenbarger Truck Eqp Co ....E 513 772-6800
Cincinnati *(G-3967)*

Kennametal Inc ....C 440 349-5151
Solon *(G-17329)*

Kilgore Manufacturing Mch Co ....G 330 491-1915
Canton *(G-2752)*

Mike Suponcic ....G 740 635-0654
Bridgeport *(G-2092)*

Nolan Company ....G 330 453-7922
Canton *(G-2789)*

Nolan Company ....G 740 269-1512
Bowerston *(G-1959)*

Npk Construction Equipment Inc .....D 440 232-7900
Bedford *(G-1449)*

Penn Machine Company ....E 814 288-1547
Twinsburg *(G-18996)*

Pneumatic Parts Co ....F 330 923-6063
Stow *(G-17788)*

SMI Holdings Inc ....D 740 927-3464
Pataskala *(G-15985)*

Terrasource Global Corporation ....D 330 923-5254
Cuyahoga Falls *(G-8054)*

Warren Fabricating Corporation ....D 330 847-0596
Warren *(G-19621)*

Zen Industries Inc ....E 216 432-3240
Cleveland *(G-6493)*

P
R
O
D
U
C
T

MACHINERY: Pack-Up Assemblies, Wheel Overhaul

Aot Inc .... E 937 323-9669
Springfield *(G-17517)*

Haeco Inc .... F 513 722-1030
Loveland *(G-12356)*

MACHINERY: Packaging

Accu Pak Mfg Inc .... G 330 644-3015
Akron *(G-26)*

Advanced Poly-Packaging Inc ...... E 330 785-4000
Akron *(G-33)*

Andy Pac Inc .... G 440 748-8800
Columbia Station *(G-6578)*

Atlas Vac Machine Co LLC .... E 513 407-3513
Cincinnati *(G-3426)*

Audion Automation Ltd .... E 216 267-1911
Berea *(G-1602)*

Audion Automation Ltd .... E 216 267-1911
Berea *(G-1603)*

Automated Packg Systems Inc ..... D 330 342-2000
Bedford *(G-1401)*

Automated Packg Systems Inc ..... C 330 626-2313
Streetsboro *(G-17842)*

Automation Solutions Inc .... G 614 235-4060
Columbus *(G-6790)*

Boggs Graphic Equipment LLC .... G 440 564-9675
Maple Heights *(G-12728)*

Combi Packaging Systems Llc ..... D 330 456-9333
Canton *(G-2664)*

Crown Closures Machinery .... E 740 681-6593
Lancaster *(G-11701)*

Ctm Integration Incorporated ...... E 330 332-1800
Salem *(G-16887)*

Darifill Inc .... F 614 890-3274
Westerville *(G-20208)*

Dover Corporation .... G 513 696-1790
Mason *(G-13010)*

Euclid Products Co Inc .... G 440 942-7310
Willoughby *(G-20482)*

Exact Equipment Corporation ...... F 215 295-2000
Columbus *(G-6645)*

Food Equipment Mfg Corp .... E 216 672-5859
Bedford Heights *(G-1484)*

G L Industries Inc .... E 513 874-1233
Hamilton *(G-10696)*

Gunnison Associates LLC .... G 330 562-5230
Aurora *(G-923)*

Hadsell Chemical Proc LLC .... E 740 941-1792
Waverly *(G-19710)*

Heat Seal LLC .... E 216 341-2022
Cleveland *(G-5491)*

Hill & Griffith Company .... G 513 921-1075
Cincinnati *(G-3882)*

Impackt .... G 513 559-1488
Cincinnati *(G-3913)*

Kaufman Engineered Systems Inc ... D 419 878-9727
Waterville *(G-19661)*

Kaws Inc .... E 513 521-8292
Cincinnati *(G-3973)*

Kennedy Group Incorporated ...... G 440 951-7660
Willoughby *(G-20520)*

Kolinahr Systems Inc .... F 513 745-9401
Blue Ash *(G-1823)*

Madgar Genis Corp .... G 330 848-6950
Barberton *(G-1125)*

Millwood Inc .... E 614 717-9099
Powell *(G-16479)*

Millwood Inc .... F 513 860-4567
West Chester *(G-19901)*

Millwood Inc .... E 330 393-4400
Vienna *(G-19370)*

Millwood Natural LLC .... D 330 393-4400
Vienna *(G-19371)*

MTS Medication Tech Inc .... G 440 238-0840
Strongsville *(G-17943)*

Nilpeter Usa Inc .... C 513 489-4400
Cincinnati *(G-4156)*

Pack Line Corp .... F 212 564-0664
Cleveland *(G-5960)*

Pneumatic Scale Corporation ...... C 330 923-0491
Cuyahoga Falls *(G-8033)*

Reactive Resin Products Co .... E 419 666-6119
Perrysburg *(G-16146)*

Rpmi Packaging Inc .... F 513 398-4040
Lebanon *(G-11835)*

Switchback Group Inc .... E 330 523-5200
Richfield *(G-16641)*

System Packaging of Glassline .... C 419 666-9712
Perrysburg *(G-16151)*

Vistech Mfg Solutions LLC .... F 513 933-9300
Lebanon *(G-11848)*

Vmi Americas Inc .... E 330 929-6800
Stow *(G-17815)*

W/S Packaging Group Inc .... E 513 459-2400
Mason *(G-13102)*

MACHINERY: Paint Making

Bethel Engineering and Eqp Inc ... E 419 568-1100
New Hampshire *(G-14833)*

Bethel Engineering and Eqp Inc ... E 419 568-7976
New Hampshire *(G-14834)*

Cohesant Inc .... E 216 910-1700
Beachwood *(G-1262)*

Fawcett Co Inc .... G 330 659-4187
Richfield *(G-16623)*

General Fabrications Corp .... E 419 625-6055
Sandusky *(G-16970)*

Nutro Corporation .... D 440 572-3800
Cleveland *(G-5923)*

Nutro Inc .... E 440 572-3800
Strongsville *(G-17947)*

Woodman Agitator Inc .... F 440 937-9865
Avon *(G-1021)*

MACHINERY: Paper Industry Miscellaneous

Aleris Recycling Inc .... G 216 910-3400
Beachwood *(G-1254)*

Baumfolder Corporation .... D 937 492-1281
Sidney *(G-17169)*

Coater Services Inc .... E 330 499-1407
Canton *(G-2662)*

Comco Machinery Inc .... C 513 248-8000
Milford *(G-14132)*

Custom Threading Systems LLC ... G 937 846-1405
New Carlisle *(G-14799)*

Elite Mill Service & Cnstr .... G 513 422-4234
Trenton *(G-18790)*

J E Doyle Company .... D 330 564-0743
Norton *(G-15515)*

Kadant Black Clawson Inc .... D 513 229-8100
Mason *(G-13052)*

Loroco Industries Inc .... E 513 554-0356
Cincinnati *(G-4033)*

Magna Machine Co .... C 513 851-6900
Cincinnati *(G-4052)*

Mtr Martco LLC .... D 513 424-5307
Middletown *(G-14065)*

National Oilwell Varco LP .... A 937 454-3200
Dayton *(G-8520)*

Rebiltco Inc .... G 513 424-2024
Middletown *(G-14081)*

Rumford Paper Company .... G 937 242-9230
Miamisburg *(G-13856)*

Tri-Mac Mfg & Svcs Co .... F 513 896-4445
Hamilton *(G-10749)*

Universal Precision Products ...... E 330 633-6128
Akron *(G-457)*

Vail Rubber Works Inc .... F 513 705-2060
Middletown *(G-14093)*

MACHINERY: Pharmaciutical

Enerfab Inc .... G 513 771-2300
Cincinnati *(G-3705)*

McFlusion Inc .... G 800 341-8616
Twinsburg *(G-18982)*

Patientss Consumers Phrm Inc .... G 937 813-7800
Dayton *(G-8565)*

MACHINERY: Photographic Reproduction

Tameran Inc .... E 440 349-7100
Solon *(G-17397)*

MACHINERY: Plastic Working

Alstart Enterprises LLC .... F 330 533-3222
Canfield *(G-2547)*

American Plastic Tech Inc .... D 440 632-5203
Middlefield *(G-13914)*

Bradford Neal Machinery Inc .... G 440 632-1393
Middlefield *(G-13918)*

Budget Molders Supply Inc .... E 216 367-7050
Macedonia *(G-12439)*

Chardon Plastics Machinery .... G 440 564-5360
Chardon *(G-3145)*

Component Mfg & Design .... F 330 225-8080
Brunswick *(G-2218)*

Dover High Prfmce Plas Inc .... E 330 343-3477
Dover *(G-8980)*

DRG Hydraulics Inc .... E 216 663-9747
Cleveland *(G-5216)*

Encore Plastics Corporation .... F 419 626-8000
Sandusky *(G-16962)*

Florida Production Engrg Inc .... C 740 420-5252
Circleville *(G-4629)*

I G Brenner Inc .... F 740 345-8845
Newark *(G-15022)*

Innovative Plastic Machinery ...... G 330 478-1825
Canton *(G-2737)*

J McCaman Enterprises Inc .... F 330 825-2401
New Franklin *(G-14825)*

Jaco Manufacturing Company ..... F 440 234-4000
Berea *(G-1622)*

Linden Industries Inc .... E 330 928-4064
Cuyahoga Falls *(G-8020)*

MI 2009 Inc .... A 513 536-2000
Batavia *(G-1204)*

Plastic Process Equipment Inc .... E 216 367-7000
Macedonia *(G-12474)*

Rebuilding & Fabricating Inc .... G 440 322-0844
Elyria *(G-9484)*

Tooltex Inc .... F 614 539-3222
Grove City *(G-10603)*

Tri Technologies Inc .... F 513 422-1300
Middletown *(G-14090)*

Vulcan Machinery Corporation .... E 330 376-6025
Akron *(G-465)*

Wentworth Mold Inc Electra .... D 937 898-8460
Vandalia *(G-19317)*

Wesco Machine Inc .... E 330 688-6973
Munroe Falls *(G-14668)*

Youngstown Plastic Tooling .... E 330 782-7222
Youngstown *(G-21254)*

Zed Industries Inc .... D 937 667-8407
Vandalia *(G-19318)*

MACHINERY: Polishing & Buffing

Areway LLC .... D 216 651-9022
Brooklyn *(G-2128)*

MACHINERY: Printing Presses

1st Choice Web Solution Inc .... G 330 503-1591
Youngstown *(G-21008)*

Advanced Web Corporation .... G 740 662-6323
Stewart *(G-17721)*

Allen Green Enterprises LLC .... G 330 339-0200
New Philadelphia *(G-14883)*

Desco Equipment Corp .... E 330 405-1581
Twinsburg *(G-18923)*

Graphic Systems Services Inc ..... E 937 746-0708
Springboro *(G-17482)*

Incorporated Trustees Gospel W ... D 216 749-1428
Cleveland *(G-5561)*

Key Blue Prints Inc .... G 614 899-6180
Columbus *(G-7259)*

Lyle Printing & Publishing Co ...... F 330 337-7172
Salem *(G-16910)*

MACHINERY: Recycling

Agmet Metals Inc .... E 440 439-7400
Oakwood Village *(G-15621)*

ARS Recycling Systems LLC .... F 330 536-8210
Lowellville *(G-12405)*

Cbg Biotech Ltd Co .... E 440 786-7667
Bedford *(G-1413)*

Continental Turf Systems Inc ...... G 419 596-4409
Continental *(G-7825)*

Glenn Hunter & Associates Inc .... D 419 822-3744
Delta *(G-8935)*

Grasan Equipment Company Inc ... D 419 526-4440
Mansfield *(G-12620)*

Ingredient Masters Inc .... G 513 231-7432
Cincinnati *(G-3920)*

Innovative Recycling Systems ..... G 440 498-9200
Solon *(G-17317)*

Master Chemical Corporation ...... D 419 874-7902
Perrysburg *(G-16121)*

Plastic Partners LLC .... G 425 765-2416
Salem *(G-16919)*

Prodeva Inc .... F 937 596-6713
Jackson Center *(G-11347)*

RSI Company .... F 216 360-9800
Beachwood *(G-1297)*

SDS National LLC .... G 330 759-8066
Youngstown *(G-21198)*

Time Is Money ....G...... 419 701-6098
   Fostoria *(G-9997)*

MACHINERY: Riveting

Fluidpower Assembly Inc ....G...... 419 394-7486
   Saint Marys *(G-16839)*

MACHINERY: Road Construction & Maintenance

American Highway Products Ltd..........F...... 330 874-3270
   Bolivar *(G-1927)*
City of Oxford ....F...... 513 523-8412
   Oxford *(G-15834)*
Concord Road Equipment Mfg Inc.......E...... 440 357-5344
   Painesville *(G-15867)*
Forge Industries Inc. ....A...... 330 782-8301
   Youngstown *(G-21089)*
Gledhill Road Machinery Co ....E...... 419 468-4400
   Galion *(G-10273)*
Gradeworks ....G...... 440 487-4201
   Willoughby *(G-20501)*
Hug Manufacturing Corporation ....G...... 419 668-5086
   Norwalk *(G-15546)*
Jcl Equipment Co Inc ....G...... 937 374-1010
   Xenia *(G-20958)*
Lake Township Trustees ....G...... 419 836-1143
   Millbury *(G-14184)*
Liverpool Township ....G...... 330 483-4747
   Valley City *(G-19211)*
Miller Curber Company LLC ....F...... 330 782-8081
   Youngstown *(G-21146)*
Power-Pack Conveyor Company ....E...... 440 975-9955
   Willoughby *(G-20576)*
Richland Twp Garage ....G...... 419 358-4897
   Bluffton *(G-1915)*

MACHINERY: Robots, Molding & Forming Plastics

CAM-Lem Inc ....G...... 216 391-7750
   Cleveland *(G-4963)*
Day-TEC Tool & Mfg Inc ....F...... 937 847-0022
   Miamisburg *(G-13797)*
Lifeformations Inc..........................E...... 419 352-2101
   Bowling Green *(G-1997)*

MACHINERY: Rubber Working

Anderson International Corp ....D...... 216 641-1112
   Stow *(G-17730)*
Conviber Inc ....F...... 330 723-6006
   Medina *(G-13393)*
French Oil Mill Machinery Co..............D...... 937 773-3420
   Piqua *(G-16266)*
Heintz Manufacturers Inc ....G...... 724 274-6300
   Medina *(G-13420)*
Hydratecs Injection Eqp Co ....G...... 330 773-0491
   Akron *(G-226)*
Kobelco Stewart Bolling Inc ....D...... 330 655-3111
   Hudson *(G-11187)*
McNeil & Nrm Inc ....D...... 330 761-1855
   Akron *(G-291)*
McNeil & Nrm Intl Inc......................D...... 330 253-2525
   Akron *(G-292)*
R A K Machine Inc ....F...... 216 631-7750
   Cleveland *(G-6080)*
R R R Development Co.....................D...... 330 966-8855
   North Canton *(G-15260)*
Rhino Rubber LLC ....F...... 877 744-6603
   North Canton *(G-15262)*
RMS Equipment LLC ....E...... 330 564-1360
   Cuyahoga Falls *(G-8042)*
Rubber City Machinery Corp ....E...... 330 434-3500
   Akron *(G-380)*
Technical Machine Products Inc ....F...... 216 281-9500
   Cleveland *(G-6300)*

MACHINERY: Saw & Sawing

Bortnick Tractor Sales Inc.................F...... 330 924-2555
   Cortland *(G-7862)*

MACHINERY: Screening Eqpt, Electric

M M Industries Inc..........................E...... 330 332-5947
   Salem *(G-16912)*
Measurement Specialties Inc ....F...... 937 885-0800
   Dayton *(G-8482)*
Midwestern Industries Inc.................C...... 330 837-4203
   Massillon *(G-13180)*

Sizetec Inc ....G...... 330 492-9682
   Canton *(G-2850)*

MACHINERY: Semiconductor Manufacturing

Altera Corporation ....G...... 330 650-5200
   Hudson *(G-11155)*
Eaton Corporation ....B...... 216 523-5000
   Cleveland *(G-5245)*
Lam Research Corporation ....C...... 937 472-3311
   Eaton *(G-9314)*

MACHINERY: Separation Eqpt, Magnetic

Decision Systems Inc ....E...... 330 456-7600
   Canton *(G-2682)*
Ohio Magnetics Inc ....E...... 216 662-8484
   Maple Heights *(G-12736)*
Peerless-Winsmith Inc.....................G...... 614 526-7000
   Dublin *(G-9122)*

MACHINERY: Service Industry, NEC

Askia Inc ....G...... 513 828-7443
   Cincinnati *(G-3419)*
C J Smith Machinery Service ....G...... 614 348-1376
   Columbus *(G-6883)*
Clark Auto Machine Shop ....G...... 216 939-0768
   Cleveland *(G-5041)*
Eagle Engineering Wtr Tech LLC ....G...... 419 345-4688
   Perrysburg *(G-16087)*
Erichar Inc ....G...... 216 402-2628
   Cleveland *(G-5293)*

MACHINERY: Sheet Metal Working

Diverse Mfg Solutions LLC ....F...... 740 363-3600
   Delaware *(G-8838)*

MACHINERY: Sifting & Screening

Rotex Global Lcc ....C...... 513 541-1236
   Cincinnati *(G-4359)*
Tyler Haver Inc ....D...... 800 255-1259
   Mentor *(G-13757)*

MACHINERY: Specialty

Devilbiss Ransburg ....F...... 419 470-2000
   Toledo *(G-18437)*
Eaton Electrical Inc........................F...... 216 433-0616
   Beachwood *(G-1269)*
Gam ....G...... 330 427-6470
   Leetonia *(G-11860)*
Life Formations Inc.........................F...... 419 352-2101
   Bowling Green *(G-1996)*
Tex-Vent Co ....G...... 614 299-1902
   Columbus *(G-7686)*

MACHINERY: Stone Working

Stoneworkd ....F...... 740 920-4099
   Newark *(G-15058)*

MACHINERY: Tapping

Midwest Specialties Inc....................F...... 419 738-8147
   Wapakoneta *(G-19501)*

MACHINERY: Textile

CA Litzler Co Inc ....E...... 216 267-8020
   Cleveland *(G-4958)*
Randy Gray ....G...... 513 533-3200
   Cincinnati *(G-4330)*
Wolf Machine Company ....E...... 513 791-5194
   Blue Ash *(G-1897)*
Xpressions LLC ....G...... 330 898-8591
   Warren *(G-19627)*

MACHINERY: Tire Retreading

American Manufacturing & Eqp ....G...... 513 829-2248
   Fairfield *(G-9642)*

MACHINERY: Tire Shredding

Affinity Information Managemet ....G...... 419 517-2055
   Sylvania *(G-18098)*
File 13 Inc...................................F...... 937 642-4855
   Marysville *(G-12943)*
Shred Away ....G...... 740 363-6327
   Delaware *(G-8887)*

MACHINERY: Wire Drawing

Arku Coil-Systems Inc ....G...... 513 985-0500
   Blue Ash *(G-1745)*
EZ Grout Corporation Inc ....E...... 740 962-2024
   Malta *(G-12536)*
Filmtec Inc ....E...... 419 435-1819
   Fostoria *(G-9972)*
Fmt Repair Service Co......................G...... 330 347-7374
   Mentor *(G-13579)*
Hoppel Fabrication Specialties ....F...... 330 823-5700
   Louisville *(G-12315)*
Kenley Enterprises LLC ....E...... 419 630-0921
   Bryan *(G-2308)*
Oma USA Inc ....G...... 330 487-0602
   Twinsburg *(G-18991)*
Shadetree Machine ....G...... 513 727-8771
   Middletown *(G-14082)*
Simon De Young Corporation ....C...... 440 834-3000
   Middlefield *(G-13991)*

MACHINERY: Woodworking

Bent Wood Solutions LLC ....G...... 330 674-1454
   Millersburg *(G-14199)*
Coe Manufacturing Company ....D...... 440 352-9381
   Painesville *(G-15865)*
General Intl Pwr Pdts LLC ....G...... 419 877-5234
   Whitehouse *(G-20340)*
McFeelys Inc................................F...... 800 443-7937
   Harrison *(G-10790)*
Rlfshop LLC.................................G...... 937 898-6070
   Dayton *(G-8634)*
Trico Enterprises LLC......................E...... 330 674-1157
   Millersburg *(G-14272)*

MACHINES: Forming, Sheet Metal

Auburn Metal Processing LLC.............E...... 315 253-2565
   Twinsburg *(G-18902)*
Jones Metal Products Company............D...... 740 545-6381
   West Lafayette *(G-20087)*

MACHINISTS' TOOLS & MACHINES: Measuring, Metalworking Type

Hykon Manufacturing Company...........G....... 330 821-8889
   Alliance *(G-517)*
Karma Metal Products Inc..................F 419 524-4371
   Mansfield *(G-12632)*
L C Smith Co ....G....... 440 327-1251
   Elyria *(G-9448)*
PMC Gage Inc...............................E....... 440 953-1672
   Willoughby *(G-20572)*
WMI Group LLC ....F 330 535-8848
   Akron *(G-474)*

MACHINISTS' TOOLS: Measuring, Precision

Cowles Tool Company LLC ....G....... 330 799-9100
   Austintown *(G-973)*
Morgan Precision Instrs LLC ....G....... 330 896-0846
   Akron *(G-303)*
Thaler Machine Company ....G...... 937 550-2400
   Springboro *(G-17509)*

MACHINISTS' TOOLS: Precision

A & B Machine Inc..........................E...... 937 492-8662
   Sidney *(G-17164)*
Angstrom Precision Metals LLC............D...... 440 255-6700
   Mentor *(G-13522)*
Apollo Manufacturing Co LLC ....E...... 440 951-9972
   Mentor *(G-13524)*
Chippewa Tool & Mfg Co ....F...... 419 849-2790
   Woodville *(G-20724)*
Kaskell Manufacturing Inc ....F...... 937 704-9700
   Springboro *(G-17485)*
Keb Industries Inc...........................G...... 440 953-4623
   Willoughby *(G-20519)*
Levan Enterprises Inc......................E...... 330 923-9797
   Stow *(G-17769)*
M A Harrison Mfg Co Inc ....F...... 440 965-4306
   Wakeman *(G-19451)*
Machining Technologies Inc ....E...... 419 862-3110
   Elmore *(G-9363)*
Midwest Ohio Tool Co ....G...... 419 294-1987
   Upper Sandusky *(G-19132)*
Myers Precision Grinding Co...............F...... 216 365-2630
   Cleveland *(G-5844)*
Pfi Precision Inc.............................E...... 937 845-3563
   New Carlisle *(G-14812)*

Employee Codes: A=Over 500 employees, B=251-500
C=101-250, D=51-100, E=20-50, F=10-19, G=3-9

2017 Harris Ohio
Industrial Directory

1559

P R O D U C T

R Dunn Mold Inc ....G....... 937 773-3388
Piqua *(G-16309)*
Schober USA Inc ....G....... 513 489-7393
Fairfield *(G-9714)*
Seco Machine Inc ....E....... 330 499-2150
North Canton *(G-15263)*

MAGAZINE STAND

Cruisin Times Magazine ....G....... 440 331-4615
Rocky River *(G-16696)*

MAGNESIUM

Air Craft Wheels LLC ....G....... 440 937-7903
Ravenna *(G-16513)*
Lite Metals Company ....E....... 330 296-6110
Ravenna *(G-16539)*
Th Magnesium Inc ....G....... 513 285-7568
Cincinnati *(G-4504)*

MAGNESIUM

Magnesium Refining Tech Inc ....E....... 419 483-9199
Cleveland *(G-5729)*
Magnesium Refining Tech Inc ....E....... 419 483-9199
Bellevue *(G-1552)*

MAGNETIC INK & OPTICAL SCANNING EQPT

Applied Vision Corporation ....D....... 330 926-2222
Cuyahoga Falls *(G-7969)*

MAGNETIC RESONANCE IMAGING DEVICES: Nonmedical

Alliance Healthcare Svcs Inc ....D....... 330 493-6747
Canton *(G-2598)*
Mansfield Imaging Center LLC ....F....... 419 756-8899
Mansfield *(G-12642)*
Summit Diagnostic Imaging LLC ....E....... 513 233-3320
Cincinnati *(G-4475)*

MAGNETIC TAPE, AUDIO: Prerecorded

News Reel Inc ....G....... 614 469-0700
Columbus *(G-7390)*

MAGNETS: Ceramic

Electrodyne Company Inc ....F....... 513 732-2822
Batavia *(G-1180)*

MAGNETS: Permanent

Automatic Equipment Corp ....F....... 513 771-3833
West Chester *(G-19983)*
Dura Magnetics Inc ....F....... 419 882-0591
Sylvania *(G-18106)*
Fenix Magnetics Inc ....G....... 415 308-0134
Lakewood *(G-11663)*
Flexmag Industries Inc ....D....... 740 373-3492
Marietta *(G-12784)*
Magnum Magnetics Corporation ....C....... 740 373-7770
Marietta *(G-12801)*
Ohio Magnetics Inc ....E....... 216 662-8484
Maple Heights *(G-12736)*
Specialty Magnetics LLC ....G....... 330 468-8834
Macedonia *(G-12484)*
Sulo Enterprises Inc ....F....... 440 926-3322
Grafton *(G-10437)*
Walker Magnetics Group Inc ....E....... 614 492-1614
Columbus *(G-7747)*
Walker National Inc ....E....... 614 492-1614
Columbus *(G-7748)*
Winkle Industries Inc ....D....... 330 823-9730
Alliance *(G-554)*

MAIL PRESORTING SVCS

Johnson Brothers Holdings LLC ....G....... 614 868-5273
Columbus *(G-7240)*

MAIL-ORDER HOUSE, NEC

American Frame Corporation ....D....... 419 893-5595
Maumee *(G-13222)*
Communication Concepts Inc ....G....... 937 426-8600
Beavercreek *(G-1326)*
Kencraft Co Inc ....G....... 419 536-0333
Toledo *(G-18542)*
Loctote LLC ....G....... 614 407-0882
Blacklick *(G-1700)*

Paddock Corporation ....G....... 440 543-0631
Chagrin Falls *(G-3110)*
Pardson Inc ....F....... 740 373-5285
Marietta *(G-12813)*

MAIL-ORDER HOUSES: Books, Exc Book Clubs

Scott Fetzer Company ....F....... 440 892-3000
Westlake *(G-20306)*
Stadvec Inc ....G....... 330 644-7724
Barberton *(G-1150)*

MAIL-ORDER HOUSES: Cards

Mantapart ....G....... 330 549-2389
New Springfield *(G-14951)*

MAIL-ORDER HOUSES: Cheese

Guggisberg Cheese Inc ....E....... 330 893-2550
Millersburg *(G-14219)*

MAIL-ORDER HOUSES: Computers & Peripheral Eqpt

Systemax Manufacturing Inc ....C....... 937 368-2300
Dayton *(G-8694)*

MAIL-ORDER HOUSES: Educational Splys & Eqpt

Bendon Inc ....D....... 419 207-3600
Ashland *(G-712)*
E-Z Grader Company ....G....... 440 247-7511
Chagrin Falls *(G-3057)*

MAIL-ORDER HOUSES: Food

Coons Homemade Candies ....G....... 740 496-4141
Harpster *(G-10765)*
Tech Solutions LLC ....G....... 419 852-7190
Celina *(G-3020)*

MAIL-ORDER HOUSES: Gift Items

Krema Products Inc ....G....... 614 889-4824
Dublin *(G-9097)*

MAIL-ORDER HOUSES: Novelty Merchandise

Silk Screen Special TS Inc ....G....... 740 246-4843
Thornville *(G-18199)*

MAIL-ORDER HOUSES: Record & Tape, Music Or Video Club

Dove Cds Inc ....G....... 330 928-3430
Tallmadge *(G-18143)*

MAIL-ORDER HOUSES: Tools & Hardware

Diy Holster LLC ....G....... 419 921-2168
Elyria *(G-9405)*

MAILING & MESSENGER SVCS

A Z Printing Inc ....G....... 513 745-0700
Cincinnati *(G-3339)*
Allen Green Enterprises LLC ....G....... 330 339-0200
New Philadelphia *(G-14883)*
Richardson Printing Corp ....D....... 740 373-5362
Marietta *(G-12824)*

MAILING LIST: Compilers

Brothers Publishing Co LLC ....E....... 937 548-3330
Greenville *(G-10490)*
Cpmm Services Group Inc ....F....... 614 447-0165
Columbus *(G-6996)*
Haines & Company Inc ....C....... 330 494-9111
North Canton *(G-15237)*

MAILING MACHINES WHOLESALERS

Copier Resources Inc ....G....... 614 268-1100
Columbus *(G-6981)*

MAILING SVCS, NEC

Aero Fulfillment Services Corp ....D....... 800 225-7145
Mason *(G-12979)*
Bindery & Spc Pressworks Inc ....D....... 614 873-4623
Plain City *(G-16326)*

Bpm Realty Inc ....E....... 614 221-6811
Columbus *(G-6852)*
Buckeye Business Forms Inc ....G....... 614 882-1890
Westerville *(G-20141)*
Covap Inc ....F....... 513 793-1855
Blue Ash *(G-1769)*
Dayton Mailing Services Inc ....E....... 937 222-5056
Dayton *(G-8279)*
Eg Enterprise Services Inc ....F....... 216 431-3300
Cleveland *(G-5260)*
Fine Line Graphics Corp ....C....... 614 486-0276
Columbus *(G-7085)*
Macke Brothers Inc ....D....... 513 771-7500
Cincinnati *(G-4048)*
Marco Printed Products Co Inc ....G....... 937 433-5680
Dayton *(G-8478)*
Porath Business Services Inc ....F....... 216 626-0060
Cleveland *(G-6021)*
Power Management Inc ....E....... 937 222-2909
Dayton *(G-8580)*
Print All Inc ....G....... 419 534-2880
Toledo *(G-18658)*

MANAGEMENT CONSULTING SVCS: Automation & Robotics

Recognition Robotics Inc ....F....... 440 590-0499
Elyria *(G-9485)*
Scott Systems International ....G....... 740 383-8383
Marion *(G-12898)*

MANAGEMENT CONSULTING SVCS: Business

5me LLC ....E....... 513 719-1600
Cincinnati *(G-3285)*
5me Holdings LLC ....G....... 859 534-4872
Cincinnati *(G-3286)*
Crimson Gate Consulting Co ....G....... 614 805-0897
Dublin *(G-9066)*
Salient Systems Inc ....E....... 614 792-5800
Dublin *(G-9138)*

MANAGEMENT CONSULTING SVCS: Construction Project

Elite Property Group LLC ....F....... 216 316-8222
Cleveland *(G-5272)*
Kbc Services ....F....... 513 693-3743
Loveland *(G-12365)*
Mc Cully Supply & Sales Inc ....G....... 330 497-2211
Canton *(G-2775)*

MANAGEMENT CONSULTING SVCS: Corporation Organizing

Comex North America Inc ....D....... 303 307-2100
Cleveland *(G-5103)*
Pwi Inc ....F....... 732 212-8110
New Albany *(G-14770)*

MANAGEMENT CONSULTING SVCS: General

Faith Guiding Cafe LLC ....F....... 614 245-8451
New Albany *(G-14758)*
Quarrymasters Inc ....G....... 330 612-0474
Canton *(G-2830)*

MANAGEMENT CONSULTING SVCS: Industrial

4r Enterprises Incorporated ....G....... 330 923-9799
Cuyahoga Falls *(G-7960)*
Alloy Extrusion Company ....E....... 330 677-4946
Kent *(G-11427)*
I C Consultants Inc ....F....... 216 731-9992
Cleveland *(G-5545)*
Stellar Industrial Tech Co ....G....... 740 654-7052
Lancaster *(G-11756)*

MANAGEMENT CONSULTING SVCS: Industry Specialist

Bar Codes Unlimited Inc ....G....... 937 434-2633
Dayton *(G-8181)*
Chemsultants International Inc ....G....... 440 974-3080
Mentor *(G-13543)*
Ketman Corporation ....G....... 330 262-1688
Wooster *(G-20795)*
Telex Communications Inc ....F....... 419 865-0972
Toledo *(G-18718)*

MANAGEMENT CONSULTING SVCS: New Products & Svcs

Akron Centl Engrv Mold Mch Inc............E....... 330 794-8704
Akron *(G-37)*

MANAGEMENT CONSULTING SVCS: Public Utilities

Sabre Energy Corporation ....G...... 740 685-8266
Lore City *(G-12294)*

MANAGEMENT CONSULTING SVCS: Real Estate

Acer Contracting LLC.............................G...... 702 236-5917
Columbus *(G-6688)*

MANAGEMENT CONSULTING SVCS: Training & Development

Hard Chrome Plating Consultant ....G...... 216 631-9090
Cleveland *(G-5480)*
Honda of America Mfg Inc ....C...... 937 644-0724
Marysville *(G-12951)*
Leidos Inc ....D...... 937 431-2400
Beavercreek *(G-1348)*

MANAGEMENT CONSULTING SVCS: Transportation

CPC Logistics Inc ....D...... 513 874-5787
Fairfield *(G-9657)*
Ds Express Carriers Inc ....G...... 419 433-6200
Norwalk *(G-15534)*

MANAGEMENT SERVICES

Babcock & Wilcox Company ....A...... 330 753-4511
Barberton *(G-1104)*
Cardinal Health Inc ....A...... 614 757-5000
Dublin *(G-9057)*
Ccw Group Pacesetter Inc ....C...... 740 474-0122
Circleville *(G-4624)*
CFM Religion Pubg Group LLC ....E...... 513 931-4050
Cincinnati *(G-3520)*
Coal Services Inc ....D...... 740 795-5220
Powhatan Point *(G-16488)*
Eleet Cryogenics Inc............................E...... 330 874-4009
Bolivar *(G-1933)*
Instantwhip-Columbus Inc ....E...... 614 871-9447
Grove City *(G-10564)*
Key Principal Partners Corp ....F...... 888 539-3322
Cleveland *(G-5651)*
Kurtz Bros Compost Services ....E...... 330 864-2621
Akron *(G-263)*
Leadec Corp ....E...... 513 731-3590
Blue Ash *(G-1826)*
Majestic Steel Management Co ....E...... 440 786-2666
Cleveland *(G-5732)*
Ohio Designer Craftsmen Entps............F...... 614 486-7119
Columbus *(G-7419)*
Pazco Inc ....E...... 216 447-9581
Cleveland *(G-5982)*
Pf Management Inc ....G...... 513 874-8741
West Chester *(G-20036)*
Revolution Group Inc ....D...... 614 212-1111
Westerville *(G-20182)*
Special Mtls RES & Tech Inc ....G...... 440 777-4024
North Olmsted *(G-15347)*

MANAGEMENT SVCS, FACILITIES SUPPORT: Environ Remediation

Alpha Omega Bioremediation LLC.......F....... 614 287-2600
Columbus *(G-6728)*
Tetra Tech Inc ....F....... 330 286-3683
Canfield *(G-2578)*

MANAGEMENT SVCS: Administrative

Instantwhip Foods Inc ....F...... 614 488-2536
Columbus *(G-7195)*
Media Procurement Services Inc...........G...... 513 977-3000
Cincinnati *(G-4077)*

MANAGEMENT SVCS: Business

Ohio Cllbrtive Lrng Sltons Inc ....E...... 216 595-5289
Beachwood *(G-1286)*

MANAGEMENT SVCS: Construction

Ameridian Specialty Services...............E....... 513 769-0150
Cincinnati *(G-3396)*
Elite Property Group LLC ....F....... 216 316-8222
Cleveland *(G-5272)*
Eric Allshouse LLC ....G....... 330 533-4258
Canfield *(G-2554)*
Protective Industrial Polymers ....F....... 440 327-0015
North Ridgeville *(G-15396)*

MANAGEMENT SVCS: Financial, Business

Dana Companies LLC............................G...... 419 931-9086
Perrysburg *(G-16082)*
Dome Energicorp ....G...... 440 892-4900
Westlake *(G-20265)*
Jmac Inc..F...... 614 436-2418
Columbus *(G-7235)*

MANHOLES & COVERS: Metal

Ej Usa Inc ....G...... 614 871-2436
Grove City *(G-10556)*
Ej Usa Inc ....F...... 330 782-3900
Youngstown *(G-21076)*

MANICURE PREPARATIONS

Hair & Nail Impressions.......................G...... 937 399-0221
Springfield *(G-17567)*

MANIFOLDS: Pipe, Fabricated From Purchased Pipe

Propipe Technologies Inc ....E...... 513 424-5311
Middletown *(G-14079)*
Rexarc International Inc ....E...... 937 839-4604
West Alexandria *(G-19781)*

MANNEQUINS

Denton Atd Inc ....E...... 567 265-5200
Huron *(G-11220)*

MANUFACTURED & MOBILE HOME DEALERS

Pro Fab Industries Inc ....G...... 317 297-0461
Dundee *(G-9179)*

MANUFACTURING INDUSTRIES, NEC

4S Company ....F...... 330 792-5518
Youngstown *(G-21009)*
A-Buck Manufacturing Inc ....G...... 937 687-3738
New Lebanon *(G-14839)*
Abby Industries LLC ....G...... 513 502-9865
Eaton *(G-9298)*
Access Manufacturing Svcs LLC ....G...... 330 659-9893
Richfield *(G-16612)*
Accu Pak Mfg Inc ....G...... 330 644-3015
Akron *(G-26)*
Accurate Automatic Mfg Ltd ....G...... 330 435-4575
Creston *(G-7937)*
Ace Assembly Packaging Inc ....E...... 330 866-9117
Waynesburg *(G-19722)*
Actual Industries LLC...........................G...... 614 379-2739
Columbus *(G-6693)*
Aerovent Inc ....G...... 937 473-3789
Covington *(G-7917)*
Alt Fuel LLC ....G...... 419 865-4196
Toledo *(G-18334)*
American Pioneer Manufacturing..........G...... 330 457-1400
New Waterford *(G-14967)*
Arrowhead Industries ....G...... 440 349-2846
Solon *(G-17261)*
Birge Heavy Industries Ltd ....E...... 440 821-3249
Elyria *(G-9382)*
Blackhawk Industries ....F...... 918 610-4719
Brunswick *(G-2213)*
Blue Creek Renewables LLC ....G...... 419 576-7855
Paulding *(G-16001)*
BMC of Barfield Inc ....G...... 513 860-4455
Hamilton *(G-10676)*
Bomb Mfg LLC ....G...... 419 559-9689
Fremont *(G-10131)*
Buckbuilt Manufacturing Co ....F...... 330 764-3363
Medina *(G-13383)*
Burton Bottling Company Inc ....E...... 216 681-0025
Cleveland *(G-4950)*
C&H Industries ....G...... 330 899-0001
Canton *(G-2632)*

CNB Machining and Mfg LLC................G...... 330 877-7920
Hartville *(G-10819)*
Connelly Industries LLC.......................G...... 330 468-0675
Macedonia *(G-12443)*
Continental Fan Mfg ....G...... 937 233-5524
Huber Heights *(G-11144)*
Creation Industries LLC ....G...... 440 554-6286
Middlefield *(G-13925)*
Dem Manufacturing LLC ....F...... 440 564-7160
Newbury *(G-15088)*
Devault Industries LLC ....G...... 330 456-6070
Canton *(G-2685)*
Duramax Marine Industries ....G...... 419 668-3728
Norwalk *(G-15536)*
Dynamic Manufacturing ....G...... 419 564-8738
Shelby *(G-17135)*
Eagle Burgmann Industries ....G...... 513 563-7325
Cincinnati *(G-3681)*
Eaglehead Manufacturing Co ....G...... 440 951-0400
Eastlake *(G-9267)*
Elaire Corporation ....G...... 419 843-2192
Toledo *(G-18451)*
Energizer Battery Mfg Inc ....G...... 330 527-2191
Garrettsville *(G-10321)*
Fallen Oak Candles Inc ....G...... 419 204-8162
Celina *(G-2997)*
Faw Industries ....G...... 216 651-9595
Cleveland *(G-5327)*
Fbr Industries Inc ....G...... 330 701-7425
Mineral Ridge *(G-14304)*
Frugal Systems ....G...... 419 957-7863
Carey *(G-2918)*
Gen Two Industries LLC ....G...... 419 624-8803
Sandusky *(G-16969)*
Grant Solutions ....G...... 937 344-5558
Tipp City *(G-18280)*
Green Door Industries LLC ....G...... 614 558-1663
Blacklick *(G-1696)*
Groff Industries ....F...... 216 634-9100
Cleveland *(G-5460)*
HCC Industries ....G...... 513 334-5585
Cincinnati *(G-3872)*
Highland Technologies LLC...................G...... 513 739-3510
Mount Orab *(G-14580)*
Housing & Emrgncy Lgstcs Plnnr.........E...... 209 201-7511
Lisbon *(G-12122)*
J S Manufacturing LLC ....G...... 330 815-2136
Kent *(G-11473)*
J-Fab ....G...... 740 384-2649
Wellston *(G-19764)*
Jrf Industries Ltd ....G...... 330 665-3130
Copley *(G-7849)*
Jrw Manufacturing ....G...... 330 628-2994
Akron *(G-244)*
JW Manufacturing ....G...... 419 375-5536
Fort Recovery *(G-9957)*
Kenton Industries Ltd ....G...... 915 603-2139
Cleveland *(G-5647)*
Kiser Industries llc ....G...... 937 332-6723
Troy *(G-18853)*
L E P D Industries Ltd ....G...... 614 985-1470
Powell *(G-16476)*
Leyshon Miller Industries LLC ....F...... 740 432-2969
Cambridge *(G-2463)*
Linebacker Inc.......................................G...... 614 340-1446
Columbus *(G-7298)*
M & R Industries Inc ....G...... 440 897-7950
Brecksville *(G-2062)*
Maca Mold & Machine Co Inc ....G...... 330 854-0292
Canal Fulton *(G-2507)*
Manufacturing Company LLC ....G...... 414 708-7583
Cincinnati *(G-4056)*
MCS Mfg LLC ....G...... 419 923-7535
Lyons *(G-12432)*
Midwest Stamping & Mfg Co..................G...... 419 298-2394
Edgerton *(G-9333)*
Morris Technologies ....F...... 330 384-3084
Akron *(G-304)*
NI Mfg & Distribution Sys In ....G...... 513 422-5216
Middletown *(G-14102)*
Norris North Manufacturing ....G...... 330 691-0449
Canton *(G-2791)*
Norton Manufacturing Co Inc ....F...... 419 435-0411
Fostoria *(G-9990)*
Ohio Manufacturing EXT Partnr ....G...... 614 644-8788
Columbus *(G-7422)*
Oveco Industries Electrica ....G...... 740 381-3326
Richmond *(G-16648)*
Pdi Constellation LLC ....G...... 216 271-7344
Solon *(G-17359)*

PRODUCT

Pegasus Industries ....G....... 740 772-1049
Chillicothe (G-3259)

Plx Industries Inc ....G....... 330 896-7373
Uniontown (G-19095)

Powersonic Industries LLC ....F....... 513 429-2339
Cincinnati (G-4257)

Premier Seals Mfg....................G....... 330 861-1060
Akron (G-349)

Quality Compound Mfg ....G....... 440 353-0150
North Ridgeville (G-15398)

R and D Industries Unlimited ......G....... 937 502-1374
Xenia (G-20969)

Rbs Mfg Inc ....F....... 330 426-9486
East Palestine (G-9243)

Reiser Manufacturing ....G....... 330 846-8003
New Waterford (G-14973)

Restless Noggins Mfg LLC ....G....... 330 526-6908
North Canton (G-15261)

Rmw Industries Inc ....G....... 440 439-1971
Bedford Heights (G-1493)

Royal Mfg ....G....... 419 902-8222
Findlay (G-9886)

RPM Industries ....G....... 440 268-8077
Elyria (G-9489)

S & H Industries Inc ....G....... 216 831-0550
Cleveland (G-6146)

Sdi Industries ....G....... 513 561-4032
Cincinnati (G-4394)

Seavival LLC ....G....... 330 252-1151
Akron (G-398)

Shafts Mfg ....G....... 440 942-6012
Willoughby (G-20595)

Sharc Industries ....G....... 216 272-0668
Columbia Station (G-6600)

Sheridan Mfg of Ohio LLC..........G....... 419 825-2950
Swanton (G-18090)

Smith & Mills Shapers Inc ....F....... 513 541-4031
Cincinnati (G-4428)

Softpoint Industries ....G....... 330 668-2645
Copley (G-7855)

Soldier Tech & Armor RES LLC ....G....... 330 896-5217
Akron (G-407)

Solomon Industries LLC ....G....... 937 558-5334
Troy (G-18877)

Stone & Sullivan Industries ....F....... 513 896-1976
Hamilton (G-10742)

Texstone Industries ....G....... 419 722-4664
Findlay (G-9900)

Thapa Industries ....G....... 419 234-3498
Lima (G-12104)

Thomas Mfg ....G....... 330 758-2384
Youngstown (G-21220)

Thoroughbred Gt Mfg LLC ....F....... 330 533-0048
Canfield (G-2579)

Tommy B Manufacturing Inc ....G....... 330 745-4539
Barberton (G-1155)

Treadway Manufacturing LLC ......G....... 937 264-8447
Dayton (G-8722)

Ttr Manufacturing ....G....... 440 366-5005
Elyria (G-9503)

Tuffy Manufacturing ....G....... 330 940-2356
Cuyahoga Falls (G-8058)

V Mast Manufacturing Inc ....G....... 330 409-8116
Canton (G-2894)

Valentino Industries LLC ....G....... 330 523-7216
Richfield (G-16644)

Vandiley Industries Ltd ....G....... 419 618-1970
Tiffin (G-18251)

Vermilion Dock Masters ....G....... 440 244-5370
Vermilion (G-19337)

Vic Maroscher ....F....... 330 332-4958
Salem (G-16934)

Visual Education Association......G....... 937 325-5503
Springfield (G-17673)

Voodoo Industries ....G....... 440 653-5333
Avon Lake (G-1054)

Waterloo Industries Inc ....G....... 800 833-8851
Cleveland (G-6449)

Wellington Manufacturing ....G....... 440 647-1162
Wellington (G-19757)

Wheeler Embroidery ....G....... 740 550-9751
Ironton (G-11305)

Willoughby Manufacturing Inc ....G....... 330 402-8217
New Waterford (G-14976)

Woodson Distribution LLC ....G....... 937 864-9013
Xenia (G-20989)

Yoder Manufacturing ....G....... 740 504-5028
Howard (G-11125)

MAPS

Hampton Publishing Company......G....... 513 777-9543
Liberty Township (G-11964)

Sentinel USA Inc ....F....... 740 345-6412
Newark (G-15052)

MAPS & CHARTS, WHOLESALE

Ckm Ventures LLC ....G....... 216 623-0370
Cleveland (G-5040)

MARBLE, BUILDING: Cut & Shaped

Al-Co Products Inc 419 399-3867
Latty (G-11767)

Columbus Marble Products Inc ....F....... 614 766-2786
Dublin (G-9063)

Custom Cast Marbleworks Inc ....E....... 513 769-6505
Cincinnati (G-3625)

Engineered Marble Inc ....G....... 614 308-0041
Columbus (G-7057)

Heritage Marble of Ohio Inc ....E....... 614 436-1464
Columbus (G-7151)

Ohio Tile & Marble Co ....E....... 513 541-4211
Cincinnati (G-4180)

Piqua Granite & Marble Co Inc ....G....... 937 773-2000
Piqua (G-16304)

Suburban Marble and Granite Co ....G....... 216 281-5557
Cleveland (G-6259)

MARINAS

Mariners Landing Inc ....F....... 513 941-3625
Cincinnati (G-4060)

Tack-Anew Inc ....E....... 419 734-4212
Port Clinton (G-16417)

MARINE CARGO HANDLING SVCS

Eae Logistics Company LLC ....G....... 440 417-4788
Madison (G-12505)

McGinnis Inc ....C....... 740 377-4391
South Point (G-17440)

McNational Inc ....E....... 740 377-4391
South Point (G-17441)

Rayle Coal Co ....G....... 740 695-2197
Saint Clairsville (G-16805)

MARINE HARDWARE

Great Midwest Yacht Co ....G....... 740 965-4511
Sunbury (G-18061)

Hydromotive Engineering Co ....G....... 330 425-4266
Twinsburg (G-18956)

Minderman Marine Products Inc ....G....... 419 732-2626
Port Clinton (G-16406)

Racelite South Coast Inc ....F....... 216 581-4600
Maple Heights (G-12739)

Worthignton Products Inc ....G....... 330 452-7400
Canton (G-2903)

MARINE PROPELLER REPAIR SVCS

Minderman Marine Products Inc ....G....... 419 732-2626
Port Clinton (G-16406)

MARINE RELATED EQPT

Duramax Marine LLC ....D....... 440 834-5400
Hiram (G-11034)

MARINE SPLY DEALERS

Great Midwest Yacht Co ....G....... 740 965-4511
Sunbury (G-18061)

Jacks Marine Inc ....G....... 440 997-5060
Ashtabula (G-814)

MARINE SPLYS WHOLESALERS

Hydromotive Engineering Co ....G....... 330 425-4266
Twinsburg (G-18956)

MARKETS: Meat & fish

D & H Meats Inc ....G....... 419 387-7767
Vanlue (G-19319)

John Stehlin & Sons Co Inc ....F....... 513 385-6164
Cincinnati (G-3955)

Kmart Supercenter ....G....... 440 974-7300
Cleveland (G-5660)

Riesbeck Food Markets Inc.........C....... 740 695-3401
Saint Clairsville (G-16806)

Strasburg Provision Inc ....E....... 330 878-1059
Strasburg (G-17830)

MARKING DEVICES

Ace Rubber Stamp & Off Sup Co ....E....... 216 771-8483
Cleveland (G-4690)

Akron Paint & Varnish Inc ....D....... 330 773-8911
Akron (G-50)

Bishop Machine Tool & Die ....F....... 740 453-8818
Zanesville (G-21280)

Boehm Inc ....E....... 614 875-9010
Grove City (G-10546)

Dayton Stencil Works Company.....E....... 937 223-3233
Dayton (G-8287)

E C Shaw Co ....E....... 513 721-6334
Cincinnati (G-3677)

East Cleveland Rubber Stamp ......G....... 216 851-5050
Cleveland (G-5239)

Garvey Products Inc ....E....... 513 771-8710
West Chester (G-20009)

Hathaway Stamp & Ident Co of C ....F....... 513 621-1052
Cincinnati (G-3870)

Identity Holding Company LLC ......C....... 216 514-1277
Cleveland (G-5548)

Inner Products Sales Inc ....E....... 216 581-4141
Bedford (G-1431)

Jerry Pulfer ....G....... 937 778-1861
Piqua (G-16283)

Mark Rite Co ....G....... 330 757-7229
Youngstown (G-21141)

Marking Devices Inc ....E....... 216 861-4498
Cleveland (G-5748)

Master Marking Company Inc ....F....... 330 688-6797
Stow (G-17772)

Microcom Corporation ....E....... 740 548-6262
Lewis Center (G-11907)

Monode Marking Products Inc ....F....... 419 929-0346
New London (G-14861)

Monode Steel Stamp Inc ....G....... 419 929-3501
New London (G-14862)

Quick As A Wink Printing Co ....F....... 419 224-9786
Lima (G-12079)

Raschke Engraving Inc ....G....... 330 677-5544
Kent (G-11512)

REA Elektronik Inc ....F....... 440 232-0555
Bedford (G-1456)

Sprinter Marking Inc ....F....... 740 453-1000
Zanesville (G-21356)

Superior Steel Stamp Co ....G....... 216 431-6460
Cleveland (G-6271)

Taradon Rubber Co Inc ....F....... 330 896-3143
Akron (G-428)

Technology and Services Inc ....G....... 740 626-2020
Chillicothe (G-3280)

The Metal Marker Mfg Co ....F....... 440 327-2300
North Ridgeville (G-15405)

Volk Corporation ....G....... 513 621-1052
Cincinnati (G-4570)

MARKING DEVICES: Canceling Stamps, Hand, Rubber Or Metal

Telesis Technologies Inc ....C....... 740 477-5000
Circleville (G-4647)

MARKING DEVICES: Date Stamps, Hand, Rubber Or Metal

Desmond Engraving Co Inc ....G....... 216 265-8338
Cleveland (G-5186)

MARKING DEVICES: Embossing Seals & Hand Stamps

Hathaway Stamp Co ....F....... 513 621-1052
Cincinnati (G-3871)

Royal Acme Corporation ....E....... 216 241-1477
Cleveland (G-6136)

System Seals Inc ....D....... 440 735-0200
Cleveland (G-6284)

Ulrich Rubber Stamp Company ....G....... 419 339-9939
Elida (G-9359)

MARKING DEVICES: Embossing Seals, Corporate & Official

Williams Steel Rule Die Co ....F....... 216 431-3232
Cleveland (G-6464)

(G-0000) Company's Geographic Section entry number

MARKING DEVICES: Figures, Metal

Infosight Corporation ....D 740 642-3600
Chillicothe *(G-3245)*
Lectroetch Co ....F 440 934-1249
Sheffield Village *(G-17125)*
Mark-All Enterprises LLC ....E 800 433-3615
Akron *(G-284)*

MARKING DEVICES: Letters, Metal

All-Craft Wellman Products ....F 440 946-9646
Willoughby *(G-20428)*

MARKING DEVICES: Numbering Stamps, Hand, Rubber Or Metal

Quality Rubber Stamp Inc ....G 614 235-2700
Columbus *(G-7536)*

MARKING DEVICES: Pads, Inking & Stamping

Innovative Ceramic Corp ....G 330 385-6515
East Liverpool *(G-9219)*

MARKING DEVICES: Screens, Textile Printing

Marathon Mfg & Sup Co ....D 330 343-2656
New Philadelphia *(G-14911)*

MARKING DEVICES: Stationary Embossers, Personal

Global Partners USA Co Inc ....G 513 276-4981
West Chester *(G-19878)*

MARKING DEVICES: Textile Making Stamps, Hand, Rubber/Metal

Ccsi Inc ....G 800 742-8535
Akron *(G-114)*
Greg G Wright & Sons LLC ....E 513 721-3310
Cincinnati *(G-3852)*

MASQUERADE OR THEATRICAL COSTUMES STORES

Adyl Inc ....G 330 797-8700
Austintown *(G-968)*
Costume Specialists Inc ....E 614 464-2115
Columbus *(G-6987)*
Costume Specialists Inc ....G 614 464-2115
Columbus *(G-6988)*

MASSAGE MACHINES, ELECTRIC: Barber & Beauty Shops

Vandalia Massage Therapy ....G 937 890-8660
Vandalia *(G-19315)*

MASSAGE PARLORS

Oil Bar LLC ....F 614 880-3950
Columbus *(G-6657)*

MASTIC ROOFING COMPOSITION

Chemspec Ltd ....F 330 896-0355
Uniontown *(G-19079)*

MASTS: Cast Aluminum

Non-Ferrous Casting Co ....G 937 228-1162
Dayton *(G-8525)*
Precision Aluminum Inc ....E 330 335-2351
Wadsworth *(G-19429)*

MATERIAL GRINDING & PULVERIZING SVCS NEC

Ace Grinding Co ....G 440 951-6760
Willoughby *(G-20424)*
Centerless Grinding Service ....G 216 251-4100
Cleveland *(G-5003)*
Erichar Inc ....G 216 402-2628
Cleveland *(G-5293)*
Fleig Enterprises Inc ....G 216 361-8020
Cleveland *(G-5355)*
Melvin Grain Co ....G 937 382-1249
Wilmington *(G-20670)*

Puritan Systems Inc ....E 330 686-0527
Stow *(G-17794)*
Resource Recycling Inc ....F 419 222-2702
Lima *(G-12081)*

MATERIALS HANDLING EQPT WHOLESALERS

American Solving Inc ....G 440 234-7373
Brookpark *(G-2150)*
Bobco Enterprises Inc ....F 419 867-3560
Toledo *(G-18374)*
Bud Corp ....G 740 967-9992
Johnstown *(G-11394)*
Delta Crane Systems Inc ....F 937 324-7425
Springfield *(G-17542)*
Forte Indus Eqp Systems Inc ....E 513 398-2800
Mason *(G-13022)*
Great Lakes Power Products Inc ....D 440 951-5111
Mentor *(G-13596)*
Innovative Hdlg & Metalfab LLC ....E 419 882-7480
Sylvania *(G-18112)*
Intelligrated Systems LLC ....A 513 701-7300
Mason *(G-13046)*
Mes Material Hdlg Systems LLC ....G 740 477-8920
Circleville *(G-4633)*
Mmh Americas Inc ....G 414 764-6200
Springfield *(G-17605)*
Mmh Holdings Inc ....G 937 525-5533
Springfield *(G-17606)*
Ohio Mechanical Handling Co ....F 330 773-5165
Akron *(G-325)*
Scott-Randall Systems Inc ....F 937 446-2293
Sardinia *(G-17033)*

MATS & MATTING, MADE FROM PURCHASED WIRE

Kadee Industries Newco Inc ....F 440 439-8650
Bedford *(G-1435)*

MATS OR MATTING, NEC: Rubber

DTR Equipment Inc ....F 419 692-3000
Delphos *(G-8907)*
Durable Corporation ....D 419 668-8138
Norwalk *(G-15535)*
Garro Tread Corporation ....G 330 376-3125
Akron *(G-198)*
Ludlow Composites Corporation ....G 419 332-5531
Fremont *(G-10168)*
R C Musson Rubber Co ....E 330 773-7651
Akron *(G-362)*
R T H Processing Inc ....D 419 692-3000
Delphos *(G-8916)*
Space-Links Inc ....E 330 788-2401
Youngstown *(G-21206)*
Ultimate Rb Inc ....F 419 692-3000
Delphos *(G-8922)*

MATS, MATTING & PADS: Auto, Floor, Exc Rubber Or Plastic

Crown Dielectric Inds Inc ....C 614 224-5161
Columbus *(G-7001)*

MATS, MATTING & PADS: Nonwoven

Absorbcore LLC ....G 440 614-0457
North Olmsted *(G-15324)*
Durable Corporation ....D 419 668-8138
Norwalk *(G-15535)*
Spacelinks Enterprises Inc ....D 330 788-2401
Youngstown *(G-21207)*
Tranzonic Companies ....C 216 535-4300
Richmond Heights *(G-16656)*
Tranzonic Companies ....C 440 446-0643
Cleveland *(G-6350)*
Zahler Enterprises LLC ....G 614 870-7872
Columbus *(G-7785)*

MATS: Table, Plastic & Textile

A & W Table Pad Co ....F 800 541-0271
Cleveland *(G-4667)*

MATTRESS STORES

Homecare Mattress Inc ....F 937 746-2556
Franklin *(G-10027)*

MEAT & FISH MARKETS: Food & Freezer Plans, Meat

Links Country Meats ....G 419 683-2195
Crestline *(G-7931)*

MEAT & FISH MARKETS: Freezer Provisioners, Meat

Dumas Meats Inc ....G 330 628-3438
Mogadore *(G-14373)*

MEAT & MEAT PRDTS WHOLESALERS

Fresh Mark Inc ....B 330 832-7491
Massillon *(G-13136)*
Fresh Mark Inc ....B 330 834-3669
Massillon *(G-13135)*
Kenosha Beef International Ltd ....C 614 771-1330
Columbus *(G-7256)*
Robert Winner Sons Inc ....E 419 582-4321
Yorkshire *(G-21006)*
Tri-State Beef Co Inc ....E 513 579-1722
Cincinnati *(G-4521)*

MEAT CUTTING & PACKING

Acme Steak & Seafood Inc ....F 330 270-8000
Youngstown *(G-21016)*
Baltic Country Meats ....G 330 897-7025
Baltic *(G-1065)*
C J Kraft Enterprises Inc ....E 740 653-9606
Lancaster *(G-11694)*
Canaan Country Meats ....G 330 435-4778
Creston *(G-7938)*
Case Farms of Ohio Inc ....C 330 359-7141
Winesburg *(G-20702)*
Caven and Sons Meat Packing Co ....F 937 368-3841
Conover *(G-7822)*
D & H Meats Inc ....G 419 387-7767
Vanlue *(G-19319)*
Dee-Jays Cstm Butchering Proc ....G 740 694-7492
Fredericktown *(G-10099)*
Empire Packing Company LP ....D 513 942-5400
West Chester *(G-20000)*
Fresh Mark Inc ....A 330 332-8508
Salem *(G-16893)*
Fresh Mark Inc ....B 330 834-3669
Massillon *(G-13135)*
Gortons Inc ....E 216 362-1050
Cleveland *(G-5439)*
Hartville Locker Service Inc ....G 330 877-9547
Hartville *(G-10823)*
Heffelfingers Meats Inc ....E 419 368-7131
Jeromesville *(G-11384)*
Horst Packing Inc ....G 330 482-2997
Columbiana *(G-6620)*
Industrial Packaging Products ....G 440 734-2663
Cleveland *(G-5567)*
J M Meat Processing ....G 740 259-3030
Mc Dermott *(G-13342)*
Jacoby Packing Co ....G 419 924-2684
West Unity *(G-20130)*
John Morrell & Co ....C 513 782-3800
Cincinnati *(G-3953)*
John Stehlin & Sons Co Inc ....F 513 385-6164
Cincinnati *(G-3955)*
Jones Processing ....G 330 772-2193
Hartford *(G-10814)*
Karn Meats Inc ....E 614 252-3712
Columbus *(G-7251)*
King Kold Inc ....E 937 836-2731
Englewood *(G-9529)*
Links Country Meats ....G 419 683-2195
Crestline *(G-7931)*
Mahan Packing Co Inc ....E 330 889-2454
Bristolville *(G-2099)*
Mannings Packing Co ....G 937 446-3278
Sardinia *(G-17030)*
Marshallville Packing Co Inc ....E 330 855-2871
Marshallville *(G-12918)*
Mc Connells Market ....G 740 765-4300
Richmond *(G-16647)*
New Riegel Cafe Inc ....E 419 595-2255
New Riegel *(G-14947)*
Northside Meat Co Inc ....G 513 681-4111
Cincinnati *(G-4163)*
Ohio Packing Company ....D 614 445-0627
Columbus *(G-7426)*
Ohio Packing Company ....D 614 445-0627
Columbus *(G-7427)*

PRODUCT

Oiler Processing ....G...... 740 892-2640
  Utica (G-19195)
Patrick M Davidson ....G...... 513 897-2971
  Waynesville (G-19733)
Premium Meats Inc ....F...... 330 394-8651
  Warren (G-19589)
Presslers Meats Inc ....F...... 330 644-5636
  Akron (G-350)
Reuss Meats Inc ....F...... 513 874-3200
  Fairfield (G-9710)
Robert Winner Sons Inc ....E...... 419 582-4321
  Yorkshire (G-21006)
Rxpert Consultants LLC ....G...... 614 579-9384
  Columbus (G-7580)
Shaker Valley Foods Inc ....E...... 216 961-8600
  Cleveland (G-6182)
Shirer Brothers Meats ....G...... 740 796-3214
  Adamsville (G-9)
Smokin TS Smokehouse ....G...... 440 577-1117
  Jefferson (G-11371)
Strasburg Provision Inc ....E...... 330 878-1059
  Strasburg (G-17830)
Sugar Creek Packing Co ....B...... 740 335-7440
  Wshngtn CT Hs (G-20927)
Sugar Creek Packing Co ....B...... 937 268-6601
  Dayton (G-8687)
Sugar Creek Packing Co ....C...... 513 874-4422
  West Chester (G-19950)
Sugar Creek Packing Co ....B...... 513 874-4422
  West Chester (G-19951)
Sunny Side Meats ....G...... 419 387-7812
  Vanlue (G-19320)
Tempac LLC ....G...... 513 505-9700
  West Chester (G-19954)
Tri-State Beef Co Inc ....E...... 513 579-1722
  Cincinnati (G-4521)
Trumbull Locker Plant Inc ....G...... 440 474-4631
  Rock Creek (G-16686)
V H Cooper & Co Inc ....B...... 419 678-4853
  Saint Henry (G-16823)
Werling and Sons Inc ....F...... 937 338-3281
  Burkettsville (G-2370)
Whitefeather Meats LLC ....G...... 330 435-6300
  Creston (G-7944)
Winesburg Meats Inc ....G...... 330 359-5092
  Winesburg (G-20708)
Youngs Locker Service Inc ....F...... 740 599-6833
  Danville (G-8093)

MEAT MARKETS

A To Z Portion Ctrl Meats Inc ....E...... 419 358-2926
  Bluffton (G-1906)
Caven and Sons Meat Packing Co ....F...... 937 368-3841
  Conover (G-7822)
Hoffman Meat Processing ....G...... 419 864-3994
  Cardington (G-2911)
Honeybaked Ham Company ....E...... 513 583-9700
  Cincinnati (G-3895)
John Krusinski ....F...... 216 441-0100
  Cleveland (G-5619)
Lee Williams Meats Inc ....E...... 419 729-3893
  Toledo (G-18555)
Marshallville Packing Co Inc ....E...... 330 855-2871
  Marshallville (G-12918)
Mc Connells Market ....G...... 740 765-4300
  Richmond (G-16647)
Old Country Sausage Kitchen ....G...... 216 662-5988
  Cleveland (G-5936)
Pettisville Meats Inc ....F...... 419 445-0921
  Pettisville (G-16183)
Pine Ridge Processing ....G...... 740 749-3166
  Fleming (G-9913)
Trumbull Locker Plant Inc ....G...... 440 474-4631
  Rock Creek (G-16686)
Winesburg Meats Inc ....G...... 330 359-5092
  Winesburg (G-20708)

MEAT PRDTS: Bacon, Side & Sliced, From Purchased Meat

Sugar Creek Packing Co ....B...... 740 335-7440
  Wshngtn CT Hs (G-20927)
Sugar Creek Packing Co ....B...... 937 268-6601
  Dayton (G-8687)
Sugar Creek Packing Co ....C...... 513 874-4422
  West Chester (G-19950)

MEAT PRDTS: Cooked Meats, From Purchased Meat

King Kold Inc ....E...... 937 836-2731
  Englewood (G-9529)

MEAT PRDTS: Corned Beef, From Slaughtered Meat

Signature Beef LLC ....G...... 740 468-3579
  Pleasantville (G-16375)

MEAT PRDTS: Cured, From Slaughtered Meat

Troyers Trail Bologna Inc ....E...... 330 893-2414
  Dundee (G-9183)

MEAT PRDTS: Dried Beef, From Purchased Meat

Amish Wedding Foods Inc ....E...... 330 674-9199
  Millersburg (G-14193)
Weaver Meats Inc ....F...... 440 639-1954
  Painesville (G-15938)

MEAT PRDTS: Frozen

Frank Brunckhorst Company LLC ....G...... 614 662-5300
  Groveport (G-10622)
Jtm Provisions Company Inc ....B...... 513 367-4900
  Harrison (G-10787)
Martin-Brower Company LLC ....B...... 513 773-2301
  West Chester (G-19898)
Sunrise Foods Inc ....E...... 614 276-2880
  Columbus (G-7667)
Zartic LLC ....D...... 513 874-8741
  West Chester (G-20072)

MEAT PRDTS: Hams & Picnics, From Slaughtered Meat

Honey Baked Ham Company LLC ....G...... 513 474-0022
  Cincinnati (G-3894)

MEAT PRDTS: Luncheon Meat, From Purchased Meat

Fink Meat Company Inc ....G...... 937 390-2750
  Springfield (G-17558)

MEAT PRDTS: Pork, Cured, From Purchased Meat

Williams Pork Co Op ....G...... 419 682-9022
  Stryker (G-18010)

MEAT PRDTS: Pork, From Slaughtered Meat

Robert Winner Sons Inc ....G...... 937 548-7513
  Greenville (G-10520)
V H Cooper & Co Inc ....C...... 419 375-4116
  Fort Recovery (G-9961)

MEAT PRDTS: Prepared Beef Prdts From Purchased Beef

Advancepierre Foods Inc ....B...... 513 874-8741
  Blue Ash (G-1734)
Brinkman Turkey Farms Inc ....F...... 419 365-5127
  Findlay (G-9802)
Fresh Mark Inc ....B...... 330 834-3669
  Massillon (G-13135)
Pierre Holding Corp ....G...... 513 874-8741
  West Chester (G-20037)
Wild Joes Inc ....G...... 513 681-9200
  Cincinnati (G-4594)

MEAT PRDTS: Prepared Pork Prdts, From Purchased Meat

Brentmoor Hams LLC ....G...... 513 677-0813
  Loveland (G-12344)
D D D Hams Inc ....G...... 440 487-9572
  Solon (G-17281)
Schad Meats Inc ....G...... 513 520-4888
  Cincinnati (G-4385)

MEAT PRDTS: Sausages, From Purchased Meat

Edelmann Provision Company ....D...... 513 881-5800
  Harrison (G-10776)
Lous Sausage Ltd ....F...... 216 752-5060
  Cleveland (G-5710)
Mama Mias Foods Inc ....G...... 216 281-2188
  Cleveland (G-5737)
Old Country Sausage Kitchen ....G...... 216 662-5988
  Cleveland (G-5936)
Raddells Sausage ....G...... 216 486-1944
  Cleveland (G-6085)
Rays Sausage ....G...... 216 921-8782
  Cleveland (G-6092)

MEAT PRDTS: Sausages, From Slaughtered Meat

Bob Evans Farms Inc ....D...... 937 372-4493
  Xenia (G-20939)
Bob Evans Farms Inc ....F...... 740 245-5305
  Bidwell (G-1673)
Bob Evans Farms Inc ....B...... 614 491-2225
  New Albany (G-14750)
V H Cooper & Co Inc ....E...... 419 678-4853
  Saint Henry (G-16824)

MEAT PRDTS: Snack Sticks, Incl Jerky, From Purchased Meat

Johns Jerky & Snack Meats LLC ....G...... 937 207-7008
  South Charleston (G-17426)
Simply Unique Snacks LLC ....G...... 513 223-7736
  Cincinnati (G-4422)

MEAT PRDTS: Veal, From Slaughtered Meat

Buckeye Veal Services ....G...... 740 489-5145
  Wooster (G-20755)
Dalton Veal ....G...... 330 828-8337
  Dalton (G-8066)
Ohio Farms Packing Co Ltd ....G...... 330 435-6400
  Creston (G-7942)

MEAT PROCESSED FROM PURCHASED CARCASSES

A To Z Portion Ctrl Meats Inc ....E...... 419 358-2926
  Bluffton (G-1906)
Advancepierre Foods Inc ....G...... 513 874-8741
  West Chester (G-19977)
Advancperre Foods Holdings Inc ....G...... 800 969-2747
  Blue Ash (G-1735)
American Foods Group LLC ....E...... 513 733-8898
  Cincinnati (G-3388)
Carl Rittberger Sr Inc ....E...... 740 452-2767
  Zanesville (G-21287)
Caven and Sons Meat Packing Co ....F...... 937 368-3841
  Conover (G-7822)
Cincinnati Meat Processing Inc ....D...... 513 682-6000
  Cincinnati (G-3559)
Dirussos Sausage Inc ....E...... 330 744-1208
  Youngstown (G-21070)
Dumas Meats Inc ....G...... 330 628-3438
  Mogadore (G-14373)
Empire Packing Company LP ....D...... 513 942-5400
  West Chester (G-20000)
Fresh Mark Inc ....B...... 330 832-7491
  Massillon (G-13136)
Fresh Mark Inc ....A...... 330 332-8508
  Salem (G-16893)
Hoffman Meat Processing ....G...... 419 864-3994
  Cardington (G-2911)
Honeybaked Ham Company ....E...... 513 583-9700
  Cincinnati (G-3895)
Hormel Foods Corp Svcs LLC ....E...... 513 563-0211
  Cincinnati (G-3898)
John Krusinski ....F...... 216 441-0100
  Cleveland (G-5619)
John Stehlin & Sons Co Inc ....F...... 513 385-6164
  Cincinnati (G-3955)
Karn Meats Inc ....E...... 614 252-3712
  Columbus (G-7251)
Keith Grimm ....G...... 419 899-2725
  Sherwood (G-17146)
Kenosha Beef International Ltd ....C...... 614 771-1330
  Columbus (G-7256)
Keystone Foods LLC ....C...... 419 257-2341
  North Baltimore (G-15193)

Kings Command Foods LLC..........D...... 937 526-3553
  Versailles *(G-19350)*
Kraft Heinz Foods Company.........B...... 740 622-0523
  Coshocton *(G-7896)*
Lee Williams Meats Inc...............E...... 419 729-3893
  Toledo *(G-18555)*
Marshallville Packing Co Inc........E...... 330 855-2871
  Marshallville *(G-12918)*
Ohio Packing Company................D...... 614 445-0627
  Columbus *(G-7427)*
Patrick M Davidson......................G...... 513 897-2971
  Waynesville *(G-19733)*
Peggys Pride...................................G...... 614 464-2511
  Columbus *(G-7475)*
Perfettes Sausage LLC................G...... 330 792-0775
  Youngstown *(G-21169)*
Pettisville Meats Inc....................F...... 419 445-0921
  Pettisville *(G-16183)*
Queen City Sausage & Provision.......E...... 513 541-5581
  Cincinnati *(G-4320)*
Robert Winner Sons Inc...............E...... 419 582-4321
  Yorkshire *(G-21006)*
Sausage Shoppe............................G...... 216 351-5213
  Cleveland *(G-6163)*
Steven Yant...................................G...... 937 596-0497
  Jackson Center *(G-11348)*
Strasburg Provision Inc...............E...... 330 878-1059
  Strasburg *(G-17830)*
Sugar Creek Packing Co................G...... 513 874-4422
  West Chester *(G-19951)*
Tea Hills Gourmet Chicken Pdts.......G...... 419 685-1689
  Loudonville *(G-12305)*
Tri-State Beef Co Inc....................E...... 513 579-1722
  Cincinnati *(G-4521)*
White Castle System Inc..............B...... 614 228-5781
  Columbus *(G-7761)*
Youngs Locker Service Inc...........F...... 740 599-6833
  Danville *(G-8093)*

MEATS, PACKAGED FROZEN: Wholesalers

A To Z Portion Ctrl Meats Inc......E...... 419 358-2926
  Bluffton *(G-1906)*
Frank Brunckhorst Company LLC.......G...... 614 662-5300
  Groveport *(G-10622)*
White Castle System Inc..............B...... 614 228-5781
  Columbus *(G-7761)*

MECHANICAL INSTRUMENT REPAIR SVCS

Fmt Repair Service Co...................G...... 330 347-7374
  Mentor *(G-13579)*

MEDIA BUYING AGENCIES

Pixslap Inc...................................G...... 937 559-2671
  Middletown *(G-14076)*

MEDIA: Magnetic & Optical Recording

CD Solutions Inc.........................G...... 937 676-2376
  Pleasant Hill *(G-16369)*

MEDICAL & HOSPITAL EQPT WHOLESALERS

Askia Inc......................................G...... 513 828-7443
  Cincinnati *(G-3419)*
Biorx LLC.....................................C...... 866 442-4679
  Cincinnati *(G-3450)*
Homecare Mattress Inc.................F...... 937 746-2556
  Franklin *(G-10027)*
Julius Zorn Inc.............................D...... 330 923-4999
  Cuyahoga Falls *(G-8015)*
Smiths Medical North America.......G...... 614 210-7300
  Dublin *(G-9146)*
Wbc Group LLC.............................C...... 866 528-2144
  Hudson *(G-11207)*

MEDICAL & HOSPITAL SPLYS: Radiation Shielding Garments

Hall Safety Apparel Inc.................F...... 740 922-3671
  Uhrichsville *(G-19051)*
Tradex International Inc...............D...... 216 651-4788
  Cleveland *(G-6345)*

MEDICAL & SURGICAL SPLYS: Atomizers, Medical

Acela Biomedical..........................F...... 937 544-8618
  Winchester *(G-20689)*

Whiteford Industries Inc...............F...... 419 381-1155
  Toledo *(G-18774)*

MEDICAL & SURGICAL SPLYS: Bandages & Dressings

Beiersdorf Inc..............................C...... 513 682-7300
  West Chester *(G-19984)*
Jobskin Div of Torbot Group.........E...... 419 724-1475
  Toledo *(G-18535)*
Tytek Medical Inc.........................G...... 513 247-2002
  Blue Ash *(G-1885)*

MEDICAL & SURGICAL SPLYS: Belts, Surg, Sanitary & Corrective

Steris Corporation.........................C...... 440 352-8724
  Mentor *(G-13731)*

MEDICAL & SURGICAL SPLYS: Braces, Elastic

Daishin Industrial Co....................G...... 614 766-9535
  Dublin *(G-9067)*
Motion Mobility & Design Inc.........F...... 330 244-9723
  North Canton *(G-15251)*

MEDICAL & SURGICAL SPLYS: Braces, Orthopedic

ABI Orthtc/Prosthetic Labs Ltd.......E...... 330 758-1143
  Youngstown *(G-21013)*
Akron Orthotic Solutions Inc.........G...... 330 253-3002
  Akron *(G-49)*
Anatomical Concepts Inc...............F...... 330 757-3569
  Youngstown *(G-21026)*
Arthur W Guilford III Inc..............G...... 216 362-1350
  Cleveland *(G-4837)*
Brace Sp Prsthtic Orthtic Ctrs.......F...... 513 421-5653
  Cincinnati *(G-3465)*
Bracemart LLC..............................G...... 440 353-2830
  North Ridgeville *(G-15362)*
Cole Orthotics Prosthetic Ctr.........G...... 419 476-4248
  Toledo *(G-18405)*
Faretec Inc...................................F...... 440 350-9510
  Painesville *(G-15880)*
Findlay American Prosthetic &.......G...... 419 424-1622
  Findlay *(G-9822)*
Lexington Prosthetic Ortotics.......G...... 803 939-0097
  Galena *(G-10246)*
North Cast Orthtics Prsthetics.......F...... 440 233-4314
  Lorain *(G-12263)*
Orthotics & Prosthetics Rehab.......F...... 330 856-2553
  Warren *(G-19585)*

MEDICAL & SURGICAL SPLYS: Clothing, Fire Resistant & Protect

Apex Fire Services LLC.................G...... 614 274-6400
  Columbus *(G-6761)*
Barton-Carey Medical Products.......E...... 419 887-1285
  Maumee *(G-13230)*
Chester West Holdings Inc............C...... 800 647-1900
  Sharonville *(G-17113)*
Serena Safety.................................G...... 440 572-4481
  Columbia Station *(G-6599)*
Wcm Holdings Inc.........................G...... 513 705-2100
  Cincinnati *(G-4581)*

MEDICAL & SURGICAL SPLYS: Cosmetic Restorations

Anderson Cosmetic & Vein Inst.......G...... 513 624-7900
  Cincinnati *(G-3402)*

MEDICAL & SURGICAL SPLYS: Foot Appliances, Orthopedic

Northestrn OH Foot & Ankl Asoc.......G...... 330 633-3445
  Tallmadge *(G-18161)*
Stable Step LLC............................E...... 513 825-1888
  West Chester *(G-19948)*

MEDICAL & SURGICAL SPLYS: Grafts, Artificial

Evanko Wm/Barringer Richd DDS.......G...... 330 336-6693
  Wadsworth *(G-19405)*
Interplex Medical LLC....................E...... 513 248-5120
  Milford *(G-14154)*

Osteonovus Inc.............................G...... 617 717-8867
  Toledo *(G-18622)*

MEDICAL & SURGICAL SPLYS: Hosiery, Support

Julius Zorn Inc.............................D...... 330 923-4999
  Cuyahoga Falls *(G-8015)*

MEDICAL & SURGICAL SPLYS: Limbs, Artificial

Capital Prosthetic &.....................F...... 614 451-0446
  Columbus *(G-6899)*
Capital Prosthetic &.....................G...... 567 560-2051
  Mansfield *(G-12574)*
Capital Prosthetic &.....................G...... 740 453-9545
  Zanesville *(G-21286)*
Capital Prosthetic &.....................G...... 614 451-0446
  Columbus *(G-6900)*
Capital Prosthetic &.....................G...... 740 522-3331
  Newark *(G-14991)*
Fidelity Orthopedic Inc.................G...... 937 228-0682
  Dayton *(G-8341)*
Hanger Prsthetcs & Ortho Inc.......G...... 440 605-0232
  Mayfield Heights *(G-13316)*
Hanger Prsthetcs & Ortho Inc.......G...... 330 670-8263
  Akron *(G-214)*
Hanger Prsthetcs & Ortho Inc.......G...... 614 471-8210
  Gahanna *(G-10208)*
Hanger Prsthetcs & Ortho Inc.......G...... 440 842-4251
  Cleveland *(G-5477)*
Hanger Prsthetcs & Ortho Inc.......G...... 330 374-9544
  Akron *(G-215)*
Hanger Prsthetcs & Ortho Inc.......G...... 330 856-6990
  Warren *(G-19556)*
Hanger Prsthetcs & Ortho Inc.......G...... 740 383-2163
  Marion *(G-12872)*
Hanger Prsthetcs & Ortho Inc.......G...... 419 522-0055
  Marion *(G-12871)*
Hanger Prsthetcs & Ortho Inc.......G...... 740 454-6215
  Zanesville *(G-21317)*
Lower Limb Centers LLC................G...... 440 365-2502
  Elyria *(G-9456)*
Novacare Inc.................................G...... 216 704-4817
  Beachwood *(G-1285)*
Out On A Limb...............................G...... 513 432-5091
  Cincinnati *(G-4202)*
Rowley J F Prosth & Orth Lab.......G...... 513 861-3705
  Cincinnati *(G-4361)*
Swanson Orthotic & Prosthetic.......G...... 419 690-0026
  Oregon *(G-15719)*
Yanke Bionics Inc.........................E...... 330 762-6411
  Akron *(G-475)*
Yanke Bionics Inc.........................G...... 330 668-4070
  Akron *(G-476)*

MEDICAL & SURGICAL SPLYS: Live Preservers, Exc Cork & Inflat

Beaufort Rfd Inc...........................F...... 330 239-4331
  Sharon Center *(G-17102)*

MEDICAL & SURGICAL SPLYS: Orthopedic Appliances

Acor Orthopaedic Inc....................D...... 216 662-4500
  Cleveland *(G-4695)*
Canton Orthotic Laboratory..........G...... 330 833-0955
  Canton *(G-2644)*
Central Ohio Orthtic Prsthetic.......G...... 614 659-1580
  Dublin *(G-9060)*
Depuy Orthopaedics Inc...............E...... 937 274-5850
  Dayton *(G-8299)*
DPM Orthodontics Inc...................G...... 330 673-0334
  Kent *(G-11451)*
Earthwalk Orthotic........................F...... 330 837-6569
  Massillon *(G-13128)*
Gaitwell Orthotics Pedorthics.......G...... 513 829-2217
  Cincinnati *(G-3793)*
Matplus Ltd...................................G...... 440 352-7201
  Painesville *(G-15900)*
Opc Inc..G...... 419 531-2222
  Toledo *(G-18620)*
Orthotic and Prosthetics Svc.........G...... 330 723-6679
  Medina *(G-13454)*
Osteo Solution.............................G...... 614 485-9790
  Westerville *(G-20177)*
S R T Prosthetics & Orthotics.......G...... 419 272-3102
  Edon *(G-9345)*

PRODUCT

Yanke Bionics Inc ....G..... 330 833-0955
  Massillon (G-13212)
Zimme Ortho Surgi Produ Inc ....D...... 800 321-5533
  Dover (G-9025)

MEDICAL & SURGICAL SPLYS: Personal Safety Eqpt

Beeline Purchasing LLC ....G...... 513 703-3733
  Mason (G-12989)
Orion Holdings LLC ....G...... 513 871-4344
  Cincinnati (G-4196)
Targeting Customer Safety Inc ....G...... 330 865-9593
  Akron (G-429)
Washington Laboratories Inc ....G...... 330 452-4928
  Canton (G-2901)

MEDICAL & SURGICAL SPLYS: Prosthetic Appliances

Ace Prosthetics Inc ....G...... 614 291-8325
  Columbus (G-6687)
Advanced Arm Dynamics ....G...... 440 617-6601
  Westlake (G-20245)
American Orthopedics Inc ....E...... 614 291-6454
  Columbus (G-6741)
Biocare Orthopedic ....G...... 614 754-7514
  Canal Winchester (G-2520)
Catech Inc ....E...... 937 439-0432
  Dayton (G-8215)
Hanger Prsthetcs & Ortho Inc ....F...... 419 841-9852
  Toledo (G-18495)
Hanger Prsthetcs & Ortho Inc ....G...... 937 773-2441
  Piqua (G-16269)
Hanger Prsthetcs & Ortho Inc ....F...... 937 228-5462
  Dayton (G-8384)
Hanger Prsthetcs & Ortho Inc ....G...... 740 266-6400
  Steubenville (G-17697)
Hanger Prsthetcs & Ortho Inc ....G...... 740 369-2424
  Marysville (G-12947)
Hanger Prsthetcs & Ortho Inc ....G...... 740 654-1884
  Lancaster (G-11722)
Luminaud Inc ....G...... 440 255-9082
  Mentor (G-13637)
Materials Engineering & Dev ....G...... 937 884-5118
  Brookville (G-2191)
Miller Prsthtics Orthotics LLC ....G...... 740 421-4211
  Belpre (G-1591)
Neu Prosthetics & Orthotics ....G...... 740 363-3522
  Delaware (G-8874)
O & P Options LLC ....G...... 513 791-7767
  Montgomery (G-14434)
Ohio Willow Wood Company ....C...... 740 869-3377
  Mount Sterling (G-14601)
Ortho Prosthetic Center ....G...... 419 352-8161
  Bowling Green (G-2005)
Orthotic Prosthetic Center ....G...... 419 531-2222
  Toledo (G-18621)
Prosthetic Design Inc ....G...... 937 836-1464
  Englewood (G-9537)
Synthetic Body Parts Inc ....G...... 440 838-0985
  Brecksville (G-2075)
Touch Life Centers LLC ....G...... 614 388-8075
  Hilliard (G-10988)
Western Reserve Orthodontics & ....F...... 330 792-6826
  Austintown (G-977)

MEDICAL & SURGICAL SPLYS: Respiratory Protect Eqpt, Personal

MST Inc ....G...... 419 542-6645
  Hicksville (G-10903)

MEDICAL & SURGICAL SPLYS: Splints, Pneumatic & Wood

Avalign Technologies Inc ....F...... 419 542-7743
  Hicksville (G-10900)

MEDICAL & SURGICAL SPLYS: Stretchers

Midmark Corporation ....A...... 937 526-3662
  Versailles (G-19352)
S K M L Inc ....G...... 330 220-7565
  Valley City (G-19228)

MEDICAL & SURGICAL SPLYS: Technical Aids, Handicapped

Forbes Rehab Services Inc ....G...... 419 589-7688
  Mansfield (G-12606)

Ohio State University ....G...... 614 293-3600
  Columbus (G-7433)
Southpaw Enterprises Inc ....E...... 937 252-7676
  Moraine (G-14531)
Visualy Imp Exp Wm Isues Fr Gr ....G...... 216 561-6864
  Cleveland (G-6422)

MEDICAL & SURGICAL SPLYS: Trusses, Orthopedic & Surgical

Lifes Products Inc ....G...... 740 965-9711
  Sunbury (G-18066)

MEDICAL & SURGICAL SPLYS: Welders' Hoods

Kuhlmanns Fabrication ....G...... 513 967-4617
  Hamilton (G-10717)
M-Co Welling ....G...... 330 897-1374
  Stone Creek (G-17724)
Sfl Enterprises Inc ....G...... 513 239-6822
  Loveland (G-12385)

MEDICAL CENTERS

Buses International ....F...... 440 233-4091
  Lorain (G-12235)

MEDICAL EQPT REPAIR SVCS, NON-ELECTRIC

Elite Biomedical Solutions LLC ....F...... 513 207-0602
  Cincinnati (G-3301)

MEDICAL EQPT: CAT Scanner Or Computerized Axial Tomography

Deerfield Medical Imaging LLC ....G...... 513 271-5717
  Mason (G-13009)
Imageiq Inc ....F...... 855 462-4347
  Cleveland (G-5551)

MEDICAL EQPT: Defibrillators

Nkh Life Safety LLC ....F...... 513 688-7100
  Cincinnati (G-4159)

MEDICAL EQPT: Diagnostic

Aeiou Scientific LLC ....G...... 614 325-2103
  Columbus (G-6699)
Baby Love Prenatal Imaging LLC ....G...... 419 905-7935
  Delphos (G-8901)
Broad Street Imaging ....G...... 614 621-9100
  Columbus (G-6643)
Diagnostic Hybrids Inc ....C...... 740 593-1784
  Athens (G-861)
Ebisyn Medical Inc ....G...... 609 759-1101
  Dublin (G-9071)
Eoi Inc ....F...... 740 201-3300
  Lewis Center (G-11897)
Filament LLC ....G...... 614 732-0754
  Columbus (G-7083)
Flotbi Inc ....G...... 216 619-5928
  Cleveland (G-5359)
Sense Diagnostics LLC ....G...... 513 515-3853
  Cincinnati (G-4405)
Smiths Medical Pm Inc ....F...... 614 210-7300
  Dublin (G-9147)
Sonogage Inc ....F...... 216 464-1119
  Cleveland (G-6220)
Transdermal Inc ....F...... 440 241-1846
  Gates Mills (G-10338)
World Wide Medical Physics Inc ....G...... 419 266-7530
  Perrysburg (G-16172)
Ysi Incorporated ....D...... 937 767-7241
  Yellow Springs (G-21005)

MEDICAL EQPT: Electromedical Apparatus

Cleveland Medical Devices Inc ....E...... 216 426-0365
  Cleveland (G-5068)
Great Lkes Nrotechnologies Inc ....E...... 216 520-1537
  Cleveland (G-5456)
Imalux Corporation ....F...... 216 502-0755
  Cleveland (G-5553)

MEDICAL EQPT: Electrotherapeutic Apparatus

Ep Technologies LLC ....F...... 234 208-8967
  Akron (G-171)

MEDICAL EQPT: Laser Systems

Hair Science Systems LLC ....G...... 513 231-8284
  Cincinnati (G-3862)
Infinity Trichology Center ....G...... 937 281-0555
  Kettering (G-11581)
Medical Quant USA Inc ....F...... 440 542-0761
  Solon (G-17333)
Scallywag Tag ....G...... 513 922-4999
  Cincinnati (G-4383)

MEDICAL EQPT: MRI/Magnetic Resonance Imaging Devs, Nuclear

Alltech Med Systems Amer Inc ....E...... 440 424-2240
  Solon (G-17255)
Elastance Imaging LLC ....G...... 614 579-9520
  Columbus (G-7049)
Gvi Medical Devices Corp ....F...... 330 963-4083
  Twinsburg (G-18951)
Magnetic Resonance Tech ....G...... 440 942-2922
  Willoughby (G-20532)

MEDICAL EQPT: Pacemakers

Cardiac Arrhythmia Associates ....G...... 330 759-8169
  Youngstown (G-21043)
University Crdc & Thrc Grp ....F...... 216 844-3053
  Cleveland (G-6393)

MEDICAL EQPT: Patient Monitoring

GE Medical Systems Information ....G...... 216 663-2110
  Warrensville Heights (G-19633)
Valued Relationships Inc ....B...... 800 860-4230
  Franklin (G-10061)

MEDICAL EQPT: Sterilizers

Pure Light Technology LLC ....G...... 513 779-7474
  West Chester (G-20042)
Steris Corporation ....D...... 440 354-2600
  Mentor (G-13736)
Steris Corporation ....A...... 440 354-2600
  Mentor (G-13733)

MEDICAL EQPT: Ultrasonic Scanning Devices

Axiomed Spine Corp ....F...... 216 587-5566
  Cleveland (G-4879)
Century Biotech Partners Inc ....G...... 614 746-6998
  Dublin (G-9061)
Flocel Inc ....G...... 216 619-5903
  Cleveland (G-5358)
Imaging Center East Main ....G...... 614 566-8120
  Columbus (G-7183)
Neurowave Systems Inc ....G...... 216 361-1591
  Cleveland (G-5875)
Nuvasive Manufacturing LLC ....E...... 937 343-0400
  Fairborn (G-9627)
Open Sided Mri Cleveland LLC ....G...... 804 217-7114
  Westlake (G-20290)

MEDICAL EQPT: X-Ray Apparatus & Tubes, Radiographic

General Electric Company ....D...... 216 663-2110
  Cleveland (G-5414)

MEDICAL INSURANCE CLAIM PROCESSING: Contract Or Fee Basis

Acu-Serve Corp ....G...... 330 923-5258
  Cuyahoga Falls (G-7961)
Merry X-Ray Chemical Corp ....G...... 614 219-2011
  Hilliard (G-10960)

MEDICAL SUNDRIES: Rubber

Formco Inc ....G...... 330 966-2111
  Canton (G-2706)
Philpott Rubber LLC ....E...... 330 225-3344
  Brunswick (G-2243)
Premiere Medical Resources Inc ....F...... 330 923-5899
  Cuyahoga Falls (G-8036)

MEDICAL TRAINING SERVICES

M R I Education Foundation ....C...... 513 281-3400
  Cincinnati (G-4043)

MEDICAL, DENTAL & HOSP EQPT, WHOLESALE: X-ray Film & Splys

Philips Medical Systems Clevel ....B 440 247-2652
Cleveland (G-6001)

MEDICAL, DENTAL & HOSPITAL EQPT, WHOL: Dentists' Prof Splys

Triage Ortho Group ....G 937 653-6431
Urbana (G-19185)

MEDICAL, DENTAL & HOSPITAL EQPT, WHOL: Hospital Eqpt & Splys

Jones Metal Products Company ....E 740 545-6341
West Lafayette (G-20088)
Kempf Surgical Appliances Inc ....E 513 984-5758
Montgomery (G-14433)

MEDICAL, DENTAL & HOSPITAL EQPT, WHOL: Hosptl Eqpt/Furniture

Access To Independence Inc ....G 330 296-8111
Ravenna (G-16512)
Electro-Cap International Inc ....F 937 456-6099
Eaton (G-9305)
Key Mobility Services Ltd ....G 937 374-3226
Xenia (G-20959)
Pdi Communication Systems Inc ....D 937 743-6010
Springboro (G-17495)

MEDICAL, DENTAL & HOSPITAL EQPT, WHOL: Surgical Eqpt & Splys

Cardinal Health Inc ....A 614 757-5000
Dublin (G-9057)
Haag-Streit Holding Us Inc ....E 513 336-7255
Mason (G-13033)

MEDICAL, DENTAL & HOSPITAL EQPT, WHOLESALE: Diagnostic, Med

Thermo Fisher Scientific Inc ....C 800 871-8909
Oakwood Village (G-15630)
Tosoh America Inc ....B 614 539-8622
Grove City (G-10604)

MEDICAL, DENTAL & HOSPITAL EQPT, WHOLESALE: Med Eqpt & Splys

Eoi Inc ....F 740 201-3300
Lewis Center (G-11897)
Faretec Inc ....F 440 350-9510
Painesville (G-15880)
Mill Rose Laboratories Inc ....E 440 974-6730
Mentor (G-13656)

MEDICAL, DENTAL & HOSPITAL EQPT, WHOLESALE: Safety

Beeline Purchasing LLC ....G 513 703-3733
Mason (G-12989)

MEDICAL, DENTAL & HOSPITAL EQPT, WHOLESALE: Therapy

Viewray Incorporated ....D 440 703-3210
Oakwood Village (G-15631)

MEDICAL, DENTAL/HOSPITAL EQPT, WHOL: Veterinarian Eqpt/Sply

Berlin Industries Inc ....F 330 549-2100
North Lima (G-15310)

MELAMINE RESINS: Melamine-Formaldehyde

Next Specialty Resins Inc ....E 517 547-4600
Toledo (G-18606)
Plastic Compounders Inc ....E 740 432-7371
Cambridge (G-2472)

MEMBERSHIP HOTELS

American Guild of English Hand ....G 937 438-0085
Cincinnati (G-3389)

MEMBERSHIP ORGANIZATIONS, CIVIC, SOCIAL/FRAT: Social Assoc

Family Motor Coach Assn Inc ....E 513 474-3622
Cincinnati (G-3738)

MEMBERSHIP ORGANIZATIONS, NEC: Bowling club

Greater Cincinnati Bowl Assn ....E 513 761-7387
Cincinnati (G-3847)

MEMBERSHIP ORGANIZATIONS, NEC: Flying Club

Institute Mthmtical Statistics ....G 216 295-2340
Shaker Heights (G-17090)

MEMBERSHIP ORGANIZATIONS, NEC: Personal Interest

American Guild of English Hand ....G 937 438-0085
Cincinnati (G-3389)

MEMBERSHIP ORGANIZATIONS, REL: Christian & Reformed Church

Buses International ....F 440 233-4091
Lorain (G-12235)
Calvary Christian Ch of Ohio ....E 740 828-9000
Frazeysburg (G-10071)

MEMBERSHIP ORGANIZATIONS, RELIGIOUS: Brethren Church

Society of The Precious Blood ....E 419 925-4516
Celina (G-3018)

MEMBERSHIP ORGANIZATIONS, RELIGIOUS: Nonchurch

Incorporated Trst Gspl Wk Scty ....D 216 749-2100
Cleveland (G-5560)

MEMORIALS, MONUMENTS & MARKERS

Artistic Memorials Ltd ....G 419 873-0433
Perrysburg (G-16066)
Fostoria Monument Co ....G 419 435-0373
Fostoria (G-9978)
Linden Monuments ....G 419 468-4130
Galion (G-10279)

MEN'S & BOYS' CLOTHING STORES

Benchmark Prints ....F 419 332-7640
Fremont (G-10129)
S F Mock & Associates LLC ....F 937 438-0196
Dayton (G-8644)

MEN'S & BOYS' CLOTHING WHOLESALERS, NEC

Chester West Holdings Inc ....C 800 647-1900
Sharonville (G-17113)
Fine Line Embroidery Company ....G 440 331-7030
Rocky River (G-16699)
McCc Sportswear Inc ....E 513 583-9210
West Chester (G-20025)
Totes Isotoner Corporation ....F 513 682-8200
West Chester (G-20059)

MEN'S & BOYS' SPORTSWEAR CLOTHING STORES

Jakes Sportswear Ltd ....G 740 746-8356
Sugar Grove (G-18012)
Lion Clothing Inc ....G 419 692-9981
Delphos (G-8914)
Locker Room Lettering Ltd ....G 419 359-1761
Castalia (G-2977)
Sports Express ....G 330 297-1112
Ravenna (G-16559)

MEN'S & BOYS' SPORTSWEAR WHOLESALERS

Activewares ....G 419 994-5932
Loudonville (G-12295)
Barbs Graffiti Inc ....E 216 881-5550
Cleveland (G-4889)

METAL FABRICATORS: Architechtural

Design Original Inc ....F 937 596-5121
Jackson Center (G-11339)
Precision Imprint ....G 740 592-5916
Athens (G-882)
R & A Sports Inc ....E 216 289-2254
Euclid (G-9603)
Unisport Inc ....F 419 529-4727
Ontario (G-15696)

MEN'S & BOYS' WORK CLOTHING WHOLESALERS

Hands On International LLC ....G 513 502-9000
Mason (G-13034)

METAL & STEEL PRDTS: Abrasive

Cleveland Granite & Marble LLC ....E 216 291-7637
Cleveland (G-5063)
Innovation Sales LLC ....G 330 239-0400
Medina (G-13426)
Steel Warehouse of Ohio LLC ....D 888 225-3760
Cleveland (G-6246)
Tomson Steel Company ....E 513 420-8600
Middletown (G-14089)

METAL COMPONENTS: Prefabricated

Metal Seal Precision Ltd ....C 440 205-0016
Mentor (G-13654)
St Marys Iron Works Inc ....F 419 300-6300
Saint Marys (G-16857)

METAL CUTTING SVCS

Aetna Plastics Corp ....G 330 274-2855
Mantua (G-12706)
Dbcr Inc ....E 330 920-1900
Cuyahoga Falls (G-7986)
Exact Cutting Service Inc ....E 440 546-1319
Brecksville (G-2048)
Gerdau Macsteel Atmosphere Ann ....D 330 478-0314
Canton (G-2713)
Independent Steel Company LLC ....E 330 225-7741
Valley City (G-19207)
Laserflex Corporation ....D 614 850-9600
Hilliard (G-10958)
Precision Strip Inc ....D 937 667-6255
Tipp City (G-18293)
Quality Tube Service Inc ....F 419 237-3014
Fayette (G-9778)
Quest Technologies Inc ....F 937 743-1200
Franklin (G-10047)
Scot Industries Inc ....E 330 262-7585
Wooster (G-20832)
Trojon Gear Inc ....F 937 254-1737
Dayton (G-8729)

METAL DETECTORS

Ceia Usa Ltd ....E 330 405-3190
Twinsburg (G-18909)
Ohio Magnetics Inc ....E 216 662-8484
Maple Heights (G-12736)

METAL FABRICATORS: Architechtural

A & E Butscha Co ....G 513 761-1919
Cincinnati (G-3329)
A & G Manufacturing Co Inc ....E 419 468-7433
Galion (G-10250)
Annin & Co ....D 740 622-4447
Coshocton (G-7878)
Armor Consolidated Inc ....C 513 923-5260
Mason (G-12982)
Armor Metal Group Mason Inc ....C 513 769-0700
Mason (G-12983)
Art Fremont Iron Co ....G 419 332-5554
Fremont (G-10125)
Bauer Corporation ....E 800 321-4760
Wooster (G-20746)
Blevins Metal Fabrication Inc ....E 419 522-6082
Mansfield (G-12567)
Courtad Inc ....G 330 274-3100
Aurora (G-913)
Cozmyk Enterprises Inc ....F 614 231-1370
Columbus (G-6994)
Cramers Inc ....E 330 477-4571
Canton (G-2670)
Debra-Kuempel Inc ....D 513 271-6500
Cincinnati (G-3645)
Decor Architectural Products ....G 419 537-9493
Toledo (G-18432)

Dover Tank and Plate Company ....E...... 330 343-4443
  Dover (G-8982)
E B P Inc ....E...... 216 241-2550
  Cleveland (G-5230)
Federal Iron Works Company ....E...... 330 482-5910
  Columbiana (G-6616)
Finelli Ornamental Iron Co ....F...... 440 248-0050
  Cleveland (G-5347)
Friends Ornamental Iron Co ....G...... 216 431-6710
  Cleveland (G-5382)
Geist Co Inc ....E...... 216 771-2200
  Cleveland (G-5406)
Gem City Metal Tech LLC ....E...... 937 252-8998
  Dayton (G-8362)
Gem Ornamental Iron Co ....G...... 216 661-6965
  Cleveland (G-5408)
GL Nause Co Inc ....E...... 513 722-9500
  Loveland (G-12353)
Graber Metal Works Inc ....E...... 440 237-8422
  North Royalton (G-15422)
Granite Industries Inc ....D...... 419 445-4733
  Archbold (G-679)
Gwp Holdings Inc ....D...... 513 860-4050
  Fairfield (G-9662)
Harsco Corporation ....E...... 740 387-1150
  Marion (G-12873)
Hrh Door Corp ....C...... 330 828-2291
  Dalton (G-8070)
Indian Creek Fabricators Inc ....E...... 937 667-7214
  Tipp City (G-18283)
James C Denier Co Inc ....G...... 513 385-6272
  Cincinnati (G-3939)
Jerry Harolds Doors Unlimited ....G...... 740 635-4949
  Bridgeport (G-2090)
Jim Denigris & Sons Ldscpg ....G...... 440 449-5548
  Cleveland (G-5615)
John A & William J Wiechart ....G...... 419 647-4617
  Spencerville (G-17461)
Joyce Manufacturing Co ....D...... 440 239-9100
  Berea (G-1624)
Lakeway Mfg Inc ....E...... 419 433-3030
  Huron (G-11232)
Langdon Inc ....E...... 513 733-5955
  Cincinnati (G-4011)
Lifetime Ironworks LLC ....G...... 419 443-0567
  Tiffin (G-18227)
M F Y Inc ....F...... 330 747-1334
  Youngstown (G-21137)
Mack Iron Works Company ....E...... 419 626-3712
  Sandusky (G-16984)
Mataco ....G...... 440 546-8355
  Broadview Heights (G-2114)
Metal Craft Docks Inc ....G...... 440 286-7135
  Mentor (G-13653)
Metal Maintenance Inc ....F...... 513 661-3300
  Cleves (G-6521)
Michaels Pre-Cast Con Pdts ....F...... 513 683-1292
  Loveland (G-12374)
Modern Builders Supply Inc ....C...... 330 729-2690
  Youngstown (G-21147)
Momentive Prfmce Mtls Qrtz Inc ....C...... 440 878-5700
  Strongsville (G-17941)
Newman Brothers Inc ....E...... 513 242-0011
  Cincinnati (G-4151)
Quality Architectural and Fabr ....F...... 937 743-2923
  Franklin (G-10046)
Rezmann Karoly ....G...... 216 441-4357
  Cleveland (G-6110)
Royalton Archtctral Fbrication ....F...... 440 582-0400
  North Royalton (G-15447)
Sausser Steel Company Inc ....F...... 419 422-9632
  Findlay (G-9888)
Schwab Welding Inc ....G...... 513 353-4262
  Cincinnati (G-4390)
Security Fence Group Inc ....E...... 513 681-3700
  Cincinnati (G-4395)
Sewah Studios Inc ....F...... 740 373-2087
  Marietta (G-12827)
Sine Wall LLC ....G...... 919 453-2011
  West Chester (G-19946)
Southern Ornamental Iron Co ....G...... 937 278-4319
  Dayton (G-8663)
Spillman Company ....E...... 614 444-2184
  Columbus (G-7644)
Stephens Pipe & Steel LLC ....C...... 740 869-2257
  Mount Sterling (G-14604)
Swanton Wldg Machining Co Inc ....D...... 419 826-4816
  Swanton (G-18091)
T E Martindale Enterprises ....G...... 614 253-6826
  Columbus (G-7673)

Tim Calvin Access Controls ....G...... 740 494-4200
  Radnor (G-16508)
Triangle Precision Industries ....D...... 937 299-6776
  Dayton (G-8723)
Van Dyke Custom Iron Inc ....G...... 614 860-9300
  Columbus (G-7732)
Viking Fabricators Inc ....E...... 740 374-5246
  Marietta (G-12848)
Wendell August Gift Sp & Forge ....F...... 330 893-3713
  Berlin (G-1653)
Wright Brothers Inc ....F...... 513 731-2222
  Cincinnati (G-4606)

METAL FABRICATORS: Plate

A A S Amels Sheet Meta L Inc ....E...... 330 793-9326
  Youngstown (G-21010)
A & E Butscha Co ....G...... 513 761-1919
  Cincinnati (G-3329)
A & G Manufacturing Co Inc ....E...... 419 468-7433
  Galion (G-10250)
A M Castle & Co ....D...... 330 425-7000
  Bedford (G-1394)
A Metalcraft Associates Inc ....G...... 937 693-4008
  Botkins (G-1949)
A P O Holdings Inc ....D...... 330 455-8925
  Canton (G-2585)
Acme Boiler Co Inc ....E...... 216 961-2471
  Cleveland (G-4691)
Advance Industrial Mfg Inc ....D...... 614 871-3333
  Grove City (G-10539)
Advanced Welding Co ....E...... 937 746-6800
  Franklin (G-10005)
Alpha Sintered Metals LLC ....F...... 330 220-5800
  Brunswick (G-2204)
American Tank & Fabricating Co ....D...... 216 252-1500
  Cleveland (G-4796)
Apex Welding Incorporated ....F...... 440 232-6770
  Bedford (G-1398)
Ares Inc ....D...... 419 635-2175
  Port Clinton (G-16393)
Armor Consolidated Inc ....C...... 513 923-5260
  Mason (G-12982)
Armor Metal Group Mason Inc ....C...... 513 769-0700
  Mason (G-12983)
Babcock & Wilcox Company ....A...... 330 753-4511
  Barberton (G-1104)
Baxter Holdings Inc ....E...... 513 860-3593
  Hamilton (G-10673)
Bico Akron Inc ....D...... 330 794-1716
  Mogadore (G-14369)
BJ Equipment Ltd ....F...... 614 497-1776
  Columbus (G-6834)
Blackwood Sheet Metal Inc ....G...... 614 291-3115
  Columbus (G-6839)
Blevins Metal Fabrication Inc ....E...... 419 522-6082
  Mansfield (G-12567)
Boochers Inc ....G...... 937 667-3414
  Tipp City (G-18265)
Breitinger Company ....C...... 419 526-4255
  Mansfield (G-12569)
Brighton Truedge ....E...... 513 771-2300
  Cincinnati (G-3474)
Brown-Singer Co ....F...... 513 422-9619
  Middletown (G-14024)
C & C Fabrication Inc ....E...... 419 354-3535
  Bowling Green (G-1975)
C & R Inc ....E...... 614 497-1130
  Groveport (G-10617)
C A Joseph Co ....C...... 330 532-4646
  Irondale (G-11287)
C Imperial Inc ....E...... 937 669-5620
  Tipp City (G-18268)
CA Litzler Co Inc ....E...... 216 267-8020
  Cleveland (G-4958)
Capital Tool Company ....E...... 216 661-5750
  Cleveland (G-4971)
Cardinal Pumps Exchangers Inc ....F...... 330 332-8558
  Salem (G-16878)
Ceco Environmental Corp ....E...... 513 874-8915
  West Chester (G-19987)
Ceco Group Inc ....E...... 513 458-2600
  Cincinnati (G-3510)
Cleveland Track Material Inc ....F...... 216 641-4000
  Cleveland (G-5083)
Commercial Mtal Fbricators Inc ....E...... 937 233-4911
  Dayton (G-8239)
Containment Solutions Inc ....C...... 419 874-8765
  Perrysburg (G-16078)
Contech Cnstr Pdts Hldings Inc ....G...... 513 645-7000
  West Chester (G-19839)

Contech Engnered Solutions Inc ....A...... 513 645-7000
  West Chester (G-19840)
Contech Engnered Solutions LLC ....D...... 513 645-7000
  Middletown (G-14032)
Contech Engnered Solutions LLC ....C...... 513 645-7000
  West Chester (G-19841)
Cramers Inc ....E...... 330 477-4571
  Canton (G-2670)
Curtiss-Wright Flow Ctrl Corp ....D...... 513 528-7900
  Cincinnati (G-3298)
David S Rodgers ....G...... 740 490-5843
  Plain City (G-16334)
Debra-Kuempel Inc ....D...... 513 271-6500
  Cincinnati (G-3645)
Defiance Metal Products Co ....B...... 419 784-5332
  Defiance (G-8785)
Deibel Manufacturing LLC ....G...... 330 482-3351
  Leetonia (G-11859)
Dover Tank and Plate Company ....E...... 330 343-4443
  Dover (G-8982)
Eagle Wldg & Fabrication Inc ....E...... 440 946-0692
  Willoughby (G-20478)
Eaton Fabricating Company Inc ....E...... 440 926-3121
  Grafton (G-10425)
Ebner Furnaces Inc ....D...... 330 335-2311
  Wadsworth (G-19404)
Efco Corp ....E...... 614 876-1226
  Columbus (G-7048)
Ellis & Watts Intl LLC ....G...... 513 752-9000
  Batavia (G-1183)
En-Hanced Products Inc ....G...... 614 882-7400
  Westerville (G-20213)
Fabco Inc ....E...... 419 421-4740
  Findlay (G-9820)
Fabrication Shop Inc ....F...... 419 435-7934
  Fostoria (G-9970)
Falls Welding & Fabg Inc ....G...... 330 253-3437
  Akron (G-180)
Farasey Steel Fabricators Inc ....F...... 216 641-1853
  Cleveland (G-5324)
Fulton Equipment Co ....G...... 419 290-5393
  Toledo (G-18475)
General Technologies Inc ....E...... 419 747-1800
  Mansfield (G-12612)
General Tool Company ....C...... 513 733-5500
  Cincinnati (G-3820)
GL Nause Co Inc ....E...... 513 722-9500
  Loveland (G-12353)
Graber Metal Works Inc ....E...... 440 237-8422
  North Royalton (G-15422)
Grenga Machine & Welding ....G...... 330 743-1113
  Youngstown (G-21104)
H P E Inc ....F...... 330 833-3161
  Massillon (G-13145)
Halvorsen Company ....E...... 216 341-7500
  Cleveland (G-5473)
Hammelmann Corporation ....F...... 937 859-8777
  Miamisburg (G-13814)
I L R Inc ....G...... 216 587-2212
  Cleveland (G-5546)
Indian Creek Fabricators Inc ....E...... 937 667-7214
  Tipp City (G-18283)
Industrial Container Svcs LLC ....E...... 513 921-2056
  Cincinnati (G-3916)
Industrial Container Svcs LLC ....E...... 513 921-8811
  Cincinnati (G-3917)
Industrial Container Svcs LLC ....D...... 614 864-1900
  Blacklick (G-1699)
Ironman Metalworks LLC ....G...... 614 907-6629
  Groveport (G-10628)
J B Kepple Sheet Metal ....G...... 740 393-2971
  Mount Vernon (G-14624)
Jergens Inc ....C...... 216 486-5540
  Cleveland (G-5610)
Jh Industries Inc ....E...... 330 963-4105
  Twinsburg (G-18961)
Kard Welding Inc ....E...... 419 628-2598
  Minster (G-14356)
Kendall Holdings Ltd ....E...... 614 486-4750
  Columbus (G-7255)
Kirk & Blum Manufacturing Co ....C...... 513 458-2600
  Cincinnati (G-3992)
Kirk & Blum Manufacturing Co ....E...... 419 782-9885
  Defiance (G-8798)
Langdon Inc ....E...... 513 733-5955
  Cincinnati (G-4011)
Lapham-Hickey Steel Corp ....E...... 614 443-4881
  Columbus (G-7286)
Lion Industries LLC ....E...... 740 699-0012
  Saint Clairsville (G-16794)

Long-Stanton Mfg Company ....E 513 874-8020
West Chester *(G-19895)*

Louis Arthur Steel Company ....G 440 997-5545
Geneva *(G-10352)*

Louis Arthur Steel Company ....G 440 997-5545
Uniontown *(G-19091)*

M T Metals LLC ....G 330 809-6465
Massillon *(G-13169)*

Mack Iron Works Company ....E 419 626-3712
Sandusky *(G-16984)*

McGill Airpressure LLC ....G 614 882-5455
Columbus *(G-7332)*

Metal Fabricating Corporation ....D 216 631-8121
Cleveland *(G-5787)*

Midwestern Industries Inc ....C 330 837-4203
Massillon *(G-13180)*

Moore Mr Specialty Company ....G 330 332-1229
Salem *(G-16916)*

Munroe Incorporated ....G 330 755-7216
Struthers *(G-17995)*

Myers Industries Inc ....C 330 336-6621
Wadsworth *(G-19420)*

Nbw Inc ....E 216 377-1700
Cleveland *(G-5864)*

New Wayne Inc ....G 740 453-3454
Zanesville *(G-21333)*

Northwest Installations Inc ....E 419 423-5738
Findlay *(G-9869)*

Oil Skimmers Inc ....E 440 237-4600
North Royalton *(G-15440)*

P B Fabrication Mech Contr ....F 419 478-4869
Toledo *(G-18631)*

Parker-Hannifin Corporation ....F 330 336-3511
Wadsworth *(G-19427)*

Pcy Enterprises Inc ....E 513 241-5566
Cincinnati *(G-4219)*

Pioneer Pipe Inc ....B 740 376-2400
Marietta *(G-12816)*

Prout Boiler Htg & Wldg Inc ....E 330 744-0293
Youngstown *(G-21180)*

Pucel Enterprises Inc ....D 216 881-4604
Cleveland *(G-6061)*

R B Mfg Co ....F 419 626-9464
Sandusky *(G-16999)*

Retays Welding Company ....E 440 327-4100
North Ridgeville *(G-15400)*

Sausser Steel Company Inc ....F 419 422-9632
Findlay *(G-9888)*

Schweizer Dipple Inc ....D 440 786-8090
Cleveland *(G-6167)*

Skinner Sales Group Inc ....E 440 572-8455
Strongsville *(G-17966)*

Snair Co ....F 614 873-7020
Plain City *(G-16360)*

Spradlin Bros Welding Co ....F 800 219-2182
Springfield *(G-17650)*

St Lawrence Steel Corporation ....E 330 562-9000
Streetsboro *(G-17878)*

Standard Welding & Steel Pdts ....F 330 273-2777
Medina *(G-13482)*

Steel & Alloy Utility Pdts Inc ....E 330 530-2220
Mc Donald *(G-13348)*

Steve Vore Welding and Steel ....F 419 375-4087
Fort Recovery *(G-9959)*

Sticker Corporation ....F 440 946-2100
Willoughby *(G-20606)*

Swagelok Company ....D 440 349-5934
Solon *(G-17392)*

Swanton Wldg Machining Co Inc ....D 419 826-4816
Swanton *(G-18091)*

Thermogenics Corp ....G 513 247-7963
Cincinnati *(G-4505)*

Triangle Precision Industries ....D 937 299-6776
Dayton *(G-8723)*

TW Tank LLC ....G 419 334-2664
Fremont *(G-10189)*

Universal Rack & Equipment Co ....E 330 963-6776
Twinsburg *(G-19033)*

Val-Co Pax Inc ....D 717 354-4586
Coldwater *(G-6573)*

Verhoff Machine & Welding Inc ....C 419 596-3202
Continental *(G-7829)*

Viking Fabricators Inc ....E 740 374-5246
Marietta *(G-12848)*

Vortec Corporation ....E 513 686-8210
Blue Ash *(G-1891)*

Warren Fabricating Corporation ....D 330 847-0596
Warren *(G-19621)*

Washington Products Inc ....F 330 837-5101
Massillon *(G-13211)*

Wcr Inc ....E 937 223-0703
Fairborn *(G-9635)*

Will-Burt Company ....E 330 682-7015
Orrville *(G-15772)*

Will-Burt Company ....B 330 682-7015
Orrville *(G-15770)*

METAL FABRICATORS: Sheet

A A S Amels Sheet Meta L Inc ....E 330 793-9326
Youngstown *(G-21010)*

A & C Welding Inc ....E 330 762-4777
Peninsula *(G-16032)*

A & E Butscha Co ....G 513 761-1919
Cincinnati *(G-3329)*

A & G Manufacturing Co Inc ....E 419 468-7433
Galion *(G-10250)*

A C Shutters Inc ....G 216 429-2424
Cleveland *(G-4669)*

A M Castle & Co ....D 330 425-7000
Bedford *(G-1394)*

Accufab Inc ....G 513 942-1929
West Chester *(G-19796)*

Acro Tool & Die Company ....D 330 773-5173
Akron *(G-29)*

Advance Metal Products Inc ....F 216 741-1800
Cleveland *(G-4709)*

Advanced Welding Co ....E 937 746-6800
Franklin *(G-10005)*

Aerolite Extrusion Company ....D 330 782-1127
Youngstown *(G-21018)*

Ahemco LLC ....F 513 385-0555
Cincinnati *(G-3368)*

Ahner Fabricating & Shtmtl Inc ....E 419 626-6641
Sandusky *(G-16945)*

Akron Foundry Co ....E 330 745-3101
Barberton *(G-1095)*

Alan Manufacturing Inc ....G 330 262-1555
Wooster *(G-20737)*

Aleris Rolled Products Inc ....D 740 983-2571
Ashville *(G-848)*

All Metal Fabricators Inc ....F 216 267-0033
Cleveland *(G-4755)*

Allen County Fabrication Inc ....E 419 227-7447
Lima *(G-11986)*

Allfab Inc ....F 614 491-4944
Columbus *(G-6723)*

Allied Mask and Tooling Inc ....G 419 470-2555
Toledo *(G-18329)*

Alloy Fabricators Inc ....E 330 948-3535
Lodi *(G-12156)*

Alro Steel Corporation ....E 419 720-5300
Toledo *(G-18331)*

Aluminum Color Industries Inc ....E 330 536-6295
Lowellville *(G-12404)*

Aluminum Extruded Shapes Inc ....C 513 563-2205
Cincinnati *(G-3383)*

AMD Fabricators Inc ....E 440 946-8855
Willoughby *(G-20429)*

American Frame Corporation ....D 419 893-5595
Maumee *(G-13222)*

Ampp Incorporated ....C 419 666-4747
Perrysburg *(G-16065)*

Anchor Metal Processing Inc ....F 216 362-6463
Cleveland *(G-4804)*

Anchor Metal Processing Inc ....E 216 362-1850
Cleveland *(G-4805)*

Andy Russo Jr Inc ....F 440 585-1456
Wickliffe *(G-20354)*

Anro Logistics Inc ....G 614 428-7490
Westerville *(G-20138)*

Antique Auto Sheet Metal Inc ....E 937 833-4422
Brookville *(G-2174)*

Armor Consolidated Inc ....E 513 923-5260
Mason *(G-12982)*

Armor Metal Group Mason Inc ....C 513 769-0700
Mason *(G-12983)*

Austintown Metal Works Inc ....F 330 259-4673
Youngstown *(G-21028)*

Autoneum North America Inc ....B 419 693-0511
Oregon *(G-15703)*

Avon Lake Sheet Metal Co ....E 440 933-3505
Avon Lake *(G-1025)*

Aztec Manufacturing Inc ....G 330 783-9747
Youngstown *(G-21030)*

B Y G Industries Inc ....G 216 961-5436
Cleveland *(G-4884)*

B-R-O-T Incorporated ....E 216 267-5335
Cleveland *(G-4886)*

Bainter Machining Company ....G 740 653-2422
Lancaster *(G-11691)*

Baltimore Fabricators Inc ....G 740 862-6016
Baltimore *(G-1080)*

Bayloff Stmped Pdts Knsman Inc ....D 330 876-4511
Kinsman *(G-11608)*

Berran Industrial Group Inc ....E 330 253-5800
Akron *(G-89)*

Bickers Metal Products Inc ....E 513 353-4000
Miamitown *(G-13884)*

BJ Equipment Ltd ....F 614 497-1776
Columbus *(G-6834)*

Blesco Services ....G 614 871-4900
Mount Sterling *(G-14596)*

Blevins Metal Fabrication Inc ....E 419 522-6082
Mansfield *(G-12567)*

Bob Lanes Welding Inc ....F 740 373-3567
Marietta *(G-12767)*

Bogie Industries Inc Ltd ....E 330 745-3105
Akron *(G-95)*

Breitinger Company ....C 419 526-4255
Mansfield *(G-12569)*

Buckeye Metal Works Inc ....F 614 239-8000
Columbus *(G-6873)*

Bud Corp ....G 740 967-9992
Johnstown *(G-11394)*

Budde Sheet Metal Works Inc ....E 937 224-0868
Dayton *(G-8202)*

Burt Manufacturing Company Inc ....C 330 762-0061
Akron *(G-105)*

Busch & Thiem Inc ....E 419 625-7515
Sandusky *(G-16952)*

C A Joseph Co ....E 330 532-4646
Irondale *(G-11287)*

C G C Systems Inc ....G 330 678-3261
Kent *(G-11437)*

C-N-D Industries Inc ....E 330 478-8811
Massillon *(G-13118)*

Cbr Industrial Llc ....G 419 645-6447
Wapakoneta *(G-19483)*

Centria Inc ....D 740 432-7351
Cambridge *(G-2451)*

Chagrin Metal Fabricating Inc ....G 440 946-6342
Eastlake *(G-9262)*

Champion Window Co of Toledo ....E 419 841-0154
Perrysburg *(G-16077)*

Chute Source LLC ....F 330 475-0377
Akron *(G-123)*

Cinfab LLC ....C 513 396-6100
Cincinnati *(G-3575)*

Cleveland Steel Specialty Co ....E 216 464-9400
Bedford Heights *(G-1481)*

Collier Well Eqp & Sup Inc ....F 330 345-3968
Wooster *(G-20760)*

Commercial Mtal Fbricators Inc ....E 937 233-4911
Dayton *(G-8239)*

Compco Industries Incorporated ....D 330 482-6488
Columbiana *(G-6614)*

Contech Engnered Solutions Inc ....A 513 645-7000
West Chester *(G-19840)*

Contech Engnered Solutions LLC ....D 513 645-7000
Middletown *(G-14032)*

Contech Engnered Solutions LLC ....G 614 477-1171
Columbus *(G-6977)*

Contech Engnered Solutions LLC ....C 513 645-7000
West Chester *(G-19841)*

Contour Forming Inc ....E 740 345-9777
Newark *(G-14996)*

COW Industries Inc ....E 614 443-6537
Columbus *(G-6992)*

Cramers Inc ....E 330 477-4571
Canton *(G-2670)*

CRC Metal Products ....G 740 966-0475
Johnstown *(G-11397)*

Custom Crete ....G 740 726-2433
Waldo *(G-19465)*

Custom Metal Shearing Inc ....F 937 233-6950
Dayton *(G-8260)*

Datco Mfg Company Inc ....E 330 781-6100
Youngstown *(G-21065)*

David Cox ....G 740 254-4858
Gnadenhutten *(G-10405)*

Decor Architectural Products ....G 419 537-9493
Toledo *(G-18432)*

Delafoil Pennsylvania Inc ....D 610 327-9565
Perrysburg *(G-16083)*

Di Lorio Sheet Metal Inc ....F 216 961-3703
Cleveland *(G-5187)*

Die-Cut Products Co ....E 216 771-6994
Cleveland *(G-5193)*

Dimensional Metals Inc ....D 740 927-3633
Reynoldsburg *(G-16586)*

Dover Tank and Plate Company .... E 330 343-4443
Dover (G-8982)

Duct Fabricators Inc .... G 216 391-2400
Cleveland (G-5219)

Ducts Inc .... E 216 391-2400
Cleveland (G-5220)

Duro Dyne Midwest Corp .... B 513 870-6000
Hamilton (G-10685)

Dynamic Weld Corporation .... E 419 582-2900
Osgood (G-15785)

E & K Products Co Inc .... G 216 631-2510
Cleveland (G-5229)

E B P Inc .... E 216 241-2550
Cleveland (G-5230)

Eagle Wldg & Fabrication Inc .... E 440 946-0692
Willoughby (G-20478)

Eaton Fabricating Company Inc .... E 440 926-3121
Grafton (G-10425)

Ebner Furnaces Inc .... D 330 335-2311
Wadsworth (G-19404)

Elsass Fabricating Ltd .... G 937 394-7169
Anna (G-622)

Enterprise Welding & Fabg Inc .... C 440 354-4128
Mentor (G-13574)

F M Sheet Metal Fabrication .... G 937 362-4357
Quincy (G-16503)

Fabco Inc .... E 419 421-4740
Findlay (G-9820)

Fabcraft Inc .... G 440 286-6700
Chardon (G-3152)

Fabricating Solutions Inc .... F 330 486-0998
Twinsburg (G-18933)

Fabrication Unlimited LLC .... G 937 492-3166
Sidney (G-17189)

Fabtech Ohio .... G 440 942-0811
Willoughby (G-20484)

Falcon Industries Inc .... E 330 723-0099
Medina (G-13409)

Famous Industries Inc .... C 740 397-8842
Mount Vernon (G-14622)

Firestone Sheet Metal Inc .... G 330 337-9551
Salem (G-16890)

First Francis Company Inc .... E 440 352-8927
Painesville (G-15881)

Flood Heliarc Inc .... F 614 835-3929
Groveport (G-10621)

Franck and Fric Incorporated .... D 216 524-4451
Cleveland (G-5377)

Franklin Frames and Cycles .... G 740 763-3838
Newark (G-15008)

Fred Winner .... E 419 582-2421
New Weston (G-14977)

Fulton Equipment Co .... G 419 290-5393
Toledo (G-18475)

G T Metal Fabricators Inc .... F 440 237-8745
Cleveland (G-5388)

Galion LLC .... E 419 468-5214
Galion (G-10268)

Galion-Godwin Truck Bdy Co LLC .... D 330 359-5495
Millersburg (G-14217)

Gaspar Inc .... D 330 477-2222
Canton (G-2711)

Gem City Metal Tech LLC .... E 937 252-8998
Dayton (G-8362)

General Technologies Inc .... E 419 747-1800
Mansfield (G-12612)

General Tool Company .... C 513 733-5500
Cincinnati (G-3820)

George Manufacturing Inc .... E 513 932-1067
Lebanon (G-11801)

Gilson Screen Incorporated .... E 419 256-7711
Malinta (G-12534)

GL Nause Co Inc .... E 513 722-9500
Loveland (G-12353)

Glunt Industries Inc .... C 330 399-7585
Warren (G-19555)

GNI Erectors .... G 614 465-7260
Galloway (G-10314)

Gomech Ltd .... G 419 419-4446
Maumee (G-13261)

Graber Metal Works Inc .... E 440 237-8422
North Royalton (G-15422)

Great Day Improvements LLC .... G 330 468-0700
Macedonia (G-12456)

Gunderson Rail Services LLC .... E 330 792-6521
Youngstown (G-21106)

Gundlach Sheet Metal Works Inc .... E 419 626-4525
Sandusky (G-16971)

Gwp Holdings Inc .... D 513 860-4050
Fairfield (G-9662)

H B Products Inc .... E 937 492-7031
Sidney (G-17191)

Hall Company .... E 937 652-1376
Urbana (G-19160)

Halls Sheet Metal Fabrication .... G 740 965-9264
Galena (G-10243)

Halvorsen Company .... E 216 341-7500
Cleveland (G-5473)

Harray LLC .... E 888 568-8371
Cincinnati (G-3867)

Harrison Mch & Plastic Corp .... E 330 569-3128
Garrettsville (G-10323)

Hartley Machine Inc .... G 330 821-0343
Alliance (G-513)

Hartzell Manufacturing Co Inc .... E 937 859-5955
Miamisburg (G-13815)

Heidtman Steel Products Inc .... E 216 641-6995
Cleveland (G-5494)

Hidaka Usa Inc .... E 614 889-8611
Dublin (G-9084)

Hoffman Machining & Repair LLC .... G 419 547-9204
Clyde (G-6540)

Holgate Metal Fab Inc .... F 419 599-2000
Napoleon (G-14682)

Home Sheet Metal & Roofing Co .... G 419 562-7806
Bucyrus (G-2348)

Hvac Inc .... F 330 343-5511
Dover (G-8991)

Indian Creek Fabricators Inc .... E 937 667-7214
Tipp City (G-18283)

Induction Iron Incorporated .... G 330 501-8852
Youngstown (G-21114)

Industrial Hanger Conveyor Co .... G 419 332-2661
Fremont (G-10158)

Industrial Mill Maintenance .... E 330 746-1155
Youngstown (G-21115)

Isaiah Industries Inc .... E 937 773-9840
Piqua (G-16280)

Izit Cain Sheet Metal Corp .... E 937 667-6521
Tipp City (G-18284)

J & L Welding Fabricating Inc .... F 330 393-9353
Warren (G-19561)

J B Kepple Sheet Metal .... G 740 393-2971
Mount Vernon (G-14624)

Jacobs Mechanical Co .... C 513 681-6800
Cincinnati (G-3937)

Jeffery A Burns .... E 419 845-2129
Caledonia (G-2439)

Jh Industries Inc .... E 330 963-4105
Twinsburg (G-18961)

Jim Nier Construction Inc .... F 740 289-3925
Piketon (G-16222)

Johnson-Nash Metal Pdts Inc .... F 513 874-7022
Fairfield (G-9671)

Joining Metals Inc .... F 440 259-1790
Perry (G-16051)

Joseph T Ryerson & Son Inc .... D 513 542-5800
Columbus (G-7245)

Kerber Sheetmetal Works Inc .... F 937 339-6366
Troy (G-18852)

Kettering Roofing & Shtmtl .... F 513 281-6413
Cincinnati (G-3986)

Kilroy Company .... D 440 951-8700
Eastlake (G-9278)

Kirk Williams Company Inc .... D 614 875-9023
Grove City (G-10568)

Knight Manufacturing Co Inc .... E 740 676-5516
Shadyside (G-17082)

Korda Manufacturing Inc .... D 330 262-1555
Wooster (G-20797)

Kramer Power Equipment Co .... F 937 456-2232
Eaton (G-9313)

Kuhlman Engineering Co .... F 419 243-2196
Toledo (G-18549)

L&M Sheet Metal Ltd .... G 513 858-6173
Fairfield (G-9676)

Lake Shore Electric Corp .... E 440 232-0200
Bedford (G-1438)

Lima Sheet Metal Machine & Mfg .... E 419 229-1161
Lima (G-12045)

Locker Konnection Services LLC .... G 419 334-3956
Fremont (G-10166)

Long-Stanton Mfg Company .... E 513 874-8020
West Chester (G-19895)

Louis Arthur Steel Company .... G 440 997-5545
Geneva (G-10352)

Louis Arthur Steel Company .... G 440 997-5545
Uniontown (G-19091)

Lowry Furnace Company Inc .... G 330 745-4822
Akron (G-276)

LSI Industries Inc .... E 513 793-3200
Blue Ash (G-1829)

Lt Enterprises of Ohio LLC .... E 330 526-6908
North Canton (G-15247)

Lund Equipment Co Inc .... E 330 659-4800
Bath (G-1238)

M H EBY Inc .... E 614 879-6901
West Jefferson (G-20081)

M3 Technologies Inc .... F 216 898-9936
Cleveland (G-5721)

Mack Iron Works Company .... E 419 626-3712
Sandusky (G-16984)

Maines Brothers Tin Shop .... G 937 393-1633
Hillsboro (G-11008)

Mantych Metalworking Inc .... E 937 258-1373
Dayton (G-8111)

Marsam Metalfab Inc .... E 330 405-1520
Twinsburg (G-18978)

Martina Metal LLC .... E 614 291-9700
Columbus (G-7321)

McGill Airflow LLC .... F 614 829-1200
Columbus (G-7331)

McWane Inc .... B 740 622-6651
Coshocton (G-7897)

Medway Tool Corp .... E 937 335-7717
Troy (G-18857)

Meese Inc .... D 440 998-1202
Ashtabula (G-819)

Mestek Inc .... D 419 288-2703
Holland (G-11072)

Mestek Inc .... D 419 288-2703
Bradner (G-2029)

Met L Fab Inc .... F 513 561-4289
Cincinnati (G-4088)

Metal Technology Systems Inc .... G 513 563-1882
Cincinnati (G-4089)

Metal-Max Inc .... G 330 673-9926
Kent (G-11489)

Metalworking Group Holdings .... C 513 521-4119
Cincinnati (G-4091)

Metlweb .... E 513 563-8822
Cincinnati (G-4093)

Metrodeck Inc .... F 513 541-4370
Cincinnati (G-4095)

Michael Fabricating Inc .... G 330 325-8636
Rootstown (G-16724)

Mid-Ohio Products Inc .... D 614 771-2795
Hilliard (G-10962)

Midwest Metal Fabricators .... F 419 739-7077
Wapakoneta (G-19499)

Midwest Metal Fabricators .... F 419 739-7077
Wapakoneta (G-19500)

Midwest Metal Products LLC .... E 614 539-7322
Grove City (G-10573)

Mika Metal Fabricating Co .... E 440 951-5500
Willoughby (G-20549)

Mike Loppe .... F 937 969-8102
Tremont City (G-18789)

Mings Heating & AC .... G 216 721-2007
Cleveland (G-5821)

Modern Ice Equipment & Sup Co .... E 513 367-2101
Cincinnati (G-4115)

MRS Industrial Inc .... E 614 308-1070
Columbus (G-7372)

Muehlenkamp Properties Inc .... E 513 745-0874
Cincinnati (G-4130)

N Wasserstrom & Sons Inc .... C 614 228-5550
Columbus (G-7377)

Nel-Ack Sheet Metal Inc .... G 440 357-7844
Painesville (G-15903)

Niles Manufacturing & Finshg .... C 330 544-0402
Niles (G-15171)

Nissin Precision N Amer Inc .... D 937 836-1910
Englewood (G-9536)

Norstar Aluminum Molds Inc .... D 440 632-0853
Middlefield (G-13977)

North Coast Profile Inc .... G 330 823-7777
Alliance (G-531)

Northwest Installations Inc .... E 419 423-5738
Findlay (G-9869)

Northwind Industries Inc .... E 216 433-0666
Cleveland (G-5916)

Nufab Sheet Metal .... G 937 235-2030
Dayton (G-8535)

Ohio Blow Pipe Company .... E 216 681-7379
Cleveland (G-5930)

Ohio Gratings Inc .... B 330 477-6707
Canton (G-2799)

Ohio Steel Sheet & Plate Inc .... E 800 827-2401
Hubbard (G-11136)

Ohio Trailer Inc F 330 392-4444
Warren *(G-19584)*
Options Plus Incorporated F 740 694-9811
Fredericktown *(G-10108)*
P & L Metalcrafts LLC F 330 793-2178
Youngstown *(G-21160)*
P B Fabrication Mech Contr F 419 478-4869
Toledo *(G-18631)*
Parker-Hannifin Corporation F 330 336-3511
Wadsworth *(G-19427)*
Patterson & Sons Inc F 419 281-0897
Nova *(G-15579)*
Paul Wilke & Son Inc F 513 921-3163
Cincinnati *(G-4217)*
Pcy Enterprises Inc E 513 241-5566
Cincinnati *(G-4219)*
Pei Liquidation Company C 330 467-4267
Macedonia *(G-12470)*
Pei Liquidation Company E 615 781-5020
Macedonia *(G-12471)*
Pennant Moldings Inc C 937 584-5411
Sabina *(G-16775)*
Phillips Awning Co G 740 653-2433
Lancaster *(G-11738)*
Phillips Manufacturing Co D 330 652-4335
Niles *(G-15173)*
Phillips Shtmtl Fabrications G 937 223-2722
Dayton *(G-8572)*
Pioneer Fabrication G 419 737-9464
Alvordton *(G-558)*
Plas-Tanks Industries Inc E 513 942-3800
Hamilton *(G-10730)*
Precise Metal Form Inc F 419 636-5221
Bryan *(G-2319)*
Precision Mtal Fabrication Inc D 937 235-9261
Dayton *(G-8587)*
Precision Steel Services Inc D 419 476-5702
Toledo *(G-18654)*
Precision Welding Corporation E 216 524-6110
Cleveland *(G-6037)*
Premier Stamping and Assembly G 440 293-8961
Williamsfield *(G-20416)*
Priest Millwright Service G 937 780-3405
Leesburg *(G-11856)*
Production Manufacturing Inc E 513 892-2331
Hamilton *(G-10731)*
Prototype Fabricators Co G 216 252-0080
Cleveland *(G-6058)*
Providence Group Inc E 440 350-4615
Mentor *(G-13703)*
Quality Craftsman Inc F 740 474-9685
Circleville *(G-4639)*
Quality Steel Fabrication F 937 492-9503
Sidney *(G-17213)*
Quass Sheet Metal Inc G 330 477-4841
Canton *(G-2831)*
R B Mfg Co F 419 626-9464
Sandusky *(G-16999)*
R L Torbeck Industries Inc D 513 367-0080
Harrison *(G-10800)*
Raka Corporation D 419 476-6572
Toledo *(G-18671)*
Range One Products & Fabg F 330 533-1151
Canfield *(G-2571)*
Rapid Machine Inc F 419 737-2377
Pioneer *(G-16243)*
Related Metals Inc G 330 799-4866
Canfield *(G-2572)*
Rexam Beverage Can Company C 419 334-4461
Fremont *(G-10178)*
Rezmann Karoly G 216 441-4357
Cleveland *(G-6110)*
Ridge Enterprises Inc G 740 867-3456
Chesapeake *(G-3190)*
Ridgeview Sheet Metal G 330 674-3768
Millersburg *(G-14259)*
Robinson Fin Machines Inc E 419 674-4152
Kenton *(G-11567)*
Rockwell Metals Company LLC F 440 242-2420
Lorain *(G-12273)*
Roconex Corporation F 937 339-2616
Troy *(G-18868)*
Romar Metal Fabricating Inc G 740 682-7731
Oak Hill *(G-15606)*
Royalton Archtctral Fbrication F 440 582-0400
North Royalton *(G-15447)*
S & B Metal Products Inc E 330 487-5790
Twinsburg *(G-19015)*
S & D Architectural Metals G 440 582-2560
North Royalton *(G-15451)*
S & G Manufacturing Group LLC C 614 529-0100
Hilliard *(G-10977)*
S & R Sheet Metal G 937 865-9236
Dayton *(G-8642)*
Sausser Steel Company Inc F 419 422-9632
Findlay *(G-9888)*
Schoonover Industries Inc E 419 289-8332
Ashland *(G-776)*
Schweizer Dipple Inc D 440 786-8090
Cleveland *(G-6167)*
Selmco Metal Fabricators Inc F 937 498-1331
Sidney *(G-17224)*
Seneca Sheet Metal Company F 419 447-8434
Tiffin *(G-18244)*
Shaffer Metal Fab Inc E 937 492-1384
Sidney *(G-17225)*
Sheet Angle Bar Met Fbrication G 513 829-8600
Fairfield *(G-9716)*
Sheet Metal Products Co Inc E 440 392-9000
Mentor *(G-13722)*
Shriner Sheet Metal Inc F 330 435-6735
Creston *(G-7943)*
Sidney Manufacturing Company E 937 492-4154
Sidney *(G-17227)*
Smith Rn Sheet Metal Shop Inc E 740 653-5011
Lancaster *(G-11753)*
Snair Co F 614 873-7020
Plain City *(G-16360)*
Somerville Manufacturing Inc E 740 336-7847
Marietta *(G-12834)*
Spradlin Bros Welding Co F 800 219-2182
Springfield *(G-17650)*
Staber Industries Inc E 614 836-5995
Groveport *(G-10645)*
Standard Technologies LLC D 419 332-6434
Fremont *(G-10183)*
Starr Fabricating Inc D 330 394-9891
Vienna *(G-19376)*
Steel & Alloy Utility Pdts Inc E 330 530-2220
Mc Donald *(G-13348)*
Steelial Wldg Met Fbrction Inc E 740 669-5300
Vinton *(G-19383)*
Steve Vore Welding and Steel F 419 375-4087
Fort Recovery *(G-9959)*
Suburban Metal Products Inc F 740 474-4237
Circleville *(G-4644)*
Sulecki Precision Products F 440 255-5454
Mentor *(G-13740)*
Super Sheet Metal G 330 482-9045
Leetonia *(G-11866)*
Swanton Wldg Machining Co Inc D 419 826-4816
Swanton *(G-18091)*
Systech Handling Inc F 419 445-8226
Archbold *(G-696)*
Tangent Air Inc E 740 474-1114
Circleville *(G-4645)*
Tectum Inc C 740 345-9691
Newark *(G-15063)*
Tendon Manufacturing Inc E 216 663-3200
Cleveland *(G-6305)*
Tex-Tyler Corporation E 419 729-4951
Toledo *(G-18720)*
TL Industries Inc C 419 666-8144
Northwood *(G-15490)*
Tool & Die Systems Inc E 440 327-5800
North Ridgeville *(G-15406)*
Torok Supply Company G 330 799-6677
Youngstown *(G-21224)*
Tower Tool & Manufacturing Co F 330 425-1623
Twinsburg *(G-19028)*
Tri-Fab Inc E 330 337-3425
Salem *(G-16931)*
Tri-Mac Mfg & Svcs Co F 513 896-4445
Hamilton *(G-10749)*
Tri-State Fabricators Inc E 513 752-5005
Amelia *(G-587)*
Triangle Precision Industries D 937 299-6776
Dayton *(G-8723)*
Tricor Industrial Inc D 330 264-3299
Wooster *(G-20841)*
Tru Form Metal Products Inc G 216 252-3700
Cleveland *(G-6368)*
Unison Industries LLC D 937 426-4676
Alpha *(G-555)*
Universal Steel Company D 216 883-4972
Cleveland *(G-6392)*
V & S Schuler Engineering Inc D 330 452-5200
Canton *(G-2893)*
V M Systems Inc D 419 535-1044
Toledo *(G-18763)*
Valley Metal Works Inc E 513 554-1022
Cincinnati *(G-4553)*
Verhoff Machine & Welding Inc C 419 596-3202
Continental *(G-7829)*
Vicart Prcsion Fabricators Inc E 614 771-0080
Hilliard *(G-10992)*
Visual Information Institute F 937 376-4361
Xenia *(G-20985)*
Vortex Metals Ltd G 216 365-2300
Warrensville Heights *(G-19636)*
W & W Custom Fabrication Inc G 513 353-4617
Hamilton *(G-10755)*
W J Egli Company Inc F 330 823-3666
Alliance *(G-551)*
Waino Sheet Metal Inc G 330 945-4226
Stow *(G-17816)*
Warner Fabricating Inc F 330 848-3191
Wadsworth *(G-19443)*
Warren Fabricating Corporation D 330 847-0596
Warren *(G-19621)*
Waterville Sheet Metal Company G 419 878-5050
Waterville *(G-19670)*
Weber Technologies Inc E 440 946-8833
Eastlake *(G-9297)*
Wheeler Sheet Metal Inc G 419 668-0481
Norwalk *(G-15566)*
Will-Burt Company B 330 682-7015
Orrville *(G-15770)*
William Weber G 440 350-9397
Painesville *(G-15941)*
Worthington Steel Company G 513 702-0130
Middletown *(G-14100)*
Ysd Industries Inc D 330 792-6521
Youngstown *(G-21260)*

METAL FABRICATORS: Structural, Ship

Morrison Custom Welding Inc F 330 264-0626
Wooster *(G-20811)*

METAL FINISHING SVCS

Allen Aircraft Products Inc E 330 296-1531
Ravenna *(G-16515)*
Aluminum Color Industries Inc E 330 536-6295
Lowellville *(G-12404)*
Amac Enterprises Inc C 216 362-1880
Parma *(G-15954)*
Anodizing Specialists Inc F 440 951-0257
Mentor *(G-13523)*
Atom Blasting & Finishing Inc G 440 235-4765
Columbia Station *(G-6580)*
Autocoat G 419 636-3830
Bryan *(G-2280)*
Bar Processing Corporation D 330 872-0914
Newton Falls *(G-15129)*
Bill J Jernigan Inc D 937 264-1598
Vandalia *(G-19283)*
Chrome & Speed Cycle LLC G 937 429-5656
Beavercreek *(G-1323)*
Cleveland Finishing Inc G 440 572-5475
Strongsville *(G-17904)*
CMF Custom Metal Finishers G 513 821-8145
Cincinnati *(G-3592)*
Electro Polish Company Inc E 937 222-3611
Dayton *(G-8322)*
Equinox Enterprises LLC F 419 627-0022
Sandusky *(G-16964)*
Foundry Support Operation F 440 951-4142
Mentor *(G-13581)*
Gateway Metal Finishing Inc E 216 267-2580
Cleveland *(G-5401)*
H & R Metal Finishing Inc G 440 942-6656
Willoughby *(G-20502)*
Hayes Metalfinishing Inc G 937 228-7550
Dayton *(G-8386)*
Heatstar G 440 701-1031
Mentor *(G-13600)*
Jotco Inc G 513 721-4943
Mansfield *(G-12630)*
Kel-Mar Inc E 419 806-4600
Bowling Green *(G-1994)*
M I P Inc F 330 744-0215
Youngstown *(G-21138)*
Metal Finishers Inc F 937 492-9175
Sidney *(G-17201)*
Metal Improvement Company LLC E 330 425-1490
Twinsburg *(G-18985)*
Micro Metal Finishing LLC D 513 541-3095
Cincinnati *(G-4100)*
Northeast Coatings Inc F 330 784-7773
Tallmadge *(G-18159)*

Oerlikon Blzers Cating USA Inc ... E ... 330 220-7716
Brunswick *(G-2240)*
Ohio Anodizing Company Inc ... F ... 614 252-7855
Columbus *(G-7414)*
P & J Manufacturing Inc ... F ... 419 241-7369
Toledo *(G-18630)*
REA Polishing Inc ... D ... 419 470-0216
Toledo *(G-18672)*
Russell Products Co Inc ... G ... 330 535-3391
Akron *(G-386)*
Stricker Refinishing Inc ... G ... 216 696-2906
Cleveland *(G-6253)*
Superfinishers Inc ... G ... 330 467-2125
Macedonia *(G-12492)*
Tablox Inc ... G ... 440 953-1951
Willoughby *(G-20608)*
Tatham Schulz Incorporated ... E ... 216 861-4431
Cleveland *(G-6295)*
Toledo Metal Finishing Inc ... G ... 419 661-1422
Northwood *(G-15491)*
Trans-Acc Inc ... E ... 513 793-6410
Blue Ash *(G-1883)*
Weber Technologies Inc ... E ... 440 946-8833
Eastlake *(G-9297)*

METAL MINING SVCS

Alloy Metal Exchange LLC ... E ... 216 478-0200
Bedford Heights *(G-1477)*
Hopedale Mining LLC ... E ... 740 937-2225
Hopedale *(G-11118)*
Metokote Corporation ... G ... 419 996-7800
Lima *(G-12058)*
Mining Reclamation Inc ... F ... 740 327-5555
Dresden *(G-9033)*

METAL RESHAPING & REPLATING SVCS

A Metalcraft Associates Inc ... G ... 937 693-4008
Botkins *(G-1949)*
Machine Tool Design & Fab LLC ... F ... 419 435-7676
Fostoria *(G-9984)*
Space Age Coatings LLC ... G ... 937 275-5117
Dayton *(G-8665)*

METAL SERVICE CENTERS & OFFICES

A J Oster Foils LLC ... D ... 330 823-1700
Alliance *(G-486)*
A M Castle & Co ... D ... 330 425-7000
Bedford *(G-1394)*
Aluminum Line Products Company ... D ... 440 835-8880
Westlake *(G-20249)*
American Ir Met Cleveland LLC ... E ... 216 266-0518
Cleveland *(G-4786)*
American Tank & Fabricating Co ... D ... 216 252-1500
Cleveland *(G-4796)*
Atlas Bolt & Screw Company LLC ... C ... 419 289-6171
Ashland *(G-709)*
Canfield Coating LLC ... C ... 330 533-3311
Canfield *(G-2550)*
Canfield Metal Coating Corp ... D ... 330 702-3876
Canfield *(G-2551)*
Clifton Steel Company ... D ... 216 662-6111
Maple Heights *(G-12731)*
D & D Metal Supply Inc ... F ... 513 272-1246
Cincinnati *(G-3629)*
D T Kothera Inc ... G ... 440 632-1651
Middlefield *(G-13930)*
EPI of Cleveland Inc ... G ... 330 468-2872
Twinsburg *(G-18929)*
General Steel Corporation ... F ... 216 883-4200
Cleveland *(G-5421)*
Graber Metal Works Inc ... E ... 440 237-8422
North Royalton *(G-15422)*
Hynes Industries Inc ... C ... 330 799-3221
Youngstown *(G-21111)*
Industrial Wire Rope Sup Inc ... G ... 513 941-2443
Cincinnati *(G-3919)*
Kirtland Capital Partners LP ... E ... 216 593-0100
Beachwood *(G-1276)*
Matandy Steel & Metal Pdts LLC ... D ... 513 844-2277
Hamilton *(G-10723)*
Materion Brush Inc ... E ... 440 960-5660
Lorain *(G-12260)*
Mid-America Steel Corp ... E ... 800 282-3466
Cleveland *(G-5805)*
Modern Welding Co Ohio Inc ... E ... 740 344-9425
Newark *(G-15035)*
Monarch Steel Company Inc ... E ... 216 587-8000
Cleveland *(G-5830)*
National Bronze and Metals ... E ... 440 277-1226
Lorain *(G-12261)*
Ohio Steel Sheet & Plate Inc ... E ... 800 827-2401
Hubbard *(G-11136)*
Panacea Products Corporation ... E ... 614 850-7000
Columbus *(G-7456)*
Perfection Metal Co ... G ... 216 641-0949
Cleveland *(G-5992)*
Samuel Steel Pickling Company ... E ... 330 963-3777
Twinsburg *(G-19016)*
Springtime Manufacturing ... G ... 419 697-3720
Toledo *(G-18702)*
Stein Inc ... D ... 440 277-6148
Lorain *(G-12281)*
Summit Resources Group Inc ... G ... 330 653-3992
Hudson *(G-11203)*
The Mansfield Strl & Erct Co ... F ... 419 522-5911
Mansfield *(G-12695)*
Thyssenkrupp Materials NA Inc ... D ... 216 883-8100
Independence *(G-11277)*
Tomson Steel Company ... E ... 513 420-8600
Middletown *(G-14089)*
Tricor Industrial Inc ... D ... 330 264-3299
Wooster *(G-20841)*
Tsk America Co Ltd ... F ... 513 942-4002
West Chester *(G-20062)*
Watteredge LLC ... D ... 440 933-6110
Avon Lake *(G-1055)*
Western Reserve Metals Inc ... E ... 330 448-4092
Masury *(G-13218)*
Worthington Industries Inc ... C ... 513 539-9291
Monroe *(G-14420)*
Worthngton Stelpac Systems LLC ... C ... 614 438-3205
Columbus *(G-7778)*
Worthngton Stl Cmpny-Baltimore ... E ... 410 574-5835
Worthington *(G-20901)*

METAL SLITTING & SHEARING

Cctm Inc ... G ... 513 934-3533
Lebanon *(G-11788)*
Crest Products Inc ... F ... 440 942-5770
Mentor *(G-13556)*
Custom Metal Shearing Inc ... F ... 937 233-6950
Dayton *(G-8260)*
Metal Shredders Inc ... E ... 937 866-0777
Miamisburg *(G-13830)*
Pettit W T & Sons Co Inc ... G ... 330 539-6100
Girard *(G-10392)*
Samuel Steel Pickling Company ... E ... 330 963-3777
Twinsburg *(G-19016)*
Shear Service Inc ... G ... 216 341-2700
Cleveland *(G-6185)*

METAL SPINNING FOR THE TRADE

Artistic Metal Spinning Inc ... G ... 216 961-3336
Cleveland *(G-4839)*
Atra Metal Spinning Inc ... F ... 440 354-9525
Painesville *(G-15853)*
Dayton United Metal Spinners ... F ... 937 222-6732
Tipp City *(G-18275)*
Deshler Metal Working Co Inc ... G ... 419 278-0472
Deshler *(G-8949)*
Elyria Mtal Spnning Fbrication ... G ... 440 323-8068
Elyria *(G-9414)*
Gem City Metal Tech LLC ... E ... 937 252-8998
Dayton *(G-8362)*
Hukon Manufacturing Company ... G ... 513 721-5562
Cincinnati *(G-3901)*
Imperial Metal Spinning Co ... G ... 216 524-5020
Cleveland *(G-5557)*
J Schrader Co ... F ... 216 961-2890
Cleveland *(G-5601)*
Lewark Metal Spinning Inc ... E ... 937 275-3303
Dayton *(G-8457)*
McGlennon Metal Products Inc ... F ... 614 252-7114
Columbus *(G-7335)*
Ottawa Products Co ... E ... 419 836-5115
Curtice *(G-7958)*
Toledo Metal Spinning Company ... E ... 419 535-5931
Toledo *(G-18733)*

METAL STAMPING, FOR THE TRADE

Accurate Tool Co Inc ... G ... 330 332-9448
Salem *(G-16868)*
Acro Tool & Die Company ... D ... 330 773-5173
Akron *(G-29)*
Amclo Group Inc ... C ... 216 791-8400
Cleveland *(G-4776)*
American Tool and Die Inc ... F ... 419 726-5394
Toledo *(G-18346)*
Andre Corporation ... E ... 574 293-0207
Mason *(G-12981)*
Boehm Pressed Steel Company ... E ... 330 220-8000
Valley City *(G-19200)*
Brainin-Advance Industries LLC ... E ... 513 874-9760
West Chester *(G-19821)*
Central Ohio Metal Stampi ... E ... 614 861-3332
Columbus *(G-6918)*
Cleveland Metal Stamping Co ... F ... 440 234-0010
Berea *(G-1607)*
Continental Business Entps Inc ... F ... 440 439-4400
Cleveland *(G-5123)*
D & L Manufacturing ... G ... 440 428-1627
Madison *(G-12503)*
Dependable Stamping Company ... E ... 216 486-5522
Cleveland *(G-5184)*
Dyco Manufacturing Inc ... F ... 419 485-5525
Montpelier *(G-14444)*
Eagle Precision Products LLC ... G ... 440 582-9393
North Royalton *(G-15418)*
Eisenhauer Manufacturing Co ... E ... 419 238-0081
Van Wert *(G-19256)*
Ernst Metal Technologies LLC ... E ... 937 434-3133
Moraine *(G-14485)*
Exline Manufacturing Co Inc ... G ... 937 866-1515
Miamisburg *(G-13808)*
Falls Stamping & Welding Co ... C ... 330 928-1191
Cuyahoga Falls *(G-7996)*
Falls Tool & Die Incorporated ... G ... 330 633-4884
Akron *(G-179)*
Famous Industries Inc ... D ... 740 685-2592
Byesville *(G-2401)*
Faull & Son LLC ... F ... 330 652-4341
Niles *(G-15152)*
G & M Metal Products Inc ... G ... 513 863-3353
Hamilton *(G-10695)*
Guarantee Specialties Inc ... D ... 216 451-9744
Strongsville *(G-17923)*
H&M Mtal Stamping Assembly Inc ... F ... 216 898-9030
Brookpark *(G-2163)*
Hill Manufacturing Inc ... E ... 419 335-5006
Wauseon *(G-19682)*
Hpl Stampings Inc ... G ... 440 582-9794
Cleveland *(G-5531)*
Impact Industries Inc ... E ... 440 327-2360
North Ridgeville *(G-15380)*
Independent Stamping Inc ... E ... 216 251-3500
Cleveland *(G-5563)*
Interlake Industries Inc ... G ... 440 942-0800
Willoughby *(G-20512)*
K & H Industries LLC ... F ... 513 921-6770
Cincinnati *(G-3964)*
K & L Die & Manufacturing ... G ... 419 895-1301
Greenwich *(G-10532)*
Knowlton Manufacturing Co Inc ... F ... 513 631-7353
Cincinnati *(G-3999)*
L & W Inc ... D ... 734 397-6300
Avon *(G-999)*
L C I Inc ... G ... 330 948-1922
Lodi *(G-12163)*
La Ganke & Sons Stamping Co ... F ... 216 451-0278
Columbia Station *(G-6590)*
Lextech Industries Ltd ... G ... 216 883-7900
Cleveland *(G-5694)*
Mahoning Valley Manufacturing ... E ... 330 537-4492
Beloit *(G-1584)*
Mark True Engraving Co ... G ... 216 651-7700
Cleveland *(G-5745)*
Master Products Company ... D ... 216 341-1740
Cleveland *(G-5760)*
Metal Fabricating Corporation ... D ... 216 631-8121
Cleveland *(G-5787)*
Neway Stamping & Mfg Inc ... D ... 440 951-8500
Willoughby *(G-20554)*
Ohi-TEC Manufacturing Inc ... E ... 937 882-6144
Dayton *(G-8542)*
Ohio Gasket and Shim Co Inc ... E ... 330 630-0626
Akron *(G-323)*
Ohio Valley Manufacturing Inc ... D ... 419 522-5818
Mansfield *(G-12662)*
Paramount Stamping & Wldg Co ... D ... 216 631-1755
Cleveland *(G-5964)*
Pfahl Gauge & Manufacturing Co ... G ... 330 633-8402
Akron *(G-337)*
Quality Stamping Products Co ... F ... 216 441-2700
Cleveland *(G-6075)*
R L Rush Tool & Pattern Inc ... G ... 419 562-9849
Bucyrus *(G-2356)*

RB&w Manufacturing LLC ....G....... 740 363-1971
Delaware (G-8881)

RB&w Manufacturing LLC ....F....... 234 380-8540
Streetsboro (G-17870)

Regal Metal Products Co ....E....... 330 868-6343
Minerva (G-14339)

Ronfeldt Associates Inc ....D....... 419 382-5641
Toledo (G-18680)

Ronlen Industries Inc ....E....... 330 273-6468
Brunswick (G-2255)

Sadler Corporation ....G....... 330 688-7400
Stow (G-17796)

Schott Metal Products Company ....D....... 330 773-7873
Akron (G-397)

Service Stampings Inc ....E....... 440 946-2330
Willoughby (G-20593)

Stolle Machinery Company LLC ....C....... 937 497-5400
Sidney (G-17230)

Stuebing Automatic Machine Co ....E....... 513 771-8028
Cincinnati (G-4473)

Sunfield Inc ....D....... 740 928-0404
Hebron (G-10887)

Superior Steel Stamp Co ....E....... 216 431-6460
Cleveland (G-6271)

Supply Technologies LLC ....C....... 440 947-2100
Cleveland (G-6274)

Transue & Williams Stampg Corp ....D....... 330 821-5777
Alliance (G-546)

Transue Williams Stamping Inc ....G....... 330 270-0891
Austintown (G-976)

Transue Williams Stamping Inc ....G....... 330 829-5007
Alliance (G-547)

Triad Metal Products Company ....D....... 216 676-6505
Chagrin Falls (G-3128)

United Die & Mfg Co ....E....... 330 938-6141
Sebring (G-17056)

Universal Industrial Pdts Inc ....F....... 419 737-9584
Pioneer (G-16245)

V K C Inc ....F....... 440 951-9634
Mentor (G-13764)

Weber Technologies Inc ....E....... 440 946-8833
Eastlake (G-9297)

Winco Stamping Inc ....G....... 937 859-5522
Miamisburg (G-13881)

WLS Stamping Co ....D....... 216 271-5100
Cleveland (G-6472)

METAL STAMPINGS: Ornamental

Catania Medallic Specialty ....E....... 440 933-9595
Avon Lake (G-1026)

Connaughton Wldg & Fence LLC ....G....... 513 867-0230
Hamilton (G-10680)

Pacific Manufacturing Tenn Inc ....E....... 513 900-7862
Jackson (G-11324)

METAL STAMPINGS: Patterned

Durivage Pattern & Mfg Co ....E....... 419 836-8655
Williston (G-20420)

Hynes Modern Pattern Co Inc ....G....... 937 322-3451
Springfield (G-17579)

Mallory Pattern Works Inc ....G....... 419 726-8001
Toledo (G-18572)

Q Model Inc ....E....... 330 673-0473
Barberton (G-1144)

Seilkop Industries Inc ....E....... 513 761-1035
Cincinnati (G-4398)

METAL TREATING COMPOUNDS

Broco Products Inc ....G....... 216 531-0880
Cleveland (G-4933)

Ferrum Industries Inc ....G....... 440 519-1768
Twinsburg (G-18935)

Foseco Inc ....G....... 440 826-4548
Cleveland (G-5374)

Magnesium Technologies Corp ....G....... 330 659-3003
Independence (G-11266)

ND Industries Inc ....F....... 330 425-3167
Twinsburg (G-18989)

Northern Chem Binding Corp Inc ....G....... 216 781-7799
Cleveland (G-5909)

Qualico Inc ....G....... 216 271-2550
Cleveland (G-6067)

METAL TREATING: Cryogenic

Cryoplus Inc ....G....... 330 683-3375
Wooster (G-20761)

METAL, TITANIUM: Sponge & Granules

Advanced Materials Products ....G....... 330 650-4000
Hudson (G-11154)

Hamilton Rti Inc ....G....... 330 652-9951
Niles (G-15157)

METAL: Battery

Cleanlife Energy LLC ....F....... 216 661-7872
Cleveland (G-5044)

METALS SVC CENTERS & WHOL: Structural Shapes, Iron Or Steel

Blackburns Fabrication Inc ....E....... 614 875-0784
Columbus (G-6838)

METALS SVC CENTERS & WHOLESALERS: Bars, Metal

Ambassador Steel Corporation ....F....... 740 382-9969
Marion (G-12854)

METALS SVC CENTERS & WHOLESALERS: Cable, Wire

Radix Wire Co ....D....... 216 731-9191
Cleveland (G-6086)

METALS SVC CENTERS & WHOLESALERS: Casting, Rough, Iron/Steel

Ferralloy Inc ....E....... 440 250-1900
Cleveland (G-5335)

METALS SVC CENTERS & WHOLESALERS: Copper

Anchor Bronze and Metals Inc ....E....... 440 549-5653
Cleveland (G-4802)

J W Harris Co Inc ....F....... 216 481-8100
Euclid (G-9587)

METALS SVC CENTERS & WHOLESALERS: Ferroalloys

Howmet Corporation ....E....... 800 242-9898
Newburgh Heights (G-15074)

METALS SVC CENTERS & WHOLESALERS: Ferrous Metals

Masters Group Inc ....G....... 440 893-1900
Chagrin Falls (G-3103)

Premier Metal Trading LLC ....G....... 440 247-9494
Chagrin Falls (G-3068)

METALS SVC CENTERS & WHOLESALERS: Flat Prdts, Iron Or Steel

H & D Steel Service Inc ....E....... 440 237-3390
North Royalton (G-15423)

Major Metals Company ....E....... 419 886-4600
Mansfield (G-12639)

METALS SVC CENTERS & WHOLESALERS: Foundry Prdts

CA Picard Surface Engrg Inc ....F....... 440 366-5400
Elyria (G-9386)

Shells Inc ....G....... 330 808-5558
Wadsworth (G-19440)

METALS SVC CENTERS & WHOLESALERS: Iron & Steel Prdt, Ferrous

Akers America Inc ....G....... 330 757-4100
Poland (G-16382)

Fpt Cleveland LLC ....C....... 216 441-3800
Cleveland (G-5376)

Joseph T Ryerson & Son Inc ....D....... 513 542-5800
Columbus (G-7245)

Supply Dynamics LLC ....F....... 513 965-2000
Loveland (G-12392)

METALS SVC CENTERS & WHOLESALERS: Lead

Victory White Metal Company ....F....... 216 641-2575
Cleveland (G-6416)

METALS SVC CENTERS & WHOLESALERS: Misc Nonferrous Prdts

Cleveland Tungsten Inc ....G....... 440 786-0800
Bedford (G-1415)

HM Wire International Inc ....G....... 330 244-8501
Canton (G-2729)

METALS SVC CENTERS & WHOLESALERS: Pipe & Tubing, Steel

G & C Drainage Supplies Inc ....G....... 513 563-8616
Cincinnati (G-3788)

L B Industries Inc ....E....... 330 750-1002
Struthers (G-17994)

McWane Inc ....B....... 740 622-6651
Coshocton (G-7897)

Pipe Products Inc ....D....... 513 587-7532
West Chester (G-19915)

METALS SVC CENTERS & WHOLESALERS: Plates, Metal

Loveman Steel Corporation ....D....... 440 232-6200
Bedford (G-1439)

METALS SVC CENTERS & WHOLESALERS: Rails & Access

James C Denier Co Inc ....G....... 513 385-6272
Cincinnati (G-3939)

METALS SVC CENTERS & WHOLESALERS: Rope, Wire, Exc Insulated

Cambridge Cable Service Co ....G....... 740 685-5775
Byesville (G-2396)

Samsel Rope & Marine Supply Co ....E....... 216 241-0333
Cleveland (G-6156)

METALS SVC CENTERS & WHOLESALERS: Sheets, Metal

Rockwell Metals Company LLC ....F....... 440 242-2420
Lorain (G-12273)

METALS SVC CENTERS & WHOLESALERS: Stampings, Metal

Ohio Engineering and Mfg Sls ....G....... 937 855-6971
Germantown (G-10371)

Stamped Steel Products Inc ....F....... 330 538-3951
North Jackson (G-15299)

Tig Wood & Die Inc ....F....... 937 849-6741
New Carlisle (G-14815)

Troy West LLC ....G....... 937 339-2192
Troy (G-18882)

METALS SVC CENTERS & WHOLESALERS: Steel

Alro Steel Corporation ....E....... 419 720-5300
Toledo (G-18331)

Alro Steel Corporation ....E....... 937 253-6121
Dayton (G-8149)

American Posts LLC ....E....... 419 720-0652
Toledo (G-18344)

AT&f Nuclear Inc ....G....... 216 252-1500
Cleveland (G-4852)

Benjamin Steel Company Inc ....E....... 937 233-1212
Springfield (G-17522)

Bico Akron Inc ....D....... 330 794-1716
Mogadore (G-14369)

Buckeye Metals Industries Inc ....F....... 216 663-4300
Cleveland (G-4943)

Columbia Steel and Wire Inc ....G....... 330 468-2709
Northfield (G-15463)

Contractors Steel Company ....E....... 330 425-3050
Twinsburg (G-18919)

Coventry Steel Services Inc ....F....... 216 883-4477
Cleveland (G-5136)

Efco Corp ....E....... 614 876-1226
Columbus (G-7048)

PRODUCT

Grenga Machine & Welding ....F 330 743-1113
Youngstown *(G-21104)*
Independent Steel Company LLC ....E 330 225-7741
Valley City *(G-19207)*
Lakewood Steel Inc ....F 440 965-4226
Wakeman *(G-19450)*
Lapham-Hickey Steel Corp ....E 614 443-4881
Columbus *(G-7286)*
Latrobe Spcialty Mtls Dist Inc ....D 330 609-5137
Vienna *(G-19366)*
Louis Arthur Steel Company ....G 440 997-5545
Geneva *(G-10352)*
Louis Arthur Steel Company ....G 440 997-5545
Uniontown *(G-19091)*
Master-Halco Inc ....E 513 869-7600
Fairfield *(G-9680)*
Metals USA Crbn Flat Rlled Inc .....D 937 882-6354
Springfield *(G-17604)*
Metals USA Crbn Flat Rlled Inc .....C 330 264-8416
Wooster *(G-20806)*
Metrodeck Inc ....F 513 541-4370
Cincinnati *(G-4095)*
Miller Consolidated Industries ....E 937 294-2681
Moraine *(G-14507)*
North American Steel Company ......E 216 475-7300
Cleveland *(G-5890)*
Precision Steel Services Inc ....D 419 476-5702
Toledo *(G-18654)*
Sausser Steel Company Inc ....F 419 422-9632
Findlay *(G-9888)*
Scot Industries Inc ....E 330 262-7585
Wooster *(G-20832)*
St Lawrence Steel Corporation ......E 330 562-9000
Streetsboro *(G-17878)*
Universal Steel Company ....D 216 883-4972
Cleveland *(G-6392)*
Westfield Steel Inc ....D 937 322-2414
Springfield *(G-17677)*
Worthington Steel Company ....G 513 702-0130
Middletown *(G-14100)*

METALS SVC CENTERS & WHOLESALERS: Tubing, Metal

Swagelok Company ....D 440 349-5934
Solon *(G-17392)*
Tubular Techniques Inc ....G 614 529-4130
Hilliard *(G-10989)*

METALS SVC CTRS & WHOLESALERS: Aluminum Bars, Rods, Etc

Alanod Westlake Metal Ind Inc ......E 440 327-8184
North Ridgeville *(G-15356)*
Aluminum Bearing Co of America ....G 216 267-8560
Cleveland *(G-4773)*
Loxcreen Company Inc ....F 513 539-2255
Middletown *(G-14056)*

METALS: Precious NEC

Metallic Resources Inc ....E 330 425-3155
Twinsburg *(G-18987)*

METALS: Precious, Secondary

Auris Noble LLC ....G 330 321-6649
Fairlawn *(G-9739)*
Auris Noble LLC ....G 330 685-3748
Akron *(G-77)*
Materion Brush Inc ....D 216 486-4200
Mayfield Heights *(G-13317)*
Materion Corporation ....D 216 486-4200
Mayfield Heights *(G-13318)*

METALS: Primary Nonferrous, NEC

Aci Industries Ltd ....E 740 368-4160
Delaware *(G-8815)*
American Friction Tech LLC ....D 216 823-0861
Cleveland *(G-4781)*
American Spring Wire Corp ....C 216 292-4620
Bedford Heights *(G-1478)*
Bradley Metal Fabrication ....F 216 881-7400
Shaker Heights *(G-17085)*
Galt Alloys Inc Main Ofc ....G 330 453-4678
Canton *(G-2710)*
General Electric Company ....D 330 343-8841
Dover *(G-8987)*
H C Starck Inc ....E 216 692-6990
Euclid *(G-9583)*

Rhenium Alloys Inc ....D 440 365-7388
North Ridgeville *(G-15401)*
Rml Tool Inc ....G 216 941-1615
Cleveland *(G-6120)*
Rti Finance Corp ....G 330 652-9952
Niles *(G-15178)*
Swift Manufacturing Co Inc ....G 740 237-4405
Ironton *(G-11302)*

METALWORK: Miscellaneous

Advance Industrial Mfg Inc ....E 614 871-3333
Grove City *(G-10539)*
Architctral Rfuse Slutions LLC ....G 330 733-3996
Akron *(G-72)*
Arrow Tru-Line Inc ....D 419 636-7013
Bryan *(G-2279)*
BMA Metals Group Inc ....G 513 874-5152
West Chester *(G-19819)*
Buckeye Stamping Company ....D 614 445-0059
Columbus *(G-6875)*
Burghardt Metal Fabg Inc ....F 330 794-1830
Akron *(G-104)*
CMF Custom Metal Finishers ....G 513 821-8145
Cincinnati *(G-3592)*
Concast Birmingham Inc ....D 440 965-4455
Wakeman *(G-19446)*
Custom Manufacturing Solutions ....G 937 372-0777
Dayton *(G-8259)*
Dan Novak ....G 440 269-1741
Willoughby *(G-20469)*
Fabrication Group LLC ....E 216 251-1125
Cleveland *(G-5318)*
Fortin Welding & Mfg Inc ....E 614 291-4342
Columbus *(G-7094)*
Friesingers Inc ....G 740 452-9480
Zanesville *(G-21312)*
Harvey Brothers Inc ....F 513 541-2622
Cincinnati *(G-3868)*
Lwr Enterprises Inc ....G 740 984-0036
Waterford *(G-19650)*
Markley Enterprises LLC ....E 513 771-1290
Cincinnati *(G-4061)*
Matteo Aluminum Inc ....E 440 585-5213
Wickliffe *(G-20372)*
Meibuhr Co Inc ....G 440 942-9375
Willoughby *(G-20543)*
Metal Sales Manufacturing Corp ....E 440 576-9070
Jefferson *(G-11367)*
Mk Metal Products Inc ....E 419 756-3644
Mansfield *(G-12650)*
Omco Holdings Inc ....E 440 944-2100
Wickliffe *(G-20375)*
Simcote Inc ....E 740 382-5000
Marion *(G-12902)*
Skinner Sales Group Inc ....E 440 572-8455
Strongsville *(G-17966)*
Tallmadge Spinning & Metal Co ......F 330 794-2277
Akron *(G-427)*
Trulite GL Alum Solutions LLC ....D 614 876-1057
Columbus *(G-7712)*
Ventari Corporation ....E 937 278-4269
Miamisburg *(G-13874)*
Ver-Mac Industries Inc ....E 740 397-6511
Mount Vernon *(G-14654)*
Watteredge LLC ....D 440 933-6110
Avon Lake *(G-1055)*
Will-Burt Company ....E 330 682-7015
Orrville *(G-15772)*
Will-Burt Company ....B 330 682-7015
Orrville *(G-15770)*

METALWORK: Ornamental

Beauty Cft Met Fabricators Inc ....F 440 439-0710
Bedford *(G-1405)*
Fortin Welding & Mfg Inc ....E 614 291-4342
Columbus *(G-7094)*
Jason Incorporated ....F 513 860-3400
Hamilton *(G-10711)*
L & L Ornamental Iron Co ....E 513 353-1930
Cleves *(G-6520)*
P & L Metalcrafts LLC ....F 330 793-2178
Youngstown *(G-21160)*
Tarrier Steel Company Inc ....E 614 444-4000
Columbus *(G-7679)*

METALWORKING MACHINERY WHOLESALERS

Advanced Tech Utilization Co ....F 440 238-3770
Strongsville *(G-17884)*

Analytic Stress Relieving Inc ....G 804 271-7198
Northwood *(G-15476)*
Patton Industries Inc ....G 419 331-5658
Elida *(G-9354)*
Stuebing Automatic Machine Co ......E 513 771-8028
Cincinnati *(G-4473)*

METEOROLOGICAL INSTRUMENT REPAIR SVCS

Electric Speed Indicator Co ....F 216 251-2540
Cleveland *(G-5265)*

METER READERS: Remote

Matvest Inc ....E 614 487-8720
Columbus *(G-7327)*

METERING DEVICES: Flow Meters, Impeller & Counter Driven

Bif Co LLC ....F 330 564-0941
Akron *(G-92)*

METERING DEVICES: Gas Meters, Domestic & Large Cap, Indl

Gilbarco Catlow LLC ....G 937 898-3236
Tipp City *(G-18279)*

METERING DEVICES: Gasoline Dispensing

CNG Fueling LLC ....G 330 772-2403
Brookfield *(G-2121)*

METERING DEVICES: Water Quality Monitoring & Control Systems

Brooks Manufacturing ....G 419 244-1777
Toledo *(G-18382)*
Ernst Flow Industries LLC ....F 732 938-5641
Strongsville *(G-17918)*
Fred W Hanks Company ....G 216 731-1774
Cleveland *(G-5380)*

METERS: Pyrometers, Indl Process

Marlin Manufacturing Corp ....D 216 676-1340
Cleveland *(G-5749)*
Ralph A Felice Inc ....G 330 468-0482
Macedonia *(G-12479)*

METERS: Resistance

Harris Instrument Corporation ....G 740 369-3580
Delaware *(G-8857)*

MGMT CONSULTING SVCS: Matls, Incl Purch, Handle & Invntry

Midwest Motor Supply Co ....C 800 233-1294
Columbus *(G-7351)*
Streamside Materials Llc ....G 419 423-1290
Findlay *(G-9896)*

MICA PRDTS

Dayton Wright Composite ....G 937 469-3962
Dayton *(G-8292)*
Fillous & Ruppel Inc ....G 216 431-0470
Cleveland *(G-5344)*

MICROCIRCUITS, INTEGRATED: Semiconductor

Crishtronics Llc ....G 440 572-8318
Strongsville *(G-17908)*
Smart Microsystems Ltd ....F 440 366-4257
Elyria *(G-9493)*

MICROPHONES

C T I Audio Inc ....D 440 593-1111
Brooklyn Heights *(G-2133)*
Cad Audio LLC ....F 440 349-4900
Solon *(G-17275)*

MICROPROCESSORS

AT&T Corp ....G 513 792-9300
Cincinnati *(G-3423)*
General Nano LLC ....G 513 309-5947
Cincinnati *(G-3819)*

Intel Industries LLC .... G 614 551-5702
Cincinnati *(G-3926)*

Ki Intel LLC .... G 740 200-9000
Sunbury *(G-18065)*

Salient Systems Inc .... E 614 792-5800
Dublin *(G-9138)*

MICROPUBLISHER

Promatch Solutions LLC .... F 937 299-0185
Springboro *(G-17500)*

MICROSCOPES

FT Group Inc .... E 937 746-6439
Cincinnati *(G-3786)*

MICROWAVE COMPONENTS

Berry Investments Inc .... G 937 293-0398
Moraine *(G-14469)*

Idcomm LLC .... G 661 250-4081
Willoughby Hills *(G-20639)*

MILITARY INSIGNIA

Gayston Corporation .... C 937 743-6050
Miamisburg *(G-13812)*

Staco Energy Products Co .... G 937 253-1191
Miamisburg *(G-13863)*

MILL PRDTS: Structural & Rail

Cleveland Track Material Inc .... D 216 641-4000
Cleveland *(G-5082)*

Cleveland Track Material Inc .... F 216 641-4000
Cleveland *(G-5083)*

Pemjay Inc .... E 740 254-4591
Gnadenhutten *(G-10409)*

MILLINERY SUPPLIES: Sweat Bands, Hat/Cap, From Purchsd Mtrls

Sweaty Bands LLC .... E 513 871-1222
Cincinnati *(G-4489)*

MILLINERY SUPPLIES: Veils & Veiling, Bridal, Funeral, Etc

Jls Funeral Home .... F 614 625-1220
Columbus *(G-7234)*

MILLING: Cereal Flour, Exc Rice

Ardent Mills LLC .... F 419 994-4181
Loudonville *(G-12296)*

Friends of Bears Mill Inc .... G 937 548-5112
Greenville *(G-10500)*

Grain Craft Inc .... E 216 621-3206
Cleveland *(G-5444)*

Keynes Bros Inc .... E 740 385-6824
Logan *(G-12181)*

MILLING: Chemical

Triaxis Machine & Tool LLC .... G 440 230-0303
North Royalton *(G-15457)*

MILLING: Grains, Exc Rice

Sunrise Cooperative Inc .... F 419 929-1568
Wakeman *(G-19453)*

MILLS: Ferrous & Nonferrous

North Coast Profile Inc .... G 330 823-7777
Alliance *(G-531)*

Sentek Corporation .... G 614 586-1123
Columbus *(G-7608)*

MILLWORK

7&7 Woodworking .... G 330 347-6574
Wooster *(G-20729)*

7d Marketing Inc .... F 330 721-8822
Medina *(G-13362)*

A & J Woodworking .... G 888 572-9561
Sugarcreek *(G-18014)*

A & J Woodworking Inc .... G 419 695-5655
Delphos *(G-8898)*

A & M Woodworking .... G 330 893-1331
Millersburg *(G-14189)*

A C Shutters Inc .... G 216 429-2424
Cleveland *(G-4669)*

A W S Incorporated .... G 419 352-5397
Bowling Green *(G-1962)*

Ace Lumber Company .... F 330 744-3167
Youngstown *(G-21015)*

Adams Custom Woodworking .... F 513 761-1395
Cincinnati *(G-3355)*

Advantage Tent Fittings Inc .... F 740 773-3015
Chillicothe *(G-3226)*

Ailes Millwork Inc .... F 330 678-4300
Kent *(G-11424)*

Aj Stineburg Wdwkg Studio LLC .... G 614 526-9480
Columbus *(G-6706)*

American Home Products LLC .... G 800 684-3434
Cleveland *(G-4784)*

Art Woodworking & Mfg Co .... E 513 681-2986
Cincinnati *(G-3415)*

Automated Bldg Components Inc .... E 419 257-2152
North Baltimore *(G-15191)*

Baird Brothers Sawmill Inc .... G 330 533-3122
Canfield *(G-2549)*

Beechvale Laminating .... F 330 674-2804
Millersburg *(G-14198)*

Berlin Woodworking .... G 330 893-3234
Millersburg *(G-14202)*

Berry Woodworking .... F 513 734-6133
Amelia *(G-569)*

Bomba S Custom Woodworking ..... G 330 699-9075
Uniontown *(G-19078)*

Brogan Machine Shop .... G 513 683-9054
Loveland *(G-12345)*

Bruewer Woodwork Mfg Co .... D 513 353-3505
Cleves *(G-6507)*

Buckeye Products .... G 740 969-4718
Amanda *(G-560)*

Bwd Woodwork LLC .... G 740 335-9766
Wshngtn CT Hs *(G-20903)*

C & W Custom Wdwkg Co Inc .... E 513 891-6340
Blue Ash *(G-1757)*

Carter-Jones Lumber Company ...... C 330 674-9060
Millersburg *(G-14211)*

Cassady Woodworks Inc .... E 937 256-7948
Dayton *(G-8099)*

Cincinnati Woodworks Inc .... G 513 241-6412
Cincinnati *(G-3570)*

Cindoco Wood Products Co .... G 937 444-2504
Mount Orab *(G-14577)*

Corns Quality Woodworking LLC .... G 419 589-4899
Mansfield *(G-12585)*

Cortland Hardwood Products LLC ... E 330 638-3232
Cortland *(G-7865)*

Country Comfort Woodworking .... G 330 695-4408
Fredericksburg *(G-10081)*

Cox Interior Inc .... G 614 473-9169
Columbus *(G-6993)*

Creative Millwork Ohio Inc .... E 440 992-3566
Ashtabula *(G-799)*

Creative Woodworks .... G 330 897-1432
Sugarcreek *(G-18021)*

Crowes Cabinets .... G 330 536-2545
Lowellville *(G-12406)*

Curves and More Woodworking ...... G 614 239-7837
Columbus *(G-7003)*

Darby Creek Millwork Co .... G 614 873-3267
Plain City *(G-16331)*

Dendratec Ltd .... G 330 473-4878
Dalton *(G-8067)*

Denoon Lumber Company LLC .... D 740 768-2220
Bergholz *(G-1641)*

Design-N-Wood LLC .... G 937 419-0479
Sidney *(G-17177)*

Display Dynamics Inc .... F 937 832-2830
Englewood *(G-9516)*

Dlwoodworking .... G 740 927-2693
Pataskala *(G-15969)*

Door Fabrication Services Inc .... G 937 454-9207
Vandalia *(G-19290)*

Dublin Millwork Co Inc .... E 614 889-7776
Dublin *(G-9069)*

Dutch Heritage Woodcraft .... E 330 893-2211
Berlin *(G-1648)*

Ernest Warther and Sons Inc .... F 330 343-7513
Dover *(G-8984)*

Farmstead Acres Woodworking ...... G 330 695-6492
Fredericksburg *(G-10086)*

Fdi Cabinetry LLC .... G 513 353-4500
Cleves *(G-6514)*

Fifth Avenue Lumber Co .... D 614 833-6655
Canal Winchester *(G-2524)*

Fixture Dimensions Inc .... G 513 360-7512
Middletown *(G-14041)*

Flottemesch Anthony & Son .... F 513 561-1212
Cincinnati *(G-3762)*

Forum III Inc .... F 513 961-5123
Cincinnati *(G-3773)*

Gdw Woodworking LLC .... G 513 494-3041
South Lebanon *(G-17429)*

Gerstenslager Construction .... G 330 832-3604
Massillon *(G-13139)*

Gross & Sons Custom Millwork ..... G 419 227-0214
Lima *(G-12020)*

Hawk Engine & Machine .... G 440 582-0900
North Royalton *(G-15424)*

Hj Systems Inc .... F 614 351-9777
Columbus *(G-7161)*

Hoehnes Custom Woodworking ...... G 937 693-8008
Anna *(G-623)*

Holes Custom Woodworking .... G 419 586-8171
Celina *(G-3002)*

Holmes Lumber & Bldg Ctr Inc ...... C 330 674-9060
Millersburg *(G-14231)*

Hrh Door Corp .... D 440 593-5226
Conneaut *(G-7809)*

Huntington Hardwood Lbr Co Inc ... G 440 647-2283
Wellington *(G-19748)*

Hyde Park Lumber Company .... E 513 271-1500
Cincinnati *(G-3903)*

Idx Corporation .... C 937 401-3225
Dayton *(G-8400)*

Inter Cab Corporation .... G 216 351-0770
Cleveland *(G-5576)*

J A H Woodworking LLC .... G 740 266-6949
Bloomingdale *(G-1723)*

Jeld-Wen Inc .... B 740 397-1144
Mount Vernon *(G-14625)*

Jeld-Wen Inc .... C 740 964-1431
Etna *(G-9557)*

Jeld-Wen Inc .... E 740 397-3403
Mount Vernon *(G-14626)*

Jh Woodworking LLC .... G 330 276-7600
Killbuck *(G-11595)*

John M Hand .... G 937 902-1327
West Alexandria *(G-19780)*

Judy Mills Company Inc .... E 513 271-4241
Cincinnati *(G-3962)*

L J Smith Inc .... C 740 269-2221
Bowerston *(G-1958)*

Liechty Specialties Inc .... G 419 445-6696
Archbold *(G-683)*

Lima Millwork Inc .... E 419 331-3303
Elida *(G-9351)*

Lj Woodworking .... G 330 359-3216
Dundee *(G-9175)*

M H Woodworking LLC .... G 330 893-3929
Millersburg *(G-14243)*

Maple Hill Woodworking .... G 330 674-2500
Millersburg *(G-14245)*

Marsh Industries Inc .... E 330 308-8667
New Philadelphia *(G-14912)*

Martin Bauder Woodworking LLC .... G 513 735-0659
Milford *(G-14160)*

Menard Inc .... F 513 250-4566
Cincinnati *(G-4084)*

Menard Inc .... E 419 998-4348
Lima *(G-12053)*

Midwest Woodworking Co Inc .... E 513 631-6684
Cincinnati *(G-4106)*

Miller and Slay Wdwkg LLC .... G 513 265-3816
Mason *(G-13063)*

Miller Manufacturing Inc .... E 330 852-0689
Sugarcreek *(G-18028)*

Mills Customs Woodworks .... G 216 407-3600
Cleveland *(G-5818)*

Millwood Wholesale Inc .... F 330 359-6109
Dundee *(G-9177)*

Millwork Designs Inc .... G 740 335-5203
Wshngtn CT Hs *(G-20917)*

Millwork Fabricators Inc .... G 937 299-5452
Moraine *(G-14508)*

Morey Woodworking LLC .... G 937 623-5280
Piqua *(G-16293)*

Mount Hope Planing .... F 330 359-0538
Millersburg *(G-14250)*

Nagele Manufacturing Co Inc .... E 216 433-1100
Cleveland *(G-5849)*

National Access Design LLC .... F 513 351-3400
Cincinnati *(G-4137)*

Nauvoo Custom Woodworking .... G 440 632-9502
Middlefield *(G-13974)*

North View Woodworking .... G 330 359-6286
Dundee *(G-9178)*

P
R
O
D
U
C
T

Noteworthy Woodworking ....G...... 330 297-0509
Ravenna (G-16545)

Oak Front Inc ....G...... 330 948-4500
Lodi (G-12167)

Ohio Woodworking Co Inc ....G...... 513 631-0870
Cincinnati (G-4181)

P & T Millwork Inc ....E...... 440 543-2151
Chagrin Falls (G-3109)

Paragon Woodworking LLC ....G...... 614 402-1459
Columbus (G-7461)

Peninsula Hardwoods Inc ....G...... 330 657-2701
Peninsula (G-16039)

Pj Woodwork LLC ....G...... 419 886-0008
Bellville (G-1574)

Premium Panel & Tread ....G...... 330 695-9979
Fredericksburg (G-10090)

R Carney Thomas ....G...... 740 342-3388
New Lexington (G-14853)

Rebsco Inc ....F...... 937 548-2246
Greenville (G-10517)

Renewal By Andersen LLC ....G...... 614 781-9600
Columbus (G-6658)

Rinos Woodworking Shop Inc ......F...... 440 946-1718
Willoughby (G-20589)

Riverside Cnstr Svcs Inc ....E...... 513 723-0900
Cincinnati (G-4349)

Robertson Cabinets Inc ....E...... 937 698-3755
West Milton (G-20110)

Roettger Hardwood Inc ....F...... 937 693-6811
Kettlersville (G-11589)

Roy Holtzapple John Johns ....G...... 419 657-2460
Wapakoneta (G-19504)

S & S Panel ....G...... 330 412-6735
Orrville (G-15761)

Sauder Wdwkg Co Welfare Tr ......G...... 419 446-2711
Archbold (G-693)

Scarred Hands Wood Creations ....G...... 740 975-2835
Etna (G-9562)

Schreiner Cstm Stairs & Mllwk .....G...... 419 435-8935
Fostoria (G-9994)

Select Woodworking Inc ....G...... 513 948-9901
Cincinnati (G-4402)

Shade Youngstown & Aluminum Co ....G...... 330 782-2373
Youngstown (G-21200)

Sheridan Woodworks Inc ....F...... 216 663-9333
Cleveland (G-6188)

Stainwood Products ....F...... 440 244-1352
Lorain (G-12280)

Stein Inc ....F...... 419 747-2611
Mansfield (G-12683)

Stephen M Trudick ....E...... 440 834-1891
Burton (G-2385)

Stoney Acres Woodworking Llc .....G...... 440 834-0717
Burton (G-2386)

Stony Point Hardwoods ....F...... 330 852-4512
Sugarcreek (G-18040)

Stratton Creek Wood Works LLC ....F...... 330 876-0005
Kinsman (G-11612)

Summit Millwork LLC ....G...... 330 920-4000
Cuyahoga Falls (G-8051)

Swartz Woodworking ....G...... 330 359-6359
Millersburg (G-14266)

T & D Thompson Inc ....E...... 740 332-8515
Laurelville (G-11772)

Timberlane Woodworking ....G...... 419 895-9945
Greenwich (G-10537)

Turnwood Industries Inc ....E...... 330 278-2421
Hinckley (G-11031)

Versailles Building Supply ....G...... 937 526-3238
Versailles (G-19358)

Village Woodworking ....G...... 740 326-4461
Fredericktown (G-10115)

Volpe Millwork Inc ....G...... 216 581-0200
Cleveland (G-6427)

Walnut Creek Woodworking LLC ....G...... 513 504-3520
Bethel (G-1665)

Wittrock Wdwkg & Mfg Co Inc .....D...... 513 891-5800
Blue Ash (G-1896)

Woodcraft Industries Inc ....C...... 440 632-9655
Middlefield (G-14007)

Woodcraft Industries Inc ....D...... 440 437-7811
Orwell (G-15783)

Woodland Woodworking ....G...... 330 897-7282
Baltic (G-1079)

Woodworks Unlimited ....G...... 740 574-4523
Franklin Furnace (G-10070)

Wyman Woodworking ....G...... 614 338-0615
Columbus (G-7779)

Yoder Lumber Co Inc ....G...... 330 893-3121
Millersburg (G-14288)

Yoder Woodworking ....G...... 740 399-9400
Butler (G-2394)

Yutzy Woodworking Ltd ....G...... 330 359-6166
Millersburg (G-14292)

MINE & QUARRY SVCS: Nonmetallic Minerals

M G Q Inc ....G...... 419 992-4236
Tiffin (G-18229)

Stoepfel Drilling Co ....G...... 419 532-3307
Ottawa (G-15811)

MINE DEVELOPMENT SVCS: Nonmetallic Minerals

Robin Industries Inc ....E...... 330 893-3501
Berlin (G-1652)

MINE EXPLORATION SVCS: Nonmetallic Minerals

Fgb International LLC ....G...... 440 359-0000
Cleveland (G-5341)

Sandy Creek Mining Co Inc ....G...... 419 435-5891
Fostoria (G-9993)

MINE PREPARATION SVCS

Strata Mine Services LLC ....F...... 740 695-0488
Saint Clairsville (G-16811)

MINE PUMPING OR DRAINING SVCS: Nonmetallic Minerals

Tresslers Plumbing LLC ....G...... 419 784-2142
Defiance (G-8812)

MINERAL WOOL

Autoneum North America Inc ......B...... 419 693-0511
Oregon (G-15703)

Brendons Fiber Works ....G...... 614 353-6599
Columbus (G-6854)

Corrosion Resistant Technology ....G...... 440 543-1320
Chagrin Falls (G-3083)

Johns Manville Corporation ....B...... 419 878-8111
Waterville (G-19660)

Johns Manville Corporation ....C...... 419 784-7000
Defiance (G-8796)

Johns Manville Corporation ....C...... 419 878-8111
Defiance (G-8797)

McGill Airpressure LLC ....G...... 614 882-5455
Columbus (G-7332)

Midwest Acoust-A-Fiber Inc ....E...... 740 363-6247
Delaware (G-8871)

Nitto Denko Auto Ohio Inc ....C...... 937 773-4820
Piqua (G-16295)

Owens Corning ....G...... 419 248-8000
Navarre (G-14723)

Owens Corning Sales LLC ....C...... 740 328-2300
Newark (G-15043)

Owens Corning Sales LLC ....E...... 614 539-0830
Grove City (G-10581)

Owens Corning Sales LLC ....D...... 614 399-3915
Mount Vernon (G-14635)

Premier Manufacturing Corp ....D...... 216 941-9700
Cleveland (G-6041)

Refractory Specialties Inc ....E...... 330 938-2101
Sebring (G-17050)

Sorbothane Inc ....E...... 330 678-9444
Kent (G-11530)

Tectum Inc ....C...... 740 345-9691
Newark (G-15063)

MINERAL WOOL INSULATION PRDTS

Fibreboard Corporation ....C...... 419 248-8000
Toledo (G-18470)

MINERALS: Ground Or Otherwise Treated

Cimbar Performance Mnrl WV LLC ....E...... 330 532-2034
Wellsville (G-19774)

MINERALS: Ground or Treated

6062 Holdings LLC ....G...... 216 359-9005
Beachwood (G-1252)

Acme Company ....D...... 330 758-2313
Poland (G-16381)

Advanced Quartz Fabrication ....F...... 440 350-4567
Chardon (G-3138)

Aluchem Inc ....E...... 513 733-8519
Cincinnati (G-3382)

Edw C Levy Co ....E...... 330 484-6328
Canton (G-2695)

Edw C Levy Co ....E...... 419 822-8286
Delta (G-8931)

EMD Millipore Corporation ....C...... 513 631-0445
Norwood (G-15572)

GRB Holdings Inc ....D...... 937 236-3250
Dayton (G-8377)

Industrial Quartz Corp ....F...... 440 942-0909
Mentor (G-13606)

Mineral Met Inc ....G...... 216 641-3555
Cleveland (G-5820)

Premier Silica LLC ....E...... 740 659-2241
Glenford (G-10400)

Premier Silica LLC ....E...... 740 599-7773
Howard (G-11124)

Seaforth Mineral & Ore Co Inc .....F...... 216 292-5820
Cleveland (G-6176)

MINIATURES

Precise Models Inc ....G...... 440 365-5701
Elyria (G-9480)

MINING EXPLORATION & DEVELOPMENT SVCS

Omega Cementing Co ....G...... 330 695-7147
Apple Creek (G-646)

MINING MACHINERY & EQPT WHOLESALERS

J & A Machine ....G...... 330 424-5235
Lisbon (G-12123)

Unified Scrn & Crush-Oh Inc ....G...... 937 836-3201
Englewood (G-9541)

MINING MACHINES & EQPT: Augers

Brydet Development Corporation ....E...... 740 623-0455
Coshocton (G-7883)

Horizontal Eqp Manufacturing ....G...... 330 264-2229
Wooster (G-20784)

MINING MACHINES & EQPT: Bits, Rock, Exc Oil/Gas Field Tools

Jennmar McSweeney LLC ....C...... 740 377-3354
South Point (G-17439)

MINING MACHINES & EQPT: Cages, Mine Shaft

Dover Conveyor Inc ....E...... 740 922-9390
Midvale (G-14106)

Tema Systems Inc ....E...... 513 489-7811
Cincinnati (G-4501)

MINING MACHINES & EQPT: Crushers, Stationary

Grasan Equipment Company Inc ....D...... 419 526-4440
Mansfield (G-12620)

MINING MACHINES & EQPT: Rock Crushing, Stationary

Irock Crushers LLC ....G...... 866 240-0201
Cleveland (G-5587)

MINING MACHINES & EQPT: Shuttle Cars, Underground

Buzz N Shuttle Service ....G...... 740 223-0567
Marion (G-12860)

MINING SVCS, NEC: Bituminous

Duncan Brothers Drilling Inc ....F...... 330 426-9507
East Palestine (G-9234)

Duncan Brothers Drilling Inc ....F...... 330 426-9507
East Palestine (G-9235)

MIRRORS: Motor Vehicle

Beach Manufacturing Co ....C...... 937 882-6372
Donnelsville (G-8960)

Commercial Vehicle Group Inc............A...... 614 289-5360
New Albany (G-14753)
Domair Transmore Inc............................F...... 513 771-1516
Cincinnati (G-3662)
Tiger Mirror Corporation.......................G...... 419 855-3146
Clay Center (G-4654)

MISSILES: Ballistic, Complete

Lockheed Martin Corporation................B...... 330 796-2800
Akron (G-273)

MIXING EQPT

Duplex Mill & Manufacturing Co............E...... 937 325-5555
Springfield (G-17548)
Quikstir Inc..F...... 419 732-2601
Port Clinton (G-16410)

MIXTURES & BLOCKS: Asphalt Paving

A United..G...... 330 782-6005
Youngstown (G-21011)
Action Blacktop Sealcoating &............G...... 937 667-4769
Tipp City (G-18259)
All Coatings Co Inc................................G...... 330 821-3806
Alliance (G-489)
Allied Corporation Inc............................G...... 330 425-7861
Twinsburg (G-18898)
Aluminum Coating Manufacturers.......E...... 216 341-2000
Cleveland (G-4774)
Asphalt Fabrics & Specialties...............G...... 440 786-1077
Solon (G-17262)
Asphalt Materials Inc.............................G...... 740 373-3040
Marietta (G-12764)
Asphalt Services & Cnstr.......................G...... 330 995-6044
Aurora (G-907)
Atlas Roofing Corporation......................C...... 937 746-9941
Franklin (G-10008)
Baileys Asphalt Sealing.........................F...... 740 453-9409
South Zanesville (G-17453)
Barrett Paving Materials Inc..................C...... 513 271-6200
Middletown (G-14101)
Bluffton Stone Co...................................E...... 419 358-6941
Bluffton (G-1909)
Bowerston Shale Company.....................E...... 740 269-2921
Bowerston (G-1957)
Brewer Company....................................E...... 614 279-8688
Columbus (G-6855)
Brewer Company....................................G...... 800 394-0017
Milford (G-14127)
Brown Construction & Paving................G...... 513 494-0095
Morrow (G-14544)
Buckeye Sealcoating..............................F...... 330 658-3377
Doylestown (G-9027)
Central Ohio Asphalt LLC.......................G...... 419 768-4211
Chesterville (G-3224)
D and D Asp Sealcoating LLC................G...... 614 288-3597
Pickerington (G-16189)
Erie Materials Inc..................................G...... 419 483-4648
Castalia (G-2975)
Hanson Aggregates Midwest LLC..........G...... 419 983-2211
Bloomville (G-1728)
Hanson Aggregates Midwest LLC..........G...... 419 878-2006
Waterville (G-19659)
Holmes Supply Corp..............................G...... 330 279-2634
Holmesville (G-11105)
Hy-Grade Corporation............................E...... 216 341-7711
Cleveland (G-5541)
Image Pavement Maintenance...............E...... 937 833-9200
Brookville (G-2187)
John R Jurgensen Co.............................G...... 937 293-3112
Springfield (G-17582)
Kokosing Materials Inc..........................E...... 740 745-3341
Saint Louisville (G-16827)
Koksing Material Inc..............................G...... 330 721-2775
Medina (G-13434)
Lake Erie Asphalt Paving Inc.................G...... 440 526-5191
Brecksville (G-2060)
M & B Asphalt Company Inc...................G...... 419 992-4235
Tiffin (G-18228)
Mansfield Asphalt Paving Inc.................F...... 740 453-0721
Zanesville (G-21327)
Mar-Zane Inc..F...... 740 453-0721
Zanesville (G-21328)
Mar-Zane Inc..G...... 740 782-1240
Bethesda (G-1666)
Mar-Zane Inc..G...... 740 685-5118
Byesville (G-2407)
Mar-Zane Inc..G...... 330 626-2079
Mantua (G-12716)

Marathon Petroleum Company LP........B...... 330 478-5000
Canton (G-2767)
Marathon Petroleum Company LP........F...... 419 422-2121
Findlay (G-9855)
Massillon Asphalt Co.............................G...... 330 833-6330
Massillon (G-13173)
Miller Bros Paving Inc...........................F...... 419 445-1015
Archbold (G-687)
Newton Asphalt Paving Inc....................F...... 330 878-5648
Strasburg (G-17826)
Reading Rock Inc...................................C...... 513 874-2345
West Chester (G-20045)
Rutland Township..................................G...... 740 742-2805
Bidwell (G-1678)
Seal Master Corporation........................E...... 330 673-8410
Kent (G-11525)
Shelly and Sands Inc.............................G...... 330 743-8850
Youngstown (G-21201)
Shelly and Sands Inc.............................D...... 740 859-2104
Rayland (G-16575)
Shelly Company.....................................G...... 740 246-6315
Thornville (G-18196)
Shelly Materials Inc...............................G...... 419 229-2741
Lima (G-12090)
Shelly Materials Inc...............................G...... 740 246-5009
Thornville (G-18197)
Shelly Materials Inc...............................G...... 419 273-2510
Forest (G-9922)
Sidwell Materials Inc.............................C...... 740 849-2394
Zanesville (G-21354)
Smalls Asphalt Paving Inc.....................G...... 740 427-4096
Gambier (G-10318)
Stark Materials Inc................................E...... 330 497-1648
Canton (G-2856)
Stoneco Inc..G...... 419 393-2555
Oakwood (G-15619)
Thorworks Industries Inc.......................E...... 419 626-4375
Sandusky (G-17015)
Valley Asphalt Corporation....................G...... 513 381-0652
Morrow (G-14552)
Valley Asphalt Corporation....................G...... 937 335-3664
Troy (G-18884)
York Paving Co......................................F...... 740 594-3600
Athens (G-891)

MOBILE COMMUNICATIONS EQPT

Eei Acquisition Corp..............................E...... 440 564-5484
Newbury (G-15089)
Sagequest LLC.......................................D...... 216 896-7243
Solon (G-17374)

MOBILE HOME & TRAILER REPAIR

Advanced Rv LLC...................................G...... 440 283-0405
Willoughby (G-20425)

MOBILE HOMES

C & C Mobile Homes LLC.......................G...... 740 663-5535
Waverly (G-19704)
Ellis & Watts Intl LLC.............................G...... 513 752-9000
Batavia (G-1183)
Holiday Homes Inc.................................F...... 513 353-9777
Harrison (G-10782)
Mobile Conversions Inc.........................F...... 513 797-1991
Amelia (G-580)
Skyline Corporation...............................C...... 330 852-2483
Sugarcreek (G-18039)
Sun Communities Inc.............................G...... 740 548-1942
Lewis Center (G-11922)

MOBILE HOMES, EXC RECREATIONAL

Manufactured Housing Entps Inc...........C...... 419 636-4511
Bryan (G-2313)

MODELS

Advance Products...................................F...... 419 882-8117
Sylvania (G-18097)
Consolidated Pattern Works Inc............G...... 330 434-6060
Akron (G-127)
Morris Technologies Inc.........................C...... 513 733-1611
Cincinnati (G-4123)
Scott Models Inc....................................F...... 513 771-8005
Cincinnati (G-4391)

MODELS: Airplane, Exc Toy

Ohio Model Planes.................................G...... 937 372-0603
Xenia (G-20965)

MODELS: General, Exc Toy

3-D Technical Services Inc.....................E...... 937 746-2901
Franklin (G-10004)
Anza Inc...G...... 513 542-7337
Cincinnati (G-3406)
Debolt Machine Inc................................G...... 740 454-8082
Zanesville (G-21298)
Jack R Stiner Models & Pattern............G...... 330 494-1730
Canton (G-2744)
King Model Company..............................E...... 330 633-0491
Akron (G-259)
Model Engineering Company..................G...... 330 644-3450
Barberton (G-1132)

MODULES: Computer Logic

John B Allen..G...... 614 488-7122
Columbus (G-7238)

MOLDED RUBBER PRDTS

Action Rubber Co Inc.............................F...... 937 866-5975
Dayton (G-8134)
Aeroquip-Vickers Inc.............................G...... 216 523-5000
Cleveland (G-4722)
American Pro-Mold Inc..........................E...... 330 336-4111
Wadsworth (G-19394)
American Rubber Products Co................G...... 440 461-0900
Solon (G-17258)
ARC Rubber Inc.....................................C...... 440 466-4555
Geneva (G-10343)
C & M Rubber Co Inc.............................F...... 937 299-2782
Dayton (G-8203)
Cardinal Rubber Company Inc................E...... 330 745-2191
Barberton (G-1113)
Chardon Custom Polymers LLC..............F...... 440 285-2161
Chardon (G-3143)
Clark Rbr Plastic Intl Sls Inc.................D...... 440 953-9514
Mentor (G-13544)
Cleveland Rubber Products LLC..............G...... 440 564-7100
Newbury (G-15084)
Columbus Gasket Co Inc........................G...... 614 878-6041
Columbus (G-6953)
Contitech Usa Inc..................................F...... 330 664-7000
Fairlawn (G-9748)
Custom Rubber Corporation...................D...... 216 391-2928
Cleveland (G-5151)
Datwyler Sling Sltions USA Inc..............D...... 937 387-2800
Vandalia (G-19289)
Eaton-Aeroquip Llc................................C...... 216 523-5000
Cleveland (G-5254)
Enduro Rubber Company........................G...... 330 296-9603
Ravenna (G-16529)
Hhi Company Inc....................................G...... 330 455-3983
Canton (G-2727)
Hytech Silicone Products Inc..................G...... 330 297-1888
Ravenna (G-16533)
Ier Fujikura Inc.....................................C...... 330 425-7121
Macedonia (G-12458)
Jet Rubber Company..............................E...... 330 325-1821
Rootstown (G-16723)
K F D Inc...G...... 330 773-4300
Akron (G-246)
Karman Rubber Company........................E...... 330 864-2161
Akron (G-251)
Lauren International Ltd.........................C...... 330 339-3373
New Philadelphia (G-14908)
Lauren Manufacturing LLC.....................B...... 330 339-3373
New Philadelphia (G-14909)
Luxx Ultra-Tech Inc...............................G...... 330 483-6051
Medina (G-13438)
Macdivitt Rubber Company LLC..............E...... 440 259-5937
Perry (G-16054)
MPS Manufacturing Company LLC..........G...... 330 343-1435
New Philadelphia (G-14917)
Mullins Rubber Products Inc..................D...... 937 233-4211
Dayton (G-8514)
Neff-Perkins Company...........................C...... 440 632-1658
Middlefield (G-13975)
Newact Inc...F...... 513 321-5177
Batavia (G-1213)
Noster Rubber Company Inc...................F...... 419 299-3387
Van Buren (G-19240)
Park-Ohio Holdings Corp........................F...... 440 947-2000
Cleveland (G-5966)
Park-Ohio Industries Inc........................C...... 440 947-2000
Cleveland (G-5967)
Park-Ohio Products Inc..........................D...... 216 961-7200
Cleveland (G-5969)
Plabell Rubber Products Corp................F...... 419 691-5878
Toledo (G-18646)

PRODUCT

Profile Rubber Corporation ....F 330 239-1703
Wadsworth (G-19431)
Q Model Inc ....E 330 673-0473
Barberton (G-1144)
Qualiform Inc ....E 330 336-6777
Wadsworth (G-19432)
R C A Rubber Company ....D 330 784-1291
Akron (G-361)
Raydar Inc of Ohio ....E 330 334-6111
Wadsworth (G-19435)
Robin Industries Inc ....C 330 359-5418
Winesburg (G-20707)
Robin Industries Inc ....C 330 695-9300
Fredericksburg (G-10092)
Robin Industries Inc ....G 216 267-3554
Cleveland (G-6124)
Robin Industries Inc ....E 330 893-3501
Berlin (G-1652)
Rubber Associates Inc ....D 330 745-2186
New Franklin (G-14831)
Rubber-Tech Inc ....F 937 274-1114
Dayton (G-8640)
Sorbothane Inc ....E 330 678-9444
Kent (G-11530)
Sumiriko Ohio Inc ....C 419 358-2121
Bluffton (G-1916)
Sur-Seal Corporation ....C 513 574-8500
Cincinnati (G-4485)
Taradon Rubber Co Inc ....F 330 896-3143
Akron (G-428)
TMI Inc ....E 330 270-9780
Youngstown (G-21223)
Tristan Rubber Molding Inc ....E 330 499-4055
North Canton (G-15278)
Universal Polymer & Rubber Ltd ....C 440 632-1691
Middlefield (G-14000)
Vernay Manufacturing Inc ....E 937 767-7261
Yellow Springs (G-21000)
Woodlawn Rubber Co ....F 513 489-1718
Blue Ash (G-1898)
Yokohama Inds Amricas Ohio Inc ....D 440 352-3321
Painesville (G-15944)

MOLDING COMPOUNDS

20/20 Custom Molded Plast ....D 419 485-2020
Montpelier (G-14437)
A Schulman Inc ....F 330 630-3315
Akron (G-20)
A Schulman Inc ....C 330 630-0308
Akron (G-21)
Ada Solutions Inc ....E 440 576-0423
Jefferson (G-11355)
Buckeye Polymers Inc ....E 330 948-3007
Lodi (G-12158)
Clyde Tool & Die Inc ....G 419 547-9574
Clyde (G-6538)
Dentsply International Inc ....D 419 865-9497
Maumee (G-13256)
Dihbowles Inc ....F 330 478-2503
Canton (G-2692)
Flex Technologies Inc ....E 330 897-6311
Baltic (G-1071)
Hadsell Chemical Proc LLC ....E 740 941-1792
Waverly (G-19710)
Hpc Holdings LLC ....F 330 666-3751
Fairlawn (G-9753)
Incredible Solutions Inc ....F 330 898-3878
Warren (G-19559)
Jain America Foods Inc ....G 614 850-9400
Columbus (G-7222)
Jain America Holdings Inc ....G 614 850-9400
Columbus (G-7223)
JMS Industries Inc ....E 937 325-3502
Springfield (G-17581)
Kiley Mold Company LLC ....G 513 875-3223
Fayetteville (G-9784)
L-K Industry Inc ....E 937 526-3000
Versailles (G-19351)
Meggitt (erlanger) LLC ....D 513 851-5550
Cincinnati (G-4080)
Mold Surface Textures ....G 330 678-8590
Kent (G-11494)
Pace Mold & Machine LLC ....G 330 879-1777
Massillon (G-13192)
Pro Mold Design Inc ....G 440 352-1212
Mentor (G-13697)
Resinoid Engineering Corp ....D 847 673-1050
Hebron (G-10881)
Rochling Glastic Composites LP ....C 216 486-0100
Cleveland (G-6125)

Stopol Equipment Sales LLC ....G 440 499-0030
Brunswick (G-2258)

MOLDING SAND MINING

Kistler Instrument Corp ....G 937 268-5920
Dayton (G-8442)
Standex International Corp ....E 513 871-3777
Cincinnati (G-4457)

MOLDINGS & TRIM: Metal, Exc Automobile

Aluminum Color Industries Inc ....E 330 536-6295
Lowellville (G-12404)

MOLDINGS & TRIM: Wood

A & B Wood Design Assoc Inc ....G 330 721-2789
Wadsworth (G-19385)
Armstrong Custom Moulding Inc ....G 740 922-5931
Uhrichsville (G-19045)
Fairfield Woodworks Ltd ....G 740 689-1953
Lancaster (G-11715)

MOLDINGS OR TRIM: Automobile, Stamped Metal

American Quality Molds LLC ....G 513 276-7345
Hamilton (G-10665)
American Trim LLC ....A 419 228-1145
Sidney (G-17167)
Angell-Demmel North Amer Corp ....D 937 461-5800
Dayton (G-8158)
Florida Production Engrg Inc ....D 937 996-4361
New Madison (G-14869)
M-Tek Inc ....A 419 209-0399
Upper Sandusky (G-19130)
Pennant Companies ....B 614 451-1782
Columbus (G-7476)

MOLDINGS, ARCHITECTURAL: Plaster Of Paris

Richtech Industries Inc ....G 440 937-4401
Avon (G-1009)
Stephen R Lilley ....G 513 899-4400
Morrow (G-14551)

MOLDINGS: Picture Frame

Frame USA ....E 513 577-7107
Cincinnati (G-3776)
Ginnys Custom Framing Gallery ....G 419 468-7240
Galion (G-10272)
House of 10000 Picture Frames ....G 937 254-5541
Dayton (G-8393)

MOLDS: Gray, Ingot, Cast Iron

Anchor Glass Container Corp ....C 740 452-2743
Zanesville (G-21272)
Ellwood Engineered Castings Co ....C 330 568-3000
Hubbard (G-11130)
Kenton Iron Products Inc ....E 419 674-4178
Kenton (G-11554)
Kenton Iron Products Inc ....E 419 674-4178
Kenton (G-11555)

MOLDS: Indl

Akron Centl Engrv Mold Mch Inc ....E 330 794-8704
Akron (G-37)
Alpha Tool & Mold Inc ....F 440 473-2343
Cleveland (G-4769)
American Cube Mold Inc ....G 330 558-0044
Hinckley (G-11022)
Amerimold Inc ....G 330 628-2190
Mogadore (G-14367)
Anchor Foundry & Machine Inc ....G 330 453-3441
Canton (G-2603)
Barberton Mold & Machine Co ....G 330 745-8559
Barberton (G-1108)
Borke Mold Specialist Inc ....F 513 870-8000
West Chester (G-19820)
Broadway Companies ....E 937 890-1888
Dayton (G-8197)
C & D Tool Inc ....G 440 942-8463
Eastlake (G-9260)
Caliber Mold and Machine Inc ....E 330 633-8171
Akron (G-107)
Camden Concrete Products ....G 937 456-1229
Eaton (G-9302)

Canton Pattern & Mold Inc ....G 330 455-4316
Canton (G-2645)
Century Die Company LLC ....D 419 332-2693
Fremont (G-10136)
Cincinnati Mold Incorporated ....G 513 922-1888
Cincinnati (G-3561)
Creative Foam Dayton Mold ....G 937 279-9987
Dayton (G-8249)
Cubic Blue Inc ....G 330 638-2999
Cortland (G-7866)
Deca Manufacturing Co Inc ....D 419 884-0071
Mansfield (G-12594)
Diversified Mold Castings LLC ....E 216 663-1814
Cleveland (G-5199)
Durivage Pattern & Mfg Co ....E 419 836-8655
Williston (G-20420)
Elliott Mfg Co ....F 937 833-4430
Brookville (G-2182)
Erickson-Huff Tool and Die ....G 740 596-4036
Mc Arthur (G-13331)
Estee Mold & Die Inc ....E 937 224-7853
Dayton (G-8332)
Esterle Mold & Machine Co Inc ....E 330 686-1685
Stow (G-17748)
Exodus Mold & Machine Inc ....G 330 854-0282
Canal Fulton (G-2501)
Faith Tool & Manufacturing ....G 440 951-5934
Willoughby (G-20485)
Ferriot Inc ....C 330 786-3000
Akron (G-185)
H&M Machine & Tool LLC ....E 419 776-9220
Toledo (G-18491)
Herbert Machine Works Inc ....D 330 929-4297
Akron (G-221)
High Tech Mold & Machine Co ....F 330 896-4466
Uniontown (G-19087)
J & H Corporation ....G 440 357-5982
Painesville (G-15893)
J Tek Tool & Mold Inc ....F 419 547-9476
Clyde (G-6541)
Kent Mold and Manufacturing Co ....E 330 673-3469
Kent (G-11480)
King Machine of Akron Inc ....E 330 762-7116
Akron (G-258)
Liberty Die Cast Molds Inc ....F 740 666-7492
Ostrander (G-15788)
Lightning Mold & Machine Inc ....F 440 593-6460
Conneaut (G-7813)
Magnum Molding Inc ....G 937 368-3040
Conover (G-7824)
Mallory Pattern Works Inc ....G 419 726-8001
Toledo (G-18572)
Martz Mold & Machine Inc ....G 330 928-2159
Cuyahoga Falls (G-8024)
Maumee Pattern Company Inc ....E 419 693-4968
Toledo (G-18579)
Mercury Machine Co ....D 440 349-3222
Solon (G-17335)
Micro Mold Co Inc ....G 330 325-2373
Ravenna (G-16540)
Milacron Holdings Corp ....E 513 487-5000
Blue Ash (G-1841)
Mold Crafters Inc ....G 937 426-3179
Dayton (G-8505)
Mold Solutions ....G 800 948-4947
Oberlin (G-15645)
National Mold Remediation ....G 614 231-6653
Columbus (G-7384)
Nichols Mold Inc ....G 330 297-9719
Ravenna (G-16544)
Norwalk Precast Molds Inc ....E 419 668-1639
Norwalk (G-15557)
Numerics Unlimited Inc ....E 937 849-0100
New Carlisle (G-14810)
Oakley Die & Mold Co ....E 513 754-8500
Mason (G-13070)
Penco Tool LLC ....E 440 998-1116
Ashtabula (G-829)
Pendleton Mold & Machine LLC ....G 440 998-0041
Ashtabula (G-830)
Perfection Mold & Machine Co ....F 330 784-5435
Twinsburg (G-19000)
Plastic Mold Technology Inc ....G 330 848-4921
Barberton (G-1139)
Pyramid Mold Inc ....G 330 673-5200
Kent (G-11509)
Quality Mold Inc ....D 330 645-6653
Akron (G-357)
Retco Mold & Machine ....F 330 633-5725
Tallmadge (G-18167)

Reuther Mold & Mfg Co Inc ....D 330 923-5266
  Cuyahoga Falls *(G-8041)*

Ron-Al Mold & Machine Inc ....F 330 673-7919
  Kent *(G-11519)*

Seaway Pattern Mfg Inc ....E 419 865-5724
  Toledo *(G-18689)*

Slabe Tool Company ....G 740 439-1647
  Cambridge *(G-2476)*

Superior Mold & Die Co ....E 330 688-8251
  Munroe Falls *(G-14666)*

Tech Mold & Tool Co Inc ....G 937 667-8851
  Tipp City *(G-18304)*

Tempcraft Corporation ....C 216 391-3885
  Cleveland *(G-6303)*

Tom Smith Industries Inc ....C 937 832-1555
  Clayton *(G-4663)*

Tracker Machine Inc. ....G 330 482-4086
  Columbiana *(G-6635)*

Tree City Mold & Machine Co ....G 330 673-9807
  Kent *(G-11538)*

Turbo-Mold Inc ....G 440 352-2530
  Painesville *(G-15934)*

Velocity Concept Dev Group LLC ....G 740 685-2637
  Byesville *(G-2412)*

XCEL Mold and Machine Inc ....F 330 499-8450
  Canton *(G-2905)*

Yugo Mold Inc ....F 330 606-0710
  Akron *(G-479)*

MOLDS: Plastic Working & Foundry

Allen Mold & Die Inc ....G 440 944-1819
  Willowick *(G-20646)*

Aspec Inc ....G 513 561-9922
  Cincinnati *(G-3420)*

Basilius Inc ....E 419 536-5810
  Toledo *(G-18364)*

Case Pattern Co Inc ....G 216 531-0744
  Cleveland *(G-4987)*

Centerline Tool & Machine ....G 937 222-3600
  Dayton *(G-8221)*

Circle Mold Incorporated ....E 330 633-7017
  Tallmadge *(G-18138)*

Data Mold and Tool Inc ....G 419 878-9861
  Waterville *(G-19655)*

De-Lux Mold & Machine Inc ....G 330 678-1030
  Kent *(G-11447)*

Delco Corporation ....E 330 896-4220
  Akron *(G-145)*

Diamond Mold & Die Co ....F 330 633-5682
  Tallmadge *(G-18141)*

Diemaster Tool & Mold Inc ....F 330 467-4281
  Macedonia *(G-12445)*

Diversified Tool Systems ....G 419 845-2143
  Caledonia *(G-2436)*

Eger Products Inc ....D 513 753-4200
  Amelia *(G-575)*

Enterprise Plastics Inc ....E 330 346-0496
  Kent *(G-11456)*

Founder Service & Mfg Co ....F 330 584-7759
  Deerfield *(G-8773)*

Green Machine Tool Inc ....F 937 253-0771
  Dayton *(G-8106)*

Hamilton Mold & Machine Co ....E 216 732-8200
  Cleveland *(G-5474)*

Industrial Mold Inc ....E 330 425-7374
  Twinsburg *(G-18959)*

Justin P Straub LLC ....G 513 761-0282
  Cincinnati *(G-3963)*

Liqui-Box Corporation ....C 419 209-9085
  Upper Sandusky *(G-19129)*

Match Mold & Machine Inc ....E 330 830-5503
  Massillon *(G-13176)*

Midwest Mold & Texture Corp ....E 513 732-1300
  Batavia *(G-1205)*

Milacron Plas Tech Group LLC ....C 513 536-2000
  Batavia *(G-1208)*

Milacron Plas Tech Group LLC ....C 937 444-2532
  Mount Orab *(G-14583)*

Pace Mold & Machine LLC ....G 330 879-1777
  Massillon *(G-13192)*

Premiere Mold and Machine Co ....G 330 874-3000
  Bolivar *(G-1942)*

Preuss Mold & Die ....G 419 729-9100
  Toledo *(G-18656)*

Promold Inc ....F 330 633-3532
  Tallmadge *(G-18165)*

Prospect Mold & Die Company ....D 330 929-3311
  Cuyahoga Falls *(G-8037)*

Ross Special Products Inc ....F 937 335-8406
  Troy *(G-18869)*

Shelburne Corp ....G 216 321-9177
  Shaker Heights *(G-17094)*

Skribs Tool and Die Inc ....E 440 951-7774
  Mentor *(G-13724)*

Thomas Tool & Mold Company ....F 614 890-4978
  Westerville *(G-20237)*

Universal Tire Molds Inc ....E 330 253-5101
  Akron *(G-458)*

Vinyltech Inc ....E 330 538-0369
  North Jackson *(G-15302)*

Ward Mold & Machine ....G 740 472-5303
  Woodsfield *(G-20722)*

Wentworth Mold Inc Electra ....D 937 898-8460
  Vandalia *(G-19317)*

MOLYBDENUM SILICON, EXC MADE IN BLAST FURNACES

H C Starck Inc ....B 216 692-3990
  Euclid *(G-9584)*

MONORAIL SYSTEMS

Webb-Stiles Company ....D 330 225-7761
  Valley City *(G-19237)*

MONUMENTS: Concrete

Art Columbus Memorial Inc ....G 614 221-9333
  Columbus *(G-6773)*

Jackson Monument Inc ....G 740 286-1590
  Jackson *(G-11316)*

MONUMENTS: Cut Stone, Exc Finishing Or Lettering Only

Dodds Monument Inc ....G 937 372-2736
  Xenia *(G-20948)*

Solon Granite Memorial Works ....G 440 248-6606
  Solon *(G-17384)*

MOPS: Floor & Dust

Guardian Co Inc ....G 216 721-2262
  Cleveland *(G-5464)*

Ha-Ste Manufacturing Co Inc ....E 937 968-4858
  Union City *(G-19071)*

Impact Products LLC ....C 419 841-2891
  Toledo *(G-18518)*

MOTION PICTURE & VIDEO PRODUCTION SVCS

David Esrati ....G 937 228-4433
  Dayton *(G-8266)*

Province of St John The Baptis ....D 513 241-5615
  Cincinnati *(G-4301)*

MOTION PICTURE EQPT

Da-Lite Screen Company LLC ....E 574 267-8101
  Blue Ash *(G-1774)*

Eprad Inc ....G 419 666-3266
  Perrysburg *(G-16093)*

MOTION PICTURE PRODUCTION & DISTRIBUTION: Television

Estreamz Inc ....E 513 278-7836
  Cincinnati *(G-3719)*

MOTOR & GENERATOR PARTS: Electric

Electrocraft Arkansas Inc ....D 501 268-4203
  Gallipolis *(G-10294)*

Parker-Hannifin Corporation ....C 330 336-3511
  Wadsworth *(G-19425)*

Ramco Electric Motors Inc ....D 937 548-2525
  Greenville *(G-10516)*

Swiger Coil Systems Ltd ....C 216 362-7500
  Cleveland *(G-6280)*

Wabtec Corporation ....C 216 362-7500
  Cleveland *(G-6437)*

MOTOR HOMES

Advanced Rv LLC ....G 440 283-0405
  Willoughby *(G-20425)*

Airstream Inc ....B 937 596-6111
  Jackson Center *(G-11337)*

MOTOR REBUILDING SVCS, EXC AUTOMOTIVE

Integrated Power Services LLC ....E 513 863-8816
  Hamilton *(G-10707)*

Joe Baker Equipment Sales ....G 513 451-1327
  Cincinnati *(G-3948)*

MOTOR REPAIR SVCS

Bar1 Motorsports ....F 614 284-3732
  Marysville *(G-12933)*

General Electric Intl Inc ....G 410 737-7228
  Cincinnati *(G-3816)*

Home Service Station Inc ....G 419 678-2612
  Coldwater *(G-6565)*

Southwest Electric Co ....F 330 875-7000
  Louisville *(G-12330)*

MOTOR SCOOTERS & PARTS

Dana Companies LLC ....G 419 931-9086
  Perrysburg *(G-16082)*

Huffy Corporation ....D 937 865-2800
  Centerville *(G-3043)*

MOTOR VEHICLE ASSEMBLY, COMPLETE: Ambulances

Braun Industries Inc ....C 419 232-7020
  Van Wert *(G-19246)*

Horton Enterprises Inc ....G 614 539-8181
  Grove City *(G-10563)*

La Boit Specialty Vehicles ....E 614 231-7640
  Gahanna *(G-10216)*

MOTOR VEHICLE ASSEMBLY, COMPLETE: Autos, Incl Specialty

Auto Expo USA of Cleveland ....G 216 889-3000
  Cleveland *(G-4863)*

Brookville Roadster Inc ....E 937 833-4605
  Brookville *(G-2176)*

Electro Prime Assembly Inc ....F 419 476-0100
  Rossford *(G-16738)*

Farber Specialty Vehicles Inc ....C 614 863-6470
  Reynoldsburg *(G-16589)*

General Motors LLC ....A 330 824-5000
  Warren *(G-19553)*

Great Lakes Assemblies LLC ....D 937 645-3900
  East Liberty *(G-9200)*

Honda of America Mfg Inc ....A 937 642-5000
  Marysville *(G-12950)*

Honda of America Mfg Inc ....B 937 642-5000
  Marysville *(G-12952)*

K K Racing Chassis ....G 330 628-2930
  Akron *(G-247)*

Magic Dragon Machine Inc ....G 614 539-8004
  Grove City *(G-10570)*

P C Workshop Inc ....D 419 399-4805
  Paulding *(G-16012)*

Pittsburgh Glass Works LLC ....C 419 569-7521
  Crestline *(G-7934)*

Star Fab Inc ....E 330 482-1601
  Columbiana *(G-6634)*

Toledo Molding & Die Inc ....D 419 720-3500
  Toledo *(G-18735)*

Universal Composite LLC ....E 614 507-1646
  Sunbury *(G-18077)*

Weastec Incorporated ....G 614 734-9645
  Dublin *(G-9165)*

Weiss Motors ....G 330 678-5585
  Kent *(G-11542)*

Wyatt Specialties Inc ....G 614 989-5362
  Circleville *(G-4650)*

MOTOR VEHICLE ASSEMBLY, COMPLETE: Bus/Large Spclty Vehicles

Buses International ....F 440 233-4091
  Lorain *(G-12235)*

MOTOR VEHICLE ASSEMBLY, COMPLETE: Buses, All Types

Aftermarket Parts Company LLC ....B 740 369-1056
  Delaware *(G-8818)*

Eldorado National Kansas Inc ....G 937 596-6849
  Jackson Center *(G-11340)*

Petermann ....G 419 925-5404
  Maria Stein *(G-12760)*

Employee Codes: A=Over 500 employees, B=251-500
C=101-250, D=51-100, E=20-50, F=10-19, G=3-9

2017 Harris Ohio
Industrial Directory

1579

PRODUCT

Thor Industries Inc ....E 937 596-6111
Jackson Center *(G-11349)*

MOTOR VEHICLE ASSEMBLY, COMPLETE: Cars, Armored

Hyq Technologies LLC ....G 513 225-6911
Oxford *(G-15837)*
Svm America Ltd ....E 937 218-7591
Maineville *(G-12532)*

MOTOR VEHICLE ASSEMBLY, COMPLETE: Fire Department Vehicles

Antram Fire Equipment ....G....330 525-7171
North Georgetown *(G-15286)*
Bethlehem Fire and Rescue Inc............G....330 879-5800
Navarre *(G-14710)*
Columbus Fire Fighters Union ....G....614 481-8900
Columbus *(G-6951)*
Copley Fire & Rescue Assn ....E 330 666-6464
Copley *(G-7843)*
Reberland Equipment Inc ....F 330 698-5883
Apple Creek *(G-648)*
Sutphen Corporation ....C 800 726-7030
Dublin *(G-9150)*
United Fire Apparatus Corp ....G....419 645-4083
Cridersville *(G-7947)*

MOTOR VEHICLE ASSEMBLY, COMPLETE: Hearses

Accubuilt Inc ....C 419 224-3910
Lima *(G-11980)*
Accubuilt Inc ....C 419 224-3910
Lima *(G-11981)*
Eagle Coach Inc ....D 513 797-4100
Amelia *(G-573)*

MOTOR VEHICLE ASSEMBLY, COMPLETE: Military Motor Vehicle

AM General LLC ....G....937 704-0160
Franklin *(G-10006)*
Mbm Industries Ltd ....G....937 522-0719
Beavercreek Township *(G-1385)*

MOTOR VEHICLE ASSEMBLY, COMPLETE: Mobile Lounges

Gerling and Associates Inc ....D 740 965-6200
Sunbury *(G-18060)*
Obs Inc ....F 330 453-3725
Canton *(G-2796)*

MOTOR VEHICLE ASSEMBLY, COMPLETE: Snow Plows

Marc Industries Inc ....G....440 944-9305
Willoughby *(G-20536)*

MOTOR VEHICLE ASSEMBLY, COMPLETE: Truck & Tractor Trucks

Navistar Inc...C 937 390-5848
Springfield *(G-17612)*
Navistar Inc...D 937 390-5653
Springfield *(G-17614)*
Navistar Inc...D 937 390-4774
Springfield *(G-17615)*
Navistar Inc...G....513 733-8500
Cincinnati *(G-4142)*
Paccar Inc ....A 740 774-5111
Chillicothe *(G-3257)*

MOTOR VEHICLE ASSEMBLY, COMPLETE: Truck Tractors, Highway

Navistar Inc...D 937 390-2800
Springfield *(G-17613)*
Navistar Inc...E 937 390-5704
Springfield *(G-17616)*

MOTOR VEHICLE ASSEMBLY, COMPLETE: Wreckers, Tow Truck

Lawsons Towing & Auto Wrckg............F 216 883-9050
Cleveland *(G-5688)*

MOTOR VEHICLE DEALERS: Automobiles, New & Used

American Honda Motor Co Inc ....C 937 332-6100
Troy *(G-18803)*
Doug Marine Motors Inc ....E 740 335-3700
Wshngtn CT Hs *(G-20907)*
Jeff Wyler Chevrolet Inc ....B 513 752-3447
Batavia *(G-1194)*
Jmac Inc..F 614 436-2418
Columbus *(G-7235)*

MOTOR VEHICLE DEALERS: Cars, Used Only

D & D Classic Auto Restoration ....E 937 473-2229
Covington *(G-7921)*
Sammartino Welding & Auto Sls ....G....330 782-6086
Youngstown *(G-21196)*
Tuffy Manufacturing ....G....330 940-2356
Cuyahoga Falls *(G-8058)*

MOTOR VEHICLE DEALERS: Pickups & Vans, Used

Life Star Rescue Inc.............................E 419 238-2507
Van Wert *(G-19266)*

MOTOR VEHICLE DEALERS: Pickups, New & Used

Knippen Chrysler Dodge Jeep ....E 419 695-4976
Delphos *(G-8909)*

MOTOR VEHICLE DEALERS: Trucks, Tractors/Trailers, New & Used

Friess Welding Inc ....F 330 644-8160
Akron *(G-195)*
Steubenville Truck Center Inc...............E 740 282-2711
Steubenville *(G-17715)*
Tbone Sales LLC ....E 330 897-6131
Baltic *(G-1077)*
Tiger General LLC ....D 330 239-4949
Medina *(G-13489)*
Trailer One Inc ....G....330 723-7474
Medina *(G-13490)*

MOTOR VEHICLE DEALERS: Vans, New & Used

Steves Vans & Accessories LLC ....G....740 374-3154
Marietta *(G-12836)*

MOTOR VEHICLE PARTS & ACCESS: Acceleration Eqpt

Yachiyo of America Inc..........................D 614 876-3220
Columbus *(G-7781)*

MOTOR VEHICLE PARTS & ACCESS: Air Conditioner Parts

Delphi Automotive Systems LLC ....B 330 306-1000
Warren *(G-19542)*
Ftd Investments LLC ....C 937 833-2161
Brookville *(G-2184)*
Hanon Systems Usa LLC ....C 313 920-0583
Carey *(G-2919)*
Mahle Behr Dayton LLC ....B 937 369-2900
Dayton *(G-8470)*
Majestic Trailers Inc ....F 330 798-1698
Akron *(G-280)*
Taiho Corporation of America................C 419 443-1645
Tiffin *(G-18246)*

MOTOR VEHICLE PARTS & ACCESS: Axel Housings & Shafts

Angstrom Automotive Group LLC.........G....440 255-6700
Mentor *(G-13521)*
Jae Tech Inc ....D 330 698-2000
Apple Creek *(G-640)*
Ktsdi LLC ....G....330 783-2000
North Lima *(G-15318)*
Omsi Transmissions Inc ....G....330 405-7350
Twinsburg *(G-18993)*
Pdi Ground Support Systems Inc ....D 216 271-7344
Solon *(G-17360)*

MOTOR VEHICLE PARTS & ACCESS: Bearings

Green Acquisition LLC ....E 440 930-7600
Avon *(G-997)*
Kyklos Bearing Intl LLC ....B 419 627-7000
Sandusky *(G-16977)*
S & A Precision Bearing Inc ....C 440 930-7600
Avon *(G-1010)*

MOTOR VEHICLE PARTS & ACCESS: Body Components & Frames

ARE Inc ....B 330 830-7800
Massillon *(G-13111)*
Beasley Fiberglass Inc ....G....440 357-6644
Painesville *(G-15861)*
Core Automotive Tech LLC ....C 614 870-5000
Columbus *(G-6982)*
David Boswell ....E 614 441-2497
Columbus *(G-7014)*
Frontier Tank Center Inc ....E 330 659-3888
Richfield *(G-16624)*
Gerich Fiberglass Inc ....E 419 362-4591
Mount Gilead *(G-14560)*
Green Tokai Co Ltd ....A 937 833-5444
Brookville *(G-2185)*
Karg Fiberglass Inc...............................G....330 494-2611
Middlebranch *(G-13901)*
Magna Modular Systems Inc ....D 419 324-3387
Toledo *(G-18570)*
Oakley Industries Sub Assembly ....E 419 661-8888
Northwood *(G-15486)*
Tower Automotive Operations I ....C 419 483-1500
Bellevue *(G-1564)*
TS Tech USA Corporation ....C 614 577-1088
Reynoldsburg *(G-16610)*
Vivid Wraps LLC ....G....513 515-8386
Cincinnati *(G-4569)*

MOTOR VEHICLE PARTS & ACCESS: Booster Cables, Jump-Start

Noco Company ....B 216 464-8131
Solon *(G-17350)*
SMH Manufacturing Inc ....F 419 884-0071
Lexington *(G-11952)*

MOTOR VEHICLE PARTS & ACCESS: Brakes, Air

Bendix Spcer Fndtion Brake LLC ....C 440 329-9709
Elyria *(G-9380)*
Eaton Corporation ....C 216 281-2211
Cleveland *(G-5247)*
Johnson Welded Products Inc ....C 937 652-1242
Urbana *(G-19166)*

MOTOR VEHICLE PARTS & ACCESS: Clutches

Pt Tech Inc..D 330 239-4933
Sharon Center *(G-17108)*
Westfield Steel Inc ....D 937 322-2414
Springfield *(G-17677)*

MOTOR VEHICLE PARTS & ACCESS: Connecting Rods

TRW Automotive Inc ....E 216 750-2400
Cleveland *(G-6371)*
Usui International Corporation ....G....513 448-0410
Sharonville *(G-17115)*

MOTOR VEHICLE PARTS & ACCESS: Cylinder Heads

All Pro Alum Cylinder Heads ....G....740 967-7761
Johnstown *(G-11387)*
Done Right Engine & Machine ....G....440 582-1366
Cleveland *(G-5206)*

MOTOR VEHICLE PARTS & ACCESS: Electrical Eqpt

Eaton Corporation ....B 440 523-5000
Beachwood *(G-1267)*
Enhanced Mfg Solutions LLC ....D 440 476-1244
Brecksville *(G-2047)*

Mrs Electronic Inc ....F 937 660-6767
Dayton *(G-8513)*

Stoneridge Inc ....A 419 884-1219
Lexington *(G-11953)*

Supplier Park Industries LLC ....D 440 476-1244
Brecksville *(G-2074)*

Utv Hitchworks Llc ....G 513 615-8568
Maineville *(G-12533)*

Weastec Incorporated ....C 937 393-6800
Hillsboro *(G-11018)*

MOTOR VEHICLE PARTS & ACCESS: Engines & Parts

Alegre Inc ....F 937 885-6786
Miamisburg *(G-13782)*

Areway LLC ....D 216 651-9022
Brooklyn *(G-2128)*

Custom Fab ....G 330 825-3586
Norton *(G-15509)*

Custom Speed Parts Inc ....F 440 238-3260
Strongsville *(G-17909)*

Detroit Toledo Fiber LLC ....F 248 647-0400
Toledo *(G-18436)*

Dexol Industries Inc ....G 330 633-4477
Akron *(G-148)*

Eaton Corporation ....B 216 523-5000
Cleveland *(G-5245)*

Eaton Corporation ....C 216 416-2500
Cleveland *(G-5246)*

Fetters Racing Engine Inc ....F 937 698-6411
Union *(G-19066)*

Flaming River Industries Inc ....F 440 826-4488
Berea *(G-1616)*

Ford Motor Company ....A 419 226-7000
Lima *(G-12014)*

Fram Group Operations LLC ....D 419 661-6700
Perrysburg *(G-16097)*

Gregory Auto Service ....G 513 248-0423
Loveland *(G-12355)*

Gt Technologies Inc ....C 419 782-8955
Defiance *(G-8792)*

Gt Technologies Inc ....D 419 324-7300
Toledo *(G-18489)*

Hite Parts Exchange Inc ....E 614 272-5115
Columbus *(G-7160)*

Interstate-Mcbee LLC ....G 800 321-4234
Cleveland *(G-5584)*

Keihin Thermal Tech Amer Inc .....B 740 869-3000
Mount Sterling *(G-14599)*

Lakota Racing ....G 330 627-7255
Carrollton *(G-2959)*

Lorain County Auto Systems Inc ...D 248 442-6800
Elyria *(G-9454)*

Lorain County Auto Systems Inc ...E 440 960-7470
Lorain *(G-12256)*

Pro Gram Engineering Corp ....G 330 745-1004
Barberton *(G-1143)*

Qualitor Inc ....G 248 204-8600
Lima *(G-12078)*

Satco Inc ....G 330 630-8866
Tallmadge *(G-18168)*

Soundwich Inc ....D 216 486-2666
Cleveland *(G-6221)*

Supercharger Systems Inc ....G 216 676-5800
Brookpark *(G-2170)*

Switzer Performance Engrg ....F 440 774-4219
Oberlin *(G-15648)*

Tenneco Automotive Oper Co Inc ...D 937 781-4940
Kettering *(G-11587)*

Vanderpool Motor Sports ....G 513 424-2166
Middletown *(G-14094)*

W W Williams Company LLC ....F 330 659-3084
Richfield *(G-16645)*

MOTOR VEHICLE PARTS & ACCESS: Engs & Trans,Factory, Rebuilt

Recon Systems LLC ....G 330 484-8444
East Canton *(G-9196)*

MOTOR VEHICLE PARTS & ACCESS: Frames

Chantilly Development Corp ....F 419 243-8109
Toledo *(G-18393)*

Scott Emerson ....G 330 372-1040
Warren *(G-19599)*

MOTOR VEHICLE PARTS & ACCESS: Fuel Pumps

Bergstrom Company Ltd Partnr .....E 440 232-2282
Cleveland *(G-4905)*

Manuel Tamargo ....G 330 456-3080
Akron *(G-282)*

MOTOR VEHICLE PARTS & ACCESS: Fuel Systems & Parts

Interstate Diesel Service Inc ....C 216 881-0015
Cleveland *(G-5582)*

Onix Corporation ....E 800 844-0076
Perrysburg *(G-16136)*

MOTOR VEHICLE PARTS & ACCESS: Gas Tanks

Buckley Manufacturing Company ...F 513 821-4444
Cincinnati *(G-3485)*

MOTOR VEHICLE PARTS & ACCESS: Gears

All Wright Enterprises LLC ....G 440 259-5656
Perry *(G-16047)*

Cincinnati Gearing Systems Inc ...C 513 527-8600
Cincinnati *(G-3554)*

Gear Company of America Inc ....D 216 671-5400
Cleveland *(G-5404)*

Geartec Inc ....G 440 953-3900
Willoughby *(G-20497)*

Ig Watteeuw Usa LLC ....F 740 588-1722
Zanesville *(G-21321)*

Scs Gearbox Inc ....F 419 483-7278
Bellevue *(G-1557)*

Trojon Gear Inc ....F 937 254-1737
Dayton *(G-8729)*

MOTOR VEHICLE PARTS & ACCESS: Heaters

Hdt Expeditionary Systems Inc ....G 216 438-6111
Solon *(G-17308)*

Jbar A/C Inc ....F 216 447-4294
Cleveland *(G-5609)*

Lintern Corporation ....E 440 255-9333
Mentor *(G-13635)*

MOTOR VEHICLE PARTS & ACCESS: Ice Scrapers & Window Brushes

OReilly Equipment LLC ....G 440 564-1234
Newbury *(G-15101)*

MOTOR VEHICLE PARTS & ACCESS: Instrument Board Assemblies

New Sabina Industries Inc ....B 937 584-2433
Sabina *(G-16774)*

MOTOR VEHICLE PARTS & ACCESS: Manifolds

Atlas Industries Inc ....D 419 447-4730
Tiffin *(G-18206)*

Mueller Gas Products ....D 513 424-5311
Middletown *(G-14066)*

MOTOR VEHICLE PARTS & ACCESS: Mufflers, Exhaust

Chestnut Holdings Inc ....G 330 849-6503
Akron *(G-122)*

Dreison International Inc ....C 216 362-0755
Cleveland *(G-5215)*

Faurecia Automotive Holdings ......A 419 727-5000
Toledo *(G-18461)*

Faurecia Exhaust Systems LLC .....C 419 727-5000
Toledo *(G-18463)*

Faurecia Exhaust Systems LLC .....C 330 824-2807
Warren *(G-19549)*

Faurecia USA Holdings Inc ....A 419 727-5000
Toledo *(G-18464)*

Josh L Derksen ....G 937 548-0080
Greenville *(G-10507)*

Riker Products Inc ....C 419 729-1626
Toledo *(G-18676)*

Supertrapp Industries Inc ....D 216 265-8400
Cleveland *(G-6273)*

MOTOR VEHICLE PARTS & ACCESS: Power Steering Eqpt

Maval Industries LLC ....C 330 405-1600
Twinsburg *(G-18981)*

Steer & Gear Inc ....E 614 231-4064
Columbus *(G-7655)*

MOTOR VEHICLE PARTS & ACCESS: Propane Conversion Eqpt

Superior Energy Systems LLC ......F 440 236-6009
Columbia Station *(G-6601)*

MOTOR VEHICLE PARTS & ACCESS: Pumps, Hydraulic Fluid Power

Eaton Corporation ....B 216 523-5000
Beachwood *(G-1268)*

Eaton Corporation ....B 216 920-2000
Cleveland *(G-5249)*

MOTOR VEHICLE PARTS & ACCESS: Sanders, Safety

Doran Mfg LLC ....F 513 681-5424
Cincinnati *(G-3664)*

MOTOR VEHICLE PARTS & ACCESS: Tie Rods

Mid-West Fabricating Co ....C 740 969-4411
Amanda *(G-563)*

Mid-West Fabricating Co ....G 740 681-4411
Lancaster *(G-11729)*

MOTOR VEHICLE PARTS & ACCESS: Tire Valve Cores

31 Inc ....D 740 498-8324
Newcomerstown *(G-15107)*

MOTOR VEHICLE PARTS & ACCESS: Trailer Hitches

White Mule Company ....E 740 382-9008
Ontario *(G-15697)*

MOTOR VEHICLE PARTS & ACCESS: Transmission Housings Or Parts

Oerlikon Friction Systems ....C 937 449-4000
Dayton *(G-8540)*

MOTOR VEHICLE PARTS & ACCESS: Transmissions

Florence Alloys Inc ....G 330 745-9141
Barberton *(G-1115)*

Goodale Auto-Truck Parts Inc ....E 614 294-4777
Columbus *(G-7125)*

MOTOR VEHICLE PARTS & ACCESS: Water Pumps

ASC Holdco Inc ....G 330 899-0340
Canton *(G-2607)*

ASC Industries Inc ....E 330 899-0340
North Canton *(G-15220)*

Hytec Automotive Ind LLC ....F 614 527-9370
Columbus *(G-7175)*

Hytec-Debartolo LLC ....F 614 527-9370
Columbus *(G-7176)*

MOTOR VEHICLE PARTS & ACCESS: Wheel rims

Wheel Group Holdings LLC ....G 614 253-6247
Columbus *(G-7760)*

MOTOR VEHICLE PARTS & ACCESS: Windshield Frames

T L H Windshield Repair ....G
Botkins *(G-1955)*

**P
R
O
D
U
C
T**

MOTOR VEHICLE PARTS & ACCESS: Winter Fronts

Bug-Barrier Screen Corp....................G....... 330 723-2551
  Medina (G-13384)

MOTOR VEHICLE PARTS & ACCESS: Wiring Harness Sets

Carlton-Bates Company ....G....... 937 384-0426
  Miamisburg (G-13789)
Connective Design Incorporated........F....... 937 746-8252
  Miamisburg (G-13793)
Designed Harness Systems Inc ....F....... 937 599-2485
  Bellefontaine (G-1527)
G S Wiring Systems Inc ....G....... 419 423-7111
  Findlay (G-9829)
GSW Manufacturing Inc ....B....... 419 423-7111
  Findlay (G-9834)
Matrix Cable and Mould ....G....... 513 832-2577
  Cincinnati (G-4067)
Ohio Harness LLC..............................G....... 937 292-7355
  Bellefontaine (G-1537)
Sumitomo Elc Wirg Systems Inc ....E....... 937 642-7579
  Marysville (G-12974)

MOTOR VEHICLE SPLYS & PARTS WHOLESALERS: New

Anest Iwata Usa Inc ....G....... 513 755-3100
  Hamilton (G-10670)
ARE Inc ....B....... 330 830-7800
  Massillon (G-13111)
Contitech North America Inc ....E....... 440 225-5363
  Akron (G-129)
Custer Products Limited ....F....... 330 490-3158
  North Canton (G-15225)
D-G Custom Chrome LLC ....D....... 513 531-1881
  Cincinnati (G-3634)
Dexol Industries Inc ....G....... 330 633-4477
  Akron (G-148)
Doran Mfg LLC ....F....... 513 681-5424
  Cincinnati (G-3664)
Faurecia Exhaust Systems LLC ....C....... 419 727-5000
  Toledo (G-18463)
G S Wiring Systems Inc ....G....... 419 423-7111
  Findlay (G-9829)
Gear Star American Performance ....G....... 330 434-5216
  Akron (G-200)
Goodyear Tire & Rubber Company ......A....... 330 796-2121
  Akron (G-207)
Legacy Supplies Inc ....F....... 330 405-4565
  Twinsburg (G-18971)
Mac Trailer Manufacturing Inc ....C....... 330 823-9900
  Alliance (G-525)
Neff Machinery and Supplies ....E....... 740 454-0128
  Zanesville (G-21331)
Pioneer Automotive Tech Inc ....C....... 937 746-2293
  Springboro (G-17497)
Qualitor Inc ....G....... 248 204-8600
  Lima (G-12078)
Safe Systems Inc ....G....... 216 661-1166
  Cleveland (G-6154)
Thyssenkrupp Bilstein Amer Inc ....E....... 513 881-7600
  West Chester (G-19958)
Tk Holdings Inc ....E....... 937 778-9713
  Piqua (G-16315)

MOTOR VEHICLE SPLYS & PARTS WHOLESALERS: Used

Mac Trailer Manufacturing Inc ....C....... 330 823-9900
  Alliance (G-525)

MOTOR VEHICLE: Hardware

R H Industries Inc ....E....... 216 281-5210
  Cleveland (G-6083)

MOTOR VEHICLE: Radiators

Albright Radiator Inc ....G....... 330 264-8886
  Wooster (G-20738)
Mahle Behr Service America LLC..........G....... 937 369-2610
  Xenia (G-20962)

MOTOR VEHICLE: Shock Absorbers

Pullman Company.................................E....... 419 499-2541
  Milan (G-14115)

Thyssenkrupp Bilstein Amer Inc ....C....... 513 881-7600
  Hamilton (G-10747)

MOTOR VEHICLE: Wheels

Aap St Marys Corp ....A....... 419 394-7840
  Saint Marys (G-16830)
Dayton Wheel Concepts Inc................E....... 937 438-0100
  Dayton (G-8290)
Forgeline Inc ....F....... 937 299-0298
  Moraine (G-14488)
Goodrich Corporation ....A....... 937 339-3811
  Troy (G-18833)
Oe Exchange LLC ....G....... 440 266-1639
  Mentor (G-13671)

MOTOR VEHICLES & CAR BODIES

Airstream Inc ....B....... 937 596-6111
  Jackson Center (G-11337)
American Honda Motor Co Inc ....C....... 937 332-6100
  Troy (G-18803)
AMP Electric Vehicles Inc ....F....... 513 360-4704
  Loveland (G-12339)
Antique Auto Sheet Metal Inc ....E....... 937 833-4422
  Brookville (G-2174)
Autowax Inc ....G....... 440 334-4417
  Strongsville (G-17894)
Bartley Lawn Service LLC ....E....... 937 435-8884
  West Carrollton (G-19791)
Bobbart Industries Inc ....E....... 419 350-5477
  Sylvania (G-18101)
Comprehensive Logistics Co Inc ....E....... 330 793-0504
  Youngstown (G-21055)
D & D Classic Auto Restoration ....E....... 937 473-2229
  Covington (G-7921)
Dakkota Integrated Systems LLC ....E....... 517 694-6500
  Toledo (G-18425)
Ford Motor Company............................A....... 440 933-1215
  Avon Lake (G-1029)
Ford Motor Company............................A....... 216 587-7700
  Cleveland (G-5368)
Galion-Godwin Truck Bdy Co LLC ....D....... 330 359-5495
  Millersburg (G-14217)
General Motors LLC..............................A....... 216 265-5000
  Cleveland (G-5419)
Honda of America Mfg Inc ....C....... 937 644-0724
  Marysville (G-12951)
JLW - TW Corp ....G....... 216 361-5940
  Avon (G-998)
Ogara Hess Eisenhardt ....G....... 513 346-1300
  West Chester (G-19907)
Rikenkaki America Corporation ....G....... 614 336-2744
  Dublin (G-9133)
Toledo Pro Fiberglass Inc ....G....... 419 241-9390
  Toledo (G-18740)
Workhorse Group Inc ....F....... 513 297-3640
  Loveland (G-12401)

MOTOR VEHICLES, WHOLESALE: Ambulances

Life Star Rescue Inc ....E....... 419 238-2507
  Van Wert (G-19266)

MOTOR VEHICLES, WHOLESALE: Commercial

Kelley Brothers Roofing Inc..................F....... 330 273-3700
  Medina (G-13432)

MOTOR VEHICLES, WHOLESALE: Fire Trucks

Fire Safety Services Inc.......................F....... 937 686-2000
  Huntsville (G-11213)

MOTOR VEHICLES, WHOLESALE: Trailers for passenger vehicles

Mr Trailer Sales Inc ....G....... 330 339-7701
  Dover (G-9004)

MOTOR VEHICLES, WHOLESALE: Trailers, Truck, New & Used

Bulk Carrier Trnsp Eqp Co ....E....... 330 339-3333
  New Philadelphia (G-14887)
M & W Trailers Inc ....F....... 419 453-3331
  Ottoville (G-15824)

M H EBY Inc ....E....... 614 879-6901
  West Jefferson (G-20081)
Mac Manufacturing Inc ....A....... 330 823-9900
  Alliance (G-523)
Mac Manufacturing Inc ....C....... 330 829-1680
  Salem (G-16913)
Mac Trailer Manufacturing Inc ....C....... 330 823-9900
  Alliance (G-525)

MOTOR VEHICLES, WHOLESALE: Truck bodies

Ace Truck Equipment Co ....E....... 740 453-0551
  Zanesville (G-21264)
Brown Industrial Inc ....E....... 937 693-3838
  Botkins (G-1951)
J W Devers & Son Inc ....E....... 937 854-3040
  Trotwood (G-18797)
Schodorf Truck Body & Eqp Co ....E....... 614 228-6793
  Columbus (G-7596)
Venco Venturo Industries LLC ....E....... 513 772-8448
  Cincinnati (G-4561)

MOTOR VEHICLES, WHOLESALE: Trucks, Noncommercial

Cipted Corp ....D....... 412 829-2120
  Monroe (G-14397)

MOTOR VEHICLES, WHOLESALE: Trucks, commercial

United Fire Apparatus Corp ....G....... 419 645-4083
  Cridersville (G-7947)
Youngstown-Kenworth Inc.....................E....... 330 534-9761
  Hubbard (G-11143)

MOTORCYCLE & BICYCLE PARTS: Frames

Franklin Frames and Cycles ....G....... 740 763-3838
  Newark (G-15008)

MOTORCYCLE ACCESS

B&D Truck Parts Sls & Svcs LLC ....G....... 419 701-7041
  Fostoria (G-9968)
Newman Technology Inc ....C....... 419 525-1856
  Mansfield (G-12656)
Outback Cycle Shack LLC ....G....... 513 554-1048
  Cincinnati (G-4203)
Thomas D Epperson ....G....... 937 855-3300
  Germantown (G-10374)

MOTORCYCLE DEALERS

Wholecycle Inc ....E....... 330 929-8123
  Peninsula (G-16045)

MOTORCYCLE DEALERS

Hot Shot Motor Works M LLC ....G....... 419 294-1997
  Upper Sandusky (G-19125)

MOTORCYCLE PARTS & ACCESS DEALERS

Gear Star American Performance ....G....... 330 434-5216
  Akron (G-200)
McIntosh Machine................................G....... 937 687-3936
  New Lebanon (G-14844)
Spiegler Brake Systems USA LLC ....G....... 937 291-1735
  Dayton (G-8670)

MOTORCYCLE PARTS: Wholesalers

Behlke Dalene ....G....... 330 399-6780
  Warren (G-19528)
McIntosh Machine................................G....... 937 687-3936
  New Lebanon (G-14844)

MOTORCYCLE REPAIR SHOPS

Alvords Yard & Garden Eqp ....G....... 440 286-2315
  Chardon (G-3140)
Outback Cycle Shack LLC ....G....... 513 554-1048
  Cincinnati (G-4203)
Sinners N Saints LLC ....G....... 614 231-7467
  Columbus (G-7625)

MOTORCYCLES & RELATED PARTS

Beasley Fiberglass Inc ....G....... 440 357-6644
  Painesville (G-15861)

(G-0000) Company's Geographic Section entry number

Cherhire Choppers ....G...... 740 362-0695
Delaware (G-8834)
Cobra Motorcycles Mfg ....E...... 330 207-3844
North Lima (G-15312)
Heritage Tool ....F...... 513 753-7300
Loveland (G-12358)
Shumaker Racing Components...........G...... 419 238-0801
Van Wert (G-19270)
Sinners N Saints LLC ....G...... 614 231-7467
Columbus (G-7625)
Sunstar Engrg Americas Inc ....E...... 937 746-8575
Springboro (G-17508)
Tc Bros Choppers LLC ....G...... 419 265-9399
Wauseon (G-19695)

MOTORCYCLES: Wholesalers

Ktm North America Inc ....D...... 440 985-3553
Amherst (G-600)
Wholecycle Inc ....E...... 330 929-8123
Peninsula (G-16045)

MOTORS: Electric

ABM Drives Inc ....G...... 513 576-1300
Loveland (G-12336)
American Mitsuba Corporation ....G...... 989 779-4962
Dublin (G-9042)
American Mitsuba Corporation ....G...... 989 779-4962
Dublin (G-9043)
Ametek Technical & Indus Pdts..........D...... 330 677-3754
Kent (G-11429)
Dcm Manufacturing Inc ....E...... 216 265-8006
Cleveland (G-5178)
Dreison International Inc...................C...... 216 362-0755
Cleveland (G-5215)
Franklin Electric Co Inc ....A...... 614 794-2266
Dublin (G-9077)
Globe Motors Inc...........................D...... 937 228-3171
Dayton (G-8370)
Hannon Company ....D...... 330 456-4728
Canton (G-2723)
Nidec Motor Corporation ....C...... 575 434-0633
Akron (G-315)
Palesh & Associates Inc ....G...... 440 942-9168
Willoughby (G-20566)
Reuland Electric Co ....G...... 513 825-7314
Cincinnati (G-4340)
Siemens Industry Inc ....C...... 513 841-3100
Cincinnati (G-4417)

MOTORS: Generators

Aadco Instruments Inc ....G...... 513 467-1477
Cleves (G-6505)
Ametek Inc....................................G...... 302 636-5401
Worthington (G-20857)
Ametek Florcare Specialty Mtrs ....F...... 330 677-3786
Kent (G-11428)
Ares Inc ....D...... 419 635-2175
Port Clinton (G-16393)
Chemequip Sales Inc ....E...... 330 724-8300
Akron (G-120)
City Machine Technologies Inc..........F...... 330 747-2639
Youngstown (G-21047)
City Machine Technologies Inc..........E...... 330 740-8186
Youngstown (G-21048)
Dayton-Phoenix Group Inc...............C...... 937 496-3900
Dayton (G-8293)
Econ-O-Machine Products Inc ....G...... 937 882-6307
Donnelsville (G-8961)
Energy Technologies Inc ....D...... 419 522-4444
Mansfield (G-12600)
Freeman Enclosure Systems LLC......C...... 877 441-8555
Batavia (G-1187)
GE Aviation Systems LLC ....B...... 937 898-5881
Vandalia (G-19293)
General Electric Company ....D...... 216 883-1000
Cleveland (G-5412)
Gleason Metrology Systems Corp ......E...... 937 384-8901
Dayton (G-8365)
Globe Motors Inc...........................C...... 334 983-3542
Dayton (G-8368)
Globe Motors Inc...........................C...... 937 228-3171
Dayton (G-8369)
Grand-Rock Company Inc ....E...... 440 639-2000
Painesville (G-15884)
Gunter Electric LLC ....G...... 304 253-4671
Athens (G-871)
Hurst Auto-Truck Electric ....G...... 216 961-1800
Cleveland (G-5538)

Industrial and Mar Eng Svc Co ....F...... 740 694-0791
Fredericktown (G-10104)
Intellitronix Corporation ....E...... 440 210-7645
Eastlake (G-9276)
JD Power Systems LLC ....F...... 614 317-9394
Hilliard (G-10955)
Lake Shore Electric Corp ....E...... 440 232-0200
Bedford (G-1438)
Linde Hydraulics Corporation ....E...... 330 533-6801
Canfield (G-2562)
Michael Bradley Apparatus LLC ....F...... 740 374-6255
Marietta (G-12807)
Ohio Magnetics Inc ....E...... 216 662-8484
Maple Heights (G-12736)
Ohio Semitronics Inc ....D...... 614 777-1005
Hilliard (G-10967)
Peerless-Winsmith Inc ....B...... 330 399-3651
Dublin (G-9121)
Peerless-Winsmith Inc ....G...... 614 526-7000
Dublin (G-9122)
R Gordon Jones Inc ....G...... 740 986-8381
Williamsport (G-20418)
Regal Beloit America Inc ....C...... 937 667-2431
Tipp City (G-18296)
Stateline Power Corp ....F...... 937 547-1006
Greenville (G-10524)
Tigerpoly Manufacturing Inc..............B...... 614 871-0045
Grove City (G-10601)
Tremont Electric Incorporated ....G...... 888 214-3137
Cleveland (G-6355)
Vanner Holdings Inc ....D...... 614 771-2718
Hilliard (G-10991)
Waibel Electric Co Inc ....F...... 740 964-2956
Etna (G-9553)

MOTORS: Pneumatic

Vickers International Inc ....E...... 419 867-2200
Maumee (G-13307)

MOTORS: Starting, Automotive & Aircraft

Mitsubishi Elc Auto Amer Inc ....B...... 513 573-6614
Mason (G-13065)

MOTORS: Torque

Alliance Torque Converters Inc ....G...... 937 222-3394
Dayton (G-8147)

MOUNTING RINGS, MOTOR Rubber Covered Or Bonded

Yusa Corporation ....A...... 740 335-0335
Washington Court Hou (G-19641)

MOUTHWASHES

Oasis Consumer Healthcare LLC ....G...... 216 394-0544
Cleveland (G-5924)

MOVING SVC: Local

C P S Enterprises Inc ....F...... 216 441-7969
Cleveland (G-4957)

MOWERS & ACCESSORIES

California Grounds Care LLC ....G...... 513 207-0244
Cincinnati (G-3494)
Friesen Fab and Equipment...............G...... 614 873-4354
Plain City (G-16340)
Tri-Tech Mfg LLC ....G...... 419 238-0140
Delphos (G-8921)

MUSEUMS

Brewster Sugarcreek Twp Histo ....F...... 330 767-0045
Brewster (G-2084)

MUSIC BROADCASTING SVCS

Musair Ohio ....G...... 330 455-2800
Massillon (G-13183)

MUSIC DISTRIBUTION APPARATUS

Q Music USA LLC ....G...... 239 995-5888
North Olmsted (G-15343)

MUSIC RECORDING PRODUCER

Tiny Lion Music Groups ....G...... 419 874-7353
Perrysburg (G-16160)

MUSICAL INSTRUMENT REPAIR

Fifth Avenue Fret Shop LLC ....G...... 614 481-8300
Columbus (G-7082)
Loft Violin Shop ....F...... 614 267-7221
Columbus (G-7303)
Paul Bartel ....G...... 513 541-2000
Cincinnati (G-4216)

MUSICAL INSTRUMENTS & ACCESS: Carrying Cases

L M Engineering Inc ....E...... 330 270-2400
Youngstown (G-21130)

MUSICAL INSTRUMENTS & ACCESS: NEC

Bbb Music LLC ....G...... 740 772-2262
Chillicothe (G-3228)
Belco Works Inc ....B...... 740 695-0500
Saint Clairsville (G-16782)
Conn-Selmer Inc ....B...... 440 946-6100
Willoughby (G-20462)
D Picking & Co ....G...... 419 562-5016
Bucyrus (G-2337)
DC Music......................................G...... 330 385-0468
East Liverpool (G-9211)
Engels Machining LLC ....G...... 419 485-1500
Montpelier (G-14445)
Loft Violin Shop ....F...... 614 267-7221
Columbus (G-7303)
New Cleveland Group Inc.................G...... 216 932-9310
Cleveland (G-5876)
The W L Jenkins Company ....F...... 330 477-3407
Canton (G-2869)
Tremelo ....G...... 330 823-6359
Alliance (G-548)
Waits Instruments LLC ....G...... 513 600-5996
Cincinnati (G-4575)

MUSICAL INSTRUMENTS & ACCESS: Pipe Organs

C E Kegg Inc ....G...... 330 877-8800
Hartville (G-10818)
J Zamberlan & Co ....G...... 740 765-9028
Steubenville (G-17700)
Lima Pipe Organ Co Inc ....G...... 419 331-5461
Elida (G-9352)
Peebles - Herzog Inc ....G...... 614 279-2211
Columbus (G-7474)
The Holtkamp Organ Co ....F...... 216 741-5180
Cleveland (G-6314)

MUSICAL INSTRUMENTS & PARTS: Brass

Brooks Manufacturing......................G...... 419 244-1777
Toledo (G-18382)
Conn-Selmer Inc ....E...... 216 391-7723
Cleveland (G-5115)

MUSICAL INSTRUMENTS & PARTS: Percussion

Universal Percussion Inc ....F...... 330 482-5750
Columbiana (G-6636)

MUSICAL INSTRUMENTS & PARTS: String

McHael D Goronok String Instrs..........G...... 216 421-4227
Cleveland (G-5769)
Paul Bartel ....G...... 513 541-2000
Cincinnati (G-4216)
S I T Strings Co Inc ....E...... 330 434-8010
Akron (G-391)
Sperzel Inc ....E...... 216 281-6868
Cleveland (G-6225)

MUSICAL INSTRUMENTS & SPLYS STORES

Bbb Music LLC ....G...... 740 772-2262
Chillicothe (G-3228)
Loft Violin Shop ....F...... 614 267-7221
Columbus (G-7303)
Paul Bartel ....G...... 513 541-2000
Cincinnati (G-4216)
S I T Strings Co Inc ....E...... 330 434-8010
Akron (G-391)
Stewart-Macdonald Mfg Co ....E...... 740 592-3021
Athens (G-885)
Universal Percussion Inc ....F...... 330 482-5750
Columbiana (G-6636)

P
R
O
D
U
C
T

Willis Music Company ....F 513 671-3288
Cincinnati **(G-4597)**

MUSICAL INSTRUMENTS & SPLYS STORES: *String instruments*

Fifth Avenue Fret Shop LLC ....G 614 481-8300
Columbus **(G-7082)**

MUSICAL INSTRUMENTS WHOLESALERS

McHael D Goronok String Instrs ....G 216 421-4227
Cleveland **(G-5769)**

MUSICAL INSTRUMENTS: *Banjos & Parts*

Stewart-Macdonald Mfg Co ....E 740 592-3021
Athens **(G-885)**

MUSICAL INSTRUMENTS: *Bells*

Bell Industries ....F 513 353-2355
Harrison **(G-10769)**
Commercial Music Service Co ....G 740 746-8500
Sugar Grove **(G-18011)**
Hisey Bells ....G 740 333-7669
Greenfield **(G-10480)**

MUSICAL INSTRUMENTS: *Carillon Bells*

I T Verdin Co ....E 513 241-4010
Cincinnati **(G-3906)**
I T Verdin Co ....E 513 241-4010
Cincinnati **(G-3907)**
I T Verdin Co ....E 513 559-3947
Cincinnati **(G-3908)**

MUSICAL INSTRUMENTS: *Guitars & Parts, Electric & Acoustic*

Earthquaker Devices LLC ....F 330 252-9220
Akron **(G-160)**
Fifth Avenue Fret Shop LLC ....G 614 481-8300
Columbus **(G-7082)**
Garys Classic Guitars ....G 513 891-0555
Loveland **(G-12351)**

MUSICAL INSTRUMENTS: *Keyboards*

D C Ramey Piano Co ....G 708 602-3961
Marysville **(G-12940)**

MUSICAL INSTRUMENTS: *Keyboards & Parts|*

Watson Meeks and Company ....G 937 378-2355
Georgetown **(G-10367)**

MUSICAL INSTRUMENTS: *Organ Parts & Materials*

A R Schopps Sons Inc ....E 330 821-8406
Alliance **(G-487)**

MUSICAL INSTRUMENTS: *Organs*

Schantz Organ Company ....E 330 682-6065
Orrville **(G-15762)**
Victor Organ Company ....G 330 792-1321
Youngstown **(G-21238)**

MUSICAL INSTRUMENTS: *Recorders, Musical*

Belmont County of Ohio ....G 740 699-2140
Saint Clairsville **(G-16783)**

MUSICAL INSTRUMENTS: *Violins & Parts*

Peter Zaret & Sons Violins ....G 440 461-1411
Cleveland **(G-5995)**

NAIL SALONS

Nail Art ....G 614 899-7155
Westerville **(G-20225)**

NAME PLATES: *Engraved Or Etched*

Auld Company ....E 614 454-1010
Columbus **(G-6786)**
Etched Metal Company ....E 440 248-0240
Solon **(G-17290)**

Hathaway Stamp & Ident Co of C ....F 513 621-1052
Cincinnati **(G-3870)**
Industrial and Mar Eng Svc Co ....F 740 694-0791
Fredericktown **(G-10104)**
Laserdealer Inc ....G 440 357-8419
Mentor **(G-13630)**
Roemer Industries Inc ....D 330 448-2000
Masury **(G-13216)**
Ryder Engraving Inc ....G 740 927-7193
Pataskala **(G-15982)**
Signature Partners Inc ....F 419 678-1400
Coldwater **(G-6571)**
Visionmark Nameplate Co LLC ....E 419 977-3131
New Bremen **(G-14796)**

NAMEPLATES

Auld Company ....E 614 454-1010
Columbus **(G-6786)**
Brainerd Industries Inc ....E 937 228-0488
Miamisburg **(G-13786)**
Cubbison Company ....D 330 793-2481
Youngstown **(G-21059)**
Greg G Wright & Sons LLC ....E 513 721-3310
Cincinnati **(G-3852)**
Metalphoto of Cincinnati Inc ....E 513 772-8281
Cincinnati **(G-4090)**
Specialty Nameplate Corp ....F 614 444-6876
Columbus **(G-7636)**
Vmi Liquidating Inc ....G 937 492-3100
Sidney **(G-17232)**
Woodrow Corp ....G 937 322-7696
Springfield **(G-17681)**

NATIONAL SECURITY FORCES

Dla Document Services ....G 216 522-3535
Cleveland **(G-5201)**
Dla Document Services ....E 937 257-6014
Dayton **(G-8104)**

NATIONAL SECURITY, GOVERNMENT: *Air Force*

Air Force US Dept of ....B 937 656-2354
Dayton **(G-8095)**

NATIONAL SECURITY, GOVERNMENT: *Army*

United States Dept of Army ....D 419 221-9500
Lima **(G-12108)**

NATURAL GAS DISTRIBUTION TO CONSUMERS

City of Lancaster ....E 740 687-6670
Lancaster **(G-11697)**
National Gas & Oil Company ....G 740 344-2102
Newark **(G-15036)**
National Gas & Oil Corporation ....E 740 344-2102
Newark **(G-15037)**

NATURAL GAS LIQUIDS PRODUCTION

H & S Operating Company Inc ....G 330 830-8178
Winesburg **(G-20704)**
Markwest Energy Partners LP ....G 740 942-0463
Cadiz **(G-2419)**
Markwest Utica Emg LLC ....G 740 942-4810
Jewett **(G-11386)**

NATURAL GAS POWER BROKER

Metals Recovery Services LLC ....G 614 870-0364
Columbus **(G-7342)**

NATURAL GAS PRODUCTION

B & J Drilling Company Inc ....G 740 599-6700
Danville **(G-8083)**
Buckeye Franklin Co ....F 330 859-2465
Zoarville **(G-21370)**
Chevron Ae Resources LLC ....E 330 896-8510
Uniontown **(G-19080)**
Columbia Midstream Group LLC ....F 330 542-1095
New Middletown **(G-14875)**
Edco Producing ....G 419 947-2515
Mount Gilead **(G-14558)**
Interstate Gas Supply Inc ....D 614 659-5000
Dublin **(G-9090)**
National Gas & Oil Company ....G 740 344-2102
Newark **(G-15036)**

RCM Engineering Company ....G 330 666-0575
Akron **(G-368)**
Southeastern Natural Gas Co ....G 740 385-8583
Logan **(G-12195)**
Temple Oil & Gas Company ....G 740 452-7878
Crooksville **(G-7954)**
Williams Partners LP ....C 330 966-3674
North Canton **(G-15284)**

NATURAL GAS TRANSMISSION

Belden & Blake Corporation ....E 330 602-5551
Dover **(G-8968)**
Columbia Energy Group ....G 614 460-4683
Columbus **(G-6945)**
Koch Knight LLC ....D 330 488-1651
East Canton **(G-9194)**
National Gas & Oil Company ....G 740 344-2102
Newark **(G-15036)**
National Gas & Oil Corporation ....E 740 344-2102
Newark **(G-15037)**

NATURAL GAS TRANSMISSION & DISTRIBUTION

Ngo Development Corporation ....F 740 622-9560
Coshocton **(G-7901)**

NATURAL GASOLINE PRODUCTION

Husky Marketing and Supply Co ....E 614 210-2300
Dublin **(G-9087)**
RCM Engineering Company ....G 330 666-0575
Akron **(G-368)**

NATURAL PROPANE PRODUCTION

A Plus Propane LLC ....G 419 399-4445
Paulding **(G-15998)**
Consolidated Gas Coop Inc ....G 419 946-6600
Mount Gilead **(G-14557)**
Nimco Inc ....G 740 596-4477
Mc Arthur **(G-13332)**

NAUTICAL REPAIR SVCS

Canvas Specialty Mfg Co ....G 216 881-0647
Cleveland **(G-4968)**
Loadmaster Trailer Company ....F 419 732-3434
Port Clinton **(G-16403)**
North Sails Toledo LLC ....F 419 726-2933
Toledo **(G-18608)**

NAVIGATIONAL SYSTEMS & INSTRUMENTS

Ball Aerospace & Tech Corp ....C 937 429-5005
Beavercreek **(G-1321)**
Cedar Elec Holdings Corp ....G 513 870-8500
West Chester **(G-19824)**
L3 Technologies Inc ....G 937 223-3285
Dayton **(G-8449)**
Tmw Systems Inc ....F 615 986-1900
Cleveland **(G-6328)**
Trimble Inc ....F 937 233-8921
Dayton **(G-8726)**
U S Army Corps of Engineers ....F 740 537-2571
Toronto **(G-18786)**

NET & NETTING PRDTS

Murray Fabrics Inc ....F 216 881-4041
Cleveland **(G-5840)**

NETTING: *Cargo*

Patches LLC ....G 513 304-4882
Williamsburg **(G-20410)**

NEW & USED CAR DEALERS

Bwi North America Inc ....E 937 253-1130
Kettering **(G-11577)**

NEWS DEALERS & NEWSSTANDS

Advance Reporter ....G 419 485-4851
Montpelier **(G-14438)**

NEWS SYNDICATES

Ohio News Network ....D 614 460-3700
Columbus **(G-7423)**
Plain Dealer Publishing Co ....G 614 228-8200
Columbus **(G-7488)**

NEWSSTAND

Caxton New Stand ....G...... 216 861-1600
Cleveland (G-4996)
Gazette Publishing Company ....F...... 419 335-2010
Wauseon (G-19679)
Journal Register Company ....C...... 440 245-6901
Lorain (G-12251)

NICKEL ALLOY

Allied Mask and Tooling Inc ....G...... 419 470-2555
Toledo (G-18329)
Chris Nckel Cstm Ltherwork LLC ....G...... 614 262-2672
Columbus (G-6927)
Eric Nickel ....G...... 614 818-2488
Westerville (G-20151)
Robert Nickel ....G...... 419 448-8256
Tiffin (G-18240)
Steven Nickel ....G...... 419 732-3377
Port Clinton (G-16415)

NIPPLES: Rubber

Novatex North America Inc ....D...... 419 282-4264
Ashland (G-757)
Ppafco Inc ....F...... 614 488-7259
Columbus (G-7507)

NITRILE RUBBERS: Butadiene-Acrylonitrile

Tradex International Inc ....D...... 216 651-4788
Cleveland (G-6345)

NONCURRENT CARRYING WIRING DEVICES

Akron Foundry Co ....E...... 330 745-3101
Barberton (G-1095)
Arnco Corporation ....C...... 800 847-7661
Elyria (G-9375)
Barracuda Technologies Inc ....F...... 216 469-1566
Aurora (G-910)
Bud Industries Inc ....G...... 440 946-3200
Willoughby (G-20447)
Erico Inc ....E...... 440 248-0100
Solon (G-17287)
Power Shelf LLC ....G...... 419 775-6125
Plymouth (G-16378)
Red Seal Electric Co ....E...... 216 941-3900
Cleveland (G-6095)
Regal Beloit America Inc ....C...... 419 352-8441
Bowling Green (G-2013)
Rochling Glastic Composites LP ....C...... 216 486-0100
Cleveland (G-6125)
Vertiv Co ....G...... 440 288-1122
Lorain (G-12290)
Zekelman Industries Inc ....C...... 740 432-2146
Cambridge (G-2483)

NONDURABLE GOODS WHOLESALERS, NEC

La Mfg Inc ....G...... 513 577-7200
Cincinnati (G-4009)

NONFERROUS: Rolling & Drawing, NEC

API Machining Fabrication Inc ....G...... 740 369-0455
Delaware (G-8821)
BCi and V Investments Inc ....D...... 330 538-0660
North Jackson (G-15287)
Bunting Bearings LLC ....E...... 419 522-3323
Mansfield (G-12572)
Canton Drop Forge Inc ....B...... 330 477-4511
Canton (G-2638)
Consolidated Metal Pdts Inc ....C...... 513 251-2624
Cincinnati (G-3604)
Contour Forming Inc ....E...... 740 345-9777
Newark (G-14996)
Curtiss-Wright Flow Ctrl Corp ....D...... 216 267-3200
Cleveland (G-5148)
Economy Flame Hardening Inc ....G...... 216 431-9333
Cleveland (G-5255)
Economy Straightening Service ....G...... 216 432-4410
Cleveland (G-5256)
Fusion Incorporated ....E...... 440 946-3300
Willoughby (G-20495)
G A Avril Company ....F...... 513 641-0566
Cincinnati (G-3790)
Gem City Metal Tech LLC ....E...... 937 252-8998
Dayton (G-8362)
General Electric Company ....C...... 330 793-3911
Youngstown (G-21095)

Kilroy Company ....D...... 440 951-8700
Eastlake (G-9278)
Mestek Inc ....D...... 419 288-2703
Bradner (G-2029)
Metal Merchants Usa Inc ....G...... 330 723-3228
Medina (G-13447)
Nova Machine Products Inc ....C...... 216 267-3200
Middleburg Heights (G-13907)
Patriot Special Metals Inc ....G...... 330 538-9621
North Jackson (G-15296)
Patriot Special Metals Inc ....D...... 330 580-9600
Canton (G-2809)
Titanium Metals Corporation ....A...... 740 537-1571
Toronto (G-18785)

NONMETALLIC MINERALS & CONCENTRATE WHOLESALERS

Seaforth Mineral & Ore Co Inc ....F...... 216 292-5820
Cleveland (G-6176)

NONMETALLIC MINERALS DEVELOPMENT & TEST BORING SVC

Barr Engineering Incorporated ....F...... 614 892-0162
Columbus (G-6807)
Barr Engineering Incorporated ....E...... 614 714-0299
Columbus (G-6808)

NONMETALLIC MINERALS: Support Activities, Exc Fuels

Aluchem of Jackson Inc ....E...... 740 286-2455
Jackson (G-11309)
Masters Group Inc ....G...... 440 893-1900
Chagrin Falls (G-3103)

NOTEBOOKS, MADE FROM PURCHASED MATERIALS

CCL Label Inc ....E...... 440 878-7000
Brunswick (G-2215)

NOTIONS: Pins, Straight, Steel Or Brass

Cailin Dev Ltd Lblty Co ....F...... 216 408-6261
Cleveland (G-4962)

NOVELTIES

Mibtach Enterprises Inc ....G...... 513 941-0387
Cincinnati (G-4098)
Tiger Cat Furniture ....G...... 330 220-7232
Brunswick (G-2262)

NOVELTIES & SPECIALTIES: Metal

Dimensional Fabricating Inc ....G...... 513 482-7440
Cincinnati (G-3655)
Extreme Marine ....G...... 330 963-7800
Twinsburg (G-18932)

NOVELTIES, DURABLE, WHOLESALE

Baker Plastics Inc ....G...... 330 743-3142
Youngstown (G-21031)
Club 513 LLC ....G...... 800 530-2574
Cincinnati (G-3591)

NOVELTIES: Leather

Cromwell Aleene ....G...... 937 547-2281
Greenville (G-10496)
Dpi Inc ....G...... 419 273-1400
Forest (G-9919)

NOVELTIES: Plastic

Baker Plastics Inc ....G...... 330 743-3142
Youngstown (G-21031)
CM Paula Company ....E...... 513 759-7473
Mason (G-13002)
Quality Innovative Pdts LLC ....G...... 330 990-9888
Akron (G-356)
Yachiyo of America Inc ....D...... 614 876-3220
Columbus (G-7781)

NOVELTY SHOPS

Silk Screen Special TS Inc ....G...... 740 246-4843
Thornville (G-18199)
Wild Berry Incense Inc ....F...... 513 523-8583
Oxford (G-15846)

NOZZLES: Fire Fighting

Element14 US Holdings Inc ....G...... 330 523-4280
Richfield (G-16622)
Premier Farnell Holding Inc ....E...... 330 523-4273
Richfield (G-16633)
Sensible Products Inc ....G...... 330 659-4212
Richfield (G-16637)

NOZZLES: Spray, Aerosol, Paint Or Insecticide

Exair Corporation ....E...... 513 671-3322
Cincinnati (G-3729)
J & J Performance Inc ....F...... 330 567-2455
Shreve (G-17159)
Vortec Corporation ....E...... 513 686-8210
Blue Ash (G-1891)

NUCLEAR DETECTORS: Solid State

Rexon Components Inc ....F...... 440 585-7086
Cleveland (G-6109)

NUCLEAR FUELS SCRAP REPROCESSING

C Soltesz Co ....G...... 614 529-5494
Columbus (G-6885)

NUCLEAR REACTORS: Military Or Indl

Babcock & Wilcox Nuclr Oprtns ....F...... 330 860-1010
Barberton (G-1105)
Babcock & Wilcox Powr Generatn ....E...... 330 753-4511
Barberton (G-1106)
Firstenergy Corp ....E...... 419 321-7114
Oak Harbor (G-15590)
Firstnrgy Nclear Gnration Corp ....G...... 330 761-4370
Akron (G-189)
Gayston Corporation ....C...... 937 743-6050
Miamisburg (G-13812)

NUCLEAR SHIELDING: Metal Plate

Laird Technologies Inc ....G...... 234 806-0105
Warren (G-19569)

NURSERIES & LAWN & GARDEN SPLY STORE, RET: Fountain, Outdoor

Custom Fountains Inc ....F...... 513 398-1447
Mason (G-13007)
Fountain Specialists Inc ....G...... 513 831-5717
Milford (G-14142)

NURSERIES & LAWN & GARDEN SPLY STORE, RET: Lawn/Garden Splys

Markers Inc ....G...... 440 933-5927
Avon Lake (G-1039)
Rw Sidley Inc ....G...... 330 545-1964
Girard (G-10394)

NURSERIES & LAWN & GARDEN SPLY STORES, RETAIL

Riverview Productions Inc ....G...... 740 441-1150
Gallipolis (G-10308)

NURSERIES & LAWN & GARDEN SPLY STORES, RETAIL: Fertilizer

Centerra Co-Op ....E...... 419 281-2153
Ashland (G-717)
Centerra Co-Op ....E...... 800 362-9598
Jefferson (G-11358)
Crop Production Services Inc ....G...... 614 873-4253
Milford Center (G-14181)
Harvest Land Co-Op Inc ....G...... 937 884-5526
Verona (G-19338)
Insta-Gro Manufacturing Inc ....G...... 419 845-3046
Caledonia (G-2438)
K M B Inc ....E...... 330 889-3451
Bristolville (G-2098)
Mid-Wood Inc ....F...... 419 257-3331
North Baltimore (G-15195)
New Eezy-Gro Inc ....F...... 419 927-6110
Upper Sandusky (G-19136)
Ohigro Inc ....E...... 740 726-2429
Waldo (G-19467)
Premier Feeds LLC ....G...... 937 584-2411
Sabina (G-16776)

Employee Codes: A=Over 500 employees, B=251-500
C=101-250, D=51-100, E=20-50, F=10-19, G=3-9

2017 Harris Ohio
Industrial Directory

PRODUCT

1585

NURSERIES & LAWN & GARDEN SPLY STORES, RETAIL: *Lawn Ornament*

Wilsons Country Creations .... F 330 377-4190
Killbuck (G-11602)

NURSERIES & LAWN & GARDEN SPLY STORES, RETAIL: *Top Soil*

Kurtz Bros Inc .... E 614 491-0868
Groveport (G-10632)

Mad River Topsoil Inc .... G 937 882-6115
Springfield (G-17598)

NURSERIES & LAWN/GARDEN SPLY STORE, RET: *Lawnmowers/Tractors*

Albright Saw Company Inc .... G 740 887-2107
Londonderry (G-12225)

T JS Oil & Gas Inc .... G 740 623-0192
Coshocton (G-7912)

NURSERY & GARDEN CENTERS

Alvords Yard & Garden Eqp .... G 440 286-2315
Chardon (G-3140)

Buckeye Tractor Company Corp .... G 419 659-2162
Columbus Grove (G-7791)

Dittmar Sales and Service .... G 740 653-7933
Lancaster (G-11709)

Gardenscape .... E 419 445-6561
Archbold (G-676)

Mel Stevens U-Cart Concrete .... G 419 478-2600
Toledo (G-18582)

Mulch World .... G 419 873-6852
Perrysburg (G-16123)

NURSING CARE FACILITIES: *Skilled*

Biorx LLC .... C 866 442-4679
Cincinnati (G-3450)

NUTRITION SVCS

Abbott Laboratories .... A 614 624-3191
Columbus (G-6671)

NUTS: *Metal*

Facil North America Inc .... C 330 487-2500
Twinsburg (G-18934)

Industrial Nut Corp .... D 419 625-8543
Sandusky (G-16973)

Jerry Tools Inc .... F 513 242-3211
Cincinnati (G-3944)

Lear Mfg Co Inc .... F 440 324-1111
Elyria (G-9451)

Ramco Specialties Inc .... D 330 653-5135
Hudson (G-11195)

Telefast Industries Inc .... D 440 826-0011
Berea (G-1638)

Wheel Group Holdings LLC .... G 614 253-6247
Columbus (G-7760)

NYLON FIBERS

Dowco LLC .... E 330 773-6654
Akron (G-155)

Ohio Plastics Belting Co .... G 330 882-6764
New Franklin (G-14828)

OFCS & CLINICS,MEDICAL DRS: *Specl, Physician Or Surgn, ENT*

Akron Ent Hearing Services Inc .... G 330 762-8959
Akron (G-41)

OFFICE EQPT WHOLESALERS

Friends Service Co Inc .... G 800 427-1704
Kent (G-11459)

Friends Service Co Inc .... D 419 427-1704
Findlay (G-9828)

Friends Service Co Inc .... F 800 427-1704
Dayton (G-8352)

Giesecke & Devrient Amer Inc .... C 330 425-1515
Twinsburg (G-18947)

Media Procurement Services Inc .... G 513 977-3000
Cincinnati (G-4077)

Mpc Inc .... F 440 835-1405
Westlake (G-20284)

Pinnacle Sales Inc .... G 440 777-2544
Westlake (G-20295)

Symatic Inc .... E 330 225-1510
Brunswick (G-2260)

Wasserstrom Company .... F 614 228-2233
Columbus (G-7751)

William J Dupps .... G 419 734-2126
Port Clinton (G-16419)

Xerox Corporation .... B 513 554-3200
Blue Ash (G-1902)

OFFICE EQPT, WHOL: *Check Writing, Signing/Endorsing Mach*

Cummins - Allison Corp .... G 440 824-5050
Cleveland (G-5146)

OFFICE EQPT, WHOLESALE: *Blueprinting*

Robert Becker Impressions Inc .... F 419 385-5303
Toledo (G-18678)

OFFICE EQPT, WHOLESALE: *Duplicating Machines*

Xpress Print Inc .... F 330 494-7246
Louisville (G-12335)

OFFICE EQPT, WHOLESALE: *Typewriter & Dictation*

Cleveland Business Supply LLC .... G 888 831-0088
Broadview Heights (G-2108)

OFFICE EQPT, WHOLESALE: *Typewriters*

Essential Pathways Ohio LLC .... G 330 518-3091
Youngstown (G-21079)

OFFICE FIXTURES: *Exc Wood*

Acrylicon Inc .... G 614 263-2086
Columbus (G-6691)

Intelitool Manufacturing Svcs .... G 440 953-1071
Willoughby (G-20511)

OFFICE FIXTURES: *Wood*

Bruewer Woodwork Mfg Co .... D 513 353-3505
Cleves (G-6507)

M21 Industries LLC .... D 937 781-1377
Dayton (G-8465)

Mock Woodworking Company LLC .... E 740 452-2701
Zanesville (G-21329)

OFFICE FURNITURE REPAIR & MAINTENANCE SVCS

American Office Services Inc .... G 440 899-6888
Westlake (G-20252)

Recycled Systems Furniture Inc .... E 614 880-9110
Worthington (G-20884)

OFFICE MACHINES, NEC

Buynix .... G 216 551-3485
Cleveland (G-4954)

OFFICE SPLY & STATIONERY STORES

Fedex Office & Print Svcs Inc .... E 419 866-5464
Toledo (G-18466)

Paper Occasions .... G 614 761-8880
Dublin (G-9116)

The Rubber Stamp Shop .... G 419 478-4444
Toledo (G-18722)

OFFICE SPLY & STATIONERY STORES: *Office Forms & Splys*

Ace Rubber Stamp & Off Sup Co .... E 216 771-8483
Cleveland (G-4690)

Avon Lake Printing .... G 440 933-2078
Avon Lake (G-1024)

COS Blueprint Inc .... F 330 376-0022
Akron (G-130)

Go Calendars .... G 513 755-1555
Liberty Township (G-11962)

Gordons Graphics Inc .... G 330 863-2322
Malvern (G-12546)

Hathaway Stamp Co .... F 513 621-1052
Cincinnati (G-3871)

Hubbard Company .... E 419 784-4455
Defiance (G-8794)

Info-Graphics Inc .... G 440 498-1640
Solon (G-17315)

Murr Corporation .... F 330 264-2223
Wooster (G-20813)

O Connor Office Pdts & Prtg .... G 740 852-2209
London (G-12216)

Pep Pony Express Printing Inc .... G 513 542-4882
Cincinnati (G-4222)

Print Craft Inc .... G 513 931-6828
Cincinnati (G-4270)

Quick Tech Graphics Inc .... F 937 743-5952
Springboro (G-17502)

SPAOS Inc .... G 937 890-0783
Dayton (G-8666)

Warren Printing & Off Pdts Inc .... F 419 523-3635
Ottawa (G-15814)

OFFICE SPLY & STATIONERY STORES: *School Splys*

Marsh Industries Inc .... E 330 308-8667
New Philadelphia (G-14912)

OFFICE SPLYS, NEC, WHOLESALE

Supply International Inc .... G 740 282-8604
Steubenville (G-17718)

Wasserstrom Company .... F 614 228-2233
Columbus (G-7751)

Wasserstrom Company .... B 614 737-8472
Columbus (G-7750)

William J Dupps .... G 419 734-2126
Port Clinton (G-16419)

OFFICES & CLINICS OF DOCTORS OF MEDICINE: *Dermatologist*

M D Complete Prof Skincare .... G 513 965-3760
Terrace Park (G-18181)

OFFICES & CLINICS OF DOCTORS OF MEDICINE: *Surgeon*

University Crdc & Thrc Grp .... F 216 844-3053
Cleveland (G-6393)

OFFICES & CLINICS OF DRS OF MED: *Cardiologist & Vascular*

Cardiac Arrhythmia Associates .... G 330 759-8169
Youngstown (G-21043)

OFFICES & CLINICS OF DRS OF MED: *Physician/Surgeon, Int Med*

Westerville Endoscopy Ctr LLC .... F 614 568-1666
Westerville (G-20194)

OIL & GAS FIELD EQPT: *Drill Rigs*

Buckeye Companies .... E 740 452-3641
Zanesville (G-21282)

Kelley Brothers Roofing Inc .... F 330 273-3700
Medina (G-13432)

OIL & GAS FIELD MACHINERY

Allied Machine Works Inc .... G 740 454-2534
Zanesville (G-21270)

Appalachian Equipment Co LLC .... G 330 345-2251
Wooster (G-20739)

Baker Hughes C/O Tangoe Inc .... G 304 884-6442
Hubbard (G-11127)

Cameron International Corp .... G 740 654-4260
Lancaster (G-11695)

Cyclone Supply Company Inc .... G 330 204-0313
Dover (G-8974)

Electric Design For Indust Inc .... E 740 401-4000
Belpre (G-1586)

Enercon Systems Inc .... G 305 213-3997
Elyria (G-9419)

H P E Inc .... F 330 833-3161
Massillon (G-13145)

Hughes Christensen .... G 330 455-2140
Canton (G-2731)

Midflow Services LLC .... E 330 674-2399
Millersburg (G-14246)

Midflow Services LLC .... G 330 567-3108
Shreve (G-17161)

N & N Oil ....G 740 743-2848
  Somerset (G-17417)
National Oilwell Varco Inc ....E 440 577-1225
  Pierpont (G-16213)
Ohio Energy Assets Inc ....G 740 332-9511
  Laurelville (G-11771)
Oil Skimmers Inc ....E 440 237-4600
  North Royalton (G-15440)
Pride of Hills Mfg Inc ....D 330 567-3108
  Big Prairie (G-1683)
Pride of Hills Mfg Inc ....E 800 345-1744
  Killbuck (G-11598)
Reberland Equipment Inc ....F 330 698-5883
  Apple Creek (G-648)
Robbins & Myers Inc ....F 937 454-3200
  Dayton (G-8636)
Saint-Gobain Norpro Corp ....C 330 673-5860
  Stow (G-17798)
Smith International Inc ....F 570 368-2130
  Strasburg (G-17829)
Smith International Inc ....G 330 497-2999
  Uniontown (G-19098)
Tech Tool Inc ....F 330 674-1176
  Millersburg (G-14267)
Terra Sonic International LLC ....E 740 374-6608
  Marietta (G-12840)
Timco Inc ....F 740 685-2594
  Byesville (G-2410)

OIL ABSORPTION Eqpt

Lamor Corporation ....F 440 871-8000
  Westlake (G-20281)

OIL FIELD MACHINERY & EQPT

Condition Monitoring Supplies ....G 216 941-6868
  Strongsville (G-17906)
H & S Company Inc ....F 419 394-4444
  Celina (G-2999)
Multi Products Company ....E 330 674-5981
  Millersburg (G-14252)

OIL FIELD SVCS, NEC

Altier Brothers Inc ....F 740 347-4329
  Corning (G-7860)
Appalachian Oilfield Svcs LLC ......G 337 216-0066
  Sardis (G-17035)
Atec Diversfd Wldg Fabrication .....G 937 546-4399
  Wilmington (G-20655)
Belden & Blake Corporation ....E 330 602-5551
  Dover (G-8968)
Bishop Well Service Corp ....G 330 264-2023
  Wooster (G-20748)
BJ Oilfield Services Ltd ....G 419 768-2408
  Cardington (G-2908)
Countryside Pumping Inc ....G 330 628-0058
  Mogadore (G-14371)
Dansco Mfg & Pmpg Unit Svc LP ....G 330 452-3677
  Canton (G-2678)
Decker Well Service LLC ....G 740 678-2970
  Fleming (G-9912)
Dover Atwood Corp ....G 330 809-0630
  Massillon (G-13125)
Echo Drilling Inc ....G 740 498-8560
  Newcomerstown (G-15112)
Everflow Eastern Partners LP ....G 330 537-3863
  Salem (G-16889)
Global Oilfield Services LLC ....G 419 756-8027
  Mansfield (G-12613)
Granger Pipeline Corporation ....G 330 454-8095
  Canton (G-2718)
HI Oilfield Services LLC ....G 740 783-1156
  Caldwell (G-2427)
Infinity Oilfield Services LLC ....G 570 567-7027
  Newcomerstown (G-15116)
James Engineering Inc ....G 740 373-9521
  Marietta (G-12794)
Killbuck Oilfield Services ....G 330 276-6706
  Killbuck (G-11596)
Loken Oil Field Services LLC ....G 740 749-3495
  Marietta (G-12799)
Maan Power Services LLC ....E 740 609-3020
  Bridgeport (G-2091)
Mac Oil Field Service Inc ....F 330 674-7371
  Millersburg (G-14244)
Northeastern Oilfield Svcs LLC ......G 330 581-3304
  Canton (G-2794)
Ohio Natural Gas Services Inc ....G 740 796-3305
  Zanesville (G-21336)

Petrox Inc ....F 330 653-5526
  Streetsboro (G-17867)
R & J Drilling Company Inc ....G 740 763-3991
  Frazeysburg (G-10076)
Sanders Fredrick Excvtg Co Inc .....G 330 297-7980
  Ravenna (G-16555)
Stonebridge Oilfield Svcs LLC ....D 740 373-6134
  Marietta (G-12837)
Stratagraph Ne Inc ....E 740 373-3091
  Marietta (G-12838)
Surveying Cannon Land ....G 740 342-2835
  New Lexington (G-14856)
Tk Gas Services Inc ....G 740 826-0303
  New Concord (G-14822)
Trico Corporation ....E 216 642-3223
  Cleveland (G-6364)
Triple J Oilfield Services LLC ....G 740 483-9030
  Hannibal (G-10764)
W Pole Contracting Inc ....F 330 325-7177
  Ravenna (G-16570)
Wenger Pipeline Construction ....E 330 828-8803
  Dalton (G-8080)
Williams John F Oil Field Svcs ......G 740 622-7692
  Jackson (G-11333)
Wolfe Creek Farms ....G 740 962-4563
  Malta (G-12538)

OIL ROYALTY TRADERS

U S Fuel Development Co ....G 614 486-0614
  Columbus (G-7716)

OIL TREATING COMPOUNDS

Lubrizol Corporation ....A 440 943-4200
  Wickliffe (G-20370)

OILS & ESSENTIAL OILS

Natural Essentials Inc ....E 330 562-8022
  Aurora (G-937)
Oil Bar LLC ....G 614 501-9815
  Columbus (G-7439)

OILS & GREASES: Blended & Compounded

Blendzall Inc ....G 740 633-1333
  Martins Ferry (G-12922)
Cambridge Mill Products Inc ....G 330 863-1121
  Malvern (G-12539)
Chemical Solvents Inc ....E 216 741-9310
  Cleveland (G-5025)
Cincinnati - Vulcan Company ....D 513 242-5300
  Cincinnati (G-3535)
Digilube Systems Inc ....F 937 748-2209
  Springboro (G-17479)
Etna Products Incorporated ....E 440 543-9845
  Chagrin Falls (G-3087)
Into Great Brands Inc ....F 888 771-5656
  Gahanna (G-10213)
Metal Forming Lubricants Inc ....G 440 458-5730
  Elyria (G-9461)
New Vulco Mfg & Sales Co LLC .....D 513 242-2672
  Cincinnati (G-4149)
Phymet Inc ....F 937 743-8061
  Springboro (G-17496)
US Industrial Lubricants Inc ....E 513 541-2225
  Cincinnati (G-4547)
Wallover Enterprises Inc ....E 440 238-9250
  Strongsville (G-17981)
Wallover Oil Company Inc ....E 440 238-9250
  Strongsville (G-17982)

OILS & GREASES: Lubricating

A & M Products ....G 419 595-2092
  Tiffin (G-18201)
Advanced Engine Tech LLC ....G 937 439-0224
  Bellbrook (G-1503)
Amsoil Inc ....G 614 274-9851
  Columbus (G-6746)
Anchor Chemical Co Inc ....G 440 871-1660
  Westlake (G-20254)
Apex Advanced Technologies LLC ...G 216 898-1595
  Cleveland (G-4818)
BLaster Corporation ....E 216 901-5800
  Cleveland (G-4916)
Borchers Americas Inc ....D 440 899-2950
  Westlake (G-20258)
Chemical Methods Inc ....E 216 476-8400
  Strongsville (G-17901)
Commercial Lubricants Inc ....G 614 475-5952
  Columbus (G-6971)

Douglas W & B C Richardson ....G 440 247-5262
  Chagrin Falls (G-3055)
Dubro Oil Corporation ....G 216 696-2646
  Cleveland (G-5218)
Eni USA R & M Co Inc ....F 330 723-6457
  Medina (G-13405)
Ensign Product Company Inc ....E 216 341-5911
  Cleveland (G-5284)
Fuchs Lubricants Co ....E 330 963-0400
  Twinsburg (G-18938)
Functional Products Inc ....E 330 963-3060
  Macedonia (G-12452)
G W Smith and Sons Inc ....E 937 253-5114
  Dayton (G-8105)
Ha-International LLC ....E 419 537-0096
  Toledo (G-18492)
Jtm Products Inc ....E 440 287-2302
  Solon (G-17324)
Maintenance + Inc ....F 330 264-6262
  Wooster (G-20801)
Mar Mor Inc ....G 216 961-6900
  Cleveland (G-5740)
McGlaughlin Oil Compny/Fas Lube ...E 614 231-2518
  Columbus (G-7334)
North Shore Strapping Inc ....E 216 661-5200
  Brooklyn Heights (G-2144)
Oil Etc Inc ....G 513 933-8280
  Lebanon (G-11822)
Oliver Chemical Co Inc ....G 513 541-4540
  Cincinnati (G-4185)
Paramount Products ....G 419 832-0235
  Grand Rapids (G-10442)
Perma-Fix of Dayton Inc ....E 937 268-6501
  Dayton (G-8571)
Petroliance LLC ....C 216 441-7200
  Cleveland (G-5999)
Plasti-Kote Co Inc ....C 330 725-4511
  Medina (G-13459)
Quaker Chemical Corporation ....D 513 422-9600
  Middletown (G-14080)
R and J Corporation ....E 440 871-6009
  Westlake (G-20299)
Reladyne Inc ....E 513 489-6000
  Blue Ash (G-1862)
Renite Company ....F 614 253-5509
  Columbus (G-7554)
Shooters Choice LLC ....G 440 834-8888
  Middlefield (G-13990)
Spec Mask Ohio LLC ....G 440 522-3055
  Kirtland (G-11616)
Specialty Technologies Inc ....G 330 638-0744
  Cortland (G-7875)
Starchem Inc ....G 513 458-8262
  Cincinnati (G-4458)
State Industrial Products Corp ....B 877 747-6986
  Cleveland (G-6239)
Triad Energy Corporation ....E 740 374-2940
  Marietta (G-12844)
United Lubricants Corporation ....D 513 422-9600
  Middletown (G-14092)
Ventco Inc ....E 440 834-8888
  Middlefield (G-14001)
Wallover Enterprises Inc ....E 440 238-9250
  East Liverpool (G-9228)

OILS: Cutting

Dnd Emulsions Inc ....G 419 525-4988
  Mansfield (G-12595)
M B Industries Inc ....G 419 738-4769
  Wapakoneta (G-19496)
Master Chemical Corporation ....D 419 874-7902
  Perrysburg (G-16121)

OILS: Lubricating

Lube Depot ....G 330 854-6345
  Canal Fulton (G-2506)
Novagard Solutions Inc ....F 216 881-3890
  Cleveland (G-5917)
Sports Care Products Inc ....G 216 663-8110
  Cleveland (G-6227)

OILS: Lubricating

Advanced Fluids Inc ....G 216 692-3050
  Cleveland (G-4713)
Aerospace Lubricants Inc ....F 614 878-3600
  Columbus (G-6701)
Aml Industries Inc ....E 330 399-5000
  Warren (G-19523)

OILS: Lubricating

Bechem Lubrication Tech LLC ....G....... 440 543-9845
Chagrin Falls (G-3077)
Diversified Technology Inc ....G....... 330 722-4995
Medina (G-13403)
J J Merlin Systems Inc ....G....... 330 666-8609
Copley (G-7848)
Lcp Tech Inc ....G....... 513 271-1389
Cincinnati (G-4017)
Melanda Inc ....G....... 330 833-0517
Massillon (G-13179)
Petroliance ....G....... 614 475-5952
Columbus (G-7480)
Universal Oil Inc ....E....... 216 771-4300
Cleveland (G-6391)
Western Reserve Lubricants ....G....... 440 951-5700
Painesville (G-15939)

OINTMENTS

Dr Hess Products LLC ....G....... 800 718-8022
Ashland (G-729)

OLEFINS

Lyondell Chemical Company ....D....... 513 530-4000
Cincinnati (G-4042)

ON-LINE DATABASE INFORMATION RETRIEVAL SVCS

EW Scripps Company ....E....... 513 977-3000
Cincinnati (G-3728)

OPENERS, BOTTLE Stamped Metal

Doan Machinery & Eqp Co Inc ....G....... 216 932-6243
University Heights (G-19108)

OPERATOR TRAINING, COMPUTER

Computer Workshop Inc ....E....... 614 798-9505
Dublin (G-9065)

OPERATOR: Apartment Buildings

Dela-Glassware Ltd LLC ....G....... 740 369-6737
Delaware (G-8835)
Power Management Inc ....E....... 937 222-2909
Dayton (G-8580)

OPERATOR: Nonresidential Buildings

Great Lakes Management Inc ....G....... 216 883-6500
Cleveland (G-5454)
Kedar D Army ....G....... 419 238-6929
Van Wert (G-19262)
Power Management Inc ....E....... 937 222-2909
Dayton (G-8580)
Pubco Corporation ....D....... 216 881-5300
Cleveland (G-6059)
Wernli Realty Inc ....D....... 937 258-7878
Beavercreek (G-1384)

OPHTHALMIC GOODS

Bsa Industries Inc ....D....... 614 846-5515
Columbus (G-6869)
Bulk Molding Compounds Inc ....D....... 419 874-7941
Perrysburg (G-16071)
Classic Optical Labs Inc ....C....... 330 759-8245
Youngstown (G-21052)
Cleveland Hoya Corp ....D....... 440 234-5703
Berea (G-1606)
DMV Corporation ....G....... 740 452-4787
Zanesville (G-21299)
Jerold Optical Inc ....G....... 216 781-4279
Cleveland (G-5611)
Lake Cable Optical Lab ....G....... 330 497-3022
Canton (G-2758)
Luxottica Retail N Amer Inc ....C....... 614 409-9381
Lockbourne (G-12149)
Mileti Optical Inc ....G....... 440 884-6333
Cleveland (G-5815)
Oakley Inc ....D....... 949 672-6560
Dayton (G-8537)
Opti Vision Inc ....G....... 330 650-0919
Hudson (G-11191)
Rx Frames N Lenses Ltd ....G....... 513 557-2970
Cincinnati (G-4370)
Steiner Eoptics Inc ....D....... 937 426-2341
Miamisburg (G-13865)
Terminal Optical Lab ....G....... 216 289-7722
Euclid (G-9610)

Usv Optical Inc ....G....... 614 717-0238
Dublin (G-9160)

OPHTHALMIC GOODS, NEC, WHOLESALE: Contact Lenses

Lens AC ....E....... 888 248-5367
Columbus (G-7291)

OPHTHALMIC GOODS, NEC, WHOLESALE: Lenses

Toledo Optical Laboratory Inc ....D....... 419 248-3384
Toledo (G-18738)

OPHTHALMIC GOODS: Lenses, Ophthalmic

Volk Optical Inc ....D....... 440 942-6161
Mentor (G-13768)

OPTICAL GOODS STORES

Central Optical Inc ....E....... 330 783-9660
Youngstown (G-21046)
Mileti Optical Inc ....G....... 440 884-6333
Cleveland (G-5815)

OPTICAL GOODS STORES: Eyeglasses, Prescription

Jerold Optical Inc ....G....... 216 781-4279
Cleveland (G-5611)
Opti Vision Inc ....G....... 330 650-0919
Hudson (G-11191)

OPTICAL INSTRUMENTS & APPARATUS

Harris Instrument Corporation ....G....... 740 369-3580
Delaware (G-8857)
Trevi Technology Inc ....G....... 614 754-7175
Columbus (G-7708)

OPTICAL INSTRUMENTS & LENSES

Cleveland Hoya Corp ....D....... 440 234-5703
Berea (G-1606)
Genvac Aerospace Corp ....F....... 440 646-9986
Cleveland (G-5424)
Gooch & Housego (florida) LLC ....D....... 321 242-7818
Cleveland (G-5437)
Gooch & Housego (ohio) LLC ....D....... 216 486-6100
Highland Heights (G-10914)
Greenlight Optics LLC ....E....... 513 247-9777
Loveland (G-12354)
Holte Eyeware ....G....... 513 321-4000
Cincinnati (G-3890)
Hoya Optical Labs ....G....... 440 239-1924
Berea (G-1619)
Krendl Machine Company ....D....... 419 692-3060
Delphos (G-8910)
Lens AC ....E....... 888 248-5367
Columbus (G-7291)
Mercury Iron & Steel ....F....... 440 349-1500
Solon (G-17334)
Point Source Inc ....F....... 937 855-6020
Germantown (G-10373)
Punch Components Inc ....F....... 419 224-1242
Lima (G-12077)
Uvisir Inc ....G....... 216 374-9376
Beachwood (G-1304)
Volk Optical Inc ....D....... 440 942-6161
Mentor (G-13768)
Vsp Lab Columbus ....E....... 614 409-8900
Lockbourne (G-12152)
Wilson Optical Laboratory Inc ....E....... 440 357-7000
Mentor (G-13769)

OPTICAL SCANNING SVCS

Contractor Tools Online LLC ....G....... 614 264-9392
New Albany (G-14754)

OPTOMETRIC EQPT & SPLYS WHOLESALERS

Hoya Optical Labs ....G....... 440 239-1924
Berea (G-1619)

OPTOMETRISTS' OFFICES

Holte Eyeware ....G....... 513 321-4000
Cincinnati (G-3890)

ORAL PREPARATIONS

Biocurv Medical Instruments ....G....... 330 451-1628
Canton (G-2623)

ORDNANCE

Advanced Innovation & Mfg Inc ....G....... 330 308-6360
New Philadelphia (G-14882)
American Apex Corporation ....F....... 614 652-2000
Plain City (G-16319)
Ares Inc ....D....... 419 635-2175
Port Clinton (G-16393)
Excelitas Technologies Corp ....C....... 937 865-4621
Miamisburg (G-13807)
General Dynamics-Ots Inc ....C....... 937 746-8500
Springboro (G-17481)
Hi-Tech Solutions LLC ....G....... 216 331-3050
Cleveland (G-5511)
Ordnance Cleaning Systems LLC ....G....... 440 205-0677
Mentor (G-13674)

ORGAN TUNING & REPAIR SVCS

Lima Pipe Organ Co Inc ....G....... 419 331-5461
Elida (G-9352)
Peebles - Herzog Inc ....G....... 614 279-2211
Columbus (G-7474)
Victor Organ Company ....G....... 330 792-1321
Youngstown (G-21238)

ORGANIZATIONS: Civic & Social

Eagles Club ....G....... 740 962-6490
McConnelsville (G-13349)

ORGANIZATIONS: Medical Research

Mp Biomedicals LLC ....C....... 440 337-1200
Solon (G-17340)
University Crdc & Thrc Grp ....F....... 216 844-3053
Cleveland (G-6393)

ORGANIZATIONS: Physical Research, Noncommercial

Sunpower Inc ....D....... 740 594-2221
Athens (G-887)

ORGANIZATIONS: Professional

American Ceramic Society ....E....... 614 890-4700
Westerville (G-20137)

ORGANIZATIONS: Religious

C A I R Ohio ....G....... 513 281-8200
Blue Ash (G-1758)
Pines Manufacturing Inc ....E....... 440 835-5553
Westlake (G-20294)
Saint Ctherines Metalworks Inc ....G....... 216 409-0576
Cleveland (G-6155)
Sunday School Software ....G....... 614 527-8776
Hilliard (G-10984)
World Harvest Church Inc ....G....... 614 837-1990
Canal Winchester (G-2542)

ORGANIZATIONS: Scientific Research Agency

Innovative Weld Solutions Ltd ....G....... 937 545-7695
Dayton (G-8408)
Performnce Plymr Solutions Inc ....F....... 937 298-3713
Moraine (G-14512)

ORNAMENTS: Christmas Tree, Exc Electrical & Glass

Sterling Collectables Inc ....G....... 419 892-5708
Mansfield (G-12684)

ORNAMENTS: Lawn

Gececo Inc ....E....... 614 861-4479
Columbus (G-7106)
Twin Oaks Barn ....F....... 330 893-3126
Dundee (G-9184)

ORTHOPEDIC SUNDRIES: Molded Rubber

Foot Logic Inc ....G....... 330 699-0123
Uniontown (G-19084)

OUTBOARD MOTORS & PARTS

Hemco Inc ....G 419 499-4602
Milan (G-14112)

OUTLETS: Electric, Convenience

Alert Safety Lite Products Co ....F 440 232-5020
Cleveland (G-4750)

Deals ....G 937 293-7429
Dayton (G-8294)

OVENS: Core Baking & Mold Drying

Miller Core 2 Inc ....G 330 359-0500
Beach City (G-1249)

OVENS: Laboratory

Ignio Systems LLC ....F 419 708-0503
Toledo (G-18516)

PACKAGE DESIGN SVCS

Amatech Inc ....E 614 252-2506
Columbus (G-6729)

Austin Foam Plastics Inc ....E 614 921-0824
Columbus (G-6789)

Diversipak Inc ....G 513 321-7884
Cincinnati (G-3658)

PACKAGED FROZEN FOODS WHOLESALERS, NEC

Koch Meat Co Inc ....B 513 874-3500
Fairfield (G-9674)

Lori Holding Co ....E 740 342-3230
New Lexington (G-14848)

PACKAGING & LABELING SVCS

A-Z Packaging Company ....F 614 444-8441
Columbus (G-6670)

Ace Assembly Packaging Inc ....E 330 866-9117
Waynesburg (G-19722)

Advanced Specialty Products ....D 419 882-6528
Bowling Green (G-1966)

Amros Industries Inc ....E 216 433-0010
Cleveland (G-4799)

Baumfolder Corporation ....D 937 492-1281
Sidney (G-17169)

BDS Packaging Inc ....G 937 643-0530
Moraine (G-14468)

Bernard Laboratories Inc ....E 513 681-7373
Cincinnati (G-3447)

C A P Industries Inc ....F 937 773-1824
Piqua (G-16254)

Crane Consumables LLC ....G 513 539-9980
Middletown (G-14034)

Cusc International Ltd ....G 513 881-2000
Hamilton (G-10682)

D C S Specialty Packaging Inc ....F 937 615-0100
Piqua (G-16258)

Domino Foods Inc ....D 216 432-3222
Cleveland (G-5205)

Fedex Office & Print Svcs Inc ....F 937 335-3816
Troy (G-18827)

First Choice Packaging Inc ....C 419 333-4100
Fremont (G-10145)

G L Industries Inc ....E 513 874-1233
Hamilton (G-10696)

G S K Inc ....G 937 547-1611
Greenville (G-10501)

Groff Industries ....F 216 634-9100
Cleveland (G-5460)

Hunt Products Inc ....E 440 667-2457
Newburgh Heights (G-15075)

Iron Wind Metals Co LLC ....G 513 870-0606
Cincinnati (G-3932)

Joseph T Snyder Industries ....G 216 883-6900
Cleveland (G-5623)

Lawnview Industries Inc ....C 937 653-5217
Urbana (G-19168)

Magnaco Industries Inc ....E 216 961-3636
Lodi (G-12166)

Ohio Gasket and Shim Co Inc ....E 330 630-0626
Akron (G-323)

Outsourcing Services Inc ....F 330 963-2710
Solon (G-17357)

Pactiv LLC ....C 614 771-5400
Columbus (G-7454)

Pro-Pet LLC ....G 419 394-3374
Saint Marys (G-16850)

Production Support Inc ....F 937 526-3897
Russia (G-16768)

Richland Newhope Industries ....C 419 774-4400
Mansfield (G-12671)

Safecor Health LLC ....F 781 933-8780
Columbus (G-7583)

Satco Inc ....G 330 630-8866
Tallmadge (G-18168)

Stadvec Inc ....G 330 644-7724
Barberton (G-1150)

Systems Pack Inc ....E 330 467-5729
Macedonia (G-12493)

Tekni-Plex Inc ....E 419 491-2407
Holland (G-11088)

Teva Womens Health Inc ....C 513 731-9900
Cincinnati (G-4503)

Tko Mfg Services Inc ....E 937 299-1637
Moraine (G-14535)

Unique Packaging & Printing ....F 440 785-6730
Mentor (G-13759)

Universal Packg Systems Inc ....B 513 732-2000
Batavia (G-1231)

Universal Packg Systems Inc ....E 513 735-4777
Batavia (G-1232)

Universal Packg Systems Inc ....B 513 674-9400
Cincinnati (G-4542)

VIP-Supply Chain Solutions LLC ......G 513 454-2020
West Chester (G-19970)

Welch Packaging Group Inc ....E 614 870-2000
Columbus (G-7755)

PACKAGING MATERIALS, WHOLESALE

B B Bradley Company Inc ....G 614 777-5600
Columbus (G-6796)

Ball Corporation ....F 330 534-7418
Hubbard (G-11129)

Bemis Company Inc ....E 330 923-5281
Akron (G-87)

Cambridge Packaging Inc ....E 740 432-3351
Cambridge (G-2449)

Century Marketing Corporation ....C 419 354-2591
Bowling Green (G-1978)

Custom Products Corporation ....D 440 528-7100
Solon (G-17280)

Diversified Products & Svcs ....C 740 393-6202
Mount Vernon (G-14619)

Evergreen Packaging Inc ....G 440 235-7200
Olmsted Falls (G-15675)

Kapstone Container Corporation ......C 330 562-6111
Aurora (G-928)

Ohio Packaging ....E 330 833-2884
Massillon (G-13186)

Packaging Plus Inc ....G 304 429-5900
Dayton (G-8562)

Putnam Plastics Inc ....G 937 866-6261
Dayton (G-8603)

Samuel Strapping Systems Inc ....D 740 522-2500
Heath (G-10855)

Skybox Packaging LLC ....D 419 525-7209
Mansfield (G-12680)

Storopack Inc ....E 513 874-0314
West Chester (G-20056)

Systems Pack Inc ....E 330 467-5729
Macedonia (G-12493)

PACKAGING MATERIALS: Paper

ABC Packaging Direct LLC ....G 440 934-1477
Avon (G-979)

Adaptive Data Inc ....F 937 436-2343
Centerville (G-3032)

American Corrugated Pdts Inc ....C 614 870-2000
Columbus (G-6735)

American Corrugated Pdts Inc ....G 800 248-6840
Columbus (G-6736)

Angell-Demmel North Amer Corp ....D 937 461-5800
Dayton (G-8158)

Austin Tape and Label Inc ....D 330 928-7999
Stow (G-17731)

Bemis Company Inc ....E 419 334-9465
Fremont (G-10128)

Bollin & Sons Inc ....E 419 693-6573
Toledo (G-18376)

Cole Pak Inc ....D 937 652-3910
Urbana (G-19152)

Crabar/Gbf Inc ....C 419 943-2141
Leipsic (G-11868)

Creative Packaging LLC ....C 740 452-8497
Zanesville (G-21295)

Custom Products Corporation ....D 440 528-7100
Solon (G-17280)

Dayton Fruit Tree Label Co ....G 937 223-4650
Dayton (G-8274)

Douglas Michalske ....G 216 631-0567
Cleveland (G-5210)

E-Z Stop Service Center ....D 330 448-2236
Brookfield (G-2123)

Engineered Films Division ....F 419 884-8150
Mansfield (G-12601)

Esperia Holdings LLC ....G 714 249-7888
Oak Harbor (G-15589)

Euclid Products Co Inc ....G 440 942-7310
Willoughby (G-20482)

Gauntlet Awards & Engraving ....G 937 890-5811
Dayton (G-8357)

Georgia-Pacific LLC ....C 740 477-3347
Circleville (G-4631)

Gt Industrial Supply Inc ....E 513 771-7000
Cincinnati (G-3856)

Harris & Company Inc ....F 330 332-4127
Salem (G-16899)

Hooven - Dayton Corp ....D 937 233-4473
Miamisburg (G-13818)

Hunt Products Inc ....E 440 667-2457
Newburgh Heights (G-15075)

International Paper Company ....C 740 363-9882
Delaware (G-8862)

Jerry Pulfer ....G 937 778-1861
Piqua (G-16283)

Joseph T Snyder Industries ....G 216 883-6900
Cleveland (G-5623)

Kapstone Container Corporation ......C 330 562-6111
Aurora (G-928)

Kay Toledo Tag Inc ....D 419 729-5479
Toledo (G-18541)

Kroy LLC ....C 216 426-5600
Cleveland (G-5666)

Liqui-Box Corporation ....C 419 289-9696
Ashland (G-750)

Loroco Industries Inc ....E 513 891-9544
Blue Ash (G-1828)

Marlen Manufacturing & Dev Co ......E 216 292-7546
Bedford (G-1442)

Multi-Color Corporation ....D 513 943-0080
Batavia (G-1212)

National Glass Service Group ....F 614 652-3699
Dublin (G-9109)

Newpage Group Inc ....E 937 242-9500
Miamisburg (G-13841)

Nilpeter Usa Inc ....C 513 489-4400
Cincinnati (G-4156)

North American Plas Chem Inc ....E 216 531-3400
Euclid (G-9595)

Novacel Inc ....C 937 335-5611
Troy (G-18858)

Novacel Inc ....E 413 283-3468
Troy (G-18859)

Paxar Corporation ....G 937 681-4541
Dayton (G-8567)

Perfect Packaging ....G 419 662-1700
Northwood (G-15487)

Perfection Packaging Inc ....G 614 866-8558
Gahanna (G-10226)

Plastic Works Inc ....F 440 331-5575
Cleveland (G-6014)

Plastipak Packaging Inc ....B 937 596-6142
Jackson Center (G-11344)

Prime Industries Inc ....E 440 288-3626
Lorain (G-12268)

Raven Industries Inc ....G 937 323-4625
Springfield (G-17634)

Safeway Packaging Inc ....D 419 629-3200
New Bremen (G-14793)

Schilling Graphics Inc ....E 419 468-1037
Galion (G-10286)

Schwarz Partners Packaging LLC ....F 317 290-1140
Sidney (G-17222)

Shurtape Technologies LLC ....B 440 937-7000
Avon (G-1011)

Shurtech Brands LLC ....C 440 937-7000
Avon (G-1012)

Signode Industrial Group LLC ....E 513 248-2990
Loveland (G-12387)

Sonoco Products Company ....E 419 448-4428
Tiffin (G-18245)

Sonoco Products Company ....E 614 759-8400
Columbus (G-7631)

Sourcepac Inc ....G 614 899-0744
Westerville (G-20234)

Springdot Inc ....D 513 542-4000
Cincinnati (G-4448)

PRODUCT

Storopack Inc ....E....... 513 874-0314
West Chester (G-20056)
Stretchtape Inc ....E....... 216 486-9400
Cleveland (G-6251)
Superior Label Systems Inc ....B....... 513 336-0825
Mason (G-13092)
Tce International Ltd ....F....... 800 962-2376
Perry (G-16059)
Tcp Inc ....G....... 330 836-4239
Fairlawn (G-9764)
Tech/III Inc ....E....... 513 482-7500
Cincinnati (G-4497)
Therm-O-Packaging Suppliers ....F....... 440 543-5188
Chagrin Falls (G-3126)
Thomas Products Co Inc ....E....... 513 756-9009
Cincinnati (G-4507)
Virgail Industries Inc ....G....... 740 928-6001
Hebron (G-10894)
Westrock Cp LLC ....B....... 513 745-2400
Blue Ash (G-1893)
Zebco Industries Inc ....F....... 740 654-4510
Lancaster (G-11763)
Zech Printing Industries Inc ....E....... 937 748-2776
Cincinnati (G-4618)

PACKAGING MATERIALS: Paper, Coated Or Laminated

Central Coated Products Inc ....D....... 330 821-9830
Alliance (G-503)
Central Ohio Paper & Packg Inc ....G....... 614 492-8956
Groveport (G-10618)
Central Ohio Paper & Packg Inc ....F....... 419 621-9239
Huron (G-11219)
Inno-Pak Holding Inc ....G....... 740 363-0090
Delaware (G-8861)
Proampac LLC ....E....... 513 671-1777
Cincinnati (G-4275)
Retterbush Graphic and Packg ....E....... 513 779-4466
West Chester (G-19931)
Sterling Paper Company Inc ....F....... 513 242-3678
Monroe (G-14414)

PACKAGING MATERIALS: Paperboard Backs For Blister/Skin Pkgs

Ample Industries Inc ....C....... 937 746-9700
Franklin (G-10007)

PACKAGING MATERIALS: Plastic Film, Coated Or Laminated

Amatech Inc ....E....... 614 252-2506
Columbus (G-6729)
Command Plastic Corporation ....F....... 800 321-8001
Tallmadge (G-18139)
Cpg - Ohio LLC ....D....... 513 825-4800
Cincinnati (G-3616)
Engineered Films Division ....G....... 419 884-8150
Lexington (G-11950)
Future Polytech Inc ....E....... 419 763-1352
Saint Henry (G-16816)
Johnson Energy Company ....G....... 937 435-5401
Miamisburg (G-13822)
Next Design & Build LLC ....G....... 330 907-3042
Akron (G-314)
Next Generation Films Inc ....C....... 419 884-8150
Lexington (G-11951)
Packaging Material Direct Inc ....G....... 989 482-8400
Solon (G-17358)
Polychem Corporation ....C....... 440 357-1500
Mentor (G-13691)
Polychem Corporation ....C....... 440 357-1500
Mentor (G-13692)
Richards and Simmons Inc ....G....... 614 268-3909
Columbus (G-7561)
Sonoco Prtective Solutions Inc ....G....... 419 420-0029
Findlay (G-9891)
Universal Packg Systems Inc ....B....... 513 674-9400
Cincinnati (G-4542)
Universal Packg Systems Inc ....B....... 513 732-2000
Batavia (G-1231)
Universal Packg Systems Inc ....E....... 513 735-4777
Batavia (G-1232)

PACKAGING MATERIALS: Polystyrene Foam

American Foam Products Inc ....E....... 440 352-3434
Painesville (G-15850)
Archbold Container Corp ....C....... 800 446-2520
Archbold (G-664)

Arlington Rack & Packaging Co ....G....... 419 476-7700
Toledo (G-18355)
B B Bradley Company Inc ....E....... 440 354-2005
Painesville (G-15860)
B B Bradley Company Inc ....G....... 614 777-5600
Columbus (G-6796)
Cryovac Inc ....F....... 513 771-7770
West Chester (G-19849)
Fabricated Packaging Mtls Inc ....G....... 740 681-1750
Lancaster (G-11712)
Fabricated Packaging Mtls Inc ....F....... 740 654-3492
Lancaster (G-11713)
Foam Concepts & Design Inc ....E....... 513 860-5589
West Chester (G-19866)
Greif Packaging LLC ....D....... 740 549-6000
Delaware (G-8854)
Hinkle Manufacturing Inc ....D....... 419 666-5550
Perrysburg (G-16107)
Hitti Enterprises Inc ....F....... 440 243-4100
Cleveland (G-5514)
Packages Anything Anywhere ....G....... 937 298-1939
Dayton (G-8561)
Plastic Works Inc ....F....... 440 331-5575
Cleveland (G-6014)
Skybox Packaging LLC ....D....... 419 525-7209
Mansfield (G-12680)
Special Design Products Inc ....E....... 614 272-6700
Columbus (G-7634)
Storopack Inc ....E....... 513 874-0314
West Chester (G-20056)
Thermal Visions Inc ....G....... 740 587-4025
Granville (G-10467)
Truechoicepack Corp ....E....... 937 630-3832
Dayton (G-8732)
Zebco Industries Inc ....F....... 740 654-4510
Lancaster (G-11763)
Zing Pac Inc ....E....... 440 248-7997
Cleveland (G-6495)

PACKAGING: Blister Or Bubble Formed, Plastic

A Aabaco Plastics Inc ....F....... 216 663-9494
Cleveland (G-4668)
MTS Medication Tech Inc ....G....... 440 238-0840
Strongsville (G-17943)
Republic Rings Inc ....G....... 440 238-2622
Strongsville (G-17957)
Rohrer Corporation ....C....... 330 335-1541
Wadsworth (G-19438)
Sonoco Prtective Solutions Inc ....D....... 419 420-0029
Findlay (G-9892)
Truechoicepack Corp ....E....... 937 630-3832
Dayton (G-8732)

PACKING & CRATING SVC

A Z Printing Inc ....G....... 513 745-0700
Cincinnati (G-3339)
Bates Metal Products Inc ....D....... 740 498-8371
Port Washington (G-16422)
Caravan Packaging Inc ....F....... 440 243-4100
Cleveland (G-4974)
Forrest Enterprises Inc ....G....... 937 773-1714
Piqua (G-16265)
Lefco Worthington LLC ....E....... 216 432-4422
Cleveland (G-5691)
Third Party Service Ltd ....F....... 419 872-2312
Perrysburg (G-16158)
Vista Industrial Packaging LLC ....D....... 800 454-6117
Columbus (G-7743)

PACKING MATERIALS: Mechanical

Excelsior Solutions ....G....... 937 848-2569
Spring Valley (G-17467)
Produce Packaging Inc ....C....... 216 391-6129
Cleveland (G-6052)

PACKING SVCS: Shipping

American Health Packaging ....D....... 614 492-8177
Columbus (G-6738)
Contract Pckg Dist Specialists ....F....... 513 942-0300
West Chester (G-19993)
Forest City Companies Inc ....E....... 216 586-5279
Cleveland (G-5369)
Global Packaging & Exports Inc ....G....... 513 454-2020
West Chester (G-19877)
McElroy Contract Packaging ....F....... 330 262-0855
Wooster (G-20804)

McNerney & Associates LLC ....E....... 513 241-9951
Cincinnati (G-4070)
Overseas Packing LLC ....F....... 440 232-2917
Bedford (G-1451)
Packaging Plus Inc ....G....... 304 429-5900
Dayton (G-8562)
Reynolds Industries Inc ....E....... 330 889-9466
West Farmington (G-20075)
World Express Packaging Corp ....G....... 216 634-9000
Cleveland (G-6479)

PADDING: Foamed Plastics

Aqua Lily Products LLC ....F....... 951 246-9610
Willoughby (G-20439)
J P Industrial Products Inc ....E....... 330 424-3388
Lisbon (G-12126)
Team Wendy LLC ....D....... 216 738-2518
Cleveland (G-6297)

PADS: Athletic, Protective

Soccer Centre Owners Ltd ....E....... 419 893-5425
Maumee (G-13296)
Tuffy Pad Company Inc ....F....... 330 688-0043
Stow (G-17813)

PAILS: Shipping, Metal

Cleveland Steel Container Corp ....E....... 330 656-5600
Streetsboro (G-17845)

PAINT & PAINTING SPLYS STORE

American Indus Maintanence ....G....... 937 254-3400
Dayton (G-8154)
Schilling Enamels Company ....G....... 216 252-6242
Cleveland (G-6164)
Schilling Enterprises Inc ....G....... 216 252-6242
Cleveland (G-6165)
Sherwin-Williams Company ....A....... 216 566-2000
Cleveland (G-6189)
Sherwin-Williams Company ....G....... 440 282-2310
Lorain (G-12275)
Sherwin-Williams Company ....G....... 614 539-8456
Grove City (G-10594)
Sherwin-Williams Company ....E....... 440 846-4328
Strongsville (G-17965)
Sherwin-Williams Company ....G....... 216 662-3300
Cleveland (G-6190)
Sherwin-Williams Company ....G....... 330 528-0124
Hudson (G-11198)
Sherwn-Wllams Auto Fnshes Corp ......C....... 216 332-8330
Cleveland (G-6191)
Sherwn-Wllams Intl Hldings Inc ....G....... 216 566-2000
Cleveland (G-6192)

PAINT DRIERS

Ferro Corporation ....D....... 216 577-7144
Bedford (G-1423)

PAINT STORE

Comex North America Inc ....D....... 303 307-2100
Cleveland (G-5103)
Fort Loramie Cast Stone Pdts ....G....... 937 420-2257
Fort Loramie (G-9931)
PPG Architectural Finishes Inc ....G....... 330 477-8165
Canton (G-2817)
Prints & Paints Flr Cvg Co Inc ....E....... 419 462-5663
Galion (G-10283)
Sherwin-Williams Company ....G....... 330 253-6625
North Canton (G-15264)

PAINTING SVC: Metal Prdts

Advance Paint Technology Inc ....G....... 216 676-8770
Cleveland (G-4710)
Alsco Metals Corporation ....E....... 740 983-2571
Dennison (G-8942)
Astro-Coatings Inc ....E....... 330 755-1414
Struthers (G-17990)
Austin Finishing Co Inc ....G....... 216 883-0326
Cleveland (G-4859)
Balser Inc ....G....... 567 444-4737
Archbold (G-667)
Benco Industries Inc ....G....... 440 572-3555
Strongsville (G-17896)
Brilliant Colorworks LLC ....G....... 800 566-4162
Columbus (G-6862)
Bta of Motorcars Inc ....G....... 440 716-1000
North Olmsted (G-15328)

C L S Finishing Inc............................F 330 784-4134
  Tallmadge (G-18136)

Carboline Company.........................G...... 513 896-1919
  Fairfield (G-9650)

Colonial Surface Solutions Inc ......D 419 659-5639
  Columbus Grove (G-7793)

Colonial Surface Solutions Inc ......E 419 358-0129
  Bluffton (G-1910)

Creative Powder Coatings ....G...... 440 322-8197
  Elyria (G-9398)

Duffee Finishing Inc.......................G...... 740 965-4848
  Sunbury (G-18059)

Fayette Industrial Coatings ....E 419 636-1773
  Bryan (G-2295)

Final Finish Corp............................G...... 440 439-3303
  Macedonia (G-12450)

Herbert E Orr Company...................C 419 399-4866
  Paulding (G-16005)

Heritage Industrial Finshg Inc ....D 330 798-9840
  Akron (G-222)

Kars Ohio LLC ....G...... 614 655-1099
  Pataskala (G-15973)

Lima Sandblasting & Pntg Co ....C 419 331-2939
  Lima (G-12044)

Newsome & Work Metalizing Co ......F 330 376-7144
  Akron (G-313)

Newtons Paint & Body......................G...... 740 352-9334
  Lucasville (G-12423)

Parker Trutec Incorporated ....D 937 653-8500
  Urbana (G-19172)

Precision Coatings Systems ....E 937 642-4727
  Marysville (G-12963)

Procoat Painting Inc ....G...... 513 735-2500
  Batavia (G-1218)

Production Paint Finishers Inc ....D 937 448-2627
  Bradford (G-2026)

Russell Products Co Inc...................E 330 633-5252
  Akron (G-385)

Sapa Extrusions North Amer LLC ....C 888 935-5759
  Sidney (G-17221)

Seacor Painting Corporation ....G...... 330 755-6361
  Campbell (G-2491)

Spectrum Metal Finishing Inc ....D 330 758-8358
  Youngstown (G-21211)

Springco Metal Coatings Inc ....C 216 251-7023
  Cleveland (G-6228)

Star Fab Inc ....C 330 533-9863
  Canfield (G-2576)

Tendon Manufacturing Inc ....E 216 663-3200
  Cleveland (G-6305)

Tool & Die Systems Inc ....E 440 327-5800
  North Ridgeville (G-15406)

Tri-State Fabricators Inc..................E 513 752-5005
  Amelia (G-587)

PAINTS & ADDITIVES

Akron Paint & Varnish Inc ....D 330 773-8911
  Akron (G-50)

All Coatings Co Inc ....G...... 330 821-3806
  Alliance (G-489)

Aluminum Coating Manufacturers ....E 216 341-2000
  Cleveland (G-4774)

American Paint Recyclers LLC ....G...... 888 978-6558
  Middle Point (G-13897)

Avion Manufacturing Company ....G...... 330 220-1989
  Brunswick (G-2207)

Axalt Powde Coati Syste Usa I ....F 614 600-4104
  Hilliard (G-10929)

Brinkman LLC ....F 419 204-5934
  Lima (G-11997)

Cansto Paint and Varnish Co............G...... 216 231-6115
  Cleveland (G-4966)

Certon Technologies Inc ....F 440 786-7185
  Bedford (G-1414)

Coloramics LLC................................E 614 876-1171
  Hilliard (G-10942)

Comex North America Inc ....D 303 307-2100
  Cleveland (G-5103)

Continental Products Company ....E 216 383-3932
  Euclid (G-9573)

Continental Products Company ....E 216 531-0710
  Cleveland (G-5126)

Dap Products Inc ....C 937 667-4461
  Tipp City (G-18274)

Filament LLC ....G...... 614 732-0754
  Columbus (G-7083)

Kalcor Coatings Company ....E 440 946-4700
  Willoughby (G-20518)

Karyall-Telday Inc ....E 216 281-4063
  Cleveland (G-5633)

Npa Coatings Inc.............................C 216 651-5900
  Cleveland (G-5921)

Sheffield Bronze Paint Corp ....E 216 481-8330
  Cleveland (G-6186)

Spectrum Dispersions Inc ....F 330 296-0600
  Ravenna (G-16558)

Suncolor Corporation ....G...... 330 499-7010
  North Canton (G-15270)

Thorworks Industries Inc ....E 419 626-4375
  Sandusky (G-17015)

Toledo Paint & Chemical Co.............G...... 419 244-3726
  Toledo (G-18739)

Valspar Corporation ....C 330 830-6000
  Massillon (G-13209)

PAINTS & ALLIED PRODUCTS

Akzo Nobel Coatings Inc ....C 614 294-3361
  Columbus (G-6709)

Akzo Nobel Coatings Inc ....C 614 294-3361
  Columbus (G-6711)

Akzo Nobel Inc ....C 205 323-5201
  Columbus (G-6712)

Americhem Inc ....D 330 929-4213
  Cuyahoga Falls (G-7965)

Aps-Materials Inc ....D 937 278-6547
  Dayton (G-8161)

Basic Coatings LLC ....F 419 241-2156
  Bowling Green (G-1971)

Bollin & Sons Inc ....E 419 693-6573
  Toledo (G-18376)

Cansto Coatings Ltd ....F 216 231-6115
  Cleveland (G-4965)

Cleveland Pigment Blending LLC ......G...... 330 794-6960
  Akron (G-126)

Consolidated Coatings Corp ....E 216 514-7596
  Cleveland (G-5118)

Creative Commercial Finishing ....G...... 513 722-9393
  Loveland (G-12347)

Deco Plas Properties LLC ....E 419 485-0632
  Montpelier (G-14443)

Envirnmntal Prtctive Ctngs LLC ....G...... 740 363-6180
  Ostrander (G-15786)

Ferro Corporation ....G...... 216 481-0238
  Cleveland (G-5338)

Fuchs Lubricants Co ....E 330 963-0400
  Twinsburg (G-18938)

General Electric Company ....D 216 268-3846
  Cleveland (G-5417)

Genvac Aerospace Corp ....F 440 646-9986
  Cleveland (G-5424)

Harrison Paint Company ....E 330 455-5120
  Canton (G-2724)

Henkel Corporation..........................C 216 475-3600
  Cleveland (G-5498)

Hexpol Compounding LLC ....C 440 834-4644
  Burton (G-2376)

Hoover & Wells Inc ....C 419 691-9220
  Toledo (G-18511)

Kardol Quality Products LLC ....C 513 933-8206
  Blue Ash (G-1822)

Leonhardt Plating Company ....F 513 242-1410
  Cincinnati (G-4020)

Mameco International Inc ....F 216 752-4400
  Cleveland (G-5738)

Matrix Sys Auto Finishes LLC ....D 248 668-8135
  Massillon (G-13177)

Meggitt (erlanger) LLC ....D 513 851-5550
  Cincinnati (G-4080)

Mid America Chemical Corp ....G...... 216 749-0100
  Cleveland (G-5803)

Myko Industries...............................E 216 431-0900
  Cleveland (G-5845)

Parker Trutec Incorporated ....F 937 653-8500
  Urbana (G-19172)

Perstorp Polyols Inc ....C 419 729-5448
  Toledo (G-18641)

Pittsburgh Glass Works LLC ....B 419 683-2400
  Crestline (G-7933)

Plasti-Kote Co Inc ....C 330 725-4511
  Medina (G-13459)

Polymerics Inc.................................G...... 330 434-6665
  Cuyahoga Falls (G-8034)

Polynt Composites USA Inc ....E 816 391-6000
  Sandusky (G-16997)

Polyone Corporation ....C 419 668-4844
  Norwalk (G-15559)

PPG Architectural Finishes Inc ....G...... 216 328-1581
  Cleveland (G-6025)

PPG Architectural Finishes Inc ....G...... 330 477-8165
  Canton (G-2817)

PPG Industries Inc...........................E 330 825-0831
  Barberton (G-1140)

PPG Industries Inc...........................D 440 572-2800
  Strongsville (G-17951)

PPG Industries Inc...........................G...... 740 774-8734
  Chillicothe (G-3264)

PPG Industries Inc...........................E 216 671-7793
  Cleveland (G-6026)

PPG Industries Inc...........................C 740 474-3161
  Circleville (G-4637)

PPG Industries Inc...........................E 740 774-7600
  Chillicothe (G-3265)

PPG Industries Inc...........................F 740 774-7600
  Chillicothe (G-3266)

PPG Industries Inc...........................E 419 683-2400
  Crestline (G-7935)

PPG Industries Inc...........................E 513 231-3200
  Cincinnati (G-4259)

PPG Industries Inc...........................E 740 474-3945
  Circleville (G-4638)

PPG Industries Inc...........................E 513 829-6006
  Fairfield (G-9703)

PPG Industries Inc...........................E 513 661-5220
  Cincinnati (G-4260)

PPG Industries Inc...........................G...... 614 277-0620
  Grove City (G-10584)

PPG Industries Inc...........................G...... 614 921-9228
  Hilliard (G-10972)

PPG Industries Inc...........................E 513 424-1241
  Middletown (G-14077)

PPG Industries Inc...........................E 513 984-6761
  Cincinnati (G-4261)

PPG Industries Inc...........................E 614 939-2365
  Columbus (G-7509)

PPG Industries Inc...........................E 614 268-2609
  Columbus (G-7510)

PPG Industries Inc...........................E 513 779-2727
  West Chester (G-20039)

PPG Industries Inc...........................E 513 242-3050
  Cincinnati (G-14262)

PPG Industries Inc...........................E 614 501-7360
  Reynoldsburg (G-16597)

PPG Industries Inc...........................E 330 262-9741
  Wooster (G-20822)

PPG Industries Inc...........................E 513 576-3100
  Milford (G-14168)

PPG Industries Inc...........................E 330 824-2537
  Warren (G-19588)

PPG Industries Ohio Inc ....E 740 363-9610
  Delaware (G-8878)

PPG Industries Ohio Inc ....D 216 486-5300
  Euclid (G-9600)

PPG Industries Ohio Inc ....A 216 671-0050
  Cleveland (G-6027)

Priest Services Inc ....G...... 440 333-1123
  Mayfield Heights (G-13321)

Prism Powder Coatings Ltd ....E 330 225-5626
  Brunswick (G-2249)

Ramon Robinson ....G...... 330 883-3244
  Vienna (G-19374)

Republic Powdered Metals Inc ....D 330 225-3192
  Medina (G-13467)

RPM Consumer Holding Company .....G...... 330 273-5090
  Medina (G-13470)

RPM International Inc ....D 330 273-5090
  Medina (G-13471)

Ruscoe Company ....E 330 253-8148
  Akron (G-383)

Schilling Enamels Company ....G...... 216 252-6242
  Cleveland (G-6164)

Schilling Enterprises Inc ....G...... 216 252-6242
  Cleveland (G-6165)

Sherwin-Williams Company ....A 216 566-2000
  Cleveland (G-6189)

Sherwin-Williams Company ....G...... 440 282-2310
  Lorain (G-12275)

Sherwin-Williams Company ....G...... 330 253-6625
  North Canton (G-15264)

Sherwin-Williams Company ....E 614 539-8456
  Grove City (G-10594)

Sherwin-Williams Company ....E 440 846-4328
  Strongsville (G-17965)

Sherwin-Williams Company ....G...... 216 662-3300
  Cleveland (G-6190)

Sherwin-Williams Company ....G...... 330 528-0124
  Hudson (G-11198)

Sherwn-Wllams Auto Fnshes Corp ...C 216 332-8330
  Cleveland (G-6191)

Sherwn-Wllams Intl Hldings Inc ....G...... 216 566-2000
  Cleveland (G-6192)

PRODUCT

Teknol Inc ....D...... 937 264-0190
Dayton (G-8708)

The Euclid Chemical Company ....D...... 216 531-9222
Cleveland (G-6310)

Tremco Incorporated ....B...... 216 292-5000
Beachwood (G-1303)

Universal Urethane Pdts Inc ....D...... 419 693-7400
Toledo (G-18760)

Wooster Products Inc ....D...... 330 264-2844
Wooster (G-20850)

Xim Products Inc ....E...... 440 871-4737
Westlake (G-20323)

Zircoa Inc ....C...... 440 248-0500
Cleveland (G-6498)

PAINTS, VARNISHES & SPLYS WHOLESALERS

Continental Products Company ....E...... 216 531-0710
Cleveland (G-5126)

Cto Inc ....G...... 330 785-1130
Akron (G-134)

Finishmaster Inc ....D...... 614 228-4328
Columbus (G-7086)

Myko Industries ....G...... 216 431-0900
Cleveland (G-5845)

Teknol Inc ....D...... 937 264-0190
Dayton (G-8708)

PAINTS, VARNISHES & SPLYS, WHOLESALE: Paints

C A P Industries Inc ....F...... 937 773-1824
Piqua (G-16254)

Comex North America Inc ....D...... 303 307-2100
Cleveland (G-5103)

Jmac Inc ....F...... 614 436-2418
Columbus (G-7235)

Matrix Sys Auto Finishes LLC ....D...... 248 668-8135
Massillon (G-13177)

PAINTS, VARNISHES & SPLYS, WHOLESALE: Stain

Tridico Silk Screen & Sign Co...........G...... 419 526-1695
Mansfield (G-12700)

PAINTS: Asphalt Or Bituminous

Parkins Asphalt Sealing ....G...... 419 422-2399
Findlay (G-9876)

PAINTS: Marine

Precisions Paint Systems LLC ....F...... 740 894-6224
South Point (G-17444)

PAINTS: Oil Or Alkyd Vehicle Or Water Thinned

Akzo Nobel Coatings Inc......................F...... 937 322-2671
Springfield (G-17515)

Axalta Coating Systems LLC ....E...... 419 478-1211
Toledo (G-18361)

Mansfield Paint Co Inc ....F...... 330 725-2436
Medina (G-13439)

Waterlox Coatings Corporation ....F...... 216 641-4877
Cleveland (G-6450)

PALLET REPAIR SVCS

Able Pallet Mfg & Repr ....F...... 614 444-2115
Columbus (G-6681)

George Biniker Wooden Pallets ....F...... 419 666-3185
Perrysburg (G-16101)

Langston Pallets ....G...... 937 492-8769
Sidney (G-17198)

Lumberjack Pallet Recycl LLC...........G...... 513 821-7543
Cincinnati (G-4039)

Martin Pallet Inc ....E...... 330 832-5309
Massillon (G-13172)

PALLETIZERS & DEPALLETIZERS

Intelligrated Systems Ohio LLC...........A...... 513 701-7300
Mason (G-13047)

PALLETS

A & M Pallet ....F...... 937 295-3093
Russia (G-16760)

A2z Pallets LLC......................G...... 513 652-9026
Cincinnati (G-3340)

AAA Plastics and Pallets Ltd ....G...... 330 844-2556
North Lawrence (G-15305)

Akron Crate and Pallet LLC ....G...... 330 524-8955
Kent (G-11425)

American Built Custom Pallets ....G...... 330 532-4780
Lisbon (G-12116)

At Pallet......................G...... 330 264-3903
Wooster (G-20742)

B & B Pallet Co......................G...... 419 435-4530
Fostoria (G-9967)

B M Pallets......................G...... 740 634-2659
Hillsboro (G-10996)

Bonded Pallets......................G...... 513 541-1855
Cincinnati (G-3459)

Buy The Pallet LLC......................G...... 440 521-0073
Broadview Heights (G-2107)

Carrillo Pallets LLC......................G...... 513 942-2210
Cincinnati (G-3503)

CC Pallets LLC......................G...... 513 442-8766
Terrace Park (G-18179)

Cleveland Cstm Pllet Crate Inc ....E...... 216 881-1414
Cleveland (G-5055)

Clover Pallet LLC......................G...... 330 454-5592
Canton (G-2660)

Contreras Pallets ....G...... 567 277-2447
Toledo (G-18412)

Crosscreek Pallet Co......................G...... 440 632-1940
Middlefield (G-13926)

Daves Pallets ....G...... 740 525-4938
Belpre (G-1585)

Dj Pallets......................G...... 216 701-9183
Columbia Station (G-6588)

Fisher Pallet......................G...... 440 632-0863
Middlefield (G-13934)

Garys Pallet Sales......................G...... 330 569-7676
Hiram (G-11035)

H & K Pallet Services......................G...... 937 608-1140
Xenia (G-20954)

Hillside Pallet......................G...... 440 272-5425
Windsor (G-20700)

J & K Pallet Inc......................G...... 937 526-5117
Versailles (G-19349)

J&R Pallet Ltd......................G...... 740 226-1112
Waverly (G-19712)

Joe Barrett......................G...... 216 385-2384
East Liverpool (G-9220)

L N S Pallets......................G...... 330 936-7507
Navarre (G-14718)

Lawrence Pallets & Solutions ....G...... 740 259-4283
Lucasville (G-12421)

Leroy Yutzy......................G...... 937 386-2872
Winchester (G-20694)

Montgomerys Pallet Service ....G...... 330 297-6677
Ravenna (G-16542)

Mt Eaton Pallet Ltd......................E...... 330 893-2986
Millersburg (G-14251)

Mulch World......................G...... 419 873-6852
Perrysburg (G-16123)

Oakmoor Pallet......................G...... 216 926-1858
Westlake (G-20287)

Oakmoor Pallet......................G...... 440 385-7340
Westlake (G-20288)

Ohio State Pallet Corp......................G...... 614 332-3961
Homer (G-11113)

Pallet Guys......................G...... 440 897-3001
North Royalton (G-15441)

Pallet Pros......................G...... 440 537-9087
Grafton (G-10434)

Paul E Cekovich......................G...... 330 424-3213
Lisbon (G-12132)

Precise Pallets LLC......................G...... 513 560-8236
Batavia (G-1217)

Quality Pllets Recyclables LLC ....G...... 419 396-3244
Carey (G-2926)

S & S Pallets......................G...... 513 967-7432
Milford (G-14171)

Schnider Pallet LLC......................G...... 440 632-5346
Middlefield (G-13987)

Smith Pallets......................G...... 937 564-6492
Versailles (G-19357)

Specialty Pallet & Design Ltd ....E...... 330 857-0257
Orrville (G-15768)

T&A Pallets Inc......................G...... 330 968-4743
Ravenna (G-16564)

Tri State Pallet Inc......................F...... 937 746-8702
Franklin (G-10060)

Troyers Pallet Shop......................G...... 330 897-1038
Fresno (G-10201)

Universal Pallets Inc......................G...... 614 444-1095
Columbus (G-7724)

Valley View Pallets Partners ....G...... 740 393-9282
Danville (G-8092)

Van Wert Pallets LLC......................G...... 419 203-1823
Van Wert (G-19275)

Worthington Pallet......................G...... 614 888-1573
Worthington (G-20899)

PALLETS & SKIDS: Wood

A W Taylor Lumber Incorporated ....F...... 440 577-1889
Pierpont (G-16210)

Able Pallet Mfg & Repr ....F...... 614 444-2115
Columbus (G-6681)

Arrowhead Pallets LLC......................F...... 440 693-4241
Middlefield (G-13915)

B J Pallett......................G...... 419 447-9665
Tiffin (G-18208)

Belco Works Inc......................B...... 740 695-0500
Saint Clairsville (G-16782)

Brookhill Center Industries ....C...... 419 876-3932
Ottawa (G-15790)

Buck Creek Pallet......................G...... 937 653-3098
Urbana (G-19149)

Buckeye Pallett......................G...... 330 359-5919
Millersburg (G-14204)

Chep (usa) Inc......................E...... 614 497-9448
Columbus (G-6924)

Clark Rm Inc......................E...... 419 425-9889
Findlay (G-9808)

Cs Products......................G...... 330 452-8566
Canton (G-2672)

Custom Palet Manufacturing ....G...... 440 693-4603
Middlefield (G-13927)

D P Products Inc......................G...... 440 834-9663
Middlefield (G-13929)

Emergency Products & RES Inc ....G...... 330 673-5003
Kent (G-11455)

Forrest Rawlins......................G...... 740 778-3366
Wheelersburg (G-20330)

Grant Street Pallet Inc......................G...... 330 424-0355
Lisbon (G-12120)

Hacker Wood Products Inc ....G...... 513 737-4462
Hamilton (G-10700)

Haessly Lumber Sales Co ....D...... 740 373-6681
Marietta (G-12788)

Hann Box Works......................E...... 740 962-3752
McConnelsville (G-13351)

Hann Manufacturing Inc ....E...... 740 962-3752
McConnelsville (G-13352)

Hinchcliff Lumber Company ....G...... 440 238-5200
Strongsville (G-17925)

Hines Builders Inc......................F...... 937 335-4586
Troy (G-18834)

Hope Timber Pallet Recycl Inc...........E...... 740 344-1788
Newark (G-15021)

J E Johnson Pallett Inc......................G...... 614 424-9663
Columbus (G-7217)

J I T Pallets Inc......................G...... 330 424-0355
Lisbon (G-12124)

Ken Harper......................C...... 740 439-4452
Byesville (G-2406)

Kountry Pride Enterprises ....G...... 330 868-3345
Minerva (G-14330)

Litco International Inc......................E...... 330 539-5433
Vienna (G-19368)

Litco Manufacturing LLC ....G...... 330 539-5433
Warren (G-19573)

Lumberjack Pallet Recycl LLC ....G...... 513 821-7543
Cincinnati (G-4039)

Melt Inc......................G...... 330 426-3545
Negley (G-14731)

Mid Ohio Wood Recycling Inc ....G...... 419 673-8470
Kenton (G-11558)

Middlefield Pallet Inc......................E...... 440 632-0553
Middlefield (G-13961)

Midtown Pallet & Recycling ....E...... 419 241-1311
Toledo (G-18585)

Millwood Inc......................D...... 330 857-3075
Apple Creek (G-645)

Mjc Enterprises Inc......................G...... 330 669-3744
Sterling (G-17684)

Morgan Wood Products Inc ....F...... 614 336-4000
Powell (G-16480)

Oak Chips Inc......................G...... 740 947-4159
Waverly (G-19714)

Olympic Forest Products Co ....F...... 216 421-2775
Cleveland (G-5940)

P R U Industries Inc......................F...... 937 746-8702
Franklin (G-10043)

Packaging Plus Inc ....G....... 304 429-5900
Dayton (G-8562)
Pallet Distributors Inc.........................D....... 330 852-3531
Sugarcreek (G-18030)
Pallet World Inc ....E....... 419 874-9333
Perrysburg (G-16144)
Plains Precut Ltd ....G....... 330 893-3300
Millersburg (G-14255)
Premier Pallet & Recycling ....F....... 330 767-2221
Navarre (G-14724)
Prime Wood Craft Inc ....F....... 216 738-2222
Brunswick (G-2248)
Quadco Rehabilitation Center ....B....... 419 682-1011
Stryker (G-18006)
Quadco Rehabilitation Center ....D....... 419 445-1950
Archbold (G-691)
Rettig Family Pallets Inc......................F....... 419 264-1540
Holgate (G-11040)
Richland Newhope Industries...............C....... 419 774-4400
Mansfield (G-12671)
San Pallet LLC ....G....... 937 271-5308
Troy (G-18871)
Shaw Pallets & Specialties...................G....... 740 498-7892
Newcomerstown (G-15123)
Specialty Pallet Entps LLC ....G....... 419 673-0247
Kenton (G-11569)
Sugarcreek Pallett................................G....... 330 852-9812
Sugarcreek (G-18043)
Troymill Manufacturing Inc ....F....... 440 632-5580
Middlefield (G-13997)
Tusco Hardwoods LLC ....F....... 330 852-4281
Sugarcreek (G-18047)
Ultimate Pallet & Trucking LLC.............G....... 440 693-4090
Middlefield (G-13999)
Weaver Pallet Ltd ....G....... 330 682-4022
Apple Creek (G-652)
Wjf Enterprises LLC..............................F....... 513 871-7320
Cincinnati (G-4601)
Woodford Logistics ....D....... 513 417-8453
South Charleston (G-17427)
Yoder Lumber Co Inc ....E....... 330 674-1435
Millersburg (G-14289)
Zak Box Co Inc ....G....... 216 961-5636
Cleveland (G-6491)

PALLETS: Corrugated

Jordon Auto Service & Tire Inc.............G....... 216 214-6528
Cleveland (G-5622)

PALLETS: Plastic

Marcum Development LLC......................G....... 330 466-8231
Wooster (G-20802)
Mye Automotive Inc ....G....... 330 253-5592
Akron (G-308)
Myers Industries Inc ....E....... 330 253-5592
Akron (G-309)
Quality Frp Fabrications........................G....... 440 942-9067
Willoughby (G-20582)

PALLETS: Wooden

A & D Wood Products Inc.......................G....... 419 331-8859
Elida (G-9349)
A & M Pallet Shop Inc ....F....... 440 632-1941
Middlefield (G-13911)
A-Z Packaging Company.........................F....... 614 444-8441
Columbus (G-6670)
Anderson Pallet & Packg Inc ....E....... 937 962-2614
Lewisburg (G-11931)
Buckeye Diamond Logistics Inc ....C....... 937 462-8361
South Charleston (G-17424)
Cabot Lumber Inc ....G....... 740 545-7109
West Lafayette (G-20085)
Caesarcreek Pallets Ltd ....F....... 937 416-4447
Jamestown (G-11351)
Cimino Box Inc ....G....... 216 961-7377
Cleveland (G-5033)
Coblentz Brothers Inc............................E....... 330 857-7211
Apple Creek (G-634)
Cottonwood Pallet Inc ....G....... 419 468-9703
Galion (G-10260)
Cox Wood Product Inc ....F....... 740 372-4735
Otway (G-15829)
D M Pallet Service Inc ....F....... 614 491-0881
Columbus (G-7006)
Damar Products Inc ....G....... 937 492-9023
Sidney (G-17174)
Damar Products Inc ....F....... 937 492-9023
Sidney (G-17175)

Dan S Miller & David S Miller ....G....... 937 464-9061
Belle Center (G-1512)
Fox Hollow Pallet ....G....... 937 386-2872
Winchester (G-20693)
Franks Sawmill Inc.................................F....... 419 682-3831
Stryker (G-18003)
Gallagher Lumber Co ....G....... 330 274-2333
Mantua (G-12710)
Gardner Lumber Co Inc ....F....... 740 254-4664
Tippecanoe (G-18313)
George Biniker Wooden Pallets ....F....... 419 666-3185
Perrysburg (G-16101)
Gross Lumber Inc ....E....... 330 683-2055
Apple Creek (G-638)
Halliday Holdings Inc ....E....... 740 335-1430
Wshngtn CT Hs (G-20910)
Hershberger Manufacturing....................E....... 440 272-5555
Windsor (G-20699)
Hope Timber & Marketing Group..........F....... 740 344-1788
Newark (G-15019)
Ifco Systems North America Inc ....D....... 330 669-2726
Smithville (G-17240)
Ifco Systems Us LLC ....E....... 513 769-0377
Hamilton (G-3910)
Inca Presswood-Pallets Ltd ....E....... 330 343-3361
Dover (G-8992)
Industrial Hardwood Inc.........................G....... 419 666-2503
Perrysburg (G-16111)
Inland Hardwood Corporation................D....... 740 373-7187
Marietta (G-12793)
Iron City Wood Products Inc...................E....... 330 755-2772
Youngstown (G-21121)
J & L Wood Products Inc ....E....... 937 667-4064
Tipp City (G-18286)
J D L Hardwoods ....E....... 440 272-5630
Middlefield (G-13943)
JIT Packaging Inc...................................G....... 330 562-8080
Aurora (G-927)
Joe Gonda Company Inc ....F....... 440 458-6000
Elyria (G-9443)
Kenneth Schrock ....E....... 937 544-7566
West Union (G-20123)
Lake Wood Product Inc...........................G....... 419 832-0150
Grand Rapids (G-10441)
Langston Pallets ....G....... 937 492-8769
Sidney (G-17198)
Lima Pallet Company Inc ....E....... 419 229-5736
Lima (G-12041)
Martin Pallet Inc ....E....... 330 832-5309
Massillon (G-13172)
Mid Ohio Wood Products Inc...................G....... 740 323-0427
Newark (G-15033)
Miller Pallet Company.............................G....... 937 464-4483
Belle Center (G-1514)
Millwood Inc ....E....... 614 409-9680
Columbus (G-7355)
Millwood Inc ....E....... 330 359-5220
Dundee (G-9176)
Nwp Manufacturing Inc ....F....... 419 894-6871
Waldo (G-19466)
Ohio Wood Recycling Inc ....G....... 614 491-0881
Columbus (G-7437)
Pallet & Cont Corp of Amer ....G....... 419 255-1256
Toledo (G-18634)
Pallet Specs Plus LLC ....F....... 513 351-3200
Norwood (G-15573)
Pallets-Fm-N-plc-packaging Inc ....E....... 937 526-9333
Versailles (G-19355)
Parks West Pallet Llc ....G....... 440 693-4651
Middlefield (G-13979)
Pettits Pallets Inc ....G....... 614 351-4920
Derby (G-8947)
Precision Pallet Inc ....G....... 419 381-8191
Ottawa Hills (G-15818)
Queen City Pallets ....F....... 513 200-6426
Cincinnati (G-4318)
R C Family Wood Products......................G....... 937 295-2393
Fort Loramie (G-9935)
Raber Lumber Co....................................G....... 330 893-2797
Charm (G-3184)
Russell L Garber ....G....... 937 548-6224
Greenville (G-10521)
S & M Products ....G....... 419 272-2054
Blakeslee (G-1708)
S & S Pallett..G....... 740 372-0238
Mc Dermott (G-13343)
Schaefer Box & Pallet Co ....E....... 513 738-2500
Hamilton (G-10736)
Schrock John ....G....... 937 544-8457
West Union (G-20125)

Sealco Inc ....G....... 740 922-4122
Uhrichsville (G-19058)
Silvesco Inc ....F....... 740 373-6661
Marietta (G-12830)
Slats and Nails Inc ....G....... 330 866-1008
East Sparta (G-9255)
Southeast Ohio Timber Pdts Co.............G....... 740 344-2570
Zanesville (G-21355)
Southern Ohio Lumber LLC ....E....... 614 436-4472
Peebles (G-16025)
Sterling Industries Inc ....F....... 419 523-3788
Ottawa (G-15810)
Stony Point Hardwoods ....F....... 330 852-4512
Sugarcreek (G-18040)
Stumptown Lbr Pallet Mills Ltd ....G....... 740 757-2275
Somerton (G-17421)
T & D Thompson Inc ....E....... 740 332-8515
Laurelville (G-11772)
Terry Lumber and Supply Co ....F....... 330 659-6800
Peninsula (G-16043)
Thomas J Weaver Inc ....F....... 740 622-2040
Coshocton (G-7913)
Timber Products Inc ....E....... 440 693-4098
Middlefield (G-13995)
Tolson Pallet Mfg Inc ....F....... 937 787-3511
Gratis (G-10468)
Traveling & Recycle Wood Pdts ....F....... 419 968-2649
Middle Point (G-13899)
Tri State Pallet Inc ....G....... 937 323-5210
Springfield (G-17667)
Van Orders Pallet Company Inc..............F....... 419 875-6932
Swanton (G-18094)
Winesburg Hardwood Lumber Co............E....... 330 893-2705
Dundee (G-9186)
Yoder Lumber Co Inc ....D....... 330 893-3121
Millersburg (G-14288)

PAN GLAZING SVC

Russell T Bundy Associates Inc.............E....... 419 526-4454
Mansfield (G-12674)

PANEL & DISTRIBUTION BOARDS & OTHER RELATED APPARATUS

Acorn Technology Corporation ....E....... 216 663-1244
Cleveland (G-4697)
Hosler Maps Inc ....G....... 937 855-4173
Germantown (G-10369)
Jeff Bonham Electric Inc ....E....... 937 233-7662
Dayton (G-8425)

PANEL & DISTRIBUTION BOARDS: Electric

Assembly Works Inc................................G....... 419 433-5010
Huron (G-11217)
Industrial Solutions Inc ....E....... 614 431-8118
Lewis Center (G-11900)
Osborne Coinage Company.....................D....... 513 681-5424
Cincinnati (G-4197)
Spectra-Tech Manufacturing Inc ....E....... 513 735-9300
Batavia (G-1225)

PANELS & SECTIONS: Prefabricated, Concrete

Aetna Plastics Corp ....G....... 330 274-2855
Mantua (G-12706)

PANELS: Building, Metal

Otter Group LLC.....................................F....... 937 315-1199
Dayton (G-8554)

PANELS: Building, Plastic, NEC

Clearsonic Manufacturing Inc................G....... 330 650-1420
Hudson (G-11164)
Remram Recovery LLC ....F....... 740 667-0092
Tuppers Plains (G-18886)
Tema Isenmann Inc................................G....... 859 252-0613
Cincinnati (G-4500)

PANELS: Building, Wood

Ecoponics Group LLC.............................G....... 330 819-1233
Kent (G-11453)
Premier Construction Company..............E....... 513 874-2611
Fairfield (G-9704)
Thomas Panels Inc ....F....... 330 758-2384
Youngstown (G-21221)

PRODUCT

PANELS: Wood

Carter Woodcraft Center .... G 330 872-6474
Newton Falls (G-15130)

PAPER & BOARD: Die-cut

A G Ruff Paper Specialties Co .... G 513 891-7990
Blue Ash (G-1731)

A H Pelz Co .... G 216 861-1882
Cleveland (G-4674)

Art Guild Binders Inc .... E 513 242-3000
Cincinnati (G-3414)

Buckeye Boxes Inc .... D 614 274-8484
Columbus (G-6870)

Ccw Group Pacesetter Inc .... C 740 474-0122
Circleville (G-4624)

Commercial Cutng Graphics LLC .... D 419 526-4800
Mansfield (G-12583)

Consuetudo Abscisum Inc .... G 419 281-8002
Ashland (G-725)

Cornerstone Indus Holdings .... G 440 893-9144
Chagrin Falls (G-3054)

Cutting Edge Cnverted Pdts Inc .... E 888 720-3343
Toledo (G-18420)

D A Stirling Inc .... G 330 923-3195
Cuyahoga Falls (G-7985)

Georgia-Pacific LLC .... C 740 477-3347
Circleville (G-4631)

Harris & Company Inc .... F 330 332-4127
Salem (G-16899)

Harris Paper Crafts Inc .... F 614 299-2141
Columbus (G-7145)

Honeymoon Paper Products Inc .... D 513 755-7200
Fairfield (G-9666)

Hunt Products Inc .... E 440 667-2457
Newburgh Heights (G-15075)

Kent Adhesive Products Co .... D 330 678-1626
Kent (G-11475)

Keyah International Trdg LLC .... E 937 399-3140
Springfield (G-17586)

Lam Pro Inc .... F 216 426-0661
Cleveland (G-5678)

McElroy Contract Packaging .... F 330 262-0855
Wooster (G-20804)

Nordec Inc .... D 330 940-3700
Stow (G-17784)

Paxar Corporation .... G 937 681-4541
Dayton (G-8567)

Printers Bindery Services Inc .... D 513 821-8039
Cincinnati (G-4271)

R W Michael Printing Co .... G 330 923-9277
Akron (G-363)

Rohrer Corporation .... C 330 335-1541
Wadsworth (G-19438)

Spencer-Walker Press Inc .... F 740 344-6110
Newark (G-15055)

Springdot Inc .... D 513 542-4000
Cincinnati (G-4448)

Stuart Company .... F 513 621-9462
Cincinnati (G-4471)

Vya Inc .... E 513 772-5400
Cincinnati (G-4573)

PAPER CONVERTING

American Paper Converting LLC .... F 419 729-4782
Toledo (G-18343)

Buckeye Paper Co Inc .... E 330 477-5925
Canton (G-2630)

Buschman Corporation .... F 216 431-6633
Cleveland (G-4951)

Davidson Converting Inc .... G 330 626-2118
Streetsboro (G-17848)

Domtar Paper Company LLC .... D 740 333-0003
Wshngtn CT Hs (G-20906)

Fibercorr Mills LLC .... D 330 837-5151
Massillon (G-13131)

Gemini Fiber Corporation .... D 330 874-4131
Bolivar (G-1935)

Graphic Paper .... E 419 526-4123
Mansfield (G-12619)

Greif Inc .... D 330 879-2101
Navarre (G-14714)

Harris Paper Crafts Inc .... F 614 299-2141
Columbus (G-7145)

Kent Adhesive Products Co .... D 330 678-1626
Kent (G-11475)

Media Procurement Services Inc .... G 513 977-3000
Cincinnati (G-4077)

Millcraft Group LLC .... D 216 441-5500
Cleveland (G-5817)

Mondi Akrosil LLC .... C 740 653-4102
Lancaster (G-11731)

Paper Systems Incorporated .... C 937 746-6841
Springboro (G-17494)

Pmco LLC .... C 513 825-7626
West Chester (G-19916)

Rivercor LLC .... E 330 784-1113
Akron (G-375)

Signode Industrial Group LLC .... E 513 248-2990
Loveland (G-12387)

Stumps Converting Inc .... F 419 492-2542
New Washington (G-14965)

Van Deleigh Industries LLC .... G 419 467-2244
Sylvania (G-18129)

PAPER MANUFACTURERS: Exc Newsprint

Appvion Inc .... B 937 859-8261
West Carrollton (G-19790)

Evergreen Packaging Inc .... G 440 235-7200
Olmsted Falls (G-15675)

Georgia-Pacific LLC .... C 330 794-4444
Mogadore (G-14376)

Honey Cell Inc Mid West .... E 513 360-0280
Monroe (G-14405)

International Paper Company .... C 800 473-0830
Middletown (G-14049)

International Paper Company .... B 877 447-2737
Milford (G-14153)

International Paper Company .... G 440 428-5116
Madison (G-12507)

International Paper Company .... C 513 248-6365
Loveland (G-12362)

International Paper Company .... F 740 439-3527
Byesville (G-2404)

International Paper Company .... G 419 675-2534
Kenton (G-11551)

International Paper Company .... C 513 248-6000
Loveland (G-12363)

International Paper Company .... B 419 673-0711
Kenton (G-11553)

Kimberly-Clark Corporation .... C 513 864-3780
Cincinnati (G-3989)

Metro Recycling Company .... G 513 251-1800
Cincinnati (G-4094)

Mohawk Fine Papers Inc .... E 440 969-2000
Ashtabula (G-822)

Newpage Energy Services LLC .... A 877 855-7243
Miamisburg (G-13840)

Package Design & Mfg Inc .... F 513 874-7364
West Chester (G-20034)

Resolute FP US Inc .... B 216 961-3900
Cleveland (G-6107)

Resolute FP US Inc .... B 614 443-6300
Columbus (G-7557)

Resolute FP US Inc .... B 513 242-3671
Cincinnati (G-4338)

Veritiv Operating Company .... C 513 242-0800
Fairfield (G-9728)

Verso Corporation .... D 901 369-4105
Miamisburg (G-13875)

Wausau Paper Corp .... C 513 217-3623
Middletown (G-14096)

West Carrollton Converting Inc .... D 937 859-3621
Dayton (G-8753)

Westrock Cp LLC .... B 740 622-0581
Coshocton (G-7915)

PAPER NAPKINS WHOLESALERS

Canton Sterilized Wiping Cloth .... G 330 455-5179
Canton (G-2648)

PAPER PRDTS: Book Covers

Unique Covers .... G 419 925-9600
Maria Stein (G-12761)

PAPER PRDTS: Feminine Hygiene Prdts

Procter & Gamble Company .... C 513 983-1100
Cincinnati (G-4278)

PAPER PRDTS: Infant & Baby Prdts

Qpi Cincinnati LLC .... G 513 755-2670
West Chester (G-19924)

PAPER PRDTS: Napkins, Made From Purchased Materials

Gibson Greetings Inc .... G 216 252-7300
Cleveland (G-5428)

Tri Con Distribution LLC .... G 937 399-3312
Springfield (G-17666)

PAPER PRDTS: Napkins, Sanitary, Made From Purchased Material

Health Care Products Inc .... E 419 678-9620
Coldwater (G-6562)

Procter & Gamble Far East Inc .... C 513 983-1100
Cincinnati (G-4289)

Tranzonic Companies .... B 216 535-4300
Richmond Heights (G-16657)

PAPER PRDTS: Sanitary

B & B Necessities .... G 330 995-0489
Aurora (G-909)

Georgia-Pacific LLC .... F 513 336-4200
Mason (G-13027)

Giant Industries Inc .... E 419 531-4600
Toledo (G-18480)

Kimberly-Clark Corporation .... C 513 794-1005
West Chester (G-19888)

Linsalata Capital Partners Fun .... G 440 684-1400
Cleveland (G-5703)

Little Busy Bodies LLC .... E 513 351-5700
Cincinnati (G-4029)

Playtex Manufacturing Inc .... D 937 498-4710
Sidney (G-17209)

Procter & Gamble Paper Pdts Co .... F 513 983-1100
Cincinnati (G-4291)

Procter & Gamble Paper Pdts Co .... E 513 983-2222
Cincinnati (G-4292)

Tranzonic Companies .... C 216 535-4300
Richmond Heights (G-16656)

Tranzonic Companies .... C 440 446-0643
Cleveland (G-6350)

Tz Acquisition Corp .... A 216 535-4300
Richmond Heights (G-16658)

Wausau Ppr Towel & Tissue LLC .... C 513 424-2999
Middletown (G-14097)

PAPER PRDTS: Tampons, Sanitary, Made From Purchased Material

Cbl Products .... G 216 321-2599
Cleveland (G-4997)

Tambrands Sales Corp .... C 513 983-1100
Cincinnati (G-4492)

PAPER PRDTS: Towels, Napkins/Tissue Paper, From Purchd Mtrls

Aci Industries Converting Ltd .... E 740 368-4160
Delaware (G-8816)

Novex Products Incorporated .... E 440 244-3330
Lorain (G-12264)

PGT Healthcare LLP .... G 513 983-1100
Cincinnati (G-4234)

Procter & Gamble Company .... C 513 934-3406
Oregonia (G-15722)

Procter & Gamble Company .... C 513 626-2500
Blue Ash (G-1857)

Procter & Gamble Company .... B 513 983-1100
Cincinnati (G-4277)

Procter & Gamble Company .... C 513 634-9110
West Chester (G-19923)

Procter & Gamble Company .... B 513 983-1100
Cincinnati (G-4286)

Procter & Gamble Company .... C 410 527-5735
Grove City (G-10586)

PAPER PRDTS: Wrappers, Blank, Made From Purchased Materials

Btw LLC .... G 419 382-4443
Toledo (G-18383)

The Magic Seal Paper Pdts Co .... F 614 299-1185
Columbus (G-7691)

PAPER, WHOLESALE: Printing

Marco Printed Products Co Inc .... G 937 433-5680
Dayton (G-8478)

PAPER: Adding Machine Rolls, Made From Purchased Materials

Jr Kennel Mfg .... G 937 780-6104
Leesburg (G-11853)

PAPER: Adhesive

Ameri-Cal Corporation ....F 330 725-7735
Medina (G-13368)
Avery Dennison Corporation ....C 440 358-4691
Painesville (G-15856)
CCL Label Inc ....C 216 676-2703
Cleveland (G-4998)
CCL Label Inc ....E 440 878-7000
Brunswick (G-2215)
GBS Corp ....C 330 863-1828
Malvern (G-12545)
ID Images LLC ....D 330 220-7300
Brunswick (G-2234)
Kent Adhesive Products Co ....D 330 678-1626
Kent (G-11475)
Miller Studio Inc ....D 330 339-1100
New Philadelphia (G-14916)
Morgan Adhesives Company LLC ....B 330 688-1111
Stow (G-17775)
Stretchtape Inc ....E 216 486-9400
Cleveland (G-6251)
Technicote Inc ....E 800 358-4448
Miamisburg (G-13868)
Technicote Westfield Inc ....D 937 859-4448
Miamisburg (G-13869)
Unitherm Inc ....G 937 278-1900
Dayton (G-8738)

PAPER: Book

P H Glatfelter Company ....D 740 772-3111
Chillicothe (G-3256)

PAPER: Building, Insulating & Packaging

Avery Dennison Corporation ....C 440 358-4691
Painesville (G-15856)

PAPER: Building, Insulation

Owens Corning Sales LLC ....D 614 399-3915
Mount Vernon (G-14635)

PAPER: Cardboard

Derby Fabg Solutions LLC ....E 937 498-4054
Sidney (G-17176)
Valley Converting Co Inc ....E 740 537-2152
Toronto (G-18787)

PAPER: Chemically Treated, Made From Purchased Materials

Oliver Products Company ....F 513 860-6880
Hamilton (G-10729)

PAPER: Cigarette

Thedkahn LLC ....G 239 961-8757
Amelia (G-586)

PAPER: Cloth, Lined, Made From Purchased Materials

Tekni-Plex Inc ....E 419 491-2407
Holland (G-11088)

PAPER: Coated & Laminated, NEC

21st Century Printers Inc ....G 513 771-4150
Cincinnati (G-3322)
3 Sigma Corporation ....D 937 440-3400
Troy (G-18801)
3M Company ....D 330 725-1444
Medina (G-13361)
A-1 Printing Inc ....F 419 562-3111
Bucyrus (G-2330)
Adcraft Decals Inc ....E 216 524-2934
Cleveland (G-4702)
Admiral Products Company Inc ....E 216 671-0600
Cleveland (G-4706)
Ahlstrom West Carrollton LLC ....C 937 859-3621
Dayton (G-8140)
All-Seasons Paper Company ....E 440 826-1700
Cleveland (G-4760)
Avery Dennison Corporation ....B 440 358-3700
Painesville (G-15857)
Avery Dennison Corporation ....G 216 267-8700
Cleveland (G-4871)
Avery Dennison Corporation ....G 800 282-8379
Painesville (G-15858)

Avery Dennison Corporation ....D 440 358-3408
Painesville (G-15859)
Bemis Company Inc ....E 419 334-9465
Fremont (G-10128)
Bemis Company Inc ....E 330 923-5281
Akron (G-87)
Boehm Inc ....E 614 875-9010
Grove City (G-10546)
Bollin & Sons Inc ....E 419 693-6573
Toledo (G-18376)
CCL Label Inc ....B 440 878-7277
Strongsville (G-17900)
Central Coated Products Inc ....D 330 821-9830
Alliance (G-503)
Deco Tools Inc ....E 419 476-9321
Toledo (G-18430)
Gary I Teach Jr ....G 614 582-7483
London (G-12210)
GBS Corp ....G 330 929-8050
Stow (G-17758)
Giesecke & Devrient Amer Inc ....F 330 405-8442
Twinsburg (G-18946)
Giesecke & Devrient Amer Inc ....C 330 425-1515
Twinsburg (G-18947)
Hall Company ....E 937 652-1376
Urbana (G-19160)
Harris & Company Inc ....F 330 332-4127
Salem (G-16899)
Illinois Tool Works Inc ....C 937 393-4271
Hillsboro (G-11004)
Kardol Quality Products LLC ....G 513 933-8206
Blue Ash (G-1822)
Lam Pro Inc ....F 216 426-0661
Cleveland (G-5678)
Laminate Technologies Inc ....D 419 448-0812
Tiffin (G-18226)
Loroco Industries Inc ....E 513 891-9544
Blue Ash (G-1828)
Marlen Manufacturing & Dev Co ....E 216 292-7546
Bedford (G-1442)
Miami Valley Paper LLC ....E 937 746-6451
Franklin (G-10036)
Mr Label Inc ....E 513 681-2088
Cincinnati (G-4128)
Newpage Energy Services LLC ....A 877 855-7243
Miamisburg (G-13840)
Newpage Holding Corporation ....A 877 855-7243
Miamisburg (G-13842)
Nilpeter Usa Inc ....C 513 489-4400
Cincinnati (G-4156)
Novolex Holdings Inc ....D 740 397-2555
Mount Vernon (G-14634)
Ohio Laminating & Binding Inc ....E 614 771-4868
Hilliard (G-10966)
Paxar Corporation ....G 937 681-4541
Dayton (G-8567)
Pilot Production Solutions LLC ....G 513 602-1467
Mason (G-13073)
Roemer Industries Inc ....G 330 448-2000
Masury (G-13216)
RR Donnelley & Sons Company ....E 440 774-2101
Oberlin (G-15647)
Sensical Inc ....D 216 641-1141
Solon (G-17378)
Superior Label Systems Inc ....B 513 336-0825
Mason (G-13092)
The Rubber Stamp Shop ....G 419 478-4444
Toledo (G-18722)
Thomas Products Co Inc ....E 513 756-9009
Cincinnati (G-4507)
Waytek Corporation ....E 937 743-6142
Franklin (G-10065)

PAPER: Coated, Exc Photographic, Carbon Or Abrasive

Appvion Inc ....B 937 859-8261
West Carrollton (G-19790)
Imerys Usa Inc ....E 920 687-0872
Blue Ash (G-1813)
Troy Laminating & Coating Inc ....D 937 335-5611
Troy (G-18881)

PAPER: Corrugated

Gatton Packaging Inc ....G 419 886-2577
Bellville (G-1569)

PAPER: Enameled, Made From Purchased Materials

Coating Applications Intl LLC ....G 513 956-5222
Cincinnati (G-3594)

PAPER: Envelope

Crown Envelope LLC ....G 513 771-5070
Cincinnati (G-3621)

PAPER: Fine

Blue Ridge Paper Products Inc ....C 440 235-7200
Olmsted Falls (G-15674)
Greif Inc ....C 330 879-2936
Massillon (G-13143)
Newpage Holding Corporation ....A 877 855-7243
Miamisburg (G-13842)
Verso Paper Holding LLC ....B 877 855-7243
Miamisburg (G-13876)

PAPER: Gummed, Made From Purchased Materials

Thomas Tape and Supply Company .....F 937 325-6414
Springfield (G-17663)

PAPER: Milk Filter

Ken AG Inc ....E 419 281-1204
Ashland (G-747)

PAPER: Newsprint

B & B Paper Converters Inc ....F 216 941-8100
Cleveland (G-4880)

PAPER: Packaging

Ampac Plastics LLC ....B 513 671-1777
Cincinnati (G-3399)
D C S Specialty Packaging Inc ....F 937 615-0100
Piqua (G-16258)
Duracorp LLC ....E 740 549-3336
Lewis Center (G-11896)
Graphic Paper Products Corp ....D 937 325-5503
Springfield (G-17564)
JMJ Paper Inc ....F 216 941-8100
Avon Lake (G-1034)
Ranpak Corp ....C 440 354-4445
Concord Township (G-7799)

PAPER: Parchment

Ahlstrom West Carrollton LLC ....C 937 859-3621
Dayton (G-8140)

PAPER: Printer

Eagle Wright Innovations Inc ....G 937 640-8093
Moraine (G-14482)
Kn8designs LLC ....G 859 380-5926
Cincinnati (G-3997)
Transmit Identity LLC ....G 330 576-4732
Stow (G-17810)

PAPER: Specialty

T J Target ....G 330 658-3057
Doylestown (G-9031)

PAPER: Specialty Or Chemically Treated

BASF Corporation ....E 216 867-1040
Independence (G-11251)
Gvs Industries Inc ....G 513 887-8660
Hamilton (G-10699)
Novolyte Technologies Inc ....E 216 867-1040
Cleveland (G-5920)

PAPER: Tissue

Novolex Holdings Inc ....D 740 397-2555
Mount Vernon (G-14634)
Novolex Holdings Inc ....B 937 746-1933
Franklin (G-10041)

PAPER: Waxed, Made From Purchased Materials

Novolex Holdings Inc ....D 740 397-2555
Mount Vernon (G-14634)

PRODUCT

PAPER: Wrapping

Plus Mark LLC ....E 216 252-6770
Cleveland *(G-6018)*

PAPER: Wrapping & Packaging

Hanchett Paper Company ....E 513 782-4440
Cincinnati *(G-3865)*

Polymer Packaging Inc ....D 330 832-2000
Massillon *(G-13195)*

Welch Packaging Group Inc ....E 614 870-2000
Columbus *(G-7755)*

Westrock Cp LLC ....B 513 745-2586
Cincinnati *(G-4589)*

Westrock CP LLC ....C 937 898-2115
Dayton *(G-8754)*

PAPERBOARD

Ball Corporation ....D 330 244-2800
Canton *(G-2615)*

Buckeye Boxes Inc ....D 614 274-8484
Columbus *(G-6870)*

Caraustar Industries Inc ....E 513 871-7112
Cincinnati *(G-3497)*

Caraustar Industries Inc ....E 330 665-7700
Copley *(G-7841)*

Caraustar Industries Inc ....D 740 862-4167
Baltimore *(G-1081)*

Churmac Industries Inc ....E 740 773-5800
Chillicothe *(G-3234)*

Corpad Company Inc ....D 419 522-7818
Mansfield *(G-12586)*

Fibercorr Mills LLC ....D 330 837-5151
Massillon *(G-13131)*

G S K Inc ....G 937 547-1611
Greenville *(G-10501)*

Georgia-Pacific LLC ....C 740 477-3347
Circleville *(G-4631)*

Greif Paper Packg & Svcs LLC ....D 740 549-6000
Delaware *(G-8855)*

International Paper Company ....C 740 383-4061
Marion *(G-12877)*

International Paper Company ....C 740 363-9882
Delaware *(G-8862)*

Loroco Industries Inc ....E 513 891-9544
Blue Ash *(G-1828)*

Martin Paper Products Inc ....E 740 756-9271
Carroll *(G-2944)*

Miami Valley Paper LLC ....F 937 746-6451
Franklin *(G-10036)*

National Bias Fabric Co ....E 216 361-0530
Cleveland *(G-5853)*

P & R Specialty Inc ....E 937 773-0263
Piqua *(G-16297)*

Pactiv LLC ....C 614 771-5400
Columbus *(G-7454)*

Safeway Packaging Inc ....D 419 629-3200
New Bremen *(G-14793)*

Sonoco Products Company ....C 330 688-8247
Munroe Falls *(G-14665)*

Sonoco Products Company ....D 740 927-2525
Johnstown *(G-11404)*

Sonoco Products Company ....E 614 759-8470
Columbus *(G-7631)*

Sonoco Products Company ....D 513 455-6003
Blue Ash *(G-1870)*

Valley Converting Co Inc ....E 740 537-2152
Toronto *(G-18788)*

Westrock Cp LLC ....E 614 445-6850
Columbus *(G-7759)*

Westrock Mwv LLC ....C 937 495-6323
Kettering *(G-11588)*

PAPERBOARD CONVERTING

Caraustar Industries Inc ....F 216 961-5060
Cleveland *(G-4973)*

Caraustar Industries Inc ....E 330 665-7700
Copley *(G-7841)*

Corrchoice Inc ....D 330 833-5705
Massillon *(G-13122)*

E-Z Grader Company ....G 440 247-7511
Chagrin Falls *(G-3057)*

Formica Corporation ....E 513 786-3400
Cincinnati *(G-3772)*

Oak Hills Carton Co ....E 513 948-4200
Cincinnati *(G-4171)*

Ohio Packaging ....E 330 833-2884
Massillon *(G-13186)*

Outhouse Paper Etc Inc ....G 937 382-2800
Waynesville *(G-19732)*

Paper Service Inc ....F 330 227-3546
Lisbon *(G-12131)*

Roberds Converting Co Inc ....E 513 683-6667
Loveland *(G-12381)*

Vemuri International LLC ....G 513 483-6300
Cincinnati *(G-4559)*

PAPERBOARD PRDTS: Container Board

Multi-Color Corporation ....C 513 396-5600
Cincinnati *(G-4131)*

Westrock Converting Company ....C 513 860-0225
West Chester *(G-19973)*

PAPERBOARD PRDTS: Folding Boxboard

Custom Aluminum Boxes ....G 440 864-2664
Elyria *(G-9400)*

Folding Carton Service Inc ....F 419 281-4099
Ashland *(G-734)*

Graphic Packaging Intl Inc ....C 513 424-4200
Middletown *(G-14044)*

Graphic Packaging Intl Inc ....C 440 248-4370
Solon *(G-17301)*

Smith-Lustig Paper Box Mfg Co ....E 216 621-0453
Bedford *(G-1462)*

PAPERBOARD PRDTS: Packaging Board

National Carton & Coating Co ....D 937 347-1042
Xenia *(G-20964)*

PAPERBOARD PRDTS: Specialty Board

Third Party Service Ltd ....F 419 872-2312
Perrysburg *(G-16158)*

PAPERBOARD PRDTS: Stencil Board

Quilting Creations Intl ....E 330 874-4741
Bolivar *(G-1945)*

PAPERBOARD: Corrugated

Westrock Cp LLC ....B 740 622-0581
Coshocton *(G-7915)*

PAPETERIES & WRITING PAPER SETS

Selco Industries Inc ....C 419 861-0336
Holland *(G-11085)*

PARKING GARAGE

Youngstown Letter Shop Inc ....G 330 793-4935
Youngstown *(G-21253)*

PARKING METERS

Parking & Traffic Control SEC ....F 440 243-7565
Cleveland *(G-5977)*

PARTICLEBOARD: Laminated, Plastic

Amerilam Laminating ....G 440 235-4687
Cleveland *(G-4797)*

Miller Manufacturing Inc ....E 330 852-0689
Sugarcreek *(G-18028)*

Wico Products Inc ....G 937 783-0000
Blanchester *(G-1718)*

PARTITIONS & FIXTURES: Except Wood

3-D Technical Services Inc ....E 937 746-2901
Franklin *(G-10004)*

B-R-O-T Incorporated ....E 216 267-5335
Cleveland *(G-4886)*

Benko Products Inc ....E 440 934-2180
Sheffield Village *(G-17121)*

Bud Industries Inc ....E 440 946-3200
Willoughby *(G-20447)*

Component Systems Inc ....E 216 252-9292
Cleveland *(G-5113)*

Control Electric Co ....E 216 671-8010
Columbia Station *(G-6586)*

Crescent Metal Products Inc ....C 440 350-1100
Mentor *(G-13555)*

Custom Millcraft Corp ....E 513 874-7080
West Chester *(G-19851)*

Display Dynamics Inc ....F 937 832-2830
Englewood *(G-9516)*

Environmental Wall Systems ....G 440 542-6600
Hudson *(G-11170)*

Gallo Displays Inc ....E 216 431-9500
Cleveland *(G-5393)*

GMR Furniture Services Ltd ....F 216 244-5072
Parma *(G-15959)*

Gwp Holdings Inc ....D 513 860-4050
Fairfield *(G-9662)*

HP Manufacturing Company Inc ....D 216 361-6500
Cleveland *(G-5530)*

Integral Design Inc ....F 216 524-0555
Cleveland *(G-5574)*

Kellogg Cabinets Inc ....E 614 833-9596
Canal Winchester *(G-2529)*

M/W International Inc ....F 440 526-6900
Brecksville *(G-2063)*

Marlite Inc ....C 330 343-6621
Dover *(G-8998)*

Marlite Inc ....C 330 343-6621
Dover *(G-8999)*

Midmark Corporation ....A 937 526-3662
Versailles *(G-19352)*

Mro Built Inc ....D 330 526-0555
North Canton *(G-15252)*

Myers Industries Inc ....C 330 336-6621
Wadsworth *(G-19420)*

Ohio Displays Inc ....F 216 961-5600
Elyria *(G-9470)*

Organized Living Inc ....E 513 489-9300
Cincinnati *(G-4194)*

Panacea Products Corporation ....D 614 429-6320
Columbus *(G-7457)*

Pfi Displays Inc ....E 330 925-9015
Rittman *(G-16681)*

Pucel Enterprises Inc ....D 216 881-4604
Cleveland *(G-6061)*

Rack Processing Company Inc ....E 937 294-1911
Moraine *(G-14521)*

Stanley Industrial & Auto LLC ....C 614 755-7089
Westerville *(G-20187)*

Sunrise Cooperative Inc ....E 419 683-4600
Crestline *(G-7936)*

Ternion Inc ....E 216 642-6180
Cleveland *(G-6307)*

Valley Plastics Co Inc ....E 419 666-2349
Toledo *(G-18764)*

W J Egli Company Inc ....F 330 823-3666
Alliance *(G-551)*

Witt-Gor Inc ....G 419 659-2151
Columbus Grove *(G-7798)*

PARTITIONS WHOLESALERS

Door Fabrication Services Inc ....E 937 454-9207
Vandalia *(G-19290)*

Partitions Plus LLC ....F 419 422-2600
Findlay *(G-9877)*

Tri-State Supply Co Inc ....F 614 272-6767
Columbus *(G-7709)*

PARTITIONS: Nonwood, Floor Attached

Mills Company ....E 740 375-0770
Marion *(G-12885)*

Tri County Tarp Inc ....E 419 288-3350
Bradner *(G-2030)*

PARTITIONS: Solid Fiber, Made From Purchased Materials

Cole Pak Inc ....D 937 652-3910
Urbana *(G-19152)*

PARTITIONS: Wood & Fixtures

A & J Woodworking Inc ....G 419 695-5655
Delphos *(G-8898)*

Accent Manufacturing Inc ....F 330 724-7704
Norton *(G-15500)*

Action Group Inc ....D 614 868-8868
Blacklick *(G-1686)*

Amtekco Industries Inc ....G 614 228-6525
Columbus *(G-6750)*

Automated Bldg Components Inc ....E 419 257-2152
North Baltimore *(G-15191)*

Brower Products Inc ....D 937 563-1111
Cincinnati *(G-3482)*

Case Crafters Inc ....G 937 667-9473
Tipp City *(G-18271)*

Cassady Woodworks Inc ....E 937 256-7948
Dayton *(G-8099)*

Crane Plumbing LLC ....E 419 522-4211
Mansfield *(G-12587)*

Creative Products Inc ....E 419 866-5501
  Holland *(G-11049)*
D Lewis Inc ....G...... 740 695-2615
  Saint Clairsville *(G-16788)*
Diversified Products & Svcs ....C 740 393-6202
  Mount Vernon *(G-14619)*
Fleetwood Custom Countertops ....F 740 965-9833
  Johnstown *(G-11398)*
Forum III Inc ....F 513 961-5123
  Cincinnati *(G-3773)*
Geograph Industries Inc ....E 513 202-9200
  Harrison *(G-10780)*
Hawthorne Caravan & Assoc LLC ....F 440 366-9065
  Elyria *(G-9428)*
Home Stor & Off Solutions Inc ....F 216 362-4660
  Cleveland *(G-5521)*
Kitchens By Rutenschroer Inc ....F 513 251-8333
  Cincinnati *(G-3994)*
LE Smith Company ....D 419 636-4555
  Bryan *(G-2310)*
Leiden Cabinet Company LLC ....E 330 878-7790
  Strasburg *(G-17825)*
Lima Millwork Inc ....E 419 331-3303
  Elida *(G-9351)*
Nagele Manufacturing Co Inc ....E 216 433-1100
  Cleveland *(G-5849)*
Partitions Plus LLC ....F 419 422-2600
  Findlay *(G-9877)*
Profac Inc ....C 440 942-0205
  Mentor *(G-13698)*
Reserve Millwork Inc ....E 216 531-6982
  Bedford *(G-1457)*
Riceland Cabinet Inc ....D 330 601-1071
  Wooster *(G-20829)*
Symatic Inc ....E 330 225-1510
  Brunswick *(G-2260)*
Thomas Cabinet Shop Inc ....F 937 847-8239
  Dayton *(G-8711)*
Thomas Hora ....G 740 622-1386
  Fresno *(G-10200)*
Trumbull Industries Inc ....E 330 434-6174
  Akron *(G-448)*
Wine Cellar Innovations LLC ....C 513 321-3733
  Cincinnati *(G-4599)*
Wood Specialists ....G 440 639-9797
  Mentor *(G-13772)*
Xxx Intrntional Amusements Inc ....G 216 671-6900
  Cleveland *(G-6487)*

PARTS: Metal

Allpass Corporation ....F 440 998-6300
  Ashtabula *(G-792)*
Centerline Machine Inc ....G 937 322-4887
  Springfield *(G-17529)*
Cleveland Steel Specialty Co ....E 216 464-9400
  Bedford Heights *(G-1481)*
Clifton Steel Company ....D 216 662-6111
  Maple Heights *(G-12731)*
Diller Metals Inc ....G 419 943-3364
  Leipsic *(G-11869)*
Netshape Technologies Mim Inc ....F 440 248-5456
  Solon *(G-17348)*
Plastran Inc ....G 440 237-8404
  Cleveland *(G-6015)*
Sharon Manufacturing Inc ....E 330 239-1561
  Sharon Center *(G-17109)*
Strohecker Incorporated ....E 330 426-9496
  East Palestine *(G-9245)*

PARTY & SPECIAL EVENT PLANNING SVCS

Adyl Inc ....G 330 797-8700
  Austintown *(G-968)*

PASTES, FLAVORING

Sensus LLC ....F 513 892-7100
  Hamilton *(G-10737)*

PASTES: Metal

Ferro Corporation ....D 216 875-5600
  Mayfield Heights *(G-13313)*

PATIENT MONITORING EQPT WHOLESALERS

Neurowave Systems Inc ....G 216 361-1591
  Cleveland *(G-5875)*

PATTERNS: Indl

7 Rowe Court Properties LLC ....G 513 874-7236
  Hamilton *(G-10659)*
Aero Pattern Works ....G 937 890-3720
  Dayton *(G-8139)*
Air Power Dynamics LLC ....C 440 701-2100
  Mentor *(G-13511)*
Anger Pattern Company Inc ....G 330 882-6519
  Clinton *(G-6533)*
API Pattern Works Inc ....E 440 269-1766
  Willoughby *(G-20433)*
Boko Patterns Models & Molds ....G 937 426-9667
  Beavercreek *(G-1371)*
Cascade Pattern Company Inc ....E 440 323-4300
  Elyria *(G-9388)*
Clinton Pattern Works Inc ....F 419 243-0855
  Toledo *(G-18402)*
Colonial Patterns Inc ....E 330 673-6475
  Kent *(G-11440)*
Consolidated Pattern Works Inc ....G 330 434-6060
  Akron *(G-127)*
Dayton Pattern Inc ....G 937 277-0761
  Dayton *(G-8281)*
Design Pattern Works Inc ....G 937 252-0797
  Dayton *(G-8300)*
Design Tech Inc ....G 937 254-7000
  Dayton *(G-8301)*
Elyria Pattern Co Inc ....G 440 323-1526
  Elyria *(G-9415)*
Feiner Pattern Works Inc ....F 513 851-9800
  Cincinnati *(G-3748)*
Foster Pattern Works Inc ....G 330 482-3612
  Columbiana *(G-6617)*
Freeman Manufacturing & Sup Co ....E 440 934-1902
  Avon *(G-996)*
Geotech Pattern & Mold Inc ....G 513 683-2600
  Loveland *(G-12352)*
Glazier Pattern & Coach ....G 937 492-7355
  Houston *(G-11121)*
H&M Machine & Tool LLC ....E 419 776-9220
  Toledo *(G-18491)*
Humtown Pattern Company ....D 330 482-5555
  Columbiana *(G-6621)*
Hynes Modern Pattern Co Inc ....G 937 322-3451
  Springfield *(G-17579)*
Industrial Pattern & Mfg Co ....E 614 252-0934
  Columbus *(G-7185)*
Industrial Technologies Inc ....G 330 434-2033
  Akron *(G-232)*
J-Lenco Inc ....D 740 499-2260
  Morral *(G-14540)*
Jack R Stiner Models & Pattern ....G 330 494-1730
  Canton *(G-2744)*
Ketco Inc ....E 937 426-9331
  Beavercreek *(G-1346)*
Kohl Patterns ....G 513 353-3831
  Cleves *(G-6519)*
Lesleys Patterns Ltd ....G 937 554-4674
  Vandalia *(G-19300)*
Liberty Pattern and Mold Inc ....G 330 788-9463
  Youngstown *(G-21134)*
Lisbon Pattern Limited ....G 330 424-7676
  Lisbon *(G-12128)*
Lorain Modern Pattern Inc ....F 440 365-6780
  Elyria *(G-9455)*
Maumee Pattern Company Inc ....G 419 693-4968
  Toledo *(G-18579)*
Model Engineering Company ....G 330 644-3450
  Barberton *(G-1132)*
Mount Union Pattern Works Inc ....G 330 821-2274
  Alliance *(G-530)*
R L Rush Tool & Pattern Inc ....G 419 562-9849
  Bucyrus *(G-2356)*
Ross Aluminum Castings LLC ....F 937 492-4134
  Sidney *(G-17218)*
Seaport Mold & Casting Company ....F 419 243-1422
  Toledo *(G-18688)*
Seaway Pattern Mfg Inc ....E 419 865-5724
  Toledo *(G-18689)*
Shells Inc ....G 330 808-5558
  Wadsworth *(G-19440)*
Sherwood Rtm Corp ....G 330 875-7151
  Louisville *(G-12328)*
Spectracam Ltd ....G 937 223-3805
  Dayton *(G-8667)*
Standard Pattern Works Inc ....G 330 745-2295
  Akron *(G-414)*
Tempcraft Corporation ....C 216 391-3885
  Cleveland *(G-6303)*

Th Manufacturing Inc ....G 330 893-3572
  Millersburg *(G-14269)*
Transducers Direct Llc ....F 513 247-0601
  Cincinnati *(G-4519)*
United States Drill Head Co ....E 513 941-0300
  Cincinnati *(G-4540)*
Wendling Patterns Inc ....G 937 233-7770
  Dayton *(G-8752)*
Xi Pattern Shop Inc ....G 330 682-2981
  Orrville *(G-15773)*

PAVERS

Adairs Pavers ....G 937 454-9302
  Vandalia *(G-19277)*
Mead Paving ....G 937 322-7414
  Springfield *(G-17602)*

PAVING MATERIALS: Coal Tar, Not From Refineries

Star Seal of Ohio Inc ....G 614 870-1590
  Columbus *(G-7653)*

PAVING MATERIALS: Prefabricated, Concrete

Adler & Company Inc ....F 513 248-1500
  Cincinnati *(G-3356)*
P L M Corporation ....G 216 341-8008
  Cleveland *(G-5956)*
Pavestone LLC ....D 513 474-3783
  Cincinnati *(G-4218)*

PAVING MIXTURES

Ashland LLC ....G 513 557-3100
  Cincinnati *(G-3418)*
Asphalt Materials Inc ....F 740 374-5100
  Marietta *(G-12765)*
Specialty Technology & Res ....G 614 870-0744
  Columbus *(G-7639)*
Stoneco Inc ....G 419 693-3933
  Toledo *(G-18705)*

PAYROLL SVCS

Fields Associates Inc ....G 513 426-8652
  Cincinnati *(G-3755)*

PENCILS & PENS WHOLESALERS

Berea Hardwood Co Inc ....G 216 898-8956
  Cleveland *(G-4904)*

PENS & PARTS: Ball Point

Berea Hardwood Co Inc ....G 216 898-8956
  Cleveland *(G-4904)*

PENS & PENCILS: Mechanical, NEC

Bexley Pen Company Inc ....G 614 351-9988
  Columbus *(G-6826)*

PERFUME: Perfumes, Natural Or Synthetic

Aeroscena LLC ....F 800 671-1890
  Cleveland *(G-4723)*

PERIODICALS, WHOLESALE

Findaway World LLC ....D 440 893-0808
  Solon *(G-17292)*

PERSONAL APPEARANCE SVCS

Anderson Cosmetic & Vein Inst ....G 513 624-7900
  Cincinnati *(G-3402)*
D J Klingler Inc ....G 513 891-2284
  Cincinnati *(G-3632)*

PERSONAL CREDIT INSTITUTIONS: Financing, Autos, Furniture

Mtd Holdings Inc ....B 330 225-2600
  Valley City *(G-19220)*

PERSONAL DEVELOPMENT SCHOOL

Dialogue House Associates Inc ....G 216 342-5170
  Beachwood *(G-1266)*

PRODUCT

PERSONAL SVCS, NEC

Tanning ....G 937 233-4554
  Dayton *(G-8699)*

PEST CONTROL SVCS

A Best Trmt & Pest Ctrl Sups.............G ... 330 434-5555
  Akron *(G-17)*

Scotts Miracle-Gro Company..............B ... 937 644-0011
  Marysville *(G-12968)*

PESTICIDES

Bird Control International ....E ... 330 425-2377
  Twinsburg *(G-18905)*

Mystic Chemical Products Co ....G ... 216 251-4416
  Cleveland *(G-5846)*

PESTICIDES WHOLESALERS

A Best Trmt & Pest Ctrl Sups.............G ... 330 434-5555
  Akron *(G-17)*

PET & PET SPLYS STORES

Aquatic Technology............................F 440 236-8330
  Columbia Station *(G-6579)*

PET ACCESS: Collars, Leashes, Etc, Exc Leather

Perimeter Technologies Inc ....F ... 513 322-5453
  Cincinnati *(G-4229)*

PET COLLARS, LEASHES, MUZZLES & HARNESSES: Leather

Cornerstone Brands Inc.....................G ... 866 668-5962
  West Chester *(G-19844)*

Dog Depot ....G ... 513 771-9274
  Cincinnati *(G-3661)*

In Good Hlth & Animal Wellness ....G ... 330 908-1234
  Northfield *(G-15467)*

Tarahill Inc ....E ... 706 864-0808
  Columbus *(G-7676)*

PET SPLYS

Aquatic Technology............................F 440 236-8330
  Columbia Station *(G-6579)*

Bird Loft ....G ... 440 988-2473
  Amherst *(G-592)*

Boss Pet Products Inc........................F ... 216 332-0832
  Bedford *(G-1408)*

Canine Creations ....G ... 937 667-8576
  Tipp City *(G-18269)*

City Dog..G ... 614 228-3647
  Columbus *(G-6931)*

Condos and Trees LLC.......................G ... 419 691-2287
  Northwood *(G-15479)*

Hartz Mountain Corporation ....D ... 513 877-2131
  Pleasant Plain *(G-16372)*

Miraclecorp Products ....D ... 937 293-9994
  Moraine *(G-14509)*

Otomik Products Inc...........................G ... 877 776-5358
  Cincinnati *(G-4199)*

Ourpets Company ....G ... 440 354-6500
  Fairport Harbor *(G-9769)*

Parrot University LLC ....G ... 740 965-1965
  Sunbury *(G-18073)*

PET SPLYS WHOLESALERS

IAMS Company....................................D ... 937 962-2624
  Lewisburg *(G-11935)*

PETROLEUM & PETROLEUM PRDTS, WHOLESALE Crude Oil

Echo Drilling Inc.................................G ... 740 498-8560
  Newcomerstown *(G-15112)*

PETROLEUM & PETROLEUM PRDTS, WHOLESALE Diesel Fuel

Cac Energy Ltd ....G ... 937 867-5593
  Dayton *(G-8206)*

K2 Petroleum & Supply LLC ....G ... 937 503-2614
  Cincinnati *(G-3966)*

PETROLEUM & PETROLEUM PRDTS, WHOLESALE Engine Fuels & Oils

Sunrise Cooperative Inc.....................F ... 419 628-4705
  Minster *(G-14362)*

PETROLEUM & PETROLEUM PRDTS, WHOLESALE Fuel Oil

D W Dickey and Son Inc......................E ... 330 424-1441
  Lisbon *(G-12119)*

Santmyer Oil Co of Ashland ....G ... 330 262-6501
  Wooster *(G-20831)*

PETROLEUM & PETROLEUM PRDTS, WHOLESALE: Bulk Stations

Cincinnati - Vulcan Company ....D ... 513 242-5300
  Cincinnati *(G-3535)*

New Vulco Mfg & Sales Co LLC..........D ... 513 242-2672
  Cincinnati *(G-4149)*

Universal Oil Inc.................................E ... 216 771-4300
  Cleveland *(G-6391)*

PETROLEUM PRDTS WHOLESALERS

Bradner Oil Company Inc....................G 419 288-2945
  Wayne *(G-19721)*

Eni USA R & M Co Inc.........................F ... 330 723-6457
  Medina *(G-13405)*

Grand Aire Inc ....E ... 419 861-6700
  Swanton *(G-18084)*

Koch Knight LLC.................................D ... 330 488-1651
  East Canton *(G-9194)*

Marathon Petroleum Company LP ....B ... 330 478-5000
  Canton *(G-2767)*

Polar Inc...F ... 937 297-0911
  Moraine *(G-14516)*

Wallover Enterprises Inc ....F ... 440 238-9250
  East Liverpool *(G-9228)*

PETS & PET SPLYS, WHOLESALE

Aquatic Technology............................F ... 440 236-8330
  Columbia Station *(G-6579)*

PEWTER WARE

Quantum Jewelry Dist ....E 330 678-2222
  Kent *(G-11510)*

PHARMACEUTICAL PREPARATIONS: Druggists' Preparations

Abbott Laboratories............................A 614 624-7677
  Columbus *(G-6672)*

Abbott Laboratories............................A ... 614 624-6627
  Columbus *(G-6673)*

Abbott Laboratories............................A ... 614 624-6088
  Columbus *(G-6676)*

Abbott Nutrition Mfg Inc......................B ... 614 624-7485
  Columbus *(G-6677)*

CMC Pharmaceuticals Inc ....G ... 216 600-9430
  Cleveland *(G-5094)*

Flow Dry Technology Inc......................C ... 937 833-2161
  Brookville *(G-2183)*

Ftd Investments LLC ....C ... 937 833-2161
  Brookville *(G-2184)*

Roxane Laboratories Inc ....C ... 614 276-4000
  Columbus *(G-7574)*

PHARMACEUTICAL PREPARATIONS: Emulsions

Performanx Specialty Chem LLC ....G 614 300-7001
  Westerville *(G-20179)*

Polynt Composites USA Inc..................E ... 816 391-6000
  Sandusky *(G-16997)*

PHARMACEUTICAL PREPARATIONS: Medicines, Capsule Or Ampule

Adare Pharmaceuticals Inc ....C 937 898-9669
  Vandalia *(G-19278)*

Advanced Medical Solutions Inc ....G ... 937 291-0069
  Centerville *(G-3033)*

Aultwrks Occupational Medicine..........F ... 330 491-9675
  Canton *(G-2609)*

Buderer Drug Co ....G ... 419 626-3429
  Sandusky *(G-16950)*

Cabell Huntington ....G 740 867-2665
  Chesapeake *(G-3185)*

Casselberry Clinic Inc ....G ... 440 995-0555
  Cleveland *(G-4990)*

Dayton Laser & Aesthetic Medic..........G ... 937 208-8282
  Dayton *(G-8278)*

PHARMACEUTICAL PREPARATIONS: Pills

Fred W Albrecht Grocery Co................C 330 922-4057
  Stow *(G-17757)*

Sermonix Pharmaceuticals ....G ... 614 864-4919
  Columbus *(G-7609)*

PHARMACEUTICAL PREPARATIONS: Proprietary Drug PRDTS

Buderer Drug Company Inc ....F 419 627-2800
  Sandusky *(G-16951)*

Buderer Drug Company Inc ....F ... 419 873-2800
  Perrysburg *(G-16070)*

Buderer Drug Company Inc ....G ... 440 934-3100
  Avon *(G-987)*

Camargo Phrm Svcs LLC ....F ... 513 561-3329
  Blue Ash *(G-1761)*

Ferro Corporation ....D ... 216 875-5600
  Mayfield Heights *(G-13313)*

PHARMACEUTICAL PREPARATIONS: Solutions

Allergan Inc ....D 614 623-8140
  Powell *(G-16462)*

Sara Wood Pharmaceuticals LLC........G ... 513 833-5502
  Mason *(G-13085)*

PHARMACEUTICALS

Abbott Laboratories............................A 614 624-3078
  Columbus *(G-6674)*

Abbott Laboratories............................A ... 614 624-6627
  Columbus *(G-6675)*

Abbott Laboratories............................A ... 614 624-3191
  Columbus *(G-6671)*

Abitec Corporation ....E ... 614 429-6464
  Columbus *(G-6678)*

Aeromics Inc ....G ... 216 772-1004
  Cleveland *(G-4721)*

Affinity Therapeutics LLC ....G ... 216 224-9364
  Cleveland *(G-4728)*

Alkermes Inc.......................................E ... 937 382-5642
  Wilmington *(G-20654)*

Amerisourcebergen Corporation ....D ... 614 497-3665
  Lockbourne *(G-12145)*

Analiza Inc ....F ... 216 432-9050
  Cleveland *(G-4801)*

Aprecia Pharmaceuticals Co ....E ... 513 204-1369
  Blue Ash *(G-1744)*

Astellas Pharma Us Inc ....E ... 614 409-2953
  Groveport *(G-10615)*

Athersys Inc ....D ... 216 431-9900
  Cleveland *(G-4854)*

Barr Laboratories Inc..........................B ... 513 731-9900
  Cincinnati *(G-3437)*

BASF Corporation ....G ... 614 662-5682
  Columbus *(G-6812)*

Bellwyck Packg Solutions Inc ....G ... 513 874-1200
  West Chester *(G-19816)*

Bigmar Inc ....E ... 740 966-5800
  Johnstown *(G-11391)*

Biorx LLC ....G ... 866 442-4679
  Cincinnati *(G-3450)*

Bnoat Oncology ....G ... 330 285-2537
  Akron *(G-93)*

Bristol-Myers Squibb Company ....E ... 800 321-1335
  Columbus *(G-6642)*

Bulk Molding Compounds Inc ....D ... 419 874-7941
  Perrysburg *(G-16071)*

Calcol Inc..E ... 216 245-6301
  Shaker Heights *(G-17086)*

Caps ....G ... 216 524-0418
  Cleveland *(G-4972)*

Cardinal Health 414 LLC......................C ... 614 757-5000
  Dublin *(G-9058)*

Cardinal Health 414 LLC......................G ... 513 759-1900
  West Chester *(G-19823)*

Cardinal Health 414 LLC......................G ... 614 473-0786
  Columbus *(G-6906)*

CBS Pharmacy....................................G ... 740 366-9082
  Newark *(G-14992)*

Chester Labs Inc ....E 513 458-3871
Cincinnati *(G-3526)*

Chester Packaging LLC ....C 513 458-3840
Cincinnati *(G-3527)*

Chewrite Co ....D 937 746-5509
Springboro *(G-17476)*

Cleobrothers & Company LLC ....F 614 985-3639
Columbus *(G-6936)*

Dow Chemical Company ....F 937 254-1550
Dayton *(G-8309)*

Fluence Therapeutics ....G 216 780-5220
Akron *(G-192)*

Forest Pharmaceuticals Inc ....C 513 271-6800
Cincinnati *(G-3770)*

Forest Pharmaceuticals Inc ....C 513 271-6800
Cincinnati *(G-3771)*

Forrest Pharmaceuticals ....C 513 791-1701
Blue Ash *(G-1799)*

Gateway Biotechnology Inc ....G 314 747-7199
Rootstown *(G-16722)*

Gebauer Company ....E 216 581-3030
Cleveland *(G-5405)*

Glaxosmithkline LLC ....E 937 623-2680
Columbus *(G-7116)*

Glaxosmithkline LLC ....E 440 552-2895
North Ridgeville *(G-15376)*

Glaxosmithkline LLC ....E 330 608-2365
Copley *(G-7847)*

Glaxosmithkline LLC ....E 614 570-5970
Columbus *(G-7117)*

Glaxosmithkline LLC ....E 330 241-4447
Medina *(G-13417)*

Isp Chemicals LLC ....D 614 876-3637
Columbus *(G-7214)*

Lubrizol Advanced Mtls Inc ....F 216 447-5000
Brecksville *(G-2061)*

Medpace Holdings Inc ....G 513 579-9911
Cincinnati *(G-4079)*

Mercurio Biotec LLC ....F 214 507-8031
Dublin *(G-9102)*

Meridian Bioscience Inc ....B 513 271-3700
Cincinnati *(G-4085)*

Middletown Pharmacy Inc ....G 513 705-6252
Middletown *(G-14063)*

Mp Biomedicals LLC ....C 440 337-1200
Solon *(G-17340)*

Mvp Pharmacy ....G 614 449-8000
Columbus *(G-7375)*

N M R Inc ....G 513 530-9075
Cincinnati *(G-4135)*

N8 Medical Inc ....G 614 537-7246
Dublin *(G-9108)*

Nigerian Assn Pharmacists & PH ....G 513 861-2329
Cincinnati *(G-4155)*

Nitto Denko Avecia Inc ....F 513 679-3000
Cincinnati *(G-4158)*

Nnodum Pharmaceuticals Corp ....F 513 861-2329
Cincinnati *(G-4160)*

Norwich Overseas Inc ....F 513 983-1100
Mason *(G-13068)*

Nostrum Laboratories Inc ....E 419 636-1168
Bryan *(G-2314)*

Novartis Corporation ....D 919 577-5000
Cincinnati *(G-4165)*

Oak Tree Intl Holdings Inc ....F 702 462-7295
Elyria *(G-9469)*

Oakwood Laboratories LLC ....E 440 359-0000
Oakwood Village *(G-15626)*

Oakwood Laboratories LLC ....F 440 505-2011
Solon *(G-17352)*

Omnicare Phrm of Midwest LLC ....D 513 719-2600
Cincinnati *(G-4186)*

Organon Inc ....G 440 729-2290
Chesterland *(G-3218)*

Patenthealth LLC ....G 330 208-1111
North Canton *(G-15257)*

Patheon Pharmaceuticals Inc ....C 513 948-7942
Cincinnati *(G-4212)*

Performanx Specialty Chem LLC ....G 614 300-7001
Waverly *(G-19716)*

Pfizer Inc ....G 513 342-9056
West Chester *(G-19913)*

Pfizer Inc ....C 614 496-0990
Dublin *(G-9124)*

Pfizer Inc ....D 216 591-0642
Beachwood *(G-1290)*

Pfizer Inc ....C 937 746-3603
Franklin *(G-10044)*

Pharmacia Hepar LLC ....D 937 746-3603
Franklin *(G-10045)*

Pharmaforce Inc ....E 614 436-2222
Columbus *(G-7481)*

Pharmaforce Inc ....F 614 436-2222
Hilliard *(G-10969)*

Polgenix Inc ....G 440 537-9691
Cleveland *(G-6019)*

Principled Dynamics Inc ....G 419 351-6303
Holland *(G-11079)*

Procter & Gamble Company ....C 513 983-1100
Cincinnati *(G-4281)*

Procter & Gamble Company ....B 513 983-1100
Cincinnati *(G-4286)*

Procter & Gamble Company ....C 513 634-9110
West Chester *(G-19923)*

Procter & Gamble Company ....G 410 527-5735
Grove City *(G-10586)*

RC Outsourcing LLC ....G 330 536-8500
Lowellville *(G-12412)*

Retinagenix LLC ....G 440 808-9334
Cleveland *(G-6108)*

River City Pharma ....D 513 870-1680
Fairfield *(G-9711)*

Rohm and Haas Chemicals LLC ....G 513 733-2100
Cincinnati *(G-4356)*

Rx Institutional Services LLC ....G 330 505-1979
Mineral Ridge *(G-14310)*

Safe Rx Pharmacies Inc ....G 740 377-4162
South Point *(G-17447)*

Safecor Health LLC ....F 781 933-8780
Columbus *(G-7583)*

Sironrx Therapeutics Inc ....G 216 445-5588
Cleveland *(G-6206)*

Solvaira Specialties Inc ....D 937 652-2101
Urbana *(G-19181)*

Specialized Pharmaceuticals ....G 330 453-3067
Canton *(G-2853)*

Specialized Pharmaceuticals ....G 419 371-2081
Lima *(G-12095)*

Summit Research Group ....G 330 689-1778
Stow *(G-17806)*

Takeda Pharmaceuticals USA Inc ......G 440 238-0872
Strongsville *(G-17977)*

Tersus Pharmaceuticals ....F 440 951-2451
Mentor *(G-13745)*

Teva Womens Health Inc ....C 513 731-9900
Cincinnati *(G-4503)*

Tri-Tech Laboratories Inc ....D 740 927-2817
Johnstown *(G-11408)*

USB Corporation ....D 216 765-5000
Cleveland *(G-6401)*

Venture Therapeutics Inc ....G 614 430-3300
New Albany *(G-14775)*

Warner Chlcott Phrmcticals Inc ....F 513 983-1100
Cincinnati *(G-4579)*

Xellia Pharmaceuticals USA LLC ....E 847 986-7984
Bedford *(G-1473)*

PHARMACEUTICALS: Medicinal & Botanical Prdts

Amresco LLC ....C 440 349-2805
Cleveland *(G-4798)*

Biofocus Inc ....G 937 890-3068
Dayton *(G-8188)*

Frutarom USA Inc ....G 513 870-4900
West Chester *(G-20008)*

Graminex LLC ....F 419 278-1023
Deshler *(G-8951)*

Patenthealth LLC ....G 330 208-1111
North Canton *(G-15257)*

Plymouth Healthcare Pdts LLC ....F 440 542-0762
Solon *(G-17362)*

USB Corporation ....D 216 765-5000
Cleveland *(G-6401)*

Valley Vitamins II Inc ....E 330 533-0051
Columbus *(G-7731)*

Vdm Biochemicals LLC ....G 440 786-9400
Bedford *(G-1470)*

PHARMACIES & DRUG STORES

Buderer Drug Co ....G 419 626-3429
Sandusky *(G-16950)*

Kroger Co ....C 740 671-5164
Bellaire *(G-1499)*

Kroger Co ....C 740 264-5057
Steubenville *(G-17702)*

Kroger Co ....C 614 263-1766
Columbus *(G-7271)*

Kroger Co ....C 614 575-3742
Columbus *(G-7272)*

Kroger Co ....D 513 683-4001
Maineville *(G-12526)*

Kroger Co ....D 740 374-2523
Marietta *(G-12798)*

Kroger Co ....C 937 277-0950
Dayton *(G-8447)*

Riesbeck Food Markets Inc ....C 740 695-3401
Saint Clairsville *(G-16806)*

Specialized Pharmaceuticals ....G 419 371-2081
Lima *(G-12095)*

PHOSPHATES

Auto-Tap Inc ....E 216 671-1043
Cleveland *(G-4864)*

Scotts Company LLC ....A 937 644-3729
Marysville *(G-12967)*

PHOTOCOPY MACHINES

E-Waste Systems (ohio) Inc ....G 614 824-3057
Columbus *(G-7044)*

Xerox Corporation ....F 513 860-8600
West Chester *(G-20070)*

Xerox Corporation ....B 513 554-3200
Blue Ash *(G-1902)*

PHOTOCOPYING & DUPLICATING SVCS

A Grade Notes Inc ....G 614 766-9999
Dublin *(G-9034)*

A-A Blueprint Co Inc ....E 330 794-8803
Akron *(G-22)*

Bethart Enterprises Inc ....F 513 863-6161
Hamilton *(G-10675)*

Brooke Printers Inc ....G 614 235-6800
Lancaster *(G-11692)*

Capitol Citicom Inc ....E 614 472-2679
Columbus *(G-6903)*

Cincinnati Print Solutions LLC ....G 513 943-9500
Amelia *(G-570)*

Colortech Graphics & Printing ....G 614 766-2400
Columbus *(G-6944)*

Corporate Dcment Solutions Inc ....F 513 595-8200
Cincinnati *(G-3613)*

Curry Copy Center of Lakewood ....G 216 521-5775
Lakewood *(G-11661)*

Domicone Printing Inc ....G 937 878-3080
Fairborn *(G-9619)*

Doug Smith ....G 740 345-1398
Newark *(G-15000)*

Eg Enterprise Services Inc ....F 216 431-3300
Cleveland *(G-5260)*

Elyria Copy Center Inc ....G 440 323-4145
Elyria *(G-9412)*

Fedex Office & Print Svcs Inc ....E 937 436-0677
Dayton *(G-8339)*

Fedex Office & Print Svcs Inc ....F 330 376-6002
Akron *(G-183)*

Fedex Office & Print Svcs Inc ....E 614 621-1100
Columbus *(G-7080)*

Fedex Office & Print Svcs Inc ....E 419 866-5464
Toledo *(G-18466)*

Fedex Office & Print Svcs Inc ....E 614 898-0000
Westerville *(G-20214)*

Fedex Office & Print Svcs Inc ....E 614 575-0800
Reynoldsburg *(G-16590)*

Fedex Office & Print Svcs Inc ....E 216 573-1511
Cleveland *(G-5333)*

Fremont Quick Print ....G 419 334-8808
Helena *(G-10895)*

Geygan Enterprises Inc ....F 513 932-4222
Lebanon *(G-11803)*

Great Lakes Engraving Corp ....G 419 867-1607
Maumee *(G-13262)*

Henry Bussman ....G 614 224-0417
Columbus *(G-7150)*

Hilleary-Whitaker Inc ....G 614 766-4694
Columbus *(G-7157)*

Hoster Graphics Company Inc ....F 614 299-9770
Columbus *(G-7168)*

Instant Impressions Inc ....G 614 538-9844
Columbus *(G-7191)*

Lakota Printing Inc ....G 513 755-3666
West Chester *(G-19890)*

Monks Copy Shop Inc ....G 614 885-7228
Columbus *(G-7367)*

Montview Corporation ....G 330 723-3409
Medina *(G-13449)*

Morse Enterprises Inc ....G 513 229-3600
Mason *(G-13066)*

Pep Pony Express Printing Inc ....G 513 542-4882
Cincinnati **(G-4222)**
Print-Digital Incorporated ....G 330 686-5945
Stow **(G-17792)**
Printers Devil Inc ....F 330 650-1218
Hudson **(G-11194)**
Profile Digital Printing LLC ....E 937 866-4241
Dayton **(G-8599)**
Rhoads Printing Center Inc ....G 330 678-2042
Kent **(G-11516)**
Ricci Anthony ....G 330 758-5761
Youngstown **(G-21188)**
Technoprint Inc ....F 614 899-1403
Westerville **(G-20236)**
Zip Laser Systems Inc ....G 740 286-6613
Jackson **(G-11335)**

PHOTOELECTRIC DEVICES: Magnetic

Tytek Industries Inc ....G 513 874-7326
Blue Ash **(G-1884)**

PHOTOENGRAVING SVC

Linger Photo Engraving Corp ....G 513 579-1380
Cincinnati **(G-4026)**
Youngstown ARC Engraving Co ....E 330 793-2471
Youngstown **(G-21245)**

PHOTOFINISHING LABORATORIES

Enlarging Arts Inc ....G 330 434-3433
Akron **(G-168)**
Simply Canvas Inc ....E 330 436-6500
Akron **(G-402)**
Transimage Inc ....G 937 293-0261
Oakwood **(G-15611)**

PHOTOGRAPHIC EQPT & SPLYS

AEG Photoconductor Corporation ....D 513 874-4939
West Chester **(G-19799)**
AGFA Corporation ....C 513 829-6292
Fairfield **(G-9638)**
Anderson Industries Inc ....F 216 941-7766
Cleveland **(G-4810)**
E I Du Pont De Nemours & Co ....E 740 474-0220
Circleville **(G-4627)**
Horizons Inc Camcode Division ....E 216 714-0020
Cleveland **(G-5524)**
Jay Tackett ....G 740 779-1715
Frankfort **(G-9999)**
Tbh International ....G 440 323-4651
Elyria **(G-9499)**
Xerox Corporation C/O Genco ....G 503 582-6059
Groveport **(G-10651)**

PHOTOGRAPHIC EQPT & SPLYS WHOLESALERS

ID Card Systems Inc ....G 330 963-7446
Twinsburg **(G-18958)**

PHOTOGRAPHIC EQPT & SPLYS, WHOLESALE: Project, Motion/Slide

Eastman Kodak Company ....E 937 259-3000
Dayton **(G-8317)**

PHOTOGRAPHIC EQPT & SPLYS: Blueprint Reproduction Mach/Eqpt

Rightway Fab & Machine Inc ....G 937 295-2200
Russia **(G-16769)**

PHOTOGRAPHIC EQPT & SPLYS: Film, Cloth & Paper, Sensitized

Stretchtape Inc ....E 216 486-9400
Cleveland **(G-6251)**

PHOTOGRAPHIC EQPT & SPLYS: Graphic Arts Plates, Sensitized

Plastigraphics Inc ....F 513 771-8848
Cincinnati **(G-4243)**

PHOTOGRAPHIC EQPT & SPLYS: Lens Shades, Camera

Kay Zee Inc ....G 330 339-1268
New Philadelphia **(G-14905)**

PHOTOGRAPHIC EQPT & SPLYS: Paper & Cloth, All Types, NEC

Transimage Inc ....G 937 293-0261
Oakwood **(G-15611)**

PHOTOGRAPHIC EQPT & SPLYS: Plates, Sensitized

Horizons Incorporated ....C 216 475-0555
Cleveland **(G-5525)**

PHOTOGRAPHIC EQPT & SPLYS: Printing Eqpt

Advanced Litho Systems ....G 419 865-2652
Monclova **(G-14388)**
Ink Again ....G 419 232-4465
Van Wert **(G-19260)**

PHOTOGRAPHIC EQPT & SPLYS: Processing Eqpt

Smartcopy Inc ....G 740 392-6162
Mount Vernon **(G-14651)**

PHOTOGRAPHIC EQPT & SPLYS: Toners, Prprd, Not Chem Plnts

Gvs Industries Inc ....G 513 887-8660
Hamilton **(G-10699)**

PHOTOGRAPHIC EQPT REPAIR SVCS

Amtech Inc ....G 440 238-2141
Strongsville **(G-17888)**

PHOTOGRAPHY SVCS: Commercial

American Colorscans Inc ....E 614 895-0233
Columbus **(G-6732)**
David Esrati ....G 937 228-4433
Dayton **(G-8266)**
Golden Graphics Ltd ....F 419 673-6260
Kenton **(G-11548)**
Middlefield Sign Co ....G 440 632-0708
Middlefield **(G-13963)**
Queen City Reprographics ....C 513 326-2300
Cincinnati **(G-4319)**
Youngstown ARC Engraving Co ....G 330 793-2471
Youngstown **(G-21245)**

PHOTOGRAPHY SVCS: Portrait Studios

SMS Communications Inc ....E 216 374-6686
Shaker Heights **(G-17095)**

PHOTOGRAPHY SVCS: Still Or Video

Studs N Hip Hop ....G 614 477-0786
Columbus **(G-7663)**

PHOTOTYPESETTING SVC

DOV Graphics Inc ....E 513 241-5150
Cincinnati **(G-3668)**
HOT Graphic Services Inc ....E 419 242-7000
Northwood **(G-15483)**
Photo-Type Engraving Company ....F 614 308-1900
Columbus **(G-7483)**
Photo-Type Engraving Company ....F 614 308-7914
Columbus **(G-7484)**
Tj Metzgers Inc ....D 419 861-8611
Toledo **(G-18726)**

PHOTOVOLTAIC Solid State

Hunters Hightech Energy Systm ....G 614 275-4777
Columbus **(G-7171)**
Solar Integrated Resources LLC ....G 937 608-4498
Moraine **(G-14530)**

PHYSICAL EXAMINATION & TESTING SVCS

Broad Street Imaging ....G 614 621-9100
Columbus **(G-6643)**

PHYSICAL FITNESS CENTERS

Novacare Inc ....G 216 704-4817
Beachwood **(G-1285)**

PHYSICIANS' OFFICES & CLINICS: Medical

Dayton Laser & Aesthetic Medic ....G 937 208-8282
Dayton **(G-8278)**

PHYSICIANS' OFFICES & CLINICS: Medical doctors

Community Action Program Corp ....F 740 374-8501
Marietta **(G-12776)**
Eye Center ....E 614 228-3937
Columbus **(G-7074)**
Francisco Jaume ....G 740 622-1200
Coshocton **(G-7891)**
Lababidi Enterprises Inc ....E 330 733-2907
Akron **(G-266)**
Orthotics & Prosthetics Rehab ....F 330 856-2553
Warren **(G-19585)**
Vein Center and Medspa ....G 330 629-9400
Youngstown **(G-21236)**
Volk Optical Inc ....D 440 942-6161
Mentor **(G-13768)**

PICTURE FRAMES: Metal

Frame USA ....E 513 577-7107
Cincinnati **(G-3776)**
Frame Warehouse ....G 614 861-4582
Reynoldsburg **(G-16591)**
Nostalgic Images Inc ....E 419 784-1728
Defiance **(G-8807)**

PICTURE FRAMES: Wood

Bonfoey Co ....F 216 621-0178
Cleveland **(G-4924)**
Cass Frames Inc ....G 419 468-2863
Galion **(G-10257)**
Fenwick Gallery of Fine Arts ....G 419 475-1651
Toledo **(G-18468)**
Frame Depot Inc ....G 330 652-7865
Niles **(G-15153)**
Frame Shoppe ....G 513 232-3970
Cincinnati **(G-3775)**
Frame Warehouse ....G 614 861-4582
Reynoldsburg **(G-16591)**
Hackman Frames LLC ....F 614 841-0007
Columbus **(G-7137)**
Lazars Art Gllery Crtive Frmng ....G 330 477-8351
Canton **(G-2759)**
Wood Trader Inc ....G 216 397-7671
Cleveland Heights **(G-6503)**

PICTURE FRAMING SVCS, CUSTOM

American Frame Corporation ....D 419 893-5595
Maumee **(G-13222)**
Frame Depot Inc ....G 330 652-7865
Niles **(G-15153)**

PIECE GOODS & NOTIONS WHOLESALERS

Sysco Guest Supply LLC ....F 440 960-2515
Lorain **(G-12285)**

PIECE GOODS, NOTIONS & DRY GOODS, WHOL: Fabrics Broadwoven

Mmi Textiles Inc ....F 440 899-8050
Westlake **(G-20283)**

PIECE GOODS, NOTIONS & DRY GOODS, WHOL: Textile Converters

Db Rediheat Inc ....E 216 361-0530
Cleveland **(G-5175)**

PIECE GOODS, NOTIONS & DRY GOODS, WHOLESALE: Fabrics, Lace

Joe Busby ....G 513 821-1716
Cincinnati **(G-3949)**

PIECE GOODS, NOTIONS & DRY GOODS, WHOLESALE: Sewing Access

Embroidered ID Inc ....G 440 974-8113
Mentor **(G-13572)**

PIECE GOODS, NOTIONS & DRY GOODS, WHOLESALE: Tape, Textile

Great Lakes Textiles Inc ....E 440 439-1300
Solon *(G-17304)*

PIECE GOODS, NOTIONS & OTHER DRY GOODS, WHOL: Flags/Banners

Johnson Brothers Holdings LLC ....G 614 868-5273
Columbus *(G-7240)*

Pro Companies Inc ....G 614 738-1222
Pickerington *(G-16201)*

PIECE GOODS, NOTIONS/DRY GOODS, WHOL: Drapery Mtrl, Woven

Anthony Decorative Fabrics and ....G 937 299-4637
Moraine *(G-14466)*

Style-Line Incorporated ....E 614 291-0600
Columbus *(G-7664)*

PIGMENTS, INORGANIC: Metallic & Mineral, NEC

Harsco Corporation ....D 330 372-1781
Warren *(G-19557)*

Obron Atlantic Corporation ....D 440 954-7600
Painesville *(G-15905)*

PILOT SVCS: Aviation

Theiss Uav Solutions LLC ....G 330 584-2070
North Benton *(G-15214)*

PINS

Altenloh Brinck & Co Inc ....E 419 636-6715
Bryan *(G-2276)*

Dph Discount Pin Inc ....G 740 264-2450
Steubenville *(G-17692)*

Express Trading Pins ....G 419 394-2550
Saint Marys *(G-16838)*

Lapel Pins Unlimited LLC ....G 614 562-3218
Lewis Center *(G-11904)*

Paine Falls Centerpin LLC ....G 440 298-3202
Thompson *(G-18189)*

Patchwork People Pins Etc ....G 937 725-2981
Clarksville *(G-4652)*

Pin Oak Development LLC ....G 440 933-9862
Avon Lake *(G-1043)*

Pin Oak Estates Ltd ....G 330 657-2727
Akron *(G-339)*

Pin Point Marketing LLC ....G 330 336-5863
Wadsworth *(G-19428)*

PINS: Dowel

Dayton Superior Corporation ....C 937 866-0711
Miamisburg *(G-13798)*

PINS: Spring

H G Schneider Company ....G 614 882-6944
Westerville *(G-20216)*

PIPE & FITTING: Fabrication

Alloy Bllows Prcision Wldg Inc ....D 440 684-3000
Cleveland *(G-4767)*

American Roll Formed Pdts Corp ....C 440 352-0753
Painesville *(G-15851)*

Appian Manufacturing Corp ....E 614 445-2230
Columbus *(G-6762)*

Arem Co ....F 440 974-6740
Mentor *(G-13526)*

Atlas Industrial Contrs LLC ....B 614 841-4500
Columbus *(G-6784)*

Carter Machine Company Inc ....G 419 468-3530
Galion *(G-10256)*

Contractors Steel Company ....E 330 425-3050
Twinsburg *(G-18919)*

Crest Bending Inc ....E 419 492-2108
New Washington *(G-14959)*

Defiance Metal Products WI Inc ....C 920 426-9207
Defiance *(G-8787)*

Duro Dyne Midwest Corp ....B 513 870-6000
Hamilton *(G-10685)*

Eaton Corporation ....C 440 826-1115
Berea *(G-1613)*

Ebner Furnaces Inc ....D 330 335-2311
Wadsworth *(G-19404)*

Elliott Tool Technologies Ltd ....D 937 253-6133
Dayton *(G-8324)*

Elster Perfection Corporation ....D 440 428-1171
Geneva *(G-10346)*

Esterle Mold & Machine Co Inc ....E 330 686-1685
Stow *(G-17748)*

Ever Roll Specialties Co ....E 937 964-1302
Springfield *(G-17555)*

Famous Industries Inc ....D 740 685-2592
Byesville *(G-2401)*

Faull & Son LLC ....F 330 652-4341
Niles *(G-15152)*

Franklin Frames and Cycles ....G 740 763-3838
Newark *(G-15008)*

Hollaender Manufacturing Co ....D 513 772-8800
Cincinnati *(G-3887)*

Industrial Quartz Corp ....F 440 942-0909
Mentor *(G-13606)*

Ipsco Tubulars Inc ....G 330 448-6772
Brookfield *(G-2125)*

Jan Squires Inc ....G 440 988-7859
Amherst *(G-599)*

John H Hosking Inc ....G 513 821-1080
Middletown *(G-14052)*

Kings Welding and Fabg Inc ....E 330 738-3592
Mechanicstown *(G-13359)*

Kirtland Capital Partners LP ....E 216 593-0100
Beachwood *(G-1276)*

Lakewood Steel Inc ....F 440 965-4226
Wakeman *(G-19450)*

Lim Services LLC ....F 513 217-0801
Middletown *(G-14054)*

McJunkn Redman ....F 330 686-4988
Stow *(G-17774)*

Mitchell Piping LLC ....E 330 245-0258
Hartville *(G-10830)*

Normandy Products Company ....D 440 632-5050
Middlefield *(G-13976)*

Phillips Mfg and Tower Co ....D 419 347-1720
Shelby *(G-17140)*

Pines Manufacturing Inc ....E 440 835-5553
Westlake *(G-20294)*

Precise Tube Forming Inc ....D 440 237-3956
North Royalton *(G-15445)*

Precision Fittings LLC ....E 440 647-4143
Wellington *(G-19752)*

Qual-Fab Inc ....E 440 327-5000
Avon *(G-1005)*

Quality Mechanicals Inc ....E 513 559-0998
Cincinnati *(G-4307)*

Quality Tube Service Inc ....F 419 237-3014
Fayette *(G-9778)*

Rafter Equipment Corporation ....E 440 572-3700
Strongsville *(G-17956)*

Rbm Environmental and Cnstr ....E 419 693-5840
Oregon *(G-15715)*

Rhenium Alloys Inc ....D 440 365-7388
North Ridgeville *(G-15401)*

Riker Products Inc ....C 419 729-1626
Toledo *(G-18676)*

Scot Industries Inc ....E 330 262-7585
Wooster *(G-20832)*

Seal Tite LLC ....E 937 393-4268
Hillsboro *(G-11014)*

Sroka Industries Inc ....E 440 572-2811
Strongsville *(G-17972)*

SSP Fittings Corp ....D 330 425-4250
Twinsburg *(G-19022)*

Stripmatic Products Inc ....E 216 241-7143
Cleveland *(G-6255)*

Summers Acquisition Corp ....E 419 423-5800
Findlay *(G-9898)*

Swagelok Company ....D 440 349-5934
Solon *(G-17392)*

Swagelok Company ....D 440 349-5652
Solon *(G-17391)*

T & D Fabricating Inc ....E 440 951-5646
Eastlake *(G-9292)*

Tech Tool Inc ....F 330 674-1176
Millersburg *(G-14267)*

Thompson Culvert Company LLC ....F 513 645-7000
West Chester *(G-19956)*

TI Group Auto Systems LLC ....D 740 929-2049
Hebron *(G-10890)*

Transit Sittings of NA ....G 330 797-2516
Youngstown *(G-21227)*

Tri-America Contractors Inc ....D 740 574-0148
Wheelersburg *(G-20335)*

Tri-America Contractors Inc ....E 740 574-0148
Wheelersburg *(G-20336)*

Tri-State Fabricators Inc ....E 513 752-5005
Amelia *(G-587)*

Tristate Tubular Inc ....G 330 339-5240
New Philadelphia *(G-14937)*

U S Weatherford L P ....C 330 746-2502
Youngstown *(G-21233)*

Unison Industries LLC ....B 937 426-0621
Dayton *(G-8121)*

United Group Services Inc ....C 800 633-9690
West Chester *(G-20063)*

Vortec Corporation ....E 513 686-8210
Blue Ash *(G-1891)*

W J Egli Company Inc ....F 330 823-3666
Alliance *(G-551)*

Welded Tubes Inc ....E 440 437-5144
Orwell *(G-15782)*

Zekelman Industries Inc ....C 740 432-2146
Cambridge *(G-2483)*

PIPE & FITTINGS: Cast Iron

Advanced Metals Group LLC ....C 937 492-4134
Sidney *(G-17166)*

General Aluminum Mfg Company ....C 419 739-9300
Wapakoneta *(G-19487)*

McWane Inc ....B 740 622-6651
Coshocton *(G-7897)*

Tangent Air Inc ....E 740 474-1114
Circleville *(G-4645)*

PIPE & TUBES: Seamless

Reliacheck Manufacturing Inc ....E 440 933-6162
Avon Lake *(G-1048)*

PIPE CLEANERS

C P R Drain Cleaning Inc ....F 614 279-3445
Columbus *(G-6884)*

PIPE FITTINGS: Plastic

Cantex Inc ....D 330 995-3665
Aurora *(G-912)*

Cleveland Plastic Fabricat ....F 216 797-7300
Euclid *(G-9572)*

Elster Perfection Corporation ....D 440 428-1171
Geneva *(G-10346)*

Gadjets Inc ....G 937 274-2111
Dayton *(G-8356)*

Haviland Plastic Products Co ....E 419 622-3110
Haviland *(G-10841)*

Lenz Inc ....E 937 277-9364
Dayton *(G-8456)*

Osburn Associates Inc ....F 740 385-5732
Logan *(G-12188)*

Parker-Hannifin Corporation ....D 330 673-2700
Kent *(G-11499)*

Ppafco Inc ....F 614 488-7259
Columbus *(G-7507)*

Qube Corporation ....F 440 543-2393
Chagrin Falls *(G-3115)*

Speedline Corporation ....G 440 914-1122
Solon *(G-17386)*

PIPE JOINT COMPOUNDS

Hydratech Engineered Pdts LLC ....F 513 827-9169
Cincinnati *(G-3904)*

PIPE SECTIONS, FABRICATED FROM PURCHASED PIPE

Excel Loading Systems LLC ....G 513 265-2936
Blue Ash *(G-1790)*

John Maneely Company ....E 724 342-6851
Niles *(G-15165)*

Kottler Metal Products Co Inc ....E 440 946-7473
Willoughby *(G-20523)*

Pioneer Pipe Inc ....B 740 376-2400
Marietta *(G-12816)*

PIPE, CULVERT: Concrete

Forterra Pipe & Precast LLC ....G 330 467-7890
Macedonia *(G-12451)*

PIPE, CYLINDER: Concrete, Prestressed Or Pretensioned

Complete Cylinder Service Inc ....G 513 772-1500
Cincinnati *(G-3600)*

PRODUCT

PIPE, SEWER: Concrete

Ash Sewer & Drain Service ....G....... 330 376-9714
Akron (G-74)

L B Weiss Construction Inc ....G....... 440 205-1774
Mentor (G-13625)

PIPE: Concrete

Haviland Culvert Company ....G....... 419 622-6951
Haviland (G-10839)

Northern Concrete Pipe Inc ....F....... 419 841-3361
Sylvania (G-18122)

PIPE: Plastic

ADS Ventures Inc ....G....... 614 658-0050
Hilliard (G-10922)

Advanced Drainage of Ohio Inc ....D....... 614 658-0050
Hilliard (G-10924)

Advanced Drainage Systems Inc ....E....... 740 852-9554
London (G-12198)

Advanced Drainage Systems Inc ....D....... 513 863-1384
Hamilton (G-10662)

Advanced Drainage Systems Inc ....D....... 330 264-4949
Wooster (G-20731)

Advanced Drainage Systems Inc ....D....... 614 658-0050
Hilliard (G-10925)

Advanced Drainage Systems Inc ....E....... 419 599-9565
Napoleon (G-14669)

Advanced Drainage Systems Inc ....D....... 740 852-2980
London (G-12199)

Advanced Drainage Systems Inc ....E....... 419 424-8324
Findlay (G-9788)

Aetna Plastics Corp ....G....... 330 274-2855
Mantua (G-12706)

Baughman Tile Company ....D....... 800 837-3160
Paulding (G-16000)

Cantex Inc ....D....... 330 995-3665
Aurora (G-912)

Contech Engnered Solutions Inc ....A....... 513 645-7000
West Chester (G-19840)

Contech Engnered Solutions LLC ....D....... 513 645-7000
Middletown (G-14032)

Contech Engnered Solutions LLC ....C....... 513 645-7000
West Chester (G-19841)

Drain Products LLC ....G....... 419 230-4549
Lakeview (G-11649)

Drainage Products Inc ....E....... 419 622-6951
Haviland (G-10838)

Dura-Line Corporation ....E....... 440 322-1000
Elyria (G-9407)

Elster Perfection Corporation ....D....... 440 428-1171
Geneva (G-10346)

Fowler Products Inc ....F....... 419 683-4057
Crestline (G-7929)

Hancor Holding Corporation ....B....... 419 422-6521
Findlay (G-9836)

Hancor Inc ....B....... 614 658-0050
Hilliard (G-10950)

Hancor Inc ....D....... 419 424-8222
Findlay (G-9838)

Hancor Inc ....D....... 419 424-8225
Findlay (G-9837)

Harrison Mch & Plastic Corp ....E....... 330 569-3128
Garrettsville (G-10323)

Nupco Inc ....G....... 419 629-2259
New Bremen (G-14791)

Plas-Tanks Industries Inc ....E....... 513 942-3800
Hamilton (G-10730)

Savko Plastic Pipe & Fittings ....F....... 614 885-8420
Columbus (G-7591)

Tolloti Pipe LLC ....F....... 330 364-6627
New Philadelphia (G-14935)

Tolloti Plastic Pipe Inc ....E....... 330 364-6627
New Philadelphia (G-14936)

Tolloti Plastic Pipe Inc ....G....... 740 922-6911
Uhrichsville (G-19062)

Utility Solutions Inc ....G....... 740 369-4300
Delaware (G-8892)

PIPE: Seamless Steel

Vallourec Star LP ....C....... 330 742-6300
Youngstown (G-21235)

Zekelman Industries Inc ....C....... 740 432-2146
Cambridge (G-2483)

PIPE: Sheet Metal

American Culvert & Fabg Co ....F....... 740 432-6334
Cambridge (G-2443)

Shape Supply Inc ....G....... 513 863-6695
Hamilton (G-10738)

Siata Ds Inc ....G....... 216 503-7200
Beachwood (G-1298)

Thompson Culvert Company LLC ....F....... 513 645-7000
West Chester (G-19956)

PIPE: Water, Cast Iron

Monroe Water System ....G....... 740 472-1030
Sardis (G-17036)

PIPELINES: Crude Petroleum

Bluefoot Industrial LLC ....E....... 740 314-5299
Steubenville (G-17689)

PIPELINES: Natural Gas

Ngo Development Corporation ....F....... 740 344-3790
Newark (G-15039)

PIPES & TUBES

George Manufacturing Inc ....E....... 513 932-1067
Lebanon (G-11801)

Lokring Technology LLC ....D....... 440 942-0880
Willoughby (G-20528)

Prime Conduit Inc ....F....... 216 464-3400
Cleveland (G-6046)

PIPES & TUBES: Steel

AK Tube LLC ....C....... 419 661-4150
Walbridge (G-19456)

All Steel Structures Inc ....G....... 330 312-3131
Carrollton (G-2951)

Alro Steel Corporation ....E....... 937 253-6121
Dayton (G-8149)

Arcelormittal Tubular ....D....... 740 382-3979
Marion (G-12855)

Arcelormittal Tubular ....A....... 419 347-2424
Shelby (G-17132)

Arcelormittal USA LLC ....D....... 419 347-2424
Shelby (G-17133)

Benjamin Steel Company Inc ....E....... 937 233-1212
Springfield (G-17522)

Bull Moose Tube Company ....G....... 330 448-4878
Masury (G-13213)

Busch & Thiem Inc ....E....... 419 625-7515
Sandusky (G-16952)

Chart International Inc ....D....... 440 753-1490
Cleveland (G-5021)

Commercial Honing LLC ....D....... 330 343-8896
Dover (G-8971)

Conduit Pipe Products Company ....D....... 614 879-9114
West Jefferson (G-20077)

Contech Engnered Solutions Inc ....A....... 513 645-7000
West Chester (G-19840)

Contech Engnered Solutions LLC ....D....... 513 645-7000
Middletown (G-14032)

Contech Engnered Solutions LLC ....C....... 513 645-7000
West Chester (G-19841)

Crest Bending Inc ....E....... 419 492-2108
New Washington (G-14959)

General Machine & Saw Company ....E....... 740 375-5730
Marion (G-12867)

Jackson Tube Service Inc ....C....... 937 773-8550
Piqua (G-16282)

James O Emert Jr ....G....... 330 650-6990
Hudson (G-11185)

Jmc Steel Group ....E....... 216 910-3700
Beachwood (G-1275)

John Maneely Company ....E....... 724 342-6851
Niles (G-15165)

Kirtland Capital Partners LP ....E....... 216 593-0100
Beachwood (G-1276)

Major Metals Company ....E....... 419 886-4600
Mansfield (G-12639)

Munroe Incorporated ....G....... 330 755-7216
Struthers (G-17995)

Phillips Mfg and Tower Co ....D....... 419 347-1720
Shelby (G-17140)

PMC Industries Corp ....D....... 440 943-3300
Wickliffe (G-20383)

Shawcor Inc ....E....... 513 683-7800
Loveland (G-12386)

Sterling Pipe & Tube Inc ....C....... 419 729-9756
Toledo (G-18704)

Stryker Steel Tube LLC ....F....... 419 682-4527
Stryker (G-18008)

T & D Fabricating Inc ....E....... 440 951-5646
Eastlake (G-9292)

TI Group Auto Systems LLC ....C....... 740 929-2049
Hebron (G-10890)

Timkensteel Corporation ....G....... 330 471-7000
Canton (G-2877)

Tite Seal Case Company Inc ....G....... 440 647-2371
Wellington (G-19756)

Unison Industries LLC ....B....... 937 426-0621
Dayton (G-8121)

Welded Tubes Inc ....F....... 440 437-5144
Orwell (G-15782)

Woodsage LLC ....C....... 419 866-8000
Holland (G-11098)

Zekelman Industries Inc ....C....... 330 373-4410
Warren (G-19628)

PIPES & TUBES: Welded

PWS Welding & Mtg ....F....... 330 385-6922
East Liverpool (G-9226)

Specialty Pipe & Tube Inc ....F....... 330 505-8262
Mineral Ridge (G-14311)

PIPES OR FITTINGS: Sewer, Clay

Superior Clay Corp ....D....... 740 922-4122
Uhrichsville (G-19061)

PIPES: Steel & Iron

Youngstown Tube Co ....E....... 330 743-7414
Youngstown (G-21258)

PISTONS & PISTON RINGS

Ad Piston Ring Company LLC ....F....... 216 781-5200
Cleveland (G-4699)

Air Conversion Technology Inc ....G....... 419 841-1720
Sylvania (G-18099)

Celina Alum Precision Tech Inc ....B....... 419 586-2278
Celina (G-2989)

Dover Corporation ....G....... 440 951-6600
Mentor (G-13563)

Federal-Mogul Corporation ....C....... 740 432-2393
Cambridge (G-2457)

PMI Operating Company Inc ....B....... 440 951-6600
Mentor (G-13690)

PLACER GOLD MINING

Ivi Mining Group Ltd ....G....... 740 418-7745
Vinton (G-19382)

PLANING MILL, NEC

Walnut Creek Planing Ltd ....D....... 330 893-3244
Millersburg (G-14281)

PLANING MILLS: Millwork

Wedge Hardwood Products ....G....... 330 525-7775
Alliance (G-552)

PLANTERS: Plastic

Rubbermaid Incorporated ....C....... 330 733-7771
Mogadore (G-14383)

PLANTS, POTTED, WHOLESALE

Trumbull Locker Plant Inc ....G....... 440 474-4631
Rock Creek (G-16686)

PLANTS: Artificial & Preserved

Custom Made Palm Trees LLC ....G....... 330 633-0063
Akron (G-138)

PLAQUES: Clay, Plaster/Papier-Mache, Factory Production

Miller Studio Inc ....D....... 330 339-1100
New Philadelphia (G-14916)

PLAQUES: Picture, Laminated

Dcc Corp ....G....... 330 494-0494
Canton (G-2680)

Gerber Wood Products Inc ....G....... 330 857-3901
Kidron (G-11591)

Glass Mirror Awards Inc ....G....... 419 638-2221
Helena (G-10896)

Hafner Hardwood Connection LLC ....G....... 419 726-4828
Toledo (G-18493)

Idx Corporation ....C....... 937 401-3225
Dayton (G-8400)

Lawnview Industries Inc......................C 937 653-5217
Urbana (G-19168)

PLASMAS

Csl Plasma Inc...................................E 937 325-4200
Springfield (G-17537)
Octapharma Plasma Inc ....G 216 518-0322
Maple Heights (G-12735)
Octapharma Plasma Inc ....G 216 252-6811
Cleveland (G-5926)
Plasmacare Inc..................................G 614 231-5322
Columbus (G-7491)
Talecris Plasma Resources................G 937 275-5996
Dayton (G-8698)
Tpr Plasma Center.............................G 419 244-3910
Toledo (G-18754)

PLASTER WORK: Ornamental & Architectural

Seves Glass Block Inc.......................G 440 627-6257
Broadview Heights (G-2119)
The Fischer & Jirouch Company ....G 216 361-3840
Cleveland (G-6312)

PLASTER, ACOUSTICAL: Gypsum

Next Sales LLC..................................G 330 704-4126
Dover (G-9006)

PLASTIC COLORING & FINISHING

A Schulman Inc ....E 330 498-4840
North Canton (G-15217)
Ampacet Corporation ....E 513 247-5400
Cincinnati (G-3400)
Carolina Color Corp Ohio ....E 740 363-6622
Delaware (G-8827)

PLASTIC PRDTS

Achill Island Composites LLC ....G 440 838-1746
Brecksville (G-2033)
Bisson Custom Plastic ....G 937 653-4966
Urbana (G-19147)
Bu E Comp Inc ....G 419 284-3381
Bloomville (G-1725)
Budd Co Plastics Div ....G 419 238-4332
Van Wert (G-19247)
Giesecke & Devrient Can ....G 330 425-1515
Twinsburg (G-18948)
H P Manufacturing Co ....D 216 361-6500
Cleveland (G-5469)
Holm Industries Inc............................G 330 562-2900
Aurora (G-925)
J H Plastics......................................G 419 937-2035
Tiffin (G-18223)
Jeffrey Brandewie ....G 937 726-7765
Fort Loramie (G-9933)
Jjc Products Inc ....G 330 666-4582
Akron (G-240)
Kurzkasch Inc Wilm Div ....F 740 498-8345
Newcomerstown (G-15119)
Louis G Freeman Co ....G 513 263-1720
Batavia (G-1202)
Matrix Plastics Co Inc ....G 330 666-7730
Medina (G-13440)
Plastics Converting Solutions ....G 330 722-2537
Medina (G-13460)
Plastics Mentor LLC ....G 440 352-1357
Mentor (G-13688)
Professional Plastics Corp ....G 614 336-2498
Dublin (G-9127)
Solon..G 440 498-1798
Solon (G-17383)
Unique Plastics LLC ....G 419 352-0066
Bowling Green (G-2018)
Vlchek Plastics ....G 440 632-1631
Middlefield (G-14004)
White Co David ....G 440 247-2920
Novelty (G-15584)
Wrr Creative Concepts LLC ....G 513 659-2284
West Chester (G-19974)
Yngstn Plastic Fabrication ....G 330 743-6404
Petersburg (G-16179)

PLASTIC PRDTS REPAIR SVCS

Fetters and Son Sign Company ....G 614 299-6947
Mount Gilead (G-14559)

PLASTICIZERS, ORGANIC: Cyclic & Acyclic

Chemionics Corporation ....E 330 733-8834
Tallmadge (G-18137)

PLASTICS FILM & SHEET

Clear Packaging Films Inc ....G 513 860-9053
West Chester (G-19836)
Clopay Corporation ....G 800 282-2260
Mason (G-12999)
Clopay Corporation ....G 513 742-1984
Cincinnati (G-3589)
Clopay Plastic Products Co Inc ....D 513 770-4800
Mason (G-13000)
Dow Chemical Company ....C 419 423-6500
Findlay (G-9818)
Dow Chemical Company ....F 937 254-1550
Dayton (G-8309)
Entrotech Inc ....F 614 946-7602
Columbus (G-7062)
Graphic Art Systems Inc ....E 216 581-9050
Cleveland (G-5446)
Klockner Pentaplast Amer Inc.............D 937 548-7272
Greenville (G-10508)
Liqui-Box Corporation ....D 614 888-9280
Columbus (G-7300)
Plastic Suppliers Inc ....D 614 475-8010
Columbus (G-7494)
Plastic Suppliers Inc ....D 614 475-8010
Columbus (G-7495)
PMC Acquisitions Inc ....G 419 429-0042
Findlay (G-9879)
Polyone Corporation ....C 800 727-4338
Greenville (G-10514)
Premier Material Concepts LLC ....D 419 429-0042
Findlay (G-9880)
Renegade Materials Corporation..........E 508 579-7888
Miamisburg (G-13854)
Specialty Films Inc............................E 614 471-9100
Columbus (G-7635)
Tsp Inc..E 513 732-8900
Batavia (G-1229)
United Converting Inc.........................G 614 863-9972
Columbus (G-7719)
Valfilm LLC ....E 419 423-6500
Findlay (G-9904)

PLASTICS FILM & SHEET: Polyethylene

Blako Industries Inc...........................E 419 246-6172
Dunbridge (G-9168)
Clondalkin Group ....G 440 324-2222
Elyria (G-9395)
General Films Inc ....D 888 436-3456
Covington (G-7923)
IVEX Protective Packaging Inc ....E 937 498-9298
Sidney (G-17196)
Putnam Plastics Inc ....G 937 866-6261
Dayton (G-8603)

PLASTICS FILM & SHEET: Polypropylene

Crown Plastics Co ....D 513 367-0238
Harrison (G-10775)
Orbis Rpm LLC..................................G 740 772-6355
Chillicothe (G-3255)
Orbis Rpm LLC..................................F 419 355-8310
Fremont (G-10173)

PLASTICS FILM & SHEET: Polyvinyl

Jain America Foods Inc ....G 614 850-9400
Columbus (G-7222)
Jain America Holdings Inc ....D 614 850-9400
Columbus (G-7223)

PLASTICS FILM & SHEET: Vinyl

Champion Win Co Cleveland LLC ....E 440 899-2562
Macedonia (G-12440)
Clarkwestern Dietrich Building.............G 330 372-5564
Warren (G-19535)
Clarkwestern Dietrich Building.............G 513 870-1100
West Chester (G-19835)
Ludlow Composites Corporation ....G 419 332-5531
Fremont (G-10168)
Rotary Products Inc...........................F 740 747-2623
Ashley (G-790)
Scherba Industries Inc ....D 330 273-3200
Brunswick (G-2256)
Tradex International Inc......................D 216 651-4788
Cleveland (G-6345)

Walton Plastics Inc ....E 440 786-7711
Bedford (G-1472)
World Connections Corps....................E 419 363-2681
Rockford (G-16694)

PLASTICS FINISHED PRDTS: Laminated

Blt Inc ....F 513 631-5050
Norwood (G-15571)
Bruewer Woodwork Mfg Co ....D 513 353-3505
Cleves (G-6507)
Counter Concepts Inc ....F 330 848-4848
Doylestown (G-9028)
Designer Cntemporary Laminates ....E 440 946-8207
Willoughby (G-20473)
Fdi Cabinetry LLC ....G 513 353-4500
Cleves (G-6514)
Franklin Cabinet Company Inc ....E 937 743-9606
Franklin (G-10023)
General Electric Company ....D 740 623-5366
Coshocton (G-7893)
Idx Corporation ....C 937 401-3225
Dayton (G-8400)
Microsol Inc ....G 330 733-0086
Tallmadge (G-18154)
Quality Rubber Stamp Inc ....G 614 235-2700
Columbus (G-7536)
Southern Cabinetry Inc ....E 740 245-5992
Bidwell (G-1679)
Spring Grove Manufacturing ....F 513 542-0185
Cincinnati (G-4444)
Victory Store Fixtures Inc ....F 740 499-3494
La Rue (G-11623)

PLASTICS MATERIAL & RESINS

1999 Pvc Partner Inc..........................G 440 930-1000
Avon Lake (G-1022)
A Schulman Inc ....D 330 666-3751
Fairlawn (G-9736)
A Schulman Inc ....C 330 773-2700
Akron (G-19)
Absolute Polymers Inc ....F 888 850-0455
Salem (G-16866)
Al-Co Products Inc ....F 419 399-3867
Latty (G-11767)
American Polymer Standards ....G 440 255-2211
Mentor (G-13520)
Ametek Westchester Plastics ....C 419 739-3200
Wapakoneta (G-19478)
Arclin USA LLC ....E 419 726-5013
Toledo (G-18354)
Arizona Chemical Company LLC ....C 330 343-7701
Dover (G-8964)
Armorsource LLC ....E 740 928-0070
Hebron (G-10861)
Ashland LLC ....G 513 557-3100
Cincinnati (G-3418)
Axalta Coating Systems LLC ....E 419 478-1211
Toledo (G-18361)
Biobent Holdings LLC ....G 513 658-5560
Columbus (G-6830)
Biobent Holdings LLC ....G 513 658-5560
Columbus (G-6831)
Biothane Coated Webbing Corp ....E 440 327-0485
North Ridgeville (G-15361)
Bricolage Inc ....G 614 853-6789
Grove City (G-10547)
Cameo Countertops Inc ....G 419 865-6371
Holland (G-11048)
Capital Resin Corporation ....D 614 445-7177
Columbus (G-6901)
Chemionics Corporation ....E 330 733-8834
Tallmadge (G-18137)
Concrete Sealants Inc ....E 937 845-8776
Tipp City (G-18273)
Cornerstone Indus Holdings................G 440 893-9144
Chagrin Falls (G-3054)
Covestro LLC ....C 740 929-2015
Hebron (G-10863)
Crane Plastics Mfg Ltd ....G 614 754-3700
Columbus (G-6998)
Crown Plastics Co ....D 513 367-0238
Harrison (G-10775)
Dow Chemical Company ....C 740 533-4000
Ironton (G-11292)
Durez Corporation ....G 567 295-6400
Kenton (G-11546)
E C Shaw Co ....E 513 721-6334
Cincinnati (G-3677)
E I Du Pont De Nemours & Co ....D 740 474-0635
Circleville (G-4628)

PRODUCT

E P S Specialists Ltd Inc ....F 513 489-3676
Cincinnati *(G-3679)*

Eagle Elastomer Inc ....E 330 923-7070
Peninsula *(G-16037)*

Emerald Performance Mtls LLC .....E 330 916-6700
Cuyahoga Falls *(G-7990)*

Emerald Performance Mtls LLC .....D 330 374-2418
Akron *(G-164)*

Emerald Specialty Polymers LLC ...E 330 374-2424
Akron *(G-166)*

Ep Bollinger LLC ....A 513 941-1101
Cincinnati *(G-3712)*

Evans Adhesive Corporation Ltd ...E 614 451-2665
Columbus *(G-7070)*

Farmed Materials Inc ....G 513 680-4046
Cincinnati *(G-3740)*

Ferro Corporation ....D 216 875-5600
Mayfield Heights *(G-13313)*

Flexsys America LP ....D 330 666-4111
Akron *(G-190)*

Freeman Manufacturing & Sup Co ...E 440 934-1902
Avon *(G-996)*

Geo-Tech Polymers LLC ....F 614 797-2300
Waverly *(G-19709)*

Georgia-Pacific LLC ....E 614 491-9100
Columbus *(G-7111)*

Goldsmith & Eggleton LLC ....F 203 855-6000
Wadsworth *(G-19408)*

Grit Guard Inc ....G 937 592-9003
Bellefontaine *(G-1531)*

Hancor Inc ....D 419 424-8225
Findlay *(G-9837)*

Hggc Citadel Plas Holdings Inc .....G 330 666-3751
Fairlawn *(G-9752)*

Ic3d LLC ....G 614 260-5631
Columbus *(G-7180)*

ICP Adhesives and Sealants Inc ....G 330 753-4585
Norton *(G-15513)*

Ier Fujikura Inc ....C 330 425-7121
Macedonia *(G-12458)*

Ineos LLC ....D 419 226-1200
Lima *(G-12027)*

Ineos ABS (usa) LLC ....C 513 467-2400
Addyston *(G-10)*

Ineos USA LLC ....D 419 226-1200
Lima *(G-12029)*

Integrated Chem Concepts Inc ......G 440 838-5666
Brecksville *(G-2056)*

Intergroup International Ltd ....D 216 965-0257
Euclid *(G-9586)*

International Technical ....E 330 505-1218
Niles *(G-15161)*

Isochem Incorporated ....G 614 775-9328
New Albany *(G-14762)*

J P Industrial Products Inc ....G 330 424-1110
Lisbon *(G-12125)*

Jjc Plastics Ltd ....G 330 334-3637
Norton *(G-15516)*

Kardol Quality Products LLC ....G 513 933-8206
Blue Ash *(G-1822)*

Kathom Manufacturing Co Inc ....E 513 868-8890
Hamilton *(G-10715)*

Kraton Polymers US LLC ....B 740 423-7571
Belpre *(G-1589)*

Ltg Polymers Limited ....G 330 854-5609
Massillon *(G-13168)*

Lubrizol Advanced Mtls Inc ....E 440 933-0400
Avon Lake *(G-1037)*

Materion Brush Inc ....E 440 960-5660
Lorain *(G-12260)*

Michael Day Enterprises LLC ....G 330 335-5100
Wadsworth *(G-19419)*

Mitsubishi Chls Perf Plyrs Inc ....D 419 483-2931
Bellevue *(G-1553)*

Modern Plastics Recovery Inc ....G 419 622-4611
Haviland *(G-10842)*

Multibase Inc ....D 330 666-0505
Copley *(G-7850)*

Nano Innovations LLC ....G 614 203-5706
Columbus *(G-7379)*

Nanosperse LLC ....G 937 296-5030
Kettering *(G-11583)*

National Polymer Dev Co Inc ....F 440 708-1245
Chagrin Falls *(G-3105)*

Nexeo Solutions LLC ....F 800 531-7106
Dublin *(G-9113)*

Novo Foam Products LLC ....G 440 892-3325
Westlake *(G-20286)*

Occidental Chemical Corp ....E 513 242-2900
Cincinnati *(G-4172)*

Ohio Foam Corporation ....F 419 492-2151
New Washington *(G-14963)*

Orica Ground Support Inc ....D 740 377-9146
South Point *(G-17443)*

OSI Global Sourcing LLC ....G 614 471-4800
Columbus *(G-7447)*

Ovation Polymer Technology and ...E 330 723-5686
Medina *(G-13455)*

Owens Corning Sales LLC ....F 330 633-6735
Tallmadge *(G-18163)*

Performnce Plymr Solutions Inc ....F 937 298-3713
Moraine *(G-14512)*

Perstorp Polyols Inc ....F 419 729-5448
Toledo *(G-18641)*

Plaskolite LLC ....C 614 294-3281
Columbus *(G-7489)*

Plasti-Kemm Inc ....G 330 239-1555
Medina *(G-13458)*

Plastic Regrinders Inc ....G 740 659-2346
Glenford *(G-10399)*

Plastic Selection Group Inc ....G 614 464-2008
Columbus *(G-7492)*

Poly Green Technologies LLC ....G 419 529-9909
Ontario *(G-15694)*

Poly-Carb Inc ....G 440 248-1223
Twinsburg *(G-19003)*

Polygroup Inc ....E 877 476-5972
Maineville *(G-12531)*

Polymer Packaging Inc ....D 330 832-2000
Massillon *(G-13195)*

Polymerics Inc ....G 330 677-1131
Kent *(G-11503)*

Polymerics Inc ....E 330 434-6665
Cuyahoga Falls *(G-8034)*

Polynew Inc ....G 330 897-3202
Baltic *(G-1076)*

Polynt Composites USA Inc ....C 816 391-6000
Sandusky *(G-16997)*

Polyone Corporation ....F 740 423-7571
Belpre *(G-1594)*

Polyone Corporation ....D 440 930-3754
Avon Lake *(G-1045)*

Polyone Corporation ....D 330 834-3812
Massillon *(G-13196)*

PPG Industries Inc ....E 419 683-2400
Crestline *(G-7935)*

Premix Inc ....C 440 224-2181
North Kingsville *(G-15304)*

Prime Industries Inc ....E 440 288-3626
Lorain *(G-12268)*

Proficient Plastics Inc ....F 440 205-9700
Mentor *(G-13700)*

Rauh Polymers Inc ....F 330 376-1120
Akron *(G-367)*

Ray Fogg Construction Inc ....F 216 351-7976
Cleveland *(G-6091)*

Rohm and Haas Company ....E 513 733-2100
Cincinnati *(G-4357)*

Rohm and Haas Company ....C 937 839-4612
West Alexandria *(G-19783)*

Saco Aei Polymers Inc ....G 330 995-1600
Aurora *(G-947)*

Scott Bader Inc ....G 330 920-4410
Stow *(G-17799)*

Scott Molders Incorporated ....G 330 673-5777
Kent *(G-11524)*

Sherwood Rtm Corp ....G 330 875-7151
Louisville *(G-12328)*

Sonoco Prtective Solutions Inc ......D 419 420-0029
Findlay *(G-9892)*

Sorbothane Inc ....E 330 678-9444
Kent *(G-11530)*

STC International Co Ltd ....G 561 308-6002
Lebanon *(G-11842)*

Tembec Btlsr Inc ....E 419 244-5856
Toledo *(G-18719)*

Triple Arrow Industries Inc ....G 614 437-5588
Marysville *(G-12976)*

Uniloy Milacron Inc ....D 513 487-5000
Batavia *(G-1230)*

Vinyl Profiles Acquisition LLC ....E 330 538-0660
North Jackson *(G-15301)*

Wilsonart LLC ....E 614 876-1515
Columbus *(G-7765)*

Winsell Incorporated ....G 330 836-7421
Akron *(G-473)*

PLASTICS MATERIALS, BASIC FORMS & SHAPES WHOLESALERS

Ampacet Corporation ....E 513 247-5400
Cincinnati *(G-3400)*

Drain Products LLC ....G 419 230-4549
Lakeview *(G-11649)*

Nexeo Solutions LLC ....F 800 531-7106
Dublin *(G-9113)*

Queen City Polymers Inc ....G 937 236-2710
Dayton *(G-8607)*

Total Plastics Inc ....G 440 891-1140
Cleveland *(G-6342)*

PLASTICS PROCESSING

Accurate Plastics LLC ....F 330 346-0048
Kent *(G-11422)*

Advanced Plastic Systems Inc ....F 614 759-6550
Gahanna *(G-10202)*

Allied Plastic Co Inc ....G 419 389-1688
Toledo *(G-18330)*

AMS Global Ltd ....F 937 620-1036
West Alexandria *(G-19778)*

Angell-Demmel North Amer Corp ...D 937 461-5800
Dayton *(G-8158)*

Apollo Plastics Inc ....F 440 951-7774
Mentor *(G-13525)*

Atc Nymold Corporation ....G 440 293-4064
Andover *(G-614)*

Baldie Import and Export Corp ....G 513 503-0953
Cincinnati *(G-3435)*

Ball Bounce and Sport Inc ....B 419 289-9310
Ashland *(G-710)*

Bc Investment Corporation ....G 330 262-3070
Wooster *(G-20747)*

Bena Inc ....G 419 299-3313
Van Buren *(G-19239)*

C A Joseph Co ....G 330 385-6869
East Liverpool *(G-9204)*

Carney Plastics Inc ....G 330 746-8273
Youngstown *(G-21044)*

Carson Industries LLC ....G 419 592-2309
Napoleon *(G-14675)*

Chemigon LLC ....G 330 592-1875
Akron *(G-121)*

Claflin Company Inc ....G 330 650-0582
Hudson *(G-11163)*

Continental Strl Plas Inc ....C 440 945-4800
Conneaut *(G-7803)*

Continental Strl Plas Inc ....B 419 396-1980
Carey *(G-2917)*

Continental Strl Plas Inc ....B 419 238-4628
Van Wert *(G-19248)*

Continental Strl Plas Inc ....C 419 257-2231
North Baltimore *(G-15192)*

David Wolfe Design Inc ....F 330 633-6124
Akron *(G-142)*

Dawn Enterprises Inc ....E 216 642-5506
Cleveland *(G-5172)*

Dimcogray Corporation ....D 937 433-7600
Centerville *(G-3039)*

DJM Plastics Ltd ....F 419 424-5250
Findlay *(G-9817)*

Drummond Corp ....F 440 834-9660
Middlefield *(G-13931)*

Dyna Vac Plastics Inc ....G 937 773-0092
Piqua *(G-16262)*

Dynamic Plastics Inc ....G 937 437-7261
New Paris *(G-14879)*

Eger Products Inc ....E 513 735-1400
Batavia *(G-1179)*

Electr-Gnral Plas Corp Clumbus ....G 614 871-2915
Grove City *(G-10557)*

Encore Industries Inc ....E 419 626-8000
Sandusky *(G-16961)*

Encore Plastics Corporation ....D 740 432-1652
Cambridge *(G-2456)*

Evans Industries Inc ....F 330 453-1122
Canton *(G-2698)*

Extreme Custom Spools ....G 330 533-6936
Canfield *(G-2556)*

Fci Inc ....D 216 251-5200
Cleveland *(G-5329)*

Flambeau Inc ....C 330 239-0202
Sharon Center *(G-17106)*

Flex Technologies Inc ....D 330 359-5415
Mount Eaton *(G-14555)*

Fountain Specialists Inc ....G 513 831-5717
Milford *(G-14142)*

G I Plastek Inc G 440 230-1942
Westlake *(G-20270)*
G S K Inc G 937 547-1611
Greenville *(G-10501)*
Hanlon Industries Inc F 216 261-7056
Cleveland *(G-5479)*
Harrison Mch & Plastic Corp E 330 569-3128
Garrettsville *(G-10323)*
Hartville Plastics Inc G 330 877-9090
Hartville *(G-10824)*
HP Manufacturing Company Inc D 216 361-6500
Cleveland *(G-5530)*
J & O Plastics Inc E 330 927-3169
Rittman *(G-16676)*
Jos-Tech Inc E 330 678-3260
Kent *(G-11474)*
Joslyn Manufacturing Company E 330 467-8111
Macedonia *(G-12465)*
JPS Technologies Inc F 513 984-6400
Blue Ash *(G-1820)*
JPS Technologies Inc F 513 984-6400
Blue Ash *(G-1821)*
Kathom Manufacturing Co Inc E 513 868-8890
Hamilton *(G-10715)*
Liqui-Box Corporation C 419 289-9696
Ashland *(G-750)*
Mega Plastics Co E 330 527-2211
Garrettsville *(G-10330)*
Milacron LLC E 513 536-2000
Batavia *(G-1206)*
Mvp Plastics Inc F 330 872-4451
Middlefield *(G-13970)*
Nitrojection G 440 834-8790
Chesterland *(G-3217)*
Orbit Manufacturing Inc E 513 732-6097
Batavia *(G-1215)*
P & S Welding Co G 330 274-2850
Mantua *(G-12720)*
P S Plastics Inc F 614 262-7070
Columbus *(G-7451)*
Paragon Plastics G 330 542-9825
New Middletown *(G-14878)*
Plastic Moldings Company Llc D 513 921-5040
Blue Ash *(G-1851)*
Plastic Products and Supply G 330 744-5076
Youngstown *(G-21171)*
Plastic Works Inc G 419 433-6576
Huron *(G-11237)*
Possible Plastics Inc G 614 277-2100
Grove City *(G-10583)*
Precision Thrmplstc Componts D 419 227-4500
Lima *(G-12115)*
Preferred Solutions Inc F 216 642-1200
Seven Hills *(G-17062)*
Queen City Polymers Inc E 513 779-0990
West Chester *(G-19928)*
Queen City Polymers Inc G 937 236-2710
Dayton *(G-8607)*
Radici Plastics Usa Inc D 330 336-7611
Wadsworth *(G-19434)*
Ravago Americas LLC F 419 924-9090
West Unity *(G-20134)*
Rexles Inc G 419 732-8188
Port Clinton *(G-16411)*
Rutland Plastic Tech Inc G 614 846-3055
Columbus *(G-7578)*
Samuel Strapping Systems Inc D 740 522-2500
Heath *(G-10855)*
Solus Indus Innovations LLC G 440 356-1933
Rocky River *(G-16711)*
Solvay Spclty Polymers USA LLC E 740 373-9242
Marietta *(G-12833)*
Starks Plastics LLC G 513 541-4591
Cincinnati *(G-4459)*
Tahoma Enterprises Inc D 330 745-9016
Barberton *(G-1151)*
Tahoma Rubber & Plastics Inc D 330 745-9016
Barberton *(G-1152)*
Th Plastics Inc C 419 352-2770
Bowling Green *(G-2017)*
Todd Smith Products G 216 529-0525
Lakewood *(G-11680)*
Total Plastics Inc G 440 891-1140
Cleveland *(G-6342)*
Trilogy Plastics Inc E 440 893-5522
Chagrin Falls *(G-3129)*
Trilogy Plastics Inc G 330 875-1789
Louisville *(G-12331)*
Trimold LLC B 740 474-7591
Circleville *(G-4648)*
U S Development Corp E 570 966-5990
Kent *(G-11540)*
United Security Seals Inc E 614 443-7633
Columbus *(G-7721)*
Upl International Inc E 330 433-2860
North Canton *(G-15280)*
Valley Plastics Co Inc E 419 666-2349
Toledo *(G-18764)*
Weldon Plastics Corporation G 330 425-9660
Twinsburg *(G-19039)*
West Extrusion LLC G 330 744-0625
Campbell *(G-2494)*
Westar Plastics Llc G 419 636-1333
Bryan *(G-2327)*
Windsor Mold USA Inc E 419 483-0653
Bellevue *(G-1566)*
World Resource Solutons Corp G 614 733-3737
Plain City *(G-16364)*
Wyatt Industries LLC G 330 954-1790
Streetsboro *(G-17883)*
Y City Recycling LLC D 740 452-2500
Zanesville *(G-21364)*

PLASTICS SHEET: Packing Materials

Automated Packg Systems Inc C 330 626-2313
Streetsboro *(G-17842)*
Automated Packg Systems Inc C 216 663-2000
Cleveland *(G-4866)*
Buckeye Diamond Logistics Inc G 937 644-2194
Marysville *(G-12934)*
Cool Seal Usa LLC F 419 666-1111
Perrysburg *(G-16079)*
Kapstone Container Corporation C 330 562-6111
Aurora *(G-928)*
MAI-Weave LLC D 937 322-1698
Springfield *(G-17600)*
Plastic Works Inc G 419 433-6576
Huron *(G-11237)*
Polyone Corporation E 937 548-2133
Greenville *(G-10515)*
Professional Packaging Company E 440 238-8850
Strongsville *(G-17954)*
Raven Industries Inc G 937 323-4625
Springfield *(G-17634)*
Western Reserve Sleeve Inc E 440 238-8850
Strongsville *(G-17983)*

PLASTICS: Blow Molded

Diamond Plastics Inc D 419 759-3838
Dunkirk *(G-9187)*
Fremont Plastic Products Inc C 419 332-6407
Fremont *(G-10150)*
Klw Plastics Inc G 513 539-2673
Monroe *(G-14409)*
Marshall Plastics Inc G 937 653-4740
Urbana *(G-19169)*
Paarlo Plastics Inc D 330 494-3798
North Canton *(G-15256)*
Pinnacle Industrial Entps Inc C 419 352-8688
Bowling Green *(G-2008)*
Plastic Forming Company Inc E 330 830-5167
Massillon *(G-13194)*
Plastipak Packaging Inc C 937 596-5166
Jackson Center *(G-11345)*
Quality Blow Molding Inc D 440 458-6550
Elyria *(G-9481)*
Rez-Tech Corporation E 330 673-4009
Kent *(G-11515)*
Roto Solutions Inc D 330 279-2424
Holmesville *(G-11110)*
Thermoplastic Accessories Corp E 614 771-4777
Hilliard *(G-10987)*
Tigerpoly Manufacturing Inc B 614 871-0045
Grove City *(G-10601)*
Tmd Wek North LLC C 440 576-6940
Jefferson *(G-11374)*

PLASTICS: Cast

Flambeau Inc D 440 632-1631
Middlefield *(G-13936)*
Innovation Plastics LLC E 513 818-1771
Fostoria *(G-9980)*
Polymer Tech & Svcs Inc E 740 929-5500
Heath *(G-10851)*
S&V Industries Inc G 330 666-1986
Medina *(G-13472)*

PLASTICS: Extruded

Akron Polymer Products Inc E 330 628-5551
Akron *(G-52)*
Astra Products of Ohio Ltd D 330 296-0112
Ravenna *(G-16516)*
Axion Strl Innovations LLC F 740 452-2500
Zanesville *(G-21273)*
Buecomp Inc E 419 284-3840
Bloomville *(G-1726)*
Cell-O-Core Co E 330 239-4370
Sharon Center *(G-17104)*
Cep Holdings LLC G 330 665-2900
Fairlawn *(G-9745)*
Clark Rbr Plastic Intl Sls Inc D 440 953-9514
Mentor *(G-13544)*
Cleveland Specialty Pdts Inc E 216 281-8300
Cleveland *(G-5079)*
Creative Extruded Products Inc D 937 667-1618
Vandalia *(G-19286)*
D & D Plastics Inc F 330 376-0668
Akron *(G-139)*
Dimex LLC C 740 374-3100
Marietta *(G-12778)*
Eclipse Blind Systems Inc C 330 296-0112
Ravenna *(G-16528)*
Engineered Profiles LLC C 614 754-3700
Columbus *(G-7058)*
Erie Lake Plastic Inc F 440 333-4880
Cleveland *(G-5295)*
Extrudex Limited Partnership E 440 352-7101
Painesville *(G-15879)*
Formtech Enterprises Inc G 330 688-2171
Stow *(G-17755)*
Fowler Products Inc F 419 683-4057
Crestline *(G-7929)*
G & J Extrusions Inc G 330 753-0162
New Franklin *(G-14824)*
Hi-Tech Extrusions Ltd E 440 286-4000
Chardon *(G-3156)*
Horsemens Pride Inc E 800 232-7950
Streetsboro *(G-17857)*
Hrh Door Corp D 440 593-5226
Conneaut *(G-7809)*
Hudson Extrusions Inc E 330 653-6015
Hudson *(G-11180)*
ICO Technology Inc G 330 666-3751
Fairlawn *(G-9754)*
Imperial Plastics Inc D 330 927-5065
Rittman *(G-16675)*
Inventive Extrusions Corp E 330 874-3000
Bolivar *(G-1937)*
Lpi Legacy Plastics LLC F 270 827-1318
Cincinnati *(G-4035)*
Malish Corporation C 440 951-5356
Mentor *(G-13644)*
Mercury Plastics Inc C 440 632-5281
Middlefield *(G-13957)*
Middlefield Plastics Inc E 440 834-4638
Middlefield *(G-13962)*
Montville Plastics & Rbr LLC D 440 548-3211
Parkman *(G-15952)*
Orzen Extruded Polymers G 330 298-9550
Ravenna *(G-16547)*
Pahuja Inc D 614 864-3989
Gahanna *(G-10225)*
Plastic Extrusion Technologies E 440 632-5611
Middlefield *(G-13982)*
Polyone Corporation C 419 399-4050
Paulding *(G-16013)*
Profile Plastics Inc E 330 452-7000
Canton *(G-2827)*
Profusion Industries LLC G 800 938-2858
Fairlawn *(G-9758)*
Roppe Holding Company G 419 435-6601
Fostoria *(G-9992)*
Rowmark LLC D 419 425-8974
Findlay *(G-9884)*
Rowmark LLC D 419 429-0042
Findlay *(G-9885)*
Ryan Development Corp E 937 587-2266
Peebles *(G-16024)*
Seagate Plastics Company E 419 878-5010
Waterville *(G-19667)*
Trellborg Sling Prfiles US Inc E 330 995-9725
Aurora *(G-951)*
Universal Polymer & Rubber Ltd C 440 632-1691
Middlefield *(G-14000)*
Vts Co Ltd G 419 273-4010
Forest *(G-9924)*

PRODUCT

Win Cd Inc	F	330 929-1999
Cuyahoga Falls (G-8062)		

PLASTICS: Finished Injection Molded

ABC Plastics Inc	E	330 948-3322
Lodi (G-12154)		
Acorn Products Inc	B	614 222-4400
Columbus (G-6689)		
Advanced Plastics Inc	F	330 336-6681
Wadsworth (G-19390)		
Akron Porcelain & Plastics Co	C	330 745-2159
Akron (G-53)		
Allied Moulded Products Inc	B	419 636-4217
Bryan (G-2275)		
Associated Plastics Corp	D	419 634-3910
Ada (G-5)		
Atc Group Inc	D	440 293-4064
Andover (G-612)		
Atc Nymold Corporation	G	440 293-4064
Andover (G-615)		
B & B Molded Products Inc	E	419 592-8700
Napoleon (G-14673)		
Bourbon Plastics Inc	E	574 342-0893
Cuyahoga Falls (G-7975)		
Caraustar Industries Inc	E	330 665-7700
Copley (G-7841)		
Centrex Plastics LLC	C	419 423-1213
Findlay (G-9806)		
Continental Coml Pdts LLC	D	419 447-5000
Tiffin (G-18216)		
CP Technologies Company	E	614 866-9200
Blacklick (G-1693)		
D K Manufacturing	D	740 654-5566
Lancaster (G-11704)		
D Martone Industries Inc	E	440 632-5800
Middlefield (G-13928)		
Dak Enterprises Inc	F	740 828-3291
Marysville (G-12941)		
Design Molded Plastics Inc	C	330 963-4400
Macedonia (G-12444)		
DK Manfcturing Frazeysburg Inc	E	740 828-3291
Frazeysburg (G-10072)		
DK Manufacturing Lancaster Inc	D	740 654-5566
Lancaster (G-11710)		
Dreco Inc	C	440 327-6021
North Ridgeville (G-15370)		
Edge Plastics Inc	C	419 522-6696
Mansfield (G-12598)		
Encore Plastics Corporation	F	419 626-8000
Sandusky (G-16962)		
Endura Plastics Inc	D	440 951-4466
Kirtland (G-11613)		
Ernie Green Industries Inc	G	614 219-1423
Columbus (G-7064)		
Global Plastic Tech Inc	E	330 963-6830
Brecksville (G-2053)		
Greenville Technology Inc	A	937 548-3217
Greenville (G-10504)		
Hadlock Plastics LLC	C	440 466-4876
Geneva (G-10349)		
Illinois Tool Works Inc	D	937 332-2839
Troy (G-18843)		
Illinois Tool Works Inc	D	519 376-8886
Troy (G-18844)		
Innovations In Plastic Inc	G	216 541-6060
Cleveland (G-5571)		
International Automotive	A	419 433-5653
Huron (G-11228)		
Jack Gruber	G	740 408-2718
Cardington (G-2912)		
Jaco Manufacturing Company	F	440 234-4000
Berea (G-1622)		
Just Plastics Inc	E	419 468-5506
Galion (G-10277)		
Ka Molded Products	G	419 884-3375
Mansfield (G-12631)		
Kamco Industries	G	419 551-9211
West Unity (G-20131)		
Kamco Industries Inc	B	419 924-5511
West Unity (G-20132)		
Kasai North America Inc	F	614 356-1494
Dublin (G-9094)		
Kennick Mold & Die Inc	G	216 631-3535
Cleveland (G-5646)		
Mdi of Ohio Inc	E	937 866-2345
Miamisburg (G-13829)		
Meese Inc	D	440 998-1202
Ashtabula (G-819)		
Myers Industries Inc	E	440 632-1006
Middlefield (G-13971)		

Novatex North America Inc	D	419 282-4264
Ashland (G-757)		
Ohio Plastics Company	G	740 828-3291
Newark (G-15041)		
P P E Inc	D	440 322-8577
Elyria (G-9473)		
Plas-TEC Corp	D	419 272-2731
Edon (G-9343)		
PMC Smart Solutions LLC	F	513 921-5040
Blue Ash (G-1852)		
Precision Custom Products Inc	E	937 585-4011
De Graff (G-8769)		
Pyramid Plastics Inc	E	216 641-5904
Cleveland (G-6065)		
R A M Plastics Co Inc	E	330 549-3107
North Lima (G-15322)		
Reebar Die Casting Inc	F	419 878-7591
Waterville (G-19665)		
Revere Plas Systems Group LLC	B	419 547-6918
Clyde (G-6544)		
Sonoco Products Company	E	614 759-8470
Columbus (G-7631)		
Springfield Plastics Inc	F	937 322-6071
Springfield (G-17654)		
Stuchell Products LLC	E	330 821-4299
Alliance (G-541)		
T&M Plastics Co Inc	G	216 651-7700
Cleveland (G-6291)		
Tez Tool & Fabrication Inc	G	440 323-2300
Elyria (G-9500)		
Toledo Molding & Die Inc	D	419 470-3950
Toledo (G-18736)		
Toledo Molding & Die Inc	D	419 476-0581
Toledo (G-18737)		
Tom Smith Industries Inc	C	937 832-1555
Clayton (G-4663)		
Toth Mold & Die Inc	F	440 232-8530
Cleveland (G-6343)		
Tri-Craft Inc	E	440 826-1050
Cleveland (G-6358)		
Unique-Chardan Inc	E	419 636-6900
Bryan (G-2325)		
Venture Packaging Inc	B	419 465-2534
Monroeville (G-14430)		
Wayne Frame Products Inc	G	419 726-7715
Toledo (G-18771)		

PLASTICS: Injection Molded

Acco Brands USA LLC	A	937 495-6323
Kettering (G-11573)		
Accutech Plastic Molding Inc	G	937 233-0017
Dayton (G-8133)		
Advantage Mold Inc	G	419 691-5676
Toledo (G-18322)		
All Srvice Plastic Molding Inc	E	937 415-3674
Fairborn (G-9614)		
All Srvice Plastic Molding Inc	F	937 890-0322
Vandalia (G-19279)		
All Srvice Plastic Molding Inc	D	937 890-0322
Vandalia (G-19280)		
Allied Custom Molded Products	G	614 291-0629
Columbus (G-6724)		
Amclo Group Inc	C	216 791-8400
Cleveland (G-4776)		
American Molded Plastics Inc	F	330 872-3838
Newton Falls (G-15128)		
American Plastic Tech Inc	D	440 632-5203
Middlefield (G-13914)		
Arkay Industries Inc	E	513 360-0390
Monroe (G-14392)		
Arkay Plastics Alabama Inc	F	513 360-0390
Monroe (G-14393)		
Artisan Mold Co Inc	G	440 926-4511
Grafton (G-10419)		
Aspec Inc	G	513 561-9922
Cincinnati (G-3420)		
Auld Company	E	614 454-1010
Columbus (G-6786)		
Automation Plastics Corp	D	330 562-5148
Aurora (G-908)		
Bennett Plastics Inc	E	740 432-2209
Cambridge (G-2447)		
Berlekamp Plastics Inc	F	419 334-4481
Fremont (G-10130)		
Bloom Industries Inc	D	330 898-3878
Warren (G-19529)		
Bloomdale Plastics Co	E	419 454-5135
Bloomdale (G-1719)		
Boardman Molded Products Inc	D	330 788-2401
Youngstown (G-21032)		

Brown Company of Findlay Ltd	E	419 425-3002
Findlay (G-9803)		
Buckeye Design & Engr Svc LLC	G	419 375-4241
Fort Recovery (G-9945)		
C-Mold Inc	E	937 981-7797
Greenfield (G-10474)		
Case Industries Inc	G	330 963-7717
Twinsburg (G-18908)		
Century Mold Company Inc	D	513 539-9283
Middletown (G-14027)		
Converge Group Inc	F	419 281-0000
Ashland (G-726)		
Cosmo Corporation	D	330 359-5429
Wilmot (G-20684)		
Ctc Plastics	B	937 228-9184
Dayton (G-8255)		
Custom Molded Products LLC	G	937 382-1070
Wilmington (G-20662)		
Custom Pultrusions Inc	E	330 562-5201
Aurora (G-915)		
D J Metro Mold & Die Inc	G	440 237-1130
North Royalton (G-15416)		
D M Tool & Plastics Inc	F	937 962-4140
Brookville (G-2180)		
D M Tool & Plastics Inc	F	937 962-4140
Lewisburg (G-11932)		
Deimling/Jeliho Plastics Inc	D	513 752-6653
Amelia (G-572)		
Dinesol Plastics Inc	C	330 544-7171
Niles (G-15149)		
Dlhbowles Inc	E	330 479-7595
Canton (G-2693)		
Dlhbowles Inc	D	330 488-0716
East Canton (G-9191)		
Dlhbowles Inc	B	330 478-2503
Canton (G-2691)		
Don-Ell Corporation	G	419 841-7114
Sylvania (G-18104)		
Doyle Manufacturing Inc	D	419 865-2548
Holland (G-11055)		
Drs Industries Inc	D	419 861-0334
Holland (G-11057)		
Dublin Plastics Inc	G	216 641-5904
Cleveland (G-5217)		
Elliott Mfg Co	F	937 833-4430
Brookville (G-2182)		
Elra Industries Inc	G	513 868-6228
Hamilton (G-10688)		
Enginred Plstic Components Inc	C	513 228-0298
Lebanon (G-11797)		
Enkon LLC	F	937 898-2603
Dayton (G-8327)		
Enpress LLC	E	440 510-0108
Eastlake (G-9269)		
Ferriot Inc	C	330 786-3000
Akron (G-185)		
Frantz Medical Development Ltd	G	212 308-4860
Mentor (G-13582)		
G M R Technology Inc	E	440 992-6003
Ashtabula (G-808)		
Genesis Plastic Tech LLC	D	440 542-0722
Solon (G-17296)		
H & H Engineered Molded Pdts	D	440 415-1814
Geneva (G-10348)		
Harmony Systems and Svc Inc	D	937 778-1082
Piqua (G-16270)		
HI Tek Mold	G	440 942-4090
Mentor (G-13601)		
Hy-Tech Products	F	440 537-1257
Elyria (G-9430)		
Hycomp LLC	D	440 234-2002
Cleveland (G-5542)		
ICO Products LLC	G	419 867-3900
Holland (G-11064)		
Illinois Tool Works Inc	B	419 636-3161
Bryan (G-2302)		
Injection Molding Specialist	G	440 639-7896
Painesville (G-15890)		
Integra Enclosures Inc	G	440 269-4966
Willoughby (G-20510)		
International Supply Corp	G	513 793-0393
Cincinnati (G-3931)		
J K Plastics Co	G	440 632-1482
Middlefield (G-13944)		
Jaco Manufacturing Company	D	440 234-4000
Berea (G-1621)		
Jensar Manufacturing LLC	G	419 727-8320
Toledo (G-18533)		
Kittyhawk Molding Company Inc	E	937 746-3663
Carlisle (G-2932)		

L C Liming & Sons Inc ....G 513 876-2555
Felicity *(G-9786)*

Lancaster Commercial Pdts LLC ....E 740 286-5081
Columbus *(G-7282)*

Laszeray Technology LLC ....D 440 582-8430
North Royalton *(G-15432)*

Lee Plastic Company LLC ....G 937 456-5720
Eaton *(G-9316)*

Lion Mold & Machine Inc ....G 330 688-4248
Stow *(G-17770)*

M L C Technologies Inc ....G 513 874-7792
Hamilton *(G-10720)*

Maca Plastics Inc ....F 937 544-8618
Winchester *(G-20695)*

Mag-Nif Inc ....D 440 946-4308
Mentor *(G-13643)*

Magnum Molding Inc ....G 937 368-3040
Conover *(G-7824)*

Mahar Spar Industries Inc ....E 216 249-7143
Cleveland *(G-5731)*

Majestic Plastics Inc ....G 937 593-9500
Bellefontaine *(G-1536)*

Matrix Cable and Mould ....G 513 832-2577
Cincinnati *(G-4067)*

McCann Tool & Die Inc ....F 330 264-8820
Wooster *(G-20803)*

Mexus Holdings Inc ....F 937 832-2307
Englewood *(G-9532)*

Miami Valley Plastics Inc ....E 937 273-3200
Eldorado *(G-9346)*

Molding Dynamics Inc ....F 440 786-8100
Bedford *(G-1444)*

Moldmakers Inc ....F 419 673-0902
Kenton *(G-11559)*

National Molded Products Inc ....E 440 365-3400
Elyria *(G-9466)*

NBC Industries Inc ....F 216 651-9800
Cleveland *(G-5863)*

Nebraska Industries Corp ....E 419 335-6010
Wauseon *(G-19691)*

Nissen Chemitec America Inc ....C 740 852-3200
London *(G-12215)*

North Canton Plastics Inc ....E 330 497-0071
Canton *(G-2792)*

Northshore Mold Inc ....E 440 838-8212
Cleveland *(G-5915)*

Ohio Precision Molding Inc ....E 330 745-9393
Barberton *(G-1135)*

Omega Polymer Technologies Inc ....G 330 562-5201
Aurora *(G-939)*

Omega Pultrusions Incorporated ....C 330 562-5201
Aurora *(G-940)*

Opti Mold Inc ....G 440 248-9179
Solon *(G-17356)*

Orbis Corporation ....B 937 652-1361
Urbana *(G-19171)*

P M Machine Inc ....F 440 942-6537
Willoughby *(G-20563)*

Pace Mold & Machine LLC ....G 330 879-1777
Massillon *(G-13192)*

Pave Technology Co ....E 937 890-1592
Dayton *(G-8566)*

Performance Plastics Ltd ....E 513 321-8404
Cincinnati *(G-4227)*

Pioneer Custom Molding Inc ....E 419 737-3252
Pioneer *(G-16237)*

Pioneer Plastics Corporation ....C 330 896-2356
Akron *(G-341)*

Plastex Industries Inc ....E 419 531-0189
Toledo *(G-18647)*

Plastic Enterprises Inc ....E 440 324-3240
Elyria *(G-9478)*

Podnar Plastics Inc ....E 330 673-2255
Kent *(G-11502)*

Positool Technologies Inc ....G 330 220-4002
Brunswick *(G-2245)*

Precision Polymers Inc ....G 614 322-9951
Reynoldsburg *(G-16599)*

Preform Technologies LLC ....G 419 720-0355
Swanton *(G-18088)*

Priamus System Technology ....G 330 273-3393
Brunswick *(G-2247)*

Prime Engineered Plastics Corp ....F 330 452-5110
Canton *(G-2821)*

Progressive Molding Tech ....G 330 220-7030
Medina *(G-13464)*

Proto Plastics Inc ....E 937 667-8416
Tipp City *(G-18295)*

Proto-Mold Products Co Inc ....E 937 778-1959
Piqua *(G-16308)*

PVS Plastics Technology Corp ....E 937 233-4376
Huber Heights *(G-11151)*

R Dunn Mold Inc ....G 937 773-3388
Piqua *(G-16309)*

Rage Corporation ....D 614 771-4771
Hilliard *(G-10974)*

Raven Concealment Systems LLC ....G 440 508-9000
North Ridgeville *(G-15399)*

Recto Molded Products Inc ....D 513 871-5544
Cincinnati *(G-4334)*

Reserve Industries Inc ....E 440 871-2796
Bay Village *(G-1243)*

Resinoid Engineering Corp ....D 847 673-1050
Hebron *(G-10881)*

Retterbush Fiberglass Corp ....E 937 778-1936
Piqua *(G-16310)*

Revere Plastics Systems LLC ....B 419 547-6918
Clyde *(G-6545)*

Ro-MAI Industries Inc ....E 330 425-9090
Twinsburg *(G-19009)*

Ross Special Products Inc ....F 937 335-8406
Troy *(G-18869)*

Rotosolutions Inc ....F 419 903-0800
Ashland *(G-774)*

Royal Plastics Inc ....C 440 352-1357
Mentor *(G-13717)*

Sajar Plastics Inc ....D 440 632-5203
Middlefield *(G-13986)*

Sanborn Plastics Corp ....E 440 286-4122
Chardon *(G-3177)*

Shelly Fisher ....D 419 522-6696
Mansfield *(G-12677)*

Shiloh Industries Inc ....F 937 236-5100
Dayton *(G-8655)*

Skribs Tool and Die Inc ....E 440 951-7774
Mentor *(G-13724)*

Spectrum Plastics Corporation ....G 330 926-9766
Cuyahoga Falls *(G-8048)*

Stanley Electric US Co Inc ....B 740 852-5200
London *(G-12219)*

State Tool and Die Inc ....G 216 267-6030
Cleveland *(G-6241)*

Stewart Acquisition LLC ....E 800 376-4466
Kirtland *(G-11617)*

Stewart Acquisition LLC ....E 330 963-0322
Twinsburg *(G-19024)*

Stopol Equipment Sales LLC ....G 440 499-0030
Brunswick *(G-2258)*

Sun State Plastics Inc ....G 330 494-5220
Canton *(G-2863)*

Systems Jay LLC Nanogate ....C 419 524-3778
Mansfield *(G-12688)*

Tech II Inc ....B 937 969-7000
Urbana *(G-19183)*

Tech-Way Industries Inc ....D 937 746-1004
Franklin *(G-10058)*

Technimold Plus Inc ....G 937 492-4077
Port Jefferson *(G-16421)*

Tetra Mold & Tool Inc ....E 937 845-1651
New Carlisle *(G-14814)*

Thogus Products Company ....D 440 933-8850
Avon Lake *(G-1053)*

Tjar Innovations LLC ....G 937 347-1999
Xenia *(G-20981)*

Toledo Molding & Die Inc ....C 419 692-6022
Delphos *(G-8919)*

Treemen Industries Inc ....E 330 965-3777
Boardman *(G-1925)*

Triaxis Machine & Tool LLC ....G 440 230-0303
North Royalton *(G-15457)*

Turbo Machine & Tool Inc ....G 216 651-1940
Cleveland *(G-6375)*

US Molding Machinery Co Inc ....E 440 918-1701
Willoughby *(G-20625)*

V & R Molded Products Inc ....F 419 752-4171
Willard *(G-20403)*

Venture Plas Middlefield LLC ....E 440 834-0704
Middlefield *(G-14002)*

Venture Plastics Inc ....G 330 872-5774
Newton Falls *(G-15141)*

Vicas Manufacturing Co Inc ....E 513 791-7741
Cincinnati *(G-4568)*

Vision Color LLC ....G 419 924-9450
West Unity *(G-20136)*

Windsor Mold Inc ....E 419 484-2400
Bellevue *(G-1565)*

World Class Plastics Inc ....D 937 843-3003
Russells Point *(G-16759)*

Zehrco-Giancola Composites Inc ....G 440 576-9941
Jefferson *(G-11377)*

PLASTICS: *Molded*

Alpha Packaging Holdings Inc ....B 216 252-5595
Cleveland *(G-4768)*

American Molding Company Inc ....G 330 620-6799
Barberton *(G-1097)*

Beach Mfg Plastic Molding Div ....D 937 882-6400
New Carlisle *(G-14797)*

Cardinal Products Inc ....G 440 237-8280
North Royalton *(G-15413)*

Claycor Inc ....F 419 318-7290
Toledo *(G-18399)*

Cobra Plastics Inc ....D 330 425-3669
Macedonia *(G-12442)*

Core Composites Cincinnati LLC ....A 513 724-6111
Batavia *(G-1174)*

Core Molding Technologies Inc ....B 614 870-5000
Columbus *(G-6983)*

Country Molding ....G 440 564-5235
Newbury *(G-15085)*

Crg Plastics Inc ....F 937 298-2025
Dayton *(G-8251)*

Custom Molded Foam Products ....G 440 288-8951
Lorain *(G-12241)*

Don-Ell Corporation ....E 419 841-7114
Sylvania *(G-18103)*

Encon Inc ....G 937 890-6239
Vandalia *(G-19291)*

Industrial Farm Tank Inc ....G 937 843-2972
Lewistown *(G-11944)*

Interpak Inc ....E 440 974-8999
Mentor *(G-13611)*

Kurz-Kasch Inc ....G 740 498-8343
Newcomerstown *(G-15117)*

Lion Helmet Molding ....G 937 297-0760
Kettering *(G-11582)*

Liqui-Box Corporation ....C 419 209-9085
Upper Sandusky *(G-19129)*

Mar-Bal Inc ....D 440 543-7526
Chagrin Falls *(G-3101)*

Mar-Bal Inc ....D 440 543-7526
Chagrin Falls *(G-3102)*

Meggitt (erlanger) LLC ....D 513 851-5550
Cincinnati *(G-4080)*

Mibtach Enterprises Inc ....G 513 941-0387
Cincinnati *(G-4098)*

Midwest Molding Inc ....E 614 873-1572
Plain City *(G-16349)*

Molded Extruded ....G 216 475-5491
Bedford Heights *(G-1490)*

Molded Fiber Glass Companies ....A 440 997-5851
Ashtabula *(G-823)*

Molded Fiber Glass Companies ....B 440 997-5851
Ashtabula *(G-824)*

Molders World Inc ....F 513 469-6653
Blue Ash *(G-1843)*

Moore Industries Inc ....D 419 485-5572
Montpelier *(G-14449)*

North Coast Custom Molding Inc ....F 419 905-6447
Dunkirk *(G-9188)*

Northwest Molded Plastics ....G 419 459-4414
Edon *(G-9342)*

Palpac Industries Inc ....F 419 523-3230
Ottawa *(G-15803)*

Pilot Plastics Inc ....E 330 920-1718
Peninsula *(G-16041)*

Plastics Group Inc ....C 630 325-1210
Fremont *(G-10175)*

Podnar Plastics Inc ....E 330 673-2255
Kent *(G-11501)*

Priority Custom Molding Inc ....F 937 431-8770
Beavercreek Township *(G-1389)*

R and S Technologies Inc ....F 419 483-3691
Bellevue *(G-1555)*

Sentry Protection LLC ....G 216 228-3200
Lakewood *(G-11679)*

Step2 Company LLC ....B 866 429-5200
Streetsboro *(G-17879)*

Step2 Company LLC ....B 419 938-6343
Perrysville *(G-16176)*

Sugar Showcase ....G 330 792-9154
Youngstown *(G-21213)*

Team Amity Molds & Plastic ....D 937 667-7856
Tipp City *(G-18303)*

Trilogy Plastics Inc ....C 330 821-4700
Alliance *(G-550)*

U S Development Corp ....E 330 673-6900
Kent *(G-11541)*

Vast Mold & Tool Co Inc ....G 440 942-7585
Mentor *(G-13765)*

P
R
O
D
U
C
T

Wch Molding LLC................E.....740 335-6320
  Wshngtn CT Hs (G-20928)
West Pharmaceutical Svcs Inc............G.....513 741-3004
  Cincinnati (G-4586)
Yanfeng US Automotive.............B.....419 636-4211
  Bryan (G-2328)
Ypf Corporation.............G.....330 743-6404
  Petersburg (G-16180)

PLASTICS: Polystyrene Foam

A K Athletic Equipment Inc.............E.....614 920-3069
  Canal Winchester (G-2518)
ADS Ventures Inc.............G.....614 658-0050
  Hilliard (G-10922)
ADS Worldwide Inc.............G.....614 658-0050
  Hilliard (G-10923)
Advanced Drainage Systems Inc............D.....614 658-0050
  Hilliard (G-10925)
Amatech Inc.............E.....614 252-2506
  Columbus (G-6729)
American Corrugated Pdts Inc............C.....614 870-2000
  Columbus (G-6735)
American Corrugated Pdts Inc............E.....800 248-6840
  Columbus (G-6736)
Aqua Lily Products LLC.............E.....480 588-6731
  Willoughby (G-20438)
Arkay Industries Inc.............E.....513 360-0390
  Monroe (G-14392)
Armaly LLC.............E.....740 852-3621
  London (G-12200)
Bentley World-Packaging Ltd............F.....440 232-1100
  Bedford (G-1407)
Contract Pckg Dist Specialists............F.....513 942-0300
  West Chester (G-19993)
Custom Foam Products Inc.............E.....937 295-2700
  Fort Loramie (G-9928)
Dayton Polymeric Products Inc............D.....937 279-9987
  Dayton (G-8282)
Dow Chemical Company.............C.....740 533-4000
  Ironton (G-11292)
Dow Chemical Company.............F.....937 254-1550
  Dayton (G-8309)
Extol of Ohio Inc.............E.....419 668-2072
  Norwalk (G-15538)
Gdc Inc.............F.....574 533-3128
  Wooster (G-20775)
Hfi LLC.............B.....614 491-0700
  Canal Winchester (G-2525)
ICP Adhesives and Sealants Inc............G.....330 753-4585
  Norton (G-15513)
Interior Dnnage Spcialites Inc............F.....614 291-0900
  Columbus (G-7203)
Jain America Foods Inc.............G.....614 850-9400
  Columbus (G-7222)
Jain America Holdings Inc............D.....614 850-9400
  Columbus (G-7223)
M L B Molded Urethane Pdts LLC............G.....419 825-9140
  Swanton (G-18086)
Myers Industries Inc.............E.....330 253-5592
  Akron (G-309)
Ohio Decorative Products LLC............C.....419 647-9033
  Spencerville (G-17463)
Ohio Foam Corporation.............G.....614 252-4877
  Columbus (G-7421)
Owens Corning Sales LLC.............C.....330 634-0460
  Tallmadge (G-18162)
Palpac Industries Inc.............F.....419 523-3230
  Ottawa (G-15803)
Paragon Custom Plastics Inc............E.....419 636-6060
  Bryan (G-2318)
Plastic Fabrication Svcs Inc............G.....440 953-9990
  Willoughby (G-20570)
Plastic Forming Company Inc............E.....330 830-5167
  Massillon (G-13194)
Plymouth Foam Incorporated............E.....740 254-1188
  Gnadenhutten (G-10410)
Polycel Incorporated.............E.....614 252-2400
  Columbus (G-7503)
Precision Foam Fabrication Inc............F.....330 270-2440
  Youngstown (G-21175)
Prime Industries Inc.............E.....440 288-3626
  Lorain (G-12268)
Protective Packg Solutions LLC............F.....513 769-5777
  Cincinnati (G-4299)
S & A Industries Corporation............D.....330 733-6040
  Akron (G-390)
Sash Foam Works Inc.............G.....419 522-4074
  Mansfield (G-12676)
Scott Port-A-Fold Inc.............E.....419 748-8880
  Napoleon (G-14698)

Smithers-Oasis Company.............F.....330 945-5100
  Kent (G-11528)
Smithers-Oasis Company.............F.....330 673-5831
  Kent (G-11529)
Solo Products Inc.............F.....513 321-7884
  Cincinnati (G-4435)
Sonoco Prtective Solutions Inc............D.....419 420-0029
  Findlay (G-9892)
Technifab Inc.............E.....440 934-8324
  Avon (G-1013)
Toy & Sport Trends Inc.............F.....419 748-8880
  Napoleon (G-14700)
Trans Foam Inc.............G.....330 630-9444
  Tallmadge (G-18173)
Unique-Chardan Inc.............G.....419 636-6900
  Bryan (G-2325)
US Foam Corporation.............G.....513 528-9800
  Cincinnati (G-4545)

PLASTICS: Protein

Hexa Americas Inc.............E.....937 497-7900
  Sidney (G-17192)

PLASTICS: Thermoformed

AMD Plastics LLC.............F.....216 289-4862
  Euclid (G-9565)
Arthur Corporation.............D.....419 433-7202
  Huron (G-11216)
Comdess Company Inc.............F.....330 769-2094
  Seville (G-17073)
Corvac Composites LLC.............G.....248 807-0969
  Greenfield (G-10475)
Creative Plastics Intl.............F.....937 596-6769
  Jackson Center (G-11338)
Fabri-Form Company.............D.....740 826-5000
  New Concord (G-14818)
First Choice Packaging Inc............C.....419 333-4100
  Fremont (G-10145)
Integral Design Inc.............F.....216 524-0555
  Cleveland (G-5574)
Kurz-Kasch Inc.............C.....740 498-8343
  Newcomerstown (G-15118)
Maverick Corporation.............F.....513 469-9919
  Blue Ash (G-1835)
Pendaform Company.............E.....740 826-5000
  New Concord (G-14819)
Pendaform Company.............G.....740 826-5000
  New Concord (G-14820)
Plastikos Corporation.............E.....513 732-0961
  Batavia (G-1216)
Premix Inc.............C.....440 224-2181
  North Kingsville (G-15304)
Progrssive Molding Bolivar Inc............C.....330 874-3000
  Bolivar (G-1944)
Replex Mirror Company.............E.....740 397-5535
  Mount Vernon (G-14641)
Rlr Industries Inc.............E.....440 951-9501
  Mentor (G-13716)
Rochling Glastic Composites LP............C.....216 486-0100
  Cleveland (G-6125)
Saint-Gobain Prfmce Plas Corp............C.....330 296-9948
  Ravenna (G-16554)
Saint-Gobain Prfmce Plas Corp............C.....440 836-6900
  Solon (G-17375)
Scott Molders Incorporated............D.....330 673-5777
  Kent (G-11524)
Springseal Inc.............F.....330 626-0673
  Ravenna (G-16560)
Thermoform Products LLC.............G.....330 686-2050
  Stow (G-17808)
Tooling Tech Holdings LLC.............G.....937 295-3672
  Fort Loramie (G-9942)

PLATE WORK: For Nuclear Industry

Curtiss-Wright Flow Control............D.....513 735-2538
  Batavia (G-1175)
Curtiss-Wright Flow Control............D.....513 528-7900
  Cincinnati (G-3296)

PLATE WORK: Metalworking Trade

Alloy Engineering Company............D.....440 243-6800
  Berea (G-1600)
Hard Chrome Plating Consultant............G.....216 631-9090
  Cleveland (G-5480)
Mark One Manufacturing Ltd............G.....419 628-4405
  Minster (G-14358)
Mercury Iron & Steel.............F.....440 349-1500
  Solon (G-17334)

Rezmann Karoly.............G.....216 441-4357
  Cleveland (G-6110)

PLATEMAKING SVC: Color Separations, For The Printing Trade

Carey Color Inc.............D.....330 239-1835
  Sharon Center (G-17103)
Carey Color Inc /cincinnati............E.....513 241-5210
  Cincinnati (G-3498)
Lazer Systems Inc.............F.....513 641-4002
  Cincinnati (G-4016)
Pinnacle Graphics & Imaging............F.....216 781-1800
  Cleveland (G-6008)
Registered Images Inc.............G.....859 781-9200
  Cincinnati (G-4335)
Stevenson Color Inc.............C.....513 321-7500
  Cincinnati (G-4466)

PLATEMAKING SVC: Embossing, For The Printing Trade

Acme Printing Co Inc.............G.....419 626-4426
  Sandusky (G-16944)

PLATENS, EXC PRINTERS': Rubber, Solid Or Covered

Tmac Machine Inc.............G.....330 673-0621
  Kent (G-11537)

PLATES

Amos Press Inc.............C.....937 498-2111
  Sidney (G-17168)
Anderson & Vreeland Inc.............D.....419 636-5002
  Bryan (G-2278)
Art-American Printing Plates............E.....216 241-4420
  Cleveland (G-4836)
Bock & Pierce Enterprises............G.....513 474-9500
  Cincinnati (G-3455)
Centec Cast Metal Products............G.....419 355-1414
  Fremont (G-10135)
Century Graphics Inc.............E.....614 895-7698
  Westerville (G-20142)
Csw of Ny Inc.............F.....413 589-1311
  Sylvania (G-18102)
Custom Cntrwght Plate Proc Inc............G.....330 448-2347
  Masury (G-13214)
Customer Service Systems Inc............G.....330 677-2877
  Kent (G-11442)
Dorothy Crooker.............G.....513 385-0888
  Cincinnati (G-3665)
E C Shaw Co.............E.....513 721-6334
  Cincinnati (G-3677)
Earl D Arnold Printing Company............E.....513 533-6900
  Cincinnati (G-3685)
Econo Products Inc.............F.....330 923-4101
  Cuyahoga Falls (G-7989)
Fine Lines Laser Engraving............G.....419 337-6313
  Wauseon (G-19677)
Flexoplate Inc.............E.....513 489-0433
  Blue Ash (G-1796)
Grant John.............G.....937 298-0633
  Dayton (G-8376)
Hadronics Inc.............D.....513 321-9350
  Cincinnati (G-3861)
Harris Paper Crafts Inc.............F.....614 299-2141
  Columbus (G-7145)
Jerry Pulfer.............G.....937 778-1861
  Piqua (G-16283)
Keystone Press Inc.............G.....419 243-7326
  Toledo (G-18544)
Mark-All Enterprises LLC.............E.....800 433-3615
  Akron (G-284)
Master Marking Company Inc............F.....330 688-6797
  Stow (G-17772)
Penguin Enterprises Inc.............E.....440 899-5110
  Westlake (G-20292)
Prime Printing Inc.............E.....937 438-3707
  Dayton (G-8594)
Quality Rubber Stamp Inc.............G.....614 235-2700
  Columbus (G-7536)
R W Michael Printing Co.............G.....330 923-9277
  Akron (G-363)
Robert H Shackelford.............G.....330 364-2221
  New Philadelphia (G-14926)
Shamrock Plastics Inc.............F.....740 392-5555
  Mount Vernon (G-14646)
Springfield Engraving Company............G.....937 390-0011
  Springfield (G-17651)

Universal Urethane Pdts Inc ....D...... 419 693-7400
Toledo *(G-18760)*
West-Camp Press Inc ....D...... 614 818-6279
Westerville *(G-20241)*
Westrock CP LLC ....C...... 937 898-2115
Dayton *(G-8754)*
Williams Steel Rule Die Co ....F...... 216 431-3232
Cleveland *(G-6464)*
Wood Graphics Inc ....E...... 513 771-6300
Cincinnati *(G-4603)*

PLATES: Paper, Made From Purchased Materials

Premier Industries Inc ....E...... 513 271-2550
Cincinnati *(G-4266)*
Taylor Company ....G...... 513 271-2550
Cincinnati *(G-4496)*

PLATES: Plastic Exc Polystyrene Foam

Zehrco-Giancola Composites Inc........C...... 440 994-6317
Ashtabula *(G-847)*

PLATES: Sheet & Strip, Exc Coated Prdts

Major Metals Company ....E...... 419 886-4600
Mansfield *(G-12639)*
The Florand Company ....E...... 330 747-8986
Youngstown *(G-21219)*

PLATES: Steel

Adams Fabricating Inc ....G...... 330 866-2986
East Sparta *(G-9253)*
American Mfg & Engrg Co ....G...... 440 899-9400
Cleveland *(G-4791)*
Charles C Lewis Company ....F...... 440 439-3150
Cleveland *(G-5015)*
Churchill Steel Plate Ltd ....E...... 330 425-9000
Twinsburg *(G-18913)*
J&J Precision Fabricators.............F...... 330 482-4964
Columbiana *(G-6623)*

PLATING & FINISHING SVC: Decorative, Formed Prdts

Mechanical Finishers Inc LLC ....E...... 513 641-5419
Cincinnati *(G-4074)*

PLATING & POLISHING SVC

A J Oster Foils LLC..................D...... 330 823-1700
Alliance *(G-486)*
A-Brite LP ....D...... 216 252-2995
Cleveland *(G-4680)*
Ak-Isg Steel Coating Company..........D...... 216 429-6901
Cleveland *(G-4739)*
Allegheny Ludlum LLC ....E...... 330 875-2244
Louisville *(G-12308)*
Allen Aircraft Products Inc ....E...... 330 296-9621
Ravenna *(G-16514)*
Aluminum Extruded Shapes Inc..........C...... 513 563-2205
Cincinnati *(G-3383)*
Arcelormittal Columbus LLC ....C...... 614 492-6800
Columbus *(G-6768)*
Arem Co ....F...... 440 974-6740
Mentor *(G-13526)*
Bmd Blasting ....G...... 614 580-9468
Columbus *(G-6841)*
Carlisle and Finch Company ....E...... 513 681-6080
Cincinnati *(G-3502)*
Carter Machine Company Inc ....G...... 419 468-3530
Galion *(G-10256)*
Chemical Methods Inc ....E...... 216 476-8400
Strongsville *(G-17901)*
Cincinnati Gearing Systems Inc ....D...... 513 527-8600
Cincinnati *(G-3552)*
Classic Evolution Inc................G...... 216 440-0559
Medina *(G-13388)*
Columbus Coatings Company ....D...... 614 492-6800
Columbus *(G-6949)*
Commercial Honing LLC ....D...... 330 343-8896
Dover *(G-8971)*
Commercial Steel Treating Co ....F...... 216 431-8204
Cleveland *(G-5105)*
Crystal Koch Finishing Inc ....G...... 440 366-7526
Elyria *(G-9399)*
D-G Custom Chrome LLC ....D...... 513 531-1881
Cincinnati *(G-3634)*
Davro Ltd ....G...... 216 258-0057
Cleveland *(G-5171)*

Die Co Inc ....E...... 440 942-8856
Eastlake *(G-9265)*
E L Stone Company ....E...... 330 825-4565
Norton *(G-15510)*
Electro Prime Group LLC ....D...... 419 476-0100
Toledo *(G-18453)*
Electro Prime Group LLC ....D...... 419 666-5000
Rossford *(G-16739)*
Emerson Electric Co ....E...... 513 631-6112
Cincinnati *(G-3697)*
Etched Metal Company ....E...... 440 248-0240
Solon *(G-17290)*
Fastenal Company ....G...... 330 745-2996
Akron *(G-182)*
Future Finishes Inc ....E...... 513 860-0020
Hamilton *(G-10693)*
GRB Holdings Inc ....D...... 937 236-3250
Dayton *(G-8377)*
Hadronics Inc ....E...... 513 321-9350
Cincinnati *(G-3861)*
Hall Company ....E...... 937 652-1376
Urbana *(G-19160)*
Hartzell Manufacturing Co Inc ....E...... 937 859-5955
Miamisburg *(G-13815)*
Hercules Polishing & Plating ....F...... 330 455-8871
Canton *(G-2726)*
Highland Precision Plating ....G...... 937 393-9501
Hillsboro *(G-11002)*
J Horst Manufacturing Co ....D...... 330 828-2216
Dalton *(G-8072)*
J M Hamilton Group Inc ....F...... 419 229-4010
Lima *(G-12032)*
Jason Incorporated...................F...... 513 860-3400
Hamilton *(G-10711)*
Luke Engineering & Mfg Corp ....E...... 330 925-3344
Rittman *(G-16679)*
McGean-Rohco Inc ....D...... 216 441-4900
Newburgh Heights *(G-15076)*
Mechanical Finishing Inc ....E...... 513 641-5419
Cincinnati *(G-4075)*
Metal Improvement Company LLC........E...... 513 489-6484
Blue Ash *(G-1838)*
Metokote Corporation ....D...... 440 934-4686
Sheffield Village *(G-17127)*
Metokote Corporation ....C...... 419 221-2754
Lima *(G-12057)*
Micro Lapping & Grinding Co ....E...... 216 267-6500
Cleveland *(G-5798)*
Micro Products Co Inc ....D...... 440 943-0258
Willoughby Hills *(G-20641)*
Milestone Services Corp ....G...... 330 374-9988
Akron *(G-298)*
MPC Plastics Inc ....D...... 216 881-7220
Cleveland *(G-5835)*
Niles Manufacturing & Finshg ....C...... 330 544-0402
Niles *(G-15171)*
Ohio Decorative Products LLC..........C...... 419 647-9033
Spencerville *(G-17463)*
Ohio Metal Products Company ....E...... 937 228-6101
Dayton *(G-8545)*
Ohio Metalizing LLC ....G...... 330 830-1092
Massillon *(G-13185)*
Ohio Roll Grinding Inc ....E...... 330 453-1884
Louisville *(G-12322)*
Oliver Chemical Co Inc ....G...... 513 541-4540
Cincinnati *(G-4185)*
P & J Industries Inc.................C...... 419 726-2675
Toledo *(G-18629)*
P & L Heat Trting Grinding Inc ....E...... 330 746-1339
Youngstown *(G-21159)*
Parker Rst-Proof Cleveland Inc ....E...... 216 481-6680
Cleveland *(G-5972)*
Parker Trutec Incorporated ....D...... 937 653-8500
Urbana *(G-19172)*
Phoenix Technologies Inc ....F...... 330 630-5888
Akron *(G-338)*
Plating Resources Supply ....G...... 330 908-3949
Macedonia *(G-12475)*
Rack Processing Company Inc ....G...... 937 294-1911
Moraine *(G-14522)*
Rack Processing Company Inc ....E...... 937 294-1911
Moraine *(G-14521)*
Reifel Industries Inc................D...... 419 737-2138
Pioneer *(G-16244)*
Rite Way Black & Deburr Inc ....G...... 937 224-7762
Dayton *(G-8632)*
Samuel Steel Pickling Company ....E...... 330 963-3777
Twinsburg *(G-19016)*
Sawyer Technical Materials LLC ....E...... 440 951-8770
Willoughby *(G-20591)*

Scot Industries Inc ....E...... 330 262-7585
Wooster *(G-20832)*
Springco Metal Coatings Inc...........C...... 216 251-7023
Cleveland *(G-6228)*
Super Fine Shine Inc ....G...... 740 774-1700
Chillicothe *(G-3279)*
Teikuro Corporation ....D...... 937 327-3955
Springfield *(G-17662)*
Tri-State Fabricators Inc............E...... 513 752-5005
Amelia *(G-587)*
Vacuum Finishing Company ....F...... 440 286-4386
Chardon *(G-3182)*
Vectron Inc ....D...... 440 323-3369
Elyria *(G-9507)*
Whitaker Finishing LLC ....E...... 419 666-7746
Northwood *(G-15496)*
Whitaker Surface Systems ....E...... 419 874-1211
Northwood *(G-15497)*
Worthington Industries Inc ....C...... 513 539-9291
Monroe *(G-14420)*
Worthington Steel Company ....C...... 614 438-3210
Worthington *(G-20900)*
Worthngton Stl Cmpny-Baltimore ....E...... 410 574-5835
Worthington *(G-20901)*
Yoder Industries Inc ....C...... 937 278-5769
Dayton *(G-8766)*

PLATING COMPOUNDS

Pazco Inc ....E...... 216 447-9581
Cleveland *(G-5982)*
Plating Process Systems Inc ....G...... 440 951-9667
Mentor *(G-13689)*
Rotech Products Incorporated ....G...... 216 476-3722
Cleveland *(G-6135)*
Surtec ....G...... 440 239-9710
Brunswick *(G-2259)*

PLATING SVC: Chromium, Metals Or Formed Prdts

B & R Custom Chrome ....G...... 419 536-7215
Toledo *(G-18362)*
Chromatic Inc ....F...... 216 881-2228
Cleveland *(G-5031)*
Chrome Deposit Corporation ....E...... 513 539-8486
Monroe *(G-14395)*
Chrome Deposit Corporation ....E...... 513 539-8486
Monroe *(G-14396)*
Chrome Industries Inc ....G...... 216 771-2266
Cleveland *(G-5032)*
Customchrome Plating Inc ....F...... 440 926-3116
Grafton *(G-10423)*
Ernie Green Industries Inc ....G...... 614 219-1423
Columbus *(G-7064)*
Hale Performance Coatings Inc ....E...... 419 244-6451
Toledo *(G-18494)*
Master Chrome Service Inc ....E...... 216 961-2012
Cleveland *(G-5756)*
MPC Plating Inc ....E...... 216 881-7220
Cleveland *(G-5837)*
Plate-All Metal Company Inc ....G...... 330 633-6166
Akron *(G-342)*
Porter-Guertin Co Inc ....F...... 513 241-7663
Cincinnati *(G-4251)*
Quality Plating Co ....E...... 216 361-0151
Cleveland *(G-6072)*
R A Heller Company ....F...... 513 771-6100
Cincinnati *(G-4322)*
Raf Acquisition Co ....F...... 440 572-5999
Valley City *(G-19227)*
United Surface Finishing Inc ....G...... 330 453-2786
Canton *(G-2889)*
Youngstown Hard Chrome Plating........E...... 330 758-9721
Youngstown *(G-21252)*

PLATING SVC: Electro

Aetna Plating Co ....F...... 216 341-9111
Cleveland *(G-4726)*
Akron Plating Co Inc ....F...... 330 773-6878
Akron *(G-51)*
American Metal Coatings Inc...........E...... 216 451-3131
Cleveland *(G-4788)*
Barker Products Company ....E...... 216 249-0900
Cleveland *(G-4891)*
Beringer Plating Inc ....G...... 330 633-8409
Akron *(G-88)*
Bricker Plating Inc ....G...... 419 636-1990
Bryan *(G-2285)*
Canton Plating Co Inc ....G...... 330 452-7808
Canton *(G-2646)*

P R O D U C T

Delta Plating Inc.............................E....... 330 452-2300
Canton (G-2684)
Electro-Metallics Co..........................G....... 513 423-8091
Middletown (G-14039)
Elyria Plating Corporation.................E....... 440 365-8300
Elyria (G-9416)
Epd Enterprises Inc...........................D....... 216 961-1200
Cleveland (G-5289)
Erieview Metal Treating Co................D....... 216 663-1780
Cleveland (G-5298)
Kelly Plating Co..................................E....... 216 961-1080
Cleveland (G-5643)
Leonhardt Plating Company...............E....... 513 242-1410
Cincinnati (G-4020)
Medina Plating Corp...........................E....... 330 725-4155
Medina (G-13443)
MPC Plating Inc..................................E....... 216 881-7220
Cleveland (G-5836)
Novavision Inc....................................D....... 419 354-1427
Bowling Green (G-2003)
Ohio Electro-Polishing Co Inc............G....... 419 667-2281
Venedocia (G-19322)
Plastic Platers LLC.............................C....... 216 961-1200
Cleveland (G-6013)
Plating Technology Inc.......................D....... 937 268-6882
Dayton (G-8578)
Precious Metal Plating Co...................E....... 440 585-7117
Wickliffe (G-20384)
Roberts-Demand Corp.........................G....... 216 581-1300
Cleveland (G-6122)
Rykon Plating Inc................................G....... 440 933-3273
Avon Lake (G-1049)
Smith Electro Chemical Co..................E....... 513 351-7227
Cincinnati (G-4430)
Springfield Metal Finishing.................G....... 937 324-2353
Springfield (G-17652)
Techniplate Inc...................................F....... 216 486-8825
Cleveland (G-6301)
U S Chrome Corporation Ohio..............F....... 937 224-0548
Dayton (G-8736)
United Hard Chrome Corporation.........F....... 330 453-2786
Canton (G-2887)

PLATING SVC: NEC

Best Plating Rack Corp........................F....... 440 944-3270
Wickliffe (G-20358)
Bron-Shoe Company............................E....... 614 252-0967
Columbus (G-6867)
Cascade Plating Inc.............................G....... 440 366-4931
Elyria (G-9389)
Case Plating Inc..................................G....... 440 288-8304
Lorain (G-12237)
Cleveland Plating................................G....... 216 249-0300
Cleveland (G-5072)
Custom Brass Finishing Inc..................G....... 330 453-0888
Canton (G-2673)
Durable Plating Co..............................G....... 216 391-2132
Cleveland (G-5223)
Engineering Coatings LLC.....................G....... 419 485-0077
Montpelier (G-14446)
Hearn Plating Co Ltd...........................F....... 419 473-9773
Toledo (G-18499)
Kyron Plating Corp..............................F....... 216 221-7275
Cleveland (G-5668)
Lake County Plating Corp......................F....... 440 255-8835
Mentor (G-13627)
Lakeside Custom Plating Inc.................G....... 440 599-2035
Conneaut (G-7812)
Lustrous Metal Coatings Inc..................E....... 330 478-4653
Canton (G-2760)
M&L Plating Works LLC.........................G....... 419 255-7701
Toledo (G-18568)
Mechanical Galv-Plating Corp...............E....... 937 492-3143
Sidney (G-17200)
Metal Brite Polishing............................F....... 937 278-9739
Dayton (G-8486)
Mmf Incorporated................................F....... 614 252-2522
Columbus (G-7358)
Mmf Incorporated................................F....... 614 252-2522
Columbus (G-7359)
Moore Chrome Products Co....................E....... 419 843-3510
Sylvania (G-18119)
Nicks Plating Co Inc.............................F....... 937 773-3175
Piqua (G-16294)
Nuclear Plating Service Inc...................E....... 216 641-1109
Brecksville (G-2068)
Paxos Plating Inc.................................E....... 330 479-0022
Canton (G-2810)
Plating Perceptions Inc.........................G....... 330 425-4180
Twinsburg (G-19002)

Plating Solutions.................................G....... 513 771-1941
Cincinnati (G-4244)
Plating Technology Inc.........................F....... 937 268-6788
Dayton (G-8579)
Rawac Plating Company........................E....... 937 322-7491
Springfield (G-17635)
Sebring Industrial Plating......................G....... 330 938-6666
Sebring (G-17054)
Tubetech Inc..E....... 330 426-9476
East Palestine (G-9247)
United State Pltg Bumper Svc.................G....... 614 403-4666
Worthington (G-20892)

PLAYGROUND EQPT

Adventurous Child Inc...........................G....... 513 531-7700
Cincinnati (G-3361)
Charles V Snider & Assoc Inc..................F....... 440 877-9151
North Royalton (G-15414)
Funtown Playgrounds Inc.......................E....... 513 871-8585
Cincinnati (G-3303)
Meyer Design Inc..................................G....... 330 434-9176
Akron (G-296)
Playground Equipment Service................G....... 513 481-3776
Cincinnati (G-4245)
Ultrabuilt Play Systems Inc.....................F....... 419 652-2294
Nova (G-15580)

PLEATING & STITCHING FOR THE TRADE: Decorative & Novelty

Ideal Drapery Company Inc.....................F....... 330 745-9873
Barberton (G-1121)
Initially Yours......................................G....... 216 228-4478
Lakewood (G-11669)

PLEATING & STITCHING SVC

A Graphic Solution................................F....... 216 228-7223
Cleveland (G-4672)
Action Sports Apparel Inc.......................G....... 330 848-9300
Norton (G-15503)
Aubrey Rose Apparel LLC........................G....... 513 728-2681
Cincinnati (G-3428)
Barbs Graffiti Inc..................................E....... 216 881-5550
Cleveland (G-4889)
Big Kahuna Graphics Inc.........................G....... 330 455-2625
Canton (G-2622)
Catania Medallic Specialty.......................E....... 440 933-9595
Avon Lake (G-1026)
David Brandeberry.................................G....... 937 653-4680
Urbana (G-19156)
Design Original Inc................................F....... 937 596-5121
Jackson Center (G-11339)
Dimensions Three Inc.............................G....... 614 539-5180
Grove City (G-10554)
Fine Line Embroidery Company.................G....... 330 788-9070
Youngstown (G-21084)
Fineline Imprints Inc..............................E....... 740 453-1083
Zanesville (G-21308)
Finn Graphics Inc..................................G....... 513 941-6161
Cincinnati (G-3756)
Logan Screen Printing.............................G....... 740 385-3303
Logan (G-12185)
Robs Creative Screen Printing...................G....... 740 264-6383
Wintersville (G-20713)
Shamrock Companies Inc.........................D....... 440 899-9510
Westlake (G-20308)
Wizard Graphics Inc...............................G....... 419 354-3098
Bowling Green (G-2021)
Writely Sew LLC.....................................G....... 513 728-2682
Cincinnati (G-4609)

PLUMBERS' GOODS: Rubber

Deruijter Intl USA Inc..............................F....... 419 678-3909
Coldwater (G-6556)

PLUMBING & HEATING EQPT & SPLY, WHOL: Htg Eqpt/Panels, Solar

Hess Advanced Solutions Llc....................G....... 937 829-4794
Dayton (G-8389)
Hunters Hightech Energy Systm................G....... 614 275-4777
Columbus (G-7171)

PLUMBING & HEATING EQPT & SPLY, WHOLESALE: Hydronic Htg Eqpt

Accurate Mechanical Inc..........................E....... 740 654-5898
Lancaster (G-11683)

PLUMBING & HEATING EQPT & SPLYS WHOLESALERS

Carr Supply Co......................................G....... 937 276-2555
Dayton (G-8211)
Carter-Jones Lumber Company..................F....... 440 834-8164
Middlefield (G-13920)
Clean Water Conditioning........................G....... 614 475-4532
Columbus (G-6935)
Famous Industries Inc............................E....... 330 535-1811
Akron (G-181)
Savko Plastic Pipe & Fittings...................F....... 614 885-8420
Columbus (G-7591)
Trumbull Industries Inc..........................E....... 330 434-6174
Akron (G-448)
Trumbull Manufacturing Inc....................D....... 330 393-6624
Warren (G-19614)
US Water Company LLC...........................G....... 740 453-0604
Zanesville (G-21360)
W A S P Inc...G....... 740 439-2398
Cambridge (G-2482)
Waxman Industries Inc...........................C....... 440 439-1830
Cleveland (G-6452)
Wc Sales Inc...G....... 419 836-2300
Northwood (G-15494)
Zurn Industries LLC...............................F....... 814 455-0921
Hilliard (G-10994)

PLUMBING & HEATING EQPT & SPLYS, WHOL: Fireplaces, Prefab

Mason Structural Steel Inc.......................D....... 440 439-1040
Walton Hills (G-19474)

PLUMBING & HEATING EQPT & SPLYS, WHOL: Pipe/Fitting, Plastic

Cleveland Plastic Fabricat.......................F....... 216 797-7300
Euclid (G-9572)
Ppafco Inc..F....... 614 488-7259
Columbus (G-7507)

PLUMBING & HEATING EQPT & SPLYS, WHOL: Plumbing Fitting/Sply

Carr Supply Co......................................G....... 937 316-6300
Greenville (G-10492)
Columbus Pipe and Equipment Co............F....... 614 444-7871
Columbus (G-6962)
Empire Brass Co....................................E....... 216 431-6565
Cleveland (G-5276)
Famous Realty Cleveland Inc...................F....... 740 685-2533
Byesville (G-2402)
Ferguson Fire Fabrication Inc...................F....... 614 299-2070
Columbus (G-7081)
Mansfield Plumbing Pdts LLC...................A....... 419 938-5211
Perrysville (G-16173)
Parker-Hannifin Corporation....................B....... 937 456-5571
Eaton (G-9320)
Parker-Hannifin Corporation....................F....... 614 279-7070
Columbus (G-7462)
Winsupply Inc..F....... 937 346-0600
Springfield (G-17679)
Zekelman Industries Inc..........................C....... 740 432-2146
Cambridge (G-2483)

PLUMBING & HEATING EQPT & SPLYS, WHOL: Plumbng/Heatng Valves

Maverick Industries Inc...........................F....... 440 838-5335
Brecksville (G-2064)

PLUMBING & HEATING EQPT & SPLYS, WHOL: Water Purif Eqpt

Chandler Systems Incorporated.................D....... 419 281-5767
Ashland (G-721)
Enting Water Conditioning Inc...................E....... 937 294-5100
Moraine (G-14484)
Pelton Environmental Pdts Inc...................G....... 440 838-1221
Lewis Center (G-11909)
Wayne/Scott Fetzer Company....................C....... 800 237-0987
Harrison (G-10811)

PLUMBING & HEATING EQPT, WHOLESALE: Water Heaters/Purif

Mountain Filtration Systems.....................G....... 419 395-2526
Defiance (G-8806)

(G-0000) Company's Geographic Section entry number

PLUMBING FIXTURES

As America Inc ....C 614 497-9384
  Groveport (G-10614)
As America Inc ....G 330 337-2219
  Salem (G-16873)
As America Inc ....G 615 873-2410
  Mansfield (G-12563)
Atlantic Co ....E 440 944-8988
  Willoughby Hills (G-20637)
Carr Supply Co ....G 937 316-6300
  Greenville (G-10492)
Carr Supply Co ....G 937 276-2555
  Dayton (G-8211)
Cfrc Wtr & Enrgy Solutions Inc ....G 216 479-0290
  Cleveland (G-5011)
CMI Holding Company Crawford ....D 419 468-9122
  Galion (G-10259)
Dittmar Sales and Service ....G 740 653-7933
  Lancaster (G-11709)
Empire Brass Co ....E 216 431-6565
  Cleveland (G-5276)
Field Stone Inc ....D 937 898-3236
  Tipp City (G-18277)
Fort Recovery Industries Inc ....C 419 375-4121
  Fort Recovery (G-9951)
Fort Recovery Industries Inc ....E 419 375-3005
  Fort Recovery (G-9952)
Krendl Machine Company ....D 419 692-3060
  Delphos (G-8910)
Lsq Manufacturing Inc ....F 330 725-4905
  Medina (G-13437)
Maass Midwest Mfg Inc ....G 419 894-6424
  Arcadia (G-654)
Mansfield Plumbing Pdts LLC ....A 419 938-5211
  Perrysville (G-16173)
Next Gerenation Crimping ....G 440 237-6300
  North Royalton (G-15437)
Scotts Miracle-Gro Products ....F 937 644-0011
  Marysville (G-12970)
Trumbull Manufacturing Inc ....D 330 393-6624
  Warren (G-19614)
W A S P Inc ....E 740 439-2398
  Cambridge (G-2482)
Waxman Industries Inc ....C 440 439-1830
  Cleveland (G-6452)
Winsupply Inc ....F 937 346-0600
  Springfield (G-17679)
Zekelman Industries Inc ....C 740 432-2146
  Cambridge (G-2483)

PLUMBING FIXTURES: Brass, Incl Drain Cocks, Faucets/Spigots

American Brass Manufacturing ....E 216 431-6565
  Cleveland (G-4778)
National Brass Company Inc ....G 216 651-8530
  Cleveland (G-5854)

PLUMBING FIXTURES: Plastic

Add-A-Trap LLC ....G 330 750-0417
  Struthers (G-17988)
Bobbart Industries Inc ....E 419 350-5477
  Sylvania (G-18101)
Carolina Color Corporation ....E 740 363-6622
  Delaware (G-8828)
Certified Walk In Tubs ....F 614 436-4848
  Columbus (G-6921)
Cincinnati Machines Inc ....A 513 536-2432
  Batavia (G-1172)
Cultured Marble Inc ....G 330 549-2282
  North Lima (G-15314)
Dbhl Inc ....F 216 267-7100
  Cleveland (G-5176)
E L Mustee & Sons Inc ....D 216 267-3100
  Brookpark (G-2158)
Hancor Inc ....B 614 658-0050
  Hilliard (G-10950)
Lubrizol Advanced Mtls Inc ....F 216 447-5000
  Brecksville (G-2061)
Mansfield Plumbing Pdts LLC ....E 330 496-2301
  Big Prairie (G-1682)
Mansfield Plumbing Pdts LLC ....A 419 938-5211
  Perrysville (G-16173)
Marble Arch Products Inc ....F 937 746-8388
  Franklin (G-10034)
Meese Inc ....D 440 998-1202
  Ashtabula (G-819)
Nibco Inc ....E 513 228-1426
  Lebanon (G-11819)

Righter Plumbing ....G 614 604-7197
  Pataskala (G-15980)
Tower Industries Ltd ....E 330 837-2216
  Massillon (G-13207)

PLUMBING FIXTURES: Vitreous

Aabel Plumbing Inc ....E 937 434-4343
  Dayton (G-8127)
Accent Manufacturing Inc ....F 330 724-7704
  Norton (G-15500)
As America Inc ....G 330 337-2219
  Salem (G-16873)
As America Inc ....G 615 873-2410
  Mansfield (G-12563)
East Woodworking Company ....G 216 791-5950
  Cleveland (G-5240)
Mansfield Plumbing Pdts LLC ....A 419 938-5211
  Perrysville (G-16173)

PLUMBING FIXTURES: Vitreous China

Crane Plumbing LLC ....E 419 522-4211
  Mansfield (G-12587)

POINT OF SALE DEVICES

A & M Creative Group Inc ....E 330 452-8940
  Canton (G-2584)
J3 Systems Ltd ....G 419 562-5522
  Bucyrus (G-2351)
Outta Box Dispensers LLC ....G 937 221-7106
  Dayton (G-8556)
Puddle Shark Studios Inc ....G 440 286-2811
  Chardon (G-3173)

POLE LINE HARDWARE

Helical Line Products Co ....E 440 933-9263
  Avon Lake (G-1032)
Preformed Line Products Co ....C 440 461-5200
  Mayfield Village (G-13324)

POLICE PROTECTION

Public Safety Ohio Department ....G 440 943-5545
  Willowick (G-20650)

POLISHING SVC: Metals Or Formed Prdts

A & B Deburring Company ....F 513 723-0777
  Cincinnati (G-3328)
Aircraft Plating Corp ....E 216 781-5845
  Cleveland (G-4737)
Als Polishing Shop Inc ....G 419 476-8857
  Toledo (G-18332)
Areway Acquisition Inc ....D 216 651-9022
  Brooklyn (G-2127)
Century Plating Inc ....G 216 531-4131
  Cleveland (G-5007)
Charles J Meyers ....E 513 922-2866
  Cincinnati (G-3523)
Custom Polishing ....G 937 596-0430
  Sidney (G-17173)
Dayton United Metal Spinners ....F 937 222-6732
  Tipp City (G-18275)
Euclid Refinishing Compnay Inc ....F 440 275-3356
  Austinburg (G-960)
Faithful Mold Polishing Ex ....G 330 678-8006
  Kent (G-11458)
Finishers Inc ....G 937 773-3177
  Piqua (G-16264)
Gei of Columbiana Inc ....D 330 783-0270
  Youngstown (G-21094)
General Extrusions Inc ....D 330 783-0270
  Youngstown (G-21096)
Hy-Blast Inc ....F 513 424-0704
  Middletown (G-14045)
Indigo 48 LLC ....G 419 551-6931
  Bryan (G-2304)
Kellys Polishing Metal Finshg ....G 440 232-8800
  Bedford (G-1436)
McCrary Metal Polishing Inc ....E 937 492-1979
  Port Jefferson (G-16420)
Miami Valley Polishing ....F 937 615-9353
  Piqua (G-16292)
Miami Valley Polishing LL ....G 937 498-1634
  Sidney (G-17203)
Microsheen Corporation ....F 216 481-5610
  Cleveland (G-5801)
Microtek Finishing LLC ....E 513 766-5600
  West Chester (G-20029)

P & C Metal Polishing Inc ....E 513 771-9143
  Cincinnati (G-4206)
Shalmet Corporation ....G 440 236-8840
  Elyria (G-9492)
Sun Polishing Corp ....G 440 237-5525
  Cleveland (G-6263)
Tuckers Mold Polishing ....G 937 339-3063
  Troy (G-18883)
Wall Polishing LLC ....G 937 698-1330
  Ludlow Falls (G-12429)

POLYESTERS

E I Du Pont De Nemours & Co ....E 740 474-0220
  Circleville (G-4627)
Illinois Tool Works Inc ....C 513 489-7600
  Blue Ash (G-1812)
Maintenance Repair Supply Inc ....E 740 922-3006
  Midvale (G-14109)
Mar-Bal Inc ....D 440 543-7526
  Chagrin Falls (G-3101)
Mar-Bal Inc ....D 440 543-7526
  Chagrin Falls (G-3102)
Pet Processors LLc ....D 440 354-4321
  Painesville (G-15911)

POLYETHYLENE CHLOROSULFONATED RUBBER

Lyondell Chemical Company ....D 513 530-4000
  Cincinnati (G-4042)

POLYETHYLENE RESINS

Composite Technical Svcs LLC ....G 937 660-3783
  Kettering (G-11578)
Etna Products Incorporated ....E 440 543-9845
  Chagrin Falls (G-3087)
Pitt Plastics Inc ....D 614 868-8660
  Columbus (G-7486)

POLYMETHYL METHACRYLATE RESINS: Plexiglas

Mexichem Specialty Resins Inc ....E 440 930-1435
  Avon Lake (G-1040)
Pf Polymers LLC ....E 567 712-7046
  Lima (G-12069)

POLYPROPYLENE RESINS

Pahuja Inc ....D 614 864-3989
  Gahanna (G-10225)

POLYSTYRENE RESINS

Americas Styrenics LLC ....D 740 533-4017
  Hanging Rock (G-10761)
Deltech Polymers Corporation ....G 937 339-3150
  Troy (G-18817)
Eps Specialties Ltd Inc ....F 513 489-3676
  Cincinnati (G-3714)
Nova Chemicals Inc ....D 440 352-3381
  Painesville (G-15904)
Progressive Foam Tech Inc ....C 330 756-3200
  Beach City (G-1250)
Queen City Foam Inc ....G 513 741-7722
  Cincinnati (G-4315)

POLYTETRAFLUOROETHYLENE RESINS

Crg Plastics Inc ....F 937 298-2025
  Dayton (G-8251)

POLYURETHANE RESINS

Hfi LLC ....B 614 491-0700
  Canal Winchester (G-2525)
Hfi Manufacturing Holdings LLC ....G 614 491-0700
  Canal Winchester (G-2528)
Louisville Molded Products ....G 330 877-9740
  Hartville (G-10829)
Polymer Concepts Inc ....G 440 953-9605
  Mentor (G-13693)

POLYVINYL CHLORIDE RESINS

Aurora Plastics Inc ....D 330 422-0700
  Streetsboro (G-17840)
Crane Blending Center ....E 614 542-1199
  Columbus (G-6997)
Kirtland Cpitl Partners III LP ....G 440 585-9010
  Willoughby Hills (G-20640)

Liberty Plastics LLC ....G...... 330 627-6677
Carrollton (G-2960)
Prime Conduit Inc ....F...... 216 464-3400
Cleveland (G-6046)

POLYVINYLIDENE CHLORIDE RESINS

Great Lakes Textiles Inc ....E...... 440 439-1300
Solon (G-17304)

PONTOONS: Rubber

Survitec Group (usa) Inc ....E...... 330 239-4331
Sharon Center (G-17111)

POSTERS, WHOLESALE

Posterservice Incorporated ....E...... 513 577-7100
Cincinnati (G-4254)

POSTS: Floor, Adjustable, Metal

Gwp Holdings Inc ....D...... 513 860-4050
Fairfield (G-9662)

POTPOURRI

Rose of Sharon Enterprises ....G...... 937 862-4543
Waynesville (G-19735)

POTTERY

All Fired Up Pnt Your Own Pot ....G...... 330 865-5858
Copley (G-7839)
Bosco Pup Co LLC ....G...... 614 833-0349
Pickerington (G-16187)
Javanation ....F...... 419 584-1705
Celina (G-3003)
Mad Potter LLC ....G...... 513 770-5585
Mason (G-13057)
Yellow Springs Pottery ....F...... 937 767-1666
Yellow Springs (G-21002)

POTTING SOILS

Garick LLC ....E...... 216 581-0100
Cleveland (G-5398)
Roe Transportation Entps Inc ....G...... 937 497-7161
Sidney (G-17217)

POULTRY & POULTRY PRDTS WHOLESALERS

Borden Dairy Co Cincinnati LLC ....C...... 513 948-8811
Cincinnati (G-3461)
Just Natural Provision Company ....G...... 216 431-7922
Cleveland (G-5626)
Koch Meat Co Inc ....B...... 513 874-3500
Fairfield (G-9674)
Roots Poultry Inc ....F...... 419 332-0041
Fremont (G-10180)

POULTRY & SMALL GAME SLAUGHTERING & PROCESSING

Cal-Maine Foods Inc ....E...... 937 337-9576
Rossburg (G-16735)
Cooper Foods ....E...... 419 232-2440
Van Wert (G-19250)
Cooper Hatchery Inc ....C...... 419 238-4869
Van Wert (G-19251)
Kings Command Foods LLC ....D...... 937 526-3553
Versailles (G-19350)
Koch Meat Co Inc ....B...... 513 874-3500
Fairfield (G-9674)
Ohio Fresh Eggs LLC ....E...... 937 354-2233
Mount Victory (G-14657)
Weaver Bros Inc ....D...... 937 526-3907
Versailles (G-19360)

POULTRY SLAUGHTERING & PROCESSING

Case Farms of Ohio Inc ....C...... 330 359-7141
Winesburg (G-20702)
Case Farms of Ohio Inc ....F...... 330 878-7118
Strasburg (G-17822)
Just Natural Provision Company ....G...... 216 431-7922
Cleveland (G-5626)

POWDER: Iron

Truck Fax Inc ....G...... 216 921-8866
Cleveland (G-6369)

POWDER: Metal

Additive Metal Alloys Ltd ....G...... 800 687-6110
Holland (G-11043)
Bogie Industries Inc Ltd ....E...... 330 745-3105
Akron (G-95)
Diamond Metals Dist Inc ....E...... 216 898-7900
Cleveland (G-5189)
Duffee Finishing Inc ....G...... 740 965-4848
Sunbury (G-18059)
Eckart America Corporation ....D...... 440 954-7600
Painesville (G-15876)
J & K Powder Coating ....G...... 330 540-6145
Mineral Ridge (G-14305)
Key Finishes LLC ....G...... 614 351-8393
Columbus (G-7260)
Key Principal Partners Corp ....F...... 888 539-3322
Cleveland (G-5651)
Legacy Finishing Inc ....G...... 937 743-7278
Franklin (G-10032)
Obron Atlantic Corporation ....D...... 440 954-7600
Painesville (G-15905)
Powder Alloy Corporation ....E...... 513 984-4016
Loveland (G-12378)
Powdermet Inc ....E...... 216 404-0053
Euclid (G-9598)
Rmi Titanium Company LLC ....E...... 330 652-9952
Niles (G-15176)

POWDER: Silver

Topkote Inc ....G...... 440 428-0525
Madison (G-12512)

POWER GENERATORS

AEP Resources Inc ....E...... 614 716-1000
Columbus (G-6700)
Micropower LLC ....F...... 513 382-0100
Cincinnati (G-4101)
Td Power Systems (usa) Inc ....G...... 330 247-5264
Richfield (G-16642)
Thermelectricity LLC ....G...... 330 972-8054
Akron (G-438)

POWER SPLY CONVERTERS: Static, Electronic Applications

Bennett & Bennett Inc ....F...... 937 324-1100
Springfield (G-17523)

POWER SUPPLIES: All Types, Static

Dare Electronics Inc ....E...... 937 335-0031
Troy (G-18814)
Siglent Technologies Amer Inc ....G...... 440 398-5800
Solon (G-17380)
Tracewell Power Inc ....E...... 614 846-6175
Westerville (G-20239)
Vertiv Group Corporation ....A...... 614 888-0246
Columbus (G-7735)

POWER SUPPLIES: Transformer, Electronic Type

Cletronics Inc ....F...... 330 239-2002
Medina (G-13389)
Electric Service Co Inc ....E...... 513 271-6387
Cincinnati (G-3692)
Norlake Manufacturing Company ....D...... 440 353-3200
North Ridgeville (G-15391)
North Dixie Parts & Service ....G...... 937 275-0933
Dayton (G-8526)

POWER SWITCHING EQPT

Layerzero Power Systems Inc ....E...... 440 399-9000
Aurora (G-932)
Te Connectivity Corporation ....C...... 419 521-9500
Mansfield (G-12694)

POWER TOOLS, HAND: Drills, Port, Elec/Pneumatic, Exc Rock

Airmachinescom Inc ....G...... 330 759-1620
Youngstown (G-21019)

POWER TOOLS, HAND: Hammers, Portable, Elec/Pneumatic, Chip

Corbett R Caudill Chipping Inc ....F...... 740 596-5984
Hamden (G-10656)

POWER TRANSMISSION EQPT WHOLESALERS

Riverside Drives Inc ....E...... 216 362-1211
Cleveland (G-6118)
Stock Fairfield Corporation ....C...... 440 543-6000
Chagrin Falls (G-3122)

POWER TRANSMISSION EQPT: Mechanical

Advance Bronze Inc ....D...... 330 948-1231
Lodi (G-12155)
Advanced Pneumatics Inc ....G...... 440 953-0700
Mentor (G-13510)
Ban-Fam Industries Inc ....G...... 216 265-9588
Cleveland (G-4888)
Bdi Inc ....F...... 330 498-4980
Canton (G-2617)
Bucyrus Precision Tech Inc ....C...... 419 563-9950
Bucyrus (G-2334)
Bunting Bearings LLC ....E...... 419 522-3323
Mansfield (G-12572)
City Machine Technologies Inc ....E...... 330 740-8186
Youngstown (G-21048)
Columbus McKinnon Corporation ....D...... 330 424-7248
Lisbon (G-12118)
Custom Cltch Jint Hydrlics Inc ....E...... 216 431-1630
Cleveland (G-5149)
Drive Components ....G...... 440 234-6200
Brookpark (G-2157)
E I Du Pont De Nemours & Co ....C...... 216 901-3600
Cleveland (G-5232)
Eaton Corporation ....C...... 440 826-1115
Berea (G-1613)
Eaton Hydraulics LLC ....E...... 419 232-7777
Van Wert (G-19254)
Equipment Concepts ....E...... 937 291-9734
Dayton (G-8329)
Euclid Universal Corporation ....G...... 440 542-0960
Cleveland (G-5302)
Force Control Industries Inc ....D...... 513 868-0900
Fairfield (G-9659)
General Electric Company ....D...... 216 883-1000
Cleveland (G-5412)
General Metals Powder Co ....D...... 330 633-1226
Akron (G-203)
Geneva Gear & Machine Inc ....F...... 937 866-0318
Dayton (G-8363)
GKN Sinter Metals LLC ....C...... 740 441-3203
Gallipolis (G-10298)
Hite Parts Exchange Inc ....E...... 614 272-5115
Columbus (G-7160)
Lextech Industries Ltd ....G...... 216 883-7900
Cleveland (G-5694)
Luk Clutch Systems LLC ....E...... 330 264-4383
Wooster (G-20798)
Master Products Company ....D...... 216 341-1740
Cleveland (G-5760)
Mechanical Dynamics Analis Ltd ....E...... 440 946-0082
Euclid (G-9592)
Metro Mech Inc ....G...... 216 641-6262
Cleveland (G-5792)
Mfh Partners Inc ....F...... 440 461-4100
Cleveland (G-5795)
Morgal Machine Tool Co ....D...... 937 325-5561
Springfield (G-17607)
Nook Industries Inc ....C...... 216 271-7900
Cleveland (G-5887)
Opw Engineered Systems Inc ....D...... 888 771-9438
Lebanon (G-11824)
Penn Machine Company ....E...... 814 288-1547
Twinsburg (G-18996)
Rampe Manufacturing Company ....F...... 440 352-8995
Fairport Harbor (G-9771)
Regal Industries Inc ....G...... 440 352-9600
Painesville (G-15917)
Saf-Holland Inc ....G...... 513 874-7888
West Chester (G-20046)
Stevenson Machine Inc ....F...... 513 761-4121
Cincinnati (G-4467)
Stripmatic Products Inc ....E...... 216 241-7143
Cleveland (G-6255)
Taiho Corporation of America ....C...... 419 443-1645
Tiffin (G-18246)
Webb-Stiles Company ....D...... 330 225-7761
Valley City (G-19237)
Western Branch Diesel Inc ....E...... 330 454-8800
Canton (G-2902)
Xtek Inc ....B...... 513 733-7800
Cincinnati (G-4616)

POWER TRANSMISSION EQPT: Vehicle

Adelmans Truck Parts Corp...............E....... 330 456-0206
 Canton (G-2587)

POWERED GOLF CART DEALERS

Golf Car Company Inc ....F....... 614 873-1055
 Plain City (G-16344)

PRECAST TERRAZZO OR CONCRETE PRDTS

Ald Precast Corp.......................G....... 614 449-3366
 Columbus (G-6714)
Concrete Fealants Inc.................D....... 937 339-0549
 Troy (G-18812)
Hanson Aggregates East LLC ....F....... 937 382-2557
 Wilmington (G-20668)
Lindsay Package Systems Inc..........G....... 330 854-4511
 Canal Fulton (G-2504)
Premere Precast Products...............F....... 740 533-3333
 Ironton (G-11298)
Shock Precast ....G....... 419 426-0535
 Attica (G-896)

PRECIOUS STONES & METALS, WHOLESALE

A R Jester Co ....G....... 513 241-1465
 Cincinnati (G-3335)

PRECIPITATORS: Electrostatic

McGill Airclean LLC ....D....... 614 829-1200
 Columbus (G-7330)
McGill Corporation.....................F....... 614 829-1200
 Groveport (G-10635)
Neundorfer Inc ....E....... 440 942-8990
 Willoughby (G-20553)
United McGill Corporation ....E....... 614 829-1200
 Groveport (G-10648)

PRECISION INSTRUMENT REPAIR SVCS

Beaumont Machine LLC..............F....... 513 701-0421
 Mason (G-12988)

PRESSED FIBER & MOLDED PULP PRDTS, EXC FOOD PRDTS

Vista Industrial Packaging LLC ....D....... 800 454-6117
 Columbus (G-7743)

PRESSES

Alliance Die Design & Mfg..............G....... 330 821-2440
 Alliance (G-492)
Eae Logistics Company LLC ....G....... 440 417-4788
 Madison (G-12505)

PRESSURIZERS OR AUXILIARY EQPT: Nuclear, Metal Plate

AMF Bruns America Lp ....G....... 877 506-3770
 Hudson (G-11158)

PRESTRESSED CONCRETE PRDTS

Fabcon Companies LLC.................D....... 614 875-8601
 Grove City (G-10558)
Prestress Services Inds LLC ....E....... 614 871-2900
 Grove City (G-10585)

PRIMARY FINISHED OR SEMIFINISHED SHAPES

Dietrich Industries Inc ....C....... 330 372-2868
 Warren (G-19544)
Northeast Tubular Service Inc ....G....... 330 262-1881
 Wooster (G-20818)

PRIMARY METAL PRODUCTS

Altana ....G....... 440 954-7600
 Painesville (G-15849)
Liberty Steel Pressed Pdts LLC...........G....... 330 538-2236
 North Jackson (G-15294)
Materion Technical Mtls Inc ....D....... 216 486-4200
 Cleveland (G-5761)

PRINT CARTRIDGES: Laser & Other Computer Printers

Eco-Print Solutions LLC.................G....... 513 731-3106
 Cincinnati (G-3689)
Jay Tackett.............................G....... 740 779-1715
 Frankfort (G-9999)
Kehler Enterprises Inc.................G....... 614 889-8488
 Dublin (G-9095)
Wood County Ohio......................G....... 419 353-1227
 Bowling Green (G-2022)

PRINTED CIRCUIT BOARDS

Accurate Electronics Inc ....C....... 330 682-7015
 Orrville (G-15727)
Adonai Technologies LLC................G....... 513 560-9020
 Middletown (G-14012)
Airborn Flxble Circuits NH Inc............G....... 603 537-9500
 Akron (G-36)
Alektronics Inc ....F....... 937 429-2118
 Beavercreek (G-1368)
Avcom Smt Inc ....F....... 614 882-8176
 Westerville (G-20200)
Bud Industries Inc......................G....... 440 946-3200
 Willoughby (G-20447)
C E Electronics Inc ....D....... 419 636-6705
 Bryan (G-2289)
Cartessa Corporation ....F....... 513 738-4477
 Shandon (G-17096)
Central Systems & Control ....G....... 440 835-0015
 Cleveland (G-5005)
Chaffin Electronics Inc ....G....... 740 354-9896
 Franklin Furnace (G-10068)
Circle Prime Manufacturing ....E....... 330 923-0019
 Cuyahoga Falls (G-7980)
Circuit Center ....G....... 513 435-2131
 Dayton (G-8231)
Co- Ax Technology Inc ....C....... 440 914-9200
 Solon (G-17279)
Community RE Group-Comvet...........G....... 440 319-6714
 Ashtabula (G-798)
Debra Harbour.........................G....... 937 440-9618
 Troy (G-18816)
Deca Manufacturing Co Inc............D....... 419 884-0071
 Mansfield (G-12594)
Flextronics International Usa.............A....... 513 755-2500
 Liberty Township (G-11961)
Interactive Engineering Corp...........E....... 330 239-6888
 Medina (G-13427)
International Trade Group Inc...........G....... 614 486-4634
 Columbus (G-7207)
Journey Electronics Corp ....G....... 513 539-9836
 Monroe (G-14406)
L3 Technologies Inc ....E....... 513 943-2000
 Cincinnati (G-3311)
Lad Technology Inc ....E....... 440 461-8002
 Cleveland (G-5675)
Levison Enterprises LLC ....E....... 419 838-7365
 Millbury (G-14185)
Libra Industries Inc.....................E....... 440 974-7770
 Mentor (G-13632)
McGregor-Surmount Corporation ....C....... 937 833-6768
 Brookville (G-2193)
Philway Products Inc...................C....... 419 281-7777
 Ashland (G-765)
Precision Switching Inc.................G....... 800 800-8143
 Mansfield (G-12667)
Qualtech Technologies Inc ....E....... 440 946-8081
 Willoughby (G-20585)
S Wj Llcred ....G....... 330 938-6173
 Sebring (G-17051)
Techtron Systems Inc ....E....... 440 505-2990
 Solon (G-17401)
Tetrad Electronics Inc..................D....... 440 946-6443
 Willoughby (G-20614)
Thomas Enterprises ....G....... 330 394-4483
 Warren (G-19607)
United Circuits Inc ....F....... 440 926-1000
 Grafton (G-10438)
Viasystems Tech Corp LLC ....C....... 330 538-3900
 North Jackson (G-15300)
Visual Information Institute.............F....... 937 376-4361
 Xenia (G-20985)
Vmetro Inc ....G....... 281 584-0728
 Fairborn (G-9633)
Wurth Electronics Ics Inc ....F....... 937 415-7700
 Dayton (G-8765)

PRINTERS & PLOTTERS

Ava Graphix...........................G....... 216 409-8646
 Brunswick (G-2206)
Eprintworksplus........................G....... 513 731-3797
 Cincinnati (G-3713)
Gameday Vision ....F....... 330 830-4550
 Massillon (G-13137)
Royal Specialty Products Inc............G....... 513 841-1267
 Cincinnati (G-4362)
Small Business Products ....G....... 800 553-6485
 Cincinnati (G-4427)

PRINTERS' SVCS: Folding, Collating, Etc

Bookmasters Inc ....C....... 419 281-1802
 Ashland (G-713)
Capitol Citicom Inc ....E....... 614 472-2679
 Columbus (G-6903)
Erd Specialty Graphics Inc ....F....... 419 242-9545
 Toledo (G-18456)
Erie Laser Ink LLC ....G....... 419 346-0600
 Toledo (G-18457)
Printing Services........................E....... 440 708-1999
 Chagrin Falls (G-3114)

PRINTERS: Computer

Microcom Corporation ....E....... 740 548-6262
 Lewis Center (G-11907)

PRINTERS: Magnetic Ink, Bar Code

Hunkar Technologies Inc ....C....... 513 272-1010
 Cincinnati (G-3902)
ID Images Inc..........................G....... 330 220-7300
 Brunswick (G-2233)
M C Systems Inc ....G....... 513 336-6007
 Mason (G-13056)
Perfection Packaging Inc ....G....... 614 866-8558
 Gahanna (G-10226)

PRINTING & BINDING: Books

48 Hr Books Inc ....E....... 330 374-6917
 Akron (G-13)
All Systems Colour Inc ....G....... 937 859-9701
 Dayton (G-8144)
Bip Printing Solutions LLC ....F....... 216 832-5673
 Beachwood (G-1259)
C J Krehbiel Company..................C....... 513 271-6035
 Cincinnati (G-3493)
Hf Group LLC ....F....... 440 729-2445
 Chesterland (G-3210)
Hf Group LLC ....A....... 440 729-9411
 Chesterland (G-3211)
Hf Group LLC ....D....... 440 729-9411
 Chesterland (G-3212)
Lsc Communications Us LLC ....C....... 419 935-0111
 Willard (G-20396)

PRINTING & BINDING: Pamphlets

Morse Enterprises Inc ....G....... 513 229-3600
 Mason (G-13066)

PRINTING & BINDING: Textbooks

Amerilam Laminating ....G....... 440 235-4687
 Cleveland (G-4797)

PRINTING & EMBOSSING: Plastic Fabric Articles

Akron Felt & Chenille Mfg Co ....F....... 330 733-7778
 Akron (G-43)
Plastic Card Inc ....D....... 330 896-5555
 Uniontown (G-19093)
Solar Arts Graphic Designs ....G....... 330 744-0535
 Youngstown (G-21205)

PRINTING & ENGRAVING: Financial Notes & Certificates

Basinger Inc ....G....... 614 771-8300
 Columbus (G-6813)
Cap City Direct LLC ....F....... 614 252-6245
 Columbus (G-6894)
Fedex Office & Print Svcs Inc............F....... 937 335-3816
 Troy (G-18827)
Quick Tech Business Forms Inc...........E....... 937 743-5952
 Springboro (G-17501)

PRODUCT

Watson Haran & Company Inc .... G 937 436-1414
  Dayton *(G-8747)*

PRINTING & ENGRAVING: Invitation & Stationery

Adyl Inc .... G 330 797-8700
  Austintown *(G-968)*
Papel Couture .... G 614 848-5700
  Columbus *(G-7458)*
Paper Occasions .... G 614 761-8880
  Dublin *(G-9116)*
Shops By Todd Inc .... G 937 458-3192
  Beavercreek *(G-1360)*

PRINTING & STAMPING: Fabric Articles

Action Sports Apparel Inc .... G 330 848-9300
  Norton *(G-15503)*
Hollywood Imprints LLC .... F 614 501-6040
  Gahanna *(G-10211)*
Johnson Brothers Holdings LLC .... G 614 868-5273
  Columbus *(G-7240)*
Pro Companies Inc .... G 614 738-1222
  Pickerington *(G-16201)*
Puttco Inc .... G 937 299-1527
  Dayton *(G-8604)*

PRINTING & WRITING PAPER WHOLESALERS

Gvs Industries Inc .... G 513 887-8660
  Hamilton *(G-10699)*
Microcom Corporation .... E 740 548-6262
  Lewis Center *(G-11907)*
Millcraft Group LLC .... D 216 441-5500
  Cleveland *(G-5817)*

PRINTING INKS WHOLESALERS

Braden-Sutphin Ink Company .... G 614 443-9100
  Columbus *(G-6853)*
Eco-Print Solutions LLC .... G 513 731-3106
  Cincinnati *(G-3689)*
Kennedy Ink Company Inc .... G 937 461-5600
  Dayton *(G-8437)*

PRINTING MACHINERY

A/C Laser Technologies Inc .... F 330 784-3355
  Akron *(G-23)*
Aleris Ohio Management Inc .... F 216 910-3400
  Cleveland *(G-4747)*
Anderson & Vreeland Inc .... D 419 636-5002
  Bryan *(G-2278)*
Boggs Graphic Equipment LLC .... G 440 564-9675
  Maple Heights *(G-12728)*
Capital Track Company Inc .... G 614 595-5088
  Columbus *(G-6902)*
Comco Machinery Inc .... C 513 248-8000
  Milford *(G-14132)*
Commonwealth Aluminum Mtls LLC ..... G 216 910-3400
  Beachwood *(G-1263)*
Flexotech Graphics Inc .... F 330 929-4743
  Stow *(G-17754)*
FT Group Inc .... E 937 746-6439
  Cincinnati *(G-3786)*
Gedico International Inc .... G 937 274-2167
  Dayton *(G-8360)*
Gew Inc .... G 440 237-4439
  Cleveland *(G-5427)*
Hadronics Inc .... D 513 321-9350
  Cincinnati *(G-3861)*
Hotend Works Inc .... G 440 787-3181
  Grafton *(G-10430)*
Kase Equipment .... D 216 642-9040
  Cleveland *(G-5634)*
Nilpeter Usa Inc .... C 513 489-4400
  Cincinnati *(G-4156)*
Ohio Graphic Supply Inc .... G 937 433-7537
  Dayton *(G-8543)*
Pearce Inc .... F 216 252-0550
  Cleveland *(G-5986)*
R & D Equipment Inc .... F 419 668-8439
  Norwalk *(G-15561)*
Resource Graphics .... G 513 205-2686
  Cincinnati *(G-4339)*
Roconex Corporation .... G 937 339-2616
  Troy *(G-18868)*
Roessner Holdings Inc .... G 419 356-2123
  Fort Recovery *(G-9958)*

Rotation Dynamics Corporation .... F 937 746-4069
  Franklin *(G-10051)*
Schilling Graphics Inc .... E 419 468-1037
  Galion *(G-10286)*
Suspension Feeder Corporation .... F 419 763-1377
  Fort Recovery *(G-9960)*
Wood Graphics Inc .... E 513 771-6300
  Cincinnati *(G-4603)*

PRINTING MACHINERY, EQPT & SPLYS: Wholesalers

Anderson & Vreeland Inc .... D 419 636-5002
  Bryan *(G-2278)*
Esko-Graphics Inc .... D 937 454-1721
  Miamisburg *(G-13805)*
General Data Company Inc .... C 513 752-7978
  Cincinnati *(G-3304)*
Monode Marking Products Inc .... E 440 975-8802
  Mentor *(G-13660)*
Newfax Corporation .... G 419 893-4557
  Toledo *(G-18604)*
Newfax Corporation .... F 419 241-5157
  Toledo *(G-18603)*

PRINTING TRADES MACHINERY & EQPT REPAIR SVCS

A/C Laser Technologies Inc .... F 330 784-3355
  Akron *(G-23)*
Glen D Lala .... G 937 274-7770
  Dayton *(G-8366)*
Lazer Action Inc .... G 330 630-9200
  Akron *(G-268)*

PRINTING, COMMERCIAL Newspapers, NEC

Ckm Ventures LLC 216 623-0370
  Cleveland *(G-5040)*
Wolfe Associates Inc .... G 614 461-5000
  Columbus *(G-7771)*

PRINTING, COMMERCIAL: Business Forms, NEC

Alpha Bus Forms & Prtg LLC .... G 419 999-5138
  Lima *(G-11987)*
Cns Inc .... G 513 631-7073
  Cincinnati *(G-3593)*
Crabar/Gbf Inc .... G 419 943-2141
  Leipsic *(G-11868)*
Echographics Inc .... G 440 846-2330
  North Ridgeville *(G-15371)*
International Business Solutio .... F 937 853-0348
  Dayton *(G-8415)*
PJ Bush Associates Inc .... E 216 362-6700
  Cleveland *(G-6009)*
Reynolds and Reynolds Company .... G 937 485-4771
  Dayton *(G-8629)*
RR Donnelley & Sons Company .... B 740 928-6110
  Hebron *(G-10882)*
S F Mock & Associates LLC .... F 937 438-0196
  Dayton *(G-8644)*
Smartbill Ltd .... F 740 928-6909
  Hebron *(G-10885)*
State-Mate Company .... G 740 392-9487
  Mount Vernon *(G-14652)*

PRINTING, COMMERCIAL: Calendars, NEC

Haman Enterprises Inc .... F 614 888-7574
  Worthington *(G-20869)*

PRINTING, COMMERCIAL: Cards, Visiting, Incl Business, NEC

Bookmyer LLP .... G 419 447-3883
  Tiffin *(G-18210)*

PRINTING, COMMERCIAL: Decals, NEC

Boehm Inc .... E 614 875-9010
  Grove City *(G-10546)*
Commercial Decal of Ohio Inc .... E 330 385-7178
  East Liverpool *(G-9208)*

PRINTING, COMMERCIAL: Directories, Telephone, NEC

Ad Source Inc .... G 330 468-2934
  Peninsula *(G-16033)*

PRINTING, COMMERCIAL: Envelopes, NEC

Anthony Business Forms Inc .... F 937 253-0072
  Dayton *(G-8096)*
McDaniel Envelope Co Inc .... F 330 868-5929
  Minerva *(G-14332)*
Miami Valley Press Inc .... G 937 547-0771
  Greenville *(G-10511)*
Ohio Envelope Manufacturing Co .... E 216 267-2920
  Cleveland *(G-5933)*

PRINTING, COMMERCIAL: Imprinting

Better Living Concepts Inc .... F 330 494-2213
  Canton *(G-2621)*
Cotton Pickin Tees & Caps .... G 419 636-3595
  Bryan *(G-2291)*
Fair Publishing House Inc .... E 419 668-3746
  Norwalk *(G-15540)*
Holmes Prcut/Troyer Imprinting .... G 330 359-0000
  Dundee *(G-9173)*
John C Starr .... G 740 852-5592
  London *(G-12213)*
Middaugh Enterprises Inc .... F 330 852-2471
  Sugarcreek *(G-18026)*

PRINTING, COMMERCIAL: Invitations, NEC

Domicone Printing Inc .... G 937 878-3080
  Fairborn *(G-9619)*
Doug Smith .... G 740 345-1398
  Newark *(G-15000)*

PRINTING, COMMERCIAL: Labels & Seals, NEC

Albert Bramkamp Printing Co .... G 513 641-1069
  Cincinnati *(G-3376)*
Bar Codes Unlimited Inc .... G 937 434-2633
  Dayton *(G-8181)*
Century Marketing Corporation .... E 419 354-2591
  Bowling Green *(G-1977)*
Century Marketing Corporation .... C 419 354-2591
  Bowling Green *(G-1978)*
CMC Group Inc .... D 419 352-9567
  Bowling Green *(G-1981)*
Contemprary Image Labeling Inc .... G 513 583-5699
  Lebanon *(G-11791)*
D&D Design Concepts Inc .... F 513 752-2191
  Batavia *(G-1176)*
Donprint Inc .... E 847 573-7777
  Strongsville *(G-17911)*
Federal Barcode Label Systems .... G 440 748-8060
  North Ridgeville *(G-15373)*
Flex Pro Label Inc .... G 513 489-4417
  Blue Ash *(G-1795)*
Geygan Enterprises Inc .... F 513 932-4222
  Lebanon *(G-11803)*
Hooven - Dayton Corp .... D 937 233-4473
  Miamisburg *(G-13818)*
M PI Label Systems .... G 330 938-2134
  Sebring *(G-17047)*
Mpi Labels of Baltimore Inc .... F 330 938-2134
  Sebring *(G-17049)*
Multi-Color Corporation .... F 513 381-1480
  Batavia *(G-1211)*
Multi-Color Corporation .... D 513 943-0080
  Batavia *(G-1212)*
Scratch-Off Systems Inc .... E 216 649-7800
  Brecksville *(G-2071)*
Tech/III Inc .... E 513 482-7500
  Cincinnati *(G-4497)*
Trebnick Systems Inc .... E 937 743-1550
  Springboro *(G-17512)*
Triangle Label Inc .... G 513 242-2822
  West Chester *(G-19961)*

PRINTING, COMMERCIAL: Letterpress & Screen

Club 513 LLC .... G 800 530-2574
  Cincinnati *(G-3591)*
Hypodermic Designs LLC .... G 614 203-4048
  Columbus *(G-7174)*

PRINTING, COMMERCIAL: Literature, Advertising, NEC

Multi-Color Australia LLC .... B 513 381-1480
  Batavia *(G-1210)*
Penca Design Group Ltd .... G 440 210-4422
  Painesville *(G-15910)*

Stephens Publishing Co Inc .... G 419 626-5592
Sandusky (G-17010)

PRINTING, COMMERCIAL: Magazines, NEC

Quebecor World Johnson Hardin .... A 614 326-0299
Cincinnati (G-4312)

PRINTING, COMMERCIAL: Menus, NEC

Cleveland Menu Printing Inc .... E 216 241-5256
Cleveland (G-5069)

PRINTING, COMMERCIAL: Post Cards, Picture, NEC

Victory Postcards Inc .... G 614 764-8975
Columbus (G-7740)

PRINTING, COMMERCIAL: Promotional

Axent Graphics LLC .... G 216 362-7560
Brookpark (G-2152)
Bradleys Beacons Ltd .... G 419 447-7560
Tiffin (G-18211)
Clear Images LLC .... F 419 241-9347
Toledo (G-18400)
Corporate Supply LLC .... G 614 876-8400
Columbus (G-6986)
Dyenamo Distributing .... F 419 462-9474
Galion (G-10264)
Everythings Image Inc .... F 513 469-6727
Blue Ash (G-1789)
Exxcite Marketing Inc .... G 513 271-4550
Cincinnati (G-3733)
Hyde Brothers Prtg & Mktg LLC .... G 740 373-2054
Marietta (G-12792)
RR Donnelley & Sons Company .... G 513 552-1512
West Chester (G-19939)
Solution Ventures Inc .... G 440 242-1658
Avon Lake (G-1051)
Spectrum Embroidery Inc .... G 937 847-9905
Dayton (G-8669)
SRC Liquidation LLC .... A 937 221-1000
Dayton (G-8672)

PRINTING, COMMERCIAL: Publications

American Future Systems Inc .... F 330 758-0277
Youngstown (G-21023)
Bayard Inc .... G 937 293-1415
Moraine (G-14467)
Brahler Inc .... G 330 966-7730
Canton (G-2627)
Forward Movement Publications .... F 513 721-6659
Cincinnati (G-3774)
Heartland Publications LLC .... F 860 664-1075
Miamisburg (G-13816)
Heartland Publications LLC .... F 740 446-2342
Gallipolis (G-10300)
Jjkb Enterprises LLC .... G 513 731-4332
Cincinnati (G-3946)
ML Erectors LLC .... G 440 328-3227
Elyria (G-9464)
Penton Media Inc .... A 216 696-7000
Cleveland (G-5991)
Scriptype Publishing Inc .... E 330 659-0303
Richfield (G-16635)

PRINTING, COMMERCIAL: Screen

4d Screenprinting Ltd .... G 513 353-1070
Cleves (G-6504)
A Screen Printed Products .... G 419 352-1535
Bowling Green (G-1961)
A Special Touch Embroidery LLC ...... G 740 858-2241
Portsmouth (G-16429)
Aardvark Screen Prtg & EMB LLC ..... F 419 354-6686
Bowling Green (G-1964)
Aardvark Sportswear Inc .... G 330 793-9428
Youngstown (G-21012)
Abl Screen Printing .... G 440 914-0093
Solon (G-17247)
Ace Transfer Company .... G 937 398-1103
Springfield (G-17514)
Adcraft Decals Inc .... E 216 524-2934
Cleveland (G-4702)
Alberts Screen Print Inc .... C 330 753-7559
Norton (G-15505)
Allied Silk Screen Inc .... G 937 223-4921
Dayton (G-8148)
Alvin L Roepke .... F 419 862-3891
Elmore (G-9360)

Am Graphics .... G 330 799-7319
Youngstown (G-21022)
Anthony-Lee Screen Prtg Inc .... F 419 683-1861
Crestline (G-7928)
Art Brands LLC .... E 614 755-4278
Blacklick (G-1688)
Art Tees Inc .... G 614 338-8337
Columbus (G-6774)
Assocted Vsual Cmmncations Inc ..... E 330 452-4449
Canton (G-2608)
Atrium Corp .... G 740 966-8200
Johnstown (G-11390)
B & D Graphics Inc .... G 513 641-0855
Cincinnati (G-3431)
Benchmark Prints .... F 419 332-7640
Fremont (G-10129)
Blue Ribbon Screen Graphics .... G 216 226-6200
Avon (G-986)
Bluelogos Inc .... F 614 898-9971
Westerville (G-20203)
Bob King Sign Company Inc .... G 330 753-2679
Akron (G-94)
Buckeye Cstm Screen Print EMB ...... F 614 237-0196
Columbus (G-6872)
Bullseye Activewear Inc .... G 330 220-1720
Brunswick (G-2214)
C A I R Ohio .... G 513 281-8200
Blue Ash (G-1758)
Campbell Signs & Apparel LLC .... F 330 386-4768
East Liverpool (G-9205)
Carnegie Promotions Inc .... G 440 442-2099
Cleveland (G-4982)
Carroll Exhibit and Print Svcs .... G 216 361-2325
Cleveland (G-4985)
Centennial Screen Printing .... G 419 422-5548
Findlay (G-9805)
Cleveland Printwear Inc .... G 216 521-5500
Cleveland (G-5073)
Cold Duck Screen Prtg & EMB Co ..... G 330 426-1900
East Palestine (G-9231)
Collegiate Connection .... G 419 352-8333
Bowling Green (G-1982)
Color Process Inc .... E 440 268-7100
Strongsville (G-17905)
Columbus Humungous Apparel LLC ... G 614 824-2657
Columbus (G-6955)
Concept 9 Inc .... G 614 294-3743
Columbus (G-6976)
Custom Deco South Inc .... E 419 698-2900
Toledo (G-18418)
Custom Screen Printing .... G 330 963-3131
Twinsburg (G-18920)
Custom Sportswear Imprints LLC ..... G 330 335-8326
Wadsworth (G-19400)
Danroc Corp .... G 330 262-0712
Wooster (G-20763)
Debandale Printing Inc .... G 330 725-5122
Medina (G-13401)
Design Graphics Group Inc .... E 419 354-8717
Bowling Green (G-1984)
Drycal Inc .... G 440 974-1999
Mentor (G-13566)
Dynamic Design & Systems Inc .... G 440 708-1010
Chagrin Falls (G-3085)
E & E Nameplates Inc .... F 419 468-3617
Galion (G-10265)
Embroidme Co .... G 614 933-9194
Columbus (G-7056)
Erd Specialty Graphics Inc .... G 419 242-9545
Toledo (G-18456)
Expert TS .... G 330 263-4588
Wooster (G-20770)
First Impression Wear .... G 937 456-3900
Eaton (G-9306)
First Stop Signs and Decals .... G 330 343-1859
New Philadelphia (G-14899)
Five Star Graphics Inc .... G 330 545-5077
Girard (G-10388)
Fulton Sign & Decal Inc .... G 440 951-1515
Mentor (G-13587)
Future Screen Inc .... G 440 838-5055
Cleveland (G-5386)
Gail Berner .... G 937 322-0314
Springfield (G-17563)
Gail Zeilmann .... G 440 888-4858
Cleveland (G-5391)
Glauners Wholesale Inc .... G 216 398-7088
Cleveland (G-5432)
Glavin Industries Inc .... E 440 349-0049
Solon (G-17297)

Glen D Lala .... G 937 274-7770
Dayton (G-8366)
Good JP .... G 419 207-8484
Ashland (G-735)
Grady McCauley Incorporated .... D 330 494-9444
North Canton (G-15236)
Graphix Junction .... G 234 284-8392
Hudson (G-11176)
Gym Pro LLC .... G 740 984-4143
Waterford (G-19648)
H & H Screen Process Inc .... G 937 253-7520
Dayton (G-8381)
Hartman Distributing LLC .... D 740 616-7764
Heath (G-10847)
Hoffee John .... G 330 868-3553
Minerva (G-14325)
Homestretch Sportswear Inc .... F 419 678-4282
Saint Henry (G-16818)
Illusions Screenprinting .... G 330 263-7770
Wooster (G-20785)
Industrial Screen Process .... F 419 255-4900
Toledo (G-18522)
Innovtive Crtive Solutions LLC .... E 614 491-9638
Groveport (G-10626)
J-M Designs LLC .... G 419 794-2114
Maumee (G-13269)
Jazz Textile Impressions .... G 419 242-5940
Maumee (G-13270)
Joe Paxton .... G 614 424-9000
Columbus (G-7237)
Jones & Assoc Advg & Design .... G 330 799-6876
Youngstown (G-21127)
Kaufman Container Company .... C 216 898-2000
Cleveland (G-5636)
Kendra Screen Print .... G 440 967-8820
Vermilion (G-19330)
Kens His & Hers Shop Inc .... G 330 872-3190
Newton Falls (G-15134)
KS Designs Inc .... G 513 241-5953
Cincinnati (G-4005)
Lamar D Steiner .... G 330 466-1479
Millersburg (G-14239)
Lima Sporting Goods Inc .... E 419 222-1036
Lima (G-12046)
Locker Room Lettering Ltd .... G 419 359-1761
Castalia (G-2977)
Logos On Lee .... G 216 862-5226
Cleveland (G-5708)
LSI Industries Inc .... E 513 793-3200
Blue Ash (G-1829)
Magnetic Mktg Solutions LLC .... G 513 721-3801
Cincinnati (G-4053)
Marazita Graphics Inc .... G 330 773-6462
Akron (G-283)
Meders Special Tees .... G 513 921-3800
Cincinnati (G-4076)
Mid Ohio Screen Print Inc .... G 614 875-1774
Grove City (G-10572)
Mid West Dry Sift .... G 614 946-3797
Columbus (G-7348)
Mike B Crawford .... G 330 673-7944
Kent (G-11492)
Modern Displays Inc .... G 513 471-1639
Cincinnati (G-4114)
Mojo Sportsgear .... G 614 864-6656
Columbus (G-7362)
Moonshine Screen Printing Inc .... F 513 523-7775
Oxford (G-15840)
Morrison Sign Company Inc .... E 614 276-1181
Columbus (G-7371)
Niklee Co .... G 440 944-0082
Willoughby Hills (G-20643)
Nordec Inc .... D 330 940-3700
Stow (G-17784)
Northeastern Plastics Inc .... G 330 453-5925
Canton (G-2795)
Odyssey Spirits Inc .... F 330 562-1523
Aurora (G-938)
Off Contact Inc .... F 419 255-5546
Toledo (G-18614)
Painted Hill Inv Group Inc .... F 937 339-1756
Troy (G-18861)
Pops Printed Apparel LLC .... G 614 372-5651
Columbus (G-7504)
Precision Imprint .... G 740 592-5916
Athens (G-882)
Primal Screen Inc .... G 330 677-1766
Kent (G-11507)
Proline Screenwear .... G 440 205-3700
Mentor (G-13702)

PRODUCT

Quali-Tee Design Sports ....F 937 382-7997
Wilmington (G-20675)

Qualitee Design Sportswear Co ....F 740 333-8337
Wshngtn CT Hs (G-20922)

Richardson Supply LLC ....G 614 539-3033
Grove City (G-10589)

Rising Moon Custom Apparel ....G 614 882-1336
Westerville (G-20232)

RR Donnelley & Sons Company ....D 330 562-5250
Streetsboro (G-17872)

Rush Graphix Ltd ....G 419 448-7874
Tiffin (G-18241)

Ruthie Ann Inc ....F 800 231-3567
New Paris (G-14881)

Rutland Plastic Tech Inc ....G 614 846-3055
Columbus (G-7578)

Screen Craft Plastics ....G 440 286-4060
Chardon (G-3178)

Screen Tech Graphics ....G 740 695-7950
Saint Clairsville (G-16807)

Shirtwork ....G 937 322-7507
Springfield (G-17648)

Sign Lady Inc ....G 419 476-9191
Toledo (G-18696)

Signs By George ....G 216 394-2095
Brookfield (G-2126)

Silk Screen Special TS Inc ....G 740 246-4843
Thornville (G-18199)

Spear USA Inc ....C 513 459-1100
Mason (G-13088)

Specialtee Sportswear & Design ....G 614 877-0976
Orient (G-15724)

Specialty Printing and Proc ....F 614 322-9035
Columbus (G-7637)

Sports Express ....G 330 297-1112
Ravenna (G-16559)

SRI Ohio Inc ....D 740 653-5800
Lancaster (G-11755)

Srm Graphics Inc ....G 614 263-4433
Columbus (G-7648)

Steves Sports Inc ....G 440 735-0044
Bedford Heights (G-1494)

Studio Eleven Inc ....E 937 295-2225
Fort Loramie (G-9941)

Studs N Hip Hop ....G 614 477-0786
Columbus (G-7663)

T K L Lettering ....G 937 832-2091
Englewood (G-9540)

Tag ....G 614 921-1732
Columbus (G-7674)

Tewell & Associates ....G 440 543-5190
Chagrin Falls (G-3125)

Toledo Signs & Designs Ltd ....G 419 843-1073
Toledo (G-18742)

Transfer Express Inc ....D 440 918-1900
Mentor (G-13755)

Underground Sport Shop Inc...............F 513 751-1662
Cincinnati (G-4535)

Unisport Inc ....F 419 529-4727
Ontario (G-15696)

United Sport Apparel ....F 330 722-0818
Medina (G-13493)

Unlimited Promotions Inc ....G 513 844-2211
Fairfield (G-9727)

Uptown Dog The Inc ....G 740 592-4600
Athens (G-889)

Vgu Industries Inc ....E 216 676-9093
Cleveland (G-6414)

Viewpoint Graphic Design ....G 419 447-6073
Tiffin (G-18252)

Water Drop Media Inc ....G 234 600-5817
Vienna (G-19377)

Zenos Activewear Inc ....G 614 443-0070
Columbus (G-7787)

PRINTING, COMMERCIAL: Stationery, NEC

Vagabond Creations Inc ....G 937 298-1124
Moraine (G-14536)

PRINTING, COMMERCIAL: Tickets, NEC

Premier Southern Ticket Co Inc ....E 513 489-6700
Cincinnati (G-4267)

PRINTING, COMMERCIAL: Wrappers, NEC

Homeguard Products Inc ....G 616 846-0804
Baltimore (G-1083)

PRINTING, LITHOGRAPHIC: Advertising Posters

State-Mate Company ....G 740 392-9487
Mount Vernon (G-14652)

PRINTING, LITHOGRAPHIC: Calendars

Beach Company...............................F 740 622-0905
Coshocton (G-7882)

Novelty Advertising Co Inc ....E 740 622-3113
Coshocton (G-7903)

PRINTING, LITHOGRAPHIC: Calendars & Cards

Go Calendars..................................G 513 755-1555
Liberty Township (G-11962)

PRINTING, LITHOGRAPHIC: Color

American Colorscans Inc ....E 614 895-0233
Columbus (G-6732)

Evolution Crtive Solutions Inc.............E 513 681-4450
Cincinnati (G-3724)

Lindsey Graphics Inc.........................G 330 995-9241
Aurora (G-933)

SP Mount Printing Company ....E 216 881-3316
Cleveland (G-6223)

Valley Graphics ....G 330 652-0484
Niles (G-15187)

PRINTING, LITHOGRAPHIC: Decals

Bogart Imprinting.............................G 419 659-2840
Columbus Grove (G-7790)

Dynamic Design & Systems Inc ....G 440 708-1010
Chagrin Falls (G-3085)

Pro-Decal Inc ....G 330 484-0089
Canton (G-2825)

Schilling Graphics Inc ....E 419 468-1037
Galion (G-10286)

Sun Art Decals Inc ....E 440 234-9045
Berea (G-1636)

PRINTING, LITHOGRAPHIC: Forms & Cards, Business

Carbonless On Demandcom ....F 330 837-8611
Massillon (G-13119)

Crabar/Gbf Inc ....D 419 943-2141
Leipsic (G-11867)

Crabar/Gbf Inc ....E 740 622-0222
Coshocton (G-7887)

G A Spring Advertising......................G 330 343-9030
Dover (G-8986)

Miami Valley Press Inc ....G 937 547-0771
Greenville (G-10511)

Optimum System Products Inc...........E 614 885-4464
Westerville (G-20228)

Pro Companies Inc ....G 614 738-1222
Pickerington (G-16201)

Sandy Smittcamp..............................G 937 372-1687
Xenia (G-20971)

Victory Direct LLC ....G 614 626-0000
Gahanna (G-10240)

PRINTING, LITHOGRAPHIC: Forms, Business

Betley Printing Co.............................G 216 206-5600
Cleveland (G-4910)

GBS Corp ....C 330 863-1828
Malvern (G-12545)

Go2 Partners Inc ....E 330 650-5300
Twinsburg (G-18949)

Jaymac Systems Inc.........................G 440 498-0810
Solon (G-17320)

Quick Tab II Inc ....D 419 448-6622
Tiffin (G-18238)

PRINTING, LITHOGRAPHIC: Letters, Circular Or Form

E L Frueh Inc ....F 419 222-9741
Lima (G-12007)

Printers Emergency Service LLC ....G 513 421-7799
Cincinnati (G-4272)

PRINTING, LITHOGRAPHIC: Offset & photolithographic printing

Arnold Printing Inc............................G 330 494-1191
Canton (G-2606)

Clark Associates Inc ....G 419 334-3838
Fremont (G-10138)

Corporate Dcment Solutions Inc ....F 513 595-8200
Cincinnati (G-3613)

Eagle Advertising.............................G 216 881-0800
Cleveland (G-5236)

Hecks Direct Mail & Prtg Svc ....E 419 661-6028
Toledo (G-18503)

Kennedy Mint Inc ....D 440 572-3222
Cleveland (G-5645)

Mathews Printing Company ....F 614 444-1010
Columbus (G-7324)

Northwest Print Inc ....G 419 385-3375
Perrysburg (G-16127)

Nova Creative Group Inc ....F 937 291-8653
Dayton (G-8533)

Performa La Mar Printing Inc ....G 440 632-9800
Middlefield (G-13981)

Power Management Inc ....E 937 222-2909
Dayton (G-8580)

SMI Holdings Inc ....F 740 927-3464
Pataskala (G-15986)

Smith-Feeman Inc ....F 330 434-8882
Uniontown (G-19099)

PRINTING, LITHOGRAPHIC: On Metal

Akron Litho-Print Company Inc............F 330 434-3145
Akron (G-47)

American Inks and Coatings Co ....F 513 552-7200
Fairfield (G-9641)

Crest Craft Company ....F 513 271-4858
Blue Ash (G-1770)

Delores E OBeirn ....G 440 582-3610
Cleveland (G-5182)

Genie Repros Inc ....E 216 965-0213
Cleveland (G-5422)

Jarman Printing Company LLC ....G 330 823-8585
Alliance (G-519)

Key Press Inc ....G 513 721-1203
Cincinnati (G-3987)

Knowles Press Inc ....G 330 877-9345
Hartville (G-10827)

Meridian Arts and Graphics ....F 330 759-9099
Youngstown (G-21143)

Michael R Kelly ....G 614 491-1745
Obetz (G-15656)

Queen City Reprographics...................C 513 326-2300
Cincinnati (G-4319)

Sportsartcom ....G 330 903-0895
Copley (G-7856)

Tecnocap LLC ....D 330 392-7222
Warren (G-19604)

Youngstown Pre-Press Inc ....F 330 793-3690
Youngstown (G-21255)

PRINTING, LITHOGRAPHIC: Posters

Frame Warehouse ....G 614 861-4582
Reynoldsburg (G-16591)

PRINTING, LITHOGRAPHIC: Publications

International Cntr Artfcial or ....G 440 358-1102
Painesville (G-15891)

PRINTING, LITHOGRAPHIC: Tags

Printprod Inc ....F 937 228-2181
Dayton (G-8596)

Trebnick Systems Inc ....E 937 743-1550
Springboro (G-17512)

PRINTING, LITHOGRAPHIC: Tickets

Toledo Ticket Company ....E 419 476-5424
Toledo (G-18746)

PRINTING, LITHOGRAPHIC: Transfers, Decalcomania Or Dry

Air Waves Inc ....C 740 548-1200
Lewis Center (G-11883)

Mark-N-Mend Inc ....G 440 951-2003
Willoughby (G-20537)

Transfer Express Inc ....D 440 918-1900
Mentor (G-13755)

PRINTING: Book Music

Indian River Industries ....G...... 740 965-4377
  Sunbury (G-18064)

PRINTING: Books

Printex Incorporated ....F....... 740 773-0088
  Chillicothe (G-3268)
Quebecor World Johnson Hardin ....A...... 614 326-0299
  Cincinnati (G-4312)
RR Donnelley & Sons Company ....A...... 419 935-0111
  Willard (G-20400)

PRINTING: Books

D B Hess Company ....G...... 330 676-2006
  Kent (G-11445)
Golf Marketing Group Inc ....G...... 330 963-5155
  Twinsburg (G-18950)
Hubbard Company ....E...... 419 784-4455
  Defiance (G-8794)
J & L Management Corporation ....G...... 440 205-1199
  Mentor (G-13614)
Naomi Kight ....G...... 937 278-0040
  Dayton (G-8517)

PRINTING: Broadwoven Fabrics. Cotton

Rapid Signs & More Inc ....G...... 513 553-4040
  New Richmond (G-14944)

PRINTING: Commercial, NEC

3dlt LLC ....F....... 513 452-3358
  Cincinnati (G-3324)
A E Wilson Holdings Inc ....G...... 330 405-0316
  Twinsburg (G-18888)
A Sign For The Times Inc ....G...... 216 297-2977
  Cleveland (G-4678)
A To Z Paper Box Co ....G...... 330 325-8722
  Rootstown (G-16718)
A Z Printing Inc ....G...... 513 733-3900
  Cincinnati (G-3338)
A Z Printing Inc ....G...... 513 745-0700
  Cincinnati (G-3339)
Able Printing Company ....G...... 614 294-4547
  Columbus (G-6682)
Advanced Specialty Products ....D...... 419 882-6528
  Bowling Green (G-1966)
Aero Fulfillment Services Corp ....D...... 800 225-7145
  Mason (G-12979)
Agnone-Kelly Enterprises Inc ....G...... 800 634-6503
  Cincinnati (G-3367)
AGS Custom Graphics Inc ....D...... 330 963-7770
  Macedonia (G-12433)
Akos Promotions Inc ....G...... 513 398-6324
  Mason (G-12980)
Alfacomp Inc ....G...... 216 459-1790
  Cleveland (G-4751)
Amerigraph Llc ....G...... 614 278-8000
  Columbus (G-6743)
Ameriprint ....G...... 440 235-6094
  Olmsted Falls (G-15673)
Amtech Inc ....G...... 440 238-2141
  Strongsville (G-17888)
Anderson Graphics Inc ....E...... 330 745-2165
  Barberton (G-1098)
Appleheart ....G...... 937 384-0430
  Miamisburg (G-13784)
Ashton LLC ....F....... 614 833-4165
  Pickerington (G-16186)
Associated Graphics Inc ....F....... 614 873-1273
  Plain City (G-16321)
Atlas Printing and Embroidery ....G...... 440 882-3537
  Cleveland (G-4856)
August Graphics Inc ....G...... 216 381-5503
  Cleveland (G-4858)
Austin Tape and Label Inc ....D...... 330 928-7999
  Stow (G-17731)
Baise Enterprises Inc ....G...... 614 444-3171
  Columbus (G-6801)
Bates Printing Inc ....F....... 330 833-5830
  Massillon (G-13114)
Bemis Company Inc ....E...... 330 923-5281
  Akron (G-87)
Bindery & Spc Pressworks Inc ....D...... 614 873-4623
  Plain City (G-16326)
Bizzy Bee Printing Inc ....G...... 614 771-1222
  Columbus (G-6833)
Bock & Pierce Enterprises ....G...... 513 474-9500
  Cincinnati (G-3455)

Bohlender Engraving Company ....F....... 513 621-4095
  Cincinnati (G-3457)
Bollin & Sons Inc ....E...... 419 693-6573
  Toledo (G-18376)
Bornhorst Printing Company Inc ....G...... 419 738-5901
  Wapakoneta (G-19482)
Brakers Publishing & Prtg Svc ....G...... 440 576-0136
  Jefferson (G-11357)
Broadway Printing LLC ....G...... 513 621-3429
  Cincinnati (G-3475)
Brune Printing Co ....G...... 419 399-2756
  Paulding (G-16002)
Burns & Rink Enterprises LLC ....G...... 513 421-7799
  Cincinnati (G-3487)
Bush Inc ....E...... 216 362-6700
  Cleveland (G-4952)
C P S Enterprises Inc ....F....... 216 441-7969
  Cleveland (G-4957)
Canvas 123 Inc ....G...... 312 805-0563
  Akron (G-108)
Carbonless & Cut Sheet Forms ....F....... 740 826-1700
  New Concord (G-14817)
Carey Color Llc/Cincinnati ....G...... 513 241-5210
  Cincinnati (G-3499)
Casad Company Inc ....F....... 419 586-9457
  Coldwater (G-6555)
Cds Signs ....G...... 513 563-7446
  Cincinnati (G-3508)
Century Graphics Inc ....E...... 614 895-7698
  Westerville (G-20142)
Charles Huffman & Associates ....G...... 216 295-0850
  Warrensville Heights (G-19630)
Cincinnati Enquirer ....G...... 513 721-2700
  Cincinnati (G-3549)
Cincinnati Print Solutions LLC ....G...... 513 943-9500
  Amelia (G-570)
Cleveland Copy & Prtg Svc LLC ....G...... 216 861-0324
  Cleveland (G-5054)
Cloverleaf Office Slutions LLC ....G...... 614 219-9050
  Hilliard (G-10939)
Cnr Marketing Ltd ....G...... 937 293-1030
  Dayton (G-8233)
Coloring Book Solutions LLC ....F....... 419 281-9641
  Ashland (G-723)
Comdoc Inc ....G...... 330 899-8000
  Columbus (G-6970)
Consoldated Graphics Group Inc ....C...... 216 881-9191
  Cleveland (G-5116)
Consolidated Graphics Inc ....C...... 740 654-2112
  Lancaster (G-11699)
Consolidated Web ....G...... 216 881-7816
  Cleveland (G-5119)
Copy Cats Printing LLC ....G...... 440 345-5966
  Cleveland (G-5132)
Copy Source Inc ....G...... 937 642-7140
  Marysville (G-12939)
Corporate Dcment Solutions Inc ....F....... 513 595-8200
  Cincinnati (G-3613)
Coso Media LLC ....G...... 330 904-5889
  Hudson (G-11166)
Crabro Printing Inc ....G...... 740 533-3404
  Ironton (G-11291)
Creative Documents Solutions ....G...... 740 389-4252
  Marion (G-12864)
Creative Print Solutions LLC ....G...... 614 989-1747
  Westerville (G-20205)
Crest Graphics Inc ....F....... 513 271-2200
  Cincinnati (G-3619)
Culaine Inc ....G...... 419 345-4984
  Toledo (G-18417)
Custom Products Corporation ....C...... 440 528-7100
  Solon (G-17280)
Customer Service Systems Inc ....G...... 330 677-2877
  Kent (G-11442)
D B Hess Company ....E...... 330 678-5868
  Kent (G-11444)
D B Hess Company ....G...... 330 676-2006
  Kent (G-11445)
Danner Press Corp ....G...... 330 454-5692
  Canton (G-2677)
Dayton Mailing Services Inc ....E...... 937 222-5056
  Dayton (G-8279)
Designer Set ....G...... 937 382-8000
  Wilmington (G-20663)
Dietrich Von Hildebrand Legacy ....G...... 703 496-7821
  Steubenville (G-17691)
Digital Graphics ....G...... 330 707-1720
  Youngstown (G-21069)
Digital Shorts Inc ....G...... 937 228-1700
  Dayton (G-8304)

Digital Visuals Inc ....G...... 513 420-9466
  Middletown (G-14037)
Direct Digital Graphics Inc ....G...... 330 405-3770
  Twinsburg (G-18925)
Divine Prtg T-Shirts & More ....G...... 419 241-8208
  Toledo (G-18441)
DK & J Inc ....G...... 216 357-3090
  Cleveland (G-5200)
Docupros ....G...... 513 242-7700
  Blue Ash (G-1776)
Dominion Labels & Forms ....G...... 419 784-1041
  Defiance (G-8789)
DSC Supply Company LLC ....G...... 614 891-1100
  Westerville (G-20211)
Dupli-Systems Inc ....C...... 440 234-9415
  Strongsville (G-17913)
Durbin Minuteman Press ....G...... 513 791-9171
  Blue Ash (G-1778)
E L Frueh Inc ....F....... 419 222-9741
  Lima (G-12007)
Eagle Image Inc ....F....... 513 662-3000
  Cincinnati (G-3683)
Eastern Graphic Arts ....G...... 419 994-5815
  Loudonville (G-12297)
Emta Inc ....G...... 440 734-6464
  North Olmsted (G-15332)
Evolution Crtive Solutions LLC ....E...... 513 681-4450
  Cincinnati (G-3725)
Express Graphic Prtg & Design ....G...... 513 728-3344
  Cincinnati (G-3731)
F J Designs Inc ....E...... 330 264-1377
  Wooster (G-20771)
Fedex Office & Print Svcs Inc ....E...... 614 898-0000
  Westerville (G-20214)
Fine Line Embroidery Company ....G...... 440 331-7030
  Rocky River (G-16699)
Firelands Fas-Print LLC ....G...... 419 668-3045
  Norwalk (G-15541)
Folks Creative Printers Inc ....E...... 740 383-6326
  Marion (G-12865)
Freeport Press Inc ....C...... 740 658-3315
  Freeport (G-10118)
G Q Business Products ....G...... 513 792-4750
  Blue Ash (G-1801)
G2 Print Plus ....F....... 614 276-0500
  Columbus (G-7105)
GBS Corp ....E...... 330 929-8050
  Stow (G-17758)
GBS Corp ....C...... 330 494-5330
  North Canton (G-15233)
GCI Digital Imaging Inc ....F....... 513 521-7446
  Cincinnati (G-3802)
General Data Company Inc ....C...... 513 752-7978
  Cincinnati (G-3304)
General Theming Contrs LLC ....C...... 614 252-6342
  Columbus (G-7108)
Genesis Graphics ....G...... 937 335-5332
  Troy (G-18831)
Genesis Quality Printing Inc ....G...... 440 975-5700
  Mentor (G-13592)
Golden Graphics Ltd ....F....... 419 673-6260
  Kenton (G-11548)
Gordon Bernard Company LLC ....E...... 513 248-7600
  Milford (G-14147)
Grant John ....G...... 937 298-0633
  Dayton (G-8376)
Graphic Paper Products Corp ....G...... 937 325-3912
  Springfield (G-17566)
Graphic Stitch inc ....G...... 937 642-6707
  Marysville (G-12945)
Graphics To Go LLC ....G...... 937 382-4100
  Wilmington (G-20666)
Haines & Company Inc ....C...... 330 494-9111
  North Canton (G-15237)
Harper Engraving & Printing Co ....D...... 614 276-0700
  Columbus (G-7144)
Harris & Company Inc ....F....... 330 332-4127
  Salem (G-16899)
Hecks Direct Mail & Prtg Svc ....E...... 419 697-3505
  Toledo (G-18502)
Hilltop Printing ....G...... 419 782-9898
  Defiance (G-8793)
Hkm Direct Mkt Cmmnications Inc ....E...... 440 934-3060
  Sheffield Village (G-17122)
Hkm Direct Mkt Cmmnications Inc ....E...... 330 395-9538
  Cleveland (G-5517)
Hkm Direct Mkt Cmmnications Inc ....C...... 216 651-9500
  Cleveland (G-5516)
Hollys Custom Print Inc ....E...... 740 928-2697
  Hebron (G-10871)

Employee Codes: A=Over 500 employees, B=251-500
C=101-250, D=51-100, E=20-50, F=10-19, G=3-9

2017 Harris Ohio
Industrial Directory

1617

PRODUCT

Homestretch Inc	G	419 738-6604	
Wapakoneta (G-19488)			
Homewood Press Inc	E	419 478-0695	
Toledo (G-18510)			
Horizon Ohio Publications Inc	E	419 738-2128	
Wapakoneta (G-19489)			
Humtown Pattern Company	D	330 482-5555	
Columbiana (G-6621)			
Image Print Inc	G	614 776-3985	
Westerville (G-20158)			
Imagemart Inc	G	216 486-4767	
Cleveland (G-5552)			
Imagine This Renovations	G	330 833-6739	
Navarre (G-14716)			
Impressions - A Print Shop	G	440 449-6966	
Cleveland (G-5558)			
Inktastic Inc	F	330 345-0911	
Wooster (G-20787)			
Innomark Communications LLC	C	513 285-1040	
Miamisburg (G-13819)			
Innovtive Lbling Solutions Inc	D	513 860-2457	
Hamilton (G-10706)			
Inskeep Brothers Inc	F	614 898-6620	
Columbus (G-7189)			
Instant Impressions Inc	G	614 538-9844	
Columbus (G-7191)			
Integrity Printing	G	937 331-5390	
Dayton (G-8414)			
Intermec Technologies Corp	F	513 874-5882	
West Chester (G-19884)			
International Advg Concepts	G	440 331-4733	
Cleveland (G-5579)			
J & K Printing	G	330 456-5306	
Canton (G-2742)			
Jack G Walker	F	440 352-4222	
Mentor (G-13617)			
Jeffrey Reedy	G	614 794-9292	
Westerville (G-20219)			
Jim Davis	G	740 335-8030	
Wshngtn CT Hs (G-20914)			
Joe Sestito	G	614 871-7778	
Grove City (G-10566)			
Jscs Group Inc	G	513 563-4900	
Cincinnati (G-3961)			
Kay Toledo Tag Inc	D	419 729-5479	
Toledo (G-18541)			
Kdm Signs Inc	C	513 769-1932	
Cincinnati (G-3975)			
Kenwel Printers Inc	E	614 261-1011	
Columbus (G-7257)			
Keteli Teamwear LLC	G	740 373-7969	
Marietta (G-12797)			
Key Marketing Group	G	440 748-3479	
Grafton (G-10432)			
Keystone Printing & Copy Cat	G	740 354-6542	
Portsmouth (G-16439)			
Kramer Graphics Inc	E	937 296-9600	
Moraine (G-14499)			
Labeltek Inc	D	330 335-3110	
Wadsworth (G-19417)			
Lake Screen Printing Inc	G	440 244-5707	
Lorain (G-12254)			
Lamar Proforma	G	440 285-2277	
Chardon (G-3163)			
Landen Desktop Pubg Ctr Inc	G	513 683-5181	
Loveland (G-12370)			
Laughing Star Montessory	G	513 683-5682	
Maineville (G-12527)			
Leeper Printing Co Inc	G	419 243-2604	
Toledo (G-18556)			
Legendary Ink Inc	G	614 766-5101	
Columbus (G-7290)			
Lesher Printers Inc	E	419 332-8253	
Fremont (G-10163)			
Letterman Printing Inc	G	513 523-1111	
Oxford (G-15839)			
Liberty Sportswear LLC	G	513 755-8740	
West Chester (G-19893)			
Liming Printing Inc	F	937 374-2646	
Xenia (G-20961)			
Locker Room Inc	G	419 445-9600	
Archbold (G-684)			
Logan Screen Printing	G	740 385-3303	
Logan (G-12185)			
Loris Printing Inc	G	419 626-6648	
Sandusky (G-16981)			
M L Advertising & Design LLC	G	419 447-6523	
Tiffin (G-18230)			
Mac Printing Company	G	937 393-1101	
Hillsboro (G-11007)			
Madison Graphics	G	216 226-5770	
Cleveland (G-5726)			
Marbee Inc	G	419 422-9441	
Findlay (G-9858)			
Marcus Uppe Inc	D	216 263-4000	
Cleveland (G-5742)			
Margaret Trentman	G	513 948-1700	
Cincinnati (G-4059)			
Markethatch Co Inc	F	330 376-6363	
Akron (G-285)			
Marysville Printing Company	G	937 644-4959	
Marysville (G-12958)			
Matthew Koster	G	440 887-9000	
Valley City (G-19216)			
McPc Imaging and Printing LLC	G	419 627-9872	
Sandusky (G-16987)			
Metro Flex Inc	G	937 299-5360	
Moraine (G-14506)			
Meyers Printing & Design Inc	G	937 461-6000	
Dayton (G-8488)			
Miami Graphics Services Inc	G	937 698-4013	
West Milton (G-20108)			
Middleton Printing Co Inc	G	614 294-7277	
Gahanna (G-10219)			
Miracle Documents	G	513 651-2222	
Cincinnati (G-4111)			
Mmp Printing Inc	E	513 381-0990	
Cincinnati (G-4112)			
Morse Enterprises Inc	G	513 229-3600	
Mason (G-13066)			
Mound Printing Company Inc	G	937 866-2872	
Miamisburg (G-13838)			
Network Printing & Graphics	F	614 230-2084	
Columbus (G-7387)			
Newton Falls Printing	G	330 872-3532	
Newton Falls (G-15137)			
Nilpeter Usa Inc	C	513 489-4400	
Cincinnati (G-4156)			
Nomis Publications Inc	F	330 965-2380	
Youngstown (G-21150)			
Novex Systems LLC	G	330 659-3546	
Akron (G-320)			
Old Trail Printing Company	C	614 443-4852	
Columbus (G-7440)			
Onetouchpoint East Corp	D	513 421-1600	
Cincinnati (G-4189)			
Packaging Materials Inc	E	740 432-6337	
Cambridge (G-2471)			
Park PLC Prntg Cpyg & Dgtl IMG	G	330 799-1739	
Youngstown (G-21164)			
Park Press Direct	F	419 626-4426	
Sandusky (G-16993)			
Peebles Creative Group Inc	G	614 487-2011	
Dublin (G-9120)			
Penguin Enterprises Inc	G	440 899-5110	
Westlake (G-20292)			
Pep Pony Express Printing Inc	G	513 542-4882	
Cincinnati (G-4222)			
Perfection Printing	F	513 874-2173	
Fairfield (G-9701)			
Pexco Packaging Corp	E	419 470-5935	
Toledo (G-18642)			
Powell Prints LLC	G	614 771-4830	
Hilliard (G-10971)			
Premiere Printing & Signs Inc	G	330 688-6244	
Stow (G-17791)			
Press of Ohio Inc	E	330 678-5868	
Kent (G-11506)			
Printing Depot Inc	G	330 783-5341	
Youngstown (G-21179)			
Profile Digital Printing LLC	E	937 866-4241	
Dayton (G-8599)			
Proforma Advantage	G	440 781-5255	
Mayfield Village (G-13325)			
Proforma Steinbacher & Assoc	G	330 241-5370	
Medina (G-13463)			
Proforma Systems Advantage	G	419 224-8747	
Lima (G-12076)			
Progressive Printers Inc	D	937 222-1267	
Dayton (G-8601)			
PS Graphics Inc	G	440 356-9656	
Rocky River (G-16706)			
Quality Print Shop Inc	G	740 992-3345	
Middleport (G-14011)			
Quick As A Wink Printing Co	F	419 224-9786	
Lima (G-12079)			
R C L Enterprises Inc	G	972 390-6500	
Cincinnati (G-4323)			
R W Michael Printing Co	G	330 923-9277	
Akron (G-363)			
R&D Marketing Group Inc	G	216 398-9100	
Brooklyn Heights (G-2145)			
Research and Development Group	G	614 261-0454	
Columbus (G-7556)			
Reynolds and Reynolds Company	F	419 584-7000	
Celina (G-3017)			
RI Smith Printing Co	F	330 747-9590	
Youngstown (G-21189)			
Robert Esterman	G	513 541-3311	
Cincinnati (G-4353)			
Robert H Shackelford	G	330 364-2221	
New Philadelphia (G-14926)			
RR Donnelley & Sons Company	A	419 935-0111	
Willard (G-20400)			
Ryans Newark Leader Ex Prtg	F	740 522-2149	
Newark (G-15051)			
Sandy Smittcamp	G	937 372-1687	
Xenia (G-20971)			
Saturn Press Inc	G	440 232-3344	
Bedford (G-1460)			
Schilling Graphics Inc	G	419 468-1037	
Galion (G-10286)			
Schlabach Printing Ltd	E	330 852-4687	
Sugarcreek (G-18038)			
Sensical Inc	D	216 641-1141	
Solon (G-17378)			
Sevell + Sevell Inc	G	614 341-9700	
Columbus (G-7611)			
Silica Press Inc	G	419 843-8500	
Sylvania (G-18125)			
Slutzkers Quickprint Center	G	440 244-0330	
Lorain (G-12278)			
Small Dog Printing	G	614 777-7620	
Hilliard (G-10979)			
SMS Communications Inc	E	216 374-6686	
Shaker Heights (G-17095)			
Snyder Printing LLC	G	740 353-3947	
Portsmouth (G-16455)			
Somerset Commercial Prtg Co	G	740 536-7187	
Rushville (G-16753)			
Special Touch Midnight Press	G	740 596-5380	
South Bloomingville (G-17423)			
Spencer-Walker Press Inc	G	740 345-4494	
Newark (G-15056)			
Spencer-Walker Press Inc	G	740 344-6110	
Newark (G-15055)			
Springdot Inc	D	513 542-4000	
Cincinnati (G-4448)			
Stadvec Inc	G	330 644-7724	
Barberton (G-1150)			
Standard Register Inc	C	419 678-6000	
Coldwater (G-6572)			
Standard Register Inc	C	614 277-7500	
Grove City (G-10598)			
Standard Register Inc	E	860 870-2063	
Dayton (G-8676)			
Standout Stickers Inc	G	877 449-7703	
Medina (G-13483)			
Stephen Andrews Inc	G	330 725-2672	
Lodi (G-12170)			
Stolle Machinery Company LLC	C	937 497-5400	
Sidney (G-17230)			
Suburban Press Inc	E	216 961-0766	
Cleveland (G-6260)			
Suntwist Corp	E	800 935-3534	
Maple Heights (G-12741)			
T & L Custom Screening Inc	G	937 237-3121	
Dayton (G-8695)			
The Label Team Inc	F	330 332-1067	
Salem (G-16929)			
Thomas Allen Co	G	330 823-8487	
Alliance (G-544)			
Tj Metzgers Inc	D	419 861-8611	
Toledo (G-18726)			
Toledo Ticket Company	E	419 476-5424	
Toledo (G-18746)			
Tree Free Resources LLC	F	740 751-4844	
Marion (G-12908)			
Trinity Printing Co	F	513 469-1000	
Cincinnati (G-4526)			
US Government Publishing Off	G	614 469-5657	
Columbus (G-7727)			
Value Added Business Svcs Co	G	614 854-9755	
Jackson (G-11332)			
Vision Press Inc	G	440 357-6362	
Painesville (G-15937)			
Visual Information Institute	F	937 376-4361	
Xenia (G-20985)			
Vya Inc	E	513 772-5400	
Cincinnati (G-4573)			

Ward/Kraft Forms of Ohio Inc ....D 740 694-0015
  Fredericktown *(G-10116)*
West-Camp Press Inc ....D 614 818-6279
  Westerville *(G-20241)*
Western Ohio Graphics ....F 937 335-8769
  Troy *(G-18885)*
Western Reserve Printing ....G 330 650-9800
  Hudson *(G-11209)*
Western Roto Engravers Inc ....E 330 336-7636
  Wadsworth *(G-19444)*
Wfsr Holdings LLC ....A 877 735-4966
  Dayton *(G-8757)*
William J Dupps ....G 419 734-2126
  Port Clinton *(G-16419)*
Williams Steel Rule Die Co ....F 216 431-3232
  Cleveland *(G-6464)*
Wingate Packaging South ....E 513 745-8600
  Blue Ash *(G-1895)*
X Press Printing Services Inc ....F 440 951-8848
  Willoughby *(G-20633)*
Yi Xing Inc ....G 614 785-9631
  Columbus *(G-7784)*
Yockey Group Inc ....E 513 860-9053
  West Chester *(G-19975)*
Youngstown ARC Engraving Co ....E 330 793-2471
  Youngstown *(G-21245)*
Zippity Print ....G 216 438-0001
  Cleveland *(G-6497)*

PRINTING: Engraving & Plate

Converters/Prepress Inc ....E 937 743-0935
  Carlisle *(G-2929)*
Northmont Sign Co Inc ....G 937 890-0372
  Dayton *(G-8528)*
Roban Inc ....G 330 794-1059
  Lakemore *(G-11645)*
Sams Graphic Industries ....F 330 821-4710
  Alliance *(G-536)*

PRINTING: Flexographic

Admiral Products Company Inc ....E 216 671-0600
  Cleveland *(G-4706)*
Cincinnati Convertors Inc ....F 513 731-6600
  Cincinnati *(G-3545)*
Ebel-Binder Printing Co ....G 513 471-1067
  Cincinnati *(G-3688)*
Gateway Packaging Company ....G 419 738-5126
  Wapakoneta *(G-19486)*
Hawks & Associates Inc ....E 513 752-4311
  Cincinnati *(G-3308)*
Intermec Ultra Print Inc ....C 513 874-5882
  West Chester *(G-19885)*
Lazer Systems Inc ....F 513 641-4002
  Cincinnati *(G-4016)*
Mr Label Inc ....E 513 681-2088
  Cincinnati *(G-4128)*
Novavision Inc ....D 419 354-1427
  Bowling Green *(G-2003)*
Ohio Flexible Packaging Co ....F 513 494-1800
  South Lebanon *(G-17430)*
Samuels Products Inc ....E 513 891-4456
  Blue Ash *(G-1864)*
Seneca Label Inc ....E 440 237-1600
  Cleveland *(G-6180)*
Superior Label Systems Inc ....B 513 336-0825
  Mason *(G-13092)*
Thomas Products Co Inc ....E 513 756-9009
  Cincinnati *(G-4507)*
Warren Printing & Off Pdts Inc ....F 419 523-3635
  Ottawa *(G-15814)*
West Carrollton Parchment ....E 513 594-3341
  West Carrollton *(G-19794)*

PRINTING: Gravure, Business Form & Card

Business Fnctnality Forms Svcs ....G 614 557-9420
  Gahanna *(G-10205)*
Wilmer ....G 419 678-6000
  Coldwater *(G-6574)*

PRINTING: Gravure, Color

Hotcardscom Inc ....E 216 241-4040
  Cleveland *(G-5528)*

PRINTING: Gravure, Coupons

Clipper Magazine LLC ....G 937 534-0470
  Moraine *(G-14472)*

PRINTING: Gravure, Directories, Phone, No Publishing On-Site

Graphic Paper Products Corp ....G 937 322-7711
  Springfield *(G-17565)*

PRINTING: Gravure, Envelopes

Ohio Envelope Manufacturing Co ....E 216 267-2920
  Cleveland *(G-5933)*

PRINTING: Gravure, Forms, Business

Dupli-Systems Inc ....C 440 234-9415
  Strongsville *(G-17913)*

PRINTING: Gravure, Invitations

Miami Valley Press Inc ....G 937 547-0771
  Greenville *(G-10511)*
Revenue Management Group LLC ....G 419 993-2200
  Lima *(G-12082)*

PRINTING: Gravure, Job

Cham Cor Industries Inc ....G 740 967-9015
  Johnstown *(G-11395)*
Graphic Paper Products Corp ....D 937 325-5503
  Springfield *(G-17564)*

PRINTING: Gravure, Labels

Admiral Products Company Inc ....E 216 671-0600
  Cleveland *(G-4706)*
Anthony Business Forms Inc ....F 937 253-0072
  Dayton *(G-8096)*
E-Z Stop Service Center ....D 330 448-2236
  Brookfield *(G-2123)*
Label Print Technologies LLC ....F 800 475-4030
  Mogadore *(G-14380)*
M PI Label Systems ....G 330 938-2134
  Sebring *(G-17047)*
Mpi Labels of Baltimore Inc ....F 330 938-2134
  Sebring *(G-17049)*
Retterbush Graphic and Packg ....E 513 779-4466
  West Chester *(G-19931)*
Scratch-Off Systems Inc ....E 216 649-7800
  Brecksville *(G-2071)*

PRINTING: Gravure, Rotogravure

Angstrom Graphics Inc ....C 216 271-5300
  Cleveland *(G-4814)*
Dulle Associates ....G 513 723-9600
  Cincinnati *(G-3674)*
Lloyd F Helber ....E 740 756-9607
  Carroll *(G-2943)*
Lsc Communications Us LLC ....C 419 935-0111
  Willard *(G-20396)*
Multi-Color Australia LLC ....B 513 381-1480
  Batavia *(G-1210)*
Multi-Color Corporation ....D 513 943-0080
  Batavia *(G-1212)*
Ohio Gravure Technologies Inc ....E 937 439-1582
  Miamisburg *(G-13846)*
Quad/Graphics Inc ....A 513 932-1064
  Lebanon *(G-11830)*
Shamrock Companies Inc ....D 440 899-9510
  Westlake *(G-20308)*
Standard Register Inc ....G 866 541-0937
  Dayton *(G-8680)*
Standard Register Inc ....E 937 228-5800
  Dayton *(G-8679)*
Trebnick Systems Inc ....E 937 743-1550
  Springboro *(G-17512)*
W L Beck Printing & Design ....G 330 762-3020
  Akron *(G-467)*
Wfsr Holdings LLC ....A 877 735-4966
  Dayton *(G-8757)*
World Color (usa) Corp ....G 847 230-1547
  Oberlin *(G-15649)*

PRINTING: Laser

Data Image ....E 740 763-7017
  Heath *(G-10846)*
DCS Technologies Corporation ....E 937 743-4060
  Franklin *(G-10018)*
Laser Printing Solutions Inc ....F 216 351-4444
  Cleveland *(G-5684)*
Marketing Comm Resource Inc ....D 440 484-3010
  Willoughby *(G-20538)*

Microplex Printware Corp ....F 440 374-2424
  Bedford *(G-1443)*
Queen City Office Machine ....F 513 251-7200
  Cincinnati *(G-4317)*

PRINTING: Letterpress

A-A Blueprint Co Inc ....E 330 794-8803
  Akron *(G-22)*
Acme Printing Co Inc ....G 419 626-4426
  Sandusky *(G-16944)*
Akron Litho-Print Company Inc ....F 330 434-3145
  Akron *(G-47)*
Art Printing Co Inc ....G 419 281-4371
  Ashland *(G-705)*
Barnhart Printing Corp ....F 330 456-2279
  Canton *(G-2616)*
Berea Printing Company ....G 440 243-1080
  Berea *(G-1605)*
Betley Printing Co ....G 216 206-5600
  Cleveland *(G-4910)*
Boldman Printing LLC ....G 937 653-3431
  Urbana *(G-19148)*
Bramkamp Printing Company Inc ....E 513 241-1865
  Blue Ash *(G-1754)*
Brothers Printing Co Inc ....F 216 621-6050
  Cleveland *(G-4938)*
Cornerstone Industries Lcc ....G 513 871-4546
  West Chester *(G-19845)*
Cox Printing Co ....G 937 382-2312
  Wilmington *(G-20661)*
Dana Graphics Inc ....G 513 351-4400
  Cincinnati *(G-3638)*
Dee Printing Inc ....F 614 777-8700
  Columbus *(G-7017)*
Diocesan Publications Inc Ohio ....E 614 718-9500
  Dublin *(G-9068)*
Douglas Michalske ....G 216 631-0567
  Cleveland *(G-5210)*
DOV Graphics Inc ....E 513 241-5150
  Cincinnati *(G-3668)*
Dresden Specialties Inc ....G 740 452-7100
  Zanesville *(G-21302)*
Dresden Specialties Inc ....G 740 754-2451
  Dresden *(G-9032)*
Earl D Arnold Printing Company ....E 513 533-6900
  Cincinnati *(G-3685)*
Empire Printing Inc ....G 513 242-3900
  Cincinnati *(G-3700)*
Exact Software North Amer LLC ....C 978 539-6186
  Dublin *(G-9075)*
Exchange Printing Company ....G 330 773-7842
  Akron *(G-173)*
Foote Printing Company ....F 216 431-1757
  Cleveland *(G-5367)*
Graphic Touch Inc ....G 330 337-3341
  Salem *(G-16896)*
Great Lakes Printing Inc ....D 440 993-8781
  Ashtabula *(G-810)*
Heskamp Printing Co Inc ....G 513 871-6770
  Cincinnati *(G-3881)*
J P Quality Printing Inc ....G 216 791-6303
  Cleveland *(G-5598)*
Jarman Printing Company LLC ....G 330 823-8585
  Alliance *(G-519)*
Johnson Printing ....G 740 922-4821
  Uhrichsville *(G-19053)*
Kee Printing Inc ....G 937 456-6851
  Eaton *(G-9312)*
Kehoe Brothers Printing Inc ....G 216 351-4100
  Cleveland *(G-5641)*
Keithley Enterprises Inc ....G 937 890-1878
  Dayton *(G-8434)*
Key Press Inc ....G 513 721-1203
  Cincinnati *(G-3987)*
Keystone Press Inc ....G 419 243-7326
  Toledo *(G-18544)*
KMS 2000 Inc ....F 330 454-9444
  Canton *(G-2756)*
Krok Printing Inc ....G 330 652-8198
  Niles *(G-15166)*
Lee Corporation ....F 513 771-3602
  Cincinnati *(G-4019)*
Lilienthal Southeastern Inc ....F 740 439-1640
  Cambridge *(G-2464)*
Lsc Communications Us LLC ....C 419 935-0111
  Willard *(G-20396)*
Lund Printing Co ....G 330 628-4047
  Akron *(G-277)*
Lyle Printing & Publishing Co ....E 330 337-3419
  Salem *(G-16909)*

Employee Codes: A=Over 500 employees, B=251-500
C=101-250, D=51-100, E=20-50, F=10-19, G=3-9

2017 Harris Ohio
Industrial Directory

PRODUCT

1619

Madison Press Inc ....G....216 521-3789
Lakewood (G-11673)
Mariotti Printing Co LLC....G....440 245-4120
Lorain (G-12259)
Martin Printing Co....G....419 224-9176
Lima (G-12051)
Minuteman Press of Athens LLC....G....740 593-7393
Athens (G-878)
Nelis Printing Co....G....330 757-4114
Youngstown (G-21149)
News Gazette Printing Company....F....419 227-2527
Lima (G-12063)
Odyssey Press Inc....F....614 410-0356
Huron (G-11236)
Paragon Press....G....513 281-9911
Cincinnati (G-4211)
Post Printing Co....D....859 254-7714
Minster (G-14359)
Printcraft Inc....G....440 599-8903
Conneaut (G-7817)
Printex Incorporated....F....740 773-0088
Chillicothe (G-3268)
Rotary Printing Company....G....419 668-4821
Norwalk (G-15563)
RR Donnelley & Sons Company....E....440 774-2101
Oberlin (G-15647)
Selby Service/Roxy Press Inc....G....513 241-3445
Cincinnati (G-4400)
Shreve Printing LLC....F....330 567-2341
Shreve (G-17163)
Sitler Printer Inc....G....330 482-4463
Columbiana (G-6632)
Slimans Printery Inc....F....330 454-9141
Canton (G-2851)
Snow Printing Co Inc....F....419 229-7669
Lima (G-12093)
South End Printing Co....G....216 341-0669
Cleveland (G-6222)
Star Calendar & Printing Co....G....216 741-3223
Cleveland (G-6237)
Star Printing Company Inc....E....330 376-0514
Akron (G-415)
Starr Printing Services Inc....G....513 241-7708
Cincinnati (G-4460)
Stationery Shop Inc....G....330 376-2033
Akron (G-416)
Tope Printing Inc....G....330 674-4993
Millersburg (G-14271)
Traxium LLC....E....330 572-8200
Stow (G-17811)
Wilkinson Printing Co....G....419 238-3615
Van Wert (G-19276)
William J Bergen & Co....G....440 248-6132
Solon (G-17414)
Wirick Press Inc....G....330 273-3488
Brunswick (G-2269)
Zech Printing Industries Inc....E....937 748-2776
Cincinnati (G-4618)

PRINTING: Lithographic

1455 Group LLC....G....330 494-9074
Canton (G-2583)
4 Over LLC....F....937 610-0629
Dayton (G-8123)
A Grade Notes Inc....G....614 766-9999
Dublin (G-9034)
Action Printing Inc....G....330 963-7772
Twinsburg (G-18893)
Adcraft Decals Inc....E....216 524-2934
Cleveland (G-4702)
Admark Printing Inc....G....937 833-5111
Brookville (G-2173)
Advanatage Print Solut....G....614 519-2392
Columbus (G-6695)
Advanced Graphics of Dayton....G....937 228-2221
Dayton (G-8138)
Aero Printing Inc....G....419 695-2931
Delphos (G-8899)
Akron Thermography Inc....E....330 896-9712
Akron (G-59)
Alberts Screen Print Inc....C....330 753-7559
Norton (G-15505)
All American Screen Printing....G....419 475-0696
Toledo (G-18327)
All Print Ltd....F....440 349-6868
Solon (G-17252)
All Systems Colour Inc....G....937 859-9701
Dayton (G-8144)
Alliance Publishing Co Inc....C....330 453-1304
Alliance (G-495)
Alpha Print Specialties....G....440 282-1150
Lorain (G-12231)
AlphaGraphics 507 Inc....G....440 878-9700
Strongsville (G-17886)
Alt Control Print....G....419 841-2467
Toledo (G-18333)
Alvito Custom Imprints....G....614 846-8986
Worthington (G-20856)
Anderson Printing & Supply LLC....G....614 891-1100
Westerville (G-20199)
Angell-Demmel North Amer Corp....D....937 461-5800
Dayton (G-8158)
Angstrom Graphics Inc....C....216 271-5300
Cleveland (G-4814)
Angstrom Graphics Southeast....G....216 271-5300
Cleveland (G-4816)
Anthony Business Forms Inc....F....937 253-0072
Dayton (G-8096)
Armstrong S Printing Ex LLC....G....937 276-7794
Dayton (G-8164)
Art Pro Graphics....G....216 236-6465
Seven Hills (G-17060)
Ashland Inc Valvoline Instant....G....330 653-3926
Hudson (G-11159)
Avondale Printing Inc....G....330 477-1180
Canton (G-2610)
B2 Incorporated....G....330 244-9510
North Canton (G-15221)
Baise Enterprises Inc....G....614 444-3171
Columbus (G-6801)
Bang Printing of Ohio Inc....F....800 678-1222
Kent (G-11432)
Bansal Enterprises Inc....F....330 633-9355
Akron (G-84)
Barberton Printcraft....G....330 848-3000
Barberton (G-1109)
Barnhart Printing Corp....F....330 456-2279
Canton (G-2616)
BCT Alarm Services Inc....G....440 669-8153
Amherst (G-591)
Beckman Xmo....F....614 864-3305
Columbus (G-6818)
Belle Printing....G....937 592-5161
Bellefontaine (G-1521)
Bemis Company Inc....E....330 923-5281
Akron (G-87)
Berea Printing Company....G....440 243-1080
Berea (G-1605)
Bloch Printing Company....G....330 576-6760
Copley (G-7840)
Blue Crescent Enterprises Inc....G....440 878-9700
Strongsville (G-17897)
Blueserv Reprograhics LLC....G....937 426-6410
Beavercreek (G-1370)
Bock & Pierce Enterprises....G....513 474-9500
Cincinnati (G-3455)
Bodnar Printing Co Inc....F....440 277-8295
Lorain (G-12234)
Boehm Inc....E....614 875-9010
Grove City (G-10546)
Boehr Print....G....419 358-1350
Findlay (G-9799)
Bohlender Engraving Company....F....513 621-4095
Cincinnati (G-3457)
Bookmasters Inc....C....419 281-1802
Ashland (G-713)
Bottomline Ink Corporation....E....419 897-8000
Perrysburg (G-16068)
Box King LLC....G....937 322-8117
Springfield (G-17524)
Brandon Screen Printing....F....419 229-9837
Lima (G-11996)
Bricolage Inc....G....614 853-6789
Grove City (G-10547)
Brookville Star....G....937 833-2545
Brookville (G-2177)
Buckeye Cstm Screen Print EMB....F....614 237-0196
Columbus (G-6872)
Busson Digital Printing Inc....E....330 753-8373
Wadsworth (G-19396)
C Massouh Printing Co Inc....F....330 408-7330
Canal Fulton (G-2500)
C Massouh Printing Co Inc....G....330 832-6334
Massillon (G-13116)
Canton Graphic Arts Service....G....330 456-9868
Canton (G-2641)
Capehart Enterprises LLC....F....614 769-7746
Columbus (G-6895)
Cats Printing Inc....G....216 381-8181
Cleveland (G-4995)
Central Ohio Printing Corp....D....740 852-1616
London (G-12203)
Century Graphics Inc....E....614 895-7698
Westerville (G-20142)
Century Marketing Corporation....C....419 354-2591
Bowling Green (G-1978)
Characters Inc....G....937 335-1976
Troy (G-18808)
Child Evngelism Fellowship Inc....E....440 218-4982
Cuyahoga Falls (G-7979)
Child Evngelism Fellowship Inc....E....419 756-7799
Mansfield (G-12579)
Cincinnati Print Solutions LLC....G....513 943-9500
Amelia (G-570)
City of Cleveland....F....216 664-3013
Cleveland (G-5035)
City Printing Co Inc....E....330 747-5691
Youngstown (G-21051)
Clints Printing Inc....G....937 426-2771
Beavercreek (G-1373)
Cnb LLC....G....419 528-3109
Ontario (G-15685)
Cns Inc....G....513 631-7073
Cincinnati (G-3593)
Commercial Prtg of Greenvill....G....937 548-3835
Greenville (G-10494)
Concept Printing of Wauseon....G....419 335-6627
Wauseon (G-19674)
Consoldated Graphics Group Inc....C....216 881-9191
Cleveland (G-5116)
Copley Ohio Newspapers Inc....D....330 833-2631
Massillon (G-13121)
Copy Right of Ohio LLC....G....614 431-1303
Plain City (G-16328)
Cornerstone Printing Inc....G....614 861-2138
Reynoldsburg (G-16585)
County Classifieds....G....937 592-8847
Bellefontaine (G-1525)
Covap Inc....F....513 793-1855
Blue Ash (G-1769)
Cowgill Printing Co....G....216 741-2076
Parma (G-15955)
Crabar/Gbf Inc....E....419 269-1720
Toledo (G-18415)
Crabar/Gbf Inc....G....419 943-2141
Leipsic (G-11868)
Creative Impressions Inc....F....937 435-5296
Dayton (G-8250)
Culaine Inc....G....419 345-4984
Toledo (G-18417)
Curless Printing Company....E....937 783-2403
Blanchester (G-1712)
Curv Imaging LLC....G....614 890-2878
Westerville (G-20207)
Customer Printing Inc....F....330 629-8676
Youngstown (G-21061)
Customer Service Systems Inc....G....330 677-2877
Kent (G-11442)
Cwh Graphics LLC....G....866 241-8515
Bedford Heights (G-1482)
D & J Printing Inc....D....330 678-5868
Kent (G-11443)
D & S Crtive Cmmunications Inc....D....419 524-6699
Mansfield (G-12591)
Daily Gazette....E....937 372-4444
Xenia (G-20945)
Danner Press Corp....G....330 454-5692
Canton (G-2677)
Dansizen Printing Co Inc....G....330 966-4962
North Canton (G-15226)
Daves Printing....G....513 221-0182
Cincinnati (G-3641)
David A and Mary A Mathis....G....330 837-8611
Massillon (G-13124)
Debandale Printing Inc....G....330 725-5122
Medina (G-13401)
Deerfield Ventures Inc....G....614 875-0688
Grove City (G-10553)
Digital Color Intl LLC....E....330 762-6959
Akron (G-152)
Directconnectgroup Ltd....A....216 281-2866
Cleveland (G-5196)
Dispatch Printing Company....E....614 885-6020
Columbus (G-7030)
Dixie Flyer & Printing Co....G....937 687-0088
New Lebanon (G-14841)
Dla Document Services....G....216 522-3535
Cleveland (G-5201)
Dla Document Services....E....937 257-6014
Dayton (G-8104)

Docmann Printing & Assoc Inc ....G....... 440 975-1775
Willoughby (G-20474)
Doll Inc ....G....... 419 586-7880
Celina (G-2992)
Donnelley Financial LLC ....F....... 216 621-8384
Cleveland (G-5208)
Double b Printing LLC ....G....... 740 593-7393
Athens (G-863)
Dsk Imaging LLC ....F....... 513 554-1797
Blue Ash (G-1777)
Duncan Press Corporation ....E....... 330 477-4529
Canton (G-2694)
Dupli-Systems Inc ....C....... 440 234-9415
Strongsville (G-17913)
Durbin Minuteman Press ....G....... 513 791-9171
Blue Ash (G-1778)
Eagle Printing & Graphics LLC ....G....... 937 773-7900
Piqua (G-16263)
Edwards Electrical & Mech ....E....... 614 485-2003
Columbus (G-7047)
Emta Inc ....G....... 440 734-6464
North Olmsted (G-15332)
Enlarging Arts Inc ....G....... 330 434-3433
Akron (G-168)
Enquirer Printing Company ....G....... 513 241-1956
Cincinnati (G-3708)
Envoi Design Inc ....G....... 513 651-4229
Cincinnati (G-3711)
Etched Metal Company ....E....... 440 248-0240
Solon (G-17290)
Eugene Stewart ....G....... 937 898-1117
Dayton (G-8333)
Eurostampa North America Inc ....D....... 513 821-2275
Cincinnati (G-3721)
Excelsior Printing Co ....G....... 740 927-2934
Pataskala (G-15970)
Exec-U-Print Inc ....G....... 440 333-6484
Rocky River (G-16698)
F P C Printing Inc ....G....... 937 743-8136
Franklin (G-10020)
Fair Publishing House Inc ....E....... 419 668-3746
Norwalk (G-15540)
Fairchild Printing Co ....G....... 216 641-4192
Cleveland (G-5319)
Far Corner ....G....... 330 767-3734
Navarre (G-14712)
Fedex Corporation ....G....... 740 687-0334
Lancaster (G-11716)
Fedex Office & Print Svcs Inc ....G....... 513 777-1079
West Chester (G-19862)
Fedex Office & Print Svcs Inc ....G....... 614 356-1639
Dublin (G-9076)
Fedex Office & Print Svcs Inc ....G....... 419 841-2756
Toledo (G-18465)
Fedex Office & Print Svcs Inc ....G....... 614 478-1180
Columbus (G-7079)
Fedex Office & Print Svcs Inc ....G....... 513 754-1482
Mason (G-13021)
Fedex Office & Print Svcs Inc ....G....... 440 605-0191
Richmond Heights (G-16653)
Fedex Office & Print Svcs Inc ....F....... 330 376-6002
Akron (G-183)
Fedex Office & Print Svcs Inc ....E....... 419 866-5464
Toledo (G-18466)
Fine Print LLC ....G....... 419 702-7087
Lakeside Marblehead (G-11648)
Finn Graphics Inc ....E....... 513 941-6161
Cincinnati (G-3756)
Fleet Graphics Inc ....G....... 937 252-2552
Dayton (G-8345)
Flowers Print Inc ....G....... 937 429-3823
Beavercreek (G-1338)
Follow Print Club On Facebook ....G....... 216 707-2579
Cleveland (G-5365)
Fortec Litho Central LLC ....G....... 330 463-1265
Streetsboro (G-17853)
Fourjays Inc ....G....... 216 741-8258
Parma (G-15958)
Franchise Services Inc ....G....... 513 731-1440
Cincinnati (G-3777)
Frank J Prucha & Associates ....G....... 216 642-3838
Cleveland (G-5378)
Frankies Graphics Inc ....G....... 440 979-0824
Westlake (G-20268)
Franklins Printing Company ....F....... 740 452-6375
Zanesville (G-21311)
Friends Service Co Inc ....F....... 800 427-1704
Dayton (G-8352)
Friends Service Co Inc ....G....... 800 427-1704
Kent (G-11459)
Frisby Printing Company ....G....... 330 665-4565
Fairlawn (G-9750)
G S Link & Associates ....G....... 513 722-2457
Goshen (G-10415)
Gannett Co Inc ....C....... 740 773-2111
Chillicothe (G-3240)
Gannett Co Inc ....E....... 740 295-3435
Coshocton (G-7892)
Gannett Stllite Info Ntwrk LLC ....D....... 419 334-1012
Fremont (G-10152)
Gazette Publishing Company ....E....... 419 483-4190
Oberlin (G-15640)
Genesis Quality Printing Inc ....G....... 440 975-5700
Mentor (G-13592)
Geygan Enterprises Inc ....F....... 513 932-4222
Lebanon (G-11803)
Globus Printing & Packg Co Inc ....D....... 419 628-2381
Minster (G-14354)
Gordon Bernard Co Inc ....E....... 513 248-7600
Milford (G-14146)
Gordon Bernard Company LLC ....E....... 513 248-7600
Milford (G-14147)
Graphic Expressions Signs ....G....... 330 422-7446
Streetsboro (G-17856)
Graphic Paper Products Corp ....D....... 937 325-5503
Springfield (G-17564)
Graphic Paper Products Corp ....G....... 937 322-7711
Springfield (G-17565)
Graphic Solutions Company ....F....... 513 484-3067
Cincinnati (G-3845)
Graphic TS ....G....... 614 836-2613
Groveport (G-10624)
Grayson Graphics Inc ....G....... 740 927-7080
Pataskala (G-15971)
Great Lakes Engraving Corp ....G....... 419 867-1607
Maumee (G-13262)
Great Lakes Integrated Inc ....D....... 216 651-1500
Cleveland (G-5452)
Great Lakes Integrated Inc ....E....... 440 892-7760
Avon Lake (G-1030)
Great Lakes Lithograph ....F....... 216 651-1500
Cleveland (G-5453)
Green Leaf Printing and Design ....G....... 937 222-3634
Dayton (G-8378)
Greg Blume ....G....... 740 574-2308
Wheelersburg (G-20332)
Gregg Macmillan ....G....... 513 248-2121
Milford (G-14148)
Haines & Company Inc ....C....... 330 494-9111
North Canton (G-15237)
Haman Enterprises Inc ....F....... 614 888-7574
Worthington (G-20869)
Harris & Company Inc ....F....... 330 332-4127
Salem (G-16899)
Hartman Printing Co ....G....... 419 946-2854
Mount Gilead (G-14561)
Hawks & Associates Inc ....E....... 513 752-4311
Cincinnati (G-3308)
Headlee Enterprises Ltd ....G....... 614 785-0011
Columbus (G-6649)
Heitkamp & Kremer Printing ....G....... 419 925-4121
Celina (G-3001)
Herald Inc ....E....... 419 492-2133
New Washington (G-14960)
Herff Jones Inc ....G....... 740 821-3109
Portsmouth (G-16438)
Hilleary-Whitaker Inc ....G....... 614 766-4694
Columbus (G-7157)
Hkm Drect Mkt Cmmnications Inc ....C....... 216 651-9500
Cleveland (G-5516)
Hollys Custom Print Inc ....E....... 740 928-2697
Hebron (G-10871)
Holmes Printing Solutions LLC ....G....... 330 234-9699
Fredericksburg (G-10087)
Horizon Ohio Publications Inc ....E....... 419 738-2128
Wapakoneta (G-19489)
Hudson Printing of Medina LLC ....G....... 330 591-4800
Medina (G-13424)
Icandi Graphics LLC ....G....... 330 723-8337
Medina (G-13425)
Image Concepts Inc ....F....... 216 524-9000
Cleveland (G-5550)
Info-Graphics Inc ....G....... 440 498-1640
Solon (G-17315)
Ink Inc ....G....... 330 875-4789
Louisville (G-12316)
Ink Well ....G....... 614 861-7113
Gahanna (G-10212)
Insta-Print Inc ....G....... 216 741-6500
Cleveland (G-5573)
Instant Replay ....G....... 937 592-0534
Bellefontaine (G-1534)
Integrity Print Solutions Inc ....G....... 330 818-0161
Akron (G-233)
It XCEL Consulting LLC ....F....... 513 847-8261
West Chester (G-19886)
J & L Management Corporation ....G....... 440 205-1199
Mentor (G-13614)
Jack G Walker ....F....... 440 352-4222
Mentor (G-13617)
Jakprints Inc ....C....... 877 246-3132
Cleveland (G-5605)
Jeffrey Reedy ....G....... 614 794-9292
Westerville (G-20219)
Jk Digital Publishing LLC ....E....... 937 299-0185
Springboro (G-17484)
JM Printing ....G....... 740 412-8666
Circleville (G-4632)
Joe The Printer Guy LLC ....G....... 216 651-3880
Lakewood (G-11670)
Jones Printing Services Inc ....G....... 440 946-7300
Eastlake (G-9277)
Joseph Berning Printing Co ....F....... 513 721-0781
Cincinnati (G-3957)
K B Printing ....G....... 614 771-1222
Columbus (G-7249)
Kad Holdings Inc ....G....... 614 792-3399
Dublin (G-9093)
Kader Printing LLC ....G....... 440 668-1579
North Royalton (G-15429)
Kelly Prints LLC ....G....... 440 356-6361
North Olmsted (G-15340)
Kendall & Sons Company ....G....... 937 222-6996
Dayton (G-8436)
Key Maneuvers Inc ....G....... 440 285-0774
Chardon (G-3159)
Keystone Press Inc ....G....... 419 243-7326
Toledo (G-18544)
Keystone Printing & Copy Cat ....G....... 740 354-6542
Portsmouth (G-16439)
Keystone Printing Co ....G....... 330 385-9519
East Liverpool (G-9223)
Klingstedt Brothers Company ....F....... 330 456-8319
Canton (G-2755)
Knox County Printing Co ....G....... 740 848-4032
Galion (G-10278)
Kovacevic Printing Inc ....G....... 440 887-1000
Cleveland (G-5663)
Kuwatch Printing LLC ....G....... 513 759-5850
Liberty Twp (G-11976)
L & H Printing ....G....... 937 855-4512
Germantown (G-10370)
L & T Collins Inc ....G....... 740 345-4494
Newark (G-15029)
L B L Lithographers Inc ....G....... 440 350-0106
Painesville (G-15896)
Landen Desktop Pubg Ctr Inc ....G....... 513 683-5181
Loveland (G-12370)
Larry C White ....G....... 330 386-3228
East Liverpool (G-9224)
Lasting Impressions Printing ....G....... 216 382-8436
Twinsburg (G-18970)
Lee Corporation ....F....... 513 771-3602
Cincinnati (G-4019)
Lilienthal Southeastern Inc ....F....... 740 439-1640
Cambridge (G-2464)
Lobo Awrds Screen Prtg Graphix ....G....... 740 972-9087
Marion (G-12880)
Lorain Printing Company ....E....... 440 288-6000
Lorain (G-12258)
Loris Printing Inc ....G....... 419 626-6648
Sandusky (G-16981)
Mabar Printing Service ....G....... 419 257-3659
North Baltimore (G-15194)
Mac Printing Company ....G....... 937 393-1101
Hillsboro (G-11007)
Marco Printed Products Co ....E....... 937 433-7030
Dayton (G-8477)
Margaret Trentman ....G....... 513 948-1700
Cincinnati (G-4059)
Mass-Marketing Inc ....C....... 513 860-6200
Fairfield (G-9679)
Mc Sign Company ....C....... 440 209-6200
Mentor (G-13649)
McNerney & Associates LLC ....E....... 513 241-9951
Cincinnati (G-4070)
Mike B Crawford ....G....... 330 673-7944
Kent (G-11492)
Milo Bennett Corp ....G....... 419 874-1492
Perrysburg (G-16122)

Minuteman Press .... G 440 946-3311
Mentor (G-13658)

Minuteman Press .... G 419 782-8002
Defiance (G-8805)

Minuteman Press .... G 513 772-0500
Cincinnati (G-4109)

Minuteman Press .... G 614 337-2334
Columbus (G-7357)

Minuteman Press .... G 937 429-8610
Beavercreek (G-1352)

Minuteman Press Inc .... G 513 741-9056
Cincinnati (G-4110)

Minuteman Press of Athens LLC .... G ... 740 593-7393
Athens (G-878)

Minuteman Press of Elyria .... G 440 365-9377
Elyria (G-9463)

Minutman Press Frfeld Cnty LLC .... G ... 740 689-1992
Lancaster (G-11730)

Mizer Printing & Graphics .... G 740 942-3343
Cadiz (G-2421)

Mmp Printing Inc .... E 513 381-0990
Cincinnati (G-4112)

Monks Copy Shop Inc .... G 614 885-7228
Columbus (G-7367)

Mullin Print Solutions .... G 216 383-2901
Euclid (G-9594)

Multi-Color Australia LLC .... B 513 381-1480
Batavia (G-1210)

Network Printing & Graphics .... F 614 230-2084
Columbus (G-7387)

Newspaper Holding Inc .... D 440 998-2323
Ashtabula (G-826)

Newton Falls Printing .... G 330 872-3532
Newton Falls (G-15137)

Nickum Enterprises Inc .... G 513 561-2292
Cincinnati (G-4154)

North Coast Litho Inc .... E 216 881-1952
Cleveland (G-5897)

North Toledo Graphics LLC .... D 419 476-8808
Toledo (G-18609)

Northeast Blueprint & Sup Co .... G 216 261-7500
Cleveland (G-5903)

O T Packaging .... G 330 482-2224
Columbiana (G-6626)

Ogden Newspapers Inc .... C 330 841-1600
Warren (G-19582)

Ohio Art Company .... D 419 636-3141
Bryan (G-2315)

Olmsted Printing Inc .... G 440 234-2600
Berea (G-1631)

Onetouchpoint East Corp .... D 513 421-1600
Cincinnati (G-4189)

Orwell Printing .... G 440 285-2233
Chardon (G-3171)

Oscar Hicks .... G 937 435-4350
Dayton (G-8553)

Our Nine LLC .... G 614 844-6655
Columbus (G-7449)

Painesville Publishing Co .... G 440 354-4142
Austinburg (G-964)

Papworth Prints .... G 614 428-6137
Columbus (G-7460)

Paragraphics Inc .... E 330 493-1074
Canton (G-2806)

Patterson-Britton Printing .... G 216 781-7997
Cleveland (G-5981)

Paxar Corporation .... G 937 681-4541
Dayton (G-8567)

PDQ Printing Service .... F 216 241-5443
Cleveland (G-5985)

Peck Engraving Co .... E 216 221-1556
Cleveland (G-5987)

Peerless Printing Company .... F 513 721-4657
Cincinnati (G-4221)

Pen-Ann Corporation .... G 740 373-2054
Marietta (G-12815)

Penguin Enterprises Inc .... E 440 899-5110
Westlake (G-20292)

Phil Vedda & Sons Inc .... G 216 671-2222
Cleveland (G-6000)

Plain Dealer Publishing Co .... A 216 999-5000
Cleveland (G-6011)

Pooles Printing & Office Svcs .... G 419 475-9000
Toledo (G-18649)

Premier Printing and Packg Inc .... G 937 436-5290
Dayton (G-8589)

Premier Printing Solutions .... G 740 374-2836
Marietta (G-12819)

Press For Less Printing Firm I .... G 931 912-4606
Lebanon (G-11829)

Prestige Printing .... G 937 236-8468
Dayton (G-8590)

Print Craft Inc .... G 513 931-6828
Cincinnati (G-4270)

Print Direct For Less 2 Inc .... E 440 236-8870
Columbia Station (G-6595)

Print Factory Pll .... G 330 549-9640
North Lima (G-15321)

Print Masters Ltd .... G 740 450-2885
Zanesville (G-21346)

Print Shop Design and Print .... G 440 232-2391
Bedford (G-1454)

Print Solutions Today LLC .... G 614 848-4500
Westerville (G-20231)

Print Squad LLC .... G 440 315-5652
Strongsville (G-17953)

Print Syndicate LLC .... F 614 519-0341
Columbus (G-7518)

Print Zone .... G 513 733-0067
West Chester (G-20040)

Printex Incorporated .... F 740 773-0088
Chillicothe (G-3268)

Printex Incorporated .... G 740 947-8800
Waverly (G-19719)

Printing Center of Xenia .... G 937 372-1687
Xenia (G-20967)

Printing Connection Inc .... G 216 898-4878
Brookpark (G-2168)

Printing Express .... G 937 276-7794
Moraine (G-14517)

Printing For Less .... G 937 743-8268
Springboro (G-17499)

Printing Services .... E 440 708-1999
Chagrin Falls (G-3114)

Printmanagement Llc .... E 513 272-7000
Cincinnati (G-4273)

Printpoint Printing Inc .... G 937 223-9041
Dayton (G-8595)

Printzone .... G 513 733-0067
Cincinnati (G-4274)

Pro Printing Inc .... G 614 276-8366
Columbus (G-7521)

Professional Screen Printing .... G 740 687-0760
Lancaster (G-11742)

Profile Digital Printing LLC .... E 937 866-4241
Dayton (G-8599)

Proforma Print & Imaging .... G 216 520-8400
Dublin (G-9128)

Progressive Printers Inc .... D 937 222-1267
Dayton (G-8601)

Progressive Printing Services .... G 330 534-8501
Hubbard (G-11138)

Proimage Printing & Design LLC ...... G 937 312-9544
Xenia (G-20968)

Promatch Solutions LLC .... F 937 299-0185
Springboro (G-17500)

Province of St John The Baptis .... D 513 241-5615
Cincinnati (G-4301)

Quad/Graphics Inc .... A 513 932-1064
Lebanon (G-11830)

Quad/Graphics Inc .... C 614 276-4800
Columbus (G-7531)

Quick Tech Graphics Inc .... E 937 743-5952
Springboro (G-17502)

R Design & Printing Co .... G 614 299-1420
Columbus (G-7544)

R W Michael Printing Co .... G 330 923-9277
Akron (G-363)

R&D Marketing Group Inc .... G 216 398-9100
Brooklyn Heights (G-2145)

Red Vette Printing Company .... G 740 364-1766
Granville (G-10466)

Repro Acquisition Company LLC ...... E 216 738-3800
Cleveland (G-6104)

Reynolds and Reynolds Company ..... F 419 584-7000
Celina (G-3017)

Ricci Anthony .... G 330 758-5761
Youngstown (G-21188)

Richardson Printing Corp .... D 740 373-5362
Marietta (G-12824)

Robs Creative Screen Printing .... G 740 264-6383
Wintersville (G-20713)

Rohrer Corporation .... C 440 542-3100
Solon (G-17371)

Rotary Forms Press Inc .... E 937 393-3426
Hillsboro (G-11013)

RPI Color Service Inc .... D 513 471-4040
Cincinnati (G-4363)

RR Donnelley & Sons Company .... E 440 774-2101
Oberlin (G-15647)

RR Donnelley & Sons Company .... A 419 935-0111
Willard (G-20400)

Ruda Print & Graphics .... G 419 331-7832
Lima (G-12086)

S and K Painting .... G 330 505-1910
Niles (G-15184)

S Beckman Print & G .... E 614 864-2232
Columbus (G-7581)

Sandusky Newspapers Inc .... C 419 625-5500
Sandusky (G-17004)

Sanscan Inc .... G 330 332-9365
Salem (G-16926)

Schaffner Publication Inc .... E 419 732-2154
Port Clinton (G-16413)

Schiffer Group Inc .... G 937 694-8185
Troy (G-18872)

Schlabach Printing Ltd .... E 330 852-4687
Sugarcreek (G-18038)

Scratch Off Works .... G 440 333-4302
Rocky River (G-16709)

Screen Printing Unlimited .... G 419 621-2335
Sandusky (G-17007)

Sdg News Group Inc .... F 419 929-3411
New London (G-14865)

Seemless Design & Printing LLC ...... G 513 871-2366
Cincinnati (G-4397)

Seifert Printing Company .... G 330 759-7414
Youngstown (G-21199)

Sensical Inc .... D 216 641-1141
Solon (G-17378)

Sfc Graphics Cleveland Ltd .... E 419 255-1283
Toledo (G-18693)

Shallow Lake Corp .... G 614 883-6350
Lewis Center (G-11917)

Shawnee Systems Inc .... D 513 561-9932
Cincinnati (G-4414)

Shelby Printing Inc .... E 419 342-3171
Shelby (G-17143)

Ship Print E Sell .... G 614 459-1205
Columbus (G-7616)

Sidney Printing Works Inc .... G 513 542-4000
Cincinnati (G-4416)

Sjpm Inc .... G 614 475-4571
Gahanna (G-10233)

Slimans Printery Inc .... F 330 454-9141
Canton (G-2851)

Sourcelink Ohio LLC .... C 937 885-8000
Miamisburg (G-13862)

Southeast Publications Inc .... F 740 732-2341
Caldwell (G-2433)

Specialty Lithographing Co .... F 513 621-0222
Cincinnati (G-4440)

Springdot Inc .... D 513 542-4000
Cincinnati (G-4448)

Springfield Engraving Company .... G 937 390-0011
Springfield (G-17651)

Sprint Print Inc .... G 740 622-4429
Coshocton (G-7910)

Standard Register Inc .... E 860 870-2063
Dayton (G-8676)

Standard Register Inc .... G 937 228-5800
Dayton (G-8679)

Stapins Qick Cpy/Print Ctr LLC .... G 330 296-0123
Ravenna (G-16563)

Starr Printing Services Inc .... G 513 241-7708
Cincinnati (G-4460)

Start Printing .... G 513 424-2121
Middletown (G-14085)

Stein-Palmer Printing Co .... G 740 633-3894
Saint Clairsville (G-16809)

Stephen Andrews Inc .... G 330 725-2672
Lodi (G-12170)

Stepping Stone Enterprises Inc .... F 419 472-0505
Toledo (G-18703)

Stevenson Color Inc .... C 513 321-7500
Cincinnati (G-4466)

Stick-It Graphics LLC .... G 330 407-0142
New Philadelphia (G-14930)

Streamline Printing .... G 740 549-0330
Lewis Center (G-11921)

Swimmer Printing Inc .... G 216 623-1005
Cleveland (G-6281)

Syndicate Printers Inc .... G 513 779-3625
West Chester (G-19952)

T D Dynamics Inc .... F 216 881-0800
Cleveland (G-6288)

T H E B Inc .... G 216 391-4800
Cleveland (G-6290)

Tce International Ltd .... F 800 962-2376
Perry (G-16059)

Tcp Inc ....G 330 836-4239
  Fairlawn (G-9764)
Technoprint Inc ....F 614 899-1403
  Westerville (G-20236)
Thrifty Print ....G 440 360-7826
  North Olmsted (G-15349)
Timely Tours Inc ....G 419 734-3751
  Port Clinton (G-16418)
Tiny Printing Co ....G 614 920-0800
  Pickerington (G-16208)
Tj Metzgers Inc ....D 419 861-8611
  Toledo (G-18726)
Tradewinds Prin Twear ....G 740 214-5005
  Roseville (G-16733)
Tri-State Publishing Company ....E 740 283-3686
  Steubenville (G-17719)
Tribune Printing Inc ....G 419 542-7764
  Hicksville (G-10909)
Ultimate Printing Co Inc ....G 330 847-2941
  Warren (G-19616)
United Trade Printers LLC ....E 614 326-4829
  Dublin (G-9158)
University of Cincinnati ....F 513 556-5042
  Cincinnati (G-4543)
V & C Enterprises Co ....G 614 221-1412
  Columbus (G-7729)
Valley Printing & Graphics ....G 330 364-5010
  Dover (G-9023)
Variety Printing ....G 216 676-9815
  Brookpark (G-2171)
Vectra Inc ....F 614 351-6868
  Columbus (G-7733)
Villager Publishing Co Inc ....G 330 527-5761
  Garrettsville (G-10335)
Vision Graphix Inc ....G 440 835-6540
  Westlake (G-20318)
Visual Art Graphic Services ....E 330 274-2775
  Mantua (G-12725)
Vya Inc ....G 513 772-5400
  Cincinnati (G-4573)
W C Sims Co Inc ....G 937 325-7035
  Springfield (G-17674)
Warren Printing & Off Pdts Inc ....F 419 523-3635
  Ottawa (G-15814)
Welch Publishing Co ....E 419 874-2528
  Perrysburg (G-16168)
West Bend Printing & Pubg Inc ....G 419 258-2000
  Antwerp (G-632)
West-Camp Press Inc ....D 614 818-6279
  Westerville (G-20241)
Western Reserve Graphics ....G 440 729-9527
  Chesterland (G-3223)
Westrock Commercial LLC ....G 419 476-9101
  Toledo (G-18773)
Wfsr Holdings LLC ....A 877 735-4966
  Dayton (G-8757)
Wholesale Printers Ltd ....G 440 354-5788
  Painesville (G-15940)
Williams Design & Printing Ser ....G 937 320-9449
  Beavercreek (G-1365)
Williams Executive Entps Inc ....G 440 887-1000
  Middleburg Heights (G-13910)
Wilson Prtg Graphics of London ....G 740 852-5934
  London (G-12224)
Woodrow Manufacturing Co ....E 937 399-9333
  Springfield (G-17682)
Youngs Screenprinting & Embro ....G 330 922-5777
  Cuyahoga Falls (G-8063)
Youngstown ARC Engraving Co ....E 330 793-2471
  Youngstown (G-21245)
Zip Laser Systems Inc ....G 740 286-6613
  Jackson (G-11335)

PRINTING: Offset

21st Century Printers Inc ....G 513 771-4150
  Cincinnati (G-3322)
A & D Printing Co ....G 440 975-8001
  Willoughby (G-20421)
A F Krainz Co ....G 216 431-4341
  Cleveland (G-4671)
A-1 Printing Inc ....F 419 562-3111
  Bucyrus (G-2330)
A-A Blueprint Co Inc ....E 330 794-8803
  Akron (G-22)
Academy Graphic Comm Inc ....E 216 661-2550
  Cleveland (G-4689)
Acme Printing Co Inc ....G 419 626-4426
  Sandusky (G-16944)
Action Printing & Photography ....G 419 332-9615
  Fremont (G-10123)

Activities Press Inc ....E 440 953-1200
  Mentor (G-13509)
Adkins & Co Inc ....G 216 521-6323
  Cleveland (G-4705)
Admiral Products Company Inc ....E 216 671-0600
  Cleveland (G-4706)
Advanced Marking Systems Inc ....G 330 792-8239
  Youngstown (G-21017)
Advantage Printing Inc ....G 614 272-8259
  Columbus (G-6698)
AGS Custom Graphics Inc ....D 330 963-7770
  Macedonia (G-12433)
Allegra Print & Imaging ....F 419 427-8095
  Findlay (G-9789)
Allegra Printing & Imaging LLC ....G 440 449-6989
  Westlake (G-20248)
Allen Graphics Inc ....G 440 349-4100
  Solon (G-17253)
Allen Kenard Printing Inc ....F 440 323-7405
  Elyria (G-9369)
Allen Press ....G 614 891-4413
  Westerville (G-20198)
Alliance Printing & Publishing ....F 513 422-7611
  Middletown (G-14019)
American Printing Inc ....F 330 630-1121
  Akron (G-68)
Anderson Graphics Inc ....E 330 745-2165
  Barberton (G-1098)
Angel Prtg & Reproduction Co ....F 216 631-5225
  Cleveland (G-4812)
Angstrom Graphics Inc Midwest ....B 216 271-5300
  Cleveland (G-4815)
Ann Printing & Promotions ....G 330 399-6564
  Warren (G-19524)
Aran Inc ....G 216 464-1508
  Cleveland (G-4821)
Arens Corporation ....F 937 473-2028
  Covington (G-7918)
Arens Corporation ....G 937 473-2028
  Covington (G-7919)
Art Printing Co Inc ....G 419 281-4371
  Ashland (G-705)
Atkinson Printing Inc ....G 330 669-3515
  Wooster (G-20743)
Avon Lake Printing ....G 440 933-2078
  Avon Lake (G-1024)
B & B Printing Graphics Inc ....F 419 893-7068
  Maumee (G-13228)
Barberton Magic Press Printing ....G 330 753-9578
  Barberton (G-1107)
Baseline Printing Inc ....G 330 369-3204
  Warren (G-19526)
Bates Printing Inc ....F 330 833-5830
  Massillon (G-13114)
Bay Business Forms Inc ....F 937 322-3000
  Springfield (G-17521)
Bay Village Printing Inc ....G 440 892-2005
  Cleveland (G-4897)
Bethart Enterprises Inc ....F 513 863-6161
  Hamilton (G-10675)
Bill Wyatt Inc ....G 330 535-1113
  Mentor (G-13535)
Bindery & Spc Pressworks Inc ....D 614 873-4623
  Plain City (G-16326)
Blt Inc ....F 513 631-5050
  Norwood (G-15571)
Boldman Printing LLC ....G 937 653-3431
  Urbana (G-19148)
Bpm Realty Inc ....G 614 221-6811
  Columbus (G-6852)
Bramkamp Printing Company Inc ......E 513 241-1865
  Blue Ash (G-1754)
Brent Carter Enterprises Inc ....G 513 731-1440
  Cincinnati (G-3468)
Brentwood Printing & Sty ....G 513 522-2679
  Cincinnati (G-3469)
Broadway Offset Printing Co ....F 216 391-3800
  Cleveland (G-4932)
Brooke Printers Inc ....G 614 235-6800
  Lancaster (G-11692)
Brothers Printing Co Inc ....F 216 621-6050
  Cleveland (G-4938)
Buckeye Business Forms Inc ....G 614 882-1890
  Westerville (G-20141)
Bucyrus Graphics Inc ....F 419 562-2906
  Bucyrus (G-2333)
Capozzolo Printers Inc ....G 513 542-7874
  Cincinnati (G-3496)
Cardinal Printing Inc ....G 330 773-7300
  Akron (G-111)

Carl Graphics Company ....G 740 382-6583
  Marion (G-12861)
Charger Press Inc ....F 513 542-3113
  Miamitown (G-13886)
Cincinnati Printers Co Inc ....F 513 860-9053
  West Chester (G-19832)
Cleveland Letter Service Inc ....E 216 781-8300
  Chagrin Falls (G-3052)
Cleveland Offset Press Co Inc ....G 440 845-9137
  Cleveland (G-5071)
Cold Duck Screen Prtg & EMB Co ....G 330 426-1900
  East Palestine (G-9231)
Color Bar Printing Centers Inc ....E 216 595-3939
  Cleveland (G-5099)
Copley Ohio Newspapers Inc ....C 330 364-5577
  New Philadelphia (G-14892)
Cornerstone Industries Lcc ....G 513 871-4546
  West Chester (G-19845)
COS Blueprint Inc ....F 330 376-0022
  Akron (G-130)
Cox Printing Co ....G 937 382-2312
  Wilmington (G-20661)
Cpmm Services Group Inc ....F 614 447-0165
  Columbus (G-6996)
Crain-Tharp Printing Inc ....G 740 345-9823
  Newark (G-14998)
Crown Printing Inc ....G 740 477-2511
  Circleville (G-4626)
Curry Copy Center of Lakewood ....G 216 521-5775
  Lakewood (G-11661)
D M J F Inc ....G 440 845-1155
  Cleveland (G-5162)
Dana Graphics Inc ....G 513 351-4400
  Cincinnati (G-3638)
Daubenmires Printing ....G 513 425-7223
  Middletown (G-14036)
David Butler Tax Service ....G 419 626-8086
  Sandusky (G-16956)
Delphos Herald Inc ....D 419 695-0015
  Delphos (G-8904)
Delphos Herald Inc ....D 419 695-0015
  Delphos (G-8905)
Dewitt Group Inc ....F 614 847-5919
  Columbus (G-7024)
Distributor Graphics Inc ....G 440 260-0024
  Cleveland (G-5198)
Domicone Printing Inc ....G 937 878-3080
  Fairborn (G-9619)
Dorothy Crooker ....G 513 385-0888
  Cincinnati (G-3665)
Doug Smith ....G 740 345-1398
  Newark (G-15000)
Douglas Michalske ....G 216 631-0567
  Cleveland (G-5210)
DOV Graphics Inc ....E 513 241-5150
  Cincinnati (G-3668)
Dove Graphics Inc ....G 440 238-1800
  Cleveland (G-5212)
Downtown Print Shop ....G 419 242-9164
  Toledo (G-18443)
Dresden Specialties Inc ....G 740 452-7100
  Zanesville (G-21302)
Dresden Specialties Inc ....G 740 754-2451
  Dresden (G-9032)
Duke Graphics Inc ....E 440 946-0606
  Willoughby (G-20475)
E T & K Inc ....G 440 777-7375
  North Olmsted (G-15331)
E T & K Inc ....G 440 888-4780
  Cleveland (G-5234)
Earl D Arnold Printing Company ....E 513 533-6900
  Cincinnati (G-3685)
Easterdays Printing Center ....G 330 726-1182
  Youngstown (G-21073)
Echographics Inc ....G 440 846-2330
  North Ridgeville (G-15371)
Eg Enterprise Services Inc ....F 216 431-3300
  Cleveland (G-5260)
Elyria Copy Center Inc ....G 440 323-4145
  Elyria (G-9412)
Empire Printing Inc ....G 513 242-3900
  Cincinnati (G-3700)
Engler Printing Co ....G 419 332-2181
  Fremont (G-10144)
Enquirer Printing Co Inc ....F 513 241-1956
  Cincinnati (G-3707)
Eveready Printing Inc ....E 216 587-2389
  Cleveland (G-5307)
Exchange Printing Company ....G 330 773-7842
  Akron (G-173)

PRODUCT

Fine Line Graphics Corp	C	614 486-0276	
Columbus (G-7085)			
Flemish Investments Inc	G	419 625-4073	
Sandusky (G-16967)			
Folks Creative Printers Inc	G	740 383-6326	
Marion (G-12865)			
Foote Printing Company	F	216 431-1757	
Cleveland (G-5367)			
Fremont Quick Print	G	419 334-8808	
Helena (G-10895)			
Fx Digital Media Inc	E	216 241-4040	
Cleveland (G-5387)			
Galaxy Balloons Incorporated	C	216 476-3360	
Cleveland (G-5392)			
Galley Printing Inc	E	330 220-5577	
Brunswick (G-2228)			
Ganger Enterprises Inc	G	614 776-3985	
Westerville (G-20154)			
Gaspar Services LLC	G	330 467-8292	
Macedonia (G-12455)			
George D Kanaan & Associates	G	440 243-6410	
Berea (G-1617)			
Gergel-Kellem Company Inc	D	216 398-2000	
Cleveland (G-5425)			
Golden Graphics Ltd	F	419 673-6260	
Kenton (G-11548)			
Gordons Graphics Inc	G	330 863-2322	
Malvern (G-12546)			
Grant John	G	937 298-0633	
Dayton (G-8376)			
Graphic Touch Inc	G	330 337-3341	
Salem (G-16896)			
Graphicsource Inc	G	440 248-9200	
Solon (G-17302)			
Graphtech Communications Inc	F	216 676-1020	
Cleveland (G-5447)			
Great Lakes Printing Inc	D	440 993-8781	
Ashtabula (G-810)			
Greenwood Printing & Graphics	F	419 727-3275	
Toledo (G-18487)			
H&An LLC	G	740 435-0200	
Cambridge (G-2460)			
Harper Engraving & Printing Co	D	614 276-0700	
Columbus (G-7144)			
Harris Hawk	G	800 459-4295	
Mason (G-13036)			
Hartco Printing Company	G	614 761-1292	
Dublin (G-9083)			
Hartmann Incorporated	F	513 276-7318	
Blue Ash (G-1805)			
Hecks Direct Mail & Prtg Svc	E	419 697-3505	
Toledo (G-18502)			
Heritage Press Inc	E	419 289-9209	
Ashland (G-738)			
Heskamp Printing Co Inc	G	513 871-6770	
Cincinnati (G-3881)			
Holmes W & Sons Printing	F	937 325-1509	
Springfield (G-17574)			
Homewood Press Inc	E	419 478-0695	
Toledo (G-18510)			
Hoster Graphics Company Inc	F	614 299-9770	
Columbus (G-7168)			
HOT Graphic Services Inc	E	419 242-7000	
Northwood (G-15483)			
Howland Printing Inc	G	330 637-8255	
Cortland (G-7869)			
Hubbard Company	E	419 784-4455	
Defiance (G-8794)			
Hubbard Publishing Co	E	937 592-3060	
Bellefontaine (G-1533)			
Ideas & Ad Ventures Inc	G	513 542-7154	
Cincinnati (G-3909)			
Image Print Inc	G	614 430-8470	
Columbus (G-7182)			
In-Touch Corp	G	440 268-0881	
Cleveland (G-5559)			
Innmark Communications LLC	E	937 454-5555	
Dayton (G-8404)			
Insley Printing Inc	G	614 885-5973	
Worthington (G-20873)			
Irwin Engraving & Printing Co	G	216 391-7300	
Cleveland (G-5589)			
J & J Bechke Inc	G	440 238-1441	
Strongsville (G-17932)			
J & K Printing	G	330 456-5306	
Canton (G-2742)			
J & P Investments Inc	F	513 821-2299	
Cincinnati (G-3933)			
J P Quality Printing Inc	G	216 791-6303	
Cleveland (G-5598)			

Jim Davis	G	740 335-8030	
Wshngtn CT Hs (G-20914)			
John Kolesar and Sons Inc	G	216 221-7117	
Cleveland (G-5618)			
John S Swift Company Inc	F	513 721-4147	
Cincinnati (G-3954)			
Johnson Printing	G	740 922-4821	
Uhrichsville (G-19053)			
Joseph Scarberry	G	740 522-1551	
Newark (G-15025)			
Kahny Printing Inc	E	513 251-2911	
Cincinnati (G-3968)			
Kay Toledo Tag Inc	D	419 729-5479	
Toledo (G-18541)			
Kee Printing Inc	G	937 456-6851	
Eaton (G-9312)			
Keener Printing Inc	F	216 531-7595	
Cleveland (G-5640)			
Kehl-Kolor Inc	G	419 281-3107	
Ashland (G-746)			
Kehoe Brothers Printing Inc	G	216 351-4100	
Cleveland (G-5641)			
Keithley Enterprises Inc	G	937 890-1878	
Dayton (G-8434)			
Kennedy Graphics Inc	G	419 223-9825	
Lima (G-12035)			
Kennedy Printing Co	F	419 422-1802	
Findlay (G-9847)			
Kenwel Printers Inc	F	614 261-1011	
Columbus (G-7257)			
Kever Incorporated	G	614 552-9000	
Columbus (G-7258)			
Kevin K Tidd	G	419 885-5603	
Sylvania (G-18115)			
Kimpton Printing & Spc Co	F	330 467-1640	
Macedonia (G-12466)			
KMS 2000 Inc	F	330 454-9444	
Canton (G-2756)			
Krok Printing Inc	G	330 652-8198	
Niles (G-15166)			
Lake Erie Graphics Inc	G	216 575-1333	
Brookpark (G-2166)			
Lakota Printing Inc	G	513 755-3666	
West Chester (G-19890)			
Lanz Printing Co Inc	G	614 221-1724	
Columbus (G-7285)			
Laser Images Inc	G	419 668-8348	
Norwalk (G-15549)			
Lasting First Impressions Inc	F	513 870-6900	
West Chester (G-20020)			
Laurenee Ltd LLC	G	513 662-2225	
Cincinnati (G-4015)			
Legal News Publishing Co	E	216 696-3322	
Cleveland (G-5692)			
Letter Shop	G	937 981-3117	
Greenfield (G-10482)			
Letterman Printing Inc	G	513 523-1111	
Oxford (G-15839)			
Liming Printing Inc	F	937 374-2646	
Xenia (G-20961)			
Lsc Communications Us LLC	F	419 935-0111	
Willard (G-20396)			
Lund Printing Co	G	330 628-4047	
Akron (G-277)			
Lyle Printing & Publishing Co	E	330 337-3419	
Salem (G-16909)			
Mackland Co Inc	G	330 399-5034	
Warren (G-19575)			
Mansfield Journal Co	G	330 364-8641	
New Philadelphia (G-14910)			
Marbee Inc	G	419 422-9441	
Findlay (G-9858)			
Marco Printed Products Co Inc	G	937 433-5680	
Dayton (G-8478)			
Mariotti Printing Co LLC	G	440 245-4120	
Lorain (G-12259)			
Mark Advertising Agency Inc	F	419 626-9000	
Sandusky (G-16985)			
Marles Business Systems Inc	G	440 268-8380	
Brooklyn Heights (G-2142)			
Martin Printing Co	G	419 224-9176	
Lima (G-12051)			
Martys Print Shop	G	740 373-3454	
Marietta (G-12804)			
Marysville Printing Company	G	937 644-4959	
Marysville (G-12958)			
Master Printing Company	E	216 351-2246	
Cleveland (G-5759)			
Maumee Quick Print Inc	G	419 893-4321	
Maumee (G-13280)			

Maximum Graphix Inc	G	440 353-3301	
North Ridgeville (G-15390)			
Mc Vay Ventures Inc	G	614 890-1516	
Westerville (G-20223)			
McKinnon Printing Inc	F	330 929-5769	
Cuyahoga Falls (G-8025)			
McMath & Sheets Unlimited Inc	G	216 381-0010	
Cleveland (G-5771)			
Mercer Color Corporation	G	419 678-8273	
Coldwater (G-6568)			
Messenger Publishing Company	C	740 592-6612	
Athens (G-876)			
Metzgers	F	419 861-8611	
Toledo (G-18584)			
Middaugh Enterprises Inc	F	330 852-2471	
Sugarcreek (G-18026)			
Middleton Printing Co Inc	G	614 294-7277	
Gahanna (G-10219)			
Milford Printers	E	513 831-6630	
Milford (G-14162)			
Milford Printers	G	513 831-6630	
Milford (G-14163)			
Millstream Press Inc	F	419 422-9745	
Findlay (G-9863)			
Mmp Toledo	F	419 472-0505	
Toledo (G-18588)			
Montview Corporation	G	330 723-3409	
Medina (G-13449)			
Morse Enterprises Inc	G	513 229-3600	
Mason (G-13066)			
Muir Graphics Inc	G	309 673-7034	
Sylvania (G-18120)			
Murr Corporation	F	330 264-2223	
Wooster (G-20813)			
Mustang Printing	G	419 592-2746	
Napoleon (G-14690)			
Nari Inc	G	440 960-2280	
Monroeville (G-14427)			
National Bank Note Company	G	216 281-7792	
Cleveland (G-5852)			
Nelis Printing Co	G	330 757-4114	
Youngstown (G-21149)			
Newhouse & Faulkner Inc	G	513 721-1660	
Cincinnati (G-4150)			
Newmast Mktg & Communications	E	614 837-1200	
Columbus (G-7389)			
Nomis Publications Inc	F	330 965-2380	
Youngstown (G-21150)			
Nta Graphics Inc	C	419 476-8808	
Toledo (G-18611)			
O Connor Office Pdts & Prtg	G	740 852-2209	
London (G-12216)			
Oak Printing Company	E	440 238-3316	
Strongsville (G-17948)			
Odyssey Press Inc	F	614 410-0356	
Huron (G-11236)			
Office Print N Copy	G	740 695-3616	
Saint Clairsville (G-16799)			
Old Trail Printing Company	C	614 443-4852	
Columbus (G-7440)			
Oliver Printing & Packg Co LLC	D	330 425-7890	
Twinsburg (G-18990)			
One-Write Company	E	740 654-2128	
Lancaster (G-11737)			
Orange Blossom Press Inc	G	216 781-8655	
Willoughby (G-20562)			
Oregon Village Print Shoppe	F	937 222-9418	
Dayton (G-8552)			
Orrville Printing Co Inc	G	330 682-5066	
Orrville (G-15752)			
Page One Group	G	740 397-4240	
Mount Vernon (G-14636)			
Painted Hill Inv Group Inc	F	937 339-1756	
Troy (G-18861)			
Paragon Press	G	513 281-9911	
Cincinnati (G-4211)			
Patio Printing Inc	G	614 785-9553	
Columbus (G-7463)			
Paul Stipkovich	G	330 499-7391	
North Canton (G-15258)			
Paul/Jay Associates	G	740 676-8776	
Bellaire (G-1500)			
Penny Printing Inc	G	330 645-2955	
Akron (G-334)			
Perrons Printing Company	E	440 236-8870	
Columbia Station (G-6593)			
Pinnacle Press Inc	F	330 453-7060	
Canton (G-2813)			
PIP and Huds LLC	G	740 208-5519	
Gallipolis (G-10307)			

PIP Printing ....G....... 440 951-2606
Willoughby (G-20569)

PM Graphics Inc ....E....... 330 650-0861
Streetsboro (G-17868)

Porath Business Services Inc ....F....... 216 626-0060
Cleveland (G-6021)

Post Printing Co ....D....... 859 254-7714
Minster (G-14359)

Preferred Printing ....G....... 937 492-6961
Sidney (G-17212)

Preisser Inc ....E....... 614 345-0199
Columbus (G-7514)

Premier Printing Corporation ....F....... 216 478-9720
Cleveland (G-6042)

Pressmark Inc ....G....... 740 373-6005
Marietta (G-12820)

Priesman Printery ....G....... 419 898-2526
Oak Harbor (G-15593)

Prime Printing Inc ....E....... 937 438-3707
Dayton (G-8594)

Print A Copy ....G....... 440 845-9039
Cleveland (G-6049)

Print All Inc ....G....... 419 534-2880
Toledo (G-18658)

Print Marketing Inc ....E....... 330 625-1500
Homerville (G-11114)

Print Shop ....G....... 740 335-8030
Wshngtn CT Hs (G-20920)

Print Shop of Canton Inc ....G....... 330 497-3212
Canton (G-2822)

Print-Digital Incorporated ....G....... 330 686-5945
Stow (G-17792)

Printcraft Inc ....G....... 440 599-8903
Conneaut (G-7817)

Printed Image ....F....... 614 221-1412
Columbus (G-7519)

Printers Devil Inc ....F....... 330 650-1218
Hudson (G-11194)

Printing Arts Press ....F....... 740 397-6106
Mount Vernon (G-14639)

Printing Express Inc ....G....... 740 532-7003
Ironton (G-11299)

Printing Service Company ....D....... 937 425-6100
Miamisburg (G-13848)

Printing System Inc ....F....... 330 375-9128
Akron (G-351)

Progressive Communications ....D....... 740 397-5333
Mount Vernon (G-14640)

Q C Printing ....G....... 419 475-4266
Toledo (G-18662)

Quality Publishing Co ....F....... 513 863-8210
Hamilton (G-10733)

Quebecor World Johnson Hardin ......A....... 614 326-0299
Cincinnati (G-4312)

Quez Media Marketing Inc ....F....... 216 910-0202
Cleveland (G-6077)

Quick As A Wink Printing Co ....F....... 419 224-9786
Lima (G-12079)

R & J Bardon Inc ....G....... 614 457-5500
Columbus (G-7541)

R & J Printing Enterprises Inc ....F....... 330 343-1242
Dover (G-9008)

R & W Printing Company ....G....... 513 575-0131
Loveland (G-12379)

R B Robinson Inc ....G....... 440 543-5547
Chagrin Falls (G-3116)

R S C Sales Company ....E....... 423 581-4916
Dayton (G-8612)

Randd Assoc Prtg & Promotions ....G....... 937 294-1874
Dayton (G-8617)

Rba Inc ....G....... 330 336-6700
Wadsworth (G-19436)

Renco Printing Inc ....G....... 216 267-5585
Cleveland (G-6100)

Rhoads Printing Center Inc ....G....... 330 678-2042
Kent (G-11516)

Robert Becker Impressions Inc ....F....... 419 385-5303
Toledo (G-18678)

Robert H Shackelford ....G....... 330 364-2221
New Philadelphia (G-14926)

Roberts Graphic Center ....G....... 330 788-4642
Youngstown (G-21191)

Robin Enterprises Company ....C....... 614 891-0250
Westerville (G-20233)

Rutobo Inc ....G....... 614 236-2948
Columbus (G-7579)

Ryans Newark Leader Ex Prtg ....F....... 740 522-2149
Newark (G-15051)

S & S Printing Service Inc ....G....... 937 228-9411
Dayton (G-8643)

S O S Graphics & Printing Inc ....G....... 614 846-8229
Worthington (G-20886)

Schuerholz Printing Inc ....G....... 937 294-5218
Dayton (G-8647)

Scorecards Unlimited LLC ....G....... 614 885-0796
Columbus (G-7602)

Scrip-Safe Security Products ....E....... 513 697-7789
Loveland (G-12384)

Selby Service/Roxy Press Inc ....G....... 513 241-3445
Cincinnati (G-4400)

Sentry Graphics Inc ....G....... 440 735-0850
Northfield (G-15471)

Sharon Printing Co Inc ....G....... 330 239-1684
Sharon Center (G-17110)

Sharp Enterprises Inc ....F....... 937 295-2965
Fort Loramie (G-9939)

Shreve Printing LLC ....F....... 330 567-2341
Shreve (G-17163)

Sitler Printer Inc ....G....... 330 482-4463
Columbiana (G-6632)

Skladany Enterprises Inc ....G....... 614 823-6883
Westerville (G-20185)

Slutzkers Quickprint Center ....G....... 440 244-0330
Lorain (G-12278)

Snow Printing Co Inc ....F....... 419 229-7669
Lima (G-12093)

Source3media Inc ....E....... 330 467-9003
Macedonia (G-12483)

South End Printing Co ....G....... 216 341-0669
Cleveland (G-6222)

SPAOS Inc ....G....... 937 890-0783
Dayton (G-8666)

Spencer-Walker Press Inc ....F....... 740 344-6110
Newark (G-15055)

Star Calendar & Printing Co ....G....... 216 741-3223
Cleveland (G-6237)

Star Printing Company Inc ....E....... 330 376-0514
Akron (G-415)

Stationery Shop Inc ....G....... 330 376-2033
Akron (G-416)

Streichers Enterprises Inc ....G....... 419 423-8606
Findlay (G-9897)

Suburban Press Inc ....E....... 216 961-0766
Cleveland (G-6260)

Summit Printing & Graphics ....G....... 330 645-7644
Akron (G-421)

Superior Impressions Inc ....G....... 419 244-8676
Toledo (G-18709)

Superprinter Inc ....G....... 440 277-0787
Lorain (G-12282)

Superprinter Ltd ....G....... 440 277-0787
Lorain (G-12283)

T & K Heins Corporation ....G....... 740 452-6006
Zanesville (G-21358)

Target Printing & Graphics ....G....... 937 228-0170
Dayton (G-8700)

Taylor Quick Print ....G....... 740 439-2208
Cambridge (G-2478)

The Gazette Printing Co Inc ....D....... 440 576-9125
Jefferson (G-11373)

The Gazette Printing Co Inc ....G....... 440 593-6030
Conneaut (G-7820)

TL Krieg Offset Inc ....E....... 513 542-1522
Cincinnati (G-4511)

Tomahawk Printing ....F....... 419 335-3161
Wauseon (G-19696)

Tomahawk Printing Inc ....F....... 419 335-3161
Wauseon (G-19697)

Tope Printing Inc ....G....... 330 674-4993
Millersburg (G-14271)

Traxium LLC ....E....... 330 572-8200
Stow (G-17811)

Ultra Impressions Inc ....G....... 440 951-4777
Mentor (G-13758)

Ultra Printing & Design Inc ....G....... 440 887-0393
Cleveland (G-6380)

United Prtrs & Lithographers ....G....... 216 771-2759
Cleveland (G-6386)

USA Quickprint Inc ....F....... 330 455-5119
Canton (G-2892)

V I P Printing & Design ....G....... 513 777-7468
West Chester (G-20066)

Vision Graphics ....G....... 330 665-4451
Copley (G-7857)

Walter Graphics Inc ....G....... 419 522-5261
Mansfield (G-12702)

Wasserstrom Company ....F....... 614 228-2233
Columbus (G-7751)

Watkins Printing Company ....E....... 614 297-8270
Columbus (G-7752)

Western Ohio Graphics ....F....... 937 335-8769
Troy (G-18885)

Whiskey Fox Corporation ....F....... 440 779-6767
North Olmsted (G-15352)

White Tiger Inc ....F....... 740 852-4873
London (G-12223)

Wilkinson Printing Co ....G....... 419 238-3615
Van Wert (G-19276)

William J Bergen & Co ....G....... 440 248-6132
Solon (G-17414)

William J Dupps ....G....... 419 734-2126
Port Clinton (G-16419)

Wirick Press Inc ....G....... 330 273-3488
Brunswick (G-2269)

Xpress Print Inc ....F....... 330 494-7246
Louisville (G-12335)

Yes Press Printing Co ....G....... 330 535-8398
Akron (G-477)

Youngstown Letter Shop Inc ....G....... 330 793-4935
Youngstown (G-21253)

Yuckon International Corp ....G....... 216 361-2103
Cleveland (G-6488)

Z P Enterprises Inc ....G....... 513 863-3393
Hamilton (G-10758)

PRINTING: Pamphlets

Digicom Inc ....G....... 216 642-3838
Independence (G-11252)

Society of The Precious Blood ....E....... 419 925-4516
Celina (G-3018)

PRINTING: Photo-Offset

Deshea Printing Company ....G....... 330 336-7601
Wadsworth (G-19402)

Gerald L Hermann Co Inc ....F....... 513 661-1818
Cincinnati (G-3822)

Henry Bussman ....G....... 614 224-0417
Columbus (G-7150)

Marshalls Thrifty Print Inc ....G....... 513 984-5513
Cincinnati (G-4062)

Newfax Corporation ....F....... 419 241-5157
Toledo (G-18603)

Newfax Corporation ....F....... 419 893-4557
Toledo (G-18604)

PRINTING: Photolithographic

Acme Duplicating Co ....G....... 216 241-1241
Cleveland (G-4692)

Friends Service Co Inc ....D....... 419 427-1704
Findlay (G-9828)

PRINTING: Rotary Photogravure

Klingstedt Brothers Company ....F....... 330 456-8319
Canton (G-2755)

Toledo Tape and Label Company ....G....... 419 536-8316
Toledo (G-18745)

PRINTING: Rotogravure

Western Roto Engravers Inc ....E....... 330 336-7636
Wadsworth (G-19444)

PRINTING: Screen, Broadwoven Fabrics, Cotton

Air Waves Inc ....C....... 740 548-1200
Lewis Center (G-11883)

Apparel Screen Printing Inc ....G....... 513 733-9495
Cincinnati (G-3408)

Ares Sportswear Ltd ....D....... 614 767-1950
Hilliard (G-10926)

Atlantis Sportswear Inc ....E....... 937 773-0680
Piqua (G-16250)

CSP Graphics Inc ....F....... 216 426-2660
Cleveland (G-5144)

Designer Awards Inc ....G....... 937 339-4444
Troy (G-18819)

Fryes Soccer Shoppe ....G....... 937 832-2230
Englewood (G-9520)

Graphic Plus ....G....... 740 701-1860
Chillicothe (G-3241)

Image Group Inc ....G....... 419 866-3300
Holland (G-11065)

Image Group of Toledo Inc ....E....... 419 866-3300
Holland (G-11066)

Phantasm Designs ....G....... 419 538-6737
Ottawa (G-15804)

Precision Imprint ....G....... 740 592-5916
Athens (G-882)

PRODUCT

Prism Prints Inc .... G 614 294-4981
  Columbus *(G-7520)*

Professional Image Inc .... F 513 984-1111
  Cincinnati *(G-4296)*

Screen Printing Show House .... G 614 252-2202
  Columbus *(G-7603)*

Shirt Stop LLC .... G 740 574-4774
  Wheelersburg *(G-20334)*

Three Cord LLC .... G 419 445-2673
  Archbold *(G-698)*

Uptown Dog The Inc .... G 740 592-4600
  Athens *(G-889)*

Zenos Activewear Inc .... G 614 443-0070
  Columbus *(G-7787)*

PRINTING: Screen, Fabric

Aardvark Graphic Enterprises L .... F 419 352-3197
  Bowling Green *(G-1963)*

ABC Lettering & Embroidery .... G 216 321-8338
  Lakewood *(G-11653)*

Activewares .... G 419 994-5932
  Loudonville *(G-12295)*

Art Works .... G 740 425-5765
  Barnesville *(G-1158)*

B D P Services Inc .... D 740 828-9685
  Nashport *(G-14703)*

Brandon Screen Printing .... F 419 229-9837
  Lima *(G-11996)*

Cal Sales Embroidery .... G 440 236-3820
  Columbia Station *(G-6582)*

Charisma Products Inc .... G 614 846-8888
  Westerville *(G-20143)*

Charizma Corp .... G 216 621-2220
  Cleveland *(G-5014)*

Charles Wisvari .... F 740 671-9960
  Bellaire *(G-1497)*

David Brandeberry .... G 937 653-4680
  Urbana *(G-19156)*

Detailed Athletic Wear Co Inc .... G 513 541-0884
  Cincinnati *(G-3651)*

Fineline Imprints Inc .... E 740 453-1083
  Zanesville *(G-21308)*

Gotcha Covered .... G 513 829-7555
  Fairfield *(G-9661)*

H & H Screen Process Inc .... G 937 253-7520
  Dayton *(G-8381)*

J&D Beck Co Inc .... G 419 224-0027
  Lima *(G-12033)*

Jakes Sportswear Ltd .... G 740 746-8356
  Sugar Grove *(G-18012)*

Jetts Embroideries .... G 937 981-3716
  Greenfield *(G-10481)*

Kiwi Promotional AP & Prtg Co .... E 330 487-5115
  Twinsburg *(G-18966)*

M & H Screen Printing .... G 740 522-1957
  Newark *(G-15031)*

Madison Group Inc .... G 216 362-9000
  Cleveland *(G-5727)*

Mr Emblem Inc .... G 419 697-1888
  Oregon *(G-15710)*

Ohio State Institute of Fin .... G 614 861-8811
  Reynoldsburg *(G-16596)*

Painted Hill Inv Group Inc .... F 937 339-1756
  Troy *(G-18861)*

Peska Inc .... F 440 998-4664
  Ashtabula *(G-831)*

Pinky & Thumb LLC .... G 614 939-5216
  New Albany *(G-14769)*

Quality Rubber Stamp Inc .... G 614 235-2700
  Columbus *(G-7536)*

Quality Spt & Silk Screen Sp .... G 513 769-8300
  Cincinnati *(G-4309)*

R & A Sports Inc .... E 216 289-2254
  Euclid *(G-9603)*

Robert Midkiff .... G 614 848-6677
  Worthington *(G-20885)*

S S T Enterprises Inc .... D 330 343-2656
  New Philadelphia *(G-14927)*

Simply Canvas Inc .... E 330 436-6500
  Akron *(G-402)*

Sroufe Healthcare Products LLC .... E 260 894-4171
  Wadsworth *(G-19442)*

Swocat Design Inc .... G 440 282-4700
  Lorain *(G-12284)*

Tee Creations .... G 937 878-2822
  Fairborn *(G-9632)*

Tim L Humbert .... F 330 497-4944
  Canton *(G-2870)*

Triage Ortho Group .... G 937 653-6431
  Urbana *(G-19185)*

Vasil Co Inc .... G 419 562-2901
  Bucyrus *(G-2362)*

Vector International Corp .... G 440 942-2002
  Mentor *(G-13766)*

Wizard Graphics Inc .... G 419 354-3098
  Bowling Green *(G-2021)*

Zide Sport Shop of Ohio Inc .... F 740 373-8199
  Marietta *(G-12852)*

PRINTING: Screen, Manmade Fiber & Silk, Broadwoven Fabric

B Richardson Inc .... F 330 724-2122
  Akron *(G-80)*

Cincinnati Advg Pdts LLC .... E 513 346-7310
  Cincinnati *(G-3537)*

Creatia Inc. .... G 937 368-3100
  Fletcher *(G-9915)*

E & E Screen Prtg & Cstm EMB .... G 614 235-2177
  Columbus *(G-7042)*

Evolution Crtive Solutions LLC .... E 513 681-4450
  Cincinnati *(G-3725)*

Fcs Graphics Inc .... G 216 771-5177
  Cleveland *(G-5330)*

Flashions Sportswear Ltd .... G 937 323-5885
  Springfield *(G-17560)*

Great Oppurtunities Inc .... G 614 868-1899
  Columbus *(G-7130)*

Phantasm Designs .... G 419 538-6737
  Ottawa *(G-15804)*

Scenic Screen .... G 419 468-3110
  Galion *(G-10285)*

Sportsco Imprinting .... G 513 641-5111
  Cincinnati *(G-4443)*

Wayne Sporting Goods .... G 937 236-6665
  Dayton *(G-8748)*

PRINTING: Thermography

A C Hadley - Printing Inc .... G 937 426-0952
  Beavercreek *(G-1314)*

Austintown Printing Inc .... G 330 797-0099
  Youngstown *(G-21029)*

Functional Imaging Ltd .... G 740 689-2466
  Lancaster *(G-11717)*

Larmax Inc .... G 513 984-0783
  Blue Ash *(G-1825)*

Sharon Printing Co Inc .... G 330 239-1684
  Sharon Center *(G-17110)*

PRODUCTS: Petroleum & coal, NEC

Citi 2 Citi Logistics .... E 614 306-4109
  Columbus *(G-6930)*

PROFESSIONAL EQPT & SPLYS, WHOLESALE: Analytical Instruments

Consolidatd Analytical Sys Inc .... F 513 542-1200
  Cleves *(G-6511)*

Mettler-Toledo Intl Fin Inc .... G 614 438-4511
  Columbus *(G-6653)*

PROFESSIONAL EQPT & SPLYS, WHOLESALE: Bank

Security Systems Eqp Corp .... G 513 758-1070
  Cincinnati *(G-4396)*

PROFESSIONAL EQPT & SPLYS, WHOLESALE: Engineers', NEC

S&V Industries Inc .... G 330 666-1986
  Medina *(G-13472)*

US Tsubaki Power Transm LLC .... C 419 626-4560
  Sandusky *(G-17019)*

PROFESSIONAL EQPT & SPLYS, WHOLESALE: Optical Goods

Essilor Laboratories Amer Inc .... E 614 274-0840
  Columbus *(G-7066)*

Hoya Optical Labs .... G 440 239-1924
  Berea *(G-1619)*

PROFESSIONAL EQPT & SPLYS, WHOLESALE: Precision Tools

Ahner Fabricating & Shtmtl Inc .... E 419 626-6641
  Sandusky *(G-16945)*

Hapco Inc .... F 330 678-9353
  Kent *(G-11469)*

Monarch Steel Company Inc .... E 216 587-8000
  Cleveland *(G-5830)*

Sp Acquisitions LLC .... E 440 205-0143
  Mentor *(G-13726)*

PROFESSIONAL EQPT & SPLYS, WHOLESALE: Scientific & Engineerg

Laser Automation Inc .... F 440 543-9291
  Chagrin Falls *(G-3099)*

PROFESSIONAL INSTRUMENT REPAIR SVCS

Certon Technologies Inc .... F 440 786-7185
  Bedford *(G-1414)*

Edmonds Elevator Company .... F 216 781-9135
  Thompson *(G-18188)*

Form-A-Chip Inc .... G 937 223-4135
  Dayton *(G-8347)*

Mettler-Toledo Intl Fin Inc .... G 614 438-4511
  Columbus *(G-6653)*

UPA Technology Inc .... F 513 755-1380
  West Chester *(G-19969)*

PROFILE SHAPES: Unsupported Plastics

ABC Inoac Exterior Systems LLC .... C 419 334-8951
  Fremont *(G-10122)*

Advanced Composites Inc .... C 937 575-9800
  Sidney *(G-17165)*

Alkon Corporation .... G 614 799-6650
  Dublin *(G-9039)*

Bobbart Industries Inc .... E 419 350-5477
  Sylvania *(G-18101)*

Deceuninck North America LLC .... B 513 539-5466
  Monroe *(G-14399)*

Duracote Corporation .... E 330 296-9600
  Ravenna *(G-16526)*

Global Manufacturing Solutions .... F 937 236-8315
  Dayton *(G-8367)*

Granger Plastic Company .... E 513 424-1955
  Middletown *(G-14043)*

HP Manufacturing Company Inc .... D 216 361-6500
  Cleveland *(G-5530)*

Inventive Extrusions Corp .... E 330 874-3000
  Bolivar *(G-1937)*

Machining Technologies Inc .... E 419 862-3110
  Elmore *(G-9363)*

Meridian Industries Inc .... D 330 673-1011
  Kent *(G-11488)*

Pexco Packaging Corp .... E 419 470-5935
  Toledo *(G-18642)*

Plasto-Tech Corporation .... F 440 323-6300
  Elyria *(G-9479)*

Roach Wood Products & Plas Inc .... G 740 532-4855
  Ironton *(G-11301)*

Wurms Woodworking Company .... E 419 492-2184
  New Washington *(G-14966)*

PROPELLERS: Boat & Ship, Cast

Advanced Propeller Systems .... G 937 409-1038
  Dayton *(G-8094)*

PROPERTY & CASUALTY INSURANCE AGENTS

Stancorp Inc .... G 330 545-6615
  Girard *(G-10396)*

PROPRIETARY STORES, NON-PRESCRIPTION MEDICINE

Kroger Co .... D 419 423-2065
  Findlay *(G-9848)*

PROTECTION EQPT: Lightning

Amidac Wind Corporation .... G 213 973-4000
  Elyria *(G-9372)*

Burkett Industries Inc .... G 419 332-4391
  Fremont *(G-10132)*

Ohio Vly Lightning Protection .... G 937 987-0245
  New Vienna *(G-14956)*

PROTECTIVE FOOTWEAR: Rubber Or Plastic

Advantage Products Corporation ....F 513 489-2283
Blue Ash (G-1736)

PUBLIC RELATIONS & PUBLICITY SVCS

Dayton Weekly News ....G....... 937 223-8060
Dayton (G-8289)
Marketing Essentials LLC ....F 419 629-0080
New Bremen (G-14789)

PUBLIC RELATIONS SVCS

Jjkb Enterprises LLC ....G....... 513 731-4332
Cincinnati (G-3946)

PUBLISHERS: Atlases

Scott Fetzer Company ....F 440 892-3000
Westlake (G-20306)

PUBLISHERS: Book

American Academic Press ....G....... 216 906-2518
Bedford (G-1396)
B & S Transport Inc ....G....... 330 767-4319
Navarre (G-14709)
B&D Productions Inc ....F 216 961-0310
Cleveland (G-4885)
Beevinwood Inc ....G....... 937 678-9910
West Manchester (G-20096)
Bendon Inc ....D 419 207-3600
Ashland (G-712)
Bookfactory LLC ....E 937 226-7100
Dayton (G-8191)
Bookmasters Inc ....C 419 281-1802
Ashland (G-713)
Carmel Trader Publishing Inc ....E 330 478-9200
Canton (G-2650)
Cengage Learning Inc ....C 513 234-5967
Mason (G-12993)
Conway Greene Co Inc ....G....... 216 619-8091
Cleveland (G-5128)
CSS Publishing Co Inc ....E 419 227-1818
Lima (G-12002)
Dalmatian Press LLC ....E 419 207-3600
Ashland (G-728)
Dreamscape Media LLC ....G....... 877 983-7326
Holland (G-11056)
Eastword Publications Dev ....G....... 216 781-9594
Cleveland (G-5241)
Elloras Cave Publishing Inc ....E 330 253-3521
Akron (G-163)
Frasernet Inc ....G....... 216 691-6686
Cleveland (G-5379)
Gareth Stevens Publishing LP...........C 800 542-2595
Strongsville (G-17922)
Grand Unification Press Inc ....G....... 330 683-1187
Orrville (G-15738)
Highlights Press Inc ....G....... 614 487-2767
Columbus (G-7156)
Hubbard Company ....E 419 784-4455
Defiance (G-8794)
Instruction & Design Concepts ....G....... 937 439-2698
Dayton (G-8412)
Just Business Inc ....F 866 577-3303
Dayton (G-8431)
Kaeden Corporation ....G....... 440 617-1400
Westlake (G-20280)
Katherine A Stull Inc ....G....... 440 349-3977
Solon (G-17327)
Kent State University ....F 330 672-7913
Kent (G-11481)
Kovels Antiques Inc ....F 216 752-2252
Cleveland (G-5664)
Lachina Publishing Svcs Inc ....E 216 292-7959
Cleveland (G-5674)
Lloyd Library & Museum ....G....... 513 721-3707
Cincinnati (G-4030)
Master Communications Inc ....G....... 208 821-3473
Blue Ash (G-1833)
Matthew Bender & Company Inc ....C 518 487-3000
Miamisburg (G-13827)
McDonald & Woodward Pubg Co ......G....... 740 321-1140
Granville (G-10460)
McGraw-Hill Global Educatn LLC........B 614 755-4151
Blacklick (G-1702)
McGraw-Hill School Education H........B 614 430-4000
Columbus (G-6652)

McNamaras Pub Inc ....G....... 216 671-8820
Cleveland (G-5772)
Micropress America LLC ....G....... 513 746-0689
Cincinnati (G-4102)
Neola Inc ....F 740 622-5341
Coshocton (G-7900)
North Coast Media LLC ....E 216 706-3700
Cleveland (G-5898)
Nurdcon LLC ....G....... 614 208-5898
Canal Winchester (G-2534)
Ohio Psychlogy Pblications Inc ....G....... 614 861-1999
Columbus (G-7429)
One Liberty Street ....G....... 419 352-6298
Bowling Green (G-2004)
Pardson Inc ....F 740 373-5285
Marietta (G-12813)
Precision Metalforming Assn ....E 216 241-1482
Independence (G-11271)
Province of St John The Baptis...........D 513 241-5615
Cincinnati (G-4301)
Reynolds Industries Group LLC...........E 614 864-6199
Blacklick (G-1704)
SC Solutions Inc ....G....... 614 317-7119
Grove City (G-10592)
Silver Maple Publications ....G....... 937 767-1259
Yellow Springs (G-20999)
Sparkpeople Inc ....F 513 651-2062
Cincinnati (G-4439)
St Media Group Intl Inc ....D 513 421-2050
Blue Ash (G-1873)
Talbot Drake Incorporated ....E 216 441-5600
Cleveland (G-6293)
Tgs International Inc ....E 330 893-2428
Millersburg (G-14268)
Vista Research Group LLC ....G....... 419 281-3927
Ashland (G-784)
Weaver Boos Consultants Inc ....F 419 933-5216
Willard (G-20404)
Woodburn Press LLC ....G....... 937 293-9245
Dayton (G-8764)
Zaner-Bloser Inc ....G....... 614 486-0221
Columbus (G-7786)

PUBLISHERS: Books, No Printing

American Legal Publishing Corp ....E 513 421-4248
Cincinnati (G-3391)
Anderson Publishing Co ....D 513 474-9305
Miamisburg (G-13783)
Asm International ....A 440 338-5151
Novelty (G-15582)
Dialogue House Associates Inc...........G....... 216 342-5170
Beachwood (G-1266)
F+w Media Inc ....B 513 531-2690
Blue Ash (G-1791)
Gie Media Inc ....E 800 456-0707
Cleveland (G-5430)
Golf Galaxy Golfworks Inc ....C 740 328-4193
Newark (G-15014)
Gray & Company Publishers ....G....... 216 431-2665
Cleveland (G-5448)
Harvey Whitney Books Company.........F 513 793-3555
Cincinnati (G-3869)
Indicator Advisory Corporation ....G....... 419 726-9000
Toledo (G-18521)
Jack C Keir Inc ....F 513 422-4860
Middletown (G-14051)
Kelley Communication Dev..................G....... 937 298-6132
Dayton (G-8435)
Ketman Corporation ....G....... 330 262-1688
Wooster (G-20795)
National Directory Morticians ....G....... 440 247-3561
Chagrin Falls (G-3065)
Neal Publications Inc ....G....... 419 874-4787
Perrysburg (G-16125)
OFA Services Inc ....F 614 884-1203
Columbus (G-7413)
Orange Frazer Press Inc ....G....... 937 382-3196
Wilmington (G-20672)
Relx Inc ....C 937 865-6800
Miamisburg (G-13853)
Relx Inc ....E 937 865-6800
Miamisburg (G-13851)
River Corp ....G....... 513 641-3355
Cincinnati (G-4348)
Teachers Publishing Group ....F 614 486-0631
Hilliard (G-10985)
Wolters Kluwer Clinical Drug................D 330 650-6506
Hudson (G-11210)

PUBLISHERS: Catalogs

Kennedy Catalogs LLC ....G....... 513 753-1518
Batavia (G-1196)

PUBLISHERS: Directories, NEC

Collegiate Directories Inc ....G....... 440 835-1172
Cleveland (G-5098)
Consumer Source Inc ....G....... 513 621-7300
Cincinnati (G-3605)
General Bar Inc ....F 440 835-2000
Westlake (G-20271)
Nomis Publications Inc ....F 330 965-2380
Youngstown (G-21150)
Snook Advertising Al Publisher ....F 614 866-3333
Reynoldsburg (G-16606)

PUBLISHERS: Directories, Telephone

All County Phone Directories ....G....... 419 865-2464
Holland (G-11044)
Ameritech Publishing Inc ....D 614 895-6123
Columbus (G-6744)
Berry Co ....F 877 742-3779
Hudson (G-11161)
Cbd Media Holdings LLC ....G....... 513 217-9483
Cincinnati (G-3507)
Champion Directories Inc ....F 419 668-1280
Norwalk (G-15530)
Christian Blue Pages ....F 937 847-2583
Miamisburg (G-13792)
Lanier & Associates Inc ....G....... 216 391-7735
Cleveland (G-5681)
Local Insight Yellow Pages Inc ....C 330 650-7100
Hudson (G-11188)
Supermedia LLC ....G....... 614 216-6566
Westerville (G-20190)

PUBLISHERS: Guides

Senior Impact Publication ....F 513 791-8800
Cincinnati (G-4404)
Shoppers Compass ....G....... 419 947-9234
Mount Gilead (G-14567)

PUBLISHERS: Magazines, No Printing

Acoustical Publications Inc ....G....... 440 835-0101
Bay Village (G-1241)
Adams Street Publishing Co ....E 419 244-9859
Toledo (G-18321)
Advanstar Communications Inc ....F 440 243-8100
North Olmsted (G-15325)
Arens Corporation ....F 937 473-2028
Covington (G-7918)
Arens Corporation ....G....... 937 473-2028
Covington (G-7919)
Baker Media Group LLC ....F 330 253-0056
Akron (G-83)
Bobit Business Media Inc ....G....... 330 899-2200
Uniontown (G-19077)
CFM Religion Pubg Group LLC ....E 513 931-4050
Cincinnati (G-3520)
City Visitor Inc ....G....... 216 661-6666
Cleveland (G-5039)
Crain Communications Inc ....E 216 522-1383
Cleveland (G-5140)
F+w Media Inc ....B 513 531-2690
Blue Ash (G-1791)
Family Motor Coaching Inc ....D 513 474-3622
Cincinnati (G-3739)
Generals Books ....G....... 614 870-1861
Columbus (G-7109)
Gie Media Inc ....E 800 456-0707
Cleveland (G-5430)
Great Lakes Publishing Company.........D 216 771-2833
Cleveland (G-5455)
Harvey Whitney Books Company..........F 513 793-3555
Cincinnati (G-3869)
Jadlyn Inc ....G....... 330 670-9545
Akron (G-238)
Kyle Publications Inc ....G....... 419 754-4234
Toledo (G-18551)
Marketing Essentials LLC ....F 419 629-0080
New Bremen (G-14789)
Meister Media Worldwide Inc...............D 440 942-2000
Willoughby (G-20544)
Organic Spa Magazine Ltd ....G....... 440 331-5750
Rocky River (G-16704)
Pardson Inc ....F 740 373-5285
Marietta (G-12813)

PRODUCT

Pink Corner Office Inc G 614 547-9350
Lewis Center *(G-11910)*

Pjl Enterprise Inc D 937 293-1415
Moraine *(G-14513)*

Pjl Enterprise Inc E 937 293-1415
Moraine *(G-14514)*

Plus Publications Inc G 740 345-5542
Newark *(G-15046)*

Province of St John The Baptis D 513 241-5615
Cincinnati *(G-4301)*

Rector Inc G 440 892-0444
Westlake *(G-20301)*

Sheep & Farm Life Inc G 419 492-2364
New Washington *(G-14964)*

Standard Publishing LLC C 513 931-4050
Cincinnati *(G-4453)*

Suburban Communications Inc E 440 632-0130
Middlefield *(G-13993)*

Toastmasters International F 937 429-2680
Dayton *(G-8118)*

Wordcross Enterprises Inc F 614 410-4140
Columbus *(G-7773)*

Xray Media Ltd G 513 751-9641
Cincinnati *(G-4615)*

PUBLISHERS: Maps

Permaguide E 330 456-8519
Canton *(G-2811)*

PUBLISHERS: Miscellaneous

360 Communications LLC G 330 329-2013
Akron *(G-12)*

Aaronyx Publishing G 419 747-2400
Mansfield *(G-12555)*

Adelphi Enterprises G 937 372-3791
Xenia *(G-20934)*

Albert Bickel G 513 530-5700
Cincinnati *(G-3375)*

Align Assess Achieve LLC G 614 505-6820
Columbus *(G-6716)*

American City Bus Journals Inc E 513 337-9450
Cincinnati *(G-3386)*

American Legal Publishing Corp E 513 421-4248
Cincinnati *(G-3391)*

Ameritech Publishing Inc E 330 896-6037
Uniontown *(G-19075)*

Amos Press Inc C 937 498-2111
Sidney *(G-17168)*

Anadem Inc G 614 262-2539
Columbus *(G-6751)*

Anderson Publishing Co D 513 474-9305
Miamisburg *(G-13783)*

AT&T Corp A 614 223-8236
Columbus *(G-6780)*

Bcmr Publications LLC G 740 441-7778
Gallipolis *(G-10291)*

Becker Gallagher Legal Pubg F 513 677-5044
Cincinnati *(G-3442)*

Blue Line Painting LLC G 440 951-2583
Cleveland *(G-4919)*

Cartoon Books Inc G 614 224-4487
Columbus *(G-6914)*

Ceja Publishing G 216 319-0268
Cleveland *(G-5000)*

Checkered Express Inc F 330 530-8169
Girard *(G-10384)*

Competitive Press Inc G 330 289-1968
Copley *(G-7842)*

Computer Workshop Inc E 614 798-9505
Dublin *(G-9065)*

Computer Workshop Inc G 216 901-0106
Cleveland *(G-5114)*

Computercrafts G 614 231-7559
Columbus *(G-6974)*

Copy Source Inc G 937 642-7140
Marysville *(G-12939)*

County Classifieds G 937 592-8847
Bellefontaine *(G-1525)*

Cox Publishing Hq G 937 225-2000
Dayton *(G-8247)*

Darby Creek Publishing F 614 873-7958
Plain City *(G-16332)*

Deward Publishing Co Ltd G 800 300-9778
Chillicothe *(G-3236)*

Diocesan Publications Inc Ohio E 614 718-9500
Dublin *(G-9068)*

Discover Publications G 614 785-1111
Columbus *(G-7029)*

Dodge Data & Analytics LLC G 513 345-8200
Cincinnati *(G-3660)*

Douthit Communications Inc E 419 621-2142
Sandusky *(G-16959)*

Douthit Communications Inc D 419 625-5825
Sandusky *(G-16958)*

Educational Publisher Inc G 614 485-0721
Columbus *(G-7046)*

Elbern Publications G 614 235-2643
Columbus *(G-7051)*

Elloras Cave Publishing Inc E 330 253-3521
Akron *(G-163)*

Express Care F 740 266-2501
Steubenville *(G-17694)*

F and W Publications Inc G 513 531-2690
Cincinnati *(G-3734)*

Fax Medley Group Inc G 513 272-1932
Cincinnati *(G-3743)*

Fire Ball Press G 614 280-0100
Columbus *(G-7087)*

Fish Express G 513 661-3000
Cincinnati *(G-3758)*

Fleetmaster Express Inc C 419 425-0666
Findlay *(G-9826)*

Franklin Covey Co G 513 792-0099
Cincinnati *(G-3779)*

Free Bird Publications Ltd G 216 673-0229
Brunswick *(G-2226)*

Gordon Bernard Co Inc E 513 248-7600
Milford *(G-14146)*

Gordon Bernard Company LLC E 513 248-7600
Milford *(G-14147)*

Gospel Trumpet Publishing G 937 548-9876
Greenville *(G-10503)*

Graphic Paper Products Corp D 937 325-5503
Springfield *(G-17564)*

Guadalupe Publishing Inc G 614 450-2474
Etna *(G-9556)*

Haines Criss Cross G 330 494-9111
North Canton *(G-15238)*

Hanover Publishing Co G 440 838-0911
Brecksville *(G-2054)*

Herff Jones LLC E 330 678-8138
Stow *(G-17762)*

Igloo Press LLC G 614 787-5528
Worthington *(G-20871)*

Immigration Law Systems Inc G 614 252-3078
Columbus *(G-7184)*

Incorporated Trustees Gospel W D 216 749-1428
Cleveland *(G-5561)*

Interweave Press LLC G 513 531-2690
Blue Ash *(G-1817)*

Johnny Chin Insurance Agency G 513 777-8695
West Chester *(G-20019)*

Kaylee Ryan Publishing LLC G 937 446-3926
Lake Waynoka *(G-11643)*

L & S Liette Express G 419 394-7077
Saint Marys *(G-16842)*

L M Berry and Company A 937 296-2121
Moraine *(G-14500)*

Lake Publishing Inc G 440 299-8500
Mentor *(G-13628)*

Lexisnexis Group C 937 865-6800
Miamisburg *(G-13825)*

Lily Tiger Press E 513 591-0817
Cincinnati *(G-4025)*

LPC Publishing Co G 216 721-1800
Cleveland *(G-5711)*

M R I Education Foundation C 513 281-3400
Cincinnati *(G-4043)*

Massie Publishing LLC G 740 446-4543
Gallipolis *(G-10305)*

Masterpiece Publisher L P G 513 948-1000
Cincinnati *(G-4065)*

Matthew R Copp G 614 276-8959
Columbus *(G-7325)*

Mia Express Inc G 330 896-8180
Akron *(G-297)*

Mp Printing & Design Inc G 740 456-2045
Portsmouth *(G-16445)*

Network Communications Inc C 614 934-1919
Gahanna *(G-10223)*

New Century Sales LLC G 513 422-3631
Middletown *(G-14070)*

North Bend Express G 513 481-4623
Cincinnati *(G-4162)*

Ogr Publishing Inc G 330 757-3020
Youngstown *(G-21153)*

Ohlinger Publishing Svcs Inc F 614 261-5360
Columbus *(G-7438)*

P&M Publishing G 740 353-3300
Portsmouth *(G-16447)*

Paula and Julies Cookbooks LLC G 614 863-1193
Columbus *(G-7469)*

Pauler Communications Inc G 440 243-1229
Richfield *(G-16631)*

Pedestrian Press G 419 244-6488
Toledo *(G-18637)*

Peebles Creative Group Inc G 614 487-2011
Dublin *(G-9120)*

Penton Business Media Inc A 216 696-7000
Cleveland *(G-5990)*

Phoenix Graphix Pubg Svcs LLC G 740 587-3659
Granville *(G-10465)*

Pixslap Inc G 937 559-2671
Middletown *(G-14076)*

Press Resource LLC G 614 794-9000
Westerville *(G-20230)*

Pressed Coffee Bar & Eatery G 330 746-8030
Youngstown *(G-21177)*

Propress Inc F 216 631-8200
Cleveland *(G-6056)*

Province of St John The Baptis D 513 241-5615
Cincinnati *(G-4301)*

Prowrite Inc G 614 864-2004
Reynoldsburg *(G-16601)*

Psa Consulting Inc G 513 382-4315
Cincinnati *(G-4302)*

Puhd G 216 244-3336
Bedford *(G-1455)*

Purebred Publishing Inc G 614 339-5393
Columbus *(G-7527)*

Quaker Express Stamping Inc F 330 332-9266
Salem *(G-16921)*

Rawhide Software Inc G 419 878-0857
Bowling Green *(G-2010)*

Rcl Publishing Group LLC G 972 390-6400
Cincinnati *(G-4333)*

Recob Great Lakes Express Inc G 216 265-7940
Cleveland *(G-6093)*

Research and Development Group G 614 261-0454
Columbus *(G-7556)*

Robs Creative Screen Printing G 740 264-6383
Wintersville *(G-20713)*

S J T Enterprises Inc E 440 617-1100
Westlake *(G-20305)*

S&P Global Inc E 216 749-9779
Cleveland *(G-6152)*

Samhain Publishing Ltd (llc) G 513 453-4688
Cincinnati *(G-4378)*

Scrambl-Gram Inc F 419 635-2321
Port Clinton *(G-16414)*

Sea Bird Publications Inc G 513 869-2200
Fairfield *(G-9715)*

Sei Inc F 513 942-6170
West Chester *(G-20048)*

Sevell + Sevell Inc G 614 341-9700
Columbus *(G-7611)*

Simon & Schuster Inc C 614 876-0371
Columbus *(G-7623)*

Singer Press G 216 595-9400
Beachwood *(G-1299)*

Snap-On Business Solutions B 330 659-1600
Richfield *(G-16639)*

Specialty Gas Publishing Inc G 216 226-3796
Cleveland *(G-6224)*

Star Brite Express Car WA G 330 674-0062
Millersburg *(G-14264)*

Starbringer Media Group Ltd G 440 871-5448
Westlake *(G-20312)*

Suburban Communications Inc E 440 632-0130
Middlefield *(G-13993)*

Success Pro Publications G 614 497-5674
Columbus *(G-7666)*

Tiny Lion Music Groups G 419 874-7353
Perrysburg *(G-16160)*

Trogdon Publishing Inc G 330 620-2407
Powell *(G-16486)*

Universal Drect Fflment Corp C 330 650-5000
Hudson *(G-11206)*

Van-Griner LLC G 419 733-7951
Cincinnati *(G-4555)*

Visual Education Association G 937 325-5503
Springfield *(G-17673)*

Wizard Publications Inc F 808 821-1214
Lancaster *(G-11762)*

Zoo Publishing Inc E 513 824-8297
Blue Ash *(G-1905)*

PUBLISHERS: Music Book

Decent Hill Publishers LLC G 216 548-1255
Hilliard *(G-10948)*

PUBLISHERS: Music Book & Sheet Music

Terewell Inc..............................G...... 216 334-6897
Cleveland (G-6306)

PUBLISHERS: Music, Sheet

American Guild of English Hand......G...... 937 438-0085
Cincinnati (G-3389)

Beckenhorst Press Inc..................G...... 614 451-6461
Columbus (G-6817)

Lorenz Corporation......................D...... 937 228-6118
Dayton (G-8460)

Ludwig Music Publishing Co..........F...... 440 926-1100
Grafton (G-10433)

PUBLISHERS: Newsletter

Pike County Paper Inc..................F...... 740 947-5522
Waverly (G-19717)

See Ya There Inc.........................G...... 614 856-9037
Millersport (G-14298)

PUBLISHERS: Newspaper

Akron Legal News Inc....................F...... 330 296-7578
Akron (G-46)

American Community Newspapers......G...... 614 888-4567
Columbus (G-6733)

Antwerp Bee-Argus......................G...... 419 258-8161
Antwerp (G-627)

Applelane Press LLC.....................G...... 440 543-6747
Chagrin Falls (G-3048)

B G News..................................E...... 419 372-2601
Bowling Green (G-1969)

Bloomville Gazette Inc...................G...... 419 426-3491
Attica (G-892)

Brecksville Broadview Gazette.........E...... 440 526-7977
Brecksville (G-2038)

Brookville Star.............................G...... 937 833-2545
Brookville (G-2177)

Brown Publishing Inc LLC...............G...... 513 794-5040
Blue Ash (G-1756)

Brv Inc.......................................F...... 513 977-3000
Cincinnati (G-3483)

Buckeye Post...............................G...... 330 724-2800
Akron (G-102)

Catholic Diocese of Columbus..........G...... 614 224-5195
Columbus (G-6916)

Chesterland News Inc....................F...... 440 729-7667
Chesterland (G-3200)

Chronicle Telegram.......................G...... 330 725-4166
Medina (G-13387)

Chronicle Your Life Story...............G...... 614 456-7576
Columbus (G-6928)

Cleveland Citizen Pubg Co.............G...... 216 861-4283
Cleveland (G-5052)

Cleveland Jewish Publ Co Fdn.........G...... 216 454-8300
Beachwood (G-1261)

Coffee News...............................G...... 330 688-0952
Stow (G-17741)

Columbus Messenger Company.......G...... 740 852-0809
London (G-12205)

Consumers News Services Inc.........C...... 740 888-6000
Lewis Center (G-11893)

Cox Newspapers LLC.....................E...... 513 696-4500
Liberty Township (G-11959)

Cox Newspapers LLC.....................D...... 937 225-2000
Dayton (G-8246)

Cox Newspapers LLC.....................D...... 513 863-8200
Liberty Township (G-11960)

Crain Communications Inc...............E...... 216 522-1383
Cleveland (G-5140)

Daily Legal News Inc......................G...... 330 747-7777
Youngstown (G-21063)

Dayton City Paper New LLC.............F...... 937 222-8855
Dayton (G-8270)

Eastern Ohio Newspapers Inc..........G...... 740 633-1131
Martins Ferry (G-12924)

EW Scripps Company.....................E...... 513 977-3000
Cincinnati (G-3728)

Fire Tetrahedron Journal.................G...... 567 220-6477
Tiffin (G-18220)

Fostoria Focus Inc........................F...... 419 435-6397
Fostoria (G-9976)

Franklin Communications Inc...........D...... 614 459-9769
Columbus (G-7097)

Full Gospel Baptist Times...............G...... 614 279-3307
Columbus (G-7102)

Gannett Co Inc............................D...... 740 452-4561
Zanesville (G-21314)

Gannett Co Inc............................C...... 419 522-3311
Mansfield (G-12609)

Gannett Stllite Info Ntwrk Inc...........D...... 513 721-2700
Cincinnati (G-3796)

Gannett Stllite Info Ntwrk Inc...........G...... 513 576-1800
Milford (G-14143)

Gannett Stllite Info Ntwrk LLC.........D...... 419 334-1012
Fremont (G-10152)

Gazette Editorial Department...........G...... 330 725-6220
Medina (G-13415)

Gazette Publishing Company...........F...... 419 335-2010
Wauseon (G-19679)

Hirt Publishing Co Inc....................E...... 419 946-3010
Mount Gilead (G-14562)

Hirt Publishing Co Inc....................F...... 419 523-5709
Ottawa (G-15795)

Holmes County Hub Inc..................G...... 330 674-1811
Millersburg (G-14230)

Horizon Publications Inc.................G...... 419 628-2369
Minster (G-14355)

Iheartcommunications Inc...............F...... 740 335-0941
Wshngtn CT Hs (G-20911)

Iheartcommunications Inc...............D...... 419 223-2060
Lima (G-12026)

James Oshea..............................G...... 614 262-3188
Columbus (G-7226)

Journal Register Company..............C...... 440 951-0000
Willoughby (G-20517)

Leaf & Thorn Press........................G...... 614 396-6055
Columbus (G-6651)

Lisa Arters.................................G...... 330 435-1804
Creston (G-7940)

Lore Inc.....................................G...... 513 969-8481
Milford (G-14159)

Marrow County Sentinel..................G...... 419 946-3010
Mount Gilead (G-14564)

Mature Living News Magazine..........G...... 419 241-8880
Toledo (G-18576)

Mickens Inc................................G...... 419 943-2590
Leipsic (G-11872)

Monroe County Beacon Inc.............F...... 740 472-0734
Woodsfield (G-20720)

Morgan County Publishing Co.........G...... 740 962-3377
McConnelsville (G-13356)

My Way Home Finder Magazine........G...... 419 841-6201
Toledo (G-18596)

Neighborhood News Pubg Co..........G...... 216 441-2141
Cleveland (G-5867)

Newspaper Solutions LLC...............G...... 937 694-9370
Englewood (G-9535)

North Coast Voice Mag..................G...... 440 415-0999
Geneva (G-10353)

Northeast Scene Inc.....................E...... 216 241-7550
Cleveland (G-5907)

Ocm LLC....................................E...... 937 247-2700
Miamisburg (G-13844)

Ogden Newspapers of Ohio Inc.......D...... 419 448-3200
Tiffin (G-18236)

Ohio News Network........................D...... 614 460-3700
Columbus (G-7423)

Outdoor News Service....................G...... 419 734-5172
Port Clinton (G-16408)

Pataskala Post.............................F...... 740 964-6226
Pataskala (G-15977)

Patriot......................................G...... 419 864-8411
Cardington (G-2913)

Perry County Tribune.....................F...... 740 342-4121
New Lexington (G-14851)

Plain Dealer Publishing Co..............F...... 216 999-5000
Cleveland (G-6010)

Plain Dealer Publishing Co..............G...... 614 228-8200
Columbus (G-7488)

Plain Dealer Publishing Co..............A...... 216 999-5000
Cleveland (G-6011)

Print Shop..................................G...... 740 335-8030
Wshngtn CT Hs (G-20920)

Progressor Times.........................G...... 419 396-7567
Carey (G-2924)

Ptr Daily LLC...............................G...... 330 673-1990
Stow (G-17793)

R & C Lortcher LLC........................G...... 419 663-1531
Norwalk (G-15560)

Royalton Recorder.......................G...... 440 237-2235
North Royalton (G-15450)

Rural Urban Record Inc..................G...... 440 236-8982
Columbia Station (G-6598)

Sandusky Newspapers Inc..............C...... 419 625-5500
Sandusky (G-17004)

Scripps Media Inc.........................D...... 513 977-3000
Cincinnati (G-4392)

Sdg News Group Inc......................F...... 419 929-3411
New London (G-14865)

Sesh Communications....................F...... 513 851-1693
Cincinnati (G-4408)

Shree Krupa Inc...........................G...... 216 781-6054
Cleveland (G-6197)

Sojourners Truth..........................F...... 419 243-0007
Toledo (G-18700)

Star Newspaper............................G...... 614 622-5930
Columbus (G-7652)

Stumbo Publishing Co....................G...... 419 529-2847
Ontario (G-15695)

The Cleveland Jewish Publ Co.........G...... 216 454-8300
Beachwood (G-1300)

The Gazette Printing Co Inc............G...... 440 593-6030
Conneaut (G-7820)

The Jeffersonian.........................G...... 740 498-7117
Newcomerstown (G-15125)

Times Bulletin Media......................F...... 419 238-2285
Van Wert (G-19272)

Times Journal..............................F...... 740 286-2187
Jackson (G-11330)

Toledo Streets Newspaper..............G...... 419 214-3460
Toledo (G-18743)

Toledo Sword Newspaper................G...... 419 932-0767
Toledo (G-18744)

Toledos Runway Rivalry Brough........G...... 419 724-6307
Toledo (G-18749)

Trogdon Publishing Inc...................E...... 330 721-7678
Medina (G-13491)

Trumbull County Legal News............G...... 330 392-7112
Warren (G-19612)

University Sports Publications..........G...... 614 291-6416
Columbus (G-7726)

Village Voice Publishing Ltd............G...... 419 537-0286
Toledo (G-18769)

Villager Publishing Co Inc...............G...... 330 527-5761
Garrettsville (G-10335)

Vindicator...................................G...... 330 755-0135
Campbell (G-2493)

Vindicator Boardman Office.............G...... 330 259-1732
Youngstown (G-21240)

Vindicator Printing Company............G...... 330 392-0176
Warren (G-19618)

Weekly Brothers Cnty Line Far.........G...... 330 674-4195
Millersburg (G-14284)

Weekly Chatter............................G...... 740 336-4704
Belpre (G-1597)

Weekly Juicery.............................G...... 513 321-0680
Cincinnati (G-4582)

Whitney House.............................G...... 614 396-7846
Worthington (G-20894)

Willard Times Junction...................F...... 419 935-0184
Willard (G-20405)

Zanesville Newspaper.....................G...... 740 452-4561
Zanesville (G-21367)

PUBLISHERS: Newspapers, No Printing

American City Bus Journals Inc.........E...... 513 337-9450
Cincinnati (G-3386)

American City Bus Journals Inc.........E...... 937 528-4400
Dayton (G-8152)

American Israelite Co.....................G...... 513 621-3145
Cincinnati (G-3390)

American Lithuanian Press...............G...... 216 531-8150
Cleveland (G-4787)

Archbold Buckeye Inc....................F...... 419 445-4466
Archbold (G-663)

Arens Corporation.........................F...... 937 473-2028
Covington (G-7918)

Arens Corporation.........................G...... 937 473-2028
Covington (G-7919)

Ashland Publishing Co....................A...... 419 281-0581
Ashland (G-708)

Boardman News...........................G...... 330 758-6397
Boardman (G-1920)

Brothers Publishing Co LLC.............E...... 937 548-3330
Greenville (G-10490)

Brown Publishing Co Inc.................G...... 740 286-2187
Jackson (G-11313)

Business First Columbus Inc............E...... 614 461-4040
Columbus (G-6878)

C L M Associates.........................G...... 440 942-8861
Willoughby (G-20451)

Chagrin Valley Publishing Co...........C...... 440 247-5335
Chagrin Falls (G-3051)

Cleveland Jewish Publ Co...............E...... 216 454-8300
Cleveland (G-5067)

Columbus Alive Inc.......................F...... 614 221-2449
Columbus (G-6947)

Employee Codes: A=Over 500 employees, B=251-500
C=101-250, D=51-100, E=20-50, F=10-19, G=3-9

P
R
O
D
U
C
T

Columbus Messenger Company .... E 614 272-5422
 Columbus *(G-6961)*
Columbus-Sports Publications .... F 614 486-2202
 Columbus *(G-6969)*
Comcorp Inc .... B 718 981-1234
 Cleveland *(G-5102)*
Coshocton County Advertiser .... G 740 295-3435
 Coshocton *(G-7884)*
Cox Newspapers LLC .... G 513 523-4139
 Oxford *(G-15835)*
Crain Communications Inc .... D 330 836-9180
 Akron *(G-133)*
Daily Fostoria Review Co .... C 419 435-6641
 Fostoria *(G-9969)*
Easy Side Publishing Co Inc .... G 216 721-1674
 Cleveland *(G-5242)*
Farmland News LLC .... F 419 445-9456
 Archbold *(G-672)*
Funny Times Inc .... G 216 371-8600
 Cleveland *(G-5383)*
Gannett Co Inc .... E 740 654-1321
 Lancaster *(G-11718)*
Gannett Co Inc .... C 740 773-2111
 Chillicothe *(G-3240)*
Gannett Co Inc .... E 419 521-7341
 Marion *(G-12866)*
Gannett Co Inc .... E 740 295-3435
 Coshocton *(G-7892)*
Gannett Co Inc .... F 419 332-5511
 Fremont *(G-10151)*
Gannett Co Inc .... F 740 349-1100
 Newark *(G-15010)*
Harrison News Herald Inc .... F 740 942-2118
 Cadiz *(G-2418)*
Impact Publications .... G 740 928-5541
 Buckeye Lake *(G-2329)*
Indian Lake Shoppers Edge .... G 937 843-6600
 Russells Point *(G-16756)*
Lake Community News .... G 440 946-2577
 Willoughby *(G-20524)*
Laprensa Publications Inc .... G 419 242-7744
 Toledo *(G-18554)*
Leader Publications Inc .... E 330 665-9595
 Fairlawn *(G-9756)*
Louisville Herald Inc .... G 330 875-5610
 Louisville *(G-12318)*
Marketing Essentials LLC .... F 419 629-0080
 New Bremen *(G-14789)*
Marysville Newspaper Inc .... G 740 943-2214
 Richwood *(G-16660)*
Mickens Inc .... G 419 533-2401
 Liberty Center *(G-11955)*
Mirror Publishing Co Inc .... E 419 893-8135
 Maumee *(G-13285)*
Napoleon Inc .... E 419 592-5055
 Napoleon *(G-14691)*
Nomis Publications Inc .... F 330 965-2380
 Youngstown *(G-21150)*
Ogden Newspapers Inc .... E 330 332-4601
 Salem *(G-16917)*
Ogden Newspapers Inc .... D 740 283-4711
 Steubenville *(G-17708)*
Ogden Newspapers Inc .... C 330 841-1600
 Warren *(G-19582)*
Outlook Publishing Inc .... F 614 268-8525
 Columbus *(G-7450)*
Peebles Messenger Newspaper .... G 937 587-1451
 Peebles *(G-16023)*
Reporter Newspaper Inc .... F 330 535-7061
 Akron *(G-371)*
Richardson Publishing Company .... F 330 753-1068
 Barberton *(G-1146)*
Shelby Daily Globe Inc .... E 419 342-4276
 Shelby *(G-17142)*
Smart Business Network Inc .... E 440 250-7000
 Cleveland *(G-6210)*
Suburban Newpapers of Dayton .... E 937 878-3993
 Xenia *(G-20976)*
Sugarcreek Budget Publishers .... F 330 852-4634
 Sugarcreek *(G-18042)*
Telegram .... F 740 286-3604
 Jackson *(G-11328)*
Toledo Journal .... G 419 472-4521
 Toledo *(G-18732)*
Travelers Vacation Guide .... G 440 582-4949
 North Royalton *(G-15456)*
Tribune Printing Inc .... G 419 542-7764
 Hicksville *(G-10909)*
Voice Media Group Inc .... D 216 241-7550
 Cleveland *(G-6425)*

Welch Publishing Co .... G 419 666-5344
 Rossford *(G-16750)*
Winkler Co Inc .... G 937 294-2662
 Dayton *(G-8761)*

PUBLISHERS: Pamphlets, No Printing

Neola Inc .... G 330 926-0514
 Stow *(G-17783)*

PUBLISHERS: Periodical, With Printing

American Ceramic Society .... E 614 890-4700
 Westerville *(G-20137)*
Babcox Media Inc .... D 330 670-1234
 Akron *(G-82)*
Hacienda Publications LLC .... G 216 202-5440
 Euclid *(G-9585)*
Incorporated Trst Gspl Wk Scty .... D 216 749-2100
 Cleveland *(G-5560)*
SC Solutions Inc .... G 614 317-7119
 Grove City *(G-10592)*

PUBLISHERS: Periodicals, Magazines

AGS Custom Graphics Inc .... D 330 963-7770
 Macedonia *(G-12433)*
Alcohol & Drug Addiction Svcs .... E 216 348-4830
 Cleveland *(G-4744)*
American Heart Association Inc .... F 419 740-6180
 Maumee *(G-13223)*
Buckeye Prep Report Magazine .... G 614 855-6977
 New Albany *(G-14752)*
Center For Inquiry Inc .... G 330 671-7192
 Peninsula *(G-16035)*
Charlotte M Peters .... G 216 798-8997
 Cleveland *(G-5017)*
Cincinnati Magazine .... G 513 421-4300
 Cincinnati *(G-3557)*
City Girl Magazine LLC .... G 216 481-4110
 Cleveland *(G-5034)*
Clipper Magazine LLC .... G 937 534-0470
 Moraine *(G-14472)*
Communication Resources Inc .... E 800 992-2144
 Canton *(G-2665)*
Construction Journal Ltd .... F 440 826-4700
 Cleveland *(G-5120)*
Crain Communications Inc .... D 330 836-9180
 Akron *(G-133)*
Dispatch Printing Company .... E 614 885-6020
 Columbus *(G-7030)*
Dominion Enterprises .... E 216 472-1870
 Cleveland *(G-5204)*
Family Values Magazine .... G 419 566-1102
 Mansfield *(G-12602)*
Graphicom Press Inc .... G 937 767-1916
 Yellow Springs *(G-20991)*
Greater Cincinnati Bowl Assn .... E 513 761-7387
 Cincinnati *(G-3847)*
Guitar Digest Inc .... F 740 592-4614
 Athens *(G-870)*
In Box Publications LLC .... G 330 592-4288
 Akron *(G-231)*
Institute Mthmtical Statistics .... G 216 295-2340
 Shaker Heights *(G-17090)*
Kaleidoscope Magazine LLC .... E 216 566-5500
 Cleveland *(G-5631)*
Kent Information Services Inc .... G 330 672-2110
 Kent *(G-11479)*
Lavish Lyfe Magazine .... G 937 938-5816
 Dayton *(G-8453)*
Legal News Publishing Co .... E 216 696-3322
 Cleveland *(G-5692)*
Marketing Directions Inc .... G 440 835-5550
 Cleveland *(G-5747)*
Matthew Bender & Company Inc .... C 518 487-3000
 Miamisburg *(G-13827)*
Miller Publishing Company .... G 937 866-3331
 Miamisburg *(G-13837)*
Ohio State University .... G 614 292-6930
 Columbus *(G-7434)*
Pearson Education Inc .... F 614 876-0371
 Columbus *(G-7471)*
Pearson Education Inc .... F 614 841-3700
 Columbus *(G-7472)*
Professional Reports Corp .... G 330 492-6063
 Canton *(G-2826)*
Reel Image .... G 937 296-9036
 Dayton *(G-8621)*
Relx Inc .... F 937 865-6800
 Miamisburg *(G-13852)*

Rubber World Magazine Inc .... F 330 864-2122
 Akron *(G-381)*
Sesh Communications .... F 513 851-1693
 Cincinnati *(G-4408)*
Sterling Associates Inc .... G 330 630-3500
 Akron *(G-418)*
Target Printing & Graphics .... G 937 228-0170
 Dayton *(G-8700)*
Telex Communications Inc .... F 419 865-0972
 Toledo *(G-18718)*
United Advg Publications Inc .... G 513 469-8818
 Cincinnati *(G-4537)*
University Sports Publications .... E 614 291-6416
 Columbus *(G-7726)*
US Brands Inc .... G 216 595-9700
 Cleveland *(G-6398)*
Vela .... G 614 500-0150
 Salesville *(G-16938)*
Welch Publishing Co .... E 419 874-2528
 Perrysburg *(G-16168)*
Z Track Magazine .... G 614 764-1703
 Dublin *(G-9167)*

PUBLISHERS: Periodicals, No Printing

Agri Communicators Inc .... E 614 273-0465
 Columbus *(G-6702)*
American Lawyers Co Inc .... F 440 333-5190
 Westlake *(G-20250)*
Amos Press Inc .... C 937 498-2111
 Sidney *(G-17168)*
Asm International .... D 440 338-5151
 Novelty *(G-15582)*
C & S Associates Inc .... E 440 461-9661
 Highland Heights *(G-10910)*
Camargo Publications Inc .... G 513 779-7177
 Cincinnati *(G-3495)*
Columbus Bride .... D 614 888-4567
 Columbus *(G-6948)*
Fontanelle Group Inc .... G 440 834-8900
 Burton *(G-2375)*
Gongwer News Service Inc .... F 614 221-1992
 Columbus *(G-7123)*
Gongwer News Service Inc .... G 614 221-1992
 Columbus *(G-7124)*
Graphic Publications Inc .... E 330 674-2300
 Millersburg *(G-14218)*
Indicator Advisory Corporation .... G 419 726-9000
 Toledo *(G-18521)*
Lorenz Corporation .... D 937 228-6118
 Dayton *(G-8460)*
National Mortgage Weekley .... G 330 674-2887
 Millersburg *(G-14253)*
Northeast Scene Inc .... E 216 241-7550
 Cleveland *(G-5907)*
Ohio Designer Craftsmen Entps .... F 614 486-7119
 Columbus *(G-7419)*
Schuster Beverage Marketing .... G 614 764-1420
 Dublin *(G-9140)*
St Media Group Intl Inc .... D 513 421-2050
 Blue Ash *(G-1873)*

PUBLISHERS: Sheet Music

Great Works Publishing Inc .... F 440 926-1100
 Grafton *(G-10428)*
Thunder Dreamer Publishing .... G 419 424-2004
 Findlay *(G-9903)*
Willis Music Company .... F 513 671-3288
 Cincinnati *(G-4597)*

PUBLISHERS: Technical Manuals

ONeil & Associates Inc .... C 937 865-0800
 Miamisburg *(G-13847)*
Resource Development Co LLC .... G 440 617-9087
 Westlake *(G-20302)*

PUBLISHERS: Technical Manuals & Papers

Elsevier Inc .... G 513 942-5070
 West Chester *(G-19855)*
Fgm Media Inc .... G 440 376-0487
 North Royalton *(G-15419)*
Walter H Drane Co Inc .... G 216 514-1022
 Beachwood *(G-1305)*

PUBLISHERS: Telephone & Other Directory

B G News .... E 419 372-2601
 Bowling Green *(G-1969)*
Begashaw & Associates .... G 614 329-1630
 Columbus *(G-6820)*

Hibu Inc ....E 614 468-7900
  Columbus (G-6650)

PUBLISHERS: Television Schedules, No Printing

Virtus Stunts LLC ....G 440 543-0472
  Chagrin Falls (G-3132)

PUBLISHERS: Textbooks, No Printing

Leap Publishing Services Inc ....F 234 738-0082
  Stow (G-17768)
Scott Fetzer Company ....F 440 892-3000
  Westlake (G-20306)

PUBLISHERS: Trade journals, No Printing

Gardner Business Media Inc ....E 513 527-8800
  Cincinnati (G-3799)
Lippincott & Peto Inc ....F 330 864-2122
  Akron (G-271)
Lyle Printing & Publishing Co ....E 330 337-3419
  Salem (G-16909)
Lyle Printing & Publishing Co ....F 330 337-7172
  Salem (G-16910)
Modern Trade Communications ....G 419 849-3109
  Woodville (G-20726)
Relx Inc ....G 937 865-6800
  Miamisburg (G-13851)

PUBLISHING & BROADCASTING: Internet Only

Clark Optimization LLC ....E 330 417-2164
  Canton (G-2658)
Deemsys Inc ....D 614 322-9928
  Gahanna (G-10206)
Evans Creative Group LLC ....G 614 657-9439
  Columbus (G-7072)
IPA Ltd ....F 614 523-3974
  Columbus (G-7210)
Latte Living ....G 440 364-2201
  Cleveland (G-5685)
Marketing Essentials LLC ....F 419 629-0080
  New Bremen (G-14789)
Organized Lightning LLC ....G 407 965-2730
  Blue Ash (G-1850)
Quadriga Americas LLC ....G 614 890-6090
  Westerville (G-20180)
Thickemz Entertainment LLC ....G 404 399-4255
  Cuyahoga Falls (G-8056)

PUBLISHING & PRINTING: Art Copy

Powerhouse Factories Inc ....F 513 719-6417
  Cincinnati (G-4256)
Publishing Group Ltd ....F 614 572-1240
  Columbus (G-7526)

PUBLISHING & PRINTING: Book Music

Swagg Productions2015llc ....F 614 815-1173
  Reynoldsburg (G-16608)

PUBLISHING & PRINTING: Books

Bearing Precious Seed ....G 513 575-1706
  Milford (G-14124)
Gardner Business Media Inc ....E 513 527-8800
  Cincinnati (G-3799)
Hamilton Arts Inc ....G 937 767-1834
  Yellow Springs (G-20992)
Kendall/Hunt Publishing Co ....D 877 275-4725
  Cincinnati (G-3982)
Kid Concoctions Company ....G 440 572-1800
  Strongsville (G-17936)
Lawpak Inc ....G 513 831-3900
  Terrace Park (G-18180)
Marysville Newspaper Inc ....E 937 644-9111
  Marysville (G-12957)
McGraw-Hill School Education H ....B 419 207-7400
  Ashland (G-753)
Northstar Publishing ....G 330 721-9126
  Medina (G-13450)
Simon & Schuster Inc ....C 614 876-0371
  Columbus (G-7623)
World Harvest Church Inc ....C 614 837-1990
  Canal Winchester (G-2542)

PUBLISHING & PRINTING: Catalogs

Chasing Fireflies LLC ....G 206 574-4500
  West Chester (G-19826)
D B Hess Company ....G 330 676-2006
  Kent (G-11445)

PUBLISHING & PRINTING: Directories, NEC

Dickman Directories Inc ....G 740 548-6130
  Lewis Center (G-11894)
Haines & Company Inc ....C 330 494-9111
  North Canton (G-15237)
Haines Publishing Inc ....D 330 494-9111
  Canton (G-2722)
RR Donnelley & Sons Company ....A 419 935-0111
  Willard (G-20400)

PUBLISHING & PRINTING: Directories, Telephone

Berry Company ....G 513 768-7800
  Cincinnati (G-3448)
Cincinnati Bell Inc ....F 513 565-2210
  Cincinnati (G-3541)
User Friendly Phone Book LLC ....E 216 674-6500
  Independence (G-11281)

PUBLISHING & PRINTING: Guides

Beaver Productions ....G 330 352-4603
  Akron (G-86)
Trogdon Publishing Inc ....E 330 721-7678
  Medina (G-13491)

PUBLISHING & PRINTING: Magazines: publishing & printing

614 Media Group LLC ....D 614 488-4400
  Columbus (G-6665)
A R Harding Publishing Company ....F 614 231-5735
  Columbus (G-6668)
Advanced Mdia Publications Inc ....F 440 260-9910
  Cleveland (G-4716)
Alternative Press Magazine Inc ....E 216 631-1510
  Cleveland (G-4771)
Angstrom Graphics Inc ....C 216 271-5300
  Cleveland (G-4814)
Bluffton News Pubg & Prtg Co ....F 419 358-8010
  Bluffton (G-1907)
Carmel Trader Publishing Inc ....E 330 478-9200
  Canton (G-2650)
Cars and Parts Magazine ....C 937 498-0803
  Sidney (G-17171)
Cruisin Times Magazine ....G 440 331-4615
  Rocky River (G-16696)
Curt Harler Inc ....G 440 238-4556
  Cleveland (G-5147)
Downey Enterprises Inc ....G 740 587-4258
  Granville (G-10457)
Family Motor Coach Assn Inc ....E 513 474-3622
  Cincinnati (G-3738)
Half Price Bks Rec Mgzines Inc ....F 614 776-5551
  Westerville (G-20217)
Half Price Bks Rec Mgzines Inc ....F 440 255-2581
  Mentor (G-13599)
Highlights For Children Inc ....C 614 486-0631
  Hilliard (G-10951)
Horizon Communications Inc ....G 330 968-6959
  Twinsburg (G-18955)
Housetrends ....G 513 794-4103
  Blue Ash (G-1809)
Kenyon Review ....G 740 427-5208
  Gambier (G-10316)
Larry C White ....G 330 386-3228
  East Liverpool (G-9224)
Marula Publishing LLC ....G 513 549-5218
  Cincinnati (G-4064)
Midwest Exposure Magazine ....G 937 626-6738
  Dayton (G-8495)
Morrison Media Group-Cmj LLP ....G 216 973-4005
  Cleveland (G-5834)
New Track Media LLC ....F 513 421-6500
  Blue Ash (G-1844)
North Coast Minority Media LLC ....E 216 407-4327
  Cleveland (G-5899)
Open House Magazine Inc ....G 614 523-7775
  Columbus (G-7443)
Peninsula Publishing LLC ....G 330 524-3359
  Peninsula (G-16040)
Prehistoric Antiquities ....G 937 747-2225
  North Lewisburg (G-15308)

PUBLISHING & PRINTING: Newspapers

Publishing Group Ltd ....F 614 572-1240
  Columbus (G-7526)
Quad/Graphics Inc ....A 513 932-1064
  Lebanon (G-11830)
Sabre Publishing ....G 440 243-4300
  Berea (G-1634)
Venue Lifestyle & Event Guide ....F 513 405-6822
  Cincinnati (G-4563)
Youngs Publishing Inc ....F 937 259-6575
  Beavercreek (G-1367)

PUBLISHING & PRINTING: Newsletters, Business Svc

Matly Digital Solutions LLC ....G 513 860-3435
  Fairfield (G-9681)
Questline Inc ....E 614 255-3166
  Dublin (G-9129)

PUBLISHING & PRINTING: Newspapers

Aak Kings Mills LLC ....G 513 598-4460
  Mason (G-12978)
Acm Ohio LLC ....G 740 286-2187
  Jackson (G-11308)
Active Daily Living LLC ....G 513 607-6769
  Cincinnati (G-3352)
Adams Publishing Group LLC ....G 740 592-6612
  Athens (G-854)
Adult Daily Living LLC ....G 330 612-7941
  Barberton (G-1093)
Advance Reporter ....G 419 485-4851
  Montpelier (G-14438)
Alliance Publishing Co Inc ....C 330 453-1304
  Alliance (G-495)
Alliance Publishing Co Inc ....F 330 868-5222
  Minerva (G-14316)
American Jrnl of Drmtpathology ....G 440 542-0041
  Solon (G-17257)
Amos Press Inc ....C 937 498-2111
  Sidney (G-17168)
Barbara A Eisenhardt ....G 614 436-9690
  Columbus (G-6806)
Bellefontaine Examiner ....F 937 592-3060
  Bellefontaine (G-1522)
Block Communications Inc ....F 419 724-6212
  Toledo (G-18372)
Brown Publishing Co ....F 937 544-2391
  West Union (G-20118)
Bryan Publishing Company ....D 419 636-1111
  Bryan (G-2288)
Buchtelite ....E 330 972-6184
  Akron (G-101)
Buckeye Lake Shopper Reporter ....G 740 246-4741
  Thornville (G-18192)
Cameco Communications ....G 937 840-9490
  Hillsboro (G-10997)
Carrollton Publishing Company ....F 330 627-5591
  Carrollton (G-2954)
Cathie D Hubbard ....E 937 593-0316
  Bellefontaine (G-1524)
Caxton New Stand ....G 216 861-1600
  Cleveland (G-4996)
Central Ohio Printing Corp ....D 740 852-1616
  London (G-12203)
Citizens USA ....G 937 280-2001
  Dayton (G-8232)
Clermont Sun Publishing Co ....G 937 444-3441
  Mount Orab (G-14578)
Construction Bulletin Inc ....G 330 782-3733
  Youngstown (G-21057)
Copley Ohio Newspapers Inc ....C 330 364-5577
  New Philadelphia (G-14892)
Copley Ohio Newspapers Inc ....D 330 833-2631
  Massillon (G-13121)
Cox Media Group Ohio Inc ....A 937 225-2000
  Dayton (G-8245)
Cox Media Group Ohio Inc ....G 937 743-6700
  Franklin (G-10016)
Cox Newspapers LLC ....F 937 866-3331
  Miamisburg (G-13794)
Cross Communications Inc ....G 937 304-0010
  Vandalia (G-19287)
Cuyahoga Co Med Examiner S Off ......G 216 721-5610
  Cleveland (G-5156)
Daily Agency Inc ....F 937 456-9808
  Eaton (G-9304)
Daily Chief Union ....F 419 294-2331
  Upper Sandusky (G-19118)
Daily Dog ....G 419 708-4923
  Holland (G-11053)

Daily Gazette .... E 937 372-4444
Xenia (G-20945)

Daily Growler Inc .... G 614 656-2337
Upper Arlington (G-19112)

Daily Needs Assistance .... F 614 824-8340
Plain City (G-16330)

Daily Needs Personal Care LLC ...... G 614 598-8383
Ashville (G-850)

Daily Reporter .... E 614 224-4835
Columbus (G-7008)

Daily Squawk LLC .... G 937 426-6247
Dayton (G-8101)

Dayton Dailey News .... F 937 743-2387
Franklin (G-10017)

Dayton Weekly News .... G 937 223-8060
Dayton (G-8289)

Defiance Publishing Co .... A 419 784-5441
Defiance (G-8788)

Delaware Gazette Company ...... D 740 363-1161
Delaware (G-8836)

Delphos Herald Inc .... D 419 695-0015
Delphos (G-8904)

Delphos Herald Inc .... G 419 399-4015
Paulding (G-16003)

Delphos Herald Inc .... D 419 695-0015
Delphos (G-8905)

Dog Daily .... G 216 624-0735
Cleveland (G-5202)

Dow Jones & Company Inc .... E 419 352-4696
Bowling Green (G-1987)

Erie Chinese Journal .... G 216 324-2959
Twinsburg (G-18930)

Euclid Media Group LLC .... E 216 241-7550
Cleveland (G-5301)

Gannett Co Inc .... C 740 345-4053
Newark (G-15009)

Gannett Co Inc .... D 513 721-2700
Cincinnati (G-3795)

Gannett Co Inc .... G 419 562-3333
Mansfield (G-12610)

Gate West Coast Ventures LLC ...... F 513 891-1000
Blue Ash (G-1802)

Gazette Publishing Company ...... E 419 483-4190
Oberlin (G-15640)

Graphic Publications Inc .... D 330 343-4377
Dover (G-8988)

Greenhills Journal .... F 513 825-2525
Cincinnati (G-3851)

Hamilton Journal News Inc .... D 513 863-8200
Liberty Township (G-11963)

Heartland Education Community ...... F 330 684-3034
Orrville (G-15739)

Heartland Publications LLC ...... F 740 446-2342
Gallipolis (G-10300)

Herald House .... G 740 967-8044
Johnstown (G-11401)

Herald Looms .... G 330 948-1080
Lodi (G-12162)

Herald Reflector Inc .... E 419 668-3771
Norwalk (G-15545)

Highschoolball Inc .... G 844 472-2551
North Royalton (G-15425)

Hirt Publishing Co Inc .... G 419 523-5709
Ottawa (G-15794)

Holland Springfield Journal ...... G 419 874-2528
Perrysburg (G-16108)

Horizon Ohio Publications Inc ...... G 419 738-2128
Wapakoneta (G-19489)

Horizon Publications Inc .... E 419 738-2128
Wapakoneta (G-19490)

Huron Hometown News .... G 419 433-1401
Huron (G-11225)

Ironton Publications Inc .... A 740 532-1441
Ironton (G-11294)

Jewish Journal Monthly Mag ...... G 330 746-3251
Youngstown (G-21126)

Job News USA .... F 614 310-1700
Columbus (G-7236)

Journal Bkr .... G 440 245-6901
Lorain (G-12250)

Journal Register Company .... C 440 245-6901
Lorain (G-12251)

Kent State University .... G 330 672-2586
Kent (G-11482)

La Voz Hispania Newspaper ...... G 614 274-5505
Columbus (G-7279)

Lakewood Observer Inc .... G 216 712-7070
Lakewood (G-11672)

Legal News Publishing Co .... E 216 696-6111
Cleveland (G-5692)

Lets Golf Daily Inc .... G 330 966-3373
North Canton (G-15246)

Lorain Journal .... G 440 245-6900
Lorain (G-12257)

Mansfield Journal Co .... G 330 364-8641
New Philadelphia (G-14910)

Mark Daily .... G 937 369-5358
Eaton (G-9318)

Marysville Newspaper Inc .... E 937 644-9111
Marysville (G-12957)

Messenger Publishing Company ...... C 740 592-6612
Athens (G-876)

Mirror .... E 419 893-8135
Maumee (G-13284)

News Democrat .... G 937 378-6161
Miamisburg (G-13843)

News Watchman & Paper .... F 740 947-2149
Waverly (G-19713)

Newspaper Holding Inc .... D 440 998-2323
Ashtabula (G-826)

Newspaper Network Central OH ...... G 419 524-3545
Mansfield (G-12657)

Ohio Community Media .... G 740 848-4064
Fredericktown (G-10107)

Ohio Newspaper Services Inc ...... F 614 486-6677
Columbus (G-7424)

Ohio Newspapers Foundation ...... G 614 486-6677
Columbus (G-7425)

Ohio University .... C 740 593-4010
Athens (G-880)

Our Daily Bread .... G 513 621-6364
Cincinnati (G-4201)

Photo Star .... G 419 495-2696
Willshire (G-20651)

Pride of Geneva .... G 440 466-5695
Geneva (G-10356)

Pulse Journal .... E 513 829-7900
Liberty Township (G-11965)

Record Publishing Co .... D 330 541-9400
Kent (G-11513)

Register Herald Office .... F 937 456-5553
Eaton (G-9321)

Ripley Bee .... G 937 392-4321
Ripley (G-16669)

Robert Tuneberg .... G 440 899-9277
Bay Village (G-1244)

Roman Cthlic Docese Youngstown ...... G 330 744-8451
Youngstown (G-21193)

Sentinel Daily .... G 740 992-2155
Pomeroy (G-16390)

Seven Hills Reporter .... G 216 524-9515
Seven Hills (G-17064)

Sound Publishing Holding Inc ...... G 330 996-3000
Akron (G-408)

Standard Printing Co Inc .... E 419 586-2371
Celina (G-3019)

Summit Street News Inc .... G 330 609-5600
Warren (G-19602)

The Beacon Journal Pubg Co ...... B 330 996-3140
Akron (G-435)

Toledo Blade Company .... B 419 724-6000
Toledo (G-18730)

Trading Post .... G 740 922-1199
Uhrichsville (G-19063)

Venice Cornerstone Newspaper ...... G 513 738-7151
Hamilton (G-10753)

Village Reporter .... G 419 485-4851
Montpelier (G-14456)

Weirton Daily Times .... F 740 283-4711
Steubenville (G-17720)

Wooster Daily Record Inc .... C 330 264-1125
Wooster (G-20849)

World Journal .... G 216 458-0988
Cleveland (G-6480)

Your Daily Bargains .... G 330 715-8324
Stow (G-17818)

Your Daily Motivation Ydm Fitn ...... G 440 954-1038
Painesville (G-15946)

PUBLISHING & PRINTING: Pamphlets

Communication Resources Inc ...... E 800 992-2144
Canton (G-2665)

Design Avenue Inc .... G 330 487-5280
Twinsburg (G-18924)

J S C Publishing .... G 614 424-6911
Columbus (G-7219)

PUBLISHING & PRINTING: Periodical Statistical Reports

City of Parma .... G 440 885-8816
Cleveland (G-5037)

PUBLISHING & PRINTING: Posters

Posterservice Incorporated ...... E 513 577-7100
Cincinnati (G-4254)

Woodburn Press LLC .... G 937 293-9245
Dayton (G-8764)

PUBLISHING & PRINTING: Shopping News

M Grafix LLC .... F 419 528-8665
Mansfield (G-12638)

PUBLISHING & PRINTING: Technical Papers

Ohio Printed Products Inc .... F 330 659-0909
Richfield (G-16630)

SC Solutions Inc .... G 614 317-7119
Grove City (G-10592)

PUBLISHING & PRINTING: Textbooks

Spanish Lngage Productions Inc ...... G 614 737-3424
Alexandria (G-481)

PUBLISHING & PRINTING: Trade Journals

Benjamin Media Inc .... E 330 467-7588
Brecksville (G-2036)

Business Journal .... F 330 744-5023
Youngstown (G-21040)

Medquest Communications Inc ...... E 216 391-9100
Cleveland (G-5776)

North Coast Business Journal ...... G 419 734-4838
Port Clinton (G-16407)

Ohio Association Realtors Inc ...... E 614 228-6675
Columbus (G-7415)

PULLEYS: Metal

Industrial Pulley & Machine Co ...... G 937 355-4910
West Mansfield (G-20099)

J L R Products Inc .... F 330 832-9557
Massillon (G-13158)

PULLEYS: Power Transmission

A J Rose Mfgco .... C 216 631-4645
Cleveland (G-4675)

A J Rose Mfgco .... C 216 631-4645
Avon (G-978)

Dependable Gear Corp .... G 440 942-4969
Eastlake (G-9264)

J L R Products Inc .... F 330 832-9557
Massillon (G-13158)

PULP MILLS

Caraustar Industries Inc .... E 216 961-5060
Cleveland (G-4973)

Caraustar Industries Inc .... D 740 862-4167
Baltimore (G-1081)

Newpage Energy Services LLC ...... A 877 855-7243
Miamisburg (G-13840)

Newpage Holding Corporation ...... A 877 855-7243
Miamisburg (G-13842)

Polymer Tech & Svcs Inc .... E 740 929-5500
Heath (G-10851)

Rumpke Transportation Co LLC ...... C 513 242-4600
Cincinnati (G-4367)

Verso Corporation .... D 901 369-4105
Miamisburg (G-13875)

Waste Parchment Inc .... E 330 674-6868
Millersburg (G-14282)

PULP MILLS: Mechanical & Recycling Processing

Flegal Brothers Inc .... F 419 298-3539
Edgerton (G-9331)

Green Recycling Works LLC ...... G 513 278-7111
Cincinnati (G-3849)

Riverview Productions Inc .... G 740 441-1150
Gallipolis (G-10308)

World Wide Recyclers Inc .... F 614 554-3296
Columbus (G-7774)

(G-0000) Company's Geographic Section entry number

PUMP SLEEVES: Rubber

Precision Component & Mch Inc.............E...... 740 867-6366
Chesapeake (G-3189)

PUMPS

A P O Holdings Inc..............................E...... 330 455-8925
Canton (G-2585)

Advanced Fuel Systems Inc ....G...... 614 252-8422
Columbus (G-6697)

All - Flo Pump Company ....E...... 440 354-1700
Mentor (G-13518)

Belden Brick Company..........................E...... 330 852-2411
Sugarcreek (G-18016)

Bergstrom Company Ltd Partnr ....E...... 440 232-2282
Cleveland (G-4905)

Blue Chip Pump Inc...............................G...... 513 871-7867
Cincinnati (G-3453)

Chaos Entertainment ....G...... 937 520-5260
Dayton (G-8225)

Cleveland Plastic Fabricat ....F...... 216 797-7300
Euclid (G-9572)

Crane Pumps & Systems Inc ....B...... 937 773-2442
Piqua (G-16257)

Curtiss-Wright Flow Ctrl Corp ....E...... 440 838-7690
Brecksville (G-2042)

Dreison International Inc ....C...... 216 362-0755
Cleveland (G-5215)

Eaton-Aeroquip Inc ....E...... 419 891-7775
Maumee (G-13258)

Eco-Flo Products Inc ....F...... 877 326-3561
Ashland (G-730)

Electro-Mechanical Mfg Co Inc ....G...... 330 864-0717
Akron (G-161)

Flow Control US Holding Corp ....G...... 800 843-5628
Cincinnati (G-3763)

Flow Control US Holding Corp ....G...... 419 289-1144
Ashland (G-733)

Flowserve Corporation...........................E...... 513 874-6990
Loveland (G-12350)

Flowserve Corporation...........................D...... 937 226-4568
Dayton (G-8346)

Frantz Medical Development Ltd ....D...... 440 205-9026
Mentor (G-13583)

General Electric Company ....D...... 216 883-1000
Cleveland (G-5412)

Giant Industries Inc ....E...... 419 531-4600
Toledo (G-18480)

Gorman-Rupp Company ....E...... 419 886-3001
Bellville (G-1570)

Gorman-Rupp Company ....B...... 419 755-1011
Mansfield (G-12614)

Gorman-Rupp Company ....B...... 419 755-1011
Mansfield (G-12615)

Gorman-Rupp Company ....G...... 419 755-1245
Mansfield (G-12616)

Hpc Manufacturing Inc ....G...... 440 322-8334
Lorain (G-12249)

Hugo Vglsang Maschinenbau GMBH....E...... 330 296-3820
Ravenna (G-16532)

Hurst Auto-Truck Electric.......................G...... 216 961-1800
Cleveland (G-5538)

Ingersoll-Rand Company ....E...... 419 633-6800
Bryan (G-2306)

Keen Pump Company Inc ....E...... 419 207-9400
Ashland (G-745)

M T Systems Inc ....G...... 330 453-4646
Canton (G-2763)

Magnum Piering Inc ....E...... 513 759-3348
West Chester (G-20022)

Neptune Chemical Pump Company ......G...... 513 870-3239
West Chester (G-19905)

Preferred Global Equipment LLC ....D...... 513 530-5800
Cincinnati (G-4265)

Pyrotek Incorporated ....C...... 440 349-8800
Aurora (G-942)

Quikstir Inc ....F...... 419 732-2601
Port Clinton (G-16410)

Robbins & Myers Inc ....C...... 937 327-3023
Springfield (G-17643)

Rumpke Transportation Co LLC.............F...... 513 851-0122
Cincinnati (G-4366)

Seepex Inc ....C...... 937 864-7150
Enon (G-9549)

Stahl Gear & Machine Co ....E...... 216 431-2820
Cleveland (G-6231)

Suburban Manufacturing Co..................D...... 440 953-2024
Eastlake (G-9290)

Swanson Industries Inc ....D...... 304 284-5199
New Philadelphia (G-14931)

Systecon Inc...D...... 513 777-7722
West Chester (G-19953)

T D Group Holdings LLC ....G...... 216 706-2939
Cleveland (G-6289)

Tark Inc ....E...... 937 434-6766
Dayton (G-8702)

Tolco Corporation...................................D...... 419 241-1113
Toledo (G-18728)

Transdigm Inc...F...... 216 291-6025
Cleveland (G-6346)

Transdigm Inc...E...... 440 352-6182
Painesville (G-15931)

Vertiflo Pump Company ....F...... 513 530-0888
Cincinnati (G-4566)

Vickers International Inc ....E...... 419 867-2200
Maumee (G-13307)

Warren Rupp Inc ....C...... 419 524-8388
Mansfield (G-12703)

Waterpro ....F...... 330 372-3565
Warren (G-19625)

Wepuko Pahnke Engineering LP ....F...... 937 390-2100
Springfield (G-17676)

PUMPS & PARTS: Indl

A & F Machine Products Co ....E...... 440 826-0959
Berea (G-1599)

Ayling and Reichert Co Consent ....E...... 419 898-2471
Oak Harbor (G-15586)

Cima Inc ....E...... 513 682-5900
Fairfield (G-9653)

Crane Co ....C...... 330 337-7861
Salem (G-16886)

E R Advanced Ceramics Inc ....E...... 330 426-9433
East Palestine (G-9237)

Fischer Global Enterprises LLC ....E...... 513 583-4900
Loveland (G-12349)

Fluid Automation Inc ....E...... 248 912-1970
North Canton (G-15232)

Gerow Equipment Company Inc............G...... 216 383-8800
Cleveland (G-5426)

Graphite Equipment Mfg Co ....G...... 216 271-9500
Solon (G-17303)

Molten Mtal Eqp Invnations LLC ....E...... 440 632-9119
Middlefield (G-13968)

Pckd Enterprises Inc ....E...... 440 632-9119
Middlefield (G-13980)

Replica Engineering Inc ....F...... 216 252-2204
Cleveland (G-6103)

Ruthman Pump and Engineering ....G...... 513 559-1901
Cincinnati (G-4369)

Valco Cincinnati Inc ....C...... 513 874-6550
West Chester (G-20067)

PUMPS & PUMPING EQPT REPAIR SVCS

Blue Chip Pump Inc...............................G...... 513 871-7867
Cincinnati (G-3453)

Certified Labs & Service Inc ....G...... 419 289-7462
Ashland (G-718)

Ohio Electric Motor Svc LLC ....G...... 419 525-2225
Mansfield (G-12661)

Thirion Brothers Eqp Co LLC ....G...... 440 357-8004
Painesville (G-15930)

Tyler Electric Motor Repair ....G...... 330 836-5537
Akron (G-451)

Wm Plotz Machine and Forge Co ....F...... 216 861-0441
Cleveland (G-6473)

PUMPS & PUMPING EQPT WHOLESALERS

Giant Industries Inc ....E...... 419 531-4600
Toledo (G-18480)

Gorman-Rupp Company ....G...... 419 755-1245
Mansfield (G-12616)

Hammelmann Corporation......................F...... 937 859-8777
Miamisburg (G-13814)

Motionsource International LLC..............F...... 440 287-7037
Solon (G-17339)

Tyler Electric Motor Repair ....G...... 330 836-5537
Akron (G-451)

PUMPS: Domestic, Water Or Sump

Certified Labs & Service Inc ....G...... 419 289-7462
Ashland (G-718)

Champion Pump Company Inc...............G...... 419 281-4500
Ashland (G-719)

City of Newark ....F...... 740 349-6765
Newark (G-14993)

Hydromatic Pumps Inc ....A...... 419 289-1144
Ashland (G-741)

Lakecraft Inc ....G...... 419 734-2828
Port Clinton (G-16402)

Wayne/Scott Fetzer Company ....C...... 800 237-0987
Harrison (G-10811)

PUMPS: Fluid Power

Alkid Corporation...................................G...... 216 896-3000
Cleveland (G-4754)

All - Flo Pump Company ....E...... 440 354-1700
Mentor (G-13518)

Custom Cltch Jint Hydrlics Inc ....F...... 216 431-1630
Cleveland (G-5149)

Eaton Hydraulics LLC ....E...... 419 232-7777
Van Wert (G-19254)

Opw Inc ....A...... 800 422-2525
West Chester (G-19910)

Parker-Hannifin Corporation..................C...... 330 740-8366
Youngstown (G-21165)

Parker-Hannifin Corporation..................E...... 440 266-2300
Mentor (G-13681)

Parker-Hannifin Corporation..................F...... 216 896-3000
Cleveland (G-5976)

Suburban Manufacturing Co..................D...... 440 953-2024
Eastlake (G-9290)

Vertiflo Pump Company ....E...... 513 530-0888
Cincinnati (G-4566)

PUMPS: Gasoline, Measuring Or Dispensing

Field Stone Inc ....D...... 937 898-3236
Tipp City (G-18277)

PUMPS: Hydraulic Power Transfer

Bosch Rexroth Corporation ....B...... 330 263-3300
Wooster (G-20751)

Eaton Corporation ....B...... 216 523-5000
Cleveland (G-5245)

Eaton Corporation ....B...... 216 416-2500
Cleveland (G-5246)

Linde Hydraulics Corporation ....E...... 330 533-6801
Canfield (G-2562)

Parker-Hannifin Corporation..................C...... 937 644-3915
Marysville (G-12962)

R & L Hydraulics Inc ....G...... 937 399-3407
Springfield (G-17632)

PUMPS: Measuring & Dispensing

Bergstrom Company Ltd Partnr ....E...... 440 232-2282
Cleveland (G-4905)

Cohesant Inc ....E...... 216 910-1700
Beachwood (G-1262)

Gojo Industries Inc ....C...... 330 255-6000
Akron (G-206)

Gojo Industries Inc ....C...... 330 255-6525
Stow (G-17760)

Gojo Industries Inc ....C...... 330 922-4522
Cuyahoga Falls (G-8005)

Graco Ohio Inc ....D...... 330 494-1313
North Canton (G-15235)

Hydro Systems Company ....G...... 513 271-8800
Milford (G-14151)

Hydro Systems Company ....E...... 513 271-8800
Cincinnati (G-3905)

Neptune Chemical Pump Company ....G...... 513 870-3239
West Chester (G-19905)

Porto Pump Inc ....G...... 740 454-2576
Zanesville (G-21343)

Precision Conveyor Technology ....F...... 440 352-3601
Perry (G-16056)

Seepex Inc ....C...... 937 864-7150
Enon (G-9549)

Tolco Corporation...................................D...... 419 241-1113
Toledo (G-18728)

Tranzonic Companies ....B...... 216 535-4300
Richmond Heights (G-16657)

Valco Cincinnati Inc ....C...... 513 874-6550
West Chester (G-20067)

Valco Cincinnati Inc ....G...... 513 874-6550
West Chester (G-20068)

PUMPS: Oil Well & Field

F E Myers Co ....G...... 419 289-1144
Ashland (G-731)

General Electric Intl Inc ....E...... 330 963-2066
Twinsburg (G-18944)

Pentair Flow Technologies LLC..............B...... 419 289-1144
Ashland (G-764)

Tat Pumps Inc..G...... 740 385-0008
Nelsonville (G-14742)

PRODUCT

Westerman Inc .... D 330 262-6946
 Wooster (G-20846)

PUMPS: Oil, Measuring Or Dispensing

Energy Manufacturing Ltd .... G 419 355-9304
 Fremont (G-10143)

PUNCHES: Forming & Stamping

Cleveland Steel Tool Company .... E 216 681-7400
 Cleveland (G-5080)
Dayton Progress Corporation .... A 937 859-5111
 Dayton (G-8284)
Miami Valley Punch & Mfg .... E 937 237-0533
 Dayton (G-8491)
Porter Precision Products Co .... D 513 385-1569
 Cincinnati (G-4250)
Stolle Machinery Company LLC .... E 937 859-4644
 Dayton (G-8684)
Tipco Punch Inc .... E 513 874-9140
 Hamilton (G-10748)

PURCHASING SVCS

Canfield Industries Inc .... G 800 554-5071
 Youngstown (G-21042)

PURIFICATION & DUST COLLECTION EQPT

Ceco Environmental Corp .... G 513 458-2606
 Blue Ash (G-1763)
Ceco Environmental Corp .... G 513 458-2600
 Cincinnati (G-3509)
Dreison International Inc .... C 216 362-0755
 Cleveland (G-5215)

PURLINS: Steel, Light Gauge

Worthington Cnstr Group Inc .... G 216 472-1511
 Cleveland (G-6481)
Worthington Mid-Rise Cnstr Inc .... E 216 472-1511
 Cleveland (G-6482)

QUARTZ CRYSTALS: Electronic

Quality Quartz Engineering Inc .... D 937 236-3250
 Dayton (G-8606)
Quality Quartz of America Inc .... G 440 352-2851
 Mentor (G-13709)
Quartz Scientific Inc .... E 360 574-6254
 Fairport Harbor (G-9770)
Sawyer Technical Materials LLC .... E 440 951-8770
 Willoughby (G-20591)
Schupp Advanced Materials LLC .... G 440 488-6416
 Willoughby (G-20592)

QUICKLIME

Huron Lime Inc .... E 419 433-2141
 Huron (G-11226)

QUILTING SVC & SPLYS, FOR THE TRADE

Just Quilt It Inc .... G 330 469-6956
 Warren (G-19564)

RABBIT SLAUGHTERING & PROCESSING

Briarwood Valley Farms .... G 419 736-2298
 Sullivan (G-18053)

RACEWAYS

Buckeye Raceway LLC .... G 614 272-7888
 Columbus (G-6874)
Highline Raceway LLC .... G 419 883-2042
 Butler (G-2391)
Hollywood Gaming At Dayton RAC ...... G 937 235-7800
 Dayton (G-8391)
Indian Lake Raceway LLC .... G 937 837-7533
 Clayton (G-4660)
Raceway Beverage LLC .... G 513 932-2214
 Lebanon (G-11831)
Raceway Petroleum Inc .... G 440 989-2660
 Lorain (G-12270)
State of Ohio Dayton Raceway .... G 937 237-7802
 Dayton (G-8682)

RACKS & SHELVING: Household, Wood

Installed Building Pdts LLC .... E 614 308-9900
 Columbus (G-7190)

RACKS: Book & Magazine, Wood

Touchpint Cmplete Slutions LLC .... G 419 919-3222
 Celina (G-3024)

RACKS: Display

Bates Metal Products Inc .... D 740 498-8371
 Port Washington (G-16422)
Busch & Thiem Inc .... E 419 625-7515
 Sandusky (G-16952)
Dwayne Bennett Industries .... G 440 466-5724
 Geneva (G-10345)
E2 Merchandising Inc .... E 513 860-5444
 West Chester (G-19998)
Jhg Retail Services LLC .... F 216 447-0831
 Cincinnati (G-3945)
Rack Processing Company Inc .... E 937 294-1911
 Moraine (G-14522)
Unarco Material Handling Inc .... E 419 384-3211
 Pandora (G-15948)
Zak Box Co Inc .... E 216 961-5636
 Cleveland (G-6491)
Zukowski Rack Co .... G 440 942-5889
 Willoughby (G-20636)

RACKS: Railroad Car, Vehicle Transportation, Steel

Smith Truck Cranes & Eqp Co .... F 330 929-3303
 Cuyahoga Falls (G-8047)

RADAR SYSTEMS & EQPT

Decibel Research Inc .... D 256 705-3341
 Beavercreek (G-1329)
Dragoon Technologies Inc .... G 937 439-9223
 Dayton (G-8310)
Dynamic Sensor Systems LLC .... G 614 430-2888
 Worthington (G-20865)
Escort Inc .... D 513 870-8500
 West Chester (G-19859)
Star Dynamics Corporation .... D 614 334-4510
 Hilliard (G-10981)
Valentine Research Inc .... E 513 984-8900
 Blue Ash (G-1888)

RADIO & TELEVISION COMMUNICATIONS EQUIPMENT

Accurate Electronics Inc .... C 330 682-7015
 Orrville (G-15727)
Commscope Technologies LLC .... C 216 272-0055
 Cleveland (G-5107)
Essential Pathways Ohio LLC .... G 330 518-3091
 Youngstown (G-21079)
G2 Digital Solutions .... F 937 241-6003
 Xenia (G-20953)
Gatesair Inc .... E 513 459-3400
 Mason (G-13025)
Greyfield Industries Inc .... F 513 860-1785
 Trenton (G-18793)
Intwine Energy Networks LLC .... G 216 970-5908
 Chagrin Falls (G-3096)
McClaflin Mobile Media LLC .... G 419 575-9367
 Bradner (G-2028)
Mentor Radio LLC .... G 216 265-2315
 Elyria (G-9460)
Northrop Grumman Systems Corp ...... B 513 881-3296
 West Chester (G-20032)
Ohio Semitronics Inc .... D 614 777-1005
 Hilliard (G-10967)
Prentke Romich Company .... C 330 202-5800
 Wooster (G-20825)
R L Drake Holdings LLC .... F 937 746-4556
 Springboro (G-17503)
Rev38 LLC .... G 937 572-4000
 West Chester (G-19932)
Shenet LLC .... E 614 563-9600
 Columbus (G-7615)
Solar Con Inc .... E 419 865-5877
 Holland (G-11086)
Sourcepoint Logistics LLC .... E 937 604-8209
 Tipp City (G-18300)
T V Specialties Inc .... F 330 364-6678
 Dover (G-9020)
Tls Corp .... E 216 574-4759
 Cleveland (G-6327)
Track-It Systems .... G 513 522-0083
 Cincinnati (G-4516)
Transel Corporation .... G 513 897-3442
 Harveysburg (G-10835)

Valco Melton Inc .... E 513 874-6550
 West Chester (G-20069)
Wirenet Inc .... F 513 774-7759
 Loveland (G-12400)

RADIO BROADCASTING & COMMUNICATIONS EQPT

Circle Prime Manufacturing .... E 330 923-0019
 Cuyahoga Falls (G-7980)
Harris Broadcast Communication .... E 513 459-3400
 Mason (G-13035)
Imagine Communications Corp .... D 513 459-3400
 Mason (G-13041)
Manchik Engineering & Co .... G 740 927-4454
 Dublin (G-9101)
Maranatha Industries Inc .... E 419 263-2013
 Payne (G-16016)
Peterson Radio Inc .... G 937 549-3731
 Manchester (G-12551)
R L Drake Company .... D 937 746-4556
 Franklin (G-10048)

RADIO BROADCASTING STATIONS

Franklin Communications Inc .... D 614 459-9769
 Columbus (G-7097)
Iheartcommunications Inc .... F 740 335-0941
 Wshngtn CT Hs (G-20911)
Iheartcommunications Inc .... D 419 223-2060
 Lima (G-12026)
Sandusky Newspapers Inc .... C 419 625-5500
 Sandusky (G-17004)

RADIO COMMUNICATIONS: Airborne Eqpt

Quasonix Inc .... E 513 942-1287
 West Chester (G-19927)

RADIO COMMUNICATIONS: Carrier Eqpt

L-3 Cmmncations Nova Engrg Inc ...... C 877 282-1168
 Mason (G-13054)

RADIO RECEIVER NETWORKS

Analynk Wireless LLC .... G 614 755-5091
 Columbus (G-6752)
Envision Radio MII .... F 216 831-3761
 Beachwood (G-1271)
Globecom Technologies Inc .... G 330 408-7008
 Canal Fulton (G-2502)
Iheartcommunications Inc .... C 513 241-1550
 Cincinnati (G-3911)

RADIO REPAIR & INSTALLATION SVCS

Peterson Radio Inc .... G 937 549-3731
 Manchester (G-12551)

RADIO, TELEVISION & CONSUMER ELECTRONICS STORES: Eqpt, NEC

House of Hindenach .... G 419 422-0392
 Findlay (G-9843)
Ohio Valley Vapor Station .... G 740 449-2288
 Saint Clairsville (G-16804)
Total Supply Solutions LLC .... G 614 989-6665
 Dublin (G-9155)

RADIO, TV & CONSUMER ELEC STORES: Automotive Sound Eqpt

Electra Sound Inc .... D 216 433-9600
 Parma (G-15957)

RADIO, TV & CONSUMER ELEC STORES: High Fidelity Stereo Eqpt

ABC Appliance Inc .... E 419 693-4414
 Oregon (G-15699)
Tune Town Car Audio .... G 419 627-1100
 Sandusky (G-17017)

RADIO, TV/CONSUMER ELEC STORES: Antennas, Satellite Dish

Gadgets Manufacturing Co .... G 937 686-5371
 Huntsville (G-11214)

RADIOS WHOLESALERS

Peterson Radio Inc ....G....... 937 549-3731
  Manchester *(G-12551)*

T V Specialties Inc ....F....... 330 364-6678
  Dover *(G-9020)*

RAILINGS: Prefabricated, Metal

A & T Ornamental Iron Company ....G....... 937 859-6006
  Miamisburg *(G-13778)*

AT&f Advanced Metals LLC ....E....... 330 684-1122
  Cleveland *(G-4851)*

Beacon Metal Fabricators Inc ....F....... 216 391-7444
  Cleveland *(G-4900)*

Glas Ornamental Metals Inc ....G....... 330 753-0215
  Barberton *(G-1118)*

Hayes Bros Ornamental Ir Works ....F....... 419 531-1491
  Toledo *(G-18498)*

Taflan Steel & Welding Inc ....G....... 740 635-0841
  Bridgeport *(G-2093)*

RAILINGS: Wood

L & L Ornamental Iron Co ....F....... 513 353-1930
  Cleves *(G-6520)*

LAtelier Custom Woodworking ....G....... 234 759-3359
  North Lima *(G-15320)*

RAILROAD CAR CUSTOMIZING SVCS

Transco Railway Products Inc ....E....... 419 726-3383
  Toledo *(G-18756)*

RAILROAD CAR RENTING & LEASING SVCS

Andersons Inc ....C....... 419 893-5050
  Maumee *(G-13224)*

Andersons Inc ....G....... 419 536-0460
  Toledo *(G-18349)*

RAILROAD CAR REPAIR SVCS

Andersons Inc ....C....... 419 893-5050
  Maumee *(G-13224)*

Andersons Inc ....G....... 419 536-0460
  Toledo *(G-18349)*

Jk-Co LLC ....E....... 419 422-5240
  Findlay *(G-9846)*

Norfolk Southern Corporation ....E....... 419 697-5070
  Oregon *(G-15712)*

RAILROAD CARGO LOADING & UNLOADING SVCS

Dale Lute Logging ....G....... 740 352-1779
  Mc Dermott *(G-13341)*

Fairway Carts Parts & More LLC ....G....... 234 209-9008
  North Canton *(G-15229)*

RAILROAD CROSSINGS: Steel Or Iron

Bridge Components Inds Inc ....G....... 614 873-0777
  Columbus *(G-6859)*

RAILROAD EQPT

A Stucki Company ....G....... 412 424-0560
  North Canton *(G-15218)*

Alliance Castings Company LLC ....E....... 330 829-5600
  Alliance *(G-491)*

Amsted Industries Incorporated ....C....... 614 836-2323
  Groveport *(G-10612)*

Amsted Rail Company Inc ....F....... 614 836-2323
  Groveport *(G-10613)*

Buck Equipment Inc ....E....... 614 539-3039
  Grove City *(G-10548)*

Dayton-Phoenix Group Inc ....C....... 937 496-3900
  Dayton *(G-8293)*

Dennis Lavender ....G....... 740 344-3336
  Newark *(G-14999)*

George R Silcott Railway Equip ....G....... 614 885-7224
  Worthington *(G-20867)*

Gunderson Rail Services LLC ....E....... 330 792-6521
  Youngstown *(G-21106)*

Johnson Bros Rubber Co Inc ....E....... 419 752-4814
  Greenwich *(G-10531)*

K & G Machine Co ....E....... 216 732-7115
  Cleveland *(G-5628)*

L B Foster Company ....E....... 330 652-1461
  Mineral Ridge *(G-14307)*

Nolan Company ....G....... 330 453-7922
  Canton *(G-2789)*

Nolan Company ....G....... 740 269-1512
  Bowerston *(G-1959)*

Prime Manufacturing Corp ....G....... 937 496-3900
  Dayton *(G-8593)*

R H Little Co ....G....... 330 477-3455
  Canton *(G-2833)*

Sperling Railway Services Inc ....F....... 330 479-2004
  Canton *(G-2855)*

Transco Railway Products Inc ....D....... 330 872-0934
  Newton Falls *(G-15140)*

Trinity Highway Products Llc ....F....... 419 227-1296
  Lima *(G-12105)*

RAILROAD EQPT & SPLYS WHOLESALERS

Amsted Industries Incorporated ....C....... 614 836-2323
  Groveport *(G-10612)*

Buck Equipment Inc ....E....... 614 539-3039
  Grove City *(G-10548)*

Ysd Industries Inc ....D....... 330 792-6521
  Youngstown *(G-21260)*

RAILROAD EQPT: Brakes, Air & Vacuum

Westinghouse A Brake Tech Corp ....D....... 419 526-5323
  Mansfield *(G-12705)*

RAILROAD EQPT: Cars & Eqpt, Dining

Standard Car Truck Company ....D....... 740 775-6450
  Chillicothe *(G-3276)*

RAILROAD EQPT: Cars & Eqpt, Interurban

Engines Inc of Ohio ....D....... 740 377-9874
  South Point *(G-17437)*

RAILROAD EQPT: Cars & Eqpt, Train, Freight Or Passenger

Rail Road Corporation ....G....... 614 771-2102
  Columbus *(G-7546)*

RAILROAD EQPT: Cars, Rebuilt

Jk-Co LLC ....E....... 419 422-5240
  Findlay *(G-9846)*

Norfolk Southern Corporation ....E....... 419 697-5070
  Oregon *(G-15712)*

Rescar Industries Inc ....F....... 630 963-1114
  Minerva *(G-14341)*

RAILROAD EQPT: Cars, Tank Freight & Eqpt

Precision Runners LLC ....E....... 330 240-5988
  Burghill *(G-2369)*

RAILROAD EQPT: Locomotives & Parts, Indl

Good Day Tools LLC ....G....... 513 578-2050
  Cincinnati *(G-3840)*

RAILROAD MAINTENANCE & REPAIR SVCS

Simpson & Sons Inc ....F....... 513 367-0152
  Harrison *(G-10802)*

Tmt Inc ....C....... 419 592-1041
  Perrysburg *(G-16161)*

RAILROAD RELATED EQPT

Youngstown Bending Rolling ....F....... 330 799-2227
  Youngstown *(G-21246)*

RAILROAD RELATED EQPT: Railway Track

Ohio Valley Trackwork Inc ....F....... 740 446-0181
  Bidwell *(G-1677)*

RAILROAD TIES: Concrete

KSA Limited Partnership ....E....... 740 776-3238
  Portsmouth *(G-16442)*

RAILROAD TIES: Wood

Koppers Ind Inc ....G....... 740 776-2149
  Portsmouth *(G-16440)*

RAMPS: Prefabricated Metal

Homecare Mattress Inc ....F....... 937 746-2556
  Franklin *(G-10027)*

Jh Industries Inc ....E....... 330 963-4105
  Twinsburg *(G-18961)*

Overhead Door Corporation ....F....... 419 294-3874
  Upper Sandusky *(G-19138)*

Upside Innovations LLC ....G....... 513 889-2492
  West Chester *(G-20065)*

Wyse Industrial Carts Inc ....F....... 419 923-7353
  Wauseon *(G-19702)*

RAZORS, RAZOR BLADES

Edgewell Per Care Brands LLC ....D....... 937 228-0105
  Dayton *(G-8319)*

Edgewell Per Care Brands LLC ....D....... 440 835-7500
  Westlake *(G-20266)*

Edgewell Per Care Brands LLC ....D....... 330 527-2191
  Garrettsville *(G-10320)*

Edgewell Per Care Brands LLC ....E....... 440 572-1336
  Cleveland *(G-5259)*

Procter & Gamble Company ....B....... 513 983-1100
  Cincinnati *(G-4277)*

REACTORS: Current Limiting

Unity Cable Technologies Inc ....G....... 419 322-4118
  Toledo *(G-18759)*

REACTORS: Saturable

Arisdyne Systems Inc ....F....... 216 458-1991
  Cleveland *(G-4829)*

REAL ESTATE AGENCIES & BROKERS

Brent Bleh Company ....G....... 513 721-1100
  Cincinnati *(G-3467)*

Coldwell Family Tree Farm ....G....... 330 506-9012
  Salineville *(G-16940)*

Lenz Inc ....E....... 937 277-9364
  Dayton *(G-8456)*

Ruscilli Real Estate Services ....F....... 614 923-6400
  Dublin *(G-9135)*

Wedco LLC ....G....... 513 309-0781
  Mount Orab *(G-14587)*

REAL ESTATE AGENCIES: Buying

Sawmill Road Management Co LLC ....E....... 937 342-9071
  Springfield *(G-17646)*

REAL ESTATE AGENCIES: Commercial

E L Ostendorf Inc ....G....... 440 247-7631
  Chagrin Falls *(G-3056)*

REAL ESTATE AGENCIES: Leasing & Rentals

Lloyd F Helber ....E....... 740 756-9607
  Carroll *(G-2943)*

Rex American Resources Corp ....C....... 937 276-3931
  Dayton *(G-8627)*

REAL ESTATE AGENTS & MANAGERS

American Dreams Inc ....G....... 740 385-4444
  Thornville *(G-18191)*

Daily Agency Inc ....F....... 937 456-9808
  Eaton *(G-9304)*

Hitti Enterprises Inc ....F....... 440 243-4100
  Cleveland *(G-5514)*

Holiday Homes Inc ....F....... 513 353-9777
  Harrison *(G-10782)*

Muehlenkamp Properties Inc ....E....... 513 745-0874
  Cincinnati *(G-4130)*

Open House Magazine Inc ....G....... 614 523-7775
  Columbus *(G-7443)*

Rona Enterprises Inc ....G....... 740 927-9971
  Pataskala *(G-15981)*

V&P Group International LLC ....F....... 703 349-6432
  Cincinnati *(G-4550)*

REAL ESTATE INVESTMENT TRUSTS

Sun Communities Inc ....G....... 740 548-1942
  Lewis Center *(G-11922)*

REAL ESTATE OPERATORS, EXC DEVELOPERS: Commercial/Indl Bldg

Afc Company ....F....... 330 533-5581
  Canfield *(G-2545)*

At Holdings Corporation ....G....... 216 692-6000
  Cleveland *(G-4850)*

Caravan Packaging Inc ....F....... 440 243-4100
  Cleveland *(G-4974)*

PRODUCT

David A Waldron & Associates ....G....... 330 264-7275
Wooster (G-20764)
DRDC Realty Inc ....G....... 419 478-7091
Toledo (G-18444)
Garland Industries Inc ....G....... 216 641-7500
Cleveland (G-5399)
Garland/Dbs Inc ....C....... 216 641-7500
Cleveland (G-5400)
Judy Mills Company Inc ....E....... 513 271-4241
Cincinnati (G-3962)
North Coast Holdings Inc....................G....... 330 535-7177
Akron (G-316)
Park Corporation ....B....... 216 267-4870
Cleveland (G-5965)
S-P Company Inc ....F....... 330 482-0200
Columbiana (G-6631)
Snyder Manufacturing Co Ltd ....G....... 330 343-4456
Dover (G-9017)
U S Development Corp.........................E....... 330 673-6900
Kent (G-11541)

REAL ESTATE OPERATORS, EXC DEVELOPERS: Property, Retail

Perry County Tribune ....F....... 740 342-4121
New Lexington (G-14851)

REALTY INVESTMENT TRUSTS

Standard Energy Company....................G....... 614 885-1901
Columbus (G-7650)

RECEIVERS: Radio Communications

CDI Industries Inc ....E....... 440 243-1100
Cleveland (G-4999)

RECHROMING SVC: Automobile Bumpers

Prince Plating Inc ....D....... 216 881-7523
Cleveland (G-6048)

RECLAIMED RUBBER: Reworked By Manufacturing Process

Goldsmith & Eggleton LLC ....F....... 203 855-6000
Wadsworth (G-19408)
Lake Erie Rubber Recycling LLC ....G....... 440 570-6027
Strongsville (G-17937)
Midwest Elastomers Inc ....D....... 419 738-8844
Wapakoneta (G-19498)
Sparton Enterprises Inc ....E....... 330 745-6088
Norton (G-15521)
Tahoma Enterprises Inc ....D....... 330 745-9016
Barberton (G-1151)
Tahoma Rubber & Plastics Inc ....D....... 330 745-9016
Barberton (G-1152)

RECORDING TAPE: Video, Blank

US Video ....G....... 440 734-6463
North Olmsted (G-15350)

RECORDS & TAPES: Prerecorded

Belkin Production ....E....... 440 247-2722
Chagrin Falls (G-3049)
Beverly Snider ....G....... 614 837-5817
Columbus (G-6824)

RECORDS OR TAPES: Masters

Q C A Inc ....F....... 513 681-8400
Cincinnati (G-4304)

RECOVERY SVC: Iron Ore, From Open Hearth Slag

Masters Group Inc ....G....... 440 893-1900
Chagrin Falls (G-3103)
Stein Inc ....D....... 440 277-6148
Lorain (G-12281)
Stein Inc ....F....... 440 526-9301
Cleveland (G-6248)
Stein Inc ....D....... 216 883-7444
Cleveland (G-6249)
Waterford Tank Fabrication Ltd............D....... 740 984-4100
Beverly (G-1672)

RECOVERY SVC: Silver, From Used Photographic Film

Metals Recovery Services LLC.............G....... 614 870-0364
Columbus (G-7342)

RECOVERY SVCS: Metal

Able Alloy Inc ....F....... 216 251-6110
Cleveland (G-4685)
Shaneway Inc ....G....... 330 868-2220
Minerva (G-14342)
Umicore Spclty Mtls Recycl LLC ....E....... 440 833-3000
Wickliffe (G-20389)

RECREATIONAL & SPORTING CAMPS

Prairie Lane Corporation......................G....... 330 262-3322
Wooster (G-20823)

RECREATIONAL DEALERS: Camper & Travel Trailers

All Power Equipment LLC......................F....... 740 593-3279
Athens (G-855)
Cecil Caudill Trailer Sls Inc ....F....... 740 574-0704
Franklin Furnace (G-10067)
Isaacs Jr Floyd Thomas ....F....... 513 899-2342
Morrow (G-14548)

RECREATIONAL SPORTING EQPT REPAIR SVCS

Balbo Industries Inc............................G....... 440 333-0630
Rocky River (G-16695)

RECREATIONAL VEHICLE PARTS & ACCESS STORES

Mitchs Welding & Hitches ....G....... 419 893-3117
Maumee (G-13286)
Steves Vans & Accessories LLC ....G....... 740 374-3154
Marietta (G-12836)

RECREATIONAL VEHICLE REPAIR SVCS

L A Productions Co LLC ....G....... 330 666-4230
Akron (G-264)

RECTIFIERS: Electronic, Exc Semiconductor

Darrah Electric Company ....E....... 216 631-0912
Cleveland (G-5168)

RECYCLABLE SCRAP & WASTE MATERIALS WHOLESALERS

A & B Iron & Metal Company ....F....... 937 228-1561
Dayton (G-8125)
Aci Industries Ltd................................E....... 740 368-4160
Delaware (G-8815)
Ascendtech Inc ....E....... 216 458-1101
Willoughby (G-20441)
Edw C Levy Co....................................E....... 330 484-6328
Canton (G-2695)
Franklin Iron & Metal Corp ....C....... 937 253-8184
Dayton (G-8350)
Homan Metals LLC..............................G....... 513 721-5010
Cincinnati (G-3891)
Imperial Alum - Minerva LLC ....D....... 330 868-7765
Minerva (G-14326)
Midwest Iron and Metal Co..................D....... 937 222-5992
Dayton (G-8496)
Rnw Holdings Inc ....E....... 330 792-0600
Youngstown (G-21190)

RECYCLING: Paper

Greif Packaging LLC............................C....... 330 879-2101
Massillon (G-13144)
Itran Electronics Recycling...................G....... 330 659-0801
Richfield (G-16628)
SMA Plastics LLC ....G....... 330 627-1377
Carrollton (G-2966)
Verso Paper Holding LLC ....B....... 877 855-7243
Miamisburg (G-13876)

REELS: Cable, Metal

Alert Stamping & Mfg Co Inc ....E....... 440 232-5020
Bedford Heights (G-1476)

Hykon Manufacturing Company...........G....... 330 821-8889
Alliance (G-517)
New American Reel Company LLC ......G....... 419 258-2900
Antwerp (G-631)

REELS: Fiber, Textile, Made From Purchased Materials

Howard B Claflin Co ....G....... 330 928-1704
Cuyahoga Falls (G-8009)

REELS: Wood

Singleton Reels Inc ....E....... 330 274-2961
Mantua (G-12722)
Sonoco Products Company ....E....... 614 759-8470
Columbus (G-7631)

REFINERS & SMELTERS: Aluminum

Continental Metal Proc Co ....F....... 216 268-0000
Cleveland (G-5124)
Continental Metal Proc Co ....E....... 216 268-0000
Cleveland (G-5125)
Gnw Aluminum Inc ....E....... 330 821-7955
Alliance (G-511)
Imco Recycling of Ohio LLC ....C....... 740 922-2373
Uhrichsville (G-19052)
Quality Molded ....C....... 330 645-6653
Akron (G-358)
Real Alloy Specialty Products ....F....... 440 563-3487
Rock Creek (G-16685)
Real Alloy Specialty Products ....E....... 440 322-0072
Elyria (G-9483)

REFINERS & SMELTERS: Brass, Secondary

G A Avril Company...............................F....... 513 641-0566
Cincinnati (G-3790)
I Schumann & Co LLC ....C....... 440 439-2300
Bedford (G-1430)
Oakwood Industries Inc ....D....... 440 232-8700
Bedford (G-1450)

REFINERS & SMELTERS: Copper

Bryan Metals LLC................................G....... 419 636-4571
Bryan (G-2286)
Sam Dong Ohio Inc ....D....... 740 363-1985
Delaware (G-8884)

REFINERS & SMELTERS: Copper, Secondary

Echo Environmental Waverly LLC ....F....... 740 286-2810
Waverly (G-19708)
River Smelting & Ref Mfg Co ....E....... 216 459-2100
Cleveland (G-6117)

REFINERS & SMELTERS: Gold

Quality Gold Inc ....B....... 513 942-7659
Fairfield (G-9706)

REFINERS & SMELTERS: Gold, Secondary

Panama Jewelers LLC ....G....... 440 376-6987
Painesville (G-15909)

REFINERS & SMELTERS: Lead, Secondary

Victory White Metal Company ....E....... 216 271-7200
Cleveland (G-6418)

REFINERS & SMELTERS: Nonferrous Metal

A & B Iron & Metal Company ....F....... 937 228-1561
Dayton (G-8125)
A J Oster Foils LLC.............................D....... 330 823-1700
Alliance (G-486)
Aci Industries Ltd................................E....... 740 368-4160
Delaware (G-8815)
Agmet LLC ....F....... 216 663-8200
Cleveland (G-4731)
Aleris Rolled Pdts Sls Corp ....E....... 216 910-3400
Cleveland (G-4748)
Aleris Rolled Products Inc ....E....... 216 910-3400
Beachwood (G-1256)
Aleris Rolled Products Inc ....D....... 740 983-2571
Ashville (G-848)
Aleris Rolled Products Inc ....D....... 740 922-2540
Uhrichsville (G-19044)
Applied Materials Finishing ....E....... 330 336-5645
Wadsworth (G-19395)

Beck Aluminum Alloys Ltd...............D......216 861-4455
Mayfield Heights (G-13311)
City Scrap & Salvage Co.................E......330 753-5051
Akron (G-124)
Clean Harbors Envmtl Svcs Inc.........F......330 425-3825
Twinsburg (G-18914)
Cohen Brothers Inc........................G......513 422-3696
Middletown (G-14031)
Fpt Cleveland LLC.........................C......216 441-3800
Cleveland (G-5376)
Franklin Iron & Metal Corp.............C......937 253-8184
Dayton (G-8350)
Fusion Automation Inc...................G......440 602-5595
Willoughby (G-20493)
Garden Street Iron & Metal.............E......513 853-3700
Cincinnati (G-3798)
Grandview Materials Inc.................G......614 488-6998
Lewis Center (G-11899)
HC Starck (ohio) Inc......................B......216 692-3990
Cleveland (G-5487)
I H Schlezinger Inc.......................E......614 252-1188
Columbus (G-7178)
Lake County Auto Recyclers............G......440 428-2886
Painesville (G-15897)
Lakeside Industrial Pdts Corp..........G......440 366-0052
Elyria (G-9449)
Masters Group Inc........................G......440 893-1900
Chagrin Falls (G-3103)
Materion Brush Inc.......................A......419 862-2745
Elmore (G-9365)
Metal Improvement Company LLC......E......513 489-6484
Blue Ash (G-1838)
Metal Shredders Inc.....................E......937 866-0777
Miamisburg (G-13830)
Metalico Akron Inc.......................E......330 376-1400
Akron (G-295)
Midwest Iron and Metal Co.............D......937 222-5992
Dayton (G-8496)
Moskowitz Bros Inc......................E......513 242-2100
Cincinnati (G-4126)
National Bronze and Metals............E......440 277-1226
Lorain (G-12261)
Ohio Valley Alloy Services Inc.........E......740 373-1900
Marietta (G-12811)
Polymet Corporation.....................E......513 874-3586
West Chester (G-20038)
Precision Strip Inc.......................C......419 674-4186
Kenton (G-11564)
R L S Corporation........................E......740 773-1440
Chillicothe (G-3270)
Real Alloy Holding Inc...................D......216 755-8800
Beachwood (G-1292)
Real Alloy Recycling Inc................E......216 755-8900
Beachwood (G-1293)
Rnw Holdings Inc.........................E......330 792-0600
Youngstown (G-21190)
Rti International Metals Inc.............D......330 471-1844
Canton (G-2845)
Rumpke Transportation Co LLC........C......513 242-4600
Cincinnati (G-4367)
Sawbrook Steel Castings Co............D......513 554-1700
Cincinnati (G-4381)
Thyssenkrupp Materials NA Inc........D......216 883-8100
Independence (G-11277)
W R G Inc.................................E......216 351-8494
Cleveland (G-6436)
Wall Colmonoy Corporation.............F......937 278-9111
Cincinnati (G-4576)

REFINERS & SMELTERS: Rhenium, Primary

H C Starck Inc............................B......216 692-3990
Euclid (G-9584)

REFINERS & SMELTERS: Silicon, Primary, Over 99% Pure

Globe Metallurgical Inc.................C......740 984-2361
Waterford (G-19647)
Silicon Processors Inc..................G......740 373-2252
Marietta (G-12829)

REFINERS & SMELTERS: Zirconium

Zircoa Inc.................................C......440 248-0500
Cleveland (G-6498)

REFINING LUBRICATING OILS & GREASES, NEC

American Ultra Specialties Inc.........F......330 656-5000
Hudson (G-11157)
Fiske Brothers Refining Co..............D......419 691-2491
Toledo (G-18471)
Wallover Oil Hamilton Inc..............F......513 896-6692
Hamilton (G-10756)

REFINING: Petroleum

Aecom Energy & Cnstr Inc..............C......419 698-6277
Oregon (G-15701)
Blanchard Pipe Line Co LLC............G......419 422-2121
Findlay (G-9796)
Blanchard Refining Company LLC......G......419 422-2121
Findlay (G-9797)
Blanchard Terminal Company LLC......G......419 422-2121
Findlay (G-9798)
Blaster Chemical Co Inc.................G......216 901-5800
Cleveland (G-4915)
BP Products North America Inc.........G......937 461-3621
Dayton (G-8192)
BP Products North America Inc.........F......419 537-9540
Toledo (G-18378)
BP Products North America Inc.........G......419 636-2249
Bryan (G-2284)
Chemours Company Fc LLC.............D......740 989-5202
Little Hocking (G-12144)
Citgo Petroleum Corporation...........G......419 698-8055
Oregon (G-15705)
Cyberutility LLC..........................G......216 291-8723
Cleveland (G-5161)
Grace Petroleum Inc....................G......330 484-0709
Canton (G-2717)
Husky Energy............................F......614 766-5633
Dublin (G-9086)
Isp Lima LLC.............................E......419 998-8700
Lima (G-12031)
K2 Petroleum & Supply LLC............G......937 503-2614
Cincinnati (G-3966)
Koch Knight LLC.........................D......330 488-1651
East Canton (G-9194)
Lima Refining Company.................B......419 226-2300
Lima (G-12042)
Lima Refining Company.................D......419 226-2300
Lima (G-12043)
Marathon Oil Company..................E......419 422-2121
Findlay (G-9854)
Marathon Petroleum Corporation......B......419 422-2121
Findlay (G-9856)
Marathon Petroleum Supply LLC.......A......419 422-2121
Findlay (G-9857)
Mid-Town Petro Acquisition LLC........G......219 728-5149
Blue Ash (G-1840)
Ohio Biofuels............................G......614 886-6518
Cincinnati (G-4174)
Seneca Petroleum Co Inc...............F......419 691-3581
Toledo (G-18692)
Standard Oil Company...................E......419 698-6200
Oregon (G-15717)
Sunoco Inc...............................E......216 912-2579
Akron (G-423)
Troy Valley Petroleum...................G......937 604-0012
Dayton (G-8730)
Vertex Refining OH LLC..................E......419 668-8373
Norwalk (G-15565)

REFLECTIVE ROAD MARKERS, WHOLESALE

Lightle Enterprises Ohio LLC...........G......740 998-5363
Frankfort (G-10001)
Lightle Enterprises Ohio LLC...........G......740 998-5363
Frankfort (G-10000)

REFRACTORIES: Brick

Minteq International Inc.................E......330 343-8821
Dover (G-9003)
Plibrico Company LLC....................E......740 682-7755
Oak Hill (G-15604)

REFRACTORIES: Cement

Castruction Company Inc................F......330 332-9622
Salem (G-16879)

REFRACTORIES: Clay

Afc Company..............................F......330 533-5581
Canfield (G-2545)
Bowerston Shale Company...............E......740 269-2921
Bowerston (G-1957)
Glen-Gery Corporation...................E......419 468-5002
Iberia (G-11243)
Glen-Gery Corporation...................D......419 845-3321
Caledonia (G-2437)
Harbisonwalker Intl Inc..................D......740 682-7711
Oak Hill (G-15597)
Harbisonwalker Intl Inc..................E......330 326-2010
Windham (G-20697)
Harbisonwalker Intl Inc..................E......513 576-6240
Batavia (G-1191)
Harbisonwalker Intl Inc..................F......330 868-4141
Minerva (G-14323)
I Cerco Inc...............................D......740 982-2050
Crooksville (G-7950)
Lakeway Mfg Inc.........................E......419 433-3030
Huron (G-11232)
Magneco/Metrel Inc......................E......330 426-9468
Negley (G-14730)
Minteq International Inc.................E......330 343-8821
Dover (G-9003)
Nock and Son Company..................G......440 871-5525
Cleveland (G-5885)
Nock and Son Company..................G......740 682-7741
Oak Hill (G-15602)
Resco Products Inc......................E......330 372-3716
Warren (G-19594)
Selas Heat Technology Co LLC..........E......800 523-6500
Streetsboro (G-17875)
Specialty Ceramics Inc..................D......330 482-0800
Columbiana (G-6633)
Stebbins Engineering & Mfg Co.........E......740 922-3012
Uhrichsville (G-19060)
Summitville Tiles Inc....................E......330 868-6463
Minerva (G-14344)
UNI-Ref United Refractories Co..........E......513 563-9955
Cincinnati (G-4536)
Wahl Refractory Solutions LLC..........D......419 334-2658
Fremont (G-10193)
Whitacre Greer Company................E......330 823-1610
Alliance (G-553)

REFRACTORIES: Graphite, Carbon Or Ceramic Bond

E I Ceramics LLC........................D......513 772-7001
Cincinnati (G-3678)

REFRACTORIES: Nonclay

A & M Refractories Inc..................E......740 456-8020
New Boston (G-14778)
Allied Mineral Products Inc.............B......614 876-0244
Columbus (G-6726)
Ets Schaefer LLC........................E......330 468-6600
Macedonia (G-12448)
Harbisonwalker Intl Inc..................D......740 682-7711
Oak Hill (G-15597)
I Cerco Inc...............................D......740 982-2050
Crooksville (G-7950)
Impact Armor Technologies LLC........F......216 706-2024
Cleveland (G-5554)
Johns Manville Corporation.............B......419 878-8111
Waterville (G-19660)
Magneco/Metrel Inc......................E......330 426-9468
Negley (G-14730)
Martin Marietta Materials Inc..........E......513 701-1140
West Chester (G-19897)
Momentive Prfmce Mtls Qrtz Inc........C......440 878-5700
Strongsville (G-17941)
Nock and Son Company..................G......440 871-5525
Cleveland (G-5885)
Ohio Vly Stmpng-Assemblies Inc........E......419 522-0983
Mansfield (G-12663)
Pyromatics Corp.........................F......440 352-3500
Mentor (G-13704)
Refractory Specialties Inc..............E......330 938-2101
Sebring (G-17050)
Resco Products Inc......................E......740 682-7794
Oak Hill (G-15605)
Ruscoe Company.........................E......330 253-8148
Akron (G-383)
Saint-Gobain Ceramics Plas Inc.........A......330 673-5860
Stow (G-17797)
UNI-Ref United Refractories Co..........E......513 563-9955
Cincinnati (G-4536)

PRODU

US Refractory Products LLC ....E 440 386-4580
North Ridgeville (G-15408)
Vacuform Inc ....E 330 938-9674
Sebring (G-17057)
Vesuvius U S A Corporation ....E 419 986-5126
Bettsville (G-1670)
Wahl Refractory Solutions LLC ....D 419 334-2658
Fremont (G-10193)
Zircoa Inc ....C 440 248-0500
Cleveland (G-6498)

REFRIGERATION & HEATING EQUIPMENT

A A S Amels Sheet Meta L Inc ....E 330 793-9326
Youngstown (G-21010)
Arthurs Refrigeration ....G 740 532-0206
Ironton (G-11290)
Bard Manufacturing Company Inc ......D 419 636-1194
Bryan (G-2281)
Beckett Air Incorporated ....D 440 327-9999
North Ridgeville (G-15359)
Budzar Industries Inc ....D 440 530-1000
Willoughby (G-20448)
C Nelson Manufacturing Co ....E 419 898-3305
Oak Harbor (G-15587)
Carrier Corporation ....E 937 275-0645
Dayton (G-8212)
Central Heating & Cooling Inc ....G 330 782-7100
Youngstown (G-21045)
Cryogenic Equipment & Svcs Inc ....F 513 761-4200
Cincinnati (G-3623)
Csafe LLC ....G 937 312-0114
Moraine (G-14473)
Daikin Applied Americas Inc ....G 614 351-9862
Columbus (G-7007)
Dmtco LLC ....G 937 324-0061
Springfield (G-17545)
Ellis & Watts Global Inds Inc ....F 513 752-9000
Batavia (G-1182)
Famous Industries Inc ....D 740 685-2592
Byesville (G-2401)
Famous Industries Inc ....C 740 397-8842
Mount Vernon (G-14622)
Fire From Ice Ventures LLC ....F 419 944-6705
Solon (G-17293)
Gould Group LLC ....G 740 807-4294
Hilliard (G-10949)
Hydro-Thrift Corporation ....E 330 837-5141
Massillon (G-13154)
Jnp Group LLC ....G 800 735-9645
Wooster (G-20791)
Liebert North America Inc ....A 614 888-0246
Columbus (G-7293)
Mahle Behr USA Inc ....A 937 369-2000
Dayton (G-8472)
Maverick Innvtive Slutions LLC ....E 419 281-7944
Ashland (G-751)
Mv Group Inc ....G 419 776-1133
Toledo (G-18594)
Prime Manufacturing Corp ....G 937 496-3900
Dayton (G-8593)
Professional Supply Inc ....F 419 332-7373
Fremont (G-10177)
RSI Company ....F 216 360-9800
Beachwood (G-1297)
Space Dynamics Corp ....E 513 792-9800
Blue Ash (G-1871)
T J F Inc ....E 419 878-4400
Waterville (G-19668)
Taiho Corporation of America ....C 419 443-1645
Tiffin (G-18246)
Thermo King Corporation ....F 478 625-7241
Chagrin Falls (G-3072)
Trane US Inc ....E 513 771-8884
Cincinnati (G-4517)
Trane US Inc ....C 614 473-3131
Columbus (G-7703)
Trane US Inc ....C 614 497-6300
Groveport (G-10647)
Trane US Inc ....D 614 473-8701
Columbus (G-7704)
United Technologies Corp ....B 330 784-5477
North Canton (G-15279)
Variflow Equipment Inc ....G 513 245-0420
Cincinnati (G-4556)
Vortec Corporation ....E 513 686-8210
Blue Ash (G-1891)

REFRIGERATION EQPT & SPLYS WHOLESALERS

Modern Ice Equipment & Sup Co ....E 513 367-2101
Cincinnati (G-4115)

REFRIGERATION EQPT & SPLYS, WHOLESALE: Beverage Dispensers

Dj Beverage Innovations Inc ....G 614 769-1569
Plain City (G-16336)
International Beverage Works ....G 614 798-5398
Columbus (G-7205)

REFRIGERATION EQPT & SPLYS, WHOLESALE: Commercial Eqpt

Hattenbach Company ....E 330 744-2732
Youngstown (G-21107)
Hattenbach Company ....D 216 881-5200
Cleveland (G-5485)

REFRIGERATION EQPT: Complete

CFC Startec LLC ....G 330 688-8316
Stow (G-17737)
Hobart Corporation ....E 937 332-3000
Troy (G-18840)
Hobart Corporation ....C 937 332-2797
Piqua (G-16277)
Northeastern Rfrgn Corp ....E 440 942-7676
Willoughby (G-20557)
NRC Inc ....E 440 975-9449
Willoughby (G-20558)
Refrigeration Industries Corp ....F 740 377-9166
South Point (G-17446)
So-Low Environmental Eqp Co ....E 513 772-9410
Cincinnati (G-4431)
Thermo King Corporation ....B 478 625-7241
Chagrin Falls (G-3071)

REFRIGERATION REPAIR SVCS

Northeastern Rfrgn Corp ....E 440 942-7676
Willoughby (G-20557)

REFRIGERATORS & FREEZERS WHOLESALERS

Arthurs Refrigeration ....G 740 532-0206
Ironton (G-11290)

REFUGEE SVCS

Jeffco Sheltered Workshop ....E 740 264-4608
Steubenville (G-17701)

REFUSE SYSTEMS

A & B Iron & Metal Company ....F 937 228-1561
Dayton (G-8125)
Capital City Oil Inc ....G 740 397-4483
Mount Vernon (G-14612)
Fpt Cleveland LLC ....C 216 441-3800
Cleveland (G-5376)
Green Vision Materials Inc ....F 440 564-5500
Newbury (G-15093)
Metalico Akron Inc ....E 330 376-1400
Akron (G-295)
Rumpke Transportation Co LLC ....F 513 851-0122
Cincinnati (G-4366)
Waste Water Pollution Control ....F 330 263-5290
Wooster (G-20844)

REGISTERS: Air, Metal

Hart & Cooley Inc ....C 937 832-7800
Englewood (G-9522)

REGULATION & ADMIN, GOVT: Facility Licensing & Inspection

National Welding & Tanker Repr ....G 614 875-3399
Grove City (G-10576)

REGULATORS: Generator Voltage

Staco Energy Products Co ....G 937 253-1191
Miamisburg (G-13863)

REGULATORS: Power

Liebert Corporation ....A 614 888-0246
Columbus (G-7292)

REHABILITATION SVCS

Clovernook Center For The Bli ....C 513 522-3860
Cincinnati (G-3590)

RELAYS & SWITCHES: Indl, Electric

Control Electric Co ....E 216 671-8010
Columbia Station (G-6586)
Controllix Corporation ....F 440 232-8757
Walton Hills (G-19472)
Rogers Industrial Products Inc ....E 330 535-3331
Akron (G-378)
Utility Relay Co Ltd ....E 440 708-1000
Chagrin Falls (G-3131)

RELAYS: Control Circuit, Ind

Industrial and Mar Eng Svc Co ....F 740 694-0791
Fredericktown (G-10104)
Omega Tek Inc ....G 419 756-9580
Mansfield (G-12664)

RELAYS: Electronic Usage

Innovative Integrations Inc ....G 216 533-5353
Mesopotamia (G-13775)
Te Connectivity Corporation ....C 419 521-9500
Mansfield (G-12694)

RELIGIOUS SPLYS WHOLESALERS

Novak J F Manufacturing Co LLC ....G 216 741-5112
Cleveland (G-5918)

REMOVERS & CLEANERS

Cahill Services Inc ....G 216 410-5595
Lakewood (G-11659)
Dolgencorp LLC ....G 740 289-4790
Piketon (G-16219)
Hytek Coatings Inc ....G 513 424-0131
Middletown (G-14046)
Janet Sullivan ....G 419 658-2333
Ney (G-15142)
Roger Hoover ....G 330 857-1815
Orrville (G-15760)

REMOVERS: Paint

Treved Exteriors ....G 513 771-3888
Cincinnati (G-4520)

RENDERING PLANT

Griffin Industries LLC ....G 216 696-2588
Cleveland (G-5459)

RENT-A-CAR SVCS

Precision Coatings Systems ....E 937 642-4727
Marysville (G-12963)

RENTAL SVCS: Business Machine & Electronic Eqpt

Pitney Bowes Inc ....D 203 426-7025
Brecksville (G-2069)
Pitney Bowes Inc ....D 740 374-5535
Marietta (G-12817)

RENTAL SVCS: Clothing

American Commodore Tuxedos ....G 440 324-2889
Elyria (G-9370)

RENTAL SVCS: Costume

Akron Design & Costume Co ....G 330 644-4849
Akron (G-40)
Costume Specialists Inc ....E 614 464-2115
Columbus (G-6987)
Costume Specialists Inc ....G 614 464-2115
Columbus (G-6988)
Promo Costumes Inc ....F 740 383-5176
Marion (G-12893)
Stagecraft Costuming Inc ....F 513 541-7150
Cincinnati (G-4451)

RENTAL SVCS: Eqpt, Theatrical

Schenz Theatrical Supply Inc ....F 513 542-6100
Cincinnati (G-4387)

RENTAL SVCS: Home Cleaning & Maintenance Eqpt

Certon Technologies Inc ....F 440 786-7185
Bedford (G-1414)

RENTAL SVCS: Motor Home

Advanced Rv LLC ....G 440 283-0405
Willoughby (G-20425)

RENTAL SVCS: Musical Instrument

Loft Violin Shop ....F 614 267-7221
Columbus (G-7303)
Paul Bartel ....G 513 541-2000
Cincinnati (G-4216)

RENTAL SVCS: Pallet

Forklifts of Americas LLC ....G 440 821-5143
Highland Heights (G-10912)

RENTAL SVCS: Saddle Horse

Victorian Farms ....G 330 628-9188
Atwater (G-903)

RENTAL SVCS: Sign

A B C Sign Inc ....F 513 241-8884
Cincinnati (G-3332)

RENTAL SVCS: Sound & Lighting Eqpt

Iacono Production Services Inc ....F 513 469-5095
Blue Ash (G-1811)
Importers Direct LLC ....E 330 436-3260
Akron (G-230)
Technical Artistry Inc ....G 614 299-7777
Columbus (G-7684)

RENTAL SVCS: Sporting Goods, NEC

McSports ....G 419 586-5555
Celina (G-3007)

RENTAL SVCS: Stores & Yards Eqpt

Golf Car Company Inc ....F 614 873-1055
Plain City (G-16344)
Showplace Inc ....G 419 468-7368
Galion (G-10287)

RENTAL SVCS: Tent & Tarpaulin

Galion Canvas Products Co ....G 419 468-5333
Galion (G-10269)
Rainbow Industries Inc ....G 937 323-6493
Springfield (G-17633)
South Akron Awning Co ....F 330 848-7611
Akron (G-409)
Tarpco Inc ....F 330 677-8277
Kent (G-11535)
Wolf G T Awning & Tent Co ....F 937 548-4161
Greenville (G-10529)

RENTAL SVCS: Trailer

Eleet Cryogenics Inc ....E 330 874-4009
Bolivar (G-1933)
Lloyd F Helber ....E 740 756-9607
Carroll (G-2943)
Mr Trailer Sales Inc ....G 330 339-7701
Dover (G-9004)

RENTAL SVCS: Vending Machine

Cuyahoga Vending Co Inc ....E 440 353-9595
North Ridgeville (G-15368)

RENTAL SVCS: Work Zone Traffic Eqpt, Flags, Cones, Etc

A & A Safety Inc ....E 513 943-6100
Amelia (G-564)
Lightle Enterprises Ohio LLC ....G 740 998-5363
Frankfort (G-10000)
Paul Peterson Company ....E 614 486-7467
Columbus (G-7467)

Paul Peterson Safety Div Inc ....E 614 486-4375
Columbus (G-7468)

RENTAL: Portable Toilet

Johnny On The Spot Inc ....E 614 497-1776
Columbus (G-7239)
Pro-Kleen Industrial Svcs Inc ....E 740 689-1886
Lancaster (G-11741)

RENTAL: Trucks, With Drivers

Hull Ready Mix Concrete Inc ....F 419 625-8070
Sandusky (G-16972)
Mulch Madness LLC ....F 330 920-9900
Aurora (G-935)

RENTAL: Video Tape & Disc

US Video ....G 440 734-6463
North Olmsted (G-15350)

REPAIR SERVICES, NEC

M C Systems Inc ....G 513 336-6007
Mason (G-13056)

REPAIR TRAINING, COMPUTER

Corporate Elevator LLC ....F 614 288-1847
Columbus (G-6985)

REPOSSESSION SVCS

Interscope Manufacturing Inc ....E 513 423-8866
Middletown (G-14050)

REPRODUCTION SVCS: Video Tape Or Disk

Markeys Audio/Visual Inc ....G 419 244-8844
Toledo (G-18573)

RESEARCH & DEVELOPMENT SVCS, COMMERCIAL: Engineering Lab

Morris Technologies Inc ....C 513 733-1611
Cincinnati (G-4123)

RESEARCH, DEV & TESTING SVCS, COMM: Chem Lab, Exc Testing

Guild Associates Inc ....E 614 798-8215
Dublin (G-9081)
Guild Associates Inc ....E 843 573-0095
Dublin (G-9082)
Heraeus Precious Metals North ....E 937 264-1000
Vandalia (G-19295)

RESEARCH, DEVEL & TEST SVCS, COMM: Sociological & Education

Community RE Group-Comvet ....G 440 319-6714
Ashtabula (G-798)

RESEARCH, DEVELOPMENT & TEST SVCS, COMM: Cmptr Hardware Dev

Ic3d LLC ....G 614 260-5631
Columbus (G-7180)
Noggin LLC ....G 440 305-6188
Cleveland (G-5886)

RESEARCH, DEVELOPMENT & TEST SVCS, COMM: Research, Exc Lab

Special Mtls RES & Tech Inc ....G 440 777-4024
North Olmsted (G-15347)

RESEARCH, DEVELOPMENT & TESTING SVCS, COMM: Agricultural

Lifestyle Nutraceuticals Ltd ....F 513 376-7218
Cincinnati (G-4022)

RESEARCH, DEVELOPMENT & TESTING SVCS, COMM: Research Lab

Applied Sciences Inc ....E 937 766-2020
Cedarville (G-2980)
Performnce Plymr Solutions Inc ....F 937 298-3713
Moraine (G-14512)
Ronald T Dodge Co ....F 937 439-4497
Dayton (G-8638)

Wrl of Indiana Inc ....A 419 289-8700
Ashland (G-786)

RESEARCH, DEVELOPMENT & TESTING SVCS, COMMERCIAL: Business

Smokeheal Inc ....G 216 255-5119
Cleveland (G-6213)

RESEARCH, DEVELOPMENT & TESTING SVCS, COMMERCIAL: Education

Instruction & Design Concepts ....G 937 439-2698
Dayton (G-8412)

RESEARCH, DEVELOPMENT & TESTING SVCS, COMMERCIAL: Energy

Fripro Energy LLC ....G 419 865-0002
Maumee (G-13259)

RESEARCH, DEVELOPMENT & TESTING SVCS, COMMERCIAL: Food

Nutralab Inc ....G 513 561-0471
Cincinnati (G-4169)

RESEARCH, DEVELOPMENT & TESTING SVCS, COMMERCIAL: Medical

Applied Medical Technology Inc ....E 440 717-4000
Brecksville (G-2034)

RESEARCH, DEVELOPMENT & TESTING SVCS, COMMERCIAL: Physical

Fenix Magnetics Inc ....G 415 308-0134
Lakewood (G-11663)
Ftech R&D North America Inc ....D 937 339-2777
Troy (G-18829)
H & N Instruments Inc ....G 740 344-4351
Newark (G-15017)
Ivac Technologies Corp ....F 216 662-4987
Cleveland (G-5592)
Leidos Inc ....D 937 431-2400
Beavercreek (G-1348)
Lubrizol Advanced Mtls Inc ....E 440 933-0400
Avon (G-1037)
Velocys Inc ....D 614 733-3300
Plain City (G-16363)

RESEARCH, DVLPT & TEST SVCS, COMM: Mkt Analysis or Research

Jscs Group Inc ....G 513 563-4900
Cincinnati (G-3961)

RESEARCH, DVLPT & TESTING SVCS, COMM: Mkt, Bus & Economic

Enerchem Incorporated ....G 513 745-0580
Cincinnati (G-3703)

RESIDENTIAL MENTAL HEALTH & SUBSTANCE ABUSE FACILITIES

Style Crest Inc ....B 419 332-7369
Fremont (G-10184)

RESIDENTIAL REMODELERS

Boyce Ltd ....G 614 236-8901
Columbus (G-6851)
Carr Supply Co ....G 937 316-6300
Greenville (G-10492)
Custom Blind Corporation ....F 937 643-2907
Dayton (G-8257)
JC Electric ....E 330 760-2915
Garrettsville (G-10325)
Winsupply Inc ....F 937 346-0600
Springfield (G-17679)

RESIDUES

Residue National LLC ....G 614 309-8963
Dublin (G-9132)

RESINS: Custom Compound Purchased

Accel Corporation ....D 440 934-7711
Avon (G-981)

PRODUCT

Advanced Composites Inc ....C 937 575-9800
Sidney (G-17165)

Aurora Plastics Inc ....D 330 422-0700
Streetsboro (G-17840)

Chemionics Corporation ....E 330 733-8834
Tallmadge (G-18137)

Chromaflo Technologies Corp ....C 440 997-0081
Ashtabula (G-795)

Chromaflo Technologies Corp ....C 513 733-5111
Cincinnati (G-3532)

Deltech Polymers Corporation ....G 937 339-3150
Troy (G-18817)

Dyneon LLC ....E 859 334-4500
Cincinnati (G-3676)

Flex Technologies Inc ....E 330 897-6311
Baltic (G-1071)

Freeman Manufacturing & Sup Co .....E 440 934-1902
Avon (G-996)

General Color Investments Inc ....D 330 868-4161
Minerva (G-14322)

Hexpol Compounding LLC ....C 440 834-4644
Burton (G-2376)

Hexpol Compounding LLC ....E 440 834-4644
Burton (G-2377)

Killian Latex Inc ....F 330 644-6746
Akron (G-256)

McCann Plastics Inc ....D 330 499-1515
Canton (G-2776)

Nanosperse LLC ....G 937 296-5030
Kettering (G-11583)

Omnova Solutions Inc ....C 330 628-6550
Mogadore (G-14382)

Polymers By Design LLC ....G 937 361-7398
Troy (G-18863)

Polyone Corporation ....F 573 468-6513
North Baltimore (G-15196)

Polyone Corporation ....C 419 668-4844
Norwalk (G-15559)

Polyone Corporation ....D 440 930-1000
Avon Lake (G-1047)

Polyone Corporation ....D 440 930-1000
North Baltimore (G-15197)

Radici Plastics Usa Inc ....D 330 336-7611
Wadsworth (G-19434)

Rutland Plastic Tech Inc ....G 614 846-3055
Columbus (G-7578)

Synthetic Rubber Technology ....G 330 494-2221
Uniontown (G-19101)

Thermafab Alloy Inc ....E 216 861-0540
Olmsted Falls (G-15677)

Tymex Plastics Inc ....E 216 429-8950
Cleveland (G-6378)

Valspar Corporation ....C 330 830-6000
Massillon (G-13209)

RESISTORS

Filnor Inc ....F 330 821-7667
Alliance (G-508)

RESISTORS & RESISTOR UNITS

Asco Power Technologies LP ....E 216 573-7600
Cleveland (G-4841)

Asco Power Technologies LP ....C 973 966-2161
Cleveland (G-4842)

RESOLVERS

Home Resolver ....G 440 886-6758
Cleveland (G-5520)

RESPIRATORS

Morning Pride Mfg LLC ....A 937 264-2662
Dayton (G-8508)

Morning Pride Mfg LLC ....G 937 264-1726
Dayton (G-8509)

RESTAURANT EQPT REPAIR SVCS

Harry C Lobalzo & Sons Inc ....E 330 666-6758
Akron (G-216)

RESTAURANT EQPT: Carts

Cateringstone ....G 513 410-1064
Cincinnati (G-3506)

Modroto ....G 800 772-7659
Ashtabula (G-821)

Quadra - Tech Inc ....D 614 445-0690
Columbus (G-7532)

RESTAURANT EQPT: Food Wagons

CC & Sj of Ohio Inc ....G 614 878-7291
Columbus (G-6917)

RESTAURANT EQPT: Sheet Metal

Architectural Sheet Metals LLC ....G 216 361-9952
Cleveland (G-4827)

D B S Stinless Stl Fabricators ....G 513 856-9600
Hamilton (G-10683)

RESTAURANTS:Full Svc, American

Elizabeths Closet ....G 513 646-5025
Maineville (G-12522)

Little Ghost Roasters ....G 614 325-2065
Columbus (G-7301)

The Great Lakes Brewing Co ....D 216 771-4404
Cleveland (G-6313)

RESTAURANTS:Full Svc, Barbecue

Barbeque Integrated Inc ....D 614 430-0572
Columbus (G-6640)

Buckeye Sauce Corporation ....F 216 751-0440
Cleveland (G-4944)

New Riegel Cafe Inc ....E 419 595-2255
New Riegel (G-14947)

RESTAURANTS:Full Svc, Chinese

Magic Wok Inc ....G 419 531-1818
Toledo (G-18569)

RESTAURANTS:Full Svc, Family, Chain

Bob Evans Farms Inc ....B 614 491-2225
New Albany (G-14750)

Skyline Chili Inc ....C 513 874-1188
Fairfield (G-9719)

RESTAURANTS:Full Svc, Family, Independent

Amish Door Inc ....C 330 359-5464
Wilmot (G-20683)

Moyer Vineyards Inc ....E 937 549-2957
Manchester (G-12550)

Robert Barr ....F 740 826-7325
New Concord (G-14821)

RESTAURANTS:Full Svc, Italian

Lloyd F Helber ....E 740 756-9607
Carroll (G-2943)

RESTAURANTS:Limited Svc, Chicken

Brewpub Restaurant Corp ....D 614 228-2537
Columbus (G-6857)

Maumee Bay Brewing Company ....E 419 243-1253
Toledo (G-18577)

RESTAURANTS:Limited Svc, Chili Stand

Gold Star Chili Inc ....E 513 631-1990
Cincinnati (G-3839)

RESTAURANTS:Limited Svc, Fast-Food, Chain

White Castle System Inc ....B 614 228-5781
Columbus (G-7761)

White Castle System Inc ....E 513 563-2290
Cincinnati (G-4591)

RESTAURANTS:Limited Svc, Ice Cream Stands Or Dairy Bars

Country Maid Ice Cream Inc ....G 330 659-6830
Richfield (G-16619)

International Brand Services ....F 513 376-8209
Cincinnati (G-3930)

Johnsons Real Ice Cream Co ....E 614 231-0014
Columbus (G-7241)

Stella Lou LLC ....F 937 935-9536
Powell (G-16483)

Youngs Jersey Dairy Inc ....B 937 325-0629
Yellow Springs (G-21003)

RESTAURANTS:Limited Svc, Lunch Counter

Milk & Honey ....F 330 492-5884
Canton (G-2782)

RESTAURANTS:Limited Svc, Pizzeria, Chain

Miami Valley Pizza Hut Inc ....E 419 586-5900
Celina (G-3009)

RESTAURANTS:Limited Svc, Pizzeria, Independent

Brinkman LLC ....F 419 204-5934
Lima (G-11997)

Wal-Bon of Ohio Inc ....F 740 423-6351
Belpre (G-1595)

RESTAURANTS:Limited Svc, Sandwiches & Submarines Shop

Circleville Oil Co ....G 740 477-3341
Circleville (G-4625)

Perfettes Sausage LLC ....G 330 792-0775
Youngstown (G-21169)

RESTAURANTS:Limited Svc, Snack Shop

Bunker Hill Cheese Co Inc ....D 330 893-2131
Millersburg (G-14207)

RESTAURANTS:Ltd Svc, Ice Cream, Soft Drink/Fountain Stands

Dari Freeze ....G 937 678-6171
West Manchester (G-20097)

RETAIL BAKERY: Bread

B L F Enterprises Inc ....F 937 642-6425
Westerville (G-20201)

Norcia Bakery ....E 330 454-1077
Canton (G-2790)

RETAIL BAKERY: Cakes

Sugar Showcase ....G 330 792-9154
Youngstown (G-21213)

RETAIL BAKERY: Cookies

Adrians Place ....G 513 651-2154
Cincinnati (G-3357)

Cookie Bouquets Inc ....G 614 888-2171
Columbus (G-6980)

Great American Cookie Company ....F 419 474-9417
Toledo (G-18486)

RETAIL BAKERY: Doughnuts

Crispie Creme of Chillicothe ....E 740 774-3770
Chillicothe (G-3235)

Dandi Enterprises Inc ....F 419 516-9070
Solon (G-17282)

Georges Donuts Inc ....G 330 963-9902
Twinsburg (G-18945)

Krispy Kreme Doughnut Corp ....F 614 798-0812
Columbus (G-7268)

McHappys Donuts of Parkersburg ....G 740 593-8744
Athens (G-875)

RETAIL BAKERY: Pastries

Meeks Pastry Shop ....G 419 782-4871
Defiance (G-8803)

RETAIL BAKERY: Pies

K & B Acquisitions Inc ....F 937 253-1163
Dayton (G-8432)

RETAIL BAKERY: Pretzels

Annes Auntie Pretzels ....E 614 418-7021
Columbus (G-6758)

Auntie Annes ....G 330 652-1939
Niles (G-15144)

RETAIL FIREPLACE STORES

Overhead Inc ....G 419 476-0300
Toledo (G-18624)

Whempys Corp ....G 614 888-6670
Worthington (G-20893)

RETAIL LUMBER YARDS

A & B Wood Design Assoc Inc ....G....... 330 721-2789
Wadsworth *(G-19385)*

Ace Lumber Company ....F 330 744-3167
Youngstown *(G-21015)*

Carter-Jones Lumber Company...........F 440 834-8164
Middlefield *(G-13920)*

Clarksville Stave & Lumber Co...........G....... 937 376-4618
Xenia *(G-20944)*

Conover Lumber Company Inc...........F 937 368-3010
Conover *(G-7823)*

Hardwood Store Inc ....G....... 937 864-2899
Enon *(G-9547)*

J D L Hardwoods.................................G....... 440 272-5630
Middlefield *(G-13943)*

K D Hardwoods Inc..............................G....... 440 834-1772
Burton *(G-2379)*

Marsh Valley Forest Pdts Ltd..............G....... 440 632-1889
Middlefield *(G-13953)*

R C Moore Lumber Co.........................F 740 732-4950
Caldwell *(G-2431)*

Regal Cabinet Inc...............................G....... 419 865-3932
Toledo *(G-18674)*

RETAIL STORES, NEC

Auntie Annes ....G....... 330 652-1939
Niles *(G-15144)*

Gannons Discount Blinds ....G....... 216 398-2761
Cleveland *(G-5394)*

RETAIL STORES: Alarm Signal Systems

Bakers Print Shop ....G....... 740 423-1717
Little Hocking *(G-12143)*

RETAIL STORES: Alcoholic Beverage Making Eqpt & Splys

Cineen Inc ....G....... 440 236-3658
Columbia Station *(G-6583)*

RETAIL STORES: Art & Architectural Splys

GBS Corp..E 330 929-8050
Stow *(G-17758)*

RETAIL STORES: Artificial Limbs

Hanger Prsthetcs & Ortho Inc..............G....... 740 454-6215
Zanesville *(G-21317)*

Novacare Inc.......................................G....... 216 704-4817
Beachwood *(G-1285)*

RETAIL STORES: Audio-Visual Eqpt & Splys

Custom Automation Technologies........G....... 614 939-4228
New Albany *(G-14755)*

Findaway World LLC ....D....... 440 893-0808
Solon *(G-17292)*

Lightyearmusiccom..............................G....... 216 929-1022
Cleveland *(G-5695)*

RETAIL STORES: Awnings

Jacqueline L Vandyke...........................G....... 740 593-6779
Athens *(G-874)*

P C R Restorations Inc ....F 419 747-7957
Mansfield *(G-12666)*

RETAIL STORES: Banners

Blang Acquisition LLC ....F 937 223-2155
Dayton *(G-8190)*

RETAIL STORES: Batteries, Non-Automotive

Battery Unlimited ....G....... 740 452-5030
Zanesville *(G-21276)*

One Wish LLC ....F 800 505-6883
Beachwood *(G-1289)*

RETAIL STORES: Business Machines & Eqpt

A/C Laser Technologies Inc ....F 330 784-3355
Akron *(G-23)*

RETAIL STORES: Cake Decorating Splys

Cake Arts Supplies ....G....... 419 472-4959
Toledo *(G-18387)*

Hartville Chocolates Inc ....F 330 877-1999
Hartville *(G-10822)*

RETAIL STORES: Children's Furniture, NEC

Foundations Worldwide Inc ....E 330 722-5033
Medina *(G-13412)*

RETAIL STORES: Christmas Lights & Decorations

Christmas Ranch LLC ....E 513 505-3865
Morrow *(G-14545)*

RETAIL STORES: Cleaning Eqpt & Splys

Akron Cotton Products Inc ....G....... 330 434-7171
Akron *(G-38)*

Chempure Products Corporation..........G....... 330 874-4300
Bolivar *(G-1930)*

Jeff Pendergrass.................................G....... 513 575-1226
Milford *(G-14156)*

Scott Fetzer Company ....E 216 228-2400
Chagrin Falls *(G-3119)*

RETAIL STORES: Communication Eqpt

Communications Aid Inc ....F 513 475-8453
Cincinnati *(G-3599)*

Transel Corporation.............................G....... 513 897-3442
Harveysburg *(G-10835)*

RETAIL STORES: Concrete Prdts, Precast

Michaels Pre-Cast Con Pdts ....F 513 683-1292
Loveland *(G-12374)*

Snyder Concrete Products Inc ....F 513 539-7686
Monroe *(G-14413)*

RETAIL STORES: Cosmetics

Safe 4 People Inc ....G....... 419 797-4087
Port Clinton *(G-16412)*

RETAIL STORES: Decals

First Stop Signs and Decals ....G....... 330 343-1859
New Philadelphia *(G-14899)*

Mike B Crawford..................................G....... 330 673-7944
Kent *(G-11492)*

RETAIL STORES: Educational Aids & Electronic Training Mat

Bendon Inc ....D....... 419 207-3600
Ashland *(G-712)*

Health Nuts Media LLC.........................G....... 818 802-5222
Cleveland *(G-5489)*

RETAIL STORES: Electronic Parts & Eqpt

Mixed Logic LLC..................................G....... 440 826-1676
Valley City *(G-19218)*

Precision Replacement LLC ....G....... 330 908-0410
Macedonia *(G-12476)*

RETAIL STORES: Engine & Motor Eqpt & Splys

DW Hercules LLC.................................E 330 830-2498
Massillon *(G-13127)*

Interstate-Mcbee LLC...........................G....... 800 321-4234
Cleveland *(G-5584)*

RETAIL STORES: Farm Eqpt & Splys

Coleman Machine Inc ....G....... 740 695-3006
Saint Clairsville *(G-16787)*

Gerber & Sons Inc...............................E 330 897-6201
Baltic *(G-1072)*

R & J AG Manufacturing Inc ....F 419 962-4707
Ashland *(G-770)*

Wollam AG Center Inc ....F 419 596-3896
Continental *(G-7830)*

RETAIL STORES: Farm Tractors

Miners Tractor Sales Inc.......................F 330 325-9914
Rootstown *(G-16725)*

RETAIL STORES: Fiberglass Materials, Exc Insulation

Toledo Pro Fiberglass Inc.....................G....... 419 241-9390
Toledo *(G-18740)*

RETAIL STORES: Fire Extinguishers

Warren Fire Equipment Inc ....E 330 824-3523
Warren *(G-19622)*

RETAIL STORES: Flags

Flag Lady Inc ....G....... 614 263-1776
Columbus *(G-7090)*

Mel Wacker Sign Inc ....G....... 330 832-1726
Massillon *(G-13178)*

RETAIL STORES: Gravestones, Finished

Ashland Monument Company Inc ....G....... 419 281-2688
Ashland *(G-706)*

RETAIL STORES: Hair Care Prdts

Natural Beauty Products Inc..................F 513 420-9400
Middletown *(G-14068)*

RETAIL STORES: Hearing Aids

Morris Maico Hearing Aid Svc ....G....... 419 232-6200
Van Wert *(G-19267)*

RETAIL STORES: Hospital Eqpt & Splys

Kempf Surgical Appliances Inc ....E 513 984-5758
Montgomery *(G-14433)*

Key Mobility Services Ltd ....G....... 937 374-3226
Xenia *(G-20959)*

RETAIL STORES: Ice

Haller Enterprises Inc...........................F 330 733-9693
Akron *(G-211)*

Home City Ice Company ....F 440 439-5001
Bedford *(G-1429)*

Home City Ice Company ....E 614 836-2877
Groveport *(G-10625)*

Home City Ice Company ....E 937 461-6028
Dayton *(G-8392)*

RETAIL STORES: Medical Apparatus & Splys

Access To Independence Inc.................G....... 330 296-8111
Ravenna *(G-16512)*

Relevium Labs Inc ....G....... 614 568-7000
Oxford *(G-15842)*

Schaerer Medical Usa Inc.....................F 513 561-2241
Cincinnati *(G-4386)*

RETAIL STORES: Monuments, Finished To Custom Order

Bell Vault & Monument Works ....E 937 866-2444
Miamisburg *(G-13785)*

Dodds Monument Inc ....G....... 937 372-2736
Xenia *(G-20948)*

Drake Monument Company ....G....... 937 399-7941
Springfield *(G-17547)*

Jackson Monument Inc ....G....... 740 286-1590
Jackson *(G-11316)*

Mayfair Granite Co Inc ....G....... 216 382-8150
Cleveland *(G-5763)*

North Hill Marble & Granite Co ....F 330 253-2179
Akron *(G-318)*

Piqua Granite & Marble Co Inc ....G....... 937 773-2000
Piqua *(G-16304)*

RETAIL STORES: Motors, Electric

Allan A Irish ....G....... 419 394-3284
Saint Marys *(G-16831)*

Big River Electric Inc ....G....... 740 446-4360
Gallipolis *(G-10292)*

C and O Electric Motor Service ....G....... 614 491-6387
Columbus *(G-6882)*

Carnation Elc Mtr Repr Sls Inc ....G....... 330 823-7116
Alliance *(G-501)*

Franks Electric Inc ....G....... 513 542-0342
Cincinnati *(G-3781)*

Lebanon Electric Motor Svc LLC...........G....... 513 932-2889
Lebanon *(G-11813)*

Lemsco Inc ....G....... 419 242-4005
Toledo *(G-18557)*

Wheatley Electric Service Co ....G....... 513 531-4951
Cincinnati *(G-4590)*

PRODUCT

RETAIL STORES: Orthopedic & Prosthesis Applications

Akron Orthotic Solutions Inc ....G....... 330 253-3002
  Akron (G-49)
Capital Prosthetic & ....G....... 740 522-3331
  Newark (G-14991)
Catech Inc ....E....... 937 439-0432
  Dayton (G-8215)
Hanger Prsthetcs & Ortho Inc ....G....... 740 654-1884
  Lancaster (G-11722)
Hanger Prsthetcs & Ortho Inc ....F....... 419 841-9852
  Toledo (G-18495)
Hanger Prsthetcs & Ortho Inc ....G....... 937 773-2441
  Piqua (G-16269)
Hanger Prsthetcs & Ortho Inc ....F....... 937 228-5462
  Dayton (G-8384)
Hanger Prsthetcs & Ortho Inc ....G....... 740 383-2163
  Marion (G-12872)
Hanger Prsthetcs & Ortho Inc ....G....... 740 266-6400
  Steubenville (G-17697)
Hanger Prsthetcs & Ortho Inc ....G....... 419 522-0055
  Marion (G-12871)
Leimkuehler Inc ....E....... 440 899-7842
  Cleveland (G-5693)
Prosthetic Design Inc ....G....... 937 836-1464
  Englewood (G-9537)

RETAIL STORES: Pet Splys

Miraclecorp Products ....D....... 937 293-9994
  Moraine (G-14509)

RETAIL STORES: Photocopy Machines

ABC Appliance Inc ....E....... 419 693-4414
  Oregon (G-15699)
Copier Resources Inc ....G....... 614 268-1100
  Columbus (G-6981)

RETAIL STORES: Picture Frames, Ready Made

Frame USA ....E....... 513 577-7107
  Cincinnati (G-3776)
House of 10000 Picture Frames...........G....... 937 254-5541
  Dayton (G-8393)

RETAIL STORES: Plumbing & Heating Splys

Carr Supply Co ....G....... 937 276-2555
  Dayton (G-8211)
Certified Walk In Tubs ....F....... 614 436-4848
  Columbus (G-6921)
Dbhl Inc ....F....... 216 267-7100
  Cleveland (G-5176)
Stevens Auto Parts & Towng ....G....... 740 988-2260
  Jackson (G-11325)

RETAIL STORES: Police Splys

Walter F Stephens Jr Inc ....E....... 937 746-0521
  Franklin (G-10063)

RETAIL STORES: Religious Goods

Incorporated Trst Gspl Wk Scty ....D....... 216 749-2100
  Cleveland (G-5560)
Strictly Stitchery Inc ....F....... 440 543-7128
  Cleveland (G-6254)

RETAIL STORES: Rock & Stone Specimens

National Lime and Stone Co ....E....... 740 387-3485
  Marion (G-12889)

RETAIL STORES: Rubber Stamps

Geygan Enterprises Inc ....F....... 513 932-4222
  Lebanon (G-11803)
Hathaway Stamp Co ....F....... 513 621-1052
  Cincinnati (G-3871)
Hirt Publishing Co Inc ....E....... 419 946-3010
  Mount Gilead (G-14562)
Kee Printing Inc ....G....... 937 456-6851
  Eaton (G-9312)
The Rubber Stamp Shop ....G....... 419 478-4444
  Toledo (G-18722)

RETAIL STORES: Safety Splys & Eqpt

Paul Peterson Safety Div Inc ....E....... 614 486-4375
  Columbus (G-7468)

R M Welding Products ....G....... 937 260-4510
  Dayton (G-8611)

RETAIL STORES: Sunglasses

Holte Eyeware ....G....... 513 321-4000
  Cincinnati (G-3890)

RETAIL STORES: Swimming Pools, Above Ground

Oliver Pool and Spa Inc ....G....... 740 264-5368
  Steubenville (G-17709)

RETAIL STORES: Technical Aids For The Handicapped

Steves Vans & Accessories LLC ....G....... 740 374-3154
  Marietta (G-12836)

RETAIL STORES: Telephone & Communication Eqpt

Securcom Inc ....E....... 419 628-1049
  Minster (G-14361)

RETAIL STORES: Telephone Eqpt & Systems

Ray Communications Inc ....G....... 330 686-0226
  Stow (G-17795)

RETAIL STORES: Tents

Rainbow Industries Inc ....G....... 937 323-6493
  Springfield (G-17633)

RETAIL STORES: Theatrical Eqpt & Splys

Schenz Theatrical Supply Inc ....F....... 513 542-6100
  Cincinnati (G-4387)

RETAIL STORES: Typewriters & Business Machines

COS Blueprint Inc ....F....... 330 376-0022
  Akron (G-130)
Golubitsky Corporation ....G....... 800 552-4204
  Cleveland (G-5436)

RETAIL STORES: Vaults & Safes

Dayton Safe Company ....G....... 937 461-3900
  Dayton (G-8286)
National Security Products ....G....... 216 566-9962
  Cleveland (G-5860)

RETAIL STORES: Water Purification Eqpt

Enting Water Conditioning Inc ....E....... 937 294-5100
  Moraine (G-14484)
K S W C Inc ....G....... 440 577-1114
  Pierpont (G-16212)
US Water Company LLC ....G....... 740 453-0604
  Zanesville (G-21360)

RETAIL STORES: Welding Splys

AT&f Nuclear Inc ....G....... 216 252-1500
  Cleveland (G-4852)
C & M Welding Services LLC ....G....... 419 584-0008
  Celina (G-2987)
Nyeco Gas Inc ....G....... 419 447-2712
  Sandusky (G-16990)
Praxair Distribution Inc ....G....... 419 422-1353
  Lima (G-12072)
Praxair Distribution Inc ....G....... 513 821-2192
  Cincinnati (G-4263)
Welders Supply Inc ....F....... 216 241-1696
  Cleveland (G-6456)

RETREADING MATERIALS: Tire

H & H Industries Inc ....G....... 740 682-7721
  Oak Hill (G-15596)

REUPHOLSTERY & FURNITURE REPAIR

Baird Cabinet Shop Inc ....G....... 330 837-9075
  Massillon (G-13113)
Fortner Upholstering Inc ....F....... 614 475-8282
  Columbus (G-7095)
Robert Mayo Industries ....G....... 330 426-2587
  East Palestine (G-9244)

REUPHOLSTERY SVCS

Central Design Services ....G....... 513 829-7027
  Fairfield (G-9652)
Office Magic Inc ....F....... 510 782-6100
  Medina (G-13452)
Wahlies Cstm Cft Drapery Uphl ....G....... 419 229-1731
  Lima (G-12111)

RHEOSTATS: Electronic

Madison Manufacturing LLC ....G....... 440 428-4630
  Madison (G-12509)

RIBBONS & BOWS

Camela Nitschke Ribbonry ....G....... 419 872-0073
  Perrysburg (G-16073)
Kam-Awards Inc ....G....... 513 631-5553
  Cincinnati (G-3971)
Nicholas Ray Enterprises LLC ....G....... 330 454-4811
  Canton (G-2788)
Sylvan Studio Inc ....G....... 419 882-3423
  Sylvania (G-18127)

RIBBONS: Machine, Inked Or Carbon

All Write Ribbon Inc ....E....... 513 753-8300
  Amelia (G-566)
Progressive Ribbon Inc ....E....... 513 705-9319
  Middletown (G-14078)

RIVETS: Metal

HI Tecmetal Group Inc ....F....... 216 881-8100
  Cleveland (G-5510)
Jenco Manufacturing Inc ....E....... 216 898-9682
  Independence (G-11261)
Kre Inc ....F....... 216 883-1600
  Twinsburg (G-18967)
North Coast Rivet Inc ....F....... 440 366-6829
  Elyria (G-9468)

ROAD CONSTRUCTION EQUIPMENT WHOLESALERS

Brewpro Inc ....G....... 513 577-7200
  Cincinnati (G-3472)

ROAD MATERIALS: Bituminous, Not From Refineries

Roof To Road LLC ....G....... 740 986-6923
  Williamsport (G-20419)

ROBOTS: Assembly Line

Advanced Design Industries Inc ....E....... 440 277-4141
  Sheffield Village (G-17120)
Air Technical Industries Inc ....E....... 440 951-5191
  Mentor (G-13512)
Ats Systems Oregon Inc ....B....... 541 738-0932
  Lewis Center (G-11885)
Computer Allied Technology Co ....E....... 614 457-2292
  Columbus (G-6973)
Fanuc America Corporation ....E....... 513 754-2400
  Mason (G-13020)
Motor Systems Incorporated ....E....... 513 576-1725
  Milford (G-14164)
Omega Automation Inc ....D....... 937 890-2350
  Dayton (G-8548)
Omega International Inc ....E....... 937 890-2350
  Dayton (G-8549)
Process Innovations Inc ....G....... 330 856-5192
  Vienna (G-19373)
Production Design Services Inc ....D....... 937 866-3377
  Dayton (G-8598)
Programmable Control Service ....F....... 740 927-0744
  Pataskala (G-15978)
Recognition Robotics Inc ....F....... 440 590-0499
  Elyria (G-9485)
Rennco Automation Systems Inc ....E....... 419 861-2340
  Holland (G-11080)
Rimrock Holdings Corporation ....E....... 614 471-5926
  Columbus (G-7564)
Rixan Associates Inc ....E....... 937 438-3005
  Dayton (G-8633)
Sas Automation LLC ....F....... 937 372-5255
  Xenia (G-20972)
Versatile Automation Tech Ltd ....G....... 330 220-2600
  Brunswick (G-2265)
Xigent Automation Systems Inc ....D....... 740 548-3700
  Lewis Center (G-11929)

Yaskawa America Inc ....C..... 937 847-6200
  Miamisburg (G-13883)

ROBOTS: Indl Spraying, Painting, Etc

Ats Ohio Inc ....C..... 614 888-2344
  Lewis Center (G-11884)
Rubberset Company ....G..... 800 345-4939
  Cleveland (G-6142)
Wiwa LP ....F..... 419 757-0141
  Alger (G-483)

ROD & BAR Aluminum

Allen Morgan Trucking & Repair ....G..... 330 336-5192
  Norton (G-15506)

RODS: Plastic

New Image Plastics Mfg Co ....G..... 330 854-3010
  Canal Fulton (G-2509)
Precision Fabrications Inc ....G..... 937 297-8606
  Sunbury (G-18074)

RODS: Rolled, Aluminum

Kaiser Aluminum Fab Pdts LLC ....C..... 740 522-1151
  Heath (G-10848)

RODS: Steel & Iron, Made In Steel Mills

American Posts LLC ....E..... 419 720-0652
  Toledo (G-18344)
Buschman Corporation ....F..... 216 431-6633
  Cleveland (G-4951)
Charter Manufacturing Co Inc ....A..... 216 883-3800
  Cleveland (G-5022)
L&H Threaded Rods Corp ....C..... 937 294-6666
  Moraine (G-14501)

RODS: Welding

Artistic Composite & Mold Co ....G..... 330 352-6632
  Litchfield (G-12137)

ROLL COVERINGS: Rubber

Niles Roll Service Inc ....F..... 330 544-0026
  Niles (G-15172)

ROLL FORMED SHAPES: Custom

American Roll Formed Pdts Corp ....C..... 440 352-0753
  Painesville (G-15851)
Ej Usa Inc ....F..... 330 782-3900
  Youngstown (G-21076)
Formasters Corporation ....F..... 440 639-9206
  Mentor (G-13580)
Hynes Industries Inc ....C..... 330 799-3221
  Youngstown (G-21111)
Lion Industries LLC ....E..... 740 699-0012
  Saint Clairsville (G-16794)
Ontario Mechanical LLC ....E..... 419 529-2578
  Ontario (G-15691)

ROLLING MILL EQPT: Finishing

Bardons & Oliver Inc ....C..... 440 498-5800
  Solon (G-17264)
Fives Bronx Inc ....D..... 330 277-1366
  North Canton (G-15231)
Grinding Equipment & McHy LLC ....F..... 330 747-2313
  Youngstown (G-21105)

ROLLING MILL EQPT: Galvanizing Lines

Multi Galvanizing LLC ....G..... 330 453-1441
  Canton (G-2784)

ROLLING MILL MACHINERY

Addisonmckee Inc ....C..... 513 228-7000
  Lebanon (G-11774)
ADS Machinery Corp ....D..... 330 399-3601
  Warren (G-19515)
Bendco Machine & Tool Co Inc ....F..... 419 628-3802
  Minster (G-14350)
Circle Machine Rolls Inc ....E..... 330 938-9010
  Sebring (G-17044)
E R Advanced Ceramics Inc ....E..... 330 426-9433
  East Palestine (G-9237)
Element Machinery LLC ....G..... 855 447-7648
  Toledo (G-18454)
Enprotech Industrial Tech LLC ....C..... 216 883-3220
  Cleveland (G-5283)

Formtek Inc ....D..... 216 292-6300
  Cleveland (G-5371)
Foseco Inc ....G..... 440 826-4548
  Cleveland (G-5374)
George A Mitchell Company ....E..... 330 758-5777
  Youngstown (G-21099)
H P E Inc ....F..... 330 833-3161
  Massillon (G-13145)
Hydranamics Inc ....D..... 419 468-3530
  Galion (G-10275)
J Horst Manufacturing Co ....D..... 330 828-2216
  Dalton (G-8072)
Kottler Metal Products Co Inc ....E..... 440 946-7473
  Willoughby (G-20523)
Leadar Roll Inc ....E..... 419 227-2200
  Lima (G-12037)
Park Corporation ....B..... 216 267-4870
  Cleveland (G-5965)
Perfecto Industries Inc ....E..... 937 778-1900
  Piqua (G-16299)
Pines Manufacturing Inc ....E..... 440 835-5553
  Westlake (G-20294)
Pines Manufacturing Inc ....E..... 440 835-5553
  Westlake (G-20293)
Rafter Equipment Corporation ....E..... 440 572-3700
  Strongsville (G-17956)
Ridge Tool Company ....A..... 440 323-5581
  Elyria (G-9486)
Ridge Tool Manufacturing Co ....A..... 440 323-5581
  Elyria (G-9488)
Rki Inc ....C..... 888 953-9400
  Mentor (G-13715)
Steel Eqp Specialists Inc ....E..... 330 829-2626
  Alliance (G-539)
Steel Eqp Specialists Inc ....D..... 330 823-8260
  Alliance (G-540)
Sticker Corporation ....F..... 440 946-2100
  Willoughby (G-20606)
Turner Machine Co ....F..... 330 332-5821
  Salem (G-16932)
United Rolls Inc ....C..... 330 456-2761
  Canton (G-2888)
Warren Fabricating Corporation ....D..... 330 847-0596
  Warren (G-19621)
Wauseon Machine & Mfg Inc ....E..... 419 337-0940
  Wauseon (G-19700)
Xtek Inc ....B..... 513 733-7800
  Cincinnati (G-4616)

ROLLING MILL ROLLS: Cast Steel

Arcelormittal Cleveland LLC ....E..... 216 429-6000
  Cleveland (G-4824)
United Engineering & Fndry Co ....F..... 330 456-2761
  Canton (G-2885)

ROLLS & ROLL COVERINGS: Rubber

Pinnacle Roller Co ....F..... 513 369-4830
  Cincinnati (G-4239)

ROOF DECKS

Interlock Industries Inc ....E..... 440 576-9070
  Jefferson (G-11361)

ROOFING MATERIALS: Asphalt

Classic Metals Ltd ....G..... 330 763-1162
  Holmesville (G-11100)
Custom Seal Inc ....E..... 419 334-1020
  Fremont (G-10140)
Garland Industries Inc ....G..... 216 641-7500
  Cleveland (G-5399)
Garland/Dbs Inc ....C..... 216 641-7500
  Cleveland (G-5400)
P C R Inc ....F..... 330 945-7721
  Akron (G-329)
Topps Products Inc ....G..... 216 271-2550
  Cleveland (G-6338)
Tremco Incorporated ....B..... 216 292-5000
  Beachwood (G-1303)

ROOFING MATERIALS: Sheet Metal

Cincinnati Gutter Supply Inc ....G..... 513 825-0500
  West Chester (G-19831)
Gutter Topper Ltd ....G..... 513 797-5800
  Batavia (G-1189)
HCC Holdings Inc ....G..... 800 203-1155
  Cleveland (G-5488)
Interstate Contractors LLC ....E..... 513 372-5393
  Mason (G-13048)

John Baird ....G..... 216 440-3595
  Spencer (G-17456)
Neal Miller ....G..... 440 296-5322
  Pierpont (G-16214)
Transtar Holding Company ....G..... 800 359-3339
  Cleveland (G-6349)

ROOFING MEMBRANE: Rubber

Hyload Inc ....F..... 330 336-6604
  Seville (G-17075)
Omnova Solutions Inc ....C..... 216 682-7000
  Beachwood (G-1287)
Republic Powdered Metals Inc ....D..... 330 225-3192
  Medina (G-13467)
RPM International Inc ....D..... 330 273-5090
  Medina (G-13471)
Soprema USA Inc ....E..... 330 334-0066
  Wadsworth (G-19441)

ROOM COOLERS: Portable

All About House ....G..... 614 725-3595
  Columbus (G-6718)
Climateright LLC ....G..... 800 725-4628
  Columbus (G-6939)

ROTORS: Motor

Yamada North America Inc ....B..... 937 462-7111
  South Charleston (G-17428)

RUBBER

Advanced Elastomer Systems LP ....D..... 330 336-7641
  Wadsworth (G-19389)
All-Tra Rubber Processing ....G..... 330 630-1945
  Tallmadge (G-18133)
Bridgestone Procurement Holdin ....A..... 337 882-1200
  Akron (G-98)
Brp Manufacturing Company ....E..... 800 858-0482
  Lima (G-11998)
Cardinal Rubber Company Inc ....E..... 330 745-2191
  Barberton (G-1113)
Concrete Sealants Inc ....E..... 937 845-8776
  Tipp City (G-18273)
Covestro LLC ....C..... 740 929-2015
  Hebron (G-10863)
Dupont Prfmce Elastomers LLC ....C..... 330 929-6934
  Stow (G-17744)
Dupont Prfmce Elastomers LLC ....C..... 330 929-6934
  Akron (G-158)
E I Du Pont De Nemours & Co ....E..... 330 929-2961
  Stow (G-17745)
Elastostar Rubber Corp ....E..... 614 841-4400
  Columbus (G-7050)
Eliokem Inc ....E..... 330 734-1100
  Fairlawn (G-9749)
Flexsys America LP ....D..... 330 666-4111
  Akron (G-190)
Gdc Inc ....F..... 574 533-3128
  Wooster (G-20775)
High Tech Elastomers Inc ....E..... 937 236-6575
  Vandalia (G-19296)
Kraton Emplyees Recreation CLB ....G..... 740 423-7571
  Belpre (G-1588)
Kraton Polymers US LLC ....B..... 740 423-7571
  Belpre (G-1589)
Meggitt (erlanger) LLC ....D..... 513 851-5550
  Cincinnati (G-4080)
Midwest Elastomers Inc ....D..... 419 738-8844
  Wapakoneta (G-19498)
Mohican Industries Inc ....F..... 330 869-0500
  Akron (G-300)
Mondo Polymer Technologies Inc ....E..... 740 376-9396
  Reno (G-16577)
Universal Urethane Pdts Inc ....D..... 419 693-7400
  Toledo (G-18760)
Vibronic ....F..... 937 274-1114
  Dayton (G-8742)
Wayne County Rubber Inc ....E..... 330 264-5553
  Wooster (G-20845)

RUBBER BANDS

Keener Rubber Company ....E..... 330 821-1880
  Alliance (G-521)

RUBBER PRDTS

Richard L Gibson ....F..... 937 964-1521
  Springfield (G-17638)

PRODUCT

University Plastic Surgery ....G....... 216 778-4450
Cleveland *(G-6394)*

RUBBER PRDTS REPAIR SVCS

Conviber Inc ....F....... 330 723-6006
Medina *(G-13393)*
Heintz Manufacturers Inc ....G....... 724 274-6300
Medina *(G-13420)*

RUBBER PRDTS: Appliance, Mechanical

Canton OH Rubber Speclty Prods........G....... 330 454-3847
Canton *(G-2642)*

RUBBER PRDTS: Automotive, Mechanical

Bridgestone APM Company ....D....... 419 294-6989
Upper Sandusky *(G-19114)*
Bridgestone APM Company ....D....... 419 294-6304
Upper Sandusky *(G-19115)*
Cardinal Rubber Company Inc ....E....... 330 745-2191
Barberton *(G-1113)*
Koneta Inc..D....... 419 739-4200
Wapakoneta *(G-19495)*
Miller Enterprises Ohio LLC ....G....... 330 852-4009
Sugarcreek *(G-18027)*
Milligan Workshops Inc ....E....... 419 353-0099
Bowling Green *(G-2002)*

RUBBER PRDTS: Mechanical

Alloy Extrusion Company ....E....... 330 677-4946
Kent *(G-11427)*
Alternative Flash Inc ....E....... 330 334-6111
Wadsworth *(G-19393)*
American Pro-Mold Inc ....E....... 330 336-4111
Wadsworth *(G-19394)*
ARC Rubber Inc ....F....... 440 466-4555
Geneva *(G-10343)*
Ashtabula Rubber Co ....C....... 440 992-2195
Ashtabula *(G-794)*
Brp Manufacturing Company ....E....... 800 858-0482
Lima *(G-11998)*
Chardon Custom Polymers LLC............F....... 440 285-2161
Chardon *(G-3143)*
Clark Rbr Plastic Intl Sls Inc ....D....... 440 953-9514
Mentor *(G-13544)*
Colonial Rubber Company ....E....... 330 296-2831
Ravenna *(G-16523)*
Contitech North America Inc ....F....... 330 664-7180
Fairlawn *(G-9747)*
Datwyler Sling Sltions USA Inc ....G....... 937 387-2800
Vandalia *(G-19289)*
Duramax Global Corp ....C....... 440 834-5400
Hiram *(G-11033)*
Elbex Corporation ....E....... 330 673-3233
Kent *(G-11454)*
Epg Inc ....E....... 330 995-5125
Aurora *(G-919)*
Epg Inc ....F....... 330 995-9725
Streetsboro *(G-17852)*
Extruded Silicon Products Inc ....E....... 330 733-0101
Mogadore *(G-14375)*
Frankes Wood Products LLC ....E....... 937 642-0706
Marysville *(G-12944)*
Harwood Rubber Products Inc ....E....... 330 923-3256
Cuyahoga Falls *(G-8008)*
Hygenic Acquisition Co ....C....... 330 633-8460
Akron *(G-228)*
Hygenic Corporation ....C....... 330 633-8460
Akron *(G-229)*
Ier Fujikura Inc ....C....... 330 425-7121
Macedonia *(G-12458)*
Jakmar Incorporated ....F....... 513 631-4303
Cincinnati *(G-3938)*
Johnson Bros Rubber Co Inc ....D....... 419 853-4122
West Salem *(G-20114)*
K-Js Mechanical Service ....F....... 419 729-1103
Toledo *(G-18536)*
Karman Rubber Company ....E....... 330 864-2161
Akron *(G-251)*
Kleen Polymers Inc ....F....... 330 336-4212
Wadsworth *(G-19415)*
Lauren Manufacturing LLC ....B....... 330 339-3373
New Philadelphia *(G-14909)*
Macdivitt Rubber Company LLC ....E....... 440 259-5937
Perry *(G-16054)*
Mantaline Corporation ....D....... 330 274-2264
Mantua *(G-12715)*
Martin Industries Inc ....E....... 419 862-2694
Elmore *(G-9364)*

Meridian Industries Inc........................D....... 330 673-1011
Kent *(G-11488)*
Midlands Millroom Supply Inc ....E....... 330 453-9100
Canton *(G-2779)*
Midwest Industrial Rubber Inc..............F....... 614 876-3110
Hilliard *(G-10963)*
Neff-Perkins Company ....C....... 440 632-1658
Middlefield *(G-13975)*
Ohio Elastomers ....G....... 440 354-9750
Perry *(G-16055)*
Ottawa Rubber Company ....F....... 419 865-1378
Holland *(G-11075)*
Plabell Rubber Products Corp ....F....... 419 691-5878
Toledo *(G-18646)*
Polycraft Products Inc ....G....... 513 353-3334
Cleves *(G-6523)*
Q Holding Company ....B....... 330 425-8472
Twinsburg *(G-19006)*
Qualiform Inc ....E....... 330 336-6777
Wadsworth *(G-19432)*
Quanex Ig Systems Inc.........................C....... 740 439-2338
Cambridge *(G-2473)*
Quanex Ig Systems Inc.........................C....... 216 910-1519
Solon *(G-17366)*
Robin Industries Inc ....E....... 330 893-3501
Berlin *(G-1652)*
Robin Industries Inc ....C....... 330 359-5418
Winesburg *(G-20707)*
Robin Industries Inc ....C....... 330 695-9300
Fredericksburg *(G-10092)*
Robin Industries Inc ....G....... 216 267-3554
Cleveland *(G-6124)*
Roboworld Molded Products LLC..........G....... 513 720-6900
West Chester *(G-19935)*
Rubber-Tech Inc...................................F....... 937 274-1114
Dayton *(G-8640)*
Saint-Gobain Prfmce Plas Corp ....B....... 614 889-2220
Dublin *(G-9137)*
Shreiner Sole Co Inc ....F....... 330 276-6135
Killbuck *(G-11599)*
Soffseal Inc ....E....... 513 367-0028
Harrison *(G-10804)*
Taradon Rubber Co Inc ....F....... 330 896-3143
Akron *(G-428)*
Tigerpoly Manufacturing Inc.................B....... 614 871-0045
Grove City *(G-10601)*
Trelleborg Wheel Systems Ameri ....E....... 866 633-8473
Akron *(G-444)*
Universal Urethane Pdts Inc ....D....... 419 693-7400
Toledo *(G-18760)*
Vertex Inc ....E....... 330 628-6230
Mogadore *(G-14387)*
Woodlawn Rubber Co ....F....... 513 489-1718
Blue Ash *(G-1898)*
Yokohama Tire Corporation ....C....... 440 352-3321
Painesville *(G-15945)*

RUBBER PRDTS: Medical & Surgical Tubing, Extrudd & Lathe-Cut

Saint-Gobain Prfmce Plas Corp............C....... 330 798-6981
Akron *(G-396)*

RUBBER PRDTS: Oil & Gas Field Machinery, Mechanical

United Feed Screws Ltd ....F....... 330 798-5532
Akron *(G-456)*
V & M Star LP ....E....... 330 742-6300
Youngstown *(G-21234)*

RUBBER PRDTS: Reclaimed

Bedell-Kraus Flexographic and............E....... 330 688-4881
Stow *(G-17735)*
Boomerang Rubber Inc ....E....... 937 693-4611
Botkins *(G-1950)*
Chemionics Corporation ....E....... 330 733-8834
Tallmadge *(G-18137)*
Econo Products Inc ....F....... 330 923-4101
Cuyahoga Falls *(G-7989)*
Flexsys America LP ....D....... 330 666-4111
Akron *(G-190)*
Gold Key Processing Inc.......................C....... 440 632-0901
Middlefield *(G-13937)*
Lanxess Corporation ....C....... 440 279-2367
Chardon *(G-3164)*
Valley Rubber Mixing Inc......................F....... 330 434-4442
Akron *(G-462)*

RUBBER PRDTS: Sheeting

Brp Manufacturing Company.................E....... 800 858-0482
Lima *(G-11998)*
Censtar Coatings Inc ....G....... 330 723-8000
West Salem *(G-20111)*

RUBBER PRDTS: Silicone

Brain Child Products LLC......................F....... 419 698-4020
Toledo *(G-18381)*
Medical Elastomer Dev Inc ....E....... 330 425-8352
Twinsburg *(G-18983)*
Shincor Silicones Inc ....G....... 330 630-9460
Akron *(G-400)*

RUBBER PRDTS: Sponge

Chalfant Sew Fabricators Inc................E....... 216 521-7922
Cleveland *(G-5012)*
Miles Rubber & Packing Company.........E....... 330 425-3888
Twinsburg *(G-18988)*

RUBBER STAMP, WHOLESALE

Northmont Sign Co Inc ....G....... 937 890-0372
Dayton *(G-8528)*
Quick As A Wink Printing Co ....F....... 419 224-9786
Lima *(G-12079)*

RUBBER STRUCTURES: Air-Supported

Truflex Rubber Products Co ....C....... 740 967-9015
Johnstown *(G-11409)*

RUST ARRESTING COMPOUNDS: Animal Or Vegetable Oil Based

Lubrizol Corporation ....E....... 440 357-7064
Painesville *(G-15898)*
Magnus International Group Inc ....G....... 216 592-8355
Chagrin Falls *(G-3100)*

RUST PROOFING SVC: Hot Dipping, Metals & Formed Prdts

Parker Rst-Proof Cleveland Inc ....E....... 216 481-6680
Cleveland *(G-5972)*

RUST REMOVERS

Skybryte Company Inc ....G....... 216 771-1590
Cleveland *(G-6209)*

RUST RESISTING

Zerust Consumer Products LLC............G....... 330 405-1965
Twinsburg *(G-19042)*

SADDLERY STORES

Old West Industries Inc ....G....... 513 889-0500
Hamilton *(G-10728)*
Paddock Corporation ....G....... 440 543-0631
Chagrin Falls *(G-3110)*

SAFE DEPOSIT BOXES

Hamilton Safe Co ....F....... 513 874-3733
Cincinnati *(G-3863)*
Hamilton Security Products Co ....G....... 513 874-3733
Cincinnati *(G-3864)*
Williamson Safe Inc ....E....... 937 393-9919
Hillsboro *(G-11019)*

SAFES & VAULTS: Metal

Cincy Safe Company ....E....... 513 900-9152
Milford *(G-14130)*
Dayton Safe Company ....G....... 937 461-3900
Dayton *(G-8286)*
Diebold Nixdorf Incorporated ....A....... 330 490-4000
North Canton *(G-15228)*
Hamilton Fabricators Inc ....E....... 513 735-7773
Batavia *(G-1190)*
Hamilton Safe Amelia ....F....... 513 753-5694
Amelia *(G-576)*
Linsalata Capital Partners Fun ....G....... 440 684-1400
Cleveland *(G-5703)*
Target Holdings Inc ....E....... 513 474-4409
Cincinnati *(G-4493)*

SAFETY EQPT & SPLYS WHOLESALERS

Chester West Holdings Inc ....C 800 647-1900
Sharonville *(G-17113)*

L-Mor Inc ....F 216 541-2224
Cleveland *(G-5672)*

Matheson Tri-Gas Inc ....E 440 365-1741
Twinsburg *(G-18980)*

Netherland Rubber Company ....F 513 733-0883
Cincinnati *(G-4146)*

Wcm Holdings Inc ....G 513 705-2100
Cincinnati *(G-4581)*

SAILBOAT BUILDING & REPAIR

Doyle Sailmaker ....G 216 486-5732
Cleveland *(G-5213)*

Dynamic Plastics Inc ....G 937 437-7261
New Paris *(G-14879)*

Great Midwest Yacht Co ....G 740 965-4511
Sunbury *(G-18061)*

SAILS

North Sails Toledo LLC ....F 419 726-2933
Toledo *(G-18608)*

R F W Holdings Inc ....G 440 331-8300
Cleveland *(G-6082)*

Ragman Inc ....G 419 255-8068
Toledo *(G-18670)*

SALT

Abraxus Salt Inc ....G 440 743-7669
Cleveland *(G-4687)*

Cargill Incorporated ....C 330 745-0031
Akron *(G-112)*

Obersons Nurs & Landscapes Inc ......F 513 894-0669
Fairfield *(G-9692)*

SALT & SULFUR MINING

Morton International LLC ....G 513 941-1578
Cincinnati *(G-4125)*

SALT MINING: Common

Cargill Incorporated ....C 216 651-7200
Cleveland *(G-4977)*

SALT: Packers'

Morton Salt Inc ....F 440 354-9901
Painesville *(G-15902)*

SAND & GRAVEL

Allen Harper ....G 740 543-3919
Amsterdam *(G-609)*

Barrett Paving Materials Inc ....C 513 271-6200
Middletown *(G-14101)*

Beck Sand & Gravel Inc ....G 330 626-3863
Ravenna *(G-16518)*

Beldex Land Company LLC ....G 740 783-3575
Dexter City *(G-8955)*

Big Bills Trucking LLC ....G 614 850-0626
Hilliard *(G-10934)*

Bonsal American Inc ....E 513 398-7300
Cincinnati *(G-3460)*

C F Poeppelman Inc ....E 937 448-2191
Bradford *(G-2025)*

Clay LBC Co ....G 740 492-5055
Newcomerstown *(G-15111)*

Fisher Sand & Gravel Inc ....G 330 745-9239
Norton *(G-15512)*

FML Resin LLC ....E 440 214-3200
Chesterland *(G-3207)*

FML Terminal Logistics LLC ....D 440 214-3200
Chesterland *(G-3209)*

Foundry Sand Service LLC ....G 330 823-6152
Sebring *(G-17045)*

Gravel Doctor of Ohio LLC ....G 844 472-8353
Millersport *(G-14293)*

Gravel-Tech ....G 513 703-3672
Morrow *(G-14546)*

Hanson Aggregates East ....G 513 353-1100
Cleves *(G-6515)*

Hanson Aggregates East LLC ....E 740 773-2172
Chillicothe *(G-3242)*

Harvest Sand and Gravel Inc ....G 330 372-4408
Warren *(G-19558)*

Hilltop Basic Resources Inc ....F 937 882-6357
Springfield *(G-17573)*

Hilltop Basic Resources Inc ....F 937 859-3616
Miamisburg *(G-13817)*

Hilltop Basic Resources Inc ....E 513 621-1500
Cincinnati *(G-3885)*

Holmes Supply Corp ....G 330 279-2634
Holmesville *(G-11105)*

James Bunnell Inc ....F 513 353-1100
Cleves *(G-6516)*

James Ryan Soloman ....G 740 659-2304
Glenford *(G-10398)*

Joe McClelland Inc ....E 740 452-3036
Zanesville *(G-21324)*

Ken Heuser & Gary Gravel ....E 513 752-4159
Cincinnati *(G-3981)*

Kenmore Construction Co Inc ....E 330 832-8888
Massillon *(G-13162)*

Marietta Martin Materials Inc ....F 919 781-4550
Brookville *(G-2189)*

Martin Marietta Materials Inc ....G 513 200-2303
Harrison *(G-10789)*

Martin Marietta Materials Inc ....E 513 701-1140
West Chester *(G-19897)*

Medina Supply Company ....E 330 723-3681
Medina *(G-13445)*

National Lime and Stone Co ....C 419 396-7671
Carey *(G-2921)*

Oeder Carl E Sons Sand & Grav ....E 513 494-1238
Lebanon *(G-11820)*

Ohio Valley Sand LLC ....G 740 661-4240
New Philadelphia *(G-14920)*

Olen Corporation ....G 330 262-6821
Wooster *(G-20819)*

Oster Sand and Gravel Inc ....G 330 494-5472
Canton *(G-2805)*

Oster Sand and Gravel Inc ....G 330 874-3322
Bolivar *(G-1940)*

Oster Sand and Gravel Inc ....G 330 833-2649
Massillon *(G-13190)*

Phillips Ready Mix Co ....D 937 426-5151
Beavercreek Township *(G-1388)*

Phoenix Asphalt Company Inc ....G 330 339-4935
Magnolia *(G-12518)*

Piketon Sand & Gravel ....G 740 289-2316
Piketon *(G-16227)*

Prairie Lane Corporation ....G 330 262-3322
Wooster *(G-20823)*

Premier Silica LLC ....E 740 599-7773
Howard *(G-11124)*

R W Sidley Incorporated ....E 440 564-2221
Newbury *(G-15102)*

Riverside Sand & Gravel Co ....G 330 673-2021
Kent *(G-11517)*

Rjw Trucking Company Ltd ....E 740 363-5343
Delaware *(G-8883)*

Robert Perez Carpentry ....G 330 497-0043
Canton *(G-2840)*

Roger Hall ....G 740 778-2861
South Webster *(G-17451)*

Rolo Sand & Gravel ....G 740 886-7407
Proctorville *(G-16491)*

Rupp Construction Inc ....F 330 855-2781
Marshallville *(G-12920)*

Shamrock Materials Inc ....F 513 988-0647
Cincinnati *(G-4411)*

Shelly and Sands Inc ....E 740 453-0721
Zanesville *(G-21351)*

Shelly Company ....G 740 246-6315
Thornville *(G-18196)*

Shelly Materials Inc ....G 330 673-3646
Kent *(G-11527)*

Shelly Materials Inc ....G 740 745-5965
Newark *(G-15053)*

Shelly Materials Inc ....D 740 246-6315
Thornville *(G-18198)*

Smith Concrete Co ....E 740 373-7441
Dover *(G-9015)*

Solomons Mines Inc ....G 330 337-0123
Salem *(G-16928)*

Stafford Gravel Inc ....E 419 298-2440
Edgerton *(G-9336)*

Stocker Concrete Company ....F 740 254-4626
Gnadenhutten *(G-10411)*

Streamside Materials Llc ....G 419 423-1290
Findlay *(G-9896)*

Tiger Sand & Gravel LLC ....F 330 833-6325
Massillon *(G-13205)*

Tri County Concrete Inc ....E 330 425-4464
Twinsburg *(G-19029)*

Turkeyfoot Hill Sand & Gravel ....G 330 899-1997
Akron *(G-449)*

W&W Rock Sand and Gravel ....G 513 266-3708
Williamsburg *(G-20413)*

Wayne Concrete Company ....F 937 545-9919
Medway *(G-13502)*

Weber Sand & Gravel Inc ....G 419 636-7920
Bryan *(G-2326)*

World Development & Conslt LLC ....G 614 805-4450
Westerville *(G-20242)*

Young Sand & Gravel Co Inc ....F 419 994-3040
Loudonville *(G-12307)*

SAND LIME PRDTS

Holmes Supply Corp ....G 330 279-2634
Holmesville *(G-11105)*

SAND MINING

Alden Sand & Gravel Co Inc ....F 330 928-3249
Cuyahoga Falls *(G-7963)*

Carl E Oeder Sons Sand & Grav ....E 513 494-1555
Lebanon *(G-11787)*

Central Ready Mix LLC ....E 513 402-5001
Cincinnati *(G-3515)*

Fenner Enterprises Inc ....G 937 698-7048
Ludlow Falls *(G-12426)*

Keeney Sand & Stone Inc ....G 440 254-4582
Painesville *(G-15894)*

L & I Natural Resources Inc ....G 513 683-2045
Loveland *(G-12369)*

Marietta Martin Materials Inc ....G 937 335-8313
Troy *(G-18856)*

Marietta Martin Materials Inc ....G 937 766-2351
Cedarville *(G-2981)*

Massillon Materials Inc ....F 330 837-4767
Dalton *(G-8074)*

National Lime and Stone Co ....G 330 339-2144
New Philadelphia *(G-14918)*

National Lime and Stone Co ....G 216 883-9840
Cleveland *(G-5857)*

Osborne Materials Company ....G 440 357-7026
Grand River *(G-10452)*

Phillips Companies ....E 937 426-5461
Beavercreek Township *(G-1386)*

Phillips Companies ....E 937 431-7987
Vandalia *(G-19308)*

S & S Aggregates Inc ....G 740 453-0721
Zanesville *(G-21349)*

Sant Sand & Gravel Co ....G 740 397-0000
Mount Vernon *(G-14644)*

Small Sand & Gravel Inc ....E 740 427-3130
Gambier *(G-10317)*

Technisand Inc ....G 440 285-3132
Chardon *(G-3181)*

Tipp Stone Inc ....G 937 890-4051
Dayton *(G-8717)*

Twinsburg Development Corp ....G 440 357-5562
Grand River *(G-10454)*

Ward Construction Co ....F 419 943-2450
Leipsic *(G-11879)*

SAND: Hygrade

Fairmount Minerals LLC ....A 269 926-9450
Chesterland *(G-3204)*

Fairmount Santrol Holdings Inc ....G 800 255-7263
Chesterland *(G-3205)*

Jim Nier Construction Inc ....F 740 289-2629
Piketon *(G-16221)*

Parry Co ....G 740 884-4893
Chillicothe *(G-3258)*

Premier Silica LLC ....E 740 659-2241
Glenford *(G-10400)*

Premier Silica LLC ....E 740 599-7773
Howard *(G-11124)*

SANDBLASTING EQPT

Hirons Memorial Works Inc ....G 937 444-2917
Mount Orab *(G-14581)*

L N Brut Manufacturing Co ....G 330 833-9045
Navarre *(G-14717)*

R Houston Son Sndblst Spclists ....E 513 367-5252
Harrison *(G-10799)*

SANDBLASTING SVC: Building Exterior

All Ohio Companies Inc ....F 216 420-9274
Cleveland *(G-4756)*

Shur Clean Usa LLC ....G 513 341-5486
Liberty Township *(G-11968)*

X-Treme Finishes Inc ....F 330 474-0614
Medina *(G-13498)*

P
R
O
D
U
C
T

SANDSTONE: Dimension

Irg Operating LLC ....E 440 963-4008
Vermilion **(G-19329)**

SANITARY SVC, NEC

Ash Sewer & Drain Service ....G 330 376-9714
Akron **(G-74)**

Gerald H Smith ....G 740 446-3455
Bidwell **(G-1676)**

N-Viro International Corp ....F 419 535-6374
Toledo **(G-18597)**

SANITARY SVCS: Environmental Cleanup

Alpha Omega Bioremediation LLC ....F 614 287-2600
Columbus **(G-6728)**

Samsel Rope & Marine Supply Co ......E 216 241-0333
Cleveland **(G-6156)**

SANITARY SVCS: Hazardous Waste, Collection & Disposal

Clean Harbors Envmtl Svcs Inc ....F 330 425-3825
Twinsburg **(G-18914)**

SANITARY SVCS: Liquid Waste Collection & Disposal

Koski Construction Co ....G 440 997-5337
Ashtabula **(G-815)**

Stellar Industrial Tech Co ....G 740 654-7052
Lancaster **(G-11756)**

SANITARY SVCS: Refuse Collection & Disposal Svcs

Montgomerys Pallet Service ....G 330 297-6677
Ravenna **(G-16542)**

SANITARY SVCS: Rubbish Collection & Disposal

Sidwell Materials Inc ....C 740 849-2394
Zanesville **(G-21354)**

SANITARY SVCS: Waste Materials, Recycling

Continental Turf Systems Inc ....G 419 596-4409
Continental **(G-7825)**

Garden Street Iron & Metal ....E 513 853-3700
Cincinnati **(G-3798)**

Grasan Equipment Company Inc ....D 419 526-4440
Mansfield **(G-12620)**

Homan Metals LLC ....G 513 721-5010
Cincinnati **(G-3891)**

Hope Timber Pallet Recycl Inc ....E 740 344-1788
Newark **(G-15021)**

Imco Recycling of Ohio LLC ....C 740 922-2373
Uhrichsville **(G-19052)**

Innovation Plastics LLC ....E 513 818-1771
Fostoria **(G-9980)**

Lumberjack Pallet Recycl LLC ....G 513 821-7543
Cincinnati **(G-4039)**

Magnus International Group Inc ....G 216 592-8355
Chagrin Falls **(G-3100)**

Metro Recycling Company ....G 513 251-1800
Cincinnati **(G-4094)**

Mondo Polymer Technologies Inc ....E 740 376-9396
Reno **(G-16577)**

Perma-Fix of Dayton Inc ....E 937 268-6501
Dayton **(G-8571)**

Polychem Corporation ....G 419 547-1400
Clyde **(G-6543)**

Resource Recycling Inc ....F 419 222-2702
Lima **(G-12081)**

Roe Transportation Entps Inc ....G 937 497-7161
Sidney **(G-17217)**

Rumpke Transportation Co LLC ....C 513 242-4600
Cincinnati **(G-4367)**

Shaneway Inc ....G 330 868-2220
Minerva **(G-14342)**

Synagro Midwest Inc ....F 937 384-0669
Miamisburg **(G-13866)**

Waste Parchment Inc ....E 330 674-6868
Millersburg **(G-14282)**

SANITARY WARE: Metal

Accent Manufacturing Inc ....F 330 724-7704
Norton **(G-15500)**

Agean Marble Manufacturing ....F 513 874-1475
West Chester **(G-19978)**

BJ Equipment Ltd ....F 614 497-1776
Columbus **(G-6834)**

Crane Plumbing LLC ....E 419 522-4211
Mansfield **(G-12587)**

Crane Plumbing LLC ....F 419 522-4211
Mansfield **(G-12588)**

Extrudex Limited Partnership ....E 440 352-7101
Painesville **(G-15879)**

SANITATION CHEMICALS & CLEANING AGENTS

Alco-Chem Inc ....E 330 253-3535
Akron **(G-61)**

Babcock & Wilcox Megtec ....C 614 258-9501
Columbus **(G-6799)**

Betco Corporation Ltd ....C 419 241-2156
Bowling Green **(G-1972)**

Boyd Sanitation ....G 740 697-7940
Roseville **(G-16727)**

Canberra Corporation ....C 419 724-4300
Toledo **(G-18388)**

Capital Chemical Co ....E 330 494-9535
Canton **(G-2649)**

Chester Packaging LLC ....E 513 458-3840
Cincinnati **(G-3527)**

Cincinnati - Vulcan Company ....D 513 242-5300
Cincinnati **(G-3535)**

Consolidated Coatings Corp ....E 216 514-7596
Cleveland **(G-5118)**

D C Filter & Chemical Inc ....G 419 626-3967
Sandusky **(G-16955)**

EMD Millipore Corporation ....C 513 631-0445
Norwood **(G-15572)**

Ferro Corporation ....D 216 577-7144
Bedford **(G-1423)**

Fuchs Lubricants Co ....E 330 963-0400
Twinsburg **(G-18938)**

Glister Inc ....G 614 252-6400
Columbus **(G-7118)**

Gojo Industries Inc ....C 330 255-6000
Akron **(G-206)**

Gojo Industries Inc ....E 330 255-6000
Cuyahoga Falls **(G-8004)**

Gojo Industries Inc ....C 330 255-6525
Stow **(G-17760)**

Gojo Industries Inc ....C 330 922-4522
Cuyahoga Falls **(G-8005)**

Henkel Corporation ....E 740 363-1351
Delaware **(G-8859)**

Henkel Corporation ....C 216 475-3600
Cleveland **(G-5498)**

Intercontinental Chemical Corp ....E 513 541-7100
Cincinnati **(G-3928)**

Jason Incorporated ....F 513 860-3400
Hamilton **(G-10711)**

Jax Wax Inc ....F 614 476-6769
Columbus **(G-7228)**

Kardol Quality Products LLC ....G 513 933-8206
Blue Ash **(G-1822)**

Kcs Cleaning Service ....F 740 418-5479
Oak Hill **(G-15599)**

Leonhardt Plating Company ....E 513 242-1410
Cincinnati **(G-4020)**

Malco Products Inc ....C 330 753-0361
Akron **(G-281)**

McGean-Rohco Inc ....D 216 441-4900
Newburgh Heights **(G-15076)**

Milsek Furniture Polish Inc ....G 330 542-2700
Petersburg **(G-16178)**

Mold Masters Intl Inc ....C 440 953-0220
Mentor **(G-13659)**

Nanofilm Ltd ....E 216 674-1430
Cleveland **(G-5851)**

National Colloid Company ....E 740 282-1171
Steubenville **(G-17706)**

New Vulco Mfg & Sales Co LLC ....D 513 242-2672
Cincinnati **(G-4149)**

Pilot Chemical Company Ohio ....E 513 733-4880
Cincinnati **(G-4237)**

Pilot Chemical Corp ....E 513 424-9700
Middletown **(G-14075)**

Polynt Composites USA Inc ....E 816 391-6000
Sandusky **(G-16997)**

Q2power Technologies Inc ....G 740 415-2073
Lancaster **(G-11743)**

Reid Asset Management Company ....E 440 942-8488
Willoughby **(G-20587)**

Smart Sonic Corporation ....G 818 610-7900
Cleveland **(G-6211)**

Spartan Chemical Company Inc ....E 419 897-5551
Maumee **(G-13297)**

State Industrial Products Corp ....B 877 747-6986
Cleveland **(G-6239)**

Sun Cleaners & Laundry Inc ....G 740 756-4749
Carroll **(G-2948)**

Tolco Corporation ....D 419 241-1113
Toledo **(G-18728)**

Tremco Incorporated ....B 216 292-5000
Beachwood **(G-1303)**

Univar USA Inc ....C 513 714-5264
West Chester **(G-20064)**

SASHES: Door Or Window, Metal

YKK AP America Inc ....F 513 942-7200
West Chester **(G-20071)**

SATELLITES: Communications

Great Lakes Telcom Ltd ....E 330 629-8848
Youngstown **(G-21103)**

Marrik Dish Company LLC ....E 419 475-6538
Toledo **(G-18574)**

Touba Satellite R US ....G 513 853-0700
Cincinnati **(G-4514)**

SAW BLADES

Blade Manufacturing Co Inc ....F 614 294-1649
Columbus **(G-6840)**

Callahan Cutting Tools Inc ....G 614 294-1649
Columbus **(G-6889)**

Dynatech Systems Inc ....E 440 365-1774
Elyria **(G-9408)**

Form-A-Chip Inc ....G 937 223-4135
Dayton **(G-8347)**

J and S Tool Incorporated ....E 216 676-8330
Cleveland **(G-5595)**

Joes Saw Shop ....G 440 834-1196
Burton **(G-2378)**

Martindale Electric Company ....E 216 521-8567
Cleveland **(G-5754)**

Regal Diamond Products Corp ....E 440 944-7700
Wickliffe **(G-20385)**

Superion Inc ....E 937 374-0033
Xenia **(G-20977)**

Uhrichsville Carbide Inc ....F 740 922-9197
Uhrichsville **(G-19064)**

Wolff Tool & Manufacturing Co ....F 440 933-7797
Avon Lake **(G-1056)**

SAWDUST & SHAVINGS

McMillion Lock & Key ....G 937 473-5342
Covington **(G-7926)**

R J Dobay Enterprises Inc ....G 440 834-4580
Burton **(G-2382)**

Sugarcreek Shavings LLC ....G 330 763-4239
Sugarcreek **(G-18044)**

SAWING & PLANING MILLS

Andy A Raber ....G 330 893-0400
Millersburg **(G-14194)**

Appalachia Wood Inc ....F 740 596-2551
Mc Arthur **(G-13328)**

Baillie Lumber Co LP ....E 419 462-2000
Galion **(G-10254)**

Barker Lumber ....G 740 289-2424
Piketon **(G-16215)**

Beaver Wood Products ....G 740 226-6211
Beaver **(G-1310)**

Blaney Hardwoods Ohio Inc ....E 740 678-8288
Vincent **(G-19378)**

Blankenship Lumber Inc ....G 740 372-0191
Otway **(G-15827)**

Bruewer Woodwork Mfg Co ....D 513 353-3505
Cleves **(G-6507)**

Cherokee Hardwoods Inc ....F 440 632-0322
Middlefield **(G-13922)**

Clarksville Stave & Lumber Co ....G 937 376-4618
Xenia **(G-20944)**

Clear Run Lumber Co ....G 740 747-2665
Marengo **(G-12748)**

Coblentz Brothers Inc ....E 330 857-7211
Apple Creek **(G-634)**

Crownover Lumber Co Inc ....D 740 596-5229
Mc Arthur **(G-13330)**

Del Holdash ....G 440 427-0611
North Olmsted **(G-15329)**

DIA Enterprises Inc ....G...... 740 802-7075
New Bloomington *(G-14777)*

Don Puckett Lumber Inc ....F 740 887-4191
Londonderry *(G-12227)*

Dues Jersey Farm ....G...... 419 678-2102
Coldwater *(G-6557)*

Frickco Inc ....G...... 740 887-2017
South Bloomingville *(G-17422)*

Gardner Lumber Co Inc ....F 740 254-4664
Tippecanoe *(G-18313)*

Gary Brown Farm & Sawmill ....G...... 740 372-5022
Otway *(G-15830)*

Gross Lumber Inc ....E 330 683-2055
Apple Creek *(G-638)*

Hartzell Hardwoods Inc ....D...... 937 773-7054
Piqua *(G-16272)*

Hess & Gault Lumber Co ....E 419 281-3105
Ashland *(G-739)*

Hillcrest Lumber Ltd ....G...... 330 359-5721
Apple Creek *(G-639)*

Kaufman Mulch Inc ....G...... 330 893-3676
Millersburg *(G-14236)*

Knisley Lumber ....F 740 634-2935
Bainbridge *(G-1061)*

Koppers Industries Inc ....E 740 776-3238
Portsmouth *(G-16441)*

Kreis Sawmill ....G...... 937 537-1248
Marysville *(G-12955)*

L Garbers Sons Sawmilling LLC ....G...... 419 335-6362
Wauseon *(G-19686)*

Lansing Bros Sawmill ....G...... 937 588-4291
Piketon *(G-16223)*

Lantz Lumber & Saw Shop ....G...... 740 286-5658
Jackson *(G-11318)*

Marathon At Sawmill ....F 614 734-0836
Columbus *(G-7317)*

Mbm Lumber ....G...... 937 459-7448
Union City *(G-19072)*

Mohler Lumber Company ....E 330 499-5461
North Canton *(G-15250)*

Ohio Valley Veneer Inc ....E 740 493-2901
Piketon *(G-16225)*

Omega Logging Inc ....G...... 330 534-0378
Hubbard *(G-11137)*

P & R Hardwoods ....G...... 937 452-3753
Camden *(G-2487)*

Piada Sawmill LLC ....G...... 614 389-2069
Dublin *(G-9125)*

Plaza At Sawmill Pl ....G...... 614 889-6121
Columbus *(G-7497)*

R & D Hilltop Lumber Inc ....E 740 342-3051
New Lexington *(G-14852)*

R M Wood Co ....G...... 419 845-2661
Mount Gilead *(G-14566)*

Raber Lumber Co ....G...... 330 893-2797
Charm *(G-3184)*

Ramona Southworth ....G...... 740 226-8202
Beaver *(G-1311)*

Residents of Sawmill Park ....G...... 614 659-6678
Dublin *(G-9131)*

Roseville Hardwood ....G...... 740 221-8712
Roseville *(G-16732)*

Runkles Sawmill LLC ....G...... 937 663-0115
Saint Paris *(G-16864)*

Salt Creek Lumber Company Inc ....G...... 330 695-3500
Fredericksburg *(G-10093)*

Saw Siefker Mill ....G...... 419 339-1956
Delphos *(G-8917)*

Sawmill Crossing ....G...... 614 766-1685
Columbus *(G-7592)*

Sawmill Eye Associates Inc ....G...... 440 724-0396
Broadview Heights *(G-2118)*

Sawmill Eye Associates Inc ....G...... 614 734-2685
Columbus *(G-7593)*

Sawmill Road Management Co LLC ....E 937 342-9071
Springfield *(G-17646)*

Sawmill Station ....G...... 614 434-6147
Dublin *(G-9139)*

Select Enterprises Inc ....F 724 588-4141
Kinsman *(G-11611)*

Siefker Sawmill ....G...... 419 339-1956
Elida *(G-9358)*

Southern Ohio Wood ....G...... 740 288-1825
Wellston *(G-19769)*

Stark Truss Company Inc ....E 330 756-3050
Beach City *(G-1251)*

Stephen M Trudick ....E 440 834-1891
Burton *(G-2385)*

Stony Point Hardwoods ....F 330 852-4512
Sugarcreek *(G-18040)*

Stutzman Brothers Sawmill ....G...... 440 272-5179
Middlefield *(G-13992)*

Superior Hardwoods of Ohio ....E 740 596-2561
Mc Arthur *(G-13333)*

Superior Hardwoods of Ohio ....D...... 740 384-6862
Jackson *(G-11327)*

Superior Hardwoods Ohio Inc ....D...... 740 384-5677
Wellston *(G-19770)*

Superior Hardwoods Ohio Inc ....E 740 439-2727
Cambridge *(G-2477)*

Supply Dynamics LLC ....F 513 965-2000
Loveland *(G-12392)*

T & D Thompson Inc ....E 740 332-8515
Laurelville *(G-11772)*

Taylor Lumber Worldwide Inc ....C...... 740 259-6222
Mc Dermott *(G-13344)*

Timbermill Ltd ....G...... 740 862-3426
Baltimore *(G-1089)*

Trumbull County Hardwoods ....E 440 632-0555
Middlefield *(G-13998)*

Tusco Hardwoods LLC ....F 330 852-4281
Sugarcreek *(G-18047)*

Valley Veneer & Lumber Co ....F 440 293-6025
Williamsfield *(G-20417)*

W O Hardwoods Inc ....G...... 740 425-1588
Barnesville *(G-1162)*

Wagner Farms & Sawmill LLC ....F 419 653-4126
Leipsic *(G-11878)*

Wappoo Wood Products Inc ....E 937 492-1166
Sidney *(G-17233)*

Wilmington Forest Products ....G...... 937 382-5013
Wilmington *(G-20682)*

Wooldridge Lumber Co ....D...... 740 289-4912
Piketon *(G-16229)*

Wrights Saw Mill ....G...... 937 773-2546
Piqua *(G-16316)*

Yoder Lumber Co Inc ....E 330 674-1435
Millersburg *(G-14289)*

Yoder Lumber Co Inc ....D...... 330 893-3131
Sugarcreek *(G-18052)*

SAWING & PLANING MILLS: Custom

Facemyer Lumber Co Inc ....F 740 992-5965
Pomeroy *(G-16389)*

Newberry Wood Enterprises Inc ....F 440 238-6127
Strongsville *(G-17945)*

United Hardwoods Ltd ....G...... 330 878-9510
Strasburg *(G-17832)*

Walnut Creek Lumber Co Ltd ....E 330 852-4559
Dundee *(G-9185)*

Weaver Lumber Co ....G...... 330 359-5091
Wilmot *(G-20687)*

SAWMILL MACHINES

Midwest Timber & Land Co Inc ....E 740 493-2400
Piketon *(G-16224)*

Trico Enterprises LLC...........................E 330 674-1157
Millersburg *(G-14273)*

SAWS & SAWING EQPT

Alvords Yard & Garden Eqp ....G...... 440 286-2315
Chardon *(G-3140)*

Rboog Industries LLC ....G...... 330 350-0396
Brunswick *(G-2252)*

Stevens Auto Parts & Towng ....G...... 740 988-2260
Jackson *(G-11325)*

SAWS: Hand, Metalworking Or Woodworking

Cammel Saw Company Inc ....F 330 477-3764
Canton *(G-2634)*

SCAFFOLDS: Mobile Or Stationary, Metal

Hansen Scaffolding LLC ....F 513 574-9000
West Chester *(G-20012)*

Sky Climber LLC ....E 740 203-3900
Delaware *(G-8888)*

Sky Climber Wind Solutions LLC ....G...... 740 203-3900
Delaware *(G-8890)*

SCALE REPAIR SVCS

Kanawha Scales & Systems Inc ....F 513 576-0700
Milford *(G-14158)*

SCALES & BALANCES, EXC LABORATORY

Etched Metal Company ....E 440 248-0240
Solon *(G-17290)*

Interface Logic Systems Inc ....G...... 614 236-8388
Columbus *(G-7202)*

Kanawha Scales & Systems Inc ....F 513 576-0700
Milford *(G-14158)*

T & S Enterprises ....E 419 424-1122
Findlay *(G-9899)*

SCALES: Indl

Exact Equipment Corporation ....F 215 295-2000
Columbus *(G-6645)*

Holtgreven Scale & Elec Corp ....F 419 422-4779
Findlay *(G-9840)*

Mettler-Toledo LLC ....D...... 614 438-4511
Worthington *(G-20878)*

Mettler-Toledo LLC ....C...... 614 438-4390
Worthington *(G-20879)*

Mettler-Toledo LLC ....C...... 614 841-7300
Columbus *(G-7343)*

Mettler-Toledo Intl Fin Inc ....E 614 438-4511
Columbus *(G-6653)*

Mettler-Toledo Intl Inc ....B...... 614 438-4511
Columbus *(G-6654)*

Scale Tech Ltd ....G...... 419 729-5240
Toledo *(G-18686)*

SCALES: Truck

LTS Metrology LLC ....E 330 425-3092
Twinsburg *(G-18975)*

Roth Transit Inc ....G...... 937 773-5051
Piqua *(G-16311)*

SCHOOL SPLYS, EXC BOOKS: Wholesalers

Lorenz Corporation...............................D...... 937 228-6118
Dayton *(G-8460)*

Zaner-Bloser Inc ....D...... 614 486-0221
Columbus *(G-7786)*

SCHOOLS & EDUCATIONAL SVCS, NEC

School House Winery LLC ....G...... 330 602-9463
Dover *(G-9012)*

SCHOOLS: Vocational, NEC

Revonoc Inc ....G...... 440 548-3491
Parkman *(G-15953)*

SCIENTIFIC EQPT REPAIR SVCS

Crystal Koch Finishing Inc ....G...... 440 366-7526
Elyria *(G-9399)*

Instrumentors Inc ....G...... 440 238-3430
Strongsville *(G-17931)*

SCIENTIFIC INSTRUMENTS WHOLESALERS

Rosemount Analytical Inc ....C...... 440 914-1261
Solon *(G-17372)*

Science/Electronics Inc ....F 937 224-4444
Dayton *(G-8648)*

SCRAP & WASTE MATERIALS, WHOLESALE: Ferrous Metal

Agmet LLC...F 216 663-8200
Cleveland *(G-4731)*

City Scrap & Salvage Co ....E 330 753-5051
Akron *(G-124)*

Cohen Brothers Inc ....G...... 513 422-3696
Middletown *(G-14031)*

Fpt Cleveland LLC ....C...... 216 441-3800
Cleveland *(G-5376)*

I H Schlezinger Inc ....E 614 252-1188
Columbus *(G-7178)*

Induction Iron Incorporated ....G...... 330 501-8852
Youngstown *(G-21114)*

Lake County Auto Recyclers ....G...... 440 428-2886
Painesville *(G-15897)*

Metalico Akron Inc ....E 330 376-1400
Akron *(G-295)*

Moskowitz Bros Inc ....E 513 242-2100
Cincinnati *(G-4126)*

SCRAP & WASTE MATERIALS, WHOLESALE: Junk & Scrap

Lawsons Towing & Auto Wrckg..............F 216 883-9050
Cleveland *(G-5688)*

PRODUCT

SCRAP & WASTE MATERIALS, WHOLESALE: Lumber Scrap

Garick LLC ....E 216 581-0100
  Cleveland (G-5398)

SCRAP & WASTE MATERIALS, WHOLESALE: Metal

R L S Corporation ....E 740 773-1440
  Chillicothe (G-3270)
Triple Arrow Industries Inc...........G 614 437-5588
  Marysville (G-12976)
Tungsten Sltons Group Intl Inc........G 440 708-3096
  Chagrin Falls (G-3130)

SCRAP & WASTE MATERIALS, WHOLESALE: Nonferrous Metals Scrap

W R G Inc ....E 216 351-8494
  Cleveland (G-6436)

SCRAP & WASTE MATERIALS, WHOLESALE: Rubber Scrap

Frankes Wood Products LLC............E 937 642-0706
  Marysville (G-12944)

SCRAP STEEL CUTTING

Geneva Liberty Steel Ltd..............D 330 740-0103
  Youngstown (G-21097)

SCREENS: Door, Metal Covered Wood

Screenmobile Inc ....G 614 868-8663
  Radnor (G-16507)

SCREENS: Door, Wood Frame

Touchstone Woodworks ....G 330 297-1313
  Ravenna (G-16566)

SCREENS: Projection

Stewart Filmscreen Corp...............E 513 753-0800
  Amelia (G-584)

SCREENS: Window, Metal

Bug-Barrier Screen Corp...............G 330 723-2551
  Medina (G-13384)
Dale Kestler ....G 513 871-9000
  Cincinnati (G-3637)
Loxcreen Company Inc ....F 513 539-2255
  Middletown (G-14056)
Renewal By Andersen LLC ....G 614 781-9600
  Columbus (G-6658)
Thermal Industries Inc ....G 216 464-0674
  Cleveland (G-6316)

SCREENS: Window, Wood Framed

Pickens Window Service Inc...........F 513 931-4432
  Cincinnati (G-4235)

SCREENS: Woven Wire

Kimmatt Corp ....G 937 228-3811
  Dayton (G-8441)
US Screen Co ....G 419 736-2400
  Sullivan (G-18055)
Yankee Wire Cloth Products Inc..........E 740 545-9129
  West Lafayette (G-20090)

SCREW MACHINE PRDTS

Abco Bar & Tube Cutting Svc ....E 513 697-9487
  Maineville (G-12520)
Abel Fbrction Prcsion Pdts Inc........F 513 681-5000
  Cincinnati (G-3344)
Abel Manufacturing Company ....F 513 681-5000
  Cincinnati (G-3345)
Accuracy Products Inc ....F 937 454-2240
  Dayton (G-8132)
Adams Automatic Inc ....F 440 235-4416
  Olmsted Falls (G-15672)
Alco Manufacturing ....G 440 322-9166
  Amherst (G-590)
All-Craft Wellman Products ....F 440 946-9646
  Willoughby (G-20428)
Amco Products Inc ....F 937 433-7982
  Kettering (G-11575)

Amerascrew Inc ....E 419 522-2232
  Mansfield (G-12559)
American Aero Components LLC ....G 937 367-5068
  Dayton (G-8150)
Amt Machine Systems Limited ....F 740 965-2693
  Columbus (G-6747)
Ashley F Ward Inc ....C 513 398-1414
  Mason (G-12984)
Atlas Machine Products Co ....G 216 228-3688
  Cleveland (G-4855)
Automatic Screw Products Co ....G 216 241-7896
  Cleveland (G-4868)
Blc Precision Machine Co Inc ....F 937 783-1406
  Blanchester (G-1710)
Bronco Machine Inc ....F 440 951-5015
  Willoughby (G-20446)
Bront Machining Inc ....E 937 228-4551
  Moraine (G-14470)
Chardon Metal Products Co...........E 440 285-2147
  Chardon (G-3144)
Clear Creek Screw Machine Corp......G 740 969-2113
  Amanda (G-562)
Condo Inc ....G 330 505-0485
  Niles (G-15148)
Condo Incorporated ....D 330 609-6021
  Warren (G-19537)
CT Ferry Screw Products I ....G 440 871-1617
  Cleveland (G-5145)
D L Salkil LLC ....G 419 841-3341
  Toledo (G-18424)
Day-Hio Products Inc ....G 937 445-0782
  Dayton (G-8267)
Dove Machine Inc ....F 440 864-2645
  Columbia Station (G-6589)
Dunham Products Inc ....F 440 232-0885
  Walton Hills (G-19473)
Eastlake Machine Products Inc ....E 440 953-1014
  Willoughby (G-20479)
Efficient Machine Pdts Corp ....E 440 268-0205
  Strongsville (G-17915)
Elgin Fastener Group LLC ....E 216 481-4400
  Cleveland (G-5271)
Elliott Oren Products Inc ....F 419 298-0015
  Edgerton (G-9328)
Elliott Oren Products Inc ....E 419 298-2306
  Edgerton (G-9329)
Elyria Manufacturing Corp ....D 440 365-4171
  Elyria (G-9413)
Engels Machining LLC ....G 419 485-1500
  Montpelier (G-14445)
Engstrom Manufacturing Inc ....F 513 573-0010
  Mason (G-13017)
Eureka Screw Machine Pdts Co ....G 216 883-1715
  Cleveland (G-5304)
Fair Field Machine Products ....F 740 756-4409
  Carroll (G-2941)
Fairfield Machined Products ....F 740 756-4409
  Carroll (G-2942)
Fairfield Screw Products Co ....G 740 653-7627
  Lancaster (G-11714)
Falmer Screw Pdts & Mfg Inc ....F 330 758-0593
  Youngstown (G-21082)
Flash Industrial Tech Ltd ....G 440 786-8979
  Cleveland (G-5353)
Forrest Machine Pdts Co Ltd ....E 419 589-3774
  Mansfield (G-12607)
Fostoria Machine Products ....G 419 435-4262
  Fostoria (G-9977)
Gent Machine Company ....F 216 481-2334
  Cleveland (G-5423)
Global Precision Parts Inc ....D 419 453-0010
  Ottoville (G-15821)
Global Precision Parts Inc ....G 260 563-9030
  Van Wert (G-19258)
Great Lakes Defense Svcs LLC ....G 216 272-3450
  University Heights (G-19109)
Gtd Machine Inc ....G 440 812-6877
  Mentor (G-13597)
H & E Machine Company ....F 614 443-7635
  Columbus (G-7133)
H & S Precision Screw Pdts Inc........E 937 437-0316
  New Paris (G-14880)
H & W Screw Products Inc ....F 937 866-2577
  Franklin (G-10026)
Hamco Manufacturing Inc ....G 440 774-1637
  Oberlin (G-15643)
Harding Machine Acquisition Co........D 937 666-3031
  East Liberty (G-9201)
Hebco Products Inc ....A 419 562-7987
  Bucyrus (G-2347)

Heller Machine Products Inc...........G 216 281-2951
  Cleveland (G-5496)
Hept Machine Inc ....G 937 890-5633
  Vandalia (G-19294)
Hi-Tech Solutions LLC ....G 216 331-3050
  Cleveland (G-5511)
Houston Machine Products Inc ....E 937 322-8022
  Springfield (G-17577)
Hy-Production Inc ....C 330 273-2400
  Valley City (G-19206)
Hyland Machine Company ....E 937 233-8600
  Dayton (G-8399)
Ilsco Corporation ....E 513 367-9100
  Harrison (G-10785)
Integrity Manufacturing Corp ....E 937 233-6792
  Dayton (G-8413)
J & M Cutting Tools Inc ....G 440 622-3900
  Mentor (G-13615)
JAD Machine Company Inc ....F 419 256-6332
  Malinta (G-12535)
Karma Metal Products Inc ....F 419 524-4371
  Mansfield (G-12632)
Kernells Autmtc Machining Inc ....E 419 588-2164
  Berlin Heights (G-1662)
Kohut Enterprises Inc ....G 440 366-6666
  Independence (G-11263)
Krausher Machining Inc ....G 440 839-2828
  Wakeman (G-19449)
Krist Krenz Machine Inc ....D 440 237-1800
  North Royalton (G-15431)
Kts-Met Bar Products Inc ....G 440 288-9308
  Lorain (G-12252)
Lake Erie Industries LLC ....E 216 255-1867
  Lakewood (G-11671)
Lear Manufacturing Inc ....G 440 327-4545
  North Ridgeville (G-15387)
Lehner Screw Machine LLC ....E 330 688-6616
  Munroe Falls (G-14662)
Lenco Industries Inc ....E 937 277-9364
  Dayton (G-8455)
Machine Tek Systems Inc ....E 330 527-4450
  Garrettsville (G-10329)
Magnetic Screw Machine Pdts..........G 937 348-2807
  Marysville (G-12956)
Mansfield Screw Mch Pdts Co ....D 419 884-1511
  Mansfield (G-12644)
Maumee Machine & Tool Corp ....E 419 385-2501
  Toledo (G-18578)
McDaniel Products Inc ....F 440 967-5630
  Vermilion (G-19333)
McDaniel Products Inc ....E 419 524-5841
  Mansfield (G-12645)
Meistermatic Inc ....D 216 481-7773
  Chesterland (G-3214)
Mettlr-Tledo Globl Hldings LLC ....G 614 438-4511
  Columbus (G-6655)
Midwest Precision LLC ....D 440 951-2333
  Eastlake (G-9282)
Morgal Machine Tool Co ....D 937 325-5561
  Springfield (G-17607)
Mosher Machine & Tool Co Inc ....E 937 258-8070
  Dayton (G-8511)
Murray Machine & Tool Inc ....G 216 267-1126
  Cleveland (G-5841)
Nook Industries Inc ....C 216 271-7900
  Cleveland (G-5887)
Obars Machine and Tool Company ......E 419 535-6307
  Toledo (G-18613)
Ohio Machined Products Inc ....F 419 264-2400
  Holgate (G-11038)
Ohio Metal Products Company ....E 937 228-6101
  Dayton (G-8545)
Ohio Screw Products Inc ....D 440 322-6341
  Elyria (G-9472)
Paramont Machine Company LLC........E 330 339-3489
  New Philadelphia (G-14921)
Parker-Hannifin Corporation ....D 218 534-3148
  Wickliffe (G-20380)
Pfi Precision Inc ....G 937 845-3563
  New Carlisle (G-14812)
Phoenix Tool & Thread Grindng ....G 216 433-7008
  Cleveland (G-6004)
Pike Machine Products Co ....E 216 731-1880
  Euclid (G-9597)
Port Clinton Manufacturing LLC ....E 419 734-2141
  Port Clinton (G-16409)
Precision Fittings LLC ....E 440 647-4143
  Wellington (G-19752)
Profile Grinding Inc ....E 216 351-0600
  Cleveland (G-6055)

(G-0000) Company's Geographic Section entry number

Qcsm LLC ....G 216 531-5960
  Euclid (G-9602)
R T & T Machining Co Inc ....F 440 974-8479
  Mentor (G-13714)
R W Screw Products Inc ....C 330 837-9211
  Massillon (G-13198)
Raka Corporation ....D 419 476-6572
  Toledo (G-18671)
Richland Screw Mch Pdts Inc ....E 419 524-1272
  Mansfield (G-12672)
Rite Machine Inc ....G 216 267-6911
  Cleveland (G-6114)
Roehlers Machine Products..............G 937 354-4401
  Mount Victory (G-14659)
Rtsi LLC ....G 440 542-3066
  Solon (G-17373)
Rural Products Inc ....G 419 298-2677
  Edgerton (G-9335)
S & S Machining Ltd ....F 419 524-9525
  Mansfield (G-12675)
Semtorq Inc ....F 330 487-0600
  Twinsburg (G-19019)
Shanafelt Manufacturing Co ....E 330 455-0315
  Canton (G-2847)
Slabe Machine Products Co..............D 440 946-6555
  Willoughby (G-20599)
Southern Adhsives Coatings Inc.......G 513 561-8440
  Cincinnati (G-4438)
Stadco Inc ....E 937 878-0911
  Fairborn (G-9630)
Standby Screw Machine Pdts Co ......B 440 243-8200
  Berea (G-1635)
Star Screw Machine Products ....G 216 361-0307
  Cleveland (G-6238)
State Machine Co Inc ....G 440 248-1050
  Cleveland (G-6240)
Summit Machine Ltd ....E 330 628-2663
  Mogadore (G-14386)
Superior Bar Products Inc ....G 419 784-2590
  Defiance (G-8811)
Superior Products Llc ....D 216 651-9400
  Cleveland (G-6269)
Supply Technologies LLC ....D 740 363-1971
  Delaware (G-8891)
Swagelok Hy-Level Company ....C 440 238-1260
  Strongsville (G-17975)
Swivel-Tek Industries LLC ....G 419 636-7770
  Bryan (G-2322)
Toledo Automatic Screw Co ....G 419 726-3441
  Toledo (G-18729)
Toledo Screw Products Inc ....G 419 841-3341
  Toledo (G-18741)
Tri-K Enterprises Inc ....G 330 832-7380
  Canton (G-2882)
Triangle Machine Products Co ....E 216 524-5872
  Cleveland (G-6361)
Trojon Gear Inc ....F 937 254-1737
  Dayton (G-8729)
Troy Manufacturing Co ....E 440 834-8262
  Burton (G-2388)
Twin Valley Metalcraft Asm LLC ....G 937 787-4634
  West Alexandria (G-19784)
United Auto Worker AFL CIO ....F 419 592-0434
  Napoleon (G-14701)
Valley Tool & Die Inc ....D 440 237-0160
  North Royalton (G-15458)
Vanamatic Company ....D 419 692-6085
  Delphos (G-8927)
Vinco Machine Products Inc ....G 216 475-6708
  Cleveland (G-6420)
Vulcan Products Co Inc ....F 419 468-1039
  Galion (G-10290)
Warren Screw Machine Inc ....E 330 609-6020
  Warren (G-19623)
Watters Manufacturing Co Inc ....G 216 281-8600
  Cleveland (G-6451)
Whirlaway Corporation ....C 440 647-4711
  Wellington (G-19758)
Whirlaway Corporation ....C 440 647-4711
  Wellington (G-19759)
Whirlaway Corporation ....E 440 647-4711
  Wellington (G-19760)
Whiteford Industries Inc ....F 419 381-1155
  Toledo (G-18774)
Wood-Sebring Corporation ....G 216 267-3191
  Cleveland (G-6475)
Z and M Screw Machine Products ......G 330 467-5822
  Garrettsville (G-10337)

SCREW MACHINES

Ken Emerick Machine Products ....G 440 834-4501
  Burton (G-2380)
Ohio CAM & Tool Co ....G 216 531-7900
  Cleveland (G-5932)
Ohio Screw Products Inc ....D 440 322-6341
  Elyria (G-9472)

SCREWS: Metal

Akko Fastener Inc ....E 513 489-8300
  Blue Ash (G-1738)
Altenloh Brinck & Co US Inc ....D 419 636-6715
  Bryan (G-2277)
Engstrom Manufacturing Inc ....F 513 573-0010
  Mason (G-13017)
Ivan Extruders Co Inc ....G 330 644-7400
  Akron (G-237)
Senco Holdings Inc ....G 800 543-4596
  Cincinnati (G-3316)
W-J Inc ....G 440 248-8282
  Solon (G-17412)

SCREWS: Wood

Hudson Fasteners Inc ....G 330 270-9500
  Youngstown (G-21110)

SEALANTS

A & M Products ....G 419 595-2092
  Tiffin (G-18201)
Aluminum Coating Manufacturers ......E 216 341-2000
  Cleveland (G-4774)
Besten Equipment Inc ....E 216 581-1166
  Solon (G-17267)
Chemmasters Inc ....E 440 428-2105
  Madison (G-12501)
Concrete Sealants Inc ....E 937 845-8776
  Tipp City (G-18273)
Davis Caulking & Sealant LLC ....G 740 286-3825
  Wellston (G-19762)
Dental Sealants ....G 440 582-3466
  North Royalton (G-15417)
Egc Enterprises Inc ....E 440 285-5835
  Chardon (G-3151)
Extendit Company ....G 330 743-4343
  Youngstown (G-21081)
Freedom Asphalt Sealant & Line ....G 937 416-1053
  Miamisburg (G-13811)
Jetcoat LLC ....E 800 394-0047
  Columbus (G-7232)
P & T Products Inc ....E 419 621-1966
  Sandusky (G-16992)
Royal Adhesives & Sealants LLC ....G 440 708-1212
  Chagrin Falls (G-3118)
Sealant Solutions ....G 614 599-8000
  Columbus (G-7605)
Signature Salants Coatings LLC ....E 513 922-8723
  Cleves (G-6525)
Tara Acquisition Group ....F 614 754-4777
  Lewis Center (G-11923)
Teknol Inc ....D 937 264-0190
  Dayton (G-8708)
Tremco Incorporated ....C 216 752-4401
  Cleveland (G-6354)
Tremco Incorporated ....B 216 292-5000
  Beachwood (G-1303)
Truseal Technologies Inc ....E 216 910-1500
  Solon (G-17408)

SEALING COMPOUNDS: Sealing, synthetic rubber or plastic

Federal Process Corporation ....E 216 464-6440
  Cleveland (G-5332)
Foam Seal Inc ....D 216 881-8111
  Cleveland (G-5363)
Leesburg Modern Sales Inc ....G 937 780-2613
  Leesburg (G-11854)
National Applied Cnstr Pdts ....G 330 644-3117
  Akron (G-310)
Novagard Solutions Inc ....F 216 881-3890
  Cleveland (G-5917)
Technical Rubber Company Inc ....B 740 967-9015
  Johnstown (G-11407)

SEALS: Hermetic

Aeroseal LLC ....E 937 428-9300
  Centerville (G-3034)

SEALS: Oil, Rubber

Federal-Mogul Corporation ....A 419 238-1053
  Van Wert (G-19257)

SEARCH & NAVIGATION SYSTEMS

Accurate Electronics Inc ....C 330 682-7015
  Orrville (G-15727)
ADB Safegate Americas LLC ....B 614 861-1304
  Columbus (G-6694)
Aviation Technologies Inc ....G 216 706-2960
  Cleveland (G-4872)
Boeing Company ....A 740 788-5805
  Newark (G-14987)
Boeing Company ....B 740 788-4000
  Newark (G-14986)
Brookpark Laboratories Inc ....G 216 267-7140
  Cleveland (G-4935)
Btc Inc ....E 740 549-2722
  Lewis Center (G-11892)
David Boswell ....E 614 441-2497
  Columbus (G-7014)
Drs Advanced Isr LLC ....C 937 429-7408
  Beavercreek (G-1330)
Drs Advanced Isr LLC ....E 603 429-0111
  Beavercreek (G-1331)
Drs Icas LLC ....E 937 429-7408
  Beavercreek (G-1332)
Drs Mobile Environmntl Svc ....G 513 943-1111
  Cincinnati (G-3299)
Enginetics Corporation ....C 937 878-3800
  Huber Heights (G-11146)
Eti Tech Inc ....F 937 832-4200
  Englewood (G-9519)
Fame Tool & Mfg Co Inc ....E 513 271-6387
  Cincinnati (G-3737)
Ferrotherm Corporation ....C 216 883-9350
  Cleveland (G-5339)
Fluid Conservation Systems ....F 513 831-9335
  Milford (G-14141)
General Dynmics Mssion Systems ......E 513 253-4770
  Beavercreek (G-1340)
Goodrich Corporation ....D 330 374-2882
  Uniontown (G-19086)
Grimes Aerospace Company ....B 937 484-2001
  Urbana (G-19158)
Harris Corporation ....C 973 284-2866
  Beavercreek (G-1344)
Heller Machine Products Inc ....G 216 281-2951
  Cleveland (G-5496)
Hept Machine Inc ....G 937 890-5633
  Vandalia (G-19294)
Lake Shore Cryotronics Inc ....C 614 891-2243
  Westerville (G-20165)
Lockheed Martin Integ ....D 330 796-2800
  Akron (G-274)
PCC Airfoils LLC ....C 216 692-7900
  Cleveland (G-5983)
Redco Instrument ....G 440 232-2132
  Cleveland (G-6096)
Reuter-Stokes Inc ....B 330 425-3755
  Twinsburg (G-19008)
Sunset Industries Inc ....E 216 731-8131
  Euclid (G-9607)
Te Connectivity Corporation ....C 419 521-9500
  Mansfield (G-12694)
Wall Colmonoy Corporation ....D 513 842-4200
  Cincinnati (G-4577)
Yost Labs Inc ....F 740 876-4936
  Portsmouth (G-16459)

SEAT BELTS: Automobile & Aircraft

Tk Holdings Inc ....E 937 778-9713
  Piqua (G-16315)

SEATING: Chairs, Table & Arm

Brocar Products Inc ....E 513 922-2888
  Cincinnati (G-3477)
Gasser Chair Co Inc ....E 330 534-2234
  Youngstown (G-21091)
Gasser Chair Co Inc ....D 330 759-2234
  Youngstown (G-21093)

SEATING: Stadium

American Office Services Inc ....G 440 899-6888
  Westlake (G-20252)
Ap-Alternatives LLC ....F 419 267-5280
  Ridgeville Corners (G-16663)

PRODUCT

SEATING: Transportation

C E White Co .... D 419 492-2157
New Washington *(G-14958)*

SECRETARIAL & COURT REPORTING

Fax Medley Group Inc .... G 513 272-1932
Cincinnati *(G-3743)*

Landen Desktop Pubg Ctr Inc .... G 513 683-5181
Loveland *(G-12370)*

Sound Communications Inc .... F 614 875-8500
Grove City *(G-10597)*

SECRETARIAL SVCS

Ohio Shelterall Inc .... F 614 882-1110
Westerville *(G-20227)*

SECURITY CONTROL EQPT & SYSTEMS

Aaron Smith .... G 330 285-1360
Akron *(G-24)*

Checkpoint Systems Inc .... C 937 281-1304
Dayton *(G-8226)*

Diebold Nixdorf Incorporated .... A 330 490-4000
North Canton *(G-15228)*

Emx Industries Inc .... E 216 518-9888
Cleveland *(G-5279)*

Habitec SEC Diversfd Alarm .... G 419 636-1155
Bryan *(G-2299)*

Henderson Partners LLC .... G 614 883-1310
Columbus *(G-7149)*

Honeywell International Inc .... A 937 484-2000
Urbana *(G-19162)*

Intelligent Biometric Controls .... G 513 239-6322
Milford *(G-14152)*

MAI Media Group Llc .... G 513 779-0604
West Chester *(G-20023)*

Modular Security Systems Inc .... G 740 532-7822
Ironton *(G-11297)*

Pentagon Protection Usa LLC .... F 614 734-7240
Dublin *(G-9123)*

Securcom Inc .... E 419 628-1049
Minster *(G-14361)*

Technlogy Install Partners LLC .... E 888 586-7040
Cleveland *(G-6302)*

Vero Security Group Ltd .... G 513 731-8376
Cincinnati *(G-4564)*

SECURITY DEVICES

1 A Lifesafer Inc .... G 513 651-9560
Blue Ash *(G-1729)*

Access 2 Communications Inc .... G 800 561-1110
Steubenville *(G-17686)*

Cincinnati Gate Systems Inc .... G 513 769-5200
Cincinnati *(G-3551)*

Everykey Inc .... G 866 798-5577
Cleveland *(G-5309)*

Executive Security Systems Inc .... G 513 895-2783
Cincinnati *(G-3730)*

Invue Security Products Inc .... C 330 456-7776
Canton *(G-2740)*

J II Fire Systems Inc .... G 513 574-0609
Cincinnati *(G-3935)*

Lindsay Precast Inc .... E 330 854-6282
Canal Fulton *(G-2505)*

Mace Security Intl Inc .... F 440 424-5321
Cleveland *(G-5723)*

Residential Electronic Svcs .... G 740 681-9150
Lancaster *(G-11745)*

Vigilant Defense .... E 513 214-1635
Mason *(G-13101)*

Viotec LLC .... G 614 596-2054
Dublin *(G-9163)*

SECURITY EQPT STORES

American Scaffolding Inc .... G 216 524-7733
Cleveland *(G-4795)*

Beeline Purchasing LLC .... G 513 703-3733
Mason *(G-12989)*

Kriss Kreations .... G 330 405-6102
Twinsburg *(G-18968)*

Warthers Music Box Bells .... G 330 343-4706
Dover *(G-9024)*

SECURITY PROTECTIVE DEVICES MAINTENANCE & MONITORING SVCS

Contingncy Prcrments Group LLC ...... G 513 204-9590
Maineville *(G-12521)*

Taupe Holdings Co .... G 614 330-4600
Dublin *(G-9153)*

SECURITY SYSTEMS SERVICES

Johnson Controls Inc .... F 513 671-6338
Cincinnati *(G-3956)*

Securcom Inc .... E 419 628-1049
Minster *(G-14361)*

Sound Communications Inc .... F 614 875-8500
Grove City *(G-10597)*

SEMICONDUCTOR CIRCUIT NETWORKS

Micro Industries Corporation .... F 740 548-7878
Columbus *(G-7347)*

Micro Industries Corporation .... D 740 548-7878
Westerville *(G-20224)*

SEMICONDUCTORS & RELATED DEVICES

Advanced Dstrbted Gnration LLC ...... G 419 530-3792
Maumee *(G-13219)*

AEG Photoconductor Corporation ...... D 513 874-4939
West Chester *(G-19799)*

Altera Corporation .... G 513 444-2021
Cincinnati *(G-3381)*

Babcock & Wilcox Megtec .... G 614 258-9501
Columbus *(G-6799)*

Biometric Information MGT LLC .... G 614 456-1296
Dublin *(G-9054)*

Communication Concepts Inc .... G 937 426-8600
Beavercreek *(G-1326)*

CPC Logistics Inc .... D 513 874-5787
Fairfield *(G-9657)*

Darrah Electric Company .... E 216 631-0912
Cleveland *(G-5168)*

First Solar Inc .... B 419 661-1478
Perrysburg *(G-16096)*

Gould Electronics Inc .... C 440 953-5000
Eastlake *(G-9271)*

Greenfield Solar Inc .... E 216 535-9200
Oberlin *(G-15642)*

Heraeus Electro-Nite Co LLC .... G 330 725-1419
Medina *(G-13421)*

Honeywell International Inc .... C 614 850-5000
Columbus *(G-7163)*

Honeywell International Inc .... D 614 850-5000
Columbus *(G-7164)*

Hyper Tech Research Inc .... F 614 481-8050
Columbus *(G-7173)*

Linear Asics Inc .... G 330 474-3920
Tallmadge *(G-18150)*

Materion Brush Inc .... D 216 486-4200
Mayfield Heights *(G-13317)*

Materion Corporation .... C 216 486-4200
Mayfield Heights *(G-13318)*

Ohio Semitronics Inc .... G 614 777-1005
Hilliard *(G-10967)*

Pepperl + Fuchs Inc .... C 330 425-3555
Twinsburg *(G-18997)*

Rbs Technologies LLC .... G 937 320-8189
Xenia *(G-20970)*

SCI Engineered Materials Inc .... E 614 486-0261
Columbus *(G-7599)*

Selectronics Incorporated .... G 440 546-5595
Brecksville *(G-2072)*

Signature Technologies Inc .... E 937 859-6323
Miamisburg *(G-13859)*

Silfex Inc .... C 937 472-3311
Eaton *(G-9323)*

Spang & Company .... E 440 350-6108
Mentor *(G-13727)*

Spb Global LLC .... G 419 931-6559
Perrysburg *(G-16150)*

Special Mtls RES & Tech Inc .... G 440 777-4024
North Olmsted *(G-15347)*

Techneglas Inc .... G 419 873-2000
Perrysburg *(G-16154)*

Ustek Incorporated .... G 614 538-8000
Columbus *(G-7728)*

Vega Technology Group LLC .... G 216 772-1434
North Canton *(G-15281)*

SENSORS: Infrared, Solid State

Madison Electric (mepco) Inc .... G 440 279-0521
Chardon *(G-3165)*

SENSORS: Radiation

Integrated Sensors LLC .... G 419 536-3212
Ottawa Hills *(G-15816)*

SENSORS: Temperature, Exc Indl Process

Krumor Inc .... F 216 328-9802
Cleveland *(G-5667)*

Lake Shore Cryotronics Inc .... C 614 891-2243
Westerville *(G-20165)*

Safe-Grain Inc .... G 513 398-2500
Loveland *(G-12383)*

SENSORS: Ultraviolet, Solid State

Transducers Direct Llc .... G 513 583-7597
Loveland *(G-12395)*

SEPARATORS: Metal Plate

Almo Process Technology Inc .... G 513 402-2566
West Chester *(G-19804)*

SEPTIC TANK CLEANING SVCS

Pro-Kleen Industrial Svcs Inc .... E 740 689-1886
Lancaster *(G-11741)*

Reed Elvin Burl II .... G 937 399-3242
Springfield *(G-17636)*

SEPTIC TANKS: Concrete

Allen Enterprises Inc .... G 740 532-5913
Ironton *(G-11288)*

Dennis Constuction Sanitation .... G 419 332-8301
Fremont *(G-10142)*

E A Cox Inc .... G 740 858-4400
Lucasville *(G-12419)*

Encore Precast LLC .... F 513 726-5678
Seven Mile *(G-17065)*

Green Forward Technologies LLC ...... G 513 607-9639
Cincinnati *(G-3848)*

J K Precast LLC .... G 740 335-2188
Wshngtn CT Hs *(G-20912)*

James Kimmey .... F 740 335-5746
Wshngtn CT Hs *(G-20913)*

Lindsay Precast Inc .... E 330 854-6282
Canal Fulton *(G-2505)*

Quaker City Septic Tanks LLC .... G 330 427-2239
Leetonia *(G-11864)*

Reed Elvin Burl II .... G 937 399-3242
Springfield *(G-17636)*

Richmond Concrete Products .... G 330 673-7892
Warren *(G-19595)*

Septic Products Inc .... G 419 282-5933
Ashland *(G-777)*

Sickels Septic Tanks Inc .... G 740 593-8302
Athens *(G-884)*

Stiger Pre Cast Inc .... G 740 482-2313
Nevada *(G-14743)*

Uniontown Septic Tanks Inc .... F 330 699-3386
Uniontown *(G-19104)*

SEPTIC TANKS: Plastic

Hancor Inc .... D 419 424-8225
Findlay *(G-9837)*

Hancor Inc .... B 614 658-0050
Hilliard *(G-10950)*

J K Precast LLC .... G 740 335-2188
Wshngtn CT Hs *(G-20912)*

SEWAGE & WATER TREATMENT EQPT

Applied Biomimetic Inc .... G 513 558-6090
Cincinnati *(G-3409)*

B L Anderson Co Inc .... G 765 463-1518
West Chester *(G-19812)*

Bleachtech LLC .... D 330 421-2134
Medina *(G-13378)*

City of Chardon .... F 440 286-2657
Chardon *(G-3147)*

City of Troy .... F 937 339-4826
Troy *(G-18809)*

Comp-U-Chem Inc .... G 740 345-3332
Newark *(G-14995)*

County of Lawrence .... F 740 867-8700
Chesapeake *(G-3186)*

De Nora Tech Inc .... D 440 710-5300
Painesville *(G-15875)*

Eagle Crusher Co Inc .... D 419 468-2288
Galion *(G-10266)*

Evoqua Water Technologies LLC .... G 262 521-8352
Milford *(G-14140)*

Flow-Liner Systems Ltd .... E 800 348-0020
Zanesville *(G-21309)*

(G-0000) Company's Geographic Section entry number

Greene County ....G...... 937 429-0127
Dayton (G-8107)

Komar Industries Inc ....E...... 614 836-2366
Groveport (G-10629)

Monarch Water Systems Inc ....F...... 937 426-5773
Beavercreek (G-1353)

Or-Tec Inc ....G...... 216 475-5225
Maple Heights (G-12737)

Pelton Environmental Pdts Inc .....G...... 440 838-1221
Lewis Center (G-11909)

Smart Sonic Corporation ....G...... 818 610-7900
Cleveland (G-6211)

Village of Somerset ....G...... 740 743-1986
Somerset (G-17420)

Village of West Alexandria ....G...... 937 839-4168
West Alexandria (G-19785)

Water & Waste Water Eqp Co ....G...... 440 542-0972
Solon (G-17413)

X-3-5 LLC ....G...... 513 489-5477
Cincinnati (G-4613)

SEWAGE FACILITIES

City of Ravenna..............................G...... 330 296-5214
Ravenna (G-16522)

SEWAGE TREATMENT SYSTEMS & EQPT

Beckman Environmental Svcs Inc ......F...... 513 752-3570
Batavia (G-1168)

City of Ravenna..............................G...... 330 296-5214
Ravenna (G-16522)

E - I Corp ....F...... 614 899-2282
Westerville (G-20146)

Mack Industries PA Inc ....F...... 330 638-7680
Vienna (G-19369)

McNish Corporation ....G...... 614 899-2282
Westerville (G-20171)

Oceco Inc ....F...... 419 447-0916
Tiffin (G-18235)

SEWER CLEANING & RODDING SVC

Beckman Environmental Svcs Inc ......F...... 513 752-3570
Batavia (G-1168)

Stevens Auto Parts & Towng ....G...... 740 988-2260
Jackson (G-11325)

SEWER CLEANING EQPT: Power

Best Equipment Co Inc ....E...... 440 237-3515
North Royalton (G-15411)

Electric Eel Mfg Co Inc ....E...... 937 323-4644
Springfield (G-17552)

SEWING CONTRACTORS

Cold Duck Screen Prtg & EMB Co........G...... 330 426-1900
East Palestine (G-9231)

Db Rediheat Inc ....E...... 216 361-0530
Cleveland (G-5175)

DCW Acquisition Inc ....F...... 216 451-0666
Cleveland (G-5179)

Ideal Drapery Company Inc............F...... 330 745-9873
Barberton (G-1121)

SEWING MACHINES & PARTS: Indl

Acb Three Inc ....G...... 614 873-4680
Plain City (G-16317)

Intelliworks Ht ....G...... 419 660-9050
Norwalk (G-15547)

Omar McDowell Co ....G...... 440 808-2280
Westlake (G-20289)

Rda Group LLC ....G...... 440 724-4347
Avon (G-1007)

SEWING, NEEDLEWORK & PIECE GOODS
STORE: Needlework Gds/Sply

Nettting Technologies LLC ....G...... 330 298-0022
Ravenna (G-16543)

SEWING, NEEDLEWORK & PIECE GOODS
STORE: Quilting Matls/Splys

Quilting Creations Intl ....E...... 330 874-4741
Bolivar (G-1945)

SEWING, NEEDLEWORK & PIECE GOODS
STORES: Knitting Splys

Yarn Shop Inc ....G...... 614 457-7836
Columbus (G-7782)

SEWING, NEEDLEWORK & PIECE GOODS
STORES: Notions, Incl Trim

Camela Nitschke Ribbonry ....G...... 419 872-0073
Perrysburg (G-16073)

SEWING, NEEDLEWORK & PIECE GOODS
STORES: Sewing & Needlework

Embroidme Co ....G...... 614 933-9194
Columbus (G-7056)

J-M Designs LLC ....G...... 419 794-2114
Maumee (G-13269)

SEXTANTS

Sextant Group Inc ....G...... 614 429-3606
Columbus (G-7613)

SHADES: Window

Cincinnati Window Shade Inc ....G...... 513 398-8510
Mason (G-12995)

Cincinnati Window Shade Inc ....F...... 513 631-7200
Cincinnati (G-3568)

Simex Inc ....G...... 304 665-1104
Columbus (G-7622)

SHAFTS: Shaft Collars

Southeastern Shafting Mfg ....F...... 740 342-4629
New Lexington (G-14854)

SHALE MINING, COMMON

Blue Jay Entps of Tscrwas Cnty...........G...... 330 874-2048
Bolivar (G-1928)

SHAPES & PILINGS, STRUCTURAL: Steel

A-1 Welding & Fabricating Inc ....F...... 440 233-8474
Lorain (G-12230)

Brenmar Construction Inc ....D...... 740 286-2151
Jackson (G-11312)

Heartland Steel Inc ....F...... 740 333-5401
Washington Court Hou (G-19639)

Steve Vore Welding and Steel ....F...... 419 375-4087
Fort Recovery (G-9959)

SHAPES: Extruded, Aluminum, NEC

Aerolite Extrusion Company............D...... 330 782-1127
Youngstown (G-21018)

Gei of Columbiana Inc ....D...... 330 783-0270
Youngstown (G-21094)

General Extrusions Inc ....D...... 330 783-0270
Youngstown (G-21096)

I R B F Company ....G...... 330 633-5100
Tallmadge (G-18147)

Kit MB Systems Inc ....E...... 330 945-4500
Akron (G-260)

Patton Aluminum Products Inc ....F...... 937 845-9404
New Carlisle (G-14811)

Vari-Wall Tube Specialists Inc................D...... 330 482-0000
Columbiana (G-6637)

SHAVING PREPARATIONS

Edgewell Personal Care LLC ....C...... 937 492-1057
Sidney (G-17183)

SHEARS

Klenk Industries Inc ....D...... 330 453-7857
Canton (G-2754)

SHEET METAL SPECIALTIES, EXC STAMPED

Allied Fabricating & Wldg Co...........E...... 614 751-6664
Columbus (G-6725)

C & R Inc ....E...... 614 497-1130
Groveport (G-10617)

Ceco Group Inc ....G...... 513 458-2600
Cincinnati (G-3510)

Columbus Steelmasters Inc ....F...... 614 231-2141
Columbus (G-6968)

Crown Electric Engrg & Mfg LLC ....E...... 513 539-7394
Middletown (G-14035)

Kirk & Blum Manufacturing Co ....C...... 513 458-2600
Cincinnati (G-3992)

Kirk & Blum Manufacturing Co ....E...... 419 782-9885
Defiance (G-8798)

Kuhn Fabricating Inc ....G...... 440 277-4182
Lorain (G-12253)

Lambert Sheet Metal Inc ....F...... 614 237-0384
Columbus (G-7281)

Midwest Fabrications Inc ....E...... 330 633-0191
Tallmadge (G-18155)

Modern Manufacturing Inc ....E...... 513 251-3600
Cincinnati (G-4116)

S L M Inc ....G...... 216 651-0666
Cleveland (G-6150)

Varmland Inc ....F...... 216 741-1510
Cleveland (G-6408)

Wolf Metals Inc ....G...... 614 461-6361
Columbus (G-7768)

SHEETING: Laminated Plastic

Great Lakes Textiles Inc ....E...... 440 201-1300
Bedford (G-1425)

Plaskolite Inc ....D...... 740 450-1109
Zanesville (G-21341)

Poly TEC East Inc ....G...... 330 799-7876
Youngstown (G-21172)

Rochling Glastic Composites LP ....C...... 216 486-0100
Cleveland (G-6125)

Schneller LLC ....D...... 330 673-1299
Kent (G-11523)

Shamrock Plastics Inc ....F...... 740 392-5555
Mount Vernon (G-14646)

SHEETS & STRIPS: Aluminum

Alcoa Inc ....C...... 330 848-4000
Barberton (G-1096)

Alcoa Inc ....F...... 216 391-3885
Cleveland (G-4743)

Alcoa Inc ....E...... 608 363-5214
Newburgh Heights (G-15068)

Arconic Inc ....C...... 330 835-6000
Mogadore (G-14368)

SHEETS: Hard Rubber

Novex Inc ....F...... 330 335-2371
Wadsworth (G-19422)

SHELLAC

Hess Advanced Technology Inc ....G...... 937 268-4377
Huber Heights (G-11148)

PPG Industries Inc ....E...... 513 576-0360
Milford (G-14167)

SHELTERED WORKSHOPS

Belco Works Inc ....B...... 740 695-0500
Saint Clairsville (G-16782)

Brookhill Center Industries............C...... 419 876-3932
Ottawa (G-15790)

Brown Cnty Bd Mntal Rtardation ....E...... 937 378-4891
Georgetown (G-10364)

Carroll Hills Industries Inc ....D...... 330 627-5524
Carrollton (G-2953)

Cincinnati Assn For The Blind...........C...... 513 221-8558
Cincinnati (G-3539)

Hopewell Industries Inc ....D...... 740 622-3563
Coshocton (G-7895)

Hunter Defense Tech Inc ....E...... 216 438-6111
Solon (G-17312)

J-Vac Industries Inc ....D...... 740 384-2155
Wellston (G-19765)

Ken Harper ....C...... 740 439-4452
Byesville (G-2406)

Monco Enterprises Inc ....A...... 937 461-0034
Dayton (G-8507)

R T Industries Inc ....G...... 937 335-5784
Troy (G-18865)

SHELVES & SHELVING: Wood

Darko Inc ....E...... 330 425-9805
Twinsburg (G-18921)

SHELVING, MADE FROM PURCHASED WIRE

Interntnal Tchncal Catings Inc...........D...... 614 449-6669
Columbus (G-7208)

K Effs Inc ....F...... 614 443-0586
Columbus (G-7250)

SHELVING: Office & Store, Exc Wood

Metrodeck Inc..............................F 513 541-4370
Cincinnati (G-4095)

Panacea Products Corporation ....E 614 850-7000
Columbus (G-7456)

SHIMS: Metal

Die-Cut Products Co......................E 216 771-6994
Cleveland (G-5193)

Ohio Gasket and Shim Co Inc.............E 330 630-0626
Akron (G-323)

Spirol International Corp..................D 330 920-3655
Stow (G-17802)

SHIP BUILDING & REPAIRING: Cargo Vessels

Manitowoc Company Inc..................G 920 746-3332
Cleveland (G-5739)

SHIP BUILDING & REPAIRING: Lighthouse Tenders

Lighthouse Youth Services Inc............F 513 961-4080
Cincinnati (G-4024)

SHIP BUILDING & REPAIRING: Tankers

Services Acquisition Co LLC...............G 330 479-9267
Dennison (G-8946)

SHIP BUILDING & REPAIRING: Tugboats

Superior Marine Ways Inc..................G 740 894-6224
South Point (G-17448)

SHIP COMPONENTS: Metal, Prefabricated

Accurate Fab LLC ....G 330 562-0566
Streetsboro (G-17833)

Navpar Inc..................................G 513 738-2230
Harrison (G-10792)

SHIPBUILDING & REPAIR

Great Lakes Group.........................C 216 621-4854
Cleveland (G-5451)

Ironhead Marine Inc ....E 419 690-0001
Toledo (G-18529)

Lake Erie Ship Repair ....F 440 624-0025
Jefferson (G-11366)

O-Kan Marine Repair Inc ....E 740 446-4686
Gallipolis (G-10306)

Oneseal Inc.................................G 973 599-1155
Perrysburg (G-16134)

Tack-Anew Inc ....E 419 734-4212
Port Clinton (G-16417)

V&P Group International LLC ....F 703 349-6432
Cincinnati (G-4550)

WH Fetzer & Sons Mfg Inc ....E 419 687-8237
Plymouth (G-16380)

SHOE MATERIALS: Counters

Bean Counter LLC ....G 419 636-0705
Bryan (G-2282)

Buckeye Counters ....G 330 682-0902
Orrville (G-15732)

Classic Countertops LLC ....G 330 882-4220
Akron (G-125)

Counter Creation Plus L L C ....G 419 826-7449
Swanton (G-18083)

Counter Method Inc ....G 614 206-3192
Sunbury (G-18058)

Counter Rhythm Group ....G 513 379-6587
Cincinnati (G-3615)

Dicks Counter D M ....G 440 322-3312
Elyria (G-9404)

Perfume Counter ....G 513 885-5989
Cincinnati (G-4228)

SHOE MATERIALS: Inner Soles

Sentinel Consumer Products Inc ....D 801 825-5671
Mentor (G-13720)

SHOE MATERIALS: Quarters

Bond Quarters Horses......................G 614 354-4028
Freeport (G-10117)

Cruise Quarters.............................G 614 777-6022
Hilliard (G-10944)

Cruise Quarters and Tours.................G 614 891-6089
Westerville (G-20206)

French Quarter LLC ....G 614 781-0588
Columbus (G-7101)

Halvey Quarter Horses ....G 614 648-0483
Blacklick (G-1697)

Home Quarters North Canto ....G 330 806-5336
North Canton (G-15240)

Latin Quarter ....G 513 271-5400
Cincinnati (G-4014)

Quarter Bistro ....G 513 271-5400
Cincinnati (G-4311)

Quarter Mile Fabrication LLC ....G 440 298-1272
Thompson (G-18190)

Randy R Wilson ....G 740 454-4440
Zanesville (G-21348)

SHOE MATERIALS: Rands

McClellan Rand L ....G 614 462-4782
Columbus (G-7329)

SHOE MATERIALS: Rubber

Remington Products Co.....................C 330 335-1571
Wadsworth (G-19437)

SHOE MATERIALS: Uppers

Fountain Pk Inn Upper Sandusky.........G 419 209-1100
Upper Sandusky (G-19123)

J Liu of Upper Arlington Inc...............G 614 313-1268
Columbus (G-7218)

Rancho Alegre Upper Arlin................G 614 273-1305
Upper Arlington (G-19113)

Selbys Upper Deck Company ....G 513 451-5981
Cincinnati (G-4401)

Upper Cut ....G 740 397-0330
Mount Vernon (G-14653)

Upper Echelon Bar LLC ....G 513 531-2814
Cincinnati (G-4544)

Upper Monument ....G 419 310-2387
Upper Sandusky (G-19143)

Upper Paw ....G 419 277-9000
Toledo (G-18762)

Upper Sandusky Senior Housing.........G 419 731-4104
Upper Sandusky (G-19144)

Upper Sarahsville LLC ....G 740 732-2071
Caldwell (G-2434)

Upperroom Action Ministries ....G 330 848-9246
Akron (G-459)

Whits Frozen Custard of Upper ....G 614 230-2213
Columbus (G-7762)

Yabos Tacos ....G 614 824-2485
Columbus (G-7780)

SHOE REPAIR SHOP

Charm Harness and Boot Ltd ....F 330 893-0402
Charm (G-3183)

Maysville Harness Shop Ltd ....G 330 695-9977
Apple Creek (G-644)

SHOE STORES

Charm Harness and Boot Ltd ....F 330 893-0402
Charm (G-3183)

Ervin Yoder ....G 330 359-5862
Mount Hope (G-14570)

Outdoor Army Store of Ashtbula.........F 440 992-8791
Ashtabula (G-828)

RG Barry Corporation......................C 614 864-6400
Pickerington (G-16203)

Vances Department Store ....G 937 549-2188
Manchester (G-12552)

Vances Department Store ....F 937 549-3033
Manchester (G-12553)

SHOE STORES: Boots, Men's

Cobblers Corner LLC........................F 330 482-4005
Columbiana (G-6610)

Hudson Leather Ltd ....G 419 485-8531
Pioneer (G-16234)

SHOE STORES: Men's

Essential Pathways Ohio LLC ....G 330 518-3091
Youngstown (G-21079)

Wagoner Stores Inc ....G 937 836-3636
Englewood (G-9544)

SHOE STORES: Women's

Robs Creative Screen Printing ....G 740 264-6383
Wintersville (G-20713)

SHOES & BOOTS WHOLESALERS

RG Barry Corporation......................C 614 864-6400
Pickerington (G-16203)

Sysco Guest Supply LLC ....F 440 960-2515
Lorain (G-12285)

SHOES: Athletic, Exc Rubber Or Plastic

NTS Enterprises Ltd ....G 513 531-1166
Cincinnati (G-4167)

SHOES: Canvas, Rubber Soled

Vans Inc......................................F 419 471-1541
Toledo (G-18765)

SHOES: Men's

Acor Orthopaedic Inc ....D 216 662-4500
Cleveland (G-4695)

Georgia Boot LLC ....D 740 753-1951
Nelsonville (G-14734)

Red Wing Shoe Company Inc ....G 419 531-1948
Toledo (G-18673)

RG Barry Corporation......................C 614 864-6400
Pickerington (G-16203)

Rocky Brands Inc...........................B 740 753-1951
Nelsonville (G-14736)

Rocky Brands Inc...........................D 740 753-1951
Nelsonville (G-14737)

Rocky Brands Inc...........................A 740 753-9100
Nelsonville (G-14738)

SHOES: Plastic Or Rubber

American Doll Accessories.................G 740 590-8458
Coolville (G-7833)

Cobblers Corner LLC.......................F 330 482-4005
Columbiana (G-6610)

Georgia Boot LLC ....D 740 753-1951
Nelsonville (G-14734)

Mulhern Belting Inc ....E 201 337-5700
Fairfield (G-9689)

Nwc HUD Corp II ....G 419 228-8400
Lima (G-12064)

Totes Isotoner Corporation ....F 513 682-8200
West Chester (G-20059)

Totes Isotoner Holdings Corp.............C 513 682-8200
West Chester (G-20060)

SHOES: Plastic Soles Molded To Fabric Uppers

Factory Direct International ....E 419 425-9636
Findlay (G-9821)

SHOES: Rubber Or Rubber Soled Fabric Uppers

Crocs Inc.....................................F 330 954-1963
Aurora (G-914)

SHOES: Women's

Acor Orthopaedic Inc ....D 216 662-4500
Cleveland (G-4695)

Georgia Boot LLC ....D 740 753-1951
Nelsonville (G-14734)

RG Barry Corporation......................C 614 864-6400
Pickerington (G-16203)

Rocky Brands Inc...........................B 740 753-1951
Nelsonville (G-14736)

SHOT PEENING SVC

Metal Improvement Company LLC.......E 513 489-6484
Blue Ash (G-1838)

National Peening ....G 216 342-9155
Bedford Heights (G-1491)

SHOWCASES & DISPLAY FIXTURES: Office & Store

Darko Inc.....................................E 330 425-9805
Twinsburg (G-18921)

Easy Board Inc...............................G 440 205-8836
Mentor (G-13570)

Pete Gaietto & Associates Inc ....D...... 513 771-0903
Cincinnati (G-4230)

SHOWER STALLS: Plastic & Fiberglass

Cfrc Wtr & Enrgy Solutions Inc ....G...... 216 479-0290
Cleveland (G-5011)

Closets By Mike ....G...... 740 607-2212
Zanesville (G-21290)

Crane Plumbing LLC ....F...... 419 522-4211
Mansfield (G-12588)

SHREDDERS: Indl & Commercial

Accushred LLC ....F...... 419 244-7473
Toledo (G-18319)

Cintas Corporation No 2 ....G...... 937 236-1506
Dayton (G-8230)

Shred Devil LLC ....G...... 740 776-1400
Portsmouth (G-16452)

Shred-It USA LLC ....G...... 614 231-7470
Columbus (G-7618)

Shred-It USA LLC ....E...... 513 699-0845
Blue Ash (G-1869)

SHUTTERS, DOOR & WINDOW: Metal

A C Shutters Inc ....G...... 216 429-2424
Cleveland (G-4669)

Installed Building Pdts LLC ....E...... 614 308-9900
Columbus (G-7190)

SHUTTERS, DOOR & WINDOW: Plastic

A C Shutters Inc ....G...... 216 429-2424
Cleveland (G-4669)

Tapco Holdings Inc ....G...... 800 771-4486
Franklin (G-10057)

SIDING & STRUCTURAL MATERIALS: Wood

Automated Bldg Components Inc ....E...... 419 257-2152
North Baltimore (G-15191)

Beiting Farms ....G...... 740 384-5127
Jackson (G-11310)

S & J Lumber Co ....E...... 740 245-5804
Thurman (G-18200)

Sphon Associates Inc ....G...... 614 741-4002
Gahanna (G-10236)

SIDING MATERIALS

American Orginal Bldg Pdts LLC ....F...... 330 786-3000
Akron (G-67)

C Green & Sons Incorporated ....F...... 740 745-2998
Saint Louisville (G-16826)

SIDING: Plastic

Alsco Metals Corporation ....E...... 740 983-2571
Dennison (G-8942)

Fibreboard Corporation ....C...... 419 248-8000
Toledo (G-18470)

Gentek Building Products Inc ....F...... 800 548-4542
Cuyahoga Falls (G-8003)

Style Crest Inc ....B...... 419 332-7369
Fremont (G-10184)

SIDING: Precast Stone

Headwaters Incorporated ....F...... 989 671-1500
Manchester (G-12549)

SIDING: Sheet Metal

Alsco Metals Corporation ....E...... 740 983-2571
Dennison (G-8942)

Amh Holdings LLC ....A...... 330 929-1811
Cuyahoga Falls (G-7966)

Gentek Building Products Inc ....F...... 800 548-4542
Cuyahoga Falls (G-8003)

Higgins Building Mtls No 2 LLC ....G...... 740 395-5410
Jackson (G-11315)

Metal Sales Manufacturing Corp ....E...... 440 576-9070
Jefferson (G-11367)

North Star Metals Mfg Co ....E...... 740 254-4567
Uhrichsville (G-19055)

Owens Corning Sales Inc ....G...... 740 983-1300
Ashville (G-853)

SIGN LETTERING & PAINTING SVCS

Akers Identity LLC ....G...... 330 493-0055
Canton (G-2596)

SIGN PAINTING & LETTERING SHOP

All Signs and Designs LLC ....G...... 216 267-8588
Cleveland (G-4758)

Art & Sign Corporation ....G...... 419 865-3336
Toledo (G-18356)

Bernard R Doyles Inc ....G...... 216 523-2288
Cleveland (G-4906)

Brent Bleh Company ....G...... 513 721-1100
Cincinnati (G-3467)

Carroll Exhibit and Print Svcs ....G...... 216 361-2325
Cleveland (G-4985)

Digimatics Inc ....G...... 419 478-0804
Toledo (G-18438)

General Theming Contrs LLC ....C...... 614 252-6342
Columbus (G-7108)

KS Designs Inc ....G...... 513 241-5953
Cincinnati (G-4005)

Medina Signs Post Inc ....G...... 330 723-2484
Medina (G-13444)

Ohio Shelterall Inc ....F...... 614 882-1110
Westerville (G-20227)

Premiere Printing & Signs Inc ....G...... 330 688-6244
Stow (G-17791)

Quick As A Wink Printing Co ....F...... 419 224-9786
Lima (G-12079)

Signery ....G...... 513 932-1938
Lebanon (G-11840)

Steven Mercer Inc ....G...... 740 623-0033
Coshocton (G-7911)

Triangle Sign Co ....G...... 513 863-2578
Hamilton (G-10751)

SIGNALS: Traffic Control, Electric

Area Wide Protective Inc ....E...... 513 321-9889
Fairfield (G-9643)

Athens Technical Specialists ....F...... 740 592-2874
Athens (G-857)

City Elyria Communication ....G...... 440 322-3329
Elyria (G-9394)

City of Canton ....E...... 330 489-3370
Canton (G-2656)

Intelligent Signal Tech ....G...... 614 530-4784
Loveland (G-12361)

K-Hill Signal Co Inc ....G...... 740 922-0421
Uhrichsville (G-19054)

MD Solutions Inc ....G...... 866 637-6588
Plain City (G-16348)

Paul Peterson Company ....E...... 614 486-4375
Columbus (G-7467)

Security Fence Group Inc ....E...... 513 681-3700
Cincinnati (G-4395)

SIGNALS: Transportation

Ds Express Carriers Inc ....G...... 419 433-6200
Norwalk (G-15534)

General Dynmics Mssion Systems ....E...... 513 253-4770
Beavercreek (G-1340)

Ohio Department Transportation ....E...... 614 351-2898
Columbus (G-7418)

Signature Technologies Inc ....E...... 937 859-6323
Miamisburg (G-13859)

SIGNS & ADVERTISING SPECIALTIES

1 Day Sign ....G...... 419 475-6060
Toledo (G-18315)

A & A Safety Inc ....E...... 513 943-6100
Amelia (G-564)

A B C Sign Inc ....F...... 513 241-8884
Cincinnati (G-3332)

A M Scheffer Signs Fab ....G...... 330 666-6674
Copley (G-7837)

A Plus Signs & Graphix ....G...... 330 848-4800
Akron (G-18)

A Sign Above Inc ....G...... 330 723-3650
Twinsburg (G-18889)

A Sign For The Times Inc ....G...... 216 297-2977
Cleveland (G-4678)

Abbot Image Solutions LLC ....G...... 937 382-6677
Wilmington (G-20652)

Accu-Sign ....G...... 216 544-2059
Broadview Heights (G-2102)

Accutech Sign Shop ....G...... 513 385-3595
Cincinnati (G-3348)

Action Enterprise ....G...... 740 522-1678
Newark (G-14978)

Ad-Pro Signs I LLC ....G...... 513 922-5046
Cincinnati (G-3354)

Adcraft Decals Inc ....E...... 216 524-2934
Cleveland (G-4702)

Advance Sign Group LLC ....E...... 614 429-2111
Columbus (G-6696)

Advertising Ideas of Ohio Inc ....G...... 330 745-6555
Barberton (G-1094)

Affinity Disp Expositions Inc ....D...... 513 771-2339
Cincinnati (G-3363)

Affinity Disp Expositions Inc ....D...... 513 771-2339
Cincinnati (G-3364)

Agile Sign & Ltg Maint Inc ....F...... 440 918-1311
Eastlake (G-9258)

Akers Identity LLC ....G...... 330 493-0055
Canton (G-2596)

Alberts Screen Print Inc ....G...... 330 753-7559
Norton (G-15505)

All Signs and Designs LLC ....G...... 216 267-8588
Cleveland (G-4758)

All Signs Express Inc ....F...... 513 489-7744
Blue Ash (G-1741)

All Signs of Chillicothe Inc ....G...... 740 773-5016
Chillicothe (G-3227)

All Star Sign Company ....E...... 614 461-9052
Columbus (G-6722)

Alvin L Roepke ....F...... 419 862-3891
Elmore (G-9360)

Am Graphics ....G...... 330 799-7319
Youngstown (G-21022)

American Awards Inc ....F...... 614 875-1850
Grove City (G-10542)

American Metal Sign ....G...... 267 521-2670
Ada (G-4)

Aq Productions Inc ....G...... 614 486-7700
Dublin (G-9046)

Archer Corporation ....G...... 330 455-9995
Canton (G-2604)

Architctral Identification Inc ....G...... 614 868-8400
Gahanna (G-10204)

Art Tees Inc ....G...... 614 338-8337
Columbus (G-6774)

Atchley Signs & Graphics ....G...... 614 421-7446
Columbus (G-6781)

Atlantic Sign Company Inc ....F...... 513 383-1504
Cincinnati (G-3425)

Auld Lang Signs Inc ....G...... 513 792-5555
Blue Ash (G-1746)

Auld Technologies LLC ....F...... 614 755-2853
Columbus (G-6788)

Auto Dealer Designs Inc ....E...... 330 374-7666
Akron (G-78)

Baker Plastics Inc ....G...... 330 743-3142
Youngstown (G-21031)

Bambeck Inc ....G...... 614 766-1000
Dublin (G-9052)

Barnes Advertising Corp ....F...... 740 453-6836
Zanesville (G-21275)

Bates Metal Products Inc ....D...... 740 498-8371
Port Washington (G-16422)

Becker Signs Inc ....G...... 330 659-4504
Richfield (G-16615)

Beebe Worldwide Graphics Sign ....G...... 513 241-2726
Blue Ash (G-1748)

Beesign Signs Inc ....G...... 614 449-3233
Columbus (G-6819)

Belco Works Inc ....B...... 740 695-0500
Saint Clairsville (G-16782)

Bench Billboard Company Inc ....G...... 513 271-2222
Cincinnati (G-3444)

Bernard R Doyles Inc ....G...... 216 523-2288
Cleveland (G-4906)

Bird Corporation ....G...... 419 424-3095
Findlay (G-9795)

Blang Acquisition LLC ....F...... 937 223-2155
Dayton (G-8190)

Bob King Sign Company Inc ....G...... 330 753-2679
Akron (G-94)

Boyer Signs & Graphics Inc ....E...... 216 383-7242
Euclid (G-9568)

Brandon Screen Printing ....F...... 419 229-9837
Lima (G-11996)

Breibach Association ....G...... 614 876-6480
Hilliard (G-10936)

Brent Bleh Company ....G...... 513 721-1100
Cincinnati (G-3467)

Brockmans Signs Inc ....G...... 513 574-6163
Cincinnati (G-3469)

Brown Cnty Bd Mntal Rtardation ....E...... 937 378-4891
Georgetown (G-10364)

Buckeye Boxes Inc ....D...... 614 274-8484
Columbus (G-6870)

P
R
O
D
U
C
T

Company		Phone
Buds Sign Shop Inc	F	330 744-5555
Youngstown (G-21039)		
Busch & Thiem Inc	E	419 625-7515
Sandusky (G-16952)		
Business Idntification Systems	G	614 841-1255
Columbus (G-6879)		
Byers Sign Co	G	614 561-1224
Columbus (G-6880)		
C A Kustoms	G	419 332-4395
Fremont (G-10133)		
C JS Signs	G	330 821-7446
Alliance (G-500)		
Campbell Signs & Apparel LLC	F	330 386-4768
East Liverpool (G-9205)		
Casad Company Inc	F	419 586-9457
Coldwater (G-6555)		
Catalog Merchandiser Inc	F	888 325-9677
Cincinnati (G-3505)		
Central Graphics Inc	G	330 928-7080
Cuyahoga Falls (G-7977)		
Century Signs	G	419 352-2666
Bowling Green (G-1979)		
Cgs Signs LLC	F	419 897-3000
Maumee (G-13233)		
Chas J Steven Inc	G	440 954-9191
Painesville (G-15864)		
Classic Sign Company Inc	G	419 420-0058
Findlay (G-9809)		
Cline Signs LLC	G	513 396-7446
Cincinnati (G-3586)		
Columbus Graphics Inc	F	614 577-9360
Reynoldsburg (G-16584)		
Creative Blast Co	G	513 251-4177
Cincinnati (G-3618)		
CTS Signs & Sales	G	419 407-5534
Oregon (G-15707)		
Custom Engraving & Screen Prtg	G	440 933-2902
Avon Lake (G-1027)		
Custom Neon & Commercial Signs	G	440 327-0225
North Ridgeville (G-15367)		
Custom Sign Center Inc	E	614 279-6700
Columbus (G-7005)		
D & D Next Day Signs Inc	G	419 537-9595
Toledo (G-18422)		
Dana Signs LLC	G	937 653-3917
Urbana (G-19155)		
Danite Holdings Ltd	E	614 444-3333
Columbus (G-7011)		
David Esrati	G	937 228-4433
Dayton (G-8266)		
Dayton Wire Products Inc	E	937 236-8000
Dayton (G-8291)		
Dee Sign Co	E	513 779-3333
West Chester (G-19852)		
Dee Sign Usa LLC	G	513 779-3333
West Chester (G-19853)		
Dern Trophies Corp	F	614 895-3260
Westerville (G-20145)		
Design Masters Inc	G	513 772-7175
Cincinnati (G-3649)		
Design Sign Inc	G	216 398-9900
Cleveland (G-5185)		
Devries & Associates Inc	F	614 890-3821
Westerville (G-20209)		
Devries & Associates Inc	G	614 860-0103
Westerville (G-20210)		
Devries & Associates Inc	G	614 860-0103
Columbus (G-7023)		
Digimatics Inc	G	419 478-0804
Toledo (G-18438)		
Digimax Signs	G	513 576-0747
Milford (G-14137)		
Direct Image Signs Inc	G	440 327-5575
North Ridgeville (G-15369)		
Discount Signs Awnings	G	740 373-3556
Marietta (G-12780)		
DJ Signs MD LLC	G	330 344-6643
Akron (G-153)		
Donald Marlo	G	937 836-4880
Dayton (G-8308)		
Downing Displays Inc	D	513 248-9800
Milford (G-14138)		
Downing Enterprises Inc	D	330 666-3888
Copley (G-7845)		
Dyverse Entertainment LLC	G	513 225-3301
Blue Ash (G-1779)		
E S Sign & Design LLC	G	330 405-4799
Twinsburg (G-18927)		
Eighth Floor Promotions	C	419 586-6433
Celina (G-2994)		

Company		Phone
Ellet Neon Sales & Service Inc	E	330 628-9907
Akron (G-162)		
Enlarging Arts Inc	G	330 434-3433
Akron (G-168)		
Etched Metal Company	E	440 248-0240
Solon (G-17290)		
Ew Publishing Company	G	440 887-0131
North Olmsted (G-15333)		
F J Designs Inc	E	330 264-1377
Wooster (G-20771)		
Fair Publishing House Inc	E	419 668-3746
Norwalk (G-15540)		
Fastsigns	G	513 489-8989
Cincinnati (G-3741)		
Fdi Cabinetry LLC	G	513 353-4500
Cleves (G-6514)		
Ffr-DSI Company	G	330 998-7800
Twinsburg (G-18936)		
Fineline Imprints Inc	E	740 453-1083
Zanesville (G-21308)		
Firehouse Sign Co Inc	G	216 267-5300
Brookpark (G-2159)		
First Stop Signs and Decals	G	330 343-1859
New Philadelphia (G-14899)		
Folks Creative Printers Inc	E	740 383-6326
Marion (G-12865)		
Forty Nine Degrees LLC	F	419 678-0100
Coldwater (G-6560)		
Fourteen Ventures Group LLC	G	937 866-2341
West Carrollton (G-19792)		
Fried Daddy	G	937 854-4542
Dayton (G-8351)		
Frontier Signs & Displays Inc	G	513 367-0813
Harrison (G-10779)		
Fultz Sign Co Inc	G	419 225-6000
Lima (G-12016)		
Gail Berner	G	937 322-0314
Springfield (G-17563)		
Galaxy Balloons Incorporated	C	216 476-3360
Cleveland (G-5392)		
Gallo Displays Inc	G	216 431-9500
Cleveland (G-5393)		
Gary Krinn	G	740 344-3695
Newark (G-15012)		
Gary Lawrence Enterprises Inc	F	330 833-7181
Massillon (G-13138)		
Gauntlet Awards & Engraving	G	937 890-5811
Dayton (G-8357)		
Gedco Inc	G	330 828-2044
Dalton (G-8069)		
Geoffrey Smith	G	614 793-1996
Dublin (G-9078)		
Geograph Industries Inc	E	513 202-9200
Harrison (G-10780)		
Ginos Awards Inc	E	216 831-5653
Cleveland (G-5431)		
Glavin Industries Inc	E	440 349-0049
Solon (G-17297)		
Global Lighting Tech Inc	E	440 922-4584
Brecksville (G-2052)		
Global Signs and Graphics Inc	G	440 230-2100
North Royalton (G-15421)		
Golden Signs and Lighting LLC	G	513 248-0895
Milford (G-14144)		
Golf Marketing Group Inc	G	330 963-5155
Twinsburg (G-18950)		
Grady McCauley Incorporated	D	330 494-9444
North Canton (G-15236)		
Granite Industries Inc	D	419 445-4733
Archbold (G-679)		
Hall Company	E	937 652-1376
Urbana (G-19160)		
Ham Signs LLC	G	937 454-9111
Dayton (G-8383)		
Hart Advertising Inc	G	419 668-1194
Norwalk (G-15543)		
Hendricks Vacuum Forming Inc	E	330 837-2040
Massillon (G-13147)		
Hollingsworth Signs Inc	G	614 875-2825
Grove City (G-10562)		
HP Manufacturing Company Inc	D	216 361-6500
Cleveland (G-5530)		
HPM Business Systems Inc	G	216 520-1330
Cleveland (G-5532)		
Identitek Systems Inc	G	330 832-9844
Massillon (G-13155)		
Impressions To Go LLC	G	614 760-0600
Dublin (G-9088)		
Industrial and Mar Eng Svc Co	F	740 694-0791
Fredericktown (G-10104)		

Company		Phone
Industrial Image	G	419 547-1417
Bellevue (G-1551)		
Inner Products Sales Inc	G	216 581-4141
Bedford (G-1431)		
Innersource Inc	F	330 799-7619
Youngstown (G-21117)		
Innovation Exhibits Inc	G	330 726-1324
Youngstown (G-21118)		
Insignia Signs Inc	G	937 866-2341
Dayton (G-8409)		
Integral Design Inc	G	216 524-0555
Cleveland (G-5574)		
J & D Berdine Signs Inc	G	330 468-0556
Macedonia (G-12461)		
Jacqueline L Vandyke	G	740 593-6779
Athens (G-874)		
Janeway Signs Inc	G	937 237-8433
Dayton (G-8422)		
JCP Signs & Graphix Inc	G	740 965-3058
Galena (G-10244)		
Jeffrey A Clark	G	419 866-8775
Holland (G-11067)		
Jeffrey L Becht Inc	G	937 264-2070
Dayton (G-8426)		
Jerry Pulfer	G	937 778-1861
Piqua (G-16283)		
Jfm Industries	G	330 550-6009
Struthers (G-17992)		
Joe Paxton	G	614 424-9000
Columbus (G-7237)		
Jones & Assoc Advg & Design	G	330 799-6876
Youngstown (G-21127)		
Jones Old Rustic Sign	E	937 643-1695
Moraine (G-14498)		
Judith C Zell	G	740 385-0386
Logan (G-12180)		
Kane Sign Co	G	330 253-5263
Akron (G-249)		
Kdm Signs Inc	C	513 769-1932
Cincinnati (G-3975)		
Kenneth J Moore	G	330 923-8313
Cuyahoga Falls (G-8016)		
Kim Phillips Sign Co LLC	G	330 364-4280
Dover (G-8995)		
King Retail Solutions Inc	F	513 729-5858
Hamilton (G-10716)		
Kingsway Art & Sign	G	330 877-6241
Hartville (G-10826)		
Kmgrafx Inc	G	513 248-4100
Loveland (G-12367)		
Koebbeco Signs LLC	G	513 923-2974
Cincinnati (G-4000)		
Krigbaum Inc	E	614 478-6472
Columbus (G-7267)		
Laad Sign & Lighting Inc	F	330 379-2297
Akron (G-265)		
Lapat Signs	G	440 277-6291
Sheffield Village (G-17124)		
Ledge Hill Signs Limited	G	440 461-4445
Cleveland (G-5690)		
Long Sign Co	G	614 294-1057
Columbus (G-7304)		
Macray Co LLC	G	937 325-1726
Springfield (G-17596)		
Magnetic Mktg Solutions LLC	G	513 721-3801
Cincinnati (G-4053)		
Maines Inc	G	937 322-2084
Springfield (G-17601)		
Massillon-Cleveland-Akron Sign	C	330 833-3165
Massillon (G-13175)		
Mayfair Granite Co Inc	G	216 382-8150
Cleveland (G-5763)		
Mc Sign Company	C	440 209-6200
Mentor (G-13649)		
McQueen Advertising Inc	G	440 967-1137
Vermilion (G-19334)		
McRd Enterprises LLC	F	740 775-2377
Chillicothe (G-3250)		
ME Signs Inc	G	419 222-7446
Lima (G-12052)		
Media Sign Company	G	513 564-9500
Cincinnati (G-4078)		
Meka Signs Enterprises Inc	G	513 942-5494
West Chester (G-20027)		
Mentor Signs & Graphics Inc	G	440 951-7446
Mentor (G-13652)		
Metromedia Technologies Inc	D	330 264-2501
Wooster (G-20807)		
Middlefield Sign Co	G	440 632-0708
Middlefield (G-13963)		

Midwest Sign Ctr ....F 330 493-7330
Canton (G-2781)

Mike B Crawford ....G 330 673-7944
Kent (G-11492)

Mike Closterman ....G 513 245-9593
Cincinnati (G-4107)

Mitchell Plastics Inc ....E 330 825-2461
Barberton (G-1131)

Moments To Remember USA LLC ....G 330 830-0839
Massillon (G-13181)

Moonlight Specialties ....G 216 464-6444
Cleveland (G-5833)

Names Unlimited Corp ....G 419 845-2005
Caledonia (G-2440)

Nauman Communications Inc ....G 740 654-0084
Lancaster (G-11732)

Next Day Sign ....G 419 537-9595
Toledo (G-18605)

Next Day Signs LLC ....G 614 764-7446
Columbus (G-7391)

Norcal Signs Inc ....G 513 779-6982
West Chester (G-19906)

North Coast Theatrical Inc ....G 330 762-1768
Akron (G-317)

Northmont Sign Co Inc ....G 937 890-0372
Dayton (G-8528)

Norton Outdoor Advertising ....E 513 631-4864
Cincinnati (G-4164)

Off The Wall Signs ....G 740 264-7759
Steubenville (G-17707)

Ohio Logos Inc ....G 614 717-0833
Dublin (G-9115)

Ohio Plastics & Safety Pdts ....G 330 882-6764
New Franklin (G-14827)

Ohio Shelterall Inc ....F 614 882-1110
Westerville (G-20227)

Oliver Signs & Graphics ....G 330 460-2996
Valley City (G-19226)

Omni Media ....G 216 687-0077
Cleveland (G-5941)

Orange Barrel Media LLC ....E 614 294-4898
Columbus (G-7445)

Painted Hill Inv Group Inc ....F 937 339-1756
Troy (G-18861)

Pfi Displays Inc ....E 330 925-9015
Rittman (G-16681)

Plastigraphics Inc ....F 513 771-8848
Cincinnati (G-4243)

Power Corp Sign Products Inc ....G 740 344-0468
Newark (G-15047)

PR Signs & Service ....G 614 252-7090
Columbus (G-7511)

Pro-Decal Inc ....G 330 484-0089
Canton (G-2825)

R & H Signs Unlimited Inc ....G 937 293-3834
Dayton (G-8608)

R Weir Inc ....G 937 438-5730
Dayton (G-8613)

Ram Z Neon ....G 330 788-5121
Youngstown (G-21185)

Rapid Signs & More Inc ....G 513 553-4040
New Richmond (G-14944)

Red Hot Studios ....G 330 609-7446
Warren (G-19592)

Redi-Quik Signs Inc ....G 614 228-6641
Columbus (G-7551)

Renoir Visions LLC ....F 419 586-5679
Celina (G-3016)

Ricks Graphic Accents Inc ....G 330 644-4455
Akron (G-374)

Rise N Shine Yard Signs ....G 330 745-5868
Barberton (G-1147)

Roderer Enterprises Inc ....G 513 942-3000
Fairfield (G-9712)

Roemer Industries Inc ....D 330 448-2000
Masury (G-13216)

Rossi Concept Arts ....G 330 453-6366
Canton (G-2843)

Royal Acme Corporation ....E 216 241-1477
Cleveland (G-6136)

S & S Sign Co ....G 614 837-1511
Canal Winchester (G-2536)

S T Custom Signs ....G 513 733-4227
Cincinnati (G-4375)

S&S Sign Service ....G 614 279-9722
Columbus (G-7582)

Sa-Mor Signs ....G 937 441-4950
Wapakoneta (G-19505)

Sabco Industries Inc ....E 419 531-5347
Toledo (G-18683)

Screen Images Inc ....G 440 779-7356
North Olmsted (G-15344)

Screen Works Inc ....E 937 264-9111
Dayton (G-8650)

Sensical Inc ....D 216 641-1141
Solon (G-17378)

Sign A Rama ....G 330 499-4653
North Canton (G-15265)

Sign A Rama ....G 614 337-6000
Gahanna (G-10232)

Sign A Rama Inc ....G 440 442-5002
Cleveland (G-6202)

Sign A Rama Inc ....G 513 671-2213
Cincinnati (G-4419)

Sign America Incorporated ....E 740 765-5555
Richmond (G-16649)

Sign Connection Inc ....G 937 435-4070
Dayton (G-8657)

Sign Design Wooster Inc ....G 330 262-8838
Wooster (G-20835)

Sign Graphics & Design ....G 513 576-1639
Milford (G-14174)

Sign Pro of Lima ....G 419 222-7767
Lima (G-12091)

Sign Shop ....G 740 474-1499
Circleville (G-4643)

Sign Smith LLC ....G 614 519-9144
Marengo (G-12755)

Sign Source USA Inc ....D 419 224-1130
Lima (G-12092)

Sign Write ....G 937 559-4388
Beavercreek (G-1361)

Signed By Josette LLC ....G 419 796-9632
Findlay (G-9889)

Signery ....G 513 932-1938
Lebanon (G-11840)

Signery2 LLC ....G 513 738-3048
Hamilton (G-10739)

Significant Impressions Inc ....G 513 874-5223
Fairfield (G-9718)

Signline Graphics & Lettering ....G 740 397-5806
Mount Vernon (G-14650)

Signmaster Inc ....G 614 777-0670
Lewis Center (G-11918)

Signs 2 Graphics ....G 740 493-2049
Piketon (G-16228)

Signs Limited LLC ....G 740 282-7715
Steubenville (G-17712)

Signs N Stuff Inc ....G 440 974-3151
Mentor (G-13723)

Signs PDQ Inc ....G 440 951-6651
Willoughby (G-20597)

Signs Unlimited ....G 614 836-7446
Logan (G-12193)

Spotted Horse Studio Inc ....G 330 533-2391
Greenford (G-10483)

Steel Valley Sign ....G 330 755-7446
Struthers (G-17999)

Steven Mercer Inc ....G 740 623-0033
Coshocton (G-7911)

Stine Consulting Inc ....G 513 723-4800
Cincinnati (G-4469)

Summco Inc ....G 330 965-7446
Youngstown (G-21215)

Super Sign Guys LLC ....G 330 477-3887
Canton (G-2864)

Super Signs Inc ....E 480 968-2200
North Bend (G-15209)

Superior Label Systems Inc ....B 513 336-0825
Mason (G-13092)

T-Top Shoppe ....G 330 343-3481
New Philadelphia (G-14932)

Tamblingson Inc ....G 419 221-3437
Lima (G-12101)

Tce International Ltd ....F 800 962-2376
Perry (G-16059)

Ternion Inc ....E 216 642-6180
Cleveland (G-6307)

Thatcher Enterprises Co Ltd ....G 614 228-2013
Columbus (G-7688)

The Hartman Corp ....G 614 475-5035
Columbus (G-7690)

Tim Boutwell ....G 419 358-4653
Bluffton (G-1917)

To A T ....G 216 621-3322
Cleveland (G-6329)

Toledo Mobile Media LLC ....G 419 389-0687
Toledo (G-18734)

Traffic Cntrl Sgnls Signs & MA ....G 740 670-7763
Newark (G-15064)

Traffic Detectors & Signs Inc ....G 330 707-9060
Youngstown (G-21226)

Tridico Silk Screen & Sign Co ....G 419 526-1695
Mansfield (G-12700)

Triumph Signs & Consulting Inc ......E 513 576-8090
Milford (G-14180)

Ultimate Signs and Graphics ....G 740 633-8928
Martins Ferry (G-12926)

Unionville Center Sign Co ....G 614 873-5834
Unionville Center (G-19105)

Unique Straight Line & Sfety S ....G 740 452-2724
Zanesville (G-21359)

United-Maier Signs Inc ....D 513 681-6600
Cincinnati (G-4541)

Visionary Signs LLC ....G 614 504-5899
Columbus (G-7742)

Visual Advantage LLC ....G 714 671-0988
Perrysburg (G-16166)

Visual Expressions Sign Co ....G 440 245-6660
Lorain (G-12291)

Vital Signs & Advertising LLC ....G 937 292-7967
Bellefontaine (G-1540)

Vsl Signs ....G 740 441-7578
Gallipolis (G-10311)

Waterford Signs Inc ....G 740 362-7446
Delaware (G-8895)

Westrock Cp LLC ....B 513 745-2400
Blue Ash (G-1893)

Wettle Corporation ....G 419 865-6923
Holland (G-11096)

WH Fetzer & Sons Mfg Inc ....E 419 687-8237
Plymouth (G-16380)

Williams Steel Rule Die Co ....F 216 431-3232
Cleveland (G-6464)

Wright John ....G 937 653-4570
Urbana (G-19188)

Yes Management Inc ....G 330 747-8593
Columbiana (G-6638)

SIGNS & ADVERTISING SPECIALTIES: Artwork, Advertising

Penca Design Group Ltd ....G 440 210-4422
Painesville (G-15910)

Platinum Productions Inc ....E 614 888-7771
Columbus (G-7496)

SIGNS & ADVERTISING SPECIALTIES: Displays, Paint Process

Custom Retail Group LLC ....G 614 409-9720
Columbus (G-7004)

Ohio Displays Inc ....F 216 961-5600
Elyria (G-9470)

SIGNS & ADVERTISING SPECIALTIES: Letters For Signs, Metal

AG Designs LLC ....G 614 506-2849
Delaware (G-8819)

Engravers Gallery & Sign Co ....G 330 830-1271
Massillon (G-13130)

Interstate Sign Products Inc ....G 419 683-1962
Crestline (G-7930)

Pro Companies Inc ....G 614 738-1222
Pickerington (G-16201)

Sign City Inc ....G 614 486-6700
Mount Gilead (G-14568)

Tillmans Entp -Signs Ship LLC ....G 440 281-9340
Elyria (G-9502)

SIGNS & ADVERTISING SPECIALTIES: Novelties

American Executive Gifts Inc ....F 330 645-4396
Akron (G-66)

Finn Graphics Inc ....E 513 941-6161
Cincinnati (G-3756)

Gerber Wood Products Inc ....G 330 857-3901
Kidron (G-11591)

Joseph A Panico & Sons Inc ....G 614 235-3188
Columbus (G-7244)

Power Media Inc ....G 330 475-0500
Akron (G-345)

Quikey Manufacturing Co Inc ....C 330 633-8106
Akron (G-360)

Ruthie Ann Inc ....F 800 231-3567
New Paris (G-14881)

PRODUCT

SIGNS & ADVERTISING SPECIALTIES: Scoreboards, Electric

Industrial Electronic Service ....F 937 746-9750
Carlisle (G-2931)

SIGNS & ADVERTISING SPECIALTIES: Signs

Abbott Signs ....G 937 393-6600
Hillsboro (G-10995)
Action Sign Inc ....G 330 966-0390
Greentown (G-10484)
Chatelain Plastics Inc ....G 419 422-4323
Findlay (G-9807)
Exchange Signs ....G 330 644-4552
Akron (G-174)
Insta Plak Inc ....F 419 537-1555
Toledo (G-18525)
Interior Graphic Systems LLC ....G 330 244-0100
Canton (G-2738)
Judco Inc ....G 440 322-6604
Elyria (G-9444)
Kessler Sign Company ....E 740 453-0668
Zanesville (G-21326)
Kessler Sign Company ....G 937 898-0633
Dayton (G-8440)
Kief Signs ....G 513 941-8800
Addyston (G-11)
Mel Wacker Sign Inc ....G 330 832-1726
Massillon (G-13178)
Morrison Sign Company Inc ....E 614 276-1181
Columbus (G-7371)
Municipal Signs and Sales Inc ......G 330 457-2421
Columbiana (G-6625)
North Hill Marble & Granite Co ....F 330 253-2179
Akron (G-318)
Paul Peterson Safety Div Inc ....E 614 486-4375
Columbus (G-7468)
Rocal Inc ....D 740 998-2122
Frankfort (G-10002)
Safety Sign Company ....E 440 238-7722
Strongsville (G-17960)
Scioto Sign Co Inc ....E 419 673-1261
Kenton (G-11568)
Signage Consultants Inc ....G 614 297-7446
Columbus (G-7620)
Standard Signs Incorporated ....F 330 467-2030
Macedonia (G-12489)
Sterling Associates Inc ....G 330 630-3500
Akron (G-418)
Vgu Industries Inc ....E 216 676-9093
Cleveland (G-6414)
Wilson Seat Company Inc ....E 513 732-2460
Batavia (G-1233)
Wurtec Manufacturing Service ....E 419 726-1066
Toledo (G-18777)

SIGNS & ADVERTSG SPECIALTIES: Displays/Cutouts Window/Lobby

Art & Sign Corporation ....G 419 865-3336
Toledo (G-18356)
BDS Packaging Inc ....D 937 643-0530
Moraine (G-14468)
Benchmark Craftsman Inc ....E 330 975-4214
Seville (G-17069)
Co Pac Services Inc ....F 216 688-1780
Cleveland (G-5095)
Genesis Display Systems Inc ....G 513 561-1440
Cincinnati (G-3821)
Hill John ....F 419 727-8666
Toledo (G-18508)
Myers and Lasch Inc ....G 440 235-2050
Cleveland (G-5843)
Skyline Exhibits Grtr Cncnt ....G 513 671-4460
Cincinnati (G-4426)

SIGNS, ELECTRICAL: Wholesalers

Sign America Incorporated ....E 740 765-5555
Richmond (G-16649)

SIGNS, EXC ELECTRIC, WHOLESALE

Atlantic Sign Company Inc ....F 513 383-1504
Cincinnati (G-3425)
Breibach Association ....G 614 876-6480
Hilliard (G-10936)
Fostoria Monument Co ....G 419 435-0323
Fostoria (G-9978)
J-M Designs LLC ....G 419 794-2114
Maumee (G-13269)

Jones & Assoc Advg & Design ......G 330 799-6876
Youngstown (G-21127)
K Ventures Inc ....F 419 678-2308
Coldwater (G-6566)
Macray Co LLC ....G 937 325-1726
Springfield (G-17596)
Sign Lady Inc ....G 419 476-9191
Toledo (G-18696)
Snyder Printing LLC ....G 740 353-3947
Portsmouth (G-16455)
Toledo Signs & Designs Ltd ....G 419 843-1073
Toledo (G-18742)
Water Drop Media Inc ....G 234 600-5817
Vienna (G-19377)

SIGNS: Electrical

American Led-Gible Inc ....F 614 851-1100
Columbus (G-6740)
Behrco Inc ....G 419 394-1612
Saint Marys (G-16832)
Brilliant Electric Sign Co Ltd ....D 216 741-3800
Brooklyn Heights (G-2132)
Cicogna Electric and Sign Co ....D 440 998-2637
Ashtabula (G-797)
Federal Heath Sign Company LLC ...D 740 369-0999
Delaware (G-8844)
Gardner Signs Inc ....F 419 385-6669
Toledo (G-18477)
Gus Holthaus Signs Inc ....E 513 861-0060
Cincinnati (G-3858)
Kasper Enterprises Inc ....G 419 829-2121
Toledo (G-18540)
Letter Graphics Sign Co Inc ....G 330 683-3903
Orrville (G-15746)
LSI Industries Inc ....E 513 793-3200
Blue Ash (G-1829)
LSI Industries Inc ....B 513 793-3200
Blue Ash (G-1830)
National Illumination Sign Corp ....F 419 866-1666
Holland (G-11074)
Ohio Awning & Manufacturing Co ....E 216 861-2400
Cleveland (G-5928)
Quality Channel Letters ....G 859 866-6500
Miamisburg (G-13850)
R M Davis Inc ....G 419 756-6719
Mansfield (G-12669)
Sign-Lite Corporation ....D 216 851-1000
Cleveland (G-6203)
Signaffects Limited LLC ....G 614 504-5324
Plain City (G-16358)
Signcom Incorporated ....E 614 228-9999
Columbus (G-7621)
Signs By George ....G 216 394-2095
Brookfield (G-2126)
Terry & Jack Neon Sign Co ....F 419 229-0674
Lima (G-12103)
Wholesale Channel Letters ....G 440 256-3200
Kirtland (G-11619)
Wide Area Media LLC ....G 440 356-3133
Westlake (G-20321)
Wilson Sign Co Inc ....F 937 253-2246
Dayton (G-8760)

SIGNS: Neon

Canton Sign Co ....G 330 456-7151
Canton (G-2647)
Columbus Sign Company ....E 614 252-3133
Columbus (G-6966)
Fetters and Son Sign Company ......G 614 299-6947
Mount Gilead (G-14559)
Medina Signs Post Inc ....G 330 723-2484
Medina (G-13444)
Moonshine Screen Printing Inc ......F 513 523-7775
Oxford (G-15840)
Neon Beach Tanning Inc ....G 440 333-3050
Rocky River (G-16702)
Neon Nights ....F 330 345-9907
Wooster (G-20815)
Ruff Neon & Lighting Maint Inc ....F 440 350-6267
Painesville (G-15920)
Triangle Sign Co ....G 513 863-2578
Hamilton (G-10751)
Warren Enterprises ....G 330 836-6119
Akron (G-468)

SILICON: Pure

Ohio Valley Specialty Company ....F 740 373-2276
Marietta (G-12812)

SILICONES

Canton OH Rubber Speclty Prods ....G 330 454-3847
Canton (G-2642)
Dow Corning Corporation ....C 330 319-1127
Copley (G-7844)
Momentive Performance Mtls Inc ....C 740 928-7010
Hebron (G-10874)
Momentive Performance Mtls Inc ....A 440 878-5705
Richmond Heights (G-16655)
Momentive Performance Mtls Inc ....B 614 986-2495
Columbus (G-7365)
Momentive Prfmce Mtls Qrtz Inc .....C 440 878-5700
Strongsville (G-17941)
Silicone Solutions Inc ....F 330 920-3125
Cuyahoga Falls (G-8045)
Silicone Solutions Inc ....G 419 720-8709
Toledo (G-18697)
Wacker Chemical Corporation ....E 330 899-0847
Canton (G-2899)

SILK SCREEN DESIGN SVCS

Alvin L Roepke ....F 419 862-3891
Elmore (G-9360)
Art & Sign Corporation ....G 419 865-3336
Toledo (G-18356)
Galaxy Balloons Incorporated ....C 216 476-3360
Cleveland (G-5392)
Good JP ....G 419 207-8484
Ashland (G-735)
Graphic TS ....G 614 836-2613
Groveport (G-10624)
Heller Acquisitions Inc ....G 937 833-2676
Brookville (G-2186)
Hollywood Imprints LLC ....F 614 501-6040
Gahanna (G-10211)
Image Industries Inc ....G 937 832-7969
Englewood (G-9524)
Kent Stow Screen Printing Inc ....F 330 923-5118
Akron (G-255)
Kimpton Printing & Spc Co ....F 330 467-1640
Macedonia (G-12466)
Liming Printing Inc ....F 937 374-2646
Xenia (G-20961)
Lion Clothing Inc ....G 419 692-9981
Delphos (G-8914)
Madison Graphics ....G 216 226-5770
Cleveland (G-5726)
Marazita Graphics Inc ....G 330 773-6462
Akron (G-283)
Newmast Mktg & Communications ...E 614 837-1200
Columbus (G-7389)
Pelz Lettering Inc ....G 419 625-3567
Sandusky (G-16996)
Professional Screen Printing ....G 740 687-0760
Lancaster (G-11742)
Quali-Tee Design Sports ....F 937 382-7997
Wilmington (G-20675)
Qualitee Design Sportswear Co ......F 740 333-8337
Wshngtn CT Hs (G-20922)
R S C Sales Company ....E 423 581-4916
Dayton (G-8612)
Red Barn Screen Printing & EMB ....F 740 474-6657
Circleville (G-4640)
Roban Inc ....G 330 794-1059
Lakemore (G-11645)
Screen Works Inc ....E 937 264-9111
Dayton (G-8650)
Tridico Silk Screen & Sign Co ....G 419 526-1695
Mansfield (G-12700)
Woodrow Manufacturing Co ....E 937 399-9333
Springfield (G-17682)

SILVERWARE & PLATED WARE

Professional Award Service ....G 513 389-3600
Cincinnati (G-4294)

SIMULATORS: Electronic Countermeasure

Lockheed Martin Corporation ....B 330 796-7000
Akron (G-272)

SIMULATORS: Flight

Technology Products Inc ....G 937 652-3412
Urbana (G-19184)

SINK TOPS, PLASTIC LAMINATED

Malco Laminated Inc ....G 513 541-8300
Cincinnati (G-4055)

SINTER: Iron

GKN Sinter Metals LLC ....C 740 441-3203
Gallipolis (G-10298)

Miba Sinter USA LLC ....F 740 962-4242
McConnelsville (G-13355)

SIZES: Indl

Ace Gasket Manufacturing Co ....G 513 271-6321
Cincinnati (G-3349)

SKIDS

J Smokin ....G 330 466-7087
Rittman (G-16677)

Ohio Box & Crate Inc ....F 440 526-3133
Burton (G-2381)

SKIDS: Wood

Built-Rite Box & Crate Inc ....E 330 263-0936
Wooster (G-20756)

Global Packaging & Exports Inc ....G 513 454-2020
West Chester (G-19877)

SKYLIGHTS

Architectural Daylighting LLC ....G 330 460-5000
Medina (G-13373)

SLAB & TILE: Precast Concrete, Floor

Redi Rock Structures Oki LLC ....G 513 965-9221
Milford (G-14169)

SLAG PRDTS

Ironics Inc ....G 330 652-0583
Niles (G-15162)

Stein Steel Mill Services Inc ....F 440 526-9301
Broadview Heights (G-2120)

SLAG: Crushed Or Ground

Allega Slag Recovery Inc ....E 216 447-0814
Cleveland (G-4763)

Brier Hill Slag Company ....F 330 743-8170
Youngstown (G-21035)

Harsco Corporation ....G 740 367-7322
Cheshire (G-3192)

R W Sidley Incorporated ....G 330 750-1661
Struthers (G-17997)

Sharon Stone Co ....G 740 374-3236
Dexter City (G-8957)

Tms International LLC ....E 330 847-0844
Warren (G-19609)

Tms International Corporation ....F 740 223-0091
Marion (G-12906)

Trans Ash Inc ....F 859 341-1528
Cincinnati (G-4518)

SLAUGHTERING & MEAT PACKING

American Foods Group LLC ....E 513 733-8898
Cincinnati (G-3388)

Carl Rittberger Sr Inc ....E 740 452-2767
Zanesville (G-21287)

Pine Ridge Processing ....G 740 749-3166
Fleming (G-9913)

SLINGS: Lifting, Made From Purchased Wire

Blacco Splcing Rgging Loft Inc ....G 614 444-2888
Columbus (G-6836)

West Equipment Company Inc ....F 419 698-1601
Toledo (G-18772)

SLIPPER SOCKS, MADE FROM PURCHASED SOCKS

Gold Toe Moretz Holdings Corp ....G 740 948-0004
Jeffersonville (G-11380)

SLIPPERS: House

Principle Business Entps Inc ....C 419 352-1551
Bowling Green (G-2009)

SLOT MACHINES

Daca Vending Wholesale LLC ....G 513 753-1600
Amelia (G-571)

SMOKE DETECTORS

Slap N Tickle LLC ....G 419 349-3226
Toledo (G-18698)

Voice Products Inc ....F 216 360-0433
Cleveland (G-6426)

SNOW PLOWING SVCS

Ioppolo Concrete Corporation ....E 440 439-6606
Bedford (G-1433)

Mapledale Farm Inc ....F 440 286-3389
Chardon (G-3166)

SNOW REMOVAL EQPT: Residential

R J Engineering Company Inc ....G 419 843-8651
Toledo (G-18667)

Russell Hunt ....F 740 264-1196
Steubenville (G-17711)

SOAP DISHES: Vitreous China

Bridgits Bath LLC ....G 937 259-1960
Dayton (G-8194)

SOAPS & DETERGENTS

AIN Industries Inc ....G 440 781-0950
Cleveland (G-4733)

Chester Packaging LLC ....C 513 458-3840
Cincinnati (G-3527)

Cincinnati - Vulcan Company ....D 513 242-5300
Cincinnati (G-3535)

Colgate-Palmolive Company ....C 212 310-2000
Cambridge (G-2452)

Cr Brands Inc ....D 513 860-5039
West Chester (G-19846)

Cresset Chemical Co Inc ....F 419 669-2041
Weston (G-20325)

Cresset Chemical Co Inc ....F 419 669-2041
Weston (G-20324)

Emco Electric International ....G 440 878-1199
Strongsville (G-17917)

Equipment Spcalists Dayton LLC ....G 937 415-2151
Dayton (G-8330)

EZ Brite Brands Inc ....F 440 871-7817
Cleveland (G-5316)

Fairy Dust Ltd Inc ....F 513 251-0065
Cincinnati (G-3736)

Foam-Tex Solutions Corp ....G 216 889-2702
Cleveland (G-5364)

Kardol Quality Products LLC ....G 513 933-8206
Blue Ash (G-1822)

Kutol Products Company Inc ....C 513 527-5500
Sharonville (G-17114)

Lubrizol Advanced Mtls Inc ....F 419 352-5565
Bowling Green (G-1998)

Mix-Masters Inc ....F 513 228-2800
Lebanon (G-11817)

New Vulco Mfg & Sales Co LLC ....D 513 242-2672
Cincinnati (G-4149)

Noveon Incorporated ....G 216 447-5000
Brecksville (G-2067)

Oliver Chemical Co Inc ....G 513 541-4540
Cincinnati (G-4185)

Pilot Chemical Corp ....E 513 424-9700
Middletown (G-14075)

Polar Inc ....F 937 297-0911
Moraine (G-14516)

Procter & Gamble Company ....A 513 626-2500
Blue Ash (G-1856)

Procter & Gamble Company ....C 513 634-9600
West Chester (G-19922)

Procter & Gamble Company 513 627-7779
Cincinnati (G-4287)

Procter & Gamble Mfg Co ....C 419 226-5500
Lima (G-12075)

Renegade Brands LLC ....G 216 342-4347
Cleveland (G-6101)

St Bernard Soap Company ....B 513 242-2227
Cincinnati (G-4450)

US Industrial Lubricants Inc ....E 513 541-2225
Cincinnati (G-4547)

Wallover Oil Company Inc ....E 440 238-9250
Strongsville (G-17982)

Washing Systems LLC ....C 800 272-1974
Loveland (G-12399)

SOCIAL SVCS: Individual & Family

County of Lake ....D 440 269-2193
Willoughby (G-20464)

SOFTWARE PUBLISHERS: Application

Ohio State University ....G 614 293-3600
Columbus (G-7433)

Our Daily Bread ....G 513 621-6364
Cincinnati (G-4201)

Trumbull Mobile Meals Inc ....F 330 394-2538
Warren (G-19615)

SOCKETS: Electric

Brooks Utility Products Group ....E 330 455-0301
Canton (G-2629)

SOFT DRINKS WHOLESALERS

Coca-Cola Bottling Co Cnsld ....D 937 878-5000
Dayton (G-8235)

P-Americas LLC ....E 419 227-3541
Lima (G-12065)

SOFTWARE PUBLISHERS: Application

Acclaimd Inc ....G 614 219-9519
Columbus (G-6684)

Advanced Prgrm Resources Inc ....E 614 761-9994
Dublin (G-9037)

Alltel Communications Corp ....G 419 784-3808
Defiance (G-8777)

Ames Development Group Ltd ....G 419 704-7812
Toledo (G-18347)

Apostrophe Apps LLC ....G 513 608-4399
Liberty Twp (G-11970)

Avasax Ltd ....G 937 694-0807
Beavercreek (G-1369)

Aver Inc ....G 877 841-2775
Columbus (G-6792)

Check Yourself LLC ....G 513 685-0868
Blue Ash (G-1764)

Click It Connect Corp ....G 440 247-4998
Chagrin Falls (G-3053)

Corporate Elevator LLC ....F 614 288-1847
Columbus (G-6985)

Crabware Ltd ....G 330 699-2305
Uniontown (G-19081)

D+h USA Corporation ....C 513 381-9400
Cincinnati (G-3633)

Dante Solutions Inc ....G 440 234-8477
Cleveland (G-5166)

Delta Media Group Inc ....E 330 493-0350
Canton (G-2683)

Eighty Six Inc ....G 800 760-0722
Huber Heights (G-11145)

Emerge Health Solutions ....G 513 204-5600
Cincinnati (G-3696)

Facilities Management Ex LLC ....F 844 664-4400
Columbus (G-7075)

Gain LLC ....G 440 396-6613
Westerville (G-20153)

Gis Dynamics LLC ....G 513 847-4931
Blue Ash (G-1803)

Gracie Plum Investments Inc ....E 740 355-9029
Portsmouth (G-16436)

Hyland Software Inc ....A 440 788-5000
Westlake (G-20278)

Idialogs LLC ....G 937 372-2890
Xenia (G-20956)

Infinite Synergy LLC ....G 330 892-8777
Poland (G-16383)

Janova LLC ....F 614 638-6785
New Albany (G-14763)

List Media Inc ....G 330 995-0864
Aurora (G-934)

Lockheed Martin Corporation ....G 614 418-1930
Columbus (G-7302)

Lync Corp ....E 513 655-7286
Cincinnati (G-4041)

Mainstream Software Inc ....F 330 963-0103
Twinsburg (G-18977)

Mamsys Consulting Services ....G 440 287-6824
Solon (G-17332)

Microstrategy Incorporated ....G 513 792-2253
Cincinnati (G-4104)

Mim Software Inc ....E 216 896-9798
Beachwood (G-1281)

Parthenon Global LLC ....G 888 332-5303
Cleveland (G-5979)

Patient Focus Systems ....G 330 655-7222
Hudson (G-11193)

Pmj Partners LLC ....G 201 360-1914
Columbus (G-7501)

Precision Castparts Corp ....G 330 868-7376
Minerva (G-14338)

Ptc Inc ....F 513 791-0330
Cincinnati (G-4303)
Qm Scientific LLP ....G 513 250-2397
Cincinnati (G-4305)
Racedirector LLC ....G 440 940-6675
Willoughby (G-20586)
Rockware Corp ....G 419 483-5649
Bellevue (G-1556)
Sas Institute Inc ....F 216 643-6719
Cleveland (G-6161)
Secure Medical Mail LLC ....G 216 269-1971
Cleveland (G-6177)
Sest Inc ....F 440 777-9777
Westlake (G-20307)
Socialpay LLC ....G 513 721-3900
Cincinnati (G-4433)
Soda Pig LLC ....G 646 241-7126
Columbus (G-7627)
Software Solutions Inc ....E 513 932-6667
Lebanon (G-11841)
Spitfire Technologies LLC ....G 937 463-7729
Dayton (G-8671)
Step It Up LLC ....G 720 289-1520
Columbus (G-7656)
Streamsavvy LLC ....G 614 256-7955
Columbus (G-7660)
Strongbasics LLC ....G 716 903-6151
Columbus (G-7662)
Tech Solutions LLC ....G 419 852-7190
Celina (G-3020)
Uninterrupted LLC ....F 216 771-2323
Akron (G-453)
Vertical Data LLC ....F 330 289-0313
Akron (G-463)
Willow Frog LLC ....G 513 861-4834
Cincinnati (G-4598)

SOFTWARE PUBLISHERS: Business & Professional

4me Group LLC ....G 513 898-1083
Cincinnati (G-3326)
Agile Global Solutions Inc ....E 916 655-7745
Independence (G-11246)
Air Force US Dept of ....B 937 656-2354
Dayton (G-8095)
Alanax Technologies Inc ....G 216 469-1545
Belmont (G-1577)
Alpps Ltd ....G 614 804-3772
Dublin (G-9040)
Application Link Inc ....F 614 934-1735
Columbus (G-6764)
Autorentalsystemscom LLC ....G 513 334-1040
Norwood (G-15570)
Bass International Sftwr LLC ....G 877 227-0155
Columbus (G-6814)
Bjond Inc ....G 614 537-7246
Columbus (G-6835)
Casentric LLC ....G 216 233-6300
Shaker Heights (G-17087)
Cincom Systems Inc ....C 513 459-1470
Mason (G-12996)
Cleveland Business Supply LLC ....G 888 831-0088
Broadview Heights (G-2108)
Clinicl Otcms Mngmnt Syst LLC ....D 330 650-9900
Broadview Heights (G-2109)
Columbus International Corp ....F 614 323-1086
Columbus (G-6957)
Contractor Tools Online LLC ....G 614 264-9392
New Albany (G-14754)
Crimson Gate Consulting Co ....G 614 805-0897
Dublin (G-9066)
Delphia Consulting LLC ....G 614 421-2000
Columbus (G-7021)
Dwllr Inc ....G 513 400-5544
West Chester (G-19854)
Echo Mobile Solutions LLC ....G 614 282-3756
Pickerington (G-16191)
Ela Holding Corporation ....G 513 200-1374
Cincinnati (G-3691)
Field Dailies LLC ....G 859 379-2120
Cincinnati (G-3754)
Infoaccessnet LLC ....E 216 328-0100
Cleveland (G-5568)
Innerapps LLC ....G 419 467-3110
Perrysburg (G-16112)
Iq Solutions Group LLC ....F 855 367-4774
Westerville (G-20161)
Jasstek Inc ....F 614 808-3600
Dublin (G-9091)

Kapios LLC ....G 567 661-0772
Toledo (G-18539)
Linestream Technologies ....G 216 862-7874
Cleveland (G-5702)
Mapsys Inc ....E 614 255-7258
Columbus (G-7316)
Monitored Therapeutics Inc ....G 614 761-3555
Dublin (G-9106)
Netpark LLC ....F 614 866-2495
Gahanna (G-10222)
Netsmart Technologies Inc ....E 440 942-4040
Solon (G-17349)
Neural Holdings LLC ....G 734 512-8865
Cincinnati (G-4147)
Nextmed Systems Inc ....E 216 674-0511
Cincinnati (G-4153)
Ohio Cllbrtive Lrng Sltons Inc ....E 216 595-5289
Beachwood (G-1286)
One Cloud Services LLC ....G 513 231-9500
Cincinnati (G-4187)
Onx Holdings LLC ....G 800 559-2497
Mayfield Heights (G-13320)
Onx USA LLC ....D 440 569-2300
Cleveland (G-5943)
Pakra LLC ....F 614 477-6965
Columbus (G-7455)
Parallel Technologies Inc ....D 614 798-9700
Dublin (G-9117)
Pearl Tech Corporation ....G 614 284-8357
Dublin (G-9119)
Queen City Technologies ....F 513 253-1312
West Chester (G-20044)
Research Metrics LLC ....G 419 464-3333
Norwalk (G-15562)
Retail Management Products ....F 740 548-1725
Lewis Center (G-11914)
Showroom Tracker LLC ....G 888 407-0094
Canton (G-2848)
Simple Vms LLC ....G 888 255-8918
Cincinnati (G-4421)
Simplex-It LLC ....G 234 380-1277
Stow (G-17800)
Softura Legal Solutions LLC ....G 614 220-5611
Columbus (G-7629)
Spearfysh Inc ....F 330 487-0300
Twinsburg (G-19021)
Symantec Corporation ....G 614 793-3060
Dublin (G-9151)
Tmw Systems Inc ....C 216 831-6606
Mayfield Heights (G-13322)
Turning Technologies LLC ....C 330 746-3015
Youngstown (G-21231)
Turning Technologies LLC ....G 330 746-3015
Youngstown (G-21232)
Westmount Technology Inc ....G 216 328-2011
Independence (G-11284)
Workflex Solutions LLC ....G 513 257-0215
Cincinnati (G-4604)
Zipscene LLC ....D 513 201-5174
Cincinnati (G-4619)
Znode Inc ....F 614 468-7900
Columbus (G-6662)

SOFTWARE PUBLISHERS: Computer Utilities

Asterena Corporation ....G 937 605-6470
Dayton (G-8167)
Elytus Ltd ....F 614 824-4985
Columbus (G-7054)
Sark Technologies LLC ....G 216 932-3171
Cleveland (G-6160)

SOFTWARE PUBLISHERS: Education

360water Inc ....G 614 294-3600
Columbus (G-6663)
American Grphcal Sftwr Systems ....G 440 729-0018
Chesterland (G-3198)
Butler Tech Career Dev Schools ....F 513 867-1028
Hamilton (G-10679)
Efab Technologies LLC ....G 937 429-1401
Beavercreek (G-1335)
Flypaper Studio Inc ....G 602 801-2208
Cincinnati (G-3765)
Jst LLC ....G 614 423-7815
Westerville (G-20164)
Learning Egg LLC ....G 330 207-8663
North Jackson (G-15293)
Lost Technology LLP ....G 513 685-0054
West Chester (G-19896)

Noggin LLC ....G 440 305-6188
Cleveland (G-5886)
Skillsoft Corporation ....D 216 524-5200
Independence (G-11275)
Southwestern Ohio Instruction ....F 937 746-6333
Dayton (G-8664)
Vitalrock LLC ....G 888 596-8892
Rocky River (G-16713)

SOFTWARE PUBLISHERS: Home Entertainment

Cake LLC ....G 614 592-7681
Dublin (G-9056)
Estreamz Inc ....E 513 278-7836
Cincinnati (G-3719)
Jack A Byte Mltmdia Gaming LLC ....G 937 321-1716
Englewood (G-9527)
Liquid Shock Games LLC ....G 386 627-0840
Elyria (G-9453)
Mirus Adapted Tech LLC ....E 614 402-4585
Dublin (G-9103)
Polygon Spaceship ....G 440 506-0403
Amherst (G-606)
Wonderful Failure LLC ....G 440 666-0919
Lakewood (G-11682)

SOFTWARE PUBLISHERS: NEC

252 Tattoo ....G 440 235-6699
Columbia Station (G-6577)
About Time Software Inc ....F 614 759-6295
Pickerington (G-16185)
Accumulus Software ....G 937 435-0861
Dayton (G-8131)
Actipro Software LLC ....G 888 922-8477
Broadview Heights (G-2103)
Acu-Serve Corp ....G 330 923-5258
Cuyahoga Falls (G-7961)
Advant-E Corporation ....F 937 429-4288
Beavercreek (G-1316)
American Dreams Inc ....G 740 385-4444
Thornville (G-18191)
Ampersand International Inc ....G 216 831-3500
Beachwood (G-1257)
Apex Solutions Inc ....G 419 843-3434
Toledo (G-18352)
Applied Systems Inc ....E 513 943-0000
Milford (G-14121)
Arges ....G 440 574-1305
Oberlin (G-15634)
Assisted Patrol LLC ....G 937 369-0080
Beavercreek (G-1318)
Associated Software Cons Inc ....E 440 826-1010
Middleburg Heights (G-13902)
Atr Distributing Company ....F 513 353-1800
Cincinnati (G-3427)
Auto Des Sys Inc ....E 614 488-7984
Upper Arlington (G-19110)
Besttransportcom Inc ....E 614 888-2378
Worthington (G-20858)
Callcopy Inc ....G 614 340-3346
Columbus (G-6890)
Carenection LLC ....G 614 468-6045
Columbus (G-6907)
Caring Things Inc ....G 614 749-9084
Columbus (G-6908)
Cimx LLC ....E 513 248-7700
Cincinnati (G-3534)
Citynet Ohio LLC ....G 614 364-7881
Columbus (G-6932)
Clientrax Technology Solutions ....F 614 875-2245
Grove City (G-10549)
Clinical Computing Inc ....F 513 651-3803
Cincinnati (G-3587)
Cluster Software Inc ....F 614 760-9380
Columbus (G-6940)
Coffing Corporation ....E 513 919-2813
Liberty Twp (G-11972)
Commercial Transportation Svcs ....G 216 267-2000
Cleveland (G-5106)
Computer System Enhancement ....G 513 251-6791
Cincinnati (G-3603)
Compuware Corporation ....D 614 847-8212
Columbus (G-6975)
Concept Xxi Inc ....F 216 831-2121
Beachwood (G-1264)
Corillian Payment Solutions ....F 419 244-8048
Toledo (G-18413)
Creative Microsystems Inc ....D 937 836-4499
Englewood (G-9515)

D+h USA Corporation E 937 435-2335
Miamisburg *(G-13796)*
Datatrak International Inc E 440 443-0082
Mayfield Heights *(G-13312)*
Deadbolt Software G 614 679-2093
Columbus *(G-7016)*
Digionyx LLC G 614 594-9897
London *(G-12209)*
Digisoft Systems Corporation G 937 833-5016
Brookville *(G-2181)*
Digital Controls Corporation D 513 746-8118
Miamisburg *(G-13801)*
Drb Systems LLC D 330 645-3299
Akron *(G-157)*
Edict Systems Inc E 937 429-4288
Beavercreek *(G-1334)*
Einstruction Corp G 940 565-0004
Youngstown *(G-21074)*
Einstruction Corporation D 330 746-3015
Youngstown *(G-21075)*
Electronic Vision Inc E 740 592-2433
Athens *(G-864)*
Elynx Holdings LLC G 513 612-5969
Cincinnati *(G-3693)*
EMC Corporation D 513 794-9624
Blue Ash *(G-1783)*
EMC Corporation E 216 606-2000
Independence *(G-11254)*
Empyracom Inc E 330 744-5570
Canfield *(G-2553)*
Engineering Methods Inc E 513 563-0400
Cincinnati *(G-3706)*
Equipsync LLC G 216 367-6640
Cleveland *(G-5292)*
Esko-Graphics Inc D 937 454-1721
Miamisburg *(G-13805)*
Exact Software North Amer LLC C 978 539-6186
Dublin *(G-9075)*
Explorys Inc D 216 767-4700
Cleveland *(G-5315)*
Flexnova Inc E 216 288-6961
Cleveland *(G-5356)*
Forcam Inc F 513 878-2780
Cincinnati *(G-3768)*
Foundation Software Inc D 330 220-8383
Strongsville *(G-17920)*
Fusionstorm G 614 431-8000
Columbus *(G-6647)*
Health Nuts Media LLC G 818 802-5222
Cleveland *(G-5489)*
Healthedge Software Inc G 614 431-3711
Powell *(G-16473)*
Honeywell International Inc D 513 745-7200
Cincinnati *(G-3897)*
ICC Systems Inc G 614 524-0299
Sunbury *(G-18063)*
Igc Software F 614 759-9148
Reynoldsburg *(G-16595)*
Image Integrations Systems F 419 872-0003
Perrysburg *(G-16109)*
Incessant Software Inc G 614 206-2211
Lancaster *(G-11723)*
Innovative Apps Ltd G 330 687-2888
New Albany *(G-14761)*
Innovative Bus Cmpt Solutions G 937 832-3969
Englewood *(G-9525)*
Intelligent Mobile Support Inc F 440 600-7343
Solon *(G-17318)*
Intellinetics Inc F 614 388-8908
Columbus *(G-7201)*
Interactive Fincl Solutions F 419 335-1280
Wauseon *(G-19683)*
Intermec Technologies Corp F 513 874-5882
West Chester *(G-19884)*
Intersoft Group Inc F 216 765-7351
Cleveland *(G-5581)*
Investment Systems Company G 440 247-2865
Chagrin Falls *(G-3061)*
Jack C Keir Inc F 513 422-4860
Middletown *(G-14051)*
Jehm Technologies Inc G 440 355-5558
Lagrange *(G-11628)*
King Software Systems G 330 562-1135
Aurora *(G-931)*
Kronos Incorporated F 614 528-2200
Columbus *(G-7273)*
Kronos Incorporated G 216 867-5609
Independence *(G-11264)*
Mae Consulting G 513 531-8100
Cincinnati *(G-4050)*
Marxware Computing Services F 216 661-5263
Cleveland *(G-5755)*
Mathematical Business Systems G 440 237-2345
Broadview Heights *(G-2115)*
Matrix Management Solutions C 330 470-3700
Canton *(G-2773)*
McGaw Technology Inc G 216 521-3490
Lakewood *(G-11675)*
Merkur Group Inc G 937 429-4288
Beavercreek *(G-1351)*
Miami Valley Eductl Cmpt Assn F 937 767-1468
Yellow Springs *(G-20995)*
Microsoft Corporation E 614 719-5900
Columbus *(G-6656)*
Microsoft Corporation E 216 986-1440
Cleveland *(G-5802)*
Microsoft Corporation D 513 339-2800
Mason *(G-13062)*
Mindcrafted Systems Inc G 440 821-2245
Cleveland *(G-5819)*
Network Savvy Ltd G 419 843-1122
Toledo *(G-18600)*
No Surprises Software Inc G 855 462-6448
Columbus *(G-7394)*
Northrop Grmmn Spce & Mssn Sys D 937 259-4956
Dayton *(G-8529)*
Now Software Inc G 614 783-4517
New Albany *(G-14767)*
Ohio Distinctive Enterprises E 614 459-0453
Columbus *(G-7420)*
Open Text Inc E 614 658-3588
Hilliard *(G-10968)*
Optimal Office Solutions LLC G 201 257-8516
Cincinnati *(G-4190)*
Optimzed Prdctvity Sltions LLC G 513 444-2156
Cincinnati *(G-4192)*
Oracle Corporation C 513 826-5632
Beavercreek *(G-1355)*
Oracle Corporation G 440 264-1620
Cleveland *(G-5945)*
Oracle Systems Corporation E 513 826-6000
Blue Ash *(G-1849)*
Oracle Systems Corporation G 937 427-5495
Beavercreek *(G-1356)*
Pathfinder Computer Systems G 330 928-1961
Barberton *(G-1138)*
Pathos LLC G 440 497-7278
Chesterland *(G-3219)*
Patrick J Burke & Co E 513 455-8200
Cincinnati *(G-4215)*
Patriot Software Inc F 877 968-7147
Canton *(G-2808)*
Patterson Colburne G 419 866-5544
Holland *(G-11077)*
Paul/Jay Associates G 740 676-8776
Bellaire *(G-1500)*
Pdmb Inc G 513 522-7362
Cincinnati *(G-4220)*
Peco II Inc D 614 431-0694
Columbus *(G-7473)*
Perennial Software Inc F 440 247-5602
Chagrin Falls *(G-3067)*
Perfect Probate G 513 791-4100
Cincinnati *(G-4223)*
Pkg Technologies Inc G 513 967-2783
Lebanon *(G-11828)*
Posm Software LLC G 859 274-0041
Columbus *(G-7505)*
Preemptive Solutions LLC E 216 732-5895
Cleveland *(G-6040)*
Proepo Software Ltd G 937 243-3825
Wshngtn CT Hs *(G-20921)*
Profile Imaging Columbus LLC G 614 222-2888
Columbus *(G-7523)*
Profound Logic Software Inc G 937 439-7925
Dayton *(G-8600)*
Protel Systems and Svcs LLC G 419 893-2440
Maumee *(G-13289)*
Protel Systems and Svcs LLC G 419 913-0825
Toledo *(G-18661)*
Pwi Inc F 732 212-8110
New Albany *(G-14770)*
Quayle Consulting Inc G 614 868-1363
Pickerington *(G-16202)*
Queen City Software Inc G 513 469-1424
Cincinnati *(G-4321)*
R & L Software LLC G 513 847-4942
Monroe *(G-14412)*
R&D Software Services Inc G 513 755-8851
Liberty Twp *(G-11978)*
Reichard Software Corp G 614 537-8598
Dublin *(G-9130)*
Retalix Inc C 937 384-2277
Miamisburg *(G-13855)*
Revolution Group Inc D 614 212-1111
Westerville *(G-20182)*
Reynolds and Reynolds Company F 937 485-2805
Beavercreek *(G-1379)*
Rhino Tech Software LLC G 614 456-9321
Pickerington *(G-16204)*
S L C Software Services G 513 922-4303
Cincinnati *(G-4374)*
Sanctuary Software Studio Inc E 330 666-9690
Fairlawn *(G-9759)*
SC Elearning LLC D 513 852-6841
Cincinnati *(G-4382)*
Seapine Software Inc E 513 754-1655
Mason *(G-13087)*
Sherwin Software Solutions G 440 498-8010
Solon *(G-17379)*
Sigmatek Systems LLC D 513 674-0005
Cincinnati *(G-4418)*
Softchoice Corporation G 614 224-4123
Columbus *(G-7628)*
Software Authority Inc G 216 236-0200
Cleveland *(G-6217)*
Software Management Group E 513 618-2165
Cincinnati *(G-4434)*
Software To Systems Inc G 513 893-4367
Fairfield *(G-9720)*
Specialized Business Sftwr Inc E 440 542-9145
Solon *(G-17385)*
Splicenet Inc G 513 563-3533
West Chester *(G-20053)*
Starwin Industries Inc E 937 293-8568
Dayton *(G-8681)*
Steve Schaefer G 513 792-9911
Cincinnati *(G-4465)*
Sunday School Software G 614 527-8776
Hilliard *(G-10984)*
Symantec Corporation D 216 643-6700
Independence *(G-11276)*
Tahoe Interactive Systems Inc F 614 891-2323
Westerville *(G-20235)*
Tarigma Corporation F 614 436-3734
Columbus *(G-7677)*
Tata America Intl Corp B 513 677-6500
Milford *(G-14177)*
Technosoft Inc F 513 985-9877
Blue Ash *(G-1880)*
Tekdog Inc G 614 737-3743
Columbus *(G-7685)*
Teradata Corporation B 866 548-8348
Miamisburg *(G-13870)*
Terrene Labs G 404 408-2241
Mason *(G-13097)*
Thinkware Incorporated E 513 598-3300
Cincinnati *(G-4506)*
Timekeeping Systems Inc F 216 595-0890
Solon *(G-17406)*
To Scale Software LLC E 513 253-0053
Mason *(G-13099)*
Trapeze Software Group Inc G 905 629-8727
Beachwood *(G-1302)*
Triad Governmental Systems E 937 376-5446
Xenia *(G-20983)*
United Computer Group Inc G 216 520-1333
Independence *(G-11280)*
Veeam Software Corporation G 678 353-2140
Columbus *(G-6661)*
Vertex Computer Systems Inc F 513 662-6888
Cincinnati *(G-4565)*
Virtual Boss Inc G 419 872-7686
Perrysburg *(G-16165)*
Virtual Hold Technology LLC D 330 666-1181
Akron *(G-464)*
W L Arehart Computing Systems G 937 383-4710
Wilmington *(G-20681)*
Web3box Software LLC G 330 794-7397
Tallmadge *(G-18176)*
Wentworth Solutions F 440 212-7696
Brunswick *(G-2266)*
Wentworth Technologies LLC F 440 212-7696
Brunswick *(G-2267)*
Wififace LLC G 419 754-4816
Toledo *(G-18775)*
Wissman & Wood Incorporated G 513 793-6222
Cincinnati *(G-4600)*
Workspeed Management LLC E 917 369-9025
Solon *(G-17415)*

PRODUCT

Employee Codes: A=Over 500 employees, B=251-500
C=101-250, D=51-100, E=20-50, F=10-19, G=3-9
2017 Harris Ohio
Industrial Directory
1659

Zebu Compliance Solutions Inc ....E 740 355-9029
Portsmouth *(G-16460)*

SOFTWARE PUBLISHERS: Operating Systems

Computer Zoo Inc ....G...... 937 310-1474
Bellbrook *(G-1504)*
Magic Interface Ltd ....G...... 440 498-3700
Solon *(G-17330)*
North Coast Security Group LLC ....G...... 614 887-7255
Columbus *(G-7399)*
Tech-E-Z LLC ....G...... 419 692-1700
Delphos *(G-8918)*

SOFTWARE PUBLISHERS: Publisher's

Capitol Citicom Inc ....E 614 472-2679
Columbus *(G-6903)*
Exponentia US Inc ....E 614 944-5103
Columbus *(G-7073)*
Ezshred LLC ....G...... 440 256-7640
Kirtland *(G-11614)*
Hardmagic ....F 415 390-6232
Marietta *(G-12789)*
Nsa Technologies LLC ....C 330 576-4600
Akron *(G-321)*
Rawhide Software Inc ....G...... 419 878-0857
Bowling Green *(G-2010)*
Torah Tech Inc ....G...... 614 570-6298
Columbus *(G-7699)*
Trivantis Corporation...........................D 513 929-0188
Cincinnati *(G-4528)*

SOFTWARE TRAINING, COMPUTER

A Graphic Solution ....F 216 228-7223
Cleveland *(G-4672)*
Carey Color Llc/Cincinnati ....F 513 241-5210
Cincinnati *(G-3499)*
Cleveland Business Supply LLC ....G...... 888 831-0088
Broadview Heights *(G-2108)*
Computer Workshop Inc ....G...... 216 901-0106
Cleveland *(G-5114)*
Tekdog Inc ....G...... 614 737-3743
Columbus *(G-7685)*

SOLAR CELLS

Isofoton North America Inc ....F 419 591-4330
Napoleon *(G-14685)*
Mok Industries LLC...............................G...... 614 934-1734
Columbus *(G-7363)*
Redhawk Energy Systems LLC ....G...... 740 927-8244
Pataskala *(G-15979)*
UIC Energy LLC....................................G...... 614 839-0250
Columbus *(G-7718)*

SOLAR HEATING EQPT

Infinity Plus...G...... 937 828-1350
Mechanicsburg *(G-13357)*
Iosil Energy Corporation ....F 614 295-8680
Groveport *(G-10627)*
Rbi Solar Inc ....G...... 513 242-2051
Cincinnati *(G-4332)*
Shark Solar LLC...................................G...... 216 630-7395
Medina *(G-13479)*
Willard Kelsey Solar Group LLC...........E 419 931-2001
Perrysburg *(G-16170)*

SOLDERING EQPT: Electrical, Exc Handheld

Fusion Automation Inc ....G...... 440 602-5595
Willoughby *(G-20493)*

SOLDERING EQPT: Electrical, Handheld

Hutchinson-Stevens Inc ....G...... 216 281-8585
Cleveland *(G-5540)*

SOLDERS

Fusion Automation Inc ....G...... 440 602-5595
Willoughby *(G-20493)*
Metallic Resources Inc ....E 330 425-3155
Twinsburg *(G-18987)*
Victory White Metal Company ....D 216 271-1400
Cleveland *(G-6417)*

SOLENOIDS

Electromotive Inc ....G...... 330 688-6494
Stow *(G-17746)*

SOLES, BOOT OR SHOE: Rubber, Composition Or Fiber

Shreiner Sole Co Inc.............................F 330 276-6135
Killbuck *(G-11599)*

SOLVENTS

Appalachian Solvents LLC....................G...... 740 680-3649
Cambridge *(G-2445)*
Babcock & Wilcox Megtec ....G...... 614 340-4154
Columbus *(G-6800)*

SOLVENTS: Organic

Tedia Company Inc ....D 513 874-5340
Fairfield *(G-9723)*

SONAR SYSTEMS & EQPT

Raytheon Company ....F 937 429-5429
Beavercreek *(G-1359)*

SOUND EFFECTS & MUSIC PRODUCTION: Motion Picture

Swagg Productions2015llc ....F 614 815-1173
Reynoldsburg *(G-16608)*

SOUND EQPT: Electric

Fernandes Enterprises LLC ....F 937 890-6444
Dayton *(G-8340)*
Holland Assocts LLC DBA Archou........F 513 891-0006
Cincinnati *(G-3888)*
Mixed Logic LLC ....G...... 440 826-1676
Valley City *(G-19218)*

SOUND REPRODUCING EQPT

Background Music & Sound Inc............G...... 937 898-9871
Dayton *(G-8180)*
Pioneer North America Inc ....B 937 746-6600
Springboro *(G-17498)*

SOUVENIR SHOPS

Modern China Inc ....E 330 938-6104
Sebring *(G-17048)*

SOUVENIRS, WHOLESALE

Victory Postcards Inc ....G...... 614 764-8975
Columbus *(G-7740)*

SOYBEAN PRDTS

Archer-Daniels-Midland Company ....E 419 435-6633
Fostoria *(G-9966)*
Bunge North America Foundation........D 740 383-1181
Marion *(G-12859)*
Cargill Incorporated ....D 937 498-4555
Sidney *(G-17170)*
Pioneer Hi-Bred Intl Inc ....E 419 748-8051
Grand Rapids *(G-10443)*
Schlessman Seed Co.............................E 419 499-2572
Milan *(G-14116)*
Solae LLC ....G...... 419 483-5340
Bellevue *(G-1561)*

SPACE PROPULSION UNITS & PARTS

Morton International LLC ....G...... 937 222-3860
Dayton *(G-8510)*

SPACE RESEARCH & TECHNOLOGY PROGRAMS ADMINISTRATION

Weldon Pump Acquition LLC.................E 440 232-2282
Oakwood Village *(G-15633)*

SPACE VEHICLE EQPT

Curtiss-Wright Controls ....E 937 252-5601
Fairborn *(G-9618)*
General Electric Company ....B 513 977-1500
Cincinnati *(G-3813)*
Gleason Metrology Systems Corp ....E 937 384-8901
Dayton *(G-8365)*
Grimes Aerospace Company ....B 937 484-2001
Urbana *(G-19158)*
Industrial Quartz Corp ....F 440 942-0909
Mentor *(G-13606)*

L-3 Communications Cincinnati...........A 513 573-6100
Mason *(G-13055)*
Lockheed Martin Integ ....D 330 796-2800
Akron *(G-274)*
Lord Corporation ....C 937 278-9431
Dayton *(G-8459)*
Metalex Manufacturing Inc ....C 513 489-0507
Blue Ash *(G-1839)*
Millat Industries Corp ....D 937 434-6666
Dayton *(G-8501)*
Morris Bean & Company ....C 937 767-7301
Yellow Springs *(G-20996)*
Sunpower Inc ....D 740 594-2221
Athens *(G-887)*
Te Connectivity Corporation ....C 419 521-9500
Mansfield *(G-12694)*
US Aeroteam Inc ....E 937 458-0344
Dayton *(G-8740)*

SPARK PLUGS: Internal Combustion Engines

Fram Group Operations LLC ....D 419 661-6700
Perrysburg *(G-16097)*

SPARK PLUGS: Porcelain

Fram Group Operations LLC ....G...... 937 316-3000
Greenville *(G-10499)*

SPEAKER MONITORS

UNI Corp ....E 330 489-6500
Canton *(G-2883)*

SPEAKER SYSTEMS

Janszen Loudspeaker Ltd ....G...... 614 448-1811
Columbus *(G-7227)*
Phantom Sound ....F 513 759-4477
Mason *(G-13072)*
Technical Artistry Inc ....G...... 614 299-7777
Columbus *(G-7684)*

SPECIALIZED LIBRARIES

Lloyd Library & Museum ....G...... 513 721-3707
Cincinnati *(G-4030)*

SPECIALTY FOOD STORES: Coffee

Boston Stoker Inc ....G...... 937 890-6401
Vandalia *(G-19284)*
Generations Coffee Company LLC ....E 440 546-0901
Brecksville *(G-2051)*

SPECIALTY FOOD STORES: Dried Fruit

CWC Partners LLC ....G...... 567 208-1573
Findlay *(G-9815)*
Hershbergers Dutch Market LLP..........E 740 489-5322
Old Washington *(G-15671)*

SPECIALTY FOOD STORES: Eggs & Poultry

Roots Poultry Inc ....F 419 332-0041
Fremont *(G-10180)*

SPECIALTY FOOD STORES: Health & Dietetic Food

Aggregate Tersornance LLC ....G...... 330 418-4751
Canton *(G-2590)*
Manco Inc ....G...... 937 962-2661
Lewisburg *(G-11937)*
Premier Tanning & Nutrition ....G...... 419 342-6259
Shelby *(G-17141)*

SPEED CHANGERS

Great Lakes Power Products Inc...........D 440 951-5111
Mentor *(G-13596)*
Peerless-Winsmith Inc..........................G...... 614 526-7000
Dublin *(G-9122)*

SPINDLES: Textile

American Precision Spindles ....G...... 267 436-6000
Cleveland *(G-4792)*

SPONGES, ANIMAL, WHOLESALE

Armaly LLC..E 740 852-3621
London *(G-12200)*

(G-0000) Company's Geographic Section entry number

SPONGES: Bleached & Dyed

AK Mansfield ....B 419 755-3011
Mansfield (G-12556)

SPONGES: Plastic

3M Company ....C 440 323-6161
Elyria (G-9366)

SPOOLS: Indl

P & R Specialty Inc ....E 937 773-0263
Piqua (G-16297)

SPORTING & ATHLETIC GOODS: Balls, Baseball, Football, Etc

Wilson Sporting Goods Co ....C 419 634-9901
Ada (G-7)

SPORTING & ATHLETIC GOODS: Bases, Baseball

Black Wing Shooting Center LLC ....G 740 363-7555
Delaware (G-8825)

SPORTING & ATHLETIC GOODS: Basketball Eqpt & Splys, NEC

American Sports Design Company ....D 937 865-5431
Centerville (G-3035)
Boatfun Sports Inc ....G 513 379-0506
Liberty Township (G-11958)
Huffy Corporation ....D 937 865-2800
Centerville (G-3043)
Shoot-A-Way Inc ....F 419 294-4654
Upper Sandusky (G-19141)

SPORTING & ATHLETIC GOODS: Bows, Archery

Lakota Industries Inc ....G 937 532-6394
Xenia (G-20960)

SPORTING & ATHLETIC GOODS: Boxing Eqpt & Splys, NEC

Argrov Box Co ....G 513 217-5900
Middletown (G-14021)

SPORTING & ATHLETIC GOODS: Camping Eqpt & Splys

M&M Great Adventures LLC ....G 937 344-1415
Westerville (G-20169)
Rockbridge Outfitters ....G 740 654-1956
Lancaster (G-11748)

SPORTING & ATHLETIC GOODS: Cases, Gun & Rod

Raven Concealment Systems LLC ....G 440 508-9000
North Ridgeville (G-15399)

SPORTING & ATHLETIC GOODS: Crossbows

Hunters Manufacturing Co Inc ....E 330 628-9245
Mogadore (G-14377)

SPORTING & ATHLETIC GOODS: Decoys, Duck & Other Game Birds

Fowl Foolers LLC ....G 419 797-2412
Port Clinton (G-16400)

SPORTING & ATHLETIC GOODS: Driving Ranges, Golf, Electronic

Cabin Creek Golf ....G 330 852-4879
Sugarcreek (G-18018)
Golf Dome ....G 440 543-1211
Chagrin Falls (G-3089)
Mudbrook Golf Center ....G 419 433-2945
Huron (G-11234)

SPORTING & ATHLETIC GOODS: Dumbbells & Other Weight Eqpt

Equipment Guys Inc ....F 614 871-9220
Newark (G-15004)

SPORTING & ATHLETIC GOODS: Fishing Eqpt

Bay Area Products Inc ....G 419 732-2147
Port Clinton (G-16394)

SPORTING & ATHLETIC GOODS: Fishing Tackle, General

Barnett Spouting Inc ....G 330 644-0853
Akron (G-85)
Ebsco Industries Inc ....F 513 398-2149
Mason (G-13012)

SPORTING & ATHLETIC GOODS: Flies, Fishing, Artificial

Red Barakuda LLC ....G 614 596-5432
Columbus (G-7550)

SPORTING & ATHLETIC GOODS: Guards, Football, Soccer, Etc

Tri County Vking Warriors ....E 330 646-4632
Warren (G-19610)

SPORTING & ATHLETIC GOODS: Gymnasium Eqpt

Rockys Gym ....G 330 965-0464
Youngstown (G-21192)

SPORTING & ATHLETIC GOODS: Hooks, Fishing

Duff Farm ....G 740 742-2182
Langsville (G-11764)

SPORTING & ATHLETIC GOODS: Hunting Eqpt

Ghostblind Industries Inc ....G 740 374-6766
Marietta (G-12785)
Kabler Farms ....G 513 732-0501
Batavia (G-1195)
Lem Products Holding LLC ....E 513 202-1188
West Chester (G-19892)

SPORTING & ATHLETIC GOODS: Masks, Hockey, Baseball, Etc

Hofmanns Lures Inc ....G 937 684-0338
Ansonia (G-625)

SPORTING & ATHLETIC GOODS: Pigeons, Clay Targets

Lasermark LLC ....G 513 312-9889
Dayton (G-8452)

SPORTING & ATHLETIC GOODS: Pools, Swimming, Exc Plastic

Bradley Enterprises Inc ....G 330 875-1444
Louisville (G-12311)
Imperial On-Pece Fibrgls Pools ....F 740 747-2971
Ashley (G-788)
Imperial Pools Inc ....D 513 771-1506
Cincinnati (G-3915)
Uniwall Manufacturing Co ....F 330 875-1444
Louisville (G-12332)

SPORTING & ATHLETIC GOODS: Pools, Swimming, Plastic

GL International LLC ....C 330 744-8812
Youngstown (G-21101)

SPORTING & ATHLETIC GOODS: Reels, Fishing

Reelflyrodcom ....G 937 434-8472
Dayton (G-8622)

SPORTING & ATHLETIC GOODS: Shafts, Golf Club

1 Iron Golf Inc ....G 419 662-9336
Celina (G-2984)

Board of Park Commissioners ....G 216 635-3200
Cleveland (G-4920)
Grey Hawk Golf Club ....E 440 355-4844
Lagrange (G-11626)
The Salem Golf Club ....G 330 332-0346
Salem (G-16930)
Zwf Golf LLC ....E 937 767-5621
Fairborn (G-9636)

SPORTING & ATHLETIC GOODS: Shooting Eqpt & Splys, General

Drop Zone Ltd ....G 234 806-4604
Warren (G-19546)
Ohio Sporting Goods LLC ....G 330 548-5911
Cuyahoga Falls (G-8030)

SPORTING & ATHLETIC GOODS: Skateboards

Careless Heart Enterprises ....G 740 654-9999
Lancaster (G-11696)
Konkrete City Skateboards ....G 513 231-0399
Cincinnati (G-4001)
Martini Skate & Snow ....G 216 371-0155
Cleveland Heights (G-6500)
Trilo Inc ....E 937 276-4288
Dayton (G-8725)

SPORTING & ATHLETIC GOODS: Soccer Eqpt & Splys

Soccer First Inc ....G 614 889-1115
Dublin (G-9148)
Soccer Village Inc ....G 513 451-8500
Cincinnati (G-4432)

SPORTING & ATHLETIC GOODS: Target Shooting Eqpt

Apex Target Systems LLC ....G 877 224-6692
Tiffin (G-18204)
Target Thompson Technology ....G 330 699-8000
Uniontown (G-19102)

SPORTING & ATHLETIC GOODS: Targets, Archery & Rifle Shooting

Challenge Targets ....G 859 462-5851
Batavia (G-1170)

SPORTING & ATHLETIC GOODS: Team Sports Eqpt

Shoot A Way Inc ....F 419 294-4654
Upper Sandusky (G-19140)

SPORTING & ATHLETIC GOODS: Tennis Eqpt & Splys

Total Tennis Inc ....G 614 488-5004
Columbus (G-7701)

SPORTING & ATHLETIC GOODS: Track & Field Athletic Eqpt

Achilles Running Shop LLC ....G 440 942-2059
Mentor (G-13507)
Field Specialties ....G 440 635-0064
Chardon (G-3153)

SPORTING & ATHLETIC GOODS: Water Sports Eqpt

Kent Sporting Goods Co Inc ....D 419 929-7021
New London (G-14860)
Rain Drop Products Llc ....E 419 207-1229
Ashland (G-771)
Royal Spa Columbus ....G 614 529-8569
Lewis Center (G-11915)
Wake Nation ....F 513 887-9253
Fairfield (G-9730)

SPORTING & RECREATIONAL GOODS & SPLYS WHOLESALERS

Activewares ....G 419 994-5932
Loudonville (G-12295)
Advantage Tent Fittings Inc ....F 740 773-3015
Chillicothe (G-3226)

PRODUCT

Akron Felt & Chenille Mfg Co .... F 330 733-7778
   Akron (G-43)
Balbo Industries Inc .... G 440 333-0630
   Rocky River (G-16695)
Berry Investments Inc .... G 937 293-0398
   Moraine (G-14469)
Great Oppurtunities Inc .... G 614 868-1899
   Columbus (G-7130)
Hershberger Lawn Structures .... F 330 674-3900
   Millersburg (G-14221)
House of Awards and Sports .... G 419 422-7877
   Findlay (G-9842)
Just Basic Sports Inc .... G 330 264-7771
   Wooster (G-20793)
McSports .... G 419 586-5555
   Celina (G-3007)
Phoenix Bat Company .... G 614 873-7776
   Plain City (G-16354)
R & A Sports Inc .... E 216 289-2254
   Euclid (G-9603)
Roy L Bayes .... G 614 274-6729
   Columbus (G-7575)
T J Target .... G 330 658-3057
   Doylestown (G-9031)
Total Tennis Inc .... G 614 488-5004
   Columbus (G-7701)
Toy & Sport Trends Inc .... E 419 748-8880
   Napoleon (G-14700)
Zebec of North America Inc .... E 513 829-5533
   Fairfield (G-9735)

SPORTING & RECREATIONAL GOODS, WHOLESALE: Athletic Goods

Garick LLC .... E 216 581-0100
   Cleveland (G-5398)

SPORTING & RECREATIONAL GOODS, WHOLESALE: Bowling

Action Sports Apparel Inc .... G 330 848-9300
   Norton (G-15503)
Done-Rite Bowling Service Co .... E 440 232-3280
   Bedford (G-1420)

SPORTING & RECREATIONAL GOODS, WHOLESALE: Fitness

Ball Bounce and Sport Inc .... B 419 289-9310
   Ashland (G-710)
Suarez Corporation Industries .... E 330 494-4282
   Canton (G-2861)

SPORTING & RECREATIONAL GOODS, WHOLESALE: Golf

Tim Boutwell .... G 419 358-4653
   Bluffton (G-1917)

SPORTING & RECREATIONAL GOODS, WHOLESALE: Golf & Skiing

Golf Galaxy Golfworks Inc .... C 740 328-4193
   Newark (G-15014)

SPORTING & RECREATIONAL GOODS, WHOLESALE: Gymnasium

A K Athletic Equipment Inc .... E 614 920-3069
   Canal Winchester (G-2518)

SPORTING & RECREATIONAL GOODS, WHOLESALE: Hot Tubs

Royal Spa Columbus .... G 614 529-8569
   Lewis Center (G-11915)

SPORTING & RECREATIONAL GOODS, WHOLESALE: Hunting

Ghostblind Industries Inc .... G 740 374-6766
   Marietta (G-12785)

SPORTING & RECREATIONAL GOODS, WHOLESALE: Spa

Agean Marble Manufacturing .... F 513 874-1475
   West Chester (G-19978)

SPORTING GOODS

Advanced Fitness Inc .... G 513 563-1000
   Cincinnati (G-3358)
Al-Co Products Inc .... F 419 399-3867
   Latty (G-11767)
All Sport Services Corporation .... G 216 361-1965
   Cleveland (G-4759)
American Heritage Billiards .... G 330 626-3710
   Streetsboro (G-17839)
American Whistle Corporation .... F 614 846-2918
   Columbus (G-6742)
Arem Co .... F 440 974-6740
   Mentor (G-13526)
Backyard Scoreboards LLC .... G 513 702-6561
   Middletown (G-14023)
Baseball Card Corner .... G 513 677-0464
   Loveland (G-12340)
Bracemart LLC .... G 440 353-2830
   North Ridgeville (G-15362)
Coulter Ventures Llc .... E 614 358-6190
   Columbus (G-6990)
Creighton Sports Center Inc .... G 740 865-2521
   New Matamoras (G-14873)
Daisys Pillows LLC .... G 937 776-6968
   Dayton (G-8265)
Europa Sports Products Inc .... F 440 846-9571
   Strongsville (G-17919)
Foot Locker Retail Inc .... G 513 671-4085
   Cincinnati (G-3767)
Galaxy Balloons Incorporated .... C 216 476-3360
   Cleveland (G-5392)
Golf Car Company Inc .... F 614 873-1055
   Plain City (G-16344)
Gym Pro LLC .... G 740 984-4143
   Waterford (G-19648)
H & H of Milford Ohio LLC .... G 513 576-9004
   Milford (G-14149)
Hibbett Sporting Goods Inc .... G 330 837-9272
   Massillon (G-13149)
Hoistech LLC .... G 440 327-5379
   North Ridgeville (G-15379)
House of Awards and Sports .... G 419 422-7877
   Findlay (G-9842)
Just Basic Sports Inc .... G 330 264-7771
   Wooster (G-20793)
L A Productions Co LLC .... G 330 666-4230
   Akron (G-264)
Line Drive Sportz-Lcrc LLC .... G 419 794-7150
   Maumee (G-13276)
M C Sports .... F 419 874-2990
   Rossford (G-16742)
Mc Alarney Pool Spas and Billd .... E 740 373-6698
   Marietta (G-12806)
McSports .... G 419 586-5555
   Celina (G-3007)
Meridian Industries Inc .... D 330 359-5447
   Winesburg (G-20706)
Ohio Table Pad Company .... F 419 872-6400
   Perrysburg (G-16130)
Otomik Products Inc .... G 877 776-5358
   Cincinnati (G-4199)
Packaging Plus Inc .... G 304 429-5900
   Dayton (G-8562)
R L Y Inc .... G 513 385-1950
   Cincinnati (G-4326)
Ready To Haul Columbus LLC .... F 614 329-5161
   Streetsboro (G-17871)
Shooting Range Supply LLC .... G 440 576-7711
   Jefferson (G-11370)
Smart 3d Solutions LLC .... G 330 972-7840
   Akron (G-405)
Toy & Sport Trends Inc .... E 419 748-8880
   Napoleon (G-14700)
U S Development Corp .... E 570 966-5990
   Kent (G-11540)
Unique-Chardan Inc .... E 419 636-6900
   Bryan (G-2325)
Vf Outdoor LLC .... G 614 337-1147
   Columbus (G-7738)
Victory Athletics Inc .... G 330 274-2854
   Mantua (G-12724)
Voll Hockey Inc .... G 216 521-4625
   Lakewood (G-11681)
Wholesale Bait Co Inc .... F 513 863-2380
   Fairfield (G-9732)
Zebec of North America Inc .... E 513 829-5533
   Fairfield (G-9735)

SPORTING GOODS STORES, NEC

Art Tees Inc .... G 614 338-8337
   Columbus (G-6774)
Balbo Industries Inc .... G 440 333-0630
   Rocky River (G-16695)
Ernst Sporting Gds Minster LLC .... G 937 526-9822
   Versailles (G-19346)
Fried Daddy .... G 937 854-4542
   Dayton (G-8351)
Highpoint Firearms .... E 419 747-9444
   Mansfield (G-12625)
Hoffee John .... G 330 868-3553
   Minerva (G-14325)
Joe Sestito .... G 614 871-7778
   Grove City (G-10566)
Johndavid D Jones .... G 740 264-0176
   Wintersville (G-20711)
Lakeside Sport Shop Inc .... G 330 637-2862
   Cortland (G-7870)
Lima Sporting Goods Inc .... E 419 222-1036
   Lima (G-12046)
Lion Clothing Inc .... G 419 692-9981
   Delphos (G-8914)
McSports .... G 419 586-5555
   Celina (G-3007)
National Bullet Co .... G 800 317-9506
   Eastlake (G-9284)
Peska Inc .... F 440 998-4664
   Ashtabula (G-831)
Quality Spt & Silk Screen Sp .... G 513 769-8300
   Cincinnati (G-4309)
Sports Express .... G 330 297-1112
   Ravenna (G-16559)
Sunset Golf LLC .... E 419 994-5563
   Tallmadge (G-18171)
T J Target .... G 330 658-3057
   Doylestown (G-9031)
T K L Lettering .... G 937 832-2091
   Englewood (G-9540)
Target Holdings Inc .... E 513 474-4409
   Cincinnati (G-4493)

SPORTING GOODS STORES: Ammunition

Reloading Supplies Corp .... G 440 228-0367
   Ashtabula (G-836)

SPORTING GOODS STORES: Baseball Eqpt

Phoenix Bat Company .... G 614 873-7776
   Plain City (G-16354)

SPORTING GOODS STORES: Camping Eqpt

Outdoor Army Store of Ashtbula .... F 440 992-8791
   Ashtabula (G-828)
Vance Adams .... G 330 424-9670
   Lisbon (G-12134)

SPORTING GOODS STORES: Firearms

762mm Firearms LLC .... G 440 655-8572
   Wadsworth (G-19384)
R & S Monitions Inc .... G 614 846-0597
   Columbus (G-7542)
Smokin Guns LLC .... G 440 324-4003
   Elyria (G-9494)

SPORTING GOODS STORES: Hunting Eqpt

Butera Manufacturing Inc .... F 440 516-3698
   Willoughby Hills (G-20638)

SPORTING GOODS STORES: Playground Eqpt

Hershberger Lawn Structures .... F 330 674-3900
   Millersburg (G-14221)

SPORTING GOODS STORES: Skateboarding Eqpt

Trilo Inc .... E 937 276-4288
   Dayton (G-8725)

SPORTING GOODS STORES: Soccer Splys

Fryes Soccer Shoppe .... G 937 832-2230
   Englewood (G-9520)

SPORTING GOODS STORES: Team sports Eqpt

Locker Room Inc .... G 419 445-9600
Archbold (G-684)

Wayne Sporting Goods .... G 937 236-6665
Dayton (G-8748)

SPORTING GOODS: Archery

Foster Manufacturing .... G 513 735-9770
Batavia (G-1185)

SPORTS APPAREL STORES

Aardvark Sportswear Inc .... G 330 793-9428
Youngstown (G-21012)

Activewares .... G 419 994-5932
Loudonville (G-12295)

All Sport Printwear Inc .... F 330 887-6505
Westfield Center (G-20243)

Collegiate Connection .... G 419 352-8333
Bowling Green (G-1982)

Essential Pathways Ohio LLC .... G 330 518-3091
Youngstown (G-21079)

Mypro Apparel LLC .... G 419 462-9464
Ontario (G-15690)

Quali-Tee Design Sports .... F 937 382-7997
Wilmington (G-20675)

Quality Spt & Silk Screen Sp .... G 513 769-8300
Cincinnati (G-4309)

Shoot A Way Inc .... F 419 294-4654
Upper Sandusky (G-19140)

Silk Screen Special TS Inc .... G 740 246-4843
Thornville (G-18199)

Sports Express .... G 330 297-1112
Ravenna (G-16559)

Swocat Design Inc .... G 440 282-4700
Lorain (G-12284)

T K L Lettering .... G 937 832-2091
Englewood (G-9540)

T-Top Shoppe .... G 330 343-3481
New Philadelphia (G-14932)

Tee Creations .... G 937 878-2822
Fairborn (G-9632)

Trd Leathers .... G 216 631-6233
Cleveland (G-6352)

Unisport Inc .... F 419 529-4727
Ontario (G-15696)

Uptown Dog The Inc .... G 740 592-4600
Athens (G-889)

SPOUTING: Plastic & Fiberglass Reinforced

C B & S Spouting Inc .... G 937 866-1600
Miamisburg (G-13788)

SPRAYING & DUSTING EQPT

Cipar Inc .... G 216 910-1700
Beachwood (G-1260)

Paratus Supply Inc .... G 330 745-3600
Barberton (G-1137)

United Air Specialists Inc .... C 513 891-0400
Blue Ash (G-1886)

Wiwa LLC .... F 419 757-0141
Alger (G-482)

SPRAYING EQPT: Agricultural

Yocom Brothers .... G 937 653-8767
Cable (G-2414)

SPRAYS: Self-Defense

Mace Personal Def & SEC Inc .... E 440 424-5321
Cleveland (G-5722)

Mace Security Intl Inc .... F 440 424-5321
Cleveland (G-5723)

SPRINGS: Coiled Flat

Euclid Spring Co .... E 440 943-3213
Wickliffe (G-20365)

Golden Spring Co Inc .... F 937 848-2513
Bellbrook (G-1509)

Rassini Chassis Systems LLC .... D 419 485-1524
Montpelier (G-14452)

Timac Manufacturing Company .... F 937 372-3305
Xenia (G-20980)

SPRINGS: Cold Formed

Solon Manufacturing Company .... E 440 286-7149
Chardon (G-3180)

SPRINGS: Leaf, Automobile, Locomotive, Etc

E & L Spring Shop .... G 440 632-1439
Middlefield (G-13933)

Liteflex LLC .... E 937 836-7025
Englewood (G-9530)

SPRINGS: Mechanical, Precision

Kern-Liebers Usa Inc .... D 419 865-2437
Holland (G-11070)

Spring Works Inc .... E 614 351-9345
Columbus (G-7646)

Stalder Spring Works Inc .... F 937 322-6120
Springfield (G-17656)

Twist Inc .... C 937 675-9581
Jamestown (G-11353)

Twist Inc .... E 937 675-9581
Jamestown (G-11354)

Wire Products Company Inc .... C 216 267-0777
Cleveland (G-6469)

Yost Superior Co .... E 937 323-7591
Springfield (G-17683)

SPRINGS: Precision

B & P Spring Production Co .... F 216 486-4260
Cleveland (G-4881)

Tadd Spring Co Inc .... E 440 572-1313
Strongsville (G-17976)

SPRINGS: Steel

Accurate Tool Co Inc .... G 330 332-9448
Salem (G-16868)

Crawford Manufacturing Company ...... F 330 897-1060
Baltic (G-1068)

Dayton Progress Corporation .... A 937 859-5111
Dayton (G-8284)

Elyria Spring & Specialty Inc .... E 440 323-5502
Elyria (G-9417)

Formed Metal Products Inc .... F 440 775-0819
Oberlin (G-15639)

Hendrickson International Corp .... D 740 929-5600
Hebron (G-10870)

Jamestown Industries Inc .... D 330 779-0670
Youngstown (G-21125)

Kern-Liebers Usa Inc .... D 419 865-2437
Holland (G-11070)

Matthew Warren Inc .... E 614 418-0250
Columbus (G-7326)

Precision Products Group Inc .... D 330 698-4711
Apple Creek (G-647)

Service Spring Corp .... D 419 838-6081
Maumee (G-13292)

Tadd Spring Co Inc .... E 440 572-1313
Strongsville (G-17976)

Torsion Control Product .... C 248 597-9997
Dayton (G-8721)

Tremac Corporation .... E 937 372-8662
Xenia (G-20982)

SPRINGS: Torsion Bar

Napoleon Spring Works Inc .... C 419 445-1010
Archbold (G-688)

SPRINGS: Wire

A & W Spring Co Inc .... G 937 222-7284
Dayton (G-8126)

Barnes Group Inc .... G 440 526-5900
Brecksville (G-2035)

Barnes Group Inc .... E 419 891-9292
Maumee (G-13229)

Bloomingburg Spring & Wire For .... E 740 437-7614
Bloomingburg (G-1720)

Dayton Progress Corporation .... A 937 859-5111
Dayton (G-8284)

Elyria Spring & Specialty Inc .... E 440 323-5502
Elyria (G-9417)

Kern-Liebers Texas Inc .... E 419 865-2437
Holland (G-11069)

Matthew Warren Inc .... E 614 418-0250
Columbus (G-7326)

Ohio Wire Form & Spring Co .... F 614 444-3676
Columbus (G-7436)

Precision Products Group Inc .... D 330 698-4711
Apple Creek (G-647)

Protech Electric LLC .... F 937 427-0813
Beavercreek (G-1357)

Regal Spring Co .... G 614 278-7761
Columbus (G-7552)

Solon Manufacturing Company .... E 440 286-7149
Chardon (G-3180)

Spring Team Inc .... D 440 275-5981
Austinburg (G-966)

Springtime Manufacturing .... G 419 697-3720
Toledo (G-18702)

Supro Spring & Wire Forms Inc .... E 330 722-5628
Medina (G-13485)

The Reliable Spring Wire Frms .... E 440 365-7400
Elyria (G-9501)

Trupoint Products .... F 330 204-3302
Sugarcreek (G-18046)

SPRINKLER SYSTEMS: Field

Mih Marketing Group Inc .... F 740 942-0411
Cadiz (G-2420)

Siteone Landscape Supply LLC .... G 330 220-8691
Brunswick (G-2257)

SPRINKLING SYSTEMS: Fire Control

Cae Ransohoff Inc .... G 513 870-0100
West Chester (G-19986)

Fire Fab Corporation .... G 330 759-9834
Girard (G-10386)

Fire Foe Corp .... G 330 759-9834
Girard (G-10387)

Gould Fire Protection Inc .... G 419 957-2416
Findlay (G-9832)

Radco Fire Protection Inc .... G 419 476-0102
Toledo (G-18668)

Viking Group Inc .... G 937 443-0433
Dayton (G-8743)

SPROCKETS: Power Transmission

Abl Products Inc .... F 216 281-2400
Cleveland (G-4684)

Akron Gear & Engineering Inc .... E 330 773-6608
Akron (G-45)

Martin Sprocket & Gear Inc .... D 419 485-5515
Montpelier (G-14448)

Robertson Manufacturing Co .... E 216 531-8222
Cleveland (G-6123)

STACKING MACHINES: Automatic

Air Technical Industries Inc .... E 440 951-5191
Mentor (G-13512)

STAGE LIGHTING SYSTEMS

Iacono Production Services Inc .... F 513 469-5095
Blue Ash (G-1811)

Importers Direct LLC .... E 330 436-3260
Akron (G-230)

STAINED GLASS ART SVCS

Whitney Stained Glass Studio .... G 216 348-1616
Cleveland (G-6461)

STAINLESS STEEL

Aco Polymer Products Inc .... E 440 285-7000
Mentor (G-13508)

Allegheny Ludlum LLC .... E 330 875-2244
Louisville (G-12308)

Bcast Stainless Products LLC .... F 614 873-3945
Plain City (G-16325)

Challenger Hardware Company .... F 216 591-1141
Brooklyn Heights (G-2134)

Grace Metals Ltd .... G 234 380-1433
Hudson (G-11175)

Latrobe Spcialty Mtls Dist Inc .... D 330 609-5137
Vienna (G-19366)

Mtr Martco LLC .... D 513 424-5307
Middletown (G-14065)

North American Steel Company .... E 216 475-7300
Cleveland (G-5890)

North Jckson Specialty Stl LLC .... E 330 538-9621
North Jackson (G-15295)

Premier Metal Trading LLC .... G 440 247-9494
Chagrin Falls (G-3068)

Qual-Fab Inc .... E 440 327-5000
Avon (G-1005)

PRODUCT

Robert James Sales Inc ....F 330 425-9116
　Twinsburg *(G-19010)*

STAINLESS STEEL WARE

Online Engineering Corporation ....G....... 513 561-8878
　Amelia *(G-581)*

STAIR TREADS: Rubber

Safeguard Technology Inc ....E 330 995-5200
　Streetsboro *(G-17873)*

STAIRCASES & STAIRS, WOOD

Great Lakes Stair & Mllwk Co ....G....... 330 225-2005
　Hinckley *(G-11024)*
Heartland Stairway Ltd ....G....... 330 279-2554
　Millersburg *(G-14220)*
Hinckley Wood Products ....F 330 220-9999
　Hinckley *(G-11025)*
Jaco Inc ....G....... 513 722-3947
　Loveland *(G-12364)*
Kacy Stairs ....F 740 599-5201
　Howard *(G-11123)*
Shawnee Wood Products Inc ....G....... 440 632-1771
　Middlefield *(G-13989)*
Woodcraft Manufacturing Co ....E 740 927-6609
　Pataskala *(G-15992)*

STAMPED ART GOODS FOR EMBROIDERING

Anything Personalized ....G....... 330 655-0723
　Twinsburg *(G-18900)*
Graphix Junction ....G....... 234 284-8392
　Hudson *(G-11176)*
Vasil Co Inc ....G....... 419 562-2901
　Bucyrus *(G-2362)*

STAMPING: Fabric Articles

Big Kahuna Graphics Inc ....G....... 330 455-2625
　Canton *(G-2622)*

STAMPINGS: Automotive

A J Rose Mfgco ....C 216 631-4645
　Cleveland *(G-4675)*
A J Rose Mfgco ....C 216 631-4645
　Avon *(G-978)*
AMG Industries LLC ....D 740 397-4044
　Mount Vernon *(G-14605)*
Anchor Tool & Die Co ....B 216 362-1850
　Cleveland *(G-4806)*
Antique Auto Sheet Metal Inc ....E 937 833-4422
　Brookville *(G-2174)*
Arcelormittal Tailored Blanks ....D 419 737-3180
　Pioneer *(G-16233)*
Artiflex Manufacturing LLC ....F 419 547-9211
　Clyde *(G-6537)*
Cleveland Die & Mfg Co ....D 440 243-3404
　Cleveland *(G-5059)*
Cleveland Metal Processing Inc ....C 440 243-3404
　Cleveland *(G-5070)*
Cole Tool & Die Company ....E 419 522-1272
　Ontario *(G-15686)*
Defiance Metal Products Co ....B 419 784-5332
　Defiance *(G-8785)*
Defiance Metal Products Co ....B 419 784-5332
　Defiance *(G-8786)*
Defiance Stamping Co ....D 419 782-5781
　Napoleon *(G-14677)*
E & W Enterprises Powell Inc ....D 937 346-0800
　Springfield *(G-17549)*
Elyria Spring & Specialty Inc ....E 440 323-5502
　Elyria *(G-9417)*
Emerson Electric Co ....E 513 631-6112
　Cincinnati *(G-3697)*
Exact-Tool & Die Inc ....E 216 676-9140
　Cleveland *(G-5311)*
Falls Stamping & Welding Co ....C 330 928-1191
　Cuyahoga Falls *(G-7996)*
Falls Stamping & Welding Co ....F 216 771-9635
　Cleveland *(G-5323)*
Falls Tool & Die Incorporated ....G....... 330 633-4884
　Akron *(G-179)*
Feintool Cincinnati Inc ....C 513 247-0110
　Blue Ash *(G-1793)*
Feintool US Operations Inc ....C 513 247-4061
　Blue Ash *(G-1794)*
Findlay Products Corporation ....C 419 423-3324
　Findlay *(G-9825)*

Ford Motor Company ....A 216 587-7700
　Bedford *(G-1424)*
Ford Motor Company ....A 216 587-7700
　Cleveland *(G-5368)*
Fuserashi Intl Tech Inc ....E 330 273-0140
　Valley City *(G-19204)*
Gamco Componets Group LLC ....G....... 440 593-1500
　Conneaut *(G-7804)*
General Motors LLC ....B 330 824-5840
　Warren *(G-19554)*
Gt Technologies Inc ....D 419 324-7300
　Toledo *(G-18489)*
Guarantee Specialties Inc ....D 216 451-9744
　Strongsville *(G-17923)*
Hayford Technologies ....D 419 524-7627
　Mansfield *(G-12622)*
Hercules Acquisition Corp ....E 419 287-3223
　Pemberville *(G-16027)*
Honda of America Mfg Inc ....C 937 644-0724
　Marysville *(G-12951)*
Jatdco LLC ....G....... 440 238-6570
　Strongsville *(G-17933)*
L & W Inc ....D 734 397-6300
　Avon *(G-999)*
Lakepark Industries Inc ....C 419 752-4471
　Greenwich *(G-10533)*
Langenau Manufacturing Company ......F 216 651-3400
　Cleveland *(G-5680)*
Merrick Manufacturing II LLC ....G....... 937 222-7164
　Dayton *(G-8485)*
Metal Products Company ....E 330 652-2558
　Niles *(G-15168)*
N N Metal Stampings Inc ....E 419 737-2311
　Pioneer *(G-16235)*
Nasg Ohio LLC ....F 419 634-3125
　Ada *(G-6)*
Navistar Inc ....D 937 390-2800
　Springfield *(G-17613)*
Nebraska Industries Corp ....E 419 335-6010
　Wauseon *(G-19691)*
Northern Stamping Co ....C 216 883-8888
　Cleveland *(G-5912)*
Northern Stamping Co ....C 216 642-8081
　Cleveland *(G-5913)*
Oerlikon Friction Systems ....E 937 233-7002
　Dayton *(G-8539)*
Oerlikon Friction Systems ....E 937 233-9191
　Dayton *(G-8541)*
Ohio Stamping & Machine LLC ....C 937 322-3880
　Springfield *(G-17619)*
P & A Industries Inc ....E 419 422-7070
　Findlay *(G-9875)*
Progressive Stamping Inc ....C 419 453-1111
　Ottoville *(G-15825)*
Quaker Mfg Corp ....C 330 332-4631
　Salem *(G-16922)*
R K Industries Inc ....E 419 523-5001
　Ottawa *(G-15806)*
Sapa Extrusions North Amer LLC ....C 888 935-5759
　Sidney *(G-17221)*
Select International Corp ....G....... 937 233-9191
　Dayton *(G-8653)*
Shiloh Industries Inc ....E 330 558-2300
　Valley City *(G-19232)*
Shiloh Industries Inc ....A 440 647-2100
　Wellington *(G-19755)*
Shiloh Industries Inc ....A 330 558-2000
　Valley City *(G-19233)*
Shiloh Industries Inc ....G....... 330 558-2600
　Valley City *(G-19234)*
Shiloh Industries Inc ....A 330 558-2600
　Valley City *(G-19235)*
SSP Industrial Group Inc ....G....... 330 665-2900
　Fairlawn *(G-9761)*
Stamco Industries Inc ....E 216 731-9333
　Cleveland *(G-6233)*
Stripmatic Products Inc ....E 216 241-7143
　Cleveland *(G-6255)*
Styner+bienz US Inc ....G....... 216 362-1850
　Cleveland *(G-6258)*
Sulzer Transmission Tech ....G....... 937 449-4000
　Dayton *(G-8688)*
Sunrise Cooperative Inc ....E 419 683-4600
　Crestline *(G-7936)*
T A Bacon Co ....F 216 851-1404
　Chesterland *(G-3220)*
Taylor Metal Products Co ....C 419 522-3471
　Mansfield *(G-12693)*
Tfo Tech Co Ltd ....C 740 426-6381
　Jeffersonville *(G-11382)*

Tower Automotive Operations I ....B 419 358-8966
　Bluffton *(G-1918)*
Trucut Incorporated ....D 330 938-9806
　Sebring *(G-17055)*
TS Trim Industries Inc ....E 614 837-4114
　Canal Winchester *(G-2539)*
TS Trim Trimold Inc ....G....... 614 920-1927
　Canal Winchester *(G-2540)*
Valley Tool & Die Inc ....D 440 237-0160
　North Royalton *(G-15458)*
Vr Waverly Inc ....D 740 947-7763
　Waverly *(G-19720)*
Wrena LLC ....E 937 667-4403
　Tipp City *(G-18312)*
Yachiyo of America Inc ....D 614 876-3220
　Columbus *(G-7781)*
Zip Tool & Die Inc ....F 216 267-1117
　Cleveland *(G-6496)*

STAMPINGS: Metal

A J Rose Mfgco ....C 216 631-4645
　Cleveland *(G-4675)*
A J Rose Mfgco ....C 216 631-4645
　Avon *(G-978)*
A-1 Manufacturing Corp ....G....... 216 475-6084
　Maple Heights *(G-12726)*
A-Stamp Industries LLC ....E 419 633-0451
　Bryan *(G-2273)*
AAA Stamping Inc ....E 216 749-4494
　Cleveland *(G-4681)*
Abl Products Inc ....F 216 281-2400
　Cleveland *(G-4684)*
Advanced Technology Corp ....C 440 293-4064
　Andover *(G-611)*
Agb LLC ....G....... 419 924-5216
　West Unity *(G-20126)*
AJD Holding Co ....D 330 405-4477
　Twinsburg *(G-18895)*
Allied Tool & Die Inc ....F 216 941-6196
　Cleveland *(G-4766)*
Amaroq Inc ....G....... 419 747-2110
　Mansfield *(G-12558)*
Amcraft Inc ....G....... 419 729-7900
　Toledo *(G-18335)*
American Guard Co Inc ....F 440 354-1400
　Geneva *(G-10342)*
American Tool & Mfg Co ....F 419 522-2452
　Mansfield *(G-12561)*
American Trim LLC ....A 419 228-1145
　Sidney *(G-17167)*
American Trim LLC ....G....... 419 996-4703
　Lima *(G-11989)*
American Trim LLC ....D 419 739-4349
　Wapakoneta *(G-19476)*
American Trim LLC ....D 419 738-9664
　Wapakoneta *(G-19477)*
American Trim LLC ....D 419 996-4729
　Lima *(G-11990)*
American Trim LLC ....D 419 996-4703
　Lima *(G-11991)*
American Trim LLC ....E 419 228-1145
　Lima *(G-11992)*
Ampex Metal Products Company ....E 216 267-9242
　Brookpark *(G-2151)*
Amtekco Industries Inc ....G....... 614 228-6525
　Columbus *(G-6750)*
Anchor Fabricators Inc ....E 937 836-5117
　Clayton *(G-4656)*
Anchor Tool & Die Co ....D 216 362-1850
　Cleveland *(G-4807)*
Anchor Tool & Die Co ....B 216 362-1850
　Cleveland *(G-4806)*
Anderson Industries Inc ....F 216 941-7766
　Cleveland *(G-4810)*
Angell-Demmel North Amer Corp ....D 937 461-5800
　Dayton *(G-8158)*
Anomatic Corporation ....B 740 522-2203
　New Albany *(G-14745)*
Arrow Tru-Line Inc ....D 419 636-7013
　Bryan *(G-2279)*
Artiflex Manufacturing LLC ....B 330 262-2015
　Wooster *(G-20741)*
Artisan Tool & Die Corp ....E 216 883-2769
　Cleveland *(G-4838)*
Atlantic Durant Technology Inc ....G....... 440 238-6931
　Strongsville *(G-17890)*
Atlantic Tool & Die Company ....C 440 238-6931
　Strongsville *(G-17891)*
Atlantic Tool & Die Company ....C 330 769-4500
　Seville *(G-17068)*

(G-0000) Company's Geographic Section entry number

Atlantic Tool & Die Company ....C 330 239-3700
Sharon Center (G-17101)
Automatic Stamp Products Inc ....F 216 781-7933
Cleveland (G-4869)
Ayling and Reichert Co Consent ....E 419 898-2471
Oak Harbor (G-15586)
Banner Metals Group Inc ....D 614 291-3105
Columbus (G-6805)
Barnes Group Inc ....G 440 526-5900
Brecksville (G-2035)
Bates Metal Products Inc ....D 740 498-8371
Port Washington (G-16422)
Bayloff Stmped Pdts Knsman Inc ....D 330 876-4511
Kinsman (G-11608)
Bellevue Manufacturing Company ....G 419 483-3190
Bellevue (G-1546)
Brainerd Industries Inc ....E 937 228-0488
Miamisburg (G-13786)
Breitinger Company ....C 419 526-4255
Mansfield (G-12569)
Brw Tool Inc ....F 419 394-3371
Saint Marys (G-16835)
Buckeye Metals Industries Inc ....F 216 663-4300
Cleveland (G-4943)
Buckley Manufacturing Company ....F 513 821-4444
Cincinnati (G-3485)
C & C Fabrication Inc ....G 419 354-3535
Bowling Green (G-1975)
Camelot Manufacturing Inc ....F 419 678-2603
Coldwater (G-6554)
Case Industries Inc ....G 330 963-7717
Twinsburg (G-18908)
Cleveland Die & Mfg Co ....D 440 243-3404
Middleburg Heights (G-13904)
Cole Tool & Die Company ....E 419 522-1272
Ontario (G-15686)
Com-Corp Industries Inc ....D 216 431-6266
Cleveland (G-5101)
Commercial Vehicle Group Inc ....C 740 676-6542
Shadyside (G-17080)
Compco Industries Incorporated ....D 330 482-6488
Columbiana (G-6614)
Contour Forming Inc ....E 740 345-9777
Newark (G-14996)
Cubbison Company ....D 330 793-2481
Youngstown (G-21059)
Customformed Products Inc ....F 937 388-0480
Miamisburg (G-13795)
Dayton Tool Co Inc ....E 937 222-5501
Dayton (G-8288)
Dayton Tractor & Crane ....G 937 317-5014
Xenia (G-20946)
Deerfield Manufacturing Inc ....E 513 398-2010
Mason (G-13008)
Delafoil Pennsylvania Inc ....D 610 327-9565
Perrysburg (G-16083)
Delta Tool & Die Stl Block Inc ....F 419 822-5939
Delta (G-8930)
Die Co Inc ....E 440 942-8856
Eastlake (G-9265)
Die-Matic Corporation ....D 216 749-4656
Brooklyn Heights (G-2138)
Die-Mension Corporation ....F 330 273-5872
Brunswick (G-2221)
Dove Die and Stamping Company ....E 216 267-3720
Cleveland (G-5211)
Duro Dyne Midwest Corp ....B 513 870-6000
Hamilton (G-10685)
E C Shaw Co ....E 513 721-6334
Cincinnati (G-3677)
Elliott Oren Products Inc ....E 419 298-2306
Edgerton (G-9329)
Elyria Spring & Specialty Inc ....E 440 323-5502
Elyria (G-9417)
Emerson Electric Co ....E 513 631-6112
Cincinnati (G-3697)
Ernie Green Industries Inc ....G 614 219-1423
Columbus (G-7064)
Even Heat Mfg Ltd ....F 330 695-9351
Fredericksburg (G-10085)
Exact-Tool & Die Inc ....E 216 676-9140
Cleveland (G-5311)
F & G Tool and Die Co ....E 937 746-3658
Franklin (G-10019)
F C Brengman and Assoc LLC ....E 740 756-4308
Carroll (G-2940)
Federal-Mogul Valve Train Inte ....E 330 628-6700
Brunswick (G-2224)
Feinblanking Limited Inc ....G 513 860-2100
West Chester (G-19863)
Feintool US Operations Inc ....C 513 247-4061
Blue Ash (G-1794)
Findlay Products Corporation ....C 419 423-3324
Findlay (G-9825)
Flood Heliarc Inc ....F 614 835-3929
Groveport (G-10621)
Formasters Corporation ....F 440 639-9206
Mentor (G-13580)
Formed Metal Products Inc ....F 440 775-0819
Oberlin (G-15639)
Formetal Inc ....F 419 898-2211
Oak Harbor (G-15591)
Fremont Plastic Products Inc ....C 419 332-6407
Fremont (G-10150)
Frepeg Industries Inc ....F 440 255-8595
Mentor (G-13585)
Fulton Industries Inc ....D 419 335-3015
Wauseon (G-19678)
Fulton Manufacturing Inds LLC ....E 440 546-1435
Brecksville (G-2050)
G & W Products LLC ....C 513 860-4050
Fairfield (G-9660)
Gb Fabrication Company ....E 419 347-1835
Shelby (G-17136)
Gb Fabrication Company ....E 419 896-3191
Shiloh (G-17148)
Gb Manufacturing Company ....D 419 822-5323
Delta (G-8934)
General Technologies Inc ....E 419 747-1800
Mansfield (G-12612)
Gentzler Tool & Die Corp ....E 330 896-1941
Akron (G-205)
Gottschall Tool & Die Inc ....E 330 332-1544
Salem (G-16895)
Gt Technologies Inc ....D 419 324-7300
Toledo (G-18489)
Guardian Engineering & Mfg Co ....G 419 335-1784
Wauseon (G-19680)
Gwp Holdings Inc ....D 513 860-4050
Fairfield (G-9662)
Hamlin Steel Products LLC ....D 330 753-7791
Akron (G-213)
Hawthorne Caravan & Assoc LLC ....F 440 366-9065
Elyria (G-9428)
Hayford Technologies ....D 419 524-7627
Mansfield (G-12622)
Hercules Acquisition Corp ....E 419 287-3223
Pemberville (G-16027)
Herd Manufacturing Inc ....E 216 651-4221
Cleveland (G-5503)
Ice Industries Inc ....G 513 398-2010
Mason (G-13040)
Ice Industries Inc ....E 419 842-3612
Sylvania (G-18110)
Imperial Die & Mfg Co ....F 440 268-9080
Strongsville (G-17929)
Interlake Stamping Ohio Inc ....E 440 942-0800
Willoughby (G-20513)
International Trade Group Inc ....G 614 486-4634
Columbus (G-7207)
J B Stamping Inc ....E 216 631-0013
Cleveland (G-5597)
J Williams & Associates Inc ....G 330 887-1392
Westfield Center (G-20244)
JD Norman Industries Inc ....D 216 671-8000
Brooklyn (G-2129)
Jet Stream International Inc ....E 330 505-9988
Niles (G-15164)
Jones Metal Products Company ....D 740 545-6381
West Lafayette (G-20087)
K & B Stamping & Manufacturing ....G 937 778-8875
Piqua (G-16284)
Kelch Manufacturing Corp ....G 440 366-5060
Elyria (G-9446)
Knight Manufacturing Co Inc ....G 740 676-5516
Shadyside (G-17082)
Kreider Corp ....D 937 325-8787
Springfield (G-17592)
Lakepark Industries Inc ....C 419 752-4471
Greenwich (G-10533)
Langenau Manufacturing Company ....F 216 651-3400
Cleveland (G-5680)
Larosa Die Engineering Inc ....G 513 284-9195
Cincinnati (G-4012)
Liberty Steel Industries Inc ....D 330 372-6363
Warren (G-19570)
Liberty Steel Industries Inc ....E 330 372-6363
Warren (G-19571)
Logan Machine Company ....D 330 633-6163
Akron (G-275)
Long-Stanton Mfg Company ....E 513 874-8020
West Chester (G-19895)
Malin Wire Co ....E 216 267-9080
Cleveland (G-5735)
Malin Wire Co ....G 216 267-9080
Cleveland (G-5734)
Mansfield Industries Inc ....E 419 524-1300
Mansfield (G-12643)
Marc V Concepts Inc ....F 419 782-6505
Defiance (G-8801)
Matco Tools Corporation 1 ....B 330 929-4949
Stow (G-17773)
Maumee Assembly & Stamping LLC ....D 419 304-2887
Maumee (G-13278)
McAfee Tool & Die Inc ....E 330 896-9555
Uniontown (G-19092)
Medina Blanking Inc ....C 330 558-2300
Valley City (G-19217)
Merrick Manufacturing II LLC ....G 937 222-7164
Dayton (G-8485)
Metal & Wire Products Company ....E 330 332-9448
Salem (G-16914)
Metal Products Company ....E 330 652-6201
Niles (G-15169)
Metal Stampings Unlimited ....F 937 328-0206
Springfield (G-17603)
Mic-Ray Metal Products Inc ....F 216 791-2206
Cleveland (G-5796)
Mid-America Steel Corp ....E 800 282-3466
Cleveland (G-5805)
Modern Pipe Supports Corp ....E 216 361-1666
Cleveland (G-5828)
Monode Steel Stamp Inc ....G 419 929-3501
New London (G-14862)
Monode Steel Stamp Inc ....F 440 975-8802
Mentor (G-13661)
Morgal Machine Tool Co ....D 937 325-5561
Springfield (G-17607)
Mtd Holdings Inc ....B 330 225-2600
Valley City (G-19220)
Nebraska Industries Corp ....E 419 335-6010
Wauseon (G-19691)
New Bremen Machine & Tool Co ....E 419 629-3295
New Bremen (G-14790)
New Holland Engineering Inc ....G 740 495-5200
New Holland (G-14835)
Nicholas Press Sales LLC ....G 440 652-6604
Brunswick (G-2239)
Niles Manufacturing & Finshg ....C 330 544-0402
Niles (G-15171)
Norplas Industries Inc ....B 419 662-3317
Northwood (G-15485)
Northern Stamping Co ....C 216 883-8888
Cleveland (G-5912)
Northwind Industries Inc ....E 216 433-0666
Cleveland (G-5916)
Norwood Medical ....G 937 228-4101
Dayton (G-8530)
Norwood Medical ....C 937 228-4101
Dayton (G-8531)
Norwood Tool Company ....D 937 228-4101
Dayton (G-8532)
Ohio Associated Entps LLC ....E 440 354-3148
Painesville (G-15908)
Omni Manufacturing Inc ....D 419 394-7424
Saint Marys (G-16846)
Omni Manufacturing Inc ....F 419 394-7424
Saint Marys (G-16847)
Orick Stamping ....D 419 331-0600
Elida (G-9353)
P & A Industries Inc ....C 419 422-7070
Findlay (G-9875)
Pacific Manufacturing Ohio Inc ....B 513 860-3900
Fairfield (G-9696)
Parker-Hannifin Corporation ....F 330 336-3511
Wadsworth (G-19427)
Pax Machine Works Inc ....C 419 586-2337
Celina (G-3012)
Peerless Metal Products Inc ....E 216 431-6905
Cleveland (G-5988)
Pennant Moldings Inc ....C 937 584-5411
Sabina (G-16775)
Pentaflex Inc ....C 937 325-5551
Springfield (G-17626)
Pettit W T & Sons Co Inc ....G 330 539-6100
Girard (G-10392)
Phillips Mch & Stamping Corp ....G 330 882-6714
New Franklin (G-14829)
Pilot-Run Stamping Company ....E 440 255-8821
Mentor (G-13687)

PRODUCT

Precision Fabg & Stamping ....G....... 740 453-7310
Zanesville (G-21345)

Precision Metal Products Inc ....F 216 447-1900
Cleveland (G-6036)

Premier Stamping and Assembly ....G...... 440 293-8961
Williamsfield (G-20416)

Production Products Inc ....D..... 419 659-2978
Columbus Grove (G-7797)

Progress Tool & Stamping Inc ....E...... 419 628-2384
Minster (G-14360)

Progressive Machine Die Inc ....E...... 330 405-6600
Macedonia (G-12478)

Quaker Mfg Corp ....C..... 330 332-4631
Salem (G-16922)

Quality Fabricated Metals Inc ....E...... 330 332-7008
Salem (G-16923)

Quality Metal Products Inc ....G...... 440 355-6165
Lagrange (G-11636)

Quality Tool Company ....E...... 419 476-8228
Toledo (G-18663)

R K Metals Ltd ....E...... 513 874-6055
Fairfield (G-9708)

Racelite South Coast Inc ....F 216 581-4600
Maple Heights (G-12739)

Range Kleen Mfg Inc ....B..... 419 331-8000
Elida (G-9356)

Rapid Machine Inc ....F 419 737-2377
Pioneer (G-16243)

Regal Metal Products Co ....F 330 868-6343
Minerva (G-14340)

Rezmann Karoly ....G...... 216 441-4357
Cleveland (G-6110)

Ridge Tool Manufacturing Co ....A..... 440 323-5581
Elyria (G-9488)

Rittal Corp ....C..... 937 399-0500
Urbana (G-19176)

Rittal Corp ....F 937 399-0500
Springfield (G-17639)

Rjm Stamping Co ....F 614 443-1191
Columbus (G-7565)

Roemer Industries Inc ....D..... 330 448-2000
Masury (G-13216)

Ronfeldt Manufacturing LLC ....E...... 419 382-5641
Toledo (G-18681)

S-P Company Inc ....F 330 482-0200
Columbiana (G-6631)

Scott Fetzer Company ....C..... 216 267-9000
Cleveland (G-6168)

Sectional Stamping Inc ....B..... 440 647-2100
Wellington (G-19754)

Select Industries Corporation ....C..... 937 233-9191
Dayton (G-8652)

Seven Ranges Mfg Corp ....E...... 330 627-7155
Carrollton (G-2965)

Shiloh Automotive Inc ....E...... 330 558-2600
Valley City (G-19230)

Shiloh Corporation ....B..... 330 558-2600
Valley City (G-19231)

Shiloh Industries Inc ....G...... 330 558-2600
Valley City (G-19234)

Shiloh Industries Inc ....A..... 330 558-2600
Valley City (G-19235)

Smithville Manufacturing Co ....E...... 330 345-5818
Wooster (G-20836)

Stamped Steel Products Inc ....F 330 538-3951
North Jackson (G-15299)

Steel Forming Inc ....C..... 714 532-6321
Youngstown (G-21212)

Stolle Properties Inc ....A..... 513 932-8664
Blue Ash (G-1875)

Stripmatic Products Inc ....E...... 216 241-7143
Cleveland (G-6255)

Suburban Manufacturing Co ....D..... 440 953-2024
Eastlake (G-9290)

Superior Metal Products Inc ....E...... 419 228-1145
Lima (G-12099)

T & D Fabricating Inc ....E...... 440 951-5646
Eastlake (G-9292)

T & W Stamping Inc ....G...... 330 270-0891
Youngstown (G-21216)

Takk Industries Inc ....F 513 353-4306
Cincinnati (G-4491)

Talan Products Inc ....D..... 216 458-0170
Cleveland (G-6292)

Talent Tool & Die Inc ....E...... 440 239-8777
Berea (G-1637)

Taylor Metal Products Co ....C..... 419 522-3471
Mansfield (G-12693)

The Reliable Spring Wire Frms ....E...... 440 365-7400
Elyria (G-9501)

The W L Jenkins Company ....F 330 477-3407
Canton (G-2869)

Toledo Tool and Die Co Inc ....E...... 419 476-4422
Toledo (G-18747)

Tool & Die Systems Inc ....E...... 440 327-5800
North Ridgeville (G-15406)

Torr Metal Products Inc ....E...... 216 671-1616
Cleveland (G-6339)

Treaty City Industries Inc ....F 937 548-9000
Greenville (G-10525)

Trucut Incorporated ....D..... 330 938-9806
Sebring (G-17055)

TRW Automotive US LLC ....E...... 216 750-2400
Cleveland (G-6372)

TRW Automotive US LLC ....D..... 419 726-5599
Toledo (G-18758)

TRW Automotive US LLC ....B..... 216 332-7100
Cleveland (G-6373)

Twist Inc ....E...... 937 675-9581
Jamestown (G-11353)

Twist Inc ....E...... 937 675-9581
Jamestown (G-11354)

United Tool and Machine Inc ....F 937 843-5603
Lakeview (G-11650)

Universal Metal Products Inc ....C..... 440 943-3040
Wickliffe (G-20391)

Universal Metal Products Inc ....E...... 419 287-3223
Pemberville (G-16031)

Valley Tool & Die Inc ....D..... 440 237-0160
North Royalton (G-15458)

Varbros LLC ....E...... 216 267-5200
Cleveland (G-6406)

Verhoff Machine & Welding Inc ....E...... 419 596-3202
Continental (G-7829)

W H Heimkreiter Manufacturing ....E...... 513 681-9192
Cincinnati (G-4574)

W M Inc ....E...... 330 427-6115
Washingtonville (G-19644)

Washington Products Inc ....F 330 837-5101
Massillon (G-13211)

Wedge Products Inc ....B..... 330 405-4477
Twinsburg (G-19038)

Weiss Industries Inc ....E...... 419 526-2480
Mansfield (G-12704)

Welage Corporation ....F 513 681-2300
Cincinnati (G-4583)

Wellington Industries ....D..... 734 942-1060
Maumee (G-13308)

Westlake Tool & Die Mfg Co ....D..... 440 934-5305
Avon (G-1019)

Willow Hill Industries LLC ....D..... 440 942-3003
Willoughby (G-20631)

Winzeler Stamping Co ....D..... 419 485-3147
Montpelier (G-14458)

Wire Products Company Inc ....E...... 216 267-0777
Cleveland (G-6469)

Wisco Products Incorporated ....E...... 937 228-2101
Dayton (G-8763)

WLS Fabricating Co ....E...... 440 449-0543
Cleveland (G-6471)

Zip Tool & Die Inc ....F 216 267-1117
Cleveland (G-6496)

STANDS & RACKS: Engine, Metal

St Marys Iron Works Inc ....F 419 300-6300
Saint Marys (G-16857)

STARTERS & CONTROLLERS: Motor, Electric

MA Flynn Associates LLC ....G...... 513 893-7873
Hamilton (G-10721)

STARTERS: Electric Motor

M Technologies ....F 330 477-9009
Canton (G-2764)

STARTERS: Motor

Charles Auto Electric Co Inc ....G...... 330 535-6269
Akron (G-118)

H W Fairway International Inc ....E...... 330 678-2540
Kent (G-11467)

Ohio Generator Remanufacturing ....G...... 330 875-6677
Louisville (G-12321)

STATIC ELIMINATORS: Ind

Takk Industries Inc ....F 513 353-4306
Cincinnati (G-4491)

STATIONARY & OFFICE SPLYS, WHOL: Albums, Scrapbooks/Binders

S O S Graphics & Printing Inc ....G...... 614 846-8229
Worthington (G-20886)

STATIONARY & OFFICE SPLYS, WHOL: Writing Instruments & Splys

Boehm Inc ....E...... 614 875-9010
Grove City (G-10546)

STATIONARY & OFFICE SPLYS, WHOLESALE: Inked Ribbons

Jay Tackett ....G...... 740 779-1715
Frankfort (G-9999)

Microcom Corporation ....E...... 740 548-6262
Lewis Center (G-11907)

STATIONARY & OFFICE SPLYS, WHOLESALE: Marking Devices

Advanced Marking Systems Inc ....G...... 330 792-8239
Youngstown (G-21017)

REA Elektronik Inc ....F 440 232-0555
Bedford (G-1456)

The Rubber Stamp Shop ....G...... 419 478-4444
Toledo (G-18722)

STATIONARY & OFFICE SPLYS, WHOLESALE: Office Filing Splys

Corporate Supply LLC ....G...... 614 876-8400
Columbus (G-6986)

STATIONER'S SUNDRIES: Rubber

Custom Stamp Makers Inc ....G...... 216 351-1470
Cleveland (G-5152)

STATIONERY & OFFICE SPLYS WHOLESALERS

AW Faber-Castell Usa Inc ....D..... 216 643-4660
Cleveland (G-4877)

Covap Inc ....F 513 793-1855
Blue Ash (G-1769)

Dewitt Group Inc ....F 614 847-5919
Columbus (G-7024)

Easterdays Printing Center ....G...... 330 726-1182
Youngstown (G-21073)

Ed Thomas ....G...... 937 325-4300
Springfield (G-17551)

Friends Service Co Inc ....F 800 427-1704
Dayton (G-8352)

Friends Service Co Inc ....G...... 800 427-1704
Kent (G-11459)

Friends Service Co Inc ....D..... 419 427-1704
Findlay (G-9828)

G A Spring Advertising ....G...... 330 343-9030
Dover (G-8986)

Go Calendars ....G...... 513 755-1555
Liberty Township (G-11962)

Gvs Industries Inc ....G...... 513 887-8660
Hamilton (G-10699)

Lawpak Inc ....G...... 513 831-3900
Terrace Park (G-18180)

Lindsey Graphics Inc ....G...... 330 995-9241
Aurora (G-933)

Queen City Office Machine ....F 513 251-7200
Cincinnati (G-4317)

Quick Tab II Inc ....D..... 419 448-6622
Tiffin (G-18238)

Scratch-Off Systems Inc ....E...... 216 649-7800
Brecksville (G-2071)

Standard Register Inc ....G...... 937 228-5800
Dayton (G-8679)

Value Added Business Svcs Co ....G...... 614 854-9755
Jackson (G-11332)

Westrock Commercial LLC ....G...... 419 476-9101
Toledo (G-18773)

Z P Enterprises Inc ....G...... 513 863-3393
Hamilton (G-10758)

STATIONERY ARTICLES: Pottery

Larose Industries LLC ....E...... 419 237-1600
Fayette (G-9776)

STATIONERY PRDTS

CCL Label Inc ....C 216 676-2703
　Cleveland (G-4998)
Keeler Enterprises Inc ....G 330 336-7601
　Wadsworth (G-19412)
Nature Friendly Products LLC ....G 216 464-5490
　Cleveland (G-5861)
Primary Colors Design Corp ....G 419 903-0403
　Ashland (G-768)
Westrock Mwv LLC ....A 937 495-6323
　Dayton (G-8755)

STATIONERY: Made From Purchased Materials

American Greetings Corporation ....A 216 252-7300
　Cleveland (G-4782)
Century Intermediate Holdg Co ....F 216 252-7300
　Cleveland (G-5006)
CM Paula Company ....E 513 759-7473
　Mason (G-13002)

STATUARY & OTHER DECORATIVE PRDTS: Nonmetallic

Aquablok Ltd ....F 419 402-4170
　Swanton (G-18080)
Fireline Inc ....E 330 259-0647
　Youngstown (G-21085)
Fireline Inc ....D 330 743-1164
　Youngstown (G-21086)

STATUARY GOODS, EXC RELIGIOUS: Wholesalers

Custom Fountains Inc ....F 513 398-1447
　Mason (G-13007)
Mazzolini Artcraft Co Inc ....F 216 431-7529
　Cleveland (G-5767)
Wilsons Country Creations ....F 330 377-4190
　Killbuck (G-11602)

STATUES: Nonmetal

B & B Cast Stone Co Inc ....G 740 697-0008
　Roseville (G-16726)
Mazzolini Artcraft Co Inc ....F 216 431-7529
　Cleveland (G-5767)

STEAM SPLY SYSTEMS SVCS INCLUDING GEOTHERMAL

BT Investments II Inc ....G 937 434-4321
　Dayton (G-8200)

STEEL & ALLOYS: Tool & Die

American Steel & Alloys LLC ....E 330 847-0487
　Warren (G-19521)
Ernst Metal Technologies LLC ....E 937 434-3133
　Moraine (G-14485)
Esm Products Inc ....G 937 492-4644
　Celina (G-2996)
Hi-Tech Wire Inc ....D 419 678-8376
　Saint Henry (G-16817)
Kind Special Alloys Us LLC ....G 330 788-2437
　Youngstown (G-21128)
L-K Industry Inc ....E 937 526-3000
　Versailles (G-19351)
Nichidai America Corporation ....E 419 423-7511
　Findlay (G-9867)
Romarc Enterprises Inc ....G 419 287-4837
　Pemberville (G-16030)
S & J Precision Inc ....G 937 296-0068
　Moraine (G-14524)
Thrift Tool Inc ....G 937 275-3600
　Dayton (G-8714)
Unlimited Machine and Tool LLC ....F 419 269-1730
　Toledo (G-18761)
WH Fetzer & Sons Mfg Inc ....E 419 687-8237
　Plymouth (G-16380)

STEEL Electrometallurgical

Nuflux LLC ....G 330 399-1122
　Cortland (G-7872)

STEEL FABRICATORS

A & E Butscha Co ....G 513 761-1919
　Cincinnati (G-3329)

A & G Manufacturing Co Inc ....E 419 468-7433
　Galion (G-10250)
A+ Engineering Fabrication Inc ....F 419 832-0748
　Grand Rapids (G-10439)
A-1 Fabricators Finishers LLC ....D 513 724-0383
　Batavia (G-1163)
Accu-Tech Manufacturing Co ....G 330 848-8100
　Akron (G-27)
Ace Boiler & Welding Co Inc ....G 330 745-4443
　Barberton (G-1092)
Advance Industrial Mfg Inc ....E 614 871-3333
　Grove City (G-10539)
Advance Industries Group LLC ....E 216 741-1800
　Cleveland (G-4707)
Advanced Onsight Welding Svcs ....G 513 924-1400
　Cincinnati (G-3359)
Air Heater Seal Company Inc ....E 740 984-2146
　Waterford (G-19645)
Akron Rebar Co ....E 330 745-7100
　Akron (G-54)
Albert Freytag Inc ....E 419 628-2018
　Minster (G-14349)
Alcon Industries Inc ....D 216 961-1100
　Cleveland (G-4745)
Allied Fabricating & Wldg Co ....E 614 751-6664
　Columbus (G-6725)
Alro Steel Corporation ....C 937 253-6121
　Dayton (G-8149)
Alsteel Fabricators Inc ....F 330 652-4344
　Mineral Ridge (G-14302)
Alufab Inc ....G 513 528-7281
　Cincinnati (G-3293)
AM Warren LLC ....G 330 841-2800
　Warren (G-19520)
Ambassador Steel Corporation ....F 740 382-9969
　Marion (G-12854)
Ameco USA Metal Fabrication ....E 440 899-9400
　Cleveland (G-4777)
American Ir Met Cleveland LLC ....E 216 266-0518
　Cleveland (G-4786)
American Steel Assod Pdts Inc ....D 419 531-9471
　Toledo (G-18345)
Ameridian Specialty Services ....E 513 769-0150
　Cincinnati (G-3396)
Amrod Bridge & Iron LLC ....E 330 530-8230
　Mc Donald (G-13346)
Amtank Armor LLC ....E 216 252-1500
　Cleveland (G-4800)
Amtech Tool and Machine Inc ....E 330 758-8215
　Youngstown (G-21024)
Anstine Machining Corp ....F 330 821-4365
　Alliance (G-496)
Ap-Alternatives LLC ....E 419 267-5280
　Ridgeville Corners (G-16663)
Appian Manufacturing Corp ....E 614 445-2230
　Columbus (G-6762)
Applied Energy Tech Inc ....E 419 537-9052
　Maumee (G-13227)
Applied Engneered Surfaces Inc ....F 440 366-0440
　Elyria (G-9374)
Arcalloy Metal Fabrication ....G 800 822-9402
　Akron (G-71)
Arctech Fabricating Inc ....G 937 525-9353
　Springfield (G-17518)
Armor Consolidated Inc ....C 513 923-5260
　Mason (G-12982)
Armor Metal Group Mason Inc ....C 513 769-0700
　Mason (G-12983)
Arrow Fabricating Co ....E 216 641-0490
　Novelty (G-15581)
Ashco Manufacturing Inc ....G 419 838-7157
　Toledo (G-18357)
Aster Elements Inc ....E 440 942-2799
　Mentor (G-13527)
Astro-TEC Mfg Inc ....E 330 854-2209
　Canal Fulton (G-2497)
Avenue Fabricating Inc ....E 513 752-1911
　Batavia (G-1165)
Banks Manufacturing Company ....F 440 458-8661
　Grafton (G-10420)
Bauer Corporation ....E 800 321-4760
　Wooster (G-20746)
Bcfab Inc ....E 419 532-2899
　Fort Jennings (G-9925)
Berran Industrial Group Inc ....E 330 253-5800
　Akron (G-89)
Best Fab Co ....G 440 328-3254
　Elyria (G-9381)
Best Process Solutions Inc ....E 330 220-1440
　Brunswick (G-2212)

Bethel Engineering and Eqp Inc ....E 419 568-1100
　New Hampshire (G-14833)
Bickers Metal Products Inc ....E 513 353-4000
　Miamitown (G-13884)
Bird Equipment LLC ....E 330 549-1004
　North Lima (G-15311)
Bison Wldg & Fabrication Inc ....E 440 944-4770
　Wickliffe (G-20360)
Blackburns Fabrication Inc ....E 614 875-0784
　Columbus (G-6838)
Blevins Metal Fabrication Inc ....E 419 522-6082
　Mansfield (G-12567)
Boardman Steel Inc ....D 330 758-0951
　Columbiana (G-6607)
Bradley Metal Fabrication Llc ....F 216 881-7400
　Cleveland (G-4930)
Breitinger Company ....C 419 526-4255
　Mansfield (G-12569)
Brilex Industries Inc ....C 330 744-1114
　Youngstown (G-21037)
Brilex Industries Inc ....D 330 744-1114
　Youngstown (G-21036)
Buck Equipment Inc ....E 614 539-3039
　Grove City (G-10548)
Buckeye Fbricators of Leetonia ....G 330 427-0330
　Leetonia (G-11858)
Buckeye Steel Incorporated ....F 740 425-2306
　Barnesville (G-1159)
Burghardt Manufacturing Inc ....G 330 253-7590
　Akron (G-103)
Burghardt Metal Fabg Inc ....F 330 794-1830
　Akron (G-104)
C A Joseph Co ....F 330 532-4646
　Irondale (G-11287)
C-N-D Industries Inc ....E 330 478-8811
　Massillon (G-13118)
Camelot Manufacturing Inc ....F 419 678-2603
　Coldwater (G-6554)
CCM Welding Inc ....G 330 630-2521
　Akron (G-113)
Ceco Environmental Corp ....E 513 874-8915
　West Chester (G-19987)
Central Ohio Fabricators LLC ....E 740 393-3892
　Mount Vernon (G-14613)
Chagrin Vly Stl Erectors Inc ....E 440 975-1556
　Willoughby (G-20455)
Champion Bridge Company ....E 937 382-2521
　Wilmington (G-20658)
Charles Mfg Co ....F 330 395-3490
　Warren (G-19534)
Charles Ray Evans ....F 740 967-3669
　Johnstown (G-11396)
Chattanooga Laser Cutting LLC ....E 513 779-7200
　Cincinnati (G-3524)
Chc Manufacturing Inc ....E 513 821-7757
　Cincinnati (G-3525)
Chc Manufacturing Inc ....G 614 527-1606
　Columbus (G-6923)
Christman Fabricators Inc ....G 330 477-8077
　Canton (G-2654)
Cincinnati Industrial McHy Inc ....C 513 923-5600
　Mason (G-12994)
Cincy Glass Inc ....G 513 241-0455
　Cincinnati (G-3573)
Clermont Steel Fabricators LLC ....D 513 732-6033
　Batavia (G-1173)
Cleveland City Forge Inc ....E 440 647-5400
　Wellington (G-19739)
Clifton Steel Company ....D 216 662-6111
　Maple Heights (G-12731)
Clipsons Metal Working Inc ....G 513 772-6393
　Cincinnati (G-3588)
Cohen Brothers Inc ....G 513 422-3696
　Middletown (G-14031)
Com-Fab Inc ....E 740 857-1107
　Plain City (G-16327)
Commercial Mtal Fbricators Inc ....E 937 233-4911
　Dayton (G-8239)
Concord Fabricators Inc ....E 614 875-2500
　Grove City (G-10550)
Contech Engnered Solutions Inc ....A 513 645-7000
　West Chester (G-19840)
Contech Engnered Solutions LLC ....D 513 645-7000
　Middletown (G-14032)
Contech Engnered Solutions LLC ....C 513 645-7000
　West Chester (G-19841)
Continental GL Sls & Inv Group ....B 614 679-1201
　Powell (G-16469)
County of Lake ....D 440 269-2193
　Willoughby (G-20464)

PRODUCT

Coventry Steel Services Inc	F	216 883-4477	Cleveland (G-5136)
Cramers Inc	E	330 477-4571	Canton (G-2670)
Creative Fab & Welding LLC	E	937 780-5000	Leesburg (G-11851)
Curtiss-Wright Flow Control	D	513 528-7900	Cincinnati (G-3297)
D T Kothera Inc	G	440 632-1651	Middlefield (G-13930)
Dal-Little Fabricating Inc	G	216 883-3323	Cleveland (G-5163)
Davis Fabricators Inc	E	419 898-5297	Oak Harbor (G-15588)
De-Ko Inc	G	440 951-2585	Willoughby (G-20472)
Debra-Kuempel Inc	D	513 271-6500	Cincinnati (G-3645)
Debs Welding & Fabrication	G	330 376-2242	Akron (G-143)
Defiance Metal Products WI Inc	C	920 426-9207	Defiance (G-8787)
Diamond Mfg Bluffton Ltd	D	419 358-0129	Bluffton (G-1911)
Diamond Wipes Intl Inc	G	419 562-3575	Bucyrus (G-2338)
Diversifd OH Vlly Eqpt & Srvcs	F	740 458-9881	Clarington (G-4651)
DMC Welding Incorporated	G	330 877-1935	Hartville (G-10820)
Dover Conveyor Inc	E	740 922-9390	Midvale (G-14106)
Dover Tank and Plate Company	E	330 343-4443	Dover (G-8982)
Dracool-Usa Inc	E	937 743-5899	Carlisle (G-2930)
Dwayne Bennett Industries	G	440 466-5724	Geneva (G-10345)
E B P Inc	E	216 241-2550	Cleveland (G-5230)
E W Welding & Fabricating	G	440 826-9038	Berea (G-1612)
E-Pak Manufacturing LLC	D	800 235-1632	Wooster (G-20769)
Ebner Furnaces Inc	D	330 335-2311	Wadsworth (G-19404)
Egypt Structural Steel Proc	E	419 628-2375	Minster (G-14352)
Electromech Technologies LLC	B	216 706-2960	Cleveland (G-5270)
Emh Inc	E	330 220-8600	Valley City (G-19203)
EPI of Cleveland Inc	G	330 468-2872	Twinsburg (G-18929)
Erico International Corp	A	440 349-2630	Solon (G-17288)
Erico International Corp	B	440 248-0100	Solon (G-17289)
Evers Welding Co Inc	E	513 385-7352	Cincinnati (G-3723)
F M Machine Co	E	330 773-8237	Akron (G-177)
Fab Shop Inc	G	513 860-1332	Hamilton (G-10690)
Fabco Inc	E	419 421-4740	Findlay (G-9820)
Falls Welding & Fabg Inc	G	330 253-3437	Akron (G-180)
Fastfeed Corp	G	330 948-7333	Lodi (G-12160)
Fenix Fabrication Inc	E	330 745-8731	Akron (G-184)
Fiedeldey Stl Fabricators Inc	E	513 353-3300	Cincinnati (G-3751)
Fincom Corporation	G	330 456-8341	Canton (G-2703)
Flex-Strut Inc	D	330 372-9999	Warren (G-19551)
Foster Products Inc	G	513 735-9770	Batavia (G-1186)
Franck and Fric Incorporated	D	216 524-4451	Cleveland (G-5377)
Fulton Equipment Co	G	419 290-5393	Toledo (G-18475)
G & R Welding & Machining	G	937 323-9353	Springfield (G-17562)
G & W Products LLC	C	513 860-4050	Fairfield (G-9660)
Galion-Godwin Truck Bdy Co LLC	D	330 359-5495	Millersburg (G-14217)
Gardner Metal Craft Inc	G	513 539-4538	Monroe (G-14402)
Garland Welding Co Inc	F	330 536-6506	Lowellville (G-12408)
Gb Fabrication Company	E	419 347-1835	Shelby (G-17136)
Gen III	G	614 737-8744	Columbus (G-7107)
General Steel Corporation	F	216 883-4200	Cleveland (G-5421)
George Steel Fabricating Inc	E	513 932-2887	Lebanon (G-11802)
Gilson Machine & Tool Co Inc	E	419 592-2911	Napoleon (G-14678)
GL Nause Co Inc	E	513 722-9500	Loveland (G-12353)
Glenwood Erectors Inc	G	330 652-9616	Niles (G-15156)
Gokoh Corporation	F	937 339-4977	Troy (G-18832)
Gold Star Met Fabg & Repr Inc	F	440 353-3233	North Ridgeville (G-15377)
Goyal Industries Inc	E	419 522-7099	Mansfield (G-12618)
Graber Metal Works Inc	E	440 237-8422	North Royalton (G-15422)
Green Point Metals Inc	E	937 743-4075	Franklin (G-10025)
Grenga Machine & Welding	F	330 743-1113	Youngstown (G-21104)
Griffin Industries LLC	G	216 696-2588	Cleveland (G-5459)
Gunderson Rail Services LLC	E	330 792-6521	Youngstown (G-21106)
H B Products Inc	E	937 492-7031	Sidney (G-17191)
Halman Inc	F	440 992-4239	Ashtabula (G-811)
Halvorsen Company	E	216 341-7500	Cleveland (G-5473)
Hanson Concrete Products Ohio	E	614 443-4846	Columbus (G-7143)
Hays Fabricating & Welding	E	937 325-0031	Springfield (G-17568)
Herman Manufacturing LLC	F	216 251-6400	Cleveland (G-5504)
High Production Technology LLC	F	419 591-7000	Napoleon (G-14680)
Holgate Metal Fab Inc	F	419 599-2000	Napoleon (G-14682)
Horizon Metals Inc	E	440 235-3338	Berea (G-1618)
Horning Steel Co	G	330 633-0028	Tallmadge (G-18146)
Howden North America Inc	E	330 721-7374	Medina (G-13422)
Hr Machine LLC	G	937 222-7644	Beavercreek (G-1345)
Hunkar Technologies Inc	C	513 272-1010	Cincinnati (G-3902)
Hynes Industries Inc	C	330 799-3221	Youngstown (G-21111)
Hyq Technologies LLC	G	513 225-6911	Oxford (G-15837)
Indian Creek Fabricators Inc	E	937 667-7214	Tipp City (G-18283)
Industrial Hanger Conveyor Co	G	419 332-2661	Fremont (G-10158)
Industrial Mill Maintenance	E	330 746-1155	Youngstown (G-21115)
Ironfab LLC	F	614 443-3900	Columbus (G-7211)
Ironhead Fabg & Contg Inc	D	419 690-0000	Toledo (G-18528)
J & L Specialty Steel Inc	G	330 875-6200	Louisville (G-12317)
J & L Welding Fabricating Inc	F	330 393-9353	Warren (G-19561)
J A Donadee Corporation	E	330 533-3305	Canfield (G-2559)
J A McMahon Incorporated	E	330 652-2588	Niles (G-15163)
J Horst Manufacturing Co	D	330 828-2216	Dalton (G-8072)
J P Suggins Mobile Welding	E	216 566-7131	Cleveland (G-5599)
Jab Sales Inc	G	440 446-0606	Cleveland (G-5603)
James C Denier Co Inc	G	513 385-6272	Cincinnati (G-3939)
Jayron Fabrication LLC	G	740 335-3184	Leesburg (G-11852)
Jh Industries Inc	E	330 963-4105	Twinsburg (G-18961)
Joe Rees Welding	G	937 652-4067	Urbana (G-19165)
Jomac Ltd	G	330 627-7727	Carrollton (G-2958)
JR Manufacturing Inc	C	419 375-8021	Fort Recovery (G-9956)
Js Fabrications Inc	G	419 333-0323	Fremont (G-10161)
Kecoat LLC	F	330 527-0215	Garrettsville (G-10327)
Kedar D Army	G	419 238-6929	Van Wert (G-19262)
Kellys Welding & Fabricating	G	440 593-6040	Conneaut (G-7811)
Kings Welding and Fabg Inc	E	330 738-3592	Mechanicstown (G-13359)
Kirk Welding & Fabricating	G	216 961-6403	Cleveland (G-5658)
Kirwan Industries Inc	G	513 333-0766	Cincinnati (G-3993)
Kottler Metal Products Co Inc	E	440 946-7473	Willoughby (G-20523)
Kramer Power Equipment Co	F	937 456-2232	Eaton (G-9313)
L & W Inc	D	734 397-6300	Avon (G-999)
Lake Erie Ship Repair	F	440 624-0025	Jefferson (G-11366)
Langdon Inc	E	513 733-5955	Cincinnati (G-4011)
Lapham-Hickey Steel Corp	E	614 443-4881	Columbus (G-7286)
Laserflex Corporation	D	614 850-9600	Hilliard (G-10958)
Lauren Yoakam	G	440 365-3952	Elyria (G-9450)
Lazarus Steel LLC	G	216 391-3245	Cleveland (G-5689)
Lefeld Welding & Stl Sups Inc	E	419 678-2397	Coldwater (G-6567)
Lideco LLC	G	330 539-9333	Vienna (G-19367)
Lilly Industries Inc	E	419 946-7908	Mount Gilead (G-14563)
Livingston & Company Ltd	G	513 553-6430	New Richmond (G-14941)
Louis Arthur Steel Company	G	440 997-5545	Geneva (G-10352)
Louis Arthur Steel Company	G	440 997-5545	Uniontown (G-19091)
Lyco Corporation	E	330 534-3330	Lowellville (G-12410)
M & H Fabricating Co Inc	F	937 325-8708	Springfield (G-17593)
M & M Fabrication Inc	F	740 779-3071	Chillicothe (G-3249)
M & W Welding Inc	G	614 224-0501	Columbus (G-7307)
Machine Tool & Fab Corp	F	419 435-7676	Fostoria (G-9983)
Mad River Fabricating Ltd	G	937 322-6521	Springfield (G-17597)
Magnesium Products Group Inc	G	310 971-5799	Maumee (G-13277)
Magnum Piering Inc	E	513 759-3348	West Chester (G-20022)
Mahoning Valley Fabricators	F	330 793-8995	Austintown (G-975)
Manifold & Phalor Inc	E	614 920-1200	Canal Winchester (G-2531)
Manitowoc Company Inc	G	920 746-3332	Cleveland (G-5739)
Marc Industries Inc	G	440 944-9305	Willoughby (G-20536)
Marsam Metalfab Inc	E	330 405-1520	Twinsburg (G-18978)
Martina Metal LLC	E	614 291-9700	Columbus (G-7321)
Marysville Steel Inc	E	937 642-5971	Marysville (G-12959)
Mason Structural Steel Inc	D	440 439-1040	Walton Hills (G-19474)
Masonite International Corp	G	937 454-9308	Vandalia (G-19304)
Maverick Innvtive Slutions LLC	E	419 281-7944	Ashland (G-752)

Mc Brown Industries Inc ....F 419 963-2800
Findlay (G-9859)

McNeil Group Inc ....E 614 298-0300
Columbus (G-7338)

McNeil Holdings LLC ....G 614 298-0300
Columbus (G-7339)

McWane Inc ....B 740 622-6651
Coshocton (G-7897)

Mercury Iron & Steel ....F 440 349-1500
Solon (G-17334)

Metal Dynamics Co ....G 330 601-0748
Wooster (G-20805)

Metal Man Inc ....G 614 830-0968
Groveport (G-10636)

Metal Sales Manufacturing Corp ....E 440 576-9070
Jefferson (G-11367)

Metlweb ....E 513 563-8822
Cincinnati (G-4093)

Miami Steel Fabricators Inc ....G 937 299-5550
Dayton (G-8489)

Mikes Welding ....G 937 675-6587
Jamestown (G-11352)

Miracle Welding Inc ....G 513 746-9977
Franklin (G-10037)

Mobile Mini Inc ....F 614 449-8655
Columbus (G-7360)

Mohican Steel Fabricators Inc ....G 419 994-4802
Loudonville (G-12300)

Monnig Welding Co ....G 513 241-5156
Cincinnati (G-4119)

Nct Technologies Group Inc ....E 937 882-6800
New Carlisle (G-14808)

Neidert Fabricating Inc ....G 330 753-3331
Barberton (G-1133)

New Wayne Inc ....G 740 453-3454
Zanesville (G-21333)

Northeast Ohio Contractors LLC ....G 216 269-7881
Cleveland (G-5906)

Northern Boiler Company ....F 216 961-3033
Cleveland (G-5908)

Northern Manufacturing Co Inc ....C 419 898-2821
Oak Harbor (G-15592)

Northwest Installations Inc ....E 419 423-5738
Findlay (G-9869)

Northwind Industries Inc ....E 216 433-0666
Cleveland (G-5916)

Ohio Gratings Inc ....B 330 477-6707
Canton (G-2799)

Ohio Steel Industries Inc ....E 740 927-9500
Pataskala (G-15975)

Ohio Structures Inc ....E 330 547-7705
Berlin Center (G-1657)

Ohio Structures Inc ....E 330 533-0084
Canfield (G-2568)

Olson Sheet Metal Cnstr Co ....G 330 745-8225
Barberton (G-1136)

Outotec Oyj ....E 440 783-3336
Strongsville (G-17949)

Overhead Door Corporation ....D 740 383-6376
Marion (G-12892)

Ozone Systems Svcs Group Inc ....G 513 899-4131
Morrow (G-14550)

P & L Metalcrafts LLC ....F 330 793-2178
Youngstown (G-21160)

P B Fabrication Mech Contr ....F 419 478-4869
Toledo (G-18631)

Pcy Enterprises Inc ....E 513 241-5566
Cincinnati (G-4219)

Perfections Fabricators Inc ....F 440 365-5850
Elyria (G-9477)

Perry Welding Service Inc ....F 330 425-2211
Twinsburg (G-19001)

Phillips & Sons Welding & Fabg ....G 440 428-1625
Geneva (G-10355)

Phoenix Metal Works Inc ....G 937 274-5555
Dayton (G-8573)

Pioneer Machine Inc ....G 330 948-6500
Lodi (G-12168)

Pioneer Pipe Inc ....B 740 376-2400
Marietta (G-12816)

PJs Fabricating Inc ....E 330 478-1120
Canton (G-2814)

Pjs Towing Inc ....E 330 478-1120
Canton (G-2815)

Porters Welding Inc ....F 740 452-4181
Zanesville (G-21342)

Precision International LLC ....E 330 793-0900
Akron (G-348)

Precision Quincy Shelters Inc ....B 888 312-5442
Mason (G-13076)

Precision Steel Services Inc ....D 419 476-5702
Toledo (G-18654)

Precision Welding & Mfg ....F 937 444-6925
Mount Orab (G-14585)

Precision Welding Corporation ....E 216 524-6110
Cleveland (G-6037)

Pro Fab Industries Inc ....G 317 297-0461
Dundee (G-9179)

Pro-Fab Inc ....E 330 644-0044
Akron (G-352)

Production Support Inc ....F 937 526-3897
Russia (G-16768)

Professional Fabricators Inc ....G 216 362-1208
Cleveland (G-6054)

Pucel Enterprises Inc ....D 216 881-4604
Cleveland (G-6061)

Q S I Fabrication ....G 419 832-1680
Grand Rapids (G-10444)

Qc Industrial Inc ....G 740 642-5004
Chillicothe (G-3269)

Quality Steel Fabrication ....F 937 492-9503
Sidney (G-17213)

R L Torbeck Industries Inc ....D 513 367-0080
Harrison (G-10800)

R S V Wldg Fbrcation Machining ....F 419 592-0993
Napoleon (G-14694)

Rads LLC ....F 330 671-0464
Berea (G-1633)

Railing Crafters Ltd ....G 440 506-9336
Painesville (G-15915)

Rance Industries Inc ....F 330 482-1745
Columbiana (G-6629)

RB Fabricators Inc ....F 330 779-0263
Youngstown (G-21186)

Rbm Environmental and Cnstr ....E 419 693-5840
Oregon (G-15715)

Redbuilt LLC ....E 740 363-0870
Delaware (G-8882)

Republic Storage Systems LLC ....C 330 438-5800
Canton (G-2839)

Retays Welding Company ....E 440 327-4100
North Ridgeville (G-15400)

Rezmann Karoly ....G 216 441-4357
Cleveland (G-6110)

Richard Steel Company Inc ....G 216 520-6390
Cleveland (G-6111)

Ripley Metalworks Ltd ....E 937 392-4992
Ripley (G-16670)

Rittman Inc ....D 330 927-6855
Rittman (G-16682)

Riwco Corp ....F 937 322-6521
Springfield (G-17641)

Robs Welding Technologies Ltd ....G 937 890-4963
Dayton (G-8637)

Rol- Fab Inc ....E 216 662-2500
Cleveland (G-6130)

Romar Metal Fabricating Inc ....G 740 682-7731
Oak Hill (G-15606)

Rose Metal Industries LLC ....F 216 881-3355
Cleveland (G-6132)

Rose Metal Industries LLC ....E 216 426-8615
Cleveland (G-6133)

Royal Welding Inc ....G 513 829-9353
Fairfield (G-9713)

Rti International Metals Inc ....G 330 544-9470
Niles (G-15179)

S & G Manufacturing Group LLC ....C 614 529-0100
Hilliard (G-10977)

Sausser Steel Company Inc ....F 419 422-9632
Findlay (G-9888)

Sautter Brothers ....G 419 468-7443
Galion (G-10284)

Schoonover Industries Inc ....E 419 289-8332
Ashland (G-776)

Seeburger Greenhouse ....G 419 832-1834
Grand Rapids (G-10446)

Service Iron & Steel Company ....G 330 253-9147
Akron (G-399)

Shaffer Metal Fab Inc ....E 937 492-1384
Sidney (G-17225)

Sharon Manufacturing Inc ....E 330 239-1561
Sharon Center (G-17109)

Signa Stortech Systems Inc ....E 214 357-0411
Canton (G-2849)

Sintered Metal Industries Inc ....F 330 650-4000
Hudson (G-11199)

Skinner Sales Group Inc ....E 440 572-8455
Strongsville (G-17966)

Snair Co ....F 614 873-7020
Plain City (G-16360)

Somerville Manufacturing Inc ....E 740 336-7847
Marietta (G-12834)

Specialty Steel Solutions ....G 567 674-0011
Kenton (G-11570)

Spradlin Bros Welding Co ....F 800 219-2182
Springfield (G-17650)

Ss Metal Fabricators Inc ....G 937 226-9957
Dayton (G-8673)

St Lawrence Steel Corporation ....E 330 562-9000
Streetsboro (G-17878)

Stainless Specialties Inc ....E 440 942-4242
Eastlake (G-9287)

Starr Fabricating Inc ....D 330 394-9891
Vienna (G-19376)

Steel & Alloy Utility Pdts Inc ....E 330 530-2220
Mc Donald (G-13348)

Steel Eqp Specialists Inc ....D 330 823-8260
Alliance (G-540)

Steel Quest Inc ....G 513 772-5030
Cincinnati (G-4462)

Steelcon LLC ....G 330 457-4003
New Waterford (G-14975)

Steelial Wldg Met Fbrction Inc ....E 740 669-5300
Vinton (G-19383)

Steeltec Products LLC ....E 216 681-1114
Cleveland (G-6247)

Steve Vore Welding and Steel ....F 419 375-4087
Fort Recovery (G-9959)

Stock Mfg & Design Co Inc ....D 513 353-3600
Cleves (G-6528)

Straightaway Fabrications Ltd ....E 419 281-9440
Ashland (G-780)

Suburban Metal Products Inc ....F 740 474-4237
Circleville (G-4644)

Suburban Stl Sup Co Ltd Partnr ....G 317 783-6555
Columbus (G-7665)

Sulecki Precision Products ....F 440 255-5454
Mentor (G-13740)

Summers Acquisition Corp ....G 419 423-5800
Findlay (G-9898)

Superior Soda Service LLC ....G 937 657-9700
Beavercreek (G-1381)

Superior Welding Co ....F 614 252-8539
Columbus (G-7669)

Surface Recovery Tech LLC ....F 937 879-5864
Fairborn (G-9631)

T & K Welding Co Inc ....G 216 432-0221
Cleveland (G-6287)

Taflan Steel & Welding Inc ....G 740 635-0841
Bridgeport (G-2093)

Tarrier Steel Company Inc ....E 614 444-4000
Columbus (G-7679)

Tech Dynamics Inc ....F 419 666-1666
Perrysburg (G-16153)

Tech Systems Inc ....E 419 878-2100
Waterville (G-19669)

The Mansfield Strl & Erct Co ....F 419 522-5911
Mansfield (G-12695)

The Mansfield Strl & Erct Co ....G 419 747-6571
Mansfield (G-12696)

Thomas Steel Inc ....E 419 483-7540
Bellevue (G-1563)

Transco Railway Products Inc ....D 330 872-0934
Newton Falls (G-15140)

Tri-America Contractors Inc ....E 740 574-0148
Wheelersburg (G-20335)

Tri-Fab Inc ....E 330 337-3425
Salem (G-16931)

Tri-State Fabricators Inc ....E 513 752-5005
Amelia (G-587)

Triangle Precision Industries ....D 937 299-6776
Dayton (G-8723)

Tru-Fab Inc ....F 937 435-1733
Dayton (G-8731)

Tru-Form Steel & Wire Inc ....E 765 348-5001
Toledo (G-18757)

U M D Automated Systems Inc ....D 740 694-8614
Fredericktown (G-10113)

Union Fabricating & Machine Co ....G 419 626-5963
Sandusky (G-17018)

Unique Fabrications Inc ....F 419 355-1700
Fremont (G-10192)

Updegraff Inc ....G 216 621-7600
Cleveland (G-6395)

Upright Steel LLC ....E 216 923-0852
Cleveland (G-6396)

V & S Schuler Engineering Inc ....D 330 452-5200
Canton (G-2893)

Valco Industries Inc ....E 937 399-7400
Springfield (G-17672)

Verhoff Machine & Welding Inc .... C 419 596-3202
Continental *(G-7829)*

Vicon Fabricating Company Ltd .... E 440 205-6700
Mentor *(G-13767)*

Viking Fabricators Inc .... E 740 374-5246
Marietta *(G-12848)*

W & W Custom Fabrication Inc .... G 513 353-4617
Cleves *(G-6532)*

Warren Fabricating Corporation .... D 330 847-0596
Warren *(G-19621)*

Wauseon Machine & Mfg Inc .... D 419 337-0940
Wauseon *(G-19700)*

Wecan Fabricators LLC .... G 740 667-0731
Tuppers Plains *(G-18887)*

Welage Corporation .... F 513 681-2300
Cincinnati *(G-4583)*

Weldfab Inc .... G 440 563-3310
Rock Creek *(G-16687)*

Welding Improvement Company .... G 330 424-9666
Lisbon *(G-12135)*

Weldtec Inc .... F 419 394-9440
Celina *(G-3027)*

Weldtec Ltd .... G 419 394-9440
Celina *(G-3028)*

Wernke Wldg & Stl Erection Co .... F 513 353-4173
North Bend *(G-15210)*

Westwood Fbrction Shtmetal Inc .... G 937 837-0494
Dayton *(G-8756)*

White Machine & Mfg Co 740 453-3444
Zanesville *(G-21362)*

Whole Shop Inc .... F 330 630-5305
Tallmadge *(G-18177)*

Winston Campbell LLC .... G 614 274-7015
Columbus *(G-7766)*

Wirenet Inc .... F 513 774-7759
Loveland *(G-12400)*

Wiseman Bros Fabg & Stl Ltd .... F 740 988-5121
Beaver *(G-1313)*

Witt Industries Inc .... D 513 871-5700
Mason *(G-13103)*

Wm Lang & Sons Company .... F 513 541-3304
Cincinnati *(G-4602)*

Woodbury Welding Inc .... G 937 968-3573
Union City *(G-19073)*

Worthington Industries Inc .... C 513 539-9291
Monroe *(G-14420)*

Worthngton Stelpac Systems LLC .... G 937 747-2370
North Lewisburg *(G-15309)*

Ysd Industries Inc .... D 330 792-6521
Youngstown *(G-21260)*

Ziegler Engineering Inc .... G 440 582-8515
North Royalton *(G-15461)*

Zimmerman Shtmtl Stl & Wldg .... G 419 335-3806
Wauseon *(G-19703)*

STEEL MILLS

AK Steel Corporation .... B 419 755-3011
Mansfield *(G-12557)*

AK Steel Corporation .... B 740 450-5600
Zanesville *(G-21267)*

AK Steel Corporation .... A 740 829-2206
Coshocton *(G-7877)*

AK Steel Corporation .... B 513 425-3694
Middletown *(G-14014)*

AK Steel Corporation .... F 513 425-3593
Middletown *(G-14015)*

AK Steel Corporation .... D 513 425-5000
West Chester *(G-19801)*

AK Steel Corporation .... G 513 231-2552
Cincinnati *(G-3373)*

AK Steel Corporation .... B 513 425-4200
West Chester *(G-19802)*

AK Steel Holding Corporation .... B 513 425-5000
West Chester *(G-19803)*

Akers America Inc .... G 330 757-4100
Poland *(G-16382)*

Alba Manufacturing Inc .... D 513 874-0551
Fairfield *(G-9640)*

Alro Steel Corporation .... E 937 253-6121
Dayton *(G-8149)*

American Culvert & Fabg Co .... F 740 432-6334
Cambridge *(G-2443)*

American Processing LLC .... E 216 486-4600
Cleveland *(G-4793)*

Amthor Steel Inc .... G 330 759-0200
Youngstown *(G-21025)*

Arcelormittal Cleveland LLC .... C 216 429-6000
Cleveland *(G-4823)*

Arcelormittal USA LLC .... D 330 659-9100
Richfield *(G-16614)*

Barberton Steel Industries Inc .... E 330 745-6837
Barberton *(G-1110)*

Benjamin Steel Company Inc .... E 937 233-1212
Springfield *(G-17522)*

C & R Inc .... E 614 497-1130
Groveport *(G-10617)*

Canton Drop Forge Inc .... B 330 477-4511
Canton *(G-2638)*

Cohen Brothers Inc .... G 513 422-3696
Middletown *(G-14031)*

Community Care On Wheels .... F 330 882-5506
Clinton *(G-6535)*

Contractors Steel Company .... E 330 425-3050
Twinsburg *(G-18919)*

Csc Ltd .... G 330 841-6011
Warren *(G-19538)*

Diversifd OH Vlly Eqpt & Srvcs .... F 740 458-9881
Clarington *(G-4651)*

E D M Star-One Inc .... F 440 647-0600
Wellington *(G-19740)*

Eastern Automated Piping .... G 740 535-8184
Mingo Junction *(G-14348)*

Egypt Structural Steel Proc .... E 419 628-2375
Minster *(G-14352)*

Elster Perfection Corporation .... D 440 428-1171
Geneva *(G-10346)*

Famous Industries Inc .... C 740 397-8842
Mount Vernon *(G-14622)*

Franklin Iron & Metal Corp .... E 937 253-8184
Dayton *(G-8350)*

Fulton County Processing Ltd .... D 419 822-9266
Delta *(G-8933)*

Garden Street Iron & Metal .... E 513 853-3700
Cincinnati *(G-3798)*

Grenga Machine & Welding .... F 330 743-1113
Youngstown *(G-21104)*

Hadronics Inc .... D 513 321-9350
Cincinnati *(G-3861)*

Harvard Coil Processing Inc .... C 216 883-6366
Cleveland *(G-5484)*

Holgate Metal Fab Inc .... F 419 599-2000
Napoleon *(G-14682)*

Humble Construction Co .... E 614 888-8960
Columbus *(G-7169)*

Ideal Steel Inc .... E 937 525-9161
Springfield *(G-17580)*

International Steel Group .... C 330 841-2800
Warren *(G-19560)*

Jck Industries .... E 419 433-6277
Huron *(G-11229)*

John Maneely Company .... E 724 342-6851
Niles *(G-15165)*

Lapham-Hickey Steel Corp .... E 614 443-4881
Columbus *(G-7286)*

Liverpool Coil Processing Inc .... C 330 558-2600
Valley City *(G-19210)*

Long View Steel Corp .... F 419 747-1108
Mansfield *(G-12637)*

Lukjan Metal Products Inc .... C 440 599-8127
Conneaut *(G-7814)*

McWane Inc .... B 740 622-6651
Coshocton *(G-7897)*

Metals USA Crbn Flat Rlled Inc .... D 330 264-8416
Wooster *(G-20806)*

Metals USA Crbn Flat Rlled Inc .... D 937 882-6354
Springfield *(G-17604)*

Mid-America Steel Corp .... E 800 282-3466
Cleveland *(G-5805)*

Ohio Gratings Inc .... B 330 477-6707
Canton *(G-2799)*

Ohio Pickling & Processing LLC .... D 419 241-9601
Toledo *(G-18616)*

Ohio Valley Alloy Services Inc .... E 740 373-1900
Marietta *(G-12811)*

Pendleton Mold & Machine LLC .... G 440 998-0041
Ashtabula *(G-830)*

Pioneer Equipment Company .... F 330 857-6340
Dalton *(G-8078)*

Pioneer Pipe Inc .... E 740 376-2400
Marietta *(G-12816)*

Precision Laser & Forming .... F 419 943-4350
Leipsic *(G-11873)*

Precision Specialty Metals Inc .... D 323 475-3200
Worthington *(G-20883)*

Precision Strip Inc .... D 937 667-6255
Tipp City *(G-18293)*

Quality Bar Inc .... F 330 755-0000
Struthers *(G-17996)*

Racelite South Coast Inc .... E 216 581-4600
Maple Heights *(G-12739)*

Republic Steel Inc .... E 440 277-2000
Lorain *(G-12272)*

Rti Alloys .... G 330 652-9952
Niles *(G-15177)*

Samuel Steel Pickling Company .... G 330 963-3777
Twinsburg *(G-19016)*

Schaefer Group Inc .... G 419 897-2883
Perrysburg *(G-16147)*

Sedlak .... G 330 908-2200
Richfield *(G-16636)*

Sertek LLC .... D 614 504-5828
Dublin *(G-9143)*

Shear Service Inc 216 341-2700
Cleveland *(G-6185)*

Shear Tech Steel LLC 419 726-6174
Toledo *(G-18694)*

Stainless Specialties Inc .... E 440 942-4242
Eastlake *(G-9287)*

Stein Inc .... F 440 526-9301
Cleveland *(G-6248)*

Timken Receivables Corporation .... G 234 262-3000
North Canton *(G-15275)*

Timkensteel Corporation .... B 330 471-7000
Canton *(G-2876)*

Timkensteel Corporation .... G 330 517-7300
Akron *(G-441)*

Timkensteel Corporation .... C 330 438-3000
Canton *(G-2878)*

Timkensteel Corporation .... D 937 456-8002
Eaton *(G-9324)*

Timkensteel Corporation .... B 330 438-3000
Canton *(G-2879)*

United States Steel Corp .... A 440 240-2500
Lorain *(G-12287)*

Universal Urethane Pdts Inc .... D 419 693-7400
Toledo *(G-18760)*

V & S Schuler Engineering Inc .... D 330 452-5200
Canton *(G-2893)*

Western Reserve Metals Inc .... E 330 448-4092
Masury *(G-13218)*

Witt Industries Inc .... D 513 871-5700
Mason *(G-13103)*

Wodin Inc .... E 440 439-4222
Cleveland *(G-6474)*

Worthington Industries Inc .... C 513 539-9291
Monroe *(G-14420)*

Worthington Steel Company .... C 614 438-3210
Worthington *(G-20900)*

Worthngton Stl Cmpny-Baltimore .... E 410 574-5835
Worthington *(G-20901)*

Zekelman Industries Inc .... C 740 432-2146
Cambridge *(G-2483)*

Zekelman Industries Inc .... C 330 373-4410
Warren *(G-19628)*

STEEL SHEET: Cold-Rolled

Worthngton Stl Cmpny-Baltimore .... E 410 574-5835
Worthington *(G-20901)*

STEEL, COLD-ROLLED: Flat Bright, From Purchased Hot-Rolled

Clark Grave Vault Company .... C 614 294-3761
Columbus *(G-6933)*

Geneva Liberty Steel Ltd .... D 330 740-0103
Youngstown *(G-21097)*

STEEL, COLD-ROLLED: Sheet Or Strip, From Own Hot-Rolled

Matandy Steel & Metal Pdts LLC .... D 513 844-2277
Hamilton *(G-10723)*

Steel Technologies LLC .... E 419 523-5199
Ottawa *(G-15809)*

Superior Forge & Steel Corp .... D 419 222-4412
Lima *(G-12098)*

STEEL, COLD-ROLLED: Strip NEC, From Purchased Hot-Rolled

Centaur Inc .... G 419 469-8000
Toledo *(G-18392)*

Greer Steel Company .... C 330 343-8811
Dover *(G-8989)*

H S Processing LP .... G 216 641-6995
Cleveland *(G-5470)*

Heidtman Steel Products Inc .... E 419 691-4646
Toledo *(G-18505)*

Worthington Industries Inc .... C 614 438-3210
Worthington *(G-20896)*

Worthington Industries Inc ....F....... 614 438-3113
Columbus (G-7776)

Worthington Steel Company ....C....... 216 441-8300
Cleveland (G-6483)

STEEL, COLD-ROLLED: Strip Or Wire

Bekaert Corporation ....C....... 330 683-5060
Orrville (G-15729)

Worthington Steel Company ....C....... 614 438-3210
Worthington (G-20900)

STEEL, HOT-ROLLED: Sheet Or Strip

Centaur Inc ....G....... 419 469-8000
Toledo (G-18392)

Heidtman Steel Products Inc ....D....... 419 385-0636
Toledo (G-18506)

Heidtman Steel Products Inc ....E....... 419 691-4646
Toledo (G-18505)

Ohio Steel Sheet & Plate Inc ....E....... 800 827-2401
Hubbard (G-11136)

STEEL: Cold-Rolled

AK Steel Corporation.......................B....... 740 450-5600
Zanesville (G-21267)

AK Steel Corporation.......................A....... 740 829-2206
Coshocton (G-7877)

Akers America Inc ....G....... 330 757-4100
Poland (G-16382)

All Ohio Threaded Rod Co Inc ....E....... 216 426-1800
Cleveland (G-4757)

Allegheny Ludlum LLC ....E....... 330 875-2244
Louisville (G-12308)

Alro Steel Corporation ....E....... 937 253-6121
Dayton (G-8149)

Bar Processing Corporation ....D....... 330 872-0914
Newton Falls (G-15129)

Bcs Metal Prep LLC ....E....... 440 663-1100
Solon (G-17266)

Benjamin Steel Company Inc ....E....... 937 233-1212
Springfield (G-17522)

Cincinnati Cold Drawn Inc ....G....... 513 874-3296
West Chester (G-19830)

Consolidated Metal Pdts Inc ....C....... 513 251-2624
Cincinnati (G-3604)

Denne Industries Inc........................E....... 440 365-0600
Elyria (G-9401)

Dietrich Industries Inc ....E....... 614 438-3210
Worthington (G-20864)

Elgin Fastener Group LLC ....E....... 216 481-4400
Cleveland (G-5271)

Ferrolux Metals Co Ohio LLC ....G....... 216 671-6161
Macedonia (G-12449)

Formetal Inc....................................F....... 419 898-2211
Oak Harbor (G-15591)

Independent Steel Company LLC........G....... 330 225-7741
Valley City (G-19207)

Lakeway Mfg Inc ....E....... 419 433-3030
Huron (G-11232)

LLC Ring Masters ....E....... 330 832-1511
Massillon (G-13167)

Mid-America Steel Corp ....E....... 800 282-3466
Cleveland (G-5805)

MSC Walbridge Coatings Inc ....C....... 419 666-6130
Walbridge (G-19461)

Pilot-Run Stamping Company ....E....... 440 255-8821
Mentor (G-13687)

Precision Strip Inc ....C....... 419 674-4186
Kenton (G-11564)

Raco Cutting Inc ....G....... 937 293-1228
Moraine (G-14523)

Republic Steel Inc ....F....... 330 837-7024
Massillon (G-13199)

Steel Technologies LLC ....D....... 440 946-8666
Willoughby (G-20605)

Superior Forge & Steel Corp ....D....... 419 222-4412
Lima (G-12098)

Tecumseh Redevelopment Inc ....G....... 330 659-9100
Richfield (G-16643)

Thomas Steel Strip Corporation ....B....... 330 841-6429
Warren (G-19608)

Thompson Steel Company Inc ....D....... 419 399-4803
Paulding (G-16014)

Western Reserve Metals Inc ....E....... 330 448-4092
Masury (G-13218)

Worthington Industries Inc ....F....... 614 438-3190
Columbus (G-7777)

Worthington Industries Inc ....A....... 614 438-3077
Worthington (G-20897)

Worthington Industries Lsg LLC ....G....... 614 438-3210
Worthington (G-20898)

STEEL: Galvanized

Arcelormittal Obetz LLC.....................E....... 614 492-8287
Columbus (G-6769)

Arrowstrip Inc..................................E....... 740 633-2609
Martins Ferry (G-12921)

Columbus Processing Co LLC ....G....... 614 492-8287
Columbus (G-6963)

Gregory Roll Form Inc ....D....... 330 477-4800
Canton (G-2720)

Majestic Steel Management Co ....E....... 440 786-2666
Cleveland (G-5732)

Worthington Industries Inc ....D....... 419 822-2500
Delta (G-8941)

STEERING SYSTEMS & COMPONENTS

American Showa Inc.........................A....... 937 783-4961
Blanchester (G-1709)

Industrial Steering Pdts Inc ....G....... 419 636-3300
Bryan (G-2305)

Yamada North America Inc ....B....... 937 462-7111
South Charleston (G-17428)

STENCILS

Stencilsmith LLC ....G....... 614 876-4350
Hilliard (G-10983)

STEREOGRAPHS: Photographic Message Svcs

Octsys Security Corp ....G....... 614 470-4510
Columbus (G-7412)

STITCHING SVCS

Wizard Graphics Inc ....G....... 419 354-3098
Bowling Green (G-2021)

STITCHING SVCS: Custom

B Richardson Inc..............................F....... 330 724-2122
Akron (G-80)

Pelz Lettering Inc ....G....... 419 625-3567
Sandusky (G-16996)

STONE: Cast Concrete

Outdoor Supply................................G....... 440 256-3338
Kirtland (G-11615)

Rock Decor Company ....G....... 330 857-7625
Orrville (G-15759)

STONE: Crushed & Broken, NEC

Melvin Stone Company LLC ....G....... 937 453-2032
Sabina (G-16773)

Rockhold Stone Quarry Inc.................G....... 937 358-2224
West Mansfield (G-20103)

STONE: Dimension, NEC

Connolly Construction Co Inc ....G....... 937 644-8831
Marysville (G-12936)

Heritage Marble of Ohio Inc ....E....... 614 436-1464
Columbus (G-7151)

Jim Nier Construction Inc ....F....... 740 289-2629
Piketon (G-16221)

North Hill Marble & Granite Co ....F....... 330 253-2179
Akron (G-318)

Ohio Beauty Inc...............................G....... 330 644-2241
Akron (G-322)

STONE: Quarrying & Processing, Own Stone Prdts

Briar Hill Stone Company...................E....... 330 377-5100
Glenmont (G-10402)

Canton Cut Stone Co.........................G....... 330 456-8408
North Canton (G-15223)

Cardinal Aggregate ....F....... 419 872-4380
Perrysburg (G-16075)

Custar Stone Co...............................F....... 419 669-4327
Napoleon (G-14676)

D J Decorative Stone Inc...................G....... 937 848-6462
Bellbrook (G-1505)

Hanson Aggregates East LLC ....E....... 937 364-2311
Hillsboro (G-10999)

Trustone Distributors Co...................G....... 513 469-0335
Cincinnati (G-4531)

Waller Brothers Stone Company.........E....... 740 858-1948
Mc Dermott (G-13345)

STONES, SYNTHETIC: Gem Stone & Indl Use

Cultured Marble Inc ....G....... 330 549-2282
North Lima (G-15314)

Southwest Greens Ohio LLC ....F....... 614 389-6042
Columbus (G-7633)

STONEWARE PRDTS: Pottery

Beaumont Brothers Stoneware ....G....... 740 982-0055
Crooksville (G-7949)

Clay Burley Products Co ....E....... 740 452-3633
Roseville (G-16728)

Clay Burley Products Co ....G....... 740 697-0221
Roseville (G-16729)

Ohio Stoneware LLC ....F....... 740 450-4415
Zanesville (G-21337)

Spirit of Clay ....G....... 440 684-0001
Cleveland (G-6226)

Stoneware Palace Ltd ....G....... 614 529-6974
Columbus (G-7659)

STORE FIXTURES, EXC REFRIGERATED: Wholesalers

Bobs Custom Str Interiors LLC ....G....... 567 316-7490
Toledo (G-18375)

Leiden Cabinet Company LLC.............E....... 330 878-7790
Strasburg (G-17825)

Starks Plastics LLC ....G....... 513 541-4591
Cincinnati (G-4459)

STORE FIXTURES: Exc Wood

Bobs Custom Str Interiors LLC ....G....... 567 316-7490
Toledo (G-18375)

Cap & Associates Incorporated..........C....... 614 863-3363
Columbus (G-6893)

Dell Fixtures Inc ....E....... 614 449-1750
Columbus (G-7020)

Heat Seal LLC ....C....... 216 341-2022
Cleveland (G-5491)

Modern Store Fixtures Inc ....F....... 330 427-6906
Garrettsville (G-10331)

Richard B Linneman ....G....... 513 922-5537
Cincinnati (G-4342)

STORE FIXTURES: Wood

Allied Plastic Co Inc ....G....... 419 389-1688
Toledo (G-18330)

Artistic Finishes Inc ....F....... 440 951-7850
Willoughby (G-20440)

Baker Store Equipment Company........F....... 216 475-5900
Shaker Heights (G-17084)

Cap & Associates Incorporated..........C....... 614 863-3363
Columbus (G-6893)

CIP International Inc ....D....... 513 874-9925
West Chester (G-19833)

Custom Surroundings Inc...................F....... 330 483-9020
Valley City (G-19202)

Display Dynamics Inc ....F....... 937 832-2830
Englewood (G-9516)

Leiden Cabinet Company LLC.............C....... 330 425-8555
Twinsburg (G-18972)

Modern Designs Inc..........................G....... 330 644-1771
Akron (G-299)

Norton Industries Inc........................F....... 888 357-2345
Lakewood (G-11676)

Prestige Store Interiors Inc ....D....... 419 476-2106
Toledo (G-18655)

Richard B Linneman ....G....... 513 922-5537
Cincinnati (G-4342)

Rivercity Woodworking Inc.................G....... 513 860-1900
West Chester (G-19934)

STORE FRONTS: Prefabricated, Metal

Fab Tech Inc ....G....... 330 926-9556
Brecksville (G-2049)

STORES: Auto & Home Supply

Brp Inc...G....... 440 988-4398
Amherst (G-593)

Contitech North America Inc ....E....... 440 225-5363
Akron (G-129)

Doug Marine Motors Inc....................E....... 740 335-3700
Wshngtn CT Hs (G-20907)

Knippen Chrysler Dodge Jeep ....E 419 695-4976
Delphos (G-8909)

Mr Trailer Sales Inc ....G 330 339-7701
Dover (G-9004)

Pattons Truck & Heavy Eqp Svc ....F 740 385-4067
Logan (G-12189)

Public Safety Concepts LLC ....G 614 733-0200
Plain City (G-16355)

Support Svc LLC ....G 419 617-0660
Lexington (G-11954)

Vintage Electric Ltd Inc ....F 419 472-9349
Toledo (G-18770)

York Fabrication & Machine ....G 419 483-6275
Bellevue (G-1567)

STORES: Drapery & Upholstery

M C L Window Coverings Inc ....G 513 868-6000
Hamilton (G-10719)

STRAINERS: Line, Piping Systems

Insulpro Inc ....F 614 262-3768
Columbus (G-7200)

Pipelines Inc ....G 330 448-0000
Masury (G-13215)

STRAPPING

Alacriant Inc ....D 330 562-7191
Streetsboro (G-17835)

Alacriant Inc ....E 330 562-7191
Streetsboro (G-17836)

Drawn Metals Corp ....F 937 433-6151
Dayton (G-8311)

North Shore Strapping Inc ....E 216 661-5200
Brooklyn Heights (G-2144)

Shipping Room Products Inc ....G 216 531-4422
Cleveland (G-6195)

Voss Industries Inc ....C 216 771-0870
Cleveland (G-6429)

Warren Steel Specialties Corp ....F 330 399-8360
Warren (G-19624)

Youngstown Specialty Mtls Inc ....G 330 259-1110
Youngstown (G-21256)

STRAPS: Bindings, Textile

Db Rediheat Inc ....E 216 361-0530
Cleveland (G-5175)

STRAPS: Braids, Textile

Amfm Inc ....E 440 953-4545
Willoughby (G-20431)

Vacuflo Factory ....G 330 875-2450
Louisville (G-12333)

STRAPS: Spindle Banding

Grove Engineered Products Inc ....E 419 659-5939
Columbus Grove (G-7794)

STRAPS: Webbing, Woven

Champion Webbing Company Inc ....G 330 920-1007
Cuyahoga Falls (G-7978)

STRIPS: Copper & Copper Alloy

Stoutheart Corporation ....G 401 434-7640
Chagrin Falls (G-3123)

STRUCTURAL SUPPORT & BUILDING MATERIAL: Concrete

High Concrete Group LLC ....C 937 748-2412
Springboro (G-17483)

Jet Stream International Inc ....E 330 505-9988
Niles (G-15164)

National Center For Composite ....E 937 297-9450
Dayton (G-8518)

STUCCO

Roberts Group Inc ....G 614 486-0497
Columbus (G-7569)

STUDIOS: Artist

Dimensional Works of Art ....G 330 657-2681
Peninsula (G-16036)

STUDIOS: Artists & Artists' Studios

4w Services ....F 614 554-5427
Hebron (G-10859)

B&D Truck Parts Sls & Svcs LLC ....G 419 701-7041
Fostoria (G-9968)

Terewell Inc ....G 216 334-6897
Cleveland (G-6306)

STUDS & JOISTS: Sheet Metal

Clarkdietrich Bldg Systems LLC ....C 513 870-1100
West Chester (G-19834)

Clarkwestern Dietrich Building ....G 330 372-5564
Warren (G-19535)

Clarkwestern Dietrich Building ....G 513 870-1100
West Chester (G-19835)

J N Linrose Mfg LLC ....C 513 867-5500
Hamilton (G-10709)

Matandy Steel & Metal Pdts LLC ....D 513 844-2277
Hamilton (G-10723)

STYRENE

Americas Styrenics LLC ....D 740 533-4017
Hanging Rock (G-10761)

SUBDIVIDERS & DEVELOPERS: Real Property, Cemetery Lots Only

Patriot Holdings Unlimited LLC ....G 740 574-2112
Wheelersburg (G-20333)

SUBPRESSES, METALWORKING

Central Machinery Company LLC ....F 740 387-1289
Marion (G-12862)

SUNDRIES & RELATED PRDTS: Medical & Laboratory, Rubber

Abeon Medical Corporation ....G 440 262-6000
Brecksville (G-2032)

Fenner Dunlop Port Clinton Inc ....C 419 635-2191
Port Clinton (G-16399)

Gdc Inc ....F 574 533-3128
Wooster (G-20775)

Guardian Manufacturing Co LLC ....E 419 933-2711
Willard (G-20395)

Hygenic Acquisition Co ....C 330 633-8460
Akron (G-228)

Hygenic Corporation ....C 330 633-8460
Akron (G-229)

Newell Brands Inc ....G 330 733-1184
Kent (G-11496)

Ohio Foam Corporation ....E 330 799-4553
Youngstown (G-21155)

Pritt Enterprises Inc ....F 330 453-2142
Canton (G-2823)

SUNROOFS: Motor Vehicle

CR Laurence Co Inc ....G 440 248-0003
Cleveland (G-5139)

SUNROOMS: Prefabricated Metal

Better Living Sunrooms NW Ohio ....G 419 692-4526
Delphos (G-8902)

SUPERMARKETS & OTHER GROCERY STORES

C J Kraft Enterprises Inc ....E 740 653-9606
Lancaster (G-11694)

Hershbergers Dutch Market LLP ....E 740 489-5322
Old Washington (G-15671)

Ingles Logging ....G 740 379-2909
Patriot (G-15995)

Kmart Supercenter ....G 440 974-7300
Cleveland (G-5660)

Nestle Prepared Foods Company ....A 440 248-3600
Solon (G-17344)

Nestle Prepared Foods Company ....D 440 349-5757
Solon (G-17345)

SURFACE ACTIVE AGENTS

BASF Corporation ....G 614 662-5682
Columbus (G-6812)

Henkel Corporation ....C 440 250-7700
Westlake (G-20275)

Pilot Chemical Corp ....F 513 326-0600
Cincinnati (G-4238)

SURFACE ACTIVE AGENTS: Emulsifiers, Exc Food & Pharmaceuticl

Berghausen Corporation ....E 513 541-5631
Cincinnati (G-3445)

SURFACE ACTIVE AGENTS: Oils & Greases

Southern Express Lubes Inc ....F 937 278-5807
Dayton (G-8662)

SURGICAL & MEDICAL INSTRUMENTS WHOLESALERS

Ashton Pumpmatic Inc ....G 937 424-1380
Dayton (G-8165)

Axon Medical LLC ....E 216 276-0262
Medina (G-13374)

Pure Light Technology LLC ....G 513 779-7474
West Chester (G-20042)

Rultract Inc ....G 216 524-2990
Cleveland (G-6144)

SURGICAL APPLIANCES & SPLYS

Isomedix Inc ....F 440 354-2600
Mentor (G-13612)

Marlen Manufacturing & Dev Co ....G 216 292-7060
Bedford (G-1441)

Steris Corporation ....G 440 354-2600
Mentor (G-13732)

Steris Corporation ....G 330 686-4550
Stow (G-17804)

Steris Corporation ....C 440 354-2600
Mentor (G-13734)

Steris Corporation ....G 440 354-2600
Mentor (G-13735)

Steris Corporation ....G 440 354-2600
Mentor (G-13737)

Surgical Appliance Inds Inc ....C 513 271-4594
Cincinnati (G-4488)

SURGICAL APPLIANCES & SPLYS

Acor Orthopaedic Inc ....G 440 532-0117
Cleveland (G-4696)

Action Prosthetics LLC ....G 937 548-9100
Greenville (G-10487)

Axon Medical LLC ....E 216 276-0262
Medina (G-13374)

Bulk Molding Compounds Inc ....D 419 874-7941
Perrysburg (G-16071)

Cardinal Health Inc ....A 614 757-5000
Dublin (G-9057)

Cleveland Medical Devices Inc ....E 216 426-0365
Cleveland (G-5068)

Comprhnsive Brace Limb Ctr LLC ....G 330 337-8333
Salem (G-16885)

Deco Tools Inc ....E 419 476-9321
Toledo (G-18430)

Dentronix Inc ....E 330 916-7300
Cuyahoga Falls (G-7987)

Doling & Associates Dental Lab ....E 937 254-0075
Dayton (G-8307)

Dynamic Control North Amer Inc ....G 440 979-0657
North Olmsted (G-15330)

Ethicon Inc ....C 513 786-7000
Blue Ash (G-1787)

Foot Logic Inc ....G 330 699-0123
Uniontown (G-19084)

Francisco Jaume ....G 740 622-1200
Coshocton (G-7891)

Frohock-Stewart Inc ....E 440 329-6000
North Ridgeville (G-15375)

Gelok International Corp ....F 419 352-1482
Dunbridge (G-9169)

Gendron Wheel LLC ....G 419 445-6060
Archbold (G-677)

Gottfried Medical Inc ....E 419 474-2973
Toledo (G-18484)

Guardian Manufacturing Co LLC ....E 419 933-2711
Willard (G-20395)

Hanger Prosthetics & Orthotics ....D 614 436-3516
Columbus (G-6648)

Hanger Prsthetcs & Ortho Inc ....G 740 446-6879
Gallipolis (G-10299)

Hanger Prsthetcs & Ortho Inc ....F 614 481-8351
Columbus (G-7142)

(G-0000) Company's Geographic Section entry number

Hanger Prsthetcs & Ortho Inc...............G.......740 354-4775
  Portsmouth (G-16437)
Integrated Med Solutions Inc.............D.......440 269-6984
  Mentor (G-13609)
Invacare Canadian Holdings LLC.........G.......440 329-6000
  Elyria (G-9434)
Invacare Corporation...........................A.......440 329-6000
  Elyria (G-9435)
Invacare Corporation...........................D.......800 333-6900
  Elyria (G-9436)
Invacare Corporation...........................F.......440 329-6000
  North Ridgeville (G-15381)
Invacare Corporation (tw)....................E.......440 329-6000
  North Ridgeville (G-15382)
Invacare Holdings Corporation ....G.......440 329-6000
  Elyria (G-9438)
Invacare International Corp ....G.......440 329-6000
  Elyria (G-9439)
Joint Vue LLC......................................G.......614 640-3350
  Columbus (G-7243)
Jones Metal Products Company ....D.......740 545-6381
  West Lafayette (G-20087)
Jones Metal Products Company ....E.......740 545-6341
  West Lafayette (G-20088)
Kempf Surgical Appliances Inc ....E.......513 984-5758
  Montgomery (G-14433)
Kufbag Inc ....G.......614 589-8687
  Westerville (G-20221)
Leimkuehler Inc...................................E.......440 899-7842
  Cleveland (G-5693)
M & S Acquistion Co LLC.....................E.......440 951-8700
  Mentor (G-13638)
Marlen Manufacturing & Dev Co..........E.......216 292-7546
  Bedford (G-1442)
Meridian Industries Inc ....D.......330 673-1011
  Kent (G-11488)
Optimus LLC..E.......513 918-2320
  Cincinnati (G-4191)
Optimus LLC..G.......937 454-1900
  Dayton (G-8551)
Orthotic and Prostetic Spc..................F.......216 531-2773
  Euclid (G-9596)
Philips Medical Systems Clevel...........B.......440 247-2652
  Cleveland (G-6001)
Schaerer Medical Usa Inc....................F.......513 561-2241
  Cincinnati (G-4386)
Smith & Nephew Inc ....E.......513 821-5888
  Cincinnati (G-4429)
Smiths Medical Asd Inc ....E.......800 796-8701
  Dublin (G-9144)
Sroufe Healthcare Products LLC..........E.......260 894-4171
  Wadsworth (G-19442)
Surgical Appliance Inds Inc ....E.......937 392-4301
  Ripley (G-16671)
Thomas Products Co Inc......................E.......513 756-9009
  Cincinnati (G-4507)
Tilt 15 Inc ....D.......330 239-4192
  Sharon Center (G-17112)
Tranzonic Companies ....B.......216 535-4300
  Richmond Heights (G-16657)
Weber Orthopedic Inc..........................G.......440 934-1812
  Avon (G-1018)
X-Spine Systems Inc............................D.......937 847-8400
  Miamisburg (G-13882)
Zimmer Inc...C.......614 508-6000
  Columbus (G-7788)

SURGICAL EQPT: See Also Instruments

3M Company...B.......513 248-1749
  Milford (G-14118)
Atricure Inc..C.......513 755-4100
  Mason (G-12985)
Ethicon Endo-Surgery Inc ....A.......513 337-7000
  Blue Ash (G-1786)
Ethicon US LLC....................................E.......513 337-7000
  Blue Ash (G-1788)
Gqi Inc...G.......330 830-9805
  Massillon (G-13141)
Mill-Rose Company..............................C.......440 255-9171
  Mentor (G-13657)
Rultract Inc ....G.......216 524-2990
  Cleveland (G-6144)
Scottcare Corporation ....E.......216 362-0550
  Cleveland (G-6175)
United States Endoscopy......................G.......440 639-4494
  Mentor (G-13760)
United States Endoscopy......................F.......440 639-4494
  Mentor (G-13761)

SURGICAL IMPLANTS

Bahler Medical Inc ....E.......614 873-7600
  Plain City (G-16323)
Hammill Manufacturing Co ....D.......419 476-0789
  Maumee (G-13264)
Mosher Medical Inc ....G.......330 668-2252
  Akron (G-305)
Osteosymbionics LLC..........................F.......216 881-8500
  Cleveland (G-5950)

SURVEYING & MAPPING: Land Parcels

Barr Engineering Incorporated.............E.......614 714-0299
  Columbus (G-6808)
Dlz Ohio Inc ....C.......614 888-0040
  Columbus (G-7033)

SURVEYING INSTRUMENTS WHOLESALERS

Zaenkert Surveying Essentials.............G.......513 738-2917
  Okeana (G-15668)

SUSPENSION SYSTEMS: Acoustical, Metal

One Wish LLC......................................F.......800 505-6883
  Beachwood (G-1289)

SVC ESTABLISH EQPT, WHOLESALE: Carpet/Rug Clean Eqpt & Sply

Jeff Pendergrass..................................G.......513 575-1226
  Milford (G-14156)

SVC ESTABLISHMENT EQPT & SPLYS WHOLESALERS

AIN Industries Inc ....G.......440 781-0950
  Cleveland (G-4733)
Friends Service Co Inc ....F.......800 427-1704
  Dayton (G-8352)
Friends Service Co Inc ....G.......800 427-1704
  Kent (G-11459)
K-O-K Products Inc ....F.......740 548-0526
  Galena (G-10245)
Vandalia Massage Therapy ....G.......937 890-8660
  Vandalia (G-19315)

SVC ESTABLISHMENT EQPT, WHOL: Cleaning & Maint Eqpt & Splys

Ace-Tex Enterprises Inc ....F.......513 829-8899
  Hamilton (G-10661)
Judco Inc ....G.......440 322-6604
  Elyria (G-9444)
Zircon Industries Inc............................G.......216 595-0200
  Cleveland (G-6499)

SVC ESTABLISHMENT EQPT, WHOL: Concrete Burial Vaults & Boxes

Allen Enterprises Inc ....G.......740 532-5913
  Ironton (G-11288)
Baxter Burial Vault Service ....E.......513 641-1010
  Cincinnati (G-3440)
Bell Burial Vault Co..............................G.......513 896-9044
  Hamilton (G-10674)
Shaw Wilbert Vaults LLC......................G.......740 498-7438
  Newcomerstown (G-15124)

SVC ESTABLISHMENT EQPT, WHOLESALE: Beauty Parlor Eqpt & Sply

Sally Beauty Supply LLC.......................G.......330 823-7476
  Alliance (G-535)

SVC ESTABLISHMENT EQPT, WHOLESALE: Firefighting Eqpt

A-1 Sprinkler Company Inc ....D.......937 859-6198
  Miamisburg (G-13779)
Action Coupling & Eqp Inc....................D.......330 279-4242
  Holmesville (G-11099)
Antram Fire Equipment ....G.......330 525-7171
  North Georgetown (G-15286)
Fire Safety Services Inc........................F.......937 686-2000
  Huntsville (G-11213)
Merrick Manufacturing II LLC ....G.......937 222-7164
  Dayton (G-8485)
Sutphen Corporation............................C.......800 726-7030
  Dublin (G-9150)

United Fire Apparatus Corp ....G.......419 645-4083
  Cridersville (G-7947)
Warren Fire Equipment Inc ....G.......937 866-8918
  Miamisburg (G-13878)

SVC ESTABLISHMENT EQPT, WHOLESALE: Restaurant Splys

Dmi Products Inc ....G.......440 951-1828
  Mentor (G-13561)
Martin-Brower Company LLC ....B.......513 773-2301
  West Chester (G-19898)
Touchpint Cmplete Slutions LLC...........G.......419 919-3222
  Celina (G-3024)
Wasserstrom Company ....B.......614 737-8472
  Columbus (G-7750)

SVC ESTABLISHMENT EQPT, WHOLESALE: Shredders, Indl & Comm

Cummins - Allison Corp ....G.......440 824-5050
  Cleveland (G-5146)

SWEEPING COMPOUNDS

Nwp Manufacturing Inc ....F.......419 894-6871
  Waldo (G-19466)

SWIMMING POOL ACCESS: Leaf Skimmers Or Pool Rakes

Spa Pool Covers Inc ....G.......440 235-9981
  North Royalton (G-15452)

SWIMMING POOL EQPT: Filters & Water Conditioning Systems

Baleco International Inc ....E.......513 353-3000
  North Bend (G-15202)
Clean Water Conditioning ....G.......614 475-4532
  Columbus (G-6935)

SWIMMING POOLS, EQPT & SPLYS: Wholesalers

Baleco International Inc ....E.......513 353-3000
  North Bend (G-15202)
Bradley Enterprises Inc ....G.......330 875-1444
  Louisville (G-12311)
Mc Alarney Pool Spas and Blld ....E.......740 373-6698
  Marietta (G-12806)

SWITCHBOARDS & PARTS: Power

Vacuum Electric Switch Co Inc..............G.......330 374-5156
  Akron (G-461)

SWITCHES

Saia-Burgess Lcc.................................D.......937 898-3621
  Vandalia (G-19310)

SWITCHES: Electric Power

Temple Israel ....G.......330 762-8617
  Akron (G-434)
Wes-Garde Components Group Inc ......G.......614 885-0319
  Westerville (G-20240)

SWITCHES: Electric Power, Exc Snap, Push Button, Etc

Lake Shore Electric Corp ....E.......440 232-0200
  Bedford (G-1438)

SWITCHES: Electronic

Black Box Corporation...........................E.......614 825-7400
  Lewis Center (G-11890)
Don-Ell Corporation..............................E.......419 841-7114
  Sylvania (G-18103)
Hall Company ....E.......937 652-1376
  Urbana (G-19160)
Quality Switch Inc ....E.......330 872-5707
  Newton Falls (G-15138)
Specialty Switch Co ....F.......330 427-3000
  Youngstown (G-21210)

SWITCHES: Electronic Applications

Contact Industries Inc ....E.......419 884-9788
  Lexington (G-11949)

PRODUCT

SWITCHES: Flow Actuated, Electrical

SCC Instruments ....G 513 856-8444
Hamilton (G-10735)

SWITCHES: Knife, Electric

Filnor Inc ....F 330 821-7667
Alliance (G-508)

SWITCHES: Thermostatic

Great Lakes Management Inc ....G 216 883-6500
Cleveland (G-5454)

Twinsource LLC ....F 440 248-6800
Solon (G-17410)

SWITCHES: Time, Electrical Switchgear Apparatus

All Pack Services LLC ....F 614 935-0964
Grove City (G-10541)

SWITCHGEAR & SWITCHBOARD APPARATUS

Asco Power Technologies LP ....E 216 573-7600
Cleveland (G-4841)

Asco Power Technologies LP ....C 973 966-2161
Cleveland (G-4842)

Bud Industries Inc ....G 440 946-3200
Willoughby (G-20447)

CDI Industries Inc ....E 440 243-1100
Cleveland (G-4999)

Delta Systems Inc ....C 330 626-2811
Streetsboro (G-17850)

Emerson Network Power ....F 740 833-8630
Delaware (G-8842)

Empire Power Systems Co ....G 440 796-4401
Madison (G-12506)

Fabriweld Corporation ....G 419 668-3358
Norwalk (G-15539)

Flood Heliarc Inc ....F 614 835-3929
Groveport (G-10621)

General Electric Company ....D 216 883-1000
Cleveland (G-5412)

Ida Controls ....G 440 785-8457
Willoughby (G-20508)

Mercury Iron & Steel ....F 440 349-1500
Solon (G-17334)

Myers Controlled Power LLC ....C 330 834-3200
North Canton (G-15253)

Precision Switching Inc ....G 800 800-8143
Mansfield (G-12667)

Roemer Industries Inc ....D 330 448-2000
Masury (G-13216)

Schneider Electric Usa Inc ....C 513 755-5503
Liberty Township (G-11967)

Schneider Electric Usa Inc ....C 513 755-4231
West Chester (G-19942)

Schneider Electric Usa Inc ....D 513 755-5000
West Chester (G-19943)

Siemens Industry Inc ....D 937 593-6010
Bellefontaine (G-1539)

Spb Global LLC ....G 419 931-6559
Perrysburg (G-16150)

Technology Products Inc ....G 937 652-3412
Urbana (G-19184)

Toledo Transducers Inc ....E 419 724-4170
Holland (G-11090)

SWITCHGEAR & SWITCHGEAR ACCESS, NEC

Hyundai Ideal Electric Co ....C 419 520-3314
Mansfield (G-12626)

SWITCHING EQPT: Radio & Television Communications

Pole/Zero Acquisition Inc ....C 513 870-9060
West Chester (G-19917)

SYNAGOGUES

Temple Israel ....G 330 762-8617
Akron (G-434)

SYNTHETIC RESIN FINISHED PRDTS, NEC

Amrex Inc ....G 330 678-7050
Kent (G-11430)

Orbis Corporation ....C 440 974-3857
Mentor (G-13673)

Printing 3d Parts Inc ....G 330 759-9099
Youngstown (G-21178)

Reactive Resin Products Co ....E 419 666-6119
Perrysburg (G-16146)

SYRUPS, DRINK

Coca-Cola Refreshments USA Inc .....C 419 476-6622
Toledo (G-18404)

Dominion Liquid Tech LLC ....E 513 272-2824
Cincinnati (G-3663)

Slush Puppie ....D 513 771-0940
West Chester (G-20050)

SYRUPS, FLAVORING, EXC DRINK

Cleveland Syrup Corp ....G 330 963-1900
Twinsburg (G-18916)

SYSTEMS ENGINEERING: Computer Related

Leidos Inc ....D 937 431-2400
Beavercreek (G-1348)

North Coast Security Group LLC ....G 614 887-7255
Columbus (G-7399)

SYSTEMS INTEGRATION SVCS

Advanced Prgrm Resources Inc ....E 614 761-9994
Dublin (G-9037)

Creative Microsystems Inc ....D 937 836-4499
Englewood (G-9515)

Data Processing Sciences Corp ....D 513 791-7100
Cincinnati (G-3640)

Elynx Holdings LLC ....G 513 612-5969
Cincinnati (G-3693)

Generic Systems Inc ....F 419 841-8460
Holland (G-11062)

Kc Robotics Inc ....E 513 860-4442
West Chester (G-19887)

Smartronix Inc ....F 216 378-3300
Northfield (G-15472)

Splicenet Inc ....G 513 563-3533
West Chester (G-20053)

Systemax Manufacturing Inc ....C 937 368-2300
Dayton (G-8694)

Ucr LLC ....F 937 253-8898
Dayton (G-8120)

SYSTEMS INTEGRATION SVCS: Local Area Network

Complete Network Solutions Inc ....G 330 328-2596
Stow (G-17742)

SYSTEMS INTEGRATION SVCS: Office Computer Automation

Innovative Integrations Inc ....G 216 533-5353
Mesopotamia (G-13775)

Westmount Technology Inc ....G 216 328-2011
Independence (G-11284)

SYSTEMS SOFTWARE DEVELOPMENT SVCS

CHI Corporation ....F 440 498-2300
Cleveland (G-5026)

Cincinnati Ctrl Dynamics Inc ....G 513 242-7300
Cincinnati (G-3547)

Deemsys Inc ....D 614 322-9928
Gahanna (G-10206)

Drb Systems LLC ....D 330 645-3299
Akron (G-157)

Image Integrations Systems ....F 419 872-0003
Perrysburg (G-16109)

List Media Inc ....G 330 995-0864
Aurora (G-934)

Medforall LLC ....G 614 947-0791
Columbus (G-7340)

Online Mega Sellers Corp ....G 888 384-6468
Toledo (G-18619)

Pinnacle Data Systems Inc ....C 614 748-1150
Groveport (G-10641)

TABLE OR COUNTERTOPS, PLASTIC LAMINATED

Archer Counter Design Inc ....G 513 396-7526
Cincinnati (G-3410)

E J Skok Industries ....E 216 292-7533
Bedford (G-1422)

Form-A-Top Products Inc ....G 440 779-9452
North Olmsted (G-15334)

Formware Inc ....G 614 231-9387
Columbus (G-7093)

Helmart Company Inc ....G 513 941-3095
Cincinnati (G-3876)

Scio Laminated Products Inc ....E 740 945-1321
Scio (G-17038)

Shur Fit Distributors Inc ....E 937 746-0567
Franklin (G-10053)

Summit Custom Cabinets ....G 740 345-1734
Newark (G-15061)

Tenkotte Tops Inc ....G 513 738-7300
Harrison (G-10810)

Tri-Co Industries ....G 740 927-1928
Pataskala (G-15988)

Wilsonart LLC ....E 614 876-1515
Columbus (G-7765)

Youngstown Curve Form Inc ....F 330 744-3028
Youngstown (G-21250)

TABLES: Lift, Hydraulic

Machine Tool Corporation ....G 513 863-4920
Hamilton (G-10722)

TABLETS & PADS: Newsprint, Made From Purchased Materials

Steel City Corporation ....E 330 792-7663
Ashland (G-779)

TABLETS: Bronze Or Other Metal

All-Craft Wellman Products ....F 440 946-9646
Willoughby (G-20428)

TABLEWARE OR KITCHEN ARTICLES: Commercial, Fine Earthenware

Us Inc ....G 513 791-1162
Blue Ash (G-1887)

West Ohio Tool & Mfg LLC ....G 419 678-4745
Saint Henry (G-16825)

TABLEWARE: Plastic

Berman Industries Inc ....F 513 874-7477
Blue Ash (G-1749)

TABLEWARE: Vitreous China

Libbey Inc ....C 419 325-2100
Toledo (G-18561)

TACKS: Steel, Wire Or Cut

Robertson Incorporated ....G 937 323-3747
Springfield (G-17644)

TAGS & LABELS: Paper

Century Marketing Corporation ....C 419 354-2591
Bowling Green (G-1978)

Federal Barcode Label Systems ....G 440 748-8060
North Ridgeville (G-15373)

Hooven - Dayton Corp ....D 937 233-4473
Miamisburg (G-13818)

Kay Toledo Tag Inc ....G 419 729-5479
Toledo (G-18541)

Kennedy Group Incorporated ....D 440 951-7660
Willoughby (G-20520)

Label Aid Inc ....F 419 433-2888
Huron (G-11231)

Orbytel Print and Packg Inc ....G 216 267-8734
Cleveland (G-5946)

Warren Printing & Off Pdts Inc ....F 419 523-3635
Ottawa (G-15814)

TAGS: Paper, Blank, Made From Purchased Paper

Paxar Corporation ....G 937 681-4541
Dayton (G-8567)

TANK & BOILER CLEANING SVCS

Rbm Environmental and Cnstr ....E 419 693-5840
Oregon (G-15715)

TANK REPAIR & CLEANING SVCS

Amko Service Company...............E...... 330 364-8857
Midvale (G-14105)
Kars Ohio LLC..............................G...... 614 655-1099
Pataskala (G-15973)
National Welding & Tanker Repr..........G...... 614 875-3399
Grove City (G-10576)
Ohio Hydraulics Inc.....................E...... 513 771-2590
Cincinnati (G-4178)
Sabco Industries Inc....................E...... 419 531-5347
Toledo (G-18683)

TANK REPAIR SVCS

Corrotec Inc............................E...... 937 325-3585
Springfield (G-17536)
Frontier Tank Center Inc................G...... 330 659-3888
Richfield (G-16624)

TANKS & OTHER TRACKED VEHICLE CMPNTS

American Apex Corporation...............F...... 614 652-2000
Plain City (G-16319)
Joint Systems Mfg Ctr...................G...... 419 221-9580
Lima (G-12034)
Sugartree Square Mercantile.............G...... 740 345-3882
Newark (G-15060)
Tencate Advanced Armor USA Inc..........D...... 740 928-0326
Hebron (G-10888)
Tessec Manufacturing Svcs LLC...........E...... 937 985-3552
Dayton (G-8710)
United States Dept of Army..............D...... 419 221-9500
Lima (G-12108)
US Yachiyo Inc..........................C...... 740 223-3134
Marion (G-12910)
Weldon Pump Acquition LLC...............E...... 440 232-2282
Oakwood Village (G-15633)

TANKS: Cryogenic, Metal

Amko Service Company....................E...... 330 364-8857
Midvale (G-14105)
Eleet Cryogenics Inc....................E...... 330 874-4009
Bolivar (G-1933)
Fiba Technologies Inc...................D...... 330 602-7300
Midvale (G-14107)

TANKS: For Tank Trucks, Metal Plate

Elliott Machine Works Inc...............E...... 419 468-4709
Galion (G-10267)
Jacp Inc................................G...... 513 353-3660
Miamitown (G-13888)
Liquid Luggers LLC......................E...... 330 426-2538
East Palestine (G-9241)
Macleod Inc.............................G...... 513 771-9560
Miamitown (G-13889)

TANKS: Fuel, Including Oil & Gas, Metal Plate

Convault of Ohio Inc....................G...... 614 252-8422
Columbus (G-6979)
Dragon Products Ltd.....................G...... 330 345-3968
Wooster (G-20767)
Fabstar Tanks Inc.......................F...... 419 587-3639
Grover Hill (G-10652)
North High Marathon.....................G...... 937 444-1894
Mount Orab (G-14584)

TANKS: Lined, Metal

Hamilton Tanks LLC......................F...... 614 445-8446
Columbus (G-7139)
Modern Welding Co Ohio Inc..............E...... 740 344-9425
Newark (G-15035)
Polymer Steel Corp......................E...... 330 562-6906
Streetsboro (G-17869)

TANKS: Military, Including Factory Rebuilding

General Dynamics Land...................B...... 419 221-7000
Lima (G-12018)

TANKS: Plastic & Fiberglass

AB Plastics Inc.........................G...... 513 576-6333
Milford (G-14119)
Aco Polymer Products Inc................E...... 440 285-7000
Mentor (G-13508)

Air Plastics Inc........................F...... 513 469-1074
Blue Ash (G-1737)
Alliance Equipment Company Inc..........F...... 330 821-2291
Alliance (G-493)
Composite Advantage LLC.................G...... 937 723-9031
Dayton (G-8240)
Elkhart Plastics........................E...... 419 965-2103
Ohio City (G-15661)
Industrial Container Svcs LLC...........E...... 513 921-2056
Cincinnati (G-3916)
Kar-Del Plastics Inc....................G...... 419 289-9739
Ashland (G-744)
Norwesco Inc............................F...... 740 335-6236
Wshngtn CT Hs (G-20918)
Norwesco Inc............................F...... 740 654-6402
Lancaster (G-11735)
R L Industries Inc......................D...... 513 874-2800
West Chester (G-19929)
RTS Companies (us) Inc..................E...... 440 275-3077
Austinburg (G-965)

TANKS: Standard Or Custom Fabricated, Metal Plate

Aetna Plastics Corp.....................G...... 330 274-2855
Mantua (G-12706)
Buckeye Fabricating Co..................E...... 937 746-9822
Springboro (G-17475)
Central Fabricators Inc.................E...... 513 621-1240
Cincinnati (G-3514)
Compco Industries Incorporated..........D...... 330 482-6488
Columbiana (G-6614)
Dabar Industries LLC....................F...... 614 873-3949
Plain City (G-16329)
Enerfab Inc.............................B...... 513 641-0500
Cincinnati (G-3704)
Hason USA Corp..........................E...... 513 248-0287
Milford (G-14150)
Hershey Machine.........................G...... 330 674-2718
Millersburg (G-14222)
M & H Fabricating Co Inc................G...... 937 325-8708
Springfield (G-17594)
Manco Manufacturing Co..................G...... 419 925-4152
Maria Stein (G-12759)
Modern Sheet Metal Works Inc............E...... 513 353-3666
Miamitown (G-13890)
Rebsco Inc..............................F...... 937 548-2246
Greenville (G-10517)
S-P Company Inc.........................F...... 330 482-0200
Columbiana (G-6631)
Tonns Fabrication.......................G...... 614 989-5097
Orient (G-15725)

TANKS: Storage, Farm, Metal Plate

Industrial Farm Tank Inc................E...... 937 843-2972
Lewistown (G-11944)
Rcr Partnership.........................G...... 419 340-1202
Genoa (G-10362)

TANNING SALON EQPT & SPLYS, WHOLESALE

Success Technologies Inc................G...... 614 761-0008
Powell (G-16484)

TANNING SALONS

Kahuna Bay Spray Tan LLC................G...... 419 386-2387
Toledo (G-18537)
Premier Tanning & Nutrition.............G...... 419 342-6259
Shelby (G-17141)

TAPE DRIVES

CHI Corporation.........................F...... 440 498-2300
Cleveland (G-5026)

TAPES, ADHESIVE: Medical

Medco Labs Inc..........................F...... 216 292-7546
Cleveland (G-5775)
Mt Pleasant Pharmacy LLC................G...... 216 672-4377
Bedford (G-1446)

TAPES: Fabric

Piland Parts............................G...... 330 686-3083
Stow (G-17787)

TAPES: Insulating

Denizen Inc.............................F...... 937 615-9561
Piqua (G-16261)

TAPES: Magnetic

Magnet Technology Inc...................G...... 513 932-4416
Lebanon (G-11814)
Magnetnotes Ltd.........................G...... 419 593-0060
Toledo (G-18571)

TAPES: Plastic Coated

Buschman Corporation....................F...... 216 431-6633
Cleveland (G-4951)
Shaheen Oriental Rug Co Inc.............F...... 330 493-9000
Canton (G-2846)

TAPES: Pressure Sensitive

Austin Tape and Label Inc...............D...... 330 928-7999
Stow (G-17731)
Beiersdorf Inc..........................C...... 513 682-7300
West Chester (G-19984)
Cortape Inc.............................F...... 330 929-6700
Cuyahoga Falls (G-7982)
D M V Supply Corporation................G...... 330 847-0450
Warren (G-19540)
Hooven - Dayton Corp....................D...... 937 233-4473
Miamisburg (G-13818)
Progressive Labels LLC..................F...... 570 688-9636
Willoughby (G-20580)
Shurtape Technologies LLC...............B...... 440 937-7000
Avon (G-1011)

TARPAULINS

Custom Tarpaulin Products Inc...........F...... 330 758-1801
Youngstown (G-21060)
Electra Tarp Inc........................F...... 330 477-7168
Canton (G-2696)
Lesch Boat Cover Canvas Co LLC..........G...... 419 668-6374
Norwalk (G-15550)
Tarpco Inc..............................F...... 330 677-8277
Kent (G-11535)

TARPAULINS, WHOLESALE

Berlin Truck Caps Ltd...................F...... 330 893-2811
Millersburg (G-14201)
Shur-Co LLC.............................G...... 330 297-0888
Ravenna (G-16556)

TATTOO PARLORS

252 Tattoo..............................G...... 440 235-6699
Columbia Station (G-6577)

TAX RETURN PREPARATION SVCS

David Butler Tax Service................G...... 419 626-8086
Sandusky (G-16956)

TECHNICAL INSTITUTE

Borman Enterprises Inc..................F...... 216 459-9292
Cleveland (G-4926)

TECHNICAL MANUAL PREPARATION SVCS

ONeil & Associates Inc..................C...... 937 865-0800
Miamisburg (G-13847)
Prowrite Inc............................G...... 614 864-2004
Reynoldsburg (G-16601)
Revonoc Inc.............................G...... 440 548-3491
Parkman (G-15953)

TELECOMMUNICATION EQPT REPAIR SVCS, EXC TELEPHONES

AT&T Corp...............................A...... 614 223-8236
Columbus (G-6780)
Vertiv Co...............................G...... 440 288-1122
Lorain (G-12290)

TELECOMMUNICATION SYSTEMS & EQPT

7signal Solutions Inc...................E...... 330 761-3515
Akron (G-15)
Alcatel Co..............................G...... 818 878-4485
Westerville (G-20197)
AT&T Corp...............................G...... 513 792-9300
Cincinnati (G-3423)

PRODUCT

Cutting Edge Technologies Inc ....E 216 574-4759
  Cleveland (G-5154)
DTE Inc.......................................E 419 522-3428
  Mansfield (G-12597)
Electrodata Inc ....F 216 663-3333
  Bedford Heights (G-1483)
Fremont Plastic Products Inc ....C 419 332-6407
  Fremont (G-10150)
Greyfield Industries Inc ....F 513 860-1785
  Trenton (G-18793)
Mitel (delaware) Inc.........................E 513 733-8000
  West Chester (G-19902)
Peco II Inc ....D 614 431-0694
  Columbus (G-7473)
Prentke Romich Company ....C 330 202-5800
  Wooster (G-20825)
Pro Oncall Technologies LLC ....F 614 761-1400
  Dublin (G-9126)
Tls Corp ....E 216 574-4759
  Cleveland (G-6327)
Vertiv Co ....G 440 288-1122
  Lorain (G-12290)
Vertiv Co ....G 440 460-3600
  Cleveland (G-6410)
Viasat Inc ....D 216 706-7800
  Independence (G-11282)

TELECOMMUNICATIONS CARRIERS & SVCS: Wired

AT&T Corp ....G 513 792-9300
  Cincinnati (G-3423)
AT&T Corp ....A 614 223-8236
  Columbus (G-6780)
Byrd Prcurement Specialist Inc ....G 419 936-0019
  Swanton (G-18082)
Data Processing Sciences Corp ....D 513 791-7100
  Cincinnati (G-3640)
Kraft Electrical Contg Inc ....E 614 836-9300
  Groveport (G-10630)
Kraftmaid Trucking Inc ....D 440 632-2531
  Middlefield (G-13949)

TELEMETERING EQPT

Advanced Telemetrics Intl...................F 937 862-6948
  Spring Valley (G-17466)
Douglas J Hall ....G 614 261-8871
  Columbus (G-7035)
Grace Automation Services Inc ....G 330 567-3108
  Big Prairie (G-1681)

TELEPHONE BOOTHS, EXC WOOD

Ray Communications Inc ....G 330 686-0226
  Stow (G-17795)

TELEPHONE CENTRAL OFFICE EQPT: Dial Or Manual

Kentrox Inc ....D 614 798-2000
  Dublin (G-9096)

TELEPHONE EQPT INSTALLATION

Crase Communications Inc..................F 419 468-1173
  Galion (G-10262)
Johnson Brothers Holdings LLC...........G 614 868-5273
  Columbus (G-7240)
Mitel (delaware) Inc.........................E 513 733-8000
  West Chester (G-19902)

TELEPHONE EQPT: Modems

Black Box Corporation ....E 614 825-7400
  Lewis Center (G-11890)
C Dcap Modem Line ....G 419 748-7409
  Mc Clure (G-13334)
C Dcap Modem Line ....G 440 685-4302
  North Bloomfield (G-15215)
Lisa Modem ....G 216 551-3365
  Cleveland (G-5706)
Procomsol Ltd ....G 216 221-1550
  Lakewood (G-11677)

TELEPHONE EQPT: NEC

Arnco Corporation ....C 800 847-7661
  Elyria (G-9375)
Commercial Electric Pdts Corp ....E 216 241-2886
  Cleveland (G-5104)

Siemens Energy Inc.........................G 740 393-8464
  Mount Vernon (G-14649)

TELEPHONE SET REPAIR SVCS

DTE Inc......................................E 419 522-3428
  Mansfield (G-12597)

TELEPHONE STATION EQPT & PARTS: Wire

Ocs Telecom LLC...........................F 740 503-5939
  Hilliard (G-10965)

TELEPHONE SWITCHING EQPT: Toll Switching

Crase Communications Inc..................F 419 468-1173
  Galion (G-10262)

TELEPHONE: Fiber Optic Systems

Cotsworks LLC ....E 440 446-8800
  Highland Heights (G-10911)
Preformed Line Products Co ....C 440 461-5200
  Mayfield Village (G-13324)

TELEPHONE: Sets, Exc Cellular Radio

Minor Corporation ....G 216 291-8723
  Cleveland (G-5822)

TELEVISION BROADCASTING & COMMUNICATIONS EQPT

Nissin Precision N Amer Inc ....D 937 836-1910
  Englewood (G-9536)
Pdi Communication Systems Inc ....D 937 743-6010
  Springboro (G-17495)
Punch Components Inc ....E 419 224-1242
  Lima (G-12077)

TELEVISION BROADCASTING STATIONS

Block Communications Inc..................F 419 724-6212
  Toledo (G-18372)
Dispatch Printing Company ....C 740 548-5331
  Lewis Center (G-11895)
EW Scripps Company ....E 513 977-3000
  Cincinnati (G-3728)

TELEVISION REPAIR SHOP

Electra Sound Inc ....D 216 433-9600
  Parma (G-15957)

TELEVISION: Closed Circuit Eqpt

Diamond Electronics Inc ....C 740 652-9222
  Lancaster (G-11706)
Musair Ohio ....G 330 455-2800
  Massillon (G-13183)

TEMPORARY HELP SVCS

Cima Inc ....E 513 682-5900
  Fairfield (G-9653)
Production Design Services Inc ....D 937 866-3377
  Dayton (G-8598)

TENT REPAIR SHOP

J & W Canvas Company ....G 330 652-7678
  Mineral Ridge (G-14306)

TENTS: All Materials

Celina Tent Inc ....E 419 586-3610
  Celina (G-2990)
Embedee LLC ....G 419 678-7007
  Coldwater (G-6558)

TERMINAL BOARDS

Osborne Coinage Company ....D 513 681-5424
  Cincinnati (G-4197)

TEST BORING SVCS: Nonmetallic Minerals

Longyear Company ....E 740 373-2190
  Marietta (G-12800)
Tom Hudson ....G 937 393-1285
  Hillsboro (G-11016)

TEST BORING, METAL MINING

Hahs Factory Outlet.........................E 330 405-4227
  Twinsburg (G-18953)

TESTERS: Battery

Battery Unlimited ....G 740 452-5030
  Zanesville (G-21276)
Zts Inc ....F 513 271-2557
  Cincinnati (G-4620)

TESTERS: Environmental

Auto Technology Company ....F 440 572-7800
  Strongsville (G-17892)
Blue Water Satellite Inc ....G 419 372-0160
  Toledo (G-18373)
Bry-Air Inc ....E 740 965-2974
  Sunbury (G-18056)
Environ International Cor ....G 440 834-1460
  Burton (G-2374)
Northcoast Environmental Labs ....G 330 342-3377
  Streetsboro (G-17865)
Reuter-Stokes Inc ....B 330 425-3755
  Twinsburg (G-19008)

TESTERS: Gas, Exc Indl Process

Compliant Healthcare Tech LLC ....F 216 255-9607
  Cleveland (G-5111)
Compliant Healthcare Tech LLC ....E 216 255-9607
  Cleveland (G-5112)

TESTERS: Physical Property

Omega Automation Inc ....D 937 890-2350
  Dayton (G-8548)
Omega International Inc ....E 937 890-2350
  Dayton (G-8549)
Plating Test Cell Supply Co ....G 216 486-8400
  Cleveland (G-6017)
Pressco Technology Inc ....D 440 498-2600
  Cleveland (G-6044)
Test Mark Industries Inc ....F 330 426-2200
  East Palestine (G-9246)

TESTERS: Water, Exc Indl Process

CST Zero Discharged Car Wash S ....G 740 947-5480
  Waverly (G-19706)
Ysi Incorporated.............................D 937 767-7241
  Yellow Springs (G-21005)

TESTING SVCS

Data Analysis Technologies.................G 614 873-0710
  Plain City (G-16333)
Orton Edward Jr Crmic Fndation ....E 614 895-2663
  Westerville (G-20176)

TEXTILE & APPAREL SVCS

Eagle Rock Brand Cons LLC ....G 614 403-4802
  Plain City (G-16338)

TEXTILE FABRICATORS

Ver Mich Ltd.................................G 330 493-7330
  Canton (G-2896)

TEXTILE FINISHING: Chem Coat/Treat, Man, Broadwoven, Cotton

Mmi Textiles Inc ....F 440 899-8050
  Westlake (G-20283)

TEXTILE FINISHING: Chemical Coating Or Treating, Narrow

Creative Commercial Finishing ....G 513 722-9393
  Loveland (G-12347)

TEXTILE FINISHING: Decorative, Man Fiber & Silk, Broadwoven

Wizard Graphics Inc ....G 419 354-3098
  Bowling Green (G-2021)

TEXTILE FINISHING: Napping, Manmade Fiber & Silk, Broadwoven

Tranzonic Companies ....C 216 535-4300
  Richmond Heights (G-16656)

Tranzonic Companies ....C 440 446-0643
Cleveland (G-6350)
Tz Acquisition Corp ....A 216 535-4300
Richmond Heights (G-16658)

TEXTILE: Finishing, Cotton Broadwoven

Duracote Corporation ....E 330 296-9600
Ravenna (G-16526)
Resistflame Acquisition Corp ....G 513 561-5223
Cincinnati (G-4337)

TEXTILE: Finishing, Raw Stock NEC

Nettting Technologies LLC ....G 330 298-0022
Ravenna (G-16543)
Pelz Lettering Inc ....G 419 625-3567
Sandusky (G-16996)

TEXTILES

Mmi Textiles Inc ....F 440 899-8050
Westlake (G-20283)

TEXTILES: Jute & Flax Prdts

Big Productions Inc ....G 440 775-0015
Oberlin (G-15635)
Construction Techniques Inc ....F 216 267-7310
Cleveland (G-5121)

TEXTILES: Tops & Top Processing, Manmade Or Other Fiber

Cusc International Ltd ....G 513 881-2000
Hamilton (G-10682)

TEXTILES: Tops, Combing & Converting

Tops Inc ....G 440 954-9451
Mentor (G-13749)

THEATRICAL LIGHTING SVCS

Iacono Production Services Inc ....F 513 469-5095
Blue Ash (G-1811)

THEATRICAL PRODUCTION SVCS

North Coast Theatrical Inc ....G 330 762-1768
Akron (G-317)

THEATRICAL SCENERY

Scarefactory Inc ....F 614 252-8000
Columbus (G-7594)
Schell Scenic Studio Inc ....G 614 444-9550
Columbus (G-7595)

THEATRICAL TALENT & BOOKING AGENCIES

Thickemz Entertainment LLC ....G 404 399-4255
Cuyahoga Falls (G-8056)

THERMISTORS, EXC TEMPERATURE SENSORS

Measurement Specialties Inc ....F 937 427-1231
Beavercreek (G-1374)

THERMOCOUPLES

Blaze Technical Services Inc ....E 330 923-0409
Stow (G-17736)
Heraeus Electro-Nite Co LLC ....G 330 725-1419
Medina (G-13421)
L H Marshall Co ....F 614 294-6433
Columbus (G-7277)
Roberts Group Inc ....G 614 486-0497
Columbus (G-7569)

THERMOCOUPLES: Indl Process

Cleveland Electric Labs Co ....E 800 447-2207
Twinsburg (G-18915)
Geocorp Inc ....E 419 433-1101
Huron (G-11222)
MR&e Ltd ....G 419 872-8180
Toledo (G-18593)

THERMOELECTRIC DEVICES: Solid State

Melcor Corporation ....C 609 393-4178
Cleveland (G-5779)

THERMOMETERS: Indl

T P F Inc ....G 513 761-9968
Cincinnati (G-4490)

THERMOMETERS: Medical, Digital

ARC Drilling Inc ....F 216 525-0920
Cleveland (G-4822)
Corcadence Inc ....G 216 702-6371
Beachwood (G-1265)

THERMOPLASTIC MATERIALS

Amros Industries Inc ....E 216 433-0010
Cleveland (G-4799)
Denney Plastics Machining LLC ....F 330 308-5300
New Philadelphia (G-14894)
Dow Chemical Company ....D 937 839-4612
West Alexandria (G-19779)
Dow Chemical Company ....F 937 254-1550
Dayton (G-8309)
Eaton Corporation ....C 330 562-9111
Aurora (G-917)
Hexpol Compounding LLC ....E 440 834-4644
Burton (G-2377)
Polyone Corporation ....D 440 930-1000
Avon Lake (G-1044)
Polyone Corporation ....D 440 930-1000
Avon Lake (G-1047)
Ppl Holding Company ....E 216 514-1840
Cleveland (G-6028)
Versa-Pak Ltd ....E 419 586-5466
Celina (G-3026)

THERMOPLASTICS

Bulk Molding Compounds Inc ....D 419 874-7941
Perrysburg (G-16071)
McHenry Industries Inc ....E 330 799-8930
Youngstown (G-21142)
Parker-Hannifin Corporation ....C 330 296-2871
Ravenna (G-16548)
Plextrusions Inc ....G 330 668-2587
North Ridgeville (G-15394)
Techniform Industries Inc ....E 419 332-8484
Fremont (G-10186)
V & A Process Inc ....F 440 288-8137
Lorain (G-12288)

THERMOSETTING MATERIALS

Current Inc ....G 330 392-5151
Warren (G-19539)
Hexion Inc ....B 614 225-4000
Columbus (G-7152)
Hexion Inc ....G 614 759-6227
Gahanna (G-10210)
Hexion LLC ....B 614 225-4000
Columbus (G-7153)
Momentive Performance Mtls Inc ....B 614 986-2495
Columbus (G-7365)

THREAD: Embroidery

Alvin L Roepke ....F 419 862-3891
Elmore (G-9360)

THREAD: Rubber

West & Barker Inc ....E 330 652-9923
Niles (G-15189)

TIES, FORM: Metal

Puritas Metal Products Inc ....F 440 353-1917
North Ridgeville (G-15397)
Tig Welding Specialties Inc ....G 216 621-1763
Cleveland (G-6324)

TILE: Brick & Structural, Clay

Armstrong World Industries Inc ....D 614 771-9307
Hilliard (G-10927)
Hanson Aggregates East LLC ....F 937 382-2557
Wilmington (G-20668)
Kepcor Inc ....F 330 868-6434
Minerva (G-14327)

LBC Clay Co LLC

LBC Clay Co LLC ....G 330 674-0674
Millersburg (G-14240)
Minteq International Inc ....E 330 343-8821
Dover (G-9003)
Morgan Advanced Ceramics Inc ....C 440 232-8604
Bedford (G-1445)
Resco Products Inc ....E 740 682-7794
Oak Hill (G-15605)
Stebbins Engineering & Mfg Co ....E 740 922-3012
Uhrichsville (G-19060)

TILE: Clay, Drain & Structural

Baughman Tile Company ....D 800 837-3160
Paulding (G-16000)
Clay Logan Products Company ....D 740 385-2184
Logan (G-12172)

TILE: Clay, Roof

Ludowici Roof Tile Inc ....D 740 342-1995
New Lexington (G-14849)
Nr Lee Restoration Ltd ....G 419 692-2233
Delphos (G-8915)

TILE: Drain, Clay

Haviland Drainage Products Co ....F 419 622-4611
Haviland (G-10840)

TILE: Sand Lime

Carmeuse Lime Inc ....G 216 961-1010
Cleveland (G-4980)

TILE: Vinyl, Asbestos

Texas Tile Manufacturing LLC ....E 713 869-5811
Solon (G-17404)

TILE: Wall & Floor, Ceramic

Artfinders ....G 330 264-7706
Wooster (G-20740)
Ironrock Capital Incorporated ....D 330 484-4887
Canton (G-2741)
Wccv Floor Coverings Inc ....E 330 688-0114
Peninsula (G-16044)

TILE: Wall, Ceramic

Florida Tile Inc ....G 513 891-1122
Blue Ash (G-1797)
Florida Tile Inc ....G 614 436-2511
Columbus (G-7091)
Florida Tile Inc ....G 937 293-5151
Miamisburg (G-13809)

TIN

Tin Indian Performance ....G 216 214-5485
Uniontown (G-19103)
Tin Shed LLC ....G 330 636-2524
Willard (G-20402)
Tin Wizard Heating and Cooling ....G 330 468-7884
Macedonia (G-12494)
Tin-Sau LLC ....G 419 586-8886
Celina (G-3023)

TIN-BASE ALLOYS, PRIMARY

Gdc Industries LLC ....G 937 367-7229
Beavercreek (G-1339)

TIRE & INNER TUBE MATERIALS & RELATED PRDTS

American Airless Inc ....E 614 552-0146
Reynoldsburg (G-16580)
Grove Engineered Products Inc ....G 419 659-5939
Columbus Grove (G-7794)
Troy Engineered Components and ....G 937 335-8070
Vandalia (G-19312)
Truflex Rubber Products Co ....C 740 967-9015
Johnstown (G-11409)
Yrp Industries Inc ....G 330 533-2524
Youngstown (G-21259)

TIRE & TUBE REPAIR MATERIALS, WHOLESALE

Myers Industries Inc ....E 330 253-5592
Akron (G-309)

Technical Rubber Company Inc ....B 740 967-9015
Johnstown *(G-11407)*

TIRE CORD & FABRIC

Akro Polychem Inc ....G 330 864-0360
Fairlawn *(G-9737)*
ARC Abrasives Inc ....D 800 888-4885
Troy *(G-18805)*
Cleveland Canvas Goods Mfg Co ....D 216 361-4567
Cleveland *(G-5050)*
Mfh Partners LLC ....F 440 461-4100
Cleveland *(G-5795)*

TIRE CORD & FABRIC: Indl, Reinforcing

Midwest Precision Products ....F 440 237-9500
Cleveland *(G-5811)*

TIRE DEALERS

A & A Discount Tire ....G 330 863-1936
Carrollton *(G-2950)*
Bkt USA Inc ....F 330 836-1090
Fairlawn *(G-9743)*
Bridgestone Ret Operations LLC ....F 330 379-6220
Akron *(G-99)*
Garro Tread Corporation ....G 330 376-3125
Akron *(G-198)*
Goodyear Tire & Rubber Company ....C 216 265-1800
Cleveland *(G-5438)*
Gregs Eagle Tire Co Inc ....G 330 837-1983
Massillon *(G-13142)*
Mid-Wood Inc ....F 419 257-3331
North Baltimore *(G-15195)*
Q T Columbus LLC ....G 800 758-2410
Columbus *(G-7528)*
QT Equipment Company ....E 330 724-3055
Akron *(G-355)*

TIRE RECAPPING & RETREADING

Goodyear Tire & Rubber Company .....A 330 796-2121
Akron *(G-207)*

TIRE SUNDRIES OR REPAIR MATERIALS: Rubber

31 Inc ....D 740 498-8324
Newcomerstown *(G-15107)*
PPG Industries Inc ....G 614 921-9228
Hilliard *(G-10972)*
Technical Rubber Company Inc ....B 740 967-9015
Johnstown *(G-11407)*

TIRES & INNER TUBES

B & S Transport Inc ....G 330 767-4319
Navarre *(G-14709)*
BF Diversified Svcs ....G 330 869-5203
Akron *(G-91)*
Bkt USA Inc ....F 330 836-1090
Fairlawn *(G-9743)*
Bridgestone Americas Inc ....E 330 379-7000
Akron *(G-97)*
Bridgestone Firestone ....G 614 523-2259
Columbus *(G-6641)*
Bridgestone Ret Operations LLC ....F 330 379-6220
Akron *(G-99)*
Buckman Machine Works Inc ....G 330 525-7665
Homeworth *(G-11115)*
Continental Tire Americas LLC ....G 419 633-4221
Bryan *(G-2290)*
Contitech North America Inc ....E 440 225-5363
Akron *(G-129)*
Cooper Tire & Rubber Company ....D 419 424-4384
Findlay *(G-9813)*
F M P Enterprises Inc ....G 330 920-8059
Cuyahoga Falls *(G-7994)*
Goodrich Corporation ....G 216 429-4655
Brooklyn Heights *(G-2140)*
Goodyear Tire & Rubber Company .....A 330 796-2121
Akron *(G-207)*
Goodyear Tire & Rubber Company ....C 216 265-1800
Cleveland *(G-5438)*
Gregs Eagle Tire Co Inc ....G 330 837-1983
Massillon *(G-13142)*
Intertex World Resources Inc ....G 770 214-5551
Canton *(G-2739)*
Titan Tire Corporation ....B 419 633-4221
Bryan *(G-2323)*
Umd Contractors Inc ....F 740 694-8614
Fredericktown *(G-10114)*

TIRES & TUBES WHOLESALERS

B & S Transport Inc ....G 330 767-4319
Navarre *(G-14709)*
Bridgestone Firestone ....G 614 523-2259
Columbus *(G-6641)*
Chestnut Holdings Inc ....G 330 849-6503
Akron *(G-122)*
Rhino Rubber LLC ....F 877 744-6603
North Canton *(G-15262)*
Sumitomo Rubber Usa LLC ....E 419 347-1067
Shelby *(G-17144)*

TIRES: Auto

C N C Wholesale ....G 330 832-9525
Massillon *(G-13117)*
Chemspec Ltd ....F 330 896-0355
Uniontown *(G-19079)*
Cooper Tire & Rubber Company ....A 419 423-1321
Findlay *(G-9811)*
Cooper Tire & Rubber Company ....E 419 424-4202
Findlay *(G-9812)*
Cooper Tire Vhcl Test Ctr Inc ....E 419 423-1321
Findlay *(G-9814)*
Sumitomo Rubber Usa LLC ....E 419 347-1067
Shelby *(G-17144)*

TIRES: Indl Vehicles

Trelleborg Wheel Systems Ameri ....E 866 633-8473
Akron *(G-444)*

TIRES: Plastic

Rhino Rubber LLC ....F 877 744-6603
North Canton *(G-15262)*

TITANIUM MILL PRDTS

Rmi Titanium Company LLC ....E 330 652-9952
Niles *(G-15176)*
Rti International Metals Inc ....G 330 652-9955
Niles *(G-15181)*
Tailwind Technologies Inc ....E 937 778-4200
Piqua *(G-16313)*
Titanium Contractors Ltd ....G 513 256-2152
Cincinnati *(G-4510)*
Titanium Industries Inc ....G 216 661-4610
Independence *(G-11278)*
Titanium Lacrosse LLC ....F 216 562-8082
Lewis Center *(G-11926)*
Titanium Trout LLC ....G 440 543-3187
Chagrin Falls *(G-3127)*
Water Star Inc ....G 440 564-1001
Newbury *(G-15106)*

TOBACCO & TOBACCO PRDTS WHOLESALERS

Butt Hut of America Inc ....G 419 443-1997
Tiffin *(G-18212)*

TOBACCO STORES & STANDS

Boston Stoker Inc ....G 937 890-6401
Vandalia *(G-19284)*
Smoke Rings Inc ....G 419 420-9966
Findlay *(G-9890)*

TOBACCO: Chewing & Snuff

Ev Liquids LLC ....G 614 622-9617
Columbus *(G-7069)*
Great Midwest Tobacco Inc ....G 513 745-0450
Cincinnati *(G-3846)*
Smoke Rings Inc ....G 419 420-9966
Findlay *(G-9890)*

TOBACCO: Cigarettes

Avail Vapor LLC ....G 440 716-6027
North Olmsted *(G-15327)*
Avail Vapor LLC ....G 440 365-5440
Elyria *(G-9377)*
Butt Hut of America Inc ....G 419 443-1997
Tiffin *(G-18212)*
Itg Brands LLC ....G 614 431-0044
Columbus *(G-7215)*
Low Bobs Discount Tobacco ....G 513 727-1430
Middletown *(G-14055)*
Memphis Smokehouse Inc ....G 216 351-5321
Cleveland *(G-5782)*

TOBACCO: Cigars

American Western Inc ....E 513 662-8802
Cincinnati *(G-3394)*
Cigars of Cincy ....G 513 931-5926
Cincinnati *(G-3533)*
Guari Inc ....G 330 733-4005
Akron *(G-208)*

TOBACCO: Smoking

Hookah Rush ....G 614 267-6463
Columbus *(G-7166)*

TOILET FIXTURES: Plastic

W T Inc ....F 419 224-6942
Lima *(G-12110)*

TOILET PREPARATIONS

Barbasol LLC ....E 419 903-0738
Ashland *(G-711)*
Bocchi Laboraties Ohio LLC ....B 661 673-8500
New Albany *(G-14751)*
Procter & Gamble Far East Inc ....C 513 983-1100
Cincinnati *(G-4289)*
Procter & Gamble Mfg Co ....F 513 983-1100
Cincinnati *(G-4290)*

TOILETRIES, COSMETICS & PERFUME STORES

Bath & Body Works LLC ....B 614 856-6000
Reynoldsburg *(G-16582)*
Olfactorium Corp Inc ....G 216 663-8831
Cleveland *(G-5938)*

TOILETRIES, WHOLESALE: Toiletries

Nehemiah Manufacturing Co LLC ....E 513 351-5700
Cincinnati *(G-4143)*
Walter F Stephens Jr Inc ....E 937 746-0521
Franklin *(G-10063)*

TOMBSTONES: Terrazzo Or Concrete, Precast

Ellinger Monument Inc ....G 740 385-3687
Rockbridge *(G-16688)*

TOOL & DIE STEEL

Anchor Pattern Company ....G 614 443-2221
Columbus *(G-6754)*
Applied Innovations ....G 330 837-5694
Massillon *(G-13109)*
B & G Tool Company ....G 614 451-2538
Columbus *(G-6795)*
B-K Tool & Design Inc ....D 419 532-3890
Kalida *(G-11412)*
Carter Scott-Browne ....E 513 398-3970
Mason *(G-12992)*
Deaks Form Tools Inc ....G 440 286-2353
Chardon *(G-3149)*
Die Services Ltd ....G 216 883-5800
Cleveland *(G-5192)*
DMG Tool & Die LLC ....G 937 407-0810
Bellefontaine *(G-1529)*
K K Tool Co ....E 937 325-1373
Springfield *(G-17583)*
Latrobe Specialty Mtls Co LLC ....E 419 335-8010
Wauseon *(G-19687)*
Louis G Freeman Co ....E 419 334-9709
Fremont *(G-10167)*
Maull Tool & Die Supply Llc ....G 513 646-4229
Loveland *(G-12373)*
Metaldyne Pwrtrain Cmpnnts Inc ....C 330 486-3200
Twinsburg *(G-18986)*
New Age Design & Tool Inc ....F 440 355-5400
Lagrange *(G-11634)*
OReilly Precision Tool Inc ....E 937 526-4677
Russia *(G-16767)*
Precision Die & Stamping Inc ....G 513 942-8220
West Chester *(G-19918)*
Precision Wood & Metal Co ....G 419 221-1512
Lima *(G-12074)*
Quality Tool Company ....E 419 476-8228
Toledo *(G-18663)*
R&D Machine Inc ....F 937 339-2545
Troy *(G-18866)*
Robs Welding Technologies Ltd ....G 937 890-4963
Dayton *(G-8637)*

Seilkop Industries Inc.............................E......513 353-3090
Miamitown **(G-13892)**

West Motorsports Inc.............................G......330 350-0375
Akron **(G-470)**

TOOL REPAIR SVCS

Harbor Freight Tools Usa Inc...............E......937 415-0770
Dayton **(G-8385)**

Lawrence Industries Inc.........................E......216 518-7000
Cleveland **(G-5687)**

T M Industries Inc.................................G......330 627-4410
Carrollton **(G-2967)**

TOOLS & EQPT: Used With Sporting Arms

C-H Tool & Die.......................................G......740 397-7214
Mount Vernon **(G-14610)**

TOOLS: Carpenters', Including Levels & Chisels, Exc Saws

Eric Mondene...G......740 965-2842
Galena **(G-10241)**

TOOLS: Hand

Acme Company.......................................D......330 758-2313
Poland **(G-16381)**

Alliance Knife Inc..................................E......513 367-9000
Harrison **(G-10768)**

Amcraft Inc..G......419 729-7900
Toledo **(G-18335)**

ASG..F......216 486-6163
Cleveland **(G-4845)**

CB Manufacturing & Sls Co Inc............D......937 866-5986
Dayton **(G-8216)**

Cleveland Iron Workers Members.........G......216 687-2290
Cleveland **(G-5066)**

Cornwell Quality Tools Company..........D......330 628-2627
Mogadore **(G-14370)**

Desmond-Stephan Mfgcompany...........E......937 653-7181
Urbana **(G-19157)**

Edgerton Forge Inc................................D......419 298-2333
Edgerton **(G-9327)**

Electric Eel Mfg Co Inc.........................E......937 323-4644
Springfield **(G-17552)**

Empire Plow Company Inc.....................E......216 641-2290
Cleveland **(G-5278)**

Everhard Products Inc...........................C......330 453-7786
Canton **(G-2699)**

Falcon Industries Inc............................E......330 723-0099
Medina **(G-13409)**

File Sharpening Company Inc................E......937 376-8268
Xenia **(G-20951)**

Furukawa Rock Drill USA Co Ltd...........E......330 673-5826
Kent **(G-11462)**

Fusion Automation Inc..........................G......440 602-5595
Willoughby **(G-20493)**

Harbor Freight Tools Usa Inc...............E......937 415-0770
Dayton **(G-8385)**

J & H Manufacturing LLC......................F......330 482-2636
Columbiana **(G-6622)**

J and S Tool Incorporated....................E......216 676-8330
Cleveland **(G-5595)**

Klawhorn Industries Inc........................G......330 335-8191
Wadsworth **(G-19414)**

Knight Ergonomics Inc..........................F......440 746-0044
Brecksville **(G-2059)**

Komar Industries Inc............................E......614 836-2366
Groveport **(G-10629)**

Martin Sprocket & Gear Inc..................D......419 485-5515
Montpelier **(G-14448)**

Matco Tools Corporation 1.....................B......330 929-4949
Stow **(G-17773)**

Midwest Knife Grinding Inc...................F......330 854-1030
Canal Fulton **(G-2508)**

Myers Industries Inc.............................E......440 632-1006
Middlefield **(G-13971)**

Myers Industries Inc.............................D......440 632-0230
Middlefield **(G-13972)**

North Coast Holdings Inc......................G......330 535-7177
Akron **(G-316)**

Panacea Products Corporation.............D......614 429-6320
Columbus **(G-7457)**

Rex International USA Inc......................E......800 321-7950
Ashtabula **(G-837)**

Ridge Tool Company.............................A......440 323-5581
Elyria **(G-9486)**

Ridge Tool Manufacturing Co...............A......440 323-5581
Elyria **(G-9488)**

Sewer Rodding Equipment Co...............E......419 991-2065
Lima **(G-12089)**

Simon Ellis Superabrasives..................G......937 226-0683
Dayton **(G-8659)**

Simonds International LLC.....................E......978 424-0100
Kimbolton **(G-11603)**

Stanley Access Tech LLC......................C......440 461-5500
Cleveland **(G-6235)**

Stanley Industrial & Auto LLC..............C......614 755-7089
Westerville **(G-20187)**

Stanley Industrial & Auto LLC..............D......614 755-7000
Westerville **(G-20188)**

Step2 Company LLC..............................B......866 429-5200
Streetsboro **(G-17879)**

Step2 Company LLC..............................B......419 938-6343
Perrysville **(G-16176)**

Stride Tool LLC.....................................C......440 247-4600
Solon **(G-17388)**

Sumitomo Elc Carbide Mfg Inc.............F......440 354-0600
Grand River **(G-10453)**

Summit Tool Company...........................D......330 535-7177
Akron **(G-422)**

Toolovation LLC....................................G......216 514-3022
Cleveland **(G-6336)**

Wright Tool Company............................C......330 848-0600
Barberton **(G-1157)**

TOOLS: Hand, Engravers'

F & B Engraving Tls & Sup LLC............G......937 332-7994
Troy **(G-18824)**

TOOLS: Hand, Hammers

Fiery Chillcom..G......800 575-4180
Akron **(G-186)**

TOOLS: Hand, Jewelers'

Abhushan LLC..G......614 789-0632
Dublin **(G-9035)**

Silver Expressions.................................G......740 687-0144
Lancaster **(G-11752)**

TOOLS: Hand, Masons'

Chrisnik Inc...G......513 738-2920
Okeana **(G-15663)**

E Z Grout Corporation...........................E......740 749-3512
Waterford **(G-19646)**

TOOLS: Hand, Mechanics

A W C Inc...G......216 831-0550
Cleveland **(G-4679)**

North Pk Innovations Group Inc...........C......440 247-4600
Solon **(G-17351)**

Oldforge Tools Inc.................................G......330 535-7177
Akron **(G-327)**

S & H Industries Inc.............................E......216 831-0550
Cleveland **(G-6145)**

TOOLS: Hand, Plumbers'

Bartter & Sons......................................G......419 651-0374
Jeromesville **(G-11383)**

Calvin Lanier...E......937 952-4221
Dayton **(G-8208)**

TOOLS: Hand, Power

Air Tool Service Company......................F......440 701-1021
Mentor **(G-13513)**

Aircraft Dynamics Corporation.............F......419 331-0371
Elida **(G-9350)**

Apex Tool Group LLC.............................C......937 222-7871
Dayton **(G-8160)**

Black & Decker (us) Inc........................G......513 772-3111
Cincinnati **(G-3452)**

Black & Decker (us) Inc........................G......614 895-3112
Columbus **(G-6837)**

Black & Decker Corporation..................E......440 842-9100
Cleveland **(G-4913)**

Campbell Hausfeld LLC.........................C......513 367-4811
Harrison **(G-10770)**

Furukawa Rock Drill USA Co Ltd...........E......330 673-5826
Kent **(G-11462)**

Galaxy Products Inc..............................G......419 843-7337
Sylvania **(G-18107)**

Gougler Industries Inc..........................C......330 673-5826
Kent **(G-11463)**

Hall-Toledo Inc......................................F......419 893-4334
Maumee **(G-13263)**

Huron Cement Products Company.........E......419 433-4161
Huron **(G-11224)**

Ingersoll-Rand Company.......................E......419 633-6800
Bryan **(G-2306)**

Michabo Inc...G......419 893-4334
Maumee **(G-13282)**

Npk Construction Equipment Inc..........D......440 232-7900
Bedford **(G-1449)**

Ohio Drill & Tool Co..............................E......330 525-7717
Homeworth **(G-11117)**

Rex International USA Inc......................E......800 321-7950
Ashtabula **(G-837)**

Ridge Tool Company.............................A......440 323-5581
Elyria **(G-9486)**

Ridge Tool Manufacturing Co...............A......440 323-5581
Elyria **(G-9488)**

Selbro Inc...F......419 483-9918
Bellevue **(G-1558)**

Senco Brands Inc..................................E......513 388-2833
Cincinnati **(G-4403)**

Senco Brands Inc..................................D......513 388-2000
Cincinnati **(G-3315)**

Sensource Global Sourcing LLC...........G......513 659-8283
Cincinnati **(G-3317)**

Sewer Rodding Equipment Co...............E......419 991-2065
Lima **(G-12089)**

Stanley Access Tech LLC......................C......440 461-5500
Cleveland **(G-6235)**

Stanley Bittinger..................................G......740 942-4302
Cadiz **(G-2422)**

Stanley Industrial & Auto LLC..............D......614 755-7000
Westerville **(G-20188)**

Suburban Manufacturing Co..................D......440 953-2024
Eastlake **(G-9290)**

Sumitomo Elc Carbide Mfg Inc.............F......440 354-0600
Grand River **(G-10453)**

Superior Pneumatic & Mfg Inc..............F......440 871-8780
Cleveland **(G-6266)**

TC Service Co..E......440 954-7500
Willoughby **(G-20609)**

Technidrill Systems Inc.........................E......330 678-9980
Kent **(G-11536)**

Triad Capital Aat LLC............................C......440 236-4163
Columbia Station **(G-6603)**

Uhrichsville Carbide Inc........................F......740 922-9197
Uhrichsville **(G-19064)**

White Industrial Tool Inc.......................F......330 773-6889
Akron **(G-471)**

Wolf Machine Company.........................E......513 791-5194
Blue Ash **(G-1897)**

Wyeth-Scott Company...........................G......740 345-4528
Newark **(G-15066)**

X-Press Tool Inc....................................E......330 225-8748
Brunswick **(G-2271)**

Zagar Inc..E......216 731-0500
Cleveland **(G-6490)**

TOOLS: Hand, Stonecutters'

Firenza Stone Inc..................................G......440 953-8883
Willoughby **(G-20488)**

TOOLS: Soldering

Luma Electric Company.........................G......419 843-7842
Sylvania **(G-18116)**

TOWELS: Fabric & Nonwoven, Made From Purchased Materials

Lawnview Industries Inc.......................C......937 653-5217
Urbana **(G-19168)**

Saturday Knight Ltd..............................D......513 641-1400
Cincinnati **(G-4379)**

TOWERS, SECTIONS: Transmission, Radio & Television

Amto Acquisition Corp...........................F......419 347-1185
Shelby **(G-17131)**

K & L Die & Manufacturing....................G......419 895-1301
Greenwich **(G-10532)**

Warmus and Associates Inc..................F......330 659-4440
Bath **(G-1240)**

TOWERS: Cooling, Sheet Metal

Obr Cooling Towers Inc.........................E......419 243-3443
Rossford **(G-16744)**

PRODUCT

TOWING & TUGBOAT SVC

Superior Marine Ways Inc ....G....... 740 894-6224
South Point **(G-17448)**

TOWING SVCS: Marine

Great Lakes Group.........................C....... 216 621-4854
Cleveland **(G-5451)**

TOYS

Advance Novelty Incorporated ....G....... 419 424-0363
Findlay **(G-9787)**
Ajj Enterprises LLC ....F....... 513 755-9562
West Chester **(G-19979)**
AW Faber-Castell Usa Inc ....D....... 216 643-4660
Cleveland **(G-4877)**
Cornpentry..................................G....... 513 741-0594
Cincinnati **(G-3612)**
Evenflo Company Inc ....D....... 937 773-3971
Troy **(G-18823)**
Evenflo Company Inc ....C....... 937 415-3300
Miamisburg **(G-13806)**
Fremont Plastic Products Inc ....C....... 419 332-6407
Fremont **(G-10150)**
Ink Factory Inc ....G....... 330 799-0888
Youngstown **(G-21116)**
Iron Wind Metals Co LLC ....G....... 513 870-0606
Cincinnati **(G-3932)**
Jackpot Festival & Gaming ....G....... 216 531-3500
Cleveland **(G-5604)**
Lawbre Co...................................G....... 330 637-3363
Cortland **(G-7871)**
Little Cottage Company..................G....... 330 893-4212
Dundee **(G-9174)**
Pioneer National Latex Inc ....D....... 419 289-3300
Ashland **(G-766)**
Resaurus Company Inc ....F....... 614 751-9352
Columbus **(G-7555)**
RPM Consumer Holding Company ....G....... 330 273-5090
Medina **(G-13470)**
Step2 Company LLC......................B....... 866 429-5200
Streetsboro **(G-17879)**
Step2 Company LLC......................B....... 419 938-6343
Perrysville **(G-16176)**
Step2 Holdings LLC ....A....... 330 656-0440
Streetsboro **(G-17880)**
The Guardtower Inc ....F....... 614 488-4311
Columbus **(G-7689)**
Todd Smith Products ....G....... 216 529-0525
Lakewood **(G-11680)**
Unique-Chardan Inc ....E....... 419 636-6900
Bryan **(G-2325)**
Vacuum Finishing Company............F....... 440 286-4386
Chardon **(G-3182)**
Watch-Us Inc ....E....... 513 829-8870
Fairfield **(G-9731)**
Wells Manufacturing Co Llc ....F....... 937 987-2481
New Vienna **(G-14957)**

TOYS & HOBBY GOODS & SPLYS, WHOLESALE: Amusement Goods

Alligator Cmpt Systems Corp ....F....... 513 542-1000
Cincinnati **(G-3380)**

TOYS & HOBBY GOODS & SPLYS, WHOLESALE: Arts/Crafts Eqpt/Sply

AW Faber-Castell Usa Inc ....D....... 216 643-4660
Cleveland **(G-4877)**
Larose Industries LLC ....E....... 419 237-1600
Fayette **(G-9776)**
Ramon Robinson ....G....... 330 883-3244
Vienna **(G-19374)**

TOYS & HOBBY GOODS & SPLYS, WHOLESALE: Balloons, Novelty

Galaxy Balloons Incorporated ....C....... 216 476-3360
Cleveland **(G-5392)**

TOYS & HOBBY GOODS & SPLYS, WHOLESALE: Dolls

Huston Gifts Dolls and Flowers.........G....... 740 775-9141
Chillicothe **(G-3244)**
Middleton Llyd Dolls Inc ....G....... 740 989-2082
Coolville **(G-7835)**

TOYS & HOBBY GOODS & SPLYS, WHOLESALE: Educational Toys

Bendon Inc ....D....... 419 207-3600
Ashland **(G-712)**

TOYS & HOBBY GOODS & SPLYS, WHOLESALE: Playing Cards

H & H of Milford Ohio LLC..................G....... 513 576-9004
Milford **(G-14149)**

TOYS & HOBBY GOODS & SPLYS, WHOLESALE: Toys & Games

Advance Novelty Incorporated ....G....... 419 424-0363
Findlay **(G-9787)**

TOYS & HOBBY GOODS & SPLYS, WHOLESALE: Toys, NEC

Ball Bounce and Sport Inc ....B....... 419 289-9310
Ashland **(G-710)**
Resaurus Company Inc ....F....... 614 751-9352
Columbus **(G-7555)**

TOYS & HOBBY GOODS & SPLYS, WHOLESALE: Video Games

Lasermark LLC..............................G....... 513 312-9889
Dayton **(G-8452)**

TOYS, HOBBY GOODS & SPLYS WHOLESALERS

Toy & Sport Trends Inc ....E....... 419 748-8880
Napoleon **(G-14700)**
Wooden Horse ....G....... 740 503-5243
Baltimore **(G-1091)**

TOYS: Dolls, Stuffed Animals & Parts

Datatex Media Dolls ....G....... 216 598-1000
Cleveland **(G-5170)**

TOYS: Kites

Premier Kites & Designs Inc ....G....... 888 416-0174
Portsmouth **(G-16449)**

TOYS: Rubber

Pioneer National Latex Inc ....D....... 419 289-3300
Ashland **(G-766)**
Plan B Toys Ltd ....G....... 614 751-6605
Groveport **(G-10642)**

TRADE SHOW ARRANGEMENT SVCS

Publishing Group Ltd ....F....... 614 572-1240
Columbus **(G-7526)**
Relx Inc ....E....... 937 865-6800
Miamisburg **(G-13851)**

TRAILERS & PARTS: Boat

Loadmaster Trailer Company ....F....... 419 732-3434
Port Clinton **(G-16403)**
Lux Corporation ....G....... 419 562-7978
Bucyrus **(G-2353)**

TRAILERS & PARTS: Horse

Mohawk Manufacturing Inc ....G....... 860 632-2345
Mount Vernon **(G-14631)**

TRAILERS & PARTS: Truck & Semi's

All A Cart Manufacturing Inc ....F....... 614 443-5544
Columbus **(G-6717)**
American Mnfcturing Operations ....G....... 419 269-1560
Toledo **(G-18342)**
Appalachian Trailer Inc ....G....... 330 277-4140
Salem **(G-16872)**
ATW Ohio LLC ....C....... 937 444-4295
Mount Orab **(G-14575)**
Bell Logistics Co ....E....... 740 702-9830
Chillicothe **(G-3229)**
Brothers Equipment Inc ....G....... 216 458-0180
Cleveland **(G-4937)**
Bruce High Performance Tran ....E....... 440 357-8964
Painesville **(G-15862)**

Containerport Group Inc ....D....... 440 333-2009
Cleveland **(G-5122)**
David Ogilbee ....G....... 740 929-2638
Hebron **(G-10864)**
Diamond Trailers Inc ....E....... 513 738-4500
Shandon **(G-17097)**
Diverse Logistics & Trnsp Inc ....E....... 513 305-1460
Cincinnati **(G-3656)**
Engineered MBL Solutions Inc ....F....... 513 724-0247
Batavia **(G-1184)**
Extreme Trailers LLC ....G....... 330 440-0026
Dover **(G-8985)**
H & H Equipment Inc ....G....... 330 264-5400
Wooster **(G-20781)**
High Tech Prfmce Trlrs Inc ....D....... 440 357-8964
Painesville **(G-15888)**
J & L Body Inc ....F....... 216 661-2323
Brooklyn Heights **(G-2141)**
Jerry Tadlock ....G....... 937 544-2851
West Union **(G-20122)**
Kenan Advantage Group Inc ....E....... 614 878-4050
Columbus **(G-7254)**
Larry Moore ....G....... 740 697-7085
Roseville **(G-16731)**
Longriders Trucking Company ....G....... 740 975-7863
Mount Vernon **(G-14629)**
Lyons ....G....... 440 224-0676
Kingsville **(G-11605)**
M & W Trailers Inc ....F....... 419 453-3331
Ottoville **(G-15824)**
Mac Manufacturing Inc ....A....... 330 823-9900
Alliance **(G-523)**
Mac Manufacturing Inc ....C....... 330 829-1680
Salem **(G-16913)**
Mac Steel Trailer Ltd ....E....... 330 823-9900
Alliance **(G-524)**
Mac Trailer Manufacturing Inc ....C....... 330 823-9900
Alliance **(G-525)**
Majestic Trailers Inc ....F....... 330 798-1698
Akron **(G-280)**
Moritz International Inc ....E....... 419 526-5222
Mansfield **(G-12653)**
Mr Trailer Sales Inc ....G....... 330 339-7701
Dover **(G-9004)**
Navarre Trailer Sales Inc ....G....... 330 879-2406
Navarre **(G-14722)**
Paccar Inc ....A....... 740 774-5111
Chillicothe **(G-3257)**
Saf-Holland Inc ....G....... 513 874-7888
West Chester **(G-20046)**
Shilling Transport ....G....... 330 948-1105
Lodi **(G-12169)**
Trailer One Inc ....G....... 330 723-7474
Medina **(G-13490)**
Trailex Inc ....F....... 330 533-6814
Canfield **(G-2580)**
Tri County Wheel and Rim Ltd ....G....... 419 666-1760
Northwood **(G-15492)**
Wabash National Corporation ....C....... 419 434-9409
Findlay **(G-9905)**
William Minnier ....G....... 614 562-8080
Canal Winchester **(G-2541)**

TRAILERS & TRAILER EQPT

Belshe Industries Inc ....F....... 937 526-4460
Versailles **(G-19340)**
Blue Ribbon Trailers Ltd ....E....... 330 538-4114
North Jackson **(G-15288)**
Cleveland Hdwr & Forging Co ....E....... 216 641-5200
Cleveland **(G-5064)**
D & A Custom Trailer Inc ....G....... 740 922-2205
Uhrichsville **(G-19047)**
Fitchville East Corp ....E....... 419 929-1510
New London **(G-14859)**
Hawkline Nevada LLC......................E....... 937 444-4295
Mount Orab **(G-14579)**
Hitch-Hiker Mfg Inc ....F....... 330 542-3052
New Middletown **(G-14877)**
Independent Trailer Services ....G....... 937 667-8900
Tipp City **(G-18282)**
Interstate Truckway Inc ....E....... 614 771-1220
Columbus **(G-7209)**
Johnny On The Spot Inc ....E....... 614 497-1776
Columbus **(G-7239)**
Liebrecht Manufacturing ....G....... 419 596-3501
Continental **(G-7827)**
M Manufacturing Inc ....G....... 330 793-6806
Youngstown **(G-21139)**
Midway Trailer Sales LLC ....G....... 419 394-4408
Saint Marys **(G-16843)**

Transglobal Inc...G....... 419 396-9079
Carey (G-2927)

TRAILERS OR VANS: Horse Transportation, Fifth-Wheel Type

Monarch Trailers Co.............................F....... 419 747-2848
Shelby (G-17138)

Pegasus Vans & Trailers Inc.................E....... 419 625-8953
Sandusky (G-16995)

TRAILERS: Bodies

East Manufacturing Corporation...........B....... 330 325-9921
Randolph (G-16509)

East Manufacturing Corporation...........F....... 330 325-9921
Randolph (G-16510)

Gerich Fiberglass Inc..............................E....... 419 362-4591
Mount Gilead (G-14560)

Haulette Manufacturing Inc..................D....... 419 586-1717
Celina (G-3000)

Heritage Manufacturing Inc...................G....... 217 854-2513
Akron (G-223)

J W Devers & Son Inc............................F....... 937 854-3040
Trotwood (G-18797)

L C Smith Co...G....... 440 327-1251
Elyria (G-9448)

Pleasant Vly Tardrop Trlrs LLC..............G....... 330 752-4425
Sugarcreek (G-18033)

Quick Loadz Delivery Sys LLC...............G....... 888 304-3946
Nelsonville (G-14735)

R J Cox Co..G....... 937 548-4699
Arcanum (G-658)

Stahl/Scott Fetzer Company...................C....... 800 277-8245
Wooster (G-20839)

TRAILERS: Camping, Tent-Type

Isaacs Jr Floyd Thomas.........................F....... 513 899-2342
Morrow (G-14548)

TRAILERS: Semitrailers, Missile Transportation

Ds Express Carriers Inc.........................G....... 419 433-6200
Norwalk (G-15534)

Pdi Ground Support Systems Inc............D....... 216 271-7344
Solon (G-17360)

TRAILERS: Semitrailers, Truck Tractors

4w Services..F....... 614 554-5427
Hebron (G-10859)

Nelson Manufacturing Company..............D....... 419 523-5321
Ottawa (G-15802)

TRANSDUCERS: Electrical Properties

D C M Industries Inc...............................F....... 937 254-8500
Dayton (G-8264)

Guitammer Company................................G....... 614 898-9370
Westerville (G-20156)

Ohio Semitronics Inc...............................D....... 614 777-1005
Hilliard (G-10967)

TRANSDUCERS: Pressure

Honeywell International Inc......................C....... 614 850-5000
Columbus (G-7163)

Honeywell International Inc......................D....... 614 850-5000
Columbus (G-7164)

Omega Engineering Inc............................E....... 740 965-9340
Sunbury (G-18072)

Sensotec LLC..G....... 614 481-8616
Hilliard (G-10978)

TRANSFORMERS: Distribution

Darrah Electric Company..........................E....... 216 631-0912
Cleveland (G-5168)

TRANSFORMERS: Distribution, Electric

Clark Substations LLC..............................E....... 330 452-5200
Canton (G-2659)

Tesa Inc...G....... 614 847-8200
Lewis Center (G-11925)

TRANSFORMERS: Electric

Control Transformer Inc............................E....... 330 637-6015
Cortland (G-7864)

Delta Transformer Inc...............................G....... 513 242-9400
Cincinnati (G-3647)

Nautilus Hyosung America Inc..................G....... 937 203-4900
Miamisburg (G-13839)

Schneider Electric Usa Inc........................C....... 513 755-4231
West Chester (G-19942)

Schneider Electric Usa Inc........................D....... 513 755-5000
West Chester (G-19943)

Transcontinental Electric LLC....................G....... 614 496-4379
Columbus (G-7705)

Vida Ve Corp..G....... 614 203-2607
Dublin (G-9162)

TRANSFORMERS: Florescent Lighting

H Left Company..G....... 216 361-6348
Cleveland (G-5468)

TRANSFORMERS: Furnace, Electric

Ajax Tocco Magnethermic Corp.................C....... 330 372-8511
Warren (G-19517)

TRANSFORMERS: Ignition, Domestic Fuel Burners

Alfred J Buescher Jr.................................G....... 216 752-3676
Cleveland (G-4752)

TRANSFORMERS: Machine Tool

Pioneer Transformer Company...................G....... 419 737-2304
Pioneer (G-16239)

TRANSFORMERS: Meters, Electronic

Spectre Sensors Inc.................................G....... 440 250-0372
Westlake (G-20309)

Spectre Sensors Inc.................................G....... 440 250-0616
Westlake (G-20310)

TRANSFORMERS: Power Related

ABB Inc...D....... 440 585-8500
Wickliffe (G-20347)

ABB Inc...D....... 513 874-4730
West Chester (G-19795)

Acuity Brands Lighting Inc.........................B....... 740 349-4343
Newark (G-14979)

Contact Industries Inc..............................E....... 419 884-9788
Lexington (G-11949)

Custom Coil & Transformer Co...................E....... 740 452-5211
Zanesville (G-21297)

Eaton Leasing Corporation........................G....... 216 382-2292
Beachwood (G-1270)

Energy Developments Inc..........................G....... 440 774-6816
Oberlin (G-15638)

Fishel Company..D....... 614 850-4400
Columbus (G-7089)

Fostoria Bshngs Inslators Corp..................G....... 419 435-7514
Fostoria (G-9973)

Fostoria Bushings Inc...............................G....... 419 435-7514
Fostoria (G-9974)

General Electric Company.........................D....... 216 883-1000
Cleveland (G-5412)

Hannon Company......................................D....... 330 456-4728
Canton (G-2723)

Japlar Group Inc......................................F....... 513 791-7192
Cincinnati (G-3942)

Lake Shore Electric Corp...........................E....... 440 232-0200
Bedford (G-1438)

Matlock Electric Co Inc.............................E....... 513 731-9600
Cincinnati (G-4066)

Morlan & Associates Inc...........................E....... 614 889-6152
Hilliard (G-10964)

Norlake Manufacturing Company................D....... 440 353-3200
North Ridgeville (G-15391)

Ohio Semitronics Inc.................................D....... 614 777-1005
Hilliard (G-10967)

Otc Services Inc.......................................D....... 330 871-2444
Louisville (G-12323)

Power House Electric Sup LLC...................G....... 419 523-6614
Ottawa (G-15805)

Precision Switching Inc.............................G....... 800 800-8143
Mansfield (G-12667)

Qualtek Electronics Corp...........................C....... 440 951-3300
Mentor (G-13710)

Schneider Electric Usa Inc........................B....... 513 523-4171
Oxford (G-15843)

Siemens Industry Inc................................D....... 937 593-6010
Bellefontaine (G-1539)

TRANSFORMERS: Specialty

LTI Power Systems....................................E....... 440 327-5050
Elyria (G-9457)

TRANSFORMERS: Voltage Regulating

Transformer Associates Limited.................G....... 330 430-0750
Canton (G-2881)

Voltage Regulator Sales & Svcs................G....... 937 878-0673
Fairborn (G-9634)

TRANSLATION & INTERPRETATION SVCS

Advanced Translation/Cnsltng....................E....... 440 716-0820
Westlake (G-20246)

Asist Inc..F....... 614 451-6744
Columbus (G-6777)

Technical Translation Services...................E....... 440 942-3130
Willoughby (G-20611)

TRANSMISSION FLUID, MADE FROM PURCHASED MATERIALS

Koki Laboratories Inc...............................E....... 330 773-7669
Akron (G-262)

TRANSMISSIONS: Motor Vehicle

A & H Automotive Industries......................G....... 614 235-1759
Columbus (G-6666)

Ada Technologies Inc................................C....... 419 634-7000
Ada (G-3)

Capital Core Inc.......................................G....... 800 223-1884
Dayton (G-8209)

Comprehensive Logistics Co Inc................E....... 440 934-3517
Avon (G-990)

Custom Cltch Jint Hydrlics Inc...................F....... 216 431-1630
Cleveland (G-5149)

Dayton Superior Pdts Co Inc.....................G....... 937 332-1930
Troy (G-18815)

FCA US LLC...A....... 419 661-3500
Perrysburg (G-16094)

Gear Star American Performance................G....... 330 434-5216
Akron (G-200)

Metro Mech Inc...G....... 216 641-6262
Cleveland (G-5792)

TRANSPORTATION EPQT & SPLYS, WHOLESALE: Combat Vehicles

Unity Cable Technologies Inc.....................G....... 419 322-4118
Toledo (G-18759)

TRANSPORTATION EPQT & SPLYS, WHOLESALE: Nav Eqpt & Splys

Cedar Elec Holdings Corp..........................G....... 513 870-8500
West Chester (G-19824)

TRANSPORTATION EPQT & SPLYS, WHOLESALE: Tanks & Tank Compnts

Eleet Cryogenics Inc.................................E....... 330 874-4009
Bolivar (G-1933)

TRANSPORTATION EQPT & SPLYS WHOLESALERS, NEC

Dircksen and Associates Inc......................G....... 614 238-0413
Columbus (G-7027)

Omsi Transmissions Inc.............................G....... 330 405-7350
Twinsburg (G-18993)

TRANSPORTATION EQUIPMENT, NEC

Besl Specialized Carrier............................G....... 740 599-6305
Danville (G-8084)

Cleveland Wheels......................................D....... 440 937-6211
Avon (G-989)

TRANSPORTATION PROG REG & ADMIN, GOVT: Licensing Agencies

Barbara A Lieurance..................................G....... 937 382-2864
Wilmington (G-20656)

TRANSPORTATION PROGRAM REGULATION & ADMIN, GOVT: State

Transportation Ohio Department...................G....... 740 927-2285
Pataskala (G-15987)

P
R
O
D
U
C
T

TRANSPORTATION PROGRAMS REGULATION & ADMINISTRATION SVCS

Ohio Department Transportation.........E........ 614 351-2898
　Columbus (G-7418)

TRANSPORTATION SVCS, AIR, NONSCHEDULED: Air Cargo Carriers

Grand Aire Inc ....E........ 419 861-6700
　Swanton (G-18084)

TRANSPORTATION SVCS, NEC

Anro Logistics Inc ....G........ 614 428-7490
　Westerville (G-20138)

TRANSPORTATION: Air, Scheduled Passenger

Grand Aire Inc ....E........ 419 861-6700
　Swanton (G-18084)
Ruhe Sales Inc ....F........ 419 943-3357
　Leipsic (G-11876)

TRANSPORTATION: Horse-Drawn

Victorian Farms ....G........ 330 628-9188
　Atwater (G-903)

TRAPS: Animal, Iron Or Steel

Butera Manufacturing Inc..................F........ 440 516-3698
　Willoughby Hills (G-20638)
Butera Manufacturing Inds ....G........ 216 761-8800
　Cleveland (G-4953)
Smarty Company LLC ....E........ 614 890-6090
　Westerville (G-20186)

TRAVEL TRAILERS & CAMPERS

Airstream Inc ....B........ 937 596-6111
　Jackson Center (G-11337)
ARE Inc ....C........ 330 830-7800
　Massillon (G-13112)
ARE Inc ....B........ 330 830-7800
　Massillon (G-13111)
C&C Trailer Park ....G........ 330 823-7733
　Salem (G-16877)
Capitol City Trailers Inc ....D........ 614 491-2616
　Obetz (G-15651)
Cecil Caudill Trailer Sls Inc ....F........ 740 574-0704
　Franklin Furnace (G-10067)
D W Truax Enterprise Inc ....G........ 740 695-2596
　Saint Clairsville (G-16789)
Gerich Fiberglass Inc ....E........ 419 362-4591
　Mount Gilead (G-14560)
Hybrid Trailer Co LLC ....G........ 419 433-3022
　Huron (G-11227)
Jeff Couchs Campers LLC ....G........ 513 863-7000
　Hamilton (G-10712)

TRAVELER ACCOMMODATIONS, NEC

Amish Door Inc ....C........ 330 359-5464
　Wilmot (G-20683)
John Purdum ....G........ 513 897-9686
　Waynesville (G-19731)
Norstar Aluminum Molds Inc ....D........ 440 632-0853
　Middlefield (G-13977)

TRAYS: Plastic

Fastformingcom LLC ....F........ 330 927-3277
　Rittman (G-16674)

TROPHIES, NEC

All American Trophy ....G........ 614 231-8824
　Columbus (G-6719)
B & B Trophies & Awards ....G........ 330 225-6193
　Brunswick (G-2209)
Ginos Awards Inc ....E........ 216 831-5653
　Cleveland (G-5431)
Lawnview Industries Inc ....C........ 937 653-5217
　Urbana (G-19168)
Regal Trophy & Awards Company ......G........ 877 492-7531
　Sidney (G-17214)
Tempo Manufacturing Company ....G........ 937 773-6613
　Piqua (G-16314)

TROPHIES, PLATED, ALL METALS

Behrco Inc ....G........ 419 394-1612
　Saint Marys (G-16832)

TROPHIES, STAINLESS STEEL

Hr Machine LLC ....G........ 937 222-7644
　Beavercreek (G-1345)

TROPHIES, WHOLESALE

American Awards Inc ....F........ 614 875-1850
　Grove City (G-10542)
Behrco Inc ....G........ 419 394-1612
　Saint Marys (G-16832)
Dern Trophies Corp ....F........ 614 895-3260
　Westerville (G-20145)
Sharonco Inc ....G........ 419 882-3443
　Sylvania (G-18124)

TROPHIES: Metal, Exc Silver

Company Front Awards ....G........ 440 636-5493
　Middlefield (G-13924)
Dern Trophies Corp ....F........ 614 895-3260
　Westerville (G-20145)
Hit Trophy Inc ....G........ 419 445-5356
　Archbold (G-681)
Mid Ohio Trophy & Awards ....G........ 419 756-2266
　Mansfield (G-12647)
P S Superior Inc ....F........ 216 587-1000
　Cleveland (G-5958)
Ray Rieser Trophy Co ....G........ 614 279-1128
　Columbus (G-7549)

TROPHY & PLAQUE STORES

Auld Crafters Inc ....G........ 614 221-6825
　Columbus (G-6787)
B & B Trophies & Awards ....G........ 330 225-6193
　Brunswick (G-2209)
Behrco Inc ....G........ 419 394-1612
　Saint Marys (G-16832)
Designer Awards Inc ....G........ 937 339-4444
　Troy (G-18819)
Fineline Imprints Inc ....E........ 740 453-1083
　Zanesville (G-21308)
Fried Daddy ....G........ 937 854-4542
　Dayton (G-8351)
Gauntlet Awards & Engraving ....G........ 937 890-5811
　Dayton (G-8357)
Greg Blume ....G........ 740 574-2308
　Wheelersburg (G-20332)
Gym Pro LLC ....G........ 740 984-4143
　Waterford (G-19648)
Hit Trophy Inc ....G........ 419 445-5356
　Archbold (G-681)
Initially Yours ....G........ 216 228-4478
　Lakewood (G-11669)
Jakes Sportswear Ltd ....G........ 740 746-8356
　Sugar Grove (G-18012)
Joe Paxton ....G........ 614 424-9000
　Columbus (G-7237)
John C Starr ....G........ 740 852-5592
　London (G-12213)
L S Manufacturing Inc ....G........ 614 885-7988
　Worthington (G-20876)
M & M Engraving ....G........ 216 749-7166
　Cleveland (G-5716)
Mid Ohio Trophy & Awards ....G........ 419 756-2266
　Mansfield (G-12647)
Minotas Trophies & Awards ....G........ 440 720-1288
　Cleveland (G-5823)
Play All LLC ....G........ 440 992-7529
　Ashtabula (G-833)
Quali-Tee Design Sports ....F........ 937 382-7997
　Wilmington (G-20675)
Qualitee Design Sportswear Co ....F........ 740 333-8337
　Wshngtn CT Hs (G-20922)
Ray Rieser Trophy Co ....G........ 614 279-1128
　Columbus (G-7549)
Sun Shine Awards ....F........ 740 425-2504
　Barnesville (G-1161)
The Hartman Corp ....G........ 614 475-5035
　Columbus (G-7690)

TRUCK & BUS BODIES: Ambulance

Alterntive Spport Appratus LLC ....G........ 740 922-2727
　Midvale (G-14103)
Halcore Group Inc ....C........ 614 539-8181
　Grove City (G-10561)

TRUCK & BUS BODIES: Automobile Wrecker Truck

Miller Industries Inc ....G........ 937 293-2223
　Dayton (G-8503)
Rke Trucking Co ....F........ 614 891-1786
　Westerville (G-20183)

TRUCK & BUS BODIES: Bus Bodies

Gerich Fiberglass Inc ....E........ 419 362-4591
　Mount Gilead (G-14560)

TRUCK & BUS BODIES: Car Carrier

Kilar Manufacturing Inc ....E........ 330 534-8961
　Hubbard (G-11133)

TRUCK & BUS BODIES: Cement Mixer

Kimble Mixer Company ....D........ 330 308-6700
　New Philadelphia (G-14907)
McNeilus Truck and Mfg Inc ....G........ 614 868-0760
　Gahanna (G-10218)
McNeilus Truck and Mfg Inc ....E........ 513 874-2022
　Fairfield (G-9683)

TRUCK & BUS BODIES: Dump Truck

Daniel Wagner ....G........ 740 942-2928
　Cadiz (G-2416)
Friesen Transfer Ltd ....G........ 614 873-5672
　Plain City (G-16341)
Kruz Inc ....E........ 330 878-5595
　Dover (G-8996)
Unlimted Rcovery Solutions LLC ....E........ 419 868-4888
　Wauseon (G-19699)

TRUCK & BUS BODIES: Garbage Or Refuse Truck

Arts Rolloffs & Refuse Inc ....G........ 419 991-3730
　Lima (G-11994)

TRUCK & BUS BODIES: Motor Vehicle, Specialty

Bush Specialty Vehicles Inc ....F........ 937 382-5502
　Wilmington (G-20657)
Columbus Mobility Specialist ....G........ 614 825-8996
　Worthington (G-20861)
Willard Machine & Welding Inc ....F........ 330 467-0642
　Macedonia (G-12495)

TRUCK & BUS BODIES: Tank Truck

Bosserman Automotive Engrg LLC .....G........ 419 722-2879
　Findlay (G-9800)
Johnny On The Spot Inc ....E........ 614 497-1776
　Columbus (G-7239)
Marengo Fabricated Steel Ltd ....F........ 419 253-2119
　Marengo (G-12752)
Reberland Equipment Inc ....F........ 330 698-5883
　Apple Creek (G-648)
Tremcar USA Inc ....D........ 330 878-7708
　Strasburg (G-17831)

TRUCK & BUS BODIES: Truck Beds

Able Industries Inc ....G........ 614 252-1050
　Columbus (G-6680)
Crosco ....G........ 330 477-1999
　Canton (G-2671)
River City Body Company ....F........ 513 772-9317
　Cincinnati (G-4347)
Zie Bart Rhino Linings Toledo ....G........ 419 841-2886
　Toledo (G-18780)

TRUCK & BUS BODIES: Truck Cabs, Motor Vehicles

Valco Industries Inc ....E........ 937 399-7400
　Springfield (G-17672)

TRUCK & BUS BODIES: Truck, Motor Vehicle

Brown Industrial Inc ....E........ 937 693-3838
　Botkins (G-1951)

Cipted Corp ....D 412 829-2120
Monroe (G-14397)

Elliott Machine Works Inc ....E 419 468-4709
Galion (G-10267)

Kaffenbarger Truck Eqp Co ....C 937 845-3804
New Carlisle (G-14804)

Neiss Body & Equipment Corp ....G 330 828-2409
Dalton (G-8075)

Schodorf Truck Body & Eqp Co ....E 614 228-6793
Columbus (G-7596)

Venco Venturo Industries LLC ....E 513 772-8448
Cincinnati (G-4561)

TRUCK & BUS BODIES: Utility Truck

Q T Columbus LLC ....G 800 758-2410
Columbus (G-7528)

QT Equipment Company ....E 330 724-3055
Akron (G-355)

TRUCK & BUS BODIES: Van Bodies

Ellis & Watts Intl LLC ....G 513 752-9000
Batavia (G-1183)

Ford Motor Company.......................A 440 933-1215
Avon Lake (G-1029)

TRUCK BODIES: Body Parts

ARE Accessories LLC ....A 330 830-7800
Massillon (G-13110)

ARE Inc ....B 330 830-7800
Massillon (G-13111)

Bair Bodies & Trailers Inc ....G 330 343-4853
Dover (G-8966)

Brothers Body and Eqp LLC ....F 419 462-1975
Galion (G-10255)

Cota International Inc ....F 937 526-5520
Versailles (G-19344)

H & H Truck Parts LLC ....G 216 642-4540
Cleveland (G-5467)

Kaffenbarger Truck Eqp Co ....E 513 772-6800
Cincinnati (G-3967)

Kimble Custom Chassis Company ....D 877 546-2537
New Philadelphia (G-14906)

Mancor Ohio Inc ....E 937 228-6141
Dayton (G-8474)

Mancor Ohio Inc ....D 937 228-6141
Dayton (G-8475)

Proform Group Inc ....D 614 332-9654
Columbus (G-7524)

Silverado Trucks & Accessories ....G 937 492-8862
Sidney (G-17228)

Wilson Seat Company Inc ....E 513 732-2460
Batavia (G-1233)

TRUCK BODY SHOP

Q T Columbus LLC ....G 800 758-2410
Columbus (G-7528)

QT Equipment Company ....E 330 724-3055
Akron (G-355)

TRUCK DRIVER SVCS

Industrial Repair & Mfg Inc ....E 419 822-4232
Delta (G-8936)

TRUCK GENERAL REPAIR SVC

M & W Trailers Inc ....F 419 453-3331
Ottoville (G-15824)

Top Notch Fleet Services LLC ....G 419 260-4057
Maumee (G-13303)

TRUCK PAINTING & LETTERING SVCS

Design Masters Inc ....G 513 772-7175
Cincinnati (G-3649)

Ham Signs LLC ....G 937 454-9111
Dayton (G-8383)

J & L Body Inc ....F 216 661-2323
Brooklyn Heights (G-2141)

Mike B Crawford............................G 330 673-7944
Kent (G-11492)

Sign Lady Inc ....G 419 476-9191
Toledo (G-18696)

TRUCK PARTS & ACCESSORIES: Wholesalers

Adelmans Truck Parts Corp ....E 330 456-0206
Canton (G-2587)

Adelmans Truck Parts Corp ....F 216 362-0500
Canton (G-2588)

Buyers Products Company ....C 440 974-8888
Mentor (G-13540)

Buyers Products Company ....G 440 974-8888
Mentor (G-13542)

East Manufacturing Corporation ....B 330 325-9921
Randolph (G-16509)

Kaffenbarger Truck Eqp Co ....C 937 845-3804
New Carlisle (G-14804)

Malone Specialty Inc ....F 440 255-4200
Mentor (G-13645)

Mytee Products Inc ....F 440 591-4301
Aurora (G-936)

Perkins Motor Service Ltd ....F 440 277-1256
Lorain (G-12267)

Silverado Trucks & Accessories ....G 937 492-8862
Sidney (G-17228)

Youngstown-Kenworth Inc.................E 330 534-9761
Hubbard (G-11143)

TRUCKING & HAULING SVCS: Animal & Farm Prdt

Pro-Pet LLC ....G 419 394-3374
Saint Marys (G-16850)

TRUCKING & HAULING SVCS: Contract Basis

Kmj Leasing Ltd ....E 614 871-3883
Orient (G-15723)

TRUCKING & HAULING SVCS: Garbage, Collect/Transport Only

Werlor Inc ....E 419 784-4285
Defiance (G-8814)

TRUCKING & HAULING SVCS: Heavy Machinery, Local

J & A Machine ....G 330 424-5235
Lisbon (G-12123)

TRUCKING & HAULING SVCS: Liquid, Local

Mac Oil Field Service Inc ....F 330 674-7371
Millersburg (G-14244)

TRUCKING & HAULING SVCS: Machinery, Heavy

L A Productions Co LLC ....G 330 666-4230
Akron (G-264)

TRUCKING & HAULING SVCS: Mail Carriers, Contract

Glenn Michael Brick........................F 740 391-5735
Flushing (G-9916)

TRUCKING, ANIMAL

Yemaneh Musie ....G 614 506-3687
Columbus (G-7783)

TRUCKING, AUTOMOBILE CARRIER

Akron Centl Engrv Mold Mch Inc..........E 330 794-8704
Akron (G-37)

Jatdco LLC ....G 440 238-6570
Strongsville (G-17933)

TRUCKING, DUMP

Carl E Oeder Sons Sand & Grav..........E 513 494-1555
Lebanon (G-11787)

Edw C Levy Co ....E 419 822-8286
Delta (G-8931)

Kirby and Sons Inc ....F 419 927-2260
Upper Sandusky (G-19128)

Roe Transportation Entps Inc ....G 937 497-7161
Sidney (G-17217)

Silverado Trucks & Accessories ....G 937 492-8862
Sidney (G-17228)

TRUCKING: Except Local

Bc Investment Corporation ....G 330 262-3070
Wooster (G-20747)

Buckeye Energy Resources Inc ....G 740 452-9506
Zanesville (G-21283)

Chagrin Vly Stl Erectors Inc................F 440 975-1556
Willoughby (G-20455)

Custom Built Crates Inc ....E 513 248-4422
Milford (G-14135)

Ds Express Carriers Inc ....G 419 433-6200
Norwalk (G-15534)

Flegal Brothers Inc ....F 419 298-3539
Edgerton (G-9331)

Oeder Carl E Sons Sand & Grav ....E 513 494-1238
Lebanon (G-11820)

Parobek Trucking Co ....G 419 869-7500
West Salem (G-20116)

The Euclid Chemical Company ....E 800 321-7628
Cleveland (G-6309)

TRUCKING: Local, With Storage

M G Q Inc ....E 419 992-4236
Tiffin (G-18229)

Pro-Hoe Utility LLC ....G 740 892-4765
Johnstown (G-11403)

Resource Recycling Inc ....F 419 222-2702
Lima (G-12081)

TRUCKING: Local, Without Storage

Collier Well Eqp & Sup Inc ....F 330 345-3968
Wooster (G-20760)

Corbett R Caudill Chipping Inc.............F 740 596-5984
Hamden (G-10656)

Erichar Inc ....G 216 402-2628
Cleveland (G-5293)

Fairway Carts Parts & More LLC ....G 234 209-9008
North Canton (G-15229)

Haul-Away Containers Inc ....G 440 546-1879
Richfield (G-16626)

Hershberger Manufacturing................G 440 272-5555
Windsor (G-20699)

M & R Redi Mix Inc ....E 419 445-7771
Pettisville (G-16181)

Olen Corporation ....G 740 745-5865
Saint Louisville (G-16829)

Parobek Trucking Co ....G 419 869-7500
West Salem (G-20116)

R J Dobay Enterprises Inc ....G 440 834-4580
Burton (G-2382)

Rjw Trucking Company Ltd.................E 740 363-5343
Delaware (G-8883)

Roth Transit Inc.............................G 937 773-5051
Piqua (G-16311)

Third Party Service Ltd.....................F 419 872-2312
Perrysburg (G-16158)

Ward Construction Co ....F 419 943-2450
Leipsic (G-11879)

TRUCKS & TRACTORS: Industrial

Belden Brick Company......................E 330 852-2411
Sugarcreek (G-18016)

Canton Elevator Inc ....D 330 833-3600
North Canton (G-15224)

City Machine Technologies Inc............F 330 747-2639
Youngstown (G-21047)

Crescent Metal Products Inc ....C 440 350-1100
Mentor (G-13555)

Falls Welding & Fabg Inc ....G 330 253-3437
Akron (G-180)

Fame Tool & Mfg Co Inc ....E 513 271-6387
Cincinnati (G-3737)

Foerster Instruments Inc ....F 330 332-9100
Salem (G-16891)

Forte Indus Eqp Systems Inc ....E 513 398-2800
Mason (G-13022)

G & T Manufacturing Co ....F 440 639-7777
Mentor (G-13588)

General Electric Company ....B 513 977-1500
Cincinnati (G-3813)

Gradall Industries Inc ....C 330 339-2211
New Philadelphia (G-14901)

Grand Harbor Yacht Sales & Svc ....G 440 442-2919
Cleveland (G-5445)

Harsco Corporation ....E 740 387-1150
Marion (G-12873)

Hendrickson Usa LLC......................C 330 456-7288
Canton (G-2725)

Hobart Brothers Company ....A 937 332-5439
Troy (G-18836)

Jh Industries Inc ....E 330 963-4105
Twinsburg (G-18961)

Kinetic Technologies Inc ....F 440 943-4111
Wickliffe (G-20369)
Lange Precision Inc ....F 513 530-9500
Blue Ash (G-1824)
Leebaw Manufacturing Company .....F 330 533-3368
Canfield (G-2561)
Martin Sprocket & Gear Inc ....D 419 485-5515
Montpelier (G-14448)
McCullough Industries Inc ....E 800 245-9490
Kenton (G-11556)
MH Logistics Corp ....D 513 681-2200
West Chester (G-20028)
Miller Products Inc ....E 330 308-5934
New Philadelphia (G-14915)
Miners Tractor Sales Inc ....F 330 325-9914
Rootstown (G-16725)
Mitchs Welding & Hitches ....G 419 893-3117
Maumee (G-13286)
Parker Elwell Ltd ....G 216 881-5042
Cleveland (G-5970)
Parobek Trucking Co ....G 419 869-7500
West Salem (G-20116)
Perfecto Industries Inc ....E 937 778-1900
Piqua (G-16299)
Pollock Research & Design Inc .....E 330 332-3300
Salem (G-16920)
Pucel Enterprises Inc ....D 216 881-4604
Cleveland (G-6061)
R B Mfg Co ....F 419 626-9464
Sandusky (G-16999)
Saf-Holland Inc ....G 513 874-7888
West Chester (G-20046)
Scott-Randall Systems Inc ....F 937 446-2293
Sardinia (G-17033)
Snair Co ....F 614 873-7020
Plain City (G-16360)
Sroka Inc ....E 440 572-2811
Strongsville (G-17971)
Stock Fairfield Corporation ....C 440 543-6000
Chagrin Falls (G-3122)
Sweet Manufacturing Company .....E 937 325-1511
Springfield (G-17659)
Tarpco Inc ....F 330 677-8277
Kent (G-11535)
Trailer Component Mfg Inc ....E 440 255-2888
Mentor (G-13753)
Transco Railway Products Inc ....E 419 726-3383
Toledo (G-18756)
Waltco Lift Corp ....C 330 633-9191
Tallmadge (G-18175)
Webb-Stiles Company ....D 330 225-7761
Valley City (G-19237)
Youngstown-Kenworth Inc ....E 330 534-9761
Hubbard (G-11143)

TRUCKS, INDL: Wholesalers

Tri-Mac Mfg & Svcs Co ....F 513 896-4445
Hamilton (G-10749)

TRUCKS: Forklift

Foerster Systems Inc ....F 330 332-9100
Salem (G-16892)
Forklifts of Americas LLC ....G 440 821-5143
Highland Heights (G-10912)
Integrity Industrial Eqp Inc ....G 937 238-9275
Huber Heights (G-11149)
Marlow-2000 Inc ....F 216 362-8500
Cleveland (G-5751)
Precision Equipment Llc ....G 330 220-7600
Brunswick (G-2246)

TRUCKS: Indl

Chemtrans Logistics Inc ....G 419 447-8041
Tiffin (G-18215)
Elliott Machine Works Inc ....E 419 468-4709
Galion (G-10267)
Grand Aire Inc ....E 419 861-6700
Swanton (G-18084)
Newsafe Transport Service Inc .....F 740 387-1679
Marion (G-12890)
Surplus Freight Inc ....G 614 235-7660
Gahanna (G-10237)
Triumphant Enterprises Inc ....E 513 617-1668
Goshen (G-10417)
Yemaneh Musie ....G 614 506-3687
Columbus (G-7783)

TRUSSES & FRAMING: Prefabricated Metal

C Green & Sons Incorporated ....F 740 745-2998
Saint Louisville (G-16826)
Shrock Prefab LLC ....F 740 599-9401
Danville (G-8091)

TRUSSES: Wood, Floor

Khempco Bldg Sup Co Ltd Partnr ...D 740 549-0465
Delaware (G-8865)
Woodcraft Floor & Roof Trusses ....G 740 927-9015
Pataskala (G-15991)

TRUSSES: Wood, Roof

Automated Bldg Components Inc ....E 419 257-2152
North Baltimore (G-15191)
Buckeye Components LLC ....G 330 482-5163
Columbiana (G-6608)
Building Concepts Inc ....F 419 298-2371
Edgerton (G-9326)
Columbus Roof Trusses Inc ....E 614 272-6464
Columbus (G-6964)
Columbus Roof Trusses Inc ....F 740 763-3000
Newark (G-14994)
Fifth Avenue Lumber Co ....D 614 833-6655
Canal Winchester (G-2524)
Four Js Bldg Components LLC ....F 740 886-6112
Scottown (G-17039)
M & G Truss Rafters ....G 740 667-3166
Coolville (G-7834)
Ohio Valley Truss Co ....E 937 393-3995
Hillsboro (G-11010)
Ohio Valley Truss Co ....G 937 393-3995
Hillsboro (G-11011)
Pioneer Homes Inc ....F 419 737-2371
Pioneer (G-16238)
Proline Truss ....F 419 895-9980
Shiloh (G-17154)
R & L Truss Inc ....F 419 587-3440
Grover Hill (G-10653)
Redbuilt LLC ....E 740 363-0870
Delaware (G-8882)
Schilling Truss Inc ....F 740 984-2396
Beverly (G-1671)
Stark Truss Company Inc ....E 740 335-4156
Washington Court Hou (G-19640)
Stark Truss Company Inc ....D 419 298-3777
Edgerton (G-9337)
Stark Truss Company Inc ....F 330 478-2100
Canton (G-2858)
Strait & Lamp Lumber Co Inc ....D 614 833-6655
Canal Winchester (G-2537)
Thomas Do-It Center Inc ....E 740 446-2002
Gallipolis (G-10310)
Waynedale Truss and Panel Co .....E 330 698-7373
Apple Creek (G-651)

TRUST MANAGEMENT SVC, EXC EDUCATIONAL, RELIGIOUS & CHARITY

OFA Services Inc ....F 614 884-1203
Columbus (G-7413)

TUB CONTAINERS: Plastic

Plas-Tanks Industries Inc ....E 513 942-3800
Hamilton (G-10730)

TUBE & PIPE MILL EQPT

Atkore Plastic Pipe Corp ....D 330 627-8002
Carrollton (G-2952)
Formtek Inc ....D 216 292-4460
Cleveland (G-5372)
Graebener Group Tech Ltd ....G 419 591-7033
Napoleon (G-14679)
Pipeline Automation Syste Inc ....G 419 462-8833
Galion (G-10282)

TUBE & TUBING FABRICATORS

Beaverson Machine Inc ....G 419 923-8064
Delta (G-8929)
Benjamin Steel Company Inc ....E 937 233-1212
Springfield (G-17522)
Chardon Metal Products Co ....E 440 285-2147
Chardon (G-3144)
Cleveland Plastic Fabricat ....F 216 797-7300
Euclid (G-9572)
Dekay Fabricators Inc ....E 330 793-0826
Youngstown (G-21066)

Fabcraft Inc ....G 440 286-6700
Chardon (G-3152)
H-P Products Inc ....E 330 875-7193
Louisville (G-12313)
Hycom Inc ....E 330 753-2330
Barberton (G-1120)
Hydra-TEC Inc ....G 330 225-8797
Brunswick (G-2232)
Hydro Tube Enterprises Inc ....D 440 774-1022
Oberlin (G-15644)
Kenley Enterprises LLC ....E 419 630-0921
Bryan (G-2308)
Machine Dynamics & Engrg Inc .....D 330 868-5603
Minerva (G-14331)
Moss Vale Inc ....F 513 939-1970
Fairfield (G-9687)
Parker-Hannifin Corporation ....B 937 456-5571
Eaton (G-9320)
Precision Cutoff LLC ....C 419 866-8000
Holland (G-11078)
S-P Company Inc ....F 330 482-0200
Columbiana (G-6631)
Sanoh America Inc ....D 419 425-2600
Findlay (G-9887)
Stam Inc ....E 440 974-2500
Mentor (G-13729)
Tomco Machining Inc ....E 937 264-1943
Dayton (G-8718)
Unison Industries LLC ....D 937 426-4676
Alpha (G-555)
Unison Industries LLC ....A 937 426-0621
Dayton (G-8122)
United Metal Fabricators Inc ....E 216 662-2000
Maple Heights (G-12742)
Unity Tube Inc ....F 330 426-4282
East Palestine (G-9248)
US Tubular Products Inc ....D 330 832-1734
North Lawrence (G-15307)
Woodsage Corporation ....D 419 476-3553
Holland (G-11097)

TUBES: Finned, For Heat Transfer

Fin Tube Products Inc ....F 330 334-3736
Wadsworth (G-19406)

TUBES: Generator, Electron Beam, Beta Ray

Fripro Energy LLC ....G 419 865-0002
Maumee (G-13259)

TUBES: Hard Rubber

Crushproof Tubing Co ....E 419 293-2111
Mc Comb (G-13337)
Usui International Corporation ....E 513 448-0410
Cincinnati (G-4548)

TUBES: Paper

A T Tube Company Inc ....G 330 336-8706
Wadsworth (G-19386)
Acme Spirally Wound Paper Pdts ....F 216 267-2950
Cleveland (G-4694)
Advanced Paper Tube Inc ....F 216 281-5691
Cleveland (G-4717)
Caraustar Industrial and Con ....E 330 868-4111
Minerva (G-14318)
Caraustar Industries Inc ....E 330 665-7700
Copley (G-7841)
Erie Container Corporation ....G 216 631-1650
Cleveland (G-5294)
Midwest Specialty Pdts Co Inc ......F 513 874-7070
Fairfield (G-9685)
Ohio Paper Tube Co ....F 330 478-5171
Canton (G-2802)

TUBES: Paper Or Fiber, Chemical Or Electrical Uses

Newkor Inc ....E 216 631-7800
Cleveland (G-5880)

TUBES: Steel & Iron

Crest Bending Inc ....E 419 492-2108
New Washington (G-14959)
Kirtland Capital Partners LP ....E 216 593-0100
Beachwood (G-1276)
Middletown Tube Works Inc ....D 513 727-0080
Middletown (G-14064)
Phillips Mfg and Tower Co ....D 419 347-1720
Shelby (G-17140)

Systems Jay LLC Nanogate ....E 419 747-1096
Mansfield *(G-12689)*
Universal Metals Cutting Inc ....G 330 580-5192
Canton *(G-2890)*

TUBES: Wrought, Welded Or Lock Joint

Tubetech Inc ....E 330 426-9476
East Palestine *(G-9247)*
United Tube Corporation ....D 330 725-4196
Medina *(G-13494)*
Welded Tubes Inc ....G 216 378-2092
Orwell *(G-15781)*

TUBING: Copper

Arem Co ....F 440 974-6740
Mentor *(G-13526)*

TUBING: Electrical Use, Quartz

Great Lakes Glasswerks Inc ....G 440 358-0460
Painesville *(G-15885)*
Unity Cable Technologies Inc ....G 419 322-4118
Toledo *(G-18759)*

TUBING: Flexible, Metallic

Tubular Techniques Inc ....G 614 529-4130
Hilliard *(G-10989)*
Wayne Trail Technologies Inc ....D 937 295-2120
Fort Loramie *(G-9944)*

TUBING: Glass

Glasstech Inc ....C 419 661-9500
Perrysburg *(G-16103)*
Jack Pine Studio ....G 614 291-0699
Columbus *(G-7220)*
Techneglas Inc ....G 419 873-2000
Perrysburg *(G-16155)*

TUBING: Plastic

Akron Polymer Products Inc ....E 330 628-5551
Akron *(G-52)*
Alkon Corporation ....D 419 355-9111
Fremont *(G-10124)*
Dlhbowles Inc ....D 330 488-0716
East Canton *(G-9191)*
Dlhbowles Inc ....B 330 478-2503
Canton *(G-2691)*
Kentak Products Company ....D 330 386-3700
East Liverpool *(G-9221)*
Kentak Products Company ....E 330 382-2000
East Liverpool *(G-9222)*
Kentak Products Company ....G 330 532-6211
East Palestine *(G-9240)*
Normandy Products Company ....D 440 632-5050
Middlefield *(G-13976)*
Quality Poly Corp ....F 330 453-9559
Canton *(G-2829)*
Universal Plastics Inc ....E 440 942-7510
Mentor *(G-13762)*

TUBING: Rubber

Eagle Elastomer Inc ....E 330 923-7070
Peninsula *(G-16037)*
Meridian Industries Inc ....D 330 359-5447
Winesburg *(G-20706)*
Meridian Industries Inc ....D 330 673-1011
Kent *(G-11488)*
Meteor Sealing Systems LLC ....C 330 343-9595
Dover *(G-9001)*
Sml Inc ....G 330 668-6555
Akron *(G-406)*

TUBING: Seamless

Mid-Ohio Tubing LLC ....E 419 883-2066
Butler *(G-2392)*
Mid-Ohio Tubing LLC ....D 419 886-0220
Bellville *(G-1572)*

TUGBOAT SVCS

Shelly Materials Inc ....G 330 673-3646
Kent *(G-11527)*
Shelly Materials Inc ....D 740 246-6315
Thornville *(G-18198)*

TUNGSTEN CARBIDE POWDER

Castlebar Corporation ....G 330 451-6511
Canton *(G-2651)*
Cleveland Tungsten Inc ....G 440 786-0800
Bedford *(G-1415)*
Tungsten Sltons Group Intl Inc ....G 440 708-3096
Chagrin Falls *(G-3130)*

TUNGSTEN MILL PRDTS

Castlebar Corporation ....G 330 451-6511
Canton *(G-2651)*
General Electric Company ....D 330 343-8841
Dover *(G-8987)*
H C Starck Inc ....B 216 692-3990
Euclid *(G-9584)*
Rhenium Alloys Inc ....D 440 365-7388
North Ridgeville *(G-15401)*

TURBINE GENERATOR SET UNITS: Hydraulic, Complete

Kw River Hydroelectric I LLC ....G 513 673-2251
Cincinnati *(G-4007)*

TURBINES & TURBINE GENERATOR SET UNITS, COMPLETE

Northel Usa LLC ....G 740 973-0309
Newark *(G-15040)*

TURBINES & TURBINE GENERATOR SETS

Alin Machining Company Inc ....E 740 223-0200
Marion *(G-12853)*
Arete Innovative Solutions LLC ....G 513 503-2712
Morrow *(G-14543)*
Argosy Wind Power Ltd ....G 440 539-1345
Aurora *(G-906)*
Camfil USA Inc ....G 937 773-0866
Piqua *(G-16255)*
Eaton Leasing Corporation ....G 216 382-2292
Beachwood *(G-1270)*
Fluidpower Assembly Inc ....G 419 394-7486
Saint Marys *(G-16839)*
General Electric Company ....F 513 243-9317
West Chester *(G-19874)*
Metalex Manufacturing Inc ....C 513 489-0507
Blue Ash *(G-1839)*
Pfpc Enterprises Inc ....B 513 941-6200
Cincinnati *(G-4233)*
R H Industries Inc ....E 216 281-5210
Cleveland *(G-6083)*
Siemens Energy Inc ....B 740 393-8897
Mount Vernon *(G-14648)*
Td Power Systems (usa) Inc ....G 330 247-5264
Richfield *(G-16642)*

TURBINES & TURBINE GENERATOR SETS & PARTS

Aero Propulsion Support Inc ....E 513 367-9452
Harrison *(G-10766)*
GE Aviation Systems LLC ....C 937 898-9600
Dayton *(G-8358)*

TURBINES: Gas, Mechanical Drive

On-Power Inc ....E 513 228-2100
Lebanon *(G-11823)*
Teledyne Technologies Inc ....D 419 470-3000
Toledo *(G-18717)*

TURBINES: Hydraulic, Complete

Fluid System Service Inc ....G 216 651-2450
Cleveland *(G-5361)*
Fusion Incorporated ....E 440 946-3300
Willoughby *(G-20494)*
Parker Triad Store ....D 937 293-4080
Moraine *(G-14511)*

TURBINES: Steam

Steam Turb Alte Reso ....E 740 387-5535
Marion *(G-12903)*

TURNSTILES

Controlled Access Inc ....F 330 273-6185
Hinckley *(G-11023)*

TWINE PRDTS

R C Packaging Systems ....F 248 684-6363
Mentor *(G-13711)*

TYPE: Rubber

Farmed Materials Inc ....G 513 680-4046
Cincinnati *(G-3740)*

TYPESETTING SVC

21st Century Printers Inc ....G 513 771-4150
Cincinnati *(G-3322)*
A-1 Printing Inc ....F 419 562-3111
Bucyrus *(G-2330)*
A-A Blueprint Co Inc ....E 330 794-8803
Akron *(G-22)*
Activities Press Inc ....G 440 953-1200
Mentor *(G-13509)*
Advanced Translation/Cnsltng ....E 440 716-0820
Westlake *(G-20246)*
AGS Custom Graphics Inc ....D 330 963-7770
Macedonia *(G-12433)*
Ajeh & Company Unlimited ....G 440 729-2367
Chesterland *(G-3196)*
Alfacomp Inc ....G 216 459-1790
Cleveland *(G-4751)*
Anderson Graphics Inc ....E 330 745-2165
Barberton *(G-1098)*
Anthony Business Forms Inc ....F 937 253-0072
Dayton *(G-8096)*
Art Printing Co Inc ....G 419 281-4371
Ashland *(G-705)*
Art Tees Inc ....G 614 338-8337
Columbus *(G-6774)*
Asist Inc ....F 614 451-6744
Columbus *(G-6777)*
Baise Enterprises Inc ....G 614 444-3171
Columbus *(G-6801)*
Beer Communications Inc ....G 419 756-6882
Mansfield *(G-12566)*
Bill Wyatt Inc ....G 330 535-1113
Mentor *(G-13535)*
Bindery & Spc Pressworks Inc ....D 614 873-4623
Plain City *(G-16326)*
Blt Inc ....F 513 631-5050
Norwood *(G-15571)*
Bock & Pierce Enterprises ....G 513 474-9500
Cincinnati *(G-3455)*
Boldman Printing LLC ....G 937 653-3431
Urbana *(G-19148)*
Bookmasters Inc ....C 419 281-1802
Ashland *(G-713)*
Brothers Publishing Co LLC ....E 937 548-3330
Greenville *(G-10490)*
Camelot Typesetting Company ....G 216 574-8973
Cleveland *(G-4964)*
Canton Graphic Arts Service ....G 330 456-9868
Canton *(G-2641)*
Capozzolo Printers Inc ....G 513 542-7874
Cincinnati *(G-3496)*
Carlisle Prtg Walnut Creek Ltd ....E 330 852-9922
Sugarcreek *(G-18020)*
Clints Printing Inc ....G 937 426-2771
Beavercreek *(G-1373)*
Cold Duck Screen Prtg & EMB Co ....G 330 426-1900
East Palestine *(G-9231)*
Colortech Graphics & Printing ....F 614 766-2400
Columbus *(G-6944)*
Consoldated Graphics Group Inc ....C 216 881-9191
Cleveland *(G-5116)*
Copley Ohio Newspapers Inc ....C 330 364-5577
New Philadelphia *(G-14892)*
Cornerstone Industries Lcc ....G 513 871-4546
West Chester *(G-19845)*
COS Blueprint Inc ....F 330 376-0022
Akron *(G-130)*
Crabar/Gbf Inc ....G 419 943-2141
Leipsic *(G-11868)*
Customer Service Systems Inc ....G 330 677-2877
Kent *(G-11442)*
D & S Crtive Cmmunications Inc ....D 419 524-6699
Mansfield *(G-12591)*
Daily Gazette ....E 937 372-4444
Xenia *(G-20945)*
Daubenmires Printing ....G 513 425-7223
Middletown *(G-14036)*
Debandale Printing Inc ....G 330 725-5122
Medina *(G-13401)*
Dorothy Crooker ....G 513 385-0888
Cincinnati *(G-3665)*

PRODUCT

Douglas Michalske.....G..... 216 631-0567
Cleveland (G-5210)
Dove Cds Inc.....G..... 330 928-3430
Tallmadge (G-18143)
E L Frueh Inc.....F..... 419 222-9741
Lima (G-12007)
Earl D Arnold Printing Company.....E..... 513 533-6900
Cincinnati (G-3685)
Easterdays Printing Center.....G..... 330 726-1182
Youngstown (G-21073)
Emta Inc.....G..... 440 734-6464
North Olmsted (G-15332)
Eugene Stewart.....G..... 937 898-1117
Dayton (G-8333)
Fedex Office & Print Svcs Inc.....E..... 937 436-0677
Dayton (G-8339)
Fedex Office & Print Svcs Inc.....E..... 614 621-1100
Columbus (G-7080)
Fedex Office & Print Svcs Inc.....F..... 614 575-0800
Reynoldsburg (G-16590)
Fedex Office & Print Svcs Inc.....E..... 216 573-1511
Cleveland (G-5333)
Fedex Office & Print Svcs Inc.....E..... 419 866-5464
Toledo (G-18466)
Flexoplate Inc.....E..... 513 489-0433
Blue Ash (G-1796)
Frank J Prucha & Associates.....G..... 216 642-3838
Cleveland (G-5378)
Franklins Printing Company.....F..... 740 452-6375
Zanesville (G-21311)
Gazette Publishing Company.....E..... 419 483-4190
Oberlin (G-15640)
Genesis Quality Printing Inc.....G..... 440 975-5700
Mentor (G-13592)
George D Kanaan & Associates.....G..... 440 243-6410
Berea (G-1617)
Geygan Enterprises Inc.....F..... 513 932-4222
Lebanon (G-11803)
Graphic Image.....G..... 937 320-0302
Beavercreek (G-1341)
Graphic Touch Inc.....G..... 330 337-3341
Salem (G-16896)
Greg Blume.....G..... 740 574-2308
Wheelersburg (G-20332)
Harlan Graphic Arts Svcs Inc.....E..... 513 251-5700
Cincinnati (G-3866)
Hecks Direct Mail & Prtg Svc.....E..... 419 697-3505
Toledo (G-18502)
Hilleary-Whitaker Inc.....G..... 614 766-4694
Columbus (G-7157)
Hkm Drect Mkt Cmmnications Inc.....C..... 216 651-9500
Cleveland (G-5516)
Homewood Press Inc.....E..... 419 478-0695
Toledo (G-18510)
Hubbard Publishing Co.....E..... 937 592-3060
Bellefontaine (G-1533)
Image Industries Inc.....G..... 937 832-7969
Englewood (G-9524)
Imprints.....F..... 330 650-0467
Hudson (G-11181)
Jack G Walker.....F..... 440 352-4222
Mentor (G-13617)
Jim Davis.....G..... 740 335-8030
Wshngtn CT Hs (G-20914)
Kad Holdings Inc.....G..... 614 792-3399
Dublin (G-9093)
Keener Printing Inc.....F..... 216 531-7595
Cleveland (G-5640)
Kehl-Kolor Inc.....E..... 419 281-3107
Ashland (G-746)
Kevin K Tidd.....G..... 419 885-5603
Sylvania (G-18115)
Keystone Press Inc.....G..... 419 243-7326
Toledo (G-18544)
Keystone Printing & Copy Cat.....G..... 740 354-6542
Portsmouth (G-16439)
La Dua Inc.....G..... 440 243-9600
Olmsted Twp (G-15679)
Landen Desktop Pubg Ctr Inc.....G..... 513 683-5181
Loveland (G-12370)
Larry C White.....G..... 330 386-3228
East Liverpool (G-9224)
Laurenee Ltd LLC.....G..... 513 662-2225
Cincinnati (G-4015)
Lee Corporation.....F..... 513 771-3602
Cincinnati (G-4019)
Legal News Publishing Co.....E..... 216 696-3322
Cleveland (G-5692)
Liming Printing Inc.....F..... 937 374-2646
Xenia (G-20961)
Lund Printing Co.....G..... 330 628-4047
Akron (G-277)
M Web Type Inc.....G..... 614 272-8973
Columbus (G-7310)
Margaret Trentman.....G..... 513 948-1700
Cincinnati (G-4059)
Middleton Printing Co Inc.....G..... 614 294-7277
Gahanna (G-10219)
Mmp Printing Inc.....E..... 513 381-0990
Cincinnati (G-4112)
Montview Corporation.....G..... 330 723-3409
Medina (G-13449)
Nari Inc.....G..... 440 960-2280
Monroeville (G-14427)
Network Printing & Graphics.....F..... 614 230-2084
Columbus (G-7387)
Newfax Corporation.....F..... 419 241-5157
Toledo (G-18603)
Newspaper Holding Inc.....D..... 440 998-2323
Ashtabula (G-826)
Old Trail Printing Company.....C..... 614 443-4852
Columbus (G-7440)
Onetouchpoint East Corp.....D..... 513 421-1600
Cincinnati (G-4189)
Orange Blossom Press Inc.....G..... 216 781-8655
Willoughby (G-20562)
Orrville Printing Co Inc.....G..... 330 682-5066
Orrville (G-15752)
Painesville Publishing Co.....G..... 440 354-4142
Austinburg (G-964)
Paul/Jay Associates.....G..... 740 676-8776
Bellaire (G-1500)
Penguin Enterprises Inc.....E..... 440 899-5110
Westlake (G-20292)
Performa La Mar Printing Inc.....G..... 440 632-9800
Middlefield (G-13981)
Pooles Printing & Office Svcs.....G..... 419 475-9000
Toledo (G-18649)
Preisser Inc.....E..... 614 345-0199
Columbus (G-7514)
Prime Printing Inc.....E..... 937 438-3707
Dayton (G-8594)
Printed Image.....F..... 614 221-1412
Columbus (G-7519)
Printing Arts Press.....F..... 740 397-6106
Mount Vernon (G-14639)
Progressive Communications.....D..... 740 397-5333
Mount Vernon (G-14640)
Quad/Graphics Inc.....C..... 614 276-4800
Columbus (G-7531)
Quick As A Wink Printing Co.....F..... 419 224-9786
Lima (G-12079)
Quick Tab II Inc.....D..... 419 448-6622
Tiffin (G-18238)
Quick Tech Graphics Inc.....E..... 937 743-5952
Springboro (G-17502)
R & W Printing Company.....G..... 513 575-0131
Loveland (G-12379)
R B Robinson Inc.....G..... 440 543-5547
Chagrin Falls (G-3116)
R W Michael Printing Co.....G..... 330 923-9277
Akron (G-363)
Registered Images Inc.....G..... 859 781-9200
Cincinnati (G-4335)
Ricci Anthony.....G..... 330 758-5761
Youngstown (G-21188)
River Corp.....G..... 513 641-3355
Cincinnati (G-4348)
Robert Esterman.....G..... 513 541-3311
Cincinnati (G-4353)
Robin Enterprises Company.....C..... 614 891-0250
Westerville (G-20233)
Robs Creative Screen Printing.....G..... 740 264-6383
Wintersville (G-20713)
Royal Acme Corporation.....E..... 216 241-1477
Cleveland (G-6136)
RR Donnelley & Sons Company.....G..... 614 221-8385
Columbus (G-7576)
Ryans Newark Leader Ex Prtg.....F..... 740 522-2149
Newark (G-15051)
S O S Graphics & Printing Inc.....G..... 614 846-8229
Worthington (G-20886)
Sandy Smittcamp.....G..... 937 372-1687
Xenia (G-20971)
Sharon Printing Co Inc.....G..... 330 239-1684
Sharon Center (G-17110)
Sjpm Inc.....G..... 614 475-4571
Gahanna (G-10233)
South End Printing Co.....G..... 216 341-0669
Cleveland (G-6222)
Spencer-Walker Press Inc.....F..... 740 344-6110
Newark (G-15055)
Springfield Engraving Company.....G..... 937 390-0011
Springfield (G-17651)
St Media Group Intl Inc.....D..... 513 421-2050
Blue Ash (G-1873)
Stationery Shop Inc.....G..... 330 376-2033
Akron (G-416)
Stumbo Publishing Co.....G..... 419 529-2847
Ontario (G-15695)
Suburban Press Inc.....E..... 216 961-0766
Cleveland (G-6260)
Target Business Services.....F..... 614 866-4065
Pickerington (G-16207)
Target Printing & Graphics.....G..... 937 228-0170
Dayton (G-8700)
Technical Translation Services.....G..... 440 942-3130
Willoughby (G-20611)
Tim L Humbert.....F..... 330 497-4944
Canton (G-2870)
Ulrich Rubber Stamp Company.....G..... 419 339-9939
Elida (G-9359)
W L Beck Printing & Design.....G..... 330 762-3020
Akron (G-467)
Watkins Printing Company.....E..... 614 297-8270
Columbus (G-7752)
West-Camp Press Inc.....D..... 614 818-6279
Westerville (G-20241)
Western Roto Engravers Inc.....E..... 330 336-7636
Wadsworth (G-19444)
Wfsr Holdings LLC.....A..... 877 735-4966
Dayton (G-8757)
Winkler Co Inc.....G..... 937 294-2662
Dayton (G-8761)
Youngstown ARC Engraving Co.....E..... 330 793-2471
Youngstown (G-21245)

TYPESETTING SVC: Computer

Henderson Builders Inc.....G..... 419 665-2684
Gibsonburg (G-10377)
Heritage Press Inc.....E..... 419 289-9209
Ashland (G-738)
Plott Graphic Directions Inc.....G..... 614 475-0217
Columbus (G-7500)
Wolters Kluwer Clinical Drug.....D..... 330 650-6506
Hudson (G-11210)

ULTRASONIC EQPT: Cleaning, Exc Med & Dental

Cleaning Tech Group LLC.....C..... 513 870-0100
West Chester (G-19990)
Magnus Engineered Eqp LLC.....E..... 440 942-8488
Willoughby (G-20533)
Smart Sonic Corporation.....G..... 818 610-7900
Cleveland (G-6211)

UMBRELLAS & CANES

Tmb Enterprises LLC.....F..... 419 243-2189
Holland (G-11089)

UNDERCOATINGS: Paint

Kars Ohio LLC.....G..... 614 655-1099
Pataskala (G-15973)

UNIFORM SPLY SVCS: Indl

Cintas Corporation.....A..... 513 459-1200
Cincinnati (G-3577)
Cintas Corporation.....D..... 513 631-5750
Cincinnati (G-3578)
Cintas Corporation No 2.....D..... 330 966-7800
Canton (G-2655)
Cintas Sales Corporation.....B..... 513 459-1200
Cincinnati (G-3579)

UNIFORM STORES

Fechheimer Brothers Company.....C..... 513 793-7819
Blue Ash (G-1792)
K Ventures Inc.....F..... 419 678-2308
Coldwater (G-6566)
Kip-Craft Incorporated.....D..... 216 898-5500
Cleveland (G-5656)

UNISEX HAIR SALONS

Fantastic Sams Hair Care Salon.....G..... 740 456-4296
Portsmouth (G-16435)

Hair & Nail Impressions..................G...... 937 399-0221
Springfield *(G-17567)*

UNIVERSITY

Kent State University......................F...... 330 672-7913
Kent *(G-11481)*

Kent State University......................G...... 330 672-2586
Kent *(G-11482)*

Ohio State University.....................F...... 614 292-6930
Columbus *(G-7434)*

Ohio State University.....................E...... 614 292-7656
Columbus *(G-7431)*

Ohio State University.....................E...... 614 292-4139
Columbus *(G-7432)*

Ohio University.............................C...... 740 593-4010
Athens *(G-880)*

University of Cincinnati.................F...... 513 556-5042
Cincinnati *(G-4543)*

UNSUPPORTED PLASTICS: Floor Or Wall Covering

Koroseal Interior Products LLC.............C...... 330 668-7600
Fairlawn *(G-9755)*

UPHOLSTERY WORK SVCS

Berlin Boat Covers.........................G...... 330 547-7600
Berlin Center *(G-1654)*

Casco Mfg Solutions Inc...................D...... 513 681-0003
Cincinnati *(G-3504)*

Tops Inc..G...... 440 954-9451
Mentor *(G-13749)*

URANIUM ORE MINING, NEC

Centrus Energy Corp........................C...... 740 897-2457
Piketon *(G-16217)*

USED BOOK STORES

Half Price Bks Rec Mgzines Inc............F...... 440 255-2581
Mentor *(G-13599)*

USED CAR DEALERS

Cars and Parts Magazine...................C...... 937 498-0803
Sidney *(G-17171)*

Core Automotive Tech LLC.................G...... 614 870-5000
Columbus *(G-6982)*

Dawn Enterprises Inc.......................E...... 216 642-5506
Cleveland *(G-5172)*

Knippen Chrysler Dodge Jeep.............E...... 419 695-4976
Delphos *(G-8909)*

United Ignition Wire Corp..................G...... 216 898-1112
Cleveland *(G-6385)*

USED MERCHANDISE STORES: Musical Instruments

Fifth Avenue Fret Shop LLC................G...... 614 481-8300
Columbus *(G-7082)*

USED MERCHANDISE STORES: Rare Books

The Bookseller Inc...........................G...... 330 865-5831
Akron *(G-436)*

UTENSILS: Cast Aluminum

Quality Match Plate Co......................F...... 330 889-2462
Southington *(G-17454)*

UTENSILS: Cast Aluminum, Cooking Or Kitchen

Calphalon Corporation......................E...... 419 666-8700
Rossford *(G-16737)*

Range Kleen Mfg Inc.........................B...... 419 331-8000
Elida *(G-9356)*

UTILITY TRAILER DEALERS

Custom Way Welding Inc....................F...... 937 845-9469
New Carlisle *(G-14800)*

Jerry Tadlock.................................G...... 937 544-2851
West Union *(G-20122)*

Lux Corporation..............................G...... 419 562-7978
Bucyrus *(G-2353)*

Mr Trailer Sales Inc..........................G...... 330 339-7701
Dover *(G-9004)*

Navarre Trailer Sales Inc...................G...... 330 879-2406
Navarre *(G-14722)*

OReilly Equipment LLC......................G...... 440 564-1234
Newbury *(G-15101)*

VACUUM CLEANER STORES

ABC Appliance Inc............................E...... 419 693-4414
Oregon *(G-15699)*

Carbonless & Cut Sheet Forms............F...... 740 826-1700
New Concord *(G-14817)*

VACUUM CLEANERS: Household

Edwards Vacuum LLC........................G...... 440 248-4453
Solon *(G-17284)*

GMI Holdings Inc.............................B...... 330 821-5360
Mount Hope *(G-14571)*

H-P Products Inc.............................E...... 330 875-7193
Louisville *(G-12313)*

J K Plastics Co................................G...... 440 632-1482
Middlefield *(G-13944)*

Kirby Sales Company Inc...................B...... 216 228-2400
Cleveland *(G-5657)*

Powerclean Equipment Company.........G...... 513 202-0001
Cleves *(G-6524)*

Rent A Mom Inc...............................F...... 216 901-9599
Seven Hills *(G-17063)*

Scott Fetzer Company.......................B...... 216 228-2403
Cleveland *(G-6169)*

Scott Fetzer Company.......................E...... 216 252-1190
Cleveland *(G-6170)*

Scott Fetzer Company.......................B...... 440 871-2160
Cleveland *(G-6171)*

Scott Fetzer Company.......................C...... 440 439-1616
Cleveland *(G-6172)*

Scott Fetzer Company.......................D...... 216 281-1100
Cleveland *(G-6173)*

Scott Fetzer Company.......................D...... 216 433-7797
Cleveland *(G-6174)*

Scott Fetzer Company.......................E...... 440 871-2160
Avon Lake *(G-1050)*

Scott Fetzer Company.......................E...... 216 228-2400
Chagrin Falls *(G-3119)*

Stanley Steemer Intl Inc....................C...... 614 764-2007
Dublin *(G-9149)*

Western/Scott Fetzer Company...........C...... 440 871-2160
Westlake *(G-20319)*

Western/Scott Fetzer Company...........E...... 440 892-3000
Westlake *(G-20320)*

VACUUM CLEANERS: Indl Type

Dinkmar Inc....................................G...... 419 468-8516
Galion *(G-10263)*

Fimco Services LLC..........................E...... 330 830-1413
Massillon *(G-13132)*

Hi-Vac Corporation..........................G...... 740 374-2306
Marietta *(G-12790)*

Metropolitan Envmtl Svcs Inc.............D...... 614 771-1881
Hilliard *(G-10961)*

VALUE-ADDED RESELLERS: Computer Systems

Quayle Consulting Inc.......................G...... 614 868-1363
Pickerington *(G-16202)*

VALVE REPAIR SVCS, INDL

Aj Fluid Power Sales & Sup Inc............G...... 440 255-7960
Mentor *(G-13514)*

VALVES

Brooks Manufacturing........................G...... 419 244-1777
Toledo *(G-18382)*

Buckeye BOP LLC.............................G...... 740 498-9898
Newcomerstown *(G-15110)*

Michael N Wheeler...........................F...... 740 377-9777
South Point *(G-17442)*

Northcoast Process Contrls Inc............G...... 440 498-0542
Cleveland *(G-5901)*

Oylair Specialty..............................G...... 614 873-3968
Plain City *(G-16353)*

VALVES & PARTS: Gas, Indl

Honeywell International Inc ....A...... 937 484-2000
Urbana *(G-19162)*

VALVES & PIPE FITTINGS

Air Tool Service Company ....F...... 440 701-1021
Mentor *(G-13513)*

Alloy Bllows Prcision Wldg Inc ....D...... 440 684-3000
Cleveland *(G-4767)*

Amaltech Inc...................................G...... 440 248-7500
Solon *(G-17256)*

Auto-Valve Inc.................................E...... 937 854-3037
Dayton *(G-8172)*

Bowes Manufacturing Inc...................F...... 216 378-2110
Solon *(G-17271)*

Calvin J Magsig...............................G...... 419 862-3311
Elmore *(G-9361)*

Crane Pumps & Systems Inc...............B...... 937 773-2442
Piqua *(G-16256)*

Cylinders & Valves Inc......................G...... 440 238-7343
Strongsville *(G-17910)*

Eaton Corporation............................C...... 330 274-0743
Aurora *(G-916)*

Edward W Daniel LLC........................E...... 440 647-1960
Wellington *(G-19742)*

Fcx Performance Inc.........................E...... 614 324-6050
Columbus *(G-7078)*

General Aluminum Mfg Company...........C...... 419 739-9300
Wapakoneta *(G-19487)*

H P E Inc.......................................F...... 330 833-3161
Massillon *(G-13145)*

Hydro-Aire Inc.................................C...... 440 323-3211
Elyria *(G-9431)*

Iii Williams LLC................................G...... 440 721-8191
Chardon *(G-3158)*

Impaction Co...................................G...... 440 349-5652
Solon *(G-17313)*

Kirtland Capital Partners LP ....E...... 216 593-0100
Beachwood *(G-1276)*

Lsq Manufacturing Inc......................F...... 330 725-4905
Medina *(G-13437)*

Machine Component Mfg.....................F...... 330 454-4566
Canton *(G-2765)*

Mack Iron Works Company..................E...... 419 626-3712
Sandusky *(G-16984)*

Northcoast Valve and Gate Inc............G...... 440 392-9910
Mentor *(G-13669)*

Nupro Company...............................C...... 440 951-9729
Willoughby *(G-20559)*

O E M Hydraulics Inc.........................G...... 740 454-1201
Zanesville *(G-21335)*

Oceco Inc.......................................F...... 419 447-0916
Tiffin *(G-18235)*

Opw Engineered Systems Inc..............D...... 888 771-9438
Lebanon *(G-11824)*

Parker-Hannifin Corporation...............C...... 216 531-3000
Cleveland *(G-5974)*

Piersante and Associates...................G...... 330 533-9904
Canfield *(G-2569)*

Precision Fittings LLC........................E...... 440 647-4143
Wellington *(G-19752)*

Robbins & Myers Inc.........................B...... 937 327-3111
Springfield *(G-17642)*

Robeck Fluid Power Co.......................D...... 330 562-1140
Aurora *(G-944)*

Ruthman Pump and Engineering ....E...... 937 783-2411
Blanchester *(G-1716)*

Simplex Time Recorder LLC.................D...... 419 861-0661
Maumee *(G-13293)*

Stelter and Brinck Inc.......................E...... 513 367-9300
Harrison *(G-10805)*

Stephens Pipe & Steel LLC.................C...... 740 869-2257
Mount Sterling *(G-14604)*

Superior Holding LLC.........................G...... 216 651-9400
Cleveland *(G-6265)*

Superior Products LLC........................D...... 216 651-9400
Cleveland *(G-6270)*

Superior Products Llc........................D...... 216 651-9400
Cleveland *(G-6269)*

Swagelok..G...... 440 349-5657
Solon *(G-17389)*

Swagelok Company............................E...... 440 944-8988
Willoughby Hills *(G-20645)*

Swagelok Company............................E...... 440 473-1050
Cleveland *(G-6278)*

Swagelok Company............................F...... 440 442-6611
Cleveland *(G-6277)*

Swagelok Company............................D...... 440 349-5934
Solon *(G-17392)*

Tech Tool Inc..................................F...... 330 674-1176
Millersburg *(G-14267)*

Thogus Products Company...................D...... 440 933-8850
Avon Lake *(G-1053)*

Employee Codes: A=Over 500 employees, B=251-500
C=101-250, D=51-100, E=20-50, F=10-19, G=3-9

2017 Harris Ohio
Industrial Directory

1687

PRODUCT

VALVES & PIPE FITTINGS

Tylok International Inc ....D...... 216 261-7310
Cleveland (G-6377)
Waxman Industries Inc ....C...... 440 439-1830
Cleveland (G-6452)
William Powell Company ....E...... 513 852-2000
Cincinnati (G-4596)
Zeiger Industries ....E...... 330 484-4413
Canton (G-2906)

VALVES & REGULATORS: Pressure, Indl

Manico Inc ....G...... 440 946-5333
Willoughby (G-20534)
Rogers Industrial Products Inc ....E...... 330 535-3331
Akron (G-378)
Swagelok Company ....D...... 440 248-4600
Willoughby Hills (G-20644)
Swagelok Company ....A...... 440 248-4600
Solon (G-17390)
Swagelok Company ....D...... 440 349-5652
Solon (G-17391)
Swagelok Company ....E...... 440 349-5836
Solon (G-17393)
Tylok International Inc ....D...... 216 261-7310
Cleveland (G-6377)
William Powell Company ....E...... 513 852-2000
Cincinnati (G-4596)

VALVES: Aerosol, Metal

Accurate Mechanical Inc ....E...... 740 654-5898
Lancaster (G-11683)
Deltec Incorporated ....E...... 513 732-0800
Batavia (G-1177)
Humble Construction Co ....E...... 614 888-8960
Columbus (G-7169)
J Feldkamp Design Build Ltd ....E...... 513 870-0601
Fairfield (G-9670)
Mab Fabrication Inc ....G...... 855 622-3221
Harrison (G-10788)
Mk Trempe Corporation ....E...... 937 492-3548
Sidney (G-17204)
North American Steel Company ....E...... 216 475-7300
Cleveland (G-5890)
Titan Metal Fabricators ....F...... 513 755-3394
Liberty Township (G-11969)
Tosoh SMD Inc ....G...... 614 875-7912
Grove City (G-10605)
Tosoh SMD Inc ....C...... 614 875-7912
Grove City (G-10606)

VALVES: Aircraft

Manufacturing Division Inc ....G...... 330 533-6835
Canfield (G-2564)

VALVES: Aircraft, Fluid Power

Taiyo America Inc ....F...... 419 300-8811
Saint Marys (G-16858)

VALVES: Aircraft, Hydraulic

Aerocontrolex Group Inc ....D...... 440 352-6182
Cleveland (G-4719)
Parker-Hannifin Corporation ....C...... 419 542-6611
Hicksville (G-10905)
Valvole America LLC ....G...... 330 464-8872
Medina (G-13495)

VALVES: Control, Automatic

Flow Technology Inc ....C...... 513 745-6000
Cincinnati (G-3764)
Precision Q Systems LLC ....G...... 614 286-5142
Westerville (G-20229)

VALVES: Engine

Eaton Usev Holding Company ....G...... 216 523-5000
Cleveland (G-5253)

VALVES: Fluid Power, Control, Hydraulic & pneumatic

Aj Fluid Power Sales & Sup Inc ....G...... 440 255-7960
Mentor (G-13514)
Cfrc Wtr & Enrgy Solutions Inc ....G...... 216 479-0290
Cleveland (G-5011)
Dana Incorporated ....B...... 419 887-3000
Maumee (G-13246)
Dana Limited ....B...... 630 697-3783
Maumee (G-13249)

DNC Hydraulics LLC ....F...... 419 963-2800
Rawson (G-16573)
Hy-Production Inc ....C...... 330 273-2400
Valley City (G-19206)
National Aviation Products Inc ....D...... 330 688-6494
Stow (G-17779)
National Machine Company ....C...... 330 688-6494
Stow (G-17780)
Parker-Hannifin Corporation ....B...... 440 366-5100
Elyria (G-9475)
Parker-Hannifin Corporation ....B...... 216 896-3000
Cleveland (G-5973)
Parker-Hannifin Corporation ....F...... 216 896-3000
Cleveland (G-5976)
Ruthman Pump and Engineering ....G...... 513 559-1901
Cincinnati (G-4369)
SMC Corporation of America ....E...... 330 659-2006
Richfield (G-16638)
Valv-Trol Company ....F...... 330 686-2800
Stow (G-17814)
Valveco Inc ....D...... 330 337-9535
Salem (G-16933)

VALVES: Hard Rubber

Vertex Inc ....E...... 330 628-6230
Mogadore (G-14387)

VALVES: Indl

Alkon Corporation ....E...... 614 799-6650
Dublin (G-9039)
Bosch Rexroth Corporation ....B...... 330 263-3300
Wooster (G-20751)
Canfield Industries Inc ....G...... 800 554-5071
Youngstown (G-21042)
Clark-Reliance Corporation ....G...... 440 572-7408
Strongsville (G-17903)
Cleveland Valve & Gauge Co LLC ....G...... 216 362-1702
Cleveland (G-5084)
Curtiss-Wright Flow Control ....D...... 513 735-2538
Batavia (G-1175)
Curtiss-Wright Flow Control ....D...... 513 528-7900
Cincinnati (G-3296)
Curtiss-Wright Flow Control ....D...... 513 528-7900
Cincinnati (G-3297)
Dayton Air Control Pdts LLC ....G...... 937 254-4441
Moraine (G-14476)
Emerson Network Power System ....G...... 614 841-6309
Westerville (G-20150)
Kaman Industrial Tech Corp ....G...... 740 779-9201
Chillicothe (G-3248)
Keen Manufacturing Inc ....G...... 330 427-0045
Washingtonville (G-19642)
Maass Midwest Mfg Inc ....G...... 419 894-6424
Arcadia (G-654)
Machine Component Mfg ....F...... 330 454-4566
Canton (G-2765)
Nupro Company ....C...... 440 951-9729
Willoughby (G-20559)
Parker-Hannifin Corporation ....C...... 419 542-6611
Hicksville (G-10905)
Parker-Hannifin Corporation ....C...... 937 644-3915
Marysville (G-12962)
Phoenix Partners LLC ....E...... 734 654-2201
Ottawa Hills (G-15817)
Richards Industries Inc ....C...... 513 533-7340
Cincinnati (G-4344)
Russments Inc ....G...... 513 602-5035
Cincinnati (G-4368)
Ruthman Pump and Engineering ....E...... 937 783-2411
Blanchester (G-1716)
Seawin Inc ....D...... 419 355-9111
Fremont (G-10182)
Shan-Rod Inc ....E...... 419 588-2066
Berlin Heights (G-1663)
Transdigm Inc ....G...... 216 706-2939
Cleveland (G-6347)
Vickers International Inc ....E...... 419 867-2200
Maumee (G-13307)
Waxman Industries Inc ....C...... 440 439-1830
Cleveland (G-6452)
Xomox Corporation ....E...... 513 947-1200
Batavia (G-1235)

VALVES: Nuclear Power Plant, Ferrous

Alkon Corporation ....D...... 419 355-9111
Fremont (G-10124)

VALVES: Plumbing & Heating

Xomox Corporation ....E...... 936 271-6500
Cincinnati (G-4614)

VALVES: Regulating & Control, Automatic

Fisher Controls Intl LLC ....G...... 513 285-6000
West Chester (G-19864)
Hunt Valve Company Inc ....E...... 330 337-9535
Salem (G-16901)
Hunt Valve Company Inc ....E...... 330 337-9535
Salem (G-16902)
Sherwood Valve LLC ....D...... 216 264-5028
Cleveland (G-6194)
Viking Group Inc ....G...... 937 443-0433
Dayton (G-8743)

VALVES: Regulating, Process Control

Akron Steel Fabricators Co ....E...... 330 644-0616
Akron (G-57)
Clark-Reliance Corporation ....C...... 440 572-1500
Strongsville (G-17902)
Digital Automation Associates ....G...... 419 352-6977
Bowling Green (G-1986)
Hearth Products Controls Co ....F...... 937 436-9800
Dayton (G-8108)
Xomox Corporation ....G...... 513 745-6000
Blue Ash (G-1903)

VALVES: Water Works

Zal Air Products Inc ....G...... 440 237-7155
Cleveland (G-6492)

VAN CONVERSIONS

Key Mobility Services Ltd ....G...... 937 374-3226
Xenia (G-20959)
Mobile Conversions Inc ....F...... 513 797-1991
Amelia (G-580)
National Fleet Svcs Ohio LLC ....F...... 440 930-5177
Avon Lake (G-1041)
Steves Vans & Accessories LLC ....G...... 740 374-3154
Marietta (G-12836)

VANADIUM ORE MINING, NEC

AMG Vanadium LLC ....G...... 740 435-4600
Cambridge (G-2444)

VARIETY STORES

Dolgencorp LLC ....G...... 740 289-4790
Piketon (G-16219)
Wagoner Stores Inc ....G...... 937 836-3636
Englewood (G-9544)

VARNISHES, NEC

David E Easterday and Co Inc ....F...... 330 359-0700
Wilmot (G-20685)
Superior Printing Ink Co Inc ....G...... 216 328-1720
Cleveland (G-6268)

VASES: Pottery

Annies Mud Pie Shop LLC ....G...... 513 871-2529
Cincinnati (G-3405)

VAULTS & SAFES WHOLESALERS

National Security Products ....G...... 216 566-9962
Cleveland (G-5860)

VEHICLES: All Terrain

All Power Equipment LLC ....F...... 740 593-3279
Athens (G-855)
Branham Motorsports LLC ....G...... 937 428-6040
Dayton (G-8193)
Kolpin Outdoors Corporation ....G...... 330 328-0772
Cuyahoga Falls (G-8018)
Polaris Industries Inc ....E...... 937 283-1200
Wilmington (G-20673)
Premier Uv Products LLC ....G...... 330 715-2452
Cuyahoga Falls (G-8035)
Wholecycle Inc ....E...... 330 929-8123
Peninsula (G-16045)

VEHICLES: Recreational

Aerodynamic Systems ....G...... 440 463-8820
Chagrin Falls (G-3076)

Kedar D Army ....G....... 419 238-6929
Van Wert (G-19262)
R V Spa LLC ....G....... 440 284-4800
Elyria (G-9482)
Rv Xpress Inc ....G....... 937 418-0127
Piqua (G-16312)
Thor Industries Inc ....E....... 937 596-6111
Jackson Center (G-11349)

VENDING MACHINE OPERATORS: Cigarette

Priority Vending Inc ....G....... 216 361-4100
Cleveland (G-6050)

VENDING MACHINE OPERATORS: Sandwich & Hot Food

Sanese Services Inc ....E....... 330 494-5900
Warren (G-19597)

VENDING MACHINES & PARTS

AVI Food Systems Inc ....E....... 513 860-4191
Fairfield (G-9644)
AVI Food Systems Inc ....E....... 440 327-1944
North Ridgeville (G-15358)
Giant Industries Inc ....E....... 419 531-4600
Toledo (G-18480)
Innovative Vend Solutions LLC ....E....... 866 931-9413
Dayton (G-8407)
Michele Mellen ....G....... 740 369-1422
Powell (G-16478)
Reeces Las Vegas Supplies ....G....... 937 274-5000
Dayton (G-8620)
Tranzonic Companies ....B....... 216 535-4300
Richmond Heights (G-16657)
Ve Global Vending Inc ....F....... 216 785-2611
Cleveland (G-6409)

VENETIAN BLIND REPAIR SHOP

Miles Pk Vntian Blind Shds Mfg ....G....... 216 239-0850
Beachwood (G-1279)

VENETIAN BLINDS & SHADES

Miles Pk Vntian Blind Shds Mfg ....G....... 216 239-0850
Beachwood (G-1279)
Shade Youngstown & Aluminum Co .....G....... 330 782-2373
Youngstown (G-21200)

VENTILATING EQPT: Metal

Famous Industries Inc ....E....... 330 535-1811
Akron (G-181)

VENTILATING EQPT: Sheet Metal

L C Systems Inc ....G....... 614 235-9430
Dublin (G-9098)
Thermo Vent Manufacturing Inc ....F....... 330 239-0239
Medina (G-13487)

VENTURE CAPITAL COMPANIES

Linsalata Capital Partners Fun ....G....... 440 684-1400
Cleveland (G-5703)
Victoria Ventures Inc ....G....... 330 793-9321
Youngstown (G-21239)

VESSELS: Process, Indl, Metal Plate

AT&f Advanced Metals LLC ....E....... 330 684-1122
Cleveland (G-4851)
Columbiana Boiler Company LLC ....E....... 330 482-3373
Columbiana (G-6612)
Columbiana Holding Co Inc ....E....... 330 482-3373
Columbiana (G-6613)

VETERINARY PHARMACEUTICAL PREPARATIONS

Berlin Industries Inc ....F....... 330 549-2100
North Lima (G-15310)
Scicompro - LLC ....G....... 513 680-8686
Mason (G-13086)

VETERINARY PRDTS: Instruments & Apparatus

Rockdale Systems LLC ....G....... 513 379-3577
Cincinnati (G-4355)

Suarez Corporation Industries ....E....... 330 494-4282
Canton (G-2861)

VIBRATORS, ELECTRIC: Beauty & Barber Shop

HK Technologies ....G....... 330 337-9710
Cleveland (G-5515)

VIBRATORS: Concrete Construction

Minnich Manufacturing Co Inc ....E....... 419 903-0010
Mansfield (G-12649)

VIBRATORS: Interrupter

Karrier Company Inc ....G....... 330 823-9597
Alliance (G-520)

VIDEO & AUDIO EQPT, WHOLESALE

Dayton Audio LLC ....G....... 937 743-3000
Springboro (G-17478)
Technical Artistry Inc ....G....... 614 299-7777
Columbus (G-7684)

VIDEO CAMERA-AUDIO RECORDERS: Household Use

Array Telepresence Inc ....G....... 800 779-7480
West Chester (G-19809)

VIDEO TAPE PRODUCTION SVCS

Master Communications Inc ....G....... 208 821-3473
Blue Ash (G-1833)
World Harvest Church Inc ....C....... 614 837-1990
Canal Winchester (G-2542)

VIDEO TRIGGERS EXC REMOTE CONTROL TV DEVICES

Ops Wireless ....G....... 419 396-4041
Carey (G-2923)

VIDEO TRIGGERS: Remote Control TV Devices

Universal Electronics Inc ....D....... 330 487-1110
Twinsburg (G-19032)

VINYL RESINS, NEC

BCi and V Investments Inc ....D....... 330 538-0660
North Jackson (G-15287)
Polyone Corporation ....D....... 440 933-2000
Avon Lake (G-1046)
Polyone Corporation ....D....... 440 930-1000
North Baltimore (G-15197)

VISES: Machine

Bee Jax Inc ....G....... 330 373-0500
Warren (G-19527)

VISUAL COMMUNICATIONS SYSTEMS

Findaway World LLC ....D....... 440 893-0808
Solon (G-17292)

VITAMINS: Pharmaceutical Preparations

Eyescience Labs LLC ....G....... 614 885-7100
Powell (G-16471)
Libido Edge Labs LLC ....G....... 740 344-1401
Newark (G-15030)
Vitamin Shoppe Inc ....E....... 440 238-5987
Strongsville (G-17980)

VOCATIONAL REHABILITATION AGENCY

Quadco Rehabilitation Center ....B....... 419 682-1011
Stryker (G-18006)
Quadco Rehabilitation Center ....D....... 419 445-1950
Archbold (G-691)

VOCATIONAL TRAINING AGENCY

Hard Chrome Plating Consultant ....G....... 216 631-9090
Cleveland (G-5480)
Jeffco Sheltered Workshop ....E....... 740 264-4608
Steubenville (G-17701)

WALL COVERINGS: Rubber

Koroseal Interior Products LLC ....C....... 330 668-7600
Fairlawn (G-9755)

WALLPAPER & WALL COVERINGS

4 Walls Com LLC ....F....... 216 432-1400
Cleveland (G-4666)
Wolff House Art Papers Inc ....G....... 740 501-3766
Mount Vernon (G-14656)

WALLS: Curtain, Metal

Midwest Curtainwalls Inc ....D....... 216 641-7900
Cleveland (G-5809)
Wt Acquisition Company Ltd ....E....... 513 577-7980
Cincinnati (G-4610)
YKK AP America Inc ....F....... 513 942-7200
West Chester (G-20071)

WAREHOUSING & STORAGE FACILITIES, NEC

Comprehensive Logistics Co Inc ....E....... 330 793-0504
Youngstown (G-21055)
Contract Pckg Dist Specialists ....F....... 513 942-0300
West Chester (G-19993)
Kuhlman Corporation ....E....... 419 897-6000
Maumee (G-13273)
Lefco Worthington LLC ....E....... 216 432-4422
Cleveland (G-5691)
Littlern Corporation ....G....... 330 848-8847
Barberton (G-1124)
Route 14 Storage Inc ....G....... 330 296-0084
Ravenna (G-16553)
SH Bell Company ....F....... 412 963-9910
East Liverpool (G-9227)
Vista Industrial Packaging LLC ....D....... 800 454-6117
Columbus (G-7743)

WAREHOUSING & STORAGE, REFRIGERATED: Cold Storage Or Refrig

Youngs Locker Service Inc ....F....... 740 599-6833
Danville (G-8093)

WAREHOUSING & STORAGE, REFRIGERATED: Frozen Or Refrig Goods

Oiler Processing ....G....... 740 892-2640
Utica (G-19195)
Pettisville Meats Inc ....F....... 419 445-0921
Pettisville (G-16183)

WAREHOUSING & STORAGE: Farm Prdts

Growmark Fs LLC ....F....... 330 386-7626
East Liverpool (G-9216)
JJ Delong & Associates Inc ....G....... 216 861-4727
Cleveland (G-5616)

WAREHOUSING & STORAGE: General

Aero Fulfillment Services Corp ....D....... 800 225-7145
Mason (G-12979)
Efco Corp ....E....... 614 876-1226
Columbus (G-7048)
G & J Pepsi-Cola Bottlers Inc ....D....... 740 593-3366
Athens (G-867)
Klosterman Baking Co ....F....... 513 398-2707
Mason (G-13053)
Ohio Valley Alloy Services Inc ....E....... 740 373-1900
Marietta (G-12811)
Service Iron & Steel Company ....G....... 330 253-9147
Akron (G-399)
Sumitomo Rubber Usa LLC ....E....... 419 347-1067
Shelby (G-17144)

WAREHOUSING & STORAGE: General

Alegre Inc ....F....... 937 885-6786
Miamisburg (G-13782)
Atotech USA Inc ....D....... 216 398-0550
Cleveland (G-4857)
Ccw Group Pacesetter Inc ....C....... 740 474-0122
Circleville (G-4624)
Cooper Tire Vhcl Test Ctr Inc ....E....... 419 423-1321
Findlay (G-9814)
Dayton Bag & Burlap Co ....F....... 937 253-1722
Dayton (G-8268)
Fuchs Lubricants Co ....E....... 330 963-0400
Twinsburg (G-18938)

Employee Codes: A=Over 500 employees, B=251-500
C=101-250, D=51-100, E=20-50, F=10-19, G=3-9

2017 Harris Ohio
Industrial Directory

PRODUCT

1689

WAREHOUSING & STORAGE: General (cont'd)

Growmark Fs LLC ....F 330 386-7626
East Liverpool (G-9216)

Ingersoll-Rand Company ....E 419 633-6800
Bryan (G-2306)

Malleys Candies Inc ....E 216 529-6262
Cleveland (G-5736)

Michigan Sugar Company ....G 419 423-1666
Findlay (G-9860)

P-Americas LLC ....C 330 746-7652
Youngstown (G-21161)

Parker-Hannifin Corporation ....A 216 531-3000
Cleveland (G-5975)

SH Bell Company ....E 412 963-9910
East Liverpool (G-9227)

The Euclid Chemical Company ....F 216 531-9222
Cleveland (G-6311)

Tmarzetti Company ....C 614 277-3577
Grove City (G-10602)

Vectra Inc ....F 614 351-6868
Columbus (G-7733)

Victory White Metal Company ....E 216 271-7200
Cleveland (G-6418)

WAREHOUSING & STORAGE: Self Storage

Cusc International Ltd ....G 513 881-2000
Hamilton (G-10682)

John D Oil and Gas Company ....G 440 255-6325
Mentor (G-13620)

McMillion Lock & Key ....G 937 473-5342
Covington (G-7926)

WARM AIR HEATING & AC EQPT & SPLYS, WHOLESALE Air Filters

Cincinnati A Flter Sls Svc Inc ....E 513 242-3400
Cincinnati (G-3536)

Swift Filters Inc ....E 440 735-0995
Oakwood Village (G-15628)

WARM AIR HEATING & AC EQPT & SPLYS, WHOLESALE Furnaces, Elec

Bcast Stainless Products LLC ....F 614 873-3945
Plain City (G-16325)

WARM AIR HEATING/AC EQPT/SPLYS, WHOL Warm Air Htg Eqpt/Splys

Air-Rite Inc ....E 216 228-8200
Cleveland (G-4735)

Anson Co ....G 216 524-8838
Bedford (G-1397)

Shape Supply Inc ....G 513 863-6695
Hamilton (G-10738)

Wood Stove Shed ....G 419 562-1545
Bucyrus (G-2365)

WASHERS

Buck Eye Pressure Wash ....G 419 385-9274
Toledo (G-18384)

Die-Cut Products Co ....E 216 771-6994
Cleveland (G-5193)

Pressure Washer Mfrs Assn ....G 216 241-7333
Cleveland (G-6045)

Pro Roof Washers ....G 440 521-2622
Cleveland (G-6051)

WASHERS: Metal

Andre Corporation ....E 574 293-0207
Mason (G-12981)

Atlas Bolt & Screw Company LLC ....C 419 289-6171
Ashland (G-709)

Master Products Company ....D 216 341-1740
Cleveland (G-5760)

WASHERS: Rubber

Clearly Visible Mobile Wash ....G 440 543-9299
Chagrin Falls (G-3080)

Die-Cut Products Co ....E 216 771-6994
Cleveland (G-5193)

WASHERS: Spring, Metal

Connell Limited Partnership ....D 877 534-8986
Northfield (G-15464)

Solon Manufacturing Company ....E 440 286-7149
Chardon (G-3180)

WATCH & CLOCK STORES

Quality Gold Inc ....B 513 942-7659
Fairfield (G-9706)

WATCH REPAIR SVCS

White Jewelers ....G 330 264-3324
Wooster (G-20848)

WATER BOTTLES: Rubber

Manufacturers Representatives ....G 513 467-6669
West Chester (G-20024)

WATER HEATERS

RAD Technologies Incorporated ....F 513 641-0523
Cincinnati (G-4328)

U S Thermal Inc ....G 513 777-7763
West Chester (G-19966)

WATER PURIFICATION EQPT: Household

CST Zero Discharged Car Wash S ....G 740 947-5480
Waverly (G-19706)

De Nora Holdings Us Inc ....B 440 710-5300
Painesville (G-15873)

Evoqua Water Technologies LLC ....E 614 491-4000
Groveport (G-10620)

R D Baker Enterprises Inc ....G 937 461-5225
Dayton (G-8609)

WATER PURIFICATION PRDTS: Chlorination Tablets & Kits

Clearwater One LLC ....F 216 554-4747
Cleveland (G-5046)

West-Ward Pharmaceuticals Corp ....G 614 276-4000
Columbus (G-7758)

WATER SOFTENER SVCS

Delta Control Inc ....G 937 277-3444
Dayton (G-8297)

US Water Company LLC ....G 740 453-0604
Zanesville (G-21360)

WATER SOFTENING WHOLESALERS

R D Baker Enterprises Inc ....G 937 461-5225
Dayton (G-8609)

WATER SPLY: Irrigation

ATI Irrigation LLC ....G 937 750-2976
Troy (G-18806)

WATER SUPPLY

American Water Services Inc ....G 440 243-9840
Strongsville (G-17887)

Aqua Pennsylvania Inc ....G 440 257-6190
Mentor On The Lake (G-13773)

City of Athens ....E 740 592-3344
Athens (G-858)

City of Middletown ....F 513 425-7781
Middletown (G-14030)

City of Troy ....F 937 339-4826
Troy (G-18809)

Greene County ....G 937 429-0127
Dayton (G-8107)

Samco Technologies Inc ....G 216 641-5288
Newburgh Heights (G-15079)

Victory White Metal Company ....E 216 271-7200
Cleveland (G-6418)

WATER TREATMENT EQPT: Indl

Ameriwater LLC ....E 937 461-8833
Dayton (G-8157)

Aqua Pennsylvania Inc ....G 440 257-6190
Mentor On The Lake (G-13773)

Buckeye Field Supply Ltd ....G 513 312-2343
Cincinnati (G-3484)

City of Athens ....E 740 592-3344
Athens (G-858)

City of Marietta ....E 740 374-6864
Marietta (G-12774)

City of Middletown ....F 513 425-7781
Middletown (G-14030)

City of Xenia ....E 937 376-7269
Xenia (G-20943)

Clearwater Systems Inc ....F 330 262-5515
Wooster (G-20758)

Coldwell Wilcox Tech LLC ....G 513 758-1010
Cincinnati (G-3596)

County of Lake ....F 440 428-1794
Madison (G-12502)

Eps Wastewater LLC ....G 859 689-4300
Milford (G-14139)

Hempy Water Conditioning Inc ....G 419 273-2531
Forest (G-9921)

Hempy Water Conditioning Inc ....G 419 448-8885
Tiffin (G-18222)

Hempy Water Conditioning Inc ....G 419 529-4002
Ontario (G-15688)

J & K Wade Ltd ....G 419 352-6163
Bowling Green (G-1992)

K S W C Inc ....G 440 577-1114
Pierpont (G-16212)

Kinetico Incorporated ....E 440 564-7167
Newbury (G-15098)

Larrys Water Conditioning ....G 419 887-0290
Maumee (G-13275)

Layne Heavy Civil Inc ....E 513 424-7287
Middletown (G-14053)

Mt Vernon Cy Wastewater Trtmnt ....F 740 393-9502
Mount Vernon (G-14633)

N-Viro International Corp ....F 419 535-6374
Toledo (G-18597)

Neil Barton ....G 614 889-9933
Dublin (G-9111)

Norwalk Wastewater Eqp Co ....E 419 668-4471
Norwalk (G-15558)

Reynolds & Co Inc ....G 937 592-8300
Bellefontaine (G-1538)

Samco Technologies Inc ....G 216 641-5288
Newburgh Heights (G-15079)

The Mahoning Valley Sani Dst ....D 330 799-6315
Mineral Ridge (G-14312)

Tipton Environmental Intl Inc ....F 513 735-2777
Batavia (G-1228)

Trionetics Inc ....G 216 812-3570
Brooklyn Heights (G-2148)

Under Pressure Systems Inc ....G 330 602-4466
New Philadelphia (G-14938)

Veolia Water Technologies Inc ....D 937 890-4075
Vandalia (G-19316)

Waste Water Pollution Control ....F 330 263-5290
Wooster (G-20844)

Water Poll Control ....E 740 383-4446
Marion (G-12912)

Water Treatment Dept ....G 937 498-8180
Sidney (G-17234)

Western Rserve Wtr Systems Inc ....D 216 341-9797
Newburgh Heights (G-15080)

William R Hague Inc ....D 614 836-2115
Groveport (G-10649)

Willow Water Treatment Inc ....G 440 254-6313
Painesville (G-15942)

WATER: Distilled

Distillata Company ....D 216 771-2900
Cleveland (G-5197)

Rambasek Realty Inc ....F 937 228-1189
Dayton (G-8616)

WATER: Mineral, Carbonated, Canned & Bottled, Etc

Diverse Acquisitions Group LLC ....F 888 232-1546
Centerville (G-3040)

WATER: Pasteurized & Mineral, Bottled & Canned

Natural Country Farms Inc ....G 330 753-2293
Akron (G-311)

Your Bottled Water LLC ....G 740 443-6079
Piketon (G-16230)

WATERPROOFING COMPOUNDS

Republic Powdered Metals Inc ....D 330 225-3192
Medina (G-13467)

RPM International Inc ....D 330 273-5090
Medina (G-13471)

Truco Inc ....B 216 631-1000
Cleveland (G-6370)

(G-0000) Company's Geographic Section entry number

WEATHER STRIP: Sponge Rubber

Canton OH Rubber Speclty Prods.........G....... 330 454-3847
Canton *(G-2642)*

WEATHER STRIPS: Metal

M-D Building Products Inc...................B....... 513 539-2255
Middletown *(G-14057)*

WEIGHING MACHINERY & APPARATUS

Advance Weight System Inc ....F....... 440 926-3691
Grafton *(G-10418)*
Hobart Corporation..............................E....... 937 332-3000
Troy *(G-18840)*
Hobart Corporation..............................C....... 937 332-2797
Piqua *(G-16277)*

WELDING & CUTTING APPARATUS & ACCESS, NEC

Accurate Machining & Welding ....G....... 937 584-4518
Sabina *(G-16772)*
Airgas...G....... 330 345-1257
Wooster *(G-20732)*
Buckeye State Welding & Fabg ....E....... 440 322-0344
Elyria *(G-9385)*
Firelands Manufacturing LLC ....F....... 419 687-8237
Plymouth *(G-16376)*
J T E Corp ....G....... 937 454-1112
Dayton *(G-8418)*
Lima Equipment Co ....G....... 419 222-4181
Lima *(G-12040)*
Luvata Ohio Inc ....D....... 740 363-1981
Delaware *(G-8870)*
M B Industries Inc ....G....... 419 738-4769
Wapakoneta *(G-19496)*
Miller Weldmaster Corporation..........D....... 330 833-6739
Navarre *(G-14719)*
O E Meyer Co ....G....... 419 332-6931
Fremont *(G-10171)*
Otto Konigslow Mfg Co ....F....... 216 851-7900
Cleveland *(G-5952)*
Postle Industries Inc ....E....... 216 265-9000
Cleveland *(G-6022)*
PWS Welding & Mtg ....F....... 330 385-6922
East Liverpool *(G-9226)*
Quality Components Inc........................F....... 440 255-0606
Mentor *(G-13706)*
Weld-Action Company Inc ....G....... 330 372-1063
Warren *(G-19626)*

WELDING EQPT

Accurate Manufacturing Company ....E....... 614 878-6510
Columbus *(G-6685)*
Aerowave Inc..G....... 440 731-8464
North Ridgeville *(G-15355)*
AK Fabrication Inc ....F....... 330 458-1037
Canton *(G-2595)*
American Weldquip Inc ....F....... 330 239-0317
Sharon Center *(G-17100)*
Campbell Hausfeld LLC ....C....... 513 367-4811
Harrison *(G-10770)*
Dennis Corso Co Inc............................G....... 330 673-2411
Kent *(G-11448)*
Fusion Incorporated ....E....... 440 946-3300
Willoughby *(G-20495)*
Halls Welding & Supplies Inc..............G....... 330 385-9353
East Liverpool *(G-9217)*
Hobart Brothers Company ....A....... 937 332-5439
Troy *(G-18836)*
Hobart Brothers Company ....F....... 937 773-5869
Piqua *(G-16276)*
Hobart Brothers Company ....G....... 937 332-5338
Troy *(G-18837)*
Hobart Brothers Company ....G....... 937 332-5023
Troy *(G-18838)*
Imax Industries Inc ....F....... 440 639-0242
Painesville *(G-15889)*
Lincoln Electric Company ....F....... 216 481-8100
Cleveland *(G-5697)*
Lincoln Electric Holdings Inc..............C....... 216 481-8100
Cleveland *(G-5698)*
Lincoln Electric Intl Holdg Co ....E....... 216 481-8100
Euclid *(G-9590)*
Nelson Stud Welding Inc ....B....... 440 329-0400
Elyria *(G-9467)*
Owen & Sons...G....... 513 726-5406
Seven Mile *(G-17066)*

Peco Holdings Corp...............................F....... 937 667-4451
Tipp City *(G-18292)*
Polymet Corporation.............................E....... 513 874-3586
West Chester *(G-20038)*
Process Development Corp ....E....... 937 890-3388
Dayton *(G-8597)*
Process Equipment Co Tipp City ....D....... 937 667-7105
Tipp City *(G-18294)*
Select-Arc Inc ....C....... 937 295-5215
Fort Loramie *(G-9938)*
Semtorq Inc ....F....... 330 487-0600
Twinsburg *(G-19019)*
Sherbrooke Metals ....E....... 440 942-3520
Willoughby *(G-20596)*
Spiegelberg Manufacturing Inc ....E....... 440 324-3042
Strongsville *(G-17970)*
Stryver Mfg Inc ....E....... 937 854-3048
Trotwood *(G-18799)*
Taylor - Winfield Corporation ....D....... 330 259-8500
Hubbard *(G-11140)*
Taylor-Winfield Tech Inc ....E....... 330 259-8500
Youngstown *(G-21218)*
Tokin America Corporation ....G....... 513 644-9743
West Chester *(G-19959)*
Westside Supply Co Inc ....E....... 216 267-9353
Brookpark *(G-2172)*
Wiederhold Wldg & Fabrication ....E....... 513 875-3755
Fayetteville *(G-9785)*
Wonder Weld Inc ....G....... 614 875-1447
Orient *(G-15726)*

WELDING EQPT & SPLYS WHOLESALERS

Airgas Usa LLC ....F....... 419 228-2828
Lima *(G-11983)*
Airgas Usa LLC ....G....... 440 232-6397
Oakwood Village *(G-15622)*
Airgas USA LLC ....E....... 937 228-8594
Dayton *(G-8142)*
Airgas USA LLC ....G....... 419 726-2719
Toledo *(G-18325)*
Bickett Machine and Supply Inc ....G....... 740 353-5710
Portsmouth *(G-16431)*
Delille Oxygen Company ....G....... 937 325-9595
Springfield *(G-17541)*
Halls Welding & Supplies Inc..............G....... 330 385-9353
East Liverpool *(G-9217)*
Jerrys Welding Supply Inc ....G....... 937 364-1500
Hillsboro *(G-11006)*
Lefeld Welding & Stl Sups Inc ....E....... 419 678-2397
Coldwater *(G-6567)*
Matheson Tri-Gas Inc ....E....... 513 727-9638
Middletown *(G-14060)*
Matheson Tri-Gas Inc ....F....... 330 425-4407
Twinsburg *(G-18979)*
Matheson Tri-Gas Inc ....F....... 419 865-8881
Holland *(G-11071)*
Praxair Distribution Inc ....G....... 419 422-1353
Lima *(G-12072)*
Praxair Distribution Inc ....G....... 513 821-2192
Cincinnati *(G-4263)*
Praxair Distribution Inc ....G....... 937 283-3400
Wilmington *(G-20674)*
Praxair Distribution Inc ....G....... 419 221-0517
Lima *(G-12073)*
Salem Welding & Supply Company ....G....... 330 332-4517
Salem *(G-16925)*
Sausser Steel Company Inc ....F....... 419 422-9632
Findlay *(G-9888)*
T & D Fabricating Inc ....G....... 440 951-5646
Eastlake *(G-9292)*
Weld-Action Company Inc ....G....... 330 372-1063
Warren *(G-19626)*
Welders Supply Inc ....F....... 216 241-1696
Cleveland *(G-6456)*
Weldparts Inc ....F....... 513 530-0064
Blue Ash *(G-1892)*
Wright Brothers Inc ....F....... 513 731-2222
Cincinnati *(G-4606)*

WELDING EQPT & SPLYS: Gas

Rexarc International Inc ....E....... 937 839-4604
West Alexandria *(G-19781)*

WELDING EQPT & SPLYS: Generators, Arc Welding, AC & DC

Lincoln Electric Company ....A....... 216 481-8100
Euclid *(G-9589)*

WELDING EQPT & SPLYS: Resistance, Electric

Weldparts Inc ....F....... 513 530-0064
Blue Ash *(G-1892)*

WELDING EQPT & SPLYS: Spot, Electric

Retek Inc ....G....... 440 937-6282
Avon *(G-1008)*

WELDING EQPT & SPLYS: Wire, Bare & Coated

Lincoln Electric Holdings Inc..............A....... 440 255-7696
Mentor *(G-13634)*
Techalloy Inc ....E....... 410 633-9300
Euclid *(G-9609)*

WELDING EQPT REPAIR SVCS

ARS Recycling Systems LLC................F....... 330 536-8210
Lowellville *(G-12405)*
Hannon Company ....E....... 740 453-0527
Zanesville *(G-21318)*
Hannon Company ....G....... 330 343-7758
Dover *(G-8990)*
Lyco Corporation ....E....... 330 534-3330
Lowellville *(G-12410)*
Quality Components Inc........................F....... 440 255-0606
Mentor *(G-13706)*
Unified Scrn & Crush-Oh Inc ....E....... 937 836-3201
Englewood *(G-9541)*

WELDING EQPT: Electric

Fanuc America Corporation ....E....... 513 754-2400
Mason *(G-13020)*
Midwest Fasteners Inc ....D....... 937 866-0463
Miamisburg *(G-13835)*
Production Products Inc ....D....... 419 659-2978
Columbus Grove *(G-7797)*
Tech-Sonic Inc ....F....... 614 792-3117
Columbus *(G-7683)*

WELDING EQPT: Electrical

Izit Cain Sheet Metal Corp ....G....... 937 667-6521
Tipp City *(G-18284)*
PWS Welding & Mtg ....F....... 330 385-6922
East Liverpool *(G-9226)*
Technical Sales & Solution ....G....... 614 793-9612
Dublin *(G-9154)*

WELDING MACHINES & EQPT: Ultrasonic

Cecil C Peck Co.....................................F....... 330 785-0781
Akron *(G-116)*

WELDING REPAIR SVC

A & C Welding Inc.................................E....... 330 762-4777
Peninsula *(G-16032)*
A & G Manufacturing Co Inc ....E....... 419 468-7433
Galion *(G-10250)*
A Metalcraft Associates Inc ....G....... 937 693-4008
Botkins *(G-1949)*
Abbott Tool Inc ....E....... 419 476-6742
Toledo *(G-18318)*
Advanced Onsight Welding Svcs ....G....... 513 924-1400
Cincinnati *(G-3359)*
Advanced Welding Co ....E....... 937 746-6800
Franklin *(G-10005)*
Aetna Welding Co Inc ....G....... 216 883-1801
Cleveland *(G-4727)*
Aircraft Welding Inc ....G....... 440 951-3863
Willoughby *(G-20426)*
Albright Radiator Inc ....G....... 330 264-8886
Wooster *(G-20738)*
All American Welding Co ....G....... 614 224-7752
Columbus *(G-6720)*
All Do Weld & Fab LLC ....G....... 740 477-2133
Circleville *(G-4622)*
All-Type Welding & Fabrication ....E....... 440 439-3990
Cleveland *(G-4761)*
Allied Fabricating & Wldg Co................E....... 614 751-6664
Columbus *(G-6725)*
Alloy Unlimited Weld ....G....... 330 506-8375
Canfield *(G-2546)*
Amptech Machining & Welding ....G....... 419 652-3444
Nova *(G-15576)*
ARC Solutions Inc.................................F....... 419 542-9272
Hicksville *(G-10899)*

PRODUCT

Arctech Fabricating Inc ....E 937 525-9353	Creative Fabrication Ltd ....G 740 262-5789	Garland Welding Co Inc ....F 330 536-6506
Springfield *(G-17518)*	Richwood *(G-16659)*	Lowellville *(G-12408)*
Arnolds Repair Shop ....G 740 373-5313	Creative Mold and Machine Inc ......E 440 338-5146	Gaspar Inc ....D 330 477-2222
Marietta *(G-12762)*	Newbury *(G-15087)*	Canton *(G-2711)*
Athens Mold and Machine Inc ......D 740 593-6613	Crest Bending Inc ....E 419 492-2108	General Technologies Inc ....E 419 747-1800
Akron *(G-76)*	New Washington *(G-14959)*	Mansfield *(G-12612)*
Auglaize Welding Company Inc ....G 419 738-4422	Custom Machine Inc ....E 419 986-5122	General Tool Company ....C 513 733-5500
Wapakoneta *(G-19480)*	Tiffin *(G-18217)*	Cincinnati *(G-3820)*
Auto-Tap Inc ....E 216 671-1043	Custom Way Welding Inc ....G 937 845-9469	George Steel Fabricating Inc ....E 513 932-2887
Cleveland *(G-4864)*	New Carlisle *(G-14800)*	Lebanon *(G-11802)*
Automation Welding System ....G 330 263-1176	D & G Welding Inc ....G 419 445-5751	Gilson Machine & Tool Co Inc ....G 419 592-2911
Wooster *(G-20744)*	Archbold *(G-670)*	Napoleon *(G-14678)*
B & B Welding ....G 419 968-2743	D & M Welding & Radiator ....G 740 947-9032	Glenridge Machine Co ....E 440 975-1055
Middle Point *(G-13898)*	Waverly *(G-19707)*	Willoughby *(G-20499)*
Baker Built Products Inc ....G 419 965-2646	Dalin Auto Service ....G 440 997-3301	Greber Machine Tool Inc ....G 440 322-3685
Ohio City *(G-15660)*	Ashtabula *(G-801)*	Elyria *(G-9427)*
Baker Welding Llc ....G 614 252-6100	Davenport Service Group Inc ....G 440 487-9353	Greggs Specialty Services ....F 419 478-0803
Columbus *(G-6803)*	Mentor *(G-13559)*	Toledo *(G-18488)*
Baughmans Machine & Weld Shop ....G 330 866-9243	David Cox ....G 740 254-4858	Grodhaus & Young Inc ....F 330 866-3321
Waynesburg *(G-19723)*	Gnadenhutten *(G-10405)*	Waynesburg *(G-19725)*
Bayloff Stmped Pdts Knsman Inc ....D 330 876-4511	Dayton Brick Company Inc ....F 937 293-4189	Gurina Company ....G 614 279-3891
Kinsman *(G-11608)*	Moraine *(G-14477)*	Columbus *(G-7132)*
Bear Welding Services LLC ....F 740 630-7538	Dayton United Metal Spinners ....F 937 222-6732	H & H Machine Shop Akron Inc ....E 330 773-3327
Caldwell *(G-2424)*	Tipp City *(G-18275)*	Akron *(G-209)*
Bens Welding Service Inc ....G 937 878-4052	Dbcr Inc ....G 330 920-1900	H & K Fabricating ....G 330 767-4279
Fairborn *(G-9615)*	Cuyahoga Falls *(G-7986)*	Navarre *(G-14715)*
Blackwood Sheet Metal Inc ....G 614 291-3115	Delta Machine & Tool Co ....E 216 524-2477	H & L Welding Service Inc ....G 740 862-3520
Columbus *(G-6839)*	Cleveland *(G-5183)*	Columbus *(G-7134)*
Blevins Metal Fabrication Inc ....E 419 522-6082	Des Eck Welding ....G 330 698-7271	Habco Tool and Dev Co Inc ....E 440 946-5546
Mansfield *(G-12567)*	Apple Creek *(G-636)*	Mentor *(G-13598)*
Bob Lanes Welding Inc ....F 740 373-3567	Diamond Welding Co Inc ....G 216 251-1679	Hackworth Electric Motors Inc ....G 330 345-6049
Marietta *(G-12767)*	Cleveland *(G-5190)*	Wooster *(G-20782)*
Breitinger Company ....C 419 526-4255	Diversified Welding Services ....G 419 382-1433	Harris Welding and Machine Co ....F 419 281-8351
Mansfield *(G-12569)*	Toledo *(G-18440)*	Ashland *(G-736)*
Broadway Welding & Fabrication ......G 513 821-0004	Dover Fabrication and Burn Inc ....G 330 339-1057	Harris Welding and Machine Co ....G 419 281-9623
Cincinnati *(G-3476)*	New Philadelphia *(G-14895)*	Ashland *(G-737)*
Brocks Welding & Repair Svc ....G 740 453-3943	Dover Machine Co ....F 330 343-4123	Hartley Machine Inc ....G 330 821-0343
Zanesville *(G-21281)*	Dover *(G-8981)*	Alliance *(G-513)*
Bse Welding & Fabricating LLC ....F 419 547-1043	Drabik Manufacturing Inc ....E 216 267-1616	HI Tecmetal Group Inc ....E 216 881-8100
Vickery *(G-19361)*	Cleveland *(G-5214)*	Cleveland *(G-5508)*
Buckeye Welding ....G 330 674-0944	Duco Tool & Die Inc ....E 419 628-2031	HI Tecmetal Group Inc ....E 440 373-5101
Millersburg *(G-14206)*	Minster *(G-14351)*	Wickliffe *(G-20368)*
C & M Welding Services LLC ....G 419 584-0008	Duray Machine Co Inc ....F 440 277-4119	HI Tecmetal Group Inc ....E 440 946-2280
Celina *(G-2987)*	Amherst *(G-597)*	Willoughby *(G-20504)*
C & R Inc ....E 614 497-1130	Durisek Enterprises Inc ....E 216 281-3898	Hi-Tek Manufacturing Inc ....C 513 459-1094
Groveport *(G-10617)*	Cleveland *(G-5225)*	Mason *(G-13037)*
C O Welding & Fabrication Inc ....G 419 394-3293	Dynamic Specialties Inc ....G 440 946-2838	Highs Welding Inc ....G 937 464-3029
Saint Marys *(G-16836)*	Mentor *(G-13568)*	Belle Center *(G-1513)*
C Stoneman Corporation ....G 440 942-3325	Dynamic Weld Corporation ....E 419 582-2900	Hobart Bros Stick Electrode ....C 937 332-5375
Eastlake *(G-9261)*	Osgood *(G-15785)*	Troy *(G-18835)*
C-N-D Industries Inc ....E 330 478-8811	E & M Liberty Welding Inc ....G 330 866-2338	Hoffman Machining & Repair LLC .....G 419 547-9204
Massillon *(G-13118)*	Waynesburg *(G-19724)*	Clyde *(G-6540)*
Camelot Manufacturing Inc ....F 419 678-2603	E & R Welding Inc ....F 440 329-9387	Holdren Brothers Inc ....F 937 465-7050
Coldwater *(G-6554)*	Berlin Heights *(G-1661)*	West Liberty *(G-20092)*
Cardinal Welding Inc ....G 330 426-2404	E L Davis Inc ....G 419 268-2004	Holdsworth Industrial Fabg ....G 330 874-3945
East Palestine *(G-9229)*	Celina *(G-2993)*	Bolivar *(G-1936)*
Carol J Guiler ....G 614 252-6920	E W Welding & Fabricating ....G 440 826-9038	Hyneks Machine and Welding ....G 419 281-7966
Columbus *(G-6910)*	Berea *(G-1612)*	Ashland *(G-742)*
Carter Manufacturing Co Inc ....E 513 398-7303	Eagle Machine and Welding Inc ....G 740 345-5210	Independent Machine & Wldg Inc ....G 937 339-7330
Mason *(G-12991)*	Newark *(G-15001)*	Troy *(G-18845)*
Case-Maul Manufacturing Co ....F 419 524-1061	Eagle Wldg & Fabrication Inc ....E 440 946-0692	Innovative Wldg & Design LLC ....G 330 581-1316
Mansfield *(G-12577)*	Willoughby *(G-20478)*	Alliance *(G-518)*
Certified Welding Co ....F 216 961-5410	East End Welding Company ....C 330 677-6000	J & A Machine ....G 330 424-5235
Cleveland *(G-5009)*	Kent *(G-11452)*	Lisbon *(G-12123)*
Chipmatic Tool & Machine Inc ....D 419 862-2737	Euclid Welding Co Inc ....E 216 289-0714	J & L Welding Fabricating Inc ....F 330 393-9353
Elmore *(G-9362)*	Cleveland *(G-5303)*	Warren *(G-19561)*
Chore Anden ....G 330 695-2300	Fab-Tech Machine Inc ....G 937 473-5572	J & S Industrial Mch Pdts Inc ....D 419 691-1380
Fredericksburg *(G-10080)*	Covington *(G-7922)*	Toledo *(G-18531)*
City Machine Technologies Inc ....F 330 747-2639	Fabrication Shop Inc ....F 419 435-7934	J A B Welding Service Inc ....F 740 453-5868
Youngstown *(G-21047)*	Fostoria *(G-9970)*	Zanesville *(G-21322)*
Cleveland Welding & Fabg LLC ....G 440 364-5137	Fabrication Unlimited LLC ....G 937 492-3166	J P Suggins Mobile Welding ....E 216 566-7131
Cleveland *(G-5085)*	Sidney *(G-17189)*	Cleveland *(G-5599)*
Clipsons Metal Working Inc ....G 513 772-6393	Falls Stamping & Welding Co ....C 330 928-1191	James G Morehouse ....G 513 752-2236
Cincinnati *(G-3588)*	Cuyahoga Falls *(G-7996)*	Milford *(G-14155)*
Cmt Machining & Fabg LLC ....F 937 652-3740	Farnsworth Engineering ....F 330 385-1745	Jerl Machine Inc ....D 419 873-0270
Urbana *(G-19151)*	East Liverpool *(G-9215)*	Perrysburg *(G-16114)*
Columbus Mobile Welding ....G 614 352-6052	Fosbel Inc ....C 216 362-3900	Jerrys Welding Supply Inc ....G 937 364-1500
Centerburg *(G-3029)*	Brookpark *(G-2161)*	Hillsboro *(G-11006)*
Columbus Pipe and Equipment Co .....F 614 444-7871	Fosbel Holding Inc ....E 216 362-3900	JJ Delong & Associates Inc ....G 216 861-4727
Columbus *(G-6962)*	Cleveland *(G-5373)*	Cleveland *(G-5616)*
Compton Metal Products Inc ....D 937 382-2403	Fred Winner ....G 419 582-2421	JMw Welding and Mfg ....E 330 484-2428
Wilmington *(G-20660)*	New Weston *(G-14977)*	Canton *(G-2748)*
Comptons Precision Machine ....F 937 325-9139	Fredrick Welding & Machining ....F 614 866-9650	Johns Welding & Towing Inc ....F 419 447-8937
Springfield *(G-17535)*	Reynoldsburg *(G-16592)*	Tiffin *(G-18225)*
Connaughton Wldg & Fence LLC ......G 513 867-0230	Friess Welding Inc ....F 330 644-8160	Jrs Hydraulic & Welding ....G 614 497-1100
Hamilton *(G-10680)*	Akron *(G-195)*	Columbus *(G-7246)*
County Wide Welding LLC ....G 440 564-1333	G B Welding & Metal Fabg Co ....G 937 444-2091	K & J Machine Inc ....F 740 425-3282
Newbury *(G-15086)*	Fayetteville *(G-9782)*	Barnesville *(G-1160)*
Creative Fab & Welding LLC ....E 937 780-5000	G M P Welding and Fabricating ....F 513 825-7861	K & M Tool & Machine Co Inc ....G 440 572-5130
Leesburg *(G-11851)*	Cincinnati *(G-3792)*	Strongsville *(G-17934)*

2017 Harris Ohio
Industrial Directory

(G-0000) Company's Geographic Section entry number

K-M-S Industries Inc ....E 440 243-6680
Brookpark (G-2165)
Kedar D Army ....G 419 238-6929
Van Wert (G-19262)
Kellys Welding & Fabricating ....G 440 593-6040
Conneaut (G-7811)
Kendel Welding & Fabrication ....G 330 834-2429
Massillon (G-13161)
Kings Welding and Fabg Inc ....E 330 738-3592
Mechanicstown (G-13359)
Kirbys Auto & Truck Repair ....G 513 934-3999
Lebanon (G-11812)
Kirk Welding & Fabricating ....G 216 961-6403
Cleveland (G-5658)
Kottler Metal Products Co Inc ....E 440 946-7473
Willoughby (G-20523)
Kramer Power Equipment Co ....F 937 456-2232
Eaton (G-9313)
Kys Welding & Fabrication ....G 513 702-9081
Loveland (G-12368)
L B Industries Inc ....E 330 750-1002
Struthers (G-17994)
Lakecraft Inc ....G 419 734-2828
Port Clinton (G-16402)
Lanes Welding & Repair ....G 740 397-2525
Mount Vernon (G-14628)
Laserflex Corporation ....D 614 850-9600
Hilliard (G-10958)
Liberty Casting Company LLC ....D 740 363-1941
Delaware (G-8869)
Lima Sheet Metal Machine & Mfg ....E 419 229-1161
Lima (G-12045)
Logan Welding Inc ....G 740 385-9651
Logan (G-12186)
Long-Stanton Mfg Company ....E 513 874-8020
West Chester (G-19895)
Lostcreek Tool & Machine Inc ....F 937 773-6022
Piqua (G-16287)
Lukens Blacksmith Shop ....G 513 821-2308
Cincinnati (G-4038)
Lunar Tool & Mold Inc ....F 440 237-2141
North Royalton (G-15434)
M & M Concepts Inc ....G 937 355-1115
West Mansfield (G-20100)
M & W Welding Inc ....G 614 224-0501
Columbus (G-7307)
M S Welding ....G 419 925-4141
Maria Stein (G-12758)
Maintenance and Repair Fabg Co ....G 330 478-1149
Massillon (G-13171)
Majestic Tool and Machine Inc ....E 440 248-5058
Solon (G-17331)
Manufacturing Concepts ....F 330 784-9054
Tallmadge (G-18151)
Marsam Metalfab Inc ....E 330 405-1520
Twinsburg (G-18978)
Martin Welding LLC ....F 937 687-3602
New Lebanon (G-14843)
Matheson Tri-Gas Inc ....E 440 365-1741
Twinsburg (G-18980)
Mc Elwain Industries Inc ....G 419 532-3126
Ottawa (G-15800)
McDannald Welding & Machining ....G 937 644-0300
Marysville (G-12960)
McIntosh Machine ....G 937 687-3936
New Lebanon (G-14844)
Mecca Rebuilding & Welding Co ....G 419 476-8133
Toledo (G-18581)
Mercers Welding Inc ....G 330 533-3373
Canfield (G-2565)
Meta Manufacturing Corporation ....E 513 793-6382
Blue Ash (G-1837)
Microweld Engineering Inc ....F 614 847-9410
Worthington (G-20880)
Mike Loppe ....F 937 969-8102
Tremont City (G-18789)
Mikes Automotive LLC ....G 937 233-1433
Dayton (G-8500)
Mikes Welding ....G 937 675-6587
Jamestown (G-11352)
Miller Welding Inc ....G 330 364-6173
Dover (G-9002)
Millwrght Wldg Fbrication Svcs ....F 740 533-1510
Kitts Hill (G-11621)
Mitchell Welding LLC ....G 740 259-2211
Lucasville (G-12422)
Monnig Welding Co ....G 513 241-5156
Cincinnati (G-4119)
Montgomery & Montgomery LLC ....G 330 858-9533
Akron (G-301)

National Welding & Tanker Repr ....G 614 875-3399
Grove City (G-10576)
National Welding & Tanker Repr ....G 614 875-3399
Grove City (G-10577)
New Tech Welding Inc ....G 937 426-4801
Beavercreek (G-1354)
Norman Noble Inc ....C 216 761-2133
Cleveland (G-5889)
Northwind Industries Inc ....E 216 433-0666
Cleveland (G-5916)
Oaks Welding Inc ....G 330 482-4216
Columbiana (G-6627)
Oceco Inc ....F 419 447-0916
Tiffin (G-18235)
Ohio Hydraulics Inc ....E 513 771-2590
Cincinnati (G-4178)
Ohio State University ....E 614 292-4139
Columbus (G-7432)
Ohio Trailer Inc ....F 330 392-4444
Warren (G-19584)
Ohio Trailer Supply Inc ....G 614 471-9121
Columbus (G-7435)
Paul Wilke & Son Inc ....F 513 921-3163
Cincinnati (G-4217)
Penco Tool LLC ....E 440 998-1116
Ashtabula (G-829)
Pentaflex Inc ....C 937 325-5551
Springfield (G-17626)
Perry Welding Service Inc ....F 330 425-2211
Twinsburg (G-19001)
Phillips & Sons Welding & Fabg ....G 440 428-1625
Geneva (G-10355)
Phillips Mfg and Tower Co ....D 419 347-1720
Shelby (G-17140)
Phoenix Industries & Apparatus ....F 513 722-1085
Loveland (G-12377)
Precision Mtal Fabrication Inc ....D 937 235-9261
Dayton (G-8587)
Precision Reflex Inc ....F 419 629-2603
New Bremen (G-14792)
Precision Welding Corporation ....E 216 524-6110
Cleveland (G-6037)
Pro Fab Welding Service LLC ....G 937 272-2142
Moraine (G-14518)
Product Tooling Inc ....G 740 524-2061
Sunbury (G-18075)
Prout Boiler Htg & Wldg Inc ....E 330 744-0293
Youngstown (G-21180)
Quality Welding Inc ....E 419 483-6067
Bellevue (G-1554)
Quick Service Welding & Mch Co ....F 330 673-3818
Kent (G-11511)
R & M Welding Co ....G 330 264-4788
Wooster (G-20826)
R M Welding Products ....G 937 260-4510
Dayton (G-8611)
R S V Wldg Fbrcation Machining ....F 419 592-0993
Napoleon (G-14694)
Ray Townsend ....G 440 968-3617
Montville (G-14461)
Rbm Environmental and Cnstr ....E 419 693-5840
Oregon (G-15715)
Rl Alto Mfg Inc ....F 740 914-4230
Marion (G-12895)
Ridge Engineering Inc ....G 513 681-5500
Cincinnati (G-4346)
Ridge Enterprises Inc ....G 740 867-3456
Chesapeake (G-3190)
Ridge Machine & Welding Co ....G 740 537-2821
Toronto (G-18784)
RJR & Associates Inc ....G 419 237-2220
Fayette (G-9779)
Robert Alten Inc ....G 740 653-2640
Lancaster (G-11747)
Robert E Moore ....G 513 367-0006
Harrison (G-10801)
Romar Metal Fabricating Inc ....G 740 682-7731
Oak Hill (G-15606)
Rose Metal Industries LLC ....F 216 881-3355
Cleveland (G-6132)
Rosie S Welding ....G 614 506-2475
Reynoldsburg (G-16603)
Rush Welding & Machine Inc ....G 740 354-7874
Portsmouth (G-16450)
S & S Spring Shop ....G 800 619-4652
Mount Perry (G-14594)
Salem Welding & Supply Company ....G 330 332-4517
Salem (G-16925)
Sauerwein Welding ....G 513 563-2979
Cincinnati (G-4380)

Schmidt Machine Company ....E 419 294-3814
Upper Sandusky (G-19139)
Schwab Welding Inc ....G 513 353-4262
Cincinnati (G-4390)
Selinick Co ....G 440 632-1788
Middlefield (G-13988)
Selzer Tool & Die Inc ....G 440 365-4124
Elyria (G-9491)
Semtorq Inc ....F 330 487-0600
Twinsburg (G-19019)
Sheet Angle Bar Met Fbrication ....G 513 829-8600
Fairfield (G-9716)
Simpson & Sons Inc ....F 513 367-0152
Harrison (G-10802)
Slabe Tool Company ....G 740 439-1647
Cambridge (G-2476)
Slade Gardner ....G 440 355-8015
Lagrange (G-11637)
Smith Springs Inc ....G 800 619-4652
Mount Perry (G-14595)
Smp Welding LLC ....F 440 205-9353
Mentor (G-13725)
Somerville Manufacturing Inc ....E 740 336-7847
Marietta (G-12834)
Spradlin Bros Welding Co ....F 800 219-2182
Springfield (G-17650)
Steubenville Truck Center Inc ....E 740 282-2711
Steubenville (G-17715)
Steve Vore Welding and Steel ....F 419 375-4087
Fort Recovery (G-9959)
Stryker Welding ....G 419 682-2301
Stryker (G-18009)
Suburban Metal Products Inc ....F 740 474-4237
Circleville (G-4644)
Superior Weld and Fabg Co Inc ....G 216 249-5122
Cleveland (G-6272)
Systech Handling Inc ....F 419 445-8226
Archbold (G-696)
Systems Jay LLC Nanogate ....B 419 747-4161
Mansfield (G-12691)
T & L Welding LLC ....G 937 498-9170
Sidney (G-17231)
T & R Welding Systems Inc ....F 937 228-7517
Dayton (G-8696)
T&T Welding ....G 513 615-1156
Loveland (G-12393)
Tbone Sales LLC ....E 330 897-6131
Baltic (G-1077)
Temperature Controls Company ....F 330 773-6633
Akron (G-433)
Tendon Manufacturing Inc ....E 216 663-3200
Cleveland (G-6305)
Thomas Entps of Georgetown ....G 937 378-6300
Georgetown (G-10366)
Tig Welding Specialties Inc ....G 216 621-1763
Cleveland (G-6324)
Timothy Sasser ....G 740 260-9499
Byesville (G-2411)
Tri-Weld Inc ....F 216 281-6009
Cleveland (G-6359)
Triangle Precision Industries ....D 937 299-6776
Dayton (G-8723)
Tru-Fab Technology Inc ....F 440 954-9760
Willoughby (G-20620)
TW Tank LLC ....G 419 334-2664
Fremont (G-10190)
Two M Precision Co Inc ....E 440 946-2120
Willoughby (G-20623)
Valley Machine Tool Co Inc ....E 513 899-2737
Morrow (G-14553)
Van Burens Welding & Machine ....G 740 787-2636
Glenford (G-10401)
Viking Fabricators Inc ....E 740 374-5246
Marietta (G-12848)
Waldock Eqp Sls & Svc Inc ....G 419 426-7771
Attica (G-897)
Warlock Inc ....G 614 471-4055
Columbus (G-7749)
Waxler Machine Tool Company ....G 419 422-1240
Findlay (G-9906)
Wayne Trail Technologies Inc ....D 937 295-2120
Fort Loramie (G-9944)
Webers Body & Frame ....G 937 839-5946
West Alexandria (G-19786)
Weldcraft Products Co ....F 937 233-6141
Dayton (G-8750)
Weldfab Inc ....G 440 563-3310
Rock Creek (G-16687)
Welding Consultants Inc ....G 614 258-7018
Columbus (G-7756)

PRODUCT

Employee Codes: A=Over 500 employees, B=251-500
C=101-250, D=51-100, E=20-50, F=10-19, G=3-9

2017 Harris Ohio
Industrial Directory

1693

Welding Equipment Repair Co ....G..... 330 536-2125
Lowellville (G-12414)
Weldments Inc ....F..... 937 235-9261
Dayton (G-8751)
Wenrick Machine and Tool Corp ....F..... 937 667-7307
Tipp City (G-18311)
Westerman Acquisition Co LLC ....E..... 330 264-2447
Wooster (G-20847)
Wg Mobile Welding LLC ....G..... 440 720-1940
Highland Heights (G-10921)
Whitt Machine Inc ....F..... 513 423-7624
Middletown (G-14098)
Wonder Weld Inc ....G..... 614 875-1447
Orient (G-15726)
Worleys Machine & Fab Inc ....G..... 740 532-3337
Hanging Rock (G-10762)

WELDING SPLYS, EXC GASES: Wholesalers

Airgas Usa LLC ....G..... 440 232-6397
Oakwood Village (G-15622)
Airgas USA LLC ....G..... 419 726-2719
Toledo (G-18325)
Delille Oxygen Company ....E..... 614 444-1177
Columbus (G-7018)
Matheson Tri-Gas Inc ....E..... 440 365-1741
Twinsburg (G-18980)
Retek Inc ....G..... 440 937-6282
Avon (G-1008)

WELDING TIPS: Heat Resistant, Metal

Arete Innovative Solutions LLC ....G..... 513 503-2712
Morrow (G-14543)
Ben James Enterprises Inc ....G..... 330 477-9353
Canton (G-2620)
Ohio Laser LLC ....E..... 614 873-7030
Plain City (G-16352)

WELDMENTS

A H Marty Co Ltd ....F..... 216 641-8950
Cleveland (G-4673)
A-1 Welding & Fabricating Inc ....F..... 440 233-8474
Lorain (G-12230)
All American Welding Co ....G..... 614 224-7752
Columbus (G-6720)
Dj S Weld ....G..... 330 432-2206
Uhrichsville (G-19049)
Fred Winner ....G..... 419 582-2421
New Weston (G-14977)
Loveman Steel Corporation ....D..... 440 232-6200
Bedford (G-1439)
M & M Certified Welding Inc ....F..... 330 467-1729
Macedonia (G-12467)

WELL CURBING: Concrete

Creative Curbing America LLC ....G..... 419 738-7668
Wapakoneta (G-19484)

WET CORN MILLING

Tate Lyle Ingrdnts Amricas LLC ....D..... 937 235-4074
Dayton (G-8704)

WHEELBARROWS

Acorn Products Inc ....B..... 614 222-4400
Columbus (G-6689)

WHEELCHAIR LIFTS

Access To Independence Inc ....G..... 330 296-8111
Ravenna (G-16512)
Key Mobility Services Ltd ....G..... 937 374-3226
Xenia (G-20959)
Serving Veterans Mobility Inc ....G..... 937 746-4788
Franklin (G-10052)
Steves Vans & Accessories LLC ....G..... 740 374-3154
Marietta (G-12836)

WHEELCHAIRS

American Ride Wheelchair Coach ....G..... 216 276-1700
Cleveland (G-4794)
Columbus Prescr Rehabilitation ....G..... 614 294-1600
Westerville (G-20204)
Healthwares Manufacturing ....F..... 513 353-3691
Cincinnati (G-3874)
Invacare Corporation ....F..... 440 329-6000
Elyria (G-9437)
JI Safety LLC ....G..... 440 582-5866
Broadview Heights (G-2112)

Rees Wheelchair Mobility Svc ....G..... 330 923-2345
Akron (G-370)
Reliable Wheelchair Trans ....G..... 216 390-3999
Beachwood (G-1296)
Wilson Mobility LLC ....G..... 216 921-9457
Cleveland (G-6465)

WHEELS

Allen Alloys ....G..... 330 422-1814
Streetsboro (G-17837)
Dan Nemes American Racing ....G..... 216 749-4203
Brooklyn Heights (G-2137)
Ferguson Fire Fabrication Inc ....F..... 614 299-2070
Columbus (G-7081)

WHEELS & BRAKE SHOES: Railroad, Cast Iron

Amsted Industries Incorporated...........C..... 614 836-2323
Groveport (G-10612)
Engines Inc of Ohio ....D..... 740 377-9874
South Point (G-17437)

WHEELS & GRINDSTONES, EXC ARTIFICIAL: Abrasive

Everett Industries Inc ....E..... 330 372-3700
Warren (G-19548)
Regal Diamond Products Corp ....E..... 440 944-7700
Wickliffe (G-20385)
Schumann Enterprises Inc ....E..... 216 267-6850
Cleveland (G-6166)
Unisand Incorporated ....E..... 330 722-0222
Medina (G-13492)

WHEELS & PARTS

Ernie Green Industries Inc ....G..... 614 219-1423
Columbus (G-7064)
Marion Industries Inc ....A..... 740 223-0075
Marion (G-12883)
Martin Wheel Co Inc ....D..... 330 633-3278
Tallmadge (G-18153)
Pacific Industries USA Inc ....E..... 513 860-3900
Fairfield (G-9695)
Production Turning LLC ....G..... 937 424-0034
Moraine (G-14520)

WHEELS, GRINDING: Artificial

Action Super Abrasive Pdts Inc ....E..... 330 673-7333
Kent (G-11423)
Performance Superabrasives LLC ....G..... 440 946-7171
Mentor (G-13685)

WHEELS: Abrasive

Buckeye Abrasive Inc ....F..... 330 753-1041
Barberton (G-1112)
Maxion Wheels Sedalia LLC ....F..... 330 794-2300
Akron (G-290)
Research Abrasive Products Inc ....E..... 440 944-3200
Wickliffe (G-20386)

WHEELS: Buffing & Polishing

B & P Polishing Inc ....F..... 330 753-4202
Barberton (G-1102)
United Buff & Supply Co Inc ....G..... 419 738-2417
Wapakoneta (G-19510)
Wright Buffing Wheel Company ....G..... 330 424-7887
Lisbon (G-12136)

WHEELS: Disc, Wheelbarrow, Stroller, Etc, Stamped Metal

Axis Corporation ....F..... 937 592-1958
Bellefontaine (G-1520)
Byer Steel Rebar Inc ....E..... 513 821-6400
Cincinnati (G-3492)
Ibi Brake Products Inc ....G..... 440 543-7962
Chagrin Falls (G-3094)

WHEELS: Iron & Steel, Locomotive & Car

Plymouth Locomotive Svc LLC ....G..... 419 896-2854
Shiloh (G-17152)
Xtek Inc ....B..... 513 733-7800
Cincinnati (G-4616)

WHEELS: Railroad Car, Cast Steel

Engines Inc of Ohio ....D..... 740 377-9874
South Point (G-17437)

WHEELS: Water

Muller Engine & Machine Co................G..... 937 322-1861
Springfield (G-17610)

WHIRLPOOL BATHS: Hydrotherapy

Meridienne International Inc ....G..... 330 274-8317
Mantua (G-12717)

WHISTLES

Rays Whistle Stop ....G..... 740 965-2085
New Albany (G-14771)

WICKING

Community Action Program Corp ....F..... 740 374-8501
Marietta (G-12776)

WINCHES

American Power Pull Corp ....G..... 419 335-7050
Wauseon (G-19671)
David Round Company Inc ....G..... 330 656-1600
Streetsboro (G-17847)
Wyeth-Scott Company ....G..... 740 345-4528
Newark (G-15066)

WINDINGS: Coil, Electronic

Adkel Corp ....G..... 740 452-6973
Zanesville (G-21266)
M2m Imaging Corporation ....F..... 440 684-9690
Cleveland (G-5720)

WINDMILLS: Electric Power Generation

Surenergy LLC ....F..... 419 626-8000
Sandusky (G-17011)

WINDMILLS: Farm Type

Ohio Windmill & Pump Co Inc ....G..... 330 547-6300
Berlin Center (G-1658)

WINDOW & DOOR FRAMES

A B Siemer Inc ....B..... 614 888-8855
Columbus (G-6667)
Desco Corporation ....G..... 614 888-8855
New Albany (G-14757)
Dj & Woodies Vinyl Frontier ....G..... 740 623-2818
Coshocton (G-7888)
Lean Factory America LLC ....G..... 513 297-3086
Cincinnati (G-4018)
Midwest Curtainwalls Inc ....D..... 216 641-7900
Cleveland (G-5809)

WINDOW FRAMES & SASHES: Plastic

Champion Opco LLC ....B..... 513 924-4858
Cincinnati (G-3521)
Champion Opco LLC ....D..... 419 740-5193
Maumee (G-13234)
Champion Window Co of Akron ....E..... 330 474-3024
Macedonia (G-12441)
Vinylmax Corporation ....D..... 800 847-3736
Hamilton (G-10754)
Vinylume Products Inc ....D..... 330 799-2000
Youngstown (G-21242)

WINDOW FRAMES, MOLDING & TRIM: Vinyl

Builder Tech Wholesale LLC ....G..... 419 535-7606
Toledo (G-18385)
Comfort Line Ltd ....D..... 419 729-8520
Toledo (G-18407)
Duo-Corp ....E..... 330 549-2149
North Lima (G-15315)
Great Lakes Window Inc ....A..... 419 666-5555
Walbridge (G-19458)
Laird Plastics Inc ....F..... 614 272-0777
Columbus (G-7280)
Larmco Windows Inc ....E..... 216 502-2832
Cleveland (G-5683)
Modern Builders Supply Inc ....C..... 330 729-2690
Youngstown (G-21147)
O A R Vinyl Windows & Siding ....G..... 440 636-5573
Middlefield (G-13978)

Owens Corning ....A 419 248-8000
 Toledo (G-18625)
Owens Corning Sales LLC ....A 419 248-8000
 Toledo (G-18626)
Soft-Lite LLC ....C 330 528-3400
 Streetsboro (G-17876)
Stanek E F and Assoc Inc ....C 216 341-7700
 Macedonia (G-12490)
Tsp Inc ....E 513 732-8900
 Batavia (G-1229)
Vinyl Design Corporation ....E 419 283-4009
 Holland (G-11095)

WINDOW FURNISHINGS WHOLESALERS

Cincinnati Window Shade Inc ....G 513 398-8510
 Mason (G-12995)
Cincinnati Window Shade Inc ....F 513 631-7200
 Cincinnati (G-3568)

WINDOW SCREENING: Plastic

Gateway Industrial Pdts Inc ....F 440 324-4112
 Elyria (G-9425)
Hang-It-All Curtain System LLC ....G 614 275-0954
 Columbus (G-7140)

WINDOWS: Frames, Wood

American Woodwork Specialty Co .....E 937 263-1053
 Dayton (G-8156)
Bay World International Inc ....E 419 525-2222
 Mansfield (G-12565)

WINDOWS: Wood

M21 Industries LLC ....D 937 781-1377
 Dayton (G-8465)
Ply Gem Industries Inc ....C 937 492-1111
 Sidney (G-17210)
Yoder Window & Siding Ltd ....F 330 695-6960
 Fredericksburg (G-10095)

WINDSHIELD WIPER SYSTEMS

Visible Solutions Inc ....G 440 925-2810
 Westlake (G-20317)

WINDSHIELDS: Plastic

Few Atmtive GL Applcations Inc ....G 234 249-1880
 Wooster (G-20772)
J & B Rogers Inc ....G 937 669-2677
 Tipp City (G-18285)

WINE & DISTILLED ALCOHOLIC BEVERAGES WHOLESALERS

Victoria Ventures Inc ....G 330 793-9321
 Youngstown (G-21239)

WINE CELLARS, BONDED: Wine, Blended

Georgetown Vineyards LLC ....F 740 435-3222
 Cambridge (G-2458)
Muirfield Wine Company LLC ....G 614 799-9222
 Dublin (G-9107)

WIRE

Advance Industries Group LLC ....E 216 741-1800
 Cleveland (G-4707)
AJD Holding Co ....D 330 405-4477
 Twinsburg (G-18895)
Bekaert Corporation ....C 330 683-5060
 Orrville (G-15729)
Bekaert Corporation ....F 330 683-5060
 Orrville (G-15730)
Bekaert Corporation ....E 330 835-5124
 Fairlawn (G-9740)
Bekaert Corporation ....G 330 867-3325
 Fairlawn (G-9741)
Bekaert North America MGT Corp ......E 330 867-3325
 Fairlawn (G-9742)
Brushes Inc ....E 216 267-8084
 Cleveland (G-4942)
Cambridge Cable Service Co ....G 740 685-5775
 Byesville (G-2396)
DC Controls LLC ....G 513 225-0813
 West Chester (G-19997)
Falcon Fab and Finishes LLC ....G 740 820-4458
 Lucasville (G-12420)
Hawthorne Wire Ltd ....F 216 712-4747
 Lakewood (G-11667)

Injection Alloys Incorporated ....F 513 422-8819
 Middletown (G-14047)
Madsen Wire Products Inc ....E 937 829-6561
 Dayton (G-8468)
Merchants Metals LLC ....E 513 942-0268
 West Chester (G-19900)
Reinforcement Systems Ohio LLC ......G 330 469-6958
 Warren (G-19593)
Wire Holdings LLC ....E 216 731-9191
 Cleveland (G-6467)

WIRE & CABLE: Aluminum

Max Mighty Inc ....F 937 862-9530
 Spring Valley (G-17468)

WIRE & CABLE: Nonferrous, Automotive, Exc Ignition Sets

Delphi Automotive Systems LLC ....B 248 813-2000
 Warren (G-19541)

WIRE & CABLE: Nonferrous, Building

Ribbon Technology Corporation ....F 614 864-5444
 Gahanna (G-10228)

WIRE & WIRE PRDTS

4-Sure Wire Products Inc ....G 440 563-9263
 Rock Creek (G-16684)
Able Fence of Columbus Inc ....G 614 253-8587
 Columbus (G-6679)
Alcan Corporation ....E 440 460-3307
 Cleveland (G-4741)
Amanda Manufacturing ....C 740 385-6893
 Logan (G-12171)
Bloomingburg Spring & Wire For ....G 740 437-7614
 Bloomingburg (G-1720)
Busch & Thiem Inc ....E 419 625-7515
 Sandusky (G-16952)
C & F Fabrications Inc ....G 937 666-3234
 East Liberty (G-9199)
Canron Manufacturing Inc ....F 330 497-1131
 Greentown (G-10485)
Clamps Inc ....E 419 729-2141
 Toledo (G-18398)
Columbus McKinnon Corporation ......D 330 424-7248
 Lisbon (G-12118)
Dayton Wire Products Inc ....E 937 236-8000
 Dayton (G-8291)
Die Co Inc ....D 440 942-8856
 Eastlake (G-9265)
Dolin Supply Co ....E 304 529-4171
 South Point (G-17436)
Eagle Wire Works Inc ....F 216 341-8550
 Cleveland (G-5238)
Efco Corp ....E 614 876-1226
 Columbus (G-7048)
Elyria Spring & Specialty Inc ....E 440 323-5502
 Elyria (G-9417)
Engineered Wire Products Inc ....C 419 294-3817
 Upper Sandusky (G-19121)
Ever Roll Specialties Co ....E 937 964-1302
 Springfield (G-17555)
Falcon Fab and Finishes LLC ....G 740 820-4458
 Lucasville (G-12420)
Fence One Inc ....F 216 441-2600
 Cleveland (G-5334)
Friends Ornamental Iron Co ....G 216 431-6710
 Cleveland (G-5382)
Gateway Concrete Forming Svcs ....D 513 353-2000
 Miamitown (G-13887)
General Chain & Mfg Corp ....E 513 541-6005
 Cincinnati (G-3812)
General Electric Company ....D 330 343-8841
 Dover (G-8987)
Gr Group Sales Inc ....G 216 961-3773
 Cleveland (G-5441)
Industrial Wire Rope Sup Inc ....G 513 941-2443
 Cincinnati (G-3919)
J B Kepple Sheet Metal ....G 740 393-2971
 Mount Vernon (G-14624)
JD Norman Industries Inc ....D 216 671-8000
 Brooklyn (G-2129)
John A & William J Wiechart ....G 419 647-4617
 Spencerville (G-17461)
Malin Wire Co ....E 216 267-9080
 Cleveland (G-5734)
Marik Spring Inc ....F 330 564-0617
 Tallmadge (G-18152)

Mazzella Lifting Tech Inc ....D 440 239-7000
 Cleveland (G-5765)
McM Ind Co Inc ....F 216 292-4506
 Beachwood (G-1278)
McM Ind Co Inc ....E 216 641-6300
 Cleveland (G-5770)
Meese Inc ....E 440 998-1202
 Ashtabula (G-819)
Mueller Electric Company Inc ....E 216 771-5225
 Akron (G-307)
Ohio Wire Form & Spring Co ....F 614 444-3676
 Columbus (G-7436)
Options Plus Incorporated ....F 740 694-9811
 Fredericktown (G-10108)
Organized Living Inc ....E 513 489-9300
 Cincinnati (G-4194)
Panacea Products Corporation ....E 614 850-7000
 Columbus (G-7456)
Panacea Products Corporation ....D 614 429-6320
 Columbus (G-7457)
Parker-Hannifin Corporation ....F 330 336-3511
 Wadsworth (G-19427)
Polymet Corporation ....E 513 874-3586
 West Chester (G-20038)
Premier Manufacturing Corp ....D 216 941-9700
 Cleveland (G-6041)
Production Plus Corp ....G 614 492-8811
 Obetz (G-15658)
Pwp Inc ....E 216 251-2181
 Cleveland (G-6064)
Qualtek Electronics Corp ....C 440 951-3300
 Mentor (G-13710)
Range One Products & Fabg ....F 330 533-1151
 Canfield (G-2571)
RFS Fabrication ....G 419 547-0650
 Clyde (G-6546)
Royal Wire Products Inc ....D 440 237-8787
 North Royalton (G-15446)
Saxon Products Inc ....G 419 241-6771
 Toledo (G-18685)
Schweizer Dipple Inc ....D 440 786-8090
 Cleveland (G-6167)
Spring Team Inc ....D 440 275-5981
 Austinburg (G-966)
Starr Fabricating Inc ....D 330 394-9891
 Vienna (G-19376)
Stephens Pipe & Steel LLC ....C 740 869-2257
 Mount Sterling (G-14604)
Stolle Machinery Company LLC ....E 937 859-4644
 Dayton (G-8684)
T & R Welding Systems Inc ....F 937 228-7517
 Dayton (G-8696)
Therm-O-Link Inc ....D 330 527-2124
 Garrettsville (G-10334)
Tyler Haver Inc ....E 440 974-1047
 Mentor (G-13756)
Ver-Mac Industries Inc ....E 740 397-6511
 Mount Vernon (G-14654)
W J Egli Company Inc ....F 330 823-3666
 Alliance (G-551)
Wire Products Company Inc ....D 216 267-0777
 Cleveland (G-6468)
Wrwp LLC ....F 330 425-3421
 Twinsburg (G-19041)
Yost Superior Co ....E 937 323-7591
 Springfield (G-17683)

WIRE CLOTH & WOVEN WIRE PRDTS, MADE FROM PURCHASED WIRE

Ofco Inc ....D 740 622-5922
 Coshocton (G-7904)
Unified Scrn & Crush-Oh Inc ....G 937 836-3201
 Englewood (G-9541)

WIRE FABRIC: Welded Steel

American Manufacturing Inc ....F 419 531-9471
 Toledo (G-18340)
S & S Wldg Fabg Machining Inc ....E 330 392-7878
 Newton Falls (G-15139)

WIRE FENCING & ACCESS WHOLESALERS

Agratronix LLC ....E 330 562-2222
 Streetsboro (G-17834)
D&M Fencing LLC ....G 419 604-0698
 Spencerville (G-17459)
Richards Whl Fence Co Inc ....E 330 773-0423
 Akron (G-373)
Security Fence Group Inc ....E 513 681-3700
 Cincinnati (G-4395)

PRODUCT

WIRE MATERIALS: Aluminum

Alcan Corporation..................E........ 440 460-3307
Cleveland *(G-4741)*

WIRE MATERIALS: Copper

Alcan Corporation..................E........ 440 460-3307
Cleveland *(G-4741)*

American Wire & Cable Company........E....... 440 235-1140
Olmsted Twp *(G-15678)*

Commconnect.....................G........ 937 414-0505
Dayton *(G-8238)*

Republic Wire Inc...................D........ 513 860-1800
West Chester *(G-19930)*

WIRE MATERIALS: Steel

Advance Wire Forming Inc............F........ 216 432-3250
Cleveland *(G-4711)*

American Wire & Cable Company........E........ 440 235-1140
Olmsted Twp *(G-15678)*

Ametco Manufacturing Corp...........E........ 440 951-4300
Willoughby *(G-20430)*

Bayloff Stmped Pdts Knsman Inc.......D........ 330 876-4511
Kinsman *(G-11608)*

Butler Processing Inc................E........ 513 874-1400
Hamilton *(G-10678)*

Ceco Machine & Tool.................G........ 937 264-3047
Dayton *(G-8217)*

Contour Forming Inc.................E........ 740 345-9777
Newark *(G-14996)*

Custom Cltch Jint Hydrlics Inc.........F........ 216 431-1630
Cleveland *(G-5149)*

D M L Steel Tech....................F........ 513 737-9911
Liberty Twp *(G-11973)*

Dayton Superior Corporation..........C........ 937 866-0711
Miamisburg *(G-13798)*

Engineered Wire Products Inc..........C........ 419 294-3817
Upper Sandusky *(G-19121)*

File Sharpening Company Inc..........E........ 937 376-8268
Xenia *(G-20951)*

Garda Arch Fab LLC.................G........ 216 431-6300
Cleveland *(G-5395)*

Genesis Steel Corp.................G........ 740 282-2300
Steubenville *(G-17696)*

Glebus Alloys LLC...................F........ 330 867-9999
Stow *(G-17759)*

Hawthorne Wire Services Ltd..........G........ 216 712-4747
Lakewood *(G-11668)*

JR Manufacturing Inc................C........ 419 375-8021
Fort Recovery *(G-9956)*

Master-Halco Inc...................E........ 513 869-7600
Fairfield *(G-9680)*

McHenry Industries Inc...............E........ 330 799-8930
Youngstown *(G-21142)*

Midwestern Industries Inc.............C........ 330 837-4203
Massillon *(G-13180)*

Noco Company.....................B........ 216 464-8131
Solon *(G-17350)*

Partners Manufacturing Group.........G........ 419 468-8516
Galion *(G-10281)*

Polymet Corporation................E........ 513 874-3586
West Chester *(G-20038)*

Republic Steel Wire Proc LLC..........E........ 440 996-0740
Solon *(G-17368)*

Republic Wire Inc...................D........ 513 860-1800
West Chester *(G-19930)*

Summit Engineered Products..........F........ 330 854-5388
Canal Fulton *(G-2514)*

Tru-Form Steel & Wire Inc............E........ 765 348-5001
Toledo *(G-18757)*

WIRE PRDTS: Ferrous Or Iron, Made In Wiredrawing Plants

American Spring Wire Corp...........C........ 216 292-4620
Bedford Heights *(G-1478)*

Fenix LLC.........................F........ 419 739-3400
Fostoria *(G-9971)*

Seneca Wire Group Inc...............G........ 419 435-9261
Fostoria *(G-9996)*

WIRE PRDTS: Steel & Iron

Falcon Fab and Finishes LLC..........G........ 740 820-4458
Lucasville *(G-12420)*

North Shore Strapping Inc............E........ 216 661-5200
Brooklyn Heights *(G-2144)*

Trupoint Products..................F........ 330 204-3302
Sugarcreek *(G-18046)*

Wire Holdings LLC..................G........ 216 731-9191
Cleveland *(G-6467)*

WIRE WINDING OF PURCHASED WIRE

Providence Rees Inc.................E........ 614 833-6231
Columbus *(G-7525)*

WIRE, FLAT: Strip, Cold-Rolled, Exc From Hot-Rolled Mills

American Spring Wire Corp...........C........ 216 292-4620
Bedford Heights *(G-1478)*

Hynes Industries Inc.................C........ 330 799-3221
Youngstown *(G-21111)*

WIRE: Communication

AT&T Corp........................G........ 513 792-9300
Cincinnati *(G-3423)*

Ohio Associated Entps LLC...........E........ 440 354-3148
Painesville *(G-15908)*

Solexy Usa LLC....................G........ 513 860-5465
West Chester *(G-20051)*

Xponet Inc........................E........ 440 354-6617
Painesville *(G-15943)*

WIRE: Magnet

HM Wire International Inc.............E........ 330 244-8501
Canton *(G-2729)*

Master Magnetics Inc................F........ 740 373-0909
Marietta *(G-12805)*

WIRE: Mesh

Midwestern Industries Inc.............C........ 330 837-4203
Massillon *(G-13180)*

WIRE: Nonferrous

Alcan Corporation..................E........ 440 460-3307
Cleveland *(G-4741)*

American Wire & Cable Company........E........ 440 235-1140
Olmsted Twp *(G-15678)*

Arnco Corporation..................C........ 800 847-7661
Elyria *(G-9375)*

Astro Industries Inc.................E........ 937 429-5900
Beavercreek *(G-1319)*

Composite Concepts Inc..............E........ 440 247-3844
Mason *(G-13005)*

Connectors Unlimited Inc.............E........ 440 357-1161
Painesville *(G-15868)*

Electra - Cord Inc..................D........ 330 832-8124
Massillon *(G-13129)*

Electrovations Inc..................E........ 330 274-3558
Aurora *(G-918)*

Legrand North America LLC...........B........ 937 224-0639
Moraine *(G-14503)*

Mueller Electric Company Inc..........E........ 216 771-5225
Akron *(G-307)*

Murphy Industries Inc................E........ 740 387-7890
Marion *(G-12887)*

Radix Wire Co.....................E........ 216 731-9191
Cleveland *(G-6086)*

Radix Wire Co.....................D........ 216 731-9191
Cleveland *(G-6087)*

Radix Wire Company.................E........ 330 995-3677
Aurora *(G-943)*

Schneider Electric Usa Inc............B........ 513 523-4171
Oxford *(G-15843)*

Scott Fetzer Company...............C........ 216 267-9000
Cleveland *(G-6168)*

Therm-O-Link Inc..................D........ 330 527-2124
Garrettsville *(G-10334)*

Therm-O-Link Inc..................E........ 330 393-7600
Warren *(G-19605)*

Therm-O-Link of Texas Inc...........E........ 330 393-4300
Warren *(G-19606)*

Veteran Industries LLC...............G........ 937 751-2133
Columbus *(G-7737)*

Vulkor Incorporated.................E........ 330 393-7600
Warren *(G-19619)*

WIRE: Nonferrous, Appliance Fixture

General Electric Company............D........ 330 343-8841
Dover *(G-8987)*

WIRE: Steel, Insulated Or Armored

Euclid Steel & Wire Inc...............F........ 216 731-6744
Euclid *(G-9580)*

Marlin Thermocouple Wire Inc.........E........ 440 835-1950
Cleveland *(G-5750)*

Ram Sensors Inc...................G........ 440 835-3540
Westlake *(G-20300)*

Ram Sensors Inc...................F........ 440 835-3540
Cleveland *(G-6089)*

WIRE: Wire, Ferrous Or Iron

Solon Specialty Wire Co..............E........ 440 248-7600
Cleveland *(G-6219)*

WIRING DEVICES WHOLESALERS

Astro Industries Inc.................E........ 937 429-5900
Beavercreek *(G-1319)*

WOMEN'S & CHILDREN'S CLOTHING WHOLESALERS, NEC

Chester West Holdings Inc............C........ 800 647-1900
Sharonville *(G-17113)*

Fine Line Embroidery Company.........G........ 440 331-7030
Rocky River *(G-16699)*

McCc Sportswear Inc................E........ 513 583-9210
West Chester *(G-20025)*

Rita Fishel Inc.....................E........ 740 775-1957
Chillicothe *(G-3272)*

Zimmer Enterprises Inc...............E........ 937 428-1057
Dayton *(G-8768)*

WOMEN'S & GIRLS' SPORTSWEAR WHOLESALERS

Barbs Graffiti Inc..................E........ 216 881-5550
Cleveland *(G-4889)*

Design Original Inc.................F........ 937 596-5121
Jackson Center *(G-11339)*

Precision Imprint..................G........ 740 592-5916
Athens *(G-882)*

R & A Sports Inc...................E........ 216 289-2254
Euclid *(G-9603)*

Unisport Inc......................F........ 419 529-4727
Ontario *(G-15696)*

WOMEN'S CLOTHING STORES

Rita Fishel Inc.....................E........ 740 775-1957
Chillicothe *(G-3272)*

WOMEN'S CLOTHING STORES: Ready-To-Wear

Mypro Apparel LLC.................G........ 419 462-9464
Ontario *(G-15690)*

WOMEN'S SPORTSWEAR STORES

Locker Room Lettering Ltd............G........ 419 359-1761
Castalia *(G-2977)*

Sports Express....................G........ 330 297-1112
Ravenna *(G-16559)*

WOOD & WOOD BY-PRDTS, WHOLESALE

77 Coach Supply Ltd................E........ 330 674-1454
Millersburg *(G-14187)*

Cindoco Wood Products Co...........G........ 937 444-2504
Mount Orab *(G-14577)*

Gross Lumber Inc..................E........ 330 683-2055
Apple Creek *(G-638)*

WOOD CHIPS, PRODUCED AT THE MILL

Miller Logging Inc..................E........ 330 279-4721
Holmesville *(G-11109)*

WOOD PRDTS

Global Wood Products LLC...........G........ 440 442-5859
Highland Heights *(G-10913)*

Gregoire Moulin...................G........ 614 861-4582
Reynoldsburg *(G-16593)*

Growers Choice Ltd.................G........ 330 262-8754
Shreve *(G-17156)*

Kennewegs Wood Products...........G........ 330 832-1540
Massillon *(G-13163)*

R M Wood Co.....................G........ 419 845-2661
Mount Gilead *(G-14566)*

Wooden Creations..................... 419 874-6367
Perrysburg *(G-16171)*

WOOD PRDTS: Applicators

Woodcor America Inc .... G 614 277-2930
Grove City *(G-10610)*

WOOD PRDTS: Baskets, Fruit & Veg, Round Stave, Till, Etc

Longaberger Company .... A 740 828-4000
Frazeysburg *(G-10075)*

WOOD PRDTS: Door Trim

Mohican Wood Products .... G 740 599-5655
Butler *(G-2393)*

WOOD PRDTS: Engraved

Minotas Trophies & Awards .... G 440 720-1288
Cleveland *(G-5823)*
Solid Dimensions Inc .... G 419 663-1134
Norwalk *(G-15564)*

WOOD PRDTS: Furniture Inlays, Veneers

Wurms Woodworking Company .... E 419 492-2184
New Washington *(G-14966)*

WOOD PRDTS: Ladders & Stepladders

Bc Investment Corporation .... G 330 262-3070
Wooster *(G-20747)*

WOOD PRDTS: Laundry

Dalton Wood Products Inc .... G 330 682-0727
Orrville *(G-15734)*

WOOD PRDTS: Mantels

Universal Production Corp .... C 740 522-1147
Newark *(G-15065)*

WOOD PRDTS: Moldings, Unfinished & Prefinished

Clark Wood Specialties Inc .... G 330 499-8711
Clinton *(G-6534)*
J McCoy Lumber Co Ltd .... F 937 587-3423
Peebles *(G-16022)*
J McCoy Lumber Co Ltd .... G 937 544-2968
West Union *(G-20121)*
K D Hardwoods Inc .... G 440 834-1772
Burton *(G-2379)*
Laborie Enterprises LLC .... G 419 686-6245
Portage *(G-16425)*
Seneca Millwork Inc .... E 419 435-6671
Fostoria *(G-9995)*

WOOD PRDTS: Mulch Or Sawdust

American Wood Fibers Inc .... E 740 420-3233
Circleville *(G-4623)*
BR Mulch Inc .... G 937 667-8288
Tipp City *(G-18266)*
Chromascape Inc .... E 330 998-7574
Twinsburg *(G-18912)*
Garick LLC .... E 216 581-0100
Cleveland *(G-5398)*
Hope Timber & Marketing Group .... F 740 344-1788
Newark *(G-15019)*
Hope Timber Mulch Inc .... G 740 344-1788
Newark *(G-15020)*
Mulch Madness LLC .... F 330 920-9900
Aurora *(G-935)*
National Pallet & Mulch LLC .... F 937 237-1643
Dayton *(G-8521)*
Roe Transportation Entps Inc .... G 937 497-7161
Sidney *(G-17217)*

WOOD PRDTS: Mulch, Wood & Bark

Hauser Services Llc .... E 440 632-5126
Middlefield *(G-13941)*
Irvine Wood Recovery Inc .... E 513 831-0060
Miamiville *(G-13894)*
Kaufman Mulch Inc .... G 330 893-3676
Millersburg *(G-14236)*
Latham Lumber & Pallet Co Inc .... F 740 493-2707
Latham *(G-11766)*
Mad River Topsoil Inc .... G 937 882-6115
Springfield *(G-17598)*
Mulch Makers of Ohio Inc .... G 330 753-3090
Norton *(G-15518)*

Mulch Man .... E 937 866-5370
Dayton *(G-8114)*
Scotts Company LLC .... A 937 644-3729
Marysville *(G-12967)*
Yoder Lumber Co Inc .... D 330 893-3121
Millersburg *(G-14288)*

WOOD PRDTS: Novelties, Fiber

F J Designs Inc .... E 330 264-1377
Wooster *(G-20771)*
Good Wood Inc .... G 740 484-1500
Belmont *(G-1579)*

WOOD PRDTS: Plugs

Sealco Inc .... G 740 922-4122
Uhrichsville *(G-19058)*

WOOD PRDTS: Reed, Rattan, Wicker & Willow ware, Exc Furnitr

Buhi Imports .... G 440 224-0013
North Kingsville *(G-15303)*

WOOD PRDTS: Saddle Trees

Red Lion Nursery Inc .... G 937 704-9840
Lebanon *(G-11832)*

WOOD PRDTS: Signboards

Blang Acquisition LLC .... F 937 223-2155
Dayton *(G-8190)*
R T Communications Inc .... G 330 726-7892
Youngstown *(G-21183)*
Sign Technologies LLC .... G 937 439-3970
Dayton *(G-8658)*
Signature Sign Co Inc .... F 216 426-1234
Cleveland *(G-6204)*

WOOD PRDTS: Survey Stakes

Adco Products Inc .... D 937 339-6267
Tipp City *(G-18261)*
Lawnview Industries Inc .... G 937 653-5217
Urbana *(G-19168)*
Zaenkert Surveying Essentials .... G 513 738-2917
Okeana *(G-15668)*

WOOD PRDTS: Trophy Bases

Company Front Awards .... G 440 636-5493
Middlefield *(G-13924)*
Hit Trophy Inc .... G 419 445-5356
Archbold *(G-681)*
L S Manufacturing Inc .... G 614 885-7988
Worthington *(G-20876)*

WOOD PRDTS: Veneer Work, Inlaid

Decorative Veneer Inc .... G 216 741-5511
Cleveland *(G-5180)*

WOOD PRDTS: Washboards, Wood & Part Wood

Columbus Washboard Company Ltd .... F 740 380-3828
Logan *(G-12173)*

WOOD PRDTS: Weather Strip, Wood

Action Industries Ltd .... F 216 252-7800
Cleveland *(G-4698)*

WOOD PRODUCTS: Reconstituted

Aristocrat Industries Inc .... F 740 694-2752
Mount Vernon *(G-14608)*
Decker Custom Wood Llc .... G 419 332-3464
Fremont *(G-10141)*
Ohio Plywood Box .... G 513 242-9125
Cincinnati *(G-4179)*
Profile Products LLC .... F 330 452-2630
Canton *(G-2828)*

WOOD TREATING: Millwork

Couch Business Development Inc .... F 937 253-1099
Dayton *(G-8244)*
Joseph Sabatino .... G 330 332-5879
Salem *(G-16904)*

WOOD TREATING: Structural Lumber & Timber

Clark Rm Inc .... E 419 425-9889
Findlay *(G-9808)*
Luxus Products LLC .... G 937 444-6500
Mount Orab *(G-14582)*

WOOD TREATING: Wood Prdts, Creosoted

Wood Duck Enterprises Ltd .... G 937 426-0506
Beavercreek *(G-1366)*

WOODWORK & TRIM: Exterior & Ornamental

Lehman & Sons .... G 330 857-7404
Orrville *(G-15745)*

WOODWORK & TRIM: Interior & Ornamental

Hoover Group .... G 419 525-3159
Shiloh *(G-17149)*
LE Smith Company .... D 419 636-4555
Bryan *(G-2310)*
Pete Emmert Co .... G 740 455-3924
Nashport *(G-14706)*
Pleasant Valley Wdwkg LLC .... G 440 636-5860
Middlefield *(G-13983)*
Richardson Woodworking .... G 614 893-8850
Blacklick *(G-1705)*

WOODWORK: Carved & Turned

Baker McMillen Co .... D 330 923-8300
Stow *(G-17733)*
Mark Nelson .... F 740 282-5334
Steubenville *(G-17704)*
Mollard Conducting Batons Inc .... F 330 659-7081
Bath *(G-1239)*
Smith P K Woodcarving LLC .... G 513 271-7077
Louisville *(G-12329)*
Todd W Goings .... G 740 389-5842
Marion *(G-12907)*

WOODWORK: Interior & Ornamental, NEC

Cincinnati Wood Products Co .... G 513 542-0569
Cincinnati *(G-3569)*
Joe P Fischer Woodcraft .... G 513 530-9600
Blue Ash *(G-1819)*
Mandi A Tripp .... G 740 380-1216
Rockbridge *(G-16689)*
Sawdust .... G 740 862-0612
Baltimore *(G-1088)*
Stull Woodworks .... G 937 698-8181
Ludlow Falls *(G-12428)*
Sylvan Forge Inc .... G 440 237-3626
North Royalton *(G-15453)*
V & W Woodcraft .... G 330 674-0073
Millersburg *(G-14276)*

WOODWORK: Ornamental, Cornices, Mantels, Etc.

Reserve Millwork Inc .... E 216 531-6982
Bedford *(G-1457)*
Trimtec Systems Ltd .... F 614 820-0340
Grove City *(G-10607)*

WOOL: Felted

Ohio Table Pad of Indiana .... E 419 872-6400
Perrysburg *(G-16132)*

WORD PROCESSING EQPT

Cap Data Supply Inc .... G 216 252-2280
Cleveland *(G-4969)*

WOVEN WIRE PRDTS, NEC

Mazzella Lifting Tech Inc .... F 513 772-4466
Cincinnati *(G-4069)*
Roy I Kaufman Inc .... G 740 382-0643
Marion *(G-12896)*
Utility Wire Products Inc .... F 216 441-2180
Cleveland *(G-6403)*

WRENCHES

Bergman Safety Spanner Co Inc .... G 419 691-1462
Northwood *(G-15478)*
Buckeye Gear Co .... F 216 292-7998
Chagrin Falls *(G-3078)*

Employee Codes: A=Over 500 employees, B=251-500
C=101-250, D=51-100, E=20-50, F=10-19, G=3-9

2017 Harris Ohio
Industrial Directory

1697

PRODUCT

Norbar Torque Tools Inc....................F........ 440 953-1175
  Willoughby **(G-20555)**

X-RAY EQPT & TUBES

Comet Technologies USA Inc ....F 234 284-7849
  Hudson **(G-11165)**
Dentsply International Inc ....D 419 865-9497
  Maumee **(G-13256)**
Metro Design Inc ....F 440 458-4200
  Elyria **(G-9462)**

North Coast Medical Eqp Inc ....F 440 243-2722
  Berea **(G-1629)**
Philips Medical Systems Clevel.............B 440 247-2652
  Cleveland **(G-6001)**
Yxlon ....G 234 284-7862
  Hudson **(G-11211)**

X-RAY EQPT REPAIR SVCS

Metro Design Inc ....F 440 458-4200
  Elyria **(G-9462)**

YARN & YARN SPINNING

Specilty Fbrics Converting Inc ....E 706 637-3000
  Fairlawn **(G-9760)**
Yarn Shop Inc......................................G....... 614 457-7836
  Columbus **(G-7782)**

YARN: Manmade & Synthetic Fiber, Twisting Or Winding

US Greentech ....G 513 371-5520
  Cincinnati **(G-4546)**